123rd edition
Published by Kelly's Directories
Reed Business Information Ltd
Windsor Court
East Grinstead House
East Grinstead
West Sussex
RH19 1XA

Tel: (01342) 335866
Fax: (01342) 335671
E-mail: kellys.listdata@reedinfo.co.uk

ISBN 978-0-610-00679-1
ISSN 1467-1220

For further information & enquiries please ring:

CD & Book Orders: **0800 0185 882**
General Enquiries: **01342 335 866**

Reed Business Information

Typeset by DCS
Printed and bound by CLOWES

Introduction

Kelly's Industrial Directory remains an essential business-to-business tool for every purchaser and supplier throughout the UK and globally.

Updated throughout the year by a dedicated editorial team there are over 87,000 companies classified under more than 18,000 headings, that buyers and specifiers alike continue to turn to when they need quick access to important and accurate business information.

Comprehensive and easy to use

Any industrial company within the UK is entitled to appear in the Kelly's Industrial Directory free of charge, therefore this remains one of the most comprehensive and easy to use business-to-business directories available.

Industrial Products & Services

In this section, there are over 87,000 companies listed under more than 18,000 product headings - this really does allow you instant access to the product or supplier you're searching for - saving you a great deal of time on research. Including full address and telecommunication details, there is also a products and services index that will speed your search.

Company Information

Here you will find full postal address, telecommunication details and trade descriptions for over 87,000 UK companies. Data change indicators enable you to see at a glance if a company's information has changed. You will also find the company e-mail, web address and product description which allows quick and easy cross referencing to the relevant headings in the Products and Services Volume.

Kelly's is used constantly by Purchasers and Suppliers to search for a particular product or service and is a trusted source of business leads for your sales and marketing activity.

Contents & How To Use

Kelly's Industrial Directory is divided into 2 sections

Section 1

Industrial Products and Services

Product and Service headings listed alphabetically provide details of UK companies, including telecommunication details.

Section 2

Company Information

An alphabetical listing of all the companies that appear in the Products and Services Section. Each company entry includes nature of business, address, telecommunication details, e-mail & web addresses (where available). Product headings also appear allowing you to cross-reference with the Products and Services Section.

To find suppliers of a product or service
Turn to the Products and Services Section and select the appropriate heading. The product and service headings are listed in strict alphabetical order.

To find details of a company
Go to the Company Information Section, where companies are listed in alphabetical order.

Section 1 Products & Services

100 TO 1500 TONNES CAPACITY HYDRAULIC PRESSES

Bruderer Ltd, Cradock Industrial Estate, Cradock Road, Luton, LU4 0JF Tel: (01582) 560300 Fax: (01582) 570611 E-mail: mail@bruderer.co.uk

100 TO 500 TONNES CAPACITY MECHANICAL PRESSES

Bruderer Ltd, Cradock Industrial Estate, Cradock Road, Luton, LU4 0JF Tel: (01582) 560300 Fax: (01582) 570611 E-mail: mail@bruderer.co.uk

▶ Formost Machinery Services, Holly Lane Industrial Estate, Atherstone, Warwickshire, CV9 2QX Tel: (01827) 721010 Fax: (01827) 721012

1000 DEGREES C FLAME RETARDANT (FR) TAPES

Fireprotect Chester Ltd, Factory Road, Sandycroft, Deeside, Clwyd, CH5 2QJ Tel: (01244) 536595 Fax: (01244) 533592 E-mail: sales@fireprotect.co.uk

180 DEGREE STACKER NARROW AISLE FORKLIFT TRUCKS

Hyster Europe, Flagship House, Reading Road North, Fleet, Hampshire, GU51 4WD Tel: (01252) 810261 Fax: (01252) 770702 E-mail: sales@hyster.co.uk

Translift Holdings plc, 22 Padgets Lane, Redditch, Worcestershire, B98 0RB Tel: (01527) 527411 Fax: (01527) 510177 E-mail: sales@translift.co.uk

19 INCH ENCLOSURES

Ad Tek Products Ltd, 35 Broton Drive, Halstead, Essex, CO9 1HB Tel: (01787) 474470 Fax: (01787) 475880 E-mail: ad-tek@lineone.net

Data & Power Solutions, Unit 1 The Monarch Centre, Venture Way, Priorswood Industrial Estate, Taunton, Somerset, TA2 8DE Tel: (01823) 275100 Fax: (01823) 275002 E-mail: sales@dataandpower.com

Enclosure Systems Ltd, Platt Industrial Estate, Maidstone Road, Borough Green, Sevenoaks, Kent, TN15 8JA Tel: (01732) 886552 Fax: (01732) 886443 E-mail: sales@enclosures.co.uk

▶ Tempa Pano UK, Unit 5, Centre 21 Industrial Estate, Bridge Lane, Woolston, Warrington, WA1 4AW Tel: 0845 4941730 Fax: (01925) 810386 E-mail: info@tempapano.co.uk

24 HOUR EMERGENCY BUILDING SERVICES

▶ Alexandra Locksmiths, 11 Palace Court Gardens, London, N10 2LB Tel: (020) 8883 1555 E-mail: pau.@alexandralocksmiths.co.uk

500 TO 1000 TONNES CAPACITY MECHANICAL PRESSES

▶ Formost Machinery Services, Holly Lane Industrial Estate, Atherstone, Warwickshire, CV9 2QX Tel: (01827) 721010 Fax: (01827) 721012

Pearson Panke Equipment Ltd, 1 3 Halegrove Gardens, Mill Hill, London, NW7 3LR Tel: (020) 8959 3232 Fax: (020) 8959 5613 E-mail: sales@pearsonpanke.co.uk

70 SHORE HARDNESS HIGH TEAR SILICONE INSULATED CABLES

▶ Mapra Technik Co., Unit D13, The Seedbed Centre, Langston Road, Loughton, Essex, IG10 3TQ Tel: (020) 8508 4207 Fax: (020) 8502 5107 E-mail: info@mapra.co.uk

ABATTOIR PLANT ENGINEERING OR FABRICATION

Abachem Engineering Ltd, Jessop Way, Newark, Nottinghamshire, NG24 2ER Tel: (01636) 676483 Fax: (01636) 708632

Bishops Castle Meat Ltd, Love Lane Industrial Estate, Bishops Castle, Shropshire, SY9 5DW Tel: (01588) 638770 Fax: (01588) 638008 E-mail: bcmeats@btopenworld.com

E.A. Bitterling Ltd, Poulton Drive, Daleside Road Industrial Estate, Nottingham, NG2 4BN Tel: 0115-986 2934 Fax: 0115-986 3027 E-mail: info@bitterling.co.uk

Brassington & Co., Easing Moor Farm, Thorncliffe Road, Thorncliffe, Leek, Staffordshire, ST13 7LW Tel: (01538) 300243 Fax: (01538) 300333

C G Duffy & Sons, 6 Ratcliffe Road, Fakenham, Norfolk, NR21 8AY Tel: (01328) 862990 Fax: (01328) 853438

Cheshire Fabrications, Villa Farm, Sound Lane, Sound, Nantwich, Cheshire, CW5 8BE Tel: (01270) 780707 Fax: (01270) 780707

Country Vale Products, Bath Road, Bridgwater, Somerset, TA6 4PW Tel: (01823) 271011 Fax: (01823) 431059

Duerden, Lindal Moor Abbatior, Lindal In Furness, Ulverston, Cumbria, LA12 0LT Tel: (01229) 465619 Fax: (01229) 467218

F D Statton & Son, Stone Farm, Hatherleigh, Okehampton, Devon, EX20 3LU Tel: (01837) 810237 Fax: (01840) 261216

F Drury & Sons Ltd, The Abattoir, Tockenham Corner, Tockenham, Swindon, SN4 7PF Tel: (01793) 852467 Fax: (01793) 848470

Fairfield Meat Co., Maelor Abattoir, Bedwell Road, Wrexham, Clwyd, LL13 0TS Tel: (01978) 661794 Fax: (01978) 661774 E-mail: admin@fairfieldmeats.ffs.co.uk

G R Evans & Co., The Abbatoir, Ty Gwyn, Corwen, Clwyd, LL21 9BU Tel: (01490) 412999 Fax: (01490) 413071

Jaspers Treburley Ltd, Treburley, Launceston, Cornwall, PL15 9PU Tel: (01579) 370461 Fax: (01579) 370192 E-mail: admin@jaspersbeef.co.uk

W. Lloyd Williams & Sons, Poplar Terrace, Machynlleth, Powys, SY20 8BY Tel: (01654) 702106 Fax: (01654) 702106

Lockerbie & Wilkinson Engineering Ltd, Alexandra Works, Locarno Road, Tipton, West Midlands, DY4 9SD Tel: 0121-557 1861 Fax: 0121-557 4804 E-mail: locwiltipton@aol.com

R Bennett & Sons, Fal Valley Tannery, Grampound, Truro, Cornwall, TR2 4RX Tel: (01726) 882417

Wards Welding & Fabrications, Cranfield Road, Woburn Sands, Milton Keynes, MK17 8UR Tel: (01908) 586505 Fax: (01908) 587505 E-mail: steve@wardsweldingandfsnet.co.uk

ABATTOIR SERVICES

A B P Scotland Ltd, Whitburn Road, Bathgate, West Lothian, EH48 2HR Tel: (01506) 632722 Fax: (01506) 632802

▶ Abdullah Musa & Sons Ltd., Head Office: Musa House, 262 Deepdale Road, Preston, PR1 6QB Tel: 01772 700005 Fax: 01772 705550 E-mail: info@musagroup.co.uk

▶ The Arran Lamb Co., The Abattoir, Blackwaterfoot, Isle of Arran, KA27 8EZ Tel: (01770) 850264 Fax: (01770) 850264 E-mail: iain@arranlamb.com

Fowler Bros, Brook Farm, Marsh Road, Burnham-on-Crouch, Essex, CM0 8NA Tel: (01621) 782877

ABOVE GROUND DETECTORS

Rokonet UK Ltd, Commerce Way, Whitbrook Way, Middleton, Manchester, M24 2SS Tel: (01527) 576765 Fax: 0161-655 5501 E-mail: sales@riscogroup.co.uk

ABOVE GROUND SWIMMING POOLS

Aquaplan, South Cadleigh House, Beech Road, Ivybridge, Devon, PL21 9HN Tel: (01752) 892908 Fax: (01752) 892908

ABRASION RESISTANT OPTICAL COATINGS

▶ Siltint Ind Ltd, 124 Longley Lane, Sharston, Manchester, M22 4SP Tel: 0161-945 4000 Fax: 0161-945 4040 E-mail: info@siltint.com

ABRASION RESISTANT STEEL PLATE

Corus Construction & Industrial UK Ltd, Brigg Road, Scunthorpe, South Humberside, DN16 1BP Tel: (01724) 404040 Fax: (01724) 402191E-mail: andrew.page@corusgroup.com

P & D Northern Steels Ltd, Mosshey Street, Shaw, Oldham, OL2 8QL Tel: (01706) 848811 Fax: (01706) 841153 E-mail: sales@pdnorthern.co.uk

Quenched & Tempered Steels Ltd, 60 Green Road, Leeds, LS6 4JP Tel: 0113-225 0400 Fax: 0113-228 6333 E-mail: sales@qandtsteels.fsnet.co.uk

Swedish Steel, De Salis Court, De Salis Drive, Hampton Lovett, Droitwich, Worcestershire, WR9 0QE Tel: (01905) 795794 Fax: (01905) 794736 E-mail: ssabuk@ssab.com

ABRASION RESISTANT STEEL PROFILE CUTTING

Energy Alloys UK Ltd, Canklow Meadows Industrial Estate, West Bawtry Road, Rotherham, South Yorkshire, S60 2XN Tel: (01709) 788000 Fax: (01709) 788030 E-mail: uksales@ealloys.com

ABRASIVE BELT OR BAND GRINDING MACHINES

Crescent Machinery Ltd, Unit 1 Moderna Business Park, Moderna Way, Mytholmroyd, Hebden Bridge, West Yorkshire, HX7 5QQ Tel: (01422) 884888 Fax: (01422) 881338 E-mail: info@crescentmachinery.co.uk

Surface Technology Products Ltd, 244 Heneage Street, Birmingham, B7 4LY Tel: 0121-359 4322 Fax: 0121-359 1817 E-mail: sales@surtech.co.uk

ABRASIVE BELTS OR DISCS OR ROLLS OR SHEETS

3M Abrasive Systems, 3 M Centre, Cain Road, Bracknell, Berkshire, RG12 8HT Tel: (01344) 858974 Fax: (01344) 858195 E-mail: abrasives.uk@mmm.com

Abacon Ltd, 2 Atlas Way, Sheffield, S4 7QQ Tel: 0114-256 2266 Fax: 0114-256 2268 E-mail: sales@abacon.co.uk

▶ Apex Industrial Ltd, 14 Faraday Road, Glenrothes, Fife, KY6 2RU Tel: (01592) 771676 Fax: (01592) 774674

▶ Bilbo Tools Ltd, Steamhouse Group, 555 White Hart Lane, London, N17 7RN Tel: 020 88196076 E-mail: sales@bilbotools.com

▶ Bodyshop Consumables Ltd, Wilne Road, Long Eaton, Nottingham, NG10 3AN Tel: 0115-946 1571 E-mail: orders@bodyshopconsumables.co.uk

C P L, 2 St. James Road, Brackley, Northamptonshire, NN13 7XY Tel: (01280) 706661 Fax: (01280) 706671 E-mail: canonbury@canonbury.com

Cambridge Manufacturing Services, 3 Hale Close, Melbourn, Royston, Hertfordshire, SG8 6ET Tel: (01763) 260070 Fax: (01763) 260070 E-mail: cammas_uk@yahoo.co.uk

DCB Abrasives & Industrial Ltd, Unit 12 Vale Business Park, Llandow, Cowbridge, South Glamorgan, CF71 7PF Tel: (01446) 772902 Fax: (01446) 775863

Drake Tooling & Abrasives Ltd, Unit 12 Chantry Park, Cowley Road, Nuffield Industrial Park, Poole, Dorset, BH17 0UJ Tel: (01202) 666467 Fax: (01202) 666468 E-mail: drake@poolebranch.co.uk

Fixings & Power Tools Direct Ltd, Tunbridge Wells Tool Room Stag Trade Park, Longfield Road, Tunbridge Wells, Kent, TN2 3BF Tel: (0800) 365598 Fax: (01892) 520888 E-mail: sales@fixings-direct.co.uk

▶ Hermes Abrasives Ltd, Wyncolls Road, Severalls Industrial Park, Colchester, CO4 9LW Tel: (01206) 754400 Fax: (01206) 754401 E-mail: jason.banner@btinternet.com

▶ K C W International Ltd, 394A Wingletye Lane, Hornchurch, Essex, RM11 3DB Tel: (01708) 455224 Fax: (0871) 6614761 E-mail: kcwinternational@btinternet.com

Lloyds British Testing plc, Wincomblee Road, Walker, Newcastle upon Tyne, NE6 3QQ Tel: 0191-262 9844 Fax: 0191-263 8868 E-mail: sales@lloydsgroup.co.uk

Mirka Abrasives Ltd, 7 Holdom Avenue, Bletchley, Milton Keynes, MK1 1QU Tel: (01908) 375533 Fax: (01908) 376611 E-mail: sales.uk@mirka.com

Wasp Supplies Ltd, Richardson Bottoms, Progress Way, Chalton, Luton, LU4 9TR Tel: (01582) 566560 Fax: (01582) 566056 E-mail: sale@waspsupplies.co.uk

ABRASIVE BLASTING, *See headings for particular types such as Shot*

ABRASIVE BLOCKS

Bonded Abrasives Ltd, Green Street, Macclesfield, Cheshire, SK10 1JQ Tel: (01625) 429009 Fax: (01625) 610076 E-mail: p.d.bailey@btinternet.com

▶ D G S Abrasives Division, 189-191 New Road, Portsmouth, PO2 7QU Tel: (023) 9266 1481 Fax: (023) 9267 3476 E-mail: south@dgsabrasives.co.uk

DCB Abrasives & Industrial Ltd, Unit 12 Vale Business Park, Llandow, Cowbridge, South Glamorgan, CF71 7PF Tel: (01446) 772902 Fax: (01446) 775863

Draper Tools Ltd, Hursley Road, Chandler's Ford, Eastleigh, Hampshire, SO53 1YF Tel: (023) 8026 6355 Fax: (023) 8026 0784 E-mail: sales@draper.co.uk

Sia Abrafoam Ltd, Keys Road, Nixs Hill Industrial Estate, Alfreton, Derbyshire, DE55 7FQ Tel: (01773) 832524 Fax: (01773) 520776 E-mail: info@sia-abrafoam.co.uk

ABRASIVE CLEANING

▶ Kleeneze Ltd, 1A St Georges Avenue, Herne Bay, Kent, CT6 8JU Tel: (01227) 360903 Fax: (0870) 4325666 E-mail: julie@kleeneze-option.co.uk

ABRASIVE COATED FOAM

Clomac Ltd, 4 Hills House, Wellington Road, Wavertree, Liverpool, L15 4JN Tel: 0151-734 5400 Fax: 0151-734 2333 E-mail: info@clomac.co.uk

Sia Abrafoam Ltd, Keys Road, Nixs Hill Industrial Estate, Alfreton, Derbyshire, DE55 7FQ Tel: (01773) 832524 Fax: (01773) 520776 E-mail: info@sia-abrafoam.co.uk

ABRASIVE COATED PRODUCTS

3M Abrasive Systems, 3 M Centre, Cain Road, Bracknell, Berkshire, RG12 8HT Tel: (01344) 858974 Fax: (01344) 858195 E-mail: abrasives.uk@mmm.com

Abacon Ltd, 2 Atlas Way, Sheffield, S4 7QQ Tel: 0114-256 2266 Fax: 0114-256 2268 E-mail: sales@abacon.co.uk

Cambridge Manufacturing Services, 3 Hale Close, Melbourn, Royston, Hertfordshire, SG8 6ET Tel: (01763) 260070 Fax: (01763) 260070 E-mail: cammas_uk@yahoo.co.uk

Central Polishing Supplies, Unit 33 Innage Park, Abeles Way, Holly Lane Industrial Estate, Atherstone, Warwickshire, CV9 2QX Tel: (01827) 714839 Fax: (01827) 714839 E-mail: c.polishing@talk21.com

▶ D G S Abrasives Division, 189-191 New Road, Portsmouth, PO2 7QU Tel: (023) 9266 1481 Fax: (023) 9267 3476 E-mail: south@dgsabrasives.co.uk

Hermes Abrasives Ltd, Wyncolls Road, Severalls Industrial Park, Colchester, CO4 9LW Tel: (01206) 754400 Fax: (01206) 754401 E-mail: huk@hermes-abrasives.com

Lloyds British Testing plc, Wincomblee Road, Walker, Newcastle upon Tyne, NE6 3QQ Tel: 0191-262 9844 Fax: 0191-263 8868 E-mail: sales@lloydsgroup.co.uk

Meister Abrasives UK Ltd, High March Industrial Estate, Daventry, Northamptonshire, NN11 4PG Tel: (01327) 703813 Fax: (01327) 871617E-mail: sales@master-abrasives.co.uk

Mirka Abrasives Ltd, 7 Holdom Avenue, Bletchley, Milton Keynes, MK1 1QU Tel: (01908) 375533 Fax: (01908) 376611 E-mail: sales.uk@mirka.com

P B Abrasives Ltd, 4 Gilston Road, Saltash, Cornwall, PL12 6TW Tel: (01752) 846713 Fax: (01752) 848771

S A I T Abrasives (UK) Ltd, Regent Street, Narborough, Leicester, LE19 2DL Tel: 0116-286 2325 Fax: 0116-275 0081 E-mail: info@sait-abrasives.co.uk

Saint-Gobain Abrasives, Doxey Road, Stafford, ST16 1EA Tel: (01785) 223281 Fax: (01785) 213487 E-mail: sales.gloucester.uk@saint-gobain.com

Sal Abrasives Technologies, 7 Drumhead Road, Chorley North Industrial Park, Chorley, Lancashire, PR6 7BX Tel: (01257) 271914 Fax: (01257) 260702 E-mail: sales@salgroup.co.uk

Sia Abrafoam Ltd, Keys Road, Nixs Hill Industrial Estate, Alfreton, Derbyshire, DE55 7FQ Tel: (01773) 832524 Fax: (01773) 520776 E-mail: info@sia-abrafoam.co.uk

Walther Trowal Ltd, 3 Spedding Road, Fenton Industrial Estate, Fenton, Stoke-on-Trent, ST4 2SN Tel: (01782) 412111 Fax: (01782) 744267 E-mail: enquires@metaret.co.uk

ABRASIVE CUTTING OFF

D G S Grinding Wheels & Machines Ltd, 90-92 Dovedale Road, Wolverhampton, WV4 6RA Tel: (01902) 661111 Fax: (01902) 880311 E-mail: sales@dgsabrasives.co.uk

Oil States MCS Ltd, Bouthwood Road, Sowerby Woods Industrial Estate, Barrow-in-Furness, Cumbria, LA14 4RD Tel: (01229) 825080 Fax: (01229) 839791 E-mail: owen-osmotherly@osmcs-bat.co.uk

United Abrasives Ltd, Unit 1 Charles Street, Walsall, WS2 9LZ Tel: (01922) 625544 Fax: (01922) 626345 E-mail: unitedabrasives@btconnect.com

ABRASIVE CUTTING OFF MACHINES

Benetec Cutting Tools, Unit 5b Midland Trading Estate, Consul Road, Rugby, Warwickshire, CV21 1PB Tel: (01788) 561133 Fax: (01788) 560223 E-mail: sales@benetecmetlab.com

Birkett Cutmaster Ltd, PO Box 30, Cleckheaton, West Yorkshire, BD19 5LY Tel: (01274) 870311 Fax: (01274) 862754 E-mail: bryn.pritchard@birkett-cutmaster.co.uk

Midland Machine Knives Ltd, Unit 17 Baltic Works, Effingham Road, Sheffield, S9 3QA Tel: 0114-244 8952 Fax: 0114-243 2437

ABRASIVE CUTTING OFF SEGMENTS OR DISCS OR BLADES

Arcorundum Grinding Wheel Co., Toll End Road, Tipton, West Midlands, DY4 0HF Tel: (0845) 6347171 Fax: (0845) 6347170

ABRASIVE EQUIPMENT CONTACT WHEELS

Equip (Midlands) Ltd, Byron Street, Buxton, Derbyshire, SK17 6NT Tel: (01298) 22233 Fax: (01298) 72097

ABRASIVE FLAP DISCS

▶ A T A Grinding Processes Ltd, 37 Dalsetter Avenue, Drumchapel, Glasgow, G15 8TE Tel: 0141-940 4720 Fax: 0141-940 4721 E-mail: ata@atagrinding.co.uk

Garryson Ltd, Spring Road, Ibstock, Leicestershire, LE67 6LR Tel: (01530) 261145 Fax: (01530) 262801 E-mail: sales@garryson.co.uk

ABRASIVE HONING STICKS

Abrahone Engineering, Unit 4 Thornes Trading Estate, Wakefield, West Yorkshire, WF1 5QN Tel: (01924) 378733 Fax: (01924) 200014 E-mail: abrahone@btconnect.com

ABRASIVE MOUNTED POINTS

Garryson Ltd, Spring Road, Ibstock, Leicestershire, LE67 6LR Tel: (01530) 261145 Fax: (01530) 262801 E-mail: sales@garryson.co.uk

Meister Abrasives UK Ltd, High March Industrial Estate, Daventry, Northamptonshire, NN11 4PG Tel: (01327) 703813 Fax: (01327) 871617E-mail: sales@master-abrasives.co.uk

Morrisflex Ltd, London Road, Braunston, Daventry, Northamptonshire, NN11 7HX Tel: (01788) 891777 Fax: (01788) 891629 E-mail: sales@morrisflex.co.uk

ABRASIVE POWDERS OR GRAINS

DDSM Tools, Cartersfield Road, Waltham Abbey, Essex, EN9 1JD Tel: (01992) 651607 Fax: (01992) 701105 E-mail: ddsm@netcomuk.co.uk

Kuhmichel U K, Friars Mill, Friars Terrace, Stafford, ST17 4AU Tel: (01785) 252200 Fax: (01785) 252100 E-mail: andrew.shepphaerd@kuhmichel.com

▶ Logitech Ltd, Erskine Ferry Road, Old Kilpatrick, Glasgow, G60 5EU Tel: (01389) 875444 Fax: (01389) 879042

Reliable Techniques Ltd, Unit 59 Parkhouse Industrial Estate West, Brick Kiln Lane, Newcastle, Staffordshire, ST5 7AS Tel: (01782) 565002 Fax: (01782) 565001 E-mail: optics@reliabletechniques.fsnet.co.uk

Washington Mills Electro Minerals Ltd, Mosley Road, Trafford Park, Manchester, M17 1NR Tel: 0161-848 0271 Fax: 0161-872 2974 E-mail: sales@washingtonmills.co.uk

ABRASIVE PRODUCTS, *See also headings for particular types*

Abacon Ltd, 2 Atlas Way, Sheffield, S4 7QQ Tel: 0114-256 2266 Fax: 0114-256 2268 E-mail: sales@abacon.co.uk

Abrasive Services & Stockists, 18 Baldock Road, Stotfold, Hitchin, Hertfordshire, SG5 4NZ Tel: (01462) 730886 Fax: (01462) 733354

▶ AbTec Industries Ltd, Unit 4, Venture Court, Boleness Road, Wisbech, Cambridgeshire, PE13 2XQ Tel: (01945) 585500 Fax: (01945) 585052 E-mail: sales@abrasivetechnology.net

Alansons Industrial Supplies, 7 Flowers Hill, Bristol, BS4 5JJ Tel: 0117-971 1364 Fax: (0870) 7773272

Allfix Ltd, 2 Leyland Road, Poole, Dorset, BH12 5HB Tel: (01202) 519066 Fax: (01202) 518353 E-mail: sales@allfix.co.uk

Andrew Beattie & Co, 332 Chipstead Valley Road, Coulsdon, Surrey, CR5 3BE Tel: (01737) 557811

▶ Apex Industrial Ltd, 14 Faraday Road, Glenrothes, Fife, KY6 2RU Tel: (01592) 771676 Fax: (01592) 774674

B C Abrasives Ltd, Cleeton Cottage, Cleeton St. Mary, Kidderminster, Worcestershire, DY14 0QU Tel: (01584) 891202 Fax: (01584) 891002 E-mail: bcabrasives2@btconnect.com

Besco Industrial Supplies Ltd, Unit 3, The Glenmore Centre, Eurolink Industrial Centre, Castle Road, Sittingbourne, Kent, ME10 3GL Tel: (0845) 2960050 Fax: (0845) 2960056 E-mail: sales@besco.co.uk

Bryant Welding Supplies, PO Box 100, Southampton, SO40 9LA Tel: (023) 8086 7789 Fax: (023) 8066 3688 E-mail: sales@bryantwelding.co.uk

Build Centre Ltd, Unit 8 Etna Court, Falkirk, FK2 9ED Tel: (01324) 611787 Fax: (01324) 621375 E-mail: sales@buildcentre.co.uk

C B S Power Tools Ltd, 2 Bramhall Place, Storeys Bar Road, Peterborough, PE1 5YS Tel: (01733) 343031 Fax: (01733) 897151 E-mail: sales@cbspowertools.co.uk

Cambridge Manufacturing Services, 3 Hale Close, Melbourn, Royston, Hertfordshire, SG8 6ET Tel: (01763) 260070 Fax: (01763) 260070 E-mail: cammas_uk@yahoo.co.uk

Cameo Abrasives, Unit 4 Langley Drive, Chester Road Industrial Estate, Castle Bromwich, B35 7AD Tel: 0121-747 7100 Fax: 0121-748 5000

Carroll Tools Ltd, 16-18 Factory Lane, Croydon, CR0 3RL Tel: (020) 8781 1268 Fax: (020) 8781 1278 E-mail: info@carrolltools.com

▶ Carters Consumables Ltd, 70 Princess Street, Castle Gresley, Swadlincote, Derbyshire, DE11 9LA Tel: (01283) 550500

Couldridge Industrial Supplies, Crucible Close, Mushet Industrial Park, Coleford, Gloucestershire, GL16 8RE Tel: (01594) 833177 Fax: (01594) 837423

County Abrasive Supplies, 7 Bawden Road, Bodmin, Cornwall, PL31 1PT Tel: (01208) 75121 Fax: (01208) 76358

Cromwell Tools Ltd, Gorman House, James Street, Righead Industrial Estate, Bellshill, Lanarkshire, ML4 3LU Tel: (01698) 746974 Fax: (01698) 841988 E-mail: glasgow@cromwell-tools.co.uk

Crystal Abrasive Products & Co. Ltd, Clamark House, 63 Stalker Lees Road, Sheffield, S11 8NP Tel: 0114-266 6281 Fax: 0114-268 5336 E-mail: info@crystal-abrasives.com

▶ D G S Abrasives Division, 189-191 New Road, Portsmouth, PO2 7QU Tel: (023) 9266 1481 Fax: (023) 9267 3476 E-mail: south@dgsabrasives.co.uk

DCB Abrasives & Industrial Ltd, Unit 12 Vale Business Park, Llandow, Cowbridge, South Glamorgan, CF71 7PF Tel: (01446) 772902 Fax: (01446) 775863

Derbyshire Industrial Sales Ltd, Unit 17 Vanguard Trading Estate, Britannia Road, Chesterfield, Derbyshire, S40 2TZ Tel: (01246) 208963 Fax: (01246) 277139

Drake Tooling & Abrasives Ltd, Unit 12 Chantry Park, Cowley Road, Nuffield Industrial Park, Poole, Dorset, BH17 0UJ Tel: (01202) 666467 Fax: (01202) 666468 E-mail: drake@poolebranch.co.uk

Draper Tools Ltd, Hursley Road, Chandler's Ford, Eastleigh, Hampshire, SO53 1YF Tel: (023) 8026 6355 Fax: (023) 8026 0784 E-mail: sales@draper.co.uk

E C Hopkins, Unit 34 Stretford Motorway Estate, Stretford, Manchester, M32 0ZH Tel: 0161-866 9122 Fax: 0161-866 9121 E-mail: sales@echopkins.com

Ervin Amasteel Ltd, George Henry Road, Tipton, West Midlands, DY4 7BZ Tel: 0121-522 2777 Fax: 0121-522 2927 E-mail: info@ervinamasteel.com

Essex Fixing & Abrasives Supplies Ltd, Unit 12 Featherby Way, Purdey's Industrial Estate, Rochford, Essex, SS4 1LD Tel: (01702) 549222 Fax: (01702) 541465

Euro Safety & Abrasives, Unit 3, 13 Cobham Road, Ferndown Industrial Estate, Wimborne, Dorset, BH21 7TE Tel: (01202) 870661 Fax: (01202) 870095

Faint Gobain Abrasives, Doxey Road, Stafford, ST16 1EA Tel: (01785) 222000 Fax: (0845) 6026215

FineCal (Cymru) Ltd, 3 Rhymney River Bridge Road, Rumney, Cardiff, CF23 9AF Tel: (029) 2046 2644 Fax: (029) 2048 4522 E-mail: sales@finecal.co.uk

Finecal Distributors, 2 Temple Trading Estate, Cole Road, Bristol, BS2 0UG Tel: 0117-971 1111 Fax: 0117-977 2326 E-mail: sales@finecal.co.uk

Finishing Aids & Tools, Unit 25 Woolfold Industrial Estate, Mitchell Street, Bury, Lancashire, BL8 1SF Tel: 0161-705 1300 Fax: 0161-763 1959

Finishing Components Co., 1-8 Silverdale, Meadow Road, Worthing, West Sussex, BN11 2RZ Tel: (01903) 205155 Fax: (01903) 205166 E-mail: finishingcomponents@supanet.com

Fixings & Power Tools Direct Ltd, Tunbridge Wells Tool Room Stag Trade Park, Longfield Road, Tunbridge Wells, Kent, TN2 3BF Tel: (0800) 365598 Fax: (01892) 520888 E-mail: sales@fixings-direct.co.uk

G M A Garnet UK Ltd, PO Box 9, Middlewich, Cheshire, CW10 9FD Tel: (01606) 836233 Fax: (01606) 836610 E-mail: sales@gmagarnet.co.uk

▶ Gold Medal (Romsey) Ltd, Unit 25, Romsey Industrial Estate, Greatbridge Road, Romsey, Hampshire, SO51 0HR Tel: (01794) 519933 Fax: (01794) 519991 E-mail: information@goldmedalco.com

Thomas Graham & Sons Ltd, Maple Works, Northgate, White Lund Estate, Morecambe, Lancashire, LA3 3AZ Tel: (01524) 69112 Fax: (01524) 841076 E-mail: morecambe@thomas-graham.co.uk

Grinding Centre, 62 Berkeley Street, Glasgow, G3 7DS Tel: 0141-564 8888 Fax: 0141-564 1084 E-mail: sales@thegrindingcentre.co.uk

Hallmark Fraulo Ltd, Units 55-56, Hillgrove Business Park, Nazeing Road, Nazeing, Waltham Abbey, Essex, EN9 2HB Tel: (01992) 899025 Fax: (01992) 899026 E-mail: info@hallmarkfraulo.co.uk

Industrial Abrasives & Tool Co. Ltd, Amberwood, Wantage Road, Harwell, Didcot, Oxfordshire, OX11 0LL Tel: (01235) 834850 Fax: (01235) 832857 E-mail: trudy@industrialabrasives.net

Ipc Fixings, 1 National Road, Hunslet Business Park, Leeds, LS10 1TD Tel: 0113-277 9444 Fax: 0113-277 9555

Jeaton Tapes & Abrasives Ltd, Unit 1, Manchester Mill Industrial Estate, Geoffrey St, Preston, PR1 5NR Tel: (01772) 703636 Fax: (01772) 701271 E-mail: sales@jeaton.co.uk

The Jemma Tools Group Ltd, Bell Lane, Bayton Road Industrial Estate, Uckfield, East Sussex, TN22 1QL Tel: (01825) 761711 Fax: (01825) 767568 E-mail: info@jemmatools.co.uk

Jemma Tools Kent Ltd, 16 Willesborough Industrial Park, Willesborough, Ashford, Kent, TN24 0TD Tel: (01233) 639600 Fax: (01233) 637300 E-mail: sales@jemma-kent.co.uk

▶ Lamplan Industries Ltd, Unit 5, Pettings Court Farm, Hodsoll Street, Sevenoaks, Kent, TN15 7LH Tel: (01732) 824829 Fax: (01732) 824828 E-mail: jbroad@lamsplan.com

Lloyds British Testing plc, Wincomblee Road, Walker, Newcastle upon Tyne, NE6 3QQ Tel: 0191-262 9844 Fax: 0191-263 8868 E-mail: sales@lloydsgroup.co.uk

▶ Logitech Ltd, Erskine Ferry Road, Old Kilpatrick, Glasgow, G60 5EU Tel: (01389) 875444 Fax: (01389) 879042

MacGregor & Moir, Unit 4, 95 Westburn Drive, Cambuslang, Glasgow, G72 7NA Tel: 0141-643 3636 Fax: 0141-641 8505 E-mail: info@macgregorandmoir.com

Martract, Ardent Link, Humber Bridge Industrial Estate, Humber Bridge Industrial Estat, Barton-upon-Humber, South Humberside, DN18 5RN Tel: (01652) 632172 Fax: (01652) 660295 E-mail: info@martract.co.uk

Matglen Ltd, Unit 48 Milmead Industrial Centre, Mill Mead Road, London, N17 9QU Tel: (020) 8801 7799 Fax: (020) 8801 7985 E-mail: sales@matglen.demon.co.uk

Meister Abrasives UK Ltd, High March Industrial Estate, Daventry, Northamptonshire, NN11 4PG Tel: (01327) 703813 Fax: (01327) 871617E-mail: sales@meister-abrasives.co.uk

▶ Mineral Crushing & Classification Ltd, Unit 5, Airfield Industrial Estate, Newport Road, Seighford, Stafford, ST18 9NR Tel: (01785) 281113 Fax: (01785) 281114 E-mail: info@mineralcrushing.co.uk

Mirka Abrasives Ltd, 7 Holdom Avenue, Bletchley, Milton Keynes, MK1 1QU Tel: (01908) 375533 Fax: (01908) 376611 E-mail: sales.uk@mirka.com

Noritake (UK) Ltd, 26 Heathfield, Stacey Bushes, Milton Keynes, MK12 6HR Tel: (01908) 318446 Fax: (01908) 320932 E-mail: china@noritake.co.uk

Peter Walters (U K) Ltd, Brindley Road, Dodwells Bridge Industrial Estate, Hinckley, Leicestershire, LE10 3BY Tel: (01455) 631707 Fax: (01455) 611360 E-mail: pwuk@peter-wolters.com

Preline Ltd, Rutherford Square, Brucefield Industrial Estate, Livingston, West Lothian, EH54 9BU Tel: (01506) 412297 Fax: (01506) 416536 E-mail: sales@preline.co.uk

Pumex (UK) Ltd, Hall Road, Aylesford, Maidstone, Kent, ME20 7QZ Tel: (01622) 882022 Fax: (01622) 882441 E-mail: info@pumex.co.uk

Quick Wood UK, Station Road, Braughing, Ware, Hertfordshire, SG11 2PB Tel: (01920) 822922 Fax: (01920) 822909

Reliable Techniques Ltd, Unit 59 Parkhouse Industrial Estate West, Brick Kiln Lane, Newcastle, Staffordshire, ST5 7AS Tel: (01782) 565002 Fax: (01782) 565001 E-mail: optics@reliabletechniques.fsnet.co.uk

ABRASIVE PRODUCTS – *continued*

Gordon Richards Tools (Birmingham), Unit 28, Roman Way, Coles Hill, Birmingham, B46 1HQ Tel: 0121-328 5454 Fax: 0121-322 2148
S A I T Abrasives (UK) Ltd, Regent Street, Narborough, Leicester, LE19 2DL Tel: 0116-286 2325 Fax: 0116-275 0081 E-mail: info@sait-abrasives.co.uk
Sal Abrasives Technologies, 7 Drumhead Road, Chorley North Industrial Park, Chorley, Lancashire, PR6 7BX Tel: (01257) 271914 Fax: (01257) 260702 E-mail: sales@salgroup.co.uk
Saunders & Co. Ltd, 35-39 Trinity Street, Sheffield, S3 7AJ Tel: 0114-276 6733 Fax: 0114-275 0307
Swift Abrasive Wheels, Toll End Road, Tipton, West Midlands, DY4 0HF Tel: 0121-557 8337 Fax: 0121-520 4770 E-mail: swiftandwhitmore@virgin.net
▶ Treibacher Schleifmittel UK, Claremont House, 12-14 Claremont Road, West Byfleet, Surrey, KT14 6DY Tel: (01932) 347499 Fax: (01932) 354081
United Abrasives Ltd, Unit 1 Charles Street, Walsall, WS2 9LZ Tel: (01922) 625544 Fax: (01922) 626345 E-mail: unitedabrasives@btconnect.com
Vapormatt Ltd, Monarch Centre, Venture Way, Priorswood Industrial Est, Taunton, Somerset, TA2 8DE Tel: (01823) 257976 Fax: (01823) 336446 E-mail: sales@vapormatt.com
White Milne & Co., Baird Avenue, Dundee, DD2 3XG Tel: (01382) 814822 Fax: (01382) 813751 E-mail: sales@whitemilne.co.uk
Robert Wilcox (Abrasives) Ltd, 19 Desborough Avenue, High Wycombe, Buckinghamshire, HP11 2RS Tel: (01494) 530533 Fax: (01494) 524532
Wolverhampton Abrasives, Orgreave Drive, Sheffield, S13 9NR Tel: (0800) 0853085 Fax: 0114-254 0913E-mail: gritsales@aol.com

ABRASIVE RESISTANT COATINGS

▶ Survair South Manchester Ltd, 17 Hawthorn Lane, Ashton-On-Mersey, Sale, Cheshire, M33 5WW Tel: 0161-286 9629 E-mail: brian.kiely@survair.co.uk

ABRASIVE RESISTANT HOSES

Masterflex Technical Hoses Ltd, Unit G & H Prince Of Wales, Vulcan St, Oldham, OL1 4ER Tel: 0161 6268066

ABRASIVE TOOLS

▶ Bilbo Tools Ltd, Steamhouse Group, 555 White Hart Lane, London, N17 7RN Tel: 020 88196076 E-mail: sales@bilbotools.com
Crystal Abrasive Products & Co. Ltd, Clamark House, 63 Stalker Lees Road, Sheffield, S11 8NP Tel: 0114-266 6281 Fax: 0114-268 5336 E-mail: info@crystal-abrasives.com
▶ Hahl Extrusions Ltd, St Helens Industrial Estate, Bishop Auckland, County Durham, DL14 9AD Tel: (01388) 661818 Fax: (01388) 450733 E-mail: sales@hahl-extrusions.co.uk
S K S Paint & Equipment Ltd, 11 Redehall Road, Smallfield, Horley, Surrey, RH6 9PY Tel: (01342) 843688 Fax: (01342) 842140 E-mail: sks@sks-group.co.uk

ABRASIVE WHEEL TRAINING

▶ A 1 Hire & Sales Ltd, 76 Old Wareham Road, Poole, Dorset, BH12 4QR Tel: (01202) 736899 Fax: (01202) 732726 E-mail: sales@a1hire.co.uk
▶ Abacus Safety Training, 7 Pennywort Grove, Harrogate, North Yorkshire, HG3 2XJ Tel: (01423) 550413 Fax: (01423) 552355 E-mail: info@abacussafetytraining.com
▶ AES Training Services, 1 Lower Bar, Newport, Shropshire, TF10 7BE Tel: (01952) 812535 Fax: (01952) 272233 E-mail: safety@aes-training.com
Citrus Training Ltd, 16 Bentley Court, Finedon Road Industrial Estate, Wellingborough, Northamptonshire, NN8 4BQ Tel: (0870) 8503505 Fax: (01933) 228876 E-mail: develop@citrustraining.com
Keith Cook Training Services, Madonna Villa, Oaks Road, Coalville, Leicestershire, LE67 5UN Tel: (01509) 506913 Fax: 01509 506913 E-mail: admin@kcts.me.uk
▶ Drury P S M Ltd, Ashfield House, Stewart Close, Bradford, West Yorkshire, BD2 2EE Tel: (01274) 626200 Fax: (01274) 626222 E-mail: info@drurypsm.com
First Choice Training & Development Ltd, 37 Langdale Crescent Eston, Grange Middlesbrough, Middlesbrough, Cleveland, TS6 7RB Tel: (01642) 511877 E-mail: firstchoicetraining@ntlwolrd.com
▶ Hitss Safety Training Ltd, Foxgloves, Millers Lane, Hornton, Banbury, Oxfordshire, OX15 6BS Tel: (01295) 678200 Fax: (01295) 670252 E-mail: sales@hitss.co.uk
▶ Jupiter Safety Management Ltd, 36 Shelley Road, Reddish, Stockport, Cheshire, Stockport, Cheshire, SK5 6JG Tel: 0161 442 4359 Fax: 0161 442 4359 E-mail: ccork-jupitersafety@fsmail.net
▶ M Spiller, 43 Linmere Walk, Houghton Regis, Dunstable, Bedfordshire, LU5 5PS Tel: (01582) 866363 Fax: (01582) 656046 E-mail: mike@michaelspiller.co.uk
▶ Panad Ltd, Unit 27, Brierley Business Centre, Mirion St, Crewe, CW1 2AZ Tel: (01270) 253533 Fax: (01270) 253544 E-mail: panad.limited@ntlworld.com
▶ Prospects Business Training Ltd, Prospects House, 10 Fairfax Drive, Westcliff-on-Sea, Essex, SS0 9AR Tel: (01702) 214100 Fax: (01702) 390488 E-mail: jane_trent@prospectscollege.co.uk
▶ Trans Plant Mastertrain, Schovella, Cliff Road, Gorran Haven, St. Austell, Cornwall, PL26 6JN Tel: (01392) 426242 Fax: (01392) 205006 E-mail: geoff_fox@hotmail.com
Walker Training, Park Farm Road, Park Farm Industrial Estate, Folkestone, Kent, CT19 5DY Tel: (01303) 850186 Fax: (01303) 850908 E-mail: walkertraining@hotmail.com

ABRASIVE WHEELS

▶ Abacus Safety Training, 7 Pennywort Grove, Harrogate, North Yorkshire, HG3 2XJ Tel: (01423) 550413 Fax: (01423) 552355 E-mail: info@abacussafetytraining.com
Abrasive Blades Ltd, 4 Greenhill Crescent, Watford Business Park, Watford, WD18 8RE Tel: (01923) 223248 Fax: (01923) 210234
Consort Abrasives Products Ltd, Swallowfields, Welwyn Garden City, Hertfordshire, AL7 1JD Tel: (01707) 330319 Fax: (01707) 376697 E-mail: consortabrasives@btconnect.com
Crystal Abrasive Products & Co. Ltd, Clamark House, 63 Stalker Lees Road, Sheffield, S11 8NP Tel: 0114-266 6281 Fax: 0114-268 5336 E-mail: info@crystal-abrasives.com
D G S Grinding Wheels & Machines Ltd, 90-92 Dovedale Road, Wolverhampton, WV4 6RA Tel: (01902) 661111 Fax: (01902) 880311 E-mail: sales@dgsabrasives.co.uk
Disco Hi-Tec, Second Floor, 151 London Road, East Grinstead, West Sussex, RH19 1ET Tel: (01342) 313165 Fax: (01342) 313177 E-mail: sales.uk@discoeurope.com
Garryson Ltd, Spring Road, Ibstock, Leicestershire, LE67 6LR Tel: (01530) 261145 Fax: (01530) 262801 E-mail: sales@garryson.co.uk
Jewel Abrasives, Stanley Street, Worksop, Nottinghamshire, S81 7HX Tel: (01909) 472650 Fax: (01909) 532186
Kayson Green Ltd, 9 Commerce Park, Commerce Way, Colchester, CO2 8HX Tel: (01206) 751500 Fax: (01206) 791916 E-mail: abrasives@kaysongreen.co.uk
Klingspor Abrasives Ltd, Dukeries Close, Worksop, Nottinghamshire, S81 7DN Tel: (01909) 504400 Fax: (01909) 504405 E-mail: sales@klingspor.co.uk
P B R (Abrasives) Ltd, The Quadrant, 99 Parkway Avenue, Sheffield, S9 4WG Tel: 0114-243 3700 Fax: 0114-243 3527 E-mail: sales@pbrabrasives.com
Swift Abrasive Wheels, Toll End Road, Tipton, West Midlands, DY4 0HF Tel: 0121-557 8337 Fax: 0121-520 4770 E-mail: swiftandwhitmore@virgin.net

ABS ELECTRICALLY ACTUATED BUTTERFLY VALVES

Frenstar, Unit 240 Ordinance Business Park, Aerodrome Road, Gosport, Hampshire, PO13 0FG Tel: (01329) 233445 Fax: (01329) 233450 E-mail: info@frenstar.co.uk

ABS ENCLOSURES

Mainframe Communications Ltd, Network House, Journeymans Way, Temple Farm Industrial Estate, Southend-On-Sea, SS2 5TF Tel: (01702) 443800 Fax: (01702) 443801 E-mail: sales@mainframecomms.co.uk

ABS MOULDING/EXTRUSION COMPOUNDS

▶ National Centre For Product Design & Development Research, Llandaff Campus, 200 Western Avenue, Cardiff, CF5 2YB Tel: (029) 2041 6725 Fax: (029) 2041 6973 E-mail: info-pdr@uwic.ac.uk

ABS PLASTIC MATERIALS

Betterware UK Ltd, Stanley House, Park Lane, Castle Vale, Birmingham, B35 6LJ Tel: (0845) 1294500 Fax: (0845) 1294654 E-mail: info@betterware.co.uk
C & H Plastics Ltd, Burrel Road, St. Ives, Cambridgeshire, PE27 3LE Tel: (01480) 496959 Fax: (01480) 492105 E-mail: sales@chplastics.co.uk
Chesterfield Plastics, 61 Foljambe Avenue, Chesterfield, Derbyshire, S40 3EY Tel: (01246) 540670 Fax: (01246) 540106 E-mail: clive.cooper1@virgin.net
Country Plastics Injection Moulding Services, 2 Weensland Mill, Weensland Road, Hawick, Roxburghshire, TD9 9PS Tel: (01450) 377583 Fax: (01450) 376065
Linpac Plastics Ltd, Pegrams Road, Harlow, Essex, CM18 7QU Tel: (01279) 451148 Fax: (01279) 451187
Plastic Parts Centre, Unit 2 St. Lukes Business Estate, St. Luke'S Place, Glasgow, G5 0TS Tel: 0141-420 3806 Fax: 0141-420 3806 E-mail: scotlandsales@plastic-parts.co.uk
Sabic Plastics, Bo'Ness Road, Grangemouth, Stirlingshire, FK3 9XF Tel: (01324) 483490 Fax: (01324) 667265
Stepart Plastics, Riverside House, Wye Business Park, Churchfield Way, Wye, Ashford, Kent, TN25 5BX Tel: (01233) 813353 E-mail: stepart@tiscali.co.uk
Stirling Moulded Composites Ltd, Unit 10 Alliance Business Park, Corporation Street, Accrington, Lancashire, BB5 0RR Tel: (01254) 395550 Fax: (01254) 398584 E-mail: daryl@stirlingmoulded.com
WHS Halo, Water Orton Lane, Minworth, Sutton Coldfield, West Midlands, B76 9BW Tel: 0121-749 3000 Fax: 0121-749 2511 E-mail: info@whs-halo.co.uk

ABS PLASTIC SHEETS

▶ Amari Plastics PLC, Holmes House, 24-30 Baker Street, Weybridge, Surrey, KT13 8AU Tel: 01932 835000 Fax: 01932 835002 E-mail: ho@amariplastics.com
S & D Solutions (UK) Ltd, Unit 3, New Line Road, Kirkby-In-Ashfield, NG17 8JQ Tel: (01623) 752837 Fax: (01623) 757584 E-mail: sale@sndsolutions.co.uk
▶ V S P Ltd, 4 Malling Walk, Bottesford, Scunthorpe, North Lincolnshire, DN16 3SS Tel: (01724) 335005 Fax: (01724) 338981 E-mail: enquiries@vspuk.com

ABSEILING DIFFICULT ACCESS CONSULTANCY

Access Training Services Ltd, Unit 4, 45 Mowbray Street, Sheffield, S3 8EN Tel: 0114-273 1333 Fax: 0114-280 2010 E-mail: info@the-access-group.com
Geotex Ground Services Ltd, PO Box 5071, Market Harborough, Leicestershire, LE16 7WJ Tel: (01858) 545111 Fax: (01858) 545914 E-mail: sales@geotex.co.uk
Oceaneering International Services Ltd, Pitmedden Road, Dyce, Aberdeen, AB21 0DP Tel: (01224) 770444 Fax: (01224) 771583
Reflex Print & Design Ltd, Unit 4 Kiln Hill Industrial Estate, Slaithwaite, Huddersfield, HD7 5JS Tel: (01484) 846950 Fax: (01484) 847644
Rope Access Specialists Ltd, Newtate, Florence Court Demesne, Enniskillen, County Fermanagh, BT92 1DB Tel: (028) 6634 8443 Fax: (028) 6634 8081
Total Access UK Ltd, Units 5b/C, Raleigh Hall Indust Estate, Eccleshall, Stafford, ST21 6JL Tel: (01785) 850333 Fax: (01785) 850339 E-mail: sales@totalaccess.co.uk
▶ Richard Turner Ltd, 101 Coupe Lane, Old Tupton, Chesterfield, Derbyshire, S42 6HA Tel: (01246) 861738 Fax: (01246) 863587 E-mail: info@ropeaccessuk.com
Vertical Access Ltd, Tame Bank,, Unit E211 Warmco Industry Park, East Gate,, Manchester Road,, Mossley, Ashton-under-Lyne, Lancashire, OL5 9AY Tel: (01457) 838722 Fax: (01457) 833881 E-mail: info@verticalaccess.co.uk
Vertical Technology Ind Rope Access Specialists, Unit 15 Wren Centre, Westbourne Road, Emsworth, Hampshire, PO10 7SU Tel: (01243) 377599 Fax: (01243) 377227 E-mail: admin@vertical-technology.com

ABSOLUTE ENCODERS

British Encoder Products Co., Unit 33, Whitegate Industrial Estate, Wrexham, Clwyd, LL13 8UG Tel: (01978) 262100 Fax: (01978) 262101 E-mail: sales@brit-encoder.com
Computer Optical Products, 45 Leaver Road, Henley-On-Thames, Oxfordshire, RG9 1UW Tel: (01491) 412055 Fax: (01491) 413006 E-mail: sales@sensortronic.co.uk
Hohner Automation Ltd, Unit 15 Whitegate Industrial Estate, Whitegate Road, Wrexham, Clwyd, LL13 8UG Tel: (01978) 363888 Fax: (01978) 364586 E-mail: uksales@hohner.com
Siko Ltd, Unit 6, Cod Beck Estate, Dalton, Thirsk, North Yorkshire, YO7 3HR Tel: (01845) 578845 Fax: (01845) 577781 E-mail: sales@siko-uk.com
T R Controls Ltd, 12a Oak Industrial Park, Chelmsford Road, Dunmow, Essex, CM6 1XN Tel: (01371) 876187 Fax: (01371) 876287 E-mail: alan@trcontrols.co.uk

ABSORBENTS, *See also particular types, such as Oil; Chemical etc*

C.P. Burns & Associates Ltd, Peter's Farm, Helmdon, Brackley, Northants, NN13 5QH Tel: (01295) 768271 Fax: (01295) 768298 E-mail: enquiries@burnsassociates.demon.co.uk
Elcef Fibre, 9 Oundle Road, Chesterton, Peterborough, PE7 3UA Tel: (01733) 233293 Fax: (01733) 235351 E-mail: info@spillshop.co.uk
Fosse, 12 Enderby Road Industrial Estate, Whetstone, Leicester, LE8 6HZ Tel: 0116-286 7844 Fax: (0870) 2247842 E-mail: sales@fosse.co.uk
New Pig Ltd, Hogs Hill, Watt Place, Hamilton International Technology Park, Blantyre, Glasgow, G72 0AH Tel: (0800) 919900 Fax: (0800) 7315071 E-mail: pigpen@newpig.com
▶ SES Consultants, PO Box 5513, Ilkeston, Derbyshire, DE7 9ZT Tel: 0115-875 0848 Fax: 0115-875 0849
Steetley Bentonite & Absorbents Ltd, Woburn Road, Woburn Sands, Milton Keynes, MK17 8TU Tel: (01908) 583939 Fax: (01908) 585231

ACCELERATION TRANSDUCERS

Bruel & Kjaer Ltd, Bedford House, Rutherford Close, Stevenage, Hertfordshire, SG1 2ND Tel: (01438) 739000 Fax: (01438) 739099 E-mail: ukinfo@bksv.com
Monitran Ltd, 33 Hazlemere Road, Penn, High Wycombe, Buckinghamshire, HP10 8AD Tel: (01494) 816569 Fax: (01494) 812256 E-mail: sales@monitran.co.uk
Tilt Measurement Ltd, Horizon House Baldock Industrial Estate, London Road, Baldock, Hertfordshire, SG7 6NG Tel: (01462) 894566 Fax: (01462) 895990 E-mail: sales@tilt-measurement.com

ACCELEROMETERS, *See also headings for particular types*

Analog Devices Ltd, Rothwell House, Pembroke Road, Newbury, Berkshire, RG14 1BX Tel: (01635) 555400 Fax: (01635) 555401 E-mail: hilary.abbott@analog.com
Atex Ltd, 4 Thames Park, Lester Way, Wallingford, Oxfordshire, OX10 9TA Tel: (01491) 839999 Fax: (01491) 839466 E-mail: contactuk@atex-f1.com
Bruel & Kjaer Ltd, Bedford House, Rutherford Close, Stevenage, Hertfordshire, SG1 2ND Tel: (01438) 739000 Fax: (01438) 739099 E-mail: ukinfo@bksv.com
▶ Celsum Technologies Ltd, Willow House, 17 Braemar Close, Mountsorrel, Loughborough, Leicestershire, LE12 7ES Tel: 0116-210 6319 Fax: (0870) 1206319 E-mail: sales@celsum.com
Ferranti Technologies Group Ltd, Cairo Mill, Greenacres Road, Oldham, OL4 3JA Tel: 0161-624 0281 Fax: 0161-624 5244 E-mail: sales@ferranti-technologies.co.uk
J A E Europe Ltd, Coliseum Business Centre, Riverside Way, Camberley, Surrey, GU15 3YL Tel: (01276) 404000 Fax: (01276) 404010 E-mail: sales@jae.co.uk
Livingston Services plc, Livingston House, 2-6 Queens Road, Teddington, Middlesex, TW11 0LR Tel: (020) 8943 1142 Fax: (020) 8977 6431 E-mail: info@livingston.co.uk
Monitran Ltd, 33 Hazlemere Road, Penn, High Wycombe, Buckinghamshire, HP10 8AD Tel: (01494) 816569 Fax: (01494) 812256 E-mail: sales@monitran.co.uk
Sensonics Ltd, North Bridge Road, Berkhamsted, Hertfordshire, HP4 1EF Tel: (01442) 876833 Fax: (01442) 876477 E-mail: sales@sensonics.co.uk
Sensors UK Ltd, 135-137 Hatfield Road, St. Albans, Hertfordshire, AL4 0DH Tel: (01727) 861110 Fax: (01727) 844272 E-mail: admin@sensorsuk.com

ACCESS CONTROL CARDS

▶ 020 Locksmiths Ltd, 19 Third Avenue, London, E17 9QJ Tel: (020) 8223 0396 Fax: (020) 8521 5470 E-mail: info@020locksmiths.com
Automate UK, 9 Hill La Industrial Estate, Markfield, Leicestershire, LE67 9PN Tel: (01530) 249444 Fax: (01530) 249444 E-mail: sales@automateuk.co.uk
Bewator Ltd, Albany Street, Newport, Gwent, NP20 5XW Tel: (08713) 860800 Fax: (01633) 850893 E-mail: sales@bewator.co.uk
British Security Technologies, 19 Hackford Walk, 119-123 Hackford Road, London, SW9 0QT Tel: (01424) 883275 E-mail: britsectec@aol.com
Carter Voce Access Control Ltd, 111 Chiltern Drive, Surbiton, Surrey, KT5 8LS Tel: (020) 8339 9111 Fax: (020) 8390 1727
Future Access Technologies, 18 Cherry Lane, Pond Park, Lisburn, County Antrim, BT28 3JT Tel: (028) 9262 9689 Fax: (028) 9267 6573 E-mail: info@futureaccess.co.uk
G E Security Ltd, Unit 5, Ashton Gate, Ashton Road, Harold Hill, Romford, RM3 8UF Tel: (01708) 381496 Fax: (0870) 7773049
GARDSEC, Unit 82, 571 Finchley Road, Hampsted, London, NW3 7BN Tel: (020) 7183 3999 Fax: (0871) 4334090 E-mail: gardsec@gmail.com
Group 4 Security Systems Ltd, Challenge House, Northway LaneInternational Drive, Tewkesbury, Gloucestershire, GL20 8UQ Tel: (01684) 274874 Fax: (01684) 294845
Group 4 Technology Ltd, Challenge House, International Drive, Tewkesbury, Gloucestershire, GL20 8UQ Tel: (01684) 277175 Fax: (01684) 294845 E-mail: sales@group4technology.com

ACCESS CONTROL CARDS – *continued*

▶ Intelligent Access Systems Ltd, 16 Gladstone Terrace, Boldon Colliery, Tyne & Wear, NE35 9HL Tel: 0191-536 9255 Fax: 0191-536 9255E-mail: laurance.laidlaw@homecall.co.uk

▶ J M H Technology LLP, Unit 3, Highlands Farm, Berden, Bishop's Stortford, Hertfordshire, CM23 1AB Tel: (0845) 0537457 Fax: (07092) 002578 E-mail: sales@jmhtechnology.co.uk

Kalamazoo Secure Solutions Ltd, Northfield, Birmingham, B31 2NY Tel: 0121-256 2222 Fax: 0121-256 2249 E-mail: kalamazoo@ksp.co.uk

▶ Multilink Access Control Systems Ltd, 71 Hampermill Lane, Watford, WD19 4NT Tel: (01923) 224900 Fax: (01923) 224970 E-mail: info@multilinksecurity.co.uk

New Parking Solutions, Unit 81, Pembroke Centre, Cheney Manor Industrial Estate, Swindon, SN2 2PQ Tel: (01793) 700608 Fax: (01793) 700608 E-mail: sales@newparkingsolutions.co.uk

N-Force Security Solutions, 95 Lambert Road, Grimsby, North East Lincolnshire, DN32 0NR Tel: (01472) 604609 E-mail: sales@n-force.co.uk

P A C International Ltd, 1 Park Gate Close, Bredbury Park Way, Bredbury, Stockport, Cheshire, SK6 2SZ Tel: 0161-494 1331 Fax: 0161-430 8658 E-mail: info@pac.co.uk

▶ Total Security Northern, 3 Conyers Avenue, Chester le Street, County Durham, DH2 2HQ Tel: 0191-387 3117 Fax: 0191-387 3117 E-mail: totalnorthern@hotmail.com

John Wainwright Systems Ltd, Third Avenue, Midsomer Norton, Radstock, BA3 4XD Tel: (01761) 414700 Fax: (01761) 414722 E-mail: post@jwsltd.co.uk

ACCESS CONTROL EQUIPMENT

▶ Ace Security Systems Ltd, 12 Triumph Way, Kempston, Bedford, MK42 7QB Tel: (01234) 854455 Fax: (01234) 855345 E-mail: sales@acesecurity.co.uk

ACCESS CONTROL GATES

▶ The Garage Door & Gate Automation Co., Unit 7 Block D, Isle of Man Business Park, Isle of Man, IM2 2QY Tel: (01624) 624122 Fax: (01624) 623877 E-mail: info@manxgaragedoors.com

ACCESS CONTROL SYSTEMS

▶ A P T Ski Data Ltd, The Power House, Chantry Place, Harrow, Middlesex, HA3 6NY Tel: (020) 8421 2211 Fax: (020) 8428 6622 E-mail: info@skidata.com

Assaabloy Hospitality Ltd, Unit 21 Stadium Way, Tilehurst, Reading, RG30 6BX Tel: 0118-945 2200 Fax: 0118-945 1375 E-mail: uk@vcegroup.com

▶ Ace Security Systems Ltd, 12 Triumph Way, Kempston, Bedford, MK42 7QB Tel: (01234) 854455 Fax: (01234) 855345 E-mail: sales@acesecurity.co.uk

▶ Combined Security, 79 Pickford Lane, Bexleyheath, Kent, DA7 4RW Tel: (020) 8304 6111 Fax: (020) 8304 6555 E-mail: info@combinedsecurity.co.uk

Controlled Access Storage Cabinets Ltd, Ford House, Dewing Road, Rackheath Industrial Estate, Rackheath, Norwich, NR13 6PS Tel: (01603) 722770 Fax: (01603) 722771 E-mail: sales@casc-ltd.com

▶ E D S Systems North Wales Ltd, Heathfield, Padeswood Road, Buckley, Clwyd, CH7 2JL Tel: (01244) 541056 Fax: (0870) 7052350 E-mail: admin@edssystems.com

Hansett Electronics, 38 Kimpton Road, Sutton, Surrey, SM3 9QP Tel: (020) 8644 1777 E-mail: hansett@aol.com

Iti Security, Aylesford Business Centre, High Street, Aylesford, Kent, ME20 7AX Tel: (01732) 522090 E-mail: sales@itisecurity.co.uk

▶ Raytel Security Systems Ltd, 3 Block 5 Oakbank Industrial Estate, Garscube Road, Glasgow, G20 7LU Tel: 0141-332 4232 Fax: 0141-332 6952 E-mail: sales@raytelsecurity.co.uk

▶ Smartlock Access Control Ltd, 3A Thame Road, Long Crendon, Aylesbury, Buckinghamshire, HP18 9AS Tel: (01844) 201145 Fax: (01844) 201155 E-mail: sales@smart-lock.co.uk

Specialized Security Products Ltd, Unit 18, Park Farm Industrial Estate, Ermine Street, Buntingford, Hertfordshire, SG9 9AZ Tel: (01763) 274223 Fax: (01763) 273515 E-mail: sales@specialized-security.co.uk

▶ Telecor UK, 21 Coopers Court, Newport Pagnell, Buckinghamshire, MK16 8JS Tel: (01908) 211782 Fax: (01908) 216946 E-mail: chris.jones@telecor.co.uk

▶ Trinity Protection Systems Ltd, Old Mill House, Oil Mill Lane, Clyst St. Mary, Exeter, EX5 1AG Tel: (01392) 874455 Fax: (01392) 875546 E-mail: info@trinityprotection.co.uk

ACCESS EQUIPMENT

A1 Top Spares, 15 Walton Way, Brandon, Suffolk, IP27 0HP Tel: (01842) 814524 Fax: (01842) 811666

▶ Access Sales International, 9 Kings Lodge Drive, Mansfield, Nottinghamshire, NG18 5GZ Tel: (01623) 624411 Fax: (01623) 624415 E-mail: sales@asionline.co.uk

Access Training Services Ltd, Unit 4, 45 Mowbray Street, Sheffield, S3 8EN Tel: 0114-273 1333 Fax: 0114-280 2010 E-mail: info@the-access-group.com

▶ Alba Hire & Sales, 5 Broughton Industrial Estate, Broughton Mills Road, Bretton, Chester, CH4 0BY Tel: (01244) 661820 Fax: (01244) 661763

A-Plant Powered Access, Trent Lane, Nottingham, NG2 4DS Tel: 0115-948 3348 Fax: 0115-950 8275

C & G Platforms Ltd, PO Box 14, Mirfield, West Yorkshire, WF14 8XH Tel: (01924) 498660 Fax: (01924) 491778 E-mail: sales@candgplatforms.co.uk

▶ Caladonian Plant, Unit 9 Harlaw Way, Harlaw Road Industrial Estate, Inverurie, Aberdeenshire, AB51 4SG Tel: (01467) 623616 Fax: (01467) 624411

▶ Can London Ltd, Unit A Springhead Enterprise Park, Springhead Road, Northfleet, Gravesend, Kent, DA11 8HB Tel: (01474) 538100 Fax: (01474) 538101 E-mail: info@canlondon.co.uk

Cape Hire Ltd, Unit 4 Eastmoors, Cardiff, CF24 2EE Tel: (029) 2049 3184 Fax: (029) 2049 3186

Carlisle Engineering Ltd, Edgeworth House, 20 High Street, Northchurch, Berkhamsted, Hertfordshire, HP4 3LS Tel: (01442) 874534 Fax: (01442) 878525 E-mail: info@accessequipment.net

Chislett Hire, Enterprise Way, Pinchbeck, Spalding, Lincolnshire, PE11 3YR Tel: (01775) 725778 Fax: (01775) 767523 E-mail: sales@chislett.co.uk

Clow Group Ltd, Garratts Lane, Cradley Heath, West Midlands, B64 5AW Tel: 0121-559 5222 Fax: 0121-559 0330 E-mail: clowgroup@btconnect.com

Colmil Plant & Equipment Co. Ltd, Abbotsford Road, Gateshead, Tyne & Wear, NE10 0LF Tel: 0191-469 4926 Fax: 0191-469 6084 E-mail: sales@colmil.fsnet.co.uk

E T C, 250 Queensferry Road, Edinburgh, EH4 2BR Tel: 0131-332 1616 Fax: 0131-343 6161 E-mail: etclocks@aol.com

Elap Engineering Ltd, Fort Street, Accrington, Lancashire, BB5 1QG Tel: (01254) 871599 Fax: (01254) 389992 E-mail: mail@elap.co.uk

▶ Electrogate Ltd, Unit 4, Ahed Trading Estate, Dewsbury Road, Ossett, West Yorkshire, WF5 9ND Tel: (01924) 283322 Fax: (01924) 283344 E-mail: info@electrogate.co.uk

▶ Euracess Ltd, Unit 6, Trubodys Yard, 121 London Road, Warmley, Bristol, BS30 5NA Tel: 0117-960 9497 Fax: 0117-960 9497

Eye Bolt Testing Services, 41 West Hill Drive, Dartford, DA1 3DU Tel: (01322) 402200 Fax: (01322) 402201

Hewden Instant Access Ltd, Staceys Yard, Station Road, Langley, Slough, SL3 6DB Tel: (01753) 548849 Fax: (01753) 540655

Hi-Reach Wales, Moy Road Industrial Estate, Taffs Well, Cardiff, CF15 7QR Tel: (029) 2081 3413 Fax: (029) 2081 3848

Roy Hopwood Ltd, Hibbert Street, Whitehill Industrial Estate, Stockport, Cheshire, SK4 1NS Tel: 0161-429 6066 Fax: 0161-429 6166 E-mail: info@rhf.co.uk

HSS Lift & Shift, 772 London Road, Alvaston, Derby, DE24 8UT Tel: (01332) 755699 Fax: (01332) 756715

Hyprosteps Ltd, Unit 6-7 Brandon Business Centre, Putney Close, Brandon, Suffolk, IP27 0PA Tel: (01842) 815972 Fax: (01842) 815347 E-mail: hyprosteps@aol.com

▶ Independent Access Supplies Ltd, 115B, Burcott Road, Bristol, BS11 8AD Tel: 0117-982 6800 Fax: 0117-982 1555

Introland Ltd, Access House, 2 Bilton Road, Erith, Kent, DA8 2AN Tel: (01322) 339595 Fax: (01322) 339994 E-mail: enquiries@introland-testing.com

Keysecure UK Ltd, 39-40 Seymour Road, Nuneaton, Warwickshire, CV11 4JD Tel: (024) 7637 4888 Fax: (024) 7637 4666 E-mail: info@keysecure-uk..com

Linkcare Ltd, Unit 15 Chiltern Business Village, Arundel Road, Uxbridge, Middlesex, UB8 2SN Tel: (01895) 232626 Fax: (01895) 251001 E-mail: linkcare@hotmail.com

Loxam Access Ltd, Unit 12a, Glaisdale Point, Glaisdale Parkway, Nottingham, NG8 4GP Tel: 0115-900 8855 Fax: 0115-900 8880 E-mail: abishop@loxam-access.co.uk

Mr Plant Hire plc, 120 Hertford Road, Enfield, Middlesex, EN3 5AX Tel: (020) 8351 3434 Fax: (020) 8351 3636 E-mail: info@mrplanthire.co.uk

▶ Planet Platform Western Ltd, Peel House, Peel Road, Skelmersdale, Lancashire, WN8 9PT Tel: (01695) 559980 Fax: (01695) 559960

Planet Platforms Ltd, 146 Wakefield Road, Ossett, West Yorkshire, WF5 9AR Tel: (01924) 263377 Fax: (01924) 267090 E-mail: enquiries@planetplatforms.co.uk

Potteries Towers, Unit 10 Norton Industrial Estate, Bellerton Lane, Stoke-on-Trent, ST6 8ED Tel: (01782) 537263 Fax: (01782) 537213

Powerclimber UK Ltd, Unit 27 Cromer Industrial Estate, Middleton, Manchester, M24 2LT Tel: 0161-654 0999 Fax: 0161-653 0555

▶ Powered Access Ltd, Block 3, Unit 3B Central Avenue, Blantyre Industrial Estate, Blantyre, Glasgow, G72 0UZ Tel: (01698) 820300 Fax: (01698) 829988 E-mail: info@poweredaccessuk.com

▶ Pure Hire & Sales, 167 Hampton Road, London, E4 8NS Tel: (020) 8524 5115 Fax: (020) 8523 8751 E-mail: sales@purehire.co.uk

▶ Real Access Platforms, Acorn Centre, 51 High Street, Grimethorpe, Barnsley, South Yorkshire, S72 7LR Tel: (01226) 781666 Fax: (01226) 781333

▶ S C A Marine Ltd, 5 Millstream Trading Estate, Christchurch Road, Ringwood, Hampshire, BH24 3SB Tel: (0870) 6077772 Fax: (08702) 417124

Securi Plex Ltd, Swordfish Way, Sherburn in Elmet, Leeds, LS25 6NG Tel: (01977) 680700 Fax: (01977) 680701 E-mail: business@securi-plex.co.uk

▶ SGB, Alfreton Road, Derby, DE21 4AP Tel: (01332) 831661 Fax: (01332) 835810

▶ Skyform, Unit 7C, Beechcroft Farm Industrial Estate, Chapel Wood Road, Ash, Sevenoaks, Kent, TN15 7HX Tel: (01474) 879990

▶ Standfast Access Equipement, Brendon Road, Bristol, BS3 4PX Tel: 0117-953 9533

Top Man Access & Handling, 22 Lenside Drive, Bearsted, Maidstone, Kent, ME15 8UE Tel: (01622) 730540 Fax: (01622) 730540 E-mail: sales@topmanaccess.co.uk

Total Access UK Ltd, Units 5b/C, Raleigh Hall Indust Estate, Eccleshall, Stafford, ST21 6JL Tel: (01785) 850333 Fax: (01785) 850339 E-mail: sales@totalaccess.co.uk

▶ Woodgates Chartered Certified Accountants, 100, London Road, Leicester, LE2 0QS Tel: 0116-254 3718 Fax: 0116-275 6575

ACCESS EQUIPMENT HIRE

D W Hire, 41 Home Rule Road, Locks Heath, Southampton, SO31 6LH Tel: (01489) 581269 Fax: (01489) 559321 E-mail: dwhireaccess@aol.com

▶ M & S Hire Ltd, Unit 11c Dolphin Park, Cremers Road, Sittingbourne, Kent, ME10 3HB Tel: (01795) 429731 Fax: (01795) 427790

ACCESS GATES

▶ Cotswold Forge, 2 Exmouth Street, Cheltenham, Gloucestershire, GL53 7NS Tel: (01242) 242754 Fax: (01242) 242754 E-mail: sales@cotswoldforge.com

ACCESS HARDWARE

Extra Trade UK Ltd, 22 Sherwell Rise, Allerton, Bradford, West Yorkshire, BD15 7AP Tel: 01274 481994 Fax: 01274 547989 E-mail: extratradeuk@btinternet.com

ACCESS PANELS, FLOOR

▶ Syd Pollard Commercial Interiors, 98 Marlowe Road, Worthing, West Sussex, BN14 8EZ Tel: (01903) 533483 Fax: (01903) 533483 E-mail: info@partitions.org.uk

ACCESS PLATFORM HIRE

2 Cousins Access Ltd, Shell House, Watlington Road, Cowley, Oxford, OX4 6NF Tel: (01865) 779778 Fax: (01865) 401041 E-mail: keith@2cousins.co.uk

▶ Ainscough Crane Hire Ltd, Rugby Road, Princethorpe, Rugby, Warwickshire, CV23 9PN Tel: (01926) 634786 Fax: (01926) 634763 E-mail: coventry@ainscough.co.uk

▶ Already Hire Ltd, 469 Malton Avenue, Slough, SL1 4QU Tel: (01753) 512333 Fax: (01753) 533303

Altitude Access, Burma Road, Blidworth, Mansfield, Nottinghamshire, NG21 0RT Tel: (01623) 796969 Fax: (01623) 793008 E-mail: info@altitudeaccess.co.uk

A-Plant Powered Access, Trent Lane, Nottingham, NG2 4DS Tel: 0115-948 3348 Fax: 0115-950 8275

▶ Beechwood Hire & Sales Ltd, 264-272 Corporation Rd, Newport, Gwent, NP19 0DZ Tel: (01633) 244444 Fax: (01633) 251111 E-mail: sales@beechwoodhire.co.uk

Central Access Ltd, Unit 21, Hazelford Way, Newstead, Nottingham, NG15 0DQ Tel: (01623) 750500 Fax: (01623) 750400 E-mail: info@central-access.co.uk

D W Hire, 41 Home Rule Road, Locks Heath, Southampton, SO31 6LH Tel: (01489) 581269 Fax: (01489) 559321 E-mail: dwhireaccess@aol.com

Alan Drew Ltd, 8 Caxton Way, The Watford Bussiness Park, Watford, WD18 8JX Tel: (01923) 817933 Fax: (01923) 237824 E-mail: alandrew@onet.co.uk

Steven Edwards Engineering Ltd, 3A Linden Road, Dunstable, Bedfordshire, LU5 4NZ Tel: (01582) 609411 Fax: (01582) 609411 E-mail: steven.edwards347@ntlworld.com

Go Hire Access Ltd, 6 Droicon Industrial Estate, Portway Road, Rowley Regis, West Midlands, B65 9BY Tel: 0121-559 0660 Fax: 0121-559 0770 E-mail: dudley@gohireaccess.co.uk

▶ H & P Hire, 5 Black Stick Road, Killyhevlin Industrial Estate, Enniskillen, County Fermanagh, BT74 4EB Tel: (028) 6632 2250 Fax: (028) 6632 3326 E-mail: ronnie@handphire.co.uk

Hewden Crane Hire Ltd, Willowbridge Lane, Castleford, West Yorkshire, WF10 5NJ Tel: (01977) 664300 Fax: (01977) 664306

Hewden Hire Centres Ltd, 39-40 New Summer Street, Birmingham, B19 3QN Tel: 0121-359 4282 Fax: 0121-333 6866

Hewden Plant Hire Ltd, 21-23 Willis Way, Poole, Dorset, BH15 3SR Tel: (01202) 674371 Fax: (01202) 665560

Higher Platforms South Ltd, Archers Fields, Burnt Mills Industrial Estate, Basildon, Essex, SS13 1DH Tel: (01268) 525566 Fax: (01268) 525544

Newlins Access Ltd, Long Close Farm, Wimborne Road, Walford, Wimborne, Dorset, BH21 1NR Tel: (01202) 885300 Fax: (01202) 885400 E-mail: office@newlinaccess.co.uk

Northern Access Ltd, Unit D Avondale Way, Wakefield, West Yorkshire, WF2 7QU Tel: (01924) 385869 Fax: (01924) 385868 E-mail: sales@northernaccess.co.uk

Northern Platforms Ltd, 8 Hind Heath Road, Wheelock, Sandbach, Cheshire, CW11 3LG Tel: (01270) 761954 Fax: (01270) 761954 E-mail: jc.wood@npl.com

▶ R Bell, 14 Birch Close, North Walsham, Norfolk, NR28 0UD Tel: (01692) 409080 Fax: (0800) 7832212 E-mail: contact@rbellplatformhire.co.uk

Safe T Reach Ltd, Crucible Road, Corby, Northamptonshire, NN17 5TS Tel: (01536) 267686 Fax: (01536) 267686

▶ Towable Access, 11a Ramshill Road, Scarborough, North Yorkshire, YO11 2LN Tel: (01723) 370399 Fax: (01723) 370399 E-mail: Rick_Nightingale@hotmail.com

Universal Aerial Platforms, Swinbourne Road, Burnt Mills Industrial Estate, Basildon, Essex, SS13 1GZ Tel: (01268) 722700 Fax: (01268) 722706 E-mail: basildon@universalplatforms.com

ACCESS PLATFORM OPERATOR TRAINING

▶ AES Training Services, 1 Lower Bar, Newport, Shropshire, TF10 7BE Tel: (01952) 812535 Fax: (01952) 272233 E-mail: safety@aes-training.com

Keith Cook Training Services, Madonna Villa, Oaks Road, Coalville, Leicestershire, LE67 5UN Tel: (01509) 506913 Fax: 01509 506913 E-mail: admin@kcts.me.uk

Alan Drew Ltd, 8 Caxton Way, The Watford Bussiness Park, Watford, WD18 8JX Tel: (01923) 817933 Fax: (01923) 237824 E-mail: alandrew@onet.co.uk

▶ JH Training Services Ltd, 7 Baron Court, Peterborough, PE4 7ZE Tel: (07752) 847195

▶ Jupiter Safety Management Ltd, 36 Shelley Road, Reddish, Stockport, Cheshire, Stockport, Cheshire, SK5 6JG Tel: 0161 442 4359 Fax: 0161 442 4359 E-mail: ccork-jupitersafety@fsmail.net

Northern Platforms Ltd, 8 Hind Heath Road, Wheelock, Sandbach, Cheshire, CW11 3LG Tel: (01270) 761954 Fax: (01270) 761954 E-mail: jc.wood@npl.com

▶ UK Operators Ltd, The Pin Mill, New Street, Charfield, Wotton-under-Edge, Gloucestershire, GL12 8ES Tel: (01453) 843121 Fax: (01453) 843079 E-mail: reception@ukoperators.co.uk

Universal Aerial Platforms, Swinbourne Road, Burnt Mills Industrial Estate, Basildon, Essex, SS13 1GZ Tel: (01268) 722700 Fax: (01268) 722706 E-mail: basildon@universalplatforms.com

ACCESS PLATFORMS, *See also headings for particular types*

▶ Access Design & Engineering, Halesfield 18, Telford, Shropshire, TF7 4JS Tel: (01952) 588788 Fax: (01952) 685139 E-mail: sales@access-design.co.uk

▶ Bruno's Access, 20 Regent Street, Treorchy, Mid Glamorgan, CF42 6PP Tel: (01443) 777997 Fax: (01443) 777997 E-mail: brunopink@aol.co.uk

▶ Caladonian Plant, Unit 9 Harlaw Way, Harlaw Road Industrial Estate, Inverurie, Aberdeenshire, AB51 4SG Tel: (01467) 623616 Fax: (01467) 624411

Canal Engineering Ltd, Lenton Lane, Nottingham, NG7 2PQ Tel: 0115-986 6321 Fax: 0115-986 0211 E-mail: enquiries@canalengineering.co.uk

Easi Uplifts (Aerials) Ltd, 16 Johnstone Street, Bellshill, Lanarkshire, ML4 1DE Tel: (01698) 308899 Fax: (01698) 308800 E-mail: ronan.maclennen@heightforhire.ie

Steven Edwards Engineering Ltd, 3A Linden Road, Dunstable, Bedfordshire, LU5 4NZ Tel: (01582) 609411 Fax: (01582) 609411 E-mail: steven.edwards347@ntlworld.com

Ellis Welding & Fabrications, Ollershaw Lane, Marston, Northwich, Cheshire, CW9 6ES Tel: (01606) 45405 Fax: (01606) 40237 E-mail: sales@e-w-l.com

ACCESS PLATFORMS – *continued*

Fibergrate Composite Structures Ltd, Wass Way, Eaglescliffe, Stockton-on-Tees, Cleveland, TS16 0RG Tel: (01642) 784747 Fax: (01642) 784748 E-mail: info@fibergrate.co.uk

▶ Genie UK Ltd, The Maltings, Wharf Road, Grantham, Lincolnshire, NG31 6BH Tel: (01476) 584333 Fax: (01476) 584334 E-mail: infoeurope@genieind.com

▶ Haas Tek, Broomhouse Industrial Park, Kirkburn, Dryfe Road, Lockerbie, Dumfriesshire, DG11 2RF Tel: (01576) 203074 Fax: (01576) 204594 E-mail: info@haas-tek.co.uk

King Highway Products Ltd, Riverside, Market Harborough, Leicestershire, LE16 7PX Tel: (01858) 467361 Fax: (01858) 467161 E-mail: sales@skyking.co.uk

Minianchor, 3 Toledo Works, Neepsend Lane, Sheffield, S3 8UL Tel: 0114-275 6211 Fax: 0114-249 6211 E-mail: info@minianchorltd.co.uk

Oil & Steel UK Ltd, Rotherfield House, 7 Fairmile, Henley-on-Thames, Oxfordshire, RG9 2JR Tel: (01491) 411022 Fax: (01491) 411554 E-mail: info@oilandsteel.co.uk

▶ Smith & Austin Engineering Products Ltd, 11 Church Road, Hayling Island, Hampshire, PO11 0NN Tel: (023) 9246 2451 Fax: (023) 9246 1431

Tadweld Ltd, Station Estate, Station Road, Tadcaster, North Yorkshire, LS24 9SG Tel: (01937) 832865 Fax: (01937) 835823 E-mail: info@tadweld.co.uk

▶ Towable Access, 11a Ramshill Road, Scarborough, North Yorkshire, YO11 2LN Tel: (01723) 370399 Fax: (01723) 370399 E-mail: Rick_Nightingale@hotmail.com

▶ Voyager Site Services, Ashton Clough Road, Liversedge, West Yorkshire, WF15 6JX Tel: (07870) 588297 E-mail: voyagersiteservices@aol.com

ACCESS SCAFFOLDING

Boulton Ltd, Cannon Business Park, Darkhouse Lane, Bilston, West Midlands, WV14 8XQ Tel: (01902) 385300 Fax: (01902) 385330 E-mail: info@boultonlimited.com

▶ Rilmac Scaffolding Ltd, Crofton Drive, Allenby Road Industrial Estate, Lincoln, LN3 4NJ Tel: 01522 531711 Fax: 01522 510291 E-mail: enquiries@rilmac.co.uk

▶ Rilmac Scaffolding Ltd, Brigg Road, Scunthorpe, North Lincolnshire, DN16 1AX Tel: (01724) 845888 Fax: (01724) 876005 E-mail: enquiries@rilmac.co.uk

S G B Ltd, 40 Bayton Road, Exhall, Coventry, CV7 9EJ Tel: (024) 7636 2255 Fax: (024) 7658 8042 E-mail: info@sgb.co.uk

ACCESS SYSTEMS

Mastclimbers (Scotland) Ltd, Denmark Street Industrial Estate, 97a Hawthorn Street, Glasgow, G22 6HY Tel: 0141-336 3344 Fax: 0141-336 3355 E-mail: sales@mastclimbers.co.uk

▶ Safe Access, 136 Derbyshire Lane, Sheffield, S8 8SE Tel: 0114-280 2020 Fax: 0114-280 2010 E-mail: info@the-access-group.com

ACCIDENT INSURANCE

▶ Insurance for Car Hire, Trans-World House, 0 City Road, London, EC1Y 2BP Tel: (020) 7012 6300 Fax: (020) 7012 6315 E-mail: iskra@webfactory.bg

▶ Utopia Mortgage Solutions, The Bearings, Bowbridge Road, Newark, Nottinghamshire, NG24 4BZ Tel: (01636) 593990 Fax: (08700) 501222E-mail: craig@utopia4mortgages.co.uk

ACCIDENT INVESTIGATION

▶ Accidents Revisited, 12 Kariba Close, Chesterfield, Derbyshire, S41 0FP Tel: (01246) 207285 Fax: (0871) 242 9547 E-mail: accidents.revisited@tiscali.co.uk

Luckett Investigation, 14 Barnfield Way, Stafford, ST17 4NB Tel: 01785 602075 Fax: 01785 602075 E-mail: info@luckett-investigation.co.uk

Renaissance, 1 Emperor Way, Exeter Business Park, Exeter Business Park, Exeter, EX1 3QS Tel: (01803) 404047 Fax: 01392 434047 E-mail: enquiries@commercial-investigation.com

ACCOMMODATION MODULE FURNISHING OR FITTING SERVICES

▶ Aston Carpets, 7 Polmorla Walk, Wadebridge, Cornwall, PL27 7NS Tel: (01208) 812184 Fax: (01208) 816137 E-mail: enquiries@astons-online.co.uk

ACCOMMODATION MODULE HIRE

▶ Accommadata Cabins Direct, Unit 1, Crowland Street Industrial Estate, Russell Road, Blowick, Southport, Merseyside, PR9 7AS Tel: (01704) 540956 Fax: (01704) 220247 E-mail: accommadata@churchtown.co.uk

Add Plant Ltd, Grovehill Road, Beverley, East Yorkshire, HU17 0JN Tel: (01482) 867227 Fax: (01482) 872868 E-mail: hire@addplant.karoo.co.uk

Balfour Beatty Power Networks Ltd, PO Box 5064 West Service Road, Derby, DE21 7ZP Tel: (01332) 661494 Fax: (01332) 288312

Cabin Centre Ltd, Sandtoft Industrial Estate, Belton Road Road, Sandtoft, Doncaster, South Yorkshire, DN9 1PN Tel: (01427) 873285 Fax: (01427) 874248 E-mail: sales@cabincentreltd.co.uk

County Hire & Sales, Wymeswold Industrial Park, Wymeswold Road, Burton-on-the-Wolds, Loughborough, Leicestershire, LE12 5TY Tel: (01509) 881152 Fax: (01509) 889413

G E Capital Modular Space Ltd, 2a Pioneer Works, Crabtree Manorway, Belvedere, Kent, DA17 6AH Tel: (020) 8312 4000 Fax: (020) 8311 7643

H B Rentals Ltd, Howe Moss Drive, Kirkhill Industrial Estate, Dyce, Aberdeen, AB21 0GL Tel: (01224) 772304 Fax: (01224) 772641 E-mail: sales@dm-accommodation.com

Marske Site Services Ltd, Suite 311, The Innovation Centre, Vienna Court, Kirkleatham Business Park, Redcar, Cleveland, TS10 5SH Tel: (01642) 777993 Fax: (01642) 777994 E-mail: tim.mccullagh@marske.com

Wide Range Services Ltd, Alexandra Dock, Hull, HU9 1TA Tel: (01482) 898261 Fax: (01482) 587271 E-mail: sales@wrshull.co.uk

Wraith Accommodation P.L.C., Accommodation House, Main Street, Torksey, Lincoln, LN1 2EE Tel: (01427) 718000 Fax: (01427) 718921 E-mail: sales@wraith.co.uk

ACCOMMODATION MODULE PARTITIONING OR PANELLING OR DOORS

▶ DKF Iinteriors, Royce Road, Peterborough, PE1 5YB Tel: (0845) 6443145 Fax: (0845) 6443146 E-mail: info@dkfiinteriors.com

Encon Insulation Ltd, Buchanans Warehouse, Chittening Industrial Estate, Chittening, Bristol, BS11 0YB Tel: 0117-980 2100 Fax: 0117-980 2101

▶ Liverpool Cubicles & Washroom Systems Ltd, Unit 5-7 Luton Street, Liverpool, L5 9XR Tel: 0151-298 1509 Fax: 0151-298 2276 E-mail: liverpoolcubicle@aol.com

Westgate Factory Dividers, PO Box 21, Stafford, ST16 3DD Tel: (01785) 242171

ACCOMMODATION MODULE REFURBISHMENT

H B Rentals Ltd, Howe Moss Drive, Kirkhill Industrial Estate, Dyce, Aberdeen, AB21 0GL Tel: (01224) 772304 Fax: (01224) 772641 E-mail: sales@dm-accommodation.com

North Offshore Ltd, Saltire House, Blackness Avenue, Altens Industrial Estate, Aberdeen, AB12 3PG Tel: (01224) 871906 Fax: (01224) 878828 E-mail: northoffshore@northgroup.co.uk

▶ Rouge Interiors Ltd, 19 Hoblands, Haywards Heath, West Sussex, RH16 3SB Tel: (01444) 415695 Fax: (01444) 416823 E-mail: info@rougeinteriors.co.uk

ACCOMMODATION MODULES

Accommodations, Lion House, 6 Hawthorn Road, Newcastle upon Tyne, NE3 4DE Tel: 0191-213 2131 Fax: 0191-213 2211 E-mail: sales@accomodationsuk.co.uk

Addacabin Ltd, Southend, Thornton, Kirkcaldy, Fife, KY1 4ED Tel: (01592) 774387 Fax: (01592) 779474 E-mail: info@addacabin.co.uk

Burntisland Fabrications, Seaforth Place, West Shore, Burntisland, Fife, KY3 9AU Tel: (01592) 222000 Fax: (01592) 874688 E-mail: enquiries@bifab.co.uk

▶ Elliott Group Ltd, Oliver Road, Grays, Essex, RM20 3ED Tel: (01708) 681500 Fax: (01708) 681519 E-mail: info@elliotthire.co.uk

▶ Elliott Group Ltd, Oliver Road, Grays, Essex, RM20 3ED Tel: (01708) 681500 Fax: (01708) 681519 E-mail: info@elliotthire.co.uk

Elliott Group Ltd, Chaddock Lane, Worsley, Manchester, M28 1DP Tel: 0161-790 3721 Fax: 0161-703 8294 E-mail: info@elliotthire.co.uk

▶ Elliott Group Ltd, King Charles Business Park Old Newton Road, Heathfield Industrial Estate, Heathfield, Newton Abbot, Devon, TQ12 6UT Tel: (01626) 834377 Fax: 0117-982 2832 E-mail: info@elliotthire.co.uk

▶ Elliott Group Ltd, Normandy Way, Marchwood, Southampton, SO40 4PB Tel: (023) 8087 3819 Fax: (023) 8087 3820 E-mail: info@elliotthire.co.uk

▶ Elliott Hire, Victoria Road, Avonmouth, Bristol, BS11 9DB Tel: 0117-916 3400 Fax: 0117-982 2832 E-mail: info@elliotthire.co.uk

Elliott Hire, Victoria Road, Avonmouth, Bristol, BS11 9DB Tel: 0117-916 3400 Fax: 0117-982 2832 E-mail: info@elliotthire.co.uk

▶ Elliott Hire, Yard 1, 2, 3, 4, Camp Industrial Estate, East Calder, Livingston, West Lothian, EH53 0EP Tel: (01698) 801580 Fax: (01698) 811708 E-mail: info@elliotthire.co.uk

Elliott Hire, Manor Drive, Peterborough, PE4 7AP Tel: (01733) 298600 Fax: (01733) 573543 E-mail: info@elliotthire.co.uk

Elliotthire, Chittening Industrial Estate, Avonmouth, Bristol, BS11 0YB Tel: 0117 916 3400 Fax: 0117 982 2832 E-mail: info@elliotthire.co.uk

Elliotthire, Scotter Road South, Bottesford, Scunthorpe, South Humberside, DN17 2BW Tel: (01724) 279660 Fax: (01724) 848384 E-mail: info@elliotthire.co.uk

▶ Elliotthire Portable Accom Hire, Charville Lane, Hayes, Middlesex, UB4 8PD Tel: (020) 8845 6958 Fax: (020) 8841 1138 E-mail: info@elliotthire.co.uk

▶ Elliotthire Portable Accom Hire, Charville Lane, Hayes, Middlesex, UB4 8PD Tel: (020) 8845 6958 Fax: (020) 8841 1138 E-mail: info@elliotthire.co.uk

H B Rentals Ltd, Howe Moss Drive, Kirkhill Industrial Estate, Dyce, Aberdeen, AB21 0GL Tel: (01224) 772304 Fax: (01224) 772641 E-mail: sales@dm-accommodation.com

Lydney Containers Ltd, Unit 14 Lydney Industrial Estate, Harbour Road, Lydney, Gloucestershire, GL15 4EJ Tel: (01594) 842378 Fax: (01594) 843213 E-mail: info@lydneycontainers.co.uk

Marske Site Services Ltd, Suite 311, The Innovation Centre, Vienna Court, Kirkleatham Business Park, Redcar, Cleveland, TS10 5SH Tel: (01642) 777993 Fax: (01642) 777994 E-mail: tim.mccullagh@marske.com

▶ S G B plc, 86-88 Gresham Road, London, SW9 7NP Tel: (020) 7924 9000 Fax: (020) 7738 4144

▶ S G B plc, Richmond Walk, Plymouth, PL1 4LT Tel: (01752) 561575 Fax: (01752) 606892

▶ S G B Rovacabin, Green Lane, Felling, Gateshead, Tyne & Wear, NE10 0EZ Tel: (0800) 585383 Fax: 0191-469 5175

▶ S G B Rovacabin, 12 Dunnswood Road, Wardpark South, Cumbernauld, Glasgow, G67 3EN Tel: (01236) 729601 Fax: (01236) 738005

▶ S G B Rovacabin, 609 London Road, Grays, Essex, RM20 3BJ Tel: (0800) 585383 Fax: (01708) 869560

S G B Rovacabin, B Peterley Road, Cowley, Oxford, OX4 2TZ Tel: (01865) 337200 Fax: (01865) 337201 E-mail: rovasales@sgb.co.uk

▶ S G B Rovacabin Haydock, Anglezarke Road, Sankey Valley Industrial Estate, Newton-le-Willows, Merseyside, WA12 8DJ Tel: (0800) 585383 Fax: (01925) 291045

▶ S G B Rovacabin Hire Ltd, Ainleys Industrial Estate, Huddersfield Road, Elland, West Yorkshire, HX5 9BZ Tel: 0161-620 3047 Fax: (01454) 322948

▶ S G B Rovacabin Hire Ltd, Ainleys Industrial Estate, Huddersfield Road, Elland, West Yorkshire, HX5 9BZ Tel: 0161-620 3047 Fax: (01422) 379142

▶ SGB Rovacabin, Unit 54 Hobbs Industrial Estate, Newchapel, Lingfield, Surrey, RH7 6HN Tel: (01342) 833869 Fax: (01342) 835550

Grant Westfield Ltd, 3 Westfield Avenue, Edinburgh, EH11 2QH Tel: 0131-337 6262 Fax: 0131-337 2859 E-mail: sales@grantwestfield.co.uk

Wide Range Services Ltd, Alexandra Dock, Hull, HU9 1TA Tel: (01482) 898261 Fax: (01482) 587271 E-mail: sales@wrshull.co.uk

ACCOMMODATION OR BUSINESS MULTIPLE POST BOXES

▶ A M Mouldings, Lower Copy, Allerton Road, Allerton, Bradford, West Yorkshire, BD15 7QQ Tel: (01274) 547844 Fax: (01274) 483350 E-mail: j.barraclough@btinternet.com

▶ Stephen Clark Fabrication Ltd, Castle Street, Alloa, Clackmannanshire, FK10 1EU Tel: (01259) 729729 Fax: (01259) 210000 E-mail: sales@scfabs.com

ACCOUNT BOOKS

▶ Isosceles Finance, PO Box 2898, Ascot, Berkshire, SL5 0UW Tel: (01344) 622169 Fax: (0871) 661 6557 E-mail: info@isoscelesfinance.co.uk

▶ Officepoint Fivestar, 326 Kensal Road, London, W10 5BZ Tel: (020) 8969 8348 Fax: (020) 8969 8349 E-mail: sales@officepointfivestar.com

Rippin's Books, 77 Coleman Road, Leicester, LE5 4LE Tel: 0116-246 0044 Fax: 0116-246 0404

Sheerspeed Accounting Services, 45 Highgate, Kendal, Cumbria, LA9 4ED Tel: (01539) 720807 Fax: (01539) 740516 E-mail: linxroger@aol.com

Turpin Barker Armstrong, 1 Westmead Road, Sutton, Surrey, SM1 4LA Tel: (020) 8661 7878 Fax: (020) 8661 0598 E-mail: tba@turpinba.co.uk

George Vyner Ltd, PO Box 1, Holmfirth, HD9 7YP Tel: (01484) 685221 Fax: (01484) 688538

▶ Wave Accounting Solutions Limited, 15 Lara Close, Throop, Bournemouth, BH8 0HB Tel: 07970 476709 E-mail: gordon@waveaccountingsolutions.co.uk

ACCOUNTANCY INSTITUTIONS

Datatec Computer Services West Midlands Ltd, 121 Brownswall Road, Dudley, West Midlands, DY3 3NS Tel: (01902) 666144 Fax: (01902) 666146 E-mail: mail@datateclimted.co.uk

▶ Graham Paul, 372-374 Cyncoed Road, Cardiff, CF23 6SA Tel: (029) 2068 1980 Fax: (029) 2068 1981

Institute of Chartered Accountants of Scotland, CA House, 21 Haymarket Yards, Edinburgh, EH12 5BH Tel: 0131-347 0100 Fax: 0131-347 0105 E-mail: enquiries@icas.org.uk

Institute of Chartered Accountants-England & Wales, PO Box 433, London, EC2P 2BJ Tel: (020) 7920 8100 Fax: (020) 7920 0547 E-mail: feedback@icaew.co.uk

Technology Management (Midlands) Ltd, The Old Rectory, 57 Waterloo Road, Wolverhampton, WV1 4QH Tel: (01902) 578300 Fax: (01902) 578301 E-mail: admin@tecman.co.uk

ACCOUNTANCY SERVICES

▶ Accountancy Services, 16 Grosvenor Avenue, Newquay, Cornwall, TR7 1BQ Tel: (01637) 876795 Fax: (01637) 876795 E-mail: info@accountancyservices.uk.net

▶ Clickbooks Accountancy Services, Rowe Leyes Furlong, Rothley, Leicester, LE7 7LS Tel: 0116-230 1173 Fax: 0116-230 1173 E-mail: info@clickbooksaccountancy.co.uk

ACCOUNTANTS

▶ AbbeyHill Associates, 40 Tunbridge, Emersons Green, Bristol, BS16 7EX Tel: 0117 3730098 E-mail: info@abbeyhillassociates.co.uk

▶ Accounts Plus, 25 Elm Tree Road, Cosby, Leicester, LE9 1SR Tel: 0116-286 7874 Fax: 0116-286 7874

▶ Account-Wryte Ltd, Suite 105, York House, 2-4 York Road, Felixstowe, Suffolk, IP11 7QG Tel: (01394) 277888 Fax: (0871) 2771548 E-mail: accountwryteltd@yahoo.co.uk

Adam Beeny Halson, 4 Sudley Road, Bognor Regis, West Sussex, PO21 1EU Tel: (01243) 865661 Fax: (01243) 841533 E-mail: info@adamsbeeny.com

▶ Adam & Co Financial Management, 1 Edmund Street, Bradford, West Yorkshire, BD5 0BH Tel: (01274) 744877 Fax: (01274) 741966 E-mail: Profit@Advice.Tv

▶ Alex Parker & Co. Ltd, 11 Eagle Brow, Lymm, Cheshire, WA13 0LP Tel: (01925) 758889 Fax: (01925) 758894 E-mail: info@alexparker.co.uk

Ase Ltd, Stanley House, Acorn Business Park Heaton Lane, Stockport, Cheshire, SK4 1AS Tel: 0161-429 1500 Fax: 0161-480 3382 E-mail: info@aselcd.co.uk

▶ B & C Services, Premier House, 46 Victoria Road, Burgess Hill, West Sussex, RH15 9LR Tel: 01444 248474 Fax: 01444 870146 E-mail: info@redwellassociates.co.uk

Alan Bell & Partners Ltd, Manor House, Front St South, Trimdon, Trimdon Station, County Durham, TS29 6LY Tel: (01429) 883664 Fax: (01429) 883664 E-mail: abell@criticalstrategy.com

▶ Bookkeeper Blandford Dorset accountant, 9 The Pebbles, Chettle Village, Blandford Forum, Dorset, DT11 8DB Tel: (01258) 830624 E-mail: info@bookkeeper.org.uk

▶ Bosworth Business Management Limited, 37 Northumberland Avenue, Market Bosworth, Nuneaton, Warwickshire, CV13 0RJ Tel: 07050 369499 E-mail: contact@bbml.org

▶ BresnanWalsh, 1 Water Street, Liverpool, L2 0RD Tel: 0151 236 1494 Fax: 0151 258 1516 E-mail: mail@bresnanwalsh.co.uk

▶ C K R, 74-76 West Street, Erith, Kent, DA8 1AF Tel: (01322) 445200 Fax: (01322) 439242 E-mail: ckr@accountant.com

▶ C Todd & Co, Riverdale House, 89 Graham Road, Ranmoor, Sheffield, S10 3GP Tel: 0114 2306565 Fax: 0114 2309932 E-mail: chris@c-todd.co.uk

▶ Calcutt Matthews Ltd, 30 North Street, Ashford, Kent, TN24 8JR Tel: (01233) 623300 Fax: (01233) 623400 E-mail: reception@calcutt-m.co.uk

▶ Cert Tax Accounting, 47 Clarence Road, Chesterfield, Derbyshire, S40 1LQ Tel: (01246) 200255

▶ Corporate Turnaround Services, 30 Nicholds Close, Bilston, West Midlands, WV14 9JS Tel: (07813) 102014 Fax: (0870) 1681652 E-mail: paul_brindley@talk21.com

▶ Coulsons Chartered Accountants, 2 Belgrave Crescent, Scarborough, North Yorkshire, YO11 1UB Tel: (01723) 364141 Fax: (01723) 376010 E-mail: postmaster@coulsons.co.uk

ACCOUNTANTS – *continued*

▶ Culwick & Co, 69 Southend Road, Hockley, Essex, SS5 4PZ Tel: (01702) 200939 Fax: (01702) 207258 E-mail: info@culwick.com

▶ D G Owens Ltd, 34 Saxon Way, Old Windsor, Windsor, Berkshire, SL4 2PU Tel: (01753) 856762 Fax: 01753 856762 E-mail: jon@dgowens.co.uk

▶ David Evans Ltd, Unit 2 The Old Saw Mill, Clitheroe, Lancashire, BB7 1LY Tel: (01200) 428460 Fax: (0870) 4601595 E-mail: david@evansaccountants.com

▶ David Kirk Ltd, Rock Head House, Cowdale, Buxton, Derbyshire, SK17 9SE Tel: 01298 78413 Fax: 01298 78429 E-mail: davidkirkltd@btconnect.com

▶ The Fletcher Thompson Practice Limited, Mill House, 21 High Street, Ely, Cambs, CB7 5XR Tel: 0870 2323130 Fax: 0870 2323120 E-mail: info@fletcher-thompson.co.uk

▶ Garbetts Ltd, 2 New Road, Brading, Sandown, Isle of Wight, PO36 0DT Tel: (01983) 400350 Fax: (01983) 404016 E-mail: office@garbetts.com

▶ Garner Associates, 138 Bromham Road, Bedford, MK40 2QW Tel: (01234) 354508 Fax: (01234) 349588 E-mail: email@garnerassociates.co.uk

▶ Greyhound Business Systems Ltd, PO Box 5306, Leicester, LE2 4SS Tel: 0116-271 8808 Fax: 0116-271 8808 E-mail: sales@greyhound-business.co.uk

Hamiltons Accountants & Business Advisors, Meriden House, 6 Great Cornbow, Halesowen, West Midlands, B63 3AB Tel: 0121-585 6655 Fax: 0121-585 6228 E-mail: enquiries@hamiltons-group.co.uk

▶ Helen Agutter, 1 Bedford Place, Brighton, BN1 2PT Tel: (01273) 231310 Fax: (01273) 231310 E-mail: helen.agutter@ntlworld.com

High Energy Financial Management Ltd, Windmill House, Windmill Hill, Pudsey, West Yorkshire, LS28 8JQ Tel: 0113-303 0404 E-mail: info@hefm.co.uk

▶ Hills, Eddystone House, Aberderfyn Road, Johnstown, Wrexham, Clwyd, LL14 1PB Tel: (01978) 846609 Fax: (01978) 843954 E-mail: sales@hillsaccountants.supanet.com

▶ Howell Wade, 55 Church Road, London, SW19 5DQ Tel: (020) 8947 6912 Fax: (020) 8947 4936 E-mail: mail@howellwade.com

Hussains Accountants, 38 Devonshire Street, Keighley, West Yorkshire, BD21 2AU Tel: (01535) 661700 Fax: (01535) 662664 E-mail: info@hussains.biz

K A Javid, 49 Hydepark Street, Glasgow, G3 8BW Tel: 0141-248 8666 Fax: 0141-248 7555 E-mail: sales@kajavid.com

▶ Kumar & Co., 255-261 Horn Lane, London, W3 9EH Tel: (020) 8993 7771 Fax: (020) 8993 0057 E-mail: anil@kumar.co.uk

▶ Lakin Accounting Services Ltd, Manor Lodge, Teeton, Northampton, NN6 8LH Tel: (01604) 505563 Fax: 01604 505563 E-mail: louise@lakinltd.go-plus.net

▶ Marray & Mcintyre, Hawthorn House, 1 Medlicott Close, Corby, Northamptonshire, NN18 9NF Tel: (01536) 747888 Fax: (01536) 747744 E-mail: mail@marrayandmcintyre.co.uk

▶ Montgomery Swann Ltd, Scotts Sufferance Wharf, 1 Mill Street, London, SE1 2DE Tel: (020) 7237 0537 Fax: (020) 7237 2661 E-mail: s.bradshaw@montgomeryswann.com

Moore Stephens International Ltd, St Paul's, 8-12 Warwick Lane, London, EC4P 4BN Tel: (020) 7248 4499 Fax: (020) 7334 7976 E-mail: postmaster@moorestephens.com

▶ Morgan Hamilton Chartered Certified Accountants, Sheridan House, 17 St Anns Road, Harrow, Middlesex, HA1 1JU Tel: (020) 8515 7970 Fax: (020) 8515 7979 E-mail: info@morganhamilton.com

▶ Neil Webster & Co. Ltd, 14 Finkle Street, Kendal, Cumbria, LA9 4AB Tel: (01539) 731518 Fax: (01539) 725602 E-mail: info@neilwebster.co.uk

▶ Nicolson's Chartered Accountants, 49-50 Bayhead, Stornoway, Isle of Lewis, HS1 2DZ Tel: (01851) 700362 Fax: (01851) 700092 E-mail: sales@nicolsonmaps.com

▶ Nieman Walters, 7 Bourne Court Southend Road, Woodford Green, Essex, IG8 8HD Tel: (020) 8550 3131 Fax: (020) 8550 6020 E-mail: howard@nwnaccounts.com

▶ Osborne Sheen LLP, 73 Celandine Avenue,, Locks Heath, Southampton, SO31 6WZ Tel: 07740 901848

▶ Parmar Udai & Co., 29 New Way Road, London, NW9 6PL Tel: (020) 8931 0504 E-mail: info@udaiparmar.co.uk

▶ Pisces Accounts, Doe House Farm, Bradfield, Sheffield, S6 6LE Tel: 0114 2851384 E-mail: alanoakes@piscesaccounts.co.uk

Pricewaterhousecoopers, 1 Enbankment Place, London, WC2N 6RH Tel: (020) 7583 5000 Fax: (020) 7822 4652 E-mail: info@pcwglobal.com

▶ Pritchard Newport Accountants, Unit, Wingbury Courtyard Business Village, Wingrave, Aylesbury, Buckinghamshire, HP22 4LW Tel: (01296) 688022 E-mail: admin@pritchardnewport.co.uk

▶ ProSolutions Ltd, 3 Sunningdale Court, Crowstone Road, Westcliff-on-Sea, Essex, SS0 8LJ Tel: (0845) 4566854 Fax: (0870) 4608025 E-mail: enquiries@prosolutionsltd.com

Rahman Company, 9 Rampart Street, London, E1 2LA Tel: (020) 7790 0608 Fax: (020) 7790 8140

Raydon Associates Ltd, Hadleigh Farm, Raydon, Ipswich, IP7 5PZ Tel: (01473) 652679 Fax: (01473) 652679 E-mail: hfhraydon@btinternet.com

▶ Robinson Reed Layton, Peat House, Newham Road, Truro, Cornwall, TR1 2DP Tel: (01872) 276116 Fax: (01872) 222172 E-mail: info@rrl-truro.co.uk

▶ Saffery Champness, 40 Melville Street, Edinburgh, EH3 7TW Tel: 0131-225 2741 Fax: 0131-225 5376

Shah & Co., 15 Stanier Street, Swindon, SN1 5QU Tel: (01793) 524084 E-mail: shahco@mrshah.com

▶ Slaney & Co., 3 Queen Street, Worksop, Nottinghamshire, S80 2AW Tel: (01909) 472105 Fax: (01909) 482907 E-mail: worksop@slaneyandco.co.uk

Solvers Accounting Services Ltd, Bridge House, 119-123 Station Road, Hayes, Middlesex, UB3 4BX Tel: (020) 8589 0786 Fax: (020) 8561 9034 E-mail: mail@taxsolvers.co.uk

Tancred Solutions, 32b High Causeway, Whittlesey, Peterborough, PE7 1AJ Tel: (01733) 350925 Fax: (01733) 350832 E-mail: info@tancredsolutions.com

▶ Tax & Figures, Hamilton House, 111 Marlowes, Hemel Hempstead, Hertfordshire, HP1 1BB Tel: (01442) 450480 E-mail: robert@taxandfigures.com

▶ Teeac Associates, Unit 205 Camberwell Business Centre, Lomond Grove, London, SE5 7HN Tel: (020) 7708 2396 Fax: (0870) 7656230 E-mail: info@teeac.com

▶ W Accountancy Ltd, 369 Hertford Road, Enfield, Middlesex, EN3 5JW Tel: (020) 8804 0478 Fax: (020) 8804 0221 E-mail: c.wheatley@waccountancy.co.uk

W Accountancy Ltd, Victoria Rdknaphill, Knaphill, Woking, Surrey, GU21 2AA Tel: (01483) 797901 Fax: (01483) 797899 E-mail: m.wood@waccountancy.co.uk

▶ Williams Accountants, 27 Torrington Avenue, Stafford, ST17 0HZ Tel: (01785) 608179 Fax: (01785) 608179 E-mail: williams.accountants@ntlworld.com

▶ Williams, Jenkins & Co. Ltd, 3 Hannah Street, Porth, Rhondda Cynon Taff, CF39 9PU Tel: (01443) 688046 Fax: (01443) 688046 E-mail: info@williamjenkins.info

ACCOUNTING COMPUTER SOFTWARE

Advanced Digital Technology UK Ltd, Unit 10 Lord Wilmot House, Bristol Road, Bumpers Farm, Chippenham, Wiltshire, SN14 6LH Tel: (01249) 653654 Fax: (01249) 659258

Amethyst Associates Ltd, The Old Barn, Oak House, Main Road, Farthinghoe, Brackley, Northamptonshire, NN13 5PB Tel: (01295) 714056 Fax: (0870) 1219961 E-mail: geoff.wenmouth@amethystassociates.co.uk

Andrews Computer Services Ltd, Nash House, London Road, Hemel Hempstead, Hertfordshire, HP3 9SR Tel: (01442) 241200 Fax: (01442) 241201 E-mail: admin@andrews-computers.com

Asset Business Systems Ltd, 8a Milburn Road, Bournemouth, BH4 9HJ Tel: (01202) 757599 Fax: (01202) 757588 E-mail: davemac@assetsystems.co.uk

Aw Computer Systems Ltd, 16 Dundry Lane, Winford, Bristol, BS40 8AN Tel: (01275) 474591 Fax: (0870) 9004911 E-mail: awcs@dial.pipex.com

Base 2 Professional Ltd, 1 Bracklinn Road, Callander, Perthshire, FK17 8EH Tel: (01877) 331331 Fax: (01877) 331711

Business Intelligence International Ltd, 37 Kirkton St, Carluke, Lanarkshire, ML8 4AD Tel: 01555 750783 Fax: 01555 770168 E-mail: sales@businessit.net

C B W Associates Ltd, 15 Station Rise, Marlow, Buckinghamshire, SL7 1EJ Tel: (01628) 482282 E-mail: bm.watson@btclick.com

C P L, Anglo House, Worcester Road, Stourport-On-Severn, Worcestershire, DY13 9AW Tel: (01299) 877004 Fax: (01299) 877226 E-mail: enquiries@computerproof.co.uk

Capstone Systems, Oak Mead, Honington, Bury St. Edmunds, Suffolk, IP31 1RE Tel: (01359) 268711 Fax: (01359) 268870 E-mail: dcg@capstonesystems.co.uk

Clarke Computer Systems, 43 Cannock Road, Burntwood, Staffordshire, WS7 0BL Tel: (01543) 670756 Fax: (01543) 670756 E-mail: info@clarkecomputers.co.uk

Command Alkon Ltd, 21 St Annes Road, St Annes Park, St. Annes Park, Bristol, BS4 4AB Tel: 0117-972 4777 Fax: 0117-972 4888

Computential Computer Systems, 70 Norris Road, Sale, Cheshire, M33 3QR Tel: 0161-969 2663

Comtek Accounts Ltd, Venture House Venture Court, Boleness Road, Wisbech, Cambridgeshire, PE13 2XQ Tel: (01945) 464854 Fax: (01945) 465575 E-mail: accounts@comtekaccounts.com

Cpio Ltd, Arden House The Courtyard, Gorsey Lane, Coleshill, Birmingham, B46 1JA Tel: (01675) 467046 Fax: (01675) 467682 E-mail: rcf@cpio.co.uk

▶ Datadesk Computer Services Ltd, 21 Anniesdale Avenue, Stepps, Glasgow, G33 6DW Tel: 0141-779 9162 Fax: 0141-779 9083 E-mail: info@datadesk.it

Datapro Software Ltd, North Street, Portslade, Brighton, BN41 1DH Tel: (01273) 886000 Fax: (01273) 886066 E-mail: sales@datapro.co.uk

Datavalley Sales Ltd, 32 London Road, Southborough, Tunbridge Wells, Kent, TN4 0QA Tel: (01892) 514545 Fax: (01892) 518282 E-mail: sales@datavalley.co.uk

Dean Microcomputers Ltd, 1 Abenhall Technolgy Centre, Abenhall Road, Mitcheldean, Gloucestershire, GL17 0DT Tel: (01594) 542116 Fax: (01594) 542643 E-mail: mary@deanmicros.co.uk

Econintel Treasury Systems Ltd, The Octagon, 27 Middleborough, Colchester, CO1 1TG Tel: (01206) 760033 Fax: (01206) 760133 E-mail: colchester@econintel.com

Ensign Advanced Systems Ltd, 56 Regent Road, Leicester, LE1 6YD Tel: 0116-254 9444 E-mail: ensignsys@aol.com

Farmdata Ltd, Westertown, Rothienorman, Inverurie, Aberdeenshire, AB51 8US Tel: (01467) 671457 Fax: (01467) 671448 E-mail: sales@farmdata.co.uk

Financial Management Systems (UK) P.L.C., 4 Hillbrow House, Linden Drive, Liss, Hampshire, GU33 7RJ Tel: (01730) 894789 Fax: (01730) 892387 E-mail: info@fmsuk.com

Flexible Management Systems Ltd, Fielden Ho, 28 London Bridge St, London, SE1 9SG Tel: (020) 7378 6788 Fax: (020) 7357 0577

Gateway Computing, Whitehouse, 114 Hendford Hill, Yeovil, Somerset, BA20 2RF Tel: (01935) 424356 Fax: (01935) 420549

▶ Hebron (UK) Ltd, Oxford Road, Yeovil, Somerset, BA21 5HR Tel: (01935) 403000 Fax: (01935) 403025 E-mail: info@hebron.co.uk

Hexagon Software Ltd, Unit 8 Highnam Business Centre, Highnam, Gloucester, GL2 8DN Tel: (01608) 811801 Fax: (01608) 811852 E-mail: sales@hexagon.co.uk

I C S Software Ltd, The Square, Ramsbury, Marlborough, Wiltshire, SN8 2PE Tel: (01672) 521212 Fax: (01672) 521002 E-mail: mike@folio2000.co.uk

▶ I T C (Epos) Ltd, Barnsley Business & Innovation Centre, Innovation Way, Barnsley, South Yorkshire, S75 1JL Tel: (01226) 731785 Fax: (01226) 731867 E-mail: sales@itcepos.co.uk

Impaq UK Ltd, Lantern House, Walnut Tree Close, Guildford, Surrey, GU1 4TX Tel: (01483) 466900 Fax: (01483) 466901 E-mail: enquiries@impaq.co.uk

Innovise Software Ltd, Hellier House, Wychbury Court, Brierley Hill, West Midlands, DY5 1TA Tel: (01384) 484032 Fax: (01277) 822566 E-mail: info@innovise.com

Integration Services Ltd, 119 Kingston Road, Leatherhead, Surrey, KT22 7SU Tel: (01372) 227400 Fax: (01372) 225120 E-mail: sales@isluk.com

▶ ITMAX Ltd, Abbey Drive, Abbots Langley, Hertfordshire, WD5 0TL Tel: (01923) 464105 Fax: (01923) 464106 E-mail: bash@itmax.co.uk

▶ JH Acounting Services, 15 Lunt Place, Bilston, West Midlands, WV14 7AH Tel: (07801) 429827E-mail: enquiries@jh-accounting.co.uk

Kaniko Computing, 23 Edward Road, Harrow, Middlesex, HA2 6QB Tel: (020) 8861 6543 Fax: (020) 8861 6543 E-mail: kanikoc@aol.com

Keystone Software Developments Ltd, 84 Commercial Road, Grantham, Lincolnshire, NG31 6DB Tel: (01476) 562447 E-mail: info@keystonesoftware.co.uk

▶ Kingsword Ltd, Unit 5, The Boundary Business Park, Wheatley Road, Garsington, Oxford, OX44 9EJ Tel: (01865) 361840 Fax: (01865) 361850 E-mail: sales@cssg.co.uk

L P C Computer Solutions, Unit 2 Buslingthorpe Green, Leeds, LS7 2HG Tel: 0113-262 2626 Fax: 0113-262 6622 E-mail: len@lpconline.co.uk

Mclellan Software Design Ltd, 18 Carlton Business Centre, Carlton, Nottingham, NG4 3AA Tel: 0115-961 7676 Fax: 0115-961 6866 E-mail: sales@msdmagic.co.uk

Marsden's Computer Systems, Unit 168 Glenfield Park Lomeshaye Business Village, Turner Road, Nelson, Lancashire, BB9 7DR Tel: (01282) 616176 Fax: (01282) 616152 E-mail: info@marsdens.net

Matrica, Unit 30 Cannon Wharf Business Park, 35 Evelyn Street, London, SE8 5RT Tel: (020) 7536 2950 Fax: (020) 7237 0044

MCC Ltd, 2 Milford Road, Sherburn in Elmet, Leeds, LS25 6AF Tel: (01977) 682880 Fax: (0870) 0518693 E-mail: tim@mccltd.org.uk

Merlin Software International Ltd, 6 Bancombe Road, Somerton, Somerset, TA11 6SB Tel: (01458) 271300 Fax: (01458) 224044 E-mail: info@caliburn-software.com

▶ Metaphorix Ltd, 3 Temple Court, Temple Way, Coleshill, Birmingham, B46 1HH Tel: (01675) 432400 Fax: (01675) 465571 E-mail: enquiries@metaphorix.co.uk

Mican Ltd, Oakmere, Horsemans Green, Whitchurch, Shropshire, SY13 3DY Tel: (01948) 830069

Midsoft Computer Systems, Aston Lane, Aston, Stone, Staffordshire, ST15 0BW Tel: (01785) 818054 Fax: (01785) 817513 E-mail: sales@midsoft.co.uk

Misys P.L.C., Burleigh House, Chapel Oak, Salford Priors, Evesham, Worcestershire, WR11 8SP Tel: (01386) 871373 Fax: (01386) 871045

Nike Consultants Ltd, Raynor House, 6 Raynor Road, Wolverhampton, WV10 9QY Tel: (01902) 566200 Fax: (01902) 566201 E-mail: sales@nike.co.uk

Pegasus Group Public Ltd Company, Orion House, Orion Way, Kettering, Northamptonshire, NN15 6PE Tel: (01536) 495000 Fax: (01536) 495001 E-mail: sales@pegasus.co.uk

Peter Saxon & Co., 362 Church Road, London, SW19 2QF Tel: (07956) 379622 Fax: (020) 8648 7829 E-mail: peter@petersaxton.co.uk

Phil Partners Micro Help, 8 Bleak Hill Way, Mansfield, Nottinghamshire, NG18 5EZ Tel: (01623) 651444 Fax: (01623) 633661 E-mail: philj@microhelpuk.net

Practice Engine Group Ltd, The Stables, Byford, Hereford, HR4 7JU Tel: (01981) 590410 Fax: (01981) 590411 E-mail: sales@praceng.com

Redview Computers, 17A North End, Longhoston, Alnwick, Northumberland, NE66 3AG Tel: (01665) 572027 E-mail: tom@redview.co.uk

Soft Brands ' Evolution, Glenfield Park 2, Blakewater Road, Blackburn, BB1 5QH Tel: (01254) 724400 Fax: (01254) 724404 E-mail: joanne.slater@softbrands.com

Sovereign Software Solutions Ltd, 12 Bank Crescent, Burntwood, Staffordshire, WS7 4TL Tel: (01543) 677070 Fax: (01543) 677671 E-mail: info@sovsoft.co.uk

Spectrum Colors, Merrivale House, Kinburn Drive, Egham Hill, Egham, Surrey, TW20 0BD Tel: (01784) 431273 Fax: (01784) 431103 E-mail: sales@spectrum.co.uk

Star Computer Group plc, King Edward Court, 23 High Street, Sutton Coldfield, West Midlands, B72 1XS Tel: 0121-355 6171 Fax: 0121-354 4656 E-mail: info@starplc.co.uk

Star Seaford, 10 Broad Street, Seaford, East Sussex, BN25 1ND Tel: (01323) 490565 Fax: (01323) 491599

Stone & Associates, 40 Beaulieu Drive, Pinner, Middlesex, HA5 1NG Tel: (020) 8866 8631 E-mail: sales@stone-associates.co.uk

Strategy In Computing Ltd, Mooring Business Centre Willows End House, 9 Carolus Creek, Penn Island, Milton Keynes, MK15 8AZ Tel: (01908) 201202 Fax: (01908) 201170 E-mail: reply@strategy-in-computing.co.uk

Sum-It Computer Systems Ltd, Samuel House, Chinnor Road, Thame, Oxfordshire, OX9 3NU Tel: (01844) 213003 Fax: (01844) 214722 E-mail: sales@sum-it.co.uk

Technology Services Group Edinburgh, Pentland Estate, Straiton, Edinburgh, EH20 9QW Tel: 0131-448 2400 Fax: 0131-448 0064 E-mail: enquiries@tsg.com

X K O Group P.L.C., Clyde House, 16 Milburn Avenue, Oldbrook, Milton Keynes, MK6 2WA Tel: (01908) 295400 Fax: (01908) 393633

X-GL Systems Ltd, 24 Hunters Reach, Waltham Cross, Hertfordshire, EN7 6HQ Tel: (01992) 638763 Fax: (0870) 0521734 E-mail: sales@xgl.com

Xirtek, Matrix House, Langley Road, Chippenham, Wiltshire, SN15 1BT Tel: (01249) 767710 Fax: (01249) 766767 E-mail: info@matrixeng.co.uk

Zipzap Ltd, Unit 18 Exchange Road, Lincoln, LN6 3JZ Tel: (01522) 684705 Fax: (01522) 684627 E-mail: sales@zipzap.co.uk

ACCOUNTING PERSONNEL RECRUITMENT AGENCIES/ CONSULTANTS/SERVICES

ADSEC Booke Keeping Services, PO Box 88, Cardiff, CF72 0AE Tel: 0845 230 1423 E-mail: email@adsec.co.uk

▶ Alliance Resourcing Ltd, 14 Paul Street, Taunton, Somerset, TA1 3PF Tel: (01823) 48 998 Fax: (08700) 100582 E-mail: contact@allianceresourcing.com

▶ Austin Banks Ltd, Hutton Business Centre, Suite 1a High Street, Bentley, Doncaster, South Yorkshire, DN5 9QP Tel: (01302) 822228 Fax: 01302 822237 E-mail: james@austinbanks.co.uk

▶ Badger Associates Ltd, Pottergate Street, Aslacton, Norwich, NR15 2JU Tel: 01508 536013 Fax: 0871 7501925 E-mail: info@badgerassociates.co.uk

▶ Berber Ltd, 18 Rosebank, Lymm Warrington, Lymm, Cheshire, WA13 0JH Tel: (07961) 905903 E-mail: nicksteed@supanet.com

▶ Blue Enterprises, 130 Shaftesbury Avenue, London, W1D 5EU Tel: (0845) 3702583 Fax: (0845) 3702584 E-mail: info@blue-enterprises.co.uk

▶ Blue Fire Consulting Ltd, Il Palazzo 7 Water Street, Liverpool, L2 0RD Tel: (0870) 7521080 Fax: (0870) 7521090 E-mail: sales@bluefireconsulting.co.uk

Blue Tree Recruitment, Suite 3 The Sanctuary, 23 Oak Hill Grove, Surbiton, Surrey, KT6 6DU Tel: (020) 8399 4908 Fax: (020) 8399 4909 E-mail: claire@bluetreerecruitment.co.uk

▶ Bond Williams Professional Recruitment, 23 Hinton Road, Bournemouth, BH1 2EF Tel: (01202) 201700 Fax: (01202) 201645 E-mail: enquiry@bondwilliams.co.uk

▶ Brighter Recruiting, Elmsland House, Kirk Hammerton, York, YO26 8BX Tel: (01423) 331535 Fax: (01423) 331536 E-mail: recruiting@brighter-recruiting.co.uk

▶ Byron Finance, 41 London Road, Reigate, Surrey, RH2 9QE Tel: (01737) 228777 Fax: (01737) 735200 E-mail: recruitment@byronfinance.com

ACCOUNTING PERSONNEL RECRUITMENT AGENCIES/ CONSULTANTS/SERVICES – *continued*

▶ Calibre Recruitment, Unit 10 River Court Brighouse Business Village, Brighouse Road, Middlesbrough, Cleveland, TS2 1RT Tel: (01642) 244020 Fax: (01642) 243480 E-mail: careers@calibre-recruitment.co.uk

▶ Cameron Wallace - International Accountancy Recruiters, Caledonia Business Centre, Caledonia House, Evanton Drive, Glasgow, G46 8JT Tel: 0141 270 9713 E-mail: info@cameronwallace.com

▶ Career Finder, Church Drive, Hucknall, Nottingham, NG15 7BX Tel: 0115-840 1105 E-mail: support@look4jobs.net

▶ Chameleon Personnel Services Ltd, 1 West Street, Leighton Buzzard, Bedfordshire, LU7 1DA Tel: (01525) 218068 Fax: (01525) 218067 E-mail: info@chameleonpersonnel.co.uk

▶ Chequers Personnel, Wiltshire House, 121 High Street, Marlborough, Wiltshire, SN8 1LZ Tel: (01672) 519194 Fax: 01672 519195 E-mail: info@chequers-personnel.co.uk

▶ City Associates, Centre Gate, Colston Avenue, Bristol, BS1 4TR Tel: 0117-317 8133 Fax: 0117-317 8134 E-mail: sales@city-associates.co.uk

▶ CityJobs, Langstone technology park, Langstone road, Havant, Hampshire, PO9 1SA Tel: 0870 774 8847 E-mail: Kelly@receptional.com

CV Honesty Box, 64 Burghley Street, Bourne, Lincolnshire, PE10 9NG Tel: (01778) 420407 E-mail: info@cvhonestybox.co.uk

▶ D I Recruitment, 8 Dig Street, Ashbourne, Derbyshire, DE6 1GF Tel: (01335) 342354 Fax: (01335) 300179 E-mail: info@direcruitment.co.uk

▶ Delaney Ditchfield Recruitment, 17 Shires Mead, Verwood, Dorset, BH31 6LD Tel: 01202 825676 E-mail: info@delaneyditchfield.co.uk

▶ Ebor Nannies Ltd, No 1 Ebor House, Dike Ray Close, Haxby, York, YO32 3WJ Tel: (01904) 767777 Fax: (01904) 767700 E-mail: jane@ebornannies.co.uk

▶ Employment Enjoyment Ltd, 6 Shurdington Road, Cheltenham, Gloucestershire, GL53 0DJ Tel: 01242 252337 Fax: 01242 580451 E-mail: info@employment-enjoyment.co.uk

▶ Equinox Financial Search & Selection, Unity House, Clive Street, Bolton, BL1 1ET Tel: (0870) 9192457 Fax: (0870) 9192458 E-mail: iwright@equinox-financial.co.uk

▶ FinanceCVs.co.uk, 18 Bedfordshire Down, Warfield, Bracknell, Berkshire, RG42 3UA Tel: (07006) 300980 E-mail: info@financecvs.co.uk

▶ Fresh Start Recruitment UK, Ashfield Avenue, Mansfield, Nottinghamshire, NG18 2AE Tel: (01623) 404525 Fax: 01623 404234 E-mail: mansfield@barecruitment.co.uk

▶ Human Resources Consultancy, 50 Keedwell Hill, Long Ashton, Bristol, BS41 9DR Tel: (01275) 540510 Fax: (01275) 540510 E-mail: melaniehall@hrc-bristol.co.uk

▶ International Recruitment Bureau Ltd., Address 274 Hither green lane, London, SE13 6T Tel: 07776 472126 Fax: 02086 959200

▶ Ips Recruitment, 39 westgate, Grantham, Lincolnshire, NG31 6LY Tel: 01476 568225 Fax: 01476 565548 E-mail: dan.nash@ips-recruitment.co.uk

▶ Jobsearch Northern Ireland, PO Box 05, Ballymena, County Antrim, BT44 9YF Tel: 028276 41743

Just Accountancy Ltd, 5 Crwys Place, Plasnewydd Cardiff, Cardiff, CF24 4NS Tel: (029) 2045 0874 Fax: (029) 2045 0874 E-mail: justyn.withey@justaccountancy.com

▶ Just Recruit (UK) Ltd, Viking Industrial Park, Tedco Business Centre, Jarrow, Tyne & Wear, NE32 3DT Tel: 0191-428 3336 Fax: 0191-428 3356 E-mail: mark@justrecruit.co.uk

▶ Key Associate Group, Orbit House Second Floor, Albert Street, Eccles, Manchester, M30 0BL Tel: 0161-707 9448 Fax: (0870) 2320090 E-mail: Natasha.Karimi@Keyassociategroup.com

▶ Grant Lawson Ltd, Albany House, 14 Shute End, Wokingham, Berkshire, RG40 1BJ Tel: 0118-979 6023 Fax: (07092) 382965

▶ Liberty Consulting, 8 Cromwell Road, Hove, East Sussex, BN3 3WB Tel: (0845) 0090044 Fax: (0845) 0090045 E-mail: vicky@liberty-consulting.co.uk

▶ Management Consultancy 4 Limited, 7-111 Fleet Street, London, EC4A 2AB Tel: 0 870 770 9116 Fax: 0 870 770 9117 E-mail: info@mc4.co.uk

▶ Marble Recruitment Ltd, Dominions House, Queen Street, Cardiff, CF10 2AR Tel: (029) 2038 3837 Fax: (029) 2038 3847 E-mail: paul@marblerecruitment.co.uk

▶ Nicholas Andrews Employment & Recruitment, 1 Whitehall Quay, Leeds, LS1 4HR Tel: 0113-245 6717 Fax: 0113-244 8242 E-mail: richardmhenley@aol.com

▶ Now Accountancy, 14 Drake Walk, Brigantine Place, Cardiff, CF10 4AN Tel: (029) 2048 9966 Fax: (029) 2049 7722 E-mail: info@nowaccountancy.com

▶ Now Recruitment Ltd, 5 The Square, Broad Street, Birmingham, B15 1AS Tel: 0121-693 9408 E-mail: info@nowrecruitment.com

▶ O J M Recruitment, Gresham House, 7 Veryan, Fareham, Hampshire, PO14 1NN Tel: (0845) 8330875 Fax: (0845) 8330873 E-mail: info@ojmrecruitment.com

▶ Parker Robinson Recruitment Ltd, The Imex Business Park, Shobnall Road, Burton-On-Trent, Staffordshire, DE14 2AU Tel: (01283) 543406 Fax: (01283) 519191 E-mail: owen@parkerrobinson.co.uk

▶ Platinum Permanent Recruitment, 1 Emperor Way, Exeter Business Park, Exeter, EX1 3QS Tel: (01392) 314053 Fax: (01392) 314224 E-mail: rayseo@gmail.com

Prime50plus, PO Box 5050, Huddersfield, HD1 4WB Tel: (0845) 4562201 E-mail: paul.kern@prime50plus.co.uk

Raegurn Group Ltd, Ruby House, Ruby Place, Aberdeen, AB10 1QZ Tel: (01224) 625050 Fax: (01224) 626840 E-mail: heather.milne@raeburn.com

▶ RD Financial Recruitment, St.Stephens House, Arthur Road, Windsor, Berkshire, SL4 1Ry Tel: 01753 621902 Fax: 01753 621901 E-mail: paul@rdfr.co.uk

▶ Recadnet, Minerva Road, London, NW10 6HJ Tel: (0870) 2240656 E-mail: admin@recadnet.com

Redgoldfish Jobs, Cornelius House, Whitehouse Court, Cannock, Staffordshire, WS11 3DA Tel: (01543) 468800 Fax: (01543) 468900 E-mail: info@redgoldfish.co.uk

▶ SAF- Recuitment, Marvell Rise, Harrogate, North Yorkshire, HG1 3LT Tel: (01423) 550756 E-mail: stuart@saf-recruitment.com

▶ Salestarget.co.uk, Holden House, 57 Rathbone Place, London, W1T 1LD Tel: 020 7769 9200 Fax: 020 7769 9008 E-mail: info@salestarget.co.uk

SF Group, 4 Millennium Way West, Nottingham, NG8 6AS Tel: 0115-911 2082 Fax: 0115-975 8087 E-mail: registrations@registrations.com

▶ Anna Shaw Associates Ltd, 9 Tramway Drive, Sutton-on-Sea, Mablethorpe, Lincolnshire, LN12 2GS Tel: (01507) 440278 Fax: (01507) 440278 E-mail: info@annashawassociates.co.uk

▶ Darren Snell, Ground Floor, Clair House, Haywards Heath, West Sussex, RH16 3DP Tel: (01444) 415559 Fax: (01444) 415180 E-mail: enquiries@artconsulting.com

▶ Spectrum Personnel Ltd, 154 Merry Street, Motherwell, Lanarkshire, ML1 1NA Tel: (01698) 304545 Fax: (01698) 304646 E-mail: garytelfer@spectrum-personnel.com

▶ Stafforce Recruitment, 39A Minerva Road, London, NW10 6HJ Tel: (020) 8537 9070 Fax: (020) 8537 9071 E-mail: parkroyal@stafforce.co.uk

Stirling Recruitment, 49 Old Steine, Brighton, BN1 1NH Tel: (01273) 324255 Fax: (01273) 325656 E-mail: info@duneofficerecruitment.co.uk

▶ theACCOUNTANCYjob.com, PO Box 2448, Slough, SL1 1ZB Tel: 0870 8701193 Fax: 0870 8701194 E-mail: coz.dauncey@theACCOUNTANCYjob.com

▶ TMP & Associates Ltd, Sedgecombe House, Garfield Road, Camberley, Surrey, GU15 2JG Tel: 01276 684007 Fax: 01276 684010 E-mail: mike@tmpandass.com

▶ Top Language Jobs, 770-780 Great Cambridge Road, Enfield, Middlesex, EN1 3RN Tel: (020) 8363 3334

▶ Travail Employment Group Ltd, 7 St. Johns Hill, Shrewsbury, SY1 1JD Tel: (01743) 235532 Fax: (01743) 236327 E-mail: shrewsbury@travailshrewsbury.co.uk

▶ Triple S Recruitment Ltd, Heath Business Technical Park, Runcorn, Cheshire, WA7 4QX Tel: (01928) 576925 E-mail: info@boxpeople.co.uk

▶ W S S Associates Ltd, 23 Austin Friars, London, EC2N 2QP Tel: (020) 31707837 E-mail: accounts@wss-associates.com

▶ Williams Hall Ltd, St. George's House, 14 George Street, Huntingdon, Cambridgeshire, PE29 3BD Tel: (01480) 426515 Fax: (0871) 9942705 E-mail: info@williamshall.co.uk

The Work Shop, 7 High Street, Ringwood, Hampshire, BH24 1AB Tel: (01425) 489393 Fax: (01425) 489402 E-mail: sales@thework-shop.net

ACCOUNTING SYSTEM SOFTWARE

Adobe Systems (U K) Ltd, 3 Roundwood Avenue, Stockley Park, Uxbridge, Middlesex, UB11 1AY Tel: (020) 8606 4000 Fax: (020) 8606 4004 E-mail: jobs@adobe.co.uk

Ama Business Systems Ltd, The Old Tabernacle, Palmyra Road, Bristol, BS3 3JQ Tel: 0117-923 1133 Fax: 0117-923 1144 E-mail: sales@ama-it.com

Anjec Computer Services, The Mansard Suite The Robbins Building, Albert Street, Rugby, Warwickshire, CV21 2AA Tel: (01788) 540484 Fax: (01788) 540493 E-mail: anjec@via-anjec.co.uk

Asset Business Systems Ltd, 8a Milburn Road, Bournemouth, BH4 9HJ Tel: (01202) 757599 Fax: (01202) 757588 E-mail: davemac@assetsystems.co.uk

B H Associates 2000 Ltd, Cromwell House, Elland Road, Brighouse, West Yorkshire, HD6 2RG Tel: (01756) 700138 Fax: (01422) 371337 E-mail: sales@bhassociates.sagehost.co.uk

Banks Software Ltd, 74 Forest Road, Oldbury, West Midlands, B68 0EF Tel: 0121-421 8295 E-mail: sales@banks-software.co.uk

C N S, Earley, Reading, RG10 8NF Tel: 0118-940 1313 Fax: 0118-940 3754 E-mail: enquire@cnscommunications.co.uk

Data One Ltd, Unit 12 Loughborough Technology Centre, Epinal Way, Loughborough, Leicestershire, LE11 3GE Tel: (01509) 215662 Fax: (01509) 212571 E-mail: danny@dataone.ltd.uk

Datapro Software Ltd, North Street, Portslade, Brighton, BN41 1DH Tel: (01273) 886000 Fax: (01273) 886066 E-mail: sales@datapro.co.uk

Datavalley Sales Ltd, 32 London Road, Southborough, Tunbridge Wells, Kent, TN4 0QA Tel: (01892) 514545 Fax: (01892) 518282 E-mail: sales@datavalley.co.uk

De Facto Software Ltd, The Rutherford Centre, 8 Dunlop Road, Ipswich, IP2 0UG Tel: (01473) 230202 Fax: (01473) 230247 E-mail: sales@defactosoftware.com

Delta Comtech Ltd, Artillery House, Gunco Lane, Macclesfield, Cheshire, SK11 7JL Tel: (01625) 430055 Fax: (0870) 2200568 E-mail: sales@delta-comtech.co.uk

▶ The E R P Group, Bliss House, 251 Dewsbury Road, Ossett, West Yorkshire, WF5 9QF Tel: (0870) 3339032 Fax: (01924) 280117 E-mail: sales@theerpgroup.co.uk

Ensign Advanced Systems Ltd, 56 Regent Road, Leicester, LE1 6YD Tel: 0116-254 9444 E-mail: ensignsys@aol.com

Gateway Computing, Whitehouse, 114 Hendford Hill, Yeovil, Somerset, BA20 2RF Tel: (01935) 424356 Fax: (01935) 420549

Ibex Systems Maidstone Ltd, Mill House Quarry Wood Industrial Estate, Mills Road, Aylesford, Kent, ME20 7NA Tel: (01622) 791991 Fax: (01622) 882900 E-mail: sales@ibexsystems.co.uk

Impaq UK Ltd, Lantern House, Walnut Tree Close, Guildford, Surrey, GU1 4TX Tel: (01483) 466900 Fax: (01483) 466901 E-mail: enquiries@impaq.co.uk

Infor, Needles House, Birmingham Road, Studley, Warwickshire, B80 7AS Tel: (01527) 496200 Fax: (01527) 496300

Integration Services Ltd, 119 Kingston Road, Leatherhead, Surrey, KT22 7SU Tel: (01372) 227400 Fax: (01372) 225120 E-mail: sales@isluk.com

▶ JH Acounting Services, 15 Lunt Place, Bilston, West Midlands, WV14 7AH Tel: (07801) 429827E-mail: enquiries@jh-accounting.co.uk

L P C Computer Solutions, Unit 2 Buslingthorpe Green, Leeds, LS7 2HG Tel: 0113-262 2626 Fax: 0113-262 6622 E-mail: len@lpconline.co.uk

Lyquidity Solutions, Ground Floor Office Suite, 16 Lynton Road, New Malden, Surrey, KT3 5EE Tel: (020) 7043 2777 Fax: (0870) 1373744 E-mail: sarah.seddon@lyquidity.com

Maxima, Stonepail Court, Stonepail Road, Gatley, Cheadle, Cheshire, SK8 4EX Tel: 0161-491 3700 Fax: 0161-491 2859

Minerva Software, Cedar Lodge, Mill Road, Peasenhall, Saxmundham, Suffolk, IP17 2LJ Tel: (01728) 660411 Fax: (01728) 660385 E-mail: sales@minervasoftware.com

Oasys, Unit 1, Briar Close, Bramble Lane, Wye, Ashford, Kent, TN25 5HB Tel: (01233) 812050 Fax: (01233) 812082 E-mail: enquiries@o-a-sys.co.uk

Pegasus Group Public Ltd Company, Orion House, Orion Way, Kettering, Northamptonshire, NN15 6PE Tel: (01536) 495000 Fax: (01536) 495001 E-mail: sales@pegasus.co.uk

Phil Partners Micro Help, 8 Bleak Hill Way, Mansfield, Nottinghamshire, NG18 5EZ Tel: (01623) 651444 Fax: (01623) 633661 E-mail: philj@microhelpuk.net

Plastics Software Ltd, Unit 1, Farmcroft, Farnham Lane, Haslemere, Surrey, GU27 1HD Tel: (01428) 656595 Fax: (01428) 656595 E-mail: sales@plasware.co.uk

Professional Accounting Systems Ltd, 52 High House Drive, Lickey, Birmingham, B45 8ET Tel: 0121-445 2200 Fax: 0121-447 8586

Redview Computers, 17A North End, Longhoston, Alnwick, Northumberland, NE66 3AG Tel: (01665) 572027 E-mail: tom@redview.co.uk

Sci-sys Ltd, Clothier Road, Bristol, BS4 5SS Tel: 0117-971 7251 Fax: 0117-972 1846 E-mail: marketing@scisys.co.uk

Smart People Time plc, Node Court, Drivers End, Codicote, Hitchin, Hertfordshire, SG4 8TR Tel: (01438) 822222 Fax: (01438) 822240 E-mail: info@smarthumanlogistics.com

Strategix, Regatta Place, Marlow Road, Bourne End, Buckinghamshire, SL8 5TD Tel: (01628) 532565 Fax: (01628) 551490 E-mail: strategix@tissoft.co.uk

Talos Ltd, Prospect House, 20 High Street, Brasted, Westerham, Kent, TN16 1RG Tel: (01959) 561124 Fax: (01959) 561402 E-mail: info@quantus.co.uk

Trymdata Computer Systems, 157 Redland Road, Bristol, BS6 6YE Tel: (0845) 2308075

▶ Vision Software Solutions Ltd, 49 Westfields, St Albans, St. Albans, Hertfordshire, AL3 4LS Tel: (01727) 817220 E-mail: sales@vision-software.co.uk

▶ WinIT Consultancy Ltd, West Mills, Newbury, Berkshire, RG14 5HG Tel: (0870) 2000635 Fax: (0870) 2000755 E-mail: robin@winitconsultancy.co.uk

Xperience Support Ltd, 11 Ferguson Drive, Knockmore Hill Industrial Park, Lisburn, County Antrim, BT28 2EX Tel: (028) 9267 7533 Fax: (028) 9267 2887 E-mail: info@xperience-group.com

ACCOUNTING SYSTEMS

▶ Accounting Products Ltd, 16 Lynton Road, New Malden, Surrey, KT3 5EE Tel: (020) 7043 2777 Fax: (0870) 1373744 E-mail: sarah.seddon@accountingproducts.co.uk

▶ Advanced Media Engineering Ltd, Sannerville Chase, Main Road, Exminster, Exeter, EX6 8AT Tel: (01392) 824022 Fax: (01392) 824838 E-mail: sales@amesolutions.co.uk

Concord Computer Services, Meridian Centre, King St, Oldham, OL8 1EZ Tel: 0161-627 2370 Fax: 0161-628 9429 E-mail: enq@concordservices.co.uk

▶ Evaluation Centre, 15 Chiltern Business Centre, 63-65 Woodside Road, Amersham, Buckinghamshire, HP6 6AA Tel: (0870) 9088767 Fax: (0870) 1340931 E-mail: info@pmp.co.uk

Imperial Business Systems, 7 Hill Street, Bristol, BS1 5PU Tel: 0117-925 1700 Fax: 0117-925 2515 E-mail: ibs@imperial.co.uk

▶ Metaphorix Ltd, 3 Temple Court, Temple Way, Coleshill, Birmingham, B46 1HH Tel: (01675) 432400 Fax: (01675) 465571 E-mail: enquiries@metaphorix.co.uk

▶ Nieman Walters, 7 Bourne Court Southend Road, Woodford Green, Essex, IG8 8HD Tel: (020) 8550 3131 Fax: (020) 8550 6020 E-mail: howard@nwnaccounts.com

Sheerspeed Accounting Services, 45 Highgate, Kendal, Cumbria, LA9 4ED Tel: (01539) 720807 Fax: (01539) 740516 E-mail: linxroger@aol.com

Xirtek, Matrix House, Langley Road, Chippenham, Wiltshire, SN15 1BT Tel: (01249) 767710 Fax: (01249) 766767 E-mail: info@matrixeng.co.uk

ACCOUNTS PAYABLE ACCOUNTANCY

▶ A L B Accountancy, 4 Brighton Road, Horsham, West Sussex, RH13 5BA Tel: (01403) 255788 Fax: (01403) 255704 E-mail: info@franaccounts.co.uk

▶ Accounting Taxation & Business Services, 58 Queen Elizabeth Drive, Beccles, Suffolk, NR34 9LP Tel: (01502) 713362 Fax: (01502) 714366 E-mail: mail@atbs1.co.uk

▶ Culwick & Co, 69 Southend Road, Hockley, Essex, SS5 4PZ Tel: (01702) 200939 Fax: (01702) 207258 E-mail: info@culwick.com

▶ Tax & Figures, Hamilton House, 111 Marlowes, Hemel Hempstead, Hertfordshire, HP1 1BB Tel: (01442) 450480 E-mail: robert@taxandfigures.com

▶ Wave Accounting Solutions Limited, 15 Lara Close, Throop, Bournemouth, BH8 0HB Tel: 07970 476709 E-mail: gordon@waveaccountingsolutions.co.uk

ACCOUNTS TRAINING, COMPUTERISED

▶ Pittmans Accounting Services, Parhema, Lees Court Road, Sheldwich, Faversham, Kent, ME13 0LY Tel: 01795 531085 Fax: 01795 531085 E-mail: info@pittmansage.co.uk

▶ System Fixers, The Heathers, Mildenhall, Marlborough, Wiltshire, SN8 2LR Tel: (08700) 733150 E-mail: mds@the-sf.com

▶ Workforce Systems, Unit 13 Nortex Business Centre, 105 Chorley Old Road, Bolton, BL1 3AS Tel: (01204) 842225 Fax: (01204) 497197 E-mail: sales@workforce.co.uk

ACCUMULATING CONVEYOR SYSTEMS

Excel Automation Ltd, Gregorys Bank, Worcester, WR3 8AB Tel: (01905) 721500 Fax: (01905) 613024 E-mail: information@excel-automation.co.uk

Handling Technology, 11 Cavendish Road, Halesowen, West Midlands, B62 0DB Tel: 0121-421 6153 Fax: 0121-423 1709

Jervis B Webb Co. Ltd, Swan Valley Way, Northampton, NN4 8BD Tel: (0845) 1270222 Fax: (0845) 1270221 E-mail: sales@jervisbwebb.co.uk

Logan Teleflex UK Ltd, Sutton Road, Kingston Upon Hull, Hull, HU7 0DR Tel: (01482) 785600 Fax: (01482) 785699 E-mail: marketing@loganteleflex.co.uk

Serpecon Ltd, 22 Fairmile Road, Halesowen, West Midlands, B63 3QJ Tel: 0121-550 5950 Fax: 0121-550 6222 E-mail: serpecon@btinternet.com

ACCUMULATOR (HYDRAULIC/ HYDROPNEUMATIC) MAINTENANCE AND RECERTIFICATION

Yarl Hydracentre Ltd, Scarth Road, Sowerby Wood Industrial Estate, Barrow-In-Furness, Cumbria, LA14 4RF Tel: (01229) 845560 Fax: (01229) 845561 E-mail: yarl@hydracentre.com

ACCUMULATORS, HYDRAULIC/ HYDROPNEUMATIC

Fawcett Christie Hydraulics Ltd, Sandycroft Industrial Estate, Chester Road, Sandycroft, Deeside, Clwyd, CH5 2QP Tel: (01244) 535515 Fax: (01244) 533002 E-mail: sales@fch.co.uk

Fluid Power Centre Ltd, 4th Avenue Zone 2, Deeside Industrial Park, Deeside, Clwyd, CH5 2NR Tel: (01244) 289231 Fax: (01244) 289232

Hydac Technology Ltd, Woodstock Road, Charlbury, Charlbury, Chipping Norton, Oxfordshire, OX7 3ES Tel: (01608) 811211 Fax: (01608) 811259E-mail: info@hydac.co.uk

Morton & Bone Services, PO Box 1, Gairloch, Ross-Shire, IV21 2AY Tel: (01445) 712322 Fax: (01445) 712310 E-mail: stopsurge@aol.com

Pulsation Dampers At Pulseguard Ltd, Unit 1, Greg Street Industrial Centre, Greg Street, Reddish, Stockport, Cheshire, SK5 7BS Tel: 0161-480 9625 Fax: 0161-480 9627 E-mail: sales@pulsation-dampers.co.uk

Quality Hydraulic Power Ltd, Unit 5 Chelford Close, Sealand Industrial Estate, Chester, CH1 4NE Tel: (01244) 393500 Fax: (01244) 393501 E-mail: sales@qhp.co.uk

ACETAL STOCKHOLDERS

Industrial Plastic Supplies Ltd, 3 Milestone Court, Stanningley, Pudsey, West Yorkshire, LS28 6HE Tel: 0113-257 2222 Fax: 0113-257 2222 E-mail: sales@industrialplastics.co.uk

Metals South West, 10 Bradley Lane, Newton Abbot, Devon, TQ12 1LZ Tel: (01626) 362026 Fax: (01626) 332220

ACETATE SHEET/FILM

▶ Polyester Converters Ltd, 49-53 Glengall Road, Peckham, London, SE15 6NF Tel: (020) 7740 9740 Fax: (020) 7277 5654 E-mail: sales@psggroup.co.uk

ACETIC ACID

A H Marks & Co. Ltd, Wyke Lane, Wyke, Bradford, West Yorkshire, BD12 9EJ Tel: (01274) 691234 Fax: (01274) 691176 E-mail: info@ahmarks.com

Tennants Distribution, Gelderd Road, Birstall, Batley, West Yorkshire, WF17 9LY Tel: (01924) 474447 Fax: (01924) 477842 E-mail: sales.leeds@tennantsdistribution.com

ACID OR CHEMICAL OR CORROSION RESISTING CEMENT

John Lord Holdings Ltd, Wellington Cement Works, Ainsworth Road, Bury, Lancashire, BL8 2RS Tel: 0161-764 4617 Fax: 0161-763 1873 E-mail: enquiries@john-lord.co.uk

North East Slag Cement Ltd, 97 Godstone Road, Caterham, Surrey, CR3 6RE Tel: (01883) 331071

ACID OR CORROSION RESISTANT FLOORING

Ancorite, Moston Road, Sandbach, Cheshire, CW11 3AB Tel: (01270) 761720 Fax: (01270) 761697

Epoxy Products, 7 Haviland Road, Ferndown Industrial Estate, Wimborne, Dorset, BH21 7RZ Tel: (01202) 891899 Fax: (01202) 896983 E-mail: sales@epoxyproducts.co.uk

John Lord Holdings Ltd, Wellington Cement Works, Ainsworth Road, Bury, Lancashire, BL8 2RS Tel: 0161-764 4617 Fax: 0161-763 1873 E-mail: enquiries@john-lord.co.uk

Kemtile Ltd, Unit C3, Taylor Business Park, Risley, Warrington, WA3 6BL Tel: (01925) 763045 Fax: (01925) 763381 E-mail: all@kemtile.co.uk

R P S Industrial Flooring Contractors Ltd, Woodhouse, Packhorse Lane, Headley Heath, Birmingham, B38 0DN Tel: (01564) 824900 Fax: (01564) 823447

ACID PROOF IMMERSION HEATERS

E. Braude (London) Ltd, Liberta House, Scotland Hill, Sandhurst, Berkshire, GU47 8JR Tel: (01252) 876123 Fax: (01252) 875281 E-mail: sales@braude.co.uk

ACID PUMPS

Bradford Cylinders Ltd, Soho Works, Allerton Road, Bradford, West Yorkshire, BD8 0BA Tel: (01274) 495611 Fax: (01274) 547119 E-mail: sales@bradfordcylinders.co.uk

David Bedlington Ltd, Flemingate Works, Flemingate, Beverley, North Humberside, HU17 0NZ Tel: (01482) 867590 Fax: (01482) 866472

Lutz (UK) Ltd, Gateway Estate, West Midlands Freeport, Birmingham, B26 3QD Tel: 0121-782 2662 Fax: 0121-782 2680 E-mail: lutzpump@aol.com

Sterling Fluid Systems UK Ltd, Atlantic Street, Broadheath, Altrincham, Cheshire, WA14 5DH Tel: 0161-928 6371 Fax: 0161-925 2129 E-mail: sales@sterlingfluid.com

Vanton Pumps Ltd, Unit 6 Radnor Park Industrial Centre, Back Lane, Congleton, Cheshire, CW12 1JJ Tel: (01260) 277040 Fax: (01260) 280605 E-mail: vanton@btinternet.com

ACID RESISTANT PROTECTIVE CLOTHING

Advance Workwear & Disposables Ltd, Unit 12a South Leicester Industrial Estate, Ellistown, Coalville, Leicestershire, LE67 1EU Tel: (01530) 263321 Fax: (01530) 262623 E-mail: info@advanceworkwear.com

Haqson Corporation, 12 Neville Road, Wirral, Merseyside, CH62 7JE Tel: 0151-334 9796

Hurricane Protective Clothing, Tame Valley Industrial Estate, Wilnecote, Tamworth, Staffordshire, B77 5DQ Tel: (01827) 250808 Fax: (01827) 250808 E-mail: hurricane@mgrubber.com

Mcconville Bros, 55-57 Kilvergan Road, Lurgan, Craigavon, County Armagh, BT66 6LJ Tel: (028) 3834 1452 Fax: (028) 3834 8892

ACID RESISTANT TANKS

Brooks Composites Ltd, Percival Lane, Runcorn, Cheshire, WA7 4DS Tel: (01928) 574776 Fax: (01928) 577067 E-mail: sales@brooks-composites.co.uk

Niplast Tanks, 187 Higher Hillgate, Stockport, Cheshire, SK1 3JG Tel: 0161-477 6777 Fax: 0161-429 8413 E-mail: contactus@niplast.com

Plastic Tanks & Fabrications Ltd, Unit 5, Stone Lane Industrial Estate, Wimborne, Dorset, BH21 1HD Tel: (01202) 888133 Fax: (01202) 886288 E-mail: ptf@avnet.co.uk

ACIDS, *See also other headings for particular acids*

Albion Chemicals Ltd, 46-50 Sydney Street West, Belfast, BT13 3GX Tel: (028) 9078 7450 Fax: (028) 9075 2500 E-mail: sales@albionchemicals.co.uk

Caldic UK Ltd, Stainsby Close, Holmewood Industrial Estate, Holmewood, Chesterfield, Derbyshire, S42 5UG Tel: (01246) 854111 Fax: (01246) 856222 E-mail: info@caldic.com

▶ The Scottish Crop Research Institute, Invergowrie, Dundee, DD2 5DA Tel: (01382) 562731 Fax: (01382) 562426

ACIDS, FATTY, DISTILLED

▶ Oleo Solutions Ltd, Westminster Business Centre, 10 Great North Way, Neter Poppleton, York, YO26 ^RB Tel: (01904) 520106 Fax: (01904) 520105 E-mail: garry.turner@oleosolutions.com

ACOUSTIC CEILING CLEANING MACHINES

▶ Cleanceil, 46 Owen Road, Kirkdale, Liverpool, L4 1RW Tel: 0870 910 1602 E-mail: enquiries@cleanceil.co.uk

Host Von Schrader, Unit 6 Capenhurst Technology Park, Capenhurst, Chester, CH1 6EH Tel: 0151-347 1900 Fax: 0151-347 1901 E-mail: host@hostvs.co.uk

ACOUSTIC CEILING CONSTRUCTORS OR MANUFACTURERS OR CONTRACTORS

Armstrong UK Investments, Armstrong House, 38 Market Square, Uxbridge, Middlesex, UB8 1NG Tel: (01895) 251122 Fax: (01895) 231571

Arrow Ceilings Ltd, A9 Hucknall Road, Nottingham, NG5 1FD Tel: 0115-985 7016 Fax: 0115-985 6883 E-mail: mail@arrowceilings.co.uk

Midland Tool Manufacturing Co. Ltd, Unit 13, Belle Eau Park, Bilsthorpe, Newark, Nottinghamshire, NG22 8TX Tel: (01623) 870411 Fax: (01623) 871857 E-mail: midlandtoolmans@msn.com

Quality Conveyors Ltd, 10 Elland Lane, Elland, West Yorkshire, HX5 9DU Tel: (01422) 377166 Fax: (01422) 377238

ACOUSTIC CEILING TILES

Burgess Architectural Products Ltd, Brookfield Road, Burbage, Hinckley, Leicestershire, LE10 2LL Tel: (01455) 618787 Fax: (01455) 251061 E-mail: info@burgessceilings.co.uk

C E P Ceilings Ltd, Welshmill Lane, Frome, Somerset, BA11 2LL Tel: (01373) 463185 Fax: (01373) 461437

C E P Ceilings Ltd, Common Road Industrial Estate, Verulam Road, Stafford, ST16 3EA Tel: (01785) 223435 Fax: (01785) 251309 E-mail: cep@cepgroup.co.uk

ACOUSTIC CONSULTANCY OR DESIGN

A B Dust Control Ltd, 79-81 High Street, Albrighton, Wolverhampton, WV7 3JA Tel: (01902) 373155 Fax: (01902) 373133 E-mail: abdustconltd@aol.com

A M S Acoustics, Rayleigh House, 21 Queen Annes Place, Enfield, Middlesex, EN1 2QB Tel: (020) 8886 4060 Fax: (020) 8360 2640 E-mail: info@amsacoustics.co.uk

Acia Engineering, 39 Garners Lane, Stockport, Cheshire, SK3 8SD Tel: 0161-487 2225 Fax: (0871) 9941778 E-mail: ian@acia-acoustics.co.uk

Acoustic Consultancy Services, 2 Belhaven Terrace Lane, Glasgow, G12 9LZ Tel: 0141-339 7536 Fax: 0141-339 7536 E-mail: andywatson@talk21.com

Acoustic Control Systems, 64 Cromley Road, High Lane, Stockport, Cheshire, SK6 8BU Tel: (01663) 764409 Fax: (01663) 764409 E-mail: sales@acousticcontrol.co.uk

Acoustic Design Consultancy, Aldham House, Lady La Industrial Estate, Hadleigh, Ipswich, IP7 6BQ Tel: (01473) 824452 Fax: (01473) 824408 E-mail: adc@acoustic.co.uk

Acoustic & Engineer Consultants Ltd, 1 Stockport Road, Marple, Stockport, Cheshire, SK6 6BD Tel: 0161-449 5900 Fax: 0161-449 5901 E-mail: kaw@aecltd.co.uk

Acoustic & Noise Partnership, Penburn House, 25a Upper Dock Street, Newport, Gwent, NP20 1DL Tel: (01633) 252957 Fax: (01633) 252958 E-mail: paul@acoustics-and-noise.co.uk

Acoustical Investigation & Research Organisation Ltd, Duxons Turn, Hemel Hempstead, Hertfordshire, HP2 4SB Tel: (01442) 247146 Fax: (01442) 256749 E-mail: airo@bcs.org.uk

Acoustics Noise & Vibration, Hastings House, Auckland Park, Bletchley, Milton Keynes, MK1 1BU Tel: (01908) 642811 Fax: (01908) 642800 E-mail: info@anv.uk.com

Arup Acoustics, 8 St Thomas Street, Winchester, Hampshire, SO23 9HE Tel: (01962) 829900 Fax: (01962) 867270 E-mail: rob.harris@arup.com

ATCO Noise Management Ltd, PO Box 3, Newcastle Upon Tyne, NE20 9WY Tel: (01661) 825379 Fax: (01661) 825379 E-mail: jerry.kinver@atconoise.com

Audio & Acoustics, United House, North Road, London, N7 9DP Tel: (020) 7700 2900 Fax: (020) 7700 6900 E-mail: sales@audioandacoustics.com

Belair Research Ltd, Broadway, Bourne, Cambridge, CB23 2TA Tel: (01954) 718366 Fax: (01954) 718355 E-mail: brl@acoustical.co.uk

Burau Verater Ltd, 91 Winchester Road, Chandlers Ford, Eastleigh, Hampshire, SO53 2GG Tel: (023) 8024 2300 Fax: (023) 8024 2399

C A D (Sales) Ltd, Unit 6, Waldegraves Business Park, West Mersea, Colchester, CO5 8SE Tel: (01206) 386611 Fax: (01206) 385959

Cole Jarman Associates, John Cree House, 24b High Street, Addlestone, Surrey, KT15 1TN Tel: (01932) 829007 Fax: (01932) 829003 E-mail: info@colejarman.com

Compliance Modules Ltd, Platts La Industrial Estate, Burscough, Ormskirk, Lancashire, L40 7TP Tel: (0791) 7407559 Fax: (01704) 891501 E-mail: sales@compliancemodules.co.uk

Cullum Detuners Ltd, Adams Close, Heanor Gate Industrial Park, Heanor, Derbyshire, DE75 7SW Tel: (01773) 717341 Fax: (01773) 760601 E-mail: sales.enquiries@cullum.co.uk

Custom Audio Design, Ridgeway Office Park, Bedford Road, Petersfield, Hampshire, GU32 3QF Tel: (01730) 269572 Fax: (0870) 7479878 E-mail: sales@customaudiodesigns.co.uk

D 4 S Fabrications Ltd, 19 Morses Lane, Brightlingsea, Colchester, CO7 0SF Tel: (01206) 303668 Fax: (01206) 304835 E-mail: ab@d4sfabrication.co.uk

Deane Austin Associates, PO Box 274, Aldershot, Hampshire, GU11 1TT Tel: (01252) 333727 Fax: (01252) 337266 E-mail: daa@tacitus.co.uk

Denis R Robinson & Associates, 169 Sherwood Avenue, Northampton, NN2 8TB Tel: (01604) 843807 Fax: (01604) 843807 E-mail: denis-rr@skynet.co.uk

Equus Partnership Ltd, Park House, 15-19 Greenhill CR, Watford, WD18 8PH Tel: (01923) 213625 Fax: (01923) 213863 E-mail: acoustix@equuspartnership.co.uk

Galloway Acoustics, Low Mill Lane, Ravensthorpe Industrial Estate, Dewsbury, West Yorkshire, WF13 3LN Tel: (01924) 498818 Fax: (01924) 498414 E-mail: sales.dewsbury@gallowaygroup.co.uk

Hann Tucker Associates Ltd, Duke House, Duke Street, Woking, Surrey, GU21 5BA Tel: (01483) 770595 Fax: (01483) 729565 E-mail: enquiries@hanntucker.co.uk

Hepworth Acoustics Ltd, 5 Bankside, Crosfield Street, Warrington, WA1 1UP Tel: (01925) 579100 Fax: (01925) 579150 E-mail: enquiries@hepworth-acoustics.co.uk

Hodgson & Hodgson Group, Audio House, Progress Road, Sands Industrial Estate, High Wycombe, Buckinghamshire, HP12 4JD Tel: (01494) 519000 Fax: (01494) 465274 E-mail: ecomax@easynet.co.uk

I A C (Industrial Acoustics Company) Ltd, I A C House, Moorside Road, Winchester, Hampshire, SO23 7US Tel: (01962) 873000 Fax: (01962) 873123 E-mail: info@iacl.co.uk

Innervisions, Po Box 9, Retford, Nottinghamshire, DN22 7GZ Tel: (01777) 702913

▶ Isvr Consulting, University Road, Southampton, SO17 1BJ Tel: (023) 8059 2162 Fax: (023) 8059 2728 E-mail: consultancy@isvr.co.uk

▶ Peter Lloyd & Associates, 18 Demesne Road, Holywood, County Down, BT18 9NB Tel: (028) 9042 8080 Fax: (028) 9042 8063 E-mail: LloydSound@aol.com

Martec Environmental Consultants Ltd, Waterbrow Wood, Gressingham, Lancaster, LA2 8LX Tel: (01524) 222000 Fax: (07970) 137469 E-mail: sales@noise.sh

Noico Ltd, Patrick House, Station Road, Hook, Hampshire, RG27 9HU Tel: (01256) 766207 Fax: (01256) 768413 E-mail: sales@noico.co.uk

Noise Insulation & Measurement Services, High Darkdale House, Slaggyford, Brampton, Cumbria, CA8 7NW Tel: (01434) 381394 Fax: (01434) 382634 E-mail: noise@cwcom.net

Norwest Acoustic Contractors, 9 Kirkstone Court, Congleton, Cheshire, CW12 4JW Tel: (01260) 280430 Fax: (01260) 280430 E-mail: norwestacoustics@btinternet.com

Otodynamics Ltd, 36-38 Beaconsfield Road, Hatfield, Hertfordshire, AL10 8BB Tel: (01707) 267540 Fax: (01707) 262327 E-mail: enquiries@oae-ilo.co.uk

▶ Peninsular Acoustics, 114 Shrewsbury Road, Prenton, Merseyside, CH43 8SP Tel: 0151-652 6270 Fax: 0151-652 6270 E-mail: noise@btconnect.com

Qinetiq, Cody Technology Park, Ively Road, Farnborough, Hampshire, GU14 0LX Tel: 08700 100942 Fax: (01252) 393399 E-mail: contactus@qinetiq.com

Chris Reading Associates, 6 Charfield Close, Winchester, Hampshire, SO22 4PZ Tel: (07802) 618656 Fax: (01962) 861496 E-mail: consult@cvrassociates.freeserve.co.uk

S T L Midlands Ltd, 80 Lockhurst Lane, Coventry, CV6 5PZ Tel: (024) 7658 4800 Fax: (024) 7658 4848 E-mail: enquiries@stl-ltd.com

Sonardyne Group Ltd, Ocean House, Blackbush Business Park, Yateley, Hampshire, GU46 6GD Tel: (01252) 872288 Fax: (01252) 876100 E-mail: sales@sonardyne.co.uk

▶ Sound Control Services, White Lodge Farm, Nottingham Road, Ab Kettleby, Melton Mowbray, Leicestershire, LE14 3JB Tel: (01664) 823704 Fax: (01664) 823663 E-mail: sales@soundcontrolservices.co.uk

Sound Research Laboratories Ltd, Holbrook House, Holbrook Hall Park, Little Waldingfield, Sudbury, Suffolk, CO10 0TH Tel: (01787) 247595 Fax: (01787) 248420 E-mail: srl@soundresearch.co.uk

▶ Sound Space Design, Unit 2 St. George's Court, 131 Putney Bridge Road, London, SW15 2PA Tel: (020) 8877 5868 Fax: (020) 8875 9385 E-mail: acoustics@soundspacedesign.co.uk

Stream Environmental, 100-102 Headstone Road, Harrow, Middlesex, HA1 1PF Tel: (020) 8933 6611 Fax: (020) 8424 8001 E-mail: sales@streamenvironmental.co.uk

Tek Ltd, Unit 14, Tyseley Industrial Estate, Seeleys Road, Birmingham, B11 2LQ Tel: 0121-766 5005 Fax: 0121-766 5010 E-mail: sales@tek.ltd.uk

ACOUSTIC CONTROL OR MONITORING OR MEASURING EQUIPMENT

Acoustics Noise & Vibration, Hastings House, Auckland Park, Bletchley, Milton Keynes, MK1 1BU Tel: (01908) 642811 Fax: (01908) 642800 E-mail: info@anv.uk.com

J & S Marine Ltd, Riverside Road, Pottington Business Park, Barnstaple, Devon, EX31 1LY Tel: (01271) 337500 Fax: (01271) 337501 E-mail: sales@jsmarine.co.uk

Nendle Acoustics Ltd, 153 High Street, Aldershot, Hampshire, GU11 1TT Tel: (01252) 344222 Fax: (01252) 333782 E-mail: info@nendle.co.uk

ACOUSTIC CONTROL OR MONITORING OR MEASURING EQUIPMENT – *continued*

Noise Insulation & Measurement Services, High Darkdale House, Slaggyford, Brampton, Cumbria, CA8 7NW Tel: (01434) 381394 Fax: (01434) 382634 E-mail: noise@cwcom.net

▶ Reef Inc, P.O.Box 185, Manchester, M41 6XG Tel: 0870 211 9888

ACOUSTIC CONTROL VENTILATORS

Airforce Ventilation Products, 3 Brunel Gate, West Portway Industrial Estate, Andover, Hampshire, SP10 3SL Tel: (01264) 358101 Fax: (01264) 358404 E-mail: enquiries@airforcevp.com

R W Simon Ltd, Hatchmoor Industrial Estate, Torrington, Devon, EX38 7HP Tel: (01805) 623721 Fax: (01805) 624578 E-mail: info@rwsimon.co.uk

ACOUSTIC COVERS/HOODS, COMPUTER ETC

Apcom Computer Services Ltd, 104 Newbury Gardens, Epsom, Surrey, KT19 0PD Tel: (020) 8224 9015 Fax: (020) 8224 9015 E-mail: atul@apcom.co.uk

▶ J R K Computer Supplies, Unit 27 Wombourne Enterprise Park, Bridgnorth Road, Wombourne, Wolverhampton, WV5 0AL Tel: (01902) 326426 Fax: (01902) 326323 E-mail: jrkkay@talk21.com

ACOUSTIC DOORS

Accent Hansen, Greengate Industrial Estate, Greenside Way, Middleton, Manchester, M24 1SW Tel: 0161-284 4100 Fax: 0161-655 3119 E-mail: operations@accenthansen.co.uk

Acoustic Engineering Services (UK) Ltd, PO Box 322, West Byfleet, Surrey, KT14 6YN Tel: (01932) 352733 Fax: (01932) 355265 E-mail: sales@aesuk.co.uk

Environmental Silencing Ltd, D5 Fleming Road, Hinckley, Leicestershire, LE10 3DU Tel: (01455) 617067 Fax: (01455) 615633 E-mail: contact@enviromental-silencing.fsnet.co.uk

Envirosound Ltd, 8 Murrell Green Business Park, London Road, Hook, Hampshire, RG27 9GR Tel: (01256) 760775 Fax: (01256) 760754 E-mail: sales@envirosound.co.uk

Pendle Doors Ltd, Plumbe Street, Burnley, Lancashire, BB11 3AG Tel: (01254) 870850 Fax: (01282) 703027 E-mail: info@pendledoors.co.uk

Replacement Door Co. Ltd, 24 Millfield, Livingston, West Lothian, EH54 7AR Tel: 01506 411434

ACOUSTIC ENCLOSURES

A E Engineering Services, 8 Eye Green Industries, Crowland Road, Eye, Peterborough, PE6 7SZ Tel: (01733) 223355 Fax: (01733) 222330 E-mail: tony@aeengineering.co.uk

Acoustic Enclosures Co. Ltd, Unit 3 Waldergraves Business Park, Waldergraves Lane, West Mersey, Colchester, CO5 8SE Tel: (01206) 384377 Fax: (01206) 384611 E-mail: acoustic.enclosures@btinternet.com

Bradgate Containers Ltd, Leicester Road, Shepshed, Loughborough, Leicestershire, LE12 9EG Tel: (01509) 508678 Fax: (01509) 503224 E-mail: sales@bradgate.co.uk

Compliance Modules Ltd, Platts La Industrial Estate, Burscough, Ormskirk, Lancashire, L40 7TP Tel: (0791) 7407559 Fax: (01704) 891501 E-mail: sales@compliancemodules.co.uk

Pennine Forge, Peel Park Works, Peel Park View, Bradford, West Yorkshire, BD3 0JY Tel: (01274) 642248 Fax: (01274) 634132

ACOUSTIC ENGINEERING

Amcc Electronic Engineers, 15 Enterprise Industrial Estate, Station Road West, Ash Vale, Aldershot, Hampshire, GU12 5QJ Tel: (01252) 377723 Fax: (01252) 377724 E-mail: enquiries@amcc.co.uk

Custom Audio Design, Ridgeway Office Park, Bedford Road, Petersfield, Hampshire, GU32 3QF Tel: (01730) 269572 Fax: (0870) 7479878 E-mail: sales@customaudiodesigns.co.uk

Euro Acoustics Holdings Ltd, 54 Trevean Way, Newquay, Cornwall, TR7 1TW Tel: (01637) 852172 Fax: (01637) 853960 E-mail: alan@euro-acoustics.com

Man Acoustics, Walrow Industrial, Commerce Way, Highbridge, Somerset, TA9 4AG Tel: (01278) 789335 Fax: (01278) 735385

Mech Tool Engineering Ltd, Whessoe Road, Darlington, County Durham, DL3 0QT Tel: (01325) 355141 Fax: (01325) 487053 E-mail: info@mechtool.co.uk

▶ Modern Fordayne Fire Protection Ltd, Crofton Drive, Lincoln, LN3 4NJ Tel: (01522) 531711 Fax: (01522) 510291 E-mail: sales@rilmac.co.uk

ACOUSTIC EQUIPMENT

▶ A V Calibration Ltd, 13C Old Bridge Way, Shefford, Bedfordshire, SG17 5HQ Tel: (01462) 638600 Fax: (01462) 638601 E-mail: lab@avcalib.co.uk

Bradgate Containers Ltd, Leicester Road, Shepshed, Loughborough, Leicestershire, LE12 9EG Tel: (01509) 508678 Fax: (01509) 503224 E-mail: sales@bradgate.co.uk

Environmental Silencing Ltd, D5 Fleming Road, Hinckley, Leicestershire, LE10 3DU Tel: (01455) 617067 Fax: (01455) 615633 E-mail: contact@enviromental-silencing.fsnet.co.uk

Fulcrum Systems, Hillbottom Road, Sands Industrial Estate, High Wycombe, Buckinghamshire, HP12 4HJ Tel: (0845) 4304060 Fax: (01494) 473324 E-mail: sales@fulcrum-systems.co.uk

▶ Inter County Office Furniture, 20-21 Woodside Industrial Park, Works Road, Letchworth Garden City, Hertfordshire, SG6 1LA Tel: (01462) 675609 Fax: (01462) 687025 E-mail: sales@intercounty.com

Mech Tool Engineering Ltd, Whessoe Road, Darlington, County Durham, DL3 0QT Tel: (01325) 355141 Fax: (01325) 487053 E-mail: info@mechtool.co.uk

ACOUSTIC EQUIPMENT HIRE

Dynamic Positioning Services Ltd, Unit 2, Denmore Place, Bridge Of Don, Aberdeen, AB23 8JS Tel: (01224) 226850 Fax: (01224) 226851 E-mail: egrant@dynamic-positioning.co.uk

ACOUSTIC FOAM PRODUCTS

Caligen Foam Ltd, Broad Oak, Accrington, Lancashire, BB5 2BS Tel: (01254) 355000 Fax: (01254) 355111 E-mail: info@caligen.co.uk

Siderise Holdings Ltd, Unit 21 Lady Lane Industrial Estate, Hadleigh, Ipswich, IP7 6BQ Tel: (01473) 827695 Fax: (01473) 824143 E-mail: oem@siderise.com

ACOUSTIC INSULATION CONTRACTORS, *See headings under Acoustic; also Noise; also Sound*

ACOUSTIC INSULATION MATERIALS

Aardvark Transatlantic Ltd, 106 New Road, Ascot, Berkshire, SL5 8QH Tel: (01344) 882314 Fax: (01344) 884506 E-mail: atlmonoglass@aol.com

Audio Agency Europe, PO Box 4601, Kiln Farm, Milton Keynes, MK19 7ZN Tel: (01908) 510123 Fax: (01908) 511123 E-mail: info@audioagencyeurope.com

Christie & Grey Ltd, Morley Road, Tonbridge, Kent, TN9 1RA Tel: (01732) 371100 Fax: (01732) 359666 E-mail: sales@christiegrey.com

Custom Audio Design, Ridgeway Office Park, Bedford Road, Petersfield, Hampshire, GU32 3QF Tel: (01730) 269572 Fax: (0870) 7479878 E-mail: sales@customaudiodesigns.co.uk

Custom Foams, Deans Rd, Wolverton Industry, Milton Keynes, MK12 5NA Tel: (01908) 312331 Fax: (01908) 220715 E-mail: sales@customfoams.co.uk

Euro Acoustics Holdings Ltd, 54 Trevean Way, Newquay, Cornwall, TR7 1TW Tel: (01637) 852172 Fax: (01637) 853960 E-mail: alan@euro-acoustics.com

Foam Techniques Ltd, 39 Booth Drive, Park Farm South, Wellingborough, Northamptonshire, NN8 6GR Tel: (01933) 400096 Fax: (01933) 400095 E-mail: sales@foamtechniques.co.uk

H P Chemie Pelzer UK Ltd, Speke Hall Avenue, Liverpool, L24 1UU Tel: 0151-448 2300 Fax: (08702) 429393

▶ Modern Fordayne Fire Protection Ltd, Crofton Drive, Lincoln, LN3 4NJ Tel: (01522) 531711 Fax: (01522) 510291 E-mail: sales@rilmac.co.uk

Perkins Contracts Ltd, Knights Court, South Chailey, Lewes, East Sussex, BN8 4QF Tel: (01273) 401401 Fax: (01273) 401400 E-mail: info@perkinscontracts.co.uk

Rieter Automotive Great Britain Ltd, Keller House, Hereward Rise, Halesowen, West Midlands, B62 8AN Tel: 0121-504 4500 Fax: 0121-504 4521 E-mail: steve.nash@rieterauto.com

Rocon Foam Products Ltd, 14 Shrub Hill, Worcester, WR4 9EL Tel: (01905) 26616 Fax: (01905) 612319 E-mail: sales@roconfoam.co.uk

Siderise Holdings Ltd, Unit 21 Lady Lane Industrial Estate, Hadleigh, Ipswich, IP7 6BQ Tel: (01473) 827695 Fax: (01473) 824143 E-mail: oem@siderise.com

Vitec, Oldham Road, Middleton, Manchester, M24 2DB Tel: 0161-653 8231 Fax: 0161-654 8942 E-mail: vitec@kay-metzeler.co.uk

Warren Insulation, Blackthorne Road, Colnbrook, Slough, SL3 0DU Tel: (01753) 687272 Fax: (01753) 681623 E-mail: heathrow@warren.co.uk

ACOUSTIC LOUVRES

▶ Avon Solar Control Ltd, Avon House, Kineton Road Industrial Estate, Southam, Warwickshire, CV47 0DR Tel: (01926) 818992 Fax: (01926) 811676 E-mail: enquiries@avonsolarcontrol.co.uk

ACOUSTIC MOULDINGS

Eiger (UK) Ltd, Unit 12, Landsdown Industrial Estate, Cheltenham, Gloucestershire, GL51 8PL Tel: (01242) 245678 Fax: (01242) 224643 E-mail: valform@aol.com

ACOUSTIC PANELS

Amman Valley Fabrication Ltd, Llandeilo Road, Llandybie, Ammanford, Dyfed, SA18 3JG Tel: (01269) 851266 Fax: (01269) 851340

Mech Tool Engineering Ltd, Whessoe Road, Darlington, County Durham, DL3 0QT Tel: (01325) 355141 Fax: (01325) 487053 E-mail: info@mechtool.co.uk

▶ Pellco Partitions, Church Lane, Challock, Ashford, Kent, TN25 4BU Tel: (01233) 740777 Fax: (01233) 740577E-mail: info@pellco.co.uk

ACOUSTIC SCREENS

▶ Pellco Partitions, Church Lane, Challock, Ashford, Kent, TN25 4BU Tel: (01233) 740777 Fax: (01233) 740577E-mail: info@pellco.co.uk

ACOUSTIC TELEPHONE HOODS

Burgess Architectural Products Ltd, Brookfield Road, Burbage, Hinckley, Leicestershire, LE10 2LL Tel: (01455) 618787 Fax: (01455) 251061 E-mail: info@burgessceilings.co.uk

Storacall Teleacoustics, 6 Enterprise Way, Cheltenham Trade Park, Cheltenham, Gloucestershire, GL51 8LZ Tel: (01242) 570995 Fax: (01242) 226131 E-mail: storacall.telea@btinternet.com

ACOUSTIC THERMAL INSULATING MATERIALS

Lancaster GTB Systems Ltd, 32 Europa Way, Lund Industrial Estate, Lancaster, LA1 5QP Tel: (01524) 599600 Fax: (01524) 599699 E-mail: info@lancastergtb.com

ACOUSTIC TRANSDUCERS

Chelsea Technologies Group, 55 Central Avenue, West Molesey, Surrey, KT8 2QZ Tel: (020) 8941 0044 Fax: (020) 8941 9349 E-mail: sales@chelsea.co.uk

Plastic Sensor Technology Ltd, 1 Vicarage Lane, The Bourne, Farnham, Surrey, GU9 8HN Tel: (01252) 724110 Fax: (01252) 716110 E-mail: pingpoint@btinternet.com

ACRYLIC AQUARIUM TANKS

▶ acrylic aquarium co (UK), 3 Fitzstephen Road, Dagenham, Essex, RM8 2YP Tel: 020 8593 3305 E-mail: info@aquariummasters.freeserve.co.uk

▶ Aqualease Ltd, Wigan Road, Leyland, PR25 5XW Tel: (0845) 3905904 E-mail: info@aqualease.co.uk

▶ AquariumHire.co.uk, PO Box 156, Sevenoaks, Kent, TN15 0WA Tel: (01732) 760991 Fax: (01732) 760992 E-mail: goldfish@aquariumhire.co.uk

World Of Water, Mulbrooks, Hailsham, East Sussex, BN27 2RH Tel: (01323) 442400 Fax: (01323) 848400

ACRYLIC CONSULTANTS OR DESIGNERS

▶ First Source & Supply Ltd, Unit 1 High Hall Farm, Oxley Hill, Heybridge, Maldon, Essex, CM9 8ES Tel: (01621) 810893 Fax: (01621) 840054 E-mail: info@firstsourcesupply.co.uk

▶ Logix Retail Display & Design Consultancy, Unit 15, Arlington Way, Dalton, Huddersfield, HD5 9TF Tel: (01484) 533548 E-mail: logix_gareth@fsmail.net

Lucite International Speciality Polymers & Resins Ltd, Horndale Avenue, Aycliffe Industrial Estate, Aycliffe Industrial Park, Newton Aycliffe, County Durham, DL5 6YE Tel: (01325) 300990 Fax: (01325) 314925

Stanley Plastics Ltd, Units 4-7, Holmbush Industrial Estate, Midhurst, West Sussex, GU29 9HX Tel: (01730) 816221 Fax: (01730) 812877 E-mail: sales@stanleyplastics.co.uk

▶ Studio Art, 65 The Parkway, Cottingham, North Humberside, HU16 5HD Tel: (07834) 839727 E-mail: info@studioartwork.co.uk

ACRYLIC EMBEDMENTS

Rubert & Co. Ltd, Acru Works, Demmings Road, Cheadle, Cheshire, SK8 2PG Tel: 0161-428 5855 Fax: 0161-428 1146 E-mail: info@rubert.co.uk

Stanley Plastics Ltd, Units 4-7, Holmbush Industrial Estate, Midhurst, West Sussex, GU29 9HX Tel: (01730) 816221 Fax: (01730) 812877 E-mail: sales@stanleyplastics.co.uk

ACRYLIC ENCAPSULATION MATERIALS

▶ M J K Acrylics, Unit 8b Whinfield Industrial Estate, Rowlands Gill, Tyne & Wear, NE39 1EH Tel: (01207) 549999 Fax: (01207) 549999 E-mail: mjkacrylics@btinternet.com

ACRYLIC FABRICATORS

▶ Daventry Guarding, 3 Siddeley Way, Royal Oak, Daventry, Northamptonshire, NN11 8PA Tel: (01327) 312880 Fax: (01327) 312881 E-mail: gareth@dglfabs.com

Eurolux Plastics Ltd, Unit 7 Station Road, Tolleshunt D'Arcy, Maldon, Essex, CM9 8TQ Tel: (01621) 868787 Fax: (01621) 868857 E-mail: euroluxplastic@ukonline.co.uk

Fibresports Glass Fibre, 34 Bowlers Croft, Basildon, Essex, SS14 3ED Tel: (01268) 282723 Fax: (01268) 282273 E-mail: fibresports@aol.com

▶ Imperial Design UK Ltd, Hanson Close, Middleton, Manchester, M24 2HD Tel: 0161-643 2266 E-mail: sales@displaydesgins.net

▶ Ino-Plaz Ltd, Unit B2 Chamberlain Business Centre, Chamberlain Road, Hull, HU8 8HL Tel: (01482) 225996 Fax: (01482) 225920 E-mail: sales@ino-plaz.co.uk

Project Plastics Ltd, 9 Grange Way Business Park, Grange Way, Colchester, CO2 8HF Tel: (01206) 868696 Fax: (01206) 793737 E-mail: project.plastics@btinternet.com

▶ Retail Engineering Design Ltd, Unit 2, Pioneer Park, Clough Road, Hull, HU6 7HW Tel: (01482) 333803 Fax: (01482) 333809 E-mail: info@redltd.karoo.co.uk

Screenprint Plus Ltd, Morton Peto Road, Harfreys Industrial Estate, Great Yarmouth, Norfolk, NR31 0LT Tel: (01493) 440292 Fax: (01493) 440269 E-mail: sales@screenprintplus.co.uk

Stanley Plastics Ltd, Units 4-7, Holmbush Industrial Estate, Midhurst, West Sussex, GU29 9HX Tel: (01730) 816221 Fax: (01730) 812877 E-mail: sales@stanleyplastics.co.uk

P.J. Wilkes Plastics Ltd, Unit 12A Izons Industrial Estate, Oldbury Road, West Bromwich, West Midlands, B70 9BS Tel: 0121-525 4224 Fax: 0121-525 2242 E-mail: pjw@pjwsigns.freeserve.co.uk

ACRYLIC FABRICS

A M Fabrics, 15 Sulgrave Road, Leicester, LE5 0LH Tel: 0116-274 2128 Fax: 0116-274 2790

ACRYLIC FURNITURE

Brockwood Collection, Brockwood Hill Farm, Park Lane, Audley, Stoke-On-Trent, ST7 8HR Tel: (01782) 722569 Fax: (01782) 722569 E-mail: louise@brockwood.freeserve.co.uk

Carlton House International Ltd, 19 Ayleswater, Aylesbury, Buckinghamshire, HP19 0FD Tel: (01296) 399507 Fax: (01296) 399507

Chalon UK Ltd, Hambridge Mill, Hambridge, Langport, Somerset, TA10 0BP Tel: (01458) 254600 Fax: (01458) 251192

Contrast Upholstery, Cobden Mill, Whalley Road, Sabden, Clitheroe, Lancashire, BB7 9DZ Tel: (01282) 778122 Fax: (01282) 771925

Goodwood Furniture Design Ltd, 74 Farndon Road, Newark, Nottinghamshire, NG24 4SE Tel: (01636) 706593

Graeme Scott Furniture, 11 Westcombe, Bideford, Devon, EX39 3JQ Tel: (01237) 424227 Fax: (01237) 470432

Mclay Furniture, Little Trodgers Lane, Mayfield, East Sussex, TN20 6PN Tel: (01435) 872877 Fax: (01435) 872817

Mark Griffiths Furniture Maker, Unit 4 Sewells Farm, Barcombe, Lewes, East Sussex, BN8 5TJ Tel: (01273) 401611 Fax: (01273) 628290

Michael Tyler Furniture Co. Ltd, Woodlands Way, The Ridge, Hastings, East Sussex, TN34 2RY Tel: (01424) 756675 Fax: (01424) 751436

Monk Furniture, Cottage Street Mill, Cottage Street, Macclesfield, Cheshire, SK11 8DZ Tel: (01625) 422525 Fax: (01625) 503919

Oxleaze Workshop, Nempnett Thrubwell, Blagdon, Bristol, BS40 7UZ Tel: (01761) 462927

ACRYLIC FURNITURE – *continued*

Pine Plus, 1 G E C Industrial Estate, Beanacre Road, Melksham, Wiltshire, SN12 8RP Tel: (01225) 707777

S L Furnishing, 16 Church Walk, Lurgan, Craigavon, County Armagh, BT67 9AA Tel: (028) 3832 6556 Fax: (028) 3832 6556

Shaw & Riley Ltd, Station Yard, New Road, Hessay, York, YO26 8JS Tel: (01904) 738700 Fax: (01904) 738001

Mark Stoddart International Designer, Ladybank House, Girvan, Ayrshire, KA26 9JJ Tel: (01292) 443103 Fax: (01292) 441266 E-mail: info@markstoddart.com

T J Smith, 9-9a Forge Lane, Headcorn, Ashford, Kent, TN27 9QG Tel: (01622) 891025

Technacryl Ltd, Shakenhurst, Cleobury Mortimer, Kidderminster, Worcestershire, DY14 9AR Tel: (01299) 832406 Fax: (01299) 832676

ACRYLIC MACHINING/CASTING/ ENGINEERING SERVICES

▶ Av-Tech Manufacturing Co. Ltd, Unit 33 London Road Industrial Estate, Baldock, Hertfordshire, SG7 6NG Tel: (01462) 893336 Fax: (01462) 893336

Hamar Acrylic Fabrications Ltd, 238-240 Bethnal Green Road, London, E2 0AA Tel: (020) 7739 2907 Fax: (020) 7739 7807

Moulded Acrylic Products, 4 Brook Farm, Horsham Road, Cowfold, Horsham, West Sussex, RH13 8AH Tel: (01403) 865220 Fax: (01403) 865224 E-mail: sales@mouldedacrylic.co.uk

Northern Cast Acrylics Ltd, 1 Aston Fields Road, Whitehouse Industrial Estate, Runcorn, Cheshire, WA7 3DL Tel: (01928) 790209 Fax: (01928) 790210 E-mail: nca@ncaltd.co.uk

ACRYLIC MODELS

A H Designs, Mountain Ash, Rhydyfoel Road, Llanddulas, Abergele, Clwyd, LL22 8EG Tel: (01492) 512765 Fax: (01492) 512662

Fine Form Architects Design & Model Makers, Searsons F M, Cordys Lane, Trimley, Felixstowe, Suffolk, IP11 0UD Tel: (01394) 672299 Fax: (01394) 672289 E-mail: sales@fineform.co.uk

Imagineering, Sittingbourne Research Centre Room 30 Building 940, Security, Sittingbourne, Kent, ME9 8AG Tel: (01795) 479120 Fax: (01795) 479120 E-mail: tom@imagineering1.co.uk

Mobile Marine Models, Drinsey Nook, Lincoln, LN1 2JJ Tel: (01522) 704485

ACRYLIC PLAQUES

Abbey Engraving, Unit 15 New Horizon Business Centre, Barrows Road, Harlow, Essex, CM19 5FN Tel: (01279) 626277 Fax: (01279) 626277 E-mail: info@abbeyengraving.co.uk

Anglia Sign Casting Co., 4 Horsbeck Industrial Estate, Horsbeck Way, Horsford, Norwich, NR10 3SS Tel: (01603) 897111 Fax: (01603) 897011

J A M Y Ltd, Unit 17 Roman Way Small Business Park, London Road, Godmanchester, Huntingdon, Cambridgeshire, PE29 2LN Tel: (01480) 456391 Fax: (01480) 414959 E-mail: sales@jamy.co.uk

ACRYLIC POLYMERS

Distrupol, 119 Guildford Street, Chertsey, Surrey, KT16 9AL Tel: (01932) 566033 Fax: (01932) 560363 E-mail: info@distrupol.com

Distrupol Ltd, Distrupol, Marston Road, Wolverhampton, WV2 4LN Tel: (01902) 426839 Fax: (01902) 426852 E-mail: info@distrupol.com

Lucite International Speciality Polymers & Resins Ltd, Horndale Avenue, Aycliffe Industrial Estate, Aycliffe Industrial Park, Newton Aycliffe, County Durham, DL5 6YE Tel: (01325) 300990 Fax: (01325) 314925

Rhodia Sealants Ltd, 4 Pomeroy Drive, Oadby, Leicester, LE2 5NE Tel: 0116-206 3400 Fax: 0116-206 3460 E-mail: rhodia.sealants@eu.rohodia.com

ACRYLIC PRODUCTS, CAST

Amari Plastics P.L.C., 11-12 Hillman Close, Hornchurch, Essex, RM11 2SJ Tel: (01708) 452525 Fax: (01708) 437030 E-mail: el@amariplastics.com

Amari Plastics plc, Wednesbury One, Blackcountry New Road, Wednesbury, West Midlands, WS10 7NZ Tel: 0121-567 3400 Fax: 0121-567 3401 E-mail: bm@amariplastics.com

J A M Y Ltd, Unit 17 Roman Way Small Business Park, London Road, Godmanchester, Huntingdon, Cambridgeshire, PE29 2LN Tel: (01480) 456391 Fax: (01480) 414959 E-mail: sales@jamy.co.uk

Moulded Acrylic Products, 4 Brook Farm, Horsham Road, Cowfold, Horsham, West Sussex, RH13 8AH Tel: (01403) 865220 Fax: (01403) 865224 E-mail: sales@mouldedacrylic.co.uk

Northern Cast Acrylics Ltd, 1 Aston Fields Road, Whitehouse Industrial Estate, Runcorn, Cheshire, WA7 3DL Tel: (01928) 790209 Fax: (01928) 790210 E-mail: nca@ncaltd.co.uk

ACRYLIC SHEET FABRICATORS

Anglo Fabrications Ltd, Saxon Way, Melbourn, Royston, Hertfordshire, SG8 6DN Tel: (01763) 260872 Fax: (01763) 262615 E-mail: sales@anglofabrication.com

Encore Of Gloucester Ltd, 5 Francis Woodcock Trading Estate, 277 Barton Street, Gloucester, GL1 4JE Tel: (01452) 503079 Fax: (01452) 310177 E-mail: j-mckee@btconnect.com

Engineering Plastic Services, 23a Eliot Street, Bootle, Merseyside, L20 4PD Tel: 0151-922 3243 Fax: 0151-922 6306

Fibresports Glass Fibre, 34 Bowlers Croft, Basildon, Essex, SS14 3ED Tel: (01268) 282723 Fax: (01268) 282273 E-mail: fibresports@aol.com

Hamar Acrylic Fabrications Ltd, 238-240 Bethnal Green Road, London, E2 0AA Tel: (020) 7739 2907 Fax: (020) 7739 7807

Heaven Dowsett & Co. Ltd, 197 Shady Lane, Birmingham, B44 9ES Tel: 0121-360 0345 Fax: 0121-360 7328 E-mail: richarddowsett@heavendowsett.com

▶ Imperial Design UK Ltd, Hanson Close, Middleton, Manchester, M24 2HD Tel: 0161-643 2266 E-mail: sales@displaydesgins.net

J D Sign & Display Ltd, Unit 34 Adams Industrial Estate, Dickerage Lane, New Malden, Surrey, KT3 3SF Tel: (020) 8949 4468 Fax: (020) 8949 7758E-mail: john@jdsignanddisplay.com

Limar Solutions Ltd, Imperial Works, King Street, Enderby, Leicester, LE19 4NT Tel: 0116-284 9019 Fax: 0116-275 0564 E-mail: steve@limarsolutions.co.uk

Northern Plastics 84 Ltd, Mount Street, Hyde, Cheshire, SK14 1NT Tel: 0161-368 2968 Fax: 0161-368 2183 E-mail: np84ltd@btconnect.com

▶ Peron Plastics, Unit 10 Dunscar Industrial Estate, Blackburn Road, Egerton, Bolton, BL7 9PQ Tel: (01204) 597546 Fax: (01204) 596928 E-mail: sales@peronplastics.co.uk

Ridgeway Plastics (Iver) Ltd, Unit 7B Waldeck House, Waldeck Road, Maidenhead, Berkshire, SL6 8BR Tel: (01628) 636621 Fax: (01628) 636621

Swan Signs Ltd, Lynton House, Golden Hill, Leyland, PR25 3NN Tel: (01772) 455011 Fax: (01772) 457936

Technacryl Ltd, Shakenhurst, Cleobury Mortimer, Kidderminster, Worcestershire, DY14 9AR Tel: (01299) 832406 Fax: (01299) 832676

ACRYLIC SHEETS

Atuglas International, Swadlincote, Derbyshire, DE11 1BD Tel: (0870) 5403050 E-mail: maureen.cairns@atuglasint.com

Hamar Acrylic Fabrications Ltd, 238-240 Bethnal Green Road, London, E2 0AA Tel: (020) 7739 2907 Fax: (020) 7739 7807

Industrial Plastic Supplies Ltd, 3 Milestone Court, Stanningley, Pudsey, West Yorkshire, LS28 6HE Tel: 0113-257 2222 Fax: 0113-257 2222 E-mail: sales@industrialplastics.co.uk

Irpen UK Ltd, Block A Bescot Industrial Estate, Woden Road West, Wednesbury, West Midlands, WS10 7SG Tel: 0121-556 5534 Fax: 0121-556 1744 E-mail: sales@irpenuk.demon.co.uk

Lewis & Mason Plastics, Unit 47 Business Development Centre, Stafford Park 4, Telford, Shropshire, TF3 3BA Tel: (01952) 210322 Fax: (01952) 292647 E-mail: info@lewis-mason-plastics.co.uk

Lucite International Speciality Polymers & Resins Ltd, Horndale Avenue, Aycliffe Industrial Estate, Aycliffe Industrial Park, Newton Aycliffe, County Durham, DL5 6YE Tel: (01325) 300990 Fax: (01325) 314925

Plastic Formers Ltd, Unit 1, King Street, Stockport Road, Denton, Manchester, M34 6PF Tel: 0161-320 7200 Fax: 0161-335 0109 E-mail: enquiries@plasticformers.co.uk

Polybron Plastics Ltd, Unit 4c Loughborough Motorway Trading Estate, Gelders Hall Road, Shepshed, Loughborough, Leicestershire, LE12 9NH Tel: (01509) 507123 Fax: (01509) 507594 E-mail: sales@polybron.co.uk

Robert Horne Group Plc, Huntsman House, Mansion Close, Moulton Park, Northampton, NN3 6LA Tel: (01604) 495333 Fax: (01604) 673495 E-mail: terry.cattle@roberthorne.co.uk

Sign Trade Supplies, Britannia House, Granville Road, Maidstone, Kent, ME14 2BJ Tel: (01622) 689410 Fax: (01622) 689416 E-mail: orders@signtradesupplies.co.uk

Sol Systems, Unit 4 Mallorie House, Beaumont Road, Banbury, Oxfordshire, OX16 1RH Tel: (01295) 255536 Fax: (01295) 276492 E-mail: bworsley@btinternet.com

ACRYLIC TUBES

Aluminium & Plastics Ltd, 29a Marlborough Road, Newport, Gwent, NP19 0PZ Tel: (01633) 259188 Fax: (01633) 212217

Northern Cast Acrylics Ltd, 1 Aston Fields Road, Whitehouse Industrial Estate, Runcorn, Cheshire, WA7 3DL Tel: (01928) 790209 Fax: (01928) 790210 E-mail: nca@ncaltd.co.uk

ACRYLIC YARN

Ahmad Textiles, Ahmad House, Downham Street, Bradford, West Yorkshire, BD3 9QY Tel: (01274) 727069 Fax: (01274) 390407 E-mail: info@ahmadtextiles.co.uk

B S K Ltd, Murdock Rd, Bedford, MK41 7PD Tel: (01234) 217096 Fax: (01234) 271537 E-mail: info@bsk.co.uk

Fabrics & Yarns Macclesfield Ltd, Hulley Road, Macclesfield, Cheshire, SK10 2LP Tel: (01625) 427311 Fax: (01625) 424769

K.Azmeh (Textiles) Ltd, Richmond House, Richmond Grove, Manchester, M13 0LN Tel: 0161-274 4827 Fax: 0161-274 4815 E-mail: info@katuk.com

SGL Technic Ltd, Muir of Ord Industrial Estate, Great North Road, Muir of Ord, Ross-Shire, IV6 7UA Tel: (01463) 870000 Fax: (01463) 871402

▶ Technical Textiles Executive, Batchworth Lock House, 99 Church Street, Rickmansworth, Hertfordshire, WD3 1JJ Tel: 01923 498001 E-mail: info@technicaltextiles.co.uk

▶ Textile Innovations Ltd, 14 Swan Court, Paradise Street, Oxford, OX1 1JB Tel: (01865) 201108 Fax: (01865) 201108 E-mail: mtemirov@yandex.ru

ACTIVATED ALUMINA

GeeJay Chemicals Ltd, 1 Beamish Close, Sandy, Bedfordshire, SG19 1SD Tel: (01767) 682774 Fax: (01767) 699697 E-mail: sales@geejaychemicals.co.uk

ACTIVATED CARBON

C P L Carbon Link, Sterling House, 2 Park Street, Wigan, Lancashire, WN3 5HE Tel: (01942) 824240 Fax: (01942) 824133 E-mail: support@activated-carbon.com

▶ Carbon Enterprises Ltd, 77A High St, Esher, Surrey, KT10 9QA Tel: (01372) 462892 Fax: (01372) 467043 E-mail: ce@carbonenterprises.co.uk

Chemviron Carbon Ltd, 434 London Road, Grays, Essex, RM20 4DH Tel: (01375) 381711 Fax: (01375) 389644 E-mail: info@chemvironcarbon.com

▶ HB Carbon (UK), Room C2 College Business Centre, The College, Uttoxeter New Road, Derby, DE22 3WZ Tel: (01332) 869310 E-mail: enquiry@hbcarbon.co.uk

Jacobi Carbons, 3 Moss Industrial Estate, St. Helens Road, Leigh, Lancashire, WN7 3PT Tel: (01942) 670600 Fax: (01942) 670605 E-mail: infouk@jacobi.net

Norit UK Ltd, Clydesmill Place, Cambuslang Industrial Estate, Clydesmill Industrial Estate, Glasgow, G32 8RF Tel: 0141-641 8841 Fax: 0141-641 8411 E-mail: fisher.martin.nl@norit.com

Sutcliffe Speakman Ltd, Edgar House, Lockett Road, Ashton-In-Makerfield, Wigan, Lancashire, WN4 8DE Tel: (01942) 275400 Fax: (01942) 275600 E-mail: immisioncontrols@waterlink.com

ACTIVATED CARBON ADSORPTION SYSTEMS

▶ Carbon Enterprises Ltd, 77A High St, Esher, Surrey, KT10 9QA Tel: (01372) 462892 Fax: (01372) 467043 E-mail: ce@carbonenterprises.co.uk

ACTIVE ELECTRONIC COMPONENTS

Comstock Electronics Ltd, Unit 6 Paycocke Road, Quatro Park, Basildon, Essex, SS14 3GH Tel: (01268) 295555 Fax: (01268) 523455 E-mail: celsales@comstock.co.uk

ACTIVITIES OR SPORTS UNDERWEAR

▶ one-wear Disposable underwear, po box 48611, London, NW8 7WZ Tel: (020) 7722 0687 E-mail: ask@one-wear.co.uk

ACTUATED VALVES

Actreg UK Ltd, 2 & 3 Henson Close, Telford Way Industrial Estate, Kettering, Northamptonshire, NN16 8PZ Tel: (01536) 412525 Fax: (01536) 521616 E-mail: sales@actreg.co.uk

Alpha Controls Ltd, Hindley Industrial Estate, Off Swan Lane, Hindley Green, Wigan, Lancashire, WN2 4HR Tel: (01942) 525833 Fax: (01942) 523413 E-mail: technicalsales@alphacontrols.co.uk

Bells Engineering Products Ltd, 874 Plymouth Road, Slough, SL1 4LP Tel: (01753) 567788 Fax: (01753) 567799 E-mail: bells.engineering@virgin.net

Bonomi UK Ltd, The Fluid Power Centre, Watling Street, Nuneaton, Warwickshire, CV11 6BQ Tel: (024) 7635 4535 Fax: (024) 7635 4143 E-mail: sales@bonomi.co.uk

Clayton & Co Penistone Ltd, Westhorpe Works, Halifax Road, Sheffield, S36 7EY Tel: (01226) 763130 Fax: (01226) 370145

Damar Group Ltd, Unit 15-19, Mill Road, Radstock, BA3 5TX Tel: (01761) 439111 Fax: (01761) 439123 E-mail: info@damarnet.com

Flow Control Co. Ltd, Cooper Drive, Springwood Industrial Estate, Braintree, Essex, CM7 2RF Tel: (01376) 321211 Fax: (01376) 321222 E-mail: flowcontrolco@lineone.net

Forac, Unit 8 9 Riverbank Business Centre, Old Shoreham Road, Shoreham-by-Sea, West Sussex, BN43 5FL Tel: (01273) 467100 Fax: (01273) 467101 E-mail: sales@forac.co.uk

G R Controls, 19 109 Sydenham Road, Birmingham, B11 1DG Tel: 0121-773 8007 Fax: 0121-773 8007 E-mail: grcontrols1@yahoo.co.uk

Indachem Process Valves Ltd, The Valve Centre Calder Road, Ravensthorpe, Dewsbury, West Yorkshire, WF13 3JS Tel: (01924) 438353 Fax: (01924) 438373

Invicta Valves Ltd, Units 10-11, Boxmend, Bircholt Road, Parkwood Industrial Estate, Maidstone, Kent, ME15 9XT Tel: (01622) 754613 Fax: (01622) 750436 E-mail: sales@invictavalves.co.uk

John Clark Ltd, Portrack Grange Road, Stockton-on-Tees, Cleveland, TS18 2PH Tel: (01642) 602288 Fax: (01642) 603388 E-mail: sales@jcvltd.com

Kits & Bits, Reform Street, Sutton-in-Ashfield, Nottinghamshire, NG17 5DB Tel: (01623) 442524 Fax: (01623) 442545 E-mail: kitsandbitsltd@aol.com

Leeds Valve Co. Ltd, Caledonia Road, Batley, West Yorkshire, WF17 5NH Tel: (01924) 428000 Fax: (01924) 428001 E-mail: sales@leedsvalve.com

Process Control Equipment, 45 Dukesway, Teesside Industrial Estate, Stockton-on-Tees, Cleveland, TS17 9LT Tel: (01642) 768250

Process Valve Supplies Ltd, 2 Ringtail Industrial Estate, Tollgate Road, Burscough, Ormskirk, Lancashire, L40 8RT Tel: (01704) 894403 Fax: (01704) 897046 E-mail: sales@processvalve.co.uk

Q Controls, Waterton House, Stoneywood, Bucksburn, Aberdeen, AB21 9HX Tel: (01224) 715464 Fax: (01224) 716079 E-mail: sales@jbpipeline.co.uk

SAFI Ltd, 35 Holton Road, Holton Heath Trading Park, Poole, Dorset, BH16 6LT Tel: (01202) 624618 Fax: (01202) 628500 E-mail: sales@safi-limited.com

Valvestock, 2 Fielder Drive, Fareham, Hampshire, PO14 1JG Tel: (01329) 283425 Fax: (01329) 822741 E-mail: enquiries@valvestock.co.uk

Western Automation Ivac, 5 Colemans Bridge, Witham, Essex, CM8 3HP Tel: (01376) 511808 Fax: (01376) 500862 E-mail: sales@waivac.co.uk

ACTUATORS, *See also headings for particular types*

Actuation Valve & Controls, 8 Woodward Road, Knowsley Industrial Park, Liverpool, L33 7UZ Tel: 0151-547 1221 Fax: 0151-547 1222 E-mail: chris@actuation.co.uk

Bonomi UK Ltd, The Fluid Power Centre, Watling Street, Nuneaton, Warwickshire, CV11 6BQ Tel: (024) 7635 4535 Fax: (024) 7635 4143 E-mail: sales@bonomi.co.uk

D J Automation Engineering Ltd, 11d Old Bridge Way, Shefford, Bedfordshire, SG17 5HQ Tel: (01462) 813703 Fax: (01462) 816810 E-mail: enquiries@djautomation.co.uk

Indachem Process Valves Ltd, The Valve Centre Calder Road, Ravensthorpe, Dewsbury, West Yorkshire, WF13 3JS Tel: (01924) 438353 Fax: (01924) 438373

LINAK UK Ltd, Actuation House, Crystal Drive, Sandwell Business Park, Smethwick, West Midlands, B66 1RJ Tel: 0121-544 2211 Fax: 0121-544 2552E-mail: sales@linak.co.uk

Poynton Valves Ltd, 81a Coppice Road, Poynton, Stockport, Cheshire, SK12 1SL Tel: (01625) 871014 Fax: (01625) 879814 E-mail: sales@poyntonvalves.com

Score Europe Ltd, Glenugie Engineering Works, Burnhaven, Peterhead, Aberdeenshire, AB42 0YX Tel: (01779) 480000 Fax: (01779) 481111 E-mail: adm@score-group.com

ACTUATORS, DOOR LOCK

▶ 3D Group, 3D Group, 165 Westdale Lane, Mapperley, Nottingham, NG3 6DH Tel: 0115-952 2772 E-mail: ddkeypro@hotmail.com

▶ indicates data change since last edition

ADAPTERS

Emulation Technology UK Ltd, 78 Asheridge Road, Chesham, Buckinghamshire, HP5 2PY Tel: (01494) 791336 Fax: (01494) 792336
▶ Laptopshop IT Ltd, 12-14 Valley Bridge Road, Clacton-on-Sea, Essex, CO15 4AD Tel: (01255) 422033 Fax: (01255) 470300 E-mail: sales@laptopshop.co.uk
Melcom Electronics, Elliott House, Gogmore Lane, Chertsey, Surrey, KT16 9AP Tel: (01932) 565544 Fax: (01932) 569988 E-mail: melcomsales@melcom.co.uk
▶ Robins Air Team, Unit 22, Llanelli Workshops, Trostre Industrial Park, Llanelli, Dyfed, SA14 9UU Tel: (0800) 0131440 Fax: (01554) 746569 E-mail: robin@robinsairteam.co.uk
Tyco Electronics, Head Office, Faraday Road, Swindon, SN3 5HH Tel: (01793) 528171 Fax: (01793) 572516 E-mail: PICUK@tycoelectronics.com

ADAPTERS, GAME, WIRELESS

▶ Freedom Wireless Ltd, Bedford Heights, Manton Lane, Bedford, MK41 7PH Tel: 08707 480153 E-mail: info@freedom-wireless.co.uk

ADAPTERS, GIGABIT NETWORK

▶ E-Linc Technologies Ltd, 3 Farrington Crescent, Lincoln, LN6 0YG Tel: (01522) 567765 E-mail: neil@elinc.co.uk

ADAPTERS, MEDIA, WIRELESS

▶ Freedom Wireless Ltd, Bedford Heights, Manton Lane, Bedford, MK41 7PH Tel: 08707 480153 E-mail: info@freedom-wireless.co.uk

ADAPTERS, PERIPHERAL COMPONENT INTERCONNECT (PCI), WIRELESS

▶ Freedom Wireless Ltd, Bedford Heights, Manton Lane, Bedford, MK41 7PH Tel: 08707 480153 E-mail: info@freedom-wireless.co.uk

ADAPTERS, PERSONAL COMPUTER (PC) MONITOR

Astra Distribution Ltd, 29 Roseberry Crescent, Great Ayton, Middlesbrough, Cleveland, TS9 6EP Tel: (01642) 724367 E-mail: info@astradistribution.com
▶ Blue.com, 76 Landedmans, Westhoughton, Bolton, BL5 2QJ Tel: 07841 708495 E-mail: pfreek@10Blue.com
▶ Cream Computers UK Ltd, The Red House, Kingswood Park, Bonsor Drive, Tadworth, Surrey, KT20 6AY Tel: (01737) 377220 Fax: (01737) 377221 E-mail: ray@creamcomputers.com
▶ Digit Computers, PO Box 47761, London, NW10 5UN Tel: (08700) 420490 Fax: (070) 92844761 E-mail: info@digitcomputers.co.uk
▶ J R K Computer Supplies, Unit 27 Wombourne Enterprise Park, Bridgnorth Road, Wombourne, Wolverhampton, WV5 0AL Tel: (01902) 326426 Fax: (01902) 326323 E-mail: jrkkay@talk21.com
Marketmix, Unit 12, Leigh Indoor Market Hall, Albion Street, LEIGH, Lancashire, WN7 4PG Tel: (01942) 677777 Fax: (07902) 045895 E-mail: rob@marketmix.co.uk
▶ Pc Option Ltd, 19 Ragdale Road, Bulwell, Nottingham, NG6 8GP Tel: (0870) 3501560 Fax: 0115-877 8603 E-mail: info@pcoption.co.uk
▶ PC Payless, 3 Farmfield Road, Bromley, BR1 4NE Tel: (020) 8480 1118
▶ Peach Data Services P.L.C., Lakeside, Festival Park, Stoke-on-Trent, ST1 5RY Tel: (01782) 267484 Fax: (01782) 267454 E-mail: john.burnett@peachdata.co.uk
Realtime Online, Blackstone Road, Huntingdon, Cambs, PE29 6EF Tel: (01480) 435881 Fax: (01480) 411120 E-mail: sales@realtimeltd.co.uk
Response It Services, 31 Prospect Place, Epsom, Surrey, KT17 1WW Tel: (0870) 2642062 E-mail: simon@response-it.co.uk
▶ Somerset Computers, 168 Southdown Road, Southdown, Bath, BA2 1JL Tel: 01225 424887

ADDITIVE INJECTION SYSTEMS

Enraf Fluid Technology Ltd, 6 Pennant Park, Standard Way, Fareham, Hampshire, PO16 8XU Tel: (01329) 825823 Fax: (01329) 825824 E-mail: info@enraf.com

ADDITIVES, ENGINE OIL

▶ Performance Oils Ltd, 40 Broad Walk, Hounslow, TW5 9AQ Tel: (020) 8737 0649 Fax: (020) 8577 3974 E-mail: greenlynx@blueyonder.co.uk

ADDITIVES, ENGINE OIL, COLLOIDAL PTFE

Intro Marketing Ltd, Old Freight Depot, Roberts Road, Doncaster, South Yorkshire, DN4 0JW Tel: (01302) 320269 Fax: (01302) 340678 E-mail: sales@intro.co.uk

ADDRESSABLE EMERGENCY LIGHTING SYSTEMS

▶ City Fire Protection Ltd, 30 Ansdell Drive, Brockworth, Gloucester, GL3 4BU Tel: (0800) 0730250 Fax: (01452) 530669 E-mail: info@cityfireprotection.co.uk

ADDRESSABLE FIRE ALARM SYSTEMS

▶ Cook Facilities Ltd, Technology Centre, 20 Westgate, Morecambe, Lancashire, LA3 3LN Tel: (01524) 402090 Fax: (01524) 418269 E-mail: sales@cookfire.co.uk
▶ East Riding Electrical Ltd, Unit 4b Colt Business Park Havelock Street, Hull, HU3 4TU Tel: (01482) 326553 Fax: (01482) 326553 E-mail: enquires@e-r-e.co.uk
▶ Elektrek Services Ltd, 19 Manning Road, Felixstowe, Suffolk, IP11 2AY Tel: (01394) 270777 Fax: 01394 670189 E-mail: mail@elektrek.com
▶ J R H Electrical Contractors Ltd, Unit A, Ashleigh Mews, Woodland Grove, Blackpool, FY3 9HD Tel: (01253) 390002 Fax: (01253) 390003 E-mail: info@jrh-electrical.com
▶ Kentec, Unit 25 Fawkes Avenue, Dartford Trade Park, Dartford, DA1 1JQ Tel: (01322) 222121 Fax: (01322) 291794 E-mail: sales@kentec.co.uk

ADDRESSING MACHINES

Renaddress Ltd, Target House, Lea Road, Waltham Abbey, Essex, EN9 1AE Tel: (01992) 712592 Fax: (01992) 760902 E-mail: reg@target-sys.co.uk

ADHESIVE APPLICATION OR COATING EQUIPMENT

2KM UK Ltd, 11 Sherwood House, Sherwood Road, Aston Fields Trading Estate, Bromsgrove, Worcestershire, B60 3DR Tel: (01527) 834720 Fax: (01527) 834729 E-mail: sales@2km.co.uk
AWE Newtech Ltd, Brunel Drive, Northern Road Industrial Estate, Newark, Nottinghamshire, NG24 2EG Tel: (01636) 703793 Fax: (01636) 701210 E-mail: sales@awe-newtech.com
▶ Eurotrade Global Ltd, 4 Julian Place, Docklands, London, E14 3AT Tel: (020) 7515 5499 Fax: (020) 7531 1412 E-mail: etguk@btinternet.com
Flexible Heating Hoses Ltd, Unit Z Sapcote Trading Centre, 68 Wyrley Road, Aston, Birmingham, B6 7BN Tel: 0121-250 2525 Fax: 0121-250 2526 E-mail: sales@flexible-heated-hoses.co.uk
H H S Gluing Systems, Peterborough Business Park, Lynch Wood, Peterborough, PE2 6FZ Tel: (01733) 391333 Fax: (01733) 391555 E-mail: sales@hhsuk.co.uk
Intertronics Electronic Equipment Component, 17a Station Field Industrial Estate, Kidlington, Oxfordshire, OX5 1JD Tel: (01865) 842842 Fax: (01865) 842172 E-mail: enquiries@intertronics.co.uk
Kleinmichel, Birds Hill, Letchworth Garden City, Hertfordshire, SG6 1JE Tel: (01462) 677611 Fax: (0870) 7626539 E-mail: uk-sales@kleinmichel.com
W.H. Leary Ltd, Bentalls, Basildon, Essex, SS14 3BX Tel: (01268) 535800 Fax: (01268) 535808 E-mail: sales.europe@whleary.com
Liquid Control Ltd, Stewarts Road, Finedon Road Industrial Estate, Wellingborough, Northamptonshire, NN8 4RJ Tel: (01933) 277571 Fax: (01933) 440273 E-mail: sales@liquidcontrol.co.uk
Meter Mix Systems Ltd, Unit 1 Brindley Close, Rushden, Northamptonshire, NN10 6EN Tel: (01933) 354500 Fax: (01933) 354506
Metix (UK) Ltd, Saxon House, Henson Way, Telford Way Industrial Estate, Kettering, Northamptonshire, NN16 8PX Tel: (01536) 312990 Fax: (01536) 312985 E-mail: sales@metix.co.uk
Nordson UK Ltd, Wenman Road, Thame, Oxfordshire, OX9 3SW Tel: (01844) 264500 Fax: (01844) 215358 E-mail: salesoxf@uk.nordson.com
Power Adhesives Ltd, 1 Lords Way, Basildon, Essex, SS13 1TN Tel: (01268) 885800 Fax: (01268) 885810 E-mail: sales@poweradhesives.com
Quma Systems Ltd, 7 Frarydene, Emsworth, Hampshire, PO10 8HU Tel: (01243) 373746 Fax: (01243) 379730 E-mail: quma.systems@btinternet.com
R & A Stevens, 2 Church Terrace, Bures, Suffolk, CO8 5ED Tel: (01787) 227291 Fax: (01787) 228252 E-mail: stevens.ra@virgin.net
Rocep Pressure Packs Ltd, Rocep Drive, Renfrew, PA4 8XY Tel: 0141-885 2222 Fax: 0141-886 7464 E-mail: info@rocep.com
S & D Sealants Cotswold, St. James Trading Estate, Barton Street, Gloucester, GL1 4JJ Tel: (01452) 504344 Fax: (01452) 504355
Valco Cincinnati, Unit 7-8 Hortonwood 32, Telford, Shropshire, TF1 7YN Tel: (01952) 677911 Fax: (01952) 677945 E-mail: sales@valco.co.uk
Wey Adhesives Ltd, Unit 45 Murrell Green Business Park, London Road, Hook, Hampshire, RG27 9GR Tel: (01256) 766661 Fax: (01256) 766667 E-mail: sales@weyadhesives.com

ADHESIVE APPLICATION SYSTEMS

▶ Tecno Incollaggi UK Ltd, 4 Warren Court, Stapleford, Nottingham, NG9 8EY Tel: (07866) 477542 Fax: 0115-875 2670 E-mail: info@tecnoinc.co.uk

ADHESIVE APPLICATION/ COATING EQUIPMENT SPARE PARTS

Highland Scientific, Unit 16 Bedford Business Centre, Mile Road, Bedford, MK42 9TW Tel: (01234) 216636 Fax: (01234) 271991 E-mail: sales@highland-scientific.com
R & A Stevens, 2 Church Terrace, Bures, Suffolk, CO8 5ED Tel: (01787) 227291 Fax: (01787) 228252 E-mail: stevens.ra@virgin.net

ADHESIVE APPLICATION/ COATING EQUIPMENT, AQUEOUS DISPERSIONS

▶ Bondrite Adhesives Ltd, Unit 12, Meadow Lane Industrial Estate, Gordon Road, Loughborough, Leicestershire, LE11 1JP Tel: (01509) 262121 Fax: (01509) 262122 E-mail: sales@bondrite.co.uk
H H S Gluing Systems, Peterborough Business Park, Lynch Wood, Peterborough, PE2 6FZ Tel: (01733) 391333 Fax: (01733) 391555 E-mail: sales@hhsuk.co.uk

ADHESIVE APPLICATION/ COATING EQUIPMENT, HOT MELT (HMA)

Adhesives International Ltd, Northleigh Business Park, Woodstock Road, North Leigh, Witney, Oxfordshire, OX29 6RN Tel: (01993) 882749 Fax: (01993) 883887 E-mail: info@adhesivesintnl.com
Bea Fastening Systems Ltd, Waterside Road, Beverley, North Humberside, HU17 0ST Tel: (01482) 889911 Fax: (01482) 871804 E-mail: sales@uk.bea-group.com
▶ Bondrite Adhesives Ltd, Unit 12, Meadow Lane Industrial Estate, Gordon Road, Loughborough, Leicestershire, LE11 1JP Tel: (01509) 262121 Fax: (01509) 262122 E-mail: sales@bondrite.co.uk
FineCal (Cymru) Ltd, 3 Rhymney River Bridge Road, Rumney, Cardiff, CF23 9AF Tel: (029) 2046 2644 Fax: (029) 2048 4522 E-mail: sales@finecal.co.uk
H H S Gluing Systems, Peterborough Business Park, Lynch Wood, Peterborough, PE2 6FZ Tel: (01733) 391333 Fax: (01733) 391555 E-mail: sales@hhsuk.co.uk
Hawkes Technical Ltd, Spencer Parade, Stanwick, Wellingborough, Northamptonshire, NN9 6QJ Tel: (01933) 622492 Fax: (01933) 624092 E-mail: info@hawkestechnical.com
Power Adhesives Ltd, 1 Lords Way, Basildon, Essex, SS13 1TN Tel: (01268) 885800 Fax: (01268) 885810 E-mail: sales@poweradhesives.com
R & A Stevens, 2 Church Terrace, Bures, Suffolk, CO8 5ED Tel: (01787) 227291 Fax: (01787) 228252 E-mail: stevens.ra@virgin.net
Robatech UK Ltd, The Street, Broughton Gifford, Melksham, Wiltshire, SN12 8PH Tel: (01225) 783456 Fax: (01225) 783400 E-mail: sales@robatech.co.uk
Stapling Centre P.L.C., Rapesco House, One Connections Business Place, Otford Road, Sevenoaks, Kent, TN14 5DF Tel: (01732) 464800 Fax: (01732) 464888
Valco Cincinnati, Unit 7-8 Hortonwood 32, Telford, Shropshire, TF1 7YN Tel: (01952) 677911 Fax: (01952) 677945 E-mail: sales@valco.co.uk
Wey Adhesives Ltd, Unit 45 Murrell Green Business Park, London Road, Hook, Hampshire, RG27 9GR Tel: (01256) 766661 Fax: (01256) 766667 E-mail: sales@weyadhesives.com

ADHESIVE APPLICATION/ COATING MONITORING/ QUALITY CONTROL DETECTION SYSTEMS

Elcometer Instruments Ltd, Edge Lane, Droylsden, Manchester, M43 6BU Tel: 0161-371 6000 Fax: 0161-371 6010 E-mail: sales@elcometer.com

ADHESIVE APPLICATION/ COATING SERVICES

A T London Ltd, 218 Hornsey Road, London, N7 7LL Tel: (020) 7607 3512 Fax: (020) 7607 3522 E-mail: sales@atlondonltd.co.uk
Cherrie Adhesive Coatings Ltd, Unit 14 Raikes Clough Industrial, Estate Raikes Lane, Bolton, BL3 1RP Tel: (01204) 371645 Fax: (01204) 371645
Premier Coatings & Converters, West Portway, Andover, Hampshire, SP10 3LF Tel: (01264) 358633 Fax: (01264) 334701 E-mail: sales@pcc-ltd.com
Raleigh Adhesive Coatings, Unit 1c Raleigh Hall Industrial Estate, Eccleshall, Stafford, ST21 6JL Tel: (01785) 852824 Fax: (01785) 851358
Webmaster Ltd, Units 5-6 Astra Industrial Centre, Royle Barn Road, Rochdale, Lancashire, OL11 3DT Tel: (01706) 656122 Fax: (01706) 764400 E-mail: sales@webmasterltd.co.uk

ADHESIVE COATED PRODUCTS

Warrender Products, 284 Chepstow Road, Newport, Gwent, NP19 8NN Tel: (01633) 278336 Fax: (01633) 666986

ADHESIVE CONSULTANTS/ ADVISORY SERVICES

Adhesive Technical Services Ltd, Beacon Hill Industrial Estate, Botany Way, Purfleet, Essex, RM19 1SR Tel: (01708) 867355 Fax: (01708) 869804 E-mail: sales@adhtechnical.com
Alansons Industrial Supplies, 7 Flowers Hill, Bristol, BS4 5JJ Tel: 0117-971 1364 Fax: (0870) 7773272
▶ Bondrite Adhesives Ltd, Unit 12, Meadow Lane Industrial Estate, Gordon Road, Loughborough, Leicestershire, LE11 1JP Tel: (01509) 262121 Fax: (01509) 262122 E-mail: sales@bondrite.co.uk

ADHESIVE DESIGN

Adhesive Technical Services Ltd, Beacon Hill Industrial Estate, Botany Way, Purfleet, Essex, RM19 1SR Tel: (01708) 867355 Fax: (01708) 869804 E-mail: sales@adhtechnical.com
Bluefrog Design, 21 St Margarets Street, Leicester, LE1 3EB Tel: 0116-253 0612 Fax: 0116-226 5737 E-mail: mail@bluefrogdesign.co.uk

ADHESIVE DISPENSERS OR MIXERS

Ellsworth Adhesives Ltd, 2 Kelvin South BSNS Park, Glasgow, G75 0YG Tel: (01355) 231122 Fax: (01355) 235266 E-mail: info@ellsworthadhesives.co.uk
Liquid Control Ltd, Stewarts Road, Finedon Road Industrial Estate, Wellingborough, Northamptonshire, NN8 4RJ Tel: (01933) 277571 Fax: (01933) 440273 E-mail: sales@liquidcontrol.co.uk
Metix (UK) Ltd, Saxon House, Henson Way, Telford Way Industrial Estate, Kettering, Northamptonshire, NN16 8PX Tel: (01536) 312990 Fax: (01536) 312985 E-mail: sales@metix.co.uk

ADHESIVE GLAZING TAPES

Venture Tape Europe, 5-6 Faraday Close, Drayton Fields Industrial Estate, Daventry, Northamptonshire, NN11 8RD Tel: (01327) 876555 Fax: (01327) 876444 E-mail: jaeanne@venturetape.co.uk

ADHESIVE MATERIALS, RAW/ BASE

Resad Polymers Ltd, 53 Royce Close, West Portway Industrial Estate, Andover, Hampshire, SP10 3TS Tel: (01264) 334633 Fax: (01264) 332639 E-mail: sales@resad.co.uk

ADHESIVE MIXERS

Fillworth (UK) Ltd, Unit 2, Baltic Road, Felling, Gateshead, Tyne & Wear, NE10 0SB Tel: 0191-500 0230 Fax: 0191-500 0231 E-mail: mail@fillworth.com

Meter Mix Systems Ltd, Unit 1 Brindley Close, Rushden, Northamptonshire, NN10 6EN Tel: (01933) 354500 Fax: (01933) 354506

ADHESIVE PACKING AND FILLING CONTRACT SERVICES, TUBE/APPLICATOR

C B Baggs Ltd, 1 Claremont Industrial Estate, London, NW2 1AL Tel: (020) 8905 5111 Fax: (020) 8905 5222 E-mail: info@cbbaggs.co.uk

Cedesa Ltd, Chater Lea Building, Icknield Way, Letchworth Garden City, Hertfordshire, SG6 1WT Tel: (01462) 480764 Fax: (01462) 480765 E-mail: neil.wildon@cedesa.co.uk

Co Ordinated Packaging Ltd, 3-4 Robert Way, Wickford, Essex, SS11 8DD Tel: (01268) 570551 Fax: (01268) 570611

ADHESIVE PACKING AND FILLING EQUIPMENT

R C S Filling Machines Ltd, Unit 1 Brand Street, Nottingham, NG2 3GW Tel: 0115-985 1717 Fax: 0115-985 1948 E-mail: sales@rcsfilling.com

ADHESIVE PRINTED TAPES

Allstat Ltd, Bowmans Trading Estate, Bessemer Drive, Stevenage, Hertfordshire, SG1 2DL Tel: (01438) 759084 Fax: (01438) 740958 E-mail: info@allstat.co.uk

Compat Europe Ltd, 24 Harnham Trading Estate, Salisbury, SP2 8NW Tel: (01722) 326411 Fax: (01722) 326413 E-mail: compat@tesco.net

Fillmore Packaging Ltd, Unit 15, Bowthorpe Industrial Estate, Norwich, NR5 9JE Tel: (01603) 745911 Fax: (01603) 747519 E-mail: sales.norwich@fillmorepackaging.co.uk

Limpet Printed Tapes Ltd, The Causeway, Bassingbourn, Royston, Hertfordshire, SG8 5JB Tel: (01763) 252420 Fax: (01763) 252421 E-mail: print@limpettapes.com

Links Labels & Tapes Ltd, Pinfold Road, Bourne, Lincolnshire, PE10 9HT Tel: (01778) 426282 Fax: (01778) 425003 E-mail: enquiries@linkslabels-tapes.co.uk

Morrison Adhesive Tapes Ltd, PO Box 2279, Glasgow, G33 9AE Tel: 0141-779 5648 E-mail: morrisontapes@tiscali.co.uk

Pakprint Tapes Ltd, Woodlands, Dale Street, Longwood, Huddersfield, HD3 4TG Tel: (01484) 644884 Fax: (01484) 460094 E-mail: gat@pakprint.co.uk

PBL Packaging, 6 Maple Business Park, Walter Street, Birmingham, B7 5ET Tel: 0121-327 7757 Fax: 0121-328 3382

Scappa (U K) Ltd, The Woodside Estate, Dunstable, Bedfordshire, LU5 4TP Tel: (01582) 478111 Fax: (01582) 471085 E-mail: carole.price@scapatapes.com

Swallow Tapes Ltd, 2 Cotton Hall Barns, Middlewich Road, Holmes Chapel, Crewe, CW4 7ET Tel: (01477) 535599 Fax: (01477) 535440 E-mail: sales@swallowtapes.sagehost.co.uk

Tritel Ltd, Unit 1 Bolney Grange Business Park, Hickstead, Haywards Heath, West Sussex, RH17 5PB Tel: (01444) 871188 Fax: (01444) 871199 E-mail: sales@tritel.co.uk

Watershed Packaging Ltd, Westpoint, Westland Square, Leeds, LS11 5SS Tel: 0113-277 0606 Fax: 0113-277 7174 E-mail: sales@watershed-packaging.co.uk

ADHESIVE SEALING PRODUCTS

▶ Anixper Luton, Unit 10, Sundon Business Park, Dencora Way, Luton, LU3 3HP Tel: (01582) 491748 Fax: (01582) 491280 E-mail: luton.adesco@infast.com

Chemence Ltd, 13 Princewood Road, Earlstrees Industrial Estate, Corby, Northamptonshire, NN17 4XD Tel: (01536) 402600 Fax: (01536) 400266 E-mail: sales@chemence.com

Scappa (U K) Ltd, The Woodside Estate, Dunstable, Bedfordshire, LU5 4TP Tel: (01582) 478111 Fax: (01582) 471085 E-mail: carole.price@scapatapes.com

Sword Sealant Services Ltd, 8 Fryern Wood, Chaldon, Caterham, Surrey, CR3 5AR Tel: (01883) 348311 Fax: (01883) 340872 E-mail: swordsealant@btconnet.com

ADHESIVE TAPE APPLICATION EQUIPMENT

Forward & Thompson Ltd, Atlas Road, North York Trading Estate, Clifton Moor, York, YO30 4UR Tel: (01904) 690999 Fax: (01904) 690960

Snow Hunter Automation, PO Box 260, Scarborough, North Yorkshire, YO12 5YA Tel: (07944) 085848 Fax: (01723) 371696 E-mail: john@snowhunter.freeserve.co.uk

ADHESIVE TAPE CONVERTERS

A & B Converters, 8a Common Lane, Sawston, Cambridge, CB22 3HW Tel: (01223) 830026 Fax: (01223) 830026 E-mail: ab_converters@hotmail.com

Action Tapes Ltd, Red Scar Industrial Estate, Longridge Road, Ribbleton, Preston, PR2 5NE Tel: (01280) 700591 Fax: (01280) 700590 E-mail: sales@prestec.co.uk

Adhere Industrial Tapes Ltd, Unit 1 Whitehall Road, Whitehall Industrial Estate, Colchester, CO2 8WA Tel: (01206) 871999 Fax: (01206) 871998 E-mail: sales@adhere.co.uk

Adhesive Tape Manufacturing Co Ltd, 2 Bilston Industrial Estate, Oxford Street, Bilston, West Midlands, WV14 7EG Tel: (01902) 409598 Fax: (01902) 409599 E-mail: sales@atmuk.co.uk

BDK Industrial Products, Levington Park, Bridge Road, Levington, Ipswich, IP10 0JE Tel: (01473) 659059 Fax: (01473) 659104 E-mail: sales@bdk.uk.com

General Fabrications Ltd, 26 Orphanage Road, Birmingham, B24 9HT Tel: 0121-377 6070 Fax: 0121-377 7175 E-mail: info@genfab.co.uk

▶ Kwikgrip Ltd, Denaby Main Industrial Estate, Denaby Main, Doncaster, South Yorkshire, DN12 4LH Tel: (01709) 772422 E-mail: sales@kwikgrip.co.uk

▶ Lohmann Adhesive Tape Systems, Cane End Lane, Bierton, Aylesbury, Buckinghamshire, HP22 5BH Tel: (01296) 337888 Fax: (01296) 337772 E-mail: info@lohmann-tapes.co.uk

Parafix, Spencer Road, Church Hill Industrial Estate, Lancing, West Sussex, BN15 8UA Tel: (01903) 750000 Fax: (01903) 767728 E-mail: sales@parafix.co.uk

Polar Seal Tapes & Conversions, Guildford Road Industrial Estate, Guildford Road, Farnham, Surrey, GU9 9PZ Tel: (01252) 726000 Fax: (01252) 728125

▶ Sealking UK Ltd, Centrum House, Engine Lane, Brownhills, Walsall, WS8 7TE Tel: (01543) 453453 Fax: (01543) 452542 E-mail: uksales@seal-king-europe.com

Tecman Speciality Materials, Eastgate House, Moreton Road, Longborough, Moreton-in-Marsh, Gloucestershire, GL56 0QJ Tel: (01451) 830044 Fax: (01451) 830230

R.A. Wood Adhesive Tapes Ltd, Unit 2 Waterside Business Centre, Wolverhampton Road, Cannock, Staffordshire, WS11 1SN Tel: (01543) 578331 Fax: (01543) 572301

ADHESIVE TAPE DISPENSERS

Adpac Packaging Supplies, 63d Milton Park, Milton, Abingdon, Oxfordshire, OX14 4RX Tel: (01553) 612130 Fax: (01235) 832821 E-mail: enquiries@adpac.co.uk

Armalines Ltd, Unit 11 Saracen Estate, Mark Road, Hemel Hempstead, Hertfordshire, HP2 7BJ Tel: (01442) 241334 Fax: (01442) 264261 E-mail: armalinesltd@aol.com

Brenmark Holdings Ltd, 1 Newbridge Road, St Annes, Bristol, BS4 4GH Tel: 0117-971 3121 Fax: 0117-971 3428 E-mail: info@brenmark.co.uk

▶ Essex Tape, 45 Canvey Road, Leigh-on-Sea, Essex, SS9 2PA Tel: (01702) 479729 E-mail: john@essextape.co.uk

Isca-Bags, 47 Marsh Green Road, Marsh Barton, Exeter, EX2 8PN Tel: (01392) 275906 Fax: (01392) 435028 E-mail: info@isca-bags.com

Pakprint Tapes Ltd, Woodlands, Dale Street, Longwood, Huddersfield, HD3 4TG Tel: (01484) 644884 Fax: (01484) 460094 E-mail: gat@pakprint.co.uk

ADHESIVE TAPE PRODUCTION MACHINERY

D K Engineering Services, 7 Enterprise Industrial Estate, Enterprise Road, Waterlooville, Hampshire, PO8 0BB Tel: (023) 9259 3947 Fax: (023) 9259 3948 E-mail: sales@dkeltd.co.uk

ADHESIVE TAPES

Abaco Industrial Tapes, Marnic House, 37 Shooters Hill Road, Blackheath, London, SE3 7HS Tel: (020) 8858 8100 Fax: (020) 8305 1401 E-mail: tapes@marnic.com

Action Tapes Ltd, Red Scar Industrial Estate, Longridge Road, Ribbleton, Preston, PR2 5NE Tel: (01280) 700591 Fax: (01280) 700590 E-mail: sales@prestec.co.uk

Adhere Industrial Tapes Ltd, Unit 1 Whitehall Road, Whitehall Industrial Estate, Colchester, CO2 8WA Tel: (01206) 871999 Fax: (01206) 871998 E-mail: sales@adhere.co.uk

▶ Adhesive Coatings, Eagle Technology Park, Queensway, Rochdale, Lancashire, OL11 1TQ Tel: (01706) 356125 Fax: (01706) 524853 E-mail: postbox@adhesive-coatings.co.uk

Adhesive Tape Manufacturing Co Ltd, 2 Bilston Industrial Estate, Oxford Street, Bilston, West Midlands, WV14 7EG Tel: (01902) 409598 Fax: (01902) 409599 E-mail: sales@atmuk.co.uk

Adtech Ltd, 6 East Street, Braintree, Essex, CM7 3JJ Tel: (01376) 346511 Fax: (01376) 349871 E-mail: sales@adtechltd.co.uk

Alba Self Adhesive Tape Supply Co. Ltd, 10 Rhynie Road, Broughty Ferry, Dundee, DD5 1RH Tel: (01382) 731100 Fax: (01382) 731100 E-mail: frank@albatapes.co.uk

Anca Industrial Supplies Ltd, Unit 16 Forge Trading Estate, Mucklow Hill, Halesowen, West Midlands, B62 8TP Tel: 0121-503 0919 Fax: 0121-585 5483 E-mail: admin@anca.co.uk

Anixter Adhesives, 3 Edmond Road, Sheffield, S2 4EB Tel: 0114-275 1496 Fax: 0114-269 7171 E-mail: sheffield.adesco@infast.com

Armalines Ltd, Unit 11 Saracen Estate, Mark Road, Hemel Hempstead, Hertfordshire, HP2 7BJ Tel: (01442) 241334 Fax: (01442) 264261 E-mail: armalinesltd@aol.com

B N D Abrasives & Tapes Ltd, Unit 3a Stephenson Close, Andover, Hampshire, SP10 3RU Tel: (01264) 354133 Fax: (01264) 323873 E-mail: info@bnd-abrasives.co.uk

Boddingtons Ltd, Blackwater Trading Estate, The Causeway, Maldon, Essex, CM9 4GG Tel: (01621) 874200 Fax: (01621) 874299 E-mail: sales@boddingtons-ltd.com

Breamfold Packaging Ltd, 129 Richmond Road, London, E8 3NJ Tel: (020) 7249 6735 Fax: (020) 7249 6737 E-mail: sales@breamfoldpackaging.co.uk

Bristol Industrial Protection Ltd, Avonmouth Docks Estate, Chittening, Bristol, BS11 0YB Tel: 0117-982 7418 Fax: 0117-923 5961 E-mail: eip@netgates.co.uk

Bruce Douglas Ultratape Ltd, Kilspindie Road, Dunsinane Industrial Estate, Dundee, DD2 3JP Tel: (01382) 832999 Fax: (01382) 833422 E-mail: sales@ultratape.com

Castle Packaging Ltd, Bott Lane, Walsall, WS1 2JG Tel: (01922) 625451 Fax: (01922) 722202 E-mail: sales@castlepackaging.co.uk

Cheshire Adhesives Tapes & Packaging, New Road, Winsford, Cheshire, CW7 2NU Tel: (01606) 863228 Fax: (01606) 863139 E-mail: bullfinchgroup@freeuk.com

Cleaning & Packaging Supplies (Worcester), A Perrywood Trading Park, Wylds Lane, Worcester, WR5 1DZ Tel: (01905) 763500 Fax: (01905) 763363 E-mail: cps.worcs@btinternet.com

Coastline Adhesive Tapes Ltd, 8 Skye Road, Shaw Farm Industrial Estate, Shawfarm Industrial Estate, Prestwick, Ayrshire, KA9 2TA Tel: (01292) 470289 Fax: (01292) 671287 E-mail: sales@coastlinetapes.co.uk

Coating & Converting Solutions Ltd, Bloomfield Park, Bloomfield Road, Tipton, West Midlands, DY4 9AP Tel: 0121-557 1155 Fax: 0121-557 9997 E-mail: sales@coatingconverting.co.uk

Colt Staplers, 10 Bunting Close, Mitcham, Surrey, CR4 4ND Tel: (020) 8687 5500 Fax: (020) 8687 5501 E-mail: sales@coltstaplers.co.uk

Compat Europe Ltd, 24 Harnham Trading Estate, Salisbury, SP2 8NW Tel: (01722) 326411 Fax: (01722) 326413 E-mail: compat@tesco.net

▶ D & P Shop, 76 Huddersfield Road, Elland, West Yorkshire, HX5 9AA Tel: (01422) 310552 Fax: (01422) 310552 E-mail: sales@dandpshop.co.uk

Davis & Moore, 5 Bute Street, Salford, M50 1DU Tel: 0161-737 1166 Fax: 0161-736 4038

Double Sided Tapes, 47 Copland Medows, Totnes, Devon, TQ9 6ES Tel: (01803) 863022 Fax: (01803) 863022

East Anglian Fine Weld Ltd, Unit 1, St. Margarets Way, Stukeley Meadows Industrial Estate, Huntingdon, Cambridgeshire, PE29 6EB Tel: (01480) 453412 Fax: (01480) 434952 E-mail: sales@eafw.co.uk

▶ Essex Tape, 45 Canvey Road, Leigh-on-Sea, Essex, SS9 2PA Tel: (01702) 479729 E-mail: john@essextape.co.uk

▶ Everfast Products, Unit 47 Barkston House, Croydon Street, Leeds, LS11 9RT Tel: 0113-242 5835 Fax: 0113-242 5836 E-mail: sales@everfastproducts.co.uk

Fantas Tak Ltd, 2-6 Station Road, Shipley, West Yorkshire, BD18 2JL Tel: (01274) 466666 Fax: (01274) 466664 E-mail: sales@fantastak.com

Fensell Properties Ltd, Oak Lodge, Homedowns, Tewkesbury, Gloucestershire, GL20 7BQ Tel: (01684) 273091 Fax: (01684) 273090 E-mail: simonbillinghurst@yahoo.com

Finecal Distributors, 2 Temple Trading Estate, Cole Road, Bristol, BS2 0UG Tel: 0117-971 1111 Fax: 0117-977 2326 E-mail: sales@finecal.co.uk

Fosseway Technical Tapes, 8 Ladywood Works, Leicester Road, Lutterworth, Leicestershire, LE17 4HD Tel: (01455) 550515 Fax: (01455) 550122 E-mail: sales@fossewaytapes.co.uk

Frankly Packaging, Unit 25-27 Delph Industrial Estate, Delph Road, Brierley Hill, West Midlands, DY5 2UA Tel: (01384) 263328 Fax: (01384) 79283 E-mail: frankley@brierleyhill55.freeserve.co.uk

General Fabrications Ltd, 26 Orphanage Road, Birmingham, B24 9HT Tel: 0121-377 6070 Fax: 0121-377 7175 E-mail: info@genfab.co.uk

Global Packaging Ltd, 9 Lockwood Way, Black Horse Lane, London, E17 5RB Tel: (020) 8531 3130 Fax: (020) 8503 2319

Samuel Grant Ltd, 146-148 Garnet Road, Leeds, LS11 5LA Tel: 0113-270 7221 Fax: 0113-277 9867 E-mail: sales@samuelgrant.co.uk

Hadleigh Enterprises Ltd, Unit 11, Buckingham Square, Wickford, Essex, SS11 8YQ Tel: (01268) 572255 Fax: (01268) 572121 E-mail: info@hadleigh.u-net.com

Halewood Business Forms, Fountain House South Horizon West, Canal View Road, Newbury, Berkshire, RG14 5XF Tel: (01635) 231641 Fax: (01635) 231664 E-mail: halewood@tape27.freeserve.co.uk

Heskins Tapes, Churchill Road, Brinscall, Chorley, Lancashire, PR6 8RQ Tel: (01254) 832266 Fax: (01254) 832476 E-mail: mail@heskins.com

Hi Bond Tapes Ltd, 1 Crucible Road, Corby, Northamptonshire, NN17 5TS Tel: (01536) 260022 Fax: (01536) 260044 E-mail: sales@hi-bondtapes.co.uk

Hopson Packaging Ltd, 135 High Street, Newton-le-Willows, Merseyside, WA12 9SQ Tel: (01925) 222533 Fax: (01925) 222711

I B S Ltd, 30 Glenburn Road, East Kilbride, Glasgow, G74 5BA Tel: (01355) 244555 Fax: (01355) 241974 E-mail: sales@tapes.co.uk

Industrial Self Adhesives Ltd, Robey Close, Linby, Nottingham, NG15 8AA Tel: 0115-968 1895 Fax: 0115-963 2821 E-mail: sales@isatape.co.uk

Isola Manufacturing Co (Wythenshaw) Ltd, Harper Road, Wythenshawe, Manchester, M22 4RG Tel: 0161-998 2294 Fax: 0161-946 0390 E-mail: isola.sales@nu-pax.com

J I T Industrial Products Ltd, 16 Melford Road, Righead Industrial Estate, Bellshill, Lanarkshire, ML4 3LR Tel: (01698) 748290 Fax: (01698) 749141 E-mail: sales@jitwebsite.com

Jeaton Tapes & Abrasives Ltd, Unit 1, Manchester Mill Industrial Estate, Geoffrey St, Preston, PR1 5NR Tel: (01772) 703636 Fax: (01772) 701271 E-mail: sales@jeaton.co.uk

Kingfisher Tapes Ltd, Unit 3 Kents Avenue, Hemel Hempstead, Hertfordshire, HP3 9XH Tel: (01442) 212624 Fax: (01442) 241057

Laserpack Cartons & Cases Ltd, Unit 4, Llandygai Industrial Estate, Bangor, Gwynedd, LL57 4YH Tel: (0845) 2575758 Fax: (0845) 2575759 E-mail: sales@laserpack.co.uk

Le Mark Self Adhesives Ltd, Houghton Hill Industries, Houghton Hill Farm, Houghton, Huntingdon, Cambridgeshire, PE28 2DH Tel: (01480) 494540 Fax: (01480) 494206 E-mail: info@lemark.co.uk

▶ Leete & French, Unit 1 Reginald Street, Stoke-on-Trent, ST6 1DU Tel: (01782) 575710 Fax: (01782) 835363 E-mail: tapes@leeteandfrench.co.uk

Lewis Industrial Products, 25 Lichfield Close, New Arley, Coventry, Warwickshire, CV7 8PU Tel: (01676) 541792 Fax: (01676) 541184 E-mail: lewislip@aol.com

Marnic P.L.C., Armstrong Road, London, SE18 6RS Tel: (020) 8312 7200 Fax: (020) 8312 7250 E-mail: tapes@marnic.com

North British Tapes Ltd, Unit 5 Locomotion Way, Camperdown Industrial Estate, Newcastle upon Tyne, NE12 5US Tel: 0191-268 6272 Fax: 0191-268 7400

Northumbrian Packaging, Gear House, Saltmeadows Road, Gateshead, Tyne & Wear, NE8 3AH Tel: 0191-490 3372 Fax: 0191-490 3372 E-mail: northpackaging@fsbdial.co.uk

▶ P & L Tapes Ltd, 39 The Airfield, Little Staughton, Bedford, MK44 2BN Tel: (01234) 376421 Fax: (01234) 376115 E-mail: nickckd1@aol.com

▶ Paint Protection Systems, 10 Oak Rd, Withington, Manchester, M20 3DA Tel: (07949) 094708 Fax: 0161-448 9240 E-mail: tim@paintprotectionsystems.co.uk

Parafix, Spencer Road, Church Hill Industrial Estate, Lancing, West Sussex, BN15 8UA Tel: (01903) 750000 Fax: (01903) 767728 E-mail: sales@parafix.co.uk

Polar Seal Tapes & Conversions, Guildford Road Industrial Estate, Guildford Road, Farnham, Surrey, GU9 9PZ Tel: (01252) 726000 Fax: (01252) 728125

Premier Coatings & Converters, West Portway, Andover, Hampshire, SP10 3LF Tel: (01264) 358633 Fax: (01264) 334701 E-mail: sales@pcc-ltd.com

Prima Tapes & Labels Ltd, Prima House, Faraday Way, Orpington, Kent, BR5 3QW Tel: (01689) 816111 Fax: (01689) 816010 E-mail: sales@prima-tapes.com

Protective Tapes, Vale Park, Hamil Road, Stoke-on-Trent, ST6 1AW Tel: (01782) 833560 Fax: (01782) 833550 E-mail: sales@protective-tapes.co.uk

▶ Proton Supplies, Unit 18 Allshots Enterprises, Woodhouse Lane, Kelvedon, Colchester, CO5 9DF Tel: (01376) 584000 Fax: (01376) 583444 E-mail: sales@apcsolutionsuk.com

▶ R W Greeff, Neilson Road, Gateshead, Tyne & Wear, NE10 0EW Tel: 0191-490 0110 Fax: 0191-490 0261

Saffron Tape Design, Epsilon House, 27 Fulfen Way, Saffron Walden, Essex, CB11 4DW Tel: (01799) 520170 Fax: (01799) 520170 E-mail: saffrontapedesign@tiscali.co.uk

▶ Sealking UK Ltd, Centrum House, Engine Lane, Brownhills, Walsall, WS8 7TE Tel: (01543) 453453 Fax: (01543) 452542 E-mail: uksales@seal-king-europe.com

Self Adhesive Supplies Ltd, 9 Southview Park, Caversham, Reading, RG4 5AF Tel: 0118-948 3833 Fax: 0118-948 1089 E-mail: sales@selfadhesive.co.uk

Shand Higson & Co. Ltd, Lees Road, Knowsley Industrial Park North, Knowsley, Liverpool, L33 7SE Tel: 0151-549 2210 Fax: 0151-549 1405 E-mail: sales@shandhigson.co.uk

ADHESIVE TAPES – *continued*

▶ Stable Tapes, 557 Aspley Lane, Nottingham, NG8 5RX Tel: 0115-929 8782 Fax: 0115-929 8783

▶ Steratape Ltd, Carnaby Industrial Estate, Lancaster Road, Carnaby, Bridlington, East Yorkshire, YO15 3QY Tel: (01262) 603721 Fax: (01262) 400028 E-mail: carl@steratape.com

Swallow Tapes Ltd, 2 Cotton Hall Barns, Middlewich Road, Holmes Chapel, Crewe, CW4 7ET Tel: (01477) 535599 Fax: (01477) 535440 E-mail: sales@swallowtapes.sagehost.co.uk

▶ Swiftec, Pennine House, Tilson Road, Roundthorn Industrial Estate, Manchester, M23 9GF Tel: 0161-945 1500 Fax: (0800) 0740005

Taurus Packaging, Meadow Lane, Little Houghton, Northampton, NN7 1AH Tel: (01604) 891707 Fax: (01604) 891708 E-mail: tauruspackaging@hotmail.com

Tecman Speciality Materials, Eastgate House, Moreton Road, Longborough, Moreton-in-Marsh, Gloucestershire, GL56 0QJ Tel: (01451) 830044 Fax: (01451) 830230

tesa UK Ltd, Yeomans Drive, Blakelands, Milton Keynes, MK14 5LS Tel: 0845 4941752 Fax: (01908) 211555 E-mail: ukenquiry@tesa.com

Trade Grade Products Ltd, 10 Victory Close Woolsbridge Indust Estate, Verwood, Wimborne, Dorset, BH21 6SX Tel: (01202) 820177 Fax: (01202) 814011 E-mail: sales@theglue.co.uk

U K Tapes Ltd, 5 Cooper Drive, Springwood Industrial Estate, Braintree, Essex, CM7 2RF Tel: (01376) 349090 Fax: (01376) 348989 E-mail: sales@uktapes.com

Venture Tape Europe, 5-6 Faraday Close, Drayton Fields Industrial Estate, Daventry, Northamptonshire, NN11 8RD Tel: (01327) 876555 Fax: (01327) 876444 E-mail: jaeanne@venturetape.co.uk

Watershed Packaging Ltd, Westpoint, Westland Square, Leeds, LS11 5SS Tel: 0113-277 0606 Fax: 0113-277 7174 E-mail: sales@watershed-packaging.co.uk

Welsh Boxes of Swansea Ltd, Bruce Road, Swansea Industrial Estate, Fforestfach, Swansea, SA5 4HX Tel: (01792) 586527 Fax: (01792) 585410 E-mail: sales@welshboxes.co.uk

West Packaging Ltd, Cornish Street, Sheffield, S6 3AA Tel: 0114-276 0555 Fax: 0114-275 7590 E-mail: info@westpack.co.uk

William Hayes Ltd, Bankfield Works, Haley Hill, Halifax, West Yorkshire, HX3 6ED Tel: (01422) 365034 Fax: (01422) 345497 E-mail: enquiries@williamhayes.co.uk

ADHESIVE TAPES, CONVERTED, DIECUT SHAPES

▶ Lohmann Adhesive Tape Systems, Cane End Lane, Bierton, Aylesbury, Buckinghamshire, HP22 5BH Tel: (01296) 337888 Fax: (01296) 337772 E-mail: info@lohmann-tapes.co.uk

ADHESIVE TAPES, KRAFT PAPER

▶ Dreamcrafts Ltd, 107 Thistledene, Thames Ditton, Surrey, KT7 0YW Tel: (020) 8873 2893 Fax: (020) 8873 2893 E-mail: sales@dreamcraftstore.co.uk

ADHESIVE TAPES, PHOTOLUMINESCENT, SAFETY ETC

Globright Ltd, 530 Woodbridge Road, Ipswich, IP4 4PN Tel: (01473) 721561 Fax: (01473) 714069 E-mail: sales@globritephotoluminescent.com

▶ Kemco Technology, Acorn House, Tonbridge Road, Bough Beech, Edenbridge, Kent, TN8 7AU Tel: (01892) 870077 Fax: (01892) 870777 E-mail: info@kemcotech.com

ADHESIVES, *See also headings for particular types*

▶ 5 Star Adhesives, P O Box 96, Liverpool, L17 3BY Tel: 0151-733 7182 Fax: 0151-733 7182 E-mail: info@glue-shop.com

The Adhesive Co., 51 Church Walk South, Swindon, SN2 2JE Tel: (01793) 537816 Fax: (01793) 537816 E-mail: sales@theadhesivecompany.co.uk

Adhesive & Coating Supplies, Sherborne St West, Salford, M3 7LF Tel: 0161-835 1420 Fax: 0161-839 3543 E-mail: sales@chemipat.co.uk

Adseal, 2 Charnwood Park, Foreshore Road, Cardiff, CF10 4LZ Tel: (029) 2047 1200 Fax: (029) 2047 1230 E-mail: adseallt d@btconnect.com

Adtech Ltd, 6 East Street, Braintree, Essex, CM7 3JJ Tel: (01376) 346511 Fax: (01376) 349871 E-mail: sales@adtechltd.co.uk

Akzo Nobel Industrial Coatings Ltd, Crown House, Hollins Road, Darwen, Lancashire, BB3 0BG Tel: (01254) 760760 Fax: (01254) 701092 E-mail:

Alansons Industrial Supplies, 7 Flowers Hill, Bristol, BS4 5JJ Tel: 0117-971 1364 Fax: (0870) 7773272

▶ Aldcroft Adhesives Ltd, Unit 13A Horwich Loco Industrial Estate, Chorley New Road, Horwich, Bolton, BL6 5UE Tel: (01204) 668282 Fax: (01204) 668780 E-mail: info@aldcroftadhesives.com

▶ Anixter Industrial - Barrow, Unit 2D Ashburner Way, Walney Road Industrial Estate, Barrow-In-Furness, Cumbria, LA14 5UZ Tel: (01229) 825871 Fax: (01229) 827442

Anixter Industrial - Chesterfield, Brimington Road North, Chesterfield, Derbyshire, S41 9BE Tel: (01246) 452188 Fax: (01246) 455778 E-mail: chesterfield.sales@alistairindustrial.com

Apollo Chemicals Holdings Ltd, Sandy Way, Amington Industrial Estate, Tamworth, Staffordshire, B77 4DS Tel: (01827) 54281 Fax: (01827) 53030 E-mail: sales@apolloadhesives.com

Ashland Foundry Products, Vale Industrial Estate, Kidderminster, Worcestershire, DY11 7QU Tel: (01562) 821300 Fax: (01562) 740785

Bondex Adhesives & Coatings Ltd, C.P Farms, Woburn Road, Wootton, Bedford, MK43 9EL Tel: (01234) 757763 Fax: (01234) 765550

▶ Bostik Findley Ltd, Common Road, Stafford, ST16 3EH Tel: (01785) 272727 Fax: (01785) 257236 E-mail: jackie.scarfe@bostikfindley.com

Brenmark Holdings Ltd, 1 Newbridge Road, St Annes, Bristol, BS4 4GH Tel: 0117-971 3121 Fax: 0117-971 3428 E-mail: info@brenmark.co.uk

By Design Sealants, D The Business Centre, Faringdon Avenue, Romford, RM3 8EN Tel: (01708) 377010 Fax: (01708) 377080 E-mail: info@byds.co.uk

Ceramic Tiles Ltd, Unit 46, Bosshall Business Park, Bosshall Road, Ipswich, IP1 5BN Tel: (01473) 745478 Fax: (01473) 240133 E-mail: customer.support@ceramic-tiles.co.uk

Chemence Ltd, 13 Princewood Road, Earlstrees Industrial Estate, Corby, Northamptonshire, NN17 4XD Tel: (01536) 402600 Fax: (01536) 400266 E-mail: sales@chemence.com

Cheshire Adhesives Tapes & Packaging, New Road, Winsford, Cheshire, CW7 2NU Tel: (01606) 863228 Fax: (01606) 863139 E-mail: bullfinchgroup@freeuk.com

Coastline Adhesive Tapes Ltd, 8 Skye Road, Shaw Farm Industrial Estate, Shawfarm Industrial Estate, Prestwick, Ayrshire, KA9 2TA Tel: (01292) 470289 Fax: (01292) 671287 E-mail: sales@coastlinetapes.co.uk

Couldridge Industrial Supplies, Crucible Close, Mushet Industrial Park, Coleford, Gloucestershire, GL16 8RE Tel: (01594) 833177 Fax: (01594) 837423

Danfast, English Street, Hull, HU3 2DZ Tel: (01482) 599333 Fax: (01482) 599321 E-mail: enquiries@danfast.co.uk

Delta Adhesives Ltd, 2 Lakeside Industrial Estate, Lakeside Road, Leeds, LS12 4QP Tel: 0113-279 6966 Fax: 0113-231 0828 E-mail: info@delta-adhesives.co.uk

▶ David Deverill, 172 Spendmore Lane, Coppull, Chorley, Lancashire, PR7 5BX Tel: (01257) 793196 Fax: (01257) 793196

Don Industrial Supplies Ltd, Unit 17 Guildhall Industrial Estate, Sandall Stones Road, Kirk Sandall Industrial Estate, Doncaster, South Yorkshire, DN3 1QR Tel: (01302) 884086 Fax: (01302) 887458 E-mail: donindust@aol.com

Dowell Enterprises Ltd, Unit 6 & 7, 549 Eskdale Road, Uxbridge, Middlesex, UB8 2RT Tel: (01895) 811422 Fax: (01895) 811423 E-mail: sales@glue-4u.co.uk

Ellsworth Adhesives Ltd, 2 Kelvin South BSNS Park, Glasgow, G75 0YG Tel: (01355) 231122 Fax: (01355) 235266 E-mail: info@ellsworthadhesives.co.uk

Essex Fixing & Abrasives Supplies Ltd, Unit 12 Featherby Way, Purdey's Industrial Estate, Rochford, Essex, SS4 1LD Tel: (01702) 549222 Fax: (01702) 541465

Euro Safety & Abrasives, Unit 3, 13 Cobham Road, Ferndown Industrial Estate, Wimborne, Dorset, BH21 7TE Tel: (01202) 870661 Fax: (01202) 870095

Excel Adhesives, 18 Low Farm Place, Moulton Park Industrial Estate, Northampton, NN3 6HY Tel: (01604) 648484 Fax: (01604) 790370

F Ball & Co. Ltd, Churnetside Business Park, Station Road, Cheddleton, Leek, Staffordshire, ST13 7RS Tel: (01538) 361633 Fax: (01538) 361622 E-mail: webmaster@f-ball.co.uk

F D Products, 1-5 Olympus Park Business Centre, Quedgeley, Gloucester, GL2 4NF Tel: (01452) 722944 Fax: (01452) 722825

Fast 10 Adhesives, Hollytree House, Leeds Road, Tadcaster, North Yorkshire, LS24 9NL Tel: (07949) 274474 Fax: (01937) 832337 E-mail: nrockcliff@fast10.co.uk

Firmafix Fastenings, Unit 3, Pioneer Park Clough Road, Hull, HU8 8BB Tel: (01482) 224334 Fax: (01482) 224341 E-mail: sales@firmafix.com

▶ G Seal, Peatburn Avenue, Heanor, Derbyshire, DE75 7RL Tel: (01773) 761579 Fax: (01773) 711788

General Fabrications Ltd, 26 Orphanage Road, Birmingham, B24 9HT Tel: 0121-377 6070 Fax: 0121-377 7175 E-mail: info@genfab.co.uk

Geocel Ltd, Western Wood Way, Langage Business Park, Plympton, Plymouth, PL7 5BG Tel: (01752) 202060 Fax: (01752) 202065 E-mail: info@geocel.co.uk

Gluegunsdirect.Com Ltd, Regent House, Regent Street, Oldham, OL1 3TZ Tel: 0161-627 1001 Fax: 0161-627 5072 E-mail: sales@gluegunsdirect.com

▶ Gluemart Ltd, Robins Farm, Matson Lane, Matson, Gloucester, GL4 6DZ Tel: (01452) 423883 Fax: (01452) 308229 E-mail: sales@gluemart.co.uk

Grosvenor Electronic Supplies, Priory Tec Park Saxon Way, Priory Park, Hessle, North Humberside, HU13 9PB Tel: (01482) 627327 Fax: (01482) 627328 E-mail: sales@grosvenor-group.com

Hallmark Fraulo Ltd, Units 55-56, Hillgrove Business Park, Nazeing Road, Nazeing, Waltham Abbey, Essex, EN9 2HB Tel: (01992) 899025 Fax: (01992) 899026 E-mail: info@hallmarkfraulo.co.uk

Hampshire Tile Warehouse Ltd, Hollybush Industrial Park, Hollybush Lane, Aldershot, Hampshire, GU11 2PX Tel: (01252) 333333 Fax: (0800) 3284481E-mail: admin@htw.co.uk

Hyloc Ltd, Unit 5, Jensen Court, Astmoor, Runcorn, Cheshire, WA7 1SQ Tel: (01928) 590110 Fax: (01928) 590905 E-mail: info@hyloc.com

Industrial Fasteners Ltd, Chilcott Avenue, Brynmenyn Industrial Estate, Brynmenyn, Bridgend, CF32 9RQ Tel: (01656) 724775 Fax: (01656) 729612

▶ Industrial Fasteners Ltd, Unit 10 Sundon Business Park, Dencora Way, Luton, LU3 3HP Tel: (01582) 563100 Fax: (01582) 563040 E-mail: sales@anixterfasteners.com

▶ Industrial Fasteners Ltd, 7 Bell Park Bell Close, Newnham Industrial Estate, Plympton, Plymouth, PL7 4TA Tel: (01752) 341100 Fax: (01752) 346012

▶ Industrial Fasteners Ltd, 6 Station Road, Thatcham, Berkshire, RG19 4RB Tel: (01635) 865885 Fax: (01635) 871511

Industrial Links Ltd, Unit 19 Ventura Place, Poole, Dorset, BH16 5SW Tel: (01202) 632996 Fax: (01202) 632997 E-mail: sales@industrial-links.com

Industria Engineering Products Ltd, 45 Kelvin Way, West Bromwich, West Midlands, B70 7TP Tel: 0121-525 2988 Fax: 0121-525 3607 E-mail: sales@industria.co.uk

Ingram Foundry Industries Ltd, Unit E1 Dudley Central Trading Estate, Shaw Road, Dudley, West Midlands, DY2 8QX Tel: (01384) 253022 Fax: (01384) 213339 E-mail: sales@ingram-industries.com

John Young, 7 Cranbrook Court, Avenue Two, Witney, Oxfordshire, OX28 4YP Tel: (01993) 700337 Fax: (01993) 778123 E-mail: john-young1@btconnect.com

K M S Adhesives, Hamlin Way, King's Lynn, Norfolk, PE30 4NG Tel: (01553) 774100 Fax: (01553) 774165

Laybond Products Ltd, Riverside, Chester, CH4 8RS Tel: (01244) 674774 Fax: (01244) 682218 E-mail: sales-info@laybond.com

Machine Sales & Services Ltd, 23 Cowley Road, Nuffield Industrial Estate, Poole, Dorset, BH17 0UJ Tel: (01202) 686238 Fax: (01202) 686661 E-mail: enquiries@machinesalesandservices.co.uk

Med-Lab International Ltd, Copeland Street, Derby, DE1 2PU Tel: (01332) 349094 Fax: (01332) 371237 E-mail: sales@med-lab.co.uk

M-Tec, 3 Craven Court, Canada Road, Byfleet, West Byfleet, Surrey, KT14 7JL Tel: (01932) 354100 Fax: (01932) 340200 E-mail: m.tec@lineone.net

Ney Ltd, Middlemarch Business Park Coventry Trading Estate, Siskin Drive, Middlemarch Business Park, Coventry, CV3 4FJ Tel: (024) 7630 8100 Fax: (024) 7630 8102 E-mail: info@ney.co.uk

North British Tapes Ltd, Unit 5 Locomotion Way, Camperdown Industrial Estate, Newcastle upon Tyne, NE12 5US Tel: 0191-268 6272 Fax: 0191-268 7400

Robatech UK Ltd, The Street, Broughton Gifford, Melksham, Wiltshire, SN12 8PH Tel: (01225) 783456 Fax: (01225) 783400 E-mail: sales@robatech.co.uk

Rubbarite Ltd, 23-27 Boundary Street, Liverpool, L5 9ZQ Tel: 0151-298 1038 Fax: 0151-298 1910 E-mail: rubbarite@btconnect.com

Sheppy Ltd, Rushenden Road, Queenborough, Kent, ME11 5HH Tel: (01795) 580181 Fax: (01795) 580649 E-mail: sales@sheppy.ltd.uk

Strongbond Adhesives Ltd, Beehive Works, Hollins Lane, Bury, Lancashire, BL9 8AA Tel: 0161-766 2618 Fax: 0161-767 9024 E-mail: sales@strongbond.co.uk

Techsil Ltd, Unit 30 Bidavon Industrial Estate, Waterloo Road, Bidford-on-Avon, Alcester, Warwickshire, B50 4JN Tel: (01789) 773232 Fax: (01789) 774239 E-mail: sales@techsil.co.uk

ThreeBond Europe SAS, 5 Newmarket Court, Kingston, Milton Keynes, MK10 0AS Tel: (01908) 285000 Fax: (01908) 285001 E-mail: mark.beeson@threebond.co.uk

Trade Grade Products Ltd, 10 Victory Close Woolsbridge Indust Estate, Verwood, Wimborne, Dorset, BH21 6SX Tel: (01202) 820177 Fax: (01202) 814011 E-mail: sales@theglue.co.uk

▶ Trimseal Mastiq Applicators, Eastcote, Brixham Road, Paignton, Devon, TQ4 7BD Tel: (01803) 524511 Fax: (01803) 524511

Unibond, Apollo Court, 2 Bishops Square Business Park, Hatfield, Hertfordshire, AL10 9EY Tel: (01707) 289041 Fax: (01707) 289099

Wey Adhesives Ltd, Unit 45 Murrell Green Business Park, London Road, Hook, Hampshire, RG27 9GR Tel: (01256) 766661 Fax: (01256) 766667 E-mail: sales@weyadhesives.com

ADHESIVES, SURFACE MOUNT (SM)

Henkel, Technologies House, Wood La End, Hemel Hempstead, Hertfordshire, HP2 4RQ Tel: (01442) 278000 Fax: (01442) 278071 E-mail: customer.enquiry@henkel.com

ADJUSTABLE FRICTION CLUTCHES

Raybestos G B F Ltd, Unit 1 Preserve Works, Jubilee Way, Thackley Old Rd, Shipley, W. Yorkshire, BD18 1QB Tel: (01274) 597332 Fax: (01274) 597357 E-mail: info@raybestosgbf.freeserve.co.uk

ADJUSTABLE SEAT MECHANISMS

Isringhausen GB Ltd, Second Avenue, Redwither Industrial Complex, Redwither Business Park, Wrexham, Clwyd, LL13 9XQ Tel: (01978) 666300 Fax: (01978) 660192 E-mail: isrigb@isrigb.co.uk

Pullmaflex (U K) Ltd, Heol Las, Ammanford, Dyfed, SA18 3ED Tel: (01269) 592301 Fax: (01269) 593262 E-mail: info@pullmaflex.com

ADJUSTABLE SHELVING

E Z Rect Ltd, Witan Park, Avenue Two, Witney, Oxfordshire, OX28 4FH Tel: (01993) 779494 Fax: (01993) 704111 E-mail: sales@e-z-rect.com

Redirack Ltd, Wharf Road, Kilnhurst, Mexborough, South Yorkshire, S64 5SU Tel: (01709) 584711 Fax: (01709) 589821 E-mail: sales@redirack.co.uk

T P G Storage, 7 Hudsons Way, Canvey Island, Essex, SS8 9FE Tel: (01268) 696336 Fax: (01268) 514048

ADJUSTABLE SPEED PULLEYS

R G Wylie & Co. Ltd, Vanguard Way, Shoeburyness, Southend-on-Sea, SS3 9QY Tel: (01702) 296751 Fax: (01702) 297560 E-mail: rg.wylie@dtconect.com

Renold Gears, Station Road, Milnrow, Rochdale, Lancashire, OL16 3LS Tel: (01706) 751000 Fax: (01706) 751001

ADSORPTION MEDIA, WASTE WATER TREATMENT

Colloid Treatment Technologies, Rovert House, Water Tower Road, Clayhill Light Industrial Park, Neston, CH64 3US Tel: 0151-336 7775 Fax: 0151-336 7733E-mail: colltreat@aol.com

ADVANCED LUBRICANTS

Danoil Ltd, 94 Owl Lane, Ossett, West Yorkshire, WF5 9AU Tel: (01924) 263128 Fax: (01924) 264078

GBR Technology Ltd, 6 Jupiter House, Calleva Park, Aldermaston, Reading, RG7 8NN Tel: 0118-982 0567 Fax: 0118-982 0590 E-mail: sales@gbrtech.co.uk

Wymark Ltd, Runnings Road Ind Estate, Cheltenham, Gloucestershire, GL51 9NQ Tel: 01242 520966

ADVANCED MATERIAL BLADES

Saint-Gobain Abrasives Ltd, Albert Drive, Burgess Hill, West Sussex, RH15 9TN Tel: (01444) 259400 Fax: (01444) 232407 E-mail: sales@nimbus-diamond.co.uk

ADVANCED STRUCTURAL COMPOSITE MATERIALS

Composite Tooling & Structures Ltd, Lola House, Clebe Road, Huntingdon, Cambridgeshire, PE29 7DS Tel: (01480) 459378 Fax: (01480) 455585

ADVANCED STRUCTURAL MATERIAL COMPOSITE COMPONENTS

AIM Composites Ltd, Pembroke Avenue, Waterbeach, Cambridge, CB5 9QR Tel: (01223) 441000 Fax: (01223) 862336 E-mail: sales@aimcomposites.com
Aviation Tool Corporation P.L.C, Airport Works, Green Lane, Hounslow, TW4 6DE Tel: (020) 8570 9664 Fax: (020) 8570 9660 E-mail: atctools@aol.com
Cobham Composites Ltd, Davey House, Gelders Ha, Shepshed, Loughborough, Leicestershire, LE12 9NH Tel: (01509) 504541 Fax: (01509) 507563
Crompton Technology Group Ltd, Thorp Park Thorpe Way, Banbury, Oxfordshire, OX16 4SU Tel: (01295) 220130 Fax: (01295) 220138 E-mail: info@ctgltd.co.uk
Custom Composites Ltd, Hugo Street, Rochdale, Lancashire, OL11 2PH Tel: (01706) 526255 Fax: (01706) 350187 E-mail: mail@customcom.co.uk
Cytec Engineered Materials Ltd, Abenbury Way, Wrexham Industrial Estate, Wrexham, Clwyd, LL13 9UZ Tel: (01978) 665200 Fax: (01978) 665222 E-mail: info@cytec.com
Heatcon Composite Systems (Europe) Ltd, Blackstone Road, Stukeley Meadows Industrial Estate, Huntingdon, Cambridgeshire, PE29 6EF Tel: (01480) 410740 Fax: (01480) 433195 E-mail: ukinfo@heatcon.com
Northshore Composites Ltd, Brockhampton Road, Havant, Hampshire, PO9 1JU Tel: (023) 9247 1428 Fax: (023) 9245 2228 E-mail: info@northshore-composites.co.uk
Performance Composites Ltd, Unit 13a The Old Sawmills, Halves Lane, East Coker, Yeovil, Somerset, BA22 9JJ Tel: (01935) 864098 Fax: (01935) 863807 E-mail: sms@performance-composites.com
Sigmatex (UK) Ltd, Unit 3, The Trafalgar Centre, Belfield Road, Rochdale, Lancashire, OL16 2UX Tel: (01706) 631128 Fax: (01706) 523691 E-mail: sigmatex@sigmatex.co.uk
Technical Resin Bonders Ltd, 12 Clifton Road, Huntingdon, Cambridgeshire, PE29 7EN Tel: 0845 5314225 Fax: (01480) 414992 E-mail: sales@trbonders.co.uk

ADVANCED STRUCTURAL MATERIAL ENGINEERING

G D Engineering, Retford Road, Worksop, Nottinghamshire, S80 2PY Tel: (01909) 482323 Fax: (01909) 477902
H Beesley Ltd, Commercial Square, Freemans Common, Leicester, LE2 7SR Tel: 0116-255 4233 Fax: 0116-255 4366 E-mail: enquiries@hbeesley.co.uk
▶ T P Aspinall & Sons Ltd, Middleton Business Park, Middleton Road, Middleton, Morecambe, Lancashire, LA3 3PW Tel: (01524) 852883 Fax: (01524) 853303 E-mail: enquiries@aspinall.co.uk

ADVERTISEMENT COPYWRITING

Clarity Communications, Barley Mow Passage, London, W4 4PH Tel: 0845 355 1178 Fax: 0870 706 4834 E-mail: enquiries@claritycomms.com
J W T, 1 Knightsbridge Green, London, SW1X 7NW Tel: (020) 7656 7000 Fax: (020) 7656 7010
▶ More than Words Media Ltd, 17 Greens Farm Lane, Billericay, Essex, CM11 2EZ Tel: (0783) 5001534 E-mail: info@morethanwordsmedia.com
▶ St Creative Ltd, 102 Frimley House 5 The Parade, Frimley High Street, Frimley, Camberley, Surrey, GU16 7HY Tel: (0845) 3301920 Fax: (01276) 507157 E-mail: sales@st-creative.co.uk
▶ Standard English, Clark House, Higher Kingsbury, Milborne Port, Sherborne, Dorset, DT9 5EB Tel: (07709) 935909 Fax: (0870) 7461291 E-mail: lisa@galventures.com
Words That Sell, 45 Sherrardspark Road, Welwyn Garden City, Herts, AL8 7LD Tel: 01707 887989 Fax: 07050 663664 E-mail: mel@wordsthatsell.co.uk
▶ write4me.co.uk, St Martin's Studios, Greenbank Road, Ashton Village, Sale, Cheshire, M33 5PL Tel: 0845 054 8585

ADVERTISING AGENCIES

▶ The Ad Studio, 23 Martlet Close, Cherque Farm, Lee on the Solent, Gosport, Hampshire, PO13 8FP Tel: 02392 553442 Fax: 08715 227697 E-mail: info@theadstudio.co.uk
▶ Adverteyes, 109 Tennyson Avenue, Harrogate, North Yorkshire, HG1 3LE Tel: (01423) 508430 E-mail: adverteyes@adverteyes.biz
Art Workshop NW Ltd, Unit 20 Kingston Mill, Chestergate, Stockport, Cheshire, SK3 0AL Tel: 0161-429 9445 Fax: 0161-480 0218
▶ Buzz Connections, Unit 19 Govan Workspace, Harmony Row, Glasgow, G51 3BA Tel: 0141-440 2600 Fax: 0141-445 3217 E-mail: info@buzzconnections.co.uk
▶ CabAds - Taxi Advertising, Unit 1A, West Craigs Industrial Estate, Turnhouse Road, Edinburgh, EH12 0BD Tel: (0845) 2268595 Fax: (0845) 2268595 E-mail: info@cabads.co.uk
Cane Communications Ltd, River Side House, Turnac Avenue, Woking, Surrey, GU22 0AJ Tel: (01483) 727150 Fax: (01483) 223311
Cia, 1 Paris Garden, London, SE1 8NU Tel: (020) 7633 9999 Fax: (020) 7803 2001
▶ Discount-Line Ltd, 5 Witches Linn, Ardrossan, Ayrshire, KA22 8NP Tel: (0845) 1223110 E-mail: discount.line@btinternet.com
Doner Cardwell Hawkins, 26 Emerald Street, London, WC1N 3QS Tel: (020) 7405 4611 Fax: (020) 7437 3961 E-mail: doner@donermail.co.uk
▶ Geek Pixel Ads, c/o NTB Global Trading, 2nd Floor, 145-157 St. John Street, London, EC1V 4PY Tel: (0845) 3104486 E-mail: sales@geek-pixelads.com
Gildersons Ltd, 31-35 Pitfield Street, London, N1 6HB Tel: (020) 7324 0180 Fax: (020) 7490 4333 E-mail: studio@gildersons.co.uk
▶ Go2Devon, 21 Meadow Court, Ballasalla, Isle of Man, IM9 2DP Tel: (01624) 823768 E-mail: info-fountain@manx.net
▶ Guava Ltd, Hurst Grove, Sandford Lane, Hurst, Reading, RG10 0SQ Tel: 0118-932 1100 Fax: 0118-932 1222 E-mail: info@guava.co.uk
▶ H G S Marketing, Elmgrove Lodge, 47A Elmgrove Road, Weybridge, Surrey, KT13 8PB Tel: (01932) 829419 E-mail: info@hgsmarketing.com
▶ Horrex Davis Design Associates Ltd, 6 Dorset Street, London, W1U 6QL Tel: (020) 7486 8132 Fax: (020) 7487 2936 E-mail: design@hdda.co.uk
Impact Design & Advertising, 113 Bradbury Road, Solihull, West Midlands, B92 8AL Tel: 0121-707 4774 Fax: 0121-706 1663 E-mail: steve@impactida.com
Intermediate Ltd, 3RD Floor, 21 Great Chapel Street, London, W1F 8FP Tel: (020) 7432 7040 Fax: (020) 7437 1843 E-mail: info@intermediate.co.uk
Key Note Ltd, Field House, 72 Oldfield Road, Hampton, Middlesex, TW12 2HQ Tel: (020) 8481 8750 Fax: (020) 8783 0049 E-mail: sales@keynote.co.uk
▶ Klick Solutions, Pinfold Lane, Penkridge, Stafford, ST19 5AP Tel: (0845) 2620052 Fax: (01785) 716829 E-mail: enquiries@klicksolutions.co.uk
Marathon P R Ltd, 2 West Street, Epsom, Surrey, KT18 7RG Tel: (01372) 727030 Fax: (01372) 744150 E-mail: ray@marathonpr.co.uk
▶ Marketing Direct, 26 Makendon Street, Hebburn, Tyne & Wear, NE31 1RF Tel: 0191 4836090 E-mail: md_marketingdirect@yahoo.co.uk
Newsquest Media Ltd, Reliance House, Long St, Dursley, Gloucestershire, GL11 4LF Tel: (01453) 544000 Fax: (01453) 540212 E-mail: reporters@dursleygazette.co.uk
▶ Nicholson Martin, 4 Thorley Hall Stables, Bishop's Stortford, Hertfordshire, CM23 4BE Tel: (0844) 4155508 Fax: (0844) 4155509 E-mail: gill@nicholsonmartin.co.uk
Ogilvy Interactive Ltd, 10 Carbot Square, Canary Wharf, London, E14 4QB Tel: (020) 7345 3999 Fax: (020) 7345 3888
Online Awareness, Balmoral Court, 22 Balmoral Road, Stockport, Cheshire, SK4 4DJ Tel: 0161-432 3669 Fax: 0161-718 9462 E-mail: enquiries@online-awareness.com
▶ The Palmer & Rose Partnership, Maree House, 149 New Road, Booker, High Wycombe, Buckinghamshire, HP12 4RH Tel: (01494) 637499 Fax: (01494) 452630 E-mail: info@palmer-rose.co.uk
▶ Phoenix Design Print, 56 Wilbury Way, Hitchin, Hertfordshire, SG4 0TP Tel: (01462) 427500 Fax: (01462) 427501 E-mail: mark@pcsltd.org.uk
▶ PJM Advertising Ltd, 9 Rempstone Barns, Rempstone, Corfe Castle, Wareham, Dorset, BH20 5JH Tel: (01929) 481520 Fax: (01929) 481519 E-mail: office@pjmsouth.co.uk
Saatchi & Saatchi, 80 Charlotte St, London, W1A 1AQ Tel: (020) 7636 5060 Fax: (020) 7436 1998
Slater, 13 Fort Dunlop, Birmingham, B24 9FD Tel: 0121-384 9700 Fax: 0121-384 9790 E-mail: golleyslater@golleyslater.co.uk
Strange & Dawson Advertising Ltd, Ninth Floor Clifton Heights, Triangle West, Clifton, Bristol, BS8 1EJ Tel: 0117-925 3830 Fax: 0117-925 3851
T C S Media (North) Ltd, Camellia House, 76 Water Lane, Wilmslow, Cheshire, SK9 5BB Tel: (01625) 536795 Fax: (01625) 536796 E-mail: staff@tcsnorth.com
▶ WFCA Integrated Ltd, Cobden House, 25 London Road, Tunbridge Wells, Kent, TN1 1DA Tel: (01892) 511085 Fax: (01892) 512180 E-mail: info@wfca.co.uk

ADVERTISING CALENDARS

Allan & Bertram Ltd, Cuffley Gate, Sopers Road, Cuffley, Hertfordshire, EN6 4RY Tel: (01707) 876677 Fax: (01707) 877960
Argonaut Press, Kendalls Buildings, Birmingham Road, Stratford-upon-Avon, Warwickshire, CV37 0AQ Tel: (01789) 414478 Fax: (01789) 414478 E-mail: john@argonautpress.co.uk
Beaver Business Gifts, 5 Telford Road, Middlesbrough, Cleveland, TS3 8BL Tel: (01642) 252890 Fax: (01642) 773277
Bemrose Booth, PO Box 18, Derby, DE21 6XG Tel: (01332) 294242 Fax: (01332) 290366 E-mail: promote@bemrose.co.uk
▶ Calendar Lady Promotions Ltd, 2 Barnfield Cottages, Upton Bishop, Ross-on-Wye, Herefordshire, HR9 7TZ Tel: (01989) 780727 Fax: (01989) 780276 E-mail: info@calendarlady.co.uk
▶ Captive Calendars, 12 Fairway*, Sawbridgeworth, Hertfordshire, CM21 9NJ Tel: 01279 319769
G B Promotional Products Ltd, The Old Smoke House Potter Street, Sandwich, Kent, CT13 9DR Tel: (01304) 619390 Fax: (01304) 619391 E-mail: sales@gbpromotionalproducts.co.uk
Judges Postcards Ltd, 176 Bexhill Road, St. Leonards-on-Sea, East Sussex, TN38 8BN Tel: (01424) 420919 Fax: (01424) 438538 E-mail: sales@judges.co.uk
Moments Calendars, Wayzgoose Drive, Derby, DE21 6ST Tel: (01332) 285911 Fax: (01332) 285912 E-mail: sales@moments.co.uk
Motiv Business Gifts, 28 Moor Lane, Loughborough, Leicestershire, LE11 1BA Tel: (01509) 262272 Fax: (01509) 267276
Mouth & Foot Painting Artists, 9 Inverness Place, London, W2 3JG Tel: (020) 7229 4491 Fax: (020) 7229 7052
Offset Marketing, 2 Speedwell Close, Chandler's Ford, Eastleigh, Hampshire, SO53 4BT Tel: (023) 8027 4444 Fax: (023) 8027 0112
Reeves Calendar, Knowling Mead, Tenby, Dyfed, SA70 8ED Tel: (01834) 842652 Fax: (01834) 842337 E-mail: info@reeve-calendars.com
Rose Colchester Ltd, Clough Road, Severalls Industrial Park, Colchester, CO4 9QT Tel: (01206) 844500 Fax: (01206) 845872 E-mail: sales@rosecalendars.co.uk

ADVERTISING CREATIVE DESIGN CONSULTANTS/ PRODUCERS/SERVICES

▶ 3D Illustration - Digital Illustration Specialists, South View, 43 Queens Road, Accrington, Lancashire, BB5 6AR Tel: (01254) 381027 E-mail: team@3dillustration.co.uk
▶ The Ad Studio, 23 Martlet Close, Cherque Farm, Lee on the Solent, Gosport, Hampshire, PO13 8FP Tel: 02392 553442 Fax: 08715 227697 E-mail: info@theadstudio.co.uk
▶ Arclid.Com Ltd, 506 Building 1, Radway Green Venture Park, Crewe, CW2 5PR Tel: (0844) 8009672 Fax: (01270) 750524 E-mail: info@arclid.com
Azure Blue Design, 61 Viceroy Court, Wilmslow Road, Didsbury, Manchester, M20 2RH Tel: (07886) 443129 E-mail: sales@azure-blue.co.uk
B-Looney, Buck House, Sunnyside Road, Chesham, Buckinghamshire, HP5 2AR Tel: (01494) 793904 Fax: (01494) 791268 E-mail: balloons@b-loony.co.uk
▶ CabAds - Taxi Advertising, Unit 1A, West Craigs Industrial Estate, Turnhouse Road, Edinburgh, EH12 0BD Tel: (0845) 2268595 Fax: (0845) 2268595 E-mail: info@cabads.co.uk
▶ Creative Place Ltd, 4 Millfield House, Woodshots Meadow, Watford, WD18 8SS Tel: (01923) 227272 Fax: (01923) 246556 E-mail: sales@thecreativeplace.co.uk
▶ Design Forte, Harewood Cottage, Main Street, Weeton, Leeds, LS17 0AY Tel: (01423) 734856 E-mail: chris@designforte.co.uk
▶ Easy Tiger Creative Ltd, 25-27 Greenwich Market, Greenwich, London, SE10 9HZ Tel: (020) 8305 9292 E-mail: studio@easytigercreative.com
▶ Envisage Design Ltd, Brick Kiln Lane, Basford, Stoke-on-Trent, ST4 7BS Tel: (01782) 219922 Fax: (01782) 289580E-mail: info@enviz.co.uk
Finger Prints, Unit 3 Andrews Court, Andrews Way, Barrow-in-Furness, Cumbria, LA14 2UE Tel: (01229) 432959 Fax: (01229) 431955 E-mail: info@fingerprints.co.uk
Gildersons Ltd, 31-35 Pitfield Street, London, N1 6HB Tel: (020) 7324 0180 Fax: (020) 7490 4333 E-mail: studio@gildersons.co.uk
▶ GnD Creations, 6 Peterborough Rd, Whittlesey, Peterborough, PE7 1NJ Tel: 01733 206520 E-mail: design@gndcreations.com
▶ Grove Creative Ltd, 15 Wentworth Grove, Winsford, Cheshire, CW7 2LJ Tel: (01606) 553793 E-mail: info@grovecreative.co.uk
▶ Guava Ltd, Hurst Grove, Sandford Lane, Hurst, Reading, RG10 0SQ Tel: 0118-932 1100 Fax: 0118-932 1222 E-mail: info@guava.co.uk
▶ IDVE Design, 2 Hillside Road, HASTINGS, East Sussex, TN34 2QT Tel: 0845 2571965 E-mail: contact@idve.co.uk
Impact Design & Advertising, 113 Bradbury Road, Solihull, West Midlands, B92 8AL Tel: 0121-707 4774 Fax: 0121-706 1663 E-mail: steve@impactida.com
▶ In-Toon Ltd, 17b Beacon Hill, London, N7 9LY Tel: (020) 7609 2071 E-mail: enquiries@intoononline.com
J W T, 1 Knightsbridge Green, London, SW1X 7NW Tel: (020) 7656 7000 Fax: (020) 7656 7010
▶ Jonk Design & Film Boutique, 30 High Street, Eton, Windsor, Berkshire, SL4 6AX Tel: (07793) 122586 Fax: (01753) 840240 E-mail: info@jonkproductions.com
▶ Juni Design & Artwork, 16 Manea Close, Lower Earley, Reading, RG6 4JN Tel: 0118-986 8064 Fax: 0118-986 8064 E-mail: ashton_dave@hotmail.com
▶ Kaptive Animation Studios, 73 Attlee Road, Walsall, WS2 0EX Tel: (01922) 867443 E-mail: kris@kaptive.co.uk
Kiosk, No. 2, 43 High Street, Leamington Spa, Warwickshire, CV31 1LN Tel: (01926) 776282
▶ Limegreentangerine, 57 Cowbridge Road East, Cardiff, CF11 9AE Tel: (029) 2046 2544 E-mail: info@limegreentangerine.co.uk
▶ Logix Retail Display & Design Consultancy, Unit 15, Arlington Way, Dalton, Huddersfield, HD5 9TF Tel: (01484) 533548 E-mail: logix_gareth@fsmail.net
▶ Marketing Direct, 26 Makendon Street, Hebburn, Tyne & Wear, NE31 1RF Tel: 0191 4836090 E-mail: md_marketingdirect@yahoo.co.uk
▶ Oasis Design Studio, 1 Culzean Glen, Larne, County Antrim, BT40 2HF Tel: (028) 2827 0668 Fax: (028) 2827 0668 E-mail: info@oasisdesignstudio.co.uk
▶ Open Creation, Fermoy House, Shepley Road, Barnt Green, Birmingham, B45 8JN Tel: 0121 2882205 E-mail: mail@opencreation.co.uk
▶ Pentacor plc, Capital House 4 Parkhouse Business Centre, Desborough Park Road, High Wycombe, Buckinghamshire, HP12 3DJ Tel: (01494) 898300 Fax: (01494) 898301 E-mail: info@pentacor.co.uk
▶ Phoenix Design Print, 56 Wilbury Way, Hitchin, Hertfordshire, SG4 0TP Tel: (01462) 427500 Fax: (01462) 427501 E-mail: mark@pcsltd.org.uk
▶ Pixel Perfect, The White House, Copse Road, Haslemere, Surrey, GU27 3QQ Tel: (01428) 643500 E-mail: sales@pixelperfect.co.uk
▶ PJM Advertising Ltd, 9 Rempstone Barns, Rempstone, Corfe Castle, Wareham, Dorset, BH20 5JH Tel: (01929) 481520 Fax: (01929) 481519 E-mail: office@pjmsouth.co.uk
▶ Premedian.com, Ivy House, Main Street, Leyburn, North Yorkshire, DL8 4EX Tel: 01969 625674 E-mail: ttalbot@premedian.com
▶ Principal Image, Cherry Tree Lane, Rostherne, Altrincham, Cheshire, WA14 3RZ Tel: (01565) 830213 Fax: (01565) 830214 E-mail: info@principalimage.com
▶ Ripe, Science & Technology Centre Earley Gate, Whiteknights Road, Reading, RG6 6BZ Tel: 0118-935 7316 Fax: 0118-926 7917 E-mail: sales@ripe.org.uk
▶ Rye Design, 107-109 High Street, Rochester, Kent, ME1 1JS Tel: (01634) 818168 Fax: (01634) 818178 E-mail: sales@ryedesign.co.uk
▶ Sea Design, Lansdowne Road, Falmouth, Cornwall, TR11 4BE Tel: (01326) 311658 E-mail: info@sea-studio.com
▶ Studio K, The Lodge, 145 Westgate, Cleckheaton, West Yorkshire, BD19 5EJ Tel: 01274 861433 E-mail: imelda@studiok.fsbusiness.co.uk
▶ Talk Marketing Ltd, Stockton Business Centre, Brunswick Street, Stockton-on-Tees, Cleveland, TS18 1DW Tel: (01642) 345133 Fax: (01642) 345135 E-mail: talkmarketing@fsbdial.co.uk
▶ Ti-Visual Ltd, 4 Greenfields, Upton, Chester, CH2 1LN Tel: (01244) 382287 Fax: 0870 1357161 E-mail: info@ti-visual.co.uk
▶ Topform Visual Communication Ltd, 2 The Courtyard, Lamdin Road, Bury St. Edmunds, Suffolk, IP32 6NU Tel: (01284) 747399 Fax: (01284) 747401 E-mail: sales@topformonline.co.uk
▶ Travisbead, 611 South Eighth Street, Milton Keynes, MK9 3DE Tel: (01908) 231401 E-mail: info@travisbead.com
▶ WFCA Integrated Ltd, Cobden House, 25 London Road, Tunbridge Wells, Kent, TN1 1DA Tel: (01892) 511085 Fax: (01892) 512180 E-mail: info@wfca.co.uk
▶ White Cat, 7 Micheldever Gardens, Whitchurch, Hampshire, RG28 7JY Tel: (01256) 892952 E-mail: kimbyatt@whitecatdesign.biz

ADVERTISING DRAWING SERVICES

▶ Flameboy Graphix, 9 Halliday Drive, Armley, Leeds, LS12 3PA Tel: 01132 891205 Fax: 0113 891205 E-mail: info@flameboygraphix.co.uk

ADVERTISING GIFT/BUSINESS INCENTIVE/SOUVENIR DESIGNERS, PRODUCERS ETC

A D Litho, Unit 3 Wycombe Industrial Mall, West End Street, High Wycombe, Buckinghamshire, HP11 2QY Tel: (01494) 536117 Fax: (01494) 531298 E-mail: adlitho@aol.com
A G Products, 4-5 North Bar Street, Banbury, Oxfordshire, OX16 0TB Tel: (01295) 259608 Fax: (01295) 271787 E-mail: steve@agproducts.co.uk
A L Atack Ltd, Church Street, Ossett, West Yorkshire, WF5 9DG Tel: (01924) 263358 Fax: (01924) 281546
Acorn Hip Flasks Ltd, Reliance Works, 62 Northwood Street, Birmingham, B3 1TT Tel: (0777) 9724408 Fax: 0121-233 4336 E-mail: peter@hipflasks.co.uk
Actionpoint Packaging Materials, The Old Brickfields, Otterham Quay Lane, Rainham, Gillingham, Kent, ME8 8NA Tel: (01634) 373736

ADVERTISING GIFT/BUSINESS INCENTIVE/SOUVENIR DESIGNERS, PRODUCERS ETC – *continued*

AdGiftsOnline, 17 The Barracks, Barracks Road, Newcastle, Staffordshire, ST5 1LG Tel: (01782) 713177 Fax: (01782) 715431 E-mail: sales@adgiftsonline.com

Adline Personalised Products, Sterling House, 20 Renfield Street, Glasgow, G2 5AP Tel: 0141-248 4411 Fax: 0141-248 4411 E-mail: sales@adlinepersonalised.com

Advanta Marketing Ltd, 190 Cromwell Road, Newport, Gwent, NP19 0HP Tel: (01633) 292939 Fax: (01633) 292938 E-mail: sales@advantamarketing.co.uk

Allan & Bertram Ltd, Cuffley Gate, Sopers Road, Cuffley, Hertfordshire, EN6 4RY Tel: (01707) 876677 Fax: (01707) 877960

Angel Multimedia, 32 Blue Street, Carmarthen, Dyfed, SA31 3LE Tel: (01267) 221175 Fax: (01267) 223196 E-mail: sales@angelmm.co.uk

▶ Arclid.Com Ltd, 506 Building 1, Radway Green Venture Park, Crewe, CW2 5PR Tel: (0844) 8009672 Fax: (01270) 750524 E-mail: info@arclid.com

Ashprint London Ltd, 46 South Building 56 Magnet Road, East Lane, Wembley, Middlesex, HA9 7RG Tel: (020) 8904 6479 Fax: (020) 8908 0315 E-mail: sales@ashprint-international.co.uk

Balloons Direct, Lyn Court, The Common, Holt, Trowbridge, Wiltshire, BA14 6QL Tel: (01225) 784040

Banbury Badges Ltd, Brooklands, Brook Street, Moreton Pinkney, Daventry, Northamptonshire, NN11 3SL Tel: (01295) 768758 Fax: (01295) 768759 E-mail: info@banburybadges.co.uk

Base 1 Ltd, 41-43 Roebuck Road, Hainault Industrial Estate, Ilford, Essex, IG6 3TU Tel: (020) 8500 5649 Fax: (020) 8559 9456 E-mail: phil@base1.co.uk

Herbert Baumann Ltd, Bago Ho, 11-15 Chase Rd, Park Royal, London, NW10 6PT Tel: (020) 8955 6400 Fax: (020) 8883 3833

Beaumont PPS Ltd, 537 Sauchiehall Street, Glasgow, G3 7PQ Tel: 0141-226 3411 Fax: 0141-221 9249 E-mail: sales@beaumontpps.com

Beaver Business Gifts, 5 Telford Road, Middlesbrough, Cleveland, TS3 8BL Tel: (01642) 252890 Fax: (01642) 773277

B-Looney, Buck House, Sunnyside Road, Chesham, Buckinghamshire, HP5 2AR Tel: (01494) 793904 Fax: (01494) 791268 E-mail: balloons@b-loony.co.uk

▶ Nigel Brand, Unit H, Tollgate Business Centre, Tollgate Industrial Estate, Stafford, ST16 3HS Tel: (01785) 259988 E-mail: penshop@premierprint.uk.com

Branston Plastics Ltd, 60 Spencer Street, Birmingham, B18 6DS Tel: 0121-236 8253 Fax: 0121-236 8253

Brenton Handbags Ltd, Darren Mill, Wash Lane, Bury, Lancashire, BL9 7DU Tel: 0161-764 8528 Fax: 0161-763 1503 E-mail: info@brentonbags.com

BTC Group Ltd, Unit 9 Millington Road, Hayes, Middlesex, UB3 4AZ Tel: (020) 8569 2250 Fax: (020) 8587 3350 E-mail: sales@btcgroup.co.uk

Burnham Signs Ltd, Burnham Way, London, SE26 5AG Tel: (020) 8659 1525 Fax: (020) 8659 4707 E-mail: sales@burnhamsigns.com

▶ Business Baubles, North Oast, Reed Court Farm, Hunton Road, Tonbridge, Kent, TN12 9SX Tel: (01622) 820005 Fax: (01622) 820006 E-mail: sales@businessbaubles.com

▶ Cardtoon Creations, 7 Kiln Crescent, Bishop Middleham, Ferryhill, County Durham, DL17 9AP Tel: (07747) 746123 E-mail: sales@cardsgifts.co.uk

The Carole Group Ltd, Oaklands Business Centre, Oaklands Park, Wokingham, Berkshire, RG41 2FD Tel: 0118-977 1424 Fax: 0118-977 2479 E-mail: sales@carolegroup.com

Carter Advertising, 11 Kirkhouse Road, Blanefield, Glasgow, G63 9BX Tel: (01360) 770235 Fax: (01360) 770235 E-mail: sales@carteradvertising.co.uk

Cathian Leather Goods, Compstall Mills Estate, Andrew Street, Compstall, Stockport, Cheshire, SK6 5HN Tel: 0161-427 4871 Fax: 0161-427 4871 E-mail: cathian@ukonline.co.uk

Chimo Holdings, White Rose Works, 61 Eyre Lane, Sheffield, S1 3GF Tel: 0114-272 4656 Fax: 0114-249 0922 E-mail: sales@chimoholdings.co.uk

City Screen Print Ltd, Unit 2 Sextant Park Neptune Close, Medway City Estate, Rochester, Kent, ME2 4LU Tel: (01634) 297779 Fax: (01634) 294264 E-mail: info@cityscreenprint.co.uk

▶ Clanroots, Braeside, 162 High Street, Gardenstown, Banff, AB45 3YW Tel: (01261) 851059 E-mail: nda@clanroots.co.uk

▶ Colintonwigglys, 51 Redford Road, Colinton, Edinburgh, EH13 0AD Tel: 0131-441 2454 Fax: 0131-441 2454 E-mail: james@colintonwigglys.com

Colorphaze, 73 Bunting Road, Northampton, NN2 6EE Tel: (01604) 792001 E-mail: sales@colorphaze.co.uk

Conquest Products, 29 Whitley Street, Reading, RG2 0EG Tel: 0118-987 4635 Fax: 0118-987 4638 E-mail: phil@conquestproducts.co.uk

Cook Hammond & Kell Ltd, Whittington House, 764-768 Holloway Road, London, N19 3JQ Tel: (020) 7281 2161 Fax: (020) 7281 4117

▶ Corporate Executive Gifts Ltd, Unit K, Houndswood Gate, Harper Lane, Radlett, Hertfordshire, WD7 7HU Tel: (01923) 852330 Fax: (01923) 859946 E-mail: sales@corporateexecutivegifts.com

Cougar Designs, 6A Bart Street, Sparkhill, Birmingham, B11 4SA Tel: 0121-773 9491 Fax: 0121-771 0464

Craigdon Business Gifts, Advertising House, Burghmuir Circle, Inverurie, Aberdeenshire, AB51 4FS Tel: (01467) 622943 Fax: (01467) 620286 E-mail: sales@craigdon.com

Creative Promotions, 79 West Regent Street, Glasgow, G2 2AW Tel: 0141-332 7471 Fax: 0141-331 2801 E-mail: enquiries@creativepromotions.co.uk

Credit Card Keys Ltd, 37 Sovereign Road, Kings Norton Business Centre, Birmingham, B30 3HN Tel: 0121-451 3911 Fax: 0121-451 3133 E-mail: sales@cckeys.co.uk

Crown Products International Ltd, Innovation House, Cobnar Wood Close, Chesterfield, Derbyshire, S41 9RQ Tel: (01246) 451451 Fax: (01246) 260122 E-mail: sales@crownproducts.demon.co.uk

D & N Design, 2 Weston Road, Thames Ditton, Surrey, KT7 0HN Tel: (020) 8398 9639 Fax: (020) 8398 9639

Darby Rosettes & Trophies, 5 Goulburn Road, Norwich, NR7 9UX Tel: (01603) 440694 Fax: (01603) 440687

Denham Wine Ltd, 1-3 Law Lane, Halifax, West Yorkshire, HX3 9QU Tel: (01422) 356146 Fax: (01422) 380224

▶ Design Wise, Matrix House, Constitution Hill, Leicester, LE1 1PL Tel: 0116-262 8678 Fax: 0116-262 8678 E-mail: info@designwise.org.uk

DJH Engineering Ltd, Consett Business Park, Consett, County Durham, DH8 6BP Tel: (01207) 500050 Fax: (01207) 599757 E-mail: sales@djhpewterworks.co.uk

E H Advertising Ltd, Castlethorpe Court, Castlethorpe, Brigg, North Lincolnshire, DN20 9LG Tel: (01652) 650100 Fax: (01652) 650035 E-mail: eh.advertising@virgin.net

Elite Screen Printing & Embroidery Ltd, 45 Sartoris Road, Rushden, Northamptonshire, NN10 9TL Tel: (01933) 315930 Fax: (01933) 418364 E-mail: elitetex@aol.com

Ellenell Promotions Ltd, 1b Shrubbery Road, London, N9 0QQ Tel: (020) 8887 0000 Fax: (020) 8887 0001 E-mail: sales@ellenell.com

Epik Incentives, Unit 13 Silver End Business Park, Brettell Lane, Brierley Hill, West Midlands, DY5 3LG Tel: (01384) 77310 Fax: (01384) 481975E-mail: sales@epik.co.uk

Everts International Ltd, Second Avenue, Flixborough Industrial Estate, Flixborough, Scunthorpe, South Humberside, DN15 8SD Tel: (01724) 282525 Fax: (01724) 282526 E-mail: info@evertsballoon.co.uk

▶ Expatboxes, Robyn's Way, Edenbridge, Kent, TN8 5SE Tel: (07840) 891880 E-mail: info@expatboxes.com

▶ Feathers Favours, 16 Burnpark, Catrine, Mauchline, Ayrshire, KA5 6ER Tel: (01290) 553105 E-mail: enquires@feathersfavours.co.uk

Filofax Time Management, Unit 3 Victoria Gardens, Burgess Hill, West Sussex, RH15 9NB Tel: (01444) 238100 Fax: (01444) 238119 E-mail: enquiries@filofax.co.uk

Flipstick (International) Ltd, 40a Rowland Street, Rugby, Warwickshire, CV21 2BW Tel: (01788) 542109 Fax: (01788) 542116 E-mail: info@flipstick.co.uk

Formula Incentives Ltd, 1 Lockside Office Park, Lockside Road, Preston, PR2 2YS Tel: (01772) 721122 Fax: (01772) 326850 E-mail: sales@incentives.co.uk

Forward Group plc, 57 Buckland Road, London, E10 6QS Tel: (020) 8558 7110 Fax: (020) 8558 5974E-mail: sales@forward-group.co.uk

Harpercollins Pubrs Ophelia House, Fulham Palace Road, London, W6 8JA Tel: (020) 8741 7070 Fax: (020) 8307 4440 E-mail: vibecke.olsen@harpercollins.co.uk

Harrod Business Promotions Ltd, 3 Goodwood Rise, Marlow BTM, Marlow, Buckinghamshire, SL7 3QE Tel: (01628) 891133 Fax: (01628) 891134 E-mail: sales@harrodpromotions.com

Harwell Enterprises Ltd, 43 Platts Eyot, Hampton, Middlesex, TW12 2HF Tel: (020) 8783 0666 Fax: (020) 8941 6977 E-mail: sales@harwell.co.uk

Hedgerow Publishing Ltd, 325 Abbeydale Road, Sheffield, S7 1FS Tel: 0114-255 4873 Fax: 0114-250 9400 E-mail: sales@hedgerow.co.uk

Horton & Newberry (Sales & Marketing) Ltd, 53a High Street Wanstead, London, E11 2AA Tel: (020) 8989 5903 Fax: (020) 8530 4118 E-mail: sales@hortonandnewberry.co.uk

E. Hulme & Son Ltd, 13-15 Cecil Street, Walsall, WS4 2BD Tel: (01922) 622082 Fax: (01922) 722442

I M I Cornelius, 39-41 Nuffield Way, Abingdon, Oxfordshire, OX14 1AE Tel: (01235) 555123 Fax: (01235) 555456

I S Enterprises International, Clement House, Commerce Way, Colchester, CO2 8HY Tel: (01206) 798131 Fax: (01206) 791186 E-mail: sales@isenterprisesintl.co.uk

▶ IDVE Design, 2 Hillside Road, HASTINGS, East Sussex, TN34 2QT Tel: 0845 2571965 E-mail: contact@idve.co.uk

Image Matters, Unit B12, Laser Quay, Rochester, Kent, ME2 4HU Tel: (01634) 296400 Fax: (01634) 296444 E-mail: sales@imagematters.co.uk

Impakt Stationers, Unit 12 Endeavour Way, Croydon, CR0 4TR Tel: (020) 8684 5777 Fax: (020) 8684 5999 E-mail: sales@impakt.co.uk

IMPAMARK, 1Dammerwick Farm, Marsh Road, Burnham-On-Crouch, Essex, CM0 8AG Tel: (01621) 783550 Fax: (01621) 784548 E-mail: info@impamark.co.uk

▶ IM-Press Promotions Ayr Ltd, 3 Barclaugh Drive, Coylton, Ayr, KA6 6HS Tel: (01292) 570495 Fax: (01292) 570495 E-mail: im-pressayr@btconnect.com

Initial Incentives, Unit 4, Parr Road, Stanmore, Middlesex, HA7 1NP Tel: (020) 8381 3300 Fax: (020) 8381 3700 E-mail: sales@initialonline.com

▶ Ink Promotions Ltd, 225 High Road, Woodford, London, E18 2PB Tel: (020) 8505 2510 Fax: (020) 8181 7537 E-mail: sales@inkpromotions.co.uk

Inprints (Screenprinters) Ltd, 32-36 Garden St, Sheffield, S1 4BJ Tel: 0114-272 7733 Fax: 0114-272 1976 E-mail: sales@inprints.co.uk

Insignia Ltd, 1-6 Chalice Close, Wallington, Surrey, SM6 9RU Tel: (020) 8669 3122 Fax: (020) 8669 7192 E-mail: sales@insigniauk.com

▶ Interknickers Ltd, 21 Claremont Drive, Coalville, Coalville, Leicestershire, LE67 2ND Tel: (01530) 460316 E-mail: interknickers@btinternet.com

Interlogo London Ltd, High Street, Newport, Isle of Wight, PO30 1BQ Tel: (01983) 522470 Fax: (01983) 532891 E-mail: sales@interlogo.co.uk

▶ IPNV Limited, PO Box 6882, Kettering, Northants, NN15 6WR Tel: 0845 070 1765 E-mail: info@ipnv.co.uk

J S M Business Gifts, 9 St. Albans Road, Gloucester, GL2 5FW Tel: (01452) 310030 Fax: (01452) 304454

Jack Nadel, 23 Pembridge Square, London, W2 4DR Tel: (020) 7535 3400 Fax: (020) 7353 4310 E-mail: jn-ap@activepromotions.com

▶ Juni Design & Artwork, 16 Manea Close, Lower Earley, Reading, RG6 4JN Tel: 0118-986 8064 Fax: 0118-986 8064 E-mail: ashton_dave@hotmail.com

Kingfob, 4 John Street, Walsall, WS2 8AF Tel: (01922) 722561 Fax: (01922) 722442 E-mail: artwork@keyfob.co.uk

L & H Promotional Ltd, 1A Barton Heys Road, Formby, Liverpool, L37 2EZ Tel: (01704) 873550 Fax: (01704) 878812 E-mail: pual@lhapm.com

Lancewich Promotional Items, Unit 14 Wellington Business Park, Dukes Ride, Crowthorne, Berkshire, RG45 6LS Tel: (01344) 753550 Fax: (01344) 753551 E-mail: sales@lancewich.co.uk

Lericoat Ltd, Unit 18, Addington Park Industrial Estate, Little Addington, Kettering, Northamptonshire, NN14 4AS Tel: (01933) 651618 Fax: (01933) 652112 E-mail: rob.britten@lericoat.co.uk

Lowe Aston Partnership, Moorlands Lane, Saltash, Cornwall, PL12 4HL Tel: (01752) 842233 Fax: (01752) 848060 E-mail: info@loweaston.co.uk

LP Marketing Ltd, Millenium House, Junction Road, Sheffield, S11 8XB Tel: 0114-268 2812 Fax: 0114-268 2812

M T M Promotional, 287 Palatine Road, Northenden, Manchester, M22 4ET Tel: 0161-946 9200 Fax: 0161-946 9209 E-mail: info@mtmpromotional.co.uk

Maccravats Ltd, Byrons Lodge, Byrons Lane, Macclesfield, Cheshire, SK11 7JW Tel: (01625) 422079 Fax: (01625) 614641 E-mail: maccravats@yahoo.com

Map Marketing Ltd, 92-104 Carnwath Road, London, SW6 3HW Tel: (020) 7526 2322 Fax: (020) 7371 0473 E-mail: sales@mapmarketing.com

Marketing Solutions, 51 Castleton Road, Ilford, Essex, IG3 9QW Tel: (020) 8590 2703 Fax: (020) 8597 4911 E-mail: mktsolutions@hotmail.com

Marks Of Distinction, 55 Central Avenue, West Molesey, Surrey, KT8 2QZ Tel: (020) 8941 5533 Fax: (020) 8941 5575 E-mail: lbrind@chelsea.co.uk

Mister Tee's Rock Stop, 65 Blackwell Street, Kidderminster, Worcestershire, DY10 2EL Tel: (01562) 515291

Mitreprize Ltd, Mitre House, 96-98 Braemar Avenue, South Croydon, Surrey, CR2 0QB Tel: (020) 8668 4999 Fax: (020) 8668 1487 E-mail: info@mitreprize.co.uk

Moores of London Ltd, Third Floor, Elizabeth House, 54-58 High Street, Edgware, Middlesex, HA8 7EJ Tel: (020) 8731 2120 Fax: (020) 8731 2121 E-mail: sales@mooreslondon.co.uk

Moulded Acrylic Products, 4 Brook Farm, Horsham Road, Cowfold, Horsham, West Sussex, RH13 8AH Tel: (01403) 865220 Fax: (01403) 865224 E-mail: sales@mouldedacrylic.co.uk

▶ Nauticality Nautical Gifts, Albrighton, Wolverhampton, WV7 3WL Tel: (01902) 373217 Fax: (01902) 375317 E-mail: nauticalitygift@aol.com

Network Promotions, 5 Braehead Business Units, Braehead Road, Linlithgow, West Lothian, EH49 6EP Tel: (01506) 845797 Fax: (01506) 845149

Nicholson Promotional Supplies, 198a Halfway Street, Sidcup, Kent, DA15 8DJ Tel: (020) 8308 1818 Fax: (020) 8309 5718 E-mail: jeff.nps@btinternet.com

Offset Marketing, 2 Speedwell Close, Chandler's Ford, Eastleigh, Hampshire, SO53 4BT Tel: (023) 8027 4444 Fax: (023) 8027 0112

Oldeani Ltd, Unit 2a Hoffmanns Way, Chelmsford, CM1 1GU Tel: (01245) 262611 Fax: (01245) 262885 E-mail: sales@oldeani.com

P K A Promotions Ltd, 6 South Folds Road, Corby, Northamptonshire, NN18 9EU Tel: (01536) 461122 Fax: (01536) 744668 E-mail: sales@pkapromotions.com

P M W Gifts, Springfield House, Water Lane, Wilmslow, Cheshire, SK9 5BG Tel: (01625) 536036 Fax: (01625) 536320 E-mail: sales@pmwgifts.co.uk

Pathway Insentives Ltd, 47 Keats Way, Rushden, Northamptonshire, NN10 6EE Tel: (01933) 350244 Fax: (01933) 350255 E-mail: pathway@harryg.freeserve.co.uk

Pegasus Plastics UK Ltd, Unit 24 Eldon Way, Paddock Wood, Tonbridge, Kent, TN12 6BE Tel: (01892) 832326 Fax: (01892) 832328 E-mail: sales@pegasusplastics.co.uk

Pennine Products, Marsh House, Market Place, Honley, Holmfirth, HD9 6NG Tel: (01484) 666303 Fax: (01484) 663260 E-mail: sales@pennineproducts.co.uk

▶ Pewter Art Online Giftware Specialist Ltd, 492 Chigwell Road, Woodford Green, Essex, IG8 8PA Tel: (07801) 531553 Fax: (020) 8504 4528 E-mail: sales@yourpewter.com

Plastech Print Ltd, Debdale Lane, Keyworth, Nottingham, NG12 5HN Tel: 0115-937 4041 Fax: 0115-937 3426 E-mail: sales@plastechprint.co.uk

The PP Group, Dukesway, Teeside Industrial Estate, Thornaby, Stockton-On-Tees, Cleveland, TS17 9LT Tel: (01642) 765566 Fax: (01642) 760692 E-mail: sales@ppgroup.co.uk

Premier Promotional Services, 38 Bearton Road, Hitchin, Hertfordshire, SG5 1UE Tel: (01462) 442288 Fax: (01462) 458883 E-mail: sales@premierpromotional.co.uk

▶ PresentstoGo Christening & Birthday Gifts Co., Sunnywood Drive, Haywards Heath, West Sussex, RH16 4PE Tel: 01444 415096 E-mail: jw@presentstogo.co.uk

Printform Direct Ltd, 8 Longbridge, Willesborough, Ashford, Kent, TN24 0TA Tel: (01233) 639898 Fax: (01233) 636866 E-mail: sales@printform.co.uk

Promo Branding Ltd, New Southgate Industrial Estate, Lower Park Road, London, N11 1QD Tel: (020) 8361 8820 Fax: (020) 8361 8821 E-mail: sales@promobranding.co.uk

Promocan, Plaistow Road, Loxwood, Billingshurst, West Sussex, RH14 0TS Tel: (01403) 753453 Fax: 0845 6120655 E-mail: tmursell@promocan.co.uk

Promotional Fabrics Ltd, The Maltings, School Lane, Amersham, Buckinghamshire, HP7 0ES Tel: (01494) 724172 Fax: (01494) 725283 E-mail: enquiries@amershamfabrics.com

Promotional Products Specialities Scotland Ltd, 537 Sauchiehall Street, Glasgow, G3 7PQ Tel: 0141-221 2420 Fax: 0141-221 9249 E-mail: sales@beaumontpps.com

R J Smith Ltd, 41-42 Tenby St North, Birmingham, B1 3EG Tel: 0121-233 2160 Fax: 0121-233 9630E-mail: sales@rjs-ltd.com

Rafferty Hospitality Products Ltd, Unit 1 Shepherds Drive, Carnbane Industrial Estate, Newry, County Down, BT35 6JQ Tel: (028) 3025 2205 Fax: (028) 3025 2206 E-mail: sales@raffertyhospitality.com

Richards & Philips Ltd, Century House, Vickers Business Centre, Priestley Road, Basingstoke, Hampshire, RG24 9RA Tel: 01256 358651 Fax: 01256 333369 E-mail: sales@richards-philips.co.uk

B. Sanders (Bromsgrove) Ltd, 4 Sherwood Road, Aston Fields Industrial Estate, Bromsgrove, Worcestershire, B60 3DR Tel: (01527) 575757 Fax: (01527) 575539

▶ Shimmee, Plough Road, Great Bentley, Colchester, CO7 8LG Tel: (01206) 250400 Fax: (01206) 250410 E-mail: sales@shimmee.co.uk

Shreds, Station Yard, Station Road, Digby, Lincoln, LN4 3NF Tel: (01526) 320450 Fax: (01526) 320452 E-mail: information@shreds.co.uk

Silver Crane Co., 34a Black Moor Road, Ebblake Industrial Estate, Verwood, Dorset, BH31 6BB Tel: (01202) 825155 Fax: (01202) 823300 E-mail: sales@silvercrane.co.uk

▶ Sky High Leisure Hot Air Balloon Team, Watery Lane Cottage, Wrexham, LL13 OSL Tel: (0845) 3302994 E-mail: info@skyhighleisure.com

Source Ltd, The Old Stables, 10 Beulah Road, London, SW19 3SB Tel: (020) 8540 4201 Fax: (020) 8540 7380 E-mail: sales@sbsource.co.uk

Southern Platform, Unit 16 Vulcan Business Centre, Vulcan Way, New Addington, Croydon, CR0 9UG Tel: (01689) 800181 Fax: (01689) 800401 E-mail: sales@southernplatforms.co.uk

Special Efx Ltd, Ettington Park Bus Centre, Stratford-upon-Avon, Warwickshire, CV37 8BT Tel: (01789) 450005

Squeezyball Merchandising, 2 The Linen House, 253 Kilburn Lane, London, W10 4BQ Tel: (0870) 7512538 Fax: (020) 8960 6077 E-mail: sales@squeezyball.com

Starline, Mowbray Drive, Blackpool, FY3 7UN Tel: (01253) 307100 Fax: (01253) 307149 E-mail: sales@starlinesales.co.uk

Steel City Marketing Ltd, Allen Street, Sheffield, S3 7AW Tel: 0114-275 4150 Fax: 0114-275 0010 E-mail: sales@steel-city.co.uk

ADVERTISING GIFT/BUSINESS INCENTIVE/SOUVENIR DESIGNERS, PRODUCERS ETC – *continued*

▶ Talk Marketing Ltd, Stockton Business Centre, Brunswick Street, Stockton-on-Tees, Cleveland, TS18 1DW Tel: (01642) 345133 Fax: (01642) 345135 E-mail: talkmarketing@fsbdial.co.uk

Tetley Specialist Printers, 11 Wakelins End, Cookham, Maidenhead, Berkshire, SL6 9TQ Tel: (01628) 520047 Fax: (01628) 520047

TMS Corporate Awards, 2-4 Kathleen Road, Southampton, SO19 8EX Tel: (023) 8043 8866 Fax: (023) 8068 5604 E-mail: tms@trophyman.co.uk

Nigel Tooley Ltd, PO Box 91, Ashtead, Surrey, KT21 1YX Tel: (01372) 278620 E-mail: coincabinet@btconnect.com

▶ Total Merchandise Ltd, Standen House, Fishponds Lane, Holbrook, Ipswich, IP9 2QZ Tel: (01702) 540043 Fax: (01473) 327537 E-mail: sales@totalmerchandise.co.uk

Touchline Promotions Ltd, 17 Rayleas Close, London, SE18 3JN Tel: (020) 8856 1115 Fax: (020) 8319 3035 E-mail: touchproms@aol.com

Tommy Tucker Ltd, Barnham House, Aurillac Way, Hallcroft Industrial Estate, Retford, Nottinghamshire, DN22 7PX Tel: (01777) 705141 Fax: (01777) 860859 E-mail: sales@mgagency.demon.co.uk

Walsall Gold Blocking Service, John Street, Walsall, WS2 8AF Tel: (01922) 630031 Fax: (01922) 722855

Wessex Crystal, Unit 4 Silver End Industrial Estate, Brierley Hill, West Midlands, DY5 3LA Tel: (01384) 481390 Fax: (01384) 481600

Westbrook Marketing Ltd, 24 The Dean, Alresford, Hampshire, SO24 9AZ Tel: (01962) 733122 Fax: (01962) 733122 E-mail: sales@westbrookmarketing.co.uk

WH Smith Retail Ltd, Greenbridge Road, Swindon, SN3 3LD Tel: (01793) 616161 Fax: (01793) 426410 E-mail: info@whsmithonline.com

Wild Things, 12 Denmark Road, Exeter, EX1 1SL Tel: (01392) 493775 Fax: (01392) 413538 E-mail: info@wildthingsgifts.com

Worldwide Ideas Ltd, Ideas House Station Estate, Eastwood Close, London, E18 1RT Tel: (020) 8530 7171 Fax: (020) 8530 7365 E-mail: sales@worldwideideas.co.uk

Yorkshire Post, 7-11 Manor Row, Bradford, West Yorkshire, BD1 4PB Tel: (01274) 721571 Fax: (01274) 370165 E-mail: sales@topfile.fsnet.co.uk

ADVERTISING GRAPHIC DESIGN

▶ 3G Creative Graphic Design Glasgow Scotland, Design House, 7 Woodside Crescent, Glasgow, GL3 7UL Tel: 0141-332 3892 Fax: 0141-332 2233 E-mail: g3creative@tiscali.co.uk

▶ Base Creative Ltd, 46 Parkway, Dorking, Surrey, RH4 1EU Tel: (01306) 875447 E-mail: info@base-creative.co.uk

▶ Angela Berry, Hag Hill Rise, Taplow, Maidenhead, Berkshire, SL6 0LS Tel: (01628) 661073 Fax: (01628) 661073 E-mail: design@angelaberry.co.uk

▶ The Conservatory, Spitfire Studios, 63-71 Collier Street, London, N1 9BE Tel: (020) 7278 3222 E-mail: studio@theconservatory.co.uk

▶ design indeed, Top flat, 80 Cavendish Road, London, N4 1RS Tel: 0794 4231340 E-mail: info@design-indeed.co.uk

▶ Exposure, Marketing and Design Services, 12 FieldFare, Billericay, Essex, CM11 2PA Tel: 01277 621474 E-mail: paula@exposureonline.co.uk

▶ Eye For Design, PO BOX 4657, Shrewsbury, SY1 9AD Tel: 01743 353536 E-mail: sales@eyefor.co.uk

▶ Fingertip Designs, 17 Hildenley Close, Scarborough, North Yorkshire, YO12 5DU Tel: (01723) 351668 E-mail: fingertipdesigns@yahoo.co.uk

▶ G D Sign, 62 West Street, Gorseinon, Swansea, SA4 4AF Tel: (01792) 549172 E-mail: sales@gdsign.co.uk

▶ High Kite, Fordham, Linden Avenue, Odiham, Hook, Hampshire, RG29 1AW Tel: (01256) 704876 E-mail: info@highkite.co.uk

▶ Idealogic, Focal Point, 88 Coronation Avenue, Bath, BA2 2JP Tel: 01225 483322 Fax: 01225 483322 E-mail: kirstie@idealogicuk.com

▶ Jarman Design Associates Ltd, The Barn Churchill Farm, Church Hill, Whaddon, Milton Keynes, MK17 0LZ Tel: (01908) 867398 Fax: (01908) 503884 E-mail: info@jdadesign.co.uk

▶ Jonk Design & Film Boutique, 30 High Street, Eton, Windsor, Berkshire, SL4 6AX Tel: (07793) 122586 Fax: (01753) 840240 E-mail: info@jonkproductions.com

▶ Kingston Publishing Services, Broadway House, 105 Ferensway, Hull, HU1 3UN Tel: (01482) 602600 Fax: (01482) 216816 E-mail: sue.brightman@kcom.com

MMV Design, 30 Rosewood Court, Rothwell, LEEDS, LS26 0XG Tel: 0113 2825831 E-mail: enquiries@mmvdesign.co.uk

Sapio Solutions, New Brook House, 385 Alfreton Road, Nottingham, NG7 5LR Tel: 0115-875 8837 Fax: 0115-875 9900 E-mail: info@wowdesignsolutions.com

▶ Snafu Design, 8 South Street, Torrington, Devon, EX38 8HE Tel: (01805) 623387 E-mail: rob@snafudesign.co.uk

▶ Thumbprint Design, 37 St. Leonards Street, Stamford, Lincolnshire, PE9 2HL Tel: (07949) 330316 E-mail: enquiry@thumb-print.co.uk

▶ Urbansoul Design, Kingfisher Centre, Futures Park, Bacup, Lancashire, OL13 0BB Tel: (01706) 877899 Fax: (01706) 877899 E-mail: info@urbansouldesign.co.uk

▶ White Cat, 7 Micheldever Gardens, Whitchurch, Hampshire, RG28 7JY Tel: (01256) 892952 E-mail: kimbyatt@whitecatdesign.biz

▶ The Workroom Ltd, 28 Waterside, 44-48 Wharf Road, London, N1 7UX Tel: (020) 7608 0840 Fax: (020) 7608 0850 E-mail: admin@workroom.co.uk

Ziggurat Design, Hall Farm Barn, Carleton Forehoe, Norwich, NR9 4AL Tel: (01603) 757600 E-mail: info@zigguratdesign.co.uk

ADVERTISING MEDIA BUYING

Austin West Communications Ltd, New Premier House, 150 Southampton Row, London, WC1B 5AL Tel: (020) 7278 7878 Fax: (020) 7278 0238

▶ Nicholson Martin, 4 Thorley Hall Stables, Bishop's Stortford, Hertfordshire, CM23 4BE Tel: (0844) 4155508 Fax: (0844) 4155509 E-mail: gill@nicholsonmartin.co.uk

ADVERTISING SALES MANAGEMENT

Stanton Media Sales, 10 Grazing Lane, Redditch, Worcestershire, B97 5PE Tel: (01527) 404295 Fax: (01527) 540503 E-mail: sales@stantonmedia.co.uk

ADVERTISING SERVICES, INDOOR

▶ Baiss & Co Advances, 2 St. Peters Street, Ipswich, IP1 1XB Tel: (01473) 400033 E-mail: info@baiss.co.uk

ADVERTISING SIGNS

Trojan, 3 Lyon Road, Hersham Trading Estate, Walton-On-Thames, Surrey, KT12 3PU Tel: (01932) 232400 Fax: (01932) 267987 E-mail: info@trojansigns.com

Abbey Signs, Unit 1, The Yarn Barn, Upper Manor Road, Preston, Paignton, Devon, TQ3 2TP Tel: (01803) 559029 Fax: (01803) 666010 E-mail: sales@abbey4signs.com

C H Reynolds & Sons Ltd, 1358 Stratford Road, Hall Green, Birmingham, B28 9EH Tel: 0121-777 3675 Fax: 0121-777 4883 E-mail: reysigns@aol.com

Chadfield Signs, 6 Highfield Road, Stockton-on-Tees, Cleveland, TS18 5HG Tel: (01642) 582082

Cowen Signs, 65 Old Chester Road, Birkenhead, Merseyside, CH41 9AW Tel: 0151-647 8081 Fax: 0151-666 1087 E-mail: sales@cowen-signs.co.uk

Easter Road Plastics Signs Division, 289 Easter Road, Edinburgh, EH6 8LQ Tel: 0131-555 6446 Fax: 0131-553 3975

Excel Graphics Ltd, Unit 20 Finch Drive, Braintree, Essex, CM7 2SF Tel: (01376) 551199 Fax: (01376) 322899

Graphic Metal Co., 3 Lyon Road, Walton-on-Thames, Surrey, KT12 3PU Tel: (01932) 254669 Fax: (01932) 252628

Hertford Sign Services, Unit 4 Dicker Mill, Hertford, SG13 7AA Tel: 01920 877655 Fax: 01920 877654

Impact Signs, 2 Mugiemoss Road, Bucksburn, Aberdeen, AB21 9HH Tel: (01224) 684488 Fax: (01224) 684400

J D Signs, PO Box 317, Camberley, Surrey, GU17 0QG Tel: (01276) 600562 Fax: (01273) 600562

Morelli Birmingham, 1 Stratford St North, Birmingham, B11 1BY Tel: 0121-772 7100 Fax: 0121-772 7713 E-mail: headoffice@morelli.co.uk

Mr Signs, 7a Austin Fields, King's Lynn, Norfolk, PE30 1PH Tel: (01553) 761100 Fax: (01553) 773535

Multisigns, Unit 6, Southern Avenue, Leominster, Herefordshire, HR6 0QF Tel: (01432) 353333 Fax: (01568) 612379 E-mail: multi_signs_uk@yahoo.com

The Newport Sign Company Ltd, 47 Dolphin Street, Newport, Gwent, NP20 2AT Tel: (01633) 263301 Fax: (01633) 676497 E-mail: bernie@aol.com

R C Marble & Sons Ltd, 158a Ovenden Road, Halifax, West Yorkshire, HX3 5QG Tel: (01422) 345990 E-mail: sales@rcmarble.co.uk

Raymac Signs Ltd, Prospect Works, Showfield Lane, Malton, North Yorkshire, YO17 6BT Tel: (01653) 600015 Fax: (01653) 691600 E-mail: sales@raymac.co.uk

Scorpio Signs & Designs, Unit 28 Leeway Court, Leeway Industrial Estate, Newport, Gwent, NP19 4SJ Tel: (01633) 277599 Fax: (01633) 279669 E-mail: scorpiosigns@tiscalr.co.uk

Sign A Rama, Unit A Whiteknights Retail Centre, Shinfield Road, Reading, RG2 8HA Tel: 0118-931 1122 Fax: 0118-931 4040 E-mail: reading@sign-a-rama.co.uk

Sign & Design, 13 Crannog Lane, Oban, Argyll, PA34 4HB Tel: (01631) 562622 Fax: (01631) 562338 E-mail: sales@signx.com

Sign Here, Unit 1 & 2, 179 Fosse Road North, Leicester, LE3 5EZ Tel: 0116-225 9977 Fax: 0116-225 9966 E-mail: sales@sign-here.co.uk

Sign It, 302 Union Road, Oswaldtwistle, Accrington, Lancashire, BB5 3JD Tel: (01254) 396325 Fax: (01254) 396325

Sign Maker, 82 York Road, Woking, Surrey, GU22 7XR Tel: (01483) 714389 Fax: (01483) 714389 E-mail: info@thesignmaker.co.uk

Signs Now, Unit 6 Kenn Court, Roman Farm Road, Hengrove, Bristol, BS4 1UL Tel: 0117-964 6644 Fax: 0117-964 6655 E-mail: sales@342.signsnow.co.uk

Signs4you, 35 East St, Crediton, Devon, EX17 3AY Tel: 01363 776877 Fax: 01363 776877 E-mail: shsigns@aol.com

Simply Read, Stanley Road, Hartlepool, Cleveland, TS25 1QP Tel: (01429) 868866 Fax: (01429) 868866 E-mail: sales@simply-read.com

Solway Signs & Shop Equipment, 79 Blackwell Road, Carlisle, CA2 4AJ Tel: (01228) 528865 Fax: (01228) 528865 E-mail: solway.signs@tiscali.co.uk

Speedy Signs, 1 Moor Lane, Dungannon, County Tyrone, BT71 6HS Tel: (028) 8772 7511 Fax: (028) 8772 9511

Style Engravers, Unit 2 Warneford Avenue, Ossett, West Yorkshire, WF5 9NJ Tel: (01924) 270506 Fax: (01924) 265156 E-mail: sales@engravers.fsbusiness.co.uk

Tower Signs, 2 Railway Yard, Railway Street, Ballymena, County Antrim, BT42 2AF Tel: (028) 2565 8306 Fax: (028) 2565 8306

Tribune Graphics Ltd, Unit 11 New Road Industrial Estate, Grace Road, Sheerness, Kent, ME12 1DB Tel: (01795) 580261 Fax: (01795) 663318 E-mail: mail@tribunegraphics.co.uk

Write On Signs, Kilda Road, Perth, PH1 3FL Tel: (01738) 630007 Fax: (01738) 449191 E-mail: info@write-on-signs.com

AERIAL AMPLIFIERS

Antiference, Eastern Avenue, Lichfield, Staffordshire, WS13 7SB Tel: (01889) 272600 Fax: (01296) 84284 E-mail: sales@antiference.co.uk

Fringe Electronics Ltd, 50 Mansfield Rd, Clipstone Village, Mansfield, Nottinghamshire, NG21 9EQ Tel: (01623) 643802 Fax: (01623) 625407 E-mail: enquiries@fringeelectronics.co.uk

Hi-Tech Aerials, 5 Golden Noble Hill, Colchester, CO1 2AG Tel: (0800) 3897091 Fax: (0800) 3897091 E-mail: info@hitechaerials.co.uk

▶ Maxview Ltd, Common Lane, Setch, King's Lynn, Norfolk, PE33 0AT Tel: (01553) 813300 Fax: (01553) 813301 E-mail: sales@maxview.ltd.uk

Meridian Services Ltd, 94a Ash Road, Aldershot, Hampshire, GU12 4EY Tel: (01252) 318893 Fax: (01252) 336969

▶ T & D Electronics, 5 Liscombe Road, Dunstable, Bedfordshire, LU5 4PL Tel: (01582) 672134 E-mail: enquiries@tnd-electronics.co.uk

AERIAL ANTENNAS

Harada Industries Europe Ltd, Bell Heath Way, Birmingham, B32 3BZ Tel: 0121-423 2222 Fax: 0121-423 2121E-mail: hie@harada.co.uk

Jaybeam Ltd, Rutherford Drive, Park Farm South, Wellingborough, Northamptonshire, NN8 6AX Tel: (01933) 408408 Fax: (01933) 408404 E-mail: sales@jaybeamwireless.com

M G Sanders Co. Ltd, Newcastle Street, Stone, Staffordshire, ST15 8JU Tel: (01785) 815544 Fax: (01785) 815642 E-mail: sales@mgsanders.co.uk

Panorama Antennas Ltd, 61 Frogmore, London, SW18 1HF Tel: (020) 8877 4444 Fax: (020) 8877 4477 E-mail: sales@panorama.co.uk

Precision Antennas Ltd, Masons Road, Stratford-upon-Avon, Warwickshire, CV37 9NU Tel: (01789) 266131 Fax: (01789) 298497 E-mail: sales@precision-antennas.co.uk

Renair Antennae Ltd, 11-15 Chase Road, London, NW10 6PT Tel: (020) 8965 3001 Fax: (020) 8965 5773 E-mail: sales@renair.co.uk

Sigma Wireless (UK) Ltd, Unit 6, Bridgegate Business Park, Gatehouse Way, Aylesbury, Buckinghamshire, HP19 8XN Tel: (01296) 505505 Fax: (01296) 505500 E-mail: infouk@sigma.ie

H.R. Smith Technical Development Ltd, Street Court, Kingsland, Leominster, Herefordshire, HR6 9QA Tel: (01568) 708744 Fax: (01568) 708713 E-mail: sales@hr-smith.com

South Midlands Communications Ltd, SM House, School Close, Chandler's Ford, Eastleigh, Hampshire, SO53 4RA Tel: (023) 8024 6200 Fax: (023) 8024 6206 E-mail: sales@smc-comms.com

TVM Systems, 2 Newgate Court, Paradise Street, Coventry, CV1 2RU Tel: (024) 7625 7875 Fax: (024) 7625 6433 E-mail: sales@tvm-systems.co.uk

AERIAL INSTALLATION CONTRACTORS

▶ A B Aerials, 38 Old Farm Road, Poole, Dorset, BH15 3LW Tel: (01202) 250550 Fax: (01202) 680626 E-mail: sales@abaerials.co.uk

▶ A World of Digital, 104 Walton Road, Chesterfield, Derbyshire, S40 3BY Tel: (01246) 229585 E-mail: aworldofdigital@aol.com

Active Aerials & Systems, 53 Rugeley Road, Armitage, Rugeley, Staffordshire, WS15 4AR Tel: 01543 307072 E-mail: active.systems@ntlworld.com

▶ Aerialek, 42-44 Ulverston Road, Dalton-In-Furness, Cumbria, LA15 8EF Tel: (01229) 463168

C & D Aerials, 25 Howard Avenue, Rochester, Kent, ME1 2AW Tel: (01634) 844448

Eagle Aerials, Mount Pleasant, Chapel Lane, Cannock Wood, Rugeley, Staffordshire, WS15 4SE Tel: (01543) 684558 Fax: (01543) 684558

▶ Eden Group, 43 Ellens Glen Road, Edinburgh, EH17 7QJ Tel: 0131-664 3906 Fax: 0131-658 1038 E-mail: Lynne@edengroup.co.uk

G P Aerials (1955) Ltd, 7 Maida Vale Business Centre, Maida Vale Road, Cheltenham, Gloucestershire, GL53 7ER Tel: (01242) 515216 Fax: (01242) 519125 E-mail: gp.aerials@virgin.net

Hi-Tech Aerials, 5 Golden Noble Hill, Colchester, CO1 2AG Tel: (0800) 3897091 Fax: (0800) 3897091 E-mail: info@hitechaerials.co.uk

▶ J S C Installations, Charlton Avenue, Eccles, Manchester, M30 0JQ Tel: 0161-211 9842 E-mail: enquiries@jscinstallations.co.uk

M F T Co Ltd, 22 Bedford Road, Lower Stondon, Henlow, Bedfordshire, SG16 6EA Tel: (01462) 850536 Fax: (01462) 851522 E-mail: sales@mftsat.co.uk

R T M Ltd, 1-4 Morris Close, Park Farm North, Wellingborough, Northamptonshire, NN8 6XF Tel: (01933) 673066 Fax: (01933) 678933 E-mail: sales@rtm-uk.com

▶ Silver Television Ltd, 22 Green Street, Saltcoats, Ayrshire, KA21 5HQ Tel: (01294) 461508 Fax: (01294) 464829 E-mail: iain@silvertv.plus.com

Skyforce Ltd, Old Mill Lane Industrial Estate, 15 Millway, Mansfield, Nottinghamshire, NG19 9AL Tel: (0800) 622752 Fax: (01623) 420672

Southern Antennae Ltd, 15 Grosvenor Road, Broadstairs, Kent, CT10 2BT Tel: (01843) 865673 Fax: (01843) 864542 E-mail: sales@southern-antenna.demon.co.uk

T V A Installations Stockport Ltd, Waterloo House, Hopes Carr, Stockport, Cheshire, SK1 3BL Tel: 0161-480 2265 Fax: 0161-480 6720 E-mail: tva@btconnect.com

▶ Ward Aerial Installations Ltd, 181 Woodhouse Road, London, N12 9AY Tel: (020) 8368 0077 E-mail: office@wardaerials.co.uk

AERIAL MASTS OR TOWERS

Precision Antennas Ltd, Masons Road, Stratford-upon-Avon, Warwickshire, CV37 9NU Tel: (01789) 266131 Fax: (01789) 298497 E-mail: sales@precision-antennas.co.uk

AERIAL SURVEYING

▶ Flight Logistics, The Cabair Building, Elstree Aerodrome, Borehamwood, Hertfordshire, WD6 3AW Tel: (0870) 620 8046 Fax: (0870) 620 8047 E-mail: operations@flight-logistics.co.uk

FR Aviation Services Ltd, Bournemouth Airport, Hurn, Christchurch, Dorset, BH23 6NE Tel: (01202) 409100 Fax: (01202) 576709 E-mail: fra-marketing@dial.pipex.com

▶ Giraffic, Manor Barn, Wilsthorpe, Stamford, Lincolnshire, PE9 4PE Tel: (01778) 560670 Fax: (01778) 560670 E-mail: giraffic@ndirect.co.uk

Image Aviation, 12A Court Park, Thurlestone, Kingsbridge, Devon, TQ7 3LX Tel: (01548) 562324 E-mail: fotos967@hotmail.com

▶ Infoterra Ltd, Atlas House, 41 Wembley Road, Leicester, LE3 1UT Tel: 0116-273 2391 Fax: 0116-273 2400 E-mail: info@infoterra-global.com

London Aerial Photo Library, Chobham, Woking, Surrey, GU24 8HU Tel: (01276) 855997 Fax: (01276) 855455 E-mail: info@londonaerial.co.uk

Plowman Craven & Associates, 141 Lower Luton Road, Harpenden, Hertfordshire, AL5 5EQ Tel: (01582) 765566 Fax: (01582) 765370 E-mail: sbarnes@plowmancraven.co.uk

Sky Films, 49 Butt Lane, Hinckley, Leicestershire, LE10 1LB Tel: (01455) 890081 Fax: (01455) 611227 E-mail: admin@skyfilmsnational.co.uk

AERIALS AND AERIAL COMPONENTS

Active Aerials & Systems, 53 Rugeley Road, Armitage, Rugeley, Staffordshire, WS15 4AR Tel: 01543 307072 E-mail: active.systems@ntlworld.com

AERIALS AND AERIAL COMPONENTS – *continued*

E M R Windings Ltd, Units 5 & 6, Kiln Park Industrial Park, Searle Crescent, Weston-super-Mare, Somerset, BS23 3XP Tel: (01934) 631374 Fax: (01934) 622698 E-mail: lee.graham@emrelectronics.co.uk

Engineered Composites Ltd, 41 Hope St., Chester, CH4 8BU Tel: (01244) 676000 Fax: (01244) 677267 E-mail: info@engineered-composites.co.uk

Hi-Tech Aerials, 5 Golden Noble Hill, Colchester, CO1 2AG Tel: (0800) 3897091 Fax: (0800) 3897091 E-mail: info@hitechaerials.co.uk

Maplin Electronics P.L.C., National Distribution Centre, Valley Road, Wombwell, Barnsley, South Yorkshire, S73 0BS Tel: (0870) 4296000 Fax: (0870) 4296001 E-mail: sales@maplin.co.uk

Nippon Antenna Europe, Venture House, Bone Lane, Newbury, Berkshire, RG14 5SH Tel: (01635) 30001 Fax: (01635) 35406 E-mail: nae@nippon-antenna.co.uk

Shelley (Halesowen) Ltd, 39 The Old Woodyard, Hagley Hall Hagley, Hagley, Stourbridge, West Midlands, DY9 9LQ Tel: (01562) 885905 Fax: (01562) 884941

Skyforce Ltd, Old Mill Lane Industrial Estate, 15 Millway, Mansfield, Nottinghamshire, NG19 9AL Tel: (0800) 622752 Fax: (01623) 420672

Z S Electroniques Europe, 235 Liscard Road, Wallasey, Merseyside, CH44 5TH Tel: 0151-637 1778 Fax: 0151-691 1477

AERONAUTICAL CUTTING TOOLS

Mapal Ltd, Swift Park, Old Leicester Road, Rugby, Warwickshire, CV21 1DZ Tel: (01788) 574700 Fax: (01788) 569551

AERONAUTICAL DESIGNING/ ENGINEERING SERVICES

Aerospace Composite Technologies Ltd, Percival Way, London Luton Airport, Luton, LU2 9PQ Tel: (01582) 731441 Fax: (01582) 423456 E-mail: gkn@ts.aero.gknplc.com

Aircraft Materials Ltd, Llangeinor, Bridgend, Mid Glamorgan, CF32 8PL Tel: (01656) 727000 Fax: (01656) 721100

Arrow Aviation Services Ltd, Little Stone, Thorverton, Exeter, EX5 5LL Tel: (01884) 855327 Fax: (01884) 855249 E-mail: arrow@eclipse.co.uk

Aviation Jersey Ltd, Beaumont, St. Peter, Jersey, JE3 7BR Tel: (01534) 725301 Fax: (01534) 759449 E-mail: sales@aviationjersey.com

Aviation Tool Corporation P.L.C, Airport Works, Green Lane, Hounslow, TW4 6DE Tel: (020) 8570 9664 Fax: (020) 8570 9660 E-mail: atctools@aol.com

B A E Systems plc, Stirling Square, 6 Carlton Gardens, London, SW1Y 5AD Tel: (01252) 373232 Fax: (01252) 383000

▶ B & D Patterns Ltd, Alan Bray Close, Hinckley, Leicestershire, LE10 3BP Tel: (01455) 445500 Fax: (01455) 445501 E-mail: sales@bdpatterns.co.uk

Babcock Defence Services, Hangar 4, RAF Leeming, Leeming, Northallerton, North Yorkshire, DL7 9NJ Tel: (01677) 425952 Fax: (01677) 425952

Busy Bee Aero Engineering, Sibson Airfield, Sibson, Peterborough, PE8 6NE Tel: (01832) 280579 Fax: (01832) 280579

▶ C F S Aeroproducts, Alvis Works, Bubbenhall Road, Baginton, Coventry, CV8 3BB Tel: (024) 7630 5873 Fax: (024) 7630 2088 E-mail: mslater@cfsaeroproducts.co.uk

Chevron Technical Services Ltd, Beta Court, 2 Harper Road, Sharston Industrial Area, Manchester, M22 4QE Tel: 0161-902 9029 Fax: 0161-945 0945 E-mail: info@chevrontechnicalservices.com

▶ E & R S Engineering Services, Park Road South, Havant, Hampshire, PO9 1HB Tel: (023) 9236 7777 Fax: (023) 9236 7776 E-mail: sales@e-r-s.com

Edgley Sailplanes Ltd, Furzelease Farm, Tisbury Row, Tisbury, Salisbury, SP3 6RZ Tel: (01747) 870509 Fax: (01747) 870509 E-mail: edgleysailplanes@argonet.co.uk

European Aviation Air Charter Ltd, European House, Bournemouth Int Airport, Hurn, Christchurch, Dorset, BH23 6EA Tel: (01202) 581111 Fax: (01202) 578333 E-mail: sales@eaac.co.uk

G E Aviation, Wobaston Road, Wolverhampton, WV9 5EW Tel: (01902) 397700 Fax: (01902) 394394

G E D Designs, 400 Aviation Park West, Bournemouth Int Airp, Hurn, Christchurch, Dorset, BH23 6NW Tel: (01202) 578537 Fax: (01202) 578537

G K N Aerospace Services, Ferry Road, East Cowes, Isle of Wight, PO32 6RA Tel: (01983) 294101 Fax: (01983) 291006 E-mail: info@gknwae.com

G K N Export Services Ltd, PO Box 55, Redditch, Worcestershire, B98 0TL Tel: (01527) 517715 Fax: (01527) 517700 E-mail: information@gkn.com

Gardner Aerospace Ltd, Hagher Clough Works, Hargher Street, Burnley, Lancashire, BB11 4EG Tel: (01282) 416466 Fax: (01282) 450363

H G Aerospace Engineering Ltd, 30-31 Castleham Road, St. Leonards-on-Sea, East Sussex, TN38 9NS Tel: (01424) 853444 Fax: (01424) 851690 E-mail: sales@hgaerospace.com

H.V. Wooding Ltd, Range Road Industrial Estate, Hythe, Kent, CT21 6HG Tel: (01303) 264471 Fax: (01303) 262408 E-mail: sales@hvwooding.co.uk

Hanley Smith Ltd, 7 South Road, Harlow, Essex, CM20 2AP Tel: (01279) 414446 Fax: (01279) 635101 E-mail: info@hanleysmith.co.uk

Hull Aero, Unit 14 The Street, Catfield, Great Yarmouth, Norfolk, NR29 5AA Tel: (01692) 582888 Fax: (01692) 580850

Hyde Aero Products Ltd, Ashton Street, Dukinfield, Cheshire, SK16 4RR Tel: 0161-343 5844 Fax: 0161-343 5833 E-mail: enquiries@hydeaero.co.uk

Jade Air P.L.C., Hanger 1, Shoreham Airport, Shoreham-by-Sea, West Sussex, BN43 5FF Tel: (01273) 464013 Fax: (01273) 465184 E-mail: info@jadeair.co.uk

Kearsley Airways Holdings Ltd, 8 Temple Gardens, London, NW11 0LL Tel: (020) 8458 7299 Fax: (020) 8458 9945 E-mail: mehta@kalair.co.uk

Larchfield Ltd Graphics Division, 18-20 East Street, Tonbridge, Kent, TN9 1HA Tel: (01732) 369757 Fax: (01732) 369767 E-mail: sales@larchfieldgraphics.net

M B Aerospace Ltd, Unit 9, P O Box 11, Heasandford Industrial Estate, Burnley, Lancashire, BB10 2TG Tel: (01282) 446600 Fax: (01282) 439318

Marshall Aerospace International Services Ltd, Airport House, Newmarket Road, Cambridge, CB5 8RX Tel: (01223) 373737 Fax: (01223) 321032E-mail: sales@marshallaerospace.com

Monarch Aircraft Engineering Ltd, London Luton Airport, Percival Way, Luton, LU2 9NU Tel: (01582) 424211

Morson Projects Ltd, 37 Liverpool Road, Irlam, Manchester, M44 6TB Tel: 0161-777 4000 Fax: 0161-777 4001 E-mail: enquiries@morson-projects.co.uk

Dr R.K. Nangia, West Point, 78 Queens Road, Maggs Ho, Bristol, BS8 1QX Tel: 0117-987 3995 Fax: 0117-987 3995

Nelson Tool Co Stockport Ltd, Stringer Street, Stockport, Cheshire, SK1 2NZ Tel: 0161-480 6004 Fax: 0161-476 2325 E-mail: info@nelsontool.co.uk

Preci Spark Ltd, School Street, Syston, Leicester, LE7 1HN Tel: 0116-260 7911 Fax: 0116-260 9461E-mail: andrerussell@preci-spark.uk.com

▶ Reheat International Ltd, Caker Stream Road, Alton, Hampshire, GU34 2QF Tel: (01420) 80633 Fax: (01420) 80644 E-mail: sales@reheat.co.uk

Rotadata Ltd, Bateman Street, Derby, DE23 8JQ Tel: (01332) 348008 Fax: (01332) 331023 E-mail: sales@rotadata.com

SPS Technologies Ltd, Troon Industrial Area, 191 Barkby Road, Leicester, LE4 9HX Tel: 0116-276 8261 Fax: 0116-274 0243

Stanworth Engineers Ltd, Brown Street, Burnley, Lancashire, BB11 1PN Tel: (01282) 421427 Fax: (01282) 458318 E-mail: info@stanworth.co.uk

Stop Choc Ltd, Banbury Avenue, Slough, SL1 4LR Tel: (01753) 533223 Fax: (01753) 693724 E-mail: sales@stop-choc.co.uk

Tenencia Aerospace Design, Hangar 6, Coventry Airport, Coventry, CV8 3AZ Tel: (024) 7688 2695 E-mail: info@tenencia.co.uk

Tindon Engineering Ltd, Unit 4 Little Snoring Airfield, Thursford Road, Little Snoring, Fakenham, Norfolk, NR21 0JL Tel: (01328) 878809 Fax: (01328) 878004

TRW Aeronautical Systems Lucas Areospace, 4 Bruce Street, Belfast, BT2 7LA Tel: (028) 9044 5800 Fax: (028) 9044 5801

Unison Engine Components, 1 Bentley Wood Way, Network 65 Business Park, Hapton, Burnley, Lancashire, BB11 5TG Tel: (01282) 831199 Fax: (01282) 422989

James Wilson Ltd, Broom Road Business Park, Broom Road, Poole, Dorset, BH12 4PA Tel: (01202) 731731 Fax: (01202) 736736 E-mail: enquiries@james.wilson-ltd.com

AERONAUTICAL FABRICATORS

Bae Systems Defence Systems Ltd, Warwick House, P O Box 87, Farnborough, Hampshire, GU14 6YU Tel: (01252) 373232 Fax: (01252) 383000

G K N Export Services Ltd, PO Box 55, Redditch, Worcestershire, B98 0TL Tel: (01527) 517715 Fax: (01527) 517700 E-mail: information@gkn.com

Marshall Aerospace International Services Ltd, Airport House, Newmarket Road, Cambridge, CB5 8RX Tel: (01223) 373737 Fax: (01223) 321032E-mail: sales@marshallaerospace.com

Meggitt P.L.C., Atlantic House, 3 Aviation Park West, Bournemouth International Airport, Hurn, Christchurch, Dorset, BH23 6EW Tel: (01202) 597597 Fax: (01202) 597555

AERONAUTICAL INSTRUMENTS

Rotadata Ltd, Bateman Street, Derby, DE23 8JQ Tel: (01332) 348008 Fax: (01332) 331023 E-mail: sales@rotadata.com

AERONAUTICAL MACHINING SERVICES

J.S. Chinn Engineering Co. Ltd, Faraday Road, Harrowbrook Industrial Estate, Hinckley, Leicestershire, LE10 3DE Tel: (01455) 238333 Fax: (01455) 890585 E-mail: enquiries@jschinn.com

Middlesex Group Ltd, Telford Road, Houndmills Industrial Estate, Basingstoke, Hampshire, RG21 6YU Tel: (01256) 353711 Fax: (01256) 842613 E-mail: sales@middlesex.co.uk

Mussett Group Ltd, Beccles Industrial Estate, Loddon, Norwich, NR14 6JD Tel: (01508) 522500 Fax: (01508) 528769 E-mail: enquire@mussett.co.uk

Quick Edge Engineering, Grosvenor Works, Windmill Lane, Denton, Manchester, M34 3LA Tel: 0161-335 0331 Fax: 0161-335 0332 E-mail: keith@quickedge.co.uk

Sommerwest Technical Services Ltd, 32 Garrett Road, Lynx Trading Estate, Yeovil, Somerset, BA20 2TJ Tel: 01935 412595

AERONAUTICAL SOFTWARE CONSULTANTS OR DESIGNERS

Russell Adams Ltd, Beechwood House, Tanners Lane, Berkswell, Coventry, CV7 7DA Tel: (024) 7685 6400 Fax: (024) 7685 6401 E-mail: sales@russelladams.com

Resource Engineering Projects, Waterlinks House, Richard Street, Birmingham, B7 4AA Tel: 0121-678 7880 Fax: 0121-678 7899 E-mail: technical@topmode.co.uk

Resource Management Systems, Mexborough Business Centre, College Road, Mexborough, South Yorkshire, S64 9JP Tel: (01709) 578300 Fax: (01709) 578010 E-mail: sales@rmsuk.co.uk

▶ Sean's Usability Co., Level 5, 5 St Helen's Place, Bishopsgate, London, EC3A 6AU Tel: (020) 7036 0378

AEROSOL CANS

3M Neotechnic Ltd, UpBrooks, Clitheroe, Lancashire, BB7 1NX Tel: (01200) 422251 Fax: (01200) 428993 E-mail: neotechnic@mmm.com

Aerocan (UK) Ltd, Folly Road, Roundway, Devizes, Wiltshire, SN10 2HT Tel: (01380) 727006 Fax: (01380) 732440

AEROSOL COMPONENTS

Graeme Paisley Ltd, Herberts Farmhouse, Quay Lane, Hanley Castle, Worcester, WR8 0BS Tel: (01684) 594066 Fax: (01684) 594066 E-mail: graeme.paisley@btinternet.com

Springpart Manufacturing Ltd, 50 Heming Road, Redditch, Worcestershire, B98 0EA Tel: (01527) 527302 Fax: (01527) 520215 E-mail: info@springpart.com

AEROSOL FILLING EQUIPMENT MANUFRS

▶ Aerofill, 33-35 Clayton Road, Hayes, Middlesex, UB3 1RU Tel: (020) 8848 4501 Fax: (020) 8561 3308 E-mail: sales@aerofill.com

AEROSOL FILLINGS

Breakwells Paints Ltd, 1 Harden Road, Walsall, WS3 1EL Tel: (01922) 400444 Fax: (01922) 400555 E-mail: sales@breakwellspaints.co.uk

Shirley Jones & Associates Ltd, C The Courtyard, Lonesome Lane, Reigate, Surrey, RH2 7QT Tel: (01737) 244844 Fax: (01737) 243266

AEROSOL PAINTS

▶ Colorite Paint Co. Ltd, 169 Boston Road, Hanwell, London, W7 3QJ Tel: (020) 8579 3381 Fax: (020) 8567 5158 E-mail: info@colorite.co.uk

AEROSOL VALVE SPRINGS

Springpart Manufacturing Ltd, 50 Heming Road, Redditch, Worcestershire, B98 0EA Tel: (01527) 527302 Fax: (01527) 520215 E-mail: info@springpart.com

AEROSOL VALVES

3M Neotechnic Ltd, UpBrooks, Clitheroe, Lancashire, BB7 1NX Tel: (01200) 422251 Fax: (01200) 428993 E-mail: neotechnic@mmm.com

Coster Aerosols Ltd, Babbage Rd, Stevenage, Hertfordshire, SG1 2EQ Tel: (01438) 367763 Fax: (01438) 728305 E-mail: sales.uk@coster.com

Lindal Valve Co. Ltd, Cherrycourt Way, Leighton Buzzard, Bedfordshire, LU7 4UH Tel: (01525) 381155 Fax: (01525) 383304

Precision Valve UK, Precision House, Bakewell Road, Lynch Wood, Peterborough, PE2 6XU Tel: (01733) 238181 Fax: (01733) 238553

AEROSOLS, DOMESTIC

Hydrokem Aerosols Ltd, Hickmans Road, Birkenhead, Merseyside, CH41 1JH Tel: 0151-630 4414 Fax: 0151-638 2353 E-mail: sales@hydrokem.co.uk

Keen World Marketing Ltd, 1 Northbrook Street, Newbury, Berkshire, RG14 1DJ Tel: (01635) 34600 Fax: (01635) 33360 E-mail: info@keen-newport.com

Miswa Chemicals Ltd, Caswell Road, Brackmills Industrial Estate, Northampton, NN4 7PW Tel: (01604) 701111 Fax: (01604) 701120 E-mail: sales@miswa.com

Reabrook Ltd, Rawdon Road, Moira, Swadlincote, Derbyshire, DE12 6DA Tel: (01283) 221044 Fax: (01283) 225731 E-mail: sales@greenhill.co.uk

Statestrong Ltd, Boundary Road, Lytham St. Annes, Lancashire, FY8 5LT Tel: (01253) 741806 Fax: (01253) 794542

AEROSPACE ADHESIVES

Aerospheres (UK) Ltd, Aerospace House, 2A Tudor Road, Harrow, Middlesex, HA3 5PE Tel: (020) 8863 8578 Fax: (020) 8427 1005 E-mail: sales@aerospheres.com

Dippon Label Co. Ltd, 125 Dartmouth Middleway, Aston, Birmingham, B7 4UA Tel: 0121-359 8183 Fax: 0121-359 2749 E-mail: sales@dippon.co.uk

Polymer Systems Technology Ltd, 6 Vernon Building, Westbourne Street, High Wycombe, Buckinghamshire, HP11 2PX Tel: (01494) 446610 Fax: (01494) 528611 E-mail: sales@silicone-polymers.co.uk

AEROSPACE AIR CONDITIONING (AC) EQUIPMENT

Honeywell The Oval, Bunford Lane, Yeovil, Somerset, BA20 2YD Tel: (01935) 475181 Fax: (01935) 427600 E-mail: angus.maclean@honeywell.com

AEROSPACE BEARINGS

▶ Aero Fasteners Co. Ltd, Unit 2, Block 4 Northherbour, Ayr, KA1 8BN Tel: (0870) 0509005 Fax: (0870) 0509006 E-mail: aerofastuk@btconnect.com

F K F UK Ltd, Strode Road, Clevedon, Avon, BS21 6QQ Tel: (01275) 876021 Fax: (01275) 878480 E-mail: mail@fkf.co.uk

N M B Minebea UK Ltd, Doddington Road, Lincoln, LN6 3RA Tel: (01522) 500933 Fax: (01522) 500975

Snfa Bearings Ltd, Wotton Road, Charfield, Wotton-under-Edge, Gloucestershire, GL12 8SP Tel: (01453) 843501 Fax: (01453) 842577 E-mail: sales@snfa-bearings.co.uk

AEROSPACE BOLTS AND NUTS

▶ Aero Fasteners Co. Ltd, Unit 2, Block 4 Northherbour, Ayr, KA1 8BN Tel: (0870) 0509005 Fax: (0870) 0509006 E-mail: aerofastuk@btconnect.com

AEROSPACE COMPONENT MACHINING

Castle Precision Engineering Glasgow Ltd, 241 Drakemire Drive, Glasgow, G45 9SZ Tel: 0141-634 1377 Fax: 0141-634 3678 E-mail: sales@castleprecision.com

Dupaul Engineering, Unit 5a Bone Lane, Newbury, Berkshire, RG14 5SH Tel: (01635) 31770 Fax: (01635) 521048 E-mail: dupaul@dupaul-eng.co.uk

Marshall Aerospace International Services Ltd, Airport House, Newmarket Road, Cambridge, CB5 8RX Tel: (01223) 373737 Fax: (01223) 321032E-mail: sales@marshallaerospace.com

AEROSPACE COMPONENTS,

See also headings for particular types

Aerospace Systems & Technologies Group Ltd, Unit 24 Number One Industrial Estate, Consett, County Durham, DH8 6SR Tel: (01207) 582811 Fax: (01207) 582812 E-mail: enquiries@cav-aerospace.net

▶ Burwood Aviation Supplies, Fairoaks Airport, Chobham, Woking, Surrey, GU24 8HU Tel: (01276) 855966 Fax: (01276) 855977 E-mail: sales@burwoodaviation.co.uk

C M L Group Ltd, Price Street, Birkenhead, Merseyside, CH41 3PT Tel: 0151-647 5531 Fax: 0151-650 0668 E-mail: enquiries@cml-group.com

AEROSPACE COMPONENTS – *continued*

Chelton Radomes Witney Ltd, Avenue One, Station Lane, Witney, Oxfordshire, OX28 4XS Tel: (01993) 778881 Fax: (01993) 776089 E-mail: sales@radomeswitney.co.uk

Composite Tooling & Structures Ltd, Lola House, Clebe Road, Huntingdon, Cambridgeshire, PE29 7DS Tel: (01480) 459378 Fax: (01480) 455585

E S L Engineers (Basildon) Ltd, Woolaston Way, Basildon, Essex, SS13 1DJ Tel: (01268) 727777 Fax: (01268) 728866 E-mail: sales@eslengineers.co.uk

Express Engineering Thompson Ltd, Kingsway North, Team Valley Trading Estate, Gateshead, Tyne & Wear, NE11 0EG Tel: 0191-487 2021 Fax: 0191-487 3172 E-mail: sales@express-group.co.uk

H.V. Wooding Ltd, Range Road Industrial Estate, Hythe, Kent, CT21 6HG Tel: (01303) 264471 Fax: (01303) 262408 E-mail: sales@hvwooding.co.uk

International Precision Products, Station Yard, Thame, Oxfordshire, OX9 3UH Tel: (01844) 217678 Fax: (01844) 215495 E-mail: ask@ippbv.com

Jet Blades & Engineering, Maguire Industrial Estate, 219 Torrington Avenue, Coventry, CV4 9HN Tel: (024) 7646 6841 Fax: (024) 7647 4215 E-mail: info@jetblades.com

Middlesex Group Ltd, Telford Road, Houndmills Industrial Estate, Basingstoke, Hampshire, RG21 6YU Tel: (01256) 353711 Fax: (01256) 842613 E-mail: sales@middlesex.co.uk

Volvo Aero Services, The Mill, Abbey Mill Business Park, Lower Eashing, Godalming, Surrey, GU7 2QJ Tel: (0870) 2422436 Fax: (01483) 523799

AEROSPACE CONNECTORS

Globe Electronics (UK) Ltd, 19 Westmorland Drive, Warfield, Bracknell, Berkshire, RG42 3QJ Tel: (01344) 420775 Fax: (01344) 421194 E-mail: globeuk@btinternet.com

AEROSPACE ENGINEERING

Aerospace Systems & Technologies Group Ltd, Unit 24 Number One Industrial Estate, Consett, County Durham, DH8 6SR Tel: (01207) 582811 Fax: (01207) 582812 E-mail: enquiries@cav-aerospace.net

▶ Heward Microjets Ltd, 8 Beagle Court, Cottenham, Cambridge, CB24 8RS Tel: (01526) 322266 E-mail: pheward@yahoo.com

AEROSPACE FANS

Airscrew Ltd, 111 Windmill Road, Sunbury-on-Thames, Middlesex, TW16 7EF Tel: (01932) 765822 Fax: (01932) 761098 E-mail: airscrew@ametek.co.uk

AEROSPACE FORGINGS

Firth Rixson P.L.C, PO Box 644, Sheffield, S9 1JD Tel: 0114-219 3000 Fax: 0114-219 1111 E-mail: info@firthrixson.com

AEROSPACE HEAT EXCHANGERS

Serck Aviation, Oscar House, Wharfdale Road, Tyseley, Birmingham, B11 2DG Tel: 0121-623 6000 Fax: 0121-623 6100 E-mail: john.felton@dunlop-aerospace.com

AEROSPACE INDUSTRY PERSONNEL RECRUITMENT AGENCIES OR CONSULTANTS

Kinetic plc, Duckworth House, Talbot Road, Stretford, Manchester, M32 0FP Tel: 0161-872 2333 Fax: 0161-872 2444 E-mail: info@kinetic-plc.co.uk

Strongfield Technologies Ltd, Strongfield House, Unit 2 Inovation Park, 89 Manor Farm Road, Wembley, Middlesex, HA0 1BA Tel: (020) 8813 2684 Fax: (020) 8799 8901 E-mail: anu@strongfield.com

AEROSPACE INDUSTRY PRESSINGS

G & O Springs Ltd, Broad Ground Road, Lakeside, Redditch, Worcestershire, B98 8YP Tel: (01527) 523764 Fax: (01527) 527920 E-mail: steve@g-o-springs.com

AEROSPACE LIGHTING TRANSFORMERS

TRI Technology Ltd, 15 Cowlairs, Southglade Business Park, Hucknall Road, Nottingham, NG5 9RA Tel: 0115-977 0707 Fax: 0115-977 0606 E-mail: enquiries@tritechnology.co.uk

AEROSPACE MAGAZINES

Airline Business, Quadrant House, The Quadrant, Brighton Road, Sutton, Surrey, SM2 5AS Tel: (020) 8652 3500

AEROSPACE PAINT FINISHING

▶ Eurospray Ltd, 2 Crompton Road, Glenrothes, Fife, KY6 2SF Tel: (01592) 770055 Fax: (01592) 770066 E-mail: admin@eurospray.sol.co.uk

AEROSPACE SEALS

Neomet Ltd, 92 Cross Lane, Marple, Stockport, Cheshire, SK6 7PZ Tel: 0161-427 7741 Fax: 0161-449 0080 E-mail: fkirk@neomet.org

AEROSPACE TEST EQUIPMENT

Bodycote Materials Engineering, White Cross Industrial Estate, South Road, Lancaster, LA1 4XQ Tel: (01524) 841070 Fax: (01524) 62983 E-mail: sales-uk@bodycote-mt.com

AFTER BUILDER CLEANING

▶ L Razec, 82 Oakdale Road, Poole, Dorset, BH15 3LQ Tel: (07716) 529694 E-mail: contact@razec.co.uk

AGAR-AGAR

F. Gutkind & Co. Ltd, Suite F8, Oxford Centre For Innovation, Mill Street, Oxford, OX2 0JX Tel: (01865) 812031 Fax: (01865) 249261 E-mail: info@fgutkind.com

▶ Koenig & Wiegand, 45 Sarisbury Close, Tadley, Hampshire, RG26 3SZ Tel: 0118-981 9481 Fax: (020) 7117 3273 E-mail: s.hewett@koenig-wiegand.de

AGGREGATE CRUSHERS

▶ A & S Crushing Services Ltd, Theedhams Farm, Steeple Road, Southminster, Essex, CM0 7BD Tel: 01621 772620

Red Rhino Crushers, Unit 3 Triangle Business Park, Quilters Way, Stoke Mandeville, Aylesbury, Buckinghamshire, HP22 5BL Tel: (0870) 6064949 Fax: (0870) 6063939 E-mail: info@redrhinocrushers.net

AGGREGATE SUPPLIERS SOFTWARE

Kirkland Ltd, 95 Main Street, Golspie, Sutherland, KW10 6TG Tel: (01408) 633109 Fax: (01408) 634468 E-mail: mark@kirkland.ltd.uk

▶ View2IT Ltd, 4, Edge Close, Weybridge, Surrey, KT13 0SZ Tel: 01932 851016 E-mail: info@view2it.co.uk

AGGREGATE TEST EQUIPMENT, *See also headings for particular types*

▶ Q A Equipment Ltd, Hutton Place, Grasslot, Maryport, Cumbria, CA15 8ED Tel: (01900) 812777 Fax: (0870) 7598333 E-mail: sales@qaequipment.co.uk

AGGREGATES

Aggregate Industries UK Ltd, Hulland Ward, Ashbourne, Derbyshire, DE6 3ET Tel: (01335) 372222 Fax: (01335) 370074

Alfa Aggregates Products Ltd, Kingsley Works, Kingsley, Stoke-on-Trent, ST10 2DG Tel: (01538) 754773 Fax: (01538) 750280 E-mail: alpha.aggregates@btopenworld.com

Bardon Aggregates Ltd, Thorney Mill Road, West Drayton, Middlesex, UB7 7EZ Tel: (01895) 442852 Fax: (01895) 421464

Barker Bros Aggregates Ltd, The Green, Railway Road, Downham Market, Norfolk, PE38 9DY Tel: (01366) 382525 Fax: (01366) 383002

Brand & Rae Ltd, Russell Mill, Springfield, Cupar, Fife, KY15 5QX Tel: (01334) 652828 Fax: (01334) 655967

Brennans Of Wiltshire Ltd, Harepath Farm, Burbage, Marlborough, Wiltshire, SN8 3BT Tel: (01672) 810380 Fax: (01672) 811157 E-mail: bofwilts@aol.com

Brett Aggregates Ltd, Brett House, Bysing Wood Road, Faversham, Kent, ME13 7UD Tel: (01795) 594051 Fax: (01795) 594027

Brett Aggregates, North Sea Terminal, Cliffe, Rochester, Kent, ME3 7SX Tel: (01634) 220631 Fax: (01634) 220067

Brett Specialised Aggregates, Sturry Quarry, Fordwich Road, Sturry, Canterbury, Kent, CT2 0BW Tel: (0845) 6080572 Fax: (0845) 6080573 E-mail: sales@brett-specialised-aggregates.co.uk

Buckingham Aggregates Ltd, Unit 6 Ballmoor, Buckingham Industrial Estate, Buckingham, MK18 1RT Tel: (01280) 817611 Fax: (01280) 817749

Builder Center Ltd, Windsor Road, Bedford, MK42 9SU Tel: (01234) 272292 Fax: (01234) 365395 E-mail: peter.abbott@wolseley.co.uk

Builder Center Ltd, Finmere Road, Eastbourne, East Sussex, BN22 8QJ Tel: (01323) 725121 Fax: (01323) 738879

Builder Center Ltd, Conway Street, Hove, East Sussex, BN3 3LA Tel: (01273) 778778 Fax: (01273) 722413

Builder Center Ltd, 80 Low Hill, Liverpool, L6 1BT Tel: 0151-263 5544 Fax: 0151-263 1432

Builder Center Ltd, Cradle Hill Industrial Estate, Alfriston Road, Seaford, East Sussex, BN25 2AT Tel: (01323) 893243 Fax: (01323) 891072

Builder Center Ltd, 591 Sedlescombe Road North, St. Leonards-on-Sea, East Sussex, TN37 7PY Tel: (01424) 756946 Fax: (01424) 751481

C E D Ltd, 728 London Road, Grays, Essex, RM20 3LU Tel: (01708) 867237 Fax: (01708) 867230 E-mail: sales@ced.ltd.uk

C & G Concrete Ltd, Mansgate Hill, Caistor, Market Rasen, Lincolnshire, LN7 6NT Tel: (01472) 851281 Fax: (01472) 851117

Chap Quarries (Aberdeen) Ltd, Westhill Industrial Estate, Westhill, Aberdeenshire, AB32 6TQ Tel: (01224) 748500 Fax: (01224) 748501 E-mail: mail@chap.co.uk

▶ Chas Long & Son, Woodside, Great North Road, Brompton, Richmond, North Yorkshire, DL10 7JL Tel: (01748) 811359

D P Passmore Ltd, Hunts Lane, London, E15 2QE Tel: (020) 8555 7676 Fax: (020) 8534 4470

Day Group Ltd, Transport Avenue, Great West Road, Brentford, Middlesex, TW8 9HF Tel: (01483) 725100 Fax: (020) 8380 9700 E-mail: email@daygroup.co.uk

William Gabriel Ltd, Bloomfield Road, Bloomfield, Tipton, West Midlands, DY4 9BS Tel: 0121-520 2502 Fax: 0121-522 2913

Gardenscape, Rye Road, Newenden, Cranbrook, Kent, TN18 5QG Tel: (0800) 854663 Fax: (01797) 253554 E-mail: gerald@bourne.uk.com

Gibson Bros, Magherally, Banbridge, County Down, BT32 4YN Tel: (028) 4066 2771 Fax: (028) 4062 6704 E-mail: liam@gibbros.freeserve.co.uk

Grundon Waste Management Ltd, Goulds Grove, Ewelme, Wallingford, Oxfordshire, OX10 6PJ Tel: (01491) 834311 Fax: (01491) 832272 E-mail: enquiries@grundin.com

Hanson Aggregates Ltd, Ashby Road East, Shepshed, Loughborough, Leicestershire, LE12 9BU Tel: (01509) 507050 Fax: (01509) 504120

Hanson Aggregates Ltd, Marine Parade, Southampton, SO14 5JF Tel: (023) 8023 7210 Fax: (023) 8082 8248

Hanson Aggregates Ltd, Clifford House, York Road, Wetherby, West Yorkshire, LS22 7NS Tel: (01937) 581977 Fax: (01937) 545889 E-mail: sales.orderswest@hanson-aggregates.com

Hanson Aggregates Ltd, Grovesend, Tytherington, Wotton-under-Edge, Gloucestershire, GL12 8UW Tel: (01454) 416161 Fax: (01454) 411821

Hanson Q P E, Mill Pond St, Ross-on-Wye, Herefordshire, HR9 7AP Tel: (01989) 563363

Harrison Jewitt Ltd, Flat, The Brickyard, Scotter Road South, Scunthorpe, South Humberside, DN17 2BT Tel: (01724) 281453 Fax: (01724) 281453 E-mail: sales@jewittonline.co.uk

Hoddam Contracting Co. Ltd, Hoddom Road, Ecclefechan, Lockerbie, Dumfriesshire, DG11 3BY Tel: (01576) 300634 Fax: (01576) 300798

Howie Minerals Ltd, Dornie Quarry, Torlundy, Fort William, Inverness-Shire, PH33 6SW Tel: (01397) 702227 Fax: (01397) 702308 E-mail: blaurie@howie-forest.co.uk

J J Prior (Transport) Ltd, Ballat Quay, Fingringhoe, Colchester, CO5 7DB Tel: (01206) 729412 Fax: (01206) 729551 E-mail: sales@jjprior.co.uk

John Owen Aggregates Ltd, Unit 11 Monksbridge Trading Estate, Outgang Lane, Dinnington, Sheffield, S25 3QZ Tel: (01909) 564191 Fax: (01909) 564234

Kendall Bros Portsmouth Ltd, Kendalls Wharf, Eastern Road, Portsmouth, PO3 5LY Tel: (023) 9266 2801 Fax: (023) 9267 0889 E-mail: sales@kendalls.co.uk

L E W Diecastings Ltd, Trows Lane, Rochdale, Lancashire, OL11 2UF Tel: (01706) 632218 Fax: (01706) 643714 E-mail: alan@lew.co.uk

Lafarge Aggregates Ltd, Riverside House, Upper Quay, Fareham, Hampshire, PO16 0LY Tel: (01329) 235717 Fax: (01329) 822697

Lafarge Redland Aggregates Ltd, The Business Centre, Watermead Business Park, Syston, Leicester, LE7 1WA Tel: (01509) 882088 Fax: (01707) 356141

Midland Quarry Products Ltd, Leicester Road, Whitwick, Coalville, Leicestershire, LE67 5GR Tel: (01530) 832244 Fax: (01530) 832299 E-mail: sales@mqp.co.uk

Minelco, 3 Riverside Business Centre, Brighton Road, Shoreham-by-Sea, West Sussex, BN43 6RE Tel: (01273) 452331 Fax: (01273) 464741 E-mail: info@minelco.com

Minilco Specialities Ltd, Bowesfield Industrial Estate, Bowesfield Lane, Stockton-on-Tees, Cleveland, TS18 3HJ Tel: (01642) 674375 Fax: (01642) 614379

Pumex (UK) Ltd, Hall Road, Aylesford, Maidstone, Kent, ME20 7QZ Tel: (01622) 882022 Fax: (01622) 882441 E-mail: info@pumex.co.uk

R M C Materials Ltd, Tannochside Park, Uddingston, Glasgow, G71 5PH Tel: (01698) 811100 Fax: (01698) 816068

▶ Riskend Aggregates Ltd, 1 Garrell Avenue, Kilsyth, Glasgow, G65 9PZ Tel: (01236) 823015 Fax: (01236) 823256 E-mail: enquiries@riskend.co.uk

▶ Sheehan Haulage, Woodstock Road, Yarnton, Kidlington, Oxfordshire, OX5 1PH Tel: (01865) 379931

Smiths Concrete Ltd, Southam Road, Banbury, Oxfordshire, OX16 2RR Tel: (01295) 278177 Fax: (01295) 271402 E-mail: info@smithsconcrete.co.uk

▶ Tarmac Central Ltd, Pant Quarry, Halkyn, Holywell, Clwyd, CH8 8BP Tel: (01352) 780441 Fax: (01352) 781207

Tarnac Ltd, Cairneyhill Quarry, Caldercruix, Airdrie, Lanarkshire, ML6 8NX Tel: (01236) 842351 Fax: (01236) 843950

Travis Perkins plc, Sydenham Wharf, Lower Bristol Road, Bath, BA2 3EE Tel: (01225) 446110 Fax: (01225) 442796 E-mail: bath@travisperkins.co.uk

Travis Perkins plc, Chamberlayne Road, London, NW10 3NB Tel: (020) 8964 9000 Fax: (020) 8969 0702 E-mail: enquiries@travisperkins.com

Travis Perkins plc, Manchester Road, Whitehill Industrial Estate, Whitehall Industrial Estate, Stockport, Cheshire, SK4 1NY Tel: 0161-480 0881 Fax: 0161-477 3658

United Marine Aggregates Ltd, Uma House, Shopwhyke Road, Chichester, West Sussex, PO20 2AD Tel: (01243) 817200 Fax: (01243) 817216 E-mail: info@umag.co.uk

Water Hall Group plc, Paralel House, 32 London Road, Guildford, Surrey, GU1 2AB Tel: (01483) 452333 Fax: (01483) 452322

G. Webb Haulage Ltd, Station Road, Longstanton, Cambridge, CB4 5DS Tel: (01954) 260691 Fax: (01954) 261211 E-mail: sales@gwebb.uk.com

Yeoman Aggregates Ltd, Stone Terminal, Horn Lane, London, W3 9EH Tel: (020) 8896 6820 Fax: (020) 8896 6811

AGRICULTURAL ADVERTISING

▶ Farmgear Ltd, The Old Vicarage, Church Close, Boston, Lincolnshire, PE21 6NE Tel: (0845) 6440228 Fax: (0845) 6520124 E-mail: info@farmgear.co.uk

AGRICULTURAL AIR CONDITIONING (AC) EQUIPMENT

Agricultural & Mobile Air Conditioning Ltd, Avening Road, Nailsworth, Stroud, Gloucestershire, GL6 0BS Tel: (01453) 832884 Fax: (01453) 832040 E-mail: sales@ama-airconditioning.co.uk

Eastfield Engineering Ltd, PO Box 232, Stafford, ST19 5QY Tel: (01785) 714794 Fax: (01785) 711373 E-mail: sales@eastfield-engineering.com

Plant Mart Ltd, 7 Langhedge Lane Industrial Estate, Langhedge Lane, London, N18 2TQ Tel: (020) 8366 7375 Fax: (020) 8803 0814 E-mail: sales@aircon4u.co.uk

AGRICULTURAL BALERS

Chandlers Farm Equipment Ltd, Boston Road, Horncastle, Lincolnshire, LN9 6JN Tel: (01507) 527211 Fax: (01507) 524498 E-mail: enquries@chandlersfe.co.uk

Claas UK Ltd, Saxham, Bury St. Edmunds, Suffolk, IP28 6QZ Tel: (01284) 763100 Fax: (01284) 769839 E-mail: info-uk@claas.com

John Deere Ltd, Harby Road, Langar, Nottingham, NG13 9HT Tel: (01949) 860491 Fax: (01949) 860490

AGRICULTURAL BUILDING ERECTORS, *See Agricultural Engineering Services*

AGRICULTURAL BUILDINGS, *See also headings for particular types*

E C N (UK) Ltd, Mambury Moor Estate, Buckland Brewer, Bideford, Devon, EX39 5NL Tel: (01237) 451002 Fax: (01237) 451002

AGRICULTURAL CANVAS MESH WIND BREAKS

John M Carter Ltd, Winchester Road Industrial Estate, Kimbell Road, Basingstoke, Hampshire, RG22 4AB Tel: (01256) 324434 Fax: (01256) 816209 E-mail: info@johnmcarterltd.co.uk

AGRICULTURAL CELLAR CONTRACTORS

E Just & Son, Waterlog Farm, Spondon Road, Dale Abbey, Ilkeston, Derbyshire, DE7 4PQ Tel: (01332) 662994 Fax: (01332) 662994

Philip Sidford, Bridzor Farm, Wardour, Tisbury, Salisbury, SP3 6RN Tel: (01747) 870456 Fax: (01747) 871656 E-mail: pjs@sidford.com

AGRICULTURAL CHEMICAL FORMULATION AND PACKING

▶ Jovia Ltd, 3 Linden Crescent, Great Ayton, Middlesbrough, Cleveland, TS9 6AF Tel: (01642) 723211 Fax: (01642) 724681

AGRICULTURAL CHEMICAL PRODUCTS

Agrovista UK Ltd, Broadway Drive, Halesworth, Suffolk, IP19 8QR Tel: (01986) 875181 Fax: (01986) 875483

Banks Cargill Agriculture Ltd, Unit 6 Bury Road Industrial Estate, Ramsey, Huntingdon, Cambridgeshire, PE26 1NF Tel: (01487) 813361 Fax: (01487) 814600

Bayer, 230 Science Park, Milton Road, Cambridge, CB4 0WB Tel: (01223) 226500 Fax: (01223) 426240

Billericay Farm Services Ltd, School Road, Downham, Billericay, Essex, CM11 1QU Tel: (01268) 710237 Fax: (01268) 711040 E-mail: sales@bfs.uk.com

Boothmans (Agriculture) Ltd, 6 Hereward, Cherry Holt Road, Bourne, Lincolnshire, PE10 9LA Tel: (01778) 394040 Fax: (01778) 394499 E-mail: info@boothman.co.uk

Brown Butlin, Northons Lane, Holbeach, Spalding, Lincolnshire, PE12 7QA Tel: (01406) 422666 Fax: (01406) 422757

Certis, The Crown Business Park, Old Dalby, Melton Mowbray, Leicestershire, LE14 3NQ Tel: (01664) 820052 Fax: (01664) 820216 E-mail: enquiry@luxan.co.uk

Ciba Specialty Chemicals plc, Charter Road, Macclesfield, Cheshire, SK10 2NX Tel: (01625) 665000 Fax: (01625) 619637

Clynderwen & Cardiganshire Farmers Ltd, Main St, Clynderwen, Dyfed, SA66 7NW Tel: (01437) 563441 Fax: (01437) 563745 E-mail: info@ccfagri.co.uk

Countrywide Farmers P.L.C., Brickhouse Lane, Stoke Prior, Bromsgrove, Worcestershire, B60 4LX Tel: (01527) 831663 Fax: (01527) 570290 E-mail: enquiries@countrywidefarmers.co.uk

Countrywide Farmers P.L.C., Lady Lane, Blunsdon, Swindon, SN2 4DN Tel: (01793) 722888 Fax: (01793) 706011

Countrywide Stores, Hook Norton Road, Chipping Norton, Oxfordshire, OX7 5TE Tel: (01608) 642071 Fax: (01608) 645125 E-mail: enquiries@countrywidefarmers.co.uk

Croda Chemicals International Ltd, Cowick Hall, Snaith, Goole, North Humberside, DN14 9AA Tel: (01405) 860551 Fax: (01405) 861767

Crop Chemicals Ltd, Drem Airfield, North Berwick, East Lothian, EH39 5AW Tel: (01620) 842170 Fax: (01620) 843596 E-mail: enquires@cropchemicals.co.uk

Cropchem Wholesale (S.W.) Ltd, Tamar House, Thornbury Road, Estover, Plymouth, PL6 7TT Tel: (01752) 695363 Fax: (01752) 695969

Cropwise Ltd, Saxelby Lodge, Saxelby Road, Old Dalby, Melton Mowbray, Leicestershire, LE14 3NA Tel: (01664) 823535 Fax: (01664) 823536

CSC Crop Protection Ltd, Schoolcroft, Culbokie, Dingwall, Ross-Shire, IV7 8JH Tel: (01349) 877557 Fax: (01349) 877533 E-mail: enquiries@csccrop.com

Kevin Derry Agrochemicals, 10 West Mount, Tadcaster, North Yorkshire, LS24 9LB Tel: (01937) 832037

Dow Mirfield, Steanard Lane, Mirfield, West Yorkshire, WF14 8HZ Tel: (01924) 493861 Fax: (01924) 490972 E-mail: enquiries@dow.com

Du Pont UK Ltd, Wedgewood Way, Stevenage, Hertfordshire, SG1 4QN Tel: (01438) 734000 Fax: (01438) 734836 E-mail: enquiries@dupontpharma.com

Dyfed Seeds Ltd, Old Llangunnor Rd, Carmarthen, Dyfed, SA31 2BJ Tel: (01267) 237309 Fax: (01267) 238400 E-mail: mail@dyfedseeds.freeserve.co.uk

Fluorochem Ltd, Wesley Street, Glossop, Derbyshire, SK13 7RY Tel: (01457) 865698 Fax: (01457) 869360 E-mail: enquiries@fluorochem.co.uk

Frontier, 51a Hallgate, Holbeach, Spalding, Lincolnshire, PE12 7JA Tel: (01406) 422606 Fax: (01406) 423780

FSC Agronomy, Lancaster Park, Newborough Road, Needwood, Burton-on-Trent, Staffordshire, DE13 9PD Tel: (01283) 575571 Fax: (01283) 575574 E-mail: nigel.francis@masstock.co.uk

Gallagher Power Fence (UK) Ltd, Curriers Close, Coventry, CV4 8AW Tel: (0870) 2010101 Fax: (0870) 0111545 E-mail: info@gallagher.co.uk

Headland Agrochemicals Ltd, Rectors Lane, Pentre, Deeside, Clwyd, CH5 2DH Tel: (01244) 537370 Fax: (01244) 532097 E-mail: john.hughes@headlandmanufacturing.com

J Todd & Son, Summerbridge, Harrogate, North Yorkshire, HG3 4JN Tel: (01423) 780319 Fax: (01423) 780431 E-mail: jtoddshop@aol.com

▶ Kemira Growhow UK Ltd, Ince, Chester, CH2 4LB Tel: 0151-357 2777 Fax: 0151-357 1755 E-mail: kemira-growhow.uk@kemira-growhow.com

Masstock Arable UK Ltd, Station Road, Andoversford, Cheltenham, Gloucestershire, GL54 4LZ Tel: (01242) 821100 Fax: (01242) 820807

Microbial Developments Ltd, Spring La North, Malvern, Worcestershire, WR14 1BU Tel: (01684) 891055 Fax: (01684) 891060 E-mail: info@micdev.com

Micromix Solutions Ltd, Coachgap Lane, Langar, Nottingham, NG13 9HP Tel: (01949) 861087 Fax: (01949) 861061 E-mail: info@micromixsolutions.com

P H Chandler, Heybridge Farm, Uttoxeter Road, Tean, Stoke-on-Trent, ST10 4LN Tel: (01538) 722127 Fax: (01538) 723949

H. & C. Pearce & Sons Ltd, Farndon Road, Market Harborough, Leicestershire, LE16 9NP Tel: (01858) 432704 Fax: (01858) 466026 E-mail: info@hcpearce.co.uk

Robertson Crop Services Ltd, Scotsburn Road, Kildary, Invergordon, Ross-Shire, IV18 0NJ Tel: (01862) 842552 Fax: (01862) 842700

Ross Feed Ltd, Industrial Estate West, 2 Wonastow Road, Monmouth, Gwent, NP25 5AH Tel: (01600) 715448 Fax: (01600) 712480

Ryehill Farmservice, Unit 77 Manchester Road, Pocklington Industrial Estate, Pocklington, York, YO42 1NR Tel: (01759) 307447 Fax: (01759) 301155

Sprayrite, Greshop Industrial Estate, Forres, Morayshire, IV36 2GW Tel: (01309) 674217 Fax: (01309) 675262

Syngenta Crop Protection UK Ltd, CPC4 Capital Park, Fulbourn, Cambridge, CB21 5XE Tel: (01223) 883400 Fax: (01223) 882195 E-mail: cropmarketing-uk@syngenta.com

United Agri Products Ltd, London Road, Dunkirk, Faversham, Kent, ME13 9LR Tel: (01227) 753713 Fax: (01227) 753719

United Agri Products Ltd, Balboughty Farm, Perth, PH2 6AA Tel: (01738) 555400 Fax: (01738) 555401

United Agri Products Ltd, Fresh Winds Farm, Long Lane, Telford, Shropshire, TF6 6HD Tel: (01952) 260012 Fax: (01952) 260337

United Agriproducts Ltd, Robsheugh Farm, Milbourne, Newcastle upon Tyne, NE20 0JQ Tel: (0870) 4114666 Fax: (0870) 4114667

Universal Crop Protection Ltd, Park House, Maidenhead Road, Cookham, Berkshire, SL6 9DS Tel: (01628) 526083 Fax: (01628) 810457 E-mail: enquiries@unicrop.com

Wallace Of Kelso Ltd, Bowmont Street, Kelso, Roxburghshire, TD5 7EA Tel: (01573) 224131 Fax: (01573) 226145 E-mail: info@wallaceofkelso.co.uk

AGRICULTURAL CHEMICAL PRODUCTS RESEARCH/ TESTING SERVICES

Huntingdon Life Sciences, Occold, Eye, Suffolk, IP23 7PX Tel: (01480) 892000 Fax: (01379) 651165 E-mail: sales@ukorg.huntingdon.com

S G S UK Ltd, 7TH Floor, Westgate House, West Gate, London, W5 1YY Tel: (020) 8991 3410 Fax: (020) 8991 3417 E-mail: rolandstephan@sgsgroup.com

AGRICULTURAL CLEANING SERVICES

J B Services Ltd, Mill Street, Stowupland, Stowmarket, Suffolk, IP14 5BJ Tel: (01449) 673232 Fax: (01449) 770981 E-mail: jb@jbsltd.freeserve.co.uk

AGRICULTURAL CONSTRUCTION MACHINERY

▶ Hortec Solutions, Bromyard Road, Ledbury, Herefordshire, HR8 1LG Tel: (01531) 636511 Fax: (01531) 632172

McConnel Ltd, Temeside Works, Ludlow, Shropshire, SY8 1JL Tel: (01584) 873131 Fax: (01584) 876463 E-mail: sales@mcconnel.com

AGRICULTURAL CONSULTANTS/ TECHNICAL SERVICES

A & B Contractors Devon Ltd, Porte Farm Kentisbury, Kentisbury, Barnstaple, Devon, EX31 4NL Tel: (01271) 882006 Fax: (01271) 882006 E-mail: info@aandbcontractors.co.uk

A & B M Suffield & Sons, Homelea Farm, Bearley Road, Aston Cantlow, Henley-in-Arden, West Midlands, B95 6LD Tel: (01789) 488040 Fax: (01789) 488971

A C Dare & Partners, Higher Knapp Farm, Knapp, North Curry, Taunton, Somerset, TA3 6AY Tel: (01823) 490747 Fax: (01823) 490747

A D Billington, Greenbank Farm, Limes Lane, Whitley, Warrington, WA4 4DU Tel: (01925) 730285

A D Milburn, Brookside, Whitbeck, Millom, Cumbria, LA19 5UP Tel: (01229) 718638

A G & R L Cornes, Hollins Farm, Station Road, Halmer End, Stoke-on-Trent, ST7 8AR Tel: (01782) 722804 Fax: (01782) 721445

A & J Nightingale, Big House Farm, Breach Oak Lane, Fillongley, Coventry, CV7 8DE Tel: (01676) 540252 Fax: (01676) 540252

A J Wright Agricultural Services, Mickleton, Chipping Campden, Gloucestershire, GL55 6PS Tel: (01386) 438536 Fax: (01386) 438536

A K & L F Hutchings, The Barton, Thornbury, Holsworthy, Devon, EX22 7DD Tel: (01409) 261373

A R Clay, Low Farm, Littlebeck, Whitby, North Yorkshire, YO22 5EY Tel: (01947) 893574 Fax: (01947) 893574

A & R Milton, Arable View, Udny Green, Ellon, Aberdeenshire, AB41 7RS Tel: (01651) 843123 Fax: (01651) 842501

A S S Stephens, Long Meadow, Stoke Orchard, Cheltenham, Gloucestershire, GL52 7RY Tel: (01242) 680629

Adas Gleadthorpe Grange, Gleadthorpe, Meden Vale, Mansfield, Nottinghamshire, NG20 9PF Tel: (01623) 844331 Fax: (01623) 844472

Ag-Bag Systems, Cleaveanger, Coldridge, Crediton, Devon, EX17 6BE Tel: (01363) 83996

Agricultural Contracting Services Ltd, Buddington Farm, Buddington La, Easebourne, Midhurst, W. Sussex, GU29 0QP Tel: 01730 812441 Fax: 01730 812441

▶ Aja Services, 32 Talbot Street, Church Gresley, Swadlincote, Derbyshire, DE11 9PG Tel: (01283) 214204 Fax: (01283) 214204

Allison Farming Partnership, Thistledown Farm House, Amesbury Road, Newton Toney, Salisbury, SP4 0HN Tel: (01980) 629246 Fax: (01980) 629246

Andrew Tyler, Berthlwyd, Maesymeillion, Llandysul, Dyfed, SA44 4NG Tel: (01545) 590590

Anker Of Ellington, Unit 16 Brook Farm, Thrapston Road, Ellington, Huntingdon, Cambridgeshire, PE28 0AE Tel: (01480) 890990 Fax: (01480) 890988 E-mail: enquiries@ankerofcoates.co.uk

Aubourn, Rolfes House, 60 Milford Street, Salisbury, SP1 2BP Tel: (01722) 426850 Fax: (01722) 426851 E-mail: salisbury@aubourn-consultancy.co.uk

G. Auger & Son, Old Post Ho, The Street, Hartlip, Sittingbourne, Kent, ME9 7TH Tel: 01795 842490 Fax: 01795 845490

B G Saunders & Son, Orchard View, Long Lane, Maidenhead, Berkshire, SL6 3TA Tel: (01628) 621491

B & G Spreaders, Back Meadow Cottage, 23, Denham, Bury St. Edmunds, Suffolk, IP29 5EW Tel: (01284) 811082 Fax: (01284) 810234 E-mail: phorner@jhbunn.co.uk

B & M Services, 7 Pioneer Way, Lincoln, LN6 3DH Tel: (01522) 695272 Fax: (01522) 500092

B & S Adams, Fairy Cross, Bideford, Devon, EX39 5DA Tel: (01237) 451254 Fax: (01237) 451254

B S R Wickens, Hambridge Farm, Martley, Worcester, WR6 6QT Tel: (01886) 812228 Fax: (01886) 812228

B & V Fowler, Lowmans Farm, Beacon, Honiton, Devon, EX14 4TX Tel: (01404) 42683 Fax: (01404) 47411

Backlane Farm, Back Lane Farm, Back Lane, Goosnargh, Preston, PR3 2WE Tel: (01772) 782247 Fax: (01772) 782247

Bainbridge Farms, Donkin Rigg, Cambo, Morpeth, Northumberland, NE61 4LA Tel: (01670) 774246 Fax: (01670) 774246

Barretts Leisure Buildings Ltd, 347 Leverington Common, Leverington, Wisbech, Cambridgeshire, PE13 5JR Tel: (01945) 410361 Fax: (01945) 419038 E-mail: enquiries@barretts-leisure.co.uk

Beak Bros, Clover Cottage, 3 Butts Road, Ryde, Isle of Wight, PO33 3JH Tel: (01983) 611509 Fax: (01983) 611509

Bennie Contracts, Leafy Lodge, Bridgecastle, Bathgate, West Lothian, EH48 3DR Tel: (01501) 730369 Fax: (01501) 730369

Beverley Analytical Laboratories, Hull Bridge Mills, Tickton, Beverley, North Humberside, HU17 9SB Tel: (01964) 542144 Fax: (01964) 543060E-mail: admin@beverlyanalytical.co.uk

Boarder Contract Services, Castlemains, Duns, Berwickshire, TD11 3TP Tel: (01361) 882809 Fax: (01361) 882871

Boothmans (Agriculture) Ltd, 6 Hereward, Cherry Holt Road, Bourne, Lincolnshire, PE10 9LA Tel: (01778) 394040 Fax: (01778) 394499 E-mail: info@boothman.co.uk

James Boville, 35 Culnafay Road, Toomebridge, Antrim, BT41 3QG Tel: (028) 2587 8213 Fax: (028) 2587 8213

Bridley Equestrian Centre, Berry Lane, Worplesdon, Guildford, Surrey, GU3 3QG Tel: (01483) 232272 Fax: (01483) 232070 E-mail: pan.edwards@bridleyec.demon.co.uk

George Briggs & Son, Wirswall, Whitchurch, Shropshire, SY13 4LF Tel: (01948) 663733

Buchan Agricultural Consultants, Fridayhill, Maud, Peterhead, Aberdeenshire, AB42 4QQ Tel: (01771) 637721 Fax: (01771) 637888 E-mail: bac.ltd@farmline.com

A.G. Bunker & Sons, Old House Stud Farm, Station Road, Stanbridge, Leighton Buzzard, Bedfordshire, LU7 9JF Tel: (01525) 210984 Fax: (01525) 210984

C Clayton, The Brindles, Frolesworth, Lutterworth, Leicestershire, LE17 5EL Tel: (01455) 209350

C J Smith, 21 Stoneleigh Court, Westcroft, Milton Keynes, MK4 4BS Tel: (01908) 502386 Fax: (01908) 502386

C L Hichins & Sons, Carn Farm, Morvah, Pendeen, Penzance, Cornwall, TR19 7TT Tel: (01736) 788309

C T & E F Thomas, 12 Greenbank Terrace, Callington, Cornwall, PL17 7BU Tel: (01579) 384643

J.& M. Cartney, Currarie Farm, Lendalfoot, Girvan, Ayrshire, KA26 0JB Tel: (01465) 891213 E-mail: moraghornse@aol.com

Cattletech, Leeds Road, Hambleton, Selby, North Yorkshire, YO8 9HJ Tel: (01757) 708870 Fax: (01757) 213604

Centaur Grain Ltd, Barrow Hill Barns, Barrow Hill, Goodworth Clatford, Andover, Hampshire, SP11 7RG Tel: (01264) 356666 Fax: (01264) 350200 E-mail: sales@centaurgrain.com

R.A.C. Chandler Contractors Ltd, Villiers Farm, Frisby Road, Hoby, Melton Mowbray, Leicestershire, LE14 3DS Tel: (01664) 434813 Fax: (01664) 434134

Martin Clark Consultants, Trendle Cottage, Trendal Street, Sherborne, Dorset, DT9 3NT Tel: (01935) 815777 Fax: (0870) 1360933 E-mail: victor@cahor.plus.com

Clive Powell & Co, Franksbridge, Llandrindod Wells, Powys, LD1 5SA Tel: (01982) 570297

Clynderwen & Cardiganshire Farmers Ltd, Main St, Clynderwen, Dyfed, SA66 7NW Tel: (01437) 563441 Fax: (01437) 563745 E-mail: info@ccfagri.co.uk

Coates Bros, Manor Farm, Watlington Road, Runcton Holme, King's Lynn, Norfolk, PE33 0EJ Tel: (01553) 810463 Fax: (01553) 811549 E-mail: enquiries@coates-bros.co.uk

Countrywide Farmers plc, Church Street, Melksham, Wiltshire, SN12 6LS Tel: (01225) 701470 Fax: (01225) 702318 E-mail: info@countrywidefarmers.co.uk

Crop Services Ltd, Elie Road, Pitscottie, Cupar, Fife, KY15 5TE Tel: (01334) 828303 Fax: (01334) 828564

D A & N D Towers, Spacey Houses Farm, Spacey Houses, Harrogate, North Yorkshire, HG3 1LD Tel: (01423) 879076

D C Contracts, Kennoway, Leven, Fife, KY8 5SG Tel: (01333) 352500 Fax: (01333) 352500

D C F M Quotas Ltd, 1 Bridge Street, Boston, Lincolnshire, PE21 8QF Tel: (01205) 310644 Fax: (01205) 310645 E-mail: post@dcfm.com

D E Spencer & Sons, Nupend, Nupend, Stonehouse, Gloucestershire, GL10 3SS Tel: (01453) 822764 Fax: (01453) 792600

D M Mcclurg, Blakeley Hill Farm, North Bitchburn, Crook, County Durham, DL15 8AP Tel: (01388) 603608 Fax: (01388) 603608

D & P Bingham, 40 Ballymartin Road, Templepatrick, Ballyclare, County Antrim, BT39 0BS Tel: (028) 9443 2452

D Pither, Cirencester Road, Brockworth, Gloucester, GL3 4TN Tel: (01452) 864714 Fax: (01452) 864714

Darrow Farm Supplies Ltd, Darrow Wood Farm, Shelfanger Road, Diss, Norfolk, IP22 4XY Tel: (01379) 640331 Fax: (01379) 641331

David Chapman, Lynn House, Mill Lane, Sutton St. James, Spalding, Lincolnshire, PE12 0EJ Tel: (01945) 440273 Fax: (01945) 440273

David J Tremain, Millside, Bridge, St. Columb, Cornwall, TR9 6BE Tel: (01637) 880352

David M Petherick, Higher Thorne Farm, Down St. Mary, Crediton, Devon, EX17 6EB Tel: (01363) 82487 Fax: (01363) 82487

Dean, Wester Clockeasy, Urquhart, Elgin, Morayshire, IV30 8LP Tel: (01343) 842210 Fax: (01343) 843198

Derek E Dye, 33 Station Road, Long Sutton, Spalding, Lincolnshire, PE12 9BP Tel: (01406) 363107 Fax: (01406) 363107

J.D. & C.W. Dyer, Penrock, Llandovery, Dyfed, SA20 0DZ Tel: 01550 720956

E G Hingston & Son, Wilburton Farm, Ivybridge, Devon, PL21 9LB Tel: (01752) 880416

E Haste, Stoneleigh Farm, Shebbear, Beaworthy, Devon, EX21 5QT Tel: (01409) 281230 Fax: (01409) 281880 E-mail: haste@stoneleighsfnet.co.uk

E S Harrison & Sons, The Willows, Haven Bank, New York, Lincoln, LN4 4XR Tel: (01205) 280336 Fax: (01205) 280336

E W Contracting Ltd, East Wick Farm, Wootton Rivers, Marlborough, Wiltshire, SN8 4NS Tel: (01672) 810255 Fax: (01672) 810884

East Of Scotland Farmers Ltd, Forfar Road, Coupar Angus, Blairgowrie, Perthshire, PH13 9AW Tel: (01828) 627264 Fax: (01828) 627002 E-mail: r.barron@eosf.co.uk

Eifionydd Farmers Association Ltd, Station Road, Penygroes, Caernarfon, Gwynedd, LL54 6NW Tel: (01286) 880234 Fax: (01286) 880234

▶ indicates data change since last edition

AGRICULTURAL CONSULTANTS/ TECHNICAL SERVICES – *continued*

▶ EnSynch Environmental Consultancy, North End, Hale Road, Woodgreen, Fordingbridge, Hampshire, SP6 2AN Tel: (07855) 581132 E-mail: peter.carpenter@ensynch.co.uk

Eric J Pothan, Worcester Road, Torton, Kidderminster, Worcestershire, DY11 7RR Tel: (01299) 250449

F E C Services Ltd, National Agricultural Centre, Stoneleigh Park, Kenilworth, Warwickshire, CV8 2LS Tel: (024) 7669 6512 Fax: (024) 7669 6360 E-mail: sales@farmenergy.com

F R R Ltd, Brockley Combe Road, Backwell, Bristol, BS48 3DR Tel: (01934) 862861 Fax: (01934) 863666

Fairhead Wones, Beccles Road, Hales, Norwich, NR14 6SR Tel: (01508) 548244 Fax: (01508) 548942

Fisher W.H Agricultural Contractor, Intack House, Ivegill, Carlisle, CA4 0QF Tel: (01697) 476373

Fishleighs Of Galsworthy, Galsworthy, Buckland Brewer, Bideford, Devon, EX39 5NP Tel: (01409) 261231 Fax: (01409) 261231

Frank Brewer & Son, Moorgate Farm, Dinckley, Blackburn, BB6 8AN Tel: (01254) 248858 Fax: (01254) 246916

Fullpoint Probe Services, 170 Heath Road, Ipswich, IP4 5SR Tel: (01473) 717810 Fax: (01473) 717863 E-mail: sales@fullpoint.net

G A Wisbey & Son Ltd, Tile Hall Farm, Little Sampford, Saffron Walden, Essex, CB10 2SA Tel: (01371) 830313 Fax: (01371) 831478

G Bayne, North Lodge, Wolflee, Hawick, Roxburghshire, TD9 9TE Tel: (01450) 860357

G Clements & Sons, Redbourne Mere, Kirton Lindsey, Gainsborough, Lincolnshire, DN21 4LE Tel: (01652) 648787 Fax: (01652) 649494

G D E Associates UK, Causeway House, The Causeway, Great Hawksley, Colchester, CO6 4EJ Tel: (01206) 272999 Fax: (01206) 272998 E-mail: consult@gde.co.uk

G & D Matthews, Sycamore House, Leaveslake Drove, West Pinchbeck, Spalding, Lincolnshire, PE11 3QJ Tel: (01775) 640230 Fax: (01775) 640230

G D White & Partners, Old Post Office, Broomfield, Bridgwater, Somerset, TA5 2EH Tel: (01823) 451348

G J Orford & Partners, Hill Farm, Lopham Road, Fersfield, Diss, Norfolk, IP22 2BJ Tel: (01379) 687326 Fax: (01379) 688077 E-mail: gjorfordpartners@btconnect.com

G R M International Ltd, 4TH Floor, 57-59 Gloucester Place, London, W1U 8JH Tel: (020) 7486 3800 Fax: (020) 7486 3859 E-mail: info@grminternationa.co.uk

Frederick Garrett & Sons, Slittingmill Farm, Staveley Lane, Staveley, Chesterfield, Derbyshire, S43 3YQ Tel: (01246) 432294

Garwood Cleaning Services, West Hyde, Brook Road, Tillingham, Southminster, Essex, CM0 7SB Tel: (01621) 779507 Fax: (01621) 779507

Gilbert H Elson, The Bungalow, Stretton Lodge, Stretton, Oakham, Leicestershire, LE15 7QS Tel: (01780) 410430 Fax: (01780) 410430

Godwin, Wick Farm, Luckington, Chippenham, Wiltshire, SN14 6PW Tel: (07754) 726553 Fax: (01454) 238019

Graham D Davies, Cwmgeifr, Llandilo Graban, Builth Wells, Powys, LD2 3SJ Tel: (01982) 560246 Fax: (01982) 560246

Grange Arable Consultancy, Peplow Grange, Peplow, Market Drayton, Shropshire, TF9 3JT Tel: (01952) 541633 Fax: (01952) 541633

John Griffith, Pant Hwfa, Llanllechid, Bangor, Gwynedd, LL57 3LA Tel: (01248) 600344 Fax: (01248) 602909

H Gilbert, Whiteridden Farm, Kilbirnie, Ayrshire, KA25 7JY Tel: (01505) 684162 Fax: (01505) 684162

H R & W E Burnell & Son, Bathealton, Taunton, Somerset, TA4 2BG Tel: (01398) 361266

W.W. & B.T. Harrison, Moorthorpe Farm, Drumacre Lane East, Longton, Preston, PR4 4SD Tel: (01772) 613373

W.J. Heard, Ford Farm, Seven Crosses, Tiverton, Devon, EX16 5NW Tel: 01884 254250

Hindhay Agricultural Services, Green Lane Farm, Coningsby Lane, Fifield, Maidenhead, Berkshire, SL6 2PF Tel: (01628) 621160 Fax: (01628) 635861 E-mail: office@hindhay.co.uk

G.W. Hogarth, Town End Farm, Glassonby, Penrith, Cumbria, CA10 1DU Tel: (01768) 898317

Leslie Houston, 25 Ballylig Road, Broughshane, Ballymena, County Antrim, BT43 7HH Tel: (028) 2586 1068

Howton Contractors Ltd, Howton Farm, Pillaton, Saltash, Cornwall, PL12 6QY Tel: (01579) 350781 Fax: (01579) 351420

Ron Hughes, Glanfaes, Llanybydder, Dyfed, SA40 9TZ Tel: (01570) 480376 Fax: (01570) 480376

Humberts, Mansfield House, Silver Street, Taunton, Somerset, TA1 3DN Tel: (01823) 331234 Fax: (01823) 332034 E-mail: taunton.ag@humberts.co.uk

I Johns & Sons, Leafield Pig Farm, Purrants Lane, Leafield, Witney, Oxfordshire, OX29 9PN Tel: (01993) 878526

I & M Findlay, Broadgate, Mouswald, Dumfries, DG1 4LY Tel: (01387) 830241 Fax: (01387) 830241

Ian Crawford, Whitelees Road, Lanark, ML11 7LD Tel: (01555) 664432 Fax: (01555) 661262 E-mail: sales@signsandsafety.com

Independent Agronomy Ltd, 60 Stowupland Road, Stowmarket, Suffolk, IP14 5AL Tel: (01449) 677294 Fax: (01449) 771245 E-mail: tanya@indagronomy.co.uk

J B Contracting Ltd, Orchard House, Green End, Stretham, Ely, Cambridgeshire, CB6 3LF Tel: (01353) 648509 Fax: (01353) 648509

J & D Mcadam Ltd, Lawmuir Farm, Sheardale, Dollar, Clackmannanshire, FK14 7LY Tel: (01259) 750014 Fax: (01259) 750014

J E Evans, Velindre Park, Pencader, Dyfed, SA39 9HP Tel: (01559) 384242

J E Unwin, Pultheley Bank, Hyssington, Montgomery, Powys, SY15 6AX Tel: (01588) 650645 Fax: (01588) 650645

J Gadd, 20 Rancliffe Avenue, Keyworth, Nottingham, NG12 5HY Tel: 0115-937 3155 Fax: 0115-937 3155

J L & S A Edwards, Wood Cottage, Lacon Street, Prees, Whitchurch, Shropshire, SY13 2EP Tel: (01948) 840264

J Lawrie, Balchalum Farm, Errol, Perth, PH2 7RR Tel: (01821) 670311 Fax: (01821) 670311

J & M G Smith, Manor Farm, York Lane, Morthen, Rotherham, South Yorkshire, S66 9JH Tel: (01709) 544632 Fax: (01709) 544632

J & M Rule, Sparnon Gate, Redruth, Cornwall, TR16 4JB Tel: (01209) 216460

J P Griffiths, Newton Hall Farm, Saughall Massie Road, West Kirby, Wirral, Merseyside, CH48 1PQ Tel: 0151-625 5990 Fax: 0151-625 5775

J S Ridgway & Sons, The Oaklands Broadhay Lane, Lower Heath, Prees, Whitchurch, Shropshire, SY13 2BJ Tel: (01948) 840355 Fax: (01948) 840355

J Strefford & Son, Atcham Grange, Atcham, Shrewsbury, SY5 6QF Tel: (01743) 761567 Fax: (01743) 761570

J & T James, Cilpostau, Cilycwm, Llandovery, Dyfed, SA20 0HH Tel: (01550) 720716

James P Wilson & Sons, Millmannoch Farm, Drongan, Ayr, KA6 6HF Tel: (01292) 570239 Fax: (01292) 570239

▶ Jennings, Stream Cottages, Staunton-on-Arrow, Leominster, Herefordshire, HR6 9HR Tel: (01544) 388816 Fax: (01544) 388816 E-mail: peterjennings@farmmanagement.co.uk

John M Warbeck, Glenburn, Canonbie, Dumfriesshire, DG14 0YF Tel: (01387) 372218

Jon Macrae, Lynjon, Lundy Green, Hempnall, Norwich, NR15 2NU Tel: (01508) 499400

R. Jones & Son, Greenhill Farm, Elson, Ellesmere, Shropshire, SY12 9EZ Tel: 01691 690252

K Bell, 3 Sunnyside Farm Trading Estate, Martcombe Road, Easton-in-Gordano, Bristol, BS20 0QQ Tel: (01275) 373238

K G Consultants Ltd, Cessford, Kelso, Roxburghshire, TD5 8EG Tel: (01573) 440218 Fax: (01573) 440372

K J Thulborn Ltd, New Yard, Totnes Road, Paignton, Devon, TQ4 7HD Tel: (01803) 551217 Fax: (01803) 663722

K T Mcpartlin & Sons, The Barrocks, Ramsey Road, Farcet, Peterborough, PE7 3DR Tel: (01733) 844557

K W Barnett, 88 Main Street, Hutton Buscel, Scarborough, North Yorkshire, YO13 9LL Tel: (01723) 864375 Fax: (01723) 864375

K W Tilt & Sons, Whitehouse Farm, Hockley Brook Lane, Belbroughton, Stourbridge, West Midlands, DY9 0AH Tel: (01562) 730375

▶ Kemira Growhow UK Ltd, Ince, Chester, CH2 4LB Tel: 0151-357 2777 Fax: 0151-357 1755 E-mail: kemira-growhow.uk@kemira-growhow.com

▶ Kernon Countryside Consultants, Brook Cottage, Purton Stoke, Swindon, SN5 4JE Tel: (01793) 771333 Fax: (01793) 778384 E-mail: sales@kernon.co.uk

Kevin Johnson Contracting, 4 Church Road, Wittering, Peterborough, PE8 6AG Tel: (01780) 782924 Fax: (01780) 782924 E-mail: info@sandhill-gardencentre.co.uk

King Bros, Cross Lane, Salterforth, Barnoldswick, Lancashire, BB18 5UD Tel: (01282) 813118 Fax: (01282) 851984 E-mail: peter.kingbros@btconnect.com

L C Teague, Colliers Hill, Little Rissington, Cheltenham, Gloucestershire, GL54 2ND Tel: (01451) 820591 Fax: (01451) 822449

Land Use Consultancy Services, 16 Springdale Road, Market Weighton, York, YO43 3JT Tel: (01430) 871489 Fax: (01430) 871489 E-mail: skinglucs@aol.com

▶ Landmark Environmental Ltd, Myerscough Hall, St. Michaels Road, Bilsborrow, Preston, PR3 0RY Tel: (01995) 642109 Fax: (01995) 642108 E-mail: info@land-mark.co.uk

Leslie Dick & Sons Ltd, Linkfield Farm, Airth, Falkirk, FK2 8QT Tel: (01324) 831335 Fax: (01324) 831335

Lincolnshire Machinery Ring Ltd, Cannon St House, Cannon Street, Louth, Lincolnshire, LN11 9NL Tel: (01507) 600888 Fax: (01507) 611888

Little & Little, 16 St Marks Road, Henley-on-Thames, Oxfordshire, RG9 1LJ Tel: (01491) 572533

M Hibbert, Windmill Farm, Dale, Haverfordwest, Dyfed, SA62 3QX Tel: (01646) 636428 E-mail: sheila.hibbert@tesco.net

M J Beskeen, 1872 Melton Road, Rearsby, Leicester, LE7 4YS Tel: (01664) 424799 Fax: (01664) 424799

M J Curwood, Wards Cross, Broadclyst, Exeter, EX5 3DB Tel: (01404) 822264 Fax: (01404) 822264

M J Madkins, Thornborough Road, Nash, Milton Keynes, MK17 0HN Tel: (01296) 712938 Fax: (01296) 712938

M J Richardson, Newholme Farm, High Street, Hatfield, Doncaster, South Yorkshire, DN7 6RS Tel: (01302) 840518

M L Hughes, Bryn Olwen, Llanfair Road, Abergele, Clwyd, LL22 8PB Tel: (07850) 401762 Fax: (01745) 832243

M & M Bell, Techmuiry, Fraserburgh, Aberdeenshire, AB43 7BD Tel: (01346) 541289 Fax: (01346) 541454

M & P Williams, Little Toldish Farm, Moorland Road, Indian Queens, St. Columb, Cornwall, TR9 6HJ Tel: (01726) 860664 Fax: (01726) 860401

M S R Kirk, Leagate Road, Gipsey Bridge, Boston, Lincolnshire, PE22 7BU Tel: (01205) 280516

M V Shepherd, Sibson Lane, Shenton, Nuneaton, Warwickshire, CV13 6DD Tel: (01455) 212670 Fax: (01455) 213707

M W Furlong & Co., Ridley Farm, Bardon Mill, Hexham, Northumberland, NE47 7BP Tel: (01434) 344531 Fax: (01434) 344531

M W Nash & Partners, Smoky Farm, Staplegrove, Taunton, Somerset, TA2 6SL Tel: (01823) 451298 Fax: (01823) 451870

Masdar International Ltd, Masdar House, 1 Reading Road, Hook, Hampshire, RG27 0RP Tel: 0118-973 0750 Fax: 0118-973 0002 E-mail: masdar@masdar.com

John Masters, Trenay, Two Waters Foot, Liskeard, Cornwall, PL14 6HX Tel: (01208) 821248

Mattacott Dairy Engineers, 4 Collaford Farm Business Units, Plympton, Plymouth, PL7 5BD Tel: (01752) 881000 Fax: (01752) 881000

William Meyrick Jones, Fronhaul, Cwm Golau, Cyfronydd, Welshpool, Powys, SY21 9EZ Tel: (01938) 810419

Michael G Harris, Greenway, Rowden Mill Lane, Stourton Caundle, Sturminster Newton, Dorset, DT10 2JT Tel: (01963) 362302

Morgan Bros, Colomendy, Church Stoke, Montgomery, Powys, SY15 6ST Tel: (01588) 620279 Fax: (01588) 620279

Norden Agricultural Contractors, Paper House Farm, Ashworth Road, Rochdale, Lancashire, OL11 5UP Tel: (01706) 642727

O G Davies & Sons, Maes Yr Hedydd, Meidrim, Carmarthen, Dyfed, SA33 5QY Tel: (01994) 231041 Fax: (01994) 231041

O M F Partnership, Old Manor Farm, Spring Lane, Little Bourton, Banbury, Oxfordshire, OX17 1RB Tel: (01295) 758857 Fax: (01295) 758131 E-mail: oldmanorfarm@ukonline.co.uk

Ogborne K.R, West Cleave, Germansweek, Beaworthy, Devon, EX21 5AL Tel: (01837) 871339

P Smith, Rushton Spencer, Macclesfield, Cheshire, SK11 0RX Tel: (01782) 513294 Fax: (01782) 513294

P Tuckwell Ltd, Ardleigh Hall, Dedham Road, Ardleigh, Colchester, CO7 7LG Tel: (01206) 231293 Fax: (01206) 231218 E-mail: ardleigh@tuckwell.co.uk

P.R. Parker, Lea Green Farm, Long La, Scorton, Preston, PR3 1DB Tel: (01524) 791397 Fax: (01524) 791397

A.J. Parton, Field House Farm, Slindon, Stafford, ST21 6LX Tel: (01782) 791305 Fax: (01782) 791305

John Peak & Sons, Three Bells, Church Road, Frating, Colchester, CO7 7HE Tel: (01206) 250543 Fax: (01206) 250543

Phil Morgan Contracting, Blue Barns, Church Stoke, Montgomery, Powys, SY15 6EN Tel: (01588) 620355 Fax: (01588) 620355

PLG Agronomy, Bishops Tawton, Barnstaple, Devon, EX32 0EA Tel: (01271) 831003 Fax: (01271) 830826

Porter Agriculture, Gowers Farm, Tumblers Green, Braintree, Essex, CM77 8AZ Tel: (07831) 447102 Fax: (01376) 334375 E-mail: mike@porterag.co.uk

▶ Quantech Solutions, Howe Farm, Malton, North Yorkshire, YO17 6RG Tel: (01653) 694490 Fax: (01653) 694490 E-mail: sam.hoste@quantechsolutions.co.uk

R A Lewis, Galltyllan Farm, Penegoes, Machynlleth, Powys, SY20 8DF Tel: (01654) 702083

R A Roberts, Llawr Y Pant Hall, Selattyn, Oswestry, Shropshire, SY10 7HX Tel: (01691) 653913

R & D Hope, 9 Caulside, Canonbie, Dumfriesshire, DG14 0RT Tel: (01387) 371297

R G & I M Heaman, Remberton Farm, Cullompton, Devon, EX15 1LY Tel: (07768) 651417

R G Stokes & Son, Bellwood, Shobdon, Leominster, Herefordshire, HR6 9NJ Tel: (01568) 708642 Fax: (01568) 708642

R O Williams & Son, Dyers Lane, Iron Acton, Bristol, BS37 9XT Tel: (01454) 228663 Fax: (01454) 228663

R P Hill, Kidmore Lane, Waterlooville, Hampshire, PO7 6JY Tel: (023) 9263 2644

R Simeon, Dalts Farm House, Daltes Lane, St. Osyth, Clacton-on-Sea, Essex, CO16 8SA Tel: (01255) 821874 Fax: (01255) 821874 E-mail: robsimeon@aol.com

Richard Ingram Land Drainage, 10 Church Lane, Gaddesby, Leicester, LE7 4WE Tel: (01664) 840480 Fax: (01664) 840480

A.R. Richards Ltd, Cobscott Farm, Norton In Hales, Market Drayton, Shropshire, TF9 3TW Tel: (01630) 653757

▶ RJT Consultancy, 6 The Oaks, Kitlings Lane, Stafford, ST17 0LE Tel: (01785) 660000 Fax: (01785) 660000

Robert Caerwen Evans, 10 Friars Avenue, Oswestry, Shropshire, SY11 2JJ Tel: (01691) 661611 Fax: (01691) 661611

Roger Sorrell, Shipton Gorge, Bridport, Dorset, DT6 4NJ Tel: (01308) 897861 Fax: (01308) 897861

M.A. Roper & Sons, Paer Tree Cottage, Town Road, Fleggburgh, Great Yarmouth, Norfolk, NR29 3AB Tel: (01493) 368176 Fax: (01493) 369807

Rural Development Service, Southgate Street, Bury St. Edmunds, Suffolk, IP33 2BD Tel: (01284) 750102 Fax: (01284) 753658

Rural Development Services Ltd, 54 Church Road, Gracehill, Ballymena, County Antrim, BT42 2NL Tel: (028) 2565 1283 Fax: (028) 2563 0103 E-mail: sales@farmrelief.co.uk

S B Lawrence, 5 Long Lane, Over Peover, Knutsford, Cheshire, WA16 8XB Tel: (01565) 722655

S C Marsh Ltd, 2 Dorchester Road, Maiden Newton, Dorchester, Dorset, DT2 0AY Tel: (01300) 320268 Fax: (01300) 320268

S Gray & Son, Chapel Farm, Galhampton, Yeovil, Somerset, BA22 7AB Tel: (01963) 440347 Fax: (01963) 440347 E-mail: yarlington1@btopenworld.com

S W Witham & Sons, The Forge, Blacksmiths Lane, Erpingham, Norwich, NR11 7QF Tel: (01263) 761404

Scotgrain Agriculture Ltd, Rosehall, Turriff, Aberdeenshire, AB53 4HD Tel: 01888 568765

Scottish Agronomy Ltd, Arlary Farmhouse, Milnathort, Kinross, KY13 9SJ Tel: (01577) 862759 Fax: (01577) 865129

Scottish Woolgrowers, Newton Road, Novar, Evanton, Dingwall, Ross-Shire, IV16 9XQ Tel: (01349) 830678 Fax: (01349) 830546 E-mail: mail@britishwool.org.uk

Sidney J George & Son, Moat Cottage, Beguildy, Knighton, Powys, LD7 1YU Tel: (01547) 510233 Fax: (01547) 510233

Sykes R.O, 62b Feltwell Road, Southery, Downham Market, Norfolk, PE38 0NS Tel: (01366) 377591 Fax: (01366) 377592

T & A Dale, Underhill Farm, Shatterford, Bewdley, Worcestershire, DY12 1TH Tel: (01299) 861285

T G & A L Evans, Cross Inn Hall, Llanfihangel-Ar-Arth, Pencader, Dyfed, SA39 9JX Tel: (01559) 384304

T J K Harries, Lletty Dryw, Felinfoel, Llanelli, Dyfed, SA14 8NX Tel: (01554) 758777 Fax: (01554) 758777 E-mail: lletydryw@tiscali.co.uk

T & J White, High Onn House, High Onn, Church Eaton, Stafford, ST20 0AX Tel: (01952) 691223

T M Barker & Son, High Lane, Beadlam/Nawton, Nawton, York, YO62 7SP Tel: (01439) 770367

T N Sneath & Sons, Cross Lanes, Pinchbeck, Spalding, Lincolnshire, PE11 3SN Tel: (01775) 640373 Fax: (01775) 640125 E-mail: richard@tn-sneath.co.uk

T & S Services, 32 Wimblington Road, Doddington, March, Cambridgeshire, PE15 0TJ Tel: (01354) 740025

S. & M. Taylor, Lower Ozzings Farm, Shelley, Huddersfield, HD8 8NA Tel: (01484) 863492

Thomas Bros, Lowlands, Nash, Newport, Gwent, NP18 2DA Tel: (01633) 276316 Fax: (01633) 276316

Upu Industries Ltd, 1 Quillyburn Business Park, Banbridge Road, Dromore, County Down, BT25 1BY Tel: (028) 9269 9020 Fax: (028) 9269 9029 E-mail: info@steve-orr.com

W Campbell, 11 Kedar Bank, Mouswald, Dumfries, DG1 4LU Tel: (01387) 830239

W E Atkins & Sons, Abbey Fields, Rocester, Uttoxeter, Staffordshire, ST14 5JX Tel: (01889) 590922 Fax: (01889) 591700

W Hume & Son, Hillside House, Norham, Norham, Berwick-upon-Tweed, TD15 2JZ Tel: (07753) 937070 Fax: (01289) 382435

W J O Rees, King Heriot, Solva, Haverfordwest, Dyfed, SA62 6XN Tel: (01437) 721313

W R Suckling & Sons, 6 Chapel Street, Steeple Bumpstead, Haverhill, Suffolk, CB9 7DQ Tel: (01440) 730227

W & T Clayson, Henbury Close, Henbury, Elham, Canterbury, Kent, CT4 6NL Tel: (01303) 840233 Fax: (01303) 840160

Geoff Ward, Glantanat Isaf, Llangedwyn, Oswestry, Shropshire, SY10 9LQ Tel: (01691) 780278

Wedderspoon Processes Ltd, Eassie Station, Eassie, Forfar, Angus, DD8 1SG Tel: (01307) 840396 Fax: (01307) 840404

Welsh Agricultural Office, Plas Y Ffynnon, Cambrian Way, Brecon, Powys, LD3 7HP Tel: (01874) 625123 Fax: (01874) 622737

Willington Crop Services, Woodend, Rattlesden Road, Drinkstone Green, Bury St. Edmunds, Suffolk, IP30 9TL Tel: (01449) 736602 Fax: (01449) 737352 E-mail: info@willingtoncropservices.co.uk

Wright Bros, Farley, Matlock, Derbyshire, DE4 5LQ Tel: (01629) 582687 Fax: (01629) 582687 E-mail: tax@farmersweekly.net

AGRICULTURAL CROP AERATION EQUIPMENT

Alvan Blanch Development Co. Ltd, Chelworth, Malmesbury, Wiltshire, SN16 9SG Tel: (01666) 577333 Fax: (01666) 577339 E-mail: info@alvanblanch.co.uk

CSC Crop Protection Ltd, Gooseberry Farm, Whinney Hill, Stockton-on-Tees, Cleveland, TS21 1BQ Tel: (01642) 588585 Fax: (01642) 570597 E-mail: sales@csccrop.co.uk

AGRICULTURAL CROP AERATION EQUIPMENT - *continued*

J Angus & Partners, 44 Portaferry Road, Kircubbin, Newtownards, County Down, BT22 2RY Tel: (028) 4278 8272

West Engineering Ltd, Olympus Close, Ipswich, IP1 5LN Tel: (01473) 467930 Fax: (01473) 467931 E-mail: west@engineering40.fsbusiness.co.uk

AGRICULTURAL CROP DRYING EQUIPMENT

Terry Johnson Ltd, Cranmore Lane, Holbeach, Spalding, Lincolnshire, PE12 7HT Tel: (01406) 422286 Fax: (01406) 426356

Welvent Ltd, Whisby Way, Whisby Road, Lincoln, LN6 3LQ Tel: (01522) 693008 Fax: (01522) 500429 E-mail: enquiries@welvent.com

AGRICULTURAL DRAIN PIPE AND FITTINGS

John Tucker & Son, Lockyers Farm, Mudgley, Wedmore, Somerset, BS28 4TY Tel: (01934) 712594 Fax: (01934) 712594

AGRICULTURAL ENGINEERING SERVICES

A & B M Suffield & Sons, Homelea Farm, Bearley Road, Aston Cantlow, Henley-in-Arden, West Midlands, B95 6LD Tel: (01789) 488040 Fax: (01789) 488971

A E Huddleston, Mardale, Quernmore, Lancaster, LA2 9EG Tel: (01524) 66914 Fax: (01524) 66914

A G & G C Gibson, Forge House, Old Forge Lane, West Rasen, Market Rasen, Lincolnshire, LN8 3LS Tel: (01673) 842891 Fax: (01673) 842891

A & M Engineering, Merlins Cross, Pembroke, Dyfed, SA71 4AG Tel: (01646) 685169 Fax: (01646) 622060

A M Phillip Ltd, Ardlaw Garage, Fraserburgh, Aberdeenshire, AB43 7DA Tel: (01346) 541351 Fax: (01346) 541703

A Robinson, Gelt Hall Farm, Castle Carrock, Brampton, Cumbria, CA8 9LT Tel: (01228) 670260 Fax: (01228) 670260

A Stone, Unit 11 Camp Industrial Estate, Rycote Lane, Milton Common, Thame, Oxfordshire, OX9 2NP Tel: (01844) 278966

A T Oliver & Sons Ltd, Home Park Works, Station Road, Kings Langley, Hertfordshire, WD4 8LW Tel: (01923) 265211 Fax: (01923) 261759

A T Oliver & Sons Ltd, Wandon End Works, Wandon End, Luton, LU2 8NY Tel: (01582) 727111 Fax: (01582) 729763 E-mail: ato@atoliver.co.uk

A T Osborne Ltd, Wytchwood, Shelley Lane, Ower, Romsey, Hampshire, SO51 6ZL Tel: (023) 8081 4340 Fax: (023) 8081 2941

A W Green Agricultural Engineers, Stable Works, Climpsetts Farm, Robertsbridge, East Sussex, TN32 5SP Tel: (01580) 860630 Fax: (01580) 860630

A W Warner & Sons Ltd, Guilton Lodge, Guilton, Ash, Canterbury, Kent, CT3 2HS Tel: (01304) 812396 Fax: (01304) 813635

A Woods Agricultural Engineers, Pipwell Gate, Holbeach, Spalding, Lincolnshire, PE12 8BA Tel: (01406) 426108 Fax: (01406) 490101 E-mail: woodsagri@tiscali.co.uk

Acorn Industrial Developments, 3 Wallbrook Court, Netherwood Road, Rotherwas Industrial Estate, Hereford, HR2 6JG Tel: (01432) 276600 Fax: (01432) 341268

▶ George Agar, Church Road, Ravenscar, Scarborough, North Yorkshire, YO13 0LZ Tel: (01723) 870966 Fax: (01723) 870771

Agricar Ltd, 6 Lochside Road, Forfar, Angus, DD8 3JE Tel: (01307) 462281 Fax: (01307) 467199 E-mail: derek.johnston@agricar.co.uk

Agricar Ltd, Station Road, Laurencekirk, Kincardineshire, AB30 1BE Tel: (01561) 378888 Fax: (01561) 378032 E-mail: admin@agricar-laurencekirk.co.uk

Agricar Ltd, West Huntingtower, Almondbank, Perth, PH1 3NP Tel: (01738) 583249 Fax: (01738) 583869 E-mail: admin@agricar.co.uk

▶ Agri-Care Engineering Ltd, 25 Summerhouse View, Yeovil, Somerset, BA21 4DJ Tel: (07708) 863282 E-mail: agricare276@hotmail.com

Agricon Engineers Ltd, Station Road, Kirk Hammerton, York, YO26 8DN Tel: (01423) 330014 Fax: (01423) 331347

Agricultural & Commercial Supplies Ltd, 2 Healey Lane Mill, Healey Lane, Batley, West Yorkshire, WF17 7SH Tel: (01924) 420354 Fax: (01924) 420357

Agrihire, Moors Farm, Moors Lane, Bourton-on-the-Water, Cheltenham, Gloucestershire, GL54 2HA Tel: (01451) 821292 Fax: (01451) 821292 E-mail: sales@agrihire.co.uk

Alan C Cowan, Hartburn, Morpeth, Northumberland, NE61 4EN Tel: (01670) 772555 Fax: (01670) 772655

Alasdair Grigor, Albion Works, Fortrose, Ross-Shire, IV10 8SS Tel: (01381) 620571 Fax: (01381) 620571

Albar Construction Ltd, 115 Burys Bank Road, Crookham Common, Thatcham, Berkshire, RG19 8DE Tel: (01635) 867713 Fax: (01635) 867730

Nick Allday, Broadley Works, Stoke Gabriel, Totnes, Devon, TQ9 6PU Tel: (01803) 782742 Fax: (01803) 782742

Alwen Garage, Llanfihangel Glyn Myfyr, Corwen, Clwyd, LL21 9UH Tel: (01490) 420567 Fax: (01490) 420418

Andrew C Alston & Son Ltd, Benston Smithy, Cumnock, Ayrshire, KA18 4QA Tel: (01290) 421234 Fax: (01290) 425889

Andrew Thomas, Crossgates, Llandrindod Wells, Powys, LD1 6RF Tel: (01597) 851810 Fax: (01597) 851810

Anthony Pickard, The Depot, Weeton Lane, Harewood, Leeds, LS17 9LP Tel: 0113-288 6524 Fax: 0113-288 6524

Askham Motors Ltd, Gilwilly Road Industrial Estate, Gilwilly Industrial Estate, Penrith, Cumbria, CA11 9BF Tel: (01768) 892233 Fax: (01768) 895522

B & B Tractors, Windmill House Farm, Forest Road, Warsop, Mansfield, Nottinghamshire, NG20 0EP Tel: (01623) 847171 Fax: (01623) 847485 E-mail: enquiries@bbtractors.co.uk

B Clatworthy & Sons, Greyhouse Farm, St Brides Wentlodge, Newport, Gwent, NP10 8SQ Tel: (01633) 680235 Fax: (01633) 680235

B Preece & Son, Plowden Mill, Plowden, Lydbury North, Shropshire, SY7 8BG Tel: (01588) 680279

G.E. Baker (UK) Ltd, Heath Road, Woolpit, Bury St. Edmunds, Suffolk, IP30 9RN Tel: (01359) 240529 Fax: (01359) 242086 E-mail: baker@quality-equipment.co.uk

Neville Barnes Ltd, Padmoor Lane, Upton, Gainsborough, Lincolnshire, DN21 5NH Tel: (01427) 838245 Fax: (01427) 838417

Bellerby Engineering Ltd, 6 Queens Gardens, Hornsea, North Humberside, HU18 1AU Tel: (01964) 532176 Fax: (01964) 532176

Ben Burgess Beeston, Dereham Road, Beeston, King's Lynn, Norfolk, PE32 2LE Tel: (01328) 701347 Fax: (01328) 700111 E-mail: beestonsales@benburgess.co.uk

A.W. Blake Ltd, Commerce Road, Black Park Industrial Park, Stranraer, Wigtownshire, DG9 7DF Tel: (01776) 706665 Fax: (01776) 889669

Breckhouse Engineering, Middle Farm, Sproxton, York, YO62 5EF Tel: (01439) 770579 Fax: (01439) 770772

Brookthorpe Engineering, Tiltups End, Horsley, Stroud, Gloucestershire, GL6 0QE Tel: (01453) 832420 Fax: (01453) 832420

Gordon Brown, White Hill, Springfield, Enniskillen, County Fermanagh, BT74 8AL Tel: (028) 6634 1717 Fax: (028) 6634 1717

Brucklay Garage, Maud, Peterhead, Aberdeenshire, AB42 4RA Tel: (01771) 613500 Fax: (01771) 613789

Burton Engineering, Burton, Chippenham, Wiltshire, SN14 7LT Tel: (01454) 218431 Fax: (01454) 218431

H.E. Butters & Co., Baldwins Gate, Newcastle, Staffordshire, ST5 5DA Tel: (01782) 680253

C E Davis Marshfield Ltd, 94 High Street, Marshfield, Chippenham, Wiltshire, SN14 8LS Tel: (01225) 891444 Fax: (01225) 891910

C F Dodson Ltd, Birch Close, Charlton Marshall, Blandford Forum, Dorset, DT11 9AJ Tel: (01258) 488955

C G C Agricultural & Motor Engineers, Five Down, Puddock Road, Warboys, Huntingdon, Cambridgeshire, PE28 2UB Tel: (01487) 823248 Fax: (01487) 823248 E-mail: sales@cgcagricultural.co.uk

C Griffiths & Son, The Foundry, Brimfield, Ludlow, Shropshire, SY8 4NG Tel: (01584) 711264 Fax: (01584) 711805 E-mail: sales@autogasdevelopmentsltd.co.uk

C J Keitch Engineering, Dunkeswell Airfield, Dunkeswell Industrial Estate, Honiton, Devon, EX14 4LH Tel: (01404) 891796 Fax: (01404) 891796 E-mail: sales@cjkeitchengineering.co.uk

C O P Autogas Ltd, Somersall Mill, Grove Lane, Doveridge, Ashbourne, Derbyshire, DE6 5PB Tel: (01283) 585240 Fax: (01283) 585738

C & O Tractors Ltd, West Street, Wilton, Salisbury, SP2 0DG Tel: (01722) 742141 Fax: (01722) 744497 E-mail: admin@candotractors.co.uk

C P C Engineers Ltd, Adderley Road, Market Drayton, Shropshire, TF9 3SW Tel: (01630) 652904 Fax: (01630) 652904

C T Hayton Ltd, Sandylands Road, Kendal, Cumbria, LA9 6EX Tel: (01539) 721518 Fax: (01539) 722977 E-mail: sales@cthayton.co.uk

C T M Root Crop Systems - Harpley Engineering Ltd, Cross Street, Harpley, King's Lynn, Norfolk, PE31 6TJ Tel: (01485) 520355 Fax: (01485) 520062 E-mail: sales@ctmharpley.co.uk

Campmuir Ltd, Bourtie Works, Inverurie, Aberdeenshire, AB51 0HL Tel: (01467) 621591 Fax: (01467) 624414 E-mail: richard@campmuir.com

Canalside Autos, Unit 6, Finnington Lane, Feniscowles, Blackburn, BB2 5JD Tel: (01254) 200170

Challinor & Sons, Malverne, Church Bank, Goostrey, Crewe, CW4 8PG Tel: (01477) 533282 Fax: (01260) 276924

A.M. & B.J. Chattaway, Meriden Mill Farm, Meriden, Coventry, CV7 7LJ Tel: (01675) 442564 Fax: (01675) 443120 E-mail: info@waterinthegarden.co.uk

Chiltern Agricultural Services, Blackhorse, Checkendon, Reading, RG8 0TE Tel: (01491) 682456

Claas UK Ltd, Saxham, Bury St. Edmunds, Suffolk, IP28 6QZ Tel: (01284) 763100 Fax: (01284) 769839 E-mail: info-uk@claas.com

Coar Agricultural Services, Settle Road, Newsholme, Clitheroe, Lancashire, BB7 4JF Tel: (01200) 445187 Fax: (01200) 445187

George Colliar Ltd, Middle Balado, Balado, Kinross, KY13 0NH Tel: (01577) 863173 Fax: (01577) 864768 E-mail: colliar@harleys.co.uk

Collings Bros Of Abbotsley Ltd, 3-5 Prospect Way, Chatteris, Cambridgeshire, PE16 6TZ Tel: (01354) 694169 Fax: (01354) 694218 E-mail: sales@collingbrothers.co.uk

Collings Bros Of Abbotsley Ltd, Potton Road, Abbotsley, St. Neots, Cambridgeshire, PE19 6TZ Tel: (01767) 677316 Fax: (01767) 677451 E-mail: sales@collingsbrothers.co.uk

Combine Fabrications Ltd, Fen Lane, Long Bennington, Newark, Nottinghamshire, NG23 5ED Tel: (01400) 281506 Fax: (01400) 282100 E-mail: enquiries@combinefabs.co.uk

▶ Continental Soil Technology, The Old Dairy, Chavenage Estate, Tetbury, Gloucestershire, GL8 8XY Tel: (0845) 6034136 Fax: E-mail: info@continentalsoiltechnology.com

Morris Corfield & Co. Ltd, Westington, Docklow, Leominster, Herefordshire, HR6 0SJ Tel: (01885) 488884 Fax: (01885) 483888

Country West Trading Ltd, Northgate, Barnstaple Street, Bideford, Devon, EX39 4AE Tel: (01237) 424373 Fax: (01237) 425054

Cranworth Farm Services, High Common, Cranworth, Thetford, Norfolk, IP25 7SX Tel: (01362) 820391 Fax: (01362) 820077 E-mail: sales@c-f-s.info

D C Merrett, The Grain Store Castle Lane, Epney, Saul, Gloucester, GL2 7LN Tel: (01452) 740782 Fax: (01452) 741496 E-mail: info@dcmerrett.co.uk

D Canavan, 66 Mountjoy Road, Dungannon, County Tyrone, BT71 5EF Tel: (028) 8774 7666 Fax: (028) 8774 7666

D H Willis & Sons Ltd, Carrbeck House, Gilling West, Richmond, North Yorkshire, DL10 5LN Tel: (01748) 822714 Fax: (01748) 822714

D Henderson, 12 Acomb Industrial Estate, Acomb, Hexham, Northumberland, NE46 4SA Tel: (01434) 601966 Fax: (01434) 601966

D Highland, Salthill View, Clitheroe, Lancashire, BB7 1NY Tel: (01200) 423300

D I Gubb, Sunnymead, Culmbridge Road, Hemyock, Cullompton, Devon, EX15 3QP Tel: (01823) 680553

D & J Simpson, Eassie Smithy, Eassie, Forfar, Angus, DD8 1SG Tel: (01307) 840325

D Murrie & Son, 42 Main Street, Methven, Perth, PH1 3PU Tel: (01738) 840477 Fax: (01738) 840477

D R Fox, Grange Farm, Stillingfleet Road, Escrick, York, YO19 6EB Tel: (01904) 728668

D R Harrod, 79 Denford Road, Ringstead, Kettering, Northamptonshire, NN14 4DF Tel: (01933) 626260 Fax: (01933) 460072

D Stretton, High Barns, Isley Walton, Castle Donington, Derby, DE74 2RL Tel: (01332) 810757

D Theakstone, Lawrence Cottage, Beningbrough, York, YO30 1BZ Tel: (01904) 470550 Fax: (01904) 470566

Dacre Agriculture Ltd, Astwood Road, Cranfield, Bedford, MK43 0AT Tel: (01234) 751591 Fax: (01234) 750745 E-mail: sales@dacreag.co.uk

David A Clifford, 118 Maescader, Pencader, Dyfed, SA39 9HR Tel: (01559) 384891 Fax: (01559) 384891

David R Howells, Maes Y Gelli, Penybont, Carmarthen, Dyfed, SA33 6QA Tel: (01994) 484257

Denleys Agricultural & Motor Engineers, Awliscombe, Honiton, Devon, EX14 3PU Tel: (01404) 841237 Fax: (01404) 841311 E-mail: info@agricultural-parts.co.uk

Donald C Speakman, Brendon, Monkland, Leominster, Herefordshire, HR6 9DB Tel: (01568) 720235 Fax: (01568) 720235

Downes C.R Agricultural Engineer, Lower House, Llandrinio, Llanymynech, Powys, SY22 6SH Tel: (01691) 830407

Drews of Dinton Ltd, Dinton, Salisbury, SP3 5EH Tel: (01722) 716377 Fax: (01722) 716489

James Duke, Little Ham Barn, Ham Road, Ham, Chichester, West Sussex, PO20 7NY Tel: (01243) 641441 Fax: (01243) 641708 E-mail: dairytec@dircon.co.uk

Robert Dykes & Son, Burnside Works, Westend, Thornhill, Stirling, FK8 3PS Tel: (01786) 850242 Fax: (01786) 850740

E Bowden & Sons, Little Woodland, Old Newton Road, Bovey Tracey, Newton Abbot, Devon, TQ13 9DT Tel: (01626) 833374 Fax: (01626) 832144 E-mail: ebowden@btconnect.com

E Darley, Darfield House, Hull Road, Hemingbrough, Selby, North Yorkshire, YO8 6QJ Tel: (01757) 638233

E Hughes, Bryn Eden, Caeathro, Caernarfon, Gwynedd, LL55 2SG Tel: (01286) 675401 Fax: (01286) 672816

E & J D Alderson, The Old Power House Garage, Wensley Station, Preston under Scar, Leyburn, North Yorkshire, DL8 4AQ Tel: (01969) 624160

E S Harrison & Sons, The Willows, Haven Bank, New York, Lincoln, LN4 4XR Tel: (01205) 280336 Fax: (01205) 280336

Eaton Berry Ltd, Bridge Farm, Reading Road, Arborfield, Reading, RG2 9HT Tel: 0118-976 1076 Fax: 0118-976 0479 E-mail: info@eatonberry.com

Edwards Engineering (Perth) Ltd, Glenearn Road, Perth, PH2 0NJ Tel: (01738) 627101 Fax: (01738) 630769 E-mail: mail@edwardsengineering.co.uk

Ellesmere Farm Machinery, Cambrian House, Frankton, Ellesmere, Shropshire, SY12 9HE Tel: (01691) 690307 Fax: (01691) 690307

Ellis Dawe & Son, The Forge, Rye Street, Birtsmorton, Malvern, Worcestershire, WR13 6AS Tel: (01684) 833235 Fax: (01684) 833840 E-mail: sales@ellisdawe.co.uk

Elnor Engineering, Checkley, Nantwich, Cheshire, CW5 7QA Tel: (01270) 520282

L. Evans & Son (Hereford) Ltd, Crown House, Canon Pyon, Hereford, HR4 8PE Tel: (01432) 830285 Fax: (01432) 830285

F J Banks & Sons, Oldstead Grange, Oldstead, York, YO61 4BJ Tel: (01347) 868634 E-mail: enquiries@spillsave.co.uk

F W & A J Beckwith, 69 Clotherholme Road, Ripon, North Yorkshire, HG4 2DN Tel: (01765) 600587 Fax: (01765) 602215

F W Stennett & Sons, New House, High Road, Swilland, Ipswich, IP6 9LP Tel: (01473) 785815 Fax: (01473) 785403

Farm & Forestry Equipment, 44 Stuart Street, Ardersier, Inverness, IV2 7RS Tel: (01667) 462608 Fax: (01667) 462902

Farmplus Construction Ltd, Shay Lane, Longridge, Preston, PR3 3BT Tel: (01772) 785252 Fax: (01772) 782944 E-mail: enquiries@farmplus.co.uk

Fawcett Agriculture, Ireby Hall, Cowan Bridge, Carnforth, Lancashire, LA6 2JH Tel: (01524) 242222 Fax: (01524) 42239 E-mail: richard@fawcetts.net

Fix It Engineering, North Back Lane, Terrington, York, YO60 6NS Tel: (01653) 648446 Fax: (01653) 648293

R.B. Flett Ltd, Central Garage, Watten, Wick, Caithness, KW1 5XG Tel: (01955) 621255 Fax: (01955) 621260

Forest & Field Engineering, The Workshop, Mains of Arthurstone Farm, Meigle, Blairgowrie, Perthshire, PH12 8QY Tel: (01828) 640606 Fax: (01828) 640899 E-mail: fm@ffengineering.co.uk

Foster Agricultural Services, Wingfield, Diss, Norfolk, IP21 5QT Tel: (01379) 384479 Fax: (01379) 384188

Francis Bugler Ltd, Rimpton Road, Marston Magna, Yeovil, Somerset, BA22 8DP Tel: (01935) 850426 Fax: (01935) 851376 E-mail: all@mardentractors.co.uk

Frankie Wainman, Foster Cliffe Farm South, Low Lane, Silsden, Keighley, West Yorkshire, BD20 9JH Tel: (01535) 652487 Fax: (01535) 658286

Fraser C Robb, Arendale, Stirling Road, Drymen, Glasgow, G63 0AA Tel: (01360) 660688 Fax: (01360) 660814 E-mail: admin@frasercrobb.com

G Bryan Jones Ltd, Love La Industrial Estate, Bishops Castle, Shropshire, SY9 5DW Tel: (01588) 638638 Fax: (01588) 638741 E-mail: sales@gbj1.freeserve.co.uk

G & D Engineering Moulton Ltd, Spalding Gate, High Road, Moulton, Spalding, Lincolnshire, PE12 6NT Tel: (01406) 370570 Fax: (01406) 370456

G H East & Sons, Little London House, Little London, North Kelsey, Market Rasen, Lincolnshire, LN7 6JP Tel: (01652) 678116 Fax: (01652) 678116

G & J Peck Ltd, Main Street, Mareham-le-Fen, Boston, Lincolnshire, PE22 7QJ Tel: (01507) 568484 Fax: (01507) 568585

G Jones, Mayville, Pulford Lane, Dodleston, Chester, CH4 9NN Tel: (01244) 660691 Fax: (01244) 660691

G & S Thomson, Dubford, Turriff, Aberdeenshire, AB53 8AJ Tel: (01888) 562500 Fax: (01888) 568672

Gardiners, The Batts, Frosterley, Bishop Auckland, County Durham, DL13 2SE Tel: (07711) 356444 Fax: (01388) 527295

GB Farm Services, D Park Farm, Colchester Road, Elmstead, Colchester, CO7 7BA Tel: (01206) 822734 Fax: (01206) 822734

Gerald Hallet, Long Acre, Closworth Road, Halstock, Yeovil, Somerset, BA22 9SY Tel: (01935) 891616 Fax: (01935) 891617 E-mail: hallettlandrover@btconnect.com

Glover J Agricultural Contractor, Hollies Farm, Ashbourne, Derbyshire, DE6 2FF Tel: (01889) 590351 Fax: (01889) 590351

Glyn V Thomas, Church View, Mathry, Haverfordwest, Dyfed, SA62 5HA Tel: (01348) 831391 Fax: (01348) 831389

Goodrowes Of Chichester Ltd, 6 The Hornet, Chichester, West Sussex, PO19 7JQ Tel: (01243) 784411 Fax: (01243) 784339 E-mail: goodrowesltd@aol.com

Gordon James Engineers Ltd, Old Station Yard, Newton Stewart, Wigtownshire, DG8 9AL Tel: (01988) 840201 Fax: (01988) 840670 E-mail: nsparts@jgordon.co.uk

Grangewards Agricultural Engineers, 454 Hern Road Ramsey St Marys, Ramsey St. Marys, Ramsey, Huntingdon, Cambridgeshire, PE26 2TJ Tel: (01733) 844590

W. Grant, 122 Main Street, Aberchirder, Huntly, Aberdeenshire, AB54 7TD Tel: (01466) 780227 Fax: (01466) 780227

Gurney Reeve & Co. Ltd, Station Road, Spooner Row, Wymondham, Norfolk, NR18 9SR Tel: (01953) 603303 Fax: (01953) 601331 E-mail: sales@sweepersuton.co.uk

H Cooper & Sons Bristol, Westerleigh Road, Yate, Bristol, BS37 8QA Tel: (01454) 312081 Fax: (01454) 318880E-mail: info@hcooper.net

AGRICULTURAL ENGINEERING SERVICES – *continued*

H R N Tractors Ltd, South Road, Insch, Aberdeenshire, AB52 6XF Tel: (01464) 820661 Fax: (01464) 820082 E-mail: sales@hrntractors.com

Hadrian Farm Services Ltd, 6 Mcmullen Road, Darlington, County Durham, DL1 1ZY Tel: (01325) 350038 Fax: (01325) 354527

John Halliday & Sons, Chapelton Smithy, Borgue, Kirkcudbright, DG6 4SN Tel: (01557) 870200 Fax: (01557) 870200

Hamilton Bros Engineering Ltd, Barmore Road, Tarbert, Argyll, PA29 6TT Tel: (01880) 820249 Fax: (01880) 820249

Bernard Hancock, Rolle Quay, Barnstaple, Devon, EX31 1JE Tel: (01271) 345545 Fax: (01271) 378777 E-mail: rolle.quay@tiscali.co.uk

Hardy J, 64a Ballinderry Bridge Road, Coagh, Cookstown, County Tyrone, BT80 0BT Tel: (028) 8673 7134 Fax: (028) 8673 7134

Harper & Eede Ltd, Broyle House, The Broyle, Ringmer, Lewes, East Sussex, BN8 5NN Tel: (01273) 812707 Fax: (01273) 814040 E-mail: sales@harperandeede.co.uk

Haynes Agricultural Ltd, Parkwood Industrial Estate, Sutton Road, Maidstone, Kent, ME15 9NH Tel: (01622) 755726 Fax: (01622) 672634 E-mail: agrienquiries@haynesgrp.co.uk

Henderson Grass Machinery Ltd, Bye-Pass Road, Haddington, East Lothian, EH41 3PQ Tel: (01620) 823171 Fax: (01620) 826696 E-mail: info@hendersongm.co.uk

M.R. Hendy, Middle Hill Farm, Langford Budville, Wellington, Somerset, TA21 0RS Tel: 01823 400476

Henry R Taylor, 21 Church Lane, Rasharkin, Ballymena, County Antrim, BT44 8QZ Tel: (028) 2957 1316

Heylin Engineering, Cartref, Four Crosses, Llanymynech, Powys, SY22 6RG Tel: (01691) 830440 Fax: (01691) 830410

Hircocks Engineers Ltd, College Lodge Works, Wisbech St. Mary, Wisbech, Cambridgeshire, PE13 4SW Tel: (01945) 450404 Fax: (01945) 450595 E-mail: sales@hircocks.com

Bruce Hopkins Ltd, Shenington Airfield, Shenington, Banbury, Oxfordshire, OX15 6NZ Tel: (01295) 680711 Fax: (01295) 680780 E-mail: bruce@brucehopkins.co.uk

Howard & Sons, Forge Workshop, Moor Road, North Owersby, Market Rasen, Lincolnshire, LN8 3PR Tel: (01673) 828888 Fax: (01673) 828888

Howat John Agricultural Contractors, Rosemount, Closeburn, Thornhill, Dumfriesshire, DG3 5JH Tel: (01387) 740338

Hutchinson & Mudd, Tower Hill, Grewelthorpe, Ripon, North Yorkshire, HG4 3DS Tel: (01765) 658580 Fax: (01765) 658580

Arthur Ibbett Ltd, River Lane, Great Paxton, St. Neots, Cambridgeshire, PE19 6RD Tel: (01480) 473452 Fax: (01480) 405026 E-mail: aibbet@lineone.net

J A Friend & Son, 35 Parkwood Road, Tavistock, Devon, PL19 0HH Tel: (01822) 613726

J Anderson, Bridge End Cottage, Ebchester, Consett, County Durham, DH8 9JA Tel: (01207) 560208

J Burroughs, Bird Lime Farm, Porton, Salisbury, SP4 0NB Tel: (01980) 611389 Fax: (01980) 611826

J C Griffiths & Son, The Green, Bronllys Road, Talgarth, Brecon, Powys, LD3 0HH Tel: (01874) 711317 Fax: (01497) 847144

J Davies & Son, Gwastod Abbot, New Inn, Pencader, Dyfed, SA39 9AZ Tel: (01559) 384886 Fax: (01559) 384814 E-mail: jdavies.pencader@btconnect.com

J H Young, West Moor, Felton, Morpeth, Northumberland, NE65 9QE Tel: (01670) 787255

J Humphrey & Son, Bleak House Farm, Allens Drove, Gorefield, Wisbech, Cambridgeshire, PE13 4PB Tel: (01945) 410644 Fax: (01945) 410644

J J Clarke & Son, Lake View, Walesby, Market Rasen, Lincolnshire, LN8 3UW Tel: (01673) 838497 Fax: (01673) 838721

J J Westaby & Partners, Cape Farm, Sheriff Hutton, York, YO60 6RT Tel: (01347) 878703 Fax: (01347) 878771 E-mail: hydrapower@mcmail.com

J Parlour & Son, South Otterington, Northallerton, North Yorkshire, DL7 9HJ Tel: (01609) 773607 Fax: (01609) 778405 E-mail: johns@jparlour.fslife.co.uk

J Rutherford Earlston Ltd, Swinton Mill Farm, Coldstream, Berwickshire, TD12 4JS Tel: (01890) 840458 Fax: (01890) 840461 E-mail: smill@rutherford-earlston.co.uk

J T Harrison, Druary, Back Lane, Holme-on-Spalding-Moor, York, YO43 4AU Tel: (01430) 860252 Fax: (01430) 860252

J W Mortimer, Horseshoe Inn, Egton, Whitby, North Yorkshire, YO21 1TZ Tel: (01947) 895520 Fax: (01947) 895520

J Wardle & Son Ltd, Boothferry Road, Howden, Goole, North Humberside, DN14 7DZ Tel: (01430) 430388 Fax: (01430) 423049

J Webber, Coles Lane Farm, Shaftesbury, Dorset, SP7 0PY Tel: (01747) 851717 Fax: (01747) 855635

J White Fabrications, South Cowton, Northallerton, North Yorkshire, DL7 0JB Tel: (01325) 378207 Fax: (01325) 378271

James Gordon Engineers Ltd, Heathhall Industrial Estate, Heathhall, Dumfries, DG1 3PH Tel: (01387) 261024 Fax: (01387) 272640 E-mail: dfsales@jgordon.co.uk

John A Seale Ltd, New Barn Offices, Quin Hay Farm, Froxfield, Petersfield, Hampshire, GU32 1BZ Tel: (01730) 827416 Fax: (01730) 827207 E-mail: info.jasealeltd@virgin.net

John W Doubleday Ltd, Jekils Bank, Holbeach, Spalding, Lincolnshire, PE12 8SQ Tel: (01406) 540344 Fax: (01406) 540262 E-mail: graham.collishaw@btclick.com

Jomac Engineering Ltd, The Airfield, Martin Moor, Metheringham, Lincoln, LN4 3BQ Tel: (01526) 378278 Fax: (01526) 378329 E-mail: sales@jomacengineering.sageweb.co.uk

Jones & Edwards Agricultural Engineers Ltd, Bausley House Farm Coedway, Crew Green, Shrewsbury, SY5 9AS Tel: (01743) 884363

K H & D Bosomworth, The Forge, Melmerby, Ripon, North Yorkshire, HG4 5HH Tel: (01765) 640270 Fax: (01765) 640880

K & M Arrowsmith, 81 West Street, Alford, Lincolnshire, LN13 9HT Tel: (01507) 463258 Fax: (01507) 462312 E-mail: steve@kandmarrowsmith.fsnet.co.uk

K W Timmins, The Cottage, Tillbridge Road, Sturton by Stow, Lincoln, LN1 2BP Tel: (01427) 788009 Fax: (01427) 787374

Ken G Lundy, 38 Annaboe Road, Portadown, Craigavon, County Armagh, BT62 4HW Tel: (028) 3887 0681 Fax: (028) 3887 0861

Keytons, Newton Road, Sudbury, Suffolk, CO10 6RN Tel: (01787) 882338

Kit Speakman, Witham Road, Little Braxted, Witham, Essex, CM8 3EU Tel: (01376) 515164 Fax: (01376) 515165 E-mail: kit@ksmltd.co.uk

L F & H F Harrison, Brandon Parva, Norwich, NR9 4DY Tel: (01603) 759281 Fax: (01603) 759420

L Parry & Sons, Gorse Hall New Farm, Promised Land Lane, Rowton, Chester, CH3 6AZ Tel: (01244) 335880 Fax: (01244) 335856

Lamberhurst Engineering Ltd, Priory Farm, Parsonage Lane, Lamberhurst, Tunbridge Wells, Kent, TN3 8DS Tel: (0845) 6121141 Fax: (0845) 6121142 E-mail: info@lameng.com

R.W. Lambert, 1 Woodlands Terrace, Threshfield, Skipton, North Yorkshire, BD23 5EU Tel: 01756 752208

Lancare Engineering Ltd, Lancare Park, Pelynt, Looe, Cornwall, PL13 2LT Tel: (01503) 220209 Fax: (01503) 220144 E-mail: ellott@lancarefarmfsnet.com

▶ Landfill Services, Lyneburn Industrial Estate, Halbeath Place, Dunfermline, Fife, KY11 4JT Tel: (01383) 739073 Fax: (01383) 739073

Leach Bros, Old Market Field Industrial Estate, Witheridge, Tiverton, Devon, EX16 8TA Tel: (01884) 861120 Fax: (01884) 860902 E-mail: leachbrothers@aol.com

Lincolnshire Motors Ltd, Windsor Road, Fairfield Industrial Estate, Louth, Lincolnshire, LN11 0LF Tel: (01507) 604061 Fax: (01507) 605609 E-mail: sales@lincsmotors.co.uk

Llansilin Tractors, Bwlch, Llansilin, Oswestry, Shropshire, SY10 7JW Tel: (01691) 791460 Fax: (01691) 791243

George Long Ltd, New Close Works, Easingwold, York, YO61 3DG Tel: (01347) 821657

Lothian Harvesters Ltd, 2c Hospital Road, Haddington, East Lothian, EH41 3BH Tel: (01620) 825738 Fax: (01620) 824224

▶ M A Engineering, Boughton Farm, Stoke Ferry, King's Lynn, Norfolk, PE33 9ST Tel: (01366) 502205

M & C (Agricultural) Ltd, Norwich Road, Swaffham, Norfolk, PE37 8DD Tel: (01760) 722607 Fax: (01760) 725435 E-mail: itaylor@mcagri.co.uk

M Davies, Tyrafon, Pentrefelin, Sennybridge, Brecon, Powys, LD3 8TU Tel: (01874) 638124 Fax: (01874) 638124

M Fairnington, A Berwick Road, Wooler, Northumberland, NE71 6AH Tel: (01668) 282027 Fax: (01668) 282439

M G Agricultural Ltd, Innage Park, Abeles Way, Holly Lane Industrial Estate, Atherstone, Warwickshire, CV9 2QX Tel: (01827) 712703 Fax: (01827) 718800

M G C Engineering Ltd, Bradfords Quay, Wadebridge, Cornwall, PL27 6DB Tel: (01208) 812585 Fax: (01208) 814066 E-mail: mgceng@tiscali.co.uk

M Honour, Mead Farm, Mead Road, Barford St. John, Banbury, Oxfordshire, OX15 0PW Tel: (01295) 721809 Fax: (01295) 721809

M J Andrew, Tamsquite House, St. Tudy, Bodmin, Cornwall, PL30 3PU Tel: (01208) 850261 Fax: (01208) 850261

M J & H M Roberts, The Smithy Bungalow, Bromyard Road, Bringsty, Worcester, WR6 5TA Tel: (01885) 482775

M J Pringle, Main Street, Radcliffe, Morpeth, Northumberland, NE65 0JB Tel: (01665) 711702 Fax: (01665) 711702

M K M Agriculture, Sun Valley Works, Woodend, Marston Moretaine, Bedford, MK43 0NJ Tel: (01234) 768889 Fax: (01234) 767935 E-mail: info@mkmagri.com

M W Partridge & Co. Ltd, 60 High Street, Hadleigh, Ipswich, IP7 5EE Tel: (01473) 822333 Fax: (01473) 828009 E-mail: sales@partridgemw.co.uk

Mac Fabrication, Tregarth Farm, Camelford, Cornwall, PL32 9TX Tel: (01840) 212234 E-mail: aaron_macleod@hotmail.com

Mccaskie Farm Supplies Ltd, 4 Munro Road, Springkerse Industrial Estate, Stirling, FK7 7UU Tel: (01786) 474481 Fax: (01786) 464099 E-mail: admin@mccaskie.co.uk

Macdonald's Engineers Ltd, 11-13 Linden Walk, Louth, Lincolnshire, LN11 9HT Tel: (01507) 603566 Fax: (01507) 603565

Major Equipment Ltd, Middleton Road, Middleton, Morecambe, Lancashire, LA3 3JJ Tel: (01524) 850501 Fax: (01524) 850502 E-mail: ukinfo@major-grasscare.com

Marrs Of Methlick, Methlick, Ellon, Aberdeenshire, AB41 7DS Tel: (01651) 806910 Fax: (01651) 806911 E-mail: marrsofmethlick@btconnect.com

N.& G. Marsh, Unit 12, Meadow Industrial Estate, Reach Road, Burwell, Cambridge, CB25 0GH Tel: (01638) 741354 Fax: (01638) 743424

Phil Masland, Coxs Yard, Taunton Road, Wellington, Somerset, TA21 9HG Tel: (01823) 666160 Fax: (01823) 666160

Masons, Cornmarket, Louth, Lincolnshire, LN11 9QD Tel: (01507) 350500 Fax: (01507) 600561 E-mail: info@patricia-williams.com

Mekanag, Shepards Grove, Stanton, Bury St. Edmunds, Suffolk, IP31 2AR Tel: (01359) 250415 Fax: (01359) 250464 E-mail: neio.smith@shelbourne.com

Meyrick & Powell Ltd, Llangenny, Llangenny, Crickhowell, Powys, NP8 1HD Tel: (01873) 812074 Fax: (01873) 812074

Mick Furniss Agricultural Engineering, Higham Fields Farm, Basin Bridge Lane, Higham-on-the-Hill, Nuneaton, Warwickshire, CV13 6ET Tel: (01455) 213124

Mill Garage, Walkington, Beverley, North Humberside, HU17 8RT Tel: (01482) 868365 Fax: (01482) 865232

Mitchell Industries Ltd, Unit 18H, Hilton Business Park, The Mease, Hilton, Derby, DE65 5JD Tel: (01283) 731100 Fax: (01283) 734309 E-mail: danny.hall@mitchell-industries.co.uk

Mole Valley Farmers Ltd, The Forge, Church Street, Witheridge, Tiverton, Devon, EX16 8AP Tel: (01884) 860478 Fax: (01884) 860769

Moore Bros, Finkle Street, Market Weighton, York, YO43 3JL Tel: (01430) 872521

Morgan Engineering, The Workshop, Grange Farm, Whittington, King's Lynn, Norfolk, PE33 9TF Tel: (01366) 500947 Fax: (01366) 501554

Morris Bufton & Co., 6 Gravel Hill, Ludlow, Shropshire, SY8 1QL Tel: (01584) 872244 Fax: (01584) 873910

Morspan Ltd, Woodside Industrial Estate, Usk, Gwent, NP15 1SS Tel: (01291) 672334 Fax: (01291) 673928 E-mail: richard@morspan.co.uk

Mountains Of Boston, Marsh Farm, Wythes Lane, Fishtoft, Boston, Lincolnshire, PE21 0RG Tel: (01205) 351054 Fax: (01205) 366004

Murch Bros (Engineers) Ltd, Bridge Works, Umberleigh, Devon, EX37 9AA Tel: (01769) 560369 Fax: (01769) 560759

Newtown Engineering, Garleigh Road, Rothbury, Morpeth, Northumberland, NE65 7RG Tel: (01669) 620755 Fax: (01669) 620478 E-mail: enqs@newtownengineering.com

Eric Norman, Mill Cottage, Newburgh, Coxwold, York, YO61 4AS Tel: (01347) 868255

O V Garland & Sons Ltd, The Forge, Dark Lane, North Wootton, Shepton Mallet, Somerset, BA4 4AQ Tel: (01749) 890288 Fax: (01749) 890288

Oakes Brothers Ltd, Fareham Road, Wickham, Fareham, Hampshire, PO17 5DH Tel: (01329) 832345 Fax: (01329) 833944

Oakes Bros Ltd, Ridgeway Works, Stanmore Road, East Ilsley, Newbury, Berkshire, RG20 7LU Tel: (01635) 281222 Fax: (01635) 281200

Oakes Brothers, Cowdown Farm, Micheldever, Winchester, Hampshire, SO21 3DN Tel: (01962) 794100 Fax: (01962) 794118

Oakley Coachbuilders, High Cross, Ware, Hertfordshire, SG11 1AD Tel: (01920) 466781 Fax: (01920) 467895 E-mail: sales@oakleyhorseboxes.co.uk

Brian Otterburn Agricultural Engineers, Danby House, High Street, Harome, York, YO62 5JE Tel: (01439) 770265 Fax: (01439) 770525 E-mail: ian@brianotterburn.force9.co.uk

P A Moston, 1 Holly House Estate, Middlewich Road, Cranage, Middlewich, Cheshire, CW10 9LT Tel: (01606) 737464 Fax: (01606) 738300

P A Turney, The Corner Unit, Gatehouse Way, Aylesbury, Buckinghamshire, HP19 8DB Tel: (01296) 398005 Fax: (01296) 433005

P A Turney Ltd, Middleton Stoney, Bicester, Oxfordshire, OX25 4AB Tel: (01869) 343333 Fax: (01869) 343540

P A Turney Ltd, Edmonds Close, Denington Industrial Estate, Wellingborough, Northamptonshire, NN8 2QY Tel: (01933) 443333 Fax: (01933) 443340

P B Engineering, Ysgyborwen Farm Bungalow, Llantrisant, Usk, Gwent, NP15 1LU Tel: (01291) 673274 Fax: (01291) 673274

P H Griffiths & Son, Birch Orchard, Bettws Newydd, Usk, Gwent, NP15 1JN Tel: (01873) 880336

P & J Smith Agricultural, Brook Farm, Redisham, Beccles, Suffolk, NR34 8NF Tel: (01986) 781505 Fax: (01986) 781505

P & P Drysdale, Darnoch Farm, Dunkeld, Perthshire, PH8 0JE Tel: (01350) 727467 Fax: (01350) 727467 E-mail: drysdale467@tiscali.co.uk

P R Salmon, Red House Farm, Station Road, Onneley, Crewe, CW3 9QQ Tel: (01782) 750255 Fax: (01782) 750255

Pat C G Wilson, Loanleven Farm, Almondbank, Perth, PH1 3NF Tel: (01738) 583370 Fax: (01738) 583546

A.P. Pavers, Britania House, Goliath Road, Coalville, Leicestershire, LE67 3FT Tel: (01530) 510980 Fax: (01530) 516890

Peacock & Binnington, High Street, Corringham, Gainsborough, Lincolnshire, DN21 5QP Tel: (01427) 838696 Fax: (01427) 838411

Richard Pearson Ltd, Priory Road, Freiston, Boston, Lincolnshire, PE22 0JZ Tel: (01205) 760383 Fax: (01205) 761064 E-mail: info@richardpearson.com

G. & J. Peck Ltd, Elsoms Way, Pinchbeck, Spalding, Lincolnshire, PE11 3JG Tel: (01775) 724343 Fax: (01775) 722073 E-mail: ssales@peck.co.uk

Pecks Agri-Trac, Wardentree Park, Pinchbeck, Spalding, Lincolnshire, PE11 3ZN Tel: (01775) 712310 Fax: (01775) 722073 E-mail: sales@peck.co.uk

Phil Light Tractors, Tipplefield Farm, Brickworth Road, Whiteparish, Salisbury, SP5 2QG Tel: (01794) 884141 Fax: (01794) 884141

Michael Pickles, Camp House Farm, Moor Road, Bramhope, Leeds, LS16 9HL Tel: 0113-284 2242

F.J. Pirie & Co. Ltd, Unit 2 Palmermount Works, Bypass Road, Dundonald, Kilmarnock, Ayrshire, KA2 9BL Tel: (01563) 850325 Fax: (01563) 851081

Player N, Caravan, Tanhouse Farm, Redstocks, Melksham, Wiltshire, SN12 6RF Tel: (01380) 828867 Fax: (01380) 828961

Price Bros, 1 Ross Road, Abergavenny, Gwent, NP7 5LT Tel: (01873) 853827 Fax: (01873) 853827

Pugh Bros, Frondeg Farm, Rhostyllen, Wrexham, Clwyd, LL14 4NB Tel: 01978 759719

Q Mac Engineering, 161 Ballymaguire Road, Stewartstown, Dungannon, County Tyrone, BT71 5NN Tel: (028) 8673 7312

Quoditch Engineering Ltd, Sycamore House, Ashwater, Beaworthy, Devon, EX21 5EF Tel: (01409) 211516

R A Mcmullen, 3a Ballyvannon Road, Ballinderry Upper, Lisburn, County Antrim, BT28 2LD Tel: (028) 9442 3133 Fax: (028) 9445 2830

R B Lyttle, 60 Station Road, Garvagh, Coleraine, County Londonderry, BT51 5LA Tel: (028) 2955 8264 Fax: (028) 2955 7043

R C Billington Farmer, Stubbins Farm, Preston, PR3 0PL Tel: (01995) 640467 Fax: (01995) 640073

R Couch, Bodwen Farm, Bodwen, Bodmin, Cornwall, PL30 4QU Tel: (01208) 72507 Fax: (01208) 851264

R D B Services, The Forge, Ockendon Road, North Ockendon, Upminster, Essex, RM14 3PS Tel: (01708) 852319 Fax: (01708) 851610

R & E Parry & Sons Agricultural Contractors, Fron Farm, Llangoed, Beaumaris, Gwynedd, LL58 8PA Tel: (01248) 490032

R G Clark & Sons, Hemnall Street, Epping, Essex, CM16 4LW Tel: (01992) 572081

R & G Lawrie, Old Philpstoun, Linlithgow, West Lothian, EH49 7RY Tel: (01506) 834205 Fax: (01506) 834205

R G Linton, 83 Edenbane Road, Garvagh, Coleraine, County Londonderry, BT51 5NA Tel: (028) 2955 8489

R H Bunner & Son Ltd, Arthur Street, Montgomery, Powys, SY15 6RA Tel: (01686) 668308 Fax: (01686) 668564 E-mail: sales@rhbunner.co.uk

R H Matthews & Sons, The Firs, Hempstead Road, Holt, Norfolk, NR25 6DQ Tel: (01263) 712239 Fax: (01263) 712239

R Lancaster & Son, 21 Bryning Lane, Wrea Green, Preston, PR4 2WJ Tel: (01772) 684222

R Palfrey & Sons, Engineering Works, Sandford, Crediton, Devon, EX17 4PN Tel: (01363) 84494 Fax: (01363) 85219

R S M Beare Stoke Canon, Coads Green, Launceston, Cornwall, PL15 7LY Tel: (01566) 782100 Fax: (01566) 782012

R T C Agricultural Ltd, Newton Hollows, Frodsham, WA6 6HY Tel: (01928) 740493 Fax: (01928) 740593 E-mail: sales@rtc-agricultural.co.uk

R Tincknell & Son Ltd, Brinsea Road, Congresbury, Bristol, BS49 5JG Tel: (01934) 832318 Fax: (01934) 834569 E-mail: sales.congresbury@tincknellag.com

R Todd, Ramshaw, Bishop Auckland, County Durham, DL14 0PE Tel: (01388) 833117

R V W Pugh Ltd, Mellington, Church Stoke, Montgomery, Powys, SY15 6TQ Tel: (01588) 620545 Fax: (01588) 620515 E-mail: rvwpugh@farmersweekly.net

R W Crawford Agricultural Machinery Ltd, 42-44 Cutlers Road, South Woodham Ferrers, Chelmsford, CM3 5XJ Tel: (01245) 322733 Fax: (01245) 322241 E-mail: sales@rwcrawford.co.uk

R W Marsh Ltd, Station Road, Brigg, South Humberside, DN20 8HX Tel: (01652) 651810 Fax: (01652) 650822 E-mail: c.rothery@rwmarsh.co.uk

R W Marsh, London Road, Sleaford, Lincolnshire, NG34 8NX Tel: (01529) 303093 Fax: (01529) 413363 E-mail: sales@rwmarsh.com

Ramsay Soil Injection Ltd, Units 2 & 3 Moorlands Trading Estate, Moor Lane, Metheringham, Lincoln, LN4 3HX Tel: (01526) 328663 Fax: (01526) 323529 E-mail: ramsay.soil@btclick.com

Ratcliffe & Son, Westport Iron Works, Foundry Road, Malmesbury, Wiltshire, SN16 0AW Tel: (01666) 823222 Fax: (01666) 823222

Ravenhill Farm Services, Beech Business Park, Tillington Road, Hereford, HR4 9QJ Tel: (01432) 352333 Fax: (01432) 278042 E-mail: hereford.sales@ravenhill.co.uk

Richards Bros, Noyadd, Cilmery, Builth Wells, Powys, LD2 3NT Tel: (01982) 552308

AGRICULTURAL ENGINEERING SERVICES – *continued*

Rickerby Ltd, Currock Road, Carlisle, CA2 4AU Tel: (01228) 527521 Fax: (01228) 533008 E-mail: martyn.henderson@rickerby.net
Rickerby Ltd, Brunswick Road, Penrith, Cumbria, CA11 7JP Tel: (01768) 863718 Fax: (01768) 899117 E-mail: sales@rickerby.net
Ringlink Scotland Ltd, 10 High Street, Laurencekirk, Kincardineshire, AB30 1AE Tel: (01561) 378231 Fax: (01561) 378231
Ripon Farm Service Ltd, Station Road, Ottringham, Hull, HU12 0BJ Tel: (01964) 622351 Fax: (01964) 624078 E-mail: ottsales@r-f-s.com
Rippon Farm Services, Dalesgate Works, Skipton Road, Cross Hills, Keighley, West Yorkshire, BD20 7BX Tel: (01535) 632661 Fax: (01535) 633752 E-mail: sales@r-f-s.com
J.M. Roberts, Ragley View, Allimore Lane, Alcester, Warwickshire, B49 5PR Tel: (01789) 762920 Fax: (01789) 762920
Robertsons Of Tain Ltd, Williamson Street, Wick, Caithness, KW1 5EU Tel: (01955) 602296 Fax: (01955) 603401 E-mail: sales@robertsonsoftain.co.uk
Robin Sharp Agricultural Engineers, The Dean, Alresford, Hampshire, SO24 9BH Tel: (01962) 734400 Fax: (01962) 734873 E-mail: robinsharp25@tiscali.co.uk
Dave Rose, 65 Horseshoe Lane, Kirton, Boston, Lincolnshire, PE20 1LW Tel: (01205) 722167 Fax: (01205) 723615
Rosewell Engineers, Stockwitch Lodge, Bridgehampton, Yeovil, Somerset, BA22 8HN Tel: (01935) 840838 Fax: (01935) 840552
S G E (Seal) Ltd, Church Street, Seal, Sevenoaks, Kent, TN15 0AT Tel: (01732) 761724 Fax: (01732) 761422 E-mail: sales@sgeseal.com
S H Coates, Selly Hill Depot, Guisborough Road, Whitby, North Yorkshire, YO21 1SG Tel: (01947) 820569
S W Brown, Topley Farm, Rushbury, Church Stretton, Shropshire, SY6 7EQ Tel: (01584) 841356 Fax: (01584) 841356
Wilfred Scruton Ltd, Providence Foundry, Foxholes, Driffield, North Humberside, YO25 3QQ Tel: (0844) 4770405 Fax: (01262) 470335 E-mail: sales@wilfredscruton.co.uk
Sellar Agricultural, Victoria Road, Maud, Peterhead, Aberdeenshire, AB42 4NL Tel: (01771) 613481 Fax: (01771) 613672
Sharmans Of Stamford, Barnack Road, Stamford, Lincolnshire, PE9 2NA Tel: (01780) 762916 Fax: (01780) 752159
T. Sherriff & Co. Ltd, West Barns, Dunbar, East Lothian, EH42 1UN Tel: (01368) 863708 Fax: (01368) 864799 E-mail: j.w.sherriff@talk21.com
Short & Abbott Ltd, Agricultural Workshop, Bridge Mill, Bridgerule, Holsworthy, Devon, EX22 7EL Tel: (01288) 381485 Fax: (01288) 381486 E-mail: gary@shortandabbott.fsnet.co.uk
Smillie & Cuthbertson Ltd, 17 James Little St, Kilmarnock, Ayrshire, KA1 4AU Tel: 01563 521819
Smithfield Tractors Builth Wells Ltd, Llanelwedd, Builth Wells, Powys, LD2 3SR Tel: (01982) 553221 Fax: (01982) 552048 E-mail: sales@smithfieldtractors.co.uk
South West Tractors Ltd, Thorne Cross Farm, Cheriton Bishop, Exeter, EX6 6HA Tel: (01647) 24007 Fax: (01647) 24107 E-mail: chris@southwesttractors.co.uk
Southam Agricultural Services, Fields Farm, Station Road, Southam, Warwickshire, CV47 2DH Tel: (01926) 813426 Fax: (01926) 817908 E-mail: sales@southamagri.co.uk
Southern Tractors, Ruthwell, Dumfries, DG1 4NZ Tel: (01387) 870216 Fax: (01387) 870306
Stalham Engineering Co. Ltd, The Green, Stalham, Norwich, NR12 9QG Tel: (01692) 580513 Fax: (01692) 581770 E-mail: mgn@stalhameng.co.uk
Stanley Charleston, Treglossack Farm, St. Keverne, Helston, Cornwall, TR12 6PS Tel: (01326) 280017 Fax: (01326) 280017
Sterma M, Reed Point, Sutterton, Boston, Lincolnshire, PE20 2EP Tel: (01205) 460418
Steven Cambage, Willow Garth, Roecliffe, York, YO51 9LY Tel: (01423) 323640
W. Stewart, 126 Irish Hill Road, Newtownabbey, Co. Antrim, BT36 5SH Tel: (028) 9083 6047
Stockshop Livestock Equipment Ltd, Lodge Trading Estate, Broadclyst Station, Exeter, EX5 3BS Tel: (01392) 460077 Fax: (01392) 460966 E-mail: nathalie.andre@stockshop.co.uk
Stubbings Bros., Chale Green, Ventnor, Isle Of Wight, PO38 2JN Tel: (01983) 551443 Fax: (01983) 551400 E-mail: sales@stubbings-bros.co.uk
Andrew Studley, Castle Lodge Farm, Llancarfan, Barry, South Glamorgan, CF62 3AW Tel: (01446) 781229
Surrey Engineering, Lambs Green, Rusper, Horsham, West Sussex, RH12 4RG Tel: (01293) 871594 Fax: (01293) 871401
T Burden, New Workshop, Wood Lane, North Wheatley, Retford, Nottinghamshire, DN22 9BQ Tel: (01427) 880094 Fax: (01427) 880094
T C Hillier, 17 High Street, Oxted, Surrey, RH8 9LW Tel: (01883) 712355 Fax: (01883) 714966
T F M Engineering, 1 Ghyll Mill, Beehive Lane, New Hutton, Kendal, Cumbria, LA8 0AJ Tel: (01539) 733881 Fax: (01539) 721616
T H Horn Ltd, Copthorne Farm, Woods Lane, Eagland Hill, Preston, PR3 6BB Tel: (01995) 600150
T H White Ltd, Newton, Thornbury, Bristol, BS35 1LG Tel: (01454) 417007 Fax: (01454) 414126
T H White Ltd, Nursteed Road, Devizes, Wiltshire, SN10 3EA Tel: (01380) 722381 Fax: (01380) 729147 E-mail: enquiries@thwhite.co.uk
T H White Ltd, Ross Road, Huntley, Gloucester, GL19 3EX Tel: (01452) 830303 Fax: (01452) 830984
T H White Ltd, Sherston Works, Knockdown, Tetbury, Gloucestershire, GL8 8QY Tel: (01454) 238181 Fax: (01454) 238772
T J Agricultural Ltd, Bridge Farm, Holt Lane, Ashby Magna, Lutterworth, Leicestershire, LE17 5NJ Tel: (01455) 202414 Fax: (01455) 202414
T M Robinson & Sons, Heads Nook, Brampton, Cumbria, CA8 9DW Tel: (01228) 670318
T S G Ltd, Rumbridge Street, Totton, Southampton, SO40 9DR Tel: (023) 8030 4300 Fax: (023) 8066 7763 E-mail: sales@tsg.com
T Wilson & Sons, The Barracks, Abbeytown, Wigton, Cumbria, CA7 4SY Tel: (01697) 361628 Fax: (01697) 361622
Taylor & Braithwaite Ltd, Dyke Nook, Sandford, Appleby-in-Westmorland, Cumbria, CA16 6NS Tel: (01768) 341400 Fax: (01768) 341488 E-mail: principal@t-and-b.co.uk
Thomas Corrie, Balmaclellan, Castle Douglas, Kirkcudbrightshire, DG7 3QE Tel: (01644) 420265
Thomas Sherriff & Co. Ltd, Wagonway Road, Alnwick, Northumberland, NE66 2NP Tel: (01665) 603555 Fax: (01665) 510558
Thomas Sherriff & Co. Ltd, Eccles Service Station, Coldstream, Berwickshire, TD12 4LX Tel: (01890) 840550
Thomas Sherriff & Co. Ltd, 150-162 Galashiels Road, Stow, Galashiels, Selkirkshire, TD1 2RA Tel: (01578) 730282 Fax: (01578) 730284
Thurlow Nunn Standen Ltd, Lisle Lane, Ely, Cambridgeshire, CB7 4AE Tel: (01353) 662871 Fax: (01353) 663480 E-mail: agsales@tnsgroup.co.uk
R. Tincknell & Son Ltd, PO Box 9, Wells, Somerset, BA5 1TQ Tel: (01749) 683150 Fax: (01749) 583160
R. Tincknell & Son Agricultural Ltd, Glastonbury Road, Wells, Somerset, BA5 1TQ Tel: (01749) 683150 Fax: (01749) 683160
John Wallis Titt & Co. Ltd, Manor Road, Frome, Somerset, BA11 4BQ Tel: (01373) 463594 Fax: (01373) 451382
Tong Engineering Ltd, Ashby Road, Spilsby, Lincolnshire, PE23 5DW Tel: (01790) 752771 Fax: (01790) 753611 E-mail: sales@tongpeal.com
D.H. Townsend & Co. Ltd, Unit 1, St Andrews Industrial Estate, Bridport, Dorset, DT6 3DL Tel: (01308) 423305 Fax: (01308) 427913 E-mail: dhtownsendeng@aol.com
Tripp Batt & Co. Ltd, Hepworth Road, Stanton, Bury St. Edmunds, Suffolk, IP31 2BT Tel: (01359) 250268 Fax: (01359) 251603
Truro Tractors Ltd, Treburley, Launceston, Cornwall, PL15 9PU Tel: (01579) 371133 Fax: (01579) 371010
Tullibaridine, Castleton Road, Auchterarder, Perthshire, PH3 1JS Tel: (01764) 662696 Fax: (01764) 662011
Upton Farm Services, Tewkesbury Road, Upton-Upon-Severn, Worcester, WR8 0PU Tel: (01684) 591071
Vaughan Agri, Yellowham Wood, Dorchester, Dorset, DT2 8FA Tel: (01305) 849000 Fax: (01305) 849222
W A Daw & Son, Hans Farm, Ruckinge, Ashford, Kent, TN26 2PX Tel: (01233) 732311
W E Scorgie & Son, Balrownie Smithy, Menmuir, Brechin, Angus, DD9 7RG Tel: (01356) 660229 Fax: (01356) 660229
W G Banham & Sons, Springlea, Half Moon Lane, Redgrave, Diss, Norfolk, IP22 1RU Tel: (01379) 898438 Fax: (01379) 898438
W J Brown Agricultural Services Ltd, Dunecht, Westhill, Aberdeenshire, AB32 7BS Tel: (01330) 860870 Fax: (01330) 860870
W J Shields & Sons, Hall Farm, Main Street, Shipton by Beningbrough, York, YO30 1AA Tel: (01904) 470263 Fax: (01904) 471872
W & W H Pettit, Lawnswood Cowbit Road, Spalding, Lincolnshire, PE12 6AA Tel: (01775) 723411 Fax: (01775) 713064
Waen Agricultural Sales, Waen, Llanbedr Dyffryn Clwyd, Ruthin, Clwyd, LL15 1SR Tel: (01824) 705571 Fax: (01824) 705243 E-mail: lindadyer@waenagriculturalsales.fsnet.co.uk
Mark Weatherhead Ltd, Helions Road, Steeple Bumpstead, Haverhill, Suffolk, CB9 7DU Tel: (01440) 730377 Fax: (01440) 730777
Mark Weatherhead Ltd, Garden Walk, Royston, Hertfordshire, SG8 7HT Tel: (01763) 242361 Fax: (01763) 245106
T.H. White Ltd, London Road, Marlborough, Wiltshire, SN8 2RN Tel: 01672 512328
▶ Whites Of Skendleby, 1, Fordington Water Works, Fordington, Alford, Lincs, LN13 0HQ Tel: (01790) 753904 Fax: (01790) 752565
Whites Of Skendleby, Skendleby, Spilsby, Lincolnshire, PE23 4QE Tel: (07774) 658100 Fax: (01754) 890270 E-mail: diggerdjw@aol.com
Wilks Bros, Murthly, Perth, PH1 4HG Tel: (01738) 710381 Fax: (01738) 710581
Willow Agricultural Engineers, Willow Farm, Newchurch, Romney Marsh, Kent, TN29 0DY Tel: (01303) 874490 Fax: (01303) 874763
P. Withers Agricultural, Moat End Farm House, Hindlip Lane, Clains, Worcester, WR3 8SA Tel: (01905) 458159
J. Wood & Son Ltd, Kirkby Mills Industrial Estate, Kirby Mills, Kirkbymoorside, York, YO62 6NL Tel: (01751) 433434 Fax: (01751) 433094 E-mail: sales@johnwoods.co.uk
J. Wood & Son, 24 Dove Way, Kerkby Mills Industrial Estate, Kirkby Morside, York, YO62 6QR Tel: (01751) 433434 Fax: (01751) 433094 E-mail: admin@johnwoods.co.uk
Trevor Woodliffe, Treveen House, Meltonby, York, YO42 1PN Tel: (01759) 304202 Fax: (01759) 304202
Woods Engineering, Dunn Farm, Littleham, Bideford, Devon, EX39 5HR Tel: (01237) 473338 Fax: (01237) 473338
Wye Valley Tractors Ltd, Tanyard Lane, Ross-on-Wye, Herefordshire, HR9 7BH Tel: (01989) 562486 Fax: (01989) 566030 E-mail: wvt1@aol.com
Yorkshire Handlers Ltd, Unit 3 Fryors Close, Murton, York, YO19 5UY Tel: (01904) 489988 Fax: (01904) 489061 E-mail: sales@yorkshirehandlers.co.uk
Alistair Young Engineering Ltd, The Engineering Works, Dunphail, Forres, Morayshire, IV36 2QQ Tel: (01309) 611335 Fax: (01309) 611369 E-mail: sale@youngengineering.co.uk
R.H. Young, The Sheiling, The Camps, Kirknewton, Midlothian, EH27 8DN Tel: (01506) 880413 Fax: (01506) 881253

AGRICULTURAL EQUIPMENT ACCESSORIES

▶ Brice-Baker Group, Rookery Road, The Lane, Wyboston, Bedford, MK44 3AX Tel: (01480) 216618 Fax: (01480) 406226 E-mail: info@bricebaker.co.uk
McConnel Ltd, Temeside Works, Ludlow, Shropshire, SY8 1JL Tel: (01584) 873131 Fax: (01584) 876463 E-mail: sales@mcconnel.com

AGRICULTURAL EQUIPMENT LUBRICANTS

C P L Petroleum Ltd, Prince Regent Way, Diss, Norfolk, IP22 4GW Tel: (01379) 652235 Fax: (01379) 643529 E-mail: diss@cplpetroleum.co.uk
Danoil Ltd, 94 Owl Lane, Ossett, West Yorkshire, WF5 9AU Tel: (01924) 263128 Fax: (01924) 264078
Q8 Fuel Care, Estuary Road, King's Lynn, Norfolk, PE30 2HH Tel: (01553) 614800 Fax: (01553) 614835 E-mail: enquiries@q8fuelcare.co.uk
Q8 Fuels Care, 10 Midurst Road, Fernhurst, Haslemere, Surrey, GU27 3EE Tel: (01428) 652218 Fax: (01428) 652250
Total Butler Ltd, Sandy Lane, Sudbury, Suffolk, CO10 7HL Tel: (01787) 371511 Fax: (01787) 370780
Total Butler, Haybrook, Halesfield 9, Telford, Shropshire, TF7 4QW Tel: (01952) 680168 Fax: (01952) 588351

AGRICULTURAL EQUIPMENT WHEELS

D & S Factors Ltd, 1 Pinder Lane, Donington, Spalding, Lincolnshire, PE11 4SN Tel: (01775) 820309 Fax: (01775) 821263 E-mail: dsfactor@globalnet.co.uk
Fieldens plc, Star House, Onehouse, Stowmarket, Suffolk, IP14 3EL Tel: (01449) 675071 Fax: (01449) 678282 E-mail: sales@fieldens.co.uk
R G Carey, Mill Lane, Hooe, Battle, East Sussex, TN33 9HS Tel: (01424) 892051 Fax: (01424) 892051
Titan Distribution (UK) Ltd, North Florida Road, Haydock Industrial Estate, St. Helens, Merseyside, WA11 9UB Tel: (01942) 715333 Fax: (01942) 715111 E-mail: enquiries@titandistributionuk.com

AGRICULTURAL ESTATE AGENTS

▶ Croft Sales, East Durran, Castletown, Thurso, Caithness, KW14 8TE Tel: (01847) 821405 Fax: (01847) 821153 E-mail: jim@jimmacmillan.co.uk
New Forest Estate Agents, New Forest Estate Agents, PO Box 5561, Ringwood, Hampshire, BH24 2ZS Tel: 08700 11 68 55 E-mail: info@NewForestEstateAgents.com
▶ The New Forest Estate Agents, PO Box 5561, Ringwood, Hampshire, BH24 2ZS Tel: 08700 11 45 75 Fax: 08700 11 45 76 E-mail: info@NewForestEstateAgents.com

AGRICULTURAL FABRICATION OR SHEET METALWORK

A G Lester & Sons Ltd, Unit 1 Erskine Street, Birmingham, B7 4RU Tel: 0121-359 1018 Fax: 0121-359 1018 E-mail: info@aglesterandsons.sagenet.co.uk
G.E. Baker (UK) Ltd, Heath Road, Woolpit, Bury St. Edmunds, Suffolk, IP30 9RN Tel: (01359) 240529 Fax: (01359) 242086 E-mail: baker@quality-equipment.co.uk
Butt Bros, Charlton Musgrove, Wincanton, Somerset, BA9 8HP Tel: (01963) 31771
▶ D M S Stainless Fabrications Ltd, 1 St Peters Works, St Peters Road, Maidenhead, Berkshire, SL6 7QU Tel: (01628) 777391 Fax: (01628) 777396 E-mail: sales@dmslaserprofiles.co.uk
Harry Dalby Engineering Incoporating Dalby Sheetmetal, Gloucester Crescent, Wigston, Leicestershire, LE18 4YQ Tel: 0116-291 6000 Fax: 0116-291 6001 E-mail: enquiries@dalby.co.uk
▶ Fab Tech Automotive Ltd, Unit 5-6 Lichfield Trading Estate, Lagrange, Tamworth, Staffordshire, B79 7XD Tel: (01827) 66602 Fax: (01827) 66168 E-mail: sales@fabtechauto.co.uk
G R Owen & Son, Gilfach Yard, Chwilog, Pwllheli, Gwynedd, LL53 6SL Tel: (01766) 810320 Fax: (01766) 810320
▶ Investment Castings Ltd, 130 Great North Road, Birchwood Industrial Estate, Hatfield, Hertfordshire, AL9 5JN Tel: (01707) 262871 Fax: (01707) 271565 E-mail: investmentcastings130@yahoo.co.uk
Knee Agricultural Machinery, Ashton Mills, West Ashton Road, Trowbridge, Wiltshire, BA14 7BB Tel: (01225) 753894 Fax: (01225) 762208 E-mail: info@kamengineering.co.uk
Laserit Ltd, Unit 26 Beeches Industrial Estate, Lavenham Road, Yate, Bristol, BS37 5QX Tel: (01454) 318585 Fax: (01454) 318541 E-mail: sales@laserit.co.uk
Melhuish & Bateman Ltd, 5 Flowers Hill Close, Bristol, BS4 5LF Tel: 0117-977 1450 Fax: 0117-971 7388 E-mail: melhuishbateman@aol.com
Moughton Engineering Services, Units 12-13, Faraday Road, Great Yarmouth, Norfolk, NR31 0NF Tel: (01493) 650195 Fax: (01493) 650199
▶ Perlam Sheet Metal Work, Wandle Trading Estate, Mill Green Road, Mitcham, Surrey, CR4 4HZ Tel: (020) 8685 9276 Fax: (020) 8640 0551 E-mail: sales@perlamsheetmetal.co.uk
▶ Raybrook Sheet Metal Works Ltd, 9 Towerfield Close, Shoeburyness, Southend-on-Sea, SS3 9QP Tel: (01702) 293208 Fax: (01702) 297628 E-mail: info@raybrook.com
▶ Rilmac Fabrication Ltd, Crofton Drive, Allenby Road Industrial Estate, Lincoln, LN3 4NJ Tel: (01522) 531711 Fax: (01522) 510291 E-mail: enquiries@rilmac.co.uk
Unit Construction, 41 Cardinal Close, Tonbridge, Kent, TN9 2EN Tel: (01732) 355250 Fax: (01892) 355984

AGRICULTURAL FARM CONSTRUCTORS

Agritask Construction Ltd, Tanhouse Farm, Rusper Road, Newdigate, Dorking, Surrey, RH5 5BX Tel: (01306) 631334 Fax: (01306) 631891 E-mail: info@agritask.co.uk
Alec Williams, Forden, Welshpool, Powys, SY21 8TS Tel: (01938) 580329 Fax: (01938) 580329
B C Agricultural Services, 26 Corsend Road, Hartpury, Gloucester, GL19 3BP Tel: (01452) 700521 Fax: (01452) 700521 E-mail: bcagricultural@btconnect.com
Bentley Contracts, Brook Farm, Thorrington Road, Great Bentley, Colchester, CO7 8QP Tel: (01206) 250213
C J & B Parr & Sons, Mill Farm, Pilham Lane, Corringham, Gainsborough, Lincolnshire, DN21 5RB Tel: (01427) 838253 Fax: (01427) 838253
Cook Contracting, Ednam West Mill, Ednam, Kelso, Roxburghshire, TD5 7QL Tel: (01573) 223840 Fax: (01573) 224995
D M Adams, Coombe Farm, Llanvair Discoed, Chepstow, Gwent, NP16 6LN Tel: (01291) 641792 Fax: (01291) 641792
Edwards & Farmer Ltd, Chatford, Bayston Hill, Shrewsbury, SY3 0AY Tel: (01743) 658669 Fax: (01743) 718126
F C Garlick & Sons, Garway Hill, Hereford, HR2 8RT Tel: (01981) 580365 Fax: (01981) 580365
Family Farm Development Ltd, Milestone Centre Termon Business Park Quarry Road, Sixmilecross, Omagh, County Tyrone, BT79 9AL Tel: (028) 8076 1719 Fax: (028) 8076 1779 E-mail: familyfarm@btconnect.com
Fenland Shops Ltd, Jubilee Garage, Abbey Road, Bourne, Lincolnshire, PE10 9EF Tel: (01778) 423041 Fax: (01778) 423041
G & O D Thomas & Sons, Castle Road, Richards Castle, Ludlow, Shropshire, SY8 4EW Tel: (01584) 831244 Fax: (01584) 831382
H Raley & Sons, Hill Farm, Escrick Road, Stillingfleet, York, YO19 6HT Tel: (01904) 728665 Fax: (01904) 728665
Harts Farm Enterprises, Highgrove Farm House, Main Road, Bosham, Chichester, West Sussex, PO18 8EH Tel: (01243) 573232
J A & F Bullock Saddlery, North Moor, Easingwold, York, YO61 3NB Tel: (01347) 823430 Fax: (01347) 823430
J B Browning & Son, 32 Boultons Lane, Redditch, Worcestershire, B97 5NY Tel: (01527) 543116
J G Paxton & Sons Ltd, Roman Road, Brandon, Durham, DH7 8UF Tel: (01609) 783331 Fax: (01609) 783332 E-mail: northallerton@paxtons.co.uk

AGRICULTURAL FARM CONSTRUCTORS – *continued*

J Keeling & Sons, Church Road, Ramsden Bellhouse, Billericay, Essex, CM11 1RH Tel: (01268) 733037 Fax: (01268) 572835

J & M Bodman, Cuckoo Corner, Urchfont, Devizes, Wiltshire, SN10 4RA Tel: (01380) 840273 Fax: (01380) 840126

J R Marshall Farmer, Lower Mead Farm, Newton Abbot, Devon, TQ13 7LJ Tel: (01364) 652466 Fax: 01364 652466

J T Simkins & Son, Chapel Farm, Chapel Road, Meppershall, Shefford, Bedfordshire, SG17 5NG Tel: (01462) 813330

Jaques International, Orchard End, Shobdon, Leominster, Herefordshire, HR6 9NE Tel: (01568) 708644 Fax: (01568) 708166 E-mail: sales@jacquesint.com

W.I.S. Jones, Birds Hill Factory, Llandeilo, Dyfed, SA19 6SG Tel: 01558 822691

L R & Sons, Laindon Common Road, Little Burstead, Billericay, Essex, CM12 9SY Tel: (01277) 652381 Fax: (01277) 652381 E-mail: lrandsons@aol.com

Lillechurch Farms & Contracting Ltd, Lillechurch Road, Higham, Rochester, Kent, ME3 7HW Tel: (01634) 222332 Fax: (01634) 222344

Lock Bros, Rouses Farm, Calves Lane, Stoke By Nayland, Colchester, CO6 4RR Tel: (01206) 262340

▶ M G Sutton, Grendon House Farm, Warton Lane, Grendon, Atherstone, Warwickshire, CV9 3DT Tel: (01827) 892295 Fax: (01827) 892432 E-mail: lee.sutton@btinternet.com

M & M Ducksbury, 95 Newcastle Street, Tuxford, Newark, Nottinghamshire, NG22 0LN Tel: (01777) 870289 Fax: (01777) 872932

Moor 'N Dales, Chop Gate, Middlesbrough, Cleveland, TS9 7JB Tel: (01642) 778203

N M Farley & Sons, Gaddon Spring Farm, Uffculme, Cullompton, Devon, EX15 3DL Tel: (01884) 840402 Fax: (01884) 840402

J. Norman & Son, Riverside & Leigh Farm, Exton, Dulverton, Somerset, TA22 9LD Tel: (01643) 851385 Fax: (01643) 851385

P J Gerring, Home Farm, Buckland, Faringdon, Oxfordshire, SN7 8RG Tel: (01367) 870245 Fax: (01367) 870245 E-mail: peter.gerring@btconnect.com

Clifford Pye Ltd, Lomond, Holt Road, Cawston, Norwich, NR10 4HS Tel: (01603) 871213 Fax: (01603) 871713 E-mail: cyeltdcawston@farming.co.uk

R A Newman & Sons, Indemnifying Farm, Chastleton, Moreton-in-Marsh, Gloucestershire, GL56 0SP Tel: (01608) 674288 Fax: (01608) 674573

R F Roberts, Selattyn, Oswestry, Shropshire, SY10 7DY Tel: (01691) 659716 Fax: (01691) 650129

S & J Kidson, 7 Ingramgate, Thirsk, North Yorkshire, YO7 1DF Tel: (01845) 524610

R.J. Sparks, 2 Winfield Gro, Newdigate, Dorking, Surrey, RH5 5AZ Tel: 01306 631256

W J Higgins & Son, Middlegate Farm, Pitney, Langport, Somerset, TA10 9AQ Tel: (01458) 250475 Fax: (01458) 251010

AGRICULTURAL GATES

B F T Northern, Units 14-16, Bassington Industrial Estate, Cramlington, Northumberland, NE23 8AD Tel: (01670) 737645 Fax: (01670) 736558

Curtis & Shaw, Cowbeech, Hailsham, East Sussex, BN27 4JE Tel: (01323) 833441 Fax: (01323) 833072 E-mail: sales@curtisandshaw.co.uk

D & E Fabrications Ltd, Latteridge Road, Iron Acton, Bristol, BS37 9TL Tel: (01454) 228810 Fax: (01454) 228810

Golden Soney Agri Fencing, The Gables, Golden Soney, Tockholes, Darwen, Lancashire, BB3 0NL Tel: (01254) 773648

Hazelwood Products Wattle Hurdles, Golden Dell, Golden Dell, Herriard, Basingstoke, Hants, RG25 2PE Tel: (01256) 381266

Mount Trading Co. Ltd, Glan Yr Afon Industrial Estate, Llanbadarn Fawr, Aberystwyth, Dyfed, SY23 3JQ Tel: (01970) 611919 Fax: (01970) 627062

Suffolk Gate Co., Bridge Farm, Rushbrooke, Bury St. Edmunds, Suffolk, IP30 0BP Tel: (01284) 388399 Fax: (01284) 388400 E-mail: sales@suffolkgatecompany.co.uk

Tarporley Gates, Moorcroft, Clotton, Tarporley, Cheshire, CW6 0EG Tel: (01829) 781444

AGRICULTURAL GLOBAL POSITIONING SYSTEMS (GPS)

▶ GPS4Less, The Chimneys, Dauntsey Lock, Chippenham, Wiltshire, SN15 4HD Tel: (0845) 4309207 Fax: (0845) 4309208 E-mail: sales@gps4less.co.uk

▶ Precise Solutions, Cote House, Wetheral, Carlisle, CA4 8HZ Tel: (01228) 562234 Fax: (01228) 501912 E-mail: derekjohnston@precise-solutions.co.uk

AGRICULTURAL HAND IMPLEMENTS

A Morris & Sons Ltd, The Iron Mills, Dunsford, Exeter, EX6 7EE Tel: (01647) 252352

Ralph Martindale & Co. Ltd, Strawberry Lane, Willenhall, West Midlands, WV13 3RS Tel: (01902) 826826 Fax: (01902) 826827 E-mail: crocodile@ralphmartindale.co.uk

Rawral Engineering, The Roost, Three Gates Rd, Fawkham, Longfield, Kent, DA3 8NZ Tel: 01474 704238 Fax: 01474 704238

AGRICULTURAL INDUSTRY PUBLIC RELATIONS

Amcort Ltd, Field House, McMichaels Way, Hurst Green, Etchingham, East Sussex, TN19 7HJ Tel: (01580) 860500 Fax: (01580) 860171 E-mail: info@amcort.com

▶ Chrome Consulting Ltd, 26 Fitzroy Square, London, W1T 6BT Tel: 020 7323 1610 E-mail: enquiries@chromeconsulting.com

AGRICULTURAL INFORMATION OR RESEARCH ORGANISATIONS

British Institute of Agricultural Consultants, Estate Office, Torry Hill, Milstead, Sittingbourne, Kent, ME9 0SP Tel: (01795) 830100 Fax: (01795) 830243 E-mail: info@biac.co.uk

Burkard Scientific (Sales) Ltd, PO Box 55, Uxbridge, Middlesex, UB8 2RT Tel: (01895) 230056 Fax: (01895) 230058 E-mail: sales@burkardscientific.co.uk

National Institute Of Agricultural Botany, Folley Hill, Itchen Stoke, Alresford, Hampshire, SO24 9TF Tel: (01962) 779521 Fax: (01962) 779543

Tekpro Ltd, Laundry Loke, North Walsham, Norfolk, NR28 0BD Tel: (01692) 403403 Fax: (01692) 404955 E-mail: sales@catchpole.co.uk

U L G Northumbrian Ltd, Gables House, 62 Kenilworth Road, Leamington Spa, Warwickshire, CV32 6JX Tel: (01926) 452464 Fax: (01926) 452465 E-mail: ulg@ulg.co.uk

AGRICULTURAL LABORATORY/ FIELD INSTRUMENTS

▶ Rhys International, Unit 41 42 Halliwell Industrial Estate, Rossini Street, Bolton, BL1 8DL Tel: (01204) 848430 Fax: (01294) 848431 E-mail: info@rhysinternational.co.uk

AGRICULTURAL LIME

John Bourne & Co. Ltd, Rye Road, Newenden, Cranbrook, Kent, TN18 5QG Tel: (01797) 252298 Fax: (01797) 253115 E-mail: enquiries@bourne.uk.com

Longcliffe Quarries Ltd, Longcliffe, Brassington, Matlock, Derbyshire, DE4 4BZ Tel: (01629) 540284 Fax: (01629) 540569 E-mail: sales@longcliffe.co.uk

Tarff Valley Ltd, Main Street, Glenluce, Newton Stewart, Wigtownshire, DG8 0PL Tel: (01581) 300555 Fax: (01581) 300553

West Norfolk Superlime Co. Ltd, Station Road, Hillington, King's Lynn, Norfolk, PE31 6DG Tel: (01485) 600269 Fax: (01485) 609622 E-mail: info@westnorfolk.com

Yorkshire Roadstone Lightwater Quarrys Ltd, Potgate Quarry, North Stainley, Ripon, North Yorkshire, HG4 3JN Tel: (01765) 635435 Fax: (01765) 635413

AGRICULTURAL LIVESTOCK TRAILERS

▶ Dawson's Trailers, Sunny-Vale, Far Westhouse, Ingleton, Carnforth, Lancashire, LA6 3NR Tel: (01524) 241372 E-mail: sydney@dawsonstrailers.f9.co.uk

▶ New Forest Horse Boxes Ltd, Peartree Cottage, Arnewood Bridge Road, Sway, Lymington, Hampshire, SO41 6ER Tel: (01590) 682633 Fax: (01590) 683497 E-mail: sales@newforesthorseboxes.co.uk

AGRICULTURAL MACHINERY COUPLING SYSTEMS

Agricultural Machinery & Repairs, Station Yard, Bootle Station, Bootle, Millom, Cumbria, LA19 5XB Tel: (01229) 718364

Burdens Group, Main Road, Old Leake, Boston, Lincolnshire, PE22 9AT Tel: (01205) 870011 Fax: (01205) 871252

Earnvale Tractors Ltd, Townhead, Balbeggie, Perth, PH2 6ET Tel: (01821) 640444 Fax: (01821) 640525 E-mail: earnvale.tractors@btinternet.com

F S Foot & Son, Fourways Farm, Northbrook, Micheldever, Winchester, Hampshire, SO21 3AH Tel: (01962) 774209 Fax: (01962) 774796

Global Recycling Solutions Ltd, Unit 2, Cook House, Brunel Drive, Newark, Nottinghamshire, NG24 2FB Tel: (0870) 7708540 Fax: (0870) 7708541 E-mail: sales@globalrecycling.eu

J T Pegg & Sons Ltd, The Garage, Bigsbys Corner, Saxmundham, Suffolk, IP17 1RP Tel: (01728) 604668 Fax: (01728) 604120

R Mcateer, 7 Tullaghmore Road, Coalisland, Dungannon, County Tyrone, BT71 4PN Tel: (028) 8774 0504 Fax: (028) 8774 0504

R W Marsh Ltd, The Forge, Markham Moor, Retford, Nottinghamshire, DN22 0QU Tel: (01777) 838888 Fax: (01777) 838000

AGRICULTURAL MACHINERY SPARE PARTS AND WEARING PARTS

A J S Machine Sales & Spares Ltd, 22 Exeter Road, Urmston, Manchester, M41 0RE Tel: 0161-747 7436 Fax: 0161-718 0952

A M Phillip Trucktech, Muiryfaulds, Forfar, Angus, DD8 1XP Tel: (01307) 820255 Fax: (01307) 820417 E-mail: agritech@amphillip.co.uk

A T Oliver & Sons Ltd, Wandon End Works, Wandon End, Luton, LU2 8NY Tel: (01582) 727111 Fax: (01582) 729763 E-mail: ato@atoliver.co.uk

AE Carbide Ltd, Cheltenham, GL53 8RA Tel: (01242) 539707 E-mail: a.emberson@btinternet.com

Agricultural Machinery Nantwich Ltd, Millstone Lane, Nantwich, Cheshire, CW5 5PJ Tel: (01270) 624141 Fax: (01270) 624140 E-mail: sales@ag-mac.co.uk

Agriservices, Unit N3 Blackpole Trading Estate East, Blackpole Road, Worcester, WR3 8SG Tel: (01905) 754929 Fax: (01905) 754929 E-mail: agriservices@bitsmail.co.uk

Agrispares, 116 Haven Road, Haverfordwest, Dyfed, SA61 1DP Tel: (01437) 764863

Agrispares, 62 Gortin Road, Omagh, County Tyrone, BT79 7HT Tel: (028) 8224 3793 Fax: (028) 8224 6050

Alexander & Duncan Ltd, Southern Avenue, Leominster, Herefordshire, HR6 0QB Tel: (01568) 613434 Fax: (01568) 613736 E-mail: simon@alexanderandduncan.co.uk

Beeversales Components Ltd, Aurillac Way, Retford, Nottinghamshire, DN22 7PX Tel: (01777) 700611 Fax: (01777) 701799 E-mail: sales@beeversales.com

Bepco UK Ltd, Unit 2, Hatton Gardens Industrial Estate, Kington, Herefordshire, HR5 3RB Tel: (01544) 231144 Fax: (01544) 231484 E-mail: jbrett@bepco.co.uk

Broomhill Agricultural Spares, BA Country Store, Lyne Of Skene, Dunecht, Westhill, Aberdeenshire, AB32 7DA Tel: (01330) 860840 Fax: (01330) 860841

C E Davis Marshfield Ltd, 94 High Street, Marshfield, Chippenham, Wiltshire, SN14 8LS Tel: (01225) 891444 Fax: (01225) 891910

Carpenter Goodwin Ltd, 31 Bridge Street, Leominster, Herefordshire, HR6 8DU Tel: (01568) 616266 Fax: (01568) 616276 E-mail: sales@carpentergoodwin.co.uk

D & P D Upton, Park Farm, Six Hills Road, Six Hills, Melton Mowbray, Leicestershire, LE14 3PR Tel: (01509) 880284 Fax: (01509) 889222 E-mail: roy@sixhills.freeserve.co.uk

E G Coles & Son, Station Yard, Station Road, Semley, Shaftesbury, Dorset, SP7 9AN Tel: (01747) 854777 Fax: (01747) 855610 E-mail: sales@candotractors.co.uk

Patrick Edwards, Langley Farm, Langley Lane, Little Clanfield, Bampton, Oxfordshire, OX18 2RZ Tel: (01367) 810259 Fax: (01367) 810545

Essex Tractor Co. Ltd, Birchwood Road, Cock Clarks, Chelmsford, CM3 6RF Tel: (01621) 828880 Fax: (01621) 828944 E-mail: sales@tractor.net

Flails Direct Ltd, Marsh Lane, Laughterton, Lincoln, LN1 2JX Tel: (01427) 717449 Fax: (01427) 718016 E-mail: eng-hire@dial.pipex.com

Griff Chains Ltd, Quarry Road, Dudley Wood, Dudley, West Midlands, DY2 0ED Tel: (01384) 569415 Fax: (01384) 410580 E-mail: sales@griffchains.co.uk

Holmwood Tractors, Norfolk Garage, Horsham Road, Holmwood, Dorking, Surrey, RH5 4ER Tel: (01306) 888627

Kramp UK Ltd, Station Business Park, London Road, Biggleswade, Bedfordshire, SG18 8QB Tel: (01767) 602602 Fax: (01767) 602620 E-mail: info.agri.uk@kramp.com

M & C (Agricultural) Ltd, Norwich Road, Swaffham, Norfolk, PE37 8DD Tel: (01760) 722607 Fax: (01760) 725435 E-mail: itaylor@mcagri.co.uk

Marshall Farm Machinery, Rugby Road, Leicester, LE9 7TB Tel: (01788) 832300 Fax: (01455) 888179 E-mail: sales@marshallfarmmachinery.co.uk

▶ Geoff Matthews Engineers, Unit 17 Pavilion Workshops, Holmewood Industrial Park, Park Road, Holmewood, Chesterfield, Derbyshire, S42 5UY Tel: (01246) 851118 Fax: (01246) 855502 E-mail: enquiries@gmengineers.co.uk

Payne & Pool, 15c Deverill Road Trading Est, Deverill Rd, Sutton Veny, Warminster, Wilts, BA12 7BZ Tel: 01985 840912

Stephen Peachey Agricultural Engineering, Highwood Farm, Main Road, Rookley, Ventnor, Isle Of Wight, PO38 3NH Tel: (01983) 721333 Fax: (01983) 721588

R C F Bolt & Nut Co. Ltd, Park Lane East, Tipton, West Midlands, DY4 8RF Tel: 0121-522 2353 Fax: 0121-522 2304 E-mail: rcf@dial.pipex.com

▶ Ranell Ltd, Unit 7a Beckingham Business Park, Tolleshunt Major, Maldon, Essex, CM9 8LZ Tel: (01621) 869048 Fax: (01621) 868978 E-mail: info@ranell.com

RNG Agdrive Ltd, Unit 5-6 Linton Trading Estate, Worcester Road, Bromyard, Herefordshire, HR7 4QT Tel: (01885) 483662 Fax: (01885) 482080 E-mail: rng@eur-ist.co.uk

Southam Agricultural Services, Fields Farm, Station Road, Southam, Warwickshire, CV47 2DH Tel: (01926) 813426 Fax: (01926) 817908 E-mail: sales@southamagri.co.uk

Spaldings Trustees Ltd, 25-35 Sadler Road, Lincoln, LN6 3XJ Tel: (01522) 500600 Fax: (01522) 509300 E-mail: sales@spaldings.co.uk

Sparex Agricultural Machinery, 56 Seskanore Road, Omagh, County Tyrone, BT78 1RW Tel: (028) 8225 2565 Fax: (028) 8225 2946 E-mail: inpost@sparex.co.uk

▶ Tim Gittoes, Station Yard, Llandrindod Wells, Powys, LD1 5BE Tel: (01597) 823255

W E Wilde & Co. Ltd, Unit 12 Cropper Row, Alton Road, Ross-on-Wye, Herefordshire, HR9 5LA Tel: (01989) 565100 Fax: (01989) 764326 E-mail: wilde.coltd@virgin.net

Wye Valley Tractors Ltd, Tanyard Lane, Ross-on-Wye, Herefordshire, HR9 7BH Tel: (01989) 562486 Fax: (01989) 566030 E-mail: wvt1@aol.com

AGRICULTURAL MACHINERY/ EQUIPMENT/IMPLEMENT HIRE

Agri - Hire Ltd, Fidgeons Farm, Bullen Lane, Bramford, Ipswich, IP8 4JJ Tel: (01473) 744088 Fax: (01473) 240740 E-mail: agrihire@agrihire.co.uk

Alexander & Duncan Ltd, Southern Avenue, Leominster, Herefordshire, HR6 0QB Tel: (01568) 613434 Fax: (01568) 613736 E-mail: simon@alexanderandduncan.co.uk

B W Services Ltd, St. James Road, Goffs Oak, Waltham Cross, Hertfordshire, EN7 6TR Tel: (01707) 872099 Fax: (01707) 876440 E-mail: pwservices@btinternet.com

Bradley D.B.& D.K Farmers, Thelbridge Hall, Witheridge, Tiverton, Devon, EX16 8NZ Tel: (01884) 860226

Bucket & Grab Handling Ltd, Bevington Farm, Belchamp Otten, Sudbury, Suffolk, CO10 7BE Tel: (01787) 278781 Fax: (01787) 278783

Class (UK) Ltd, 9 Harvest Road, Newbridge, Midlothian, EH28 8PN Tel: 0131-333 3237 Fax: 0131-333 4845

G A Robson & Son, Carlton Husthwaite, Thirsk, North Yorkshire, YO7 2BP Tel: (01845) 501581 Fax: (01845) 501520 E-mail: tim.robson@fwi.co.uk

Haynes Agricultural Kent Ltd, Mill Lane, Eastry, Sandwich, Kent, CT13 0JS Tel: (01304) 611112 Fax: (01304) 619006 E-mail: sales@rpv.org.uk

Hayward United Farmers Ltd, Benacre Road, Ellough, Beccles, Suffolk, NR34 7XD Tel: (01502) 475111 Fax: (01502) 476533 E-mail: steve@hufl.co.uk

▶ J Henry & Son, Shinny Road, Macosquin, Coleraine, County Londonderry, BT51 4PS Tel: (028) 7086 8505 Fax: (028) 7086 8811 E-mail: slles@agriplant.co.uk

James R Georgeson, Guidibest, Latheron, Caithness, KW5 6DQ Tel: (01593) 741300 Fax: (01593) 741300

Kennet Croft Contractors, Islandstone Lane, Hurst, Reading, RG10 0RJ Tel: 0118-934 1921 Fax: (01889) 344305

R C Boreham & Co., Woodfield Farm, Pleshey, Chelmsford, CM3 1HU Tel: (01245) 231320 Fax: (01245) 231435 E-mail: sales@rcboreham.co.uk

R L Smith & Sons Ltd, Herriot Bank Farm, Whitsome, Duns, Berwickshire, TD11 3NB Tel: (01890) 870241 Fax: (01890) 870369 E-mail: sales@rlsmithandsons.co.uk

S & J Webster, Spring Farm, Chellaston, Derby, DE73 6UE Tel: (01332) 700255 Fax: (01332) 690511

South Anglia Marketing Co. Ltd, Eastlodge, 110 Dunmow Road, Bishop's Stortford, Hertfordshire, CM23 5HN Tel: (01279) 656523 Fax: (01279) 653179 E-mail: enquires@sancoshrim.com

Tarporley Tractors, Rode Street, Tarporley, Cheshire, CW6 0EF Tel: (01829) 733487 Fax: (01829) 733606

AGRICULTURAL MACHINERY/ EQUIPMENT/IMPLEMENT IMPORT/EXPORT MERCHANTS OR AGENTS

A T Oliver & Sons Ltd, Home Park Works, Station Road, Kings Langley, Hertfordshire, WD4 8LW Tel: (01923) 265211 Fax: (01923) 261759

Agriservices, Unit N3 Blackpole Trading Estate East, Blackpole Road, Worcester, WR3 8SG Tel: (01905) 754929 Fax: (01905) 754929 E-mail: agriservices@bitsmail.co.uk

Broadwood International, Trading Estate, Oakhanger Road, Bordon, Hampshire, GU35 9HH Tel: (01420) 478111 Fax: (01420) 483000 E-mail: info@wessexmachinery.co.uk

Burdens Group, Main Road, Old Leake, Boston, Lincolnshire, PE22 9AT Tel: (01205) 870011 Fax: (01205) 871252

AGRICULTURAL MACHINERY/ EQUIPMENT/IMPLEMENT IMPORT/ EXPORT MERCHANTS OR AGENTS

– *continued*

C Bright, Elms Farm, Mount Bures, Bures, Suffolk, CO8 5BA Tel: (01787) 227730 Fax: (01787) 229027
E W Allen, Hallgarth Garage, High Pittington, Durham, DH6 1AT Tel: 0191-372 0313 Fax: 0191-372 2440 E-mail: ewallentractors@fsmail.net
East Anglian Tractors Ltd, Arkesden Road, Clavering, Saffron Walden, Essex, CB11 4QU Tel: (01799) 550268 Fax: (01799) 550874 E-mail: sales@eatractors.co.uk
Essex Tractor Co. Ltd, Birchwood Road, Cock Clarks, Chelmsford, CM3 6RF Tel: (01621) 828880 Fax: (01621) 828944 E-mail: sales@tractor.net
George Hamilton Machinery, 100 Barnish Road, Randalstown, Antrim, BT41 2NL Tel: (028) 9447 2269 Fax: (028) 9447 9191 E-mail: georgehamilton.mchy@bttinternet.com
Gregoire Besson UK Ltd, Bourne Road Carlby, Stamford, Lincolnshire, PE9 4NP Tel: (01778) 590223 Fax: (01778) 590645 E-mail: bill@gregoire-besson.co.uk
Kverneland Group UK Ltd, Walkers Lane, Lea Green, St. Helens, Merseyside, WA9 4AF Tel: (01744) 853200 Fax: (01744) 853400 E-mail: sales@kvernelandgroup.com
Landmec Ltd, Redlake Trading Estate, Ivybridge, Devon, PL21 0EZ Tel: (01752) 891285 Fax: (01752) 891392 E-mail: info@landmecpottinger.co.uk
Major Equipment Ltd, Middleton Road, Middleton, Morecambe, Lancashire, LA3 3JJ Tel: (01524) 850501 Fax: (01524) 850502 E-mail: ukinfo@major-grasscare.com
Richard Pearson Ltd, Priory Road, Freiston, Boston, Lincolnshire, PE22 0JZ Tel: (01205) 760383 Fax: (01205) 761064 E-mail: info@richardpearson.com
Phillip Trim, Frensham, Chamberlaynes, Bere Regis, Wareham, Dorset, BH20 7LS Tel: (01929) 472192 Fax: (01929) 472555
Rekord Sales Great Britain Ltd, Manor Road, Mancetter, Atherstone, Warwickshire, CV9 1RJ Tel: (01827) 712424 Fax: (01827) 715133 E-mail: sales@rekord.com
Rogers & Taylor Agricultural & Equestrian Supplies, Blaenddol, Bow Street, Dyfed, SY24 5BH Tel: (01970) 828680 Fax: (01970) 828680 E-mail: rogersandtaylor@equestrianet.co.uk
Standen Reflex Ltd, Hereward Works, 47-49 Station Road, Ely, Cambridgeshire, CB7 4BP Tel: (01353) 666200 Fax: (01353) 666202 E-mail: sales@standenreflex.com
Technical Help to Exporters, 389 Chiswick High Road, London, W4 4AL Tel: (020) 8996 7474 Fax: (020) 8996 7048 E-mail: the@bsi-global.com

AGRICULTURAL MACHINERY/ EQUIPMENT/IMPLEMENT MANUFRS

A B E Specialist Products, Haymoor Hall, Wybunbury Lane, Wybunbury, Nantwich, Cheshire, CW5 7HD Tel: (01270) 841174 Fax: (01270) 841128 E-mail: enquiries@haymoorleisure.co.uk
A J S Machine Sales & Spares Ltd, 22 Exeter Road, Urmston, Manchester, M41 0RE Tel: 0161-747 7436 Fax: 0161-718 0952
A T Landquip, Lonmay, Fraserburgh, Aberdeenshire, AB43 8RN Tel: (01346) 532492 Fax: (01346) 532547 E-mail: sales@atlandquip.com
A T Oliver & Sons Ltd, Wandon End Works, Wandon End, Luton, LU2 8NY Tel: (01582) 727111 Fax: (01582) 729763 E-mail: ato@atoliver.co.uk
Agco International Ltd, PO Box 62, Coventry, CV4 0GF Tel: (024) 7669 4400 Fax: (024) 7685 2495
Agricultural Machinery Nantwich Ltd, Millstone Lane, Nantwich, Cheshire, CW5 5PJ Tel: (01270) 624141 Fax: (01270) 624140 E-mail: sales@ag-mac.co.uk
Agrimech Farming Ltd, Willow Farm, Common Lane, Church Fenton, Tadcaster, North Yorkshire, LS24 9QR Tel: (01937) 557779 Fax: (01937) 557093
Agriservices, Unit N3 Blackpole Trading Estate East, Blackpole Road, Worcester, WR3 8SG Tel: (01905) 754929 Fax: (01905) 754929 E-mail: agriservices@bitsmail.co.uk
Alexander & Duncan Ltd, Southern Avenue, Leominster, Herefordshire, HR6 0QB Tel: (01568) 613434 Fax: (01568) 613736 E-mail: simon@alexanderandduncan.co.uk
G.A. Allen & Co., 131 Grovehill Road, Banbridge, County Down, BT32 5AB Tel: (028) 4065 1303 Fax: (028) 4065 1370
Alvan Blanch Development Co. Ltd, Chelworth, Malmesbury, Wiltshire, SN16 9SG Tel: (01666) 577333 Fax: (01666) 577339 E-mail: info@alvanblanch.co.uk
Amazone Ltd, Blyth Road, Harworth, Doncaster, South Yorkshire, DN11 8NE Tel: (01302) 751 200 Fax: (01302) 751 202 E-mail: info@amazone.co.uk
Arcusin UK, Walnut Tree House, Oxton, Southwell, Nottinghamshire, NG25 0SZ Tel: (07790) 989024 Fax: 0115-965 5970 E-mail: stephen@arcusin.com
Arter Bros Ltd, Barham Services, Folkestone Road, Barham, Canterbury, Kent, CT4 6EX Tel: (01227) 831356 Fax: (01227) 832060 E-mail: sales@arterbros.co.uk
Ashfield & Wilson, Charlemont Street, Moy, Dungannon, County Tyrone, BT71 7SL Tel: (028) 8778 4671 Fax: (028) 8778 4391 E-mail: ashfieldwilson@btconnect.com
B K Grain Handling Engineers, Littlecoate Road, Froxfield, Marlborough, Wiltshire, SN8 3JY Tel: (01488) 684154 Fax: (01488) 684455 E-mail: info@bkgrain.co.uk
Banbury Farm General Supplies Ltd, Grove Farm Building, Burton Dassett, Southam, Warwickshire, CV47 2AB Tel: (01295) 770707 Fax: (01295) 770787
Beaconsfield Products Halesowen Ltd, Foxoak Street, Cradley Heath, West Midlands, B64 5DE Tel: (01384) 569571 Fax: (01384) 566328 E-mail: sales@beacoproducts.co.uk
Ben Burgess Beeston, Dereham Road, Beeston, King's Lynn, Norfolk, PE32 2LE Tel: (01328) 701347 Fax: (01328) 700111 E-mail: beestonsales@benburgess.co.uk
▶ Ben Burgess Newmarket Ltd, Windmill Hill, Exning, Newmarket, Suffolk, CB8 7NP Tel: (01638) 577877 Fax: (01638) 577977 E-mail: newmarket@benburgess.co.uk
Ben Singer Machinery, Woolley Grange Farm, Woolley Green, Bradford-On-Avon, Wiltshire, BA15 1TY Tel: (01225) 866487 Fax: (01225) 865742 E-mail: ben@woolley59.fsnet.co.uk
Bexwell Tractors Ltd, Bexwell, Downham Market, Norfolk, PE38 9LU Tel: (01366) 383301 Fax: (01366) 384930 E-mail: admin@bexwell-tractors.co.uk
The Big Bale Company North Ltd, Heck Lane, Great Heck, Goole, North Humberside, DN14 0BL Tel: (01405) 862240 Fax: (01405) 862328 E-mail: northern.straw@virgin.net
Blakemore & Chell Ltd, New Street, Leek, Staffordshire, ST13 6EB Tel: (01538) 382387 Fax: (01538) 399726
Bomford Turner Ltd, Station Road, Salford Priors, Evesham, Worcestershire, WR11 8SW Tel: (01789) 773383 Fax: (01789) 773238 E-mail: sales@bomford-turner.com
Border Shearing Supplies, The Hagg, Cornhill-on-Tweed, Northumberland, TD12 4RT Tel: (01890) 850219 Fax: (01890) 850219
Boston Tractors Ltd, Eagle Iron Works, Creake Road, Sculthorpe, Fakenham, Norfolk, NR21 9NH Tel: (01328) 862333 Fax: (01328) 856249
John Bownes Ltd, Courthouse Farm, Swanlow Lane, Darnhall, Winsford, Cheshire, CW7 4BS Tel: (01606) 592639 Fax: (01606) 861410 E-mail: sales@jbownes.co.uk
Boyd & Sons Bendooragh Ltd, 80 Bann Road, Bendoragh, Ballymoney, County Antrim, BT53 7LP Tel: (028) 2766 3116 Fax: (028) 2766 3116
Broadwood International, Trading Estate, Oakhanger Road, Bordon, Hampshire, GU35 9HH Tel: (01420) 478111 Fax: (01420) 483000 E-mail: info@wessexmachinery.co.uk
Francis Bugler Ltd, Barrowfield, Broadwindsor Road, Beaminster, Dorset, DT8 3PP Tel: (01308) 862239 Fax: (01308) 863511 E-mail: info@buglers.co.uk
Burden Groundcare, 7 Main Street, North Kyme, Lincoln, LN4 4DF Tel: (01526) 860060 Fax: (01526) 861347 E-mail: sales@burdens.com
Burdens Distribution Ltd, Spalding Road, Sutterton, Boston, Lincolnshire, PE20 2EX Tel: (01205) 460466 Fax: (01205) 460122 E-mail: sales@burdens.com
Burdens Group, Main Road, Old Leake, Boston, Lincolnshire, PE22 9AT Tel: (01205) 870011 Fax: (01205) 871252
C E Davis Marshfield Ltd, 94 High Street, Marshfield, Chippenham, Wiltshire, SN14 8LS Tel: (01225) 891444 Fax: (01225) 891910
C Hanson & Son, Aynhams Hill, Bracewell, Skipton, North Yorkshire, BD23 3JS Tel: (01200) 445905
C R Allen, Lower Hoddern Farm, Glynn Road, Peacehaven, East Sussex, BN10 8AP Tel: (01273) 584987 Fax: (01273) 580904
C T M Root Crop Systems - Harpley Engineering Ltd, Cross Street, Harpley, King's Lynn, Norfolk, PE31 6TJ Tel: (01485) 520355 Fax: (01485) 520062 E-mail: sales@ctmharpley.co.uk
C W F Country Wide, Station Approach, Wrexham, Clwyd, LL11 2AA Tel: (01978) 361561 Fax: (01978) 364328 E-mail: enquiries@nwf.co.uk
C W Trading, Units 1-4 Danes Grave, Cottam, Driffield, North Humberside, YO25 3BG Tel: (01377) 267400 Fax: (01377) 267444
Chandlers Farm Equipment Ltd, Boston Road, Horncastle, Lincolnshire, LN9 6JN Tel: (01507) 527211 Fax: (01507) 524498 E-mail: enqruies@chandlersfe.co.uk
Chelford Farm Supplies Ltd, 2 Chelford Farm Supplies Ltd, Knutsford Road, Chelford, Macclesfield, Cheshire, SK11 9AS Tel: (01625) 861588 Fax: (01625) 861235 E-mail: sales@chelfordfarmsupplies.fsbusiness.co.uk
Clovelly Contractors, Huntshaw Barton, Huntshaw, Torrington, Devon, EX38 7HH Tel: (01805) 623255 Fax: (01805) 625225
Clwyd Agricultural, Terfyn Farm, Caerwys Road, Cwm Dyserth, Rhyl, Clwyd, LL18 6HT Tel: (01745) 571018 Fax: (01745) 571002
Collings Bros Of Abbotsley Ltd, 3-5 Prospect Way, Chatteris, Cambridgeshire, PE16 6TZ Tel: (01354) 694169 Fax: (01354) 694218 E-mail: sales@collingbrothers.co.uk
▶ Compact Tractor World, 3 Three Cocks Lane, Offenham, Evesham, Worcestershire, WR11 8RY Tel: (01386) 761166
▶ Compass Tractors Ltd, Manor Farm, Hele, Taunton, Somerset, TA4 1AH Tel: (01823) 462999 Fax: (01823) 462998
▶ Continental Soil Technology, The Old Dairy, Chavenage Estate, Tetbury, Gloucestershire, GL8 8XY Tel: (0845) 6034136 Fax: E-mail: info@continentalsoiltechnology.com
John Cornthwaite Farm Machinery Ltd, The Auction Mart, Pilling, Preston, PR3 6AH Tel: (01253) 790771 Fax: (01253) 790839 E-mail: enquiries.pilling@cornthwaites.co.uk
Cornwall Farmers Ltd, Three Milestone Industrial Estate, Truro, Cornwall, TR4 9LD Tel: (01872) 274301 Fax: (01872) 260484 E-mail: enquiries@cornwallfarmers.co.uk
Countrywide Farmers P.L.C., Lady Lane, Blunsdon, Swindon, SN2 4DN Tel: (01793) 722888 Fax: (01793) 706011
Countrywide Stores, Hook Norton Road, Chipping Norton, Oxfordshire, OX7 5TE Tel: (01608) 642071 Fax: (01608) 645125 E-mail: enquiries@countrywidefarmers.co.uk
Cousins of Emneth Ltd, The Forge, Hungate Road, Emneth, Wisbech, Cambridgeshire, PE14 8DE Tel: (01945) 584600 Fax: (01945) 584616 E-mail: sales@cousinsofemneth.co.uk
Cowan Bros, 11 Monnaboy Road, Eglinton, Londonderry, BT47 3AZ Tel: (028) 7181 0699 Fax: (028) 7181 1429
Cragg's Of Conder Green, Thurnham, Thurnham, Lancaster, LA2 0BD Tel: (01524) 751946 Fax: (01524) 752378 E-mail: craggsofconder@tiscali.co.uk
Crop Chemicals Ltd, Drem Airfield, North Berwick, East Lothian, EH39 5AW Tel: (01620) 842170 Fax: (01620) 843596 E-mail: enquires@cropchemicals.co.uk
Curtis & Shaw, Cowbeech, Hailsham, East Sussex, BN27 4JE Tel: (01323) 833441 Fax: (01323) 833072 E-mail: sales@curtisandshaw.co.uk
D B I, Marsh La, Burgh le Marsh, Skegness, Lincs, PE24 5AG Tel: (01754) 811777 Fax: (01754) 811555
D G Marketing, Ditchford Mill Farm, Todenham, Moreton-In-Marsh, Gloucestershire, GL56 9NU Tel: (01608) 650399 Fax: (01608) 650560 E-mail: graham@farmline.com
D Hinds, Low Wood Farm, Bewerley, Harrogate, North Yorkshire, HG3 5BT Tel: (01423) 712065 Fax: (01423) 711984
D & K Singer, Fordoun, Fordoun, Laurencekirk, Kincardineshire, AB30 1JR Tel: (01561) 320639 Fax: (01561) 320690 E-mail: dksinger@freeserve.co.uk
D S Logan, 25 Duneoin Road, Cullybackey, Ballymena, County Antrim, BT42 1PL Tel: (028) 2588 0297 Fax: (028) 2588 1041 E-mail: kuhn@dslogan.wanadoo.co.uk
Dales Contractors Ltd, Rough Heys Farm, Rough Heys Lane, Henbury, Macclesfield, Cheshire, SK11 9PF Tel: (01625) 501529 Fax: (01625) 501403 E-mail: dales@farmline.com
Dalton ID Systems Ltd, Dalton House, Newtown Road, Henley-on-Thames, Oxfordshire, RG9 1HG Tel: (0800) 838882 Fax: (0800) 7311957 E-mail: sales@dalton.co.uk
Danagri - 3 S Ltd, Wenlock Road, Bridgnorth, Shropshire, WV16 4QR Tel: (01746) 762777 Fax: (01746) 764777 E-mail: info@danagri-3s.com
David Charles Whitaker, Killatree Farm, Holsworthy, Devon, EX22 6LP Tel: (01409) 253539 Fax: (01409) 253539
David Johnson Lutterworth Ltd, Upper Bruntingthorpe, Lutterworth, Leicestershire, LE17 5QZ Tel: 0116-247 8349 Fax: 0116-247 8349
Davies Implements Ltd, Blaenteg, Llwynderi, Trevaughan, Carmarthen, Dyfed, SA31 3QN Tel: (01267) 237726 Fax: (01267) 238696 E-mail: davies@implements.preserve.co.uk
Day & Coles Agricultural Ltd, Newton Close, Park Farm, Wellingborough, Northamptonshire, NN8 6UW Tel: (01933) 673900 Fax: (01933) 675858
John Day Engineering Ltd, Welford Works, Easton, Newbury, Berkshire, RG20 8EA Tel: (01488) 608666 Fax: (01488) 608781
John Deeny Ltd, 123 Learmount Road, Claudy, Londonderry, BT47 4AL Tel: (028) 7133 8229 Fax: (028) 7133 8039
John Deere Ltd, Harby Road, Langar, Nottingham, NG13 9HT Tel: (01949) 860491 Fax: (01949) 860490
Dennis Shingler & Son, Agricultural Service Station, Cyfronydd, Welshpool, Powys, SY21 9EW Tel: (01938) 850270 Fax: (01938) 850387
S.T.A. Dinnis, 25 Meadow Drive, Bude, Cornwall, EX23 8HZ Tel: (01288) 355006 Fax: (01288) 355006
Ernest Doe & Sons Ltd, Whempstead Road, Benington, Stevenage, Hertfordshire, SG2 7BZ Tel: (01438) 869251 Fax: (01438) 869302 E-mail: ernestdoe@benington.com
Ernest Doe & Sons Ltd, Industrial Estate, Valleyside, Wymondham, Norfolk, NR18 0NN Tel: (01953) 602982 Fax: (01953) 601270 E-mail: rossjohnson@ernestdoe.com
Dolphine Ventilation, The Green, Barrow, Bury St. Edmunds, Suffolk, IP29 5AA Tel: (01284) 810563 Fax: (01284) 811119 E-mail: dolphineventilation@btinternet.com
Alan Dunlop, 2 Killyleagh Road, Killinchy, Newtownards, County Down, BT23 6TA Tel: (028) 9754 1440 Fax: (028) 9754 1644 E-mail: bill_dunlop@btinternet.com
E Bowden & Sons, Little Woodland, Old Newton Road, Bovey Tracey, Newton Abbot, Devon, TQ13 9DT Tel: (01626) 833374 Fax: (01626) 832144 E-mail: ebowden@btconnect.com
E C Reese Agricultural Ltd, Rose Brook, Pwlltrap, St. Clears, Carmarthen, SA33 4AR Tel: (01994) 230560 Fax: (01994) 230133
E O Culverwell Ltd, Station Road, Robertsbridge, East Sussex, TN32 5DG Tel: (01580) 880567 Fax: (01580) 881022 E-mail: cars@eo-culverwell.ltd.uk
Eastern Farm Implements Ltd, Bourne Road, Carlby, Stamford, Lincolnshire, PE9 4LW Tel: (01778) 590215 Fax: (01778) 590282
Eaton Tractors Ltd, High Street, Little Paxton, St. Neots, Cambridgeshire, PE19 6HD Tel: (01480) 473121 Fax: (01480) 404585
Evans Bros Agriparts, Agricultural Parts, Cefn Mabws, Llanrhystud, Dyfed, SY23 5BD Tel: (01974) 272260 Fax: (01974) 272537
I.N. Evans & Son, Tegfan Garage, 30 Carmarthen Road, Llandeilo, Dyfed, SA19 6RS Tel: (01558) 822542 Fax: (01558) 822337
F Dunn, 84 Newtownards Road, Donaghadee, County Down, BT21 0PT Tel: (028) 9188 3243 Fax: (028) 9188 8483
F M Taylor, High Whinnow Farm, Whinnow Road, Thursby, Carlisle, CA5 6QL Tel: (01697) 342191 Fax: (01697) 345005 E-mail: ftaylor.machinery@virgin.net
Farm Machines & Agricultural, Holwell Barton, Neopardy, Crediton, Devon, EX17 5EP Tel: (01363) 774209 Fax: (01363) 774261
▶ FarmEquip.co.uk, Strichen, Fraserburgh, Aberdeenshire, AB43 6NY Tel: (01771) 637413
▶ FarmEquip.co.uk, 16 Camperdown Road, Boathpark, Nairn, IV12 5AR Tel: (01667) 456842
▶ Farmgear Ltd, The Old Vicarage, Church Close, Boston, Lincolnshire, PE21 6NE Tel: (0845) 6440228 Fax: (0845) 6520124 E-mail: info@farmgear.co.uk
Farmline Agricultural Supplies, 11 Kinallen Road, Dromara, Dromore, County Down, BT25 2NL Tel: (028) 9753 3422 Fax: (028) 9753 3555
Fleming Agri Products, New Buildings Industrial Estate, Victoria Road, Newbuildings, Londonderry, BT47 2SX Tel: (028) 7134 2637 Fax: (028) 7134 4735 E-mail: info@fleming-agri.co.uk
Fuel Wood Harvesting, Weirburn House, Abbey St Bathans, Duns, Berwickshire, TD11 3TX Tel: (01361) 840251 Fax: (01361) 840248 E-mail: wsj.dobie@btconnect.com
Gallagher Power Fence (UK) Ltd, Curriers Close, Coventry, CV4 8AW Tel: (0870) 2010101 Fax: (0870) 0111545 E-mail: info@gallagher.co.uk
Glenside Tractors Ltd, Millknowe, Campbeltown, Argyll, PA28 6NJ Tel: (01586) 553624 Fax: (01586) 554923 E-mail: glensidetractors@btinternet.com
Grampian A T VS, Inverythan Garage, Fyvie, Turriff, Aberdeenshire, AB53 8JU Tel: (01888) 511511 Fax: (01888) 511511 E-mail: rena.findlay@btinternet.com
Gregsons, Brookside, Drointon Road, Rugeley, Staffordshire, WS15 3NX Tel: (01889) 500572 Fax: (01889) 500415
Griffiths & Co., Gwar Y Rhos, Y Ffor, Pwllheli, Gwynedd, LL53 6NF Tel: (01766) 810334 Fax: (01766) 810248
Gwynedd Farm Machinery Ltd, Dinas, Caernarfon, Gwynedd, LL54 5UG Tel: (01286) 830009 Fax: (01286) 831498 E-mail: sales@gwyneddfarmmachinery.co.uk
H Kane & Son, 31 Legavara Road, Ballintoy, Ballycastle, County Antrim, BT54 6NG Tel: (028) 2076 2613 Fax: (028) 2076 2027 E-mail: sales@hunterkaneandson.com
H M Howard & Sons, Manor Farm, Close Lane, Marston, Devizes, Wiltshire, SN10 5SN Tel: (01380) 723986 Fax: (01380) 730600 E-mail: howardagri@btconnect.com
H West Prees Ltd, Lower Heath, Prees, Whitchurch, Shropshire, SY13 2BT Tel: (01948) 840465 Fax: (01948) 841055 E-mail: sales@harrywest.co.uk
▶ Hauler Europe Ltd, Moll Springs, Netherton, Huddersfield, HD4 7DN Tel: (01484) 660291 Fax: (01484) 660295
▶ Haynes Agricultural Ltd, Squires Farm Industrial Estate, Easons Green, Uckfield, East Sussex, TN22 5RB Tel: (01825) 841100 Fax: (01825) 841122 E-mail: sales@haynesgrp.co.uk
Haynes Agricultural Kent Ltd, 1 The Street, Appledore, Ashford, Kent, TN26 2BU Tel: (01233) 758395 Fax: (01233) 758242 E-mail: j.burt@haynesgrp.co.uk
Hayward United Farmers Ltd, Benacre Road, Ellough, Beccles, Suffolk, NR34 7XD Tel: (01502) 475111 Fax: (01502) 476533 E-mail: steve@hufl.co.uk
▶ Henderson Grass Machinery Ltd, Tweedbank Industrial Estate, Tweedbank, Galashiels, Selkirkshire, TD1 3RS Tel: (01896) 753870 Fax: (01896) 752598
HFS Engineering Ltd, 20 Dorsey Road, Cullyhanna, Newry, County Down, BT35 0QA Tel: (028) 3086 8228
Hillam Farm Machinery, Brookside Works, Brick Street, Cleckheaton, West Yorkshire, BD19 5LD Tel: (01274) 870632 Fax: (01274) 862815 E-mail: geanne@hilams.freeserve.co.uk
Joseph Hillary Ltd, Station Road, Aspatria, Wigton, Cumbria, CA7 3JW Tel: (01697) 320251 Fax: (01697) 321180 E-mail: duncan@josephhilary.co.uk

▶ indicates data change since last edition

AGRICULTURAL MACHINERY/ EQUIPMENT/IMPLEMENT MANUFRS

– continued

Holtractors Ltd, 1 St.Andrews Close, Golden Cross, Hailsham, East Sussex, BN27 3UB Tel: (01323) 841024 Fax: (01323) 441196 E-mail: holtractors@hotmail.com

I D Rawlinson Contractors, Marton, Ulverston, Cumbria, LA12 0NR Tel: (01229) 465665 Fax: (01229) 465665

Inta-Trac UK Ltd, Little London, Halifax, West Yorkshire, HX3 7ST Tel: (01422) 206333 Fax: (01422) 204486 E-mail: sales@intatrac.co.uk

Ireland's Farm Machinery Ltd, Bramley House, Old Bolingbroke, Spilsby, Lincolnshire, PE23 4EX Tel: (01790) 763424 Fax: (01790) 763540 E-mail: jonathan.ireland@btinternet.com

J B Edlington & Co Ltd, Carr Lane, Gainsborough, Lincolnshire, DN21 1LF Tel: (01427) 616869 Fax: (01427) 616869 E-mail: paul@edlington.com

J G Paxton & Sons Ltd, Front Street, Pity Me, Durham, DH1 5DE Tel: 0191-384 7111 Fax: 0191-386 7806 E-mail: peter@jgpaxtonandsons.ibcos.net

J G Plant, Brackla Industrial Estate, Bridgend, Mid Glamorgan, CF31 2AQ Tel: (01656) 652299

J H Morse Ltd, Morfa Lane, Carmarthen, Dyfed, SA31 3AX Tel: (01267) 234704 Fax: (01267) 221376

J J Machines, 38 Hinksley Road, Flitwick, Bedford, MK45 1HH Tel: (01525) 717600 Fax: (01525) 716816

J & W Tait Ltd, Sparrowhawk Road, Hatston Industrial Estate, Kirkwall, Orkney, KW15 1GE Tel: (01856) 872490 Fax: (01856) 873076

J Wilson Agriculture, 75 Drumcroon Road, Garvagh, Coleraine, County Londonderry, BT51 4ED Tel: (028) 7086 8430 Fax: (028) 7086 8803 E-mail: cowcomfort@wilsonagri.co.uk

James Gordon Engineers Ltd, Dalbeattie Road, Castle Douglas, Kirkcudbrightshire, DG7 1HZ Tel: (01556) 502338 Fax: (01556) 504178 E-mail: admin@jgordon.co.uk

James & Powell, Little Ton Farm, Tredunnock, Usk, Gwent, NP15 1LY Tel: (01633) 450550 Fax: (01633) 450424

Tom Jefferson, Far Long Park Farm, Long Park, Carlisle, CA6 4JP Tel: (01228) 675451 Fax: (01228) 675363

Gwili Jones & Sons, Maesyfelin Business Park, Lampeter, Dyfed, SA48 8LS Tel: (01570) 423777 Fax: (01570) 423355

Julian Mousley, Llwyncelyn Uchaf, Llangynin, St. Clears, Carmarthen, SA33 4LA Tel: (01994) 230550 Fax: (01994) 230235

K J Joyce, Canaan, Chale Green, Ventnor, Isle of Wight, PO38 2JN Tel: (01983) 551381 Fax: (01983) 551440

Kent Harvest Centre, Bayley Wood, Great Chart, Ashford, Kent, TN26 1JJ Tel: (01233) 822300 Fax: (01233) 822301 E-mail: steve_lewis@southernharvesters.co.uk

Kentra Grain Systems Ltd, Station Road, Kirk Hammerton, York, YO26 8DN Tel: (01423) 330085 Fax: (01423) 331347 E-mail: kentra@graindriers.com

Kuhn Farm Machinery (UK) Ltd, Stafford Park 7, Telford, Shropshire, TF3 3BQ Tel: (01952) 239300 Fax: (01952) 290091 E-mail: infouk@kuhn.co.uk

Landmec-Pottinger Ltd, Cantrell Works, Bittaford, Ivybridge, Devon, PL21 0EZ Tel: (01752) 891285 Fax: (01752) 891392 E-mail: info@landmecpottinger.co.uk

Landtecnics Ltd, Unit18, Orchard Place Business, Comp Road, Wrotham Heath, Sevenoaks, Kent, TN15 8QX Tel: (01732) 885700 Fax: (01732) 882255 E-mail: landtecnics@btconnect.com

Lely (UK) Ltd, 1 Station Road, St. Neots, Cambridgeshire, PE19 1QH Tel: (01480) 226810 Fax: (01480) 226811 E-mail: ag.sales.uk@lely.com

Samuel Lewis Ltd, PO Box 65, Cradley Heath, West Midlands, B64 5PS Tel: 0121-561 2157 Fax: 0121-561 5273

Linklater Engineering, Stenness, Stenness, Stromness, Orkney, KW16 3JZ Tel: (01856) 851000 Fax: (01856) 851080 E-mail: enquiries@linklaterengineering.co.uk

Llandissilio Garage, Modyrllys, Llandissilio, Clynderwen, Dyfed, SA66 7TG Tel: (01437) 563225 Fax: (01437) 563709

Lloyd Ltd, Myers Lane, Penrith, Cumbria, CA11 9DP Tel: (01768) 863806 Fax: (01768) 865664 E-mail: lloyd.ltd@lineone.net

Lower Quinton Garages Ltd, Back Lane, Lower Quinton, Stratford-upon-Avon, Warwickshire, CV37 8SX Tel: (01789) 720265 Fax: (01789) 721489 E-mail: lqg@lqgltd.co.uk

Mccaskie Farm Supplies Ltd, Fossowey Garage, Crook of Devon, Drum, Kinross, KY13 0PR Tel: (01577) 840272 Fax: (01577) 840694

McCormick Tractors International Ltd, Wheatley Hall Road, Doncaster, South Yorkshire, DN2 4PE Tel: (01302) 366631 Fax: (01302) 733491 E-mail: bridget.kenny@mccormick-intl.com

Mccullagh Farm Machinery, 206 Derrylin Road, Bellanaleck, Enniskillen, County Fermanagh, BT92 2BA Tel: (028) 6634 8213 Fax: (028) 6634 8013

Machine Mart Ltd, Machine Mart House, Derwent Street, Derby, DE1 2ED Tel: (01332) 290931 Fax: (01332) 366531 E-mail: sales@machinemart.co.uk

B.W. Mack (Machinery) Ltd, Barroway Drove, Downham Market, Norfolk, PE38 0AL Tel: (01366) 324256 Fax: (01366) 324431 E-mail: info@bwmack.co.uk

▶ Mclaren Tractors Ltd, Strathpeffer Road, Dingwall, Ross-Shire, IV15 9QF Tel: (01349) 867210 Fax: (01349) 866738

N.& G. Marsh, Unit 12, Meadow Industrial Estate, Reach Road, Burwell, Cambridge, CB25 0GH Tel: (01638) 741354 Fax: (01638) 743424

Marston Agricultural Services Ltd, Toll Bar Road, Marston, Grantham, Lincolnshire, NG32 2HT Tel: (01400) 250226 Fax: (01400) 250540 E-mail: sales@mas-trailers-group.co.uk

Maxwell Emsworth Ltd, Elsted Station, Elsted, Midhurst, West Sussex, GU29 0JT Tel: (01730) 812662 Fax: (01730) 813560

Mitchell Industries Ltd, Unit 1 Brindley Close, Tollgate Industrial Park, Stafford, ST16 3HS Tel: (01785) 242341 Fax: (01785) 222616

Mix It Stirrers, Little Chillaton, Loddiswell, Kingsbridge, Devon, TQ7 4EG Tel: (01548) 550298

Mona Tractor Co. Ltd, Gilfach Yard, Chwilog, Pwllheli, Gwynedd, LL53 6SL Tel: (01766) 810222 Fax: (01766) 810999 E-mail: monatractors@mtchwilog.fsnet.co.uk

Morgans, Mile End Business Park, Maesbury Road Industrial Estate, Oswestry, Shropshire, SY10 8NN Tel: (01691) 657700 Fax: (01691) 680681 E-mail: emailsales@morgans-machinery.co.uk

Motokov UK Ltd, Bergen Way, North Lynn Industrial Estate, King's Lynn, Norfolk, PE30 2JG Tel: (01553) 817700 Fax: (01553) 691201

Moulton Engineering Ltd, Swepstone Road, Heather, Coalville, Leicestershire, LE67 2RE Tel: (01530) 262504 Fax: (01530) 260399

Murley Agricultural Supplies Ltd, Crab Apple Way, Vale Park, Evesham, Worcestershire, WR11 1GP Tel: (01386) 765657 Fax: (01386) 765029 E-mail: sales@murley-agri.co.uk

N C Engineering Co. Ltd, 2 Killyrudden Road, Hamiltonsbawn, Armagh, BT61 9SF Tel: (028) 3887 1970 Fax: (028) 3887 0362 E-mail: nc.a.engineering@btinternet.com

Neil Bath, Sedgemoor House, Othery, Bridgwater, Somerset, TA7 0QL Tel: 01823 698810 Fax: (01823) 698004 E-mail: neilbath@btinternet.com

New Barn Farm, Whaddon Lane, Hilperton, Trowbridge, Wiltshire, BA14 7RN Tel: (01225) 777053

Niagri Engineering Ltd, Station Road, Lakenheath, Brandon, Suffolk, IP27 9AA Tel: (01842) 862500 Fax: (01842) 862501 E-mail: info@niagri.co.uk

Norman F Ogg, West Kinwhirrie, Kirriemuir, Angus, DD8 4QA Tel: (01575) 540234 Fax: (01575) 540235

Norman Raw Farm Machinery, The Forge, Rudgate, Whixley, York, YO26 8AL Tel: (01423) 330391 Fax: (01423) 331422

Oakes Brothers Ltd, Fareham Road, Wickham, Fareham, Hampshire, PO17 5DH Tel: (01329) 832345 Fax: (01329) 833944

Olesen Agriculture Limited, 32 Papermakers, Overton, Basingstoke, Hampshire, RG25 3NS Tel: (01256) 771887 Fax: (01256) 771956 E-mail: sales@olesenagri.co.uk

Robert O'Neill, 1 Queen Street, Ayr, KA8 0DW Tel: (01292) 260888 Fax: (01292) 619726

Opico Ltd, Cherry Holt Road, Bourne, Lincolnshire, PE10 9LA Tel: (01778) 421111 Fax: (01778) 425080E-mail: ask@opico.co.uk

P A Turney Ltd, Middleton Stoney, Bicester, Oxfordshire, OX25 4AB Tel: (01869) 343333 Fax: (01869) 343540

P A Turney Ltd, Worcester Road Industrial Estate, Chipping Norton, Oxfordshire, OX7 5XW Tel: (01608) 642131 Fax: (01608) 644413

P Jeffrey & Sons, Rosebank, Hutton, Berwick-upon-Tweed, TD15 1TS Tel: (01289) 386398

Palmers Agricultural Ltd, Redwall Farm, Redwall Lane, Linton, Maidstone, Kent, ME17 4AX Tel: (01622) 749819 Fax: (01622) 749829 E-mail: sales@johndeartractors.com

Paramaeth Agricultural Merchants, Unit 9 Penyrorsedd Industrial Estate, Llangefni, Gwynedd, LL77 7JD Tel: (01248) 724959 Fax: (01248) 724092

P.J. Parmiter & Sons Ltd, Station Works, Tisbury, Salisbury, SP3 6QZ Tel: (01747) 870821 Fax: (01747) 871171 E-mail: mail@parmiter.co.uk

Peacock & Binnington, Old Foundry, Brigg, South Humberside, DN20 8NR Tel: (01652) 600200 Fax: (01652) 657532 E-mail: sales@peacock.co.uk

Peacock & Binnington, Old Foundry, Brigg, South Humberside, DN20 8NR Tel: (01652) 600200 Fax: (01652) 657532 E-mail: sales@peacock.co.uk

G.W.J. Pluess Ltd, Trevoutter, Poundstock, Bude, Cornwall, EX23 0DH Tel: (01288) 361368 Fax: (01288) 361361

Port Agric Ltd, Unit 5 Hailsham Industrial Park, Diplocks Way, Hailsham, East Sussex, BN27 3JF Tel: (01323) 841207 Fax: (01323) 844942 E-mail: sales@portagric.co.uk

Jim Price Machinery Ltd, Farmore Mills, Shrewsbury Road, Craven Arms, Shropshire, SY7 9QG Tel: (01588) 673746 Fax: (01588) 672956

Pureclad, 9 Rake Top Avenue, Higham, Burnley, Lancashire, BB12 9BB Tel: (07710) 934133 Fax: (01282) 773712

R B M Agricultural Ltd, Waterloo Works, Jameson Bridge Street, Market Rasen, Lincolnshire, LN8 3EW Tel: (01673) 844079 Fax: (01673) 844632 E-mail: steveplewesrbm@btconnect.com

R & R Shepherd, 227 Pilling Lane, Preesall, Poulton-le-Fylde, Lancashire, FY6 0HH Tel: (01253) 811101

Ralph Martindale & Co. Ltd, Strawberry Lane, Willenhall, West Midlands, WV13 3RS Tel: (01902) 826826 Fax: (01902) 826827 E-mail: crocodile@ralphmartindale.co.uk

Randell NFM Ltd, 3 Maurice Gaymer Road, Attleborough, Norfolk, NR17 2QZ Tel: (01953) 452468 Fax: (01953) 453229 E-mail: enquiries@randallnfm.co.uk

Reekie Lothian, Haddington Road, Tranent, East Lothian, EH33 1DZ Tel: (01875) 615355 Fax: (01875) 615012

Reekie (Stirling), 19 Kerse Road, Stirling, FK7 7SY Tel: (01786) 445577 Fax: (01786) 447138

Rekord Sales Great Britain Ltd, Manor Road, Mancetter, Atherstone, Warwickshire, CV9 1RJ Tel: (01827) 712424 Fax: (01827) 715133 E-mail: sales@rekord.com

Rickerby Agricultural Machinery, Elmsfield Park, Holme, Carnforth, Lancashire, LA6 1RJ Tel: (01539) 563416 Fax: (01539) 563248 E-mail: rob.bell@rickerby.net

Ringlink Scotland Ltd, New Elgin Road, Elgin, Morayshire, IV30 6BE Tel: (01343) 550123 Fax: (01343) 551665

Ripon Farm Services, Dallamires Lane, Ripon, North Yorkshire, HG4 1TT Tel: (01765) 692255 Fax: (01765) 606475 E-mail: sales@riponlandrover.co.uk

Risborough Agricultural Services Ltd, Woodway, Princes Risborough, Buckinghamshire, HP27 0NN Tel: (01844) 275275 Fax: (01844) 274264 E-mail: sales@risag.com

Riverlea Tractors Ltd, Riverlea, Crymych, Dyfed, SA41 3QX Tel: (01239) 831733 Fax: (01239) 831668 E-mail: sales@riverlea.co.uk

Riverlea Tractors Ltd, Millfield, Whitland, Dyfed, SA34 0QQ Tel: (01994) 240644 Fax: (01994) 240747 E-mail: sales@riverlea.co.uk

Roben Equipment, PO Box 4021, Milton Keynes, MK14 5YD Tel: (01908) 217306 Fax: (01908) 617775

Robertsons Of Milnathort Ltd, New Road, Milnathort, Kinross, KY13 9XT Tel: (01577) 863342 Fax: (01577) 863342 E-mail: willie@electricfencingonline.co.uk

Ross Farm Machinery Ltd, Usk Road, Raglan, Usk, Gwent, NP15 2HJ Tel: (01291) 690205 Fax: (01291) 690177 E-mail: ragland@rossfarm.co.uk

RS Agribusiness Ltd, Balstone Farm, Ibworth, Tadley, Hampshire, RG26 5TJ Tel: (01256) 850777 Fax: (01256) 850930 E-mail: info@rmhmixers.co.uk

Russells Ltd, Eden Works, Old Malton, Malton, North Yorkshire, YO17 6RD Tel: (01653) 698000 Fax: (01653) 605499 E-mail: sales@russells.uk.com

Ryetec Industrial Equipment Ltd, 12-13 Town Green Lane, Settrington, Malton, North Yorkshire, YO17 8NR Tel: (01944) 768232 Fax: (01944) 768199 E-mail: info@ryetec.co.uk

S L S Trailors, 29A Shanliss Road, Stewartstown, Dungannon, County Tyrone, BT71 5PZ Tel: (028) 8774 6078 Fax: (028) 8774 6078 E-mail: slsengineering@tiscali.co.uk

S & W Agricultural Services, Royd Moor Farm, Royd Moor Lane, Badsworth, Pontefract, West Yorkshire, WF9 1AZ Tel: (01977) 610943 Fax: (01977) 612891

Same Deuts Fahr (U K) Ltd, Barby Lane, Barby, Rugby, Warwickshire, CV23 8TD Tel: (01788) 891892 Fax: (01788) 891387 E-mail: info@sdf.co.uk

Saville Tractors Ltd, 67 Moira Road, Hillsborough, County Down, BT26 6DX Tel: (028) 9268 2220 Fax: (028) 9268 9333 E-mail: info@savillemac.com

Wilfred Scruton Ltd, Providence Foundry, Foxholes, Driffield, North Humberside, YO25 3QQ Tel: (0844) 4770405 Fax: (01262) 470335 E-mail: sales@wilfredscruton.co.uk

Sean Murray, 9 Sandbank Road, Hilltown, Newry, County Down, BT34 5XU Tel: (028) 4063 0736 Fax: (028) 4063 0736

Sellar Agriculture Ltd, Seabank Road, Invergordon, Ross-Shire, IV18 0HE Tel: (01349) 852577 Fax: (01349) 853856

Seward Agricultural Machinery Ltd, Sinderby Station, Thirsk, North Yorkshire, YO7 4LB Tel: (01845) 567407 Fax: (01845) 567680

Sharmans Agricultural Ltd, College Farm, Gonerby Moor, Grantham, Lincolnshire, NG32 2AB Tel: (01476) 562561 Fax: (01476) 590343

Sharmans Of Stamford, Barnack Road, Stamford, Lincolnshire, PE9 2NA Tel: (01780) 762916 Fax: (01780) 752159

Shelbourne Reynolds Engineering Ltd, Shepherds Grove Industrial Estate, Stanton, Bury St. Edmunds, Suffolk, IP31 2AR Tel: (01359) 250415 Fax: (01359) 250464 E-mail: info@shelbourne.com

Simba International Ltd, Woodbridge Road, Sleaford, Lincolnshire, NG34 7EW Tel: (01529) 304654 Fax: (01529) 413468 E-mail: sales@simba.co.uk

South Cave Tractors Ltd, Main Road, Brough, North Humberside, HU15 2RD Tel: (01430) 424233 Fax: (01430) 424200 E-mail: tony.levitt@btconnect.com

Southdown Tractors, Burndell Road, Yapton, Arundel, West Sussex, BN18 0HR Tel: (01243) 551835 Fax: (01243) 553517

Specialised Wheel Services, Buntings Lane, Methwold, Thetford, Norfolk, IP26 4PR Tel: (01366) 727393 Fax: (01366) 728256 E-mail: lisag@fieldens.co.uk

Springhill Mills, 12 Harts Road, Haddenham, Aylesbury, Buckinghamshire, HP17 8HJ Tel: (01844) 299406 Fax: (01844) 299406 E-mail: gbsmr521@attgolbal.net

Standen Engineering Ltd, Hereward Works, 47-49 Station Road, Ely, Cambridgeshire, CB7 4BP Tel: (01353) 661111 Fax: (01353) 662370 E-mail: sales@standen.co.uk

Stanley Agriculture, Thorn Rise Farm, Sandon Road, Hopton, Stafford, ST18 9TH Tel: (01785) 229140 Fax: (01785) 251620

Startin Tractors Ltd, Ashby Road, Twycross, Atherstone, Warwickshire, CV9 3PW Tel: (01827) 880088 Fax: (01827) 880572 E-mail: sales@startintractors.co.uk

Stockfarm Supplies, 1 Highfield Close, Stockport, Cheshire, SK3 8UB Tel: 0161-483 1011

Symtag, Unit 9, Mendip Industrial Estate, Mendip Road, Rooksbridge, Axbridge, Somerset, BS26 2UG Tel: (01934) 750410 Fax: (01934) 750404 E-mail: info@symtag.co.uk

T Alun Jones & Son, Danycapel, Dryslwyn, Carmarthen, Dyfed, SA32 8SD Tel: (01558) 668383 Fax: (01558) 668024

T J Mckenna & Son Ltd, 54 Reclain Road, Dungannon, County Tyrone, BT70 3BS Tel: (028) 8775 8600 Fax: (028) 8775 8981

T Roberts & Sons, Trout Farm, Llanfyllin, Powys, SY22 5LZ Tel: (01691) 648420 Fax: (01691) 648420

T W Relph & Sons Ltd, Moore House, Yanwath, Penrith, Cumbria, CA10 2LA Tel: (01768) 864308 Fax: (01768) 890916 E-mail: johnwrelph@hotmail.com

Tanton Ltd, Lodge Farm, Bowl Road, Charing, Ashford, Kent, TN27 0HB Tel: (0870) 7461300 Fax: (0870) 7461900 E-mail: sales@tanton.ltd.uk

Tay Forth Machinery Ring, Newhill Farm, Glenfarg, Perth, PH2 9QN Tel: (01577) 830616 Fax: (01577) 80663 E-mail: admin@tayforth.co.uk

Teagle Machinery Ltd, Blackwater, Truro, Cornwall, TR4 8HQ Tel: (01872) 560592 Fax: (01872) 561166 E-mail: sales@teagle.co.uk

Tekpro Ltd, Laundry Loke, North Walsham, Norfolk, NR28 0BD Tel: (01692) 403403 Fax: (01692) 404955 E-mail: sales@catchpole.co.uk

Thurlow Nunn Standen Ltd, Lisle Lane, Ely, Cambridgeshire, CB7 4AE Tel: (01353) 662871 Fax: (01353) 663480 E-mail: agsales@tnsgroup.co.uk

Tooby, Hereford Road, Ledbury, Herefordshire, HR8 2PR Tel: (01531) 635656

Townson Tractors Ltd, West End, Kendal Road, Hellifield, Skipton, North Yorkshire, BD23 4HE Tel: (01729) 850374 Fax: (01729) 850315 E-mail: sales@townsontractors.co.uk

Tractor Service, 548 Galleywood Road, Chelmsford, CM2 8BX Tel: (07889) 461892 Fax: (01245) 492471

Tramspread Agricultural Machinery, Hobbies Lane, Mendlesham, Stowmarket, Suffolk, IP14 5SZ Tel: (01449) 766133 Fax: (01449) 766155 E-mail: tramspread@yahoo.co.uk

Traymaster Ltd, New Road, Catfield, Great Yarmouth, Norfolk, NR29 5BQ Tel: (01692) 582100 Fax: (01692) 582211

Tripp Batt & Co. Ltd, Hepworth Road, Stanton, Bury St. Edmunds, Suffolk, IP31 2BT Tel: (01359) 250268 Fax: (01359) 251603

TRP, Pride Parkway, Sleaford Business Park, Sleaford, Lincolnshire, NG34 8GL Tel: (01529) 300111 Fax: (01529) 300310 E-mail: info@trp.uk.com

Tryac Electrical Engineers, Unit 3 Isaac Newton Way, Grantham, Lincolnshire, NG31 9RT Tel: (01476) 576434 Fax: (01476) 578416

Sam Turner & Sons Ltd, Darlington Road, Northallerton, North Yorkshire, DL6 2XB Tel: (01609) 772422 Fax: (01609) 770653 E-mail: clothing@sam-turner.co.uk

Tuthill Temperley, Wardington House, Wardington, Banbury, Oxfordshire, OX17 1SD Tel: (01295) 750513 Fax: (01295) 750036 E-mail: george.tuthill@wardington.com

Vapormatic Company Limited, P O Box 58, Exeter, EX2 7NB Tel: (01392) 435461 Fax: (01392) 438445 E-mail: sales@vapormatic.com

Votex Hereford Ltd, Redhill Depot, Ross Road, Hereford, HR2 8BH Tel: (01432) 274361 Fax: (01432) 352743 E-mail: sales@votex.co.uk

W H James & Son Ltd, Cross House, Crymych, Dyfed, SA41 3UJ Tel: (01239) 831233 Fax: (01239) 831415

Waen Agricultural Sales, Waen, Llanbedr Dyffryn Clwyd, Ruthin, Clwyd, LL15 1SR Tel: (01824) 705571 Fax: (01824) 705243 E-mail: lindadyer@waenagriculturalsales.fsnet.co.uk

West Engineering Ltd, Olympus Close, Ipswich, IP1 5LN Tel: (01473) 467930 Fax: (01473) 467931 E-mail: west@engineering40.fsbusiness.co.uk

Richard Western Ltd, The Durbans, Apsey Green, Framlingham, Woodbridge, Suffolk, IP13 9RP Tel: (01728) 723224 Fax: (01728) 724291 E-mail: sales@richard-western.co.uk

Whites Of Braunston, 38 High Street, Braunston, Oakham, Leicestershire, LE15 8QU Tel: (01572) 722517 Fax: (01572) 755900

William W Kerr, Mosshill, Ayr, KA6 6AJ Tel: (01292) 267376 Fax: (01292) 289645

AGRICULTURAL MACHINERY/ EQUIPMENT/IMPLEMENT MANUFRS

– continued

J. Wood & Son, 24 Dove Way, Kerkby Mills Industrial Estate, Kirkby Morside, York, YO62 6QR Tel: (01751) 433434 Fax: (01751) 433094 E-mail: admin@johnwoods.co.uk

Woodway Farm Machinery, Woodway Farm, Little Lane, Princes Risborough, Buckinghamshire, HP27 9NW Tel: (01844) 345375 Fax: (01844) 274081

Wye Valley Tractors Ltd, Tanyard Lane, Ross-on-Wye, Herefordshire, HR9 7BH Tel: (01989) 562486 Fax: (01989) 566030 E-mail: wvt1@aol.com

AGRICULTURAL MACHINERY/ EQUIPMENT/IMPLEMENT, USED

Addisons, North Holme, Main Street, Bonby, Brigg, South Humberside, DN20 0PY Tel: (01652) 618661 Fax: (01652) 618575

B C Thornell, Churchleaze, Codrington Road, Westerleigh, Bristol, BS37 8RQ Tel: (01454) 316935 Fax: (01454) 329642 E-mail: manc@bcthornell.fsnet.co.uk

Alistair Campbell, Wembly, Bridge of Marnoch, Huntly, Aberdeenshire, AB54 7UN Tel: (01466) 780826 Fax: (01466) 780230

Collings Bros Of Abbotsley Ltd, 3-5 Prospect Way, Chatteris, Cambridgeshire, PE16 6TZ Tel: (01354) 694169 Fax: (01354) 694218 E-mail: sales@collingbrothers.co.uk

East Anglian Tractors Ltd, Arkesden Road, Clavering, Saffron Walden, Essex, CB11 4QU Tel: (01799) 550268 Fax: (01799) 550874 E-mail: sales@eatractors.co.uk

Patrick Edwards, Langley Farm, Langley Lane, Little Clanfield, Bampton, Oxfordshire, OX18 2RZ Tel: (01367) 810259 Fax: (01367) 810545

Hayward United Farmers Ltd, Benacre Road, Ellough, Beccles, Suffolk, NR34 7XD Tel: (01502) 475111 Fax: (01502) 476533 E-mail: steve@hufl.co.uk

J G F Machinery, Windamoore Farm, Doras Green Lane, Ewshot, Farnham, Surrey, GU10 5DZ Tel: (01252) 851266 Fax: (01252) 850968 E-mail: sales@jgfmachinery.co.uk

▶ J Henry & Son, Shinny Road, Macosquin, Coleraine, County Londonderry, BT51 4PS Tel: (028) 7086 8505 Fax: (028) 7086 8811 E-mail: slles@agriplant.co.uk

John E Hitchings Hereford Ltd, Twyford Road, Rotherwas Industrial Estate, Hereford, HR2 6JR Tel: (01432) 272584 Fax: (01432) 353072 E-mail: enquiries@hitchingsofhereford.co.uk

Kent Harvest Centre, Bayley Wood, Great Chart, Ashford, Kent, TN26 1JJ Tel: (01233) 822300 Fax: (01233) 822301 E-mail: steve_lewis@southernharvesters.co.uk

R W Crawford Agricultural Machinery Ltd, 42-44 Cutlers Road, South Woodham Ferrers, Chelmsford, CM3 5XJ Tel: (01245) 322733 Fax: (01245) 322241 E-mail: sales@rwcrawford.co.uk

S & W Agricultural Services, Royd Moor Farm, Royd Moor Lane, Badsworth, Pontefract, West Yorkshire, WF9 1AZ Tel: (01977) 610943 Fax: (01977) 612891

AGRICULTURAL MAGAZINES

Avery Dennison, Unit 7, Astra Centre, Edinburgh Way, Harlow, Essex, CM20 2BN Tel: (01279) 786000 Fax: (01279) 786100 E-mail:

AGRICULTURAL MANAGEMENT CONSULTANCY

▶ Direct Farming & Rural Solutions Ltd, Newton House, Birch Way, Easingwold, York, YO61 3FB Tel: (01347) 822776 Fax: 01347 822776 E-mail: nola@dfrs.co.uk

AGRICULTURAL MERCHANTS

A C Burn Ltd, Mounthooly, Jedburgh, Roxburghshire, TD8 6TJ Tel: (01835) 850250 Fax: (01835) 850250

A Handley & Partners, Townsditch, Rossett, Wrexham, LL12 0AN Tel: (01978) 760341 Fax: (01978) 760341

A J Wyatt Animal Feeds & Supplies, Stowey House Farm, Stowey, Bishop Sutton, Bristol, BS39 5TQ Tel: (01275) 333312 Fax: (01275) 332013

A M Farm Supplies, Unit 6, 154 Newlands, Witney, Oxfordshire, OX28 3JH Tel: (01993) 772574 Fax: (01993) 706499

A M Handling Ltd, Burneston, Bedale, North Yorkshire, DL8 2JW Tel: (01845) 567233 Fax: (01845) 567360

A M S Glaswall Ltd, Shielhill Works, Loch Thom Road, Inverkip, Greenock, Renfrewshire, PA16 9NB Tel: (01475) 520170 Fax: (01475) 521653 E-mail: enquiries@glaswall.pluf.com

A Nichols Cowmills Ltd, Station Road, Yate, Bristol, BS37 4AD Tel: (01454) 313788 Fax: (01454) 326692 E-mail: general@anichols.co.uk

A & P Hill Fruit Ltd, Oakleigh, Thorn Road, Marden, Tonbridge, Kent, TN12 9EJ Tel: (01622) 728404 Fax: (01622) 832492 E-mail: graham@aphillfruit.co.uk

A R Gane & Sons, West Lydford, Somerton, Somerset, TA11 7DL Tel: (01963) 240501 Fax: (01963) 240502

Afb Farm Supplies, Sheriff House, Nantwich Road, Stanthorne, Middlewich, Cheshire, CW10 0LH Tel: (01606) 836464 Fax: (01606) 837676

Agricentre, Redhill, Bristol, BS40 5TG Tel: (01934) 863123 Fax: (01934) 862891 E-mail: redhill@agricentre.net

Agricentre, Castle Gate Business Park, Old Sarum, Salisbury, SP4 6QX Tel: (01722) 320316 Fax: (01722) 325613

Agricultural Brokerage Company Ltd, 18 Camp Hill Close, Dallamires Industrial Estate, Ripon, North Yorkshire, HG4 1QY Tel: (01765) 608522 Fax: (01765) 608040 E-mail: agricsupply@agriculturalsupply.co.uk

Agrispares Ni Ltd, 701 Feeny Road, Feeny, Londonderry, BT47 4SU Tel: (028) 7778 1522 Fax: (028) 7778 1631

Agronomy Services, 31 Mortimer Dr, Orleton, Ludlow, Shropshire, SY8 4JW Tel: 01568 780990 Fax: 01568 780990

Agrovista UK Ltd, Unit 2f Heathlands Industrial Estate, Liskeard, Cornwall, PL14 4DH Tel: (01579) 343142 Fax: (01579) 340258

Alan J I & M D James, Tegfan, Cilrhedyn, Llanfyrnach, Dyfed, SA35 0AB Tel: (01239) 698373 Fax: (01239) 698473

Howard Allen Seeds, 42 Calvertstown Road, Portadown, Craigavon, County Armagh, BT63 5NY Tel: (028) 3832 3213 Fax: (028) 3834 5583 E-mail: info@howardallen-seeds.com

Allied Grain (South) Ltd, Church Lane, Godmersham, Canterbury, Kent, CT4 7DS Tel: (01227) 731161 Fax: (01227) 731157

Robin Appel Ltd, The Town House, The Square, Bishops Waltham, Southampton, SO32 1AF Tel: (01489) 896388 Fax: (01489) 896602 E-mail: enquiries@robin-appel.com

Armstrong Richardson & Co.Limited, Mount Pleasant Way, Stokesley Business Park, Stokesley, Middlesbrough, Cleveland, TS9 5NZ Tel: (01642) 718280 Fax: (01642) 710993 E-mail: sales@armstrongrichardson.co.uk

B A T A Lloyds Ltd, 7 Norwood, Beverley, North Humberside, HU17 9ET Tel: (01482) 868135 Fax: (01482) 861173

B & B Contractors Ltd, Tamar Ridge, Cox Park, Coxpark, Gunnislake, Cornwall, PL18 9BD Tel: (01822) 834397 Fax: (01822) 834397

B E Williams Ltd, Sennybridge, Brecon, Powys, LD3 8RR Tel: (01874) 636711 Fax: (01874) 638902

B H James, Great Penlan, Brilley, Whitney-on-Wye, Hereford, HR3 6JW Tel: (01497) 831224

Ball Bros, 42 Church Road, Dromara, Dromore, County Down, BT25 2NS Tel: (028) 9753 2379 Fax: (028) 9753 2379

Banbury Farm General Supplies Ltd, Grove Farm Building, Burton Dassett, Southam, Warwickshire, CV47 2AB Tel: (01295) 770707 Fax: (01295) 770787

Banks Cargill Agriculture Ltd, Unit 7 Spalding Road Business Park, Bourne, Lincolnshire, PE10 9LF Tel: (01778) 422454 Fax: (01778) 426200

Barlow Farm Services Ltd, New Farm, Wilkin Hill, Barlow, Dronfield, Derbyshire, S18 7TE Tel: 0114-289 0209 Fax: 0114-289 1496

Bartholomews Specialist Distribution Ltd, Bognor Road, Chichester, West Sussex, PO19 7TT Tel: (01243) 539224 Fax: (01243) 536341 E-mail: agri@bartholomews.co.uk

Bartram Mowers, Bluebell Road, Norwich, NR4 7LG Tel: (01603) 458916 Fax: (01603) 250643 E-mail: sales@bartrammowers.co.uk

L.M. Bateman & Co. Ltd, Five Bridges, Cullompton, Devon, EX15 1QP Tel: (01884) 33453 Fax: (01884) 34410 E-mail: info@lmbateman.co.uk

Baxter Avey & Co. Ltd, The Hill House, Castor, Peterborough, PE5 7BS Tel: (01733) 380597 Fax: (01733) 380365 E-mail: william.baxter@virgin.net

Thomas Bell & Sons (Corn Merchants) Ltd, PO Box 5, Brigg, South Humberside, DN20 8RA Tel: (01652) 652933 Fax: (01652) 651313

Robert Blair, 50 Waterfall Road, Larne, County Antrim, BT40 3NQ Tel: (028) 2827 6898

Border Farm Supplies Ltd, Turfford Park, Earlston, Berwickshire, TD4 6GZ Tel: (01896) 848911 Fax: (01896) 848006

T.A. Bowkett, 3 Cox Industustrial Estate, Three Cocks, Brecon, Powys, LD3 0SD Tel: (01497) 851650 Fax: (01497) 847766

H.E.L.& H.M. Bradley & Son, Waddings Farm, Knighton-on-teme, Tenbury Wells, Worcs, WR15 8LY Tel: 01584 781243

Brandsby Agricultural Trading Association Ltd, Station Yard, Green Lane, Lebberston, Scarborough, North Yorkshire, YO11 3PF Tel: (01723) 584455 Fax: (01723) 586247

Brandsby Agricultural Trading Association Ltd, Ruswarp, Whitby, North Yorkshire, YO21 1NJ Tel: (01947) 602522 Fax: (01947) 602522

Brandsby Agricultural Trading Association Ltd, Sawmill Lane, Helmsley, York, YO62 5DQ Tel: (01439) 770372 Fax: (01439) 770372

Bridgman, Market Fields, Kilkhampton, Bude, Cornwall, EX23 9QZ Tel: (01288) 321777 Fax: (01288) 321211 E-mail: info@bridgmans.co.uk

Brock Farm Supplies, Foxhouses Farm Cottage, Long Lane, Scorton, Preston, PR3 1DB Tel: (01524) 791170

Burgess Agricultural Engineers Ltd, 1 Dyffryn Trading Estate, Rhyl Road, Denbigh, Clwyd, LL16 5SJ Tel: (01745) 816776 Fax: (01745) 812772 E-mail: denbigh@burgessae.co.uk

C A Davies & Sons Ltd, Dovefields, Uttoxeter, Staffordshire, ST14 8AE Tel: (01889) 564844 Fax: (01889) 568578

C C Moore & Co. Ltd, Church Hill, Sturminster Newton, Dorset, DT10 2RL Tel: (01963) 362234 Fax: (01963) 363837

C Cromie, 31 Reservoir Road, Banbridge, County Down, BT32 4LD Tel: (028) 4066 2448 Fax: (028) 4062 9291 E-mail: thomas@futuregenetics.co.uk

C Davidson Agricultural Contractors, Lincote, Southwaite, Carlisle, CA4 0EP Tel: (01697) 473506

C R Supplies, 143 Ballysnod Road, Larne, County Antrim, BT40 3NP Tel: (028) 2827 8800 Fax: (028) 2827 8800

C W G Ltd, Priory Depot, Uffington Road, Stamford, Lincolnshire, PE9 2HD Tel: (01780) 762543 Fax: (01780) 755152 E-mail: sales@cwg.co.uk

Cae Gwyn Farm Supplies, Caegwyn, Harford, Llanwrda, Dyfed, SA19 8EA Tel: (01558) 650318

Campmuir Ltd, Leanaig Road, Conon Bridge, Dingwall, Ross-shire, IV7 8BE Tel: (01349) 866021 Fax: (01349) 866020 E-mail: campuir@dinwald.net

Carmarthen & Pumpsaint Farmers Ltd, Myrtle Hill, Pensarn, Carmarthen, Dyfed, SA31 2NG Tel: (01267) 236794 Fax: (01267) 230721

Carmarthen & Pumpsaint Farmers Ltd, Station Yard, Station Road, Llangadog, Dyfed, SA19 9LS Tel: (01550) 777281 Fax: (01550) 777955

D.M. Carnegie Precast, Steelstrath, Laurencekirk, Kincardineshire, AB30 1RN Tel: (01674) 840288 Fax: (01674) 840395

Carrs Billington Agriculture Ltd, 78-80 Stirling Road, Milnathort, Kinross, KY13 9UZ Tel: (01577) 862381 Fax: (01577) 863057

Carrs Billington Agriculture Ltd, Highland House, St Catherines Road, Perth, PH1 5YA Tel: (01738) 643022 Fax: (01738) 643022

Chelford Farm Supplies Ltd, 2 Chelford Farm Supplies Ltd, Knutsford Road, Chelford, Macclesfield, Cheshire, SK11 9AS Tel: (01625) 861588 Fax: (01625) 861235 E-mail: sales@chelfordfarmsupplies.fsbusiness.co.uk

Cheviot Farmers Trading Co. Ltd, Greensfield Park, Willowburn Avenue, Alnwick, Northumberland, NE66 2DD Tel: (01665) 603117 Fax: (01665) 603119

Clynderwen & Cardiganshire Farmers Ltd, Main St, Clynderwen, Dyfed, SA66 7NW Tel: (01437) 563441 Fax: (01437) 563745 E-mail: info@ccfagri.co.uk

Clynderwen & Cardiganshire Farmers Ltd, Hermon Road, Crymych, Dyfed, SA41 3QE Tel: (01239) 831203 Fax: (01239) 831363

Clynderwen & Cardiganshire Farmers Ltd, Station Road, Letterston, Haverfordwest, Dyfed, SA62 5SY Tel: (01348) 840208 Fax: (01348) 841030

Clynderwen & Cardiganshire Farmers Ltd, Heol Maengwyn, Machynlleth, Powys, SY20 8EA Tel: (01654) 702448 Fax: (01654) 703685

Clynderwen & Cardiganshire Farmers Ltd, Spring Gardens, Narberth, Dyfed, SA67 7BT Tel: (01834) 860369 Fax: (01834) 869185

Clynderwen & Cardiganshire Farmers Ltd, Hebron, Whitland, Dyfed, SA34 0XP Tel: (01994) 419238 Fax: (01994) 419238

Coastal Grains Ltd, Station Road, Belford, Northumberland, NE70 7DT Tel: (01668) 213609 Fax: (01668) 213609 E-mail: terence@coastalgrains.fsnet.co.uk

Colin Rayner Green, The Street, Beachamwell, Swaffham, Norfolk, PE37 8BD Tel: (01366) 328275 Fax: (01366) 328853 E-mail: colin@rayner-green.sfnet.co.uk

Comonin Garage, Mitchel Troy, Monmouth, Gwent, NP25 4BL Tel: (01600) 740623 Fax: (01600) 740623

Cornwall Farmers Ltd, School Road, Praze, Camborne, Cornwall, TR14 0LB Tel: (01209) 831431 Fax: (01209) 832212

Cornwall Farmers Ltd, Otterham Station, Otterham, Camelford, Cornwall, PL32 9SW Tel: (01840) 261235 Fax: (01840) 261369

Cornwall Farmers Ltd, Station Yard, Liskeard, Cornwall, PL14 4DX Tel: (01579) 343446 Fax: (01579) 345645 E-mail: info@cornwallfarmers.co.uk

Cornwall Farmers Ltd, Three Milestone Industrial Estate, Truro, Cornwall, TR4 9LD Tel: (01872) 274301 Fax: (01872) 260484 E-mail: enquiries@cornwallfarmers.co.uk

Corwen Farmers Ltd, Station Yard, Corwen, Clwyd, LL21 0EG Tel: (01490) 412272 Fax: (01490) 412431 E-mail: enquiries@corwenfarmers.co.uk

Country Supplies, Hundred House, Llandrindod Wells, Powys, LD1 5RY Tel: (01982) 570200

Countrywide Farmers P.L.C., Brickhouse Lane, Stoke Prior, Bromsgrove, Worcestershire, B60 4LX Tel: (01527) 831663 Fax: (01527) 570290 E-mail: enquiries@countrywidefarmers.co.uk

Countrywide Farmers plc, Church Street, Melksham, Wiltshire, SN12 6LS Tel: (01225) 701470 Fax: (01225) 702318 E-mail: info@countrywidefarmers.co.uk

Countrywide Farmers P.L.C., Lady Lane, Blunsdon, Swindon, SN2 4DN Tel: (01793) 722888 Fax: (01793) 706011

Countrywide Stores, Old Gloucester Road, Thornbury, Bristol, BS35 3UH Tel: (01454) 260406 Fax: (01454) 260749

Countrywide Stores, Hook Norton Road, Chipping Norton, Oxfordshire, OX7 5TE Tel: (01608) 642071 Fax: (01608) 645125 E-mail: enquiries@countrywidefarmers.co.uk

Countrywide Stores P.L.C., Station Road, Stockton, Southam, Warwickshire, CV47 8HA Tel: (01926) 812513 Fax: (01926) 815105

Countrywide Stores, Grange Mill, Abergavenny Road, Raglan, Usk, Gwent, NP15 2AA Tel: (01291) 690056 Fax: (01291) 690378

Cropwise (North) Ltd, Unit 2a Greensfield Park Industrial Estate, Alnwick, Northumberland, NE66 2DD Tel: (01665) 510022 Fax: (01665) 510901

D Evans, The Poplars, Redhall Lane, Penley, Wrexham, Clwyd, LL13 0NA Tel: (01978) 710756

D & I Bridgman & Son Ltd, Down View, Newton St. Petrock, Torrington, Devon, EX38 8LS Tel: (01409) 261321 Fax: (01409) 261520 E-mail: mike@bridgmans.co.uk

D M B Farm & Garden Ltd, Riverbank Indust Park, Downshire Road, Newry, County Down, BT34 1DX Tel: (028) 3026 2354 Fax: (028) 3026 2658

D Mcconnell & Sons, Muiredge, Coaltown of Burnturk, Cupar, Fife, KY15 7TR Tel: (01337) 830246 Fax: (01337) 830246

D Reynolds Agricultural Engineers, 7 High Street, Bromyard, Herefordshire, HR7 4AA Tel: (01885) 483241 Fax: (01885) 483409

D T Jones & Son, Plas Yn Rhal, Llanbedr Dyffryn Clwyd, Ruthin, Clwyd, LL15 2UY Tel: (01824) 702955 Fax: (01824) 704585

Dalgarno Chemicals & Oils, Newton of Thainstone, Kintore, Inverurie, Aberdeenshire, AB51 0YG Tel: (01467) 632673 Fax: (01467) 633016 E-mail: dalgarnochemicals@btconnect.com

Dalgety Arable Ltd, Throws Farm, Stebbing, Dunmow, Essex, CM6 3AQ Tel: (01371) 856431 Fax: (01371) 856616 E-mail: throws.farm@dalgety.co.uk

DBC Agriculture Supplies, 3 Old Jewson Yard, Edenwall, Coalway, Coleford, Gloucestershire, GL16 7HN Tel: (01594) 835625 Fax: (01594) 835625

Deering Agri-Supplies Ltd, Cortrasna, Roslea, Rosslea, Enniskillen, County Fermanagh, BT92 7FU Tel: (028) 6775 1232 Fax: (028) 6775 1987

▶ Denis Brinicombe Ltd, Fordton Trading Estate, Crediton, Devon, EX17 3BZ Tel: (01363) 775115 Fax: (01363) 776761 E-mail: sales@brinicombe.co.uk

Direct Farm Marketing Ltd, Saxon Way, Melbourn, Royston, Hertfordshire, SG8 6DN Tel: (01763) 263031 Fax: (01763) 262504

Dods Of Haddington Ltd, Backburn, Haddington, East Lothian, EH41 4NN Tel: (01620) 823305 Fax: (01620) 824406

Doltons Silos & Storage Ltd, Water Eaton, Oxford, OX2 8HA Tel: (01865) 552914

Dovetail UK Ltd, 16 Hill Crescent, Dudleston Heath, Ellesmere, Shropshire, SY12 9NA Tel: (01691) 690407 Fax: (01691) 690419

E A Bell Ltd, 45a Church Road, Kells, Ballymena, County Antrim, BT42 3JU Tel: (028) 2589 2164

E C Reese Agricultural Ltd, Rose Brook, Pwlltrap, St. Clears, Carmarthen, SA33 4AR Tel: (01994) 230560 Fax: (01994) 230133

E George & Sons, Pontdolgoch, Caersws, Powys, SY17 5JE Tel: (01686) 688231 Fax: (01686) 688811 E-mail: info@egeorge.co.uk

E Hubert Agricultural Contractors Ltd, Dunt Avenue, Hurst, Reading, RG10 0SY Tel: 0118-934 1114 Fax: 0118-934 1114

E J Churchill, Fall Farm, Stanford Bridge, Worcester, WR6 6SJ Tel: (01886) 853240

E M Worts & Son, Little Mill, Disserth, Builth Wells, Powys, LD2 3TN Tel: (01982) 551426 Fax: (01982) 551601

East Down Farmers Ltd, 20 Tullynaskeagh Road, Downpatrick, County Down, BT30 7EU Tel: (028) 4484 1463 Fax: (028) 4484 1463

Eastern Forge Agriculture Ltd, Eastern Forge, Stockwell Gate, Whaplode, Spalding, Lincolnshire, PE12 6UE Tel: (01406) 422731 Fax: (01406) 424245 E-mail: eforge@nippymail.co.uk

▶ John Ebbage Seeds Ltd, The Stable Yard, Ryston Hall, Ryston, Downham Market, Norfolk, PE38 0AA Tel: (01366) 387877 Fax: (01366) 384285 E-mail: info@ebbageseeds.co.uk

▶ D.J. Edwards, Boduan, Pwllheli, Gwynedd, LL53 6DT Tel: (01758) 720815 Fax: (01758) 720881

Gordon Edwards & Sons, Fferm, Llanfwrog, Ruthin, Clwyd, LL15 2DB Tel: (01824) 702822 Fax: (01824) 702822 E-mail: edwfferm1@freeserve.co.uk

Geraint Evans A'i Fabion, Fronhaul, Llanpumsaint, Carmarthen, Dyfed, SA33 6LX Tel: (01267) 253244 Fax: (01267) 253244

Exmoor Farm Supplies, Carnarvon Arms Garage, Market Close, Brushford, Dulverton, Somerset, TA22 9AG Tel: (01398) 323933 Fax: (01398) 323327

F Waites & Sons, Harper Street, Driffield, North Humberside, YO25 6LY Tel: (01377) 253310 Fax: (01377) 253310

Fane Valley Co-Operative Society Ltd, Alexander Road, Armagh, BT61 7JJ Tel: (028) 3752 2344 Fax: (028) 3752 7876 E-mail: contact@fanevalley.co.uk

Fane Valley Co-Operative Society Ltd, 61 Clare Road, Tandragee, Craigavon, County Armagh, BT62 2EZ Tel: (028) 3755 1223 Fax: (028) 3755 1223

AGRICULTURAL MERCHANTS – *continued*

Farm Direct, 2 Westfield Terrace, Main Road, Flimby, Maryport, Cumbria, CA15 8QW Tel: (01900) 819923 Fax: (01900) 819936

Farmway Ltd, Albion Mill, Albion Street, Driffield, North Humberside, YO25 6QA Tel: (01377) 249700 Fax: (01377) 249709

Farmway Ltd, Chirnside, Duns, Berwickshire, TD11 3LJ Tel: (01890) 819400 Fax: (01890) 819409

▶ Farmway Ltd, Golden Lion Lane, Market Place, Leyburn, North Yorkshire, DL8 5AS Tel: (01969) 621300 Fax: (01969) 621309

Farmway Machinery Ltd, Cock Lane, Piercebridge, Darlington, County Durham, DL2 3TJ Tel: (01325) 374000 Fax: (01325) 374094 E-mail: csd@farmway.co.uk

Fenland Shops Ltd, Jubilee Garage, Abbey Road, Bourne, Lincolnshire, PE10 9EF Tel: (01778) 423041 Fax: (01778) 423041

Forsyths Of Wooler Ltd, Bridge End, South Road, Wooler, Northumberland, NE71 6QE Tel: (01668) 281567

Frank B Forman & Sons, The Mill, Rotten Row, Theddlethorpe, Mablethorpe, Lincolnshire, LN12 1NX Tel: (01507) 473472 Fax: (01507) 473701

Frontier Agriculture Ltd, Red Shute Mill, Hermitage, Thatcham, Berkshire, RG18 9QU Tel: (01635) 204100 Fax: (01635) 201417

Furness & South Cumberland Supply Association Ltd, Foxfield, Broughton-in-Furness, Cumbria, LA20 6BX Tel: (01229) 716229 Fax: (01229) 716860

Furness & South Cumberland Supply Association Ltd, Neville Street, Ulverston, Cumbria, LA12 0BJ Tel: (01229) 582122

G A Swinbank, Thorndale Farm, Melsonby, Richmond, North Yorkshire, DL10 5NJ Tel: (01325) 377318 Fax: (01325) 377796

Gardiner Icm, Lower Oldmill, Hatton, Auchterless, Turriff, Aberdeenshire, AB53 8BN Tel: (01888) 560044 Fax: (01888) 544948

George A Mackay, Benachie, Halkirk, Caithness, KW12 6UL Tel: (01847) 831636

Gillett Cook Ltd, Wildwinds Barn, London Road, Teynham, Sittingbourne, Kent, ME9 9JY Tel: (01795) 532235 Fax: (01795) 538868

Gleadell Agriculture Ltd, Lindsey House, Hemswell Cliff, Gainsborough, Lincolnshire, DN21 5TH Tel: (01427) 421200 Fax: (01427) 421230

Gortavoy Feeds & Farm Supplies, 73 Shanmaghry Road, Pomeroy, Dungannon, County Tyrone, BT70 2TT Tel: (028) 8775 9283 Fax: (028) 8775 9570 E-mail: info@gortavoyfeeds.co.uk

Grainfarmers Uap Ltd, Lark Whistle Farm Road, Michelldever Station, Micheldever, Winchester, Hampshire, SO21 3BG Tel: (01962) 794000 Fax: (01962) 794001

Arthur S. Griffiths, 2B Wonastow Road, Monmouth, Gwent, NP25 5AH Tel: (01600) 712626

H Colvin & Sons, 82 Ballybollen Road, Ahoghill, Ballymena, County Antrim, BT42 2RF Tel: (028) 7965 0222 Fax: (028) 7965 0217 E-mail: hcolvinandson@aol.com

H S Harper & Sons, 11 Kinallen Road, Dromara, Dromore, County Down, BT25 2NL Tel: (028) 9753 2677 Fax: (028) 9753 3555

H V Bowen & Sons Transport Ltd, Dwyrhiew Mill, New Mills, Newtown, Powys, SY16 3BS Tel: (01686) 650242 Fax: (01686) 650727

H W Feeds, Pantygarn, Eglwyswrw, Crymych, Pembrokeshire, SA41 3SY Tel: (01239) 891516 Fax: (01239) 891516

H Walton, Old Goole Mill, South Park Road, Goole, North Humberside, DN14 8BD Tel: (01405) 762928 Fax: (01405) 763542

Hampshire Grain Ltd, Overton Road, Micheldever Station, Winchester, Hampshire, SO21 3AN Tel: (01962) 774531 Fax: (01962) 774531 E-mail: info@hampshire-grain.co.uk

M . Hancock & Son Ltd, Hanover Mills, Mersham, Ashford, Kent, TN25 6NU Tel: (01233) 720871 Fax: (01233) 721200 E-mail: mhancockson@btinternet.com

Hanslope Land Link Ltd, White House, Bruisyard, Saxmundham, Suffolk, IP17 2EE Tel: (01728) 638082 Fax: (01728) 638741

Harbro Ltd, Unit 6 Admiralty Site, Corpach, Fort William, Inverness-Shire, PH33 7NA Tel: (01397) 772434 Fax: (01397) 773159

Harbro Ltd, Steven Road, Huntly, Aberdeenshire, AB54 8SX Tel: (01466) 793405 Fax: (01466) 794575

Harbro Ltd, Unit 2 Station Road Industrial Estate, Mintlaw, Peterhead, Aberdeenshire, AB42 5EE Tel: (01771) 622627 Fax: (01771) 622903 E-mail: sales@harbro.co.uk

Harbro Country Stores, Agricultural Centre, Staney Hill Industrial Estate, Lerwick, Shetland, ZE1 0QY Tel: (01595) 693744 Fax: (01595) 696741

Hay & Brecon Farmers Ltd, The Old Station, Newport Street, Hay-On-Wye, Hereford, HR3 5BH Tel: (01497) 820516 Fax: (01497) 821007 E-mail: farmershay@aol.com

Hay & Brecon Farmers Ltd, Station Yard, Llandrindod Wells, Powys, LD1 5BE Tel: (01597) 824851 Fax: (01597) 823914

Heard Oke & Letheren, Market Place, Hatherleigh, Okehampton, Devon, EX20 3JN Tel: (01837) 810576 Fax: (01837) 810605

Hilltop Seeds, Clayhanger, Tiverton, Devon, EX16 7NT Tel: (01398) 361387

Isca Agriculture, Venn Ottery, Ottery St. Mary, Devon, EX11 1RY Tel: (01404) 811200 Fax: (01404) 811222 E-mail: enquireries@isca-kinver.co.uk

Ivanhoe Feeds Ltd, Ashby Road, Boundary, Swadlincote, Derbyshire, DE11 7BA Tel: (01283) 212300 Fax: (01283) 221836

J C Hammond Ltd, The Windmill, Ringstead Road, Heacham, King's Lynn, Norfolk, PE31 7JA Tel: (01485) 570274 Fax: (01485) 572973

J Clarke, Upper Southwick Farm, Southwick, Mark, Highbridge, Somerset, TA9 4LQ Tel: (01278) 783708 Fax: (01278) 783708

J E Simpson & Son, Fir Tree Farm, Bramley Grange, Grewelthorpe, Ripon, North Yorkshire, HG4 3DL Tel: (01765) 658383 Fax: (01765) 658600

J J Melley & Sons (Welsh Feeds), Penybanc Stores, Maes Y Bont Road, Gorslas, Llanelli, Dyfed, SA14 7NA Tel: (01269) 842224 Fax: (01269) 842224

J & J Ransley, Golden Wood Farm, Brisley Lane, Ruckinge, Ashford, Kent, TN26 2PW Tel: (01233) 733189 Fax: (01233) 731002

J R K Campbell & Co., Camling, Tynron, Thornhill, Dumfriesshire, DG3 4JS Tel: (01848) 330419 Fax: (01848) 330833

J S Hubbuck Ltd, Anick Road, Hexham, Northumberland, NE46 4JS Tel: (01434) 601673 Fax: (01434) 605609 E-mail: catherine@hubbucks.freeserve.co.uk

J & V Dalton Ltd, Dalmark House, Eye, Peterborough, PE6 7UD Tel: (01733) 222391 Fax: (01733) 223246 E-mail: sales@dalmark.co.uk

Albert E. James & Son Ltd, Barrow Mill, Barrow Street, Barrow Gurney, Bristol, BS48 3RU Tel: (01275) 463496 Fax: (01275) 463791

James Tainsh & Sons, Drummondernoch Farm, Comrie, Crieff, Perthshire, PH6 2JB Tel: (01764) 670337 Fax: (01764) 670397

Jersey Farmers (Trading) Union Ltd, 20 Commercial Buildings, St. Helier, Jersey, JE2 3NB Tel: (01534) 733277 Fax: (01534) 768916 E-mail: jstush@jasonmiles.co.uk

Jim Hall, Jacksoms Lane, Langley Burrell, Chippenham, Wiltshire, SN15 5LU Tel: (01249) 750291 Fax: (01249) 750291

Ernie Jobling, 25 St Pauls Drive, Brompton on Swale, Richmond, North Yorkshire, DL10 7HQ Tel: (01748) 818550 Fax: (01748) 818550

John Foad & Co., 30 Westbere Lane, Westbere, Canterbury, Kent, CT2 0HH Tel: (01227) 713333 Fax: (01227) 712600

Kam Farming Ltd, Forston Farm, Forston, Dorchester, Dorset, DT2 7AB Tel: (01305) 257795 Fax: (01305) 889906 E-mail: kamfarming@aol.com

Kashif Export Company (International) Ltd, 2 Livesey Hill, Shenley Lodge, Milton Keynes, MK5 7EG Tel: (01908) 674758 Fax: (01908) 678139 E-mail: sales@kashifexport.co.uk

Kingdom Agribusiness, 7 Douglas Cresent, Kinross, KY13 8TJ Tel: (01577) 863396

L F Smith, Pink Road, Lacey Green, Princes Risborough, Buckinghamshire, HP27 0PG Tel: (01844) 343901

L L Morgan, Dolidrey, Llanddewi, Llandrindod Wells, Powys, LD1 6SE Tel: (01597) 851378 Fax: 01597 851378

Lachlan Macgregor Feeds, 1 Cross Street, Callander, Perthshire, FK17 8EA Tel: (01877) 331218 Fax: (01877) 331414

Laycocks Animal Health, Showfield Lane, Malton, North Yorkshire, YO17 6BT Tel: (01653) 600328 Fax: (01653) 690338

Leominster Farm Supplies Ltd, 17 Broad Street, Leominster, Herefordshire, HR6 8DB Tel: (01568) 612277 Fax: (01568) 616993 E-mail: hintonscountry@btinternet.com

Lewis Bros, The Grove, Hollyhurst, Leebotwood, Church Stretton, Shropshire, SY6 7JP Tel: (01694) 751212 Fax: (01694) 751212

Lewis Crofters Ltd, Island Road, Stornoway, Isle Of Lewis, HS1 2RD Tel: (01851) 702350 Fax: (01851) 703077

John Loader (Wessex) Ltd, Station Mill, Ashford Road, Fordingbridge, Hampshire, SP6 1BY Tel: (01425) 652394 Fax: (01425) 652625 E-mail: info@wessex-feeds.co.uk

M G Agricultural Ltd, Innage Park, Abeles Way, Holly Lane Industrial Estate, Atherstone, Warwickshire, CV9 2QX Tel: (01827) 712703 Fax: (01827) 718800

M S Souch, 55 Brize Norton Road, Minster Lovell, Witney, Oxfordshire, OX29 0SG Tel: (01993) 775386 Fax: (01993) 709635

M T W Pritchard, Yew Tree Cottage, Hillgates, Hereford, HR2 8JG Tel: (01981) 540828

M W Farm Supplies, 61 Holme Road, Market Weighton, York, YO43 3EW Tel: (01430) 872899 Fax: (01430) 872093

Mccash's Country Store, 1 Feus Road, Perth, PH1 2AS Tel: (01738) 623245 Fax: (01738) 451011 E-mail: info@mccash.uk.com

Samuel McCausland Ltd, Commercial Road, Banbridge, County Down, BT32 3ES Tel: (028) 4066 2277 Fax: (028) 4066 2288 E-mail: sales@mccauslands.co.uk

Mckelvey Bros, 34-36 Lisburn Street, Ballynahinch, County Down, BT24 8BD Tel: (028) 9756 5680 Fax: (028) 9756 5680

Mcveigh Parker & Co Ltd, Southend Road, Southend, Reading, RG7 6HA Tel: (0845) 1207755 Fax: 0118-974 4123 E-mail: sales@mcveighparker.co.uk

Mcveigh-Parker & Co. Ltd, Six Acre Farm, Stane Street, Adversane, Billingshurst, West Sussex, RH14 9JR Tel: (01403) 784250 Fax: (01403) 786394 E-mail: sales@mcveighparker.co.uk

Maelor Feeds Ltd, Pandy Farm, Whitchurch Road, Bangor-on-Dee, Wrexham, Clwyd, LL13 0BL Tel: (01978) 780280 Fax: (01978) 780150

Malmesbury Farm Supplies Ltd, Whitewalls, Easton Grey, Malmesbury, Wiltshire, SN16 0RD Tel: (01666) 822254 Fax: (01666) 826129

Martins Feeds & Farm Supplies, Nutts Corner Road, Aldergrove, Crumlin, County Antrim, BT29 4BT Tel: (028) 9082 5239 Fax: (028) 9082 5239

Maryland Farm, Main Road, Whissendine, Oakham, Leicestershire, LE15 7ER Tel: (01664) 474155 Fax: (01664) 474155

Ian Mason, Station Road, Hillington, King's Lynn, Norfolk, PE31 6DH Tel: (01485) 600496 Fax: (01485) 601412

Masstock Arable (Uk) Ltd, Moreton Mill, Moreton, Ongar, Essex, CM5 0DP Tel: (01277) 899700 Fax: (01277) 898206 E-mail: jane.cable@masstock.co.uk

Maunder & Sons Ltd, Scarne Industrial Estate, Launceston, Cornwall, PL15 9HS Tel: (01566) 773079 Fax: (01566) 776823

Medforth & Co. Ltd, 190 Hilderthorpe Road, Bridlington, North Humberside, YO15 3HD Tel: (01262) 673003 Fax: (01262) 679706 E-mail: johnbifton@btconnect.com

Mid England Agriculture Ltd, Hopyard Farm, Lubbesthorpe, Enderby, Leicester, LE19 4AZ Tel: 0116-263 0208 Fax: 0116-263 0121

Mole Avon Trading Ltd, Station Yard, Axminster, Devon, EX13 5PF Tel: (01297) 32441 Fax: (01297) 35818 E-mail: axminster@moleavon.co.uk

Mole Avon Trading Ltd, Mill Street, Crediton, Devon, EX17 1HL Tel: (01363) 774786 Fax: (01363) 773695 E-mail: admin@moleavon.co.uk

Mole Valley Farmers Ltd, The Forge, Church Street, Witheridge, Tiverton, Devon, EX16 8AP Tel: (01884) 860478 Fax: (01884) 860769

Tony Monkhouse, Heatherview, Hill End, Frosterley, Bishop Auckland, County Durham, DL13 2SU Tel: (01388) 528726

Montgomerie Feeds, Dryholme, Silloth, Wigton, Cumbria, CA7 4PZ Tel: (01697) 331396 Fax: (01697) 331272

Morton Contracts Ltd, The Dial House, Holly Bush Hill, Great Bentley, Colchester, CO7 8RN Tel: (01255) 820333

N B Camber, Harley, Harley, Shrewsbury, SY5 6LN Tel: (01952) 510524 Fax: (01952) 510222 E-mail: sales@cambers.com

N B Seed Processors Ltd, Willow Farm, Little Hale Fen, Sleaford, Lincolnshire, NG34 9BG Tel: (01529) 460021 Fax: (01529) 461740

N J Meagor, Trelawder, St. Minver, Wadebridge, Cornwall, PL27 6RF Tel: (01208) 813235 Fax: (01208) 816392 E-mail: nickpoultry@aol.com

N R & P J Haywood, Battenhurst Road, Stonegate, Wadhurst, East Sussex, TN5 7DU Tel: (01580) 200571 Fax: (01580) 200920

N W F Agriculture Ltd, Wardle, Nantwich, Cheshire, CW5 6AQ Tel: (0800) 262397 Fax: (01829) 260061 E-mail: enquiries@nwfagriculture.co.uk

N W F Country Store, Bert Smith Way, Adderley Road Industrial Estate, Market Drayton, Shropshire, TF9 3SN Tel: (01630) 655766 Fax: (01630) 658413

A. Nichols (Cowmills) Ltd, 8 London Road, Warmley, Bristol, BS30 5JF Tel: 0117-967 1447

Norman Ltd, 19 Commercial Buildings, St. Helier, Jersey, JE1 1BU Tel: (01534) 883388 Fax: (01534) 883334 E-mail: sales@normans.je

Oliver Seeds Ltd, Unit 3 Saxilby Enterprise Park, Skellingthorpe Road, Saxilby, Lincoln, LN1 2LR Tel: (01522) 706500 Fax: (01522) 706509 E-mail: enquiries@oliver-seeds.co.uk

Orchard Farm, Hurst Lane, Auckley, Doncaster, South Yorkshire, DN9 3NW Tel: (01302) 770206

Tim Osborne, Kenegie Home Farm, Gulval, Penzance, Cornwall, TR20 8YN Tel: (01736) 362515 Fax: (01736) 362515

Peter Owens, Frigidaile Mill, Great Smeaton, Northallerton, North Yorkshire, DL6 2NF Tel: (01609) 881941 Fax: (01609) 881941 E-mail: peterowens@home.3b.co.uk

P W Agriculture, 37 Cartlett, Haverfordwest, Dyfed, SA61 2LH Tel: (01437) 763553 Fax: (01437) 779095

R.C. Pardoe, Hill Farm, Putley, Ledbury, Herefordshire, HR8 2RF Tel: (01531) 670552 Fax: (01531) 670552 E-mail: robertpardoe@aol.com

Parkhead Farms, Maryculter, Aberdeen, AB12 5GL Tel: (01224) 733240 Fax: (01224) 733240

Parnell Lang Ltd, Copplestone Mills, Copplestone, Crediton, Devon, EX17 5NF Tel: (01363) 84561 Fax: (01363) 84147 E-mail: sales@ernest-charles.com

H. & C. Pearce & Sons Ltd, Aylesbury Road, Thame, Oxfordshire, OX9 3AS Tel: (01844) 212034 Fax: (01844) 261358 E-mail: info@hcpearce.co.uk

A.R. Pearson & Son, Hilltop Farm, Blankney, Lincoln, LN4 3BH Tel: 01526 378358

Perkins Ltd, Unit 17, Finnimore Trading Estate, Ottery St. Mary, Devon, EX11 1NR Tel: (01404) 812605 Fax: (01404) 815300 E-mail: fwp@fwperkins.prestel.co.uk

Phoenix Agronomy Ltd, The Stables, Featherbed Lane, Wighill Park, Tadcaster, North Yorkshire, LS24 8BN Tel: (01937) 832200 Fax: (01937) 834968

J. Pickard & Co. (Burrington) Ltd, Burrington, Umberleigh, Devon, EX37 9JJ Tel: (01769) 520279 Fax: (01769) 520424 E-mail: graham@pickards.co.uk

Portek Ltd, Blease Farm, Old Hutton, Kendal, Cumbria, LA8 0LU Tel: (01539) 722628 Fax: (01539) 741282 E-mail: sales@portek.co.uk

Powells Of Coolham Ltd, The Mill, Coolham, Horsham, West Sussex, RH13 8GR Tel: (01403) 741226 Fax: (01403) 741784

R A Owen & Sons, Minavon, Llandinam, Powys, SY17 5DG Tel: (01686) 688271 Fax: (01686) 688057 E-mail: info@raowenandsons.co.uk

R B Montague & Sons, Edmont, Preston-on-Wye, Hereford, HR2 9JT Tel: (01981) 500310 Fax: (01981) 500310

R C Boreham & Co., Woodfield Farm, Pleshey, Chelmsford, CM3 1HU Tel: (01245) 231320 Fax: (01245) 231435 E-mail: sales@rcboreham.co.uk

R D Musgrave & Sons, Edder Acres Farm, Shotton Colliery, Durham, DH6 2QB Tel: 0191-526 2965

R H Bunner & Son Ltd, Arthur Street, Montgomery, Powys, SY15 6RA Tel: (01686) 668308 Fax: (01686) 668564 E-mail: sales@rhbunner.co.uk

R H Miller Agricultural Ltd, 64-66 Old Town, Peebles, EH45 8JE Tel: (01721) 720711 Fax: (01721) 729968

R M Addy & Sons, 127 Station Road, Deeping St. James, Peterborough, PE6 8RQ Tel: (01778) 343314 Fax: 01778 343314

R M Welch & Son Ltd, Fountainbrae, Monifieth, Dundee, DD5 4DU Tel: (01382) 532139 Fax: (01382) 535138 E-mail: bruce@welchseeds.co.uk

R Riddles Bros, 35 Castlewarren Road, Dunamanagh, Strabane, County Tyrone, BT82 0PJ Tel: (028) 7139 8242 Fax: (028) 7139 8529

R W F Huxter, Filford Farm, Filford, Bridport, Dorset, DT6 5JW Tel: (01308) 488651

Rathfriland Farmers Co-Operative Society Ltd, Bog Road, Rathfriland, Newry, County Down, BT34 5DT Tel: (028) 4063 8493 Fax: (028) 4063 1539

Ray Wilson & Co., The Myrtles, Pious Drove, Upwell, Wisbech, Cambridgeshire, PE14 9AN Tel: (01945) 772352 Fax: (01945) 772375

George Rees, North Street, Caerwys, Mold, Clwyd, CH7 5AW Tel: (01352) 720111

S C A T S, Winterborne Kingston, Blandford Forum, Dorset, DT11 9AZ Tel: (01929) 471789 Fax: (01929) 472202 E-mail: info@scatscountrystores.co.uk

S D West, Lower Pensworth Farm, Redlynch, Salisbury, SP5 2JU Tel: (01725) 510322 Fax: (01752) 510325

S K Dodson, 2 Lower Green, Dane End, Ware, Hertfordshire, SG12 0PJ Tel: (01920) 830652 Fax: (01920) 830652

S Mcconnell, 50 Glenavy Road, Lisburn, County Antrim, BT28 3UT Tel: (028) 9267 3757 Fax: (028) 9260 2590

S Mason & Co., Bryndolau, Pumpsaint, Llanwrda, Dyfed, SA19 8BX Tel: (01558) 650230 Fax: (01558) 650230

S Ransley & Sons, Elite, Hornash Lane, Shadoxhurst, Ashford, Kent, TN26 1HU Tel: (01233) 732921 Fax: (01233) 732921

S T Rawlings & Son, Puddletown, Haselbury Plucknett, Crewkerne, Somerset, TA18 7NZ Tel: (01460) 72466

S & W Agricultural Services, Royd Moor Farm, Royd Moor Lane, Badsworth, Pontefract, West Yorkshire, WF9 1AZ Tel: (01977) 610943 Fax: (01977) 612891

S Walters, Bearley Lane, Tintinhull, Yeovil, Somerset, BA22 8PE Tel: (01935) 822033 Fax: (01935) 826767

Saracen Horse Feeds, The Forstal, Beddow Way, Aylesford, Kent, ME20 7BT Tel: (01622) 718487 Fax: (01622) 790321 E-mail: info@saracen-horse-feeds.co.uk

Scats, Hectors Way, Newbury, Berkshire, RG14 5AB Tel: (01635) 43436 Fax: (01635) 528502

Scotgrain Agriculture Ltd, Grampian Road, Elgin, Morayshire, IV30 1XJ Tel: (01343) 543281 Fax: (01343) 550849

Seller Agricultural Ltd, Dundee Road, Letham, Forfar, Angus, DD8 2PP Tel: (01307) 818545 Fax: (01307) 818939 E-mail: admin@sellerle.net.uk

J.R. Serpell & Son, Blackpool Farm, Yealmpton, Plymouth, PL8 2LF Tel: (01752) 348376 E-mail: enquiries@serpells.co.uk

Sharpe Haltham, Autumn Lodge, Wood Enderby Lane, Haltham, Horncastle, Lincolnshire, LN9 6JH Tel: (01507) 568485 Fax: (01507) 568485

William Shearer, 71 Victoria Street, Kirkwall, Orkney, KW15 1DQ Tel: (01856) 873189 Fax: (01856) 870892

Shropshire Highland Seeds, Brockton Store, Brockton, Lydbury North, Shropshire, SY7 8BA Tel: (01588) 680371 Fax: (01588) 680345

R. Simcock Excavations, Delight Farm, Barkisland, Halifax, W. Yorkshire, HX4 0DZ Tel: (01422) 822260 Fax: (01422) 822260

Springfields Supplies, 11 Bangor Road, Overton, Wrexham, Clwyd, LL13 0HB Tel: (01978) 710291 Fax: (01978) 710292 E-mail: sales@springfieldsupplies.co.uk

Spunhill Farm Sales, Ruthin Road, Mold, Clwyd, CH7 1QQ Tel: (01352) 759189

John Sturman Ltd, Park Street, Rowley Regis, West Midlands, B65 0LU Tel: 0121-559 1175 Fax: 0121-559 1175

Sugarich, Wildmoor Mill Farm, Mill Lane, Wildmoor, Bromsgrove, Worcestershire, B61 0BX Tel: (01527) 576077 Fax: (01527) 575269

AGRICULTURAL MERCHANTS – *continued*

Swarland Grain Driers Ltd, Kitswell Dene, Felton, Morpeth, Northumberland, NE65 9NZ Tel: (01670) 787698 Fax: (01670) 787281 E-mail: richard@swarlandgrange.fsnet.co.uk

T D Ladd & Son, Belle Vue, Clynderwen, Dyfed, SA66 7NQ Tel: (01437) 563217 Fax: (01437) 563217

▶ T Denne & Sons Ltd, Hanover Mill, The Forstal, Mersham, Ashford, Kent, TN25 6NU Tel: (01233) 720871 Fax: (01233) 721200

T Denne & Sons Ltd, Whitehill, Bilting, Ashford, Kent, TN25 4HB Tel: (01233) 812237 Fax: (01233) 813327 E-mail: p.den@btinternet.com

T Dixon & Son, Newbiggin-on-Lune, Kirkby Stephen, Cumbria, CA17 4NT Tel: (01539) 623229 Fax: (01539) 623229

T G Builders Merchants, Tattenhall Road, Tattenhall, Chester, CH3 9BD Tel: (01829) 770421 Fax: (01829) 770879 E-mail: admin@tggroup.co.uk

T M Lusby & Son, Willowdene, Main Road, Saltfleetby, Louth, Lincolnshire, LN11 7SS Tel: (01507) 338604 Fax: (01507) 338750

T Moxon, Icknield Street, Beoley, Redditch, Worcestershire, B98 9AL Tel: (01527) 585073 Fax: (01527) 585073

T R Noble, Summerfield Farm, Hawsker, Whitby, North Yorkshire, YO22 4LA Tel: (01947) 602677 Fax: (01947) 602677

T S G Ltd, Rumbridge Street, Totton, Southampton, SO40 9DR Tel: (023) 8030 4300 Fax: (023) 8066 7763 E-mail: sales@tsg.com

Tarff Valley Ltd, Tarff Station House, Ringford, Castle Douglas, Kirkcudbrightshire, DG7 2AN Tel: (01557) 820247 Fax: (01557) 820249

Tayside Grain Co. Ltd, 6 St. Catherines Road, Perth, PH1 5SE Tel: (01738) 623121 Fax: (01738) 630419

Teviot Town & Country Supplies, 22 Oliver Cresent, Hawick, Roxburghshire, TD9 9BQ Tel: (01450) 371699 Fax: (01450) 371699

Thomas Lowe & Sons Corn Merchants Ltd, 36 Pine View, Winstanley, Wigan, Lancashire, WN3 6DF Tel: (01942) 211909

Tony Cullimore Services, Berkeley Heath, Berkeley, Gloucestershire, GL13 9EW Tel: (01453) 810220 Fax: (01453) 811987

Torre Feeds, Camboree House, Exton, Exeter, EX3 0PN Tel: (01392) 874488 Fax: (01392) 876278 E-mail: torre.feeds@talk21.com

Towns & Carnie Ltd, The Ward, Huntly, Aberdeenshire, AB54 4QU Tel: (01466) 792413 Fax: (01466) 792413

Sam Turner & Sons Ltd, Darlington Road, Northallerton, North Yorkshire, DL6 2XB Tel: (01609) 772422 Fax: (01609) 770653 E-mail: clothing@sam-turner.co.uk

Tynedale Farm Services, Townfoot, Longtown, Carlisle, CA6 5LY Tel: (01228) 792377 Fax: (01228) 792377

▶ UK Animal Livestock, Unit D2, Whitwood Enterprise Park, Whitwood Lane, Whitwood, Castleford, W. Yorkshire, WF10 5PX Tel: (01977) 667222 Fax: (01977) 667333

Ulster Livestock Care, 13 Ballygonny Road West, Moneymore, Magherafelt, County Londonderry, BT45 7NS Tel: (028) 8673 7500 Fax: (028) 8673 6426

Union Grain Storage Ltd, Kirmans Marsh Farm, Marsh Lane, Orby, Skegness, Lincolnshire, PE24 5JA Tel: (01754) 810222

W C Stopher, Homeview, Halesworth Road, Redisham, Beccles, Suffolk, NR34 8NF Tel: (01986) 781253

W C Thornton & Son Ltd, Brook House, Garstang Road, Bilsborrow, Preston, PR3 0RD Tel: (01995) 640212 Fax: (01995) 641063

W D Lewis & Sons, 90-92 Bridge Street, Lampeter, Dyfed, SA48 7AG Tel: (01570) 422540 Fax: (01570) 423644 E-mail: sales@wdlewis.co.uk

W Glen & Son, Errol, Perth, PH2 7TE Tel: (01821) 642878 Fax: (01821) 642878

W H Evans, Melinllecheiddior, Garndolbenmaen, Gwynedd, LL51 9EZ Tel: (01766) 530635 Fax: (01766) 530635

W H Sallis & Sons, Llechryd, Cardigan, Dyfed, SA43 2QL Tel: (01239) 682220

W N Lindsay Ltd, Gladsmuir Granary, Gladsmuir, Tranent, East Lothian, EH33 1EJ Tel: (01875) 852151 Fax: (01875) 852926 E-mail: enquiries@wnlindsay.com

W S Shearing & Sons, Southfield Holdings, Amesbury Road, Weyhill, Andover, Hampshire, SP11 8ED Tel: (01264) 772974

Henry Waddington Ltd, The Stores, Halton West, Skipton, North Yorkshire, BD23 4LL Tel: (01729) 850206 Fax: (01729) 850658

Walter Bailey Par Ltd, St Andrews Road, Par, Cornwall, PL24 2LX Tel: (01726) 812245 Fax: (01726) 812246

Welsh Farm Supplies Ltd, Gorseland, North Road, Aberystwyth, Dyfed, SY23 2AR Tel: (01970) 636433 Fax: (01970) 611494 E-mail: enquiries@wfsagri.net

William Lillico & Sons Ltd, The Forstal, Beddow Way, Aylesford, Kent, ME20 7BT Tel: (01622) 718487 Fax: (01622) 882475 E-mail: post@lillico.co.uk

William Mciver & Son, 1 Hawthorn Terrace, Bishop Middleham, Ferryhill, County Durham, DL17 9AX Tel: 0191-377 1001 Fax: 0191-377 1002E-mail: enquiries@wmmcivorandson.com

Woodheads Seeds Ltd, Little Airmyn, Selby, North Yorkshire, YO8 8PT Tel: (01757) 617000 Fax: (01757) 618888 E-mail: woodheads@zoom.co.uk

Woody's Timber & Building Supplies Ltd, Kirkham Road, Freckleton, Preston, PR4 1HY Tel: (01772) 683737 Fax: (01772) 686104

Charles Wright & Sons Ltd, Church Road, Old Leake, Boston, Lincolnshire, PE22 9NU Tel: (01205) 870434 Fax: (01205) 871240

Wynnstay & Clwyd Farmers P.L.C., The Roe, St. Asaph, Clwyd, LL17 0LB Tel: (01745) 582527 Fax: (01745) 584538

Wynnstay Group plc, 1 Maesyllan, Llanidloes, Powys, SY18 6DF Tel: (01686) 412696 Fax: (01686) 412696

Wynnstay Group P L C, Eagle House, Llansantffraid, Powys, SY22 6AQ Tel: (01691) 828512 Fax: (01691) 828690 E-mail: info@wynnstayplc.co.uk

Wynnstay Group plc, Llanidloes Road, Newtown, Powys, SY16 1ET Tel: (01686) 626379 Fax: (01686) 626679

Wynnstay Group plc, Park Road, Ruthin, Clwyd, LL15 1NQ Tel: (01824) 704900 Fax: (01824) 705846

Wynnstay Group plc, Severn Road, Welshpool, Powys, SY21 7AY Tel: (01938) 552591 Fax: (01938) 556279

Wynnstay Stores, Watergate Street, Llanfair Caereinion, Welshpool, Powys, SY21 0RG Tel: (01938) 810525 Fax: (01938) 810256

AGRICULTURAL MINI DIGGER TRANSPORTATION VEHICLES

▶ Milbank Trucks Ltd, Airfield, Earls Colne, Colchester, CO6 2NS Tel: (01787) 224226 Fax: (01787) 220533

AGRICULTURAL MIXING MACHINES

Bratherton Manufacturers' Agents, 4 Old Park Road, Sheffield, S8 7DT Tel: 0114-274 9922 Fax: 0114-274 9933 E-mail: richard.bratherton@btinternet.com

AGRICULTURAL PHOTOGRAPHERS

▶ Pascal Molliere Photography, 6 Egham Court, Grove Road, Surbiton, Surrey, KT6 4DW Tel: 020 8390 5890 E-mail: pascal@pascalphoto.co.uk

▶ Paul Harness, 41 Pondfields Drive, Kippax, Leeds, LS25 7HJ Tel: 0113-286 0909 E-mail: sales@paulharness.freeserve.co.uk

AGRICULTURAL POWER TAKE OFF EQUIPMENT

Wood Auto Supplies, 4B Locksley Drive, Belfast, BT10 0BH Tel: (028) 9060 5880 Fax: (028) 9060 0376

AGRICULTURAL POWER TRANSMISSION EQUIPMENT

Comer Industries (UK) Ltd, Units 2-3, Heath Road, Merrylees Industrial Estate, Desford, Leicester, LE9 9FE Tel: (01530) 231504 Fax: (01530) 231503 E-mail: sales@comer.co.uk

AGRICULTURAL SECRETARIAL STAFF RECRUITMENT

BSC Sales Specialists, BSC House, 16 Blackfriars Street, Salford, M3 5BQ Tel: 0161-834 6234 Fax: 0161-835 3114

AGRICULTURAL SPRAY CHEMICAL PRODUCTS

Boothmans (Agriculture) Ltd, 6 Hereward, Cherry Holt Road, Bourne, Lincolnshire, PE10 9LA Tel: (01778) 394040 Fax: (01778) 394499 E-mail: info@boothman.co.uk

Farm Services Ltd, Old Rifle Range, Common Lane, Fradley, Lichfield, Staffordshire, WS13 8NQ Tel: (01543) 251307 Fax: (01543) 410777

Headland Agrochemicals Ltd, Rectors Lane, Pentre, Deeside, Clwyd, CH5 2DH Tel: (01244) 537370 Fax: (01244) 532097 E-mail: john.hughes@headlandmanufacturing.com

Syngenta Crop Protection UK Ltd, CPC4 Capital Park, Fulbourn, Cambridge, CB21 5XE Tel: (01223) 883400 Fax: (01223) 882195 E-mail: cropmarketing-uk@syngenta.com

AGRICULTURAL SPRAY EQUIPMENT

Allman Sprayers Ltd, Birdham Business Park, Birdham Road, Chichester, West Sussex, PO20 7BT Tel: (01243) 512511 Fax: (01243) 511171 E-mail: sales@allman-sprayers.co.uk

Anglia Sprayers Ltd, Unit 60, Lancaster Way, Ely, Cambridgeshire, CB6 3NP Tel: (01353) 666615 Fax: (01353) 668763 E-mail: mail@angliasprayers.co.uk

Claxton Engineering Co., 1 Buckminster Lane, Skillington, Grantham, Lincolnshire, NG33 5EY Tel: (01476) 860870 Fax: (01476) 861681 E-mail: claxtonsprayers@lineone.net

Cleanacres Machinery Ltd, Hazleton, Cheltenham, Gloucestershire, GL54 4DX Tel: (01451) 860721 Fax: (01451) 860139 E-mail: info@cleanacres.co.uk

Cleveland Crop Sprayers Ltd, Platform 1, Station Road, Duns, Berwickshire, TD11 3EJ Tel: (01361) 883418 Fax: (01361) 882082 E-mail: info@gambetti.co.uk

Kilnwick Sprayers Ltd, Thorpefield Farm, Thorpe le Street, York, YO42 4LN Tel: (01430) 871222 Fax: (01430) 871333 E-mail: sales@kilnwkk.sagehost.co.uk

Landmec Ltd, Redlake Trading Estate, Ivybridge, Devon, PL21 0EZ Tel: (01752) 891285 Fax: (01752) 891392 E-mail: info@landmecpottinger.co.uk

Micron Sprayers Ltd, Bromyard Industrial Estate, Bromyard, Herefordshire, HR7 4HS Tel: (01885) 482397 Fax: (01885) 483043 E-mail: micron@micron.co.uk

Spindrift Ltd, Unit 17 Park Farm, Hundred Acre Lane, Wivelsfield Green, Haywards Heath, West Sussex, RH17 7RU Tel: (01273) 890932 Fax: (01273) 890931 E-mail: lockerlexus@aol.com

Spraycare, Roughton Moor, Woodhall Spa, Lincolnshire, LN10 6YQ Tel: (01526) 353671 Fax: (01526) 353963 E-mail: sales@spraycare.com

AGRICULTURAL SPRAY PROTECTIVE CLOTHING, *See Protective Clothing etc*

AGRICULTURAL STAFF RECRUITMENT

▶ Central European Staffing, Thanet Way, Whitstable, Kent, CT5 3JF Tel: (01227) 771888 Fax: (01227) 771666 E-mail: sales@centraleuropeanstaffing.co.uk

AGRICULTURAL STOCKBREEDING INSTRUMENTS

Kruuse UK Ltd, 14A Moor Lane Trading Estate, Sherburn In Elmet, Leeds, LS25 6ES Tel: (01977) 681523 Fax: (01977) 683537 E-mail: kruuse.uk@kruuse.com

AGRICULTURAL TEST EQUIPMENT

Ele International, Chartmoor Road, Leighton Buzzard, Bedfordshire, LU7 4WG Tel: (01525) 249200 Fax: (01525) 249249 E-mail: ele@eleint.co.uk

AGRICULTURAL TOOL HIRE

▶ H S S Service Hire Group Ltd, 816 Oxford Road, Reading, RG30 1EL Tel: 0118-950 8882 Fax: 0118-975 0841

▶ HSS Hire, Wakefield Road, Bradford, West Yorkshire, BD4 7LX Tel: (01274) 308055 Fax: (01274) 724773

▶ HSS Hire, 119 West Street, Glasgow, G5 8BA Tel: 0141-429 6141 Fax: 0141-429 1342

▶ HSS Hire, 151 Abbey Lane, Leicester, LE4 5NZ Tel: 0116-268 1441 Fax: 0116-268 1257

AGRICULTURAL TOYS

▶ www.farmmodels.co.uk, The Old Manor Farmhouse, Lower Road, Edington, Westbury, Wiltshire, BA13 4QW Tel: (01380) 831459 Fax: (01380) 830659 E-mail: office@farmmodels.co.uk

AGRICULTURAL TRACTOR ACCESSORIES/FITTINGS

Bepco UK Ltd, Unit 2, Hatton Gardens Industrial Estate, Kington, Herefordshire, HR5 3RB Tel: (01544) 231144 Fax: (01544) 231484 E-mail: jbrett@bepco.co.uk

Ernest Doe & Sons Ltd, Whempstead Road, Benington, Stevenage, Hertfordshire, SG2 7BZ Tel: (01438) 869251 Fax: (01438) 869302 E-mail: ernestdoe@benington.com

Ernest Doe & Sons Ltd, Industrial Estate, Valleyside, Wymondham, Norfolk, NR18 0NN Tel: (01953) 602982 Fax: (01953) 601270 E-mail: rossjohnson@ernestdoe.com

Drews of Dinton Ltd, Dinton, Salisbury, SP3 5EH Tel: (01722) 716377 Fax: (01722) 716489

Gurney Reeve & Co. Ltd, Station Road, Spooner Row, Wymondham, Norfolk, NR18 9SR Tel: (01953) 603303 Fax: (01953) 601331 E-mail: sales@sweepersuton.co.uk

H M Howard & Sons, Manor Farm, Close Lane, Marston, Devizes, Wiltshire, SN10 5SN Tel: (01380) 723986 Fax: (01380) 730600 E-mail: howardagri@btconnect.com

H R N Tractors Ltd, Denside, Turriff, Aberdeenshire, AB53 8BJ Tel: (01888) 562101 Fax: (01888) 568940 E-mail: mail@hrmtractors.com

Luk Aftermarket Service Ltd, Holme Lacy Road, Hereford, HR2 6BQ Tel: (01432) 264264 Fax: (01432) 275146 E-mail: sales@luk.co.uk

AGRICULTURAL TRACTOR DISC MOWERS

▶ F N R GROUNDCARE, F N R GROUNDCARE, LYNN ROAD, WISBECH, CAMBS, PE14 7AP Tel: 01945 581576 E-mail: enquires@fnrgroundcare.co.uk

AGRICULTURAL TRACTOR DRUM MOWERS

▶ F N R GROUNDCARE, F N R GROUNDCARE, LYNN ROAD, WISBECH, CAMBS, PE14 7AP Tel: 01945 581576 E-mail: enquires@fnrgroundcare.co.uk

AGRICULTURAL TRACTOR EXPORT MERCHANTS OR AGENTS

Adams Cundell Engineers Ltd, The Coach House, Wicken, Milton Keynes, MK19 6DH Tel: (01908) 562191 Fax: (01908) 260461 E-mail: info@aceplant.co.uk

John E Hitchings Hereford Ltd, Twyford Road, Rotherwas Industrial Estate, Hereford, HR2 6JR Tel: (01432) 272584 Fax: (01432) 353072 E-mail: enquiries@hitchingsofhereford.co.uk

Ripon Farm Service Ltd, Station Road, Ottringham, Hull, HU12 0BJ Tel: (01964) 622351 Fax: (01964) 624078 E-mail: ottsales@r-f-s.com

AGRICULTURAL TRACTOR HAY TEDDERS

H M Howard & Sons, Manor Farm, Close Lane, Marston, Devizes, Wiltshire, SN10 5SN Tel: (01380) 723986 Fax: (01380) 730600 E-mail: howardagri@btconnect.com

AGRICULTURAL TRACTOR LAND PACKERS

Flails Direct Ltd, Marsh Lane, Laughterton, Lincoln, LN1 2JX Tel: (01427) 717449 Fax: (01427) 718016 E-mail: eng-hire@dial.pipex.com

AGRICULTURAL TRACTOR SEATS

Milsco Manufacturing Ltd, Harrington Way, Bermuda Park, Nuneaton, Warwickshire, CV10 7SH Tel: (024) 7658 0400 Fax: (024) 7658 0401 E-mail: info@milsco.co.uk

AGRICULTURAL TRACTOR TYRES

Trelleborg Wheel Systems (UK) Ltd, Resolution Road, Flagstaff 42, Ashby-de-la-Zouch, Leicestershire, LE65 1DW Tel: (01530) 565656 Fax: (01530) 565630 E-mail: info.tws.uk@trelleborg.com

AGRICULTURAL TRACTORS

Agco International Ltd, PO Box 62, Coventry, CV4 0GF Tel: (024) 7669 4400 Fax: (024) 7685 2495

Alan C Cowan, Hartburn, Morpeth, Northumberland, NE61 4EN Tel: (01670) 772555 Fax: (01670) 772655

John Bownes Ltd, Courthouse Farm, Swanlow Lane, Darnhall, Winsford, Cheshire, CW7 4BS Tel: (01606) 592639 Fax: (01606) 861410 E-mail: sales@jbownes.co.uk

AGRICULTURAL TRACTORS - *continued*

W. Burns Tractors Ltd, Blaircochrane, West Linton, Peeblesshire, EH46 7BD Tel: (01968) 673003 Fax: (01968) 678663 E-mail: wburnstractors@btinternet.com
Chandlers Farm Equipment Ltd, Boston Road, Horncastle, Lincolnshire, LN9 6JN Tel: (01507) 527211 Fax: (01507) 524498 E-mail: enquiries@chandlersfe.co.uk
John Cornthwaite Farm Machinery Ltd, The Auction Mart, Pilling, Preston, PR3 6AH Tel: (01253) 790771 Fax: (01253) 790839 E-mail: enquiries.pilling@cornthwaites.co.uk
John Deere Ltd, Harby Road, Langar, Nottingham, NG13 9HT Tel: (01949) 860491 Fax: (01949) 860490
Ernest Doe & Sons Ltd, Industrial Estate, Valleyside, Wymondham, Norfolk, NR18 0NN Tel: (01953) 602982 Fax: (01953) 601270 E-mail: rossjohnson@ernestdoe.com
G W J Weir & Son, 54 Mullybrannon Road, Dungannon, County Tyrone, BT71 7ER Tel: (028) 8772 3205 Fax: (028) 8772 7555 E-mail: weirtrset@aol.com
Hallmark Tractors Ltd, Smisby Road, Ashby-de-la-Zouch, Leicestershire, LE65 2UE Tel: (01530) 412811 Fax: (01530) 412512 E-mail: sales@tractors.co.uk
▶ Haynes Agricultural Ltd, Squires Farm Industrial Estate, Easons Green, Uckfield, East Sussex, TN22 5RB Tel: (01825) 841100 Fax: (01825) 841122 E-mail: sales@haynesgrp.co.uk
Inta-Trac UK Ltd, Little London, Halifax, West Yorkshire, HX3 7ST Tel: (01422) 206333 Fax: (01422) 204486 E-mail: sales@intatrac.co.uk
John E Hitchings Hereford Ltd, Twyford Road, Rotherwas Industrial Estate, Hereford, HR2 6JR Tel: (01432) 272584 Fax: (01432) 353072 E-mail: enquiries@hitchingsofhereford.co.uk
Kent Harvest Centre, Bayley Wood, Great Chart, Ashford, Kent, TN26 1JJ Tel: (01233) 822300 Fax: (01233) 822301 E-mail: steve_lewis@southernharvesters.co.uk
Kubota (UK) Ltd, Dormer Road, Thame, Oxfordshire, OX9 3UN Tel: (01844) 214500 Fax: (01844) 216685 E-mail: sales@kubota.co.uk
Lincolnshire Motors Ltd, Windsor Road, Fairfield Industrial Estate, Louth, Lincolnshire, LN11 0LF Tel: (01507) 604061 Fax: (01507) 605609 E-mail: sales@lincsmotors.co.uk
M S W Machinery (International) Ltd, 84 St James Lane, London, N10 3RD Tel: (020) 8883 0734 Fax: E-mail: michael@mswmc.co.uk
Mcalerney Brian Farmer, 20 Clanmaghery Road, Ballyward, Castlewellan, County Down, BT31 9RR Tel: (028) 4065 0281 Fax: (028) 4065 0653
McCormick Tractors International Ltd, Wheatley Hall Road, Doncaster, South Yorkshire, DN2 4PE Tel: (01302) 366631 Fax: (01302) 733491 E-mail: bridget.kenny@mccormick-intl.com
R H Wilson, 8 Derryhollagh Lane, Randalstown, Antrim, BT41 3HT Tel: (028) 7965 0614
R W Crawford Agricultural Machinery Ltd, 42-44 Cutlers Road, South Woodham Ferrers, Chelmsford, CM3 5XJ Tel: (01245) 322733 Fax: (01245) 322241 E-mail: sales@rwcrawford.co.uk
R W Marsh, London Road, Sleaford, Lincolnshire, NG34 8NX Tel: (01529) 303093 Fax: (01529) 413363 E-mail: sales@rwmarsh.com
Teme Valley Tractors Ltd, Castle Works, Wigmore, Leominster, Herefordshire, HR6 9UJ Tel: (01568) 770208 Fax: (01568) 770207 E-mail: bsmart@temevalley.co.uk
Terex UK Ltd, Central Boulevard, Prologis Park, Coventry, CV6 4BX Tel: (024) 7633 9400 Fax: (024) 7633 9500 E-mail: enquiries@terexce.com

AGRICULTURAL TRAILER ACCESSORIES/FITTINGS

John Day Engineering Ltd, Welford Works, Easton, Newbury, Berkshire, RG20 8EA Tel: (01488) 608666 Fax: (01488) 608781
Drews of Dinton Ltd, Dinton, Salisbury, SP3 5EH Tel: (01722) 716377 Fax: (01722) 716489
Hunton Legg (Running Gear) Ltd, Bridge Works, Bruisyard, Saxmundham, Suffolk, IP17 2DT Tel: (01728) 663010 Fax: (01728) 664057 E-mail: sales@huntonlegg.co.uk
Maypole Ltd, 54 Kettles Wood Drive, Birmingham, B32 3DB Tel: 0121-423 3011 Fax: 0121-423 3020 E-mail: maypole@maypole.ltd.uk
Spenco Engineering Co Ltd, Clyst Honiton, Exeter, EX5 2DX Tel: (01392) 369795 Fax: (01392) 364439 E-mail: post@spenco.co.uk
▶ Wolds Trailers, Millington Heights, Millington, York, YO42 1UB Tel: 01759 368225 Fax: 01759 369906 E-mail: millingtonheights@hotmail.com

AGRICULTURAL TRAILERS

Bateson Trailers Ltd, Doodfield Works, Windlehurst Road, Marple, Stockport, Cheshire, SK6 7EN Tel: 0161-426 0500 Fax: 0161-426 0245 E-mail: sales@bateson-trailers.co.uk
John Day Engineering Ltd, Welford Works, Easton, Newbury, Berkshire, RG20 8EA Tel: (01488) 608666 Fax: (01488) 608781
▶ Garden Machinery Direct, 4 Newtown Road, Worcester, WR5 1HF Tel: (01905) 619522 Fax: (01905) 726241 E-mail: sales@gardenmachinerydirect.co.uk
Hunton Legg (Running Gear) Ltd, Bridge Works, Bruisyard, Saxmundham, Suffolk, IP17 2DT Tel: (01728) 663010 Fax: (01728) 664057 E-mail: sales@huntonlegg.co.uk
Kay Trailers, 27 Stirling Road, Milnathort, Kinross, KY13 9XS Tel: (01577) 862493 Fax: (01577) 864864 E-mail: dropbox@kaytrailers.co.uk
Portequip Ltd, Penninghame Home Farm, Penninghame, Newton Stewart, Wigtownshire, DG8 6RD Tel: (01671) 402775 Fax: (01671) 403791
Reform & Weld, Building A, Gobowen, Oswestry, Shropshire, SY10 7JZ Tel: (01691) 650479 Fax: (01691) 650461
T F M Engineering, 1 Ghyll Mill, Beehive Lane, New Hutton, Kendal, Cumbria, LA8 0AJ Tel: (01539) 733881 Fax: (01539) 721616
Warwick Bros Alresford Ltd, The Dean, Alresford, Hampshire, SO24 9BN Tel: (01962) 732681 Fax: (01962) 735385 E-mail: info@warwicktrailers.co.uk
Wesbroom Engineering Ltd, 173 Mersea Road, Colchester, CO2 8PN Tel: (01206) 576959 Fax: (01206) 573788
Richard Western Ltd, The Durbans, Apsey Green, Framlingham, Woodbridge, Suffolk, IP13 9RP Tel: (01728) 723224 Fax: (01728) 724291 E-mail: sales@richard-western.co.uk
▶ Wolds Trailers, Millington Heights, Millington, York, YO42 1UB Tel: 01759 368225 Fax: 01759 369906 E-mail: millingtonheights@hotmail.com

AGRICULTURAL VEHICLE TYRES

Anchor Tyres, Unit 6, Oakwood Industrial Park, Gatwick Road, Crawley, West Sussex, RH10 9AZ Tel: (01293) 544577 Fax: (01293) 527477
Fieldens plc, Star House, Onehouse, Stowmarket, Suffolk, IP14 3EL Tel: (01449) 675071 Fax: (01449) 678282 E-mail: sales@fieldens.co.uk
Kalvin Tyre Co. Ltd, 259 High Road, Broxbourne, Hertfordshire, EN10 6PZ Tel: (01992) 462728
Kirkby (Tyres) Ltd, Speke Hall Avenue, Speke, Liverpool, L24 1UU Tel: (07734) 870892 Fax: 0151-486 5391 E-mail: sales@kirkbytyres.co.uk
Maxxis International, 9 Farthing Road Industrial Estate, Sproughton Road, Ipswich, IP1 5AA Tel: (01473) 742333 Fax: (01473) 742414
▶ Sam Moreton & Sons, Burnt Heath Farm, Long Itchington Road, Offchurch, Leamington Spa, Warwickshire, CV33 9AX Tel: (01926) 632269 Fax: (01926) 632023 E-mail: sales@farmerstyre.co.uk
Titan Distribution (UK) Ltd, North Florida Road, Haydock Industrial Estate, St. Helens, Merseyside, WA11 9UB Tel: (01942) 715333 Fax: (01942) 715111 E-mail: enquiries@titandistributionuk.com
▶ Tyre-Finder (ITBUK), Inhurst Avenue, Waterlooville, Hampshire, PO7 7QS Tel: (0845) 2301966 Fax: (0845) 2301966 E-mail: info@tyre-finder.co.uk
Watts Industrial Tyres plc, 9a Brindley Road, Bayton Road Industrial Estate, Coventry, CV7 9EP Tel: (024) 7664 5222 Fax: (024) 7636 7111
Watts Industrial Tyres plc, 9 Spencer Street, Grimsby, South Humberside, DN31 3AA Tel: (01472) 362589 Fax: (01472) 352772
Watts Industrial Tyres plc, Albion Road, West Bromwich, West Midlands, B70 8AX Tel: 0121-553 5451 Fax: 0121-500 5079 E-mail: westbrom@watts.co.uk

AGRO-INDUSTRIAL CONSULTANTS/TECHNICAL SERVICES

Booker Tate Ltd, Masters Court, Church Road, Thame, Oxfordshire, OX9 3FA Tel: (01844) 251000 Fax: (01844) 251020 E-mail: info@booker-tate.co.uk
D J A Parry, Gorsgoch, Llanybydder, Dyfed, SA40 9TH Tel: (01545) 590215
Tamar Crop Services Ltd, Howton Farm, Pillaton, Saltash, Cornwall, PL12 6QY Tel: (01579) 350001 Fax: (01579) 351420 E-mail: enquiries@tamarcropservices.co.uk

AIR BAGS, MOTOR VEHICLE

JS Auto Repairs, 137 Picasso Way, Shoeburyness, Southend-on-Sea, SS3 9UY Tel: (07779) 799027 Fax: (01702) 316137 E-mail: cs@jsautorepairs.co.uk

AIR BLAST COOLERS

▶ Howford Hydraulics, Old Howford Road, Catrine, Ayrshire, KA5 5JX Tel: (01290) 551428 Fax: (01290) 550549 E-mail: sales@howford.demon.co.uk
Trans Tronic, Whitting Valley Road, Old Whittington, Chesterfield, Derbyshire, S41 9EY Tel: (01246) 264260 Fax: (01246) 455281 E-mail: sales@trans-tronic.co.uk
Transtherm Ltd, 12 Banner Park, Wickmans Drive, Coventry, CV4 9XA Tel: (024) 7647 1120 Fax: (024) 7647 1125 E-mail: sales@transtherm.ltd.uk

AIR BLOWERS

Corsair Vacuum Systems Ltd, The Avenue, Endon, Stoke-On-Trent, ST9 9BY Tel: (01782) 504459 Fax: (01782) 504459 E-mail: corsair@vacpumps.co.uk

AIR BREATHING FILTERS

Air Safety Ltd, Vickers Industrial Estate, Mellishaw Lane, Morecambe, Lancashire, LA3 3EN Tel: (01524) 388696 Fax: (01524) 33386 E-mail: sales@airsafetymedical.com
Kiwi Products Dartford Ltd, 12 Dickens Court, Enterprise Close, Medway City Estate, Rochester, Kent, ME2 4LY Tel: (01634) 718484 Fax: (01634) 718484 E-mail: enquiries@kiwiproducts.co.uk
Nationwide Filter Co. Ltd, Unit 16 First Quarter, Blenheim Road, Epsom, Surrey, KT19 9QN Tel: (01372) 728548 Fax: (01372) 742831

AIR CARGO HANDLING SERVICES

Am Safe Ltd, Tamian Way, Hounslow, TW4 6BL Tel: (020) 8572 0321 Fax: (020) 8572 2096 E-mail: sales@am-safe.co.uk
Arrowfreight Ltd, Unit D3, Crossgate Drive, Queens Drive Industrial Estate, Nottingham, NG2 1LW Tel: 0115-986 8031 Fax: 0115-986 0607 E-mail: info@arrowfreight.com
D A S Air Cargo Ltd, North Elm Park Court Tilgate Forest Business Centre, Crawley, West Sussex, RH11 9BP Tel: (01293) 540303 Fax: (01293) 514036 E-mail: sales@dasair.com
Saxon Lifts Ltd, Grand Union Works, Whilton Locks, Whilton, Daventry, Northamptonshire, NN11 2NH Tel: (01327) 843355 Fax: (01327) 843887 E-mail: sales@saxonlifts.com
Turkish Airlines, 125 Pall Mall, London, SW1Y 5EA Tel: (020) 7766 9300 Fax: (020) 7976 1733 E-mail: turkishairlines.uk@btinternet.com

AIR CHARTER AGENTS OR BROKERS

Air Partner Insurance Consultants Ltd, Platinum House Gatwick Road, Crawley, West Sussex, RH10 9RP Tel: (01293) 549555 Fax: (01293) 536810 E-mail: france@airpartner.com
The Cabair Group Ltd, Elstree Aerodrome, Elstree, Borehamwood, Hertfordshire, WD6 3AW Tel: (020) 8236 2400 Fax: (020) 8207 0995 E-mail: group@cabair.com
Chapman Freeborn Airchartering Ltd, 5 Hobart Place, London, SW1W 0HU Tel: (020) 7393 1234 Fax: (020) 7393 1275 E-mail: info@chapman-freeborn.com
Dolphin Maritime & Aviation Services Ltd, 16 The Broadway, Stanmore, Middlesex, HA7 4DW Tel: (020) 8954 8800 Fax: (020) 8954 8844 E-mail: intfo@dolphin-maritime.com
International Skycharter Ltd, Diamond House, 36-38 Hatton Garden, London, EC1N 8EB Tel: (020) 7242 9501 Fax: (020) 7405 4255 E-mail: sales@skycharter.co.uk
John Gardiner Airfreight Ltd, 14 Mount Road, Feltham, Middlesex, TW13 6AR Tel: (020) 8894 3537 Fax: (020) 8894 3542 E-mail: john@johngardinerfreight.com
Skydrift Ltd, Norwich Airport, Norwich, NR6 6EP Tel: (01603) 407424 Fax: (01603) 418687 E-mail: ops@skydrift.co.uk
▶ Sovereign Business Integration, 1a Chalk Lane, Cockfosters, Barnet, Hertfordshire, EN4 9JQ Tel: (020) 8216 3333 Fax: (020) 8216 3300 E-mail: jhambleton@sovereign-plc.co.uk
Twinjet Aircraft Sales Ltd, Essex House, Proctor Way, Luton, LU2 9PE Tel: (01582) 452888 Fax: (01582) 400098 E-mail: jets@twinjet.co.uk
▶ UK Air, 3000 Aviator Way, Manchester Airport, Manchester, M41 0TN Tel: 0161-266 1116 E-mail: ian.wilde@flyukair.com
▶ Winged Bull Aviation, 5, Norway House, 22 Cockspur Street, Trafalgar Square, London, SW1Y 5BN Tel: 0870 850 3395 Fax: 0870 850 3396 E-mail: fly@bullwings.com

AIR CHARTER OPERATORS/ SERVICES

Aeromega Ltd, Hanger 1, Stapleford Aerodrome, Stapleford Tawney, Romford, RM4 1SJ Tel: (01708) 688361 Fax: (01708) 688566 E-mail: enquiries@aeromega.com
Air Contractors, Ema Cargo West, East Midland Int Airport, Castle Donington, Derby, DE74 2TR Tel: (01332) 857850 Fax: (01332) 857859 E-mail: info@aircontractors.com
Air Partner Insurance Consultants Ltd, Platinum House Gatwick Road, Crawley, West Sussex, RH10 9RP Tel: (01293) 549555 Fax: (01293) 536810 E-mail: france@airpartner.com
British Airways plc, PO Box 365, West Drayton, Middlesex, UB7 0GB Tel: (020) 8759 5511 Fax: (020) 8738 9800
Carill Aviation Ltd, Southampton International Airport, Southampton, SO18 2NL Tel: (023) 8062 7225 E-mail: enquiries@carillavation.co.uk
Centreline Air Charter Ltd, Bristol Flying Centre, Bristol International Airport, Bristol, BS48 3DP Tel: (01275) 474357 Fax: (01275) 476539 E-mail: operations@centrelineair.co.uk
Donington Aviation Engineering, East Midlands Airport, Castle Donington, Derby, DE74 2SA Tel: (01332) 812694 Fax: (01332) 812726
Eastern Air Executive Ltd, Sturgate Airfield, Heapham, Gainsborough, Lincolnshire, DN21 5PA Tel: (01427) 838280 Fax: (01427) 838416
Eurojet Aviation Ltd, Belfast Int Airport, Belfast, BT29 4AB Tel: (028) 9442 2888 Fax: (028) 9442 2640 E-mail: engineering@eurojet.co.uk
Freight Co. International Ltd, Unit 5 Howe Moss Drive, Dyce, Aberdeen, AB21 0GL Tel: (01224) 771881 Fax: (01224) 770730 E-mail: info@freightco-group.co.uk
Humberside International Airport Ltd, Humberside Int Airport, Kirmington, Ulceby, South Humberside, DN39 6YH Tel: (01652) 688456 Fax: (01652) 680524 E-mail: m.mumby@humbairport.co.uk
Isles Of Scilly Steamship Co. Ltd, Hugh Street, St. Mary's, Isles of Scilly, TR21 0LJ Tel: (01720) 422357 Fax: (01720) 422192
Kuehne & Nagel Ltd, St.Andrews House, St.Andrews Road, Avonmouth, Bristol, BS11 9DQ Tel: 0117-982 7101 Fax: 0117-982 4606 E-mail: knbrs.fa@kuehne-nagel.com
Monarch Airlines Ltd, Prospect House, Prospect Way, London Luton Airport, Luton, LU2 9NU Tel: (01582) 400000 Fax: (01582) 398323 E-mail: reservation@monarchairlines.com
Northern Executive Aviation Ltd, Hangar 7, Western Maintenance Area, Manchester Airport, Manchester, M90 5NE Tel: 0161-436 6666 Fax: 0161-436 3450 E-mail: info@northernexec.com
Rangemile (Air Commuter) Ltd, Coventry Airport, Coventry, CV8 3AZ Tel: (024) 7630 4452 Fax: (024) 7663 9031 E-mail: rangemile@air-commuter.co.uk
Signature Aircraft Engineering, Hangar Road, Denham Airfield, Uxbridge, Middlesex, UB9 5DF Tel: (01895) 834777 Fax: (01252) 864399
Skydrift Ltd, Norwich Airport, Norwich, NR6 6EP Tel: (01603) 407424 Fax: (01603) 418687 E-mail: ops@skydrift.co.uk
▶ Sovereign Business Integration, 1a Chalk Lane, Cockfosters, Barnet, Hertfordshire, EN4 9JQ Tel: (020) 8216 3333 Fax: (020) 8216 3300 E-mail: jhambleton@sovereign-plc.co.uk
Twinjet Aircraft Sales Ltd, Essex House, Proctor Way, Luton, LU2 9PE Tel: (01582) 452888 Fax: (01582) 400098 E-mail: jets@twinjet.co.uk
▶ UK Air, 3000 Aviator Way, Manchester Airport, Manchester, M41 0TN Tel: 0161-266 1116 E-mail: ian.wilde@flyukair.com
Volga-Dnepr UK Ltd, Endeavour House, Coopers End Road, London Stansted Airport, Stansted, Essex, CM24 1HA Tel: (01279) 661166 Fax: (01279) 661103 E-mail: dennis.gliznoutsa@volga-dnepr.co.uk
Westair Flying Services Ltd, Blackpool Airport, Blackpool, FY4 2QX Tel: (01253) 404925 Fax: (01253) 401121 E-mail: services@westair.uk.com
▶ Winged Bull Aviation, 5, Norway House, 22 Cockspur Street, Trafalgar Square, London, SW1Y 5BN Tel: 0870 850 3395 Fax: 0870 850 3396 E-mail: fly@bullwings.com

AIR CIRCUIT BREAKERS (CB)

G E Power Controls Ltd, East Lancashire Road, Liverpool, L10 5HB Tel: 0151-524 1122 Fax: 0151-523 7007 E-mail: gepcuk.sales@gepc.ge.com

AIR CLEANER/PURIFIERS, DOMESTIC, ELECTRIC APPLIANCES

▶ Elbow Grease Cleaners, Kestrel House, Gurnell Grove, West Ealing, London, W13 0AD Tel: 020 82211300 Fax: 020 85030400 E-mail: info@elbowgreasecleaners.co.uk
Sterling Electrical Centre, 16 North Street, Leighton Buzzard, Bedfordshire, LU7 1EN Tel: (01525) 376895 Fax: (01525) 853358 E-mail: peter.sinclair@shop4electricals.co.uk

AIR CLEANERS, ELECTROSTATIC

▶ Adremit Ltd, Unit 2, Whalley Industrial Park, Barrow, Clitheroe, Lancashire, BB7 1QA Tel: (01254) 822021 Fax: (01254) 825720 E-mail: info@adremit.co.uk

AIR COMPRESSOR CONTROL EQUIPMENT

AIRLINK, 15 Masefield Avenue, Portsmouth, PO6 4PD Tel: 02392 851396 Fax: 02392 376662 E-mail: airlink@elite.co.uk

▶ Gardner Denver Alton Ltd, Larkfield Trading Estate, New Hythe Lane, Larkfield, Aylesford, Kent, ME20 6SW Tel: (01622) 716816 Fax: (01622) 715115 E-mail: ukinfo@eu.gardnerdenver.com

▶ Hyrdrovane Air Compressor Services, 1d North Crescent, London, E16 4TG Tel: (020) 7473 3424 Fax: (020) 7511 0194 E-mail: sales@awphillips.co.uk

▶ Merseyside Compressor Services, 3 Atherton Road, Liverpool, L9 7EL Tel: 0151-523 2160 Fax: 0151-523 2413 E-mail: mikefoley.mcs@tiscali.co.uk

▶ A.W. Phillips Ltd, Unit L OYO Business Unit, Hindmans Way, Dagenham, Essex, RM9 6LN Tel: (020) 8517 0902 Fax: (020) 8517 0832 E-mail: sales@awphillips.co.uk

AIR COMPRESSOR HIRE

A C L Engineering Ltd, Anglia House, Sandown Road Industrial Estate, Watford, WD24 7UA Tel: (01923) 249444 Fax: (01923) 242368 E-mail: sales@aclengineering.co.uk

Aggreko UK Ltd, Exchange House, Watling Street, Bridgtown, Cannock, Staffordshire, WS11 0BN Tel: (01543) 437777 Fax: (01543) 437788 E-mail: doncaster@aggreko.co.uk

Air Controls & Compressors Ltd, 9 Trafalgar Court, Widnes, Cheshire, WA8 0SZ Tel: 0151-423 1750 Fax: 0151-495 2079 E-mail: sales@accltd.com

Air Equipment, 5 Kings Road, Flitwick, Bedford, MK45 1ED Tel: (01525) 723700 Fax: (01525) 723737 E-mail: info@air-equipment.co.uk

Air For Hire Ltd, Frederick House, Anchor Lane, Bilston, West Midlands, WV14 9NE Tel: (01902) 887262 Fax: (01902) 884632

Air Technique Ltd, Eagle Centre, 1 Progress Way, Luton, LU4 9TR Tel: (01582) 495151 Fax: (01582) 495152 E-mail: sales@air-technique.co.uk

▶ Airpac Air Compressors, Mugiemoss Road, Bucksburn, Aberdeen, AB21 9NP Tel: (01224) 715008 Fax: (01224) 714290 E-mail: airpac.rentals@vpplc.com

Airquick Newark Ltd, Northern Road, Newark, Nottinghamshire, NG24 2EU Tel: (01636) 640480 Fax: (01636) 701216 E-mail: info@airquick.co.uk

▶ Already Hire Ltd, 469 Malton Avenue, Slough, SL1 4QU Tel: (01753) 512333 Fax: (01753) 533303

Anglian Compressors & Equipment Ltd, Storeys Bar Road, Peterborough, PE1 5YS Tel: (01733) 349993 Fax: (01733) 564983 E-mail: business@angliancomp.co.uk

Chelmer Pneumatics, Unit 8, Moss Rd, Freebournes Industrial Estate, Witham, Essex, CM8 3UQ Tel: (01376) 500595 Fax: (01376) 501589 E-mail: sales@chelmerpneumatics.co.uk

Compressor Engineering Sales Ltd, Cunliffe Drive Industrial Estate, Cunliffe Drive, Kettering, Northamptonshire, NN16 8LD Tel: (01536) 520339 Fax: (01536) 310061

D E Horn Pneumatic Services, Air Centre, Park Street, Ivybridge, Devon, PL21 9DW Tel: (01752) 893531 Fax: (01752) 690449 E-mail: sales@dehorn.co.uk

E H Roberts & Co Southend Ltd, 251-255 Church Road, Benfleet, Essex, SS7 4QP Tel: (01268) 752811 Fax: (01268) 793416

Exploration Electronics Ltd, Suffolk Road, Great Yarmouth, Norfolk, NR31 0ER Tel: (01493) 412040 Fax: (01493) 412044 E-mail: info@exploration-electronics.co.uk

Gloucester Conpressed Air Specialists Ltd, Staunton Court Business Park, Ledbury Road, Staunton, Gloucester, GL19 3QS Tel: (01452) 840042 Fax: (01452) 840260

H P C Engineering Plc, Victoria Gardens, Victoria Gardens Industrial Estate, Burgess Hill, West Sussex, RH15 9RQ Tel: (01444) 241671 Fax: (01444) 247304 E-mail: info@hpcplc.co.uk

▶ H & P Hire, 5 Black Stick Road, Killyhevlin Industrial Estate, Enniskillen, County Fermanagh, BT74 4EB Tel: (028) 6632 2250 Fax: (028) 6632 3326 E-mail: ronnie@handphire.co.uk

Motivair Compressors Ltd, Brittania Road, Waltham Cross, Hertfordshire, EN8 7NU Tel: (01992) 704300 Fax: (01992) 704170 E-mail: enquiries@leachlewis.co.uk

Plant Hire Ltd, Unit 3, Aquarius Business Park, Priestley Way, London, NW2 7AN Tel: (020) 8208 3838 Fax: (020) 8450 3716

▶ Pneumatic Tools & Compressors Ltd, Acton Road, Long Eaton, Nottingham, NG10 1FU Tel: 0115-973 4099 Fax: 0115-946 3030 E-mail: info@pneumatictools.sagehost.co.uk

Pump Action Ltd, 19 Hutchison Road, Edinburgh, EH14 1RA Tel: 0131-444 0888 Fax: 0131-444 2888 E-mail: enquiries@pumpactionltd.co.uk

Rodwell H T B, Bentalls, Basildon, Essex, SS14 3SD Tel: (01268) 286646 Fax: (01268) 287799 E-mail: sales@rodwell-autoclave.com

Servair Ltd, Unit 6 Blackpole Trad Est East Blackpole, Worcester, WR3 8SG Tel: 01905 755400

AIR COMPRESSOR INSTALLATION

Allube Ltd, Thorncliffe Park Estate, Chapeltown, Sheffield, S35 2PH Tel: 0114-245 4979 Fax: 0114-257 0377 E-mail: sales@allube.co.uk

Compressor Systems South West Ltd, 5 Riverside Business Park, St Annes Road, St. Annes Park, Bristol, BS4 4ED Tel: 0117-977 4531 Fax: 0117-972 3650 E-mail: sales@compressorsystems.co.uk

▶ Everquip Garage Equipment Ltd, Tex Works, Wyke St, Hull, HU9 1PA Tel: (01482) 226699 Fax: (01482) 211184 E-mail: info@everquip.co.uk

▶ Pneumatic Tools & Compressors Ltd, Acton Road, Long Eaton, Nottingham, NG10 1FU Tel: 0115-973 4099 Fax: 0115-946 3030 E-mail: info@pneumatictools.sagehost.co.uk

▶ Scorpion Compressed Air Co. Ltd, 9 Partington Street, Morris Green, Bolton, BL3 3LE Tel: (01204) 431846 E-mail: info@scorpioncompressors.co.uk

Thorite, Thorite House, Laisterdyke, Bradford, West Yorkshire, BD4 8BZ Tel: (01274) 663471 Fax: (01274) 668296 E-mail: info@thorite.co.uk

AIR COMPRESSOR MAINTENANCE OR REPAIR

A & B Air Systems Ltd, Unit 41 Abenbury Way, Wrexham Industrial Estate, Wrexham, Clwyd, LL13 9UZ Tel: (01978) 661999 Fax: (01978) 664330 E-mail: sales@ab-airsystems.co.uk

Air Equipment, 5 Kings Road, Flitwick, Bedford, MK45 1ED Tel: (01525) 723700 Fax: (01525) 723737 E-mail: info@air-equipment.co.uk

Air Methods Ltd, Frederick House, Anchor Lane, Bilston, West Midlands, WV14 9NE Tel: (01902) 884466 Fax: (01902) 884632 E-mail: sales@airmethods.co.uk

Airchannel Ltd, Unit 10, Blackburn Industrial Estate, Blackburn, Aberdeen, AB21 0RX Tel: (01224) 790895 Fax: (01224) 790921 E-mail: enquiries@airchannel.co.uk

Airchannel Ltd, Unit 5, Smithies Mill, Bradford Road, Batley, West Yorkshire, WF17 8NS Tel: (01924) 475740 Fax: (01924) 475177 E-mail: enquiries@airchannel.co.uk

Airchannel, Unit 16, Hurworth Road, Aycliffe Industrial Park, Aycliffe, Newton Aycliffe, County Durham, DL5 6UD Tel: (01325) 321237 Fax: (01325) 318397 E-mail: aycliife@woodsidecompressors.co.uk

Airquick Newark Ltd, Northern Road, Newark, Nottinghamshire, NG24 2EU Tel: (01636) 640480 Fax: (01636) 701216 E-mail: info@airquick.co.uk

Babcock PTI, Lorne Road, Larbert, Stirlingshire, FK5 4AT Tel: (01324) 552599 Fax: (01324) 562006

C & P Services Northern Ltd, 11 Burtonwood Industrial Centre, Phipps Lane, Burtonwood, Warrington, WA5 4HX Tel: (01925) 229118 Fax: (01925) 228022 E-mail: info@candpservices.co.uk

Caledonian Air Service, St. Andrews Works, Bonnyhill Road, Bonnybridge, Stirlingshire, FK4 2EJ Tel: (01324) 812122 Fax: (01324) 812128 E-mail: caledonian@airservice.fsnet.co.uk

Central Air International Ltd, 47-59 Green Lane, Small Heath, Birmingham, B9 5BU Tel: 0121-773 5630 Fax: 0121-773 1378 E-mail: info@centralaircompressors.com

Chelmer Pneumatics, Unit 8, Moss Rd, Freebournes Industrial Estate, Witham, Essex, CM8 3UQ Tel: (01376) 500595 Fax: (01376) 501589 E-mail: sales@chelmerpneumatics.co.uk

Chiltern Air Services, 6 Pleckspool Cottage, Henton, Chinnor, Oxfordshire, OX39 4AE Tel: (01844) 351486 Fax: (01844) 351486

Compressed Air Contracts, 5b Alleysbank Road, Rutherglen, Glasgow, G73 1LX Tel: 0141-647 0007 Fax: 0141-647 9090 E-mail: glasgow@economatics.co.uk

Compressor Engineering Sales Ltd, Cunliffe Drive Industrial Estate, Cunliffe Drive, Kettering, Northamptonshire, NN16 8LD Tel: (01536) 520339 Fax: (01536) 310061

Compressor Service & Repairs Ltd, 9 Delph Road Indust Estate, Brierley Hill, West Midlands, DY5 1HD Tel: (01384) 480762 Fax: (01384) 480762

Compressor Specialists, 118 Alcester Road, Stratford-upon-Avon, Warwickshire, CV37 9DP Tel: (01789) 205635 Fax: (01789) 205635 E-mail: compressorspecialist@hotmail.com

Cooper Freer Ltd, Kenilworth Drive, Oadby, Leicester, LE2 5LG Tel: 0116-271 0401 E-mail: sales@cooperfreer.co.uk

D E Horn Pneumatic Services, Air Centre, Park Street, Ivybridge, Devon, PL21 9DW Tel: (01752) 893531 Fax: (01752) 690449 E-mail: sales@dehorn.co.uk

▶ Economatics, Victoria Industrial Estate, Victoria Road West, Hebburn, Tyne & Wear, NE31 1UB Tel: 0191-428 7070 Fax: 0191-414 9312 E-mail: mail@marshall-branson.co.uk

G & M Venditti Compressors Ltd, Unit 1 Park Road, Bury, Lancashire, BL9 5BQ Tel: 0161-764 5667 Fax: 0161-764 1316

Gloucester Conpressed Air Specialists Ltd, Staunton Court Business Park, Ledbury Road, Staunton, Gloucester, GL19 3QS Tel: (01452) 840042 Fax: (01452) 840260

▶ Grant Pneumatic Services, Malvern Road, Maidenhead, Berkshire, SL6 7RD Tel: (01628) 621161 Fax: (01628) 784419 E-mail: info@grantpneumatics.co.uk

Kettering Compressed Air Services Ltd, 16 Cross Street, Kettering, Northamptonshire, NN16 9DQ Tel: (01536) 516482 Fax: (01536) 411842 E-mail: sales@kcas.co.uk

Martlets Machinery Ltd, Winnell Manor Road, Winnell Trading Estate, Winchester, Hampshire, SO23 0RF Tel: (01962) 856655 Fax: (01962) 841683 E-mail: enquiries@martletsairpower.com

▶ Paramount Services Co., PO Box 4739, Reading, RG6 1XA Tel: (0870) 3214801 Fax: (0870) 3214802 E-mail: info@paramount-services.co.uk

▶ Pneumatic Tools & Compressors Ltd, Acton Road, Long Eaton, Nottingham, NG10 1FU Tel: 0115-973 4099 Fax: 0115-946 3030 E-mail: info@pneumatictools.sagehost.co.uk

▶ Scorpion Compressed Air Co. Ltd, 9 Partington Street, Morris Green, Bolton, BL3 3LE Tel: (01204) 431846 E-mail: info@scorpioncompressors.co.uk

Servair Ltd, Unit 6 Blackpole Trad Est East Blackpole, Worcester, WR3 8SG Tel: 01905 755400

Shiremoor Compressors & Electrical Services Ltd, 11 Front Street, Seghill, Cramlington, Northumberland, NE23 7TQ Tel: 0191-237 7177 Fax: 0191-237 7178 E-mail: sylvo@talktalk.net

Thorite, Thorite House, Laisterdyke, Bradford, West Yorkshire, BD4 8BZ Tel: (01274) 663471 Fax: (01274) 668296 E-mail: info@thorite.co.uk

Wessex Compressor Services, B1 46 Holton Road, Holton Heath Trading Park, Poole, Dorset, BH16 6LT Tel: (01202) 624877 Fax: (01202) 625827 E-mail: office@wessexcompressors.co.uk

AIR COMPRESSOR PIPEWORK INSTALLATION

Aircat Ltd, Unit A1, Milestone Business Park, Oslo Road, Sutton Fields Industrial Estate, Hull, HU7 0YN Tel: (01482) 878878 Fax: (01482) 878801 E-mail: sales@aircat.karoo.co.uk

Airite Compressor Supplies & Services, Unit 1 Petersfield Works, 1357B Stratford Rd, Hall Green, Birmingham, B28 9HW Tel: 0121-778 5772 Fax: 0121-778 5773

Compressor Specialists, 118 Alcester Road, Stratford-upon-Avon, Warwickshire, CV37 9DP Tel: (01789) 205635 Fax: (01789) 205635 E-mail: compressorspecialist@hotmail.com

▶ Everquip Garage Equipment Ltd, Tex Works, Wyke St, Hull, HU9 1PA Tel: (01482) 226699 Fax: (01482) 211184 E-mail: info@everquip.co.uk

▶ Grant Pneumatic Services, Malvern Road, Maidenhead, Berkshire, SL6 7RD Tel: (01628) 621161 Fax: (01628) 784419 E-mail: info@grantpneumatics.co.uk

Perfect Pipework Ltd, 49 Rabans Close, Rabans Lane Industrial Area, Aylesbury, Buckinghamshire, HP19 8RS Tel: (01296) 399330 Fax: (01296) 487029 E-mail: sales@perfectpipework.co.uk

AIR COMPRESSOR RECONDITIONING SERVICES

Airite Compressor Supplies & Services, Unit 1 Petersfield Works, 1357B Stratford Rd, Hall Green, Birmingham, B28 9HW Tel: 0121-778 5772 Fax: 0121-778 5773

Dowding & Mills plc, Camp Hill, Birmingham, B12 0JJ Tel: 0121-766 6161 Fax: 0121-773 2345 E-mail: group.birmingham@dowdingandmills.com

AIR COMPRESSORS, *See also headings for particular types*

A & B Air Systems Ltd, Unit 41 Abenbury Way, Wrexham Industrial Estate, Wrexham, Clwyd, LL13 9UZ Tel: (01978) 661999 Fax: (01978) 664330 E-mail: sales@ab-airsystems.co.uk

A C L Engineering Ltd, Anglia House, Sandown Road Industrial Estate, Watford, WD24 7UA Tel: (01923) 249444 Fax: (01923) 242368 E-mail: sales@aclengineering.co.uk

Advanced Security Data Electrical, 26 West Street, Bognor Regis, West Sussex, PO21 1XE Tel: (01243) 841626 Fax: (01243) 820372 E-mail: info@advancedelectricaluk.com

Air Controls & Compressors Ltd, 9 Trafalgar Court, Widnes, Cheshire, WA8 0SZ Tel: 0151-423 1750 Fax: 0151-495 2079 E-mail: sales@accltd.com

Air Equipment, 5 Kings Road, Flitwick, Bedford, MK45 1ED Tel: (01525) 723700 Fax: (01525) 723737 E-mail: info@air-equipment.co.uk

Air Methods Ltd, Frederick House, Anchor Lane, Bilston, West Midlands, WV14 9NE Tel: (01902) 884466 Fax: (01902) 884632 E-mail: sales@airmethods.co.uk

Air Power Centre, Unit B4 Anchorage Business Park, Chain Caul Way, Ashton-on-Ribble, Preston, PR2 2YL Tel: (01772) 728513 Fax: (01772) 736506 E-mail: apcpreston@airpowercentre.com

Air Response Ltd, Unit 8b Camp Industrial Estate, Rycote Lane, Milton Common, Thame, Oxfordshire, OX9 2NP Tel: (01844) 279870 Fax: (01844) 278669

Air Systems Ltd, 20-22 Grafton Road, Sparkbrook, Birmingham, B11 1JP Tel: 0121-772 1561 Fax: 0121-766 8727

Air Technique Ltd, Eagle Centre, 1 Progress Way, Luton, LU4 9TR Tel: (01582) 495151 Fax: (01582) 495152 E-mail: sales@air-technique.co.uk

▶ Aircare Compressor Services Ltd, 5 B Crucible Road, Corby, Northamptonshire, NN17 5TS Tel: (01536) 403808 Fax: (01536) 403860

Aircat Ltd, Unit A1, Milestone Business Park, Oslo Road, Sutton Fields Industrial Estate, Hull, HU7 0YN Tel: (01482) 878878 Fax: (01482) 878801 E-mail: sales@aircat.karoo.co.uk

Airchannel Ltd, Unit 10, Blackburn Industrial Estate, Blackburn, Aberdeen, AB21 0RX Tel: (01224) 790895 Fax: (01224) 790921 E-mail: enquiries@airchannel.co.uk

Airchannel Ltd, Unit 5, Smithies Mill, Bradford Road, Batley, West Yorkshire, WF17 8NS Tel: (01924) 475740 Fax: (01924) 475177 E-mail: enquiries@airchannel.co.uk

Airchannel, Unit 16, Hurworth Road, Aycliffe Industrial Park, Aycliffe, Newton Aycliffe, County Durham, DL5 6UD Tel: (01325) 321237 Fax: (01325) 318397 E-mail: aycliife@woodsidecompressors.co.uk

Airco Pneumatics Ltd, Malmesbury Road, Kingsditch Trading Estate, Cheltenham, Gloucestershire, GL51 9PL Tel: (01242) 690480 Fax: (01242) 690490 E-mail: info@aircopneumatics.co.uk

Airflow Compressors & Pneumatics Ltd, 100 Lord Street, Leigh, Lancashire, WN7 1BY Tel: (01942) 673529 Fax: (01942) 604672 E-mail: mail@airflow-compressors.co.uk

Airite Compressor Supplies & Services, Unit 1 Petersfield Works, 1357B Stratford Rd, Hall Green, Birmingham, B28 9HW Tel: 0121-778 5772 Fax: 0121-778 5773

▶ Airman Engineering Services Ltd, 10 Boleyn Court, Manor Park, Runcorn, Cheshire, WA7 1SR Tel: (01928) 571945 Fax: (01928) 571946 E-mail: sales@airman-otd.co.uk

▶ Airpac Air Compressors, Mugiemoss Road, Bucksburn, Aberdeen, AB21 9NP Tel: (01224) 715008 Fax: (01224) 714290 E-mail: airpac.rentals@vpplc.com

Airquick Newark Ltd, Northern Road, Newark, Nottinghamshire, NG24 2EU Tel: (01636) 640480 Fax: (01636) 701216 E-mail: info@airquick.co.uk

Anglian Compressors & Equipment Ltd, Storeys Bar Road, Peterborough, PE1 5YS Tel: (01733) 349993 Fax: (01733) 564983 E-mail: business@angliancomp.co.uk

Arb Sales, 13 School Street, Hazel Grove, Stockport, Cheshire, SK7 4RA Tel: 0161-483 9661 Fax: 0161-483 6160 E-mail: sales.arb@ntlworld.com

Associated Compressor Engineers, Sheffield Street, Stockport, Cheshire, SK4 1RU Tel: 0161-476 3800 Fax: 0161-476 6300 E-mail: sales@acecompressors.com

Aztech Components Ltd, 78 Atcham Close, Winyates East, Redditch, Worcestershire, B98 0NZ Tel: (01527) 500151 Fax: (01527) 500151 E-mail: sales@aztech.uk.net

B C A S Ltd, Unit 8 Thames Park, Lester Way, Wallingford, Oxfordshire, OX10 9TA Tel: (01491) 821737 Fax: (01491) 821730 E-mail: sales@bcaslimited.co.uk

Babcock PTI, Lorne Road, Larbert, Stirlingshire, FK5 4AT Tel: (01324) 552599 Fax: (01324) 562006

W. Bateman & Co., Garstang Rd, Barton, Preston, PR3 5AA Tel: (01772) 862948 Fax: (01772) 861639 E-mail: sales@bateman-sellarc.co.uk

Beds Compressor Service Ltd, Unit 4h, Cambridge Road Industrial Estate, Bedford, MK42 0LJ Tel: (01234) 364446 Fax: (01234) 217344

Best Pneumatics Ltd, Units 6-7, Short Way, Thornbury Industrial Estate, Thornbury, Bristol, BS35 3UT Tel: (01454) 415761 Fax: (01454) 414607

Burford Engineering, 11 Denesway, Meopham, Gravesend, Kent, DA13 0EA Tel: (01474) 815228 Fax: 07970 086211 E-mail: pete@burfordair.co.uk

Central Air International Ltd, 47-59 Green Lane, Small Heath, Birmingham, B9 5BU Tel: 0121-773 5630 Fax: 0121-773 1378 E-mail: info@centralaircompressors.com

Chelmer Pneumatics, Unit 8, Moss Rd, Freebournes Industrial Estate, Witham, Essex, CM8 3UQ Tel: (01376) 500595 Fax: (01376) 501589 E-mail: sales@chelmerpneumatics.co.uk

Chiltern Air Services, 6 Pleckspool Cottage, Henton, Chinnor, Oxfordshire, OX39 4AE Tel: (01844) 351486 Fax: (01844) 351486

CompAir UK Ltd, Claybrook Drive, Washford Industrial Estate, Redditch, Worcestershire, B98 0DS Tel: (01527) 525522 Fax: (01527) 521140 E-mail: sales@compair.com

Compressed Air Contracts, 5b Alleysbank Road, Rutherglen, Glasgow, G73 1LX Tel: 0141-647 0007 Fax: 0141-647 9090 E-mail: glasgow@economatics.co.uk

Compressed Air Management, 74a Regent Road, Bootle, Merseyside, L20 8DB Tel: 0151-933 7565 Fax: 0151-922 2962 E-mail: canb@btconnect.com

Compressor Engineering Sales Ltd, Cunliffe Drive Industrial Estate, Cunliffe Drive, Kettering, Northamptonshire, NN16 8LD Tel: (01536) 520339 Fax: (01536) 310061

AIR COMPRESSORS – *continued*

Compressor Service & Repairs Ltd, 9 Delph Road Indust Estate, Brierley Hill, West Midlands, DY5 1HD Tel: (01384) 480762 Fax: (01384) 480762

Compressor Specialists, 118 Alcester Road, Stratford-upon-Avon, Warwickshire, CV37 9DP Tel: (01789) 205635 Fax: (01789) 205635 E-mail: compressorspecialist@hotmail.com

Compressor Systems South West Ltd, 5 Riverside Business Park, St Annes Road, St. Annes Park, Bristol, BS4 4ED Tel: 0117-977 4531 Fax: 0117-972 3650 E-mail: sales@compressorsystems.co.uk

Compressors & Systems Suppliers Ltd, Cane End Lane, Bierton, Aylesbury, Buckinghamshire, HP22 5BH Tel: (01296) 415000 Fax: (01296) 434363 E-mail: graham@cass-air.co.uk

Compressors & Washers Ltd, James David Building, 134 Widemarsh Street, Hereford, HR4 9HN Tel: (01432) 268799 Fax: (01432) 279922 E-mail: sales@compressorsandwashers.co.uk

D E Horn Pneumatic Services, Air Centre, Park Street, Ivybridge, Devon, PL21 9DW Tel: (01752) 893531 Fax: (01752) 690449 E-mail: sales@dehorn.co.uk

Danum Supplies, Kelham Street, Doncaster, South Yorkshire, DN1 3RE Tel: (01302) 344475

Durr Technik (UK) Ltd, Unit 5, Ashmead Business Centre, Ashmead Road, Keynsham, Bristol, BS31 1SX Tel: 0117-986 0414 Fax: 0117-986 0416 E-mail: info@durrtechnik.co.uk

E R P Power Products Ltd, Cannon House, Reform Street, Hull, HU2 8EF Tel: (01482) 227479 Fax: (01482) 588556 E-mail: enquries@erpuk.com

Eastern Compressors Ltd, 1-9 Drapers Road, South Woodham Ferrers, Chelmsford, CM3 5UH Tel: (01245) 320624 Fax: (01245) 328700 E-mail: enquiries@easterns.co.uk

▶ Economatics, Victoria Industrial Estate, Victoria Road West, Hebburn, Tyne & Wear, NE31 1UB Tel: 0191-428 7070 Fax: 0191-414 9312 E-mail: mail@marshall-branson.co.uk

Economatics Industrial Ltd, Epic House, Darnall Road, Sheffield, S9 5AA Tel: 0114-281 3344 Fax: 0114-243 9306 E-mail: group@economatics.co.uk

Economatics (Industrial) Ltd, Unit 6 Alders Court, Watchmead, Welwyn Garden City, Hertfordshire, AL7 1LT Tel: (01707) 322622 Fax: (01707) 330724 E-mail: ailsford@economatics.co.uk

Fini (UK) Ltd, Unit A5 & A6, Greenwood Court, Veasey Close, Attleborough Fields Industrial Estate, Nuneaton, Warwickshire, CV11 6RT Tel: (024) 7632 2850 Fax: (024) 7634 9607 E-mail: finicompressors@yahoo.co.uk

G & M Venditti Compressors Ltd, Unit 1 Park Road, Bury, Lancashire, BL9 5BQ Tel: 0161-764 5667 Fax: 0161-764 1316

G P Compressed Air Services, Unit 2, Bodmin Road, Wyken, Coventry, CV2 5DB Tel: (024) 7662 2200 Fax: (024) 7662 2300 E-mail: info@gpair.co.uk

Gatley Engineering Pneumatics Ltd, Unit 6d Lowick Close, Hazel Grove, Stockport, Cheshire, SK7 5ED Tel: 0161-483 8615 Fax: 0161-456 5285

GF Compressors, Unit 4 Wainwright Street, Birmingham, B6 5TG Tel: 0121-326 9122 Fax: 0121-327 4492 E-mail: sales@gfcompressors.co.uk

Gloucester Conpressed Air Specialists Ltd, Staunton Court Business Park, Ledbury Road, Staunton, Gloucester, GL19 3QS Tel: (01452) 840042 Fax: (01452) 840260

▶ Grant Pneumatic Services, Malvern Road, Maidenhead, Berkshire, SL6 7RD Tel: (01628) 621161 Fax: (01628) 784419 E-mail: info@grantpneumatics.co.uk

Grimes Industrial Machinery & Equipment Solutions Ltd, 199 Hyde End Rd, Spencers Wood, Reading, RG7 1BU Tel: 0118-988 4825 Fax: 0118-988 4825 E-mail: grimesindmach@aol.com

H & M Compressors & Pumps Ltd, B Enterprise Centre, Paycocke Road, Basildon, Essex, SS14 3DY Tel: (01268) 531288 Fax: (01268) 532013 E-mail: hmcompressos@tiscali.co.uk

Hawco Direct, 8 Cranfield Road, Lostock Industrial Estate, Lostock, Bolton, BL6 4SB Tel: (01204) 675000 Fax: (01204) 675010 E-mail: catalogue@hawcodirect.co.uk

J & J Pneumatics Ltd, Hillbottom Road, Sands Industrial Estate, High Wycombe, Buckinghamshire, HP12 4HJ Tel: (01494) 530291 Fax: (01494) 463062 E-mail: sales@jjp.co.uk

Gordon Jolly, Belvedere, Harray, Orkney, KW17 2LQ Tel: (01856) 771440 Fax: (01856) 771440

W. & M. Joyce Engineers (Taurus Equipment) Ltd, Steele Road, London, NW10 7AR Tel: (020) 8965 2521 Fax: (020) 8961 0242 E-mail: barry@taurus-equipment.co.uk

Kestrel Equipment Ltd, 21-23, Scott Road, Luton, LU3 3BF Tel: (01582) 563600 Fax: (01582) 563323 E-mail: info@kestrelequipment.co.uk

Kettering Compressed Air Services Ltd, 16 Cross Street, Kettering, Northamptonshire, NN16 9DQ Tel: (01536) 516482 Fax: (01536) 411842 E-mail: sales@kcas.co.uk

Lancashire & Cheshire Garage Equipment Services, Progress House, 7 Longshut Lane West, Stockport, Cheshire, SK2 6RX Tel: 0161-477 6715 Fax: 0161-477 6151 E-mail: enquiries@garageequipment.biz

Leicester Compressor Services, 28 Boston Road, Leicester, LE4 1AU Tel: 0116-235 2906 Fax: 0116-235 2077 E-mail: leicestercompressors@fsnet.co.uk

M B Air Systems, 149 Glasgow Road, Wishaw, Lanarkshire, ML2 7QJ Tel: (01698) 355711 Fax: (01698) 359299 E-mail: sales@mbairsystems.co.uk

M E C-Air (Pneumatics & Hydraulics) Ltd, Unit 5c, Enterprise Way, Five Lane Ends, Bradford, West Yorkshire, BD10 8EW Tel: (01274) 621037 Fax: (01274) 621230

Marshall Brewson Ltd, 6 Westside Industrial Estate, South Humberside Industrial Estate, Grimsby, South Humberside, DN31 2TG Tel: (01472) 359001 Fax: (01472) 359954 E-mail: sales@marshallbrewson.co.uk

Maziak Compressor Services Ltd, 1 Stanton Close, Finedon Road Industrial Estate, Wellingborough, Northamptonshire, NN8 4HN Tel: (01933) 222000 Fax: (01933) 222200 E-mail: sales@maziak.co.uk

Motivair Compressors Ltd, 9 Mount Road Industrial Estate, Mount Road, Feltham, Middlesex, TW13 6AR Tel: (020) 8744 8833 Fax: (020) 8744 8822 E-mail: international@motivair.co.uk

Motivair Compressors Ltd, Brittania Road, Waltham Cross, Hertfordshire, EN8 7NU Tel: (01992) 704300 Fax: (01992) 704170 E-mail: enquiries@leachlewis.co.uk

Multi Pneumatics, Motivair House, Crompton Court, Attwood Road, Burntwood, Staffordshire, WS7 3GG Tel: (0845) 0096161 Fax: (0845) 0096162 E-mail: enquiries@multi-pneumatics.co.uk

Nitto Kohki Europe Co. Ltd, Unit 21, Empire Centre, Imperial Way, Watford, WD24 4TS Tel: (01923) 239005 Fax: (01923) 248815 E-mail: nitto-uk@jais.co.uk

Normair Compressor Engineering Ltd, 8 Rippleside Commercial Estate, Barking, Essex, IG11 0RJ Tel: 020 89848893

Oscott Air Ltd, Sherlock Street, Birmingham, B5 6LT Tel: 0121-622 2789 Fax: 0121-666 6012 E-mail: sales@oscottair.com

Pipe Fabrication Equipment Services, Unit 4, Townley Business Park, Hanson Street, Middleton, Manchester, M24 2UF Tel: 0161-653 7459 Fax: 0161-654 7286

R D Equipment, 9 Bownham Mead, Rodborough Common, Stroud, Gloucestershire, GL5 5DZ Tel: (01453) 872623 E-mail: rdequipment@tesco.net

Rep Air Services, Unit 23 Monarch Way, Loughborough, Leicestershire, LE11 5XG Tel: (01509) 213452 Fax: (01509) 212102 E-mail: sales@rep-air.co.uk

▶ Robins Air Team, Unit 22, Llanelli Workshops, Trostre Industrial Park, Llanelli, Dyfed, SA14 9UU Tel: (0800) 0131440 Fax: (01554) 746569 E-mail: robin@robinsairteam.co.uk

Rodwell H T B, Bentalls, Basildon, Essex, SS14 3SD Tel: (01268) 286646 Fax: (01268) 287799 E-mail: sales@rodwell-autoclave.com

Rogers Duncan Engineering Ltd, 396 Hillington Road, Hillington Industrial Estate, Glasgow, G52 4BL Tel: 0141-882 6211 Fax: 0141-882 5818 E-mail: info@duncanrogers.com

S A C Marine International Ltd, 36 Ridleys Cross, Astley, Stourport-on-Severn, Worcestershire, DY13 0RF Tel: (01299) 825908 Fax: (01299) 878699 E-mail: sacmarine.com

Servair Ltd, Unit 6 Blackpole Trad Est East Blackpole, Worcester, WR3 8SG Tel: 01905 755400

Shiremoor Compressors & Electrical Services Ltd, 11 Front Street, Seghill, Cramlington, Northumberland, NE23 7TQ Tel: 0191-237 7177 Fax: 0191-237 7178 E-mail: sylvo@talktalk.net

Simm Engineering Group, Gilbertson Works, Jessell Street, Sheffield, S9 3HY Tel: 0114-244 0764 Fax: 0114-244 2725 E-mail: sales@simmengineeringgroup.co.uk

T A Industries Ltd, Gibson Road, Caenby Corner Estate, Hemswell Cliff, Gainsborough, Lincolnshire, DN21 5TL Tel: (01427) 668436 Fax: (01427) 668101

Thorite Ltd, 55 Lowfields Road, Leeds, LS12 6BS Tel: 0113-244 4554 Fax: 0113-242 4700 E-mail: leeds@thorite.co.uk

▶ Top Gun Tools & Fixings, Amy Johnson Way, Blackpool, FY4 2RP Tel: (01253) 400900 Fax: (01253) 400900 E-mail: sales@topgun.co.uk

Wessex Compressor Services, B1 46 Holton Road, Holton Heath Trading Park, Poole, Dorset, BH16 6LT Tel: (01202) 624877 Fax: (01202) 625827 E-mail: office@wessexcompressors.co.uk

Western Automation, Western House, Ipswich Road, Cardiff, CF23 9AQ Tel: (029) 2048 8446 Fax: (029) 2047 1843 E-mail: sales@appliedautomation.co.uk

Wilson Air Pneumatics, Unit 1 Southall Enterprise Centre, Bridge Rd, Southall, Middx, UB2 4AE Tel: (020) 8893 5050 Fax: (020) 8893 5011

Woodside Pneumatics Ltd, Stirling Road Industrial Estate, Dykehead Road, Airdrie, Lanarkshire, ML6 7UJ Tel: (01236) 756171 Fax: (01236) 751210 E-mail: sales@woodside-compressors.co.uk

▶ Wraith Engineering, Unit 43 Station Road Workshops, Station Road, Kingswood, Bristol, BS15 4PJ Tel: 0117-910 9919 Fax: 0117-981 1279 E-mail: sales@wraith-engineering.co.uk

Wrekin Pneumatics Telford Ltd, Park Road, Dawley Bank, Telford, Shropshire, TF4 2BE Tel: (01952) 505566 Fax: (01952) 504703 E-mail: wrekin@interramp.co.uk

AIR CONDITIONING (AC) ACCESSORIES

A C S Air Conditioning Services, 153 Peperharow Road, Godalming, Surrey, GU7 2PR Tel: (01483) 415935 Fax: (01483) 860549 E-mail: sales@acsairconsvs.co.uk

A R C S Ltd, Unit 3 Cwmtawe Business Park, Pontardawe, Swansea, SA8 4EZ Tel: (01792) 869660 Fax: (01792) 869550 E-mail: arcsltd@btconnect.com

▶ ACI Watford Ltd Air Conditioning, 1st Floor, 462-464 St Albans Road, Watford, WD24 6SR Tel: 01923 440265 Fax: 01923 440999 E-mail: Aciwatford@hotmail.com

▶ Advanced Ergonomic Technologies Ltd, 201-203 London Road, East Grinstead, West Sussex, RH19 1HA Tel: (01342) 310400 Fax: (01342) 310401 E-mail: aet@flexiblespace.com

▶ Advanced Refrigeration, Millcroft, Monteach Road, Methlick, Ellon, Aberdeenshire, AB41 7JT Tel: (01224) 773774 Fax: (0845) 2805554 E-mail: info@advanced-refrigeration.co.uk

▶ Air Conditioning Corporation (Midlands) Ltd, Unit G11, Roden Street, Nottingham, NG3 1JH Tel: (0800) 2343506 E-mail: enquiries@airconcorp.co.uk

Air Conditioning & Refrigeration Services Ltd, 16 Brunel Street, Newcastle upon Tyne, NE4 7AH Tel: 0191-273 7700 Fax: 0191-256 8700 E-mail: acr@16brunel.sfnet.co.uk

Air Terminal Ltd, 80 Deansgate Lane, Timperley, Altrincham, Cheshire, WA14 1SP Tel: 0161-928 8918 Fax: 0161-926 8234

▶ Airconditioning Birmingham, 8 Turton Gardens, Redditch, Worcestershire, B96 6JB Tel: 01527 892823 Fax: 01527 892823 E-mail: sales@airconditioningbirmingham.co.uk

Airconstruct Midlands Ltd, Littleton Drive, Cannock, Staffordshire, WS12 4TS Tel: (01543) 572300 Fax: (01543) 574090 E-mail: sales@airconstruct.co.uk

Airway Solutions, Unit 18 Uveco Business Centre, Dock Road, Birkenhead, Merseyside, CH41 1FD Tel: 0151-630 0650 Fax: 0151-630 4050 E-mail: sunhill@airwaysolutions.co.uk

▶ Angali Shipping & Trading Co. Ltd, 18 Exeter Street, London, WC2E 7DU Tel: (020) 7379 9002 Fax: (020) 7379 9004 E-mail: ast@angali.co.uk

B B J Engineering Ltd, Apex Way, Diplocks Industrial Estate, Hailsham, East Sussex, BN27 3WA Tel: (01323) 848842 Fax: (01323) 848846 E-mail: sandy@aspenpumps.com

Beta Air, Unit 6, Cheltenham Trade Park, Arle Road, Cheltenham, Gloucestershire, GL51 8LZ Tel: (01242) 570995 Fax: (01242) 226131 E-mail: betaair.storacall@btinternet.com

C T Refrigeration Services, 16 Linton Dann Close, Hoo, Rochester, Kent, ME3 9DQ Tel: (01634) 250915 Fax: (01634) 255181

C. Caswell Engineering Services Ltd, Knowsley Road Industrial Estate, Knowsley Road, Haslingden, Rossendale, Lancashire, BB4 4RR Tel: (01706) 227935 Fax: (01706) 210282 E-mail: enquiries@caswell.com

Celsius Cooling, The Hollies, Swanley Lane, Ravensmoor, Nantwich, Cheshire, CW5 8PZ Tel: (01270) 626453 Fax: 01270 624759

Climate Centers Ltd, Unit 8 Brickyard Business Park, Excelsior Road, Off Western Avenue, Cardiff, CF14 3AT Tel: (029) 2062 0033 Fax: (029) 2069 1155

D G Collins, Hillcrest, Oughterby, Carlisle, CA5 6JH Tel: (01228) 576563 Fax: (01228) 576563

Diffusion Environmental Systems Ltd, Unit 14 Sherrington Way, Basingstoke, Hampshire, RG22 4DQ Tel: (01256) 352250 Fax: 01256 817815

Elyo UK Ltd, 1 Sampson Road North, Birmingham, B11 1BL Tel: 0121-773 8421 Fax: 0121-773 2082

▶ Everest Cooling Services, 11 Brunshaw Avenue, Burnley, Lancashire, BB10 4LT Tel: (01282) 685223 Fax: (01282) 685223 E-mail: info@everestcooling.com

▶ Excel Refrigeration, Unit 2, Angel Park, Chester Le Street, County Durham, DH2 1AQ Tel: 0191-492 1929

Express Refrigeration Contractors Ltd, 2 Princess Street, Immingham, South Humberside, DN40 1LN Tel: (01469) 574561 Fax: (01469) 574628

▶ Focus Air Conditioning, Unit Laker Hosue Canning Street, Maidstone, Kent, ME14 2RX Tel: 01622 690559 Fax: 01622 690559 E-mail: focusac@talktalk.net

Frost Duval Ltd, Stanley Works, Stanley Road, Sidcup, Kent, DA14 4DQ Tel: (020) 8300 2483 Fax: (020) 8300 5754

G A C Services, 79 The Downs, Nottingham, NG11 7DX Tel: 0115-981 9501 Fax: 0115-981 9501

▶ Harrisons Electrical Mechanical & Property Services Ltd, Harrison House, Sheep Walk, Langford Road, Biggleswade, Bedfordshire, SG18 9RB Tel: (01767) 600259 Fax: (01767) 600269 E-mail: info@harrisonselec.co.uk

Just Cold Services Ltd, 117 Old Farleigh Road, South Croydon, Surrey, CR2 8QD Tel: (020) 8657 2334 Fax: (020) 8651 1580

▶ Manhatten Heights, 108 Buckstones Road, Shaw, Oldham, OL2 8DN Tel: (01706) 849752 Fax: (01706) 299209 E-mail: sales@manheights.co.uk

Sirocco Air Co. Ltd, Unit 4, Carew Street Industrial Estate, London, SE5 9DF Tel: (020) 7326 1272 Fax: (020) 7326 1272

Three Counties Refrigeration Ltd, PO Box 42, Saffron Walden, Essex, CB10 2BQ Tel: (01799) 523811 Fax: (01799) 523800

▶ Turn Key Air Conditoning Ltd, Unit S, Network Centre, Hebburn, Tyne & Wear, NE31 1SF Tel: 0191-496 3990 Fax: 0191-496 3991 E-mail: enquires@tkac.co.uk

V A C Contracting Ltd, 3 Barton Industrial Estate, Faldo Road, Barton-le-Clay, Bedford, MK45 4RP Tel: (01582) 883980 Fax: (01582) 883981

Ventair Ltd, Wednesbury Trading Estate, Darlaston Road, Wednesbury, West Midlands, WS10 7JN Tel: 0121-502 5518 Fax: 0121-556 6737

▶ www.aircon4less.co.uk, 8 Cannon Lane, Pinner, Middlesex, HA5 1HR Tel: 0845 257 4358 E-mail: admin@aircon4less.co.uk

AIR CONDITIONING (AC) CHILLERS

DPAC UK Ltd, Unit 14a, E Space North, 181 Wisbech Road, Littleport, Ely, Cambridgeshire, CB6 1RA Tel: (0845) 2576380 Fax: (0845) 2576375 E-mail: sales@dpacuk.co.uk

Interklima Ltd, Darby House, 62 Bletchingley Road, Merstham, Redhill, RH1 3DN Tel: (01737) 644270 Fax: (01737) 644250 E-mail: info@interklima.co.uk

AIR CONDITIONING (AC) CLEANING EQUIPMENT

Elgin Refrigeration Services Ltd, Unit 1, Linkwood Industrial Estate, Elgin, Morayshire, IV30 1HY Tel: (01343) 543116 Fax: (01343) 549910

Holmes Products, 1 Francis Grove, London, SW19 4DT Tel: (020) 8879 4850 Fax: (020) 8947 8272

R G K (UK) Ltd, Champfleurie House, Linlithgow, West Lothian, EH49 6NB Tel: (01506) 847999 Fax: (01506) 847174 E-mail: sales@rgk.co.uk

AIR CONDITIONING (AC) COIL MAINTENANCE OR REPAIR

▶ ACI Watford Ltd Air Conditioning, 1st Floor, 462-464 St Albans Road, Watford, WD24 6SR Tel: 01923 440265 Fax: 01923 440999 E-mail: Aciwatford@hotmail.com

▶ Air Care, 125 New Bridge Street, Newcastle upon Tyne, NE1 2SW Tel: 0191-261 1144 Fax: 0191-261 1188 E-mail: info@aircare-services.co.uk

▶ Air Conditioning Corporation (Midlands) Ltd, Unit G11, Roden Street, Nottingham, NG3 1JH Tel: (0800) 2343506 E-mail: enquiries@airconcorp.co.uk

Air Conditioning & Refrigeration Services Ltd, 16 Brunel Street, Newcastle upon Tyne, NE4 7AH Tel: 0191-273 7700 Fax: 0191-256 8700 E-mail: acr@16brunel.sfnet.co.uk

▶ Airconditioning Birmingham, 8 Turton Gardens, Redditch, Worcestershire, B96 6JB Tel: 01527 892823 Fax: 01527 892823 E-mail: sales@airconditioningbirmingham.co.uk

C F Environmental Services Ltd, Unit 3, Bentley Park, Blacknest, Alton, Hampshire, GU34 4PX Tel: (01420) 22622 Fax: (01420) 22612 E-mail: sales@cfes.co.uk

Formost Air Conditioning Ltd, Unit 9 Wilford Lane Industrial Estate, Ruddington Lane, Wilford, Nottingham, NG11 7EP Tel: 0115-945 5033 Fax: 0115-974 5527 E-mail: smurphy@formost.co.uk

▶ Fueltech Gas & Oil Boiler service, The Bungalow, Upper Clwyd street, Ruthin, Denbighshire, LL15 1HY Tel: 0845 0942715 Fax: 01824 709537 E-mail: fueltech@tiscali.co.uk

▶ L & M Refrigeration, Unit 3, Thesiger Close, Worthing, West Sussex, BN11 2RN Tel: (0871) 2882665 Fax: (01903) 214296 E-mail: admin@lmrefrigeration.co.uk

Robins Refrigeration Ltd, Units 18A & B, Chapman Way, Tunbridge Wells, Kent, TN2 3EF Tel: (01892) 537291 Fax: (01892) 549794 E-mail: sue@robinsrefrigeration.co.uk

▶ Turn Key Air Conditoning Ltd, Unit S, Network Centre, Hebburn, Tyne & Wear, NE31 1SF Tel: 0191-496 3990 Fax: 0191-496 3991 E-mail: enquires@tkac.co.uk

AIR CONDITIONING (AC) COMPONENTS

A C R Heat Transfer Ltd, Rollesby Road, King's Lynn, Norfolk, PE30 4LN Tel: (01553) 763371 Fax: (01553) 771322 E-mail: acrheat@msn.com

▶ ACI Watford Ltd Air Conditioning, 1st Floor, 462-464 St Albans Road, Watford, WD24 6SR Tel: 01923 440265 Fax: 01923 440999 E-mail: Aciwatford@hotmail.com

▶ Advanced Ergonomic Technologies Ltd, 201-203 London Road, East Grinstead, West Sussex, RH19 1HA Tel: (01342) 310400 Fax: (01342) 310401 E-mail: aet@flexiblespace.com

AIR CONDITIONING (AC) COMPONENTS – *continued*

▶ Advanced Refrigeration, Millcroft, Monteach Road, Methlick, Ellon, Aberdeenshire, AB41 7JT Tel: (01224) 773774 Fax: (0845) 2805554 E-mail: info@advanced-refrigeration.co.uk

Agm, 32 Teesdale Road, Ridgeway, Sheffield, S12 3XH Tel: 0114-248 9198 Fax: 0114-247 2551 E-mail: agm1ac@aol.com

Air Conditioning & Refrigeration Services Ltd, 16 Brunel Street, Newcastle upon Tyne, NE4 7AH Tel: 0191-273 7700 Fax: 0191-256 8700 E-mail: acr@16brunel.sfnet.co.uk

Air Diffusion Ltd, 164 Great North Road, Hatfield, Hertfordshire, AL9 5JN Tel: (01707) 272601 Fax: (01707) 274951 E-mail: hatfield@air-diffusion.co.uk

▶ Airconditioning Birmingham, 8 Turton Gardens, Redditch, Worcestershire, B96 6JB Tel: 01527 892823 Fax: 01527 892823 E-mail: sales@airconditioningbirmingham.co.uk

Aspen Pumps Ltd, Aspen Building, Apex Way, Hailsham, East Sussex, BN27 3WA Tel: (01323) 848842 Fax: (01323) 848846

Belimo Automation UK Ltd, Unit 10 Shepperton Business Park, Govett Avenue, Shepperton, Middlesex, TW17 8BA Tel: (01932) 260460 Fax: (01932) 269222 E-mail: welcome@belimo.co.uk

East Kirkby Refrigeration & Air Conditioning Ltd, The Retreat, Station Road, Sibsey, Boston, Lincolnshire, PE22 0SB Tel: (01205) 353351 Fax: (01205) 750910

Environmental Commissioning & Services Ltd, 6-8 Godstone Road, Whyteleafe, Surrey, CR3 0EA Tel: (020) 8763 1888 Fax: (020) 8763 1884

▶ Greenbox Heat Exchangers, 11 Wassage Way, Hampton Lovett, Droitwich, Worcestershire, WR9 0NX Tel: (01905) 777050 Fax: (01905) 777051 E-mail: sales@greenbox.uk.com

▶ HRP Ltd, Unit 18 Britannia Industrial Estate, Poyle Road, Colnbrook, Slough, SL3 0BH Tel: (01753) 688100 Fax: (01753) 688101

Refrigeration Spares Ltd, 31 Harrow Road, London, E11 3PT Tel: (020) 8555 1321 Fax: (020) 8519 8219

▶ Turn Key Air Conditoning Ltd, Unit S, Network Centre, Hebburn, Tyne & Wear, NE31 1SF Tel: 0191-496 3990 Fax: 0191-496 3991 E-mail: enquires@tkac.co.uk

Westbury Financial Management, Hall Farm Estate, Gadbrook Road, Betchworth, Surrey, RH3 7AH Tel: (01306) 611611 Fax: (01306) 611613 E-mail: sales@westburyfilters.co.uk

▶ www.aircon4less.co.uk, 8 Cannon Lane, Pinner, Middlesex, HA5 1HR Tel: 0845 257 4358 E-mail: admin@aircon4less.co.uk

AIR CONDITIONING (AC) COMPRESSOR MAINTENANCE OR RECONDITIONING OR REMANUFACTURING OR REPAIR

▶ Advanced Refrigeration, Millcroft, Monteach Road, Methlick, Ellon, Aberdeenshire, AB41 7JT Tel: (01224) 773774 Fax: (0845) 2805554 E-mail: info@advanced-refrigeration.co.uk

▶ Air Conditioning Corporation (Midlands) Ltd, Unit G11, Roden Street, Nottingham, NG3 1JH Tel: (0800) 2343506 E-mail: enquiries@airconcorp.co.uk

Coglan Air Conditioning, Church Lane, Worting, Basingstoke, Hampshire, RG23 8PX Tel: (01256) 464158 Fax: (01256) 811876 E-mail: clive@coglanaircon.com

Corby Refrigeration & Mechanical Services, Gordon House, Dale Street, Corby, Northamptonshire, NN17 2BQ Tel: (01536) 265273 Fax: (01536) 205881 E-mail: enquiries@corbyrefrigeration.co.uk

▶ Cube Airconditioning Ltd, Hillcrest 2 Pirbright Road, Normandy, Guildford, Surrey, GU3 2AG Tel: (01483) 811169 E-mail: info@cubeacltd.com

D A C Air Conditioning Ltd, 4 Butler Way, Stanningley, Pudsey, West Yorkshire, LS28 6EA Tel: 0113-236 2101 Fax: 0113-236 2087 E-mail: info@dacairconditioning.co.uk

Envirotech Services Ltd, Envirotech House, 1 Main Road, Edenbridge, Kent, TN8 6JE Tel: (01732) 865171 Fax: (01732) 865057 E-mail: info@esl.gb.com

F T Refrigeration Ltd, 166 Old Road, Stockport, Cheshire, SK4 1TD Tel: 0161-480 4825 Fax: 0161-480 4825

▶ Focal Projects Ltd, 4 Waterside Business Park, Armitage Road, Rugeley, Staffordshire, WS15 1LJ Tel: (01889) 586150 Fax: (01889) 575374 E-mail: sales@focalprojects.co.uk

▶ Fueltech Gas & Oil Boiler service, The Bungalow, Upper Clwyd street, Ruthin, Denbighshire, LL15 1HY Tel: 0845 0942715 Fax: 01824 709537 E-mail: fueltech@tiscali.co.uk

Ghai's Services, 14 Wood End Green Road, Hayes, Middlesex, UB3 2SH Tel: (020) 8569 3721 Fax: (020) 8569 3723

H B S Ltd, 3 Sycamore Close, Maidenhead, Berkshire, SL6 3HU Tel: (01628) 636849 Fax: (01628) 777218 E-mail: hbs.ltd@lineone.net

J & E Hall Ltd, 3 28 Botley Road, Hedge End, Southampton, SO30 2HE Tel: (01489) 890200 Fax: (01489) 788292 E-mail: g.warn@jehall.co.uk

▶ L & M Refrigeration, Unit 3, Thesiger Close, Worthing, West Sussex, BN11 2RN Tel: (0871) 2882665 Fax: (01903) 214296 E-mail: admin@lmrefrigeration.co.uk

▶ Manhatten Heights, 108 Buckstones Road, Shaw, Oldham, OL2 8DN Tel: (01706) 849752 Fax: (01706) 299209 E-mail: sales@manheights.co.uk

Optimum Air Conditioning, 1c Lyon Way, Greenford, Middlesex, UB6 0BN Tel: (020) 8813 1144 Fax: (0870) 8503132

Orbit Maintainence UK Ltd, Studio 6 The Mews, 46 Church Rd, Barnes, London, SW13 0DQ Tel: (020) 8563 2086 Fax: (020) 8563 2838

▶ Paramount Services Co., PO Box 4739, Reading, RG6 1XA Tel: (0870) 3214801 Fax: (0870) 3214802 E-mail: info@paramount-services.co.uk

Polar Car Air Conditioning, 178 Bury New Road, Whitefield, Manchester, M45 6QF Tel: 0161-798 4884 Fax: 0161-796 7673

S R Air Conditioning Services, 11 New Road, Church Crookham, Fleet, Hampshire, GU52 6BH Tel: (01252) 622620

Sabreglen Ltd, Unit 22 Marlowe Business Centre, Batavia Road, London, SE14 6BQ Tel: (020) 8694 1144 Fax: (020) 8694 8698 E-mail: sales@sabreglen.co.uk

Seymour Refrigeration, 5 Hedgeway, Guildford, Surrey, GU2 7RB Tel: (01483) 567645

SRS Cooling, Archard House, Waverley Road, Weymouth, Dorset, DT3 5HL Tel: (01305) 750020 Fax: (01305) 750021 E-mail: sales@southernrefrigeration.freeserve.co.uk

AIR CONDITIONING (AC) CONSULTANCY OR DESIGN

A C R C Ltd, The Courtyard, North Street, Wigston, Leicestershire, LE18 1PS Tel: 0116-257 0066 Fax: 0116-257 0099 E-mail: info@acrcltd.co.uk

A C S Ltd, Victoria Court, Kent Street, Nottingham, NG1 3LZ Tel: 0115-958 3100 Fax: 0115-958 3199 E-mail: aspeckcooling@hotmail.com

▶ A C S, Oakleigh, Smithy Lane, Pentre Bychan, Wrexham, Clwyd, LL14 4EN Tel: (01978) 846173 Fax: (01978) 846262

▶ A C S Wade Ltd, Unit B6, Pinfold Industrial Estate, Rhyl, Clwyd, LL18 2YR Tel: (01745) 342998 Fax: (01745) 336006 E-mail: mail@acswade.co.uk

Accent Services Air Conditioning Ltd, 4 Brooklands Close, Sunbury-on-Thames, Middlesex, TW16 7DX Tel: (01932) 765648 Fax: (01932) 788706 E-mail: info@accent.ac.co.uk

Accord Air Systems, Lawmans Centre, 28-32 Beddington Lane, Croydon, CR0 4TB Tel: (020) 8401 2058 Fax: (020) 8401 2059 E-mail: accordair@lineone.net

Adcock Refrigeration & Air Conditioning Ltd, 22 Mason Road, Norwich, NR6 6RF Tel: (01603) 786900 Fax: (01603) 418147

Air Conditioning Design Ltd, Unit 6, Manchester Road, Haslingden, Rossendale, Lancashire, BB4 6LB Tel: (01706) 219101 Fax: (01706) 219190

▶ Air Conditioning Solutions UK Ltd, Concept Park, Watling Street, Towcester, Northamptonshire, NN12 7YD Tel: (01327) 810510 Fax: (01327) 811529 E-mail: info@airconsolutions.co.uk

Air-Conditioning & Refrigeration Concerns, 5 Mingarry, Birtley, Chester Le Street, County Durham, DH3 2JB Tel: 0191-410 3594 Fax: 0191-410 8504

▶ Airflow Air Conditioning Ltd, St. Sidwells, Canworthy Water, Launceston, Cornwall, PL15 8UA Tel: (01566) 781777 Fax: (01566) 781777 E-mail: sales@airflowaircon.co.uk

Andersons Ltd, 1 Weston Road, Guildford, Surrey, GU2 8AU Tel: (01483) 578887 Fax: (01483) 578885 E-mail: johnschluter@btconnect.com

Andrew Engineering Ltd, Unit 4, Cobnar Wood Close, Chesterfield, Derbyshire, S41 9RQ Tel: (0845) 1267873 Fax: (0845) 1267874 E-mail: sales@andrew-eng.co.uk

Asadul Ltd, Hop House, West Bergholt, Colchester, CO6 3TJ Tel: (01206) 241600

Automated Systems, 1-3 Mossley Road, Grasscroft, Oldham, OL4 4HH Tel: (0870) 2402771 Fax: (0870) 2402773 E-mail: stevepage@automatedsystem.org

Berks & Bucks Air Conditioning, Unit G2 Rose Business Estate, Marlow Bottom Road, Marlow, Buckinghamshire, SL7 3ND Tel: (01628) 472267 Fax: (01628) 472262 E-mail: info@berksbucksaircon.co.uk

▶ Blygold Air Conditioning Consultants, 4 Beacon Road, Poulton Industrial Estate, Poulton-le-Fylde, Lancashire, FY6 8JE Tel: (01253) 890666 Fax: (01253) 890222

Bry-Kol Group of Companies, 10 Newcastle Street, Burslem, Stoke-On-Trent, ST6 3QF Tel: (01782) 577991 Fax: (01782) 577511 E-mail: info@bry-Kol.co.uk

C F Environmental Services Ltd, Unit 3, Bentley Park, Blacknest, Alton, Hampshire, GU34 4PX Tel: (01420) 22622 Fax: (01420) 22612 E-mail: sales@cfes.co.uk

C H Lindsey & Son Ltd, Brunel Way, Severalls Industrial Park, Colchester, CO4 9QW Tel: (01206) 844567 Fax: (01206) 844483 E-mail: info@lindsey-aircon.com

Caledonian Building Services South East Ltd, 31 Slewins Lane, Hornchurch, Essex, RM11 2BZ Tel: (01708) 454305 Fax: (01708) 437375

▶ Ceilite Air Conditioning Ltd, 1 The Alcorns, Cambridge Road, Stansted, Essex, CM24 8DF Tel: (01279) 815503 Fax: (01279) 813971 E-mail: sales@ceilte.com

Celsius Air Conditioning, 1 Well Street, Heywood, Lancashire, OL10 1NT Tel: (01706) 367500 Fax: (01706) 367355 E-mail: sales@celsiusair.co.uk

▶ Charttape Ltd, 14 Witt Road, Fair Oak, Eastleigh, Hampshire, SO50 7FR Tel: (07836) 671676 Fax: (023) 8069 6743 E-mail: charttape@btinternet.com

Chilli Group, Station Road Industrial Estate, Mauchline, Ayrshire, KA5 5EU Tel: (01290) 550362 Fax: (01290) 552677 E-mail: mail@chilliref.co.uk

Cleanair Group Ltd, Technology House, 5 Newton Close, Drayton Fields, Daventry, Northamptonshire, NN11 5RR Tel: (01327) 301383 Fax: (01327) 301384 E-mail: info@cleanair.com

▶ Clwyd Refrigeration Ltd, Conwy Morfa Enterprise Park, Parc Caer Seion, Conwy, Gwynedd, LL32 8FA Tel: (01492) 572323 Fax: (01492) 582626 E-mail: sevice@clwydrefrigeration.com

Colgijan Merault Ltd, PO Box 56, Evesham, Worcestershire, WR11 3FR Tel: (01386) 760009 Fax: (01386) 442779

Cooling Heating Electrical Services, 18 Old Pawlett Road, West Huntspill, Highbridge, Somerset, TA9 3RH Tel: (07970) 565026 Fax: (01278) 795511 E-mail: sales@chesuk.com

Coolus Services, 95 Front Lane, Upminster, Essex, RM14 1XN Tel: (01708) 641333 Fax: (01708) 641233 E-mail: sales@coolus-services.co.uk

Creative Retail Solutions Ltd, 33 - 35 Chapel Road, Parkstone, Poole, Dorset, BH14 0JU Tel: (01202) 710842 Fax: (01202) 710845 E-mail: mary@creativeretailsolutiuons.co.uk

▶ Cube Airconditioning Ltd, Hillcrest 2 Pirbright Road, Normandy, Guildford, Surrey, GU3 2AG Tel: (01483) 811169 E-mail: info@cubeacltd.com

Cudd Bentley Consulting, Ashurst Manor, Church Lane, Ascot, Berkshire, SL5 7DD Tel: (01344) 628821 Fax: (01344) 623448 E-mail: reception@ascot.cbp.co.uk

▶ D & E Technical Services Ltd, 15 Whistler Road, Eaton Ford, St. Neots, Cambridgeshire, PE19 7RT Tel: (01480) 474430 Fax: (01480) 386474 E-mail: enquiries@de-techservices.co.uk

Daventry Refrigeration, 4 Cross Lane, Braunston, Daventry, Northamptonshire, NN11 7HH Tel: (01788) 890469 Fax: (01788) 891453

Delrac Acs, Fairman Law House, 1-3 Park Terrace, Worcester Park, Surrey, KT4 7JZ Tel: (020) 8335 3141 Fax: (020) 8337 5539 E-mail: enquiries@delrac-acs.co.uk

Design Installation Service Electrical Ltd, P O Box 137, Cheltenham, Gloucestershire, GL53 7ZF Tel: (01242) 533100 Fax: (01242) 221187

Direct Cooling & Heating Services Ltd, 1 Northbank Avenue, Cambuslang, Glasgow, G72 7TG Tel: 0141-641 7788 Fax: 0141-641 8333

Ducted Air Systems Ltd, 101 Sadler Road, Lincoln, LN6 3RS Tel: (01522) 682239 Fax: (01522) 883002 E-mail: nev@ductedair.com

Ensys Ltd, Unit 10 Rivermead, Thatcham, Berkshire, RG19 4EP Tel: (01635) 872227 Fax: (01635) 872206 E-mail: sales@ensys.co.uk

Ers, 21 Upton Cresent, Basingstoke, Hampshire, RG21 5SW Tel: (01256) 465604 Fax: (01256) 473737

Essex Electric Ltd, 46 Hanbury Road, Chelmsford, CM1 3TL Tel: (01245) 251291 Fax: (01245) 354051

Franklin M & E Services Ltd, 6 Hoffmanns Way, Chelmsford, CM1 1GU Tel: (01245) 505050 Fax: (01245) 505051 E-mail: me@franklingroup.co.uk

Hadrian Air Conditioning & Refrigeration Co. Ltd, 3 Rosse Close, Parsons Industrial Estate, Washington, Tyne & Wear, NE37 1ET Tel: 0191-415 0055 Fax: 0191-415 0888 E-mail: sales@hadrian-air.co.uk

Hesflo Installations Ltd, 6 Dial Lane, Bristol, BS16 5UH Tel: 0117-970 1930 Fax: 0117-970 1931 E-mail: design@hesflo.co.uk

Ice Guard Group, Mold Road, Cefn-y-Bedd, Wrexham, Clwyd, LL12 9UL Tel: (01978) 761881 Fax: (01978) 761789

J M Air Conditioning Ltd, 23 Tollgate Avenue, Redhill, RH1 5HR Tel: 01737 772200 Fax: 01737 772300 E-mail: jmacltd@aol.com

Jack Elam, Barton Road, Wisbech, Cambridgeshire, PE13 4TP Tel: (01945) 419090 Fax: (01945) 419088 E-mail: sales@jack-elam.co.uk

Kirwin Airconditioning Ltd, B Riffa Business Park, Harrogate Road, Leathley, Otley, West Yorkshire, LS21 2RZ Tel: 0113-284 3667 Fax: 0113-284 3093

▶ L & M Refrigeration, Unit 3, Thesiger Close, Worthing, West Sussex, BN11 2RN Tel: (0871) 2882665 Fax: (01903) 214296 E-mail: admin@lmrefrigeration.co.uk

▶ London Hermetics P.L.C., Unit 42, Weir Road, Durnsford Industrial Estate, London, SW19 8UG Tel: (020) 8947 0886 Fax: (020) 8947 1007 E-mail: sales@lh-plc.co.uk

Mcveigh Technical Solutions Ltd, PO Box 407, Leicester, LE3 8ZA Tel: 0116-232 1181 Fax: 0116-232 1186

Macwhirter Ltd, 5 Stoke View Business Park, Stoke View Road, Bristol, BS16 3AE Tel: 0117-939 6661 Fax: 0117-939 6662 E-mail: sales@macwhirter.co.uk

Mansfield Refrigeration & Air Conditioning Co. Ltd, Dallas Street, Mansfield, Nottinghamshire, NG18 5SZ Tel: (01623) 626168 Fax: (01623) 420915

Orbit Maintainence UK Ltd, Studio 6 The Mews, 46 Church Rd, Barnes, London, SW13 0DQ Tel: (020) 8563 2086 Fax: (020) 8563 2838

Orostream Applied Contracting Ltd, Park Road, Crowborough, East Sussex, TN6 2QT Tel: (01892) 665888 Fax: (01892) 663218 E-mail: oracl@aol.com

Polar Air Ltd, Huntingdon House, 278-290 Huntingdon Street, Nottingham, NG1 3LY Tel: 0115-955 0055 Fax: 0115-955 7037

Protechnical Services, 28 Rose Bushes, Epsom, Surrey, KT17 3NX Tel: (01737) 361135 Fax: (01737) 361135 E-mail: info@protechnical.co.uk

PWB Industrial Heating Services Ltd, Unit 14 Dawkins Road, Poole, Dorset, BH15 4JY Tel: (01202) 682500 Fax: (01202) 682565 E-mail: enquiries@pwbltd.co.uk

Reefworld Aquarium & Pond Supplies, 219 Fir Tree Road, Epsom, Surrey, KT17 3LB Tel: (01737) 370777 Fax: (01737) 212777 E-mail: sales@reefworld.co.uk

S A S Refrigeration Ltd, 137-139 Harrowdene Road, Wembley, Middlesex, HA0 2JH Tel: (020) 8385 1355 Fax: (020) 8385 1344

Shivers Installation Ltd, 2 The Old School House, Southdown Road, Seaford, East Sussex, BN25 4JS Tel: (01323) 899888 Fax: (01323) 896810

Southern Sales & Services Ltd, Sterling House, Mayflower Close, Chandler's Ford, Eastleigh, Hampshire, SO53 4AR Tel: (023) 8026 1188 Fax: (023) 8025 4054 E-mail: jules@southernsales.co.uk

▶ T R Commissioning Ltd, 11-13 High Street, Caterham, Surrey, CR3 5UE Tel: (01883) 347374 Fax: (01883) 342887

Whitecross Engineering Ltd, Columbia House, Columbia Drive, Worthing, West Sussex, BN13 3HD Tel: (01903) 690807 Fax: (01903) 690807

AIR CONDITIONING (AC) CONTROL SYSTEMS

▶ Cadamp Ltd, Wharfedale House, Great Pasture Lane, Burley in Wharfedale, Ilkley, West Yorkshire, LS29 7DB Tel: (01943) 863884 Fax: (01943) 862630 E-mail: info@cadamp.co.uk

▶ Climater Center, Unit 10, Stockton Close, Minworth Industrial Park, Minworth, Sutton Coldfield, West Midlands, B76 1DH Tel: 0121-351 7777 Fax: 0121-351 5835

Engineered Solutions, Unit 2, North Court, Armstrong Road, Maidstone, Kent, ME15 6JZ Tel: (01622) 750650 Fax: (01622) 355199 E-mail: sales@engsolutions.co.uk

Honeywell Control Systems Ltd, 150 Aztec West, Almondsbury, Bristol, BS32 4UB Tel: (01454) 848048 Fax: (01454) 848049

Systems Controls & Instruments UK Ltd, Manx House, Bousley Rise, Ottershaw, Chertsey, Surrey, KT16 0JX Tel: (01932) 875225 Fax: (01932) 875227 E-mail: info@sciuk.co.uk

AIR CONDITIONING (AC) CONTROLS AND MONITORS

Air Conditioning Distribution Ltd, Clarence Street, Cleckheaton, West Yorkshire, BD19 5HJ Tel: (01274) 862804 Fax: (01274) 862807 E-mail: sales@acd.co.uk

Birch Sales & Marketing Ltd, 41 Green Lane, Burnham, Slough, SL1 8DZ Tel: (01628) 661475 Fax: (01628) 667999 E-mail: bob@birch-sales.co.uk

Cooling Point Ltd, 12 Sheldrake Close, Dukinfield, Cheshire, SK16 5QG Tel: 0161-338 2629 Fax: 0161-338 2628

▶ Cube Airconditioning Ltd, Hillcrest 2 Pirbright Road, Normandy, Guildford, Surrey, GU3 2AG Tel: (01483) 811169 E-mail: info@cubeacltd.com

Honeywell Control Systems Ltd, 150 Aztec West, Almondsbury, Bristol, BS32 4UB Tel: (01454) 848048 Fax: (01454) 848049

I E C Services, Spinney Lodge, Birch Lane, Ascot, Berkshire, SL5 8RF Tel: (01344) 883440 Fax: (01344) 890856

Intandem Systems Ltd, Watton Farm, Watton Lane, Droxford, Southampton, SO32 3QU Tel: (01489) 877630 Fax: (01489) 877632 E-mail: inbox@intandem.org.uk

J L Aircon Ltd, 15-21 Risborough Street, London, SE1 0HG Tel: (020) 7657 7976 Fax: (020) 7657 7769

Key Controls Ltd, Unit 6 Spring Street, Keighley, West Yorkshire, BD21 3LE Tel: (01535) 604133 Fax: (01535) 604341

Kooltech Ltd, 433 Hillington Road, Hillington Industrial Estate, Glasgow, G52 4BL Tel: 0141-883 0447 Fax: 0141-883 5642 E-mail: sales@kooltech.co.uk

Mac Marney Refrigeration & Air Conditioning Ltd, The Old Forge, Stone Street, Crowfield, Ipswich, IP6 9SZ Tel: (01449) 760560 Fax: (01449) 760590 E-mail: sales@macmarney.co.uk

AIR CONDITIONING (AC) CONTROLS AND MONITORS –

continued

Northern Refrigeration, 17 Moray Street, Wick, Caithness, KW1 5QF Tel: (01955) 603240 Fax: (01955) 604785 E-mail: j1mer@btopenworld.com

Sauter Automations, Inova House Hampshire Int Business Park, Crockford Lane, Chineham, Basingstoke, Hampshire, RG24 8WH Tel: (01256) 374400 Fax: (01256) 374455 E-mail: info@uk.sauter-bc.com

Smart Cool Systems (UK) Ltd, Westgate, 104 High Street, Alton, Hampshire, GU34 1EN Tel: (01420) 544868 Fax: (01420) 544723 E-mail: enquries@smartcool.co.uk

Stock Electronics Ltd, 10 Edison Road, Salisbury, SP2 7NU Tel: (01722) 321758 Fax: (01722) 413079 E-mail: enquiries@stockelectronics.co.uk

Uxbridge Engineering Co. Ltd, Robinswood, Dukes Kiln Drive, Gerrards Cross, Buckinghamshire, SL9 7HD Tel: (01753) 889511 Fax: (01753) 880118 E-mail: enquiries@uxbridge-eng.demon.co.uk

AIR CONDITIONING (AC) DESIGN OR INSTALLATION OR COMMISSIONING

A A C, Unit 24, AK Business Park, Russell Road, Southport, Merseyside, PR9 7SA Tel: (01704) 505213 Fax: (01704) 506480 E-mail: info@allairconditioning.net

A B S Ltd, New House, Christchurch Road, Ringwood, Hampshire, BH24 3AP Tel: (01425) 477777 Fax: (01425) 474400 E-mail: first@absme.co.uk

A C 2000, North Bridge Place, Frog Island, Leicester, LE3 5BG Tel: 0116-262 0411 Fax: 0116-251 8967 E-mail: aircon@ac2000.co.uk

A C Engineers Ltd, Unit 7, Mill Industrial Estate, Kings Coughton, Alcester, Warwickshire, B49 5QG Tel: (01789) 763956 Fax: (01789) 400565 E-mail: ace@acegroup.co.uk

A C Mechanical Services Ltd, 16 Kingdom Close, Fareham, Hampshire, PO15 5TJ Tel: (01489) 579016 Fax: (01489) 579018 E-mail: info@acms.co.uk

A C R C Ltd, The Courtyard, North Street, Wigston, Leicestershire, LE18 1PS Tel: 0116-257 0066 Fax: 0116-257 0099 E-mail: info@acrcltd.co.uk

▶ A C S, Oakleigh, Smithy Lane, Pentre Bychan, Wrexham, Clwyd, LL14 4EN Tel: (01978) 846173 Fax: (01978) 846262

A C S Environmental UK Ltd, Caxton Point, Caxton Way, Stevenage, Hertfordshire, SG1 2XU Tel: (01438) 353415 Fax: (01438) 362973

▶ A C S Wade Ltd, Unit B6, Pinfold Industrial Estate, Rhyl, Clwyd, LL18 2YR Tel: (01745) 342998 Fax: (01745) 336006 E-mail: mail@acswade.co.uk

A D Buildings Ltd, 2A Crown Street, Redbourn, St. Albans, Hertfordshire, AL3 7JU Tel: (01582) 794842 Fax: (01582) 793889 E-mail: adbuildings@connectfree.co.uk

A D Installation, 14 North Road, Dartford, DA1 3NA Tel: (01322) 223648 Fax: (01322) 419501

A E R Cooling Ltd, 21 Woburn St, Ampthill, Bedford, MK45 2HP Tel: (01525) 403221 Fax: (01525) 406060

▶ A K D Systems Ltd, 69 Peffer Place, Edinburgh, EH16 4BB Tel: 0131-621 6000 Fax: 0131-621 8200 E-mail: info@akdsystems.co.uk

A K S Air Conditioning Ltd, 4 Edinburgh Road, Formby, Liverpool, L37 6EP Tel: (01704) 833755 Fax: (01704) 833422

Aairecool Technical Services Ltd, 3 Eastfield Farm Road, Penicuik, Midlothian, EH26 8EZ Tel: (01968) 679365 Fax: (01968) 679316 E-mail: aairecool@btconnect.com

Accent Services Air Conditioning Ltd, 4 Brooklands Close, Sunbury-on-Thames, Middlesex, TW16 7DX Tel: (01932) 765648 Fax: (01932) 788706 E-mail: info@accent.ac.co.uk

Ace General Engineering Cornwall Ltd, Quarry Park Road, Newquay, Cornwall, TR7 2NY Tel: (01637) 873324 Fax: (01637) 876904

Acm Air Conditioning, Unit 10 Armley Workshops, Pickering Street, Leeds, LS12 2QG Tel: 0113-203 8240 Fax: 0113-279 7088

Acme Refrigeration Ltd, Cunliffe Road, Whitebirk Industrial Estate, Blackburn, BB1 5ST Tel: (01254) 277999 Fax: (01254) 277988 E-mail: email@acmerefrigeration.co.uk

Acrol Air Conditioning Co. Ltd, Salt Meadows Road, East Gateshead Industrial Estate, Gateshead, Tyne & Wear, NE8 3AH Tel: 0191-477 7999 Fax: 0191-477 7222 E-mail: sales@acrolairconditioningco.co.uk

Acrol Air Conditioning Services Ltd, Unit 49b, Leechmare East Industrial Estate, Sunderland, SR2 9TE Tel: 0191-523 6441 Fax: 0191-523 6425 E-mail: mail@aacs.demon.co.uk

Adcock Refrigeration & Air Conditioning Ltd, 152 London Road, Copford, Colchester, CO6 1BQ Tel: (01206) 212502 Fax: (01206) 212080 E-mail: mail20@adcock.co.uk

Adms, 151 Albury Road, Redhill, RH1 3LW Tel: (01737) 645319 Fax: (01737) 219640 E-mail: adms@ntlworld.com

Advance Cryo Refrigeration Services, 37 St Catherines Avenue, Luton, LU3 1QG Tel: (01582) 416036 Fax: (01582) 454782 E-mail: ade@advanecryo1945.fsnet.co.uk

Advanced, PO Box 6433, Birmingham, B30 3HG Tel: 0121-459 3838 Fax: 0121-459 1415

Agm, 32 Teesdale Road, Ridgeway, Sheffield, S12 3XH Tel: 0114-248 9198 Fax: 0114-247 2551 E-mail: agm1ac@aol.com

▶ Air Care, 125 New Bridge Street, Newcastle upon Tyne, NE1 2SW Tel: 0191-261 1144 Fax: 0191-261 1188 E-mail: info@aircare-services.co.uk

Air Care Mechanical Services Ltd, 297 Avenue Road Extension, Clarendon Park, Leicester, LE2 3ER Tel: 0116-270 9707 Fax: 0116-270 5737 E-mail: sales@aircaremechanical.co.uk

▶ Air Chilled Solutions, 40 Stoneleigh Court, Westcroft, Milton Keynes, MK4 4BT Tel: 01908 526585 Fax: 01908 526585 E-mail: info@airchilledsolutions.co.uk

Air Con, 30 Woodbrook Road, Springhead, Oldham, OL4 4BS Tel: 0161-678 8862 Fax: 0161-678 8862

Air Conditioning (Jersey), 9 New Street, St Helier, Jersey, JE2 3RA Tel: (01534) 870022 Fax: (01534) 870044

Air Conditioning Services, 15 Torland Road, Plymouth, PL3 5TS Tel: (01752) 778985 Fax: (01752) 778985

Air Cool Engineering Ltd, Unit G, Aghanloo Industrial Estate, Aghanloo Road, Limavady, County Londonderry, BT49 0HE Tel: (028) 7776 7114 Fax: (028) 7776 7115 E-mail: sales@ni.aircool.co.uk

Air Cool Engineering Midlands Ltd, Fairway House, Vulcan Road, Solihull, West Midlands, B91 2JY Tel: 0121-711 4700 Fax: 0121-711 4757 E-mail: dsteele@aircoolmidlands.co.uk

Air Handling Systems Ltd, Unit 3-5 Furnace Industrial Estate, Shildon, County Durham, DL4 1QB Tel: (01388) 776287 Fax: (01388) 775494 E-mail: general@ahs.uk.com

Air Improve Ltd, Unit 4 City Business Centre, Hyde Street, Winchester, Hampshire, SO23 7TA Tel: (01962) 841366 Fax: (01962) 840185 E-mail: enquiries@airimprove.ltd.uk

Air Quality Control Ltd, Ground Floor, 339 Hollinwood Avenue, Manchester, M40 0JA Tel: 0161-688 6880 Fax: 0161-682 6864 E-mail: admin@aqc-ltd.co.uk

Air Supply Systems Ltd, 8 Harmony Square, Glasgow, G51 3LW Tel: 0141-440 2121 Fax: 0141-440 0330

Aircon Refrigeration Ltd, 35e Dukesway, Teesside Industrial Estate, Stockton-on-Tees, Cleveland, TS17 9LT Tel: (01642) 760565 Fax: (01642) 764011 E-mail: aircon.refrigeration@btinternet.com

Airconaire Ltd, Unit 6 Deacon Trading Centre, Knight Road, Rochester, Kent, ME2 2AU Tel: (01634) 711264 Fax: (01634) 717100 E-mail: info@airconaire.co.uk

Air-Conditioning & Refrigeration Concerns, 5 Mingarry, Birtley, Chester Le Street, County Durham, DH3 2JB Tel: 0191-410 3594 Fax: 0191-410 8504

Aireserve Air Conditioning, Airrex House, Hambledon Road, Hambledon, Waterlooville, Hampshire, PO7 4QX Tel: (023) 9223 3300 Fax: (023) 9223 8555 E-mail: dfarr@mail.aireserv.com

Airmaster, 49A High Street, Beighton, Sheffield, S20 1EE Tel: 0114-288 9911 Fax: 0114-288 9922 E-mail: team@airmaster.uk.com

Airtech Air Conditioning Services Ltd, Devon House, Eastbourne Road, Lingfield, Surrey, RH7 6JJ Tel: (01342) 836000 Fax: (01342) 835930 E-mail: ac@airtech.uk.com

▶ Airtek Air Conditioning & Technical Services Ltd, Designer House, 44 Lorraine Road, Timperley, Altrincham, Cheshire, WA15 7NB Tel: 0161-904 9333 Fax: 0161-904 8558

Airtemp A.C. Ltd, 18 Theaklen Drive, Ponswood Industrial Estate, St. Leonards-on-Sea, East Sussex, TN38 9AZ Tel: (0845) 8725657 Fax: (0845) 8725658 E-mail: sales@airtempac.co.uk

Aldridge Mechanical Services, 244 Goldcroft, Yeovil, Somerset, BA21 4DA Tel: (01935) 420162 Fax: (01935) 420162

Anderson Refrigeration, 30 Gartclush Gardens, Bannockburn, Stirling, FK7 8QA Tel: (01786) 817677 Fax: (01786) 817677 E-mail: enquiries@andersonrefrigeration.co.uk

Andersons Ltd, 1 Weston Road, Guildford, Surrey, GU2 8AU Tel: (01483) 578887 Fax: (01483) 578885 E-mail: johnschluter@btconnect.com

Andrew Engineering Ltd, Unit 4, Cobnar Wood Close, Chesterfield, Derbyshire, S41 9RQ Tel: (0845) 1267873 Fax: (0845) 1267874 E-mail: sales@andrew-eng.co.uk

Andrew Young Auto Electrical & Air Con Specialists, 4 Prospect Business Park, Langston Road, Loughton, Essex, IG10 3TR Tel: (020) 8508 5880 Fax: (020) 8502 3530

Anglia Air Conditioning Ltd, 7 Fletcher Way, Weston Road, Norwich, NR3 3ST Tel: (01603) 787383 Fax: (01603) 403480 E-mail: sales@anglia-aircon.co.uk

Aqua Mechanical Services Ltd, Aqua House, Rose & Crown Road, Swavesey, Cambridge, CB4 5RB Tel: (01954) 230948 Fax: (01954) 230593 E-mail: group@aqua.co.uk

▶ Arden Environmental Ltd, The Arden Centre, Little Alne, Wootton Wawen, Henley-In-Arden, West Midlands, B95 6HW Tel: (01789) 488555 Fax: (01789) 488122 E-mail: enquiries@ardenair.com

Argent F M Ltd, Unit 8, Penarth Centre, London, SE15 1TW Tel: (0870) 8900399 Fax: (0870) 8900398 E-mail: info@argent.fm.co.uk

Argon Arc Ltd, South Nelson Road, South Nelson Industrial Estate, Cramlington, Northumberland, NE23 1WF Tel: (01670) 707888 Fax: (01670) 707889 E-mail: argonarc@btinternet.com

Arnold James St Albans Ltd, 1 Metro Centre, Ronsons Way, Sandridge, St. Albans, Hertfordshire, AL4 9QT Tel: (01727) 851477 Fax: (01727) 842912

Arrow Refrigeration & Air Conditioning, 54 Chesterton Close, Redditch, Worcestershire, B97 5XS Tel: (01527) 541420 Fax: (01527) 543843 E-mail: arrowcooling@tiscali.com

Aspen Air Conditioning Ltd, Apex Way, Hailsham, East Sussex, BN27 3WA Tel: (0800) 376 0767 Fax: (01323) 849 966 E-mail: info@aspen-ac.co.uk

Aspen Contracts Ltd, 333 London Road, Hadleigh, Essex, SS7 2BT Tel: (01702) 428899 Fax: (01702) 551899 E-mail: enquiries@aspencontracts.com

▶ Aster Maintenance, 3 Kings Road, Fleet, Hampshire, GU51 3DL Tel: (01252) 816111 Fax: (01252) 816070

Atrium Facilities Management Ltd, Atrium House, Oakfields, Guildford, Surrey, GU3 3AT Tel: (01483) 889090 Fax: (01483) 889091 E-mail: info@atriumfm.co.uk

Automated Systems, 1-3 Mossley Road, Grasscroft, Oldham, OL4 4HH Tel: (0870) 2402771 Fax: (0870) 2402773 E-mail: stevepage@automatedsystem.org

B T S Scotland Ltd, 15 Croft Road, Balmore, Torrance, Glasgow, G64 4AL Tel: (01360) 620761 Fax: (01360) 622236

B W Fabrications Ltd, 3 Market Side, Albert Road, St. Philips, Bristol, BS2 0XS Tel: 0117-972 4002 Fax: 0117-972 3094 E-mail: bwfabrications@hotmail.com

Bartlett Refrigeration Ltd, Marsh Green Road West, Marsh Barton Trading Estate, Exeter, EX2 8PT Tel: (01392) 203000 Fax: (01392) 203001 E-mail: sales@bartlett.uk.com

Batchelor Air Conditioning, 3 Stilebrook Road, Olney, Buckinghamshire, MK46 5EA Tel: (01234) 241781 Fax: (01234) 241781

▶ B-Dacs Ltd, 1 Cameron Gate, 145 New Edinburgh Road, Uddingston, Glasgow, G71 6NF Tel: (01698) 801181 Fax: (01698) 801111

Beaven & Sons Ltd, 183 Westgate Street, Gloucester, GL1 2RN Tel: (01452) 314384 Fax: (01452) 300195

Berks & Bucks Air Conditioning, Unit G2 Rose Business Estate, Marlow Bottom Road, Marlow, Buckinghamshire, SL7 3ND Tel: (01628) 472267 Fax: (01628) 472262 E-mail: info@berksbucksaircon.co.uk

Birdsall Services Ltd, 6 Frogmore Road, Apsley, Hemel Hempstead, Hertfordshire, HP3 9RW Tel: (01442) 212501 Fax: (01442) 248989 E-mail: lynne.culliton@birdsall.co.uk

Borahurst Ltd, Devonshire House, 31 Holmesdale Road, Reigate, Surrey, RH2 0BJ Tel: (01737) 221733 Fax: (01737) 223512 E-mail: info@borahurst.com

Bradley Refrigeration Ltd, 929 Abbeydale Road, Sheffield, S7 2QD Tel: 0114-236 9971 Fax: 0114-236 8681 E-mail: ecroft@bradley-refrigeration.com

Braywhite & Co. Ltd, Halligan Buildings, Johnstone Street, Birmingham, B19 1SZ Tel: 0121-551 6001 Fax: 0121-511 7120 E-mail: info@braywhite.co.uk

Breeze Cool Air Conditioning & Refrigeration Ltd, 37 Amberley Road, Macclesfield, Cheshire, SK11 8LX Tel: (01625) 511336 Fax: (01625) 511288 E-mail: enquiries@breezecool.co.uk

▶ Brewfitt Refrigeration & Air Conditioning, International House, Penistone Road, Fenay Bridge, Huddersfield, HD8 0LE Tel: (01484) 340800 Fax: (01484) 340900 E-mail: sales@brewfitt.com

Brifrost Engineering, 9 The Drive, Wheathampstead, St. Albans, Hertfordshire, AL4 8LE Tel: (01438) 832402 Fax: (01438) 833526

Brimalk Ltd, Unit 8, Apollo, Lichfield Road Industrial Estate, Tamworth, Staffordshire, B79 7TA Tel: (01827) 51550 Fax: (01827) 51188 E-mail: sales@brimalk.co.uk

Buchan Refrigeration, Ivy Place, Worthing, West Sussex, BN11 3LN Tel: (01903) 204655 Fax: (01903) 204657

C C N Ltd, Spence Mills, Mill Lane, Leeds, LS13 3HE Tel: 0113-236 0033 Fax: 0113-236 0069 E-mail: info@ccn-ac.co.uk

C F Environmental Services Ltd, Unit 3, Bentley Park, Blacknest, Alton, Hampshire, GU34 4PX Tel: (01420) 22622 Fax: (01420) 22612 E-mail: sales@cfes.co.uk

C & M Environmental Ltd, 52 Strathmore Road, Glasgow, G22 7DW Tel: 0141-336 7774 Fax: 0141-336 5559 E-mail: enfor@cmenvironmental.co.uk

C S Environmental Services, 270 Manchester Road, Audenshaw, Manchester, M34 5GJ Tel: 0161-371 1638 Fax: 0161-371 7081

Caledonian Building Services South East Ltd, 31 Slewins Lane, Hornchurch, Essex, RM11 2BZ Tel: (01708) 454305 Fax: (01708) 437375

Camrose Air Conditioning Ltd, Unit D4 Brunswick Place, Cranbourne Lane, Basingstoke, Hampshire, RG21 3NN Tel: 0845 4941703 Fax: (01256) 322801 E-mail: peter@camroseair.co.uk

Harry Carr Ltd, Armstrong Street, Grimsby, North East Lincolnshire, DN31 1LG Tel: (01472) 246600 Fax: (01472) 240466 E-mail: engineers@harrycarr.co.uk

Carter Refrigeration, 111-115 Marsh Lane, Bootle, Merseyside, L20 4JD Tel: 0151-922 2342 Fax: 0151-922 4004 E-mail: liverpool.contracts@crrs.co.uk

Cascade Systems (UK) Ltd, Unit 10, West Place, West Road, Harlow, Essex, CM20 2GY Tel: (01279) 626695 Fax: (01279) 626799 E-mail: infocascade@aol.com

▶ Ceilite Air Conditioning Ltd, 1 The Alcorns, Cambridge Road, Stansted, Essex, CM24 8DF Tel: (01279) 815503 Fax: (01279) 813971 E-mail: sales@ceilte.com

Celsius Air Conditioning, 1 Well Street, Heywood, Lancashire, OL10 1NT Tel: (01706) 367500 Fax: (01706) 367355 E-mail: sales@celsiusair.co.uk

Centre Bar Concepts, Willow House, New Road, Droitwich, Worcestershire, WR9 0PQ Tel: (01299) 851649 Fax: (01299) 851550 E-mail: centrebarconcept@aol.com

Cevac & Co., 4 Marechal Niel Parade, Main Road, Sidcup, Kent, DA14 6QF Tel: (020) 8308 0808 Fax: (020) 8308 0181

Chill The World Ltd, Myler Court, 156-158 Marsh Road, Leagrave, Luton, LU3 2QL Tel: (01582) 593377 Fax: (01322) 436238 E-mail: sales@chilloutaircon.com

Chillaire Ltd, Unit 1, Veasey Close, Attleborough Fields Industrial Estate, Nuneaton, Warwickshire, CV11 6RT Tel: (024) 7632 0300 Fax: (024) 7632 0400 E-mail: g.fowler@chillaire.co.uk

Chiller Box Ltd, Unit 6, Carbery Enterprise Park, 36 White Hart Lane, Tottenham, London, N17 8DP Tel: (0800) 8491188 E-mail: mail@chillerbox.com

▶ Chiswell Fireplaces Ltd, 192 Watford Road, St. Albans, Hertfordshire, AL2 3EB Tel: (01727) 859512 Fax: (01727) 836343 E-mail: sales@chiswellfireplaces.com

City Air Conditioning Ltd, 6 Palace Industrial Estate, Bircholt Road, Maidstone, Kent, ME15 9XU Tel: (01622) 692338 Fax: (01622) 672377 E-mail: cityair@cityairltd.co.uk

City Engineering Ltd, 9 Cygnus Business Centre, Dalmeyer Road, London, NW10 2XA Tel: (020) 8451 4930 Fax: (020) 8459 1120 E-mail: roul@cityengineering.fsnet.uk

Climate Services, Intersection House, 110-120 Birmingham Road, West Bromwich, West Midlands, B70 6RP Tel: 0121-524 8825 Fax: 0121-524 8823 E-mail: mail@climate-services.co.uk

Clivet Aircon Ltd, Unit F5 Railway Triangle, Walton Road, Portsmouth, PO6 1TG Tel: (023) 9238 1235 Fax: (023) 9238 1243 E-mail: info@clivetaircon.co.uk

Clover Technical Services, 4 Valiant Way, Lairdside Technology Park, Birkenhead, Merseyside, CH41 9HS Tel: 0151-650 1551 Fax: 0151-650 1213 E-mail: sales@cloveruk.com

▶ Clwyd Refrigeration Ltd, Conwy Morfa Enterprise Park, Parc Caer Seion, Conwy, Gwynedd, LL32 8FA Tel: (01492) 572323 Fax: (01492) 582626 E-mail: sevice@clwydrefrigeration.com

Cold Service Ltd, Avonside House, Kingfisher Park, Blashford, Ringwood, Hampshire, BH24 3NX Tel: (01425) 485700 Fax: (01425) 485701 E-mail: enquiries@coldservice.co.uk

Comserve Ltd, Comserve House, 54 Watling Street, Radlett, Hertfordshire, WD7 7NN Tel: (01923) 853269 Fax: (01923) 857370 E-mail: service@comserve.co.uk

Conditioned Environment Contracts Ltd, Ander House, 245 Acton Lane, London, NW10 7NR Tel: (020) 8453 1010 Fax: (020) 8965 8469 E-mail: sales@coolinguk.com

Connolly Refrigeration Ltd, 13 Howlett Way, Thetford, Norfolk, IP24 1HZ Tel: (01842) 766655 Fax: (01842) 763497 E-mail: sales@connollyrefrigeration.co.uk

Cool Air Co, 14 Seaforth Avenue, New Malden, Surrey, KT3 6JP Tel: (020) 8949 5259 Fax: (020) 8949 4490 E-mail: coolairco@aol.com

▶ Cool Concerns Ltd, Unit 12, Priesthawes Farm, Hailsham Road, Polegate, East Sussex, BN26 6QU Tel: (01323) 768768 Fax: (01323) 768768

Cool Heat Services, 167 Hullbridge Road, South Woodham Ferrers, Chelmsford, CM3 5LN Tel: (01245) 321615 Fax: (01245) 328981

▶ Cool Temp Ltd, Unit 1+2 Bedford Park, Banbury Road, Scunthorpe, South Humberside, DN16 1UL Tel: (01724) 868300 Fax: (01724) 279439 E-mail: service@cooltemp.co.uk

Cool Therm (U K) Ltd, Unit 5, 121 London Road, Warmley, Bristol, BS30 5NA Tel: 0117-961 0006 Fax: 0117-947 8642 E-mail: sales@cooltherm.co.uk

Coolburn Air Conditioning Ltd, Betsoms, The Avenue, Westerham, Kent, TN16 2EE Tel: (01959) 563361 Fax: (01959) 562786 E-mail: coolburn@tiscali.co.uk

Coolco Refrigeration Ltd, Unit 18 Green Lane Industrial Estate, Second Avenue, Small Heath, Birmingham, B9 5QP Tel: 0121-771 3373 Fax: 0121-771 3687 E-mail: coolcoltd@btconnect.com

Coolheat Ltd, Dovedale House, 16 Butts Road, Alton, Hampshire, GU34 1NB Tel: (01420) 82410 Fax: (01420) 541747 E-mail: sales@coolheatltd.co.uk

Cooling Heating Electrical Services, 18 Old Pawlett Road, West Huntspill, Highbridge, Somerset, TA9 3RH Tel: (07970) 565026 Fax: (01278) 795511 E-mail: sales@chesuk.com

Cool-Tec Services, 17 Sandford La Industrial Estate, Sandford Lane, Wareham, Dorset, BH20 4DY Tel: (01305) 268881 Fax: (01929) 554786 E-mail: sales@cool-tec.co.uk

▶ indicates data change since last edition

AIR CONDITIONING (AC) DESIGN OR INSTALLATION OR COMMISSIONING – *continued*

Coolus Services, 95 Front Lane, Upminster, Essex, RM14 1XN Tel: (01708) 641333 Fax: (01708) 641233 E-mail: sales@coolus-services.co.uk

Corby Refrigeration & Mechanical Services, Gordon House, Dale Street, Corby, Northamptonshire, NN17 2BQ Tel: (01536) 265273 Fax: (01536) 205881 E-mail: enquiries@corbyrefrigeration.co.uk

Cordell Engineering, 26-28 Elmtree Road, Teddington, Middlesex, TW11 8ST Tel: (020) 8943 8884 Fax: (020) 8943 8852

Coverite Air Conditioning Services Ltd, Unit 17 Coldart Business Centre, Dartford, DA1 2HZ Tel: (01322) 270989 Fax: (01322) 278203 E-mail: info@coverite-ac.co.uk

Cryotec Air Conditioning, Unit 4 Wolf Business Park, Alton Road Industrial Estate, Ross-on-Wye, Herefordshire, HR9 5NB Tel: (0800) 3892369 Fax: (01989) 764401 E-mail: info@cryotec.co.uk

Curaim (UK) Ltd, Units 11-12 Cockridden Farm Industrial Estate, Brentwood Road, Herongate, Brentwood, Essex, CM13 3LH Tel: (01277) 811003 Fax: (01277) 811522 E-mail: curaim@aol.com

Cutts Refrigeration Ltd, Rowbrook Farm, Ryton, Dorrington, Shrewsbury, SY5 7NR Tel: (01743) 718871 Fax: (01743) 718040

▶ D & E Technical Services Ltd, 15 Whistler Road, Eaton Ford, St. Neots, Cambridgeshire, PE19 7RT Tel: (01480) 474430 Fax: (01480) 386474 E-mail: enquiries@de-techservices.co.uk

D & J Air Conditioning Services Ltd, 5 Long Wood Road, Trafford Park, Manchester, M17 1PZ Tel: 0161-872 1033 Fax: 0161-848 0587 E-mail: info@djaircon.co.uk

D & S Air Conditioning Ltd, 5-6 Millbrook Close, Northampton, NN5 5JF Tel: (01604) 586482 Fax: (01604) 586477 E-mail: admin@dandsairconditioning.co.uk

▶ Dammy Air Ltd, 43 Old Farm Close, Hounslow, TW4 7AB Tel: (020) 8572 9841 Fax: (020) 8230 0937

Delta Air Conditioning (Reading) Ltd, 20-22 Richfield Avenue, Reading, RG1 8EQ Tel: (020) 8893 4700

Delta Environmental Ltd, Delta House Stanney Mill Industrial Park, Dutton Green, Little Stanney, Chester, CH2 4SA Tel: 0151-357 1121 Fax: 0151-357 2480 E-mail: sales@deltaenvironmental.net

▶ Deltec Maintenance Ltd, Unit R Taywood Enterprise Centre, Duchess Place, Rutherglen, Glasgow, G73 1DR Tel: 0141-647 6676 Fax: 0141-647 6643

Direction Fire Ltd, 5 First Quarter, Blenheim Road, Epsom, Surrey, KT19 9QN Tel: (01372) 744499 Fax: (01372) 741188 E-mail: angellinaw@directionfire.co.uk

Ducatt Heating Co. Ltd, Platts Road, Stourbridge, West Midlands, DY8 4YT Tel: (01384) 394641 Fax: (01384) 440455 E-mail: info@ducattheating.co.uk

Ductwork By Design Ltd, Unit 7, 193 Garth Rd, Morden, Surrey, SM4 4LZ Tel: (020) 8330 0091 Fax: (020) 8330 0103 E-mail: info@dbdltd.com

Ductwork Projects Ltd, Unit 303-305 Woolsbridge Industrial Park, Woolsbridge Industrial Estate, Three Legged Cross, Wimborne, Dorset, BH21 6SX Tel: (01202) 823621 Fax: (01202) 823744 E-mail: enquiries@dpl-kvd.co.uk

E F R Refrigeration, 695 High Road, Ilford, Essex, IG3 8RH Tel: (020) 8590 0022 Fax: (020) 8599 2870 E-mail: danney535@fsmail.net

E M S Ltd, 15-29 Eyre Street Hill, London, EC1R 5LB Tel: (020) 7837 4707 Fax: (020) 7833 8299 E-mail: enquiries@ems-maintenance.co.uk

Eastleigh Domestic Appliance Services, 53 Twyford Road, Eastleigh, Hampshire, SO50 4HH Tel: (023) 8064 4984 Fax: (023) 8061 2799 E-mail: sales@eastleigh-services.co.uk

Eastwood Air Conditioning Ltd, Eastwood House, Hubert Street, Aston, Birmingham, B6 4BA Tel: 0121-380 0555 Fax: 0121-359 8152 E-mail: sales@eastwoodgroup.co.uk

Easy Cool Refrigeration Ltd, 30 Eleanor Crescent, Newcastle, Staffordshire, ST5 3SA Tel: (01782) 628750 Fax: (01782) 628750 E-mail: info@rsm-reallycool.co.uk

Eaton-Williams Holdings Ltd, Station Road, Edenbridge, Kent, TN8 6EG Tel: (01732) 866055 Fax: (01732) 863461 E-mail: peter.dewdney@eaton-williams.com

Eldapoint Ltd, Sub-Station Road, Felixstowe, Suffolk, IP11 3JB Tel: (01394) 613110 Fax: (01394) 613218 E-mail: sales@eldapoint.co.uk

▶ Electro-Freeze Ltd, Summerhill Quarry, Douglas, Isle of Man, IM2 4PF Tel: (01624) 673921 Fax: (01624) 662312 E-mail: sales@electrofreeze.4mg.com

Elyo UK Industrial Ltd, Unit 3-4 Sheffield Airport Business Park, Europa Link, Sheffield, S9 1XU Tel: 0114-280 0000 Fax: 0114-280 0099 E-mail: sheffield@elyo.co.uk

Enright Engineering Services, Unit 8 Team Valley Business Centre, Earlsway, Team Valley Trading Estate, Gateshead, Tyne & Wear, NE11 0QH Tel: 0191-482 0002 Fax: 0191-482 0027 E-mail: info@enrightengineering.co.uk

Ensol Ltd, 344 St Helens Road, Bolton, BL3 3RP Tel: (01204) 660064 Fax: (01204) 660043 E-mail: sales@ensol.co.uk

Ensys Ltd, Unit 10 Rivermead, Thatcham, Berkshire, RG19 4EP Tel: (01635) 872227 Fax: (01635) 872206 E-mail: sales@ensys.co.uk

Envirogroup Installation, 34 Osier Road, Spalding, Lincolnshire, PE11 1UU Tel: (01775) 761344 Fax: (01775) 766011 E-mail: kevin.savage@virgin.net

Environmental Cooling Systems, PO Box 652, Aylesbury, Buckinghamshire, HP22 5XD Tel: (01296) 633315 Fax: (01296) 633316

Eres Ltd, 264 Maybank Road, London, E18 1ES Tel: (020) 8504 1188 Fax: (020) 8504 1192

Ergro Mechanical Services, Wallgrove House, Hooley Lane, Redhill, RH1 6DG Tel: (01737) 770001 Fax: (01737) 771900 E-mail: info@ergro.co.uk

Ers, 21 Upton Cresent, Basingstoke, Hampshire, RG21 5SW Tel: (01256) 465604 Fax: (01256) 473737

Essex Electric Ltd, 46 Hanbury Road, Chelmsford, CM1 3TL Tel: (01245) 251291 Fax: (01245) 354051

E-Tech Group (HVAC Div), The E-Tech Centre, Boundary Road, Great Yarmouth, Norfolk, NR31 0LY Tel: (01493) 419800 Fax: (01493) 419805 E-mail: etech-hvac@etechcentre.com

Etherington Air Conditioning Ltd, 44 Potternewton Mount, Leeds, LS7 2DR Tel: 0113-262 1112 Fax: 0113-262 5075 E-mail: graham@etheringtonac.co.uk

Eventemp (Midlands) Ltd, Carrwood Road, Chesterfield Trading Estate, Sheepbridge, Chesterfield, Derbyshire, S41 9QB Tel: (01246) 453685 Fax: (01246) 260359 E-mail: enquiries@eventempmidland.ltd.uk

▶ Fair To Air, Shearwater, Trelawney Road, Ponsanooth, Truro, Cornwall, TR3 7EN Tel: (01872) 870455 Fax: (01872) 870455

Fan Maintenance Ltd, Eastern Works 4 Eastern Road, Walthamstow, London, E17 9DU Tel: (020) 8521 1856 Fax: (020) 8521 9421

Farebrother Group Ltd, Ridgeway House, Progress Way, Denton, Manchester, M34 2GP Tel: 0161-320 0056 Fax: 0161-320 5010 E-mail: farebrother@farebrother.co.uk

Farrelly Facilities & Engineering Ltd, Facilities House, 386-388 Boldmere Road, Sutton Coldfield, West Midlands, B73 5EZ Tel: 0121-382 9988 Fax: 0121-382 4155 E-mail: sales@farrellyfacilities.com

First In Service Ltd, Windsor Industrial Estate, Rupert Street, Birmingham, B7 4PR Tel: 0121-333 3301 Fax: 0121-333 3302 E-mail: sellis@firstinservice.co.uk

Fletcher, Jubilee Lodge, Jubilee Way, Chessington, Surrey, KT9 1TR Tel: (020) 8391 1876 Fax: (020) 8391 1876

Formost Air Conditioning Ltd, Unit 9 Wilford Lane Industrial Estate, Ruddington Lane, Wilford, Nottingham, NG11 7EP Tel: 0115-945 5033 Fax: 0115-974 5527 E-mail: smurphy@formost.co.uk

Franklin M & E Services Ltd, 6 Hoffmanns Way, Chelmsford, CM1 1GU Tel: (01245) 505050 Fax: (01245) 505051 E-mail: me@franklingroup.co.uk

Frise M S & Sons Ltd, 7 Trowbridge Road, Westbury, Wiltshire, BA13 3AY Tel: (01373) 826333 Fax: (01373) 826444 E-mail: sales@frise.co.uk

G B A Electrical Ltd, 3 Williams Way, West Row, Bury St. Edmunds, Suffolk, IP28 8QB Tel: (01638) 718289 Fax: (01638) 718289

G T Building Services Ltd, Unit 2, Bath Bridge Business Park, Bath Road, Bridgwater, Somerset, TA6 4SZ Tel: (01278) 455266 Fax: (01278) 455269

▶ G8 Environmental Solutions Ltd, B3 Kingsfisher House Kingsway, Team Valley Trading Estate, Gateshead, Tyne & Wear, NE11 0JQ Tel: 0191-482 8760 Fax: 0191-482 8761 E-mail: enquiries@g8environmental.com

Gatwick Park Mechanical Services Ltd, P.O. Box 371, Caterham, Surrey, CR3 6UE Tel: (01883) 347133 Fax: (01883) 343813 E-mail: info@gatwickpark.com

Gazelle Ventures Ltd, 276B New Road, Croxley Green, Rickmansworth, Hertfordshire, WD3 3HH Tel: (01923) 720466 Fax: (01923) 720411 E-mail: sales@gazelleventures.co.uk

GK Maintenance, Leamore Industrial Estate, 8 Wall End Close, Walsall, WS2 7PH Tel: (01922) 479462 Fax: (01922) 404842 E-mail: staff@gkmaintenance.co.uk

▶ Glenfield Air Conditioning Ltd, 139a Dominion Road, Glenfield, Leicester, LE3 8JB Tel: 0116-231 4117 Fax: 0116-231 4117 E-mail: darren.web@glenfield96.fsnet.co.uk

▶ Griffiths Air Conditioning & Electrical Contractors, 115 Station Road, Burton Latimer, Kettering, Northamptonshire, NN15 5PA Tel: (01536) 420666 Fax: (01536) 721133 E-mail: griffiths.aircon@ntlworld.com

Gryson Air Conditioning Equipment Ltd, Unit 37 Penmaen Small Business Centre, Penmaen Road, Pontllanfraith, Blackwood, Gwent, NP12 2DZ Tel: (01495) 221200 Fax: (01495) 228432 E-mail: enquiries@gryson-aircon.com

▶ Guardian Environmental, 117 Clophill Road, Maulden, Bedford, MK45 2AE Tel: (01525) 862528 Fax: (01525) 862163 E-mail: val.barnes@guardian.uk.com

H & D Air Conditioning Ltd, 133 Royal George Road, Burgess Hill, West Sussex, RH15 9TD Tel: (01444) 232552 Fax: (01444) 246568 E-mail: brighton@mail.aireserv.com

Hadrian Air Conditioning & Refrigeration Co. Ltd, 3 Rosse Close, Parsons Industrial Estate, Washington, Tyne & Wear, NE37 1ET Tel: 0191-415 0055 Fax: 0191-415 0888 E-mail: sales@hadrian-air.co.uk

Hale Refrigeration, Unit 8 Paper Mill End Industrial Estate, Birmingham, B44 8NH Tel: 0121-344 3345 Fax: 0121-344 3346 E-mail: halerefrigeration@compuserve.com

J.L. Harrison & Son (Air Conditioning) Ltd, Unit 17, Olympic Business Centre, Paycocke Road, Basildon, Essex, SS14 3EX Tel: (01268) 532414 Fax: (01268) 532415 E-mail: info@chillerservices.co.uk

Harrison-Page Refrigeration Ltd, 63 Lion Road, Bexleyheath, Kent, DA6 8NN Tel: (020) 8303 7484

Hawkes Refrigeration Engineers, 2 Gibcracks, Basildon, Essex, SS14 1PE Tel: (01268) 556663 Fax: (01268) 584525 E-mail: sales@refrigeration-uk.com

Healey Duct Installations Ltd, 11 Clayton Road, Brighton, BN2 9ZP Tel: (01273) 691955 Fax: (01273) 691955 E-mail: bjhealey@aol.com

Heat Works Ltd, Unit 2 Moorend Indust Estate, Bradford Road, Cleckheaton, West Yorkshire, BD19 3TT Tel: (01274) 852900 Fax: (01274) 852911 E-mail: info@heatworks.co.uk

Heating & Ventilating Services Ltd, 50 Park Lane, Basford, Nottingham, NG6 0DT Tel: 0115-978 1445 Fax: 0115-978 1596

Hensall Mechanical Services (Holdings) Ltd, Roall, Goole, North Humberside, DN14 0NA Tel: (01977) 661318 Fax: (01977) 662127 E-mail: enquiries@hensall.com

Heronridge Services (Nottingham) Ltd, Units 2, Palm Court, Palm Street, New Basford, Nottingham, NG7 7HU Tel: 0115-979 0644 Fax: 0115-979 0438 E-mail: sales@heronridge.co.uk

Hesflo Installations Ltd, 6 Dial Lane, Bristol, BS16 5UH Tel: 0117-970 1930 Fax: 0117-970 1931 E-mail: design@hesflo.co.uk

Howard Environmental Services, Unit 5 Faygate Business Centre, Faygate, Horsham, West Sussex, RH12 4DN Tel: (01293) 852211 Fax: (01293) 852244

▶ Hpa Services, 267 Wickham Street, Welling, Kent, DA16 3LS Tel: (020) 8855 5666

Huntley Refrigeration & Air-Conditioning, 80 Broad Street, Coventry, CV6 5AZ Tel: (024) 7666 5252 Fax: (024) 7627 7102 E-mail: sales@huntleyrefrigeration.co.uk

Hussmann (Europe) Ltd, 4-5 Bonville Road, Brislington, Bristol, BS4 5NF Tel: 0117-971 2121 Fax: 0117-971 9098

Hymas Refrigeration & Catering Ltd, 178 Grove Green Road, London, E11 4EL Tel: (020) 8539 4222 E-mail: hymas_ref@fsmail.net

Ice Guard Group, Mold Road, Cefn-y-Bedd, Wrexham, Clwyd, LL12 9UL Tel: (01978) 761881 Fax: (01978) 761789

▶ Iceberg Building Services Ltd, 1 Station Court, Station Approach, Wickford, Essex, SS11 7AT Tel: (01268) 739450 Fax: (01268) 739459 E-mail: iceberg@btconnect.com

Indoor Controlled Ltd, 250-252 Tiverton Road, Birmingham, B29 6BU Tel: 0121-472 2480 Fax: 0121-414 1107

Indtherm Ltd, 120 Wellington Road, Dudley, West Midlands, DY1 1UB Tel: (01384) 456666 Fax: (01384) 456666 E-mail: action@indtherm.co.uk

Industrial Air Control Ltd, Bath Lodge, Park Street, Royton, Oldham, OL2 6QN Tel: 0161-626 0242 Fax: 0161-627 0231 E-mail: sales@iacontrol.co.uk

Industrial Cooling Equipment Ltd, 101 Chadwick Road, Astmore Industrial Estate, Runcorn, Cheshire, WA7 1PW Tel: (01928) 568800 Fax: (01928) 568822 E-mail: sales@ice-ltd.co.uk

Initial Building Services, Unit 5 Kings Castle Business Park, The Drove, Bridgwater, Somerset, TA6 4AG Tel: (01278) 444487

Inviron Ltd, 17 Portman Road, Ipswich, IP1 2BP Tel: (01473) 219921 Fax: (01473) 231317

▶ J & D Hall Ltd, Questor House, 191 Hawley Road, Dartford, DA1 1PU Tel: (01322) 223456 Fax: (01322) 394421

▶ J & E Hall Ltd, Unit 94 Christian Mill Business Park, Tamerton Foliot Road, Plymouth, PL6 5DS Tel: (01752) 776840 Fax: (01752) 776840

J & E Hall Ltd, 2 Fairbrother Street, Salford, M5 3EN Tel: 0161-872 7022 Fax: 0161-371 0555

J M Air Conditioning Ltd, 23 Tollgate Avenue, Redhill, RH1 5HR Tel: 01737 772200 Fax: 01737 772300 E-mail: jmacltd@aol.com

Jack Elam, Barton Road, Wisbech, Cambridgeshire, PE13 4TP Tel: (01945) 419090 Fax: (01945) 419088 E-mail: sales@jack-elam.co.uk

Jersey Electricity Co. Ltd, PO Box 45, Jersey, JE4 8NY Tel: (01534) 505000 Fax: (01534) 505011 E-mail: jec@jec.co.uk

John Carter Salt Lane Ltd, 6-10 Salt Lane, Salisbury, SP1 1EE Tel: (01722) 322407 Fax: (01722) 412146 E-mail: enquiry@john-carters.co.uk

▶ JPW, 302-304 Derby Road, Bootle, Merseyside, L20 8LN Tel: 0151-922 7070 Fax: 0151-922 7049

K M Services Ltd, 16 Bourne Industrial Estate, Wrotham Road, Borough Green, Sevenoaks, Kent, TN15 8DG Tel: (01732) 882280 Fax: (01732) 886011

Keeble Heating & Air Conditioning, 41 Rectory Grove, Wickford, Essex, SS11 8ER Tel: (01268) 735830 Fax: (01268) 735973

Kroyair Ltd, 262 Moseley Road, Birmingham, B12 0BX Tel: 0121-440 5383 Fax: 0121-446 4236 E-mail: info@kroyair.fsnet.co.uk

▶ L J & S Services, 87 Westminster Gardens, Eye, Peterborough, PE6 7SP Tel: (01733) 222235 Fax: (01733) 223743

L & R, 69 Rockingham Rd, Uxbridge, Middx, UB8 2UA Tel: (01895) 272523 Fax: (01895) 273664

Lee Air Conditioning Services Ltd, Lee House, Lower Road, Kenley, Surrey, CR8 5NH Tel: (020) 8660 5022 Fax: (020) 8668 0296 E-mail: nick.taylor@leeac.co.uk

Leicester Ventilation Systems Ltd, 19 Batten Street, Leicester, LE2 7PA Tel: 0116-224 0244 Fax: 0116-224 0247 E-mail: leisvent@aol.com

▶ London Cooling, 50 Northbourne Road, Gillingham, Kent, ME8 6QH Tel: (01634) 372345

A. Longworth & Sons Ltd, 55 Waverley Road, Sale, Cheshire, M33 7AY Tel: 0161-973 8398 Fax: 0161-905 1095

M & J Lossos Co. Ltd, 31 Beethoven St, London, W10 4LJ Tel: (020) 8969 1367 Fax: (020) 8968 8913 E-mail: admin@kaloricheater.co.uk

M J N Ltd, Davis House, 69-73 High Street, Croydon, CR9 1PY Tel: (020) 8686 5577 Fax: (020) 8681 3114 E-mail: jhipwell@mjncolston.co.uk

M S Air Movement, Unit 2a Hexton Manor Stables, Hexton, Hitchin, Hertfordshire, SG5 3JH Tel: (01582) 883662 Fax: (01582) 881009 E-mail: info@msairmovement.co.uk

McAlpine Grant Ilco, Osney Mead Industrial Estate, Oxford, OX2 0ER Tel: (01865) 251225 Fax: (01865) 791877 E-mail: info@mglitd.co.uk

Mcdowall Air Conditioning, Middlemore La West, Walsall, WS9 8EJ Tel: (01922) 454955 Fax: (01922) 454815 E-mail: sales@mcdowalls.co.uk

MacFarlane Environmental Ltd, Unit 20, East Belfast Enterprise Park, Belfast, BT5 4GX Tel: (028) 9045 7961 Fax: (028) 9045 9275 E-mail: macfarlane@btinternet.com

Macwhirter Ltd, 5 Stoke View Business Park, Stoke View Road, Bristol, BS16 3AE Tel: 0117-939 6661 Fax: 0117-939 6662 E-mail: sales@macwhirter.co.uk

▶ Maintenance Service Direct Ltd, Birmingham Road, Alvechurch, Birmingham, B48 7AJ Tel: 0121-447 8464 Fax: 0121-447 8463 E-mail: msd-ltd@btconnect.com

Major Refrigeration & Air Conditioning Services Ltd, 6 Broadway Road, Evesham, Worcestershire, WR11 1BH Tel: (01386) 49342 Fax: (01386) 45232 E-mail: info@majorcooling.co.uk

▶ Manhatten Heights, 108 Buckstones Road, Shaw, Oldham, OL2 8DN Tel: (01706) 849752 Fax: (01706) 299209 E-mail: sales@manheights.co.uk

Mansfield Refrigeration & Air Conditioning Co. Ltd, Dallas Street, Mansfield, Nottinghamshire, NG18 5SZ Tel: (01623) 626168 Fax: (01623) 420915

▶ Marlow Air Conditioning, N Rose Business Estate, 54 Marlow Bottom Road, Marlow, Buckinghamshire, SL7 3ND Tel: (01628) 472250 Fax: (01628) 487760 E-mail: enqs@marlowaircon.co.uk

Murray Martin Services Ltd, Unit 3 Block 2 River Place, Paddockholm Industrial Estate, Kilbirnie, Ayrshire, KA25 7EN Tel: (01505) 684822 Fax: (01505) 683005 E-mail: enquiries@murraymartinservices.co.uk

Mastercool Southern Ltd, 7a Baker Street, Ampthill, Bedford, MK45 2QE Tel: (01525) 840689 Fax: 01525 840699 E-mail: mastercool15@btopenworld.com

MBS, 24 Hanson Close, Middleton, Manchester, M24 2HD Tel: 0161-643 6151 Fax: 0161-643 6151

Mellor Bromley, 141 Barkby Road, Leicester, LE4 9LW Tel: 0116-276 6636 Fax: 0116-246 0426 E-mail: dbloxam@mellorbromley.co.uk

Met Anglia Ltd, Unit 2 Garrod Drive Industrial Estate, Fakenham, Norfolk, NR21 8NN Tel: (01328) 862026 Fax: (01328) 855961

Micra Air Conditioning Services, 9 Vicarage Road, Woodford Green, Essex, IG8 8NH Tel: (020) 8505 0749 Fax: (020) 8504 5490 E-mail: micraair@tiscali.co.uk

Miracle Astec Ltd, PO Box 119, Horsham, West Sussex, RH12 4YZ Tel: (01403) 255140 Fax: (01403) 260855

▶ Mooreserve, 5 Castlecroft, Norton Canes, Cannock, Staffordshire, WS11 9WS Tel: (01543) 275300

N A Cullen & Co. Ltd, Hayhills Road, Silsden, Keighley, West Yorkshire, BD20 9NE Tel: (01535) 654968 Fax: (01535) 655590 E-mail: nacul@lineone.net

N J R Installations Ltd, Chapel Street, Dudley, West Midlands, DY2 9PN Tel: (01384) 455555 Fax: (01384) 456177

Nationwide-ACR Ltd, 279-281 Leeds Road, Nelson, Lancashire, BB9 8EJ Tel: (0845) 6120611 Fax: (01282) 603016 E-mail: info@nationwide-acr.co.uk

Natural A C Ltd, 10 Ringwood Drive, Leigh-on-Sea, Essex, SS9 5HG Tel: (01702) 526154 Fax: (01702) 526154 E-mail: natural@aircond.freeserve.co.uk

NCS, Prizet Lodge, Helsington, Kendal, Cumbria, LA8 8AA Tel: (01539) 561666 Fax: (01539) 561999

B.C. Neill Air Conditioning Ltd, Brentwood Cronton Road, Prescot, Merseyside, L35 1SA Tel: 0151-423 3967 Fax: 0151-423 3978 E-mail: bcneill@tuscally.co.uk

Newsome Holdings Ltd, Calderbank, Saddleworth Road, Elland, West Yorkshire, HX5 0RY Tel: (01422) 371711 Fax: (01422) 377372 E-mail: enquiries@newsome.ltd.uk

North Sea Ventilation Ltd, West Carr Lane, Hull, HU7 0BW Tel: (01482) 834050 Fax: (01482) 834060 E-mail: enquiries@nsv.co.uk

AIR CONDITIONING (AC) DESIGN OR INSTALLATION OR COMMISSIONING – *continued*

Oakwood Technology Group, Ill Road, Cheadle Hulme, Cheadle, Cheshire, SK8 6GN Tel: 0161-488 4343 Fax: 0161-488 4086 E-mail: sales@oakwoodair.co.uk

Oasis Air Conditioning Ltd, 80 Bramhall Lane, Davenport, Stockport, Cheshire, SK2 6JG Tel: 0161-477 1003 Fax: 0161-477 3110 E-mail: sales@oasisairconditioning.com

OilanHeat (Maintenance) Ltd, 161 High Street, Aldershot, Hampshire, GU11 1TT Tel: (01252) 329789 Fax: (01252) 342804 E-mail: ac@lowbeck.com

Omega Environmental Technologies UK Ltd, 47 Bowness Crescent, London, SW15 3QN Tel: (020) 8870 9911 Fax: (020) 8549 1256 E-mail: omegaeurope@hotmail.com

Orbit Maintainence UK Ltd, Studio 6 The Mews, 46 Church Rd, Barnes, London, SW13 0DQ Tel: (020) 8563 2086 Fax: (020) 8563 2838

▶ Orion Air Conditioning & Refrigeration, 16 Barkers Piece, Marston Moretaine, Bedford, MK43 0LZ Tel: (07905) 967307 Fax: (01234) 765580 E-mail: info@orionair.co.uk

Oxford Refrigeration & Air Conditioning Ltd, 78-81 Magdalen Road, Oxford, OX4 1RF Tel: (01865) 424424 Fax: (01865) 424425 E-mail: ian.law@oracoxford.co.uk

P H Services Ltd, 37 Limberline Spur, Portsmouth, PO3 5DX Tel: (023) 9269 3448 Fax: (023) 9263 9094 E-mail: huntphill@aol.com

P S I (Resources) Ltd, Unit 3, Barlow Street, Walkden, Manchester, M28 3BQ Tel: 0161-703 8911 Fax: 0161-703 8995 E-mail: sales@p-s-i.co.uk

▶ Palace Tech Ltd, B14 Culpeper Close, Medway City Estate, Rochester, Kent, ME2 4HU Tel: (01634) 294200 Fax: (01634) 715432 E-mail: palt1994@aol.com

Peachman Refrigeration Ltd, 2 Jupiter Road, Norwich, NR6 6SU Tel: (01603) 789574 Fax: (01603) 789574 E-mail: mail@peachman.co.uk

▶ Perkins R & Sons, 201 London Central Markets, London, EC1A 9LH Tel: (020) 7329 4612 Fax: (020) 7329 4192 E-mail: info@rperkins.co.uk

Pert Building Services Ltd, 31 Bunbury Road, Northfield, Birmingham, B31 2DR Tel: 0121-411 2333 Fax: 0121-411 2600 E-mail: barrieroberts@pert-aircon.co.uk

Phil Kool, Graynoth Place, Otham Street, Otham, Maidstone, Kent, ME15 8RL Tel: (01622) 862123 Fax: (01622) 862160

Phoenix Ventilation & Engineering Ltd, Unit 6 Camphill Industrial Estate, Camphill Road, West Byfleet, Surrey, KT14 6EW Tel: (01932) 336125 Fax: (01932) 336132 E-mail: sales@phoenixventilation.co.uk

Pidra Environments Ltd, 23 Avebury Avenue, Sherbourne Park Estate, Choppington, Northumberland, NE62 5HE Tel: 0191-267 7111 Fax: 0191-267 7222 E-mail: david@pidra.ltd.uk

Polar Air Ltd, Huntingdon House, 278-290 Huntingdon Street, Nottingham, NG1 3LY Tel: 0115-955 0055 Fax: 0115-955 7037

Polarcool Refrigeration Ltd, Unit K1 Beckingham Business Park, Tolleshunt Major, Maldon, Essex, CM9 8LZ Tel: (01621) 868584 Fax: (01621) 868989 E-mail: sales@polarcool.co.uk

Preston Refrigeration Ltd, Units 3-4 Chantry Industrial Estate, Kingsbury Road, Curdworth, Sutton Coldfield, West Midlands, B76 9EE Tel: (01675) 470899 Fax: (01675) 470838

Quality Air Conditioning Ltd, 4 Orlando Court, Vicarage Lane, Walton on the Naze, Essex, CO14 8PA Tel: (01255) 672777 Fax: (01255) 676777 E-mail: shaun@qualityac.co.uk

R T Refrigaration & Air Conditioning, 1a Rowan Trade Park, Neville Road, Bradford, West Yorkshire, BD4 8TQ Tel: (01274) 737248 Fax: (01274) 309767

Rayvac Refrigeration Services, East Thurrock Road, Grays, Essex, RM17 6SP Tel: (01375) 390113 Fax: (01375) 381381 E-mail: keithneall@btopenworld.com

▶ React Building Services, Unit E3, Park Lane, Birmingham, B35 6LJ Tel: 0121-748 3666

Redbay Projects Ltd, 15 Dalton Court, Astmoor Industrial Estate, Runcorn, Cheshire, WA7 1PU Tel: (01928) 581782 Fax: (01928) 580619 E-mail: redbayprojects@aol.com

Redfern & Birchall, 6 Fernhill Street, Bury, Lancashire, BL9 5BG Tel: 0161-764 4929 Fax: 0161-764 4929

Reefworld Aquarium & Pond Supplies, 219 Fir Tree Road, Epsom, Surrey, KT17 3LB Tel: (01737) 370777 Fax: (01737) 212777 E-mail: sales@reefworld.co.uk

▶ Refrigeration & Heat Pump Services Ltd, Unit 7a Canalside Industrial Park, Kinoulton Road, Cropwell Bishop, Nottingham, NG12 3BE Tel: 0115-989 9985 Fax: 0115-989 1730

Refrigeration On The Wolds, Albion Street, Driffield, North Humberside, YO25 6PZ Tel: (01377) 252518

Refrigeration Service (Ruislip) Ltd, 288 West End Road, Ruislip, Middlesex, HA4 6LS Tel: (01895) 622286 Fax: (01895) 622259

Regency Building Services Ltd, 33 Station Road, Ingrebourne, Romford, RM3 0DQ Tel: (01708) 341114 Fax: (08707) 770664 E-mail: info@rbsmail.co.uk

Risby Air Conditioning Co. Ltd, Princes Road, Bourne End, Buckinghamshire, SL8 5HZ Tel: (01628) 850123 Fax: (01628) 850122 E-mail: info@risby.co.uk

Riverside Group, Tondu Road, Bridgend, Mid Glamorgan, CF31 4JA Tel: (01656) 656541 Fax: (01656) 662077 E-mail: emma@riverequip.co.uk

Rossal A/C Ltd, Systems House, 47 Palace Road, Bromley, BR1 3JU Tel: (020) 8466 0088 Fax: (020) 8466 1697 E-mail: rossalltd@aol.com

Rosser & Russell Building Services Ltd, Orbit House, 1-6 Ritz Parade, London, W5 3RD Tel: (020) 8982 2222 Fax: (020) 8982 2331

Rsy Air Conditioning Ltd, Refrigeration House, Potter Hill, Rotherham, South Yorkshire, S61 4NU Tel: (01709) 553355 Fax: (01709) 740814 E-mail: info@rsyaircon.co.uk

S G L Systems Ltd, Milton Industrial Estate, Lesmahagow, Lanark, ML11 0JN Tel: (01555) 894449 Fax: (01555) 894227

S I A S Building Services Ltd, Unit 4 Knowle Spring Industrial Estate, South Street, Keighley, West Yorkshire, BD21 1AQ Tel: (01535) 611336 Fax: (01535) 611361 E-mail: consultants@siasbuildingservices.co.uk

S & P Darwell Ltd, Scarborough Business Park, Hopper Hill Road, Eastfield, Scarborough, North Yorkshire, YO11 3YS Tel: (01723) 582000 Fax: (01723) 582828 E-mail: cad@darwells.fsnet.co.uk

S V M Consulting Engineers Ltd, 10 Kensworth Gate, Garden Road, Dunstable, Bedfordshire, LU6 3HS Tel: (01582) 660090 Fax: (01582) 660091 E-mail: solutions@svm.co.uk

Saunders & Taylor Ltd, 9 Boston Court, Kansas Avenue, Salford, M50 2GN Tel: 0161-848 9393 Fax: 0161-848 9696 E-mail: enquiries@saunders-taylor.co.uk

Sayes & Co. Ltd, Richardshaw Road, Grangefield Industrial Estate, Stanningley, Pudsey, West Yorkshire, LS28 6BR Tel: 0113-257 8411 Fax: 0113-256 9275 E-mail: contact@sayesandcoltd.co.uk

Scomo (Heating & Ventilating) Ltd, Escon House, 8 Fieldings Road, Cheshunt, Waltham Cross, Hertfordshire, EN8 9TL Tel: (01992) 635515 Fax: (01992) 635168 E-mail: esl@8escon.fsnet.co.uk

Scotford & Teasdale, Unit 8 Thames Park, Lester Way, Wallingford, Oxfordshire, OX10 9TA Tel: 01491 821737 Fax: 01491 821730

Serco Electrical Ltd, 93 Canwick Road, Lincoln, LN5 8HE Tel: (01522) 874874 Fax: (01522) 514732

Service Systems Ltd, 178 Oxford Road, Basford, Newcastle, Staffordshire, ST5 0QB Tel: (01782) 711077 Fax: (01782) 638538 E-mail: enquiries@servicesystemsltd.co.uk

Serviceplan Ltd, 1 Windmill Business Village, Brooklands Close, Sunbury-on-Thames, Middlesex, TW16 7DY Tel: (01932) 787871 Fax: (01932) 781071 E-mail: info@serviceplan.ltd.uk

Shelbourne Letheby & Co. Ltd, 154 New Kings Road, London, SW6 4LZ Tel: (020) 7736 4211 Fax: (020) 7371 0634

Simer Environmental Services Ltd, 15 Arnside Road, Waterlooville, Hampshire, PO7 7UP Tel: (023) 9225 8059 Fax: (023) 9226 7059 E-mail: sales@simer-environmental.co.uk

Simply Refrigeration & Air Conditioning Ltd, 10 Samsons Close, Brightlingsea, Colchester, CO7 0RP Tel: (0800) 0265140 Fax: (0870) 0520855 E-mail: info@simply-fridge.demon.co.uk

J.E. Smith (Higham Ferrers) Ltd., 24 Saffron Road, Higham Ferrers, Rushden, Northamptonshire, NN10 8ED Tel: (01933) 312495 Fax: (01933) 410424 E-mail: aircon@jesmith.sagehost.co.uk

▶ Sole Air, 25 Lacewing Close, Pinewood, Ipswich, IP8 3UD Tel: (01473) 602888

South East Cooling Ltd, 6 Southwinds House, Barrack Lane, Bognor Regis, West Sussex, PO21 4BZ Tel: (01243) 268888 Fax: (01243) 268843E-mail: sales@southeast-cooling.co.uk

Southern & Redfern Ltd, Forward House, Mount Street, Bradford, West Yorkshire, BD3 9SR Tel: (01274) 733333 Fax: (01274) 731300 E-mail: bernard.davis@southern-redfern.co.uk

Sperring Engineering Ltd, Unit 14, Knightcott Industrial Estate, Banwell, Avon, BS29 6JN Tel: (01934) 820233 Fax: (01934) 820374 E-mail: info@sperringengineering.co.uk

SRS Cooling, Archard House, Waverley Road, Weymouth, Dorset, DT3 5HL Tel: (01305) 750020 Fax: (01305) 750021 E-mail: sales@southernrefrigeration.freeserve.co.uk

Sterling Environmental Engineering Ltd, Sterling House, 12 Gate Lane, Sutton Coldfield, West Midlands, B73 5TT Tel: 0121-321 2244 Fax: 0121-321 3151 E-mail: enquiries@sterling.uk.com

Swift Maintenance Services, Unit 2 Albert Street, Wednesbury, West Midlands, WS10 7EW Tel: 0121-505 4001 Fax: 0121-502 2065

T H Companies Ltd, 1 Moat Farm Business Center, Turkey Cock Lane, Stanway, Colchester, CO3 8ND Tel: (01206) 212825 Fax: (01206) 212824 E-mail: sales@thcompanies.co.uk

T M P Northern Ltd, 281 Beckenham Road, Beckenham, Kent, BR3 4RL Tel: (020) 8676 0011 Fax: (020) 8676 0783 E-mail: sales@tmp-ltd.co.uk

T T F (Scotland) Ltd, 4 Block 3 12 King's Haugh, Peffermill Road, Edinburgh, EH16 5UY Tel: 0131-652 0030 Fax: 0131-661 0550 E-mail: admin@ttf-aircon.com

Tameside Refrigeration & Air Conditioning Ltd, 2 Gate Centre Bredbury Park Way, Bredbury Park Industrial Estate, Bredbury, Stockport, Cheshire, SK6 2SN Tel: 0161-406 8995 Fax: 0161-406 8997

Taprex, 2-6 Victor Road, Harrow, Middlesex, HA2 6PU Tel: (020) 8863 4698

Team National Ltd, Triumph House, Birmingham Road, Millisons Wood, Coventry, CV5 9AZ Tel: (01676) 526000 Fax: (01676) 522966 E-mail: sales@teamnational.co.uk

Thermal Transfer (Northern) Ltd, Thermal Transfer House, 2 Railway Street, Glossop, Derbyshire, SK13 7AG Tel: (01457) 854341 Fax: (01457) 868357 E-mail: ttglossop@compuserve.co.uk

Thermal Transfer (U K) Ltd, Scottish Enterprise Technology Park, Rankine Avenue, East Kilbride, Glasgow, G75 0QF Tel: (01355) 234567 Fax: (01355) 266466

Thermalair Ltd, 6 Lundy Court, Rougham Industrial Estate, Rougham, Bury St. Edmunds, Suffolk, IP30 9ND Tel: (01359) 271444 Fax: (01359) 271445 E-mail: enquiries@thermalairltd.co.uk

▶ Thorn Air Conditioning, Unit 27, Vastre Industrial Estate, Newtown, Powys, SY16 1DZ Tel: (01686) 623100 Fax: (01686) 623200

Tideside Ltd, 5 Bow Exchange, Yeo Street, London, E3 3QR Tel: (020) 7987 4652 Fax: (020) 7987 8612 E-mail: enquiries@tideside.co.uk

TP Refrigeration, 2 George Street, Leighton Buzzard, Bedfordshire, LU7 3JX Tel: (01525) 376629 Fax: (01525) 851200 E-mail: tprefrig@aol.com

Triac Air Conditioning Ltd, Shrubbery House, 47 Prospect Hill, Redditch, Worcestershire, B97 4BS Tel: (01527) 591199 Fax: (01527) 596284

Tropair Engineering Ltd, Building 528, Biggin Hill Airport, Biggin Hill, Westerham, Kent, TN16 3BN Tel: (01959) 576767 Fax: (01959) 540033 E-mail: tropairmail@aol.com

TTF Air Conditioning Ltd, 5 Tower Road, Washington, Tyne & Wear, NE37 2SH Tel: 0191-416 4525 Fax: 0191-416 4650 E-mail: cg-ttssales@jci.com

▶ U P S Direct, 6 Camross Drive, Shrewsbury, SY1 3XH Tel: (01743) 243833 Fax: (01743) 340555 E-mail: ghollis@upsdirect.com

Universal Cooling Ltd, Unit 1a West End Business Park, Oswaldtwistle, Accrington, Lancashire, BB5 4WE Tel: (01254) 396005 Fax: (01254) 396055 E-mail: sales@universalcooling.co.uk

Uxbridge Engineering Co. Ltd, Robinswood, Dukes Kiln Drive, Gerrards Cross, Buckinghamshire, SL9 7HD Tel: (01753) 889511 Fax: (01753) 880118 E-mail: enquiries@uxbridge-eng.demon.co.uk

George Varcas & Partners, Windshield, Brimpton Common, Reading, RG7 4RU Tel: 0118-981 4983 Fax: 0118-981 7138 E-mail: paul@varcas.co.uk

Ventitherm Ltd, 121 Park Road, London, W4 3EX Tel: (020) 8994 5583 Fax: (020) 8994 8221

W R Refrigeration Ltd, 8 Buckingham Court, Springfield, Chelmsford, CM2 6XW Tel: (01245) 463405 Fax: (01245) 463411

West Mercia Air Conditioning Ltd, 29a Tarsmill Court, Rotherwas Industrial Estate, Hereford, HR2 6JZ Tel: (01432) 358489 Fax: (01432) 358489 E-mail: sales@wmaircon.com

Western Refrigeration Services Ltd, 46 Aldercombe Road, Bristol, BS9 2QL Tel: 0117-968 3964 Fax: 0117-968 3964

Western Refrigeration Co. (Taunton), 53 Hamilton Road, Taunton, Somerset, TA1 2EL Tel: (01823) 272347 Fax: (01823) 272368 E-mail: sales@westfridge.sagehost.co.uk

Whitecross Engineering Ltd, Columbia House, Columbia Drive, Worthing, West Sussex, BN13 3HD Tel: (01903) 690807 Fax: (01903) 690807

Woodside Air Conditioning Ltd, 81 Woodside Business Park, Shore Road, Birkenhead, Merseyside, CH42 1EP Tel: 0151-650 2369 Fax: 0151-650 2375 E-mail: desau@merseymail.com

World of Catering, 684-692 Lea Bridge Road, London, E10 6AW Tel: (020) 8556 5038 Fax: (020) 8558 9410 E-mail:

Wyatts, 62 Footshill Road, Bristol, BS15 8EZ Tel: 0117-967 1836 Fax: 0117-935 2106 E-mail: info@wyatts-butchers.co.uk

Y2k Maintenance Ltd, 1 The Business Park, Chichester Road, Romiley, Stockport, Cheshire, SK6 4BL Tel: 0161-494 9333 Fax: 0161-494 9555 E-mail: russell@y2kaircon.co.uk

AIR CONDITIONING (AC) DUCTING OR DUCTS

A S Contracts Ltd, Warstock Road, Birmingham, B14 4RS Tel: 0121-436 7969 Fax: 0121-436 7970

Agm, 32 Teesdale Road, Ridgeway, Sheffield, S12 3XH Tel: 0114-248 9198 Fax: 0114-247 2551 E-mail: agm1ac@aol.com

▶ Arden Environmental Ltd, The Arden Centre, Little Alne, Wootton Wawen, Henley-In-Arden, West Midlands, B95 6HW Tel: (01789) 488555 Fax: (01789) 488122 E-mail: enquiries@ardenair.com

Berks & Bucks Air Conditioning, Unit G2 Rose Business Estate, Marlow Bottom Road, Marlow, Buckinghamshire, SL7 3ND Tel: (01628) 472267 Fax: (01628) 472262 E-mail: info@berksbucksaircon.co.uk

Birch Sales & Marketing Ltd, 41 Green Lane, Burnham, Slough, SL1 8DZ Tel: (01628) 661475 Fax: (01628) 667999 E-mail: bob@birch-sales.co.uk

▶ D & E Technical Services Ltd, 15 Whistler Road, Eaton Ford, St. Neots, Cambridgeshire, PE19 7RT Tel: (01480) 474430 Fax: (01480) 386474 E-mail: enquiries@de-techservices.co.uk

E Chambers Mechanical Engineering Ltd, 32 Regal Drive, Soham, Ely, Cambridgeshire, CB7 5BE Tel: (01353) 624126 Fax: (01353) 624127 E-mail: info@ecl-ductwork.co.uk

Envirogroup Installation, 34 Osier Road, Spalding, Lincolnshire, PE11 1UU Tel: (01775) 761344 Fax: (01775) 766011 E-mail: kevin.savage@virgin.net

Excell Metal Spinning Ltd, 27 Gunners Buildings, Limberline Road, Portsmouth, PO3 5BJ Tel: +44 (023) 9266 6456 Fax: +44 (023) 9266 5456 E-mail: excellmetal@btconnect.com

▶ K C G Installations Ltd, 20 Burrish Street, Droitwich, Worcestershire, WR9 8HX Tel: (01905) 770531 E-mail: enquiries@kcg-installations.com

M S Air Movement, Unit 2a Hexton Manor Stables, Hexton, Hitchin, Hertfordshire, SG5 3JH Tel: (01582) 883662 Fax: (01582) 881009 E-mail: info@msairmovement.co.uk

▶ Raybrook Sheet Metal Works Ltd, 9 Towerfield Close, Shoeburyness, Southend-on-Sea, SS3 9QP Tel: (01702) 293208 Fax: (01702) 297628 E-mail: info@raybrook.com

Sansome Construction, Bond Street, Southampton, SO14 5AN Tel: (023) 8022 2349

Vaughan Engineering Group Ltd, Aercon Works, 556 Antrim Road, Newtownabbey, County Antrim, BT36 4RF Tel: (028) 9083 7441 Fax: (028) 9034 2469 E-mail: info@vaughan-group.co.uk

Ventilate Ltd, Solent Industrial Estate, Shamblehurst Lane, Hedge End, Southampton, SO30 2FX Tel: (01489) 782262 Fax: (01489) 781822 E-mail: info@peelfabs.co.uk

W H Scuffham Refrigeration Engineers, 95 West Street, Boston, Lincolnshire, PE21 8RE Tel: (01205) 310163 Fax: (01205) 310165

West Engineering Ltd, Olympus Close, Ipswich, IP1 5LN Tel: (01473) 467930 Fax: (01473) 467931 E-mail: info@westengineering.co.uk

Woodhouse Environmental Services, 18 Yardley Road, Hedge End, Hedge End, Southampton, SO30 0HQ Tel: 0808 100 1630 Fax: (01489) 790100 E-mail: info@woodhouseservices.co.uk

AIR CONDITIONING (AC) EQUIPMENT, *See also headings for particular types*

A F R Refrigeration Ltd, Units 5-6 Delta Business Park, 10 Smugglers Way, London, SW18 1EG Tel: (020) 8875 1999 Fax: (020) 8875 0125 E-mail: sales@afr.co.uk

▶ A1 Air Systems, Unit 4, 111-117 Sydenham Road, Birmingham, B11 1DG Tel: 0121-773 2525

Accent Services Air Conditioning Ltd, 4 Brooklands Close, Sunbury-on-Thames, Middlesex, TW16 7DX Tel: (01932) 765648 Fax: (01932) 788706 E-mail: info@accent.ac.co.uk

Acson International, Hansard Gate, West Meadows, Derby, DE21 6JN Tel: 0845 601 2015 Fax: (01332) 371061 E-mail: marketing@jehall.co.uk

▶ Active Air Conditioning Ltd, Braehead Centre, Blackness Avenue, Altens Industrial Estate, Aberdeen, AB12 3PG Tel: (01224) 870777 Fax: (01224) 870888 E-mail: info@active-aircon.co.uk

Adcock Refrigeration & Air Conditioning Ltd, 5 Industrial Estate, London Road, Pampisford, Cambridge, CB22 3XX Tel: (01223) 834189 Fax: (01223) 837116 E-mail: enquiries@adcock.co.uk

Adcock Refrigeration & Air Conditioning Ltd, Unit 15, Business Science Park, Nunns Corner, Grimsby, South Humberside, DN34 5FQ Tel: (01472) 870559 Fax: (01472) 751966 E-mail: julianlloyd@adcock.co.uk

Adcock Refrigeration & Air Conditioning Ltd, 22 Mason Road, Norwich, NR6 6RF Tel: (01603) 786900 Fax: (01603) 418147

Air And Water Centre.Com, Artex Avenue, Rustington, Littlehampton, West Sussex, BN16 3LN Tel: (01903) 858657 Fax: (01903) 850345 E-mail: sales@airandwatercentre.com

▶ Air Care, 125 New Bridge Street, Newcastle upon Tyne, NE1 2SW Tel: 0191-261 1144 Fax: 0191-261 1188 E-mail: info@aircare-services.co.uk

Air Conditioning Agency, 7 Tabernacle Walk, Blandford Forum, Dorset, DT11 7DL Tel: (01258) 455522 Fax: (01258) 455622 E-mail: info@airconagency.co.uk

Air Handlers Northern Ltd, Bute Street, Salford, M50 1DU Tel: 0161-745 8888 Fax: 0161-745 9900 E-mail: sales@airhandlers.com

Air Handling Equipment Ltd, 23 Cotton Street, Liverpool, L3 7DY Tel: 0151-236 2910 Fax: 0151-236 2910 E-mail: sales@ahe.co.uk

Aircon Refrigeration Ltd, 35e Dukesway, Teesside Industrial Estate, Stockton-on-Tees, Cleveland, TS17 9LT Tel: (01642) 760565 Fax: (01642) 764011 E-mail: aircon.refrigeration@btinternet.com

▶ Aircool Building Services Ltd, 244 Shenley Road, Borehamwood, Hertfordshire, WD6 1TJ Tel: (0845) 1658071

Aire Sales Scotland, The Mews, 19 Sandyford Place Lane, Glasgow, G3 7HS Tel: 0141-204 4750 Fax: 0141-204 4755

AIR CONDITIONING (AC) EQUIPMENT – *continued*

▶ Aireco Airconditioning Ltd, 59 Burnhams Close, Andover, Hampshire, SP10 4NJ Tel: (0870) 4320920 Fax: (0870) 4320634

Aireserve Air Conditioning, Airrex House, Hambledon Road, Hambledon, Waterlooville, Hampshire, PO7 4QX Tel: (023) 9223 3300 Fax: (023) 9223 8555 E-mail: dfarr@mail.aireserv.com

▶ Airflo Distribution Ltd, Unit 16, Norton Enterprise Park, Whittle Road, Salisbury, SP2 7YS Tel: (01722) 415535 Fax: (01722) 415390

Airtemp A.C. Ltd, 18 Theaklen Drive, Ponswood Industrial Estate, St. Leonards-on-Sea, East Sussex, TN38 9AZ Tel: (0845) 8725657 Fax: (0845) 8725658 E-mail: sales@airtempac.co.uk

▶ Airwell Air Conditioning Equipment, Unit 5 Hurtmore Heights Commercial Centre, Hurtmore Road, Hurtmore, Godalming, Surrey, GU7 2FD Tel: (01483) 418282 Fax: (01483) 425826

Albion Cooling Systems Ltd, 33 Albion Road, Westcliff-on-Sea, Essex, SS0 7DP Tel: (01702) 392361 Fax: (01702) 392361 E-mail: info@albioncoolingsystems.com

Alpha, Goudhurst Road, Marden, Tonbridge, Kent, TN12 9NW Tel: (01622) 832488 Fax: (01622) 832488

Amp Air Conditioning Ltd, Blenheim House Blenheim Court, Brownfields, Welwyn Garden City, Hertfordshire, AL7 1AD Tel: (01707) 378670 Fax: (01707) 378699 E-mail: info@ampair.co.uk

Arrow Group, Smalls Hill Road, Norwood Hill, Horley, Surrey, RH6 0HR Tel: (01293) 863024 Fax: (01293) 864003 E-mail: gatwick@arrow.co.uk

Arun Environmental, Batten Street, Aylestone Road, Leicester, LE2 7PB Tel: 0116-283 0020 Fax: 0116-244 0430 E-mail: tomwhalley@arunenvironmental.co.uk

▶ Aspen A C Ltd, Apex Way, Hailsham, East Sussex, BN27 3WA Tel: (0800) 0377220 Fax: (01323) 849966 E-mail: info@aspen-ac.co.uk

B A P Air Co Ltd, 10a West St, Southend-on-Sea, SS2 6HJ Tel: (01702) 347222 Fax: (01702) 331508

Bac Air Conditioning Ltd, Lea Vale, South Normanton, Alfreton, Derbyshire, DE55 3NA Tel: (01773) 814670 Fax: (01773) 814680

Beta Air, Unit 6, Cheltenham Trade Park, Arle Road, Cheltenham, Gloucestershire, GL51 8LZ Tel: (01242) 570995 Fax: (01242) 226131 E-mail: betaair.storacall@btinternet.com

▶ Brewfitt Refrigeration & Air Conditioning, International House, Penistone Road, Fenay Bridge, Huddersfield, HD8 0LE Tel: (01484) 340800 Fax: (01484) 340900 E-mail: sales@brewfitt.com

Caledonian Building Services South East Ltd, 31 Slewins Lane, Hornchurch, Essex, RM11 2BZ Tel: (01708) 454305 Fax: (01708) 437375

Carman (Air Conditioning) Ltd, Winters Cottage, Magdalen Laver, Ongar, Essex, CM5 0EW Tel: (01279) 412314

▶ Charmeldon Air Conditioning Equipment, Unit B Roe Cross Industrial Park, Mottram, Hyde, Cheshire, SK14 6NB Tel: (01457) 764666 Fax: (01457) 764999 E-mail: n-shenton@charmeldon.com

▶ Chiswell Fireplaces Ltd, 192 Watford Road, St. Albans, Hertfordshire, AL2 3EB Tel: (01727) 859512 Fax: (01727) 836343 E-mail: sales@chiswellfireplaces.com

City Engineering Ltd, 9 Cygnus Business Centre, Dalmeyer Road, London, NW10 2XA Tel: (020) 8451 4930 Fax: (020) 8459 1120 E-mail: roul@cityengineering.fsnet.uk

Climate Center, 63 Pritchett Street, Birmingham, B6 4EX Tel: 0121-333 3636 Fax: 0121-359 8497 E-mail: gk.aston@wolseley.co.uk

Climate Services, Unit 1 Bold Street, Sheffield, S9 2LQ Tel: 0114-261 0111 Fax: 0114-261 8949

Cool Hire Services, Whittingham House, Hazel Road, Ash Green, Aldershot, Hampshire, GU12 6HR Tel: (01252) 333669 Fax: (01252) 310004

Cool Therm (U K) Ltd, Unit 5, 121 London Road, Warmley, Bristol, BS30 5NA Tel: 0117-961 0006 Fax: 0117-947 8642 E-mail: sales@cooltherm.co.uk

Coolair Equipment plc, Coolair House, Broadway, Dukinfield, Cheshire, SK16 4UR Tel: 0161-343 6000 Fax: 0161-339 1077

▶ Cooling Direct Ltd, Unit 10 Arrow Industrial Estate, Eelmoor Road, Farnborough, Hampshire, GU14 7QH Tel: (0871) 8712266 Fax: (01252) 511242 E-mail: sales@coolingdirect.com

Coolwell Ltd, 87 Ribbleton Avenue, Preston, PR2 6DA Tel: (01772) 651144 Fax: (01772) 652025E-mail: coolwellaircon@btconnect.com

Daikin Air Conditioning East Ltd, The Old Stable, Station Road, Arlesey, Bedfordshire, SG15 6RG Tel: (01462) 834999 Fax: (01462) 731208

Daikin Airconditioning UK Ltd, The Heights, Brooklands, Weybridge, Surrey, KT13 0NY Tel: (0845) 6419000 Fax: (0845) 641009 E-mail: sales@daikin.co.uk

Daikin Airconditioning UK Ltd, The Heights, Brooklands, Weybridge, Surrey, KT13 0NY Tel: (0845) 6419000 Fax: (0845) 6419009 E-mail: marketing@daikin.co.uk

Dean & Wood Ltd, Unit 1, Camwal Road, St. Philips, Bristol, BS2 0UZ Tel: 0117-971 7413 Fax: 0117-972 1561

Delrac Acs, Fairman Law House, 1-3 Park Terrace, Worcester Park, Surrey, KT4 7JZ Tel: (020) 8335 3141 Fax: (020) 8337 5539 E-mail: enquiries@delrac-acs.co.uk

Denman Group Ltd, Wolvers Home Farm, Ironsbottom, Sidlow, Reigate, Surrey, RH2 8QG Tel: (01293) 863100 Fax: (01293) 863808 E-mail: info@denmanrest.co.uk

Direct Air Supplies Ltd, 4 Brocklebank Industrial Estate, Brocklebank Road, London, SE7 7SX Tel: (020) 8853 2186 Fax: (020) 8293 5539 E-mail: direct.air@virgin.net

▶ Dysk Air Conditioning Equipment, Unit 3 40 Coldharbour Lane, Harpenden, Hertfordshire, AL5 4UN Tel: (01582) 463420

E H S International Ltd, E H S House, Lyons Road, Trafford Park, Manchester, M17 1RN Tel: 0161-872 4541 Fax: 0161-872 5491 E-mail: enquiries@ehs-intl.co.uk

Eastwood Air Conditioning Ltd, Eastwood House, Hubert Street, Aston, Birmingham, B6 4BA Tel: 0121-380 0555 Fax: 0121-359 8152 E-mail: sales@eastwoodgroup.co.uk

Eaton-Williams Holdings Ltd, Station Road, Edenbridge, Kent, TN8 6EG Tel: (01732) 866055 Fax: (01732) 863461 E-mail: peter.dewdney@eaton-williams.com

▶ Elliott Environmental, Unit 10, Brympton Way, Lynx West Trading Estate, Yeovil, Somerset, BA20 2HP Tel: (01935) 413700 Fax: (01935) 413722 E-mail: jim@e-e-s.co.uk

Ellson Environmental Ltd, 263 Edinburgh Road, Newhouse, Motherwell, Lanarkshire, ML1 5RU Tel: (01698) 831234 Fax: (01698) 834148 E-mail: sales@ellson-env.com

Elyo UK Ltd, 1 Sampson Road North, Birmingham, B11 1BL Tel: 0121-773 8421 Fax: 0121-773 2082

Envirogroup Installation, 34 Osier Road, Spalding, Lincolnshire, PE11 1UU Tel: (01775) 761344 Fax: (01775) 766011 E-mail: kevin.savage@virgin.net

▶ Exmoor Air Conditioning Equipment, Windrush, West Anstey, South Molton, Devon, EX36 3NU Tel: (01398) 341134

Fans & Spares Ltd, 1 Midas Business Centre, Wantz Road, Dagenham, Essex, RM10 8PS Tel: (020) 8595 5226 Fax: (020) 8593 4257 E-mail: info@fansandspares.co.uk

Foster Environmental Ltd, Scotter Road South, Bottesford, Scunthorpe, South Humberside, DN17 2BW Tel: (01724) 270717 Fax: (01724) 271410 E-mail: darren@forsterac.co.uk

Four Seasons Control Ltd, Astley Way, Astley La Industrial Estate, Swillington, Leeds, LS26 8XT Tel: 0113-286 5222 Fax: 0113-287 6759

Fuelboss Air Conditioning, The Maltings, Westbury Leigh, Westbury, Wiltshire, BA13 3SF Tel: (01373) 858188 Fax: (01373) 858444 E-mail: sales@fuelboss.co.uk

Fujitsu General UK Co Ltd, Unit 150 Centennial Park, Centennial Avenue, Elstree, Borehamwood, Hertfordshire, WD6 3SG Tel: (020) 8731 3450 Fax: (020) 8731 3451

▶ G D K Agencies, Hawthorne House, Malmesbury Road, Leigh, Swindon, SN6 6RH Tel: (01793) 759333 Fax: (01793) 759444 E-mail: geoffkay@gdkagencies.co.uk

G T Thermal Ltd, 36 Lanehead Road, Stoke-on-Trent, ST1 5PT Tel: (01782) 279504 Fax: (01782) 279005

G W Air Conditioning, 36 Lodge Avenue, Croydon, CR0 4JZ Tel: (020) 8686 6226 Fax: (020) 8686 2657 E-mail: sales@gwac.co.uk

Gallay Ltd, Paterson Road, Finedon Road Industrial Estate, Wellingborough, Northamptonshire, NN8 4BZ Tel: (01933) 224801 Fax: (01933) 279902 E-mail: sales@gallay.co.uk

Georges Industrial Services Ltd, 49 Theobald Street, Borehamwood, Hertfordshire, WD6 4RZ Tel: (020) 8207 2455 Fax: (020) 8207 4877 E-mail: london@airconditioningdirect.com

Global Refrigeration & Air Conditioning Co. Ltd, Unit 41, 3 Halifax Road, Metropolitan Centre, Greenford, Middlesex, UB6 8XU Tel: (020) 8575 7557 Fax: (020) 8566 6342 E-mail: enquiries@globalrefrigeration.co.uk

D.B. Green Ltd, Brook House, Southdown Business Park, Brooks Road, Lewes, East Sussex, BN7 2BY Tel: (01273) 480251 Fax: (01273) 480252 E-mail: sales@dbgreen.co.uk

Hadrian Air Conditioning & Refrigeration Co. Ltd, 3 Rosse Close, Parsons Industrial Estate, Washington, Tyne & Wear, NE37 1ET Tel: 0191-415 0055 Fax: 0191-415 0888 E-mail: sales@hadrian-air.co.uk

Harbec Services, 1A Leaphill Road, Pokesdown, Bournemouth, BH7 6LS Tel: (01202) 417725 Fax: (01202) 417732 E-mail: sales@harbec.co.uk

Hitachi Home Electronics (Europe) Ltd, Whitebrook Park, Lower Cookham Road, Maidenhead, Berkshire, SL6 8YA Tel: (01628) 643000 Fax: (01628) 778322

Holders Ltd, 55-59 Bensham Grove, Thornton Heath, Surrey, CR7 8DD Tel: (07802) 377122 Fax: (020) 8653 3011 E-mail: sales@holders.ltd.uk

Holmes Refrigeration, 443 Banbury Road, Oxford, OX2 8ED Tel: (01865) 552073 Fax: (01865) 310848

Howvale Ltd, 53 Bridgford Road, West Bridgford, Nottingham, NG2 6AU Tel: 0115-945 5050 Fax: 0115-945 5511

▶ HRP Ltd, Unit 18 Britannia Industrial Estate, Poyle Road, Colnbrook, Slough, SL3 0BH Tel: (01753) 688100 Fax: (01753) 688101

HT Cooling services, 65 Park View, Moulton, Northampton, NN3 7UZ Tel: (01604) 645135 Fax: (01604) 645135 E-mail: colin.htcooling@btopenworld.com

Hushon UK Ltd, A6 Railway Triangle, Walton Road, Drayton, Portsmouth, PO6 1TN Tel: (023) 9232 4335 Fax: (023) 9232 4348 E-mail: sales@hushonuk.co.uk

Ice Refrigeration Ltd, Spring Court House, High Street, Stapleford, Nottingham, NG9 8AG Tel: 0114-230 6555 Fax: 0115-949 9275 E-mail: john@agrice.co.uk

Industrial Cooling Equipment Ltd, 101 Chadwick Road, Astmoore Industrial Estate, Runcorn, Cheshire, WA7 1PW Tel: (01928) 568800 Fax: (01928) 568822 E-mail: sales@ice-ltd.co.uk

Industrial Pneumatic Services Liverpool Ltd, 13 Dunnings Bridge Road, Bootle, Merseyside, L30 6TE Tel: 0151-525 9381 Fax: 0151-525 1982

K G Projects, 40 Trenance Road, St. Austell, Cornwall, PL25 5AN Tel: (01726) 61119 Fax: (01726) 871110

K L S Ltd, 22-23 Austin Fields, King's Lynn, Norfolk, PE30 1PH Tel: (01553) 772935 Fax: (01553) 769118 E-mail: sales@klsonline.co.uk

Kensa Engineering Ltd, Tin Pit, Mabe Burnthouse, Penryn, Cornwall, TR10 9JH Tel: (01326) 377627 Fax: (01326) 374470 E-mail: info@kensaengineering.com

Kingsford Services Ltd, Bromley Road, Elmstead, Colchester, CO7 7BY Tel: (01206) 827653 Fax: (01206) 827654 E-mail: enquiries@kingsfordservices.co.uk

Kool It Services Ltd, 85-87 Wellington Road, Eccles, Manchester, M30 9GW Tel: 0161-707 2580 Fax: 0161-288 0135

L J W Air Conditioning Ltd, 2 Post Office Lane, Rugeley, Staffordshire, WS15 2UP Tel: (01889) 582422 Fax: (01889) 583423 E-mail: hvac@ljw.co.uk

M G Building Services Engineers Ltd, 31a High Street, Alcester, Warwickshire, B49 5AF Tel: (01789) 400270 Fax: (01789) 400396 E-mail: mgbse@globalnet.co.uk

Mcdowall Air Conditioning, Middlemore La West, Walsall, WS9 8EJ Tel: (01922) 454955 Fax: (01922) 454815 E-mail: sales@mcdowalls.co.uk

Macqueen Air Conditioning Ltd, 39-41 Carrholm Road, Leeds, LS7 2NQ Tel: 0113-393 0287 Fax: 0113-393 0284 E-mail: sales@macqueen-ac.co.uk

Merritt Air Conditioning, 44 Birchwood Drive, Dartford, DA2 7NF Tel: (01322) 525485 Fax: (01322) 524203 E-mail: fredmerrittac@aol.com

Modern Conditioning Services Ltd, Church Lane, West Bromwich, West Midlands, B71 1BX Tel: 0121-553 4001 Fax: 0121-500 5102

Montgomery Refrigeration Ltd, 5 Falcon Road, Adelaide Industrial Estate, Belfast, BT12 6RD Tel: (028) 9066 2111 Fax: (028) 9068 1130 E-mail: service@montgomery-ltd.co.uk

New Century Air Conditioning & Refrigeration Ltd, 30 Station Road, Stoke Mandeville, Aylesbury, Buckinghamshire, HP22 5UL Tel: (01296) 614878 Fax: (01296) 613619 E-mail: sales@newcenturycooling.co.uk

▶ O E M Group Ltd, London Business Innovation Centre, Innova Science Park, Mollison Avenue, Enfield, Middlesex, EN3 7XH Tel: (020) 8344 8777 Fax: (020) 8344 8778 E-mail: steve@secureseal.com

Oakwood Technology Group, Ill Road, Cheadle Hulme, Cheadle, Cheshire, SK8 6GN Tel: 0161-488 4343 Fax: 0161-488 4086 E-mail: sales@oakwoodair.co.uk

Oc Mechanical Services, 4 Broadwater Road, Worthing, West Sussex, BN14 8AE Tel: (01903) 232147 Fax: 01903 232147

▶ Ocean Air Distribution, Prospect Close, Lowmoor Business Park, Kirkby-in-Ashfield, Nottingham, NG17 7LF Tel: (01623) 727414 Fax: (01623) 727419 E-mail: info@oceanair.uk.com

▶ Orion Air Conditioning & Refrigeration, 16 Barkers Piece, Marston Moretaine, Bedford, MK43 0LZ Tel: (07905) 967307 Fax: (01234) 765580 E-mail: info@orionair.co.uk

P H Services Ltd, 37 Limberline Spur, Portsmouth, PO3 5DX Tel: (023) 9269 3448 Fax: (023) 9263 9094 E-mail: huntphill@aol.com

P V F Installations & Services, Division Lane, Blackpool, FY4 5DZ Tel: (01253) 792408 Fax: (01253) 792408

▶ Pacair, Unit 1, Eastman Way, Hemel Hempstead Industrial Estate, Hemel Hempstead, Hertfordshire, HP2 7DU Tel: (0870) 2405767 Fax: (01442) 251401 E-mail: sales@pacair.co.uk

Panasonic Air Conditioning, Panasonic House, Willoughby Road, Bracknell, Berkshire, RG12 8FP Tel: (01344) 853186 Fax: (01344) 853217 E-mail: nicky.dopson@panasonic.co.uk

Parker Air Conditioning Ltd, Gloucester House, Clarence Court, Rushmore Hill, Orpington, Kent, BR6 7LZ Tel: (01689) 858787 Fax: (01689) 858966 E-mail: parker.ac@btinternet.com

Parker Mechanical Services, 15 Waverley Drive, Camberley, Surrey, GU15 2DJ Tel: (01276) 65407 Fax: (01276) 65408

Parts Center, Unit C Tamar Road, Bristol, BS2 0TX Tel: 0117-972 1376 Fax: 0117-977 6399 E-mail: nrs-bristol@climatecentre.co.uk

Phoenix Air Conditioning Co. Ltd, Unit 2 Chichester Road, Romiley, Stockport, Cheshire, SK6 4BL Tel: 0161-430 7878 Fax: 0161-430 7979 E-mail: tony@crs-limited.co.uk

Polar Air Ltd, Huntingdon House, 278-290 Huntingdon Street, Nottingham, NG1 3LY Tel: 0115-955 0055 Fax: 0115-955 7037

Polarcold Refrigeration Ltd, 2 The Parade, Tattenham Way, Burgh Heath, Tadworth, Surrey, KT20 5NG Tel: 01737 373367 Fax: 01737 373387 E-mail: info@polarcold.co.uk

▶ Portable Air Conditioning Solutions Ltd, 1 Mill Way, Bushey, WD23 2AF Tel: (0845) 1658071

▶ Portable Air Conditioning Solutions Ltd, 1 Longfield Cottages, Killicks, Cranleigh, Surrey, GU6 7BB Tel: (0845) 1658071

▶ Portable Air Conditioning Solutions Ltd, 43 Richings Way, Iver, Buckinghamshire, SL0 9DB Tel: (0845) 1658071

▶ Portable Air Conditioning Solutions Ltd, 10 Barley Mow Passage, London, W4 4PH Tel: (0845) 1658071

▶ Portable Air Conditioning Solutions Ltd, 10 Warwick Road, West Drayton, Middlesex, UB7 9BZ Tel: (0845) 1658071

R G K (UK) Ltd, Champfleurie House, Linlithgow, West Lothian, EH49 6NB Tel: (01506) 847999 Fax: (01506) 847174 E-mail: sales@rgk.co.uk

Rabtherm International Ltd, Unit 11, Empire Close, Aldridge, Walsall, WS9 8XZ Tel: (01922) 743273 Fax: (01922) 743119 E-mail: bgas@rabtherm.co.uk

Rapid Envelopes, Potters Bar, Herts, EN6 4SP Tel: (01707) 878783

Reefworld Aquarium & Pond Supplies, 219 Fir Tree Road, Epsom, Surrey, KT17 3LB Tel: (01737) 370777 Fax: (01737) 212777 E-mail: sales@reefworld.co.uk

Refrigeration Mitton Ltd, Polar House, East Norfolk Street, Carlisle, CA2 5JL Tel: (01228) 522481 Fax: (01228) 514897

Regency Refrigeration, 5 Medina Way, Kidsgrove, Stoke-on-Trent, ST7 4TJ Tel: (01782) 773103

Riseborough Refrigeration Service Ltd, 164 Glenroy Street, Roath, Cardiff, CF24 3LA Tel: (029) 2049 6007 Fax: (029) 2049 2409

S W Heating Equipment Ltd, Environmental Centre, 98 Holmesdale Street, Cardiff, CF11 7BU Tel: (029) 2023 7654 Fax: (029) 2023 7685 E-mail: mail@swgroup.org.uk

▶ Servcool Air Conditioning Equipment, 17 Upper Station Road, Bristol, BS16 4LY Tel: 0117-956 8444 Fax: 0117-956 4141 E-mail: sales@servcool.co.uk

South East Cooling Ltd, 6 Southwinds House, Barrack Lane, Bognor Regis, West Sussex, PO21 4BZ Tel: (01243) 268888 Fax: (01243) 268843E-mail: sales@southeast-cooling.co.uk

Southern Sales & Services Ltd, Sterling House, Mayflower Close, Chandler's Ford, Eastleigh, Hampshire, SO53 4AR Tel: (023) 8026 1188 Fax: (023) 8025 4054 E-mail: jules@southernsales.co.uk

Space Airconditioning plc, Willway Court, 1 Opus Park, Moorfield Road, Guildford, Surrey, GU1 1SZ Tel: 01483 504883 Fax: 01483 574835 E-mail: marketing@spaceair.co.uk

Stream Environmental, 100-102 Headstone Road, Harrow, Middlesex, HA1 1PF Tel: (020) 8933 6611 Fax: (020) 8424 8001 E-mail: sales@streamenvironmental.co.uk

SWM Distribution Ltd, 5 Goodwood Road, Eastleigh, Hampshire, SO50 4NT Tel: (023) 8065 3283 Fax: (023) 8065 3285 E-mail: info@swm.co.uk

Syntonic Construction Ltd, 63-65 Penge Road, London, SE25 4EJ Tel: (020) 8778 7838 Fax: (020) 8659 5418 E-mail: neal.etchells@btconnect.com

Teccom Ltd, Howbury Centre, Crayford, Dartford, DA1 4RQ Tel: (0845) 8900844 E-mail: info@teccom.ltd.uk

Technical Concepts Ltd, The Neutralle Centre, 4 Eastman Way, Stevenage, Hertfordshire, SG1 4UH Tel: (0870) 5686824 Fax: (01438) 311200

Thermal Solutions, 3 Orchard Avenue, Poole, Dorset, BH14 8AH Tel: (01202) 715792 Fax: (01202) 718134 E-mail: sales@thermalsolutions.co.uk

Thermocold Mechanical Services Ltd, Unit 11 Albion Business Park, Spring Road, Smethwick, Warley, West Midlands, B66 1LY Tel: 0121-525 5887

Thermofrost Cryo P.L.C., Robert Fawkes Ho, Rea Street South, Birmingham, B5 6LB Tel: 0121-666 4700 Fax: 0121-622 7268 E-mail: admin@thermofrostcryo.co.uk

Thermofrost Cryo plc, Ernest Avenue, London, SE27 0DA Tel: (020) 8670 3663 Fax: (020) 8761 8081E-mail: info@thermofrostcryo.co.uk

Total Ventilation Solutions Ltd, Unit 10, Midland Oak Trading Estate, Marlissa Drive, Coventry, CV6 6HQ Tel: (024) 7666 2255 Fax: (024) 7666 2255

Trade Supplies, Trade House, Freestone Road, Bristol, BS2 0QN Tel: 0117-972 8230 Fax: 0117-972 8231

Trend Refrigeration Ltd, Holt Lane, Liverpool, L27 2YB Tel: 0151-487 9278 Fax: 0151-487 9254

Vicforge Air Systems Ltd, Lufton 2000, Yeovil, Somerset, BA22 8HS Tel: 01935 428387

Walter Meirer (UK) Ltd, Highlands Road, Shirley, Solihull, West Midlands, B90 4NL Tel: (0871) 6630664 Fax: (0871) 6631664 E-mail: uk.climate@waltermeier.com

Warwick Fraser, Unit 9 Alfold Business Centre, Loxwood Road, Alfold, Cranleigh, Surrey, GU6 8HP Tel: (01403) 753069 Fax: (01403) 752469 E-mail: sales@warwickfraser.co.uk

AIR CONDITIONING (AC) EQUIPMENT - *continued*

Western Air Ltd, Bencroft View House, Studley Hill, Studley, Calne, Wiltshire, SN11 9NL Tel: (01249) 817579 Fax: (01249) 819006

AIR CONDITIONING (AC) EQUIPMENT CLEANING SERVICES

A R E Refrigeration & Air Conditioning, 1 Elcho Place, Port Seton, Prestonpans, East Lothian, EH32 0DL Tel: (01875) 813947 Fax: (01875) 813947

Air Conditioning & Refrigeration Services, Lynfelde, 14 East Street, Long Buckby, Northampton, NN6 7RA Tel: (01327) 843192 Fax: (01327) 843192 E-mail: aircon1@supanet.com

Chapman Ventilators Ltd, 9 Bridge Gate Centre, Martinfield, Welwyn Garden City, Hertfordshire, AL7 1JG Tel: (01707) 372858 Fax: (01707) 325001

Climatic Engineering, 1 Cannon Road, Heathfield Industrial Estate, Newton Abbot, Devon, TQ12 6SG Tel: (01626) 203686 Fax: (01626) 203687 E-mail: sales@climaticengineering.co.uk

Halson Refrigeration, 9 Tonacliffe Way, Whitworth, Rochdale, Lancashire, OL12 8SN Tel: (01706) 344557 Fax: (01706) 344557

Hevertech, Unit 2 Treefield Industrial Estate, Gelderd Road, Morley, Leeds, LS27 7JU Tel: 0113-238 3355 Fax: 0113-253 5443 E-mail: enquiries@hevertech.co.uk

Houghton Refrigeration, 24 Birkhall Avenue, Inchinnan, Renfrew, PA4 9QA Tel: 0141-812 1434 Fax: 0141-812 1434

I C Refrigeration & Air Conditioning, 12 Broad Meadow, Ipswich, IP8 3SP Tel: (01473) 680629 Fax: (01473) 680629

Ice Boys Ltd, Unit 8, IO Centre, Fingle Drive, Stonebridge, Milton Keynes, MK13 0AT Tel: (01908) 211099 Fax: (01908) 320700 E-mail: sales@iceboys.co.uk

▶ K & S Services, Dam House, Astley Hall Drive, Tyldesley, Manchester, M29 7TX Tel: (01942) 881222 Fax: (01942) 881222 E-mail: enq@ksservices.com

Micra Air Conditioning Services, 9 Vicarage Road, Woodford Green, Essex, IG8 8NH Tel: (020) 8505 0749 Fax: (020) 8504 5490 E-mail: micraair@tiscali.co.uk

Co Ordit Building Services Ltd, Barn Lodge, Shuttleworth Lane, Cosby, Leicester, LE9 1RF Tel: (01455) 208200 Fax: (01455) 201881 E-mail: sales@co-ordit.com

Planned Maintenance Engineers Ltd, Unit 2, Site 5B, Ocean Way, Cardiff, CF24 5HF Tel: (029) 2022 0602 Fax: (029) 2089 5598 E-mail: info@pme.co.uk

Quentrall Engineering Co. Ltd, 597 High Road, London, N12 0DY Tel: (020) 8445 0751 Fax: (020) 8446 9639

R W Vesey Ltd, 734 Melton Road, Thurmaston, Leicester, LE4 8BD Tel: 0116-269 6241 Fax: 0116-269 6243 E-mail: info@vesey-airflow.com

S N G Control Systems Ltd, 41 Dryden Terrace, Loanhead, Midlothian, EH20 9JH Tel: 0131-440 0416 Fax: 0131-440 0416

Specific Environments Ltd, Gallows Lane, High Wycombe, Buckinghamshire, HP12 4BX Tel: (01494) 464411 Fax: (01494) 523933 E-mail: sel@specific-environments.co.uk

Swiftclean (UK) Ltd, Aviation Way, Southend-On-Sea, SS2 6UN Tel: (01702) 531221 Fax: (01702) 531220 E-mail: info@swiftclean.co.uk

Total Environmental Network Ltd, 9-11 Monmouth Street, Bridgwater, Somerset, TA6 5EQ Tel: (01278) 444643 Fax: (01278) 444718 E-mail: admin@total-environmentalnetwork.co.uk

TTF Air Conditioning Ltd, 5 Tower Road, Washington, Tyne & Wear, NE37 2SH Tel: 0191-416 4525 Fax: 0191-416 4650 E-mail: cg-ttssales@jci.com

AIR CONDITIONING (AC) EQUIPMENT REGASSING

▶ A C S, Oakleigh, Smithy Lane, Pentre Bychan, Wrexham, Clwyd, LL14 4EN Tel: (01978) 846173 Fax: (01978) 846262

▶ Acs Air Conditioning Solutions, 3 Law Close, Littleport, Ely, Cambridgeshire, CB6 1TS Tel: (01353) 860360 Fax: (01353) 860360 E-mail: www.info@qualityacs.co.uk

▶ Adcock Group Ltd, Midland House, Vicarage Farm Road, Peterborough, PE1 5UH Tel: (01733) 344300 Fax: (01733) 312919 E-mail: mail25@adcock.co.uk

▶ Air Mechanical Contractors, 14 Hemming Street, Kidderminster, Worcestershire, DY11 6NA Tel: (07917) 324325 Fax: (01562) 634303 E-mail: info@airuk.biz

▶ Artic Building Services Ltd, Artic House, Business Park, Green Lane, London, SE9 3TL Tel: (020) 8851 0111 Fax: (020) 8517 0011

▶ Everest Cooling Services, 11 Brunshaw Avenue, Burnley, Lancashire, BB10 4LT Tel: (01282) 685223 Fax: (01282) 685223 E-mail: info@everestcooling.com

▶ Focus Air Conditioning, Unit Laker Hosue Canning Street, Maidstone, Kent, ME14 2RX Tel: 01622 690559 Fax: 01622 690559 E-mail: focusac@talktalk.net

AIR CONDITIONING (AC) EQUIPMENT REPAIR

A C 2000 Ltd, 224 Blackbird Road, Leicester, LE4 0AG Tel: 0116-224 2425 Fax: 0116-224 2426 E-mail: acleicester@ac2000.co.uk

▶ Acs Air Conditioning Solutions, 3 Law Close, Littleport, Ely, Cambridgeshire, CB6 1TS Tel: (01353) 860360 Fax: (01353) 860360 E-mail: www.info@qualityacs.co.uk

▶ Adcock Group Ltd, Midland House, Vicarage Farm Road, Peterborough, PE1 5UH Tel: (01733) 344300 Fax: (01733) 312919 E-mail: mail25@adcock.co.uk

▶ Air Conditioning Solutions UK Ltd, Concept Park, Watling Street, Towcester, Northamptonshire, NN12 7YD Tel: (01327) 810510 Fax: (01327) 811529 E-mail: info@airconsolutions.co.uk

▶ Air Mechanical Contractors, 14 Hemming Street, Kidderminster, Worcestershire, DY11 6NA Tel: (07917) 324325 Fax: (01562) 634303 E-mail: info@airuk.biz

▶ Airconditioning & Chiller Co. Ltd, The Corner House, Northfield Avenue, Pleasley Vale, Mansfield, Nottinghamshire, NG19 8SG Tel: 01623 658580 Fax: 01623 659506 E-mail: sales@airconditioning-chiller.co.uk

▶ Artic Building Services Ltd, Artic House, Business Park, Green Lane, London, SE9 3TL Tel: (020) 8851 0111 Fax: (020) 8517 0011

▶ Everest Cooling Services, 11 Brunshaw Avenue, Burnley, Lancashire, BB10 4LT Tel: (01282) 685223 Fax: (01282) 685223 E-mail: info@everestcooling.com

▶ Focus Air Conditioning, Unit Laker Hosue Canning Street, Maidstone, Kent, ME14 2RX Tel: 01622 690559 Fax: 01622 690559 E-mail: focusac@talktalk.net

▶ Neil Sharp, Riverside Close, Weston-Super-Mare, Avon, BS22 7RZ Tel: (01934) 519278 Fax: (01934) 519278

AIR CONDITIONING (AC) EQUIPMENT SPARE PARTS

Acrol Air Conditioning Co. Ltd, Salt Meadows Road, East Gateshead Industrial Estate, Gateshead, Tyne & Wear, NE8 3AH Tel: 0191-477 7999 Fax: 0191-477 7222 E-mail: sales@acrolairconditioningco.co.uk

▶ Car Air Conditioning Services, 104 Bennett Way, Dartford, DA2 7JU Tel: (01474) 705370 E-mail: bobr@caraircon.co.uk

Compac Services Ne Ltd, Compac House, 173 Victoria Road, South Shields, Tyne & Wear, NE33 4NW Tel: 0191-454 9090 Fax: 0191-454 1212 E-mail: sales@compac.co.uk

Connolly Refrigeration Ltd, 13 Howlett Way, Thetford, Norfolk, IP24 1HZ Tel: (01842) 766655 Fax: (01842) 763497 E-mail: sales@connollyrefrigeration.co.uk

Industrial Cooling Equipment Ltd, 101 Chadwick Road, Astmore Industrial Estate, Runcorn, Cheshire, WA7 1PW Tel: (01928) 568800 Fax: (01928) 568822 E-mail: sales@ice-ltd.co.uk

▶ L V V Services Ltd, 31 Preswylfa Court, Merthyrmawr Road, Bridgend, Mid Glamorgan, CF31 3NX Tel: (01656) 658195 Fax: (01656) 658195 E-mail: stevemagill@btopenworld.com

Macqueen Air Conditioning Ltd, 39-41 Carrholm Road, Leeds, LS7 2NQ Tel: 0113-393 0287 Fax: 0113-393 0284 E-mail: sales@macqueen-ac.co.uk

▶ Tenways Engineering Services Ltd, 31 St. Marys Road, London, NW11 9UE Tel: (020) 8922 5468 Fax: (020) 8201 8022 E-mail: sales@tenwayseng.co.uk

AIR CONDITIONING (AC) HEAT EXCHANGERS

▶ Titan-Lite Motorsport, 36 Coleshill Ind Est, Station Rd, Coleshill, Birmingham, B46 1JP Tel: 01675 - 466060 Fax: 01675 - 467675 E-mail: info@titan-lite.com

AIR CONDITIONING (AC) INDUSTRIAL EQUIPMENT HIRE

Aggreko UK Ltd, Exchange House, Watling Street, Bridgtown, Cannock, Staffordshire, WS11 0BN Tel: (01543) 437777 Fax: (01543) 437788 E-mail: doncaster@aggreko.co.uk

Aireserve Air Conditioning, Airrex House, Hambledon Road, Hambledon, Waterlooville, Hampshire, PO7 4QX Tel: (023) 9223 3300 Fax: (023) 9223 8555 E-mail: dfarr@mail.aireserv.com

Airflo Enviorental, Kelham Street, Doncaster, South Yorkshire, DN1 3TA Tel: (01302) 730000 Fax: (01302) 321222

Andrews Sykes Hire Ltd, Unit F17 Ashmount Business Park, Upper Fforest Way, Swansea Enterprise Park, Swansea, SA6 8QR Tel: (01792) 701701 Fax: (01792) 701700

Andrews Sykes Hire Ltd, Premier House, Darlington Street, Wolverhampton, WV1 4JJ Tel: (01902) 328700 Fax: (01902) 422466 E-mail: info@andrews-sykes.com

Chill The World Ltd, Myler Court, 156-158 Marsh Road, Leagrave, Luton, LU3 2QL Tel: (01582) 593377 Fax: (01322) 436238 E-mail: sales@chilloutaircon.com

Chiller Rental Services, Wigan Road, Leyland, PR25 5XW Tel: (01772) 643040 Fax: (01772) 643041 E-mail: info@chiller-rental.com

Clivet Aircon Ltd, Unit F5 Railway Triangle, Walton Road, Portsmouth, PO6 1TG Tel: (023) 9238 1235 Fax: (023) 9238 1243 E-mail: info@clivetaircon.co.uk

Coolburn Air Conditioning Ltd, Betsoms, The Avenue, Westerham, Kent, TN16 2EE Tel: (01959) 563361 Fax: (01959) 562786 E-mail: coolburn@tiscali.co.uk

Cooling Equipment Hire Ltd, 1144 Manchester Road, Rochdale, Lancashire, OL11 2XX Tel: (01706) 643003 Fax: (01706) 643005 E-mail: info@cool-equip.co.uk

Georges Industrial Services Ltd, 49 Theobald Street, Borehamwood, Hertfordshire, WD6 4RZ Tel: (020) 8207 2455 Fax: (020) 8207 4877 E-mail: london@airconditioningdirect.com

H & D Air Conditioning Ltd, 133 Royal George Road, Burgess Hill, West Sussex, RH15 9TD Tel: (01444) 232552 Fax: (01444) 246568 E-mail: brighton@mail.aireserv.com

Heventech Mechanical Service Ltd, 3 Redbridge Enterprise Centre, Thompson Close, Ilford, Essex, IG1 1TY Tel: (0845) 1298565 E-mail: sales@heventech.co.uk

Nortech Services Ltd, Drypool Way, Hull, HU9 1NL Tel: (01482) 327791 Fax: (01482) 320550 E-mail: sales@nortech.co.uk

Phoenix Ventilation & Engineering Ltd, Unit 6 Camphill Industrial Estate, Camphill Road, West Byfleet, Surrey, KT14 6EW Tel: (01932) 336125 Fax: (01932) 336132 E-mail: sales@phoenixventilation.co.uk

Rapid Climate Control Ltd, 423 Becontree Avenue, Dagenham, Essex, RM8 3UH Tel: 0121-543 6211 Fax: (020) 8590 8303 E-mail: info@rapidclimatecontrol.com

AIR CONDITIONING (AC) LIFTING CONTRACTORS

Power Lifting Services Limited, Linen Hall, 162-168 Regent Street, London, W1B 5TG Tel: 0207 0383881 Fax: 0207 0383845 E-mail: powerlifting@btinternet.com

AIR CONDITIONING (AC) MAINTENANCE

▶ A C S Wade Ltd, Unit B6, Pinfold Industrial Estate, Rhyl, Clwyd, LL18 2YR Tel: (01745) 342998 Fax: (01745) 336006 E-mail: mail@acswade.co.uk

Advanced, PO Box 6433, Birmingham, B30 3HG Tel: 0121-459 3838 Fax: 0121-459 1415

Air Supply Systems Ltd, 8 Harmony Square, Glasgow, G51 3LW Tel: 0141-440 2121 Fax: 0141-440 0330

Air-Conditioning & Refrigeration Concerns, 5 Mingarry, Birtley, Chester Le Street, County Durham, DH3 2JB Tel: 0191-410 3594 Fax: 0191-410 8504

Airtech Air Conditioning Services Ltd, Devon House, Eastbourne Road, Lingfield, Surrey, RH7 6JJ Tel: (01342) 836000 Fax: (01342) 835930 E-mail: ac@airtech.uk.com

Aldridge Mechanical Services, 244 Goldcroft, Yeovil, Somerset, BA21 4DA Tel: (01935) 420162 Fax: (01935) 420162

▶ bjsedgwick.com, 23 Meadowbrook Close, Norwich, NR1 2HJ Tel: (01603) 618514 E-mail: barry@supasedg.freeserve.co.uk

Breeze Cool Air Conditioning & Refrigeration Ltd, 37 Amberley Road, Macclesfield, Cheshire, SK11 8LX Tel: (01625) 511336 Fax: (01625) 511288 E-mail: enquiries@breezecool.co.uk

Chiller Box Ltd, Unit 6, Carbery Enterprise Park, 36 White Hart Lane, Tottenham, London, N17 8DP Tel: (0800) 8491188 E-mail: mail@chillerbox.com

Clivet Aircon Ltd, Unit F5 Railway Triangle, Walton Road, Portsmouth, PO6 1TG Tel: (023) 9238 1235 Fax: (023) 9238 1243 E-mail: info@clivetaircon.co.uk

Coverite Air Conditioning Services Ltd, Unit 17 Coldart Business Centre, Dartford, DA1 2HZ Tel: (01322) 270989 Fax: (01322) 278203 E-mail: info@coverite-ac.co.uk

Curaim (UK) Ltd, Units 11-12 Cockridden Farm Industrial Estate, Brentwood Road, Herongate, Brentwood, Essex, CM13 3LH Tel: (01277) 811003 Fax: (01277) 811522 E-mail: curaim@aol.com

Denco Air Ltd, Unit 1, Clifton Lane, Sutton Weaver, Runcorn, Cheshire, WA7 3EZ Tel: (01928) 713240 Fax: (01928) 719762

▶ E Jordon Refrigeration Ltd, Refrigeration House, Quebec Street, Oldham, OL9 6QL Tel: 0161-622 9700 Fax: 0161-622 9709 E-mail: sales@jordon.co.uk

Ensol Ltd, 344 St Helens Road, Bolton, BL3 3RP Tel: (01204) 660064 Fax: (01204) 660043 E-mail: sales@ensol.co.uk

Ers, 21 Upton Cresent, Basingstoke, Hampshire, RG21 5SW Tel: (01256) 465604 Fax: (01256) 473737

Gatwick Park Mechanical Services Ltd, P.O. Box 371, Caterham, Surrey, CR3 6UE Tel: (01883) 347133 Fax: (01883) 343813 E-mail: info@gatwickpark.com

Gryson Air Conditioning Equipment Ltd, Unit 37 Penmaen Small Business Centre, Penmaen Road, Pontllanfraith, Blackwood, Gwent, NP12 2DZ Tel: (01495) 221200 Fax: (01495) 228432 E-mail: enquiries@gryson-aircon.com

Jack Elam, Barton Road, Wisbech, Cambridgeshire, PE13 4TP Tel: (01945) 419090 Fax: (01945) 419088 E-mail: sales@jack-elam.co.uk

Jackson Refrigeration, Unit 19, Cossall Industrial Estate, Solomon Road, Ilkeston, Derbyshire, DE7 5UA Tel: 0115-944 4898 Fax: 0115-944 4981 E-mail: katejackson@jacksonrefrigeration.co.uk

Mastercool Southern Ltd, 7a Baker Street, Ampthill, Bedford, MK45 2QE Tel: (01525) 840689 Fax: 01525 840699 E-mail: mastercool15@btopenworld.com

Regency Building Services Ltd, 33 Station Road, Ingrebourne, Romford, RM3 0DQ Tel: (01708) 341114 Fax: (08707) 770664 E-mail: info@rbsmail.co.uk

Stewart Anthony, Data House, 2 Waldeck Road, Dartford, DA1 1UA Tel: (01322) 293005 Fax: (01322) 293879 E-mail: peterdavison@stewartanthony.co.uk

Topaz Refrigeration & Air Conditioning, 113 Main Road, Marchwood, Southampton, SO40 4UZ Tel: (023) 8086 5202 Fax: (023) 8066 7562

TTF Air Conditioning Ltd, 5 Tower Road, Washington, Tyne & Wear, NE37 2SH Tel: 0191-416 4525 Fax: 0191-416 4650 E-mail: cg-ttssales@jci.com

York Refrigeration Ltd, 10 Longwall Avenue, Queens Drive Industrial Estate, Nottingham, NG2 1NA Tel: 0115-986 1046 Fax: 0115-934 0101

AIR CONDITIONING (AC) MAINTENANCE OR SERVICING EQUIPMENT

A R C Technical Services, 8a Watersedge, Frodsham, WA6 7NQ Tel: (01928) 731106 Fax: (01928) 732066

Airtemp A.C. Ltd, 18 Theaklen Drive, Ponswood Industrial Estate, St. Leonards-on-Sea, East Sussex, TN38 9AZ Tel: (0845) 8725657 Fax: (0845) 8725658 E-mail: sales@airtempac.co.uk

Javac UK Ltd, 6 Drake Court, Middlesbrough, Cleveland, TS2 1RS Tel: (01642) 232880 Fax: (01642) 232870E-mail: info@javac.co.uk

M E C Air Conditioning, 60 Chatterley Drive, Kidsgrove, Stoke-on-Trent, ST7 4LL Tel: (01782) 785721

Mac Air Conditioning Ltd, Unit 11 Maple Park, Essex Road, Hoddesdon, Hertfordshire, EN11 0EX Tel: (01992) 478100 Fax: (01992) 478200 E-mail: sales@macair.co.uk

Raco Air Conditioning, Addison Industrial Estate, Blaydon-on-Tyne, Tyne & Wear, NE21 4TE Tel: 0191-440 4400 Fax: 0191-440 4401

South East Cooling Ltd, 6 Southwinds House, Barrack Lane, Bognor Regis, West Sussex, PO21 4BZ Tel: (01243) 268888 Fax: (01243) 268843E-mail: sales@southeast-cooling.co.uk

AIR CONDITIONING (AC) MOTOR CAR OR VEHICLE EQUIPMENT OR SYSTEMS INSTALLATION

Agricultural & Mobile Air Conditioning Ltd, Avening Road, Nailsworth, Stroud, Gloucestershire, GL6 0BS Tel: (01453) 832884 Fax: (01453) 832040 E-mail: sales@ama-airconditioning.co.uk

▶ Ariazone, Princess of Wales Court Seaway Drive, Seaway Parade Industrial Estate, Port Talbot, West Glamorgan, SA12 7BT Tel: (01639) 822111 Fax: (01639) 822192 E-mail: sales@arizone.co.uk

Atmospheric Products, 7 Bold Industrial Estate, Lunts Heath Road, Widnes, Cheshire, WA8 5RZ Tel: (0870) 2430203 Fax: (0870) 2430204 E-mail: apluk@hotmail.com

B P V Servicing, The Workshop, Ely Avenue, Slough, SL1 3AE Tel: (01753) 692386 Fax: (01753) 692383

Bonair Air Conditioning, 8 Westfield Close Rawreth Industrial Estate, Rawreth Lane, Rayleigh, Essex, SS6 9RL Tel: (01268) 782828 Fax: (01268) 783287 E-mail: mike@bonair.co.uk

Cold Start Ltd, Little Tennis St South, Nottingham, NG2 4EU Tel: 0115-950 5095 Fax: 0115-950 5096 E-mail: sue@coldstart.freeserve.co.uk

Moss Hydraulics, Mount Pleasant Farm, Icknield Street, Kings Norton, Birmingham, B38 0EH Tel: (01564) 822254 Fax: (01564) 822254 E-mail: robinmoss@blackgraves.freeserve.co.uk

▶ newcar4me.com, Camelot House, Bredbury Park Way, Bredbury Park Industrial Estate, Bredbury, Stockport, Cheshire, SK6 2SN Tel: (0870) 9905583 Fax: (0870) 9905584 E-mail: alex.hamilton@newcar4me.com

Sinclair Systems Ltd, 74 Bewsey Street, Warrington, WA2 7JE Tel: (01925) 575543 Fax: (0845) 4567025 E-mail: info@sinclairsystems.co.uk

AIR CONDITIONING (AC) MOTOR CAR OR VEHICLE EQUIPMENT OR SYSTEMS INSTALLATION – *continued*

South Eastern Auto Ltd, Bridge Industrial Centre, Wharf Road, Tovil, Maidstone, Kent, ME15 6RR Tel: (01622) 690010 Fax: (01622) 690683 E-mail: seaes@aol.com

AIR CONDITIONING (AC) OR VENTILATION DIFFUSERS

Integral, Norris House, Crawhall Road, Newcastle upon Tyne, NE1 2BB Tel: 0191-261 1071 Fax: 0191-232 8069 E-mail: mnew@integral.co.uk

AIR CONDITIONING (AC) SERVICES

Air Supply, 7 Steatite Way, Stourport-On-Severn, Worcestershire, DY13 8PQ Tel: (01299) 825336 Fax: (01299) 825336
Airite Southern Ltd, 1 Milners Upper Street, Leeds Village, Maidstone, Kent, ME17 1GZ Tel: (01622) 861411 Fax: (01622) 861415 E-mail: airiteec@btconnect.com
Airtight Ductwork Ltd, New Town, Kington Magna, Gillingham, Dorset, SP8 5EU Tel: (01747) 838777 Fax: (01747) 838999 E-mail: info@airtightductwork.co.uk
Alldales Drive Systems Ltd, Little Cross, Church Street, Warnham, Horsham, West Sussex, RH12 3QR Tel: (01403) 218787 Fax: (01403) 218833 E-mail: sales@alldales.co.uk
Central Aircoil Service Ltd, 5 Icknield Street, Bidford On Avon, Alcester, Warwickshire, B50 4BX Tel: (01789) 774558 Fax: (01789) 774559 E-mail: sales@central-aircoil.co.uk
Compac Services Ne Ltd, Compac House, 173 Victoria Road, South Shields, Tyne & Wear, NE33 4NW Tel: 0191-454 9090 Fax: 0191-454 1212 E-mail: sales@compac.co.uk
Daventry Refrigeration, 4 Cross Lane, Braunston, Daventry, Northamptonshire, NN11 7HH Tel: (01788) 890469 Fax: (01788) 891453
Henson Refrigeration Service, 6 Olympus Square, London, E5 8PL Tel: (020) 8533 5322 Fax: (020) 7686 0851
J & E Hall Ltd, 22 Lorn Street, Birkenhead, Merseyside, CH41 6AR Tel: 0151-647 6974 Fax: 0151-666 1873
Jackson Refrigeration, Unit 19, Cossall Industrial Estate, Solomon Road, Ilkeston, Derbyshire, DE7 5UA Tel: 0115-944 4898 Fax: 0115-944 4981 E-mail: katejackson@jacksonrefrigeration.co.uk
▶ Mcmahon Air Conditioning, The Popples, Clifford Road, Bramham, Wetherby, West Yorkshire, LS23 6RN Tel: (01937) 844203 Fax: (01937) 844203
Mitsubishi Electric Europe, Unit 12 Mercury Park, Mercury Way, Urmston, Manchester, M41 7LY Tel: 0161-866 6060 Fax: 0161-866 6081
Plant Mart Ltd, 7 Langhedge Lane Industrial Estate, Langhedge Lane, London, N18 2TQ Tel: (020) 8366 7375 Fax: (020) 8803 0814 E-mail: sales@aircon4u.co.uk
▶ Priory, 38 Old Priory Road, Bournemouth, BH6 3AQ Tel: (07766) 900820 E-mail: davidquinn@prioryrefrigeration.com
Quality Air Conditioning Ltd, 4 Orlando Court, Vicarage Lane, Walton on the Naze, Essex, CO14 8PA Tel: (01255) 672777 Fax: (01255) 676777 E-mail: shaun@qualityac.co.uk
▶ Tenways Engineering Services Ltd, 31 St. Marys Road, London, NW11 9UE Tel: (020) 8922 5468 Fax: (020) 8201 8022 E-mail: sales@tenwayseng.co.uk
▶ Watco Refrigeration Ltd, Unit 1 Hardengreen Industrial Estate, Dalkeith, Midlothian, EH22 3NX Tel: 0131-561 9502 Fax: 0131-561 9503

AIR CONDITIONING (AC) SYSTEM MAINTENANCE

▶ Air Conditioning Solutions, Dipmans Lodge, Brinkton Road, East Haddon, Northampton, NN6 8DS Tel: (01604) 770660 Fax: (01604) 770036
Artic Air Refrigeration & Air Conditioning, 14 Bell Mead, Studley, Warwickshire, B80 7SH Tel: (01527) 857578 Fax: (01527) 857578
Camrose Air Conditioning Ltd, Unit D4 Brunswick Place, Cranbourne Lane, Basingstoke, Hampshire, RG21 3NN Tel: 0845 4941703 Fax: (01256) 322801 E-mail: peter@camroseair.co.uk
Cool Air Co, 14 Seaforth Avenue, New Malden, Surrey, KT3 6JP Tel: (020) 8949 5259 Fax: (020) 8949 4490 E-mail: coolairco@aol.com
▶ Dac Air Conditioning, Carrington Business Park, Manchester Road, Carrington, Manchester, M31 4DD Tel: 0161-776 4484 Fax: 0161-776 4485
Ensol Ltd, 344 St Helens Road, Bolton, BL3 3RP Tel: (01204) 660064 Fax: (01204) 660043 E-mail: sales@ensol.co.uk
Riseborough Refrigeration Service Ltd, 164 Glenroy Street, Roath, Cardiff, CF24 3LA Tel: (029) 2049 6007 Fax: (029) 2049 2409
Simply Refrigeration & Air Conditioning Ltd, 10 Samsons Close, Brightlingsea, Colchester, CO7 0RP Tel: (0800) 0265140 Fax: (0870) 0520855 E-mail: info@simply-fridge.demon.co.uk

AIR CONDITIONING (AC) SYSTEMS

▶ 3D Air Sales Ltd Scotland, McGregor House, South Bank Business Park, Kirkintilloch, Glasgow, G66 1XF Tel: 0141-777 5007 Fax: 0141-777 5009
Allistone Electrical, 24 Eastbourne Road, Willingdon, Eastbourne, East Sussex, BN20 9LD Tel: (01323) 502998 Fax: (01323) 502998
▶ I M A Cooling Systems, Hamburg Way, North Lynn Industrial Estate, King's Lynn, Norfolk, PE30 2ND Tel: (01553) 767446 Fax: (01553) 767457

AIR CONDITIONING (AC) UNITS

Airconaire Ltd, Unit 6 Deacon Trading Centre, Knight Road, Rochester, Kent, ME2 2AU Tel: (01634) 711264 Fax: (01634) 717100 E-mail: info@airconaire.co.uk
Coldlink, 18 Wellesley Road, Tharston, Norwich, NR15 2PD Tel: (01508) 532277 Fax: (01508) 532377
▶ Cooleasy.co.uk, Ixus House, Ogmore Terrace, Bridgend, Mid Glamorgan, CF31 1SU Tel: (0870) 4581818 Fax: (0870) 4581919 E-mail: info@cooleasy.co.uk
▶ I M A Cooling Systems Ltd, Unit A3-A4, 156 St. Albans Road, Sandridge, St. Albans, Hertfordshire, AL4 9LP Tel: (01727) 840090 Fax: (01727) 830679 E-mail: reception@imacooling.co.uk
Warwick Fraser, Unit 9 Alfold Business Centre, Loxwood Road, Alfold, Cranleigh, Surrey, GU6 8HP Tel: (01403) 753069 Fax: (01403) 752469 E-mail: sales@warwickfraser.co.uk

AIR CONSERVATION NOZZLES

O.N. Beck & Co. Ltd, 104 Fox Lane, Palmers Green, London, N13 4AX Tel: (020) 8886 3444 Fax: (020) 8886 9218 E-mail: sales@onbeck.co.uk

AIR COOLED CHILLERS

Transtherm Ltd, 12 Banner Park, Wickmans Drive, Coventry, CV4 9XA Tel: (024) 7647 1120 Fax: (024) 7647 1125 E-mail: sales@transtherm.ltd.uk

AIR COOLED CONDENSERS

Hamon UK Ltd, Units1-2 Ropery Park, Alferd Street, Hull, HU3 2DF Tel: (01482) 787767 Fax: (01482) 706151 E-mail: info.huk@hamon.com

AIR COOLED TRANSFORMERS

S T L Transtech Ltd, 64-66 Percy Road, Leicester, LE2 8FN Tel: 0116-283 3321 Fax: 0116-283 0730 E-mail: transtechsales@stlgroup.org
A.C. Simpson (Transformers) 1981 Ltd, Unit 20, Olds Close, Watford, WD18 9RU Tel: (01923) 777495 Fax: (01923) 771257 E-mail: info@acstx.co.uk
Transmag Power Transformers Ltd, 66-72 Lower Essex Street, Birmingham, B5 6SU Tel: 0121-622 3217 Fax: 0121-622 3217 E-mail: sales@transmag-transformers.co.uk

AIR COOLERS

▶ AKS Heat Transfer Services, Sheffield Road, Woodhouse Mill, Sheffield, S13 9WH Tel: 0114-269 4002 Fax: 0114-293 9164 E-mail: tech@aksheattransfer.com
Becool Radiators Ltd, Paterson Road, Wellingborough, Northamptonshire, NN8 4BZ Tel: (01933) 230420 Fax: (01933) 279902 E-mail: sales@gallay.co.uk
Custom Coils, Newgate Lane, Fareham, Hampshire, PO14 1AR Tel: (01329) 822222 Fax: (01329) 821238 E-mail: sales@custom-coils.co.uk
NRF (UK) Ltd, Lamport Drive, Heartlands Business Park, Daventry, Northamptonshire, NN11 5YH Tel: (01327) 300242 Fax: (01327) 300225 E-mail: sales@nrf.co.uk
Russell Ltd, 125 Business Park, Llanthony Road, Gloucester, GL2 5JQ Tel: (01452) 312851 Fax: (01452) 306388 E-mail: info@russell.co.uk
Searle Manufacturing Co., 20 Davis Way, Newgate Lane, Fareham, Hampshire, PO14 1AR Tel: (01329) 823344 Fax: (01329) 821242 E-mail: sales@searle.co.uk

AIR COURIER SERVICES

▶ Courier Please Ltd, Suite 44, 468 Walton Road, West Molesey, Surrey, KT8 8AE Tel: (07890) 454428 Fax: (0208) 3390859 E-mail: info@acourierplease.co.uk
▶ D & R Couriers, Building 2, 47 Skelwith Road, Marton, Blackpool, FY3 9UL Tel: 01253 312713 Fax: 01253 312713 E-mail: richard@dandrcouriers.co.uk
Direct Despatch International Ltd, D D I House, 1-21 Elkstone Road, London, W10 5NT Tel: (020) 7724 4000 Fax: (020) 8964 8244 E-mail: sales@ddi.co.uk
Direct Link South, 38 Millbrook Road East, Southampton, SO15 1HY Tel: (023) 8033 1541 E-mail: louis.roe@dirlinks.freeserve.co.uk
▶ Express Courier Services, Unit 8d Northwood Business Park, Newport Road, Cowes, Isle of Wight, PO31 8PE Tel: (01983) 299944 Fax: (01983) 299944 E-mail: info@ecs-iow.co.uk
Fedex, Unit A2 Skyway 14, Calder Way, Poyle, Slough, SL3 0BQ Tel: (01753) 689589 Fax: (01753) 681647
Global Logistics Systems Ltd, 448 Oakshot Place, Bamber Bridge, Preston, PR5 8AT Tel: (01772) 626400 Fax: (01772) 627251
▶ Kellylink Ltd, Unit 2, Arrow Road North, Lakeside, Redditch, Worcestershire, B98 8NT Tel: (01527) 62222 Fax: (01527) 62222 E-mail: info@kellylink.co.uk
Mailflight Ltd, Unit 2 Central Way, Feltham, Middlesex, TW14 0RX Tel: (020) 8893 1477 Fax: (020) 8893 1459 E-mail: ops@mfcourier.com
▶ PSL Couriers, Briarfield Gardens, Bradford, West Yorkshire, BD18 2BE Tel: (07890) 194132 E-mail: pslcouriers@yahoo.co.uk
S M B Couriers, 683 Tonbridge Road, Barming, Maidstone, Kent, ME16 9DQ Tel: (07930) 281229 E-mail: info@smbcouriers.com
▶ Southern Despatch, 87 Palmerston Road, Bournemouth, BH1 4HP Tel: (01202) 394357 Fax: (01202) 398954 E-mail: sales@southerndespatch.co.uk
▶ Speedy Parcels, Field Way, Greenford, Middlesex, UB6 8UN Tel: (020) 8813 4111 Fax: (020) 8833 7222
▶ Peter Watson, 57 Euston Grove, Crow, Ringwood, Hampshire, BH24 1FB Tel: (07866) 737655 E-mail: tasminservices@tiscali.co.uk
▶ World Courier, Sea Containers House, 20 Upper Ground, London, SE1 9PD Tel: (020) 7717 1400 Fax: (020) 7928 7105 E-mail: contact@worldcourier.com

AIR CURTAINS

Air Curtain Engineering Ltd, 15-29 Air Street Hill, London, EC1R 5LB Tel: (020) 7833 2940 Fax: (020) 7833 8299
Biddle Air Curtains Ltd, St Mary's Road, Nuneaton, Warwickshire, CV11 5AU Tel: (024) 7638 4233 Fax: (024) 7637 3621 E-mail: info@biddle-air.co.uk
Thermoscreens Ltd, St. Marys Road, Nuneaton, Warwickshire, CV11 5AU Tel: (024) 7638 4646 Fax: (024) 7638 8578 E-mail: sales@thermoscreens.com

AIR DIFFUSION EQUIPMENT

Air Diffusion Sales Northern Ltd, Unit 39 Sefton La Industrial Estate, Liverpool, L31 8BX Tel: 0151-527 2525 Fax: 0151-527 2717
▶ Elite Ceiling Manufacturers Ltd, Ridgeway Industrial Estate, Iver, Buckinghamshire, SL0 9HU Tel: (01753) 654411 Fax: (01753) 630002 E-mail: henry@ecmuk.com
G D L Air Systems Ltd, Air Diffusion Works, Woolley Bridge Road, Hadfield, Glossop, Derbyshire, SK13 1AB Tel: (01457) 861538 Fax: (01457) 866010 E-mail: sales@grille.co.uk
Gilberts Blackpool Ltd, Gilair Works, Clifton Road, Blackpool, FY4 4QT Tel: (01253) 766911 Fax: (01253) 767941 E-mail: sales@gilbertsblackpool.com
J C Vents Ltd, J.C. House, Hurricane Way, Wickford Business Park, Wickford, Essex, SS11 8YB Tel: (01268) 561122 Fax: (01268) 560606 E-mail: sales@jcvents.co.uk
Krantz Systems Ltd, 61-67 Rectory Road, Wivenhoe, Colchester, CO7 9ES Tel: (01206) 827171 Fax: (01206) 826936 E-mail: kjr@d4s.co.uk
Lindab Ltd, Unit 9 - 10 Carousel Way, Riverside Business Park, Northampton, NN3 9HG Tel: (01604) 788350 Fax: (01604) 788351
Trox UK Ltd, Caxton Way, Thetford, Norfolk, IP24 3SQ Tel: (01842) 754545 Fax: (01842) 763051 E-mail: sales@troxuk.co.uk

AIR DRIVEN FANS

O.N. Beck & Co. Ltd, 104 Fox Lane, Palmers Green, London, N13 4AX Tel: (020) 8886 3444 Fax: (020) 8886 9218 E-mail: sales@onbeck.co.uk
Grimes Industrial Machinery & Equipment Solutions Ltd, 199 Hyde End Rd, Spencers Wood, Reading, RG7 1BU Tel: 0118-988 4825 Fax: 0118-988 4825 E-mail: grimesindmach@aol.com
Sonic Air Systems (Europe) Ltd, 227 Sunderland Road, South Shields, Tyne & Wear, NE34 6AL Tel: 0191-455 1628 Fax: 0191-427 1994 E-mail: priley@sonicairsystems.com

AIR DRYER SPARE PARTS

▶ Global Drying Systems Ltd, Parkhall Road, Longton, Stoke-on-Trent, ST3 5AT Tel: (01782) 370200 Fax: (01782) 370222 E-mail: neilbeckett@cobwebworld.co.uk

AIR DUCT HEATERS

▶ Air Diffusion Technology, 52 London Road, Oadby, Leicester, LE2 5DH Tel: 0116-272 1231 Fax: 0116-271 4441 E-mail: info@euro-air.co.uk

AIR EXPANDING SHAFTS

Airmat Machinery Ltd, 43 Bridgeman Terrace, Wigan, Lancashire, WN1 1TT Tel: (01942) 493563 Fax: (01942) 496276 E-mail: info@airmat-machinery.co.uk

AIR FILTERS

Airclean Ltd, PO Box 147, Maidstone, Kent, ME14 2LA Tel: (01622) 832777 Fax: (01622) 832507 E-mail: info@airclean.co.uk
Camfil Ltd, Knowsley Road, Haslingden, Rossendale, Lancashire, BB4 4EG Tel: (01706) 238000 Fax: (01706) 226736 E-mail: info@camfil.com
Cleanair Group Ltd, Technology House, 5 Newton Close, Drayton Fields, Daventry, Northamptonshire, NN11 5RR Tel: (01327) 301383 Fax: (01327) 301384 E-mail: info@cleanair.com
Davis Industrial (Filters) Ltd, 21d Holmethorpe Avenue, Redhill, RH1 2NB Tel: (0845) 2735025 Fax: (0845) 2735026 E-mail: sales@davisfilters.co.uk
Dolphin Enterprises, 4 Eddington Drive, Newton Mearns, Glasgow, G77 5AX Tel: 0141-639 4551 Fax: 0141-639 4551 E-mail: dolphinenterprizes@btconnect.com
E M M UK Ltd, Old Road, Southam, Warwickshire, CV47 1RA Tel: (01926) 812419 Fax: (01926) 817425 E-mail: sales@emm.co.uk
Euro Filter, Hare Park Mills, 46 Hare Park Lane, Liversedge, West Yorkshire, WF15 8EP Tel: (01623) 412412 Fax: (01623) 412455 E-mail: sales@eurofilter.co.uk
Eurotech Filtration Ltd, 15 Furlong Lane, Stoke-on-Trent, ST6 3LE Tel: (01782) 836667 Fax: (01782) 834830
Filterite Ltd, Unit E Alfred Court Saxon Business Park, Hanbury Road, Stoke Prior, Bromsgrove, Worcestershire, B60 4AD Tel: (01527) 836201 Fax: (01527) 836202 E-mail: sales.filterite@tesco.net
Filtermax Filtration Services Ltd, Unit 17, Bradwell Works, Davenport Street, Stoke-on-Trent, ST6 4LL Tel: (01782) 816300 Fax: (01782) 790767 E-mail: sales@filterspares.com
HVDS, Site B Hixon Industrial Estate, Church Lane, Hixon, Stafford, ST18 0PY Tel: (01889) 270079 Fax: (01889) 271616
Induction Technology Group Ltd, Unit B Quinn Close, Coventry, CV3 4LH Tel: (024) 7630 5386 Fax: (024) 7630 7999 E-mail: sales@itgairfilters.com
Jasun Filtration plc, Riverside House, Parrett Way, Bridgwater, Somerset, TA6 5LB Tel: (01278) 452277 Fax: (01278) 450873 E-mail: info@jfilters.com
K & N Filters Europe Ltd, John Street, Warrington, WA2 7UB Tel: (01925) 636950 Fax: (01925) 418948E-mail: kn@knfilters.com
Lockertex, Church Street, Warrington, WA1 2SU Tel: (01925) 642709 Fax: (01925) 630431 E-mail: sales@lockertex.co.uk
Longar Industries Ltd, Unit 25 Glenmore Business Park, Colebrook Way, Andover, Hampshire, SP10 3GZ Tel: (01264) 332993 Fax: (01264) 332994 E-mail: enquires@longar.co.uk
M C Air Filtration Ltd, Motney Hill Road, Gillingham, Kent, ME8 7TZ Tel: (01634) 388333 Fax: (01634) 379384 E-mail: sales@mcaf.co.uk
Master Filtration Ltd, 7 Arden Press Way, Letchworth Garden City, Hertfordshire, SG6 1LH Tel: (01462) 675844 Fax: (01462) 480852 E-mail: sales@master-filtration.co.uk
Millipore (UK) Ltd, Units 3-5 The Court Yard, Hattes Lane, Watford, WD18 8YH Tel: (0870) 9004645 Fax: (0870) 9004646 E-mail: csr_uk@millipore.com
John Morfield Ltd, Unit 98 Sadler Foster Way, Teeside Industrial Estate, Stockton-on-Tees, Cleveland, TS17 9JY Tel: (01642) 760555 Fax: (01642) 750391 E-mail: enquiries@johnmorfield.co.uk
Nationwide Filter Co. Ltd, Unit 16 First Quarter, Blenheim Road, Epsom, Surrey, KT19 9QN Tel: (01372) 728548 Fax: (01372) 742831
P S I Global Ltd, Bowburn South Industrial Estate, Bowburn, Durham, DH6 5AD Tel: 0191-377 0550 Fax: 0191-377 0769 E-mail: sales@psiglobal.co.uk
Patent Filtration Ltd, 10 Chartmoor Road, Leighton Buzzard, Bedfordshire, LU7 4WG Tel: 01525 384858

AIR FILTERS – *continued*

Premaberg Manufacturing Ltd, 22-24 High St, Halstead, Essex, CO9 2AP Tel: (01787) 475651 Fax: (01787) 475046 E-mail: sales@premaberg.com

Sogefi Filtration Ltd, Llantrisant Industrial Estate, Llantrisant, Pontyclun, Mid Glamorgan, CF72 8YU Tel: (01443) 223000 Fax: (01443) 225459 E-mail: stuart.hobbs@sogefifiltration.com

Sttop Filters Ltd, Woodmere, 7 Moor Close, Acton Trussell, Stafford, ST17 0QZ Tel: (01785) 714687 Fax: (01785) 716499 E-mail: peter@sttopfilters.co.uk

AIR FILTRATION EQUIPMENT

A A F-Mcquay UK Ltd, Bassington Lane, Cramlington, Northumberland, NE23 8AF Tel: (01670) 713477 Fax: (01670) 714370

Altair Filter Technology Ltd, Omega Park, Alton, Hampshire, GU34 2QE Tel: (01420) 541188 Fax: (01420) 541298 E-mail: info@altairfilter.com

C T P Wipac Ltd, London Road, Buckingham, MK18 1BH Tel: (01280) 822800 Fax: (01280) 822802 E-mail: sales@wipac.com

Camfil Ltd, Knowsley Road, Haslingden, Rossendale, Lancashire, BB4 4EG Tel: (01706) 238000 Fax: (01706) 226736 E-mail: info@camfil.com

Davis Industrial (Filters) Ltd, 21d Holmethorpe Avenue, Redhill, RH1 2NB Tel: (0845) 2735025 Fax: (0845) 2735026 E-mail: sales@davisfilters.co.uk

Donaldson Filter Components Ltd, Oslo Road, Hull, HU7 0YN Tel: (01482) 835213 Fax: (01482) 835411 E-mail: info@donaldson.com

Emcel Filters Ltd, Blatchford Road, Horsham, West Sussex, RH13 5RA Tel: (01403) 253215 Fax: (01403) 259881 E-mail: filtration@emcelfilters.co.uk

Envirocare Services Ltd, 5 Stratfield Park, Elettra Avenue, Waterlooville, Hampshire, PO7 7XN Tel: (023) 9264 4700 Fax: (023) 9264 4677 E-mail: info@envirocare-services.com

Ernest Morrison & Co., Unit 13 Loughside Industrial Estate, Dargan CR, Belfast, BT3 9JP Tel: (028) 9077 7093 Fax: (028) 9077 6299

Eurotech Filtration Ltd, 15 Furlong Lane, Stoke-on-Trent, ST6 3LE Tel: (01782) 836667 Fax: (01782) 834830

Filtair Ltd, 9 Brookvale Trading Estate, Moor Lane, Birmingham, B6 7AQ Tel: 0121-356 9595 Fax: 0121-356 9538

Filterite Ltd, Unit E Alfred Court Saxon Business Park, Hanbury Road, Stoke Prior, Bromsgrove, Worcestershire, B60 4AD Tel: (01527) 836201 Fax: (01527) 836202 E-mail: sales.filterite@tesco.net

Filtermist International Ltd, Faraday Drive, Bridgnorth, Shropshire, WV15 5BA Tel: (01746) 765361 Fax: (01746) 766882 E-mail: sales@filtermist.com

▶ Filtration Medic, 15 Hughes Place, Warrington, WA2 0EJ Tel: 01925 453228 E-mail: info@filtrationmedic.co.uk

Filtrex Environmental, Unit 18 Burnt Mill Industrial Estate, Elizabeth Way, Harlow, Essex, CM20 2HS Tel: (01279) 457590 Fax: (01279) 457591

HVDS, Site B Hixon Industrial Estate, Church Lane, Hixon, Stafford, ST18 0PY Tel: (01889) 270079 Fax: (01889) 271616

Hydrasun Ltd, Hydrasun House, 392 King Street, Aberdeen, AB24 3BU Tel: (01224) 618618 Fax: (01224) 618701 E-mail: info@hydrasun.com

Industrial Pneumatic Services Liverpool Ltd, 13 Dunnings Bridge Road, Bootle, Merseyside, L30 6TE Tel: 0151-525 9381 Fax: 0151-525 1982

Lockertex, Church Street, Warrington, WA1 2SU Tel: (01925) 642709 Fax: (01925) 630431 E-mail: sales@lockertex.co.uk

Lovewell Blake, Wrenrock House, The Street, Felthorpe, Norwich, NR10 4AB Tel: (01603) 755389 Fax: (01760) 725070

M I F Filter Systems Ltd, M I F Ho, Waterfall Lane Trading Estate, Cradley Heath, West Midlands, B64 6PU Tel: 0121-561 5380 Fax: 0121-561 3711 E-mail: sales@mif-filters.com

Midland Diving Equipment Ltd, 57 Sparkenhoe Street, Leicester, LE2 0TD Tel: 0116-212 4262 Fax: 0116-212 4263 E-mail: info@midlanddiving.com

Norit UK Ltd, Clydesmill Place, Cambuslang Industrial Estate, Clydesmill Industrial Estate, Glasgow, G32 8RF Tel: 0141-641 8841 Fax: 0141-641 8411 E-mail: fisher.martin.nl@norit.com

Sangre Engineering Ltd, Unit 32c The Washford Industrial Estate, Heming Road, Redditch, Worcestershire, B98 0DH Tel: (01527) 524782 Fax: (01527) 510323 E-mail: sales@sangre.co.uk

Servais Silencers, 409 Harlestone Road, Northampton, NN5 6PB Tel: (01604) 754888 Fax: (01604) 759548

Trox UK Ltd, Caxton Way, Thetford, Norfolk, IP24 3SQ Tel: (01842) 754545 Fax: (01842) 763051 E-mail: sales@troxuk.co.uk

Westbury Financial Management, Hall Farm Estate, Gadbrook Road, Betchworth, Surrey, RH3 7AH Tel: (01306) 611611 Fax: (01306) 611613 E-mail: sales@westburyfilters.co.uk

AIR FILTRATION EQUIPMENT OR SYSTEM INSTALLATION OR INSPECTION OR MAINTENANCE OR REFURBISHMENT

Environmental Elements (UK) Ltd, Unit 2 Moor Street, Burton-on-Trent, Staffordshire, DE14 3SU Tel: (01283) 740536 Fax: (01283) 563969 E-mail: dcormack@eec1.com

Filtermist International Ltd, Faraday Drive, Bridgnorth, Shropshire, WV15 5BA Tel: (01746) 765361 Fax: (01746) 766882 E-mail: sales@filtermist.com

High Tech Environmental Engineering Ltd, Environmental House, Cross Street, Standish, Wigan, Lancashire, WN6 0HQ Tel: (01257) 426969 Fax: (01257) 426812

AIR FLOTATION EQUIPMENT

Aerogo UK Ltd, 11a Orchard Road, Royston, Hertfordshire, SG8 6HL Tel: (01763) 249349 Fax: (0870) 4014546 E-mail: sales@aerogo-uk.co.uk

AIR FLOW INDICATORS

Concept Engineering Ltd, 7 Woodlands Business Park, Woodlands Park Avenue, Maidenhead, Berkshire, SL6 3UA Tel: (01628) 825555 Fax: (01628) 826261 E-mail: info@concept-smoke.co.uk

▶ West Controls Ltd, 14 Manstone Mead, Sidmouth, Devon, EX10 9RX Tel: 01395 512816 Fax: 01395 513532 E-mail: sales@westcontrols.co.uk

AIR FREIGHT FORWARDERS/ FORWARDING AGENTS

A Hartrodt UK Ltd, Unit 2 Pump Lane Industrial Estate, Hayes, Middlesex, UB3 3NB Tel: (020) 8848 3545 Fax: (020) 8561 0940 E-mail: london@hartrodt.co.uk

Access Shipping Ltd, Rainham House Rainham Trading Estate, New Road, Rainham, Essex, RM13 8RA Tel: (01708) 521113 Fax: (01708) 521151 E-mail: access-shipping@cnsmail.co.uk

Active International Movements Ltd, 380 Ringwood Road, Poole, Dorset, BH12 3LT Tel: (01202) 307349 Fax: (01202) 743707 E-mail: sales@activefreight.co.uk

Adeptstar Shipping Ltd, Estate House, Marsh Way, Fairview Industrial Park, Rainham, Essex, RM13 8UH Tel: (01708) 550909 Fax: (01708) 551945 E-mail: adeptstar@shipping-ltd.fsnet.co.uk

Air Menzies International Ltd, 5 The Enterprise Centre, Kelvin Lane, Crawley, West Sussex, RH10 9PT Tel: (01293) 658000 Fax: (01293) 551114 E-mail: info@airmenzies.com

Airocean Freight Ltd, 6-9 Spring Road, Smethwick, West Midlands, B66 1PE Tel: 0121-580 6730 Fax: 0121-525 5296 E-mail: info@airoceanfreight.co.uk

Airworld International, 2 The Faraday Centre, Faraday Road, Crawley, West Sussex, RH10 9PX Tel: (01293) 510007 Fax: (01293) 521361 E-mail: airsales@allport.co.uk

Allport Ltd, 2 The Faraday Centre, Faraday Road, Crawley, West Sussex, RH10 9PX Tel: (01293) 510246 Fax: (01293) 562044 E-mail: info@allport.co.uk

Anglia Forwarding Group Ltd, The Anglian Centre, Blackwater Close, Rainham, Essex, RM13 8UA Tel: (01708) 527000 Fax: (01708) 524881 E-mail: london@anglia-forwarding.co.uk

Arends International Ltd, Sankey Valley Industrial Estate, Anglezarke Road, Newton-le-Willows, Merseyside, WA12 8DJ Tel: (01925) 223323 Fax: (01925) 229800 E-mail: sales@arends.co.uk

Ark Forwarding Ltd, Unit 13 Brittania Industrial Estate, Poyle Road, Slough, SL3 0BH Tel: (01753) 685454 Fax: (01753) 684093 E-mail: sales@airfreight.co.uk

Arrowfreight Ltd, Unit D3, Crossgate Drive, Queens Drive Industrial Estate, Nottingham, NG2 1LW Tel: 0115-986 8031 Fax: 0115-986 0607 E-mail: info@arrowfreight.com

Atlantis Forwarding Ltd, 1607 Pershore Road, Stirchley, Birmingham, B30 2JF Tel: 0121-451 1588 Fax: 0121-433 4034 E-mail: enquiries@atlantisltd.co.uk

B A X Global Ltd, Unitair Centre, Great South West Road, Feltham, Middlesex, TW14 8NT Tel: (020) 8899 3000 Fax: (020) 8899 3111

Balloon Flights Co, Dovecote House, Gaulby Lane, Kings Norton, Leicester, LE7 9BA Tel: 0116-259 6990 E-mail: bookings@balloonflightscompany.co.uk

Bernard Group Ltd, Bernard House 52-54 Peregrine Road, Hainault, Ilford, Essex, IG6 3SZ Tel: (020) 8501 2599 Fax: (020) 8559 9922 E-mail: corporate@bernardgroup.plc.uk

Binoray Ltd, Elm Grove, London, SW19 4HL Tel: (020) 8946 5157 Fax: (020) 8944 1476 E-mail: sales@binoray.co.uk

Chiltern Airfreight, Poyle Road, Colnbrook, Slough, SL3 0AY Tel: (01753) 680845 Fax: 01753 681094

Chiltern Cargo Services Ltd, Willen Works, Willen Road, Newport Pagnell, Bucks, MK16 0DG Tel: (01908) 611222 Fax: (01908) 612221 E-mail: admin@chiltern.cargo.co.uk

Coleshill Freight Services Ltd, Coleshill Freight Terminal, Station Road, Coleshill, Birmingham, B46 1JJ Tel: (01675) 463869 Fax: (01675) 465727 E-mail: john@coleshillfreight.com

▶ Connexion World Cargo, Unit 3 Blackburn Trading Estate, Northumberland Close, Stanwell, Staines, Middlesex, TW19 7LN Tel: (01784) 263000 Fax: (01784) 263111 E-mail: info@connexcargo.com

Crest Freight Forwarding Ltd, 76 High Street, Stony Stratford, Milton Keynes, MK11 1AH Tel: (01908) 307655 Fax: (01908) 307656 E-mail: sales@crestfreight.co.uk

Crete Shipping, 42 Battersea Rise, London, SW11 1EE Tel: (020) 7223 1244 Fax: (020) 7924 3895 E-mail: sales@creteshipping.co.uk

Cromac Smith Ltd, 34-40 Warwick Road, Kenilworth, Warwickshire, CV8 1HE Tel: (01926) 865800 Fax: (01926) 865808 E-mail: albatros@cromacsmith.com

Damco Sea & Air Ltd, Suite 20 Orwell House, Ferry Lane, Felixstowe, Suffolk, IP11 3QP Tel: (01394) 675989 Fax: (01394) 674208 E-mail: sales@damcomar.com

Danzas AEI Intercontinental, 18-32 London Road, Staines, Middlesex, TW18 4BP Tel: (01784) 871118 Fax: (01784) 871158 E-mail: mark.oxtoby@gb.danzas.com

Davies Turner & Co. Ltd, Unit C16 Taylors Court, Parkgate, Rotherham, South Yorkshire, S62 6NU Tel: (01709) 529709 Fax: (01709) 529710E-mail: paulknight@daviesturner.co.uk

Davies Turner & Co. Ltd, 184 Portswood Road, Southampton, SO17 2NJ Tel: (023) 8055 5955 Fax: (023) 8055 5644 E-mail: mikerees@daviesturner.co.uk

Delivered On Time, 4 Mercury Centre, Central Way, Feltham, Middlesex, TW14 0RN Tel: (020) 8890 5511 Fax: (020) 8890 5533 E-mail: sales@shand.co.uk

Dunwoody Airline Services Ltd, East Midlands International Airport, 70 Argosy Road, Castle Donington, Derby, DE74 2SA Tel: (01332) 811967 Fax: (01332) 850405 E-mail: accounts@baregionalcargo.com

Dyce Carrier, Kirkton Avenue, Dyce, Aberdeen, AB21 0BF Tel: (01224) 723571 Fax: (01224) 770328E-mail: info@dycecar.fsbuisiness.co.uk

Eurogate International Forwarding Co. Ltd, Garret Green Freight Depot, Bannerley Road, Birmingham, B33 0SL Tel: 0121-785 0270 Fax: 0121-785 0271 E-mail: birmingham@eurogate.co.uk

Europa Worldwide Logistics, Europa House, 68 Hailey Rd, Erith, Kent, DA18 4AU Tel: (020) 8311 5000 Fax: (020) 8310 4805 E-mail: sales@europa-worldwide.co.uk

▶ Europa Worldwide Services, Europa House, 46 Tilton Road, Birmingham, B9 4PP Tel: 0121-766 8000 Fax: 0121-771 4669 E-mail: sales@europa-worldwide.co.uk

Exel Freight Management UK Ltd, Great South West Road, Feltham, Middlesex, TW14 8NE Tel: (020) 8750 7000 Fax: (020) 8890 8444 E-mail: derrick.froom@exel.com

Export Centre, Unit 72 Wimbledon Stadium Business Centre, Rosemary Road, London, SW17 0BA Tel: (020) 8947 6767 Fax: (020) 8944 1414 E-mail: info@london-frieght.co.uk

Express Forwarders Ltd, 9 Meadowbrook Industrial Centre, Crawley, West Sussex, RH10 9SA Tel: (01293) 551642 Fax: (01293) 553375 E-mail: sales@expressforwarders.co.uk

Fedex, Unit A2 Skyway 14, Calder Way, Poyle, Slough, SL3 0BQ Tel: (01753) 689589 Fax: (01753) 681647

Foremost International Ltd, Unit C Mill Mead, Staines, Middlesex, TW18 4UQ Tel: (01784) 464319 Fax: (01784) 466418 E-mail: ops@foremost-worldcargo.co.uk

Frans Maas (U K) Ltd, 36 North Quay, Great Yarmouth, Norfolk, NR30 1JE Tel: (01493) 336600 Fax: (01493) 858730 E-mail: sales@fmaas.co.uk

Freight Co. International Ltd, Unit 5 Howe Moss Drive, Dyce, Aberdeen, AB21 0GL Tel: (01224) 771881 Fax: (01224) 770730 E-mail: info@freightco-group.co.uk

Future Forwarding Co. Ltd, Building 305, World Freight Terminal, Manchester Airport, Manchester, M90 5PY Tel: 0161-436 8181 Fax: 0161-499 0654 E-mail: andreadelves@futureforwarding.com

▶ G B Shipping & Forwarding Ltd, Meridian House, Alexandra Dock North, Grimsby, North East Lincolnshire, DN31 3UA Tel: (01472) 345551 Fax: (01472) 346927 E-mail: shipping@gbagroup.com

G K N Freight Services Ltd, Equity House, 128-136 High St, Edgware, Middlesex, HA8 7EL Tel: (020) 8905 6688 Fax: (020) 8905 6951 E-mail: info.fsl@gkndriveline.com

Garrick Freight International Ltd, 6-8 Furrow La, London, E9 6JS Tel: (020) 8985 2789 Fax: (020) 8985 4961

Geologistics Ltd, Royal Court, 81 Tweedy Road, Bromley, BR1 1TW Tel: (020) 8460 5050 Fax: (020) 8461 8884 E-mail: prandall@geo-logistics.com

Geologistics Ltd, Unit 12 The Brunel Centre, Newton Road, Crawley, West Sussex, RH10 9TU Tel: (01293) 652900 Fax: (01293) 652901 E-mail: gatwick@geo-logistics.com

Glennfreight Services Ltd, 9 Enterprise Court, Metcalf Way, Crawley, West Sussex, RH11 7RW Tel: (01293) 437770 Fax: (01293) 437775 E-mail: info@glennfreight.co.uk

Gondrand U.K., Gondrand House, 2 Oriental Road, London, E16 2BZ Tel: (020) 7540 2000 Fax: (020) 7540 2001 E-mail: info@gondrand.co.uk

Goodrem Nicholson, Export House, Rowley Road, Coventry, CV3 4FR Tel: (024) 7630 5601 Fax: (024) 7630 4663 E-mail: colin@goodrem.co.uk

Guernsey Freight Services, Airport Complex, Forest, Guernsey, GY8 0DJ Tel: (01481) 238180 Fax: (01481) 235479

Hamnett Machinery Removals, Gibbet Street, Halifax, West Yorkshire, HX2 0AR Tel: (01422) 345571 Fax: (01422) 346766 E-mail: hamnett@btinternet.com

HazMat Logistics Ltd, Unit 3, Links Industrial Estate, Popham Close, Hanworth, Feltham, Middlesex, TW13 6JE Tel: (020) 8898 1654 Fax: (020) 8898 1643 E-mail: info@hazmatlogistics.co.uk

Higgs International, Unit 7, Thameside Industrial Estate, London, E16 2HB Tel: (020) 7867 9944 Fax: (020) 7511 1976 E-mail: sales@higgs.co.uk

Immediate Transportation Co. Ltd, First Floor, St Nicholas House, Chappel St, Liverpool, L2 8TX Tel: 0151-227 4521 Fax: 0151-236 8036 E-mail: itcolhr@itcolhr.co.uk

Immediate Transportation Co. Ltd, Mckay Trading Estate, Blackthorne Road, Colnbrook, Slough, SL3 0AH Tel: (01753) 684644 Fax: (01753) 683338 E-mail: itcolhr@itcolhr.co.uk

Inchcape Shipping Services UK Ltd, East Side Locks, Immingham Dock, Immingham, South Humberside, DN40 2LZ Tel: (01469) 571400 Fax: (01469) 571309

Inchcape Shipping Services UK Ltd, Main Gate, 1 Sheerness Docks, Sheerness, Kent, ME12 1RT Tel: (01795) 660556 Fax: (01795) 580121

▶ Independent Freight Solutions Ltd, 91 Chaytor Drive, Chapel End, Nuneaton, Warwickshire, CV10 9SU Tel: (024) 7639 8663 Fax: (024) 7639 2757 E-mail: ifsltd@btconnect.com

Instone Air Services Ltd, Charity Farm, Pulborough Road, Cootham, Pulborough, West Sussex, RH20 4HP Tel: (01903) 740101 Fax: (01903) 740102 E-mail: sales@instoneair.com

▶ J D Freight Ltd, Unit 3, Hurricane Way, Slough, SL3 8AG Tel: (01753) 545556 Fax: 01753 545557 E-mail: lee.tuppen@jdfreight.co.uk

John Gardiner Airfreight Ltd, 14 Mount Road, Feltham, Middlesex, TW13 6AR Tel: (020) 8894 3537 Fax: (020) 8894 3542 E-mail: john@johngardinerfreight.com

John Pipe Ltd, 380 Ringwood Road, Poole, Dorset, BH12 3LT Tel: (01202) 715888 Fax: (01202) 743707 E-mail: david.pipe@johnpipe.co.uk

K Line Air Service UK Ltd, Building 100 Beverley Road, East Midland Int Airport, Castle Donington, Derby, DE74 2SA Tel: (01332) 850888 Fax: (01332) 812185 E-mail: ema@uk.klinelogistics.com

▶ Kamino Ltd, 3b Gatwick Metro Centre, Balcombe Road, Horley, Surrey, RH6 9GA Tel: (01293) 874444 Fax: (01293) 874454

Kuehne & Nagel Ltd, St.Andrews House, St.Andrews Road, Avonmouth, Bristol, BS11 9DQ Tel: 0117-982 7101 Fax: 0117-982 4606 E-mail: knbrs.fa@kuehne-nagel.com

L B Freight Ltd, 36 Prescott Street, Halifax, West Yorkshire, HX1 2QW Tel: (01422) 351217 Fax: (01422) 330209 E-mail: sales@lbfreight.co.uk

Laser Vision, 52 North Street, Bedminster, Bristol, BS3 1HJ Tel: 0117-963 2963 E-mail: laservisioncouk@aol.com

Linc Freight Management, 8 Capital Industrial Centre, Fulmar Way, Wickford, Essex, SS11 8YW Tel: (01438) 746766 Fax: (01438) 369125 E-mail: linc@lincfreight.co.uk

Maina Freight Forwarders plc, 5 Featherstone Industrial Estate, Dominion Road, Southall, Middlesex, UB2 5DP Tel: (020) 8843 1977 Fax: (020) 8571 5628E-mail: info@maina.com

Menlow Worldwide, Unit 19 Airlinks Industrial Estate, Spitfire Way, Heston, Hounslow, TW5 9NR Tel: (020) 8260 6000 Fax: (020) 8260 6170 E-mail: stewartinnes@menlowworldwide.com

▶ MJ Freight Solutions Ltd, 7 Bristol Close, Rayleigh, Essex, SS6 9RZ Tel: 01268 780637 Fax: 01268 780653 E-mail: Jo@mjfreightsolutions.co.uk

Moonbridge Air Project S A Freight Ltd, Unit 9, Ascot Road, Bedfont, Feltham, Middlesex, TW14 8QH Tel: (01784) 259555 Fax: (01784) 259599 E-mail: administrator@moonbridge.co.uk

O R T Forwarding Ltd, Unit 24 Bourne Road Industrial Park, Bourne Road, Dartford, DA1 4BZ Tel: (01322) 555486 Fax: (01322) 528528 E-mail: enquiries@ort.co.uk

▶ On-Line Shipping Ltd, Unit 3 Argonaut Park, Galleymead Road, Colnbrook, Slough, SL3 0EN Tel: (01753) 687702 Fax: (01753) 684404 E-mail: paul@onlineshippingltd.co.uk

P E L Agencies Ltd, 7 Longbridge Industrial Park, Floating Bridge Road, Southampton, SO14 3FL Tel: (023) 8022 8934 Fax: (023) 8022 4389 E-mail: info@pelagencies.co.uk

Panalpina World Transport Ltd, Great South West Road, Feltham, Middlesex, TW14 8NE Tel: (020) 8587 9000 Fax: (020) 8587 9200

Pegasus, 86-92 Stewarts Road, London, SW8 4UG Tel: (020) 7622 2222 Fax: (020) 7622 1616 E-mail: sales@pegasus-couriers.com

AIR FREIGHT FORWARDERS/ FORWARDING AGENTS – *continued*

▶ Peters & May Ltd, Prysmian House, Dew Lane, Eastleigh, Hampshire, SO50 9PX Tel: (023) 8048 0501 Fax: (01752) 775699 E-mail: enquiriesplh@petersandmay.com

Phoenix International Freight Services, Trent Lane Indust Estate Unit 2, Sycamore Road, Castle Donnington, Derby, DE74 2LL Tel: (01332) 817350 Fax: (01332) 850530

Pinnacle International Freight Ltd, C Mortimer Road, Narborough, Leicester, LE19 2GA Tel: 0116-286 6566 Fax: 0116-286 7928 E-mail: lecmail@pif.co.uk

John Pipe Ltd, Mayflower Close, Chandler's Ford, Eastleigh, Hampshire, SO53 4AR Tel: (023) 8036 0100 Fax: (023) 8027 3080 E-mail: sales@johnpipe.co.uk

Power Packing Export Services Ltd, Pinhoe Trading Estate, Venny Bridge, Exeter, EX4 8JN Tel: (01392) 468088 Fax: (01392) 467987 E-mail: mail@powerpacking.co.uk

▶ Premier, 24 Brunel Way, Fareham, Hampshire, PO15 5SD Tel: (01489) 565577 Fax: (01489) 565588 E-mail: sales@psap.co.uk

R H Group, Building 110, East Midlands Airport, Castle Donington, Derby, DE74 2SA Tel: (01332) 811348 Fax: (01332) 811938 E-mail: penny.rowe@rhfreight.co.uk

R & T Shipping Ltd, 2nd Floor, Holegate House, Holegate Court, Western Road, Romford, RM1 3JS Tel: (0870) 7745612 Fax: (0870) 7745602

Redbourn International Forwarding Ltd, 43A Adelaide Street, Luton, LU1 5BD Tel: (01582) 425611 Fax: (01582) 405705 E-mail: office@redbourninternational.co.uk

Redfern Transports Ltd, Mount Street Mill, Mount Street, Bradford, West Yorkshire, BD3 9RJ Tel: (01274) 392721 Fax: (01274) 370851 E-mail: sales@redferntransports.co.uk

Regional Freight Services Ltd, Airport Business Centre, Regional House, Norwich, NR6 6BS Tel: (01603) 414125 Fax: (01603) 402542 E-mail: rfs@regfrt.co.uk

S D V UK Ltd, Building 673, Spur Road, Feltham, Middlesex, TW14 0SL Tel: (020) 8831 4900 Fax: (020) 8890 1111 E-mail: sdvlhr@sdv.co.uk

Samfreight Ltd, Bath Road, West Drayton, Middlesex, UB7 0DB Tel: (020) 8750 2300 Fax: (020) 8750 2301 E-mail: lee.george@samfreight.co.uk

Sandrair International Ltd, 18 Shield Road, Ashford, Middlesex, TW15 1AU Tel: (01784) 242081 Fax: (01784) 243335 E-mail: info@heathrow.sandrair.com

Schenkers Ltd, Schenkers House, Great South West Road, Feltham, Middlesex, TW14 8NT Tel: (020) 8890 8899 Fax: (020) 8751 0141 E-mail: enquires@schenker.com

▶ Sea Wing Cargo Services Ltd, Unit 1, Lakeside Industrial Estate, Colnbrook By Pass, Colnbrook, Slough, SL3 0ED Tel: (01753) 763488 Fax: (01753) 763489 E-mail: admin@seawing.co.uk

Sealandair Transport Co., 101 Stephenson Street, London, E16 4SA Tel: (020) 7511 2288 Fax: (020) 7511 1466 E-mail: frt@sealandair.com

Service Air Cargo Ltd, Dyce Airport, Dyce, Aberdeen, AB21 0PB Tel: (01224) 770518 Fax: (01224) 724737 E-mail: abzcargo@servisair.co.uk

▶ Shuttle Bridge Logistics Ltd, Unit 15, Angerstein Business Park, Horn Lane, Greenwich, London, SE10 0RT Tel: 020 84655757 Fax: 020 84655858 E-mail: shuttlebridgeuk@yahoo.co.uk

▶ Spanish Removals, Hellman House, Lakeside Estate, Colnbrook, Slough, SL3 0EL Tel: (0870) 4202950 Fax: (08704) 202951 E-mail: info@spanishremovals.com

Spatial Air Brokers & Forwarders Ltd, Unit 7c Willow Farm Business Park, Castle Donington, Derby, DE74 2TW Tel: (01332) 850925 Fax: (01332) 812427 E-mail: sales@the-spatial-group.com

Staley Radford & Co. Ltd, Blackburn House, 22-26 Eastern Road, Romford, RM1 3PJ Tel: (01708) 737333 Fax: (01708) 737334

Sutch & Searle Shipping Ltd, Highwood Road, Writtle, Chelmsford, CM1 3PT Tel: (01245) 421770 Fax: (01245) 422734 E-mail: keith.davis@sutchanddsearle.com

T S International Freight Forwarders Ltd, Halesfield 19, Telford, Shropshire, TF7 4QT Tel: (01952) 586467 Fax: (01952) 680048 E-mail: info@tsinternational.com

Team Relocations plc, Drury Way, Brentpark, Neasden, London, NW10 0JN Tel: (020) 8784 0100 Fax: (020) 8451 0061

U T I Ltd, Skyway 14, Calder Way, Colnbrook, Slough, SL3 0BQ Tel: (01753) 681212 Fax: (01753) 764450

Unitrans International Ltd, Woodfield House, Hatmill Lane, Brenchley, Tonbridge, Kent, TN12 7AE Tel: (01892) 723270 Fax: (01892) 724188 E-mail: robert-fogg@unitrans.fsnet.co.uk

Vanstead, Unit 6 Manor Farm Road, Birmingham, B11 2HT Tel: 0121-707 4929 Fax: 0121-707 2155 E-mail: office@vanstead.com

Walker Freight Services Ltd, 8-9 Blackthorne Cresent, Colnbrook, Slough, SL3 0QR Tel: (01753) 683288 Fax: (01753) 681917 E-mail: sales@walker-freight.com

Wells & Root Ltd, Parker Drive, Leicester, LE4 0JP Tel: 0116-235 3535 Fax: 0116-235 3910 E-mail: enquiries@wellsandroot.co.uk

AIR FREIGHT HANDLING EQUIPMENT

Owen Holland Engineering Ltd, Holland Way, Blandford Forum, Dorset, DT11 7TA Tel: (01258) 452461 Fax: (01258) 480169 E-mail: sales@owenholland.com

AIR FRESHENERS

▶ Admart Promotions, Saracens House Business Centre, 25 St. Margarets Green, Ipswich, IP4 2BN Tel: (01473) 735094 Fax: (01473) 735121 E-mail: sales@admartpromotions.co.uk

Bunzl Cleaning & Hygiene Supplies, Bone Lane, Newbury, Berkshire, RG14 5SH Tel: (01635) 528550 Fax: (01635) 528822 E-mail: newbury@bunzlchs.co.uk

Millwood Marketing, Fivefield House, Bennetts Road, Keresley End, Coventry, CV7 8HX Tel: (024) 7633 1433 Fax: (024) 7633 5663

AIR GUN PELLETS

Lincoln Jeffries Ltd, Summer Lane, Birmingham, B19 3TH Tel: 0121-359 3343 Fax: 0121-359 3343

Keens Guns, 117 Bridgend Road, Aberkenfig, Bridgend, Mid Glamorgan, CF32 9AP Tel: (01656) 720807 Fax: (01656) 724889 E-mail: sales@keenstackleandguns.co.uk

Lanes Pelletts Ltd, The Raylor Centre, James Street, York, YO10 3DW Tel: (01904) 430051 Fax: (01904) 765483

Portsmouth Gun Centre, 295 London Road, Portsmouth, PO2 9HF Tel: (023) 9266 0574 Fax: (023) 9264 4666

AIR GUNS

Keens Guns, 117 Bridgend Road, Aberkenfig, Bridgend, Mid Glamorgan, CF32 9AP Tel: (01656) 720807 Fax: (01656) 724889 E-mail: sales@keenstackleandguns.co.uk

AIR HANDLING EQUIPMENT

Air Design Developments Ltd, Unit 37 Westley Grange, Chartwell Drive, Wigston, Leics, LE18 2FL Tel: 0116-281 3491 Fax: 0116-288 5428

Air Handlers Northern Ltd, Bute Street, Salford, M50 1DU Tel: 0161-745 8888 Fax: 0161-745 9900 E-mail: sales@airhandlers.com

Air Handling Equipment Ltd, 23 Cotton Street, Liverpool, L3 7DY Tel: 0151-236 2910 Fax: 0151-236 2910 E-mail: sales@ahe.co.uk

Air Vent Technology Ltd, Unit 1 Regents Court, Walworth Industrial Estate, Andover, Hampshire, SP10 5NX Tel: (01264) 356415 Fax: (01264) 337854 E-mail: avtltd@btopenworld.com

Birmingham Air Conditioning Ltd, Firswood Road, Birmingham, B33 0TG Tel: 0121-786 1842 Fax: 0121-786 2689E-mail: bhamair@aol.com

Daikin Airconditioning UK Ltd, The Heights, Brooklands, Weybridge, Surrey, KT13 0NY Tel: (0845) 6419000 Fax: (0845) 6419009 E-mail: marketing@daikin.co.uk

Owen Holland Engineering Ltd, Holland Way, Blandford Forum, Dorset, DT11 7TA Tel: (01258) 452461 Fax: (01258) 480169 E-mail: sales@owenholland.com

Hushon UK Ltd, A6 Railway Triangle, Walton Road, Drayton, Portsmouth, PO6 1TN Tel: (023) 9232 4335 Fax: (023) 9232 4348 E-mail: sales@hushonuk.co.uk

Imofa UK Ltd, New Coach House, 21 Grange Way, Colchester, CO2 8HF Tel: (01206) 505909 Fax: (01206) 794095 E-mail: sales@imofa.co.uk

Nationwide Air Systems Ltd, Bolney Grange Industrial Park, Bolney, Haywards Heath, West Sussex, RH17 5PB Tel: (01444) 230308

North Sea Ventilation Ltd, West Carr Lane, Hull, HU7 0BW Tel: (01482) 834050 Fax: (01482) 834060 E-mail: enquiries@nsv.co.uk

Reycol S V C Ltd, Unit 6 Lagley Wharfe, Kings Langley, Watford, WD18 9EQ Tel: (01923) 262522 E-mail: reycolsvc@aol.com

Scientaire Thermal Systems Ltd, 40C Heath Road, Twickenham, TW1 4BZ Tel: (020) 8891 0450 Fax: (020) 8892 9168

V E S Andover Ltd, Eagle Close, Chandler Ford Industrial Estate, Eastleigh, Hampshire, SO53 4NF Tel: (0870) 2404340 Fax: (0870) 2404550 E-mail: vesltd@ves.co.uk

AIR HANDLING EQUIPMENT MAINTENANCE OR REPAIR

A M P Wire Ltd, Sun Iron Works, Ward Street, Chadderton, Oldham, OL9 9EX Tel: 0161-620 7250 Fax: 0161-688 5566 E-mail: pam@ampwire.co.uk

Bells Heat Transfer Ltd, Factory Road, Blaydon-on-Tyne, Tyne & Wear, NE21 5SA Tel: 0191-414 6789 Fax: 0191-414 5890 E-mail: bells.heat.transfer@talk21.com

AIR HEATERS, *See also headings for particular types*

Broughton Electroair Products, Clive Works, Edward Street, Redditch, Worcestershire, B97 6HA Tel: (01527) 597567 Fax: (01527) 67603 E-mail: sales@broughtoneap.com

F A T I International Ltd, 9 Wight Way, Selsey, Chichester, West Sussex, PO20 0UD Tel: (01243) 606007 Fax: (01243) 606007 E-mail: fatiint@btconnect.com

Process Heating Services, 12 Noddington Avenue, Lichfield, Staffordshire, WS14 9NQ Tel: (01543) 432661 Fax: (01543) 432782 E-mail: sales@processheatingservices.com

Winterwarm UK Ltd, Unit H3, Taylor Industrial Estate, Risley, Warrington, WA3 6BL Tel: (01925) 765799 Fax: (01925) 762996 E-mail: enquiries@winterwarm.com

AIR HIGH PRESSURE VALVES

Dynamic Controls Ltd, Union Street, Royton, Oldham, OL2 5JD Tel: 0161-633 3933 Fax: 0161-633 4113 E-mail: sales@dynamiccontrols.co.uk

Hale Hamilton Ltd, Cowley Road, Uxbridge, Middlesex, UB8 2AF Tel: (01895) 236525 Fax: (01895) 231407 E-mail: enquiries@halehamilton.com

AIR IONISERS

Group 100 Electronics, 145 Avon Road, Worcester, WR4 9AH Tel: (01905) 22875 Fax: (01905) 22875

AIR JACKS

Load Moving Systems, Pitts House, Grange Road, Duxford, Cambridge, CB2 4QE Tel: (01223) 839930 Fax: (01223) 839940 E-mail: info@loadmovingsystems.co.uk

AIR KNIFE DRYERS

Secomak Holdings Ltd, Unit 330, Centennial Park, Elstree, Borehamwood, Hertfordshire, WD6 3TJ Tel: (020) 8732 1300 Fax: (020) 8732 1301 E-mail: sales@secomak.com

AIR KNIVES

C P A Ltd, Calderhead Road, Shotts, Lanarkshire, ML7 4EQ Tel: (01501) 825024 Fax: (01501) 825029 E-mail: cpa@cpa-group.com

Lechler Ltd, 1 Fell Street, Sheffield, S9 2TP Tel: 0114-249 2020 Fax: 0114-249 3600 E-mail: info@lechler.com

Meech Air Technology, 2 Network Point, Range Road, Witney, Oxfordshire, OX29 0YN Tel: (01993) 706700 Fax: (01993) 776977 E-mail: sales@meech.com

Spraying Systems Ltd, Farnham Business Park, Weydon Lane, Farnham, Surrey, GU9 8QT Tel: (01252) 727200 Fax: (01252) 712211 E-mail: info.uk@spray.com

AIR LINE COMPANIES

Aeroflot Russian International Airlines, 70 Piccadilly, London, W1J 8SB Tel: (020) 7355 2233 Fax: (020) 7355 2323 E-mail: infres@aeroflot.co.uk

Air Algerie, 10 Baker Street, London, W1U 3BT Tel: (020) 7486 8068 Fax: (020) 7487 5709

Air Contractors, Ema Cargo West, East Midland Int Airport, Castle Donington, Derby, DE74 2TR Tel: (01332) 857850 Fax: (01332) 857859 E-mail: info@aircontractors.com

Air Mauritius, 49 Conduit Street, London, W1S 2YS Tel: (020) 7434 4375 Fax: (020) 7439 4101 E-mail: reservations@airmauritiusuk.com

Alitalia, 2a Cains Lane, Feltham, Middlesex, TW14 9RL Tel: (020) 8745 8200 Fax: (020) 8745 8299 E-mail: sales@alitalia.co.uk

Austrian Airlines, 10 Wardour St, London, W1D 6BQ Tel: (020) 7434 7380 Fax: (020) 7434 7363

Belfast International Airport Ltd, Belfast International Airport, Belfast, BT29 4AB Tel: (028) 9442 2888 Fax: (028) 9445 2096 E-mail: info@bial.co.uk

British Airways plc, PO Box 365, West Drayton, Middlesex, UB7 0GB Tel: (020) 8759 5511 Fax: (020) 8738 9800

Cathay Pacific Airlines, 3 Shortlands, London, W6 8AQ Tel: (020) 8834 8888 Fax: (020) 8741 6118 E-mail: sales@cathaypacific.com

Continental Airlines, Beulah Court, Albert Road, Horley, Surrey, RH6 7HP Tel: (0845) 6076760 Fax: (01293) 773726

D A S Air Cargo Ltd, North Elm Park Court Tilgate Forest Business Centre, Crawley, West Sussex, RH11 9BP Tel: (01293) 540303 Fax: (01293) 514036 E-mail: sales@dasair.com

Egyptair, 296 Regent Street, London, W1B 3PH Tel: (020) 7580 5477 Fax: (020) 7637 4328 E-mail: habib@egyptair.com.eg

El Al Israel Airlines, 16 Upper Woburn Place, London, WC1H 0AF Tel: (020) 7121 1560 Fax: (020) 7121 1470

Hawaiian Airlines Reservations, The Office at Pond View, Downyard, Compton Pauncefoot, Yeovil, Somerset, BA22 7EL Tel: (0844) 4844336 Fax: (01933) 315702 E-mail: reservations@hawaiianair.co.uk

Iran Air, 73 Piccadilly, London, W1J 8QX Tel: (020) 7493 8618 Fax: (020) 7408 1360

Jat Airways, 7 Dering Street, London, W1S 1AE Tel: (020) 7629 6629 Fax: (020) 7629 6500 E-mail: sales@jatlondon.com

Korean Air, 67-68 Piccadilly, London, W1J 0HJ Tel: (020) 7495 2299 Fax: (020) 7495 1616 E-mail: sales@koreanair.com

Logan Air Ltd, Kirkwall Airport, Kirkwall Aerodrome, Kirkwall, Orkney, KW15 1TH Tel: (01856) 872420 Fax: (01856) 872420

▶ Malev Hungarian Airlines P.L.C., 22-25A First Floor, Sackville St, London, W1S 3DR Tel: (0870) 9090577 Fax: (020) 7734 8116 E-mail: london@malev.hu

Monarch Airlines Ltd, Prospect House, Prospect Way, London Luton Airport, Luton, LU2 9NU Tel: (01582) 400000 Fax: (01582) 398323 E-mail: reservation@monarchairlines.com

Northern Executive Aviation Ltd, Hangar 7, Western Maintenance Area, Manchester Airport, Manchester, M90 5NE Tel: 0161-436 6666 Fax: 0161-436 3450 E-mail: info@northernexec.com

Northwest Air Lines Inc, Oakfield Court, Consort Way, Horley, Surrey, RH6 7AF Tel: (01293) 778400 Fax: (01293) 824871

Olympic Airways, 11 Conduit Street, London, W1S 2LP Tel: (0870) 6060460 Fax: (020) 7629 9891

Pakistan International Airlines, 1-15 King Street, London, W6 9HR Tel: (020) 8741 8066 Fax: (020) 8741 9376 E-mail: longrpk@piac.com.pk

Qantas Airways Ltd, Qantas House, 395-403 King Street, London, W6 9NJ Tel: (020) 8846 0466 Fax: (020) 8746 3317

Royal Air Maroc, 205 Regent Street, London, W1B 4HB Tel: (020) 7439 4361 Fax: (020) 7734 6183 E-mail: ramlondon@btinternet.com

Royal Jordanian Airlines, 32 Brook Street, London, W1K 5DL Tel: (020) 7878 6444 Fax: (020) 7629 4069

Singapore Airlines, 578-586 Chiswick High Road, London, W4 5RP Tel: (020) 8563 6767 Fax: (020) 8563 6753

South African Airways, St. Georges House, 61 Conduit Street, London, W1S 2NE Tel: (020) 7312 5005 Fax: (020) 7312 5008 E-mail: carriehopkins@lon.flysaa.com

Syrian Arab Airlines, 27 Albemarle Street, London, W1S 4BJ Tel: (020) 7493 2851 Fax: (020) 7493 2119

Thai Airways International P.L.C., 41 Albemarle Street, London, W1S 4BF Tel: (020) 7491 7953 Fax: (020) 7409 1463

Turkish Airlines, 125 Pall Mall, London, SW1Y 5EA Tel: (020) 7766 9300 Fax: (020) 7976 1733 E-mail: turkishairlines.uk@btinternet.com

Virgin Atlantic Airways Ltd, The Office, Manor Royal, Crawley, West Sussex, RH10 9NU Tel: (01293) 616161 Fax: (01293) 561721 E-mail: sales@virgin-atlantic.com

Volga-Dnepr UK Ltd, Endeavour House, Coopers End Road, London Stansted Airport, Stansted, Essex, CM24 1HA Tel: (01279) 661166 Fax: (01279) 661103 E-mail: dennis.gliznoutsa@volga-dnepr.co.uk

AIR MOTORS

Briggs Bros Engineers Ltd, 39 Walkers Road, Moons Moat North Industrial Estate, Redditch, Worcestershire, B98 9HD Tel: (01527) 66779 Fax: (01527) 596130 E-mail: sales@briggsairmotors.com

Dynatork Air Motors Ltd, Merchant Drive, Hertford, SG13 7BL Tel: (01992) 501900 Fax: (01992) 509890 E-mail: dynatork@huco.com

Tool Repair Services, Unit 51 The Sir Robert Peel Mill, Mill Lane, Fazeley, Tamworth, Staffordshire, B78 3QD Tel: (01827) 286322 Fax: (01827) 259101 E-mail: toolrepairs@hotmail.com

AIR OPERATED DOUBLE DIAPHRAGM (AODD) PUMPS

Interco Lubrication Services, 28 Harwood Court, Riverside Park Industrial Estate, Middlesbrough, Cleveland, TS2 1PU Tel: (01642) 247157 Fax: (01642) 247157 E-mail: chas_ophield@lineone.net

▶ Pump Supply & Repair Group, Armstrong Hall, Wharton Rd, Winsford, Cheshire, CW7 3AD Tel: 0161-794 8038 Fax: 0161-794 8052 E-mail: salesc@pumpgroup.co.uk

Tapflo UK Ltd, B The Apex Centre, Church Lane, Colden Common, Winchester, Hampshire, SO21 1TN Tel: (01962) 717131 Fax: (01962) 717130 E-mail: mick@tapflo-demon.co.uk

Tri Ark, Burnham Business Park, Springfield Road, Burnham-on-Crouch, Essex, CM0 8TE Tel: (01621) 781144 Fax: (01621) 781155 E-mail: sales@tri-ark.com

AIR PRESSURE CONTROL EQUIPMENT

Apreco Ltd, Bruff Works, Suckley, Worcester, WR6 5DR Tel: (01886) 884090 Fax: (01886) 884099 E-mail: info@apreco.co.uk

AIR PUMPS

G B M Products, 4 Octavian Way, Team Valley Trading Estate, Gateshead, Tyne & Wear, NE11 0HZ Tel: 0191-487 8004 Fax: 0191-487 1655
E-mail: info@gbmproducts.sagehost.co.uk

Tri Ark, Burnham Business Park, Springfield Road, Burnham-on-Crouch, Essex, CM0 8TE Tel: (01621) 781144 Fax: (01621) 781155
E-mail: sales@tri-ark.com

Viking Pump Ltd, Viking House, Dannemore Drive, Sheffield, S9 5DF Tel: 0114-244 7701 Fax: 0114-243 2614

AIR PURIFICATION/ DEODORISING PLANT/ EQUIPMENT

Aircare, PO Box 2425, Slough, SL2 1WF Tel: (020) 8566 7000 Fax: (01753) 518167

John Godrich, Pellow House, Old Street, Ludlow, Shropshire, SY8 1NU Tel: (01584) 873153 Fax: (01584) 872424
E-mail: johngodrich@johngodrich.co.uk

Hanovia Uv Ltd, 145 Farnham Road, Slough, SL1 4XB Tel: (01753) 515300 Fax: (01753) 534277 E-mail: sales@hanovia.com

AIR PURIFIERS

E H S International Ltd, E H S House, Lyons Road, Trafford Park, Manchester, M17 1RN Tel: 0161-872 4541 Fax: 0161-872 5491
E-mail: enquiries@ehs-intl.co.uk

Sly Filters Europe Ltd, 16 The Warren, East Goscote, Leicester, LE7 3XA Tel: 0116-260 8187 Fax: 0116-264 0543
E-mail: sly@ridgep.fsbusiness.co.uk

AIR QUALITY MONITORING EQUIPMENT

Air Quality Assurance, 1 Dunnings Lane, Rochester, Kent, ME1 1YB Tel: (01634) 832895 Fax: (01634) 832882

Codel International Ltd, Station Yard, Station Road, Bakewell, Derbyshire, DE45 1GE Tel: (01629) 814351 Fax: (0870) 0566307
E-mail: sales@codel.co.uk

Resmar Ltd, 39 Dean Street, Winsford, Cheshire, CW7 1HG Tel: (01606) 863399 Fax: (01606) 558200 E-mail: wyn@resmar.co.uk

AIR RECEIVERS/RESERVOIRS

A J Metal Products Ltd, Cookley Wharf Industrial Estate, Bay 11, Leys Rd, Brierley Hill, West Midlands, DY5 3UP Tel: (01384) 74301 Fax: (01384) 485772
E-mail: sales@ajmetals.co.uk

C P E (Pressure Vessels) Ltd, Apollo, Lichfield Road Industrial Estate, Tamworth, Staffordshire, B79 7TA Tel: 01827 68710 Fax: (01827) 54396
E-mail: sales@cpe-ltd.com

Hartley & Sugden, Atlas Works, Gibbet Street, Halifax, West Yorkshire, HX1 4DB Tel: (01422) 355651 Fax: (01422) 359636

Hoval Ltd, North Gate, Newark, Nottinghamshire, NG24 1JN Tel: (01636) 672711 Fax: (01636) 673532 E-mail: boilersales@hoval.co.uk

Rednal Industries Ltd, Mile Oak Industrial Estate, Maesbury Road, Oswestry, Shropshire, SY10 8GA Tel: (01691) 659601 Fax: (01691) 655021 E-mail: sales@rednall.co.uk

AIR SAMPLING EQUIPMENT

Data Loop Ltd, Beare Green Court, Dorking, Surrey, RH5 4SL Tel: +44 (0) 1306 711088 Fax: +44 (0) 1306 713108
E-mail: sales@data-loop.co.uk

Quantitech Ltd, 3 Old Wolverton Road, Old Wolverton, Milton Keynes, MK12 5NP Tel: (01908) 227722 Fax: (01908) 227733
E-mail: quant@quantitech.co.uk

AIR SEPARATORS

Linde Cryoplants Ltd, Blackwater Way, Aldershot, Hampshire, GU12 4DR Tel: (01252) 331351 Fax: (01252) 343062
E-mail: info@linde-lcl.com

AIR SET IRON CASTINGS

J T & E Castings Ltd, Leyland Mill Lane, Wigan, Lancashire, WN1 2SA Tel: (01942) 241966 Fax: (01942) 492136
E-mail: enquiries@jte-castings.co.uk

Thomas Dudley Group Ltd, PO Box 28, Dudley, West Midlands, DY1 4SN Tel: 0121-557 5411 Fax: 0121-557 5345
E-mail: info@thomasdudley.co.uk

AIR SHAFTS

Fife Tidland Ltd, 70-72 Manchester Road, Denton, Manchester, M34 3PR Tel: 0161-320 2000 Fax: 0161-320 4513
E-mail: sales_uk@maxcess.de

AIR SHOWERS, CLEAN ROOM PRE-ENTRY

Cleanroom Supplies Ltd, Violet House, Cumrew, Carlisle, CA8 9DD Tel: (01768) 896800 Fax: 01228 830100

AIR SKATES

Load Moving Systems, Pitts House, Grange Road, Duxford, Cambridge, CB2 4QE Tel: (01223) 839930 Fax: (01223) 839940
E-mail: info@loadmovingsystems.co.uk

AIR SPRINGS

A & B Pneumatics, 117 Halftown Road, Lisburn, County Antrim, BT27 5RF Tel: (028) 9268 3440 Fax: (028) 9268 3440
E-mail: abpneumaticsltd@hotmail.com

AIR TO AIR HEAT EXCHANGERS

▶ Greenbox Heat Exchangers, 11 Wassage Way, Hampton Lovett, Droitwich, Worcestershire, WR9 0NX Tel: (01905) 777050 Fax: (01905) 777051 E-mail: sales@greenbox.uk.com

AIR TOOL REPAIR

▶ DM Tyre Supplies, In2Connect house, Acton Road, Nottingham, NG10 1NJ Tel: 07779 765614 Fax: 0115 9284912
E-mail: dmtyrsupplies@btopenworld.com

AIR TRAFFIC CONTROL (ATC) SIMULATORS

A M S, John Sutcliffe Building, Donibristle Industrial Park, Hillend, Dunfermline, Fife, KY11 9JX Tel: (01383) 821921 Fax: (01383) 824227

Pandect Precision Components Ltd, Wellington Road, High Wycombe, Buckinghamshire, HP12 3PX Tel: (01494) 526303 Fax: (01494) 465557
E-mail: enquiries@pandect.demon.co.uk

AIR TRAFFIC CONTROL (ATC) TRAINING

▶ Copperchase Ltd, 1 Ventura Centre, Ventura Place, Poole, Dorset, BH16 5SW Tel: (01202) 774500 Fax: (01202) 774540
E-mail: support@copperchase.co.uk

AIR TRANSPORT CONSULTANTS OR ECONOMIC ADVISERS

Amba Forwarding Ltd, 6 Trafalgar Business Centre, River Road, Barking, Essex, IG11 0JU Tel: (020) 8591 1600 Fax: (020) 8591 1700
E-mail: info@ambaforwarding.com

Avintair Ltd, 150 Regent St, London, W1B 5SJ Tel: (020) 7439 4767 Fax: (020) 7439 4067

Baines Simmons Ltd, Fairoaks Airport, Chobham, Woking, Surrey, GU24 8HX Tel: (01276) 855412 Fax: (01276) 856285
E-mail: bob@bainessimmons.com

▶ Beaky.net, 35 Vaughan Drive, Kemsley, Sittingbourne, Kent, ME10 2UB Tel: (07729) 163996 Fax: (01795) 438113

Business Air Centre Ltd, The Terminal Building, Gloucestershire Airport, Cheltenham, Gloucestershire, GL51 6SR Tel: (01452) 859500 Fax: (01452) 715010
E-mail: charter@businessaircentre.co.uk

Ifs Global Logistics Ltd, I F S Logistics Park, Seven Mile Straight, Muckamore, Antrim, BT41 4QE Tel: (028) 9446 4211 Fax: (028) 9446 7723 E-mail: sales@antrim.ifsgroup.com

Intavia Ltd, 1 The Brunel Centre, Newton Road, Crawley, West Sussex, RH10 9TU Tel: (01293) 544706 Fax: (01293) 615800
E-mail: aia@intavia.co.uk

J E Bernard & Co. Ltd, Unit 4-5 Lakeside Industrial Estate, Colnbrook By Passage, Colnbrook, Slough, SL3 0EE Tel: (01753) 683161 Fax: (01753) 681624
E-mail: corporate@bernardgroup.plc.uk

Virgin Atlantic Airways Ltd, The Office, Manor Royal, Crawley, West Sussex, RH10 9NU Tel: (01293) 616161 Fax: (01293) 561721
E-mail: sales@virgin-atlantic.com

Vivair Ltd, South View House, 252 High Street, Croydon, CR0 1NF Tel: (020) 8225 1120 Fax: (020) 8260 0054
E-mail: laura.davies@dialaflight.co.uk

AIR VALVE ACTUATORS

Intex Controls Ltd, Tonbridge Road, Hadlow, Tonbridge, Kent, TN11 0AH Tel: (01732) 850360 Fax: (01732) 852133
E-mail: sales@stonel.impex.com

AIR VENTS

▶ Boatcoat, Fox House, Whimple Street, Plymouth, PL1 2DH Tel: (01752) 227333 Fax: (01752) 227333
E-mail: sales@boatcoat.co.uk

▶ Seconsolar Ltd, Alexandra Building Business & Innovation Centre, Wearfield, Sunderland Enterprise Park, Sunderland, SR5 2TH Tel: 0191-516 6554 Fax: 0191-516 6558
E-mail: info@seconsolar.com

AIR-SEA RESCUE EQUIPMENT

Beaufort Air Sea Equipment Ltd, Beaufort Road, Birkenhead, Merseyside, CH41 1HQ Tel: 0151-652 9151 Fax: 0151-653 6639
E-mail: cgreen@rfdbeaufort.com

▶ Specialist Training Consultants Ltd, The Sycamores, 7 Rugby Close, Seaford, East Sussex, BN25 3PQ Tel: (01323) 873043 Fax: (01323) 872308
E-mail: pgwilliam@aol.com

AIRBORNE ODOUR ABSORPTION SYSTEMS

Mist-Air Environmental Systems, PO Box 10, Oswestry, Shropshire, SY10 9JF Tel: (07071) 666000 Fax: (01691) 828499
E-mail: info@mist-air.co.uk

AIRBRUSHES

Airbrush Co Ltd, 7 Marlborough Road, Lancing, West Sussex, BN15 8UF Tel: (0870) 0660445 Fax: (08700) 660817
E-mail: sales@airbrushes.com

AIRCRAFT ACCESSORIES

A E M Ltd, Unit 6001, Taylors End, Long Border Road, Stansted Airport, Stansted, Essex, CM24 1RB Tel: (01279) 680030 Fax: (01279) 680040 E-mail: info@aem.co.uk

Airbase Interiors (U K) Ltd, Vincent Street, Crewe, CW1 4AA Tel: (01270) 581556 Fax: (01270) 251407
E-mail: sales@airbaseservices.co.uk

Airbase Services UK Ltd, Gatwick Gate Industrial Estate, Lowfield Heath, Crawley, West Sussex, RH11 0TG Tel: (01293) 553337 Fax: (01293) 530600
E-mail: reception@airbase-interiors.com

Aviall Product Services Ltd, Unit 10 Polygon Business Centre, Blackthorne Road, Colnbrook, Slough, SL3 0QT Tel: (01753) 689090 Fax: (01753) 680755

Cavendish Resources, 57 Chaldon Road, London, SW6 7NH Tel: (020) 7381 0276 Fax: (020) 7386 8183

AIRCRAFT BRAKING SYSTEMS

▶ Aircraft Braking Systems Europe Ltd, 683-685 Stirling Road, Slough, SL1 4ST Tel: (01753) 696006 Fax: (01753) 696012
E-mail: awitney@absel.co.uk

AIRCRAFT BROKERS/DEALERS/ TRADERS

The Cabair Group Ltd, Elstree Aerodrome, Elstree, Borehamwood, Hertfordshire, WD6 3AW Tel: (020) 8236 2400 Fax: (020) 8207 0995 E-mail: group@cabair.com

Dolphin Maritime & Aviation Services Ltd, 16 The Broadway, Stanmore, Middlesex, HA7 4DW Tel: (020) 8954 8800 Fax: (020) 8954 8844
E-mail: intfo@dolphin-maritime.com

Skydrift Ltd, Norwich Airport, Norwich, NR6 6EP Tel: (01603) 407424 Fax: (01603) 418687
E-mail: ops@skydrift.co.uk

AIRCRAFT BUILDERS

B N Group Ltd, Bembridge Airport, Bembridge, Isle of Wight, PO35 5PR Tel: (020) 3371 4000 Fax: (01983) 873246
E-mail: customer.services@britten-norman.com

AIRCRAFT CATERING SERVICE VEHICLES

Grease Guardian, Greenbank Industrial Estate, Newry, County Down, BT34 2PB Tel: (028) 3026 6616 Fax: (028) 3026 3233
E-mail: gg@fmenvironmental.com

AIRCRAFT CATERING/GALLEY EQUIPMENT

Falcon Food Service Equipment, PO Box 37, Stirling, FK9 5PY Tel: (01786) 455200 Fax: (01786) 469454
E-mail: info@afefalcon.com

Grease Guardian, Greenbank Industrial Estate, Newry, County Down, BT34 2PB Tel: (028) 3026 6616 Fax: (028) 3026 3233
E-mail: gg@fmenvironmental.com

AIRCRAFT COATINGS/FINISHES

Liverpool Auto Service, Unit 12b Weaver Industrial Estate, Blackburne Street, Liverpool, L19 8JA Tel: 0151-427 5707 Fax: 0151-427 5707

Med-Lab International Ltd, Copeland Street, Derby, DE1 2PU Tel: (01332) 349094 Fax: (01332) 371237
E-mail: sales@med-lab.co.uk

AIRCRAFT COATINGS/FINISHES REMOVAL CONTRACTORS

A I M Group plc, 16 Carlton Cresent, Southampton, SO15 2ES Tel: (023) 8033 5111 Fax: (023) 8022 9733

AIRCRAFT COMPONENT ENGRAVERS

Gem Engraving, 33 Hayes Close, Wimborne, Dorset, BH21 2JJ Tel: (01202) 881907 Fax: (01202) 887691
E-mail: sales@gemengraving.co.uk

AIRCRAFT COMPONENT OVERHAUL SERVICES

▶ Airbase GSE (UK) Ltd, Bedfont Trading Estate, Bedfont Road, Feltham, Middlesex, TW14 8EB Tel: (0870) 2405576 Fax: (020) 8751 0952
E-mail: enquiries@airbasegse.co.uk

AIRCRAFT COMPONENTS

Adams Aviation Supply Co. Ltd, Hunter House Churchill Way, Biggin Hill Airport, Biggin Hill, Westerham, Kent, TN16 3BN Tel: (01959) 576129 Fax: (01959) 576660
E-mail: mail@adamsaviation.com

Aero Dart Ltd, 5 Brook Road, Benfleet, Essex, SS7 5JB Tel: (01268) 566111 Fax: (01268) 565222 E-mail: direct@aerodart.ndirect.co.uk

AIM Composites Ltd, Pembroke Avenue, Waterbeach, Cambridge, CB5 9QR Tel: (01223) 441000 Fax: (01223) 862336
E-mail: sales@aimcomposites.com

Aim Engineering Ltd, Melandra Road, Brookfield, Glossop, Derbyshire, SK13 6JE Tel: (01457) 862505 Fax: (01457) 861753
E-mail: sdada@aimeng.co.uk

Aircraft Components Equipment & Supplies Ltd, 171 Upper Halliford Road, Shepperton, Middlesex, TW17 8SN Tel: (01932) 701417 Fax: (01932) 701419
E-mail: neil@acraftcomponants.co.uk

Almec E A S Ltd, Knowl Piece, Wilbury Way, Hitchin, Hertfordshire, SG4 0TY Tel: (01462) 436330 Fax: (01462) 437160
E-mail: enquiries@almec-eas.com

Autofour Precision Engineering Ltd, 5 Alstone Trading Estate, Alstone Lane, Cheltenham, Gloucestershire, GL51 8HF Tel: (01242) 582064 Fax: (01242) 224374
E-mail: info@autofour.co.uk

Aviation Spares Ltd, 2 Haviland Road, Ferndown Industrial Estate, Wimborne, Dorset, BH21 7RF Tel: (01202) 875336 Fax: (01202) 894290 E-mail: sales@aviation-spares.co.uk

Aviation Tool Corporation P.L.C, Airport Works, Green Lane, Hounslow, TW4 6DE Tel: (020) 8570 9664 Fax: (020) 8570 9660
E-mail: atctools@aol.com

B H W Components Ltd, 1a-2b Unit, Worthington Way, Wigan, Lancashire, WN3 6XE Tel: (01942) 821205 Fax: (01942) 821377
E-mail: info@hampson-industries.plc.uk

AIRCRAFT COMPONENTS – *continued*

Boldvale Engineering Ltd, Unit 15 Cambridge Industrial Estate Montague Road, Hanwell, London, W7 3PG Tel: (020) 8840 2398 Fax: (020) 8566 3125 E-mail: john.dwight@boldvaleeng.co.uk
Bramlands Aviation Ltd, Bramlands Stables, Bramlands Lane, Woodmancote, Henfield, West Sussex, BN5 9TQ Tel: (01273) 494774 Fax: (01273) 494799 E-mail: sales@bramlands.com
C A V Aerospace Ltd, Unit 11, Ashville Way, Whetstone, Leicester, LE8 6NU Tel: 0116-284 1520 Fax: 0116-286 7493 E-mail: sales@cav-aerospace.net
Chelton Ltd, 4th Avenue, Chelton Centre Fieldhouse Lane, Marlow, Buckinghamshire, SL7 1TF Tel: (01628) 472072 Fax: (01628) 482255 E-mail: mkt@chelton.co.uk
Cobham Composites Ltd, Davey House, Gelders Ha, Shepshed, Loughborough, Leicestershire, LE12 9NH Tel: (01509) 504541 Fax: (01509) 507563
Commercial Aerospace Services Co. Ltd, Aviation Centre, Star Estate, Horsham, West Sussex, RH13 8RA Tel: (01403) 711444 Fax: (01403) 711582 E-mail: judith@casco.aero
Eaton Corporation, 2 Broad Ground Road, Redditch, Worcestershire, B98 8YS Tel: (01527) 517555 Fax: (01527) 517556 E-mail: paulsmith@eaton.com
Electro-mec (Reading) Ltd, 28 Portman Road, Reading, RG30 1EA Tel: 0118-958 2035 Fax: 0118-950 5049 E-mail: info@electromec.co.uk
Field International Ltd, Radfield House, 18-20 Nuffield Road, Nuffield Industrial Estate, Poole, Dorset, BH17 0RB Tel: (01202) 676331 Fax: (01202) 684043 E-mail: sales@fieldinternational.com
Flexal Springs UK, 179 Park Avenue, London, NW10 7XH Tel: (020) 8453 0867 Fax: (020) 8961 9181 E-mail: flexalspringsuk@btconnect.com
Ford Component Manufacturing Ltd, East Side, Tyne Dock, South Shields, Tyne & Wear, NE33 5ST Tel: 0191-454 0141 Fax: 0191-456 0028 E-mail: sales@fordcomps.co.uk
G E Aviation, Kings Avenue, Hamble, Southampton, SO31 4NF Tel: (023) 8045 3371 Fax: (023) 8074 4042 E-mail: sales@smiths-aerospace.com
G K M (Aerospace) Ltd, Unit 2 Wollaston Way, Burnt Mills Industrial Estate, Basildon, Essex, SS13 1DJ Tel: (01268) 727278 Fax: (01268) 725772 E-mail: gkm@gkm-aero.demon.co.uk
G K N Aerospace Transparancy Systems Ltd, Eckersall Road, Birmingham, B38 8SR Tel: 0121-606 4100 Fax: 0121-458 6880
Gardner Aerospace Basildon Ltd, 2-4 Rowhedge Close, Basildon, Essex, SS13 1QQ Tel: (01268) 729311 Fax: (01268) 728951 E-mail: info@gardener-aerospace-basildon.com
Gardner Aerospace Wales Ltd, Forge Industrial Estate, Maesteg, Mid Glamorgan, CF34 0AY Tel: (01656) 812100 Fax: (01656) 812101 E-mail: info@gardner-aerospace.com
Goodrich Corporation Rohr Aero Services, Bae Systems, Building 38, Glasgow Prestwick Intnl Airpor, Prestwick, Ayrshire, KA9 2GW Tel: (01292) 670200 Fax: (01292) 672854 E-mail: info@bfgoodrich.com
Graves Aircraft Components Ltd, 2 Lightning Way, Birmingham, B31 3PJ Tel: 0121-475 5181 Fax: 0121-411 1071
Harmon Precision Grinding, 55 Haviland Road, Ferndown Industrial Estate, Ferndown Industrial Estate, Wimborne, Dorset, BH21 7PY Tel: (01202) 654198 Fax: (01202) 654199 E-mail: info@harmon.co.uk
Hollycroft Engineering Ltd, 7 Teal Business Park, Dodwells Road, Hinckley, Leicestershire, LE10 3BZ Tel: (01455) 635845 Fax: (01455) 250273 E-mail: sales@hollycrofteng.freeserve.co.uk
Hyde Precision Components Ltd, Oldham Street, Denton, Manchester, M34 3SA Tel: 0161-337 9242 Fax: 0161-335 0787 E-mail: sales@hyde-precision.co.uk
Inflite The Jet Centre, Hanger 173, First Avenue, London Stansted Airport, Stansted, Essex, CM24 1RY Tel: (01279) 831000 Fax: (01279) 837900E-mail: swan@stanstead.demon.co.uk
J S Cantrill Designs & Manufacturing Holdings Ltd, Chosen View Road, Cheltenham, Gloucestershire, GL51 9LT Tel: (01242) 515794 Fax: (01242) 579265 E-mail: sales@cantrillmanufacturing.com
Jet Blades & Engineering, Maguire Industrial Estate, 219 Torrington Avenue, Coventry, CV4 9HN Tel: (024) 7646 6841 Fax: (024) 7647 4215 E-mail: info@jetblades.com
L A S Aero Ltd, Oakhampton Point, Exeter Road Industrial Estate, Okehampton, Devon, EX20 1UA Tel: (01837) 658081 Fax: (01837) 658080 E-mail: sales@lasaero.com
Linread Northbridge, Crossgate Road, Redditch, Worcestershire, B98 7TD Tel: (01527) 525719 Fax: (01527) 526881 E-mail: info@linreadnorthbridge.co.uk
Loades Dynamics Ltd, Abbey Industrial Estate, Bodmin Road, Coventry, CV2 5DB Tel: (024) 7661 6146 Fax: (024) 7662 2211 E-mail: sales@loades.com
M E L Aviation Ltd, Lawrence Walter House, Addison Road, Chilton Industrial Estate, Sudbury, Suffolk, CO10 2YW Tel: (01787) 373282 Fax: (01787) 310812 E-mail: info@melaviation.co.uk
Magellan Aerospace Bournemouth, 510 Wallisdown Road, Bournemouth, BH11 8QN Tel: (01202) 517411 Fax: (01202) 530886
Maydown Precision Engineering Ltd, 11 Carrakeel Drive, Maydown, Londonderry, BT47 6UH Tel: (028) 7186 0531 Fax: (028) 7186 0496 E-mail: info@maydown.com
North West Precision Forms Ltd, Unit 3a Ebenezer Street, Birkenhead, Merseyside, CH42 1NH Tel: 0151-643 8534 Fax: 0151-643 8539 E-mail: mail@northwestprec.demon.co.uk
P E Thomas Precision Ltd, Glan Road, Porthcawl, Mid Glamorgan, CF36 5DF Tel: (01656) 783555 Fax: (01656) 783555 E-mail: p.e.thomas@talk21.com
P & S Tools, Spring La South, Malvern, Worcestershire, WR14 1AT Tel: (01684) 563632 Fax: (01684) 560825 E-mail: info@pstools.co.uk
Pattonair Ltd, Kingsway Business Park, Forsyth Road, Sheerwater, Woking, Surrey, GU21 5SA Tel: (01483) 774600 Fax: (01483) 774619 E-mail: sales@pattonair.com
Penny & Giles Aerospace Ltd, 1 Airfield Road, Christchurch, Dorset, BH23 3TH Tel: (01202) 409409 Fax: (01202) 484846 E-mail: mike.carling@pennyandgiles.com
Precimatic Ltd, 2 Balthane Industrial Estate, Balthane, Ballasalla, Isle of Man, IM9 2AQ Tel: (01624) 823030 Fax: (01624) 824600
R D Aviation Ltd, Oxford Airport, Kidlington, Oxfordshire, OX5 1QX Tel: (01865) 841441 Fax: (01865) 842495 E-mail: sales@afeonline.com
Raldon Precision Engineering Ltd, 9 Morcom Road, Birmingham, B11 2JE Tel: 0121-707 5757 Fax: 0121-706 7290 E-mail: sales@raldonengineering.com
Repaircraft plc, The Common, Cranleigh, Surrey, GU6 8LU Tel: (01483) 273536 Fax: (01483) 278078 E-mail: hq@repaircraft.co.uk
Saywell International, Aviation House, Woods Way, Goring-by-Sea, Worthing, West Sussex, BN12 4QY Tel: (01903) 705700 Fax: (01903) 705701 E-mail: sales@saywell.co.uk
Sky Trade International Ltd, Cheriton Fitzpaine, Crediton, Devon, EX17 4BQ Tel: (01363) 866573 Fax: (01363) 866860
Smith Aerospace Actuation Systems, Arle Court, Cheltenham, Gloucestershire, GL51 0TP Tel: (01242) 221155 Fax: (01242) 277577
Stanworth Engineers Ltd, Brown Street, Burnley, Lancashire, BB11 1PN Tel: (01282) 421427 Fax: (01282) 458318 E-mail: info@stanworth.co.uk
Summit, Unit 5 Vulcan Road, Solihull, West Midlands, B91 2JY Tel: 0121-709 1898 Fax: 0121-711 1429 E-mail: enquires@summit-precision.co.uk
▶ Swift Aerospace Ltd, Metro Centre, Ronsons Way, St. Albans, Hertfordshire, AL4 9QT Tel: (01727) 868293 Fax: (01727) 868292 E-mail: sales@swiftaero.com
Tierway Systems Ltd, 17 Grenville Meadows, Lostwithiel, Cornwall, PL22 0JS Tel: (01208) 871114 Fax: (01208) 871114
Trak Precision Grinders Ltd, St. Georges Way, Bermuda Industrial Estate, Nuneaton, Warwickshire, CV10 7JS Tel: (024) 7634 7117 Fax: (024) 7637 4808 E-mail: enquiries@trakltd.co.uk
Trent Aero Engineering Ltd, 9 Argosy Road, East Midland Int Airport, Castle Donington, Derby, DE74 2SA Tel: (01332) 812348 Fax: (01332) 812954 E-mail: sales@trentaero.co.uk
Trinity Aerospace Engineering Ltd, Bilton Road, Kingsland Industrial Park, Basingstoke, Hampshire, RG24 8LJ Tel: (01256) 840276 Fax: (01256) 840278 E-mail: sales@trinityaero.co.uk
V T Aerospace Ltd Ltd, 15 Cobham Road, Ferndown Industrial Estate, Wimborne, Dorset, BH21 7PE Tel: (01202) 893500 Fax: (01202) 895331 E-mail: airwork@bta.co.uk
The Vision Corporation, PO Box 3010, Wokingham, Berkshire, RG41 5FY Tel: 0118-978 4483 Fax: 0118-978 4283 E-mail: sales@vision-corporation.co.uk

AIRCRAFT COMPOSITE MOULDING SYSTEMS

Crompton Technology Group Ltd, Thorp Park Thorpe Way, Banbury, Oxfordshire, OX16 4SU Tel: (01295) 220130 Fax: (01295) 220138 E-mail: info@ctgltd.co.uk
Rolls-Royce P.L.C., PO Box 31, Derby, DE24 8BJ Tel: (01332) 349077 Fax: (01332) 291118

AIRCRAFT DISMANTLING SERVICES

H M Sales, Templewood Estate, Stock Road, West Hanningfield, Chelmsford, CM2 8LA Tel: (01277) 840172 Fax: (01702) 333492 E-mail: info@hmsales.co.uk

AIRCRAFT EJECTION SEATS

Martin-Baker Aircraft Co. Ltd, Lower Road, Higher Denham, Uxbridge, Middlesex, UB9 5AJ Tel: (01895) 832214 Fax: (01895) 832587 E-mail: amartin@martin-baker.co.uk

AIRCRAFT ELECTRICAL EQUIPMENT/SYSTEMS

Avionics Mobile Services Ltd, 6 Park Industrial Estate, Frogmore, St. Albans, Hertfordshire, AL2 2DR Tel: (01727) 872605 Fax: (01727) 872605 E-mail: sales@avionics-mobile.co.uk
Firth Rixson P.L.C, PO Box 644, Sheffield, S9 1JD Tel: 0114-219 3000 Fax: 0114-219 1111 E-mail: info@firthrixson.com
Penny & Giles Aerospace Ltd, 1 Airfield Road, Christchurch, Dorset, BH23 3TH Tel: (01202) 409409 Fax: (01202) 484846 E-mail: mike.carling@pennyandgiles.com
Sycos (UK) Ltd, Kensworth Gate, Garden Road, Dunstable, Bedfordshire, LU6 3JD Tel: (01582) 600640 Fax: (01582) 665210 E-mail: sales@sycos.co.uk
Ultra Electronics Electrics, Kingsditch Lane, Cheltenham, Gloucestershire, GL51 9PG Tel: (01242) 221166 Fax: (01242) 221167 E-mail: admin@ultra-electronics.com

AIRCRAFT ELECTRICAL EQUIPMENT/SYSTEMS MAINTENANCE/REPAIR/ OVERHAUL SERVICES

Akki Aviation Services Ltd, Turweston Aerodrome, Biddlesden Road, Westbury, Brackley, Northamptonshire, NN13 5YD Tel: (01280) 706616 Fax: (01280) 840033 E-mail: akki@globalnet.co.uk
Aviation Spares Ltd, 2 Haviland Road, Ferndown Industrial Estate, Wimborne, Dorset, BH21 7RF Tel: (01202) 875336 Fax: (01202) 894290 E-mail: sales@aviation-spares.co.uk
Avionics Mobile Services Ltd, 6 Park Industrial Estate, Frogmore, St. Albans, Hertfordshire, AL2 2DR Tel: (01727) 872605 Fax: (01727) 872605 E-mail: sales@avionics-mobile.co.uk
▶ C F S Aeroproducts, Alvis Works, Bubbenhall Road, Baginton, Coventry, CV8 3BB Tel: (024) 7630 5873 Fax: (024) 7630 2088 E-mail: mslater@cfsaeroproducts.co.uk
I A E Ltd, 2 Hanger, Cranfield Airfield, Cranfield, Bedford, MK43 0JR Tel: (01234) 750661 Fax: (01234) 751731E-mail: sales@iae.org.uk
Kearsley Airways Ltd, Romeera House, London Stansted Airport, Stansted, Essex, CM24 1QL Tel: (01279) 871000 Fax: (01279) 871187 E-mail: sales@kalair.co.uk
Turner Aviation Ltd, Spiersbridge Terrace, Thornliebank, Glasgow, G46 8JQ Tel: 0141-638 2265 Fax: 0141-638 9694 E-mail: enquiries@turner-aviation.co.uk

AIRCRAFT ELECTRONIC EQUIPMENT/SYSTEMS

Avionics Mobile Services Ltd, 6 Park Industrial Estate, Frogmore, St. Albans, Hertfordshire, AL2 2DR Tel: (01727) 872605 Fax: (01727) 872605 E-mail: sales@avionics-mobile.co.uk

AIRCRAFT EMERGENCY EVACUATION TRAINING SIMULATORS

EDM Ltd, Brunel House, 1 Thorp Road, Newton Heath, Manchester, M40 5BJ Tel: 0161-203 3150 Fax: 0161-202 2500 E-mail: reception@edm.ltd.uk

AIRCRAFT ENGINE COMPONENTS

Adams Aviation Supply Co. Ltd, Hunter House Churchill Way, Biggin Hill Airport, Biggin Hill, Westerham, Kent, TN16 3BN Tel: (01959) 576129 Fax: (01959) 576660 E-mail: mail@adamsaviation.com
Aircraft Spares and Materials Ltd, 6 Armstrong Road, Manor Trading Estate, Benfleet, Essex, SS7 4PW Tel: (01268) 792681 Fax: (01268) 795375 E-mail: spares@airsam.clara.net
Arden Precision Ltd, 5 Maidwell Drive, Shirley, Solihull, West Midlands, B90 4QN Tel: 0121-683 5200 Fax: 0121-683 5210
Commercial Aerospace Services Co. Ltd, Aviation Centre, Star Estate, Horsham, West Sussex, RH13 8RA Tel: (01403) 711444 Fax: (01403) 711582 E-mail: judith@casco.aero
Dowty Aerospace Propellers, Anson Business Park, Cheltenham Road East, Gloucester, GL2 9QN Tel: (01452) 716000 Fax: (01452) 716001
Eaton Corporation, 2 Broad Ground Road, Redditch, Worcestershire, B98 8YS Tel: (01527) 517555 Fax: (01527) 517556 E-mail: paulsmith@eaton.com
Hampson Aerospace, 129 Scudamore Road, Leicester, LE3 1UQ Tel: 0116-232 2233 Fax: 0116-232 2311E-mail: sales@mibert.com
Kigass Aero Components Ltd, Montague Road, Warwick, CV34 5LW Tel: (01926) 493833 Fax: (01926) 401456 E-mail: enquiries@kigassaero.co.uk
Neomet Ltd, 92 Cross Lane, Marple, Stockport, Cheshire, SK6 7PZ Tel: 0161-427 7741 Fax: 0161-449 0080 E-mail: fkirk@neomet.org
Trent Aero Engineering Ltd, 9 Argosy Road, East Midland Int Airport, Castle Donington, Derby, DE74 2SA Tel: (01332) 812348 Fax: (01332) 812954 E-mail: sales@trentaero.co.uk

AIRCRAFT ENGINES

Hamilton Sundstrand International Corporation, Kingfisher House, 160-162 High Street, Egham, Surrey, TW20 9HP Tel: (01784) 414600 Fax: (01784) 438092 E-mail: alison.doran@hs.utc.com
I T P S A, North York Trading Estate, Kettlestring Lane, York, YO30 4XF Tel: (01904) 690644 Fax: (01904) 690653 E-mail: sales@itp.es
Neomet Ltd, 92 Cross Lane, Marple, Stockport, Cheshire, SK6 7PZ Tel: 0161-427 7741 Fax: 0161-449 0080 E-mail: fkirk@neomet.org
Rolls Royce Plc, P O Box 3, Bristol, BS34 7QE Tel: 0117-979 1234 Fax: 0117-979 7575
Rolls Royce plc, Building 316, Viscount Way, London Heathrow Airport, Hounslow, TW6 2RQ Tel: (020) 8897 6534 Fax: (020) 8897 0328

AIRCRAFT EQUIPMENT/ SYSTEMS, *See also headings for particular types*

▶ Dawnthrive, Unit 7 Belbins Business Park, Cupernham Lane, Romsey, Hampshire, SO51 7JF Tel: (01794) 830352 Fax: (01794) 523539 E-mail: info@dawnthrive.com
Volvo Aero Services, The Mill, Abbey Mill Business Park, Lower Eashing, Godalming, Surrey, GU7 2QJ Tel: (0870) 2422436 Fax: (01483) 523799

AIRCRAFT EVACUATION TRAINING, *See Simulator, Aircraft Emergency*

AIRCRAFT FITTINGS OR ACCESSORIES

Airline Services Ltd, Canberra House, Robeson Way, Sharston Green Business Park, Manchester, M22 4SX Tel: 0161-495 6900 Fax: 0161-495 6969 E-mail: enquiries@airline-services.com
M G R Foamtex Ltd, 10 Jefferson Way, Thame, Oxfordshire, OX9 3SZ Tel: (01844) 260005 Fax: (01844) 260157 E-mail: sales@mgrfoamtex.co.uk

AIRCRAFT FLIGHT DECK INSTRUMENTATION

Adams Aviation Supply Co. Ltd, Hunter House Churchill Way, Biggin Hill Airport, Biggin Hill, Westerham, Kent, TN16 3BN Tel: (01959) 576129 Fax: (01959) 576660 E-mail: mail@adamsaviation.com
Fylde Electronic Laboratories Ltd, 49-51 Fylde Road, Preston, PR1 2XQ Tel: (01772) 257560 Fax: (01772) 821530E-mail: sales@fylde.com
Jeppesen UK Ltd, Alteon House, Crawley Business Quarter, Manor Royal, Crawley, West Sussex, RH10 9AD Tel: (01293) 842400 E-mail: david.forsythe@jeppesen.com

AIRCRAFT FLOORING

Aim Aviation Henshalls Ltd, Abbot Close, Byfleet, West Byfleet, Surrey, KT14 7JT Tel: (01932) 351011 Fax: (01932) 352792 E-mail: c.herrington@aim-henshalls.co.uk

AIRCRAFT FLYING CONTROL SYSTEMS

G E Aviation, Wobaston Road, Wolverhampton, WV9 5EW Tel: (01902) 397700 Fax: (01902) 394394
Honeywell The Oval, Bunford Lane, Yeovil, Somerset, BA20 2YD Tel: (01935) 475181 Fax: (01935) 427600 E-mail: angus.maclean@honeywell.com
SKS Uk Ltd, Tweed Road, Clevedon, Avon, BS21 6QQ Tel: (01275) 876021 Fax: (01275) 878480 E-mail: mail@ampep.co.uk

AIRCRAFT FREIGHT CHARTERING

Air Contractors, Ema Cargo West, East Midland Int Airport, Castle Donington, Derby, DE74 2TR Tel: (01332) 857850 Fax: (01332) 857859 E-mail: info@aircontractors.com
Centreline Air Charter Ltd, Bristol Flying Centre, Bristol International Airport, Bristol, BS48 3DP Tel: (01275) 474357 Fax: (01275) 476539 E-mail: operations@centrelineair.co.uk

AIRCRAFT FREIGHT CHARTERING

– *continued*

D A S Air Cargo Ltd, North Elm Park Court Tilgate Forest Business Centre, Crawley, West Sussex, RH11 9BP Tel: (01293) 540303 Fax: (01293) 514036 E-mail: sales@dasair.com
Davies Turner & Co. Ltd, Dartford Freight Terminal, Edison's Park, Dartford, DA2 6QJ Tel: (01322) 277558 Fax: (01322) 289063 E-mail: webmaster@daviesturner.co.uk
Dyce Carrier, Kirkton Avenue, Dyce, Aberdeen, AB21 0BF Tel: (01224) 723571 Fax: (01224) 770328E-mail: info@dycecar.fsbuisiness.co.uk
▶ NTS International Express Ltd, 3 Capel Close, Leacon Road, Ashford, Kent, TN23 4GY Tel: (01233) 637722 Fax: (01233) 637733 E-mail: ashford@nts-express.co.uk

AIRCRAFT FUEL CONTROL/ MANAGEMENT SYSTEMS

Avia Technique Ltd, 1 Fishponds Estate, Fishponds Road, Wokingham, Berkshire, RG41 2QJ Tel: 0118-978 9789 Fax: 0118-979 4511 E-mail: sales@intertechnique.co.uk
Eaton Aerospace Ltd, Abbey Park, Southampton Road, Titchfield, Fareham, Hampshire, PO14 4QA Tel: (01329) 853000 Fax: (01329) 853797
Kearsley Airways Ltd, Romeera House, London Stansted Airport, Stansted, Essex, CM24 1QL Tel: (01279) 871000 Fax: (01279) 871187 E-mail: sales@kalair.co.uk

AIRCRAFT FUEL SYSTEMS

Aljac Fuelling Components, Pitfield House, Station Approach, Shepperton, Middlesex, TW17 8AN Tel: (01932) 269869 Fax: (01932) 269230 E-mail: sales@aljac.com
Flightline Support Ltd, 49 Brize Norton Road, Minster Lovell, Witney, Oxfordshire, OX29 0SG Tel: (01993) 776564 Fax: (01993) 778953 E-mail: ray@flightline-support.co.uk

AIRCRAFT GRAPHICS

Graphic Innovation Ltd, 35 Chequers Hill, Amersham, Buckinghamshire, HP7 9DQ Tel: (01494) 431500 Fax: (01494) 431500 E-mail: info@graphicinnovation.com

AIRCRAFT GROUND HANDLING EQUIPMENT

A Searle, Unit 24 Bourne Road Industrial Park, Bourne Road, Dartford, DA1 4BZ Tel: (01322) 529119 Fax: (01322) 528528 E-mail: sales@asearle.co.uk
Aircraft Ground Equipment Supply Ltd, 4 Sheepcoft Lane, Whitemoor, Holt, Wimborne, Dorset, BH21 7DA Tel: (01202) 848511 Fax: (01202) 848522 E-mail: tim@aircraftaccess.com
Frank Brown & Son (Luton) Ltd, 87-105 Wingate Road, Luton, LU4 8QA Tel: (01582) 597246 Fax: (01582) 505959 E-mail: enquiries@frankbrown.co.uk
E C Hallam Engineering Leicester Ltd, Beaufield Smeeton Road, Kibworth, Leicester, LE8 0LG Tel: 0116-279 2330 E-mail: carey@hallam-eng.freeserve.co.uk
Houchin Aerospace Ltd, Hilton Road, Ashford, Kent, TN23 1DZ Tel: (01233) 623211 Fax: (01223) 638403 E-mail: sales@houchinaero.com
Mcnaughton Dynamics Ltd, 9 Carters Lane, Long Crendon, Aylesbury, Buckinghamshire, HP18 9DE Tel: (01844) 208333 Fax: (01844) 201552 E-mail: sales@mcnaughton.co.uk
Oldbury Engineering Co. Ltd, Bridge Works, Balcombe Road, Horley, Surrey, RH6 9HT Tel: (01293) 820600 Fax: (01293) 822610 E-mail: oldburyaero@compuserve.com
▶ Smith & Austin Engineering Products Ltd, 11 Church Road, Hayling Island, Hampshire, PO11 0NN Tel: (023) 9246 2451 Fax: (023) 9246 1431

AIRCRAFT GROUND SUPPORT EQUIPMENT

A Searle, Unit 24 Bourne Road Industrial Park, Bourne Road, Dartford, DA1 4BZ Tel: (01322) 529119 Fax: (01322) 528528 E-mail: sales@asearle.co.uk
Aircraft Maintenance Ltd, Eagle House, Village Farm Industrial Estate, Pyle, Bridgend, Mid Glamorgan, CF33 6NU Tel: (01656) 743700 Fax: (01656) 744265 E-mail: office@amssgse.co.uk
Aircraft Unit Engineering Co. Ltd, 10 Horatius Way, Silver Wing Industrial Estate, Croydon, CR0 4RU Tel: (020) 8686 7755 Fax: (020) 8681 3837 E-mail: office@aircraftunit.com
▶ B C Aviation, Old Lamb House, Walton Elms, Marnhull, Sturminster Newton, Dorset, DT10 1QG Tel: (01258) 820491 Fax: (01258) 821464 E-mail: sales@bcaviation.co.uk
Frank Brown & Son (Luton) Ltd, 87-105 Wingate Road, Luton, LU4 8QA Tel: (01582) 597246 Fax: (01582) 505959 E-mail: enquiries@frankbrown.co.uk
Flight Refueling, Brook Road, Wimborne, Dorset, BH21 2BJ Tel: (01202) 882121 Fax: (01202) 880096 E-mail: sales@cobham.com
Flightline Support Ltd, 49 Brize Norton Road, Minster Lovell, Witney, Oxfordshire, OX29 0SG Tel: (01993) 776564 Fax: (01993) 778953 E-mail: ray@flightline-support.co.uk
Penny & Giles Aerospace Ltd, 1 Airfield Road, Christchurch, Dorset, BH23 3TH Tel: (01202) 409409 Fax: (01202) 484846 E-mail: mike.carling@pennyandgiles.com
Reliant Design Development Co. Ltd, 60 Woolmer Way, Bordon, Hampshire, GU35 9QF Tel: (01420) 478341 Fax: (01420) 489322 E-mail: sales@rdd.co.uk
▶ Tru-Gen Ltd, Linwood Grange, Martin Moor, Metheringham, Lincoln, LN4 3BQ Tel: (01526) 378154 Fax: (01526) 378637 E-mail: arther@tru-gen.fsnet.co.uk
Viking Trailers Ltd, Taylor Holme Industrial Estate, Bacup, Lancashire, OL13 0LE Tel: (01706) 875139 Fax: (01706) 875277 E-mail: sales@vikingtrailers.co.uk

AIRCRAFT GROUND SUPPORT EQUIPMENT CONSULTANTS OR DESIGNERS

Aircraft Ground Equipment Supply Ltd, 4 Sheepcoft Lane, Whitemoor, Holt, Wimborne, Dorset, BH21 7DA Tel: (01202) 848511 Fax: (01202) 848522 E-mail: tim@aircraftaccess.com
Aircraft Maintenance Ltd, Eagle House, Village Farm Industrial Estate, Pyle, Bridgend, Mid Glamorgan, CF33 6NU Tel: (01656) 743700 Fax: (01656) 744265 E-mail: office@amssgse.co.uk
Frank Brown & Son (Luton) Ltd, 87-105 Wingate Road, Luton, LU4 8QA Tel: (01582) 597246 Fax: (01582) 505959 E-mail: enquiries@frankbrown.co.uk
Field International Ltd, Radfield House, 18-20 Nuffield Road, Nuffield Industrial Estate, Poole, Dorset, BH17 0RB Tel: (01202) 676331 Fax: (01202) 684043 E-mail: sales@fieldinternational.com
Flightline Support Ltd, 49 Brize Norton Road, Minster Lovell, Witney, Oxfordshire, OX29 0SG Tel: (01993) 776564 Fax: (01993) 778953 E-mail: ray@flightline-support.co.uk

AIRCRAFT GROUND TEST EQUIPMENT

Aim UK Ltd, 21 Lincoln Road, Cressex Business Park, High Wycombe, Buckinghamshire, HP12 3RB Tel: (01494) 446844 Fax: (01494) 449324 E-mail: salesuk@aim-online.com
Aircraft Maintenance Ltd, Eagle House, Village Farm Industrial Estate, Pyle, Bridgend, Mid Glamorgan, CF33 6NU Tel: (01656) 743700 Fax: (01656) 744265 E-mail: office@amssgse.co.uk
Hydraulic Technical Services Ltd, 10-12 Galleymead Road, Colnbrook, Slough, SL3 0EN Tel: (01753) 689689 Fax: (01753) 689700 E-mail: info@hydraulictechnical.co.uk

AIRCRAFT HANGAR DOORS

▶ John Reid & Sons Ltd, Structural House, 6-106 Reid St, Christchurch, Dorset, BH23 2BT Tel: (01202) 483333 Fax: (01202) 470103 E-mail: sales@reidsteel.co.uk

AIRCRAFT HANGARS

▶ John Reid & Sons Ltd, Structural House, 6-106 Reid St, Christchurch, Dorset, BH23 2BT Tel: (01202) 483333 Fax: (01202) 470103 E-mail: sales@reidsteel.co.uk

AIRCRAFT HEAD-UP DISPLAY (HUD) EQUIPMENT

Hayward & Green Aviation Ltd, Unit 1 & 2 Terrys Cross Farm, Horn Lane Woodmancote, Woodmancote, Henfield, West Sussex, BN5 9SA Tel: (01273) 492237 Fax: (01273) 493898

AIRCRAFT HIRE

Diamond Aircraft UK Ltd, Gamston Airfield, Gamston, Retford, Nottinghamshire, DN22 0QL Tel: (01777) 839200 Fax: (01777) 839300 E-mail: diamond@diamondair.co.uk
▶ Panoramix Aviation Rentals Ltd, 30 Silver Hill Road, Sheffield, S11 9JG Tel: 0114 2621140 Fax: 0114 2621556 E-mail: sales@panoramixltd.freeserve.co.uk
Tayside Aviation, Riverside Drive, Dundee, DD2 1UH Tel: (01382) 668838 Fax: (01382) 644531
Twinjet Aircraft Sales Ltd, Essex House, Proctor Way, Luton, LU2 9PE Tel: (01582) 452888 Fax: (01582) 400098 E-mail: jets@twinjet.co.uk
Volga-Dnepr UK Ltd, Endeavour House, Coopers End Road, London Stansted Airport, Stansted, Essex, CM24 1HA Tel: (01279) 661166 Fax: (01279) 661103 E-mail: dennis.gliznoutsa@volga-dnepr.co.uk

AIRCRAFT HYDRAULIC CONTROL EQUIPMENT

Expedite Precision Tools Ltd, Island Farm Avenue, West Molesey, Surrey, KT8 2UZ Tel: (020) 8979 0474 Fax: (020) 8783 1977 E-mail: expedite@btopenworld.com

AIRCRAFT HYDRAULIC EQUIPMENT

Honeywell The Oval, Bunford Lane, Yeovil, Somerset, BA20 2YD Tel: (01935) 475181 Fax: (01935) 427600 E-mail: angus.maclean@honeywell.com
Smith Aerospace Actuation Systems, Arle Court, Cheltenham, Gloucestershire, GL51 0TP Tel: (01242) 221155 Fax: (01242) 277577

AIRCRAFT IMPORT OR EXPORT

▶ Dimensionize Ltd, 145-157 St. John Street, London, EC1V 4PY Tel: (0870) 7538485 Fax: (0870) 7538483 E-mail: contact@dimensionize.com

AIRCRAFT IN-FLIGHT ENTERTAINMENT SYSTEMS

Edo MBM Technology Ltd, Emblem House, Home Farm Business Park, Brighton, BN1 9HU Tel: (01273) 810500 Fax: (01273) 810565 E-mail: info@edombmtech.co.uk

AIRCRAFT INDUSTRY CHEMICALS

Aerospheres (UK) Ltd, Aerospace House, 2A Tudor Road, Harrow, Middlesex, HA3 5PE Tel: (020) 8863 8578 Fax: (020) 8427 1005 E-mail: sales@aerospheres.com
Dasic International Ltd, Winchester Hill, Romsey, Hampshire, SO51 7YD Tel: (01794) 512419 Fax: (01794) 522346 E-mail: sales@dasicinter.com
Kurion Technologies Ltd, 43 Brunel Close, Drayton Fields Industrial Estate, Daventry, Northamptonshire, NN11 8RB Tel: (01327) 876600 Fax: (01327) 705131 E-mail: sales@kurion.co.uk

AIRCRAFT INSTRUMENT MAINTENANCE/REPAIR SERVICES

Aviation Spares Ltd, 2 Haviland Road, Ferndown Industrial Estate, Wimborne, Dorset, BH21 7RF Tel: (01202) 875336 Fax: (01202) 894290 E-mail: sales@aviation-spares.co.uk
Honeywell Aerospace Ltd, Edison Road, Basingstoke, Hampshire, RG21 6QD Tel: (01256) 722200 Fax: (01256) 722201 E-mail: richard.davies@honeywell.com
I A E Ltd, 2 Hanger, Cranfield Airfield, Cranfield, Bedford, MK43 0JR Tel: (01234) 750661 Fax: (01234) 751731E-mail: sales@iae.org.uk
Inflight (Southend) Ltd, North Hangar, Aviation Way, Southend-On-Sea, SS2 6UN Tel: (01702) 348601 Fax: (01702) 541534
Kearsley Airways Ltd, Romeera House, London Stansted Airport, Stansted, Essex, CM24 1QL Tel: (01279) 871000 Fax: (01279) 871187 E-mail: sales@kalair.co.uk
Marilake Instruments Ltd, Building 97, Bournemouth International Airport, Christchurch, Dorset, BH23 6SE Tel: (01202) 570055 Fax: (01202) 581369 E-mail: phil@mailake.com
Pandect Instrument Laboratories Ltd, Wellington Road, Cressex Business Park, High Wycombe, Buckinghamshire, HP12 3PX Tel: (01494) 526301 Fax: (01494) 464503 E-mail: enquiries@pandect.demon.co.uk

AIRCRAFT INSTRUMENT TEST EQUIPMENT

G E Sensing, Fir Tree Lane, Groby, Leicester, LE6 0FH Tel: 0116-231 7100 Fax: 0116-231 7101
Honeywell Aerospace Ltd, Edison Road, Basingstoke, Hampshire, RG21 6QD Tel: (01256) 722200 Fax: (01256) 722201 E-mail: richard.davies@honeywell.com
H.R. Smith Techtest Ltd, Street Court, Kingsland, Leominster, Herefordshire, HR6 9QA Tel: (01568) 708744 Fax: (01568) 708713 E-mail: sales@hr-smith.com

AIRCRAFT INSTRUMENTS

Fenns (Farnborough) Ltd, 77 Alexandra Road, Farnborough, Hampshire, GU14 6BN Tel: (01252) 541221 Fax: (01252) 512890 E-mail: info@fennprint.co.uk

AIRCRAFT INTERIOR DESIGNERS/FABRICATORS/ FURNISHERS

A I M Group plc, 16 Carlton Cresent, Southampton, SO15 2ES Tel: (023) 8033 5111 Fax: (023) 8022 9733
Aim Aviation Ltd, Building 138, Bournemouth International, Airport, Christchurch, Dorset, BH23 6NW Tel: (01202) 599666 Fax: (01202) 599677 E-mail: enquiries@aim-aviation.co.uk
Aim Aviation Henshalls Ltd, Abbot Close, Byfleet, West Byfleet, Surrey, KT14 7JT Tel: (01932) 351011 Fax: (01932) 352792 E-mail: c.herrington@aim-henshalls.co.uk
Airline Services Ltd, Canberra House, Robeson Way, Sharston Green Business Park, Manchester, M22 4SX Tel: 0161-495 6900 Fax: 0161-495 6969 E-mail: enquiries@airline-services.com
Benson Lund Ltd, Aviation Way, Southend Airport, Southend-on-Sea, SS2 6UN Tel: (01702) 547683 Fax: (01702) 530884 E-mail: bensonsales@ipeco.co.uk
▶ Chameleon Products Ltd, 8 Grange Close, Bradley Stoke, Bristol, BS32 0AH Tel: (01425) 655952 Fax: (01425) 655607 E-mail: tsw@chameleonproducts.net
▶ DesignCambridge, Jesus Lane, Cambridge, CB5 8BA Tel: (01223) 367206 E-mail: chris@designcambridge.com
Flying Service Engineering (Sales) Ltd, 5 Springfield Road, Chesham, Buckinghamshire, HP5 1PP Tel: (01494) 786666 Fax: (01494) 791813 E-mail: fsee@talk21.com
Frank Guy, Bidston House, Astwith Close, Holmewood, Chesterfield, Derbyshire, S42 5UR Tel: (01246) 851222 Fax: (01246) 851225 E-mail: sales@frank-guy.co.uk
Interiair Aircraft Services, Elstree Aerodrome, Elstree, Borehamwood, Hertfordshire, WD6 3AW Tel: (020) 8953 1995 Fax: (020) 8953 3029 E-mail: interiair@aol.com
M G R Foamtex Ltd, 10 Jefferson Way, Thame, Oxfordshire, OX9 3SZ Tel: (01844) 260005 Fax: (01844) 260157 E-mail: sales@mgrfoamtex.co.uk
Percival Aviation, Sapphire House, 15 Barnes Wallis Road, Fareham, Hampshire, PO15 5TT Tel: (01489) 564378 Fax: (01489) 569050 E-mail: info@percival-aviation.co.uk
Spencer & Co., The Green, Long Lawford, Rugby, Warwickshire, CV23 9BL Tel: (01788) 560782 Fax: (01788) 537917 E-mail: enquiries@spencerfurniture.co.uk

AIRCRAFT JIGS

Cma Tools Burnley Ltd, Belle Vue Mill, Westgate, Burnley, Lancashire, BB11 1SD Tel: (01282) 423619 Fax: (01282) 427944 E-mail: cmatools@airtime.co.uk
Conway Precision Engineering Group Ltd, 106 Tame Road, Birmingham, B6 7EZ Tel: 0121-327 8037 Fax: 0121-328 4885 E-mail: design@gauges.co.uk
Harvey Manchester Ltd, Oldham Street, Denton, Manchester, M34 3SW Tel: 0161-336 3951 Fax: 0161-336 3936 E-mail: sales@harveymanchester.com

AIRCRAFT LANDING GEAR

Messier-Dowty Ltd, Cheltenham Road East, Gloucester, GL2 9QH Tel: (01452) 712424 Fax: (01452) 713821 E-mail: peter.hall@messier-dowty.com

AIRCRAFT LANDING GEAR MAINTENANCE/REPAIR SERVICES

▶ Hi Chrome (Europe) Ltd, Heathenford Industrial Estate, Widowhill Road, Burnley, Lancashire, BB10 2TT Tel: (01282) 418300 Fax: (01282) 418310 E-mail: sales@hycrome.com
Rotable Repairs Group Ltd, Unit 1/4, Britannia Business Park, Comet Way, Southend-on-Sea, SS2 6GE Tel: (01702) 529888 Fax: (01702) 523580 E-mail: info@rotablerepairs.com

AIRCRAFT MAINTENANCE ACCESS PLATFORMS

▶ Smith & Austin Engineering Products Ltd, 11 Church Road, Hayling Island, Hampshire, PO11 0NN Tel: (023) 9246 2451 Fax: (023) 9246 1431

▶ indicates data change since last edition

AIRCRAFT MAINTENANCE AND REPAIR MATERIALS

A E M Ltd, Unit 6001, Taylors End, Long Border Road, Stansted Airport, Stansted, Essex, CM24 1RB Tel: (01279) 680030 Fax: (01279) 680040 E-mail: info@aem.co.uk

Aerospheres (UK) Ltd, Aerospace House, 2A Tudor Road, Harrow, Middlesex, HA3 5PE Tel: (020) 8863 8578 Fax: (020) 8427 1005 E-mail: sales@aerospheres.com

Atc Lasham Ltd, Lasham Airfield, Lasham, Alton, Hampshire, GU34 5SP Tel: (01256) 356123 Fax: (01256) 467487 E-mail: sales@atclasham.co.uk

Flybe, Jack Walker House, Clyst Honiton, Exeter, EX5 2HL Tel: (01392) 366669 Fax: (01392) 366151 E-mail: caroline.fletcher@flybe.com

Tatenhill Aviation Ltd, Tatenhill Airfield, Newborough Road, Needwood, Burton-on-Trent, Staffordshire, DE13 9PD Tel: (01283) 575283 Fax: (01283) 575650

AIRCRAFT MAINTENANCE SUPPORT SYSTEMS

Expedite Precision Tools Ltd, Island Farm Avenue, West Molesey, Surrey, KT8 2UZ Tel: (020) 8979 0474 Fax: (020) 8783 1977 E-mail: expedite@btopenworld.com

AIRCRAFT MAINTENANCE/ REPAIR SPECIALIST SERVICES

A E M Ltd, Unit 6001, Taylors End, Long Border Road, Stansted Airport, Stansted, Essex, CM24 1RB Tel: (01279) 680030 Fax: (01279) 680040 E-mail: info@aem.co.uk

A J D Engineering Ltd, Moat Farm, Church Road, Milden, Ipswich, IP7 7AF Tel: (01449) 740544 Fax: (01449) 741584

Aerofab Restorations, Bourne Park Estate, Hurstbourne Tarrant, Andover, Hampshire, SP11 0DG Tel: (01264) 736635 Fax: (01264) 736636

Airline Services Ltd, Canberra House, Robeson Way, Sharston Green Business Park, Manchester, M22 4SX Tel: 0161-495 6900 Fax: 0161-495 6969 E-mail: enquiries@airline-services.com

Aviation Salvage International Ltd, Unit 2 Valley Court, Basingstoke Road, Beech, Alton, Hampshire, GU34 4BH Tel: (01420) 84183 Fax: (01420) 544266 E-mail: info@airsalvage.co.uk

Avtech Ltd, Building 170 Churchill Way, Biggin Hill Airport, Biggin Hill, Westerham, Kent, TN16 3BN Tel: (01959) 575679 Fax: (01959) 576968 E-mail: avtech@btconnect.com

Bond Air Services Ltd, Boreham Airfield, Boreham, Chelmsford, CM3 3BG Tel: (01245) 362627 Fax: (01245) 362624

Bradfor Aircraft Services, Forestbrook Mill, Forestbrook Avenue, Rostrevor, Newry, County Down, BT34 3BX Tel: (028) 4173 8835 Fax: (028) 4173 8694 E-mail: patricia@bradfor.co.uk

Bramlands Aviation Ltd, Bramlands Stables, Bramlands Lane, Woodmancote, Henfield, West Sussex, BN5 9TQ Tel: (01273) 494774 Fax: (01273) 494799 E-mail: sales@bramlands.com

Caledonian Airborne Engineering Ltd, Dove Hanger Ninian Road, Aberdeen Airport, Aberdeen, AB21 0PD Tel: (01224) 772071 Fax: (01224) 773800 E-mail: cae.line@bt.internet.com

Caledonian Airbourne Systems Ltd, 6 Ninian Road, Dyce, Aberdeen, AB21 0PD Tel: (01224) 722274 Fax: (01224) 722896

Chromalloy Prestwick, Liberator House, Glasgow Prestwick Intnl Airport, Prestwick, Ayrshire, KA9 2PT Tel: (01292) 678400 Fax: (01292) 474989

Cse Citation Centre, Hanger 100 North West Sector, Bournemouth International Airpo, Hurn, Christchurch, Dorset, BH23 6NW Tel: (01202) 573243 Fax: (01202) 581579 E-mail: info@cse-aviation.com

Eastern Air Executive Ltd, Sturgate Airfield, Heapham, Gainsborough, Lincolnshire, DN21 5PA Tel: (01427) 838280 Fax: (01427) 838416

Forg Welding & Engineering Co. Ltd, 4 Block 2 Mariner Way, Felnex Industrial Estate, Newport, Gwent, NP19 4PQ Tel: (01633) 274690 Fax: (01633) 270975 E-mail: sales@forg.co.uk

FR Aviation Services Ltd, Bournemouth Airport, Hurn, Christchurch, Dorset, BH23 6NE Tel: (01202) 409100 Fax: (01202) 576709 E-mail: fra-marketing@dial.pipex.com

G E Caledonian Ltd, Shawfarm Industrial Estate, Monument Cresent, Prestwick, Ayrshire, KA9 2RX Tel: (01292) 673000 Fax: (01292) 673001 E-mail: d.crews@ae.ge.com

Holdcroft Aviation Services Ltd, Hinton In The Hedges Airfield, Steane, Brackley, Northamptonshire, NN13 5NS Tel: (01295) 810287 Fax: (01295) 812247

Honeywell Aerospace Ltd, Enterprise Way, Aviation Park, Hurn, Christchurch, Dorset, BH23 6EW Tel: (01202) 581818 Fax: (01202) 581919 E-mail: sales@honeywell.com

I A E Ltd, 2 Hanger, Cranfield Airfield, Cranfield, Bedford, MK43 0JR Tel: (01234) 750661 Fax: (01234) 751731E-mail: sales@iae.org.uk

Inflight (Southend) Ltd, North Hangar, Aviation Way, Southend-On-Sea, SS2 6UN Tel: (01702) 348601 Fax: (01702) 541534

Light Aircraft Engineering Elstree Ltd, Elstree Aerodrome, Elstree, Borehamwood, Hertfordshire, WD6 3AW Tel: (020) 8953 9341 Fax: (020) 8207 4540

M K Aero Support Ltd, Andrews Field, Stebbing, Dunmow, Essex, CM6 3TH Tel: (01371) 856796 Fax: (01371) 856855 E-mail: mkaerosupport@btconnect.com

Mclean Aviation, Rufforth Airfield, Rufforth, York, YO23 3NA Tel: (01904) 738653 Fax: (01904) 738146

National Air Traffic Services, Atlantic House, Sherwood Road, Prestwick, Ayrshire, KA9 2NR Tel: (01292) 479800 Fax: (01292) 692733

Neam Ltd, Hangar 7, Western Maintenance Area, Manchester Airport, Manchester, M90 5NE Tel: 0161-436 6666 Fax: 0161-493 9976 E-mail: sales@northernexec.com

Newbury Aeroplane Company Aircraft Repairs, Unit 2, Denford Manor, Lower Denford, Hungerford, Berkshire, RG17 0UN Tel: (01488) 682949 Fax: (01488) 682949

Northern Executive Aviation Ltd, Hangar 7, Western Maintenance Area, Manchester Airport, Manchester, M90 5NE Tel: 0161-436 6666 Fax: 0161-436 3450 E-mail: info@northernexec.com

Old Sarum Engineering, Hangar 3, Old Sarum Airfield, Old Sarum, Salisbury, SP4 6DZ Tel: (01722) 415618 Fax: (01722) 323702 E-mail: enquiries@oldsarumflying.co.uk

Pacific Scientific, Howarth Road, Maidenhead, Berkshire, SL6 1AP Tel: (01628) 682200 Fax: (01628) 682250 E-mail: custadmin@pacscieurope.com

Prestige Air Engineers Ltd, Kinnesswood, Withybush Road, Haverfordwest, Dyfed, SA62 4BN Tel: (01437) 766126 Fax: (01437) 765151 E-mail: p.air@btconnect.com

Qualitair Engineering Services Ltd, Francis Court, High Ditch Road, Fen Ditton, Cambridge, CB5 8TE Tel: (01223) 295111 Fax: (01223) 295112 E-mail: info@swynfordpaddocks.com

Serco Defence, Bartley Wood Business Park, Bartley Way, Hook, Hampshire, RG27 9XA Tel: (01256) 745900 Fax: (01256) 745995 E-mail: enquiries@serco.com

Sigma Aerospace Ltd, 12 Imperial Way, Croydon, CR9 4LE Tel: (020) 8688 7777 Fax: (020) 8688 6603 E-mail: info@sigmaaerospace.com

Southdown Composites Ltd, Lasham Airfield, Lasham, Alton, Hampshire, GU34 5SR Tel: (01256) 381359 Fax: (01256) 381359 E-mail: sales@southdowncomposites.com

T G Aviation Ltd, Manston Airport, Manston, Ramsgate, Kent, CT12 5BN Tel: (01843) 823656 Fax: (01843) 822024 E-mail: info@tgaviation.com

Roger Targett, Nympsfield, Stonehouse, Gloucestershire, GL10 3TX Tel: (01453) 860861 Fax: (01453) 860861

Tatenhill Aviation Ltd, Tatenhill Airfield, Newborough Road, Needwood, Burton-on-Trent, Staffordshire, DE13 9PD Tel: (01283) 575283 Fax: (01283) 575650

Trinity Aerospace Engineering Ltd, Bilton Road, Kingsland Industrial Park, Basingstoke, Hampshire, RG24 8LJ Tel: (01256) 840276 Fax: (01256) 840278 E-mail: sales@trinityaero.co.uk

Vintage Engine Technology Ltd, Fullers Hill, Little Gransden, Sandy, Bedfordshire, SG19 3BP Tel: (01767) 651794 Fax: (01767) 651794

AIRCRAFT MECHANICAL EQUIPMENT

Expedite Precision Tools Ltd, Island Farm Avenue, West Molesey, Surrey, KT8 2UZ Tel: (020) 8979 0474 Fax: (020) 8783 1977 E-mail: expedite@btopenworld.com

AIRCRAFT METAL

Advanced Metals International Ltd, Odhams Trading Estate, St.Albans Road, Watford, WD24 7RT Tel: (01923) 205599 Fax: (01923) 205588 E-mail: sales@advancedmetals.com

All Metal Services Ltd, 6 Horton Industrial Park, Horton Road, West Drayton, Middlesex, UB7 8JD Tel: (01895) 444066 Fax: (01895) 420963 E-mail: london@allmetal.co.uk

C M Alloys, Peartree Business Centre, Cobham Road, Ferndown Industrial Estate, Wimborne, Dorset, BH21 7PT Tel: (01202) 850370 Fax: (01202) 850379

T W Metals Ltd, Unit 43 Nursling Industrial Estate, Majestic Road, Nursling, Southampton, SO16 0AF Tel: (023) 8073 9333 Fax: (023) 8073 9601 E-mail: enquiries@twmetals.co.uk

AIRCRAFT NAVIGATIONAL INSTRUMENTS

Thales Avionics Ltd, 88 Bushey Road, London, SW20 0JW Tel: (020) 8946 8011 Fax: (020) 8946 3014

AIRCRAFT PART MAINTENANCE AND REPAIR

Bramlands Aviation Ltd, Bramlands Stables, Bramlands Lane, Woodmancote, Henfield, West Sussex, BN5 9TQ Tel: (01273) 494774 Fax: (01273) 494799 E-mail: sales@bramlands.com

AIRCRAFT PILOT TRAINING

▶ Flight Academy Scotland.com, Building 25, Inverness Airport, Inverness, IV2 7JB Tel: 01667 461181 Fax: 01667 462202

AIRCRAFT PROPELLERS

Newton Propeller, Unit 26 Ddole Road Industrial Estate, Llandrindod Wells, Powys, LD1 6DF Tel: (01597) 824420 Fax: (01597) 824420 E-mail: sales@newtonpropeller.co.uk

Skycraft Services Ltd, Albany House, 12 Silver Street, Litlington, Royston, Hertfordshire, SG8 0QE Tel: (01763) 852150 Fax: (01763) 852593

AIRCRAFT REFUELLING EQUIPMENT

Aljac Fuelling Components, Pitfield House, Station Approach, Shepperton, Middlesex, TW17 8AN Tel: (01932) 269869 Fax: (01932) 269230 E-mail: sales@aljac.com

Kigass Aero Components Ltd, Montague Road, Warwick, CV34 5LW Tel: (01926) 493833 Fax: (01926) 401456 E-mail: enquiries@kigassaero.co.uk

AIRCRAFT REFUELLING HOSES

Ideal Hose & Safety Ltd, Spring Lane, Northampton, NN1 2JW Tel: (01604) 621964 Fax: (01604) 232936 E-mail: sales@idealhose.co.uk

AIRCRAFT REFUELLING VEHICLES

Gatwick Refuelling Services Ltd, Perimeter Road North, London Gatwick Airport, Gatwick, West Sussex, RH6 0JE Tel: (01293) 527044 Fax: (01293) 514669

AIRCRAFT RIVETS

Clevedon Fasteners Ltd, Reddicap Trading Estate, Sutton Coldfield, West Midlands, B75 7BU Tel: 0121-378 0619 Fax: 0121-378 3186 E-mail: sales@clevedon-fasteners.co.uk

AIRCRAFT SAFETY EQUIPMENT

Am Safe Ltd, Tamian Way, Hounslow, TW4 6BL Tel: (020) 8572 0321 Fax: (020) 8572 2096 E-mail: sales@am-safe.co.uk

Britax International Holdings Ltd, Seton House, Warwick Technology Park, Warwick, CV34 6DE Tel: (01926) 400040 Fax: (01926) 406350 E-mail: info@britax.com

Mistura Systems, 217 Kingsbury Road, London, NW9 9PQ Tel: (020) 8511 1854 Fax: (020) 8205 0055 E-mail: safety@mistura.co.uk

Percival Aviation, Sapphire House, 15 Barnes Wallis Road, Fareham, Hampshire, PO15 5TT Tel: (01489) 564378 Fax: (01489) 569050 E-mail: info@percival-aviation.co.uk

Seaweather Aviation Services Ltd, 625-649 Princes Road, Dartford, DA2 6EF Tel: (01322) 275513 Fax: (01322) 292639 E-mail: safety@seaweather.co.uk

AIRCRAFT SEATS

Benson Lund Ltd, Aviation Way, Southend Airport, Southend-on-Sea, SS2 6UN Tel: (01702) 547683 Fax: (01702) 530884 E-mail: bensonsales@ipeco.co.uk

Flying Service Engineering (Sales) Ltd, 5 Springfield Road, Chesham, Buckinghamshire, HP5 1PP Tel: (01494) 786666 Fax: (01494) 791813 E-mail: fsee@talk21.com

Flying Services, Newtown Industrial Estate, Cross Keys, Newport, Gwent, NP11 7PZ Tel: (01495) 272712 Fax: (01495) 270211

Ipeco Europe, Aviation Way, Southend-on-Sea, SS2 6UN Tel: (01702) 549371 Fax: (01702) 540782 E-mail: sales@ipeco.co.uk

AIRCRAFT SERVICING EQUIPMENT

Aeroparts International Ltd, 2 George House, Beam Heath Way, Nantwich, Cheshire, CW5 6GD Tel: (01270) 620260 Fax: (01270) 620261 E-mail: sales@aeroparts-international.com

Houchin Aerospace Ltd, Hilton Road, Ashford, Kent, TN23 1DZ Tel: (01233) 623211 Fax: (01223) 638403 E-mail: sales@houchinaero.com

M E L Aviation Ltd, Lawrence Walter House, Addison Road, Chilton Industrial Estate, Sudbury, Suffolk, CO10 2YW Tel: (01787) 373282 Fax: (01787) 310812 E-mail: info@melaviation.co.uk

▶ Tru-Gen Ltd, Linwood Grange, Martin Moor, Metheringham, Lincoln, LN4 3BQ Tel: (01526) 378154 Fax: (01526) 378637 E-mail: arther@tru-gen.fsnet.co.uk

AIRCRAFT SHEET METALWORK ENGINEERS OR FABRICATORS

Airbus, Chester Road, Broughton, Chester, CH4 0DR Tel: (01244) 520444 Fax: (01244) 523000

Beagle Aircraft Ltd, Stony Lane, Christchurch, Dorset, BH23 1EX Tel: (01202) 482296 Fax: (01202) 499449

Boldvale Engineering Ltd, Unit 15 Cambridge Industrial Estate Montague Road, Hanwell, London, W7 3PG Tel: (020) 8840 2398 Fax: (020) 8566 3125 E-mail: john.dwight@boldvaleeng.co.uk

C W Fletcher & Sons Ltd, Sterling Works, Mansfield Road, Wales Bar, Sheffield, S26 5PQ Tel: 0114-294 2200 Fax: 0114-294 2211

▶ CTL Components, Falcon House, 19 Deer Park Road, London, SW19 3UX Tel: (020) 8543 0911 Fax: (020) 8540 0034 E-mail: info@ctl-components.com

Elder Repetition Sheet Metal Ltd, 30 Oxford Road, Denham, Uxbridge, Middlesex, UB9 4DQ Tel: (01895) 258968 Fax: (01895) 252651 E-mail: sales@eldersheetmetal.co.uk

R.H.H. Franks (New Milton) Ltd, Stem Lane, Gore Road, New Milton, Hampshire, BH25 5NE Tel: (01425) 614730 Fax: (01425) 616472 E-mail: johnh@rhhfranks.co.uk

Gardner Aerospace Wales Ltd, Forge Industrial Estate, Maesteg, Mid Glamorgan, CF34 0AY Tel: (01656) 812100 Fax: (01656) 812101 E-mail: info@gardner-aerospace.com

Lightning Aerospace Ltd, Falkland Close, Charter Avenue Industrial Estate, Coventry, CV4 8AU Tel: (024) 7646 1238 Fax: (024) 7646 4745 E-mail: info@lightningaerospace.co.uk

M J Sections Ltd, Unit 5 Marriott Road Industrial Estate, Netherton, Dudley, West Midlands, DY2 0JZ Tel: (01384) 230444 Fax: (01384) 456086 E-mail: sales@mjsections.co.uk

Sascal Displays Ltd, Unit 1 Hayes Metro Centre, Springfield Road, Hayes, Middlesex, UB4 0LE Tel: (020) 8573 0303 Fax: (020) 8569 1515 E-mail: sales@sascal.com

Stewart & Allen Ltd, The Runnings, Cheltenham, Gloucestershire, GL51 9NW Tel: (01242) 523298 Fax: (01242) 226416

▶ Tom Lee, Unit 6 Littleton Trading Estate, Littleton Lane, Shepperton, Middlesex, TW17 0NF Tel: 01932 569939 Fax: 01932 569939E-mail: info@media-construction.co.uk

Trent Aero Engineering Ltd, 9 Argosy Road, East Midland Int Airport, Castle Donington, Derby, DE74 2SA Tel: (01332) 812348 Fax: (01332) 812954 E-mail: sales@trentaero.co.uk

Viper Metal Products Ltd, Oldmixon Cresent, Weston-super-Mare, Avon, BS24 9AX Tel: (01934) 621912 Fax: (01934) 614347 E-mail: tony@viparmetal.co.uk

James White & Son (Engineering) Co. Ltd, Commercial Road, Reading, RG2 0RU Tel: 0118-987 3421 Fax: 0118-975 0521 E-mail: mark@jameswhite.freeserve.co.uk

AIRCRAFT STARTING EQUIPMENT

Houchin Aerospace Ltd, Hilton Road, Ashford, Kent, TN23 1DZ Tel: (01233) 623211 Fax: (01223) 638403 E-mail: sales@houchinaero.com

▶ Tru-Gen Ltd, Linwood Grange, Martin Moor, Metheringham, Lincoln, LN4 3BQ Tel: (01526) 378154 Fax: (01526) 378637 E-mail: arther@tru-gen.fsnet.co.uk

AIRCRAFT STEEL TUBES

▶ PFAMetals.com, 2 Stone Circle Road, Northampton, NN3 8RF Tel: (01604) 671536 Fax: (01604) 670831 E-mail: sales@pfametals.com

AIRCRAFT TEST EQUIPMENT

▶ Avery Hardoll, Holland Way, Blandford Forum, Dorset, DT11 7BJ Tel: (01258) 486600 Fax: (01258) 486601 E-mail: sales@meggittfuelling.com

AIRCRAFT TEST EQUIPMENT – *continued*

M E L Aviation Ltd, Lawrence Walter House, Addison Road, Chilton Industrial Estate, Sudbury, Suffolk, CO10 2YW Tel: (01787) 373282 Fax: (01787) 310812 E-mail: info@melaviation.co.uk

Reliant Design Development Co. Ltd, 60 Woolmer Way, Bordon, Hampshire, GU35 9QF Tel: (01420) 478341 Fax: (01420) 489322 E-mail: sales@rdd.co.uk

Zener Designs Cheltenham Ltd, Exmouth Street, Cheltenham, Gloucestershire, GL53 7NS Tel: (01242) 527394 Fax: 01242 221871 E-mail: sales@zenerdesigns.com

AIRCRAFT TEXTILE FITTINGS AND ACCESSORIES

▶ Red Plc, Unit1a, Canalside Industrial Estate, Woodbine St East, Rochdale, Lancashire, OL16 5LB Tel: (01706) 525623 Fax: (01706) 860590 E-mail: info@red-plc.co.uk

AIRCRAFT TYRES

Dunlop Aftrica Marketing UK Ltd, 40 Fort Parkway, Birmingham, B24 9HL Tel: 0121-384 8800 Fax: 0121-377 7150 E-mail: datlsales@compuserve.com

AIRCRAFT WEAPON ARMING SYSTEMS

A E I Systems Ltd, 1 Kings Ride Park, Kings Ride, Ascot, Berkshire, SL5 8AP Tel: (01344) 636200 Fax: (01344) 636205 E-mail: info@airequip.co.uk

AIRCRAFT WEAPON CARRIAGE SYSTEMS

A E I Systems Ltd, 1 Kings Ride Park, Kings Ride, Ascot, Berkshire, SL5 8AP Tel: (01344) 636200 Fax: (01344) 636205 E-mail: info@airequip.co.uk

Edo MBM Technology Ltd, Emblem House, Home Farm Business Park, Brighton, BN1 9HU Tel: (01273) 810500 Fax: (01273) 810565 E-mail: info@edombmtech.co.uk

AIRCRAFT, PISTON ENGINE

Flightplan Ltd, PO Box 1159, Farnborough, Hampshire, GU14 6XA Tel: (01252) 52 62 82 Fax: (01252) 52 62 89 E-mail: info@flightplan.org.uk

AIRLESS PAINT SPRAYING EQUIPMENT

Air Industrial Developments Ltd, Union Street, Kencrick Way, West Bromwich, West Midlands, B70 6DB Tel: 0121-553 4446 Fax: 0121-525 5983 E-mail: paint.sales@airind.co.uk

Gray Campling Ltd, 91a Southcote Road, Bournemouth, BH1 3SN Tel: (01202) 291828 Fax: (01202) 297304 E-mail: sales@graycampling.co.uk

AIRLESS SPRAY TIPS

Exitflex (UK) Ltd, 5 Airfield Road, Airfield Industrial Estate, Christchurch, Dorset, BH23 3TG Tel: (01202) 478334 Fax: (01202) 488110 E-mail: sales@exitflex.co.uk

AIRPORT BAGGAGE HANDLING SYSTEMS

Dematic Ltd, Beaumont Rd, Banbury, Oxon, OX16 1QZ Tel: (01295) 274600 Fax: (01295) 274808 E-mail: sd.uk.ma-marketing@siemens.com

▶ Robson Handling Technology Ltd, Coleford Road, Darnall, Sheffield, S9 5PA Tel: 0114-244 4221 Fax: 0114-243 3066 E-mail: info@robson.co.uk

AIRPORT CONSULTING ENGINEERS

Engineering & Development Consultants Ltd, Keruing Cedar, Chess Hill, Loudwater, Rickmansworth, Hertfordshire, WD3 4HU Tel: (01923) 776567 Fax: (01923) 721438 E-mail: gmcrook@lineone.net

AIRPORT EQUIPMENT

Metalite Aviation Lighting, Winster Grove, Great Barr, Birmingham, B44 9EJ Tel: 0121-360 2222 Fax: 0121-366 6003 E-mail: sales@metaliteaviation.com

AIRPORT MAINTENANCE CONTRACTORS

Interserve Engineering Services Ltd, Intersection House, 110-120 Birmingham Road, West Bromwich, West Midlands, B70 6RP Tel: 0121-500 5000 Fax: 0121-525 5574 E-mail: info@interserve-eng.com

Tilbury Douglas Projects Ltd, 395 George Road, Erdington, Birmingham, B23 7RZ Tel: 0121-344 3900 Fax: 0121-344 4801 E-mail: enquiries@tilbury.co.uk

AIRPORT PARKING

▶ Help-ME-Park.com, 7th Floor, Norfolk House, South Terminal, Gatwick Airport, Crawley, West Sussex, RH6 0NN Tel: 0870 3006009 E-mail: info@help-me-park.com

▶ Skypark, Sycamore Trading Estate, Squires Gate Lane, Blackpool, FY4 3RL Tel: (01253) 310647 Fax: (01253) 362858 E-mail: webmaster@skyparksecure.com

AIRPORT RUNWAY DEMOLITION

▶ Frac Roc, Islwyn, Lon Gernant, Menai Bridge, Anglesey, LL59 5SU Tel: (01248) 717999 Fax: (01248) 717999 E-mail: rockbusters@btinternet.com

AIRPORT SECURITY EQUIPMENT

▶ International Consultants on Targeted Security, South Block, Tavistock House, Tavistock Square, London, WC1H 9LG Tel: 0207 8747576 Fax: 0207 8747599 E-mail: mark.salter_uk@icts.co.uk

AIRPORT TERMINAL CONCOURSE AND SHOP FITTERS AND FURNISHERS

▶ Amj Services UK Ltd, 21a Whirlow Grove, Whirlow, Sheffield, S11 9NR Tel: 0114-249 8380 Fax: 0114 2817979 E-mail: tony@amjservices.com

Derrywood Display, 3-6 Tuxford Road, Leicester, LE4 9TZ Tel: 0116-276 0006 Fax: 0116-276 0007 E-mail: info@derrywooddisplay.co.uk

▶ Henderson Global Imports Ltd, Limpet House, Itchenor Road Itchenor, Chichester, West Sussex, PO20 7DH Tel: (01243) 513511 Fax: (01243) 512359 E-mail: sales@hgimports.com

▶ PCS, Unit 60-62 Stephenson Way, Formby Business Park, Formby, Liverpool, L37 8EG Tel: (01704) 879204 Fax: (01704) 879204 E-mail: webdevelopment@pcsflooring.com

▶ Quinn Interiors Ltd, Number 4, Moorhey Street, Oldham, OL4 1JD Tel: 0161-785 3150 E-mail: sales@quinninteriors.co.uk

AIRPORT TRANSPORTATION OR DELIVERY OR COLLECTION SERVICES

▶ Aylesbury Limousines, 279 Tring Road, Aylesbury, Buckinghamshire, HP20 1PH Tel: (01296) 484051 Fax: (01296) 420791 E-mail: lisa@aylesburylimousines.co.uk

▶ Prop Logistics, 3 Faraday Court, Park Farm Industrial Estate, Wellingborough, Northamptonshire, NN8 6XY Tel: (01933) 401641 Fax: (01933) 402474

▶ White Heather Taxis Ltd, Brackencroft, Auchtercairn, Gairloch, Ross-shire, IV21 2BS Tel: 01445 712608 Fax: 01445 712608 E-mail: whiteheathertaxis@btinternet.com

AIRPORT TRUCKING/DELIVERY/ COLLECTION SERVICES, INTER-AIRPORT

▶ Airport 24 7, 152-154 Coles Green Road, London, NW2 7HD Tel: (020) 8208 4880 Fax: (020) 8452 0701 E-mail: renata@exclusiveairports.com

▶ Aylesbury Limousines, 279 Tring Road, Aylesbury, Buckinghamshire, HP20 1PH Tel: (01296) 484051 Fax: (01296) 420791 E-mail: lisa@aylesburylimousines.co.uk

▶ Excel Chauffeur Services, Warrington Business Park, Long Lane, Warrington, WA2 8TX Tel: (0871) 2881433 Fax: (0871) 2881433 E-mail: enquiries@xl-cars.co.uk

▶ Travel Wright, 2 Masons Way, Barnoldswick, Lancashire, BB18 6DU Tel: (01282) 815111 Fax: (01282) 850044 E-mail: info@travelwright.co.uk

▶ UK County Couriers Ltd, 21 Malvern Drive, Ilford, Essex, IG3 9DP Tel: (0870) 4460810 Fax: (0870) 4460740 E-mail: ukcountycouriers@btinternet.com

AIRTIGHTNESS OR LEAKAGE OF BUILDING TESTING TO REGULATION L2

▶ Building Sciences Ltd, The Carriage House, School Road, Ardington, Wantage, Oxfordshire, OX12 8PQ Tel: (01235) 835323 Fax: (01235) 863220 E-mail: sborland@buildingsciences.co.uk

ALARM ANNUNCIATORS

Annicom Electronic Equipment Component, Highview, High Street, Bordon, Hampshire, GU35 0AX Tel: (01420) 487788 Fax: (01420) 487799 E-mail: sale@annicom.com

ALARM CONTROL SYSTEMS

E.D.C. International Ltd, Brook House Station Road, Pangbourne, Reading, RG8 7AN Tel: 0118-984 2040 Fax: 0118-984 5300 E-mail: sales@edcinternational.com

ALARM (MOTOR CAR/VEHICLE) SYSTEMS ENGINEERS, INSTALLATION OR SERVICE

▶ Alanco Motor Services Ltd, Goldmartin Garage, Sampys Mill, Mawnan Smith, Falmouth, Cornwall, TR11 5EW Tel: (01326) 250394 Fax: (01326) 250394 E-mail: info@alanco.co.uk

Benfells Ltd, Durham Road, Blackpool, FY1 3QB Tel: (01253) 295500 Fax: (01253) 295100

Bridgwater Electronics Ltd, Unit 15 Westmans Industrial Estate, Love Lane, Burnham-on-Sea, Somerset, TA8 1EY Tel: (01278) 789552 Fax: (01278) 789782 E-mail: sales@bridgwater-electronics.co.uk

Britania Towing, Unit 2 Kensington Road, Canterbury, Kent, CT1 1QZ Tel: (01227) 457010 Fax: (01227) 784080

Car Alarm Centre, Unit 5 Hatton Garden Industrial Estate, Johnson Street, Liverpool, L3 2BR Tel: 0151-227 1241 Fax: 0151-236 4673

Car Spares Cheshunt Ltd, Delamare Road, Cheshunt, Waltham Cross, Hertfordshire, EN8 9AP Tel: (01992) 639844 Fax: (01992) 623871 E-mail: sales@carspares.co.uk

▶ D & B Mairs Car Trimmers, 734 Stockport Road West, Bredbury, Stockport, Cheshire, SK6 2EE Tel: 0161-494 8874 E-mail: dbmairs@ntlworld.com

▶ Hunt Grange Landrover, Vale Rise, Tonbridge, Kent, TN9 1TB Tel: (01732) 353637 Fax: (01732) 376000 E-mail: enquiries@huntgrange.co.uk

▶ In Car Discount, Festival House, Jessop Avenue, Cheltenham, Gloucestershire, GL50 3SH Tel: (0870) 7606110 Fax: (01684) 292200 E-mail: sales@incardiscount.co.uk

JS Auto Repairs, 137 Picasso Way, Shoeburyness, Southend-on-Sea, SS3 9UY Tel: (07779) 799027 Fax: (01702) 316137 E-mail: cs@jsautorepairs.co.uk

K A R Alarms, 4 Lindsey Road, Denham, Uxbridge, Middlesex, UB9 5BP Tel: (01895) 834217 Fax: (01895) 835725

Lion Alarms, Castle Street, Chorley, Lancashire, PR7 3BU Tel: (01257) 266102 Fax: (01257) 249355

Mark Evans Electrical & Security, 165c Soundwell Road, Bristol, BS16 4RS Tel: 0117-956 0695 Fax: 0117-956 0695

Moving Sound & Security, 151-153 Burnley Road, Accrington, Lancashire, BB5 6DH Tel: (01254) 393331 Fax: 01254 398539 E-mail: sales@movingsound-security.co.uk

Precision Alarms, Pauls Court, 12b Meppel Avenue, Canvey Island, Essex, SS8 9RZ Tel: (01268) 696787 Fax: (01268) 696922 E-mail: sales@precisionalarms.co.uk

▶ Select Telecommunications Ltd, 1 Lynn Road, Littleport, Ely, Cambridgeshire, CB6 1QG Tel: (0800) 0832228 Fax: (0870) 0337000 E-mail: info@selecttelecom.demon.co.uk

South Bank Alarms Ltd, 47 Church Lane, Humberston, Grimsby, South Humberside, DN36 4HZ Tel: (01472) 210031 Fax: (01472) 230772

South Coast Alarms Ltd, 54 Overcombe Drive, Weymouth, Dorset, DT3 6QF Tel: (01305) 832614 E-mail: admin@southcoastalarms.co.uk

ALARM SOUNDER

▶ CNA Electronic Systems, Unit 25, Furnace Industrial Estate, Shildon, County Durham, DL4 1QB Tel: (01388) 778051 E-mail: info@talking-alarms.co.uk

Live-Link Communications Ltd, 6 Milrig Cottage, Kirknewton, Midlothian, EH27 8DE Tel: (01506) 884404 Fax: (01506) 884406 E-mail: nursecallalarms@aol.com

Nationwide Cables, Unit 34, Minworth Industrial Park, Forge Lane, Minworth, Sutton Coldfield, West Midlands, B76 1AH Tel: 0121-313 1001 Fax: 0121-351 4851

ALARM SYSTEM INSTALLATION OR MONITORING OR SERVICING

1st Alert Alarm Systems, 44a Rhone Road, Dungannon, County Tyrone, BT71 7EN Tel: (028) 8778 9669 Fax: (028) 8778 9703 E-mail: info@1st-alertalarms.co.uk

4c Security Systems Ltd, 7 Fern Hill, Benllech, Tyn-y-Gongl, Gwynedd, LL74 8UE Tel: (01248) 853525 Fax: (01248) 853525 E-mail: sales@4csecurity.co.uk

A & S Alarms, 25 Rothbury Gardens, Plymouth, PL6 8TU Tel: (01752) 700284

Abacus Security Systems, 38 Randall Road, Kenilworth, Warwickshire, CV8 1JY Tel: (01926) 851322

Acorn Security Alarms Ltd, Swan House, Bonds Mill, Stonehouse, Gloucestershire, GL10 3RF Tel: (01453) 794050 Fax: (01453) 794051 E-mail: info@acornsecurityalarms.co.uk

▶ Alarm Guard, PO Box 156, Plymouth, PL1 4WY Tel: (0845) 6123130 Fax: (0871) 4332264 E-mail: paul@alarmguard.co.uk

Alarm Installations, Unit 11 Moorside Maltings, Burton Row, Leeds, LS11 5NX Tel: 0113-271 1944 Fax: 0113-271 1902

Alarm Security, 150 Hunter Dr, Bletchley, Milton Keynes, MK2 3NF Tel: 01908 642653 Fax: 01908 642653

Aztek Services Ltd, Unit 8 Hall Barn Industrial Estate, Isleham, Ely, Cambridgeshire, CB7 5RB Tel: (01638) 781799 Fax: (01638) 781768 E-mail: sales@aztekservices.co.uk

B & D Electrical Security & Surveillance Ltd, Unit 12 Grinnall Business Centre, Sandy Lane, Stourport-on-Severn, Worcestershire, DY13 9QB Tel: (01299) 822758 Fax: (01299) 827995

Barnet Lock & Security, 123-125 Baker Street, Enfield, Middlesex, EN1 3HA Tel: (020) 8342 0040 Fax: (020) 8342 0230 E-mail: barnetlock@btconnect.com

Berkeley Guard Ltd, The Pottery, Ham Lane, Baughurst, Tadley, Hampshire, RG26 5SD Tel: 0118-981 1428 Fax: 0118-981 0487 E-mail: info@berkeleyguard.com

Blaby Electrical Ltd, 12 Waterloo Crescent, Wigston, Leicestershire, LE18 3QH Tel: 0116-288 3493 Fax: 0116-288 4138 E-mail: beba@btconnect.com

Ble Ltd, Church Street, Eckington, Sheffield, S21 4BH Tel: (01246) 436361 Fax: (01246) 436726 E-mail: sales@blegroup.co.uk

C & G Alarms, 1 Spencer Street, Barnsley, South Yorkshire, S70 1QX Tel: (01226) 203139 Fax: (01226) 203139

Cartel Security, Chesham Close, Romford, RM7 7PJ Tel: (01708) 756100 Fax: (01708) 756200 E-mail: sales@openviewgroup.com

Castle Alarms, Millennium House, Boundary Bank, Kendal, Cumbria, LA9 5RR Tel: (01539) 731394 Fax: (01539) 735367 E-mail: sales@fp.castlealarms.f9.co.uk

Ceaton Security Services, The Lodge, 128 Newport Road, Cardiff, CF24 1DH Tel: (029) 2047 2288 Fax: (029) 2047 3377

Central Home Alarms, 66 Strowan Road, Comrie, Crieff, Perthshire, PH6 2EH Tel: (01764) 670540 Fax: (01764) 679652

Centurion Security System, Centurion House, Park Road West, Huddersfield, HD4 5RX Tel: (01484) 321321 Fax: (01484) 351888 E-mail: sales@centurion.net

Cleggys Electrics, 3 Sharpe Close, Barton-upon-Humber, South Humberside, DN18 5TL Tel: (01652) 636066 E-mail: jrclegg147@aol.com

Crimecure Burglar Alarm Systems, Enterprise House, 27a North Street, Crewkerne, Somerset, TA18 7AL Tel: (01460) 77582 Fax: (01460) 77582 E-mail: ken@crimecure.fsnet.co.uk

D A C Services, 45 Ross Avenue, Dalgety Bay, Dunfermline, Fife, KY11 9YN Tel: (01383) 820700 Fax: (0871) 2421081

D A S Alarms, 34 Water Lane, Ashton-on-Ribble, Preston, PR2 2NL Tel: (01772) 728900 Fax: (01772) 728300

D C Security, 3 Litherland Road, Sale, Cheshire, M33 2PE Tel: 0161-926 9955 Fax: 0161-286 1633

D D D Security Systems Ltd, Security House, Mile Lane, Coventry, CV1 2NL Tel: (024) 7652 5525 Fax: (024) 7652 5104 E-mail: admin@dddltd.com

Darlington Alarm Centre, 78 Heathfield Park, Middleton St. George, Darlington, County Durham, DL2 1LW Tel: (01325) 354500 E-mail: sales@darlingtonalarmcentre.co.uk

Discount Security Wholesalers Ltd, 217 Manchester Road, Oldham, OL8 4QY Tel: 0161-682 6869 Fax: 0161-682 8787

Duchy Alarms, Silverwell, Blackwater, Truro, Cornwall, TR4 8JG Tel: (01872) 560560 Fax: (01872) 560041 E-mail: irg@duchyalarms.co.uk

Eastman Car Alarm & Sounds, 428 Green Lane, Ilford, Essex, IG3 9LD Tel: (020) 8597 8000 E-mail: eastman@onetel.com

ALARM SYSTEM INSTALLATION OR MONITORING OR SERVICING –

continued

Electrical & Alarm Services, Colebrook Road, Plympton, Plymouth, PL7 4AA Tel: (01752) 337271 Fax: (01752) 337271 E-mail: easdale@eurobell.co.uk

Elite Security, 168 Crowmere Road, Shrewsbury, SY2 5LA Tel: (01743) 441010 Fax: (01743) 341739

Evasafe Products Ltd, Farren Court, Cowfold, Horsham, West Sussex, RH13 8BP Tel: (01403) 864486 Fax: (01403) 864873 E-mail: info@evasafe.co.uk

Expo Link Alarms Ltd, 35 Knowley Road, Beach Hill, Wigan, Lancashire, WN6 7PZ Tel: (01942) 494004 Fax: (01942) 825991 E-mail: sales@linkalarms.co.uk

▶ Express Security Systems, 88 Vallance Road, London, E1 5BW Tel: (020) 7377 6565 Fax: (020) 7900 1691 E-mail: marketing@etsuk.co.uk

Fortress Lock & Safe Co., 107 Brixton Hill, London, SW2 1AA Tel: (020) 8674 6657 Fax: (020) 8674 6439 E-mail: info@fortresslock.co.uk

P.F. Friend & Son Ltd, 3 Rolle Cottages, Rolle Street, Barnstaple, Devon, EX31 1JL Tel: (01271) 343058 Fax: (01271) 325319 E-mail: pffriend@hotmail.co.uk

Gardit Alarms, 18 Oakwood Mews, Worksop, Nottinghamshire, S80 3PF Tel: (01909) 475341

Gardner Security Ltd, Vine House, Elmbridge Road, Cranleigh, Surrey, GU6 8EL Tel: (01483) 277474 Fax: (01483) 272739 E-mail: sales@statedigitaluk..co.uk

Glendale Security Systems, Unit 3 62 Muirs, Kinross, KY13 8AU Tel: (01577) 863525 Fax: (01577) 863524

Guardian Alarms Ltd, 20-22 Sydenham Road, Croydon, CR0 2EF Tel: (020) 8686 8777 Fax: (020) 8686 9777 E-mail: sales@guardianalarms.co.uk

Guardian Security, 1 North Lane, Sandgate, Folkestone, Kent, CT20 3AS Tel: (01303) 226452 Fax: (01303) 248399 E-mail:

Hadleigh Burglar Alarm Co., Essex House, Josselin Road, Burnt Mills Industrial Estate, Basildon, Essex, SS13 1EL Tel: (01268) 727173 Fax: (01268) 728553 E-mail: sales@hadleigh-security.co.uk

Harrison Locks, Pump Street, Worcester, WR1 2QX Tel: (01905) 20999 Fax: (01527) 892612 E-mail: harrison.lock@btinternet.com

Hi-Tech Security Services Ltd, Fortune Business Park, Brook Lane, Worthing, West Sussex, BN12 5JD Tel: (01903) 709000 Fax: (01903) 709002E-mail: cust.serv@guardianhitech.com

Holman Security Systems, 1 Mill View, Hinckley, Leicestershire, LE10 0HE Tel: (01455) 251025 Fax: (01455) 890059

Home Securities, 55 Piccadilly, Stoke-on-Trent, ST1 1EA Tel: (01782) 204646 Fax: (01782) 204646 E-mail: homesecurities@btconnect.com

Initial Electronic Security Systems Ltd, Wilson House, Waterberry Drive, Waterlooville, Hampshire, PO7 7XX Tel: (023) 9223 0566 Fax: (023) 9223 0567

Intruder Security Services, Security House 6-7 The Downs, Great Dunmow, Dunmow, Essex, CM6 1DS Tel: (01279) 758870 Fax: (01371) 879201 E-mail: info@intruder.co.uk

P. Jackson, 8 Robin Royd Grove, Mirfield, West Yorkshire, WF14 0LB Tel: (01924) 492388 Fax: (01924) 492388

K M Birch Security Systems, 25 Corville Road, Halesowen, West Midlands, B62 9TJ Tel: 0121-421 5874 Fax: 0121-421 5874

Keyways Security Systems Ltd, Keyways House, 337 Hale Road, Hale Barns, Altrincham, Cheshire, WA15 8SX Tel: 0161-980 6655 Fax: 0161-904 0768 E-mail: info@keyways.co.uk

Kingsley Security, 1 Town Street, Farsley, Pudsey, West Yorkshire, LS28 5EN Tel: 0113-255 6996 Fax: 0113-255 6919 E-mail: sales@kingslysecurity.co.uk

L & P Security & Electrical Services Ltd, Suite F1 St James House, 6 Overcliffe, Gravesend, Kent, DA11 0EF Tel: (01474) 351038 Fax: (01474) 353880

Laser Alarms, 23 The Lane, Awsworth, Nottingham, NG16 2QP Tel: 0115-932 4658

▶ Lincs Electrical Services, 6 Buttler Way, Sleaford, Lincolnshire, NG34 7PA Tel: (01529) 309505 E-mail: lincelectrical@tiscali.co.uk

Mcclymont Intruder Alarms, 106 Essex Road, Liverpool, L36 1XP Tel: 0151-482 1527 Fax: 0151-482 1527

Masterguard Security Services Ltd, Masterguard House, 1 Ipsley Street, Redditch, Worcestershire, B98 7AR Tel: (01527) 65344 Fax: (01527) 63888 E-mail: mastergaurd_2000@yahoo.co.uk

Mayfair Security, Adelaide House Vivars Way, Canal Road, Selby, North Yorkshire, YO8 8BE Tel: (01757) 701596 Fax: (01757) 212442 E-mail: sales@mayfairsecurity.co.uk

Minder Alarm Co., 1 Market Place, Penistone, Sheffield, S36 6DA Tel: (01226) 370100 Fax: (01226) 764994 E-mail: minderalarmsltd@btconnect.com

Mono Alarm Installations, New Hall, Liverpool Road, Eccles, Manchester, M30 7LJ Tel: 0161-786 2649 Fax: 0161-786 2648 E-mail: sales@thewhitegroup.co.uk

Multiplex Security Communications Ltd, 32-34 Constitution Hill, Birmingham, B19 3JT Tel: 0121-236 6977

N K M Fire Protection Ltd, Broadford Oast, Goudhurst Road, Tonbridge, Kent, TN12 8ET Tel: (01892) 724242 Fax: (01892) 723242

Oakpark Alarms, Bayard Place, Verwood Road, Three Legged Cross, Wimborne, Dorset, BH21 6RJ Tel: (01202) 827776 Fax: (01202) 827776 E-mail: oakpark@fsbdial.co.uk

Octagon Security, 87 High Road, Ickenham, Uxbridge, Middlesex, UB10 8LH Tel: (01895) 624545 Fax: (01895) 624546 E-mail: sales@octogan.ltc.co.uk

P H Electrical, 5 Crawshaw Avenue, Sheffield, S8 7DZ Tel: 0114-274 7823

P J S Electrical, 11 Unity Avenue, Hessle, North Humberside, HU13 9NF Tel: (01482) 649123 Fax: (01482) 627281 E-mail: info@pjse.co.uk

Perimeter Security Solutions, Roeacre House, Fir Street, Heywood, Lancashire, OL10 1NW Tel: (0870) 8508739 Fax: (01706) 627767

Pound Hill Security Ltd, 8 Balliol Close, Crawley, West Sussex, RH10 3TE Tel: (01293) 883821 Fax: (01293) 883821 E-mail: poundshillsecurity@freenet.co.uk

S & G Tate, 3 Pigot Road, Denbigh, Clwyd, LL16 3DG Tel: (01745) 814024 Fax: (01745) 814024

S P I Security, 16 Saltmarket, Glasgow, G1 5LY Tel: 0141-564 1634 Fax: 0141-564 1636

Saddleworth Burglar Alarm Systems, 162 Wall Hill Road, Dobcross, Oldham, OL3 5BL Tel: (01457) 870773

Sandal Security Services Ltd, Otters Holt, Durkar, Wakefield, West Yorkshire, WF4 3QE Tel: (01924) 250350 Fax: (01924) 256217 E-mail: sales@sandalsecurity.co.uk

Seaton Fire & Security, 11 Dorking Close, Blyth, Northumberland, NE24 3LX Tel: (01670) 797030 Fax: (01670) 797030

Security Patrol Services Ltd, Roseland, Church Lane, Norton, Worcester, WR5 2PS Tel: (01905) 821000 Fax: (01905) 821408

SHS, 4 The Centre, The Broadway, Farnham Common, Slough, SL2 3QQ Tel: (01753) 643451 Fax: (01753) 647140

Sia Ni Ltd, 134 Finaghy Road South, Belfast, BT10 0DG Tel: (028) 9029 8999 Fax: (028) 9029 1617 E-mail: sales@sia.uk.com

A.J. Sibthorpe & Co. Ltd, 22-42 Freshwater Road, Dagenham, Essex, RM8 1RY Tel: (020) 8597 7000 Fax: (020) 8597 7300

South Eastern Security, 90 Canterbury Road, Hawkinge, Folkestone, Kent, CT18 7BN Tel: (01303) 891155 Fax: (01303) 891155 E-mail: enquiries@southeasternsecurity.co.uk

Southern Monitoring Services Ltd, 212-218 London Road, Waterlooville, Hampshire, PO7 7AJ Tel: (0870) 2422220 Fax: (0870) 2433330 E-mail: info@security-house.demon.co.uk

Sovereign Alarms Ltd, 142 Saltdean Vale, Saltdean, Brighton, BN2 8HF Tel: (01273) 301303 Fax: (01273) 300937

Surrey Security Systems, 37 Woodbridge Hill, Guildford, Surrey, GU2 9AA Tel: (01483) 303012 Fax: (01483) 303013

Switch Alarms, 8 Boothroyden Road, Middleton, Manchester, M24 4RY Tel: 0161-653 2541

T Alarms, Little Adelaide Farm, Lower Road, East Farleigh, Maidstone, Kent, ME15 0JN Tel: (01622) 729439 Fax: 01622 729439

Team Technology (South West) Ltd, Riverside Road, Pottington Business Park, Barnstaple, Devon, EX31 1TE Tel: (01271) 370420 Fax: (01271) 375977 E-mail: sales@teamtechnologysw.co.uk

Television Installation Services (Mansfield) Ltd, Old Mill Lane Industrial Estate, Mansfield Woodhouse, Mansfield, Nottinghamshire, NG19 9BG Tel: (01623) 425800 Fax: (01623) 650767 E-mail: sales@tisnet.co.uk

Tollgate Security Ltd, 16 Claverton Buildings, Bath, BA2 4LD Tel: (01225) 444328 E-mail: sales@tollgatesecurity.co.uk

Total Security, 7 The Greys, March, Cambridgeshire, PE15 9HN Tel: (01354) 652936

Trident Alarms, 23 Hawksmoor Dr, Perton, Wolverhampton, WV6 7TL Tel: 01902 743494 Fax: 01902 688557

Trust Alarms, 3 Poot Hall Syke, Dewhirst Road, Rochdale, Lancashire, OL12 0AS Tel: (01706) 357050

Universal Securities CCTV Ltd, 47a/49 Newbold Road, Chesterfield, Derbyshire, S41 7PL Tel: (01246) 555893 Fax: (01246) 239997

Vocalvale Ltd, 2 Yarmouth Road, Hemsby, Great Yarmouth, Norfolk, NR29 4NJ Tel: (01493) 732575 Fax: (01493) 730795

Wilson Alarms, Ruyton XI Towns, Shrewsbury, SY4 1WX Tel: (0845) 2306966 Fax: (0845) 2306967 E-mail: enquiries@wilson-alarms.co.uk

ALARM SYSTEMS, *See also headings for particular types*

A D K (Northwest) Ltd, 215 Accrington Road, Blackburn, BB1 2AQ Tel: (01254) 278999 Fax: (01254) 278970 E-mail: jemimah@london.com

▶ Alarm Guard, PO Box 156, Plymouth, PL1 4WY Tel: (0845) 6123130 Fax: (0871) 4332264 E-mail: paul@alarmguard.co.uk

Alert Alarms, 16 Church Parade, Canvey Island, Essex, SS8 9RQ Tel: (01268) 696534 Fax: (01268) 680785 E-mail: alertalarms@blueyonder.co.uk

Archer Electrical Services, 9 Parkdale Avenue, Wednesbury, West Midlands, WS10 9BG Tel: 0121-556 7024

B S Security, PO Box 115, Fareham, Hampshire, PO15 5TT Tel: (01489) 885870 Fax: (01489) 889801 E-mail: enquiries@bssecurity.co.uk

Barrier Surveillance Services, 77 Main Street, Shildon, County Durham, DL4 1AN Tel: (01388) 776833 Fax: (01388) 775886

Britannic Security Systems Ltd, The Exchange, Haslucks Green Road, Shirley, Solihull, West Midlands, B90 2EL Tel: 0121-744 0770 Fax: (0870) 2000772 E-mail: information@britannic-security.com

C M S Alarms, 603 Newport Road, Cardiff, CF3 4FA Tel: (029) 2079 5697 Fax: (029) 2079 5796

Ceaton Security Services, The Lodge, 128 Newport Road, Cardiff, CF24 1DH Tel: (029) 2047 2288 Fax: (029) 2047 3377

Christie Intruder Alarms Ltd, Security House, 212-218 London Road, Waterlooville, Hampshire, PO7 7AJ Tel: (023) 9226 5111 Fax: (023) 9226 5112 E-mail: enquiries@ciaalarms.co.uk

Civic Alarms Ltd, 79 Main Rd, Long Hanborough, Witney, Oxon, OX29 8JX Tel: 01993 883448 Fax: 01993 883661

Direct Alarm, 10 Limetree Avenue, Grimsby, South Humberside, DN33 2BB Tel: (01472) 278816

Discount Security Wholesalers Ltd, 217 Manchester Road, Oldham, OL8 4QY Tel: 0161-682 6869 Fax: 0161-682 8787

Initial Electronic Security Systems Ltd, Unit 22 Sea Vixen Industrial Estate, 3 Wilverley Road, Christchurch, Dorset, BH23 3RU Tel: (01202) 484172 Fax: (01202) 475828 E-mail: christchurch@ies.uk.com

Initial Electronic Security Systems Ltd, Wilson House, Waterberry Drive, Waterlooville, Hampshire, PO7 7XX Tel: (023) 9223 0566 Fax: (023) 9223 0567

Intruder 2000 Group Ltd, 47a Newbold Rd, Newbold, Chesterfield, Derbyshire, S41 7PG Tel: 01246 272023 Fax: 01246 239997

J W Alarms, 17 Crayke Road, Stockton-on-Tees, Cleveland, TS18 4EY Tel: (01642) 601131 Fax: (01642) 601131

K J W Alarms, 26A Church Road, Lilleshall, Newport, Shropshire, TF10 9HE Tel: (01952) 604757

M S I Alarms Ltd, Communications House, 9 Llewelyn Avenue, Llandudno, Gwynedd, LL30 2ER Tel: (01492) 860050 Fax: (01492) 870009 E-mail: solutions@msi.uk.net

MB Fire Protection, Unit 22 Bourne Road Industrial Park, Bourne Road, Dartford, DA1 4BZ Tel: (01322) 523399 Fax: (01322) 528883

Micromark Burglar Alarm Systems, Unit B1 Senator Point, South Boundary Road, Knowsley Industrial Park, Liverpool, L33 7RS Tel: (0870) 2413029 Fax: 0151-547 2266

N-Force Security Solutions, 95 Lambert Road, Grimsby, North East Lincolnshire, DN32 0NR Tel: (01472) 604609 E-mail: sales@n-force.co.uk

NSIN, 394A Poulton Road, Wallasey, Merseyside, CH44 4BT Tel: 0151-638 5575 Fax: 0151-637 1588

Octagon Security, 87 High Road, Ickenham, Uxbridge, Middlesex, UB10 8LH Tel: (01895) 624545 Fax: (01895) 624546 E-mail: sales@octogan.ltc.co.uk

Riscr Group, Commerce House, Whitbrook Way, Stakehill Distribution Park, Middleton, Manchester, M24 2SS Tel: 0161-655 5555 Fax: 0161-655 5599 E-mail: sales@riscrgroup.co.uk

Sandal Security Services Ltd, Otters Holt, Durkar, Wakefield, West Yorkshire, WF4 3QE Tel: (01924) 250350 Fax: (01924) 256217 E-mail: sales@sandalsecurity.co.uk

Sigma Electrical, 66 Cardinal Avenue, St. Budeaux, Plymouth, PL5 1UT Tel: (01752) 704529 Fax: (01752) 367515

South Coast Alarms Ltd, 54 Overcombe Drive, Weymouth, Dorset, DT3 6QF Tel: (01305) 832614 E-mail: admin@southcoastalarms.co.uk

Tritech Security & Electrical Services, 22 Muriel Street, Barrhead, Glasgow, G78 1QB Tel: 0141-881 1100 Fax: 0141-881 4449

Uni Fire Seurities, 9 Moor St Trading Estate, Brierley Hill, West Midlands, DY5 3SS Tel: (01432) 353400 Fax: (0800) 0723868 E-mail: admin@uni-fire.co.uk

Van Gadgets, 137 Heston Road, Hounslow, TW5 0RD Tel: (0870) 3833388 Fax: (020) 8572 8510 E-mail: sales@vangadgets.co.uk

Vision UK, PO BOX 501, DARTFORD, DA4 0LG Tel: 01322 866313 Fax: 01322 864816 E-mail: info@vision-uk.co.uk

Westcountry Security Exeter Ltd, 15 Billacombe Road, Plymouth, PL9 7HN Tel: (0870) 8500432 Fax: (01752) 492591 E-mail: sales@westcountrysecurity.co.uk

ALARM SYSTEMS, AMUSEMENT/VENDING MACHINE

Acorn Security Systems, Royal Insurance Building, 6 The Strand, Derby, DE1 1BA Tel: (01332) 370561

Speed Alarm Ltd, 94-98 Sandon Street, Nottingham, NG7 7AN Tel: 0115-978 0791 Fax: 0115-942 2423 E-mail: sales@speedalarm.com

ALARM SYSTEMS, MOTOR CAR/VEHICLE

▶ Advanced Car Audio & Security, Unit 36 Vulcan Road South, Norwich, NR6 6AF Tel: (01603) 789896 Fax: (01603) 789467

▶ Ams, 25 Challenge Enterprise Centre, Sharps Close, Portsmouth, PO3 5RJ Tel: (023) 9266 9600 Fax: (023) 9267 9743 E-mail: danny@automotivesecurity.co.uk

Autonix, 64 Brackley Square, Woodford Green, Essex, IG8 7LL Tel: (020) 8498 9797 Fax: (020) 8491 6331

Bridgwater Electronics Ltd, Unit 15 Westmans Industrial Estate, Love Lane, Burnham-on-Sea, Somerset, TA8 1EY Tel: (01278) 789552 Fax: (01278) 789782 E-mail: sales@bridgwater-electronics.co.uk

▶ Car Alarm Service Ltd, Drakes Lane Industrial Estate, Drakes Lane, Boreham, Chelmsford, CM3 3BE Tel: (01245) 362754

Car Connection, Unit 7b, Sovereign Way Dock Road, Birkenhead, Merseyside, CH41 1DL Tel: 0151-652 4317 Fax: 0151-652 4317 E-mail: carconnection@talktalkbusiness.net

Car Radio & Security Centre Halifax, 6 Trinity Road, Halifax, West Yorkshire, HX1 2QF Tel: (01422) 363207 Fax: (01422) 321450

Car Spares Cheshunt Ltd, Delamare Road, Cheshunt, Waltham Cross, Hertfordshire, EN8 9AP Tel: (01992) 639844 Fax: (01992) 623871 E-mail: sales@carspares.co.uk

Chapelhouse Farm, Roaring Gate Lane, Hale, Altrincham, Cheshire, WA15 8TZ Tel: 0161-903 9016 Fax: 0161-980 4303 E-mail: info@chapelhouseairportparking.co.uk

▶ D & B Mairs Car Trimmers, 734 Stockport Road West, Bredbury, Stockport, Cheshire, SK6 2EE Tel: 0161-494 8874 E-mail: dbmairs@ntlworld.com

▶ Delta Distributors, Unit 10 Win Business Park, Canal Quay, Newry, County Down, BT35 6PH Tel: (028) 3026 7555 Fax: (028) 3026 8814 E-mail: sales@deltadistributors.co.uk

Driveshield Ltd, Stockton Business Centre, 70-74 Brunswick Street, Stockton-on-Tees, Cleveland, TS18 1DW Tel: (01642) 608464 Fax: (07092) 077805

▶ In Car Centre Ltd, Unit 2 Magnet Road, Wembley, Middlesex, HA9 7RG Tel: (020) 8908 0777 Fax: (020) 8904 8465 E-mail: sales@incarcentre.com

In Car Music, 605 High Road Leyton, London, E10 6RF Tel: (020) 8558 6221 Fax: (020) 8556 3948 E-mail: sales@incarmusic.co.uk

▶ Infotrack Ltd, Trackcom House 2 Newmarket Court, Chippenham Drive, Kingston, Milton Keynes, MK10 0AQ Tel: (01908) 288285 Fax: (01908) 288280 E-mail: info@infotrack.com

John Kleis Car Hi-Fi Communications, 248 Basingstoke Road, Reading, RG2 0HN Tel: 0118-986 6224 Fax: (0870) 7702870 E-mail: sales@johnkleis.com

L S UK Ltd, 124 Anlaby Road, Hull, HU3 2JH Tel: (01482) 610977 Fax: (01482) 219818 E-mail: kvssales@aol.co.uk

M A Distributors Ltd, Industrial House, Conway Street, Hove, East Sussex, BN3 3LW Tel: (01273) 720129 Fax: (01273) 820915 E-mail: ash@ma-d.net

▶ Millertech, Unit 7 Bondor Business Centre, London Road, Baldock, Hertfordshire, SG7 6HP Tel: (01462) 896417 Fax: (01462) 490435

▶ Mobile Systems Ltd, 1 Four Turnings Cottages, Preston Road, Wingham Canterbury, Canterbury, Kent, CT3 1EU Tel: (01227) 720011 E-mail: sales@mobilesystemsltd.com

North London Car Sounds Vhcle Security Systems, PO Box 302, Welwyn Garden City, Hertfordshire, AL8 7NQ Tel: (01707) 371681 E-mail: info@piranha-alarms.co.uk

▶ Orbital Communications, 11 Fountain Parade, Mapplewell, Barnsley, South Yorkshire, S75 6FW Tel: (01226) 388157 Fax: (0845) 6444864 E-mail: info@orbitalcomms.com

▶ Premier Car Systems Ltd, Units 18-19, The Stacey Bushes Trading Centre, Erica Road, Stacey Bushes, Milton Keynes, MK12 6HS Tel: (01908) 220337

R S Audio & Alarms, 86-88 College Road, Perry Barr, Birmingham, B44 8DA Tel: 0121-603 1938 Fax: 0121-331 4404 E-mail: info@rsaudio.co.uk

▶ Secure Ice, 159, Marsh Road, Luton, LU3 2QL Tel: (01582) 507860

▶ Neil Sharp, Riverside Close, Weston-Super-Mare, Avon, BS22 7RZ Tel: (01934) 519278 Fax: (01934) 519278

▶ Sound & Secure, Robins Park, Loddiswell, Kingsbridge, Devon, TQ7 4RT Tel: (07966) 033718 E-mail: jason@soundandsecure.freeserve.co.uk

▶ Speedline Graphics, 81 Queens Road, Buckhurst Hill, Essex, IG9 5BW Tel: (020) 8504 8070 E-mail: speedline1@hotmail.co.uk

▶ Street Workz, Silver Wing Industrial Estate, Horatius Way, Croydon, CR0 4RU Tel: (020) 8603 7272 Fax: (020) 8603 7272

Toad plc, National Control Centre, Drake Road, Mitcham, Surrey, CR4 4HQ Tel: (020) 8710 7770 Fax: (020) 8710 7708 E-mail: info@toad.co.uk

Transfit, 572 Wilmslow Road, Manchester, M20 3DB Tel: 0161-367 7559 Fax: 0161-491 6124 E-mail: sales@transfit.com

ALARM SYSTEMS, MOTOR CAR/VEHICLE – *continued*

W A S O 2000, 15 Park Avenue, Cheadle Hulme, Cheadle, Cheshire, SK8 6EU Tel: (0870) 9027979 Fax: 0161-428 1790 E-mail: sales@waso.co.uk

ALARMS, WARNING LIGHTS

▶ Cannoc Electrical, Unit 5 Martindale Industrial Estate, Hawks Green, Cannock, Staffordshire, WS11 7XN Tel: (01543) 505104 Fax: (01543) 466034 E-mail: sales@cannockelectrical.com

ALARMS, WARNING LIGHTS, FORK LIFT TRUCK

▶ Log-It Systems Ltd, 12 Sycamore Close, Retford, Nottinghamshire, DN22 7JP Tel: (0800) 7834625 Fax: (0800) 3281240 E-mail: sales@logitsystems.com

ALBUMS

▶ FotoStation, 146 High Street, Ruislip, Middlesex, HA4 8LJ Tel: (01895) 674000 E-mail: info@fotostation.co.uk

ALCOHOL BROKERS

▶ Kegmaster.Co.Uk, 77 Warwick Road, Sparkhill, Birmingham, B11 4RB Tel: 0121-247 5347 Fax: 0121-247 5347 E-mail: sales@kegmaster.co.uk

ALGINATES

Alec Tiranti Ltd, 3 Pipers Court, Berkshire Drive, Thatcham, Berkshire, RG19 4ER Tel: 0118-930 2775 Fax: (0845) 1232101 E-mail: enquiries@tiranti.co.uk

ALIGNMENT BEARINGS

W G Keyte & Sons Ltd, Daux Road, Billingshurst, West Sussex, RH14 9SP Tel: (01403) 782276

ALL TERRAIN CRANES

▶ J. Thomas (Southern) Ltd, Bankside House, Henfield Road, Small Dole, Henfield, West Sussex, BN5 9XQ Tel: (01273) 494848 Fax: (01273) 497804 E-mail: cranes@jthomas.co.uk

ALL TERRAIN VEHICLE ATTACHMENTS

▶ Profile Events, Whiskett Hill, Barkisland, Halifax, West Yorkshire, HX4 0BN Tel: (01422) 371385 Fax: (01422) 371385 E-mail: sales@profileevents.co.uk

▶ Quad-X, 37 Carnearney Road, Ahoghill, Ballymena, County Antrim, BT42 2PJ Tel: (028) 2587 2800 Fax: (028) 2587 8744 E-mail: info@quad-x.com

ALLOY DIE CASTINGS

Aluminium Service Co. (Warwick) Ltd, Millers Road, Warwick, CV34 5AE Tel: (01926) 491824 Fax: (01926) 410072

Bridgnorth Castings Ltd, Alveley Industrial Estate, Alveley, Bridgnorth, Shropshire, WV15 6HG Tel: (01746) 781177 Fax: (01746) 781188 E-mail: vp32@dial.pipex.com

ALLOY IRON CASTINGS

Brad Ken Uk Ltd, Heath Road, Wednesbury, West Midlands, WS10 8JL Tel: 0121-526 4111 Fax: 0121-526 4174

Cerdic Foundries Ltd, Beeching Close, Chard, Somerset, TA20 1BB Tel: (01460) 64301 Fax: (01460) 63961 E-mail: sales@cerdicfoundries.co.uk

Ductile Castings Ltd, Trent Foundary, Dawes Lane, Scunthorpe, South Humberside, DN15 6UW Tel: (01724) 862152 Fax: (01724) 280461 E-mail: info@ductile.co.uk

George Taylor & Co (Hamilton) Ltd, Kemp St, Hamilton, Lanarkshire, ML3 6PQ Tel: (01698) 284949 Fax: (01698) 891285 E-mail: office@gtham.co.uk

Hillsyde Foundry (Staffordshire) Ltd, Apedale Works, Rowhurst Industrial Estate, Chesterton, Newcastle, Staffordshire, ST5 6BD Tel: (01782) 564411 Fax: (01782) 562546 E-mail: sales@hillsyde.com

Jennings Winch & Foundry Co. Ltd, Tatham Street, Sunderland, SR1 2AG Tel: 0191-567 4408 Fax: 0191-510 1549 E-mail: jwf.co.ltd@aol.com

L E W Diecastings Ltd, Trows Lane, Rochdale, Lancashire, OL11 2UF Tel: (01706) 632218 Fax: (01706) 638473 E-mail: alan@lew.co.uk

Taylormade Castings Ltd, Cobridge Road, Stoke-on-Trent, ST1 5JP Tel: (01782) 261537 Fax: (01782) 261262 E-mail: tmcstoke@ukonline.co.uk

ALLOY METAL (NON FERROUS) PRODUCERS

Anglo Blackwells Ltd, Ditton Road, Widnes, Cheshire, WA8 0NT Tel: 0151-495 1400 Fax: 0151-495 4201 E-mail: sales@angloblackwells.com

Britannia Refined Metals Ltd, Britannia Works, Botany Road, Northfleet, Gravesend, Kent, DA11 9BG Tel: (01474) 538200 Fax: (01474) 538203

F E Mottram Ltd, Oakes Green, Stevenson Road, Sheffield, S9 3XG Tel: 0114-244 6723 Fax: 0114-242 5344 E-mail: ferrometals@femottram.co.uk

F E Mottram Non Ferrous Ltd, Radnor Park Industrial Estate, Congleton, Cheshire, CW12 4XE Tel: (01260) 271122 Fax: (01260) 271324 E-mail: info@femottram.co.uk

Luton Metal Castings, 3b Holly Street Trading Estate, Holly Street, Luton, LU1 3XG Tel: (01582) 451817 Fax: (01582) 723798

Novelis U.K Ltd, Castle Works, Rogerstone, Newport, Gwent, NP10 9YD Tel: (01633) 202020 Fax: (01633) 202000 E-mail: bunworth@novelis.com

Whitehead Alloys Ltd, 4 Buck Street, Middlesbrough, Cleveland, TS2 1LW Tel: (01642) 223606 Fax: (01642) 246137 E-mail: whiteheadalloys@btconnect.com

ALLOY STEEL

Advanced Metals International Ltd, Odhams Trading Estate, St.Albans Road, Watford, WD24 7RT Tel: (01923) 205599 Fax: (01923) 205588 E-mail: sales@advancedmetals.com

Eurosteel & Allied Ltd, 61 Washford Road, Sheffield, S9 3XW Tel: 0114-242 0066 Fax: 0114-242 0077 E-mail: frank@gsbaceroltd.co.uk

Ferrari Stainless & Alloys Ltd, Unit 89, Woolsbridge Industrial Park, Three Legged Cross, Wimborne, Dorset, BH21 6SU Tel: (01202) 823346 Fax: (01202) 823903

Goodwin Alloy Products, Goodwin House, Leek Road, Hanley, Stoke-On-Trent, ST1 3NR Tel: (01782) 220260 Fax: (01782) 228060 E-mail: goodwinplc@goodwin.co.uk

Heymark Metals Ltd, Becklands Close, Bar Lane, Roecliffe, York, YO51 9NR Tel: (01423) 323388 Fax: (01423) 326888 E-mail: enquiries@heymark.co.uk

Ims UK, International House, Saltley Trading Estate, Saltley, Birmingham, B8 1BB Tel: 0121-326 3100 Fax: 0121-326 3105

Ovako Ltd, Unit 2 Yorks Park, Blowers Green Road, Dudley, West Midlands, DY2 8UL Tel: (01384) 213940 E-mail: graham.butler@ovako.com

Premier Alloys, Newbridge Industrial Estate, Newbridge, Midlothian, EH28 8PJ Tel: 0131-333 4140 Fax: 0131-333 4727 E-mail: premier_alloys@mih.co.uk

RTR Handelsgesellschaft, 8 Kingsway House, Kingsway, Team Valley Trading Estate, Gateshead, Tyne & Wear, NE11 0HW Tel: 0191-491 1292 Fax: 0191-491 1246 E-mail: sales@rtr.co.uk

Schlolz+Bickenbach UK Ltd, Speedwell Industrial Estate, Staveley, Chesterfield, Derbyshire, S43 3JW Tel: (01246) 280280 Fax: (01246) 280445

Special Quality Alloys Ltd, Colwall St, Sheffield, S9 3WP Tel: 0114-243 4366 Fax: 0114-244 1199 E-mail: sales@specialqualityalloys.com

Van Leeuwen Tubes Ltd, Unit 7 Provincial Park, Nether Lane, Ecclesfield, Sheffield, S35 9ZX Tel: 0114-257 7577 Fax: 0114-257 0639 E-mail: sales@vanleeuwen.nl

Woodberry Chillcott & Co. Ltd, Unit 17 Court Road Industrial Estate, Cwmbran, Gwent, NP44 3AS Tel: (01633) 869311 Fax: (01633) 874676 E-mail: cwmbran@woodberrychillcott.co.uk

Woodberry Chillcott & Co. Ltd, 6 Spinnaker Road, Hempsted, Gloucester, GL2 5FD Tel: (01452) 418341 Fax: (01452) 300362 E-mail: sales@woodberrychillcott.co.uk

Woodberry Chillcott & Co. Ltd, Unit 6 Langage Industrial Estate, Eastern Wood Road, Plympton, Plymouth, PL7 5ET Tel: (01752) 343421 Fax: (01752) 346947 E-mail: plymouth@woodberrychillcott.co.uk

Woodberry Chillcott & Co. Ltd, 5 Mountbatten Business Park, Jackson Close, Portsmouth, PO6 1UR Tel: (023) 9238 8031 Fax: (023) 9237 3615 E-mail: portsmouth@woodberrychillcott.co.uk

ALLOY STEEL CASTINGS

Alfa, Rockwood, Keldholme, York, YO62 6NB Tel: (01751) 432953 Fax: (01751) 432518

Ampo UK, Holly Tree Cottage, Stocks Lane, Welshampton, Ellesmere, Shropshire, SY12 0NT Tel: (01948) 710764 Fax: (01948) 710914 E-mail: ampouk@aol.com

Blantyre Castings Ltd, Block 9a West Avenue, Blantyre, Glasgow, G72 0UZ Tel: (01698) 829572 Fax: (01698) 824093 E-mail: blantyrecastings@btconnect.com

Ceramicast Precision Investment Castings Ltd, Castings House, Boundary Road, Woking, Surrey, GU21 5BX Tel: (01483) 751666 Fax: (01483) 751888 E-mail: sales@ceramicast.com

Darwins Holdings Ltd, Fitzwilliam Works, Sheffield Road, Sheffield, S9 1RL Tel: 0114-244 8421 Fax: 0114-256 1775

▶ H I Quality Steel Castings Ltd, Foundry Street, Wittington Moor, Chesterfield, Derbyshire, S41 9AX Tel: (01246) 260303 Fax: (01246) 260245 E-mail: steven@hiqsc.com

▶ Investment Castings Ltd, 130 Great North Road, Birchwood Industrial Estate, Hatfield, Hertfordshire, AL9 5JN Tel: (01707) 262871 Fax: (01707) 271565 E-mail: investmentcastings130@yahoo.co.uk

Polycast Ltd, Clocktower Buildings, Shore Road, Warsash, Southampton, SO31 9GQ Tel: (01489) 885560 Fax: (01489) 885608 E-mail: sales@polycast.ltd.uk

▶ Precision Products (Cumberland) Ltd, Highmill, Alston, Cumbria, CA9 3HT Tel: (01434) 381228 Fax: (01434) 381038 E-mail: sales@shawprocess.co.uk

ALTERNATING CURRENT (AC) CONTACTORS

Forward Microsystems Leicester Ltd, 40 Northgate Street, Leicester, LE3 5BY Tel: 0116-262 7974 Fax: 0116-262 4864 E-mail: sales@formicro.co.uk

ALTERNATING CURRENT (AC) CONTROL COIL MODULAR BLOCK CONTACTORS

Enbray Cooper (UK) Ltd, Derwent Drive, Derwent Howe Industrial Estate, Workington, Cumbria, CA14 3YW Tel: (01900) 68173 Fax: (01900) 68189 E-mail: sales@enbray.co.uk

ALTERNATING CURRENT (AC) ELECTRIC MOTOR DRIVES

Inviron Ltd, Deben House, 1 Selsdon Way, City Harbour, London, E14 9GL Tel: (020) 7515 5511 Fax: (020) 7515 5551 E-mail: admin@inviron.co.uk

ALTERNATING CURRENT (AC) ELECTRIC MOTORS

Bancroft & Co., 5 Stairbridge Court, Stairbridge Lane, Bolney, Haywards Heath, West Sussex, RH17 5PA Tel: (01444) 248884 Fax: (01444) 242767 E-mail: sales@bancroft.co.uk

Bennett Electrical Co, 6-8 Reginald St, Burslem, Stoke-on-Trent, ST6 1DU Tel: (01782) 825281 Fax: (01782) 575120 E-mail: motors@bennettelectrical.com

Brook Crompton, St. Thomas Road, Huddersfield, HD1 3LJ Tel: (01484) 557200 Fax: (01484) 557201 E-mail: csc@brookcrompton.com

Camis Motors & Drives, Wallows Industrial Estate, Brierley Hill, West Midlands, DY5 1QA Tel: (01384) 480645 Fax: (01384) 480745 E-mail: sales@camis.com

Chamjtes Ltd, Mason Fold, Lea Lane, Lea Town, Preston, PR4 0RN Tel: (01772) 726975 Fax: (01772) 721277 E-mail: john@chamjets.com

Control Techniques, Business Development Centre, Stafford Park 4, Telford, Shropshire, TF3 3BA Tel: (01952) 213727 Fax: (01952) 213701 E-mail: uksales@controltechniques.com

Crouzet Ltd, Intec 3, Wade Road, Basingstoke, Hampshire, RG24 8NE Tel: (01256) 318900 Fax: (01256) 318901 E-mail: sales@crouzet.com

Electric Motor Rewinds, 6 Upper Wharf, Fareham, Hampshire, PO16 0LZ Tel: (01329) 233154 Fax: (01329) 280679

Electrical Repairs & Rewind Service Ltd, 2 Charlotte Street, Wakefield, West Yorkshire, WF1 1UL Tel: (01924) 365117 Fax: (01924) 200268

Euromotor Ltd, 5 Bolney Grange Business Park, Stairbridge Lane, Bolney, Haywards Heath, West Sussex, RH17 5PB Tel: (07000) 226276 Fax: (07002) 668677 E-mail: sales@euromotor.net

Fraser & Macdonald Electric Motors Ltd, 176 Woodville Street, Glasgow, G51 2RN Tel: 0141-445 3874 Fax: 0141-425 1135 E-mail: frasmcd@aol.com

Gibbons Drive Systems Ltd, Woodrolfe Road, Tollesbury, Maldon, Essex, CM9 8RY Tel: (01621) 868138 Fax: (01621) 868188 E-mail: sales@gibbonsdrives.co.uk

Koncar, Unit 43, Brittania Way, Enterprise Industrial Pk, Lichfield, Staffs, WS14 9UY Tel: (01543) 255995 Fax: (01543) 250316

LEMAC Ltd, Hospital Road, Haddington, East Lothian, EH41 3PD Tel: (01620) 828700 Fax: (01620) 828730 E-mail: info@lemac.com

The Morley Electrical Engineering Co. Ltd, Bradford Road, Stanningley, Pudsey, West Yorkshire, LS28 6QB Tel: 0113-257 1734 Fax: 0113-257 0751 E-mail: sales@morleymotors.com

Powerplus Electric Motors, 5 Clydesmuir Industrial Estate, Clydesmuir Road, Cardiff, CF24 2QS Tel: (029) 2046 1602 Fax: (029) 2048 4820 E-mail: sales@powerpluselectricmotors.co.uk

Premium Power Units Ltd, Block 10, Unit 4, Beardmore Way, Clydebank, Dunbartonshire, G81 4HT Tel: 0141-952 4344 Fax: 0141-952 6350 E-mail: sales@premiumpowerunits.co.uk

Rossi Gearmotors Ltd, Unit 8-9 Phoenix Park, Bayton Road Industrial Estate, Coventry, CV7 9QN Tel: (024) 7664 4646 Fax: (024) 7664 4535 E-mail: sales@rossigears.com

S E W Eurodrive Ltd, Beckbridge Road, Normanton Industrial Estate, Normanton, West Yorkshire, WF6 1QR Tel: (01924) 893855 Fax: (01924) 893702 E-mail: sales@sew-eurodrive.co.uk

Slater Drive Systems Ltd, 6a Dukesway, Prudhoe, Northumberland, NE42 6PQ Tel: (01661) 835566 Fax: (01661) 833868 E-mail: sales@slater-drives.com

Tyco Networks (UK) Ltd, Wheatley Hall Road, Doncaster, South Yorkshire, DN2 4NB Tel: (01302) 812712 Fax: (01302) 364738

Weg Electric Motors UK Ltd, Unit 28 29, Walkers Road, Moons Moat North Industrial Estate, Redditch, Worcestershire, B98 9HE Tel: (01527) 596748 Fax: (01527) 591133 E-mail: wegsales@wegelectricmotors.co.uk

Zeitlauf, Treetops House, Gillotts Lane, Henley-On-Thames, Oxfordshire, RG9 1PT Tel: (01491) 579118 Fax: (01491) 412211 E-mail: sales@acdcsystems.com

ALTERNATING CURRENT (AC) ELECTRIC MOTORS TO SPECIFICATION

Koncar, Unit 43, Brittania Way, Enterprise Industrial Pk, Lichfield, Staffs, WS14 9UY Tel: (01543) 255995 Fax: (01543) 250316

ALTERNATING CURRENT (AC) GENERATORS

Amco Marelli Ltd, Meadow Lane, Loughborough, Leicestershire, LE11 1NB Tel: (01509) 615518 Fax: (01509) 615514 E-mail: sales@amco.fki-et.com

Cummins Generator Technologies, Barnack Road, Stamford, Lincolnshire, PE9 2NB Tel: (01780) 484000 Fax: (01780) 484100 E-mail: info@cumminsgeneratortechnologies.com

Driftgate 2000 Ltd, Little End Road, Eaton Socon, St. Neots, Cambridgeshire, PE19 8JH Tel: (01480) 470400 Fax: (01480) 470401 E-mail: sales@dg2k.co.uk

ALTERNATING CURRENT (AC) GENERATORS OVER 10 KVA

Cummins Generator Technologies, Barnack Road, Stamford, Lincolnshire, PE9 2NB Tel: (01780) 484000 Fax: (01780) 484100 E-mail: info@cumminsgeneratortechnologies.com

ALTERNATING CURRENT (AC) GENERATORS UP TO 10 KVA

Cummins Generator Technologies, Barnack Road, Stamford, Lincolnshire, PE9 2NB Tel: (01780) 484000 Fax: (01780) 484100 E-mail: info@cumminsgeneratortechnologies.com

ALTERNATING CURRENT (AC) MOTOR CONTROLLER INVERTERS

Crompton Controls Ltd, Monckton Road, Wakefield, West Yorkshire, WF2 7AL Tel: (01924) 368251 Fax: (01924) 367274 E-mail: sales@cromptoncontrols.co.uk

Merlin Equipment, Unit 4, Cabot Business Village, Holyrood Close, Cabot Lane, Poole, Dorset, BH17 7BA Tel: (01202) 697979 Fax: (01202) 691919 E-mail: sales@merlinequipment.com

Nord Gear Ltd, 11 Barton Lane, Abingdon, Oxfordshire, OX14 3NB Tel: (01235) 534404 Fax: (01235) 534414 E-mail: info@nord.uk.com

Seltec Automation, Subway Street, Hull, HU3 4EL Tel: (01482) 225297 Fax: (01482) 212470 E-mail: sales@seltec.co.uk

SSD Drives Ltd, New Courtwick Lane, Wick, Littlehampton, West Sussex, BN17 7RZ Tel: (01903) 737000 Fax: (01903) 737100 E-mail:

ALTERNATING CURRENT (AC) POWER SUPPLIES

Harrison & Greenwood Transformers Ltd, Mill Lane, Halifax, West Yorkshire, HX3 6TR Tel: (01422) 329003 Fax: (01422) 329009

ALTERNATING CURRENT (AC) TO ALTERNATING CURRENT (AC) CONVERTERS

Powerco (International) Ltd, 1 Strawberry Vale, Twickenham, TW1 4RY Tel: (0208) 831 6634 Fax: (0208) 891 6435 E-mail: radin.powerco@virgin.net

ALTERNATING CURRENT (AC) TO DIRECT CURRENT (DC) CONVERTERS

Alfatronix Ltd, 29 Newtown Business Park, Albion Close, Poole, Dorset, BH12 3LL Tel: (01202) 715517 Fax: (01202) 715122 E-mail: sales@alfatronix.co.uk

Power One, 24 Upper High Street, Worthing, West Sussex, BN11 1DL Tel: (01903) 823323 Fax: (01903) 823324 E-mail: sales@powerone.com

Powerfactor Ltd, 8 Pear Tree Farm, Townsend, Marsh Gibbon, Bicester, Oxfordshire, OX27 0EY Tel: (01869) 278585 Fax: (01869) 278989 E-mail: sales@powerfactor.co.uk

ALTERNATING CURRENT (AC) TO DIRECT CURRENT (DC) POWER SUPPLIES

▶ Haredata Electronics Ltd, 14 Crown House, Hornbeam Square North, Hornbeam Park, Harrogate, North Yorkshire, HG2 8PB Tel: (01423) 853180 Fax: (01423) 853199 E-mail: sales@haredata.co.uk

ALTERNATING CURRENT (AC) TO DIRECT CURRENT (DC) TRANSFORMERS

Demeter Windings, Beehive Lane, Chelmsford, CM2 9TE Tel: (01245) 344544 Fax: (01245) 265344 E-mail: demeterw@lycos.co.uk

ALTERNATIVE DISPUTE RESOLUTION (ADR) SERVICES

▶ Compromitto, 151 West George St, Glasgow, G2 2JJ Tel: 0141 2284737

▶ Soma Contract Services Ltd, 6 The Green, Dunchurch, Rugby, Warwickshire, CV22 6NX Tel: (01788) 817811 Fax: (01788) 817282 E-mail: maggieholman@somacontracts.co.uk

ALTERNATIVE FUELS, BIODIESEL

▶ Bioroute Ltd, Flint House, 25 Charing Cross, Norwich, NR2 4AX Tel: (01603) 724714 Fax: (01603) 724700 E-mail: biodiesel@bioroute.co.uk

ALTERNATIVE FUND INVESTMENT MANAGEMENT

W H Ireland Ltd, 11 St James's Square, Manchester, M2 6WH Tel: 0161-832 2174 Fax: 0161-833 0935 E-mail: laurie.beavers@wh-ireland.co.uk

ALTERNATIVE MEDICINES

▶ At The Source, 192 Clarendon Park Road, Leicester, LE2 3AF Tel: 0116-270 6255 E-mail: beverley@atthesource.co.uk

▶ Awareness Centre Of Natural Health, 41 Abbeville Road, London, SW4 9JX Tel: (020) 8673 8844 Fax: (020) 8673 8844 E-mail: sales@awarness.com

Balham Wholefoods & Health Store, 8 Bedford Hill, London, SW12 9RG Tel: (020) 8673 4842

Countryworld Ltd, Common Lane, Culcheth, Warrington, WA3 4EH Tel: (01925) 765448

Depeche Mode Laboratories, 8 Chestnut Close, Maidenhead, Berkshire, SL6 8SY Tel: (01628) 674644 Fax: (01628) 789640 E-mail: info@depeche-mode.co.uk

▶ Erasmus Foundation, Moat House, Banyards Green, Laxfield, Woodbridge, Suffolk, IP13 8ER Tel: (01986) 798682 E-mail: julia@erasmus-foundation.org

Firefly Tonics Ltd, 1 Petersham Mews, London, SW7 5NR Tel: (020) 7052 9720 Fax: (020) 7052 9729 E-mail: info@fireflytonics.com

Health Leads UK Ltd, 2 St. Clears Business Park, Tenby Road, St. Clears, Carmarthen, SA33 4JW Tel: (01994) 231940 Fax: (01994) 231941 E-mail: mail@healthleadsuk.com

▶ Isis Centre, 3 Dorset Street, Brighton, BN2 1WA Tel: (01273) 626644 E-mail: info@isiscentre.co.uk

▶ Karma Times Limited, PO Box 9066, Chelmsford, CM3 8WU Tel: 07963 844171 E-mail: enquires@karma-times.co.uk

Maheono Alternative Therapies, 99 Reading Road, Yateley, Hampshire, GU46 7LR Tel: (01252) 861351 Fax: E-mail: info@maheono.com

Medico-Oil Co, 29 Penhale Road, Eastbourne, East Sussex, BN22 7JX Tel: (01323) 646777 Fax: (01323) 646777 E-mail: sales@medico-oil.fsnet.co.uk

▶ Rotherham Reiki, 6 Rowan Rise, Maltby, Rotherham, South Yorkshire, S66 8BZ Tel: (01709) 817008 E-mail: rotherhamreiki@tiscali.co.uk

Safeandsound, Alma House, Perranporth, Cornwall, TR6 2QT Tel: (07854) 825599 E-mail: allysafeandsound@hotmail.co.uk

The Sea of Tranquillity (Elaine Gradone), 42 Seaview Crescent, Edinburgh, EH15 2LT Tel: 0131 6696772 E-mail: info@theseaoftranquility.co.uk

▶ Touch Alternative Health, PO Box 4462, London, W1A 7NX Tel: 020 7935 2205 Fax: 020 7935 2008 E-mail: getintouch@londontouch.com

▶ www.Nutritionzone.co.uk, Unit 5, Mill Road Industrial Estate, Linlithgow Bridge, Linlithgow, West Lothian, EH49 7QY Tel: (01506) 848968 E-mail: admin@nutrtionzone.co.uk

ALUMINISED CARBON STEEL COILS

Phoenix Steel Services Ltd, Units 3-4, Charlotte Street, Dudley, West Midlands, DY1 1TD Tel: (01384) 458866 Fax: (01384) 455576 E-mail: sales@phoenixsteelservices.co.uk

ALUMINIUM ACCESS COVERS OR GRATING

Rhodes Engineering Group Ltd, High Street Mills, High Street, Heckmondwike, West Yorkshire, WF16 0DL Tel: (01924) 410740 Fax: (01924) 410164 E-mail: tranter@rhodesengineering.co.uk

ALUMINIUM AIRCRAFT COMPONENTS

Ipeco Holdings Ltd, Aviation Way, Southend-on-Sea, SS2 6UN Tel: (01702) 209258 Fax: (01702) 542279

ALUMINIUM ALLOY OR ALUMINIUM TREADPLATES

▶ Eltherington Group Ltd, Dansom Lane, Hull, HU8 7LA Tel: (01482) 320336 Fax: (01482) 317824 E-mail: info@eltherington.co.uk

ALUMINIUM ALLOY PRESSURE DIE CASTINGS

Alzin Engineering Ltd, Century Works, Briggate, Elland, West Yorkshire, HX5 9HG Tel: (01422) 373456 Fax: (01422) 373813 E-mail: info@alzin.co.uk

B S C (Diecasting) Ltd, Fryers Close, Walsall, WS3 2XQ Tel: (01922) 710070 Fax: (01922) 408008 E-mail: tech@bscdiecasting.co.uk

Chem-Trend (UK) Ltd, Hough Mills, Bradford Road, Halifax, West Yorkshire, HX3 7BN Tel: (0870) 3504708 Fax: (0870) 3509427 E-mail: uksales@chemtrend.com

L C L Castings Ltd, Showfield Lane, Malton, North Yorkshire, YO17 6BT Tel: (01653) 694436 Fax: (01653) 600224 E-mail: sales@lcl-castings.co.uk

Norfran Aluminium Ltd, West Chirton Trading Estate, North Shields, Tyne & Wear, NE29 7TY Tel: 0191-258 2611 Fax: 0191-257 1549 E-mail: jb@norfran.co.uk

Alexander Pollock Ltd, Hospital Road, Haddington, East Lothian, EH41 3PD Tel: (01620) 823344 Fax: (01620) 824252 E-mail: jstewart@alexander-pollock.co.uk

Taylor Group, 25 St. Marys Road, Dundee, DD3 9DJ Tel: (01382) 826763 Fax: (01382) 832238 E-mail: info@tgdiecasting.co.uk

W Hallam Castings Ltd, Coulman Road Industrial Estate, Thorne, Doncaster, South Yorkshire, DN8 5JU Tel: (01405) 813006 Fax: (01405) 813786 E-mail: sales@hallamcastings.co.uk

ALUMINIUM ARCHITECTURAL WINDOWS

North 4 Design, Unit 12, 2 Somerset Road, London, N17 9EJ Tel: (020) 8885 4404 Fax: (0870) 1308374 E-mail: websales@north4.co.uk

▶ Solex Manufacturing, Unit 8, Tower Road, Gluther Industrial Estate, Washington, Tyne & Wear, NE37 2SH Tel: 0191-419 4499 Fax: 0191-419 4466 E-mail: sales@solexltd.com

ALUMINIUM BOXES

▶ Nova Aluminium, 11 Lawfords Gate, Bristol, BS2 0DY Tel: 0117-955 6463 Fax: 0117-955 6472 E-mail: sales@nova-aluminium.com

ALUMINIUM BRASS TUBE FITTINGS

Flowflex Components Ltd, Samuel Blaser Works, Tongue Lane Industrial Estate, Buxton, Derbyshire, SK17 7LR Tel: (01298) 77211 Fax: (01298) 72362 E-mail: flowflex@compuserve.com

Marine Engineering Pipworks, Leechmere East Industrial Estate, Sunderland, SR2 9TE Tel: 0191-521 1941 Fax: 0191-523 6954 E-mail: info@mepsun.com

ALUMINIUM BRAZING

Electrobase RP Ltd, 7 Maxim Road, Dartford, DA1 4BG Tel: (01322) 555938 Fax: (01322) 555099 E-mail: sales@electrobaserp.co.uk

Ipeco Engineering Ltd, Aviation Way, Southend-on-Sea, SS2 6UN Tel: (01702) 544939 Fax: (01702) 546480

Stuart Engineering, Unit B4 Chadwell Heath Industrial Park, Kemp Road, Dagenham, Essex, RM8 1SL Tel: (020) 8590 7412 Fax: (020) 8598 1787

ALUMINIUM BRIDGES

B A E Systems Land Systems (Bridging) Ltd, P O Box 37, Wolverhampton, WV4 6YN Tel: (01902) 405050 Fax: (01902) 355354 E-mail: kathryn.fisher@baesystems.com

ALUMINIUM BRONZE

Ampco Metal Ltd, 17 Binns Close, Coventry, CV4 9TB Tel: (024) 7646 7011 Fax: (024) 7646 1455 E-mail: info@ampcometal.co.uk

Columbia Metals Ltd, 19 High Street, Earls Barton, Northampton, NN6 0JG Tel: (01604) 810317 Fax: (01604) 812494 E-mail: sales@columbiametals.co.uk

Salmon Consultancy, Littlewood Farm, Cheddleton, Leek, Staffordshire, ST13 7LB Tel: (01538) 361010 Fax: (01538) 361011 E-mail: salmonconsult@btconnect.com

ALUMINIUM BRONZE ALLOYS

Salmon Consultancy, Littlewood Farm, Cheddleton, Leek, Staffordshire, ST13 7LB Tel: (01538) 361010 Fax: (01538) 361011 E-mail: salmonconsult@btconnect.com

ALUMINIUM BRONZE BOLTS AND NUTS

J Cooke Engineering Ltd, Ashwell Street, Baldock, Hertfordshire, SG7 5QT Tel: (01462) 742236 Fax: (01462) 742188 E-mail: sales@jcooke.co.uk

ALUMINIUM BRONZE CASTINGS

Crowncast Ltd, Rushenden Road, Queenborough, Kent, ME11 5HD Tel: (01795) 662722 Fax: (01795) 666552 E-mail: crowncast@whsmithnet.co.uk

J I Blackburn Foundry Ltd, Grove Works, West Road, Bridport, Dorset, DT6 5JT Tel: (01308) 459040 Fax: (01308) 459040

J T Barker & Sons Ltd, Leeds Foundries, Westland Square, Leeds, LS11 5SS Tel: 0113-271 6837 Fax: 0113-270 6901

Longton Light Alloys Ltd, Foxley Lane, Stoke-on-Trent, ST2 7EH Tel: (01782) 536615 Fax: (01782) 533415 E-mail: info@aluminium-castings.com

White Eagle Foundry Ltd, 199 Cuckfield Road, Hurstpierpoint, Hassocks, West Sussex, BN6 9RT Tel: (01273) 832062 Fax: (01273) 833628 E-mail: wef@wef.co.uk

ALUMINIUM BRONZE DIE CASTINGS

Eutectic Alloy Castings Wolverhampton Ltd, Units 25-26, Wood Street, Park Village, Wolverhampton, WV10 9DS Tel: (01902) 726699 Fax: (01902) 726692

V T L Automotors Ltd, Ellen Holme, Luddendenfoot, Halifax, West Yorkshire, HX2 6EL Tel: (01422) 882561 Fax: (01422) 883323

ALUMINIUM BRONZE FORGINGS

Cerro (Manganese Bronze) Ltd, PO Box 22, Ipswich, IP2 0EG Tel: (01473) 252127 Fax: (01473) 218229 E-mail: sales@scerromb.com

T J Smith & Son Grinding Services Ltd, 17 Clifton Street, Sheffield, S9 2DQ Tel: 0114-244 8335 Fax: 0114-244 8336 E-mail: sales@precision-grinding.co.uk

ALUMINIUM BRONZE RODS

Cerro (Manganese Bronze) Ltd, PO Box 22, Ipswich, IP2 0EG Tel: (01473) 252127 Fax: (01473) 218229 E-mail: sales@scerromb.com

T J Smith & Son Grinding Services Ltd, 17 Clifton Street, Sheffield, S9 2DQ Tel: 0114-244 8335 Fax: 0114-244 8336 E-mail: sales@precision-grinding.co.uk

ALUMINIUM CABINETS

D N Brettle Cabinet Makers, 2 Burgage Garden Workshop, Burgage, Southwell, Nottinghamshire, NG25 0EP Tel: (01636) 816036

Furniture Works, Pullens Farm, Lamberhurst Road, Horsmonden, Tonbridge, Kent, TN12 8ED Tel: (01892) 723474

T M Arlidge, New Road, Whaley Bridge, High Peak, Derbyshire, SK23 7JG Tel: (01663) 734230 Fax: (01663) 734230

ALUMINIUM CANS

Aerocan (UK) Ltd, Folly Road, Roundway, Devizes, Wiltshire, SN10 2HT Tel: (01380) 727006 Fax: (01380) 732440

Carnaudmetalbox, Golf Course Lane, Leicester, LE3 1TX Tel: 0116-291 3300 Fax: 0116-291 3312

ALUMINIUM CASTINGS

▶ A1 Outsource Ltd, 32 St. Ives Road, Coventry, CV2 5FZ Tel: (07903) 857799 E-mail: mitin@a1outsource.co.uk

Alpac Alloys Holdings Ltd, Dale Street, Burton-on-Trent, Staffordshire, DE14 3TE Tel: (01283) 567737 Fax: (01283) 512359 E-mail: peter@alpacgroup.com

Alphacast Ltd, 139 Park Road, Halesowen, West Midlands, B63 2NR Tel: (01384) 634542 E-mail: alphacast@btconnect.com

C & J Castings, 42 Bayton Road, Exhall, Coventry, CV7 9EJ Tel: (024) 7636 3031 Fax: (024) 7636 3556 E-mail: clive@42baytonroad.freeserve.co.uk

Castech (UK) Ltd, Unit 10 Manor Farm, Main Road, Newport Pagnell, Buckinghamshire, MK16 9JS Tel: 01234 391973 Fax: 01234 391185 E-mail: info@castech.co.uk

Holden Aluminium Technologies Ltd, Linton Trading Estate, Bromyard, Herefordshire, HR7 4QT Tel: (01885) 482222 Fax: (01885) 482000 E-mail: info@alloy.uk.com

▶ Opticast (UK) Ltd, Pipers Road, Park Farm Industrial Estate, Redditch, Worcestershire, B98 0HU Tel: (01527) 528400 Fax: (01527) 528700 E-mail: opticastuk@bntconnect.com

Star Metal Polishing Ltd, Hilton Trading Estate, Birmingham New Road, Wolverhampton, WV4 6BW Tel: (01902) 408455

Surecast Devizes Ltd, Roundway Mill, London Road, Devizes, Wiltshire, SN10 2EA Tel: (01380) 723402 Fax: (01380) 729063 E-mail: sales@surecast.co.uk

▶ Zeus Group, Sunrise Business Park, High Street, Wollaston, Stourbridge, West Midlands, DY8 4ZZ Tel: (01384) 446400 Fax: (01384) 446446 E-mail: sales@zeuscasting.com

ALUMINIUM CEILING TILES

Craftwork Industries Ltd, 98 Lower Richmond Road, London, SW15 1LN Tel: (020) 8780 1798 Fax: (020) 8780 1861 E-mail: sales@craftwork-interiors.co.uk

ALUMINIUM CHLORIDE SOLUTION

Pearl Chemicals Ltd, The White House, Darlaston Park, Stone, Staffordshire, ST15 0ND Tel: (01785) 819747 Fax: (01785) 811567 E-mail: g.dee@pearlchem.co.uk

ALUMINIUM CHLOROHYDRATE

Alembic Ltd, Unit 6, Wimbourne Buildings, Atlantic Way, Barry, South Glamorgan, CF63 3RA Tel: (01446) 733174 Fax: (01446) 733184E-mail: david@alembic.freeserve.co.uk

E C Gulbrandsen Ltd, Water Lane, Ancaster, Grantham, Lincolnshire, NG32 3QS Tel: (01400) 230700 Fax: (01400) 230601

ALUMINIUM COATED MIRRORS

Specialist Mirror Shop, Mediterranean Village, Metrocentre, Gateshead, Tyne & Wear, NE11 9XG Tel: 0191-460 9328

ALUMINIUM COATED STEEL

Bondcote Ltd, Unit 15, Lister Road Industrial Estate, Sherrington Way, Basingstoke, Hampshire, RG22 4DQ Tel: (01256) 465983 Fax: (01256) 328818 E-mail: mail@bondcote.co.uk

ALUMINIUM COATING SERVICES

B & T Printed Circuits Services Ltd, B&T House, 27 Eastways, Witham, Essex, CM8 3YG Tel: (01376) 519500 Fax: (01376) 500388 E-mail: btcircuits@clara.co.uk

ALUMINIUM COMPONENT FINISHING SERVICES

Edmo, Netherton Road, Overross Industrial Estate, Ross-on-Wye, Herefordshire, HR9 7QQ Tel: (01989) 564215 Fax: (01989) 564644E-mail: sales@edmoengineering.co.uk

Rhodes Barrellings, Unit 4, Victoria Avenue, Borrowash, Derby, DE72 3HE Tel: (07718) 160144 Fax: (01332) 666090 E-mail: rhodesbarrelling@aol.com

ALUMINIUM CONSERVATORIES

▶ 1st APS Conservatory Roof Repairs, Crawford Place, New Road, Staines, Middlesex, TW18 3DH Tel: (01784) 464613 Fax: (01784) 464663

Allard Windows & Doors, Unit 3b Conners Yard, Crowborough Hill, Crowborough, East Sussex, TN6 2DA Tel: (01892) 665224 Fax: (01892) 669545 E-mail: john.allard@btclick.com

Conservatory World, Unit 1, Speedwell Unit, Nelson Road Industrial Estate, Dartmouth, Devon, TQ6 9SZ Tel: (01803) 839330 Fax: (01803) 835803

▶ Durabuild Glazed Structures Ltd, Carlton Road, Coventry, CV6 7FL Tel: (024) 7666 9169 Fax: (024) 7666 9170 E-mail: enquiries@durabuild.co.uk

▶ Ezze UK Ltd, 619 Sewall Highway, Coventry, CV6 7JE Tel: (024) 7666 7755 Fax: (024) 7672 7819 E-mail: wah@ezzeconsevatories.com

Forestdale Windows Ltd, 4 Lakeside, Neptune Close, Medway City Estate, Rochester, Kent, ME2 4LT Tel: (01634) 717860 Fax: (01634) 719399 E-mail: pjenn59165@aol.com

▶ GR8-conservatories.co.uk, PO BOX 697, Telford, Shropshire, TF7 9AL Tel: 01952 282069 Fax: 0845 2802071 E-mail: info@gr8-services.co.uk

Guernsey Glass & Window, Industrial Estate, Braye Road, St. Sampson, Guernsey, GY2 4WX Tel: (01481) 243535 Fax: (01481) 243390 E-mail: gsyglass@guernsey.net

Lafford & Leavey, Arrowhead Road, Reading, RG7 4XB Tel: 0118-930 3333 Fax: 0118-932 3707 E-mail: sales@1afford.com

Oak Valley Fabrications, The Workshop, rear of 91 Chesterfield Road, North Wingfield, Chesterfield, Derbyshire, S42 5LF Tel: 0782 117 9985

▶ Spooner Bros, Hawksworth Trading Estate, Swindon, SN2 1EJ Tel: (01793) 336333 Fax: (01793) 336333 E-mail: Sales@spoonerbrothers.co.uk

ALUMINIUM CONSTRUCTION PRODUCTS, *See headings for particular types such as Doors; Windows*

ALUMINIUM CONTAINERS

▶ Barum & Dewer Ltd, Unit 11 Two Rivers Industrial Estate, Braunton Road, Barnstaple, Devon, EX31 1JY Tel: (01271) 375197 Fax: (01271) 344870

Light Alloy Ltd, 85 Dales Road, Ipswich, IP1 4JR Tel: (01473) 740445 Fax: (01473) 240002 E-mail: sales@lightalloy.co.uk

Record Dimensions Co., Kelvedon House, Hall Lane, Knutsford, Cheshire, WA16 7AE Tel: (01565) 873300 Fax: (01565) 873000 E-mail: sales@rdco.co.uk

ALUMINIUM COOKWARE

Beagle Cookware, 72-78 Stour Street, Birmingham, B18 7AJ Tel: 0121-454 3323 Fax: 0121-454 3342

Red Rose Cookware Ltd, Unit 7-9 11-15 Francis Avenue, Bournemouth, BH11 8NX Tel: (01202) 575900 Fax: (01202) 582120

ALUMINIUM CURTAIN WALLING

▶ Architectural Glazed Facades Ltd, Wellington House, East Road, Cambridge, CB1 1BH Tel: (01223) 451051 Fax: (01223) 566781 E-mail: office@agfacades.co.uk

▶ MTW Architectural, Trinity Business Park, Turner Way, Wakefield, West Yorkshire, WF2 8EF Tel: (01924) 239100 Fax: (01924) 239600 E-mail: neville.taylor@mtwarchitectural.co.uk

Queniborough Aluminium Services Ltd, 1489 Melton Road, Queniborough, Leicester, LE7 3FP Tel: 0116-260 6005 Fax: 0116-260 3005 E-mail: tonybeall@btconnect.com

ALUMINIUM CUTTING SERVICES

All Metal Services Ltd, 6 Horton Industrial Park, Horton Road, West Drayton, Middlesex, UB7 8JD Tel: (01895) 444066 Fax: (01895) 420963 E-mail: london@allmetal.co.uk

The Aluminium Cutting Company Ltd, 2 94 Kitchener Road, High Wycombe, Buckinghamshire, HP11 2SW Tel: (01494) 448790 Fax: (01494) 448794

Arrow Metals Ltd, 200 High Street, Boston Spa, Wetherby, West Yorkshire, LS23 6BT Tel: (01937) 845066 Fax: (01937) 845897 E-mail: arrowmetalsltd@aol.com

Contracut Cutting Services, Unit 19 Mill House Lane, Triangle, Sowerby Bridge, West Yorkshire, HX6 3LN Tel: (01422) 835313 Fax: (01422) 835320 E-mail: scott.thewlis@tiscali.co.uk

Control Waterjet Cutting, Unit 18 Telford Crescent, Speedwell Industrial Estate, Staveley, Chesterfield, Derbyshire, S43 3PF Tel: (01246) 284000 Fax: (01246) 284003 E-mail: sales@controlwaterjet.co.uk

Laser Process Ltd, Upper Keys, Keys Park Road, Hednesford, Cannock, Staffordshire, WS12 2GE Tel: (01543) 495000 Fax: (01543) 495001 E-mail: sales@laserprocess.co.uk

Redditch Lasercutting Ltd, 9 Broad Ground Road, Redditch, Worcestershire, B98 8YP Tel: (01527) 510474 Fax: (01527) 510432

ALUMINIUM DEOXIDISING PRODUCTS, OF STEEL

F E Mottram Ltd, Oakes Green, Stevenson Road, Sheffield, S9 3XG Tel: 0114-244 6723 Fax: 0114-242 5344 E-mail: ferrometals@femottram.co.uk

ALUMINIUM DIE CASTINGS

Ferndowne, Reform Industrial Estate, Maidenhead, Berkshire, SL6 8BY Tel: (01628) 630211 Fax: (01628) 623459

ALUMINIUM DOORS

Agostino Ferrari UK Ltd, Units H & L Strawberry Street Industrial Estate, Strawberry Street, Hull, HU9 1EN Tel: (01482) 594450 Fax: (01482) 594455 E-mail: info@aferrariuk.com

Albro Windows, Albro House, 59 Palmerston Road, Harrow, Middlesex, HA3 7RR Tel: (020) 8863 7383 Fax: (020) 8427 6248

▶ Charter Commercial Windows & Doors, Hoo Farm Industrial Estate, Worcester Road, Kidderminster, Worcestershire, DY11 7RA Tel: (01562) 745940 Fax: (01562) 66596 E-mail: info@chartercommercial.com

Custom Made (U K) Ltd, Oldends Hall, Oldends Lane, Stonehouse, Gloucestershire, GL10 3RQ Tel: (01453) 826884 Fax: (01453) 791259 E-mail: info@custommade.co.uk

Door Maintenance Co. Ltd, Unit 8, Curran Industrial Estate, Curran Road, Cardiff, CF10 5DF Tel: (029) 2066 5539 Fax: (029) 2066 8207E-mail: rpickford@harlechdoors.net

East Yorkshire Glazing Co. Ltd, Wiltshire Road, Hull, HU4 6QQ Tel: (01482) 561101 Fax: (01482) 565307 E-mail: eygsales@eygsales.com

FOCUS Windows Ltd, Unit A Technology Centre, White Oak Square, London Road, Swanley, Kent, BR8 7AG Tel: (01322) 614551 Fax: (01322) 613366

▶ G S M Aluminium Ltd, 16 Maria Street, Burley in Wharfedale, Ilkley, West Yorkshire, LS29 7JA Tel: (01943) 862307 Fax: (01943) 863168 E-mail: gerald@gsmltd.co.uk

Glamalco Ltd, Ipswich Road, Cardiff, CF23 9UR Tel: (029) 2049 7808 Fax: (029) 2047 1796 E-mail: info@glamalco.co.uk

Glass Northampton Ltd, 25-29 Bailiff Street, Northampton, NN1 3DX Tel: (01604) 233343 Fax: (01604) 233298 E-mail: admin@glassnorthampton.co.uk

▶ Harper Window Systems Ltd, The Gables, Ash Lane, Alvechurch, Birmingham, B48 7TT Tel: 0121-445 0104 Fax: 0121-445 3138 E-mail: enquiries@harperwindows.co.uk

K G Smoke Dispersal, 3 Foundry Lane, Horsham, West Sussex, RH13 5PX Tel: (01403) 242299 Fax: (01403) 255577 E-mail: kgsmoke@hotmail.co.uk

Kingsland Construction Ltd, 8 Cookley Wharf, Leys Road, Brierley Hill, West Midlands, DY5 3UP Tel: (01384) 482945 Fax: (01384) 482955 E-mail: sales@kingslandaluminium.co.uk

Leay Ltd, Unit 3 Lake Road, Quarry Wood, Aylesford, Kent, ME20 7TQ Tel: (01622) 882345 Fax: (01622) 882208 E-mail: enquiries@leay.com

Lye Valley Windows & Doors, 4 Stour Vale Road Industrial Estate, Stour Vale Road, Stourbridge, West Midlands, DY9 8PN Tel: (01384) 892952 Fax: (01384) 422626

M D S Architectural Fabrications Ltd, Unit 3a Brandon Way, West Bromwich, West Midlands, B70 8JB Tel: 0121-525 3338 Fax: 0121-525 3348

Micron Aluminium Doors Ltd, Micron House, 45 Leesons Hill, St. Mary Cray, Orpington, Kent, BR5 2LF Tel: (01689) 833501 Fax: (01689) 836188 E-mail: info@micronwindows.co.uk

N T S Aluminium Systems Ltd, Gainsford Drive, Halesowen, West Midlands, B62 8BQ Tel: 0121-501 3814 Fax: 0121-585 5492

Q Glazing Ltd, 83-89 Western Road, Wood Green, London, N22 6US Tel: (020) 8888 7733 Fax: (020) 8888 7744 E-mail: mail@qglazing.com

Reglaze Windows Ltd, 49-51 Collingdon Street, Luton, LU1 1RT Tel: (01582) 730847 Fax: (01582) 417615

▶ Right Units Ltd, Imperial Way, Watford, WD24 4YH Tel: (01923) 224477 Fax: (01923) 211119 E-mail: info@rightunits.com

S J Aluminium Fabrications, Unit E., Area 6, Fort Fareham Business Park, Fareham, Hampshire, PO14 1AH Tel: (01329) 220828 Fax: (01329) 220828 E-mail: sales@shop-frontage.com

Structura UK Ltd, Phoenix Works, Davis Road, Chessington, Surrey, KT9 1TH Tel: (020) 8397 4361 Fax: (020) 8391 5805 E-mail: sales@structura-uk.com

Technal, Units 2-4 Hudswell Road, Hunslet, Leeds, LS10 1AG Tel: 0113-296 1400 Fax: 0113-296 1414 E-mail: leeds@technal.co.uk

Welglaze Ltd, Watermill Industrial Estate, Aspenden Road, Buntingford, Hertfordshire, SG9 9JS Tel: (01763) 271811 Fax: (01763) 273108 E-mail: sales@welgaurd.co.uk

▶ Xtral Ltd, Pelham Works, Pelham Street, Wolverhampton, WV3 0BJ Tel: (01902) 425040

ALUMINIUM DOUBLE GLAZED WINDOWS

5 Star Windows & Conservatories Ltd, The Old Stores, Stanklyn Lane, Summerfield, Kidderminster, Worcestershire, DY11 7RY Tel: (01562) 66955 Fax: (01562) 66955 E-mail: sales@5star-online.co.uk

▶ Capital Windows Manfacturing, Unit 9, Sarum Complex, Salisbury Road, Uxbridge, Middlesex, UB8 2RZ Tel: (01895) 271061

▶ Finesse PVC U Ltd, Arburn House Chapel Place, Dentonholme Trading Estate, Carlisle, CA2 5DF Tel: (01228) 522581 Fax: (01228) 810947 E-mail: info@finessegroup.co.uk

▶ H & P Double Glazing Ltd, Kelsall Street, Oldham, OL9 6HR Tel: 0161-678 9144 E-mail: enquires@hpdoubleglazing.co.uk

▶ Smokeson Glass, Dart Mills, Buckfastleigh, Devon, TQ11 0NF Tel: (01364) 644673 Fax: (01364) 642162 E-mail: mail@smokesonglass.co.uk

ALUMINIUM DRAIN OR SANITARY PIPES

Alumasc Exterior Building Products, White House Works, Bold Road, Sutton, St. Helens, Merseyside, WA9 4JG Tel: 01744 648400 Fax: 01744 648401 E-mail: info@alumasc-exteriors.co.uk

ALUMINIUM ENCLOSURES

W.H Crossley Ltd, Newby Road Industrial Estate, Newby Road, Hazel Grove, Stockport, Cheshire, SK7 5DA Tel: 0161-456 3767 Fax: 0161-483 0602

▶ www.caelectrocomps.co.uk, 36 Park Lane, Bishop's Stortford, Hertfordshire, CM23 3NH Tel: (01279) 656051 Fax: (01279) 656051 E-mail: chris@caelectrocomps.co.uk

ALUMINIUM EXTRUSION DIES

Eroga Die Co. Ltd, 6a Eastbrook Road Trading Estate, Eastbrook Road, Gloucester, GL4 3DB Tel: (01452) 524039 Fax: (01452) 500615 E-mail: mail@erogadie.com

Extrusion Form Tools Ltd, Malvern View Business Park, Stella Way, Bishops Cleeve, Cheltenham, Gloucestershire, GL52 7DQ Tel: (01242) 673377 Fax: (01242) 677711 E-mail: ash@extrusionformtools.com

ALUMINIUM EXTRUSION MACHINING CENTRES

Amech Engineering Ltd, Dudley Road, Yarm Road Industrial Estate, Darlington, County Durham, DL1 4GG Tel: (01325) 488884 Fax: (01325) 382525 E-mail: info@amech.net

ALUMINIUM EXTRUSION MACHINING SERVICES

Advanced Engineering Techniques Ltd, 9-15 Holbrook Avenue, Holbrook Industrial Estate, Holbrook, Sheffield, S20 3FF Tel: 0114-247 5725 Fax: 0114-247 5726 E-mail: sales@aetuk.com

Creative Aluminium, 2 Tower View, Egremont, Cumbria, CA22 2BN Tel: (0778) 5950889 Fax: (0870) 2206938 E-mail: sales@creativealuminium.com

ALUMINIUM EXTRUSION MACHINING SERVICES, CNC

Advanced Engineering Techniques Ltd, 9-15 Holbrook Avenue, Holbrook Industrial Estate, Holbrook, Sheffield, S20 3FF Tel: 0114-247 5725 Fax: 0114-247 5726 E-mail: sales@aetuk.com

ALUMINIUM EXTRUSION MANUFRS

Alcoa (Europe), Southam Road, Banbury, Oxfordshire, OX16 2SN Tel: (01295) 454444 Fax: (01295) 454454

Almaco S.A., PO Box 22, Selby, North Yorkshire, YO8 9YX Tel: (01757) 705979 Fax: (01757) 706383 E-mail: mark.hurst@khass.fsbusiness.co.uk

Ashfield Extrusion Ltd, B Field Industrial Estate, Clover Street, Kirkby-in-Ashfield, Nottingham, NG17 7LH Tel: (01623) 757333 Fax: (01623) 751771 E-mail: ashfield.sales@btconnect.com

Capalex, Cleator Moor, Cumbria, CA25 5QB Tel: (01946) 811771 Fax: (01946) 813681 E-mail: sales@capalex.com

▶ Cold Formed Products Ltd, 24 St. Mary's Road, London, E13 9AD Tel: (020) 8471 2727 Fax: (020) 8470 1706 E-mail: sales@cfp.biz

Creative Aluminium, 2 Tower View, Egremont, Cumbria, CA22 2BN Tel: (0778) 5950889 Fax: (0870) 2206938 E-mail: sales@creativealuminium.com

Edmo, Netherton Road, Overross Industrial Estate, Ross-on-Wye, Herefordshire, HR9 7QQ Tel: (01989) 564215 Fax: (01989) 564644E-mail: sales@edmoengineering.co.uk

Galup Ltd, 48 Elmsdale Road, Wooton, Bedford, MK43 9JU Tel: (01234) 768805 Fax: (01234) 767532 E-mail: sales@galupltd.co.uk

Gilmour Extrusion Ltd, 6 Greenhill Industrial Estate, Coatbridge, Lanarkshire, ML5 2AG Tel: (01236) 426165 Fax: (01236) 423263 E-mail: sales@monklandsextrusion.com

Holton Conform Ltd, Albany House, Elliott Road, Bournemouth, BH11 8JH Tel: (01202) 581881 Fax: (01202) 581789 E-mail: enquiries@holton-conform.com

Hulett Aluminium International, Securehold Business Centre, Studley Road, Redditch, Worcestershire, B98 7LG Tel: (01527) 516222 Fax: (01527) 517199 E-mail: sales@hulett-hydro.co.za

Hydro Aluminium Extrusion Ltd, Pantglas Industrial Estate, Bedwas, Caerphilly, Mid Glamorgan, CF83 8DR Tel: (029) 2085 4600 Fax: (029) 2086 3728 E-mail: haeuk@hydro.com

Hydro Static Extrusions Ltd, Arran Road, North Muirton Industrial Estate, Perth, PH1 3DX Tel: (01738) 629381 Fax: (01738) 633933 E-mail: sales@hydrostatic.co.uk

Ingimex Ltd, Halesfield 19, Telford, Shropshire, TF7 4QT Tel: (01952) 585833 Fax: (01952) 580940 E-mail: sales@ingimex.com

Kawneer UK Ltd, Astmoor Industrial Estate, Runcorn, Cheshire, WA7 1QQ Tel: (01928) 502500 Fax: (01928) 502501 E-mail: sales@kawneereurope.com

Luxfer Gas Cylinders, Colwick Industrial Estate, Nottingham, NG4 2BH Tel: 0115-980 3800 Fax: 0115-980 3899 E-mail: info@luxfercylinders.com

N B Metals Ltd, Unit 10 Blenhiem Court, Brownfields, Welwyn Garden City, Hertfordshire, AL7 1AD Tel: (01707) 324472 Fax: (01707) 324473 E-mail: info@nbmetals.co.uk

S A P A Profiles Ltd, Sawpit Lane, Tibshelf, Alfreton, Derbyshire, DE55 5NH Tel: (01773) 872761 Fax: (01773) 874389 E-mail: info@sapagroup.com

Sapa Profiles Ltd, Tewkesbury Road, Cheltenham, Gloucestershire, GL51 9DT Tel: (01242) 521641 Fax: (01242) 513304 E-mail: info.profiles.uk@sapagroup.com

ALUMINIUM EXTRUSION MILLING SERVICES, CNC

▶ Av-Tech Manufacturing Co. Ltd, Unit 33 London Road Industrial Estate, Baldock, Hertfordshire, SG7 6NG Tel: (01462) 893336 Fax: (01462) 893336
Earhtech Engineering Ltd, Unit 1, Grovebury Place Estate, Grovebury Road, Leighton Buzzard, Bedfordshire, LU7 4SH Tel: (01525) 374362 Fax: (01525) 377304

ALUMINIUM EXTRUSION POWDER COATING SERVICES

▶ CMT Industrial Powdercoaters, 27 Dencora Way, Luton, LU3 3HP Tel: (01582) 575494 Fax: (01582) 584297 E-mail: cmtpowdercoaters@aol.com
Colourtec Powder Coatings, 23a Willow Road, Colnbrook, Slough, SL3 0BS Tel: (01753) 683820 Fax: (01753) 680020
Gwent Powder Coatings Ltd, Unit 37 Springvale Industrial Estate, Cwmbran, Gwent, NP44 5BD Tel: (01633) 860901 Fax: (01633) 872030 E-mail: gpowdercoatings@btconnect.com
▶ Hca, Unit 6 Kingsway, Andover, Hampshire, SP10 5LQ Tel: (01264) 351640 Fax: (01264) 350302 E-mail: adam@hcacoating.co.uk
▶ M K Powder Coatings, 5 Cordingley Street, Bradford, West Yorkshire, BD4 0PP Tel: (01274) 680099 Fax: (01274) 680099
Vertik-al Ltd, Yardley Brook Industrial Park, Lea Ford Road, Shard End, Birmingham, B33 9TX Tel: 0121-608 7171 Fax: 0121-693 7787 E-mail: vertikalltd@aol.com

ALUMINIUM EXTRUSION SAWING SERVICES

Capalex, Cleator Moor, Cumbria, CA25 5QB Tel: (01946) 811771 Fax: (01946) 813681 E-mail: sales@capalex.com
▶ Multi Metals Ltd, Belgrave Street, Bellshill Industrial Estate, Bellshill, Lanarkshire, ML4 3JA Tel: (01698) 841199 Fax: (01698) 841812 E-mail: sales@multimetals.com
Prosaw Ltd, Telford Way, Kettering, Northamptonshire, NN16 8UN Tel: (01536) 410999 Fax: (01536) 410080 E-mail: sales@prosaw.co.uk

ALUMINIUM EXTRUSION STOCKHOLDERS

Aluminium Droitwich, 7 Judge Court, Berry Hill, Berry Hill Industrial Estate, Droitwich, Worcestershire, WR9 9AB Tel: (01905) 794620 Fax: (01905) 797863
C M Alloys, Peartree Business Centre, Cobham Road, Ferndown Industrial Estate, Wimborne, Dorset, BH21 7PT Tel: (01202) 850370 Fax: (01202) 850379
Corus, Wakefield Road, Leeds, LS10 1AY Tel: 0113-276 0660 Fax: 0113-272 7197
Corus, Colndale Road, Colnbrook, Slough, SL3 0HL Tel: (01753) 683131 Fax: (01753) 684372 E-mail: customer-services@corusgroup.com
Corus Service Centre, The Steelpark, Steelpark Way, Wolverhampton, WV11 3SR Tel: (01902) 484200 Fax: (01902) 484049
Creative Aluminium, 2 Tower View, Egremont, Cumbria, CA22 2BN Tel: (0778) 5950889 Fax: (0870) 2206938 E-mail: sales@creativealuminium.com
Dore Metal Services Ltd, Unit 2 Dolphin Park Cremers Road, Sittingbourne, Kent, ME10 3HB Tel: (01795) 473551 Fax: (01795) 429473 E-mail: ian@doremetals.co.uk
L A Metals Ltd, Roebuck Lane, Smethwick, West Midlands, B66 1BY Tel: 0121-553 6846 Fax: 0121-553 3270
▶ M G Supplies Ltd, Unit Y Smarden Business Estate, Smarden, Ashford, Kent, TN27 8QL Tel: (01233) 770500 Fax: (01233) 770100 E-mail: sales@mgsupplies.com
Metal Mouldings Ltd, Unit 6, North Street, Walsall, WS2 8AU Tel: (01922) 615225 Fax: (01922) 632763
▶ Multi Metals Ltd, Belgrave Street, Bellshill Industrial Estate, Bellshill, Lanarkshire, ML4 3JA Tel: (01698) 841199 Fax: (01698) 841812 E-mail: sales@multimetals.com
▶ Smith Metal Centres, Unit 7-10, Eldon Road, Beeston, Nottingham, NG9 6DZ Tel: 0115-925 4801 Fax: 0115-925 5370 E-mail: nottingham-sales@smithmetal.com
▶ Smiths Metal Centres Ltd, Straton Business Park, London Road, Biggleswade, Bedfordshire, SG18 8QB Tel: (01767) 604704 Fax: 01767 600466 E-mail: sales@smithsselect.com
▶ Smiths Metal Centres Ltd, Straton Business Park, London Road, Biggleswade, Bedfordshire, SG18 8QB Tel: (01767) 604704 Fax: (01767) 315271 E-mail: biggleswade@smithmetal.com
▶ Smiths Metal Centres Ltd, Straton Business Park, London Road, Biggleswade, Bedfordshire, SG18 8QB Tel: (01767) 604704 Fax: (01767) 312885 E-mail: sales@smithshp.com
▶ Smiths Metal Centres Ltd, 10 Unicorn Park, Unicorn Park Avenue, Brislington, Bristol, BS4 4EX Tel: 0117-971 2800 Fax: 0117-971 6300 E-mail: info@smithsmetal.com
▶ Smiths Metal Centres Ltd, 3 Epsom Court, Leeds Twenty Seven Industrial Estate, Bruntcliffe Avenue, Morley, Leeds, LS27 0LL Tel: 0113-307 5167 Fax: 0113-307 5327 E-mail: leeds@smithmetal.com
▶ Smiths Metal Centres Ltd, 8-9 Cedar Trade Park, Cobham Road, Ferndown Industrial Estate, Wimborne, Dorset, BH21 7SD Tel: (01202) 893755 Fax: (01202) 893712 E-mail: ferndown@smithmetal.com
▶ Smiths Profiles, Cheltenham Film Studios, Arle Court, Hatherley Lane, Cheltenham, Gloucestershire, GL51 6PN Tel: (01242) 541380 Fax: (01242) 515480 E-mail: sales@smithsprofiles.com
Transtar Metals Ltd, Transtar (Europe) House, 1 Meredews, Letchworth Garden City, Hertfordshire, SG6 1WH Tel: (01462) 687650 Fax: (01462) 684642 E-mail: sales@transtarmetals.com

ALUMINIUM FABRICATORS

A H Fabrication, Thorn Office Centre, Thorn Business Park, Rotherwas, Hereford, HR2 6JT Tel: (01432) 354704 Fax: (01432) 359762 E-mail: alexahfabs@fairadsl.co.uk
A I S Sheet Metal Ltd, Hoo Farm Industrial Estate, Worcester Road, Kidderminster, Worcestershire, DY11 7RA Tel: (01562) 820700 Fax: (01562) 829401 E-mail: sales@aissheetmetal.co.uk
A M Profiles Ltd, Hardwick View Road, Homewood Industrial Estate, Holmewood, Chesterfield, Derbyshire, S42 5SA Tel: (01246) 856000 Fax: (01246) 855105 E-mail: sales@amprofiles.com
▶ Aaf, Unit D1 Royal Pennine Trading Estate, Lynroyle Way, Rochdale, Lancashire, OL11 3EX Tel: (01706) 869238 Fax: (01706) 860059
Ab Light Engineering, Hollygrove Farm, Upper Northam Drive, Hedge End, Southampton, SO30 4BG Tel: (023) 8046 6657 Fax: (023) 8046 6657
Able Steel Fabrications Ltd, Unit 1 Park Street, Gosport, Hampshire, PO12 4UH Tel: (023) 9242 5425 Fax: (023) 9242 5444
Ace Engineers Ltd, Albert Road, Morley, Leeds, LS27 8LD Tel: 0113-252 2611 Fax: 0113-238 0274 E-mail: sales@ace-engineers.co.uk
James Aiken (Sheetmetal) Ltd, 10 Wellington Street, Aberdeen, AB11 5BT Tel: (01224) 572555 Fax: (01224) 571214 E-mail: enquiries@jasm.com
▶ Aire Valley Architectural, 1 Parkwood Street, Keighley, West Yorkshire, BD21 4QH Tel: (01535) 683290 Fax: (01535) 683299
Albann Ltd, Unit 69 Third Avenue, Heatherhouse Industrial Estate, Irvine, Ayrshire, KA12 8HN Tel: (01294) 272311 Fax: (01294) 276677 E-mail: sales@albann.co.uk
Alifab, New Hall Mills, Milton Road, Stoke-on-Trent, ST1 6LE Tel: (01782) 544844 Fax: (01782) 544866 E-mail: sales@alifab.co.uk
Alifabs Woking Ltd, 4 Kernel Court, Walnut Tree Close, Guildford, Surrey, GU1 4UD Tel: (01483) 546547 Fax: (01483) 546548 E-mail: sales@alifabs.com
▶ Allisport Ltd, Little Northend, Newent Lane, Huntley, Gloucester, GL19 3HG Tel: (01452) 751187 Fax: (01452) 830226
Altech Services, 1 Cemetery Road, Houghton Regis, Dunstable, Bedfordshire, LU5 5BZ Tel: (01582) 472882 Fax: (01582) 471887
Aluminium Copper & Stainless Co. Ltd, 22-24 Crittall Road, Witham, Essex, CM8 3DR Tel: (01376) 513419 Fax: (01376) 511615
The Aluminium Cutting Company Ltd, 2 94 Kitchener Road, High Wycombe, Buckinghamshire, HP11 2SW Tel: (01494) 448790 Fax: (01494) 448794
Aluminium Droitwich, 7 Judge Court, Berry Hill, Berry Hill Industrial Estate, Droitwich, Worcestershire, WR9 9AB Tel: (01905) 794620 Fax: (01905) 797863
Aluminium Sashes Ltd, Barnett Way, Barnwood, Gloucester, GL4 3RT Tel: (01452) 616581 Fax: (01452) 371923
Argent Engineering Services Ltd, 52 Stockholm Road, Hull, HU7 0XW Tel: (01482) 838698 Fax: (01482) 838668
Argent Fabrications Ltd, Unit 4 Avery Dell, Lifford Lane, Birmingham, B30 3DZ Tel: 0121-459 9617 Fax: 0121-458 6604 E-mail: enquiries@argentfabs.com
Azimex Fabrications Ltd, Cartwright Road, Northampton, NN2 6HF Tel: (01604) 717712 Fax: (01604) 791087
B A E Systems Land Systems (Bridging) Ltd, P O Box 37, Wolverhampton, WV4 6YN Tel: (01902) 405050 Fax: (01902) 355354 E-mail: kathryn.fisher@baesystems.com
Barton Fabrication Ltd, Harbour Road Trading Estate, Portishead, Bristol, BS20 7BL Tel: (01275) 845901 Fax: (01275) 849462 E-mail: barton.fabrication@virgin.net
Bayswater Tubes & Sections Ltd, The Tube Mills, Pencoed, Bridgend, Mid Glamorgan, CF35 6UG Tel: (01656) 860581 Fax: (01656) 860906 E-mail: sales@aluminiumtubes.com
▶ Bell Bros Pudsey Ltd, Green Lane, Pudsey, West Yorkshire, LS28 8JN Tel: 0113-256 5715 Fax: 0113-256 9255E-mail: info@bellbros.com
Bolenda Engineering Ltd, Birds Hill, Clopton, Woodbridge, Suffolk, IP13 6SE Tel: (01473) 601982 Fax: (01473) 690954 E-mail: lee@bolenda.ndo.co.uk
Bradford Welding & Sheet Metal Co. Ltd, 340b Thornton Road, Bradford, West Yorkshire, BD8 8LD Tel: (01274) 480288 Fax: (01274) 480284
▶ C M C Aluminium Systems, Unit 4-5 Calow Brook Drive, Hasland, Chesterfield, Derbyshire, S41 0DR Tel: (01246) 555255 Fax: (01246) 555266 E-mail: sales@cmcaluminium.co.uk
▶ Caltak Aluminium Systems, 9 Napier Square, Houstoun Industrial Estate, Livingston, West Lothian, EH54 5DG Tel: (01506) 444644 Fax: (01506) 444700
Camlock Engineering Ltd, Unit 12F, Thorn Business Park, Rotherwas, Hereford, HR2 6JT Tel: (01432) 279553 Fax: (01432) 266010 E-mail: camlock@tactronics.com
Chum Engineering Ltd, Churchill Way, Trafford Park, Manchester, M17 1BS Tel: 0161-872 3253 Fax: 0161-872 0484 E-mail: info@chumengineering.co.uk
Class Panel Ltd, Colder Wharfe Works, Huddersfield Road, Ravensthorpe, Dewsbury, West Yorkshire, WF13 3JW Tel: (01924) 430034 Fax: (01924) 430596 E-mail: enquiries@qm-architectural.co.uk
Clow Group Ltd, 185 Broad Street, Glasgow, G40 2QR Tel: 0141-554 1739 Fax: 0141-551 0813 E-mail: clow@ladders-direct.co.uk
Colamet Manufacturing Ltd, 870 South St, Whiteinch, Glasgow, G14 0SY Tel: 0141-959 1183 Fax: 0141-958 1173 E-mail: info@booth-muirie.co.uk
Crossman Engineering Ltd, Downsview Road, Wantage, Oxfordshire, OX12 9FA Tel: (01235) 772885 Fax: (01235) 772886 E-mail: sales@crossmaneng.co.uk
Cruz Yardy Engineering, Roundwell Works, Dereham Road, New Costessey, Norwich, NR5 0SQ Tel: (01603) 746774 Fax: (01603) 746774
D J Stanton Engineering Ltd, Station Road, Hook Norton, Banbury, Oxfordshire, OX15 5LS Tel: (01608) 737452 Fax: (01608) 737051
Dane Architectural Ltd, Viking Works, Hamsterley, Newcastle Upon Tyne, NE17 7SY Tel: (01207) 565000 Fax: (01207) 565010 E-mail: info@danearchitectural.co.uk
Davley Fabrications Ltd, Drakes Indust Estate, Shay Lane, Ovenden, Halifax, West Yorkshire, HX3 6RL Tel: (01422) 355982 Fax: (01422) 355984 E-mail: sales@davleyfabrications.co.uk
Delta, 15 Brook Road, Kimbolton, Huntingdon, Cambridgeshire, PE28 0LR Tel: (01480) 861154 Fax: (01480) 861134 E-mail: info@deltafabrications.com
▶ Dendrite Fabrications, 18 Gordon Close, Leek, Staffordshire, ST13 8NZ Tel: (07785) 325342 Fax: (01538) 384789 E-mail: jasonbanks@worldonline.co.uk
▶ Dunnett Hook Aluminium Ltd, Hill Street, Ashton-under-Lyne, Lancashire, OL7 0PZ Tel: 0161-339 2639 Fax: 0161-343 1634
Duration Windows, Charfleets Road, Canvey Island, Essex, SS8 0PQ Tel: (01268) 681612 Fax: (01268) 510058 E-mail: sales@duration.co.uk
Edmo, Netherton Road, Overross Industrial Estate, Ross-on-Wye, Herefordshire, HR9 7QQ Tel: (01989) 564215 Fax: (01989) 564644E-mail: sales@edmoengineering.co.uk
Ellis Welding & Fabrications, Ollershaw Lane, Marston, Northwich, Cheshire, CW9 6ES Tel: (01606) 45405 Fax: (01606) 40237 E-mail: sales@e-w-l.com
▶ Eltherington Group Ltd, Dansom Lane, Hull, HU8 7LA Tel: (01482) 320336 Fax: (01482) 317824 E-mail: info@eltherington.co.uk
Empire Glass Co. Ltd, Unit 17, Saville Rd, Peterborough, PE3 7PR Tel: (01733) 260880 Fax: (01733) 262458
Engineering Metal Services Ltd, 4 Bradley Fold Trading Estate, Radcliffe Moor Road, Bradley Fold, Bolton, BL2 6RT Tel: (01204) 361811 Fax: (01204) 523697 E-mail: emslimited@emslimited.free-online.co.uk
Euro Aluminium Systems Ltd, Bradley Junction Industrial Estate, Leeds Road, Huddersfield, HD2 1UR Tel: (01484) 429987 Fax: (01484) 429937 E-mail: info@euroalisys.freeserve.co.uk
▶ Extruct 2000 Ltd, Unit 6 Francis Woodcock Trading Estate, Barton Street, Gloucester, GL1 4JD Tel: (01452) 303100 Fax: (01452) 303475
▶ Extruded Windows Systems, River Street, Bolton, BL2 1BX Tel: (01204) 454455 Fax: (01204) 454456 E-mail: david.coleman@ewsbolton.co.uk
Feldman Fabrication Co. Ltd, Unit 83, Owen Road Industrial Estate, Owen Road, Willenhall, West Midlands, WV13 2PX Tel: 0121-526 4434 Fax: 0121-526 4201 E-mail: feldmanfabs@btconnect.com
Fife Fabrications Ltd, 29 Rutherford Road, Glenrothes, Fife, KY6 2RT Tel: (01592) 776700 Fax: (01592) 772101 E-mail: sales@fifab.co.uk
Freeman & Proctor, PO Box 22, Nuneaton, Warwickshire, CV11 4XY Tel: (024) 7638 2032 Fax: (024) 7637 4353 E-mail: info@freemanandproctor.co.uk
Fulwood Fabrications Ltd, Farndale Road, Staveley, Chesterfield, Derbyshire, S43 3YN Tel: (01246) 477346 Fax: (01246) 280035 E-mail: sales@fulwood.uk.com
G J D Fabrications Ltd, Units 3-4 Holt Street, Newton Heath, Manchester, M40 5AX Tel: 0161-277 9610 Fax: 0161-203 4322 E-mail: doangraham@aol.com
Glamalco Ltd, Ipswich Road, Cardiff, CF23 9UR Tel: (029) 2049 7808 Fax: (029) 2047 1796 E-mail: info@glamalco.co.uk
GNT Engineering, Golden Triangle Industrial Estate, Harrison Street, Widnes, Cheshire, WA8 8TN Tel: 0151-420 3420 Fax: 0151-423 1579 E-mail: geoff@gntfab.fsnet.co.uk
Grant & Livingston Ltd, Kings Road, Canvey Island, Essex, SS8 0RA Tel: (01268) 696855 Fax: (01268) 697018 E-mail: gandl.canvey@btconnect.com
Greengate Metal Components Ltd, Greengate, Middleton, Manchester, M24 1RU Tel: 0161-653 3443 Fax: 0161-643 4991 E-mail: sales@greengatemetal.co.uk
H B Aluminium Fabrications Ltd, California House, Leathley Road, Leeds, LS10 1BG Tel: 0113-243 8195 Fax: 0113-242 2561 E-mail: admin@hb-aluminium.co.uk
H Snelson Engineers Ltd, Nat Lane, Winsford, Cheshire, CW7 3BS Tel: (01606) 553580 Fax: (01606) 861084 E-mail: sales@snelsons.co.uk
Hardie Secure Products Ltd, 17 Station Road, Flitwick, Bedford, MK45 1JT Tel: (01525) 716736 Fax: (01525) 716736 E-mail: hsfabrications@msn.com
Heavey & Co Engineers Ltd, Fielding Street, Eccles, Manchester, M30 0GJ Tel: 0161-789 1469 Fax: 0161-787 8226 E-mail: gedheavey@supanet.com
Hercules C S M D, Unit 14-16 Nelson Road, Townstal Industrial Estate, Dartmouth, Devon, TQ6 9LA Tel: (01803) 833736 Fax: (01803) 834846 E-mail: herculescsmd@aol.com
Hiatco Ltd, West Road, Annfield Plain, Stanley, County Durham, DH9 8NJ Tel: (01207) 282314 Fax: (01207) 283599 E-mail: hiatco@btinternet.com
Hodson Engineering, 16 Second Drove Industrial Estate, Peterborough, PE1 5XA Tel: (01733) 562323 Fax: (01733) 562323
Horsham Sheet Metal, Foundry Lane, Horsham, West Sussex, RH13 5PX Tel: (01403) 264137 Fax: (01403) 272386 E-mail: sales@horshamsheetmetal.co.uk
Hydro Aluminium Extrusion Ltd, Pantglas Industrial Estate, Bedwas, Caerphilly, Mid Glamorgan, CF83 8DR Tel: (029) 2085 4600 Fax: (029) 2086 3728 E-mail: haeuk@hydro.com
Hydro Automotive Structures, Williamson Road, Worcester, WR5 1SG Tel: (01905) 363700 Fax: (01905) 363715 E-mail: Alan.Blizzard@Hydro.com
Ilford Engineering Co. Ltd, Bentalls, Basildon, Essex, SS14 3BY Tel: (01268) 526756 Fax: (01268) 531485
Imi Components, Nobel Way, Witton, Birmingham, B6 7ES Tel: 0121-344 5800 Fax: 0121-344 3056
Ingimex Ltd, Halesfield 19, Telford, Shropshire, TF7 4QT Tel: (01952) 585833 Fax: (01952) 580940 E-mail: sales@ingimex.com
▶ Insight Architectural Glazing Ltd, Insight House, Wesley Street, Langley Mill, Nottingham, NG16 4AL Tel: (01773) 767772 Fax: (01773) 767987 E-mail: enquireies@aluminium-shopfronts.co.uk
▶ J B Products, Redhill Works, 200 Prospect Row, Dudley, West Midlands, DY2 8SG Tel: (01384) 240234 Fax: (01384) 240235
J M S Flagpoles, Ireland Industrial Estate, Adelphi Way, Staveley, Chesterfield, Derbyshire, S43 3LS Tel: (01246) 472949 Fax: (01246) 280476 E-mail: sales@bannerbox.co.uk
J W Baker & Sons Bradford Ltd, Premier Works, Newman Street, Bradford, West Yorkshire, BD4 9NT Tel: (01274) 651650 Fax: (01274) 681984 E-mail: bakerfabrications@btconnect.com
Scott James Commercial Ltd, 10-12 Armstrong Close, St. Leonards-on-Sea, East Sussex, TN38 9ST Tel: (0500) 441066 Fax: (01424) 853911 E-mail: sales@scott-james.freeserve.co.uk
K J B Engineering (West Tanfield) Ltd, Unit 2 The Sawmills, West Tanfield, Ripon, North Yorkshire, HG4 5JU Tel: (01677) 470511 Fax: (01677) 470811 E-mail: sales@kjblaser.co.uk
K & S Aluminium Ltd, Bent Street, Kearsley, Bolton, BL4 9DH Tel: (01204) 577769 Fax: (01204) 579340 E-mail: info@ksaluminium.co.uk
Lathe Trays Fabricators Ltd, Station Road, Rowley Regis, West Midlands, B65 0JX Tel: 0121-559 1115 Fax: (0870) 4202912 E-mail: admin@lathetrays.co.uk
Lester Engineering Ltd, Rathdown Road, Lissue Industrial Estate, Lisburn, County Antrim, BT28 2RE Tel: (028) 9262 1681 Fax: (028) 9262 1681
Letchford Swifts Ltd, Leamore Lane, Walsall, WS2 7BU Tel: (01922) 402460 Fax: (01922) 402460
Leton Engineering, Unit 14 Cockshades Farm, Stock Lane, Wybunbury, Nantwich, Cheshire, CW5 7HA Tel: (01270) 841977 Fax: (01270) 569226 E-mail: sales@1eton.net
Llandaff Engineering Co. Ltd, Paper Mill Road, Canton, Cardiff, CF11 8PH Tel: (029) 2083 8300 Fax: (029) 2056 5125 E-mail: majenkins@llandaffeng.com

ALUMINIUM FABRICATORS – *continued*

▶ Logic Aluminium Systems Ltd, Unit12 Moorbridge Court, Hucknall Lane, Bulwell, Nottingham, NG6 8AJ Tel: 0115-975 0800 Fax: 0115-975 0822 E-mail: info@logicaluminium.co.uk

M G B Press Break Sections Ltd, Dawley Brook Road, Kingswinford, West Midlands, DY6 7BD Tel: (01384) 400717 Fax: (01384) 400747

Magnum Aluminium Products (1993) Ltd, Units 3-4 Blackwater Close, Marsh Way, Rainham, Essex, RM13 8RH Tel: (01708) 522417 Fax: (01708) 525840 E-mail: gary@magnumaluminium.co.uk

▶ Matrix Aluminium Fabrications, 4 Robert Leonard Industrial Site, Stock Road, Southend-on-Sea, SS2 5QD Tel: (01702) 613490 Fax: (01702) 619406

Mayrock Fabrications, Old Airfield, Crail, Anstruther, Fife, KY10 3XL Tel: (01333) 450980 Fax: (01333) 450980

N C M P Ltd, 4 Falcon Way, Feltham, Middlesex, TW14 0XJ Tel: (020) 8751 0986 Fax: (020) 8751 5793 E-mail: ncmp-feltham@ncmp.co.uk

N J Aluminium, 223 Bowling Back Lane, Bradford, West Yorkshire, BD4 8SJ Tel: (01274) 733393 Fax: (01274) 732221

Nimgrove Ltd, 8 Anglesey Business Park, Littleworth Road, Cannock, Staffordshire, WS12 1NR Tel: (01543) 426926 Fax: (01543) 426872 E-mail: sales@nimgrove.co.uk

P K D Precision Sheet Metal Ltd, Unit 7 Furlong Industrial Estate, Dain Street, Stoke-on-Trent, ST6 3LN Tel: (01782) 824800 Fax: (01782) 811746 E-mail: sales@pkdsheetmetal.co.uk

Phoenix Marine Ltd, 2 Marrowbone Slip, Sutton Rd, Plymouth, PL4 0HX Tel: (01752) 267428 Fax: (01752) 267415 E-mail: info@phoenix316.com

PMF, N Quarry Road, Newhaven, East Sussex, BN9 9DG Tel: (01273) 517333 Fax: (01273) 517222 E-mail: sales@pmfdesigns.co.uk

Premier Sheet Metal & Engineering Co. Ltd, 4 Premier Building, Brockhampton Road, Havant, Hampshire, PO9 1JU Tel: (023) 9247 2633 Fax: (023) 9249 8210 E-mail: sales@premiersheetmetal.co.uk

Professional Welding Services Ltd, 80-82 Cobham Road, Ferndown Industrial Estate, Wimborne, Dorset, BH21 7RW Tel: (01202) 895080 Fax: (01202) 861463 E-mail: sales@prowelding.co.uk

Promat U.K Ltd, Wellingborough, Northamptonshire, NN8 6XS Tel: (01933) 271476 Fax: (01933) 276790

Q Glazing Ltd, 83-89 Western Road, Wood Green, London, N22 6US Tel: (020) 8888 7733 Fax: (020) 8888 7744 E-mail: mail@qglazing.com

▶ Quadrille Services Ltd, 18 Riverside Way, Dewsbury, West Yorkshire, WF13 3LG Tel: (01924) 491633 Fax: (01924) 499073

▶ Quality Interior Components, Radclive Road, Gawcott, Buckingham, MK18 4JB Tel: (01280) 818950 Fax: (01280) 818955 E-mail: sales@qictrims.co.uk

Queniborough Aluminium Services Ltd, 1489 Melton Road, Queniborough, Leicester, LE7 3FP Tel: 0116-260 6005 Fax: 0116-260 3005 E-mail: tonybeall@btconnect.com

R S M Engineering Tamworth Ltd, Unit 14 Two Gates Industrial Estate, Watling Street, Two Gates, Tamworth, Staffordshire, B77 5AE Tel: (01827) 250816 Fax: (01827) 287898

Ralloy Engineering Ltd, The Industrial Estate, York Road, Sheriff Hutton, York, YO60 6RZ Tel: (01347) 878987 Fax: (01347) 878997

Risuda Fabrications Ltd, Hare Street, Hopwood Lane, Halifax, West Yorkshire, HX1 4DJ Tel: (01422) 369782 Fax: (01422) 348251

Rpa, Unit 3 Adams Close, Heanor, Derbyshire, DE75 7SW Tel: (01773) 764509 Fax: (01773) 764509

Rylandes Engineering Ltd, Broomfield Barn, Coolham Road, Shipley, Horsham, West Sussex, RH13 8PF Tel: (01403) 741268 Fax: (01403) 741605 E-mail: sales@rylandesengineering.co.uk

S A Jones, Unit 3 Gwyrfai Mills, Bontnewydd, Caernarfon, Gwynedd, LL54 7UN Tel: (01286) 678683 Fax: (01286) 678683

Sam's Fabrication, Unit 17 Morgan Way, Bowthorpe Employment Area, Norwich, NR5 9JJ Tel: (01603) 743252 Fax: (01603) 746927 E-mail: sales@samsfabrications.co.uk

Sapa Pressweld Ltd, Spinnaker Park, Spinnaker Road, Hempsted, Gloucester, GL2 5DG Tel: (01452) 502502 Fax: (01452) 503503 E-mail: sales@pressweld.co.uk

Sheet Tech Fabrications, 6 Doman Road, Camberley, Surrey, GU15 3DF Tel: (01276) 684800 Fax: (01276) 20696 E-mail: cliffdottson@sheettech.fsnet.co.uk

Spa Aluminium Ltd, Unit 1, Chapman Way, Tunbridge Wells, Kent, TN2 3EG Tel: (01892) 533911 Fax: (01892) 542019 E-mail: sales@spaaluminium.co.uk

Alan Spear Ltd, Broadley Park Road, Roborough, Plymouth, PL6 7EZ Tel: (01752) 696500 Fax: (01752) 696777 E-mail: info@alanspear.co.uk

Specfab (Pershore) Ltd, Unit 5A, Pershore Trading Estate, Pershore, Worcestershire, WR10 2DD Tel: (01386) 552790 Fax: (01386) 556827 E-mail: sales@specfab.co.uk

Speedfab Ltd, Unit 10, Credenda Road, West Bromwich, West Midlands, B70 7JE Tel: 0121-541 1761 Fax: 0121-544 0028 E-mail: speedfabltd@aol.com

Stainless & Alloy Products Ltd, 8 Greets Green Road Industrial Estate, Greets Green Road, West Bromwich, West Midlands, B70 9EW Tel: 0121-557 0033 Fax: 0121-557 7775

Stuart Engineering, Unit B4 Chadwell Heath Industrial Park, Kemp Road, Dagenham, Essex, RM8 1SL Tel: (020) 8590 7412 Fax: (020) 8598 1787

Swindon Engineering Metalworkers, Unit 10 Bramble Close, Swindon, SN2 8DW Tel: (01793) 641808 Fax: (01793) 513029

T A M Engineering, Leverington Common, Leverington, Wisbech, Cambridgeshire, PE13 5JG Tel: (01945) 410494 Fax: (01945) 410476

T W Steam & Heating Services Ltd, Unit 7-8 Rennys Lane, Durham, DH1 2RS Tel: 0191-384 1400 Fax: 0191-386 4251

Teme Valley Engineering, 1-3 Rosemary Lane, Leintwardine, Craven Arms, Shropshire, SY7 0LP Tel: (01547) 540321 Fax: (01547) 540486

▶ Trent Aluminium Systems, Unit K3 Prospect Close, Lowmoor Business Park, Kirkby-in-Ashfield, Nottingham, NG17 7LF Tel: (01623) 755666 Fax: (01623) 759222 E-mail: trentalu@btconnect.com

Trueline Engineering Services Ltd, Unit 15 King Street Trading Estate, Middlewich, Cheshire, CW10 9LF Tel: (01606) 836961 Fax: (01606) 836528

▶ Vulcan Aluminium Ltd, 37A Copenhagen Road, Hull, HU7 0XQ Tel: (01482) 830500

W F E Ltd, Crossley Road, Crossley Road, Heaton Chapel, Stockport, Cheshire, SK4 5BD Tel: 0161-432 0281 Fax: 0161-431 3575 E-mail: wfel@hs.utc.com

W F Joy & Co. Ltd, Unit 1a Parnall Industrial Estate, Parnall Road, Bristol, BS16 3JF Tel: 0117-958 5865 Fax: 0117-958 5865

W.H Crossley Ltd, Newby Road Industrial Estate, Newby Road, Hazel Grove, Stockport, Cheshire, SK7 5DA Tel: 0161-456 3767 Fax: 0161-483 0602

Warwick Engineering, 3 River Gardens, Feltham, Middlesex, TW14 0RD Tel: (020) 8844 2268 Fax: (020) 8751 0509

Watermark Systems UK Ltd, 18 Cotton Brook Road, Derby, DE23 8YJ Tel: (01332) 366000 Fax: (01332) 372006 E-mail: sales@watermark-uk.com

Wells Fabrications & Developments Ltd, Unit 39a Wyrley Trading Estate, Wyrley Road, Birmingham, B6 7DB Tel: 0121-327 3354 Fax: 0121-327 3418 E-mail: ian.godwin@btconnect.com

Werneth Manufacturing Co., Unit 2 Dawson Street, Redfern Industrial Estate, Hyde, Cheshire, SK14 1RD Tel: 0161-368 3079 Fax: 0161-368 3079

Wessex Guild, 26-36 Horton Road, West Drayton, Middlesex, UB7 8JE Tel: (01895) 449595 Fax: (01895) 431665 E-mail: cmf@lineonewest.co.uk

West Riding Aluminium Ltd, Unit 1 Young Street Industrial Estate, Young Street, Bradford, West Yorkshire, BD8 9RE Tel: (01274) 499761 Fax: (01274) 481678 E-mail: wra@eurotelbroadband.com

Winstanley & Co. Ltd, Racecourse Road, Pershore, Worcestershire, WR10 2DG Tel: (01386) 552278 Fax: (01386) 556531 E-mail: winstanleyco@compuserve.com

Woodmet Anodisers Ltd, Globe Lane, Dukinfield, Cheshire, SK16 4RQ Tel: 0161-339 1943 Fax: 0161-343 1610

Wragg Bros Ltd, Robert Way, Wickford, Essex, SS11 8DQ Tel: (01268) 732607 Fax: (01268) 768499 E-mail: wragg.bros@btclick.com

Wright Aluminium Systems Ltd, Unit 9, Prince Consort Industrial Estate, Hebburn, Tyne & Wear, NE31 1EH Tel: 0191-430 0835 Fax: 0191-483 3062

ALUMINIUM FASTENERS

Components & Technology, Unit M Valley Way, Market Harborough, Leicestershire, LE16 7PS Tel: (01858) 439503 Fax: (01858) 466536 E-mail: sales@coldform.co.uk

Components & Technology, Unit M Valley Way, Market Harborough, Leicestershire, LE16 7PS Tel: (01858) 439503 Fax: (01858) 466536 E-mail: sales@coldform.co.uk

▶ Engineering Services Fasteners Ltd, Parson Street, Keighley, West Yorkshire, BD21 3HD Tel: (01535) 665414 Fax: (01535) 608377 E-mail: sales@engservfast.co.uk

ALUMINIUM FINISHING SERVICES TO THE TRADE

A P N Polishing, Unit 9, 54 Shernall Street, London, E17 9HP Tel: (020) 8520 3538 Fax: (020) 8520 3538

A P Robinson Ltd, 6c Fitzherbert Spur, Farlington, Portsmouth, PO6 1TT Tel: (023) 9238 3427 Fax: (023) 9222 1238 E-mail: aprobinson@btnet.com

Advanced Colour Coatings Ltd, Bannerley Road, Garretts Green, Birmingham, B33 0SL Tel: +44 (0) 121-789 6991 Fax: +44 (0) 121-789 6992 E-mail: enquiry@accoatings.co.uk

Armadillo Coatings, Unit 3A, Victor Business Centre, Arthur Street, Redditch, Worcestershire, B98 8JY Tel: (01527) 526855 Fax: (01527) 502856E-mail: msalter@aol.com

Badger Anodising Ltd, 52-54 Bissell Street, Birmingham, B5 7HP Tel: 0121-622 1850 Fax: 0121-622 1218 E-mail: sales@badgeranodising.co.uk

Barley Chalu Ltd, Ayton Road, Wymondham, Norfolk, NR18 0QH Tel: (01953) 602771 Fax: (01953) 606631 E-mail: sales@barleychalu.co.uk

Colne Anodising Co. Ltd, Calder Mill, Green Road, Colne, Lancashire, BB8 8AL Tel: (01282) 867300 Fax: (01282) 867407 E-mail: sales@colneanodising.co.uk

Colour Powder Coatings Ltd, Westwood House, 10 Westwood Avenue, Colevalley Business Park, Birmingham, B11 3RF Tel: 0121-772 3878 Fax: 0121-772 2697 E-mail: stevemay@colourpodercoatings.co.uk

Hard Anodising Ltd, Firs Industrial Estate, Kidderminster, Worcestershire, DY11 7QN Tel: (01562) 865158 Fax: (01562) 66118 E-mail: sales@hard-anodising.co.uk

▶ Jackson & Keay Ltd, Private Road No. 7, Colwick Industrial Estate, Colwick, Nottingham, NG4 2JW Tel: 0115-961 7113 Fax: 0115-961 8664

Lustre Anodising Co. Ltd, Units 22-24, Cannon Business Park, Gough Road, Coseley, Bilston, West Midlands, WV14 8XR Tel: (01902) 494455 Fax: (01902) 494411 E-mail: info@lustre-anodising.co.uk

Metal Finishing Ltd, Station Street, Town Wharf Business Park, Walsall, WS2 9JZ Tel: (01922) 720720 Fax: (01922) 723400 E-mail: sales@lbparkes.net

Powder Coatings Ltd, 215 Tyburn Road, Birmingham, B24 8NB Tel: 0121-250 2145 Fax: 0121-250 2154 E-mail: roger@abbeyland.co.uk

Sillavan Metal Polishes, Sillavan Works, Wood Street, Bury, Lancashire, BL8 2SL Tel: 0161-797 6666 Fax: 0161-797 3454 E-mail: bury@sillavan.co.uk

Vertik-al Ltd, Yardley Brook Industrial Park, Lea Ford Road, Shard End, Birmingham, B33 9TX Tel: 0121-608 7171 Fax: 0121-693 7787 E-mail: vertikalltd@aol.com

Warley Polishing Ltd, James Scott Road, Halesowen, West Midlands, B63 2QT Tel: (01384) 634036 Fax: (01384) 411025 E-mail: sales@warleypolishing.co.uk

ALUMINIUM FITTINGS AND HARDWARE

Allied Glazing Systems Ltd, 60 Cyclops Street, Sheffield, S4 8EH Tel: 0114-243 3595 Fax: 0114-243 2298 E-mail: info@allied-glazing.co.uk

John Monaghan (Midlands) Ltd, Unit 5 Cavendish, Lichfield Road Industrial Estate, Tamworth, Staffordshire, B79 7XH Tel: (01827) 302480 Fax: (01827) 62164 E-mail: info@monaghanmidlands.co.uk

Market Metals, Unit 1 Senate Place, Whitworth Road, Stevenage, Hertfordshire, SG1 4QS Tel: (01438) 740512 Fax: (01438) 740513 E-mail: sales@marketmetals.co.uk

ALUMINIUM FLAGSTAFFS

▶ Flags of the World, 41 Fisher Street, Stranraer, Wigtownshire, DG9 7LH Tel: 01776 700266 Fax: 0845 4664222 E-mail: sales@flagsoftheworld.co.uk

▶ The Wooden Flagpole Co., The Croft, West Street, Wiveliscombe, Somerset, TA4 2JP Tel: 01984 624794 Fax: 01984 624532 E-mail: mark.stoddart@btconnect.com

ALUMINIUM FLAT PANEL CLADDING SYSTEMS

▶ Nelson Associates, 186 Seacliff Road, Bangor, County Down, BT20 5HA Tel: (028) 9145 6109 Fax: (028) 9145 6109 E-mail: clivenelson@btinternet.com

Queniborough Aluminium Services Ltd, 1489 Melton Road, Queniborough, Leicester, LE7 3FP Tel: 0116-260 6005 Fax: 0116-260 3005 E-mail: tonybeall@btconnect.com

ALUMINIUM FOIL, *See also other headings under Aluminium Foil*

Novelis UK Ltd, Stourbridge Road, Bridgnorth, Shropshire, WV15 6AW Tel: (01746) 765757 Fax: (01746) 761860

Quality Foods Ltd, Hammerton Street, Bradford, West Yorkshire, BD3 9RD Tel: (01274) 393328 Fax: (01274) 730194

ALUMINIUM FOIL BOTTLE CAPS OR CLOSURES

Alcoa C S I (UK) Ltd, Kelvin Way, West Bromwich, West Midlands, B70 7LB Tel: 0121-532 5000 Fax: 0121-553 3710 E-mail: ciaran.martin@alcoa.com

Aluminium Capping Services Ltd, 30-32 Singer Way, Kempston, Bedford, MK42 7AF Tel: (01234) 843301 Fax: (01234) 841820 E-mail: sales@aluminiumcapping.com

▶ Bapco Closures, Unit 267, Jurby Industrial Estate, Jurby, Isle of Man, IM7 3BD Tel: (01624) 896166 Fax: (0870) 1383885 E-mail: info@bapcoclosures.com

Croxson William & Son Ltd, Alpha Place, Garth Road, Morden, Surrey, SM4 4LX Tel: (020) 8337 2945 Fax: (020) 8337 6783 E-mail: exports@croxsons.com

Metal Closures Ltd, Po Box 32, West Bromwich, West Midlands, B70 7HY Tel: (0870) 7605553

ALUMINIUM FOIL CAPPING MACHINES

Aluminium Capping Services Ltd, 30-32 Singer Way, Kempston, Bedford, MK42 7AF Tel: (01234) 843301 Fax: (01234) 841820 E-mail: sales@aluminiumcapping.com

ALUMINIUM FOIL CONTAINER TOOLING

▶ CS Press Tools Ltd, Unit 23 Nutwood Trading Estate, Limestone Cottage Lane, Sheffield, S6 1NJ Tel: 0114-234 8563 Fax: 0114-234 6290 E-mail: david@cspresstools.co.uk

D G C Engineering UK Ltd, Unit 7 Building 6, Stanmore Industrial Estate, Bridgnorth, Shropshire, WV15 5HP Tel: (01746) 767133 Fax: (01746) 767133

R J Clark, Unit 7 Enterprise Trading Est, Pedmore Road, Brierley Hill, West Midlands, DY5 1TX Tel: (01384) 480290 Fax: (01384) 481961

ALUMINIUM FOIL CONTAINERS

Coppice Alupack Ltd, Isfryn Industrial Estate, Blackmill, Bridgend, Mid Glamorgan, CF35 6EQ Tel: (01656) 840711 Fax: (01656) 841552 E-mail: enquiries@coppicealupack.com

▶ Food Pac Ltd, 2 Enderby Road Industrial Estate, Whetstone, Leicester, LE8 6HZ Tel: 0116-275 0836 Fax: 0116-275 0834

▶ Restaurant Supplies Ltd, 10 Kishorn Court, Glenrothes, Fife, KY7 6ES Tel: (01592) 749149 Fax: (01592) 749149 E-mail: sales@restaurantsuppliesltd.com

Reynards UK Ltd, Greengate, Middleton, Manchester, M24 1RU Tel: 0161-653 7700 Fax: 0161-655 3891 E-mail: swood@reynards.com

William Walton & Sons, 152 Stamford Street Central, Ashton-under-Lyne, Lancashire, OL6 6AD Tel: 0161-330 1506

ALUMINIUM FOIL LABELS

C & S Nameplate Co. Ltd, 37 Vale Road, Portslade, Brighton, BN41 1GD Tel: (01273) 419646 Fax: (01273) 411316 E-mail: sales@candsnameplate.com

Marcon Concepts Ltd, Building 16a, Greenwich Road, Newport, Gwent, NP20 2NN Tel: (0870) 0853790 Fax: (0870) 0853799 E-mail: enq@marconconcepts.co.uk

ALUMINIUM FOIL LAMINATED BAGS

▶ Antalis Ltd, Gateway House, Interlink Way West, Bardon Hill, Coalville, Leicestershire, LE67 1LE Tel: (0870) 6079014 Fax: (0870) 6073160 E-mail: contact@antalis.co.uk

ALUMINIUM FOIL LIDS

Coppice Alupack Ltd, Isfryn Industrial Estate, Blackmill, Bridgend, Mid Glamorgan, CF35 6EQ Tel: (01656) 840711 Fax: (01656) 841552 E-mail: enquiries@coppicealupack.com

ALUMINIUM FOIL, PACKAGING/ CATERING ETC

Alcan Packaging Materials, The Sawmill, Eridge Road, Eridge Green, Tunbridge Wells, Kent, TN3 9JR Tel: (01892) 509100 Fax: (01892) 509190

Coppice Alupack Ltd, Isfryn Industrial Estate, Blackmill, Bridgend, Mid Glamorgan, CF35 6EQ Tel: (01656) 840711 Fax: (01656) 841552 E-mail: enquiries@coppicealupack.com

Grease Guardian, Greenbank Industrial Estate, Newry, County Down, BT34 2PB Tel: (028) 3026 6616 Fax: (028) 3026 3233 E-mail: gg@fmenvironmental.com

Hilton Heath Agencies, 67 High Street, Great Missenden, Buckinghamshire, HP16 0AL Tel: (01494) 865120 Fax: (01494) 866152 E-mail: j.hilton@tiscali.co.uk

Maxim Group Ltd, The New Mill, 16 Gateforth Lane, Hambleton, Selby, North Yorkshire, YO8 9HP Tel: (01757) 228822 Fax: (01757) 228844 E-mail: info@themaximgroupltd.com

Wrapex Ltd, Unit 6 Lodge Causeway Trading Estate, Lodge Causeway, Bristol, BS16 3JB Tel: 0117-965 7000 Fax: 0117-958 6886 E-mail: sales@wrapex.co.uk

ALUMINIUM FORGINGS

Cerro Ems Ltd, Liverpool Street, Birmingham, B9 4DS Tel: 0121-772 6515 Fax: 0121-772 6126

▶ Cold Formed Products Ltd, 24 St. Mary's Road, London, E13 9AD Tel: (020) 8471 2727 Fax: (020) 8470 1706 E-mail: sales@cfp.biz

ALUMINIUM FORMING SERVICES

Holden Aluminium Technologies Ltd, Linton Trading Estate, Bromyard, Herefordshire, HR7 4QT Tel: (01885) 482222 Fax: (01885) 482000 E-mail: info@alloy.uk.com

Hydro Automotive Structures, Williamson Road, Worcester, WR5 1SG Tel: (01905) 363700 Fax: (01905) 363715 E-mail: Alan.Blizzard@Hydro.com

Proform Aluminium Bending Ltd, Unit 1 Boundry Court, Gilbert Way, Burma Road, Blidworth, Mansfield, Nottinghamshire, NG21 0RT Tel: (01623) 491926 Fax: (01623) 491927 E-mail: proformalu@btconnect.com

ALUMINIUM FOUNDERS/ ALUMINIUM FOUNDRY

Cygma Manufacturing, Unit B7- B9 Greengate Industrial Estate, Greenside Way, Middleton, Manchester, M24 1SW Tel: 0161-654 9777 Fax: 0161-654 9181 E-mail: cygmaplc@aol.com

Hadleigh Castings Ltd, Pond Hall Road, Hadleigh, Ipswich, IP7 5PW Tel: (01473) 827281 Fax: (01473) 827879 E-mail: info@hadleighcastings.com

Jighand Ltd, 5c Thames Road, London, E16 2EZ Tel: (020) 7473 1400 Fax: (020) 7473 1372 E-mail: patsy@jighand.com

Painter & Son Ltd, Pope Iron Road, Worcester, WR1 3HB Tel: (01905) 22787 Fax: (01905) 24181

Roston Castings, Mill Lane, Ellastone, Ashbourne, Derbyshire, DE6 2HF Tel: (01335) 324368 Fax: (01335) 324544 E-mail: sales@rostoncastings.co.uk

▶ Ulster Castings Ltd, 2-4 Bridge St, Comber, Newtownards, County Down, BT23 5AT Tel: (028) 9187 2372 Fax: (028) 9187 0088 E-mail: jneedham@ulstercastings.com

ALUMINIUM FRAME PANELLING

ALUMAS, Ackhurst Road, Chorley, Lancashire, PR7 1NH Tel: (01257) 266687 Fax: (01257) 267562 E-mail: alumas@nisltd.com

ALUMINIUM FRAMED WINDOWS

A W S Group Plc, Systems House, Hoo Farm Industrial Estate, Worcester Road, Kidderminster, Worcestershire, DY11 7RA Tel: (01562) 743700 Fax: (01562) 829775 E-mail: info@awsgroupplc.co.uk

A W S Turner-Fain Ltd, Roman Acre House, West Bank, Berry Hill Industrial Estate, Droitwich, Worcestershire, WR9 9AE Tel: (01905) 774267 Fax: (01905) 775565 E-mail: aws@turnerfainltd.co.uk

Albann Ltd, Unit 69 Third Avenue, Heatherhouse Industrial Estate, Irvine, Ayrshire, KA12 8HN Tel: (01294) 272311 Fax: (01294) 276677 E-mail: sales@albann.co.uk

Albro Windows, Albro House, 59 Palmerston Road, Harrow, Middlesex, HA3 7RR Tel: (020) 8863 7383 Fax: (020) 8427 6248

Alliance Group (Bristol) Ltd, Unit 303 Central Park, Petherton Road, Hengrove, Bristol, BS14 9BZ Tel: (01275) 892882 Fax: (01275) 892766 E-mail: general@alliancegroupbristol.co.uk

▶ Alumet Systems (U K) Ltd, Bourne End, Kineton Road Industrial Estate, Southam, Warwickshire, CV47 0NA Tel: (01926) 811677 Fax: (01926) 811676

Alumeta Glazing Systems Ltd, 123a Gorton Road, Stockport, Cheshire, SK5 6EE Tel: 0161-431 9998 Fax: 0161-431 9195 E-mail: mailbox.alumeta@btopenworld.com

Aluminium Sashes Ltd, Barnett Way, Barnwood, Gloucester, GL4 3RT Tel: (01452) 616581 Fax: (01452) 371923

Anglian Home Improvements Ltd, PO Box 65, Norwich, NR6 6EJ Tel: (01603) 787000 Fax: (01603) 422298 E-mail: matt.carey@angliangroup.com

Aristrobes, 37-41 Glenbank Pl, Belfast, BT14 8AL Tel: (028) 9039 1900

Armour Custom Services Ltd, K Holder Road, Aldershot, Hampshire, GU12 4RH Tel: (01252) 350280 Fax: (01252) 350682 E-mail: info@totalinstallations.co.uk

Avdon Bristol Ltd, Ashton Vale Road, Bristol, BS3 2HT Tel: 0117-953 3300 Fax: 0117-966 4948 E-mail: sales@avdon.co.uk

B H W Glass, The Gables, Church Road, Partridge Green, Horsham, West Sussex, RH13 8JS Tel: (01403) 713757 Fax: (01403) 864932 E-mail: enquiries@bhwglass.co.uk

Bromsgrove Glass & Windows Ltd, Sherwood Road, Aston Fields Industrial Estate, Bromsgrove, Worcestershire, B60 3DR Tel: (01527) 836777 Fax: (01527) 579148 E-mail: enquiries@bromsgroveglass.co.uk

C A P Aluminium Systems Ltd, Systems House, Spon Lane, West Bromwich, West Midlands, B70 6AA Tel: 0121-525 1000 Fax: 0121-525 5010

C B Metal Casements Ltd, Beardmore Place, Clydebank, Dunbartonshire, G81 4HS Tel: 0141-952 6431 Fax: 0141-941 1952 E-mail: cdmetal@supanet.co.uk

▶ Charter Commercial Windows & Doors, Hoo Farm Industrial Estate, Worcester Road, Kidderminster, Worcestershire, DY11 7RA Tel: (01562) 745940 Fax: (01562) 66596 E-mail: info@chartercommercial.com

Clivnars Ltd, Pindar Road, Hoddesdon, Hertfordshire, EN11 0EA Tel: (01992) 467710 Fax: (01992) 467866 E-mail: sales@clivnars.co.uk

Crescent Glass Ltd, Derby Road, Burton-On-Trent, Staffordshire, DE14 1RX Tel: (01283) 563070 Fax: (01283) 566898 E-mail: info@longlifewindows.co.uk

Crown Windows Ltd, Manor Works, Brunel Road, Newton Abbot, Devon, TQ12 4PB Tel: (01626) 332288 Fax: (01626) 333440 E-mail: sales@crown-windows.co.uk

Custom Made (U K) Ltd, Oldends Hall, Oldends Lane, Stonehouse, Gloucestershire, GL10 3RQ Tel: (01453) 826884 Fax: (01453) 791259 E-mail: info@custommade.co.uk

Diamond Windows, 25 The Fairways, New River Trading Estate, Cheshunt, Waltham Cross, Hertfordshire, EN8 0NL Tel: (01992) 635162 Fax: (01992) 623300

Dorma UK Ltd, Unit 3 Cala Trading Estate, Ashton Vale Road, Ashton, Bristol, BS3 2HA Tel: 0117-963 9014 Fax: 0117-953 3462

Dorset Glass Co. Ltd, 51 Nuffield Road, Nuffield Industrial Estate, Poole, Dorset, BH17 0RJ Tel: (01202) 673926 Fax: (01202) 684394 E-mail: duncan@dorsetglass.co.uk

East Yorkshire Glazing Co. Ltd, Wiltshire Road, Hull, HU4 6QQ Tel: (01482) 561101 Fax: (01482) 565307 E-mail: eygsales@eygsales.com

Ebbfix Ltd, Lancaster Road, Carnaby Industrial Estate, Carnaby, Bridlington, North Humberside, YO15 3QY Tel: (01262) 603714 Fax: (01262) 400510 E-mail: info@ic-systems.co.uk

Euro Aluminium Systems Ltd, Bradley Junction Industrial Estate, Leeds Road, Huddersfield, HD2 1UR Tel: (01484) 429987 Fax: (01484) 429937 E-mail: info@euroalisys.freeserve.co.uk

Forestdale Windows Ltd, 4 Lakeside, Neptune Close, Medway City Estate, Rochester, Kent, ME2 4LT Tel: (01634) 717860 Fax: (01634) 719399 E-mail: pjenn59165@aol.com

Glamalco Ltd, Ipswich Road, Cardiff, CF23 9UR Tel: (029) 2049 7808 Fax: (029) 2047 1796 E-mail: info@glamalco.co.uk

Glass Northampton Ltd, 25-29 Bailiff Street, Northampton, NN1 3DX Tel: (01604) 233343 Fax: (01604) 233298 E-mail: admin@glassnorthampton.co.uk

Hyatol Windows Ltd, 24 West Station Industrial Estate, Spital Road, Maldon, Essex, CM9 6EB Tel: (01621) 857685 Fax: (01621) 850971

K G Smoke Dispersal, 3 Foundry Lane, Horsham, West Sussex, RH13 5PX Tel: (01403) 242299 Fax: (01403) 255577 E-mail: kgsmoke@hotmail.co.uk

K G Smoke Dispersal, 3 Foundry Lane, Horsham, West Sussex, RH13 5PX Tel: (01403) 242299 Fax: (01403) 255577 E-mail: kgsmoke@hotmail.co.uk

Karters Joinery Ltd, 96 Vallentin Rd, London, E17 3JH Tel: 020 85217815 Fax: 020 85217815

Kellett Engineering Co. Ltd, Hill Top Road, Leeds, LS12 3PX Tel: 0113-263 9041 Fax: 0113-231 0717 E-mail: klt@btconnect.co.uk

Leay Ltd, Unit 3 Lake Road, Quarry Wood, Aylesford, Kent, ME20 7TQ Tel: (01622) 882345 Fax: (01622) 882208 E-mail: enquiries@leay.com

Lye Valley Windows & Doors, 4 Stour Vale Road Industrial Estate, Stour Vale Road, Stourbridge, West Midlands, DY9 8PN Tel: (01384) 892952 Fax: (01384) 422626

M D S Architectural Fabrications Ltd, Unit 3a Brandon Way, West Bromwich, West Midlands, B70 8JB Tel: 0121-525 3338 Fax: 0121-525 3348

M & L Homestyle Ltd, Lupin Works, Worcester Road, Kidderminster, Worcestershire, DY10 1JR Tel: (01562) 755333 Fax: (01562) 745559

Magnum Aluminium Products (1993) Ltd, Units 3-4 Blackwater Close, Marsh Way, Rainham, Essex, RM13 8RH Tel: (01708) 522417 Fax: (01708) 525840 E-mail: gary@magnumaluminium.co.uk

Marsland & Co. Ltd, Commerce Way, Station Road, Edenbridge, Kent, TN8 6EE Tel: (01732) 862501 Fax: (01732) 866737 E-mail: sales@marsland-windows.co.uk

NL Windows, 12 Pollard Street, Lofthouse, Wakefield, West Yorkshire, WF3 3HG Tel: (01924) 823314 Fax: (01924) 871766

Norking Aluminium Ltd, Tickhill Road, Doncaster, South Yorkshire, DN4 8QG Tel: (01302) 855907 Fax: (01302) 310204 E-mail: sales@norking.com

R & M Enterprise Windows Ltd, Unit 2 Thames House, Middlegreen Trading Estate, Langley, Slough, SL3 6DF Tel: (01753) 526334 Fax: (01753) 517694 E-mail: info@randmwindows.fsnet.co.uk

Reglaze Windows Ltd, 49-51 Collingdon Street, Luton, LU1 1RT Tel: (01582) 730847 Fax: (01582) 417615

▶ Right Units Ltd, Imperial Way, Watford, WD24 4YH Tel: (01923) 224477 Fax: (01923) 211119 E-mail: info@rightunits.com

Roman Windows & Doors Ltd, Unit 3 Fir Ralph Trade Centre, Hopton Industrial Estate, London Road, Devizes, Wiltshire, SN10 2FD Tel: (01380) 729000 Fax: (01380) 729038 E-mail: romanwindows@romanglass.co.uk

S J Aluminium Fabrications, Unit E., Area 6, Fort Fareham Business Park, Fareham, Hampshire, PO14 1AH Tel: (01329) 220828 Fax: (01329) 220828 E-mail: sales@shop-frontage.com

Saint Gobain Solaglas Ltd, Catkin Way, Greenfields Industrial Estate, Bishop Auckland, County Durham, DL14 9TF Tel: (01388) 603667 Fax: (01388) 600594 E-mail: solaglas.gpd@saint-gobain-glass.com

Schuco International KG, Whitehall Avenue, Kingston, Milton Keynes, MK10 0AL Tel: (01908) 282111 Fax: (01908) 282124 E-mail: info@schueco.de

Season Master Windows Ltd, 1 Oaks Industrial Estate, Coventry Road, Narborough, Leicester, LE19 2GF Tel: 0116-286 7970 Fax: 0116-284 1693 E-mail: sales@seasonmasterwindows.co.uk

Superseal Windows Ltd, 5 Bridge Street, Castledawson, Magherafelt, County Londonderry, BT45 8AD Tel: (028) 7946 9606 Fax: (028) 7946 9796

Technal, Units 2-4 Hudswell Road, Hunslet, Leeds, LS10 1AG Tel: 0113-296 1400 Fax: 0113-296 1414 E-mail: leeds@technal.co.uk

Technal Viking, J The Lodden Centre, Wade Road, Basingstoke, Hampshire, RG24 8FL Tel: (01256) 724900 Fax: (01256) 724949 E-mail: sales@tachnal.co.uk

Unique Windows Ltd, Perry Road, Harlow, Essex, CM18 7NR Tel: (01279) 420385 Fax: (01279) 420387E-mail: sales@uniquewindowsltd.co.uk

W G Spink & Sons, 1 Harrow Road, Hereford, HR4 0EH Tel: (01432) 272575 Fax: (01432) 342361

Welglaze Ltd, Watermill Industrial Estate, Aspenden Road, Buntingford, Hertfordshire, SG9 9JS Tel: (01763) 271811 Fax: (01763) 273108 E-mail: sales@welgaurd.co.uk

West Leigh Ltd, 11-13 Spa Road, London, SE16 3RB Tel: (020) 7232 0030 Fax: (020) 7232 1763 E-mail: info@west-leigh.co.uk

Wigan Aluminium Windows Co. Ltd, 7 Bridge Mills Rochdale Road, Edenfield, Ramsbottom, Bury, Lancashire, BL0 0RE Tel: (01706) 822993 Fax: (01706) 822436

▶ Xtral Ltd, Pelham Works, Pelham Street, Wolverhampton, WV3 0BJ Tel: (01902) 425040

ALUMINIUM HANDRAILS

Apex Architectural Aluminium, Broadleigh Park, Broadleigh Lane, Stoke Gabriel, Totnes, Devon, TQ9 6PU Tel: (01803) 782929 Fax: (01803) 782929

ALUMINIUM HEAT EXCHANGERS

G D M Heat Transfer Ltd, Boston Industrial Estate, Power Station Road, Rugeley, Staffordshire, WS15 2HS Tel: (01889) 574880 Fax: (01889) 575074 E-mail: sales@gdmcoolers.co.uk

NRF (UK) Ltd, Lamport Drive, Heartlands Business Park, Daventry, Northamptonshire, NN11 5YH Tel: (01327) 300242 Fax: (01327) 300225 E-mail: sales@nrf.co.uk

Specialist Heat Exchangers Ltd, Freeman Road, North Hykeham, Lincoln, LN6 9AP Tel: (01522) 881100 Fax: (01522) 684900 E-mail: info@specheat.co.uk

Thermal Solutions, 3 Orchard Avenue, Poole, Dorset, BH14 8AH Tel: (01202) 715792 Fax: (01202) 718134 E-mail: sales@thermalsolutions.co.uk

ALUMINIUM HIGH PRESSURE CASTINGS

The Alumasc Group Plc, Station Road, Burton Latimer, Kettering, Northamptonshire, NN15 5JP Tel: (01536) 383848 Fax: (01536) 723835 E-mail: info@alumascprecision.co.uk

ALUMINIUM LABELS

Inotec UK, Unit 1, Viking Close, Hull, HU10 6DZ Tel: (01482) 654466 Fax: (01482) 655004

The Manchester Rubber Stamp Company Ltd, 63 Red Bank, Manchester, M8 8RD Tel: 0161-834 1988 Fax: 0161-835 1529 E-mail: geoff@mrsengravers.co.uk

R C Perry & Co. Ltd, Unit 4 Worthington Way, Wigan, Lancashire, WN3 6XE Tel: (01942) 494012 Fax: (01942) 494021 E-mail: inquiries@rcperry.co.uk

ALUMINIUM LADDERS

C A Brown, 5 Young Street Industrial Estate, Young Street, Bradford, West Yorkshire, BD8 9RE Tel: (01274) 488099 Fax: (01274) 498868 E-mail: sales@castortruckladder.co.uk

Chase Manufacturing Ltd, Unit 52 Enterprise Way, Newport, Gwent, NP20 2AQ Tel: (01633) 841088 Fax: (01633) 243087 E-mail: sales@chaseladders.co.uk

Globe Ladders, Vincent Street, Birmingham, B12 9SG Tel: 0121-440 6636 Fax: 0121-440 5475 E-mail: info@globeladders.co.uk

Hewitt Ladders Ltd, 37 Melrose Street, Leicester, LE4 6FD Tel: 0116-266 3304 Fax: 0116-261 3033 E-mail: hewittladdersltd@btconnect.com

Kings Cross Truck, 41 Leighlands, Crawley, West Sussex, RH10 3DN Tel: (01293) 873767 Fax: (01293) 873767 E-mail: sales@kingscrosstruck.co.uk

The Ladder Man, City Ladder Works, Victoria Road, Fenton, Stoke-On-Trent, ST4 2HS Tel: 0800 197 3839 Fax: (01782) 410172 E-mail: info@theladderman.co.uk

Layher Ltd, Works Road, Letchworth Garden City, Hertfordshire, SG6 1WL Tel: (01462) 475100 Fax: (01462) 475101 E-mail: info@layher.com

▶ LFI Ladder & Fencing Industries (Newent) Ltd, Horsefair Lane, Newent, Glos, GL18 1RP Tel: (01531) 820541 Fax: (01531) 821161 E-mail: sales@lfi-ladders.co.uk

▶ Loadlift Ltd, Winchester House, Winchester Road, Frinton-on-Sea, Essex, CO13 9JB Tel: (01255) 671187 Fax: (01255) 672236 E-mail: sales@loadlift.com

Lyte Ladders & Towers, Wind Road, Ystradgynlais, Swansea, SA9 1AF Tel: (01639) 846816 Fax: (01639) 841541 E-mail: sales@lyteladders.co.uk

Youngman Group, The Causeway, Heybridge, Maldon, Essex, CM9 4LJ Tel: (01621) 745900 Fax: (01621) 745710 E-mail: youngmansales@youngmangroup.com

ALUMINIUM LOCKERS

Elite Lockers Ltd, Daniel Street, Oldham, OL1 3NS Tel: 0161-620 4787 Fax: 0161-620 4733 E-mail: info@elitelockers.co.uk

ALUMINIUM MASTER ALLOYS

Anglo Blackwells Ltd, Ditton Road, Widnes, Cheshire, WA8 0NT Tel: 0151-495 1400 Fax: 0151-495 4201 E-mail: sales@angloblackwells.com

ALUMINIUM MASTS

Selden Masts Ltd, Lederle Lane, Gosport, Hampshire, PO13 0FZ Tel: (01329) 504000 Fax: (01329) 504049 E-mail: info@seldenmast.co.uk

ALUMINIUM MILLED PARTS

▶ Helix Precision Machining, Unit 18, Unitfactory Estate, Hull, HU8 7QF Tel: (01482) 323131 Fax: (01482) 226639 E-mail: office@helixprecision.co.uk

ALUMINIUM MODULAR FRAMES

ALUMAS, Ackhurst Road, Chorley, Lancashire, PR7 1NH Tel: (01257) 266687 Fax: (01257) 267562 E-mail: alumas@nisltd.com

ALUMINIUM MOULDS

Crowthorne Numerical Control Ltd, 13 St Georges Industrial Estate, Wilton Road, Camberley, Surrey, GU15 2QW Tel: (01276) 20076 Fax: (01276) 685344 E-mail: info@crowthornenc.com

Cwmbran Engineering Services, Unit 38 John Baker Close, Llantarnam Industrial Park, Cwmbran, Gwent, NP44 3AX Tel: (01633) 871616 Fax: (01633) 861052 E-mail: sales@cesmoulds.co.uk

Dekton Components Leicester Ltd, All Saints Road, Leicester, LE3 5AB Tel: 0116-251 8387 Fax: 0116-253 2824 E-mail: mouldmakers@dekton.co.uk

Toolcraft Plastics Swindon Ltd, 2 Argyle Commercial Centre, 1-5 Argyle Street, Swindon, SN2 8AR Tel: (01793) 641040 Fax: (01793) 615483 E-mail: help@toolcraft.co.uk

ALUMINIUM OR ALLOY RIVETS

Clevedon Fasteners Ltd, Reddicap Trading Estate, Sutton Coldfield, West Midlands, B75 7BU Tel: 0121-378 0619 Fax: 0121-378 3186 E-mail: sales@clevedon-fasteners.co.uk

ALUMINIUM OXIDES

B C Abrasives Ltd, Cleeton Cottage, Cleeton St. Mary, Kidderminster, Worcestershire, DY14 0QU Tel: (01584) 891202 Fax: (01584) 891002 E-mail: bcabrasives2@btconnect.com

ALUMINIUM PANELS

▶ Northern Automotive Systems Ltd, Gilwern Park Industrial Estate, T Y Mawr Road, Gilwern, Abergavenny, Gwent, NP7 0EB Tel: (01873) 832263 Fax: (01873) 832034 E-mail: info@norcorp.com

ALUMINIUM PARTITIONING

A J B Partitioning & Ceiling, 13 Long Lane, Billesdon, Leicester, LE7 9AL Tel: 0116-259 6347 E-mail: ajb@billesdon.fsbusiness.co.uk

A30 Interiors, 167 Cannon Workshops, 3 Cannon Drive, London, E14 4AS Tel: (0800) 3161000 Fax: (0207) 719 844 E-mail: enq@a30interiors.com

Avon Partitioning Services, Unit 10 Evercreech Way, Highbridge, Somerset, TA9 4AR Tel: (01278) 788575 Fax: (01278) 782252 E-mail: enquiries@avonpartitioning.co.uk

D L Storage Handling Ltd, 20 Jessops Riverside, 800 Brightside Lane, Sheffield, S9 2RX Tel: 0114-244 0202 Fax: 0114-244 1222 E-mail: sales@thedlcompany.com

Drum Interior Systems Ltd, 2 Thatchers Close, Horley, Surrey, RH6 9LE Tel: (01293) 774422 Fax: (01293) 775204E-mail: isiparts@aol.com

Flexi-Plan Partitions Ltd, Unit J1, Halesfield 19, Telford, Shropshire, TF7 4QT Tel: (01952) 586126 Fax: (01952) 581174 E-mail: flexplanpartitions@btopenworld.com

Hemming & Morris (Shopfitters) Ltd, 60 Lincoln Road, Olton, Birmingham, B27 6NZ Tel: 0121-706 5740 Fax: 0121-706 6192 E-mail: sales@hemmingmorris.co.uk

Kaba Hufcor Operable Partitions, Trent Lane, Castle Donington, Derby, DE74 2NP Tel: (0870) 0005250 Fax: (01332) 811059 E-mail: hufcoruk@dial.pipex.com

Linco PC Ltd, Edge Lane Street, Royton, Oldham, OL2 6DS Tel: 0161-624 7098 Fax: 0161-678 6162 E-mail: info@lincopc.com

Moss Projects Ltd, Victoria House, 28-32 Desborough Street, High Wycombe, Buckinghamshire, HP11 2NF Tel: (01494) 535238 Fax: (01494) 535248 E-mail: info@moss.ltd.uk

Percy Lane Ltd, Lichfield Road, Tamworth, Staffordshire, B79 7TL Tel: (01827) 63821 Fax: (01827) 310159 E-mail: sales@percy-lane.co.uk

ALUMINIUM PASTES

Eckart UK, Unit C The Sidings, Station Road, Ampthill, Bedford, MK45 2QY Tel: (01525) 409520 Fax: (01525) 409521 E-mail: sales@eckart.co.uk

Orange Chemicals Ltd, 34 St.Thomas Street, Winchester, Hampshire, SO23 9HJ Tel: (01962) 842525 Fax: (01962) 841101 E-mail: brianorange@orangechem.co.uk

Silberline Ltd, Banbeath Industrial Estate, Leven, Fife, KY8 5HD Tel: (01333) 424734 Fax: (01333) 421369 E-mail: info@silberline.co.uk

Wolstenholme Bidco Ltd, Springfield House, Lower Eccleshill Road, Darwen, Lancashire, BB3 0RP Tel: (01254) 873888 Fax: (01254) 703430 E-mail: sales@wolstenholme-int.com

ALUMINIUM PATIO DOORS

▶ Origin Frames, Unit 9 Lincolns Park Business Centre, Lincoln Road, Cressex Business Park, High Wycombe, Buckinghamshire, HP12 3RD Tel: (0845) 4506662 Fax: (0845) 4506663 E-mail: info@originframes.co.uk

ALUMINIUM PLANT CONTRACTORS OR DESIGNERS

Elumatec UK Ltd, 2 Europa Business Park, Maidstone Road, Kingston, Milton Keynes, MK10 0BD Tel: (01908) 580800 Fax: (01908) 580825 E-mail: sales@elumatec.co.uk

K Home International Ltd, Ingram House, Allensway, Stockton-on-Tees, Cleveland, TS17 9HA Tel: (01642) 765421 Fax: (01642) 760721 E-mail: enquiry@khomeint.co.uk

ALUMINIUM PLATE

Bristol Steel Stockholders Ltd, Unit 13-14 Avonbridge Trading Estate, Atlantic Road, Bristol, BS11 9QD Tel: 0117-982 8131 Fax: 0117-982 8137 E-mail: steel@bristolsteel.co.uk

Durbin Metal Industries Ltd, Unit 0, Lawrence Drive, Stover Trading Estate, Bristol, BS37 5PG Tel: (01454) 322668 Fax: (01454) 317415 E-mail: sales@durbinmetals.co.uk

M G Non-Ferrous Products Ltd, 2 Station Road, Stratford St Mary, Colchester, CO7 6WZ Tel: (01206) 337429 Fax: (01206) 337413 E-mail: mgnf@dial.pipex.com

Metal Goods Wales Ltd, North Road, Bridgend Industrial Estate, Bridgend, Mid Glamorgan, CF31 3TP Tel: (01656) 647755 Fax: (01656) 647744 E-mail: sales@metalgoods.co.uk

ALUMINIUM POWDER COATING SERVICES

Aluminium Services Ltd, Aizlewood Road, Sheffield, S8 0YX Tel: 0114-255 3055 Fax: 0114-255 3798 E-mail: ast-info@btconnect.com

▶ CMT Industrial Powdercoaters, 27 Dencora Way, Luton, LU3 3HP Tel: (01582) 575494 Fax: (01582) 584297 E-mail: cmtpowdercoaters@aol.com

▶ E Reg Coatings, 4 Trans Britannia Industrial Estate, Farrington Road, Burnley, Lancashire, BB11 5SW Tel: (01282) 838378 Fax: (01282) 838015 E-mail: eregcoatings@aol.com

Edmo, Netherton Road, Overross Industrial Estate, Ross-on-Wye, Herefordshire, HR9 7QQ Tel: (01989) 564215 Fax: (01989) 564644E-mail: sales@edmoengineering.co.uk

Edmo, Netherton Road, Overross Industrial Estate, Ross-on-Wye, Herefordshire, HR9 7QQ Tel: (01989) 564215 Fax: (01989) 564644E-mail: sales@edmoengineering.co.uk

▶ Hca, Unit 6 Kingsway, Andover, Hampshire, SP10 5LQ Tel: (01264) 351640 Fax: (01264) 350302 E-mail: adam@hcacoating.co.uk

▶ M K Powder Coatings, 5 Cordingley Street, Bradford, West Yorkshire, BD4 0PP Tel: (01274) 680099 Fax: (01274) 680099

▶ The Powdertech Group, 108 Churchill Road, Bicester, Oxfordshire, OX26 4XD Tel: (01869) 320600 Fax: (01869) 246330 E-mail: lisa.r@powdertech.co.uk

R M S Engineering Prestwick Ltd, 5 Glenburn Industrial Estate, Shawfarm Road, Prestwick, Ayrshire, KA9 2NS Tel: (01292) 671160 Fax: (01292) 671404 E-mail: info@rmstainlesssteelexhausts.com

▶ S & E Mechanical & Fabrication Services Ltd, Dawes Lane, Scunthorpe, South Humberside, DN15 6UW Tel: (01724) 277408 Fax: (01724) 855669 E-mail: paulcloseartistic@hotmail.co.uk

▶ Serene Paints, Serene Works, 67 Victoria Road, Burgess Hill, West Sussex, RH15 9YL Tel: (01444) 870011 Fax: (01444) 871433 E-mail: sales@serenepaints.co.uk

ALUMINIUM POWDERS

Aluminium Powder Co. Ltd, Forge Lane, Minworth Industrial Park, Minworth, Sutton Coldfield, West Midlands, B76 1AH Tel: 0121-351 4686 Fax: 0121-351 7604 E-mail: enquiries@alpoco.co.uk

Debdale Metal Powders Ltd, Waterhouse Road, Manchester, M18 7HZ Tel: 0161-231 1504 Fax: 0161-223 2763 E-mail: info@debdale.com

Eckart UK, Unit C The Sidings, Station Road, Ampthill, Bedford, MK45 2QY Tel: (01525) 409520 Fax: (01525) 409521 E-mail: sales@eckart.co.uk

ALUMINIUM PRECISION ENGINEERED PARTS

R E Cross & Co. Ltd, Joule Road, Basingstoke, Hampshire, RG21 6XH Tel: (01256) 465878 Fax: (01256) 817743 E-mail: sales@recross.co.uk

Westrup (UK) Ltd, 30 North Street, Wetherby, West Yorkshire, LS22 6NN Tel: (01937) 581365 Fax: (01937) 586904 E-mail: info@westrup.co.uk

ALUMINIUM PRECISION TURNED PARTS

C & J Industries, Northern House, Station Approach, Hitchin, Hertfordshire, SG4 9UW Tel: (01462) 452414 Fax: (01462) 421105

ALUMINIUM PRESSURE VESSELS

Feldbinder (UK) Ltd, Sutton Bridge, Spalding, Lincolnshire, PE12 9XE Tel: (01406) 353500 Fax: (01406) 353510 E-mail: sales@feldbinder.co.uk

Forster & Hales Ltd, 24 Wadsworth Road, Greenford, Middlesex, UB6 7JD Tel: (020) 8998 9057 Fax: (020) 8998 2922 E-mail: sales@forsterandhales.com

ALUMINIUM PRODUCT DESIGN SERVICES

▶ Crossroads Design Ltd, 4 Sanctus Court, Stratford-upon-Avon, Warwickshire, CV37 6DL Tel: (01789) 551682 Fax: (01789) 551682 E-mail: info@crossroadsdesign.co.uk

Inspire2Design Limited, 17C Mill Road, Stourport-on-Severn, Worcestershire, DY13 9BG Tel: (01299) 827646 E-mail: info@inspire2design.co.uk

ALUMINIUM PRODUCTS, *See also headings for particular products*

▶ Altex, 58 Tailors Court, Temple Farm Industrial Estate, Southend-on-Sea, SS2 5SX Tel: (01702) 602220 Fax: (01702) 602215 E-mail: sales@altex-uk.com

Bailey, Blatchford Close, Horsham, West Sussex, RH13 5RF Tel: (01403) 261844

Rimstock plc, Church Lane, West Bromwich, West Midlands, B71 1BY Tel: 0121-525 2525 Fax: 0121-553 1083

W K L Glass, High House Farm, Barling Road, Barling Magna, Southend-on-Sea, SS3 0LZ Tel: (01702) 217539 Fax: (01702) 217539

ALUMINIUM PROFILE CUTTING SERVICES

The Aluminium Cutting Company Ltd, 2 94 Kitchener Road, High Wycombe, Buckinghamshire, HP11 2SW Tel: (01494) 448790 Fax: (01494) 448794

Laser Process Ltd, Upper Keys, Keys Park Road, Hednesford, Cannock, Staffordshire, WS12 2GE Tel: (01543) 495000 Fax: (01543) 495001 E-mail: sales@laserprocess.co.uk

Laserit Ltd, Unit 26 Beeches Industrial Estate, Lavenham Road, Yate, Bristol, BS37 5QX Tel: (01454) 318585 Fax: (01454) 318541 E-mail: sales@laserit.co.uk

Redditch Lasercutting Ltd, 9 Broad Ground Road, Redditch, Worcestershire, B98 8YP Tel: (01527) 510474 Fax: (01527) 510432

Roscope Ltd, Telford Way, Telford Way Industrial Estate, Kettering, Northamptonshire, NN16 8UN Tel: (01536) 415644 Fax: (01536) 316929E-mail: roscope.sales@btconnect.com

ALUMINIUM PROFILES

▶ Alumnium Profiles UK, Unit 5, Peckleton Lane Business Park, Peckleton Common, Leicester, LE9 7RN Tel: (01455) 823304 Fax: (01455) 828186 E-mail: sales@kjnltd.co.uk

▶ G S M Aluminium Ltd, 16 Maria Street, Burley in Wharfedale, Ilkley, West Yorkshire, LS29 7JA Tel: (01943) 862307 Fax: (01943) 863168 E-mail: gerald@gsmltd.co.uk

ALUMINIUM PROFILES, ANODISED

▶ Alumnium Profiles UK, Unit 5, Peckleton Lane Business Park, Peckleton Common, Leicester, LE9 7RN Tel: (01455) 823304 Fax: (01455) 828186 E-mail: sales@kjnltd.co.uk

ALUMINIUM PROFILES, EXTRUSION

▶ Alumnium Profiles UK, Unit 5, Peckleton Lane Business Park, Peckleton Common, Leicester, LE9 7RN Tel: (01455) 823304 Fax: (01455) 828186 E-mail: sales@kjnltd.co.uk

ALUMINIUM RAINWATER GOODS

Alifabs Woking Ltd, 4 Kernel Court, Walnut Tree Close, Guildford, Surrey, GU1 4UD Tel: (01483) 546547 Fax: (01483) 546548 E-mail: sales@alifabs.com

C G L Systems, 2 Young Place, East Kilbride, Glasgow, G75 0TD Tel: (01355) 235561 Fax: (01355) 247189 E-mail: sales@cglsystems.co.uk

Dales Fabrication Ltd, Crompton Road, Ilkeston, Derbyshire, DE7 4BG Tel: 0115-930 1521 Fax: 0115-930 7625 E-mail: technical@dales-eaves.co.uk

J.W.D. Rainwater Systems Ltd, Captain Clarke Road, Broadway Industrial Estate, Hyde, Stockport, Cheshire, SK1 4QG Tel: 0161-351 9990 Fax: 0161-351 9992 E-mail: info@rainwatergoods.co.uk

Konaflex Ltd, Unit 2 Northcote Road, Stechford, Birmingham, B33 9BE Tel: 0121-783 9778 Fax: 0121-784 8026E-mail: konaflex@aol.com

Lupton Fabrications Ltd, Unit A Aquatite House, Water Lane, Leeds, LS11 9UD Tel: 0113-242 6872 Fax: 0113-242 6874 E-mail: sales@lupton.uk.com

M R (Site Services) Ltd, Unit 6, Worcester Trading Estate, Blackpole, Worcester, WR3 8HR Tel: (01905) 755055 Fax: (01905) 755053 E-mail: info@mrsiteservices.com

N R S Ltd, 14 Lysander Road, Bowerhill, Melksham, Wiltshire, SN12 6SP Tel: (01225) 709408 Fax: (01225) 708719 E-mail: info@n-rs.co.uk

Sotech Ltd, 4 Mill Hill, North West Industrial Estate, Peterlee, County Durham, SR8 2HR Tel: 0191-587 2287 Fax: 0191-518 0703 E-mail: mail@sotech-optima.co.uk

Specialised Fixing (East Anglia) Ltd, Unit 9, Farthing Road, Ipswich, IP1 5AP Tel: (01473) 461461 Fax: (01473) 240518 E-mail: spencer.priestley@omnico.co.uk

E. Stephens Gutter Repairs, Little Clanfield Mill, Little Clanfield, Bampton, Oxfordshire, OX18 2RX Tel: (01367) 810380 Fax: (01367) 810390 E-mail: sales@gutter-repairs.co.uk

Traction Equipment (Stafford) Ltd, Glover Street, Stafford, ST16 2NY Tel: (01785) 223355 Fax: (01785) 211074 E-mail: call@tractionequipment.co.uk

ALUMINIUM ROLL CAGES

▶ Ra'Alloy Trading Company Ltd, Hortonwood 10, Telford, Shropshire, TF1 7ES Tel: (01952) 677877 Fax: (01952) 677883 E-mail: sales@raalloy.com

ALUMINIUM ROOF FLASHING

Kingspan Ltd, Greenfield Business Park 2, Greenfield, Holywell, Flintshire, CH8 7GJ Tel: (01352) 716100 Fax: (01352) 710161 E-mail: sales@kingspanpanels.com

Lupton Fabrications Ltd, Unit A Aquatite House, Water Lane, Leeds, LS11 9UD Tel: 0113-242 6872 Fax: 0113-242 6874 E-mail: sales@lupton.uk.com

ALUMINIUM ROOFING CONTRACTORS

Central Cladding Systems Ltd, Unit C4 Staverton Technology Park, Gloucester Road, Staverton Technology Park, Cheltenham, Gloucestershire, GL51 6TQ Tel: (01452) 856252 Fax: (01452) 856136 E-mail: ccs@centralcladding.co.uk

Clonshall Ltd, Whiteacre House, 97 Whiteacre Road, Ashton-under-Lyne, Lancashire, OL6 9PJ Tel: 0161-339 9637 Fax: 0161-343 1036 E-mail: adrian.young@clonshall.co.uk

ALUMINIUM SCAFFOLD TOWERS

▶ Scaffold-towers.com, Unit 9 Haysbridge Farm, Brickhouse Lane, South Godstone, Godstone, Surrey, RH9 8JW Tel: (01342) 844218 Fax: (01342) 844588 E-mail: dan@scaffoldtowershop.co.uk

ALUMINIUM SCAFFOLDING

Ably Shelters Ltd, 1700 Blueprint, Dundas Spur, Portsmouth, PO3 5RW Tel: (023) 9244 8040 Fax: (023) 9244 8049 E-mail: sales@ablyshelters.co.uk

Alcoa (Europe), Southam Road, Banbury, Oxfordshire, OX16 2SN Tel: (01295) 454444 Fax: (01295) 454454

Hulett Aluminium International, Securehold Business Centre, Studley Road, Redditch, Worcestershire, B98 7LG Tel: (01527) 516222 Fax: (01527) 517199 E-mail: sales@hulett-hydro.co.za

Upright International, Unit F1, Halesfield 4, Telford, Shropshire, TF7 4AP Tel: (01952) 685200 Fax: (01952) 685255 E-mail: mdavey@uprighteuro.com

ALUMINIUM SCRAP/WASTE/ DROSS RECYCLING/ MERCHANTS OR PROCESSORS

Alutrade Ltd, Tat Bank Road, Oldbury, West Midlands, B69 4NH Tel: 0121-552 0330 Fax: 0121-552 0166 E-mail: info@alutrade.co.uk

Commercial Engineering Metals Ltd, Unit 5 & 6, Shawbank Industrial Estate, Lakeside, Redditch, Worcestershire, B98 7YN Tel: (01527) 529145 Fax: (01527) 510236

▶ Environmental Waste Controls P.L.C., Laurel House, Kitling Road, Knowsley Business Park, Prescot, Merseyside, L34 9JA Tel: (0845) 4562456 Fax: (0845) 4563998 E-mail: enquiry@ewc.eu.com

Hicks Metals & Alloys, 170-176 Fazeley Street, Birmingham, B5 5SE Tel: 0121-772 1896 Fax: 0121-771 2085

Mil-Ver Metal Co., Coronel Avenue, Longford, Coventry, CV6 6AP Tel: (024) 7666 7098 Fax: (024) 7666 2299 E-mail: steve.miles@milver.co.uk

▶ Mountain, Summit House, Northfield Road, Quarrington, Sleaford, Lincolnshire, NG34 8RT Tel: (0800) 0266936 Fax: (01529) 413857 E-mail: sales@greenmountains.co.uk

R O B A Metals Ltd, Kinwarton Farm Road, Kinwarton, Alcester, Warwickshire, B49 6EH Tel: (01789) 763232 Fax: (01789) 400660 E-mail: info@robametals.co.uk

Welmet Coral Metals, Main Road, Unstone, Dronfield, Derbyshire, S18 4AB Tel: (01246) 414907 Fax: (01246) 411777

ALUMINIUM SECTION BENDING

Proform Aluminium Bending Ltd, Unit 1 Boundry Court, Gilbert Way, Burma Road, Blidworth, Mansfield, Nottinghamshire, NG21 0RT Tel: (01623) 491926 Fax: (01623) 491927 E-mail: proformalu@btconnect.com

ALUMINIUM SHEET METAL FABRICATIONS

Wyvern Sheet Metal & Fabrications Ltd, Three Springs Trading Estate, Vincent Road, Worcester, WR5 1BW Tel: (01905) 357830 Fax: (01905) 357830 E-mail: sales@wyvernsheetmetal.wanadoo.co.uk

ALUMINIUM SHEET METAL FABRICATORS

A G Lester & Sons Ltd, Unit 1 Erskine Street, Birmingham, B7 4RU Tel: 0121-359 1018 Fax: 0121-359 1018 E-mail: info@aglesterandsons.sagenet.co.uk

▶ Bell Sheet Metal Ltd, Unit 1 Coin Street, Off Edge Lane Street Royton, Oldham, OL2 6EE Tel: 0161-627 0748 Fax: 0161-628 2511 E-mail: info@bellsheet.com

▶ D M S Stainless Fabrications Ltd, 1 St Peters Works, St Peters Road, Maidenhead, Berkshire, SL6 7QU Tel: (01628) 777391 Fax: (01628) 777396 E-mail: sales@dmslaserprofiles.co.uk

▶ Perlam Sheet Metal Work, Wandle Trading Estate, Mill Green Road, Mitcham, Surrey, CR4 4HZ Tel: (020) 8685 9276 Fax: (020) 8640 0551 E-mail: sales@perlamsheetmetal.co.uk

▶ Raybrook Sheet Metal Works Ltd, 9 Towerfield Close, Shoeburyness, Southend-on-Sea, SS3 9QP Tel: (01702) 293208 Fax: (01702) 297628 E-mail: info@raybrook.com

V & F Sheetmetal Co. Ltd, Unit 22-25, Mitchell Close, Segensworth East, Fareham, Hampshire, PO15 5SE Tel: (01489) 577786 Fax: (01489) 889008 E-mail: sales@vandf.co.uk

W.H Crossley Ltd, Newby Road Industrial Estate, Newby Road, Hazel Grove, Stockport, Cheshire, SK7 5DA Tel: 0161-456 3767 Fax: 0161-483 0602

ALUMINIUM SHELVING

Tebrax Ltd, International House, Cray Avenue, Orpington, Kent, BR5 3RY Tel: (01689) 897766 Fax: (01689) 896789 E-mail: brackets@tebrax.co.uk

ALUMINIUM SHOP FRONT FITTINGS

Alumeta Glazing Systems Ltd, 123a Gorton Road, Stockport, Cheshire, SK5 6EE Tel: 0161-431 9998 Fax: 0161-431 9195 E-mail: mailbox.alumeta@btopenworld.com

Andrew Mark Ltd, Tredgar Wharf, Hancock Road, London, E3 3DA Tel: (020) 8981 2224 Fax: (020) 8980 7037 E-mail: sales@amarka.co.uk

Architectural Aluminium Systems Ltd, Sandleheath Industrial Estate, 6 Old Brickyard Road, Sandleheath, Fordingbridge, Hampshire, SP6 1PA Tel: (01425) 654080 Fax: (01425) 652038

Ayrshire Shop Fronts Ltd, Unit 3 & 4, Moorfield Industrial Estate, Kilmarnock, Ayrshire, KA2 0DP Tel: (01563) 542991 Fax: (01563) 538195

Billenness Keith Ltd, 22 Birch Road, Eastbourne, East Sussex, BN23 6PD Tel: (01323) 411028 Fax: (01323) 411704 E-mail: keith@kbglass.fsnet.co.uk

C A P Aluminium Systems Ltd, Systems House, Spon Lane, West Bromwich, West Midlands, B70 6AA Tel: 0121-525 1000 Fax: 0121-525 5010

DLT Shop Front & Shutter Systems Ltd, Shaw Road, Dudley, West Midlands, DY2 8TS Tel: (01384) 455277 Fax: (01384) 458847 E-mail: sales@weatherite-group.co.uk

Greenberg Glass Ltd, 10 Bard St, Birmingham, B11 4SA Tel: 0121-753 1900 Fax: 0121-772 3683 E-mail: website@greenbergglass.co.uk

Greenberg Glass Contract Ltd, unit 33 Dunes Way, Liverpool, L5 9RJ Tel: 0151-207 2574 Fax: 0151-298 1050

H B Aluminium Fabrications Ltd, California House, Leathley Road, Leeds, LS10 1BG Tel: 0113-243 8195 Fax: 0113-242 2561 E-mail: admin@hb-aluminium.co.uk

HW Architectural Ltd, Birds Royd Lane, Birds Royd Lane, Brighouse, West Yorkshire, HD6 1NG Tel: (01484) 717677 Fax: (01484) 400148 E-mail: info@hwa.co.uk

Scott James Commercial Ltd, 10-12 Armstrong Close, St. Leonards-on-Sea, East Sussex, TN38 9ST Tel: (0500) 441066 Fax: (01424) 853911 E-mail: sales@scott-james.freeserve.co.uk

M M C Ltd, 2ND Floor, Guide Bridge Mill, South Street, Ashton-Under-Lyne, Lancashire, OL7 0HU Tel: 0161-343 1740 Fax: 0161-343 1741 E-mail: pats@mmc93.co.uk

N T S Aluminium Systems Ltd, Gainsford Drive, Halesowen, West Midlands, B62 8BQ Tel: 0121-501 3814 Fax: 0121-585 5492

Nason Foster Ltd, Moor Lane, Birmingham, B6 7HH Tel: 0121-356 5693 Fax: 0121-356 3818 E-mail: sales@nasonfoster.co.uk

Norking Aluminium Ltd, Tickhill Road, Doncaster, South Yorkshire, DN4 8QG Tel: (01302) 855907 Fax: (01302) 310204 E-mail: sales@norking.com

Northgate Aluminium Systems, Park Road East, Calverton, Nottingham, NG14 6LL Tel: 0115-965 5655 Fax: 0115-965 2227 E-mail: info@dalesidegroup.com

Prestige Glazing Services Ltd, Unit 2 Shuttleworth Court, Shuttleworth Road, Elm Farm Industrial Estate, Bedford, MK41 0EN Tel: (01234) 346454 Fax: (01234) 219063 E-mail: prestigeglazing@btconnect.com

S G Aluminium Ltd, Unit B Sett End Road West, Shadsworth Business Park, Blackburn, BB1 2QJ Tel: (01254) 691600 Fax: (01253) 340526 E-mail: info@sg-aluminium.co.uk

S J Aluminium Fabrications, Unit E., Area 6, Fort Fareham Business Park, Fareham, Hampshire, PO14 1AH Tel: (01329) 220828 Fax: (01329) 220828 E-mail: sales@shop-frontage.com

Skyglass Ltd, Morgans Yard, Arundel Road Industrial Estate, Uxbridge, Middlesex, UB8 2RP Tel: (01895) 234432 Fax: (01895) 271118

Trojan Aluminium Ltd, 7 Burton Close, Falcon Road Industrial Estate, Norwich, NR6 6AY Tel: (01603) 426024 Fax: (01603) 417882 E-mail: sale@trojanaluminium.co.uk

The Window Glass Company Bristol Ltd, 11 Emery Road, Bristol, BS4 5PF Tel: 0117-977 9292 Fax: 0117-977 9299 E-mail: mail@windowglass.co.uk

ALUMINIUM SHOWER ACCESSORIES

Matki Public Ltd Company, Churchward Road, Yate, Bristol, BS37 5PL Tel: (01454) 322888 Fax: (01454) 315284 E-mail: sales@matki.co.uk

ALUMINIUM SIGNS

1st Call Rotosign Ltd, Pressmetal House, St Augustines Business Park, Whitstable, Kent, CT5 2QJ Tel: (01227) 794490 Fax: (01227) 794488 E-mail: sales@amp-uk.co.uk

Decor Signs, Unit 22 Oldbury Business Centre, Oldbury Road, Cwmbran, Gwent, NP44 3JU Tel: (01633) 866349 Fax: (01633) 866349 E-mail: marketing@decorsigns.co.uk

P B Signs & Designs, 88 Walthew Lane, Platt Bridge, Wigan, Lancashire, WN2 5AL Tel: (01942) 866240 Fax: (01942) 866240

Resistek Ltd, 46 Holton Road, Holton Heath Trading Park, Poole, Dorset, BH16 6LT Tel: (01202) 625605 Fax: (01202) 632438 E-mail: sales@resistek.co.uk

Sign A Rama, 1 Parker Street, Warrington, WA1 1LT Tel: (01925) 445577 Fax: (01925) 244555 E-mail: signarama.warrington@talk21.com

Staffordshire Signs & Graphics Ltd, 154 Lime Lane, Pelsall, Walsall, WS3 5AP Tel: (01543) 373006 Fax: (01543) 374550 E-mail: richard@signs-and-graphics.co.uk

ALUMINIUM SLIDING DOORS

▶ MOGdesign Ltd, Tilden House 5, 22 Comeragh Road, London, W14 9HP Tel: (020) 7386 8539 Fax: (020) 7381 1127 E-mail: info@mogdesign.co.uk

ALUMINIUM SLUGS

Galup Ltd, 48 Elmsdale Road, Wooton, Bedford, MK43 9JU Tel: (01234) 768805 Fax: (01234) 767532 E-mail: sales@galupltd.co.uk

ALUMINIUM SMELTERS/ REFINERS/PROCESSORS

Alcan Primary Europe, Lochaber Smelter, Fort William, Inverness-Shire, PH33 6TH Tel: (01397) 902233 Fax: (01397) 902200

Alcan Smelting & Power (UK), Lynemouth Smelter, Ashington, Northumberland, NE63 9YH Tel: (01670) 393811 Fax: (01670) 393956

Baker Metals Ltd, Great Northern Road, Derby, DE1 1LT Tel: (01332) 340186 Fax: (01332) 344130

Hydro Aluminium Deeside Ltd, Bridge Road, Wrexham Industrial Estate, Wrexham, Clwyd, LL13 9PS Tel: (01978) 660231 Fax: (01978) 661125 E-mail: hydro.deeside@hydro.com

R O B A Metals Ltd, Kinwarton Farm Road, Kinwarton, Alcester, Warwickshire, B49 6EH Tel: (01789) 763232 Fax: (01789) 400660 E-mail: info@robametals.co.uk

ALUMINIUM SMELTING FURNACES

Alcan Smelting & Power (UK), Lynemouth Smelter, Ashington, Northumberland, NE63 9YH Tel: (01670) 393811 Fax: (01670) 393956

Hengelmolen Engineering Ltd, Great Bridge Industrial Estate, Tipton, West Midlands, DY4 0HR Tel: 0121-520 1181 Fax: 0121-557 5201 E-mail: hengelmolen@btconnect.com

ALUMINIUM SPINNINGS

Midland Spinanpress Co. Ltd, 5 Sydney Road, Bordesley Green, Birmingham, B9 4QB Tel: 0121-772 6804 Fax: 0121-766 8580

Steel Spinnings Ltd, 94-96 Steward Street, Birmingham, B18 7AF Tel: 0121-456 3737 Fax: 0121-452 1616 E-mail: info@steelspinnings.com

ALUMINIUM STAIR NOSINGS

Gradus Carpets Ltd, Chapel Mill, Park Green, Macclesfield, Cheshire, SK11 7LZ Tel: (01625) 859000 Fax: (01625) 850352 E-mail: sales@gradusworld.com

Trimplex, Mulberry Way, Belvedere, Kent, DA17 6AN Tel: (020) 8312 0400 Fax: (020) 8312 1400 E-mail: saftytread@btconnect.com

ALUMINIUM STAIRCASES

Apex Architectural Aluminium, Broadleigh Park, Broadleigh Lane, Stoke Gabriel, Totnes, Devon, TQ9 6PU Tel: (01803) 782929 Fax: (01803) 782929

ALUMINIUM STANDING SEAM ROOFING SYSTEMS

▶ Solar Century, 91-94 Lower Marsh, London, SE1 7AB Tel: (020) 7803 0100 Fax: (08707) 358101 E-mail: info@solarcentury.co.uk

ALUMINIUM STOCKHOLDERS,

See also headings for particular products under Aluminium/Alloy

A S C Metals Ltd, 3 Jackdaw Close, Crow Lane Industrial Estate, Northampton, NN3 9ER Tel: (01604) 415036 Fax: (01604) 415019

A S C Metals Ltd, 20a Maxwell Road, Peterborough, PE2 7JD Tel: (01733) 370626 Fax: (01733) 370392

A S C Metals Ltd, Shaw Road, Bushbury, Wolverhampton, WV10 9LA Tel: (01902) 371700 Fax: (01902) 424324

A S D Metal Services, Suit 107, 1111 Parkway, Whiteley, Fareham, Hampshire, PO15 7AB Tel: (01489) 611660 Fax: (01489) 611750

A S D Metal Services, Tunstall Road, Biddulph, Stoke-on-Trent, ST8 6JZ Tel: (01782) 515152 Fax: (01782) 522240 E-mail: asdmetalservices@asdplc.co.uk

Ace Engineers Ltd, Albert Road, Morley, Leeds, LS27 8LD Tel: 0113-252 2611 Fax: 0113-238 0274 E-mail: sales@ace-engineers.co.uk

Agora Metals Ltd, Millfields Road, Wolverhampton, WV4 6JQ Tel: (01902) 402134 Fax: (01902) 403737 E-mail: mark@parkrow-alloys.co.uk

Alloy Sales Ltd, B G K House, Travellers Lane, North Mymms, Hatfield, Hertfordshire, AL9 7HF Tel: (01707) 268222 Fax: (01707) 274655 E-mail: info@alloysales.co.uk

▶ Alpha Windows Ltd, 30 Town Lane, Denton, Manchester, M34 6LE Tel: 0161-335 0129 Fax: 0161-337 8717

Aluminium Droitwich, 7 Judge Court, Berry Hill, Berry Hill Industrial Estate, Droitwich, Worcestershire, WR9 9AB Tel: (01905) 794620 Fax: (01905) 797863

Aluminium Stockholders Association, Broadway House, Calthorpe Road, Five Ways, Birmingham, B15 1TN Tel: 0121-456 4938 Fax: 0121-456 4937 E-mail: asa@alfed.org.uk

Aluminium Supply Aerospace, 1 Totteridge Lane, London, N20 0EX Tel: (020) 8700 2000 Fax: (020) 8700 2099 E-mail:

Anglia Alloys Ltd, Unit 5 Riverside Industrial Estate, Riverside Road, Gorleston, Great Yarmouth, Norfolk, NR31 6PU Tel: (01493) 651028 Fax: (01493) 655391

Arrow Metals Ltd, 200 High Street, Boston Spa, Wetherby, West Yorkshire, LS23 6BT Tel: (01937) 845066 Fax: (01937) 845897 E-mail: arrowmetalsltd@aol.com

Asc Metals Lincoln Ltd, Westminster Industrial Estate, Station Road, North Hykeham, Lincoln, LN6 3QY Tel: (01522) 501777 Fax: (01522) 501700 E-mail: sales@ascmetals.com

Asd, Station Road, Stalbridge, Sturminster Newton, Dorset, DT10 2RW Tel: (01963) 362066 Fax: (01963) 363260 E-mail: yeovil@asdplc.co.uk

Azimex Fabrications Ltd, Cartwright Road, Northampton, NN2 6HF Tel: (01604) 717712 Fax: (01604) 791087

BACO Metal Centres, Unit 1 Lombard Centre, Kirkhill Pl, Dyce, Aberdeen, AB21 0GU Tel: (01224) 802600 Fax: (01224) 802699 E-mail: bmc.marketing@british-aluminium.ltd.uk

Baco Metal Centres, Edison Road, Elm Farm Industrial Estate, Bedford, MK41 0HU Tel: (01234) 684100 Fax: (01234) 684199 E-mail: bmc.sales@alcoa.com

Baco Metal Centres, Coegnant Close, Brackla Industrial Estate, Bridgend, Mid Glamorgan, CF31 2AH Tel: (01656) 683900 Fax: (01656) 683999 E-mail: bridgend@bacometalcentres.co.uk

Baco Metal Centres, Unit 14 St Andrews Trading Estate, Third Way, Avonmouth, Bristol, BS11 9YE Tel: 0117-948 2600 Fax: 0117-948 2699 E-mail: bmc.sales@alcoa.com

Baco Metal Centres, 13 Concorde Road, Norwich, NR6 6BJ Tel: (01603) 243900 Fax: (01603) 243999 E-mail: norwich@blackburnsm.com

Baco Metal Centres, 1 Eagle Road, Plympton, Plymouth, PL7 5JY Tel: (01752) 612400 Fax: (01752) 612499 E-mail: plymouth@bacometalcentres.co.uk

Baco Metal Centres, Unit 4 Stadium Way, Tilehurst, Reading, RG30 6BX Tel: 0118-980 3300 Fax: 0118-980 3399 E-mail: bmc.sales@alcoa.com

▶ Beattie Architectural Aluminium, 2-4 Abercorn Street, Paisley, Renfrewshire, PA3 4AB Tel: 0141-561 7567

Berkshire Metals Ltd, 10-12 Armour Road, Tilehurst, Reading, RG31 6HS Tel: 0118-942 9476 Fax: 0118-942 4800

▶ Blackburns Metal Centres, Units 3-4, Haydock Lane, Haydock Industrial Estate, Haydock, St. Helens, Merseyside, WA11 9UY Tel: 0161-254 8800 Fax: (01942) 758899 E-mail: haydock@blackburnsmetalcentre.com

Blackburns Metals Ltd, 4 Wellington Road, Leeds, LS3 1LE Tel: 0113-296 1500 Fax: 0113-296 1599 E-mail: leeds@blackburnsmetals.com

Carlyle Metal Goods Ltd, Carlyle Business Park, Great Bridge Street, Swan Village, West Bromwich, West Midlands, B70 0XA Tel: 0121-525 6614 Fax: 0121-525 6770 E-mail: markcashmore@carlyleplc.co.uk

Cashmores, Upper Brook Street, Walsall, WS2 9PD Tel: (01922) 720930 Fax: (01922) 648304 E-mail: sales@cashmores.co.uk

Corus, Wakefield Road, Leeds, LS10 1AY Tel: 0113-276 0660 Fax: 0113-272 7197

Corus, Colndale Road, Colnbrook, Slough, SL3 0HL Tel: (01753) 683131 Fax: (01753) 684372 E-mail: customer-services@corusgroup.com

Corus Service Centre, The Steelpark, Steelpark Way, Wolverhampton, WV11 3SR Tel: (01902) 484200 Fax: (01902) 484049

▶ Creole Trading Ltd, 47 Esplanade, St. Helier, Jersey, JE2 3QB Tel: (01534) 619647

Direct Metal Services Ltd, 2 Swan Business Park, Sandpit Road, Dartford, DA1 5ED Tel: (01322) 287878 Fax: (01322) 287567 E-mail: info@directmetalservices.co.uk

Dore Metal Services Ltd, Unit 2 Dolphin Park Cremers Road, Sittingbourne, Kent, ME10 3HB Tel: (01795) 473551 Fax: (01795) 429473 E-mail: ian@doremetals.co.uk

Engravamet Engraving, Dock Meadow Drive, Wolverhampton, WV4 6LE Tel: (01902) 401666 Fax: (01902) 490129 E-mail: sales@engravamet.co.uk

Ferrari Stainless & Alloys Ltd, Unit 89, Woolsbridge Industrial Park, Three Legged Cross, Wimborne, Dorset, BH21 6SU Tel: (01202) 823346 Fax: (01202) 823903

H & H Alloy Sales Ltd, J A S House, Titford Lane, Rowley Regis, West Midlands, B65 0PY Tel: 0121-559 6466 Fax: 0121-559 8723 E-mail: signs@warleyholdings.co.uk

▶ Howard Lambert, Suite 15 Concorde House, Grenville Place, London, NW7 3SA Tel: (020) 8959 8813 Fax: (020) 8906 7821

Impact Metal Services Ltd, 3 Phoenix Park, Station Road, Rowley Regis, West Midlands, B65 0LJ Tel: 0121-561 2030 Fax: 0121-561 1158 E-mail: sales@impactmetal.co.uk

Industrial Metal Services Ltd, Metalstock House, Metal Stock House, Vanguard Way, Southend-on-Sea, SS3 9RE Tel: (01702) 296922 Fax: (01702) 296444 E-mail: sales@industrialmetal.co.uk

Jade Non Ferrous Metals Ltd, Metallum House, Arthur Drive, Hoo Farm Industrial Estate, Kidderminster, Worcestershire, DY11 7RA Tel: (01562) 746454 Fax: (01562) 820465 E-mail: sales@metalwarehouse.com

L A Metals Ltd, Roebuck Lane, Smethwick, West Midlands, B66 1BY Tel: 0121-553 6846 Fax: 0121-553 3270

▶ Linn Tech Scotland Ltd, Unit 15 Tartraven Place, East Mains Industrial Estate, Broxburn, West Lothian, EH52 5LT Tel: (01506) 858999 Fax: (01506) 858444

▶ Metal Fast, Unit 11, Cirrus Court, Glebe Road, Huntingdon, Cambridgeshire, PE29 7DL Tel: (01480) 451144 Fax: (01480) 420910 E-mail: sales@metalfast.co.uk

Metal Goods Wales Ltd, North Road, Bridgend Industrial Estate, Bridgend, Mid Glamorgan, CF31 3TP Tel: (01656) 647755 Fax: (01656) 647744 E-mail: sales@metalgoods.co.uk

Metal Mouldings Ltd, Unit 6, North Street, Walsall, WS2 8AU Tel: (01922) 615225 Fax: (01922) 632763

Metal Supermarket, 10 Madeley Road, Moons Moat North Industrial Estate, Redditch, Worcestershire, B98 9NB Tel: (01527) 68818 Fax: (01527) 68414 E-mail: mscredditch@aol.com

ALUMINIUM STOCKHOLDERS – *continued*

Metal Supermarkets, Unit 381a Jedburgh Court, Team Valley Trading Estate, Gateshead, Tyne & Wear, NE11 0BQ Tel: 0191-487 2144 Fax: 0191-487 2155 E-mail: gateshead@metalsupermarkets.org.uk

Metal Supermarkets Ltd, Trafford Park Way, Trafford Park, Trafford Park, Manchester, M17 1AN Tel: 0161-872 1199 Fax: 0161-872 8021 E-mail: mscmanchester@aol.com

Metal Supermarkets Coventry, Bayton Road, Exhall, Coventry, CV7 9EJ Tel: (024) 7636 6567 Fax: (024) 7636 6320 E-mail: msccoventry@aol.com

Metal Supermarkets Govan, Unit 8-9 Orton Place, Glasgow, G51 2HF Tel: 0141-440 1300 Fax: 0141-440 1308 E-mail: msgovan@aol.com

Metal Supermarkets Park Royal, Unit 11 Hanover Industrial Estate, Acton Lane, London, NW10 7NB Tel: (020) 8961 1414 Fax: (020) 8961 1419 E-mail: parkroyal@metalsupermarkets.org.uk

Metal Supermarkets Southampton, Unit 16 Mount Pleasant Industrial Estate, Mount Pleasant Road, Southampton, SO14 0SP Tel: (023) 8022 0999 Fax: (023) 8023 3449 E-mail: southampton@metalsupermarkets.org.uk

▶ Multi Metals Ltd, Belgrave Street, Bellshill Industrial Estate, Bellshill, Lanarkshire, ML4 3JA Tel: (01698) 841199 Fax: (01698) 841812 E-mail: sales@multimetals.com

Multimetals (Scotland), Unit 1 Atlantic Way, Wednesbury, West Midlands, WS10 7WW Tel: 0121-505 2323 Fax: 0121-505 2324 E-mail: enquiries@multimetals.com

N B Metals Ltd, Unit 10 Blenheim Court, Brownfields, Welwyn Garden City, Hertfordshire, AL7 1AD Tel: (01707) 324472 Fax: (01707) 324473 E-mail: info@nbmetals.co.uk

Nefco Multi Metals Ltd, Unit 19 Maun Valley Industrial Estate, Junction Road, Sutton-in-Ashfield, Nottinghamshire, NG17 5GS Tel: (01623) 551313 Fax: (01623) 551195 E-mail: nefco@btconnect.com

Opus Signs Ltd, Rollins House, Mimram Road, Hertford, SG14 1NW Tel: (01992) 501355 Fax: (01992) 501398 E-mail: sales@opussigns.co.uk

P J Metals & Plastics, Unit 4 Park Street, Kidderminster, Worcestershire, DY11 6TN Tel: (01562) 824570 Fax: (01562) 865170

Reyton Metals Ltd, 1 Malvern View Business Park, Stella Way, Cheltenham, Gloucestershire, GL52 7DQ Tel: (01242) 631000 Fax: (01242) 631110

▶ Ridgeway Architectural Glazing Ltd, 6 Onslow Mills, Trout Road, West Drayton, Middlesex, UB7 7RR Tel: (01895) 449666 Fax: (01895) 447666

Righton Ltd, Units 5-6, The Nelson Centre, Portsmouth, PO3 5SE Tel: (023) 9262 3070 Fax: (023) 9267 7502 E-mail: portsmouthsales@righton.co.uk

Rolled Alloys Ltd, Walker Industrial Park, Guide, Blackburn, BB1 2QE Tel: (01254) 582999 Fax: (01254) 582666 E-mail: sales@rolledalloys.co.uk

Round House Ltd, 57 Pinbush Road, Lowestoft, Suffolk, NR33 7NL Tel: (01502) 515220 Fax: (01502) 500954 E-mail: sales@roundhouse.biz

▶ S & G Aluminium Fabrications, Brooklands Road, Adwick-le-Street, Doncaster, South Yorkshire, DN6 7BA Tel: (01302) 330488 Fax: (01302) 330196

Service Metals East Anglia Ltd, 4 Springwood Drive, Springwood Industrial Estate, Braintree, Essex, CM7 2YN Tel: (01376) 322795 Fax: (01376) 322804

Service Metals (North) Ltd, 14 Tollpark Place, Cumbernauld, Glasgow, G68 0LN Tel: (01236) 453444 Fax: (01236) 453555

Service Metals (South) Ltd, Red Shute Hill, Hermitage, Thatcham, Berkshire, RG18 9QX Tel: (01635) 201811 Fax: (01635) 201894

▶ Sigmun, Unit 5 Dunhams Court, Dunhams Lane, Letchworth Garden City, Hertfordshire, SG6 1WB Tel: (01462) 678000 Fax: (01462) 678008

Skymetals Non Ferrous Metals, Unit 3 Trillennium Highway Point, Gorsey Lane, Coleshill, Birmingham, B46 1JU Tel: (01675) 430140 Fax: (01675) 430346 E-mail: birmingham@allmetal.co.uk

Smiths Metal Centres Ltd, 42-56 Tottenham Road, London, N1 4BZ Tel: (020) 7241 2430 Fax: (020) 7254 9608

Southend Aluminium Co., 24 Milton Road, Westcliff-on-Sea, Essex, SS0 7JX Tel: (01702) 331601 Fax: (01702) 330525

Spa Aluminium Ltd, Unit 1, Chapman Way, Tunbridge Wells, Kent, TN2 3EG Tel: (01892) 533911 Fax: (01892) 542019 E-mail: sales@spaaluminium.co.uk

Spectrum Alloys Ltd, Milton Road, Stoke-on-Trent, ST1 6LE Tel: (01782) 532800 Fax: (01782) 532809 E-mail: info@spectrumalloys.co.uk

▶ SPX Contech, Buttington Cross Enterprise Park, Buttington, Welshpool, Powys, SY21 8SL Tel: (01938) 557557 Fax: (01938) 557558

T W Metals Ltd, Unit 43 Nursling Industrial Estate, Majestic Road, Nursling, Southampton, SO16 0AF Tel: (023) 8073 9333 Fax: (023) 8073 9601 E-mail: enquiries@twmetals.co.uk

Taybroh Alloys & Stainless Steels Ltd, Unit 2 Eastington Trading Estate, Stonehouse, Gloucestershire, GL10 3RY Tel: (01453) 828991 Fax: (01453) 828988 E-mail: sales@taybrohalloys.co.uk

ThyssenKrupp Aerospace Ltd, Kiltonga Industrial Estate, Belfast Road, Newtownards, County Down, BT23 4TJ Tel: (028) 9184 4100 Fax: (028) 9184 4199

Villamead, 203 Inkerman Street, Birmingham, B7 4SA Tel: 0121-359 7498 Fax: 0121-359 7498 E-mail: villamead@aol.com

Weldit, 25-27 Bilton Way, Luton, LU1 1UU Tel: (01582) 727840 Fax: (01582) 727841

▶ Werner Synthetics Ltd, 663 Ajax Avenue, Slough, SL1 4BG Tel: (01753) 512444

Woodberry Chillcott & Co. Ltd, Unit 17 Court Road Industrial Estate, Cwmbran, Gwent, NP44 3AS Tel: (01633) 869311 Fax: (01633) 874676 E-mail: cwmbran@woodberrychillcott.co.uk

Woodberry Chillcott & Co. Ltd, 6 Spinnaker Road, Hempsted, Gloucester, GL2 5FD Tel: (01452) 418341 Fax: (01452) 300362 E-mail: sales@woodberrychillcott.co.uk

Woodberry Chillcott & Co. Ltd, Unit 6 Langage Industrial Estate, Eastern Wood Road, Plympton, Plymouth, PL7 5ET Tel: (01752) 343421 Fax: (01752) 346947 E-mail: plymouth@woodberrychillcott.co.uk

Woodberry Chillcott & Co. Ltd, 5 Mountbatten Business Park, Jackson Close, Portsmouth, PO6 1UR Tel: (023) 9238 8031 Fax: (023) 9237 3615 E-mail: portsmouth@woodberrychillcott.co.uk

ALUMINIUM STORAGE BINS

▶ Ra'Alloy Trading Company Ltd, Hortonwood 10, Telford, Shropshire, TF1 7ES Tel: (01952) 677877 Fax: (01952) 677883 E-mail: sales@raalloy.com

ALUMINIUM STRUCTURE FABRICATORS

Class Panel Ltd, Colder Wharfe Works, Huddersfield Road, Ravensthorpe, Dewsbury, West Yorkshire, WF13 3JW Tel: (01924) 430034 Fax: (01924) 430596 E-mail: enquiries@qm-architectural.co.uk

▶ Eventsi Marquees Ltd., 8 Silvermead Road, Sutton Coldfield, West Midlands, B73 5SR Tel: 0121-240 1470 E-mail: enquiries@eventsimarquees.co.uk

Hartley Botanic Ltd, Wellington Road, Greenfield, Oldham, OL3 7AG Tel: (0870) 7770320 Fax: (0870) 7770323 E-mail: info@hartleybotanic.co.uk

ALUMINIUM SULPHATES

Feralco (UK) Ltd, Ditton Road, Widnes, Cheshire, WA8 0PH Tel: 0151-802 2940 Fax: 0151-802 2999 E-mail: info@feralco.com

ALUMINIUM SUPERPLASTIC ALLOYS

Superform Aluminium, Cosgrove Close, Worcester, WR3 8UA Tel: (01905) 874300 Fax: (01905) 874301 E-mail: sales@superform-aluminium.com

ALUMINIUM SUSPENDED CEILING COMPONENTS

▶ Property Maintenance Direct, 80 Loughborough Road, Thringstone, Coalville, Leicestershire, LE67 8LP Tel: (0845) 4589871 Fax: (01530) 459513 E-mail: enquiries@propertymaintenancedirect.co.uk

ALUMINIUM TREADPLATES

Forgetec Engineering, Scatterford Smithy, Newland, Coleford, Gloucestershire, GL16 8NG Tel: (01594) 835363 Fax: (01594) 835363 E-mail: sales@forgetec.co.uk

ALUMINIUM WALL CLADDING

Ash & Lacy Building Systems, Bromford Lane, West Bromwich, West Midlands, B70 7JJ Tel: 0121-525 1444 Fax: 0121-524 8435 E-mail: kay.hall@ashandlacy.com

Chevron Lifts Ltd, The I O Centre, Barn Way, Lodge Farm Industrial Estate, Northampton, NN5 7UW Tel: (01604) 750080 Fax: (01604) 750081 E-mail: email@chevron-lift.com

Environmental Technology Ltd, Entech House, London Road, Woolmer Green, Knebworth, Hertfordshire, SG3 6JR Tel: (01438) 812812 Fax: (01438) 814224 E-mail: admin@etl-entech.co.uk

▶ Sorba UK, The Barn, Witham, Essex, CM8 2BU Tel: 01376 507750

Sotech Ltd, 4 Mill Hill, North West Industrial Estate, Peterlee, County Durham, SR8 2HR Tel: 0191-587 2287 Fax: 0191-518 0703 E-mail: mail@sotech-optima.co.uk

Superform Aluminium, Cosgrove Close, Worcester, WR3 8UA Tel: (01905) 874300 Fax: (01905) 874301 E-mail: sales@superform-aluminium.com

ALUMINIUM WELDING

Bunns Lane Welding, Bunns Lane Works, Bunns Lane, London, NW7 2AJ Tel: (020) 8959 8046

▶ Fab Serv, Unit 2, Underbank Way, Cars Industrial Estate, Haslingden, Rossendale, Lancashire, BB4 5HH Tel: (01706) 230817 Fax: (01706) 230033 E-mail: enquiries@fabserv.co.uk

Fastweld '93 Welding Services, Unit 8, Old Farm Buildings, Maiden Lane, Crayford, Dartford, DA1 4LX Tel: (01322) 553145 Fax: (01322) 553145

GNT Engineering, Golden Triangle Industrial Estate, Harrison Street, Widnes, Cheshire, WA8 8TN Tel: 0151-420 3420 Fax: 0151-423 1579 E-mail: geoff@gntfab.fsnet.co.uk

Hiatco Ltd, West Road, Annfield Plain, Stanley, County Durham, DH9 8NJ Tel: (01207) 282314 Fax: (01207) 283599 E-mail: hiatco@btinternet.com

Metalstyle Fabrications Ltd, Unit 25, Harvest Drive, South Lowestoft Industrial Estate, Lowestoft, Suffolk, NR33 7NJ Tel: (01502) 515758 Fax: (01502) 589927 E-mail: metalstylefab@btconnect.com

Oxford Welding, Unit 1 Wharf Farm Buildings, Eynsham Road, Cassington, Witney, Oxfordshire, OX29 4DB Tel: (01865) 884366 Fax: (01865) 884366

Ray Weld, Dayton Drive, Darent Industrial Park, Erith, Kent, DA8 2LE Tel: (01322) 334499

Starweld Engineering Ltd, 46 Harleston Street, Sheffield, S4 7QB Tel: 0114-272 0283 Fax: 0114-275 0383 E-mail: sales@starweld.com

Steel Engineering Services Ltd, Unit 7f Block Westway, Porterfield Road, Renfrew, PA4 8DJ Tel: 0141-885 0885 Fax: 0141-886 3322 E-mail: info@steeleng.com

Stuart Engineering, Unit B4 Chadwell Heath Industrial Park, Kemp Road, Dagenham, Essex, RM8 1SL Tel: (020) 8590 7412 Fax: (020) 8598 1787

ALUMINIUM WHEELS

Aluminium Service Co. (Warwick) Ltd, Millers Road, Warwick, CV34 5AE Tel: (01926) 491824 Fax: (01926) 410072

ALUMINIUM WINDOW HANDLES

▶ Plus Windows & Doors Ltd, Units 16 & 18 Moor Park Industrial Centre, Tolpits Lane, Watford, WD18 9SP Tel: (01923) 225855 Fax: (01923) 256106 E-mail: sales@apluswindows.co.uk

ALUMINIUM WINDOW MACHINE OR FABRICATING SYSTEMS

Apollo Upvc, 19 Aintree Road, Bootle, Merseyside, L20 9DL Tel: 0151-922 1322 Fax: 0151-922 1322

Chris Kilpin Machinery, 20 Bridgwater Court, Oldmixon Cresent, Weston-super-Mare, Avon, BS24 9AY Tel: (01934) 625850 Fax: (01934) 412816 E-mail: sales@ckmachinery.com

ALUMINIUM WRAPPING FOIL

Macleans Foils Ltd, Essex Works, Kenway, Southend-On-Sea, SS2 5DY Tel: (01702) 463566 Fax: (01702) 616954 E-mail: sales@macleansfoils.co.uk

ALUMINIUM/ALLOY BARS AND SECTIONS

Ace Engineers Ltd, Albert Road, Morley, Leeds, LS27 8LD Tel: 0113-252 2611 Fax: 0113-238 0274 E-mail: sales@ace-engineers.co.uk

All Metal Services Ltd, 6 Horton Industrial Park, Horton Road, West Drayton, Middlesex, UB7 8JD Tel: (01895) 444066 Fax: (01895) 420963 E-mail: london@allmetal.co.uk

Aluminiumwerk Unna AG, 48 Elmsdale Rd, Wootton, Bedford, MK43 9JN Tel: (01234) 768805 Fax: (01234) 767532 E-mail: sales@galupltd.co.uk

Corby Aluminium Co. Ltd, Princewood Rd, Earlstrees, Corby, Northamptonshire, NN17 4AP Tel: (01536) 262437 Fax: (01536) 204216 E-mail: sales@alishapes.co.uk

Cube Arts Ltd, 14-18 Abbotsbury Road, Morden, Surrey, SM4 5LQ Tel: (020) 8685 9108 Fax: (020) 8085 9089 E-mail: info@cubearts.com

L A Metals Ltd, Roebuck Lane, Smethwick, West Midlands, B66 1BY Tel: 0121-553 6846 Fax: 0121-553 3270

M C F Services Ltd, Units 4-5, Camden Drive, Hockley, Birmingham, B1 3LR Tel: 0121-236 8956 Fax: 0121-236 8048

N B Metals Ltd, Unit 10 Blenheim Court, Brownfields, Welwyn Garden City, Hertfordshire, AL7 1AD Tel: (01707) 324472 Fax: (01707) 324473 E-mail: info@nbmetals.co.uk

Pechiney UK Ltd, Pechiney House, The Grove, Slough, SL1 1QF Tel: (01753) 522800 Fax: (01753) 522014 E-mail: enquiries@pechiney.co.uk

S A P A Profiles Ltd, Sawpit Lane, Tibshelf, Alfreton, Derbyshire, DE55 5NH Tel: (01773) 872761 Fax: (01773) 874389 E-mail: info@sapagroup.com

Sapa Profiles Ltd, Tewkesbury Road, Cheltenham, Gloucestershire, GL51 9DT Tel: (01242) 521641 Fax: (01242) 513304 E-mail: info.profiles.uk@sapagroup.com

Service Metals East Anglia Ltd, 4 Springwood Drive, Springwood Industrial Estate, Braintree, Essex, CM7 2YN Tel: (01376) 322795 Fax: (01376) 322804

Spa Aluminium Ltd, Unit 1, Chapman Way, Tunbridge Wells, Kent, TN2 3EG Tel: (01892) 533911 Fax: (01892) 542019 E-mail: sales@spaaluminium.co.uk

ALUMINIUM/ALLOY BRAZING SHEETS AND COILS

Amag U K Ltd, Beckley Lodge Leatherhead Road, Bookham, Leatherhead, Surrey, KT23 3PD Tel: (01372) 450661 Fax: (01372) 450833 E-mail: amag.uk@amag.at

Corus, 15 Great Marlborough Street, London, W1F 7HR Tel: (020) 7717 4444 Fax: (020) 7717 4455

ALUMINIUM/ALLOY CIRCLES

W & S Allely Ltd, PO Box 58, Smethwick, West Midlands, B66 2RP Tel: 0121-558 3301 Fax: 0121-555 5194E-mail: sales@allely.co.uk

ALUMINIUM/ALLOY COILS

M G Non-Ferrous Products Ltd, 2 Station Road, Stratford St Mary, Colchester, CO7 6WZ Tel: (01206) 337429 Fax: (01206) 337413 E-mail: mgnf@dial.pipex.com

ALUMINIUM/ALLOY EXTRUSIONS

Alserco (UK) Ltd, 111 Fazeley Street, Digbeth, Birmingham, B5 5RR Tel: 0121 643 2421 Fax: 0121 633 3140 E-mail: philip.relph@tkmuk.thyssenkrupp.com

Amech Engineering Ltd, Dudley Road, Yarm Road Industrial Estate, Darlington, County Durham, DL1 4GG Tel: (01325) 488884 Fax: (01325) 382525 E-mail: info@amech.net

Corby Aluminium Co. Ltd, Princewood Rd, Earlstrees, Corby, Northamptonshire, NN17 4AP Tel: (01536) 262437 Fax: (01536) 204216 E-mail: sales@alishapes.co.uk

Plastestrip Profiles Ltd, Trenance Mill, St. Austell, Cornwall, PL25 5LZ Tel: (01726) 74771 Fax: (01726) 69238 E-mail: sales@plaspro.force9.co.uk

ALUMINIUM/ALLOY FABRICATORS

Cogent Contracts Ltd, Limekiln Lane, Birmingham, B14 4SP Tel: 0121-474 2500 Fax: 0121-474 6163 E-mail: cogentcontracts@hotmail.com

Engineering Metal Services Ltd, 4 Bradley Fold Trading Estate, Radcliffe Moor Road, Bradley Fold, Bolton, BL2 6RT Tel: (01204) 361811 Fax: (01204) 523697 E-mail: emslimited@emslimited.free-online.co.uk

Holden Aluminium Technologies Ltd, Linton Trading Estate, Bromyard, Herefordshire, HR7 4QT Tel: (01885) 482222 Fax: (01885) 482000 E-mail: info@alloy.uk.com

Imi Components, Nobel Way, Witton, Birmingham, B6 7ES Tel: 0121-344 5800 Fax: 0121-344 3056

Spirex Metal Products Ltd, Marsh Lane, Ware, Hertfordshire, SG12 9QQ Tel: (01920) 460516 Fax: (01920) 487028 E-mail: info@spirex.co.uk

ALUMINIUM/ALLOY FOIL

Bunzl Cleaning & Hygiene Supplies, Bone Lane, Newbury, Berkshire, RG14 5SH Tel: (01635) 528550 Fax: (01635) 528822 E-mail: newbury@bunzlchs.co.uk

▶ Reliance Converting Ltd, Salters Lane, Sedgefield, Stockton-on-Tees, Cleveland, TS21 3EE Tel: (01740) 621415 Fax: (01740) 621424 E-mail: sales@relianceconverting.co.uk

ALUMINIUM/ALLOY INGOT/ SECONDARY INGOTS

Brock Metal Co., Walsall Road, Norton Canes, Cannock, Staffordshire, WS11 9NR Tel: (01543) 276666 Fax: (01543) 276418 E-mail: brock@brock-metal.co.uk
Coleshill Alloy Sales Ltd, Gorsey Lane, Coleshill, Birmingham, B46 1JU Tel: (01675) 463170 Fax: (01675) 463748 E-mail: office@coleshill-aluminium.com
Evans & Reed Alloys Ltd, Anchor Road, Bilston, West Midlands, WV14 9NA Tel: (01902) 354776 Fax: (01902) 354856 E-mail: sales@evansandreid.com
J B M International Ltd, Unit 5b Hixon Industrial Estate, Church Lane, Hixon, Stafford, ST18 0PY Tel: (01889) 271491 Fax: (01889) 271191 E-mail: sales@jessebroughmetals.co.uk
Mil-Ver Metal Co., Coronel Avenue, Longford, Coventry, CV6 6AP Tel: (024) 7666 7098 Fax: (024) 7666 2299 E-mail: steve.miles@milver.co.uk
Reg Morris (Brierley Hill) Ltd, Canal Street, Brierley Hill, West Midlands, DY5 1JJ Tel: (01384) 78187 Fax: (01384) 75361
Rugeley Aluminium Products Ltd, 5a Knighton Road, Sutton Coldfield, West Midlands, B74 4NY Tel: 0121-353 0006 Fax: 0121-353 5586 E-mail: teakandco@aol.com

ALUMINIUM/ALLOY PLATE MANUFRS

▶ Alimex UK Possion In Aluminium Ltd, 6 Fingle Drive, Stonebridge, Milton Keynes, MK13 0AB Tel: (01908) 224240 Fax: (01908) 224241 E-mail: info@alimex.uk.com
Aluminium Stockholders Association, Broadway House, Calthorpe Road, Five Ways, Birmingham, B15 1TN Tel: 0121-456 4938 Fax: 0121-456 4937 E-mail: asa@alfed.org.uk
Amag U K Ltd, Beckley Lodge Leatherhead Road, Bookham, Leatherhead, Surrey, KT23 3PD Tel: (01372) 450661 Fax: (01372) 450833 E-mail: amag.uk@amag.at
Corus, 15 Great Marlborough Street, London, W1F 7HR Tel: (020) 7717 4444 Fax: (020) 7717 4455
Dore Metal Services Ltd, Unit 2 Dolphin Park Cremers Road, Sittingbourne, Kent, ME10 3HB Tel: (01795) 473551 Fax: (01795) 429473 E-mail: ian@doremetals.co.uk

ALUMINIUM/ALLOY RODS

Aluminium Stockholders Association, Broadway House, Calthorpe Road, Five Ways, Birmingham, B15 1TN Tel: 0121-456 4938 Fax: 0121-456 4937 E-mail: asa@alfed.org.uk

ALUMINIUM/ALLOY SHEET/COIL/ STRIP ETC, PRECOATED

Cooper 2005 Ltd, Great Bridge Street, West Bromwich, West Midlands, B70 0DJ Tel: 0121-521 1500 Fax: 0121-521 1526 E-mail: stevet@coopercoated.co.uk
Corus, Brockhurst Crescent, Walsall, WS5 4AX Tel: (01922) 629593 Fax: (01922) 648202
Euramax Coated Products Ltd, Brunel Road, Earlstrees Industrial Estate, Corby, Northamptonshire, NN17 4JW Tel: (01536) 400800 Fax: (01536) 400101
Hydo Aluminium U K, Unit 4 Newton Court Westrand, Pendeford Business Park, Wolverhampton, WV9 5HB Tel: (01902) 396630 Fax: (01902) 396640 E-mail: sales@hydro-aluminium.com

ALUMINIUM/ALLOY SHEETS

Agora Metals Ltd, Millfields Road, Wolverhampton, WV4 6JQ Tel: (01902) 402134 Fax: (01902) 403737 E-mail: mark@parkrow-alloys.co.uk
Alstain Metal Services Ltd, Sapcote Trading Centre, Small Heath Highway, Birmingham, B10 0HR Tel: 0121-773 5655 Fax: 0121-773 5220 E-mail: sales@alstain.co.uk
Baco Metal Centres, Edison Road, Elm Farm Industrial Estate, Bedford, MK41 0HU Tel: (01234) 684100 Fax: (01234) 684199 E-mail: bmc.sales@alcoa.com
Baco Metal Centres, Coegnant Close, Brackla Industrial Estate, Bridgend, Mid Glamorgan, CF31 2AH Tel: (01656) 683900 Fax: (01656) 683999 E-mail: bridgend@bacometalcentres.co.uk
Baco Metal Centres, Unit 14 St Andrews Trading Estate, Third Way, Avonmouth, Bristol, BS11 9YE Tel: 0117-948 2600 Fax: 0117-948 2699 E-mail: bmc.sales@alcoa.com
Baco Metal Centres, 13 Concorde Road, Norwich, NR6 6BJ Tel: (01603) 243900 Fax: (01603) 243999 E-mail: norwich@blackburnsm.com
Baco Metal Centres, 1 Eagle Road, Plympton, Plymouth, PL7 5JY Tel: (01752) 612400 Fax: (01752) 612499 E-mail: plymouth@bacometalcentres.co.uk
Baco Metal Centres, Unit 4 Stadium Way, Tilehurst, Reading, RG30 6BX Tel: 0118-980 3300 Fax: 0118-980 3399 E-mail: bmc.sales@alcoa.com
Blackburns, Fircroft Way, Edenbridge, Kent, TN8 6ES Tel: (01732) 582700 Fax: (01732) 582799 E-mail: edenbridge@blackburnsmetals.com
▶ Blackburns Metal Centres, Units 3-4, Haydock Lane, Haydock Industrial Estate, Haydock, St. Helens, Merseyside, WA11 9UY Tel: 0161-254 8800 Fax: (01942) 758899 E-mail: haydock@blackburnsmetalcentre.com
Blackburns Metals Ltd, 4 Wellington Road, Leeds, LS3 1LE Tel: 0113-296 1500 Fax: 0113-296 1599 E-mail: leeds@blackburnsmetals.com
C M Alloys, Peartree Business Centre, Cobham Road, Ferndown Industrial Estate, Wimborne, Dorset, BH21 7PT Tel: (01202) 850370 Fax: (01202) 850379
Eggleston Bros Ltd, Centurion Way Business Park, Alfreton Road, Derby, DE21 4AY Tel: (01332) 341536 Fax: (01332) 295715 E-mail: info@egglestonbros.co.uk
▶ Eltherington Group Ltd, Dansom Lane, Hull, HU8 7LA Tel: (01482) 320336 Fax: (01482) 317824 E-mail: info@eltherington.co.uk
Hydo Aluminium U K, Unit 4 Newton Court Westrand, Pendeford Business Park, Wolverhampton, WV9 5HB Tel: (01902) 396630 Fax: (01902) 396640 E-mail: sales@hydro-aluminium.com
Inmet Aluminium & Stainless Ltd, D Boomes Industrial Estate, New Road, Rainham, Essex, RM13 8BS Tel: (01708) 522673 Fax: (01708) 555743 E-mail: inmet@netcomuk.co.uk
M G Non-Ferrous Products Ltd, 2 Station Road, Stratford St Mary, Colchester, CO7 6WZ Tel: (01206) 337429 Fax: (01206) 337413 E-mail: mgnf@dial.pipex.com
Pechiney UK Ltd, Pechiney House, The Grove, Slough, SL1 1QF Tel: (01753) 522800 Fax: (01753) 522014 E-mail: enquiries@pechiney.co.uk
ThyssenKrupp Aerospace Ltd, Kiltonga Industrial Estate, Belfast Road, Newtownards, County Down, BT23 4TJ Tel: (028) 9184 4100 Fax: (028) 9184 4199

ALUMINIUM/ALLOY STOCKHOLDERS

▶ Aluminium All Parts, 1-5 Meadow Court, Pen Elm, Taunton, Somerset, TA2 6PD Tel: (01823) 323916 Fax: (01823) 323916 E-mail: alluminiumallparts@btinternet.com
Amag U K Ltd, Beckley Lodge Leatherhead Road, Bookham, Leatherhead, Surrey, KT23 3PD Tel: (01372) 450661 Fax: (01372) 450833 E-mail: amag.uk@amag.at
Corus Building Systems, Units 1-3 Fishwicks Industrial Estate, Kilbuck Lane, St. Helens, Merseyside, WA11 9SZ Tel: (01942) 295500 Fax: (01942) 272136E-mail: info@kalzip.co.uk
Evans & Reed Alloys Ltd, Anchor Road, Bilston, West Midlands, WV14 9NA Tel: (01902) 354776 Fax: (01902) 354856 E-mail: sales@evansandreid.com
F E Mottram Non Ferrous Ltd, Radnor Park Industrial Estate, Congleton, Cheshire, CW12 4XE Tel: (01260) 271122 Fax: (01260) 271324 E-mail: info@femottram.co.uk
Hydro Aluminium Deeside Ltd, Bridge Road, Wrexham Industrial Estate, Wrexham, Clwyd, LL13 9PS Tel: (01978) 660231 Fax: (01978) 661125 E-mail: hydro.deeside@hydro.com
Metal Supermarket, 10 Madeley Road, Moons Moat North Industrial Estate, Redditch, Worcestershire, B98 9NB Tel: (01527) 68818 Fax: (01527) 68414 E-mail: mscredditch@aol.com
Metal Supermarkets Ltd, Trafford Park Way, Trafford Park, Manchester, M17 1AN Tel: 0161-872 1199 Fax: 0161-872 8021 E-mail: mscmanchester@aol.com
Metal Supermarkets Coventry, Bayton Road, Exhall, Coventry, CV7 9EJ Tel: (024) 7636 6567 Fax: (024) 7636 6320 E-mail: msccoventry@aol.com
Metal Supermarkets Govan, Unit 8-9 Orton Place, Glasgow, G51 2HF Tel: 0141-440 1300 Fax: 0141-440 1308 E-mail: msgovan@aol.com
Metal Supermarkets Park Royal, Unit 11 Hanover Industrial Estate, Acton Lane, London, NW10 7NB Tel: (020) 8961 1414 Fax: (020) 8961 1419 E-mail: parkroyal@metalsupermarkets.org.uk
Metal Supermarkets Southampton, Unit 16 Mount Pleasant Industrial Estate, Mount Pleasant Road, Southampton, SO14 0SP Tel: (023) 8022 0999 Fax: (023) 8023 3449 E-mail: southampton@metalsupermarkets.org.uk
Metalweb, Unit 9, Trident Industrial Estate, Pindar Road, Hoddesdon, Hertfordshire, EN11 0WZ Tel: (020) 8804 4032 Fax: (01992) 450557 E-mail: info@metalweb.co.uk
Oldbury Aluminium Alloys Ltd, Amberway, Halesowen, West Midlands, B62 8AY Tel: 0121-504 3880 Fax: 0121-504 3889 E-mail: oaaltd@aol.com

ALUMINIUM/ALLOY STRIPS

Agora Metals Ltd, Millfields Road, Wolverhampton, WV4 6JQ Tel: (01902) 402134 Fax: (01902) 403737 E-mail: mark@parkrow-alloys.co.uk
Aluminiumwerk Unna AG, 48 Elmsdale Rd, Wootton, Bedford, MK43 9JN Tel: (01234) 768805 Fax: (01234) 767532 E-mail: sales@galupltd.co.uk
Hydo Aluminium U K, Unit 4 Newton Court Westrand, Pendeford Business Park, Wolverhampton, WV9 5HB Tel: (01902) 396630 Fax: (01902) 396640 E-mail: sales@hydro-aluminium.com
Inmet Aluminium & Stainless Ltd, D Boomes Industrial Estate, New Road, Rainham, Essex, RM13 8BS Tel: (01708) 522673 Fax: (01708) 555743 E-mail: inmet@netcomuk.co.uk
Novelis U.K Ltd, Castle Works, Rogerstone, Newport, Gwent, NP10 9YD Tel: (01633) 202020 Fax: (01633) 202000 E-mail: bunworth@novelis.com

ALUMINIUM/ALLOY TUBES

Alcoa (Europe), Southam Road, Banbury, Oxfordshire, OX16 2SN Tel: (01295) 454444 Fax: (01295) 454454
Aluminiumwerk Unna AG, 48 Elmsdale Rd, Wootton, Bedford, MK43 9JN Tel: (01234) 768805 Fax: (01234) 767532 E-mail: sales@galupltd.co.uk
Bayswater Tubes & Sections Ltd, The Tube Mills, Pencoed, Bridgend, Mid Glamorgan, CF35 6UG Tel: (01656) 860581 Fax: (01656) 860906 E-mail: sales@aluminiumtubes.com
Corby Aluminium Co. Ltd, Princewood Rd, Earlstrees, Corby, Northamptonshire, NN17 4AP Tel: (01536) 262437 Fax: (01536) 204216 E-mail: sales@alishapes.co.uk
Crossman Engineering Ltd, Downsview Road, Wantage, Oxfordshire, OX12 9FA Tel: (01235) 772885 Fax: (01235) 772886 E-mail: sales@crossmaneng.co.uk
Harbour, Unit 4 Premier Industrial Units, Castle Street, Castlepark Industrial Estate, Ellon, Aberdeenshire, AB41 9RF Tel: (01358) 722422 Fax: (01358) 722880 E-mail: harboureng@btinternet.com
Hulett Aluminium International, Securehold Business Centre, Studley Road, Redditch, Worcestershire, B98 7LG Tel: (01527) 516222 Fax: (01527) 517199 E-mail: sales@hulett-hydro.co.za
Le Guellec, Stone Road, Tittensor, Stoke-On-Trent, ST12 9HA Tel: (01782) 374111 Fax: (01782) 373488 E-mail: info@wlmetals.co.uk
M K Wheeler Ltd, Nine Lock Works, Mill Street, Brierley Hill, West Midlands, DY5 2SX Tel: (01384) 487600 Fax: (01384) 487619 E-mail: sales@vanleeuwenwheeler.co.uk
▶ M&G-GB Ltd, Caxton Way, Stevenage, Hertfordshire, SG1 2DF Tel: (01438) 747999 Fax: (01438) 747070 E-mail: mg.gb@mailbox.as
Pinnacal Aluminium Ltd, East Moons House, Oxleasow Road, East Moons Moat, Redditch, Worcestershire, B98 0RE Tel: (01527) 830424 Fax: (01527) 830425 E-mail: sales@pinnacal.co.uk
S A P A Profiles Ltd, Sawpit Lane, Tibshelf, Alfreton, Derbyshire, DE55 5NH Tel: (01773) 872761 Fax: (01773) 874389 E-mail: info@sapagroup.com
Sapa Profiles Ltd, Tewkesbury Road, Cheltenham, Gloucestershire, GL51 9DT Tel: (01242) 521641 Fax: (01242) 513304 E-mail: info.profiles.uk@sapagroup.com

ALUMINIUM/ALLOY TUBES, POWDER COATED

▶ CMT Industrial Powdercoaters, 27 Dencora Way, Luton, LU3 3HP Tel: (01582) 575494 Fax: (01582) 584297 E-mail: cmtpowdercoaters@aol.com
▶ M K Powder Coatings, 5 Cordingley Street, Bradford, West Yorkshire, BD4 0PP Tel: (01274) 680099 Fax: (01274) 680099
▶ M&G-GB Ltd, Caxton Way, Stevenage, Hertfordshire, SG1 2DF Tel: (01438) 747999 Fax: (01438) 747070 E-mail: mg.gb@mailbox.as

ALUMINIUM/ALLOY TUBES, WELDED SEAM

Bayswater Tubes & Sections Ltd, The Tube Mills, Pencoed, Bridgend, Mid Glamorgan, CF35 6UG Tel: (01656) 860581 Fax: (01656) 860906 E-mail: sales@aluminiumtubes.com
G K W Ltd, Merton Bank Road, St. Helens, Merseyside, WA9 1HP Tel: (01744) 762330 Fax: (01744) 754309 E-mail: kevin.jones@gordonkitto.co.uk

ALUMINIUM/ALLOY TURNED PARTS

A & J Precision Engineering, 3 Fenland Business Centre, Longhill Road, March, Cambridgeshire, PE15 0BL Tel: (01354) 652203 Fax: (01354) 652203 E-mail: anjprecision@tiscali.co.uk
Ardmore Construction Ltd, Bryne House, 54 Jeffreys Road, Enfield, Middlesex, EN3 7UB Tel: (020) 8805 0101 Fax: (020) 8364 7477 E-mail: millmarsh@mooregroup.co.uk
Autonic Engineering Co. Ltd, Salisbury Road, Hoddesdon, Hertfordshire, EN11 0HU Tel: (01992) 471101 Fax: (01992) 471102 E-mail: sales@autonic.co.uk
Ipeco Engineering Ltd, Aviation Way, Southend-on-Sea, SS2 6UN Tel: (01702) 544939 Fax: (01702) 546480

ALUMINIUM/ALLOY WIRE

Galup Ltd, 48 Elmsdale Road, Wooton, Bedford, MK43 9JU Tel: (01234) 768805 Fax: (01234) 767532 E-mail: sales@galupltd.co.uk

ALUMINIUM/ALLOYS, AMERICAN STANDARDS

Anglo Blackwells Ltd, Ditton Road, Widnes, Cheshire, WA8 0NT Tel: 0151-495 1400 Fax: 0151-495 4201 E-mail: sales@angloblackwells.com

AMBULANCE BUILDERS

Frank Guy, Bidston House, Astwith Close, Holmewood, Chesterfield, Derbyshire, S42 5UR Tel: (01246) 851222 Fax: (01246) 851225 E-mail: sales@frank-guy.co.uk

AMBULANCE OR HOSPITAL TROLLEYS

▶ David Hilton, Orchard Cottage, Littledown Farm, Brighton Road, Lewes, East Sussex, BN7 3JJ Tel: 01273 479799 Fax: 01273 239999 E-mail: david.hilton@ambulanceservice.gb.com
Medisco Medical Systems Ltd, Unit 13, Isis Trading Estate, Strutton Road, Swindon, SN1 2PG Tel: (01793) 692781 Fax: (01793) 491688E-mail: jim@redman-sheet-metal.co.uk

AMINO ACID ANALYSERS

Ecos Environmental, Low Moor Industrial Estate, Common Road, Low Moor, Bradford, West Yorkshire, BD12 0NB Tel: (01274) 691122 Fax: (01274) 608100 E-mail: info@ecos.co.uk

AMINO ACIDS

Croda Europe Ltd, Foundry Lane, Widnes, Cheshire, WA8 8UB Tel: 0151-423 3441 Fax: 0151-423 3441
Forum Bioscience Holdings Ltd, 41-51 Brighton Road, Redhill, RH1 6YS Tel: (01737) 773711 Fax: (01737) 770053
Health Leads UK Ltd, 2 St. Clears Business Park, Tenby Road, St. Clears, Carmarthen, SA33 4JW Tel: (01994) 231940 Fax: (01994) 231941 E-mail: mail@healthleadsuk.com

AMMETERS

The Herts Meter Co. Ltd, Unit 10 Bury Road, Hatfield, Hertfordshire, AL10 8BJ Tel: (01707) 270404 Fax: (01707) 270152 E-mail: info@hertsmeter.com

AMMONIUM CARBONATES AND BICARBONATES

Brotherton Speciality Products Ltd, Calder Vale Road, Wakefield, West Yorkshire, WF1 5PH Tel: (01924) 371919 Fax: (01924) 290408 E-mail: info@brotherton.co.uk

AMMUNITION, *See also headings for particular types*

▶ Clay Shooters Supplies, 32 St Marys Road, Market Harborough, Leicestershire, LE16 7DU Tel: (01858) 466616 Fax: (01858) 466616 E-mail: shaun@shooterssupplies.co.uk
Edgar Bros, Heather Close, Lyme Green Business Park, Macclesfield, Cheshire, SK11 0LR Tel: (01625) 613177 Fax: (01625) 615276 E-mail: admin@edgar-brothers.co.uk
Eley Ltd, Selco Way Off First Avenue, Minworth Industrial Estate, Minworth, Sutton Coldfield, West Midlands, B76 1BA Tel: 0121-313 4567 Fax: 0121-331 4173 E-mail: sales@eleyhawkltd.com
Hull Cartridge Co. Ltd, Bontoft Avenue, Hull, HU5 4HZ Tel: (01482) 342756 Fax: (01482) 346103 E-mail: sales@hullcartridge.co.uk
Lincoln Jeffries Ltd, Summer Lane, Birmingham, B19 3TH Tel: 0121-359 3343 Fax: 0121-359 3343

AMPLIFIERS, *See also headings for particular types*

B K Electronics, Unit 1 3 & 5 Comet Way, Southend-on-Sea, SS2 6TR Tel: (01702) 527572 Fax: (01702) 420243 E-mail: sales@bkelec.com

▶ Celsum Technologies Ltd, Willow House, 17 Braemar Close, Mountsorrel, Loughborough, Leicestershire, LE12 7ES Tel: 0116-210 6319 Fax: (0870) 1206319 E-mail: sales@celsum.com

▶ CLASS-UK, 12 Tadcaster Road, Dringhouses, York, YO24 1LH Tel: (01904) 709091 E-mail: steve@class-uk.com

Cord Electronics Ltd, The Pumphouse, Farley Bridge, Farley Lane, Maidstone, Kent, ME16 9NB Tel: (01622) 721444 Fax: (01622) 721555 E-mail: sales@chordelectronics.co.uk

Exposure Electronics, 59 North Street, Portslade, Brighton, BN41 1DH Tel: (01273) 423877 Fax: (01273) 430619 E-mail: info@exposurehifi.com

Linear Technology Ltd, 3 The Listons, Liston Road, Marlow, Buckinghamshire, SL7 1FD Tel: (01628) 477066 Fax: (01628) 478153

Showtech Sound & Light Design, Unit 23 Hammond Business Centre, Hammond Close, Attleborough Fields Ind Estate, Nuneaton, Warwickshire, CV11 6RY Tel: (024) 7634 8890 Fax: (024) 7634 8890 E-mail: enquiries@ssld.co.uk

AMPLIFIERS, AUDIO AND VIDEO

▶ Thames Electronics, 244 Battersea Bridge Road, London, SW11 3AA Tel: (020) 7924 5536 Fax: 020 7924 5537 E-mail: service@thameselectronics.co.uk

AMPLIFIERS, DIGITAL AUDIO

▶ Thames Electronics, 244 Battersea Bridge Road, London, SW11 3AA Tel: (020) 7924 5536 Fax: 020 7924 5537 E-mail: service@thameselectronics.co.uk

▶ Virtual Lifestyles, Virtual House, 280 Marlow Bottom, Marlow, Buckinghamshire, SL7 3PT Tel: 01628 474742 E-mail: info@virtual-lifestyles.com

AMPLIFIERS, KARAOKE

▶ Platterpuss Karaoke, 107 Station Road, Hayes, Middlesex, UB3 4BX Tel: (020) 8569 1090 Fax: (020) 8569 1036 E-mail: sales@platterpuss.com

AMPLIFIERS, LOCK-IN

Bentham Instruments Ltd, 2 Boulton Road, Reading, RG2 0NH Tel: 0118-975 1355 Fax: 0118-931 2971 E-mail: sales@bentham.co.uk

Scitec Instruments, Bartles Industrial Estate, North Street, Redruth, Cornwall, TR15 1HR Tel: (01209) 314608 Fax: (01209) 314609 E-mail: info@scitec.uk.com

AMPLIFIERS, POWER, MIXER

▶ Dale Electronics Ltd, Dale House, Wharf Road, Frimley Green, Camberley, Surrey, GU16 6LF Tel: (01252) 832600 Fax: (01252) 837010 E-mail: june@uk.minicircuits.com

AMPLIFIERS, SERVO

Intelligent Motion Control Ltd, 4 Brunel Close, Drayton Fields Industrial Estate, Daventry, Northamptonshire, NN11 8RB Tel: (01327) 307600 Fax: (01327) 300319 E-mail: info@inmoco.co.uk

AMUSEMENT EQUIPMENT, FAIRGROUND

Bounceabouts Leisure Ltd, Asfare Business Park, Hinckley Road, Wolvey, Hinckley, Leicestershire, LE10 3HQ Tel: (01455) 220886 Fax: (01455) 220988 E-mail: sales@bounceabouts.co.uk

C & S Bouncy Castles, 8 Duke Close, Nottingham, NG6 7BG Tel: 0115-976 3935

Castles In The Air, Spring Bank West, Hull, HU3 1LD Tel: (01482) 470366 Fax: (01482) 470366

D & D Leisure, Arcadia House, Glanmor Terrace, New Quay, Dyfed, SA45 9PX Tel: (01545) 560584 Fax: (01545) 561040

Dewey Automatics, Unit 12 The Rope Walk, Station Road, Ilkeston, Derbyshire, DE7 5HX Tel: 0115-930 8397 Fax: 0115-944 2397

Eastwood Automatics Cce Video Ltd, 19 James Street, Cookstown, County Tyrone, BT80 8AA Tel: (028) 8676 6100 Fax: (028) 8676 3412

Jolly Roger (Amusement Rides) Ltd, College View Works, Manby Road, Grimoldby, Louth, Lincolnshire, LN11 8HE Tel: (01507) 328856 Fax: (01507) 327060 E-mail: roger@jolly-roger.co.uk

Kossway Automatics Distributors Ltd, 8 The Ridgeway, Iver, Buckinghamshire, SL0 9HJ Tel: (01753) 655400 Fax: (01753) 630278 E-mail: sales@kosswayautomatics.co.uk

M D M Leisure Ltd, 56 Seaview Drive, Great Wakering, Southend-on-Sea, SS3 0BE Tel: (01702) 217917 Fax: (01702) 217917

Midas Leisure Cafe & Arcade, 148 High Street, Eston, Middlesbrough, Cleveland, TS6 9EN Tel: (01642) 454851 Fax: (01642) 505333

Pan Amusements, Austerlands Mill, Huddersfield Road, Austerlands, Oldham, OL4 3QB Tel: 0161-624 5578 Fax: 0161-627 5357 E-mail: info@panamusements.com

Ray-Play, 15 Victoria Rd, Bexleyheath, Kent, DA6 7LT Tel: 020 83034751

Riverside Balloons Ltd, 1 Whirlowdale Crescent, Millhouses Sheffield, Sheffield, S7 2NA Tel: 0114-262 1860 Fax: 0114-225 7446

The Rodeo Bulll Co., PO Box 312, Harrogate, North Yorkshire, HG1 4QE Tel: (01423) 541867 Fax: (01423) 541999

W Pettigrove, Chadwell Cottage, Owlswick, Princes Risborough, Buckinghamshire, HP27 9RJ Tel: (01844) 345751 Fax: (01844) 345751

Williamson Leisure, Wroxham Barns, Tunstead Rd, Hoveton, Norwich, NR12 8QU Tel: (01603) 784118 E-mail: info@wroxham-barns.co.uk

AMUSEMENT (FAIRGROUND) EQUIPMENT ENGINEERS, REFURBISHMENT SERVICES

John H Rundle Ltd, Main Road, New Bolingbroke, Boston, Lincolnshire, PE22 7LN Tel: (01205) 480431 Fax: (01205) 480132 E-mail: jhrundle@globalnet.co.uk

Kiddies Kastles, Fish Pond Trading Estate, Foundry Lane, Bristol, BS5 7UZ Tel: 0117-955 5544 Fax: 0117-955 0786

AMUSEMENT MACHINE/ EQUIPMENT MAINTENANCE/ REPAIR SERVICES

A A Automatics, Unit E1 Gadd Street, Nottingham, NG7 4BJ Tel: 0115-978 0965 Fax: 0115-978 0965

Armitage Leisure Services, 121a Acre Street, Huddersfield, HD3 3EJ Tel: (01484) 644404 Fax: (01484) 646315 E-mail: info@armitageleisure.co.uk

Claremont Automatics Ltd, 40 Oakley Road, Chinnor, Oxfordshire, OX39 4ES Tel: (01844) 353635 Fax: (01844) 352750

County Properties & Developments Ltd, 8-10 Hallcraig Street, Airdrie, Lanarkshire, ML6 6AH Tel: (01236) 757850 Fax: (01236) 757851

Gametime Leisure, 8 Fleet Business Park, Itlings Lane, Hessle, North Humberside, HU13 9LX Tel: (01482) 647979 Fax: (01482) 647979

Glen Leisure Services Ltd, Unit 1 Strathkelvin Retail Park, Bishopbriggs, Glasgow, G64 2TS Tel: 0141-762 1121 Fax: 0141-762 5126

Grampian Leisure, 5-13 Duff Street, Aberdeen, AB24 5LF Tel: (01224) 646422 Fax: (01224) 646630

Halliday Leisure Ltd, 90-94 Green Street, Ayr, KA8 8BG Tel: (01292) 267575 Fax: (01292) 267575 E-mail: halliday.leisure@virgin.net

Hayton Automatics Ltd, 36 Brookfield Way, Heanor, Derby, DE75 7NX Tel: 01773 711738 E-mail: spayne111@hotmail.co.uk

Heddleworth Amusements Ltd, 1 Clearway House Industrial Estate, Overthorpe Road, Banbury, Oxfordshire, OX16 4US Tel: (01295) 259863 Fax: (01295) 270559

K E R Videos, Chapel Buildings, Plainspot Road, Brinsley, Nottingham, NG16 5BQ Tel: (01773) 530315 Fax: (01773) 530315 E-mail: ker.videos@talk21.com

K Sime Machines, 14 Parkhills Road, Bury, Lancashire, BL9 9AX Tel: 0161-797 6723 Fax: 0161-797 6727 E-mail: office@tournament.co.uk

Kidzstuff, 60 Lansdown Crescent Lane, Cheltenham, Gloucestershire, GL50 2LD Tel: (01242) 232521 Fax: (0870) 1643904 E-mail: sales@kidzstuff.uk.com

Leisure Link Electronic Entertainment Ltd, Unit 4 Derwent Mills Commercial Park, Cockermouth, Cumbria, CA13 0HT Tel: (01900) 823029 Fax: (01900) 827691 E-mail: enquiries@leisure-link.com

M E Electronics, St Marys Works, 115 Burnmoor Street, Leicester, LE2 7JL Tel: 0116-254 8918 Fax: 0116-254 8918

Maday Automatics, 42 Boyslade Road East, Burbage, Hinckley, Leicestershire, LE10 2RQ Tel: (01455) 636848 Fax: (01455) 617516

Midland Automatics, 10 Sheffield Street, Leicester, LE3 0GX Tel: 0116-254 5515

▶ Paramount Services Co., PO Box 4739, Reading, RG6 1XA Tel: (0870) 3214801 Fax: (0870) 3214802 E-mail: info@paramount-services.co.uk

Revolution Entertainment Systems Ltd, Showell Road, Wolverhampton, WV10 9NL Tel: (01902) 713000 Fax: (01902) 711555

▶ SAS Amusements, 136-145 Central Parade, Herne Bay, Kent, CT6 8SS Tel: (01227) 375098 E-mail: info@sasamusements.co.uk

Starlight Music, 2 Humphrey Street, Ince, Wigan, Lancashire, WN2 2HS Tel: (01942) 242450 Fax: (01942) 242450

Tablesport Ltd, Unit 4 Surney Farm, Long Buckby Wharf, Long Buckby, Northampton, NN6 7PP Tel: (01327) 842546 Fax: (01327) 842737

W C A Leisure Machines Ltd, 4 Newnham Road, Plympton, Plymouth, PL7 4AN Tel: (01752) 336651 Fax: (01752) 340892

AMUSEMENT MACHINES AND EQUIPMENT

A A Automatics, Unit E1 Gadd Street, Nottingham, NG7 4BJ Tel: 0115-978 0965 Fax: 0115-978 0965

Ackland Automatics, Unit 2 Lower Union Road, Kingsbridge, Devon, TQ7 1EF Tel: (01548) 852668 Fax: (01548) 852668

Acorn Leisure, The Paddock, Tenby, Dyfed, SA70 8DJ Tel: (01834) 842931 Fax: (01834) 845174

Alan Davis Ltd, Woodland Close, Torquay, TQ2 7BD Tel: (01803) 612261 Fax: (01803) 615201E-mail: adaamusements@hotmail.com

Amusement Machines Services, Pioneer House, Northgate, Dewsbury, West Yorkshire, WF13 1AP Tel: (0800) 7837313 E-mail: peter@ams-nv.freeserve.co.uk

Apollo Leisure Ltd, 90 Hillcroft Crescent, Watford, WD19 4NY Tel: (01923) 221195 Fax: (01923) 334438 E-mail: michaelzapala@ntlworld.com

Arcade Amusements, 10 Shelley Grove, Loughton, Essex, IG10 1BY Tel: (020) 8508 8909

▶ Arcade Warehouse Com, Savile Road, Castleford, West Yorkshire, WF10 1PD Tel: (01977) 790523

Atronic International, Unit 2b The Courtyard, Alban Park, St. Albans, Hertfordshire, AL4 0LA Tel: (01727) 855966 Fax: (01727) 847957 E-mail: sales@atronic.com

Auto Amusements, 21 Stanmore Avenue, Blackpool, FY4 3LX Tel: (01253) 838838 Fax: (01253) 798835 E-mail: info@autoamusements.com

Auto Amusements Ltd, 31a Coxs Lane, Cradley Heath, West Midlands, B64 5NS Tel: (01384) 564207 Fax: (01384) 566877 E-mail: mike@auto-amusements.co.uk

Automatique Hambrid Ltd, 68-70 Elizabeth Street, Blackpool, FY1 3JH Tel: (01253) 620134

B A Amusements Ltd, Hayfield Road, Kirkcaldy, Fife, KY1 2HP Tel: (01592) 641133 Fax: (01592) 642345

Barnet Leisure 2000, 28a Westerham Avenue, London, N9 9BU Tel: (020) 8807 3598

Bell Amusements Ltd, Unit 11 Queens Park Industrial Estate, Studland Road, Northampton, NN2 6NA Tel: (01604) 708398 Fax: (01604) 714347

Bell-Fruit Games Ltd, Leen Gate, Lenton, Nottingham, NG7 2LX Tel: 0115-970 6707 Fax: 0115-978 0963 E-mail: sales@bellfruitgames.co.uk

Bournville Mot Centre Ltd, Bournville Road, Blaina, Abertillery, Gwent, NP13 3ER Tel: (01495) 290013 Fax: (01495) 290269

Braddicks Amusements Ltd, 37 Mill Street, Bideford, Devon, EX39 2JJ Tel: (01237) 471897 Fax: (01237) 424434

C Cooper & Sons Amusements, 49 Festival Walk, Spennymoor, County Durham, DL16 6AB Tel: (01388) 810272

▶ Casino Slots Leisure Centre, 144 The Centre, Feltham, Middlesex, TW13 4BS Tel: (020) 8844 1046 E-mail: richardbg@hotmail.com

▶ Churchfayre (UK) Ltd, 26 St. Davids Drive, Leigh-On-Sea, Essex, SS9 3RF Tel: (07946) 505105 E-mail: churchfayre@churchfayre.co.uk

Claremont Automatics Ltd, 40 Oakley Road, Chinnor, Oxfordshire, OX39 4ES Tel: (01844) 353635 Fax: (01844) 352750

▶ Coastal Leisure, Unit 14 College Close, Sandown, Isle of Wight, PO36 8EH Tel: (01983) 401234 E-mail: steph@coastalleisure.org.uk

▶ Coastal Leisure Derby Ltd, 17 Mason Crescent, Swadlincote, Derbyshire, DE11 8JP Tel: (01283) 551133

Coastal Leisure UK Ltd, Eagle House, Richmond Road, Southampton, SO15 3FT Tel: (023) 8022 3555 Fax: (01983) 401088 E-mail: steph@coastalleisure.org.uk

Crescent Automatics, 60 St. James St, London, W6 9RW Tel: (020) 8529 9477

Crest Amusements, St. James Street, New Bradwell, Milton Keynes, MK13 0BL Tel: (01908) 320142 Fax: (01908) 320142

Crown Direct (Scotland) Ltd, 27-33 Tobago Street, Glasgow, G40 2RH Tel: 0141-554 1111 Fax: 0141-554 1303 E-mail: enquiries@crowndirect.co.uk

Crystal Leisure Ltd, Unit 6, Stadium Close, Cardiff, CF11 8TS Tel: (029) 2023 9740 Fax: (029) 2022 5845 E-mail: sales@crystal-leisure.co.uk

▶ D C Automatics, 3 Hammond Business Centre, Hammond Close, Attleborough Fields Industrial Estate, Nuneaton, Warwickshire, CV11 6RY Tel: (024) 7634 7606 Fax: (024) 7634 7606

Deith Leisure Ltd, Unit 2, Block 5, Tweedbank, Galashiels, Selkirkshire, TD1 3RS Tel: (01896) 758342 Fax: (01896) 758059

Distinctive Developments, 1 East Parade, Sheffield, S1 2ET Tel: 0114-281 2208 Fax: 0114-281 2207 E-mail: info@distdevs.co.uk

Dragon Machines, 122 Trehafod Road, Pontypridd, Mid Glamorgan, CF37 2LY Tel: (01443) 683219 Fax: (01443) 684425

Dransfield Novelty Co. Ltd, Dransfield House, Mill Street, Leeds, LS9 8BP Tel: 0113-244 4555 Fax: 0113-234 3948

DVS Leisure, 9 High Street, Timsbury, Bath, BA2 0HT Tel: (01761) 472100 Fax: (01761) 472666 E-mail: dvsleisureuk@aol.com

Edmonton Machines Ltd, Units 14-15, Great Cambridge Industrial Estate, Enfield, Middlesex, EN1 1SH Tel: (020) 8344 4777 Fax: (020) 8344 4700

R. & K. Edwards Co. Ltd, 21 St. James Parade, Bath, BA1 1UL Tel: (01225) 421255 Fax: (01225) 469900

Electrocoin Manufacturing Ltd, Phoenix Estate, Caerphilly Road, Cardiff, CF14 4QF Tel: (029) 2061 4000 Fax: (029) 2061 8400 E-mail: info@electrocoin.co.uk

Elton Fabrications Ltd, 21A Cemetery Road, Southport, Merseyside, PR8 6RH Tel: (01704) 537853 Fax: (01704) 530100 E-mail: david.hodge@eltongames.com

Empire Games Ltd, Unit 5-7 New Street, Bridgend Industrial Estate, Bridgend, Mid Glamorgan, CF31 3UD Tel: (01656) 663300 Fax: (01656) 662200 E-mail: steve.brown@empiregames.co.uk

F Simmonds & Sons, 15 Cambridge Road, Granby Industrial Estate, Weymouth, Dorset, DT4 9TJ Tel: (01305) 786389 Fax: (07092) 871904 E-mail: fsimmonds.sons@btconnect.com

▶ Forbidden Fruits, Telford Way, Severalls Industrial Park, Colchester, CO4 9QP Tel: (01206) 514049 Fax: (0870) 1693473 E-mail: enquiry@forbiddenfruits.net

G & J Sales Ltd, G J Automatics, Hounds Road, Chipping Sodbury, Bristol, BS37 6EE Tel: (01454) 321207 Fax: (01454) 321207 E-mail: gandjsales@btconnect.com

Games Tec, Unit 4 Motorlink, Righead Industrial Estate, Bellshill, Lanarkshire, ML4 3LA Tel: (01698) 843344 Fax: (01698) 740829

Gamesoft Amusement Machines, Unit E1 South Point 2, Foreshore Road, Cardiff, CF10 4SP Tel: (029) 2045 3300 Fax: (029) 2045 3301

Gamestec, Provincial House, Hedworth Lane, Boldon Colliery, Tyne & Wear, NE35 9HS Tel: 0191-581 3233

Gamestech Ltd, Low Lane, Horsforth, Leeds, LS18 4ER Tel: 0113-258 9495 Fax: 0113-239 0072

Geematics Amusement Machines, 57 Chester Street, Flint, Clwyd, CH6 5DH Tel: (01352) 732404 Fax: (01352) 732404

Greaves Amusement Supplies, Ashfield House, 8 Enderby Road, Blaby, Leicester, LE8 4GD Tel: 0116-277 6297 Fax: 0116-278 9184

Hart-Marler Leisure, The Flaxmill, Flaxmill Lane, Pinchbeck, Spalding, Lincolnshire, PE11 3YP Tel: (01775) 725670 Fax: (01775) 714670 E-mail: benhart@btinternet.com

Hatwell's Leisure, 68 High Street, Witney, Oxfordshire, OX28 6HJ Tel: (01865) 884334 Fax: (01865) 884334

Haverfordwest Coin Operator, 3 Cromwell House, City Road, Haverfordwest, Dyfed, SA61 2EH Tel: (01437) 763094 Fax: (01437) 769177

John Icke Ltd, Margate Road, Broadstairs, Kent, CT10 2PR Tel: (01843) 603399 Fax: (01843) 603201

IG Block, 49 Nags Head Lane, Brentwood, Essex, CM14 5NL Tel: (01277) 848884 Fax: (01277) 848885 E-mail: sales@coinscope.co.uk

J B Amusements, 25 High Street, Draperstown, Magherafelt, County Londonderry, BT45 7AB Tel: (028) 7962 7011 Fax: (028) 7962 7411

J E Sheeran Amusement Arcades Ltd, 18 Argyle Street, Stonehouse, Larkhall, Lanarkshire, ML9 3LL Tel: (01698) 792711 Fax: (01698) 792786 E-mail: sales@jesheeranaa.co.uk

J P M International, B4, South Point, Foreshore Road, Cardiff, CF10 4SP Tel: 0121-717 7111 Fax: (029) 2046 7399 E-mail: customerservices@jpm.co.uk

▶ Jackpot, 20-21 Broad Street, Barry, South Glamorgan, CF62 7AD Tel: (01446) 749400

▶ John Ferguson Spares Ltd, Unit 11 All Saints Industrial Estate, All Saints Avenue, Margate, Kent, CT9 5TJ Tel: (01843) 571717 Fax: (01843) 230801 E-mail: john@jfspares.com

Jolly Roger (Amusement Rides) Ltd, College View Works, Manby Road, Grimoldby, Louth, Lincolnshire, LN11 8HE Tel: (01507) 328856 Fax: (01507) 327060 E-mail: roger@jolly-roger.co.uk

K E Automatics Ltd, 39 Rosslyn Street, Kirkcaldy, Fife, KY1 3HS Tel: (01592) 652323 Fax: (01592) 655720

K E R Videos, Chapel Buildings, Plainspot Road, Brinsley, Nottingham, NG16 5BQ Tel: (01773) 530315 Fax: (01773) 530315 E-mail: ker.videos@talk21.com

Pat Kelly Machine Rentals Ltd, 5 Glencoe Business Park, Warne Road, Weston-super-Mare, Avon, BS23 3TS Tel: (01934) 620703 Fax: (01934) 642306

Kent Coin Automatics, 6 Tontine Street, Folkestone, Kent, CT20 1JU Tel: (01303) 256047 Fax: 01303 850424

Kingsway Amusement Machines Co., Unit 1 Harper Lodge Farm, Harper Lane, Radlett, Hertfordshire, WD7 7HU Tel: (01923) 711700

AMUSEMENT MACHINES AND EQUIPMENT – *continued*

Kossway Automatics Distributors Ltd, 8 The Ridgeway, Iver, Buckinghamshire, SL0 9HJ Tel: (01753) 655400 Fax: (01753) 630278 E-mail: sales@kosswayautomatics.co.uk

L G Leisure Ltd, Old Station Yard, Tenby, Dyfed, SA70 7NG Tel: (01834) 845383 Fax: (01834) 845157

▶ Lakeland Leisure, The Old Brewery, Shore Street, Barrow-in-Furness, Cumbria, LA14 2UB Tel: (01229) 870770 Fax: (01229) 434140

Laser Leisure Ltd, Rugby Road, Brandon, Coventry, CV8 3GH Tel: (024) 7654 4095 Fax: (024) 7654 4095

Leeds Leisure Ltd, Unit 12 Springhead Mills, Springfield Road, Guiseley, Leeds, LS20 9BL Tel: (01943) 877888 Fax: (01943) 876192

Leisure Games, 13 St. Davids Road, Llandudno, Gwynedd, LL30 2UL Tel: (01492) 860100 E-mail: leisuregames@btconnect.com

Leisure Link Ltd, Unit 10 Whitehall Trading Estate, Cooksley Road, Bristol, BS5 9DN Tel: 0117-955 6743 Fax: 0117-955 0725

Leisure Link, Unit 8, Stafford Park 12, Telford, Shropshire, TF3 3BJ Tel: (01952) 292266 Fax: (01952) 292216

Leisure Link, Unit 10 Langford Way, Appleton, Warrington, WA4 4TZ Tel: (01925) 265888 Fax: (01925) 269229 E-mail: info@llg.co.uk

Lincoln Gaming, 495 Newark Road, North Hykeham, Lincoln, LN6 9NG Tel: (01522) 878697 Fax: (01522) 793008

Linland Ltd, 34 36 Fratton Road, Portsmouth, PO1 5BX Tel: (023) 9282 3037 Fax: (023) 9286 1615

M W Amusements, 26 Marine Parade, Worthing, West Sussex, BN11 3PT Tel: (01903) 210888 Fax: (01903) 214538

Mac Automatics Ltd, 38 Station Road, Kennett, Newmarket, Suffolk, CB8 7QD Tel: (01638) 750335 Fax: (01638) 552197

▶ MAXi COIN, PO BOX 1, Cramlington, Northumberland, NE23 7WU Tel: (0870) 2072077 E-mail: Info@MaxiCoin.co.uk

Meridian Leisure Services, Unit 5b 46 Holton Road, Holton Heath Trading Park, Poole, Dorset, BH16 6LT Tel: (01202) 632333 Fax: (01202) 620036 E-mail: sales@meridianleisure.co.uk

Mitre Amusement Services, SWN Yr Afon, Seiont Mill Road, Caernarfon, Gwynedd, LL55 2YL Tel: (01286) 674313

Moloney Automatics, 8 Factory Road, Bristol, BS36 1QN Tel: (01454) 776772 Fax: (01454) 776772

Neways Automatics Brecon, 25 Mill Street, Brecon, Powys, LD3 9BD Tel: (01874) 622849 Fax: (01874) 622849

Newby Automatics Ltd, Unit 1, Donachy Industrial Estate, Moor Lane, Witton, Birmingham, B6 7HH Tel: 0121-356 0322 Fax: 0121-356 9757

Nobles Amusements, 9 Union Terrace, Bury Old Road, Salford, M7 4ZH Tel: 0161-740 2367 Fax: 0161-720 7201

North Devon Leisure, Unit 1 The Old Aerodrome, Chivenor, Barnstaple, Devon, EX31 4AY Tel: (01271) 817129 Fax: (01271) 813512 E-mail: northdevonleisure@btinternet.com

Nostalgia Amusements, 22 Greenwood Close, Thames Ditton, Surrey, KT7 0BG Tel: (020) 8398 2141 Fax: (020) 8398 4343 E-mail: bdavey@globalnet.co.uk

▶ Novo Gaming UK Ltd, Tudor House, Coychurch Road, Bridgend, Mid Glamorgan, CF35 5NS Tel: (01656) 668881 Fax: (01656) 655255

P & F Amusements, 6 Springtown Road, Londonderry, BT48 0LY Tel: (028) 7130 9292 Fax: (028) 7137 7468 E-mail: sales@pandfamusements.com

P J Williams Automatics Ltd, The Cedars, Off Lodge Road, Maldon, Essex, CM9 6SJ Tel: (01621) 828795 Fax: (01621) 828795

Parkhouse Automatics, 34 Commercial Street, Maesteg, Mid Glamorgan, CF34 9DH Tel: (01656) 732403 Fax: (01656) 732478

Petron Amusements Ltd, Salisbury Road, Hoddesdon, Hertfordshire, EN11 0HU Tel: (01992) 473900 Fax: (01992) 573905 E-mail: sales@petronamusements.co.uk

The Pinball Heaven, 302B Liverpool Road, Southport, Merseyside, PR8 4PW Tel: (0870) 7465704 Fax: (0870) 7465705 E-mail: sales@pinballheaven.co.uk

Player Appeal Automatics, Summerfield, Division Lane, Blackpool, FY4 5DZ Tel: (01253) 693055 E-mail: coinop@btinternet.com

Powell's Automatics, 8 Marine Gardens, Whitley Bay, Tyne & Wear, NE26 1EQ Tel: 0191-253 1985 Fax: 0191-251 1493

Premier Amusements, 205 Station Road, Shirebrook, Mansfield, Nottinghamshire, NG20 8AF Tel: (01623) 747094 Fax: (01623) 747094

Premier Automatics Ltd, 42 West Church Street, Buckie, Banffshire, AB56 1HL Tel: (01542) 832777

Prize Coin Equipment, Central Avenue, Gretna, Dumfriesshire, DG16 5AQ Tel: (01461) 338320 Fax: (01461) 338688

Project Coin Machine Ltd, 682-684 London Road, Thornton Heath, Surrey, CR7 7HU Tel: (020) 8664 3400 Fax: (020) 8664 3449

Quality Amusements Ltd, St Augustines Business Park, Estuary Close, Whitstable, Kent, CT5 2QJ Tel: (01227) 793300 Fax: (01227) 793399 E-mail: antony@qualityamusements.co.uk

Quality Coin, Hill Cottage, Redmain, Cockermouth, Cumbria, CA13 0PZ Tel: (01900) 823393 Fax: (01900) 823391

R A L Ltd, 368 Silbury Boulevard, Milton Keynes, MK9 2AF Tel: (01908) 696100 Fax: (01908) 393865

R W D Coin Amusements, Race View, Factory Road, Enniskillen, County Fermanagh, BT74 6DT Tel: (028) 6632 5423 Fax: (028) 6632 8765

Rallin (Glasgow) Ltd, 81 James Street, Glasgow, G40 1DB Tel: 0141-554 8248 Fax: 0141-554 1266 E-mail: admin@rallin.com

Reliamatics, Units 1&2 Rear of 36, Palace Avenue, Paignton, Devon, TQ3 3HB Tel: (01803) 551944 Fax: (01803) 551944

Revolution Entertainment Systems Ltd, Showell Road, Wolverhampton, WV10 9NL Tel: (01902) 713000 Fax: (01902) 711555

Rochdale Automatics, 6 Fairview Close, Rochdale, Lancashire, OL12 7SR Tel: (01706) 658929 Fax: 01706 658929

▶ Bobb Rudd Leisure, Blencathra Business Centre, Threlkeld, Keswick, Cumbria, CA12 4TR Tel: (01768) 779761

S & S Enterprises, Unit 23, Pontymister Industrial Estate, Risca, Newport, Gwent, NP11 6NP Tel: (01633) 612727 Fax: (01633) 612727 E-mail: none@none.com

Select Amusement Sales Ltd, Farmeloan Road, Rutherglen, Glasgow, G73 1DN Tel: 0141-647 3362 Fax: 0141-643 2250 E-mail: info@selectamuse.co.uk

Showboat Casino Slots, Unit 16 Meadow Walk, Halton Lea, Runcorn, Cheshire, WA7 2BU Tel: (01928) 795549 Fax: (01928) 713757

Sims Automatics Ltd, 46 Dalsholm Road, Glasgow, G20 0TB Tel: 0141-946 0444 Fax: 0141-946 8155 E-mail: sales@simsautomatics.co.uk

Southern Counties Automatics, Great Hills Farm, Swallowfield Road, Beech Hill, Reading, RG7 2BG Tel: (01256) 882020 Fax: (01256) 881112 E-mail: ian@amusementsrus.co.uk

Stardust Leisure Ltd, 52 Holton Road, Barry, South Glamorgan, CF63 4HE Tel: (01446) 734862

T J Marshall Ltd, 11 Marsh Lane, Addlestone, Surrey, KT15 1UL Tel: (01932) 848088

T L J Automatics, Unit 21 Small Business Centre, Penmaen Road, Pontllanfraith, Blackwood, Gwent, NP12 2DZ Tel: (01495) 220745 Fax: 01495 232701

Thomas Automatics, 11 Springfield Terrace, Port Talbot, West Glamorgan, SA12 8HN Tel: (01639) 871213

Vivid Gaming Ltd, Hilton House, Marston Brewery, Shobnall Road, Burton-on-Trent, Staffordshire, DE14 2BW Tel: (01283) 500066 Fax: (01283) 845432 E-mail: sales@vivid-gaming.com

Wessex Coin Ltd, Unit 11 Hambridge Business Centre, Hambridge Lane, Newbury Berkshire, Newbury, Berkshire, RG14 5TU Tel: (01635) 37277 Fax: (01635) 550073 E-mail: wessexcoin@btconnect.com

Wilson Leisure, 27 St. Peters Road, Buckie, Banffshire, AB56 1DJ Tel: (01542) 833592 Fax: (01542) 833592

York Coin Leisure, Units 4 & 9 Roland Court, Huntington, York, YO32 9PW Tel: (01904) 750445 Fax: (01904) 767844 E-mail: yorkcoin@leisure72.fsbusiness.co.uk

AMUSEMENT MACHINES, PENNY ARCADE GAMES

Eagle Enterprises, The Retreat, Harby La, Eagle Moor, Lincoln, LN6 9DS Tel: 01522 696278

ANAESTHETIC EQUIPMENT

Cestradent Mckesson Ltd, Trident House, 110 Park Road, Chesterfield, Derbyshire, S40 2JX Tel: (01246) 276111 Fax: (01246) 230825 E-mail: mail@mckesson.plus.com

Datex Ohmeda Ltd, 71 Great North Road, Hatfield, Hertfordshire, AL9 5EN Tel: (01707) 263570 Fax: (01707) 260065

Intavent Orthofix Ltd, Burney Court, Cordwallis Park, Maidenhead, Berkshire, SL6 7BZ Tel: (01628) 594500 Fax: (01628) 789400 E-mail: enquiries@intaventorthofix.com

Med Tech, Riverside Works, Miller Row, Edinburgh, EH4 3BQ Tel: 0131-225 4295 Fax: 0131-220 4065 E-mail: med-tech@tiscali.co.uk

Smiths Medical International Ltd, Bramingham Business Park, Enterprise Way, Luton, LU3 4BU Tel: (01582) 430000 Fax: (01582) 430001 E-mail: info@pneupac.co.uk

ANAESTHETIC SPIROMETRY INSTRUMENT DESIGN SERVICES

Datex Ohmeda Ltd, 71 Great North Road, Hatfield, Hertfordshire, AL9 5EN Tel: (01707) 263570 Fax: (01707) 260065

ANALOGUE ELECTRONIC SYSTEM DESIGN

Technology Sources Ltd, 2 Signet Court, Swann Road, Cambridge, CB5 8LA Tel: (01223) 516469 Fax: (01223) 729916 E-mail: info@softsim.com

ANALOGUE PANEL METERS

Dalroad Distribution Ltd, Bramingham Business Park, Enterprise Way, Luton, LU3 4BU Tel: (01582) 505252 Fax: (01582) 560060 E-mail: sales@dalroad.com

Eukero Controls Ltd, Unit 7 Worton Court, Worton Road, Isleworth, Middlesex, TW7 6ER Tel: (020) 8568 4664 Fax: (020) 8568 4115 E-mail: info@eukero.co.uk

ANALOGUE TO DIGITAL CONVERTERS (ADC)

▶ Analogue Integration Ltd, The Old Village Store, Corston, Malmesbury, Wiltshire, SN16 0HJ Tel: (01666) 823290 Fax: (01666) 825154 E-mail: enquiry@analog.co.uk

Datel UK Ltd, 15 Campbell Court, Bramley, Tadley, Hampshire, RG26 5EG Tel: (01256) 880444 Fax: (01256) 880706 E-mail: datel.ltd@datel.com

Focusrite Audio Engineering Ltd, Windsor House, Turnpike Road, High Wycombe, Buckinghamshire, HP12 3FX Tel: (01494) 462246 Fax: (01494) 459920 E-mail: sales@focusrite.com

ANALOGUE VIDEO DISTRIBUTION AMPLIFIERS

▶ Genero Ltd, Unit 4, Ty Verlon Industrial Estate, Cardiff Road, Barry, South Glamorgan, CF63 2BE Tel: (0870) 1630700 Fax: (0870) 1630701 E-mail: genero@btinternet.com

▶ Virtual Lifestyles, Virtual House, 280 Marlow Bottom, Marlow, Buckinghamshire, SL7 3PT Tel: 01628 474742 E-mail: info@virtual-lifestyles.com

ANALYSERS, X-RAY

▶ Electron-X Ltd, 20 Burners Lane, Kiln Farm, Milton Keynes, MK11 3HB Tel: (01908) 566794 Fax: 01908 305062 E-mail: sales@electron-x.co.uk

ANALYSIS EQUIPMENT/ ANALYSER, *See also headings for particular types*

Advanced Medical Supplies Ltd, Freemantle House, Kingsclere Park, Kingsclere, Newbury, Berkshire, RG20 4SW Tel: (01635) 299857 Fax: (01635) 297546 E-mail: sales@ams-med.com

ATAC Ltd, 6 Redlands Centre, Redlands, Coulsdon, Surrey, CR5 2HT Tel: (020) 8763 9494 Fax: (020) 8763 9540 E-mail: atac@atacuk.com

C Q R Security, 125 Pasture Road, Wirral, Merseyside, CH46 4TH Tel: 0151-606 9595 Fax: 0151-606 1122 E-mail: info@cqr.co.uk

John Caunt Scientific Ltd, Oxford, OX2 6YE Tel: (01865) 511848 Fax: (01865) 310986 E-mail: johncaunt@johncaunt.com

Enviro Technology Services plc, Unit B1 Kingfisher Business Park, London Road, Thrupp, Stroud, Gloucestershire, GL5 2BY Tel: (01453) 733200 Fax: (01453) 733201 E-mail: sales@et.co.uk

Process Measurement & Analysis Ltd, Brockmill House, Carr Lane, Huddersfield, HD7 5BG Tel: 0151-649 8477 Fax: (01484) 843689 E-mail: sales@processmeasurement.uk.com

Sartec, Century Farmhouse, Reading Street, Tenterden, Kent, TN30 7HS Tel: (01233) 758157 Fax: (01233) 758158 E-mail: sales@sartec.co.uk

ANALYSIS EQUIPMENT/ ANALYSER (FLUE GAS) MAINTENANCE/REPAIR SERVICES

Gas & Environmental Services Ltd, Unit 9, Little Ridge, Welwyn Garden City, Hertfordshire, AL7 2BH Tel: (01707) 373751 Fax: (01707) 373752 E-mail: kevin.mileson@btinternet.com

ANALYTICAL CHEMISTS, *See also specialist services*

A Norman Tate & Co. Ltd, Caddick Road, Knowsley Business Park, Prescot, Merseyside, L34 9HP Tel: 0151-922 3064 Fax: 0151-922 4460

Asbestos Analysis Services Ltd, 8 Tower Quays, Tower Road, Birkenhead, Merseyside, CH41 1BP Tel: 0151-649 0541 Fax: 0151-649 0547

John Ashworth & Partners Ltd, PO Box 160, Bacup, Lancashire, OL13 0BW Tel: (01706) 879544 Fax: (01706) 647767 E-mail: johnashworth.paint@virgin.net

Beverley Analytical Laboratories, Hull Bridge Mills, Tickton, Beverley, North Humberside, HU17 9SB Tel: (01964) 542144 Fax: (01964) 543060E-mail: admin@beverlyanalytical.co.uk

Bodycoat Materials Testing, Shotton Works, Deeside Industrial Park, Deeside, Clwyd, CH5 2NH Tel: (01244) 818927 Fax: (01244) 836535 E-mail: shotton@bodycote.com

Bodycote Health Sciences, 121 Shady Lane, Great Barr, Birmingham, B44 9ET Tel: 0121-206 4100 Fax: 0121-251 4040 E-mail: healthsciences@bodycote.com

Central Metallurgical Laboratory, 53 Sussex Street, Sheffield, S4 7YY Tel: 0114-272 1735 Fax: 0114-275 6797 E-mail: neilellis@centralmet.co.uk

Central Scientific Laboratories, 445 New Cross Road, London, SE14 6TA Tel: (020) 8694 9330 Fax: (020) 8694 9163

Chemical Solutions, 474 Reigate Road, Epsom, Surrey, KT18 5XA Tel: (01737) 351777 Fax: (01737) 371606

D G Spectro Oil Analysis Company Ltd, Palace Gate, High Street, Hook, Hampshire, RG29 1NP Tel: (01256) 704000 Fax: (01256) 704006 E-mail: enquiries@jet-care.com

Ductile Steel Processors, Planetary Industrial Estate, Planetary Road, Willenhall, West Midlands, WV13 3XP Tel: (01902) 303230 Fax: (01902) 303231

Elemental Microanalysis Ltd, Okehampton Business Park, Okehampton, Devon, EX20 1UB Tel: (01837) 54446 Fax: (01837) 54544 E-mail: info@microanalysis.co.uk

Euro Test, Lennox Mall, Shirley Avenue, Vale Road, Windsor, Berkshire, SL4 5LH Tel: (01753) 867267 Fax: (01753) 867847 E-mail: southern.analytical@bodycote-mt.com

G C Laboratories Ltd, 6 Fen End, Stotfold, Hitchin, Hertfordshire, SG5 4BA Tel: (01462) 733770 Fax: (01462) 733898 E-mail: g.c.labs@btinternet.com

Herd Mundy Richardson Ltd, Oak House Bredbury Parkway, Ashton Road, Bredbury Park Industrial Estate, Stockport, Cheshire, SK6 2QN Tel: 0161-406 6767 Fax: 0161-494 8400 E-mail: sue.richardson@hmrlabs.com

Incotest, Holmer Road, Hereford, HR4 9SL Tel: (01432) 352230 Fax: (01432) 353545 E-mail: info@incotest.co.uk

Its Testing Services UK Ltd, Wellheads Crescent, Wellheads Industrial Estate, Aberdeen, AB21 7GA Tel: (01224) 723242 Fax: (01224) 722894

London & Scandinavian Metallurgical Co. Ltd, Fullerton Road, Rotherham, South Yorkshire, S60 1DL Tel: (01709) 828500 Fax: (01709) 833772 E-mail: enquiries@lsm.co.uk

Minton Treharne & Davies Ltd, Merton House The Avenue Industrial Park, Croescadarn Close, Cardiff, CF23 8HF Tel: (029) 2054 0000 Fax: (029) 2054 0111 E-mail: mtd@minton.co.uk

Pattinson Scientific Services, Scott House, Penn Street, Newcastle upon Tyne, NE4 7BG Tel: 0191-226 1300 Fax: 0191-226 1266 E-mail: pattinsonscientic@btconnect.com

S T L Midlands Ltd, 80 Lockhurst Lane, Coventry, CV6 5PZ Tel: (024) 7658 4800 Fax: (024) 7658 4848 E-mail: enquiries@stl-ltd.com

Sheffield Assay Office, 137 Portobello Street, Sheffield, S1 4DR Tel: 0114-275 5111 Fax: 0114-275 6473 E-mail: jarvisd@assayoffice.co.uk

Southern Counties Scientific Services Ltd, 15-17 Lansdowne Road, Shirley, Southampton, SO15 4HD Tel: (023) 8077 5535 Fax: (023) 8077 5545 E-mail: davidbelgrovelee@aol.com

Tickle & Reynolds, 83 Heavitree Road, Exeter, EX1 2ND Tel: (01392) 272836 Fax: (01392) 422691 E-mail: ebr@tandr.freeserve.co.uk

U F C Ltd, Synergy House, Guildhall Close, Manchester Science Park, Manchester, M15 6SY Tel: 0161-232 5500 Fax: 0161-232 5501 E-mail: info@ultrafine.co.uk

Vintec Laboratories, Bucknalls Lane, Watford, WD25 9XX Tel: (01923) 661144 Fax: (01923) 661115 E-mail: vinteclabs@aol.com

Waterfall & O'Brien, 138 Forest Road, Fishponds, Bristol, BS16 3SN Tel: 0117-958 3448 Fax: 0117-958 6776

Wickham Laboratories, Winchester Road, Wickham, Fareham, Hampshire, PO17 5EU Tel: (01329) 832511 Fax: (01329) 834262 E-mail: mail@wickhamlabs.co.uk

ANALYTICAL SERVICES, FOOD AND DRINK INDUSTRY

▶ Food & Drug Analytical Services Ltd, BioCity Nottingham, Pennyfoot Street, Nottingham, NG1 1GF Tel: 0115-912 4265 Fax: 0115-912 4267 E-mail: office@fdas.org

ANALYTICAL TEST INSTRUMENTS

Endress & Hauser Ltd, Floats Road, Roundthorn Industrial Estate, Manchester, M23 9NF Tel: 0161-286 5000 Fax: 0161-998 1841 E-mail: info@uk.endress.com

ANALYTICAL TEST INSTRUMENTS - *continued*

Keller UK Ltd, Winfrith Technology Centre, Winfrith Newburgh, Dorchester, Dorset, DT2 8ZB Tel: (01929) 401200 Fax: (07000) 329535 E-mail: sales@keller-pressure.co.uk

Leco Instruments (U K) Ltd, Newby Road Industrial Estate, Hazel Grove, Stockport, Cheshire, SK7 5DA Tel: 0161-487 5900 Fax: 0161-456 0969 E-mail: general@lecouk.com

▶ Malvern Instruments Ltd, Enigma Business Park, Grovewood Road, Malvern, Worcestershire, WR14 1XZ Tel: (01684) 892456 Fax: (01684) 892789 E-mail: info@malvern.co.uk

Sirius Analytical Instruments, Riverside Forest Row Business Park, Station Road, Forest Row, East Sussex, RH18 5DW Tel: (01342) 820720 Fax: (01342) 820725 E-mail: sales@sirius-analytical.com

Solway Instrument Services, South End, Wigton, Cumbria, CA7 9PZ Tel: (01697) 344168 Fax: (01697) 345242 E-mail: sales@solwayinstrumentservices.co.uk

ANCHOR CHAINS

Certex UK Ltd, 8 Trafford Court, Doncaster, South Yorkshire, DN1 1PN Tel: (01302) 731000 Fax: (01302) 731000 E-mail: sales@certex.co.uk

L H R Marine Ltd, Unit 3a Deemouth Business Centre, South Esplanade East, Aberdeen, AB11 9PB Tel: (01224) 248821 Fax: (01224) 248831 E-mail: info@lhrmarine.com

R & C Glen Scotland Ltd, Glen House, 29 Orleans Avenue, Glasgow, G14 9NF Tel: 0141-959 9988 Fax: 0141-959 9666 E-mail: sales@rcglen.co.uk

ANCHORAGE DEVICE SAFETY NETTING

Fastnets UK Ltd, 20l Hall End Business Park, A5 Watling Street Dordon, Dordon, Tamworth, Staffordshire, B78 1SZ Tel: (01827) 899101 Fax: (0870) 6091707 E-mail: sales@fastnetsuk.com

ANCHORS, *See also headings for particular types*

Cintech International, 11 Gold Tops, Newport, Gwent, NP20 4PH Tel: (01633) 246614 Fax: (01633) 246110 E-mail: cintec@aol.com

R & C Glen Scotland Ltd, Glen House, 29 Orleans Avenue, Glasgow, G14 9NF Tel: 0141-959 9988 Fax: 0141-959 9666 E-mail: sales@rcglen.co.uk

▶ Swiftfix, 18 Newtown Road, Southampton, SO19 9HQ Tel: (023) 8044 8444 Fax: (023) 8044 8444 E-mail: sales@swiftfix.co.uk

ANECHOIC CHAMBERS

T D K Electronics, T D K House, 5-7 Queensway, Redhill, RH1 1YB Tel: (01737) 773773 Fax: (01737) 781360

ANEMOMETERS

Air Flow Measurements Ltd, 72 Manchester Road, Kearsley, Bolton, BL4 8NZ Tel: (01204) 571499 Fax: (01204) 571734 E-mail: info@airflowmeasurements.com

Dantec Dynamics Ltd, Unit 16 Garonor Way, Portbury, Bristol, BS20 7XE Tel: (01275) 375333 Fax: (01275) 375336 E-mail: scientific@dantecdynamics.com

▶ Met-Check Ltd, 9 Churchfield Road, Chilton Industrial Estate, Sudbury, Suffolk, CO10 2YA Tel: (01787) 883138 Fax: (01787) 883139 E-mail: sales@met-check.co.uk

Vector Instruments, 115 Marsh Road, Rhyl, Clwyd, LL18 2AB Tel: (01745) 350700 Fax: (01745) 344206 E-mail: admin@windspeed.co.uk

ANEROID BAROMETERS

Day Impex Ltd, Station Road, Earls Colne, Colchester, CO6 2ER Tel: (01787) 223232 Fax: (01787) 224171 E-mail: general@day-impex.co.uk

▶ Nautical Antiques Center, 3a Hope Square, Weymouth, Dorset, DT4 8TR Tel: (01305) 777838 E-mail: info@nauticalantiques.org

▶ Rod L Fryatt, 10 Amberley Court, Lowestoft, Suffolk, NR32 4RL Tel: (01502) 560869

Russell Scientific Instruments Ltd, Rashs Green Industrial Estate, Dereham, Norfolk, NR19 1JG Tel: (01362) 693481 Fax: (01362) 698548 E-mail: sales@russell-scientific.co.uk

ANGULAR CONTACT CAGE TYPE BALL BEARINGS

I E C Ltd, 41 Harwell Road, Nuffield Industrial Estate, Poole, Dorset, BH17 0BD Tel: (01202) 680333 Fax: (01202) 680101 E-mail: info@iecltd.co.uk

ANIMAL ADHESIVES

Ace Adhesives Ltd, Shenstone Drive, Walsall, WS9 8TP Tel: (01922) 459393 Fax: (01922) 743417 E-mail: sales@aceadhesives.com

ANIMAL BEDDING

▶ Aromapetmats, Roville House, Ford Park Road, Plymouth, PL4 6RB Tel: (01752) 220541 Fax: (01752) 662876

H Eggleston Junior & Son Ltd, Lanchester, Durham, DH7 0TP Tel: (01207) 520869 Fax: (01207) 521941 E-mail: h.eggleston@onyxnet.co.uk

▶ SnuggleSafe, Unit 10, Thorgate Road, Wick, Littlehampton, West Sussex, BN17 7LU Tel: (01903) 730811 Fax: (01903) 726486 E-mail: info@lenricc21.com

Woodflakes Of Daventry Ltd, Unit 1, Hollandstone Farm, High Street, Flore, Northamptonshire, NN7 4LP Tel: (01327) 343344 Fax: (01327) 342470 E-mail: woodflakes@interface99.fsbusiness.co.uk

ANIMAL BY PRODUCT PROCESSING MACHINERY

Clutton Agricultural Ltd, Bedwell Road, Marchwiel, Wrexham, Clwyd, LL13 0TS Tel: (01978) 661871 Fax: (01978) 661756

De Smet Rosedowns Ltd, Cannon Street, Hull, HU2 0AD Tel: (01482) 329864 Fax: (01482) 325887 E-mail: info@rosedowns.co.uk

ANIMAL CARCASS INCINERATORS

▶ Majic Systems Ltd, Hine Lodge, Ransom Road, Mapperley, Nottingham, NG3 5HN Tel: 0870 753 3641 Fax: 0870 753 3651 E-mail: enquiries@majicsystems.co.uk

ANIMAL DRINKING EQUIPMENT

Hereford Utilities Ltd, Unit 1a, Techway, Wonastow Road Industrial Estate (West), Monmouth, Gwent, NP25 5JA Tel: (01600) 713330 Fax: (01600) 714440 E-mail: herefordutilities@hotmail.com

ANIMAL FEED BINDERS

A B N Ltd, 160 Moira Road, Lisburn, County Antrim, BT28 1JB Tel: (028) 9266 2611 Fax: (028) 9267 7202 E-mail: bibby@psilink.co.uk

Agil Chemicals Products, Hercules 2, Calleva Park, Aldermaston, Reading, RG7 8DN Tel: 0118-981 3333 Fax: 0118-981 0909 E-mail: sales@agil.com

Borregaard (UK) Ltd, Clayton Road, Risley Employment Area, Warrington, WA3 6QQ Tel: (01925) 285400 Fax: (01925) 285434 E-mail: marketing_europe@borregaard.com

Davidson Bros Shotts Ltd, Gray Street, Shotts, Lanarkshire, ML7 5EZ Tel: (01501) 820048 Fax: (01501) 822926 E-mail: info@davidsonsfeeds.co.uk

Equibale Pet Foods, Sutton Lane, Langley Burrell, Chippenham, Wiltshire, SN15 4LW Tel: (01249) 721500

Favour Pet Foods, 29 Magherabeg Road, Randalstown, County Antrim, BT41 2PL Tel: (028) 9447 3840 Fax: (028) 9447 2104 E-mail: info@favour.co.uk

Mcguinness Feeds, 65a Liverpool Road, Penwortham, Preston, PR1 9XD Tel: (01772) 745139 Fax: (01772) 752261

Masterfoods, Oakwell Way, Birstall, Batley, West Yorkshire, WF17 9LU Tel: (01924) 427000 Fax: (01924) 427427

Pointer Pet Foods Ltd, Chesterton Road, Eastwood Trading Estate, Rotherham, South Yorkshire, S65 1SX Tel: (01709) 820569 Fax: (01709) 837415 E-mail: office@pointerpetfoods.co.uk

ANIMAL FEED CONCENTRATES

▶ Chestnut Horse Feeds, Newnham Fields Farm, Willey, Rugby, Warwickshire, CV23 0SL Tel: (01455) 558808 Fax: (01455) 559401 E-mail: sales@anifeed.co.uk

ANIMAL FEED HAY

J Everitt & Sons, 10 Primrose Hill, Doddington, March, Cambridgeshire, PE15 0SU Tel: (01354) 740524 Fax: (01354) 741721

ANIMAL FEED PROCESSING PLANT

Andritz Sprout Ltd, Stockholm Road, Sutton Fields Industrial Estate, Hull, HU7 0XL Tel: (01482) 825119 Fax: (01482) 839806

C T M Systems Ltd, Unit 8, Arkwright Road Industrial Estate, Cambridge Road, Bedford, MK42 0LE Tel: (01234) 355700 Fax: (01234) 351155 E-mail: sales@ctm-systems.demon.co.uk

Country West Trading Ltd, Scarne Industrial Estate, Launceston, Cornwall, PL15 9HS Tel: (01566) 775488 Fax: (01566) 772434 E-mail: countrywest@excite.com

Crediton Milling Co. Ltd, Fordton Mill, Fordton, Crediton, Devon, EX17 3DH Tel: (01363) 772212 Fax: (01363) 775009 E-mail: cmc@creditonmilling.co.uk

Croston Engineering Ltd, Tarvin Mill Barrow Lane, Tarvin Sands, Tarvin, Chester, CH3 8JF Tel: (01829) 741119 Fax: (01829) 741169 E-mail: admin@croston-engineering.co.uk

Feedwell Animal Foods Ltd, Annsborough Park, Castlewellan, County Down, BT31 9NH Tel: (028) 4377 8765 Fax: (028) 4377 1420 E-mail: info@feedwell.com

Fold Hill Foods Ltd, Reg Office, Fold Hill, Stickney, Boston, Lincolnshire, PE22 8HQ Tel: (01205) 270500 Fax: (01205) 270596 E-mail: info@foldhillfoods.fsnet.co.uk

Game Engineering Ltd, Camp Road, Witham St. Hughs, Lincoln, LN6 9TW Tel: (01522) 868021 Fax: (01522) 868027 E-mail: sales@game-security-engineering.com

Locom Engineering Ltd, Units 34-35 Cranswick Industrial Estate, Beverley Road, Cranswick, Driffield, North Humberside, YO25 9PF Tel: (01377) 271474 Fax: (01377) 271535 E-mail: info@locom.co.uk

ANIMAL FEED PROCESSING PLANT SPARE PARTS/WEARING PARTS

Sevale Engineering Ltd, Business Park, Llanthony Road, Hempsted, Gloucester, GL2 5HJ Tel: (01452) 303180 Fax: (01452) 306250

Tavnitan Ltd, 11 James Watt Close, Drayton Fields Industrial Esta, Daventry, Northamptonshire, NN11 8RJ Tel: (01327) 703888 Fax: (01327) 703666 E-mail: sales@tavnitan.co.uk

ANIMAL FEED ROLLMAKERS

Silverthorne Engineering Co., Attwood Street, Stourbridge, West Midlands, DY9 8RU Tel: (01384) 897639 Fax: (01384) 423980 E-mail: t.hoskins@virgin.net

ANIMAL FEED SUPPLEMENTS

Agil Chemicals Products, Hercules 2, Calleva Park, Aldermaston, Reading, RG7 8DN Tel: 0118-981 3333 Fax: 0118-981 0909 E-mail: sales@agil.com

Agriwise, Lower Hutcherleigh, Blackawton, Totnes, Devon, TQ9 7AD Tel: (01548) 521404 Fax: (01548) 521581

All Bright & Seeds, Holyhead Road, Whiston, Albrighton, Wolverhampton, WV7 3BX Tel: (01902) 372266 Fax: (01902) 372266 E-mail: sales@equestrianessentrials.com

Country West Trading Ltd, Northgate, Barnstaple Street, Bideford, Devon, EX39 4AE Tel: (01237) 424373 Fax: (01237) 425054

Countrywide Stores, Lower Monk Street, Abergavenny, Gwent, NP7 5LU Tel: (01873) 855180 Fax: (01873) 856299

Deans Food, Finmere Mill, Chetwode, Buckingham, MK18 4JS Tel: (01280) 848551 Fax: (01280) 847812

Devenish Nutrition Ltd, 96 Duncrue Street, Belfast, BT3 9AR Tel: (028) 9035 7900 Fax: (028) 9074 8820 E-mail: info@devenishnutrition.com

Equiform, Newday House, First Avenue, Crewe, CW1 6BE Tel: (01270) 530930 Fax: (01270) 251197 E-mail: sales@equiformnutrition.co.uk

W.E. Jameson & Son Ltd, Foxholme Lane Mill, Masham Ripon, N Yorkshire, Ripon, North Yorkshire, HG4 4EL Tel: (01765) 689666 Fax: (01765) 689662

John Cook Corn Merchants Ltd, Rushton Mills, Rushton Spencer, Macclesfield, Cheshire, SK11 0RT Tel: (01260) 226233 Fax: (01260) 226363

K9 Pet Foods, 44 Station Road, Framlingham, Woodbridge, Suffolk, IP13 9EE Tel: (01728) 621054 Fax: (01728) 621122

Mccaskie Farm Supplies Ltd, 4 Munro Road, Springkerse Industrial Estate, Stirling, FK7 7UU Tel: (01786) 474481 Fax: (01786) 464099 E-mail: admin@mccaskie.co.uk

Massey Bros Feeds Ltd, Cranage Mill, Knutsford Road, Cranage, Crewe, CW4 8EE Tel: (01477) 533312 Fax: (01477) 533556 E-mail: enquiries@masseyfeeds.co.uk

Masterfoods, Oakwell Way, Birstall, Batley, West Yorkshire, WF17 9LU Tel: (01924) 427000 Fax: (01924) 427427

Nestle Purina, Chilton Industrial Estate, Windham Road, Sudbury, Suffolk, CO10 2XD Tel: (01787) 886000 Fax: (01787) 886086

Peter Owens, Frigidaile Mill, Great Smeaton, Northallerton, North Yorkshire, DL6 2NF Tel: (01609) 881941 Fax: (01609) 881941 E-mail: peterowens@home.3b.co.uk

Penleigh Irving Ltd, 25 Fairwood Road, Dilton Marsh, Westbury, Wiltshire, BA13 3SN Tel: (01373) 827649 Fax: (01373) 827077 E-mail: keratex.uk@btconnect.com

Powells Of Coolham Ltd, The Mill, Coolham, Horsham, West Sussex, RH13 8GR Tel: (01403) 741226 Fax: (01403) 741784

Pye Bibby Agriculture, Lansil Way, Canton Road, Lancaster, LA1 3QY Tel: (01524) 597200 Fax: (01524) 597219

Rumenco Ltd, Derby Road, Stretton, Burton-on-Trent, Staffordshire, DE13 0DW Tel: (01283) 511211 Fax: (01283) 546152 E-mail: sales@rumenco.co.uk

Tate & Lyle, 167 Regent Road, Kirkdale, Liverpool, L20 8DD Tel: 0151-933 1010 Fax: 0151-933 7434 E-mail: reception.athel@tateandlyle.com

ANIMAL FEEDING SYSTEMS

A J Kirby & Son, Whitchurch, Ross-on-Wye, Herefordshire, HR9 6DJ Tel: (01600) 890295 Fax: (01600) 890556

Attachments Ltd, 6 Peterborough Road, Crowland, Peterborough, PE6 0BA Tel: (01733) 210611 Fax: (01733) 211345 E-mail: sales@attachments.ltd.uk

Banbury Farm General Supplies Ltd, Grove Farm Building, Burton Dassett, Southam, Warwickshire, CV47 2AB Tel: (01295) 770707 Fax: (01295) 770787

Bildabin Agricultural Machinery, Harrison House, Benson Lane, Catforth, Preston, PR4 0HY Tel: (01772) 690575 Fax: (01772) 691681 E-mail: enquiries@bildabin.co.uk

Cobbs Country Store, Barrow House Farm, Woodcoates Lane, Darlton, Newark, Nottinghamshire, NG22 0TH Tel: (01777) 228260 Fax: (01777) 228160 E-mail: sales@cobbscountrystore.co.uk

E B Equipment Ltd, Barugh Green Road, Redbrook, Barnsley, South Yorkshire, S75 1HR Tel: (01226) 730037 Fax: (01226) 738101 E-mail: info@eb-equipment.com

J M C Aquatic Ltd, Unit 4, Commerce Way Industrial Estate, Stanbridge, Leighton Buzzard, Beds, LU7 8HJ Tel: (01525) 377307 Fax: (01525) 374266

Latchford Farm Aquatics, Latchford Farm, St. Marys Lane, Upminster, Essex, RM14 3PB Tel: (01708) 641363

Orby Engineering Ltd, 26 Seagoe Industrial Estate, Portadown, County Armagh, BT63 5QD Tel: (028) 3833 9145 Fax: (028) 3835 0540 E-mail: orbyengineering@btconnect.com

Stow Agricultural Services, Lower Swell Road, Stow on the Wold, Cheltenham, Gloucestershire, GL54 1LD Tel: (01451) 830400

Windmill Feeds & Saddlery, Mill Lane, Lewes Road, Cross in Hand, Heathfield, East Sussex, TN21 0TA Tel: (01435) 864383 Fax: (01435) 864383

ANIMAL HARNESSES, *See Saddlery etc*

ANIMAL HEALTH CARE EQUIPMENT AND SUPPLIES

Barlow Farm Services Ltd, New Farm, Wilkin Hill, Barlow, Dronfield, Derbyshire, S18 7TE Tel: 0114-289 0209 Fax: 0114-289 1496

Ceva Animal Health Ltd, 7 Awberry Court, Hatters Lane, Watford, WD18 8PE Tel: (01494) 781510 Fax: (01923) 243001

Denimex, Northdown Business Park, Ashford Road, Lenham, Maidstone, Kent, ME17 2DL Tel: (01622) 850057 Fax: (01622) 850097 E-mail: sales@denimex.co.uk

Euroclip 2000 Ltd, 2 Barrington Court, Ward Road, Brackley, Northamptonshire, NN13 7LE Tel: (01280) 840900 Fax: (01280) 840904 E-mail: sales@euroclip.fsnet.co.uk

Farmway RC Bland, Scarah Mill, Harrogate, North Yorkshire, HG3 3EB Tel: (01423) 774400 Fax: (01423) 324811 E-mail: ripley@farmway.co.uk

Green Farm Health, Romanby Road, West Garth, Northallerton, North Yorkshire, DL7 8NB Tel: (01609) 779548 Fax: (01609) 779548

Hall Shaw Farm Supplies Ltd, 46 East Green, West Auckland, Bishop Auckland, County Durham, DL14 9HJ Tel: (01388) 833678 Fax: (01388) 834883

Hay & Brecon Farmers Ltd, The Old Station, Newport Street, Hay-On-Wye, Hereford, HR3 5BH Tel: (01497) 820516 Fax: (01497) 821007 E-mail: farmershay@aol.com

ANIMAL HEALTH CARE EQUIPMENT AND SUPPLIES – *continued*

Kruuse UK Ltd, 14A Moor Lane Trading Estate, Sherburn In Elmet, Leeds, LS25 6ES Tel: (01977) 681523 Fax: (01977) 683537 E-mail: krusse.uk@kruuse.com

▶ Magnets4Life - Bioflow / Ecoflow Distributor, Manorcroft, School Road, Rayne, Braintree, Essex, CM77 6SR Tel: 01376 349993 Fax: 01376 349991 E-mail: vanessa@magnets4life.com

▶ Mediscot Online, 65 Oakbank Drive, Cumnock, Ayrshire, KA18 1BA Tel: (01290) 426438 Fax: (01563) 521077 E-mail: info@mediscot.co.uk

▶ SnuggleSafe, Unit 10, Thorgate Road, Wick, Littlehampton, West Sussex, BN17 7LU Tel: (01903) 730811 Fax: (01903) 726486 E-mail: info@lenricc21.com

ANIMAL HEALTH CARE PRODUCTS

Aquaculture Holdings Ltd, 24 26 Gold Street, Saffron Walden, Essex, CB10 1EJ Tel: (01799) 28167 Fax: (01799) 25546 E-mail: spaquaculture@spcorp.com

Bob Martin UK Ltd, 8 Wemberham Lane, Yatton, Bristol, BS48 4BS Tel: (01934) 831000 Fax: (01934) 831050 E-mail: sales@bobmartin.co.uk

Ceva Animal Health Ltd, 7 Awberry Court, Hatters Lane, Watford, WD18 8PE Tel: (01494) 781510 Fax: (01923) 243001

Elanco Animal Health Ltd, Lilly House, Priestly Road, Basingstoke, Hampshire, RG24 9NL Tel: (01256) 315000 Fax: (01256) 315081 E-mail: elancouk@lilly.com

Equiform, Newday House, First Avenue, Crewe, CW1 6BE Tel: (01270) 530930 Fax: (01270) 251197 E-mail: sales@equiformnutrition.co.uk

Fearing International, Creaton Road, Brixworth, Northampton, NN6 9BW Tel: (01604) 881491 Fax: (0800) 581606 E-mail: sales@fearing.co.uk

H V S Animal Health, 27 Inch Abbey Road, Downpatrick, County Down, BT30 9AT Tel: (028) 4461 2678 Fax: (028) 4461 4801 E-mail: info@hvsanimalhealth.com

Hay & Brecon Farmers Ltd, The Old Station, Newport Street, Hay-On-Wye, Hereford, HR3 5BH Tel: (01497) 820516 Fax: (01497) 821007 E-mail: farmershay@aol.com

▶ Health Haven, 173 Findon Road, Worthing, West Sussex, BN14 0BQ Tel: (01903) 877717 E-mail: info@health-haven.com

▶ Magnets4Life - Bioflow / Ecoflow Distributor, Manorcroft, School Road, Rayne, Braintree, Essex, CM77 6SR Tel: 01376 349993 Fax: 01376 349991 E-mail: vanessa@magnets4life.com

▶ Mediscot Online, 65 Oakbank Drive, Cumnock, Ayrshire, KA18 1BA Tel: (01290) 426438 Fax: (01563) 521077 E-mail: info@mediscot.co.uk

Osmonds, Bradeley Green, Tarporley Road, Whitchurch, Shropshire, SY13 4HD Tel: (01948) 668100 Fax: (01948) 668101 E-mail: info@osmonds.co.uk

Penleigh Irving Ltd, 25 Fairwood Road, Dilton Marsh, Westbury, Wiltshire, BA13 3SN Tel: (01373) 827649 Fax: (01373) 827077 E-mail: keratex.uk@btconnect.com

Shaws Pet Products Ltd, Unit 13 Bordesley Trading Estate, Bordesley Green Road, Birmingham, B8 1BZ Tel: 0121-326 7667 Fax: 0121-328 1734 E-mail: info@shawspet.co.uk

Steetley Bentonite & Absorbents Ltd, West Carr Road, Retford, Nottinghamshire, DN22 7ZF Tel: (01777) 712828 Fax: (01777) 700344 E-mail: hq@steetley.com

Stockcare Ltd, 83 West Street, Leven, Beverley, North Humberside, HU17 5LR Tel: (01964) 543924 Fax: (01964) 542750 E-mail: sales@goldlabeluk.com

Teemore Engineering, Teemore, Derrylin, Enniskillen, County Fermanagh, BT92 9BL Tel: (028) 6774 8377 Fax: (028) 6774 8978

Vetoquinol Ltd, Buckingham Industrial Park, Great Slade, Buckingham, MK18 1UA Tel: (01280) 814500 Fax: (01280) 825462 E-mail: sales@vetoquinol.co.uk

ANIMAL HOUSING

J Wilson Agriculture, 75 Drumcroon Road, Garvagh, Coleraine, County Londonderry, BT51 4ED Tel: (028) 7086 8430 Fax: (028) 7086 8803 E-mail: cowcomfort@wilsonagri.co.uk

▶ Simply Summerhouses, 130C High Street, Tranent, East Lothian, EH33 1HJ Tel: (01875) 613090 Fax: (01875) 617492 E-mail: enquiries@simply-summerhouses.co.uk

▶ SnuggleSafe, Unit 10, Thorgate Road, Wick, Littlehampton, West Sussex, BN17 7LU Tel: (01903) 730811 Fax: (01903) 726486 E-mail: info@lenricc21.com

▶ Wood For You, Unit 1b, Treburley Industrial Units, Launceston, Cornwall, PL15 9PU Tel: (01579) 370786 E-mail: kevin@wood-4-you.co.uk

ANIMAL IDENTIFICATION MICROCHIPS

Shearwell Ltd, Putham Farm, Wheddon Cross, Cutcombe, Minehead, Somerset, TA24 7AS Tel: (01643) 841552 Fax: (01643) 841628 E-mail: sales@shearwell.co.uk

ANIMAL PHOTOGRAPHERS

▶ Afan Digital Photography, 6A High Street, Cwmavon, Port Talbot, SA12 9LE Tel: (01639) 761025 E-mail: info@afandigital.co.uk

▶ Alex Tomlinson Photography, Alington House, Ledbury Road, Ross-on-Wye, Herefordshire, HR9 7BG Tel: 01989 563430 E-mail: enquiry@the-photographer.eclipse.co.uk

Artis Studios Ltd, The Studio 56a High Street, Sunninghill, Ascot, Berkshire, SL5 9NF Tel: (01344) 870033 E-mail: kat@artisstudios.com

▶ Aurora Imaging, Delfan, Cas-Mael, Haverfordwest, Pembrokeshire, SA62 5RJ Tel: 01348 881444 E-mail: info@photowales.com

▶ EXPOSURE, 4, Spinney Cottage, Hardwick Lane, Studley, Warwickshire, B80 7AD Tel: 0845 2304530 E-mail: enquiries@exposure-photo.com

▶ Jo Grant Photographer, St. Davids Road, Southsea, Hampshire, PO5 1QJ Tel: (023) 9283 9139

▶ Karina Hoskyns Photography, Hareshaw, The Platt, Dormansland, Lingfield, Surrey, RH7 6QX Tel: (07778) 599146 Fax: (01342) 836987 E-mail: enquiries@karinahoskynsphotos.co.uk

▶ Inspired Photography Ltd, 27 Kirkdale Mount, Leeds, LS12 6AZ Tel: 0113 2109653 E-mail: timlawton1981@yahoo.co.uk

▶ Karen Parker Photography, 87 Wolverton Road, Stony Stratford, Milton Keynes, MK11 1EH Tel: (01908) 566366 E-mail: HeadMoose@PetStockBoys.com

▶ Photo My Wedding, 16 Carnation Way, Red Lodge, Bury St. Edmunds, Suffolk, IP28 8TN Tel: (01638) 751889

R.P.L.Photography, Liverpool, L1 1EB Tel: (07947) 543764 E-mail: r.p.l.photography@mac.com

▶ Robert Irving Photography, 36 Parkway, Dorking, Surrey, RH4 1EU Tel: (01306) 879853 E-mail: info@robirvingphotography.com

▶ S D M Images, 16 Blenheim Close, Chandler's Ford, Eastleigh, Hampshire, SO53 4LD Tel: (023) 8027 6828 E-mail: info@sdmimages.co.uk

▶ Sharp Photography, 14 Devonshire Place, Brighton, BN2 1QA Tel: (07775) 895477 E-mail: info@janesharp.com

▶ Stone Studio, 45 High Street, Petersfield, Hampshire, GU32 3JR Tel: (01730) 269966 Fax: (01730) 269966 E-mail: mail@thestonestudio.co.uk

ANIMAL RUNS AND PENS

Top 'N' Tails, 19 Cross Tree Centre, Braunton, Devon, EX33 1AA Tel: (01271) 814733 Fax: (01271) 814824

ANIMATED FILM/CARTOON DESIGNERS/PRODUCERS, CINE/TELEVISION/VIDEO

▶ Ant Creations, 7 Granville Street, Market Harborough, Leicestershire, LE16 9EU Tel: 08444 778910 E-mail: nathan@antcreations.co.uk

Future Generation Services Ltd, A Future Court, George Summers Close, Medway City Estate, Rochester, Kent, ME2 4EL Tel: (01634) 718662 Fax: (01634) 718646 E-mail: services@bnol.co.uk

Iceni Productions Ltd, The Studio, Long Lane, Fradley, Lichfield, Staffordshire, WS13 8NX Tel: (01283) 792990 Fax: (01283) 792993 E-mail: sales@iceni.tv

▶ JBP Royalty Free, 40 Rempstone Drive, Chesterfield, Derbyshire, S41 0YB Tel: 01246 540341

▶ Kaptive Animation Studios, 73 Attlee Road, Walsall, WS2 0EX Tel: (01922) 867443 E-mail: kris@kaptive.co.uk

Mackinnon & Saunders Ltd, 146-148 Seamons Road, Altrincham, Cheshire, WA14 4LJ Tel: 0161-929 4441 Fax: 0161-929 1441

▶ Shelltown Productions Ltd, PO Box 21, Ballymoney, Co. Antrim, BT53 8TJ Tel: 0871 0971077 Fax: 0870 7627731 E-mail: admin@shelltown.co.uk

T Christien, 46 Strawberry Vale, Twickenham, TW1 4SE Tel: (020) 8892 3621 Fax: (020) 8891 5946 E-mail: terry@cartoonology.com

ANIMATION EQUIPMENT, CINE/TELEVISION/VIDEO

▶ Multimedia Productions Ltd, Minster Chambers, Suite 1, 37 High St, Wimborne, Dorset, BH21 1HR Tel: (01202) 882059 Fax: (01202) 881091 E-mail: info@mmpuk.com

▶ Projector Hire, 36 Parrock Avenue, Gravesend, Kent, DA12 1QQ Tel: 0798 454 3625

ANIMATION SERVICES, COMPUTER

▶ ROBBERS DOG ANIMATION, 3rd FLOOR, 168 VICTORIA STREET, BELGRAVIA, LONDON, SW1E 5LB Tel: 0207 630 6549 Fax: 0207 630 6549 E-mail: kevin@robbersdog.com

ANNUITY COMPARISON FINANCIAL SERVICES

▶ atretirement.co.uk, Tritton House, 14 Bath Road, Swindon, SN1 4BA Tel: (0870) 1904187

ANODISED ALUMINIUM, *See Anodised etc*

ANODISED ALUMINIUM COILS

Alanod Ltd, Chippenham Drive, Kingston, Milton Keynes, MK10 0AN Tel: (01908) 282044 Fax: (01908) 282033 E-mail: alanod@alanod.co.uk

ANODISED ALUMINIUM LABELS

Coventry Nameplate Co., 5 Watercall Ave, Styvechale, Coventry, CV3 5AW Tel: (024) 7669 3212 Fax: (024) 7669 3288 E-mail: markcove@dsl.pipex.com

Keraplate Ltd, 46 Holton Road, Holton Heath Trading Park, Poole, Dorset, BH16 6LT Tel: (01202) 622882 Fax: (01202) 632438 E-mail: sales@keraplate.co.uk

Panel Print Industrial Screen Printers, 7-12 Morris Road, Poole, Dorset, BH17 0GG Tel: (01202) 686575 Fax: (01202) 675733 E-mail: panelprint@btconnect.com

Peninsular Nameplates, Peninsular House, Carr Lane, Hoylake, Wirral, Merseyside, CH47 4AY Tel: 0151-632 5814 Fax: 0151-632 1090 E-mail: info@peninsular-nameplates.co.uk

ANODISED ALUMINIUM NAMEPLATES

Abbey Craftsmen, 127 Haslemere Road, Liphook, Hampshire, GU30 7BX Tel: (01428) 727187 Fax: (0800) 0561362 E-mail: terry@abbey.go-plus.net

G S M Graphic Art, Castlegarth Works, Masonic Lane, Thirsk, North Yorkshire, YO7 1PS Tel: (01845) 522184 Fax: (01845) 522206 E-mail: gsmgrapicarts@gsmgroup.co.uk

Keraplate Ltd, 46 Holton Road, Holton Heath Trading Park, Poole, Dorset, BH16 6LT Tel: (01202) 622882 Fax: (01202) 632438 E-mail: sales@keraplate.co.uk

Mega Electronics Ltd, Unit 4, The Grip, Linton, Cambridge, CB21 4XN Tel: (01223) 893900 Fax: (01223) 893894 E-mail: sales@megauk.com

Montgomery Engravers Ltd, Red Doles Road, Huddersfield, HD2 1AT Tel: (01484) 429520 Fax: (01484) 435022

The Principle Nameplate Company Ltd, Unit 19 St. Michaels Trading Estate, Bridport, Dorset, DT6 3RR Tel: (01308) 459900 Fax: (01308) 459911 E-mail: sales@platesandplaques.com

ANODISED ALUMINIUM SHEET

Alanod Ltd, Chippenham Drive, Kingston, Milton Keynes, MK10 0AN Tel: (01908) 282044 Fax: (01908) 282033 E-mail: alanod@alanod.co.uk

Deansfield Metal Finishing Co. Ltd, Colliery Road, Wolverhampton, WV1 2RD Tel: (01902) 351811 Fax: (01902) 458165 E-mail: admin@deansfield.fsbusiness.co.uk

Majestic, Queen Street, Walsall, WS2 9NU Tel: (01922) 628596 Fax: (01922) 628597 E-mail: info@majestics.org.uk

▶ Stotfold Plating Co. Ltd, Taylors Road, Stotfold, Hitchin, Hertfordshire, SG5 4AX Tel: (01462) 732158 Fax: (01462) 835330

ANODISERS/ANODISING PROCESSORS OR SERVICES

Alderney Plating Ltd, Thrush Road, Poole, Dorset, BH12 4NP Tel: (01202) 744664 Fax: (01202) 733577

Alpha, Westbury, Sherborne, Dorset, DT9 3RB Tel: (01935) 813722 Fax: (01935) 811822

Alpha Metal Finishes Ltd, Bond End Works, Yoxall, Burton-on-Trent, Staffordshire, DE13 8NL Tel: (01543) 472333 Fax: (01543) 473575 E-mail: diane@alphametalfinishesltd.co.uk

Aluminium Services Ltd, Aizlewood Road, Sheffield, S8 0YX Tel: 0114-255 3055 Fax: 0114-255 3798 E-mail: ast-info@btconnect.com

Ashton & Moore Ltd, 12 Smith Street, Hockley, Birmingham, B19 3EX Tel: 0845 618 8196 Fax: 0845 618 8197 E-mail: sales@ashton-moore.co.uk

Badger Anodising Ltd, 52-54 Bissell Street, Birmingham, B5 7HP Tel: 0121-622 1850 Fax: 0121-622 1218 E-mail: sales@badgeranodising.co.uk

John Beaumont Ltd, Riverside Mills, Firth Street, Huddersfield, HD1 3BD Tel: 0845 8510215 Fax: (01484) 435302 E-mail: peter@beaumont-ltd.co.uk

W. Birch & Son (Polishers) Ltd, 42-50 Bissell Street, Birmingham, B5 7HP Tel: 0121-666 6164 Fax: 0121-622 1218 E-mail: sales@badgeranodising.co.uk

Braintree Electro Platers Ltd, 12-13 Springwood Drive, Braintree, Essex, CM7 2YN Tel: (01376) 344265 Fax: (01376) 328927

C B F Aluminium Treatments Ltd, Claybank Road, Portsmouth, PO3 5NH Tel: (023) 9266 5253 Fax: (023) 9266 7710

C M L Group Ltd, Unit 5 Wheatland Business Park, Wheatland Lane, Wallasey, Merseyside, CH44 7ER Tel: 0151-631 5600 Fax: 0151-631 5601 E-mail: enquiries@cml-group.com

Colne Anodising Co. Ltd, Calder Mill, Green Road, Colne, Lancashire, BB8 8AL Tel: (01282) 867300 Fax: (01282) 867407 E-mail: sales@colneanodising.co.uk

Colour Anodising Ltd, Holland Street, Radcliffe, Manchester, M26 2RH Tel: 0161-723 2637 Fax: 0161-725 9252 E-mail: info@anodising.com

Colourite Anodisers Ltd, Selinas Lane, Dagenham, Essex, RM8 1ET Tel: (020) 8592 1172 Fax: (020) 8592 1171 E-mail: info@colourite.net

Davron Finishing Industries Ltd, 18 Tanners Drive, Blakelands, Milton Keynes, MK14 5BW Tel: (01908) 210799 Fax: (01908) 217211 E-mail: sales@davronfinsihing.co.uk

Deansfield Metal Finishing Co. Ltd, Colliery Road, Wolverhampton, WV1 2RD Tel: (01902) 351811 Fax: (01902) 458165 E-mail: admin@deansfield.fsbusiness.co.uk

Dispec Anodizing Ltd, Unit 4 Sough Bridge Mill, Colne Road, Barnoldswick, Lancashire, BB18 6UH Tel: (01282) 841341 Fax: (01282) 841341 E-mail: dispec@ic24.net

Dorset Aluminium Products Ltd, Poundbury West Industrial Estate, Dorchester, Dorset, DT1 2PG Tel: (01305) 265235 Fax: (01305) 260882 E-mail: sales@dorsetaluminium.com

▶ Dove Anodising Ltd, 14-16 Kelvin Place, Thetford, Norfolk, IP24 3RR Tel: (01842) 753908 Fax: (01842) 766007 E-mail: sales@doveanodising.co.uk

E V Wood Anodising Ltd, 421 Tyburn Road, Birmingham, B24 8HJ Tel: 0121-328 7646 Fax: 0121-327 1854 E-mail: carolyn@ebwood.co.uk

Ferndown Finishing Ltd, 12 Cobham Road, Ferndown Industrial Estate, Wimborne, Dorset, BH21 7PS Tel: (01202) 877755 Fax: (01202) 877744

Flexiable Surface Tecnology Ltd, Nairn Road, Deans, Livingston, West Lothian, EH54 8AY Tel: (01506) 460515 Fax: (01506) 460510

G S M Industrial Graphics, Avenue One, Witney, Oxfordshire, OX28 4BZ Tel: (01993) 776511 Fax: (01993) 778238 E-mail: gsmindustrialgraphics@gsmgroup.co.uk

H Snelson Engineers Ltd, Nat Lane, Winsford, Cheshire, CW7 3BS Tel: (01606) 553580 Fax: (01606) 861084 E-mail: sales@snelsons.co.uk

Hard Anodising Ltd, Firs Industrial Estate, Kidderminster, Worcestershire, DY11 7QN Tel: (01562) 865158 Fax: (01562) 66118 E-mail: sales@hard-anodising.co.uk

Heywood Williams Group plc, Field Mills, Red Doles Lane, Huddersfield, HD2 1YG Tel: (01484) 533142 Fax: (01484) 435175 E-mail: sales@hmfltd.co.uk

Hydro Aluminium Extrusion Ltd, Pantglas Industrial Estate, Bedwas, Caerphilly, Mid Glamorgan, CF83 8DR Tel: (029) 2085 4600 Fax: (029) 2086 3728 E-mail: haeuk@hydro.com

Hydro Aluminium Extrusion, Durham Road, Birtley, Chester le Street, County Durham, DH3 2AH Tel: 0191-301 1200 Fax: 0191-301 1234 E-mail: sales@hydro.com

Ingram & Glass Ltd, Catteshall Lane, Godalming, Surrey, GU7 1LB Tel: (01483) 415262 Fax: (01483) 426951 E-mail: patrick@ingram-glass.co.uk

Kohler Daryl Ltd, Alfred Road, Wallasey, Merseyside, CH44 7HY Tel: 0151-606 5000 Fax: 0151-638 0303 E-mail: daryl@daryl-showers.co.uk

L B Parkes Co. Ltd, Station Street, Walsall, WS2 9JZ Tel: (01922) 720720 Fax: (01922) 723400 E-mail: sales@lbparkes.co.uk

L H T Anodisers, Wallingford Road, Uxbridge, Middlesex, UB8 2SR Tel: (01895) 817700 Fax: (01895) 274275 E-mail: sales@lhtanodisers.co.uk

ANODISERS/ANODISING PROCESSORS OR SERVICES – *continued*

Lansdowne Cartmel Ltd, 3e West Way, Andover, Hampshire, SP10 5AS Tel: (01264) 353234 Fax: (01264) 359025 E-mail: lansdownecartmel@aol.com
London Colney Anodising Co. Ltd, Lyon Way, St. Albans, Hertfordshire, AL4 0LB Tel: (01727) 834231 Fax: (01727) 834232 E-mail: sales@lca.uk.com
Lustre Anodising Co. Ltd, Units 22-24, Cannon Business Park, Gough Road, Coseley, Bilston, West Midlands, WV14 8XR Tel: (01902) 494455 Fax: (01902) 494411 E-mail: info@lustre-anodising.co.uk
Mac Anodising Ltd, Unit 8 Harebridge Lane, Halton, Aylesbury, Buckinghamshire, HP22 5PF Tel: (01296) 621194 Fax: (01296) 621174 E-mail: macanodising@btconnect.com
Maidenhead Plating, 3 Martin Road, Maidenhead, Berkshire, SL6 7DE Tel: (01628) 783747 Fax: (01628) 778717
Majestic, Queen Street, Walsall, WS2 9NU Tel: (01922) 628596 Fax: (01922) 628597 E-mail: info@majestics.org.uk
Malden Plating Works Ltd, 32 Wates Way, Mitcham, Surrey, CR4 4HR Tel: (020) 8640 1272 Fax: (020) 8640 1372
Metal Finishing Ltd, Station Street, Town Wharf Business Park, Walsall, WS2 9JZ Tel: (01922) 720720 Fax: (01922) 723400 E-mail: sales@lbparkes.net
Norcot Engineering Ltd, Richmond House, Hill Street, Ashton-under-Lyne, Lancashire, OL7 0PZ Tel: 0161-339 9361 Fax: 0161-343 3069
Nu-Pro Surface Treatments, Eagle Works, London Road, Thrupp, Stroud, Gloucestershire, GL5 2BA Tel: (01453) 883344 Fax: (01453) 731597 E-mail: sales@nu-pro.com
Optical Tools For Industry, Brickfield Lane, Denbigh Road, Ruthin, Clwyd, LL15 2TN Tel: (01824) 704991 Fax: (01824) 705075 E-mail: info@optical-tools.co.uk
Poeton Cardiff Ltd, Penarth Road, Cardiff, CF11 8UL Tel: (029) 2038 8182 Fax: (029) 2038 8185 E-mail: cardiff@poeton.co.uk
Poeton Industries Ltd, Eastern Avenue, Gloucester, GL4 3DN Tel: (01452) 300500 Fax: (01452) 500400 E-mail: sales@poeton.co.uk
Portsmouth Aviation Ltd, Airport Service Road, Portsmouth, PO3 5PF Tel: (023) 9266 2251 Fax: (023) 9267 3690 E-mail: info@portav.co.uk
▶ The Powdertech Group, 108 Churchill Road, Bicester, Oxfordshire, OX26 4XD Tel: (01869) 320600 Fax: (01869) 246330 E-mail: lisa.r@powdertech.co.uk
Premier Plating Ltd, Lancaster Road, Cressex Business Park, High Wycombe, Buckinghamshire, HP12 3PY Tel: (01494) 533650 Fax: (01494) 473726 E-mail: gregmurray@premier-plating.co.uk
Quality Electro Depositors Ltd, Shield House, Gatehouse Close, Gatehouse Industrial Area, Aylesbury, Buckinghamshire, HP19 8DE Tel: (01296) 426214 Fax: (01296) 487787 E-mail: wise.wise.owls@aol.com
Sapa Pressweld Ltd, Spinnaker Park, Spinnaker Road, Hempsted, Gloucester, GL2 5DG Tel: (01452) 502502 Fax: (01452) 503503 E-mail: sales@pressweld.co.uk
Snell & Prideaux Ltd, 6-9 Ernest Street, Birmingham, B1 1NS Tel: 0121-622 3824 Fax: 0121-666 6630
South West Metal Finishing Ltd, Alphinbrook Road, Marsh Barton Trading Estate, Exeter, EX2 8TJ Tel: (01392) 258234 Fax: (01392) 421538 E-mail: swmf@eicgroup.co.uk
Stainless Plating Ltd, 24 Don Road, Sheffield, S9 2UB Tel: 0114-242 2000 Fax: 0114-242 2003 E-mail: brenda@stainlessplating.co.uk
Standard & Pochin Ltd, 6-7 Westminster Road, Wareham, Dorset, BH20 4SP Tel: 0845 1306660 Fax: (01929) 556726 E-mail: sales@standard-pochin.co.uk
Walton Plating Ltd, 118 Ashley Road, Walton-on-Thames, Surrey, KT12 1HN Tel: (01932) 221206 Fax: (01932) 246699 E-mail: enquiries@waltonplating.co.uk
▶ Wirral Fospray Ltd, Hawarden Business Park, Clwyd Close Manor Lane, Hawarden, Deeside, Clwyd, CH5 3NS Tel: (01244) 520202 Fax: (01244) 520363 E-mail: sales@wirralfospray.com
Woodmet Anodisers Ltd, Globe Lane, Dukinfield, Cheshire, SK16 4RQ Tel: 0161-339 1943 Fax: 0161-343 1610

ANODISING JIGS

Carrtech Ltd, Crossfield Road, Birmingham, B33 9HP Tel: 0121-683 2600 Fax: 0121-683 2601 E-mail: sales@carrtech.com

ANORAKS

A & S Clothing Manufacturers Ltd, 7 Mott Street, Birmingham, B19 3HD Tel: 0121-233 3625 Fax: 0121-236 2730
Aythen Fashions Co., 19 Hamstead Road, Hockley, Birmingham, B19 1BX Tel: 0121-523 2815 Fax: 0121-523 2815
Boston Anorak Co., Church Road, Freiston, Boston, Lincolnshire, PE22 0NX Tel: (01205) 769130 Fax: (01205) 769131
Mann Bros Ltd, 142 High Street, West Bromwich, West Midlands, B70 6JJ Tel: 0121-553 7156 Fax: 0121-553 1961 E-mail: info@mannbros.co.uk
R K Clothing Manufacturers Ltd, 300-306 Park Road, Hockley, Birmingham, B18 5HE Tel: 0121-551 1379 Fax: 0121-551 1379

ANTENNAS, DIRECTIONAL PANEL

▶ Specialist Antenna Solutions, Unit 19, Hillcrest Way, Buckingham Industrial Park, Buckingham, MK18 1HJ Tel: (01280) 818768 Fax: (01280) 817179 E-mail: sales@specialistantennas.co.uk

ANTENNAS, TELEVISION

CB's Aerials, Glendale, Heath Road, Holmewood, Chesterfield, Derbyshire, S42 5RB Tel: (01246) 852667 E-mail: carlboulter@aol.com

ANTI AGEING CREAM

▶ Anti Aging Laser Lite Ltd, 54 Eton Banks Court, Tangier Lane, Eton, Windsor, Berkshire, SL4 6BB Tel: (01753) 853878 Fax: (01753) 853878 E-mail: Beautylight@bellsouth.net

ANTIBLAST WINDOW FILM SUPPLY AND INSTALLATION

▶ Durable, 1 498 Reading Road, Winnersh, Wokingham, Berkshire, RG41 5EX Tel: (0870) 2402480 Fax: 0118-989 5209 E-mail: mail@durable.co.uk
▶ G P S Window Films, 32 Springside Rise, Golcar, Huddersfield, HD7 4RW Tel: (01484) 657735 Fax: (01484) 657735 E-mail: sales@gpswindowfilms.co.uk
▶ Image Tint, 31 Snowdon Avenue, Maidstone, Kent, ME14 5NW Tel: (01622) 672272 E-mail: info@imagetint.co.uk
▶ Solartek Films, Unit 10, High Street, Ware, Hertfordshire, SG12 9BA Tel: (01920) 466999 Fax: (01920) 464488 E-mail: enquiries@solartekfilms.co.uk
▶ South East Solar, Alterchrome House, Murray Road, Orpington, Kent, BR5 3QY Tel: (01689) 896345 Fax: (01689) 806549 E-mail: sales@sesolar.co.uk
Sunny Blinds, 127 Drummond Road, Skegness, Lincolnshire, PE25 3EX Tel: (01754) 896558 E-mail: sunny_blinds@btinternet.com

ANTIBODIES

▶ TCS Cellworks, Park Leys, Botolph Claydon, Buckingham, MK18 2LR Tel: (01296) 714630 Fax: 01296 713122 E-mail: office@tcscellworks.co.uk

ANTICAKING AGENTS

Oil Dri UK Ltd, Bannisters Row, Wisbech, Cambridgeshire, PE13 3HZ Tel: (01945) 581244 Fax: (01945) 581250 E-mail: sales@oil-dri.co.uk

ANTICLIMB FENCING

H.C. Hill Ltd, PO Box 137, Beckenham, Kent, BR3 4WY Tel: (020) 8650 7890 Fax: (020) 8650 0535 E-mail: enquiries@hchill.co.uk

ANTICONDENSATION HEATERS

Thames Valley Temperature Control, Unit 6 Harriar Park, South Mead Industrial Estate, Didcot, Oxham, Oxfordshire, OX11 7PL Tel: (01235) 811922 Fax: (01235) 812600

ANTICORROSION CHEMICALS

Agma Ltd, Gemini Works, Haltwhistle, Northumberland, NE49 9HA Tel: (01434) 320598 Fax: (01434) 321650 E-mail: enquiries@agma.co.uk
Fernox, Sheer Water, Forsyth Road, Woking, Surrey, GU21 5RZ Tel: (0870) 6015000 Fax: (0870) 6015005 E-mail: sales@fernox.com
Fluorochem Ltd, Wesley Street, Glossop, Derbyshire, SK13 7RY Tel: (01457) 865698 Fax: (01457) 869360 E-mail: enquiries@fluorochem.co.uk

ANTICORROSION PROTECTIVE COATINGS

Cameron Coatings Ltd, 18 Forest Vale Road, Forest Vale Industrial Estate, Cinderford, Gloucestershire, GL14 2PH Tel: (01594) 826088 Fax: (01594) 826092 E-mail: cameron@holscot.com
Corrosion Solutions Ltd, 5 Kirkhill Place, Kirkhill Industrial Estate, Dyce, Aberdeen, AB21 0GU Tel: (01224) 772694 Fax: (01224) 775810 E-mail: info@corrsol.co.uk
Corrpro Companies Europe, 4 Mill Court, The Sawmills, Durley, Southampton, SO32 2EJ Tel: (01489) 861980 Fax: (01489) 861981 E-mail: ccel@onyxnet.co.uk
Enginewise Corrosion Prevention, 3 Venture Business Park, Grimsby, South Humberside, DN31 2UW Tel: (01472) 347400 Fax: (01472) 267647 E-mail: sales@enginewise.co.uk
Kirtek Industries Ltd, Thorney Road, Crowland, Peterborough, PE6 0AL Tel: (01733) 211290 Fax: (01733) 212331 E-mail: gkerk01@fsmail.net
Line X, Unit 6, Fells Road, Team Valley Trading Estate, Gateshead, Tyne & Wear, NE11 0NN Tel: 0191-491 3010 Fax: 0191-491 3010 E-mail: andrew@linexgateshead.co.uk
Protective Finishing Group, 33 Crossgate Road, Park Farm Industrial Estate, Redditch, Worcestershire, B98 7SN Tel: (01527) 524126 Fax: (01527) 510361 E-mail: sales@profingroup.co.uk
▶ Serene Paints, Serene Works, 67 Victoria Road, Burgess Hill, West Sussex, RH15 9YL Tel: (01444) 870011 Fax: (01444) 871433 E-mail: sales@serenepaints.co.uk
Sermatech, Whisby Road, North Hykeham, Lincoln, LN6 3DL Tel: (01522) 878207 Fax: 01522 878250 E-mail: melissa.martin@sermatech.com

ANTIFATIGUE MATS

Jaymart Rubber & Plastics Ltd, Woodlands Trading Estate, Eden Vale Road, Westbury, Wiltshire, BA13 3QS Tel: (01373) 864926 Fax: (01373) 858454 E-mail: matting@jaymart.net

ANTIFOAMING AGENTS

Blackburn Chemicals Ltd, Cunliffe Road, Whitebirk Industrial Estate, Blackburn, BB1 5SX Tel: (01254) 52222 Fax: (01254) 664224 E-mail: info@bbchem.co.uk
Goldschmidt UK Ltd, Tego House, Chippenham Drive, Kingston, Milton Keynes, MK10 0AF Tel: (01908) 582250 Fax: (01908) 582254 E-mail: angus.smith@degussa.com

ANTIFRICTION MATERIALS

Transpower Drives Ltd, 4 Bridle Close, Finedon Road Industrial Estate, Wellingborough, Northamptonshire, NN8 4RN Tel: (01933) 441101 Fax: (01933) 443326 E-mail: sales@transpower.co.uk

ANTIGRAFFITI OR ANTIVANDAL PAINTS

Corroless Northern Ltd, Regent House, Regent Street, Oldham, OL1 3TZ Tel: 0161-624 4941 Fax: 0161-627 5072 E-mail: sales@kenyon-group.co.uk
Dacrylate Ltd, Lime Street, Kirkby-In-Ashfield, Nottingham, NG17 8AL Tel: (01623) 753845 Fax: (01623) 757151 E-mail: sales@dacrylate.co.uk
Stewart Wales Somerville Ltd, 28 Glenburn Road, East Kilbride, Glasgow, G74 5BA Tel: (01355) 222101 Fax: (01355) 233847 E-mail: sales@sws-ltd.com
T & R Williamson Ltd, 36 Stonebridgegate, Ripon, North Yorkshire, HG4 1TP Tel: (01765) 607711 Fax: (01765) 607908 E-mail: sales@trwilliamson.co.uk

ANTILITTER NETS

Advanced Netting, 157 St Osyth Road, Clacton-on-Sea, Essex, CO15 3HD Tel: (01255) 428988 Fax: (01255) 220668 E-mail: sales@advancednetting.co.uk
Knowle Nets Ltd, 20 East Road, Bridport, Dorset, DT6 4NX Tel: (01308) 424342 Fax: (01308) 458186 E-mail: sales@knowlenets.co.uk

ANTIMAGNETIC TOOLS

▶ Heraues Quartz Tech Ltd, 4 Tannery House, Tannery Lane, Send, Woking, Surrey, GU23 7EF Tel: (01483) 213324 Fax: (01483) 213329 E-mail: byfleet.sales@heraeus.com

ANTIMICROBIAL CHEMICALS

Biocote Ltd, Technology Centre Glaisher Drive, Wolverhampton Science Park, Wolverhampton, WV10 9RU Tel: (01902) 824450 Fax: (01902) 824453 E-mail: info@biocote.com
Ciba Specialty Chemicals P.L.C., Ashton New Road, Clayton, Manchester, M11 4AP Tel: 0161-223 1391 Fax: 0161-223 4315
Danisco Beaminster, 6 North Street, Beaminster, Dorset, DT8 3DZ Tel: (01308) 862216 Fax: (01308) 863630
Ecokem Ltd, 4 Trafalgar Court, Widnes, Cheshire, WA8 0SZ Tel: 0151-420 0172 Fax: 0151-510 5455 E-mail: dclarkson@ecokem.co.uk

ANTIMICROBIAL EPOXY POWDER COATINGS

Biocote Ltd, Technology Centre Glaisher Drive, Wolverhampton Science Park, Wolverhampton, WV10 9RU Tel: (01902) 824450 Fax: (01902) 824453 E-mail: info@biocote.com
Steritouch, Unit 15 Roseheyworth Business, Abertillery, Gwent, NP13 1SP Tel: (01495) 211400 E-mail: info@steritouch.com

ANTIMICROBIAL POWDER COATINGS

Biocote Ltd, Technology Centre Glaisher Drive, Wolverhampton Science Park, Wolverhampton, WV10 9RU Tel: (01902) 824450 Fax: (01902) 824453 E-mail: info@biocote.com
Steritouch, Unit 15 Roseheyworth Business, Abertillery, Gwent, NP13 1SP Tel: (01495) 211400 E-mail: info@steritouch.com

ANTIMICROBIAL RUBBER COMPOUNDS

Milliken Walk Off Mats, Hilton Fold Lane, Middleton, Manchester, M24 2HZ Tel: 0161-655 1380 Fax: 0161-655 1379 E-mail: mcse@milliken.com

ANTIMIST PRODUCTS, EYE WEAR

Elite Supplies, 19l Solway Trading Estate, Maryport, Cumbria, CA15 8NF Tel: (01900) 810111 Fax: (01900) 810222 E-mail: sales@elite-supplies.com
Millbride Products, 67 Fountain Road, Edgbaston, Birmingham, B17 8NP Tel: (0800) 281905 Fax: 0121-429 3231 E-mail: sales@klarit.com

ANTIMIST SAFETY GOGGLES

Millbride Products, 67 Fountain Road, Edgbaston, Birmingham, B17 8NP Tel: (0800) 281905 Fax: 0121-429 3231 E-mail: sales@klarit.com

ANTIMONIAL LEAD

H J Enthoven & Sons Ltd, Darley Dale Smelter, South Darley, Matlock, Derbyshire, DE4 2LP Tel: (01629) 733291 Fax: (01629) 733092

ANTIMONY TRIOXIDES

Chance & Hunt Ltd, Alexander House, Crown Gate, Runcorn, Cheshire, WA7 2UP Tel: (01928) 793000 Fax: (01928) 714351 E-mail: passport@chance-hunt.com

ANTIQUE BRICKS TO SPECIFICATION

Brick Bond Northern, 7 Healey New Mills, Healey Road, Ossett, West Yorkshire, WF5 8NF Tel: (01924) 266194 Fax: (01924) 266195 E-mail: admin@brickmanufacturers.com
The Brick Business Ltd, Todhills Factory, Newfield, Bishop Auckland, County Durham, DL14 8BA Tel: (01388) 603008 Fax: (01388) 450356
Chelwood Group, Adswood Road, Cheadle Hulme, Cheadle, Cheshire, SK8 5QY Tel: 0161-485 8211 Fax: 0161-486 1968 E-mail: marketing@chelwood.co.uk
Derwent Stone Products Ltd, Unit 16 Greencroft Industrial Estate, Stanley, County Durham, DH9 7XP Tel: (01207) 521482 Fax: (01207) 521455 E-mail: derwentstone@aol.com
Ibstock Brick Ltd, Swanage Factory, Godlingston, Swanage, Dorset, BH19 3DH Tel: (01929) 422257 Fax: (01929) 425786 E-mail: info@ibstock.co.uk
Ibstock Building Products Ltd, Pinhoe Factory, Harrington Lane, Exeter, EX4 8DT Tel: (01392) 466561 Fax: (01392) 466423

▶ indicates data change since last edition

ANTIQUE BRICKS TO SPECIFICATION - *continued*

Linton Brick Ltd, James Nasmyth Way, Eccles, Manchester, M30 0SF Tel: 0161-787 3700 Fax: 0161-787 3711 E-mail: sales@lintonbrick.co.uk

M & B Brick Cutting Services, Old Canal Yard, 52 Reuben Street, Stockport, Cheshire, SK4 1PS Tel: 0161-476 6939 Fax: 0161-429 7896

Mansfield Brick Co. Ltd, Sandhurst Avenue, Mansfield, Nottinghamshire, NG18 4BE Tel: (01623) 622441 Fax: (01623) 420904

Marshalls Clay Products, 4 Park Terrace, Glasgow, G3 6BY Tel: 0141-333 0985 Fax: 0141-332 6877

Selborne Brickworks, Honey Lane, Selborne, Alton, Hampshire, GU34 3BT Tel: (01420) 478752

Wienerberger Ltd, Smoke Jack Brickworks, Horsham Lane, Wallis Wood, Dorking, Surrey, RH5 5QH Tel: (01306) 627481 Fax: (01306) 627561

ANTIQUE DISPLAY CABINETS

Antique Furniture Designs Ltd, The Warehouse, Sandy Bank Road, New York, Lincoln, LN4 4YE Tel: (01526) 342821 Fax: (01526) 344186 E-mail: sales@antiquefurnituredesigns.com

▶ Antique Shop, 100 Bridge Road, Sutton Bridge, Spalding, Lincolnshire, PE12 9SA Tel: (01406) 350535 E-mail: info@theantiqueshop.co.uk

ANTIQUE FURNITURE

▶ Antique Shop, 100 Bridge Road, Sutton Bridge, Spalding, Lincolnshire, PE12 9SA Tel: (01406) 350535 E-mail: info@theantiqueshop.co.uk

Traditional Homes & Interiors, 16 Market Street, Portadown, Craigavon, County Armagh, BT62 3LD Tel: (028) 3835 2081 Fax: (028) 3835 0182

ANTIQUE METAL REPRODUCTION

▶ Brass Master Antiques, 36 Oakhill Road, Maple Cross, Rickmansworth, Hertfordshire, WD3 9RF Tel: 0771 3526495 Fax: 01923 896565 E-mail: sales@brassmasterantiques.com

J Shiner & Sons Ltd, 8 Windmill Street, London, W1T 2JE Tel: (020) 7636 0740 Fax: (020) 7580 0740 E-mail: info@j-shiner.co.uk

ANTIQUE METAL RESTORATION

▶ Brass Master Antiques, 36 Oakhill Road, Maple Cross, Rickmansworth, Hertfordshire, WD3 9RF Tel: 0771 3526495 Fax: 01923 896565 E-mail: sales@brassmasterantiques.com

▶ Unique Enamelling Services, Bee Mill, Preston Road, Ribchester, Preston, PR3 3XJ Tel: (01254) 878265 Fax: (01524) 792299 E-mail: enqiuries@ues-ltd.co.uk

ANTIQUE OR BULLION GLASS

▶ Antique Shop, 100 Bridge Road, Sutton Bridge, Spalding, Lincolnshire, PE12 9SA Tel: (01406) 350535 E-mail: info@theantiqueshop.co.uk

ANTIQUE REPRODUCTION FURNITURE

Antique Furniture Designs Ltd, The Warehouse, Sandy Bank Road, New York, Lincoln, LN4 4YE Tel: (01526) 342821 Fax: (01526) 344186 E-mail: sales@antiquefurnituredesigns.com

▶ B H Custom Made Furniture, Stowmarket, Suffolk, IP14 2AG Tel: (01449) 676004

Carrington House, Ancaster Square, Llanrwst, Gwynedd, LL26 0LD Tel: (01492) 642500 Fax: (01492) 642500 E-mail: richard@carringtonhouse.co.uk

▶ Harcourt Ltd, 465 Hornsey Road, London, N19 4DR Tel: (020) 7281 4555 Fax: (020) 7281 4888 E-mail: info@harcourt.uk.com

▶ Murray & Murray, 2-3 Boston Road, Glenrothes, Fife, KY6 2RE Tel: (01592) 774363 Fax: (01592) 774379 E-mail: kitchens@murrayandmurray.co.uk

ANTIQUE RESTORATION PRODUCTS

The Attic, 96 London Road South, Poynton, Stockport, Cheshire, SK12 1LQ Tel: (01625) 876141

C Wall, 11c St Peters Street, Ipswich, IP1 1XF Tel: (01473) 214366 Fax: (01473) 214366

E L Schofield & Son, 49 New Street, Pudsey, West Yorkshire, LS28 8PE Tel: 0113-256 5308 Fax: 0113-255 0052 E-mail: schofieldandson@aol.com

East Burn Pine, Unit 16 Eastburn Mills, Main Road, Eastburn, Keighley, West Yorkshire, BD20 7SJ Tel: (01535) 656297 Fax: (01535) 657717 E-mail: info@eastburnpine.co.uk

Greyhound Ltd, Duckfield Barn, Bakers Road, Belchamp St. Paul, Sudbury, Suffolk, CO10 7DG Tel: (01787) 277372 Fax: (01787) 278787

Jukes Boxes Unlimited, The Paddocks, Back Lane, East Langton, Market Harborough, Leicestershire, LE16 7TB Tel: (01858) 545307 Fax: (01858) 545307 E-mail: fred@jukeboxes-uk.com

T S Barrows & Son, Hamlyn Lodge, Station Road, Ollerton, Newark, Nottinghamshire, NG22 9BN Tel: (01623) 823600 E-mail: info@hamlynlodge.com

Weeks Restoration & Conservation, 7 Hurst Road, Eastbourne, East Sussex, BN21 2PJ Tel: (01323) 439899

ANTIQUE TELEPHONES

Telephone Lines Ltd, 304 High Street, Cheltenham, Gloucestershire, GL50 3JF Tel: (01242) 583699 Fax: (01242) 690033 E-mail: info@telephonelines.net

Ian Tofte Voice & Data Communications, 32 Bronte Close, Aylesbury, Buckinghamshire, HP19 8LF Tel: (01296) 487982 Fax: (01296) 488050 E-mail: itofte@tiscalli.co.uk

ANTIQUE WOOD FLOORING

▶ 1926 Trading Co. Ltd, 2 Daimler Close, Royal Oak Industrial Estate, Daventry, Northamptonshire, NN11 8QJ Tel: (01327) 312200 Fax: (01327) 310123 E-mail: sales@1926trading.co.uk

▶ Allwood Floors, 28 Faraday Road, Rugby, Warwickshire, CV22 5ND Tel: (01788) 569980 Fax: (01788) 569978 E-mail: info@allwood-floors.co.uk

Floor Coverings Of Doncaster, 2 Richmond Road, Doncaster, South Yorkshire, DN5 8TB Tel: (01302) 812198 E-mail: sales@fcdoncaster.co.uk

Holland & Welsh Ltd, Unit 13 Riverside Industrial Park, Treforest, Pontypridd, Mid Glamorgan, CF37 5TG Tel: (01443) 660255 Fax: (01443) 660651 E-mail: sales@hollandandwelsh.com

Online-Flooring.co.uk, Willoughby Coachworks, Coxes Farm Road, Billericay, Essex, CM11 2UB Tel: (01277) 633053 E-mail: sales@online-flooring.co.uk

▶ Pivotal Holdings Ltd, 143 New Bond Street, London, W1S 2TP Tel: (020) 7493 5550 Fax: (020) 7493 5559 E-mail: enquiries@pivotalwoodflooring.com

ANTIQUES

Cloughcor House Furnishings, 33 Townhall Street, Enniskillen, County Fermanagh, BT74 7BD Tel: (028) 6632 4805 Fax: (028) 6632 8828

▶ Kerlectables, Lambshear Lane, Lydiate, Liverpool, L31 2LA Tel: 07985 905717 E-mail: kerlectables@tiscali.co.uk

▶ Strachan Antiques, 40 Darnley Street, Glasgow, G41 2SE Tel: 0141-429 4411 Fax: 0141-429 4411 E-mail: sales@strachanantiques.co.uk

ANTIREFLECTIVE COATINGS

Charvo Finishing Ltd, Snaygill Industrial Estate, Keighley Road, Skipton, North Yorkshire, BD23 2QR Tel: (01756) 795028 Fax: (01756) 798473 E-mail: sales@charvo.co.uk

▶ Diamond Coatings, 11 Lodge Forge Trading Estate, Cradley Road, Cradley Heath, West Midlands, B64 7RW Tel: (01384) 566222 Fax: (01384) 562826 E-mail: enquires@diamondcoatings.co.uk

Northumbria Optical Coatings Ltd, Unit 10 Burford Way, Boldon Business Park, Boldon Colliery, Tyne & Wear, NE35 9PZ Tel: 0191-537 4888 Fax: 0191-537 4777 E-mail: sales@noc-ltd.com

ANTISCALE CHEMICALS

Fernox, Sheer Water, Forsyth Road, Woking, Surrey, GU21 5RZ Tel: (0870) 6015000 Fax: (0870) 6015005 E-mail: sales@fernox.com

ANTISEIZE COMPOUNDS

Molyslip Atlantic, Unit 1 Danebrook Court, Langford Lane, Kidlington, Oxfordshire, OX5 1LQ Tel: (01865) 370032 Fax: (01865) 372030 E-mail: enquiries@molyslip.co.uk

ANTISLIP OR SAFETY MATS

Bonar Floors Ltd, High Holborne Road, Ripley, Derbyshire, DE5 3XD Tel: (01773) 744121 Fax: (01773) 744142 E-mail: enquires@bonarfloors.com

Scotgrip (U K) Ltd, Units 8-9, North Deeside Road, Banchory, Kincardineshire, AB31 5YR Tel: (01330) 825335 Fax: (01330) 825260 E-mail: info@scotgrip.com

Soverign Rubber, Hillgate Industrial Estate, Carrington Field St, Stockport, Cheshire, SK1 3JN Tel: 0161-429 8787 Fax: 0161-480 3573E-mail: salessov@sovereign-rubber.co.uk

ANTISLIP PRODUCTS, *See also headings for particular items*

▶ Anti-Slip, 12 Morningside Terrace, Inverurie, Aberdeenshire, AB51 4FE Tel: (01467) 622721

Ashland Resources Ltd, PO Box 3694, Colchester, CO4 5QJ Tel: (01206) 273658 Fax: (01206) 273199 E-mail: sales@ashland.co.uk

G B Supplies, Dixons Farmhouse, Dixons Lane, Grimsargh, Preston, PR2 5LG Tel: (01772) 704364 Fax: (01772) 704030 E-mail: gbsupplies@aol.com

Heskins Tapes, Churchill Road, Brinscall, Chorley, Lancashire, PR6 8RQ Tel: (01254) 832266 Fax: (01254) 832476 E-mail: mail@heskins.com

▶ Magna Safety Products Ltd, Unit 1, Industrial Estate, London Road, Pampisford, Cambridge, CB22 3EE Tel: (01223) 836643 Fax: (01223) 834648 E-mail: info@magnasafety.co.uk

Pegasus Products (Leeds) Ltd, Rear of, 90 High Street, Yeadon, Leeds, LS19 7AA Tel: 0113-250 0303 Fax: 0113-261 1629 E-mail: info@pegasusproducts.co.uk

Safemate Antislip Ltd, Unit 1 Bankhead Avenue, Bucksburn, Aberdeen, AB21 9ET Tel: (01224) 716283 Fax: (01224) 714653 E-mail: safemate@ifb.co.uk

Slipstop (European) Ltd, Whitwick Business Park, Stenson Road, Coalville, Leicestershire, LE67 4JP Tel: (01530) 813500 Fax: (01530) 813400 E-mail: info@slipstop.co.uk

Slipstop (European) Ltd, Whitwick Business Park, Stenson Road, Coalville, Leicestershire, LE67 4JP Tel: (01530) 813500 Fax: (01530) 813400 E-mail: info@slipstop.co.uk

▶ Survair Yorkshire Ltd, Rose Cottage Front Street, Ingleton, Darlington, County Durham, DL2 3HL Tel: (01325) 733141 E-mail: steven.baker@survair.co.uk

▶ Swiftec, Pennine House, Tilson Road, Roundthorn Industrial Estate, Manchester, M23 9GF Tel: 0161-945 1500 Fax: (0800) 0740005

▶ Tread Safe Southern, 2a Wyncombe Road, Bournemouth, BH5 2JU Tel: (01202) 426400 Fax: (0870) 9509288

ANTISLIP STAIR TREADS

Luxtrade Ltd, Unit C5 Hilton Trading Estate, Hilton Road, Lanesfield, Wolverhampton, WV4 6DW Tel: (01902) 353182 Fax: (01902) 404628 E-mail: sales@luxtrade.co.uk

ANTISLIP TREADS

Ashland Resources Ltd, PO Box 3694, Colchester, CO4 5QJ Tel: (01206) 273658 Fax: (01206) 273199 E-mail: sales@ashland.co.uk

Fibergrate Composite Structures Ltd, Wass Way, Eaglescliffe, Stockton-on-Tees, Cleveland, TS16 0RG Tel: (01642) 784747 Fax: (01642) 784748 E-mail: info@fibergrate.co.uk

▶ Survair Yorkshire Ltd, Rose Cottage Front Street, Ingleton, Darlington, County Durham, DL2 3HL Tel: (01325) 733141 E-mail: steven.baker@survair.co.uk

▶ Tread Safe Southern, 2a Wyncombe Road, Bournemouth, BH5 2JU Tel: (01202) 426400 Fax: (0870) 9509288

ANTISLIP WOODEN DECKING

▶ DIYdeals.com, 6 The Shaw, Glossop, Derbyshire, SK13 6DE Tel: (01457) 855259 E-mail: timber@diydeals.com

ANTISTATIC BELTING

Phoenix Conveyors Ltd, Unit 6 Cobnash Industrial Estate, Kingsland, Leominster, Herefordshire, HR6 9RW Tel: (01568) 709144 Fax: (01568) 709145

ANTISTATIC BRUSHES

Cooks Brushes Ltd, 52 The Street, Old Costessey, Norwich, NR8 5DD Tel: (01603) 748339 Fax: (01603) 748339 E-mail: sales@cooks-brushes.co.uk

ANTISTATIC BUBBLE WRAP

B B S Packaging, Wakeford Farm, Aldermaston Road, Pamber End, Tadley, Hampshire, RG26 5QN Tel: (01256) 851281 Fax: (01256) 850429

Deakins Packing Co., 3 Osman House, Prince Street, Bolton, BL1 2NP Tel: (01204) 393211 Fax: (01204) 381282 E-mail: deakinspackaging@yahoo.co.uk

F D W Packaging, Allerton Mills, Allerton Road, Allerton, Bradford, West Yorkshire, BD15 7QX Tel: (01274) 491013 Fax: (01274) 481752

General Packaging Co., Unit 3 Cooksland Industrial Estate, Bodmin, Cornwall, PL31 2QB Tel: (01208) 265870 Fax: (01208) 72457 E-mail: enquiries@generalpackaging.co.uk

Isca-Bags, 47 Marsh Green Road, Marsh Barton, Exeter, EX2 8PN Tel: (01392) 275906 Fax: (01392) 435028 E-mail: info@isca-bags.com

▶ Proton Supplies, Unit 18 Allshots Enterprises, Woodhouse Lane, Kelvedon, Colchester, CO5 9DF Tel: (01376) 584000 Fax: (01376) 583444 E-mail: sales@apcsolutionsuk.com

W & M Watson, Unit 1a Clyde Industrial Estate, Glasgow, G73 1PP Tel: (01506) 852324 Fax: (01506) 855210

ANTISTATIC FLOOR COVERINGS

His Contracts, 24-28 Pritchards Road, London, E2 9AP Tel: (020) 7739 1455 Fax: (020) 7729 9438 E-mail: info@hiscontracts.co.uk

Static Safe, 6 Timmis Road, Stourbridge, West Midlands, DY9 7BQ Tel: (01384) 898599 Fax: (01384) 898577 E-mail: sse@static-safe.demon.co.uk

Woolmans Electrostatics, Sudbury Road, Bures, Suffolk, CO8 5JT Tel: (01787) 227392 Fax: (01787) 227597 E-mail: woolmansfloors@aol.com

ANTISTATIC FOAM

▶ Copex UK, 30 Princes Avenue, Walsall, WS1 2DG Tel: (01922) 649990 Fax: (01922) 649750 E-mail: copex@tiscali.co.uk

ANTISTATIC INSTRUMENTS

Everett Charles, Fence Avenue Indust Estate, Fence Avenue, Macclesfield, Cheshire, SK10 1LT Tel: (01625) 500303 Fax: (01625) 500306

ANTISTATIC MATERIALS

▶ Able Packaging Group Ltd, Firmin Coates Indust Estate, Middlewich Road, Byley, Middlewich, Cheshire, CW10 9NT Tel: (01606) 836161 Fax: (01606) 836970 E-mail: info@ablepackaging.co.uk

Charleswater Ltd, Unit C, 4th Dimension, Fourth Avenue, Letchworth Garden City, Hertfordshire, SG6 2TD Tel: (01462) 672005 Fax: (01462) 670440 E-mail: sales@vermason.co.uk

Date Electronic Supplies Ltd, Lilleshall Street, Newport, Gwent, NP19 0FB Tel: (01633) 259666 Fax: (01633) 266939 E-mail: alwin.treharne@pavecost.com

Maingrade Ltd, 9 Oakland Industrial Estate, Lower Road, Cannock, Staffordshire, WS12 2UZ Tel: (01543) 426155 Fax: (01543) 426155 E-mail: conductag@aol.com

Morris Packaging Ltd, 3a Telford Road, Ferndown Industrial Estate, Wimborne, Dorset, BH21 7QN Tel: (01202) 892623 Fax: (01202) 894903 E-mail: sales@packaging-uk.co.uk

Woolmans Electrostatics, Sudbury Road, Bures, Suffolk, CO8 5JT Tel: (01787) 227392 Fax: (01787) 227597 E-mail: woolmansfloors@aol.com

ANTISTATIC MATTING/MATS

Freudenberg Building Systems, Gilmorton Road, Lutterworth, Leicestershire, LE17 4DU Tel: (01455) 261200 Fax: (01455) 556529 E-mail: norauk@freudenberg.com

▶ Tread Safe Southern, 2a Wyncombe Road, Bournemouth, BH5 2JU Tel: (01202) 426400 Fax: (0870) 9509288

Woolmans Electrostatics, Sudbury Road, Bures, Suffolk, CO8 5JT Tel: (01787) 227392 Fax: (01787) 227597 E-mail: woolmansfloors@aol.com

ANTISTATIC PACKAGING FILM PRODUCTS

Leroy Packaging Ltd, Heasandford Mill, Netherwood Road, Burnley, Lancashire, BB10 2EJ Tel: (01282) 438016 Fax: (01282) 430289 E-mail: learoyd@learoyd.co.uk

ANTISTATIC PACKAGING PRODUCTS

▶ Boxes And Packaging (Cambridge)Ltd, Edison Road, St. Ives Industrial Estate, St. Ives, Cambridgeshire, PE27 3LF Tel: (01480) 467633 Fax: (01480) 309100 E-mail: cambridge@boxesandpackaging.com

Corstat Containers Ltd, Unit 7 Whitehill Industrial Estate, Whitehill Lane, Swindon, SN4 7DB Tel: (01793) 855168 Fax: (01793) 855209 E-mail: enquiries@corstat.co.uk

PolyPlus Packaging Ltd, Unit 1 Headley Park Ten, Headley Road East, Woodley, Reading, RG5 4SW Tel: 0845 4941732 Fax: 0118-944 8141 E-mail: sales@polypluspackaging.co.uk

S.J.M. Eurostat (U.K.) Ltd, Unit 4b, Bramhall Moor Industrial Park, Hazel Grove, Stockport, Cheshire, SK7 5BW Tel: 0161-456 6088 Fax: 0161-456 6089 E-mail: sjm@sjmeurostat.co.uk

Static Scotland Ltd, 16 Cromarty Campus, Rosyth, Dunfermline, Fife, KY11 2WX Tel: (01383) 419833 Fax: (01383) 413028 E-mail: staticscotland@aol.com

ANTISTATIC PACKAGING TAPES

Garden City Packaging Ltd, 10 Blackhorse Road, Letchworth Garden City, Hertfordshire, SG6 1HB Tel: (01462) 686200 Fax: (01462) 677042 E-mail: gcp@idnet.co.uk

ANTISTATIC POLYETHYLENE (PE) PRODUCTS

▶ Able Packaging Group Ltd, Firmin Coates Indust Estate, Middlewich Road, Byley, Middlewich, Cheshire, CW10 9NT Tel: (01606) 836161 Fax: (01606) 836970 E-mail: info@ablepackaging.co.uk

I A C Plastics, Oak Mill, Manchester Road, Dunnockshaw, Burnley, Lancashire, BB11 5PW Tel: (01706) 212225 Fax: (01706) 229926 E-mail: sales@iacplastics.com

ANTISTATIC PRODUCTS, *See also headings for particular products*

Fraser Anti Static Techniques Ltd, 1 Station Road, Pinhoe, Exeter, EX1 3SA Tel: (01398) 331114 Fax: (01398) 331411 E-mail: sales@fraser-antistatic.co.uk

▶ Simextron, 4 Clune Road, Gowkhall, Dunfermline, Fife, KY12 9NZ Tel: (01383) 853130 Fax: (01383) 853130 E-mail: simextron@tiscali.co.uk

Static Scotland Ltd, 16 Cromarty Campus, Rosyth, Dunfermline, Fife, KY11 2WX Tel: (01383) 419833 Fax: (01383) 413028 E-mail: staticscotland@aol.com

ANTISTATIC SHIELDING BAGS

B B S Packaging, Wakeford Farm, Aldermaston Road, Pamber End, Tadley, Hampshire, RG26 5QN Tel: (01256) 851281 Fax: (01256) 850429

ANTISTATIC WORK SURFACES

Charleswater Ltd, Unit C, 4th Dimension, Fourth Avenue, Letchworth Garden City, Hertfordshire, SG6 2TD Tel: (01462) 672005 Fax: (01462) 670440 E-mail: sales@vermason.co.uk

ANTISTATIC WORKBENCHES

Treston Ltd, 5b Bone Lane, Newbury, Berkshire, RG14 5SH Tel: (01635) 521521 Fax: (01635) 37452 E-mail: salesuk@treston.com

ANTISTATIC WRIST STRAPS

Edson Electronics Ltd, Unit 2, Coquet Enterprise Park, Amble, Morpeth, Northumberland, NE65 0RB Tel: (01665) 710393 Fax: (01665) 711021 E-mail: sales@edsonelectronics.co.uk

ANTITHEFT OFFICE EQUIPMENT SECURITY SYSTEMS

Ramic Engineering Co. Ltd, 96 Upper Wickham Lane, Welling, Kent, DA16 3HQ Tel: (020) 8855 7122 Fax: (020) 8854 8801 E-mail: ramengco@btconnect.com

ANTITHEFT/VANDAL PROTECTION SYSTEMS, AUTOMOTIVE INDUSTRY

Autolok Security Products Ltd, Park Lane, Royton, Oldham, OL2 6PU Tel: 0161-624 8171 Fax: 0161-627 3742 E-mail: enquiries@autolok.uk.com

ANTIVANDAL EXCAVATOR GUARDS

Jays Of Yorkshire, Green Lane, Featherstone, Pontefract, West Yorkshire, WF7 6EH Tel: (01977) 792431 Fax: (01977) 600334 E-mail: info@jaysofyorkshire.co.uk

ANTIVIBRATION CORK PRODUCTS

C Olley & Sons Ltd, Iberia House, 14 Finchley Avenue, Mildenhall, Bury St. Edmunds, Suffolk, IP28 7BJ Tel: (01638) 712076 Fax: (01638) 717304 E-mail: sales@olley-cork.com

ANTIVIBRATION MATERIALS

Electroflock Ltd, Unit 7-8 Building 33, Second Avenue, Pensnett Trading Estate, Kingswinford, West Midlands, DY6 7UG Tel: (01384) 402660 Fax: (01384) 402662 E-mail: electroflock@btinternet.com

ANTIVIBRATION MOUNTING (AVM) MANUFRS

A V M Air Spring Ltd, Unit 2A, Brook Lane Industrial Estate, Westbury, Wiltshire, BA13 4EP Tel: (01373) 858223 Fax: (01373) 858224 E-mail: info@avmspring.com

Allaway Acoustics Ltd, 1 Queens Road, Hertford, SG14 1EN Tel: (01992) 550825 Fax: (01992) 554982 E-mail: enquiries@allawayacoustics.co.uk

Amorim UK Ltd, Suite 1a Bishops Weald House, Albion Way, Horsham, West Sussex, RH12 1AH Tel: (01403) 710001 Fax: (01403) 710003 E-mail: sales@wicanders.co.uk

Anti Vibration Methods Rubber Co. Ltd, 3 Woodcock Industrial Estate, Woodcock Road, Warminster, Wiltshire, BA12 9DX Tel: (01985) 219032 Fax: (01985) 219849 E-mail: sales@antivibrationmethodsrubber.co.uk

C M T Dynamics, PO Box 36, Cradley Heath, West Midlands, B64 7DQ Tel: (01384) 563220 Fax: (01384) 563225 E-mail: sales@cmt-dynamics.co.uk

Christie & Grey Ltd, Morley Road, Tonbridge, Kent, TN9 1RA Tel: (01732) 371100 Fax: (01732) 359666 E-mail: sales@christiegrey.com

Eurovib Acoustic Products Ltd, Goodwood House, 86 Holmethorpe Avenue, Redhill, RH1 2NL Tel: (01737) 779577 Fax: (01737) 779537 E-mail: sales@eurovib.co.uk

Fabreeka International Inc, Units 8-12, Jubilee Way, Shipley, West Yorkshire, BD18 1QG Tel: (01274) 531333 Fax: (01274) 531717 E-mail: info@fabreeka-uk.com

Ferrabyrne Ltd, Fort Road Industrial Estate, Wick, Littlehampton, West Sussex, BN17 7QU Tel: (01903) 721317 Fax: (01903) 730452 E-mail: sales@ferrabyrne.co.uk

Firestone Industrial Products Inc, Church Street, Staines, Middlesex, TW18 4EP Tel: (01784) 462326 Fax: (01784) 462327 E-mail: sales@firestoneindustrial.com

J P Services, 55a High Street, Marlow, Buckinghamshire, SL7 1BA Tel: (01628) 485533 Fax: (01628) 477606 E-mail: sales@jpscientific.com

Kobo (UK) Ltd, Ketten House, Leestone Road, Sharston Industrial Area, Manchester, M22 4RH Tel: 0161-491 9840 Fax: 0161-428 1999 E-mail: info@kobo.co.uk

Maclellan Rubber, Neachells Lane, Wolverhampton, WV11 3QG Tel: (01902) 725515 Fax: (01902) 305201 E-mail: sales@maclellanrubber.com

▶ Polymax, School of Electrical & Mechanical Engineers, Budds Lane, Bordon, Hampshire, GU35 0JE Tel: (01420) 474123 Fax: (01420) 487816 E-mail: contactus@polymax.co.uk

S K Bearings Ltd, Brewery Road, Pampisford, Cambridge, CB22 3HG Tel: (01223) 832851 Fax: (01223) 837668 E-mail: enquiries@skbearings.co.uk

Sherborne Rubber Co. Ltd, Icknield Square, Ladywood, Birmingham, B16 0AB Tel: 0121-456 1565 Fax: 0121-452 1637 E-mail: sales@sherbourne.co.uk

Silvertown UK Ltd, Horninglow Road, Burton-on-Trent, Staffordshire, DE13 0SN Tel: (01283) 510510 Fax: (01283) 510052 E-mail: sales.enq@silvertown.co.uk

Stop Choc Ltd, Banbury Avenue, Slough, SL1 4LR Tel: (01753) 533223 Fax: (01753) 693724 E-mail: sales@stop-choc.co.uk

V T Technology Ltd, Park Road, Holmewood, Chesterfield, Derbyshire, S42 5UY Tel: (01246) 850828 Fax: (01246) 854083 E-mail: vehicletrim@tmat.com

Vibracoustics Ltd, Unit 1 Brook House, Cross Street, Syston, Leicester, LE7 2JG Tel: 0116-260 5700 Fax: 0116-260 5707 E-mail: mail@vibracoustics.com

ANTIVIBRATION SERVICES OR CONSULTANCY OR DESIGN OR INSTALLATION

A V M Air Spring Ltd, Unit 2A, Brook Lane Industrial Estate, Westbury, Wiltshire, BA13 4EP Tel: (01373) 858223 Fax: (01373) 858224 E-mail: info@avmspring.com

Acoustic Design Consultancy, Aldham House, Lady La Industrial Estate, Hadleigh, Ipswich, IP7 6BQ Tel: (01473) 824452 Fax: (01473) 824408 E-mail: adc@acoustic.co.uk

Christie & Grey Ltd, Morley Road, Tonbridge, Kent, TN9 1RA Tel: (01732) 371100 Fax: (01732) 359666 E-mail: sales@christiegrey.com

Fabreeka International Inc, Units 8-12, Jubilee Way, Shipley, West Yorkshire, BD18 1QG Tel: (01274) 531333 Fax: (01274) 531717 E-mail: info@fabreeka-uk.com

Hann Tucker Associates Ltd, Duke House, Duke Street, Woking, Surrey, GU21 5BA Tel: (01483) 770595 Fax: (01483) 729565 E-mail: enquiries@hanntucker.co.uk

Krantz Systems Ltd, 61-67 Rectory Road, Wivenhoe, Colchester, CO7 9ES Tel: (01206) 827171 Fax: (01206) 826936 E-mail: kjr@d4s.co.uk

Martec Environmental Consultants Ltd, Waterbrow Wood, Gressingham, Lancaster, LA2 8LX Tel: (01524) 222000 Fax: (07970) 137469 E-mail: sales@noise.sh

R B Associates, 65 Sea Mills Lane, Stoke Bishop, Bristol, BS9 1DR Tel: 0117-968 1374 Fax: 0117-968 1374 E-mail: rbass@avnet.co.uk

Robush Ltd, Bridge Farm, Ash Road, Lower Hacheston, Woodbridge, Suffolk, IP13 0AA Tel: (01728) 748336 Fax: (01728) 748332 E-mail: sales@robush.co.uk

Stop Choc Ltd, Banbury Avenue, Slough, SL1 4LR Tel: (01753) 533223 Fax: (01753) 693724 E-mail: sales@stop-choc.co.uk

Trelleborg Industrial Avs, 1 Hoods Close, Leicester, LE4 2BN Tel: 0116-267 0300 Fax: 0116-267 0301 E-mail: auto@trelleborg.com

Ulster Industrial Explosives Ltd, Unit 1 Kilroot Park, Carrickfergus, County Antrim, BT38 7PR Tel: (028) 9335 1444 Fax: (028) 9335 1474 E-mail: info@uielimited.com

Vibracoustics Ltd, Unit 1 Brook House, Cross Street, Syston, Leicester, LE7 2JG Tel: 0116-260 5700 Fax: 0116-260 5707 E-mail: mail@vibracoustics.com

ANTIVIBRATION STRUCTURAL BEARINGS

S K Bearings Ltd, Brewery Road, Pampisford, Cambridge, CB22 3HG Tel: (01223) 832851 Fax: (01223) 837668 E-mail: enquiries@skbearings.co.uk

Silvertown UK Ltd, Horninglow Road, Burton-on-Trent, Staffordshire, DE13 0SN Tel: (01283) 510510 Fax: (01283) 510052 E-mail: sales.enq@silvertown.co.uk

ANTIVIBRATION/SHOCK MOUNTS

Rycote Microphone Windshields Ltd, Libbys Drive, Stroud, Gloucestershire, GL5 1RN Tel: (01453) 759338 Fax: (01453) 764249 E-mail: info@rycote.com

Trelleborg Industrial Avs, 1 Hoods Close, Leicester, LE4 2BN Tel: 0116-267 0300 Fax: 0116-267 0301 E-mail: auto@trelleborg.com

Vibracoustics Ltd, Unit 1 Brook House, Cross Street, Syston, Leicester, LE7 2JG Tel: 0116-260 5700 Fax: 0116-260 5707 E-mail: mail@vibracoustics.com

AO SIZED PLAIN PAPER COPYING EQUIPMENT

▶ Bison Paper Ltd, Bison House, 6 Museum Street, Maidstone, Kent, ME14 1QD Tel: (01622) 677541 Fax: (01622) 687685 E-mail: mark@bisonprint.co.uk

▶ Copy Shop Newbury Ltd, Unit 1, Mill Lane, Newbury, Berkshire, RG14 5RE Tel: (01635) 49959 E-mail: sales@copyshopnewbury.co.uk

▶ Digiscans, 66 High Street, Hoddesdon, Hertfordshire, EN11 8ET Tel: (01992) 441516 Fax: 01992 450159 E-mail: admin@digiscans.co.uk

APPLIANCE TEST EQUIPMENT

Di-Log, Unit 28 Wheel Forge Way, Trafford Park, Manchester, M17 1EH Tel: 0161-877 0322 Fax: 0161-877 1614E-mail: sales@dilog.co.uk

APPLICANT TRACKING HUMAN RESOURCES (HR) SOFTWARE

▶ Logical Innovations, 24 Castle View, Airth, Falkirk, FK2 8GE Tel: (01324) 832333 E-mail: enquiries@logicalinnovations.co.uk

APPLICATION SERVICE PROVIDERS (ASP)

Cobweb Solutions Ltd, Delme Place, Cams Hall Estate, Fareham, Hampshire, PO16 8UX Tel: (0845) 2239000 Fax: (0845) 2493310 E-mail: sales@cobweb.co.uk

APPLICATION SPECIFIC INTEGRATED CIRCUIT (ASIC) SEMICONDUCTOR DESIGN ENGINEERS

Garfield Micro Electronics Ltd, Norfolk House, Herriad Business Park, Herriard, Basingstoke, Hampshire, RG25 2PN Tel: (01256) 384300 Fax: (01256) 384319 E-mail: enquiries@gfmicro.com

I C Resources Ltd, Capital House, 67 - 69 St Johns Road, Isleworth, Middlesex, TW7 6NL Tel: (020) 8400 2444 Fax: (020) 8560 2445 E-mail: enquiry@ic-resources.co.uk

Jennic Ltd, Furnival Street, Sheffield, S1 4QT Tel: 0114-281 2655 Fax: 0114-281 2951 E-mail: sales@jennic.com

Semtech Ltd, 218 St. Vincent Street, Glasgow, G2 5SG Tel: 0141-229 5570 Fax: 0141-229 5571

Swindon Silicon Systems Ltd, Radnor Street, Swindon, SN1 3PR Tel: (01793) 649400 Fax: (01793) 616215 E-mail: info@sssl.co.uk

APPLIED RESEARCH TECHNOLOGY CONSULTANTS

▶ Lairdside Laser Engineering Centre, Campbeltown Road, Birkenhead, Merseyside, CH41 9HP Tel: 0151-650 2305 Fax: 0151-650 2304 E-mail: info@llec.co.uk

▶ Sean's Usability Co., Level 5, 5 St Helen's Place, Bishopsgate, London, EC3A 6AU Tel: (020) 7036 0378

AQUARIUM ELECTRICAL EQUIPMENT

Aquacadabra Aquarium & Pond Supplies, 100 Barnehurst Road, Bexleyheath, Kent, DA7 6HG Tel: (01322) 345242 Fax: (01322) 335031

Bristol Waterworld, Wyevale Garden Centre, Hicks Gate, Keynsham, Bristol, BS31 2AD Tel: 0117-977 2955 Fax: 0117-977 2956 E-mail: sales@fishkeeper.com

Britains Aquatic Superstore Ltd, 225 Folds Road, Bolton, BL1 2TW Tel: (01204) 534343 Fax: (01204) 364642

Clear Water Koi Direct, Unit 10 Acaster Industrial Estate, Acaster Malbis, York, YO23 2TX Tel: (01904) 705536 Fax: (01904) 705536 E-mail: sales@koikeeping.com

▶ Coventry Aquatics, 59, Winsford Avenue, Allesley Park, Coventry, CV5 9JG Tel: (024) 7667 7706 Fax: (024) 7667 5052 E-mail: sales@covaquatics.co.uk

Fishy Business, Glyndley Garden Centre, Hailsham Road, Stone Cross, Pevensey, East Sussex, BN24 5BS Tel: (01323) 847868 Fax: (01323) 847868

J M C Aquatic Ltd, Unit 4, Commerce Way Industrial Estate, Stanbridge, Leighton Buzzard, Beds, LU7 8HJ Tel: (01525) 377307 Fax: (01525) 374266

▶ Seaton Pets, 31 Fore Street, Seaton, Devon, EX12 2AD Tel: (01297) 22439 Fax: (01297) 22439 E-mail: seaton.petshop@members.v21.co.uk

Splash Aquatics, 1 James Street, Pontardawe, Swansea, SA8 4LR Tel: (01792) 869779 Fax: (01792) 869779

Value House Aquatics, Units 3-7 Brethren Bank, Barnstaple, Devon, EX31 2AZ Tel: (01271) 328462 Fax: (01271) 328462

Wales Water Gardening, Croesyceiliog, Cwmbran, Gwent, NP44 2BZ Tel: (01633) 871144 Fax: 01633 873722

World Of Fishes, 31 North End, London Road, East Grinstead, West Sussex, RH19 1QJ Tel: (01342) 410636 Fax: (01342) 317085 E-mail: sales@worldoffishes.com

World Of Water, Turners Hill Road, Worth, Crawley, West Sussex, RH10 4PE Tel: (01293) 883237 Fax: (01293) 883231 E-mail: crawley@worldofwater.com

AQUARIUM LIFE SUPPORT SYSTEMS

▶ acrylic aquarium co (UK), 3 Fitzstephen Road, Dagenham, Essex, RM8 2YP Tel: 020 8593 3305 E-mail: info@aquariummasters.freeserve.co.uk

AQUARIUM SUPPLIES

Nicky's Fish, Slade House, 45 Overstone Road, Moulton, Northampton, NN3 7UU Tel: (01604) 644394

AQUARIUM TANKS

▶ acrylic aquarium co (UK), 3 Fitzstephen Road, Dagenham, Essex, RM8 2YP Tel: 020 8593 3305 E-mail: info@aquariummasters.freeserve.co.uk
▶ Aqua Rentals, 2 Silkwood Court, Ossett, West Yorkshire, WF5 9TP Tel: (01924) 237440 Fax: (01924) 237441 E-mail: enquiries@aquarentals.co.uk
Aqua Servicing Incorporating Thinktanks, 13 Ponsonby Place, London, SW1P 4PS Tel: (020) 7821 6489
Aqua Varium, 1 The Green, Ware, Hertfordshire, SG12 0QW Tel: (01920) 464442 Fax: (01920) 464442
▶ Aquafern Products, Unit 8, Chapel Lane, Hadleigh, Essex, SS7 2PP Tel: (01702) 551044 Fax: (01702) 551044
Aquajoy Aquarium & Pond Supplies, 31 Lower Morden Lane, Morden, Surrey, SM4 4SE Tel: (020) 8337 7373 Fax: (020) 8337 7373 E-mail: enquiries@aquajoy.co.uk
Aquapets, 17 Leeland Rd, London, W13 9HH Tel: 020 85672748
Aquaria Aquarium & Pond Supplies, 335 Hollinwood Avenue, Manchester, M40 0JA Tel: 0161-681 6731
Aquarium Design Centre, 476 Paisley Road, Glasgow, G5 8RE Tel: 0141-429 0044 Fax: 0141-429 0044 E-mail: aquariumdesigncentre@hotmail.com
▶ AquariumHire.co.uk, PO Box 156, Sevenoaks, Kent, TN15 0WA Tel: (01732) 760991 Fax: (01732) 760992 E-mail: goldfish@aquariumhire.co.uk
Aquatic Design Centre, 107-109 Great Portland Street, London, W1W 6QG Tel: (020) 7580 6764 Fax: (020) 7631 2033 E-mail: nick@aquaticdesign.co.uk
Aquatic Style, Wyndham CR, Cardiff, CF11 9EH Tel: (029) 2064 4519
Attwood Aquatics, 187 London Road, Hemel Hempstead, Hertfordshire, HP3 9SQ Tel: (01442) 211077 Fax: (01442) 264849 E-mail: sales@attwoodaquatics.co.uk
Blue Lagoon Aquatics, 157-159 Broad Street, Dagenham, Essex, RM10 9HX Tel: (020) 8595 9635 Fax: (020) 8592 3173
Bow Aquatic Centre, Willowbrook Garden Centre, West Buckland, Wellington, Somerset, TA21 9HX Tel: (01823) 461822 Fax: (01823) 461822
Paul Bromfield Aquatics, Maydencroft Lane, Gosmore, Hitchin, Hertfordshire, SG4 7QD Tel: (01462) 457399 Fax: (01462) 422652
Catchwater Meadow, Orby Road, Burgh le Marsh, Skegness, Lincolnshire, PE24 5JD Tel: (01754) 811097 Fax: (01754) 811151
Chenies Aquatics Ltd, The Van Hage Garden Co, Chenies, Rickmansworth, Hertfordshire, WD3 6EN Tel: (01494) 764549 Fax: (01494) 765783
Cheshire Water Life, Blakemere Craft Centre, Chester Road, Sandiway, Northwich, Cheshire, CW8 2EB Tel: (01606) 882223 Fax: (01606) 889964E-mail: sales@cheshire-waterlife.co.uk
Country Lanes Garden Centre Ltd, Country Lanes Garden Centre, Exeter Road, Stockley, Okehampton, Devon, EX20 1QH Tel: (01837) 52489 Fax: (01837) 52489
▶ Coventry Aquatics, 59, Winsford Avenue, Allesley Park, Coventry, CV5 9JG Tel: (024) 7667 7706 Fax: (024) 7667 5052 E-mail: sales@covaquatics.co.uk
The Creek Aquatic Garden Centre, 427 Walton Road, West Molesey, Surrey, KT8 2EJ Tel: (020) 8941 8758 E-mail: sales@koicarpuk.co.uk
Cuddra Aquatic Nursery Wholesale, Cuddra Nursery, St. Austell, Cornwall, PL25 3JQ Tel: (01726) 76686 Fax: (01726) 76602
Denmead Aquatic Nursery, Soake Road, Waterlooville, Hampshire, PO7 6HY Tel: (023) 9225 2671 Fax: (023) 9225 2671
Denton Aquatics, 98 Denton Street, Carlisle, CA2 5EN Tel: (01228) 526651 Fax: (01228) 526651
East Midlands Aquatics Ltd, 1 Nottingham Road, Trowell, Nottingham, NG9 3PA Tel: 0115-930 0921 Fax: 01159 300921 E-mail: tim@emaconline.co.uk
Emperor Tropicals & Water Garden Centre, 9 St Erth Road, Plymouth, PL2 3SW Tel: (01752) 706633 Fax: (01752) 313461 E-mail: sales@emperortropicals.co.uk
Erdington Aquatic Centre, 97 Church Road, Erdington, Birmingham, B24 9BE Tel: 0121-373 1100 Fax: 0121-373 1100
Finns Aquaria, 232 Warwick Road, Sparkhill, Birmingham, B11 2NB Tel: 0121-753 0162
Fins, Cressing Road, Braintree, Essex, CM77 8DH Tel: (01376) 343686 Fax: (01376) 343687 E-mail: sales@fins.co.uk
Furness Aquatics, 70a Kent Street, Barrow-in-Furness, Cumbria, LA13 9QR Tel: (01229) 870970 Fax: (01229) 580606
Peter Golding Ltd, Barton Stacey, Winchester, Hampshire, SO21 3QL Tel: (01962) 760792 Fax: (01962) 760692 E-mail: sales@petergoulding.co.uk
The Hampshire Pond Centre, 414 London Road, Portsmouth, PO2 9LB Tel: (023) 9265 0839
J M C Aquatics Ltd, 59 Stubley Lane, Dronfield, Derbyshire, S18 1PG Tel: (01246) 415275 Fax: (01246) 290486 E-mail: janet@jmc-aquatics.co.uk
Japanese Water Gardens, 251 Toton Lane, Stapleford, Nottingham, NG9 7JA Tel: 0115-939 7926 Fax: 0115-949 0451
Jaydee Aquatics, Mold Road, Cefn-y-Bedd, Wrexham, Clwyd, LL12 9UR Tel: (01978) 854254 Fax: (01978) 762051
Juwel Aquarium UK Ltd, Gateway 11 Business Park, Penfold Drive, Wymondham, Norfolk, NR18 0WZ Tel: (01953) 606363 Fax: (01953) 603839 E-mail: info@juwel-aquarium.co.uk
K.G. Products, 247 City Road, Stoke-on-Trent, ST4 2PX Tel: (01782) 844866 Fax: (01782) 744162 E-mail: enquiries@kgproducts.co.uk
Kettering Koi & Ponds Ltd, 63-65 Field Street, Kettering, Northamptonshire, NN16 8EW Tel: (01536) 515304 Fax: (01536) 515304
Kidsgrove Tropicals, 6 Hardingswood Road, Kidsgrove, Stoke-On-Trent, ST7 1EF Tel: (01782) 775947
▶ Kidzone South West Ltd, Bradley Mill, Bradley Lane, Newton Abbot, Devon, TQ12 1LZ Tel: (01626) 353081 Fax: (01626) 357516 E-mail: aquaticssouthwest@hotmail.com
Koi Joy Pet, 60-61 Nile Road, Gorleston, Great Yarmouth, Norfolk, NR31 6AS Tel: (01493) 442703 Fax: (01493) 441393
▶ Koi Logic, Forest View Nursery, St. Marys Lane, North Ockendon, Upminster, Essex, RM14 3PA Tel: (01708) 226699 E-mail: sales@koilogic.co.uk
Koi Plus, Newton Chambers Road, Thorncliffe Park Estate, Chapeltown, Sheffield, S35 2PH Tel: 0114-257 7525 Fax: 0114-257 7525 E-mail: sales@koiplus.force9.co.uk
Koi Pool, Fleetwood Road South, Thornton-Cleveleys, Lancashire, FY5 5NS Tel: (01253) 856411 Fax: (01253) 828610
Koi Water Garden, Lower Morden Lane, Morden, Surrey, SM4 4SJ Tel: (020) 8337 3337 Fax: (020) 8335 3979 E-mail: sales@koiwatergarden.com
Lilliput Aquarium, 16 St Annes Road, Blackpool, FY4 2AN Tel: (01253) 408824 Fax: (01253) 408824
Maidenhead Aquatic Centre, Bourne End Garden Centre, Hedsor Road, Bourne End, Buckinghamshire, SL8 5EE Tel: (01628) 528882 Fax: (01628) 850429
Maidenhead Aquatics Morden Water World, Morden Hall Road, Morden, Surrey, SM4 5JG Tel: (020) 8646 1066 Fax: (020) 8648 1414 E-mail: info@fishkeeper.co.uk
Maydencroft Aquatic Nurseries, Maydencroft Lane, Gosmore, Hitchin, Hertfordshire, SG4 7QD Tel: (01462) 456020 Fax: (01462) 422652
Newbury Aquatics Centre, Wyevale Garden Centre, Bath Road, Thatcham, Berkshire, RG18 3AN Tel: (01635) 869900 Fax: (01635) 874774
Newton Pet & Garden Supplies, 1-2 Bridge House, Sherborne Road, Newton Abbot, Devon, TQ12 2QX Tel: (01626) 201219 Fax: (01626) 201219
Noahs Ark Aquatics, 28 Shannon Way, Canvey Island, Essex, SS8 0PD Tel: (01268) 514001 Fax: (01268) 693064
North West Aquatics, Webbs Garden Centre, Burneside Road, Kendal, Cumbria, LA9 4RT Tel: (01539) 720041 Fax: (01539) 727328
Northern Koi & Aquatics, 196 Manchester Road, Rixton, Warrington, WA3 6EA Tel: (01925) 812028 Fax: (01925) 823266 E-mail: enquiries@northernkoi.co.uk
Novaplace Ltd, Intercel House, Main St, Overseal, Swadlincote, Derbyshire, DE12 6LG Tel: (01283) 763666 Fax: (01283) 763666 E-mail: sales@europond.co.uk
Oakhanger Aquatics, Nursery Road, Oakhanger, Crewe, CW1 5UY Tel: (01270) 872467 Fax: (01270) 884260
Peak Aquatics Ltd, Ashbourne Road Industrial Estate, Staden Lane, Buxton, Derbyshire, SK17 9SZ Tel: (01298) 24438 Fax: (01298) 27340 E-mail: peak@aquatics99.freeserve.co.uk
Pond Plants, Birley Moor Garden Centre, 27 Moor Valley, Mosborough, Sheffield, S20 5BB Tel: 0114-251 3536 Fax: 0114-251 3336
Portland Aquaria, 22 Portland Street, Chatham, Kent, ME4 5LS Tel: (01634) 841145
Q S S Aquarium & Koi Centre, 339 Wakefield Road, Bradford, West Yorkshire, BD4 7NJ Tel: (01274) 728361 Fax: (01274) 720718 E-mail: sales@qssaquarium.co.uk
Riverside Aquaria, 27 Linden Avenue, Stirling, FK7 7PQ Tel: (01786) 473450 Fax: (01786) 470843
Rosewood Pet Products Ltd, 45 Coalport Road, Broseley, Shropshire, TF12 5AN Tel: (01952) 883408 Fax: (01952) 884359 E-mail: sales@rosewoodpet.com
Sea Pet Centre Ltd, 21 Beardmore Park, Martlesham Heath, Ipswich, IP5 3RX Tel: (01473) 610969 Fax: (01473) 610265 E-mail: sales@seapets.co.uk
▶ Seaton Pets, 31 Fore Street, Seaton, Devon, EX12 2AD Tel: (01297) 22439 Fax: (01297) 22439 E-mail: seaton.petshop@members.v21.co.uk
Selective Koi Sales, 47 Waterloo Road, Hainford, Norwich, NR10 3AX Tel: (01603) 897453 Fax: (01603) 898523 E-mail: sales@selectivekoisales.co.uk
▶ System 2000 UK Ltd, 507 Bradford Road, Batley, West Yorkshire, WF17 8LL Tel: (01924) 422000 Fax: (01924) 422118 E-mail: sales@system2000.co.uk
Thringstone News, 20-22 Main Street, Thringstone, Coalville, Leicestershire, LE67 8NA Tel: (01530) 222355 Fax: 01530 222533
Top Trop Aquatics, 123 Caerleon Rd, Newport, Gwent, NP19 7BZ Tel: (01633) 254496 Fax: (01633) 254496
Tranquility Aquatics & Reptile Centre Ltd, 46-47 George Street, Brighton, BN2 1RJ Tel: (01273) 621691 Fax: (01273) 626908
Tropi Quaria, 27-29 Anglesea Road, Southampton, SO15 5QH Tel: (023) 8077 3120 Fax: (023) 8077 3120
Victoria Aquatics, 45 Victoria Road, Carlisle, CA1 2UE Tel: (01228) 535602 Fax: (01228) 535602
Water World Ltd, Chester High Road, Burton, Neston, CH64 8TF Tel: 0151-336 3616 Fax: 0151-336 7718
Waterlife Studio, Booker Garden Centre, Clay Lane, Booker, Marlow, Buckinghamshire, SL7 3DH Tel: (01494) 526865 E-mail: sales@thewaterlifestudio.co.uk
Waterside Aquatics & Koi Centres, West Park Road, Copthorne, Crawley, West Sussex, RH10 3HG Tel: (01342) 712332 Fax: (01342) 712332
Waterways, 85 Brereton Avenue, Cleethorpes, South Humberside, DN35 7RP Tel: (01472) 342475 Fax: (01507) 354513
Waterwise Aquarium & Pond Supplies, The Water Garden Centre, 144 Coggeshall Road, Marks Tey, Colchester, CO6 1HR Tel: (01206) 212310 Fax: (01206) 213084
Wayside Water Gardens, Doncaster Road, Oldcotes, Worksop, Nottinghamshire, S81 8HT Tel: (01909) 731367 Fax: (01909) 730511 E-mail: sales@waysidewatergardens.co.uk
Wet Pets Aquatic Centre, Fiskerton Road, Southwell, Nottinghamshire, NG25 0TH Tel: (01636) 816910
Wholesale Tropicals, 220 Bethnal Green Road, London, E2 0AA Tel: (020) 7739 5356 Fax: (020) 7729 2444 E-mail: tjones@xln..co.uk
World Of Water Ltd, Wood Lane, Timperley, Altrincham, Cheshire, WA15 7PJ Tel: 0161-903 9944 Fax: 0161-903 9666
World Of Water, Mulbrooks, Hailsham, East Sussex, BN27 2RH Tel: (01323) 442400 Fax: (01323) 848400
World Of Water, 93 Great Bridge Road, Romsey, Hampshire, SO51 0HB Tel: (01794) 515923 Fax: (01794) 830846
World Of Water (Nottingham), Woodlands, Lowdham Lane, Woodborough, Nottingham, NG14 6DN Tel: 0115-966 3333 Fax: 0115-966 5030
Worthing Aquatics, High Street, Angmering, Littlehampton, West Sussex, BN16 4AW Tel: (01903) 778922 Fax: (01903) 778902

AQUEOUS CLEANING EQUIPMENT

Layton Technologies, Parkhall Business Park, Parkhall Road, Weston Coyney, Stoke-on-Trent, ST3 5XA Tel: (01782) 370400 Fax: (01782) 333202 E-mail: webenquiries@laytontechnologies.com
Metalas UK Ltd, White Cottages, Fuller Street, Fairstead, Chelmsford, CM3 2AY Tel: (01245) 233715 Fax: (01245) 381866 E-mail: admin@metalas.co.uk
▶ Standard Industrial Systems Ltd, Stanton House, Eastham Village Rd, Eastham, Wirral, Merseyside, CH62 0DE Tel: (0845) 2571985 Fax: (0845) 2571986 E-mail: sales@standardindustrial.co.uk

AQUEOUS DEGREASERS

Cotswold Chemicals & Lubricants, Unit 16-17, Ryeford Industrial Estate, Ryeford, Stonehouse, Gloucestershire, GL10 2LB Tel: (01453) 825292 Fax: (01453) 791451 E-mail: sales@cotswoldchemicals.co.uk

ARABLE CONTRACTORS

E Just & Son, Waterlog Farm, Spondon Road, Dale Abbey, Ilkeston, Derbyshire, DE7 4PQ Tel: (01332) 662994 Fax: (01332) 662994

ARABLE FARMING MACHINE FABRICATION

Backmuir Trading Ltd, Backmuir Farm, Keith, Banffshire, AB55 5PE Tel: (01542) 882543 Fax: (01542) 886065 E-mail: philipsimmers@morayboadband.com
▶ M G Sutton, Grendon House Farm, Warton Lane, Grendon, Atherstone, Warwickshire, CV9 3DT Tel: (01827) 892295 Fax: (01827) 892432 E-mail: lee.sutton@btinternet.com

ARAMID FIBRE MOULDINGS

Curley Specialised Mouldings In Group, Weald House, Pattenden Lane, Marden, Tonbridge, Kent, TN12 9QJ Tel: (01622) 833181 E-mail: info@curleyuk.com

ARAMID TEXTILES

Gurit, St. Cross Business Park, Newport, Isle of Wight, PO30 5WU Tel: (01983) 828000 Fax: (01983) 828100 E-mail: info@gurit.com

ARAMID YARN

Ahmad Textiles, Ahmad House, Downham Street, Bradford, West Yorkshire, BD3 9QY Tel: (01274) 727069 Fax: (01274) 390407 E-mail: info@ahmadtextiles.co.uk
F. Harding (Macclesfield) Ltd, Kershaw Mill, Newton Street, Macclesfield, Cheshire, SK11 6QJ Tel: (01625) 429625 Fax: (01625) 612836 E-mail: sales@f-harding.com

ARBITRATION OR ADJUDICATION SERVICES

▶ CHARTER WISE LTD., 21a High Street, Lyndhurst, Hampshire, SO43 7BB Tel: 023 80284459 Fax: 023 80283888 E-mail: dick@charterwise.wanadoo.co.uk
▶ Longworth Consulting Worldwide Ltd, 12 Fairbairn Road, Livingston, West Lothian, EH54 6TS Tel: (01506) 414167 Fax: (01506) 414147 E-mail: admin@longworthconsulting.co.uk
▶ Soma Contract Services Ltd, 6 The Green, Dunchurch, Rugby, Warwickshire, CV22 6NX Tel: (01788) 817811 Fax: (01788) 817282 E-mail: maggieholman@somacontracts.co.uk

ARBITRATOR OR ARBITRATION ASSOCIATIONS

▶ CHARTER WISE LTD., 21a High Street, Lyndhurst, Hampshire, SO43 7BB Tel: 023 80284459 Fax: 023 80283888 E-mail: dick@charterwise.wanadoo.co.uk

ARBORS

▶ Picador Engineering Co. Ltd, 103 Louth Road, Holton-le-Clay, Grimsby, South Humberside, DN36 5AD Tel: (01472) 824520 Fax: (01724) 280999 E-mail: picadoreng@aol.co.uk

ARC WELDING ELECTRODES

Corewire Ltd, Poplars Farm, Station Road West, Ash Vale, Aldershot, Hampshire, GU12 5QD Tel: (01252) 517766 Fax: (01252) 515833 E-mail: info@corewire.com
Frank Langfield Ltd, Hollins Mill Lane, Sowerby Bridge, West Yorkshire, HX6 2RF Tel: (01422) 835388 Fax: (01422) 834452 E-mail: sales@langfieldwelding.com
M W A International Ltd, PO Box 17, Wednesbury, West Midlands, WS10 0AB Tel: 0121-556 6366 Fax: 0121-556 5566 E-mail: info@mwa-international.com
Premier Welding Services (North) Ltd, 8 Atlas Way, Atlas North Industrial Estate, Sheffield, S4 7QQ Tel: 0114-243 0555 Fax: 0114-243 0777 E-mail: premierwelding@btconnect.com

ARC WELDING EQUIPMENT

Britannia Welding Supplies Ltd, 7 Rotunda Estate, Aldershot, Hampshire, GU11 1TG Tel: (01252) 350866 Fax: (01252) 330938 E-mail: debbie@britweld.co.uk
Gullco International (UK) Ltd, 5 Stonecrop, North Quarry Business Park, Appley Bridge, Wigan, Lancashire, WN6 9DB Tel: (01257) 253579 Fax: (01257) 254629 E-mail: sales@gullco.co.uk
Parweld Ltd, Alton Works, Long Bank, Bewdley, Worcestershire, DY12 2UJ Tel: (01299) 266800 Fax: (01299) 266900 E-mail: info@parweld.co.uk
Pickhill Engineers Hipperholme Ltd, Broad Lea, Pickhill, Thirsk, North Yorkshire, YO7 4JU Tel: (01845) 567234 Fax: (01845) 567690 E-mail: sales@pickhill-engineers.co.uk
Rock Welding Supplies Ltd, Princes Dr Industrial Estate, Coventry Road, Kenilworth, Warwickshire, CV8 2FD Tel: (01926) 851430 Fax: (01926) 851562
T P S Fronius, 1 The Omni Business Centre, Omega Park, Alton, Hampshire, GU34 2QD Tel: (01420) 546855 Fax: (01420) 546856 E-mail: alton@tps-fronius.co.uk

ARCADE GAME HIRE

▶ Future Machines Ltd, Unit 20 Fleetway Business Park, Wadsworth Road, Greenford, Middlesex, UB6 7LF Tel: (020) 8997 4488 Fax: (020) 8997 4334 E-mail: info@leisuremachinesdirect.co.uk
▶ Leisure Direct Ltd, Unit 21, Fleetway West Business Park, 14-16 Wadsworth Road, Perivale, Greenford, Middlesex, UB6 7LD Tel: (020) 8997 2266 Fax: (020) 8997 4334 E-mail: leisuredirect@yahoo.co.uk
▶ Monkey Gaming, 7 Church Street, Highbridge, Somerset, TA9 3AE Tel: (01278) 784790
▶ UK Fun, Martland Mill Garage, Martland Mill Lane, Martland Mill, Wigan, Lancashire, WN5 0LZ Tel: (01942) 241722 Fax: (01942) 248099 E-mail: dave@uk-fun.co.uk

ARCHAEOLOGICAL GEOPHYSICAL SURVEYS

▶ Souterrain Archaeological Services Ltd, 50 Rectory Drive, Exhall, Coventry, CV7 9PD Tel: (024) 7631 1567 Fax: (01794) 523528 E-mail: gps@souterrain.biz

ARCHITECTS

Abbozzo, 24 Sandyford Place, Glasgow, G3 7NG Tel: 0141-221 5110 Fax: 0141-248 7632 E-mail: info@abbozzo.co.uk
Apex Architecture Ltd, The Old School, Viney Hill, Lydney, Gloucestershire, GL15 4ND Tel: (01594) 516161 Fax: (01594) 516145 E-mail: info@apexarchitecture.co.uk
Architectural Design, The Courtyard, 28a Great King Street, Macclesfield, Cheshire, SK11 6PL Tel: (01625) 615954 Fax: (01625) 511042 E-mail: post@archdes.co.uk
▶ C&D Industrial Services Ltd, Drovers Road, East Mains Industrial Estate, Broxburn, West Lothian, EH52 5ND Tel: (01506) 856000 Fax: (01506) 858000
▶ Christian Garnett Partners, 195 High Holborn, London, WC1V 7BD Tel: (020) 7404 7677 Fax: (020) 7404 6648 E-mail: sales@christiangarnett.com
▶ Clerici Associates, Pemberley, Ricksons Lane, West Horsley, Leatherhead, Surrey, KT24 6HU Tel: (01483) 283573 E-mail: enquiries@clerici.co.uk
Cowan Architects Ltd, 9-10 Old Stone Link, Ship Street, East Grinstead, West Sussex, RH19 4EF Tel: (01342) 410242 Fax: (01342) 313493 E-mail: info@cowan-architects.co.uk
▶ Etc Design Ltd, 2 Carriers Fold, Church Road, Wombourne, Wolverhampton, WV5 9DH Tel: (01902) 898282 Fax: (01902) 898283 E-mail: enquiries@etcarchitects.co.uk
▶ Fisher Wrathall, The Old Warehouse, Castle Hill, Lancaster, LA1 1YP Tel: (01524) 68822 Fax: (01524) 642211 E-mail: greg@fisherwrathall.co.uk
▶ Foster D Architect, 11 Isabel House, Victoria Road, Surbiton, Surrey, KT6 4JL Tel: (020) 8390 7555 Fax: (020) 8390 7555 E-mail: duncanfoster.architect@virgin.net
▶ Fowler Architects Ltd, The Studio, Jackeaves House, Tinkers Lane, Tring, Herts, HP23 6JB Tel: 01442 871496 Fax: 01442 876555
GIA Design Ltd, 46a Pevensey Road, Eastbourne, East Sussex, BN21 3HP Tel: (01323) 722131 Fax: (01323) 642940 E-mail: greg@duvacourt.co.uk
▶ Haa Design, 109 Hope Street, Glasgow, G2 6LL Tel: 0141-221 6234 Fax: 0141-221 6543
▶ Halliday Fraser Munro, 8 Victoria Street, Aberdeen, AB10 1XB Tel: (01224) 388700 Fax: (01224) 388777 E-mail: info@hfm.co.uk
▶ Harris & Johnston, 162 Brunton Gardens, Montgomery Street, Edinburgh, EH7 5ER Tel: 0131-661 3121 Fax: 0131-661 3122 E-mail: sales@harrisjohnson.co.uk
▶ Holmes Partnership, 80 Commercial Street, Edinburgh, EH6 6LX Tel: 0131-553 2111 Fax: 0131-553 1300 E-mail: edinburgh@holmespartnership.com
▶ HomeCAD Architectural Services, 2 Cumbernauld Business Park, Wardpark Road, Cumbernauld, Glasgow, G67 3JZ Tel: (0800) 0838288 Fax: (01236) 795579 E-mail: info@homecad.org
▶ Hypostyle Architects, 49 St. Vincent Cresent, Glasgow, G3 8NG Tel: 0141-204 4441 Fax: 0141-204 4897
▶ I D E- Architecture, Unit 205, Spitfire Studios, 63-71 Collier Street, London, N1 9BE Tel: (020) 7837 4000 Fax: (020) 7837 4222
▶ Larner Sing Architectural & Building Design, 29 Lower Street, Rode, Frome, Somerset, BA11 6PU Tel: (01373) 830836 Fax: (01373) 830527 E-mail: ian@larner-sing.co.uk
▶ Mcgarry Moon Architecs Ltd, 17 Drumimerick Road, Kilrea, Coleraine, County Londonderry, BT51 5SY Tel: (028) 2954 2323 Fax: (028) 2954 2323 E-mail: info@mcgarry-moon.com
Wilson Mason & Partners, 3 Chandos Street, London, W1G 9JU Tel: (020) 7637 1501 Fax: (020) 7631 0325 E-mail: enquiries@wilsonmason.co.uk
▶ Miller Architects, The Studio, 11 Gage Ridge, Forest Row, East Sussex, RH18 5HL Tel: 01342 823553 E-mail: info@millerarchitects.net
▶ Mr V Brown, Staunton Harold Hall, Melbourne Road, Staunton Harold, Ashby-de-la-Zouch, Leicestershire, LE65 1RT Tel: (0870) 4604758 E-mail: valton@valton.freeserve.co.uk
Patrick Stephenson, 47 Horringer Road, Bury St. Edmunds, Suffolk, IP33 2DQ Tel: (01284) 706090 Fax: (01284) 706090 E-mail: enquiries@patrickstephensonarchitects.co.uk
▶ Plann Architects Ltd, Studio 1 Welland Indust Estate, Valley Way, Market Harborough, Leicestershire, LE16 7PS Tel: (01858) 466946 Fax: (01858) 466879 E-mail: mcl@plann-architects.co.uk
R M J M Ltd, 83 Paul Street, London, EC2A 4UT Tel: (020) 7549 8900 Fax: (020) 7250 3131 E-mail: london@rmjm.com
▶ R Walker, 41 The Pastures, Lower Bullingham, Hereford, HR2 6EU Tel: (01432) 341636 E-mail: enquires@rwalker-plans.co.uk
George Scott Architects, 378A Belmont Road, Belfast, BT4 2NF Tel: (028) 9076 0020 Fax: (028) 9076 1731
▶ T P A Design Co. Ltd, 33a St Lukes Road, Maidenhead, Berkshire, SL6 7DN Tel: (01628) 412388 Fax: (01628) 412390 E-mail: sales@tpadesign.co.uk
▶ Thomas Building Plans, 18 Shiels Drive, Bradley Stoke, Bristol, BS32 8EA Tel: (0845) 1590089 E-mail: info@thomasbuildingplans.co.uk
▶ Vosper International Ltd, 7 Killermont View, Glasgow, G20 0TZ Tel: 0141-945 5529 E-mail: design@vosper.co.uk
▶ Wilson Kennett Partnership, College House 2 College Street, Harlow Hill, Harrogate, North Yorkshire, HG2 0AH Tel: (01423) 531183 Fax: (01423) 531184 E-mail: wkp@wkpartnership.co.uk

ARCHITECTURAL ALUMINIUM FABRICATORS

Argent Fabrications Ltd, Unit 4 Avery Dell, Lifford Lane, Birmingham, B30 3DZ Tel: 0121-459 9617 Fax: 0121-458 6604 E-mail: enquiries@argentfabs.com
Eurowindows Ltd, 12 Poley Road, Stanford-Le-Hope, Essex, SS17 0JJ Tel: (01375) 641935 Fax: (01375) 672461 E-mail: reception@euro-windows.co.uk
Evans Turner Finishes Ltd, 200 Manor Road, Erith, Kent, DA8 2AD Tel: (01322) 346911 Fax: (01322) 332706 E-mail: sales@evans-turner.com
Formes Alutek Ltd, Cromwell Road, Ellesmere Port, CH65 4LF Tel: 0151-357 1998 Fax: 0151-356 1078 E-mail: info@formesalutek.co.uk
Fox Aluminium Systems Ltd, Wentworth Way, Tankersley, Barnsley, South Yorkshire, S75 3DH Tel: (01226) 749910 Fax: (01226) 749920 E-mail: sales@foxaluminium.co.uk
Ingimex Ltd, Halesfield 19, Telford, Shropshire, TF7 4QT Tel: (01952) 585833 Fax: (01952) 580940 E-mail: sales@ingimex.com
J A G Services Ltd, 13 Reform Road, Maidenhead, Berkshire, SL6 8BY Tel: (01628) 670909 Fax: (01628) 672016 E-mail: gstuart@jagservices.fsnet.co.uk
J P J Installations Ltd, 8 Swinbourne Drive, Springwood Industrial Estate, Braintree, Essex, CM7 2YP Tel: (01376) 528111 Fax: (01376) 528222 E-mail: jpj@btconnect.com
N J Aluminium, 223 Bowling Back Lane, Bradford, West Yorkshire, BD4 8SJ Tel: (01274) 733393 Fax: (01274) 732221
Technal, Units 2-4 Hudswell Road, Hunslet, Leeds, LS10 1AG Tel: 0113-296 1400 Fax: 0113-296 1414 E-mail: leeds@technal.co.uk
Vanwest Ltd, Unit 2 High Street, Lenches Bridge, Pensnett, Kingswinford, West Midlands, DY6 8XD Tel: (01384) 400255 Fax: (01384) 400258

ARCHITECTURAL ALUMINIUM FRAMEWORK SYSTEMS

▶ Anders Glass Ltd, 30 Frederick Road, Salford, M6 6NY Tel: 0161-736 2487 Fax: 0161-745 8183E-mail: simon.anders@andersglass.co.uk
▶ G S M Aluminium Ltd, 16 Maria Street, Burley in Wharfedale, Ilkley, West Yorkshire, LS29 7JA Tel: (01943) 862307 Fax: (01943) 863168 E-mail: gerald@gsmltd.co.uk
Parkside Group Ltd, 5 Willow Business Centre, 17 Willow Lane, Mitcham, Surrey, CR4 4NX Tel: (020) 8685 9685 Fax: (020) 8646 5096 E-mail: sales@parksidegrp.co.uk
▶ S M Partnership Ltd, East Lodge, Leylands Farm, Colden Common, Winchester, Hampshire, SO21 1TH Tel: (023) 8069 3969 Fax: (023) 8069 8969 E-mail: enquiries@smpartnership.com

ARCHITECTURAL CASTING RESTORATION SERVICES

Barr & Grosvenor Ltd, Jenner Street, Wolverhampton, WV2 2AE Tel: (01902) 352390 Fax: (01902) 871342 E-mail: sales@bargrosvenorwannado.co.uk

ARCHITECTURAL CASTINGS

Castech (UK) Ltd, Unit 10 Manor Farm, Main Road, Newport Pagnell, Buckinghamshire, MK16 9JS Tel: 01234 391973 Fax: 01234 391185 E-mail: info@castech.co.uk
Derwent Castings Ltd, Derwent Foundry, Derby Road, Whatstandwell, Matlock, Derbyshire, DE4 5HG Tel: (01773) 852173 Fax: (01773) 856632 E-mail: info@derwent-foundry.co.uk
Goodwin International Ltd, Ivy House Foundry, Hanley, Stoke-on-Trent, ST1 3NR Tel: (01782) 220000 Fax: (01782) 208060 E-mail: goodwinplc@goodwin.co.uk
Minsterstone Ltd, Harts Close, Ilminster, Somerset, TA19 9DJ Tel: (01460) 52277 Fax: (01460) 57865 E-mail: varyl@minsterstone.ltd.uk
Mouldcraft Joinery Manufacturers, 5 Bridge Street, Kilrea, Coleraine, County Londonderry, BT51 5RR Tel: (028) 2954 0099 Fax: (028) 2954 0889
Sterling Precast Ltd, Springkerse Works, Springkerse Industrial Estate, Stirling, FK7 7SX Tel: (01786) 472191 Fax: (01786) 451284 E-mail: general@stirlingprecast.com

ARCHITECTURAL CONTRACTORS

Acclaim Fabrications, 7b Meadow Road, Reading, RG1 8LB Tel: 0118-939 3413 Fax: 0118-939 3413
James Aiken (Offshore) Ltd, Horizons Ho, 81 Waterloo Quay, Aberdeen, AB11 5DE Tel: (01224) 573322 Fax: (01224) 572666 E-mail: sales@aikenoffshore.com
Cowan Architects Ltd, 9-10 Old Stone Link, Ship Street, East Grinstead, West Sussex, RH19 4EF Tel: (01342) 410242 Fax: (01342) 313493 E-mail: info@cowan-architects.co.uk
Darnton Elgee Architects, Monk Fryston Hall, Monk Fryston, Leeds, LS25 5DU Tel: (01977) 681001 Fax: (01977) 681006 E-mail: email@darntonelgee.com
Mansell, Roman House, Granitehill Road, Aberdeen, AB16 7AW Tel: (01224) 717700 Fax: (01224) 698262 E-mail: info@mansell.plc.uk
▶ New Span Design & Build, 103 Kingsway, Chandler's Ford, Eastleigh, Hampshire, SO53 1FD Tel: (023) 8026 9944 Fax: (023) 8026 9940 E-mail: info@newspan.co.uk
▶ T P A Design Co. Ltd, 33a St Lukes Road, Maidenhead, Berkshire, SL6 7DN Tel: (01628) 412388 Fax: (01628) 412390 E-mail: sales@tpadesign.co.uk
▶ Vosper International Ltd, 7 Killermont View, Glasgow, G20 0TZ Tel: 0141-945 5529 E-mail: design@vosper.co.uk

ARCHITECTURAL FABRIC STRUCTURES

▶ Etc Design Ltd, 2 Carriers Fold, Church Road, Wombourne, Wolverhampton, WV5 9DH Tel: (01902) 898282 Fax: (01902) 898283 E-mail: enquiries@etcarchitects.co.uk
▶ Meliar Design, Lower Cwm Barns, Llanafan Fawr, Builth Wells, Powys, LD2 3SG Tel: 01597 860291 E-mail: info@meliar.com

ARCHITECTURAL FIBRE OPTIC LIGHTING

▶ Cristal Lighting, Priory Mill House, Leckhampstead Road, Akeley, Buckingham, MK18 5HG Tel: (01280) 860154 Fax: (01280) 860546 E-mail: sales@crystal-lighting-centre.com
▶ Scotaudio, Unit 2, Beta Centre, Stirling University Innovation Park, Stirling, FK9 4NF Tel: (01786) 442022 Fax: (01786) 458033 E-mail: andy@scotaudio.com

ARCHITECTURAL FIBREGLASS MOULDINGS

A & I Composites Ltd, Mile End Road, Colwick, Nottingham, NG4 2DW Tel: 0115-940 2228 Fax: 0115-940 2228
Exallot Ltd, Patent Drive, Moorcroft Business Park, Wednesbury, West Midlands, WS10 7XD Tel: 0121-506 7330 Fax: 0121-506 7333
G K Beaulah & Co. Ltd, 23 Park Street, Hull, HU2 8RU Tel: (01482) 223521 Fax: (01482) 216328 E-mail: info@beaulah.co.uk
Group Four Glass Fibre Co. Ltd, Unit 42 Church Road Business Centre, Church Road, Sittingbourne, Kent, ME10 3RS Tel: (01795) 429424 Fax: (01795) 476248 E-mail: info@groupfourglassfibre.co.uk
Logical Ltd, Unit 5 Avis Way, Newhaven, East Sussex, BN9 0DS Tel: (01273) 514146 Fax: (01273) 514146 E-mail: enquiries@logical-grp.co.uk
▶ M C Resources, Lune Industrial Estate, Lancaster, LA1 5QP Tel: (01524) 847272 Fax: (01524) 847878 E-mail: mcresources@tiscali.co.uk
Morrison Glass Fibre, Rose Hill Works, Rose Hill, Denton, Manchester, M34 3ZA Tel: 0161-336 0632 Fax: 0161-335 9852
Multitex G R P, Unit 5 Dolphin Industrial Estate, Salisbury, SP1 2NB Tel: (01722) 332139 Fax: (01722) 338458 E-mail: sales@multitex.co.uk
Salty Yacht Productions Ltd, Victoria Wharf, River Bank, Old Town Dock, Newport, Gwent, NP20 2BS Tel: (01633) 250652 Fax: (01633) 842267 E-mail: sales@saltyyachts.com
Tamworth Glass Fibre, Pooley Lane, Pooley Hall Farmhouse, Polesworth, Tamworth, Staffordshire, B78 1JA Tel: (01827) 331010 Fax: (01827) 330027 E-mail: m.hopkins267@ntlworld.com

ARCHITECTURAL GRANITE

▶ Cerrig Ltd, Glanydon Industrial Estate, Pwllheli, Gwynedd, LL53 5YT Tel: (01758) 612645 Fax: (01758) 612410 E-mail: sales@cerrig-granite.co.uk
▶ D Mcauley & Sons, Unit 1b Edenderry Industrial Estate, 326 Crumlin Road, Belfast, BT14 7EE Tel: (028) 9074 9797 Fax: (028) 9074 9398 E-mail: info@mcauleys.net
Alistair Mackintosh Ltd, Bannerley Road, Garretts Green Industrial Estate, Birmingham, B33 0SL Tel: 0121-784 6800 Fax: 0121-789 7068 E-mail: info@alistairmackintosh.co.uk

ARCHITECTURAL HARDWARE OR IRONMONGERS OR IRONMONGERY OR METALWORK

A Boyall Ltd, 187 High Street, Hampton Hill, Hampton, Middlesex, TW12 1NL Tel: (020) 8941 0880 Fax: (020) 8941 3718 E-mail: boyalls@ukonline.co.uk
A C Sissling Specialist Ironmongers Ltd, 20 Fitzwilliam Street, Bradford, West Yorkshire, BD4 7BL Tel: (01274) 200320 Fax: (01274) 220330 E-mail: sales@sissling-group.co.uk
A & H Brass, 209 Edgware Road, London, W2 1ES Tel: (020) 7706 2262 Fax: (020) 7402 0110 E-mail: sales@aandhbrass.co.uk
A Touch of Brass Ltd, 210 Fulham Road, London, SW10 9PJ Tel: (020) 7351 2255 Fax: (020) 7352 4682
▶ Access Hardware Ltd, Jewsons Ltd, The Slough, Spernal, Studley, Warwickshire, B80 7EN Tel: (01527) 852948 Fax: (01527) 854192 E-mail: sales@accesshardware.co.uk
Adams Rite Europe Ltd, 6 Moreton Industrial Estate, London Road, Swanley, Kent, BR8 8TZ Tel: (01322) 668024 Fax: (01322) 660996 E-mail: info@adamsrite.co.uk
Annstar Group Ltd, 57 Sutherland Road, London, E17 6BH Tel: (020) 8503 2323 Fax: (020) 8503 3947 E-mail: info@annstar.co.uk
B P S Dorline, Hermes Court, Hermes Close, Warwick, CV34 6NJ Tel: (01926) 332620 Fax: (01926) 332629 E-mail: bpsdorline@bandps.co.uk
▶ Beaver Architectural Ironmongery, Unit D 18 Imperial Way, Croydon, CR0 4RR Tel: (020) 8681 3939 Fax: (020) 8649 8213 E-mail: gary@beaverai.co.uk
Brass Tacks Fittings Ltd, 8 Kildare Close, Ruislip, Middlesex, HA4 9LG Tel: (020) 8866 8664 Fax: (020) 8866 8446 E-mail: sales@brasstacksfittings.co.uk
Build Centre, 555 South Street, Glasgow, G14 0QT Tel: 0141-954 5051 Fax: 0141-954 7322
Bunce's Home Hardware, 112-114 Chapel Road, Worthing, West Sussex, BN11 1BX Tel: (01903) 235321 Fax: (01903) 823279 E-mail: enquiries@bunce-co.co.uk
C B S (Midlands) Ltd, Kenilworth House, 118 Stourbridge Road, Dudley, West Midlands, DY1 2DP Tel: (01384) 254015 Fax: (01384) 456856
C F James Ltd, 68 Stoke Newington High Street, London, N16 7PA Tel: (020) 7254 5224 Fax: (020) 7254 3431 E-mail: cfjames@btconnect.com
C M D Ltd, Flixborough Industrial Estate, Ninth Avenue, Flixborough, Scunthorpe, South Humberside, DN15 8SL Tel: (01724) 851873 Fax: (01724) 874411 E-mail: cm.developments@virgin.net
▶ Cairney Hardware Ltd, 1 Distillery Lane, Edinburgh, EH11 2BD Tel: 0131-313 1303 Fax: 0131-313 1305 E-mail: enquiries@cairney.com
Campbell & Mabbs Liverpool Ltd, 1 Regent Street, Liverpool, L3 7BN Tel: 0151-236 1555 Fax: 0151-236 1698 E-mail: camabbs@aol.com
Cartwright Hardware, Cartwright House, Springwell Road, Leeds, LS12 1AX Tel: 0113-243 6931 Fax: 0113-242 1716 E-mail: sales@cartwrighthardware.co.uk
Chadwicks Liverpool Ltd, 62-64 Kitchen Street, Liverpool, L1 0AN Tel: 0151-709 3081 Fax: 0151-709 9115
Charles Kendrew Metal Workers Ltd, 33-35 Tower Street, Harrogate, North Yorkshire, HG1 1HS Tel: (01423) 502025 Fax: (01423) 531028 E-mail: enquiries@kendrews.co.uk
Chasmood Ltd, Unit 8 Weydown Industrial Estate, Haslemere, Surrey, GU27 1DW Tel: (01428) 641655 Fax: (01428) 641654 E-mail: info@chasmood.com
Frederick Cooper P.L.C., Great Bridge Street, West Bromwich, West Midlands, B70 0DJ Tel: 0121-521 1535 Fax: 0121-521 1536 E-mail: info@fredco.co.uk

ARCHITECTURAL HARDWARE OR IRONMONGERS OR IRONMONGERY OR METALWORK – *continued*

Croft Architectural Hardware Ltd, 23 Lower Lichfield Street, Willenhall, West Midlands, WV13 1QQ Tel: (01902) 606493 Fax: (01902) 606933 E-mail: sales@croft-arch.co.uk
Peter Crownshaw, St. Michaels Forge, Tenbury Wells, Worcestershire, WR15 8TG Tel: (01584) 811371 Fax: (01584) 811094
Cusden's, 104 Arlington Road, London, NW1 7HP Tel: (020) 7424 0349 Fax: (020) 7324 0352 E-mail: cusdens@aol.com
D F Wishart & Co. Ltd, St Clair St, Edinburgh, EH6 8LJ Tel: 0131-554 4393 Fax: 0131-553 7242 E-mail: sales@wishart.co.uk
Davis Architects Services Ltd, Units 1 & 2 Ropery Business Park, Anchor & Hope Lane, London, SE7 7RX Tel: (020) 8853 5997 Fax: (020) 8853 4137
Dorplan Architectural Ironmongers, 434-436 Mutton Lane, Potters Bar, Hertfordshire, EN6 3AT Tel: (01707) 647647 Fax: (01707) 647378
Dortrend International Ltd, Riverside Business Centre, Worcester Road, Stourport-on-Severn, Worcestershire, DY13 9BZ Tel: (01299) 827837 Fax: (01299) 827094 E-mail: sales@dortrend.co.uk
Era Products Ltd, Straight Road, Willenhall, West Midlands, WV12 5RA Tel: (01922) 490049 Fax: (01922) 494420 E-mail: bevans@era-security.com
Fairfields Supplies, Hambleden House, 8 Boulton Road, Reading, RG2 0NH Tel: (0800) 6346410 Fax: (0800) 6346409
Farmer Bros, 319 Fulham Road, London, SW10 9QL Tel: (020) 7351 0241 Fax: (020) 7351 4111
Franchi Locks & Tools Ltd, 278 Holloway Road, London, N7 6NE Tel: (020) 7607 2200 Fax: (020) 7700 4050 E-mail: info@franchi.co.uk
Furneaux Industrial Supplies Ltd, 5 Sinclair House, Hastings Street, London, WC1H 9PZ Tel: (020) 7387 8450 Fax: (020) 7388 0197 E-mail: furnlocks@fsbdial.co.uk
Gibbs & Dandy plc, 462 Bath Road, Slough, SL1 6BQ Tel: (01628) 604343 Fax: (01628) 600744 E-mail: slough@gibbsanddandy.com
Glenmarco Ltd, 189 Headstone Lane, Harrow, Middlesex, HA2 6ND Tel: (020) 8421 4025 Fax: (020) 8421 3643
Groupco Ltd, 18 Tresham Road, Orton Southgate, Peterborough, PE2 6SG Tel: (01733) 234750 Fax: (01733) 235246 E-mail: sales@groupcoltd.co.uk
▶ P.R. Hanman (Tools), The Market, Burwash Road, Heathfield, East Sussex, TN21 8RA Tel: (01435) 860760 E-mail: tools@hanman.fsnet.co.uk
Hoppe UK Ltd, Gailey Park, Gravelly Way, Standeford, Wolverhampton, WV10 7GW Tel: (01902) 484400 Fax: (01902) 484406
I R Laidlaw, The Building Centre, 26 Store Street, London, WC1E 7BT Tel: (020) 7436 0779 Fax: (020) 7436 0740 E-mail: infolondon@laidlaw.net
I R Laidlaw, Strawberry Lane Industrial Estate, Strawberry Lane, Willenhall, West Midlands, WV13 3RS Tel: (01902) 600400 Fax: (01902) 600490
Interhire Power Tool Services Ltd, Park Road, Ilkeston, Derbyshire, DE7 5DA Tel: 0115-930 6382 Fax: 0115-944 0407
Irm Bristol Ltd, Unit 1 2 Armstrong Court, Armstrong Way, Yate, Bristol, BS37 5NG Tel: (01454) 321311 Fax: (01454) 273411 E-mail: sales@irm-bristol.co.uk
J B Architectural Ironmongery Ltd, Avis Way, Newhaven, East Sussex, BN9 0DU Tel: (01273) 514961 Fax: (01273) 516764 E-mail: info@jbai.co.uk
J & M Hardware, 75 Scotland Road, Nelson, Lancashire, BB9 7UY Tel: (01282) 613460 Fax: (01282) 617928
J&T Group Ltd, PO Box 5 Victoria Works, Stoke-on-Trent, ST4 6HA Tel: (01782) 202545 Fax: (01782) 349449 E-mail: sales@storagebins.co.uk
John Monaghan (Midlands) Ltd, Unit 5 Cavendish, Lichfield Road Industrial Estate, Tamworth, Staffordshire, B79 7XH Tel: (01827) 302480 Fax: (01827) 62164 E-mail: info@monaghanmidlands.co.uk
▶ JOHN MONAGHAN (southern) Ltd, Units 24/25, Mount Pleasant Industrial Estate, Northam, Southampton, SO14 0SP Tel: (023) 8023 2238 Fax: (023) 8021 1218 E-mail: info@monaghansouthern.co.uk
▶ John Plank Ltd, 17-18 Haywards Place, Clerkenwell Green, London, EC1R 0EQ Tel: (020) 7608 0074 Fax: (020) 7608 0075 E-mail: sales@johnplanck.co.uk
John Smith & Co., PO Box 8, Aberdeen, AB11 5EA Tel: (01224) 586868 Fax: (01224) 590768 E-mail: sales@johnsmithaberdeen.co.uk
K C C, 20-21A Harbour Court, Heron Road, Sydenham Business Park, Belfast, BT3 9LE Tel: (028) 9046 9914 Fax: (028) 9046 9915 E-mail: sales@kcchardware.com
Kirby & Wells Ltd, 6 Benner Road, Pinchbeck, Spalding, Lincolnshire, PE11 3TZ Tel: (01775) 766886 Fax: (01775) 766885
Laidlaw Architectural Hardware, 7 Dakota Avenue, Salford, M50 2PU Tel: 0161-848 1700 Fax: 0161-872 9313 E-mail: info@laidlaw.net
Laidlaw Solutions Ltd, 4-5 Bonville Road, Bristol, BS4 5NF Tel: 0117-316 0460 Fax: 0117-316 0491 E-mail: gateshead@laidlaw.net
Laidlaw Solutions Ltd, T Y Cefnfar, Ocean Way, Cardiff, CF24 5PE Tel: (029) 2047 1808 Fax: (029) 2049 0250
Laidlaw Solutions Ltd, PO Box 15, Perth, PH1 3DU Tel: (01738) 620581 Fax: (01738) 633262
Lloyd Worrall London, Unit F21, Riverside Business Centre, Haldane Place, London, SW18 4UQ Tel: (020) 8874 4755 Fax: (020) 8874 4624 E-mail: sales@london.lloydworrall.co.uk
Lloyd Worrall Sheffield Ltd, 10 Fell Road, Sheffield, S9 2AL Tel: 0114-244 3350 Fax: 0114-244 4219 E-mail: sales@sheffield.lloydworrall.co.uk
Locks & Fittings Ltd, Unit 7-8 Rollingmill Business Park, Rollingmill Street, Walsall, WS2 9EQ Tel: (01922) 623200 Fax: (01922) 721086 E-mail: enquiries@locksandfittings.org.uk
M Marcus, 7 Blackbrook Industrial Estate, Peartree Lane, Dudley, West Midlands, DY2 0XW Tel: (01384) 457900 Fax: (01384) 457903 E-mail: info@m-marcus.com
▶ Marches Architectural Hardware, Ddole Road Industrial Estate, Llandrindod Wells, Powys, LD1 6DF Tel: (01597) 823822 Fax: (01597) 823821
Martin & Partners Ltd, 10-11 Regent Square, Northampton, NN1 2NQ Tel: (01604) 639466 Fax: (01604) 620552 E-mail: martin.partners@virgin.net
Moffett Thallon & Co. Ltd, 143 Northumberland Street, Belfast, BT13 2JF Tel: (028) 9032 2802 Fax: (028) 9024 1428 E-mail: info@moffett.demon.co.uk
P C P Gratings Ltd, Enterprise Drive, Four Ashes, Wolverhampton, WV10 7DF Tel: (01902) 791792 Fax: (01902) 791795 E-mail: sales@pcp.dk
P S L (Weir) Ltd, Ashcroft Road, Knowsley Industrial Estate North, Liverpool, L33 7TW Tel: 0151-547 2222 Fax: 0151-549 1060 E-mail: pslpool@hotmail.com
Parkside Group Ltd, 5 Willow Business Centre, 17 Willow Lane, Mitcham, Surrey, CR4 4NX Tel: (020) 8685 9685 Fax: (020) 8646 5096 E-mail: sales@parksidegrp.co.uk
Robert Pochin Ltd, 11 St Georges Way, Leicester, LE1 1SH Tel: 0116-251 5051 Fax: 0116-253 8829 E-mail: sales.enquiries@robertpochin.co.uk
Robert Pochin Ltd, Manor House Road, Long Eaton, Nottingham, NG10 1LR Tel: 0115-973 5155 Fax: 0115-946 1247 E-mail: sales.enquiries@robertpochin.co.uk
Poole Waite & Co. Ltd, 3 Clerkenwell Road, London, EC1M 5PE Tel: (020) 7253 8117 Fax: (020) 7490 0579 E-mail: sales@poolewaite.co.uk
▶ Q S Supplies, 72 Forest Road, Leicester, LE5 0DG Tel: 0116-251 0051 Fax: 0116-251 1611 E-mail: info@qssupplies.co.uk
Regis Reproduction Ltd, Unit 2 Station Road, Rowley Regis, Rowley Regis, West Midlands, B65 0JY Tel: 0121-561 5674 Fax: 0121-561 5680
South Western Supplies, Collett Way, Newton Abbot, Devon, TQ12 4PH Tel: (01626) 333900 Fax: (01626) 324297
Spiral Hardware Ltd, Unit 36, Wimbledon Avenue, Brandon, Suffolk, IP27 0NZ Tel: (01842) 816086 Fax: (01842) 813867 E-mail: info@spiralhardware.co.uk
▶ Temple Graphics & Hardware Supplies, 25 Temple Gardens, Rochester, Kent, ME2 2NQ Tel: (01634) 718924 Fax: (01634) 718924 E-mail: barry.hyder@btinternet.com
Till & Whitehead Ltd, Park House, 37 Ings Road, Osmondthorpe Lane, Leeds, LS9 9HG Tel: 0113-249 6641 Fax: 0113-248 8968 E-mail: leeds@tillwite.com
Trapex Hardware Ltd, Pindar Road, Hoddesdon, Hertfordshire, EN11 0DE Tel: (01992) 462150 Fax: (01992) 446736 E-mail: info@trapex.com
▶ Universal Hardware Supplies Direct Ltd, 1ADillwyn Road, Sketty, Swansea, SA2 9AQ Tel: (01792) 205050 Fax: (01792) 202255 E-mail: info@u-h-s.co.uk
Washington & Riley Ltd, 1 William Clowes Street, Stoke-on-Trent, ST6 3AR Tel: (01782) 834363 Fax: (01782) 834366 E-mail: info@washingtonandriley.ltd.uk
Yannedis Ltd, Riverside House Woodford Trading Estate, Southend Road, Woodford Green, Essex, IG8 8HQ Tel: (020) 8550 8833 Fax: (020) 8551 0026 E-mail: sales@yannedis.com

ARCHITECTURAL LIGHTING

Albany Metal Spinners, 18 Stirling Close, Washington, Tyne & Wear, NE38 8QD Tel: 0191-419 4588 Fax: 0191-416 3700 E-mail: sales@albanymetalspinners.co.uk
Autospin, Castle Trading Estate, Fareham, Hampshire, PO16 9SE Tel: (023) 9237 7737 Fax: (023) 9221 9544 E-mail: mariacrawley180@hotmail.com
Candela Traditional Lighting Ltd, 319 Long Acre, Birmingham, B7 5JT Tel: 0121-678 6700 Fax: 0121-678 6701 E-mail: sales@candela.co.uk
Designplan Lighting Ltd, 6 Wealdstone Road, Sutton, Surrey, SM3 9RW Tel: (020) 8254 2000 Fax: (020) 8644 4253 E-mail: info@designplan.co.uk
▶ Elder's Engineers, 9 Park CR, Edinburgh, EH16 6JD Tel: 0131-664 5176 Fax: 0131-664 5643
Firstlight Products Ltd, 22 Erica Road, Stacey Bushes, Milton Keynes, MK12 6HS Tel: (01908) 310221 Fax: (01908) 310229 E-mail: flp@firstlight-products.co.uk
Francis Searchlights, Union Road, Bolton, BL2 2HJ Tel: (01204) 527196 Fax: (01204) 558979 E-mail: sales@francis.co.uk
Graylands Trading Co., 38 Sherwood Road, Winnersh, Wokingham, Berkshire, RG41 5NJ Tel: 0118-989 0002 Fax: 0118-989 0003 E-mail: graylands@supernet.com
Illuma Lighting Ltd, 11a Sills Road, Castle Donington, Derby, DE74 2US Tel: (01332) 818200 Fax: (01332) 818222 E-mail: info@illuma.co.uk
▶ LED Colour Solutions Ltd, Titus House, 29 Saltaire Road, Shipley, West Yorkshire, BD18 3HH Tel: (01274) 609605 Fax: (01274) 531966 E-mail: samantha.crabtree@spacekraft.co.uk
Lighting Motions, 2 Slater Street, Oldham, OL9 6ES Tel: 0161-628 0098 Fax: 0161-620 7298 E-mail: sales@lightingmotions.com
▶ Lumino Ltd, Lumino House, Lovet Road, Harlow, Essex, CM19 5TB Tel: (01279) 635411 Fax: (01279) 626101 E-mail: info@lumino.co.uk
Malisa Lighting Ltd, Unit 4 Conqueror Court, Spilsby Road, Harold Hill, Romford, RM3 8SB Tel: (01708) 372221 Fax: (01708) 381354 E-mail: malisa@mabeys.co.uk
Noral Ltd, Unit 1 The Oaks, Mill Farm Courtyard, Stratford Road, Beechampton, Milton Keynes, MK19 6DS Tel: (01908) 561818 Fax: (01908) 569785 E-mail: lighting@noral-gb.co.uk
Universal Fibre Optics (Old Co) Ltd, 6 Home Place, Coldstream, Berwickshire, TD12 4DT Tel: (01890) 883416 Fax: (01890) 883062 E-mail: info@universal-fibre-optics.com

ARCHITECTURAL LOUVRES

▶ Avon Solar Control Ltd, Avon House, Kineton Road Industrial Estate, Southam, Warwickshire, CV47 0DR Tel: (01926) 818992 Fax: (01926) 811676 E-mail: enquiries@avonsolarcontrol.co.uk
▶ Renson Fabrications, Fairfax House, Bircholt Road, Maidstone, Kent, ME15 9SF Tel: (01622) 685658 Fax: (01622) 688762 E-mail: info@rensonuk.net

ARCHITECTURAL MEDIUM DENSITY FIBREBOARD (MDF) MOULDINGS

Fibercill, The Moorings, Hurst Business Park, Brierley Hill, West Midlands, DY5 1UX Tel: (01384) 482221 Fax: (01384) 482212 E-mail: mail@fibercill.com
Hoppings Softwood Products, Bones Lane, Newchapel, Lingfield, Surrey, RH7 6HR Tel: (01342) 844449 Fax: (01342) 844449 E-mail: sales@hoppings.co.uk
▶ Spa Laminates Limited, 59 Pepper Road, Leeds, LS10 2TH Tel: 0113-271 8311 Fax: 0113-270 3968 E-mail: info@spalaminates.co.uk

ARCHITECTURAL METALWORK BENDING

D M S Engineering Services, 32 Beverley Road, Oakengates, Telford, Shropshire, TF2 6SD Tel: (01952) 409836 Fax: (01952) 410873 E-mail: mikesarchet@blueyonder.co.uk
Proform Aluminium Bending Ltd, Unit 1 Boundry Court, Gilbert Way, Burma Road, Blidworth, Mansfield, Nottinghamshire, NG21 0RT Tel: (01623) 491926 Fax: (01623) 491927 E-mail: proformalu@btconnect.com

ARCHITECTURAL METALWORK FINISHING

D M S Engineering Services, 32 Beverley Road, Oakengates, Telford, Shropshire, TF2 6SD Tel: (01952) 409836 Fax: (01952) 410873 E-mail: mikesarchet@blueyonder.co.uk
Elgamec, Unit 9-11 Enterprise Industrial Estate, Station Road West, Ash Vale, Aldershot, Hampshire, GU12 5QJ Tel: (01252) 518177 Fax: (01252) 541331 E-mail: info@elgamec.com
Evans Turner Finishes Ltd, 200 Manor Road, Erith, Kent, DA8 2AD Tel: (01322) 346911 Fax: (01322) 332706 E-mail: sales@evans-turner.com
Stainless Equipment Co. (Metal Finishers) Ltd, Alma Road, Ponders End, Enfield, Middx, EN3 7BB Tel: (020) 8805 0884 Fax: (020) 8804 8167 E-mail: david@stainlesssteelpolishers.co.uk

ARCHITECTURAL METALWORK WELDING

A M C (Projects) Ltd, Unit 3B Pincents Kiln Industrial Park, Pincents Kiln, Reading, RG31 7SD Tel: 0118-932 3313 Fax: 0118-930 6163 E-mail: admin@amc.uk.net
radley fabrications, 16 St Michaels Drive, Roxwell, Chelmsford, CM1 4NU Tel: 01245 248983 Fax: 01245 248983 E-mail: jennick@mcgregor247.fsnet.co.uk

ARCHITECTURAL METALWORKERS OR FABRICATORS

A Hodgson Engineers & Smiths Ltd, 54 Guest Street, Leigh, Lancashire, WN7 2HD Tel: (01942) 673038 Fax: (01942) 673038 E-mail: hodgsoneng@fsnet.co.uk
A M P Metalworks, 837-839 Consort Road, London, SE15 2PR Tel: (020) 7277 5569 Fax: (020) 7635 6001 E-mail: sales@apmetalworks.co.uk
A W Jeffreys Southampton Ltd, 91-97 Dukes Road, Southampton, SO14 0ST Tel: (023) 8055 3730 Fax: (023) 8067 1345 E-mail: awj@awjefferys.co.uk
Adbeck Fabrications Ltd, Loomer Road Industrial Estate, Loomer Road, Chesterton, Newcastle, Staffordshire, ST5 7LB Tel: (01782) 565774 Fax: (01782) 565774 E-mail: adbeckfabs@aol.com
Admiral Welding Ltd, Aston Bury Farm, Aston, Stevenage, Hertfordshire, SG2 7EG Tel: (01438) 880309 Fax: (01438) 880174 E-mail: info@admiralwelding.co.uk
Alan Dawson Associates Ltd, Joseph Noble Road, Lillyhall Industrial Estate, Lillyhall, Workington, Cumbria, CA14 4JX Tel: (01900) 64433 Fax: (01900) 605911 E-mail: mail@adawson.co.uk
Alex J Cheetham Ltd, Morton Street, Failsworth, Manchester, M35 0BP Tel: 0161-681 1115 Fax: 0161-681 0339 E-mail: mark@alexjcheetham.co.uk
Alloy Fabweld Ltd, 5 Zone C Chelmsford Road Industrial Estate, Chelmsford Road, Dunmow, Essex, CM6 1HD Tel: (01371) 859544 Fax: (01371) 878608
Am PM Fabrications, Hatfield Cottage, Hardings Elms Road, Billericay, Essex, CM11 2UH Tel: (01268) 285115 Fax: (01268) 285117 E-mail: ampmfabrications@btconnect.com
Anvil Engineering, Aiskew Ironworks, Sandhill Lane, Bedale, North Yorkshire, DL8 1DU Tel: (01677) 427362 Fax: (01677) 427364 E-mail: info@anvileng.co.uk
Apollo Fabrications Ltd, Unit 20 Canalside Industrial Estate, Brettell Lane, Brierley Hill, West Midlands, DY5 3JU Tel: (01384) 484603 Fax: (01384) 484603 E-mail: ralph-apollo@supanet.com
Ark Site Fabrications, Unit 7b Greenhill Mills, Grange Road, Batley, West Yorkshire, WF17 6LH Tel: (01924) 420874 Fax: (01924) 359744 E-mail: brian@arksite.co.uk
Barrs Court Engineering Ltd, Netherwood Road, Rotherwas Industrial Estate, Hereford, HR2 6JU Tel: (01432) 353450 Fax: (01432) 353452 E-mail: paul@barrscourt.com
Bassett & Findley Ltd, Talbot Road North, Wellingborough, Northamptonshire, NN8 1QS Tel: (01933) 224898 Fax: (01933) 227731 E-mail: info@bassettandfindley.ltd.uk
Eddie Beedle Ltd, Unit 1 Jenning Street, Hull, HU8 7AN Tel: (01482) 323648 Fax: (01482) 211461
Bishop & Smith Stainless Fabrication, Unit 2 Thorn Business Park, Rotherwas, Hereford, HR2 6JT Tel: (01432) 342355 Fax: (01432) 352399E-mail: alan@bishop-smith.fsnet.co.uk
Broxap Dorothea, Rowhurst Industrial Estate, Chesterton, Newcastle, Staffordshire, ST5 6BD Tel: (01782) 564411 Fax: (01782) 565357 E-mail: sales@broxap.co.uk
Burbage Gates Ltd, Sapcote Road, Burbage, Hinckley, Leicestershire, LE10 2AU Tel: (01455) 613844 Fax: (01455) 611333 E-mail: sales@burbagegates.co.uk
C M D Ltd, Flixborough Industrial Estate, Ninth Avenue, Flixborough, Scunthorpe, South Humberside, DN15 8SL Tel: (01724) 851873 Fax: (01724) 874411 E-mail: cm.developments@virgin.net
J. Carroll & Sons, Unit 14, Lyon Gate Enterprise Park, Mouldon Road, Mitcham, Surrey, CR4 4NY Tel: (020) 8640 5424 Fax: (020) 8646 0990 E-mail: lee@jcarrolandsons.fsnet.co.uk
The Cast Iron Company Ltd, 8 Old Lodge Place, Twickenham, TW1 1RQ Tel: (020) 8744 9992 Fax: (020) 8744 1121 E-mail: info@castiron.co.uk
Ceejay Maintenance Ltd, Unit 49 Fairways Business Park, Lammas Road, London, E10 7QB Tel: (020) 8518 7644 Fax: (020) 8518 7678
Clifford Chapman Metalworks Ltd, Armstrong Estate, District 2, Washington, Tyne & Wear, NE37 1PB Tel: 0191-417 3135 Fax: 0191-417 8519 E-mail: email@cliffordchapman.com
Charles Kendrew Metal Workers Ltd, 33-35 Tower Street, Harrogate, North Yorkshire, HG1 1HS Tel: (01423) 502025 Fax: (01423) 531028 E-mail: enquiries@kendrews.co.uk
Claydon Architectural Ltd, 11-12 Claydon Industrial Park, Great Blakenham, Ipswich, IP6 0NL Tel: (01473) 831000 Fax: (01473) 832154 E-mail: sales@cam-ltd.co.uk
Claydon Associates Ltd, Edison Road, Rabans Lane Industrial Area, Aylesbury, Buckinghamshire, HP19 8TE Tel: (01296) 434611 Fax: (01296) 436334 E-mail: associates@claydon-group.co.uk
Clow Group Ltd, 90 Camlachie Street, Glasgow, G31 4AD Tel: 0141-556 6324 Fax: 0141-551 9087 E-mail: engineering@clowgroup.co.uk

ARCHITECTURAL METALWORKERS OR FABRICATORS – *continued*

Coates Holdings Ltd, 3 Brindley Road, Cardiff, CF11 8TX Tel: (029) 2034 4554 Fax: (029) 2034 4545 E-mail: coates-co@fsmail.net

▶ W. & D. Cole Ltd, Ashford Road, Bethersden, Ashford, Kent, TN26 3AT Tel: (01233) 820240 Fax: (01233) 820805 E-mail: emailus@wdcole.com

Control Waterjet Cutting, Unit 18 Telford Crescent, Speedwell Industrial Estate, Staveley, Chesterfield, Derbyshire, S43 3PF Tel: (01246) 284000 Fax: (01246) 284003 E-mail: sales@controlwaterjet.co.uk

Crofton Engineering Ltd, Cambridge Road, Linton, Cambridge, CB21 4NN Tel: (01223) 892138 Fax: (01223) 893547 E-mail: info@crofton-eng.co.uk

Peter Crownshaw, St. Michaels Forge, Tenbury Wells, Worcestershire, WR15 8TG Tel: (01584) 811371 Fax: (01584) 811094

Custom Metalwork Co Ltd, Eagle House, Essex Road, Hoddesdon, Hertfordshire, EN11 0DN Tel: (01992) 445151 Fax: (01992) 441884 E-mail: info@custom-metalwork.co.uk

D J Engineering, 4 Camp Industrial Estate, Rycote Lane, Milton Common, Thame, Oxfordshire, OX9 2NP Tel: (01844) 278749 Fax: (01844) 278749 E-mail: djjjeff@aol.com

D K O Designs, 66 Georges Road, London, N7 8HX Tel: (020) 7607 2653 Fax: (020) 7607 0515

D M S Engineering Services, 32 Beverley Road, Oakengates, Telford, Shropshire, TF2 6SD Tel: (01952) 409836 Fax: (01952) 410873 E-mail: mikesarchet@blueyonder.co.uk

Delta Balustrades, Belpher Road, Stockport, Cheshire, SK4 3QW Tel: 0161-947 4747

Dowlings Ltd, Duttons Farm, Bangors Road South, Iver, Buckinghamshire, SL0 0AY Tel: (01753) 630653 Fax: (0870) 2201684 E-mail: dowlingsltd@aol.com

Drawn Metal Ltd, 50 Swinnow Lane, Leeds, LS13 4NE Tel: 0113-256 5661 Fax: 0113-239 3194 E-mail: sales@drawnmetal.co.uk

Elder Repetition Sheet Metal Ltd, 30 Oxford Road, Denham, Uxbridge, Middlesex, UB9 4DQ Tel: (01895) 258968 Fax: (01895) 252651 E-mail: sales@eldersheetmetal.co.uk

Elite Metalcraft, 9 Walmgate Road, Perivale, Greenford, Middlesex, UB6 7LH Tel: (020) 8810 5555 Fax: (020) 8810 5133 E-mail: sales@elitemetalcraft.co.uk

Environmental Technology Ltd, Entech House, London Road, Woolmer Green, Knebworth, Hertfordshire, SG3 6JR Tel: (01438) 812812 Fax: (01438) 814224 E-mail: admin@etl-entech.co.uk

Evans Turner Finishes Ltd, 200 Manor Road, Erith, Kent, DA8 2AD Tel: (01322) 346911 Fax: (01322) 332706 E-mail: sales@evans-turner.com

Expertplan Ltd, 471-473 The Arches, Dereham Place, London, EC2A 3HJ Tel: (020) 7739 1080 Fax: (020) 7739 9384

F & J Hauck Ltd, Linney Lane, Shaw, Oldham, OL2 8HB Tel: (01706) 848797 Fax: (01706) 844973

Fabrenco Ltd, Wilton Road, Humberston, Grimsby, South Humberside, DN36 4AW Tel: (01472) 814845 Fax: (01472) 210412 E-mail: fabrenco@quista.net

Fellows, 1 Wattville Road, Smethwick, West Midlands, B66 2NU Tel: 0121-555 8550 Fax: 0121-555 8660 E-mail: trevor@hsfellowsltd.com

Forge Fabrications Ltd, The Street, Lyng, Norwich, NR9 5QZ Tel: (01603) 872088 Fax: (01603) 872744 E-mail: enquiries@forgefabrications.co.uk

Fox Architectural Ltd, Providence Street, Stourbridge, West Midlands, DY9 8HS Tel: (01384) 424744 Fax: (01384) 424745

Richard Fox & Associates, 8-28 Luton Avenue, Croydon, CR0 2BP Tel: (020) 8683 3331 Fax: (020) 8683 2223 E-mail: richard@foxsilver.net

▶ G L W Engineering & Construction, Unit 3 Wisbech Business Centre, Oldfield Lane, Friday Bridge, Wisbech, Cambridgeshire, PE14 0NX Tel: (01945) 464637 Fax: (07000) 785497 E-mail: geoff@glwengineering.co.uk

A.A. Gates Ltd, Culver Garden Centre, Cattlegate Road, Crews Hill, Enfield, Middlesex, EN2 9DS Tel: (020) 8367 3500 Fax: (020) 8342 1115 E-mail: argonarc@aol.com

Glazzard (Dudley) Ltd, The Washington Centre, Netherton, Dudley, West Midlands, DY2 9RE Tel: (01384) 233151 Fax: (01384) 250224 E-mail: acg@glazzard.co.uk

A.K. Goymer & Co. Ltd, Units 2-4, Hazlegreen Works, 62 Edward Road, New Barnet, Barnet, Hertfordshire, EN4 8AZ Tel: (020) 8440 2241 Fax: (020) 8441 8558 E-mail: admin@akgoymer.co.uk

Greaves Art Metalwork Ltd, Ireland Close, Staveley, Chesterfield, Derbyshire, S43 3PE Tel: (01246) 280672 Fax: (01246) 280673

Guilform Ltd, 5 Alban Park Industrial Estate, Hatfield Road, St. Albans, Hertfordshire, AL4 0JJ Tel: (01727) 841111 Fax: (01727) 832710

William Hawkes Ltd, 183 & 184 High St, Deritend, Birmingham, B12 0LH Tel: 0121-772 2694 Fax: 0121-772 2694

Hills Of Shoeburyness Ltd, 17 Towerfield Road, Shoeburyness, Southend-on-Sea, SS3 9QL Tel: (01702) 296321 Fax: (01702) 297072 E-mail: sales@hillsofshoeburyness.com

Howard Cole Developments Ltd, 4 Peterborough Road, Crowland, Peterborough, PE6 0BA Tel: (01733) 211351 Fax: (01733) 211441

Hubbard Architectural Metalwork Ltd, 3 Hurricane Way, Norwich, NR6 6HS Tel: (01603) 424817 Fax: (01603) 487158 E-mail: tony.hubbard@hubbardsmetalwork.co.uk

I D E SS Ltd, 3 West Road, Harlow, Essex, CM20 2BQ Tel: (01279) 400140 Fax: (01279) 400150

Ilford Engineering Co. Ltd, Bentalls, Basildon, Essex, SS14 3BY Tel: (01268) 526756 Fax: (01268) 531485

J A G Services Ltd, 13 Reform Road, Maidenhead, Berkshire, SL6 8BY Tel: (01628) 670909 Fax: (01628) 672016 E-mail: gstuart@jagservices.fsnet.co.uk

J Colburn, Aldrington Basin South, Basin Road South, Portslade, Brighton, BN41 1WF Tel: (01273) 413190 Fax: (01273) 423684

J Hill & Co. Ltd, Charlotte St, Melton Mowbray, Leicestershire, LE13 1NA Tel: (01664) 562219 Fax: (01664) 410258 E-mail: sales@hilltrident.co.uk

J S M Engineering Ltd, Units 5-7 Humber Works, Humber Road, Beeston, Nottingham, NG9 2ET Tel: 0115-922 3849 Fax: 0115-922 3865 E-mail: sales@jsmeng.com

▶ JayWolfe, 64 Kingsley Road, Northampton, NN2 7BL Tel: 01604 821066 E-mail: jay.wolfe@ntlworld.com

K B S Fabrications, 2b Vulcan Works, Leckhampton Road, Cheltenham, Gloucestershire, GL53 0AL Tel: (01242) 572507 Fax: (01242) 572507

Kilmarnock Engineers, Spittalhill Works, Ayr Road, Kilmarnock, Ayrshire, KA1 5NX Tel: (01563) 830198 Fax: (01563) 830692

Kimber Engineering Ltd, Arisdale Avenue, South Ockendon, Essex, RM15 5DP Tel: (01708) 852469 Fax: (01708) 853228 E-mail: info@kimbereng.co.uk

L M Engineering Services Ltd, Unit 226D, Redwither Industrial Complex, Wrexham, Clwyd, LL13 9XU Tel: (01978) 660111 Fax: (01978) 660227 E-mail: steel@lmeng.fsbusiness.co.uk

Lake, Muckley & Co. Ltd, The Stable, Lillyfee Farm, Lillyfee Farm Lane, Wooburn Green, High Wycombe, Buckinghamshire, HP10 0LL Tel: (01494) 673632 Fax: (01494) 673632

Letchworth Steel Construction, 29 Jubilee Trading Estate, Jubilee Road, Letchworth Garden City, Hertfordshire, SG6 1NE Tel: (01462) 480080 Fax: (01462) 481191 E-mail: lesco@aol.com

B. Levy & Co. (Patterns) Ltd, 37 Churton Street, London, SW1V 2LT Tel: (020) 7834 1073 Fax: (020) 7630 8673 E-mail: sales@blevy.com

Littlehampton Welding Ltd, S Riverside Industrial Estate, Bridge Road, Littlehampton, West Sussex, BN17 5DF Tel: (01903) 721555 Fax: (01903) 726805 E-mail: lhw@lhwelding.co.uk

Locker Wire Weavers, Farrell Street, Warrington, WA1 2WW Tel: (01925) 406600 Fax: (01925) 444386 E-mail: sales@lockerwire.co.uk

Loughboro Designs Ltd, Sandy Lane North, Wallington, Surrey, SM6 8JX Tel: (020) 8640 4343 Fax: (020) 8647 2855 E-mail: sales@loughboro-designs.co.uk

M F B Manufacturing Ltd, 7a The Stirling Centre, Market Deeping, Peterborough, PE6 8EQ Tel: 01778 343110

M G B Press Break Sections Ltd, Dawley Brook Road, Kingswinford, West Midlands, DY6 7BD Tel: (01384) 400717 Fax: (01384) 400747

M I W Fabrications Ltd, Marmi Works, 23 Grafton Road, Croydon, CR0 3RP Tel: (020) 8681 5435 Fax: (020) 8681 2839 E-mail: info@miwfabrication.co.uk

M & K Fabrication, Hillsdene, Clockhouse Lane, Romford, RM5 2RR Tel: (01708) 769004 Fax: (01708) 769005

Meltcharm Ltd, 4 Enterprise Works, Lockfield Avenue, Enfield, Middlesex, EN3 7PX Tel: (020) 8804 5779 Fax: (020) 8443 3814

Metalcraft Tottenham Ltd, 6-40 Durnford Street, London, N15 5NQ Tel: (020) 8802 1715 Fax: (020) 8802 1258 E-mail: sales@makingmetalwork.com

Metalways Ltd, 20 Churchill Way, Fleckney, Leicester, LE8 8UD Tel: 0116-240 3148 Fax: 0116-240 3013 E-mail: erica@metalwaysltd.com

Midas Technologies, Unit A Roundhouse Close, Fengate, Peterborough, PE1 5TA Tel: (01733) 342600 Fax: (01733) 346672 E-mail: sales@midastech.co.uk

▶ M-Tech Engineering, 1 Third Avenue, Greasley Street, Nottingham, NG6 8ND Tel: 0115-979 4448 Fax: 0115-979 4449 E-mail: matt@mtechengineering.co.uk

Nci, 2 Nelsons Lane, Hurst, Reading, RG10 0RR Tel: 0118-934 5316 Fax: 0118-934 2010 E-mail: info@nciservices.co.uk

Neptune Fabrications Ltd, 5 Ibrox Industrial Estate, Carmichael Street, Glasgow, G51 2QU Tel: 0141-427 3773 Fax: 0141-427 3703 E-mail: nepfab@btconnect.co.uk

On Site Services Gravesend Ltd, 1 Wharf Road, Gravesend, Kent, DA12 2RU Tel: (01474) 321552 Fax: (01474) 357778 E-mail: enquiries@onsiteservicesgravesend.co.uk

Joseph Percival & Co., Shawcross Street, Stockport, Cheshire, SK1 3EZ Tel: 0161-480 3858 Fax: 0161-480 7394

Perry & Co Hinges Ltd, Doulton Road, Cradley Heath, West Midlands, B64 5QW Tel: (01384) 414000 Fax: (01384) 411100 E-mail: aperry@hinges.co.uk

Peter S Neale, Clays Road, Sling, Coleford, Gloucestershire, GL16 8LJ Tel: (01594) 837309 Fax: (01594) 835363 E-mail: sales@peter-s-neale.demon.co.uk

Pollards Fyrespan, Units 3-5 Haslemere Business Centre, Lincoln Way, Enfield, Middlesex, EN1 1AY Tel: (020) 8443 5511 Fax: (020) 8443 3804 E-mail: info@pollardsfyrespan.co.uk

Richard Quinnell Ltd, Rowhurst Forge, Oxshott Road, Leatherhead, Surrey, KT22 0EN Tel: (01372) 375148 Fax: (01372) 386516 E-mail: rjquinnell@aol.com

radley fabrications, 16 St Michaels Drive, Roxwell, Chelmsford, CM1 4NU Tel: 01245 248983 Fax: 01245 248983 E-mail: jennick@mcgregor247.fsnet.co.uk

Renzland Forge Ltd, 83A London Road, Copford, Colchester, CO6 1LG Tel: (01206) 210212 Fax: (01206) 211290

Roberts Engineering, Bergen Way, Hull, HU7 0YQ Tel: (01482) 838240 Fax: (01482) 830697 E-mail: admin@robertsengineering.co.uk

Robertson Failsworth Ltd, Mersey Road North, Failsworth, Manchester, M35 9FF Tel: 0161-681 2469 Fax: 0161-688 0389

S T G Fabrications Ltd, Monument Way East, Woking, Surrey, GU21 5LY Tel: (01483) 769222 Fax: (01483) 769666 E-mail: stgfab@btclick.com

Sheetfabs (Nottingham) Ltd, Nottingham Road, Attenborough, Beeston, Nottingham, NG9 6DR Tel: 0115-925 8101 Fax: 0115-943 0872 E-mail: sheetfabs@sheetfabs.co.uk

Singer & James Ltd, 33 Roebuck Road, Ilford, Essex, IG6 3TZ Tel: (020) 8500 4115 Fax: (020) 8501 2456 E-mail: info@singerandjames.co.uk

Sovereign Stainless Fabrications Ltd, Canal Works, Cadman St, Sheffield, S4 7ZG Tel: 0114-276 9192 Fax: 0114-276 3700 E-mail: ssfl@sovereign-stainless.co.uk

Stace Yates Ltd, Unit 24 Bamfurlong Industrial Park, Staverton, Cheltenham, Gloucestershire, GL51 6SX Tel: (01452) 713722 Fax: (01452) 713282

Stackwell Forge, Front Road, Parson Drove, Wisbech, Cambridgeshire, PE13 4JQ Tel: (01945) 700666 Fax: (01945) 701242 E-mail: sales@stackwellforge.com

Staircase & Balustrades Ltd, Slaney Street, Oakengates, Telford, Shropshire, TF2 6ET Tel: (01952) 610370 Fax: (01952) 610370

Steel Appeal, Rear Of 116-118 Highfield Road, Blackpool, FY4 2JF Tel: (01253) 341225 Fax: (01253) 405378 E-mail: angleace@btconnect.com

Steelock Engineering Ltd, Unit 42 Pioneer Mills, Milltown Street, Radcliffe, Manchester, M26 1WN Tel: 0161-724 4066 Fax: 0161-724 4066

Stronga Ltd, Ashendene Farm, White Stubbs Lane, Bayford, Hertford, SG13 8PZ Tel: (01992) 519000 Fax: (01992) 519011 E-mail: info@stronga.co.uk

Structural Stairways Ltd, The Premier Estate, Leys Road, Brierley Hill, West Midlands, DY5 3UP Tel: (01384) 79256 Fax: (01384) 482412 E-mail: metalwork@stairways18.fsnet.co.uk

▶ Sunbeam Woodworks Ltd, 17 & 21 Sunbeam Road, Park Royal, London, NW10 6JP Tel: (020) 8357 1000 Fax: (020) 8357 1021 E-mail: admin@sunbeamgroup.com

Taylor & Russell Ltd, Stonebridge Mill, Preston Road, Longridge, Preston, PR3 3AN Tel: (01772) 782295 Fax: (01772) 785341

Thames Wire Production Ltd, Unit 11A Worton Hall, Worton Road, Isleworth, Middlesex, TW7 6ER Tel: (020) 8560 4936 Fax: (020) 8569 8145 E-mail: thameswire@btconnect.com

Thanet-Ware Kent Ltd, Ellington Works, Princes Road, Ramsgate, Kent, CT11 7RZ Tel: (01843) 591076 Fax: (01843) 586198

Thing Ama Jigs Ltd, 136 Oyster Lane, Byfleet, West Byfleet, Surrey, KT14 7JQ Tel: (01932) 340764 Fax: (01932) 351280

Thomson Pettie, Canal Bank Estate, Seabegs Road, Bonnybridge, Stirlingshire, FK4 2BP Tel: (01324) 815747 Fax: (01324) 819072

▶ Tom Lee, Unit 6 Littleton Trading Estate, Littleton Lane, Shepperton, Middlesex, TW17 0NF Tel: 01932 569939 Fax: 01932 569939E-mail: info@media-construction.co.uk

Weller Patents Development, 1-8 Grand Parade Mews Rear of, 96-110 Upper Richmond Road, London, SW15 2SP Tel: (020) 8788 6684 Fax: (020) 8788 4669

Wrought Art, 7 Gordon Road, Derby, DE23 6WR Tel: (01332) 340563 Fax: (01332) 200234

ARCHITECTURAL MODELS

3d Services Ltd, The Studio, 142 Main Street, Yaxley, Peterborough, PE7 3LB Tel: (01733) 243552 Fax: (01733) 243182

Architectural Models Ltd, 275-281 King Street, London, W6 9LZ Tel: (020) 8748 6110 Fax: (020) 8741 3719 E-mail: arcmodels@btinternet.com

Betrix Industrial Models Ltd, 18-20 Waterloo Road, Stockport, Cheshire, SK1 3BD Tel: 0161-477 1766 Fax: 0161-474 7052 E-mail: betrixmodels@aol.com

Concept Creative Services Ltd, Unit 1, Baird House, Dudley Innovation Centre, Pensnett Trading Estate, Kingswinford, West Midlands, DY6 7YA Tel: (01384) 400161 Fax: (01384) 400190 E-mail: sales@concept-models.com

Confluence Creative, Unit 23, Merryhills Enterprise Park, Park Lane, Wolverhampton, WV10 9TJ Tel: (01902) 862601 Fax: (01902) 862602 E-mail: contact@confluencecreative.co.uk

En Aid Design Workshop, Wassage Way, Hampton Lovett, Droitwich, Worcestershire, WR9 0NX Tel: (01905) 451501 Fax: (01905) 771771 E-mail: enaid@btclick.com

Robert Farrow & Associates, 7 Plough Lane, Field Lane, Teddington, Middlesex, TW11 9BN Tel: (020) 8943 4743 Fax: (020) 8943 9383 E-mail: models@rfarrow.fsbusiness.co.uk

Forvm Designs, 8 Bucklers Close, Warden, Sheerness, Kent, ME12 4PT Tel: (01795) 511100 Fax: (01795) 511734 E-mail: forvmdesigns@aol.com

Hamlin Model Making Ltd, Old Tractor Shed, Welsh Road, Offchurch, Leamington Spa, Warwickshire, CV33 9BE Tel: (01926) 614147 Fax: (01926) 612899 E-mail: sales@hamlinrpd.co.uk

Model Making & Graphic Services Ltd, 9 Bath Buildings, Montpelier, Bristol, BS6 5PT Tel: 0117-944 6050 Fax: 0117-944 5973 E-mail: mmgsltd@aol.com

▶ P R Designs, Tong Lane Bus Centre, Tong Lane, Whitworth, Rochdale, Lancashire, OL12 8BE Tel: (01706) 854264 Fax: (01706) 854264 E-mail: prdesignssales@timewarpuk.net

R P M Model Making, 3 Station Approach, Wendover, Aylesbury, Buckinghamshire, HP22 6BN Tel: (01296) 622625 Fax: (01296) 625755 E-mail: enquiries@rpm.modelmakers.co.uk

Rainford Models Ltd, Bingswood Industrial Estate, Whaley Bridge, High Peak, Derbyshire, SK23 7LY Tel: (01663) 719119 Fax: (01663) 719109 E-mail: sales@rainfordmodels.co.uk

Sussex Model Makers, 14 Hertford Close, Bognor Regis, West Sussex, PO21 5SF Tel: (01243) 841862

Thorp Modelmakers Ltd, Whitmore Lane, Sunningdale Village, Ascot, Berkshire, SL5 0NS Tel: (01344) 876776 Fax: (01344) 876583 E-mail: thorp@atomltd.com

Unit 22 Model Makers, 7 Cubitt Street, London, WC1X 0LN Tel: (020) 7278 3872 Fax: (020) 7837 8372 E-mail: mail@unit22.co.uk

York Model Making & Display Ltd, Unit 13, The Bull Commercial Centre, Stockton On The Forest, York, YO32 9LE Tel: (01904) 400358 Fax: (01904) 400358 E-mail: info@yorkmodelmaking.com

ARCHITECTURAL OR BUILDING TRADE WOODWORK

Mike Baker Timber Merchants, Boston Industrial Estate, Power Station Road, Rugeley, Staffordshire, WS15 2HS Tel: (01889) 583306 Fax: (01889) 575263

Beard Evans Joinery, Shepherd Road, Gloucester, GL2 5EL Tel: (01452) 423123 Fax: (01452) 501055 E-mail: sales@beardevansjoinery.co.uk

Norex Forest Products, Walton Street, Walton on the Hill, Tadworth, Surrey, KT20 7RR Tel: (01737) 814567 Fax: (01737) 217524 E-mail: sales@norex.co.uk

Richard Cullinan Joinery Ltd, 8 Ferrier Industrial Estate, Ferrier Street, London, SW18 1SW Tel: (020) 8871 0029 Fax: (020) 8871 0020 E-mail: richard@rcjoinery.co.uk

Rte UK Ltd, 101a Hall Farm Road, Benfleet, Essex, SS7 5JW Tel: (01268) 569393 Fax: (01268) 751753 E-mail: rte-uk@lineone.net

S R S Joinery High Wycombe Ltd, Wycombe Lane, Wooburn Green, High Wycombe, Buckinghamshire, HP10 0HE Tel: (01628) 520893 Fax: (01628) 810526

Symm & Co. Ltd, Osney Mead, Oxford, OX2 0EQ Tel: (01865) 254900 Fax: (01865) 254935 E-mail: mailbox@symm.co.uk

Vinnell & Son, 6 West Street, Great Gransden, Sandy, Bedfordshire, SG19 3AT Tel: (01767) 677267

Willey & Bunker Ltd, Park Avenue Industrial Estate, Sundon Park Road, Luton, LU3 3BP Tel: (01582) 574382 Fax: (01582) 490043 E-mail: willey&bunker@itnet.co.uk

ARCHITECTURAL OR DECORATIVE CERAMICS

Acacia Studio, PO Box 400, Crewe, CW3 9FL Tel: (01782) 752575 Fax: (01782) 752575

Broadland Ceramics, 8 Moores Industrial Estate, High Street, Stalham, Norwich, NR12 9AN Tel: (01692) 582528 Fax: (01692) 583403 E-mail: sales@broadlandceramics.co.uk

Caramex Ltd, PO Box 2599, Bishop's Stortford, Hertfordshire, CM23 2AQ Tel: (01279) 506895 Fax: (01279) 501454

Ceramic Choice, Unit 12 Mossedge Industrial Estate, Moss Road, Linwood, Paisley, Renfrewshire, PA3 3HR Tel: (01505) 336644 Fax: (01505) 335138

Ceramic Decals Ltd, Anderton Works, Port Street, Stoke-on-Trent, ST6 3PF Tel: (01782) 838000 Fax: (01782) 822993 E-mail: maxine@ceramicdetails.co.uk

Ceramic Gas Products Ltd, Albion Works, Uttoxeter Road, Stoke-on-Trent, ST3 1PH Tel: (01782) 599922 Fax: (01782) 598037 E-mail: joan@ceramicgasproducts.co.uk

▶ Ceramica Blue, 10 Blenheim Cresent, London, W11 1NN Tel: (020) 7727 0288 Fax: (020) 7221 6694 E-mail: shop@ceramicablue.co.uk

Ceramics Cafe, 6 Argyle Road, London, W13 8AB Tel: (020) 8810 4422 Fax: (020) 8810 5593

ARCHITECTURAL OR DECORATIVE CERAMICS – *continued*

Ceramiks, Hadfield Road, Cardiff, CF11 8AQ Tel: (0808) 1555629 Fax: (029) 2022 0559 E-mail: ceramiks@comptongroup.com
City Tiles Contracts Ltd, 73 Dean Court Road, Rottingdean, Brighton, BN2 7DL Tel: (01273) 390777 Fax: (01273) 390888
Claystyle Technology & Design, Mica Close, Tamworth, Staffordshire, B77 4DR Tel: (01827) 316696 Fax: (01827) 316697
Craig Bragdy Ltd, 7 Colomendy Industrial Estate, Rhyl Road, Denbigh, Clwyd, LL16 5TA Tel: (01745) 815656 Fax: (01745) 814488 E-mail: cbd@cbdmurals.co.uk
Crieff Pottery, Muthill Road, Crieff, Perthshire, PH7 4HQ Tel: (01764) 655081 Fax: (01764) 655081 E-mail: enquiries@crieff.co.uk
Crystal Ceramics Ltd, Unit 14A Whitebridge Industrial Estate, Whitebridge Lane, Stone, Staffordshire, ST15 8LQ Tel: (01785) 811545 Fax: (01785) 811545
Eastern Glazed Ceramics Ltd, Tile House, Eversley Road, Norwich, NR6 6TA Tel: (01603) 423391 Fax: (01603) 789040 E-mail: enquiries@egctiles.co.uk
Edinburgh Ceramics, 46 Balcarres Street, Edinburgh, EH10 5JQ Tel: 0131-452 8145 Fax: 0131-452 8145 E-mail: sales@tiles-by-artists.co.uk
Esmalglass (UK) Ltd, Eastfields Road, Dovefields Industrial Estate, Uttoxeter, Staffordshire, ST14 8AL Tel: (01889) 567277 Fax: (01889) 567892 E-mail: davidjohnson@esmalglass.co.uk
G G Ceramics, Newport Business Park, Audley Road, Newport, Shropshire, TF10 7DP Tel: (01952) 814071 Fax: (01952) 813025
Great Yarmouth Pottery, 18-19 Trinity Place, Great Yarmouth, Norfolk, NR30 3HA Tel: (01493) 850585
Harford Ceramics, Susan Clough Designs, 13 The Paddocks, Burke Road, Totnes, Devon, TQ9 5XT Tel: (01803) 864780 Fax: (01803) 862036
Helen Bull Ceramics Ltd, 4 Alexandria Industrial Estate, Moor Lane, Widnes, Cheshire, WA8 7AE Tel: 0151-420 7963 Fax: 0151-420 7963
I C Ceramics UK Ltd, 21 Dovedale Road, Liverpool, L18 5EP Tel: 0151-280 6732 Fax: 0151-280 6742
Image 90, Unit 12 Far Green Industrial Estate, Chell Street, Stoke-on-Trent, ST1 6AZ Tel: (01782) 215531 Fax: (01782) 215533
K Eardley, Cockpit Yard, Northington Street, London, WC1N 2NP Tel: (020) 7916 5941 Fax: (020) 7916 2455
Kirkholme Collectables, Main Street, Brandesburton, Driffield, North Humberside, YO25 8RL Tel: (01964) 543686 Fax: (01964) 543895 E-mail: sales@kirkholmecollectables.co.uk
Omegaslate UK Ltd, 2 Chirk Close, Kidderminster, Worcestershire, DY10 1YG Tel: (01562) 755824 Fax: (01562) 742979 E-mail: info@omegaslate.com
Sally Bourne Interiors, 10 Middle Lane, London, N8 8PL Tel: (020) 8340 3333 Fax: (020) 8340 9333
Stoltzman & Thomas Sculptural Ceramics, Unit F21 Park Hall Road Trading Estate, 40 Martell Road, London, SE21 8EN Tel: (020) 8670 6464 Fax: (020) 8670 6464 E-mail: stoltzmanthomas@onetel.com
Stone The Crows, Callywhite Lane, Dronfield, Derbyshire, S18 2XR Tel: (01246) 299800 Fax: (01246) 299809 E-mail: enquiries@stonethecrows.co.uk
Tingewick Pottery Ltd, Upper Street, Tingewick, Buckingham, MK18 4QJ Tel: (01280) 848250 Fax: (01280) 848250

ARCHITECTURAL OR RESTORATION MARBLE CONTRACTORS AND WORKERS

A Andrews & Sons Ltd, 324-330 Meanwood Road, Leeds, LS7 2JE Tel: 0113-262 4751 Fax: 0113-262 3337 E-mail: contracts@andrews-tiles.co.uk
Borg & Ranalli Ltd, 364a Clapham Road, London, SW9 9AR Tel: (020) 7627 3962 Fax: (020) 8947 1501
Carew, Shutterton Bridge, Exeter Road, Dawlish, Devon, EX7 0LX Tel: (01626) 864856 Fax: (01626) 867168
Castle Contracts, 1 Koln Close, Charfleets Industrial Estate, Canvey Island, Essex, SS8 0SB Tel: (01268) 696225 Fax: (01268) 512250
▶ DG Stone, 33 Farm Crescent, Wexham, Slough, SL2 5TQ Tel: 01753 524316 Fax: 01753 524316 E-mail: dgstone@hotmail.co.uk
F W Poole (Marble Mason) Ltd, 12 Larkhall Lane, London, SW4 6SP Tel: (020) 7622 5154 Fax: (020) 7622 4232 E-mail: poole.marble@virgin.net
Gormley (Marble Specialists) Ltd, Gormley House, Waxlow Road, Park Royal, London, NW10 7NU Tel: (020) 8961 5651 Fax: (020) 8961 5658 E-mail: info@gormley.co.uk
Grants Of Shoreditch Ltd, 25 Hackney Road, London, E2 7NX Tel: (020) 7729 3380 Fax: (020) 7613 3610 E-mail: sales@grantsint.com
H N D UK Ltd, Unit 15 Shrub Hill Industrial Estate, Worcester, WR4 9EL Tel: (01905) 29294 E-mail: info@hnd-uk.com
William Loxley Ltd, 1 Weoley Avenue, Birmingham, B29 6PP Tel: 0121-472 0834 Fax: 0121-472 8658
Manchester Brick Services, Haigh Avenue, Whitehill Indust Estate, Reddish, Stockport, Cheshire, SK4 1NU Tel: 0161-480 2621 Fax: 0161-480 0108
Marriott & Price Ltd, Station House Station Yard, Waterhouse Lane, Kingswood, Tadworth, Surrey, KT20 6EN Tel: (01737) 352735 Fax: (01737) 359192 E-mail: info@marriottandprice.co.uk
Midland Marble Ltd, Masonry Works, 80 Dollman Street, Birmingham, B7 4RP Tel: 0121-359 3699 Fax: 0121-333 3052 E-mail: enquiries@midlandmarbleltd.co.uk
O Toffolo & Son Ltd, 42 Temple Street, Hull, HU5 1AE Tel: (01482) 342674 Fax: (01482) 441344 E-mail: carl@toffolo.co.uk
Premier Marble Ltd, 3 Dewing Road, Rackheath Industrial Estate, Rackheath, Norwich, NR13 6PS Tel: (01603) 721995 Fax: (01603) 721948 E-mail: premarble@aol.com
R C Coppin Ltd, Unit 2 Park Drive, Braintree, Essex, CM7 1AP Tel: (01376) 550009 Fax: (01376) 551436 E-mail: sales@rccoppinltd.co.uk
UK Marble Ltd, 21 Burcott Road, Hereford, HR4 9LW Tel: (01432) 352178 Fax: (01432) 352112 E-mail: sales@ukmarble.co.uk
Versital Ltd, Victoria Mill, Bradford Road, Bolton, BL3 2HF Tel: (01204) 380780 Fax: (01204) 392831 E-mail: np@langnp.demon.co.uk

ARCHITECTURAL OR SCULPTURAL CASTINGS

Art Founders, 11 Springwood Industrial Estate, Braintree, Essex, CM7 2YP Tel: (01376) 343222 Fax: (01376) 341793 E-mail: info@msaf.co.uk
Lunt's Castings Ltd, Hawthorns Industrial Estate, Middlemore Road, Handsworth, Birmingham, B21 0BJ Tel: 0121-551 4301 Fax: 0121-523 7954 E-mail: info@luntscastings.co.uk
Morris Singer Ltd, Unit 10 Highfield Industrial Estate, Church Lane, Lasham, Alton, Hampshire, GU34 5SQ Tel: (01256) 381033 Fax: (01256) 381565 E-mail: info@morrissinger.co.uk

ARCHITECTURAL PHOTOGRAPHERS

▶ Afan Digital Photography, 6A High Street, Cwmavon, Port Talbot, SA12 9LE Tel: (01639) 761025 E-mail: info@afandigital.co.uk
▶ Alba Photography, 54 Milndavie Crescent, Strathblane, Glasgow, G63 9DF Tel: (01360) 770349
▶ Archimage Architectural Photography Ltd, Common Road, Kensworth, Dunstable, Bedfordshire, LU6 2PJ Tel: (01582) 872179 E-mail: anthony.weller@archimage.co.uk
▶ Campbell Gus, 23 Avondale Road, Rayleigh, Essex, SS6 8NJ Tel: (01268) 778519 E-mail: sales@justix.com
▶ Brian Cottam Photography, 3 Morlais Street, Roath, Cardiff, CF23 5HQ Tel: (029) 20498675 E-mail: info@briancottam.co.uk
▶ Emphasis Photography, 517 Hagley Road, Birmingham, B66 4AX Tel: 0121-558 8733 Fax: 0121-558 8755 E-mail: richard@emphasis.biz
▶ EXPOSURE, 4, Spinney Cottage, Hardwick Lane, Studley, Warwickshire, B80 7AD Tel: 0845 2304530 E-mail: enquiries@exposure-photo.com
▶ John Wilson, Ground Floor, 6 Madeira Road, London, SW16 2DF Tel: 020 8516 9582 E-mail: info@jcwilson.net
▶ Lewis Ronald, 5 Long Street, London, E2 8HN Tel: (020) 7033 9134 Fax:
▶ Photo Express, 7 Melville Terrace, Edinburgh, EH9 1ND Tel: 0131-667 2164 Fax: 0131-667 2164 E-mail: info@photo-express-edinburgh.co.uk
▶ Positive Pixels Photography, Stoneleigh, Bulford Road, Durrington, Salisbury, SP4 8DH Tel: (01980) 653138 E-mail: positive_pixels@tiscali.co.uk

ARCHITECTURAL POWDER COATING SERVICES

Ede Powder Coatings Ltd, Annie Reed Road, Beverley, North Humberside, HU17 0LF Tel: (01482) 865957 Fax: (01482) 864922 E-mail: info@edepc.com
▶ Hca, Unit 6 Kingsway, Andover, Hampshire, SP10 5LQ Tel: (01264) 351640 Fax: (01264) 350302 E-mail: adam@hcacoating.co.uk
Vertik-al Ltd, Yardley Brook Industrial Park, Lea Ford Road, Shard End, Birmingham, B33 9TX Tel: 0121-608 7171 Fax: 0121-693 7787 E-mail: vertikalltd@aol.com

ARCHITECTURAL RECLAIMED ITEMS

▶ Antique Oak Flooring Co., 94 High Street, London, N8 7NT Tel: (020) 8347 8222 Fax: (020) 8347 8333 E-mail: info@antiqueoakflooring.com
▶ Cotswold Reclamation Co., 2 Sandy Lane Court, Upper Rissington, Cheltenham, Gloucestershire, GL54 2NF Tel: (01451) 820292 Fax: (01451) 822455 E-mail: info@cotswoldreclamation.com
Solopark plc, Station Road, Pampisford, Cambridge, CB22 3HB Tel: (01223) 834663 Fax: (01223) 834780 E-mail: sales@solopark.co.uk

ARCHITECTURAL RECRUITMENT AGENCIES

1st Choice, 6 St. Ives Crescent, Sale, Cheshire, M33 3RU Tel: (07840) 344464 E-mail: firstchoicecvservices@ntlworld.com
▶ August Personnel, Sheraton House, Castle Park, Cambridge, CB3 0AX Tel: (01223) 370162 E-mail: pauline@augustpersonnel.co.uk
▶ Badger Associates Ltd, Pottergate Street, Aslacton, Norwich, NR15 2JU Tel: 01508 536013 Fax: 0871 7501925 E-mail: info@badgerassociates.co.uk
Bromak Ltd, Capitol House, 51 Churchgate, Bolton, BL1 1LY Tel: (01204) 532500 Fax: (01204) 363163 E-mail: enquiries@bromak.com
CV Honesty Box, 64 Burghley Street, Bourne, Lincolnshire, PE10 9NG Tel: (01778) 420407 E-mail: info@cvhonestybox.co.uk
▶ Exectec Solutions, National Deposit House, 11-13 Goldsmith Street, Nottingham, NG1 5JS Tel: 0115-988 1810 Fax: 0115-950 8900 E-mail: awalker@exectecsolutions.co.uk
Justengineers.Net, York House, 76 Lancaster Road, Morecambe, Lancashire, LA4 5QN Tel: (0845) 0502000 Fax: (0845) 0502001 E-mail: info@justengineers.net
Maxim Recruitment, 45 Bromley Road, London, E17 4PR Tel: (0870) 2430446 E-mail: contact@maximrecruitment.co.uk
▶ Melsystech, 1 Victoria Street, Portrush, County Antrim, BT56 8DL Tel: (0870) 8504309 Fax: (020) 8708 2490
Network Design International Ltd, 34 Mortimer Street, London, W1W 7JS Tel: (020) 7580 5151 Fax: (020) 7580 6242 E-mail: get.work@networkdesign.cc
▶ Nicholas Andrews Employment & Recruitment, 1 Whitehall Quay, Leeds, LS1 4HR Tel: 0113-245 6717 Fax: 0113-244 8242 E-mail: richardmhenley@aol.com
▶ P H D S Engineering Recruitment, 3 Silvan Court, Silvan Way, Southfields Business Park, Laindon, Basildon, Essex, SS15 6TU Tel: (01268) 455520 Fax: (01268) 455521 E-mail: info@phds.co.uk
▶ PDTS Ltd, 10 Thorlby Road Culcheth, Warrington, WA3 4JU Tel: (07916) 105654 Fax: (01925) 762428
▶ Prestige Recruitment Services Ltd, Saddlers Court, 650 Warwick Road, Solihull, West Midlands, B91 3DX Tel: 0121-244 4484 Fax: 0121-244 4494
▶ Recadnet, Minerva Road, London, NW10 6HJ Tel: (0870) 2240656 E-mail: admin@recadnet.com
▶ SAF- Recuitment, Marvell Rise, Harrogate, North Yorkshire, HG1 3LT Tel: (01423) 550756 E-mail: stuart@saf-recruitment.com
▶ SpiderWeb Recruitment Ltd, Kingfisher House, 2 Yarrow Road, Chatham, Kent, ME5 0SJ Tel: 01634 353131 E-mail: info@spiderweb-recruitment.co.uk
Staffhunt, 30 Birch Grove, Menstrie, Clackmannanshire, FK11 7DW Tel: (01786) 834776 E-mail: info@staffhunt.org
▶ Technology Resourcing, Unit 29, Surrey Technology Centre, Occam Road, Guildford, Surrey, GU2 7YG Tel: (01483) 302211 Fax: (01483) 301222 E-mail: recruit@tech-res.co.uk
▶ Travail Employment Group Ltd, 7 St. Johns Hill, Shrewsbury, SY1 1JD Tel: (01743) 235532 Fax: (01743) 236327 E-mail: shrewsbury@travailshrewsbury.co.uk
▶ www.simply-recruit.com, Baltic Works, Baltic Street, Hartlepool, Cleveland, TS25 1PW Tel: (01833) 638110 Fax: (01833) 630389 E-mail: sarahjane@simply-recruit.com

ARCHITECTURAL RIGGING SERVICES

GRM Rigging Services, 7 Tarbet Street, Gourock, Renfrewshire, PA19 1UF Tel: (01475) 638811 Fax: (01475) 638811
Solent Rigging Services Ltd, 21 Shamrock Quay, William Street, Southampton, SO14 5QL Tel: (023) 8055 0444 Fax: (023) 8023 0608

ARCHITECTURAL SERVICES

▶ C&D Industrial Services Ltd, Drovers Road, East Mains Industrial Estate, Broxburn, West Lothian, EH52 5ND Tel: (01506) 856000 Fax: (01506) 858000
▶ Designplus Kent, 59 Marshall Crescent, Broadstairs, Kent, CT10 2HR Tel: (01843) 602218 E-mail: designpluskent@btinternet.com
▶ Fowler Architects Ltd, The Studio, Jackeaves House, Tinkers Lane, Tring, Herts, HP23 6JB Tel: 01442 871496 Fax: 01442 876555
▶ G W Architectural Design & Build Services, 15 St. Ronans View, Gateshead, Tyne & Wear, NE9 7TF Tel: 0191-420 8844 Fax: 0191-420 8844 E-mail: info@drawingplans.co.uk
▶ Miller Architects, The Studio, 11 Gage Ridge, Forest Row, East Sussex, RH18 5HL Tel: 01342 823553 E-mail: info@millerarchitects.net
▶ Plan 2 Ltd, The Old Chapel, 8 High Street, Blakesley, Towcester, Northamptonshire, NN12 8RE Tel: (01327) 861101 Fax: (01327) 860944 E-mail: adrian@plan2.ltd.uk
▶ Bruce Watt, Hilltop, Harrowby, Grantham, Lincolnshire, NG31 9HA Tel: (01476) 590333 E-mail: hilltoppds@o2.co.uk

ARCHITECTURAL SIGN CONSULTANCY OR DESIGN

Bull Signs, Bayhorne Lane, Horley, Surrey, RH6 9ES Tel: (01293) 821313 Fax: (01293) 821414 E-mail: sales@bullsigns.com
Castleton Signs Ltd, 25 Mitcham Lane, London, SW16 6LQ Tel: (020) 8769 8741 Fax: (020) 8769 9699E-mail: sales@castletonsigns.co.uk
▶ De-signage, Briarwood House, 32, Briarwood Gardens, Woodlaithes Village, Rotherham, South Yorkshire, S66 3XR Tel: 01709 700309 Fax: 01709 700309 E-mail: sales@de-signage.com
▶ DesignCambridge, Jesus Lane, Cambridge, CB5 8BA Tel: (01223) 367206 E-mail: chris@designcambridge.com
▶ Enigma Signs, Unit 3 21a Sussex Road, Southport, Merseyside, PR9 0SS Tel: (01704) 545644 Fax: (01704) 536663 E-mail: info@enigmasigns.com
▶ Gardiner Design Associates, 34 Malting Mead, Endymion Road, Hatfield, Hertfordshire, AL10 8AR Tel: 07785 790312 E-mail: info@gardinerdesign.co.uk
▶ Graphisign Sign Makers, B Castle Park Industrial Estate, Bower Street, Oldham, OL1 3LN Tel: 0161-628 9997 Fax: 0161-628 9992 E-mail: mail@graphisign.co.uk
▶ J F K Signs & Stamp Maker, 67 Tylecroft Road, Norbury, London, SW16 4BL Tel: (020) 8679 5428 Fax: (020) 8679 1928
▶ Sean's Usability Co., Level 5, 5 St Helen's Place, Bishopsgate, London, EC3A 6AU Tel: (020) 7036 0378
▶ Vector Surveys, 24 Edwin Street, London, E16 1QA Tel: (020) 7474 3991 Fax: (020) 7474 3991 E-mail: pjwarr@btopenwolrd.com

ARCHITECTURAL STEEL FABRICATIONS

Adbeck Fabrications Ltd, Loomer Road Industrial Estate, Loomer Road, Chesterton, Newcastle, Staffordshire, ST5 7LB Tel: (01782) 565774 Fax: (01782) 565774 E-mail: adbeckfabs@aol.com

ARCHITECTURAL SURVEYING

▶ Aran Proplan, Aran House, Old Tarporley Road, Stretton, Warrington, WA4 4NB Tel: 01925 860002 Fax: 01925 860101 E-mail: a.newton@arangroup.com
▶ Kasway Ltd, 1 Conyers Avenue, Southport, Merseyside, PR8 4SZ Tel: 01704 551212 Fax: (01704) 551212 E-mail: mohammadi@kasway.co.uk
▶ Mcgarry Moon Architects Ltd, 17 Drumimerick Road, Kilrea, Coleraine, County Londonderry, BT51 5SY Tel: (028) 2954 2323 Fax: (028) 2954 2323 E-mail: info@mcgarry-moon.com
▶ Surveys, Sussex Innovation Centre, Science Park Square, Falmer, Brighton, BN1 9SB Tel: (01273) 704438 Fax: (01273) 704499 E-mail: sales@summitsolutions.co.uk

ARGON ARC WELDING

▶ Orbimatic UK, 7 The Manor Grove Centre, Vicarage Farm Road, Peterborough, PE1 5UH Tel: (01733) 555285 Fax: (01733) 555831

ARMATURE REWINDING/ WINDING/REPAIR SPECIALIST SERVICES

Bradford Armature Winding Co. Ltd, 429 Bowling Old Lane, Bradford, West Yorkshire, BD5 8HN Tel: (01274) 728379 Fax: (01274) 731518 E-mail: info@bawco.com
Cegelec Repair & Maintenance Services, Pyewipe, Gilbey Road, Grimsby, South Humberside, DN31 2SJ Tel: (01472) 355869 Fax: (01472) 250363 E-mail: info.uk@cegelec.com
Cleveland Electrical Co. Ltd, 50 Park Lane, Liverpool, L1 8HE Tel: 0151-709 6883 Fax: 0151-709 8861 E-mail: enquiries@cleveland-electrical.co.uk

ARMATURE REWINDING/WINDING/REPAIR SPECIALIST SERVICES – *continued*

Fulmak Rewinding Co., 236a Bennett Street, Long Eaton, Nottingham, NG10 4HH Tel: 0115-973 3216 Fax: 0115-946 9493 E-mail: fulmak@supernet.com
G E M Rewinds Ltd, 4 Welton Road, Wedgnock Industrial Estate, Warwick, CV34 5PZ Tel: (01926) 497778 Fax: (01926) 410128 E-mail: mike@gem-group.co.uk
J R S Rewinds, 71 Halifax Road, Maidenhead, Berkshire, SL6 5ES Tel: (01628) 628964 Fax: (01628) 672333
L S UK Rewind, 12 Bucklands Road, Penmill Trading Estate, Yeovil, Somerset, BA21 5EA Tel: (01935) 476255 Fax: (01935) 433627 E-mail: rewind@rgillard.wannado.co.uk
P G A Rewinds, 58 Temperance Street, Manchester, M12 6DP Tel: 0161-273 4484 Fax: 0161-273 4484
Robson & Francis Ltd, Unit 2 Hardess Street Industrial Estate, London, SE24 0HN Tel: (020) 7733 2353 E-mail: info@rewinds.co.uk
Scottish Electric (Services) Ltd, Locarno Works, Brown Street, Dundee, DD1 5EE Tel: (01382) 228071 Fax: (01382) 322898 E-mail: scot.elec.grp@btconnect.com
T K Rewinds, 21 Airfield Road, Christchurch, Dorset, BH23 3TG Tel: (01202) 476641 Fax: (01202) 480450
Wood Auto Holdings Ltd, Cromwell Works, Colne Road, Huddersfield, HD1 3ES Tel: (01484) 428261 Fax: (01484) 434933 E-mail: sales@woodauto.co.uk

ARMATURES

Specialty Electric Motor Sales, 23 Winston Business Centre, Chartwell Road, Lancing, West Sussex, BN15 8TU Tel: (01903) 765652 Fax: (01903) 765654 E-mail: info@sp-t.co.uk

ARMCHAIRS

▶ Rugby Suites & Beds, 104 Railway Terrace, Rugby, Warwickshire, CV21 3HE Tel: 01788 577335 Fax: 01788 577335

ARMOURED MILITARY VEHICLES

B A E Systems Land Syatems (Weapons & Vehicles) Ltd, Scotswood Road, Newcastle Upon Tyne, NE99 1BX Tel: 0191-273 8888 Fax: 0191-273 2324
B A S Systems Land Systems Weapons & Vehicles, PO Box 106, Telford, Shropshire, TF1 6QW Tel: (01952) 224500 Fax: (01952) 243910
Mawson Triton Mouldings Ltd, 4-8 Waterside Industrial Estate, Doulton Road, Rowley Regis, West Midlands, B65 8JG Tel: (01384) 633321 Fax: (01384) 565782 E-mail: sales@mawsontriton.co.uk
Repaircraft plc, The Common, Cranleigh, Surrey, GU6 8LU Tel: (01483) 273536 Fax: (01483) 278078 E-mail: hq@repaircraft.co.uk

ARMY SURPLUS CLOTHING

European Army Surplus, 14 Nobel Square, Burnt Mills Industrial Estate, Burnt Mills Industrial Estate, Basildon, Essex, SS13 1LS Tel: (01268) 591552 Fax: (01268) 591553 E-mail: email@europeanarmysurplus.co.uk

AROMA CHEMICALS

Czech & Speake Ltd, 244-254 Cambridge Heath Road, London, E2 9DA Tel: (020) 8983 7400 Fax: (020) 8981 7232 E-mail: sales@czechspeake.com
Frutarom UK Ltd, 3 Kingsthorne Park, Henson Way, Telford Way Industrial Estate, Kettering, Northamptonshire, NN16 8PX Tel: (01536) 532300 Fax: (01536) 532301 E-mail: sales@frutarom.co.uk
Oxford Chemicals Ltd, Zinc Works Road, Seaton Carew, Hartlepool, Cleveland, TS25 2DT Tel: (01429) 863222 Fax: (01429) 867567 E-mail: sales@oxfordchemicals.com
S R S Aromatics Ltd, Boldero Road, Moreton Hall Industrial Estate, Bury St. Edmunds, Suffolk, IP32 7BS Tel: (01284) 760818 Fax: (01284) 750224
Tessenderlo Fine Chemicals Ltd, Macclesfield Road, Leek, Staffordshire, ST13 8LD Tel: (01538) 399100 Fax: (01538) 399025 E-mail: sales@tessenderlofinechemicals.com
R.C. Treatt & Co. Ltd, Northern Way, Bury St. Edmunds, Suffolk, IP32 6NL Tel: (01284) 702500 Fax: (01284) 703809 E-mail: marketing@rctreatt.com

AROMATHERAPY PRODUCTS

Aphrodite, 1a Priory Lane, Penwortham, Preston, PR1 0AR Tel: (01772) 746555
▶ Aqua Warehouse, Unit 2, Rignals Lane, Chelmsford, CM2 8RE Tel: (0845) 4024303 Fax: (0845) 4024304 E-mail: richard@aquawarehouse.co.uk
The Body Shop International P.L.C., Watersmead, Littlehampton, West Sussex, BN17 6LS Tel: (01903) 731500 Fax: (01903) 726250 E-mail: info@bodyshop.co.uk
Bodytreats International Ltd, 21, Manor Rd, Upper Beeding, Steyning, W. Sussex, BN44 3TJ Tel: (07768) 908486 E-mail: ksinfo@bodytreats.com
▶ Caroline Hughes, 19, Carlyle Grove, Springbank, Cheltenham, Glos, GL51 0PW Tel: 01242 575670 E-mail: caroline@aromatherapy-makes-scents.co.uk
Christina May, Rotherdale, Fir Toll Road, Mayfield, East Sussex, TN20 6NB Tel: (01435) 873673 Fax: (01435) 873673 E-mail: bob@christinamay.com
Countryworld Ltd, Common Lane, Culcheth, Warrington, WA3 4EH Tel: (01925) 765448
Culpeper Ltd, Pall Mall Deposit, Unit 47, 124-128 Barlby Road, London, W10 6BL Tel: (020) 8962 3010 Fax: (020) 8969 9247 E-mail: info@culpeper.co.uk
E A Ellison & Co. Ltd, Crondal Road, Bayton Industrial Estate, Exhall, Coventry, CV7 9NH Tel: (024) 7636 1619 Fax: (024) 7637 9183 E-mail: sales@ellisons.co.uk
Fine English Toiletries Ltd, 15-17 Landsdown Road, Shirley, Southampton, SO15 4HD Tel: (023) 8077 8080 Fax: (023) 8077 5545
Fine Mood Ltd, Essentia House, Upper Bond Street, Hinckley, Leicestershire, LE10 1RS Tel: (01455) 615466 Fax: (01455) 615054 E-mail: info@shirleyprice.com
Forever Living Products UK Ltd, Longbridge Manor, Longbridge, Warwick, CV34 6RB Tel: (01926) 626600 Fax: (01926) 626636 E-mail: customerservices@flpuk.net
▶ Gifted Holistic Health & Beauty, 5a King Street, Hereford, HR4 9BW Tel: (01432) 350054 E-mail: tinamareafinley@msn.com
▶ I D Aromatics Ltd, 12 New Station Street, Leeds, LS1 5DL Tel: 0113-242 4983 Fax: 0113-243 3613 E-mail: info@idaromatics.co.uk
Nimbus Laboratories Ltd, Lower Farm Road, Moulton Park Industrial Estate, Northampton, NN3 6XF Tel: (01604) 646411 Fax: (01604) 647375 E-mail: keith@nimbus-labs.co.uk
▶ Primavera Aromatherapy Ltd, Manor House, Manor Road, Frome, Somerset, BA11 4BN Tel: (01373) 467103 Fax: (01373) 451532 E-mail: mail@primavera.co.uk
Sally Hair & Beauty Supplies, 17 Canal Road, Bradford, West Yorkshire, BD1 4AT Tel: (01274) 739261
▶ Scent-Ible Solutions, 10 Sorrento Grove, Stoke-on-Trent, ST3 5XZ Tel: (01782) 594862 Fax: (01782) 599189 E-mail: Helen@scentsiblesolutions.co.uk
▶ Serenity, 38 Clover Way, Harrogate, North Yorkshire, HG3 2WE Tel: 01423 528262 E-mail: heather@serenityofharrogate.co.uk
▶ Therapy Resources, 16 Canal Warf, Chesterfield, Derbyshire, S41 7RY Tel: 01246 551421
Welby Health Care Ltd, Units 16-17 Evans Business Centre, 53-58 South Avenue, High Blantyre Industrial Estate, Glasgow, G72 0XB Tel: (0845) 2572173 Fax: (0870) 4714144 E-mail: info@welbyhealthcare.co.uk

AROMATHERAPY SOAPS

▶ Bay House, Unit 1 New Rookery Farm, Little London, Silverstone, Towcester, Northamptonshire, NN12 8UP Tel: (01327) 856988 Fax: (01327) 856967 E-mail: sales@bay-house.co.uk
▶ Caroline Hughes, 19, Carlyle Grove, Springbank, Cheltenham, Glos, GL51 0PW Tel: 01242 575670 E-mail: caroline@aromatherapy-makes-scents.co.uk
▶ I D Aromatics Ltd, 12 New Station Street, Leeds, LS1 5DL Tel: 0113-242 4983 Fax: 0113-243 3613 E-mail: info@idaromatics.co.uk
▶ maria clark, Acacia house, lordship road, london, london, united kingdom, N16 0px Tel: 0207 502 1592 E-mail: maria@mariaclark.com
▶ Scent-Ible Solutions, 10 Sorrento Grove, Stoke-on-Trent, ST3 5XZ Tel: (01782) 594862 Fax: (01782) 599189 E-mail: Helen@scentsiblesolutions.co.uk
▶ Shelley's Wood, 41 Kirtley, Tamworth, Staffordshire, B77 2HF Tel: (01827) 739050 Fax: E-mail: shelleyswood@yahoo.co.uk

AROMATIC ESSENTIAL OILS

▶ Aromatic Ingredients Ltd, 33 Melton Road, Tollerton, NG12 4EL Tel: 0115-937 6785 Fax: 0115-937 2206 E-mail: lauramellor@aromaticingredients.com
▶ Incense Magic (UK) Ltd, 23 Baugh Gardens, Downend, Bristol, BS16 6PN Tel: 0117-970 2100 Fax: 0117-970 2100 E-mail: Enquiries@IncenseMagic.co.uk
J C Buck Ltd, 8 The Stafford Estate, Hillman Close, Hornchurch, Essex, RM11 2SJ Tel: (01708) 437099 Fax: (01708) 456761 E-mail: sales@jcbuck.co.uk
▶ Shelley's Wood, 41 Kirtley, Tamworth, Staffordshire, B77 2HF Tel: (01827) 739050 Fax: E-mail: shelleyswood@yahoo.co.uk
Welby Health Care Ltd, Units 16-17 Evans Business Centre, 53-58 South Avenue, High Blantyre Industrial Estate, Glasgow, G72 0XB Tel: (0845) 2572173 Fax: (0870) 4714144 E-mail: info@welbyhealthcare.co.uk

AROMATIC RAW MATERIAL MANUFRS

C P L Aromas, Barrington Hall, Dunmow Road, Hatfield Broad Oak, Bishop's Stortford, Hertfordshire, CM22 7LE Tel: (01279) 718573 Fax: (01279) 718527 E-mail: uk.enquiries@cplaromas.com
Carvansons LLP, Hollins Vale Works, Hollins Village, Bury, Lancashire, BL9 8QG Tel: 0161-766 3768 Fax: 0161-767 9437 E-mail: enquiries@carvansons.demon.co.uk
J C Buck Ltd, 8 The Stafford Estate, Hillman Close, Hornchurch, Essex, RM11 2SJ Tel: (01708) 437099 Fax: (01708) 456761 E-mail: sales@jcbuck.co.uk
Mercia International Fragrances Ltd, Station Road, Elmswell, Bury St. Edmunds, Suffolk, IP30 9HD Tel: (01359) 242459 Fax: (01359) 242129 E-mail: sales@merciaif.co.uk
S R S Aromatics Ltd, Boldero Road, Moreton Hall Industrial Estate, Bury St. Edmunds, Suffolk, IP32 7BS Tel: (01284) 760818 Fax: (01284) 750224
R.C. Treatt & Co. Ltd, Northern Way, Bury St. Edmunds, Suffolk, IP32 6NL Tel: (01284) 702500 Fax: (01284) 703809 E-mail: marketing@rctreatt.com

ART BOARDS

▶ Eyestorm, Units G & H, The Network Centre, Berkley Way, Hebburn, Tyne & Wear, NE31 1SF Tel: 0191-424 2242 E-mail: michael.davison@eyestorm.com

ART PORTALS

▶ Art Marine Ltd, Pythouse Upper Barn, Tisbury, Salisbury, SP3 6PA Tel: (01747) 871272 E-mail: jt@artmarine.co.uk
▶ Eyestorm, Units G & H, The Network Centre, Berkley Way, Hebburn, Tyne & Wear, NE31 1SF Tel: 0191-424 2242 E-mail: michael.davison@eyestorm.com

ART SUPPLIES

▶ Lisa J Fine Art Ltd, 4 Albion Parade, Kingswinford, West Midlands, DY6 0NP Tel: (01384) 401117 Fax: (01384) 294984 E-mail: sales@lisaj.biz

ARTESIAN WELLS, *See Water Well etc*

ARTICULATED DUMPER TRUCKS

Caterpillar Peterlee Ltd, North West Industrial Estate, Peterlee, County Durham, SR8 2HX Tel: 0191-569 2200 Fax: 0191-569 2298
Marton Dump Trucks Ltd, Oxford Road, Marton, Rugby, Warwickshire, CV23 9RU Tel: (01926) 632241 Fax: (01926) 633421 E-mail: sales@martondumptrucks.com

ARTIFICIAL FLOWER/PLANT COMPONENTS/ACCESSORIES

▶ Flowerworks Florists, 15 Windsor Street, Uxbridge, Middlesex, UB8 1AB Tel: (01895) 810885 Fax: (01895) 810008 E-mail: sales@actionflowers.com
The Neoknitting & Trim Ltd, Peter Pal House, Albion St, Leicester, LE2 5DE Tel: 0116-271 4923 Fax: 0116-271 4422 E-mail: sales@neotrims.com
▶ PHS Greenleaf, Western Industrial Estate, Lon-Y-Llyn, Caerphilly, Mid Glamorgan, CF83 1XH Tel: (029) 2085 1000 Fax: (029) 2080 9064 E-mail: enquiries@phs.co.uk

ARTIFICIAL GRASS

Bonar Yards & Fabrics Ltd, St Salvador Street, Dundee, DD3 7EU Tel: (01382) 227346 Fax: (01382) 202378 E-mail: ascott@bonaryarns.com
▶ Leisure Tech GB Ltd, 11 Hasler Place, Haslers Lane, Great Dunmow, Dunmow, Essex, CM6 1AJ Tel: (01371) 872822 E-mail: enquiries@leisuretechgb.co.uk
Support In Sport (U K) Ltd, Tavistock Works, Glasson Industrial Estate, Maryport, Cumbria, CA15 8NT Tel: (01900) 812796 Fax: (01900) 815509

ARTIFICIAL LIMB OR COMPONENT MAKERS

Chas A Blatchford & Sons Ltd, Wella Road, Basingstoke, Hampshire, RG22 4AH Tel: (01256) 316600 Fax: (01256) 329256 E-mail: sales@blatchford.co.uk
▶ Opcare Ltd, Windmill Road, Headington, Oxford, OX3 7DD Tel: (01865) 761310 Fax: (01865) 741703
Ortho Europe Ltd, Mill Lane, Alton, Hampshire, GU34 2PX Tel: (01420) 83294 Fax: (01420) 80068 E-mail: keithbell@ortho-europe.co.uk
Orthoeurope Ltd, Orth House, Kimber Road, Abingdon, Oxfordshire, OX14 1SG Tel: (01235) 555001 Fax: (01235) 555004 E-mail: info@ortho-europe.com
R S L Steeper Ltd, Disability Centre Queen Marys, Hospital, Roehampton, London, SW15 5PL Tel: (01634) 297010 Fax: (020) 8788 0137 E-mail: sales@rehab.co.uk

ARTIFICIAL SILK, *See Rayon etc*

ARTIFICIAL TEETH, FOR DENTAL PROFESSION

▶ Banchory Dental Practice, 9 Station Road, Banchory, Kincardineshire, AB31 5XX Tel: (01330) 823400 E-mail: smile@banchorydentalpractice.com
Plas-Dent Co. Ltd, Middlemore Road, Smethwick, West Midlands, B66 2DQ Tel: 0121-558 3601 Fax: 0121-555 5567 E-mail: richard@plas-dent.co.uk
Potters Bar Denture Centre, 13 The Service Road, Potters Bar, Hertfordshire, EN6 1QA Tel: (01707) 660303 E-mail: philtucker40@skynow.net
▶ Sheppey Dental Laboratory, 1a-2a Railway Terrace, Queenborough, Kent, ME11 5AY Tel: (01795) 662025 Fax: (01795) 583593
Wright Health Group Ltd, Dunsinane Avenue, Dunsinane Industrial Estate, Dundee, DD2 3QD Tel: (01382) 833866 Fax: (01382) 811042 E-mail: administrator@wright-dental.co.uk

ARTISTS CANVAS STRETCHING

▶ DPS Fine Art, 14 Hermes Way, Sleaford, Lincolnshire, NG34 7WH Tel: 01529 300452 Fax: 01529 300452 E-mail: matt@dpsfineart.co.uk
Lucy Art, 178b Batley Road, Alverthorpe, Wakefield, West Yorkshire, WF2 0AJ Tel: 01924 362009 Fax: 0870 1227055 E-mail: sales@lucyart.co.uk

ARTISTS' COLOURS

Bird & Davis Ltd, 45 Holmes Road, London, NW5 3AN Tel: (020) 7485 3797 Fax: (020) 7284 0509 E-mail: birdltd@aol.com
Colart Fine Art & Graphics Ltd, Whitefriars Avenue, Harrow, Middlesex, HA3 5RH Tel: (020) 8427 4343 Fax: (020) 8863 7177 E-mail: initial.surname@colart.co.uk

ARTISTS' MATERIALS, *See also headings for particular types*

Fred Aldous Ltd, Handicraft Centre, 37 Lever Street, Manchester, M1 1LW Tel: 0161-236 2477 Fax: 0161-236 6075 E-mail: aldous@btinternet.com
Argun Printers, 344 Mare Street, London, E8 1HA Tel: (020) 8985 7879 Fax: (020) 8985 3668 E-mail: info@argun.co.uk
▶ Art 4 U, The Colonnades, Albert Dock, Liverpool, L3 4AA Tel: 0151-708 7400 Fax: 0151-707 6800
▶ Artastik Ltd, Unit 6 Shorade Industrial Estate, New Street, Bridgtown, Cannock, Staffordshire, WS11 0DH Tel: (01543) 468434 E-mail: info@artastik.co.uk
▶ Artful Dodgers, Unit 3-4 Laneside Works, Stockclough Lane, Feniscowles, Blackburn, BB2 5JR Tel: 0161-228 2850 Fax: (01254) 207484 E-mail: sales@artfuldodgers.co.uk
Artistuff Framing Ltd, Victoria Road, Swindon, SN1 3BH Tel: (01793) 522152 Fax: (01793) 488379
▶ artstop.biz, 29 Red Lion Street, Aylsham, Norwich, NR11 6ER Tel: (01263) 734571 Fax: (01263) 735804
Artstore (Scotland) Ltd, 94 Queen Street, Glasgow, G1 3AQ Tel: 0141-221 1101 Fax: 0141-204 2902 E-mail: artstore@artstore.co.uk
Bayliss Wright Gados Ltd, 50 Park Street, Luton, LU1 3ET Tel: (01582) 722186 Fax: (01582) 727780 E-mail: baylisswright@eurotelbroadband.com
▶ Bee Inspired, 236 Windmill Avenue, Kettering, Northamptonshire, NN15 7DQ Tel: (01536) 514646
Bird & Davis Ltd, 45 Holmes Road, London, NW5 3AN Tel: (020) 7485 3797 Fax: (020) 7284 0509 E-mail: birdltd@aol.com

ARTISTS' MATERIALS – *continued*

Brian Clegg Educational Products Ltd, Regent Mill, Regent Street, Rochdale, Lancashire, OL12 0HQ Tel: (01706) 666620 Fax: (01706) 666621 E-mail: office@brianclegg.co.uk

Colart Fine Art & Graphics Ltd, Whitefriars Avenue, Harrow, Middlesex, HA3 5RH Tel: (020) 8427 4343 Fax: (020) 8863 7177 E-mail: initial.surname@colart.co.uk

Colemans, 34-36 St Giles Street, Northampton, NN1 1JW Tel: (01604) 636708 Fax: (01604) 622533

▶ Craft Corner, Velco House, The Square, Knottingley, West Yorkshire, WF11 8ND Tel: (01977) 607007 Fax: (01977) 607007

▶ Craft Daft, 9 Castle Parade, Bournemouth, BH7 6SH Tel: (01202) 488411

▶ The Crafthouse, 118-120 Outram Street, Sutton-in-Ashfield, Nottinghamshire, NG17 4FT Tel: (01623) 550011 Fax: (01623) 550011

▶ Crafty Individuals, 1 Sidelingtails, Yarm, Cleveland, TS15 9HT Tel: (01642) 789955

▶ Crafty Patch, 24-28 South Street, Boston, Lincolnshire, PE21 6HT Tel: (01205) 311103 Fax: (01205) 311649

▶ Creations, 64 High Street, North Berwick, East Lothian, EH39 4HQ Tel: (01620) 890411 Fax: (01620) 890411

▶ Creative Crafts Art3 Craft Gift, 38 Rainham Shopping Centre, Rainham, Gillingham, Kent, ME8 7HW Tel: (01634) 372200 Fax: (01634) 372200 E-mail: sales@justdoitcrafts.com

Cross's, 20 Lower Bridge Street, Canterbury, Kent, CT1 2LG Tel: (01227) 458776 Fax: (01227) 760827

Cross's, Brenchley House, Week Street, Maidstone, Kent, ME14 1RF Tel: (01622) 677436 Fax: (01622) 752254

▶ The Edg, 22 King Street, Lancaster, LA1 1JY Tel: (01524) 66029 Fax: (0871) 4337840

▶ Great Art, Normandy House, 1 Nether Street, Alton, Hampshire, GU34 1EA Tel: (01420) 593332 Fax: (01420) 593333 E-mail: welcome@greatart.co.uk

▶ Harris Moore, Unit 311 Jubilee Trade Centre, Pershore Street, Birmingham, B5 6ND Tel: 0121-248 0030 Fax: 0121-248 0030 E-mail: sales@stretchershop.co.uk

Hewitt & Booth Ltd, St Andrews Road, Huddersfield, HD1 6RZ Tel: (01484) 546621 Fax: (01484) 450580 E-mail: sales@hewittandbooth.com

▶ Hobbycraft Superstores Ltd, Unit 2 Harlech Retail Park, Cardiff Road, Newport, Gwent, NP20 3BA Tel: (01633) 652070

▶ Imagine 20 20 Ltd, 23 Eastgate, Worksop, Nottinghamshire, S80 1RH Tel: (01909) 473329 Fax: (01909) 477216 E-mail: info@imagine2020.co.uk

▶ Into Africa, The Market, Carmarthen, Dyfed, SA31 1QY Tel: (01267) 232333

Jakar International Ltd, Hillside House, 2-6 Friern Park, London, N12 9BX Tel: (020) 8445 6376 Fax: (020) 8445 2714E-mail: info@jakar.co.uk

Karma, 26 Ysguthan Road, Port Talbot, West Glamorgan, SA12 6LY Tel: (01639) 896299

Limavady Printing Co. Ltd, 26C Catherine Street, Limavady, County Londonderry, BT49 9DB Tel: (028) 7776 2051 Fax: (028) 7776 2132 E-mail: print@limprint.com

▶ Llexia Art, 196 High Street, Brentford, Middlesex, TW8 8AH Tel: (020) 8560 5550 Fax: (020) 8560 5562

▶ M Saltmarsh, 32 Monson Road, Tunbridge Wells, Kent, TN1 1LU Tel: (01892) 527512 Fax: (01892) 545592

▶ Mills Arts & Crafts, 49 South Street, Bo'Ness, West Lothian, EH51 9HA Tel: (01506) 829982

Opitec-Hobbyfix, 7 West Road, Southampton, SO19 9AH Tel: (023) 8068 2404 Fax: 023 80446991

Osborne Stationers Ltd, 27 Market Street, Wolverhampton, WV1 3AG Tel: (01902) 427071 Fax: (01902) 771070

Pisces, Westwood Studios, Marshfield Bank, Crewe, CW2 8UY Tel: (01270) 216211 Fax: (01270) 586150 E-mail: info@pisces-art.co.uk

▶ Retro Spectives, The Minories, Rother Street, Stratford-upon-Avon, Warwickshire, CV37 6NF Tel: (01789) 297706 E-mail: sales@retrospectives.co.uk

▶ Royal Brush UK Ltd, Unit K2 Peartree Industrial Park Crackley Way, Peartree Lane, Dudley, West Midlands, DY2 0UW Tel: (01384) 258188 Fax: (01384) 258770 E-mail: uk@royalbrush.com

Russell & Chapple Ltd, 68 Drury Lane, London, WC2B 5SP Tel: (020) 7836 7521 Fax: (020) 7497 0554 E-mail: sales@randc.net

▶ Scrap N Craft, 21 Blackhills Road, Peterlee, County Durham, SR8 4DW Tel: 0191-518 4200

▶ Simply Doughlightful, Unit 30 Barleylands Farm, Barleylands Road, Billericay, Essex, CM11 2UD Tel: (01268) 272766

T N Lawrence & Sons Ltd, 208 Portland Road, Hove, East Sussex, BN3 5QT Tel: (01273) 260260 Fax: (01273) 260270 E-mail: artbox@lawrence.co.uk

Taj Crafts, 2 Wellesley Avenue, Iver, Buckinghamshire, SL0 9AY Tel: (01753) 653900 E-mail: tajcrafts@btopenworld.com

Ward Philipson Group Ltd, Dunston Industrial Estate, Halifax Road, Gateshead, Tyne & Wear, NE11 9HW Tel: 0191-460 5915 Fax: 0191-460 8540 E-mail: info@wardphilipson.co.uk

ARTWORK

▶ Landreflections, Running Waters, Dorstone, Hereford, HR3 6AD Tel: (01981) 550465 E-mail: landreflections@hotmail.co.uk

▶ Lisa J Fine Art Ltd, 4 Albion Parade, Kingswinford, West Midlands, DY6 0NP Tel: (01384) 401117 Fax: (01384) 294984 E-mail: sales@lisaj.biz

ARTWORK PROTECTION MOUNTBOARD

Nelder & Southam, Mulberry Street, Stratford-upon-Avon, Warwickshire, CV37 6RS Tel: (01789) 267974 Fax: (01789) 267974

ASBESTOS AIR QUALITY TESTING

▶ A M S 2000 Ltd, Ladywell, Barnstaple, Devon, EX31 1QS Tel: (01271) 328663 Fax: (01271) 375436 E-mail: asbestos@ams-2000.co.uk

Asbestos Management Co. (Ireland) Ltd, 5 Carthall Manor, Coleraine, County Londonderry, BT51 3GR Tel: (028) 7032 1319 Fax: (028) 7032 1319 E-mail: jimb@asbestos-management-company.com

▶ M 3 Associates Ltd, 70 High Street, Houghton Regis, Dunstable, Bedfordshire, LU5 5BJ Tel: (01582) 866800 Fax: (01582) 866446 E-mail: sales@m3associates.co.uk

▶ M E M Group Plc, Edward House, Dallis Road, Ocean Park, Cardiff, CF24 5TW Tel: (029) 2049 8111 Fax: (029) 2048 4775 E-mail: info@memgroup.co.uk

▶ www.thameslabs.co.uk, The Granary, Suite 2, Brook Farm, Thrapston Road, Ellington, Huntingdon, Cambridgeshire, PE28 0AE Tel: (01480) 891800 Fax: (01480) 890008 E-mail: john@thameslabs.co.uk

ASBESTOS DUST FILTRATION EQUIPMENT

▶ Allpoint Hire Ltd, Emery Court, Heaton Mersey, Stockport, Cheshire, SK4 3GL Tel: 0161-431 8400 Fax: 0161-431 8411 E-mail: ian@allpointhire.com

Thermac Hire, Astra Park, Parkside Lane, Leeds, LS11 5SZ Tel: 0113-270 9555 Fax: 0113-270 9666 E-mail: sales@thermac.com

ASBESTOS DUST REMOVAL AND STRIPPING EQUIPMENT

A B C Insulation Co. Ltd, Alexandra Docks, Newport, Gwent, NP20 2NP Tel: (01633) 211473 Fax: (01633) 843212

Asbestostrip Innovations, Unit 12 Tufthorn Industrial Estate, Stepbridge Road, Coleford, Gloucestershire, GL16 8PJ Tel: (01594) 837755 Fax: (01594) 836633 E-mail: enquiries@asbestostrip.co.uk

Safety Industries (Oakwood) Ltd, Tonbridge Road, Harold Hill, Romford, RM3 8TS Tel: (01708) 381499 Fax: (01708) 381267 E-mail: sales@safetyindustries.co.uk

ASBESTOS DUST REMOVAL EQUIPMENT HIRE

▶ Allpoint Hire Ltd, Emery Court, Heaton Mersey, Stockport, Cheshire, SK4 3GL Tel: 0161-431 8400 Fax: 0161-431 8411 E-mail: ian@allpointhire.com

Interserve Industrial Services Ltd, PO Box 3, Redditch, Worcestershire, B98 0FH Tel: (01527) 507500 Fax: (01527) 507501

Thermac Hire, Astra Park, Parkside Lane, Leeds, LS11 5SZ Tel: 0113-270 9555 Fax: 0113-270 9666 E-mail: sales@thermac.com

ASBESTOS DUST REMOVAL OR STRIPPING

1st Choice Asbestos Removals Ltd, 21c Hellesdon Park Road, Drayton High Road, Norwich, NR6 5DR Tel: (01603) 426217 Fax: (01603) 417382 E-mail: sales@1stchoiceasbestos.co.uk

A A R Ltd, Unit 12 Langley Wharf, Railway Terrace, Kings Langley, Hertfordshire, WD4 8JE Tel: (01923) 260043 Fax: (01923) 260478 E-mail: info@aar.co.uk

A R G Europe Ltd, Unit 2, 58A Alexandra Road, Ponders End, Enfield, Middlesex, EN3 7EH Tel: (020) 8804 8008 Fax: (020) 8805 7600 E-mail: argeurope@aol.com

Sam Allon (Contracts) Ltd, Lincoln Street, Hull, HU2 0PE Tel: (01482) 320051 Fax: (01482) 216610 E-mail: user@samallon.co.uk

Alpha Asbestos Removals Ltd, 158 Hatmore Park, Londonderry, BT48 0QJ Tel: (028) 7126 9167 Fax: (028) 7136 4356 E-mail: alpha_asbestos@btconnect.com

Aptiva Ltd, Shapwick Road, Poole, Dorset, BH15 4AP Tel: (01202) 670597 Fax: (01202) 680789 E-mail: sales@aptiva.co.uk

Arca Ltd, 237 Branston Road, Burton-on-Trent, Staffordshire, DE14 3BT Tel: (01283) 531126 Fax: (01283) 568228E-mail: info@arca.org.uk

Asbestos & Insulation Co., 765 Maidstone Road, Gillingham, Kent, ME8 0LR Tel: (01634) 232221 Fax: (01634) 233221 E-mail: sales@asbestos-insulation.com

▶ C & D Industrial Services Ltd, 63 Portland Street, Mansfield Woodhouse, Mansfield, Nottinghamshire, NG19 8BE Tel: (01623) 781200 Fax: (01623) 420496

C G B Humbertherm Ltd, Middleplatt Road, Immingham, South Humberside, DN40 1AH Tel: (01469) 572726 Fax: (01469) 571728 E-mail: sales@cgbhumbertherm.com

C M C Asbestos Surveys Ltd, Elker House, Elker Lane, Billington, Clitheroe, Lancashire, BB7 9HZ Tel: (01254) 822029 Fax: (01254) 825771 E-mail: info@cmcasestossurveys.com

City Insulation Contractors Ltd, City House, Horspath Industrial Estate, Pony Road, Cowley, Oxford, OX4 2RD Tel: (01865) 715173 Fax: (01865) 770547 E-mail: info@cityins.co.uk

Cooks Insulations, Holly Cottage, 74 New Road, Tadley, Hampshire, RG26 3AN Tel: (07711) 241365 Fax: 0118-981 2552

D B Industrial Services Ltd, Lyn Castle Way, Appleton, Warrington, WA4 4ST Tel: (01606) 597151 Fax: (01606) 597152 E-mail: sales@dbigroup.co.uk

D & M Demolitions Ltd, Meek Street, Royton, Oldham, OL2 6HL Tel: 0161-652 2550 Fax: 0161-652 5203 E-mail: sales@dandmdemolitions.ltd.uk

Davis & Samson Contractors, Billet Lane, Berkhamsted, Hertfordshire, HP4 1DP Tel: (01442) 878800 Fax: (01442) 878801 E-mail: sales@davisandsamson.co.uk

Dean Dismantlers, Springhall Works, 28 West Lane, Thornton, Bradford, West Yorkshire, BD13 3HX Tel: (01274) 832600 Fax: (01274) 832566

Econ Construction Ltd, Old Maidstone Road, Sidcup, Kent, DA14 5AZ Tel: (020) 8302 4691 Fax: (020) 8308 0483 E-mail: econconstruction@aol.com

Erith Contractors Ltd, Riverside House, Maypole Crescent, Darent Industrial Park, Erith, Kent, DA8 2JZ Tel: (01322) 346811 Fax: (01322) 341978 E-mail: info@erith.net

European Asbestos Removals Ltd, 3 Norden Court, Alan Ramsbottom Way, Great Harwood, Blackburn, BB6 7UR Tel: (01254) 876686 Fax: (01254) 877000 E-mail: sales@asbestos-removers.co.uk

▶ G T C Asbestos Removal Services Ltd, Unit 9 Kirkhill Place, Kirkhill Industrial Estate, Dyce, Aberdeen, AB21 0GU Tel: (01224) 722150

George Beattie & Sons Ltd, Auchinvole Castle, Kilsyth, Glasgow, G65 0SA Tel: (01236) 823160 Fax: (01236) 823201 E-mail: info@beattie-demolition.com

Gill Demolitions Ltd, Progress Works, Hall Lane, Bradford, West Yorkshire, BD4 7DT Tel: (01274) 733011 Fax: (01274) 392879 E-mail: info@gilldemolitions.co.uk

Gordons Environmental Ltd, 66-68 Back Sneddon Street, Paisley, Renfrewshire, PA3 2BY Tel: 0141-842 1189 Fax: 0141-842 1139 E-mail: gordonsltd@aol.com

Hanson Recycling & Demolition, Sheffield Bottom, Off Station Road, Theale, Reading, RG7 4AJ Tel: 0118-957 6243

Haylock & Rolph, Unit 9 Hall Barn Road Industrial Estate, Hall Barn Road, Isleham, Ely, Cambridgeshire, CB7 5RJ Tel: (01638) 781715 Fax: (01638) 781716 E-mail: enquiries@haylockandrolph.co.uk

I C L Environmental Services Ltd, Firs Industrial Estate, Stourport Road, Kidderminster, Worcestershire, DY11 7QN Tel: (01562) 744655 Fax: (01562) 829207 E-mail: sales@iclenvironmental.co.uk

Ipswich Insulation Ltd, Station House, Station Road, Bentley, Ipswich, IP9 2DB Tel: (01473) 327288 Fax: (01473) 327288

J & J Insulations Ltd, 27a New Road, Croxley Green, Rickmansworth, Hertfordshire, WD3 3EJ Tel: (01923) 897161 Fax: (01923) 897161 E-mail: jj.insulations@virgin.net

Kershaw Insulation Ltd, Willowcroft Works, Broad Lane, Cottenham, Cambridge, CB4 8SW Tel: (01954) 250155 Fax: (01954) 251628 E-mail: sales.office@kershaw-insulation.co.uk

Knight Thermal Insulation, 54 Factory Estate, College Road, Perry Barr, Birmingham, B44 8BS Tel: 0121-356 3980 Fax: 0121-356 1688

Malrod Insulations Ltd, Glebe Mill, Library Street, Westhoughton, Bolton, BL5 3AU Tel: (01942) 811591 Fax: (01942) 814411 E-mail: enquiries@malrod.co.uk

Merryhill Envirotec Ltd, Merryhill House, Budds Lane, Romsey, Hampshire, SO51 0HA Tel: (01794) 515848 Fax: (01794) 524386 E-mail: enquiries@merryhill-idm.co.uk

Newmarket Insulation Contracts, Exchange House, Wash Road, Wickhambrook, Newmarket, Suffolk, CB8 8XQ Tel: (01440) 820612 Fax: (01440) 820628 E-mail: newmarktinscon@hotmail.com

Northwich Industrial Roofing Ltd, 4 Bridge Street, Northwich, Cheshire, CW9 7NR Tel: (01606) 43884 Fax: (01606) 43884

P W M Environmental Group, Bassett Road, Halesowen, West Midlands, B63 2RE Tel: (01384) 564866 Fax: (01384) 560945 E-mail: info@pwmills.co.uk

Phoenix Hazmat, Unit 6 Dabble Duck Industrial Estate, Shildon, County Durham, DL4 2RA Tel: (01388) 779220 Fax: (01388) 779230 E-mail: info@phoenixhazmatltd.co.uk

Powertherm Contracts Insulation Ltd, C Crown Works, Rotherham Road, Beighton, Sheffield, S20 1AH Tel: 0114-288 9119 Fax: 0114-288 9882 E-mail: powertherm@aol.com

R & F Insulations Ltd, Unit 7 Bardwells Yard, Latchingdon Road, Cold Norton, Chelmsford, CM3 6JG Tel: (01621) 828222 Fax: (01621) 828933 E-mail: sales@randf-insulation.co.uk

R H Insulation Services Ltd, Unit 14, Wingate Road, Gosport, Hampshire, PO12 4DR Tel: (023) 9250 1141 Fax: (023) 9251 1409

R L Insulations, 4 Sentinel Works, Northgate Avenue, Bury St. Edmunds, Suffolk, IP32 6AZ Tel: (01284) 760937 Fax: (01284) 755031 E-mail: info@rlinsulation.fsnet.co.uk

Rhodar Ltd, Subway Street, Hull, HU3 4EL Tel: (01482) 212723 Fax: (01482) 327309

S D Demolition Ltd, PO Box 65, Biggleswade, Bedfordshire, SG18 9BE Tel: (01767) 314166 Fax: (01767) 318511 E-mail: enquiries@sddemolition.net

S L (Thermal Insulation) Contracts & Supplies Co. Ltd, Unit 16 Blue Chalet Industrial Park, London Road, West Kingsdown, Sevenoaks, Kent, TN15 6BT Tel: (01474) 854465 Fax: (01474) 854393 E-mail: les@slcontracts.com

T.E. Scudder Ltd, Carey House, Great Central Way, Wembley, Middlesex, HA9 0HR Tel: (020) 8903 9722 Fax: (020) 8903 6311 E-mail: scudder@carey-plc.co.uk

H. Smith Engineers Ltd, Fordcroft Road, Orpington, Kent, BR5 2DB Tel: (01689) 833581 Fax: (01689) 820218 E-mail: mail@hsmith.co.uk

Solent Environmental Services Asbestos Ltd, 151-153 Long Lane, Holbury, Southampton, SO45 2NZ Tel: (023) 8089 9932 Fax: (023) 8089 9934

Southern Asbestos Services Ltd, Riverside Business Centre, River Lawn Road, Tonbridge, Kent, TN9 1EP Tel: (01732) 357468 Fax: (01732) 358377

Southern Insulations, 2 Grove Rd, Strood, Rochester, Kent, ME2 4BY Tel: (01634) 291100 Fax: (01634) 290680

Star Installation Ltd, Unit B Progress Business Centre, Cannock, Staffordshire, WS11 0JR Tel: (01543) 574146 Fax: (01543) 469312

T H Holroyd Ltd, Unit 15, Phoebe Lane Mills, Halifax, West Yorkshire, HX3 9EX Tel: (01422) 354793 Fax: (01422) 354255

Tees Insulation Ltd, 138 Lynn Street, Hartlepool, Cleveland, TS24 7LX Tel: (01429) 265433 Fax: (01429) 863149 E-mail: info@teesgroup.com

Wrightways Ltd, Beveridge Lane, Ellistown, Coalville, Leicestershire, LE67 1FB Tel: (01530) 263183 Fax: (01530) 263186 E-mail: info@wrightwaysltd.co.uk

ASBESTOS ENCAPSULATION OR CONTROL CONTRACTORS

▶ Allan Dyson Asbestos Services Ltd, Cagex House, Leyden Road, Stevenage, Hertfordshire, SG1 2BP Tel: (01438) 360656 Fax: 01438 721973 E-mail: mailbox@adas.co.uk

Asbestos Surveys & Advice, Suite 7, Cockenzie Business Centre, Edinburgh Road, Cockenzie, Prestonpans, East Lothian, EH32 0HL Tel: 0845 5314268 Fax: (01875) 819111 E-mail: info@asa-asbestos.uk.com

Dean Dismantlers, Springhall Works, 28 West Lane, Thornton, Bradford, West Yorkshire, BD13 3HX Tel: (01274) 832600 Fax: (01274) 832566

I C L Environmental Services Ltd, Firs Industrial Estate, Stourport Road, Kidderminster, Worcestershire, DY11 7QN Tel: (01562) 744655 Fax: (01562) 829207 E-mail: sales@iclenvironmental.co.uk

▶ Mamco Ltd, 6 Vernon Road, Porthcawl, Porthcawl, Mid Glamorgan, CF36 5LN Tel: (0845) 1668509 Fax: 0871-242 6223 E-mail: admin@mamco.co.uk

R & F Insulations Ltd, Unit 7 Bardwells Yard, Latchingdon Road, Cold Norton, Chelmsford, CM3 6JG Tel: (01621) 828222 Fax: (01621) 828933 E-mail: sales@randf-insulation.co.uk

▶ Safe Coatings Ltd, Bank House, High Street, Staplehurst, Tonbridge, Kent, TN12 0AE Tel: (01580) 893087 Fax: (01580) 893473 E-mail: enquiries@safecoatings.com

Southern Group (UK) Ltd, 23 Caker Stream Rd, Alton, Hampshire, GU34 2QA Tel: (01420) 88344 Fax: (01420) 88348 E-mail: info@southerngroupuk.com

ASBESTOS FREE GASKETS

British Gaskets Ltd, Bulmer Road Industrial Estate, Bulmer Road, Sudbury, Suffolk, CO10 7HJ Tel: (01787) 881188 Fax: (01787) 880595 E-mail: sales@british-gaskets.co.uk

Garlock GB Ltd, Premier Way, Lowfields Business Park, Elland, West Yorkshire, HX5 9HF Tel: (01422) 313600 Fax: (01422) 313601 E-mail: jasonsedgwick@compuserve.com

Scandura, St. James Road, Corby, Northamptonshire, NN18 8AW Tel: (01536) 267121 Fax: (01536) 266392 E-mail: sales@scandura.co.uk

▶ indicates data change since last edition

ASBESTOS HEALTH AND SAFETY CONSULTANCY

▶ National Health & Safety Company Ltd, Suite 14 - 15 Axwel House, East Mains Industrial Estate, Broxburn, West Lothian, EH52 5AU Tel: 08700 611725 Fax: 0707 5023614 E-mail: admin@nhasco.com

▶ Noble Health & Safety Consultancy Ltd, Ermington Mill, Ermington, Ivybridge, Devon, PL21 9NT Tel: (0870) 8504439 Fax: (01548) 831464 E-mail: enquiries@noblegroup.uk.com

▶ Positive Health & Safety Ltd, 218 Gazette Buildings, 168 Corporation Street, Birmingham, B4 6TF Tel: 0121-212 2020 E-mail: info@positivehands.co.uk

▶ Safe Coatings Ltd, Bank House, High Street, Staplehurst, Tonbridge, Kent, TN12 0AE Tel: (01580) 893087 Fax: (01580) 893473 E-mail: enquiries@safecoatings.com

ASBESTOS INSULATION BOARD

▶ Aels Ltd, 19 Queensbury Road, Seaham, County Durham, SR7 8AY Tel: 0191-581 2512 Fax: 0191-581 8419

▶ Ideal Handling (Stoke-on-Trent) Ltd, 73 Fern Crescent, Congleton, Cheshire, CW12 3HQ Tel: (01260) 295417 Fax: (01260) 295417 E-mail: simon@ideal-stoke-on-trent.co.uk

ASBESTOS PACKINGS & JOINTINGS

A M S (Burnham) Fluid Sealing, 30-32 Dropmore Road, Burnham, Slough, SL1 8BE Tel: (01628) 603311 Fax: (01628) 660040

E Dobson & Co Gaskets Ltd, Oakworth Road, Keighley, West Yorkshire, BD21 1QQ Tel: (01535) 607257 Fax: (01535) 608171 E-mail: sales@dobsongasket.com

ASBESTOS PRODUCTS

F G F Ltd, Fernhurst Road, Bristol, BS5 7XN Tel: 0117-951 7755 Fax: 0117-935 4231 E-mail: sales@fgfltd.co.uk

▶ Mamco Ltd, 6 Vernon Road, Porthcawl, Porthcawl, Mid Glamorgan, CF36 5LN Tel: (0845) 1668509 Fax: 0871-242 6223 E-mail: admin@mamco.co.uk

ASBESTOS REMOVAL TAPES

▶ Allpoint Hire Ltd, Emery Court, Heaton Mersey, Stockport, Cheshire, SK4 3GL Tel: 0161-431 8400 Fax: 0161-431 8411 E-mail: ian@allpointhire.com

▶ Anti Contamination Equipement Supplies, Carr Mills, Bradford Road, Batley, West Yorkshire, WF17 9JY Tel: (01924) 420750 Fax: (01924) 420530 E-mail: sales@aces.uk.com

Asbestos Surveys & Advice, Suite 7, Cockenzie Business Centre, Edinburgh Road, Cockenzie, Prestonpans, East Lothian, EH32 0HL Tel: 0845 5314268 Fax: (01875) 819111 E-mail: info@asa-asbestos.uk.com

▶ Brown & Mason Ltd, New Loom House, 101 Back Church Lane, London, E1 1LU Tel: (020) 7264 1120 Fax: (020) 7481 8244 E-mail: b&m@brownandmason.ltd.uk

Thermac Hire, Astra Park, Parkside Lane, Leeds, LS11 5SZ Tel: 0113-270 9555 Fax: 0113-270 9666 E-mail: sales@thermac.com

ASBESTOS RISK MANAGEMENT

▶ Asbestos Consultants To The Enviroment Ltd, 23 Romney Avenue, Bristol, BS7 9ST Tel: 0117-952 7609 Fax: 0117-952 0947 E-mail: info@asbestos-ace.co.uk

ASBESTOS SAMPLING

Southern Group (UK) Ltd, 23 Caker Stream Rd, Alton, Hampshire, GU34 2QA Tel: (01420) 88344 Fax: (01420) 88348 E-mail: info@southerngroupuk.com

ASBESTOS SUBSTITUTE BUILDING PRODUCTS, *See Fibre/Fibrous Cement etc*

ASBESTOS TEST SERVICES OR ANALYSTS

Airtech Analysis Ltd, 6 Sopwith CR, Hurricane Way, Wickford, Essex, SS11 8YU Tel: (01268) 562645 Fax: (01268) 570198 E-mail: airtech@dsl.pipex.com

Asbestos Analysis Services Ltd, 8 Tower Quays, Tower Road, Birkenhead, Merseyside, CH41 1BP Tel: 0151-649 0541 Fax: 0151-649 0547

Aztec Upvc Specialists, Unit 29-30, Colliery Close, Dinnington, Sheffield, S25 3QX Tel: (01909) 564946 Fax: (01909) 550418 E-mail: northfibre@aol.co.uk

Bristol Scientific Services, 7 Redcross Street, Bristol, BS2 0BA Tel: 0117-903 8666 Fax: 0117-903 8667 E-mail: labmail@sciserv.demon.co.uk

C P A Laboratories Ltd, 318 Worple Road, London, SW20 8QU Tel: (020) 8946 8621 Fax: (020) 8947 1206 E-mail: admincpa@eurofins.com

▶ Fibrecount U K Ltd, Thomas Ho, 88-90 Goodmayes Rd, Goodmayes, Ilford, Essex, IG3 9UU Tel: (020) 8597 8785 Fax: (020) 8597 5605 E-mail: info@fibrecount.co.uk

Invicta Analytical Services, Alexandra House, 5 Blyth Road, Bromley, BR1 3RS Tel: (020) 8290 5629 Fax: (020) 8290 4443 E-mail: admin@invictaas.co.uk

Midlands Asbestos Survey Services, 184 Northumberland Court, Northumberland Road, Leamington Spa, Warwickshire, CV32 6HW Tel: (01926) 434444 Fax: (01926) 430280 E-mail: info@massltd.co.uk

O H S Ltd, 11-17 Campus Road, Listerhills Science Park, Bradford, West Yorkshire, BD7 1HR Tel: (01274) 735848 Fax: (01274) 392280 E-mail: info@ohs.co.uk

▶ Safe Coatings Ltd, Bank House, High Street, Staplehurst, Tonbridge, Kent, TN12 0AE Tel: (01580) 893087 Fax: (01580) 893473 E-mail: enquiries@safecoatings.com

▶ Search Environmental Ltd, Centre Court, 1301 Stratford Road, Hall Green, Birmingham, B28 9HH Tel: (07821) 200228 Fax: 0121-702 1476 E-mail: enquiries@searchenvironmental.co.uk

UK Analytical Ltd, Lower Ground Floor, Dison Building, Buslingthorpe Lane, Leeds, LS7 2DG Tel: (0113) 2392 572 Fax: (0113) 2392 575 E-mail: uka@kirkstall.fsbusiness.co.uk

ASBESTOS WASTE OR ASBESTOS REMOVAL OR DISPOSAL OR PROCESSORS OR SERVICES OR MERCHANTS

A A R Ltd, Unit 12 Langley Wharf, Railway Terrace, Kings Langley, Hertfordshire, WD4 8JE Tel: (01923) 260043 Fax: (01923) 260478 E-mail: info@aar.co.uk

A R G Europe Ltd, Unit 2, 58A Alexandra Road, Ponders End, Enfield, Middlesex, EN3 7EH Tel: (020) 8804 8008 Fax: (020) 8805 7600 E-mail: argeurope@aol.com

Abastra Asbestos Removal Service Ltd, 19 Leigham Ave, London, SW16 2PT Tel: (020) 8677 4455 Fax: (020) 8677 4222 E-mail: eharrington@abastra.co.uk

Alpha Asbestos Removals Ltd, 158 Hatmore Park, Londonderry, BT48 0QJ Tel: (028) 7126 9167 Fax: (028) 7136 4356 E-mail: alpha_asbestos@btconnect.com

Aptiva Ltd, Shapwick Road, Poole, Dorset, BH15 4AP Tel: (01202) 670597 Fax: (01202) 680789 E-mail: sales@aptiva.co.uk

Bagnall Group Ltd, 940 Lakeside Drive, Centre Park, Warrington, WA1 1RY Tel: (01925) 651191 Fax: (01925) 651192 E-mail: admin@bagnallgroup.co.uk

C G B Humbertherm Ltd, Middleplatt Road, Immingham, South Humberside, DN40 1AH Tel: (01469) 572726 Fax: (01469) 571728 E-mail: sales@cgbhumbertherm.com

C M C Asbestos Surveys Ltd, Elker House, Elker Lane, Billington, Clitheroe, Lancashire, BB7 9HZ Tel: (01254) 822029 Fax: (01254) 825771 E-mail: info@cmcasestsossurveys.com

Colt Construction, Witty Street, Hull, HU3 4TT Tel: (01482) 581880 Fax: (01482) 215037 E-mail: info@colt-industrial.co.uk

Cooks Insulations, Holly Cottage, 74 New Road, Tadley, Hampshire, RG26 3AN Tel: (07711) 241365 Fax: 0118-981 2552

Crips Ltd, 40 Oxford Drive, Berdmonsey Street, London, SE1 2FB Tel: (020) 7403 1190 Fax: (020) 7407 4734 E-mail: enquiries@crips.co.uk

D B Industrial Services Ltd, Lyn Castle Way, Appleton, Warrington, WA4 4ST Tel: (01606) 597151 Fax: (01606) 597152 E-mail: sales@dbigroup.co.uk

Deborah Services Ltd, Thornes Moor Road, Wakefield, West Yorkshire, WF2 8PT Tel: (01924) 378222 Fax: (01924) 366250 E-mail: enquiries@deborahservices.co.uk

Erith Contractors Ltd, Riverside House, Maypole Crescent, Darent Industrial Park, Erith, Kent, DA8 2JZ Tel: (01322) 346811 Fax: (01322) 341978 E-mail: info@erith.net

European Asbestos Removals Ltd, 3 Norden Court, Alan Ramsbottom Way, Great Harwood, Blackburn, BB6 7UR Tel: (01254) 876686 Fax: (01254) 877000 E-mail: sales@asbestos-removers.co.uk

Alan Hadley Ltd, Colthrop Lacolthrop Business Park, Thatcham, Berkshire, RG19 4NB Tel: 0118-988 3266 Fax: 0118-988 4538 E-mail: waste@hadleys.co.uk

I C L Environmental Services Ltd, Firs Industrial Estate, Stourport Road, Kidderminster, Worcestershire, DY11 7QN Tel: (01562) 744655 Fax: (01562) 829207 E-mail: sales@iclenvironmental.co.uk

Industrial Insulation Services, Unit 2 Osborne Mill, Osborne Street, Oldham, OL9 6QQ Tel: 0161-626 0973 Fax: 0161-627 4846

J Cullen Thermals Ltd, 202 Deykin Avenue, Birmingham, B6 7BH Tel: 0121-327 5260 Fax: 0121-327 1124 E-mail: info@jcollenthermals.com

J E D Insulations Ltd, 529 Kingston Road, Ewell, Epsom, Surrey, KT19 0DL Tel: (020) 8661 1050 Fax: (020) 8661 1052 E-mail: jedinsulations@bt.com

Keanes Ltd, 4 Iverson Road, London, NW6 2HT Tel: (020) 7625 5555 Fax: (020) 7624 8444 E-mail: office@ballyholmeps.bangor.ni.sch.uk

L Rifkin (Liverpool) Ltd, Marsh Street, Kirkdale, Liverpool, L20 2BL Tel: 0151-922 3004 Fax: 0151-922 0780 E-mail: dhale.rifkin@cybase.co.uk

L Wynne & Co Manchester Ltd, Unit A7 The Dresser Centre, Whitworth Street, Openshaw, Manchester, M11 2NE Tel: 0161-223 2640 Fax: 0161-231 1367

▶ Lancebox Ltd, Block O Kent Kraft Industrial Estate, Lower Road, Northfleet, Gravesend, Kent, DA11 9SR Tel: (01322) 427482 Fax: (01322) 427397 E-mail: lancebox@fsmail.net

McGuinness (P.) Co. Ltd, Romdin House, Romdin Road, Ardwick, Manchester, M12 6BF Tel: 0161-273 5272 Fax: 0161-274 3884 E-mail: demolition@pmcguinness.com

▶ Mountain, Summit House, Northfield Road, Quarrington, Sleaford, Lincolnshire, NG34 8RT Tel: (0800) 0266936 Fax: (01529) 413857 E-mail: sales@greenmountains.co.uk

▶ Noble Health & Safety Consultancy Ltd, Ermington Mill, Ermington, Ivybridge, Devon, PL21 9NT Tel: (0870) 8504439 Fax: (01548) 831464 E-mail: enquiries@noblegroup.uk.com

▶ Oasis Environments Ltd, 2 Douglas Road, Horfield, Bristol, BS7 0JD Tel: 0117-951 9567 Fax: 0117-935 4467 E-mail: mail@oasis-bristol.co.uk

P W M Environmental Group, Bassett Road, Halesowen, West Midlands, B63 2RE Tel: (01384) 564866 Fax: (01384) 560945 E-mail: info@pwmills.co.uk

Pectel Group, Pectel Court, Burnt Mills Road, Basildon, Essex, SS13 1DT Tel: (01268) 591222 Fax: (01268) 590998 E-mail: info@pectel-group.co.uk

Phoenix Hazmat, Unit 6 Dabble Duck Industrial Estate, Shildon, County Durham, DL4 2RA Tel: (01388) 779220 Fax: (01388) 779230 E-mail: info@phoenixhazmatltd.co.uk

Pinnacle Insulation Ltd, Sandgate Industrial Estate, Hartlepool, Cleveland, TS25 1TZ Tel: (01429) 233828 Fax: (01429) 861047 E-mail: mark@pinnacle-aic.com

▶ Reddish Vale Installations, Albion House, Under Lane, Chadderton, Oldham, OL9 7PP Tel: 0161-688 6444 Fax: 0161-688 6448 E-mail: info@reddishvale.co.uk

Rhodar Ltd, Beza Road, Leeds, LS10 2BR Tel: 0113-270 0775 Fax: 0113-270 4124 E-mail: info@rhodar.co.uk

T.E. Scudder Ltd, Carey House, Great Central Way, Wembley, Middlesex, HA9 0HR Tel: (020) 8903 9722 Fax: (020) 8903 6311 E-mail: scudder@carey-plc.co.uk

Severn Insulation Co. Ltd, Somerton Works, Lloyd Street, Newport, Gwent, NP19 0JN Tel: (01633) 274239 Fax: (01633) 275252 E-mail: sales@severninsulation.co.uk

Shield Environmental Services, Shield House, Crown Way, Warmley, Bristol, BS30 8XJ Tel: 0117-960 6366 Fax: 0117-960 5583 E-mail: enquiries@shieldenvironmental.co.uk

Simpson Environmental Services Ltd, Simpsons Way, Stoke Poges Lane, Slough, SL1 3GD Tel: (01753) 533311 Fax: (01753) 533311 E-mail: jeff@simpsonrecycling.com

Toolbase Envrionmental, Waterloo Road, Romford, RM7 0AN Tel: (01708) 768766 Fax: (01708) 768773 E-mail: admin@toolbase.co.uk

U E S Ltd, Newark Road South, Glenrothes, Fife, KY7 4NS Tel: (01592) 773275 Fax: (01952) 773753

Weld Lag (Preston) Ltd, Unit 11 Oysten Mill, Strand Road, Preston, PR1 8UR Tel: (01772) 768858 Fax: (01772) 768865 E-mail: enquiries@weldlag.co.uk

ASBESTOS-FREE PACKINGS AND JOINTINGS

A M S (Burnham) Fluid Sealing, 30-32 Dropmore Road, Burnham, Slough, SL1 8BE Tel: (01628) 603311 Fax: (01628) 660040

E Dobson & Co Gaskets Ltd, Oakworth Road, Keighley, West Yorkshire, BD21 1QQ Tel: (01535) 607257 Fax: (01535) 608171 E-mail: sales@dobsongasket.com

Garlock GB Ltd, Premier Way, Lowfields Business Park, Elland, West Yorkshire, HX5 9HF Tel: (01422) 313600 Fax: (01422) 313601 E-mail: jasonsedgwick@compuserve.com

Klinger Ltd, Klinger Building, Wharfedale Road, Euroway Industrial Estate, Bradford, West Yorkshire, BD4 6SG Tel: (01274) 688222 Fax: (01274) 688962 E-mail: enquiries@klingeruk.co.uk

ASPHALT CLEANING CHEMICALS

Proteus Equipment Ltd, P O Box 33, Bury St. Edmunds, Suffolk, IP33 2RS Tel: (01284) 753954 Fax: (01284) 701369 E-mail: enquiries@proteusequipment.com

ASPHALT HEATERS

Cartem Ltd, Wharf Way, Glen Parva, Leicester, LE2 9TF Tel: (0870) 0665122 Fax: (0870) 0665133 E-mail: info@cartem.co.uk

ASPHALT MIXERS

Trojan Asphalt Mixers Ltd, 34 Hill La Industrial Estate, Markfield, Leicestershire, LE67 9PN Tel: (01530) 245232 Fax: (01530) 244063 E-mail: info@bitmen.co.uk

W.J.Horrod Ltd, 1 Leaway, Off Lea Bridge Road, London, E10 7QW Tel: (020) 8539 8746 E-mail: sales@wjhorrod.co.uk

ASPHALT OR BITUMEN OR BITUMINOUS MATERIAL FLOORING

The General Asphalte Company Ltd, La Brea House, Coventry Street, Birmingham, B5 5NJ Tel: 0121-643 1846 Fax: 0121-643 7134 E-mail: gacltd@talk21.com

Permanite, Cawder Quarry, Matlock, Derbyshire, DE4 2JH Tel: (01629) 580680 Fax: (01629) 57099 E-mail: info@permanite-asphalt.co.uk

Rock Asphalte, Latymer House, 2 Ravenscourt Road, London, W6 0UX Tel: (020) 8748 7881 Fax: (020) 8748 7225 E-mail: enquiries@rockasphalte.com

Sussex Asphalte, Clarendon Place, Portslade, Brighton, BN41 1DJ Tel: (01273) 417315 Fax: (01273) 422304 E-mail: info@sussexasphalte.co.uk

ASPHALT OR BITUMINOUS ROOFING CONTRACTORS

▶ Apex Roofing and building Maintenance, 28 Binley House, Highcliffe Drive, Roehampton, London, SW15 4PY Tel: 0208 392 9792 E-mail: masterson697@aol.com

▶ Bell Asphalt Company, 2e Penhill Road, Bexley, Kent, DA5 3EN Tel: (020) 8304 1901 Fax: (020) 8304 1901 E-mail: l-collins@ntlworld.com

Cavanagh Roofing Ltd, 36 Dalkeith Avenue, Glasgow, G41 5BN Tel: 0141-427 5555 Fax: 0141-427 5555

▶ Edwards Roofing, 1 Jacksonville Farm, Towyn Way West, Towyn, Abergele, Clwyd, LL22 9LG Tel: (01745) 339411 Fax: (01745) 369232 E-mail: sales@edwards-roofing.co.uk

Gillman Group Ltd, Chipstead Road, Erdington, Birmingham, B23 5HD Tel: 0121-244 4141 Fax: 0121-244 4142 E-mail: info@gillman-group.com

▶ Hi Spek Roofing Ltd, Hi-Spek House, Pitsford Road, Moulton, Northampton, NN3 7RS Tel: (01604) 492999 Fax: (01604) 492666 E-mail: info@hispekroofing.co.uk

Permanite, Cawder Quarry, Matlock, Derbyshire, DE4 2JH Tel: (01629) 580680 Fax: (01629) 57099 E-mail: info@permanite-asphalt.co.uk

ASPHALT PRODUCTION PLANT

B G Europa (U K) Ltd, Pipers Drove, Giffords Road, Newmarket, Suffolk, CB8 8PQ Tel: (01440) 821155 Fax: (01440) 821156 E-mail: sales@bgeuropa.co.uk

D & C Engineers Ltd, Unit 1, Mariner, Lichfield Road Industrial Estate, Tamworth, Staffs, B79 7UL Tel: (01827) 54824 Fax: (01827) 61203 E-mail: dandcengineers@compuseve.com

Parker Plant Ltd, PO Box 146, Leicester, LE4 6HD Tel: 0116-266 5999 Fax: 0116-261 0812 E-mail: sales@parkerplant.com

Puk Holdings Ltd, F Timothy'S Bridge, Stratford-upon-Avon, Warwickshire, CV37 9PR Tel: (01789) 206800 Fax: (01789) 206801 E-mail: puk@pukservices.co.uk

Sherwen Engineering Co. Ltd, Mile End Green, Dartford, DA2 8EB Tel: (01474) 703220 Fax: (01474) 705016 E-mail: sales@sherwen-engineering.co.uk

Westside Welding and Engineering Ltd, 9 Broadfield Place, Welwyn Garden City, Hertfordshire, AL8 6LJ Tel: 01707 332872 Fax: 01707 332872 E-mail: westsideweld@hotmail.co.uk

ASPHALT SURFACING EQUIPMENT

Amey plc, Sutton Courtenay, Abingdon, Oxfordshire, OX14 4PP Tel: (01235) 848811 Fax: (01235) 848822 E-mail: amey.fleet@amey.co.uk

Earthfair International, Cromwell House, Elland Road, Brighouse, West Yorkshire, HD6 2RG Tel: (01422) 374119 Fax: (01422) 374386 E-mail: enquiries@earthfair.co.uk

Finnpave, Thorbury Avenue, March Trading Estate, March, Cambridgeshire, PE15 0AZ Tel: (01354) 658600 Fax: (01354) 661888 E-mail: sales@finnpave.co.uk

ASPHALT SURFACING EQUIPMENT

– continued

Phoenix Engineering Co., Combe Street, Chard, Somerset, TA20 1JE Tel: (01460) 63531 Fax: (01460) 67388 E-mail: sales@phoenixeng.co.uk
Phoenix Transworld Ltd, Wharf Way, Glen Parva, Leicester, LE2 9TF Tel: (0870) 7505022 Fax: (0870) 7505033 E-mail: sales@phoenixtransworld.com

ASSEMBLERS/ASSEMBLY PRODUCTION TO THE TRADE, *See also headings for particular types such as Electromechanical; Electronic; Printed Circuit*

A J S Fasteners Ltd, 9 Maple Business Park, Walter Street, Birmingham, B7 5ET Tel: 0121-327 0660 Fax: 0121-327 3553 E-mail: sales@ajsfasteners.co.uk
Aim Engineering Ltd, Melandra Road, Brookfield, Glossop, Derbyshire, SK13 6JE Tel: (01457) 862505 Fax: (01457) 861753 E-mail: sdada@aimeng.co.uk
Altros Engineering Ltd, Birch House Commercial Square, Leigh Street, High Wycombe, Buckinghamshire, HP11 2QT Tel: (01494) 443082 Fax: (01494) 436186 E-mail: altros_uk@hotmail.com
Brookvale Manufacturing Co. Ltd, 15 Reddicap Trading Estate, Sutton Coldfield, West Midlands, B75 7DQ Tel: 0121-378 0833 Fax: 0121-311 1794 E-mail: enquiries@brookvale-manufacturing.co.uk
C T L Engineering Co. Ltd, Cromwell Road, Bredbury, Stockport, Cheshire, SK6 2RH Tel: 0161-430 3173 Fax: 0161-430 8643 E-mail: sales@ctl-eng.com
Camtronics Vale Ltd, Unit 1 Gwent Court, Victoria Park, Ebbw Vale, Gwent, NP23 8AN Tel: (01495) 352323 Fax: (01495) 352324 E-mail: info@camtronicsvale.com
F D Electronics Ltd, Unit U1, Riverside Industrial Estate, Bridge Road, Littlehampton, West Sussex, BN17 5DF Tel: (01903) 734160 Fax: (01903) 734170 E-mail: info@fd-electronics.net
Manjet Electronics, Longmeadow Works, Ringwood Road, Three Legged Cross, Wimborne, Dorset, BH21 6RD Tel: (01202) 823013 Fax: (01202) 823013
Mayview Packaging, 41 Oak Walk, Hockley, Essex, SS5 5AR Tel: (01702) 207560 Fax: (01702) 207560
Oxford Network Support, 6 Colwell Drive, Abingdon, Oxfordshire, OX14 1AU Tel: (01235) 468530 Fax: (01235) 555581 E-mail: sales@oxfordnetworksupport.com
S G Springs Ltd, 43 Crossgate Road, Park Farm Industrial Estate, Redditch, Worcestershire, B98 7SN Tel: (01527) 500955 Fax: (01527) 510278
Techman Engineering Ltd, Techman House, Broombank Park, Chesterfield Trading Estate, Sheepbridge, Chesterfield, Derbyshire, S41 9RT Tel: (01246) 261385 Fax: (01246) 453734 E-mail: enquiries@techman-engineering.co.uk
Walsall Pressings Co. Ltd, Wednesbury Road, Walsall, WS1 4JW Tel: (01922) 721152 Fax: (01922) 721106 E-mail: post@walpres.co.uk
Winpack Ltd, Unit A1 Lattersey Hill Trading Estate, Benwick Road, Whittlesey, Peterborough, PE7 2JA Tel: (01733) 208799 Fax: (01733) 204007
Yorkcraft, Tadcaster Road, Dringhouses, York, YO24 1QL Tel: (01904) 706654 Fax: (01904) 705627 E-mail: yorkcraft@york.gov.uk

ASSEMBLERS/ASSEMBLY SERVICES, ELECTRICAL

Alda Production Services Ltd, 14 Deanfield Court, Links 59 Business Park, Clitherhall, Rossendale, Lancashire, BB7 1QS Tel: (01200) 444354 Fax: (01200) 444359 E-mail: alda@alda.co.uk
Crow-Electro Instruments Ltd, 9A Connors Yard, Crowborough Hill, Crowborough, East Sussex, TN6 2DA Tel: (01892) 662078 Fax: (01892) 663983 E-mail: crowelectro@fsbdial.co.uk
Fusion Electrical Assembly, Unit 4, Station Industrial Estate, Burnham-On-Crouch, Essex, CM0 8RW Tel: (01621) 784107 Fax: (01621) 784327
St Davids Assemblies Co. Ltd, Glasfryn Road, St. Davids, Haverfordwest, Dyfed, SA62 6RY Tel: (01437) 720555 Fax: (01437) 725500 E-mail: sales@stdavidsassemblies.co.uk
Schort Industries Ltd, Trent Valley Industrial Estate, Rugeley, Staffordshire, WS15 3HA Tel: (01889) 583929 Fax: (01889) 583969 E-mail: sales@schort.co.uk
Truturn Precision Engineering (Charfield) Ltd, Units L2-L3, Bath Road Trading Estate, Lightpill, Stroud, Gloucestershire, GL5 3QF Tel: (01453) 752888 Fax: (01453) 753888 E-mail: truturn@truturn.co.uk

ASSEMBLERS/ASSEMBLY SERVICES, HAND, MISCELLANEOUS TECHNIQUES

Blue Boar, Unit D3 New Yatt Business Centre, Kite Lane, New Yatt, Witney, Oxfordshire, OX29 6TJ Tel: (01993) 868878 Fax: (01993) 868878 E-mail: helen.cook@virgin.net
S C A, Riverbank Works, Riverford Road, Glasgow, G43 1RP Tel: 0141-632 0999 Fax: 0141-632 8111

ASSEMBLY MACHINES/ SYSTEMS, AUTOMATIC

A B Precision Poole Ltd, 1 Fleets Lane, Poole, Dorset, BH15 3BZ Tel: (01202) 665000 Fax: (01202) 675965 E-mail: automation@abprecision.co.uk
A & D Group of Companies, Commerce Way, Lancing, West Sussex, BN15 8TA Tel: (01903) 763940 Fax: (01903) 763905 E-mail: sales@adauto.co.uk
Automation Conveyors Ltd, Coopies Field, Coopies Lane Industrial Estate, Morpeth, Northumberland, NE61 6JT Tel: (01670) 514354 Fax: (01670) 514328
Bauromat UK, Beauchamp Business Centre, Sparrowhawk Close, Malvern, Worcestershire, WR14 1GL Tel: (01684) 575757 Fax: (01684) 569887 E-mail: info@bauromat.co.uk
▶ Concept Automated Systems Ltd, Trinity House, 160 John Wilson Business Park, Chestfield, Whitstable, Kent, CT5 3RA Tel: (01227) 770677 Fax: (01227) 771392 E-mail: sales@conceptautomatedsystems.co.uk
Flangecombe Ltd, 147 Stringes Lane, Willenhall, West Midlands, WV13 1LW Tel: (01902) 602030 Fax: (01902) 604050 E-mail: info@flangecombe-ltd.fsbusiness.co.uk
Industrial Automation Ltd, 8 The Midway, Nottingham, NG7 2TS Tel: 0115-840 0500 Fax: 0115-840 5959 E-mail: sales@ind-auto.com
J F L Mecelec, Llanthony Road, Gloucester, GL2 5QT Tel: (01452) 413531 Fax: (01452) 307580 E-mail: mtl@mecelec.co.uk
Marlin Group Holdings, Marlin House Johnson Road, Fernsode Business Park, Ferndown Industrial Estate, Wimborne, Dorset, BH21 7SE Tel: (01202) 862900 Fax: (01202) 862901 E-mail: sales@marlin-ltd.co.uk
Mechatronic Production Systems Ltd, 2267 Coventry Road, Sheldon, Birmingham, B26 3PD Tel: 0121-742 7206 Fax: 0121-743 6882 E-mail: sales@mechatronic.co.uk
Modular Automation International Ltd, Talbot Way, Small Heath Business Park, Birmingham, B10 0HJ Tel: 0121-766 7979 Fax: 0121-766 6385 E-mail: crampton@modular.co.uk
Monk Converyors, Unit 18 Woodside Park, Catteshall Lane, Godalming, Surrey, GU7 1LG Tel: (01483) 791700 Fax: (01483) 791701 E-mail: sales@monk-converyors.co.uk
Phasa Developments, International House, Horsecroft Road, Harlow, Essex, CM19 5SU Tel: (01279) 630200 Fax: (01279) 630222 E-mail: sales@phasa.co.uk
Precision Motion (Cofil) Ltd, Unit 63, Roman Way, Longridge Road, Ribbleton, Preston, PR2 5BE Tel: (01772) 653366 Fax: (01772) 653163 E-mail: pmcofil@btconnect.com
Pumps & Ancilliaries, Churwell Vale, Shaw Cross Business Park, Dewsbury, West Yorkshire, WF12 7RD Tel: (01924) 468683 Fax: (01924) 469247
S P Automation Ltd, 3 Omega Centre, Sandford Lane, Wareham, Dorset, BH20 4DY Tel: (01929) 550465 Fax: (01929) 550522 E-mail: sales@spautomation.co.uk
S P Technology Ltd, Camperdown Industrial Park, George Buckman Drive, Dundee, DD2 3SP Tel: (01382) 880088 Fax: (01382) 880099 E-mail: info@sptechnology.co.uk
Special Purpose Equipment Ltd, 3 Loaland Business Centre, Maritime Close, Medway City Estate, Rochester, Kent, ME2 4AZ Tel: (01634) 295396 Fax: (01634) 718879 E-mail: johnlambell@special-purpose-equipment.co.uk
Unique Design Systemation, Manor Farm, Pickstock, Shifnal, Shropshire, TF10 8AH Tel: (01952) 550037 Fax: (01952) 551183 E-mail: bob@unique-design.co.uk

ASSEMBLY MACHINES/ SYSTEMS, SPECIAL PURPOSE

A B Precision Poole Ltd, 1 Fleets Lane, Poole, Dorset, BH15 3BZ Tel: (01202) 665000 Fax: (01202) 675965 E-mail: automation@abprecision.co.uk
A D M Automation, Nest Road, Gateshead, Tyne & Wear, NE10 0ES Tel: 0191-438 7888 Fax: 0191-438 7899 E-mail: sales@adm-automation.co.uk
Helbar Automation Ltd, 478 Rayleigh Rd, Eastwood, Leigh-on-Sea, Essex, SS9 5HZ Tel: (01702) 522425 Fax: (01702) 522425 E-mail: info@helbar.com
I M S Supplies Ltd, 3 Clifton Road, Huntingdon, Cambridgeshire, PE29 7EJ Tel: (01480) 411763 Fax: (01480) 417170 E-mail: imssupplies@cs.com
▶ Ingenia Solutions Ltd, 71 Victoria Road, Burgess Hill, West Sussex, RH15 9TR Tel: (01444) 876920 Fax: (01444) 876929 E-mail: sales@ingeniasolutions.co.uk
Marlin Group Holdings, Marlin House Johnson Road, Fernsode Business Park, Ferndown Industrial Estate, Wimborne, Dorset, BH21 7SE Tel: (01202) 862900 Fax: (01202) 862901 E-mail: sales@marlin-ltd.co.uk
Merlyn Electronics, Bridge Mills, Holland Street, Salford, M6 6EL Tel: 0161-745 7697 Fax: 0161-737 5615 E-mail: sales@merlyn-electronics.co.uk
Pneumatic Systems Ltd, Unit 32 Poplar Industrial Estate, Witton, Birmingham, B6 7AD Tel: 0121-344 3800 Fax: 0121 344 3866 E-mail: pneumaticsys@aol.com
▶ ProdAuto Ltd, Creative Industries, Science Park, Wolverhampton, WV10 9TG Tel: 01902 420877 Fax: (01902) 716312 E-mail: info@prodauto.co.uk
TQC Ltd, Hooton Street, Nottingham, NG3 2NJ Tel: 0115-950 3561 Fax: 0115-948 4642 E-mail: sales@tqc.co.uk
Ultra Contract Services, Camford Way, Luton, LU3 3AN Tel: (01582) 490000 Fax: (01582) 597038 E-mail: mail@ultracs.co.uk

ASSEMBLY ROBOT SYSTEMS

Labman Automation Ltd, Stokesley Industrial Park, Middlesbrough, Cleveland, TS9 5JZ Tel: 0845 4941644 Fax: (01642) 710667 E-mail: mailroom@labman.co.uk

ASSET INTEGRITY MANAGEMENT SERVICES

A W G Utility Services, Hampden House, Hitchin Road, Arlesey, Bedfordshire, SG15 6RT Tel: (01462) 731133 Fax: (01462) 834829
E M & I (Marine) Ltd, 18 Fairburn Terrace, Dyce, Aberdeen, AB21 7DT Tel: (01224) 771077 Fax: (01224) 771049E-mail: info@emiall.co.uk
P S L Energy Services Ltd, Badentoy Avenue, Badentoy Industrial Estate, Portlethen, Aberdeen, AB12 4YB Tel: (01224) 783008 Fax: (01224) 783005E-mail: sales@psles.com

ASSET INVENTORY SERVICES

▶ Sure Count Stocktakers, Unit 8, 88 Clyde Road, Didsbury, Manchester, M20 2JN Tel: 0161-448 9491 E-mail: info@surecount.co.uk

ASSET MANAGEMENT SERVICES

▶ Babtie Group Ltd, 95 Bothwell Street, Glasgow, G2 7HX Tel: 0141-204 2511 Fax: 0141-226 3109
M G H Reclaim Ltd, Unit 23 Common Bank Industrial Estate, Ackhurst Road, Chorley, Lancashire, PR7 1NH Tel: (01257) 279999 Fax: (01257) 279797 E-mail: neil@mgh-group.co.uk
M W H, Kirk Wynd House, Montgomery Place, The Village, East Kilbride, Glasgow, G74 4BF Tel: (01355) 260540 Fax: (01355) 279191 E-mail: stephen.friend@mwhglobal.com
▶ Pyramid Surveillance & Security, 6-8 Bread Street, Edinburgh, EH3 9AF Tel: 0131-229 7010 Fax: 0131-229 7074

ASSISTANT CHEF TEMPORARY STAFF RECRUITMENT AGENCIES

Orb Recruitment Ltd, PO Box 50, Manchester, M3 4EL Tel: 0161-244 5526 Fax: 0161-244 5526 E-mail: richard@premier-recruit.com
▶ Premier Recruitment International Ltd, PO Box 250, London, W1T 6DU Tel: (020) 7631 0050 Fax: 0870 288 4990 E-mail: info@premier-recruit.com
▶ Robochef Freelance Catering Services, 40 Hamill drive, Kilsyth, Glasgow, G65 0EQ Tel: (0785) 4400849 E-mail: mark@robochef.co.uk

ASTRONOMICAL TELESCOPES

▶ Sussex Astronomy Centre, 16 Mulberry Lane, Goring By Sea, Worthing, West Sussex, BN12 4JL Tel: (01903) 247317 E-mail: worthingastronomy@tiscali.co.uk

ATEX CERTIFICATION CONSULTANCY

▶ Risk Management Support, 11 The Street, Chirton, Devizes, Wiltshire, SN10 3QS Tel: (01380) 848170 Fax: (01380) 840152

ATHLETIC SHORTS

▶ A Campbell, Fernhurst Road, Milland, Liphook, Hampshire, GU30 7LU Tel: (01428) 741646 Fax: (01428) 741648

ATRIUM GLAZING CONTRACTORS

Melayway Glass Assemblies Ltd, Centennium House, Pyrford Road, West Byfleet, Surrey, KT14 6LD Tel: (01932) 349404 Fax: (01932) 349405 E-mail: info@melayway.co.uk
Space Decks Holdings Ltd, Leach Road, Chard Business Park, Chard, Somerset, TA20 1FA Tel: (01460) 260800 Fax: (01460) 66123 E-mail: skysystems@spacedecks.co.uk

ATTACHE CASES

▶ BWH Special Cases, Applebys Business Centre, 1 - 3 Mossley Road, Grasscroft, Oldham, OL4 4HH Tel: (01457) 810800 Fax: (01457) 877244 E-mail: tim.bristow@bwh-cases.co.uk
Trifibre Containers International, Mill Road, Newbourne, Woodbridge, Suffolk, IP12 4NP Tel: (01473) 811865 Fax: (01473) 811873 E-mail: mukesh@trifibre.co.uk

ATTENUATORS, *See also headings for particular types*

Tony Chapman Electronics Ltd, Hayleys Manor, Epping Upland, Epping, Essex, CM16 6PQ Tel: (01992) 578231 Fax: (01992) 576139 E-mail: sales@tceltd.co.uk
Credowan Ltd, 148 Stocks Lane, East Wittering, Chichester, West Sussex, PO20 8NT Tel: (01243) 670711 Fax: (01243) 672907 E-mail: sales@credowan.co.uk
Global Communications (UK) Ltd, Winterdale Manor, Southminster Road, Athorne, Chelmsford, CM3 6BX Tel: (01621) 743440 Fax: (01621) 743676 E-mail: info@globalcom.co.uk
Telonic Instruments Ltd, Toutley Industrial Estate, Toutley Road, Wokingham, Berkshire, RG41 1QN Tel: 0118-978 6911 Fax: 0118-979 2338 E-mail: info@telonic.co.uk

AUCTIONEERS, PROPERTY

▶ Repossessed House Sales, 31 Weavers House, Mannheim Quay, Swansea, SA1 1RU Tel: (01792) 529 575 E-mail: repossessed-house-sales@fsmail.net

AUCTIONS, COMPUTER HARDWARE

▶ Commtech It Solutions Ltd, 101 Lockhurst Lane, Godiva Trading Estate, Coventry, CV6 5SF Tel: (0871) 7112172 E-mail: sales@commtech-it.com
▶ PC Medic - Home PC Repair Service and Computer Sales, The Street, Gosfield, Halstead, Essex, CO9 1TP Tel: (01376) 321684 E-mail: info@pcmedicuk.net

AUCTIONS, ON LINE

▶ eboot auctions, 42a Stoke Road, Gosport, Hampshire, PO12 1JQ Tel: 02392 511909 E-mail: foo1952@hotmail.com
▶ Haggle4me, Omnia Offices, Sheffield, S1 2DU

AUDIBLE WARNING SIGNAL HORNS

▶ Fleet Electrical & Safety Direct Ltd, Unit 10, Commerce Business Centre, Commerce Close, West Wilts Trading Estate, Westbury, Wiltshire, BA13 4LS Tel: (01373) 823242 Fax: (01373) 823206 E-mail: sales@fleetelectrical.co.uk
J. Hudson & Co. (Whistles) Ltd, 244 Barr Street, Hockley, Birmingham, B19 3AH Tel: 0121-554 2124 Fax: 0121-551 9293 E-mail: sale@acmewhistles.co.uk
Stirling Evp Ltd, 222 West Road, Westcliff-on-Sea, Essex, SS0 9DE Tel: (01702) 300999 Fax: (01702) 303039 E-mail: info@stirlingevp.com

AUDIBLE WARNING SIGNALS

Fulleon, Llantarnam Industrial Park, Cwmbran, Gwent, NP44 3AW Tel: (01633) 628500 Fax: (01633) 866346 E-mail: sales@fulleon.co.uk
LGM Products Ltd, 18 Riverside Park Industrial Estate, Dogflud Way, Farnham, Surrey, GU9 7UG Tel: (01252) 725257 Fax: (01252) 727627 E-mail: sales@lgmproducts.com

AUDIBLE WARNING SIGNALS – *continued*

STS Alarm Systems, 435 Old Walsall Road, Birmingham, B42 1HX Tel: 0121-357 8390 Fax: 0121-686 9278

AUDIENCE RESPONSE SYSTEM HIRE

▶ Answerback Ltd, 56a Hatton Garden, London, EC1N 8HP Tel: (020) 7251 9313 E-mail: paul.krisman@answerbackinteractive.com

AUDIENCE RESPONSE SYSTEMS

▶ Answerback Ltd, 56a Hatton Garden, London, EC1N 8HP Tel: (020) 7251 9313 E-mail: paul.krisman@answerbackinteractive.com

AUDIO ALARM SYSTEMS

Advanced Safety Communications, 26b Brookfield Road, Arnold, Nottingham, NG5 7ER Tel: 0115-967 9067 Fax: 0115-956 1585 E-mail: sales@ascaudio.co.uk
Barb Security Systems, Reeds, Colliers End, Ware, Hertfordshire, SG11 1EH Tel: (0845) 2304248
Coles Electroacoustics Ltd, Pindar Road, Hoddesdon, Hertfordshire, EN11 0BZ Tel: (01992) 466685 Fax: (01992) 446583 E-mail: sales@coleselectroacoustics.com
J King Electronics Ltd, The Stables, Handsworth Road, Handsworth, Sheffield, S13 9BH Tel: 0114-242 4902 Fax: 0114-244 5100

AUDIO AMPLIFIERS

Arcam, Pembroke Avenue, Waterbeach, Cambridge, CB25 9QR Tel: (01223) 203200 Fax: (01223) 863384 E-mail: info@arcam.co.uk
▶ BF Interactive, 128 Frankwell, Shrewsbury, SY3 8JX Tel: (01743) 270444 Fax: (01743) 368381 E-mail: mitch@bfgroup.co.uk
C I E Group, Blenheim Industrial Estate, Widdowson Close, Bulwell, Nottingham, NG6 8WB Tel: 0115-977 0075 Fax: 0115-977 0081 E-mail: marketing@cie-ltd.co.uk
Carlsbro Electronics Ltd, Cross Drive, Kirkby-in-Ashfield, Nottingham, NG17 7LD Tel: 08452 582910 Fax: 01623 755436 E-mail: sales@carlsbro.co.uk
Cloud Electronics Ltd, 140 Staniforth Road, Sheffield, S9 3HF Tel: 0114-244 7051 Fax: 0114-242 5462 E-mail: info@cloud.co.uk
H W Audio Ltd, 180-198 St. Georges Road, Bolton, BL1 2PH Tel: (01204) 385199 Fax: (01204) 364057 E-mail: sales@hwaudio.co.uk
Headstock Distribution Ltd, Deal Park Road, Coombswood Industrial Estate West, Halesowen, West Midlands, B62 8HD Tel: 0121-508 6666 Fax: 0121-508 6677 E-mail: sales@laney.co.uk
Integrated Engineering Solutions Ltd, Millbrook Road West, Southampton, SO15 0HW Tel: (023) 8090 5020 Fax: (023) 8070 4073 E-mail: mail@iesl.co.uk
▶ J F Associates, Aberdeen House, 1-3 Cromwell Road, Maidenhead, Berkshire, SL6 6BJ Tel: (01628) 625709 Fax: (01628) 633269 E-mail: info@jfa.org.uk
M A J Electronics, Stallings Lane, Kingswinford, West Midlands, DY6 7HU Tel: (01384) 278646 Fax: (01384) 298877 E-mail: sales@majelectronic.co.uk
Marshall Amplifications plc, Denbigh Road, Bletchley, Milton Keynes, MK1 1DQ Tel: (01908) 375411 Fax: (01908) 376118 E-mail: jtait@marshallamps.com
Micina Technologies Group, Regent House, 40 Nelson Street, Leicester, LE1 7BA Tel: 0116-233 9944 Fax: 0116-233 9945 E-mail: mike@micina.co.uk
Peavey Electronics Ltd, Great Folds Road, Oakley Hay Industrial Estate, Corby, Northamptonshire, NN18 9ET Tel: (01536) 461234 Fax: (01536) 747222 E-mail: info@peavey-eu.com
Qmusic Ltd, 23a Airport Industrial Estate, Newcastle upon Tyne, NE3 2EF Tel: 0191-286 2039 Fax: 0191-286 0177 E-mail: info@qmusic.co.uk
Quad Electroacoustics Ltd, I A G House, Sovereign Court, Huntingdon, Cambridgeshire, PE29 6XU Tel: (0845) 4580011 Fax: (01480) 431767 E-mail: info@quad-hifi.co.uk
Studiocare Professional Audio Ltd, Unit 9, Century Building, Summers Road, Brunswick Business Park, Liverpool, L3 4BL Tel: (0845) 3458910 Fax: (0845) 3458911 E-mail: sales@studiocare.com

AUDIO ANCILLARY EQUIPMENT

Audionics Presentation Services, Alpen House, Headley Road, Grayshott, Hindhead, Surrey, GU26 6JG Tel: (01428) 713937
▶ Brilliant Hi Fi, 35 Cumberland Road, Urmston, Manchester, M41 9HR Tel: (07963) 117341 E-mail: sales@brilliancehifi.co.uk
Canford Audio, Crowther Road, Washington, Tyne & Wear, NE38 0BW Tel: 0191-418 1133 Fax: 0191-418 1001 E-mail: admin@canford.co.uk
Christian Fabrications Ltd, 5 Chase Side Crescent, Enfield, Middlesex, EN2 0JA Tel: (020) 8482 2082 Fax: (020) 8364 6488
Graff of Newark Ltd, Woodhill Road, Collingham, Newark, Nottinghamshire, NG23 7NR Tel: (01636) 893036 Fax: (01636) 893317 E-mail: sales@graffofnewark.co.uk
Harbeth Audio Ltd, 3 Lindfield Enterprise Park, Lewes Road, Lindfield, Haywards Heath, West Sussex, RH16 2LH Tel: (01444) 484371 Fax: (01444) 487629 E-mail: sound@harbeth.co.uk
Las Manchester Ltd, 91 Heaton Street, Denton, Manchester, M34 3RY Tel: 0161-336 3444
M T R Ltd, 58 Cross Road, Watford, WD19 4DQ Tel: (01923) 234050 Fax: (01923) 255746 E-mail: mtrltd@aol.com
Penridge Multi-Media Ltd, The Barn, Rashwood Meadow, Rashwood Hill, Rashwood, Droitwich, Worcestershire, WR9 0BJ Tel: (01527) 861911 Fax: (01527) 861899 E-mail: sales@penridge.com
Torus Production Services Stage & T V, 28-30 Wood Wharf, London, SE10 9BT Tel: (020) 8293 4909 Fax: (020) 8293 4933
Xta Electronics Ltd, Riverside Business Centre, Worcester Road, Stourport-on-Severn, Worcestershire, DY13 9BZ Tel: (01299) 879977 Fax: (01299) 879969 E-mail: sales@xta.co.uk

AUDIO CABINETS

Sambell Engineering Ltd, Winston Avenue, Croft, Leicester, LE9 3GQ Tel: (01455) 283251 Fax: (01455) 283908 E-mail: post@atacama-audio.co.uk

AUDIO CABLE ASSEMBLIES

Dolby Laboratories Inc, Interface Business Park, Binknoll Lane, Wootton Bassett, Swindon, SN4 8QJ Tel: (01793) 842100 Fax: (01793) 842101 E-mail: website@dolby.com
Farcroft Electronic Services Ltd, Tanglewood 88 Jobs Lane, Coventry, CV4 9ED Tel: (024) 7646 0087 Fax: (024) 7647 0369 E-mail: enquires@farcroft-uk.com
Switchcraft Incorporated, Robinson Way, Portsmouth, PO3 5TD Tel: (023) 9266 1579 Fax: (023) 9227 4731 E-mail: intsales@switchcraft.com

AUDIO CABLES

Amphenol Spectrastrip Ltd, Unit 21-23 Romsey Industrial Estate, Greatbridge Road, Romsey, Hampshire, SO51 0HR Tel: (01794) 517575 Fax: (01794) 516246 E-mail: info@spectra-strip.com
Bryant Broadcast, 70b Stafford Road, Croydon, CR0 4NE Tel: (020) 8404 4050 Fax: (020) 8404 4080 E-mail: sales@bryant-broadcast.co.uk

AUDIO CASSETTE BLANKS

Downsoft Ltd, Downsway House, Epsom Road, Ashtead, Surrey, KT21 1LD Tel: (01372) 272422 Fax: (01372) 276122 E-mail: sales@downsoft.co.uk
Emi Records UK Ltd, E M I House, 43 Brook Green, London, W6 7EF Tel: (020) 7605 5000 Fax: (020) 7605 5050 E-mail: enquiries@emirecordedmusic.co.uk

AUDIO CASSETTE DUPLICATING

House Of Caduceus Ltd, 5 Richards Ave, Lincoln, LN6 8SJ Tel: 01522 688142 Fax: 01522 688142

AUDIO CASSETTE DUPLICATING SYSTEMS

Graff of Newark Ltd, Woodhill Road, Collingham, Newark, Nottinghamshire, NG23 7NR Tel: (01636) 893036 Fax: (01636) 893317 E-mail: sales@graffofnewark.co.uk

AUDIO COMMUNICATION SYSTEMS

Advanced Safety Communications, 26b Brookfield Road, Arnold, Nottingham, NG5 7ER Tel: 0115-967 9067 Fax: 0115-956 1585 E-mail: sales@ascaudio.co.uk
Claude Systems Ltd, 4 Bellman Way, Donibristle Industrial Park, Hillend, Dunfermline, Fife, KY11 9JW Tel: (01383) 820011 Fax: (01383) 820093 E-mail: sales@claudesystems.com
M T R Ltd, 58 Cross Road, Watford, WD19 4DQ Tel: (01923) 234050 Fax: (01923) 255746 E-mail: mtrltd@aol.com
▶ Presentation Services, Cranborne Industrial Estate, Cranborne Road, Potters Bar, Hertfordshire, EN6 3JN Tel: (01707) 655131 Fax: (01707) 648131 E-mail: info@presservgroup.com

AUDIO CONFERENCING BUREAU SERVICES

▶ Arkadin UK Ltd, 26-28 Hammersmith Grove, London, W6 7JA Tel: (020) 8742 6380 Fax: (020) 8742 6355 E-mail: d.creigh@arkadin.co.uk

AUDIO CONNECTORS

Ambitron Components Ltd, 4 Station Road, Hungerford, Berkshire, RG17 0DY Tel: (01488) 685404 Fax: (01488) 685406 E-mail: sales@ambitron.co.uk
Argosy Ltd, Units 6-7, Ridgeway, Drakes Drive, Long Crendon, Buckinghamshire, HP18 9BF Tel: (01844) 202101 Fax: (01844) 202025 E-mail: sales@argosycable.com
Arrow Components, Unit 5 Mill Court, Spindle Way, Crawley, West Sussex, RH10 1TT Tel: (01293) 558900 Fax: (01293) 558901
Imperial Components, 7 Sutherland Court, Brownfields, Welwyn Garden City, Hertfordshire, AL7 1BJ Tel: (01707) 321122 Fax: (01707) 321121
Lane Electronics, Slinfold Lodge, Stane Street, Slinfold, Horsham, West Sussex, RH13 0RN Tel: (01403) 790661 Fax: (01403) 790849 E-mail: sales@fclane.com
Neutrik (UK) Ltd, Westridge Business Park, Ryde, Isle Of Wight, PO33 1QT Tel: (01983) 811441 Fax: (01983) 811439 E-mail: sales@neutrik.co.uk
Northern Connectors Ltd, Abbotsfield Road, Reginald Road Industrial Estate, St. Helens, Merseyside, WA9 4HU Tel: (01744) 815001 Fax: (01744) 814040 E-mail: sales@northern-connectors.co.uk

AUDIO EDITING EQUIPMENT

Rosswood Studios Ltd, 114 Wendover Road, Stoke Mandeville, Aylesbury, Buckinghamshire, HP22 5TE Tel: (01296) 612009 E-mail: marianne@rosswood.co.uk

AUDIO FADERS

Penny & Giles Controls Ltd, 15 Airfield Rd, Christchurch, Dorset, BH23 3TG Tel: (01202) 409409 Fax: (01202) 409475 E-mail: sales@pennyandgiles.com

AUDIO INDUCTION LOOP INSTALLATION

Strata Communications, 25 Hibson Avenue, Rochdale, Lancashire, OL12 7RU Tel: (01706) 344375 Fax: (01706) 633172 E-mail: info@stratacommunications.co.uk
Synapse Electronics, Old Crofters Yard, Combi Street, Oban, Argyll, PA34 4HU Tel: (01631) 565055

AUDIO INDUCTION LOOPS

▶ Access Disability Ltd, 55 Coronation Street, Blackpool, FY1 4NY Tel: (01253) 753300 Fax: 01253 733402 E-mail: Keith@accessdisability.co.uk
Ampetronic Ltd, Northern Road, Newark, Nottinghamshire, NG24 2ET Tel: (01636) 610062 Fax: (01636) 610063 E-mail: sales@ampetronic.com
Audio Design Services Ltd, St Davids House, Adcroft St, Higher Hillgate, Stockport, Cheshire, SK1 3HW Tel: 0161-476 1010 Fax: 0161-666 6366 E-mail: sales@ads-worldwide.net

AUDIO MIXERS

A M S Neve Ltd, Billington Road, Burnley, Lancashire, BB11 5UB Tel: (01282) 457011 Fax: (01282) 417282 E-mail: info@ams-neve.com
Cloud Electronics Ltd, 140 Staniforth Road, Sheffield, S9 3HF Tel: 0114-244 7051 Fax: 0114-242 5462 E-mail: info@cloud.co.uk
Studiocare Professional Audio Ltd, Unit 9, Century Building, Summers Road, Brunswick Business Park, Liverpool, L3 4BL Tel: (0845) 3458910 Fax: (0845) 3458911 E-mail: sales@studiocare.com

AUDIO OR HI FI EQUIPMENT OR SYSTEMS

A M S Neve Ltd, Billington Road, Burnley, Lancashire, BB11 5UB Tel: (01282) 457011 Fax: (01282) 417282 E-mail: info@ams-neve.com
Amazon Karaoke Disco, Glen Way House, Brightlingsea Road, Thorrington, Colchester, CO7 8JH Tel: (01206) 520756
Amstrad plc, Brentwood House, 169 Kings Road, Brentwood, Essex, CM14 4EF Tel: (01277) 228888 Fax: (01277) 211350 E-mail: admin@amstrad.com
Arcam, Pembroke Avenue, Waterbeach, Cambridge, CB25 9QR Tel: (01223) 203200 Fax: (01223) 863384 E-mail: info@arcam.co.uk
B & W Group Ltd, Dale Road, Worthing, West Sussex, BN11 2BH Tel: (01903) 221800 Fax: (01903) 221801 E-mail: info@bwgroup.com
Bang & Olufsen, Unit 630 Wharfdale Road, Winnersh Triangle, Wokingham, Berkshire, RG41 5TP Tel: 0118-969 2288 Fax: 0118-969 3388
Curtis Beauclair Automatics Ltd, 99 Wills Crescent, Hounslow, TW3 2JE Tel: (020) 8894 4463 Fax: (020) 8894 4463 E-mail: cutejuke@aol.com
Black Box A V Ltd, Unit 25, Aberafon Road, Baglan Industrial Park, Port Talbot, West Glamorgan, SA12 7DJ Tel: (01639) 767007 Fax: (01639) 767008 E-mail: sales@blackboxav.co.uk
Bose, Unit 1 Ambley Green, Gillingham Business Park, Gillingham, Kent, ME8 0NJ Tel: (0870) 7414500 Fax: (0870) 7414545 E-mail: shane_wheatcroft@bose.com
Carrick Marketing, 13 Mossgiel Avenue, Kilmarnock, Ayrshire, KA3 7DN Tel: (01563) 524320 Fax: (01563) 524320 E-mail: jcarrick@btconnect.com
▶ Chip Ltd, 46a Grahams Road, Falkirk, FK1 1HR Tel: (01324) 628853
Coomber Electronic Equipment Ltd, 1 Croft Walk, Worcester, WR1 3NZ Tel: (01905) 25168 Fax: (01905) 612701 E-mail: sales@coomber.co.uk
Creek Audio Ltd, 12 Avebury Court, Mark Road, Hemel Hempstead, Hertfordshire, HP2 7TA Tel: (01442) 260146 Fax: (01442) 243766
▶ Croaky Karaoke, 11 Perrylands, Charlwood, Horley, Surrey, RH6 0BL Tel: (01293) 863796 E-mail: taylormadeentertainment@btconnect.com
Cryogenics International Ltd, 7 Brunel Way, Fareham, Hampshire, PO15 5TX Tel: (01489) 886722 Fax: (01489) 575229 E-mail: alan.rjones@cryogenicsinternational.co.uk
▶ Early Riser Disco Centre, 50-52 Beulah Road, London, E17 9LQ Tel: (020) 8520 3401 Fax: (020) 8520 1073 E-mail: sales@earlyriser.co.uk
ES Repairs, Buckhurst Ave, Carshalton, Surrey, SM5 1PF Tel: (020) 8395 1536 E-mail: electrosysrep@blueyonder.co.uk
▶ Excel Audio Systems Ltd, Highfield Road, Acton, London, W3 0AJ Tel: (020) 8354 0820 Fax: (020) 8354 0834 E-mail: sales@excelaudio.co.uk
▶ Expotus Components, The Studio, Warehorne Road, Hamstreet, Ashford, Kent, TN26 2JJ Tel: (01233) 731137 Fax: (01233) 731237 E-mail: sales@expotuscomponents.com
F W Patterson Television Ltd, 21C1 Ben Nevis Estate, Claggan, Fort William, Inverness-Shire, PH33 6RU Tel: (01397) 702612 Fax: (01397) 701054 E-mail: fwpatterson@btconnect.com
Feltech Electronics Ltd, 7 Long Spring, Porters Wood, St. Albans, Hertfordshire, AL3 6PE Tel: (01727) 834888 Fax: (01727) 848704 E-mail: sales@feltech.co.uk
GFH SOUND AND VISION LTD, 39 SHERRARDS WAY, BARNET, HERTS, EN5 2BW Tel: 07815 735607 Fax: (020) 8449 6531 E-mail: garretthenderson345@hotmail.com
Greenwood Audio Visual, 1 Wolverhampton Road, Kingswinford, West Midlands, DY6 7HX Tel: (01384) 287337 Fax: (01384) 287347
Harbeth Audio Ltd, 3 Lindfield Enterprise Park, Lewes Road, Lindfield, Haywards Heath, West Sussex, RH16 2LH Tel: (01444) 484371 Fax: (01444) 487629 E-mail: sound@harbeth.co.uk
Harris & Russell, 124 East Road, London, N1 6AF Tel: (0870) 7277551 Fax: (020) 7608 2970 E-mail: harrisrussell@msn.com
▶ HPSS Pa Hire, 5 Dairycoates Industrial Estate, Wiltshire Road, Hull, HU4 6PA Tel: (01482) 221810 Fax: (01482) 221735 E-mail: hire@hpss.co.uk
J V C Forex UK Ltd, JVC House, JVC Business Park, London, NW2 7BA Tel: (020) 8450 3282 Fax: (020) 8208 4385
J V C UK Ltd, Gelderd Lane, Leeds, LS12 6AL Tel: 0113-279 5741 Fax: 0113-263 3987
Juke Box Services Ltd, Electroline House, 15 Lion Road, Twickenham, TW1 4JH Tel: (020) 8288 1700 E-mail: enquiries@jukeboxservices.co.uk
Karaoke Direct, Starlaw Road, Bathgate, West Lothian, EH47 7BW Tel: (01506) 636107 Fax: (01506) 653730 E-mail: sales@karaokedirect.co.uk
L M C Audio Systems Ltd, Unit 10 Acton Park Industrial Estate, The Vale, London, W3 7QE Tel: (020) 8743 4680 Fax: (020) 8749 9875 E-mail: sales@lmcaudio.co.uk
Leader Sound, Causeway End, Church Causeway, Potton, Sandy, Bedfordshire, SG19 2RL Tel: (01767) 262880 Fax: (01767) 262888 E-mail: info@leadersound.com
Leisuretec Distribution Ltd, Unit L3 Cherrycourt Way, Leighton Buzzard, Bedfordshire, LU7 4UH Tel: (01525) 850085 Fax: (01525) 852285 E-mail: vestax@leisuretec.co.uk

AUDIO OR HI FI EQUIPMENT OR SYSTEMS – *continued*

Linn Products Ltd, Glasgow Road, Eaglesham, Glasgow, G76 0EQ Tel: 0141-307 7777 E-mail: helpline@linn.co.uk
Martin Dawes Solutions Ltd, Martin Dawes House, Europa Boulevard, Westbrook, Warrington, WA5 7WH Tel: (01925) 555000 Fax: (01925) 494835
▶ Medion Karaoke Entertainment, 13 Hill Top View, Normanton, West Yorkshire, WF6 1LZ Tel: (01924) 211848
Meridian Audio Ltd, Stonehill, Stukeley Meadows Industrial Es, Huntingdon, Cambridgeshire, PE29 6EX Tel: (01480) 445678 Fax: (01480) 445686
Mosses & Mitchell Ltd, Unit 5, Bath Road Business Centre, Devizes, Wiltshire, SN10 1XA Tel: (01380) 722993 Fax: (01380) 728422 E-mail: sales@mosses-mitchel.com
Multi Media Medium Ltd, Bridge House, Glob Works Place, Bolton, BL2 1DG Tel: (01204) 387410 Fax: (01204) 369924
Music Works, 14 Stockport Road, Cheadle, Cheshire, SK8 2AA Tel: 0161-491 2932 Fax: 0161-428 3633
Musonic UK Ltd, Unit 13 Business Centre, Colne Way, Watford, WD24 7ND Tel: (020) 8950 5151 Fax: (020) 8950 5391 E-mail: sales@musonic.co.uk
Neat Acoustics, 29b Harmire Enterprise Park, Barnard Castle, County Durham, DL12 8XT Tel: (01833) 631021 Fax: (01833) 630022 E-mail: bob@neat.co.uk
P M D Magnetics, Avenue Farm Industrial Estate, Birmingham Road, Stratford-upon-Avon, Warwickshire, CV37 0HR Tel: (01789) 268579 Fax: (01789) 414450 E-mail: sales@pmdmagnetics.co.uk
Partington & Co., Fawkham Road, Longfield, Kent, DA3 7QP Tel: (01474) 709299 Fax: (01474) 709295E-mail: gailpart@aol.com
▶ Party Knights, 7 Stanford Road, Swindon, SN25 2AB Tel: (01793) 702880
Path Group plc, 8 Dormer Road, Thame, Oxfordshire, OX9 3UD Tel: (01844) 219000 Fax: (01844) 219099
Pioneer Technology (U K) Ltd, Pioneer House, Whitwood Common Lane, Castleford, West Yorkshire, WF10 5PE Tel: (01977) 551830 Fax: (01977) 512430
Protech Ltd, 4 Nuffield Road, St. Ives, Cambridgeshire, PE27 3LX Tel: (01325) 310520 Fax: (01480) 300670 E-mail: sales@pro-tech-ltd.co.uk
R C Snelling Investments Ltd, Blofield Corner, Blofield, Norwich, NR13 4SQ Tel: (01603) 712202 Fax: (01603) 716052 E-mail: sales@snellingtv.co.uk
R G Jones, 16 Endeavour Way, London, SW19 8UH Tel: (020) 8971 3100 Fax: (020) 8971 3101 E-mail: enquiries@rgjones.co.uk
Rega Research Ltd, 119 Park Street, Westcliff-On-Sea, Essex, SS0 7PD Tel: (01702) 333071 Fax: (01702) 432427 E-mail: service@rega.co.uk
▶ S L V, The Barn, Fifield Farm, Marslton Road, Marlston Hermitage, Thatcham, Berkshire, RG18 9UN Tel: (01635) 202500 Fax: (01635) 202088 E-mail: Info@s-l-v.co.uk
Sabre International Ltd, Unit 9, Brookside Business Centre, Church Street, Swallowfield, Reading, RG7 1TH Tel: 0118-988 8818 Fax: 0118-988 8828 E-mail: david@sabre-international.com
▶ Seven Oaks Sound Of Vision, 62 North Street, Leeds, LS2 7PN Tel: 0113-245 2775 Fax: 0113-242 5114
Sharp Electronics (UK) Ltd, Sharp House, Thorp Road, Manchester, M40 5BE Tel: 0161-205 2333 Fax: 0161-205 7076
▶ Showtime Karaoke, 14 Filbert Street, Oldham, OL1 4HQ Tel: 0161-628 2652
Sony Centre, 134 Baker Street, London, W1U 6UB Tel: (020) 7486 2526 Fax: (020) 7487 5603E-mail: admin@audiovisual4u.co.uk
Sound Image UK Ltd, 52 Milton Road, London, SW14 8JR Tel: (020) 8255 6868 E-mail: sales@choicehifi.com
Sound Leisure Ltd, Sandlees Way, Leeds, LS15 8AR Tel: (0845) 2301775 Fax: (0845) 2301776 E-mail: sales@soundleisure.com
Sound & Secure Ltd, 454-456 Thornton Road, Bradford, West Yorkshire, BD8 9BS Tel: (01274) 775005 Fax: (01274) 770051
South West Sound & Light, The Old Smithy, Cockwood, Starcross, Exeter, EX6 8RA Tel: (01626) 890806 Fax: (01626) 891465 E-mail: sales@swlighting.co.uk
Stage Two Ltd, Unit J Penfold Trading Estate, Imperial Way, Watford, WD24 4YY Tel: (01923) 230789 Fax: (01923) 255048 E-mail: info@stage-two.co.uk
Tannoy Group Ltd, Rosehall Industrial Estate, Coatbridge, Lanarkshire, ML5 4TF Tel: (01236) 420199 Fax: (01236) 428230 E-mail: enquiries@tannoy.com
Tavea Electrical Goods, Rear of 21 Finkle Street, Thirsk, North Yorkshire, YO7 1DA Tel: (01845) 524627 Fax: (01845) 525060 E-mail: shubebbard@tavea.co.uk
Total Home Entertainment International, Unit 1 Rosevale Business Park, Newcastle, Staffordshire, ST5 7QT Tel: (01782) 561000 Fax: (01782) 565400
Visual Systems, Unit 11 Brickfields Industrial Park, Kiln Lane, Bracknell, Berkshire, RG12 1NQ Tel: (01344) 427161 Fax: (01344) 860282 E-mail: sales@visualsystems.co.uk
Wats On Lighting & Sound Ltd, Upper House, Presteigne, Powys, LD8 2HG Tel: (01544) 260114 Fax: (01544) 267686
▶ Westminster Sonus, Westminster House, Herschel Centre, Church Street, Slough, SL1 1PJ Tel: (01753) 553325 Fax: (01753) 553867 E-mail: crn@westminstersonus.com

AUDIO OR HI FI EQUIPMENT OR SYSTEMS ACCESSORIES

▶ Brilliant Hi Fi, 35 Cumberland Road, Urmston, Manchester, M41 9HR Tel: (07963) 117341 E-mail: sales@brilliancehifi.co.uk
▶ Maxview Ltd, Common Lane, Setch, King's Lynn, Norfolk, PE33 0AT Tel: (01553) 813300 Fax: (01553) 813301 E-mail: sales@maxview.ltd.uk
▶ Wackiki, 7 Upper Mealough Road, Belfast, BT8 8LR Tel: 02890 817612 Fax: 02890 817613 E-mail: adam@wackiki.com

AUDIO OR HI FI EQUIPMENT OR SYSTEMS COMPONENTS

▶ Showtech Sound & Light, Unit 1k Moss Industrial Estate, Woodbine St East, Rochdale, Lancashire, OL16 5LB Tel: (01706) 347159 Fax: 01706 347912 E-mail: info@showtechuk.com

AUDIO OR HI FI EQUIPMENT OR SYSTEMS CONSULTANTS OR DESIGNERS

▶ B & H Sound Services Ltd, The Old School Studio, Crowland Road, Eye, Peterborough, PE6 7TN Tel: (01733) 223535 Fax: (01733) 223545 E-mail: sound@bhsound.co.uk
▶ Blacka Acoustics, Storage World, Reddish Road, Stockport, Cheshire, SK5 7BW Tel: 0161-477 9700 Fax: 0161-477 9300 E-mail: sales@blackaacoustics.co.uk
Hammer Film Productionltd, 131-151 Great Titchfield Street, London, W1W 5BB Tel: (020) 7637 2322 Fax: (020) 7665 6465 E-mail: pete@skylineaudiopost.com
▶ Marchant Design Associates, 28/29 Woodside Close, Amersham, Buckinghamshire, HP6 5EF Tel: 01494 725093 E-mail: business@marchantassociates.com
▶ Showtech Sound & Light, Unit 1k Moss Industrial Estate, Woodbine St East, Rochdale, Lancashire, OL16 5LB Tel: (01706) 347159 Fax: 01706 347912 E-mail: info@showtechuk.com
▶ Sonaptic Ltd, Chancery Court, Lincolns Inn, Lincoln Road, High Wycombe, Bucks, HP12 3RE Tel: 01494 429368 E-mail: mail@sonaptic.com
Toa Corporation, Unit 2 Hook Rise South Industrial Park, Hook Rise South, Surbiton, Surrey, KT6 7LD Tel: (0870) 7740987 Fax: (0870) 7770839 E-mail: info@toa.co.uk
▶ Wackiki, 7 Upper Mealough Road, Belfast, BT8 8LR Tel: 02890 817612 Fax: 02890 817613 E-mail: adam@wackiki.com

AUDIO OR HI FI EQUIPMENT OR SYSTEMS HIRE

▶ Countywide Entertainments, 63 Normandy Close, Exmouth, Devon, EX8 4PB Tel: (01395) 268263 E-mail: steve@countywideentertainments.co.uk
Cruise Controls, 18 Becconsall Drive, Crewe, CW1 4RU Tel: 0777 9265214 E-mail: info@cruisecontrols.co.uk
▶ Direct Sound Hire, Unit 52 Imex Business Park, Ormonde Street, Fenton, Stoke-on-Trent, ST4 3NP Tel: (01782) 596666 E-mail: info@directsoundhire.co.uk
▶ James Walton, Leyshon Road, Wheatley, Oxford, OX33 1XF Tel: 01865 875519 E-mail: contact@acdisco.com

AUDIO OR HI FI EQUIPMENT OR SYSTEMS IMPORT OR EXPORT MERCHANTS OR AGENTS

Audioserv Ltd, Beaver Works,, 36 Whitehouse street,, Hunslet,, Leeds, LS10 1AD Tel: 0113 2164255 E-mail: audioserv@gmail.com
▶ Prestige Imports & Logistics Ltd, Porterfield House 157 Harton Lane, South Shields, Tyne & Wear, NE34 0PW Tel: 0191 4200585 Fax: 0191 4200585 E-mail: enquries@pil-ltd.com
Technical Help to Exporters, 389 Chiswick High Road, London, W4 4AL Tel: (020) 8996 7474 Fax: (020) 8996 7048 E-mail: the@bsi-global.com
▶ Wackiki, 7 Upper Mealough Road, Belfast, BT8 8LR Tel: 02890 817612 Fax: 02890 817613 E-mail: adam@wackiki.com

AUDIO OR HI FI EQUIPMENT OR SYSTEMS MAINTENANCE OR REPAIR

Audioserv Ltd, Beaver Works,, 36 Whitehouse street,, Hunslet,, Leeds, LS10 1AD Tel: 0113 2164255 E-mail: audioserv@gmail.com
▶ HPSS Pa Hire, 5 Dairycoates Industrial Estate, Wiltshire Road, Hull, HU4 6PA Tel: (01482) 221810 Fax: (01482) 221735 E-mail: hire@hpss.co.uk
▶ J F Associates, Aberdeen House, 1-3 Cromwell Road, Maidenhead, Berkshire, SL6 6BJ Tel: (01628) 625709 Fax: (01628) 633269 E-mail: info@jfa.org.uk
Jai Electronics, 155 High Street, London, NW10 4TR Tel: (020) 8965 5080 Fax: (020) 8961 2924 E-mail: jai@beeb.net
▶ Lightspeed Entertainments, 108 Quay Road, Bridlington, East Yorkshire, YO16 4JB Tel: (07831) 192740 Fax: (01262) 679735 E-mail: lightspeed@trancefixed.fsnet.co.uk
▶ Servicesound, 31 Turkey Road, Bexhill-On-Sea, East Sussex, TN39 5HB Tel: (01424) 216245 E-mail: contact@servicesound.com

AUDIO OR HI FI EQUIPMENT OR SYSTEMS, RECORDING STUDIO

▶ Berry Street Studio, 1 Berry Street, London, EC1V 0AA Tel: (020) 7253 5885 E-mail: info@berrystreetstudio.com
▶ Classical Location Recording Services, Hope Cottage, 10 Middle Road, Berkhamsted, Hertfordshire, HP4 3EQ Tel: 01442 877698 E-mail: jules@julesmusic.co.uk
Creative Audio Design, 12 Harold Road, Hawley, Dartford, DA2 7SA Tel: (01322) 224998 E-mail: jbthecad@homecall.co.uk
▶ Excel Audio Systems Ltd, Highfield Road, Acton, London, W3 0AJ Tel: (020) 8354 0820 Fax: (020) 8354 0834 E-mail: sales@excelaudio.co.uk
Focusrite Audio Engineering Ltd, Windsor House, Turnpike Road, High Wycombe, Buckinghamshire, HP12 3FX Tel: (01494) 462246 Fax: (01494) 459920 E-mail: sales@focusrite.com
Hi-Tech Audio Ltd, 68 Turnberry Drive, Wilmslow, Cheshire, SK9 2QN Tel: (01625) 521302 Fax: (01625) 526345 E-mail: info@hitechaudio.com
▶ Minion A V, 44 Dunraven Parade, Belfast, BT5 6BT Tel: (07799) 558787 Fax: E-mail: nathanmateer@minionvideo.co.uk
▶ MLK Music, 5 Madeline Grove, Ilford, Essex, IG1 2RG Tel: 07951 302734 E-mail: info@mlkmusic.co.uk
▶ Riverside Studios, Four Horse Shoes Yard, Milnsbridge, Huddersfield, HD3 4NE Tel: (01484) 642131 E-mail: contact@riversidestudios.info
▶ SinCity Records UK, Polaris Studio's, Milestone Cottage, 61 London Road, Calne, Wiltshire, SN11 0AA Tel: 01249 816026 Fax: 01249 816026 E-mail: sincity@pobox.com

AUDIO OR HI FI EQUIPMENT OR SYSTEMS, TO SPECIFICATION

Audioserv Ltd, Beaver Works,, 36 Whitehouse street,, Hunslet,, Leeds, LS10 1AD Tel: 0113 2164255 E-mail: audioserv@gmail.com

AUDIO REPRODUCTION, LARGE SCALE, *See Sound Reproduction etc*

AUDIO STANDS

Apollo Hifi Furniture Ltd, Castle Works, High Street, Tipton, West Midlands, DY4 8HJ Tel: 0121-520 5070 Fax: 0121-522 2055 E-mail: sales@apollohifi.co.uk
Power Drive Drum Co. Ltd, Unit M1 Cherrycourt Way, Leighton Buzzard, Bedfordshire, LU7 4UH Tel: (01525) 370292 Fax: (01525) 852126 E-mail: info@mypowerdrive.com

AUDIO TECHNICAL RECORD PROCESSING

Pip Recording, Mendip View, Binhay Road, Yatton, Bristol, BS49 4HA Tel: (01934) 830301 Fax: (01934) 830302 E-mail: piprecording@aol.com
Richmond Film Services, The Old School, Park Lane, Richmond, Surrey, TW9 2RA Tel: (020) 8940 6077 Fax: (020) 8948 8326
Sprint Data Systems, Bridge Road, Ashford, Kent, TN23 1JA Tel: (01233) 665822 Fax: (01233) 665821 E-mail: sales@sprint-data.co.uk

AUDIO TEST EQUIPMENT/ SYSTEMS

Neutrik (UK) Ltd, Westridge Business Park, Ryde, Isle Of Wight, PO33 1QT Tel: (01983) 811441 Fax: (01983) 811439 E-mail: sales@neutrik.co.uk

AUDIO TRANSCRIPTION SERVICES

Audio Experts, Springboard Business Centre, Ellerbeck Way, Middlesbrough, Cleveland, TS9 5JZ Tel: (01642) 715345 Fax: (01642) 715344 E-mail: office@audio-experts.co.uk
▶ CMP Support, 46 Freshwater Drive, Poole, Dorset, BH15 4JE Tel: (01202) 245318 Fax: 01202 245318 E-mail: enquiries@cmpsupport.co.uk

AUDIO TRANSFORMERS

Crow-Electro Instruments Ltd, 9A Connors Yard, Crowborough Hill, Crowborough, East Sussex, TN6 2DA Tel: (01892) 662078 Fax: (01892) 663983 E-mail: crowelectro@fsbdial.co.uk
Danbury Electronics, 20 Cutlers Road, Saltcoats Industrial Estate, South Woodham Ferrers, Chelmsford, CM3 5XJ Tel: (01245) 328174 Fax: (01245) 328963 E-mail: danburyelectx@aol.com
E A Sowter Ltd, Old Boatyard, Cullingham Road, Ipswich, IP1 2EG Tel: (01473) 219390 Fax: (01473) 236188 E-mail: sales@sowter.co.uk
S P Wound Components Ltd, Unit 12 Stanley Green Industrial Estate, Stanley Green Esc, Poole, Dorset, BH15 3TH Tel: (01202) 682828 Fax: (01202) 682828 E-mail: spwoundcomp@boltblue.com

AUDIO VALVES

Billington Export Ltd, Units 1e-2e, Gilmans Industrial Estate, Billingshurst, West Sussex, RH14 9EZ Tel: (01403) 784961 Fax: (01403) 783519 E-mail: sales@bel-tubes.co.uk

AUDIO VISUAL AIDS

Absolute Sounds Ltd, 58 Durham Road, London, SW20 0TW Tel: (020) 8971 3909 Fax: (020) 8879 7962 E-mail: info@absolutesounds.com
Apollo Hifi Furniture Ltd, Castle Works, High Street, Tipton, West Midlands, DY4 8HJ Tel: 0121-520 5070 Fax: 0121-522 2055 E-mail: sales@apollohifi.co.uk
Audio Access Ltd, 9 Romney Road, Rottingdean, Brighton, BN2 7GG Tel: (01273) 300001 Fax: (01273) 390909 E-mail: sound@audioaccess.co.uk
Audio Visual Consultants Ltd, 107-111 Whitehouse Loan, Edinburgh, EH9 1AT Tel: 0131-447 6211 Fax: 0131-452 8372 E-mail: info@avc-edinburgh.co.uk
Blue Systems, 34 Clifton Road, Cambridge, CB1 7EB Tel: (01223) 404100 Fax: (01223) 414900
Business Presentations Ltd, Hillfoot Farm, Hitchin Road, Shefford, Bedfordshire, SG17 5JD Tel: (01462) 817406 Fax: (01462) 850130 E-mail: sally@business-presentations.co.uk
Concept Media Ltd, 172 Tonbridge Road, Wateringbury, Maidstone, Kent, ME18 5NS Tel: (01622) 817177 Fax: (01622) 817178 E-mail: enquiries@concept-media.co.uk
▶ Digital Cubed, The Hive, Nottingham, NG1 4BU Tel: (0870) 8148333 Fax: 0115-848 4612 E-mail: nicholas.timms@digitalcubed.co.uk
Drake Educational Associates Ltd, 89 St. Fagans Road, Fairwater, Cardiff, CF5 3AE Tel: (029) 2056 0333 Fax: (029) 2055 4909 E-mail: info@drakeav.com
ECT, Pangbourne, Reading, RG8 8TX Tel: 0118-984 1141 Fax: 0118-984 1847 E-mail: adam@ect-av.com
Edinburgh Camcorder Centre, 78 Haymarket Terrace, Edinburgh, EH12 5LQ Tel: 0131-313 5166 Fax: 0131-313 5182 E-mail: steven@camcordercentre.com
James & Beeching, Bartons Yard, Dunleys Hill, Odiham, Hook, Hampshire, RG29 1DP Tel: (01256) 701987 Fax: (01256) 701301
Kent Superior Pictures, Fred Martin Studio Barton Road, Dover, Kent, CT16 2ND Tel: (01304) 202827 Fax: (01384) 213824
Mcmillen UK Ltd, 60 Nelson St, Aberdeen, AB24 5ES Tel: 01224 645366 Fax: 01224 624097
Marlin Agency Ltd, 68-70 Surrey Street, Belfast, BT9 7FS Tel: (028) 9066 8233 Fax: (028) 9068 2033 E-mail: marlinni@aol.com
Picture Perfect Audio Visuals Ltd, AV House, Wallingford Road, Uxbridge, Middlesex, UB8 2RW Tel: (01895) 454 650 Fax: (01895) 454 657 E-mail: enquiries@ppav.co.uk
The Rural Media Company, Sullivan House, 72-80 Widemarsh Street, Hereford, HR4 9HG Tel: (01432) 344039 Fax: (01432) 270539 E-mail: info@ruralmedia.co.uk
T Christien, 46 Strawberry Vale, Twickenham, TW1 4SE Tel: (020) 8892 3621 Fax: (020) 8891 5946 E-mail: terry@cartoonology.com

AUDIO VISUAL AIDS – *continued*

Vanderquest Ltd, 7 Latimer Road, Teddington, Middlesex, TW11 8QA Tel: (020) 8943 2818 Fax: (020) 8943 4812 E-mail: nick@vanderquest.co.uk

AUDIO VISUAL CABINETS

▶ Axis Display LLP, Unit B, Centurion Way, Erith, Kent, DA18 4AF Tel: (020) 8319 7743 Fax: (020) 8319 7776 E-mail: sales@axisdisplay.co.uk

▶ BT Showroom, 155 Tailyour Road, Crownhill, Plymouth, PL6 5DJ Tel: (01752) 791222 E-mail: sales@btshowroom.com

▶ Fabriweld Tubular Steel Products Ltd, Gibbons Street, Harrimans Lane, Lenton Lane Industrial Estate, Nottingham, NG7 2SD Tel: 0115-942 2264 Fax: 0115-942 2267 E-mail: jamie@fabriweld.co.uk

▶ Forth It, Unit 2 Scion House, Stirling University Innovation Park, Stirling, FK9 4NF Tel: (01786) 442022 Fax: (01786) 451523 E-mail: sales@forthit.com

▶ Scotaudio, Unit 2, Beta Centre, Stirling University Innovation Park, Stirling, FK9 4NF Tel: (01786) 442022 Fax: (01786) 458033 E-mail: andy@scotaudio.com

▶ SoundAV, 9 Scriven Road, Knaresborough, North Yorkshire, HG5 9EQ Tel: (0772) 5050322 E-mail: info@soundav.co.uk

AUDIO VISUAL EQUIPMENT

▶ Aberdeen Projector Hire, 8 Albert Place, Aberdeen, AB25 1RG Tel: (01224) 261303 Fax: (01224) 261302

▶ B & H Sound Services Ltd, The Old School Studio, Crowland Road, Eye, Peterborough, PE6 7TN Tel: (01733) 223535 Fax: (01733) 223545 E-mail: sound@bhsound.co.uk

▶ BT Showroom, 155 Tailyour Road, Crownhill, Plymouth, PL6 5DJ Tel: (01752) 791222 E-mail: sales@btshowroom.com

Datatec, 31 Bollington Road, Stockport, Cheshire, SK4 5ER Tel: 0161-432 4245 Fax: 0161-442 1375 E-mail: datatec@tiscali.co.uk

▶ Glasgow Projector Hire, Unit 25, New Albion Industrial Estate, Halley Street, Glasgow, G13 4DJ Tel: 0141-435 7110 Fax: 0141-435 7109 E-mail: info@glasgow-projector-hire.co.uk

▶ H A V Solutions, 103 Maiden Place, Lower Earley, Reading, RG6 3HE Tel: (07910) 303555 Fax: 0118-947 3107

▶ Incendo Ltd, Unit H Sheen Lane, London, SW14 8AE Tel: (020) 8876 5333 Fax: (020) 8876 5322 E-mail: info@incendo.co.uk

▶ Interactive Technologies Ltd, Unit 14, Moorbrook Park, Didcot, Oxfordshire, OX11 7HP Tel: (01235) 516900 Fax: (01235) 516910 E-mail: mdew@itdisplays.com

▶ Lek Trix Enterprises, The Barn, 15 Station Street, Whetstone, Leicester, LE8 6JS Tel: 0116-286 5956 Fax: 0116-286 5956 E-mail: lektrix@aol.com

Majenta Audio Visual Ltd, Unit 2, Wills Industrial Estate, Salmon Parade, Bridgwater, Somerset, TA6 5JT Tel: (01278) 433700 Fax: (01278) 433131 E-mail: sales@majenta-av.co.uk

▶ Ovation Audio Visual Systems, Belgrave Business Centre, 45 Frederick Street, Edinburgh, EH2 1EP Tel: (0845) 6448851 Fax: 0131-666 2556 E-mail: sales@ovationaudiovisual.com

▶ Presentation Services Ltd, Unit 3, Mitre Bridge Industrial Estate, Mitre Way, London, W10 6AU Tel: (020) 8964 1440 Fax: (020) 8964 2449 E-mail: phill.dale@pslevents.com

▶ SoundAV, 9 Scriven Road, Knaresborough, North Yorkshire, HG5 9EQ Tel: (0772) 5050322 E-mail: info@soundav.co.uk

AUDIO VISUAL EQUIPMENT AND ACCESSORIES

1st Choice, Stileway Business Park, Lower Strode Road, Clevedon, Avon, BS21 6UU Tel: (01275) 871131 Fax: (01275) 871115 E-mail: fcgbristol@aol.com

A N Audio, 34 Huntingdon Street, St. Neots, Huntingdon, Cambridgeshire, PE19 1BB Tel: (01480) 472071 Fax: (01480) 386456 E-mail: sales@anaudio.co.uk

▶ A V Custom, 42 Winslow Road, Wingrave, Aylesbury, Buckinghamshire, HP22 4PS Tel: (01296) 682381 Fax: (01296) 682676

▶ A V Shopper, S1 St. James House, Vicar Lane, Sheffield, S1 2EX Tel: (0870) 7532295 Fax: 0114-223 6333 E-mail: info@avshopper.co.uk

▶ A W E Europe Ltd, Unit BI, Longmead Business Centre, Blenheim Road, Epsom, Surrey, KT19 9QQ Tel: (01372) 729777 Fax: (01372) 729767 E-mail: info@awe-europe.co.uk

▶ Absolute, Unit 11 Viewpoint, Boxley Road, Penenden Heath, Maidstone, Kent, ME14 2DZ Tel: (01622) 663345 Fax: (01622) 890419 E-mail: info@absoluteaudiosystemsltd.co.uk

Acoustic Arrangements, York Farm, Fenn Lane, Upton, Nuneaton, Warwickshire, CV13 6BL Tel: (01455) 213373 Fax: (01455) 213581 E-mail: mail@a-a.uk.com

ADI UK Ltd, Pittman Court, Pittman Way, Fulwood, Preston, PR2 9ZG Tel: (0800) 592346 Fax: (01772) 708201 E-mail: sales@theadigroup.com

▶ A-Line Audio Visual Services, Parkhill, Bucksburn, Aberdeen, AB21 7AT Tel: (01224) 723377 Fax: (01224) 723399 E-mail: sales@a-line.co.uk

Ambush Ltd, 11 Emmott Avenue, Ilford, Essex, IG6 1AL Tel: (020) 8554 0016 Fax: (020) 8554 6375 E-mail: enquiries@ambushed.com

Ampetronic Ltd, Northern Road, Newark, Nottinghamshire, NG24 2ET Tel: (01636) 610062 Fax: (01636) 610063 E-mail: sales@ampetronic.com

Amx UK Ltd, Auster Road, York, YO30 4GD Tel: (01904) 343100 Fax: (01904) 343101 E-mail: sales@amxuk.co.uk

Anders & Kern UK Ltd, Norderstedt House, James Carter Road, Mildenhall, Bury St. Edmunds, Suffolk, IP28 7RQ Tel: (01638) 510900 Fax: (01638) 510901 E-mail: info@anders-kern.co.uk

Asysco P.L.C., Asisco House, Omega Way, Egham, Surrey, TW20 8RD Tel: (01784) 487000 Fax: (01784) 487060 E-mail: info@rslav.com

▶ Audace, North Street, Stoke-sub-Hamdon, Somerset, TA14 6QR Tel: (01935) 825910 Fax: (08707) 051692

Audio Visual Consultants Ltd, 107-111 Whitehouse Loan, Edinburgh, EH9 1AT Tel: 0131-447 6211 Fax: 0131-452 8372 E-mail: info@avc-edinburgh.co.uk

▶ Av Shed, 6 West Haddon Road, Guilsborough, Northampton, NN6 8QL Tel: (0870) 2242246 Fax: (0871) 7333866 E-mail: sales@avshed.com

Av4business Ltd, PO Box 123, Batley, West Yorkshire, WF17 6ZZ Tel: (0870) 2412364 Fax: (0870) 2412232 E-mail: sales@av4business.com

Bang & Olufsen, 147 Kings Road, London, SW3 5TX Tel: (020) 7376 5222 Fax: (020) 7376 5333 E-mail: chelsea@bang-olufsen.uk.com

▶ Bang & Olufsen, 3 Market Place, Reading, RG1 2EG Tel: 0118-959 0770 Fax: 0118-959 0980

Big Screen, Church Lane, Gorleston, Great Yarmouth, Norfolk, NR31 7BG Tel: (01493) 662913 Fax: (01493) 440677 E-mail: sales@bigscreenonline.co.uk

Blue Systems, 34 Clifton Road, Cambridge, CB1 7EB Tel: (01223) 404100 Fax: (01223) 414900

Bose Ltd, 138-139 Cheshire Oaks Outlet Village, Kinsey Road, Ellesmere Port, CH65 9JJ Tel: 0151-357 8300 Fax: (08707) 415546 E-mail: cheshire_oaks@bose.com

C S P Audio Visual Ltd, Unit 55 Third Avenue, Deeside Industrial Park, Deeside, Clwyd, CH5 2LA Tel: (01244) 288322 Fax: (01244) 288344 E-mail: sales@cspaudiovisual.co.uk

Calumet Ltd, 93-103 Drummond Street, London, NW1 2HJ Tel: (0870) 6030303 E-mail: website@calumetphoto.co.uk

Camerson Productions, Deane, Basingstoke, Hampshire, RG25 3AR Tel: (01256) 780600 E-mail: richardcutler@camerson.co.uk

▶ Central Presentations Ltd, Innsworth Technology Park, Innsworth, Gloucester, GL3 1DL Tel: (01452) 731123 Fax: (01452) 731333 E-mail: dave@centralhospitality.co.uk

CH Design Installation Co. Ltd, 31 Southwold Mansions, Widley Road, London, W9 2LE Tel: (020) 7289 1792 Fax: (020) 7266 4607

Chameleon AV, Swallowfields, Welwyn Garden City, Hertfordshire, AL7 1JD Tel: (01707) 339444 Fax: (01707) 377400 E-mail: sales@chameleonav.com

▶ Clarke Automation, Quarles, Elm Lane, Roxwell, Chelmsford, CM1 4NJ Tel: (01245) 231234 Fax: (01245) 231270 E-mail: sales@clarkeautomation.com

Comm-Tec Ltd, 6 Danbury Court, Sunrise Parkway, Linford Wood East, Milton Keynes, MK14 6PL Tel: (01908) 550039 Fax: (01908) 696120 E-mail: sales@comm-tec.co.uk

Conferex Communications, Inglewood, Copsewood Lane, Stone Allerton, Axbridge, Somerset, BS26 2NS Tel: (01934) 712824 Fax: (01934) 713004 E-mail: info@conferex.co.uk

Coomber Electronic Equipment Ltd, 1 Croft Walk, Worcester, WR1 3NZ Tel: (01905) 25168 Fax: (01905) 612701 E-mail: sales@coomber.co.uk

▶ Couture Digital, Studio 12 & 13, 1b Darnley Road, London, E9 6QH Tel: (0870) 0429813 E-mail: info@couturedigital.com

▶ Creo Audio Equipment, 62 North Street, Leeds, LS2 7PN Tel: 0113-246 7373 Fax: 0113-242 5114 E-mail: sales@creo-designs.com

▶ D & T Electronics, Woodfield Road, Broadheath, Altrincham, Cheshire, WA14 4EU Tel: 0161-926 9149 Fax: (0870) 4445945 E-mail: sales@dandt.co.uk

DB Audio & Electronic Services Ltd, 5 East Point, High Street, Seal, Sevenoaks, Kent, TN15 0EG Tel: (01732) 760877 Fax: (01732) 760977

▶ Deago Audio Visual Solutions Ltd, 8 Stoney Lane, Quinton, Birmingham, B32 1AN Tel: 0121-422 3777 Fax: 0121-423 2223 E-mail: deagoavs@hotmail.com

▶ Deejay Solutions, 101 Upper Queen Street, Rushden, Northamptonshire, NN10 0BS Tel: (01933) 411777 Fax: (01933) 358721

▶ Designer Vision Ltd, Unit 75, Capitol Industrial Park, Capitol Way, London, NW9 0EW Tel: (020) 8200 1515 Fax: (020) 8200 0022

The Diamond Stylus Company Ltd, Council Street West, Llandudno, Gwynedd, LL30 1ED Tel: (01492) 860880 Fax: (01492) 860653 E-mail: sales@diamondstylus.co.uk

E T C (UK) Ltd, Unit 4A, Barking Business Centre, 25 Thames Road, Barking, Essex, IG11 0JP Tel: (020) 8477 4490 Fax: (020) 8594 1243 E-mail: info@etclondonparis.com

ECT, Pangbourne, Reading, RG8 8TX Tel: 0118-984 1141 Fax: 0118-984 1847 E-mail: adam@ect-av.com

Equation Audiovisual Ltd, Boston House, Downsview Road, Wantage, Oxfordshire, OX12 9FF Tel: (01235) 771144 Fax: (01235) 770404

Fumeo U K, The Old Warehouse, 2 Ashford Road, Brighton, BN1 6LJ Tel: (01273) 508622 Fax: (01273) 564693

Funky Junk, 409 Hornsey Road, London, N19 4EF Tel: (020) 7609 5479 Fax: (020) 7609 5483 E-mail: sales@funky-junk.co.uk

▶ Sally Gould, Paper Mill Cottages, Harcourt, Stanton upon Hine Heath, Shrewsbury, SY4 4LS Tel: (01939) 200444 Fax: (01939) 200555

Great Guns, 43-45 Camden Road, London, NW1 9LR Tel: (020) 7692 4444 Fax: (020) 7692 4422 E-mail: greatguns@greatguns.com

Gregory Audio Visual Ltd, 190 St. Aidans Avenue, Blackburn, BB2 4EA Tel: (01254) 674444 Fax: (01254) 674444 E-mail: sales@gregoryav.co.uk

▶ Gwynne TV & Electrical Services, 18-20 Benfield Way, Braintree, Essex, CM7 3YS Tel: (01376) 322567 Fax: (01376) 329666 E-mail: info@gwynne-tv.co.uk

Adam Hall Ltd, 3 The Cordwainers, Temple Farm Industrial Estate, Southend-on-Sea, SS2 5RU Tel: (01702) 613922 Fax: (01702) 617168 E-mail: sales@adamhall.co.uk

Hama Ltd, Unit 4 Cherrywood, Chineham Business Park, Basingstoke, Hampshire, RG24 8WF Tel: (01256) 374700 Fax: (01256) 374749 E-mail: sales@hama.co.uk

Harpers A V Ltd, 16 Woking Business Park, Albert Drive, Woking, Surrey, GU21 5JY Tel: (01483) 757577 Fax: (01483) 729449 E-mail: sales@harpersav.com

Hills Components Ltd, Valley Park, Olds Approach, Watford, WD18 9TL Tel: (01923) 772773 Fax: (01923) 421421 E-mail: sales@hillscomponents.co.uk

Hive Industries, 28 High Street, Arlesey, Bedfordshire, SG15 6RA Tel: (01462) 735151 Fax: (08707) 708089

Hocken Audio Visual Ltd, 5 Waterhouse Lane, Kingswood, Tadworth, Surrey, KT20 6EB Tel: (01737) 370371 Fax: (01737) 370372 E-mail: sales@hockenav.co.uk

Ikon AVS Ltd, Unit 238 Ikon Estate, Droitwich Road, Hartlebury, Kidderminster, Worcestershire, DY10 4EU Tel: (01299) 250991 Fax: (01299) 250983 E-mail: sales@ikonavs.com

Image Business Systems UK Ltd, 455 Maxwell Avenue, Harwell Intnl Business Centre, Didcot, Oxfordshire, OX11 0PY Tel: (01235) 865500 Fax: (01235) 865511 E-mail: sales@imagebusinesssystems.co.uk

Impact Europe, Europe House, 170 Windmill Road West, Sunbury-On-Thames, Middlesex, TW16 7HB Tel: (01932) 733700 Fax: (01932) 733710 E-mail: info@impact-europe.com

Impact Visuals, 1327 Stratford Road, Hall Green, Birmingham, B28 9HH Tel: 0121-702 0888 Fax: 0121-702 0889 E-mail: sales@impactvisuals.co.uk

▶ Inn Vision Multimedia Ltd, Unit 10 Viewpoint, Boxley, Penenden Heath, Maidstone, Kent, ME14 2DZ Tel: (01622) 765345 Fax: (01622) 765345 E-mail: sales@innvision.co.uk

▶ Insight Visual Systems Ltd, 1a Foxholes Avenue, Hertford, SG13 7JG Tel: (01992) 505177 Fax: (01992) 505178 E-mail: sales@insight-visual.co.uk

Integrated Circles Ltd, 8 Lebanon Road, London, SW18 1RE Tel: (020) 8874 6666 Fax: (020) 8870 4387E-mail: info@integrated-circles.com

▶ Invision, 5 Eastern Way, Bury St. Edmunds, Suffolk, IP32 7AB Tel: (01284) 749731 Fax: (01284) 747336 E-mail: info@invisionuk.com

▶ J K Audio Visual Ltd, Unit 7 Newport Business Park, Audley Avenue, Newport, Shropshire, TF10 7DP Tel: (01952) 825088

J UK E Services Ltd, Cratfield, Halesworth, Suffolk, IP19 0QL Tel: (01986) 785315 E-mail: jukeservicesltd@aol.com

JVC Professional Europe Ltd, JVC House, 12 Priestley Way, London, NW2 7BA Tel: (020) 8208 6200 Fax: (020) 8208 6260 E-mail: sales@jvcpro.co.uk

L R G Sound & Vision Ltd, 171-175 Albertbridge Road, Belfast, BT5 4PS Tel: (028) 9045 1381 Fax: (028) 9073 1478 E-mail: lrg@btconnect.com

Libec Europe Ltd, Priory House Industrial Estate, Pitsford Street, Birmingham, B18 6LX Tel: (01527) 596955 Fax: (01527) 596788 E-mail: sales@libeceurope.com

Libra Professional Broadcast, Chester House, 91-95 Alcester Road, Studley, Warwickshire, B80 7NJ Tel: (01527) 853305 Fax: (01527) 852086 E-mail: andy@libraproinfo.co.uk

▶ Lost It Productions Ltd, Crossland Court, Czar Street, Leeds, LS11 9PR Tel: 0113-245 7773 Fax: 0113-245 7773

M B Audio Visual Ltd, Unit 2c Thirsk Industrial Park, York Road, Thirsk, North Yorkshire, YO7 3BX Tel: (01845) 522322 Fax: (01845) 522322 E-mail: info@mbaudiovisual.co.uk

M J Visual Systems Ltd, Unit 1, New Bury Park, Easthampnett, Chichester, West Sussex, PO18 0JY Tel: (01243) 780816 Fax: (01243) 783562 E-mail: sales@mjvisual.co.uk

Majenta Audio Visual Ltd, Unit 2, Wills Industrial Estate, Salmon Parade, Bridgwater, Somerset, TA6 5JT Tel: (01278) 433700 Fax: (01278) 433131 E-mail: sales@majenta-av.co.uk

▶ The Media Services Co., 106 Tappesfield Road, London, SE15 3EZ Tel: (020) 7635 3459 Fax: (020) 7635 3459 E-mail: info@themediaservicescompany.com

Messages On Hold Ltd, P O Box 55, Barnet, Hertfordshire, EN4 0HF Tel: 020-8441 4920 Fax: 020-8449 2626E-mail: moh@london.com

Midland Audio Visual Ltd, 210 New Road, Rubery, Rednal, Birmingham, B45 9JA Tel: 0121-453 3141 Fax: 0121-453 4626 E-mail: sales@midlandaudiovisual.co.uk

▶ Modus Visual Communications, 85 Queens Park Avenue, Bournemouth, BH8 9LJ Tel: (01202) 422986 Fax: (01202) 394790 E-mail: sales@modusvisualcomms.co.uk

Moxhams Ltd, 56-56a Portswood Road, Southampton, SO17 2FW Tel: (023) 8055 6644 Fax: (023) 8067 1667 E-mail: john@moxhams.co.uk

▶ The Multi Room Co. Ltd, 4 Churchill House, Churchill Road, Cheltenham, Gloucestershire, GL53 7EG Tel: (01242) 539100 Fax: (01242) 539300

Myriad Audio Visual Sales Ltd, 106 Hampstead Road, London, NW1 2LS Tel: (020) 7380 0191 Fax: (020) 7388 9225 E-mail: info@myriad-av.co.uk

National Sound Reproducers Ltd, Lower Priory Farm, Clamp Hill, Stanmore, Middlesex, HA7 3JJ Tel: (020) 8954 7677 Fax: (020) 8954 9329

▶ Nebula Audio, Unit 238 Ikon Estate, Droitwich Road, Hartlebury, Kidderminster, Worcestershire, DY10 4EU Tel: (01299) 253571 Fax: (01299) 250983

▶ Newland Corporate Communications, 34 Blackstone Court, Blaydon-on-Tyne, Tyne & Wear, NE21 4HH Tel: 0191-256 6000 Fax: 0191-256 6056 E-mail: hire@newlandcc.co.uk

▶ Nexnix Ltd, Landmark House, 75 Station Road, Horsham, West Sussex, RH13 5EX Tel: (01403) 756777 Fax: (01403) 756888

▶ Nightingale Audio Systems, Unit 127 J C Albyn Complex, Burton Road, Sheffield, S3 8BZ Tel: 0114-270 1470 E-mail: sales@nightingale-audio.co.uk

P M Large Screen Services, 170 Jockey Road, Sutton Coldfield, West Midlands, B73 5PN Tel: 0121-355 5099 Fax: 0121-355 6059 E-mail: pm_bigscreen@msn.com

Paradigm Audio Visual Ltd, Box End Road, Bromham, Bedford, MK43 8LT Tel: (01234) 843388 Fax: (01234) 854477 E-mail: info@rearpro.com

▶ Platinum A V Ltd, Ground Floor, 131 Reading Road, Henley-on-Thames, Oxfordshire, RG9 1DJ Tel: (01491) 575100 Fax: (0870) 9506590 E-mail: info@avlamps.co.uk

Present (UK) Ltd, Unit 11, Northbrook Close, Gregorys Mill Street, Worcester, WR3 8BP Tel: (01905) 28999 Fax: (01905) 723392

Projected Image, Havers Road, Norwich, NR3 2DU Tel: (01603) 481100 Fax: (01603) 481105 E-mail: info@projected.co.uk

Protape Audio Equipment, 59-61 Goldney Road, London, W9 2AR Tel: (020) 7616 5500 Fax: (020) 7616 5501

Pyramid Production Services, 10 Stonehouse Street, Plymouth, PL1 3PE Tel: (01752) 257770 Fax: (01752) 261770 E-mail: info@pyramid-presentations.co.uk

Qtrax Ltd, 14 Valeside, Hertford, SG14 2AR Tel: (01992) 551484

▶ Recording Studio Design, Pages Industrial Park, Eden Way, Leighton Buzzard, Bedfordshire, LU7 4TZ Tel: (01525) 217111 Fax: (01525) 378466 E-mail: enquiries@studiomaster.com

Rex Leisure (Scotland) Ltd, 105 Bothwell Road, Hamilton, Lanarkshire, ML3 0DW Tel: (01698) 283283 Fax: (01698) 201290 E-mail: info@rexleisure.co.uk

Sarner Ltd, Metropolis House, 16 Southsea Road, Kingston Upon Thames, Surrey, KT1 2EH Tel: (0845) 0666444 Fax: (0845) 0666555 E-mail: rmagri@sarner.com

Saville Audio Visual, Scala Court, Leeds, LS10 1JD Tel: 0113-218 3600 Fax: 0113-242 6167 E-mail: leeds.hire@saville-av.com

▶ Saville Group, 3 Swallowgate Business Park, Holbrook Lane, Coventry, CV6 4BL Tel: (024) 7670 5380 Fax: (024) 7670 5381

▶ SCV Electronics Ltd, 40 Chigwell Lane, Loughton, Essex, IG10 3NY Tel: (020) 8418 0778 Fax: (020) 8418 0624 E-mail: info@scvlondon.co.uk

Sepal Ltd, 429 Lisburn Road, Belfast, BT9 7 EY Tel: (028) 9020 2333

▶ Sheffield Independent Film & Television Ltd, 5 Brown Street, Sheffield, S1 2BS Tel: 0114-272 6304 Fax: 0114-279 5225 E-mail: admin.sif@workstation.org.uk

Shep Associates, Long Barn, North End, Meldreth, Royston, Hertfordshire, SG8 6NT Tel: (01763) 261686 Fax: (01763) 262154 E-mail: sales@shep.co.uk

Show Connections Ltd, PO Box 74, Crowborough, East Sussex, TN6 3YE Tel: (01892) 653185 Fax: (01892) 652523 E-mail: sales@showconnections.com

▶ Si Fi, 463 Harrow Road, London, W10 4RG Tel: (020) 8962 0700 Fax: (020) 8964 2696 E-mail: sales@si-fi.com

AUDIO VISUAL EQUIPMENT AND ACCESSORIES – *continued*

Smartcomm Ltd, 45 Cressex Enterprise Centre, Lincoln Road, High Wycombe, Buckinghamshire, HP12 3RL Tel: (01494) 471912 Fax: (01494) 472464 E-mail: lucy.jenner@smartcomm.co.uk
Solent Audio Visual, Meadowsweet Cottage, Hambledon Road, Denmead, Waterlooville, Hampshire, PO7 6QA Tel: (023) 9223 0999 Fax: (023) 9223 0555 E-mail: colin@solentav.demon.co.uk
▶ Solutions Audio Visual Ltd, Unit 4 Bowdens Business Centre, Hambridge, Langport, Somerset, TA10 0BP Tel: (01458) 252000 Fax: (01458) 254461
▶ Soralex Technologies, London, E6 3QJ Tel: 0870-350 0065 Fax: 0870-350 0064
Sounds Wholesale Ltd, Unit 2 Park Street, Burton-on-Trent, Staffordshire, DE14 3SE Tel: (01283) 566823 Fax: (01283) 568631
Spectrum Colors, Merrivale House, Kinburn Drive, Egham Hill, Egham, Surrey, TW20 0BD Tel: (01784) 431273 Fax: (01784) 431103 E-mail: sales@spectrum.co.uk
Stavekirk Ltd, Studio, Pale Lane, Winchfield, Hook, Hampshire, RG27 8SW Tel: (01252) 844808 Fax: (01252) 844705 E-mail: enquiries@stavekirk.co.uk
▶ Surrey Home Entertainment, 6 William Road, Caterham, Surrey, CR3 5NN Tel: (01883) 345102 E-mail: surreyhomeent@btconnect.com
Surtees Presentation Services Ltd, 6 Whittle Road, Ferndown Industrial Estate, Wimborne, Dorset, BH21 7RU Tel: (01202) 890074 Fax: (01202) 890076 E-mail: sales@surteeshire.com
▶ Tech Home, 43 Church Street, Weybridge, Surrey, KT13 8DG Tel: (01932) 820521 Fax: (01932) 841205
Technical Earth Ltd, Unit 5f Atlas Business Centre, Oxgate Lane, London, NW2 7HJ Tel: (020) 8450 0303 Fax: (020) 8450 0330 E-mail: info@techearth.com
Thames Valley Visuals, Providence House, Forest Road, Binfield, Bracknell, Berkshire, RG42 4HP Tel: (01344) 867166 Fax: (01344) 868006 E-mail: enquiries@thamesvalleyvisuals.co/uk
▶ Tom Evans Audio Design Ltd, St. Margarets Park Main Entrance, Pengam Road, Aberbargoed, Bargoed, Mid Glamorgan, CF81 9FW Tel: (01443) 833570 Fax: (01443) 839977 E-mail: sales@audiodesign.co.uk
Total Sound Ltd, 3B Oxford House, Oxford Road, Llandudno, Gwynedd, LL30 1DH Tel: (01492) 877070 Fax: (01492) 877098 E-mail: totalsound2000@yahoo.co.uk
▶ Transcom Communications UK Ltd, 69-71 Cutlers Road, South Woodham Ferrers, Chelmsford, CM3 5WA Tel: (01245) 324347 Fax: (01245) 328597
TSR Disco Equipment, 74 Albany Road, Coventry, CV5 6JU Tel: (024) 7667 9929 Fax: (024) 7671 5147 E-mail: sales@t-s-r.co.uk
Video 125, High Street, Sunninghill, Ascot, Berkshire, SL5 9NG Tel: (01344) 628565 Fax: (01344) 623302 E-mail: sales@video125.co.uk
Video Makes Money Ltd, 140 Wythenshawe Road, Northenden, Manchester, M23 0PF Tel: 0161-902 9000 Fax: 0161-945 9900
Videotron Ltd, 441-443 Cranbrook Road, Ilford, Essex, IG2 6EW Tel: (020) 8554 7617 Fax: (020) 8554 0110 E-mail: phobbs@videotronltd.freeserve.co.uk
▶ View Right Visual Systems Ltd, Unit 10 Paper Mill End Industrial Estate, Birmingham, B44 8NH Tel: 0121-356 4441 Fax: 0121-356 4400 E-mail: pcallow@btconnect.com
Vision Screen Services, Bridge Cottage, Church Road, Rawreth, Wickford, Essex, SS11 8SH Tel: (01268) 765374 Fax: (01268) 765374
▶ Vision Sound & Light, 18 Barlow Park, Broughty Ferry, Dundee, DD5 3UB Tel: (01382) 480900 Fax: (01382) 480901 E-mail: info@visionsound.co.uk
Visual Impact Ltd, Unit M5, Southpoint Industrial Estate, Foreshore Road, Cardiff, CF10 4SP Fax: (029) 2049 6175 E-mail: cardiff@visuals.co.uk
Visual Systems, Unit 11 Brickfields Industrial Park, Kiln Lane, Bracknell, Berkshire, RG12 1NQ Tel: (01344) 427161 Fax: (01344) 860282 E-mail: sales@visualsystems.co.uk
Wedgwood A V Ltd, 16 Glentworth Road, Skegness, Lincolnshire, PE25 2TG Tel: (01754) 769967 Fax: (01754) 768036 E-mail: generalmanager@wedgwood-group.com
▶ West AV Solutions, 231 Knowle Avenue, Knowle, Fareham, Hampshire, PO17 5DQ Tel: (01329) 836603 E-mail: chris@westavsolutions.com
▶ Whest Audio, Acton Business Centre, School Road, London, NW10 6TD Tel: (020) 8965 4535 Fax: (020) 7681 1089
▶ Winchester Events Ltd, 272 Back Street, Winchester, Hampshire, SO23 7NN Tel: (01962) 889159 Fax: (01962) 884946 E-mail: sales@winchesterevents.co.uk
Wyeval Audio-Visual Sales, 16 Tarsmill Court, Rotherwas, Hereford, HR2 6JZ Tel: (01432) 272113 Fax: (01432) 272113
X Electrical, 4 Station Buildings, Fife Road, Kingston upon Thames, Surrey, KT1 1SW Tel: (020) 8546 1233 Fax: (020) 8549 1233
Zebra Chelsea Ltd, 18-24 Brighton Road, South Croydon, Surrey, CR2 6AA Tel: (020) 8603 0492 Fax: (020) 8688 2491 E-mail: info@zebra.uk.com

AUDIO VISUAL EQUIPMENT CONSULTANTS

Act Consultant Services, The Old Wood Mill, Church Lane Madingley, Sawston, Cambridge, CB22 3JR Tel: (01954) 210766 Fax: (01954) 211466
B B M Audio Visual Specialists Ltd, Studio 2, Northbrook, Mitcheldever, Winchester, Hampshire, SO21 3AJ Tel: (01962) 774857 Fax: (01962) 774144 E-mail: audiovisual.bbm@btinternet.com
Cook Associates Design Consultants Ltd, Unit 1 Casbrook Park, Bunny Lane, Timsbury, Romsey, Hampshire, SO51 0PG Tel: (01794) 367996
▶ Couture Digital, Studio 12 & 13, 1b Darnley Road, London, E9 6QH Tel: (0870) 0429813 E-mail: info@couturedigital.com
ECT, Pangbourne, Reading, RG8 8TX Tel: 0118-984 1141 Fax: 0118-984 1847 E-mail: adam@ect-av.com
Elan Electronics Ltd, 26 Bellfield Street, Dundee, DD1 5JA Tel: (01382) 206106 Fax: (01382) 206906
Eurosimm Ltd, Unit 9 Pilsworth Road, Heywood Distribution Park, Heywood, Lancashire, OL10 2TA Tel: (01706) 360000 Fax: (01706) 620000 E-mail: sales@eurosimm.com
I T M A B Ltd, Unit 2 Rushtons Farm Estate, Warren House Road, Wokingham, Berkshire, RG40 5RE Tel: 0118-977 5977 Fax: 0118-977 5624
Kle Audio Equipment, 218 Main Road, Goostrey, Crewe, CW4 8PE Tel: (01477) 533255 Fax: (01477) 533750
Libra Solutions Ltd, 34 Furham Field, Pinner, Middlesex, HA5 4DZ Tel: (020) 8428 2776 Fax: (020) 8428 2776 E-mail: sales@librasolutions.co.uk
▶ Media Control UK Ltd, 69 Dartmouth Middleway, Birmingham, B7 4UA Tel: 0121-333 3333 Fax: 0121-333 3347 E-mail: info@mcl-birmingham.com
▶ The Media Services Co., 106 Tappesfield Road, London, SE15 3EZ Tel: (020) 7635 3459 Fax: (020) 7635 3459 E-mail: info@themediaservicescompany.com
Retec Europe Ltd, Campus 5, Third Avenue, Letchworth Garden City, Hertfordshire, SG6 2JF Tel: (01462) 482944 Fax: (01462) 484255 E-mail: sales@retec-europe.com
Sound Network, 131-151 Great Titchfield Street, London, W1W 5BB Tel: (020) 7665 6463 Fax: (020) 7890 7071 E-mail: info@soundnetwork.co.uk
▶ Stage Electrics, Yeoford Way, Marsh Barton Trading Estate, Exeter, EX2 8LB Tel: (01392) 824100 Fax: (01392) 825230
▶ TCPIP Ltd, 78 Wrentham Street, Birmingham, B5 6QP Tel: 0121-622 5000 Fax: 0121-622 5159 E-mail: sales@tcpip.ltd.uk
Watson Productions Ltd, Gothic House, Bank Lane, Totnes, Devon, TQ9 5EH Tel: (01803) 863033 Fax: (01803) 864219
▶ West AV Solutions, 231 Knowle Avenue, Knowle, Fareham, Hampshire, PO17 5DQ Tel: (01329) 836603 E-mail: chris@westavsolutions.com
▶ Winchester Events Ltd, 272 Back Street, Winchester, Hampshire, SO23 7NN Tel: (01962) 889159 Fax: (01962) 884946 E-mail: sales@winchesterevents.co.uk

AUDIO VISUAL EQUIPMENT DRY HIRE

FT Audio Visual Ltd, Valley House, Hornbeam Park, Hookstone Road, Harrogate, North Yorkshire, HG2 8QT Tel: (01423) 810052 Fax: (01423) 810053 E-mail: info@ftav.co.uk

AUDIO VISUAL EQUIPMENT FURNITURE

Allen Malpass, 3 Pottery Road, Bovey Tracey, Newton Abbot, Devon, TQ13 9DS Tel: (01626) 835200 Fax: (01626) 835200 E-mail: allen.malpass@hotmail.co.uk
Chase AV Ltd, Unit 10, Upper Gamma, West Road, Ransomes Europark, Ipswich, IP3 9SX Tel: (01473) 279992 Fax: (01473) 279993 E-mail: sales2@chaseavdirect.co.uk
▶ Integrated Cinema Experience, 11 Chatteris Close, Stoke-on-Trent, ST3 7TX Tel: 01782 399317 Fax: 01782 399317 E-mail: icexperience@yahoo.com
Winsted Ltd, Units 7 & 8 Lovett Road, Hampton Lovett Industrial Estate, Droitwich, Worcestershire, WR9 0QG Tel: (01905) 770276 Fax: (01905) 779791 E-mail: harry@winsted.co.uk

AUDIO VISUAL EQUIPMENT HIRE

20 20 Presentations Ltd, 11 Jersey Close, Congleton, Cheshire, CW12 3TW Tel: (01260) 280308 Fax: (01260) 208309 E-mail: enquiries@20-20presentations.co.uk
2112 Systems Ltd, The Old Telephone Exchange, Longcross Road, Longcross, Chertsey, Surrey, KT16 0DP Tel: (01932) 873111 Fax: (01932) 874340 E-mail: enquiries@2112hire.com
A R B Audio & Visual Hire Ltd, Unit 4, Building G, Tingewick Road Industrial Park, Tingewick Road, Buckingham, MK18 1SU Tel: (01295) 262000 Fax: (01280) 817948 E-mail: info@arb-teamwork.com
A T Communications, 13-19 Gate Lane, Boldmere, Sutton Coldfield, West Midlands, B73 5TR Tel: 0121-354 7582 Fax: 0121-354 7669 E-mail: atc@atcomms.co.uk
Altered Images, Unit 4 Shepperton Business Park, Govett Avenue, Shepperton, Middlesex, TW17 8BA Tel: (01932) 255666 Fax: (01932) 260646 E-mail: sales@alteredimagesltd.com
Aston Acoustic Ltd, Unit 7, Bay 1 The Woodsbank Trading Estate, Woden Road West, Wednesbury, West Midlands, WS10 7SU Tel: 0121-505 6500 Fax: 0121-505 6515 E-mail: info@astonacoustic.com
Audio Visual Machines Ltd, Phoenix House, 2B Upper Teddington Road, Kingston Upon Thames, Surrey, KT1 4DY Tel: (020) 8977 8880 Fax: (020) 8977 8879 E-mail: info@avmachines.com
Audio Visual & Reprographics, 62 Donegall Street, Belfast, BT1 2GT Tel: (028) 9020 7070 Fax: (028) 9020 7071 E-mail: info@avar-online.co.uk
▶ Avc Productions Ltd, 106 Kings Road, Brighton, BN1 2FU Tel: (01273) 746555 Fax: (01273) 746447 E-mail: sales@avcworld.com
Blitz Vision Ltd, Unit 10, Centennial Avenue, Elstree, Borehamwood, Hertfordshire, WD6 3SA Tel: (020) 8327 1000 Fax: (020) 8327 1111 E-mail: info@blitzcomm.com
Carpenter Communications Group Ltd, Old Greenfield House, Greenfield, Christmas Common, Watlington, Oxfordshire, OX49 5HF Tel: (01491) 614144 Fax: (01491) 613416 E-mail: sales@carpentercomms.co.uk
Conference Presentation Systems, 92 Vernon Drive, Stanmore, Middlesex, HA7 2BL Tel: (020) 8200 6222 Fax: (020) 8200 6322
▶ Countywide Entertainments, 63 Normandy Close, Exmouth, Devon, EX8 4PB Tel: (01395) 268263 E-mail: steve@countywideentertainments.co.uk
G H A Group Ltd, 9 Dean St, London, W1D 3RW Tel: (020) 7439 8705 Fax: (020) 7437 5880 E-mail: sales@ghagroup.co.uk
Genius Sound & Vision, Unit 8 Anchorage Point, 90 Anchor & Hope Lane, London, SE7 7SQ Tel: (020) 8472 9011 Fax: (020) 8472 9012 E-mail: info@genius.uk.com
Gray Audio Visual, 34-36 Bickerton Road, London, N19 5JS Tel: (020) 7263 9561 Fax: (020) 7272 0146 E-mail: office@gray-av.co.uk
Gregory Audio Visual Ltd, 190 St. Aidans Avenue, Blackburn, BB2 4EA Tel: (01254) 674444 Fax: (01254) 674444 E-mail: sales@gregoryav.co.uk
Hammonds A V S Ltd, 34 -36 Oak End Way, Gerrards Cross, Buckinghamshire, SL9 8BR Tel: (01923) 239733 Fax: (01753) 887163
Harpers A V Ltd, 16 Woking Business Park, Albert Drive, Woking, Surrey, GU21 5JY Tel: (01483) 757577 Fax: (01483) 729449 E-mail: sales@harpersav.com
Heselwood Audio Visual, 361 Sutton Road, Maidstone, Kent, ME15 9BU Tel: (01622) 751578 Fax: (01622) 755706
Hocken Audio Visual Ltd, 5 Waterhouse Lane, Kingswood, Tadworth, Surrey, KT20 6EB Tel: (01737) 370371 Fax: (01737) 370372 E-mail: sales@hockenav.co.uk
House Of Bollywood, 117 Ladypool Road, Birmingham, B12 8LH Tel: 0121-440 7454 Fax: 0121-440 7454
Hunt & Co Hinckley Ltd, 4 Turville Close, Burbage, Hinckley, Leicestershire, LE10 2GZ Tel: (01455) 637263 Fax: (01455) 637263
I T M A B Ltd, Unit 2 Rushtons Farm Estate, Warren House Road, Wokingham, Berkshire, RG40 5RE Tel: 0118-977 5977 Fax: 0118-977 5624
Image Business Systems UK Ltd, 455 Maxwell Avenue, Harwell Intnl Business Centre, Didcot, Oxfordshire, OX11 0PY Tel: (01235) 865500 Fax: (01235) 865511 E-mail: sales@imagebusinesssystems.co.uk
Impact Visuals, 1327 Stratford Road, Hall Green, Birmingham, B28 9HH Tel: 0121-702 0888 Fax: 0121-702 0889 E-mail: sales@impactvisuals.co.uk
▶ Insight Visual Systems Ltd, 1a Foxholes Avenue, Hertford, SG13 7JG Tel: (01992) 505177 Fax: (01992) 505178 E-mail: sales@insight-visual.co.uk
Key Audio Visual Services, Black Tower Studios, 15 Bracondale, Norwich, NR1 2AL Tel: (01603) 616661 Fax: (01603) 616668 E-mail: sales@keyav.com
M J Visual Systems Ltd, Unit 1, New Bury Park, Easthampnett, Chichester, West Sussex, PO18 0JY Tel: (01243) 780816 Fax: (01243) 783562 E-mail: sales@mjvisual.co.uk
▶ M R Studio, Liverpool, L12 0WW Tel: (07876) 518390 E-mail: info@mrstudio.biz
M S I Visual Displays Ltd, 11 Fairway Business Centre, Airport Service Road, Portsmouth, PO3 5NU Tel: (023) 9265 4525 Fax: (023) 9269 8797 E-mail: sales@display-it.co.uk
Majenta Audio Visual Ltd, Unit 2, Wills Industrial Estate, Salmon Parade, Bridgwater, Somerset, TA6 5JT Tel: (01278) 433700 Fax: (01278) 433131 E-mail: sales@majenta-av.co.uk
▶ MAN Audio Services, Catherine Court Farm, Coppershell, Gastard, Corsham, Wiltshire, SN13 9PZ Tel: (01249) 701363 Fax: (01249) 701236 E-mail: matt@manaudio.co.uk
▶ Media Control UK Ltd, 69 Dartmouth Middleway, Birmingham, B7 4UA Tel: 0121-333 3333 Fax: 0121-333 3347 E-mail: info@mcl-birmingham.com
▶ The Media Services Co., 106 Tappesfield Road, London, SE15 3EZ Tel: (020) 7635 3459 Fax: (020) 7635 3459 E-mail: info@themediaservicescompany.com
Myriad Audio Visual Sales Ltd, 106 Hampstead Road, London, NW1 2LS Tel: (020) 7380 0191 Fax: (020) 7388 9225 E-mail: info@myriad-av.co.uk
Piccadilly Hire Ltd, Unit 4-5 Thorncross Close, Manchester, M15 4LU Tel: 0161-835 1999 Fax: 0161-839 5322 E-mail: man@picc.co.uk
Piccadily Hire, 100 Bagot Street, Birmingham, B4 7BA Tel: 0121-333 4300 Fax: 0121-333 4441 E-mail: erictaylor@picc.co.uk
Picture Perfect Audio Visuals Ltd, AV House, Wallingford Road, Uxbridge, Middlesex, UB8 2RW Tel: (01895) 454 650 Fax: (01895) 454 657 E-mail: enquiries@ppav.co.uk
Present (UK) Ltd, Unit 11, Northbrook Close, Gregorys Mill Street, Worcester, WR3 8BP Tel: (01905) 28999 Fax: (01905) 723392
Prestech Exhibition Services, Unit 14 Belgrave Industrial Estate, Belgrave Road, Southampton, SO17 3EA Tel: (023) 8055 0557 Fax: (023) 8055 2452 E-mail: prestech@prestech.co.uk
Pro-Comm Audio Visual Consultants, Woodilee Road Unit 9, Lenzie, Kirkintilloch, Glasgow, G66 3UU Tel: 0141-776 2094 Fax: 0141-775 3419 E-mail: sales@procomm.ic24.net
Produktion Teknik, The Rickyard, Eashing Lane, Godalming, Surrey, GU7 2QA Tel: (01483) 429490 Fax: (01483) 429094 E-mail: sales@syscoav.co.uk
Professional Audio Visual Cambridge Ltd, Ares Yard, Chapel Street, Steeple Bumpstead, Haverhill, Suffolk, CB9 7DQ Tel: (01440) 731831 Fax: (01440) 731931 E-mail: hires@proav2000.com
Sabre International Ltd, Unit 9, Brookside Business Centre, Church Street, Swallowfield, Reading, RG7 1TH Tel: 0118-988 8818 Fax: 0118-988 8828 E-mail: david@sabre-international.com
Saville Audio Visual, Scala Court, Leeds, LS10 1JD Tel: 0113-218 3600 Fax: 0113-242 6167 E-mail: leeds.hire@saville-av.com
Second Sight Video Ltd, The Old School House, Leicester Road, Sapcote, Leicester, LE9 4JE Tel: (01455) 274191 Fax: (01455) 273918 E-mail: sales@secondsight.co.uk
Sight 'N' Sound, 11 Parkdale Drive, Sowerby Bridge, West Yorkshire, HX6 3HS Tel: (01422) 822734 Fax: (01422) 822442
▶ Sorted Technical Services Ltd, Brafield on the Green, Northampton, NN7 1BT Tel: (01604) 890260 E-mail: enquiries@sortedtech.co.uk
Spyx Audio Equipment, 36 Shaftesbury Road, Coventry, CV5 6FN Tel: (024) 7667 7896 Fax: (024) 7667 7896 E-mail: spyx@btinternet.com
Surtees Bournemouth Ltd, 6 Whittle Road, Ferndown Industrial Estate, Wimborne, Dorset, BH21 7RU Tel: (01202) 890074 Fax: (01202) 890076 E-mail: hire@surteeshire.com
T T V Facilities Ltd, Unit 12A 12G, Airport Industrial Estate, Newcastle Upon Tyne, NE3 2EF Tel: 0191-214 2300 Fax: 0191-214 2301 E-mail: info@ttv.org.uk
Tapestry Audio Visual, Nordic House, Baltic Quay, Grangemouth, Stirlingshire, FK3 8TX Tel: (0845) 2308999 Fax: (01324) 489349 E-mail: sales@tapestryav.net
Universal A V Services, Guy Street, Bradford, West Yorkshire, BD4 7BB Tel: (01254) 351359 Fax: (01274) 200281
Valentine Audio Visual, 6 Myrtle Avenue, Kirkintilloch, Glasgow, G66 4HP Tel: 0141-578 9950 Fax: 0141-578 9960 E-mail: SALES@VALENTINE-AV.CO.UK
Videographics Presentation Services, 18a Lansdown Road, Swindon, SN1 3NE Tel: (01793) 527226 Fax: (01793) 481236
Videotheque, 54 Rosebank Crescent, Exeter, EX4 6EH Tel: (01392) 214064
Voiceport Ltd, 49-51 York Road, Brentford, Middlesex, TW8 0QP Tel: (020) 8568 0462 Fax: (020) 8568 4151 E-mail: info@windmillstudios.net
Walker Sound Ltd, 8 Somerset Road, Southsea, Hampshire, PO5 2NL Tel: (023) 9273 0259
Y S L Videowall Hire Ltd, Unit 11 Concorde Park, Amy Johnson Way, York, YO30 4WT Tel: (01904) 693535 Fax: (01904) 691114 E-mail: info@yslvideowallhire.co.uk

AUDIO VISUAL EQUIPMENT IMPORT/EXPORT WHOLESALE MERCHANTS OR AGENTS

Avm, 6 Hawley Lane Industrial Estate, Hawley Lane, Farnborough, Hampshire, GU14 8EH Tel: (01252) 510363 Fax: (01252) 519874 E-mail: sales@avmltd.co.uk
Feltech Electronics Ltd, 7 Long Spring, Porters Wood, St. Albans, Hertfordshire, AL3 6PE Tel: (01727) 834888 Fax: (01727) 848704 E-mail: sales@feltech.co.uk
Karachi Pine Ho, 161 Dickenson Rd, Manchester, M14 5HZ Tel: 0161-224 9444 Fax: 0161-225 1333

AUDIO VISUAL EQUIPMENT IMPORT/EXPORT WHOLESALE MERCHANTS OR AGENTS – *continued*

▶ Prestige Imports & Logistics Ltd, Porterfield House 157 Harton Lane, South Shields, Tyne & Wear, NE34 0PW Tel: 0191 4200585 Fax: 0191 4200585 E-mail: enquries@pil-ltd.com

Technical Help to Exporters, 389 Chiswick High Road, London, W4 4AL Tel: (020) 8996 7474 Fax: (020) 8996 7048 E-mail: the@bsi-global.com

Working Wall Ltd, 97A Addison Road, Enfield, Middlesex, EN3 5LA Tel: (01992) 558800 Fax: (020) 8272 5417

AUDIO VISUAL EQUIPMENT INSTALLATION CONTRACTORS

Acoustic Arrangements, York Farm, Fenn Lane, Upton, Nuneaton, Warwickshire, CV13 6BL Tel: (01455) 213373 Fax: (01455) 213581 E-mail: mail@a-a.uk.com

Audio & Acoustics, United House, North Road, London, N7 9DP Tel: (020) 7700 2900 Fax: (020) 7700 6900 E-mail: sales@audioandacoustics.com

Audio Visual Consultants Ltd, 107-111 Whitehouse Loan, Edinburgh, EH9 1AT Tel: 0131-447 6211 Fax: 0131-452 8372 E-mail: info@avc-edinburgh.co.uk

Christian Fabrications Ltd, 5 Chase Side Crescent, Enfield, Middlesex, EN2 0JA Tel: (020) 8482 2082 Fax: (020) 8364 6488

▶ Communications & Sound Systems Ltd, Unit 1, Sandhurst Barn, Sandhurst Lane, Bexhill-On-Sea, East Sussex, TN39 4RH Tel: (01424) 848400 Fax: (01424) 848300 E-mail: sales@commsandsound.com

▶ Eden Group, 43 Ellens Glen Road, Edinburgh, EH17 7QJ Tel: 0131-664 3906 Fax: 0131-658 1038 E-mail: Lynne@edengroup.co.uk

Elan Electronics Ltd, 26 Bellfield Street, Dundee, DD1 5JA Tel: (01382) 206106 Fax: (01382) 206906

Electrical & Acoustic Services Ltd, 105 Fermor Way, Crowborough, East Sussex, TN6 3BH Tel: (01892) 661950

Hocken Sound Contracts Ltd, 50 Sovereign Road, Kings Norton Business Centre, Birmingham, B30 3HN Tel: 0121-459 4242 Fax: 0121-433 5362 E-mail: sales@hockensound.co.uk

Radio Active, 24 Silverdale Ave, Westcliff-on-Sea, Essex, SS0 9BA Tel: 01702 348975 Fax: 01702 348975

Stage Two Ltd, Unit J Penfold Trading Estate, Imperial Way, Watford, WD24 4YY Tel: (01923) 230789 Fax: (01923) 255048 E-mail: info@stage-two.co.uk

Sysco Audio Equipment, The Rickyard, Eashing Lane, Godalming, Surrey, GU7 2QA Tel: (01483) 429491 Fax: (01483) 429094 E-mail: mail@systems.co.com

▶ TCPIP Ltd, 78 Wrentham Street, Birmingham, B5 6QP Tel: 0121-622 5000 Fax: 0121-622 5159 E-mail: sales@tcpip.ltd.uk

Television Installation Services (Mansfield) Ltd, Old Mill Lane Industrial Estate, Mansfield Woodhouse, Mansfield, Nottinghamshire, NG19 9BG Tel: (01623) 425800 Fax: (01623) 650767 E-mail: sales@tisnet.co.uk

Thanet Disco Centre, 16 North Foreland Road, Broadstairs, Kent, CT10 3NN Tel: (01843) 864001 Fax: (01843) 865666 E-mail: julie.jackson10@btiternet.com

AUDIO VISUAL EQUIPMENT MAINTENANCE/REPAIR SERVICES

A A Electronique Services Ltd, Unit 5, Grove Park Business Estate, Waltham Road, White Waltham, Maidenhead, Berkshire, SL6 3LW Tel: (020) 8893 1907 Fax: (020) 8893 1908

Arm A-V Services, 57 St. Johns Road, Caversham, Reading, RG4 5AL Tel: 0118-948 2559 E-mail: mekka@lentil.org

Audio Visual & Reprographics, 62 Donegall Street, Belfast, BT1 2GT Tel: (028) 9020 7070 Fax: (028) 9020 7071 E-mail: info@avar-online.co.uk

CH Design Installation Co. Ltd, 31 Southwold Mansions, Widley Road, London, W9 2LE Tel: (020) 7289 1792 Fax: (020) 7266 4607

D R V, Lower Tregenna, Newquay, Cornwall, TR8 4HS Tel: (01637) 875824 Fax: (01637) 876082 E-mail: mail@drv.com

The G D L Partnership, 90 Mell Road, Tollesbury, Maldon, Essex, CM9 8SR Tel: (01621) 862608 Fax: E-mail: gdl.prtnrs@virgin.net

Heriot Video, 8-10 Shandon Place, Edinburgh, EH11 1QL Tel: 0131-337 7513 Fax: 0131-327 9886

Pro Services Audio, 7 Pumbro, Stonesfield, Witney, Oxfordshire, OX29 8QF Tel: (01993) 891765 Fax: (01993) 891009 E-mail: psa@ggilbaud.deman.co.uk

AUDIO VISUAL SERVICES/ PROGRAMME PRODUCERS

A V Hire Shop, Unit 11, Concorde Park, Amy Johnson Way, York, YO30 4WT Tel: (01904) 693000 Fax: (01904) 691114

A V Q Ltd, Unit 26d Bull Commercial Centre, Stockton Lane, Stockton on the Forest, York, YO32 9LE Tel: (01904) 400121 Fax: (01904) 400565 E-mail: info@avq.co.uk

Aarchive Film Productions, 26 St. Johns Drive, Plymouth, PL9 9SB Tel: (01752) 404296 E-mail: enquiries@aarchive.co.uk

Alphabet Video Production, 2 The Heywoods, Chester, CH2 2RA Tel: (01244) 380744 Fax: (01244) 380744 E-mail: alan.digby@btconnect.com

Angstrom Video, 16 Chapel Lane, Northorpe, Gainsborough, Lincolnshire, DN21 4AF Tel: (01724) 763594 Fax: (01724) 763594 E-mail: sales@angstromvideo.co.uk

Antenna Audio, J307-9 Tower Bridge, Business Complex, London, SE16 4DG Tel: (020) 7740 1155 Fax: (020) 7394 6746

Apv Films, 6 Alexandra Square, Chipping Norton, Oxfordshire, OX7 5HL Tel: (01608) 641798 Fax: (01608) 642177 E-mail: artworks@apvfilms.co.uk

Audio Access Ltd, 9 Romney Road, Rottingdean, Brighton, BN2 7GG Tel: (01273) 300001 Fax: (01273) 390909 E-mail: sound@audioaccess.co.uk

▶ Audio Marketing Ltd, 11 Ravenscourt, Thorntonhall, Glasgow, G74 5AZ Tel: (0870) 3500205

▶ Aventis Audio Visual, 7 Rockfort Industrial Estate, Hithercroft Road, Wallingford, Oxfordshire, OX10 9DA Tel: (01491) 836244 Fax: (01491) 838568 E-mail: info@aventisav.com

▶ Bav Presentation Services, Rookhurst, Forest Road, Effingham Junction, Leatherhead, Surrey, KT24 5HD Tel: (01483) 280041 E-mail: info@bavltd.co.uk

Beetlenut, Abbey Barn Farm, Abbey Barn Lane, High Wycombe, Buckinghamshire, HP10 9QQ Tel: (0870) 460 5626 Fax: (0870) 460 5627 E-mail: Debbie@beetlenut.com

Caledonia Sterne & Wyld Ltd, 5 Queens Cres, Glasgow, G4 9BW Tel: 0141-353 3153 Fax: 0141 353 2435

▶ Carbon Lodge, Church Road, Catsfield, Battle, East Sussex, TN33 9QP Tel: (01424) 893333

John Clarke Productions, 3 Alma Studios, 32 - 34 Stratford Road, London, W8 6QF Tel: (020) 7937 4373 E-mail: jsc@jscprods.com

Clicks Media Studios, Amp House, Grove Road, Strood, Rochester, Kent, ME2 4BX Tel: (01634) 723838 E-mail: pjstv@blueyonder.co.uk

▶ Communicopia Productions Ltd, 27, Foundry Street, Brighton, BN1 4AT Tel: (01273) 691333 Fax: (01273) 683399

Conferex Communications, Inglewood, Copsewood Lane, Stone Allerton, Axbridge, Somerset, BS26 2NS Tel: (01934) 712824 Fax: (01934) 713004 E-mail: info@conferex.co.uk

Contact Middle East (UK) Ltd, 106 Hammersmith Grove, London, W6 7HB Tel: (020) 8846 9255 Fax: (020) 8748 0844

▶ Cre-8 Communications, 28, Church Street, Kidderminster, Worcs, DY10 2AR Tel: (01562) 741160 Fax: (01562) 741170

Describe Video Services, 21 Lesley Avenue, Canterbury, Kent, CT1 3LF Tel: (01227) 464265 Fax: (01227) 464265

Design Channel, 107 Warwick Street, Leamington Spa, Warwickshire, CV32 4QZ Tel: (01926) 435789 Fax: (01926) 430799 E-mail: sales@thedesignchannel.co.uk

Digital Networks Ltd, PO Box 24402, London, W5 4WQ Tel: (020) 8998 7293 Fax: (020) 8998 0216 E-mail: sales@dignet.co.uk

▶ Dynamic Visions, Unit 6 Whittle Road, Ferndown Industrial Estate, Wimborne, Dorset, BH21 7RU Tel: 01202 890404

▶ Eclipse Corporate Communications, 111 Hagley Road, Birmingham, B16 8LB Tel: 0121-452 5070 Fax: 0121-452 5071

F V S 2000, 72 Love Lane, Denbigh, Clwyd, LL16 3LU Tel: (01745) 814210 Fax: (01745) 814210 E-mail: sales@fvsvideo.co.uk

First Field, Unit B5 3 Bradbury Street, London, N16 8JN Tel: (020) 7690 4990 Fax: (020) 7690 4494 E-mail: firstfield@clara.co.uk

▶ Global Show Management, St. Georges Lane, Ascot, Berkshire, SL5 7ET Tel: (01344) 636421 Fax: (01344) 624041

Grapevine Productions Ltd, 2 St. Marys Avenue, Teddington, Middlesex, TW11 0HZ Tel: (020) 8943 9899 Fax: (020) 8943 1626

Hammonds A V S Ltd, 34 -36 Oak End Way, Gerrards Cross, Buckinghamshire, SL9 8BR Tel: (01923) 239733 Fax: (01753) 887163

The Hive, 37 Dean Street, London, W1D 4PT Tel: (020) 7565 1000 Fax: (020) 7494 0059

Image Video, 33 Walters Road, Llanelli, Dyfed, SA15 1LS Tel: (01554) 777416

Infinitely Presentation Services, Washbrook Meadow, Great Horwood Road, Winslow, Buckingham, MK18 3LX Tel: (01296) 712532 Fax: (01296) 712532 E-mail: sales@infinately.co.uk

Innervisions, Po Box 9, Retford, Nottinghamshire, DN22 7GZ Tel: (01777) 702913

▶ Interactive View, 15 Bowling Green Lane, London, EC1R 0BD Tel: (020) 7566 0430 Fax: (020) 7490 8404 E-mail: info@interactiveview.co.uk

▶ Jigsaw Innovations Ltd, 27 High Street, Hoddesdon, Hertfordshire, EN11 8SX Tel: (01992) 450550 Fax: (01992) 450551 E-mail: info@jigsawinnovations.co.uk

Loud Mastering Audio Post Production, Whitehall, Taunton, Somerset, TA1 1PG Tel: (01823) 353123 Fax: (01823) 353055 E-mail: info@loudmastering.com

Magic Video Co., 17 The Moat, Puckeridge, Ware, Hertfordshire, SG11 1SJ Tel: (01920) 821003 Fax: (01920) 821003 E-mail: robert-hamilton@btconnect.com

Mbptv, Saucelands Barn, Coolham, Horsham, West Sussex, RH13 8QG Tel: (01403) 741620 Fax: (01403) 741647 E-mail: sales@mbptv.com

▶ Media Control UK Ltd, 69 Dartmouth Middleway, Birmingham, B7 4UA Tel: 0121-333 3333 Fax: 0121-333 3347 E-mail: info@mcl-birmingham.com

Mintai, 14-16 Douglas Bldgs, Royal Stuart La, Cardiff, CF10 6EL Tel: 029 20489813 Fax: 029 20489784

Mirage Television Production, 53 Newington Road, Edinburgh, EH9 1QW Tel: 0131-668 2010 Fax: 0131-668 2243

▶ Mobile Movies, 28 High Street, Wymington, Rushden, Northamptonshire, NN10 9LS Tel: (01933) 411234 Fax: (01933) 411234

▶ Alex Myers and Associates, Apartment 25, 9 Kean Street, London, WC2B 4AY Tel: (020) 7379 5124 Fax: (020) 7379 0269 E-mail: info@alexmyersassociates.co.uk

Myriad Audio Visual Sales Ltd, 106 Hampstead Road, London, NW1 2LS Tel: (020) 7380 0191 Fax: (020) 7388 9225 E-mail: info@myriad-av.co.uk

▶ On Screen Productions, 33 Bridge Street, Chepstow, Gwent, NP16 5GA Tel: (01291) 636300 Fax: (01291) 636301

One To One Productions, Glasshoughton Cultural Industries Centre, Redhill Avenue, Castleford, West Yorkshire, WF10 4QH Tel: (01977) 603431 Fax: (01977) 735000 E-mail: sales@one2one-connected.com

Optimus Music, 35 Elm Road, London, SW14 7JL Tel: (020) 8878 6989 Fax: (020) 8878 2058

Orbital Media Ltd, 40 Balcombe Street, London, NW1 6ND Tel: (020) 7723 9216 Fax: 020 77233412

▶ P C I London, Unit G4, Harbour Yard, Chelsea Harbour, London, SW10 0XD Tel: (020) 7544 7500 Fax: (020) 7352 7906 E-mail: reception@pci-live.com

Pembrokeshire Video Productions, Thorne Cottage, Cresselly, Kilgetty, Dyfed, SA68 0TY Tel: (01646) 651555 Fax: (01646) 651555 E-mail: nickpudsey@pembrokeshirevideo.co.uk

Peninsula Films, 9 Saxon Road, Cambridge, CB5 8HS Tel: (01223) 460459 E-mail: sales@peninsulafilms.com

Perpetual Photophonics, 10 Park End, London, NW3 2SE Tel: (020) 7435 9880 Fax: (020) 7435 9880

Photosound Communications Ltd, Stansted Road, Birchanger, Bishop's Stortford, Hertfordshire, CM23 5PT Tel: (01279) 818400 Fax: (01279) 647746

Present (UK) Ltd, Unit 11, Northbrook Close, Gregorys Mill Street, Worcester, WR3 8BP Tel: (01905) 28999 Fax: (01905) 723392

Prospect Pictures Ltd, Wansworth Plain, London, SW18 1ET Tel: (020) 7636 1234 Fax: (020) 8877 0234 E-mail: info@prospect-uk.com

Prospect Presentations, 7 St Johns Close, Rugeley, Staffordshire, WS15 2TG Tel: (01889) 579713 Fax: (0870) 7622664 E-mail: info@prospectpresentations.co.uk

Purple Frog Media, 19 Westbourne Gardens, Hove, East Sussex, BN3 5PL Tel: (01273) 735475 Fax: (01273) 775787 E-mail: julie@purplefrogmedia.com

Ragdoll Ltd, Timothys Bridge Road, Stratford-upon-Avon, Warwickshire, CV37 9NQ Tel: (01789) 404100 Fax: (01789) 404136 E-mail: info@ragdoll.co.uk

Revolver Films, 10 Lambton Place, London, W11 2SH Tel: (020) 7243 4300 Fax: (020) 7243 4302 E-mail: info@revolvergroup.com

Robinson Video Productions, Pine Cottage Studio, New Road, St. Hilary, Penzance, Cornwall, TR20 9EA Tel: (01736) 763603 Fax: (01736) 763603E-mail: robvidff@aol.com

Savin Productions, 19 Woodlea Drive, Solihull, West Midlands, B91 1PG Tel: 0121-240 1100 Fax: 0121-240 4042 E-mail: sales@savinsproducts.com

▶ Shot In The Dark, The Lodge, Beaumont Park Road, Huddersfield, HD4 7AY Tel: (01484) 651111 Fax: (01484) 643930 E-mail: info@shotinthedark.co.uk

Sound Business Audio Ltd, Fitzroy House, Coombe Lane, Hughenden Valley, High Wycombe, Buckinghamshire, HP14 4NX Tel: (01494) 564497 Fax: (01494) 563497 E-mail: sales@soundbusinessaudio.co.uk

Speakeasy Productions Ltd, Wildwood House, Stanley, Perth, PH1 4PX Tel: (01738) 828524 Fax: (01738) 828419 E-mail: info@speak.co.uk

▶ Stalwart Productions, Barclay House, 35 Whitworth Street West, Manchester, M1 5NG Tel: 0161-228 0507 Fax: 0161-236 2836

▶ Suffolk Films Ltd, The Street, Wenhaston, Halesworth, Suffolk, IP19 9ED Tel: (01986) 875875 E-mail: sales@suffolkfilms.co.uk

Sum & Difference Ltd, 111 Yeolands Drive, Clevedon, Avon, BS21 7XL Tel: (01275) 870378 Fax: (01275) 870378 E-mail: ian.fisher@sumanddifference.co.uk

T A P Film & Video Ltd, 39 Hillmarton Road, London, N7 9JD Tel: (020) 7700 2212 Fax: (020) 7700 2624

▶ Talk Events UK Ltd, Unit 6, 229 Torrington Avenue, Coventry, CV4 9HN Tel: (024) 7646 2444 Fax: (0845) 6126013 E-mail: info@talkevents.com

▶ Talkback Thames, 20-21 Newman Street, London, W1T 1PG Tel: (020) 7861 8000 Fax: (020) 7861 8001 E-mail: sales@talkback.co.uk

Tapestream Duplication, Unit 4 Hampers Grn Indust Estate, Petworth, West Sussex, GU28 9NR Tel: (01798) 344108 Fax: (01798) 342116

Topical Television, 61 Devonshire Road, Southampton, SO15 2GR Tel: (023) 8071 2233 Fax: (023) 8033 9835

Trackline Presentation Services, 68 Alton Street, Crewe, CW2 7QB Tel: (01270) 665750 Fax: (01270) 665750 E-mail: enquires@trackline.com

TV Department Ltd, 3 Altrincham Road, Wilmslow, Cheshire, SK9 5ND Tel: (01625) 538835 Fax: (01625) 522898

Universal Sound, 25 Brancaster Lane, Purley, Surrey, CR8 1HJ Tel: (020) 8660 0990

Video Arts Group Ltd, 6-7 St. Cross Street, London, EC1N 8UA Tel: (020) 7400 4800 Fax: (020) 7400 4900 E-mail: sales@videoarts.co.uk

Video Promotions International, Stoneleigh, Fryerning, Ingatestone, Essex, CM4 0NP Tel: 01277 353734 Fax: 01277 353734

Videoactive Ltd, Mill House, Higher Wych, Malpas, Cheshire, SY14 7JR Tel: (01948) 780564 Fax: (01948) 780566 E-mail: enquiries@videoactive.co.uk

Visible Productions Ltd, Jubilee Yard, Queen Elizabeth St, London, SE1 2LP Tel: (020) 7403 9333 Fax: (020) 7403 5225

Vision Mix, The Old Dairy, Broadfield Road, Sheffield, S8 0XQ Tel: 0114-250 1007 Fax: 0114-250 1006

VPoint TV Ltd, 1 First Avenue, Sherwood Rise, Nottingham, NG7 6JL Tel: 0115-969 3636 Fax: 0115-969 3434 E-mail: mail@vpoint.tv

White Rabbit Enterprises Ltd, 94 Creynolds Lane, Monkspath, Solihull, West Midlands, B90 4ER Tel: 0121-744 3297 Fax: 0121-733 2876 E-mail: whiterabbitltd@solihull2.demon.co.uk

Wordley Production Ltd, The Warehouse, 1 High St, Penarth, South Glamorgan, CF64 1EY Tel: (029) 2070 0590 Fax: (029) 2070 0550 E-mail: sales@wordleyproduction.com

Wren Media Ltd, Lodge Farm, Gulls Green Road, Fressingfield, Eye, Suffolk, IP21 5SA Tel: (01379) 586787 Fax: (01379) 586755 E-mail: post@wrenmedia.co.uk

AUDIO VISUAL SOLUTIONS CONSULTANCY

▶ B & H Sound Services Ltd, The Old School Studio, Crowland Road, Eye, Peterborough, PE6 7TN Tel: (01733) 223535 Fax: (01733) 223545 E-mail: sound@bhsound.co.uk

▶ H A V Solutions, 103 Maiden Place, Lower Earley, Reading, RG6 3HE Tel: (07910) 303555 Fax: 0118-947 3107

▶ Incendo Ltd, Unit H Sheen Lane, London, SW14 8AE Tel: (020) 8876 5333 Fax: (020) 8876 5322 E-mail: info@incendo.co.uk

▶ Insight Visual Systems Ltd, 1a Foxholes Avenue, Hertford, SG13 7JG Tel: (01992) 505177 Fax: (01992) 505178 E-mail: sales@insight-visual.co.uk

▶ Touch of a Button, Aztec House, 137 Moldsey Avenue, West Molesey, Surrey, KT8 2RY Tel: (07976) 375911 Fax: (0870) 9778819 E-mail: enquires@touchofabutton.co.uk

AUDIO VISUAL TRANSFER SERVICES, SLIDE/VIDEO

▶ Dicsmart Disc Services, 25a Caxton Avenue, Blackpool, FY2 9AP Tel: (01253) 508670 Fax: (01253) 508670

Light Stop Ltd, 52 Furze Platt Road, Maidenhead, Berkshire, SL6 7NN Tel: (01628) 632632 Fax: (01628) 686900

AUGER BITS

▶ Akromultihire, Unit 6 Naysmyth Place, Houston Industrial Estate, Livingston, West Lothian, EH54 5EG Tel: (01506) 441991 Fax: (01506) 441856

Armeg Ltd, Callywhite Lane, Dronfield, Derbyshire, S18 2XJ Tel: (01246) 411081 Fax: (01246) 411882 E-mail: j.mowthorpe@armeg.co.uk

Footprint Tools Ltd, PO Box 19, Sheffield, S1 3HY Tel: 0114-275 3200 Fax: 0114-275 9613 E-mail: sales@footprint-tools.co.uk

Howard Richard Sales Ltd, 10 Holkham Road, Orton Southgate, Peterborough, PE2 6TE Tel: (01733) 237779 Fax: (01733) 230027 E-mail: sales@hrsales.co.uk

AUGER BITS, TREE PLANTING

▶ Tree Care Services Ltd, 29a Castle Mews, Salisbury, SP1 1TT Tel: (01722) 332250 Fax: (01722) 334947 E-mail: mailto@treecareservices.co.uk

AUGER DISPLACEMENT PILE DRIVING CONTRACTORS

Pennine Projects Ltd, New Line Industrial Estate, Bacup, Lancashire, OL13 9RW Tel: (01706) 877555 Fax: (01706) 879754
E-mail: info@pennine-group.co.uk

AUGER PLATFORMS

▶ Automatic Transmissions Ltd, Kebs Road, Todmorden, Lancashire, OL14 8SB
Tel: (01706) 812291
E-mail: autotrans@uk2.net

AUGERS

C Churchfield, Unit 7 Howsell Road Industrial Estate, Malvern, Worcestershire, WR14 1UJ
Tel: (01684) 892150 Fax: (01684) 892150

Footprint Tools Ltd, PO Box 19, Sheffield, S1 3HY Tel: 0114-275 3200 Fax: 0114-275 9613 E-mail: sales@footprint-tools.co.uk

I A C Plastics, Oak Mill, Manchester Road, Dunnockshaw, Burnley, Lancashire, BB11 5PW Tel: (01706) 212225 Fax: (01706) 229926 E-mail: sales@iacplastics.com

AUSTEMPERED DUCTILE IRON

A D I Treatments Ltd, Doranda Way Industrial Park, Doranda Way, West Bromwich, West Midlands, B71 4LE Tel: 0121-525 0303
Fax: 0121-525 0404
E-mail: aaron.rimmer@aditreatments.com

Classic Wrought Iron, Jorista, Top Road, Ilketshall St. Andrew, Beccles, Suffolk, NR34 8NN Tel: (01986) 781214 Fax: (01986) 781214

AUTHORISED INSTITUTION BANKING

Anglo Irish Bank, 10 Old Jewry, London, EC2R 8DN Tel: (020) 7710 7000 Fax: (020) 7710 7050
E-mail: enquiries@angloirishbank.co.uk

▶ Standard Chartered Africa plc, 1 Aldermanbury Square, London, EC2V 7SB Tel: (020) 7280 7500 Fax: (020) 7280 7791
E-mail: sales@standardchartered.com

AUTOCLAVE DATA LOGGING CONTROL SYSTEMS

▶ Meditrax, Group House, Bowling Hill Business Park, Quarry Road, Chipping Sodbury, Bristol, BS37 6JL Tel: (01454) 318373 Fax: (01454) 322792 E-mail: enquiries@meditrax.co.uk

Rock & Tapping Ltd, 10 Wedgwood Road, Bicester, Oxfordshire, OX26 4UL Tel: (01869) 240404 Fax: (01869) 245500
E-mail: sales@stackltd.com

AUTOCLAVE SPARE PARTS

Priorclave Ltd, 129-131 Nathan Way, Woolwich, London, SE28 0AB Tel: (020) 8316 6620
Fax: (020) 8855 0616
E-mail: sales@priorclave.co.uk

AUTOCLAVES, *See also headings for particular types*

▶ Aeroform Ltd, Dawkins Road Industrial Estate, Hamworthy, Poole, Dorset, BH15 4JW
Tel: (01202) 683496 Fax: (01202) 622033
E-mail: sales@aeroform.co.uk

▶ Baskerville, 30 Long Wood Road, Trafford Park, Manchester, M17 1PZ Tel: 0161-888 2345 Fax: 0161-888 2345
E-mail: admin@baskervilleautoclaves.co.uk

Jencons (Scientific) Ltd, Cherrycourt Way Industrial Estate, Stanbridge Road, Leighton Buzzard, Bedfordshire, LU7 4UA Tel: (01525) 372010 Fax: (01525) 379547
E-mail: export@jencons.co.uk

L T E Scientific Ltd, Greenbridge Lane, Greenfield, Oldham, OL3 7EN Tel: (01457) 876221 Fax: (01457) 870131
E-mail: info@lte-scientific.co.uk

▶ LBBC Ltd, Beechwood Street, Pudsey, West Yorkshire, LS28 6PT Tel: 0113-205 7400 Fax: 0113-256 3509 E-mail: sales@lbbc.co.uk

New Brunswick Scientific UK Ltd, 17 Alban Park, Hatfield Road, St. Albans, Hertfordshire, AL4 0JJ Tel: (01727) 853855 Fax: (01727) 835666 E-mail: sales@nbsuk.co.uk

Priorclave Ltd, 129-131 Nathan Way, Woolwich, London, SE28 0AB Tel: (020) 8316 6620
Fax: (020) 8855 0616
E-mail: sales@priorclave.co.uk

Sal Europe Ltd, Houghton Road, Grantham, Lincolnshire, NG31 6JE Tel: (01476) 515550
Fax: (01476) 515551
E-mail: general@sal-europe.com

AUTOELECTRICAL/ELECTRONIC DESIGN SERVICES/ENGINEERS

Crown Max Investments Ltd, Halesfield 19, Telford, Shropshire, TF7 4QT Tel: (01952) 581121 Fax: (01952) 588284
E-mail: info@crownmax.co.uk

▶ E M F Electronics, 146 Portsmouth Road, Lee-on-the-Solent, Hampshire, PO13 9AE
Tel: (023) 9255 6225
E-mail: sales@emf-electronics.co.uk

Farley Auto Electrics, Salisbury Road, Dartford, DA2 6EJ Tel: (01322) 276998

Gill Instruments Ltd, Saltmarsh Park, 67 Gosport Street, Lymington, Hampshire, SO41 9EG
Tel: (01590) 613500 Fax: (01590) 613501
E-mail: gill@gill.co.uk

AUTOELECTRICAL/ELECTRONIC ENGINEERING SERVICES

Auto Electrical Services, Unit 34-36 Harmill Industrial Estate, Grovebury Road, Leighton Buzzard, Bedfordshire, LU7 4FF Tel: (01525) 372330 Fax: (01525) 851685
E-mail: info@aes2.co.uk

Autoflex Ltd, 15 Steele Road, London, NW10 7AS Tel: (020) 8961 0193 Fax: (020) 8965 0856

Autolec Services, 101 Albert Street, Rugby, Warwickshire, CV21 2SW Tel: (01788) 573475
Fax: (01788) 550530
E-mail: autorug@yahoo.co.uk

Battery Centre Ltd, 224 Neath Road, Landore, Swansea, SA1 2JG Tel: (01792) 774528
Fax: (01792) 772464

A.B. Butt Ltd, Frog Island, Leicester, LE3 5AZ
Tel: 0116-251 3344 Fax: 0116-253 6377
E-mail: sales@abbutt.co.uk

C F Parkinson Ltd, Marsh Lane, Riverside Industrial Estate, Boston, Lincolnshire, PE21 7FP Tel: (01205) 313900 Fax: (01205) 310124
E-mail: nicholson-r@parkinsontech.co.uk

Carlex Ltd, Unit 19 Rivington Court, Hardwick Grange, Woolston, Warrington, WA1 4RT
Tel: (01925) 811073 Fax: (01925) 817235
E-mail: sales@carlex.co.uk

Carwood Motor Units Ltd, Herald Way, Binley Industrial Estate, Coventry, CV3 2RQ
Tel: (024) 7644 9533 Fax: (024) 7645 2074
E-mail: carwood@carwood.co.uk

Corfield Auto Electrics Ltd, Short Acre Street, Walsall, WS2 8HW Tel: (01922) 623063
Fax: (01922) 621830
E-mail: ken@corfield-auto.freeserve.co.uk

Cox Auto Electrical, 10 Abeles Way, Holly Lane Industrial Estate, Atherstone, Warwickshire, CV9 2QZ Tel: (01827) 718484 Fax: (01827) 712097
E-mail: enquiries@coxautomotive.co.uk

▶ Doubledrive Ltd, PO Box 363, Pinner, Middlesex, HA5 3ZR Tel: (020) 8429 5304
Fax: (020) 8429 0418
E-mail: info@translectrix.co.uk

Eres Ltd, 264 Maybank Road, London, E18 1ES
Tel: (020) 8504 1188 Fax: (020) 8504 1192

Horner Bros, Southgate Avenue, Mildenhall, Bury St. Edmunds, Suffolk, IP28 7AT Tel: (01638) 712587 Fax: (01638) 715121
E-mail: hornerbros@fast24.co.uk

▶ LS UK Ltd, Riverside Terrace, Aberystwyth, Dyfed, SY23 1PN Tel: (01970) 617013
Fax: (01970) 612443

MG Auto Electrics, 1 Cherry Tree Avenue, Farnworth, Bolton, BL4 9SB Tel: (01204) 705905 Fax: (01204) 707900
E-mail: sales@mgautoelectrics.co.uk

Mobile Music, Back Dawson Terrace, Harrogate, North Yorkshire, HG1 2AJ Tel: (01423) 565823
Fax: (01423) 508885

Ranburn Ltd, Tunnel Avenue, London, SE10 0PT
Tel: (020) 8858 2293 Fax: (020) 8293 4373

South Eastern Auto Ltd, Bridge Industrial Centre, Wharf Road, Tovil, Maidstone, Kent, ME15 6RR Tel: (01622) 690010 Fax: (01622) 690683 E-mail: seaes@aol.com

Storrington Auto Repairs, M J House, Old Mill Drive, Storrington, Pulborough, West Sussex, RH20 4RH Tel: (01903) 746694 Fax: (01903) 741101

Sungold Auto Electrics, Bishops Road, Newcastle upon Tyne, NE15 6RY Tel: 0191-273 5667
Fax: 0191-273 1900
E-mail: sales@sungoldautoelectrics.co.uk

Tamworth Auto Electrics Ltd, Unit 6-7 Mariner, Tamworth, Staffordshire, B79 7UL Tel: (01827) 67539 Fax: (01827) 57473

Warwickshire Ignition Services Ltd, 5 Colletts Drive, Cheltenham, Gloucestershire, GL51 8JQ Tel: (01242) 523500 Fax: (01242) 524117

AUTOELECTRICAL/ELECTRONIC EQUIPMENT AND COMPONENTS, *See also headings for particular types*

Caerbont Automotive Instruments Ltd, Caerbont, Abercrave, Swansea, SA9 1SH Tel: (01639) 732200 Fax: (01639) 732201

Cambridge (Auto Bulbs) Ltd, Unit 30 Over Industrial Park, Norman Way, Over, Cambridge, CB24 5QE Tel: (01954) 231611
Fax: (01954) 230552
E-mail: cabulbs@tesco.net

Carlex Ltd, Unit 19 Rivington Court, Hardwick Grange, Woolston, Warrington, WA1 4RT
Tel: (01925) 811073 Fax: (01925) 817235
E-mail: sales@carlex.co.uk

Colchester Fuel Injection Ltd, Haven Road, Colchester, CO2 8HT Tel: (01206) 862049
Fax: (01206) 861771
E-mail: info@colchesterfuelinjection.co.uk

Corfield Auto Electrics Ltd, Short Acre Street, Walsall, WS2 8HW Tel: (01922) 623063
Fax: (01922) 621830
E-mail: ken@corfield-auto.freeserve.co.uk

▶ Doubledrive Ltd, PO Box 363, Pinner, Middlesex, HA5 3ZR Tel: (020) 8429 5304
Fax: (020) 8429 0418
E-mail: info@translectrix.co.uk

Eurolec Components Midlands, Northmoor Industrial Park, Moor Street, Brierley Hill, West Midlands, DY5 3SU Tel: (01384) 70972
Fax: (01384) 74552
E-mail: eurolec@dial.pipex.com

Furneaux Riddall & Co. Ltd, Alchorne Place, Portsmouth, PO3 5PA Tel: (023) 9266 8621
Fax: (023) 9269 0521
E-mail: info@furneauxriddall.com

Glenbar Electrical, 2-4 North Croft Street, Paisley, Renfrewshire, PA3 4AD Tel: 0141-887 4040
Fax: 0141-889 6789

Henley Brothers UK Ltd, 27 Sunters Wood Close, Booker, High Wycombe, Buckinghamshire, HP12 4DZ Tel: (01494) 536872 Fax: (01494) 446910

Holger Christiansen UK Ltd, Unit 7-8 Glaisdale Business Centre, Glaisdale Parkway, Nottingham, NG8 4GP Tel: 0115-928 0086
Fax: 0115-928 0033

Imer Reman, 2 Whitewater Place Maun Way, Boughton Industrial Estate, Boughton, Newark, Nottinghamshire, NG22 9LD Tel: (01623) 863600 Fax: (01623) 863606
E-mail: sales@remanufacturers.co.uk

Iskra UK Ltd, Redlands, Coulsdon, Surrey, CR5 2HT Tel: (020) 8668 7141 Fax: (020) 8668 3108

Lampion & Co. Ltd, Unit 36 Hortonwood 33, Telford, Shropshire, TF1 7EX Tel: (01952) 608600 Fax: (01952) 608700
E-mail: sales@lampion.co.uk

Lindum Auto Electrical Ltd, 136 Dixon Street, Lincoln, LN6 7TX Tel: (01522) 522294
Fax: (01522) 533457
E-mail: lindumauto@aol.com

Lucas Aftermarket Operations, Stratford Road, Shirley, Solihull, West Midlands, B90 4LA
Tel: 0121-506 5000 Fax: 0121-506 5001
E-mail: enquiries@lucasestateagents.co.uk

Mitsumi (UK) Ltd, Bede Industrial Estate, Jarrow, Tyne & Wear, NE32 3HD Tel: 0191-428 0333
Fax: 0191-483 3333
E-mail: sales@mitsumi.co.uk

Monark Diesel & Electrical Products UK Ltd, 19 Hanley Workshops, Hanley Swan, Worcester, WR8 0DX Tel: (01684) 311031 Fax: (01684) 311009 E-mail: sales@monarkdiesel.co.uk

Pektron Group Ltd, Alfreton Road, Derby, DE21 4AP Tel: (01332) 832424 Fax: (01332) 833270 E-mail: info@pektron.co.uk

Robinson Seabrook Ltd, 16 Moat Way, Barwell, Leicester, LE9 8EY Tel: (01455) 846151
Fax: (01455) 846383
E-mail: rwells1047@aol.com

Rock & Tapping Ltd, 10 Wedgwood Road, Bicester, Oxfordshire, OX26 4UL Tel: (01869) 240404 Fax: (01869) 245500
E-mail: sales@stackltd.com

Stadium Consumer Products, Stadium North, Tofts Farm Industrial Estate East, Hartlepool, Cleveland, TS25 2DH Tel: (01429) 862616
Fax: (01429) 272126
E-mail: julie.morrissey@stadiumcp.co.uk

Standard Motor Product Europe, Occupation Road, Hucknall, Nottingham, NG15 6DZ
Tel: 0115-952 8000 Fax: 0115-952 0050
E-mail: sales@intermotor.co.uk

Superchips Ltd, 2-16 Homestall, Buckingham Industrial Estate, Buckingham, MK18 1XJ
Tel: (01280) 816781 Fax: (01280) 816764
E-mail: sales@superchips.co.uk

T R W Systems Ltd, Mercantile Road, Houghton Le Spring, Tyne & Wear, DH4 5PH
Tel: 0191-512 3700 Fax: 0191-512 3661
E-mail:

Wood Auto Holdings Ltd, Cromwell Works, Colne Road, Huddersfield, HD1 3ES Tel: (01484) 428261 Fax: (01484) 434933
E-mail: sales@woodauto.co.uk

Wood Auto Supplies, 4B Locksley Drive, Belfast, BT10 0BH Tel: (028) 9060 5880 Fax: (028) 9060 0376

Yorkshire Care Equipment, 6 Over Lane, Rawdon, Leeds, LS19 6DY Tel: (01423) 880399 Fax: 0113-250 7433

Zeta Controls Ltd, Telford Road, Bisecter, Oxford, OX26 4LB Tel: (01869) 322500 Fax: (01869) 322614 E-mail: sales@zetacontrols.co.uk

Zirkon Ltd, Butlers Leap, Rugby, Warwickshire, CV21 3RQ Tel: (01788) 534800 Fax: (01788) 569283 E-mail: info@zirkon.co.uk

AUTOELECTRICAL/ELECTRONIC EQUIPMENT/COMPONENT, RECONDITIONED/ REMANUFACTURED

Autolec Services, 101 Albert Street, Rugby, Warwickshire, CV21 2SW Tel: (01788) 573475
Fax: (01788) 550530
E-mail: autorug@yahoo.co.uk

Corfield Auto Electrics Ltd, Short Acre Street, Walsall, WS2 8HW Tel: (01922) 623063
Fax: (01922) 621830
E-mail: ken@corfield-auto.freeserve.co.uk

Cox Auto Electrical, 10 Abeles Way, Holly Lane Industrial Estate, Atherstone, Warwickshire, CV9 2QZ Tel: (01827) 718484 Fax: (01827) 712097
E-mail: enquiries@coxautomotive.co.uk

▶ Doubledrive Ltd, PO Box 363, Pinner, Middlesex, HA5 3ZR Tel: (020) 8429 5304
Fax: (020) 8429 0418
E-mail: info@translectrix.co.uk

Holger Christiansen UK Ltd, Unit 7-8 Glaisdale Business Centre, Glaisdale Parkway, Nottingham, NG8 4GP Tel: 0115-928 0086
Fax: 0115-928 0033

Imer Reman, 2 Whitewater Place Maun Way, Boughton Industrial Estate, Boughton, Newark, Nottinghamshire, NG22 9LD Tel: (01623) 863600 Fax: (01623) 863606
E-mail: sales@remanufacturers.co.uk

L S UK Rewind, 12 Bucklands Road, Penmill Trading Estate, Yeovil, Somerset, BA21 5EA
Tel: (01935) 476255 Fax: (01935) 433627
E-mail: rewind@rgillard.wannado.co.uk

Q H Auto Electrics, Lichfield Road, Brownhills, Walsall, WS8 6LH Tel: (01543) 377281
Fax: (01543) 361062

Warwickshire Ignition Services Ltd, 5 Colletts Drive, Cheltenham, Gloucestershire, GL51 8JQ Tel: (01242) 523500 Fax: (01242) 524117

AUTOMATED ASSEMBLY AND MANUFACTURING PLANT

Mechatronic Production Systems Ltd, 2267 Coventry Road, Sheldon, Birmingham, B26 3PD Tel: 0121-742 7206 Fax: 0121-743 6882 E-mail: sales@mechatronic.co.uk

AUTOMATED CONVEYOR SYSTEMS

Amber Industries, Amber House, Crompton Street, Chadderton, Oldham, OL9 9AA
Tel: 0161-284 2222 Fax: 0161-627 0075
E-mail: sales@amber-industries.ltd.uk

Ewab Engineering Ltd, Stafford Park 16, Telford, Shropshire, TF3 3BS Tel: (01952) 239200
Fax: (01952) 239258
E-mail: pam.berry@ewab.net

AUTOMATED CUTTING SYSTEMS

Estuary Automation Ltd, 40 Shoebury Avenue, Shoeburyness, Southend-on-Sea, SS3 9BH
Tel: (01702) 293901 Fax: (01702) 297318
E-mail: estaut@aol.com

AUTOMATED GUIDED VEHICLES (AGV)

Egemin UK Ltd, 369 Wellingborough Road, Northampton, NN1 4EU Tel: (01604) 234994
Fax: (01604) 234483
E-mail: info@egemin.co.uk

Indumat Systems Ltd, 25 Campbell Court Business Park, Bramley, Tadley, Hampshire, RG26 5EG Tel: (01256) 880228 Fax: (01256) 880338 E-mail: info.uk@ek-automation.com

▶ Kindunique Ltd, Grieves Buildings, Front Street, New Herrington, Houghton le Spring, Tyne & Wear, DH4 7AU Tel: 0191-512 0052
Fax: 0191-512 0543
E-mail: holtkindunique@dsi.pipex.com

Swisslog, 707 Stirling Road, Slough, SL1 4SY
Tel: (01753) 528545 Fax: (01753) 570407
E-mail: sales@telelift.uk.com

Swisslog Digitron Ltd, Regents Court, Farmoor Lane, Redditch, Worcestershire, B98 0SD
Tel: (01527) 517333 Fax: (01527) 517344
E-mail: info@digitron.ltd.uk

AUTOMATED HANDLING EQUIPMENT

Automation Conveyors Ltd, Coopies Field, Coopies Lane Industrial Estate, Morpeth, Northumberland, NE61 6JT Tel: (01670) 514354 Fax: (01670) 514328

Bauromat UK, Beauchamp Business Centre, Sparrowhawk Close, Malvern, Worcestershire, WR14 1GL Tel: (01684) 575757 Fax: (01684) 569887 E-mail: info@bauromat.co.uk

CKF Systems Ltd, Unit 10 St Albans Road, Empire Way, Gloucester, GL2 5FW
Tel: (01452) 424565 Fax: (01452) 423477
E-mail: sales@ckf.co.uk

Dematic Ltd, Beaumont Rd, Banbury, Oxon, OX16 1QZ Tel: (01295) 274600 Fax: (01295) 274808
E-mail: sd.uk.ma-marketing@siemens.com

Egemin UK Ltd, 369 Wellingborough Road, Northampton, NN1 4EU Tel: (01604) 234994
Fax: (01604) 234483
E-mail: info@egemin.co.uk

AUTOMATED HANDLING EQUIPMENT – *continued*

▶ Kindunique Ltd, Grieves Buildings, Front Street, New Herrington, Houghton le Spring, Tyne & Wear, DH4 7AU Tel: 0191-512 0052 Fax: 0191-512 0543 E-mail: holtkindunique@dsi.pipex.com

Rawson Automation Ltd, 42 Muskham Street, Nottingham, NG2 2HB Tel: 0115-986 2077 Fax: 0115-986 2077

Riley Product Handling Ltd, Unit 2b, Meteor Business Park Mansfield Ro, Derby, DE21 4ST Tel: (01332) 866000 Fax: (01332) 866127 E-mail: paolo.graziani@rileyproducthandling.com

▶ Teknek Manufacturing Ltd, Inchinnan Business Park, Newmains Avenue, Inchinnan, Renfrew, PA4 9RR Tel: 0141-568 8100 Fax: 0141-568 8101 E-mail: sales@teknek.com

AUTOMATED INSPECTION VISION SYSTEMS

Surface Inspection Ltd, Unit 6 St. Philips Central, Albert Road, St. Philips, Bristol, BS2 0XJ Tel: 0117-916 9900 Fax: 0117-916 9907 E-mail: sil@surface-inspection.com

AUTOMATED INSTRUMENTATION ENGINEERING

Global Instrumentation Ltd, Unit 1080 Galley Drive, Sittingbourne Research Centre, Sittingbourne, Kent, ME9 8GA Tel: (0870) 3820001 Fax: (0870) 3820002 E-mail: global@global-associates.co.uk

Process Control Systems, 17 Stourfield Road, Bournemouth, BH5 2AR Tel: (01202) 428251 Fax: (01202) 424964 E-mail: processcontrol.systems@ntlworld.com

AUTOMATED LATHE TURNING CENTRES

Emag (U.K.) Ltd, Chestnut House, Kingswood Business Park, Albrighton, Wolverhampton, WV7 3AU Tel: (01902) 373121 Fax: (01902) 376091 E-mail: sales@emag-vsc.co.uk

Emi Mec, 23 Avern Close, Tipton, West Midlands, DY4 7ND Tel: 0121-522 4823 Fax: 0121-522 4823 E-mail: sales@emi-mec.co.uk

AUTOMATED MATERIAL HANDLING EQUIPMENT

Indumat Systems Ltd, 25 Campbell Court Business Park, Bramley, Tadley, Hampshire, RG26 5EG Tel: (01256) 880228 Fax: (01256) 880338 E-mail: info.uk@ek-automation.com

S & A Industrial Equipment Ltd, The Handling Center, Cardiff, CF11 8TW Tel: (029) 2071 1171 Fax: (029) 2070 6464 E-mail: sandadirect@ukonline.co.uk

Swisslog, 707 Stirling Road, Slough, SL1 4SY Tel: (01753) 528545 Fax: (01753) 570407 E-mail: sales@teleliftuk.com

AUTOMATED OFFICE EQUIPMENT MANUFACTURE/ DISTRIBUTION, *See Office Automation and headings for particular equipment*

AUTOMATED PAINT SPRAYING EQUIPMENT

Air Industrial Developments Ltd, Union Street, Kencrick Way, West Bromwich, West Midlands, B70 6DB Tel: 0121-553 4446 Fax: 0121-525 5983 E-mail: paint.sales@airind.co.uk

▶ Europlas Coatings Ltd, Pool Road Industrial Estate, Pool Road, Nuneaton, Warwickshire, CV10 9AE Tel: (024) 7632 7257

▶ Eurospray Ltd, 2 Crompton Road, Glenrothes, Fife, KY6 2SF Tel: (01592) 770055 Fax: (01592) 770066 E-mail: admin@eurospray.sol.co.uk

Finishing Connect Ltd, 865 Plymouth Road, Slough, SL1 4LP Tel: (01753) 676788 Fax: (01753) 676790 E-mail: fincon@technocom.com

AUTOMATED PRODUCTION LINE, SHEETMETAL

Boxer Designs & Manufacturing, Unit 2 Boundary Court, Heaton Chapel, Stockport, Cheshire, SK4 5GA Tel: 0161-975 1830 Fax: 0161-431 3364 E-mail: sales@boxer-design.co.uk

▶ S M B Sheet Metal Co., Manor Farm, St Peters Road, Cowley, Uxbridge, Middlesex, UB8 3SG Tel: (01895) 440468 Fax: (01895) 422305 E-mail: mikeb@smbsheetmetal.co.uk

AUTOMATED SCREWDRIVING MACHINES

Russell Automation Engineering Ltd, The Stables, Batemans Lane, Wythall, Birmingham, B47 6NG Tel: (01564) 823513 Fax: (01564) 823238

AUTOMATED STORAGE AND RETRIEVAL CRANES

Demag Cranes & Components Ltd, Beaumont Rd, Banbury, Oxfordshire, OX16 1QZ Tel: (01295) 676100 Fax: (01295) 226106 E-mail: help@demagcranes.com

AUTOMATED WAREHOUSING SYSTEMS

A S G Services Ltd, 8 Easter Court, Europa Boulevard, Westbrook, Warrington, WA5 7ZB Tel: (01925) 710923 Fax: (01925) 712966 E-mail: info@asgservices.co.uk

Fata Automation Ltd, Elgar House, Shrub Hill Road, Worcester, WR4 9EE Tel: (01905) 613931 Fax: (01905) 613913 E-mail: info@fatagroup.it

Swisslog Digitron Ltd, Regents Court, Farmoor Lane, Redditch, Worcestershire, B98 0SD Tel: (01527) 517333 Fax: (01527) 517344 E-mail: info@digitron.ltd.uk

AUTOMATED WAREHOUSING SYSTEMS CONSULTANTS

Christian Salvesen P.L.C., Salvesen House, Lodge Way, Lodge Farm Industrial Estate, Northampton, NN5 7SL Tel: (01604) 737100

▶ First Concepts Ltd, Concept House, 7 Holly Grove, Tabley, Knutsford, Cheshire, WA16 0HR Tel: (0845) 4567684 Fax: (0845) 4567694 E-mail: info@firstconcepts.co.uk

▶ Ops Partnership, 22 Walkern Road, Stevenage, Hertfordshire, SG1 3RD Tel: (01707) 328660 Fax: (01707) 328661 E-mail: info@theopspartnership.com

AUTOMATIC AIR VENTS

▶ Seconsolar Ltd, Alexandra Building Business & Innovation Centre, Wearfield, Sunderland Enterprise Park, Sunderland, SR5 2TH Tel: 0191-516 6554 Fax: 0191-516 6558 E-mail: info@seconsolar.com

AUTOMATIC ALARM SYSTEMS

Impact Security, 304 Linthorpe Road, Middlesbrough, Cleveland, TS1 3QX Tel: (01642) 654000 Fax: (01642) 654500 E-mail: info@impact-security-uk.com

AUTOMATIC ARC WELDING EQUIPMENT

Britannia Welding Supplies Ltd, 7 Rotunda Estate, Aldershot, Hampshire, GU11 1TG Tel: (01252) 350866 Fax: (01252) 330938 E-mail: debbie@britweld.co.uk

AUTOMATIC BACKWASHING FILTERS

Forgeville Logisctics Ltd, Unit 3, Senate Place, Whitworth Road, Stevenage, Hertfordshire, SG1 4QS Tel: (01438) 369461 Fax: (01438) 743084 E-mail: sales@forgeville.co.uk

AUTOMATIC BARRIERS

B P T Automation Ltd, Unit 16 Sovereign Park, Cleveland Way, Hemel Hempstead, Hertfordshire, HP2 7DA Tel: (01442) 235355 Fax: (01442) 244729

Bailey Streetscene Ltd, Bailey Business Park, Grimshaw Lane, Bollington, Macclesfield, Cheshire, SK10 5NY Tel: (0870) 0928928 Fax: (0870) 0929929 E-mail: info@baileystreetscene.co.uk

AUTOMATIC CASE PACKING MACHINES

Cermex UK Ltd, PO Box 12, Huntingdon, Cambridgeshire, PE29 6EF Tel: (01480) 455919 Fax: (01480) 451520 E-mail: sales@cermexuk.com

AUTOMATIC CNC CONTROL SYSTEMS

A C I Europe Ltd, 16 Plover Close, Interchange Park, Newport Pagnell, Buckinghamshire, MK16 9PS Tel: (01908) 514500 Fax: (01908) 610111 E-mail: sales@aciuk.co.uk

Nee Controls, 19b White Rose Way, Gateshead, Tyne & Wear, NE10 8YX Tel: 0191-415 9751 Fax: 0191-416 1603 E-mail: sales@nee-controls.com

AUTOMATIC COMPUTER AIDED DESIGN (CAD), SCHEMATIC DIAGRAM

RH-TS Cad Services, Rosemead House, 10 Leyton Cross Road, Wilmington, Dartford, DA2 7AP Tel: 01322 225014 Fax: (07075) 209713 E-mail: enquiries@rh-ts.co.uk

AUTOMATIC CONTROL SYSTEMS

Abacus Automation, Seaview House, The Parade, Parkgate, Neston, CH64 6SB Tel: 0151-336 7754 Fax: 0151-336 7548 E-mail: mail@abacusautomation.co.uk

▶ Alpha Beta Controls Ltd, 14 Coles Lane, Sutton Coldfield, West Midlands, B72 1NE Tel: 0121-321 3844 Fax: 0121-321 3866 E-mail: sales@alphabetacontrols.co.uk

Anstee & Wear (Wales) Ltd, Foreshore Road, Cardiff, CF10 4DF Tel: (029) 2048 1831 Fax: (029) 2049 6592 E-mail: info@ansteewear.co.uk

Bryant Electrical Ltd, 3 Shamel Business Centre, Commissioners Road, Rochester, Kent, ME2 4HQ Tel: (01634) 297211 Fax: (01634) 226863 E-mail: bryant.electrical@bryantelectrical.com

C M C Controls Ltd, Chaucer Business Park, Watery Lane, Kemsing, Sevenoaks, Kent, TN15 6PL Tel: (01732) 763278 Fax: (01732) 763279 E-mail: sales@cmccontrols.co.uk

Clayton & Co Penistone Ltd, Westhorpe Works, Halifax Road, Sheffield, S36 7EY Tel: (01226) 763130 Fax: (01226) 370145

Colter Products Ltd, Unit 7 Zone C Chelmsford Road Industrial Estate, Chelmsford Road, Dunmow, Essex, CM6 1HD Tel: (01371) 876887 Fax: (01371) 875638 E-mail: sales@coltergroup.co.uk

Contromec Services Ltd, Beechcroft Farm Industrial Estate, Chapel Wood Road, Ash, Sevenoaks, Kent, TN15 7HX Tel: (01474) 871171 Fax: (01474) 871199

Cranleigh Control Co., Unit 30 Hewitts Industrial Estate, Elmbridge Road, Cranleigh, Surrey, GU6 8LW Tel: (01483) 272663 Fax: (01483) 272663 E-mail: mail@cranleighcontrol.co.uk

D D C Control Systems Ltd, Unit 1 Broadwyn Trading Estate, Waterfall Lane, Cradley Heath, West Midlands, B64 6PS Tel: 0121-561 3312 Fax: 0121-561 3541 E-mail: ian.biddle@ddccontrolsystems.co.uk

Dacs Electrical Ltd, Old Fire Station, Church Street, Connah's Quay, Deeside, Clwyd, CH5 4AS Tel: (01244) 834100 Fax: (01244) 831858 E-mail: sales@dacselectrical.co.uk

Electrical Design & Manufacturing Co. Ltd, Station Street, Whetstone, Leicester, LE8 6JS Tel: 0116-286 2165

Electronic & Technical Services Ltd, Unit 32, Price St Business Centre, Birkenhead, Merseyside, CH41 4JQ Tel: 0151-670 1897 Fax: 0151-652 9941

Electrotech Maintenance Services, Clarkswell House, Sugarswell Business Park, Shennington, Banbury, Oxon, OX15 6HW Tel: (01295) 688429 Fax: (01295) 680005 E-mail: admin@electrotech-cds.co.uk

Leicester Switch & Control Co. Ltd, Ross Walk, Leicester, LE4 5HA Tel: 0116-299 9277 Fax: 0116-299 9278 E-mail: lsc@lsandc.co.uk

Lion Lift Controls Ltd, Littleton Mill, Chew Road, Winford, Bristol, BS40 8HJ Tel: (01275) 332515 Fax: (01275) 333085 E-mail: sales@lionliftcontrols.co.uk

M C S Control Systems Ltd, Unit 4 Phoenix Park, Bayton Road Industrial Estate, Coventry, CV7 9QN Tel: (024) 7636 0211 Fax: (024) 7636 8219 E-mail: sales@mcscs.co.uk

M S M Group of Companies, Spring Vale Works, Middleton, Manchester, M24 2HS Tel: 0161-643 2462 Fax: 0161-643 3490 E-mail: info@msmgroup.org

G.E. Mitchell Electrical Ltd, Springvale, Brookfoot, Brighouse, West Yorkshire, HD6 2RW Tel: (01484) 717607 Fax: (01484) 720484 E-mail: sales@gemitchell.co.uk

Frank W. Murphy Ltd, Swichgage House, Church Road, Laverstock, Salisbury, SP1 1QZ Tel: (01722) 410055 Fax: (01722) 410088 E-mail: sales@fwmurphy.co.uk

Paktronic Engineering Co. Ltd, Alma Park Road, Grantham, Lincolnshire, NG31 9SE Tel: (01476) 567623 Fax: (01476) 566503 E-mail: info@paktronic.co.uk

R Gorton & Associates Electronics Ltd, 308-310 Slade Lane, Manchester, M19 2BY Tel: 0161-224 5650 Fax: 0161-257 2761 E-mail: gortonelectronics@btinternet.com

Rebus Control Systems Ltd, 156 Burton Road, Lincoln, LN1 3LS Tel: (01522) 882200 Fax: (01522) 882211 E-mail: sales@rebuscontrol.co.uk

Riverside Automation Ltd, 103 Carlisle St East, Sheffield, S4 8DQ Tel: 0114-270 1997 Fax: 0114-270 1998 E-mail: kcowley@zoom.co.uk

S M G Control Systems, 9 Smestow Bridge, Bridgnorth Road, Wombourne, Wolverhampton, WV5 8AY Tel: (01902) 326886 Fax: (01902) 326883 E-mail: smg@smgcontrolsystems.co.uk

Spimin Development Ltd, Spimin House, Beacon Road, Poulton Industrial Estate, Poulton-Le-Fylde, Lancashire, FY6 8HD Tel: (01253) 881001 Fax: (01253) 881019 E-mail: sales@spimin.co.uk

System Panels Ltd, 104 Dudley Road East, Oldbury, West Midlands, B69 3EB Tel: 0121-552 4418 Fax: 0121-552 4018 E-mail: sales@marwel.com

Teddington Controls Ltd, Daniels Lane, St. Austell, Cornwall, PL25 3HG Tel: (01726) 74400 Fax: (01726) 67953 E-mail: info@tedcon.com

Tour & Andersson, Unit 3 Nimbus Park Porz Avenue, Houghton Hall Park, Houghton Regis, Dunstable, Bedfordshire, LU5 5XR Tel: (01582) 866377 Fax: (01582) 865655 E-mail: samuel.coe@tourandersson.co.uk

Transmitton Ltd, Coalfield Way, Ashby-de-la-Zouch, Leicestershire, LE65 1JD Tel: (01530) 258000 Fax: (01530) 258008 E-mail: sales@transmitton.co.uk

Ucontrol Ltd, Units 24-25, Strawberry Lane Industrial Estate, Strawberry Lane, Willenhall, West Midlands, WV13 3RS Tel: (01902) 601441 Fax: (01902) 602503 E-mail: infr@ucontroll.com

AUTOMATIC CONVEYOR BELT CLEANING DEVICES

Hosch (GB) Ltd, 97 Sadler Forster Way, Teesside Industrial Estate, Stockton-On-Tees, Cleveland, TS17 9JY Tel: (01642) 751100 Fax: (01642) 751448 E-mail: mail@hosch.co.uk

AUTOMATIC DOOR SAFETY LIGHT CURTAINS

Locks & Fittings Ltd, Unit 7-8 Rollingmill Business Park, Rollingmill Street, Walsall, WS2 9EQ Tel: (01922) 623200 Fax: (01922) 721086 E-mail: enquiries@locksandfittings.org.uk

AUTOMATIC DOORS

▶ Daihatsu Entrance Systems Ltd, Unit E8 Kingfisher Business Park, Hawthorne Road, Bootle, Merseyside, L20 6PF Tel: 0151-933 9443 Fax: 0151-933 9447

Dorwingear, 107 Hospital Street, Birmingham, B19 3XA Tel: 0121-359 1744 Fax: 0121-333 3475 E-mail: dorwingearltd@btconnect.com

▶ PORTALP Automatic Doors, Unit 16, Invincible Road Industrial Estate, Farnborough, Hampshire, GU14 7QU Tel: 0845 603 1137 Fax: 0845 450 6356 E-mail: sales@metro-doors.com

Record U.K. Ltd, Smith Avenue, Garrion Business Park, Wishaw, Lanarkshire, ML2 0RY Tel: (01698) 376411 Fax: (01698) 376422 E-mail: patrick.montague@recorduk.co.uk

Rol Trac Automatic Doors Ltd, Unit 1 Brookfield Works, Quebec Street, Elland, West Yorkshire, HX5 9AP Tel: (01422) 375000 Fax: (01422) 379076 E-mail: sales@roltrac.com

AUTOMATIC DRILLING MACHINES

Halan Machine Tools & Engineering, Unit D1 Sketchley Meadows, Hinckley, Leicestershire, LE10 3EN Tel: (01455) 617226 Fax: (01455) 617226

AUTOMATIC FIRE VENTS

Bilco UK Ltd, 3 Park Farm Business Centre, Fornham Park, Fornham St. Genevieve, Bury St. Edmunds, Suffolk, IP28 6TS Tel: (01284) 701696 Fax: (01284) 702531 E-mail: admin@bilco.com

AUTOMATIC GATE LATCHES

D B Services, 19 Diamond Road, Dromore, County Down, BT25 1PH Tel: (028) 9269 2714 Fax: (028) 9269 9938 E-mail: del@dbservicesni.co.uk

AUTOMATIC GEAR SYSTEMS,
See Transmission, Automotive Automatic etc

AUTOMATIC HINGED DOOR CLOSERS

Modern Door Closures, Lloyds Bank Chambers, High Street, Littlehampton, West Sussex, BN17 5AG Tel: (01903) 724003 Fax: (01903) 739806
E-mail: tradersnetwork@btconnect.com

AUTOMATIC LATHES

B S A Machine Tools, Mackadown Lane, Kitts Green, Birmingham, B33 0LE Tel: 0121-783 4071 Fax: 0121-789 9509
E-mail: sales@bsamachinetools.co.uk
Emi Mec, 23 Avern Close, Tipton, West Midlands, DY4 7ND Tel: 0121-522 4823 Fax: 0121-522 4823 E-mail: sales@emi-mec.co.uk

AUTOMATIC LOCKING OR INTERLOCKING DOORS

Cooper and Controls Ltd, Unit 13 Cornwall Business Centre, Cornwall Road, Wigston, Leicestershire, LE18 4XH Tel: 0116-277 9940 Fax: 0116-277 6503

AUTOMATIC LUBRICATING SYSTEMS

Wymark Ltd, Runnings Road Ind Estate, Cheltenham, Gloucestershire, GL51 9NQ Tel: 01242 520966

AUTOMATIC OR ELECTRIC CURTAIN SYSTEMS

Overmatic Ltd, 13 Clifton Road, Coulsdon, Surrey, CR5 2DW Tel: (020) 8668 3076 Fax: (020) 8668 3076

AUTOMATIC OR ELECTRIC DOORS

▶ Advance Door Engineering Ltd, Malthouse Road, Tipton, West Midlands, DY4 9AE Tel: 0121-557 0611 Fax: 0121-520 1233
E-mail: sales@advancedooreng.com
Doorco Ltd, Phoenix Works, Whitefield Road, Bredbury, Stockport, Cheshire, SK6 2QR Tel: 0161-406 8660 Fax: 0161-406 8433
E-mail: info@doorco.co.uk
Dor Tech, 3 Cala Trading Estate, Ashton Vale Road, Bristol, BS3 2HA Tel: 0117-963 9014 Fax: 0117-953 3462
E-mail: online@vortech.fsnet.co.uk
Dorma UK, Wilbury Way, Hitchin, Hertfordshire, SG4 0AB Tel: (01462) 477602 Fax: (01462) 477603 E-mail: info@dorma-uk.co.uk
▶ Electrogate Ltd, Unit 4, Ahed Trading Estate, Dewsbury Road, Ossett, West Yorkshire, WF5 9ND Tel: (01924) 283322 Fax: (01924) 283344 E-mail: info@electrogate.co.uk
Guthrie Douglas Ltd, Collins Rd, Heathcote Industrial Estate, Warwick, CV34 6TF Tel: (01926) 452452 Fax: (01926) 336417
E-mail: sales@guthrie-douglas.uk.com
Horton Automatics Ltd, Hortonwood 31, Telford, Shropshire, TF1 7YZ Tel: (01952) 670169 Fax: (01952) 670181
E-mail: sales@horton-automatics.ltd.uk
Ingersoll-Rand Dor-O-Matic Ltd, Berrington Road, Sydenham Industrial Estate, Leamington Spa, Warwickshire, CV31 1NB Tel: (01926) 437000 Fax: (01926) 437005
E-mail: doromatic_sales@irco.com
▶ PORTALP Automatic Doors, Unit 16, Invincible Road Industrial Estate, Farnborough, Hampshire, GU14 7QU Tel: 0845 603 1137 Fax: 0845 450 6356
E-mail: sales@metro-doors.com
The Priory Group Ltd, Lionel Works, 89-91 Rolfe Street, Smethwick, West Midlands, B66 2AY Tel: 0121-558 6406 Fax: 0121-555 7140

AUTOMATIC OR ELECTRONIC GATES

A Markham & Sons Ltd, London Road, Bowers Gifford, Basildon, Essex, SS13 2DT Tel: (01268) 553748 Fax: (01268) 584502
E-mail: info@markhams.co.uk
AM-PM Gate Automation, View Gardens Centre, Old Chelmsford Road, Rawreth, Wickford, Essex, SS11 8SJ Tel: 01268 571400 Fax: 05601 150721
E-mail: enquiries@ampmgateautomation.co.uk
Auto Gates Scotland Ltd, 4-5 Murray Street, Paisley, Renfrewshire, PA3 1QG Tel: 0141-849 7029 Fax: 0141-849 1224
E-mail: info@auto-gatesscotland.co.uk
Automation & Security, Unit 11C, Victoria Road West Industrial Estate, Hebburn, Tyne & Wear, NE31 1UB Tel: 0191-428 0788 Fax: 0191-428 5127
B F T Northern, Units 14-16, Bassington Industrial Estate, Cramlington, Northumberland, NE23 8AD Tel: (01670) 737645 Fax: (01670) 736558
B P T Automation Ltd, Unit 16 Sovereign Park, Cleveland Way, Hemel Hempstead, Hertfordshire, HP2 7DA Tel: (01442) 235355 Fax: (01442) 244729
Came Automation Ltd, Design House, 27 Salt Hill Way, Slough, SL1 3TR Tel: (01753) 550660 Fax: (01753) 552424
E-mail: info@atlasgroup.co.uk
City Gate Automation, 32 Hetherington Road, Shepperton, Middlesex, TW17 0SP Tel: (01932) 786464 Fax: (01932) 766199
D B Services, 19 Diamond Road, Dromore, County Down, BT25 1PH Tel: (028) 9269 2714 Fax: (028) 9269 9938
E-mail: del@dbservicesni.co.uk
The Electric Gate Shop LLP, Stoneycourt Cottage, Midhopestones, Sheffield, S36 4GP Tel: (01226) 370549 Fax: (01405) 785300
E-mail: gary@theelectricgateshop.co.uk
Elite Electric Gates, Unit 16 Bottesford Lane, Orston, Nottingham, NG13 9NX Tel: (01949) 831113 Fax:
Engineering Services Electrical Ltd, Century House, Enterprise Crescent, Lisburn, County Antrim, BT28 2BP Tel: (028) 9266 4583 Fax: (028) 9266 3700
E-mail: info@electroautomation.co.uk
Erik Johnson Products, Unit 3, Klondyke Industrial Estate, Rushden Road, Queenborough, Kent, ME11 5HH Tel: (01795) 662266 Fax: (01795) 669990
Forge Group, Holbrook Commerce Park, Holbrook Close Holbrook Indust Estate, Holbrook, Sheffield, S20 3FJ Tel: 0114-248 2222 Fax: 0114-248 2222
Gate A Mation Ltd, 8 Boundary Business Centre, Boundary Way, Woking, Surrey, GU21 5DH Tel: (01483) 747373 Fax: (01483) 776688
E-mail: sales@gate-a-mation.com
▶ Gatestore (UK), 682 Anlaby Road, Hull, HU3 6UZ Tel: (0845) 2263123 Fax: (01482) 505001 E-mail: bruce@gatestore.co.uk
Gough & Kelly Ltd, 6 Hales Road, Leeds, LS12 4PL Tel: 0113-279 4801 Fax: 0113-279 8644 E-mail: sales@gough-kelly.co.uk
Gunnebo Perimiter Protection (UK) Ltd, Bishops Hull, Taunton, Somerset, TA1 5EA Tel: (01823) 271911 Fax: (01823) 335763
E-mail: info@gunnebo.co.uk
H C S Automation, 3 Alvechurch Highway, Lydiate Ash, Bromsgrove, Worcestershire, B60 1NZ Tel: 0121-453 8053 Fax: 0121-453 8053 E-mail: hcsautomation@aol.com
Heda, Unit D5, Chaucer Business Park, Kemsing, Sevenoaks, Kent, TN15 6YU Tel: (01732) 765474 Fax: (01732) 765478
Hi-Tec Controls (Bolton) Ltd, Unit 4 Riverside, Waters Meeting Road, The Valley, Bolton, BL1 8TU Tel: (01204) 392172 Fax: (01204) 391660 E-mail: info@hiteccontrols.co.uk
Madewell Products Ltd, Sandy Way, Tamworth, Staffordshire, B77 4DS Tel: (01827) 67721 Fax: (01827) 67721
E-mail: sales@madewellproducts.co.uk
Midland Control Systems, Unit 13 West Cannock Way, Cannock Chase Enterprise Centre, Hednesford, Cannock, Staffordshire, WS12 0QW Tel: (01543) 879116 Fax: (01543) 422518
Newgate (Newark) Ltd, Brunel Drive, Newark, Nottinghamshire, NG24 2DE Tel: (01636) 700172 Fax: (01636) 605400
E-mail: sales@newgate.uk.com
Nortech Ltd, Unit 14 Terrace Factory, Bassington Industrial Estate, Cramlington, Northumberland, NE23 8AD Tel: (01670) 736811 Fax: (01670) 731252
E-mail: sales@nortechgaragedoors.co.uk
Nova Automation, 75 Beardmore Way, Clydebank, Dunbartonshire, G81 4HT Tel: 0141-951 8121 Fax: 0141-951 8121
E-mail: info@novagates.co.uk
Powerdoor & Gate Ltd, High Bar Lane, Thakeham, Pulborough, West Sussex, RH20 3EH Tel: (01798) 815700 Fax: (01798) 815900 E-mail: sales@powerdoor.co.uk
Premier Gate Automation, 21 Buckwins Square, Burnt Mills Industrial Estate, Burnt Mills Industrial Estate, Basildon, Essex, SS13 1BJ Tel: (01268) 590560 Fax: (0845) 8386932
E-mail: info@premiergate.co.uk
Procter Bros Ltd, Ninelands Lane, Leeds, LS25 2BY Tel: 0113-287 6282 Fax: 0113-242 2649 E-mail: info@procter-brothers.co.uk
R T S Gate Automation, 224 Spen Lane, Gomersal, Cleckheaton, West Yorkshire, BD19 4PJ Tel: (01274) 852006 Fax: (01274) 871074 E-mail: info@rtsautomaticgates.co.uk
S E A (UK) Ltd, Unit 6A Olton Wharf, Off Richmond Road, Solihull, West Midlands, B92 7RN Tel: 0121-706 9629 Fax: 0121-764 5603 E-mail: sales@seaukltd.co.uk
Sagitech Designs Ltd, 120 Wolmer Gdns, Edgware, Middx, HA8 8QE Tel: (020) 8958 5747
Sampson & Partners Fencing, Aubrey Works, 15 Aubrey Ave, London Colney, St. Albans, Herts, AL2 1NE Tel: (01727) 822222 Fax: (01727) 826307
E-mail: primasampson@compuserve.com
Savage Gate Automation, 8 Mulberry Road, Canvey Island, Essex, SS8 0PR Tel: (01268) 698182 Fax: (01268) 511722
Scroll Gates, Southampton Road, Eastleigh, Hampshire, SO50 5QT Tel: (023) 8061 2028 Fax: (023) 8061 2028
E-mail: sales@scrollgates.com
Sidac Systems Ltd, New Road, Chorley, Bridgnorth, Shropshire, WV16 6PP Tel: (01746) 718737 Fax: (01746) 718737
E-mail: marie@cook120136.fsnet.co.uk
Wanzl Ltd, Europa House, Heathcote Lane, Heathcote, Warwick, CV34 6SP Tel: (01926) 451951 Fax: (01926) 451952
West Country Door & Gate, Harpitt Lodge, Old Village, Willand, Cullompton, Devon, EX15 2RW Tel: (01884) 32233 Fax: (01884) 33335

AUTOMATIC OR ELECTRONICALLY OPERATED DOOR CONTRACTORS OR INSTALLATION OR MAINTENANCE OR SERVICING OR SUPPLIES

Alldoors Security Systems, Church Lane, Old Basing, Basingstoke, Hampshire, RG24 7DJ Tel: (01256) 359932 Fax: (01256) 352703
Automated Garage Doors & Gates Ltd, Burnet Road, Sweet Briar Road Industrial Estate, Norwich, NR3 2BS Tel: (01603) 787069 Fax: (01603) 789209
Automatic Doors & Gates, 64 Standard Road, Hounslow, TW4 7AS Tel: (020) 8568 6781
Dor Tech, 3 Cala Trading Estate, Ashton Vale Road, Bristol, BS3 2HA Tel: 0117-963 9014 Fax: 0117-953 3462
E-mail: online@vortech.fsnet.co.uk
Engineering Services Electrical Ltd, Century House, Enterprise Crescent, Lisburn, County Antrim, BT28 2BP Tel: (028) 9266 4583 Fax: (028) 9266 3700
E-mail: info@electroautomation.co.uk
Entrus Automatic Solutions, 16 Bordon Road, Stockport, Cheshire, SK3 0UW Tel: (07971) 835277 Fax: 0161-283 9260
E-mail: entrus@hotmail.co.uk
G E Garage Doors, 31 Upper Hibbert Lane, Marple, Stockport, Cheshire, SK6 7JQ Tel: 0161-406 7667
E-mail: gegaragedoors@hotmail.co.uk
▶ Higher Elevation, 35 Union Street, Maidstone, Kent, ME14 1ED Tel: (01622) 682973
E-mail: info@higherelevation.co.uk
I R Security & Safety, 1 Berrington Road, Leamington Spa, Warwickshire, CV31 1NB Tel: (01926) 437000 Fax: (01926) 437005
E-mail: ir_customerservice@eu.irco.com
Merlyn Electronics, Bridge Mills, Holland Street, Salford, M6 6EL Tel: 0161-745 7697 Fax: 0161-737 5615
E-mail: sales@merlyn-electronics.co.uk
Midland Control Systems, Unit 13 West Cannock Way, Cannock Chase Enterprise Centre, Hednesford, Cannock, Staffordshire, WS12 0QW Tel: (01543) 879116 Fax: (01543) 422518
Oliver Overhead Doors Ltd, 8 Magdalen Close, Syresham, Brackley, Northamptonshire, NN13 5YF Tel: (01280) 850206 Fax: (01280) 850077 E-mail: sales@oliveroverhead.co.uk
▶ Openings Disability Access, 327 Holdenhurst Road, Bournemouth, BH8 8BT Tel: (01202) 309946 Fax: (01202) 727071
E-mail: doors@openings.co.uk
▶ PORTALP Automatic Doors, Unit 16, Invincible Road Industrial Estate, Farnborough, Hampshire, GU14 7QU Tel: 0845 603 1137 Fax: 0845 450 6356
E-mail: sales@metro-doors.com
QRS Ltd, Malthouse Road, Tipton, West Midlands, DY4 9AE Tel: 0121-557 3601 Fax: 0121-520 1233
Shuttersafe Roller Shutter Mnfrs, 3 Cae'R Odyn, Dinas Powys, South Glamorgan, CF64 4UF Tel: (029) 2081 1798
E-mail: shuttersafe@aol.com
Sidac Systems Ltd, New Road, Chorley, Bridgnorth, Shropshire, WV16 6PP Tel: (01746) 718737 Fax: (01746) 718737
E-mail: marie@cook120136.fsnet.co.uk
Stanair Industrial Door Services Ltd, Unit 2 Henson Way, Telford Way Industrial Estate, Kettering, Northamptonshire, NN16 8PX Tel: (01536) 482187 Fax: (01536) 411799
E-mail: admin@shiresecurity.co.uk
Windor Controls Ltd, Unit 58 Hillgrove Business Park, Nazeing, Waltham Abbey, Essex, EN9 2HB Tel: (01992) 893737 Fax: (01992) 893130
E-mail: barryrichards@windorcontrols.co.uk

AUTOMATIC OR SELF WIND CABLE DRUMS OR REELS

Bewa (UK) Ltd, Noble Square Industrial Estate, Brynmawr, Ebbw Vale, Gwent, NP23 4BS Tel: (01495) 310170 Fax: (01495) 311816
E-mail: bewauk@yahoo.co.uk
Hubbell Ltd, Brunel Drive, Stretton, Burton-On-Trent, Staffordshire, DE13 0BZ Tel: (01283) 500500 Fax: (01283) 500400
Morgan Rekofa Tinsley Division, 37 John Swains Way, Long Sutton, Spalding, Lincolnshire, PE12 9DQ Tel: (01406) 366400 Fax: (01406) 366626 E-mail: sales@morgan-rekofa.co.uk
T E L Engineering Ltd, Newby Road, Hazel Grove, Stockport, Cheshire, SK7 5DA Tel: 0161-456 6545 Fax: 0161-456 3810
E-mail: mail@trolexengineering.co.uk
Wampfler Co Ltd, Unit B4, Altrincham Business Park, Stuart Road, Broadheath, Altrincham, Cheshire, WA14 5GJ Tel: 0161-929 6032 Fax: 0161-928 9126
E-mail: wampfler.uk@wampfler.com
Youldon, 7 West Road, Harlow, Essex, CM20 2BU Tel: (01279) 774300 Fax: (01279) 774310 E-mail: sales@collins-youldon.com

AUTOMATIC OR SELF WIND HOSE REELS

Bewa (UK) Ltd, Noble Square Industrial Estate, Brynmawr, Ebbw Vale, Gwent, NP23 4BS Tel: (01495) 310170 Fax: (01495) 311816
E-mail: bewauk@yahoo.co.uk
Fluid Transfer Ltd, Nailsworth Mills Estate, Avening Road, Nailsworth, Stroud, Gloucestershire, GL6 0BT Tel: (01453) 833381 Fax: (01453) 833529
E-mail: sales@fluid-transfer.co.uk
G B M Products, 4 Octavian Way, Team Valley Trading Estate, Gateshead, Tyne & Wear, NE11 0HZ Tel: 0191-487 8004 Fax: 0191-487 1655
E-mail: info@gbmproducts.sagehost.co.uk
Interlube Systems Ltd, 85 St. Modwen Road, Plymouth, PL6 8LH Tel: (01752) 676000 Fax: (01752) 676001
E-mail: info@interlubesystems.co.uk
Samoa Ltd, Asturias House Barrs Fold Road, Wingates Industrial Estate, Westhoughton, Bolton, BL5 3XP Tel: (01942) 850600 Fax: (01204) 812160
E-mail: sales@samoa.ltd.uk

AUTOMATIC POWDER COATING EQUIPMENT

Systech UK Ltd, Willow House, Kingswood Business Park, Albrighton, Wolverhampton, WV7 3AU Tel: (01902) 373276 Fax: (01902) 373081 E-mail: john@systechuk.com

AUTOMATIC PRINTED CIRCUIT BOARD (PCB) ASSEMBLY EQUIPMENT

Auwell Electronics Ltd, Units 16-19, Oldends Industrial Estate, Oldends, Stonehouse, Gloucestershire, GL10 3RQ Tel: (01453) 791111 Fax: (01453) 791313
E-mail: enquiries@auwell.co.uk
Electronic Production Services, Lansbury Estate, 102 Lower Guildford Road, Knaphill, Woking, Surrey, GU21 2EP Tel: (01483) 487644 Fax: (01483) 486347
E-mail: epswoking@btconnect.com
Hypertec Ltd, Unit 2 Swangate, Hungerford, Berkshire, RG17 0YX Tel: (01488) 686844 Fax: (01488) 686845
E-mail: info@hypertec.co.uk
Invotec Circuits, Unit A1 Halesfield 11, Telford, Shropshire, TF7 4PH Tel: (01952) 683000 Fax: (01952) 683456
E-mail: sales@invotecgroup.com
Merlin Circuit Technology Ltd, Unit 1, Hawarden Industrial Park, Hawarden, Deeside, Clwyd, CH5 3PZ Tel: (01244) 520510 Fax: (01244) 520721 E-mail: sales@merlincircuit.co.uk
Syntech Europe Ltd, 351 Wigan Road, Bolton, BL3 5QU Tel: (01204) 659899 Fax: (01204) 659941 E-mail: andrew@syntech-europe.com

AUTOMATIC PUBLIC CONVENIENCES

Healthmatic Ltd, Redman Road, Porte Marsh Industrial Estate, Calne, Wiltshire, SN11 9PR Tel: (01249) 822063 Fax: (01249) 823140
E-mail: ops@healthmatic.com

AUTOMATIC RESET CIRCUIT BREAKERS (CB)

D V R Electrical Wholesale Ltd, Unit 1 Dawson Road, Bletchley, Milton Keynes, MK1 1LH Tel: (01908) 271555 Fax: (01908) 271367
E-mail: info@dvr.co.uk

AUTOMATIC ROTARY ASSEMBLY MACHINES

Mechatronic Production Systems Ltd, 2267 Coventry Road, Sheldon, Birmingham, B26 3PD Tel: 0121-742 7206 Fax: 0121-743 6882 E-mail: sales@mechatronic.co.uk
▶ Tecno Vibrazioni S.R.l, 83 Highgate Road, Sileby, Loughborough, Leicestershire, LE12 7PN Tel: (01509) 813401 Fax: (0870) 2364114 E-mail: info@tecno-feeders.co.uk

▶ indicates data change since last edition

AUTOMATIC SAMPLING EQUIPMENT

Axiom Quality Control Equipment, Chapel House, The Hill, Kirkby-In-Ashfield, Nottingham, NG17 8JS Tel: (01623) 759836 Fax: (01623) 755103 E-mail: info@handh-services.co.uk

Blackfive Engineering Ltd, 16 Beeston Court, Stuart Road, Manor Park, Runcorn, Cheshire, WA7 1SS Tel: (01928) 579140 Fax: (01928) 579514 E-mail: blackfive@btconnect.com

Microscal Ltd, 79 Southern Row, London, W10 5AL Tel: (020) 8969 3935 Fax: (020) 8968 7302 E-mail: info@microscal.com

Minco Sampling-Techniques (UK) Ltd, Tofts Farm Industrial Estate, Brenda Road, Hartlepool, Cleveland, TS25 2BS Tel: (01429) 273252 Fax: (01429) 232611 E-mail: enquiries@mincouk.com

AUTOMATIC SPRAY EQUIPMENT

Graphoidal Developments Ltd, Broombank Road, Chesterfield, Derbyshire, S41 9QJ Tel: (01246) 266000 Fax: (01246) 269269 E-mail: sales@graphoidal.com

AUTOMATIC SPRINKLER INSTALLATION OR SERVICING

A & F Sprinklers Ltd, Atrium House, 574 Manchester Road, Bury, Lancashire, BL9 9SW Tel: 0161-796 5397 Fax: 0161-796 6057 E-mail: lhill@afsprinklers.co.uk

Anglian Energy Services, 23 Windrush Road, Kesgrave, Ipswich, IP5 2NZ Tel: (01473) 614446 Fax: (01473) 620443 E-mail: aessprinklers@aol.com

Armstrong Priestley, 77 Holbeck Lane, Leeds, LS11 9UL Tel: 0113-244 3138 Fax: 0113-394 4041 E-mail: sales@armstrongpriestley.co.uk

Besseges Ltd, Riverside, Dukinfield, Cheshire, SK16 4HE Tel: 0161-308 3252 Fax: 0161-339 5003 E-mail: sales@besseges.co.uk

Central Fire Protection, 5 Bewsey Road, Warrington, WA2 7LN Tel: (01925) 414464 Fax: (01925) 244298 E-mail: cfp.warrington@central-fire.co.uk

T.A. Cowap & Co. Ltd, Hazel Grove Works, Guy Edge, Linthwaite, Huddersfield, HD7 5TQ Tel: (01484) 851177 Fax: (01484) 648798 E-mail: lisa@tacowap.com

D H L Ltd, Pickerings Road, Halebank Industrial Estate, Widnes, Cheshire, WA8 0NH Tel: 0151-424 5441 Fax: 0151-423 2678 E-mail: d.a.welding9@msn.com

Hall Fire Protection, Unit 2 Holloway Drive, Wardley Business Park, Worsley, Manchester, M28 2LA Tel: 0161-793 4822 Fax: 0161-794 4950 E-mail: info@hallfire.co.uk

Integral, Norris House, Crawhall Road, Newcastle upon Tyne, NE1 2BB Tel: 0191-261 1071 Fax: 0191-232 8069 E-mail: mnew@integral.co.uk

Phoenix Fire Protection Midlands Ltd, Mountfield House, High Street, Kingswinford, West Midlands, DY6 8AL Tel: (01384) 295529 Fax: (01384) 271391 E-mail: sales@phoenix-fire.co.uk

R S M Refko Installations Ltd, 8 Capstan Centre, Thurrock Park Way, Tilbury, Essex, RM18 7HH Tel: (01375) 855500 Fax: (01375) 855533

Trident Fire Protection Company Ltd, Henfold Lane, Newdigate, Dorking, Surrey, RH5 5AF Tel: (01306) 886166 Fax: (01306) 631430 E-mail: cbta@arabact.co.uk

AUTOMATIC SPRINKLERS

Anglian Energy Services, 23 Windrush Road, Kesgrave, Ipswich, IP5 2NZ Tel: (01473) 614446 Fax: (01473) 620443 E-mail: aessprinklers@aol.com

Hall Fire Protection, Unit 2 Holloway Drive, Wardley Business Park, Worsley, Manchester, M28 2LA Tel: 0161-793 4822 Fax: 0161-794 4950 E-mail: info@hallfire.co.uk

Reliable Fire Sprinkler Ltd, Unit A2 Epsom Business Park, Kiln Lane, Epsom, Surrey, KT17 1JF Tel: (01372) 728899 Fax: (01372) 724461 E-mail: rfsl@reliablesprinkler.com

AUTOMATIC SWITCHGEAR ELECTRONIC SYSTEMS

Garnham Switchgear Ltd, Unit 2 Olympus Close Business Park, Ipswich, IP1 5LJ Tel: (01473) 240407 Fax: (01473) 463730 E-mail: sales@garnhamswitchgear.co.uk

Max Wright Ltd, Woodland Works, Woodlands Road, Thundridge, Ware, Hertfordshire, SG12 0SP Tel: (01920) 461235 Fax: (01920) 466423 E-mail: maxwrightlimited@btinternet.com

AUTOMATIC TEST EQUIPMENT (ATE)

A I Electronics Ltd, Bothwell Road, Hamilton, Lanarkshire, ML3 0DW Tel: (01698) 285225 Fax: (01698) 285944 E-mail: aielec@aol.com

Aeroflex, Burnham, 1 Progress House, Progress Business Centre, Whittle Parkway, Slough, SL1 6DQ Tel: (01628) 604455 Fax: (01628) 662017

Alfa Electric Ltd, 14 Burgess Road, Ivyhouse Industrial Estate, Hastings, East Sussex, TN35 4NR Tel: (01424) 424040 Fax: (01424) 424040 E-mail: sales@alfaelectric.co.uk

ALPHR Technology Ltd, Amor Way, Dunhams Lane, Letchworth Garden City, Hertfordshire, SG6 1UG Tel: (01462) 675838 Fax: (01462) 481190 E-mail: alphr@alphrtechnology.co.uk

Analog Devices Ltd, Rothwell House, Pembroke Road, Newbury, Berkshire, RG14 1BX Tel: (01635) 555400 Fax: (01635) 555401 E-mail: hilary.abbott@analog.com

ATE Ltd, Design Office, 56 Nodes Road, Northwood, Cowes, Isle of Wight, PO31 8AD Tel: (01983) 292052

B P Instruments, Unit 1 Oak Street Trading Estate, Oak Street, Quarry Bank, Brierley Hill, West Midlands, DY5 2JQ Tel: (01384) 569531 Fax: (01384) 569531

▶ Cirris Solutions Ltd, 4 Commerce Way, Stanbridge Road, Leighton Buzzard, Bedfordshire, LU7 4RW Tel: (01525) 374466 Fax: (01525) 374468 E-mail: sales@cirris.co.uk

Clare Instruments, Dominion Way, Worthing, West Sussex, BN14 8NW Tel: (01903) 233314 Fax: (01903) 216089 E-mail: sales@clareinstruments.com

Genrad Holdings Ltd, Orion Business Park, Bird Hall Lane, Stockport, Cheshire, SK3 0XG Tel: (01483) 569933 Fax: 0161-491 9501

Indentec Hardness Testing Machines Ltd, Lye Valley Industrial Estate, Bromley Street, Lye, Stourbridge, West Midlands, DY9 8HX Tel: (01384) 896949 Fax: (01384) 424470 E-mail: mail@indentec.demon.co.uk

Ip Test Ltd, 15 The Pines Trading Estate, Broad Street, Guildford, Surrey, GU3 3BH Tel: (01483) 567218 Fax: (01483) 506054 E-mail: sales@iptest.com

M K Test Systems Ltd, Orchard Court, West Buckland, Wellington, Somerset, TA21 9LE Tel: (01823) 661100 Fax: (01823) 661160 E-mail: sales@mktest.com

Minderaty Solutions N I Ltd, 75 Belfast Road, Carrickfergus, County Antrim, BT38 8BX Tel: (028) 9335 7300 Fax: (028) 9335 7305 E-mail: infoni@mindready.com

Terotest Ltd, 33 Station Road, Ashwell, Baldock, Hertfordshire, SG7 5LG Tel: (01462) 742499 Fax: (01462) 742497 E-mail: info@terotest.com

AUTOMATIC TRAFFIC COUNTING SYSTEMS

Golden River Traffic Ltd, Talisman Road, Bicester, Oxfordshire, OX26 6HR Tel: (01869) 362800 Fax: (01869) 246858 E-mail: sales@goldenriver.com

Peek Traffic Ltd, Hazelwood House, Lime Tree Way, Chineham, Basingstoke, Hampshire, RG24 8WZ Tel: (01256) 891800 Fax: (01256) 891870 E-mail: sales@peek-traffic.co.uk

AUTOMATIC TRANSMISSION REPAIR

▶ American V8 Engines, 266 Orphanage Road, Erdington, Birmingham, B24 0BB Tel: 0121-350 1116 Fax: 0121-350 1116 E-mail: adrian@americanv8engines.co.uk

▶ Central Axle Services Midlands Ltd, 220 Montgomery Street, Birmingham, B11 1DS Tel: 0121-772 0121 Fax: 0121-772 0711

AUTOMATIC TRANSMISSION SPECIALIST SERVICES

▶ American V8 Engines, 266 Orphanage Road, Erdington, Birmingham, B24 0BB Tel: 0121-350 1116 Fax: 0121-350 1116 E-mail: adrian@americanv8engines.co.uk

AUTOMATIC URINAL FLUSHING CONTROL SYSTEMS

Boyerman Ltd, Unit C Chesham Close, Romford, RM7 7PJ Tel: (01708) 742854 Fax: (01708) 737737 E-mail: sales@boyerman.co.uk

Drainage Center Ltd, 116 London Road, Hailsham, East Sussex, BN27 3AL Tel: (01323) 442333 Fax: (01323) 847488 E-mail: sales@drainagecenter.co.uk

▶ Springwell Microelectronics Ltd, 197 Raikes Lane, Birstall, Batley, West Yorkshire, WF17 9QF Tel: (01924) 420029 Fax: (0870) 7062353 E-mail: sales@springwellmicro.co.uk

AUTOMATIC VOLTAGE STABILISERS

Sollatek (UK) Ltd, Units 10 Poyle, 14 Industrial Estate, Newlands Drive, Poyle, Slough, SL3 0DX Tel: (01753) 688300 Fax: (01753) 685306 E-mail: sales@sollatek.com

AUTOMATIC WATER FILTERS

East Midland Water Co., 3 Cannock Street, Leicester, LE4 9HR Tel: 0116-276 3334 Fax: 0116-276 3335 E-mail: sales@emwc.uk.com

H2O Group, 1 Gammons Lane, Watford, WD24 6GB Tel: (01923) 225454 Fax: (01923) 225450

AUTOMATIC WELDING EQUIPMENT

Gullco International (UK) Ltd, 5 Stonecrop, North Quarry Business Park, Appley Bridge, Wigan, Lancashire, WN6 9DB Tel: (01257) 253579 Fax: (01257) 254629 E-mail: sales@gullco.co.uk

M H Weltronic Systems Ltd, Unit 1 Crowles Ash Business Centre, Crowles Ash, Bromyard, Herefordshire, HR7 4SW Tel: (01885) 400777 Fax: (01885) 400777 E-mail: weltronic_sysltd@lineone.net

Power Electronics & Controls Ltd, 1 Kingsthorne Park, Henson Way, Telford Way Industrial Estate, Kettering, Northamptonshire, NN16 8PX Tel: (01536) 310070 Fax: (01536) 525466 E-mail: sales@powerelectronics.co.uk

T P S Fronius, 1 The Omni Business Centre, Omega Park, Alton, Hampshire, GU34 2QD Tel: (01420) 546855 Fax: (01420) 546856 E-mail: alton@tps-fronius.co.uk

TPS Fronius Ltd, 5 Simonsburn Road, Kilmarnock, Ayrshire, KA1 5LE Tel: (01563) 529435 Fax: (01563) 523510 E-mail: sales@tps-fronius.co.uk

Y P H Welding Supplies, Unit 1 Stubbins Lane, Claughton-on-Brock, Preston, PR3 0QH Tel: (01995) 604057 Fax: (01995) 604018 E-mail: alan@yphltd.co.uk

AUTOMATIC WROUGHT IRON GATES

ALL SEASONS WROUGHT IRON UK LTD, UNIT 15 PARKWAY COURT, GLAISDALE PARKWAY, BILBOROUGH, NOTTINGHAM, NG8 4GN Tel: 0115 928 6688 E-mail: jimbrowne701@hotmail.com

D B Services, 19 Diamond Road, Dromore, County Down, BT25 1PH Tel: (028) 9269 2714 Fax: (028) 9269 9938 E-mail: del@dbservicesni.co.uk

Da Plating Jigs & Light Fabrications, 16 Cornwall Road Industrial Estate, Smethwick, West Midlands, B66 2JS Tel: 0121-555 8687 Fax: 0121-555 8688 E-mail: david@daplating.wannadoo.co.uk

▶ Gate Supplies, Whittington Works, Thompson Street, Chesterfield, Derbyshire, S41 9AR Tel: (01246) 261795 Fax: 01426 261795 E-mail: sales@gatesupplies.co.uk

▶ L & L Welding, Unit E 1, St. Davids Industrial Estate, Pengam, Blackwood, Gwent, NP12 3SW Tel: (01443) 832000 Fax: (01443) 832000 E-mail: marklewiswales@yahoo.co.uk

Lloyds Fabrications, Unit 7, Star Trading Estate, Ponthir, Newport, Gwent, NP18 1PQ Tel: (01633) 430378 Fax: (01633) 430378 E-mail: sales@lloydsfabrications.co.uk

Metal Art Co., Cadgerhill, Glendaveny, Peterhead, Aberdeenshire, AB42 3DY Tel: (01779) 838888 Fax: (01779) 838333 E-mail: info@classicmetalart.co.uk

▶ Stokergate, 36 Geoffrey CR, Fareham, Hampshire, PO16 0QQ Tel: (01329) 519669 E-mail: stokers3@ntlworld.com

AUTOMATION COMPONENTS

Automation Partnership, York Way, Royston, Hertfordshire, SG8 5WY Tel: (01763) 227200 Fax: (01763) 227201 E-mail: sales@automationpartnership.com

C S L Technical Engineering Services, Office 2 Rainbow Business Centre, Phoenix Way, Swansea Enterprise Park, Swansea, SA7 9EH Tel: 01792 702200 E-mail: sales@csl-ltd.co.uk

Lane Punch Tech Ltd, 1 Apex Business Park, Diplocks Way, Hailsham, East Sussex, BN27 3JU Tel: (01323) 844777 Fax: (01323) 849091 E-mail: michelle.thompson@lanepunch.co.uk

▶ Pentangle Engineering Services Ltd, Isaac Newton Way, Grantham, Lincolnshire, NG31 9RT Tel: (01476) 572354 Fax: (01476) 590356 E-mail: nigel.rivers@pentangle-eng.co.uk

AUTOMATION COMPUTER EQUIPMENT

Bargate Computer Services, Suite 3, 84 High Street, Burton-on-Trent, Staffordshire, DE14 1LJ Tel: (01283) 510249 Fax: (01283) 512330 E-mail: bargate@internet-uk.net

Qubie Systems Ltd, 25 Streatham Common South, London, SW16 3BX Tel: 0208 764 8878 Fax: 0208 6798543

AUTOMATION CONSULTANTS

Amber Programmable Design Ltd, Newbie, Annan, Dumfriesshire, DG12 5QJ Tel: (01461) 206000 Fax: (01461) 206200 E-mail: info@apd-ltd.com

▶ Buffers & Stackers Ltd, Creative Industries Centre, Wolverhampton Science Park, Wolverhampton, WV10 9TG Tel: (01902) 420877 Fax: (01902) 716312 E-mail: info@buffstack.co.uk

D S C Controls Ltd, 8 Lea Green Business Park, Eurolink, St. Helens, Merseyside, WA9 4TR Tel: (01744) 820777 Fax: (01744) 820707 E-mail: derek@dsc-control.freeserve.co.uk

Ford Electronics Ltd, Brewood Hall, Sparrows End Lane, Brewood, Stafford, ST19 9DB Tel: (01902) 455555 E-mail: sales@fordelectronics.co.uk

Industrial Automation & Technology Ltd, 18 Malhamdale Rd, Congleton, Cheshire, CW12 2DA Tel: 01260 277993 Fax: 01260 277993

▶ P J G Creative Design Ltd, 11 Mayer Gardens, Shenley Lodge, Milton Keynes, MK5 7EN Tel: (01908) 231175 E-mail: info@pjgcreative.com

Telepresence Ltd, Lochside, Longhaven, Peterhead, Aberdeenshire, AB42 0PA Tel: (01779) 812277 Fax: (01779) 812391

AUTOMATION CONTROL EQUIPMENT

Felton Production Solutions Ltd., 87 High Street, Knaphill, Woking, Surrey, GU21 2QD Tel: (01483) 475500 Fax: (01483) 475226 E-mail: martin.felton@btinternet.com

AUTOMATION CONTROL SYSTEMS

▶ Advanced Control Systems Ltd, 140 Aberford Road, Woodlesford, Leeds, LS26 8LG Tel: 0113-282 7123 Fax: 0113-282 5252 E-mail: office@xcl.co.uk

Andross Electrics Ltd, Unit 12 Twyford Business Centre, London Road, Bishop's Stortford, Hertfordshire, CM23 3YT Tel: (01279) 657661 Fax: (01279) 506164 E-mail: sales@andross.net

Arcom Control Systems Ltd, 8 Clifton Road, Cambridge, CB1 7EA Tel: (01223) 411200 Fax: (01223) 403400 E-mail: sales@arcom.co.uk

AWE Newtech Ltd, Brunel Drive, Northern Road Industrial Estate, Newark, Nottinghamshire, NG24 2EG Tel: (01636) 703793 Fax: (01636) 701210 E-mail: sales@awe-newtech.com

B & G Controls Ltd, Broadoak Enterprise Village, Broadoak Road, Sittingbourne, Kent, ME9 8AQ Tel: (01795) 423554 Fax: (01795) 428873 E-mail: sales@bt-controls.co.uk

Cadalec Control Systems, Three Boundaries Business Park, Coventry Road, Croft, Leicester, LE9 3GP Tel: (01455) 286900 Fax: (01455) 286999 E-mail: sales@cadalec.com

Cannon Electronics & Automation Ltd, White Gates Factory, Dunmow Road, Hatfield Heath, Bishop's Stortford, Hertfordshire, CM22 7ED Tel: (01279) 730709

D S C Controls Ltd, 8 Lea Green Business Park, Eurolink, St. Helens, Merseyside, WA9 4TR Tel: (01744) 820777 Fax: (01744) 820707 E-mail: derek@dsc-control.freeserve.co.uk

Electrical Design & Automation Ltd, The Old Bakery, Main Road, Pontesbury, Shrewsbury, SY5 0RR Tel: (01743) 791986 Fax: (01743) 791555 E-mail: eda1987@aol.com

Electron Systems Ltd, Unit 5b Drum Industrial Estate, Chester le Street, County Durham, DH2 1SS Tel: 0191-492 2007 Fax: 0191-492 2009 E-mail: sales@electronsystems.com

Eproduction Solutions Ltd, Viking Road, Great Yarmouth, Norfolk, NR31 0NU Tel: (01493) 652611 Fax: (01493) 444598 E-mail: andrew.williment@ep-solutions.com

Equinox Training Solutions Ltd, 6 Darwin House Corby Gate Business Park, Priors Haw Road, Corby, Northamptonshire, NN17 5JG Tel: (01536) 409666 Fax: (0870) 7065600 E-mail: mick@equinoxac.co.uk

G E Fanuc Automation (UK) Ltd, 15 Basset Court, Loake Close, Grange Park, Northampton, NN4 5EZ Tel: (01604) 744130 Fax: (01604) 744140 E-mail: gef.uk@gefanuceur.ge.com

General Panel Systems Ltd, 1-2 Leicester Street, Bedminster, Bristol, BS3 4DE Tel: 0117-953 1500 Fax: 0117-947 1700 E-mail: info@gpspanels.co.uk

AUTOMATION CONTROL SYSTEMS

– continued

Graphic Controls, Southcombe House, Southcombe, Chipping Norton, Oxfordshire, OX7 5QH Tel: (01608) 646303 Fax: (01608) 646304 E-mail: rickfordham@btconnect.com

Intech Automation Ltd, Willow Hall Works Cote Hill, Halifax, West Yorkshire, HX2 7LZ Tel: (01422) 355885 Fax: (01422) 355885

Jetter Distributors Ltd, Leighswood House, 43 Leighswood Road, Walsall, WS9 8AH Tel: (01922) 745200 Fax: (01922) 745045 E-mail: jetteruk@btinternet.com

Lamonde Automation Ltd, Project House, Morris Road, South Nutfield, Redhill, RH1 5SA Tel: (01737) 824600 Fax: (01737) 821431 E-mail: sales@lamonde.com

Logic Systems Consultants Ltd, Logic House, Central Street, St. Helens, Merseyside, WA10 1TP Tel: (01744) 455000 Fax: (01744) 453300 E-mail: sales@logicsystems.co.uk

Micromech Systems Ltd, Units 7 & 8, Chilford Court, Braintree, Essex, CM7 2QS Tel: (01376) 333300 Fax: (01376) 552600 E-mail: sales@micromech.co.uk

Nee Controls, 19b White Rose Way, Gateshead, Tyne & Wear, NE10 8YX Tel: 0191-415 9751 Fax: 0191-416 1603 E-mail: sales@nee-controls.com

NUM (UK) Ltd, Unit 3, Fairfield Court, Seven Stars Industrial Estate, Coventry, CV3 4LJ Tel: (0871) 7504020 Fax: (0871) 7504021 E-mail: solutions@schneider-num.co.uk

Pepperl & Fuchs, 77 Ripponden Road, Oldham, OL1 4EL Tel: 0161-633 6431 Fax: 0161-624 6537 E-mail: sales@pepperl-fuchs.com

Practicon Ltd, Chapel Lane, Rode Heath, Stoke-on-Trent, ST7 3SD Tel: (01270) 876211 Fax: (01270) 878887 E-mail: sales.systems@practicon.co.uk

Syscom Motion Solution Ltd, Unit 19 Barnsley Business & Innovation Centre, Innovation Way, Barnsley, South Yorkshire, S75 1JL Tel: (01226) 771630 Fax: (01226) 771696 E-mail: info@automation.co.uk

System Automation Leicester Ltd, Claymill Buildings, Claymill Road, Leicester, LE4 9JJ Tel: 0116-246 0151 Fax: 0116-246 1772 E-mail: andy.austin@system-auto.demon.co.uk

Tes Europe Ltd, Sandyland, North End, Wisbech, Cambridgeshire, PE13 1PE Tel: (01945) 474809 Fax: (01945) 589591 E-mail: tes_europe@freenet.co.uk

AUTOMATION EQUIPMENT COMPONENTS

A S I (Auto Systems Industries) Ltd, PO Box 463, Maidstone, Kent, ME14 5PU Tel: (01622) 735781 Fax: (01622) 734686 E-mail: sales@asi.gb.com

Estuary Automation Ltd, 40 Shoebury Avenue, Shoeburyness, Southend-on-Sea, SS3 9BH Tel: (01702) 293901 Fax: (01702) 297318 E-mail: estaut@aol.com

Grupo Antonin, 795 London Road, Grays, Essex, RM20 3LH Tel: (01708) 683500 Fax: (01708) 683555

S T Robotics, Orwell House, 11 Cowley Road, Cambridge, CB4 0PP Tel: (01223) 420288 Fax: (01223) 420291 E-mail: sales@strobotics.com

AUTOMATION HANDLING EQUIPMENT

▶ Buffers & Stackers Ltd, Creative Industries Centre, Wolverhampton Science Park, Wolverhampton, WV10 9TG Tel: (01902) 420877 Fax: (01902) 716312 E-mail: info@buffstack.co.uk

Estuary Automation Ltd, 40 Shoebury Avenue, Shoeburyness, Southend-on-Sea, SS3 9BH Tel: (01702) 293901 Fax: (01702) 297318 E-mail: estaut@aol.com

Ismeca (UK) Ltd, 6 Azalea Drive, Up Hatherley, Cheltenham, Gloucestershire, GL51 3EA Tel: (01242) 863555 Fax: (0870) 7620696 E-mail: mchatfield@ismeca.uk.com

Weiss UK Ltd, 27 Manchester Drive, Leegomery, Telford, Shropshire, TF1 6XY Tel: (01952) 240953 Fax: (01952) 244442 E-mail: info@weiss.uk.com

AUTOMATION INSPECTION EQUIPMENT

ALPHR Technology Ltd, Amor Way, Dunhams Lane, Letchworth Garden City, Hertfordshire, SG6 1UG Tel: (01462) 675838 Fax: (01462) 481190 E-mail: alphr@alphrtechnology.co.uk

AUTOMATION SOFTWARE

▶ Evelogic Ltd, Centaur House, Ancells Road, Fleet, Hampshire, GU51 2UJ Tel: (0870) 1203148 Fax: (0870) 1203149 E-mail: sales@evelogic.com

AUTOMATION SPECIAL PURPOSE EQUIPMENT/ SYSTEMS CONSULTANTS OR DESIGNERS

A & B Auto Electrical Services Ltd, Unit 4 Regal Road Industrial Estate, Weasenham Lane, Wisbech, Cambridgeshire, PE13 2RQ Tel: (01945) 587022 Fax: (01945) 585300

Ak Developments, 5 Station Road, Isleham, Ely, Cambridgeshire, CB7 5QT Tel: (01638) 720727 Fax: (01638) 720724 E-mail: cse@akd.co.uk

Aston Dane P.L.C., Aston Dane House, Waterloo Road, Widnes, Cheshire, WA8 0QR Tel: 0151-423 4494 Fax: 0151-495 1089 E-mail: postbox@astondane.com

Bereton Electronics Ltd, Unit 49 Kettley Business Park, Ketley, Telford, Shropshire, TF1 5JD Tel: (01952) 253222 Fax: (01952) 244445 E-mail: mail@bereton.co.uk

Cambridge Systems Engineering Ltd, Fordham Technology Centre, 5 Station Road, Fordham, Ely, Cambridgeshire, CB7 5LW Tel: (01638) 720727 Fax: (01638) 720724 E-mail: mailbox@cseltd.co.uk

Crystal Structures Ltd, Crystal Park, Tunbridge Lane, Bottisham, Cambridge, CB25 9EA Tel: (01223) 811451 Fax: (01223) 811452 E-mail: sales@crystalstructures.co.uk

W. & H. Eves Ltd, Unit 5 The Aviary, Woodgate, Crawley Lane, Kings Bromley, Burton-on-Trent, Staffordshire, DE13 7JF Tel: (01543) 473444 Fax: (01543) 472152 E-mail: info@wheves.com

Forward & Thompson Ltd, Atlas Road, North York Trading Estate, Clifton Moor, York, YO30 4UR Tel: (01904) 690999 Fax: (01904) 690960

H G Systems Ltd, Dunston House Sheepbridge Works, Dunston Road, Chesterfield, Derbyshire, S41 9QD Tel: (01246) 260270 Fax: (01246) 450323 E-mail: sales@hgsystems.co.uk

Hasfield Systems, Yartleton Oak, Yartleton Lane, May Hill, Longhope, Gloucestershire, GL17 0RF Tel: (01452) 831881 Fax: (01452) 831881 E-mail: systems@hasfield.demon.co.uk

Household Automation Ltd, Fox Way, Pinkhurst Lane, Slinfold, Horsham, West Sussex, RH13 0QR Tel: (0870) 3300071 E-mail: afe@globalnet.co.uk

Inteck Automation Ltd, 9 Cotswold Avenue, Ipswich, IP1 4LL Tel: (07971) 885823 Fax: (01473) 286714 E-mail: inteck@aol.com

Ismeca (UK) Ltd, 6 Azalea Drive, Up Hatherley, Cheltenham, Gloucestershire, GL51 3EA Tel: (01242) 863555 Fax: (0870) 7620696 E-mail: mchatfield@ismeca.uk.com

J F L Mecelec, Llanthony Road, Gloucester, GL2 5QT Tel: (01452) 413531 Fax: (01452) 307580 E-mail: mtl@mecelec.co.uk

Luma Automation, Technology House, Blackpole Trading Estate West, Worcester, WR3 8TJ Tel: (01905) 753700 Fax: (01905) 753701 E-mail: sales@rglumagroup.co.uk

M G Automation Ltd, 16 Stratfield Park, Elettra Avenue, Waterlooville, Hampshire, PO7 7XN Tel: (023) 9226 7727 Fax: (023) 9226 7747 E-mail: sales@mgautomation.co.uk

Machine Techniques Ltd, Unit 3-5 Court Yard Workshops, Bath Street, Market Harborough, Leicestershire, LE16 9EW Tel: (01858) 434059 Fax: (01858) 433638 E-mail: sales@mactec.co.uk

Marlin Group Holdings, Marlin House Johnson Road, Fernsode Business Park, Ferndown Industrial Estate, Wimborne, Dorset, BH21 7SE Tel: (01202) 862900 Fax: (01202) 862901 E-mail: sales@marlin-ltd.co.uk

Modular Automation International Ltd, Talbot Way, Small Heath Business Park, Birmingham, B10 0HJ Tel: 0121-766 7979 Fax: 0121-766 6385 E-mail: crampton@modular.co.uk

N I S Holdings Ltd, Ackhurst Road, Chorley, Lancashire, PR7 1NH Tel: (01257) 265656 Fax: (01257) 275501 E-mail: tbromell@nisltd.com

North East Secure Electronics Ltd, North East Innovation Centre, Neilson Road, Gateshead, Tyne & Wear, NE10 0EW Tel: 0191-477 9235 Fax: 0191-478 3639 E-mail: g.ord@neic.co.uk

Performance Feeders, Lavender House, Station Road, Hammerwich, Burntwood, Staffordshire, WS7 0JZ Tel: (01543) 454055 Fax: (01543) 454047 E-mail: enquiries@performancefeeders.co.uk

▶ Powel Automation Ltd, Commerce Way, Lancing Industrial Estate, Lancing, West Sussex, BN15 8TA Tel: (01903) 762700 Fax: (01903) 763652 E-mail: sales@powel.co.uk

RH Industrial Electronics, Unit 11d Dabble Duck Industrial Estate, Shildon, County Durham, DL4 2RA Tel: (01388) 777823 Fax: (01388) 775902 E-mail: rhie@comp42.freeserve.co.uk

Riverside Automation Ltd, 61 Wostenholm Road, Sheffield, S7 1LE Tel: 0114-255 5500 Fax: 0114-255 5505 E-mail: sales@riverauto.co.uk

S P Automation Ltd, 3 Omega Centre, Sandford Lane, Wareham, Dorset, BH20 4DY Tel: (01929) 550465 Fax: (01929) 550522 E-mail: sales@spautomation.co.uk

Snow Hunter Automation, PO Box 260, Scarborough, North Yorkshire, YO12 5YA Tel: (07944) 085848 Fax: (01723) 371696 E-mail: john@snowhunter.freeserve.co.uk

Syscom Motion Solution Ltd, Unit 19 Barnsley Business & Innovation Centre, Innovation Way, Barnsley, South Yorkshire, S75 1JL Tel: (01226) 771630 Fax: (01226) 771696 E-mail: info@automation.co.uk

Weirgrove Automation Ltd, Lords Mill, Oakridge Road, High Wycombe, Buckinghamshire, HP11 2PA Tel: (01494) 448387 Fax: (01494) 530734 E-mail: weirgrove@weirgrove.co.uk

AUTOMATION SPECIAL PURPOSE EQUIPMENT/ SYSTEMS DISTRIBUTORS OR AGENTS

W. & H. Eves Ltd, Unit 5 The Aviary, Woodgate, Crawley Lane, Kings Bromley, Burton-on-Trent, Staffordshire, DE13 7JF Tel: (01543) 473444 Fax: (01543) 472152 E-mail: info@wheves.com

Global Access Technology Ltd, Unit 3a Beechwood, Lime Tree Way, Chineham, Basingstoke, Hampshire, RG24 8WA Tel: (01256) 374930 Fax: (01256) 374939 E-mail: info@aprimatic.co.uk

Keyence UK Ltd, Avebury House, 219-225 Avebury Boulevard, Milton Keynes, MK9 1AU Tel: (01908) 696900 Fax: (01908) 696777 E-mail: ukinfo@keyence.co.uk

AUTOMATION SPECIAL PURPOSE EQUIPMENT/ SYSTEMS MANUFRS/ CONSTRUCTORS, *See also headings for individual usage*

A C Automation, Hartland Avenue, Tattenhoe, Milton Keynes, MK4 3DN Tel: (01908) 501796 Fax: (01908) 501796 E-mail: sales@ac-automation.co.uk

A D M Automation, Nest Road, Gateshead, Tyne & Wear, NE10 0ES Tel: 0191-438 7888 Fax: 0191-438 7899 E-mail: sales@adm-automation.co.uk

A G R Automation Ltd, Elliot Industrial Estate, Arbroath, Angus, DD11 2NJ Tel: (01241) 872961 Fax: (01241) 871723 E-mail: agr@agr-automation.com

▶ Aaa V Systems Ltd, Unit 28 City Industrial Units, Crafton St West, Leicester, LE1 2DE Tel: 0116-262 7818 Fax: 0116-262 7818 E-mail: sales@aaavsystems.co.uk

Acorn Engineering, 6 Kingscroft Court, Ridgway, Havant, Hampshire, PO9 1LS Tel: (023) 9249 2040 Fax: (023) 9247 0377 E-mail: mail@acorn-engineering.co.uk

Adsyst (Automation) Ltd, White Lodge Court, Reading Road, Yateley, Hampshire, GU46 7RX Tel: (01252) 860600 Fax: (01252) 872015 E-mail: info@adsyst.co.uk

Air Controls Ltd, Garden Close, Langage Business Park, Plympton, Plymouth, PL7 5EU Tel: (01752) 344443 Fax: (01752) 346789 E-mail: aircontrols@eur-isp.com

Ak Developments, 5 Station Road, Isleham, Ely, Cambridgeshire, CB7 5QT Tel: (01638) 720727 Fax: (01638) 720724 E-mail: cse@akd.co.uk

ALPHR Technology Ltd, Amor Way, Dunhams Lane, Letchworth Garden City, Hertfordshire, SG6 1UG Tel: (01462) 675838 Fax: (01462) 481190 E-mail: alphr@alphrtechnology.co.uk

Atl Automation Systems, Cackle Street, Brede, Rye, East Sussex, TN31 6DY Tel: (01424) 882823 Fax: (01424) 882855

Automation Conveyors Ltd, Coopies Field, Coopies Lane Industrial Estate, Morpeth, Northumberland, NE61 6JT Tel: (01670) 514354 Fax: (01670) 514328

Automation Design & Installation Ltd, 1 Melchett Road, Kings Norton Business Centre, Birmingham, B30 3HG Tel: 0121-451 2255 Fax: 0121-459 1415 E-mail: info@adiltd.co.uk

B K Automations, 4 Talisman Business Centre, Duncan Road, Park Gate, Southampton, SO31 7GA Tel: (01489) 582712 Fax: (01489) 583294 E-mail: bkautomamation@tinyworld.co.uk

▶ Biele UK Ltd, 24 Wilton Court, Newton Aycliffe, County Durham, DL5 7PU Tel: (01325) 321478 Fax: (01325) 312537 E-mail: sales@biele.co.uk

C & L Developments, 25 Lyon Road, Walton-on-Thames, Surrey, KT12 3PU Tel: (01932) 244699 Fax: (01932) 241660 E-mail: info@cl-devs.co.uk

C N C Engineering, 69 Haviland Road, Ferndown Industrial Estate, Wimborne, Dorset, BH21 7PY Tel: (01202) 892892 Fax: (01202) 893114 E-mail: euromation@btconnect.com

Cambridge Systems Engineering Ltd, Fordham Technology Centre, 5 Station Road, Fordham, Ely, Cambridgeshire, CB7 5LW Tel: (01638) 720727 Fax: (01638) 720724 E-mail: mailbox@cseltd.co.uk

Cirrus Technologies Ltd, Heming Road, Washford Industrial Estate, Redditch, Worcestershire, B98 0DN Tel: (01527) 527882 Fax: (01527) 502074 E-mail: sales@cirrustesting.com

CodaOctopus Products Ltd, Admiral House, 29-30 Maritime Street, Edinburgh, EH6 6SE Tel: 0131-553 1380 Fax: 0131-554 7143 E-mail: info@codaoctopus.com

▶ Concept Automated Systems Ltd, Trinity House, 160 John Wilson Business Park, Chestfield, Whitstable, Kent, CT5 3RA Tel: (01227) 770677 Fax: (01227) 771392 E-mail: sales@conceptautomatedsystems.co.uk

Dunelm Supplies Ltd, Netherset Lane, Madeley, Crewe, CW3 9PF Tel: (01782) 750884 Fax: (01782) 751305 E-mail: dunelmpete@aol.co.uk

▶ E D S Developments Ltd, Unit 20, Saltash Business Park, Forge Lane, Moorlands Trading Estate, Saltash, Cornwall, PL12 6LX Tel: (01752) 847900 Fax: (01752) 837251 E-mail: info@edsdevelopments.com

Earlsdon Technology Properties Ltd, Unit 11 Spitfire Close, Coventry Business Park, Coventry, CV5 6UR Tel: (024) 7671 7062 Fax: (024) 7671 7062 E-mail: sales@e-tech.co.uk

Electrical Design & Automation Ltd, The Old Bakery, Main Road, Pontesbury, Shrewsbury, SY5 0RR Tel: (01743) 791986 Fax: (01743) 791555 E-mail: eda1987@aol.com

W. & H. Eves Ltd, Unit 5 The Aviary, Woodgate, Crawley Lane, Kings Bromley, Burton-on-Trent, Staffordshire, DE13 7JF Tel: (01543) 473444 Fax: (01543) 472152 E-mail: info@wheves.com

Fata Automation Ltd, Elgar House, Shrub Hill Road, Worcester, WR4 9EE Tel: (01905) 613931 Fax: (01905) 613913 E-mail: info@fatagroup.it

Gudel Lineartec (U.K.) Ltd, Unit 5 Wickmans Drive, Banner Lane, Coventry, CV4 9XA Tel: (024) 7669 5444 Fax: (024) 7669 5666 E-mail: info@uk.gudel.com

H B A Distribution, 3A Upper Darkley Road, Keady, Armagh, BT60 3RE Tel: (028) 3753 1155 Fax: (028) 3753 8231 E-mail: info@hba.ie

Hartford Engineering Ltd, Bradford Road, Winsford, Cheshire, CW7 2PE Tel: (01606) 860888 Fax: (01606) 860889 E-mail: he@hartford-eng.co.uk

Helbar Automation Ltd, 478 Rayleigh Rd, Eastwood, Leigh-on-Sea, Essex, SS9 5HZ Tel: (01702) 522425 Fax: (01702) 522425 E-mail: info@helbar.com

Holmes, 15 Ffordd Derwyn, Penyffordd, Chester, CH4 0JT Tel: (01244) 545532 Fax: (01244) 545532 E-mail: nigel.holmes1@virgin.net

▶ Ideas In Automation, Unit 4 Silver House, Adelphi Way, Ireland Idustrial Estate, Staysly, Chesterfield, Derbyshire, S43 3LJ Tel: (0870) 2000499 Fax: (0870) 2000599 E-mail: sales@ideas-in-automation.ltd.uk

Industrial Automation Ltd, 8 The Midway, Nottingham, NG7 2TS Tel: 0115-840 0500 Fax: 0115-840 5959 E-mail: sales@ind-auto.com

▶ Ingenia Solutions Ltd, 71 Victoria Road, Burgess Hill, West Sussex, RH15 9TR Tel: (01444) 876920 Fax: (01444) 876929 E-mail: sales@ingeniasolutions.co.uk

▶ Intelligent Interiors, Focus House, 6 Tonbridge Road, Maidstone, Kent, ME16 8RP Tel: (01622) 351070 Fax: (01622) 686894

Ismeca (UK) Ltd, 6 Azalea Drive, Up Hatherley, Cheltenham, Gloucestershire, GL51 3EA Tel: (01242) 863555 Fax: (0870) 7620696 E-mail: mchatfield@ismeca.uk.com

J F L Mecelec, Llanthony Road, Gloucester, GL2 5QT Tel: (01452) 413531 Fax: (01452) 307580 E-mail: mtl@mecelec.co.uk

Kleinmichel, Birds Hill, Letchworth Garden City, Hertfordshire, SG6 1JE Tel: (01462) 677611 Fax: (0870) 7626539 E-mail: uk-sales@kleinmichel.com

Kuka Automation & Robotics Ltd, Hereward Rise, Halesowen, West Midlands, B62 8AN Tel: 0121-585 0800 Fax: 0121-585 0900 E-mail: sales@kuka.co.uk

Luma Automation, Technology House, Blackpole Trading Estate West, Worcester, WR3 8TJ Tel: (01905) 753700 Fax: (01905) 753701 E-mail: sales@rglumagroup.co.uk

Macs, Unit 5 Ashburton Park, Wheelforge Way, Trafford Park, Manchester, M17 1EH Tel: (0845) 2607711 Fax: 0161-272 7449 E-mail: support@macs-solutions.com

Microdat Automation Co Uk Ltd, Unit2, Benyon Park Way, Leeds, LS12 6DP Tel: 0113-244 5225 Fax: 0113-244 5226 E-mail: info@microdat.co.uk

Modular Automation International Ltd, Talbot Way, Small Heath Business Park, Birmingham, B10 0HJ Tel: 0121-766 7979 Fax: 0121-766 6385 E-mail: crampton@modular.co.uk

NCMT Ltd, Ferry Works, Summer Road, Thames Ditton, Surrey, KT7 0QJ Tel: (020) 8398 4277 Fax: (020) 8398 3631

Overmatic Ltd, 13 Clifton Road, Coulsdon, Surrey, CR5 2DW Tel: (020) 8668 3076 Fax: (020) 8668 3076

▶ Parmley Graham Ltd, 1 Westleigh Business Park, Winchester Avenue, Blaby, Leicester, LE8 4EZ Tel: 0116-277 3783 Fax: 0116-277 5696 E-mail: sales@parmley-graham.co.uk

Pentland Systems, 8 Alderstone Business Park, Macmillan Road, Livingston, West Lothian, EH54 7DF Tel: (01506) 464666 Fax: (01506) 463030 E-mail: sales@pentlandsys.com

Peterson Design Ltd, 27 Mendip Drive, Frome, Somerset, BA11 2HT Tel: (01373) 465507 Fax: (01373) 465507 E-mail: enquiries@peterson.eu.com

▶ Powel Automation Ltd, Commerce Way, Lancing Industrial Estate, Lancing, West Sussex, BN15 8TA Tel: (01903) 762700 Fax: (01903) 763652 E-mail: sales@powel.co.uk

AUTOMATION SPECIAL PURPOSE EQUIPMENT/SYSTEMS MANUFRS/CONSTRUCTORS – *continued*

Proven Engineering Products Ltd, Wardhead Park, Stewarton, Kilmarnock, Ayrshire, KA3 5LH Tel: (01560) 485570 E-mail: info@provenenergy.com

Quantum Manufacturing Ltd, 1 Heathcote Way, Heathcote Industrial Estate, Warwick, CV34 6TE Tel: (01926) 885564 Fax: (01926) 450387 E-mail: info@quantumprecisiontoolmakers.co.uk

R T S, Northbank Industrial Park, Irlam, Manchester, M44 5AY Tel: 0161-777 2000 Fax: 0161-777 2095 E-mail: sales@rts-group.co.uk

Radway Control Systems, Business & Technology Centre, Radway Grn, Crewe, CW2 5PR Tel: (01270) 886176 Fax: (01270) 886275 E-mail: pjtomkinson@radway.co.uk

S P Automation Ltd, 3 Omega Centre, Sandford Lane, Wareham, Dorset, BH20 4DY Tel: (01929) 550465 Fax: (01929) 550522 E-mail: sales@spautomation.co.uk

S P Technology Ltd, Camperdown Industrial Park, George Buckman Drive, Dundee, DD2 3SP Tel: (01382) 880088 Fax: (01382) 880099 E-mail: info@sptechnology.co.uk

Schneider Electric Ltd, 120 New Cavendish Street, London, W1W 6XX Tel: (0870) 6088608 Fax: (0870) 6088606

Sewtec Automation Ltd, 3 Riverside Way, Dewsbury, West Yorkshire, WF13 3LG Tel: (01924) 494047 Fax: (01924) 480949 E-mail: sales@sewtec.co.uk

T I A Robotic Tooling Solutions, Unit 4C Derby Business Park, Canal Street, Derby, DE1 2RJ Tel: (01332) 204850 Fax: (01332) 204851 E-mail: info@tatem.co.uk

▶ Taktomat, 15, Rushley Drive, Sheffield, S17 3EL Tel: 0114-262 0480 Fax: 0114-262 0480

Tilling Engineering Ltd, 1 Dale House, Craven Road, Broadheath, Altrincham, Cheshire, WA14 5HJ Tel: 0161-926 9995 Fax: 0161-926 9995 E-mail: clive.tilling@tillingeng.co.uk

Total Solutions Ltd, 11 Sealand Road, Sealand, Chester, CH1 6BS Tel: (01244) 881818 Fax: (01244) 881991 E-mail: totalsols@aol.com

Tribal Automation Ltd, 6 Lodge Forge Trading Estate, Cradley Road, Cradley Heath, West Midlands, B64 7RW Tel: (01384) 562563 Fax: (01384) 562563

▶ Walker Precision Engineering Ltd, 4 Fullarton Drive, Glasgow East Investment Park, Glasgow, G32 8FA Tel: 0141-641 9641 Fax: 0141-646 2060

AUTOMATION SYSTEM COMPUTER SOFTWARE TO SPECIFICATION

Avon Control Engineering & Software, The Old Vicarage, Somerset Square, Nailsea, Bristol, BS48 1RN Tel: (01275) 853721 Fax: (01275) 857746 E-mail: sales@graynailsea.freeserve.co.uk

AUTOMATION SYSTEM DEVELOPMENT

Hasfield Systems, Yartleton Oak, Yartleton Lane, May Hill, Longhope, Gloucestershire, GL17 0RF Tel: (01452) 831881 Fax: (01452) 831881 E-mail: systems@hasfield.demon.co.uk

AUTOMATION SYSTEMS

Clark International Machinery Ltd, PO Box 58, Stratford-upon-Avon, Warwickshire, CV37 7YF Tel: (01789) 263636 Fax: (01789) 263637 E-mail: sales@clarkintmachinery.co.uk

Evershed Robotics Ltd, Unit D1 Hortonwood 10, Telford, Shropshire, TF1 7ES Tel: (01952) 608020 Fax: (01952) 608388 E-mail: sales@evershedrobotics.com

Household Automation Ltd, Fox Way, Pinkhurst Lane, Slinfold, Horsham, West Sussex, RH13 0QR Tel: (0870) 3300071 E-mail: afe@globalnet.co.uk

Synectics Solutions Ltd, Synectics House The Hollies, The Brampton, Newcastle, Staffordshire, ST5 0QY Tel: (01782) 664000 Fax: (01782) 664050 E-mail: enq@synectics-solutions.com

AUTOMATION SYSTEMS INTEGRATORS

Complete Industrial Services Ltd, 63 Cromwell Road, Bushbury Wolverhampton, Wolverhampton, WV10 8UT Tel: (01902) 651795 Fax: (01902) 651795 E-mail: sales@ciservices.worldonline.co.uk

Evershed Robotics Ltd, Unit D1 Hortonwood 10, Telford, Shropshire, TF1 7ES Tel: (01952) 608020 Fax: (01952) 608388 E-mail: sales@evershedrobotics.com

H G Systems Ltd, Dunston House Sheepbridge Works, Dunston Road, Chesterfield, Derbyshire, S41 9QD Tel: (01246) 260270 Fax: (01246) 450323 E-mail: sales@hgsystems.co.uk

I C P Projects Ltd, Cwm Cynon Business Park, Mountain Ash, Mid Glamorgan, CF45 4ER Tel: (01443) 477970 Fax: (01443) 476707 E-mail: sales@icpprojects.co.uk

Synectics Solutions Ltd, Synectics House The Hollies, The Brampton, Newcastle, Staffordshire, ST5 0QY Tel: (01782) 664000 Fax: (01782) 664050 E-mail: enq@synectics-solutions.com

AUTOMATION WORK HANDLING DEVICES

Parmley Graham Ltd, Unit 6 Pasadena Close Trading Estate, Hayes, Middlesex, UB3 3NQ Tel: (020) 8848 9667 Fax: (020) 8848 1968 E-mail: london@parmley-graham.co.uk

AUTOMOTIVE

▶ Daifuku Co. Ltd, 3 Waterside Drive, Langley, Slough, SL3 6EZ Tel: (01753) 581000 Fax: (01753) 582210 E-mail: sales@daifuku.co.uk

▶ G B Agencies Ltd, Alexandra Dock North, Grimsby, South Humberside, DN31 3UA Tel: (01472) 240416 Fax: (01472) 348751 E-mail: agencies@gbagroup.com

▶ JFL Automotive Ltd, Frankley Industrial Park, Tay Road, Rubery, Rednal, Birmingham, B45 0LD Tel: 0121-453 1061 Fax: 0121-460 1144

M W F Services, Kelsey Close, Attleborough Fields Industrial Estate, Nuneaton, Warwickshire, CV11 6RS Tel: (024) 7634 7774 Fax: (01858) 571196 E-mail: david_jeffrey@btopenworld.com

Slinden Services, 3 Riverside Court, Westminster Industrial Estate, Measham, Swadlincote, Derbyshire, DE12 7DS Tel: (01530) 274646 Fax: (01530) 274647 E-mail: info@slindenservices.co.uk

▶ Smartekh, 256 Carmel Road North, Darlington, County Durham, DL3 9TD Tel: (01325) 778161 E-mail: info@smartekh.co.uk

▶ Used Car Expert, 107-111 Fleet Street, London, EC4A 2AB Tel: (0870) 4442920 Fax: (0870) 4442921 E-mail: action@usedcarexpert.com

Van Gadgets, 137 Heston Road, Hounslow, TW5 0RD Tel: (0870) 3833388 Fax: (020) 8572 8510 E-mail: sales@vangadgets.co.uk

AUTOMOTIVE ADHESIVE TAPES

▶ Paint Protection Systems, 10 Oak Rd, Withington, Manchester, M20 3DA Tel: (07949) 094708 Fax: 0161-448 9240 E-mail: tim@paintprotectionsystems.co.uk

AUTOMOTIVE ADHESIVES

▶ Adhesive Applications, 2 Richmond Drive, Lichfield, Staffordshire, WS14 9SZ Tel: (01543) 255149 Fax: 01543 255149 E-mail: dancerpw@aol.com

▶ Customised Formulations Ltd, 146 Elmsfield Avenue, Norden, Rochdale, Lancashire, OL11 5XA Tel: 07840 133339 Fax: 0845 8330945 E-mail: andy@customised-formulations.co.uk

Lugg Facilities Ltd, 99-107 Hill Top, West Bromwich, West Midlands, B70 0RY Tel: 0121-556 1551 Fax: 0121-556 1552 E-mail: sales@lugg-tools.co.uk

AUTOMOTIVE ASSEMBLY MACHINES

Emerson & Renwick Ltd, Peel Bank Works, Peel Bank, Church, Accrington, Lancashire, BB5 4EF Tel: (01254) 872727 Fax: (01254) 871109 E-mail: sales@eandr.com

AUTOMOTIVE AUTOMATIC TRANSMISSION CONSTANT VARIABLE BELT SYSTEMS

Wimbledon Automatics, 182 Hartfield Road, London, SW19 3TQ Tel: (020) 8540 7780

AUTOMOTIVE BEARING GAUGES

Plastigauge, Unit 2, Gaugemaster Way, Ford, Arundel, West Sussex, BN18 0RX Tel: (01903) 882822 Fax: (01903) 884962 E-mail: sales@plastigauge.co.uk

AUTOMOTIVE BEARINGS

N T N Bearings UK Ltd, 11 Wellington Crescent, Fradley Park, Lichfield, Staffordshire, WS13 8RZ Tel: (01543) 445000 Fax: (01543) 445035 E-mail: jcd@ntn-europe.com

Technostart Ltd, 1a Clifton Avenue, London, E17 6HL Tel: (020) 8503 2778 Fax: (020) 8523 3054 E-mail: sales@technostart.co.uk

AUTOMOTIVE BOLTS AND NUTS

Disc-Lock Europe Ltd, PO Box 134, Sittingbourne, Kent, ME9 7TF Tel: (01795) 844332 Fax: (01795) 843986 E-mail: info@disc-lock.com

P K Engineering West Bromwich Ltd, Unit 3 Kelvin Way, West Bromwich, West Midlands, B70 7TN Tel: 0121-500 5847 Fax: 0121-553 1622 E-mail: sales@pk-engineering.co.uk

AUTOMOTIVE CABLES

Concordia Co. Ltd, Derwent Street, Long Eaton, Nottingham, NG10 3LP Tel: 0115-946 7400 Fax: 0115-946 1026

AUTOMOTIVE CHEMICAL PRODUCTS MANUFRS

Autosmart, 18 Holmfield, Holm Lane, Prenton, Merseyside, CH43 2NZ Tel: 0151-653 4588 Fax: 0151-512 0147

Bondaglass Voss Ltd, 158 Ravenscroft Road, Beckenham, Kent, BR3 4TW Tel: (020) 8778 0071 Fax: (020) 8659 5297 E-mail: bondaglass@btconnect.com

Brencliffe Ltd, Rossendale Road, Burnley, Lancashire, BB11 5HD Tel: (01282) 435226 Fax: (01282) 436147 E-mail: sales@brencliffe.com

High Technology Solvents UK Ltd, Millfield, Ashwells Road, Brentwood, Essex, CM15 9SF Tel: (01277) 375222 Fax: (01277) 373115 E-mail: htsukltd@aol.com

Honey Well Comsumer Products Group, Oakhurst Drive, Cheadle Heath, Stockport, Cheshire, SK3 0RZ Tel: 0161-491 7391 Fax: 0161-491 7399 E-mail: info@holtsauto.com

Intro Marketing Ltd, Old Freight Depot, Roberts Road, Doncaster, South Yorkshire, DN4 0JW Tel: (01302) 320269 Fax: (01302) 340678 E-mail: sales@intro.co.uk

Kluthe, 314 Midsummer Boulevard, Milton Keynes, MK9 2UB Tel: (01908) 440120 Fax: (01908) 440121 E-mail: info@kluthe.co.uk

Mirj Hygiene Products Ltd, Unit 3, Antelope Industrial Park, Rhydymwyn, Mold, Clwyd, CH7 5JH Tel: (01352) 741919 Fax: (01352) 741920 E-mail: sales@mirjhygiene.co.uk

Nielson Chemicals Ltd, Rawdon Road, Moira, Swadlincote, Derbyshire, DE12 6DA Tel: (01283) 222277 Fax: (01283) 225731 E-mail: info@nielsenchemicals.com

Pacer Technology Ltd, 196 Wilden Lane, Stourport-on-Severn, Worcestershire, DY13 9JR Tel: (01299) 825900 Fax: (01299) 827001 E-mail: sales@pacertechnology.com

Pneumatic Lines Ltd, Brunel House, 1 Archers Court, Huntingdon, Cambridgeshire, PE29 6XG Tel: (01480) 432104 Fax: (01480) 414534

AUTOMOTIVE CLUTCHES

Luk UK Ltd, Waleswood Road, Wales Bar, Sheffield, S26 5PN Tel: (01909) 510500 Fax: (01909) 515151 E-mail: info@luk.co.uk

Multipart Universal, 8 Stevenson Way, Sheffield, S9 3WZ Tel: 0114-261 1122 Fax: 0800 834500 E-mail: uksales@ucukltd.com

Setco Automotive UK Ltd, Lipe Clutch Division, York Avenue Haslingden, Haslingden, Rossendale, Lancashire, BB4 4HU Tel: (01706) 237200 Fax: (01706) 229585

AUTOMOTIVE COMPONENTS,

See also particular headings under Motor: Commercial Vehicle: Tractor etc

A E M Products Ltd, Unit 141 Leyland Estate, Irthlingborough Road, Wellingborough, Northamptonshire, NN8 1RA Tel: (01933) 442861 Fax: (01933) 225527 E-mail: enquiry@aem-products.co.uk

Actia UK Ltd, Unit 81, Mochdre Industrial Estate, Newtown, Powys, SY16 4LE Tel: (01686) 611150 Fax: (01686) 621068 E-mail: mail@actia.co.uk

Blaenau Plastics Ltd, Tanygrisiau Trading Estate, Tanygrisiau, Blaenau Ffestiniog, Gwynedd, LL41 3RY Tel: (01766) 833700 Fax: (01766) 833701

Robert Bosch Ltd, PO Box 98, Uxbridge, Middlesex, UB9 5HJ Tel: (01895) 834466 Fax: (01895) 838388

C P Mechanical Designs Ltd, 48 Wellington Road, Portslade, Brighton, BN41 1DT Tel: (01273) 430001 Fax: (01273) 424654 E-mail: enquiries@cpmechanical.co.uk

Castle Precision Engineering Glasgow Ltd, 241 Drakemire Drive, Glasgow, G45 9SZ Tel: 0141-634 1377 Fax: 0141-634 3678 E-mail: sales@castleprecision.com

Certwood Ltd, Laporte Way, Luton, LU4 8EF Tel: (01582) 456955 Fax: (01582) 485855 E-mail: sales@certwood.com

▶ Diamond Auto Parts, Brookbank Garage, Scotland Road, Carnforth, Lancashire, LA5 9JZ Tel: 01524 734200 Fax: 01524 734200 E-mail: sales@diamondautoparts.co.uk

Fisco Fasteners Ltd, Sirdar Road, Rayleigh, Essex, SS6 7XF Tel: (01268) 745421 Fax: (01268) 745467 E-mail: sales@fisco-fasteners.co.uk

▶ JFL Automotive Ltd, Frankley Industrial Park, Tay Road, Rubery, Rednal, Birmingham, B45 0LD Tel: 0121-453 1061 Fax: 0121-460 1144

George. W. King Ltd, Blackhorse Road, Letchworth Garden City, Hertfordshire, SG6 1GE Tel: (01462) 481180 Fax: (01462) 675847 E-mail: george.king@gwkgroup.com

M W F Services, Kelsey Close, Attleborough Fields Industrial Estate, Nuneaton, Warwickshire, CV11 6RS Tel: (024) 7634 7774 Fax: (01858) 571196 E-mail: david_jeffrey@btopenworld.com

Magel Engineering Ltd, Headley Road East, Woodley, Reading, RG5 4SN Tel: 0118-969 2351 Fax: 0118-927 2307

Marshalls Industrial Ltd, Hithercroft Road, Wallingford, Oxfordshire, OX10 9DG Tel: (01491) 834666 Fax: (01491) 839777 E-mail: sales@marshalls-industrial.co.uk

New Ventures Products, Queens Yard, Long Wittenham Road, North Moreton, Didcot, Oxfordshire, OX11 9AX Tel: (0845) 4304030 Fax: (0845) 130 5833 E-mail: sales@newventureproducts.co.uk

Omega Automotive Ltd, 4 Europa Way, Britannia Enterprise Park, Lichfield, Staffordshire, WS14 9TZ Tel: (01543) 490628 Fax: (01543) 493421 E-mail: info@omega-automotive.com

Parts 4 Cars Ltd, 991 Wolverhampton Road, Oldbury, West Midlands, B69 4RJ Tel: 0121-544 4040 Fax: 0121-544 5558 E-mail: info@davidmanners.co.uk

Raven Manufacturing Ltd, Metcalf Drive, Altham Industrial Estate, Accrington, Lancashire, BB5 5TU Tel: (01282) 770000 Fax: (01282) 770022 E-mail: sales@raven.co.uk

Steering Rack Services Ltd, 100 Borron Street, Port Dundas Business Park, Glasgow, G4 9XG Tel: 0141-353 1202 Fax: 0141-353 3159

▶ Stirling, 7 Cunningham Road, Stirling, FK7 7SW Tel: (01786) 445349 Fax: (01786) 445349 E-mail: sales@fergusons450222.com

T T Electronics, East Field Industrial Estate, Glenrothes, Fife, KY7 4NX Tel: (01592) 662200 Fax: (01592) 662299

Thyssen Krupp Automotive Systems UK Ltd, Seven Stars Industrial Estate, Wheeler Road, Whitley, Coventry, CV3 4LB Tel: (024) 7621 7700 Fax: (024) 7621 7701

Vallourec UK Ltd, George House, 121 High Street, Henley-in-Arden, West Midlands, B95 5AU Tel: (01564) 792277 Fax: (01564) 795818 E-mail: sales@vallourec.co.uk

▶ Viking International, 26-32 Millbrae Road, Langside, Glasgow, G42 9TU Tel: 0141-632 3222

Z F Lenforder UK Ltd, Heath Road, Wednesbury, West Midlands, WS10 8BH Tel: 0121-526 4441 Fax: 0121-526 3579 E-mail: roger.homer@zf.com

AUTOMOTIVE CONNECTORS

Raffenday Ltd, 11 Fleming Close, Park Farm Industrial Estate, Wellingborough, Northamptonshire, NN8 6UF Tel: (01933) 673333 Fax: (01933) 675555 E-mail: sales@raffenday.com

AUTOMOTIVE CONSTANT VELOCITY JOINTS

GKN Driveline, 5 Kingsbury Business Park, Kingsbury Road, Minworth, Sutton Coldfield, West Midlands, B76 9DL Tel: 0121-313 1661 Fax: 0121-313 2074 E-mail: ids.Minworth@gkndriveline.com

AUTOMOTIVE CONVERSION KITS, LIQUEFIED PETROLEUM GAS (LPG)

▶ EcoFuels UK Ltd, Smalleys Garage (Thorne), Selby Road, Thorne, Doncaster, South Yorkshire, DN8 4JD Tel: (0773) 0552832 Fax: (0784) 1399828 E-mail: info@EcoFuelsUK.com

▶ LPG Auto Conversions, Island Cottage, Stone, Tenterden, Kent, TN30 7JL Tel: (01233) 758014 E-mail: lpg@uk2.net

AUTOMOTIVE DESIGN/ DEVELOPMENT CONSULTANTS

Auto Design Ltd, 12 Tallon Road, Hutton, Brentwood, Essex, CM13 1TF Tel: (01277) 225000 Fax: (01277) 225002 E-mail: harvey@autodesign.co.uk

▶ Automotive Development Consultants Limited, 3 Chaucer Close, Bridgetown Gardens, Stratford-upon-Avon, Warwickshire, CV37 7PQ Tel: 07974 713316 E-mail: mattbishton@hotmail.com

▶ Drive Inc Ltd, 1 Rose Lane, Ripley, Woking, Surrey, GU23 6NE Tel: (01483) 211200 E-mail: info@drivein.co.uk

Federal Mogul Systems Protection Group, PO Box 47, Rochdale, Lancashire, OL12 7EZ Tel: (01706) 640100 Fax: (01706) 640110

Lola Cars Ltd, 12 Glebe Road, St Peters Hill, Huntingdon, Cambridgeshire, PE29 7DY Tel: (01480) 456722 Fax: (01480) 482970 E-mail: lola@lolacars.com

Ricardo UK Ltd, Midlands Technical Centre, Southam Road, Leamington Spa, Warwickshire, CV31 1FQ Tel: (01926) 319319 Fax: (01926) 319300

T R W Automotive Electronics, Eastern Avenue, Burnley, Lancashire, BB10 2AR Tel: (01282) 855500 Fax: (01282) 412436

AUTOMOTIVE DIAGNOSTIC TUNING EQUIPMENT

Actia UK Ltd, Unit 81, Mochdre Industrial Estate, Newtown, Powys, SY16 4LE Tel: (01686) 611150 Fax: (01686) 621068 E-mail: mail@actia.co.uk

Crypton Ltd, Bristol Road, Bridgwater, Somerset, TA6 4BX Tel: (01278) 436205 Fax: (01278) 450567 E-mail: sales@cryptontechnology.com

▶ Eclipse Automotive Technology Ltd, Clay House,, Horninglow Street, Burton-on-Trent, Staffordshire, DE14 1NG Tel: (0845) 4666699 Fax: 0845 4665986 E-mail: Sales@eclipseautomotivetechnology.com

AUTOMOTIVE ELECTRIC MOTORS

Cox Auto Electrical, 10 Abeles Way, Holly Lane Industrial Estate, Atherstone, Warwickshire, CV9 2QZ Tel: (01827) 718484 Fax: (01827) 712097 E-mail: enquiries@coxautomotive.co.uk

AUTOMOTIVE ELECTROMAGNETIC COMPATABILITY (EMC) TESTING

Building Research Establishment Ltd, Bucknalls Lane, Garston, Watford, WD25 9XX Tel: (01923) 664237 Fax: (01923) 664994 E-mail: enquiries@brecertification.com

Electromagnetic Testing Services, Pratts Field, Lubberhedges Lane, Stebbing, Dunmow, Essex, CM6 3BT Tel: (01371) 856061 Fax: (01371) 856144 E-mail: info@etsemc.co.uk

T U V Product Service, Snitterfield Road, Bearley, Stratford-upon-Avon, Warwickshire, CV37 0EX Tel: (01789) 731155 Fax: (01789) 731264 E-mail: mbrain@tuvps.co.uk

▶ WolfsonEMC, Cardiff University, Queens Building, Newport Road, Cardiff, CF24 3AA Tel: (029) 2087 5936 Fax: (07898) 199422 E-mail: richard@WolfsonEMC.co.uk

AUTOMOTIVE ELECTROMAGNETIC INTERFERENCE (EMI) PROTECTION PRODUCTS

J M K Ltd, Unit 9 Block 2, Vale of Leven Industrial Estate, Dumbarton, G82 3PW Tel: (01389) 751841 Fax: (01389) 751775 E-mail: jmkfilters@sol.co.uk

AUTOMOTIVE ENGINEERING,

See also headings for particular types

Co Engineering Ltd, Unit 57 Coleshill Industrial Estate, Station Road, Coleshill, Birmingham, B46 1JT Tel: (01675) 464252 Fax: (01675) 467318 E-mail: coeng@tiscali.co.uk

Expert Engineering Ltd, Queen Mary, University of London, Mile End Road, London, E1 4NS Tel: (0845) 6586933 E-mail: jshaikh@expertengineering.co.uk

Fontaine International Europe Ltd, Enterprise Way, Newton Road, Lowton, Warrington, WA3 2AG Tel: (01942) 686000 Fax: (01942) 686006 E-mail: info@fifthwheeleurope.com

George. W. King Ltd, Blackhorse Road, Letchworth Garden City, Hertfordshire, SG6 1GE Tel: (01462) 481180 Fax: (01462) 675847 E-mail: george.king@gwkgroup.com

Pi Technology, Milton Hall, Ely Road, Milton, Cambridge, CB4 6WZ Tel: (01223) 441434 Fax: (01223) 203999 E-mail: enquiries@pitechnology.com

▶ S P Engineering, 9 Keyford Court, Manor Furlong, Frome, Somerset, BA11 4BD Tel: (01373) 474740 Fax: (01373) 471417 E-mail: enquires@spengineering.co.uk

AUTOMOTIVE ENGINEERING COMPONENTS/PRODUCTS

A E M Products Ltd, Unit 141 Leyland Estate, Irthlingborough Road, Wellingborough, Northamptonshire, NN8 1RA Tel: (01933) 442861 Fax: (01933) 225527 E-mail: enquiry@aem-products.co.uk

Denso Manufacturing (Midlands) Ltd, Shaftsmoor Lane, Hall Green, Birmingham, B28 8SW Tel: 0121-777 3232 Fax: 0121-777 7232

Dura Automotive Body & Glass Systems, Unit A, Castle Bromwich Business Park, Tameside Drive, Castle Bromwich, Birmingham, B35 7AG Tel: 0121-776 7733 Fax: 0121-749 6850

Co Engineering Ltd, Unit 57 Coleshill Industrial Estate, Station Road, Coleshill, Birmingham, B46 1JT Tel: (01675) 464252 Fax: (01675) 467318 E-mail: coeng@tiscali.co.uk

Express 2 Automotive Ltd, Tanfield Industrial Estate, Tanfield Lea, Stanley, County Durham, DH9 9NX Tel: (01207) 299859 Fax: (01207) 284896 E-mail: andy.clark@express2automotive.com

G & R Engineering (Nantwich) Ltd, Tricketts Lane, Willaston, Nantwich, Cheshire, CW5 6PY Tel: (01270) 661033 Fax: (01270) 664524 E-mail: brian@gr-eng.fsnet.co.uk

▶ Gatehill Trading Ltd, 18 Gatehill Road, Northwood, Middlesex, HA6 3QD Tel: (01923) 820206 Fax: (01923) 450999 E-mail: gatehill@gtrad.co.uk

Hashimoto Forming Industry Co. Ltd, 5 Didcot Way, Boldon Business Park, Boldon Colliery, Tyne & Wear, NE35 9PD Tel: 0191-519 0088 Fax: 0191-519 0460 E-mail: admin@hashimoto.ltd.uk

Kongsberg Automotive, Callister Way, Burton-on-Trent, Staffordshire, DE14 2SY Tel: (01283) 492000 Fax: (01283) 492003 E-mail: info@ka-group.com

Malordale Engineering Ltd, Unit 10E, Britannia Estate, Leagrave Road, Luton, LU3 1RJ Tel: (01582) 421138 Fax: (01582) 412894 E-mail: tonyfuller@malordale.co.uk

Meritor Light Vehicle Systems (U K) Ltd, Roof Systems, Fordhouse Lane, Birmingham, B30 3BW Tel: 0121-459 1166 Fax: 0121-459 9808 E-mail: marco.foley@arvinmeritor.com

Omg UK Ltd, Ashton New Road, Clayton, Manchester, M11 4AT Tel: 0161-230 2540 Fax: 0161-230 2662

Power Steering Services, Units 1-2, Grinnall Business Centre, Sandy Lane Industrial Estate, Stourport-On-Severn, Worcestershire, DY13 9QB Tel: (01299) 879281 Fax: (01299) 879345 E-mail: enquiries@powersteeringservices.co.uk

Sumitomo Electrical Wiring Systems Europe Ltd, Unit1 Woodlands Business Park, Ystradgynlais, Swansea, SA9 1GW Tel: (01639) 842281 Fax: (01639) 849853

T R W Automotive Electronics, 45 College Road, Perry Barr, Birmingham, B44 8DU Tel: 0121-356 0351 Fax: 0121-344 3396

Vestatec Automotive Engineering, Unit 3-4 Chase Park, Daleside Road, Nottingham, NG2 4GT Tel: 0115-911 6767 Fax: 0115-912 6767 E-mail: admin@vestatec.co.uk

AUTOMOTIVE ENGINEERING CONSULTANTS

Careybrook Ltd, PO Box 205, Southam, Warwickshire, CV47 0ZL Tel: (01926) 813619 Fax: (01926) 814898 E-mail: cb.ltd@btinternet.com

▶ Casewest, Moorton Avenue, Burnage, Manchester, M19 2NQ Tel: 07870 409130 E-mail: enquiry@casewest.co.uk

Co Engineering Ltd, Unit 57 Coleshill Industrial Estate, Station Road, Coleshill, Birmingham, B46 1JT Tel: (01675) 464252 Fax: (01675) 467318 E-mail: coeng@tiscali.co.uk

Holmes & Mann Associates Ltd, 465 Tachbrook Road, Leamington Spa, Warwickshire, CV31 3DQ Tel: (01926) 426854 Fax: (01926) 426854 E-mail: holmes@holmes-mann.com

Jay Engineering Consultancy Ltd, 178 Aldridge Road, Streetly, Sutton Coldfield, West Midlands, B74 3TP Tel: 0121-353 6400 Fax: 0121-353 9600 E-mail: john.butler@iee.org

The Mathworks Ltd, Matrix House 10 Cowley Park, Cowley Road, Cambridge, CB4 0HH Tel: (01223) 423200 Fax: (01223) 423289 E-mail: sales@mathworks.co.uk

Pi Technology, Milton Hall, Ely Road, Milton, Cambridge, CB4 6WZ Tel: (01223) 441434 Fax: (01223) 203999 E-mail: enquiries@pitechnology.com

AUTOMOTIVE FASTENERS

A M S Connections Ltd, 14 Highmeres Road, Leicester, LE4 9LZ Tel: 0116-224 0070 Fax: 0116-224 0073 E-mail: astrid@amsconnections.co.uk

Asco Fixings Ltd, Colliery Road, West Bromwich, West Midlands, B71 4JT Tel: 0121-553 1177 Fax: 0121-553 1199 E-mail: info@ascofixings.co.uk

B A S Components Ltd, 2 Cramptons Road, Sevenoaks, Kent, TN14 5EF Tel: (01732) 450011 Fax: (01732) 455884 E-mail: info@bas-airospace.co.uk

Bonner-Regis Manufacturing Ltd, High Street, Princes End, Tipton, West Midlands, DY4 9HR Tel: 0121-522 2616 Fax: 0121-557 6864 E-mail: sales@regis-bolt.co.uk

Cirteq Ltd, Hayfield, Colne Road, Keighley, West Yorkshire, BD20 8QP Tel: (01535) 633333 Fax: (01535) 632966 E-mail: sales@cirteq.com

Commercial Body Fittings, 80 Bridge Road East, Welwyn Garden City, Hertfordshire, AL7 1JY Tel: (01707) 371161 Fax: (01707) 372603 E-mail: sales@cbf.uk.com

Components & Technology, Unit M Valley Way, Market Harborough, Leicestershire, LE16 7PS Tel: (01858) 439503 Fax: (01858) 466536 E-mail: sales@coldform.co.uk

Henrob, Second Avenue, Deeside Industrial Park, Deeside, Clwyd, CH5 2NX Tel: (01244) 837220 Fax: (01244) 837222 E-mail: sales@henrob.co.uk

▶ JFL Automotive Ltd, Frankley Industrial Park, Tay Road, Rubery, Rednal, Birmingham, B45 0LD Tel: 0121-453 1061 Fax: 0121-460 1144

Nelson Stud Welding UK, Rabans Lane Industrial Area, 47-49 Edison Road, Aylesbury, Buckinghamshire, HP19 8TE Tel: (01296) 433500 Fax: (01296) 487930 E-mail: enquiries@nelson-europe.co.uk

S F S Intect, Unit 13 Welshpool Enterprise Centre, Welshpool, Powys, SY21 7SL Tel: (01938) 556035 Fax: (01938) 556036 E-mail: hbob@sfsintec.biz

T R Fastenings Ltd, Waterside Park, Golds Hill Way, Tipton, West Midlands, DY4 0WP Tel: (0800) 7315553 Fax: (0800) 525230 E-mail: sales@trfastenings.com

Tolwood Ltd, Coatham Avenue, Aycliffe Industrial Park, Newton Aycliffe, County Durham, DL5 6DB Tel: (01325) 300777 Fax: (01325) 300399 E-mail: info@tolwood.co.uk

AUTOMOTIVE FELT

Naish Felts Ltd, Crow Lane, Wilton, Salisbury, SP2 0HD Tel: (01722) 743505 Fax: (01722) 744048 E-mail: sales@naishfelts.co.uk

AUTOMOTIVE FILTER ELEMENTS

Forgeville Logisctics Ltd, Unit 3, Senate Place, Whitworth Road, Stevenage, Hertfordshire, SG1 4QS Tel: (01438) 369461 Fax: (01438) 743084 E-mail: sales@forgeville.co.uk

AUTOMOTIVE FILTERS

Induction Technology Group Ltd, Unit B Quinn Close, Coventry, CV3 4LH Tel: (024) 7630 5386 Fax: (024) 7630 7999 E-mail: sales@itgairfilters.com

Lockertex, Church Street, Warrington, WA1 2SU Tel: (01925) 642709 Fax: (01925) 630431 E-mail: sales@lockertex.co.uk

John Morfield Ltd, Unit 98 Sadler Foster Way, Teeside Industrial Estate, Stockton-on-Tees, Cleveland, TS17 9JY Tel: (01642) 760555 Fax: (01642) 750391 E-mail: enquiries@johnmorfield.co.uk

Reading Filter Services, Richmond Road, Caversham, Reading, RG4 7PR Tel: 0118-947 6895 Fax: 0118-946 3310 E-mail: stan@readingfilters.fsworld.co.uk

AUTOMOTIVE FLUID HANDLING SYSTEMS

▶ T I Group Automotive Systems UK Ltd, Halesfield 9, Telford, Shropshire, TF7 4ET Tel: (01952) 651000 Fax: (01952) 651166 E-mail: mdebono@uk.tiauto.com

Tav Engineering Ltd, Unit 13-14 Priory Industrial Park, Airspeed Road, Christchurch, Dorset, BH23 4HD Tel: (01425) 270444 Fax: (01425) 276766 E-mail: tavengineering@crydom.com

AUTOMOTIVE FUSES

K.F. Ltd, 36 Bolina Road, London, SE16 3LF Tel: (020) 7232 2266 Fax: (020) 7232 2288 E-mail: kabletie@btinternet.com

AUTOMOTIVE GASKETS

All Marque, Unit 5 Block F, St. Michaels Industrial Estate, Widnes, Cheshire, WA8 8TL Tel: 0151-424 1984 Fax: 0151-420 3144 E-mail: sales@allmarque.co.uk

Bec Plastics, 18-20 Lenziemill Road, Cumbernauld, Glasgow, G67 2RL Tel: (01236) 781255 Fax: (01236) 781299 E-mail: enquires@becplastics.co.uk

British Gaskets Ltd, Bulmer Road Industrial Estate, Bulmer Road, Sudbury, Suffolk, CO10 7HJ Tel: (01787) 881188 Fax: (01787) 880595 E-mail: sales@british-gaskets.co.uk

▶ Power Seal Europe, Gwilliam Killands Complex, Broadway, Biddington, Bridgwater, Somerset, TA7 9JN Tel: (01278) 722095 E-mail: powersealeurope@btinternet.com

Scandura, St. James Road, Corby, Northamptonshire, NN18 8AW Tel: (01536) 267121 Fax: (01536) 266392 E-mail: sales@scandura.co.uk

AUTOMOTIVE HIGH VOLUME TURNED PARTS

Autonic Engineering Co. Ltd, Salisbury Road, Hoddesdon, Hertfordshire, EN11 0HU Tel: (01992) 471101 Fax: (01992) 471102 E-mail: sales@autonic.co.uk

Toyota Motor Manufacturing UK Ltd, Toyota Motor Manufacturing (Uk) Ltd, Derby, DE1 9TA Tel: (01332) 282121 Fax: (01332) 282801 E-mail: info@toyotauk.com

AUTOMOTIVE HOSES

Eaton Fluid Power Group, Thorns Road, Brierley Hill, West Midlands, DY5 2BQ Tel: (01384) 426320 Fax: (01384) 891506 E-mail: mark.ward@aeroquip.com

Hose Depot Direct Ltd, Units 8 Brunel Park, Blyth Road, Harworth, Doncaster, South Yorkshire, DN11 8NE Tel: (01302) 746969 Fax: (01302) 746974

Silflex Ltd, Coedcae Lane, Pontyclun, Mid Glamorgan, CF72 9HJ Tel: (01443) 238464 Fax: 01443 238464 E-mail: silflex@silflex.com

AUTOMOTIVE HYDRAULIC TRANSMISSION SYSTEMS

Nord Gear Ltd, Riverview House, Friarton Road, Perth, PH2 8DF Tel: (01738) 472023 Fax: (01738) 628855 E-mail: info@nord-uk.com

AUTOMOTIVE INDUSTRY FINISHING SERVICES

A C Refinish, Westgate Mills, White Lund Industrial Estate, Morecambe, Lancashire, LA3 3BS Tel: (01524) 60682 Fax: (01524) 39098 E-mail: sales@acrefinish.com

D J B Associates Ltd, 4-6 Roman Court, Watling Street, Bridgtown, Cannock, Staffordshire, WS11 0BN Tel: (01543) 574162 Fax: (01543) 574282

Protective Finishing Group, 33 Crossgate Road, Park Farm Industrial Estate, Redditch, Worcestershire, B98 7SN Tel: (01527) 524126 Fax: (01527) 510361 E-mail: sales@profingroup.co.uk

Truck & Bus Services, The Homestead Garage, Gresford Road, Llay, Wrexham, Clwyd, LL12 0NU Tel: (01978) 855506

AUTOMOTIVE INDUSTRY GLASS FIBRE OR FIBREGLASS MOULDINGS

A & I Composites Ltd, Mile End Road, Colwick, Nottingham, NG4 2DW Tel: 0115-940 2228 Fax: 0115-940 2228

Cheltenham Laminating Company Ltd, Unit 10, Bamfurlong Indust Park, Staverton, Cheltenham, Gloucestershire, GL51 6SX Tel: (01452) 713098 Fax: 01452 715114 E-mail: murray.derek@sky.com

Delta Styling.co.uk, Unit 12, Carlton Industrial Estate, Albion Road, Carlton, Barnsley, South Yorkshire, S71 3HW Tel: (01226) 722761

Hilton Docker Mouldings Ltd, Freedo Mill, Foxcroft Street, Littleborough, Lancashire, OL15 8LB Tel: (01706) 379358 Fax: (01706) 378546 E-mail: sales@hiltondoc.co.uk

AUTOMOTIVE INDUSTRY INSPECTION

▶ G B Agencies Ltd, Alexandra Dock North, Grimsby, South Humberside, DN31 3UA Tel: (01472) 240416 Fax: (01472) 348751 E-mail: agencies@gbagroup.com

AUTOMOTIVE INDUSTRY PLASTIC MOULDINGS

Bourbon Fabi UK Ltd, North Portway Close, Round Spinney Industrial Estate, Northampton, NN3 8RE Tel: (01604) 493126 Fax: (01604) 644547 E-mail: simon.t@bourbonfabi.co.uk
Certwood Ltd, Laporte Way, Luton, LU4 8EF Tel: (01582) 456955 Fax: (01582) 485855 E-mail: sales@certwood.com
Data Plastics, Avenue Three, Witney, Oxfordshire, OX28 4BP Tel: (01993) 700777 Fax: (01993) 700555 E-mail: sales@dataplastics.co.uk
Express 2 Automotive Ltd, Tanfield Industrial Estate, Tanfield Lea, Stanley, County Durham, DH9 9NX Tel: (01207) 299859 Fax: (01207) 284896 E-mail: andy.clark@express2automotive.com
Graingate, 2 Lockwood Close, Nottingham, NG5 9JN Tel: 0115-967 1888 Fax: 0115-967 1777 E-mail: info@graingate.co.uk
Hampson Composites Ltd, Vale Mill, Vale Street, Bolton, BL2 6QF Tel: (01204) 381626 Fax: (01204) 529457 E-mail: liz@hampson-composites.co.uk
Penspell Ltd, 1 Bradfield Road, Finedon Road Industrial Estate, Wellingborough, Northamptonshire, NN8 4HB Tel: (01933) 443605 Fax: (01933) 271489 E-mail: penspell@btclick.com
Siemens V D O Automotive Systems, Halesfield 25, Telford, Shropshire, TF7 4LP Tel: (01952) 683600 Fax: (01952) 580626 E-mail: sales@siemens.auto.com
Stuart Neal Chartered Loss Adjusters Ltd, 26 White Horse Lane, Maldon, Essex, CM9 5QP Tel: (01621) 857111 Fax: (01621) 858111 E-mail: stuartneilclaims@hotmail.com
Voestalpine Polynorm Plastics Ltd, PO Box 9, St. Helens, Merseyside, WA10 6FE Tel: (01744) 743333 Fax: (01744) 743300

AUTOMOTIVE INDUSTRY RECRUITMENT

Edwards Jeffery, Unit 57, The Enterprise Centre, Bridgend, Mid Glamorgan, CF32 9BS Tel: (0870) 2424 662 Fax: (0870) 2424 663 E-mail: enquiries@edwardsjeffery.co.uk
▶ The Engineer, St Giles House, 50 Poland Street, London, W1F 7AX Tel: (020) 7970 4114 Fax: 0207 9704193 E-mail: matt.comley@centaur.co.uk
▶ Global Automotive Recruitment, 28 Springbourne Court, Beckenham, Kent, BR3 5ED Tel: (0845) 330 9317 Fax: (0845) 330 9318 E-mail: info@garecruitment.com
▶ Manesis Search & Selection, 1 Lower Bar, Newport, Shropshire, TF10 7BE Tel: (01952) 811550 E-mail: recruit@manesis.co.uk
▶ Marble Recruitment Ltd, Dominions House, Queen Street, Cardiff, CF10 2AR Tel: (029) 2038 3837 Fax: (029) 2038 3847 E-mail: paul@marblerecruitment.co.uk

AUTOMOTIVE INDUSTRY SOFTWARE

▶ Autoconnect Contact Centre, Hewell Road, Redditch, Worcestershire, B97 6AY Tel: (01527) 61661

AUTOMOTIVE INDUSTRY TECHNICAL SUPPORT SERVICES

▶ G B Agencies Ltd, Alexandra Dock North, Grimsby, South Humberside, DN31 3UA Tel: (01472) 240416 Fax: (01472) 348751 E-mail: agencies@gbagroup.com

AUTOMOTIVE INDUSTRY TESTING SERVICES

Autolign Inspections Ltd, Unit 3 J B J Business Park, Northampton Road, Blisworth, Northampton, NN7 3DW Tel: (01604) 859424 Fax: (01604) 859428 E-mail: sales@autoligninspections.co.uk
RSG, 6 Arunside Industrial Estate, Fort Road, Arunside Industrial Estate, Littlehampton, West Sussex, BN17 7QU Tel: (01903) 715550 Fax: (01903) 715550
S G S UK Ltd, 7TH Floor, Westgate House, West Gate, London, W5 1YY Tel: (020) 8991 3410 Fax: (020) 8991 3417 E-mail: rolandstephan@sgsgroup.com

AUTOMOTIVE INTERIOR FABRIC LAMINATING/COATING SERVICES

Johnson Controls UK Automotive Ltd, 10 Hedera Road, Redditch, Worcestershire, B98 9EY Tel: (01527) 507100 Fax: (01527) 507101

AUTOMOTIVE INTERIOR TRIM

▶ Ahlstrom Chirnside Ltd, Chirnside, Duns, Berwickshire, TD11 3JW Tel: (01890) 818303 Fax: (01890) 818256 E-mail: karen.renton@ahlstrom.com
Auto Interiors, 56 Norfolk Street, Liverpool, L1 0BE Tel: 0151-708 8881 Fax: 0151-708 6002
▶ Auto Trim, 36 Dorset Close, Bletchley, Milton Keynes, MK3 7HZ Tel: (01908) 368542 E-mail: sales@autotrimmer.co.uk
Auto-Med Technologies Ltd, 127 North Gate, Nottingham, NG7 7FZ Tel: 0115-919 1234 Fax: 0115-919 1236 E-mail: sales@auto-med.com
Automotive Applied Technologies Ltd, PO Box 22, Accrington, Lancashire, BB5 0LA Tel: (01254) 357500 Fax: (01254) 357600 E-mail: info@automotive-tech.co.uk
B I Composites Halesowen Ltd, 270 Coombs Road, Halesowen, West Midlands, B62 8AA Tel: 0121-550 7577 Fax: 0121-585 5315 E-mail: bi-composites@bi-composites.co.uk
Bourbon Fabi UK Ltd, North Portway Close, Round Spinney Industrial Estate, Northampton, NN3 8RE Tel: (01604) 493126 Fax: (01604) 644547 E-mail: simon.t@bourbonfabi.co.uk
▶ C E Moore Ltd, 37 Disraeli Road, London, NW10 7AX Tel: (020) 8961 2225 Fax: (020) 8963 0122
Caligen Foam Ltd, Broad Oak, Accrington, Lancashire, BB5 2BS Tel: (01254) 355000 Fax: (01254) 355111 E-mail: info@caligen.co.uk
Intier Automotives, Tachbrook Park Industrial Estate, Apollo Way, Warwick, CV34 6RW Tel: (01926) 468800 Fax: (01926) 468801
▶ J & S Upholstery, 43 Askern Industrial Estate Moss Road, Askern, Doncaster, South Yorkshire, DN6 0DD Tel: (01302) 709926 Fax: (01302) 789112 E-mail: joanne@thetrimshack.fsnet.co.uk
▶ Northern Automotive Systems Ltd, Gilwern Park Industrial Estate, T Y Mawr Road, Gilwern, Abergavenny, Gwent, NP7 0EB Tel: (01873) 832263 Fax: (01873) 832034 E-mail: info@norcorp.com
Paint & Trim Company North Wales Ltd, Unit 1, Snow Nest Court, Tirllwyd Industrial Estate, Kinmel Bay, Rhyl, Conwy, LL18 5JA Tel: (0800) 0933277 Fax: 01745 369019 E-mail: info@paint-and-trim.com
Stuart Neal Chartered Loss Adjusters Ltd, 26 White Horse Lane, Maldon, Essex, CM9 5QP Tel: (01621) 857111 Fax: (01621) 858111 E-mail: stuartneilclaims@hotmail.com
Textile Bonding Ltd, Textile Bonding Limited, Midland Road, Higham Ferrers, Rushden, Northamptonshire, NN10 8ER Tel: (01933) 410100 Fax: (01933) 410200 E-mail: sales@textilebonding.co.uk

AUTOMOTIVE INTERIOR TRIM WIRE

Vanguard Wire Products, Victoria Wire Works, Raglan Street, Halifax, West Yorkshire, HX1 5QY Tel: (01422) 353339 Fax: (01422) 364532 E-mail: info@thinkg.co.uk

AUTOMOTIVE INTERIOR TRIMS

▶ Auto Trim, 36 Dorset Close, Bletchley, Milton Keynes, MK3 7HZ Tel: (01908) 368542 E-mail: sales@autotrimmer.co.uk

AUTOMOTIVE JIGS

G W J Engineering Ltd, 7 Ruston Road, Alma Park Industrial Estate, Grantham, Lincolnshire, NG31 9SW Tel: (01476) 568703 Fax: (01476) 578639 E-mail: enquiries@gwjengineering.co.uk
Luton Jig & Tool Co. Ltd, Unit 3 Chase Street, Luton, LU1 3QZ Tel: (01582) 725591 Fax: (01582) 735211E-mail: david@ljtco.co.uk

AUTOMOTIVE LUBRICANTS

Batoyle Freedom Group, Colne Vale Road, Milnsbridge, Huddersfield, HD3 4NT Tel: (01484) 653015 Fax: (01484) 460078 E-mail: bfgsales@aol.com
Chemi-Kal Ltd, Powerforce House, Rowland Way, Hoo Farm Industrial Estate, Kidderminster, Worcestershire, DY11 7RA Tel: (01562) 755884 Fax: (01562) 825319 E-mail: chemi-kal@globalnet.co.uk
Danoil Ltd, 94 Owl Lane, Ossett, West Yorkshire, WF5 9AU Tel: (01924) 263128 Fax: (01924) 264078
Exol Lubricants Ltd, All Saints Road, Wednesbury, West Midlands, WS10 9LL Tel: 0121-568 2340 Fax: 0121-568 6720 E-mail: sales@exol-lubricants.com
Granville Oil & Chemicals Ltd, Unit 29 Goldthorpe Industrial Estate, Commercial Road, Goldthorpe, Rotherham, South Yorkshire, S63 9BL Tel: (01709) 890099 Fax: (01709) 891121 E-mail: info@granvilleoilchem.co.uk
Lubrication Engineers UK Ltd, Latton Bush Business Ctr, Southern Way, Harlow, Essex, CM18 7BH Tel: (01763) 274253 Fax: (01763) 274253 E-mail: sales@le-lubricants.co.uk

AUTOMOTIVE MARKET RESEARCH

▶ Quality Eye, First Base, 239a Uxbridge Road, London, London, W12 9DL Tel: 0870 300 0931 Fax: 0870 486 5956 E-mail: info@qualityeye.com

AUTOMOTIVE METAL PRESSINGS

Bridgford Pressings Ltd, Building No. 3 Gotham Business Complex, Leake Road, Gotham, Nottingham, NG11 0LB Tel: 0115-983 0884 Fax: 0115-983 0155 E-mail: enquiries@bridgfordpressings.co.uk
T K A Body Stampings Ltd, Wolverhampton Road, Cannock, Staffordshire, WS11 1LY Tel: (01543) 466664 Fax: (01543) 466665 E-mail: info@tkbs.thyssenkrupp.com

AUTOMOTIVE MODELS

Brooklin Models Ltd, Unit A3, Pinesway Industrial Estate, Ivo Peters Road, Bath, BA2 3QS Tel: (01225) 332400 Fax: (01225) 447438
D K G Hobbies UK, 14 Princes Street, Southport, Merseyside, PR8 1EZ Tel: (01704) 500630 Fax: (01704) 500630
Hamlin Model Making Ltd, Old Tractor Shed, Welsh Road, Offchurch, Leamington Spa, Warwickshire, CV33 9BE Tel: (01926) 614147 Fax: (01926) 612899 E-mail: sales@hamlinrpd.co.uk
Horace Fuller Ltd, 72 Park Street, Horsham, West Sussex, RH12 1BY Tel: (01403) 265030 Fax: (01403) 217500 E-mail: sales@horacefuller.com
▶ P R Designs, Tong Lane Bus Centre, Tong Lane, Whitworth, Rochdale, Lancashire, OL12 8BE Tel: (01706) 854264 Fax: (01706) 854264 E-mail: prdesignssales@timewarpuk.net
Somerville Models, Westfield Ho, 104 High St, Billinghay, Lincoln, LN4 4ED Tel: 01526 860348 Fax: 01526 860315
Western Models Ltd, Acre Ridge, Clayhidon, Cullompton, Devon, EX15 3TW Tel: (01823) 666767 Fax: (01823) 666757 E-mail: sales@westernmodels.com

AUTOMOTIVE PAINT SPRAYING SYSTEMS

▶ Auto Refinish Systems, 70 Richardson Street, Belfast, BT6 8DY Tel: (07734) 235952 Fax: (028) 9061 5122 E-mail: robert.warnock@auto-refinish-systems.co.uk

AUTOMOTIVE PAINTS

Akzo Nobel Coatings Holdings Ltd, 136 Milton Park, Abingdon, Oxfordshire, OX14 4SB Tel: (01235) 862226 Fax: (01235) 862236 E-mail: cr@akzonobel.com
Andrews Auto Panels Ltd, Kimberley Road, Gillingham, Kent, ME7 4NE Tel: (01634) 851292
Auto Paint, 761 Little Horton Lane, Bradford, West Yorkshire, BD5 9ER Tel: (01274) 522222 Fax: (01274) 522500
Autopaints (South Wales) Ltd, 233 Penarth Road, Cardiff, CF11 6HF Tel: (029) 2022 4038 Fax: (029) 2034 4448 E-mail: gibsonm@btconnect.com
▶ Brisco Trading Ltd, Old Bankend Farm House, Touch, Stirling, FK8 3AD Tel: (01786) 474114 Fax: (01786) 474114
▶ Carlac Ltd, Green La Industrial Estate, Pelaw, Gateshead, Tyne & Wear, NE10 0UW Tel: 0191-438 0333 Fax: 0191-438 3320
Central Car Paints, 93 Crafton St East, Leicester, LE1 2DG Tel: 0116-262 9727 E-mail: info@centralcarparts.co.uk
Central Paints Automotive Ltd, Burncross Road, Chapeltown, Sheffield, S35 1RX Tel: 0114-257 8857 Fax: 0114-257 8857
Decor Centre, North Quay, Pwllheli, Gwynedd, LL53 5YR Tel: (01758) 612562 Fax: (01758) 704999 E-mail: sales@decorcentrewales.com
Kansai Paint Europe Ltd, Wembley Point, 1 Harrow Road, Wembley, Middlesex, HA9 6DE Tel: (020) 8900 5933 Fax: (020) 8900 5966 E-mail: info@kansaipaint.co.uk
Keypaint Ltd, 329 London Road, Hemel Hempstead, Hertfordshire, HP3 9AL Tel: (01442) 262915 Fax: (01442) 267734 E-mail: eurocolour@auto-net.co.uk
Lechler Coatings UK Ltd, Unit 42 Pochin Way, Middlewich, Cheshire, CW10 0GY Tel: (01606) 738600 Fax: (01606) 738517 E-mail: sales@lechler.it
N P Automotive Coatings (Europe) Ltd, Brittania Trade Park, Radway Road, Swindon, SN3 4ND Tel: (01793) 823361 Fax: (01793) 823127 E-mail: janesandman@npae.co.uk
New Inn, 95 The Highway, New Inn, Pontypool, Gwent, NP4 0PN Tel: (01495) 762823 Fax: (01495) 769807
P P G Industries UK Ltd, Needham Road, Stowmarket, Suffolk, IP14 2AD Tel: (01449) 613161 Fax: (01449) 677161

AUTOMOTIVE PRESS TOOLS

Burrhart Machinery Ltd, Cradock Road, Luton, LU4 0JF Tel: (01582) 563400 Fax: (01582) 493993 E-mail: sales@burrhart.co.uk

AUTOMOTIVE PRESSINGS

A P Smith & Son Metal Pressing Ltd, 8 Kings St, Birmingham, B19 3AR Tel: 0121-523 0011 Fax: 0121-554 7244 E-mail: sales@apsmith.co.uk
Cymarc Engineering, 5 Bessemer Way, Sawcliffe Industrial Park, Scunthorpe, South Humberside, DN15 8XE Tel: (01724) 289222 Fax: (01724) 852504 E-mail: cymarcengineering@cwcom.net
Frank Dudley Ltd, Unit 2 Wiggin Street, Hockley, Birmingham, B16 0AH Tel: 0121-523 0742 Fax: 0121-452 8159 E-mail: sales@frankdudley.com
Ex Pressed Steel Panels Ltd, Ickornshaw Mill, Ickornshaw, Cowling, Keighley, West Yorkshire, BD22 0DB Tel: (01535) 632721 Fax: (01535) 636977 E-mail: sales@steelpanels.co.uk
Prestige Engineering, 27 Thornleigh Trading Estate, Dudley, West Midlands, DY2 8UB Tel: (01384) 234488 Fax: (01384) 238884 E-mail: prestigeengineering@btconnect.com
R J Vickers & Son Ltd, 152 Soho Hill, Birmingham, B19 1AF Tel: 0121-523 6235 Fax: 0121-523 9397 E-mail: vickers.metform@virgin.net
Raven Manufacturing Ltd, Metcalf Drive, Altham Industrial Estate, Accrington, Lancashire, BB5 5TU Tel: (01282) 770000 Fax: (01282) 770022 E-mail: sales@raven.co.uk
Ricor Ltd, Arrow Works, Birmingham Road, Studley, Warwickshire, B80 7AS Tel: (01527) 857757 Fax: (01527) 857224 E-mail: ricorjrobinson@aol.com
Taylor Pressform Ltd, 21 Rigby Close, Heathcote Industrial Estate, Warwick, CV34 6TH Tel: (01926) 339507 Fax: (01926) 451306
Wagon Automotive Wantage Plant, Main Street, East Challow, Wantage, Oxfordshire, OX12 9SY Tel: (01235) 770770 Fax: (01235) 770017 E-mail: wantage@wagonautomotive.com
Walsall Pressings Co. Ltd, Wednesbury Road, Walsall, WS1 4JW Tel: (01922) 721152 Fax: (01922) 721106 E-mail: post@walpres.co.uk

AUTOMOTIVE RADIATOR HEAT EXCHANGERS

A H Fabrication, Thorn Office Centre, Thorn Business Park, Rotherwas, Hereford, HR2 6JT Tel: (01432) 354704 Fax: (01432) 359762 E-mail: alexahfabs@fairadsl.co.uk

AUTOMOTIVE SPARK PLUG TERMINALS

Federal-Mogul Camshaft Castings Ltd, Tutnalls, Lydney, Gloucestershire, GL15 5PX Tel: (01594) 842112 Fax: (01594) 841037

AUTOMOTIVE SPECIAL PURPOSE MACHINERY

Agp, Mussons Path, Luton, LU2 7RQ Tel: (01582) 735446 Fax: (01582) 400875 E-mail: alanwithy@hotmail.com
Cygnus Automotive Ltd, Unit 10, Advance Business Park, Burdock Close, Cannock, Staffordshire, WS11 7SG Tel: (01543) 573912 Fax: (01543) 572812 E-mail: sales@cygnus-automotive.co.uk
Hitachi Automotive Systems (Europe) Ltd, Aspinall Way, Middlebrook Business Park, Bolton, BL6 6JH Tel: (01204) 469879 Fax: (01204) 469748
I M S Supplies Ltd, 3 Clifton Road, Huntingdon, Cambridgeshire, PE29 7EJ Tel: (01480) 411763 Fax: (01480) 417170 E-mail: imssupplies@cs.com
Pneumatic Systems Ltd, Unit 32 Poplar Industrial Estate, Witton, Birmingham, B6 7AD Tel: 0121-344 3800 Fax: 0121 344 3866 E-mail: pneumaticsys@aol.com

AUTOMOTIVE SPECIALIST TRANSMISSION SERVICES

3d Transmissions, 5 Blackwater Trading Estate, Blackwater Way, Aldershot, Hampshire, GU12 4DJ Tel: (01252) 310413 Fax: (01252) 350572 E-mail: sales@3dtransmissions.com
A C C Automatic Transmission, 24 The Fairways, New River Trading Estate, Cheshunt, Waltham Cross, Hertfordshire, EN8 0NL Tel: (01992) 639678 Fax: (01992) 634544

AUTOMOTIVE SPECIALIST TRANSMISSION SERVICES – *continued*

A J Kane, Castlelaurie Industrial Estate, Falkirk, FK2 7XF Tel: (01324) 620827 Fax: (01324) 620827
Caterpillar Remanufacturing Ltd, Sanders Lodge Industrial Estate, Rushden, Northamptonshire, NN10 6AZ Tel: (01933) 316622 Fax: (01933) 354601 E-mail: sales@wealdstone.co.uk
D J Transmissions Ltd, Huxley Close, Newnham Industrial Estate, Plympton, Plymouth, PL7 4JN Tel: (01752) 342469 Fax: (01752) 348319 E-mail: admin@djtransmissions.co.uk
Kennering Transmission Ltd, Grendon Road, Polesworth, Tamworth, Staffordshire, B78 1NX Tel: (01827) 892517 Fax: (01827) 893914 E-mail: steve@ktl.org.uk
Midland Automatic Transmissions Ltd, Unit A1M1 Business Centre, Kettering, Northamptonshire, NN16 8TD Tel: (01536) 517866 Fax: (01536) 517764E-mail: sales@automaticgearbox.co.uk
Mitchell Diesel Ltd, Fulwood Road South, Sutton-in-Ashfield, Nottinghamshire, NG17 2JZ Tel: (01623) 550550 Fax: (01623) 551617 E-mail: sales@mitchells.co.uk
Proptech Ltd, Unit 80-81, Hartlebury Trading Estate, Hartlebury, Kidderminster, Worcestershire, DY10 4JB Tel: (01299) 251247 Fax: (01299) 251240 E-mail: proptech@btinternet.com
R G C Transmission Services Ltd, Unit 26 Westend Estate, Bruntcliffe Road, Morley, Leeds, LS27 0LJ Tel: 0113-252 3520
Ricardo UK Ltd, Midlands Technical Centre, Southam Road, Leamington Spa, Warwickshire, CV31 1FQ Tel: (01926) 319319 Fax: (01926) 319300
Roger Bayliss Transmissions, 5 Cradley Heath Factory Centre, Woods Lane, Cradley Heath, West Midlands, B64 7AB Tel: (01384) 564844 Fax: (01384) 636014
Top Gear Ltd, 80 Leicester Road, Mountsorrel, Loughborough, Leicestershire, LE12 7AN Tel: 0116-237 6606 E-mail: cars@topgear.uk.com
Truck Transmissions Ltd, Davyfield Road, Blackburn, BB1 2LU Tel: (01254) 690100 Fax: (01254) 690222 E-mail: sales@trucktransmissionsltd.co.uk

AUTOMOTIVE SPRINGS

K & L Commercials, 2 Shelah Road, Halesowen, West Midlands, B63 3PG Tel: 0121-585 1349
Skegness Springs Ltd, Hassall Road, Skegness, Lincolnshire, PE25 3TB Tel: (0845) 4305000 Fax: (01754) 610584 E-mail: sales@skegsprings.co.uk

AUTOMOTIVE STEEL STRIPS

Corus Ltd, PO Box 69, Rotherham, South Yorkshire, S60 1BN Tel: (01709) 377113 Fax: (01709) 375250 E-mail: info@corusgroup.com
Corus Ltd, PO Box 69, Rotherham, South Yorkshire, S60 1BN Tel: (01709) 377113 Fax: (01709) 375250 E-mail: bsmsales@corusgroup.com

AUTOMOTIVE TEST EQUIPMENT

Instron, Coronation Road, High Wycombe, Buckinghamshire, HP12 3SY Tel: (01494) 464646 Fax: (01494) 456123 E-mail: info_news@instron.com
Rugged Systems Ltd, 1 Compton Place, Surrey Avenue, Camberley, Surrey, GU15 3DX Tel: (01276) 686707 Fax: (01276) 684329 E-mail: jjy@rugged-systems.com
V L Test Systems Ltd, 3/4 Middle Slade, Buckingham Indust Estate, Buckingham, MK18 1WA Tel: (01280) 822488 Fax: (01280) 822489 E-mail: vltukltd@aol.com

AUTOMOTIVE TOOLS

Boar Engineering Ltd, 39a Barking Industrial Park, Alfreds Way, Barking, Essex, IG11 0TJ Tel: (020) 8594 0526 Fax: (020) 8507 8050 E-mail: boareng@aol.com
Desoutter Ltd, Eton Road, Hemel Hempstead, Hertfordshire, HP2 7DR Tel: (01442) 344300 Fax: (01442) 344600
Eastwood Die & Tool, 6 Morpeth Street, Sheffield, S3 7JL Tel: 0114-276 0454 Fax: 0114-276 0454
Garforth & Goodman Ltd, 1 Cromwell Street, Coventry, CV6 5EY Tel: (024) 7666 4680 Fax: (024) 7666 4685 E-mail: sales@garforthandgoodman.co.uk
M W F Services, Kelsey Close, Attleborough Fields Industrial Estate, Nuneaton, Warwickshire, CV11 6RS Tel: (024) 7634 7774 Fax: (01858) 571196 E-mail: david_jeffrey@btopenworld.com
Mitchell Machine Tool Services Ltd, Faraway, Church Road, Long Itchington, Southam, Warwickshire, CV47 9PR Tel: (01926) 817947 Fax: (01926) 817947
Moseley Bros Tools Ltd, Unit 5b Vaughan Trading Estate, Sedgley Road East, Tipton, West Midlands, DY4 7UJ Tel: 0121-520 6703 Fax: 0121-520 4118 E-mail: netadmin@moseleybrothers.co.uk
New Inn, 95 The Highway, New Inn, Pontypool, Gwent, NP4 0PN Tel: (01495) 762823 Fax: (01495) 769807
Rapid Tool Rec Ltd, Unit 2 Armoury Road Trading, Estate Armoury Road, Small Heath, Birmingham, B11 2RG Tel: 0121-771 1555 Fax: 0121-706 2479 E-mail: sales@rapidtool-rec.co.uk
Stanley Assembly Technologies, Gowerton Road, Brackmills, Northampton, NN4 7BW Tel: (01604) 827255 Fax: (01604) 827277 E-mail: sholliday@stanleyworks.com
Tool Connection Ltd, Unit 2, Kineton Road, Southam, Warwickshire, CV47 0DR Tel: (01926) 815999 Fax: (01926) 815888 E-mail: lesleyscott@lasertools.co.uk

AUTOMOTIVE WEBBING

Elastic Berger Ltd, Jubilee Road, Newtownards, County Down, BT23 4XW Tel: (028) 9181 3046 Fax: (028) 9181 3140 E-mail: berger@globalnet.co.uk

AUTOPSY EQUIPMENT

County Hospital & Mortuary Equipment, 13 Westfield Crescent, Brighton, BN1 8JB Tel: (01273) 885441 Fax: (01273) 240954 E-mail: county@pavilion.co.uk

AUXILIARY FIELD PERSONNEL RECRUITMENT AGENCIES/ CONSULTANTS/SERVICES

BCS Uk Ltd, Marle Place, Brenchley, Tonbridge, Kent, TN12 7HS Tel: (01892) 724534 Fax: (01892) 724099
▶ Chequers Personnel, Wiltshire House, 121 High Street, Marlborough, Wiltshire, SN8 1LZ Tel: (01672) 519194 Fax: 01672 519195 E-mail: info@chequers-personnel.co.uk
▶ Global Choices, Barkat House, 116-118 Finchley Road, London, NW3 5HT Tel: 0207 433 2501 Fax: 0207 435 1397 E-mail: info@globalchoices.co.uk
▶ Nicholas Andrews Employment & Recruitment, 1 Whitehall Quay, Leeds, LS1 4HR Tel: 0113-245 6717 Fax: 0113-244 8242 E-mail: richardmhenley@aol.com
▶ SpiderWeb Recruitment Ltd, Kingfisher House, 2 Yarrow Road, Chatham, Kent, ME5 0SJ Tel: 01634 353131 E-mail: info@spiderweb-recruitment.co.uk
Staff Smart, Goodacre Son, Church Street, Donington, Spalding, Lincolnshire, PE11 4UA Tel: (01775) 820786 Fax: (01775) 820512 E-mail: info@staffsmartuk.com
▶ Stafforce Recruitment, 39A Minerva Road, London, NW10 6HJ Tel: (020) 8537 9070 Fax: (020) 8537 9071 E-mail: parkroyal@stafforce.co.uk
▶ Travail Employment Group Ltd, 7 St. Johns Hill, Shrewsbury, SY1 1JD Tel: (01743) 235532 Fax: (01743) 236327 E-mail: shrewsbury@travailshrewsbury.co.uk

AVIATION CONSULTANCY

S H & E Ltd, 210 High Holborn, London, WC1V 7EU Tel: (020) 7242 9333 Fax: (020) 7242 9334 E-mail: sales@sh-e.com

AVIATION FINE ART PRINT PRINTING OR PUBLISHERS

▶ Art Marine Ltd, Pythouse Upper Barn, Tisbury, Salisbury, SP3 6PA Tel: (01747) 871272 E-mail: jt@artmarine.co.uk
Hill Shorter Group, 54 Roebuck Lane, West Bromwich, West Midlands, B70 6QP Tel: 0121-553 7011 Fax: 0121-500 5162 E-mail: sales@hillshorter.com
Terrane Promotions, Terrane House, Whisby Way Industrial Estate, Lincoln, LN6 3LQ Tel: (01522) 697000 Fax: (01522) 697154 E-mail: sales@terrane.co.uk

AVIATION FUEL TEST EQUIPMENT

A Searle, Unit 24 Bourne Road Industrial Park, Bourne Road, Dartford, DA1 4BZ Tel: (01322) 529119 Fax: (01322) 528528 E-mail: sales@asearle.co.uk
Aero Quality Sales Ltd, 8 Airlinks Estate, Spitfire Way, Heston, Hounslow, TW5 9NR Tel: (020) 8561 4211 Fax: (020) 8848 1568 E-mail: kgreene@mckaero.com

AVIATION INSURANCE COMPANIES

▶ Bruce Stevenson Risk Management, 38-40 New City Road, Glasgow, G4 9JT Tel: 0141 353 3539 Fax: 0141 353 3888 E-mail: mark.costello@brucestevenson.co.uk
▶ Eqi Insurance, 11a The Cross, Lymm, Cheshire, WA13 0HR Tel: 01925 751758 Fax: 01925 751538 E-mail: greg@eqi-insurance.co.uk

AVIATION REFUELLING PUMPS

Richard Hill Pumps Ltd, Brooke Road, Ridlington, Oakham, Leicestershire, LE15 9AJ Tel: (01572) 823385 Fax: (01572) 821660

AVIATION TECHNICAL SERVICES

A T Juniper Liverpool Ltd, Marshalls Works, 5-17 Bleasdale Road, Liverpool, L18 5JB Tel: 0151-733 1553 Fax: 0151-734 3166 E-mail: sales@juniper-liverpool.com
Asig, Pinfold Lane, Manchester Airport, Manchester, M90 5XA Tel: 0161-499 1316 Fax: 0161-499 3700
Baines Simmons Ltd, Fairoaks Airport, Chobham, Woking, Surrey, GU24 8HX Tel: (01276) 855412 Fax: (01276) 856285 E-mail: bob@bainessimmons.com
Paw Flying Services Ltd, 8 Hall Lane, Harrogate, North Yorkshire, HG1 3DX Tel: (01423) 560294 Fax: (01423) 560294
Serco Defence, Bartley Wood Business Park, Bartley Way, Hook, Hampshire, RG27 9XA Tel: (01256) 745900 Fax: (01256) 745995 E-mail: enquiries@serco.com
Tag Farnborough Airport Ltd, Farnborough Airport, Farnborough, Hampshire, GU14 6XA Tel: (01252) 379000 Fax: (01252) 379051 E-mail: ops@tagfarnborough.com

AWARD DESIGNERS/ PRODUCERS/SPECIALIST SERVICES

Berry Place Models Ltd, 1 Berry Place, Sebastian Street, London, EC1V 0HE Tel: (020) 7490 8222 Fax: (020) 7336 8482 E-mail: enquiries@berryplace.co.uk
▶ Jigsaw Confex Ltd, Events Office - Raincliffe Manor, Lady Ediths Drive, Scarborough, North Yorkshire, YO12 5RJ Tel: (07951) 164820 Fax: (07092) 399780 E-mail: office@jigsaw-confex.co.uk
▶ L Shailer, Hafod School House, Llanerfyl, Welshpool, Powys, SY21 0JH Tel: (01938) 820110 Fax: (01938) 820118 E-mail: info@lynshailer.co.uk
Louis Lejeune Ltd, The Rectory, 71 High Street, Wilburton, Ely, Cambridgeshire, CB6 3RA Tel: (01353) 740444 Fax: (01353) 741599
▶ Q R 8 Design, Arundel Street, Sheffield, S1 2NS Tel: 0114-221 1818 Fax: (0870) 1338957 E-mail: jerry@lampson.co.uk

AWNINGS, *See also headings for particular types*

Ashford Awnings, 4 Hilton Business Centre, Wotton Road, Ashford, Kent, TN23 6LL Tel: (01233) 624471 Fax: (01233) 624471 E-mail: ashford_awnings@hotmail.com
Automated Access Ltd, Unit F 59 Sibson Road, Birstall, Leicester, LE4 4DX Tel: 0116-267 1122 Fax: 0116-267 1122 E-mail: enquiries@automated-access-solutions.co.uk
Awnings & Blinds By Morco, Riverside, Lombard Wall, London, SE7 7SG Tel: (020) 8858 2083 Fax: (020) 8305 2431 E-mail: sales@morcoblinds.co.uk
Caseys Camping, Pool Road, Otley, West Yorkshire, LS21 1DY Tel: (01943) 465462 Fax: (01943) 850825 E-mail: sales@caseyscamping.com
Centurion Blinds Ltd, Oakdale Trading Estate, Ham Lane, Kingswinford, West Midlands, DY6 7JH Tel: (01384) 279797 Fax: (01384) 292354 E-mail: paulmorris@centruionblinds.com
Cottage Blinds Of Sedgley Ltd, Old Nail Works, Brick Street, Dudley, West Midlands, DY3 1NT Tel: (01902) 661267 Fax: (01902) 884312 E-mail: info@cottageblinds.co.uk
Deans Blinds & Awnings UK Ltd, 4 Haslemere Industrial Estate, Ravensbury Terrace, London, SW18 4SE Tel: (020) 8947 8931 Fax: (020) 8947 8336 E-mail: info@deansblinds.co.uk
Elero UK Ltd, Foundry Lane, Halebank, Widnes, Cheshire, WA8 8TZ Tel: (0870) 2404219 Fax: (0870) 2404086 E-mail: sales@elerouk.co.uk
Euro Blinds UK, King Street, Newton Abbot, Devon, TQ12 2LG Tel: (01392) 824225 Fax: (01626) 369005 E-mail: info@euroblindsdevon.co.uk
Lakeside Security Shutters, Bruce Road, Fforestfach, Swansea, SA5 4HS Tel: (01792) 561117 Fax: (01792) 587046 E-mail: sails@lakesidesecurity.co.uk
London Blind Co., 205a Long Lane, Bexleyheath, Kent, DA7 5AF Tel: (020) 8303 7964 Fax: (020) 8301 3586
North West Sunblinds, 19 Kilburn Close, Heald Green, Cheadle, Cheshire, SK8 3LP Tel: 0161-437 6808 Fax: 0161-437 6808 E-mail: nwblinds@aol.com
Oasis Blinds & Flooring, Comberton Hill, Kidderminster, Worcestershire, DY10 1QH Tel: (01562) 515445 Fax: (01562) 864278
Pritchard Ropes & Canvas Solutions Ltd, Freehold Street, Loughborough, Leicestershire, LE11 1AN Tel: (01509) 212400 Fax: (01509) 219375
James Robertshaw & Sons (1954) Ltd, Albion Works, Lark Hill, Farnworth, Bolton, BL4 9LB Tel: (01204) 574764 Fax: (01204) 705424 E-mail: sales@jamesrobertshaw.co.uk
Romford Blinds & Shutters Ltd, Danes Road, Romford, RM7 0HL Tel: (01708) 754754 Fax: (01708) 733128
Saxon Blinds Ltd, 7 Magee Street, Northampton, NN1 4JT Tel: (01604) 601888 Fax: (01604) 631212 E-mail: saxonblinds@hotmail.com
Shadewell Blinds Ltd, St Margarets Lane, Fareham, Hampshire, PO14 4BG Tel: (01329) 841199 Fax: (01329) 842299 E-mail: info@shadewell.co.uk
Sunsetters Of Nottingham, 130 Davies Road, West Bridgford, Nottingham, NG2 5HY Tel: 0115-974 4402 Fax: 0115-974 4402
Synektics Ltd, 4 Brinksway, Fleet, Hampshire, GU51 3LZ Tel: (01252) 815281 Fax: (01252) 624433 E-mail: sales@synektics.co.uk
Trueform Engineering Ltd, Unit 4 Pasadena Close, Pump Lane, Hayes, Middlesex, UB3 3NQ Tel: (020) 8561 4959 Fax: (020) 8848 1397 E-mail: sales@trueform.co.uk
Vale Blinds, 27 Main Street, Bottesford, Nottingham, NG13 0EP Tel: (01949) 845399 Fax: (01949) 845399

AXIAL FANS

Alfa Fans Ltd, Unit 7, Green Lane, Bridgtown, Cannock, Staffordshire, WS11 0JJ Tel: (01543) 466420 Fax: (01543) 462393 E-mail: sales@alfafans.co.uk
B.O.B Stevenson Ltd, Coleman Street, Derby, DE24 8NL Tel: (01332) 574112 Fax: (01332) 757286 E-mail: sales@bobstevenson.co.uk
Elta Fans, 17 Barnes Wallis Road, Fareham, Hampshire, PO15 5TT Tel: (01489) 583044 Fax: (01489) 566555 E-mail: mailbox@eltafans.co.uk
Fan Engineering (Midlands) Ltd, 19B Sandy Way, Amington Industrial Estate, Tamworth, Staffordshire, B77 4DS Tel: (01827) 57000 Fax: (01827) 64641 E-mail: fanengineering@aol.co.uk
Fan Systems Group, Witt House, Brookwoods Industrial Estate, Halifax, West Yorkshire, HX4 9BH Tel: (01422) 378120 Fax: (01422) 378672 E-mail: sales@fansystems.co.uk
Fans & Spares Ltd, 6 Brookmead Industrial Estate, Beddington Lane, Croydon, CR0 4TB Tel: (020) 8683 1241 Fax: (020) 8689 0043 E-mail: croydon@fansandspares.co.uk
Fans & Spares Ltd, Unit 2 Rosevale Road, Parkhouse Industrial Estate We, Newcastle, Staffordshire, ST5 7EF Tel: (01782) 579076 Fax: (01782) 563592 E-mail: stoke@fansandspares.co.uk
Fans & Spares Ltd, Unit 25 Whitemoor Court Industrial Estate, Whitemoor Court, Nottingham, NG8 5BY Tel: 0115-929 4104 Fax: 0115-929 2710 E-mail: nottingham@fansandspares.co.uk
▶ Fischbach Fans, 17 Siddeley Way, Royal Oak Industrial Estate, Daventry, Northamptonshire, NN11 8PA Tel: (01327) 315012 Fax: (01327) 315013 E-mail: fischbachacv@aol.com
Fral Products Ltd, 15 Dukes Close, Earls Way Industrial Estate, Thurmaston, Leicester, LE4 8EY Tel: 0116-260 1062 Fax: 0116-293 8013 E-mail: sales@multi-wing.co.uk
G T Fan Services & Repairs Ltd, Unit D Leona Industrial Estate, Nimmings Road, Halesowen, West Midlands, B62 9JQ Tel: 0121-559 1824 Fax: 0121-561 2153
▶ Howden Industrial, Braehead Industrial Estate, Old Govan Road, Renfrew, PA4 8XJ Tel: 0141-885 7500 Fax: 0141-886 1963 E-mail: marketing@howden.com
London Fan Co. Ltd, 75-81 Stirling Road, London, W3 8DJ Tel: (020) 8992 6923 Fax: (020) 8992 6928 E-mail: sales@londonfan.co.uk
Manrose Manufacturing Ltd, Albion House, Albion Close, Slough, SL2 5DT Tel: (01753) 691399 Fax: (01753) 692294 E-mail: sales@manrose.com
Moore Fans Ltd, 2-3 Claremont, Hastings, East Sussex, TN34 1HA Tel: (01424) 436815 Fax: (01424) 422789 E-mail: info@moorefans.com
N M B-Minebea (UK) Ltd, Suite 2.2, Doncastle House, Doncastle Road, Bracknell, Berkshire, RG12 8PE Tel: (01344) 426611 Fax: (01344) 485522
Nuaire Group, Western Indust Estate, Caerphilly, Mid Glamorgan, CF83 1BQ Tel: (029) 2088 5911 Fax: (029) 2088 7033 E-mail: info@nuaire.co.uk
R H F Fans Ltd, 2 Ferrous Way, Irlam, Manchester, M44 5FS Tel: 0161-776 6400 Fax: 0161-775 6566 E-mail: sales@rhf-fans.co.uk
Thermaco Ltd, Unit 5, Spring Lane North, Malvern, Worcestershire, WR14 1BU Tel: (01684) 566163 Fax: (01684) 892356 E-mail: sales@thermaco.co.uk
Torin Ltd, Drakes Way, Swindon, SN3 3JB Tel: (01793) 524291 Fax: (01793) 486570 E-mail: sales@torin-sifan.com
Vent Axia Ltd, Fleming Way, Crawley, West Sussex, RH10 9YX Tel: (01293) 526062 Fax: (01293) 551188 E-mail: info@vent-axia.com

AXIAL FANS – *continued*

Victoria Fan & Engineering Supplies Ltd, Audley Street Works, Audley Street, Mossley, Ashton-under-Lyne, Lancashire, OL5 9HW Tel: (01457) 835391 Fax: (01457) 833378 E-mail: sales@victoriafans.co.uk

AXIAL PUMPS

A B S Waste Water Treatment Technology, Unit 1 Bridges Industrial Estate, Bridge Road, Horshay, Telford, Shropshire, TF4 3EE Tel: (01952) 632030 Fax: (01952) 632040 E-mail: roger.youngman@absgroup.com

AXLE SHAFTS

F P W Axles Ltd, D4 Enfield Road, Accrington, Lancashire, BB5 6NN Tel: (01254) 383413 Fax: (01254) 390417

Heartland Extrusion Forge Ltd, Rocky Lane, Nechells, Birmingham, B7 5EU Tel: 0121-359 6861 Fax: 0121-359 2972 E-mail: enquiries@hef.co.uk

AXLES, *See also headings for particular types*

Clydesdale Forge Co., Marriott Road, Dudley, West Midlands, DY2 0LA Tel: (01384) 252587 Fax: (01384) 231005 E-mail: sales@clydesdale-forge.co.uk

K N Transmissions, Slater House Farm, Haighton Green Lane, Preston, PR2 5SQ Tel: (01772) 655550 Fax: (01772) 655520 E-mail: kntransmissions@btopenworld.com

Tyremart Agricultural Ltd, Main Road, Long Bennington, Newark, Nottinghamshire, NG23 5DJ Tel: (01400) 283820 Fax: (01400) 283137 E-mail: sales@tyremart.co.uk

AXMINSTER CARPETS

Bodigian & Co. Ltd, Wenman Road, Industrial Estate, Thame, Oxfordshire, OX9 3SD Tel: (01844) 213555 Fax: (01844) 214120 E-mail: sales@bodigianofthame.co.uk

Bondworth Ltd, Townshend Works, Puxton Lane, Kidderminster, Worcestershire, DY11 5DF Tel: (01562) 745000 Fax: (01562) 732827 E-mail: sales@bondworth.co.uk

Brintons Carpets (U S A) Ltd, PO Box 16, Kidderminster, Worcestershire, DY10 1AG Tel: (01562) 820000 Fax: (01562) 634540 E-mail: solutions@brintons.co.uk

Carpetright plc, Amberley House, New Road, Rainham, Essex, RM13 8QN Tel: (01708) 525522 Fax: (01708) 559361 E-mail: enquiries@carpetright.co.uk

Cavalier Carpets Ltd, Thompson St Industrial Estate, Blackburn, BB2 1TX Tel: (01254) 268000 Fax: (01254) 268001 E-mail: info@cavalier-carpets.co.uk

Checkmate Industries Ltd, Bridge House, 12 Bridge Street, Halstead, Essex, CO9 1HT Tel: (01787) 477272 Fax: (01787) 476334 E-mail: checkmatecarpets@btconnect.com

Ulster Carpet Mills Ltd, 322 King Street, London, W6 0RR Tel: (020) 8741 1100 Fax: (020) 8741 1640 E-mail: uclondon@ulstercarpets.com

BABY CARE APPLIANCES

▶ Angels, 9 Town Square, Syston, Leicester, LE7 1GZ Tel: 0116-269 3033

▶ Aunty Lesley's, 9 Cornerswell Road, Penarth, South Glamorgan, CF64 2UW Tel: (029) 2070 7923

▶ Baby Agency, 479 Hartshill Road, Stoke-on-Trent, ST4 6AA Tel: (01782) 626613

▶ Baby B, 155-157 Portland Road, Hove, East Sussex, BN3 5QJ Tel: (01273) 220789 Fax: (01273) 220789

Baby Daze, 132 Main Street, Lochgelly, Fife, KY5 0YF Tel: 01592 784218 Fax: 01592 784218

Baby Point Ltd, PO Box 28, Stowmarket, Suffolk, IP14 3AZ Tel: (01449) 770607 Fax: (01449) 678444 E-mail: sales@babypoint.co.uk

▶ Baby Prints, 41 Tivoli Road, Cheltenham, Gloucestershire, GL50 2TD Tel: (01242) 238029

▶ Baby Travel, St. Annes Road, Willenhall, West Midlands, WV13 1DY Tel: (01902) 366333 Fax: (01902) 366333

▶ Baby Unique, 35 King Street East, Stockport, Cheshire, SK1 1XJ Tel: 0161-477 1666 Fax: 0161-477 0666

▶ Baby World, 23 High Street, Hucknall, Nottingham, NG15 7HJ Tel: 0115-964 0008 Fax: 0115-964 0008

Babyland & Pramcots, 76 Yorkshire Street, Oldham, OL1 1SR Tel: 0161-628 9754 Fax: 0161-628 9754

Babytec International Ltd, 5B Sunrise Business, Blandford Forum, Dorset, DT11 8ST Tel: (01258) 459554 Fax: (01258) 480225 E-mail: stephenbenson@babytec.co.uk

▶ Bam-Bams, 106 Castle Street, Forfar, Angus, DD8 3HR Tel: (01307) 462244

▶ Brave Little Soldiers, The Waterside Centre, Unit 6 Abbey Meadows, Leicester, LE4 5AE Tel: 0116-251 9333 Fax: 0116-251 9335

▶ Briggs Kidz Ltd, 38 Kirkintilloch Road, Bishopbriggs, Glasgow, G64 2AL Tel: 0141-772 3322 Fax: 0141-772 3322

▶ Bumptastic Maternity Wear, Worthing Road, Lowestoft, Suffolk, NR32 4HD Tel: 01502 583568 E-mail: sarah@bumptastic.co.uk

▶ Cradle & All, 28 Rockingham Road, Kettering, Northamptonshire, NN16 8JS Tel: (01536) 410006 Fax: (01536) 410006 E-mail: sales@cradleandall.ltd.uk

▶ Cuddles The Baby Shop, 59 Sweyn Road, Cliftonville, Margate, Kent, CT9 2DD Tel: (01843) 229929 Fax: (01843) 229929 E-mail: samgregory3@msn.com3

▶ Early Years, 2 City Arcade, Coventry, CV1 3HW Tel: (024) 7663 4242

▶ First Impressions Castings, 25 High Street, Market Deeping, Peterborough, PE6 8ED Tel: (01778) 344541 Fax: (01778) 344541 E-mail: info@firstimpressionscastings.co.uk

Freedman's At Salters, 17-19 Barking Road, London, E6 1PW Tel: (020) 8472 2892 Fax: (020) 8472 2811 E-mail: enquiries@freedmansatsalters.co.uk

▶ Friday's Child, 2 Market Square, Narberth, Dyfed, SA67 7AU Tel: (01834) 869944 Fax: (01834) 869922

▶ Gilly Babies, 9-10 Springfield Centre, Kempston, Bedford, MK42 7PR Tel: (01234) 856677

Green Baby, 345 Upper Street, London, N1 0PD Tel: (0870) 2406894 Fax: (020) 7226 9244

▶ Helena's Nursery Equipment, Sligo Road, Enniskillen, County Fermanagh, BT74 7JY Tel: (028) 6632 0505

Jackel International Ltd, Dudley Lane, Cramlington, Northumberland, NE23 7RH Tel: 0191-250 1864 Fax: 0191-250 1727 E-mail: mail@jackel.co.uk

▶ Just Kids, 3 Corney Square, Penrith, Cumbria, CA11 7PX Tel: (01768) 892783 Fax: (01697) 473009

▶ K D's, 38 North Point Shopping Centre, Goodhart Road, Bransholme, Hull, HU7 4EE Tel: (01482) 879489

▶ Kai's Surprises, 5 Oliver Road, Bletchley, Milton Keynes, MK2 2SF Tel: (01908) 646008

▶ Little Angels, 54-58 Frodingham Road, Scunthorpe, South Humberside, DN15 7JN Tel: (01724) 843366 Fax: (01724) 843366 E-mail: les@littleangelsonline.wanadoo.co.uk

▶ Little Cherubs, Unit 2, Charlotte Court, Old Milton Road, New Milton, Hampshire, BH25 6DT Tel: (01425) 621316

▶ Lucy Locketts, 10 Stafford Street, Market Drayton, Shropshire, TF9 1HY Tel: 01630 657900

Phillip Merrell Agency, 51 Cleave Road, Sticklepath, Barnstaple, Devon, EX31 2DU Tel: (01271) 322175 Fax: (01271) 325414

Mothercare plc, Z10-Z11 Shopping Centre, Brent Cross, London, NW4 3FD Tel: (020) 8202 5377 Fax: (020) 8202 5467

Mothercare plc, Unit 27 The Charles Darwin Centre, Shrewsbury, SY1 1BW Tel: (01743) 272191

Mothercare plc, 6-8 Guildhall Shopping Centre, Market Square, Stafford, ST16 2BB Tel: (01785) 242603

Mothercare U.K Ltd, 71 St Johns Road, London, SW11 1QX Tel: (020) 7228 0391 E-mail: info@mothercare.com

Nursery Needs, 93 Church Lane, Marple, Stockport, Cheshire, SK6 7AW Tel: 0161-427 7707 Fax: 0161-427 2145

Paramount Contracts Ltd, St. Margarets, Bromley Green Road, Ruckinge, Ashford, Kent, TN26 2EF Tel: (01233) 733399 Fax: (01233) 733608

▶ Rock A Buy Baby, 1 Shopping Hall, 36 Sylvania Way South, Clydebank, Dunbartonshire, G81 1EA Tel: 0141-952 4506 Fax: 0141-952 4506

▶ Rock'A'Bye Baby, Cotsford Lane, Peterlee, County Durham, SR8 4JJ Tel: 0191-569 1771

▶ Something Special, 47 Hereward Cross, Peterborough, PE1 1TQ Tel: (01733) 319099 Fax: (01733) 319099

▶ Squashee Co. Ltd, 8 Portmore Lea, Ballinderry Lower, Lisburn, County Antrim, BT28 2LX Tel: (028) 9265 2985

▶ Stacks, Providence Mill, Alexandra Street, Hyde, Cheshire, SK14 1DX Tel: 0161-368 4948 Fax: 0161-368 4948

Tikkity Boo, 10 Maryport Road, Cardiff, CF23 5JX Tel: (029) 2075 7048 E-mail: sales@tikkityboo.co.uk

Young Trend, 39-41 South Bridge Street, Airdrie, Lanarkshire, ML6 6JQ Tel: (01236) 767248 Fax: (01236) 767248

▶ Yummies, 15 Bond Street, Brighton, BN1 1RD Tel: (01273) 738733 Fax: (01273) 738733

BABY CHANGING PRODUCTS

Baby Point Ltd, PO Box 28, Stowmarket, Suffolk, IP14 3AZ Tel: (01449) 770607 Fax: (01449) 678444 E-mail: sales@babypoint.co.uk

▶ Babyjacks Nursery Equipment, 40 Comberton Hill, Kidderminster, Worcestershire, DY10 1QN Tel: (01562) 741717

▶ Baskets & Bows Fingers & Toes, 22 Queen Street, Dalton-in-Furness, Cumbria, LA15 8EG Tel: (01229) 467868 Fax: (01229) 467868 E-mail: sue@basketsandbows-fingersandtoes.co.uk

▶ Cheeky Brats, 470 Coventry Road, Small Heath, Birmingham, B10 0UG Tel: (0870) 2467605 Fax: (0870) 1318974 E-mail: sales@cheekybrats.co.uk

▶ Mini Moose, Moose Hall (Private address), 69 Hewarts Lane, Rose Green, Bognor Regis, West Sussex, PO21 3DW Tel: (07891) 420383 E-mail: samantha@minimoose.co.uk

▶ Natural Child, Lower Naunton Farm, Evesham Road, Winchcombe, Cheltenham, Gloucestershire, GL54 5BZ Tel: (01242) 620988 Fax: (01242) 620988 E-mail: info@naturalchild.co.uk

▶ Oriflame Info.biz, 27 Blackthorn Avenue, Lenzie, Glasgow, G66 4DE Tel: (0845) 0090384 E-mail: oriflamebiz@hotmail.co.uk

BABY DUMMY/SOOTHER PRODUCTION EQUIPMENT

Maclaren Europe Ltd, Station Works, Station Road, Long Buckby, Northampton, NN6 7PF Tel: (01327) 842662 Fax: (01327) 844133 E-mail: info@maclaren.co.uk

BABY EQUIPMENT HIRE

▶ Mini Moose, Moose Hall (Private address), 69 Hewarts Lane, Rose Green, Bognor Regis, West Sussex, PO21 3DW Tel: (07891) 420383 E-mail: samantha@minimoose.co.uk

BABY FEEDING EQUIPMENT

▶ Cozeebee, Unit 49, Vinehall Business Centre, Vinehall Road, Robertsbridge, East Sussex, TN32 5JW Tel: (01424) 871434 E-mail: sales@cozeebee.co.uk

▶ Discount Baby Goods, 4 Mellowmead, Manaton, Newton Abbot, Devon, TQ13 9UE Tel: (01647) 221480 Fax: (01647) 221480 E-mail: sales@discountbabygoods.co.uk

▶ Mini Moose, Moose Hall (Private address), 69 Hewarts Lane, Rose Green, Bognor Regis, West Sussex, PO21 3DW Tel: (07891) 420383 E-mail: samantha@minimoose.co.uk

Planet Kids, 8 Actons Walk, Wood Street, Wigan, Lancashire, WN3 4HN Tel: (01942) 403910 Fax: (01942) 231188 E-mail: sales@planetkids.org.uk

▶ www.icbaby.com, 85 Bruce Avenue, Worthing, West Sussex, BN11 5LB Tel: (0870) 2406575 E-mail: Jane@icbaby.com

BABY FOODS

▶ Multi, Stanmore, Middlesex, HA7 3YR Tel: (0870) 0116220 Fax: (0870) 0116330 E-mail: mail@infantformula.co.uk

BABY HARNESS/STRAPS

▶ Babyjacks Nursery Equipment, 40 Comberton Hill, Kidderminster, Worcestershire, DY10 1QN Tel: (01562) 741717

▶ Baskets & Bows Fingers & Toes, 22 Queen Street, Dalton-in-Furness, Cumbria, LA15 8EG Tel: (01229) 467868 Fax: (01229) 467868 E-mail: sue@basketsandbows-fingersandtoes.co.uk

Clippa Safe Ltd, Lanthwaite Road, Nottingham, NG11 8LD Tel: 0115-921 1899 Fax: 0115-984 5554 E-mail: sales@clippasafe.co.uk

BABY HIGH CHAIRS

Babyworld, New Portreath Road, Redruth, Cornwall, TR16 4QQ Tel: (01209) 843311 Fax: (01209) 842206

BABY NAPPY/TRAINING PANTS

Kimberly Clark Ltd, 1 Tower View, Kings Hill, West Malling, Kent, ME19 4HA Tel: (01732) 594000 Fax: (01732) 594001

BABY SEATS

▶ Baby Boom 2000, Long Lane, Ickenham, Uxbridge, Middlesex, UB10 8QS Tel: (01895) 675596 Fax: (01895) 675596 E-mail: sales@babyboom2000.co.uk

▶ Baby Travel, St. Annes Road, Willenhall, West Midlands, WV13 1DY Tel: (01902) 366333 Fax: (01902) 366333

Babyworld, New Portreath Road, Redruth, Cornwall, TR16 4QQ Tel: (01209) 843311 Fax: (01209) 842206

Mothercare plc, 24-25 The Sovereign Centre, High Street, Weston-super-Mare, Avon, BS23 1HL Tel: (01934) 626977

BABY WEAR

4 Kids, 74 High St, Hanham, Bristol, BS15 3DS Tel: 0117-961 6808

▶ Baby B Gifts, 33A Wilberforce Road, London, N4 2SN Tel: 020 76908992

▶ Baby Rug, 61 Pepys Road, London, SW20 8NL Tel: (020) 8944 8674 E-mail: info@babyrug.co.uk

Babyworld, New Portreath Road, Redruth, Cornwall, TR16 4QQ Tel: (01209) 843311 Fax: (01209) 842206

Bricknells, 35 Fore Street, Bodmin, Cornwall, PL31 2JD Tel: (01208) 77088 Fax: (01208) 78497

▶ Bumps Maternity Wear, 19 Frederick Street, Sunderland, SR1 1LT Tel: 0191-565 3232 Fax: 0191 5520988 E-mail: info@bumpsmaternity.com

▶ Bumptastic Maternity Wear, Worthing Road, Lowestoft, Suffolk, NR32 4HD Tel: 01502 583568 E-mail: sarah@bumptastic.co.uk

T.W. Burrell & Sons Ltd, Abbey Park Road, Leicester, LE4 5AJ Tel: (0116) 253 8485 Fax: (0116) 251 4554

Casa Tiana Ltd, 6 Honey Hill, Emberton, Olney, Bucks, MK46 5LT Tel: 01234 717079 Fax: 01234 717079

Cooneen Textiles Ltd, 23 Cooneen Road, Fivemiletown, County Tyrone, BT75 0NE Tel: (028) 8952 1401 Fax: (028) 8952 1488 E-mail: info@cooneen.co.uk

Dynamic Fashion World, 2A Marlborough Road, Nuneaton, Warwickshire, CV11 5PG Tel: (024) 7664 2003 Fax: (024) 7664 2003 E-mail: razwan-amin@hotmail.com

Frillies Ltd, First Floor Shell Leyland, Wigan Road, Leyland, PR25 5UD Tel: (01772) 621037 Fax: (01772) 621037

Grasshopper Babywear (Wolverhampton) Ltd, Hunter Street, Wolverhampton, WV6 0QZ Tel: (01902) 426506 Fax: (01902) 426649

▶ Hats 4 Tots Ltd, 25 Longacre, Woodthorpe, Nottingham, NG5 4JS Tel: 0115-967 1371

G.H. Hurt & Son Ltd, 65 High Road, Chilwell, Nottingham, NG9 4AJ Tel: 0115-925 4080 Fax: 0115-925 5904

Kiddies World, Roseville House, Grant Avenue, Leeds, LS7 1QB Tel: 0113-243 5003 Fax: 0113-243 5004

▶ Kulfi Kids, 7 Market place, Camelford, Cornwall, PL32 9PB Tel: 01840 211144 E-mail: orders@kulfikids.co.uk

▶ M G S Consultancy, Desford Hall, Leicester Lane, Desford, Leicester, LE9 9JJ Tel: (01455) 828220 Fax: (01455) 828490

Margaret Ann Baby Wear, Ayr Street, Nottingham, NG7 4FX Tel: 0115-942 0384 Fax: 0115-970 4967

Mothercare plc, 156-160 High Street, Bromley, BR1 1HE Tel: (020) 8460 6730

Mothercare plc, 5 Underhill Walk, Burton-on-Trent, Staffordshire, DE14 1DE Tel: (01283) 567472

Mothercare plc, 123 Sauchiehall Street, Glasgow, G2 3DD Tel: 0141-332 7072 Fax: 0141-332 9485

Mothercare plc, Unit 13 White Rose Centre, High Street, Rhyl, Clwyd, LL18 1EW Tel: (01745) 343524

Mothercare plc, Stadium Way, Retail World, Parkgate, Rotherham, South Yorkshire, S60 1TG Tel: (01709) 780111

▶ Natural Child, Lower Naunton Farm, Evesham Road, Winchcombe, Cheltenham, Gloucestershire, GL54 5BZ Tel: (01242) 620988 Fax: (01242) 620988 E-mail: info@naturalchild.co.uk

▶ Nursery Needs, 15 Newton Road, Rushden, Northamptonshire, NN10 0PS Tel: (01933) 419898

▶ Peeny Weeny Baby, PO Box 71, Shanklin, Isle of Wight, PO37 6ZW Tel: (01983) 863532

Planet Kids, 8 Actons Walk, Wood Street, Wigan, Lancashire, WN3 4HN Tel: (01942) 403910 Fax: (01942) 231188 E-mail: sales@planetkids.org.uk

▶ Rockabyebabies, 201 Holton Road, Barry, South Glamorgan, CF63 4HR Tel: 01446 741185 Fax: 01446 741185

▶ Star Child, Unit 18 The Oak Business Centre, 79-93 Ratcliffe Road, Sileby, Loughborough, Leicestershire, LE12 7PU Tel: (01509) 817601 Fax: (01509) 817602 E-mail: info@starchildshoes.co.uk

▶ That's My Baby, 14-15 Orbit Centre, Ashworth Road, Bridgemead, Swindon, SN5 7YG Tel: (01793) 432111 Fax: (01793) 436724 E-mail: info@thatsmybaby.biz

▶ Three Bears Babywear, Cartwright Street, Wolverhampton, WV2 3BT Tel: (01902) 870838 Fax: (01902) 352005

Tiny Tots Ashford Ltd, 18 Elwick Road, Ashford, Kent, TN23 1PF Tel: (01233) 623511 Fax: (01233) 610636 E-mail: enquiries@tinytotsashford.co.uk

▶ Tops 2 Toes, 2 Eaton Road, West Derby, Liverpool, L12 7JJ Tel: 0151-256 6446

Tots & Teens Ltd, Unit B Cumberland Business Park, 17 Cumberland Avenue, London, NW10 7RT Tel: (020) 8965 8158 Fax: (020) 8961 6184 E-mail: contex@babybright.co.uk

Wick's Ltd, Unit 18L Ring Road, Burntwood Business Park, Burntwood, Staffordshire, WS7 3JQ Tel: (01543) 672488 Fax: (01543) 685211

BABY WEAR TRANSFERS

Britannia Transprint, 38 Burgess Road, Saffron Works, Leicester, LE2 8QL Tel: 0116-283 8485 E-mail: info@tranfereprint.co.uk

Dynamic Fashion World, 2A Marlborough Road, Nuneaton, Warwickshire, CV11 5PG Tel: (024) 7664 2003 Fax: (024) 7664 2003 E-mail: razwan-amin@hotmail.com

Trade Gaps Ltd, Kitchen Farm, Skipton Old Road, Colne, Lancashire, BB8 7ER Tel: (01282) 843740 Fax: (01282) 841776 E-mail: sales@tradegaps.com

▶ indicates data change since last edition

BACK PAIN RELIEF PRODUCTS

▶ GFilmsUK, 1, Stud Barn, Melton Park, Melton Constable, Norfolk, NR24 2NJ Tel: 01263 860901 E-mail: gfilms@homecall.co.uk

BACKGROUND DEBUG MODE (BDM) OR JTAG INTERFACES

Synergie-Cad UK Ltd, Greetwell Place, 2 Lime Kiln Way, Lincoln, LN2 4US Tel: (01522) 520222 Fax: (01522) 531222 E-mail: rogercooke@synergie-cad.co.uk

BACKHOE LOADER HIRE

Briggs & Partner Ltd, The Storth, Huddersfield Road, Elland, West Yorkshire, HX5 9JR Tel: (01422) 372515 Fax: (01422) 311093 E-mail: briggs@zen.co.uk
R Savage Plant Hire Co. Ltd, 222 St Margarets Road, Ward End, Birmingham, B8 2BG Tel: 0121-328 1100 Fax: 0121-327 3548 E-mail: enquiries@savageplanthire.co.uk

BACKING RINGS

Drain Center Civils, 386 Coleridge Road, Sheffield, S9 5DD Tel: 0114-244 0926 Fax: 0114-243 5990 E-mail: sheffield.p24@wolsley.co.uk

BACKSHELL DESIGN ENGINEERS

D.J.T. Swindon Ltd, Unit 12 Ash Phase, Kembrey Park, Kembrey Street, Swindon, SN2 8UN Tel: (01793) 432543 Fax: (01793) 435397 E-mail: djt@djt-engineering.fsnet.co.uk

BACON

▶ Border County Foods, The Old Vicarage, Crosby-On-Eden, Carlisle, CA6 4QZ Tel: (01228) 573500 Fax: (01228) 672021 E-mail: info@cumberland-sausage.net
▶ Daisyfield Foods Ltd, Wellington Street, Bury, Lancashire, BL8 2XX Tel: 0161-797 1100 Fax: 0161-797 1100
▶ Encore Catering, Blair Court, Port Dundas Business Park, 100 Borron Street, Glasgow, G4 9XE Tel: 0141-353 9148 Fax: 0141-353 9145

BACON PACKAGING SYSTEMS

F & P Bacon Packers Ltd, 50 Nowell La, Leeds, LS9 6JE Tel: 0113-248 8455 Fax: 0113-248 8455

BACTERIOLOGICAL PRODUCTS

Microbial Developments Ltd, Spring La North, Malvern, Worcestershire, WR14 1BU Tel: (01684) 891055 Fax: (01684) 891060 E-mail: info@micdev.com

BACTERIOSTATIC FILTERS

Air Safety Ltd, Vickers Industrial Estate, Mellishaw Lane, Morecambe, Lancashire, LA3 3EN Tel: (01524) 388696 Fax: (01524) 33386 E-mail: sales@airsafetymedical.com

BAD CREDIT MORTGAGE BROKERS

▶ Central Capital Mortgages, 2nd Floor, Edward Hyde Building, 38 Clarendon Road, Watford, WD17 1JJ Tel: 0800 032 23 20 E-mail: contact.us@centralcapital.com

BADGE HOLDERS

Eagle Technologies Ltd, Unit 17, The Western Centre, Western Road, Bracknell, Berkshire, RG12 1RW Tel: (01344) 303700 Fax: (01344) 303701 E-mail: sales@eagletechnologies.co.uk

BADGE HOLDERS, PLASTIC

▶ Im-Press Promotions Derby, 2 Marston Brook, Hilton, Derby, DE65 5HS Tel: (01283) 732994 Fax: 01283 732994 E-mail: im-pressderby@btconnect.com
▶ Keen Photo Supplies Ltd, Keen House Fleckney Road, Kibworth, Leicester, LE8 0HJ Tel: (01858) 431122 Fax: 0116-279 1275 E-mail: gary@keenphoto.co.uk

BADGES, *See also headings for particular types*

Badgemaster Ltd, Unit 2-8, Hazelford Way, Newstead Industrial Park, Newstead, Nottingham, NG15 0DQ Tel: (01623) 723112 Fax: (01623) 723113 E-mail: customerservices@badgemaster.co.uk
Baynham & Stanfield Badge Co. Ltd, 32b Coppice Industrial Trading Estate, Kidderminster, Worcestershire, DY11 7QY Tel: (01562) 60738 Fax: (01562) 829747 E-mail: sales@baynhambadges.co.uk
▶ C K Badges, 7 Oaklands Close, Bexleyheath, Kent, DA6 7AP Tel: (020) 8304 3758 Fax: (020) 8304 3758
Characteristic Promotional Items Ltd, Unit 2 Trenant Industrial Estate, Wadebridge, Cornwall, PL27 6HB Tel: (01208) 813813 Fax: (01208) 813168 E-mail: sales@cxnet.co.uk
Computerised Exhibition Services Badges Ltd, 31 Highbridge Road, Sutton Coldfield, West Midlands, B73 5QB Tel: 0121-354 9595 Fax: 0121-354 6227 E-mail: badgereg@aol.com
▶ Diedesign Emblems, Unit 16 Magreal Industrial Estate, Freeth Street, Birmingham, B16 0QZ Tel: 0121-455 0505 Fax: 0121-455 8484 E-mail: info@diedesign.co.uk
F & F Promotions, Lower Gunstone, Bideford, Devon, EX39 2DE Tel: (01237) 422477 Fax: (01237) 422633 E-mail: sales@rockbymail.co.uk
▶ Firmin & Sons P.L.C., Firmin House, 82-86 New Town Row, Birmingham, B6 4HU Tel: 0121-380 0800 Fax: 0121-359 3321 E-mail: sales@firmin.co.uk
G L J Badges, Unit 10 Park Trading Estate, Park Road, Hockley, Birmingham, B18 5HB Tel: 0121-554 9869 Fax: 0121-523 9395 E-mail: sales@gljbadges.co.uk
Graphic Arts Coventry, 69-71 Hearsall Lane, Coventry, CV5 6HF Tel: (024) 7667 3415
Jammy Badge Co., Clairmont, Victoria Street, Combe Martin, Ilfracombe, Devon, EX34 0JR Tel: (01271) 882524
Key Factors, 11 Cannon Grove, Fetcham, Leatherhead, Surrey, KT22 9LG Tel: (01372) 376904 Fax: (01372) 376904 E-mail: sales@keyfactors.co.uk
Korporate Creations Ltd, 151 Utney Bridge Road Shire Place, Swaffield Road, London, SW15 2NZ Tel: (020) 8870 2070 Fax: (020) 8870 2012 E-mail: info@korporate-creations.com
M & L Promotional Products Ltd, 5 Queen Street, Mirfield, West Yorkshire, WF14 8AH Tel: (01924) 498500 Fax: (01924) 497200 E-mail: sales@mlbadges.com
Manhattan Products Ltd, 89 Steward Street, Birmingham, B18 7AF Tel: 0121-454 6404 Fax: 0121-454 1497 E-mail: sales@manhattanproducts.com
Manor Enterprises, 3 Beacon Court, Birmingham Road, Kidderminster, Worcestershire, DY10 3JT Tel: (01562) 700375 Fax: 0121-358 1105
Qasco UK Ltd, 43d Brecknock Road, London, N7 0BT Tel: (020) 7267 3079 Fax: (020) 7267 4212 E-mail: sales@qasco.co.uk
▶ Recognition Express, Heytor House, Long Road East, Dedham, Colchester, CO7 6BH Tel: (01206) 321270 Fax: (08702) 851464 E-mail: sales@re-anglia.co.uk
Recognition Express, St. Michaels House, Parkgate Drive, Lancaster, LA1 3FN Tel: (01524) 846555 Fax: (01524) 843693 E-mail: sales@re-lancaster.co.uk
Recognition Express, 10-16 Victoria Parade, Urmston, Manchester, M41 9RE Tel: 0161-748 1716 Fax: 0161-755 3650 E-mail: sales@re-manchester.co.uk
Target Badges, 134 Watnall Road, Hucknall, Nottingham, NG15 7NH Tel: 0115-956 0047 Fax: 0115-956 0047 E-mail: info@targetbadges.co.uk
Jeremy Tenniswood, 36 St. Botolphs Street, Colchester, CO2 7EA Tel: (01206) 368787 Fax: (01206) 367836 E-mail: info@militaria.co.uk
Toye Kenning Spencer Stadden, 77 Warstone Lane, Birmingham, B18 6NL Tel: 0121-236 3253 Fax: 0121-236 7217 E-mail: sales@toyebirm.demon.co.uk
▶ Wee Badgers Badges, PO Box 3821, Glasgow, G46 6JY Tel: 0141-649 1207 Fax: 0141-649 1207 E-mail: info@weebadgers.com
West Country Marketing Advertising, Unit 1 Woodend Lane Industrial Estate, Stoke Lacy, Bromyard, Herefordshire, HR7 4HQ Tel: (01885) 490500 Fax: (01885) 490585 E-mail: sales@wcma.co.uk

BADGES, HEAT SEAL

▶ Keen Photo Supplies Ltd, Keen House Fleckney Road, Kibworth, Leicester, LE8 0HJ Tel: (01858) 431122 Fax: 0116-279 1275 E-mail: gary@keenphoto.co.uk

BADGES, PUBLICITY/ ADVERTISING/PROMOTIONAL

Badgers, 4 Beach Road, Emsworth, Hampshire, PO10 7JS Tel: (01243) 378147 Fax: (01243) 379408 E-mail: sales@badges4all.co.uk
Banbury Badges Ltd, Brooklands, Brook Street, Moreton Pinkney, Daventry, Northamptonshire, NN11 3SL Tel: (01295) 768758 Fax: (01295) 768759 E-mail: info@banburybadges.co.uk
Base 1 Ltd, 41-43 Roebuck Road, Hainault Industrial Estate, Ilford, Essex, IG6 3TU Tel: (020) 8500 5649 Fax: (020) 8559 9456 E-mail: phil@base1.co.uk
Better Badges, C 9 Garman Road, London, N17 0UR Tel: (020) 8365 1035 Fax: (020) 8365 1905 E-mail: john@abetterbadge.com
Big Badge Co., Old School House, Victoria Avenue, London, N3 1GG Tel: (020) 8371 8752 Fax: (020) 8371 8751 E-mail: sales@theknightgroup.com
Dodd Anderson Ltd, Graphic House, Mylord Cresent, Camperdown Industrial Estate, Newcastle upon Tyne, NE12 5UJ Tel: 0191-268 9993 Fax: 0191-268 6667 E-mail: doddanderson@btconnect.co.uk
Golden Finishes Ltd, 4 Malvern Drive, Llanishen, Cardiff, CF14 5DR Tel: (029) 2075 5733 Fax: (029) 2076 3993 E-mail: gfinishes@aol.com
K P Badges & Trophies, 4 Antrim Road, Bristol, BS9 4BS Tel: 0117-962 0191 Fax: 0117-975 4264 E-mail: sales@trophiesuk.biz
Manhattan Products Ltd, 89 Steward Street, Birmingham, B18 7AF Tel: 0121-454 6404 Fax: 0121-454 1497 E-mail: sales@manhattanproducts.com
Modern Engraving Ltd, Leese Street, Stoke-on-Trent, ST4 1AL Tel: (01782) 849055 Fax: (01782) 744565 E-mail: sales@modernengraving.co.uk
Motiv Business Gifts, 28 Moor Lane, Loughborough, Leicestershire, LE11 1BA Tel: (01509) 262272 Fax: (01509) 267276
Premier Badges, Unit 8 Little Hyde Farm, Ingatestone, Essex, CM4 0DU Tel: (01277) 355078 Fax: (01277) 355092 E-mail: sales@premierbadges.co.uk
Prestige Enterprises, PO Box 1160, Newtownabbey, County Antrim, BT36 5YP Tel: 0845 230 3818 Fax: 0845 230 3819 E-mail: sales@prestigeenterprises.com
▶ Promotional, 38 Beacon Close, Stone, Aylesbury, Buckinghamshire, HP17 8YH Tel: (01296) 747401 Fax: (01296) 747401 E-mail: sales@beaconpm.co.uk
B. Sanders (Bromsgrove) Ltd, 4 Sherwood Road, Aston Fields Industrial Estate, Bromsgrove, Worcestershire, B60 3DR Tel: (01527) 575757 Fax: (01527) 575539

BAG CLOSURE APPLICATION MACHINES

Saeloc Ltd, 9 Enterprise Court, Newton Close, Park Farm Industrial Estate, Wellingborough, Northamptonshire, NN8 6UW Tel: (01933) 678000 Fax: (01933) 678999 E-mail: sales@saeloc.co.uk

BAG SEALING MACHINES, VACUUM

▶ Advance Vacuum & Lift, 4 Beverley Avenue, Newtownards, County Down, BT23 7UE Tel: (028) 9181 8095 Fax: (028) 9182 7523 E-mail: sales@avlift.com

BAG-IN-BOX DISPENSING SYSTEMS, SOFT DRINKS

Autonumis Ltd, Cirencester Road, Tetbury, Gloucestershire, GL8 8SA Tel: (01666) 502641 Fax: (01666) 505100 E-mail: info@autonumis.co.uk
▶ Us 4 Slush Ltd, 8C Canford Business Park, Magna Road, Poole, Dorset, BH21 3AP Tel: (01202) 572104 E-mail: sales@us4slush.com

BAGGING EQUIPMENT

Advanced Dynamics Ltd, 250 Thornton Road, Bradford, West Yorkshire, BD1 2LB Tel: (01274) 220300 Fax: (01274) 308953 E-mail: info@advanceddynamics.co.uk
Brand & Rae Ltd, Russell Mill, Springfield, Cupar, Fife, KY15 5QX Tel: (01334) 652828 Fax: (01334) 655967
Chronos Richardson Ltd, Unit 1 Centurion Business Centre, Dabell Avenue, Nottingham, NG6 8WN Tel: 0115-935 1351 Fax: 0115-935 1353 E-mail: info@chronos-richardson.com
Jenton International Ltd, Unit 9 10 Evingar Industrial Estate, Ardglen Road, Whitchurch, Hampshire, RG28 7BB Tel: (01256) 892194 Fax: (01256) 896486 E-mail: sales@jenton.co.uk
Johnston Lightning Filler Ltd, K Prescot Trade Centre, Oliver Lyme Road, Prescot, Merseyside, L34 2SH Tel: 0151-430 0900 Fax: 0151-430 7350 E-mail: sales@jlf-packaging.co.uk
Sandiacre Packaging Machinery Ltd, 101 Lilac Grove, Beeston, Nottingham, NG9 1PF Tel: 0115-967 8787 Fax: 0115-967 8707 E-mail: sandiacre.uk@molins.com

BAGS, *See also headings for particular types*

Abreption Leather Products, Unit 14 Turnpike Close, Grantham, Lincolnshire, NG31 7XU Tel: (01476) 569020 Fax: (01476) 569020 E-mail: email@abreption.co.uk
▶ Air Care Products, Gosbecks Road, Colchester, CO2 9JT Tel: (01206) 564443 Fax: (01206) 564462
▶ Ambient Lounge, Elm Road, Kingston Upon Thames, Surrey, KT2 6HT Tel: (0870) 2851619 Fax: (0870) 2851613 E-mail: info@ambientlounge.com
▶ Amcor Flexibles (UK) Ltd, Keith House, South Gyle, Edinburgh, EH12 9DQ Tel: 0131-317 2600
▶ B & G Products Ltd, Norbury House Farm Buildings, Norbury, Stafford, ST20 0PB Tel: (01785) 284222 Fax: (01785) 284613
▶ B & H Plastics Ltd, Anchorage Works, New Road, Radford, Nottingham, NG7 3FR Tel: 0115-970 1655
▶ B M J Parr Packaging Ltd, Unit 22, Boston Industrial Estate, Power Station Road, Rugeley, Staffordshire, WS15 2HS Tel: (01889) 578915
▶ B P I Industrial Ardeer, Lundholm Road, Stevenston, Ayrshire, KA20 3NQ Tel: (01294) 605111 Fax: (01294) 842032
▶ Britton Packbourne Ltd, Unit 11, Ponders End Industrial Estate, Duck Lees Lane, Enfield, Middlesex, EN3 7UP Tel: (020) 8805 8000 Fax: (020) 8805 7727
▶ Caring Touch Ltd, Unit 16 Grays Farm Production Village, Grays Farm Road, Orpington, Kent, BR5 3BD Tel: (020) 8300 0770 Fax: (020) 8300 0770 E-mail: sales@caringtouch.co.uk
▶ Coopack, 12 Katmandu Road, Bromsgrove, Worcs, B60 2SP Tel: 0845 127 9877 Fax: 0845 257 0876 E-mail: sales@coopack.co.uk
Custom Bags, Unit 2b 102 Throckley Way, Middlefields Industrial Estate, South Shields, Tyne & Wear, NE34 0NU Tel: 0191-427 7766 Fax: 0191-427 7755 E-mail: sales@custombags.co.uk
▶ Dusk Crafts, 6 Sherwood, Uplyme Road, Lyme Regis, Dorset, DT7 3LS Tel: 01297 445033 E-mail: info@duskcrafts.co.uk
▶ Field Boxmore Healthcare Packaging Belfast Ltd, Enterprise Way, Hightown Indusst Estate, Newtownabbey, County Antrim, BT36 4EW Tel: (028) 9080 4000 Fax: (028) 9080 4300 E-mail: sales@boxmore.com
Jacon Ltd, 1 Brickfield Industrial Estate, New Road, Gillingham, Dorset, SP8 4LT Tel: (01747) 825858 Fax: (01747) 825634 E-mail: info@jacon.co.uk
▶ K & S Packaging, 33-37 Garman Road, London, N17 0UL Tel: (020) 8885 6677 Fax: (020) 8885 6678 E-mail: info@kspackaging.com
M1 Sport Ltd, Phoenix House, Waller Avenue, Luton, LU4 9RS Tel: (01582) 580000 Fax: (01582) 580040
Martindales Polythene Packaging Ltd, Block D, St. Michaels Industrial Estate, Widnes, Cheshire, WA8 8TL Tel: 0151-420 5355 Fax: 0151-420 5356 E-mail: sales@martindalespps.com
Paper Bag Co., Units 8 & 9 Oakfield Business Centre, Northacre Industrial Estate, Stephenson Road, Westbury, Wiltshire, BA13 4WF Tel: 01373 825834 Fax: 01373 865984 E-mail: sales@paperbagco.co.uk
Park Packaging Ltd, 2 Ashley Drive, Bothwell, Glasgow, G71 8BS Tel: (01698) 801943 Fax: (01698) 801925 E-mail: info@parkpackaging.co.uk
▶ Polybox (Stornoway) Ltd, Marybank, Isle of Lewis, HS2 0DB Tel: (01851) 704079 Fax: (01851) 704706
S Perviz & Co. Ltd, Solmar House, 7-9 Blackfriars Road, Salford, M3 7AG Tel: 0161-833 9910 Fax: 0161-839 0543 E-mail: mp@perviz.co.uk
▶ Synthetic Polybulk UK, Unit 4 Brandon House, 23-25 Brandon Street, Hamilton, Lanarkshire, ML3 6DA Tel: (01698) 527122 Fax: (01698) 527127 E-mail: jim.mccreadie@polybulk.com
▶ Thistle Sporting Goods, 25 Knightswood Terrace, Blantyre, Glasgow, G72 9BQ Tel: (01698) 829280 Fax: (01698) 829280 E-mail: jacbag@btinternet.com

BAGS, CUSTOM MADE, METAL FOIL AND PVC

E P S Logistics Technology Ltd, Staplehurst Road, Sittingbourne, Kent, ME10 1XS Tel: (01795) 424433 Fax: (01795) 426970 E-mail: sales@epslt.co.uk
P R Hunter Plastics Ltd, 5 Pembroke Road, Stocklake Indus Estate, Aylesbury, Buckinghamshire, HP20 1DB Tel: (01296) 422423 Fax: (01296) 422423 E-mail: hunter_plastics@hotmail.com

BAGS, CUSTOM MADE, NYLON

Allegro Bags, 110 Huttoft Road, Sutton-On-Sea, Mablethorpe, Lincolnshire, LN12 2RU Tel: (01507) 440192 E-mail: allegrobags@btconnect.com
Bana Bags, Market Hall, Earle Street, Crewe, CW1 2BL Tel: (01270) 255703

BAGS, CUSTOM MADE, NYLON – *continued*

C F Cases Ltd, 13 Consul Road, Rugby, Warwickshire, CV21 1PB Tel: (01788) 535484 Fax: (01788) 570933 E-mail: sales@cfcases.co.uk

Custom Bags, Unit 2b 102 Throckley Way, Middlefields Industrial Estate, South Shields, Tyne & Wear, NE34 0NU Tel: 0191-427 7766 Fax: 0191-427 7755 E-mail: sales@custombags.co.uk

Excelsior Rotational Moulding Ltd, Ferngrove Mills, Rochdale Old Road, Bury, Lancashire, BL9 7LS Tel: 0161-797 0855 Fax: 0161-763 1614 E-mail: sales@excelsior-ltd.co.uk

Geega Bags Co., 10 Stewart Street, Wolverhampton, WV2 4JW Tel: (01902) 717733 Fax: (01902) 717733

Travelstyle, 32 Chatley Street, Manchester, M3 1HX Tel: 0161-832 4865 Fax: 0161-832 6145

BAGS, FLEXIBLE INTERMEDIATE BULK CONTAINER (FIBC)

▶ Synthetic Polybulk UK, Unit 4 Brandon House, 23-25 Brandon Street, Hamilton, Lanarkshire, ML3 6DA Tel: (01698) 527122 Fax: (01698) 527127 E-mail: jim.mccreadie@polybulk.com

BAGS, GIFT, PAPER

▶ 1Gift4All, PO Box 172, Pudsey, West Yorkshire, LS28 5XT Tel: (0789) 9067059 E-mail: sales@1gift4all.com

▶ Xing Chao Ltd, 42 Milner Street, Preston, PR1 6BN Tel: (01772) 883937 Fax: 01772 883937 E-mail: info@xingchaoltd.com

BAGS, NOTEBOOK COMPUTER

▶ PC Payless, 3 Farmfield Road, Bromley, BR1 4NE Tel: (020) 8480 1118

Protec Metal Work Ltd, 7 H T H Complex, Blackwater Way, Aldershot, Hampshire, GU12 4DN Tel: (01252) 310443 Fax: (01252) 341787 E-mail: protecmetal@btconnect.com

BAGS, RECYCLED PAPER

▶ The Brand in a Box Co. Ltd, Damery Works, Damery Lane, Woodford, Berkeley, Gloucestershire, GL13 9JR Tel: (0845) 2011266 Fax: (0845) 2011265 E-mail: info@brandinabox.biz

BAGS, SHOPPING, JUTE

Paper Bag Co., Units 8 & 9 Oakfield Business Centre, Northacre Industrial Estate, Stephenson Road, Westbury, Wiltshire, BA13 4WF Tel: 01373 825834 Fax: 01373 865984 E-mail: sales@paperbagco.co.uk

▶ WineBag.co.uk, 4 Melcombe Gardens, Harrow, Middlesex, HA3 9RH Tel: (0701) 0704731 E-mail: sales@winebag.co.uk

BAGS, SHRINK WRAP

▶ Boatcoat, Fox House, Whimple Street, Plymouth, PL1 2DH Tel: (01752) 227333 Fax: (01752) 227333 E-mail: sales@boatcoat.co.uk

BAGS, VACUUM PACKING

▶ Advance Vacuum & Lift, 4 Beverley Avenue, Newtownards, County Down, BT23 7UE Tel: (028) 9181 8095 Fax: (028) 9182 7523 E-mail: sales@avlift.com

BAKERS' INGREDIENT/ PREPARED MATERIAL

Allied Bakeries Ltd, Dunnings Bridge Road, Bootle, Merseyside, L30 6TG Tel: 0151-523 7566 Fax: 0151-522 6363

Allied Bakeries, Upper Castle Street, Bradford, West Yorkshire, BD5 7RN Tel: (01274) 738822 Fax: (01274) 745446

Allied Bakeries Ltd, Deacon Road, Lincoln, LN2 4JE Tel: (01522) 528334 Fax: (01522) 537391 E-mail: ab_houghton@alliedbakeries.co.uk

Allied Bakeries Ltd, 1 Kingsmill Place, Vanwall Business Park, Maidenhead, Berkshire, SL6 4UF Tel: (01628) 764300 Fax: (01628) 764390 E-mail: information@alliedbakeries.co.uk

Allied Bakeries Ltd, Cartwright Road, Stevenage, Hertfordshire, SG1 4QA Tel: (01438) 359611 Fax: (01438) 316451

Allied Bakeries Walthamstow, Argall Avenue, Leyton, London, E10 7AB Tel: (020) 8556 1031 Fax: (020) 8558 6636 E-mail: subhirdey@alliedbakeries.com

Apetito, Crackley Way, Peartree Lane Industrial Estate, Dudley, West Midlands, DY2 0UW Tel: (01384) 254389 Fax: (01384) 456334

Asplins Oatcakes, 2 Haywood Street, Leek, Staffordshire, ST13 5JX Tel: (01538) 387556

Australian Dried Fruits Europe Ltd, 45a The Mall, London, W5 3TJ Tel: (020) 8566 2944 Fax: (020) 8566 2967E-mail: john@adfe.co.uk

B F P Wholesale Ltd, 1 Manson Square, Deans Industrial Estate, Deans, Livingston, West Lothian, EH54 8SD Tel: (01506) 462444 Fax: (01506) 419888 E-mail: sales@bfpwholesale.com

Bakels Foodservice, Granville Way, Launton Road, Bicester, Oxfordshire, OX26 4JT Tel: (01869) 247098 Fax: (01869) 242979 E-mail: bakels@bakels.com

The Bakery, Dwyran, Llanfairpwllgwyngyll, Gwynedd, LL61 6YU Tel: (01248) 430717 Fax: (01248) 430717

▶ The Bakery, The Shop, Edward Street, Stone, Staffordshire, ST15 8HN Tel: (01785) 812118

▶ Bread Co., Unit 8+9 Premier Trading Estate, Dartmouth Middleway, Birmingham, B7 4AT Tel: 0121-359 6163 Fax: 0121-359 5153 E-mail: sales@breadbin.co.uk

▶ Cappuccino & Gateau Ltd, 173 Crickelwood Broadway, London, NW2 3HT Tel: (020) 8208 4668 E-mail: cappucinogateau@ukcom.com

Cedar Glade Foods Ltd, George House, 3 St Davids Court, Kenn, Clevedon, Avon, BS21 6UP Tel: (01934) 834095 Fax: (01934) 835778 E-mail: cfoodsltd@aol.com

Chapman Foods, 57 Battlehill Road, Portadown, Craigavon, County Armagh, BT62 4ES Tel: (028) 3887 1225 Fax: (028) 3887 0088

Charmouth Village Bakery Ltd, Barrs Lane, Charmouth, Bridport, Dorset, DT6 6PS Tel: (01297) 560213

Chaucer Foods, Uppermoor Road, Allenton, Derby, DE24 9BY Tel: (01332) 362311 Fax: (01332) 295387 E-mail: derby@chaucerfoods.com

▶ City Bakers Ltd, 111 Dundas Spur, Portsmouth, PO3 5NX Tel: (023) 9263 9800

▶ Craft Bakers, 4 Empress Road, Newcastle upon Tyne, NE6 3NW Tel: 0191-234 2754 Fax: 0191-234 2764 E-mail: sales@craftbakery.co.uk

Culloden Foods Ltd, Smithton Industrial Estate, Smithton, Inverness, IV2 7WL Tel: (01463) 792421 Fax: (01463) 794939

Daveys Bakery & Confectionery Supplies, 1-2 Westside Centre, London Road, Stanway, Colchester, CO3 8PH Tel: (01206) 213333 Fax: (01206) 213335

Dawn Foods Ltd, Worcester Road, Evesham, Worcestershire, WR11 4QU Tel: (01386) 760800 Fax: (01386) 443608 E-mail: uk@dawnfoods.com

Delice De France plc, Opal Way, Stone Business Park, Stone, Staffordshire, ST15 0SS Tel: (01785) 811200 Fax: (01785) 812233

Devonshire Coffee Shop, 68 Spring Gardens, Buxton, Derbyshire, SK17 6BZ Tel: (01298) 23405 Fax: 01298 25551

Doughty Cakes, 3 Greetwell Hollow, Crofton Drive, Lincoln, LN3 4NR Tel: (01522) 543434 Fax: (01522) 543434 E-mail: doughtycakes@btconnect.com

▶ Druckers Vienna Patisserie, 100 Great Western Arcade, Birmingham, B2 5HU Tel: 0121-236 6292 Fax: 0121-236 6292

Edme Ltd, Edme House, High Street, Mistley, Manningtree, Essex, CO11 1HG Tel: (01206) 393725 Fax: (01206) 396699 E-mail: info@edme.com

Fermex International Ltd, Unit E3 Blackpole Trading Estate East, Blackpole Road, Worcester, WR3 8SG Tel: (01905) 755811 Fax: (01905) 754145 E-mail: info@fermex.co.uk

Fleming Howden Ltd, Whitemyres Avenue, Masterick Industrial Estate, Aberdeen, AB16 6HQ Tel: (01224) 692897 Fax: (01224) 683931

Fleming Howden, Unit 2, Newbridge Industrial Estate, Newbridge, Midlothian, EH28 8PJ Tel: 0131-333 6666 Fax: 0131-333 6633

Flynn's Bread Supplies, The Warehouse, Paradise Rd, Downham Market, Norfolk, PE38 9JE Tel: 01366 386511

Fox's Biscuits, Dove Valley Bakeries, Cheadle Road, Uttoxeter, Staffordshire, ST14 7BT Tel: (01889) 563131 Fax: (01889) 565379 E-mail: sales@elkes-biscuits.co.uk

G B Supplies, Unit 1 Modern House, Summer Lane, Barnsley, South Yorkshire, S70 2NP Tel: (01226) 288008 Fax: (01226) 285565

Garlands Crusty Connection, The Market Hall, High Town, Hereford, HR1 2AA Tel: (01432) 275080

GB Ingredients Ltd, The Heath Business & Technical Park, Runcorn, Cheshire, WA7 4QX Tel: (01928) 511111 Fax: (01928) 515115

▶ Greenfern Bakery Ltd, 13 Greenfern Road, Aberdeen, AB16 5PY Tel: (01224) 691335 Fax: (01224) 691881

Harries Bakery, 37 Heol Cae Gurwen, Gwaun Cae Gurwen, Ammanford, Dyfed, SA18 1HG Tel: (01269) 823268 Fax: (01269) 823268

Harvey's Sandwich & Espresso Bar, 73-75 Nantwich Road, Crewe, CW2 6AW Tel: (01270) 255255 Fax: (01270) 255602 E-mail: harveyssandwiches@btconnet.co.uk

Hero UK LLP, Bishop Dyke Road, Sherburn In Elmet, Leeds, LS25 6JA Tel: (01977) 684937 Fax: (01977) 683654 E-mail: info@supercook.co.uk

Irwin's Bakery, 5 Diviny Drive, Portadown, Craigavon, County Armagh, BT63 5WE Tel: (028) 3833 2421 Fax: (028) 3833 3918 E-mail: sales@irwinsbakery.com

J.Barton & Co.(Food Distributors)Limited, J B House, Gower Street, Farnworth, Bolton, BL4 7EY Tel: (01204) 862773 Fax: (01204) 701734

John Dwyer, 5 Arches Business Centre, Mill Road, Rugby, Warwickshire, CV21 1QW Tel: (01788) 536332 Fax: (01788) 546313

Joseph Thoueiri, 30 Shrewsbury Walk, Isleworth, Middlesex, TW7 7DE Tel: (020) 8560 6945

▶ Just Desserts & Pastries, Unit 5b 193-205 Mayfair Business Centre, Garvaghy Road, Portadown, Craigavon, County Armagh, BT62 1HA Tel: (028) 3835 1593

▶ Keemac Bakery, 2 Block 5, Whiteside Industrial Estate, Bathgate, West Lothian, EH48 2RX Tel: (01506) 655303 Fax: (01506) 655303

Kluman & Balter Ltd, 8 The I O Centre Waltham Cross, New Ford Road, Waltham Cross, Hertfordshire, EN8 7PG Tel: (01992) 704000 Fax: (01992) 768171 E-mail: customerservice@kaybeefoods.com

▶ M & L Foods, 5 First Avenue, Halstead, Essex, CO9 2EX Tel: (01787) 472048 Fax: (01787) 474110

Macphie of Glenbervie Ltd, Glenbervie, Stonehaven, Kincardineshire, AB39 3YG Tel: (01569) 740641 Fax: (01569) 740677 E-mail: cservice@macphie.com

▶ Manor Bakeries, Bellshill Road, Uddingston, Glasgow, G71 6NP Tel: (01698) 811738 Fax: (01698) 818783

Manor Bakeries Ltd, Brisbane Street, London, SE5 7NL Tel: (020) 7703 0291

▶ Mary Rose Bakery Ltd, 10, The Nelson Centre, 3100 Blueprint, Portsfield Road, Portsmouth, PO3 5SF Tel: (023) 9266 0385 Fax: (023) 9266 0385

F.W.P. Matthews Ltd, Station Road, Shipton-Under-Wychwood, Chipping Norton, Oxfordshire, OX7 6BH Tel: (01993) 830342 Fax: (01993) 831615

Mauri Products Ltd, Stockholm Road, Sutton Fields Industrial Estate, Hull, HU7 0XW Tel: (01482) 833133 Fax: (01482) 838460 E-mail: sue.fox@mauri.co.uk

Don Millers Hot Bread Kitchens, 36 Cornmarket, Derby, DE1 2DG Tel: (01332) 371434 Fax: (01332) 371434

▶ Millies Cookies Ltd, Maritime Way, St. Marys Island, Chatham, Kent, ME4 3ER Tel: (01634) 893450 Fax: (01634) 893450

▶ Millies Cookies Ltd, 13 The Liberty, Romford, RM1 3RL Tel: (01708) 735174 Fax: (01708) 735174

Mr Bagels Factory, 52-54 White Post Lane, London, E9 5EN Tel: (020) 8533 7553 Fax: (020) 8533 9633

Nichol & Laidlow Ltd, Bridge End Industrial Estate, Hexham, Northumberland, NE46 4DQ Tel: (01434) 600111 Fax: (01434) 600979

Palace Cuisine, 4 West End Industrial Estate, West End, Witney, Oxfordshire, OX28 1UB Tel: (01993) 702942 Fax: (01993) 702942 E-mail: palacecuisine@btconnect.com

▶ The Pantry, 105 High Street, Ilfracombe, Devon, EX34 9NH Tel: (01271) 862031

▶ Percy Ingles Bakery Ltd, The Pavilion, High Street, Waltham Cross, Hertfordshire, EN8 7BZ Tel: (01992) 767403

Pocklingtons Bakery Ltd, Sunnyhome, Main Road, Withern, Alford, Lincolnshire, LN13 0LD Tel: (01507) 450222 Fax: (01507) 450781

Puratos Ltd, Buckingham Industrial Estate, Buckingham, MK18 1XT Tel: (01280) 822860 Fax: (01280) 822857 E-mail: info_uk@puratos.com

Quigleys Bakery, 31-33 Grangeway, Runcorn, Cheshire, WA7 5LY Tel: (01928) 568244

Raffles Of Portsmouth, 1 Mitchell Way, Portsmouth, PO3 5PY Tel: (023) 9265 3000 Fax: (023) 9265 1770

Randal Home Bakery, 58 Main Street, Randalstown, Antrim, BT41 3BB Tel: (028) 9447 9944

▶ Rutherfords, 3 Freetown Business Park, Hudcar Lane, Bury, Lancashire, BL9 6HD Tel: 0161-797 6952 E-mail: info@rutherfordsca.co.uk

A.E. Shepherd, 108 Snakes Lane East, Woodford Green, Essex, IG8 7HY Tel: (020) 8504 1759 Fax: (020) 8504 1759

▶ Simmons Bakers Ltd, 1 Piggottshill Lane, Harpenden, Hertfordshire, AL5 1LG Tel: (01582) 713353 Fax: (01707) 274329

▶ Smithys Bakery, Unit 3, The George Shopping Centre, Crewkerne, Somerset, TA18 7LU Tel: (01460) 77962

Snackcakes, Unit X2, Herald Way, Binley Ind Est, Coventry, CV3 2RZ Tel: 024 76651991 Fax: 024 76651306

Standeven & Mathers Ltd, 49a Westfield Road, Leeds, LS3 1DF Tel: 0113-245 4578 Fax: 0113-245 4580

▶ Stevensons, 26 Barony Road, Auchinleck, Cumnock, Ayrshire, KA18 2LL Tel: (01290) 426009 Fax: (01290) 425988

Teviotdale Bakery, 369 South Road, Dundee, DD2 2RT Tel: (01382) 622361 Fax: (01382) 622076 E-mail: sales@teviotdale-bakery.co.uk

▶ Warburtons Ltd, Unit An Badentoy CR, Portlethen, Aberdeen, AB12 4YD Tel: (01224) 780808 Fax: (01224) 780808

Warburtons (Fylde) Ltd, 21 Caunce Street, Blackpool, FY1 3LA Tel: (01253) 407700 Fax: (01253) 27046

Zeelandia Holdings UK Ltd, Unit 4 Radford Way, Billericay, Essex, CM12 0DX Tel: (01277) 651966 Fax: (01277) 630074 E-mail: info@zeelandia.co.uk

BAKERS, WHOLESALE MANUFACTURING

A J Rowe Bakers, 46 Haybridge Road, Hadley, Telford, Shropshire, TF1 6LT Tel: (01952) 242029 Fax: (01952) 242029

Adamson J.F Bakers Confectioners, 29 High Street, Pittenweem, Anstruther, Fife, KY10 2LA Tel: (01333) 311336

Afton Bakery, 26 Afton Bridgend, New Cumnock, Cumnock, Ayrshire, KA18 4AU Tel: (01290) 332519

Alex R Ross & Son, 44 Chapel Street, Aberdeen, AB10 1SP Tel: (01224) 643527 Fax: (01224) 643527

Allied Bakeries Ltd, 64-66 Orby Road, Belfast, BT5 5HP Tel: (028) 9070 6160 Fax: (028) 9079 3411 E-mail: info@allliedbakeries.co.uk

Allied Bakeries Ltd, 2 Kingsway, Team Valley Trading Estate, Gateshead, Tyne & Wear, NE11 0LT Tel: 0191-491 0077 Fax: 0191-491 0953

Allied Bakeries Ltd, 1 Kingsmill Place, Vanwall Business Park, Maidenhead, Berkshire, SL6 4UF Tel: (01628) 764300 Fax: (01628) 764390 E-mail: information@alliedbakeries.co.uk

Allied Bakeries Ltd, Birmingham Road, West Bromwich, West Midlands, B71 4JH Tel: 0121-553 2988 Fax: 0121-553 3462

Allied Bakeries Walthamstow, Argall Avenue, Leyton, London, E10 7AB Tel: (020) 8556 1031 Fax: (020) 8558 6636 E-mail: subhirdey@alliedbakeries.com

Aston's Bakery, Longpark, Newton Road, Torquay, TQ2 7AL Tel: (01803) 614811

Aulds Delicious Desserts, Inchinnan Industrial Estate, 1 Barnsford Avenue, Renfrew, PA4 9RZ Tel: 0141-812 1126 Fax: 0141-812 1127 E-mail: deliciousdesserts@aulds.co.uk

Avana Bakeries Ltd, Wern Trading Estate, Rogerstone, Newport, Gwent, NP10 9YB Tel: (01633) 466400 Fax: (01633) 466466 E-mail: avanareception@rhm.com

The Bakery, Manor Gardens, Farmborough, Bath, BA2 0AS Tel: (01761) 470598 Fax: (01761) 479072E-mail: info@thebakeryrestaurant.com

Bankhead Bakery, 8 Wallace Street, Rutherglen, Glasgow, G73 2SA Tel: 0141-613 0405 Fax: 0141-613 0405 E-mail: akelly@bankheadbakery.fsnet.co.uk

Bap Factory, 2 Fitzroy Street, Cardiff, CF24 4BL Tel: (029) 2022 5255

Benita's Bread Shop, Market Place, Louth, Lincolnshire, LN11 9NR Tel: (01507) 600180 Fax: (01507) 450781

Blackfriars Bakery, 185 Gloucester Crescent, Wigston, Leicestershire, LE18 4YH Tel: 0116-278 6029 Fax: 0116-278 5348 E-mail: bfriars@blackfriarsbakery.co.uk

Bonnett's (Bakers) Ltd, 103 High Street, Somersham, Huntingdon, Cambridgeshire, PE28 3EH Tel: (01487) 840243 Fax: (01487) 740397

Elizabeth Botham & Sons, 35-39 Skinner Street, Whitby, North Yorkshire, YO21 3AH Tel: (01947) 602823 Fax: (01947) 820269

Brace Bakery Ltd, Cambrian House, Croespenmaen Industrial Estate, Kendon, Crumlin, Newport, Gwent, NP11 3AG Tel: (01495) 241400 Fax: (01495) 241441

Bread Bin, 3 Hay Street, Sunderland, SR5 1BG Tel: 0191-514 3933

The Bread Roll Company, Lyon Way, St Albans, St. Albans, Hertfordshire, AL4 0LQ Tel: (0845) 6070324 Fax: (01727) 818009 E-mail: info@breadroll.co.uk

British Bakeries Ltd, Gain Lane, Bradford, West Yorkshire, BD3 7DX Tel: (01274) 665211 Fax: (01274) 663895 E-mail: info@britishbakeries.co.uk

British Bakeries Ltd, Chaucer Road, London, E7 9NA Tel: (020) 8472 9881 Fax: (020) 8548 0842

British Bakeries Ltd, Main Road, Watnall, Nottingham, NG16 1HB Tel: 0115-938 3391 Fax: 0115-945 8274

British Bakeries Ltd, PO Box 527, Windsor, Berkshire, SL4 3HD Tel: (0870) 7288888 Fax: (01753) 791739

British Bakers, Avonmouth Way, Bristol, BS11 8DQ Tel: 0117-988 3900 Fax: 0117-988 3962 E-mail: admin@britishbakeries.co.uk

C A Bengry Ltd, Spring Road, Stoke-on-Trent, ST3 4PX Tel: (01782) 313405 Fax: (01782) 596633

Chalmers Bakery Ltd, 13-15 Auchmill Road, Bucksburn, Aberdeen, AB21 9LB Tel: (01224) 712631 Fax: (01224) 712464

Chapel Bakers, 384a Katherine Street, Ashton-under-Lyne, Lancashire, OL7 0AL Tel: 0161-330 6745 Fax: 0161-330 6745

Cornish Pasty Bakery, 54 Boar Lane, Leeds, LS1 5EL Tel: 0113-242 0121 Fax: 0113-242 0121

Cotswold Handmade Meringues, Newmarket, Nailsworth, Stroud, Gloucestershire, GL6 0RF Tel: (01453) 836611 Fax: (01453) 836622 E-mail: sales@meringues.co.uk

Country Bake House Dorset, Unit 2 Ambassador Trade Park, Five Bridges, West Stour, Gillingham, Dorset, SP8 5SE Tel: (01747) 838877 Fax: (01747) 838876

Daniel J Morgan & Son, Merydd Bakery, Llandissilio, Clynderwen, Dyfed, SA66 7TG Tel: (01437) 563297

Islwyn Davies, 120 Glynhir Road, Pontarddulais, Swansea, SA4 8PY Tel: (01792) 883149

BAKERS, WHOLESALE MANUFACTURING – *continued*

Dawn Foods Ltd, Worcester Road, Evesham, Worcestershire, WR11 4QU Tel: (01386) 760800 Fax: (01386) 443608 E-mail: uk@dawnfoods.com

Devonvale Ltd, 2 Duchy Road, Heathpark Industrial Estate, Honiton, Devon, EX14 1YD Tel: (01404) 549980 Fax: (01404) 549981 E-mail: enquiries@devonvale.com

Dickinson & Morris, P O Box 580, Leicester, LE4 1ZN Tel: 0116-235 5900 Fax: 0116-235 5711

Donaldsons Of St Andrews Ltd, 21 Crossgate, Cupar, Fife, KY15 5HA Tel: (01334) 656433 Fax: (01334) 653729

Dream Loaf Hot Bread Kitchen Ltd, 39A Market Place, Swaffham, Norfolk, PE37 7LA Tel: (01760) 722707 Fax: (01760) 725539

Druckers Vienna Patisserie, 940a Stratford Road, Sparkhill, Birmingham, B11 4BU Tel: 0121-777 3427 Fax: 0121-777 3427

E Mckinney, 154 Ballycastle Road, Coleraine, County Londonderry, BT52 2EH Tel: (028) 7034 3927

Eurobuns Holdings Ltd, 80 South Audley Street, London, W1K 1JH Tel: (020) 7491 9002 Fax: (020) 7491 9005

F A S Products, Unit 140 142 Block 15, Newhouse Industrial Estate, Newhouse, Motherwell, Lanarkshire, ML1 5RX Tel: (01698) 833780 Fax: (01698) 831300

Fedwen Bakery, Teifi Mill, Pontwelly, Llandysul, Dyfed, SA44 4AJ Tel: (01559) 362375 Fax: (01559) 363402

Fletchers Bakeries Ltd, Claywheels Lane, Sheffield, S6 1LY Tel: 0114-234 8171 Fax: 0114-232 4987 E-mail: enquiries@fletchers.co.uk

James Ford & Son, 5 Hide Hill, Berwick-upon-Tweed, TD15 1EQ Tel: (01289) 306081 Fax: (01289) 306081

James Ford & Son, 11 West Street, Norham, Berwick-upon-Tweed, TD15 2LB Tel: (01289) 382248 Fax: (01289) 382248

The Forrest, 24 The Square, Portsoy, Banff, AB45 2NX Tel: (01261) 842320 Fax: (01261) 843921 E-mail: info@forrestthebaker.co.uk

Fox's Biscuits, Dove Valley Bakeries, Cheadle Road, Uttoxeter, Staffordshire, ST14 7BT Tel: (01889) 563131 Fax: (01889) 565379 E-mail: sales@elkes-biscuits.co.uk

Freshbake Wholesale Bakery, 9 Malcolm Place, London, E2 0EU Tel: (020) 8983 4045 Fax: (020) 8880 6696

Friary Mill, Oakfield Place, Plymouth, PL4 0QA Tel: (01752) 255113 Fax: (01752) 662946

Greenhalgh's Craft Bakery Ltd, Bee Hive Industrial Estate, Crescent Road, Lostock, Bolton, BL6 4BU Tel: (01204) 696204 Fax: (01204) 669061 E-mail: info@greenhalghs.com

Greggs plc, 36 Dryden Road, Loanhead, Midlothian, EH20 9LZ Tel: 0131-440 4852 Fax: 0131-440 9918 E-mail: info@greggs.co.uk

H & J Moore, 3 Nelson Road, Fakenham, Norfolk, NR21 9EN Tel: (01328) 862088

Hannahs Pies Of Ormskirk, Bridge Street, Ormskirk, Lancashire, L39 4RJ Tel: (01695) 578385 Fax: (01695) 578385

J. Hardacre Ltd, Gannow Lane, Burnley, Lancashire, BB12 6JX Tel: (01282) 415155 Fax: (01282) 457904

Hardings Bakery, Oldlands, Alphington Street, Exeter, EX2 8AU Tel: (01392) 255062

Hindleys Bakeries, Wharf Road, Rugeley, Staffordshire, WS15 1BL Tel: (01889) 583161 Fax: (01889) 583846

Iles Bros, Blackwood Rd, Blackwood, Gwent, NP12 2BW Tel: 01495 223400

Interlink Food, Shadsworth Bakery, Sett End Road, Shadsworth Business Park, Blackburn, BB1 2PT Tel: (01254) 55495 Fax: (01254) 663602 E-mail: sales@interlinkfoods.co.uk

Irwin's Bakery, 5 Diviny Drive, Portadown, Craigavon, County Armagh, BT63 5WE Tel: (028) 3833 2421 Fax: (028) 3833 3918 E-mail: sales@irwinsbakery.com

J B Christie, Flowerhill Industrial Estate, Airdrie, Lanarkshire, ML6 6BH Tel: (01236) 761437 Fax: (01236) 770249

J G Ross Bakers Ltd, Costcutter, Elphinstone Road, Port Elphinstone, Inverurie, Aberdeenshire, AB51 3UR Tel: (01467) 620764 Fax: (01467) 623416 E-mail: info@jg-ross-bakers.co.uk

William Jackson & Son Ltd, 40 Derringham Street, Hull, HU3 1EW Tel: (01482) 224939 Fax: (01482) 588237 E-mail: sales@wjs.co.uk

Jacksons The Baker Ltd, New Hall Road, Chesterfield, Derbyshire, S40 1HE Tel: (01246) 274165 Fax: (01246) 200908 E-mail: jacksonsbakeries@hotmail.co.uk

John Bryson Keswick Ltd, 38-42 Main Street, Keswick, Cumbria, CA12 5JD Tel: (01768) 772257 Fax: (01768) 775456

Knicat Ltd, 64 Railway Road, Downham Market, Norfolk, PE38 9EL Tel: (01366) 383708

Knowlsons Of Blackpool, 20 Boome Street, Blackpool, FY4 2JX Tel: (01253) 406555 Fax: (01253) 406606

Krusty Loaf, Bakery, 2 Crescent Road, Hunstanton, Norfolk, PE36 5BU Tel: (01485) 533457

▶ L F Dangerfield Ltd, Church Street, Kings Stanley, Stonehouse, Gloucestershire, GL10 3HT Tel: (01453) 822540 Fax: (01453) 828277

La Baguette, 17 Picardy Street, Belvedere, Kent, DA17 5QQ Tel: (020) 8311 1113 Fax: (020) 8310 5179

La Rondine, 12 Queen Street, Bedford, MK40 2HA Tel: (01234) 400990 Fax: (01234) 219443

Le Pain De Paris, Unit 1/2 Off Mill Yard, Kendal, Cumbria, LA9 4QR Tel: (01539) 822102 Fax: (01539) 822420

Lees Of Scotland Ltd, North Caldeen Road, Coatbridge, Lanarkshire, ML5 4EF Tel: (01236) 441600 Fax: (01236) 441601 E-mail: sales@leesofscotland.co.uk

London Bread & Cake Co., Angel Road Works, Advent Way, London, N18 3AH Tel: (020) 8807 6773 Fax: (020) 8803 5229 E-mail: sales@londonbread.com

Mckay's Bakery, 9 High Street, Brechin, Angus, DD9 6ES Tel: (01356) 623664 Fax: (01356) 623061

Maclean's Bakery Benbecula Ltd, Maclean Bakery, Uachdar, Isle of Benbecula, HS7 5LY Tel: (01870) 602659 Fax: (01870) 603121 E-mail: macleansbakery@tiscali.co.uk

Maws Pies, 7 St. Lukes Terrace, Pallion, Sunderland, SR4 6NQ Tel: 0191-510 0822

Millies Cookies Ltd, Unit 32 The Merry Hill Centre, Brierley Hill, West Midlands, DY5 1SY Tel: (01384) 480864

Montana Bakery Ltd, Blackthorne Road, Colnbrook, Slough, SL3 0AP Tel: (01753) 760800 Fax: (01753) 760801

Morgan Bros, 95 Bethesda Road, Tumble, Llanelli, Dyfed, SA14 6LL Tel: (01269) 841576 Fax: (01269) 841576

Mubarak Food Co., 292 Leeds Road, Bradford, West Yorkshire, BD3 9QX Tel: (01274) 731754 Fax: (01274) 726161

Nash's Bakery, 63 Priory Road, Bicester, Oxfordshire, OX26 6BL Tel: (01869) 244647 Fax: (01869) 244844 E-mail: info@theoxfordbakery.com

New Crown Bakery Ltd, Callow Hill, Rock, Kidderminster, Worcestershire, DY14 9XD Tel: (01299) 266211 Fax: (01299) 266013

Oliver Adams Ltd, 262 Hillmorton Road, Rugby, Warwickshire, CV22 5BW Tel: (01788) 541104

Omonia Continental Patisserie, 129 High Cross Road, London, N17 9NU Tel: (020) 8801 1182 Fax: (020) 8801 1182

Park Cakes Bakeries Ltd, Ashton Road, Oldham, OL8 2ND Tel: 0161-633 1181 Fax: 0161-626 6199

Park Pantry, Longstone Business Park, Great Longstone, Bakewell, Derbyshire, DE45 1TD Tel: (01629) 640264 Fax: (01629) 640264 E-mail: parkpantry@btinternet.com

Peartree Pantry, Peartree Farm, Spring Lane, Hatfield Peverel, Chelmsford, CM3 2JW Tel: (01245) 381461

Peterborough Continental Bakery, 34a Towler Street, Peterborough, PE1 2TX Tel: (01733) 567075 Fax: (01733) 567654

Pie Cuisine, 5 Wemyss Road, Dysart, Kirkcaldy, Fife, KY1 2XZ Tel: (01592) 650555 Fax: (01592) 655654

▶ Prima Foods, Wheal Rose Bakery, Wheal Rose, Scorrier, Redruth, Cornwall, TR16 5BX Tel: (01209) 820321 Fax: (01209) 820402 E-mail: enquiries@primabakeries.co.uk

Provender Bakers' Shops, 103 Dartmouth Road, London, SE23 3HT Tel: (020) 8699 4046

Rachel's Bakery, Unit B2 South Point, Foreshore Road, Cardiff, CF10 4SP Tel: (029) 2045 6596

Rathbones, Durranhill Trading Estate, Brunel Way, Carlisle, CA1 3NH Tel: (01228) 527541 Fax: (01228) 515195 E-mail: bakery@robertsonsltd.freeserve.co.uk

Rayners Bakery Ltd, 12a Deer Park Road, London, SW19 3UQ Tel: (020) 8543 6695 Fax: (020) 8545 0736 E-mail: rayners@raynersgroup.fsnet.co.uk

Ree Distribution, Unit N Main Line Industrial Estate, Crooklands Road, Ackenthwaite, Milnthorpe, Cumbria, LA7 7LR Tel: (01539) 565477 Fax: (01539) 565466

Alex Robertson, 63 High Street, Edzell, Brechin, Angus, DD9 7TA Tel: (01356) 648285

Robertsons Home Bakery, 32 Colebrooke Road, Fivemiletown, County Tyrone, BT75 0QG Tel: (028) 8952 1077 Fax: (028) 8952 1077

Rothbury Home Bakery Ltd, Coquet View, Rothbury, Morpeth, Northumberland, NE65 7RZ Tel: (01669) 621273 Fax: (0870) 4581779 E-mail: sales@rothburybakery.com

St George's Bakery, Worcester Road, Corse, Gloucester, GL19 3BZ Tel: (01452) 700234 Fax: (01452) 700562

Seeds Bakery Health Store, 35 High Street, Totnes, Devon, TQ9 5NP Tel: (01803) 862526

Richard Sharrock & Sons, Allied Bakeries, Ashton Road, Bredbury, Stockport, Cheshire, SK6 2RE Tel: 0161-430 5151 Fax: 0161-406 3117

Shazminf Pies Manufacturers, 12 Gopsall Street, Leicester, LE2 0DL Tel: 0116-253 0058 Fax: 0116-212 3343

Sheldons Bakery Farnborough Ltd, 31 Queens Road, Farnborough, Hampshire, GU14 6DU Tel: (01252) 377577 Fax: (01252) 378262

Shirehampton Village Bakery, 7 High Street, Shirehampton, Bristol, BS11 0DT Tel: 0117-907 0076 Fax: 0117-907 0076

Siwgr A Sbeis Bakery, Parc Ty Gwyn, Betws Road, Nant y Rhiw, Llanrwst, Gwynedd, LL26 0PQ Tel: (01492) 641940

Soreen Ltd, Taylor Road, Urmston, Manchester, M41 7WS Tel: 0161-748 1235 Fax: 0161-746 7067

Southams Of Haworth, 202 Long Lee Lane, Keighley, West Yorkshire, BD21 4TT Tel: (01535) 603491 Fax: (01535) 647255

▶ Speciality Breads By FDC, Unit J2 Westwood Industrial Estate, Margate, Kent, CT9 4JS Tel: (01843) 209442 Fax: (01843) 231378 E-mail: sales@specialitybreads.co.uk

Sterchi's Cake Shop, 40 Murray Street, Filey, North Yorkshire, YO14 9DG Tel: (01723) 513120 E-mail: admin@sterchis.co.uk

Susan's Bakery, 6a Henry Wells Square, Hemel Hempstead, Hertfordshire, HP2 6BJ Tel: (01442) 245400 Fax: (01442) 245400

Taylor & Woodland Ltd, 5 Tree Works, Bakers Lane, West Hanningfield, Chelmsford, CM2 8LD Tel: (01277) 841792 Fax: (01277) 841793

Thain's Bakery, 341 George Street, Aberdeen, AB25 1EE Tel: (01224) 638698 Fax: (01244) 627102

W H Gayton, Gaytons Bakery, Maypole Lane, Grendon, Atherstone, Warwickshire, CV9 2BS Tel: (01827) 712538 Fax: (01827) 713340

W M Stephen Bakers Ltd, 20 Duncan Cresent, Dunfermline, Fife, KY11 4BT Tel: (01383) 626637

W Thatcher, Borron Street, Stockport, Cheshire, SK1 2JD Tel: 0161-480 3438 Fax: 0161-476 5361

Warburtons Ltd, Sholto Cresent, Righead Industrial Estate, Bellshill, Lanarkshire, ML4 3LX Tel: (01698) 741066 Fax: (01698) 741015

▶ Warburtons Ltd, 3 Christleton Court, Manor Park, Runcorn, Cheshire, WA7 1ST Tel: (01928) 579088 Fax: (01928) 579089

Woodruffs Bakery Buffet Service, 4 Deacon Road, Southampton, SO19 7PZ Tel: (023) 8044 8124

BAKERY CONVEYOR SYSTEMS

Ferguson Engineering Northern Ltd, 2 Coulton Road, Brierfield, Nelson, Lancashire, BB9 5ST Tel: (01282) 447500 Fax: (01282) 447600 E-mail: sales@f-e-n.com

BAKERY COUNTERS

British Bakeries Ltd, Toynbee Road, Eastleigh, Hampshire, SO50 9YU Tel: (0870) 7288888 Fax: (023) 8064 1612

C Holland & Sons Ltd, 71 Whitecroft Road, Meldreth, Royston, Hertfordshire, SG8 6LS Tel: (01763) 261873 Fax: (01763) 262764 E-mail: robert@holland&son.u-net.com

Glendon Products Ltd, 5 St. James Road, St. James Industrial Estate, Corby, Northamptonshire, NN18 8AL Tel: (01536) 403010 Fax: (01536) 266629 E-mail: info@glendonproducts.com

Sweetmans Retail Ltd, 59 Herbert Street, Pontardawe, Swansea, SA8 4ED Tel: (01792) 869552 Fax: (01792) 869552

BAKERY ENGINEERS, INSTALLATION OR SERVICE

Acrivarn Ltd, South Park Mills, Hare Lane, Pudsey, West Yorkshire, LS28 8DR Tel: 0113-257 8875 Fax: 0113-257 7564 E-mail: sales@acrivarn.co.uk

Belmont Bakery Machinery, Slater Lane, Watermead Works, Bolton, BL1 2TE Tel: (01204) 370743 Fax: (01204) 399355 E-mail: sales@bakerymachinery.co.uk

BRS, 8 Expodite Works, Stuart Road, Bredbury, Stockport, Cheshire, SK6 2SR Tel: 0161-430 8380 Fax: 0161-406 6634

Daly Catering & Bakery Maintenance, Unit 4 Lennox Industrial Mall, Lennox Road, Basingstoke, Hampshire, RG22 4AP Tel: (01256) 364500 Fax: (01256) 814069 E-mail: sarah.daly@daly-electrical.co.uk

Eurobake Ltd, Bee Hive Industrial Estate, Crescent Road, Lostock, Bolton, BL6 4BU Tel: (01204) 669980 Fax: (01204) 696665 E-mail: sales@eurobake.co.uk

European Process Plant Ltd, Epsom Business Park, Epsom, Surrey, KT17 1JF Tel: (01372) 745558 Fax: (01372) 745097 E-mail: sales@eppltd.co.uk

Ferguson Engineering Northern Ltd, 2 Coulton Road, Brierfield, Nelson, Lancashire, BB9 5ST Tel: (01282) 447500 Fax: (01282) 447600 E-mail: sales@f-e-n.com

Johnson & Wood, Lower Voe, Voe, Shetland, ZE2 9PX Tel: (01806) 588245 Fax: (01806) 588245

Modern Baking Systems Bristol Ltd, 26 Clothier Road, Bristol, BS4 5PS Tel: 0117-977 9494 Fax: 0117-971 9926

Wheatsheaf Technical Ltd, 3 Haycliffe Avenue, Off Moore Avenue, Bradford, West Yorkshire, BD7 4HY Tel: (01274) 577789 Fax: (0870) 912 8057 E-mail: t.rijneveld@xs4all.nl

BAKERY EQUIPMENT COATING SERVICES

Product Release Europe Ltd, Cusson Road, Knowsley Industrial Park, Liverpool, L33 7BY Tel: 0151-549 1491 Fax: 0151-548 4035

Slater Eyre, 105 Eastgate, Louth, Lincs, LN11 9QE Tel: 01507 603823 Fax: 01507 603 823

BAKERY OVENS

Tom Chandley Ltd, Windmill La Industrial Estate, Denton, Manchester, M34 3RB Tel: 0161-337 3700 Fax: 0161-335 0972 E-mail: info@chandleyovens.co.uk

Double D Bakery Engineering Ltd, 6 Simpson Road, East Mains Industrial Estate, Broxburn, West Lothian, EH52 5NP Tel: (01506) 857112 Fax: (01506) 852232 E-mail: sales@double-d.co.uk

Eurobake Ltd, Bee Hive Industrial Estate, Crescent Road, Lostock, Bolton, BL6 4BU Tel: (01204) 669980 Fax: (01204) 696665 E-mail: sales@eurobake.co.uk

Euromix UK Ltd, 56 Alexandra Road, Enfield, Middlesex, EN3 7EH Tel: (020) 8805 8224 Fax: (020) 8805 8228 E-mail: mail@euromixltd.co.uk

European Process Plant Ltd, Epsom Business Park, Epsom, Surrey, KT17 1JF Tel: (01372) 745558 Fax: (01372) 745097 E-mail: sales@eppltd.co.uk

BAKERY PLANT AND EQUIPMENT MANUFRS

Acrivarn Ltd, South Park Mills, Hare Lane, Pudsey, West Yorkshire, LS28 8DR Tel: 0113-257 8875 Fax: 0113-257 7564 E-mail: sales@acrivarn.co.uk

Atlas Food Processing Systems Ltd, Imperial House, 64 Willoughby Lane, London, N17 0SP Tel: (020) 8885 7200 Fax: (020) 8885 7219 E-mail: info@atlasfps.com

Bagfast Ltd, Unit 2, Morris Court, Colwick Industrial Estate, Nottingham, NG4 2JN Tel: 0115-940 1658 Fax: 0115-961 1714 E-mail: sales@bagfast.com

Benier (UK) Ltd, 56 Alston Drive, Bradwell Abbey, Milton Keynes, MK13 9HB Tel: (01908) 312333 Fax: (01908) 311481 E-mail: sales@benier.co.uk

Bowers Systems Ltd, 293 Wallisdown Road, Poole, Dorset, BH12 5BT Tel: (01202) 512790 Fax: (01202) 524663

Bringate Sheet Metals, Cross Green Industrial Estate, Cross Green, Leeds, LS9 0SG Tel: 0113-240 7711 Fax: 0113-240 7722 E-mail: sales@bringate.co.uk

D G C Engineering UK Ltd, Unit 7 Building 6, Stanmore Industrial Estate, Bridgnorth, Shropshire, WV15 5HP Tel: (01746) 767133 Fax: (01746) 767133

Dexmore Co Ltd, Hartshill Road, Stoke-on-Trent, ST4 7NF Tel: (01782) 846376 Fax: (01782) 414769 E-mail: sales@dexmore.co.uk

Eurobake Ltd, Bee Hive Industrial Estate, Crescent Road, Lostock, Bolton, BL6 4BU Tel: (01204) 669980 Fax: (01204) 696665 E-mail: sales@eurobake.co.uk

Euromix UK Ltd, 56 Alexandra Road, Enfield, Middlesex, EN3 7EH Tel: (020) 8805 8224 Fax: (020) 8805 8228 E-mail: mail@euromixltd.co.uk

European Process Plant Ltd, Epsom Business Park, Epsom, Surrey, KT17 1JF Tel: (01372) 745558 Fax: (01372) 745097 E-mail: sales@eppltd.co.uk

Fish In Crewe Engineering Ltd, 14 Gateway, Crewe, CW1 6YY Tel: (01270) 251200 Fax: (01270) 251300 E-mail: sales@fishincrewe.co.uk

Paul Guy & Co. Ltd, Unit 10, The Busiiness Centre, Corinium Industrial Estate, Raans Road, Amersham, Buckinghamshire, HP6 6FB Tel: (01494) 432121 Fax: (01494) 432727 E-mail: guypauluk@aol.com

▶ J B S Master Baker Ltd, Stirling Way, Northfields Industrial Estate, Peterborough, PE6 8LG Tel: (01778) 346168 Fax: (01778) 341918 E-mail: jbs@jbs-engineering.co.uk

Kilmore Agencies, 8 Keadybeg Road, Mountnorris, Armagh, BT60 2UQ Tel: (028) 3750 7440 Fax: (028) 3750 7294

Modern Baking Systems Bristol Ltd, 26 Clothier Road, Bristol, BS4 5PS Tel: 0117-977 9494 Fax: 0117-971 9926

Mono Equipment, Queensway, Swansea West Industrial Park, Swansea, SA5 4EB Tel: (01792) 561234 Fax: (01792) 561016 E-mail: sales@monoequip.com

Omega Bakery Equipment Ltd, 53 Hillmorton Rd, Rugby, Warwickshire, CV22 5AE Tel: 01788 552590

Raymond Travel, 192 High Street, Dorking, Surrey, RH4 1QR Tel: (01306) 743780 Fax: (01306) 743764 E-mail: info@raymondtravel.co.uk

Speedibake Ltd, 6 Cross Lane, Bradford, West Yorkshire, BD4 0SG Tel: (0870) 8307600 Fax: (0870) 8307601

Thomas's Bakery, 84 Southgate, Elland, West Yorkshire, HX5 0EP Tel: (01422) 372335 Fax: (01422) 377798

Thornton Industries (UK) Ltd, Thornton Ho, Dock La, Shipley, W. Yorkshire, BD17 7BE Tel: (01274) 598694 Fax: (01274) 531577 E-mail: sales@tiukltd.net

Unifiller (U K) Ltd, 2 Bridge Mills Rochdale Road, Edenfield, Ramsbottom, Bury, Lancashire, BL0 0RE Tel: (01706) 828802 Fax: (01706) 829986 E-mail: sales@unifiller.com

William Waddell Ltd, 30 Russell Street, Wishaw, Lanarkshire, ML2 7AN Tel: (01698) 355034 Fax: (01698) 374970

Weiler Beehive Europe Ltd, Unit 60 Beeches Industrial Estate, Waverley Road, Yate, Bristol, BS37 5QR Tel: (01454) 320900 Fax: (01454) 326262 E-mail: sales@weilerinc.co.uk

BAKERY TEXTILES

Filter & Press Cloth Co. Ltd, 26 Town Road, Hillchurch Street, Stoke-on-Trent, ST1 2EX Tel: (01782) 281819 Fax: (01782) 281819

BAKERY TINS

Dunnetts Ltd, 170 Kings Road, Tyseley, Birmingham, B11 2AS Tel: 0121-706 9180 Fax: 0121-706 6169 E-mail: dunnetts@dunnetts.co.uk

Fluorocarbon Bakeware Systems Ltd, Unit B, Lilac Grove, Beeston, Nottingham, NG9 1PF Tel: 0115-943 1111 Fax: 0115-943 1177 E-mail: sales@fluorocarbon.co.uk

Invicta Bakeware Ltd, Westgate Business Park, Westgate Carr Road, Pickering, North Yorkshire, YO18 8LX Tel: (01751) 473483 Fax: (01751) 476522 E-mail: sales@invictabakeware.co.uk

Prestige Industrial (Pullman International), India Mill, Clarendon Road, Skew Bridge, Blackburn, BB1 9SY Tel: (01254) 53333 Fax: (01254) 690484 E-mail: sales@prestigeindustrial.co.uk

BAKERY TRAYS AND PANS

Dunnetts Ltd, 170 Kings Road, Tyseley, Birmingham, B11 2AS Tel: 0121-706 9180 Fax: 0121-706 6169 E-mail: dunnetts@dunnetts.co.uk

Edwards & Godding Reading Ltd, 9d Loverock Road, Reading, RG30 1DZ Tel: 0118-939 3046 Fax: 0118-959 0294 E-mail: aga@edgod.globalnet.co.uk

Fluorocarbon Bakeware Systems Ltd, Unit B, Lilac Grove, Beeston, Nottingham, NG9 1PF Tel: 0115-943 1111 Fax: 0115-943 1177 E-mail: sales@fluorocarbon.co.uk

Invicta Bakeware Ltd, Westgate Business Park, Westgate Carr Road, Pickering, North Yorkshire, YO18 8LX Tel: (01751) 473483 Fax: (01751) 476522 E-mail: sales@invictabakeware.co.uk

K & N Coatings Ltd, 7 Bellingham Close, Bury, Lancashire, BL8 2TU Tel: 0161-797 2909 Fax: 0161-764 2810

BAKING TRAYS

E R Burgess Macclesfield Ltd, Brunswick Works, Lowe Street, Macclesfield, Cheshire, SK11 7NJ Tel: (01625) 423735 Fax: (01625) 502025

BALANCES, *See also headings for particular types*

Halifax Scale Co., Brighouse Road, Hipperholme, Halifax, West Yorkshire, HX3 8EF Tel: (01422) 201016 Fax: (01422) 203775 E-mail: info@halifaxscale.co.uk

Ohaus UK Ltd, 64 Boston Road, Leicester, LE4 1AW Tel: 0116-234 5075 Fax: 0116-235 9256

▶ Sartorius, Longmead Business Centre, Blenheim Road, Epsom, Surrey, KT19 9QQ Tel: (01372) 737102 Fax: (01372) 729927 E-mail: info@sartorius.co.uk

BALANCING MACHINES

A 1 Dynamic Balancing Ltd, 7-9 Hagley Road, Hayley Green, Halesowen, West Midlands, B63 1DG Tel: 0121-501 3705 Fax: 0121-501 3615 E-mail: sales@wdbltd.co.uk

C F R Giesler Ltd, Empson Street, London, E3 3LT Tel: (020) 7987 2161 Fax: (020) 7515 0483 E-mail: sales@giesler.co.uk

Coborn Engineering Co. Ltd, Chesham Close, Romford, RM7 7PJ Tel: (01708) 744666 Fax: (01708) 725187 E-mail: coborneng@aol.com

BALATA BELTING

Cozens & Cole Ltd, Spring Road, Ettingshall, Wolverhampton, WV4 6JT Tel: (01902) 405971 Fax: (01902) 497021 E-mail: sales@cozensandcole.co.uk

BALCONIES

Almura Building Products, Cantay House, 62 St. Georges Place, Cheltenham, Gloucestershire, GL50 3PN Tel: (01242) 262900 Fax: (01242) 221333 E-mail: philipmarsh@almura.co.uk

BALCONY RAILINGS

▶ A & H Wrought Iron Work, 14b Smeaton Industrial Estate, Hayfield Road, Kirkcaldy, Fife, KY1 2HE Tel: (07949) 501853 E-mail: adam.guthrie@sky.com

▶ Distinctive Gates & Railings, Enterprise House, 260 Chorley New Road, Horwich, Bolton, BL6 5NY Tel: (01204) 699675 Fax: (01204) 668300 E-mail: enquiries@bendtube.co.uk

BALERS, *See also headings for particular types*

▶ Advanced Recycling Solutions Ltd, The Factory Boswithian Road, Tolvaddon, Camborne, Cornwall, TR14 0EJ Tel: (01209) 611898 Fax: (01209) 712888 E-mail: sales@ars-chs.co.uk

C K International, 38 Eglish Road, Dungannon, County Tyrone, BT70 1LA Tel: (028) 8775 3966 Fax: (028) 8772 5528 E-mail: sales@ckinternational.co.uk

Dicom Ltd, Lydford Road, Alfreton, Derbyshire, DE55 7RQ Tel: (01773) 520565 Fax: (01773) 520881 E-mail: sales@dicom.ltd.uk

M & Y Air Systems Ltd, Twickenham Trading Centre, Rugby Road, Twickenham, TW1 1DN Tel: (020) 8892 8893 Fax: (020) 8891 6175 E-mail: sales@myairsystems.fsnet.co.uk

Mil-tek (GB) Ltd, Saville Court, Saville Place, Clifton, Bristol, BS8 4EJ Tel: (0800) 0835713 Fax: 0117-973 6797 E-mail: info@miltek-uk.co.uk

Orwak Environmental Services, Orwak Ltd, 6 Bevan Way, Smethwick, West Midlands, B66 1BZ Tel: (0800) 1693534 Fax: (0121) 565 7427

Planters Clayton Ltd, Unit 6, Rivington House, Horwich Business Park, Chorley New Road, Horwich, Bolton, BL6 5UE Tel: (01204) 690003 Fax: (01204) 690170 E-mail: office@plantersclayton.com

BALL BEARING MANUFRS, *See also headings under Ball Bearings*

Acorn Industrial Services Ltd (Midlands), Units 17-21, Bloomfield Park, Bloomfield Road, Tipton, West Midlands, DY4 9AH Tel: 0121-521 5999 Fax: 0121-521 5888 E-mail: midlands@acorn-ind.co.uk

Airport Bearing Co. Ltd, 4/5 Bennerly Court, Blenheim Industrial Estate, Bulwell, Nottingham, NG6 8UT Tel: 0115-975 7571 Fax: 0115-927 3778 E-mail: sales@abco-online.co.uk

Anglia Bearing Co. Ltd, 17 Lealand Way, Boston, Lincolnshire, PE21 7SW Tel: (01205) 357200 Fax: (01205) 351663

▶ Arc Euro Trade Ltd, 10 Archdale Street, Syston, Leicester, LE7 1NA Tel: 0116-269 5693 Fax: 0116-260 5805 E-mail: information@arceurotrade.co.uk

Arrow Engineering Supply Co. Ltd, Hunters Lane Industrial Estate, Rugby, Warwickshire, CV21 1EA Tel: (01788) 574107 Fax: (01788) 542179 E-mail: frank@fasteng.co.uk

Atlas Ball & Bearing Co. Ltd, Leamore Lane, Walsall, WS2 7DE Tel: (01922) 710515 Fax: (01922) 710575 E-mail: sales@atlasball.co.uk

Ball Bearing Centre Ltd, Unit 1-55, 57 Park Royal Road, London, NW10 7JJ Tel: (020) 8965 8833 Fax: (020) 8965 7080 E-mail: ballbrgctr@btconnect.com

Bearing & Transmission Supplies Ltd, Watling House, Sutherland Street, Stoke-on-Trent, ST4 4HS Tel: (01782) 846216 Fax: (01782) 749080 E-mail: sales@btslimited.freeserve.co.uk

Carfax Bearings Ltd, 30-34 Birmingham New Road, Wolverhampton, WV4 6RY Tel: (01902) 338111 Fax: (01902) 341334 E-mail: sale@mainlinebearings.com

Central Bearings & Transmissions Ltd, 43 Padgets Lane, Redditch, Worcestershire, B98 0RD Tel: (01527) 500803 Fax: (01527) 510462 E-mail: sales@centralbearings.com

City Transair, 58 Loughborough Road, Mountsorrel, Loughborough, Leicestershire, LE12 7AT Tel: 0116-230 0070 Fax: 0116-230 0075

Commercial Bearings Ltd, Plume Street, Birmingham, B6 7RY Tel: 0121-322 2036 Fax: 0121-327 6926 E-mail: sales@commercialbearings.co.uk

D I K Bearings & Transmissions Ltd, J Hawkhill Court, Mid Wynd, Dundee, DD1 4JG Tel: (01382) 228711 Fax: (01382) 202559 E-mail: sales@dik.sol.co.uk

Danaher Motion, Fishleigh Road, Roundswell Business Park, Barnstaple, Devon, EX31 3UD Tel: (01271) 334500 Fax: (01271) 334502 E-mail: information@tiblmail.com

Denton Engineering Co. Ltd, The Bearing Shop, 194 Talbot Road, Hyde, Cheshire, SK14 4HJ Tel: 0161-368 2097 Fax: 0161-368 0881

E B Bright Engineering Sales, Unit 1 Tennis Court Industrial Estate, Nottingham, NG2 4EW Tel: 0115-950 6570 Fax: 0115-959 0921 E-mail: brightbearings@supanet.com

Fosse Bearing Units Ltd, Bearing House, 887 Melton Road, Thurmaston, Leicester, LE4 8EF Tel: 0116-260 2548 Fax: 0116-260 2548 E-mail: fosse.bearings@btinternet.com

Gamet Bearings, Hythe Station Road, Colchester, CO2 8LD Tel: (01206) 862121 Fax: (01206) 868690 E-mail: sales@gamet-bearings.co.uk

H B Bearings Ltd, Riverside Works, Honley, Huddersfield, HD9 6PQ Tel: (01484) 665116 Fax: (01484) 662619 E-mail: sales@hb-bearings.com

Healy Bearings International Ltd, 4 Earls Close Industrial Estate, Earls Close, Thurmaston, Leicester, LE4 8FZ Tel: 0116-260 0849 Fax: 0116-260 0867 E-mail: healybearings@aol.com

Henderson Bearings, Crow Arch Lane, Ringwood, Hampshire, BH24 1NZ Tel: (01425) 477787 Fax: (01425) 478883 E-mail: sales@hendersonbearings.com

Ibd Ltd, 3 City Park Industrial Estate, Gelderd Road, Leeds, LS12 6DR Tel: 0113-279 6988 Fax: 0113-231 0336 E-mail: douglas@barclays.net

Industria Engineering Products Ltd, 45 Kelvin Way, West Bromwich, West Midlands, B70 7TP Tel: 0121-525 2988 Fax: 0121-525 3607 E-mail: sales@industria.co.uk

George Lodge & Sons Ltd, P O Box 61, Hull, HU3 2DX Tel: (01482) 329553 Fax: (01482) 223317 E-mail: sales@georgelodge.co.uk

Mike Davies Bearings Ltd, Leamore Lane, Walsall, WS2 7DE Tel: (01922) 494940 Fax: (01922) 407760 E-mail: sales@mikedaviesbearings.com

N M B-Minebea (UK) Ltd, Suite 2.2, Doncastle House, Doncastle Road, Bracknell, Berkshire, RG12 8PE Tel: (01344) 426611 Fax: (01344) 485522

N S K Ltd, Northern Road, Newark, Nottinghamshire, NG24 2JF Tel: (01636) 705298 Fax: (01636) 605000 E-mail: info-uk@nsk.com

N T N Bearings UK Ltd, 11 Wellington Crescent, Fradley Park, Lichfield, Staffordshire, WS13 8RZ Tel: (01543) 445000 Fax: (01543) 445035 E-mail: jcd@ntn-europe.com

New Hampshire Ball Bearings (Europe), Suite 2.2, Doncastle House, Doncastle Road, Bracknell, Berkshire, RG12 8PE Tel: (01344) 308888 Fax: (01344) 485522

Nottingham Engineering Products, Unit 5E, The Midway, Nottingham, NG7 2TS Tel: (0115) 986 9555 Fax: (0115) 986 9666 E-mail: sales@nepltd.co.uk

Potteries Specialist Auctions, 271 Waterloo Road, Stoke-on-Trent, ST6 3HR Tel: (01782) 286622 Fax: (01782) 213777 E-mail: potteriesltd@aol.com

R A M Ltd, Unit B3 Guy Motors Industrial Park, Park Lane, Wolverhampton, WV10 9QF Tel: (01902) 863506 Fax: (01902) 728402 E-mail: r.a.m.ltd@eur-is.co.uk

Replacement & Maintenance Supplies Ltd, Dunsford Road, Meadow La Industrial Estate, Alfreton, Derbyshire, DE55 7RH Tel: (01773) 520181 Fax: (01773) 836370

S K F (U K) Ltd, Sundon Park Road, Luton, LU3 3BL Tel: (01582) 490049 Fax: (01582) 848091 E-mail: marketing.uk@skf.com

Spheric Trafalgar Ltd, Bentley House Wiston Business Park, London Road, Ashington, Pulborough, West Sussex, RH20 3DJ Tel: (01903) 891200 Fax: (01903) 891220 E-mail: sales@ballbiz.co.uk

Spire Bearings, 94 Storforth La Trading Estate, Hasland, Chesterfield, Derbyshire, S41 0SN Tel: (01246) 274183 Fax: (01246) 202898 E-mail: sales@spirebearings.co.uk

Sprint Industrial Sales Ltd, 1 Rosehill, Willenhall, West Midlands, WV13 2AR Tel: (01902) 636106 Fax: (01902) 636137 E-mail: sprint@btclick.com

Timken (Coventry) Ltd, Progress Close, Leofric Business Park, Binley, Coventry, CV3 2TF Tel: (024) 7623 3233 Fax: (024) 7629 6991

West Engineering Services Ltd, Unit 1a Abbey Mill Business Centre, Paisley, Renfrewshire, PA1 1TJ Tel: 0141-889 2331 Fax: 0141-887 9564

▶ Wwe Solutions, Erskine Square, Hillington Industrial Estate, Glasgow, G52 4BJ Tel: 0141-585 9255 Fax: 0141-585 9254 E-mail: sales@wwesol.co.uk

Wyko Group Ltd, Amber Way, Halesowen, West Midlands, B62 8WG Tel: 0121-508 6000 Fax: 0121-508 6464 E-mail: marketing@wyko.co.uk

BALL BEARING PELLET GUNS

▶ Role'N'Play Model Shops, 174 Stafford Street, Wolverhampton, WV1 1NA Tel: (01902) 310027 E-mail: info@role-n-play.co.uk

BALL BEARINGS, BRASS

▶ HCT International Industry Limited, Unit 14,, Agecroft Network Centre, Lamplight Way, Swinton, Manchester, M27 8UJ Tel: 0161-351 6758 Fax: 0161-351 6759

BALL BEARINGS, OPEN

▶ HCT International Industry Limited, Unit 14,, Agecroft Network Centre, Lamplight Way, Swinton, Manchester, M27 8UJ Tel: 0161-351 6758 Fax: 0161-351 6759

BALL BEARINGS, SPECIAL OR NON STANDARD

DCN Bearings & Engineering, The Old Foundary, Wood Street, Lye, Stourbridge, West Midlands, DY9 8RX Tel: (01384) 896528 Fax: (01384) 896534 E-mail: sales@dcnbearings.com

S P C Bearings Ltd, Unit 39 Coneygre Industrial Estate, Tipton, West Midlands, DY4 8XP Tel: 0121-557 1371 Fax: 0121-557 3793

BALL CHAINS

Chain Products Ltd, 49 Ward Street, Birmingham, B19 3TD Tel: 0121-359 0697 Fax: 0121-359 3672 E-mail: chainproducts@aol.com

▶ English Chain Co Ltd, Chain House, Brighton Road, Godalming, Surrey, GU7 1NS Tel: (01483) 428383 Fax: (01483) 861931 E-mail: sales@englishchain.co.uk

J Collins & Co. Ltd, 25-26 Warstone Lane, Birmingham, B18 6JQ Tel: 0121-236 2958 Fax: 0121-212 0325 E-mail: evans@j-collins.com

BALL CLAY

Global Ceramic Materials Ltd, Milton Works, Leek New Road, Stoke-on-Trent, ST2 7EF Tel: (01782) 537297 Fax: (01782) 537867 E-mail: sales@gsb.net

W B B Minerals Ltd, North Devon Works, Peters Marland, Torrington, Devon, EX38 8QE Tel: (01805) 602200 Fax: (01805) 602201

BALL GRID ARRAY (BGA) ASSEMBLY SERVICES

CT Production Ltd, 32-40 Harwell Road, Nuffield Industrial Estate, Poole, Dorset, BH17 0GE Tel: (01202) 687633 Fax: (01202) 680788 E-mail: sales@ctproduction.co.uk

Norcott Technologies Ltd, Brookfield House, Tarporley Road, Norcott Brook, Warrington, WA4 4EA Tel: (01925) 247600 Fax: (01925) 247610 E-mail: sales@norcott.co.uk

BALL JOINTS

Arvin Motion Control Ltd, 15 New Star Road, Leicester, LE4 9JD Tel: 0116-274 3600 Fax: 0116-274 3620 E-mail: info@camloc.com

▶ Eurospan Engineering Ltd, 5 Wheatmoor Rise, Sutton Coldfield, West Midlands, B75 6AW Tel: 0121-378 1596 Fax: 0121-329 2542 E-mail: eurospan@blueyonder.co.uk

Evolution Automotive Components Ltd, 17 Lythalls Lane, Coventry, CV6 6FN Tel: (024) 7663 7337 Fax: (024) 7663 7351 E-mail: sales@eacparts.com

Illston & Robson Ltd, Herbert Road, Small Heath, Birmingham, B10 0QQ Tel: 0121-772 5674 Fax: 0121-766 6452 E-mail: illstonandrobson@tiscali.co.uk

M S Engineering, PO Box 255, Bedford, MK41 9BH Tel: (01234) 772255 Fax: (01234) 772266 E-mail: info@msengineering.co.uk

Tuthill Linkage Ltd, Unit 41 Suttons Industrial Park, Reading, RG6 1AZ Tel: 0118-929 9900 Fax: 0118-966 5978 E-mail: dneave@tuthill.com

Z F Lenforder UK Ltd, Heath Road, Wednesbury, West Midlands, WS10 8BH Tel: 0121-526 4441 Fax: 0121-526 3579 E-mail: roger.homer@zf.com

BALL SCREW ACTUATORS

D J Automation Engineering Ltd, 11d Old Bridge Way, Shefford, Bedfordshire, SG17 5HQ Tel: (01462) 813703 Fax: (01462) 816810 E-mail: enquiries@djautomation.co.uk

▶ Industrial Devices (GB) Ltd, Glebe House, Ratlinghope, Shrewsbury, SY5 0SN Tel: (01588) 650551 Fax: (01588) 650130 E-mail: sales@actuators-electric.co.uk

BALL SCREW MANUFRS

A F C Linear Products, Unit 45, Llantarnam Industrial Park, Cwmbran, Gwent, NP44 3AW Tel: (01633) 861414 Fax: (01633) 872039 E-mail: afc-cwmbran@fsmail.net

▶ THK UK, 1 Harrison Close, Knowlhill, Milton Keynes, MK5 8PA Tel: (01908) 303050 Fax: (01908) 303070 E-mail: sales.uk@thk.co.uk

BALL SPLINES

▶ THK UK, 1 Harrison Close, Knowlhill, Milton Keynes, MK5 8PA Tel: (01908) 303050 Fax: (01908) 303070 E-mail: sales.uk@thk.co.uk

BALL TRANSFER UNITS/BALL TABLES, CONVEYOR, MATERIALS HANDLING

Autotrack (Birmingham) Ltd, Ball Unit House Station Road Industrial Estate, Station Road, Woodchester, Stroud, Gloucestershire, GL5 5EQ Tel: (01453) 873155 Fax: (01453) 878500 E-mail: info@autotrack.co.uk

BALL TRANSFER UNITS/BALL TABLES, CONVEYOR, MATERIALS HANDLING – *continued*

Rollrite Manufacturing (Sales) Ltd, 20 Regent Parade, Birmingham, B1 3NS Tel: (0121) 236 1643 Fax: (0121) 212 1550

BALL VALVES

AC Valves & Controls Ltd, Telford Way, Stephenson Industrial Estate, Coalville, Leicestershire, LE67 3HE Tel: (01530) 832832 Fax: (01530) 838986 E-mail: markc@acvalvealliance.com

Akro Valves Co., 2 Chaucer Industrial Estate, Dittons Road, Polegate, East Sussex, BN26 6JF Tel: (01323) 485272 Fax: (01323) 485273 E-mail: info@akrovalve.co.uk

Albion Distribution Ltd, Unit 9a Fall Bank Industrial Estate, Dodworth, Barnsley, South Yorkshire, S75 3LS Tel: (01226) 729900 Fax: (01226) 288011 E-mail: dist@albiongroup.co.uk

▶ Alco Valves Ltd, Mission Works, Birds Royd Lane, Brighouse, West Yorkshire, HD6 1LQ Tel: 01484 710511 Fax: 01484 713009 E-mail: uk@alco-valves.com

Aqua-Gas Manufacturing Ltd, Arnsley Road, Weldon North Industrial Estate, Corby, Northamptonshire, NN17 5QW Tel: (01536) 275910 Fax: (01536) 204256 E-mail: fran.brody@agmc.co.uk

Bonomi UK Ltd, The Fluid Power Centre, Watling Street, Nuneaton, Warwickshire, CV11 6BQ Tel: (024) 7635 4535 Fax: (024) 7635 4143 E-mail: sales@bonomi.co.uk

Clesse (UK) Ltd, Unit 8, Planetary Industrial Estate, Wednesfield, Wolverhampton, WV13 3XQ Tel: (01902) 383233 Fax: (01902) 383234 E-mail: sales@clesse.co.uk

Conoflow Ltd, 18 Brook Road, Wimborne, Dorset, BH21 2BH Tel: (01202) 888010 Fax: (01202) 842009

Cottam & Preedy Ltd, 68 Lower City Road, Tividale, Oldbury, West Midlands, B69 2HF Tel: 0121-552 5281 Fax: 0121-552 6895 E-mail: enquiries@cottampreedy.co.uk

Flow Control Co. Ltd, Cooper Drive, Springwood Industrial Estate, Braintree, Essex, CM7 2RF Tel: (01376) 321211 Fax: (01376) 321222 E-mail: flowcontrolco@lineone.net

Flowserve Flow Control UK Ltd, Burrell Road, Haywards Heath, West Sussex, RH16 1TL Tel: (01444) 314400 Fax: (01444) 314401 E-mail: ukfcinfo@flowserve.com

Hacketts Connect Ltd, Bell Street, West Bromwich, West Midlands, B70 7BX Tel: 0121-553 0134 Fax: 0121-553 2320 E-mail: info@hackcon.demon.co.uk

Hindle Valves, Hindle Cockburns Ltd, Victoria Road, Leeds, LS11 5UG Tel: 0113-244 3741 Fax: 0113-244 1872 E-mail: sales_hindle@tyco-valves.com

Induchem, Unit 1 Greenfield Farm Industrial Estate, Congleton, Cheshire, CW12 4TR Tel: (01260) 277234 Fax: (01260) 277649 E-mail: sales@induchem.ie

International Valves Ltd, Willie Snaith Road, Newmarket, Suffolk, CB8 7GG Tel: (01638) 665000 Fax: (01638) 664000 E-mail: info@international-valves.com

Isis Fluid Control Ltd, Station Yard The Leys, Chipping Norton, Oxfordshire, OX7 5HZ Tel: (01608) 645755 Fax: (01608) 645532 E-mail: sales@isis-fluid.com

Jetseal Ballvalves Manufacturers, Unit 71, Cobham Road, Ferndown Industrial Estate, Wimborne, Dorset, BH21 7QE Tel: (01202) 897427 Fax: (01202) 890292 E-mail: office@jetseal.co.uk

John Clark Ltd, Portrack Grange Road, Stockton-on-Tees, Cleveland, TS18 2PH Tel: (01642) 602288 Fax: (01642) 603388 E-mail: sales@jcvltd.com

Kee Valves, The Old School, Outclough Road, Brindley Ford, Stoke-on-Trent, ST8 7QD Tel: (01782) 523388 Fax: (01782) 523399 E-mail: sales@keevalves.co.uk

Leengate Valves, Grange Close, Clover Nook Industrial Estate, Somercotes, Alfreton, Derbyshire, DE55 4QT Tel: (01773) 521555 Fax: (01773) 521591 E-mail: info@leengatevalves.co.uk

Legris Ltd, Unit 1210, Lansdowne Court, Brockworth, Gloucester, GL3 4AB Tel: (01452) 623500 Fax: (01452) 623501 E-mail: salesuk@legris.com

Lindal Valve Co. Ltd, Cherrycourt Way, Leighton Buzzard, Bedfordshire, LU7 4UH Tel: (01525) 381155 Fax: (01525) 383304

Martract, Ardent Link, Humber Bridge Industrial Estate, Humber Bridge Industrial Estat, Barton-upon-Humber, South Humberside, DN18 5RN Tel: (01652) 632172 Fax: (01652) 660295 E-mail: info@martract.co.uk

Metso Automation Ltd, 2 Lindenwood, Crockford Lane, Chineham, Basingstoke, Hampshire, RG24 8QY Tel: (0870) 6061478 Fax: (01256) 707661 E-mail: sales@metso.com

Oliver Valves Ltd, Haig Road, Parkgate Industrial Estate, Knutsford, Cheshire, WA16 8DX Tel: (01565) 632636 Fax: (01565) 654089 E-mail: sales@valves.co.uk

Phoceenne, Birtley House, Claremont Avenue, Woking, Surrey, GU22 7QB Tel: (01483) 742772 Fax: (01483) 742774

Pirtek, Unit 11 Liongate Enterprise Park, Morden Road, Mitcham, Surrey, CR4 4NY Tel: (020) 8640 6565 Fax: (020) 8640 2252 E-mail: pirtek.mitcham@zen.co.uk

Poynton Valves Ltd, 81a Coppice Road, Poynton, Stockport, Cheshire, SK12 1SL Tel: (01625) 871014 Fax: (01625) 879814 E-mail: sales@poyntonvalves.com

Process Valve Supplies Ltd, 2 Ringtail Industrial Estate, Tollgate Road, Burscough, Ormskirk, Lancashire, L40 8RT Tel: (01704) 894403 Fax: (01704) 897046 E-mail: sales@processvalve.co.uk

Q Controls, Waterton House, Stoneywood, Bucksburn, Aberdeen, AB21 9HX Tel: (01224) 715464 Fax: (01224) 716079 E-mail: sales@jbpipeline.co.uk

SAFI Ltd, 35 Holton Road, Holton Heath Trading Park, Poole, Dorset, BH16 6LT Tel: (01202) 624618 Fax: (01202) 628500 E-mail: sales@safi-limited.com

San Precision Engineering Co. Ltd, Units 9-10 Harnall Industrial Estate, Harnall Lane East, Coventry, CV1 5AE Tel: (024) 7622 0613 Fax: (024) 7652 0004 E-mail: sales@sanprecision.com

Trimline Valves Ltd, 6 Dales Park Drive Worsley Road, Swinton, Manchester, M27 0FP Tel: 0161-727 8128 Fax: 0161-727 9060 E-mail: harrycope@trimlinevalveslimited.co.uk

Tyco Valves & Controls Distribution (UK) Ltd, Crosby Road, Market Harborough, Leicestershire, LE16 9EE Tel: (01858) 467281 Fax: (01858) 434728 E-mail: uk_sales@tyco-valves.com

Valvestock, 2 Fielder Drive, Fareham, Hampshire, PO14 1JG Tel: (01329) 283425 Fax: (01329) 822741 E-mail: enquiries@valvestock.co.uk

BALLAST

F J Church Holdings Ltd, Centenary Works, Manor Way, Rainham, Essex, RM13 8RH Tel: (01708) 522651 Fax: (01708) 522786 E-mail: dave@fjchurch.co.uk

Phillip W. Keen Ltd, 284 High Road, Northweld, Epping, Essex, CM16 6EG Tel: (01992) 524824 Fax: (01992) 524239

C. Porter Ltd, Britannia Road, Waltham Cross, Hertfordshire, EN8 7PE Tel: (01992) 713565 Fax: (01992) 712980

Stutley Bros Ltd, Elms Depot, Stevenage Road, Little Wymondley, Hitchin, Hertfordshire, SG4 7HZ Tel: (01438) 354495 Fax: (01438) 354495 E-mail: stutleybros@aol.com

BALLET WEAR

GrooveDancewear, High Street, Chatteris, Cambridgeshire, PE16 6BE Tel: (01354) 693595E-mail: sales@groovedancewear.co.uk

BALLET/DANCE SHOES

▶ Baillando Dancewear, 12a Market Buildings, Maidstone, Kent, ME14 1HP Tel: (01622) 691190 E-mail: manager@baillando.co.uk

▶ Carrera Dancewear Ltd, 17 Sanders Lodge Industrial Estate, Wellingborough Road, Rushden, Northamptonshire, NN10 6BQ Tel: (01933) 315622 Fax: (01933) 311137 E-mail: sales@carrera.co.uk

▶ Dancemania, 431-441 Wimborne Road, Poole, Dorset, BH15 3EE Tel: (01202) 681801 E-mail: support@dancemania.biz

E Gandolfi Ltd, Mill Road, Wellingborough, Northamptonshire, NN8 1PR Tel: (01933) 224007 Fax: (01933) 227009 E-mail: gandolfisports@btconnet.com

Girls Of Elegance Ltd, Office B12, Arena Business Park, Holyrood Close, Poole, Dorset, BH17 7FL Tel: 0845 8385143 Fax: 0845 8385143 E-mail: sales@girlsofelegance.co.uk

GrooveDancewear, High Street, Chatteris, Cambridgeshire, PE16 6BE Tel: (01354) 693595E-mail: sales@groovedancewear.co.uk

▶ Hullachan Pro, 6 Milrig Road, Rutherglen, Glasgow, G73 2NH Tel: 0141-647 0257 E-mail: craig.coussins@btinternet.com

R E Ormerod & Sons Ltd, Union Mill, Bacup Road, Rossendale, Lancashire, BB4 7JN Tel: (01706) 215391 Fax: (01706) 210368

▶ Topline Dance Shoes Ltd, Havers Road, Norwich, NR3 2DU Tel: (01603) 788359 Fax: (01603) 400144

BALLOON INFLATION EQUIPMENT

Essential Karaoke, 58 Newport Road, Exeter, EX2 7EE Tel: (01392) 875865 Fax: (01392) 875865 E-mail: info@essentialballoons.co.uk

Razzamatazz, 166 West Street, Fareham, Hampshire, PO16 0EH Tel: (01329) 822051 Fax: (01329) 313232 E-mail: info@razzzmatazzfancydress.co.uk

BALLOON PRINTERS, ADVERTISING/PUBLICITY, TOY

3S Balloon Printers, Unit 9, Hortonwood 33, Telford, Shropshire, TF1 7EX Tel: (01952) 677506 Fax: (01952) 677464 E-mail: sales@3sballons.com

Ashton Balloon Centre, 34 Gerard Street, Ashton-in-Makerfield, Wigan, Lancashire, WN4 9AE Tel: (01942) 701312

Balloon Box, 9 Elizabeth Court, Collingham, Wetherby, West Yorkshire, LS22 5JL Tel: (01937) 579549 Fax: (01937) 574585 E-mail: enquiries@balloonbox.co.uk

Balloon Express UK Ltd, Dart Mills, Buckfastleigh, Devon, TQ11 0NF Tel: (01364) 643497 Fax: (01364) 642172 E-mail: ballonexpress@btconnect.com

Balloon Options, 66 Scotchman Lane, Morley, Leeds, LS27 0BJ Tel: 0113-252 3800 Fax: 0113-252 7400

▶ Balloon Print, 22 Hammond Road, Woking, Surrey, GU21 4TQ Tel: (01483) 722229 Fax: (01483) 722229 E-mail: balloons.partyworld@ntlworld.com

The Balloon Store Ltd, 106 Cheriton Road, Folkestone, Kent, CT20 2QN Tel: (01303) 256337 E-mail: info@balloonstore.com

Balloon Studio Ltd, 44 Sandhill Oval, Leeds, LS17 8EA Tel: 0113-225 5666 Fax: 0113-226 2845 E-mail: janice@balloonstudio.co.uk

Balloon Wrap & Decoration, 12 Downlands Parade, Upper Brighton Road, Worthing, West Sussex, BN14 9JH Tel: (01903) 203549 Fax: (01903) 203549

Balloons Direct, Lyn Court, The Common, Holt, Trowbridge, Wiltshire, BA14 6QL Tel: (01225) 784040

Balloons 'N' Things, 27 Essex Street, Birmingham, B5 4TR Tel: 0121-622 2331 Fax: 0121-622 1779 E-mail: david@balloons-n-things.co.uk

Balloons Worldwide Ltd, London Road, Brown Street, Alderley Edge, Cheshire, SK9 7EQ Tel: (01625) 583168 Fax: (01625) 586098

Bournemouth Balloon Co., 1440 Wimbpourne Road, Bournemouth, BH10 7AF Tel: (01202) 590890 Fax: (01202) 590890

Draper Party Products, 30 Comberton Hill, Kidderminster, Worcestershire, DY10 1QN Tel: (01562) 754973

Essential Karaoke, 58 Newport Road, Exeter, EX2 7EE Tel: (01392) 875865 Fax: (01392) 875865 E-mail: info@essentialballoons.co.uk

Everts International Ltd, Second Avenue, Flixborough Industrial Estate, Flixborough, Scunthorpe, South Humberside, DN15 8SD Tel: (01724) 282525 Fax: (01724) 282526 E-mail: info@evertsballoon.co.uk

Happy Talk, 17 Gateside Street, Hamilton, Lanarkshire, ML3 7HT Tel: (01698) 282813 Fax: (01698) 282813

Just Balloons, 2 The Steadings, Greenside, Ryton, Tyne & Wear, NE40 4JF Tel: 0191-413 6912 Fax: 0191-413 1185 E-mail: sales@just-balloons.co.uk

Kent Balloons UK Ltd, Unit 2a Underlyn Industrial Estate, Underlyn Lane, Marden, Tonbridge, Kent, TN12 9AT Tel: (01622) 832213 Fax: (01622) 832388 E-mail: sales@kentballoon.com

▶ Klick Solutions, Pinfold Lane, Penkridge, Stafford, ST19 5AP Tel: (0845) 2620052 Fax: (01785) 716829 E-mail: enquiries@klicksolutions.co.uk

▶ Lets Party Ruislip Ltd, 288 West End Road, Ruislip, Middlesex, HA4 6LS Tel: (01895) 633606 E-mail: letsparty@blueyonder.co.uk

▶ Puffin Balloons, McGregor's Way, Turnoaks Business Park, Chesterfield, Derbyshire, S40 2WB Tel: 01246 205163 Fax: 01246 270566 E-mail: sales@puffinballoons.com

Razzamatazz, 166 West Street, Fareham, Hampshire, PO16 0EH Tel: (01329) 822051 Fax: (01329) 313232 E-mail: info@razzzmatazzfancydress.co.uk

Sky Signs Ltd, Broadgate House, Church Street, Deeping St. James, Peterborough, PE6 8HD Tel: (01778) 345464 Fax: (01778) 341198 E-mail: enquiries@icarusballoons.co.uk

Wickers World Hot Air Balloon Co., The Hawthorns, Tolldish Lane, Great Haywood, Stafford, ST18 0RA Tel: (01889) 882222 Fax: (01889) 881122 E-mail: sales@wickersworld.co.uk

BALLOON PRINTING EQUIPMENT, ADVERTISING/ PUBLICITY, TOY

Balloonatics, 76 Penkville Street, Stoke-On-Trent, ST4 5AJ Tel: (01782) 844616

Essential Karaoke, 58 Newport Road, Exeter, EX2 7EE Tel: (01392) 875865 Fax: (01392) 875865 E-mail: info@essentialballoons.co.uk

BALLOONS, ADVERTISING/ PUBLICITY, HOT AIR

Ballooning Network Ltd, Vauxhall House, Coronation Road, Southville, Bristol, BS3 1RN Tel: 0117-963 7858 Fax: 0117-963 9555

▶ Balloonprint Balloons, Trevordale House, Pius Drove, Upwell, Wisbech, Cambridgeshire, PE14 9AL Tel: (01945) 773559 Fax: (0845) 0090903 E-mail: peter@balloonprint.co.uk

Cameron Balloons Ltd, St Johns Street, Bedminster, Bristol, BS3 4NH Tel: 0117-963 7216 Fax: 0117-966 1168 E-mail: sales@cameronballoons.co.uk

▶ Classic Hot Air Ballooning, Home Farm Cottage, Lenham Heath Road, Sandway, Maidstone, Kent, ME17 2HX Tel: (01622) 858956 Fax: (01622) 853817 E-mail: glen@ballooning.fsnet.co.uk

Heart Of England Balloons, Cross Lanes Farm, Walcote, Alcester, Warwickshire, B49 6NA Tel: (01789) 488219 Fax: (01789) 488366 E-mail: hoebinfo@ukballoons.com

▶ Hot Air Balloons, 1 Home Farm Cottage, Lenham Heath Road, Sandway, Maidstone, Kent, ME17 2HX Tel: (01622) 858956 Fax: (01622) 853817 E-mail: lizmeek@ballooning.fsnet.co.uk

Razzamatazz, 166 West Street, Fareham, Hampshire, PO16 0EH Tel: (01329) 822051 Fax: (01329) 313232 E-mail: info@razzzmatazzfancydress.co.uk

Scotair Balloons, The Old Farmhouse, Skirling, Biggar, Lanarkshire, ML12 6HB Tel: (01899) 860334 E-mail: info@scotair.com

▶ Sky High Leisure Hot Air Balloon Team, Watery Lane Cottage, Wrexham, LL13 OSL Tel: (0845) 3302994 E-mail: info@skyhighleisure.com

Special Occasions, Rambleside, Patmore Heath, Albury, Ware, Hertfordshire, SG11 2LY Tel: (01279) 771944 Fax: (01279) 771944

▶ Virgin Balloon Flights, Jesson House, Stafford Park 1, Telford, Shropshire, TF3 3BD Tel: (01952) 212750 Fax: (01952) 292020 E-mail: sales@virginballoonflights.co.uk

Wye Valley Aviation Ltd, Orchard House, Bridstow, Ross-on-Wye, Herefordshire, HR9 6AJ Tel: (01989) 763134 Fax: (01989) 768242

BALLOTINI

Jencons (Scientific) Ltd, Cherrycourt Way Industrial Estate, Stanbridge Road, Leighton Buzzard, Bedfordshire, LU7 4UA Tel: (01525) 372010 Fax: (01525) 379547 E-mail: export@jencons.co.uk

BALLPOINT PENS

A T Cross Ltd, Windmill Trading Estate, Thistle Road, Luton, LU1 3XJ Tel: (01582) 422793 Fax: (01582) 456097 E-mail: crossuk@cross.com

Azizoff Co. Ltd, 2 Beechfield Road, London, N4 1PE Tel: (020) 8809 6902 Fax: (020) 8800 5795 E-mail: azizoffltd@tiscali.co.uk

Sanford Europe Parker Pen Co., 52 Railway Road, Newhaven, East Sussex, BN9 0AU Tel: (01273) 513233 Fax: (01273) 514773 E-mail: enquiries@parkerpen.co.uk

Sheaffer Pen (UK) Ltd, Chaplin House, Widewater Place, Harefield, Middlesex, UB9 6NF Tel: (01895) 827100 Fax: (01895) 827101

Staedler (UK) Ltd, Cowbridge Road, Pontyclun, Mid Glamorgan, CF72 8YJ Tel: (01443) 235011 Fax: (01443) 237668 E-mail: terry.james@uk.staedler.com

Swan Stabilo Ltd, 75 Buckingham Avenue, Slough, SL1 4PN Tel: (01753) 605656 Fax: (01753) 605657 E-mail: marketing@stabilo.co.uk

BALLS, TABLE TENNIS

▶ KFL Leisure, Prospecthill, Falkirk, FK1 5LD Tel: 01324 410987 Fax: 01324 410987 E-mail: info@kflleisure.com

RJM Sports Ltd, 54 Cow Wynd, Falkirk, FK1 1PU Tel: (01324) 873804 Fax: (01324) 873804 E-mail: sales@rjmsports.co.uk

BALUSTRADE ACCESSORIES

Leicester Balustrading Co. Ltd, Unit 1, Ruding Street, Leicester, LE3 5BX Tel: 0116-299 2229 Fax: 0116-299 2122

Locker Wire Weavers, Farrell Street, Warrington, WA1 2WW Tel: (01925) 406600 Fax: (01925) 444386 E-mail: sales@lockerwire.co.uk

BALUSTRADE INSTALLATION CONTRACTORS OR FABRICATORS

Concept Balustrades Ltd, Unit 9, Papermill Road, Cardiff, CF11 8DH Tel: (029) 2022 0040 Fax: (029) 2034 4402 E-mail: enq@conceptbalustrades.co.uk

County Installations, 15 Moore Road, Church Crookham, Fleet, Hampshire, GU52 6JB Tel: (01252) 616093 Fax: (01252) 627755 E-mail: patlowe@countyinstallations.co.uk

Craufurd Engineering Services Ltd, Unit 4-5 Lower Mount Farm, Cookham, Maidenhead, Berkshire, SL6 9EE Tel: (01628) 532288 Fax: (01628) 532424

Dormar Fabrications Bilston Ltd, Jubilee House, Halesfield 2, Telford, Shropshire, TF7 4QH Tel: (01952) 585736 Fax: (01952) 684526

Fabrite Fixing, 6 Marshall's Lane, High Cross, Ware, Hertfordshire, SG11 1AH Tel: (01920) 485554 Fax: (01920) 486754

J S M Engineering Ltd, Units 5-7 Humber Works, Humber Road, Beeston, Nottingham, NG9 2ET Tel: 0115-922 3849 Fax: 0115-922 3865 E-mail: sales@jsmeng.com

Macelloy Ltd, Hawke Street, Sheffield, S9 2LN Tel: 0114-242 6704 Fax: 0114-243 1324 E-mail: info@macalloy.com

BALUSTRADE INSTALLATION CONTRACTORS OR FABRICATORS

– continued

K.C. Milner Engineering Ltd, Unit 7 Shepherd Cross Street, Bolton, BL1 3DE Tel: (01204) 843540 Fax: (01204) 493480

▶ Tecnik Railing, The Studio, 133 Grange Road, Ilford, Essex, IG1 1EZ Tel: (07947) 376267

Turnquest, Regent House, Bath Avenue, Wolverhampton, WV1 4EG Tel: (01902) 810075 Fax: (01902) 810078 E-mail: info@turnquest.co.uk

Ventfix Fabrications Ltd, Unit 54-55 Youngs Industrial Estate, Aldermaston, Reading, RG7 4PW Tel: 0118 9816246

BALUSTRADES, *See also headings under Handrail*

A M P Metalworks, 837-839 Consort Road, London, SE15 2PR Tel: (020) 7277 5569 Fax: (020) 7635 6001 E-mail: sales@apmetalworks.co.uk

All Metal Fabrications Services Ltd, Thundridge Business Park, Great Cambridge Road, Thundridge, Ware, Hertfordshire, SG12 0SS Tel: (01920) 485200 Fax: (01920) 485055

Alloy Fabweld Ltd, 5 Zone C Chelmsford Road Industrial Estate, Chelmsford Road, Dunmow, Essex, CM6 1HD Tel: (01371) 859544 Fax: (01371) 878608

Blackburn Bailey Ltd, Wantz Road, Dagenham, Essex, RM10 8PS Tel: (020) 8593 7346 Fax: (020) 8984 0813 E-mail: info@blackburngroup.co.uk

Browse Engineering Services, 34b Cowleigh Road, Malvern, Worcestershire, WR14 1QD Tel: (01684) 567125 Fax: (01684) 568240 E-mail: sales@ibrowse2.com

Broxap Dorothea, Rowhurst Industrial Estate, Chesterton, Newcastle, Staffordshire, ST5 6BD Tel: (01782) 564411 Fax: (01782) 565357 E-mail: sales@broxap.co.uk

Richard Burbidge Ltd, Whittington Road, Oswestry, Shropshire, SY11 1HZ Tel: (01691) 655131 Fax: (01691) 657694 E-mail: info@richardburbidge.co.uk

Caldwell Metalwork Fabrication, Units 10-11 Shaftsbury Industrial Estate, Icknield Way, Letchworth Garden City, Hertfordshire, SG6 1HE Tel: (01462) 670505 Fax: (01462) 670500

Ceto Engineering Ltd, Howard Road, Eaton Socon, St. Neots, Cambridgeshire, PE19 8ET Tel: (01480) 406646 Fax: (01480) 406605

Chatsworth Forge Ltd, Woods Way, Goring-by-Sea, Worthing, West Sussex, BN12 4RE Tel: (01903) 502221 Fax: (01903) 700002 E-mail: sales@chatsworthforge.co.uk

Colne Valley Engineering, Unit 12 Olds Close, Watford, WD18 9RU Tel: (01923) 776212 Fax: (01923) 896587 E-mail: alanhughes@tesco.net

D G N Design, Unit 7 270 Lakey Lane, Birmingham, B28 8RA Tel: 0121-778 6878 Fax: 0121-778 6878

D J Engineering, 4 Camp Industrial Estate, Rycote Lane, Milton Common, Thame, Oxfordshire, OX9 2NP Tel: (01844) 278749 Fax: (01844) 278749 E-mail: djjeff@aol.com

▶ Delta Balustrades, Millbuck Way, Sandbach, Cheshire, CW11 3JA Tel: (01270) 753383

Delta Balustrades, Belpher Road, Stockport, Cheshire, SK4 3QW Tel: 0161-947 4747

Edwin Clarke, Francis House, George Street, Lincoln, LN5 8LG Tel: (01522) 530912 Fax: (01522) 510929

Fire Escapes Unlimited, Unit 2 Atlas Trading Estate, Colebrook Road, Birmingham, B11 2NT Tel: 0121-772 4443 Fax: 0121-753 4222 E-mail: feunlimited@aol.com

Forge Fabrications Ltd, The Street, Lyng, Norwich, NR9 5QZ Tel: (01603) 872088 Fax: (01603) 872744 E-mail: enquiries@forgefabrications.co.uk

Form Weld Ltd, Unit 3C, Cutters Close, Narborough, Leicester, LE19 2FZ Tel: 0116-286 6654 Fax: 0116-275 0877 E-mail: formweld@btconnect.com

▶ G L W Engineering & Construction, Unit 3 Wisbech Business Centre, Oldfield Lane, Friday Bridge, Wisbech, Cambridgeshire, PE14 0NX Tel: (01945) 464637 Fax: (07000) 785497 E-mail: geoff@glwengineering.co.uk

Gabriel & Co. Ltd, Abro Works, 10 Hay Hall Road, Tyseley, Birmingham, B11 2AU Tel: 0121-248 3333 Fax: 0121-248 3330 E-mail: sales@gabrielco.com

General Services Fabrications Ltd, Sudmeadow Road, Gloucester, GL2 5HS Tel: (01452) 304515 Fax: (01452) 504729

Glazzard (Dudley) Ltd, The Washington Centre, Netherton, Dudley, West Midlands, DY2 9RE Tel: (01384) 233151 Fax: (01384) 250224 E-mail: acg@glazzard.co.uk

Glendale Developments Ltd, Unit 2a Union Road Trading Estate, Oldbury, West Midlands, B69 3EU Tel: 0121-541 1752 Fax: 0121-544 8774 E-mail: glendaledevelpoments@hotmail.com

Haddonstone Ltd, The Forge House, East Haddon, Northampton, NN6 8DB Tel: (01604) 770711 Fax: (01604) 770027 E-mail: info@haddonstone.co.uk

Handrail Design Ltd, Sail & Colour Loft, The Historic Dockyard, Chatham, Kent, ME4 4TE Tel: (01634) 817800 Fax: (01634) 817711 E-mail: enquiries@handraildesign.co.uk

William Hopkins & Sons Ltd, Gardine House, 147-149 Dollman Street, Nechells, Birmingham, B7 4RS Tel: 0121-333 3577 Fax: 0121-333 3480 E-mail: info@william-hopkins.co.uk

I M Products Ltd, 2 London Hill Farm, London Road, Stockbridge, Hampshire, SO20 6EN Tel: (01264) 810261 Fax: (01264) 810642

J & B Novak Metalcraft Ltd, White Cottage Farm, Lucas Green Road, West End, Woking, Surrey, GU24 9LZ Tel: (01483) 474979 Fax: (01483) 472487

Letchworth Steel Construction, 29 Jubilee Trading Estate, Jubilee Road, Letchworth Garden City, Hertfordshire, SG6 1NE Tel: (01462) 480080 Fax: (01462) 481191 E-mail: lesco@aol.com

Luxtrade Ltd, Unit C5 Hilton Trading Estate, Hilton Road, Lanesfield, Wolverhampton, WV4 6DW Tel: (01902) 353182 Fax: (01902) 404628 E-mail: sales@luxtrade.co.uk

Mealham Metal Products, Orchard Buildings, Chilmington Green, Great Chart, Ashford, Kent, TN23 3DL Tel: (01233) 621150 Fax: (01233) 621150

Metalcraft Tottenham Ltd, 6-40 Durnford Street, London, N15 5NQ Tel: (020) 8802 1715 Fax: (020) 8802 1258 E-mail: sales@makingmetalwork.com

Metalways Ltd, 20 Churchill Way, Fleckney, Leicester, LE8 8UD Tel: 0116-240 3148 Fax: 0116-240 3013 E-mail: erica@metalwaysltd.com

Minsterstone Ltd, Harts Close, Ilminster, Somerset, TA19 9DJ Tel: (01460) 52277 Fax: (01460) 57865 E-mail: varyl@minsterstone.ltd.uk

▶ M-Tech Engineering, 1 Third Avenue, Greasley Street, Nottingham, NG6 8ND Tel: 0115-979 4448 Fax: 0115-979 4449 E-mail: matt@mtechengineering.co.uk

Northern Joinery, Daniel Street, Whitworth, Rochdale, Lancashire, OL12 8DA Tel: (01706) 852345 Fax: (01706) 853114 E-mail: northern-joinery@compuserve.com

P J T Engineering, Unit 3 367 Bryn Road, Ashton-in-Makerfield, Wigan, Lancashire, WN4 8BS Tel: (01942) 712022 Fax: (01942) 712022 E-mail: sales@pjtengineering.gbr.cc

P & M Decorative Metal Work Ltd, Unit 1, Park Street, Oldbury, West Midlands, B69 4LQ Tel: 0121-544 8880 Fax: 0121-544 4617 E-mail: pmdeco@aol.com

P & R Engineering Midlands Ltd, Cable Street, Wolverhampton, WV2 2HX Tel: (01902) 870637 Fax: (01902) 871569

Pepcon Ltd, PO Box 272, Sunbury-on-Thames, Middlesex, TW16 6WB Tel: (01932) 788545 Fax: (01932) 788496 E-mail: sales@pepcon.org

Philton Fire & Security Ltd, 61 Lower Road, Harrow, Middlesex, HA2 0DE Tel: (020) 8864 7534 Fax: (020) 8864 8631

Premier Fabrications, St 1, 54-76 Bissell Street, Birmingham, B5 7HP Tel: 0121-693 9059 Fax: 0121-693 9058

Reddick Forge, Crawley Down Road, Felbridge, East Grinstead, West Sussex, RH19 2PS Tel: (01342) 302055 Fax: (01342) 302055 E-mail: sales@reddickforge.co.uk

Riteweld Engineering Ltd, Beaumont Road, Banbury, Oxfordshire, OX16 1RH Tel: 01295 250995 Fax: 01295 273505 E-mail: doug@riteweld.fsnet.co.uk

Roberts Welding Ltd, Readmans Industrial Estate, Station Road, East Tilbury, Tilbury, Essex, RM18 8QR Tel: (01375) 857736 Fax: (01375) 851280

Sovereign Stainless Fabrications Ltd, Canal Works, Cadman St, Sheffield, S4 7ZG Tel: 0114-276 9192 Fax: 0114-276 3700 E-mail: ssfl@sovereign-stainless.co.uk

Steel Line Ltd, 415 Petre Street, Sheffield, S4 8LL Tel: 0114-231 7330 Fax: 0114-256 0330 E-mail: enquiries@steelline.co.uk

Steel People Ltd, Unit 3e Priory Park, Mills Road, Aylesford, Kent, ME20 7PP Tel: (01622) 715900 Fax: (01622) 715905 E-mail: mail@thesteelpeople.com

Steeltech Kinetix Ltd, Dancroft Works, Gauxholme Fold, Todmorden, Lancashire, OL14 7PW Tel: (01706) 817144 Fax: (01706) 817522 E-mail: mail@steeltech-kinetix.co.uk

Supreme Ironcraft Ltd, Unit 26 Brook Road Industrial Estate, Brook Road, Rayleigh, Essex, SS6 7XL Tel: (01268) 747774 Fax: (01268) 770449

Sussex Ironcraft South Eastern Ltd, 31b Avis Way, Newhaven, East Sussex, BN9 0DJ Tel: (01273) 515931 Fax: (01273) 513811

Sutcliffe Bros Bradford Ltd, Paradise Works, 164 Sunbridge Road, Bradford, West Yorkshire, BD1 2HF Tel: (01274) 733063 Fax: (01274) 304434 E-mail: sutbros@aol.com

Thames Forge Ltd, Fullers Yard, Sheephouse Road, Maidenhead, Berkshire, SL6 8HA Tel: (01628) 622423 Fax: (01628) 622423

Town & Country Gates & Railings, Unit 6e Waterloo Industrial Estate, Gorsey Mount Street, Stockport, Cheshire, SK1 3BU Tel: 0161-429 7325 Fax: 0161-480 4388 E-mail: philbohen@aol.com

W A Mcgarrie & Son Ltd, Friarton Road, Perth, PH2 8BB Tel: (01738) 631194 Fax: (01738) 633814 E-mail: office@mcgarrie.net

W & G Metalwork Ltd, Sugarbrook Mill, Buntsford Hill, Stoke Pound, Bromsgrove, Worcestershire, B60 3AR Tel: (01527) 870752 Fax: (01527) 579930

Woking Forge Ltd, 126A High Street, Old Woking, Woking, Surrey, GU22 9JN Tel: (01483) 760313 Fax: (01483) 756332

BALUSTRADES, METAL

H L C Engineering Ltd, 4 Harvey Road, Burnt Mills Industrial Estate, Basildon, Essex, SS13 1QJ Tel: (01268) 590080 Fax: (01268) 590141E-mail: steelwork@hlcengineering.com

J S M Engineering Ltd, Units 5-7 Humber Works, Humber Road, Beeston, Nottingham, NG9 2ET Tel: 0115-922 3849 Fax: 0115-922 3865 E-mail: sales@jsmeng.com

BAMBOO HARDWOOD FLOORING

▶ The Flooring Directory, The Coach House, Lower Denbigh Road, St. Asaph, Clwyd, LL17 0EF Tel: (01745) 584868 E-mail: webmaster@carpetfitters.biz

Mainstream Maintenance Group, 256 High Street, Potters Bar, Hertfordshire, EN6 5DB Tel: (01707) 662774 Fax: (01707) 653382 E-mail: sales@mainstreamgroup.com

▶ Majestic Floors, Corner Glades, 16 Elmton Close, Leeds, LS10 3UD Tel: 0113-270 9921 E-mail: majesticfloors@hotmail.com

▶ Tongling, 6 Camellia Drive, Priorslee, Telford, Shropshire, TF2 9UA Tel: (01952) 200032 Fax: (01952) 291938 E-mail: sales@tlflooring.co.uk

BAND CLAMPS

Shire Fluid Power Ltd, 6 Racecourse Road, Pershore, Worcestershire, WR10 2EY Tel: (01386) 554744 Fax: (01386) 553743

Teconnex Ltd, Bronte Works, Chesham Street, Keighley, West Yorkshire, BD21 4LG Tel: (01535) 691122 Fax: (01535) 691133 E-mail: sales@teconnex.com

BANDING FASTENERS

S E A C, 46 Chesterfield Road, Leicester, LE5 5LP Tel: 0116-273 9501 Fax: 0116-273 8373 E-mail: enquiries@seac.uk.com

BANDPASS FILTERS

Faraday Technology Ltd, Units 22-26 Croft Road Indust Estate, Newcastle, Staffordshire, ST5 0TW Tel: (01782) 661501 Fax: (01782) 630101 E-mail: sales@faradaytech.co.uk

Trak Microwave Ltd, Dunsinane Avenue, Dunsinane Industrial Estate, Dundee, DD2 3QF Tel: (01382) 833411 Fax: (01382) 833599

BANDSAW BLADING OR BANDSAWS

Atlantic Service Co. (UK) Ltd, Pen-Y-Fan Industrial Estate, Croespenmaen, Crumlin, Newport, Gwent, NP11 4EG Tel: (01495) 246012 Fax: (01495) 248113 E-mail: sales@atlantic-service.co.uk

Bahco Metal Saws Ltd, Moorhead Way, Bramley, Rotherham, South Yorkshire, S66 1YY Tel: (01709) 731600 Fax: (01709) 731700

Bedford Saw & Tool Co., Ampthill Road, Bedford, MK42 9JP Tel: (01234) 217417 Fax: (01234) 270663 E-mail: info@bedfordsaw.co.uk

Birkett Cutmaster Ltd, PO Box 30, Cleckheaton, West Yorkshire, BD19 5LY Tel: (01274) 870311 Fax: (01274) 862754 E-mail: bryn.pritchard@birkett-cutmaster.co.uk

Burton Saw International Ltd, Trading Estate, Valmar Road, London, SE5 9NW Tel: (020) 7737 3577 Fax: (020) 7733 2368 E-mail: blades@burtonsaw.co.uk

Cromwell Tools Ltd, PO Box 14, Wigston, Leicestershire, LE18 1AT Tel: 0116-288 8888 Fax: 0116-288 8222 E-mail: sales@cromwell.co.uk

▶ Dakin-Flathers Ltd, Dakin-Flathers Ltd Boothroyds, Way, Featherstone, Pontefract, West Yorkshire, WF7 6RA Tel: (01977) 705600 Fax: (01977) 705700 E-mail: sales@dakin-flathers.com

E P S Services, Ford Road, Wiveliscombe, Taunton, Somerset, TA4 2RE Tel: (01984) 624273 Fax: (01984) 623204 E-mail: info@eps-services.co.uk

F J Cooper, Old Rumbelows Warehouse, Bryant Avenue, Romford, RM3 0AP Tel: (01708) 349036 Fax: (020) 7739 5777

H Pickles Ltd, Lincoln Road, Cressex Business Park, High Wycombe, Buckinghamshire, HP12 3RQ Tel: (01494) 520613 Fax: (01494) 465373 E-mail: sales@scsaws.co.uk

Harrison Saw & Tool Ltd, Underbank Way, Carrs Industrial Estate, Haslingden, Rossendale, Lancashire, BB4 5HR Tel: (01706) 225221 Fax: (01706) 831409 E-mail: sales@harrisonsaw.co.uk

L S Starrett Co. Ltd, Oxnam Road, Jedburgh, Roxburghshire, TD8 6LR Tel: (01835) 863501 Fax: (01835) 863018 E-mail: sales@starrett.co.uk

Lancashire Saw Co. Ltd, Imperial Mill, Gorse Street, Blackburn, BB1 3EU Tel: (01254) 51116 Fax: (01254) 672046 E-mail: info@lancashiresaw.co.uk

Prosaw Ltd, Telford Way, Kettering, Northamptonshire, NN16 8UN Tel: (01536) 410999 Fax: (01536) 410080 E-mail: sales@prosaw.co.uk

Quicksharp Services, Signal Hill Farm, Lenborough Road, Gawcott, Buckingham, MK18 4JG Tel: (01280) 822062 Fax: (08707) 778463

Sherlock Ltd, 21 Station Road, Woodley, Stockport, Cheshire, SK6 1HN Tel: 0161-430 2647 Fax: 0161-430 8008

Simonds Industries Ltd, 3 Motorway Industrial Estate, Tyler Street, Sheffield, S9 1DH Tel: 0114-243 3701 Fax: 0114-243 3879

Thames Valley Saw Services Ltd, Gravel Lane, Drayton, Abingdon, Oxfordshire, OX14 4HY Tel: (01235) 550088 Fax: (01235) 553150 E-mail: sales@tvss.co.uk

BANDSAW SERVICING EQUIPMENT

Matrix Machinery, Bermar House Unit 38 Rumer Hill Business Estate, Rumer Hill Road, Cannock, Staffordshire, WS11 0ET Tel: (01543) 466256 Fax: (01543) 466320 E-mail: jpl@matrixmachinery.fsnet.co.uk

Vollmer UK Ltd, Orchard Park Industrial Estate, Town Street, Sandiacre, Nottingham, NG10 5BP Tel: 0115-949 1040 Fax: 0115-949 0042 E-mail: admin@vollmer-uk.com

BANDSAW SHARPENING OR MAINTENANCE OR REPAIR

A A Smith Ltd, Pontefract, West Yorkshire, WF7 6WZ Tel: (0845) 3303805 Fax: (0845) 3303806 E-mail: sales@aasmith.co.uk

Bandsaw Service Ltd, Fairacres Industrial Estate, Dedworth Road, Windsor, Berkshire, SL4 4LE Tel: (01753) 862029 Fax: (01753) 830051 E-mail: saws@eclipse.co.uk

E P S Services, Ford Road, Wiveliscombe, Taunton, Somerset, TA4 2RE Tel: (01984) 624273 Fax: (01984) 623204 E-mail: info@eps-services.co.uk

Fourways Bandsaw Service, 5b Cannock Wood Industrial Estate, Cannock Wood Street, Cannock, Staffordshire, WS12 0PL Tel: (01543) 879711 Fax: (01543) 423654

H Pickles Ltd, Lincoln Road, Cressex Business Park, High Wycombe, Buckinghamshire, HP12 3RQ Tel: (01494) 520613 Fax: (01494) 465373 E-mail: sales@scsaws.co.uk

J C Tool Hire, Valley St North, Darlington, County Durham, DL1 1QE Tel: (01325) 382038 Fax: (01325) 468539 E-mail: sales@joegreeners.co.uk

M & E James, Unit 2 Hare Street, Bilston, West Midlands, WV14 7DX Tel: (01902) 408030 Fax: (01902) 490166 E-mail: saws@supanet.com

M & W Grinding Services, Unit 10 Annwood Lodge, Arterial Road, Rayleigh, Essex, SS6 7UA Tel: (01268) 590059 Fax: (01268) 590058 E-mail: mwgrinding@btconnect.com

Sawcraft UK Ltd, Penncricket Lane, Rowley Regis, West Midlands, B65 0RE Tel: 0121-561 5616 Fax: 0121-561 5691 E-mail: sales@sawcraftukltd.co.uk

Thames Valley Saw Services Ltd, Gravel Lane, Drayton, Abingdon, Oxfordshire, OX14 4HY Tel: (01235) 550088 Fax: (01235) 553150 E-mail: sales@tvss.co.uk

▶ WEST SAW SERVICES LTD, UNIT 15, BALTIC WORKS, EFFINGAM ROAD, Sheffield, S9 3QA Tel: 0114 2426620 Fax: 0114 2426620 E-mail: josilk@btinternet.com

BANDSAWING MACHINES, *See headings for particular types*

See also headings for particular types

Gate Machinery International Ltd, Handsford Court, 1 Garston Park Parade, Watford, WD25 9LQ Tel: (01923) 682874 Fax: (01923) 682875 E-mail: info@gatemachinery.com

Meba Saw Co Ltd, 27 Palmer Road, Retford, Nottinghamshire, DN22 6SS Tel: (01777) 860102 Fax: (01777) 860306 E-mail: mebasaw@btconnect.com

BANDSAWS

Atkins Saws, 53 Richmond Road, Solihull, West Midlands, B92 7RR Tel: 0121-707 1600

Gate Machinery International Ltd, Handsford Court, 1 Garston Park Parade, Watford, WD25 9LQ Tel: (01923) 682874 Fax: (01923) 682875 E-mail: info@gatemachinery.com

Machine Mart Ltd, Machine Mart House, Derwent Street, Derby, DE1 2ED Tel: (01332) 290931 Fax: (01332) 366531 E-mail: sales@machinemart.co.uk

Sawcraft UK Ltd, Penncricket Lane, Rowley Regis, West Midlands, B65 0RE Tel: 0121-561 5616 Fax: 0121-561 5691 E-mail: sales@sawcraftukltd.co.uk

BANK FURNISHING OR FITTING SERVICES

Cheshire Contracts Shopfitting Ltd, Imperial Works, 151 Bennett Street, Manchester, M12 5BH Tel: 0161-273 6253 Fax: 0161-274 3454
E-mail: enquiries@cheshire-contracts.co.uk

H & J Forbes Middlesbrough Ltd, 147 Stockton Street, Middlesbrough, Cleveland, TS2 1BU Tel: (01642) 222611 Fax: (01642) 232419
E-mail: frances@forbes-group.demon.co.uk

Mentha & Halsall (Shopfitters) Ltd, 95a Linaker St, Southport, Merseyside, PR8 5BU Tel: (01704) 530800 Fax: (01704) 500601
E-mail: info@mentha-halsall.com

Space Craft Projects Ltd, Sandbeck Way, Wetherby, West Yorkshire, LS22 7DN Tel: (01937) 584554 Fax: (01937) 580012
E-mail: info@space-craft.co.uk

BANK PERSONNEL RECRUITMENT AGENCIES/ CONSULTANTS/SERVICES

A Small Firms Loan, 21 Dapps Hill, Keynsham, Bristol, BS31 1ES Tel: (08458) 386917 Fax: (08701) 369549
E-mail: strategy@nildram.co.uk

Accountancy Divisions, 37 George Street, Croydon, CR0 1LB Tel: (020) 8686 5353 Fax: (020) 8686 2666
E-mail: croydon@hays.com

The Aristotle Corporation, Blenheim House, 56 Old Steine, Brighton, BN1 1NH Tel: (01273) 222400 Fax: (01273) 778464
E-mail: candidates@aristotlecorp.com

▶ Ashton Penny, Broadbent House, 64-65 Grosvenor Street, London, W1K 3JH Tel: (020) 7659 0600 Fax: (020) 7659 0601

▶ Badger Associates Ltd, Pottergate Street, Aslacton, Norwich, NR15 2JU Tel: 01508 536013 Fax: 0871 7501925
E-mail: info@badgerassociates.co.uk

▶ Buzz House Keeping, Trocoll House, Wakering Road, Barking, Essex, IG11 8PD Tel: (020) 8507 9906 Fax: (020) 8507 9066
E-mail: peter@buzzservices.co.uk

▶ Chequers Personnel, Wiltshire House, 121 High Street, Marlborough, Wiltshire, SN8 1LZ Tel: (01672) 519194 Fax: 01672 519195
E-mail: info@chequers-personnel.co.uk

D C Gardner Training, Nestor House, Playhouse Yard, London, EC4V 5EX Tel: (020) 7779 8917 Fax: (020) 7779 8786

E C H M, 43 Eagle Street, London, WC1R 4AT Tel: (020) 7304 9000 Fax: (020) 7304 9001

▶ Emerald Careers, 43 Temple Row, Birmingham, B2 5LS Tel: (0845) 2265857 Fax: (020) 8318 3222
E-mail: muyiwa@emeraldcareers.com

▶ Key Associate Group, Orbit House Second Floor, Albert Street, Eccles, Manchester, M30 0BL Tel: 0161-707 9448 Fax: (0870) 2320090
E-mail: Natasha.Karimi@Keyassociategroup.com

Lloyds Recruitment Ltd, 15 Dane Street, Bishop's Stortford, Hertfordshire, CM23 3BT Tel: (01279) 507310 Fax: (01279) 507310
E-mail: lloyds'recruitment@ntlworld.com

Martin Ward Anderson Ltd, 7 Savoy Court, The Strand, London, WC2R 0EL Tel: (020) 7240 2233 Fax: (020) 7240 8818
E-mail: info@martinwardanderson.com

▶ Recadnet, Minerva Road, London, NW10 6HJ Tel: (0870) 2240656
E-mail: admin@recadnet.com

▶ Darren Snell, Ground Floor, Clair House, Haywards Heath, West Sussex, RH16 3DP Tel: (01444) 415559 Fax: (01444) 415180
E-mail: enquiries@artconsulting.com

▶ Spectrum Personnel Ltd, 154 Merry Street, Motherwell, Lanarkshire, ML1 1NA Tel: (01698) 304545 Fax: (01698) 304646
E-mail: garytelfer@spectrum-personnel.com

▶ Triple S Recruitment Ltd, Heath Business Technical Park, Runcorn, Cheshire, WA7 4QX Tel: (01928) 576925
E-mail: info@boxpeople.co.uk

The Work Shop, 7 High Street, Ringwood, Hampshire, BH24 1AB Tel: (01425) 489393 Fax: (01425) 489402
E-mail: sales@thework-shop.net

Jonathan Wren & Co. Ltd, 34 London Wall, London, EC2M 5RU Tel: (020) 7309 3550 Fax: (020) 7309 3552
E-mail: career@jwren.com

BANKERS AUTOMATED CLEARING SYSTEMS (BACS) SOFTWARE

▶ Bottomline Technologies Europe Ltd, 115 Chatham Street, Reading, RG1 7JX Tel: 0118-925 8250 Fax: 0118-956 9988
E-mail: sales@bottomline.co.uk

Experience Payment, Eiger Point Swift Park, Old Leicester Road, Rugby, Warwickshire, CV21 1DZ Tel: (01788) 554800 Fax: (01788) 554900 E-mail: enquiries@eiger.co.uk

Wisbech Computer Services Ltd, 107 Norwich Road, Wisbech, Cambridgeshire, PE13 2BB Tel: (01945) 464146 Fax: (01945) 464680
E-mail: sales@wisbech.com

BANKING CONSULTANCY

R B Mentor Services, 152 West Regent Street, Glasgow, G2 2RQ Tel: 0141-248 1212 Fax: 0141-248 3324

BANKING INDUSTRY SOFTWARE

Agarwal Associates, Clockhouse, Partridge Lane, Newdigate, Dorking, Surrey, RH5 5EE Tel: (01306) 631888 Fax: (01306) 631011
E-mail: alokagarwal@nch.it

Anjec Computer Services, The Mansard Suite The Robbins Building, Albert Street, Rugby, Warwickshire, CV21 2AA Tel: (01788) 540484 Fax: (01788) 540493
E-mail: anjec@via-anjec.co.uk

C B W Associates Ltd, 15 Station Rise, Marlow, Buckinghamshire, SL7 1EJ Tel: (01628) 482282 E-mail: bm.watson@btclick.com

Peter Evans & Associates Ltd, 52 The Parade, Roath, Cardiff, CF24 3AB Tel: (029) 2040 2200 Fax: (029) 2040 2213
E-mail: info@peterevans.com

Filenet Ltd, Waterside House 4 Cowley Business Park, High Street, Cowley, Uxbridge, Middlesex, UB8 2FN Tel: (01895) 207300 Fax: (01895) 207365

Flexible Management Systems Ltd, Fielden Ho, 28 London Bridge St, London, SE1 9SG Tel: (020) 7378 6788 Fax: (020) 7357 0577

▶ Ibs Publishing Ltd, 8 Stade Street, Hythe, Kent, CT21 6BD Tel: (01303) 262636 Fax: (01303) 262646
E-mail: enquiries@ibspublishing.com

Intec Systems Blackburn Ltd, 12 Strawberry Bank, Blackburn, BB2 6AA Tel: (01254) 667106 Fax: (01254) 675925
E-mail: sales@intec-systems.co.uk

Misus Group, 1 St Georges Road, Wimbledon, London, SW19 4DR Tel: (020) 7757 6222 Fax: (020) 8944 7275
E-mail: sales@misys.com

Software Integrators Ltd, New London Bridge House, 25 London Bridge Street, London, SE1 9SG Tel: (020) 7378 9309 Fax: (020) 7378 9310
E-mail: admin@software-integrators.co.uk

Tib Co., Castlebridge Office Village, Kirtley Drive, Nottingham, NG7 1LD Tel: 0115-948 6500 Fax: 0115-948 6595 E-mail: sales@tibco.com

BANKNOTE COUNTING AND SORTING MACHINES

De La Rue Cash Systems, 7-8 Wolfe Close, Parkgate Industrial Estate, Knutsford, Cheshire, WA16 8XJ Tel: (01565) 654662 Fax: (01565) 658657
E-mail: robert.clark@uk.delarue.com

Francotyp-postalia Ltd, 130 High Street, Barkway, Royston, Hertfordshire, SG8 8EG Tel: (01763) 849360 Fax: (01763) 848900
E-mail: mike@spexecutiveagency.co.uk

J O B Export/Import Ltd, 15 Iberian Way, Camberley, Surrey, GU15 1LZ Tel: (01276) 21119 Fax: (01276) 62190

Scan Coin Ltd, Dutch House, 110 Broadway, Salford, M50 2UW Tel: 0161-873 0500 Fax: 0161-873 0501
E-mail: sales@scancoin.co.uk

BANKNOTE PAPER MAKERS

Portals, Overton Mill, Overton, Basingstoke, Hampshire, RG25 3JG Tel: (01256) 770770 Fax: (01256) 770937
E-mail: sales.portals@delarue.co.uk

BANNER CLOTHS

▶ Design Wise, Matrix House, Constitution Hill, Leicester, LE1 1PL Tel: 0116-262 8678 Fax: 0116-262 8678
E-mail: info@designwise.org.uk

Hammertex Ltd, Nationwide House, 7 Victoria Way, Burgess Hill, West Sussex, RH15 9NF Tel: (01444) 257733 Fax: (01444) 257744
E-mail: sales@hammertex.co.uk

BANNER FRAMES

▶ Piggotts, 43 London Road, Stanford Rivers, Ongar, Essex, CM5 9PJ Tel: (01277) 363262 Fax: (01277) 365162
E-mail: sales@piggott.co.uk

Sign Trade Supplies, Britannia House, Granville Road, Maidstone, Kent, ME14 2BJ Tel: (01622) 689410 Fax: (01622) 689416
E-mail: orders@signtradesupplies.co.uk

▶ Spirit Displays Ltd, 14 Victory Road Wimbledon, London, SW19 1HN Tel: (020) 8542 7279 Fax: (020) 8542 1680
E-mail: info@spirit-displays.com

BANNERS

Aaask Innobative Solutions, The Gap, Hafod Moor, Gwernaffield, Mold, Clwyd, CH7 5ET Tel: 0141-616 3333 Fax: 0141-639 5895
E-mail: sales@aaask.com

Abee Signs London Ltd, 435 Lordship Lane, London, N22 5DH Tel: (020) 8889 6126 Fax: (020) 8888 9009
E-mail: sales@abeesigns.co.uk

Allegro Bags, 110 Huttoft Road, Sutton-On-Sea, Mablethorpe, Lincolnshire, LN12 2RU Tel: (01507) 440192
E-mail: allegrobags@btconnect.com

Amazing Bunting Co., Units 1-7, 22 Pleydell Road, Northampton, NN4 8NL Tel: (01604) 675556 Fax: (01604) 675557
E-mail: sales@amazingbunting.co.uk

Assignment Signs & Nameplates, 26 Brindley Road, Dodwells Bridge Industrial Estate, Hinckley, Leicestershire, LE10 3BY Tel: (01455) 891200 Fax: (01455) 619426

Banner Warehouse, Unit 4 & 5 Knowle Business Centre, Wadhurst Road, Frant, Tunbridge Wells, Kent, TN3 9EJ Tel: (0800) 0523659 Fax: (0800) 0523658
E-mail: regencysigns@btclick.com

Bastow & Ryder Ltd, 157 Sunbridge Road, Bradford, West Yorkshire, BD1 2NU Tel: (01274) 724358

Beekay Products, 152-154 Ilderton Road, London, SE15 1NT Tel: (020) 7732 8608 Fax: (020) 7277 6996

▶ C & S Banners, 244 North Lane, Aldershot, Hampshire, GU12 4TJ Tel: (01252) 317701 Fax: (01252) 324375

▶ Chris Choi, Unit 3, Alexandra Court, Alexandra Road, Yeovil, Somerset, BA21 5AL Tel: (01935) 478175

Concept Signs, 40-42 Albert Road, Braintree, Essex, CM7 3JQ Tel: (01376) 329240 Fax: (01376) 331937
E-mail: signsconcept@aol.com

Covertech Plastics, Springfield Commerical Centre, Bagley Lane, Farsley, Pudsey, West Yorkshire, LS28 5LY Tel: 0113-255 2288 Fax: 0113-255 2381
E-mail: enquiries@cover-techleeds.co.uk

▶ Creative Graphics International, Unit 21, Weston Road Industrial Estate, Stratford-upon-Avon, Warwickshire, CV37 0AH Tel: (01789) 415141 Fax: (01789) 414160

Delta Flags Ltd, 37 Weathercock Lane, Woburn Sands, Milton Keynes, MK17 8NP Tel: (01908) 582883 Fax: (01908) 582552
E-mail: info@deltaflags.co.uk

Elite Signs, Albemarle Rd, Taunton, Somerset, TA1 1BE Tel: (01823) 366219 Fax: (01823) 251095 E-mail: signs@elitecameron.com

Ensign Flag, 42 Dunes Way, Liverpool, L5 9RJ Tel: 0151-298 1007 Fax: 0151-298 1006
E-mail: enquiries@ensignflags.com

Eventsigns Sign Makers, Unit 6 Poplar Drive, Witton, Birmingham, B6 7AD Tel: 0121-344 3141 Fax: 0121-344 3181
E-mail: eventsignsgb@aol.com

Express Services, Henson Way, Telford Way Industrial Estate, Kettering, Northamptonshire, NN16 8PX Tel: (01536) 481778 Fax: (01536) 521412
E-mail: sales@express-services.uk.com

Fair Sign Co., Unit E6 Aladdin Workspace, 426 Long Drive, Greenford, Middlesex, UB6 8UH Tel: (020) 8578 3080 Fax: (020) 8578 3082
E-mail: sales@fairsign.co.uk

Flag Services & Supply Co., 302 Westbourne Grove, Westcliff-on-Sea, Essex, SS0 0PT Tel: (01702) 333343 Fax: (01702) 343330

Flags & Banners Ltd, Springfield Industrial Estate, Burnham-on-Crouch, Essex, CM0 8TE Tel: (01621) 783221 Fax: (01621) 783532
E-mail: sales@flags-banners.co.uk

Fosco Hayes-Hurdley Ltd, Carlton House, 41 Smith Street, Hockley, Birmingham, B19 3EN Tel: 0121-554 7421 Fax: 0121-523 4452
E-mail: enquiries@foscos.co.uk

Girdwood Display, 44 St. Marys Street, Edinburgh, EH1 1SZ Tel: 0131-556 7024 Fax: 0131-557 8288
E-mail: girdwooddisplay@aol.com

Halton Print & Promotional, High Street, Knutton, Newcastle, Staffordshire, ST5 6BX Tel: (01782) 712909 Fax: (01782) 713626
E-mail: info@haltonpromotional.co.uk

Icon Display, 130-136 Maidstone Road, Sidcup, Kent, DA14 5HS Tel: (020) 8302 4921 Fax: (020) 8302 3971
E-mail: icondisplay@cix.co.uk

J & D Wilkie Ltd, Gairie Works, Bellies Brae, Kirriemuir, Angus, DD8 4BL Tel: (01575) 572502 Fax: (01575) 574564
E-mail: sales@jdwilkie.co.uk

J S W Inflatables, Unit 8, Church Hill Road, Thurmaston, Leicester, LE4 8DH Tel: 0116-264 0162 Fax: 0116-269 6814
E-mail: inflatafun@aol.com

J W Plant & Co. Ltd, 39 Ashley Road, Leeds, LS9 7AJ Tel: 0113-248 0454 Fax: 0113-235 0118 E-mail: sales@jwplant.co.uk

Mccall Promotional Products Ltd, Gorse Farm, Lutterworth Road, Bramcote, Nuneaton, Warwickshire, CV11 6QL Tel: (024) 7637 2835

Morgan Associates, Unit 15 Ilford Trading Estate, Paycocke Road, Basildon, Essex, SS14 3DR Tel: (01268) 288587 Fax: (01268) 288587
E-mail: info@ma4.co.uk

Northern Flags Ltd, Unit 1 5 Matrix Court, Leeds, LS11 5WB Tel: 0113-205 5180 Fax: 0113-205 5181 E-mail: info@northernflags.com

Omega Drapes, Unit 17 Riverside Industrial Estate, Thames Road, Barking, Essex, IG11 0ND Tel: (020) 8591 4945 Fax: (020) 8591 4139
E-mail: sales@omegadrapes.fsnet.co.uk

Peel Graphics, 104-106 Bridge Street, Heywood, Lancashire, OL10 1JG Tel: (01706) 621960 Fax: (01706) 625249
E-mail: sales@peelgraphics.co.uk

R. Billson & Sons Ltd, 431 Thurmaston Boulevard, Off Claymill Road, Leicester, LE4 9LA Tel: 0116-276 2555 Fax: 0116-276 9234

R S Covers, 57 Strand Road, Bootle, Merseyside, L20 4BG Tel: 0151-933 9059 Fax: 0151-923 2490

Sigma Signs Ltd, Unit 4B, Arun Buildings, Arundel Road, Uxbridge, Middlesex, UB8 2RP Tel: (01895) 273268 Fax: (01895) 271614
E-mail: signs@sigmasigns.com

Signline, Wayside House, Chapel Road, Meppershall, Shefford, Bedfordshire, SG17 5NQ Tel: (01462) 850718 Fax: (01462) 851212 E-mail: sales@signline.co.uk

SignRight, 157-161 West Road, Westcliff-On-Sea, Essex, SS0 9DH Tel: (01702) 308486 Fax: (0870) 7061711
E-mail: info@signright.co.uk

Spectrum Signs, 290 Northholt Road, South Harrow, Harrow, Middlesex, HA2 8EB Tel: (020) 8422 1168 Fax: (020) 8864 4220
E-mail: spectrumsigns@webtribe.net

Speedings Flags Poles & Masts, 4 Carrmere Road, Leechmere Industrial Estate, Sunderland, SR2 9TW Tel: 0191-523 9933 Fax: 0191-523 9955
E-mail: speedingsltd@btconnect.com

Stanford Signs, 13 Gideons Way, Stanford-le-Hope, Essex, SS17 8EE Tel: (01268) 753810 Fax: (01268) 753810

James Stevenson Flags Ltd, 75 Westmoreland Street, Glasgow, G42 8LH Tel: 0141-423 5757 Fax: 0141-946 3741
E-mail: john@stevensonflags.com

▶ Super Wide Digital, Cromer Industrial Estate, Hilton Fold Lane, Middleton, Manchester, M24 2LE Tel: 0161-653 6500 Fax: 0161-654 9500 E-mail: sales@super-wide.co.uk

▶ Swiftec, Pennine House, Tilson Road, Roundthorn Industrial Estate, Manchester, M23 9GF Tel: 0161-945 1500 Fax: (0800) 0740005

Thames Valley Textiles, Oddington Grange, Weston-on-the-Green, Bicester, Oxfordshire, OX25 3QW Tel: (01865) 331009 Fax: (01865) 331721 E-mail: info@tvt1.co.uk

TLC Signs, Fairfax House, Deeping St.James Road, Deeping Gate, Peterborough, PE6 9AP Tel: (01778) 349282
E-mail: sales@tlcsigns.co.uk

Trounce Ltd, New St Marks Works, St Marks Lane, Manchester, M8 4FW Tel: 0161-740 2159 Fax: 0161-721 4768
E-mail: sales@trounce.co.uk

George Tutill Ltd, 9 Higham Road, Chesham, Buckinghamshire, HP5 2AF Tel: (01494) 783938 Fax: (01494) 791241
E-mail: info@flags-tutill.co.uk

Union Industries, Whitehouse Street, Leeds, LS10 1AD Tel: 0113-244 8393 Fax: 0113-242 1307 E-mail: sales@unionindustries.co.uk

Up The Pole Ltd, 56 Meadow Road, Catshill, Bromsgrove, Worcestershire, B61 0JL Tel: (01527) 833873 Fax: (01527) 836578

▶ Vinyl Signs, 85 Clos Myddlyn, Beddau, Pontypridd, Mid Glamorgan, CF38 2JT Tel: (01443) 201871 Fax: (01443) 208474
E-mail: sales@vinylsign.biz

Wordcrafts, Unit 9 The Beaver Centre, Putney Road West, Freemans Common, Leicester, LE2 7TD Tel: 0116-255 8422 Fax: 0116-255 0624 E-mail: info@wordcrafts.co.uk

BANQUETING FURNITURE

Imperial Finishers Ltd, 8 Windmill Close, Stansted, Essex, CM24 8GH Tel: (01279) 817500 Fax: (01279) 817517

▶ Oblong Furniture Ltd, 80a York Street, Leeds, LS9 8AA Tel: 0113-242 6111 Fax: 0113-243 1858 E-mail: info@oblongfurniture.co.uk

Stencel Furniture, 315 Finchley Road, London, NW3 6EH Tel: (020) 3112 0112 Fax: (020) 3112 0112 E-mail: sales@stencel.co.uk

BANQUETING FURNITURE HIRE

B S Sales, 149 Hale Lane, Edgware, Middlesex, HA8 9QW Tel: (020) 8201 0101 Fax: (020) 8201 0022

BANQUETING SERVICES

Embassy Suite, 2 Balkerne Hill, Colchester, CO3 3AA Tel: (01206) 575910 Fax: (01206) 763042

Nisha Wear Ltd, 215-216 Bradford Street, Deritend, Birmingham, B12 0RG Tel: 0121-773 6060 Fax: 0121-773 5573

Redcliffe Catering Ltd, Westbourne Road, Edgbaston, Birmingham, B15 3TR Tel: 0121-456 2244 Fax: 0121-450 4620
E-mail: sales@redcliffe.com

BAR CODE BUSINESS SOLUTION SERVICES

▶ Bar Code Systems (London) Ltd, Lakeside House, 1 Furzeground Way, Stockley Park, Uxbridge, Middlesex, UB11 1BD Tel: (0870) 3516496 Fax: (020) 8622 3249 E-mail: robertmoorman@barcode-systems.com
Computoy Computer Consultants, 151 Boundary Road, London, E13 9PT Tel: (020) 8552 1800 Fax: (020) 8470 0909 E-mail: stephen@computoy.co.uk
Datascan Systems Ltd, Harris Business Park, Hanbury Road, Stoke Prior, Bromsgrove, Worcestershire, B60 4BD Tel: (01527) 839010 Fax: (01527) 839011 E-mail: sales@datascansystems.com
Direct Labels, Unit 2c Allans Indust Park, Coulman Street, Thorne, Doncaster, South Yorkshire, DN8 5JS Tel: (01405) 741111 Fax: (01405) 741112 E-mail: sales@directlabelsonline.co.uk
Intellident, Southgate Centre Two, Wilmslow Road, Heald Green, Cheadle, Cheshire, SK8 3PW Tel: 0161-436 9950 Fax: 0161-436 8787 E-mail: sales@intellident.co.uk
Latham Finishers Ltd, P O Box 794, Luton, LU1 4YA Tel: 01582 455322 Fax: 01582 455322
Pen Mobile Solutions, Court Farm, Moor Road, Banwell, Avon, BS29 6ET Tel: (01934) 823800 Fax: (01934) 820220 E-mail: sales@penmobile.co.uk
▶ Quick Thermal Transfer Ltd, 32 Cricketers Close, Ashington, Pulborough, West Sussex, RH20 3JQ Tel: (01903) 893308 E-mail: sales@qtt.info
Service Logic, Dunstable Road, Redbourn, St. Albans, Hertfordshire, AL3 7PR Tel: (01582) 792277 Fax: (01582) 792207 E-mail: info@servicelogic.co.uk
Worldwide Solutions Ltd, Unit 5, Alfred Court, Saxon Business Park, Hanbury Road, Stoke Prior, Bromsgrove, Worcestershire, B60 4AD Tel: (01527) 870849 Fax: (01527) 874499 E-mail: enquiries@wwsolutions.co.uk

BAR CODE EQUIPMENT AND PRODUCTS, *See also headings for particular types*

Aktec, Office 3 78-86 Pennywell Road, Old Market, Bristol, BS5 0TG Tel: 0117-935 1999 Fax: 0117-935 1950E-mail: info@akteclt d.com
Auto-Id.Co.Uk, 13 Telford Way, Severalls Industrial Park, Colchester, CO4 9QP Tel: (01206) 751349 Fax: (01206) 854332 E-mail: sales@auto-id.co.uk
Bar Codes For Business Ltd, 56 Packhorse Road, Gerrards Cross, Buckinghamshire, SL9 8EF Tel: (01753) 888833 Fax: (01753) 888834 E-mail: sales@barcodesforbusiness.co.uk
Barbuys Bar Equipment, 19 Index Drive, Dunstable, Bedfordshire, LU6 3TU Tel: (01582) 605477 Fax: (01582) 605477
Barcode Concepts, 4 Beckfield Drive, Glasgow, G33 1SF Tel: 0141-558 3311 Fax: 0141-558 3322 E-mail: 2johnl@barcodeconcept.com
Barcode Connections Ltd, 18 King Harry Lane, St. Albans, Hertfordshire, AL3 4AR Tel: (01727) 833391 Fax: (01727) 838819 E-mail: info@tele-ticket.co.uk
▶ Code-IT, Unit 11, Lea Green Business Park, Eurolink, St. Helens, Merseyside, WA9 4TR Tel: (01744) 811564 Fax: (01744) 811395 E-mail: code.it@virgin.net
Control & Traceability Systems, The Mistal Hagg Farm, Haggs Road, Follifoot, Harrogate, North Yorkshire, HG3 1EQ Tel: (01423) 810820 Fax: (01423) 810288 E-mail: info@ctsol.co.uk
▶ Data Capture & Apply Technology Ltd, PO Box 164, Brough, East Yorkshire, HU15 1AU Tel: (01482) 662626 Fax: (01482) 662626 E-mail: info@dcatonline.co.uk
DED Ltd, Mill Road, Lydd, Romney Marsh, Kent, TN29 9EJ Tel: (01797) 320636 Fax: (01797) 320273 E-mail: sales@ded.co.uk
▶ EG Coding, 9 Lochans Mill Avenue, Lochans, Stranraer, Wigtownshire, DG9 9BZ Tel: (07979) 692580 Fax: (07092) 870019 E-mail: ellisgaston@hotmail.com
▶ E-ScanShop Ltd, 25a Harris Business Park, Hanbury Road, Stoke Prior, Bromsgrove, Worcestershire, B60 4BD Tel: (0845) 6121282 Fax: (0845) 6121292 E-mail: sales@e-scanshop.com
Fontware Ltd, 25 Barnes Wallis Road, Fareham, Hampshire, PO15 5TT Tel: (01489) 505075 Fax: (0870) 0515816 E-mail: sales@fontware.com
▶ Gane Data Scan, Clayton Wood Rise, Leeds, LS16 6RF Tel: (0870) 2417356 Fax: (0870) 2417357 E-mail: sales@ganedatascan.com
▶ Innova IT Solutions, 1C Lyon Way, Greenford, Middlesex, UB6 0BN Tel: (020) 8833 7187
▶ Instone Labels Ltd, 5 Weighbridge Row, Cardiff Road, Reading, RG1 8LX Tel: 0118-956 8661 Fax: 0118-956 8662 E-mail: sales@instonelabels.com
Instrument Plastics Ltd, 33-37 Kings Grove Industrial Estate, Kings Grove, Maidenhead, Berkshire, SL6 4DP Tel: (01628) 770018 Fax: (01628) 773299 E-mail: sales@instrumentplastics.co.uk
▶ Komputrak Ltd, Redhill House, 41 Hope Street, Chester, CH4 8BU Tel: (01244) 671800 Fax: (01244) 671880
Neuroscot Ltd, 8 Meadow Street, Falkirk, FK1 1RP Tel: 0131-453 3845 Fax: 0131-453 3838 E-mail: neuroscot@compuserve.com
Pen Mobile Solutions, Court Farm, Moor Road, Banwell, Avon, BS29 6ET Tel: (01934) 823800 Fax: (01934) 820220 E-mail: sales@penmobile.co.uk
Printing & Scanning Solutions Ltd, Carradale, Kirby Road, Woking, Surrey, GU21 4RJ Tel: 01483 852581 E-mail: sales@pass-barcodes.co.uk
▶ Quick Thermal Transfer Ltd, 32 Cricketers Close, Ashington, Pulborough, West Sussex, RH20 3JQ Tel: (01903) 893308 E-mail: sales@qtt.info
Specialist Coding P.L.C., Greenbank Rd, East Tullos Ind Est, Aberdeen, AB12 3BQ Tel: 01224 894523 Fax: 01224 894358
Turton Retail Systems, 18 Hillside Avenue, Bromley Cross, Bolton, BL7 9NG Tel: (01204) 307589 Fax: (01204) 307589 E-mail: sales@turtonretail.co.uk
Unique Id Ltd, 1 Barnes Wallis Court, Wellington Road, Cressex Business Park, High Wycombe, Buckinghamshire, HP12 3PS Tel: (01494) 511022 Fax: (01494) 511033 E-mail: sales@barcodecentral.co.uk
▶ Weyfringe Labelling Systems, Longbeck Road, Marske-by-the-Sea, Redcar, Cleveland, TS11 6HQ Tel: (01642) 490121 Fax: (01642) 490385 E-mail: sales@weyfringe.co.uk
Worldwide Solutions Ltd, Unit 5, Alfred Court, Saxon Business Park, Hanbury Road, Stoke Prior, Bromsgrove, Worcestershire, B60 4AD Tel: (01527) 870849 Fax: (01527) 874499 E-mail: enquiries@wwsolutions.co.uk
Xact Prepack, Lawco House, 60 Vauxhall Road, Liverpool, L3 6DL Tel: 0151-4793070 Fax: 0151 4793022 E-mail: info@xactprepack.co.uk

BAR CODE EQUIPMENT REPAIR SERVICES

Aktec, Office 3 78-86 Pennywell Road, Old Market, Bristol, BS5 0TG Tel: 0117-935 1999 Fax: 0117-935 1950E-mail: info@akteclt d.com
Datascan Systems Ltd, Harris Business Park, Hanbury Road, Stoke Prior, Bromsgrove, Worcestershire, B60 4BD Tel: (01527) 839010 Fax: (01527) 839011 E-mail: sales@datascansystems.com
▶ EG Coding, 9 Lochans Mill Avenue, Lochans, Stranraer, Wigtownshire, DG9 9BZ Tel: (07979) 692580 Fax: (07092) 870019 E-mail: ellisgaston@hotmail.com
Pen Mobile Solutions, Court Farm, Moor Road, Banwell, Avon, BS29 6ET Tel: (01934) 823800 Fax: (01934) 820220 E-mail: sales@penmobile.co.uk
▶ S P C International, Unit 1-3, Station Road, Templecombe, Somerset, BA8 0JR Tel: (01963) 370504 Fax: (01963) 370101 E-mail: sales@spcint.com
Service Logic, Dunstable Road, Redbourn, St. Albans, Hertfordshire, AL3 7PR Tel: (01582) 792277 Fax: (01582) 792207 E-mail: info@servicelogic.co.uk

BAR CODE LABEL PRINTERS

A P L Industrial Ltd, 14 Carlisle Road, London, NW9 0HL Tel: (020) 8205 2444 Fax: (020) 8200 8037 E-mail: info@apl-industrial.co.uk
▶ Advanced Barcoding Solutions Ltd, 10-12 High Street, Burnham, Slough, SL1 7JH Tel: (0845) 1305975 Fax: (01628) 669530 E-mail: elliott.jones@abarcode.co.uk
Alliance Group, Evans Business Centre, Hartwith Way, Harrogate, North Yorkshire, HG3 2XA Tel: (01423) 504088 E-mail: sales@alliancegroup.co.uk
▶ Apex Labels UK Ltd, Oyo BSNS Units, Fishers Grove, Portsmouth, PO6 1SH Tel: (023) 9237 2220 Fax: (0845) 1307886 E-mail: andrew@apexlabels.co.uk
Columbian Press, 69 Lower Road, Kenley, Surrey, CR8 5NH Tel: (020) 8763 9088 Fax: (020) 8763 1053 E-mail: columbianpress@btinternet.com
▶ EPS Warehousing & Distribution, Euro House, St John Street, Leicester, LE1 3WL Tel: 0116-233 4545 Fax: 0116-233 8028 E-mail: g.hothi@europressing.com
▶ E-ScanShop Ltd, 25a Harris Business Park, Hanbury Road, Stoke Prior, Bromsgrove, Worcestershire, B60 4BD Tel: (0845) 6121282 Fax: (0845) 6121292 E-mail: sales@e-scanshop.com
Eurohill Labels Ltd, 195 Vale Road, Tonbridge, Kent, TN9 1SU Tel: (01732) 770700 Fax: (01732) 770779 E-mail: sales@eurohill.com
Gresham Forms Ltd, The Potting Shed Arkwright Road, Willowbrook East Industrial Estate, Willowbrook North Industrial Estate, Corby, Northamptonshire, NN17 5AE Tel: (01536) 408408 Fax: (01536) 408381 E-mail: sales@greshamticket.co.uk
▶ J H Davenport & Sons Ltd, Harehills Lane, Leeds, LS9 6JF Tel: 0113-249 5561 Fax: 0113-249 1381 E-mail: info@jhdavenport.co.uk
M.L.P.S., PO Box 27, Grantham, Lincs, NG31 6SJ Tel: (01476) 590400 Fax: (01476) 590400 E-mail: sales@mlps.co.uk
▶ MPF, The Slough, Studley, Warwickshire, B80 7EN Tel: (01527) 853840 Fax: (01527) 853843 E-mail: lee@mpfltd.co.uk
Printing & Scanning Solutions Ltd, Carradale, Kirby Road, Woking, Surrey, GU21 4RJ Tel: 01483 852581 E-mail: sales@pass-barcodes.co.uk
▶ Progressive Print Services, Firs Industrial Estate, Kidderminster, Worcestershire, DY11 7QN Tel: (01562) 747356 Fax: (01562) 747357 E-mail: sales@progressive-print.co.uk
▶ Tollgate Labels, Hyders Farm, Bonnetts Lane, Ifield, Crawley, West Sussex, RH11 0NY Tel: (01293) 551520 Fax: (01293) 551530 E-mail: sales@tollgatelabels.co.uk

BAR CODE LABEL STOCK

▶ Advanced Barcoding Solutions Ltd, 10-12 High Street, Burnham, Slough, SL1 7JH Tel: (0845) 1305975 Fax: (01628) 669530 E-mail: elliott.jones@abarcode.co.uk
Alliance Group, Evans Business Centre, Hartwith Way, Harrogate, North Yorkshire, HG3 2XA Tel: (01423) 504088 E-mail: sales@alliancegroup.co.uk
Data Teknologies Ltd, Seneca House, Buntsford Business Park, Buntsford Park Road, Bromsgrove, Worcestershire, B60 3DX Tel: (01527) 559411 Fax: (01527) 559258 E-mail: mail@datateknologies.com
Oki Buyer, 31a St. Neots Road, Eaton Ford, St. Neots, Cambridgeshire, PE19 7BA Tel: 0845 5314237 Fax: (01480) 403909 E-mail: sales@okibuyer.co.uk
▶ Thermaltran, Label House, 14 Summerfield Road, Kettering, Northamptonshire, NN15 6EN Tel: (01536) 392900 E-mail: Sales@thermaltran.co.uk
Tyco Electronics Identifications, Chapel Farm Industrial Estate, Cwmcarn/Cross Keys, Cross Keys, Newport, Gwent, NP11 7ZB Tel: (01495) 273519 Fax: (01495) 272979 E-mail: sales@tycoelectronics.com
Unique Id Ltd, 1 Barnes Wallis Court, Wellington Road, Cressex Business Park, High Wycombe, Buckinghamshire, HP12 3PS Tel: (01494) 511022 Fax: (01494) 511033 E-mail: sales@barcodecentral.co.uk
W E Mann, The Maids Head, Lynn Road, East Winch, King's Lynn, Norfolk, PE32 1NP Tel: (01553) 840965 E-mail: deemann@ntlworld.com
Webmaster Ltd, Units 5-6 Astra Industrial Centre, Royle Barn Road, Rochdale, Lancashire, OL11 3DT Tel: (01706) 656122 Fax: (01706) 764400 E-mail: sales@webmasterltd.co.uk

BAR CODE PRINTER MANUFRS

Applied Technology Development, Unit K1 Valley Way, Market Harborough, Leicestershire, LE16 7PS Tel: (01858) 461014 Fax: (01858) 461015 E-mail: mail@atduk.com
Columbian Press, 69 Lower Road, Kenley, Surrey, CR8 5NH Tel: (020) 8763 9088 Fax: (020) 8763 1053 E-mail: columbianpress@btinternet.com
Dragon Solutions UK Ltd, 55 Valley Road, Bramhall, Stockport, Cheshire, SK7 2NJ Tel: 0161-439 0610 Fax: 0161-439 9252 E-mail: sales@dragon-solutions.com
Electronic Reading Systems Ltd, 14 Wolsdon Business Park, Woburn Road Industrial Estate, Kempston, Bedford, MK42 7PW Tel: (01234) 855300 Fax: (01234) 855446 E-mail: sales@ersltd.co.uk
Genisys Group Ltd, Crockford Lane, Chineham, Basingstoke, Hampshire, RG24 8NA Tel: (01256) 816611 Fax: (01256) 816552 E-mail: sales@genisys.co.uk
▶ Progressive Print Services, Firs Industrial Estate, Kidderminster, Worcestershire, DY11 7QN Tel: (01562) 747356 Fax: (01562) 747357 E-mail: sales@progressive-print.co.uk
Synergix Peripheral Systems Ltd, Unit 3 The Sapphire Centre, Fishponds Road, Wokingham, Berkshire, RG41 2QL Tel: 0118-979 0992 Fax: 0118-989 2187 E-mail: info@synergix.co.uk
▶ Tollgate Labels, Hyders Farm, Bonnetts Lane, Ifield, Crawley, West Sussex, RH11 0NY Tel: (01293) 551520 Fax: (01293) 551530 E-mail: sales@tollgatelabels.co.uk

BAR CODE READERS

Altek Instruments Ltd, Enterprise House, 44-46 Terrace Road, Walton-on-Thames, Surrey, KT12 2SD Tel: (01932) 244110 Fax: (0870) 0548263 E-mail: info@barcodeman.com
Blackroc Systems Ltd, Drummond Road, Astonfields Industrial Estate, Stafford, ST16 3HJ Tel: (01785) 213777 Fax: (01785) 251546 E-mail: sales@blackroc.com
▶ Codepack Solutions Ltd, Woodhorn Lane, Oving, Chichester, West Sussex, PO20 2BX Tel: (01243) 792445 Fax: (01243) 792108 E-mail: sales@codepack.co.uk
Contech Electronics Ltd, Unit C Mindenhall Court, High Street, Stevenage, Hertfordshire, SG1 3BG Tel: (01438) 315757 Fax: (01438) 313679 E-mail: sales@contech.co.uk
Data Teknologies Ltd, Seneca House, Buntsford Business Park, Buntsford Park Road, Bromsgrove, Worcestershire, B60 3DX Tel: (01527) 559411 Fax: (01527) 559258 E-mail: mail@datateknologies.com
Datalogic Scanning, Datalogic House, Dunstable Road, Redbourn, St. Albans, Hertfordshire, AL3 7PR Tel: (01582) 791700 Fax: (01582) 791705 E-mail: uk.scanning@datalogic.com
Deister Electronic UK, Camel Gate, Spalding, Lincolnshire, PE12 6ET Tel: (01775) 717100 Fax: (01775) 717101 E-mail: info@deister.co.uk
Dragon Solutions UK Ltd, 55 Valley Road, Bramhall, Stockport, Cheshire, SK7 2NJ Tel: 0161-439 0610 Fax: 0161-439 9252 E-mail: sales@dragon-solutions.com
▶ E-ScanShop Ltd, 25a Harris Business Park, Hanbury Road, Stoke Prior, Bromsgrove, Worcestershire, B60 4BD Tel: (0845) 6121282 Fax: (0845) 6121292 E-mail: sales@e-scanshop.com
Industrial Controls Ltd, Unit 1 Audley Court, Lodge Way, Thetford, Norfolk, IP24 1HT Tel: (01842) 750800 Fax: (01842) 765900 E-mail: sales@industrialcontrols.co.uk
Service Logic, Dunstable Road, Redbourn, St. Albans, Hertfordshire, AL3 7PR Tel: (01582) 792277 Fax: (01582) 792207 E-mail: info@servicelogic.co.uk

BAR CODE READERS, ULTRAVIOLET (UV)

▶ Packaging Solutions Provider, 21 Pinewood Drive, Markfield Court, Markfield, Leicestershire, LE67 9RQ Tel: (01530) 243743 E-mail: bob.locke@packaginsolutionsprovider.co.uk

BAR CODE SCANNING SYSTEMS

UK Digital Storage Ltd, 91 Station Road, Forest Hall, Newcastle upon Tyne, NE12 8AQ Tel: 0191-280 0001 Fax: 0191-290 0001 E-mail: dbryce@ukdigitalstorage.com

BAR CODE SYSTEMS MANUFRS

Agamik Ltd, Cathlaw House, Bathgate, West Lothian, EH48 4NW Tel: (01506) 650163 Fax: (01506) 630216 E-mail: info@agamik.co.uk
Altek Instruments Ltd, Enterprise House, 44-46 Terrace Road, Walton-on-Thames, Surrey, KT12 2SD Tel: (01932) 244110 Fax: (0870) 0548263 E-mail: info@barcodeman.com
Barcode Connections Ltd, 18 King Harry Lane, St. Albans, Hertfordshire, AL3 4AR Tel: (01727) 833391 Fax: (01727) 838819 E-mail: info@tele-ticket.co.uk
Blackroc Systems Ltd, Drummond Road, Astonfields Industrial Estate, Stafford, ST16 3HJ Tel: (01785) 213777 Fax: (01785) 251546 E-mail: sales@blackroc.com
Britsoft Barcode Systems Ltd, 1 Kings Road, Hertford, SG13 7EY Tel: (01992) 554552 Fax: (01992) 552426 E-mail: sales@britsoft.com
Bulmers Business Machines Ltd, Royston House, 267 Cranmore Boulevard, Shirley, Solihull, West Midlands, B90 4QT Tel: 0121-745 5529 Fax: 0121-733 6180
Business Equipment Distributors, 16 Swanlow Avenue, Winsford, Cheshire, CW7 1PB Tel: (01606) 551755 Fax: (01606) 551755 E-mail: info@business-labels.co.uk
C D M, Central Boulavard, Blythe Valley Park, Solihull, West Midlands, B90 8AG Tel: (0870) 0116682 Fax: (01264) 711396 E-mail: cdmcontrol@aol.com
Codegate Ltd, Unit 3 The Sapphire Centre, Fishponds Road, Wokingham, Berkshire, RG41 2QL Tel: 0118-977 0808 Fax: 0118-989 2187 E-mail: sales@codegate.co.uk
Codeway Ltd, 13 Telford Way, Severalls Industrial Park, Colchester, CO4 9QP Tel: (01206) 756738 Fax: (01206) 756705 E-mail: sales@codeway.com
Computalabel International Ltd, 2ND Floor, 53A London Road, Leicester, LE2 0PD Tel: 0116-255 7898 Fax: 0116-255 7899 E-mail: info@computalabel.com
Computype Ltd, Oslo Road, Hull, HU7 0YN Tel: (01482) 835366 Fax: (01482) 822441 E-mail: enquiries@compu.co.uk
Data Teknologies Ltd, Seneca House, Buntsford Business Park, Buntsford Park Road, Bromsgrove, Worcestershire, B60 3DX Tel: (01527) 559411 Fax: (01527) 559258 E-mail: mail@datateknologies.com
Datalogic Scanning, Datalogic House, Dunstable Road, Redbourn, St. Albans, Hertfordshire, AL3 7PR Tel: (01582) 791700 Fax: (01582) 791705 E-mail: uk.scanning@datalogic.com
Earlsmere Id Systems Ltd, Earlsmere House, Doncaster Road, Barnsley, South Yorkshire, S71 5EH Tel: (01226) 204096 Fax: (01226) 244169 E-mail: sales@earlsmere.co.uk
Electronic Reading Systems Ltd, 14 Wolsdon Business Park, Woburn Road Industrial Estate, Kempston, Bedford, MK42 7PW Tel: (01234) 855300 Fax: (01234) 855446 E-mail: sales@ersltd.co.uk
▶ Episys Group Ltd, Newark Close, York Way, Royston, Hertfordshire, SG8 5HL Tel: (01763) 248866 Fax: (01763) 246000
Hand Held Products, 109 Dallam Court, Dallam Lane, Warrington, WA2 7LT Tel: (01925) 240055 Fax: (01925) 631280 E-mail: euro-sales@handheld.com
Image Computer Systems Ltd, 27 Cobham Road, Ferndown Industrial Estate, Wimborne, Dorset, BH21 7PE Tel: (01202) 876064 Fax: (01202) 897682 E-mail: sales@image-cs.co.uk

BAR CODE SYSTEMS MANUFRS – *continued*

▶ Label Innovations, Enfield Industrial Estate, Redditch, Worcestershire, B97 6BN Tel: (01527) 597774 Fax: (01527) 597775 E-mail: sales@label-innovations.com
Leuze Mayser Electronic Ltd, Generation Business Park, Barford Road, St. Neots, Cambridgeshire, PE19 6YQ Tel: (01480) 408500 Fax: (01480) 403808 E-mail: mail@leuzemayser.co.uk
S B Electronic Systems Ltd, Arden Grove, Harpenden, Hertfordshire, AL5 4SL Tel: (01582) 769991 Fax: (01582) 461705 E-mail: sales@telepen.co.uk
Scanner Services Ltd, 7 Bluebell Court, Woking, Surrey, GU22 0HQ Tel: (01483) 762943 Fax: (01483) 871624
Sick UK Ltd, Waldkirch House, 39 Hedley Road, St. Albans, Hertfordshire, AL1 5BN Tel: (01727) 831121 Fax: (01727) 856767 E-mail: info@sick.co.uk
Symbol Technologies Ltd, Symbol Place, Wharfedale Road, Winnersh, Wokingham, Berkshire, RG41 5TP Tel: 0118-945 7000 Fax: 0118-945 7500
Toshiba TEC Europe UK Operations, 1 Siskin House, Marlins Meadow, Croxley Business Park, Watford, WD18 8TY Tel: (01923) 233688 Fax: (01923) 233698 E-mail: administrator@toshibatec-eu.co.uk
Trackit Systems Ltd, Trival House, Unit 3 Hawthorne Park, Coal Road, Leeds, LS14 1PQ Tel: 0113-306 0306 Fax: 0113-276 0685
Zebra Technologies (Europe) Ltd, Zebra House, The Valley Centre, Gordon Road, High Wycombe, Buckinghamshire, HP13 6EQ Tel: (01494) 472872 Fax: (01494) 450103

BAR CODE TERMINALS, PALM, HAND HELD

Dragon Solutions UK Ltd, 55 Valley Road, Bramhall, Stockport, Cheshire, SK7 2NJ Tel: 0161-439 0610 Fax: 0161-439 9252 E-mail: sales@dragon-solutions.com
▶ Weyfringe Labelling Systems, Longbeck Road, Marske-by-the-Sea, Redcar, Cleveland, TS11 6HQ Tel: (01642) 490121 Fax: (01642) 490385 E-mail: sales@weyfringe.co.uk

BAR CODED LABELS

A C Labels Ltd, 3 Centurion Way Business Park, Alfreton Road, Derby, DE21 4AY Tel: (01332) 366117 Fax: (01332) 291292 E-mail: d.clouston@aclabels.co.uk
A D S Worldwide Ltd, West Carr Lane, Sutton Fields, Hull, HU7 0BW Tel: (01482) 820219 Fax: (01482) 831596 E-mail: sales@ads-worldwide.com
A S G Services Ltd, 8 Easter Court, Europa Boulevard, Westbrook, Warrington, WA5 7ZB Tel: (01925) 710923 Fax: (01925) 712966 E-mail: info@asgservices.co.uk
Argonaut Press, Kendalls Buildings, Birmingham Road, Stratford-upon-Avon, Warwickshire, CV37 0AQ Tel: (01789) 414478 Fax: (01789) 414478 E-mail: john@argonautpress.co.uk
Aries Barcoding & Labelling Ltd, Philpot House, Station Road, Rayleigh, Essex, SS6 7HH Tel: (01268) 774494 Fax: (01268) 777959 E-mail: ablltd@btconnect.com
B & M Labelling Supplies, 41 High Street, Linton, Cambridge, CB21 4HS Tel: (01223) 890569 Fax: (01223) 892366 E-mail: sales@bandmlabelling.co.uk
Blue Code Labelling Technology, Great Central Way Industrial Estate, Great Central Way, Rugby, Warwickshire, CV21 3XH Tel: (01788) 576100 Fax: (01788) 578900 E-mail: sales@bluecode.co.uk
Bridgelock Engineering & Marketing Ltd, 137 Slough Road, Datchet, Slough, SL3 9AE Tel: (01753) 549373 Fax: (01753) 580269 E-mail: sales@bridgelock.com
The Classic Label Company Ltd, Unit 9-14 Whitehall Properties, Town Gate, Wyke, Bradford, West Yorkshire, BD12 9JQ Tel: (01274) 690217 Fax: (01274) 690046 E-mail: info@classiclabels.co.uk
Computype Ltd, Oslo Road, Hull, HU7 0YN Tel: (01482) 835366 Fax: (01482) 822441 E-mail: enquiries@compu.co.uk
Control & Traceability Systems, The Mistal Hagg Farm, Haggs Road, Follifoot, Harrogate, North Yorkshire, HG3 1EQ Tel: (01423) 810820 Fax: (01423) 810288 E-mail: info@ctsol.co.uk
Ditac Ltd, 1 Latton Bush Business Centre, Southern Way, Harlow, Essex, CM18 7BH Tel: (01279) 427100 Fax: (01279) 427103
▶ Episys Group Ltd, Newark Close, York Way, Royston, Hertfordshire, SG8 5HL Tel: (01763) 248866 Fax: (01763) 246000
Eurohill Labels Ltd, 195 Vale Road, Tonbridge, Kent, TN9 1SU Tel: (01732) 770700 Fax: (01732) 770779 E-mail: sales@eurohill.com
Harlands of Hull Ltd, Burma Drive, Hull, HU9 5SD Tel: (01482) 785300 Fax: (01482) 785329 E-mail: enquiries@harlands.co.uk
Iml Labels & Systems Ltd, 6 Brookdale Road, Thorncliffe Park Estate, Chapeltown, Sheffield, S35 2PW Tel: 0114-246 5771 Fax: 0114-240 3410 E-mail: sales@iml-labels.co.uk
Inotec UK, Unit 1, Viking Close, Hull, HU10 6DZ Tel: (01482) 654466 Fax: (01482) 655004
Janda Barcode Label Services, Unit 17 Progress Business Park, Orders Lane, Kirkham, Preston, PR4 2TZ Tel: (01772) 686651 Fax: (01772) 684106 E-mail: sales@jandadigital.co.uk
Label Apeel Ltd, James House, Murrayfield Road, Leicester, LE3 1UW Tel: 0116-231 4555 Fax: 0116-231 4552 E-mail: info@labelapeel.co.uk
▶ Label Innovations, Enfield Industrial Estate, Redditch, Worcestershire, B97 6BN Tel: (01527) 597774 Fax: (01527) 597775 E-mail: sales@label-innovations.com
Label Spec, Unit 2, Drummond Crescent, Riverside Business Park, Irvine, Ayrshire, KA11 5AN Tel: (01563) 550990 Fax: (01563) 550991 E-mail: sales@labelspec.co.uk
Label-Form Ltd, Reform Road, Maidenhead, Berkshire, SL6 8BY Tel: (01628) 782082 Fax: (01628) 770879 E-mail: sales@label-form.co.uk
Labelpower Ltd, 6 Kingsbury Trading Estate, Church Lane, London, NW9 8AU Tel: (020) 8205 8255 Fax: (020) 8200 1769 E-mail: sales@labelpower.co.uk
Labels Symbology Ltd, 22 Froghall Lane, Warrington, WA2 7JR Tel: (01925) 415135 Fax: (01925) 415775
Macfarlane Group Ukltd, 22 Bentinck Street, Kilmarnock, Ayrshire, KA1 4AS Tel: (01563) 525151 Fax: (01563) 539963 E-mail: kwoodhouse@macfarlanelabels.com
Manor Marketing Label Supplies, 11 Manor Drive, Fenstanton, Huntingdon, Cambridgeshire, PE28 9QZ Tel: (01480) 462443 Fax: (01480) 359015
Maxwell Labels, Unit 8, Moorbridge Road, Bingham Industrial Estate, Nottingham, NG13 8GG Tel: (01949) 837831 Fax: (01949) 831128
Nitto UK Ltd, Unit2 Berkshire Business Centre, Berkshire Drive, Thatcham, Berkshire, RG19 4EW Tel: (01635) 872172 Fax: (01635) 872332 E-mail: nitto_uk@nittoeur.com
Nuprint Trimmings Ltd, Unit 21 Springtown Industrial Estate, Springtown Road, Londonderry, BT48 0LY Tel: (028) 7128 2080 Fax: (028) 7126 0009
Peninsular Nameplates, Peninsular House, Carr Lane, Hoylake, Wirral, Merseyside, CH47 4AY Tel: (0151-632 5814 Fax: 0151-632 1090 E-mail: info@peninsular-nameplates.co.uk
R G S Labels, Units 7 & 8, Roman Way Small Business Park, London Road, Godmanchester, Huntingdon, Cambridgeshire, PE29 2LN Tel: (01480) 456556 Fax: (01480) 456578 E-mail: sales@rgslabels.co.uk
▶ Robstock Ltd, Unit 9-10, Rope Walk, Ilkeston, Derbyshire, DE7 5HX Tel: 0115-930 3308 Fax: 0115-932 4726 E-mail: sales@robstock.co.uk
Royston Labels Ltd, 18 Orchard Road, Royston, Hertfordshire, SG8 5HD Tel: (01763) 212020 Fax: (01763) 248004 E-mail: info@roystonlabels.co.uk
S B Electronic Systems Ltd, Arden Grove, Harpenden, Hertfordshire, AL5 4SL Tel: (01582) 769991 Fax: (01582) 461705 E-mail: sales@telepen.co.uk
Secura Labels Ltd, Unit L2 Westminster Industrial Estate, Measham, Swadlincote, Derbyshire, DE12 7DS Tel: (01530) 515170 Fax: (01530) 515171 E-mail: sales@securalabels.co.uk
Simpson Label Co. Ltd, Newbattle Industrial Estate, Mayfield, Dalkeith, Midlothian, EH22 4AF Tel: 0131-654 2800 Fax: 0131-663 6185 E-mail: mail@simpsonlabel.co.uk
South East Labels, 7 Broomers Hill Park, Broomers Hill Lane, Pulborough, West Sussex, RH20 2RY Tel: (01798) 873738 Fax: (01798) 874538 E-mail: sales@southeastlabels.co.uk
▶ Tollgate Labels, Hyders Farm, Bonnetts Lane, Ifield, Crawley, West Sussex, RH11 0NY Tel: (01293) 551520 Fax: (01293) 551530 E-mail: sales@tollgatelabels.co.uk
Tormax UK Ltd, Tormax HS Unit 21 Mole Bus Park, Randalls Road, Leatherhead, Surrey, KT22 7BD Tel: (01372) 377711 Fax: (01372) 378044 E-mail: tormax@langleysystems.co.uk
Vista Labels Limited, Vista House, Hempshaw Lane, Stockport, Cheshire, SK1 4NB Tel: 0161-477 5151 Fax: 0161-477 9203 E-mail: sales@vistalabels.com
Worldmark, 4 Redwood CR, East Kilbride, Glasgow, G74 5PA Tel: (01355) 249191 Fax: (01355) 230875 E-mail: info@donprint.com
Worldmark, 4 Redwood CR, East Kilbride, Glasgow, G74 5PA Tel: (01355) 249191 Fax: (01355) 230875 E-mail: info@donprint.com

BAR FEED MAGAZINES

C S J Enterprises, Unit 96 Spring Hill Farm, Salters Lane, Lower Moor, Pershore, Worcestershire, WR10 2PE Tel: (01386) 861777 Fax: (01386) 861666 E-mail: csjent@aol.com
Hydrafeed Ltd, Talgarth House, Bond Avenue, Bletchley, Milton Keynes, MK1 1JD Tel: (01908) 376630 Fax: (01908) 647843 E-mail: info@hydrafeed.co.uk
LNS Turbo UK Ltd, Waterside Park, Valley Way, Wombwell, Barnsley, South Yorkshire, S73 0BB Tel: (01226) 270033 Fax: (01226) 270044 E-mail: sales@lnsturbouk.com
T D T Technology Ltd, Unit 20 Woodside Park, Rugby, Warwickshire, CV21 2NP Tel: (01788) 570411 Fax: (01788) 567632 E-mail: sales@tdt-technology.co.uk

BAR (LICENSED) COUNTER MOUNTS/TAPS

The Alumasc Group Plc, Station Road, Burton Latimer, Kettering, Northamptonshire, NN15 5JP Tel: (01536) 383848 Fax: (01536) 420147 E-mail: info@alumascprecision.co.uk
Wilman Marine Ltd, 510 Victoria Road, Feltham, Middlesex, TW13 7DR Tel: (020) 8890 4000 Fax: (020) 8751 4128 E-mail: wilmanuniversal@msn.com

BAR (LICENSED) DRINKS TRADE WHOLESALERS/SUPPLY SERVICES

ABCO-Anderson Beverage Co. Ltd, Unit 6B, Chevychase Court, Seaham Grange Estate, Seaham, County Durham, SR7 0PR Tel: 0191-521 3366 Fax: 0191-521 3377 E-mail: info@abcosoftdrinks.co.uk
Betarange Ltd, Leverington Road, Wisbech, Cambridgeshire, PE13 1PJ Tel: (01945) 583200 Fax: (01945) 463099
Denham Wine Ltd, 1-3 Law Lane, Halifax, West Yorkshire, HX3 9QU Tel: (01422) 356146 Fax: (01422) 380224
Greene King Brewing & Retailing Ltd, Westgate Brewery, Bury St. Edmunds, Suffolk, IP33 1QT Tel: (01284) 763222 Fax: (01284) 706502 E-mail: gregwilliams@greeneking.co.uk
▶ GSR Services, 1 Gristmill Close, Cheltenham, Gloucestershire, GL51 0PZ Tel: (01242) 708407 Fax: 01242 708407 E-mail: sales@gsrservices.co.uk
Hoyes & Son Ltd, 22 Oakland Road, Leicester, LE2 6AN Tel: 0116-270 1760 Fax: 0116-244 8727 E-mail: hoyes@fsbdial.co.uk
▶ Taylor, 150 Turner Lane, Ashton-under-Lyne, Lancashire, OL6 8SZ Tel: 0161-343 1294 Fax: 0161-339 9477 E-mail: info@taylorssupplies.com
W Hall & Son Holywell Ltd, Greenfield Road, Greenfield, Holywell, Clwyd, CH8 7QB Tel: (01352) 711444 Fax: (01352) 714793
▶ Wild West Jerky UK, Units 2-3, Eireastadh, Crowlista, Isle of Lewis, HS2 9JG Tel: (0870) 7415948 Fax: (0870) 7415948 E-mail: info@wildwestjerky.co.uk

BAR (LICENSED) HIRE

▶ Badger Bars, The Post Office, Firsby Road, Great Steeping, Spilsby, Lincolnshire, PE23 5PT Tel: 07731 576864
Chapman G, 36 Dycote Lane, Welbourn, Lincoln, LN5 0NL Tel: (01400) 272073

BAR (LICENSED) SUPPLIERS/ DISTRIBUTORS/AGENTS

Anglia Glassware & Bar Supplies, 6 Oakfield, Stebbing, Dunmow, Essex, CM6 3SX Tel: (01371) 856857 Fax: (01371) 874040 E-mail: angliaglassware@btclick.com
Barcare Supreme Ltd, 39 Railway Street, Stafford, ST16 2DS Tel: (01785) 247267 Fax: (01785) 247311
Bunzl Cleaning & Hygiene Supplies, Henson Road, Darlington, County Durham, DL1 4QD Tel: (01325) 353551 Fax: (01325) 465952 E-mail: darlington@bunzlchs.co.uk
Bunzl Lockhart Catering Equipment, Lockhart House, Brunel Road, Theale, Reading, RG7 4XE Tel: (0870) 1678678 Fax: (0870) 1678679 E-mail: marketing@bunzl.co.uk
Peter Clarke, 52 Southey Avenue, Sheffield, S5 7NL Tel: 0114-232 3381 Fax: 0114-233 7602
G E Cook & Sons Ltd, Tidings Hill Brewery, Halstead, Essex, CO9 1BL Tel: (01787) 475501 Fax: (01787) 475501
Global Foodservice Equipment Ltd, Global House, 104-108 School Road, Tilehurst, Reading, RG31 5AX Tel: (0870) 6004333 Fax: (0870) 2434334 E-mail: sales@global-fse.co.uk
Greene King Brewing & Retailing Ltd, Westgate Brewery, Bury St. Edmunds, Suffolk, IP33 1QT Tel: (01284) 763222 Fax: (01284) 706502 E-mail: gregwilliams@greeneking.co.uk
Halls Northern Ltd, Unit 9 Stadium Industrial Estate, Gateshead, Tyne & Wear, NE10 0XF Tel: 0191-378 4500 Fax: 0191-378 9796 E-mail: enquiries@hallsnorthern.co.uk
Hotelware Ltd, 14 Dobson Place, Leeds, LS11 5PG Tel: 0113-271 7885 Fax: 0113-270 8576 E-mail: sales@hotelwareltd.co.uk
Streamline Dispence Ltd, Brunel Court, Stroudwater Business Park, Stonehouse, Gloucestershire, GL10 3SW Tel: (01453) 821155 Fax: (01453) 821166 E-mail: dispense@enterprise.net
The Waverley Beer TBS Ltd, Unit 3A, Saxon Way, Wincanton Business Park, Wincanton, Somerset, BA9 9RT Tel: (01963) 34264 Fax: (01963) 435204 E-mail: admin@waverleytbs.co.uk

BARBED WIRE FENCING

▶ Treefellar Scotland, 6 Brodick Avenue, Kilwinning, Ayrshire, KA13 6RJ Tel: (01294) 554472 Fax: (01294) 542825 E-mail: admin@treefellar.co.uk

BARGE BUILDING OR REPAIR SERVICES

Arcrite Fabrications, Fleming Road, Corby, Northamptonshire, NN17 4SW Tel: (01536) 204969 Fax: (01536) 402456 E-mail: email@genbridge.fsnet.co.uk

BARITE AGGREGATES

Viaton Industries Ltd, Brassington, Wirksworth, Matlock, Derbyshire, DE4 4ES Tel: (01629) 540373 Fax: (01629) 540289 E-mail: sales@viaton.com

BARITES

J. Allcock & Sons Ltd, Textile Street, West Gorton, Manchester, M12 5DL Tel: 0161-223 7181 Fax: 0161-223 0173 E-mail: ja@allcocks.co.uk
Viaton Industries Ltd, Brassington, Wirksworth, Matlock, Derbyshire, DE4 4ES Tel: (01629) 540373 Fax: (01629) 540289 E-mail: sales@viaton.com

BAROGRAPHS

Russell Scientific Instruments Ltd, Rashs Green Industrial Estate, Dereham, Norfolk, NR19 1JG Tel: (01362) 693481 Fax: (01362) 698548 E-mail: sales@russell-scientific.co.uk

BAROMETER MAINTENANCE/ REPAIR SERVICES

▶ Horological Repair Service, 37 Green End, Denton, Manchester, M34 7PT Tel: 0161-336 5215 Fax: 0161-336 5215 E-mail: info@hrs-clocks.co.uk
Russell Scientific Instruments Ltd, Rashs Green Industrial Estate, Dereham, Norfolk, NR19 1JG Tel: (01362) 693481 Fax: (01362) 698548 E-mail: sales@russell-scientific.co.uk
Time & Motion, 1 Beckside, Beverley, North Humberside, HU17 0PB Tel: (01482) 881574

BAROMETERS, *See also headings for particular types*

Everglades International Ltd, The Old Station, Station Road, Cheddar, Somerset, BS27 3AH Tel: (01934) 744051 Fax: (01934) 743184
F W W Brown & Son, 39 Queen Street, Horbury, Wakefield, West Yorkshire, WF4 6LP Tel: (01924) 271696
Mega-Quartz UK Ltd, 25 Boshers Gardens, Egham, Surrey, TW20 9NZ Tel: (01784) 437072 Fax: (01784) 435793 E-mail: megaquartzuk@aol.com
▶ Met-Check Ltd, 9 Churchfield Road, Chilton Industrial Estate, Sudbury, Suffolk, CO10 2YA Tel: (01787) 883138 Fax: (01787) 883139 E-mail: sales@met-check.co.uk
Piplers Chandlers, The Quay, Poole, Dorset, BH15 1HF Tel: (01202) 673056 Fax: (01202) 683065 E-mail: sales@piplers.co.uk
▶ Rod L Fryatt, 10 Amberley Court, Lowestoft, Suffolk, NR32 4RL Tel: (01502) 560869
Time & Motion, 1 Beckside, Beverley, North Humberside, HU17 0PB Tel: (01482) 881574

BARREL COUPLINGS

▶ Piv Drive, Posiva Works 8 Skipping Dale Industrial Estate, Exmoor Avenue, Scunthorpe, South Humberside, DN15 8NJ Tel: (01724) 281868 Fax: (01724) 282808

BARREL DISTRIBUTORS OR AGENTS

Taylor Davis Ltd, Moat Road, West Wilts Trading Estate, Westbury, Wiltshire, BA13 4JF Tel: (01373) 864324 Fax: (01373) 858021 E-mail: sales@taylor-davis.co.uk

BARREL FINISHING AND POLISHING EQUIPMENT

Wheelabrator Group, 43-44 Gravelly Industrial Park, Tyburn Road, Birmingham, B24 8TG Tel: 0121-326 6481 Fax: 0121-328 0256 E-mail: uk-info@wheelabrator.co.uk

BARREL PLATING SERVICES

Electrolytic Plating Co. Ltd, Crown Works, Wednesbury Road, Walsall, WS1 4JJ Tel: (01922) 627466 Fax: (01922) 723844 E-mail: sales@electrolytic.co.uk
Levertech Metal Finishing Services, Green Lane, Eccles, Manchester, M30 8JJ Tel: 0161-787 7247 Fax: 0161-789 6411 E-mail: levertech@levertech.fsnet.co.uk

BARREL PUMPS

Interco Lubrication Services, 28 Harwood Court, Riverside Park Industrial Estate, Middlesbrough, Cleveland, TS2 1PU Tel: (01642) 247157 Fax: (01642) 247157 E-mail: chas_ophield@lineone.net
Lutz (UK) Ltd, Gateway Estate, West Midlands Freeport, Birmingham, B26 3QD Tel: 0121-782 2662 Fax: 0121-782 2680 E-mail: lutzpump@aol.com
Roach Pumps Ltd, Rotten Row Farm, Hambleden, Henley-on-Thames, Oxfordshire, RG9 6NB Tel: (01491) 410716 Fax: (01491) 410718 E-mail: roachpumps@aol.com

BARREL/CASK/KEG DEALERS/ RECONDITIONERS/SUPPLIERS

Joseph Brown & Sons, 72 Balvenie Street, Dufftown, Keith, Banffshire, AB55 4FS Tel: (01340) 820265 Fax: (01340) 820265 E-mail: jbvat@fsmail.net
Brownieside Coopereage, Airdrie Road, Caldercruix, Caldercruix, Airdrie, Lanarkshire, ML6 8PA Tel: (01236) 767774
▶ Edrington Distillers, Muirhall, West Calder, West Lothian, EH55 8NT Tel: (01506) 873433 Fax: (01506) 873438
▶ Essex Drums Ltd, Unit 3, Charles Street, London, E16 2BY Tel: (020) 7511 2785 Fax: (020) 7473 3975
Fishers Cooperage, 357 Shettleston Road, Glasgow, G31 5JL Tel: 0141-556 1850 Fax: 0141-556 4075
Morrow Bros Ltd, 433 Walton Summit Centre, Preston, PR5 8AU Tel: 01772 311882

BARREL/CASK/KEG WASHING/ FILLING EQUIPMENT, COMBINED

Gimson Ltd, 30 Boston Road, Leicester, LE4 1AU Tel: 0116-236 8688 Fax: 0116-236 3663 E-mail: a_sims@gimsoneng.co.uk

BARRIER ACCESS CONTROL SYSTEMS

▶ Zeag UK Ltd, 17 Deer Park Road, London, SW19 3XJ Tel: 0208 543 3281 Fax: 0208 543 5344 E-mail: info@zeaguk.com

BARRIER COATED CARTON BOARD

Bridger Packaging, Avenue One, Letchworth Garden City, Hertfordshire, SG6 2WP Tel: (01462) 636465 Fax: (01462) 636433 E-mail: postmaster@bridger.co.uk
Mayr Melnhof UK Ltd, Bourne House, Bourne Close, Calcot, Reading, RG31 7BS Tel: 0118-942 5504 Fax: 0118-942 0750

BARRIERS

Automatic Systems Equipment UK Ltd, Unit G4, Middlesex Business Centre, Bridge Road, Southall, Middlesex, UB2 4AB Tel: (020) 8744 7669 Fax: (020) 8744 7670 E-mail: sales@automaticsystems.co.uk
▶ Bauer Inner City, The Dallam Court, Dallam Lane, Warrington, WA2 7LT Tel: (01925) 428940 Fax: (01925) 244133 E-mail: info@bauerinnercity.co.uk
▶ K Guard UK Ltd, 6 Arlesey Business Park, Mill Lane, Arlesey, Bedfordshire, SG15 6RF Tel: (01462) 834834 Fax: (01462) 834835 E-mail: info@kguard.co.uk
O M Safety Fencing Supplies, 14A Wesley Street, Rodley, Leeds, LS13 1JH Tel: 0113-236 2241
Steel People Ltd, Unit 3e Priory Park, Mills Road, Aylesford, Kent, ME20 7PP Tel: (01622) 715900 Fax: (01622) 715905 E-mail: mail@thesteelpeople.com

BARRIERS, CROWD CONTROL

A Fax Ltd, Drakes Industrial Estate, Shay Lane, Ovenden, Halifax, West Yorkshire, HX3 6RL Tel: (01422) 331133 Fax: (01422) 323533 E-mail: sales@a-fax.com

BARROWS, *See also headings for particular types*

▶ Muck-trucks Scotland, PO Box 19570, Johnstone, Renfrewshire, PA9 1AD Tel: (01505) 702600 Fax: (01505) 703783 E-mail: sales@mucktruckscotland.com

BASE STATIONS, WIRELESS

▶ Actuate S C R, Manor Barn, Thurloxton, Taunton, Somerset, TA2 8RH Tel: (07971) 682097 Fax: (0870) 1336615 E-mail: info@actuate.eu.com

BASEEFA RATED CONNECTORS

Lane Electronics, Slinfold Lodge, Stane Street, Slinfold, Horsham, West Sussex, RH13 0RN Tel: (01403) 790661 Fax: (01403) 790849 E-mail: sales@fclane.com
Rota Engineering Ltd, Wellington Street, Bury, Lancashire, BL8 2BD Tel: 0161-764 0424 Fax: 0161-762 9729 E-mail: sales@rota-eng.com

BASEMENT CONVERSION AND DEVELOPMENT CONTRACTORS

▶ All Foundations Ltd, PO Box 2146, Watford, WD18 1AS Tel: (0870) 3503050 Fax: (0870) 3503060 E-mail: mail@allfoundations.co.uk
▶ Basement 4 Creating Space, 288 Oxford Road, Gomersal, Cleckheaton, West Yorkshire, BD19 4PY Tel: (0800) 1381998 Fax: (01274) 852937 E-mail: enquiries@basement4.com
▶ Biocraft Ltd, 25b Chapel Hill, Tilehurst, Reading, RG31 5BT Tel: 0118-945 1144 E-mail: sales@biocraft.co.uk
▶ Hightex Coatings, Unit 14 Chapel Farm, Hanslope Road, Hartwell, Northampton, NN7 2EU Tel: (01604) 861250 Fax: (01604) 871116 E-mail: sales@hightexcoatings.co.uk
Mercian Preservation Ltd, 74 Cinder Bank, Dudley, West Midlands, DY2 9BH Tel: (01384) 250154 Fax: (01384) 456068
▶ Polarwall, Unit 3 Old Mill Industrial Estate, Stoke Canon, Exeter, EX5 4RJ Tel: (01392) 841777 Fax: (01392) 841936 E-mail: info@polarwall.co.uk
R E Lay Construction Ltd, 146 West Street, Dunstable, Bedfordshire, LU6 1NX Tel: (01582) 608571 Fax: (01582) 472092 E-mail: admin@r-e-lay.co.uk
▶ Regency Preservation, Conbar House, Mead Lane, Hertford, SG13 7AP Tel: (01992) 509201 Fax: (01992) 552277 E-mail: enquiries@regencypreservation.co.uk
▶ Timberwise (UK) Ltd, PO Box 4198, Cardiff, CF14 8BG Tel: (0800) 991100 E-mail: cardiff@timberwise.co.uk
▶ Timberwise UK plc, Chester Enterprise Centre, Hoole Bridge, Chester, CH2 3NE Tel: (01244) 321366 Fax: (01565) 621000 E-mail: chester@timberwise.co.uk
▶ Timberwise (UK) Ltd, 19 Eagle Close, Birdwood Park, Fareham, Hants, PO16 8QX Tel: (0800) 991100 Fax: (01329) 510186 E-mail: hants@timberwise.co.uk
▶ Timberwise UK plc, Kirkfields Business Centre, Kirk Lane, Yeadon, Leeds, LS19 7ET Tel: 0113-250 4402 Fax: 0113-250 9931 E-mail: leeds@timberwise.co.uk
▶ Timberwise (UK) Ltd, 1 Norman Road, Thurmaston, Leicester, LE4 8EL Tel: (0800) 991100 Fax: 0116-269 3678 E-mail: leics@timberwise.co.uk
▶ Timberwise (UK) Ltd, Unit B16, Brunswick Business Centre, Brunswick Business Park, Sefton Street, Liverpool, L3 4BD Tel: (0800) 991100 Fax: 0151-284 6837 E-mail: liverpool@timberwise.co.uk
▶ Timberwise UK plc, 3 CWRT Roger Mostyn, Builder Street, Llandudno, Gwynedd, LL30 1DS Tel: (01492) 535065 Fax: (01492) 864004 E-mail: llandudno@timberwise.co.uk
▶ Timberwise (UK) Ltd, Bank House, 4 Wharf Road, Sale, Cheshire, M33 2AF Tel: (0800) 991100 Fax: 0161-972 0077 E-mail: sale@timberwise.co.uk
▶ Timberwise UK plc, 4 Finchwell Close, Sheffield, S13 9DF Tel: 0114-256 1411 Fax: 0114-256 1422 E-mail: sheffield@timberwise.co.uk
▶ Timberwise UK plc, 47 The Green, Cheadle, Stoke-on-Trent, ST10 1XS Tel: (01782) 599921 Fax: 0161 962 7610 E-mail: stoke@timberwise.co.uk
▶ Timberwise (UK) Ltd, 6 Rose Hill, Sutton, Surrey, SM1 3EU Tel: (0800) 991100 Fax: (020) 8641 4343 E-mail: sutton@timberwise.co.uk
▶ Timberwise (UK) Ltd, Wilwood, Smith Hill, Bishopsteignton, Teignmouth, Devon, TQ14 9QT Tel: (0800) 991100 Fax: (01935) 814436 E-mail: devon@timberwise.co.uk
▶ Timberwise (UK) Ltd, 7 Gooch Way, Worle, Weston-super-Mare, Avon, BS22 7YH Tel: (0800) 991100 Fax: (01935) 814436 E-mail: weston@timberwise.co.uk

BASEMENT WATERPROOFING SERVICES

▶ Substructure Protection Ltd, Warth Mill, Huddersfield Road, Diggle, Oldham, OL3 5PJ Tel: (01457) 878200 Fax: (01457) 879132 E-mail: sales@spsltd.co.uk

BASKETWARE

E J & S Y Barnard, 21 Nethermoor Road, Middlezoy, Bridgwater, Somerset, TA7 0PG Tel: (01823) 698536
Gough Packaging Ltd, 49 Whiffler Road, Norwich, NR3 2AW Tel: (01603) 423860 Fax: (01603) 485000 E-mail: leshgough@aol.com
Henry Gross Ltd, Willcox House, London, SE1 1LB Tel: (020) 7407 0942 Fax: (020) 7407 5942 E-mail: sales@henrygross.co.uk
Habasco International Ltd, Stafford Mills, George Street, Milnsbridge, Huddersfield, HD3 4JD Tel: (01484) 642115 Fax: (01484) 640058 E-mail: sales@habasco.net
▶ David Hembrow Basketmaker, 70 St. Albans Road, Cambridge, CB4 2HG Tel: (01223) 528563
J Johnson & Sons, The Basket Centre, Station Road, Bangor-on-Dee, Wrexham, Clwyd, LL13 0AB Tel: (01978) 780417 Fax: (01978) 780781 E-mail: sales@johnsoncanefurniture.co.uk
K S S Ltd, 122 Redriff Rd, London, SE16 6QD Tel: (020) 7232 2260 Fax: (020) 7232 2288 E-mail: kabletie@btinternet.com
L.Nicot & Company Ltd, 7 Beeches Avenue, Carshalton Beeches, Carshalton, Surrey, SM5 3LB Tel: (020) 8773 8050 Fax: (020) 8773 8070
Mellingey Mill Willowcraft Centre, Mellingey Mill, St. Issey, Wadebridge, Cornwall, PL27 7QU Tel: (01841) 540604 Fax: (01841) 540604
The Optima Co. Ltd, Robell Way, Storrington, Pulborough, West Sussex, RH20 3DW Tel: (01903) 744111 Fax: (01903) 746440 E-mail: sales@picnic-products.co.uk
Somerset Willow Co., Wireworks Estate, Bristol Road, Bridgwater, Somerset, TA6 4AP Tel: (01278) 424003 Fax: (01278) 446415 E-mail: enquires@sumersetwillows.co.uk
▶ W Gadsby & Son Ltd, Huntworth Business Park, Bridgwater, Somerset, TA6 6TS Tel: (01278) 437123 Fax: (01278) 458561 E-mail: sales@gadsby.co.uk

BASMATI RICE

Eden Valley Wholefoods, 34 The Market, Scotch Street, Carlisle, CA3 8QX Tel: (01228) 546853

BATCH AUTOMATION CONTROL SYSTEMS

Premier Controls Ltd, 48 Marlow Road, Stokenchurch, High Wycombe, Buckinghamshire, HP14 3QJ Tel: (01494) 485758 Fax: (01494) 485696

BATCH MACHINING

Alpine Precision Engineering, 27 Telford Road, Wimborne, Dorset, BH21 7RX Tel: (01202) 894478 Fax: (01202) 894441 E-mail: alan.codman@virgin.net
Heelman Ltd, Unit 17-18 Sheet Road Indust Estate, Ludlow, Shropshire, SY8 1LR Tel: (01584) 875030 Fax: (01584) 875030
K F Lever (Precision Engineering) Ltd, 56 Ash Tree Road, Southampton, SO18 1LX Tel: (023) 8055 2351 Fax: (023) 8055 3574 E-mail: klseverltd@yiscalli.co.uk
Southend Total Engineering & Fabrication, 14 Terminal Close, Shoeburyness, Southend-on-Sea, SS3 9BN Tel: (01702) 299499 Fax: (01702) 299561

BATCHING COUNTERS

Kirby Devon Ltd, Elm Tree House, Yealmbury Hill, Yealmpton, Plymouth, PL8 2JH Tel: (01752) 881717 Fax: (01752) 881710 E-mail: sales@kirbydevon.freeserve.co.uk
Vacuumatic, Brunel Way 8, Severalls Industrial Park, Colchester, CO4 9QX Tel: (01206) 841100 Fax: (01206) 841166 E-mail: sales@vacuumatic.com

BATH GIFT SETS

▶ 1Gift4All, PO Box 172, Pudsey, West Yorkshire, LS28 5XT Tel: (0789) 9067059 E-mail: sales@1gift4all.com
▶ Baby B Gifts, 33A Wilberforce Road, London, N4 2SN Tel: 020 76908992
▶ Gifts 2 Have, 7 Hunton Bridge Hill, Hunton Bridge, Kings Langley, Hertfordshire, WD4 8PX Tel: (07901) 671349 E-mail: gifts2have@lycos.co.uk
▶ Puckator Ltd, Lowman Works, East Tap House, East Taphouse, Liskeard, Cornwall, PL14 4NQ Tel: (01579) 321550 Fax: (01579) 321520 E-mail: kundenservice@puckator.de
▶ Pure Essence, 6a Woodend Mills, South Hill, Springhead, Oldham, OL4 5DR Tel: 0161-633 9988 E-mail: info@pureessence.co.uk

BATH OR SINK OR WASH BASIN PLUG CHAINS

▶ English Chain Co Ltd, Chain House, Brighton Road, Godalming, Surrey, GU7 1NS Tel: (01483) 428383 Fax: (01483) 861931 E-mail: sales@englishchain.co.uk

BATH SALTS

▶ Saat UK Ltd, 14 Chesterton Road, Brooklands, Manchester, M23 9LB Tel: 0161-945 5172 Fax: 0161-945 5172 E-mail: f.kaabipour@saatukltd.com
▶ Serenity, 38 Clover Way, Harrogate, North Yorkshire, HG3 2WE Tel: 01423 528262 E-mail: heather@serenityofharrogate.co.uk
Tara Personal Care Ltd, 28 Ryde Avenue, Hull, HU5 1QB Tel: (01482) 444999 Fax: (01482) 473395

BATH WASTES

Bailey Bros (Engineers) Ltd, 105 Hospital St, Newtown, Birmingham, B19 3XB Tel: 0121-359 8361 Fax: 0121-359 0909 E-mail: sales@cerro-ems.co.uk

BATHROBES

Bed & Bath UK Ltd, Orston Lane, Bottesford, Nottingham, NG13 0AU Tel: (01949) 844441 Fax: (01949) 844001 E-mail: sales@bedandbath.co.uk

BATHROOM AND TOILET PODS

▶ Bath Accessory Store, Jolen House, Solartron Road, Farnborough, Hampshire, GU14 7QL Tel: (01252) 794454 E-mail: sales@bath-accessory-store.com
▶ Revolutionary Pod Modules (UK) Ltd, Unit 3, Central Park, Cornwall Street, Hull, HU8 8AF Tel: (01482) 871717 Fax: (01482) 867727 E-mail: info@pod-modules.co.uk
▶ UK Bathroom Interiors, 3/4 Old Laundry, Fishergreen, Ripon, North Yorkshire, HG4 1NL Tel: (0845) 2008526 E-mail: mark@ukbathroominteriors.com

BATHROOM APPLIANCES

▶ Aquabrand Bathrooms Ltd, 16 Spinnaker Quay, Plymouth, PL9 9SA Tel: (01752) 223645 Fax: 0870 758 5877 E-mail: markthomas@aquabrand.com
▶ Bathstore.com Ltd, 87-89 Leeds Road, Harrogate, North Yorkshire, HG2 8BE Tel: (01423) 874400 Fax: (01423) 874400 E-mail: harrogate@bathstore.com
▶ Bathstore.com Ltd, Unit T4 Io Trade Centre, Hobley Drive, Swindon, SN3 4NS Tel: (01793) 834111 Fax: (01793) 834222 E-mail: swindon@bathstore.com
▶ G & L Home Improvements, 33 Butterside Road, Kingsnorth, Ashford, Kent, TN23 3PD Tel: (01233) 501815 E-mail: garry.laker@ntlworld.com
▶ Keramag Waveney Ltd, London Road, Beccles, Suffolk, NR34 8TS Tel: (01502) 716600 Fax: (01502) 717767 E-mail: ian@keramagwaveney.co.uk

BATHROOM CABINETS

▶ Atlantic Bathrooms & Kitchens, 21-23 Waterloo Road, Norwich, NR3 1EH Tel: (01603) 402222 Fax: (01603) 402022 E-mail: enquiries@atlanticbathrooms.com
▶ Bath Accessory Store, Jolen House, Solartron Road, Farnborough, Hampshire, GU14 7QL Tel: (01252) 794454 E-mail: sales@bath-accessory-store.com
▶ Bathroom Beauty Of Bolton, 509 Tonge Moor Road, Bolton, BL2 3BG Tel: (01204) 592306 Fax: (01204) 595970 E-mail: enquires@bathroombeautyofbolton.co.uk
▶ Bathroombits4u Ltd, 26 Fraiary Gardens, Newport Pagnell, Buckinghamshire, MK16 0JZ Tel: (01908) 614012 E-mail: leonmaclean@bathroombits4u.co.uk
▶ C R D Interiors Ltd, 245 High Street, Aldershot, Hampshire, GU12 4NG Tel: (01252) 319588 Fax: (01252) 310698 E-mail: crd-interiors@lycos.co.uk
▶ Casa Designer Interiors Ltd, 47 Vaughan Way, Leicester, LE1 4SG Tel: 0116-262 8001 Fax: 0116-262 8001E-mail: info@casadi.co.uk
▶ Gibbs & Dandy, PO Box 17, Luton, LU1 1YB Tel: (01582) 798798 Fax: (01582) 798799 E-mail: mail@gibbsanddandy.com

▶ indicates data change since last edition

BATHROOM CABINETS – *continued*

Hale & Murray Ltd, 3 Abingdon Road, Nuffield Industrial Estate, Poole, Dorset, BH17 0UG Tel: (01202) 678431 Fax: (01202) 687843 E-mail: admin@haleandmurray.co.uk

Harmony Fitted Furniture, Main Street, Rear of 51, Willerby, Hull, HU10 6BY Tel: (01482) 650685 Fax: (01482) 650685 E-mail: info@harmony.co.uk

Jacuzzi UK, Woodlands, Roydsdale Way, Euroway Industrial Estate, Bradford, West Yorkshire, BD4 6ST Tel: (01274) 654700 Fax: (01274) 654750

Maurice Parker Ltd, Alfred House, Alfreton Road, Derby, DE21 4AF Tel: (01332) 363422 Fax: (01332) 293455 E-mail: sales@mauriceparker.co.uk

▶ Property Maintenance Direct, 80 Loughborough Road, Thringstone, Coalville, Leicestershire, LE67 8LP Tel: (0845) 4589871 Fax: (01530) 459513 E-mail: enquiries@propertymaintenancedirect.co.uk

▶ Ranger Distribution, Copse Road, Fleetwood, Lancashire, FY7 7NY Tel: (01253) 878888 Fax: (01253) 878999 E-mail: enquires@rangeruk.co.uk

▶ Shak Ltd, Unit D Grange Road, Walthamstow, London, E17 8AH Tel: (020) 8521 2900 Fax: (020) 8521 2010 E-mail: shak@theworldofwater.com

▶ UK Bathroom Interiors, 3/4 Old Laundry, Fishergreen, Ripon, North Yorkshire, HG4 1NL Tel: (0845) 2008526 E-mail: mark@ukbathroominteriors.com

BATHROOM CABINETS, STAINLESS STEEL

▶ Bathstore.com Ltd, 87-89 Leeds Road, Harrogate, North Yorkshire, HG2 8BE Tel: (01423) 874400 Fax: (01423) 874400 E-mail: harrogate@bathstore.com

▶ Bathstore.com Ltd, Unit T4 Io Trade Centre, Hobley Drive, Swindon, SN3 4NS Tel: (01793) 834111 Fax: (01793) 834222 E-mail: swindon@bathstore.com

BATHROOM DESIGN OR INSTALLATION

A A Interior Design Ltd, 187 Downs Road, Walmer, Deal, Kent, CT14 7TL Tel: (01304) 373205 Fax: (01304) 373205 E-mail: info@aadesign.uk.com

▶ A W Bathrooms, 80 Buttershaw Lane, Bradford, West Yorkshire, BD6 2DA Tel: (07979) 300252 E-mail: awbathrooms@hotmail.com

▶ Absoloute Bathrooms Aim, 3 Warrington Road, Ashton-in-Makerfield, Wigan, Lancashire, WN4 9PL Tel: (01942) 271557

Advanced Property Solutions, 38 Riverside Steps, St. Annes Park, Bristol, BS4 4RH Tel: (07775) 671339 E-mail: anything@advancedpropertysolutions.co.uk

▶ Aquarians, 40 Bushby Close, Lancing, West Sussex, BN15 9JW Tel: (01903) 755978

▶ Barretts Bathrooms & Tiles, Derrylin, Enniskillen, County Fermanagh, BT92 9LA Tel: (028) 6774 2009 Fax: (028) 6774 8229

▶ Bath Time Creations, 23 Cherry Tree Grove, Wokingham, Berkshire, RG41 4UZ Tel: 0118-989 4194 E-mail: info@bathtimecreations.com

▶ Bathroom Beauty Of Bolton, 509 Tonge Moor Road, Bolton, BL2 3BG Tel: (01204) 592306 Fax: (01204) 595970 E-mail: enquires@bathroombeautyofbolton.co.uk

▶ Bathroom Refurbishments Specialists, 71 Beltony Drive, Crewe, CW1 4TX Tel: (01270) 255116

▶ Bathroom Studio Birtley, The Whitehouse, Durham Road, Birtley, County Durham, DH3 2QQ Tel: 0191 4922022 E-mail: enquiries@bathroomstudiobirtley.co.uk

▶ Bathstore.com Ltd, York Buildings, Edinburgh, EH2 1HY Tel: 0131-556 0333 Fax: 0131-557 4884E-mail: edinburgh.central@bathstore.com

Be Modern Ltd, Head Office, Western Approach, South Shields, Tyne & Wear, NE33 5QZ Tel: 0191-455 3571 Fax: 0191-456 5556 E-mail: justina.hathaway@bemodern.co.uk

▶ C R D Interiors Ltd, 245 High Street, Aldershot, Hampshire, GU12 4NG Tel: (01252) 319588 Fax: (01252) 310698 E-mail: crd-interiors@lycos.co.uk

▶ Casa Designer Interiors Ltd, 47 Vaughan Way, Leicester, LE1 4SG Tel: 0116-262 8001 Fax: 0116-262 8001E-mail: info@casadi.co.uk

▶ Classical Bathrooms Ltd, Little Lane, Ilkley, West Yorkshire, LS29 8EA Tel: (01943) 601118 Fax: (01943) 609354

▶ Clerkenwell Bathrooms, 266 Hackney Road, London, E2 7SJ Tel: (020) 7729 6698 Fax: (020) 7729 6698

▶ Designvan, 23 Wiltshire Drive, Wokingham, Berkshire, RG40 1TQ Tel: 0118-989 1295 E-mail: rob@designvan.com

▶ Direct Factory Bathrooms, Unit 5 Selby Business Park, Oakney Wood Road, Selby, North Yorkshire, YO8 8NB Tel: (01757) 291122 Fax: (01757) 241144

▶ DSL - installations, Unit , Farnborough Business Center, Eelmoor Road, Farnborough, Hampshire, GU14 7XA Tel: 01252 514228 Fax: 01252 547732 E-mail: info@dsl-installations.co.uk

▶ Exclusiv Fitted Interiors, 16a Longfield Road, Eglinton, Londonderry, BT47 3PY Tel: (028) 7181 1114 Fax: (028) 7181 4916

▶ First Call Plumbing, The Old Farmhouse, 9 North Street, Ipplepen, Newton Abbot, Devon, TQ12 5RT Tel: (01803) 814514 Fax: (01803) 814069 E-mail: fcplumbing@btinternet.com

▶ H2 Plumbing Ltd, Unit L24 The Old Laboratories, 2 Michael Road, London, SW6 2AD Tel: (020) 7751 3344 E-mail: info@h2plumbing.co.uk

Hadley Bathrooms, 683 London Road, Hadleigh, Benfleet, Essex, SS7 2EE Tel: (01702) 552233 Fax: (01702) 554292

▶ HPR Limited, 55 Park Lane, London, W1K 1NA Tel: 020 7409 9039 E-mail: services@hprlimited.co.uk

▶ I C Rushton, 16 Rostherne Avenue, High Lane, Stockport, Cheshire, SK6 8AR Tel: (01663) 762540 E-mail: IanCRushton@aol.com

Ideal Standard Social Club, County Road North, Hull, HU5 4HS Tel: (01482) 343852 Fax: (01482) 445886 E-mail: ideal-standard@asvr.com

John Norton & Son Ltd, 169 Rutland Road, Sheffield, S3 9PT Tel: 0114-272 1294 Fax: 0114-276 6336 E-mail: sales@nortons.co.uk

▶ Roger Kemp Associates, River View, High Street, Loxwood, Billingshurst, West Sussex, RH14 0RE Tel: (01403) 752370 E-mail: mattkemp70@hotmail.com

▶ Lochaber Kitchens, Unit 12e, Annat Industrial Estate, Fort William, Inverness-shire, PH33 7HR Tel: (01397) 702710 E-mail: info@lochaberkitchens.co.uk

▶ M Goodey, 9 Cameron Avenue, Abingdon, Oxfordshire, OX14 3SR Tel: (01235) 532875 Fax: (01235) 532875 E-mail: info@goodeyplumbingandheating.co.uk

▶ Merrows Ltd, 50b Inverness Avenue, Westcliff On Sea, Westcliff-on-Sea, Essex, SS0 9DY Tel: (01702) 347493

▶ Modern Bathroom/Kitchen Services, 12 Paroma Road, Belvedere, Kent, DA17 5AA Tel: (020) 8306 1397 E-mail: modernbathservices@tiscali.co.uk

▶ Oakland Leicester Ltd, 7-11 Welford Road, Blaby, Leicester, LE8 4FT Tel: 0116-277 2252 Fax: 0116-278 8445

Maurice Parker Ltd, Alfred House, Alfreton Road, Derby, DE21 4AF Tel: (01332) 363422 Fax: (01332) 293455 E-mail: sales@mauriceparker.co.uk

▶ Pendleton Bathroom Design Ltd, 64 Longfileds Road, Thorpe St Andrew, Norwich, NR7 0NA Tel: 01603 435070 E-mail: sales@pendletonbathroomdesign.co.uk

▶ Premier Service & Installation, Premier House, Unit 6, Station Terrace, Station Road,, Kegworth, Derbyshire, DE74 2GE Tel: 01509 670600 Fax: 01509 673275 E-mail: info@premservices.co.uk

▶ Property Etc Limited, Lombard House, 12/17 Upper Bridge Street, Canterbury, Kent, CT1 2NF Tel: 01227 766389 E-mail: enquiries@property-etc.com

▶ R & S Property Services, Unit 2, 14 Barr's Road, Taplow, Maidenhead, Berkshire, SL6 0LE Tel: (01628) 661666 E-mail: rnsa1@hotmail.com

▶ Richmonds Bathrooms, 21 Berridale Avenue, Cathcart, Glasgow, G44 3AF Tel: 0141 571 7261 E-mail: steve@richmondsbathrooms.co.uk

Tantofex Ltd, The Bathroom Works, National Avenue, Hull, HU5 4HS Tel: (01482) 346461 Fax: (01482) 445886

▶ Transform Building Services Ltd, 6 Lockyer House, Waterman St, London, SW15 1EE Tel: 020 8789 8780 Fax: 020 8789 8811 E-mail: contact@transformltd.co.uk

Wimbledon Bathrooms, 32 The Downs, Wimbledon, London, SW20 8JA Tel: (020) 8946 7521 Fax: (020) 8946 7521

BATHROOM FITTINGS OR ACCESSORIES

A.G.M. (Distributors) Ltd, 40b Ravenhill Road, Belfast, BT6 8EB Tel: (028) 9045 2613 Fax: (028) 9045 0023 E-mail: sales@agmbuckley.demon.co.uk

A & H Brass, 209 Edgware Road, London, W2 1ES Tel: (020) 7706 2262 Fax: (020) 7402 0110 E-mail: sales@aandhbrass.co.uk

▶ Accessory Store, 1617 London Road, Leigh-on-Sea, Essex, SS9 2SQ Tel: (01702) 480537 Fax: (01702) 480537

▶ Adur Bath Tubs, 5 St. Marys Road, Shoreham-by-Sea, West Sussex, BN43 5ZA Tel: (01273) 441788 Fax: (01273) 441769 E-mail: adurbathtubs@btconnect.com

Aestus Ltd, Unit 5, Strawberry Lane, Willenhall, West Midlands, WV13 3RF Tel: (01902) 632256 Fax: (01902) 635800 E-mail: sales@aestus-radiators.com

▶ Aquajoy Bathlifts Ltd, Consett Business Park, Villa Real, Consett, County Durham, DH8 6BP Tel: (01207) 501555 Fax: (01207) 599789 E-mail: info@aqua-joy.com

Aqualona Products, 50 Moxon Street, Barnet, Hertfordshire, EN5 5TS Tel: (020) 8449 7321 Fax: (020) 8449 7496 E-mail: sales@aqualona.com

Armitage Shanks Group Pension Trustees Ltd, Old Road, Armitage, Rugeley, Staffordshire, WS15 4BT Tel: (01543) 490253 Fax: (01543) 491677 E-mail: merrickj1@aseur.com

Aston Matthews Ltd, 141-147a Essex Road, London, N1 2SN Tel: (020) 7226 7220 Fax: (020) 7354 5951 E-mail: sales@astonmatthews.co.uk

▶ Barnet Bath & Kitchen Ltd, 2 Castle Road, St Albans, St. Albans, Hertfordshire, AL1 5DL Tel: (01727) 899155 Fax: (01727) 899153 E-mail: barnetbandk@aol.com

▶ Bath Accessory Store, Jolen House, Solartron Road, Farnborough, Hampshire, GU14 7QL Tel: (01252) 794454 E-mail: sales@bath-accessory-store.com

▶ Bath House, 3a Saunterne Road, Prestwick, Ayrshire, KA9 2JQ Tel: (01292) 470222

▶ Bathroom Beauty Of Bolton, 509 Tonge Moor Road, Bolton, BL2 3BG Tel: (01204) 592306 Fax: (01204) 595970 E-mail: enquires@bathroombeautyofbolton.co.uk

Bathroom City, Seeleys Road, Birmingham, B11 2LQ Tel: 0121-753 0700 Fax: 0121-753 1110 E-mail: 101460.273@compuserve.com

Bathroom Emporium, Galgate Mill, Chapel Lane, Galgate, Lancaster, LA2 0PR Tel: (01524) 752929 Fax: (01524) 751031 E-mail: sales@bathroomemporiumltd.co.uk

▶ Bathroom Outlet, 77 Bicester Road, Kidlington, Oxfordshire, OX5 2LD Tel: (01865) 847546 Fax: (01865) 370740

▶ Bathroombits4u Ltd, 26 Fraiary Gardens, Newport Pagnell, Buckinghamshire, MK16 0JZ Tel: (01908) 614012 E-mail: leonmaclean@bathroombits4u.co.uk

▶ Bathrooms To Go, Unit 9 First Avenue, Marlow, Buckinghamshire, SL7 1YA Tel: (01628) 484443 Fax: (01628) 483688

▶ Bathstore, 23 Gloucester Road, Brighton, BN1 4AD Tel: (01273) 608088 Fax: (01273) 609099

▶ Bathstore.com Ltd, 62-82 Commercial Road, London, E1 1NU Tel: (020) 7702 9898 Fax: (020) 7702 3399

▶ Bathstore.com Ltd, 455 Yarmouth Road, Slough, SL1 4HB Tel: (01753) 516400 Fax: (01753) 539800 E-mail: slough@bathstore.com

▶ Bathstore.com Ltd, 4 The Pompey Centre, Fratton Way, Southsea, Hampshire, PO4 8SL Tel: (023) 9287 7000 Fax: (023) 9287 5900

Bathstore.com Ltd, Unit 2a Felnex Trading Estate, Wallington, Surrey, SM6 7EL Tel: (01923) 694740 Fax: (020) 8773 5004 E-mail: enquiries@bathstore.com

▶ Bathtimes Bathroom Equipment, 3 New Road, Newhaven, East Sussex, BN9 0HE Tel: (01273) 513022 Fax: (01273) 513848 E-mail: info@bathtimesltd.co.uk

Be Modern Ltd, Head Office, Western Approach, South Shields, Tyne & Wear, NE33 5QZ Tel: 0191-455 3571 Fax: 0191-456 5556 E-mail: justina.hathaway@bemodern.co.uk

Beaumont Structural Consultants, Goose Green Marsh, La Rue Du Craslin, St. Peter, Jersey, JE3 7BU Tel: (01534) 822888 Fax: (01534) 822889

Bocco Ltd, Fitzroy House, Lynwood Park, Worcester Park, Surrey, KT4 7AT Tel: (020) 8330 7007 Fax: (020) 8330 3351 E-mail: bocco@lineone.net

▶ Bridge Bathrooms, Bridge Works, Stockport Road, Romiley, Stockport, Cheshire, SK6 3AN Tel: 0161-406 6454 Fax: 0161-494 2222

▶ Bubbles Bathrooms, 13 High Street, Linlithgow, West Lothian, EH49 7AB Tel: (01506) 840060

Builders Centre Sheffield Ltd, Nunnery Drive, Sheffield, S2 1TA Tel: 0114-272 4001 Fax: 0114-241 2840 E-mail: info@builderscentre.co.uk

C & S Builders Merchants Stamford Hill Ltd, 278-286 Stamford Hill, London, N16 6TY Tel: (020) 8809 5373 Fax: (020) 8800 3243

Capital Tiles Supplies Ltd, P O Box 80, Coventry, CV1 2RJ Tel: (024) 7663 3336 Fax: (024) 7663 1447

▶ Cavalier Marketing, North Dean Road, Keighley, West Yorkshire, BD22 6QY Tel: (01535) 613830 Fax: (01535) 613831

Chowart Ltd, 58 Heming Road, Redditch, Worcestershire, B98 0EA Tel: (01527) 501601 Fax: (01527) 510217 E-mail: admin@chowart.co.uk

City Plumbing Supplies Ltd, 159 Stanley Road, London, Teddington, Middlesex, TW11 8UF Tel: (020) 8943 3933 Fax: (020) 8943 2873

Clipvalve Ltd, 88 Stonefield Road, Hastings, East Sussex, TN34 1QA Tel: (01424) 425682 Fax: (01424) 438789 E-mail: enquiries@clipvalve.co.uk

F.G. Collier Kitchens & Bathrooms Ltd, 29-35 Edward Street, Westbury, Wiltshire, BA13 3BL Tel: (01373) 822227 Fax: (01373) 824704 E-mail: sales@fgcollier.com

Commercial Finishes Ltd, Birmingham Road, Redditch, Worcestershire, B97 6DY Tel: (01527) 584244 Fax: (01527) 61127 E-mail: info@cfltd.co.uk

Complete Kitchens, 56-58 Springbank Road, London, SE13 6SN Tel: (020) 8852 5926 Fax: (020) 8244 0907 E-mail: completekitchens@talk21.com

Cooper Callas Ltd, PO Box 32, Oxford, OX1 1LH Tel: (01865) 249931 Fax: (01865) 790561

▶ Coopers Bathrooms & Heating, 8 Elvin Way, Sweet Briar Road Industrial Estate, Norwich, NR3 2BB Tel: (01603) 400134 Fax: (01603) 400134

Coram Showers Ltd, Stanmore Industrial Estate, Bridgnorth, Shropshire, WV15 5HP Tel: (01746) 766466 Fax: (01746) 764140 E-mail: sales@coram.co.uk

Cronation Ltd, Carlton Business Centre, 104 Nechells Place, Birmingham, B7 5AB Tel: 0121-359 7567 Fax: 0121-359 5339 E-mail: sales@cronation.co.uk

Croydex Ltd, Central Way, Andover, Hampshire, SP10 5AW Tel: (01264) 365881 Fax: (01264) 356437 E-mail: admin@croydex.co.uk

Czech & Speake Ltd, 244-254 Cambridge Heath Road, London, E2 9DA Tel: (020) 8983 7400 Fax: (020) 8981 7232 E-mail: sales@czechspeake.com

▶ Delta Plumbing & Heating Supplies, Duchy Road, Heathpark Industrial Estate, Honiton, Devon, EX14 1YD Tel: (01404) 47040 Fax: (01404) 42237

Diamond Interior Design, Century Street, Stoke-on-Trent, ST1 5HT Tel: (01782) 212242 Fax: (01782) 202375 E-mail: sales@diamond-interior-design.co.uk

▶ Direct Bathrooms, 1 Wallis Road, Skippers Lane Industrial Estate, Middlesbrough, Cleveland, TS6 6DU Tel: (01642) 430066

▶ Discontinued Color Ltd, 30 Chandler's Walk, Dalgety Bay, Dunfermline, Fife, KY11 9FE Tel: (01383) 822335 Fax: (01383) 823800 E-mail: enquiries@discontinuedcolor.co.uk

Dolphin Bathrooms, Dolphin House, Springvale Industrial Park, Bilston, West Midlands, WV14 0QL Tel: (01902) 407000 E-mail: dolphin_reception@dolphin-mail.co.uk

▶ Easingwold Bathroom Centre, Unit 2 Easingwold Business Park, Easingwold, York, YO61 3FB Tel: (01347) 824777 Fax: (01347) 824221

▶ Eden Steam Showers., 5 Bagshot Road, Chobham, Surrey, GU24 8BP Tel: 01276 856240 Fax: 0118-979 4565 E-mail: contact@edensteamshowers.co.uk

▶ Elegant Bathroom Interiors, Unit 29 G L S Depot, Mill Mead Road, London, N17 9QQ Tel: (020) 8885 5404

Express, Unit 1b Thorn Business Park, Rotherwas, Hereford, HR2 6JT Tel: (01432) 278138 Fax: (01432) 278138

▶ Gibbs & Dandy, PO Box 17, Luton, LU1 1YB Tel: (01582) 798798 Fax: (01582) 798799 E-mail: mail@gibbsanddandy.com

Graham Builders Merchants Ltd, Bridgeman Street, Bolton, BL3 6BS Tel: (01204) 389500 Fax: (01204) 363205

Grove Plumbing & Heating Supplies Ltd, Unit 11a National Trading Estate, Bramhall Moor Lane, Hazel Grove, Stockport, Cheshire, SK7 5AA Tel: 0161-456 4495 Fax: 0161-456 2678 E-mail: sales@groveplg.co.uk

▶ H20 Bathroom Studio, 61-65 Bell Lane, Bury, Lancashire, BL9 6BB Tel: 0161-762 9119 Fax: 0161-762 9339 E-mail: mark@h2obathroomstudio.co.uk

Hadley Bathrooms, 683 London Road, Hadleigh, Benfleet, Essex, SS7 2EE Tel: (01702) 552233 Fax: (01702) 554292

Heating World, 53 Whitchurch Road, Shrewsbury, SY1 4DT Tel: (01743) 446775 Fax: (01743) 460385 E-mail: info@heatingworld.com

▶ Homestyle Direct Ltd, Unit 21 Hainault Works, Hainault Road, Little Heath, Romford, RM6 5SS Tel: (020) 8599 8080 Fax: (020) 8599 7070 E-mail: sales@homestyle-bathrooms.co.uk

Hydro 2000 Whirlpools, Avondale Way, Wakefield, West Yorkshire, WF2 7QU Tel: (01924) 387444 Fax: (01924) 387444

Ideal Standard Social Club, County Road North, Hull, HU5 4HS Tel: (01482) 343852 Fax: (01482) 445886 E-mail: ideal-standard@asvr.com

J C Quirk, 55 Waverley Road, Sale, Cheshire, M33 7AY Tel: 0161-973 6238 Fax: 0161-973 7066

Jacuzzi UK, Woodlands, Roydsdale Way, Euroway Industrial Estate, Bradford, West Yorkshire, BD4 6ST Tel: (01274) 654700 Fax: (01274) 654750

George Jones & Bros, 1-7 Lower Ashley Road, St. Agnes, Bristol, BS2 9QA Tel: 0117-955 6201 Fax: 0117-955 5503

McDonald Diecasting Ltd, Unit 21a Coneygre Industrial Estate, Birmingham New Rd, Tipton, West Midlands, DY4 8XP Tel: 0121-520 1177 Fax: 0121-557 0677 E-mail: info@mcdonald-diecasting.co.uk

Marenda Lindsey Ltd, Station Road, South Willingham, Market Rasen, Lincolnshire, LN8 6JQ Tel: (01507) 313301 Fax: (01507) 313513 E-mail: enquiries@marendalindsey.co.uk

Marleton Cross Ltd, Alpha Close, Tewkesbury, Gloucestershire, GL20 8JF Tel: (01684) 293311 Fax: (01684) 293900 E-mail: rhj@mxgroup.demon.co.uk

Mayalls of Wigan, Woodhouse Lane, Wigan, Lancashire, WN6 7TH Tel: (01942) 241711 Fax: (01942) 241271 E-mail: maywigan@travisperkins.co.uk

Midland Marble Ltd, Masonry Works, 80 Dollman Street, Birmingham, B7 4RP Tel: 0121-359 3699 Fax: 0121-333 3052 E-mail: enquiries@midlandmarbleltd.co.uk

Midland Spinanpress Co. Ltd, 5 Sydney Road, Bordesley Green, Birmingham, B9 4QB Tel: 0121-772 6804 Fax: 0121-766 8580

Moores Furniture Group Ltd, Thorp Arch Estate, Thorp Arch, Wetherby, West Yorkshire, LS23 7DD Tel: (01937) 842394 Fax: (01937) 845396

N & C Building Products Ltd, 41-51 Freshwater Road, Dagenham, Essex, RM8 1SP Tel: (020) 8586 4600 Fax: (020) 8586 4646 E-mail: head.office@nichollsandclarke.com

BATHROOM FITTINGS OR ACCESSORIES – *continued*

Olympus Distribution Ltd, Olympus Drive, Great Bridge, Tipton, West Midlands, DY4 7HY Tel: 0121-522 5600 Fax: 0121-522 5601 E-mail: sales@olympusdistribution.com

Maurice Parker Ltd, Alfred House, Alfreton Road, Derby, DE21 4AF Tel: (01332) 363422 Fax: (01332) 293455 E-mail: sales@mauriceparker.co.uk

T. Patton Ltd, 588 Lea Bridge Road, Leyton, London, E10 7DN Tel: (020) 8539 1599 Fax: (020) 8558 3578 E-mail: sales@tpatton.co.uk

▶ Phoenix Whirlpools, Scott Lane, Morley, Leeds, LS27 0NQ Tel: 0113-201 2260 Fax: 0113-202 2268

Plumbase Ltd, 123-129 Portland Road, Hove, East Sussex, BN3 5QW Tel: (01273) 746161 Fax: (01273) 424065 E-mail: john.bolton@btinternet.com

▶ Plumbcity Bathroom Equipment, 4-5 Bunting Road, Bury St. Edmunds, Suffolk, IP32 7BX Tel: (01284) 763355 Fax: (01284) 763335

Robert Pochin Ltd, 11 St Georges Way, Leicester, LE1 1SH Tel: 0116-251 5051 Fax: 0116-253 8829 E-mail: sales.enquiries@robertpochin.co.uk

Premier Bathrooms Ltd, Hewell Road, Redditch, Worcestershire, B97 6BW Tel: (01527) 67711 Fax: (01527) 594227 E-mail: info@premier-bathrooms.com

▶ Quick Gold Ltd, 52 Standard Road, London, NW10 6EU Tel: (020) 8965 1441 Fax: (020) 8965 2696

▶ Romaqua Bathroom Equipment, Unit 7-8 Craigmore Mill Industrial Estate, Craigmore Road, Bessbrook, Newry, County Down, BT35 6JR Tel: (028) 3026 2299 Fax: (0845) 1301743

▶ S B S Bathroom Centre, 34-40 Albert Street West, Grimsby, South Humberside, DN32 7SJ Tel: (01472) 241515 Fax: (01472) 241599

Shires Bathrooms Ltd, Beckside Road, Bradford, West Yorkshire, BD7 2JE Tel: (01274) 521199 Fax: (01274) 521583 E-mail: marketing@shires-bathrooms.co.uk

Showerdrape STD Ltd, Rammon House, 3 Longacre Street, Manchester, M1 2WN Tel: 0161-272 8700 Fax: 0161-272 8840 E-mail: info@showerdrape.co.uk

▶ Simply Bathrooms, Acan Way, Narborough, Leicester, LE19 2GW Tel: 0116-284 8880 Fax: 0116-284 8878 E-mail: sales@stuartplumbing.co.uk

▶ Stalwart Impex, 35 Stadium Business Centre, North End Road, Wembley, Middlesex, HA9 0AT Tel: (020) 8903 7711 Fax: 08707 66 17 19 E-mail: info@stalwartimpex.com

Thompson Plumbase, 10 Chapel Street, Redruth, Cornwall, TR15 2DE Tel: (01209) 215676 Fax: (01209) 213222

▶ Towel Rails (UK) Ltd, Unit 8, Cape Industrial Estate, Coal Hill Lane, Farsley, Pudsey, W. Yorkshire, LS28 5NA Tel: 0113-204 7540 Fax: 0113-204 7959

▶ Transform Building Services Ltd, 6 Lockyer House, Waterman St, London, SW15 1EE Tel: 020 8789 8780 Fax: 020 8789 8811 E-mail: contact@transformltd.co.uk

▶ Tring Bathrooms, 4-6 Miswell Lane, Tring, Hertfordshire, HP23 4BX Tel: (01442) 827295 Fax: (01442) 824148

Triton plc, Shepperton Business Park, Caldwell Road, Nuneaton, Warwickshire, CV11 4NR Tel: (024) 7634 4441 Fax: (024) 7634 9828 E-mail: reception@triton.plc.uk

Twyford Bathrooms Ltd, Lawton Road, Alsager, Stoke-on-Trent, ST7 2DF Tel: (01270) 879777 Fax: (01270) 873864

▶ UK Bathroom Interiors, 3/4 Old Laundry, Fishergreen, Ripon, North Yorkshire, HG4 1NL Tel: (0845) 2008526 E-mail: mark@ukbathroominteriors.com

Ultra Finishing Ltd, Heasandford Trading Estate, Burnley, Lancashire, BB10 2BE Tel: (01282) 436934 Fax: (01282) 428915 E-mail: sales@ultra-group.co.uk

▶ Universal Hardware Supplies Direct Ltd, 1ADillwyn Road, Sketty, Swansea, SA2 9AQ Tel: (01792) 205050 Fax: (01792) 202255 E-mail: info@u-h-s.co.uk

W Fayers & Sons Ltd, 76 Alfred Road, Buckhurst Hill, Essex, IG9 6DR Tel: (020) 8504 6625 Fax: (020) 8505 0626

Warwick Interiors, 4 Melbourne Industrial Estate, Watts Street, Chadderton, Oldham, OL9 9LQ Tel: 0161-624 1000 Fax: 0161-624 2247 E-mail: sales@warwickinteriors.co.uk

Waterbury Bathroom Accessories Ltd, 60 Adams Street, Birmingham, B7 4LT Tel: 0121-333 6062 Fax: 0121-333 6459 E-mail: sales@waterbury.co.uk

Wolseley Centers Ltd, Boroughbridge Road, Ripon, North Yorkshire, HG4 1SL Tel: (01765) 690690 Fax: (01765) 694516

BATHROOM FITTINGS OR ACCESSORIES DESIGN

▶ Bathstore.com Ltd, York Buildings, Edinburgh, EH2 1HY Tel: 0131-556 0333 Fax: 0131-557 4884E-mail: edinburgh.central@bathstore.com

BATHROOM FITTINGS OR ACCESSORIES IMPORT

Cactus Ceramics & Crafts, 4 Merville Garden Village, Newtownabbey, County Antrim, BT37 9TF Tel: (028) 9085 9869 Fax: (028) 9084 0113

▶ Eden Steam Showers., 5 Bagshot Road, Chobham, Surrey, GU24 8BP Tel: 01276 856240 Fax: 0118-979 4565 E-mail: contact@edensteamshowers.co.uk

Samuel Heath & Sons P.L.C., Cobden Works, Leopold Street, Birmingham, B12 0UJ Tel: 0121-772 2303 Fax: 0121-772 3334 E-mail: info@samuel-heath.com

Plumbase Ltd, 542 Millbrook Road West, Southampton, SO15 0LN Tel: (023) 8077 4499 Fax: (023) 8077 3388

▶ Stalwart Impex, 35 Stadium Business Centre, North End Road, Wembley, Middlesex, HA9 0AT Tel: (020) 8903 7711 Fax: 08707 66 17 19 E-mail: info@stalwartimpex.com

BATHROOM FURNITURE

▶ Allbits Plumbing Supplies Romney Ltd, Cinque Ports Road, New Romney, Kent, TN28 8LJ Tel: (01797) 363623 Fax: (01797) 363625 E-mail: sales@allbitsupplies.co.uk

▶ Aquabrand Bathrooms Ltd, 16 Spinnaker Quay, Plymouth, PL9 9SA Tel: (01752) 223645 Fax: 0870 758 5877 E-mail: markthomas@aquabrand.com

▶ Bathroom Deals, 102 Finlay Road, Gloucester, GL4 6TP Tel: (01452) 336250 Fax: (01452) 332338 E-mail: sales@bathroomdeals.com

▶ Bathstore.com Ltd, 87-89 Leeds Road, Harrogate, North Yorkshire, HG2 8BE Tel: (01423) 874400 Fax: (01423) 874400 E-mail: harrogate@bathstore.com

▶ Bathstore.com Ltd, Unit T4 Io Trade Centre, Hobley Drive, Swindon, SN3 4NS Tel: (01793) 834111 Fax: (01793) 834222 E-mail: swindon@bathstore.com

▶ Clayton Cabinets Ltd, The Barn, Langdale, Sampford Courtenay, Okehampton, Devon, EX20 2SY Tel: (01837) 82788 Fax: (01837) 82788 E-mail: nick@claytoncabinets.co.uk

Fine Line Interiors, Surrex Farm, Colchester Road, Coggeshall, Colchester, CO6 1RR Tel: (01376) 561611 Fax: (01376) 561110

▶ Furniture World, 283 Shirley Road, Southampton, SO15 3HT Tel: (023) 8057 1918 Fax: (023) 8077 9033 E-mail: info@fwtc.co.uk

▶ G & L Home Improvements, 33 Butterside Road, Kingsnorth, Ashford, Kent, TN23 3PD Tel: (01233) 501815 E-mail: garry.laker@ntlworld.com

▶ General Supplies Ltd, 465A Caledonian Road, Holloway, London, N7 9BA Tel: (020) 7609 6111 Fax: (020) 7609 8111 E-mail: sales@generalsupplies.com

▶ Keramag Waveney Ltd, London Road, Beccles, Suffolk, NR34 8TS Tel: (01502) 716600 Fax: (01502) 717767 E-mail: kerrina@waveneybaths.co.uk

▶ Keramag Waveney Ltd, London Road, Beccles, Suffolk, NR34 8TS Tel: (01502) 716600 Fax: (01502) 717767 E-mail: ian@keramagwaveney.co.uk

M F I UK Ltd, Southon House, 333 The Hyde, Edgeware Road, London, NW9 6TD Tel: (020) 8200 8000 Fax: (020) 8200 8636

oldcolours.co.uk, 16 Waterside Industrial Estate, Wolverhampton, WV2 2RH Tel: (01902) 402040 E-mail: sales@oldcolours.co.uk

▶ One Red Sky, Watcombe Manor Industrial Units, Ingham Lane, Watlington, Oxfordshire, OX49 5EB Tel: (01491) 614756 E-mail: customerservices@oneredsky.com

▶ P J Milligan, 54 Wilson Place, East Kilbride, Glasgow, G74 4QD Tel: (01355) 260990 E-mail: craig.hamilton@pjmilligan.com

Parkyn Interiors, 2 Bilton Grove Avenue, Harrogate, North Yorkshire, HG1 4HJ Tel: (01423) 563628

Richardson Bros, 39 Leg Street, Oswestry, Shropshire, SY11 2NN Tel: (01691) 656980 Fax: (01691) 656980

▶ Jon Riley Furniture, Moores Farmhouse, Corse Lawn, Gloucester, GL19 4LY Tel: (01452) 781074 E-mail: enquiries@jon-riley.co.uk

Sharps Bedrooms Ltd, Hylton Road, Worcester, WR2 5JW Tel: (01905) 424502

BATHROOM MIRRORS

Bocco Ltd, Fitzroy House, Lynwood Park, Worcester Park, Surrey, KT4 7AT Tel: (020) 8330 7007 Fax: (020) 8330 3351 E-mail: bocco@lineone.net

BATHROOM SCALES

Homedics Group Ltd, 211 Vale Road, Tonbridge, Kent, TN9 1SU Tel: (01732) 354828 Fax: (01732) 358631 E-mail: uksales@homedics.co.uk

BATHROOM SETS

▶ Primary Plumbing Supplies, Unit 28 Hawthorn Road Industrial Estate, Eastbourne, East Sussex, BN23 6QA Tel: (01323) 734714 Fax: (01323) 649193 E-mail: eastbourne@diycity.com

BATHROOM SINKS

oldcolours.co.uk, 16 Waterside Industrial Estate, Wolverhampton, WV2 2RH Tel: (01902) 402040 E-mail: sales@oldcolours.co.uk

BATHROOM SUITES

▶ Bathroom Deals, 102 Finlay Road, Gloucester, GL4 6TP Tel: (01452) 336250 Fax: (01452) 332338 E-mail: sales@bathroomdeals.com

▶ Bathtimes Bathroom Equipment, 3 New Road, Newhaven, East Sussex, BN9 0HE Tel: (01273) 513022 Fax: (01273) 513848 E-mail: info@bathtimesltd.co.uk

▶ Be Modern Ltd, 19 Bedesway, Jarrow, Tyne & Wear, NE32 3HQ Tel: 0191-428 0444 Fax: 0191-489 0620 E-mail: info@bemodern.co.uk

▶ Galley Matrix, 1 Waterside Industrial Park, Waterside Road, Leeds, LS10 1RW Tel: 0113-277 7788 Fax: 0113-277 5151

▶ HomeSupply.co.uk, County House, 12-13 Sussex Street, Plymouth, PL1 2HR Tel: (01752) 260607 E-mail: kellys@homesupply.co.uk

oldcolours.co.uk, 16 Waterside Industrial Estate, Wolverhampton, WV2 2RH Tel: (01902) 402040 E-mail: sales@oldcolours.co.uk

▶ Primary Plumbing Supplies, Unit 28 Hawthorn Road Industrial Estate, Eastbourne, East Sussex, BN23 6QA Tel: (01323) 734714 Fax: (01323) 649193 E-mail: eastbourne@diycity.com

Renaissance Period Mouldings, 262 Handsworth Road, Sheffield, S13 9BS Tel: 0114-244 6622 Fax: 0114-261 0472

BATHROOM TILES

▶ Dar Interiors, 11 Arches, Miles Street, London, SW8 1RZ Tel: (020) 7720 9678 Fax: (020) 7627 5129E-mail: enquiries@darinteriors.com

▶ G & L Home Improvements, 33 Butterside Road, Kingsnorth, Ashford, Kent, TN23 3PD Tel: (01233) 501815 E-mail: garry.laker@ntlworld.com

▶ Iceni Printed Tiles, 8 Transopel House, Queens Square, Attleborough, Norfolk, NR17 2AE Tel: 01953 451313 E-mail: info@icenitiles.co.uk

▶ Pietra Tile Distribution Ltd, 28 Silver Street, Bradford-on-Avon, Wiltshire, BA15 1JY Tel: (01225) 867678 Fax: (01225) 867678 E-mail: jakelewis@pietrastone.co.uk

▶ Stone Mine Ltd, 22 Blackfriars Street, Facing Travelodge, City Centre, Manchester, M3 5BQ Tel: 0161-833 2333 Fax: 0161-870 6340 E-mail: alex@stonemine.co.uk

BATHROOMS

B G Romeril Ltd, Dumaresq Street, St. Helier, Jersey, JE2 3WP Tel: (01534) 738806 Fax: (01534) 767016 E-mail: enquiry@romerils.co.je

▶ G & E Interiors, 27-29 Liverpool Road, Kidsgrove, Stoke-On-Trent, ST7 1EA Tel: (01782) 785965

▶ Goodwood Bathrooms, 1 North Farm, Church Road, North Mundham, Chichester, West Sussex, PO20 1JU Tel: (01243) 532121 Fax: (01243) 533423

▶ H J Ceramics Ltd, Armytage Road, Brighouse, West Yorkshire, HD6 1PT Tel: (01484) 380000

Hadley Bathrooms, 683 London Road, Hadleigh, Benfleet, Essex, SS7 2EE Tel: (01702) 552233 Fax: (01702) 554292

Home Form Group, Unit 1, Renley Road Retail Park, Ipswich, IP2 0AQ Tel: (01473) 226009

Jewson Ltd, Lyons Lane, Chorley, Lancashire, PR6 0PH Tel: (01257) 276211 Fax: (01257) 260098

▶ Primary Plumbing Supplies, Unit 28 Hawthorn Road Industrial Estate, Eastbourne, East Sussex, BN23 6QA Tel: (01323) 734714 Fax: (01323) 649193 E-mail: eastbourne@diycity.com

▶ Verrall & Parks, 225-227 Seaside, Eastbourne, East Sussex, BN22 7NR Tel: (01323) 737633 Fax: (01323) 745789 E-mail: sales@verrallandparks.co.uk

BATHS, ULTRASONIC CLEANING, BENCHTOP

Rotajet Systems, Richard Alan House, Shaw Cross Business Park, Dewsbury, West Yorkshire, WF12 7RD Tel: (01924) 468769 Fax: (01924) 485376 E-mail: info@rotajet.co.uk

BATHS, ULTRASONIC CLEANING, INDUSTRIAL

▶ Majestic Gates, Unit 1 Temple Street, Hull, HU5 1AD Tel: (01482) 441466 Fax: (01482) 441466 E-mail: sales@majesticgates.com

Rotajet Systems, Richard Alan House, Shaw Cross Business Park, Dewsbury, West Yorkshire, WF12 7RD Tel: (01924) 468769 Fax: (01924) 485376 E-mail: info@rotajet.co.uk

BATTERIES, *See also headings for particular types*

12 VoltZ Ltd, 5 Fleetwood St, Preston, PR2 2PT Tel: (0871) 2500555 Fax: (0871) 2500554 E-mail: help@12voltz.com

A J Mechanical Handling Services Ltd, Bridge Works, 2 North End Road, Yatton, Bristol, BS49 4AL Tel: (01934) 835835 Fax: (01934) 838999

A T S Euromaster Ltd, Vantage Point, 20 Upper Portland Street, Aston, Birmingham, B6 5TW Tel: 0121-325 7300 Fax: 0121-325 7333 E-mail: info@atseuromaster.co.uk

A T S Exhausts & Tyres (Edenbridge) Ltd, Unit 1 Monza House, Fircroft Way, Edenbridge, Kent, TN8 6EJ Tel: (01732) 867746 Fax: (01732) 868274

Aero Quality Sales Ltd, 8 Airlinks Estate, Spitfire Way, Heston, Hounslow, TW5 9NR Tel: (020) 8561 4211 Fax: (020) 8848 1568 E-mail: kgreene@mckaero.com

Anglia Battery & Filter Co., 834 London Road, Leigh-on-Sea, Essex, SS9 3NH Tel: (01702) 470262 Fax: (01702) 470335 E-mail: sales@angliabattery.co.uk

ATS Euromaster Ltd, 143 Histon Road, Cambridge, CB4 3HZ Tel: (01223) 454631 Fax: (01223) 454654 E-mail: ats@euromaster.com

Auctionelec Ltd, 20-22 Bedford Row, London, WC1R 4JS Tel: (0870) 6093195 E-mail: sales@auctionelec.com

Auto Battery Service, 59 Recreation Road, Guildford, Surrey, GU1 1HE Tel: (01483) 572316 Fax: (01483) 504965 E-mail: guildford@manbat.co.uk

Auto Tyre & Battery Co., Southern Avenue, Leominster, Herefordshire, HR6 0QF Tel: (01568) 615680

Baldock Tyres, 22 London Road Industrial Estate, Baldock, Hertfordshire, SG7 6LE Tel: (01462) 894772 Fax: (01462) 491412

Battery Services (Standby) Ltd, 71 Thomson Drive, Bearsden, Glasgow, G61 3PB Tel: (0141) 956 5575 Fax: (0141) 943 1134

Battery Specialists South East, 35 High Dewar Road, Rainham, Gillingham, Kent, ME8 8DN Tel: (01634) 262343 Fax: (01634) 262343

Bristol Batteries Ltd, 3 Dove Lane, St. Pauls, Bristol, BS2 9HP Tel: 0117-955 0536 Fax: 0117-935 1791 E-mail: admin@bristolbatteries.com

Bristol Batteries, Axis Business Centre, Westmead Trading Estate, Westmead, Swindon, SN5 7YS Tel: (01793) 616646 Fax: (01793) 490011 E-mail: sales@bristolbatteries.com

▶ Budget, 13 865 Ringwood Road, Bournemouth, BH11 8LW Tel: (01202) 582700 Fax: (01202) 573200 E-mail: info@budgetbatteries.co.uk

Builder Center Ltd, Windsor Road, Bedford, MK42 9SU Tel: (01234) 272292 Fax: (01234) 365395 E-mail: peter.abbott@wolseley.co.uk

Builder Center Ltd, 80 Low Hill, Liverpool, L6 1BT Tel: 0151-263 5544 Fax: 0151-263 1432

Builder Center Ltd, Cradle Hill Industrial Estate, Alfriston Road, Seaford, East Sussex, BN25 2AT Tel: (01323) 893243 Fax: (01323) 891072

Builder Center Ltd, 591 Sedlescombe Road North, St. Leonards-on-Sea, East Sussex, TN37 7PY Tel: (01424) 756946 Fax: (01424) 751481

Celltech, Unit 3, Bldg 6 Tameside Bus Development Centre, Windmill Lane, Denton, Manchester, M34 3QS Tel: 0161-320 8096 Fax: 0161-320 3526 E-mail: sales@celltech-battery.co.uk

Charger Bay Solutions, 7 Fitton Road, St. Germans, King's Lynn, Norfolk, PE34 3AU Tel: 07723 391485 Fax: (01553) 617619 E-mail: info@chargerbaysolutions.co.uk

▶ Clyde Space Ltd, 6.01 Kelvin Campus, West of Scotland Science Park, Glasgow, G20 0SP Tel: 0141-946 4440 Fax: 0141-945 1591 E-mail: enquiries@clyde-space.com

Computronic Controls Ltd, 41-46 Railway Terrace, Nechells, Birmingham, B7 5NG Tel: 0121-327 8500 Fax: 0121-327 8501 E-mail: sales@computroniccontrols.com

County Battery Services Ltd, Field Industrial Estate, Clover Street, Kirkby-in-Ashfield, Nottingham, NG17 7LJ Tel: (01623) 757377 Fax: (01623) 757347 E-mail: sales@countybattery.co.uk

Eastbourne Tyre Co. Ltd, Fort Road, Eastbourne, East Sussex, BN22 7SE Tel: (01323) 720222 Fax: (01323) 720018

Emergency Power Systems, Suite 16 Enterprise House, Strathkelvin Place, Kirkintilloch, Glasgow, G66 1XQ Tel: 0141-775 1815 Fax: 0141-775 1609 E-mail: sales@emergencypowersystems.co.uk

BATTERIES – *continued*

Emergency Power Systems P.L.C., Carley Drive Business Area, Westfield, Sheffield, S20 8NQ Tel: 0114-247 8369 Fax: 0114-247 8367 E-mail: sales@emergencypowersystems.co.uk
Energizer Group Ltd, Eveready House, 93 Burleigh Gardens, Southgate, London, N14 5AQ Tel: (020) 8882 8661 Fax: (020) 8882 1938
Exide Battery Services Ltd, 6 & 7 Parkway Estate, Longbridge Road, Trafford Park, Manchester, M17 1SN Tel: 0161-488 5577 Fax: 0161-786 3334 E-mail: sales@exideuk.co.uk
F S B Wholesale Ltd, Mirror Works, Cuckoo Hall Lane, London, N9 8DH Tel: (020) 8804 4333 Fax: (020) 8804 8777
Industrial Battery & Charger Services Ltd, 46 Catley Road, Sheffield, S9 5JF Tel: 0114-243 3993 Fax: 0114-242 4845 E-mail: peterpgarrat@ibcsltd.demon.co.uk
Kipling Motorist Centre, 76 Ifield Road, Crawley, West Sussex, RH11 7BQ Tel: (01293) 612211 Fax: (01293) 612444
L E W Diecastings Ltd, Trows Lane, Rochdale, Lancashire, OL11 2UF Tel: (01706) 632218 Fax: (01706) 643714 E-mail: alan@lew.co.uk
L S UK Ltd, 124 Anlaby Road, Hull, HU3 2JH Tel: (01482) 610977 Fax: (01482) 219818 E-mail: kvssales@aol.co.uk
Manbat Ltd, Unit 4D, Temple Gate Distribution Centre, Mead Street, Bristol, BS3 4RP Tel: 0117-977 6477 Fax: 0117-977 8481 E-mail: bristol@manbat.co.uk
Manbat Ltd, Foxwood Industrial Park, Chesterfield, Derbyshire, S41 9RN Tel: (01246) 452522 Fax: (01246) 452511 E-mail: chesterfield@manbat.co.uk
Mr Tyre Ltd, 1 Burton Street, Peterborough, PE1 5HA Tel: (01733) 560484 Fax: (01733) 342613
National Tyre Service Ltd, Regent House, Heaton Lane, Stockport, Cheshire, SK4 1BS Tel: 0161-480 7461 Fax: 0161-475 3540
Power Sonic Europe Ltd, 3 Buckingham Square, Hurricane Way, Wickford, Essex, SS11 8YQ Tel: (01268) 560686 Fax: (01268) 560902 E-mail: info@power-sonic.co.uk
Renatex Ltd, Nam House, 58 Spencer Street, Birmingham, B18 6DS Tel: 0121-233 9999 Fax: 0121-236 9295 E-mail: sales@renatex.com
Roadwheel Tyre & Exhaust Ltd, 468 London Road, Portsmouth, PO2 9RN Tel: (023) 9269 4741 Fax: (023) 9266 1923
Uniross Batteries, Uniross House, Old Mill Road, Portishead, Bristol, BS20 7BX Tel: (0870) 2206988 Fax: (01275) 846999 E-mail: sales@uniross.com
W B Power Source Ltd, Brandon Way, West Bromwich, West Midlands, B70 8JB Tel: 0121-525 4441 Fax: 0121-525 4446
Walmer Batteries & Signs, 36 North Barrack Road, Walmer, Deal, Kent, CT14 7DU Tel: (01304) 372164 Fax: (01304) 372233 E-mail: walmerbatteries@hotmail.com
Jim Whalley Batteries, 1 Homestead Cottage, Playhatch, Reading, RG4 9QR Tel: 0118-947 9953 Fax: 0118-947 3345

BATTERIES, ALKALINE/PRIMARY

Baruch Enterprises Ltd, Watkins House, Pegamoid Road, London, N18 2NG Tel: (020) 8803 8899 Fax: (020) 8965 5448 E-mail: info@baruch.co.uk
▶ Battech International Ltd, 83 Shropshire Street, Market Drayton, Shropshire, TF9 3DQ Tel: (0871) 5500051 E-mail: sales@bat-tech.co.uk
Celltech, Unit 3, Bldg 6 Tameside Bus Development Centre, Windmill Lane, Denton, Manchester, M34 3QS Tel: 0161-320 8096 Fax: 0161-320 3526 E-mail: sales@celltech-battery.co.uk
Energizer Group Ltd, Eveready House, 93 Burleigh Gardens, Southgate, London, N14 5AQ Tel: (020) 8882 8661 Fax: (020) 8882 1938
G P Batteries UK Ltd, Monument View, Chelston Business Park, Wellington, Somerset, TA21 9ND Tel: (01823) 660044 Fax: (01823) 665595 E-mail: sales@gpbatteries.co.uk
Newey & Eyre Ltd, Unit 15 17, Whittle Way, Crawley, West Sussex, RH10 9RW Tel: (01293) 517500 Fax: (01293) 561362 E-mail: neweyandeyre@hagemeyer.co.uk
Newey & Eyre Ltd, 62 Manners View, Newport, Isle of Wight, PO30 5FA Tel: (01983) 523481 Fax: (01983) 520723
Newionaire, 10 Cofton Road, Marsh Barton Trading Estate, Marsh Barton Trading Estate, Exeter, EX2 8QW Tel: (01392) 829180 Fax: (01392) 410358

BATTERIES, CUSTOM BUILT

G P Batteries UK Ltd, Monument View, Chelston Business Park, Wellington, Somerset, TA21 9ND Tel: (01823) 660044 Fax: (01823) 665595 E-mail: sales@gpbatteries.co.uk

BATTERIES, DRY/PRIMARY

Chiltern Batteries, 44 Camford Way, Luton, LU3 3AN Tel: (01582) 585231 Fax: (01582) 491964
Cornwall Battery Centre, 34 Threemilestone Industrial Estate, Threemilestone, Truro, Cornwall, TR4 9LD Tel: (01872) 270011 Fax: (01872) 264250 E-mail: sales@bristolbatteries.com
Energizer Ltd, Unit 2 Tanfield Lea Industrial Park, Tanfield Lea, Stanley, County Durham, DH9 9QF Tel: (01207) 290900 Fax: (01207) 292016 E-mail: pam.holder@energiser.com
Energizer Group Ltd, Eveready House, 93 Burleigh Gardens, Southgate, London, N14 5AQ Tel: (020) 8882 8661 Fax: (020) 8882 1938
Powerfactor Ltd, 8 Pear Tree Farm, Townsend, Marsh Gibbon, Bicester, Oxfordshire, OX27 0EY Tel: (01869) 278585 Fax: (01869) 278989 E-mail: sales@powerfactor.co.uk
Rayovac Europe Ltd, Watermans House, Watermans Court, Kingsbury Crescent, The Causeway, Staines, Middlesex, TW18 3BA Tel: (01784) 411411 Fax: (01784) 411412
▶ Varta Microbattery GmbH, 16 Progress Business Centre, Whittle Parkway, Slough, SL1 6DQ Tel: (01628) 607930 Fax: (01628) 607939 E-mail: uksales@varta.com

BATTERIES, INDUSTRIAL/ GENERAL PURPOSE/ ACCUMULATOR

▶ Bmib Scotland Ltd, 18 Melford Road, Righead Industrial Estate, Bellshill, Lanarkshire, ML4 3LR Tel: (01698) 844021 Fax: (01698) 845888
C M P Batteries Ltd, PO Box 1, Bolton, BL5 1DD Tel: (01204) 64111 Fax: (01204) 62981 E-mail: sales@cmpbatteries.co.uk
D C Emergency Systems Ltd, Wharf Street, Dukinfield, Cheshire, SK16 4JG Tel: 0161-343 1189 Fax: 0161-343 2235 E-mail: sales@dc-emergency.com
Diamond Accumulator Co. Ltd, The Chase, Bournemouth Park Road, Southend-on-Sea, SS2 5LW Tel: (01702) 467083
Exide Battery Services Ltd, 6 & 7 Parkway Estate, Longbridge Road, Trafford Park, Manchester, M17 1SN Tel: 0161-488 5577 Fax: 0161-786 3334 E-mail: sales@exideuk.co.uk
Exide Technologies Power Network, Unit 14 Gunnels Wood Park, Gunnels Wood Road, Stevenage, Hertfordshire, SG1 2BH Tel: (01438) 359090 Fax: (01438) 727684 E-mail: elainemcleod@eu.exide.com
L S UK Ltd, 124 Anlaby Road, Hull, HU3 2JH Tel: (01482) 610977 Fax: (01482) 219818 E-mail: kvssales@aol.co.uk
Lincon Batteries Ltd, Faraday Works, 25-26 Faraday Road, Leigh-On-Sea, Essex, SS9 5JU Tel: (01702) 528711 Fax: (01702) 421362 E-mail: batteries@lincon.co.uk
Manbat Ltd, Water Street, Abergele, Clwyd, LL22 7SL Tel: (01745) 832174 Fax: (01745) 833503 E-mail: sales@manbat.co.uk
Manbat Ltd, Unit 4D, Temple Gate Distribution Centre, Mead Street, Bristol, BS3 4RP Tel: 0117-977 6477 Fax: 0117-977 8481 E-mail: bristol@manbat.co.uk
Manbat Ltd, Foxwood Industrial Park, Chesterfield, Derbyshire, S41 9RN Tel: (01246) 452522 Fax: (01246) 452511 E-mail: chesterfield@manbat.co.uk
Manbat Ltd, Unit 1-5 Chancel Place, Store Street, Manchester, M1 2WB Tel: 0161-273 2235 Fax: 0161-273 7368 E-mail: sale@manbat.co.uk
Manbat Ltd, Lancaster Road, Shrewsbury, SY1 3LG Tel: (01743) 460792 E-mail: sales@manbat.co.uk
▶ Moltech Power Systems Ltd, Unit 20, Loomer Road, Chesterton, Newcastle, Staffordshire, ST5 7LB Tel: (01782) 566622 Fax: (01782) 576640 E-mail: rob.phillips@moltechpower.co.uk
Nersys, Stephenson Street, Newport, Gwent, NP19 4XJ Tel: (01633) 277673 Fax: (01633) 281787 E-mail: forename.surname@uk.nss.com
S E C Industrial Battery Co. Ltd, Thorney Weir House, Thorney Mill Road, Iver, Buckinghamshire, SL0 9AQ Tel: (01895) 431543 Fax: (01895) 431880 E-mail: info@secbattery.com
Shepfield Batteries Ltd, 277 Stansted Road, Bishop's Stortford, Hertfordshire, CM23 2BT Tel: (01279) 652067 Fax: (01279) 758041 E-mail: info@shieldbatteries.co.uk
Traction Batteries South East, Chilton Industrial Estate, 11 Addison Road, Sudbury, Suffolk, CO10 2YW Tel: (01787) 880011 Fax: (01787) 880770 E-mail: sales@traction-batteries.co.uk
Yuasa Battery UK Ltd, Unit 22 Rassau Industrial Estate, Rassau, Ebbw Vale, Gwent, NP23 5SD Tel: (01495) 350121 Fax: (01495) 350661 E-mail: enquires@yuasa-sales.co.uk

BATTERIES, MOTOR VEHICLE/ AUTOMOTIVE

Aghabridge Ltd, Unit 1-4 Sheldon Business Centre, Maritime Close, Medway City Estate, Rochester, Kent, ME2 4AF Tel: (01634) 294944 Fax: (01634) 294577 E-mail: ahgabridge@aol.com
Battery Centre Ltd, 224 Neath Road, Landore, Swansea, SA1 2JG Tel: (01792) 774528 Fax: (01792) 772464
D B Wilson & Co. Ltd, 1 Alleysbank Road, Rutherglen, Glasgow, G73 1AL Tel: 0141-647 0161 Fax: 0141-613 1795 E-mail: dbwilsonjr@aol.com
Daewoo International Ltd, 10TH Floor C I Tower, St. Georges Square, New Malden, Surrey, KT3 4HH Tel: (020) 8336 9130 Fax: (020) 8949 3783 E-mail: kelliedodds@daewoo.co.uk
▶ DBS Brand Factors, Unit 5, Haydock Lane, Haydock, St. Helens, Merseyside, WA11 9UY Tel: (01942) 276657 Fax: (01942) 722067 E-mail: enquiries@dbsbrandfactors.co.uk
Exide Battery Services Ltd, 6 & 7 Parkway Estate, Longbridge Road, Trafford Park, Manchester, M17 1SN Tel: 0161-488 5577 Fax: 0161-786 3334 E-mail: sales@exideuk.co.uk
L C Davis & Sons Ltd, 6 Prince Georges Road, London, SW19 2PX Tel: (020) 8648 3113 Fax: (020) 8640 8282 E-mail: info@lcdavis.com
Lincon Batteries Ltd, Faraday Works, 25-26 Faraday Road, Leigh-On-Sea, Essex, SS9 5JU Tel: (01702) 528711 Fax: (01702) 421362 E-mail: batteries@lincon.co.uk
Manbat Ltd, Water Street, Abergele, Clwyd, LL22 7SL Tel: (01745) 832174 Fax: (01745) 833503 E-mail: sales@manbat.co.uk
Manbat Ltd, Foxwood Industrial Park, Chesterfield, Derbyshire, S41 9RN Tel: (01246) 452522 Fax: (01246) 452511 E-mail: chesterfield@manbat.co.uk
Merlin Equipment, Unit 4, Cabot Business Village, Holyrood Close, Cabot Lane, Poole, Dorset, BH17 7BA Tel: (01202) 697979 Fax: (01202) 691919 E-mail: sales@merlinequipment.com
Andrew Page Ltd, Apson House, Colton Mill, Bullerthorpe Lane, Leeds, LS15 9JL Tel: 0113-397 0200 Fax: 0113-397 0295 E-mail: accounts@andrewpage.com
Shepfield Batteries Ltd, 277 Stansted Road, Bishop's Stortford, Hertfordshire, CM23 2BT Tel: (01279) 652067 Fax: (01279) 758041 E-mail: info@shieldbatteries.co.uk
Truckstop Hawkes, Unit 9 Brook Street, Redditch, Worcestershire, B98 8NG Tel: (01527) 68279 Fax: (01527) 60026 E-mail: info@truckstophawkes.co.uk
Tyreways Ltd, Church Street, Uttoxeter, Staffordshire, ST14 8AA Tel: (01889) 564216 Fax: (01889) 564213

BATTERIES, RECHARGEABLE/ SEALED, *See also headings for particular types*

G P Batteries UK Ltd, Monument View, Chelston Business Park, Wellington, Somerset, TA21 9ND Tel: (01823) 660044 Fax: (01823) 665595 E-mail: sales@gpbatteries.co.uk
Multicell International Ltd, 6 Swannington Road, Broughton Astley, Leicester, LE9 6TU Tel: (01455) 283443 Fax: (01455) 284250 E-mail: help@multicell.co.uk
Newey & Eyre Ltd, Unit 15 17, Whittle Way, Crawley, West Sussex, RH10 9RW Tel: (01293) 517500 Fax: (01293) 561362 E-mail: neweyandeyre@hagemeyer.co.uk
Newey & Eyre Ltd, 62 Manners View, Newport, Isle of Wight, PO30 5FA Tel: (01983) 523481 Fax: (01983) 520723
Newionaire, 10 Cofton Road, Marsh Barton Trading Estate, Marsh Barton Trading Estate, Exeter, EX2 8QW Tel: (01392) 829180 Fax: (01392) 410358
Ripmax Ltd, Ripmax Corner, Green Street, Enfield, Middlesex, EN3 7SJ Tel: (020) 8282 7500 Fax: (020) 8282 7501 E-mail: mail@ripmax.com

BATTERIES, RECHARGEABLE/ SEALED, LEAD ACID

Bristol Batteries Ltd, 3 Dove Lane, St. Pauls, Bristol, BS2 9HP Tel: 0117-955 0536 Fax: 0117-935 1791 E-mail: admin@bristolbatteries.com
Nersys, Stephenson Street, Newport, Gwent, NP19 4XJ Tel: (01633) 277673 Fax: (01633) 281787 E-mail: forename.surname@uk.nss.com
Power Sonic Europe Ltd, 3 Buckingham Square, Hurricane Way, Wickford, Essex, SS11 8YQ Tel: (01268) 560686 Fax: (01268) 560902 E-mail: info@power-sonic.co.uk
Pulsar Developments Ltd, Spracklen House, Dukes Place, Marlow, Buckinghamshire, SL7 2QH Tel: (01628) 473555 Fax: (01628) 474325 E-mail: sales@pulsardevelopments.com
Yuasa Battery UK Ltd, Unit 22 Rassau Industrial Estate, Rassau, Ebbw Vale, Gwent, NP23 5SD Tel: (01495) 350121 Fax: (01495) 350661 E-mail: enquires@yuasa-sales.co.uk
Yuasa Battery UK Ltd, Unit 22 Rassau Industrial Estate, Rassau, Ebbw Vale, Gwent, NP23 5SD Tel: (01495) 350121 Fax: (01495) 350661

BATTERIES, RECHARGEABLE/ SEALED, NICKEL METAL HYDRIDE

Saft, River Drive, South Shields, Tyne & Wear, NE33 2TR Tel: 0191-456 1451 Fax: 0191-456 6383 E-mail: enquiries@saftbatteries.com

BATTERY BACKUP POWER SUPPLIES

Eltek Energy (UK) Ltd, Eltek House, Maxted Road, Hemel Hempstead, Hertfordshire, HP2 7DX Tel: (01442) 219355 Fax: (01442) 245894 E-mail: uksales@eltekenergy.com
Tascom International Ltd, 1 Mars House, Calleva Park, Aldermaston, Reading, RG7 8LA Tel: 0118-982 0400 E-mail: bill.white@tascom.co.uk
V X I Power Ltd, Westminster Industrial Estate, Station Road, North Hykeham, Lincoln, LN6 3QY Tel: (01522) 500511 Fax: (01522) 500515 E-mail: sales@vxipower.com

BATTERY BACKUP/STANDBY UNITS

▶ Rectifier Technologies (UK) Limited, Unit A8, Sturmer End Industrial Estate, Sturmer Road, Haverhill, Suffolk, CB9 7UU Tel: (01440) 706777 Fax: (01440) 762810 E-mail: sales@duvine.co.uk

BATTERY CAPACITY DISCHARGE TESTING

Jade Air P.L.C., Hanger 1, Shoreham Airport, Shoreham-by-Sea, West Sussex, BN43 5FF Tel: (01273) 464013 Fax: (01273) 465184 E-mail: info@jadeair.co.uk
▶ Skylark Energy Systems Ltd, PO Box 11033, Banchory, Kincardineshire, AB31 5WS Tel: (01330) 823950 Fax: (01330) 823966 E-mail: info@skylark.co.uk

BATTERY CHARGER MAINTENANCE/REPAIR SERVICES

Charion Spares Ltd, Unit 7 Paper Mill End Industrial Estate, Birmingham, B44 8NH Tel: 0121-344 4540 Fax: 0121-344 3017 E-mail: charionspares@yahoo.co.uk

BATTERY CHARGER MANUFRS

Aero Quality Sales Ltd, 8 Airlinks Estate, Spitfire Way, Heston, Hounslow, TW5 9NR Tel: (020) 8561 4211 Fax: (020) 8848 1568 E-mail: kgreene@mckaero.com
Applied Power Techniques Ltd, 7 Maundrell Road, Calne, Wiltshire, SN11 9PU Tel: (01249) 811888 Fax: (01249) 811888
Arian Electronic Systems, 34A High St, Syston, Leicester, LE7 1GP Tel: 0116-260 7663 Fax: 0116-260 7663
B C Electrical Techniques Ltd, Stocklake, Aylesbury, Buckinghamshire, HP20 1DA Tel: (01296) 481995 Fax: (01296) 394158 E-mail: info@bcet.co.uk
C M P Batteries Ltd, PO Box 1, Bolton, BL5 1DD Tel: (01204) 64111 Fax: (01204) 62981 E-mail: sales@cmpbatteries.co.uk
Capricorn Controls, Thorpe Close, Banbury, Oxfordshire, OX16 4SW Tel: (01295) 272360 Fax: (01295) 264766 E-mail: sales@capricorn-controls.com
Computronic Controls Ltd, 41-46 Railway Terrace, Nechells, Birmingham, B7 5NG Tel: 0121-327 8500 Fax: 0121-327 8501 E-mail: sales@computroniccontrols.com
County Battery Services Ltd, Field Industrial Estate, Clover Street, Kirkby-in-Ashfield, Nottingham, NG17 7LJ Tel: (01623) 757377 Fax: (01623) 757347 E-mail: sales@countybattery.co.uk
Dartpoint Ltd, Unit 1b Kitewell Lane, Lydd, Romney Marsh, Kent, TN29 9LP Tel: (01797) 320910 Fax: (01797) 320571 E-mail: sales@dartpoint.co.uk
▶ Digilution, 1 The Hoppits, Park Lane, Puckeridge, Ware, Hertfordshire, SG11 1SG Tel: (01920) 822936 E-mail: stephen@digilution.co.uk
Erskine Systems Ltd, Salter Road, Eastfield Industrial Estate, Scarborough, North Yorkshire, YO11 3DU Tel: (01723) 583511 Fax: (01723) 581231 E-mail: sales@erskine-systems.co.uk
G E Plant Services Ltd, 10a Dawkins Road, Poole, Dorset, BH15 4JD Tel: (01202) 676463 Fax: (01202) 665725 E-mail: geplant@btinternet.com
HiSpark Batteries Golf International Ltd, 450 Chester Road North, Sutton Coldfield, W. Midlands, B73 6RG Tel: 0121-568 8887 Fax: 0121-355 7807
Jenelec Ltd, Fuller Road, Harleston, Norfolk, IP20 9EA Tel: (01379) 853666 Fax: (01379) 854414 E-mail: sales@jenelec.co.uk
M S S L Systems, Albany Road, Gateshead, Tyne & Wear, NE8 3AT Tel: 0191-477 3518 Fax: 0191-490 0264 E-mail: info@mssl.com
Mascot UK, PO Box 2090, Salisbury, SP2 2BH Tel: (01722) 504853 Fax: (01264) 396402 E-mail: andrew.parrish@mascot.no
Mastervolt UK Ltd, Winchester Hill, Romsey, Hampshire, SO51 7ND Tel: (01794) 516443 Fax: (01794) 516453 E-mail: sales@mastervolt.com

BATTERY CHARGER MANUFRS – *continued*

Multipower International Ltd, 8 Langney Green, Tattenhoe, Milton Keynes, MK4 3ES Tel: (01908) 522202 Fax: (0870) 7064855 E-mail: tech@multipower-int.com

P B Design & Developments Ltd, Unit 9-10, Hither Green, Clevedon, Avon, BS21 6XT Tel: (01275) 874411 Fax: (01275) 874428 E-mail: administrator@pbdesign.co.uk

Pag, 565 Kingston Road, London, SW20 8SA Tel: (020) 8543 3131 Fax: (020) 8540 4797 E-mail: email@paguk.com

Pe Systems, Victoria Industrial Estate, Victoria Street, Leigh, Lancashire, WN7 5SE Tel: (01942) 260330 Fax: (01942) 261835 E-mail: sales@pe-systems.co.uk

Power Systems Warehouse Ltd, Powerguard House, Grimsby Road, Louth, Lincolnshire, LN11 0SX Tel: (01507) 600688 Fax: (01507) 600621 E-mail: sales@powerguard.co.uk

Powernetics International Ltd, Jason Works, Clarence Street, Loughborough, Leicestershire, LE11 1DX Tel: (01509) 214153 Fax: (01509) 262460 E-mail: sales@powernetics.co.uk

Prepair Ltd, 11 Flowers Industrial Estate, Latimer Road, Luton, LU1 3XA Tel: (01582) 455000 Fax: (01582) 416000 E-mail: prepair@easynet.co.uk

Pulsar Developments Ltd, Spracklen House, Dukes Place, Marlow, Buckinghamshire, SL7 2QH Tel: (01628) 473555 Fax: (01628) 474325 E-mail: sales@pulsardevelopments.com

Specialist Computer Centres Ltd, Applied House, Killingbeck Drive, York Road, Leeds, LS14 6UF Tel: 0113-240 5250 Fax: 0113-240 1093

Tamura Europe Ltd, Hopton Park, London Road, Devizes, Wiltshire, SN10 2EY Tel: (01380) 731700 Fax: (01380) 731703 E-mail: business@tamura-europe.co.uk

Traction Electrical Services, Withymoor Farm, Day House Lane, Hillesley, Wotton-under-Edge, Gloucestershire, GL12 7QY Tel: (01453) 843526 Fax: (01453) 844145 E-mail: tracelec@freenetname.co.uk

Westman Systems Ltd, Unit 5-6 Thistle Park, Crossways Road, Bridgwater, Somerset, TA6 6LS Tel: (01278) 424717 Fax: (01278) 424718E-mail: westman.systems@lineone.net

BATTERY CHARGERS TO SPECIFICATION

International Components Corporation (Europe) Ltd, Pitreavie Drive, Pitreavie Business Park, Dunfermline, Fife, KY11 8UH Tel: (01383) 625030 Fax: (01383) 625040 E-mail: dhunter@iccuk.co.uk

BATTERY CHARGERS, MARINE

▶ ElecTech Solutions (East) Ltd, The Old Bakery, Keswick Road, Bacton, Norwich, NR12 0HE Tel: (07831) 107578 Fax: (0870) 7065369 E-mail: info@electechsolutions.co.uk

BATTERY CLIPS

Adroit Accessories Ltd, Henry Street, Walsall, WS2 9XU Tel: (01922) 632839 Fax: (01922) 629154 E-mail: sales@adroit-accessories.co.uk

Chidlow & Cheshire Ltd, Steward Street, Birmingham, B18 7AE Tel: 0121-454 1003 Fax: 0121-456 3935

BATTERY CLOCKS

Everglades International Ltd, The Old Station, Station Road, Cheddar, Somerset, BS27 3AH Tel: (01934) 744051 Fax: (01934) 743184

Gillett & Johnston Croydon Ltd, Unit 9a Twin Bridges Business Park, 232 Selsdon Road, South Croydon, Surrey, CR2 6PL Tel: (020) 8686 2694 Fax: (020) 8681 4028 E-mail: any@gillettjohnston.co.uk

BATTERY CONNECTORS

Electric Vehicle Systems Ltd, 11 Glover Network Centre, Spire Road, Washington, Tyne & Wear, NE37 3HB Tel: 0191-416 1286 Fax: 0191-419 3746 E-mail: info@evsystems.co.uk

Probus Electronics Ltd, Findon, Southill Lane, Pinner, Middlesex, HA5 2EQ Tel: (020) 8866 7272 Fax: (020) 8866 2999 E-mail: sales@probus.freeserve.co.uk

BATTERY LEAD

M S S L Systems, Albany Road, Gateshead, Tyne & Wear, NE8 3AT Tel: 0191-477 3518 Fax: 0191-490 0264 E-mail: info@mssl.com

Northern Electrical Connectors, Unit 8 Glover Centre, Egmont Street, Mossley, Ashton-Under-Lyne, Lancashire, OL5 9PY Tel: (01457) 837511 Fax: (01457) 835216 E-mail: martin@nec-ltd.net

BATTERY LEVEL CONTROLLERS/INDICATORS, FORK LIFT TRUCK

Curtis Instruments (U K) Ltd, Spencer Bridge Road, Northampton, NN1 2PT Tel: (01604) 629755 Fax: (01604) 629876 E-mail: barry.langsford@curtisinst.co.uk

▶ D A C Handling Solutions Ltd, Oxford Street Industrial Park, Vulcan Road, Bilston, West Midlands, WV14 7JG Tel: (0845) 6013529 Fax: (0870) 1662904 E-mail: drock@dac-handling.co.uk

Dac Handling Solutions, 10 Kestrel Park, Tallon Road, Hutton, Brentwood, Essex, CM13 1TN Tel: (01277) 223055 Fax: (01277) 222472 E-mail: info@dac-handling.co.uk

Roll-Rite Forklift Services Ltd, Unit 4, Golden Hillock Industrial Estate, 400 Golden Hillock Road, Sparkbrook, Birmingham, B11 2QG Tel: 0121-693 6301 Fax: 0121-693 6302

BATTERY MAINTENANCE/ TESTING SERVICES

Advanced Battery Care Ltd, Whittonditch Works, Whittonditch, Ramsbury, Marlborough, Wiltshire, SN8 2XB Tel: (01672) 520572 Fax: (01672) 520717 E-mail: sales@batterycare.co.uk

Astratec Electronics Ltd, 2-3 James Watt Close, Drayton Fields Industrial Estate, Daventry, Northamptonshire, NN11 8RJ Tel: (01327) 705936 Fax: (01327) 300665 E-mail: sales@astratec.co.uk

Hillstone Products Ltd, Unit 2, Portland Industrial Estate, Portland Street, Bury, Lancashire, BL9 6EY Tel: 0161-763 3100 Fax: 0161-763 3158 E-mail: sales@hillstone.co.uk

▶ Skylark Energy Systems Ltd, PO Box 11033, Banchory, Kincardineshire, AB31 5WS Tel: (01330) 823950 Fax: (01330) 823966 E-mail: info@skylark.co.uk

BATTERY MONITORING EQUIPMENT

N D S L Ltd, Unit 2 Oakfield Industrial Estate, Eynsham, Witney, Oxfordshire, OX29 4TS Tel: (01865) 884288 Fax: (01865) 884289 E-mail: sales@ndsl.co.uk

▶ Skylark Energy Systems Ltd, PO Box 11033, Banchory, Kincardineshire, AB31 5WS Tel: (01330) 823950 Fax: (01330) 823966 E-mail: info@skylark.co.uk

▶ SmartGauge Electronics, Nantwich Canal Centre, Basin End, Chester Road, Nantwich, Cheshire, CW5 8LB Tel: 07951 995475 E-mail: chris.gibson@smartgauge.co.uk

BATTERY PACKS

County Battery Services Ltd, Field Industrial Estate, Clover Street, Kirkby-in-Ashfield, Nottingham, NG17 7LJ Tel: (01623) 757377 Fax: (01623) 757347 E-mail: sales@countybattery.co.uk

Modelpower.co.uk, 3 Church Walk, Mancetter, Atherstone, Warwickshire, CV9 1PZ Tel: (01827) 711501 Fax: (01827) 700039 E-mail: internetsales@modelpower.co.uk

Ni-Cd Services, 4 Queens Park Road, Bournemouth, BH8 9BP Tel: (01202) 395404 Fax: (01202) 398393 E-mail: russellfrederick@mac.com

Power Sonic Europe Ltd, 3 Buckingham Square, Hurricane Way, Wickford, Essex, SS11 8YQ Tel: (01268) 560686 Fax: (01268) 560902 E-mail: info@power-sonic.co.uk

Ripmax Ltd, Ripmax Corner, Green Street, Enfield, Middlesex, EN3 7SJ Tel: (020) 8282 7500 Fax: (020) 8282 7501 E-mail: mail@ripmax.com

Univercell Battery Co. Ltd, Unit 9b Stafford Park 12, Telford, Shropshire, TF3 3BJ Tel: (01952) 293388 Fax: (01952) 290473 E-mail: sales@univercell-batteries.co.uk

BATTERY PACKS, NICKEL METAL HYDRIDE

Modelpower.co.uk, 3 Church Walk, Mancetter, Atherstone, Warwickshire, CV9 1PZ Tel: (01827) 711501 Fax: (01827) 700039 E-mail: internetsales@modelpower.co.uk

BATTERY POWERED FLOODLIGHTS

G J Bess & Sons Electrical Contractors, Hayes, Salcombe Hill Road, Sidmouth, Devon, EX10 8JR Tel: (01395) 514662 Fax: (01395) 514662 E-mail: g.bess@virgin.net

BATTERY PRODUCTION MACHINERY

TBS Engineering Ltd, Longhill, Elmstone Hardwicke, Cheltenham, Gloucestershire, GL51 9TY Tel: (01242) 680680 Fax: (01242) 680909 E-mail: laurie.gardiner@tbseng.co.uk

BATTERY RACKING

B P C EMEA Ltd, B P C House, Romsey Industrial Estate, Greatbridge Road, Romsey, Hampshire, SO51 0HR Tel: (01794) 521200 Fax: (01794) 521400 E-mail: sales@bpc-ups.com

BATTERY RECYCLING

Rabbitt Recycling, 27-29 New Street, Charfield, Wotton-under-Edge, Gloucestershire, GL12 8ES Tel: (01453) 844343 Fax: (01453) 521330 E-mail: info@rabbittrecycling.co.uk

BATTERY TERMINALS

Calder Industrial Materials Ltd, Jupiter Drive, Chester West Employment Park, Chester, CH1 4EX Tel: (01244) 390093 Fax: (01244) 389191 E-mail: enquiries@caldergroup.co.uk

BATTERY TEST EQUIPMENT

Mobile Communications Solutions Ltd, Unit 5-6, Station Yard, Llanrwst, Gwynedd, LL26 0EH Tel: (0845) 3626365 Fax: (0845) 3623616 E-mail: kevin.jones@mcs-cymru.co.uk

BEACH WEAR

▶ Air Assault Kiteboarding, Air Assault Ltd, Horley, Surrey, RH6 7JX Tel: 07739 733600 E-mail: info@air-assault.com

Desiree Boutique, 26 High Street, Rottingdean, Brighton, BN2 7HR Tel: (01273) 303444 Fax: (01273) 303444

Tag, Unit 1 Derby Road Business Park, Burton-on-Trent, Staffordshire, DE14 1RW Tel: (01283) 531855 Fax: (01283) 741411 E-mail: sales@taglesuire.co.uk

Triumph International Ltd, Arkwright Road, Groundwell Industrial Estate, Swindon, SN25 5BE Tel: (01793) 722200 Fax: (01793) 728341

▶ The Wetsuit Factory, 24 Bay Tree Hill, Liskeard, Cornwall, PL14 4BG Tel: (01579) 343573 Fax: (01579) 342062 E-mail: sales@thewetsuitfactory.com

BEACONS/BUOYS, RADAR

Tideland Signal Ltd, Unit B Kendal House, Victoria Way, Burgess Hill, West Sussex, RH15 9NF Tel: (01444) 872240 Fax: (01444) 872241 E-mail: sales@tidelandsignal.ltd.uk

BEAD BLASTING CONTRACTORS

Bernie Richardson, Unit 2 Abbey Manor Industrial Estate, Yeovil, Somerset, BA21 3AR Tel: (01935) 413317

Collins, Unit 5-6 Aultone Yard Industrial Estate, Aultone Way, Carshalton, Surrey, SM5 2LH Tel: (020) 8647 3123 Fax: (020) 8647 3123

Elgamec, Unit 9-11 Enterprise Industrial Estate, Station Road West, Ash Vale, Aldershot, Hampshire, GU12 5QJ Tel: (01252) 518177 Fax: (01252) 541331 E-mail: info@elgamec.com

G F L Industrial Finishing, William Kelvin Building, Claylands Road, Bishops Waltham, Southampton, SO32 1BH Tel: (01489) 897480 Fax: (01489) 897489 E-mail: sales@gfl-uk.com

Griffin & Son, 106 Pavenhill, Purton, Swindon, SN5 4DB Tel: (01793) 770807 Fax: (01793) 771807 E-mail: pete@griffinandson.uk.com

Kemach Services, 34 Singer Way, Woburn Road Industrial Estate, Kempston, Bedford, MK42 7AF Tel: (01234) 857340 Fax: (01234) 857340 E-mail: tworr46530@aol.com

Quality Coatings Ltd, Russell Street, Chadderton, Oldham, OL9 9LD Tel: 0161-620 0008 Fax: 0161-627 2746

BEARING BUSHES, *See also headings for particular types*

A C M Bearings Ltd, 2 Wath West Industrial Estate, Derwent Way, Wath-upon-Dearne, Rotherham, South Yorkshire, S63 6EX Tel: (01709) 874951 Fax: (01709) 878818 E-mail: sales@acmbearings.co.uk

BEARING DISTRIBUTORS/ AGENTS/STOCKHOLDERS

A B Seals, Unit 15 Canal Industrial Park, Canal Road, Gravesend, Kent, DA12 2PA Tel: (01474) 350777 Fax: (01474) 533314 E-mail: sales@abseals.com

Aire Bearings, 34 Bradford Road, Stanningley, Pudsey, West Yorkshire, LS28 6DD Tel: 0113-256 5676 Fax: 0113-255 4894 E-mail: sales@airebearings.co.uk

Airport Bearing Co. Ltd, 4/5 Bennerly Court, Blenheim Industrial Estate, Bulwell, Nottingham, NG6 8UT Tel: 0115-975 7571 Fax: 0115-927 3778 E-mail: sales@abco-online.co.uk

Albion Transmission, Unit 5 Industry Road, Carlton, Barnsley, South Yorkshire, S71 3PQ Tel: (01226) 726200 Fax: (01226) 726979

Alpha Safety Supplies Ltd, 18 Jeynes Road, Tewkesbury, Gloucestershire, GL20 5NG Tel: (01684) 298083 Fax: (01684) 850420 E-mail: sales@alphasafetysupplies.co.uk

Anglia Bearing Co. Ltd, Units 1 & 8, Wulfric Square, Bretton, Peterborough, PE3 8RF Tel: (01733) 268180 Fax: (01733) 268156 E-mail: angliabearings@aol.com

▶ Antifriction Components Ltd, 8-9 Days Road, St. Philips, Bristol, BS2 0QS Tel: 0117-955 2266 Fax: 0117-955 1287 E-mail: bristolsales@afc-uk.com

Apollo Bearings, 8 Priestley Way, Crawley, West Sussex, RH10 9NT Tel: (01293) 539539 Fax: (01293) 538853 E-mail: apollo.bearings@talk21.com

Atlantic Bearings Ltd, Unit 1, Milners Road, Yeadon, Leeds, LS19 7JE Tel: 0113-250 6640 Fax: 0113-250 0031 E-mail: user@atlantic-bearings.fsnet.co.uk

Bearing Brokers Ltd, Unit 13a Limestone Cottage Lane, Sheffield, S6 1NJ Tel: 0114-231 0310 Fax: 0114-232 2320 E-mail: sales@bearingbrokers.co.uk

Bearing Centre Ltd, 19 Nevanthon Road, Leicester, LE3 6DR Tel: 0116-275 7799 Fax: 0116-275 7799

Bearing & Engineering Products, 2 Downley Road, Havant, Hampshire, PO9 2NJ Tel: (023) 9247 7760 Fax: (023) 9247 7800 E-mail: adrian@1bep.co.uk

Bearing Power Ltd, 60 Church Road, Aston, Birmingham, B6 5TY Tel: 0121-327 5133 Fax: 0121-557 6644 E-mail: aperks@aol.com

Bearing Supplies Thetford, Unit 1 Brunel Way, Thetford, Norfolk, IP24 1HP Tel: (01842) 765074 Fax: (01842) 754709

Bearing Transmission & Pneumatics Ltd, 6 Chieftain Way, Tritton Road Trading Estate, Lincoln, LN6 7RY Tel: (01522) 560060 Fax: (01522) 560040 E-mail: btplimited@aol.com

Bearing & Transmission Supplies Ltd, Watling House, Sutherland Street, Stoke-on-Trent, ST4 4HS Tel: (01782) 846216 Fax: (01782) 749080 E-mail: sales@btslimited.freeserve.co.uk

Bearings & Drives Ltd, 4 Greenfield Farm Industrial Estate, Congleton, Cheshire, CW12 4TR Tel: (01260) 299744 Fax: (01260) 298285 E-mail: sales@bearingsanddrives.co.uk

Bearings Supplies, Southwell Road, Horsham St. Faith, Norwich, NR10 3JU Tel: (01603) 898918 Fax: (01603) 891801 E-mail: sales@bearing-supplies.co.uk

Beeline Engineering Products Ltd, 82 Alston Drive, Bradwell Abbey, Milton Keynes, MK13 9HF Tel: (01908) 222999 Fax: (01908) 222998 E-mail: sales@beeline.co.uk

Berkshire Bearings & Transmsns Ltd, 27-31 Meadow Road, Newbury, Berkshire, RG14 7AH Tel: (01635) 43449 Fax: (01635) 35447 E-mail: sales@bbt1.sagehost.co.uk

Beta Power Engineering Ltd, Beta House Discovery Park, Crossley Road, Stockport, Cheshire, SK4 5BN Tel: 0161-432 9995 Fax: 0161-431 7800 E-mail: beta_power@btconnect.com

Binson Bearing Co., 335 A Round Hay Road, Leeds, LS8 4HT Tel: 0113-249 0251 Fax: 0113-235 0375 E-mail: sales@binsonbearings.ssnet.co.uk

Boston Engineering Supplies & Services, Riverside Industrial Estate, Marsh Lane, Boston, Lincolnshire, PE21 7PJ Tel: (01205) 361218 Fax: (01205) 361218

Brammer Ltd, Unit A Berkeley Court Earl Russell Way, Lawrence Hill, Bristol, BS5 0BX Tel: 0117-935 0422 Fax: 0117-935 0435

Brammer Ltd, 8a Blackbrook Valley Industrial Estate, Narrowboat Way, Dudley, West Midlands, DY2 0XQ Tel: (01384) 456783 Fax: (01384) 456795 E-mail: dudley@branner.biz

Brammer Ltd, Claverton Court, Claverton Road, Roundthorn Industrial Estate, Manchester, M23 9NE Tel: 0161-953 8600 Fax: 0161-953 8680 E-mail: enquiries@bslbrammer.co.uk

Brammer Ltd, 11 Canons Road, Old Wolverton Industrial Estate, Old Wolverton, Milton Keynes, MK12 5TL Tel: (01908) 317464 Fax: (01908) 311113 E-mail: miltonkeynes@brammer.biz

Brammer Ltd, 16 Javelin Road, Airport Industrial Estate, Norwich, NR6 6HP Tel: (01603) 423756 Fax: (01603) 424693 E-mail: norwich@brammer.biz

Brammer Ltd, 25 Buckingham Avenue, Slough, SL1 4QA Tel: (01753) 537695 Fax: (01753) 572311 E-mail: slough@brammer.biz

BEARING DISTRIBUTORS/AGENTS/STOCKHOLDERS – *continued*

Brammer UK Ltd, Headway Road, Wolverhampton, WV10 6PZ Tel: (01902) 395949 Fax: (01902) 395945 E-mail: export@brammer.biz

BRT Bearings Ltd, 9 Common Bank Industrial Estate, Ackhurst Road, Chorley, Lancashire, PR7 1NH Tel: (01257) 264266 Fax: (01257) 274698

BRT Bearings Ltd, 43 Deerdykes View, Cumbernauld, Glasgow, G68 9HN Tel: (01236) 452976 Fax: (01236) 736604 E-mail: info@brt-group.com

C B C International Ltd, Coneygre Industrial Estate, Tipton, West Midlands, DY4 8XP Tel: 0121-557 3154 Fax: 0121-557 9570 E-mail: cklowe@cbcint.com

C B S Rotary Power Motion Ltd, Unit 14 Grandstand Business Centre, Westfields Trading Estate, Hereford, HR4 9NS Tel: (01432) 276630 Fax: (01432) 357140 E-mail: hereford@cbs-rpm.co.uk

C B S Rotary Power Motion Ltd, Lupin Works, Worcester Road, Kidderminster, Worcestershire, DY10 1JR Tel: (01562) 741808 Fax: (01562) 744312 E-mail: kidderminster@cbs-rpm.co.uk

Camco Engineering Ltd, Malvito House, Dale Street, Bilston, West Midlands, WV14 7JX Tel: (01902) 404090 Fax: (01902) 402070 E-mail: sales@camcoengineering.co.uk

Capco Presswork, Bel House, Shady Lane, Birmingham, B44 9ER Tel: 0121-325 1344 Fax: 0121-366 6619

Carrington Bearings & Engineering Ltd, 8 Torridge Close, Telford Way Industrial Estate, Kettering, Northamptonshire, NN16 8PY Tel: (01536) 518666 Fax: (01536) 412131 E-mail: sales@carringtonbearings.co.uk

Citadel Engineering Supplies Ltd, 14 Marlow Street, Rowley Regis, West Midlands, B65 0AY Tel: 0121-561 5557 Fax: 0121-561 5558 E-mail: sales@citadel-eng.co.uk

City Transair, 58 Loughborough Road, Mountsorrel, Loughborough, Leicestershire, LE12 7AT Tel: 0116-230 0070 Fax: 0116-230 0075

Commerce International G B Ltd, 14 Dalston Gardens, Stanmore, Middlesex, HA7 1BU Tel: (020) 8206 1133 Fax: (020) 8204 6969 E-mail: commintl@aol.com

Corby Mechanical Services Ltd, Unit C1 Priors Court, Priors Haw Road, Corby, Northamptonshire, NN17 5JG Tel: (01536) 408866 Fax: (01536) 408811 E-mail: sales@corby-mechanical.co.uk

County Bearings, 76 Hart Road, Benfleet, Essex, SS7 3PF Tel: (01268) 758933 Fax: (01268) 755058

County Industrial Supplies Ltd, County House, Chapel Street, Pontnewydd, Cwmbran, Gwent, NP44 1DL Tel: (01633) 872226 Fax: (01633) 864922 E-mail: cissales@aol.com

Ebc International Ltd, 7 Grovebury Place Estate, Leighton Buzzard, Bedfordshire, LU7 4SH Tel: (01525) 217217 Fax: (01525) 373772 E-mail: sales@ebcint.co.uk

Engineering Services, 5 Gavin Road, Widnes, Cheshire, WA8 8RE Tel: 0151-495 1317 Fax: 0151-495 1559 E-mail: sales@engineering-services.co.uk

Europa Bearings (1976) Ltd, Empire Centre, Imperial Way, Watford, WD24 4YH Tel: (01923) 255166 Fax: (01923) 234069 E-mail: sales@europabearings.freeserve.co.uk

Express Bearings & Transmissions, Anglo Trading Estate, Shepton Mallet, Somerset, BA4 5BY Tel: (01749) 330002 Fax: (01749) 330003 E-mail: sales@expressbearings.co.uk

F T L Seals Technology, Leeds Twenty-Seven Business Park, Bruntcliffe Avenue, Morley, Leeds, LS27 0TG Tel: 0113-252 1061 Fax: 0113-252 2627 E-mail: tonys@ftlseals.co.uk

First Engineering Services, Unit 1, Hare Street, Bilston, West Midlands, WV14 7DX Tel: (01902) 354735 Fax: (01902) 354805 E-mail: first.engineering@virgin.net

Force Seven Bearings, First Avenue, Team Valley Trading Estate, Gateshead, Tyne & Wear, NE11 0NU Tel: 0191-487 2421 Fax: 0191-491 0842 E-mail: force7@nbcgroup.com

Fosse Bearing Units Ltd, Bearing House, 887 Melton Road, Thurmaston, Leicester, LE4 8EF Tel: 0116-260 2548 Fax: 0116-260 2548 E-mail: fosse.bearings@btinternet.com

H B Industrial Services Ltd, 15 Kingdom Close, Fareham, Hampshire, PO15 5TJ Tel: (01489) 575222 Fax: (01489) 575666 E-mail: sales@hbindustrialservices.co.uk

Hayling Industrial Ltd, Units 8-9 Hayling Billy Business Centre, Furniss Way, Hayling Island, Hampshire, PO11 0ED Tel: (023) 9246 3868 Fax: (023) 9246 3831 E-mail: sales@haylingindustrial.com

Henderson Bearings, Crow Arch Lane, Ringwood, Hampshire, BH24 1NZ Tel: (01425) 477787 Fax: (01425) 478883 E-mail: sales@hendersonbearings.com

I B S Bearings Ltd, A1 Trading Estate, Lewisham Road, Smethwick, West Midlands, B66 2BN Tel: 0121-558 4141 Fax: 0121-555 5564

Ibd Ltd, 3 City Park Industrial Estate, Gelderd Road, Leeds, LS12 6DR Tel: 0113-279 6988 Fax: 0113-231 0336 E-mail: douglas@barclays.net

Industrial Links Ltd, Unit 19 Ventura Place, Poole, Dorset, BH16 5SW Tel: (01202) 632996 Fax: (01202) 632997 E-mail: sales@industrial-links.com

Industria Engineering Products Ltd, 45 Kelvin Way, West Bromwich, West Midlands, B70 7TP Tel: 0121-525 2988 Fax: 0121-525 3607 E-mail: sales@industria.co.uk

Inverness Bearings & Transmission, 5 Harbour Road, Inverness, IV1 1SY Tel: (01463) 243528 Fax: (01463) 225039

Itec Power Services Ltd, Itec House, 2 Berkeley Street, Ashton-under-Lyne, Lancashire, OL6 7DT Tel: 0161-343 1595 Fax: 0161-343 2341 E-mail: sales@itecpower.co.uk

J & M Belts Veebelts Bearings Oilseals, 72 Bridge Road, Grays, Essex, RM17 6BZ Tel: (01375) 373975 Fax: (01375) 391541 E-mail: sales@jmbelts.com

Kent Bearings, John Wilson Business Park Harvey Drive, Unit 128a, Chestfield, Whitstable, Kent, CT5 3QY Tel: (01227) 772111 Fax: (01227) 771444

Leeds Bearings Ltd, Unit 14, Castleton Close, Armley Road, Leeds, LS12 2DS Tel: 0113-234 1919 Fax: 0113-245 0037

Leek Bearings, 13-15 Burton Street, Leek, Staffordshire, ST13 8BU Tel: (01538) 381489 Fax: (01538) 387672

Leicester Bearing Co Ltd, Tunnel Top, 10 Putney Road, Leicester, LE2 7TF Tel: 0116-254 9886 Fax: 0116-247 1182 E-mail: enquires@leicester-bearings.co.uk

London Bearings (Kent) Ltd, Unit 2, Sabre Court, Gillingham Business Park, Gillingham, Kent, ME8 0RW Tel: (01634) 235335 Fax: (01634) 230268 E-mail: lbk.uk@btinternet.com

Longford Bearings Engineering Sales Ltd, Transmission House, 10a Lady Lane, Longford, Coventry, CV6 6AZ Tel: (024) 7636 0666 Fax: (024) 7636 0759

Main Line Bearing Co. Ltd, Chatsworth Industrial Estate, Percy Street, Leeds, LS12 1EL Tel: 0113-263 3321 Fax: 0113-279 1434 E-mail: sales@mainlinebearings.com

Mike Davies Bearings Ltd, Leamore Lane, Walsall, WS2 7DE Tel: (01922) 494940 Fax: (01922) 407760 E-mail: sales@mikedaviesbearings.com

Motion Industries UK Ltd, Unit 2 Bracken Trade Park, Duners Lane, Bury, Lancashire, BL9 9QP Tel: 0161-705 1237 Fax: 0161-705 1239E-mail: enquires@bearingsuppliers.co.uk

▶ N B C Group Ltd, Crown Works, Orleton Lane, Wellington, Telford, Shropshire, TF1 2BG Tel: (01952) 222400 Fax: (01952) 641325 E-mail: enquiries.kell04@nbcgroup.co.uk

Newstart Power Transmission, Unit 19 Tamworth Business Centre, Amber Cl, Tamworth, Staffs, B77 4RP Tel: (01827) 313737 Fax: (01827) 313838

Oxford Bearings Ltd, 41 Wedgewood Road, Bicester, Oxfordshire, OX26 4UL Tel: (01869) 249292 Fax: (01869) 241443

Pace Bearings Ltd, Unit 4 Dock Meadow Industrial Estate, Wolverhampton, WV4 6UD Tel: (01902) 409120 Fax: (01902) 409121 E-mail: pacebearings@freeserve.co.uk

Premier Bearings & Transmissions Ltd, Unit 2b Mariner, Lichfield Road Industrial Estate, Tamworth, Staffordshire, B79 7UL Tel: (01827) 60686 Fax: (01827) 60637 E-mail: sales@premierbearings.co.uk

Premier Power Products Ltd, 1 Dampier Mews Edward Close, Hounstone Business Park, Houndstone Business Park, Yeovil, Somerset, BA22 8RU Tel: (01935) 432412 Fax: (01935) 433557

R D R Bearings, 20 Ravenhill Road, Belfast, BT6 8EA Tel: (028) 9073 2321 Fax: (028) 9073 1889 E-mail: rdr@nbcgroup.co.uk

R & M Bearings Ltd, Unit 13 Manhattan Works, Dundonald Street, Dundee, DD3 7PY Tel: (01382) 455400 Fax: (01382) 454645 E-mail: sales@rmbearings.co.uk

Redhill Bearings Ltd, The White House, Brighton Road, Handcross, Haywards Heath, West Sussex, RH17 6BZ Tel: (01444) 400900 Fax: (01444) 400753 E-mail: redhillbearings@aol.com

Ringwood Machinery Spares, 16 College Road, Ringwood, Hampshire, BH24 1NX Tel: (01425) 479459

Rotary Bearing & Transmission Co. Ltd, Unit 11 Forty 8 North 48, Duncrue Street, Belfast, BT3 9BJ Tel: (028) 9074 9377 Fax: (028) 9035 2949 E-mail: sales@rotarybearings-ni.com

Rotary Motion, Unit A5, Grovelands Avenue Ind Estate, Winnersh, Wokingham, Berkshire, RG41 5LB Tel: 0118-989 0000 Fax: (0118) 989 0484 E-mail: rotmot@aol.com

S C H Bearings & Power Transmission, Unit 1 Great Bridge Business Park, Unit 1 Greatbridge Busn Park, Budds Lane, Romsey, Hampshire, SO51 0HA Tel: (01794) 830377 Fax: (01794) 830366 E-mail: sales@schgroup.com

S.I.S. Industrial Automation Ltd, 8 Amphion Court Hale Trading Estate, Lower Church Lane, Tipton, West Midlands, DY4 7HN Tel: 0121-520 7211 Fax: 0121-557 8146

Sapphire Engineering, Atlas Works, Brieryfield Road, Preston, PR1 8SR Tel: (01772) 822133 Fax: (01772) 822144

Seager Bearings Ltd, 52 Goldsmith Road, Birmingham, B14 7EL Tel: 0121-444 5391 Fax: 0121-443 5229 E-mail: sales@seager-bearings.co.uk

Southern Bearings Ltd, Unit 11 Waldeck House, Waldeck Road, Maidenhead, Berkshire, SL6 8BR Tel: (01628) 674123 Fax: (01628) 776502 E-mail: cmay@southernbearing.co.uk

Spectrum Engineering & Transmission Co. Ltd, Unit 43 Purfleet Industrial Park, London Road, Aveley, South Ockendon, Essex, RM15 4YA Tel: (01708) 861718 Fax: (01708) 867540 E-mail: bob@spectrum-engineering.co.uk

Spen Bearings, 129 Westgate, Cleckheaton, West Yorkshire, BD19 5EJ Tel: (01274) 851700 Fax: (01274) 869736 E-mail: admin@spen-bearings.co.uk

Spire Bearings, 94 Storforth La Trading Estate, Hasland, Chesterfield, Derbyshire, S41 0SN Tel: (01246) 274183 Fax: (01246) 202898 E-mail: sales@spirebearings.co.uk

Sprint Engineering Services Ltd, Unit G3 Imperial Business Estate, West Mill, Gravesend, Kent, DA11 0DL Tel: (01474) 534251 Fax: (01474) 534566 E-mail: info@sprint-uk.com

Sterling Corporation, 2 Law Street, Leicester, LE4 5GR Tel: 0116-261 0330 Fax: 0116-261 0259 E-mail: sales@sterlingbearings.com

Technostart Ltd, 1a Clifton Avenue, London, E17 6HL Tel: (020) 8503 2778 Fax: (020) 8523 3054 E-mail: sales@technostart.co.uk

Thamesdown Bearing Services, 3 Beechcroft Road, Swindon, SN2 7RD Tel: (01793) 724554 Fax: (01793) 724404 E-mail: thamesdown.bearings@wyko.co.uk

Thistle Bearings & Engineering Products Ltd, 38 Singer Road, Kelvin Industrial Estate, East Kilbride, Glasgow, G75 0XS Tel: (01355) 225491 Fax: (01355) 242502 E-mail: sales@thistlebearings.co.uk

Toogood Industrial Ltd, Unit H7, Haysbridge Business Centre, Brickhouse Lane, South Godstone, Godstone, Surrey, RH9 8JW Tel: (01342) 844188 Fax: (01342) 844220 E-mail: office@toogood.co.uk

Town & County Engineering Services Ltd, Warden Tree Lane, Pinchbeck, Spalding, Lincolnshire, PE11 3UG Tel: (01775) 725678 Fax: (01775) 767205 E-mail: sales@townandcounty.uk.com

Transmission Bearings UK Ltd, 6 Falcon Park, Basildon, Essex, SS14 3AL Tel: (01268) 533002 Fax: (01268) 522891

Transmission Design & Supply Co. Ltd, Unit 1A, Marlborough Street, Burnley, Lancashire, BB11 2HW Tel: (01282) 435143 Fax: (01282) 435160

Transpower Drives Ltd, 4 Bridle Close, Finedon Road Industrial Estate, Wellingborough, Northamptonshire, NN8 4RN Tel: (01933) 441101 Fax: (01933) 443326 E-mail: sales@transpower.co.uk

Trent Valley Bearings & Pneumatics Ltd, Transmission House, 1 South Street, Long Eaton, Nottingham, NG10 1ER Tel: 0115-973 2234 Fax: 0115-946 0817 E-mail: sales@trent-valley.co.uk

Universal Seals & Bearings Ltd, Waterloo Indust Park, Upper Brook Street, Stockport, Cheshire, SK1 3BP Tel: 0161-429 0287 Fax: 0161-477 2940

Wide Range Engineering Services Ltd, Coventry Road, Acan Way, Narborough, Leicester, LE19 2FT Tel: 0116-275 0100 Fax: 0116-275 0086 E-mail: sales@wres.co.uk

Yarmouth Bearing & Transmissions, 7 James Court, Faraday Road, Great Yarmouth, Norfolk, NR31 0NF Tel: (01493) 655505 Fax: (01493) 653640 E-mail: yarmouth.bearings@wyko.co.uk

Z V L UK Ltd, Unit 13 Manhatten Works, Dundonald Street, Dundee, DD3 7PY Tel: (01382) 458808 Fax: (01382) 458814 E-mail: sales@zklbearings.co.uk

BEARING HOUSINGS

A F S Rotel Ltd, Unit E Central Industrial Estate, St Marks Street, Bolton, BL3 6NR Tel: (01204) 388077 Fax: (01204) 386309 E-mail: info@pump-spares.co.uk

Acorn Industrial Services Ltd (Midlands), Units 17-21, Bloomfield Park, Bloomfield Road, Tipton, West Midlands, DY4 9AH Tel: 0121-521 5999 Fax: 0121-521 5888 E-mail: midlands@acorn-ind.co.uk

▶ Bri-Mac Engineering Ltd, Unit 2 Stambermill Works, Bagley Street, Lye, Stourbridge, West Midlands, DY9 7AR Tel: (01384) 423030 Fax: (01384) 422774 E-mail: sales@bri-mac.co.uk

Cast Iron Welding Service Ltd, 2 Samson Road, Hermitage Industrial Estate, Coalville, Leicestershire, LE67 3FP Tel: (01530) 811308 Fax: (01530) 835724 E-mail: sales@castironwelding.co.uk

Edwin Lowe Ltd, Perry Bridge Works, Aldridge Road, Perry Barr, Birmingham, B42 2HB Tel: 0121-356 5255 Fax: 0121-344 3172 E-mail: sales@edwinlowe.com

Transmission Of Power Ltd, 37 Sketchley Meadows, Hinckley, Leicestershire, LE10 3ES Tel: (01455) 616538 Fax: (01455) 250237

BEARING IMPORT MERCHANTS OR AGENTS

Air America (Rugby) Ltd, Midland Trading Estate, Consul Road, Rugby, Warwickshire, CV21 1PB Tel: (01788) 574555 Fax: (01788) 547997 E-mail: air.america@wyko.co.uk

Commerce International G B Ltd, 14 Dalston Gardens, Stanmore, Middlesex, HA7 1BU Tel: (020) 8206 1133 Fax: (020) 8204 6969 E-mail: commintl@aol.com

Pace Bearings Ltd, Unit 4 Dock Meadow Industrial Estate, Wolverhampton, WV4 6UD Tel: (01902) 409120 Fax: (01902) 409121 E-mail: pacebearings@freeserve.co.uk

Southern Bearings Ltd, Unit 11 Waldeck House, Waldeck Road, Maidenhead, Berkshire, SL6 8BR Tel: (01628) 674123 Fax: (01628) 776502 E-mail: cmay@southernbearing.co.uk

BEARING MANUFRS, *See also headings under Bearings*

A C M Bearings Ltd, 2 Wath West Industrial Estate, Derwent Way, Wath-upon-Dearne, Rotherham, South Yorkshire, S63 6EX Tel: (01709) 874951 Fax: (01709) 878818 E-mail: sales@acmbearings.co.uk

Acorn Industrial Services Ltd (Midlands), Units 17-21, Bloomfield Park, Bloomfield Road, Tipton, West Midlands, DY4 9AH Tel: 0121-521 5999 Fax: 0121-521 5888 E-mail: midlands@acorn-ind.co.uk

▶ Ashcroft Transmissions, 5 Stadium Industrial Estate, Cradock Road, Luton, LU4 0JF Tel: (01582) 496040 Fax: (01582) 595040

Bradford Grinders UK Ltd, Mount Street, Bradford, West Yorkshire, BD3 9SN Tel: (01274) 733141 Fax: (01274) 734610 E-mail: sales@bradfordgrinders.co.uk

Crawford Precision Engineering, Cross Court Industrial Estate, Kettering, Northamptonshire, NN16 9BN Tel: (01536) 417140 Fax: (01536) 524059 E-mail: cpeng@globalnet.co.uk

Danaher Motion, Fishleigh Road, Roundswell Business Park, Barnstaple, Devon, EX31 3UD Tel: (01271) 334500 Fax: (01271) 334502 E-mail: information@tiblmail.com

DCN Bearings & Engineering, The Old Foundary, Wood Street, Lye, Stourbridge, West Midlands, DY9 8RX Tel: (01384) 896528 Fax: (01384) 896534 E-mail: sales@dcnbearings.com

East Anglian Bearing Service Ltd, 19-21 Great Whip Street, Ipswich, IP2 8EY Tel: (01473) 602525 Fax: (01473) 688274 E-mail: sales@eabs.co.uk

Eriks UK Ltd, Industrial Distribution Service Centre, Unit 16C, Pool Industrial Estate, Redruth, Cornwall, TR15 3RH Tel: (01209) 216839 Fax: (01209) 219793 E-mail: redruth@eriks.co.uk

Esspee Fabrications Ltd, 149 Merton Bank Road, St. Helens, Merseyside, WA9 1DZ Tel: (01744) 28304 Fax: (01744) 28826 E-mail: sales@esspee.co.uk

▶ G K N P.L.C., 50 Pall Mall, London, SW1Y 5JH Tel: (020) 7930 2424 Fax: (020) 7463 2404

▶ Glenlake International Ltd, Unit F7 Lockside, Anchor Brook Industrial Park, Aldridge, Walsall, WS9 8BZ Tel: (01922) 458111 Fax: (01922) 458444

▶ Hollex (UK) Ltd, Unit 8C, 1 Sir Francis Ley Industrial E, Shaftsbury Street, Derby, DE23 8XA Tel: (01332) 340501

John Handley, Unit 2 Heath Mill Bus Centre, Wombourne, Wolverhampton, WV5 8AP Tel: (01902) 898560 Fax: (01902) 898561 E-mail: sales@johnhandleybearings.com

Koyo Bearings (Europe) Ltd, PO Box 101, Barnsley, South Yorkshire, S75 3TA Tel: (01226) 733200 Fax: (01226) 204029 E-mail: kbe@kbe.co.uk

▶ Marine & Industrial Transmissions Ltd, Weeland Road, Hensall, Goole, North Humberside, DN14 0QE Tel: (01977) 661467 Fax: (01977) 662099

▶ N B C Group Ltd, Crown Works, Orleton Lane, Wellington, Telford, Shropshire, TF1 2BG Tel: (01952) 222400 Fax: (01952) 641325 E-mail: enquiries.kell04@nbcgroup.co.uk

N S K Bearings Europe Ltd, Davy Drive, North West Industrial Estate, Peterlee, County Durham, SR8 2PW Tel: 0191-518 0777 Fax: 0191-518 0303

▶ Paddock Gear Engineering Ltd, 2 Kingsbury Link, Trinity Road, Piccadilly, Tamworth, Staffordshire, B78 2EX Tel: (01827) 875566 Fax: (01827) 875880

Premier Bearing Co. Ltd, Chaucer Street, Northampton, NN2 7HB Tel: (01604) 718107 Fax: (01604) 720654 E-mail: sales@premierbearing.co.uk

S K F (U K) Ltd, Sundon Park Road, Luton, LU3 3BL Tel: (01582) 490049 Fax: (01582) 848091 E-mail: marketing.uk@skf.com

S P C Bearings Ltd, Unit 39 Coneygre Industrial Estate, Tipton, West Midlands, DY4 8XP Tel: 0121-557 1371 Fax: 0121-557 3793

▶ Trelleborg Cealing Solutions (Rotherham), Bradmarsh Busines Park, Rotherham, South Yorkshire, S60 1BX Tel: (01709) 789800 Fax: (01709) 374819 E-mail: enquiries@orkotmarine.com

▶ Wolds Engineering Services Ltd, Unit 1d Pocklington Industrial Estate, Pocklington, York, YO42 1NR Tel: (01759) 303877 Fax: (01759) 306952 E-mail: johnoxley@btconnect.com

BEARING MOUNTING COMPONENTS, ADAPTER/WITHDRAWAL SLEEVE

Brown Rutter Ltd, Salisbury Street, Barton Hill, Bristol, BS5 9UD Tel: 0117-955 0781 Fax: 0117-941 3685 E-mail: sales@brownrutter.com

BEARING RELINING

J. H. Richards & Co. Ltd, Saltley Road, Birmingham, B7 4TD Tel: 0121-359 2257 Fax: 0121-359 7340 E-mail: andrew@jhrichards.co.uk

BEARING REMETALLING

K C Engineering Ltd, Hownsgill Drive, Consett, County Durham, DH8 9HU Tel: (01207) 583100 Fax: (01207) 581900 E-mail: sales@kceng.com
Michell Bearings, Scotswood Road, Newcastle upon Tyne, NE15 6LL Tel: 0191-273 0291 Fax: 0191-272 2787 E-mail: sales@michellbearings.com
J. H. Richards & Co. Ltd, Saltley Road, Birmingham, B7 4TD Tel: 0121-359 2257 Fax: 0121-359 7340 E-mail: andrew@jhrichards.co.uk

BEARING STEEL

Brammer Ltd, 8a Blackbrook Valley Industrial Estate, Narrowboat Way, Dudley, West Midlands, DY2 0XQ Tel: (01384) 456783 Fax: (01384) 456795 E-mail: dudley@branner.biz
Sterling Corporation, 2 Law Street, Leicester, LE4 5GR Tel: 0116-261 0330 Fax: 0116-261 0259 E-mail: sales@sterlingbearings.com
Vallourec UK Ltd, George House, 121 High Street, Henley-in-Arden, West Midlands, B95 5AU Tel: (01564) 792277 Fax: (01564) 795818 E-mail: sales@vallourec.co.uk

BEARING UNITS

N S K Ltd, Northern Road, Newark, Nottinghamshire, NG24 2JF Tel: (01636) 705298 Fax: (01636) 605000 E-mail: info-uk@nsk.com
N T N Bearings UK Ltd, 11 Wellington Crescent, Fradley Park, Lichfield, Staffordshire, WS13 8RZ Tel: (01543) 445000 Fax: (01543) 445035 E-mail: jcd@ntn-europe.com

BEARINGS TO SPECIFICATION

Countrose Bearings, PO Box 376, Birmingham, B42 2TB Tel: 0121-356 7220 Fax: 0121-356 7322 E-mail: c.bennett@tufnol.co.uk
Crawford Precision Engineering, Cross Court Industrial Estate, Kettering, Northamptonshire, NN16 9BN Tel: (01536) 417140 Fax: (01536) 524059 E-mail: cpeng@globalnet.co.uk
John Handley, Unit 2 Heath Mill Bus Centre, Wombourne, Wolverhampton, WV5 8AP Tel: (01902) 898560 Fax: (01902) 898561 E-mail: sales@johnhandleybearings.com

BEARINGS, AMERICAN STANDARDS

Air America (Rugby) Ltd, Midland Trading Estate, Consul Road, Rugby, Warwickshire, CV21 1PB Tel: (01788) 574555 Fax: (01788) 547997 E-mail: air.america@wyko.co.uk

BEARINGS, CONVEYOR

C P T Enterprises, 143 White Hart Lane, Portchester, Fareham, Hampshire, PO16 9BB Tel: (023) 9238 9521 Fax: (023) 9237 5181 E-mail: info@cptenterprises.co.uk
System Plast Ltd, Unit 3-4, Churchlands Business Park, Ufton Road, Harbury, Leamington Spa, Warwickshire, CV33 9GX Tel: (01926) 614314 Fax: (01926) 614914 E-mail: info@systemplastuk.com

BEARINGS, MARINE, STERN TUBE/RUDDER, PLASTIC

Tenmat Ltd, Ashburton Road West, Trafford Park, Manchester, M17 1RU Tel: 0161-872 2181 Fax: 0161-872 7596 E-mail: info@tenmat.com

BEARINGS, SLEEVE, BRONZE

▶ Shearwater Marine Ltd, Decoy Industrial Estate, Newton Abbot, Devon, TQ12 5ND Tel: (01626) 334980 Fax: (01626) 366250 E-mail: info@shearwater-marine.co.uk

BEARINGS, SPECIAL OR NON STANDARD

Braintree Precision Components Ltd, 2-8 Blackwell Drive, Springwood Industrial Estate, Braintree, Essex, CM7 2QJ Tel: (01376) 552989 Fax: (01376) 552995 E-mail: sales@hepco.co.uk
Capco Presswork, Bel House, Shady Lane, Birmingham, B44 9ER Tel: 0121-325 1344 Fax: 0121-366 6619
H B Bearings Ltd, Riverside Works, Honley, Huddersfield, HD9 6PQ Tel: (01484) 665116 Fax: (01484) 662619 E-mail: sales@hb-bearings.com
Henderson Bearings, Crow Arch Lane, Ringwood, Hampshire, BH24 1NZ Tel: (01425) 477787 Fax: (01425) 478883 E-mail: sales@hendersonbearings.com
Railko Ltd, Boundary Rd, Loudwater, High Wycombe, Bucks, HP10 9QU Tel: (01628) 524901 Fax: (01628) 810761 E-mail: info@railko.co.uk
Roballo Engineering Co. Ltd, 2 Mill Hill, North West Industrial Estate, Peterlee, County Durham, SR8 2HR Tel: 0191-518 5600 Fax: 0191-586 9096 E-mail: info@roballo.co.uk
S P C Bearings Ltd, Unit 39 Coneygre Industrial Estate, Tipton, West Midlands, DY4 8XP Tel: 0121-557 1371 Fax: 0121-557 3793
Trans Pennine Bearing Co., 48 Listerhills Road, Bradford, West Yorkshire, BD7 1HT Tel: (01274) 732366 Fax: (01274) 391503
Tyack Export Sales Services, 52 Davies Road, West Bridgford, Nottingham, NG2 5JA Tel: 0115-981 1633 Fax: 0115-969 6030 E-mail: martin@exportsales.net

BEARINGS, THIN-SECTION

Cooper Roller Bearings Co. Ltd, Wisbech Road, King's Lynn, Norfolk, PE30 5JX Tel: (01553) 767677 Fax: (01553) 761113 E-mail: sales@cooperbearings.com

BEARS, TOY, PROMOTIONAL

▶ Fun & Games, 17 St. Martins Walk, Dorking, Surrey, RH4 1UT Tel: (01306) 877334 Fax: (01306) 877334 E-mail: info@funandgameshop.com
▶ GotchaSomething, 44 Penrhyn Road, Far Cotton, Northampton, NN4 8ED Tel: 0845 1565470 E-mail: general@gotchasomething.co.uk

BEAUTY SALON SUPPLIES

▶ Body Perfect, 524 Blackburn Road, Bolton, BL1 8NW Tel: (01204) 308100 E-mail: enquires@bodyperfectsalon.co.uk

BEAUTY THERAPY

▶ Baiss & Co Advances, 2 St. Peters Street, Ipswich, IP1 1XB Tel: (01473) 400033 E-mail: info@baiss.co.uk
▶ The Beauty Studio, 33 Greystone Avenue, Worthing, West Sussex, BN13 1LR Tel: (01903) 262447 E-mail: wendy.greaves2@ntlworld.com
▶ Sugaring Practitioner Vanessa Williams, 24 Holland Way, Blandford Forum, Dorset, DT11 7RU Tel: 01258 458528

BED HEADBOARDS

Country Upholstery, Unit 1 Kennet Enterprise Centre, Charnham La, Hungerford, Berks, RG17 0EY Tel: (01488) 682226 Fax: (01488) 682226 E-mail: paulcho@btinternet.com
Harval Fitted Furniture, 4 Horbury Junction Industrial Estate, Calder Vale Road, Horbury, Wakefield, West Yorkshire, WF4 5ER Tel: (01924) 270121 Fax: (01924) 262115 E-mail: sales@harval.co.uk
Highland Blindcraft, 38 Ardconnel Street, Inverness, IV2 3EX Tel: (01463) 233662 Fax: (01463) 710809 E-mail: sales@highlandblindcraft.co.uk
Igoe Ltd, 100 Brooker Road, Waltham Abbey, Essex, EN9 1JL Tel: (01992) 655600 Fax: (01992) 655631 E-mail: enquiries@igoe.co.uk
Instant Home Ltd, Beaulieu House, 78 Ermine Street, Huntingdon, Cambridgeshire, PE29 3EZ Tel: 01480 432230 Fax: 01480 432868 E-mail: hollie@instanthome.co.uk
Spacemaker Bedrooms Ltd, 160-162 Hornchurch Road, Hornchurch, Essex, RM11 1QH Tel: (01708) 473020
Staples Uk Ltd, Windover Road, Huntingdon, Cambridgeshire, PE29 7EF Tel: (01480) 442222 Fax: (01480) 442266 E-mail: enquiries@staplesbeds.co.uk

BED OR BEDDING ACCESSORIES

Bedtime Bed Centre, 8 Falcon Road, Wisbech, Cambridgeshire, PE13 1AU Tel: (01945) 466788 Fax: (01945) 466788
▶ The Fun Squad, Little Firs, Carloggas, St. Mawgan, Newquay, Cornwall, TR8 4EQ Tel: (01637) 860956 E-mail: info@thefunsquad.co.uk
▶ Midas (NW) Ltd, Midas House, Porritt Street, Bury, Lancashire, BL9 6HJ Tel: 0161-764 6220 Fax: 0161-761 1293

BED SHEETS

Bed Linen Shop Southport, 65a London Street, Southport, Merseyside, PR9 0TH Tel: (01704) 501382
Broomhill Holdings Ltd, 189 Lurgan Road, Maralin, Craigavon, County Armagh, BT67 0QS Tel: (028) 3831 3000 Fax: (028) 3831 3001
Cumulus Mattress Protectors, Selinas Lane, Dagenham, Essex, RM8 1ES Tel: (020) 8592 2233 Fax: (020) 8593 3787 E-mail: enquiries@abbey-quilting.co.uk
Dorfell Textiles, 50 Cambrian Street, Manchester, M40 7EG Tel: 0161-273 7747 Fax: 0161-274 3862
John Dron Ltd, 43 Blundells Road, Bradville, Milton Keynes, MK13 7HD Tel: (01908) 311388 Fax: (01908) 222200 E-mail: sales@johndron.co.uk
Glencraft, 132 Wellington Road, Aberdeen, AB12 3LQ Tel: (01224) 873366 Fax: (01224) 894659 E-mail: sales@glencraft.co.uk
Nirmal Razai Mart & Co. Ltd, Carlisle Terrace, Bradford, West Yorkshire, BD8 8AT Tel: (01274) 775757 Fax: (01274) 771611
Oomers Ltd, 8 St. Andrew's Road, London, E17 6BD Tel: (020) 8527 8388 Fax: (020) 8527 8288 E-mail: sales@oomers.co.uk
Peter Reed Textiles Ltd, 2 Gisburn Road, Bolton By Bowland, Clitheroe, Lancashire, BB7 4NP Tel: (01282) 692416 Fax: (01200) 447708 E-mail: mreed@peterreedtextiles.com
Samuel Lamont & Sons Ltd, Victoria Street, Lurgan, Craigavon, County Armagh, BT67 9DA Tel: (028) 3832 9066 Fax: (028) 3834 3095 E-mail: mail@samuellamont.co.uk
J.V. Shabetai Ltd, 34 Charlotte Street, Manchester, M1 4FD Tel: 0161-236 7758 Fax: 0161-737 6061 E-mail: zedfred@aol.com
Slumberfleece Bedding & Blankets, Arkwright Industrial Estate, Arkwright Road, Bedford, MK42 0LE Tel: (01234) 210879 Fax: (01234) 217983 E-mail: samirvine6@netscape.net
Taunton Textiles, Yarde Pl, Taunton, Somerset, TA1 1UR Tel: 01823 324444 Fax: 01823 324444
Victoria Linen Co., 2 Hargreaves St Mill, Hargreaves Street, Haslingden, Rossendale, Lancashire, BB4 5RQ Tel: (01706) 220020 Fax: (01706) 220020 E-mail: brochure@victorialinen.co.uk

BEDROOM DOORS

▶ Bespoke Bedrooms, 68 Huntingdon Road, Chatteris, Cambridgeshire, PE16 6ED Tel: (01354) 693392 Fax: (01354) 696807 E-mail: sales@bespokebedroomfurniture.co.uk

BEDROOM FURNITURE

Allpine, Deardengate, Haslingden, Rossendale, Lancashire, BB4 5QJ Tel: (01706) 220463 Fax: (01706) 220463
▶ Avanti Fitted Kitchens Ltd, Avanti House, Hayes Lane, Stourbridge, West Midlands, DY9 8RD Tel: (01384) 893929 Fax: (01384) 896734 E-mail: avanti@callnetuk.com
B G Romeril Ltd, Dumaresq Street, St. Helier, Jersey, JE2 3WP Tel: (01534) 738806 Fax: (01534) 767016 E-mail: enquiry@romerils.co.je
Bedroom Options, 13 Wychwood Avenue, Edgware, Middlesex, HA8 6TL Tel: (020) 8952 3200 Fax: (020) 8952 3200
Bedtime Bedding Centre, 21-23 Windmill Street, Gravesend, Kent, DA12 1AS Tel: (01474) 321249 Fax: (01474) 320009 E-mail: info@wellsbedding.co.uk
Bee Line Fitted Bedrooms, 71 Station Road, Flitwick, Bedford, MK45 1JU Tel: (01525) 712090 Fax: (01525) 712090
Bensons Bed Centres Ltd, 1-5 St James Barton, Bristol, BS1 3LT Tel: 0117-927 2695
Bensons Bed Centres Ltd, Stadium Way, Retail World, Parkgate, Rotherham, South Yorkshire, S60 1TG Tel: (01709) 780030
▶ Bespoke Bedrooms, 68 Huntingdon Road, Chatteris, Cambridgeshire, PE16 6ED Tel: (01354) 693392 Fax: (01354) 696807 E-mail: sales@bespokebedroomfurniture.co.uk
Budget Furniture, Unit 1 Manor St, Manchester, M12 6HE Tel: 0161-272 6876
Bumble End Barn Old Pine, Grove Lane, Wishaw, Sutton Coldfield, West Midlands, B76 9PH Tel: 0121-351 3993 Fax: 0121-351 3993 E-mail: bumblepine@aol.com
Cita Furniture, 36 Seein Road, Sion Mills, Strabane, County Tyrone, BT82 9NJ Tel: (028) 8165 9744 Fax: (028) 8165 9744
Colemans Kitchens & Bedrooms Ltd, 178 Victoria Road, Kirkby-in-Ashfield, Nottingham, NG17 8AT Tel: (01623) 751239 Fax: (01623) 754649
▶ David Collier Fitted Furniture, Unit 5 Stirling Industrial Estate, Off Chorley New Road, Horwich, Bolton, BL6 6DU Tel: (01204) 668899 Fax: (01204) 668899 E-mail: info@davidcollier.co.uk
D M Design Ltd, 1 Deerdykes Place, Cumbernauld, Glasgow, G68 9HE Tel: (01236) 739200 Fax: (01236) 728862 E-mail: dmdesigns@ukonline.co.uk.
Detail Design, 2d Metropolitan Wharf, Wapping Wall, London, E1W 3SS Tel: (020) 7488 1669 Fax: (020) 7488 2524 E-mail: gorden@detail.co.uk
Dream Sleeper, The Lingfield Estate, Mcmullen Road, Darlington, County Durham, DL1 1RW Tel: (01325) 283105 Fax: (01325) 488502
▶ Dreams plc, Waterton Industrial Estate, Bridgend, Mid Glamorgan, CF31 3YN Tel: (01656) 668166 Fax: (01656) 662101
E C Hodge MF Ltd, Norton Road, Stevenage, Hertfordshire, SG1 2BB Tel: (01438) 357341 Fax: (01438) 361408 E-mail: echodgemflimited@aol.com
▶ Ed's Beds, 26A Front Street, Framwellgate Moor, Durham, DH1 5EJ Tel: 0191-375 7275 Fax: 0191-375 7275
Fine Line Interiors, Surrex Farm, Colchester Road, Coggeshall, Colchester, CO6 1RR Tel: (01376) 561611 Fax: (01376) 561110
Furniture Direct, Southfield Street, Nelson, Lancashire, BB9 9QA Tel: (01282) 690921 Fax: (01282) 690921
Galiform Corporate Services Ltd, Thorpe Road, Howden, Goole, North Humberside, DN14 7PA Tel: (01430) 430905 Fax: (01430) 431540
Gattzbee Kitchens, Darley Street, Darley Abbey, Derby, DE22 1DX Tel: (01332) 556699 Fax: (01332) 556699
H Postill, The Old Chapel, Fangfoss, York, YO41 5QP Tel: (01759) 368209
Hale & Murray Ltd, 3 Abingdon Road, Nuffield Industrial Estate, Poole, Dorset, BH17 0UG Tel: (01202) 678431 Fax: (01202) 687843 E-mail: admin@haleandmurray.co.uk
Harval Fitted Furniture, 4 Horbury Junction Industrial Estate, Calder Vale Road, Horbury, Wakefield, West Yorkshire, WF4 5ER Tel: (01924) 270121 Fax: (01924) 262115 E-mail: sales@harval.co.uk
Igoe Ltd, 100 Brooker Road, Waltham Abbey, Essex, EN9 1JL Tel: (01992) 655600 Fax: (01992) 655631 E-mail: enquiries@igoe.co.uk
Impact Kitchens & Bedrooms, Perseverance Mill, Bolton Road, Westhoughton, Bolton, BL5 3JQ Tel: (01942) 812331
John Sheridan & Sons, 72 Old Rossorry Road, Enniskillen, County Fermanagh, BT74 7LF Tel: (028) 6632 2510 Fax: (028) 6632 3895 E-mail: shaunsheridan@email.com
Julian Designs Ltd, 25 Southfield Road, Hinckley, Leicestershire, LE10 1UA Tel: (01455) 615800 Fax: (01455) 615800
K C & Son Construction Ltd, Amberley Way, Hounslow, TW4 6BH Tel: (020) 8577 2222 Fax: (020) 8577 2323
Kitchen Design Centre, 789 Lisburn Road, Belfast, BT9 7GX Tel: (028) 9038 1265 Fax: (028) 9068 2452 E-mail: info@kdckitchendesign.com
Kyoto Futons Ltd, Hards Lane, Frognall, Deeping St. James, Peterborough, PE6 8RP Tel: (01778) 380555 Fax: (01778) 380444
Lans Fine Furnishings, 1717 London Road, Leigh-on-Sea, Essex, SS9 2SW Tel: (01702) 480591 Fax: (01702) 480591
Lingwood Fitted Furniture, Sawmills Road, Diss, Norfolk, IP22 4GG Tel: (01379) 650040 Fax: (01379) 650813 E-mail: woodstyle@btopenworld.co.uk
▶ Lubina Kitchen Co. Ltd, Unit 2, Hythe Quay, Colchester, CO2 8JB Tel: (01206) 792807 Fax: (01206) 863728 E-mail: emmarose@lubina.co.uk
M F I UK Ltd, Southon House, 333 The Hyde, Edgeware Road, London, NW9 6TD Tel: (020) 8200 8000 Fax: (020) 8200 8636
▶ M & K Units, 4 Lisburn Street, Hillsborough, County Down, BT26 6AB Tel: (028) 9268 3085 Fax: (028) 9268 3739 E-mail: mk_units@hotmail.com
Maghera Joinery Works Ltd, 100 Glen Road, Maghera, County Londonderry, BT46 5JG Tel: (028) 7964 2501 Fax: (028) 7964 4181 E-mail: info@beavercabinets.co.uk
Maurice Lay Ltd, Fourth Way, Bristol, BS11 8DW Tel: 0117-938 1900 Fax: 0117-938 2446 E-mail: sales@mlay.co.uk
Moffett & Sons Ltd, Seymour Hill Industrial Estate, Dunmurry, Belfast, BT17 9PW Tel: (028) 9030 1411 Fax: (028) 9061 0785 E-mail: enquiries@moffett.co.uk
Mona Units, 56 Monadore Road, Claudy, Londonderry, BT47 4DP Tel: (028) 7778 1600 Fax: (028) 7778 1500 E-mail: tony@monaunits.com
Moonlight Bedrooms, Unit 4 Pocklington Industrial Estate, Pocklington, York, YO42 1NR Tel: (01759) 305620 Fax: (01759) 305620
Moores Furniture Group Ltd, Thorp Arch Estate, Thorp Arch, Wetherby, West Yorkshire, LS23 7DD Tel: (01937) 842394 Fax: (01937) 845396
Oakland Kitchens & Bedrooms Ltd, 14 Tile Cross Trading Estate, Tile Cross Road, Birmingham, B33 0NW Tel: 0121-779 5732 Fax: 0121-779 5732
Olympic Kitchens & Bedrooms, Unit 1 Tulketh Industrial Estate, Manchester, M40 9LY Tel: 0161-205 0055 Fax: 0161-205 0101
Oomers Ltd, 8 St. Andrew's Road, London, E17 6BD Tel: (020) 8527 8388 Fax: (020) 8527 8288 E-mail: sales@oomers.co.uk
P H Chandler Leyland Ltd, 5 The Forward Industrial Estate, Talbot Road, Leyland, PR25 2ZJ Tel: (01772) 421651 Fax: (01772) 621493 E-mail: carolw@phchandler.co.uk
John Peters Bed Centre, Guiseley Retail Park, Park Road, Guiseley, Leeds, LS20 8QH Tel: (01943) 879248 Fax: (01943) 879248
▶ Pine Tree, 69 Bruntcliffe Road, Morley, Leeds, LS27 0LQ Tel: 0113-252 0808 Fax: 0113-252 0808 E-mail: sales@thepinetreemorley.co.uk
Planahome Ltd, 105 High St, Golborne, Warrington, WA3 3BU Tel: (01942) 728059 Fax: (01942) 271643 E-mail: sales@planahome.co.uk
Premier Glass Co., 3a Railway Arches, Brady Street, London, E1 5DT Tel: (020) 7247 9908 Fax: 020 72479908
Princess Fitted Bedroom & Kitchen Furniture, 40 Whalebone Lane South, Dagenham, Essex, RM8 1BB Tel: (020) 8593 3884

BEDROOM FURNITURE - *continued*

Quantum Industries Ltd, D Frenbury Estate, Drayton High Road, Norwich, NR6 5DP Tel: (01603) 789000 Fax: (01603) 405476 E-mail: enquiries@selbix.co.uk

Restall Brown & Clennell Ltd, 21 North Street, Lewes, East Sussex, BN7 2PE Tel: (01273) 473612 Fax: 01273 477783 E-mail: sales@rbc-furniture.co.uk

Richardson Bros, 39 Leg Street, Oswestry, Shropshire, SY11 2NN Tel: (01691) 656980 Fax: (01691) 656980

Richardson Cardy, 44a-48 Railway Street, Lisburn, County Antrim, BT28 1XP Tel: (028) 9267 8884 Fax: (028) 9266 3509

Richwood Bedrooms, Unit 13 Bacon House Farm, Warren Road, Little Horwood, Milton Keynes, MK17 0PS Tel: (01908) 507907 Fax: (01908) 507976 E-mail: keith@richwoodbedrooms.co.uk

Royal Auping, 35 Baker Street, London, W1U 8EN Tel: (020) 7486 7154 Fax: (020) 7486 7143 E-mail: sh@misuraemme.co.uk

Sharps Bedrooms Ltd, 12 High Street, Ashford, Kent, TN24 8TD Tel: (01233) 641033

▶ Sharps Bedrooms Ltd, Albany Park, Camberley, Surrey, GU16 7PU Tel: (01276) 802000

Sharps Bedrooms Ltd, Homebase, Kingsway, Derby, DE22 3NF Tel: (01332) 383538

Sharps Bedrooms Ltd, 62-68 Eden Street, Kingston upon Thames, Surrey, KT1 1EL Tel: (020) 8546 1238

Sharps Bedrooms Ltd, Homebase, 4 The Sidings, Lincoln, LN6 7TP Tel: (01522) 512181

Sharps Bedrooms Ltd, Wood Green Shopping City, High Road, London, N22 6YD Tel: (020) 8889 1657

Sharps Bedrooms Ltd, 25 Swinton Hall Road, Swinton, Manchester, M27 4BL Tel: 0161-728 3561 Fax: 0161-728 3276

Sharps Bedrooms Ltd, Unit L Meadowhall Retail Park, Attercliffe Common, Sheffield, S9 2YZ Tel: 0114-244 4419

Sharps Bedrooms Ltd, Foss Bank, York, YO31 7JB Tel: (01904) 629574

Spacemaker Bedrooms Ltd, Ilford Trading Estate Paycocke Road, Basildon, Essex, SS14 3DR Tel: (01268) 476705 Fax: (01268) 472010 E-mail: sales@spacemakerfurniture.co.uk

Spacemaker Bedrooms Ltd, 160-162 Hornchurch Road, Hornchurch, Essex, RM11 1QH Tel: (01708) 473020

▶ Sportzone Marketing, PO Box 332, Bushey, WD23 3XZ Tel: 0700 5938868 Fax: 0700 5938869 E-mail: john@sportzone-marketing.co.uk

Sweetdreams Waterbeds, 115 Glasgow Road, Dumbarton, G82 1RG Tel: (01389) 742241 Fax: (01389) 742241 E-mail: sales@waterbeds.ws

Topline Furniture, Unit 3 Oakfield Industrial Estate, Eynsham, Witney, Oxfordshire, OX29 4TN Tel: (01865) 880799 Fax: (01865) 880744 E-mail: sales@toplinefurniture.co.uk

Turnstyle Ltd, Claypole Lane, Dry Doddington, Newark, Nottinghamshire, NG23 5HZ Tel: (01400) 282342 Fax: (01400) 282353

Ward Alan, Unit B Enderley Street, Newcastle, Staffordshire, ST5 2BS Tel: (01782) 713713 Fax: (01782) 740700

The Woodcutter, Receptional 7, Station Square, High Street, Flitwick, Bedford, MK45 1DP Tel: (01525) 715520

Woodstock, 127 Wandsworth Bridge Road, London, SW6 2TT Tel: (020) 7371 8484 Fax: (020) 7731 3676

BEDS

▶ A Barn Full Of Brass Beds, Main Road, Conisholme, Louth, Lincolnshire, LN11 7LS Tel: (01507) 358092 E-mail: brassbeds@clara.co.uk

Airsprung Furniture Group plc, Canal Road Industrial Estate, Canal Road, Trowbridge, Wiltshire, BA14 8RQ Tel: (01225) 754411 Fax: (01225) 763256 E-mail: sales@airsprungbeds.co.uk

And So To Bed Ltd, 15 Orchard Street, London, W1H 6HG Tel: (020) 7935 0225 Fax: (020) 7487 3434

Aqua Status Waterbed Centre, 112 Lower Dock Street, Newport, Gwent, NP20 2AF Tel: (01633) 842777 Fax: (01633) 842777 E-mail: waterbeds@aquastatus.co.uk

Aquaglow Waterbeds, 145 Fox Lane, Leyland, PR25 1HE Tel: (01772) 452462 Fax: (01772) 460669 E-mail: info@aquaglowwaterbeds.co.uk

Aquarest Bedding & Blankets, 86 Holden Road, Brierfield, Nelson, Lancashire, BB9 5PR Tel: (01282) 698671 Fax: (07005) 802409

Bargain Bedstores Ltd, 155 Hornsey Road, London, N7 6DU Tel: (020) 7609 6320 Fax: (020) 7278 6025

Bed Factory, 139 Regent Street, Leamington Spa, Warwickshire, CV32 4NX Tel: (01926) 426405 Fax: (01926) 314802 E-mail: admin@thebedfactory.co.uk

Bed Post, 193-195 Eltham High Street, London, SE9 1TS Tel: (020) 8294 1319 Fax: (020) 8294 1755

▶ Bed Shop, 21 Brunel Road, Manor Trading Estate, Benfleet, Essex, SS7 4PS Tel: (01268) 569155 Fax: (01268) 569156 E-mail: sales@thebedshopltd.com

▶ Bed Shops, 2a Buckland Road, Pen Mill Trading Estate, Yeovil, Somerset, BA21 5EA Tel: (01935) 431331

▶ Bedbugz Bedding & Blankets, 243-245 Dewsbury Road, Leeds, LS11 5HZ Tel: 0113-277 7753 Fax: 0113-277 7753

▶ Bedmakers Co., Unit 5-7, Clayhill, Fish Bound Industrial Trading Estate, Fishbound, Bristol, BS5 7ES Tel: 0117-965 6400 Fax: 0117-965 7300 E-mail: bedmakerbristol@aol.com

Beds Beds Bed Centre, 313-321 North End Rd, London, SW6 1NN Tel: 020 76103000 Fax: 020 73857711

Beds Beds Beds London Ltd, 313-321 North End Road, London, SW6 1NN Tel: (020) 7385 2000 Fax: (020) 7385 7711

Beds To Go London Ltd, 43 Windmill Hill, Enfield, Middlesex, EN2 7AE Tel: (020) 8363 3323 Fax: (020) 8363 5545

▶ Bedside Manor, 108 Burley Road, Leeds, LS3 1JP Tel: 0113-242 5600 Fax: 0113-242 6100

Bedtime, 691 London Road, Isleworth, Middlesex, TW7 4ES Tel: (020) 8568 2574 Fax: (020) 8568 4761 E-mail: sales@bedtimesuperstores.co.uk

Bedtime Bed Centre, 8 Falcon Road, Wisbech, Cambridgeshire, PE13 1AU Tel: (01945) 466788 Fax: (01945) 466788

Bedworld Ltd, 36 Bridge Street, Castleford, West Yorkshire, WF10 1JS Tel: (01977) 511577 Fax: (01977) 511577

Bedworld, Unit 3 Bulmer Way, Middlesbrough, Cleveland, TS1 5JT Tel: (01642) 860086 Fax: (01642) 862488 E-mail: admin@bedworld.org

▶ Bensons Bed Centres Ltd, Gallagher Retail Park, Stoney Stanton Road, Coventry, CV6 5QQ Tel: (024) 7666 1055

Bensons Bed Centres Ltd, 8 Newbury Retail Park, Pinchington Lane, Newbury, Berkshire, RG14 7HU Tel: (01635) 569893 Fax: (01635) 569893

▶ Bensons Bed Centres Ltd, 7 Sprowston Retail Park, Salhouse Road, Norwich, NR7 9AZ Tel: (01603) 301959

▶ Bensons Bed Centres Ltd, 786 Mansfield Road, Nottingham, NG5 3GG Tel: 0115-920 3852

▶ Bensons Bed Centres Ltd, Botley Road, Oxford, OX2 0HA Tel: (01865) 202795

Bensons Bed Centres Ltd, Glamorgan Vale Retail Park, Talbot Green, Pontyclun, Mid Glamorgan, CF72 8RP Tel: (01443) 222889 Fax: (01925) 237601

Bensons Bed Centres Ltd, Carpet World, Mariners Way, Ashton-on-Ribble, Preston, PR2 2YN Tel: (01772) 768565 Fax: (01772) 723027

Bensons Bed Centres Ltd, 18 Goodwood Square, Teesside Retail Park, Thornaby, Stockton-on-Tees, Cleveland, TS17 7BW Tel: (01642) 670800

Bensons Bed Centres Ltd, Unit 4 Taurus Park, Europa Boulevard, Westbrook, Warrington, WA5 7ZT Tel: (01925) 237600

Bensons Bed Centres Ltd, 6 Winterstoke Road, Weston-super-Mare, Avon, BS23 3YT Tel: (01934) 635946 Fax: (01934) 413228

Best Rest Beds, 18-20 Grosvenor Street, Manchester, M1 7JJ Tel: 0161-273 7700 Fax: 0161-273 7711

Big Table Furniture Co Op Ltd, 56 Great Western Road, London, W9 3BT Tel: (020) 7221 5058 Fax: (020) 7229 6032 E-mail: sales@bigtable.co.uk

Blindcraft, 2 Peffer Place, Edinburgh, EH16 4BB Tel: 0131-661 1205 Fax: 0131-652 2095 E-mail: sales@blindcraft.co.uk

Bumble End Barn Old Pine, Grove Lane, Wishaw, Sutton Coldfield, West Midlands, B76 9PH Tel: 0121-351 3993 Fax: 0121-351 3993 E-mail: bumblepine@aol.com

Burgess Bedding Ltd, 123 Pollard Street, Manchester, M4 7JB Tel: 0161-273 5528 Fax: 0161-273 5563

C W Jones Flooring Ltd, 10 Vale Lane, Bristol, BS3 5RU Tel: 0117-966 1454 Fax: 0117-963 9733 E-mail: info@cwjfloorings.co.uk

Camborne Mattress & Bed Centre, 85 Pendarves Street, Tuckingmill, Camborne, Cornwall, TR14 8NP Tel: (01209) 718029

▶ Cheshire Beds & Pine, 86 Wellington Road North, Stockport, Cheshire, SK4 1HW Tel: 0161-477 7712 Fax: 0161-477 7712

▶ Cinema Beds & Sofa Store, Court Ash, Yeovil, Somerset, BA20 1HG Tel: (01935) 413413 Fax: (01935) 423344

Citybeds Ltd, 17-39 Gibbins Road, London, E15 2HU Tel: (020) 8503 1503 Fax: (020) 8519 8450 E-mail: sales@citybeds.co.uk

Coborn Beds, 100 Coborn Road, London, E3 2DG Tel: (020) 8981 7530

▶ Coloroll Bedding & Blankets, 651 Rolston Road, Hornsea, North Humberside, HU18 1UT Tel: (01964) 534234

▶ Clive Davies, 4 Crispin Centre, Street, Somerset, BA16 0HP Tel: (01458) 441001 Fax: (01458) 441001 E-mail: sales@clivedaviesfurnishings.co.uk

Discount Furniture Co., Riverdale Business Park, Wheatley Hall Road, Doncaster, South Yorkshire, DN2 4PF Tel: (01302) 340049 Fax: (01302) 340049

▶ Dream, Unit 1 Boucher CR, Belfast, BT12 6HU Tel: (028) 9066 8596 Fax: (028) 9066 9765 E-mail: sales@therockinghorse.co.uk

▶ Dreams plc, Waterton Industrial Estate, Bridgend, Mid Glamorgan, CF31 3YN Tel: (01656) 668166 Fax: (01656) 662101

▶ Dreams plc, Point West Waterfront West, Dudley Road, Brierley Hill, West Midlands, DY5 1LL Tel: (01384) 572568 Fax: (01384) 262616

▶ Dreams plc, Wyrley Brook Retail Park, Walkmill Lane, Cannock, Staffordshire, WS11 0XA Tel: (01543) 570606 Fax: (01543) 570764

▶ Dreams plc, Unit 4a Cwmbran Retail Park, Cwmbran Drive, Cwmbran, Gwent, NP44 3JQ Tel: (01633) 480899 Fax: (01633) 480839

▶ Dreams plc, Southgate Retail Park, Normanton Road, Derby, DE23 6UQ Tel: (01332) 208989 Fax: (01332) 208124

▶ Dreams plc, 452-458 High Road, Ilford, Essex, IG1 1UT Tel: (020) 8478 5888

▶ Dreams plc, Unit 2a Crossley Retail Park, Carpet Trades Way, Kidderminster, Worcestershire, DY11 6DY Tel: (01562) 744144 Fax: (01562) 743022

Dreams plc, 11-12 High Street, Wraysbury, Staines, Middlesex, TW19 5DB Tel: (01784) 491174 Fax: (01784) 491175

Dura Beds, Moorebank Mills, Artillary Street, Heckmondwike, West Yorkshire, WF16 0NT Tel: (01924) 400066 Fax: (01924) 404071

Duxiana, 46 George Street, London, W1U 7DX Tel: (020) 7486 2363 Fax: (020) 7935 8080

▶ Ed's Beds, 26A Front Street, Framwellgate Moor, Durham, DH1 5EJ Tel: 0191-375 7275 Fax: 0191-375 7275

Edwardian Bedding Co., 44 Bank Street, Mexborough, South Yorkshire, S64 9LL Tel: (01709) 589673 Fax: (01709) 589673

▶ Essex Bedding Centres, Thornton Road Industrial Estate, Peall Road, Croydon, CR9 3EX Tel: (020) 8689 4430 Fax: (020) 8689 4430

Essex Beds Ltd, Time Square, Southern Hay, Basildon, Essex, SS14 1DJ Tel: (01268) 522209 Fax: (01268) 530809

Family Choice Ltd, 440 Bradford Road, Batley, West Yorkshire, WF17 5LS Tel: (01924) 422157 Fax: (01924) 422153 E-mail: sales@fcbeds.co.uk

Feather & Black, Terminus Road, Chichester, West Sussex, PO19 8ZZ Tel: (01243) 380200 Fax: (01243) 790589 E-mail: chichester@featherandblack.com

Feather & Black, Regent House, 13-15 Albert Street, Harrogate, North Yorkshire, HG1 1JX Tel: (01423) 536644 Fax: (01423) 529699

The Finsbury Springs Mattress King, 76 Gillespie Road, London, N5 1LN Tel: (020) 7226 2591 Fax: (020) 7503 8439

▶ First Bed & Pine Centre, 67 London Road, East Grinstead, West Sussex, RH19 1EQ Tel: (01342) 322700 Fax: (01342) 301252

Furniture World, Queens Road, Halifax, West Yorkshire, HX1 3NS Tel: (01422) 349860 Fax: (01422) 349860

Futon Co. Ltd, 147 Finchley Road, London, NW3 6JH Tel: (020) 7586 7444 Fax: (020) 7586 7555

Futon Co. Ltd, 100 Battersea Rise, London, SW11 1EJ Tel: (020) 7978 4498 Fax: (020) 7978 4029

Futon UK Com, 28 Far Gosford Street, Coventry, CV1 5DW Tel: (0870) 3500027 Fax: (0870) 3500027

Futons Direct, The Old Malthouse, Queen Street, Eynsham, Witney, Oxfordshire, OX29 4JD Tel: (01865) 880005 E-mail: sales@futons-direct.co.uk

Golden Night Beds Co. Ltd, Albion Mills, Bradford Road, Dewsbury, West Yorkshire, WF13 2HD Tel: (01924) 469000 Fax: (01924) 468899

▶ Good Knights Bed & Mattress Centre, 398 Chester Road, Little Sutton, Ellesmere Port, CH66 3RB Tel: 0151-339 1600 Fax: 0151-339 1600 E-mail: sales@goodknights.co.uk

Grenadine Trading Ltd, Bay 36-38 Circular Road, Storforth Lane Trading Estate, Hasland, Chesterfield, Derbyshire, S41 0QL Tel: (01246) 209391 Fax: (01246) 550718 E-mail: ben.bramley@ntworld.com

▶ Heli Beds, Newbridge Road Industrial Estate, Pontllanfraith, Blackwood, Gwent, NP12 2AN Tel: (01495) 223658 Fax: (01495) 223401

▶ Helibeds, 69 Roundponds, Melksham, Wiltshire, SN12 8EB Tel: (01793) 688999 Fax: (01225) 790990

John Henman Ltd, 81 High Street, West Wickham, Kent, BR4 0LS Tel: (020) 8777 4853

Hi-Tec Beds Ltd, Unit 2 Albion Mills, Bradford Rd, Dewsbury, West Yorkshire, WF13 2HD Tel: 01924 459393 Fax: 01924 488900

House Of Dreams, 3 Hayes Road, Paignton, Devon, TQ4 5PD Tel: (01803) 664076 Fax: (01803) 664096

Malcolm Johnston, 156 Woodville Park Industrial Estate, Woodville Street, Glasgow, G51 2RL Tel: 0141-445 2368 Fax: 0141-445 2368

Just Beds, 76 Broadway, Didcot, Oxfordshire, OX11 8AE Tel: (01235) 819188 Fax: (01235) 817978

Kayfoam Woolson, Unit 4B, Newline Industrial Estate, Bacup, Lancashire, OL13 9RW Tel: (01706) 875075 Fax: (01706) 872505 E-mail: kaywool@kayfoam.com

Lesters, 13-14 George Street, Hove, East Sussex, BN3 3YA Tel: (01273) 734686 Fax: (01273) 734686

Long Eaton, 76a Derby Road, Long Eaton, Nottingham, NG10 4LB Tel: 0115-972 1111

▶ Luxury Beds, Town Street, Batley Carr, Dewsbury, West Yorkshire, WF13 2HG Tel: (01924) 437392 Fax: (01924) 437825

▶ Manchester Beds & Appliances, 342 Oldham Road, Manchester, M40 7NS Tel: 0161-205 9922 Fax: 0161-205 1717

▶ Moonlight Beds, 2 Byron Parade, Uxbridge Road, Uxbridge, Middlesex, UB10 0LZ Tel: (020) 8756 0999 Fax: (020) 8561 9774

Norris Bedding Ltd, 86-88 Coldharbour Lane, London, SE5 9PU Tel: (020) 7274 5306 Fax: (020) 7274 5306

▶ Oxford Beds, 1a Bridge Street, Witney, Oxfordshire, OX28 1BY Tel: (01993) 771066 Fax: (01993) 771066

Pearsons Bed & Linen Centre, 238 High Road, Loughton, Essex, IG10 1RB Tel: (020) 8502 3949 Fax: (020) 8502 3949

▶ R & S Furnishings, 2 Winster Park, Corporation Road, Ilkeston, Derbyshire, DE7 4BN Tel: 0115-932 5361 Fax: 0115-932 5362

Relyon Ltd, Station Mills, Wellington, Somerset, TA21 8NN Tel: (01823) 667501 Fax: (01823) 666079 E-mail: enquries@reylon.co.uk

▶ Rise & Shine, Willow Road, Potton, Sandy, Bedfordshire, SG19 2PP Tel: (01767) 262629 Fax: (01767) 262756

A. & M. Robinson Ltd, 1008 Pollokshaws Road, Glasgow, G41 2HQ Tel: 0141-632 0959 Fax: 0141-632 1384 E-mail: enquiries@robinsonsbeds.co.uk

▶ Rugby Suites & Beds, 104 Railway Terrace, Rugby, Warwickshire, CV21 3HE Tel: 01788 577335 Fax: 01788 577335

S & A Bedding Ltd, 14 Honey Street, Cheetham Hill, Manchester, M8 8RG Tel: 0161-834 8249 Fax: 0161-834 7774

Sarlands Beds Ltd, Fletchampstead Highway, Tile Hill, Coventry, CV4 9BY Tel: 024 76717912 Fax: 024 76717912

▶ Scott Woyka Furniture, Falmouth Wharves, North Parade, Falmouth, Cornwall, TR11 2TF Tel: (01326) 311777 Fax: 01326 311777

Shabaz Bedding & Carpets, Havelock Street, Oldham, OL8 1JR Tel: 0161-620 2800 Fax: 0161-627 4744

Shelforce, Units 21-23 Erdington Industrial Park, Chester Road, Erdington, Birmingham, B24 0RD Tel: 0121-603 5262 Fax: 0121-603 2771 E-mail: sales@shelforce.co.uk

▶ Sheridan UK Ltd, 40 Gold Street, Tiverton, Devon, EX16 6PY Tel: (01884) 255997 Fax: (01884) 255997

Silent Night Beds, Longing Lane, Barnoldswick, Lancashire, BB18 6BJ Tel: (01282) 813051 Fax: (01282) 813466 E-mail: enquiries@silentnightgroup.co.uk

Silent Sleep Beds, Parkside Road, Bradford, West Yorkshire, BD5 8DY Tel: (01274) 733743 Fax: (01274) 733748 E-mail: sales@silentsleep.co.uk

Skipton Bed & Suite Centre, 17 Water Street, Skipton, North Yorkshire, BD23 1PQ Tel: (01756) 794719 Fax: (01756) 796284

Sleep At Ease Ltd, Clifton Road, Blackpool, FY4 4QZ Tel: (01253) 792600 Fax: (01253) 767590

▶ Sleep Heaven Beds, 115 Birleywood, Skelmersdale, Lancashire, WN8 9HR Tel: (01695) 722772

▶ Sleepmasters Ltd, 47-49 Stamford New Road, Altrincham, Cheshire, WA14 1DS Tel: 0161-928 3640 Fax: 0161-928 3640

Sleepmasters Ltd, Oxford Square, Blackpool, FY4 4DP Tel: (01253) 698987 Fax: (01253) 698987

Sleepmasters Ltd, 11-12 Derby Street, Burton-on-Trent, Staffordshire, DE14 2LA Tel: (01283) 512131 Fax: (01283) 512131

Sleepmasters Ltd, 8 Riverside Retail Park, Wharf Street, Warrington, WA1 2GZ Tel: (01925) 445524 Fax: (01925) 445524

Snooze UK Ltd, 14 Harcley Street, Dewsbury, West Yorkshire, WF13 2VB Tel: (01924) 467149

Soundsleep Ltd, Aloe Farm, Mile Road, Winfarthing, Diss, Norfolk, IP22 2EZ Tel: (01953) 861177 Fax: (01953) 861186 E-mail: sales@sound-sleep.co.uk

South Wales Waterbeds Ltd, 124A Lower Dock Street, Newport, Gwent, NP20 1EN Tel: (01633) 211448 Fax: (01633) 841083

Southwest Waterbeds, Church Farm Barn, East Stoke, Stoke-sub-Hamdon, Somerset, TA14 6UF Tel: (01935) 829777

Sunderland Bedding Centre, 7-9 Olive Street, Sunderland, SR1 3PE Tel: 0191-514 2056 Fax: 0191-510 1317 E-mail: sales@sunderlandbeddingcentre.co.uk

▶ Taurus Beds, 167a Finchley Road, London, NW3 6LB Tel: (020) 7372 1166 Fax: (020) 7328 7274 E-mail: admin@tauruspinebeds.co.uk

Theraposture Ltd, Unit 11 Warminster Business Park, Furnax Lane, Warminster, Wiltshire, BA12 8PE Tel: (01985) 847788 Fax: (01985) 847700

To Catch A Dream Ltd, The Ginnel, Harrogate, North Yorkshire, HG1 2RB Tel: (01423) 503060 Fax: (01423) 528111 E-mail: info@tocatchadream.net

Tony's Textiles, 56 Newborough, Scarborough, North Yorkshire, YO11 1ET Tel: (01723) 371171 Fax: (01723) 371171

Trends Furniture Centre, 499 London Road, Camberley, Surrey, GU15 3JE Tel: (01276) 22942 Fax: (01276) 675620

Turnwright Ltd, 12 & 19 Barking Industrial Park, Alfreds Way, Barking, Essex, IG11 0TJ Tel: (020) 8591 2862 Fax: (020) 8594 6999 E-mail: sales@turnwright.freeserve.co.uk

Ultrassage, Unit 25, Moor Lane Trading Estate, Sherburn in Elmet, Leeds, LS25 6ES Tel: (01977) 680000

Vokins At Home, Denton Island, Newhaven, East Sussex, BN9 9BB Tel: (01273) 612485 Fax: (01273) 612230 E-mail: info@vokinsathome.com

Warren Evans, 158a Camden Street, London, NW1 9PA Tel: (020) 7284 1132 Fax: (020) 7267 6604 E-mail: info@warrenevans.com

BEDS – *continued*

Willis Gambier, 121 Radwinter Road, Saffron Walden, Essex, CB11 3HY Tel: (01799) 510170 Fax: (01799) 510171

▶ www.saundersallotment.co.uk, 88 Dunkeld Road, Gosport, Hampshire, PO12 4NJ Tel: (023) 92 586619 E-mail: berylsau@saundersallotment.co.uk

BEDS, WATER

▶ Peter Ramsey & Sons Denholme Timber Ltd, Sawmills, Wellington Street, Laisterdyke, Bradford, West Yorkshire, BD4 8BW Tel: (01274) 656563 E-mail: info@ramsey-uk.com

▶ Waterbeds Direct, 7 Talbot Row, Euxton, Chorley, Lancashire, PR7 6HS Tel: (0808) 1001419 E-mail: sales@waterbedsdirect.co.uk

BEDSPREADS

▶ Art Exhibition Textile Ltd, 16 Dalesford, Haslingden, Rossendale, Lancashire, BB4 6QH Tel: (01706) 219550 Fax: (01706) 222218 E-mail: sales@artex-online.com

Brynkir Woollen Mill Ltd, Brynkir Woollen Factory, Golan, Garndolbenmaen, Gwynedd, LL51 9YU Tel: (01766) 530236

▶ Flamboyance, 483 Green Lanes, London, N13 4BS Tel: (0845) 8382542 Fax: (0871) 2423304E-mail: sales@FlamboyanceLtd.co.uk

BEEF

Allied Meat Importers, Stuart House, Britannia Road, Queens Gate, Waltham Cross, Hertfordshire, EN8 7TF Tel: (01992) 807950 Fax: (01992) 807951 E-mail: amiuk@alliedmeats.com

BEEKEEPING REQUISITES

C Wynne Jones, Ty Brith, Pentre Celyn, Ruthin, Clwyd, LL15 2SR Tel: (01978) 790279 Fax: (01978) 790265 E-mail: jones@tybrith.fsnet.co.uk

Steves Bees, 131 Wellington Street, Peterborough, PE1 5DU Tel: (01733) 891155 Fax: (01733) 709709 E-mail: enquiries@englishhoney.co.uk

E.H. Thorne (Beehives) Ltd, Beehive Works, Louth Road, Wragby, Market Rasen, Lincolnshire, LN8 5LA Tel: (01673) 858555 Fax: (01673) 857004 E-mail: sales@thorne.co.uk

BEER CELLAR FITTINGS/ EQUIPMENT

CFBS, 1 Progress Works, Parkwood Street, Keighley, West Yorkshire, BD21 4NX Tel: (01535) 681839 Fax: (01535) 681887 E-mail: mail@cfbs.co.uk

Cornwallis Ltd, Unit 42 Coneygre Industrial Estate, Tipton, West Midlands, DY4 8XP Tel: 0121-520 5552 Fax: 0121-520 3330 E-mail: sales@sandgroup.com

▶ Globetech Cellar Services Ltd, 20a Wilson Street, Bristol, BS2 9HH Tel: 0117-924 8444 Fax: 0117-924 8555

Hallamshire Brewery Services Ltd, Liverpool Street, Sheffield, S9 2PU Tel: 0114-243 1721 Fax: 0114-256 0130 E-mail: sam@hallamshire.u-net.co.ukj

▶ Kegless Ltd, Moffat Centre, 219 Colinton Road, Edinburgh, EH14 1DJ Tel: (07838) 241700 E-mail: info@kegless.co.uk

Harry Mason Ltd, 217 Thimble Mill Lane, Birmingham, B7 5HS Tel: 0121-328 5900 Fax: 0121-327 7257 E-mail: gt@harrymason.co.uk

BEER DISPENSER EQUIPMENT

Angram Ltd, Unit 11 Becklands Close, Bar Lane, Roecliffe, York, YO51 9NR Tel: (01423) 324555 Fax: (01423) 324955 E-mail: sales@angramltd.com

Centek International, Unit 30 Lawson Hunt Industrial Park, Guildford Road, Broadbridge Heath, Horsham, West Sussex, RH12 3JR Tel: (01403) 263323 Fax: (01403) 270651 E-mail: info@nuplas.co.uk

CFBS, 1 Progress Works, Parkwood Street, Keighley, West Yorkshire, BD21 4NX Tel: (01535) 681839 Fax: (01535) 681887 E-mail: mail@cfbs.co.uk

Cornwallis Ltd, Unit 42 Coneygre Industrial Estate, Tipton, West Midlands, DY4 8XP Tel: 0121-520 5552 Fax: 0121-520 3330 E-mail: sales@sandgroup.com

Hallamshire Brewery Services Ltd, Liverpool Street, Sheffield, S9 2PU Tel: 0114-243 1721 Fax: 0114-256 0130 E-mail: sam@hallamshire.u-net.co.ukj

I M I Cornelius, 39-41 Nuffield Way, Abingdon, Oxfordshire, OX14 1AE Tel: (01235) 555123 Fax: (01235) 555456

I M I Cornelius UK Ltd, 1-3 Tything Road East, Kinwarton, Alcester, Warwickshire, B49 6EU Tel: (01789) 763101 Fax: (01789) 763644 E-mail: sales@cornelius.com

▶ Kegless Ltd, Moffat Centre, 219 Colinton Road, Edinburgh, EH14 1DJ Tel: (07838) 241700 E-mail: info@kegless.co.uk

Microflow Europe Ltd, Globe Square, Dukinfield, Cheshire, SK16 4RF Tel: 0161-343 1557 Fax: 0161-343 3762 E-mail: sales@microfloweurope.com

R T L Enterprises, Windrush, Tormarton Road, Marshfield, Chippenham, Wiltshire, SN14 8NN Tel: (01225) 891899 Fax: (01225) 891890

BEER ENGINES

Angram Ltd, Unit 11 Becklands Close, Bar Lane, Roecliffe, York, YO51 9NR Tel: (01423) 324555 Fax: (01423) 324955 E-mail: sales@angramltd.com

Hallamshire Brewery Services Ltd, Liverpool Street, Sheffield, S9 2PU Tel: 0114-243 1721 Fax: 0114-256 0130 E-mail: sam@hallamshire.u-net.co.ukj

Harry Mason Ltd, 217 Thimble Mill Lane, Birmingham, B7 5HS Tel: 0121-328 5900 Fax: 0121-327 7257 E-mail: gt@harrymason.co.uk

▶ Singleton Services, Unit E, The Sidings Industrial Estate, Settle, North Yorkshire, BD24 9RP Tel: (01729) 823939 Fax: (01729) 823939 E-mail: sales@beerengines.com

BEER KEG

▶ Northern Ale Distributors, Holmcliffe Avenue, Bankfield Park, Huddersfield, HD4 7RN Tel: (01484) 302986 E-mail: sales@northernaledistributors.co.uk

BEER LINE CLEANING EQUIPMENT

Cellar Services, 39 Middle Park Way, Leigh Park, Havant, Hampshire, PO9 4AB Tel: (0845) 021 2337 Fax: (023) 9213 2047 E-mail: beerclear@hotmail.com

BEER MATS

▶ Magic Touch, 63 Barnton Street, Stirling, FK8 1HH Tel: (01786) 445992 Fax: (01786) 434922

BEER MATS, PAPERBOARD

Burton Beer Mats Ltd, Moor St Works, Burton-on-Trent, Staffordshire, DE14 3TA Tel: (01283) 564769 Fax: (01283) 535492 E-mail: sales@burtonbeermatsltd.co.uk

H Conduit, 4 King William Enterprise Park, King William Street, Salford, M50 3ZP Tel: 0161-877 0877 Fax: 0161-877 3434 E-mail: hconduit@btconnect.com

BEER TAP SYSTEMS

▶ Kegless Ltd, Moffat Centre, 219 Colinton Road, Edinburgh, EH14 1DJ Tel: (07838) 241700 E-mail: info@kegless.co.uk

BEER TAPS

R T L Enterprises, Windrush, Tormarton Road, Marshfield, Chippenham, Wiltshire, SN14 8NN Tel: (01225) 891899 Fax: (01225) 891890

BEESWAX BLEACHERS/ BLENDERS/REFINERS/ SUPPLIERS

Cambridge Traditional Products, Millfield, Cottenham, Cambridge, CB4 8RE Tel: (01954) 251380 Fax: (01954) 251387 E-mail: info@bees-wax.co.uk

Landauer Honey Ltd, Top Barn, Fowlmere Road, Newton, Cambridge, CB22 7PG Tel: (01223) 872444 Fax: (01223) 872512

Poth Hille & Co. Ltd, 37 High Street, London, E15 2QD Tel: (020) 8534 7091 Fax: (020) 8534 2291 E-mail: enquiries@poth-hille.co.uk

BELL FOUNDERS

Taylors Eyre & Smith Ltd, The Bell Foundry, Freehold Street, Loughborough, Leicestershire, LE11 1AR Tel: (01509) 212241 Fax: (01509) 263305 E-mail: office@taylorbells.co.uk

Whitechapel Bell Foundry Ltd, 34 Whitechapel Road, London, E1 1DY Tel: (020) 7247 2599 Fax: (020) 7375 1979 E-mail: sales@whitechapelbellfoundry.co.uk

BELL HOUSINGS

Bensons Bed Centres Ltd, Debenhams, 36 Prospect Street, Hull, HU2 8PQ Tel: (01482) 589068 Fax: (01482) 211926

BELLEVILLE SPRINGS

G.E. Bissell & Co. Ltd, Malt Mill Lane, Halesowen, West Midlands, B62 8JL Tel: 0121-559 2241 Fax: 0121-559 1168 E-mail: sales@bissell.co.uk

Longcroft Engineering Ltd, Rochdale Road Industrial Estate, Walsden, Todmorden, Lancashire, OL14 6UD Tel: (01706) 819955 Fax: (01706) 819966 E-mail: paul@longcroftengineering.co.uk

BELLOW COUPLINGS

Francis and Francis Ltd (Schmidt, Poggi & KBK), The Stables Works, Station Road, Kenley, Surrey, CR8 5JA Tel: (020) 8668 9792 Fax: (020) 8668 9793 E-mail: sales@powertransmissions.co.uk

▶ Pipeclear Ltd, Cliff Mount, Whins Lane, Simonstone, Burnley, Lancashire, BB12 7QU Tel: (01282) 776454 Fax: (01282) 779829 E-mail: stephenatpipeclear@btinternet.com

BELLOWS, *See also headings for particular types*

Boreflex Ltd, Unit 9 Gateway Court, Parkgate, Rotherham, South Yorkshire, S62 6LH Tel: (01709) 522333 Fax: (01709) 522663 E-mail: sales@boreflex.co.uk

▶ FlexEJ, 28 Hadcroft Grange, Stourbridge, West Midlands, DY9 7EP Tel: (0845) 0204323 Fax: (01384) 896875 E-mail: sales@flexej.co.uk

The Flexicon Company, 1 Larch Lea Trading Estate, Whitefield Road, Liverpool, L6 5BN Tel: 0151-260 6141 Fax: 0151-260 4477 E-mail: info@flexicon.org.uk

Hydrasun Ltd, Hydrasun House, 392 King Street, Aberdeen, AB24 3BU Tel: (01224) 618618 Fax: (01224) 618701 E-mail: info@hydrasun.com

Senior Aerospace Bird Bellows, Radnor Park Industrial Estate, Congleton, Cheshire, CW12 4UQ Tel: (01260) 271411 Fax: (01260) 270910 E-mail: info@bird-bellows.co.uk

Synthotech Elastomers Ltd, Mangham Road, Barbot Hall Industrial Estate, Rotherham, South Yorkshire, S61 4RJ Tel: (01709) 363705 Fax: (01709) 369165 E-mail: info@synthotech-rubber.co.uk

BELLOWS SEALED VALVES

Valvelink UK Ltd, 17 Cotswold Green, Stonehouse, Gloucestershire, GL10 2ES Tel: (01453) 822222 Fax: (01453) 821111

BELLOWS, FABRIC

▶ Total Maintenance Solutions, Unit 94 Silverbriar, Business & Innovation Centre, Sunderland Enterprise Park, Sunderland, SR5 2TQ Tel: 0191-516 6489 Fax: 0191-516 6499 E-mail: sales@online-tms.com

BELT BUCKLES

▶ Highland Dress Hire, 246 Brown Royd Avenue, Dalton, Huddersfield, HD5 9NW Tel: (01484) 546915 Fax: (01484) 432589 E-mail: laurie@highlandhire.co.uk

Tanside Ltd, Back Lane Farm, High London Lane, Winfarthing, Diss, Norfolk, IP22 2EF Tel: (01953) 861444 Fax: (01953) 861440 E-mail: tansideltd@btconnect.com

BELT CONVEYOR SYSTEMS

▶ 4 Conveyor Solutions Ltd, PO Box 87, Batley, West Yorkshire, WF17 9YB Tel: (01924) 422110 Fax: (01924) 422009 E-mail: enquiries@nuwavesystems.plus.com

The Belt Company Ltd, Springvale House, Doncaster Road, Askern, Doncaster, South Yorkshire, DN6 0AD Tel: (01302) 708383 Fax: (01302) 708527

Blackburn Conveyor, Delph Road, Great Harwood, Blackburn, BB6 7HT Tel: (01254) 888866 Fax: (01254) 829826

C I Logistics, 43 Wenlock Way, Troon Industrial Area, Leicester, LE4 9HU Tel: 0116-276 1691 Fax: 0116-276 9836 E-mail: sales@conveyors.co.uk

Challenger Handling Ltd, 1 Warwick Street, Hull, HU9 1ET Tel: (01482) 224404 Fax: (01482) 210808 E-mail: sales@challenger-group.co.uk

Conveyor Belt Systems Ltd, 19 Kewferry Road, Northwood, Middlesex, HA6 2NS Tel: (01923) 820121 Fax: (01923) 835699

Conveyors Direct, Unit 6, Fishburn Industrial Estate, Fishburn, Stockton-on-Tees, Cleveland, TS21 4AJ Tel: 01740 623338 Fax: 01740 622504 E-mail: sales@conveyorsdirect.co.uk

County Retail Services, 8 Grantham Road, Brighton, BN1 6EE Tel: (01273) 508858 Fax: (01273) 541853

Handling Technology, 11 Cavendish Road, Halesowen, West Midlands, B62 0DB Tel: 0121-421 6153 Fax: 0121-423 1709

Haven Equipment Co., Duncote Mill, Walcot, Telford, Shropshire, TF6 5ER Tel: (01952) 740484 Fax: (01952) 740464 E-mail: sales@havenequipment.co.uk

MK Profile Systems, 9 Cowling Business Park, Canal Side, Chorley, Lancashire, PR6 0QL Tel: (01257) 263937 Fax: (01257) 271409 E-mail: info@mkprofiles.co.uk

Modular Robotic Systems Ltd, Cale Lane, Aspull, Wigan, Lancashire, WN2 1HQ Tel: (01942) 820088 Fax: (01942) 820431 E-mail: info@modular-ltd.co.uk

Monk Conveyors, Unit 18 Woodside Park, Catteshall Lane, Godalming, Surrey, GU7 1LG Tel: (01483) 791700 Fax: (01483) 791701 E-mail: sales@monk-conveyors.co.uk

The Nicholson Group of Companies, Meridian Centre, King Street, Oldham, OL8 1EZ Tel: (08450) 540526 Fax: (08450) 540527 E-mail: enquiries@nicholson-group.co.uk

Olympic Mato Ltd, West Rose Works, St. Mewan, St. Austell, Cornwall, PL25 5SP Tel: (01726) 61141 Fax: (01726) 70211

Owens Conveyor, Westgate House, Westgate, Aldridge, Walsall, WS9 8EX Tel: (01922) 452333 Fax: (01922) 458777 E-mail: msullivan@ocon.co.uk

R F Clarke Ltd, 31 Windmill Road, Saintfield, Ballynahinch, County Down, BT24 7DX Tel: (028) 9751 2920 Fax: (028) 9751 2929 E-mail: sales@rfclarke.com

Rusmail Conveyor Systems Ltd, 33-35 Adams Street, Birmingham, B7 4LT Tel: 0121-359 1549 Fax: 0121-333 3104 E-mail: sales@rusmailconveyors.co.uk

▶ Southern Conveyors, Unit 2 Denton Slipways Site, Wharf Road, Gravesend, Kent, DA12 2RU Tel: (01474) 564145

Telford Mechanical Handling, The Woodlands, Bridge Road, Benthall, Broseley, Shropshire, TF12 5QS Tel: (01952) 884242 Fax: (01952) 884242 E-mail: paul@conaglen.fsbusiness.co.uk

Transnorm Systems Ltd, 4 Ashchurch Business Centre, Alexandra Way, Ashchurch, Tewkesbury, Gloucestershire, GL20 8TD Tel: (01684) 291100 Fax: (01684) 291550 E-mail: sales@transnorm.co.uk

BELT CONVEYORS, ELEVATOR

A J F Projects, 480 Earlham Road, Norwich, NR4 7HP Tel: (01603) 453226 Fax: (01603) 453226 E-mail: adam@ajfprojects.co.uk

▶ Westwood Dawes, 54 Cuckoo Road, Aston, Birmingham, B7 5SY Tel: 0121-327 5133 Fax: 0121-327 7256 E-mail: wd.pulleys@afc-uk.com

BELT (GARMENT) PRODUCTION MACHINES

John H King & Co. Ltd, 3 Sheaf Street, Leeds, LS10 1HD Tel: 0113-243 8890 Fax: 0113-242 2144

BELTING, TRANSMISSION, MANUFRS, *See also headings for particular types according to material used*

A S Belting Products, Headland House, Severn Road, Cardiff, CF11 9XH Tel: (029) 2022 6301 Fax: (029) 2023 7441 E-mail: asbeltings@aol.com

Airport Bearing Co. Ltd, 4/5 Bennerly Court, Blenheim Industrial Estate, Bulwell, Nottingham, NG6 8UT Tel: 0115-975 7571 Fax: 0115-927 3778 E-mail: sales@abco-online.co.uk

Alldrives Ltd, Unit 6 Mead Park River Way, Harlow, Essex, CM20 2SE Tel: (01279) 445576 Fax: (01279) 425554 E-mail: alldrives@btconnect.co.uk

Anaconda Belting Co., 2 Ashwood Place, Bean, Dartford, DA2 8BD Tel: (01474) 709784 Fax: (01474) 709896 E-mail: info@anacondabelting.co.uk

Anglia Bearing Co. Ltd, Units 1 & 8, Wulfric Square, Bretton, Peterborough, PE3 8RF Tel: (01733) 268180 Fax: (01733) 268156 E-mail: angliabearings@aol.com

Atlantic Bearings Ltd, Unit 1, Milners Road, Yeadon, Leeds, LS19 7JE Tel: 0113-250 6640 Fax: 0113-250 0031 E-mail: user@atlantic-bearings.fsnet.co.uk

Bearing Shop, Grace Road Central, Marsh Barton Trading Estate, Exeter, EX2 8QA Tel: (01392) 680880 Fax: (01392) 437131 E-mail: info@thebearingshop.co.uk

Bearings Supplies, Southwell Road, Horsham St. Faith, Norwich, NR10 3JU Tel: (01603) 898918 Fax: (01603) 891801 E-mail: sales@bearing-supplies.co.uk

Beltech Belting Mnfrs, 7 Acacia Close Business Estate, Off Cherrycourt Way, Leighton Buzzard, Bedfordshire, LU7 4QE Tel: (01525) 851155 Fax: (01525) 851156 E-mail: beltech@globalnet.co.uk

Belting & Mechanical Leather Co. Ltd, 20 Cloberfield Road, Milngavie, Glasgow, G62 7LN Tel: 0141-956 6577 Fax: 0141-956 2126 E-mail: sales@beltingmechanical.co.uk

Benson Beltings Ltd, Spenvale Works, Balme Road, Cleckheaton, West Yorkshire, BD19 4EW Tel: (01274) 851600 Fax: (01274) 851620 E-mail: sales@benson-beltings.co.uk

▶ indicates data change since last edition

BELTING, TRANSMISSION, MANUFRS – *continued*

Brammer UK Ltd, Headway Road, Wolverhampton, WV10 6PZ Tel: (01902) 395949 Fax: (01902) 395945 E-mail: export@brammer.biz

Express Bearings & Transmissions, Anglo Trading Estate, Shepton Mallet, Somerset, BA4 5BY Tel: (01749) 330002 Fax: (01749) 330003 E-mail: sales@expressbearings.co.uk

Fosse Bearing Units Ltd, Bearing House, 887 Melton Road, Thurmaston, Leicester, LE4 8EF Tel: 0116-260 2548 Fax: 0116-260 2548 E-mail: fosse.bearings@btinternet.com

Gould Pulleys & Drives Ltd, Unit 19, Worcester Road Industrial Estate, Chipping Norton, Oxfordshire, OX7 5XW Tel: (01608) 643311 Fax: (01608) 643050 E-mail: sales@gouldpulleys.com

H B Industrial Services Ltd, 15 Kingdom Close, Fareham, Hampshire, PO15 5TJ Tel: (01489) 575222 Fax: (01489) 575666 E-mail: sales@hbindustrialservices.co.uk

I B S Bearings Ltd, A1 Trading Estate, Lewisham Road, Smethwick, West Midlands, B66 2BN Tel: 0121-558 4141 Fax: 0121-555 5564

Industrial Links Ltd, Unit 19 Ventura Place, Poole, Dorset, BH16 5SW Tel: (01202) 632996 Fax: (01202) 632997 E-mail: sales@industrial-links.com

London Bearings (Kent) Ltd, Unit 2, Sabre Court, Gillingham Business Park, Gillingham, Kent, ME8 0RW Tel: (01634) 235335 Fax: (01634) 230268 E-mail: lbk.uk@btinternet.com

Potteries Specialist Auctions, 271 Waterloo Road, Stoke-on-Trent, ST6 3HR Tel: (01782) 286622 Fax: (01782) 213777 E-mail: potteriesltd@aol.com

R F Clarke Ltd, 31 Windmill Road, Saintfield, Ballynahinch, County Down, BT24 7DX Tel: (028) 9751 2920 Fax: (028) 9751 2929 E-mail: sales@rfclarke.com

R S Richardson Belting Co. Ltd, Crown Works, Staincliffe Road, Dewsbury, West Yorkshire, WF13 4SB Tel: (01924) 468191 Fax: (01924) 458065 E-mail: mail@diepress-richardson.co.uk

S C H Bearings & Power Transmission, Unit 1 Great Bridge Business Park, Unit 1 Greatbridge Busn Park, Budds Lane, Romsey, Hampshire, SO51 0HA Tel: (01794) 830377 Fax: (01794) 830366 E-mail: sales@schgroup.com

Shropshire Bearing Services, 6 Beveley Road, Oakengates, Telford, Shropshire, TF2 6AT Tel: (01952) 610157 Fax: (01952) 619669 E-mail: shropshirebearings@hotmail.com

Southern Bearings Ltd, Unit 11 Waldeck House, Waldeck Road, Maidenhead, Berkshire, SL6 8BR Tel: (01628) 674123 Fax: (01628) 776502 E-mail: cmay@southernbearing.co.uk

Spen Bearings, 129 Westgate, Cleckheaton, West Yorkshire, BD19 5EJ Tel: (01274) 851700 Fax: (01274) 869736 E-mail: admin@spen-bearings.co.uk

Transbelt Ltd, 36 Howe Street, Bootle, Merseyside, L20 8NG Tel: 0151-922 1314 Fax: 0151-922 3983 E-mail: transbelt@btconnect.com

Transmission Design & Supply Co. Ltd, Unit 1A, Marlborough Street, Burnley, Lancashire, BB11 2HW Tel: (01282) 435143 Fax: (01282) 435160

U K R Transmissions Ltd, 249 Cotmanhay Road, Ilkeston, Derbyshire, DE7 8NE Tel: 0115-932 4572 Fax: 0115-944 0585 E-mail: sales@ukrtrans.co.uk

Stewart Vaughan & Co. Ltd, Unit 21 Riverside Business Park, Lyon Road, London, SW19 2RL Tel: (020) 8544 9199 Fax: (020) 8540 8884

Zerny Engineering Co. Ltd, Unit 13-14, Olds Close, Watford, WD18 9RU Tel: (01923) 774777 Fax: (01923) 774777

BELTING, V/WEDGE

Arntz Belting Co. Ltd, Pennyburn Passage, Londonderry, BT48 0AE Tel: (028) 7126 1221 Fax: (028) 7126 3386 E-mail: abcderry@globalnet.co.uk

Challenge Power Transmission plc, Unit 1 2 Merryhills Enterprise Park, Park Lane, Wolverhampton, WV10 9TJ Tel: (01902) 866116 Fax: (01902) 866117 E-mail: uksales@challengept.com

Motion Industries UK Ltd, Unit 2 Bracken Trade Park, Duners Lane, Bury, Lancashire, BL9 9QP Tel: 0161-705 1237 Fax: 0161-705 1239E-mail: enquires@bearingsuppliers.co.uk

Pix Europe Ltd, Unit 24 Farthing Road Industrial Estate, Sproughton, Ipswich, IP1 5AP Tel: (01473) 744612 Fax: (01473) 744613 E-mail: info@pixeuro.com

R G Wylie & Co. Ltd, Vanguard Way, Shoeburyness, Southend-on-Sea, SS3 9QY Tel: (01702) 296751 Fax: (01702) 297560 E-mail: rg.wylie@dtconect.com

Whitaker Transmissions, 2 Heys Lane, Oswaldtwistle, Accrington, Lancashire, BB5 3BJ Tel: (01254) 382791 Fax: (01254) 239062

BENCH DRILLING MACHINES

D B Keighley Machinery Ltd, Vickers Place, Stanningley, Pudsey, West Yorkshire, LS28 6LZ Tel: 0113-257 4176 Fax: 0113-257 4293 E-mail: sales@dbkeighley.co.uk

BENCH SEATING

Garran Lockers Ltd, Garran House, Nantgarw Road, Caerphilly, Mid Glamorgan, CF83 1AQ Tel: (0845) 6588600 Fax: (0845) 6588601 E-mail: garran@garran-lockers.co.uk

Stacarac UK Ltd, Industrial Estate, Steeple Road, Mayland, Chelmsford, CM3 6AX Tel: (01621) 741250 Fax: (01621) 742768 E-mail: sales@stacarac.com

BENDING SERVICES, *See also headings for particular types*

Bristol Bending Sanoh Ltd, Fourth Way, Bristol, BS11 8DL Tel: 0117-982 8260 Fax: 0117-982 2040

Garwards Engineering, 8 Progress Way, Mid Suffolk Business Park, Eye, Suffolk, IP23 7HU Tel: (01379) 871337 Fax: (01379) 873041 E-mail: gareth@garwards.com

BENTONITE

Minelco, 3 Riverside Business Centre, Brighton Road, Shoreham-by-Sea, West Sussex, BN43 6RE Tel: (01273) 452331 Fax: (01273) 464741 E-mail: info@minelco.com

Minilco Specialities Ltd, Bowesfield Industrial Estate, Bowesfield Lane, Stockton-on-Tees, Cleveland, TS18 3HJ Tel: (01642) 674375 Fax: (01642) 614379

Steetley Bentonite & Absorbents Ltd, Woburn Road, Woburn Sands, Milton Keynes, MK17 8TU Tel: (01908) 583939 Fax: (01908) 585231

BENZOLE

Koppers UK Ltd, Normanby Gateway, Lysaghts Way, Scunthorpe, North Lincolnshire, DN15 9YG Tel: (01724) 281555 Fax: (01724) 281343 E-mail: kuk@koppers-eu.com

BERYLLIUM COPPER PRESSINGS

C Brandauer & Co. Ltd, 235 Bridge Street West, Birmingham, B19 2YU Tel: 0121-359 2822 Fax: 0121-359 2836 E-mail: aedwards@brandauer.co.uk

BERYLLIUM COPPER SPRINGS

S D Precision, 3 Stevenage Enterprise Centre, Orchard Road, Stevenage, Hertfordshire, SG1 3HH Tel: (01438) 361587 Fax: (01438) 721217 E-mail: sales@sdprecision.co.uk

BERYLLIUM OXIDE

C & T Fire, Stammerham Business Centre, Capel Road, Rusper, Horsham, West Sussex, RH12 4PZ Tel: (01306) 712421 Fax: (01306) 713225 E-mail: info@ctfire.co.uk

CBL Ceramics, Marble Hall Road, Milford Haven, Dyfed, SA73 2PP Tel: (01646) 697681 Fax: (01646) 690053

BEVEL GEARBOXES

Bonfiglioli UK Ltd, 3-5 Grosvenor Grange, Woolston, Warrington, WA1 4SF Tel: (01925) 852667 Fax: (01925) 852668 E-mail: sales@bonfiglioliuk.co.uk

Edgerton Gears Ltd, Park Square, Ossett, West Yorkshire, WF5 0JS Tel: (01924) 273193 Fax: (01924) 275560

BEVEL GEARS

Guest Gear Services, Higham Mead, Higham Road, Chesham, Buckinghamshire, HP5 2AF Tel: (01494) 794667 Fax: (01494) 794668 E-mail: guestgears@yahoo.com

Kingsway Engineering Ltd., Hanham Road, Bristol, BS15 8PX Tel: 0117-961 3168 Fax: 0117-960 4718 E-mail: sales@kingswayengineering.co.uk

The Reid Gear Co., Napier Street, Linwood, Paisley, Renfrewshire, PA3 3AN Tel: (01505) 321591 Fax: (01505) 321645 E-mail: info@reidgear.com

Shaw Gears, Unit 5 Duchess St Industrial Estate, Shaw, Oldham, OL2 7UX Tel: (01706) 847220 Fax: (01706) 847220

WMH Transmissions Ltd, Lichfield Road Industrial Estate, 24 Cavendish, Tamworth, Staffordshire, B79 7XH Tel: (01827) 310311 Fax: (01827) 307118 E-mail: sales@wmh-trans.co.uk

Woollacott Gears Ltd, Llay Hall Industrial Estate, Cefn-Y-Bedd, Wrexham, Clwyd, LL12 9YG Tel: (01978) 761848 Fax: (01978) 762340

BEVELLED MIRRORS

Designer Mirrors, Unit 11, Slingsby Close, Attleborough Fields Industrial Estate, Nuneaton, Warwickshire, CV11 6RP Tel: (024) 7664 1206 Fax: (024) 7664 1260

JP Glass & Decor Ltd, 3 Eastcote Industrial Estate, Field End Road, Ruislip, Middlesex, HA4 9XG Tel: (020) 8429 2999 Fax: (020) 8868 4314 E-mail: sales@jpglass.com

Mawby & King Ltd, Upperton Road, Leicester, LE2 7AY Tel: 0116-204 6000 Fax: 0116-204 6001 E-mail: sales@mawbyandking.co.uk

BEVERAGE FILLING MACHINES

P L F International, Riverside House Iconfield Park, Freshfields Road, Parkeston, Harwich, Essex, CO12 4EN Tel: (01255) 552994 Fax: (01255) 552995 E-mail: sales@plfinternational.com

BEVERAGE INDUSTRY PUMPS

Ferrier Pumps Ltd, Burlington Street, Leith, Edinburgh, EH6 5JL Tel: 0131-554 1200 Fax: 0131-553 1272 E-mail: edinburgh@ferrierpumps.co.uk

BEVERAGE MAKING WATER BOILERS

▶ Axon Enterprises Ltd, 8a & 8b St. Martins Street, Hereford, HR2 7RE Tel: (01432) 359906 Fax: (01432) 352436 E-mail: sales@axon-enterprises.co.uk

Bartlett Catering Equipment Ltd, 171 Camford Way, Luton, LU3 3AN Tel: (01582) 847462 Fax: (01582) 566172 E-mail: sales@bartlettcatering.com

Calomax Ltd, Lupton Avenue, Leeds, LS9 7DD Tel: 0113-249 6681 Fax: 0113-235 0358 E-mail: sales@calomax.co.uk

Instanta Ltd, Canning Road, Southport, Merseyside, PR9 7SN Tel: (01704) 501114 Fax: (01704) 501115 E-mail: info@instanta.com

BEVERAGE VENDING MACHINES

▶ Allied Machine Sales, 23 Saxton Lane, Saxton, Tadcaster, North Yorkshire, LS24 9QD Tel: (01937) 558560 Fax: (01937) 558642 E-mail: info@alliedmachines.co.uk

Brupac Drinks & Machine Co. Ltd, 147a Richmond Road, Crewe, CW1 4AX Tel: (01270) 587700 Fax: (01270) 501129 E-mail: sales@brupac.co.uk

Bunzl Vending Services Ltd, 19 Aintree Road, Greenford, Middlesex, UB6 7LG Tel: (020) 8998 2828 Fax: (020) 8998 0704 E-mail: enquiries@bunzlvend.com

Care Vending Services Ltd, Unit 16 Gunnels Wood Park, Gunnels Wood Road, Stevenage, Hertfordshire, SG1 2BH Tel: (01438) 760600 Fax: (01438) 760602 E-mail: sales@carevending.co.uk

Cooler Co., Enterprise Road, Raunds, Wellingborough, Northamptonshire, NN9 6JE Tel: (01933) 461046 Fax: (01933) 624494 E-mail: info@coolercompany.co.uk

Falkingham & Taylor (Vending) Ltd, 40-50 New Cleveland St, Hull, HU8 7EX Tel: (01482) 320600 Fax: (01482) 585766 E-mail: sales@st-vending.com

Incup Soft Drinks, Unit 2d Drum Industrial Estate, Chester le Street, County Durham, DH2 1SS Tel: (07966) 733394 Fax: 0191-492 0394 E-mail: sales@incupdrinks.com

Jede North East, Unit B4, Benfield Business Park, Benfield Road, Newcastle Upon Tyne, NE6 4NQ Tel: 0191-238 8000 Fax: 0191-238 8001 E-mail: jede.uk@jede.com

Local Vending Ltd, The Old Vicarage, St Johns Road, Ilkeston, Derbyshire, DE7 5PA Tel: 0115-930 8550

Manchester Vending Services Ltd, Alpha Point, Bradnor Road, Manchester, M22 4TE Tel: 0161-945 2030 E-mail: info@manvend.com

S A W Technologies Ltd, Express Works, Church St, Irthlingborough, Wellingborough, Northants, NN9 5SE Tel: 01933 653005 Fax: 01933 653391

Westomatic Vending Systems Ltd, Shaldon Road, Newton Abbot, Devon, TQ12 4TZ Tel: (01626) 323100 Fax: (01626) 332828 E-mail: mailbox@westomatic.com

BEVERAGES, *See also headings for particular types*

▶ Black Seal UK, Smallfield Road, Horne, Horley, Surrey, RH6 9JP Tel: (07932) 782435 E-mail: bermuda@blackseal.co.uk

Cater Direct Ltd, Unit 6 Pasadena Close, Hayes, Middlesex, UB3 3NQ Tel: (020) 8561 7706 Fax: (020) 8561 7748 E-mail: info@caterdirect.co.uk

Firefly Tonics Ltd, 1 Petersham Mews, London, SW7 5NR Tel: (020) 7052 9720 Fax: (020) 7052 9729 E-mail: info@fireflytonics.com

Q V S Fruits, 106 Firle Road, Eastbourne, East Sussex, BN22 8ES Tel: (01323) 737323 Fax: (01323) 737313

▶ Suncrest, Unit B Britannia Trading Estate, Printing House Lane, Hayes, Middlesex, UB3 1AP Tel: (020) 8848 0099 Fax: (020) 8848 4990 E-mail: sales@suncrestdrinks.com

▶ Wine and Spirit International Ltd, 9th Floor Hyde House, Edgware Road, Hendon, London, NW9 6LH Tel: (020) 8975 1023 Fax: (020) 8975 1025 E-mail: sales@wineandspirit.com

BIAS BINDING

T G Lewis Ltd, 15 Staveley Way, Brixworth Industrial Estate, Brixworth, Northampton, NN6 9EU Tel: (01604) 881966 Fax: (01604) 882318

BICYCLE PARKING STANDS

Autocross Plastics, Units 26-27 New Hall Hey Business Park, New Hall Hey Road, Rossendale, Lancashire, BB4 6HL Tel: (01706) 216794 Fax: (01706) 230758 E-mail: bill@euroshel.com

Broxap Mawrob, 121A-125A Sefton Street, Southport, Merseyside, PR8 5DR Tel: (01704) 513330 Fax: (01704) 500380 E-mail: sales@broxap.co.uk

Claydon Architectural Ltd, 11-12 Claydon Industrial Park, Great Blakenham, Ipswich, IP6 0NL Tel: (01473) 831000 Fax: (01473) 832154 E-mail: sales@cam-ltd.co.uk

▶ Cycle Pods Ltd, Unit 5, Hortons Way, Westerham, Kent, TN16 1BT Tel: (01959) 562633 Fax: (0560) 1130219 E-mail: info@cyclepods.co.uk

▶ Cycle-works Ltd, 2 Rances Way, Winchester, Hampshire, SO22 4PN Tel: (023) 9281 5555 Fax: (023) 9281 5544 E-mail: info@cycle-works.com

Furnitubes International Ltd, Meridian House, Royal Hill, London, SE10 8RD Tel: (020) 8378 3200 Fax: (020) 8378 3250 E-mail: sales@furnitubes.com

Kestrel Engineering, 9 Dartmouth Buildings, Fort Fareham Industrial Site, Fareham, Hampshire, PO14 1AH Tel: (01329) 233443 Fax: (01329) 284148 E-mail: alan.s.walker@talk21.com

BID MANAGEMENT CONSULTANTS

▶ Practical Bid Solutions, Genesys Court, Denton Drive, Northwich, Cheshire, CW9 7LU Tel: (01606) 353870 Fax: (0870) 4215142 E-mail: chriswhyatt@pbsl.co.uk

BIDIRECTIONAL COUNTERS

A A Electric UK Ltd, Witty Street, Hull, HU3 4TT Tel: (01482) 229880 Fax: (01482) 589644 E-mail: sales@aaelectric.co.uk

BIFURCATED FANS

Nuaire Group, Western Indust Estate, Caerphilly, Mid Glamorgan, CF83 1BQ Tel: (029) 2088 5911 Fax: (029) 2088 7033 E-mail: info@nuaire.co.uk

R H F Fans Ltd, 2 Ferrous Way, Irlam, Manchester, M44 5FS Tel: 0161-776 6400 Fax: 0161-775 6566 E-mail: sales@rhf-fans.co.uk

BIG BORE OIL COUNTRY LATHES

Charter Engineering Services, 6 Sycamore Centre, Sycamore Road, Eastwood Trading Estate, Rotherham, South Yorkshire, S65 1EN Tel: (01709) 836822 Fax: (01709) 836955 E-mail: sales@chartmach.co.uk

BILLET CASTING MACHINES

Vai UK Ltd, 7 Fudan Way, Thornaby, Stockton-on-Tees, Cleveland, TS17 6ER Tel: (01642) 662100 Fax: (01642) 606569 E-mail: contact@vai.co.uk

BILLET HEATING FURNACES

RADYNE, Molly Millars Lane, Wokingham, Berks, RG41 2PX Tel: 0118-978 3333 Fax: 0118-977 1729 E-mail: sales@radyne.co.uk

BILLIARD OR SNOOKER TABLE LIGHTING

B & W Billiards & Snooker Services Ltd, Unit 3 Sapcote Trading Centre, Powke Lane, Old Hill, Cradley Heath, West Midlands, B64 5QR Tel: (01384) 638191 Fax: (01384) 638195 E-mail: sales@bandwbilliards.co.uk

BIMETALLIC MONOCONTACT THERMOSTATS

Isis Fluid Control Ltd, Station Yard The Leys, Chipping Norton, Oxfordshire, OX7 5HZ Tel: (01608) 645755 Fax: (01608) 645532 E-mail: sales@isis-fluid.com

BIMETALLIC THERMOSTAT STRIPS

Imphy Ugine Precision UK Ltd, Wessex Road, Bourne End, Buckinghamshire, SL8 5DT Tel: (01628) 850234 Fax: (01628) 850119
Kanthal Ltd, Canal Arm, Festival Way, Stoke-on-Trent, ST1 5UR Tel: (01782) 224800 Fax: (01782) 224820 E-mail: info.uk@kanthal.se

BIN WASHING EQUIPMENT

Techtrol Ltd, Gregson Road, Stockport, Cheshire, SK5 7SS Tel: 0161-476 6955 Fax: 0161-476 2674 E-mail: mailbox@techtrol.co.uk

BINDER COVERS, RING BINDER, PLASTIC/PVC

Ashton Seals Ltd, PO Box 1030, Barnsley, South Yorkshire, S73 0YP Tel: (01226) 273700 Fax: (01226) 756774 E-mail: sales@ashtonseals.com
Corstat Containers Ltd, Unit 7 Whitehill Industrial Estate, Whitehill Lane, Swindon, SN4 7DB Tel: (01793) 855168 Fax: (01793) 855209 E-mail: enquiries@corstat.co.uk
Nolene Ltd, Brunel Road, Newton Abbot, Devon, TQ12 4PB Tel: (01626) 333800 Fax: (01626) 368168 E-mail: info@nolene.co.uk
Tennant PVC Ltd, Unit A Meadow Grove, Meadow Lane, Nottingham, NG2 3HF Tel: 0115-934 0950 Fax: 0115-934 0955 E-mail: sales@tennantpvc.co.uk

BINDING MACHINE/ ACCESSORIES DISTRIBUTORS OR AGENTS

Bennett, 1 Iremonger Road, Off London Road, Nottingham, NG2 3BL Tel: 0115-955 8000 Fax: 0115-955 8008 E-mail: sales@bennittsykes.co.uk
Bookcraft Supplies, Kennedy Way, Green Lane, Stockport, Cheshire, SK4 2JX Tel: 0161-480 2118 Fax: 0161-480 3679 E-mail: info@fjratchford.co.uk
Kolbus UK Ltd, 35 Heathfield, Stacey Bushes, Milton Keynes, MK12 6HR Tel: (01908) 317878 Fax: (01908) 310863 E-mail: sales@kolbus.co.uk
Single Source Binding Ltd, 223 East India Dock Road, London, E14 0ED Tel: (020) 7515 0539 Fax: (020) 7537 9839 E-mail: sales@single-source.co.uk

BINGO TICKET PRINTING

Thurston, Clare House, 46-48 St. Anne Street, Liverpool, L3 3DW Tel: 0151-482 2700 Fax: 0151-298 1134 E-mail: thurston@eaclare.co.uk

BINOCULAR CAMERAS

Sino West Business Consultancy Ltd, 32 William Bristow Road, Coventry, CV3 5LQ Tel: (024) 7650 2465 Fax: (024) 7650 3215 E-mail: enquiry@sinowest.co.uk

BINOCULARS

▶ Action Optics, 16 Butts Ash Gardens, Hythe, Southampton, SO45 3BL Tel: (023) 8084 2801 Fax: (023) 8084 2801 E-mail: richard@actionoptics.co.uk
▶ GX Optical, Cherry Gardens Industrial Estate, Helions Bumpstead Road, Haverhill, Suffolk, CB9 7AA Tel: 01440 714737 Fax: 01440 709421 E-mail: eurosales@gxoptical.com
David Hinds Ltd, Unit B Chiltern Industrial Estate, Grovebury Road, Leighton Buzzard, Bedfordshire, LU7 4TU Tel: (01525) 852696 Fax: (0844) 170588 E-mail: astro@dhinds.co.uk
In Focus Ltd, Wild Fowl Trust Newgrounds, Slimbridge, Gloucester, GL2 7BT Tel: (01453) 890978 Fax: (01453) 890267 E-mail: infocus@netcomuk.co.uk
Monk Optics Ltd, Wye Valley Observatory, The Old School, Brockweir, Chepstow, Gwent, NP16 7NW Tel: (01291) 689858 Fax: (01291) 689834 E-mail: advice@monkoptics.co.uk
▶ Newton Ellis & Co, 29 Cheapside, Liverpool, L2 2DY Tel: 0151-236 1391 E-mail: info@newtonellis.co.uk
Olympus UK Ltd, 2-8 Honduras St, London, EC1Y 0TX Tel: (020) 7253 2772 Fax: (020) 7251 6330 E-mail: info@olympus.uk.com
Optical Vision Ltd, Unit 3 Woolpit Business Park, Windmill Avenue, Woolpit, Bury St. Edmunds, Suffolk, IP30 9UP Tel: (01359) 244200 Fax: (01359) 244255 E-mail: info@opticalvision.co.uk
Simden Optical Ltd, Haugh Lane, Blaydon-on-Tyne, Tyne & Wear, NE21 4SA Tel: 0191-499 0122 Fax: 0191-414 4723
Stockport Binocular & Telescope Centre, Mercian Way, Stockport, Cheshire, SK3 9DF Tel: 0161-429 8002 Fax: 0161-474 0440 E-mail: tloptics@aol.com
Viking Optical Ltd, Blyth Road, Halesworth, Suffolk, IP19 8EN Tel: (01986) 875315 Fax: (01986) 874788 E-mail: viking@vikingoptical.co.uk
Watchers Binoculars & Telescopes, Devonshire Place, Kents Bank Road, Grange-over-Sands, Cumbria, LA11 7HF Tel: (01539) 535910 E-mail: watcherswildlife@aol.com

BINS, RECYCLING, PLASTIC

▶ Auto Plas UK Ltd, 10 Edgware Grove Winstanley, Wigan, Lancashire, WN3 6EF Tel: (01942) 217209 Fax: 01942 218720 E-mail: info@autoplasuk.co.uk
▶ Home Recycling Ltd, Bulton Brow, Sowerbry, Ingleby Barwick, Sowerby Bridge, West Yorkshire, HX6 2AG Tel: (0845) 6123191 Fax: (0845) 6123292 E-mail: sales@homerecycling.co.uk

BIO-ENERGETIC HEALTHCARE PRODUCTS

▶ The Bio-Energy Clinic, Maritime House, 14 - 16 Balls Road, Oxton, Birkenhead, Merseyside, CH43 5RE Tel: (07930) 933960 Fax: (0845) 8380793 E-mail: info@oxtonltd.com
▶ Bioresonance Therapy Centre, St. Justins Close, Orpington, Kent, BR5 3LU Tel: (01689) 834405 E-mail: bioresonancetherapycentre@yahoo.co.uk
▶ Health Haven, 173 Findon Road, Worthing, West Sussex, BN14 0BQ Tel: (01903) 877717 E-mail: info@health-haven.com
▶ Magnets4Life - Bioflow / Ecoflow Distributor, Manorcroft, School Road, Rayne, Braintree, Essex, CM77 6SR Tel: 01376 349993 Fax: 01376 349991 E-mail: vanessa@magnets4life.com
▶ Mediscot Online, 65 Oakbank Drive, Cumnock, Ayrshire, KA18 1BA Tel: (01290) 426438 Fax: (01563) 521077 E-mail: info@mediscot.co.uk

BIO-FUEL PROCESSING SERVICES

Harris Tobias Ltd, 3 Station Road, Stansted, Essex, CM24 8BE Tel: (01279) 647164 Fax: (01279) 647038 E-mail: info@harristobias.com

BIOCHEMICAL PREPARATIONS

Biozyme Holdings Ltd, Tnit 6 Gilchrist Thomas Estate, Bleanavon, Pontypool, Gwent, NP4 9RL Tel: (01495) 790678 Fax: (01495) 791780 E-mail: sales@biozyme.co.uk
Serotec Ltd, Unit 22 Bankside, Station Approach, Kidlington, Oxfordshire, OX5 1JE Tel: (01865) 852700 Fax: (01865) 373899 E-mail: sales@serotec.co.uk

BIOCIDAL CHEMICAL PRODUCTS/BIOCIDES

Agma Ltd, Gemini Works, Haltwhistle, Northumberland, NE49 9HA Tel: (01434) 320598 Fax: (01434) 321650 E-mail: enquiries@agma.co.uk
Bin UK Ltd, Prince Street, Bolton, BL1 2NP Tel: (01204) 366997 Fax: (01204) 366998 E-mail: uk_sales@binkemi.com
Feedwater Ltd, Tarran Road, Tarran Industrial Estate, Wirral, Merseyside, CH46 4TU Tel: 0151-606 0808 Fax: 0151-678 5459 E-mail: enquiries@feedwater.co.uk
Hawks Chemical Co. Ltd, 2 Tower Street, Hyde, Cheshire, SK14 1JW Tel: 0161-367 9441 Fax: 0161-367 9443 E-mail: sales@hawks-chem.com
Quatchem Chemicals Ltd, 1 Victoria Trading Estate, Drury Lane, Chadderton, Oldham, OL9 7PJ Tel: 0161-947 0177 Fax: 0161-947 0180 E-mail: sales@quatchem.co.uk
Rhodia Sealants Ltd, 4 Pomeroy Drive, Oadby, Leicester, LE2 5NE Tel: 0116-206 3400 Fax: 0116-206 3460 E-mail: rhodia.sealants@eu.rohodia.com
Thor Specialities UK Ltd, Wincham Avenue, Wincham, Northwich, Cheshire, CW9 6GB Tel: (01606) 818800 Fax: (01606) 818801 E-mail: info@thor.com

BIOCIDES, WATER TREATMENT

▶ Allied Industrial Services, 1 Withensfield, Wallasey, Merseyside, CH45 7NP Tel: 0151-734 4242 Fax: 0151-734 4242
▶ Cleartech Water Solutions, 1 Howard Court, East Kilbride, Glasgow, G74 4QZ Tel: (01355) 267199 Fax: (01355) 267109 E-mail: info@cleartechwater.co.uk

BIODEGRADABLE PACKAGING

Stanelco R F Technologies, Marchwood Industrial Park, Marchwood, Southampton, SO40 4PB Tel: (023) 8086 7100 Fax: (023) 8086 7070 E-mail: sales@stanelco.co.uk
Suface Specialists P.L.C., Bath Road, Bridgwater, Somerset, TA6 4PA Tel: (01278) 424321 Fax: (01278) 421999
Symphony Plastic Technologies Plc, Elstree House, Elstree Way, Borehamwood, Hertfordshire, WD6 1LE Tel: (020) 8207 5900 Fax: (020) 8207 5960 E-mail: sales@degradable.net

BIODIESEL ANALYSIS

▶ Intertek Caleb Brett Ltd, Rossmore Industrial Estate, Rosscliffe Road, Ellesmere Port, CH65 3BS Tel: 0151-355 2005 Fax: 0151-355 2006 E-mail: uklaboratory@intertek.com
▶ Intertek Caleb Brett, Caleb Brett House, 734 London Road, West Thurrock, Grays, Essex, RM20 3NL Tel: (01708) 680200 Fax: (01708) 680264 E-mail: uklaboratory@intertek.com
▶ Intertek Caleb Brett Ltd, Seal Sands, Middlesbrough, Cleveland, TS2 1UB Tel: (01642) 546669 E-mail: cbopperation.teeside@intertek.com
▶ Intertek Testing Services U K Ltd, Avonmouth Dock, Bristol, BS11 9DH Tel: 0117-982 4807 Fax: 0117-982 2290 E-mail: cb.avonmouth@intertek.com
▶ Intertek Testing Services (U K) Ltd, Western Jetty, Immingham Dock, Immingham, South Humberside, DN40 2NT Tel: (01469) 572353 Fax: (01469) 571197 E-mail: uklaboratory@intertek.com

BIODIESEL FUEL TESTING

▶ Intertek Caleb Brett Ltd, Rossmore Industrial Estate, Rosscliffe Road, Ellesmere Port, CH65 3BS Tel: 0151-355 2005 Fax: 0151-355 2006 E-mail: uklaboratory@intertek.com
▶ Intertek Caleb Brett, Caleb Brett House, 734 London Road, West Thurrock, Grays, Essex, RM20 3NL Tel: (01708) 680200 Fax: (01708) 680264 E-mail: uklaboratory@intertek.com
▶ Intertek Caleb Brett Ltd, Seal Sands, Middlesbrough, Cleveland, TS2 1UB Tel: (01642) 546669 E-mail: cbopperation.teeside@intertek.com
▶ Intertek Testing Services U K Ltd, Avonmouth Dock, Bristol, BS11 9DH Tel: 0117-982 4807 Fax: 0117-982 2290 E-mail: cb.avonmouth@intertek.com
▶ Intertek Testing Services (U K) Ltd, Western Jetty, Immingham Dock, Immingham, South Humberside, DN40 2NT Tel: (01469) 572353 Fax: (01469) 571197 E-mail: uklaboratory@intertek.com

BIOFUELS

▶ Bioroute Ltd, Flint House, 25 Charing Cross, Norwich, NR2 4AX Tel: (01603) 724714 Fax: (01603) 724700 E-mail: biodiesel@bioroute.co.uk

BIOLOGICAL DRAIN MAINTENANCE

Cleveland Biotech Ltd, 3 Vanguard Court, Preston Farm Business Pk, Stockton-on-Tees, Cleveland, TS18 3TR Tel: (01642) 606606 Fax: (01642) 606040 E-mail: bugs@clevebio.com
Hodge Separators Ltd, 1 Jennings Road, Kernick Road Industrial Estate, Penryn, Cornwall, TR10 9LY Tel: (01326) 375388 Fax: (01326) 377235 E-mail: sales@hodge-separators.com
▶ K G Drain Services Ltd, Woodlands Drive, Hoddesdon, Hertfordshire, EN11 8AZ Tel: (01992) 470203 Fax: (01992) 470204 E-mail: mail@kgdrains.co.uk

BIOLOGICAL PRODUCTS

Cleveland Biotech Ltd, 3 Vanguard Court, Preston Farm Business Pk, Stockton-on-Tees, Cleveland, TS18 3TR Tel: (01642) 606606 Fax: (01642) 606040 E-mail: bugs@clevebio.com
Field International UK, Unit 5 Gordleton Farm, Silver Street, Sway, Lymington, Hampshire, SO41 6DJ Tel: (01425) 628075 Fax: (01425) 628570 E-mail: peter@fieldsupplies.demon.co.uk
Koppert, Unit 8, 53 Hollands Road, Haverhill, Suffolk, CB9 8PJ Tel: (01440) 704488 Fax: (01440) 704487 E-mail: info@koppert.co.uk
Microbial Developments Ltd, Spring La North, Malvern, Worcestershire, WR14 1BU Tel: (01684) 891055 Fax: (01684) 891060 E-mail: info@micdev.com
Millipore UK Ltd, Fleming Road, Kirkton Campus, Livingston, West Lothian, EH54 7BN Tel: (01506) 404000 Fax: (01506) 404001 E-mail:

BIOMEDICAL INSTRUMENTATION

Biohit, Unit 1 Barton Hill Way, Torquay, TQ2 8JG Tel: (01803) 315900 Fax: (01803) 315530

BIOREMEDIATION OIL ABSORBENTS

Hanson Support Services, Scotter Road South, Bottesford, Scunthorpe, South Humberside, DN17 2BU Tel: (01724) 842637 Fax: (01724) 282411 E-mail: enquiries@hanserve.com

BIOREMEDIATION TECHNICAL SERVICES

SA&R plc, Brickfield House, High Road, Thornwood, Epping, Essex, CM16 6TH Tel: 0845 331 2426 Fax: 0845 331 2427 E-mail: info@sarplc.com
Sanctus Training, Sanctus House, Nympsfield, Stonehouse, Gloucestershire, GL10 3UP Tel: (01453) 828222 Fax: (01453) 827915 E-mail: info@sanctusltd.co.uk
▶ V H E Construction P.L.C., Phoenix House, 6 Hawthorn Park, Coal Road, Leeds, LS14 1PQ Tel: 0113 273 9200 Fax: 0113 273 9202 E-mail: s.maloney@construction.vhe.co.uk

BIOSCIENCE RESEARCH CONSULTANCY

▶ Quantech Solutions, Howe Farm, Malton, North Yorkshire, YO17 6RG Tel: (01653) 694490 Fax: (01653) 694490 E-mail: sam.hoste@quantechsolutions.co.uk

BIOTECHNOLOGICAL PLANT/ EQUIPMENT/SYSTEMS

Applied Biosystems, Lingley House, 120 Birchwood Boulevard, Birchwood, Warrington, WA3 7QH Tel: (01925) 825650 Fax: (01925) 282502 E-mail: abdirect@eur.apliedbiosystems.com
Brighton Systems Ltd, Unit 24 Euro Business Park, New Road, Newhaven, East Sussex, BN9 0DQ Tel: (01273) 515563 Fax: (01273) 611533 E-mail: sales@brightonsystems.co.uk
Hickey & Co. Ltd, Slade Green Road, Erith, Kent, DA8 2HX Tel: (01322) 347004 Fax: (01322) 335733 E-mail: sales@hickey.co.uk

BIOTECHNOLOGICAL PLANT/ EQUIPMENT/SYSTEMS COMPONENTS

William Lillico & Son Ltd, Wonham Mill, Betchworth, Surrey, RH3 7AD Tel: (01737) 247666 Fax: (01737) 246783
Swagelock London, Unit 11, Kingley Park, Station Road, Kings Langley, Hertfordshire, WD4 8GW Tel: (020) 8200 1677 Fax: (020) 8200 9819 E-mail: info@london.swagelock.com

BIOTECHNOLOGICAL RESEARCH AND DEVELOPMENT

Bibra International Ltd, Woodmansterne Road, Carshalton, Surrey, SM5 4DS Tel: (020) 8652 1000 Fax: (020) 8661 7029 E-mail: help@bibra.co.uk
Cobra Therapeutics Ltd, The Science Park, University of Keele, Keele, Newcastle, Staffordshire, ST5 5SP Tel: (01782) 714181 Fax: (01782) 714168
PPL Therapeutics plc, High Street, Roslin, Midlothian, EH25 9PP Tel: 0131-440 4777 Fax: 0131-440 4888 E-mail: info@ppl-therapeutics.com
Severn Biotech Ltd, 2 Park Lane Industrial Estate, Stourport Road, Kidderminster, Worcestershire, DY11 6TJ Tel: (01562) 825286 Fax: (01562) 825284 E-mail: admin@severnbiotech.com
Xenova, 310 Science Park, Milton Road, Cambridge, CB4 0WG Tel: (01223) 423413 Fax: (01223) 423458 E-mail: sales@xenova.co.uk

BIOTECHNOLOGY CONSULTANTS

I B A Associates, Dorford House, Perks Lane, Prestwood, Great Missenden, Buckinghamshire, HP16 0JD Tel: (01494) 865393 Fax: (01494) 865395 E-mail: miranda@ibaassociates.co.uk
B W P Technical Services Ltd, 543 Wallisdown Road, Poole, Dorset, BH12 5AD Tel: (01202) 546733 Fax: (01202) 546733 E-mail: info@hats.org.uk

BIRD BATHS

Longacres Nursery, London Road, Bagshot, Surrey, GU19 5JB Tel: (01276) 476778 Fax: (01276) 452779 E-mail: landscape@longacres.co.uk

BIRD CONTROL NETS

John Dee Humane Traps, 4 Russett Cottage, Greendale Barton, Woodbury Salterton, Exeter, EX5 1EW Tel: (01395) 233340 Fax: (01395) 233548 E-mail: desmo1@btopenworld.com
Dynamic Access, Dairy Bungalow, Sodom Lane, Dauntsey, Chippenham, Wiltshire, SN15 4JA Tel: (01249) 891878 Fax: (01249) 891878 E-mail: storm@pgen.net
Woodland Flyscreen & Bird Exclusion Products, 73a Kennel Ride, Ascot, Berkshire, SL5 7NU Tel: (01344) 886459 Fax: (01344) 886459

BIRD CONTROL SYSTEMS

▶ Breedmax.co.uk, PO Box 7774, Harlow, Essex, CM18 6WJ Tel: (01279) 324509 E-mail: sales@breedmax.co.uk

BIRD DETERRENT GELS

Hygiene Pest Control, 300 City Road, Sheffield, S2 5HQ Tel: 0114-272 2926 Fax: 0114-275 3776
Vermikil Pest Control Services Ltd, PO Box 3049, Romford, RM3 7BQ Tel: (0800) 0568834 Fax: (0800) 0568835 E-mail: contacts@vermikil.com
▶ West Yorkshire Property Development Corporation Ltd, The Drill Hall 56 Leeds Road, Ilkley, West Yorkshire, LS29 8EQ Tel: (01535) 670033 E-mail: info@verminix.co.uk

BIRD FEED

▶ Breedmax.co.uk, PO Box 7774, Harlow, Essex, CM18 6WJ Tel: (01279) 324509 E-mail: sales@breedmax.co.uk

BIRD FOODS

▶ Breedmax.co.uk, PO Box 7774, Harlow, Essex, CM18 6WJ Tel: (01279) 324509 E-mail: sales@breedmax.co.uk
▶ MIDLAND PARROTS, 160 Crescent Road, Hugglescote, Coalville, Leicestershire, LE67 2BD Tel: 01530 451682 Fax: 01530 451682 E-mail: info@midland-parrots.com

BIRD REPELLENT SYSTEMS

Peter Cox Ltd, 53 Cuckoo Road, Birmingham, B7 5SY Tel: 0121-326 6434 Fax: 0121-326 7242 E-mail: petercox.birmingham@ecolab.com
▶ Peter Cox Ltd, Suite 5, Keynes House, Alfreton Road, Derby, DE21 4AS Tel: (01332) 299222 Fax: (01332) 200066
▶ Peter Cox Ltd, Unit 1, Marybank Lane, Dundee, DD2 3DY Tel: (01382) 400242 Fax: (01382) 400262 E-mail: petercox.dundee@ecolab.com
▶ Peter Cox Ltd, John O Gaunts Trading Estate, Leeds Road, Rothwell, Leeds, LS26 0JB Tel: 0113-282 5316 Fax: 0113-393 4927 E-mail: petercox.leeds@ecolab.com
▶ Peter Cox Ltd, Unit M, Orchard Business Centre, St. Barnabas Close, Allington, Maidstone, Kent, ME16 0JZ Tel: (01622) 750081 Fax: (01622) 750083
Peter Cox Ltd, Unit 35, Viewforth Industrial Estate, The Loan, South Queensferry, West Lothian, EH30 9NS Tel: 0131-331 5030 Fax: 0131-319 1635 E-mail: peter.cox@ecolab.com
Peter Cox Ltd, Falcon House, Oakhurst Drive, Stockport, Cheshire, SK3 0XT Tel: 0161-491 3181 Fax: 0161-428 8138
Ecolab Ltd, Caerphilly Business Park, Caerphilly, Mid Glamorgan, CF83 3ED Tel: (029) 2085 2000 Fax: (029) 2086 5969
▶ Ecolab Pest Control Ltd, Falcon House, Lawnhurst Industrial Estate, Stockport, Cheshire, SK3 0XT Tel: 0161-491 3855 Fax: 0161 491 6088
▶ Ecolab Pest Prevention, Unit 47 Clifton Industrial Estate, Cherry Hinton Road, Cambridge, CB1 7ED Tel: (01223) 211303 Fax: (01223) 215151
Ecolab Pest Prevention, John O Gaunts Trading Estate, Leeds Road, Rothwell, Leeds, LS26 0JB Tel: 0113 288 7787 Fax: 0113 282 1298
▶ Ecolab Pest Prevention, Unit 5, Waterside Court, Bone Lane, Newbury, Berkshire, RG14 5SH Tel: (01635) 524780 Fax: (01635) 524761
▶ Ecolab Pest Prevention, 146 Moor Lane, Preston, PR1 1JR Tel: (01772) 563303 Fax: (01772) 561106
▶ Ecolab Services Ltd, Unit 11 Prideaux Close, Tamar View Industrial Estate, Saltash, Cornwall, PL12 6LD Tel: (01752) 841842 Fax: (01752) 840700
▶ Peter Cox Ltd, Unit 10, Avon Riverside Estate, Victoria Road, Avonmouth, Bristol, BS11 9DB Tel: 0117 938 7130 Fax: 0117 938 7137
Peter Cox Ltd, Unit 17, Engineer Park, Sandycroft, Deeside, Clwyd, CH5 2QB Tel: (01244) 538610 Fax: (01244) 534720
▶ Peter Cox, Unit 11d Station Approach, Team Valley Trading Estate, Gateshead, Tyne & Wear, NE11 0ZF Tel: 0191-487 2293 Fax: 0191-487 4804 E-mail: petercox.newcastle@ecolab.com
▶ Peter Cox Ltd, St. Andrews House, 385 Hillington Road, Hillington Industrial Estate, Glasgow, G52 4BL Tel: 0141 810 9100 Fax: 0141 810 9111
▶ Peter Cox Ltd, 103 Sadler Road, Lincoln, LN6 3RS Tel: (01522) 500214 Fax: (01522) 688838
▶ Peter Cox Ltd, 209 Century Buildings, Summers Road, Brunswick Business Park, Liverpool, L3 4BL Tel: 0151 709 1090 Fax: 0151 708 5304
▶ Peter Cox Ltd, 62h Lord Avenue, Thornaby, Stockton-on-Tees, Cleveland, TS17 9JX Tel: (01642) 769983 Fax: (01642) 769421

BIRD SEED

J E Haith Ltd, Park Street, Cleethorpes, South Humberside, DN35 7LX Tel: (01472) 357515 Fax: (01472) 242883E-mail: sales@haith.com

BIRD SUPPLIES

▶ MIDLAND PARROTS, 160 Crescent Road, Hugglescote, Coalville, Leicestershire, LE67 2BD Tel: 01530 451682 Fax: 01530 451682 E-mail: info@midland-parrots.com

BIRD TABLES

Longacres Nursery, London Road, Bagshot, Surrey, GU19 5JB Tel: (01276) 476778 Fax: (01276) 452779 E-mail: landscape@longacres.co.uk

BIRTHDAY CARDS

▶ Balloon Celebration (A), 1 Mill Lane, Broxbourne, Hertfordshire, EN10 7AZ Tel: (01992) 467555 Fax: (01920) 872719 E-mail: sales@aballooncelebration.co.uk
▶ Durrants English Wedding Collection, 6 Trevitt Close, Sleaford, Lincolnshire, NG34 8BT Tel: (01529) 302530 Fax: (01529) 302530 E-mail: info@englishweddingcollection.co.uk
▶ Knotweed Creations, 6 High Street, Bluntisham, Huntingdon, Cambridgeshire, PE28 3LD Tel: (01487) 842033 E-mail: andrea@knotweedcreations.co.uk
▶ Personal Touch, Unit 1 Moorgate, Ormskirk, Lancashire, L39 4RT Tel: (07966) 711459 Fax: 0151 2932008 E-mail: suedelane@blueyonder.co.uk

BISCUIT MACHINERY

Robinsons, Charlton House East Service Road, Raynesway, Spondon, Derby, DE21 7BF Tel: (01332) 679898 Fax: (01332) 671717 E-mail: tony@wsrobinson.com
▶ Taylor Made Machinery Ltd, 3A Canal Wharf, Station Road, Langley, Slough, SL3 6EG Tel: (01753) 591433 Fax: (01753) 591441 E-mail: sales@tmm-uk.com

BISCUITS

Bahlsen Ltd, Hannover House, Packhorse Road, Gerrards Cross, Buckinghamshire, SL9 7QE Tel: (01753) 889822 Fax: (01753) 889786
Brummells Foods Ltd, Old Ryes, Stebbing Green, Stebbing, Dunmow, Essex, CM6 3TE Tel: (01371) 856880
Burtons Foods Ltd, P O Box 39, Blackpool, FY3 7AN Tel: (01253) 394133 Fax: (01253) 300238
Campbell's Shortbread, Ancaster Square, Callander, Perthshire, FK17 8BL Tel: (01877) 330013 Fax: (01877) 331290 E-mail: sales@campbellsshortbread.co.uk
Dean's Of Huntly Ltd, Depot Road, Huntly, Aberdeenshire, AB54 8JX Tel: (01466) 792086 Fax: (01466) 792895 E-mail: sales@deans.co.uk
Farmhouse Biscuits Ltd, Brook Street, Nelson, Lancashire, BB9 9PX Tel: (01282) 613520 Fax: (01282) 694796 E-mail: sales@farmhouse-biscuits.co.uk
Fox Hill Foods, Barton Hall, Hardy Street, Eccles, Manchester, M30 7SB Tel: 0161-789 6315 Fax: 0161-787 8068
Fox's Biscuits, Wellington Street, Batley, West Yorkshire, WF17 5JE Tel: (01924) 444333 Fax: (01924) 470200
Fox's Biscuits, Dove Valley Bakeries, Cheadle Road, Uttoxeter, Staffordshire, ST14 7BT Tel: (01889) 563131 Fax: (01889) 565379 E-mail: sales@elkes-biscuits.co.uk
G C Cones, 39 Ennis Road, Redcar, Cleveland, TS10 5JY Tel: (01642) 471988 Fax: (01642) 471988
Heatherslaw Bakery, Heatherslaw Mill, Cornhill-on-Tweed, Northumberland, TD12 4TJ Tel: (01890) 820208 Fax: (01890) 820208
Hill Biscuits Ltd, Smith Street, Ashton-Under-Lyne, Lancashire, OL7 0DB Tel: 0161-330 3617 Fax: 0161-343 2108
Mcvities, Victoria Biscuit Works, 35 Clydeford Drive, Glasgow, G32 8YW Tel: 0141-550 6800 Fax: 0141-554 8601
Mcvities Group Ltd, Waxlow Road, London, NW10 7NY Tel: (020) 8965 5787 Fax: (020) 8965 8496
Millies Retail Ltd, Unit 62, The Merry Hill Centre, Brierley Hill, W. Midlands, DY5 1SY Tel: (01384) 75475 Fax: (01384) 75475
O P Chocolate Ltd, High Street, Dowlais, Merthyr Tydfil, CF48 3TB Tel: (01685) 352560 Fax: (01685) 352599 E-mail: opchoc@cemoi.com
S H S International Ltd, 1 Stubley Lane, Dronfield, Derbyshire, S18 1PE Tel: (01246) 413294 Fax: (01246) 414002
Sharp & Nickless Ltd, 77 College Street, Long Eaton, Nottingham, NG10 4NN Tel: 0115-973 2169 Fax: 0115-973 2169 E-mail: sharp@brandysnap.co.uk
Thomas Tunnock Ltd, 34 Old Mill Road, Uddingston, Glasgow, G71 7HH Tel: (01698) 813551 Fax: (01698) 815691 E-mail: sales@tunnock.co.uk
United Biscuits (UK), 54 Church Street, Caldewgate, Carlisle, CA2 5TG Tel: (020) 8234 5000 Fax: (01228) 535900
Unity Biscuits Ltd, Units 7-8 Saltley Industrial Centre, Adderley Road, Saltley, Birmingham, B8 1AW Tel: 0121-327 5588 Fax: 0121-328 2974
Wright & Co., Bramston Street, Brighouse, West Yorkshire, HD6 3AA Tel: (01484) 715166 Fax: (01484) 715166

BISMUTH ALLOYS

Lowden Metals Ltd, 7 Harvey Works Industrial Estate, Shelah Road, Halesowen, West Midlands, B63 3PG Tel: 0121-501 3596 Fax: 0121-585 5162 E-mail: enquiries@metals26.freeserve.co.uk
Mining & Chemical Products Ltd, 1-4 Nielson Road, Finedon Road Industrial Estate, Wellingborough, Northamptonshire, NN8 4PE Tel: (01933) 225766 Fax: (01933) 227814 E-mail: info@mcp-group.co.uk

BITUMEN

Nynas UK Ab, East Camperdown Street, Dundee, DD1 3LG Tel: (01382) 462211 Fax: (01382) 456846
Total Bitumen Ltd, Chain Caul Way, Preston Riversway, Ashton-on-Ribble, Preston, PR2 2TZ Tel: (01772) 729302 Fax: (01772) 724713
W J & H Crozier, 19 Outlack Road, Armagh, BT60 2AN Tel: (028) 3752 2202 Fax: (028) 3752 2283

BITUMEN EMULSIONS

Ayton Asphalte, Browick Works, Ayton Road, Wymondham, Norfolk, NR18 0RJ Tel: (01953) 602002 Fax: (01953) 604965 E-mail: sales@ayton.co.uk
Colas Ltd, Wallage Lane, Rowfant, Crawley, West Sussex, RH10 4NF Tel: (01342) 711000 Fax: (01342) 711198 E-mail: info@colas.co.uk
▶ Colas Ltd, Tan Lane, Exeter, EX2 8EG Tel: (01392) 207201 Fax: (01392) 201530 E-mail: sales@cola.co.uk
Elementis UK Ltd, Nettlehill Road, Houston Industrial Estate, Livingston, West Lothian, EH54 5DL Tel: (01506) 430331 Fax: (020) 7398 1401 E-mail: info@elementis.com

BITUMEN HEATERS

C M S Tools Ltd, Don Pedro Close, Normanton Industrial Estate, Normanton, West Yorkshire, WF6 1TD Tel: (01924) 895999 Fax: (01924) 896999 E-mail: info@cmstools.co.uk
Cartem Ltd, Wharf Way, Glen Parva, Leicester, LE2 9TF Tel: (0870) 0665122 Fax: (0870) 0665133 E-mail: info@cartem.co.uk
W.J. Farvis & Sons Ltd, Temple Works, Morley Road, Southville, Bristol, BS3 1DT Tel: 0117-966 6677 Fax: 0117-966 9893 E-mail: sales@favis.co.uk
T E C International Ltd, Molborough House, Molborough Road, Lancing, West Sussex, BN15 8UF Tel: (01903) 851920 Fax: (01903) 851910 E-mail: paulw@tecint.co.uk

BITUMEN/BITUMINOUS TEST EQUIPMENT

▶ C N S Farnell, Elstree Business Centre, Elstree Way, Borehamwood, Hertfordshire, WD6 1RX Tel: (020) 8238 6900 Fax: (020) 8238 6901 E-mail: sales@cnsfarnell.com
Wykeham Farrance International Ltd, Chiltern House, Unit 4B, Knaves Beech Business Centre, Loadwater, High Wycombe, Buckinghamshire, HP10 9QY Tel: (01628) 521000 Fax: (01628) 530300 E-mail: sales@wfi.co.uk

BITUMINOUS COMPOUNDS

Ayton Asphalte, Browick Works, Ayton Road, Wymondham, Norfolk, NR18 0RJ Tel: (01953) 602002 Fax: (01953) 604965 E-mail: sales@ayton.co.uk
Bituchem Group, Laymore Road, Forest Vale Industrial Estate, Cinderford, Gloucestershire, GL14 2YH Tel: (01594) 826768 Fax: (01594) 826948 E-mail: sales@bituchem.com
Jobling Purser Ltd, Paradise Works, Scotswood Road, Newcastle Upon Tyne, NE15 6BZ Tel: 0191-273 2331 Fax: 0191-226 0129 E-mail: info@joblingpurser.com
W.H. Keys Ltd, Hall End Works, Church Lane, West Bromwich, West Midlands, B71 1BN Tel: 0121-553 0206 Fax: 0121-500 5820 E-mail: sales@wh-keys.fsnet.com
Laybond Products Ltd, Riverside, Chester, CH4 8RS Tel: (01244) 674774 Fax: (01244) 682218 E-mail: sales-info@laybond.com

BITUMINOUS DAMP PROOF COURSES (DPC)

Icopal, Barton Dock Road, Stretford, Manchester, M32 0YL Tel: 0161-865 4444 Fax: 0161-864 1178 E-mail: marketing.uk@icopal.com
IKO Ltd, Appley Lane North, Appley Bridge, Wigan, Lancashire, WN6 9AB Tel: (01257) 255771 Fax: (01257) 252514

BITUMINOUS PAINTS

Technical Paint Services, 27 Southcote Road, Bournemouth, BH1 3SH Tel: (01202) 295570 Fax: (0845) 2301255 E-mail: sales@technicalpaintservices.com

BITUMINOUS ROOFING SHEETING

Icopal, Barton Dock Road, Stretford, Manchester, M32 0YL Tel: 0161-865 4444 Fax: 0161-864 1178 E-mail: marketing.uk@icopal.com

BITUMINOUS SOLUTION

Jobling Purser Ltd, Paradise Works, Scotswood Road, Newcastle Upon Tyne, NE15 6BZ Tel: 0191-273 2331 Fax: 0191-226 0129 E-mail: info@joblingpurser.com
W.H. Keys Ltd, Hall End Works, Church Lane, West Bromwich, West Midlands, B71 1BN Tel: 0121-553 0206 Fax: 0121-500 5820 E-mail: sales@wh-keys.fsnet.com
Liver Grease Oil & Chemical Company Ltd, 11 Norfolk Street, Liverpool, L1 0BE Tel: 0151-709 7494 Fax: 0151-709 3774 E-mail: sales@livergrease.co.uk

BLACK ALUMINIUM OXIDE LASER CUTTING

Laser Cutting Ceramics Ltd, Wide Range Works, Catley Road, Sheffield, S9 5JF Tel: 0114-249 4005 Fax: 0114-242 5194 E-mail: info@lasercutting-ceramics.co.uk

BLACK AND WHITE MASTERBATCHES

Begg & Co Thermoplastics Ltd, 71 Hailey Road, Erith, Kent, DA18 4AW Tel: (020) 8310 1236 Fax: (020) 8310 4371 E-mail: darrenw@fsmail.net
Collords Ltd, Kirkby Bank Road, Knowsley Industrial Park, Liverpool, L33 7SY Tel: 0151-546 9222 Fax: 0151-549 0489 E-mail: sales@colloids.co.uk
Performance Master Batches Ltd, Blaenant Industrial Estate, Blaenavon Road, Brynmawr, Ebbw Vale, Gwent, NP23 4BX Tel: (01495) 310583 Fax: (01495) 312158 E-mail: customer.service@pmb.co.uk

BLACK BARS, STEEL

Corus, Station Road, South Darenth, Dartford, DA4 9LD Tel: (01322) 227272 Fax: (01322) 864893
Corus, 216a Moira Road, Lisburn, County Antrim, BT28 2SN Tel: (028) 9266 0747 Fax: (028) 9266 0748
Corus Service Centre, Spittlegate Industrial Estate, Grantham, Lincolnshire, NG31 7UP Tel: (01476) 565522 Fax: (01476) 562459

BLACK PUDDING

▶ Border County Foods, The Old Vicarage, Crosby-On-Eden, Carlisle, CA6 4QZ Tel: (01228) 573500 Fax: (01228) 672021 E-mail: info@cumberland-sausage.net

BLACK STEEL BOLTS AND NUTS

Phil Holden Fasteners Ltd, 23 Swannington Road, Cottage Lane Industrial Estate, Broughton Astley, Leicester, LE9 6TU Tel: (01455) 285888 Fax: (01455) 285105 E-mail: enquiries@phs-ltd.com

BLACKBOARD/CHALKBOARD

Wilson & Garden, 38 Tollpark Road, Wardpark East, Cumbernauld, Glasgow, G68 0LW Tel: (01236) 853120 Fax: (01236) 853123 E-mail: info@wgltd.com

BLACKSMITHS

A G & G C Gibson, Forge House, Old Forge Lane, West Rasen, Market Rasen, Lincolnshire, LN8 3LS Tel: (01673) 842891 Fax: (01673) 842891
A J Sparkes, Luke Street, Berwick St. John, Shaftesbury, Dorset, SP7 0HQ Tel: (01747) 828496 Fax: (01747) 828496
A L Povey, The Forge, Owslebury Bottom, Winchester, Hampshire, SO21 1LY Tel: (01962) 777473 Fax: (01962) 777473 E-mail: alan.povey@tesco.net
A M Engineering, Old Forge, 206 Woodrow Rd, Forest, Melksham, Wilts, SN12 7RD Tel: (01225) 704230
A S Ball, Pennti Lowarn, Mount, Bodmin, Cornwall, PL30 4ET Tel: (01208) 821381 Fax: (01208) 821381
J.M. Acton RSS, Horse Shoe Farm, Creake Road, Fakenham, Norfolk, NR21 9JA Tel: (01328) 823561
Alderbury Forge, Old Road, Alderbury, Salisbury, SP5 3AR Tel: (01722) 711027 Fax: (01722) 711026
Anvil Engineering, Aiskew Ironworks, Sandhill Lane, Bedale, North Yorkshire, DL8 1DU Tel: (01677) 427362 Fax: (01677) 427364 E-mail: info@anvileng.co.uk
Arthur Black General Smiths Ltd, Clay Lane, Oldbury, West Midlands, B69 4TH Tel: 0121-552 4212 Fax: 0121-552 2208 E-mail: info@arthurblack.com
Benbow Metal Works Ltd, Townley Street, London, SE17 1DZ Tel: (020) 7701 0208 Fax: (020) 7703 3254
Blackberry Forge, Bar Forge, Barcelona, Looe, Cornwall, PL13 2JU Tel: (01503) 272886
Matthew Brown Blacksmiths Ltd, East Grange Farm, A179 Hartlepool, Hartlepool, Cleveland, TS27 4RA Tel: (01429) 865777 Fax: (01429) 865777
C H Jones & Son, 1 The Square, North Tawton, Devon, EX20 2EW Tel: (01837) 82237 Fax: (01837) 82526 E-mail: chjengineers@aol.com
C Moore, Drift End Stables, The Drift, Bourn, Cambridge, CB23 2TB Tel: (01954) 719565
▶ Caledonian Roofing Co. Ltd, Holyrood Business Park, 146 Duddingston Road West, Edinburgh, EH16 4AP Tel: 0131-538 6422 Fax: 0131-661 6253 E-mail: info@caledonianblacksmiths.com
▶ Cytek Jersey, Petit Haut Du Rue, La Rue de la Clochette, St. Martin, Jersey, JE3 6HN Tel: (01534) 855263
D C Richards Farrier, 9 Mount Pleasant, Fairford, Gloucestershire, GL7 4BA Tel: (01285) 711025 Fax: (01285) 712097
D Tobias Ltd, 50 Rogart Street, Glasgow, G40 2AA Tel: 0141-554 2348 Fax: 0141-550 1090
Davey & Jordan, 3 Jennings Road, Kernick Industrial Estate, Penryn, Cornwall, TR10 9AA Tel: (01326) 372282 Fax: (01326) 376596
Distinctive Iron Work, Forge House, Tewkesbury Road, Uckington, Cheltenham, Gloucestershire, GL51 9SX Tel: (01242) 680453 Fax: (01242) 680453
Ellis Dawe & Son, The Forge, Rye Street, Birtsmorton, Malvern, Worcestershire, WR13 6AS Tel: (01684) 833235 Fax: (01684) 833840 E-mail: sales@ellisdawe.co.uk
Charles Etherington Ltd, Hallgarth Field, Millington, York, YO42 1TX Tel: (01759) 302204
Flavell Precision Engineering Ltd, Moore Street, Wolverhampton, WV1 2HE Tel: (01902) 456583 Fax: (01902) 456583 E-mail: sales@precisionengineering.gbr.fm
The Forge, Hillier Garden Centre, Brighton Road, Horsham, West Sussex, RH13 6QA Tel: (01403) 272894 Fax: (01403) 272894
G K E Sampson & Sons, 22 Paddock Road, Newbury, Berkshire, RG14 7DG Tel: (01635) 43204
Lionel W. Gibbs (Horton) Ltd, Horley Road, Hornton, Banbury, Oxfordshire, OX15 6BW Tel: (01295) 670310 Fax: (01295) 670732
John Hally, Moray Street, Blackford, Auchterarder, Perthshire, PH4 1PY Tel: (01764) 682277 Fax: (01764) 663817
Howard Fabrications, Swainshill, Hereford, HR4 7QA Tel: (01432) 353100 Fax: (01432) 353100
I Caudwell, Church Street, Billinghay, Lincoln, LN4 4HN Tel: (01526) 861179 Fax: (01526) 861762 E-mail: emailcaudwell@globalnet.co.uk
Iron Art, Unit 1, Birch Industrial Estate, Eastbourne, East Sussex, BN23 6PH Tel: (01323) 722784 Fax: (01323) 722784 E-mail: info@iron-art.co.uk
▶ Iron Works, Old Stone Cottage, Brighton Road, Pease Pottage, Crawley, West Sussex, RH11 9BE Tel: (01293) 553005 E-mail: blacksmith@ironworks-crawley.co.uk
J A Godbold, The Forge, The Garage, Egton, Whitby, North Yorkshire, YO21 1TZ Tel: (01947) 895562 Fax: (01947) 895562
J E Matthews & Sons Ltd, Southbridge, Cotton End, Northampton, NN4 8BS Tel: (01604) 762188 Fax: (01604) 705218 E-mail: matthews@cottonendfsbusiness.co.uk
J Henty, 21a Lower Road, Eastbourne, East Sussex, BN21 1QE Tel: (01323) 721938
J & T Blacksmiths Ltd, 23-29 Kelvin Avenue, Hillington Industrial Estate, Glasgow, G52 4LT Tel: 0141-882 9528 Fax: 0141-883 7110
John Gibson & Sons Ltd, Unit 215 Heathhall Industrial Estate, Heathhall, Dumfries, DG1 3PH Tel: (01387) 254764 Fax: (01387) 266005 E-mail: gibsonblacksmith@aol.com
▶ Paul Johnson, 28 Werrington Drive, Callington, Cornwall, PL17 7TF Tel: (01579) 384764
K H Hedley, The Forge, Invershin, Lairg, Sutherland, IV27 4ET Tel: (01549) 421234 Fax: (01549) 421263 E-mail: khhedley@aol.com
Lake, Muckley & Co. Ltd, The Stable, Lillyfee Farm, Lillyfee Farm Lane, Wooburn Green, High Wycombe, Buckinghamshire, HP10 0LL Tel: (01494) 673632 Fax: (01494) 673632
Laurel Bank Forge, Woodway Lane, Claybrooke Parva, Lutterworth, Leicestershire, LE17 5BH Tel: (01455) 209379 Fax: (01455) 209379
Londonderry Farriers & Blacksmiths, The Forge, Londonderry, Northallerton, North Yorkshire, DL7 9NE Tel: (01677) 422587 Fax: (01677) 426587 E-mail: sales@forgesupplies.co.uk
Mcewan Bros Kirkintilloch Ltd, The Smithy House, Old Duntiblae Road, Glasgow, G66 3LG Tel: 0141-776 1880 Fax: 0141-776 1040 E-mail: mcewansfencing@aol.com
Marsh Forge Blacksmiths, Chapel House Farm, Offley Marsh, Bishops Offley, Stafford, ST21 6HE Tel: (01785) 280487 Fax: (01785) 280487 E-mail: info@marshforge.co.uk
Martin Works, 271 Lynn Road, Wisbech, Cambridgeshire, PE13 3DZ Tel: (01945) 589005 Fax: (01945) 474694
Melvin Bros, Unit 3 Baird Avenue, Strutherhill Industrial Estate, Larkhall, Lanarkshire, ML9 2PJ Tel: (01698) 887605 Fax: (01698) 884871 E-mail: melvinbrothers@aol.com
Mentmore Smithy, Stagg Hill, Mentmore, Leighton Buzzard, Bedfordshire, LU7 0QG Tel: (01296) 661760 Fax: (01296) 662502
Mill Green Forge, Essendon Forge, Essendon Hill, Essendon, Hatfield, Hertfordshire, AL9 6AL Tel: (01707) 271141 Fax: (01707) 271141 E-mail: chris@penstone-smith.fsnet.co.uk
P.J. Miller Ltd, The Old Baths, Main Road, Far Cotton, Northampton, NN4 8EN Tel: (01604) 767710 Fax: (01604) 764884
Moore Bros, Finkle Street, Market Weighton, York, YO43 3JL Tel: (01430) 872521
Newton Forge, Stalbridge Lane, Sturminster Newton, Dorset, DT10 2JQ Tel: (01258) 472407 Fax: (01258) 471111 E-mail: mail@newtonforge.co.uk
Charles Normandale, Warnford, Southampton, SO32 3LG Tel: (01730) 829300 Fax: (01730) 829608
Ornamental Iron Works & Forge, Unit2, Pinfold La Industrial Estate, Bridlington, North Humberside, YO16 6XS Tel: (01262) 401498 Fax: (01262) 401498 E-mail: ornamental-ironwork@bridlington.net
P Brockwell, Pocklington Industrial Estate, Pocklington, York, YO42 1NP Tel: (01759) 304742 Fax: (01759) 304742 E-mail: enquiries@brockwellfabrications.co.uk
P Handley & Sons, The Smithy, Smithy Lane, Knighton, Market Drayton, Shropshire, TF9 4HP Tel: (01630) 647268 Fax: (01630) 647268
Peter S Neale, Clays Road, Sling, Coleford, Gloucestershire, GL16 8LJ Tel: (01594) 837309 Fax: (01594) 835363 E-mail: sales@peter-s-neale.demon.co.uk
G. Potter, The Forge, Village Road, Bonchurch, Ventnor, Isle Of Wight, PO38 1RG Tel: (01983) 855233
Potters Potclais Group, Pelsall Road, Walsall, WS8 7DL Tel: (01543) 377015 Fax: (01543) 372301
Price Bros, 1 Ross Road, Abergavenny, Gwent, NP7 5LT Tel: (01873) 853827 Fax: (01873) 853827
R Thompson & Co., 12 Manderston Street, Edinburgh, EH6 8LY Tel: 0131-554 6501
R Y Thomson & Son, 15 Ash Street, Dundee, DD1 5AR Tel: (01382) 221460 Fax: (01382) 907005 E-mail: rythomson@btconnect.com
W.G. Renfrew, Unit1, Shanks Industrial Park, Blackbyres Road, Barrhead, Glasgow, G78 1EB Tel: 0141-881 1481 Fax: 0141-880 8085
Rock Forge, Whitebrook, Llanvaches, Newport, Gwent, NP20 6PN Tel: (01633) 400747
Slater & Green, Bath Mill, Byron Street, Royton, Oldham, OL2 6QZ Tel: 0161-624 7160 Fax: 0161-628 7552
Spring Grove Forge Ltd, Spring Grove Forge, Coombe Road, Puddletown, Dorchester, Dorset, DT2 8RZ Tel: (01305) 848326 Fax: (01305) 848328
Stackwell Forge, Front Road, Parson Drove, Wisbech, Cambridgeshire, PE13 4JQ Tel: (01945) 700666 Fax: (01945) 701242 E-mail: sales@stackwellforge.com
Stephen A Hughes, 2 Oak Street, Gilfach Goch, Porth, Mid Glamorgan, CF39 8UG Tel: (01443) 672111
Stewart, Elliot Industrial Estate, Arbroath, Angus, DD11 2NJ Tel: (01241) 873905 Fax: (01241) 875770 E-mail: jjselliot@fsbdial.co.uk
T & D Cruickshanks, Canal Street, Kirkintilloch, Glasgow, G66 1QY Tel: 0141-776 2043 Fax: 0141-777 7646 E-mail: tandd.cruickshanks@virgin.net
Titan Forge Ltd, 3 Shaftesbury Road, London, E10 7DA Tel: (020) 8558 9000 Fax: (020) 8558 8614
Tullibaridine, Castleton Road, Auchterarder, Perthshire, PH3 1JS Tel: (01764) 662696 Fax: (01764) 662011
▶ Tumble Forge, 76 Bethesda Road, Tumble, Llanelli, Dyfed, SA14 6LG Tel: (01269) 841612 Fax: (01269) 832107 E-mail: sales@tumbleforge.co.uk

BLACKSMITHS TOOLS

Glendale Forge, Monk Street, Thaxted, Dunmow, Essex, CM6 2NR Tel: (01371) 830466 Fax: (01371) 831419 E-mail: sales@glendaleforge.co.uk

BLADE (GUILLOTINE) SHARPENING/MAINTENANCE/ REPAIR SERVICES

Bandsaw Service Ltd, Fairacres Industrial Estate, Dedworth Road, Windsor, Berkshire, SL4 4LE Tel: (01753) 862029 Fax: (01753) 830051 E-mail: saws@eclipse.co.uk
Norman Haynes Ltd, 900 Thornton Road, Bradford, West Yorkshire, BD8 0JG Tel: (01274) 545115 Fax: (01274) 545113
Mastercut Cutting Systems Ltd, 8 Bridge St Industrial Estate, Bridge Street, Clay Cross, Chesterfield, Derbyshire, S45 9NU Tel: (01246) 860811 Fax: (01246) 866928 E-mail: info@mastercut.co.uk
North Shields Grinding, The Old Maltings, Tanners Bank, North Shields, Tyne & Wear, NE30 1JH Tel: 0191-257 2342 Fax: 0191-258 5310 E-mail: nsgrinding@aol.com
Wakefield Engineering Services, 44 Grove Park, Calder Grove, Wakefield, West Yorkshire, WF4 3BZ Tel: (01924) 277726 Fax: (01924) 281730 E-mail: derek@weserv.fsbusiness.co.uk
▶ WEST SAW SERVICES LTD, UNIT 15, BALTIC WORKS, EFFINGAM ROAD, Sheffield, S9 3QA Tel: 0114 2426620 Fax: 0114 2426620 E-mail: josilk@btinternet.com

BLADE OR SAW GRINDING MACHINES

Sawko Grinding Co., 1 Graham Cottages, Main Road, Lacey Green, Princes Risborough, Buckinghamshire, HP27 0PL Tel: (01844) 346823 Fax: (01844) 342396 E-mail: melebbles@hotmail.com
Vollmer UK Ltd, Orchard Park Industrial Estate, Town Street, Sandiacre, Nottingham, NG10 5BP Tel: 0115-949 1040 Fax: 0115-949 0042 E-mail: admin@vollmer-uk.com

BLADE/CUTTER/KNIFE PRECISION GRINDING SERVICES

M G Knife Services, 8 Avon Business Park, Lodge Causeway, Bristol, BS16 3JP Tel: 0117-958 3974 Fax: 0117-958 3997
▶ S M B Engineering Services, Unit G, Oldham Central Trading Park, Coulton Close, Oldham, OL1 4EB Tel: 0161-627 4640
Techni Grind Preston Machining Ltd, Unit 62 Red Scar Industrial Estate, Longridge Road, Ribbleton, Preston, PR2 5ND Tel: (01772) 797589 Fax: (01772) 797682 E-mail: sales@tgmeng.co.uk

BLADES, GAS TURBINE

▶ Heward Microjets Ltd, 8 Beagle Court, Cottenham, Cambridge, CB24 8RS Tel: (01526) 322266 E-mail: pheward@yahoo.com

BLANCHING EQUIPMENT

Ambit Projects Ltd, North Lynn Industrial Estate, King's Lynn, Norfolk, PE30 2JL Tel: (01553) 692977 Fax: (01553) 692997 E-mail: ambit@btinternet.com
C T M Systems Ltd, Unit 8, Arkwright Road Industrial Estate, Cambridge Road, Bedford, MK42 0LE Tel: (01234) 355700 Fax: (01234) 351155 E-mail: sales@ctm-systems.demon.co.uk

BLANK VIDEO CASSETTES

Downsoft Ltd, Downsway House, Epsom Road, Ashtead, Surrey, KT21 1LD Tel: (01372) 272422 Fax: (01372) 276122 E-mail: sales@downsoft.co.uk

BLANKETS

Allsorts, 33 Kirkby Road, Hemsworth, Pontefract, West Yorkshire, WF9 4BA Tel: (01977) 610955
Amoire Linen, 82 Beech Farm Drive, Macclesfield, Cheshire, SK10 2ER Tel: (01625) 431166 Fax: (01625) 610955 E-mail: sales@armoirelinen.co.uk
Calder Weaving Co. Ltd, Scout Road, Hebden Bridge, West Yorkshire, HX7 5HZ Tel: (01422) 882382 Fax: (01422) 883381 E-mail: sales@calderweaving.co.uk
▶ Cardboard Boxes, 1 Ivanhoe Street, Leicester, LE3 9GX Tel: 0116-275 2039
▶ Country Colonial Ltd, 82-86 Seymour Place, London, W1H 2NQ Tel: (020) 7723 0465 Fax: (020) 7723 4430 E-mail: textilediva@countrycolonial.co.uk
John Dron Ltd, 43 Blundells Road, Bradville, Milton Keynes, MK13 7HD Tel: (01908) 311388 Fax: (01908) 222200 E-mail: sales@johndron.co.uk
Natural Health Products Ltd, 1275 Stratford Road, Hall Green, Birmingham, B28 9AJ Tel: 0121-777 6000 Fax: 0121-777 6006 E-mail: mail@nhp.uk
R N Peace & Co., 103 High Street, Witney, Oxfordshire, OX28 6HZ Tel: (01993) 702434 Fax: (01993) 702434 E-mail: mrrbpeace@aol.com
S & M Myers Ltd, 100-106 Mackenzie Road, London, N7 8RG Tel: (020) 7609 0091 Fax: (020) 7609 2457
▶ Wool Duvets, Jasmine House, Saxlingham Road, Blakeney, Holt, Norfolk, NR25 7PB Tel: (01263) 741799 E-mail: enquiries@woolduvets.co.uk

BLANKS, LASER CUT

▶ Trim Profiles Ltd, C Fleming Way, Coronation Road, Cressex Business Park, High Wycombe, Buckinghamshire, HP12 3TS Tel: (01494) 440352 Fax: (01494) 448933

BLAST CLEANING CONTRACTORS OR SERVICES,

See also headings for particular types such as Shot, Grit etc

A1 Sandblasting, Reeds Farm, Cow Watering Lane, Writtle, Chelmsford, CM1 3SB Tel: (01245) 422188
Anglia Rustguard Ltd, 26 Crittall Road, Western Industrial Estate, Witham, Essex, CM8 3DR Tel: 01376 514152 Fax: 01376 512802 E-mail: angliarustguard@btconnect.com
Bonsers Cleaning Nottingham, 19a Forester Street, Netherfield, Nottingham, NG4 2LJ Tel: 0115-988 7520 Fax: (01636) 815926 E-mail: contact@bonsersrestoration.co.uk
Caliba Spraying, Wallet Street, Nottingham, NG2 3EL Tel: 0115-986 9200 Fax: 0115-986 9204 E-mail: sales@surface-coating.co.uk
Calmac Metal Finishers Ltd, Unit 10 Quay Lane Industrial Estate, Hard Way, Gosport, Hampshire, PO12 4LJ Tel: (023) 9251 1440 Fax: (023) 9252 8814
▶ Crown Cleaning Management, 1 Silver Street, Lincoln, LN2 1DY Tel: (01522) 545400 Fax: (01522) 545403 E-mail: info@crown-cleaning.com
Forward Protective Coating, Vernon St Industrial Estate, Shirebrook, Mansfield, Nottinghamshire, NG20 8SS Tel: (01623) 741910 Fax: (01623) 748730 E-mail: forwardpc@fornet.com
G D Crichton, Strathenry Mill, Leslie, Glenrothes, Fife, KY6 3HU Tel: (01592) 743181
G & N Shotblasting Ltd, Brindley Close, Drayton Fields Industrial Estate, Daventry, Northamptonshire, NN11 8RP Tel: (01327) 872569 Fax: (01327) 300878 E-mail: sales@shotblast.co.uk

BLAST CLEANING CONTRACTORS OR SERVICES – *continued*

Halls Specialised Services, Brooklyn Farm, North Hill, Horndon-on-the-Hill, Stanford-le-Hope, Essex, SS17 8QA Tel: (01375) 361408 Fax: (01375) 361448 E-mail: enquiries@hallsspecialisedservices.co.uk

Kue Group Ltd, Dick Lane, Bradford, West Yorkshire, BD4 8JW Tel: (01274) 669516 Fax: (01274) 665356

▶ Mann Restoration, 30 Gloucester Place, Witney, Oxfordshire, OX28 6LA Tel: (01993) 704679 E-mail: sales@mannrestoration.com

Masonry Cleaning Services, 1a Allpits Road, Calow, Chesterfield, Derbyshire, S44 5AU Tel: (01246) 209926 Fax: (01246) 211620 E-mail: mike@masonrycleaningservices.com

Mikris Finishers, Lower Dudbridge House, Dudbridge Road, Dudbridge, Stroud, Gloucestershire, GL5 3HF Tel: (01453) 763873 Fax: (01453) 763873

Possilpark Shotblasting Co. Ltd, 73 Dunn Street, Glasgow, G40 3PE Tel: 0141-556 6221 Fax: 0141-551 0714 E-mail: admin@possilparks.co.uk

Prepcraft, 11 Hunsdon, Welwyn Garden City, Hertfordshire, AL7 2PN Tel: (07775) 928822 Fax: (01707) 371413 E-mail: enquiries@prepcraft.co.uk

▶ Sapco, Seven Stars Road, Oldbury, West Midlands, B69 4JR Tel: 0121-544 7500 Fax: 0121-544 7499

Spa Engineering, Eastfield Fcty, Frank Perkins Way, Peterborough, PE1 2TD Tel: (01733) 345798 Fax: (01733) 345798 E-mail: spaengineering@btinternet.com

Stonbury Ltd, 4 Phoenix Enterprise Park, Grovehill Road, Beverley, North Humberside, HU17 0JG Tel: (01482) 881198 Fax: (01482) 868457 E-mail: admin@stonbury.co.uk

Sussex Blast Cleaning Ltd, 35 Industrial Estate, Station Road, Hailsham, East Sussex, BN27 2ER Tel: (01323) 849229 Fax: (01323) 442442

BLAST CLEANING CONTRACTORS/SERVICES, PLASTIC MEDIA

▶ Crown Cleaning Management, 1 Silver Street, Lincoln, LN2 1DY Tel: (01522) 545400 Fax: (01522) 545403 E-mail: info@crown-cleaning.com

BLAST CLEANING EQUIPMENT

Blastman Robotics Ltd, 68 Cunliffe Cl, Oxford, OX2 7BL Tel: (01865) 512654 Fax: (01865) 311874

CDS Consultants, Bwlch Tocyn Farm, Bwlchtocyn, Pwllheli, Gwynedd, LL53 7BN Tel: (01758) 712245 Fax: (01758) 712014 E-mail: cdsconsultants@btinternet.com

Clean Surface Ltd, 14 Highmeres Road, Leicester, LE4 9LZ Tel: 0116-224 0072 Fax: 0116-224 0074 E-mail: sales@cleansurface.co.uk

I S P C Surface Preperation Ltd, Wakefield Road, Ossett, West Yorkshire, WF5 9AW Tel: (01924) 276303 Fax: (01924) 277829 E-mail: uk-info@surfacepreperation.com

Ispc Surface Preparation Ltd, Craven Road, Craven Road, Altrincham, Cheshire, WA14 5EP Tel: 0161-928 6388 Fax: 0161-929 8017 E-mail: uk-info@wheelabrator.co.uk

Mason Morley Ltd, Spray Quip House, St Pauls Street, Morley, Leeds, LS27 9EP Tel: 0113-253 8681 Fax: 0113-252 3179 E-mail: info@masonmorley.co.uk

▶ Northern Power Clean Ltd, 26 Whitworth Drive, Aycliffe Industrial Estate, Newton Aycliffe, County Durham, DL5 6SZ Tel: (01325) 318070 Fax: (01325) 301711 E-mail: npcltd@btconnect.com

Pangborn UK Ltd, Riverside House Brymau Three Trading Estate, River Lane, Saltney, Chester, CH4 8RQ Tel: (01244) 659852 Fax: (01244) 659853 E-mail: sales@pangborn.co.uk

Pangborn (UK) Ltd, Orgreave Drive, Sheffield, S13 9NR Tel: 0114-288 0786 Fax: 0114-288 0791 E-mail: panguk@aol.com

Power Blast International, 9 Colhook Industrial Park, Petworth, West Sussex, GU28 9LP Tel: (01428) 707895 Fax: (01428) 707894 E-mail: sales@powerblast.co.uk

Quill International, Quill International Group Ltd, Castle Lane, Melbourne, Derby, DE73 8JB Tel: (01332) 863292 Fax: (01332) 863292 E-mail: sales@quillinternational.com

Surface Dynamics (UK) Ltd, 348 SPON LANE SOUTH, WEST BROMWICH, WEST MIDLANDS, B70 6AZ Tel: (0121) 553 7772 Fax: (0121) 553 4746 E-mail: sales@surfacedynamics.co.uk

Vapormatt Ltd, Monarch Centre, Venture Way, Priorswood Industrial Est, Taunton, Somerset, TA2 8DE Tel: (01823) 257976 Fax: (01823) 336446 E-mail: sales@vapormatt.com

Wheelabrator Group, 43-44 Gravelly Industrial Park, Tyburn Road, Birmingham, B24 8TG Tel: 0121-326 6481 Fax: 0121-328 0256 E-mail: uk-info@wheelabrator.co.uk

BLAST CLEANING MEDIA

Scangrit, Eastfield Road, South Killingholme, Immingham, South Humberside, DN40 3NF Tel: (01469) 574715 Fax: (01469) 571644 E-mail: sales@scangrit.co.uk

BLAST FURNACE PORTLAND CEMENT

Hanson Cement Ltd, 3160 Solihull Parkway, Birmingham Business Park, Birmingham, B37 7YN Tel: (0845) 6001616 Fax: 0121-606 1436 E-mail: customer.services@castlecement.co.uk

BLAST RELIEF PANEL SYSTEMS

Booth Industries, PO Box 50, Bolton, BL3 2RW Tel: (01204) 366333 Fax: (01204) 380888 E-mail: sales@booth-industries.co.uk

BLEACHERS TO TEXTILE TRADES

Alltex Ltd, Sladen Mill, Halifax Road, Littleborough, Lancashire, OL15 0LB Tel: (01706) 377374 Fax: (01706) 377256 E-mail: alltex@alltechsdying.co.uk

Belmont Bleaching & Dyeing Co. Ltd, Belmont Works, Egerton Road, Belmont, Bolton, BL7 8BN Tel: (01204) 811247 Fax: (01204) 811408 E-mail: info@belmont-bleaching.co.uk

Blackburn Yarn Dyers Ltd, Grimshaw Park Dye Works, Haslingden Road, Blackburn, BB2 3HN Tel: (01254) 53051 Fax: (01254) 672233 E-mail: info@bydltd.co.uk

P W Greenhalgh & Co. Ltd, Newhey Bleach & Dye Works, Milnrow, Rochdale, Lancashire, OL16 3TH Tel: (01706) 847911 Fax: (01706) 881217 E-mail: sgreenhalgh@pwgreenhalgh.com

Pollock & Cochrane Ltd, Thrushcraig Works, Rowan Street, Paisley, Renfrewshire, PA2 6RT Tel: 0141-889 2009 Fax: 0141-840 2114

Standfast Barracks, Caton Road, Lancaster, LA1 3PA Tel: (01524) 64334 Fax: (01524) 380157

BLEACHING CHEMICAL PRODUCTS

A M B Products Ltd, Marriott Road, Swinton, Mexborough, South Yorkshire, S64 8AG Tel: (01709) 583132 Fax: (01709) 587252 E-mail: amb@walterblack.co.uk

Chemische Fabrik Tubingen UK Ltd, 6 Newby Road Industrial Estate, Levens Road, Hazel Grove, Stockport, Cheshire, SK7 5DA Tel: 0161-456 3355 Fax: 0161-456 4153 E-mail: dbyrne@chtuk.co.uk

McBride P.L.C., McBride House, Penn Road, Beaconsfield, Buckinghamshire, HP9 2FY Tel: (01494) 607050 Fax: (01494) 607056

Melzone Plastic Products, 11 Sandgate High Street, Sandgate, Folkestone, Kent, CT20 3BD Tel: (01303) 248545 Fax: (01303) 248545

Zamo Household Products Ltd, 27 White Post Lane, London, E9 5EN Tel: (020) 8525 1177 Fax: (020) 8525 1166 E-mail: zamoproducts@aol.com

BLEACHING/SCOURING/ WASHING MACHINES, TEXTILE INDUSTRY

John Bradley Ltd, 1 Levens Road, Newby Road, Industrial Estate, Stockport, Cheshire, SK7 5DL Tel: 0161-483 5200 Fax: 0161-483 5101 E-mail: office@samuelbradley.com

BLEEPER COMMUNICATION SYSTEMS, *See Paging Systems etc; also Radio Communications etc*

BLENDING SYSTEMS, IN-LINE

Jiskoot Ltd, 85 Goods Station Road, Tunbridge Wells, Kent, TN1 2DJ Tel: (01892) 518000 Fax: (01892) 518100 E-mail: sales@jiskoot.com

Statiflo International Ltd, Crown Centre, Bond Street, Macclesfield, Cheshire, SK11 6QS Tel: (01625) 433100 Fax: (01625) 511376 E-mail: sales@statiflo.co.uk

BLENDING/MIXING SERVICES, INDUSTRIAL, *See also headings for particular types such as Powder*

Christeyns UK Ltd, Rutland Street, Bradford, West Yorkshire, BD4 7EA Tel: (01274) 393286 Fax: (01274) 309143 E-mail: headoffice@christeyns.co.uk

Cle-Pol Manufacturing Co. Ltd, PO Box 5, Barking, Essex, IG11 0TL Tel: (020) 8532 6900 Fax: (020) 8532 6940

Conagra Resources Europe Ltd, 3rd Floor, London, SW1W 9TR Tel: (020) 7824 8595 Fax: (020) 7824 8504

Excelsior Packers, Brookside Lane, Oswaldtwistle, Accrington, Lancashire, BB5 3NY Tel: (01254) 356622 Fax: (01254) 356677 E-mail: sales@gemweb.co.uk

Oakmere Technical Services Ltd, Unit 9, Pool Bank Business Park, High St, Chester, CH3 8JH Tel: (01829) 742100 Fax: (01829) 742109 E-mail: sales@oakmerets.com

Teeschem Manufacturing Co. Ltd, Salters Lane, Sedgefield, Stockton-on-Tees, Cleveland, TS21 3EE Tel: (01740) 620853 Fax: (01740) 622898 E-mail: admin@teeschem_mfg.co.uk

W T L International, Tunstall Road, Bosley, Macclesfield, Cheshire, SK11 0PE Tel: (01260) 223284 Fax: (01260) 223589 E-mail: sales@wtl-int.com

BLIND ACCESSORIES/ COMPONENTS

Artistic Blind Co., 115 Staple Hill Road, Bristol, BS16 5AD Tel: 0117-910 9888 Fax: 0117-910 9890 E-mail: sales@artisticblinds.co.uk

B T Blinds, 26 Winsover Road, Spalding, Lincolnshire, PE11 1EJ Tel: (01775) 760620 Fax: (01775) 760620 E-mail: info@btblinds.co.uk

Blind Ambition, 2 Brighton Way, Chippenham, Wiltshire, SN14 0YR Tel: (01249) 446868 Fax: (01249) 446868

Blinds Solutions, 30 Vale Street, Denbigh, Clwyd, LL16 3BE Tel: (01745) 815549 Fax: (01745) 812226

C F M Blindmaker Supplies Ltd, 18 20 James Road, Tyseley, Birmingham, B11 2BA Tel: (0870) 7702965 Fax: (0871) 4332309 E-mail: sales@cfmblinds.co.uk

Classique Window Blinds, Unit 2 River Place, Kilbirnie, Ayrshire, KA25 7EN Tel: (01505) 684441 Fax: (01505) 684333

Concept Systems, Unit 2, Wolsey Street, Leicester, LE4 0BS Tel: 0116-251 5181 Fax: 0116-251 5540

County Blinds & Awnings Ltd, 109 Worlds End Lane, Orpington, Kent, BR6 6AE Tel: (01689) 851093 Fax: (01689) 859779

Direct Blinds, 6 Oswald Road, Oswestry, Shropshire, SY11 1RE Tel: (01691) 670257 Fax: (01691) 679078

Fastrack Services Sun Blinds, 119 High Street, Tranent, East Lothian, EH33 1LW Tel: (0800) 0921021 Fax: (01875) 616677

Garden City Blinds, 7 Factory Place, Saltcoats, Ayrshire, KA21 5LA Tel: (01294) 604016 Fax: (01294) 604016

▶ Gilberts Fabrics & Blinds, Swan Centre, Kidderminster, Worcestershire, DY10 2DN Tel: (01562) 755255 E-mail: chrissarjeant@tiscali.co.uk

Hampshire Canopies, 12 Delme Court, Maytree Road, Fareham, Hampshire, PO16 0HX Tel: (023) 9265 0001 Fax: (01329) 239689

Harley Blinds Ltd, 13 Ryton Street, Worksop, Nottinghamshire, S80 2AY Tel: (01909) 482320 Fax: (01909) 482639

Harris Engineering, 400 Catesby Park, Kings Norton, Birmingham, B38 8SE Tel: 0121-433 3302 Fax: 0121-433 3047 E-mail: Sales@harrisengineering.co.uk

Homefair Blinds (UK) Ltd, 73-77 Newgate Street, Bishop Auckland, County Durham, DL14 7EQ Tel: (01388) 458890 Fax: (01388) 458890

Hopkins, Prospect House, Jameson Road, Birmingham, B6 7SJ Tel: (0845) 4563018 Fax: (0845) 4563019 E-mail: enquires@hopkinsfittings.co.uk

Island Blinds, 45 High Street, West Mersea, Colchester, CO5 8QA Tel: (01206) 384555 Fax: (01206) 384555

▶ Just Blinds, Unit 1 Monastery Lane, St. Helens, Merseyside, WA9 3SW Tel: (01942) 213600 Fax: (01744) 818002 E-mail: steve@just-blinds.co.uk

Kings Lynn Blinds, The Lodge, King's Lynn, Norfolk, PE33 0DR Tel: (01366) 348009 E-mail: enquiries@norfolksunblinds.co.uk

Louver-Lite Ltd, Ashton Road, Hyde, Cheshire, SK14 4BG Tel: 0161-882 5000 Fax: 0161-882 5009 E-mail: enquiries@louver-liteltd.co.uk

▶ New Look Sunblind Services, 310 Torquay Road, Paignton, Devon, TQ3 2DZ Tel: (01803) 323661 Fax: (01803) 698157 E-mail: richandjohn@newlook.wanadoo.co.uk

Reliant, Argyle Business Centre, 39 North Howard Street, Belfast, BT13 2AP Tel: (028) 9031 5193 Fax: (028) 9031 5130

Roman Blinds Ltd, Roman House, Wood Street, Macclesfield, Cheshire, SK11 6JQ Tel: (01625) 669779 Fax: (01625) 614698 E-mail: sales@romanblinds.com

Sani UK Ltd, Unit B1 Link One Industrial Park, George Henry Road, Tipton, West Midlands, DY4 7BU Tel: (01384) 251175 Fax: (01384) 251300

Shepherdson Shades Ltd, Ellesmere Business Park, Swingbridge Road, Grantham, Lincolnshire, NG31 7XT Tel: 0161-928 0220 Fax: (01476) 593600 E-mail: sales@vbcblinds.com

Sun Blinds, 42 Bellevue Road, Prestwick, Ayrshire, KA9 1NJ Tel: (01292) 477807

Turnils (U K) Ltd, The Washington Centre, Washington Street, Dudley, West Midlands, DY2 9SB Tel: (01384) 233233 Fax: (01384) 239339 E-mail: sales@turnils.com

Vision Blinds, The Quest, Ampthill Road, Houghton Conquest, Bedford, MK45 3JP Tel: (01234) 741633 Fax: (01234) 741981

Yewdale Bridge, Wickford Enterprise Centre, Enterprise Way, Wickford, Essex, SS11 8DH Tel: (01268) 570900 Fax: (01268) 732509 E-mail: sales@yewdalebridge.com

BLIND AND PARTIALLY SIGHTED PERSON AIDS AND EQUIPMENT

Hagger Electronics, Unit 7 Business Centre West, Avenue One, Letchworth Garden City, Hertfordshire, SG6 2HB Tel: (01462) 677331 Fax: (01462) 675016 E-mail: sales@hagger.co.uk

BLIND CLEANING/RENOVATING SERVICES

Ahandah Blinds, Honeymeade, Sawbridgeworth, Hertfordshire, CM21 0AR Tel: (01279) 422855 Fax: (01279) 423222

Blind Cleaning Services, Unit 5a, High St Indust Estate, Kirkintilloch, Glasgow, G66 1PU Tel: 0141-775 0133 Fax: 0141-775 0301

Bright A Blind Ltd, Unit 5, 1-3 North Road, London, N7 9HA Tel: (020) 7700 6000 Fax: (020) 7700 6303 E-mail: info@brightablind.com

Brighter Blinds & Services, 3 Croft Estate, Glasgow Road, Dennyloanhead, Bonnybridge, Stirlingshire, FK4 1QP Tel: (01324) 840654 Fax: (01324) 840860 E-mail: brighterblinds@blueyonder.co.uk

Dixons Blinds Manufacturers Ltd, Customes House, Ridley Street, Blyth, Northumberland, NE24 3AG Tel: (01670) 355011 Fax: (01670) 355011

Enviroclean Services Ltd, Unit A 5 Colville Road, London, W3 8BL Tel: (020) 8896 0088 Fax: (020) 8896 2676

Lelliotts Sunblinds Ltd, 80 Sopmting Road, Worthing, West Sussex, BN14 9ES Tel: (01273) 330077 Fax: (01903) 538052 E-mail: lelliottsblinds@btclick.com

▶ New Look Sunblind Services, 310 Torquay Road, Paignton, Devon, TQ3 2DZ Tel: (01803) 323661 Fax: (01803) 698157 E-mail: richandjohn@newlook.wanadoo.co.uk

Venetian Blind Services, 78 Bleerick Drive, Antrim, BT41 1HX Tel: (028) 9073 9309 Fax: (028) 9442 8866

W M Herdman Manufacturing Co. Ltd, Orchard Road, Finedon, Wellingborough, Northamptonshire, NN9 5JG Tel: (01933) 680416 Fax: (01933) 681369

BLIND INSTALLATION CONTRACTORS

Airedale Blinds & Shutters, 10 Wellington Street, Laisterdyke, Bradford, West Yorkshire, BD4 8BW Tel: (01274) 661266 Fax: (01274) 661222 E-mail: abs@fallers.co.uk

Betablinds Blinds & Awnings, Spooner Drive, Killamarsh, Sheffield, S21 1SH Tel: 0114-248 7262 E-mail: info@beta-blinds.co.uk

Blind Galleries, Unit 6g Skillion Business Park, Thames Road, Barking, Essex, IG11 0JP Tel: (020) 8594 4772 Fax: (020) 8594 7436 E-mail: blindgallery@aol.com

Briman Contracts Ltd, Unit 2b Building B Wembley Commercial Centre, East Lane, Wembley, Middlesex, HA9 7UR Tel: (020) 8908 0102 Fax: (020) 8904 0664 E-mail: info@briman.co.uk

Capital Blinds, Factory Place, Docklands, London, E14 3AN Tel: (0800) 0433442

Capricorn Blinds Ltd, 1072 Coventry Road, Yardley, Birmingham, B26 2DT Tel: 0121-772 5366 Fax: 0121-766 7504 E-mail: info@capricornblinds.com

D & S Blinds, 177 Stamford St Central, Ashton-under-Lyne, Lancashire, OL6 7PS Tel: 0161-339 5755 Fax: 0161-339 5755 E-mail: sales@kcblinds.co.uk

Evergreen Blinds, 2 Llanwenarth Road, Govilon, Abergavenny, Gwent, NP7 9PN Tel: (01873) 830112 Fax: (01873) 830112

Jayem Blinds, 3 Scotter Road, Bournemouth, BH7 6LY Tel: (01202) 422525 Fax: (01202) 422525 E-mail: sales@jayemblinds.co.uk

▶ Just Blinds, Unit 1 Monastery Lane, St. Helens, Merseyside, WA9 3SW Tel: (01942) 213600 Fax: (01744) 818002 E-mail: steve@just-blinds.co.uk

Kings Lynn Blinds, The Lodge, King's Lynn, Norfolk, PE33 0DR Tel: (01366) 348009 E-mail: enquiries@norfolksunblinds.co.uk

London Blind Co., 205a Long Lane, Bexleyheath, Kent, DA7 5AF Tel: (020) 8303 7964 Fax: (020) 8301 3586

▶ New Look Sunblind Services, 310 Torquay Road, Paignton, Devon, TQ3 2DZ Tel: (01803) 323661 Fax: (01803) 698157 E-mail: richandjohn@newlook.wanadoo.co.uk

Oasis Blinds & Flooring, Comberton Hill, Kidderminster, Worcestershire, DY10 1QH Tel: (01562) 515445 Fax: (01562) 864278

R N Contract Blinds, 57 Dyott Avenue, Whittington, Lichfield, Staffordshire, WS14 9NF Tel: (01543) 433433 Fax: (01543) 304047

BLIND INSTALLATION CONTRACTORS – *continued*

▶ Reflexol Conservatory Blinds Northwest, 1 Cuba Industrial Estate, Bolton Road North, Ramsbottom, Bury, Lancashire, BL0 0NE Tel: (01706) 825511 Fax: (01706) 825522 E-mail: info@reflexol.com

Shade Solutions Ltd, Oatley Trading Estate, Seymour Road, Kingswood, Bristol, BS15 1SD Tel: 0117-373 0599 Fax: 0117-330 9342 E-mail: sales@shadesolutions.co.uk

BLIND LADDER TAPE/WEBBING, VENETIAN BLIND

Bath Blind Co., Lower Bristol Road, Bath, BA2 7DL Tel: (01225) 837517 Fax: (01225) 837517E-mail: stewart.davies@ukonline.co.uk

D D Blinds, 25 Craven Park, London, NW10 8SU Tel: (020) 8961 3972

Solihull Blinds Ltd, A 85, Skelcher Road, Shirley, Solihull, West Midlands, B90 2EY Tel: 0121-733 1001 Fax: 0121-733 3062 E-mail: solihullblinds@blueyonder.co.uk

Total Blinds Ltd, Apex House, Builder St West, Llandudno, Gwynedd, LL30 1HH Tel: (01492) 875460 Fax: (01492) 871118

BLIND PRODUCTION CLOTHS AND FABRICS

Betablinds Blinds & Awnings, Spooner Drive, Killamarsh, Sheffield, S21 1SH Tel: 0114-248 7262 E-mail: info@beta-blinds.co.uk

D D Blinds, 25 Craven Park, London, NW10 8SU Tel: (020) 8961 3972

D R Blinds, 1d Linden Place, Trowbridge, Wiltshire, BA14 9AU Tel: (01225) 777385 Fax: (01225) 753754

Dutton & Gavin Textiles Ltd, 62-66 Bermondsey Street, London, SE1 3UD Tel: (020) 7403 6388 Fax: (020) 7407 5814 E-mail: sales@dutgav.fsnet.co.uk

Louver-Lite Ltd, Ashton Road, Hyde, Cheshire, SK14 4BG Tel: 0161-882 5000 Fax: 0161-882 5009 E-mail: enquiries@louver-liteltd.co.uk

Milltex Fabrics Ltd, 96 Brown Street, Newmilns, Ayrshire, KA16 9BP Tel: (01560) 322503 Fax: (01560) 323034 E-mail: sales@milltex.co.uk

▶ Tuscany Contract Fabrics, Century Park, Garrison Lane, Birmingham, B9 4NZ Tel: (07976) 616052 E-mail: tuscany_contract_fabrics@imageblinds.co.uk

BLIND RIVETING SYSTEMS

Arrow Fastener (U K) Ltd, Unit 5 ZK Park, 23 Commerce Way, Croydon, CR0 4ZS Tel: 0845 5314109 Fax: (020) 8686 9197 E-mail: arrowfast@aol.com

BLIND RIVETS

Emhart Fastening Technology Ltd, Walsall Road, Perry Barr, Birmingham, B42 1BP Tel: 0121-331 2408 Fax: 0121-356 1598 E-mail: uk.marketing@bdk.com

Fitlock, 6 Vaughan St Industrial Estate, Manchester, M12 5BT Tel: 0161-231 3724 Fax: 0161-231 7392 E-mail: sales@fitlocksystems.com

Rivetnut Technology Systems Ltd, 5 Bridgegate Business Park, Gatehouse Way, Gatehouse Industrial Area, Aylesbury, Buckinghamshire, HP19 8XN Tel: (01296) 330331 Fax: (01296) 331018 E-mail: sales@rivetnut.com

Screwplan Ltd, Hazelwood St Works, Hazelwood Street, Todmorden, Lancashire, OL14 5BW Tel: (01706) 812299 Fax: (01706) 816258 E-mail: sales@screwplan.com

BLIND SPRING BARRELS/ ROLLERS

Blindate Blinds & Awnings, 91 North Drive, Troon, Ayrshire, KA10 7DN Tel: (01292) 315905 Fax: (01292) 313377

BLINDS, *See also headings for particular types*

A & B Window Blinds Ltd, 111 Neilston Road, Paisley, Renfrewshire, PA2 6ER Tel: 0141-848 5565 Fax: 0141-842 1066 E-mail: info@ab-windowblinds.co.uk

Aaron Blinds, B 8 Chester Road, Whitby, Ellesmere Port, CH65 6RU Tel: 0151-355 2704 Fax: 0151-355 2704

Abacus, 93 Woodfield Road, Hadleigh, Benfleet, Essex, SS7 2ES Tel: (01702) 552354 Fax: 01702 551658

Abba Blinds Ltd, Unit 8 Old Mill Park, Kirkintilloch, Glasgow, G66 1SP Tel: 0141-777 7598 Fax: 0141-775 2500

Abbey Blinds, 31 St Nicholas Street, Ipswich, IP1 1TW Tel: (01473) 254591 Fax: (01359) 271340

▶ Abbey Blinds & Shading, 6 Chandler Court, Tolworth Rise South, Surbiton, Surrey, KT5 9NN Tel: (020) 8330 4558 Fax: (020) 8335 3908

Abc Blinds Ltd, 120 High Street, Staple Hill, Bristol, BS16 5HH Tel: 0117-957 1067 Fax: 0117-957 1067 E-mail: info@abcblinds.co.uk

Ace Contracts, 1 Frontier Works, 33 Queen Street, London, N17 8JA Tel: (020) 8801 9011 Fax: (020) 8801 9933 E-mail: acecontracts@btconnect.com

Advantage Blinds, Fisher's Brook, Calne, Wiltshire, SN11 9HB Tel: (01249) 813254 Fax: (01249) 811511 E-mail: sales@advantageblinds.com

Ahandah Blinds, Honeymeade, Sawbridgeworth, Hertfordshire, CM21 0AR Tel: (01279) 422855 Fax: (01279) 423222

Albany Blinds, 1 Murieston Valley, Murieston, Livingston, West Lothian, EH54 9HB Tel: (01506) 420000 Fax: (01506) 420000

Alpha Blinds, Radnor Chambers, Cheriton Place, Folkestone, Kent, CT20 2BB Tel: (01303) 244010 Fax: (01303) 244010

Alpine Blinds, 37 Lacy Street, Paisley, Renfrewshire, PA1 1QN Tel: 0141-840 4488 Fax: 0141-840 4499

Amo Blinds & Fabrics, 102 B M K Industrial Estate, Wakefield Road, Liversedge, West Yorkshire, WF15 6BS Tel: (01924) 410100 Fax: (01924) 410170 E-mail: showroom@amoblinds.co.uk

Andersons Blinds, Penrhewl Works, St. Asaph, Clwyd, LL17 0NH Tel: (01352) 752467 Fax: (01745) 584860

Apex Blinds Ltd, 46-48 Avenue Road, Lurgan, Craigavon, County Armagh, BT66 7BD Tel: (028) 3834 2525 Fax: (028) 3832 7835 E-mail: apexlinesni@hotmail.co.uk

Apollo Blinds, 195 Rosemount Place, Aberdeen, AB25 2XP Tel: (01224) 644600 Fax: (01224) 644292

Apollo Blinds Ltd, 38 South Bridge Street, Airdrie, Lanarkshire, ML6 6JA Tel: (01236) 768011 Fax: (01236) 768011

Apollo Blinds, 3 Bond Street, Bury, Lancashire, BL9 7BE Tel: 0161-761 3211 Fax: 0161-761 3211

Apollo Blinds Ltd, Unit 25 Lordswood Industrial Estate, Revenge Road, Chatham, Kent, ME5 8UD Tel: (01634) 686868 Fax: (01634) 686868 E-mail: midwayblinds@btconnect.com

Apollo Blinds Ltd, 42 Cow Wynd, Falkirk, FK1 1PU Tel: (01324) 627814 Fax: (01324) 627814

Apollo Blinds Ltd, 212 Argyle Street, Glasgow, G2 8HA Tel: 0141-226 3166 Fax: 0141-226 5444

Apollo Blinds Ltd, 101 Kilmarnock Road, Glasgow, G41 3YR Tel: 0141-649 2768 Fax: 0141-632 6428

Apollo Blinds Ltd, 160 York Road, Hartlepool, Cleveland, TS26 9DT Tel: (01429) 236666 Fax: (01429) 293004

Apollo Blinds Ltd, 19 St. Marnock Street, Kilmarnock, Ayrshire, KA1 1DZ Tel: (01563) 532452 Fax: (01563) 544473

Apollo Blinds Ltd, 254 High Street, Kirkcaldy, Fife, KY1 1LA Tel: (01592) 268841 Fax: (01592) 268841

Apollo Blinds Ltd, 102 BMK Industrial Estate, Wakefield Road, Liversedge, West Yorkshire, WF15 6BS Tel: (01924) 413010 Fax: (01924) 410170 E-mail: sales@apollo-blinds.co.uk

▶ Apollo Blinds Ltd, 4 Mallard Buildings, Station Road, New Milton, Hampshire, BH25 6HY Tel: (01425) 623624 Fax: (01425) 629709 E-mail: apolloblinds1@btconnect.com

Apollo Blinds Ltd, 197 Sandyford Road, Newcastle upon Tyne, NE2 1NP Tel: 0191-230 4156 Fax: 0191-232 4498

▶ Apollo Blinds Ltd, 73 South Methven Street, Perth, PH1 5NX Tel: (01738) 622366 Fax: (01738) 622366

Apollo Blinds Ltd, 43 King Street, Ramsgate, Kent, CT11 8NP Tel: (01843) 589849 Fax: (01843) 589849

Apollo Blinds Ltd, 35 Westfield Street, St. Helens, Merseyside, WA10 1QD Tel: (01744) 739588

Apollo Blinds Ltd, 27 Cowane Street, Stirling, FK8 1JW Tel: (01786) 472335 Fax: (01786) 472335

Apollo Blinds Ltd, 5 Boldmere Road, Sutton Coldfield, West Midlands, B73 5UY Tel: 0121-321 3337 Fax: 0121-321 3337

Apollo Blinds Ltd, 3 Horsemarket Street, Warrington, WA1 1TP Tel: (01925) 411404 Fax: (01925) 411404

Apollo Blinds Ltd, 8 Wigan Gallery, The Galleries, Wigan, Lancashire, WN1 1AR Tel: (01942) 495500 Fax: (01942) 495500

▶ Archer Blinds Ltd, 1 Lodge Street, Middleton, Manchester, M24 6AA Tel: 0161-653 3800 Fax: 0161-653 3800

Arnolds Curtains & Blinds, 2-4 Dinsdale Road, Bromborough, Wirral, Merseyside, CH62 3PY Tel: 0151-343 9696 Fax: 0151-343 1838

Art Blinds, 372 London Road, Hadleigh, Benfleet, Essex, SS7 2DA Tel: (01702) 559969 Fax: (01702) 554058

Artistic Window Blinds, Shopping Precinct, 28o Lochside Road, Dumfries, DG2 0LW Tel: (01387) 268518 Fax: (01387) 268518

Ashdown Blinds, St. Johns Road, Crowborough, East Sussex, TN6 1RT Tel: (01892) 665596 Fax: (01892) 665596

Ashley Blind Contracts, 20 Old Mill Road, Hunton Bridge, Kings Langley, Hertfordshire, WD4 8QT Tel: (01923) 270801 Fax: (01923) 270425 E-mail: action@ashleyblinds.co.uk

▶ Atlas Contract Blinds Ltd, 11a Bolton Road, Kearsley, Bolton, BL4 8DB Tel: (01204) 409580 Fax: (01204) 411304 E-mail: sales@atlasblinds.co.uk

Audyan Blinds, 2 Lynburn Industrial Estate, Halbeath Place, Dunfermline, Fife, KY11 4JT Tel: (01383) 624555 Fax: (01383) 624555

▶ Austin Marr, 7 The Nelson Centre, Portfield Road, Portsmouth, PO3 5SF Tel: (023) 9269 0900 Fax: (023) 9269 1300 E-mail: enquiries@austinmarr.co.uk

▶ Avalon Blinds, 13 Porlock Grove, Stoke-On-Trent, ST4 8TN Tel: (01782) 657878 Fax: (01782) 657878

B & D Blinds, 153 Castle Road West, Oldbury, West Midlands, B68 0EL Tel: 0121-421 1000 Fax: 0121-602 6008

B W Blinds, 127a Frankwell, Shrewsbury, SY3 8JU Tel: (01743) 341290 Fax: (01743) 341290

Baileys Blinds Ltd, 211 High Street, Gosforth, Newcastle upon Tyne, NE3 1HQ Tel: 0191-284 6284 Fax: 0191-284 1464 E-mail: baileys@btconnect.com

Baileys Blinds Ltd, Unit 15 Bellway Industrial Estate, Whitley Road, Newcastle Upon Tyne, NE12 9SW Tel: 0191-270 0501 Fax: 0191-266 8993 E-mail: info@baileys-blinds.co.uk

Baldock Blinds, 3-4 Charles Street, Wrexham, Clwyd, LL13 8BT Tel: (01978) 264441 Fax: (01978) 353638 E-mail: baldockblinds@aol.com

Ball Hill Blinds, 221 Walsgrave Road, Coventry, CV2 4HH Tel: (024) 7645 1615 Fax: (024) 7645 1615

Banbury Blinds, Bell Hill, Hook Norton, Banbury, Oxfordshire, OX15 5NG Tel: (01608) 737205 Fax: (01608) 730679

Bangor Blinds, 2 Dew Street, Menai Bridge, Gwynedd, LL59 5AU Tel: (01248) 714666 Fax: (01248) 715161 E-mail: bangorblinds@aol.com

Barton Blinds Ltd, Unit B3, Imex Enterprise Park, Rands Lane, Armthorpe, Doncaster, South Yorkshire, DN3 3DY Tel: (01302) 830810 Fax: (01302) 830810

Beacon Blinds Ltd, 15 Fore Street, Totnes, Devon, TQ9 5DA Tel: (01803) 867200 Fax: (01803) 867952

Beaubelle Interiors Urmston, 410 Flixton Road, Flat 1, Urmston, Manchester, M41 6QY Tel: 0161-749 8525 Fax: 0161-749 8525

▶ Belmont Blinds, 1 Brookside, Red Marsh Industrial Estate, Thornton-Cleveleys, Lancashire, FY5 4HD Tel: (01253) 820084 Fax: (01253) 820084 E-mail: pculley3@aol.com

Benhar Blinds, Rimmon Cottage, Benhar Road, Shotts, Lanarkshire, ML7 5BJ Tel: (01501) 821835 Fax: (01501) 821835

Austin Berridge Ltd, 2 Buckminster Road, Blackbird Road, Leicester, LE3 9AR Tel: 0116-251 9922 Fax: 0116-251 9922

Better Blind Co., Wych Fold, Hyde, Cheshire, SK14 5ED Tel: (0800) 1693765 Fax: 0161-367 9318 E-mail: info@newblinds.co.uk

Bilanco Ltd, Units 3-4, Powdrake Road, Grangemouth, Stirlingshire, FK3 9OT Tel: (01324) 473707 Fax: (01324) 471926

▶ Blind Co., Foundry House, Polmorla Road, Wadebridge, Cornwall, PL27 7NB Tel: (01208) 815000

Blind Business, Arturi's Garden Centre, Allington Lane, Fair Oak, Eastleigh, Hampshire, SO50 7DE Tel: (023) 8060 2211 Fax: (023) 8060 2211 E-mail: info@theblindbusiness.co.uk

Blind Date, 58 East Main Street, Whitburn, Bathgate, West Lothian, EH47 0RD Tel: (01501) 740166 Fax: (01501) 740166

Blind Design, 28-29 Springbank Industrial Estate, Pembroke Loop Road, Dunmurry, Belfast, BT17 0QL Tel: (028) 9030 0999 Fax: (028) 9030 0999 E-mail: blindesign@hotmail.com

Blind Design, 2a North End Grove, Portsmouth, PO2 8NG Tel: (023) 9266 4476 Fax: (023) 9267 0077

Blind Design, Northminster Business Park, Northfield Lane, Upper Poppleton, York, YO26 6QU Tel: (01904) 799647 Fax: (01904) 799793

Blind Design (Scotland) Ltd, 17 George Street, Bathgate, West Lothian, EH48 1PH Tel: (01506) 632813 Fax: (01506) 69366

Blind Design (Stirling) Ltd, Unit 5, Heren Square, Deans Industrial Estate, Livingston, West Lothian, EH54 8QY Tel: (0800) 3281791 Fax: (01506) 418229

Blind Galleries, Unit 6g Skillion Business Park, Thames Road, Barking, Essex, IG11 0JP Tel: (020) 8594 4772 Fax: (020) 8594 7436 E-mail: blindgallery@aol.com

Blind Image, 9 Auster Road, York, YO30 4XA Tel: (01904) 693069 Fax: (01904) 693569

Blind Man, 40 Stockdale Avenue, Redcar, Cleveland, TS10 5EE Tel: (01642) 488979 Fax: (01642) 488979

The Blind Man Ltd, The Stables, Great Farm, Wilstone Green, Tring, Hertfordshire, HP23 4PA Tel: (01296) 661545 Fax: (01296) 668631

▶ Blind Rack Ltd, 32 Navigation Drive, Glen Parva, Leicester, LE2 9TB Tel: 0116-242 5934

Blind Spot, 44 Hardhillock Avenue, New Elgin, Elgin, Morayshire, IV30 6UG Tel: (01343) 549939 Fax: (01343) 55522

▶ Blind Technique, 4 Kildare Close, Ruislip, Middlesex, HA4 9LG Tel: (020) 8866 6088

Blindfix, Wickens Place, Godstone Hill, Godstone, Surrey, RH9 8AP Tel: (01883) 743600 Fax: (01883) 731199

Blinding Ideas, Landsdown Lane, Torquay, TQ2 5AJ Tel: (01803) 299880 Fax: (01803) 299880 E-mail: fran_kim@feaves.freeserve.co.uk

Blinds 2000, 8 Spinney Avenue, Goostrey, Crewe, CW4 8JE Tel: (01477) 533472 Fax: (01477) 533472 E-mail: sales@blinds2000.co.uk

Blinds 2000, 98a Fountain Street, Morley, Leeds, LS27 0PH Tel: 0113-259 7741 Fax: 0113-259 7802

Blinds 2000, The Blinds Factory, Croft Road, Neath, West Glamorgan, SA11 1RW Tel: (0800) 0688876 Fax: (0800) 0688876 E-mail: rob@blinds2000.co.uk

Blinds Of Allkinds, Sussex House, Park Lane, Crowborough, East Sussex, TN6 2QN Tel: (01892) 610780

Blinds By Athena, 47 Longstone Avenue, East Linton, East Lothian, EH40 3BS Tel: (01620) 861729 Fax: (01620) 861729

Blinds By Design, 48 Park Lane, Poynton, Stockport, Cheshire, SK12 1RE Tel: (01625) 858558 Fax: (01625) 858558

Blinds By Sovereign, Sovereign House, Newsome Street, Leyland, PR25 2SY Tel: (01772) 421789 Fax: (01772) 421789 E-mail: sales@sovblinds.com

Blinds Direct, 61 Annacloy Road, Downpatrick, County Down, BT30 9AQ Tel: (028) 4483 1713 Fax: (028) 4483 1710 E-mail: sales@blinds-direct.co.uk

Blinds Direct Solar Control Systems, 20 Blue Chalet Industrial Park, West Kingsdown, Sevenoaks, Kent, TN15 6BQ Tel: (01474) 854156 Fax: (01474) 855361 E-mail: woodblinds@btconnect.com

Blinds & Co. Leeds Ltd, 64 Hall Lane, Armley, Leeds, LS12 2LH Tel: 0113-263 4186 Fax: 0113-231 1083

Blinds Solutions, 30 Vale Street, Denbigh, Clwyd, LL16 3BE Tel: (01745) 815549 Fax: (01745) 812226

Blinds Unlimited, 4 Carpenters Close, Barnet, Hertfordshire, EN5 1EX Tel: (020) 8441 3663 Fax: (020) 8449 0012 E-mail: blindsunlimited1@aol.com

Bloomfield Blinds & Curtains, 84 Bloomfield Road, Belfast, BT5 5LU Tel: (028) 9065 2524 Fax: (028) 9065 2524 E-mail: davidsonr@btconnect.com

▶ Blooms Blinds, 3 Aspen Close, Timperley, Altrincham, Cheshire, WA15 7YF Tel: 0161-980 0449 Fax: 0161-980 0437

▶ Blooms Blinds, 95 Swinton Hall Road, Swinton, Manchester, M27 4AU Tel: 0161-727 8810 Fax: 0161-980 0437 E-mail: sales@bloomsblinds.co.uk

Booths Blinds, 282 Derby Road, Chesterfield, Derbyshire, S40 2ER Tel: (01246) 207568 Fax: (01246) 278212 E-mail: enquiries@boothsblinds.co.uk

▶ Border Blinds Ltd, 103 Whalley Road, Clitheroe, Lancashire, BB7 1EE Tel: (01200) 428555 E-mail: borderblinds@tiscali.co.uk

Bowmans Blinds & Canopies, 8 Whinfield Close, Stockton-on-Tees, Cleveland, TS19 8UA Tel: (07762) 581158 Fax: (01642) 583625

▶ Brakewater Blinds, 14 Bromhead Court, Plymouth, PL6 5NJ Tel: (01752) 776636

Brega Blinds, Poplar Farm House, Charles Tye, Ringshall, Stowmarket, Suffolk, IP14 2HU Tel: (01449) 740013 Fax: (01449) 744392

Bright A Blind Ltd, Unit 5, 1-3 North Road, London, N7 9HA Tel: (020) 7700 6000 Fax: (020) 7700 6303 E-mail: info@brightablind.com

Bright Shade Blinds, 2 Bosden Fold Road, Hazel Grove, Stockport, Cheshire, SK7 4LQ Tel: 0161-487 3901 Fax: 0161-487 3901

Brighter Blinds, 59 Church Street, Walshaw, Bury, Lancashire, BL8 3BN Tel: (01204) 883301 Fax: (01204) 887073 E-mail: bighterblinds@aol.com

Brighter Blinds & Services, 3 Croft Estate, Glasgow Road, Dennyloanhead, Bonnybridge, Stirlingshire, FK4 1QP Tel: (01324) 840654 Fax: (01324) 840860 E-mail: brighterblinds@blueyonder.co.uk

Broadview Blinds Ltd, 57 Hatch Pond Road, Nuffield Industrial Estate, Poole, Dorset, BH17 0JZ Tel: (01202) 679012 Fax: (01202) 671885 E-mail: sales@broadview-blinds.co.uk

Budget Blinds Ltd, Enterprise House, Chorley New Road, Horwich, Bolton, BL6 5NY Tel: (01204) 669898 Fax: (01204) 469696

Budget Blinds, 10 Heol Cwm Ifor, Caerphilly, Mid Glamorgan, CF83 2EU Tel: (029) 2088 8763 Fax: (029) 2085 3167

Budget Blinds, 50 William Street, Cookstown, County Tyrone, BT80 8NB Tel: (028) 8676 7875 Fax: (028) 8676 7875

Budget Blinds, 119 Higher Lomax Lane, Heywood, Lancashire, OL10 4RU Tel: (01706) 369402 Fax: (01706) 625525

Budget Blinds, 4 Tangier Street, Whitehaven, Cumbria, CA28 7UZ Tel: (01946) 64287 Fax: (01946) 64287

Burgess Systems, 3 Friars Close, Whitstable, Kent, CT5 1NU Tel: (01227) 263035 Fax: (01227) 263035

Butterfly Blinds, Cambridge Road, Milton, Cambridge, CB24 6AT Tel: (0500) 011363 Fax: (01223) 425355 E-mail: butterflyblinds@tiscali.co.uk

▶ C R Blinds, 55 Warmington Road, Sheldon, Birmingham, B26 3SX Tel: 0121-244 0803 Fax: 0121-244 0803

Calypso Blinds, Unit 14 Royal Elizabeth Yard, Kirkliston, West Lothian, EH29 9EN Tel: 0131-319 1190 Fax: 0131-319 1191

Cambridge Blind Spot, 394 Mill Road, Cambridge, CB1 3NN Tel: (01223) 213984 Fax: (01223) 576657

BLINDS – *continued*

Capital Blinds, Factory Place, Docklands, London, E14 3AN Tel: (0800) 0433442

Capricorn Blinds Ltd, 1072 Coventry Road, Yardley, Birmingham, B26 2DT Tel: 0121-772 5366 Fax: 0121-766 7504 E-mail: info@capricornblinds.com

Carmarthenshire C C S C H, Pwllmarl Farm, Velindre, Llandysul, Dyfed, SA44 5YN Tel: (01559) 371629 Fax: (01559) 371188

The Caroline Blind Co., 151 Cocklaw Street, Kelty, Fife, KY4 0DH Tel: (01383) 831609 Fax: (01383) 831609

Carousel & Intersun, Nant Hall Road, Prestatyn, Clwyd, LL19 9LR Tel: (01745) 886677 Fax: (01745) 857399

Cascade Blinds, Trevol Business Park, Torpoint, Cornwall, PL11 2TB Tel: (01752) 815512 Fax: (01752) 823554 E-mail: info@cascadeblinds.co.uk

Cassidy Sunblinds Ltd, Henry Boot Way, Hull, HU4 7DY Tel: (01482) 473173 Fax: (01482) 473191E-mail: sales@cassidy-sunblinds.co.uk

Cavalcade Blinds, 34 Hope Street, Stoke-on-Trent, ST1 5BS Tel: (01782) 287674 Fax: (01782) 287674

▶ Century Blinds, Lurgan Road, Portadown, Craigavon, County Armagh, BT63 5QR Tel: (028) 3833 6776 Fax: (028) 3833 6776

Chantilly Blinds, 476 Hartshill Road, Stoke-on-Trent, ST4 6AD Tel: (0800) 0564282 Fax: (01782) 714515 E-mail: enquiries@chantillyblinds.freeserve.co.uk

Charisma, 44 Broomhead Park, Dunfermline, Fife, KY12 0PT Tel: (01383) 732183

Choose At Home Window Blinds, 36 Sackville Gardens, East Grinstead, West Sussex, RH19 2AH Tel: (01342) 328364

▶ Christchurch Blinds, 328 Wimborne Road, Bournemouth, BH9 2HH Tel: (01202) 535577

Christchurch Blinds, 58 Bargates, Christchurch, Dorset, BH23 1QL Tel: (01202) 478363 Fax: (01202) 485054

City Blinds, 1 Primacy Road, Bangor, County Down, BT19 7PQ Tel: (028) 9127 2949 Fax: (028) 9143 9101 E-mail: sales@cityblindsni.co.uk

City Blinds Blind Manufacturers, Fairbairn Street, Dundee, DD3 7JZ Tel: (01382) 877788 Fax: (01382) 737635 E-mail: km@city-blinds.co.uk

▶ Clarion Flooring & Blinds Ltd, Whitstable Park, Widnes, Cheshire, WA8 9AS Tel: 0151-420 0714 Fax: (0870) 705 1304 E-mail: info@cfab.co.uk

Classic Blinds, Unit 35b Abbeycentre, Longwood Road, Newtownabbey, County Antrim, BT37 9UH Tel: (028) 9086 2872 Fax: (028) 9081 3052 E-mail: sales@classic-blinds.com

Claxton Blinds Ltd, Beaumont Works, Sutton Road, St. Albans, Hertfordshire, AL1 5HH Tel: (01727) 840001 Fax: (01727) 840004 E-mail: claxton-blinds@btconnect.com

Clwyd Blinds Direct, Unit 5 Pistyll Farm, The Long Barn Pistyll Farm, Mold, Clwyd, CH7 4EW Tel: (01352) 757474 Fax: (01352) 758034

Colemans Blinds, 9a Bath Road, Bridgwater, Somerset, TA6 4PH Tel: (01278) 453008 Fax: (01278) 453008

Colorway Blinds Ltd, Victoria Mills, 12-16 Elder Road, Leeds, LS13 4DL Tel: 0113-255 7637 Fax: 0113-255 8342 E-mail: sales@colorway-blinds.co.uk

Concept Interiors Neston Ltd, 10 High Street, Neston, CH64 9TY Tel: 0151-336 7042 Fax: 0151-336 7042 E-mail: info@conceptinteriors.co.uk

Concorde Blind Co., 12 Worsley Road, Woburn Road Industrial Estate, Kempston, Bedford, MK42 7TN Tel: (01234) 841535 Fax: (01234) 840682 E-mail: sales@concordeblinds.com

▶ Concorde Blind & Curtain Co. Ltd, 45 Waterside Park, Old Wolverton Road, Old Wolverton, Milton Keynes, MK12 5NP Tel: (01908) 320600 Fax: (01908) 227338

▶ Conserva-Care Ltd, 40 Main Street, Egginton, Derby, DE65 6HL Tel: (0845) 0098854 Fax: (0845) 0098853 E-mail: info@conserva-care.co.uk

▶ Contract & Home Blinds Ltd, Shelco House, Northgate, Aldridge, Walsall, WS9 8TH Tel: (01922) 454345 Fax: (01922) 454410

Dave Cox, 43 Ingrave Road, Brentwood, Essex, CM15 8AZ Tel: (01277) 228240 Fax: (01277) 228240

Crystal Blinds Ltd, 6 Kirkstone Road North, Liverpool, L21 7NS Tel: 0151-525 3646 Fax: 0151-474 7733

Crystal Blinds, 166 Logan Street, Nottingham, NG6 9FU Tel: 0115-927 2025 Fax: 0115-916 1140

CS Blinds, 11 Merlin Court, Newton Industrial Estate, Carlisle, CA2 7NY Tel: (01228) 598646

Curtain & Blind Specialists, West Drive, Lancaster, LA1 5BY Tel: (01524) 383000

▶ Curtain Blinds: Custom Curtain Blinds, Redhouse Road, Moulton Park, Northampton, NN3 6AQ Tel: (01604) 497994 Fax: (01604) 497994 E-mail: blinds@saster.fsnet.co.uk

Cut Price Blinds, Burleigh Street, Glasgow, G51 3LA Tel: 0141-445 2229 Fax: 0141-445 2229

D R Blinds, 1d Linden Place, Trowbridge, Wiltshire, BA14 9AU Tel: (01225) 777385 Fax: (01225) 753754

D & S Blinds, 177 Stamford St Central, Ashton-under-Lyne, Lancashire, OL6 7PS Tel: 0161-339 5755 Fax: 0161-339 5755 E-mail: sales@kcblinds.co.uk

Damers Blinds & Awnings, 117a Radipole Lane, Weymouth, Dorset, DT4 9SS Tel: (01305) 784601 Fax: (01305) 789625 E-mail: sales@damers.com

Deans Blinds & Awnings UK Ltd, 4 Haslemere Industrial Estate, Ravensbury Terrace, London, SW18 4SE Tel: (020) 8947 8931 Fax: (020) 8947 8336 E-mail: info@deansblinds.co.uk

Decor Blindmakers, 111 High Street, Ecclesfield, Sheffield, S35 9XA Tel: 0114-246 8311 Fax: 0114-246 8311

Decora Blinds, 79-81 Andersonstown Road, Belfast, BT11 9AH Tel: (028) 9060 4646 Fax: (028) 9060 4646

Derek Stacey, 21 Great Bank Road, Rotherham, South Yorkshire, S65 3BT Tel: (01709) 837352 Fax: (01709) 837352

▶ Design Blinds, Rear of, 1346 Stratford Road, Hall Green, Birmingham, B28 9EH Tel: 0121-777 0403 Fax: (0871) 4332309

Design House, 2 Borough Road, Buckingham Road Industrial Estate, Brackley, Northamptonshire, NN13 7BE Tel: (01280) 840451 Fax: (01280) 840454 E-mail: enquiries@linearpro.ltd.uk

Designer Blinds, 45a Commercial Street, New Tredegar, Gwent, NP24 6AA Tel: (01443) 830003

▶ Designer Blinds & Awnings, 56 Beam Street, Nantwich, Cheshire, CW5 5LJ Tel: (01270) 611161 Fax: (01270) 611161

▶ Dobbs, Unit 5 Wainer Close, Lincoln, LN6 3RY Tel: (01522) 500100 Fax: (01522) 500110

▶ Doust Decor, 5 Lonsdale Road, Leamington Spa, Warwickshire, CV32 7EP Tel: (01926) 771736 Fax: (01926) 771736 E-mail: vicki@doustfamily.co.uk

Drapes & Blinds, 289 Ashley Road, Poole, Dorset, BH14 9DZ Tel: (01202) 742042 Fax: (01202) 742042

Durable, 1 498 Reading Road, Winnersh, Wokingham, Berkshire, RG41 5EX Tel: (0870) 2402480 Fax: 0118-989 5209 E-mail: mail@durable.co.uk

East Anglia Blinds Ltd, 6 Barrow Close, Sweet Briar Road Industrial Estate, Norwich, NR3 2AT Tel: (01603) 404040 Fax: (01603) 418398 E-mail: enquires@eablinds.co.uk

Eclipse Blind Systems Ltd, 10 Fountain Crescent, Inchinnan Business Park, Renfrew, PA4 9RE Tel: 0141-812 3322 Fax: 0141-812 5253 E-mail: orrd@eclipseblinds.co.uk

Elbon Blinds, 961 London Road, Leigh-on-Sea, Essex, SS9 3LB Tel: (01702) 713107 Fax: (01702) 713107

Elite Blinds, 160 Vernon Road, Nottingham, NG6 0AD Tel: 0115-942 0898 Fax: 0115-942 3442

Elite Blinds & Tracks Ltd, Unit 10 Chitterley Workshops, Silverton, Exeter, EX5 4DB Tel: (01392) 860141 Fax: (01392) 860141 E-mail: eliteblindsdevon@btconnect.com

Elite Blinds UK, 39 Whalley New Road, Blackburn, BB1 6JY Tel: (01254) 674263 Fax: (01254) 261935 E-mail: sales@eliteblindsuk.com

Elliot & Black Ltd, Red Lonning Indust Estate, Moresby, Whitehaven, Cumbria, CA28 6SJ Tel: (01946) 67139 Fax: (01946) 67139

Essex Blinds & Shutters, Brook Farm, Murthering Lane, Navestock, Romford, RM4 1HL Tel: (01277) 374100 Fax: (01277) 374100 E-mail: essexblinds@talk21.com

Euro Blinds UK, King Street, Newton Abbot, Devon, TQ12 2LG Tel: (01392) 824225 Fax: (01626) 369005 E-mail: info@euroblindsdevon.co.uk

Euroblinds Blinds & Awnings, 36-38 Clune Brae, Port Glasgow, Renfrewshire, PA14 5PA Tel: (01475) 744905 Fax: (01475) 744905 E-mail: sales@euroblinds.co.uk

Fabric Display Ltd, 11 - 12 The Parker Centre, Mansfield Road, Derby, DE21 4SZ Tel: (01332) 382420 Fax: (01332) 290676

Fabric Express Ltd, 54-76 Bissell Street, Birmingham, B5 7HP Tel: 0121-693 3733 Fax: 0121-693 4636 E-mail: info@fabricexpress.co.uk

Fereday & Pocock, 7 The Micro Centre, Gillette Way, Reading, RG2 0LR Tel: 0118-975 5222 Fax: 0118-975 3520

Fiesta Blinds & Fabrics Ltd, 1 Springgrowth Business Park, Springtown Road, Londonderry, BT48 0LY Tel: (028) 7126 2605 Fax: (028) 7137 4387

Flair Blinds Ltd, 123 Chester Road, Sunderland, SR4 7HG Tel: 0191-510 1111 Fax: 0191-510 0666

▶ Flamingo Blinds & Signs, 12 Chaseville Parade, Chaseville Park Road, London, N21 1PG Tel: (020) 8881 0751 Fax: (020) 8881 0771 E-mail: admin@flamingoblinds.co.uk

Flooring & Blinds, 20 Chester Street, Mold, Clwyd, CH7 1EG Tel: (01352) 750874 Fax: (01352) 750872

Forbes Blinds, 45 West Road, Peterhead, Aberdeenshire, AB42 2AR Tel: (01779) 470350 Fax: (01779) 470350

▶ Foyle Blinds Co., Unit 12b Springtown Industrial Estate, Springtown Road, Londonderry, BT48 0LY Tel: (028) 7137 3877 Fax: (028) 7137 3877 E-mail: sales@foyleblinds.com

Frenstar, Unit 240 Ordinance Business Park, Aerodrome Road, Gosport, Hampshire, PO13 0FG Tel: (01329) 233445 Fax: (01329) 233450 E-mail: info@frenstar.co.uk

Garden City Blinds, 7 Factory Place, Saltcoats, Ayrshire, KA21 5LA Tel: (01294) 604016 Fax: (01294) 604016

Garioch Blinds, 1 Garioch Centre, Constitution Street, Inverurie, Aberdeenshire, AB51 4UY Tel: (01467) 625494 Fax: (01467) 625494 E-mail: sale@gariochblinds.co.uk

Gee & Bee Stores & Blinds Ltd, 3 The Parade Manor Road, Cottingley Bingley, Bingley, West Yorkshire, BD16 1RP Tel: (01274) 561299

Gemini Blinds, 2 Greenmeadow Works, Ponthir Road, Caerleon, Newport, NP18 3NY Tel: (01633) 872724 Fax: (01633) 872849

Gemini Blinds, South Arcade, Chester Street, Wrexham, Clwyd, LL13 8BE Tel: (01978) 359972 Fax: (01978) 359972

Gemini Blinds & Curtains, 732 Borough Road, Birkenhead, Merseyside, CH42 9JF Tel: 0151-608 7100 Fax: 0151-608 7100

Gleniffer Blinds, 2 Quarry St, Johnstone, Renfrewshire, PA5 8DZ Tel: (01505) 324448 Fax: 01505 342013

Global Blinds, 636 Mansfield Road, Nottingham, NG5 2GA Tel: 0115-985 8181 Fax: 0115-985 8181

Grays Blinds, 44 Bridge Road, Grays, Essex, RM17 6BU Tel: (01375) 379022 Fax: (01375) 390109

Griffin Grilles & Shutters, Maryfields, Bangors Road North, Iver, Buckinghamshire, SL0 0BH Tel: (01753) 652129 Fax: (01753) 717686

Grosvenor Blinds, 23 Rhos Road, Rhos on Sea, Colwyn Bay, Clwyd, LL28 4RS Tel: (01492) 548866 Fax: (01492) 548866

Group Canopies Ltd, Ramsay Street, Coalsnaughton, Tillicoultry, Clackmannanshire, FK13 6LH Tel: (01259) 753800 Fax: (01259) 753801

Hall, 11 Back Avondale Road East, Heysham, Morecambe, Lancashire, LA3 1SW Tel: (01524) 414638 Fax: (01229) 466462

▶ Hallmark Blinds Ltd, 173 Caledonian Road, London, N1 0SL Tel: (020) 7837 8181 Fax: (020) 7833 1693 E-mail: info@hallmarkblindsltd.co.uk

Harley Blinds Ltd, 13 Ryton Street, Worksop, Nottinghamshire, S80 2AY Tel: (01909) 482320 Fax: (01909) 482639

Harmony Blinds, Harmony House, 11 Slater Street, Oldham, OL9 6ES Tel: 0161-626 9688 Fax: 0161-626 9688

Harmony Blinds Rayleigh Ltd, 128 B High Street, Rayleigh, Essex, SS6 7BU Tel: (01268) 778377 Fax: (01268) 741705

▶ Harris Engineering, 400 Catesby Park, Kings Norton, Birmingham, B38 8SE Tel: 0121-433 3302 Fax: 0121-433 3047

Harrison Blinds, 136 Long Street, Easingwold, York, YO61 3JA Tel: (01347) 822496 Fax: (01347) 823329

Henry's Blind & Carpet Centre, 77-79b Mid Street, Fraserburgh, Aberdeenshire, AB43 9JD Tel: (01346) 514357 Fax: (01346) 514357

▶ The Hessian Co., 5 Weston Avenue, Leighton Buzzard, Bedfordshire, LU7 4QY Tel: (01525) 853950 Fax: (01525) 372877 E-mail: andrew.strang@thehessiancompany.co.uk

▶ Hi Class Blinds, Aberaman Industrial Estate, Aberaman, Aberdare, Mid Glamorgan, CF44 6DA Tel: (01685) 872431 Fax: (01685) 872431

Highbury Design, 3 Catton Road, Arnold, Nottingham, NG5 7JD Tel: 0115-967 1188 E-mail: info@highburyblinds.co.uk

Hillary's Blinds Ltd, 38 Queens Arcade, Queen Street, Cardiff, CF10 4BY Tel: (029) 2022 8911 Fax: (029) 2023 3190 E-mail: sales@hillary.co.uk

Hillarys Blinds Ltd, Private Road 2, Colwick Industrial Estate, Nottingham, NG4 2JR Tel: 0115-961 7420 Fax: 0115-852 2525 E-mail: enquiries@hillarys.co.uk

Hillary's Blinds Ltd, Spire Road, Glover, Washington, Tyne & Wear, NE37 3ES Tel: 0191-461 1800 Fax: (0870) 2430451 E-mail: enquiries@hillarys.co.uk

Home Fair Blinds UK Ltd, Unit 9 Wrightson House, Thornaby, Stockton-on-Tees, Cleveland, TS17 9EP Tel: (01642) 645511 Fax: (01642) 645511

▶ Homechoice Blinds Ltd, 21a Manor Road, Southport, Merseyside, PR9 7LE Tel: (01704) 505656 Fax: (01704) 505992

Homefair Blinds, Viking Precinct, Jarrow, Tyne & Wear, NE32 3LF Tel: 0191-428 6587 Fax: 0191-521 4446

Homefair Blinds Ltd, 59 Fawcett Street, Sunderland, SR1 1SE Tel: 0191-567 8200 Fax: 0191-564 0424

Homefair Blinds North West, 3 Gorton Retail Market, Gortoncross Street, Manchester, M18 8LD Tel: 0161-231 8855 Fax: 0161-231 2828

▶ Homestyle Artprints, 9 A West Church Street, Newmilns, Ayrshire, KA16 9EG Tel: (01560) 329356

▶ Homestyle Blinds Stirling, 45 Barnton Street, Stirling, FK8 1HF Tel: (01786) 450659 Fax: (01786) 451751

Hopsuns Blinds, Hunthay Farm, Axminster, Devon, EX13 5RJ Tel: (01297) 33488 Fax: (01297) 35855

House Of Blinds, 6 Galloway Court, Falkirk, FK1 1HQ Tel: (01324) 613066 Fax: (01324) 814717 E-mail: sales@houseofblinds.co.uk

Humberside Sun Blinds Ltd, Marlin House, Kings Road, Immingham, South Humberside, DN40 1AW Tel: (01469) 574490 Fax: (01469) 578164 E-mail: humbersideblinds@aol.com

Hunter Douglas Ltd, Battersea Road, Stockport, Cheshire, SK4 3EQ Tel: 0161-432 5303 Fax: 0161-431 5087 E-mail: info.general@luxaflex-sunway.co.uk

Hunter Douglas Ltd, Unit 8a Swanscombe Business Centre, London Road, Swanscombe, Kent, DA10 0LH Tel: (01322) 624580 Fax: (01322) 624558 E-mail: info.contract@luxaflex-sunway.co.uk

Hunter Signs Ltd, 5 Pill Farm Industrial Estate, Caldicot, Gwent, NP26 5JG Tel: (01291) 430617 Fax: (01291) 430070 E-mail: alison@westbase.uk.com

Hurst Blinds, Units 6 & 7, 49 Nuffield Industrial Estate, Poole, Dorset, BH17 0RR Tel: (01202) 683300 Fax: (01202) 683300 E-mail: sales@hurstblinds.co.uk

I C Blinds Ltd, 26 Fulton Gardens, Houston, Johnstone, Renfrewshire, PA6 7NU Tel: (01505) 327802 Fax: (01698) 326633

Ichthus Blinds, 2 Hebburn Dr, Bury, Lancashire, BL8 1ED Tel: 0161-762 9599

Ideal Window Blinds, Denmark Street, Glasgow, G22 6DB Tel: 0141-336 4400 Fax: 0141-336 4400

▶ Ideal Window Blinds, 596 Alexandra Parade, Glasgow, G31 3BS Tel: 0141-550 4400 Fax: 0141-550 4400

Image Blinds, 1 Century Park, Garrison Lane, Birmingham, B9 4NZ Tel: 0121-771 3000 Fax: 0121-773 9690 E-mail: sales@imageblinds.co.uk

Indigo Shadings Solutions, Unit 4 New Way Business Centre, Oakdale Road, Wallasey, Merseyside, CH44 7HT Tel: 0151-630 3582 Fax: 0151-630 6914 E-mail: sales@indigoawnings.com

Insu, Unit 305, 183A Harrow Road, London, E11 3PX Tel: (020) 8534 4073 Fax: (020) 8555 3870 E-mail: sales@insu.co.uk

▶ J J Blinds, 32 Samson Crescent, Carluke, Lanarkshire, ML8 4RP Tel: (01555) 750436 Fax: (01555) 750436

J P Knight & Sons Ltd, 98 Frindsbury Road, Rochester, Kent, ME2 4JB Tel: (01634) 723088 Fax: (01634) 722784

Jody Blinds, 34 Garrett Road, Lynx Trading Estate, Yeovil, Somerset, BA20 2TJ Tel: (01935) 420777 Fax: (01935) 434046

Judson Blinds, 11 St. Davids Road North, Lytham St. Annes, Lancashire, FY8 2BB Tel: (01253) 727715 Fax: (01253) 727715 E-mail: blinds@judsonblinds.freeserve.co.uk

Just Blinds & Curtains, 13 Market Place, Dereham, Norfolk, NR19 2AW Tel: (01362) 695437 Fax: (01362) 691465

Just Fabrics, 29-30 Colemeadow Road, Moons Moat North Industrial Estate, Redditch, Worcestershire, B98 9PB Tel: (01527) 63246 Fax: (01527) 63247

▶ JW Blinds, 2 Hollyhill Road, Forest Vale Industrial Estate, Cinderford, Gloucestershire, GL14 2YA Tel: (01594) 829299 Fax: (01594) 829233

K A P Blinds, 6 Lower Grange, Peterhead, Aberdeenshire, AB42 2AT Tel: (01779) 474949 Fax: (01779) 474949

Kay Cee Blinds, 305 Whitmore Way, Basildon, Essex, SS14 2NW Tel: (01268) 293583 Fax: (01268) 293583 E-mail: kencarey@kayceeblinds.fsnet.co.uk

Kelly's Blinds, 115b Claude Road, London, E10 6NF Tel: (020) 8556 4147 Fax: (020) 8584 2299 E-mail: sales@kellysblinds.co.uk

Kingfisher Blinds, The Woodlands, Heol Creigiau, Efail Isaf, Pontypridd, Mid Glamorgan, CF38 1BG Tel: (01443) 208300 Fax: (01443) 208300 E-mail: enquiries@kingfisherblinds.com

Kingfisher Blinds & Curtains Ltd, Kingfisher Court, The Oaks, Coldfield Drive, Redditch, Worcestershire, B98 7ST Tel: (01527) 544844 Fax: (01527) 544648

Kings Lynn Blinds, The Lodge, King's Lynn, Norfolk, PE33 0DR Tel: (01366) 348009 E-mail: enquiries@norfolksunblinds.co.uk

▶ Kirkby Blinds, St. Chads Parade, Liverpool, L32 8RH Tel: 0151-547 3677 Fax: 0151-548 8006 E-mail: kirkby.blinds@merseymail.com

▶ Kover-It, Bath Road, Hare Hatch, Reading, RG10 9SB Tel: 0118-940 6095 Fax: (0871) 9895598

L & S Sun Blinds Ltd, 2 Holme Street, Grimsby, South Humberside, DN32 9AD Tel: (01472) 351855 Fax: (01472) 251011 E-mail: enquiries@blinds4sale.co.uk

Lelliotts Sunblinds Ltd, 80 Sopmting Road, Worthing, West Sussex, BN14 9ES Tel: (01273) 330077 Fax: (01903) 538052 E-mail: lelliottsblinds@btclick.com

Levolux Ltd, 1 Forward Drive, Harrow, Middlesex, HA3 8NT Tel: (020) 8863 9111 Fax: (020) 8863 8760 E-mail: info@levolux.com

Lloyds Blinds, Elim Stores, Llanfachraeth, Holyhead, Gwynedd, LL65 4UP Tel: (0800) 435549 Fax: (01407) 741164 E-mail: sales@lloydsblindsdirect.co.uk

London Blind Co., 205a Long Lane, Bexleyheath, Kent, DA7 5AF Tel: (020) 8303 7964 Fax: (020) 8301 3586

London Contracts Interiors Ltd, 88 Gillespie Road, London, N5 1LN Tel: (020) 7354 0077 Fax: (020) 7354 0077 E-mail: londoncontractsinteriors@hotmail.com

Lorraines Curtains Ltd, 15 Acacia Business Centre, Howard Road, London, E11 3PJ Tel: (020) 8558 5599 Fax: (020) 8558 5599

Louver-Lite Ltd, Ashton Road, Hyde, Cheshire, SK14 4BG Tel: 0161-882 5000 Fax: 0161-882 5009 E-mail: enquiries@louver-liteltd.co.uk

Lustalux Ltd, Unit A3 Anchorage Business Park, Chain Caul Way, Ashton-on-Ribble, Preston, PR2 2YL Tel: (01772) 726622 Fax: (01772) 726644 E-mail: sales@lustalux.co.uk

M J Blinds, 45 Castle Street, Tyldesley, Manchester, M29 8FP Tel: (01942) 882181 Fax: (01942) 882181

▶ indicates data change since last edition

BLINDS – *continued*

Maisun Blinds, 17 High Street, Wall Heath, Kingswinford, West Midlands, DY6 0HB Tel: (01384) 402800 Fax: (01384) 402900

▶ Manhattan Blinds, 121 Brookfield Drive, Liverpool, L9 7AJ Tel: 0151-525 1166 Fax: 0151-525 1144

Mannor Blinds & Curtains, Unit 1 Cavendish Court, Lawkholme Lane, Keighley, West Yorkshire, BD21 3DY Tel: (01535) 665520 Fax: (01535) 691919

Marann Blinds, 18 Ferndale Cresent, Kidderminster, Worcestershire, DY11 5LL Tel: (01562) 67522

Mayfair Blinds, 94 Old Church Street, Manchester, M40 2JF Tel: 0161-684 9960

Menai Blinds, Cibyn Industrial Estate, Caernarfon, Gwynedd, LL55 2BD Tel: (01286) 672595 Fax: (01286) 673937 E-mail: sales@menaiblinds.co.uk

Metro Blinds, 4 Gosford Industrial Estate, Far Gosford Street, Coventry, CV1 5ED Tel: (024) 7652 0613 Fax: (024) 7652 0613

Mico Signs & Blinds Ltd, 123 Kentish Town Road, London, NW1 8PB Tel: (020) 7284 2698 Fax: (020) 7267 5191 E-mail: sales@micosigns.co.uk

▶ Mike Goldrick Window Blinds Ltd, 13 Bramhall Lane, Stockport, Cheshire, SK2 6HT Tel: (01706) 625525 Fax: (01706) 625525

Millennium Blinds Ltd, 3 Northern Buildings, Northern Road, Portsmouth, PO6 3DL Tel: (023) 9222 0204 Fax: (023) 9222 0204

▶ Mirage Blinds, The Birches, Nook Lane, Weston, Shrewsbury, SY4 5LP Tel: (01948) 840956 Fax: (01948) 840956 E-mail: sean@mirageblinds.co.uk

Modern Blinds, 11 Bottesford Road, Scunthorpe, South Humberside, DN16 3HA Tel: (01724) 862472 Fax: (01724) 862472

Moray Firth Blinds Ltd, 24-26 Millbank Road, Munlochy, Ross-Shire, IV8 8ND Tel: (01463) 811274 Fax: (01463) 811274

▶ Natural Blinds, PO Box 2082, Gloucester, GL3 3WX Tel: 0845 056 4415 Fax: 0845 056 4415 E-mail: info@naturalblinds.co.uk

Newton Le Willows Blinds, Stall 55 Market Hall, The Galleries, Wigan, Lancashire, WN1 1PW Tel: (01942) 491494 Fax: (01942) 491494

North Devon Blinds Ltd, 131 East Reach, Taunton, Somerset, TA1 3HN Tel: (01823) 334665 Fax: (01823) 334665

North West Window Blinds, 3 Abercorn Avenue, Portrush, County Antrim, BT56 8HW Tel: (028) 7082 3499 Fax: (028) 7082 3499

Norwich Sunblinds Ltd, 8 St. Benedicts Street, Norwich, NR2 4AG Tel: (01603) 615945 Fax: (01603) 630972 E-mail: sales@norwich-sunblinds.co.uk

Nova Blinds, 28 Frances Street, Newtownards, County Down, BT23 7DN Tel: (028) 9181 8679 Fax: (028) 9181 8679 E-mail: sales@wonderfu1-blinds.co.uk

▶ Nu Look Blinds, 13 Down Business Centre Down Business Park, 46 Belfast Road, Downpatrick, County Down, BT30 9UP Tel: (028) 4461 3509 Fax: (028) 4461 3509

Oakland Supplies, Stevenage Indoor Market, St.Georges Way, Stevenage, Hertfordshire, SG1 1HP Tel: (01438) 314263 Fax: (01438) 314263

▶ Oasis, Unit 12 The Wenta Business Centre, Colne Way, Watford, WD24 7ND Tel: (01923) 201551 Fax: (01923) 201561 E-mail: sales@oasis-blinds.co.uk

▶ Oasis Blinds, 322 Rayleigh Road, Leigh-on-Sea, Essex, SS9 5PU Tel: (01702) 510300 Fax: (01702) 510300

▶ Oasis Blinds, 159 Rice Lane, Liverpool, L9 1AF Tel: 0151-523 1777 Fax: 0151-523 1777

Ocean Air Marine Ltd, 119 Third Avenue, Batchmere, Chichester, West Sussex, PO20 7LB Tel: (01243) 606909 Fax: (01243) 608300

Oriel Blinds, 9 Acorn Close, Rassau, Ebbw Vale, Gwent, NP23 5UP Tel: (01495) 350975 Fax: (01495) 350975

P & M Blinds Ltd, 94 Vallentin Road, London, E17 3JH Tel: (020) 8521 0121 Fax: (020) 8509 0754 E-mail: enquiries@pandmblinds.com

▶ Panos Furnishings, 101a-103 Whitelands Road, Ashton-under-Lyne, Lancashire, OL6 6UG Tel: 0161-368 0808 Fax: 0161-339 0006

Phoenix Blinds, 1 Wolseley Place, Edinburgh, EH8 7AD Tel: 0131-652 9963 Fax: 0131-661 6660

▶ Piccolo, 28 Chester Street, Saltney, Chester, CH4 8BJ Tel: (01244) 677002

Piccolo Blinds, 51 Princes Road, Ellesmere Port, CH65 8AT Tel: 0151-355 6644 Fax: 0151-355 6644

Pioneer Blinds, 265 Bury Old Road, Prestwich, Manchester, M25 1JA Tel: 0161-773 4447 Fax: 0161-773 4447

Pippas Blinds, 84 Mill Road, Cambridge, CB1 2AS Tel: (01223) 364001 Fax: (01733) 703334 E-mail: sales@pippasblinds.co.uk

Precision Blinds Ltd, 3 Sinclair Street, Halkirk, Caithness, KW12 6XP Tel: (01847) 831896 Fax: (01847) 831896

Premier Blinds & Awnings Ltd, 107 The Street, Fetcham, Leatherhead, Surrey, KT22 9RD Tel: (01372) 377112 Fax: (01372) 360824 E-mail: jane@blindsawnings.com

Premier Blinds Wales Ltd, 1 Tyle Teg, Heol Ty Gwyn Industrial Estate, Maesteg, Mid Glamorgan, CF34 0BQ Tel: (01656) 734800 Fax: (01656) 735582

Prestige Blinds & Interiors, Wharf Road, Newport, Gwent, NP19 8ET Tel: (01633) 263103 Fax: (01633) 243613

Rainbow Blinds, 64 Hamilton Road, Rutherglen, Glasgow, G73 3DQ Tel: 0141-613 1347 E-mail: col.stan@ntlworld.com

Raynesway Interiors, 5 227 Derby Road, Chaddesden, Derby, DE21 6SY Tel: (01332) 280585 Fax: (01332) 280585

▶ Reflexol Conservatory Blinds Northwest, 1 Cuba Industrial Estate, Bolton Road North, Ramsbottom, Bury, Lancashire, BL0 0NE Tel: (01706) 825511 Fax: (01706) 825522 E-mail: info@reflexol.com

Regal Sterling Blinds, 16 Thirlmere, Great Ashby, Stevenage, Hertfordshire, SG1 6AH Tel: (01438) 238650 E-mail: gary@regalsterling.com

Regency Blinds, 92 Wansbeck Gardens, Hartlepool, Cleveland, TS26 9JH Tel: (01429) 860057 Fax: 0191-387 5967

Reynolds Blinds, 118 London Road, Headington, Oxford, OX3 9AX Tel: (01865) 764731 Fax: (01865) 742243

Reynolds Blinds, 17 Fleet Street, Swindon, SN1 1RQ Tel: (01793) 526617 Fax: (01793) 526823

Ringway Blinds, PO Box 72, Cheadle, Cheshire, SK8 3DA Tel: 0161-437 4419

Riviera Blinds, The Maisonette, 58 St. Albans Road, Lytham St. Annes, Lancashire, FY8 1XD Tel: (01253) 726843 Fax: (01253) 726843 E-mail: info@blindsandawnings.co.uk

James Robertshaw & Sons (1954) Ltd, Albion Works, Lark Hill, Farnworth, Bolton, BL4 9LB Tel: (01204) 574764 Fax: (01204) 705424 E-mail: sales@jamesrobertshaw.co.uk

Rogers Blinds & Awnings Ltd, Unit 6 Castle Buildings, Gilston Road, Saltash, Cornwall, PL12 6TW Tel: (01752) 840616 Fax: (01752) 840571 E-mail: rogersblinds@supanet.com

Roses Venetian Blind Centre, 14 Highlands, Littleborough, Lancashire, OL15 0DS Tel: 0161-624 8596 Fax: 0161-622 1480 E-mail: info@rosesblinds.co.uk

▶ Ryedale Blinds, Unit 7 Showfield Lane, Malton, North Yorkshire, YO17 6BT Tel: (01653) 696955 Fax: (01653) 696955

Saddlers Blinds, Station Road, Cowfold, Horsham, West Sussex, RH13 8DA Tel: (01403) 865353 Fax: (01403) 865352 E-mail: sales@saddlers-blinds.co.uk

Sander-Shade Blinds Ltd, Treadaway Tech Centre, Treadaway Hill, Loudwater, High Wycombe, Buckinghamshire, HP10 9QL Tel: (01628) 529676 Fax: (01628) 521684 E-mail: sales@blindfashion.co.uk

Sandridge Blinds Ltd, 291 National Avenue, Hull, HU5 4JB Tel: (01482) 492662 Fax: (01482) 492667 E-mail: sales@sandridgeblinds.co.uk

Sapphire Blinds, Unit D4, Olympic Business Park, Drybridge Road, Dundonald, Kilmarnock, Ayrshire, KA2 9BE Tel: (01563) 850258 Fax: (01563) 850258

Second To None, 25 Olive Street, Sunderland, SR1 3PE Tel: 0191-565 9176 Fax: 0191-510 8841

Selkirk Blinds, 54 Forest Road, Selkirk, TD7 5DG Tel: (01750) 21732

▶ Shades Of Doncaster Ltd, Unit 3 Sandall Stones Road, Kirk Sandall Industrial Estate, Doncaster, South Yorkshire, DN3 1QR Tel: (01302) 887106 E-mail: tbell@shadesofdoncaster.co.uk

Shades Window Blind Specialists, 2B Chingford Road, London, E17 4PJ Tel: (020) 8527 3991 Fax: (020) 8523 4476 E-mail: info@shades-london.co.uk

Shadewell Blinds Ltd, St Margarets Lane, Fareham, Hampshire, PO14 4BG Tel: (01329) 841199 Fax: (01329) 842299 E-mail: info@shadewell.co.uk

Shading Systems Ltd, Unit F5 Innsworth Technology Park, Innsworth Lane, Gloucester, GL3 1DL Tel: (01452) 536000 Fax: (01452) 731901 E-mail: sales@shadings.co.uk

▶ Sheer Elegance Soft Furnishings, 4 Prices Way, Brackley, Northamptonshire, NN13 6NR Tel: (07919) 157365 E-mail: caroline@sheer-e.co.uk

Shellbie Blinds, 2 The Parade Cannock Road, Wednesfield, Wolverhampton, WV10 8PZ Tel: (01902) 305400 Fax: (01902) 305400

Sierra Blinds, 10 Openfields Cl, Liverpool, L26 7ZH Tel: 0151-487 3682

The Sign & Blind Centre Ltd, 24 Cavendish Road, New Malden, Surrey, KT3 6DE Tel: (020) 8337 1538 E-mail: signblindcoltd@aol.com

Silent Gliss Ltd, Pyramid Business Park, Poorhole Lane, Broadstairs, Kent, CT10 2PT Tel: (01843) 863571 Fax: (01843) 864503 E-mail: info@silentgliss.co.uk

▶ Simply Blinds, 47 Rossall Road, Thornton-Cleveleys, Lancashire, FY5 1HG Tel: (01253) 863991 Fax: (01253) 863991

Solaire Performance Films, 7 Lincoln Road, Navenby, Lincoln, LN5 0LA Tel: (01522) 811175 Fax: (01522) 811175

Solo Blinds, 5 Northumbria House, Manor Walks Shopping Centre, Cramlington, Northumberland, NE23 6UR Tel: (01670) 730077 Fax: (01670) 590555

Solo Manufacturing Ltd, 18 South Nelson Road, South Nelson Industrial Estate, Cramlington, Northumberland, NE23 1WF Tel: (01670) 733788 Fax: (01670) 590555

Solo Window Blinds, 120 London Road, Long Sutton, Spalding, Lincolnshire, PE12 9EE Tel: (01406) 364447 Fax: (01406) 364447

▶ South East Solar, Alterchrome House, Murray Road, Orpington, Kent, BR5 3QY Tel: (01689) 896345 Fax: (01689) 806549 E-mail: sales@sesolar.co.uk

South Wales Window Blind Centre Ltd, 77 Fleet Street, Swansea, SA1 3US Tel: (01792) 648334 Fax: (01792) 460334

Spectrum Blinds, Millers Avenue, Brynmenyn, Bridgend, CF32 9TD Tel: (01656) 723898 Fax: (01656) 723079

Spectrum Blinds, 519 Leeds Road, Outwood, Wakefield, West Yorkshire, WF1 2PN Tel: (0800) 0965480 Fax: (01924) 372728

Stansons Indoor Blinds, Sterling House, School Road, Hampton Hill, Hampton, Middlesex, TW12 1QL Tel: (020) 8941 8895 Fax: (020) 8979 8156

Starline Blinds West Ltd, Unit 16-17 Western Industrial Estate, Lon-Y-Llyn, Caerphilly, Mid Glamorgan, CF83 1BQ Tel: (029) 2086 0631 Fax: (029) 2086 2000 E-mail: sales@starlineblinds.co.uk

▶ Status Blinds, Unit 3, Rivington Works, Rivington Avenue, St. Helens, Merseyside, WA10 6UU Tel: (01744) 754794 Fax: (01744) 753683 E-mail: enquiries@statusblinds.co.uk

▶ Stephens Sunblinds, Unit Factory Estate, Argyle Street, Hull, HU3 1HD Tel: (01482) 321298 Fax: (01482) 321298

Stock Blinds, 38 Bedford Street, Bognor Regis, West Sussex, PO21 1RP Tel: (01243) 863091 Fax: (01243) 840976

Sun Screens Ltd, 72 Silver Street, Newport Pagnell, Buckinghamshire, MK16 0EG Tel: (01908) 216808 Fax: (01908) 210447

Sun X UK Ltd, 2 Madeira Parade, Madeira Avenue, Bognor Regis, West Sussex, PO22 8DX Tel: (01243) 826441 Fax: (01243) 829691 E-mail: sales@sun-x.co.uk

Sunline Blinds & Shutters Ltd, 1200 Lincoln Road, Peterborough, PE4 6LA Tel: (01733) 320822 Fax: (01733) 578732

Sunlite Blinds, Ravensby Road,, ,Carnoustie, Carnoustie, Angus, DD7 7KK Tel: (01307) 477888 Fax: (01382) 200833

Sunlite Blinds, 43 Foregate Street, Stafford, ST16 2PJ Tel: (01785) 259345 Fax: (01785) 253363

Sunlock Blinds & Interiors, 9 Gerald Road, Gravesend, Kent, DA12 2HT Tel: (01474) 564614 Fax: (01474) 564614

Sunningdale Blinds, 3 Henblas Street, Wrexham, Clwyd, LL13 8AE Tel: (01978) 366661

Sunrite Blinds, 11 Caledonian Lane, Aberdeen, AB11 6XF Tel: (01224) 575201 Fax: (01224) 575201 E-mail: sales@sunrite-blinds-aberdeen.com

▶ Sunrite Blinds Ltd, Caxton Way, Cromer House, Stevenage, Hertfordshire, SG1 2DF Tel: (01438) 722221 Fax: (01438) 740794

Sunseal Blinds, 8 Lymington Road, Willenhall, West Midlands, WV13 2SB Tel: (01902) 607798

Sunset Blinds, 48 Gordon Terrace, Invergordon, Ross-Shire, IV18 0DA Tel: (01349) 854888 Fax: (01349) 854777 E-mail: info@sunsetblinds.com

▶ Super Shade Blinds & Awnings, 3 Miglo Industrial Estate, Yalberton Road, Paignton, Devon, TQ4 7QW Tel: (01803) 522887 Fax: (01803) 522887 E-mail: tony@super-shade.co.uk

Supershades Blinds & Awnings, 167 Alexandra Road, Farnborough, Hampshire, GU14 6SD Tel: (01252) 518493 Fax: (01252) 518493

Supreme Blinds, 62 Shepherds Way, Rickmansworth, Hertfordshire, WD3 7NL Tel: (01923) 773461 Fax: (01923) 773461

Sure Shutters & Blinds Ltd, 24 High Street, Wallingford, Oxfordshire, OX10 0BP Tel: (01491) 824786 Fax: (01491) 824786

Synektics Ltd, 4 Brinksway, Fleet, Hampshire, GU51 3LZ Tel: (01252) 815281 Fax: (01252) 624433 E-mail: sales@synektics.co.uk

Techniblinds Ltd, 16 Plumpton Way, Carshalton, Surrey, SM5 2DG Tel: (020) 8669 1122 Fax: (020) 8669 2244 E-mail: info@techniblinds.co.uk

▶ Timber Blind Co., 37a Broadway Parade, London, N8 9DB Tel: (020) 8341 3603 Fax: 020 83413603

Todays Interiors Ltd, Mode Uk, 64 High Street, Uttoxeter, Staffordshire, ST14 7JD Tel: (01889) 568576 Fax: (01889) 569836 E-mail: lynne.kelly2@ntlworld.com

▶ Torbay Blinds Ltd, Broomhill Way, Torquay, TQ2 7QL Tel: (01803) 617300 Fax: (01803) 616200 E-mail: info@torbayblinds.co.uk

Trade Blinds, 104 Oak Road, Sittingbourne, Kent, ME10 3PR Tel: (01795) 428793

Tudor Blinds, 5 Win Business Park, Canal Quay, Newry, County Down, BT35 6PH Tel: (028) 3082 5900 Fax: (028) 3082 5588

▶ UK Blinds, 48 Moorside Crescent, Drighlington, Bradford, West Yorkshire, BD11 1HS Tel: 0113-285 2895

Val U Blinds, 17 Pilmuir Street, Dunfermline, Fife, KY12 7AJ Tel: (01383) 739476 Fax: (01383) 739476

Vale Blinds, 27 Main Street, Bottesford, Nottingham, NG13 0EP Tel: (01949) 845399 Fax: (01949) 845399

Vantana Blinds, Church Street, Glenrothes, Fife, KY7 5NF Tel: (01592) 610500

Venetian Blind Services, 78 Bleerick Drive, Antrim, BT41 1HX Tel: (028) 9073 9309 Fax: (028) 9442 8866

Vertical Tec, Unit 14 Ash Industrial Estate, Flex Meadow, Harlow, Essex, CM19 5TJ Tel: (020) 7383 3388 Fax: (01279) 413388 E-mail: sales@verticaltec.co.uk

Vision Blinds Stockport, 38b Gorton Road, Stockport, Cheshire, SK5 6AE Tel: 0161-432 2771 Fax: 0161-432 8291 E-mail: sales@vision-blinds.com

▶ Vista Blinds, 150 Sandy Row, Belfast, BT12 5EY Tel: (028) 9024 3615 Fax: (028) 9086 1433

Visual Blinds, Hollings Road, Bradford, West Yorkshire, BD8 8PJ Tel: (01274) 723772 Fax: (01274) 722567 E-mail: sales@visualblinds.co.uk

Weathercare Blinds, 33a Stevenson Road, Ipswich, IP1 2EY Tel: (01473) 221803 Fax: (01473) 280940

West End Blind Co., 152 Broadway, Cardiff, CF24 1NL Tel: (029) 2048 6774 Fax: (029) 2048 6774

Whitmar Blinds, 9a Stour Valley Close, Upstreet, Canterbury, Kent, CT3 4DB Tel: (01227) 860440 Fax: (01227) 860440

Wilmshurst Bros Ltd, North Wing New England House, New England Street, Brighton, BN1 4GH Tel: (01273) 683255 Fax: (01273) 683255 E-mail: wilmshurstbros@yahoo.co.uk

Window Shades, Claremont Building, Old Clatterbridge Road, Wirral, Merseyside, CH63 4JB Tel: (01978) 263000 Fax: (01978) 263222

▶ Windowcharm, Kent Road, Sheffield, S8 9RN Tel: (01709) 379092 Fax: 0114-255 8142

Wirral Blinds, 79 Mill Lane, Wallasey, Merseyside, CH44 5UB Tel: (0800) 0286330 Fax: 0151-638 8163

Wrexham Blinds, The Workshopd, Maes Y Garnedd, Tafarn-Y-Gelyn, Llanferres, Mold, Clwyd, CH7 5SE Tel: (01978) 359788 Fax: (01352) 810234

▶ Wrights Blinds, Highfield House, Fulwood Row, Fulwood, Preston, PR2 5RU Tel: (01772) 796836 Fax: (01772) 798353

Wyatts Blinds, Deans Farm, Stratford sub Castle, Salisbury, SP1 3YP Tel: (01722) 335985 Fax: (01722) 340492

▶ Zenith Blinds Ltd, Gazelle Buildings, Wallingford Road, Uxbridge, Middlesex, UB8 2RW Tel: (01895) 272094 Fax: (01895) 271469 E-mail: enquires@zenithblinds.co.uk

BLISTER PACK CHANGE-PART TOOLING

Electro-mec (Reading) Ltd, 28 Portman Road, Reading, RG30 1EA Tel: 0118-958 2035 Fax: 0118-950 5049 E-mail: info@electromec.co.uk

BLISTER PACKAGING

Ashton Seals Ltd, PO Box 1030, Barnsley, South Yorkshire, S73 0YP Tel: (01226) 273700 Fax: (01226) 756774 E-mail: sales@ashtonseals.com

Belgrave Press Ltd, 320 Melton Road, Leicester, LE4 7SL Tel: 0116-266 2516 Fax: 0116-261 0053 E-mail: sales@belgravepress.co.uk

D E Montfort Packaging, De Montfort Place, 18 Slater St, Leicester, LE3 5ASY Tel: 0116-242 3900 Fax: 0116-253 9055 E-mail: raithbylawrence@btconnect.com

Dekton Components Leicester Ltd, All Saints Road, Leicester, LE3 5AB Tel: 0116-251 8387 Fax: 0116-253 2824 E-mail: mouldmakers@dekton.co.uk

Delta Print & Packaging Ltd, Factory No. 10, Kennedy Way Industrial Estate, Belfast, BT11 9DT Tel: (028) 9062 8626 Fax: (028) 9030 1505 E-mail: info@deltapack.com

Hamilton Plastic Packaging, 18 Galowhill Road, Brackmills Industrial Estate, Northampton, NN4 7EE Tel: (01604) 766329 Fax: (01604) 701790 E-mail: sales@hamiltonpp.com

Strategic Sourcing International Limited, Unit A46, Western Avenue, Bridgend Industrial Estate, Bridgend, Mid Glamorgan, CF31 3RT Tel: 0870 2111195 Fax: 0870 2111197 E-mail: sales@sourcewithus.com

BLISTER PACKAGING CARDS/ PRINTING SERVICES

Arthur W. Clowes Ltd, Unit 2 Pepper Road Hazel Grove, Hazel Grove, Stockport, Cheshire, SK7 5BW Tel: 0161-483 1827 Fax: 0161-483 1827 E-mail: sales@clowesprinters.co.uk

Delta Print & Packaging Ltd, Factory No. 10, Kennedy Way Industrial Estate, Belfast, BT11 9DT Tel: (028) 9062 8626 Fax: (028) 9030 1505 E-mail: info@deltapack.com

Hart Boulton & Co. Ltd, Hampton Street, Joiners Square Industrial Estate, Stoke-on-Trent, ST1 3EX Tel: (01782) 260723 Fax: (01782) 263466

Midland Regional Printers Ltd, Nottingham Road, Nottingham, NG7 7BT Tel: 0115-955 1000 Fax: 0115-955 1012 E-mail: sales@midlandregionalprinters.co.uk

Sonoco Consumer Products Ltd, Stokes Street, Manchester, M11 4QX Tel: 0161-230 7000 Fax: 0161-230 1200E-mail: info@sonoco.com

BLISTER PACKAGING EQUIPMENT

▶ Ridat Co., Unit E1, Neath Vale Supplier Park, Resolven, Neath, West Glamorgan, SA11 4SR Tel: (0845) 0506525 Fax: (0845) 0506526 E-mail: info@ridat.com

BLISTER PACKAGING EQUIPMENT

– continued

Soudal Ltd, Telford Way, Stephenson Industrial Estate, Coalville, Leicestershire, LE67 3HE Tel: (01530) 510502 Fax: (01530) 510970 E-mail: sales@soudal.co.uk

BLISTER PACKAGING FILM

Bhor (Hallbridge Ltd), 28 Brookdene Drive, Northwood, Middlesex, HA6 3NS Tel: (020) 8961 1614 Fax: (020) 8961 1614 E-mail: hallbridge@aol.com

BLISTER PACKAGING SERVICES

Belpac Ltd, Heath Mill Road, Wombourne, Wolverhampton, WV5 8AP Tel: (01902) 897343 Fax: (01902) 893708 E-mail: sales@belpac.co.uk

Hurst Packaging Ltd, Unit 6, Cromwell Centre, Stepfield, Witham, Essex, CM8 3BZ Tel: (01376) 520642 Fax: (01376) 501757 E-mail: sales@hurstpackaging.co.uk

Mac Pac Ltd, 5 Barton Road, Stockport, Cheshire, SK4 3EG Tel: 0161-442 1642 Fax: 0161-442 1643 E-mail: sales@macpac.co.uk

Plymouth Packaging Services Ltd, Baird House, Darklake Close, Estover, Plymouth, PL6 7TJ Tel: (01752) 696330 Fax: (01752) 695589

▶ Primepac Solutions Ltd, Unit 36, Rassau Industrial Estate, Rassau, Ebbw Vale, Gwent, NP23 5SD Tel: (01495) 309367 Fax: 01495 309367 E-mail: sales@primepacsolutions.co.uk

▶ Reactive Solutions, 6 Lakeside Business Park, Pinfold Road, Thurmaston, Leicester, LE4 8AT Tel: 0116-260 3930 Fax: 0116-260 3931 E-mail: dean@reactive-solutions.com

Skincross (Cheshire) Ltd, 6 Riverside, Dukinfield, Cheshire, SK16 4HE Tel: 0161-343 7323 Fax: 0161-343 7324

Strategic Sourcing International Limited, Unit A46, Western Avenue, Bridgend Industrial Estate, Bridgend, Mid Glamorgan, CF31 3RT Tel: 0870 2111195 Fax: 0870 2111197 E-mail: sales@sourcewithus.com

Thermoform Ltd, The Larches Moor Farm Road, Airfield Industrial Estate, Ashbourne, Derbyshire, DE6 1HD Tel: (01335) 343757 Fax: (01335) 300096 E-mail: enquiries@thermoform-limited.co.uk

Westons Development, Pickering Street, Maidstone, Kent, ME15 9RT Tel: 01622 740418 Fax: 01622 743911 E-mail: dbwestons@aol.com

BLOCKING FOIL OR MATERIALS

▶ About Engineering Ltd, Thistleton Road Industrial Estate, Market Overton, Rutland, Oakham, Leicestershire, LE15 7PP Tel: (01572) 768007

▶ Downie Allison Downie Bookbinders Ltd, Unit H, Purdon Street, Partick, Glasgow, G11 6AF Tel: 0141-339 0333 Fax: 0141-337 1113 E-mail: mail@dadbookbinders.com

BLOOD PRESSURE MEASURING EQUIPMENT

A C Cossor & Son Surgical Ltd, Accoson Works, Vale Road, London, N4 1PS Tel: (020) 8800 1172 Fax: (020) 8809 5170 E-mail: accoson@accoson.com

BLOOD TEST EQUIPMENT

Drew Scientific Group plc, Unit 4 Peter Green Way Furness Business Park, Barrow-in-Furness, Cumbria, LA14 2PE Tel: (01229) 432089 Fax: (01229) 432096 E-mail: sales@drew-scientific.com

Hypoguard Ltd, Dock Lane, Melton, Woodbridge, Suffolk, IP12 1PE Tel: (01394) 387333 Fax: (01394) 380152 E-mail: enquiries@hypoguard.co.uk

Owen Mumford Holdings Ltd, Brook Hill, Woodstock, Woodstock, Oxfordshire, OX20 1TU Tel: (01993) 812021 Fax: (01993) 813466 E-mail: info@owenmumford.co.uk

Radiometer Ltd, Manor Court, Manor Royal, Crawley, West Sussex, RH10 9FY Tel: (01293) 517599 Fax: (01293) 531597 E-mail: sales@radiometer.co.uk

The Tintometer Ltd, Lovibond House, Solar Way, Solstice Park, Amesbury, Salisbury, SP4 7SZ Tel: (01980) 664800 Fax: (01980) 625412 E-mail: sales@tintometer.com

Vitech Scientific Ltd, Unit 14 Huffwood Trading Estate, Partridge Green, Horsham, West Sussex, RH13 8AU Tel: (01403) 710479 Fax: (01403) 710382 E-mail: sales@vitech.co.uk

BLOOM CASTING MACHINES

Vai UK Ltd, 7 Fudan Way, Thornaby, Stockton-on-Tees, Cleveland, TS17 6ER Tel: (01642) 662100 Fax: (01642) 606569 E-mail: contact@vai.co.uk

BLOTTING PAPER

Manuscript Pen Co. Ltd, New Road, Highley, Bridgnorth, Shropshire, WV16 6NN Tel: (01746) 861236 Fax: (01746) 862737 E-mail: manuscript@calligraphy.co.uk

Thomas & Green Ltd/Konos Gmbh, 81 Orchard Way, Burmell, Cambridge, CB25 0EQ Tel: 07768 682210 Fax: 01638 605146 E-mail: richard.start@ntlworld.com

BLOUSES

A E Mccandless & Co. Ltd, 23 Bishop Street, Londonderry, BT48 6PR Tel: (028) 7136 2071 Fax: (028) 7126 8996

abacus Careerwear Ltd, Unit D6 Newton Business Park, Cartwright Street, Hyde, Cheshire, SK14 4EH Tel: 0161-351 1211 Fax: 0161-367 8819 E-mail: alan@abacus-careerwear.co.uk

Denby Dale Shirt Co. Ltd, The Old School House, Spark Lane, Mapplewell, Barnsley, South Yorkshire, S75 6AB Tel: (01226) 390211 Fax: (01226) 388192 E-mail: charles@denbydaleshirt.co.uk

Dewhirst Corporate Clothing, 3 Burdon Drive, North West Industrial Estate, Peterlee, County Durham, SR8 2JH Tel: 0191-518 1888 Fax: 0191-586 3167

Double Two Ltd, Thornes Wharf Lane, Wakefield, West Yorkshire, WF1 5RQ Tel: (01924) 375651 Fax: (01924) 290096 E-mail: double2@wsg.co.uk

Graham Hunter (Shirts) Ltd, Springtown Road, Springtown Industrial Estate, Londonderry, BT48 0LY Tel: (028) 7126 2542 Fax: (028) 7126 3556 E-mail: info@hunterapparelsolutions.com

Kathrina Fashions (Marketing) Ltd, 41-45 Little Donegall Street, Belfast, BT1 2JD Tel: (028) 9032 6963 Fax: (028) 9023 3427 E-mail: kathrina@tinyonline.co.uk

▶ lastseason.com, 12 Myton Crescent, Warwick, CV34 6QA Tel: (01926) 313175 E-mail: info@lastseason.com

M T Developments Lancashire Ltd, Cornfield Cliffe, Industry Street, Darwen, Lancashire, BB3 0HA Tel: (01254) 873837 Fax: (01254) 775268 E-mail: info@aprons.co.uk

Polyfashion Ltd, 34 Parliament Street, Small Heath, Birmingham, B10 0QJ Tel: 0121-772 7754 Fax: 0121-766 6744 E-mail: info@polyfashion.co.uk

Revelation Shirts Ltd, Bewsey Street, Warrington, WA2 7JF Tel: (01925) 634372 Fax: (01925) 418438 E-mail: infomation@revelationshirts.co.uk

Roman Originals plc, 29 Inkerman Street, Birmingham, B7 4SB Tel: 0121-380 1900 Fax: 0121-380 1912 E-mail: enquires@romanoriginal.co.uk

Saville Row Shirt Co (Castledowsan) Ltd, Curran Road, Castledawson, Magherafelt, County Londonderry, BT45 8AF Tel: (028) 7946 5000 Fax: (028) 7946 8074

BLOWER FANS, *See Blower etc*

BLOWER HIRE

Industrial Blowers Services Ltd, Trumpers Way, London, W7 2QA Tel: (020) 8571 3988 Fax: (020) 8571 3955 E-mail: sales@ibsblowers.com

BLOWER MAINTENANCE/ REPAIR SERVICES

Adams Ricardo Ltd, Millbrook Road, Yate, Bristol, BS37 5PB Tel: (01454) 311646 Fax: (01454) 324114 E-mail: sales@adamsricardo.com

Crosshall Engineering Ltd, 1 Wellington Street, Liverpool, L3 6JH Tel: 0151-207 4292 Fax: 0151-298 1447 E-mail: sales@crosshall.com

▶ Howden Process Compressors Donkin Division, Holmewood Industrial Park, Park Road, Holmewood, Chesterfield, Derbyshire, S42 5UY Tel: (01246) 859053 Fax: (01246) 859054 E-mail: hdb.sales@howden.com

Industrial Blowers Services Ltd, Trumpers Way, London, W7 2QA Tel: (020) 8571 3988 Fax: (020) 8571 3955 E-mail: sales@ibsblowers.com

BLOWERS, *See also headings under Fan*

Adams Ricardo Ltd, Millbrook Road, Yate, Bristol, BS37 5PB Tel: (01454) 311646 Fax: (01454) 324114 E-mail: sales@adamsricardo.com

Air & Gas Blowers, 22 Hitch Lowes, Chelford, Macclesfield, Cheshire, SK11 9SR Tel: (01625) 860146 Fax: (01625) 860147

B.O.B Stevenson Ltd, Coleman Street, Derby, DE24 8NL Tel: (01332) 574112 Fax: (01332) 757286 E-mail: sales@bobstevenson.co.uk

Barloworld Vacuum Technology P.L.C, Harbour Road, Gosport, Hampshire, PO12 1BG Tel: (0870) 0107666 Fax: (0870) 0106916 E-mail: marketing@barloworldvt.com

C P A Ltd, Calderhead Road, Shotts, Lanarkshire, ML7 4EQ Tel: (01501) 825024 Fax: (01501) 825029 E-mail: cpa@cpa-group.com

Dresser Roots-Holmes Operations, PO Box B7, Huddersfield, HD1 6RB Tel: (01484) 422222 Fax: (01484) 422668 E-mail: dmd_roots@dresser.co.uk

▶ Garden Machinery Direct, 4 Newtown Road, Worcester, WR5 1HF Tel: (01905) 619522 Fax: (01905) 726241 E-mail: sales@gardenmachinerydirect.co.uk

▶ Gardner Denver (Alton) Ltd, Unit 1, Waterbrook Estate, Waterbrook Road, Alton, Hampshire, GU34 2UD Tel: (01420) 544184 Fax: (01420) 544183 E-mail: ukinfo@eu.gardnerdenver.com

Gardner Denver UK Ltd, PO Box 468, Bradford, West Yorkshire, BD5 7HW Tel: (01274) 715240 Fax: (01274) 715241

Houston's Of Cupar Ltd, Station House, Station Road, Cupar, Fife, KY15 5HX Tel: (01334) 655331 Fax: (01334) 656437 E-mail: sales@houstons.co.uk

Howden Industrial, Braehead Industrial Estate, Old Govan Road, Renfrew, PA4 8XJ Tel: 0141-885 7500 Fax: 0141-886 1963 E-mail: hpc.sales@howden.com

▶ Howden Process Compressors Donkin Division, Holmewood Industrial Park, Park Road, Holmewood, Chesterfield, Derbyshire, S42 5UY Tel: (01246) 859053 Fax: (01246) 859054 E-mail: hdb.sales@howden.com

Industrial Blowers Services Ltd, Trumpers Way, London, W7 2QA Tel: (020) 8571 3988 Fax: (020) 8571 3955 E-mail: sales@ibsblowers.com

Kiloheat Ltd, The Industrial Estate, Enterprise Way, Edenbridge, Kent, TN8 6HF Tel: (0870) 0435207 Fax: (01732) 866370 E-mail: sales@kiloheat.co.uk

Royston Fan Co. Ltd, Lumen Road, Royston, Hertfordshire, SG8 7AF Tel: (01763) 241400 Fax: (01763) 245654 E-mail: alan@roystonfan.co.uk

Secomak Holdings Ltd, Unit 330, Centennial Park, Elstree, Borehamwood, Hertfordshire, WD6 3TJ Tel: (020) 8732 1300 Fax: (020) 8732 1301 E-mail: sales@secomak.com

Sifan System Ltd, Northwood Road, Windrush Industrial Park, Witney, Oxfordshire, OX29 7EE Tel: 01993 771336 Fax: 01993 771336

Thelcastle Ltd, Unit 14, Newhaven Business Park, Barton Lane, Eccles, Manchester, M30 0HH Tel: 0161 7880345

Torin Ltd, Drakes Way, Swindon, SN3 3JB Tel: (01793) 524291 Fax: (01793) 486570 E-mail: sales@torin-sifan.com

TransAirVac International Ltd, PO Box 491, Newcastle, Staffordshire, ST5 0TW Tel: (01782) 710282 Fax: (01782) 710126 E-mail: office@transairvac.com

Vantage Power Drives Ltd, 244 Bromford Lane, West Bromwich, West Midlands, B70 7HX Tel: 0121-500 5525 Fax: 0121-553 2629

BLOWERS, STAINLESS STEEL

Hadron Engineering Ltd, Building 8/4 Carlson Suite, Vantage Point Business Village, Mitcheldean, Gloucestershire, GL17 0DD Tel: (01594) 546440 Fax: (01594) 546441 E-mail: info@hadronengineering.co.uk

BLOWING AGENTS

Huntsman, Hitchen Lane, Shepton Mallet, Somerset, BA4 5TZ Tel: (01749) 335200 Fax: (01749) 344221

West & Senior Ltd, Milltown Street, Radcliffe, Manchester, M26 1WE Tel: 0161-724 7131 Fax: 0161-724 9519 E-mail: david.brown@westsenior.co.uk

BLOWN POLYETHYLENE (PE) FILM EXTRUSION TO SPECIFICATION

Tech Folium Ltd, Triumph Trading Park, Speke Hall Road, Speke, Liverpool, L24 9GQ Tel: 0151-486 4300 Fax: 0151-486 3335

BLOWOUT PREVENTERS

Cooper Energy Services, Mondial House, 5 Mondial Way, Hayes, Middlesex, UB3 5AR Tel: (020) 8990 1900 Fax: (020) 8990 1911

BLOWTORCHES

Bullfinch (Gas Equipment) Ltd, Diadem Works, Kings Road, Tyseley, Birmingham, B11 2AJ Tel: 0121-706 6301 Fax: 0121-707 0995 E-mail: sales@bullfinch-gas.co.uk

BLUE CHEESE

Ashley Chase Estate Ltd, Parks Farm, Litton Cheney, Dorchester, Dorset, DT2 9AZ Tel: (01308) 482580 Fax: (01308) 482662 E-mail: cheese@fordfarm.com

BLUETOOTH WIRELESS TECHNOLOGY SYSTEMS

C S W Erlang Ltd, Unit 10, Green Farm, Fritwell, Bicester, Oxfordshire, OX27 7QU Tel: (01869) 345050 Fax: (01869) 345954 E-mail: mandy.jenkins@erlangcsw.co.uk

T D K Systems Europe Ltd, 126 Colindale Avenue, London, NW9 5HD Tel: (020) 8938) 1000 Fax: (020) 8905 8606 E-mail: info@tdksys.com

BOARD CUTTING MACHINERY

Homag UK Ltd, 10c Sills Road, Castle Donington, Derby, DE74 2US Tel: (0870) 2433244 Fax: (01332) 856400 E-mail: sales@homag-uk.co.uk

BOARDROOM DESIGN OR PLANNING CONSULTANTS

▶ Foxley Tagg Planning Ltd, Corinth House, Bath Road, Cheltenham, Gloucestershire, GL53 7SL Tel: (01242) 222107 Fax: (01242) 222112 E-mail: mail@ftlplanning.co.uk

BOAT ACCESSORIES, CANAL/ NARROW ETC

A B E Specialist Products, Haymoor Hall, Wybunbury Lane, Wybunbury, Nantwich, Cheshire, CW5 7HD Tel: (01270) 841174 Fax: (01270) 841128 E-mail: enquiries@haymoorleisure.co.uk

A G Lester & Sons Ltd, Unit 1 Erskine Street, Birmingham, B7 4RU Tel: 0121-359 1018 Fax: 0121-359 1018 E-mail: info@aglesterandsons.sagenet.co.uk

Colecraft Engineering Ltd, The Old Timber Yard, Southam Road, Long Itchington, Southam, Warwickshire, CV47 9QL Tel: (01926) 817070 Fax: (01926) 815124 E-mail: sales@colecraft.co.uk

Fox's Marina Ipswich Ltd, The Strand, Ipswich, IP2 8SA Tel: (01473) 689111 Fax: (01473) 601737E-mail: foxsmarina@oystermarine.com

High Line Yachting Ltd, Mansion Lane, Iver, Buckinghamshire, SL0 9RG Tel: (01753) 651496 Fax: (01753) 630095 E-mail: sales@high-line.co.uk

BOAT BUILDERS OR REPAIRERS, *See also other nearby headings for particular types*

▶ A & R Way Boatbuilding, 5 Creag Ghlas, Cairnbaan, Lochgilphead, Argyll, PA31 8UE Tel: (01546) 606657 Fax: (01546) 606326 E-mail: arway@tiscali.co.uk

Aldeburgh Boatyard Co. Ltd, Fort Green, Aldeburgh, Suffolk, IP15 5DE Tel: (01728) 452019 Fax: (01728) 452019

Amble Boat Co. Ltd, The Boatyard, 14 Coquet Street, Amble, Morpeth, Northumberland, NE65 0DJ Tel: (01665) 710267 Fax: (01665) 711354 E-mail: sales@ambleboat.co.uk

Arcrite Fabrications, Fleming Road, Corby, Northamptonshire, NN17 4SW Tel: (01536) 204969 Fax: (01536) 402456 E-mail: email@genbridge.fsnet.co.uk

Ardfern Yacht Centre, Ardfern, Lochgilphead, Argyll, PA31 8QN Tel: (01852) 500636 Fax: (01852) 500624 E-mail: office@ardfernyacht.co.uk

Ardmaleish Boatbuilding Co Ltd, Ardmaleish, Port Bannatyne, Isle of Bute, PA20 0QY Tel: (01700) 502007 Fax: (01700) 502257 E-mail: info@ardmaleishboatbuilding.co.uk

▶ B W M Ribs, Satchell Lane, Hamble, Southampton, SO31 4HQ Tel: (023) 8045 4719 Fax: (023) 8045 4719

Bangor Yacht Services, 98 Warren Road, Donaghadee, County Down, BT21 0PQ Tel: (028) 9188 8600 Fax: (028) 9188 8481

Barry Cousins, High House Wharf, Heyford Lane, Weedon, Northampton, NN7 4SF Tel: (01327) 342300 Fax: (01327) 342300

Barton Cruisers, Welford Road, Barton, Bidford-on-Avon, Alcester, Warwickshire, B50 4NP Tel: (01789) 772003 Fax: (01789) 772112

Bay Class Yachts Ltd, Conyer Wharf, Teynham, Sittingbourne, Kent, ME9 9HN Tel: (01795) 520787 Fax: (01795) 520788

Baymarine Industrial Services Ltd, Aqua-Plan House, Burt Street, Cardiff, CF10 5FZ Tel: (029) 2045 3700 Fax: (029) 2045 0077

Beaves & Son, Haroden, Woodrolfe Road, Tollesbury, Maldon, Essex, CM9 8SD Tel: (01621) 868870

Birchwood Marine Ltd, Fulwood Road North, Sutton-in-Ashfield, Nottinghamshire, NG17 2NB Tel: (01623) 515133 Fax: (01623) 440328 E-mail: info@birchwood.co.uk

Black Country Narrow Boats, Waterside Cottage, Prestwood Drive, Stourbridge, West Midlands, DY7 5QT Tel: (01384) 872135 Fax: (01384) 878968

Black Swan Restoration Ltd, 27 Gloucester Street, Coventry, CV1 3BZ Tel: (024) 7625 6061 Fax: (024) 7625 6061

▶ indicates data change since last edition

BOAT BUILDERS OR REPAIRERS – *continued*

Bloodaxe Boats, 9 Somerton Industrial Park, Newport Road, Cowes, Isle of Wight, PO31 8PB Tel: (01983) 298716 Fax: (01983) 299397 E-mail: sales@bloodaxeboats.co.uk

Blue Boats Boat Yard, Bryher, Isles of Scilly, TR23 0PR Tel: (01720) 423095 Fax: (01720) 423011

Blue C Marine Ltd, Firs Industrial Estate, Kidderminster, Worcestershire, DY11 7QN Tel: (01562) 746336 Fax: (01562) 742255 E-mail: info@bluecmarine.com

Boat Harbour London Ltd, 40 High Street Colliers Wood, London, SW19 2AB Tel: (020) 8542 5857 Fax: (020) 8542 0284

The Boatworks, Benson, Wallingford, Oxfordshire, OX10 8SJ Tel: (01491) 833526

Bonwitco Boatbuilders, Torr Quarry Industrial Estate, East Allington, Totnes, Devon, TQ9 7QQ Tel: (01548) 521561 Fax: (01548) 521560 E-mail: franciswills@aol.com

Braidbar Boats Ltd, Lyme Road, Poynton, Stockport, Cheshire, SK12 1TH Tel: (01625) 873471

▶ Brayzel Narrow Boats, Nateby Crossing Lane, Nateby, Preston, PR3 0JJ Tel: (01995) 601515 Fax: (01995) 601515

Bridge Boats Ltd, Fry's Island, De Montfort Road, Reading, RG1 8DG Tel: 0118-959 0346 Fax: 0118-959 1114 E-mail: sales@bridgeboats.com

Bridgend Boat Co., Western Hangar, Lawrence Road, Plymouth, PL9 9SJ Tel: (01752) 404082 Fax: (01752) 403405

Broadland Passenger Craft, George Smith & Sons, The Rhond, Hoveton, Norwich, NR12 8UE Tel: (01603) 782527 Fax: (01603) 784124

Broom Boats Ltd, Brundall, Norwich, NR13 5PX Tel: (01603) 712334 Fax: (01603) 714803 E-mail: enquiries@broomboats.com

John Broom Boats Ltd, Covey Lane, Surlingham, Norwich, NR14 7AL Tel: (01508) 538929 Fax: (01508) 538909 E-mail: info@johnbroom.co.uk

Buccaneer Boats & Mouldings, Unit 20 The Forge Industrial Park, North Roskear, Camborne, Cornwall, TR14 0AW Tel: (01209) 710398 Fax: (01209) 710398

Buchan Hall & Mitchell, Reclaimed Ground, Fraserburgh, Aberdeenshire, AB43 9TD Tel: (01346) 513336 Fax: (01346) 513345

Buckie Shipyard Ltd, Commercial Road, Buckie, Banffshire, AB56 1UR Tel: (01542) 832727 Fax: (01542) 831825 E-mail: office@buckieshipyard.com

Bucklers Hard Boat Builders Ltd, The Agamemnon Yard, Bucklers Hard, Beaulieu, Brockenhurst, Hampshire, SO42 7XB Tel: (01590) 616214 Fax: (01590) 616267

Burghead Boat Centre, Findhorn Boat Yard, Findhorn, Forres, Morayshire, IV36 3YE Tel: (01309) 690099 Fax: (01309) 690165

▶ C & J Marine Services Ltd, Stephenson Street, Wallsend, Tyne & Wear, NE28 6UE Tel: 0191-295 0072

C Toms & Son Ltd, East Hill, East Street, Polruan, Fowey, Cornwall, PL23 1PB Tel: (01726) 870232 Fax: (01726) 870318

Cambrian Marine Services Ltd, Ferry Road, Cardiff, CF11 0JL Tel: (029) 2034 3459 Fax: (029) 2034 5116 E-mail: cambrianmarine@aol.com

Canal Cruising Co. Ltd, Crown Street, Stone, Staffordshire, ST15 8QN Tel: (01785) 813982 Fax: (01785) 819041 E-mail: kwyatt5745@aol.com

Caterelle Ltd, Downs Road Boat Yard, Downs Road, Maldon, Essex, CM9 5HG Tel: (01621) 853330 Fax: (01621) 853330

Chelsea Yacht & Boat Co. Ltd, Anchor House, 106 Cheyne Walk, London, SW10 0DG Tel: (020) 7352 1427 Fax: (020) 7352 1428

Clare Lallow, 3 Medina Road, Cowes, Isle of Wight, PO31 7BU Tel: (01983) 292112 Fax: (01983) 281180 E-mail: lallows@lallowsboatyard.com

Coastal Marine (Boatbuilders) Ltd, Browns Bank, Eyemouth, Berwickshire, TD14 5DQ Tel: (01890) 750328 Fax: (01890) 751325

Colecraft Engineering Ltd, The Old Timber Yard, Southam Road, Long Itchington, Southam, Warwickshire, CV47 9QL Tel: (01926) 817070 Fax: (01926) 815124 E-mail: sales@colecraft.co.uk

Cordeal Ltd, 89 High Street, Cowes, Isle of Wight, PO31 7AW Tel: (01983) 298745 Fax: (01983) 291598E-mail: jcboats@aol.com

Corpach Boatbuilding Co. Ltd, Corpach, Fort William, Inverness-Shire, PH33 7NN Tel: (01397) 772861 Fax: (01397) 772765

Corvette Marine Ltd, 19 Station Road, Reedham, Norwich, NR13 3TA Tel: (01493) 701260 Fax: (01493) 701455 E-mail: sales@corvettemarine.co.uk

Cory Environmental Municipal Services, Riverside, London, SE7 7SU Tel: (020) 8858 2008 Fax: (020) 8858 2107

Cox's Boatyard Ltd, Staithe Road, Barton Turf, Norwich, NR12 8AZ Tel: (01692) 536206 Fax: (01692) 536206 E-mail: info@coxsboatyard.co.uk

Creekside Boatyard Ltd, Creekside Boatyard, Old Mill Creek, Dartmouth, Devon, TQ6 0HN Tel: (01803) 832649

Crown Cruisers Ltd, Yacht Station, Somerleyton, Lowestoft, Suffolk, NR32 5QW Tel: (01502) 730335 Fax: (01502) 730310

▶ Culture Boats, Unit 43 Weaver Industrial Estate, Blackburn Street, Liverpool, L19 8JA Tel: 0151-494 1234 Fax: 0151-494 9494

Cygnus Marine Ltd, 6 Annear Road, Penryn, Cornwall, TR10 9ER Tel: (01326) 372970 Fax: (01326) 374585 E-mail: info@cygnusmarine.co.uk

▶ D B Boat Fitting Ltd, Braunston Marina Trade Centre, The Wharf, Braunston, Daventry, Northamptonshire, NN11 7JH Tel: (01788) 891727 Fax: (01788) 891727 E-mail: lyn@dbboatfitting.co.uk

Dale Sailing Co Ltd, Brunel Quay, Neyland, Milford Haven, Dyfed, SA73 1PY Tel: (01646) 601061 Fax: (01646) 601061 E-mail: enquiries@dale-sailing.co.uk

Darthaven Marina Ltd, Brixham Road, Kingswear, Dartmouth, Devon, TQ6 0SG Tel: (01803) 752733 Fax: (01803) 752722

Deben Cruises, The Quay, Waldringfield, Woodbridge, Suffolk, IP12 4QZ Tel: (01473) 736260 Fax: (01473) 736260

Delta Power Services, Newby Road Industrial Estate, Newby Road, Hazel Grove, Stockport, Cheshire, SK7 5DR Tel: 0161-456 6588 Fax: 0161-456 6686 E-mail: cdyas@deltarib.u-net.com

▶ Dex Tamar Marine, 3, The Mews, Chapeldown Road, Torpoint, Cornwall, PL11 2NW Tel: (01752) 812214 Fax: (01752) 812666

Douglas Marine Ltd, Becconsall Lane, Hesketh Bank, Preston, PR4 6RR Tel: (01772) 812462 Fax: (01772) 812462 E-mail: ray@douglas-marine.co.uk

Dover Yacht Co. Ltd, Custom House Quay, Dover, Kent, CT17 9DG Tel: (01304) 201073 Fax: (01304) 207458 E-mail: peter.butler6@btinternet.com

E C Landamore & Co. Ltd, Elanco Works, Marsh Road, Hoveton, Norwich, NR12 8UH Tel: (01603) 782212 Fax: (01603) 784166

Eel Pie Island Slipways Ltd, Eel Pie Island, Twickenham, TW1 3DY Tel: (020) 8891 4481 Fax: (020) 8891 4481

Egerton Narrow Boats Ltd, Edge Lane, Stretford, Manchester, M32 8HW Tel: 0161-864 1066 Fax: 0161-864 1066 E-mail: sales@egertonnarrowboats.co.uk

Elephant Boatyard Ltd, Lands End Road, Bursledon, Southampton, SO31 8DN Tel: (023) 8040 3268 Fax: (023) 8040 5085

Emsworth Shipyard Ltd, Thorney Road, Emsworth, Hampshire, PO10 8BP Tel: (01243) 375211 Fax: (01243) 377259 E-mail: sales@tarquin-boats.com

Eton Racing Boats, Brocas Street, Eton, Windsor, Berkshire, SL4 6BW Tel: (01753) 671294 Fax: (01753) 671293

Exe Boat Store Marine Ltd, 6 Camperdown Terrace, Exmouth, Devon, EX8 1EJ Tel: (01395) 263095 Fax: (01395) 263095

Fairline Boats plc, Barnwell Road, Oundle, Peterborough, PE8 5PA Tel: (01832) 273661 Fax: (01832) 273432 E-mail: sales@fairline.com

Falmouth Boat Construction Ltd, Little Falmouth, Flushing, Falmouth, Cornwall, TR11 5TJ Tel: (01326) 374309 Fax: (01326) 377689 E-mail: bernie@fal-boat.demon.co.uk

Farndon Marina, North End, Farndon, Newark, Nottinghamshire, NG24 3SX Tel: (01636) 705483 Fax: (01636) 701457 E-mail: sales@farndonmarina.co.uk

Felix Engineering, Central Avenue, Lee Mill Industrial Estate, Ivybridge, Devon, PL21 9PE Tel: (01752) 698031 Fax: (01752) 690694

Felixstowe Ferry Boat Yard Ltd, The Ferry, Felixstowe, Suffolk, IP11 9RZ Tel: (01394) 282173 Fax: (01394) 282173

Ferry Boat Yard, Ferry Boatyard, Lower Upnor, Upnor, Rochester, Kent, ME2 4XA Tel: (01634) 723272

Fiddlers Ferry Boatyard, Ferry Boatyard, Fiddlers Ferry, Penketh, Warrington, WA5 2UJ Tel: (01925) 727519 Fax: (01925) 727519

Firmhelm Ltd, Pwllheli Boatyard, Outer Harbour, Pwllheli, Gwynedd, LL53 5AY Tel: (01758) 612244 Fax: (01758) 614790 E-mail: enqieries@firmhelm.com

Fowey Boat Yard, 10 Passage Street, Fowey, Cornwall, PL23 1DE Tel: (01726) 832194

Freshwater Cruisers, Riverside Estate, Brundall, Norwich, NR13 5PS Tel: (01603) 717355 Fax: (01603) 717355

G Hewitt, Greenway, Stiffkey, Wells-next-the-Sea, Norfolk, NR23 1QF Tel: (01328) 830078

G & J Reeves, Coventry Bridge Yard, Tomlow Road, Stockton, Southam, Warwickshire, CV47 8HX Tel: (01926) 815581 Fax: (01926) 811675 E-mail: julie@reevesboatsfsnet.co.uk

G R P Mouldings, Oakley Wharf, Porthmadog, Gwynedd, LL49 9AS Tel: (01766) 514353 Fax: (01766) 514353 E-mail: info@grpcanopies.co.uk

Gary Chabot, Newhaven Marina, West Quay, Newhaven, E. Sussex, BN9 9BY Tel: 01273 611076 Fax: 01273 611076

Gemini Industries UK Ltd., 18-20 Canterbury Road,, Whitstable, Kent, CT5 4EY Tel: 01406 350572 E-mail: info@geminiindustries.co.uk

George Wilson & Sons Ltd, Thames Street, Sunbury-on-Thames, Middlesex, TW16 6AQ Tel: (01932) 782067 Fax: (01932) 782067

Goodchild Marine Services, Burgh Castle Yacht Station, Butt Lane, Burgh Castle, Great Yarmouth, Norfolk, NR31 9PZ Tel: (01493) 782301 Fax: (01493) 782306 E-mail: info@goodchildmarine.co.uk

Gosport Boatyard Ltd, Harbour Road, Gosport, Hampshire, PO12 1BJ Tel: (023) 9252 6534 Fax: (023) 9258 6216

Grand Junction Boat Co., Canal Maintenance Yard, Blisworth Arm, Blisworth, Northampton, NN7 3EF Tel: (01604) 858043 Fax: (01604) 858043

Green Marine Ltd, Waterloo Road, Lymington, Hampshire, SO41 9DB Tel: (01590) 672356 Fax: (01590) 679124 E-mail: high@greenmarine.co.uk

Gweek Quay Boatyard, Gweek, Helston, Cornwall, TR12 6UF Tel: (01326) 221657 Fax: (01326) 221685 E-mail: info@gweek-quay.com

H Attrill & Sons Isle Of Wright Ltd, The Duver, St. Helens, Ryde, Isle of Wight, PO33 1YB Tel: (01983) 872319 Fax: (01983) 874313 E-mail: attrillboats@aol.com

H J Mears & Son Boat Builders, The Harbour, Axmouth, Seaton, Devon, EX12 4AA Tel: (01297) 20964 Fax: (01297) 20964

Haines Marine Construction, Old Mill Works, The Street, Catfield, Great Yarmouth, Norfolk, NR29 5DH Tel: (01692) 582180 Fax: (01692) 582441 E-mail: bob@hainesmarine.co.uk

Frank Halls & Son, Mill Lane, Walton on the Naze, Essex, CO14 8PF Tel: (01255) 675596 Fax: (01255) 677772

Harbour Marine Services Ltd, Blackshore, Southwold, Suffolk, IP18 6TA Tel: (01502) 724721 Fax: (01502) 722060 E-mail: johnbuckley@harbourmarine.uk.com

Hardy Marine Ltd, Gaymers Way, North Walsham, Norfolk, NR28 0AN Tel: (01692) 408700 Fax: (01692) 406483 E-mail: sales@hardymarine.co.uk

Harold Hayles Yarmouth Ltd, The Quay, Bridge Road, Yarmouth, Isle of Wight, PO41 0RS Tel: (01983) 760373 Fax: (01983) 760666 E-mail: info@spurscutters.co.uk

George Harris, The Towing Path, Oxford, OX4 4EL Tel: (01865) 243870 Fax: (01865) 243870 E-mail: info@harrisracing.co.uk

Hayling Pontoons Ltd, Mill Rithe, Hayling Island, Hampshire, PO11 0QQ Tel: (023) 9246 3592 Fax: (023) 9246 4432 E-mail: haylingyacht@mcmail.com

Henwood & Dean, Greenlands Farm, Dairy Lane, Hambleden, Henley-on-Thames, Oxfordshire, RG9 3AS Tel: (01491) 571692 Fax: (01491) 411514

Heritage Boatbuilders, Kings Road, Evesham, Worcestershire, WR11 3BU Tel: (01386) 48882 Fax: (01386) 48882 E-mail: enquiries@heritageboatbuilders.co.uk

Honnor Marine Ltd, Caxton Street, Heywood, Lancashire, OL10 1AL Tel: (01706) 368068 Fax: (01706) 623189 E-mail: info@honnormarine.co.uk

J Buchan & Sons Ltd, 2 Baltic Place, Peterhead, Aberdeenshire, AB42 1TF Tel: (01779) 475395 Fax: (01779) 479763

▶ J D Narrow Boats, Unit 20, Mount Industrial Estate, Mount Road, Stone, Staffordshire, ST15 8LL Tel: (01785) 815559 Fax: (01785) 815559

J F Donne, 865 Wolseley Road, Plymouth, PL5 1JX Tel: (01752) 362517

J & G Forbes Ltd, Balaclava Quay, Fraserburgh, Aberdeenshire, AB43 9EB Tel: (01346) 518641 Fax: (01346) 571152

J & G Forbes Ltd, Balaclava Quay, Fraserburgh, Aberdeenshire, AB43 9EB Tel: (01346) 518641 Fax: (01346) 571152 E-mail: jforbesco@aol.com

J K Marine, Dell Quay Yard, Dell Quay Road, Chichester, West Sussex, PO20 7EB Tel: (01243) 785954 Fax: (01243) 781567 E-mail: info@dellquay.com

J S B Tarbert Ltd, 24 Harbour Street, Tarbert, Argyll, PA29 6UD Tel: (01880) 820180 Fax: (01880) 820180

Jackson Yacht Services Ltd, Le Boulevard, St. Aubin, Jersey, JE3 8AB Tel: (01534) 743819 Fax: (01534) 745952 E-mail: sales@jacksonyatch.com

Janousek Racing Boats Ltd, 1a Abbot Close, Byfleet, West Byfleet, Surrey, KT14 7JN Tel: (01932) 353421 Fax: (01932) 336381

Barry Jones & Son, Rotherwood, 235 Botley Rd, Southampton, SO19 0NL Tel: 023 80406396

K G Mccoll & Co. Ltd, Kilmelford Yachthaven, Kilmelford, Oban, Argyll, PA34 4XD Tel: (01852) 200248 Fax: (01852) 200343 E-mail: info@kilmelfordyachthaven.co.uk

K & K Mouldings Ltd, Bridge Road, Ely, Cambridgeshire, CB7 4DY Tel: (01353) 663726 Fax: (01353) 668766 E-mail: sales@bridgeboatyard.com

Kegworth Marine, Kingston Lane, Kegworth, Derby, DE74 2FS Tel: (01509) 672300 Fax: (01509) 672300

Kingsley Farrington, Whitlingham Lane, Trowse, Norwich, NR14 8TR Tel: (01603) 666545 Fax: (01603) 666545

Kirton Kayaks Ltd, Marsh Lane, Lords Meadow Industrial Estate, Crediton, Devon, EX17 1ES Tel: (01363) 773295 Fax: (01363) 775908 E-mail: sales@kirton-kayaks.co.uk

L D C Racing Sail Boats, Trafalgar Close, Chandler's Ford, Eastleigh, Hampshire, SO53 4BW Tel: (023) 8027 4500 Fax: (023) 8027 4800 E-mail: info@ldcracingsailboats.co.uk

Langley Mill Boat Yard Ltd, Derby Road, Langley Mill, Nottingham, NG16 4AA Tel: (01773) 760758

Lower Park Marina Ltd, Kelbrook Road, Barnoldswick, Lancashire, BB18 5TB Tel: (01282) 815883 Fax: (01282) 816421

Ludham Bridge Services, Ludham Bridge, Ludham, Great Yarmouth, Norfolk, NR29 5NX Tel: (01692) 630486

Lymington Yacht Haven Ltd, Kings Saltern Road, Lymington, Hampshire, SO41 3QD Tel: (01590) 677071 Fax: (01590) 678186 E-mail: admin@havenboatyard.com

M D Heard, Tregatreath Yacht Yard, Tregatreath, Mylor Bridge, Falmouth, Cornwall, TR11 5NS Tel: (01326) 374441 Fax: (01326) 372469

James McCaughey (Boatbuilders) Ltd, Harbour Quay, Wick, Caithness, KW1 5EP Tel: (01955) 602858 Fax: (01955) 602858

J. Mccaughry Ltd, Harbour Quay, Wick, Caithness, KW1 5EP Tel: 01955 603701

Mackay Boatbuilders Arbroath Ltd, The Boatyard, Old Shore Head, Arbroath, Angus, DD11 1BB Tel: (01241) 872879 Fax: (01241) 872879 E-mail: mackayboatbuilders@connectfree.co.uk

Mckellars Slipway Ltd, Shore Road, Kilcreggan, Helensburgh, Dunbartonshire, G84 0JL Tel: (01436) 842334

Mallaig Boatbuilding & Engineering Co. Ltd, Harbour Slipways, Mallaig, Inverness-Shire, PH41 4QS Tel: (01687) 462304 Fax: (01687) 462378

▶ Manxboats.com, Unit 5,, Balderton Court, Balthane Industrial Estate, Ballasalla, Isle Of Man, IM9 2AJ Tel: (01624) 825040 E-mail: manxboats@manx.net

Marine Aid, Tidesreach Convent Meadows Caravan Park, The Quay, Christchurch, Dorset, BH23 1BD Tel: (01202) 477484 Fax: (01202) 477484

Maritime Workshop, 50 Ferrol Road, Gosport, Hampshire, PO12 4UG Tel: (023) 9252 7805 Fax: (023) 9258 6822 E-mail: maritimeworkshop@btconnect.com

Martham Boat Building & Development Co. Ltd, Cess Road, Martham, Great Yarmouth, Norfolk, NR29 4RF Tel: (01493) 740249 Fax: (01493) 740065 E-mail: info@marthamboats.com

Mashford Bros Ltd, Shipbuilding Yard, Cremyll, Torpoint, Cornwall, PL10 1HY Tel: (01752) 822232 Fax: (01752) 823059 E-mail: mashfords@btconnect.com

Meeching Boats, Denton Island, Newhaven, East Sussex, BN9 9BA Tel: (01273) 514907 Fax: (01273) 514907

Mike's Boatyard Ltd, 17 High Street, Old Leigh, Leigh-On-Sea, Essex, SS9 2EN Tel: (01702) 713151 Fax: (01702) 480092

Milburn Boats, Bridge Grounds, Shuckburgh Road, Staverton, Daventry, Northamptonshire, NN11 6BG Tel: (01327) 702164 Fax: (01327) 702258 E-mail: enquiries@milburnboats.co.uk

Miller Methil Ltd, 40 Links Road, Lundin Links, Leven, Fife, KY8 6AU Tel: (01333) 422694 Fax: (01333) 426330 E-mail: millermethil@btconnect.com

▶ MiTi Co, Ford Mill farm, Woolsery, Bideford, Devon, EX39 5RF Tel: (01409) 241289 E-mail: mikeivory@miticompany.co.uk

Multimarine Composites Ltd, Foss Quarry, Mill Road, Millbrook, Torpoint, Cornwall, PL10 1EN Tel: (01752) 823513 Fax: (01752) 823179 E-mail: info@multimarine.co.uk

Narrowcraft Ltd, Robeys Lane, Alvecote, Tamworth, Staffordshire, B78 1AS Tel: (01827) 898585 Fax: (01825) 897700 E-mail: sales@narrowboat.co.uk

▶ NB Marine, Ainwee, Rahane, Helensburgh, Dunbartonshire, G84 0QW Tel: (020) 7870 6247 E-mail: mail@nbmairne.co.uk

Newson Boatbuilders Ltd, 3 Sea Lake Road, Lowestoft, Suffolk, NR32 3LQ Tel: (01502) 574902 Fax: (01502) 574902 E-mail: keith@newson.co.uk

Nex Craft Ltd, Gabriels Wharf, Castle Road, Maidstone, Kent, ME16 0LT Tel: (01622) 674971 Fax: (01732) 886769

Alexander Noble & Sons Ltd, Boatsbuilders, Girvan, Ayrshire, KA26 9HL Tel: (01465) 712223 Fax: (01465) 715089 E-mail: noble@boatbuilders.fsbusiness.co.uk

Norman Pearn & Co. Ltd, Mill Pool Boatyard, Bridgend, Looe, Cornwall, PL13 2AE Tel: (01503) 262244 Fax: (01503) 262244 E-mail: sales@looeboats.co.uk

Offshore Steel Boats, The Boat Yard, Waterside Road, Barton-upon-Humber, South Humberside, DN18 5BD Tel: (01652) 635864 Fax: (01652) 635864

Orion Narrow Boats Ltd, Ashwood, Kingswinford, West Midlands, DY6 0AQ Tel: (01384) 401464 Fax: (01384) 401464 E-mail: info@narrowboatsearch.co.uk

Orkney Boats Ltd, Unit 1 Ford La Business Park, Ford, Arundel, West Sussex, BN18 0UZ Tel: (01243) 551456 Fax: (01243) 551914 E-mail: enquiries@orkneyboatsltd.co.uk

▶ Ottersports, Cedar House, Hunston, Bury St. Edmunds, Suffolk, IP31 3EP Tel: (01359) 244366 Fax: (01359) 244366 E-mail: info@ottersports.co.uk

Outhill Boat Builders Ltd, Outhill Boats, Henley Road, Outhill, Studley, Warwickshire, B80 7DU Tel: (01527) 853798 Fax: (01527) 854510 E-mail: outhillsales@aol.com

Ovington Boats Ltd, Mariners Lane, North Shields, Tyne & Wear, NE30 4AT Tel: 0191-257 6011 Fax: 0191-257 8489

P&I, Hillside Garage, Hill Corner Road, Chippenham, Wiltshire, SN15 1DP Tel: (01249) 652998 E-mail: diana@boatshop.fsnet.co.uk

▶ Parkol Marine Engineering Ltd, Eskside Wharf, Church St, Whitby, North Yorkshire, YO22 4AE Tel: (01947) 602669 E-mail: info@parkol.freeserve.co.uk

Penrhos Marine, The Boat Yard, Aberdovey, Gwynedd, LL35 0RY Tel: (01654) 767478

Performance Sailcraft (Europe) Ltd, Station Works, Station Road, Long Buckby, Northampton, NN6 7PF Tel: (01327) 841600 Fax: (01327) 841651 E-mail: info@lasersailing.com

Tony Perry, Red Bull Basin, 17 Congleton Road South, Church Lawton, Stoke-on-Trent, ST7 3AJ Tel: (01782) 779033

BOAT BUILDERS OR REPAIRERS – *continued*

Peter Freebody & Co., Mill Lane, Hurley, Maidenhead, Berkshire, SL6 5ND Tel: (01628) 824382 Fax: (01628) 820238 E-mail: peterfreebody@btconnect.com

Peter Nicholls, Braunston Marina Trade Centre, The Wharf, Braunston, Daventry, Northamptonshire, NN11 7JH Tel: (01788) 899109 Fax: (01788) 899109 E-mail: enquiry@steelboats.com

Pickwell & Arnold, Unit 10 Nanholme Mill, Shaw Wood Road, Todmorden, Lancashire, OL14 6DA Tel: (01706) 812411 Fax: (01706) 812411

J.L. Pinder & Son Ltd, 138 Hanbury Road, 8-11 The Old Basin, Stoke Prior, Bromsgrove, Worcestershire, B60 4JZ Tel: (01527) 876438 Fax: (01527) 576435 E-mail: sales@jlpindersandsons.co.uk

Piper Boats Ltd, Unit 2a, 6 Prospect Way Knypersley, Stoke-on-Trent, ST8 7PL Tel: (01782) 510610 Fax: (01782) 512332

Plancraft Marine Ltd, 4 Little Shellwood Farm, Clayhill Road, Leigh, Reigate, Surrey, RH2 8PA Tel: (01306) 611100 Fax: (01306) 611101 E-mail: sales@plancraft.co.uk

Porter & Haylett Ltd, Viaduct Works, Wroxham, Norwich, NR12 8RX Tel: (01603) 782472 Fax: (01603) 783089 E-mail: sales@connoisseurafloat.com

Purewell Fish Farming Equipment, Units 13-14 Wicormarine, Cranleigh Road, Portchester, Fareham, Hampshire, PO16 9DR Tel: (01329) 829100 Fax: (01329) 829100

▶ Quayline Boats Ltd, Unit 9 Silk Mead, Hare Street, Buntingford, Hertfordshire, SG9 0DX Tel: (01763) 848700 Fax: (01763) 848700

Quayside Marine Ltd, Mill Lane, Lymington, Hampshire, SO41 9AZ Tel: (01590) 679582 Fax: (01590) 679582 E-mail: quaysidemarine@btconnect.com

R & D Fabrications, Units 65-67 Boughton Industrial Estate, New Ollerton, Newark, Nottinghamshire, NG22 9LD Tel: (01623) 862473 Fax: (01623) 862866 E-mail: sheila@randdfabs.fsnet.co.uk

R W Davis & Son Ltd, Junction Dry Dock, Canal Bank, Saul, Gloucester, GL2 7LA Tel: (01452) 740233 Fax: (01452) 741307 E-mail: sales@rwdavis.co.uk

▶ Reaction International Ltd, PO Box 617, Southampton, SO16 4RP Tel: (023) 8023 1111 Fax: (023) 8023 1111 E-mail: sales@hovpod.com

Reading Marine Co. Ltd, Aldermaston Wharf, Wharf Side, Padworth, Reading, RG7 4JS Tel: 0118-971 3666 Fax: 0118-971 4271 E-mail: sales@readingmarine.com

Red Bay Boats Ltd, Coast Road, Cushendall, Ballymena, County Antrim, BT44 0QW Tel: (028) 2177 1331 Fax: (028) 2177 1474 E-mail: info@redbayboats.com

Reiver Boat, Rescue Station House, South Moor, Stanley, County Durham, DH9 6AA Tel: (01207) 283040 Fax: (01207) 283040

Retreat Boatyard Topsham Ltd, Retreat Drive, Topsham, Exeter, EX3 0LS Tel: (01392) 874720 Fax: (01392) 876182 E-mail: sales@retreatboatyard.co.uk

▶ Ribtec, Collingwood Road, Dartmouth, Devon, TQ6 9JY Tel: (01803) 832060 Fax: (01803) 839090 E-mail: sales@ribi.co.uk

Richardsons Boatbuilders, Island Harbour Marina, Mill Lane, Binfield, Newport, Isle of Wight, PO30 2LA Tel: (01983) 821095 Fax: (01983) 522372 E-mail: info@richardsonsyacht.co.uk

Rispond Marine, 6 Craft Village, Balnakeil, Durness, Lairg, Sutherland, IV27 4PT Tel: (01971) 511722 Fax: (01971) 511722 E-mail: rispond@aol.com

Robertsons Of Woodbridge Boat Builders Ltd, Lime Kiln Quay, Woodbridge, Suffolk, IP12 1BD Tel: (01394) 382305 Fax: (01394) 388788 E-mail: mike@robertsons-boatyard.co.uk

Rowsell Sails, 24 Camperdown Terrace, Exmouth, Devon, EX8 1EH Tel: (01395) 263911 Fax: (01395) 263911

Rushworth Racing Dinghies, 141 Blandford Road, Poole, Dorset, BH15 4AT Tel: (01202) 776877 Fax: (01202) 483085 E-mail: sales@rushworthracing.co.uk

S W Durham Steelcraft Ltd, Old Colliery Buildings, Trimdon Grange Industrial Estate, Trimdon Grange, Trimdon Station, County Durham, TS29 6PA Tel: (01429) 881300 Fax: (01429) 883184

Sagar Marine Ltd, Victoria Works, Wharfe Street, Brighouse, West Yorkshire, HD6 1PP Tel: (01484) 714541 Fax: (01484) 400683

Sanderson Boat Hire, Riverside, Reedham, Norwich, NR13 3TE Tel: (01493) 700242 Fax: (01493) 701705 E-mail: sanderson_marine@amserve.com

Scarborough Marine Engineers Ltd, 35-36 Sandside, Scarborough, North Yorkshire, YO11 1PQ Tel: (01723) 375199 Fax: (01723) 379734E-mail: info@scarboroughmarine.co.uk

Scorpion Ribs Ltd, Haven Quay, Mill Lane, Lymington, Hampshire, SO41 9AZ Tel: (01590) 677080 Fax: (01590) 671911 E-mail: sales@scorpionribs.com

Sealine International Ltd, Whitehouse Road, Kidderminster, Worcestershire, DY10 1HT Tel: (01562) 740900 Fax: (01562) 747709 E-mail: info@sealine.com

Seamark Nunn & Co., 400 High Road, Trimley St. Martin, Felixstowe, Suffolk, IP11 0SG Tel: (01394) 275327 Fax: (01394) 670329 E-mail: sales@seamarknunn.com

The Select Yacht Group Ltd, Rock, Wadebridge, Cornwall, PL27 6NT Tel: (01208) 862666 Fax: (01208) 862375 E-mail: info@selectyachts.co.uk

Shadow Boatbuilders Ltd, Riverside Estate, Brundall, Norwich, NR13 5PL Tel: (01603) 712362 Fax: (01603) 717770 E-mail: swancraft@rjd.co.uk

Shakespeare International Marine Ltd, Station Road, Hartlebury, Kidderminster, Worcestershire, DY11 7YJ Tel: (01299) 250685 Fax: (01299) 250509

Shepperton Marina Ltd, Shepperton Marina, Felix Lane, Shepperton, Middlesex, TW17 8NS Tel: (01932) 243722 Fax: (01932) 243152 E-mail: sales@boatshowrooms.com

Silverline Marine, Riverside Estate, Brundall, Norwich, NR13 5PL Tel: (01603) 712247 Fax: (01603) 716990

▶ Silvers Marine Ltd, Silverhills, Rosneath, Helensburgh, Dunbartonshire, G84 0RW Tel: (01436) 831222 Fax: (01436) 831879 E-mail: enquiries@silversmarine.co.uk

Raymond Sims Ltd, Trent Side North, West Bridgford, Nottingham, NG2 5FA Tel: 0115-981 0992

Sirius Yachts Ltd, Sandy La Industrial Estate, Stourport-on-Severn, Worcestershire, DY13 9QB Tel: (01299) 871048 Fax: (01299) 871048 E-mail: bryan@siriusyachts.com

▶ Soar Valley Steel Boats, Brimington Road, Chesterfield, Derbyshire, S41 7JG Tel: (01246) 274125 Fax: (01246) 274125

South Ferriby Marina Ltd, South Ferriby Marina, Red Lane, South Ferriby, Barton-Upon-Humber, South Humberside, DN18 6JH Tel: (01652) 635620 Fax: (01652) 660517 E-mail: tfertuson_ie@yahoo.co.uk

▶ South Holland Marine & Fabrication Ltd, Poplars Farm, Donington Road, Swineshead, Boston, Lincolnshire, PE20 3HL Tel: (01529) 460758 Fax: (01529) 460927 E-mail: info@southhollandmarine.co.uk

John South (Boats) Ltd, 89 Condover Industrial Estate, near Shrewsbury, Dorrington, Shrewsbury, SY5 7NH Tel: (01743) 718415 Fax: (01743) 718415

South River Marine, Reed Lane, St. Olaves, Great Yarmouth, Norfolk, NR31 9HG Tel: (01493) 488469 Fax: (01493) 488499 E-mail: southrivermarine@broadlyboats.com

▶ Spirit Yachts, New Cut East, Ipswich, IP3 0EA Tel: (01473) 214715 Fax: (01473) 214713

Staniland Marina, Staniland Marina, Lock Hill, Thorne, Doncaster, South Yorkshire, DN8 5EP Tel: (01405) 813150 Fax: (01405) 740592 E-mail: sales@staniland-marina.co.uk

Stephen Goldsbrough Boats, 200 Kenilworth Road, Knowle, Solihull, West Midlands, B93 0JJ Tel: (01564) 778210 Fax: (01564) 770557 E-mail: russ@sgboats.com

Stone Adrian, Cowes Yacht Haven, Cowes, Isle of Wight, PO31 7BD Tel: (01983) 297898 Fax: (01983) 280499 E-mail: adrianstone.yachts@virgin.net

Stone Boat Building Co. Ltd, Newcastle Road, Stone, Staffordshire, ST15 8JZ Tel: (01785) 812688 Fax: (01785) 811317 E-mail: sales@stoneboatbuilding.co.uk

Streethay Wharf Ltd, Burton Road, Streethay, Lichfield, Staffordshire, WS13 8LT Tel: (01543) 414808 Fax: (01543) 414770

Sutton & Smith Ltd, Bullmans Wharf, Great Wakering, Southend-on-Sea, SS3 0DA Tel: (01702) 219422 Fax: (01702) 219050

▶ T E C Marine Mouldings Ltd, Prout Industrial Estate, Point Road, Canvey Island, Essex, SS8 7TJ Tel: (01268) 680606 Fax: (01268) 684592

T Trevethicks, Gregory Street, Nottingham, NG7 2NP Tel: 0115-978 3467 Fax: 0115-978 3467

Tamar Inflatables, Unit 4b, Restormel Industrial Estate, Lostwithiel, Cornwall, PL22 0HG Tel: (01208) 873777 Fax: (01208) 873774 E-mail: ce.banyard@btconnect.com

▶ Tay Boats, Newlands View, Scone, Perth, PH2 6NW Tel: (01738) 551890

TLC, Conwy Marina, Ellis Way, Conwy, Gwynedd, LL32 8GU Tel: (01492) 580820 Fax: (01492) 580820

Tom Jones Boatbuilders Ltd, Romney Lock Boathouse, Romney Lock, Windsor, Berkshire, SL4 6HU Tel: (01753) 860699 Fax: (01753) 856982

Tough Surveys Ltd, 27 Ferry Road, Teddington, Middlesex, TW11 9NN Tel: (020) 8977 4494 Fax: (020) 8977 7546 E-mail: johntough@ctinternet.com

Traditional Shipwright Services Ltd, Westons Point Boat Yard, Turks Lane, Sandbanks Road, Parkstone, Poole, Dorset, BH14 8EW Tel: (01202) 748029 E-mail: paulk0611@aol.com

Tremlett Ski Craft Ltd, Odhams Wharf, Topsham, Exeter, EX3 0PD Tel: (01392) 873680 Fax: (01392) 876277

Tropical Engineering, Unit 8, Saunders Drive, Cowes, Isle of Wight, PO31 8HU Tel: (01983) 280456 Fax: (01983) 281844 E-mail: office@tropicalengineering.co.uk

Valley Canoe Products Ltd, Private Road 4, Colwick Industrial Estate, Nottingham, NG4 2JT Tel: 0115-961 4995 Fax: 0115-961 4970 E-mail: ceakayak@globalnet.co.uk

Voyager Yachts Ltd, Southdown Quay, Millbrook, Torpoint, Cornwall, PL10 1HG Tel: (01752) 823329 Fax: (01752) 822354

VT Halmatic Ltd, Hamilton Road, Cosham, Portsmouth, PO6 4PX Tel: (023) 9253 9600 Fax: (023) 9253 9601 E-mail: info@halmatic.com

W C Hunkin & Sons, 1 Passage Lane, Fowey, Cornwall, PL23 1JS Tel: (01726) 832874 Fax: (01726) 832001

W Trout & Son, Boat House, Ferry Road, Topsham, Exeter, EX3 0JJ Tel: (01392) 873044 Fax: (01392) 875176 E-mail: wtrout1@tiscali.co.uk

Weltonfield Narrowboats, Welton, Daventry, Northamptonshire, NN11 2LG Tel: (01327) 842282 Fax: (01327) 843754 E-mail: enquiries@weltonfield.co.uk

Willow Bay Boats, Low House Farm, Cleabarrow, Windermere, Cumbria, LA23 3NA Tel: (01539) 442741 E-mail: sales@willowbayboats.co.uk

Windboats Marine Ltd, Grange Walk, Wroxham, Norwich, NR12 8RX Tel: (01603) 782236 Fax: (01603) 784106 E-mail: windboats@aol.com

Winder Boats, Kensington Street, Keighley, West Yorkshire, BD21 1PW Tel: (01535) 604980 Fax: (01535) 605371 E-mail: guy@winderboats.freeserve.co.uk

Woods Dyke Boat Yard, Lower Street, Horning, Norwich, NR12 8PF Tel: (01692) 630461 Fax: (01692) 631415 E-mail: sales@woodsdyke-boatyard.co.uk

Wootton Bridge Industries Ltd, 10 Medina Court, Arctic Road, Cowes, Isle of Wight, PO31 7XD Tel: (01983) 280707 Fax: (01983) 280785

Working Boats UK Ltd, 12 High Street, Fordington, Dorchester, Dorset, DT1 1JZ Tel: (01305) 257488 Fax: (01305) 257488 E-mail: chris@working-boats.co.uk

BOAT CENTREBOARDS

Crompton Technology Group Ltd, Thorp Park Thorpe Way, Banbury, Oxfordshire, OX16 4SU Tel: (01295) 220130 Fax: (01295) 220138 E-mail: info@ctgltd.co.uk

BOAT CONSTRUCTION KITS

▶ CRAIGCAT UK LIMITED, P.O. BOX 131, LYMINGTON, HAMPSHIRE, SO41 9UG Tel: 07770 546250 Fax: 01590 610527 E-mail: enquiries@craigcat.co.uk

Deans Marine, Conquest Drove, Farcet, Peterborough, PE7 3DH Tel: (01733) 244166 Fax: (01733) 244166 E-mail: deansmarine@yahoo.co.uk

▶ Ottersports, Cedar House, Hunston, Bury St. Edmunds, Suffolk, IP31 3EP Tel: (01359) 244366 Fax: (01359) 244366 E-mail: info@ottersports.com

Steelkit, Abberleri Boatyard, Ynyslas, Borth, Dyfed, SY24 5JU Tel: (01970) 871713 Fax: (01970) 871879E-mail: info@steelkit.com

Topper International Ltd, Kingsnorth Industrial Estate, Wotton Road, Ashford, Kent, TN23 6LN Tel: (01233) 629186 Fax: (01233) 645897 E-mail: info@toppersailboats.com

BOAT COVERS

Arun Sails Ltd, The Sail Centre Southfields Industrial Estate, Delling Lane, Bosham, Chichester, West Sussex, PO18 8NW Tel: (01243) 573185 Fax: (01243) 573032 E-mail: arun@sailmakers.com

Bisset & Ross, Riverside Drive, Aberdeen, AB11 7SL Tel: (01224) 580659 Fax: (01224) 583295

▶ Blue Sails, Garage Street, Llandudno, Conwy, LL30 1DW Tel: (01492) 879914

▶ Cut N Cover, The Barn Workshop, Pamphill Dairy, Pamphill, Wimborne, Dorset, BH21 4ED Tel: (01202) 881122 E-mail: wayne@cutncover.fsnet.co.uk

East Coast Sales Limited, Woolverstone Marina, Woolverstone, Ipswich, IP9 1AS Tel: (01473) 780007 Fax: (01473) 780007

Flexicovers, The Courtyard, Thrush Road, Poole, Dorset, BH12 4NP Tel: (01202) 721309 Fax: (01202) 733047 E-mail: sales@flexicovers.co.uk

Garland Sails, 246a Soundwell Road, Bristol, BS15 1PN Tel: 0117-935 3233 Fax: 0117-935 3233 E-mail: garlandsails@ukonline.co.uk

Jeckells & Son Ltd, Riverside Road, Hoveton, Norwich, NR12 8UQ Tel: (01603) 784488 Fax: (01603) 783234 E-mail: jeckellstrimmers@ukgateway.net

North Dingle Made Up Textiles, 4a Orwell Road, Liverpool, L4 1RQ Tel: 0151-944 1482 Fax: 0151-944 1482

Sanders Sails, Bath Road, Lymington, Hampshire, SO41 3RU Tel: (01590) 673981 Fax: (01590) 676026

Sparks Marine Trimmers, Old School House, Thame Road, Chilton, Aylesbury, Buckinghamshire, HP18 9LX Tel: (01844) 208731 Fax: (01844) 208510

Vinall Covers, 64 Hammonds Way, Totton, Southampton, SO40 3HF Tel: (023) 8086 9411 Fax: (023) 8086 9411 E-mail: kbh47@hotmail.com

BOAT COVERS, CANVAS

▶ Blue Sails, Garage Street, Llandudno, Conwy, LL30 1DW Tel: (01492) 879914

▶ The Coverworks, Dartside Quay, Galmpton Creek, Galmpton, Brixham, Devon, TQ5 0EH Tel: (01803) 844003 E-mail: james@thecoverworks.eclipse.co.uk

▶ Cut N Cover, The Barn Workshop, Pamphill Dairy, Pamphill, Wimborne, Dorset, BH21 4ED Tel: (01202) 881122 E-mail: wayne@cutncover.fsnet.co.uk

BOAT DISTRIBUTORS OR AGENTS

Avoncraft Ltd, 12 West Burrowfield, Welwyn Garden City, Hertfordshire, AL7 4TW Tel: (01707) 330000 Fax: (01707) 333026 E-mail: sales@avoncraft.co.uk

Branson Boats Design, Crease Drove, Crowland, Peterborough, PE6 0BN Tel: (01733) 211966 Fax: (01733) 211966 E-mail: bransonboats@btinternet.com

Broom Boats Ltd, Brundall, Norwich, NR13 5PX Tel: (01603) 712334 Fax: (01603) 714803 E-mail: enquiries@broomboats.com

Cambrian Marine Services Ltd, Ferry Road, Cardiff, CF11 0JL Tel: (029) 2034 3459 Fax: (029) 2034 5116 E-mail: cambrianmarine@aol.com

Chas Newens Marine Co. Ltd, The Boathouse, Embankment, London, SW15 1LB Tel: (020) 8788 4587 Fax: (020) 8780 2339 E-mail: sales@chastheboat.co.uk

Cyclops Technologies Ltd, Durban Road, Bognor Regis, West Sussex, PO22 9QT Tel: (01243) 841123 Fax: (01243) 829321 E-mail: sales@cyclopstech.co.uk

▶ D B Boat Fitting Ltd, Braunston Marina Trade Centre, The Wharf, Braunston, Daventry, Northamptonshire, NN11 7JH Tel: (01788) 891727 Fax: (01788) 891727 E-mail: lyn@dbboatfitting.co.uk

Dartmouth Boating Centre, South Embankment, Dartmouth, Devon, TQ6 9BH Tel: (01803) 832093 Fax: (01803) 835135

Deacons, Bridge Road, Bursledon, Southampton, SO31 8FR Tel: (023) 8040 2253 Fax: (023) 8040 5665 E-mail: info@deaconsboatyard.co.uk

Debbage Yachting Services, New Cut West, Ipswich, IP2 8HN Tel: (01473) 601169 Fax: (01473) 603184

Dickies, Garth Road, Bangor, Gwynedd, LL57 2SE Tel: (01248) 363414 Fax: (01248) 354169 E-mail: info@dickies.co.uk

Dorset Yacht Co., Lake Drive, Poole, Dorset, BH15 4DT Tel: (01202) 674534 Fax: (01202) 677518 E-mail: sales@bostonwhaler.co.uk

Euroscot Seafood Services, The Fish Market, Milford Haven, Dyfed, SA73 3AT Tel: 01646 697733 Fax: 01646 694001

Fox's Marina Ipswich Ltd, The Strand, Ipswich, IP2 8SA Tel: (01473) 689111 Fax: (01473) 601737E-mail: foxsmarina@oystermarine.com

Gibbs, Sandhills Meadow, Shepperton, Middlesex, TW17 9HY Tel: (01932) 242977 Fax: (01932) 222817 E-mail: sales@gibbsmarine.co.uk

Harleyford Aggregates, Harleyford, Henley Road, Marlow, Buckinghamshire, SL7 2DY Tel: (01628) 475976 Fax: (01628) 481640 E-mail: info@harleyford.co.uk

Kelpie Boats, Hobbs Point, Pembroke Dock, Dyfed, SA72 6TR Tel: (01646) 683661 Fax: (01646) 621398 E-mail: martin@kelpieboats.com

L H Jones & Son Ltd, Low Road, St. Ives, Cambridgeshire, PE27 5ET Tel: (01480) 494040 Fax: (01480) 495280 E-mail: info@jonesboatyard.co.uk

Mccready's Sailboats Ltd, Priory Park, Holywood, County Down, BT18 0LG Tel: (028) 9042 1821 Fax: (028) 9042 2998 E-mail: sales@mccreadysailboats.co.uk

Nottingham Offshore Marine, 35 Carlton Hill, Carlton, Nottingham, NG4 1BG Tel: 0115-961 2336 E-mail: jon.dann@tesco.net

Offshore Powerboats Ltd, 1 Lymington Yacht Haven, Kings Saltern Road, Lymington, Hampshire, SO41 3QD Tel: (01590) 677955 Fax: (01590) 671890 E-mail: chris@offshorepowerboats.co.uk

Peters plc, Chichester Marina, Chichester, West Sussex, PO20 7EJ Tel: (01243) 512831 Fax: (01243) 511382 E-mail: sales@petersplc.com

Princess International Sales & Service Ltd, Billing Wharf, Cogenhoe, Northampton, NN7 1NH Tel: (01604) 890559 Fax: (01604) 891202 E-mail: sales@princess.co.uk

R Y B Marine Sales Ltd, Maidenhead Road, Windsor, Berkshire, SL4 5HT Tel: (01753) 851717 Fax: (01753) 868172 E-mail: sales@ryb.co.uk

S B S Ltd, Woden Road, Wolverhampton, WV10 0AS Tel: (01902) 455655 Fax: (01902) 453760 E-mail: sales@sbstrailers.co.uk

Shepperton Marina Ltd, Shepperton Marina, Felix Lane, Shepperton, Middlesex, TW17 8NS Tel: (01932) 243722 Fax: (01932) 243152 E-mail: sales@boatshowrooms.com

Ship Shape Marine, 314-316 London Road, Hazel Grove, Stockport, Cheshire, SK7 4RF Tel: 0161-483 0666 Fax: 0161-483 0666

Tom Jones Boatbuilders Ltd, Romney Lock Boathouse, Romney Lock, Windsor, Berkshire, SL4 6HU Tel: (01753) 860699 Fax: (01753) 856982

Walkers Yacht Chandlery, 1 Brunel Road, Leigh-on-Sea, Essex, SS9 5JL Tel: (01702) 421321 Fax: (01702) 421321

West Bay Small Boat Supplies, Unit 8a The Old Timber Yard, West Bay, Bridport, Dorset, DT6 4EL Tel: (01308) 459511 Fax: (01308) 459511 E-mail: westbaysmallboats@supanet.com

BOAT DISTRIBUTORS OR AGENTS

– continued

White Water The Canoe Centre, Shepperton Marina, Felix Lane, Shepperton, Middlesex, TW17 8NS Tel: (01932) 247978 Fax: (01932) 241368
E-mail: whitewater@canoecentre.demon.co.uk

▶ Www.Boat-Stands.Co.Uk, Unit 3 Millview Barn, Off Grange Road, Bursledon, Southampton, SO31 8GD Tel: (023) 8045 2100
E-mail: info@boat-stands.com

Yacht Marina Ltd, Naburn Marina, Naburn, York, YO19 4RW Tel: (01904) 621021 Fax: (01904) 611950 E-mail: info@yachtservice.co.uk

BOAT FITTINGS

Aldeburgh Boatyard Co. Ltd, Fort Green, Aldeburgh, Suffolk, IP15 5DE Tel: (01728) 452019 Fax: (01728) 452019

C & B Marine Ltd, Chichester Marina, Chichester, West Sussex, PO20 7EJ Tel: (01243) 511273 Fax: (01243) 511273

Cables Direct Ltd, C Industrial Estate, Heage Road, Ripley, Derbyshire, DE5 3GH
Tel: (01773) 514514 Fax: (01773) 514515
E-mail: sales@cablesdirect.co.uk

Clamcleats Ltd, Watchmead, Welwyn Garden City, Hertfordshire, AL7 1AP Tel: (01707) 330101 Fax: (01707) 321269
E-mail: sales@clamcleat.com

▶ Compass Marine Services, 156 South Street, Lancing, West Sussex, BN15 8AU Tel: (01903) 761773

Cooney Marine Intl Ltd, Telford Way, Telford Way Industrial Estate, Kettering, Northamptonshire, NN16 8UN Tel: (01536) 484481 Fax: (01536) 411580 E-mail: sales@cooneymarine.co.uk

CSB Lifting & Marine Products, 3 Station Road Industrial Estate, Station Road, Rowley Regis, West Midlands, B65 0JY Tel: 0121-559 5112 Fax: 0121-559 4173

D Steer Fabrication, 4 Riverside Avenue West, Lawford, Manningtree, Essex, CO11 1UN
Tel: (01206) 391767 Fax: (01206) 391767
E-mail: thesteers@virgin.net

▶ First Stop Marine Services, Galmpton, Brixham, Devon, TQ5 0EH Tel: (01803) 846333 Fax: (01803) 846333

Fox's Marina Ipswich Ltd, The Strand, Ipswich, IP2 8SA Tel: (01473) 689111 Fax: (01473) 601737E-mail: foxsmarina@oystermarine.com

▶ H2o Sports, 5 Harbour Masters Building, Pwllheli, Gwynedd, LL53 5AY Tel: (01758) 612867 Fax: (01758) 612685

Hollywood Marine Ltd, 176 Highfield Road, Hall Green, Birmingham, B28 0HS Tel: 0121-777 7573 Fax: 0121 7778386

Holts, Embankment, London, SW15 1LB
Tel: (020) 8789 5557 Fax: (020) 8789 8365
E-mail: sales@holtallen.com

I Y E England Ltd, 1 Towerfield Road, Shoeburyness, Southend-on-Sea, SS3 9QE
Tel: (01702) 291291 Fax: (01702) 291391
E-mail: info@iye-england.co.uk

Jasper Covers Ltd, The Mews, Heathfield Road, Portsmouth, PO2 8AG Tel: (023) 9271 1358 Fax: (023) 9261 2085

Mccready's Sailboats Ltd, Priory Park, Holywood, County Down, BT18 0LG Tel: (028) 9042 1821 Fax: (028) 9042 2998
E-mail: sales@mccreadysailboats.co.uk

▶ Manxboats.com, Unit 5,, Balderton Court, Balthane Industrial Estate, Ballasalla, Isle Of Man, IM9 2AJ Tel: (01624) 825040
E-mail: manxboats@manx.net

Martex Boat Equipment, Hillside, Church Minshull, Nantwich, Cheshire, CW5 6EA
Tel: (01270) 522251 Fax: (01270) 522616

Owen Sails Ltd, Tralee Bay, Benderloch, Oban, Argyll, PA37 1QR Tel: (01631) 720485 Fax: (01631) 720545
E-mail: info@owensails.com

P & H Co., Station Road, West Hallam, Ilkeston, Derbyshire, DE7 6HB Tel: 0115-932 0155 Fax: 0115-932 7177
E-mail: sales@phseakayaks.com

Puffer Parts Ltd, Hall Terrace, Riddlesden, Keighley, West Yorkshire, BD21 4HB
Tel: (01535) 605703 Fax: (01535) 606229
E-mail: sales@pufferparts.co.uk

Reeds Of Cambridge, 70 Water Street, Cambridge, CB4 1PA Tel: (01223) 425348 Fax: (01223) 566717
E-mail: reedsofcambridge@dsl.tipex.com

Reliance Marine, Marine Centre, South Parade, West Kirby, Wirral, Merseyside, CH48 0QG
Tel: 0151-625 5219 Fax: 0151-625 6779
E-mail: sales@reliance.com

▶ Shipmates, 2 Newcomen Road, Dartmouth, Devon, TQ6 9AF Tel: (01803) 839292 Fax: (01803) 832538
E-mail: admin@chandlery.co.uk

Sparks Marine Trimmers, Old School House, Thame Road, Chilton, Aylesbury, Buckinghamshire, HP18 9LX Tel: (01844) 208731 Fax: (01844) 208510

Technisol Ltd, Unit B14 Little Heath Industrial Estate, Old Church Road, Coventry, CV6 7NB
Tel: (024) 7668 0088 Fax: (024) 7658 1144
E-mail: sales@technisolltd.co.uk

W4 Ltd, Unit B, Ford Lane Industrial Estate, Arundel, West Sussex, BN18 0DF Tel: (01243) 553355 Fax: (01243) 553540
E-mail: enquiries@w4limited.com

BOAT HEATERS

Mikuni Heating UK Ltd, Unit 6 Second Avenue, Southampton, SO15 0LP Tel: (023) 8052 8777 Fax: (023) 8052 8800
E-mail: sales@mikuniheating.com

Whispair, Unit 31 Romsey Industrial Estate, Greatbridge Road, Romsey, Hampshire, SO51 0HR Tel: (01794) 523999 Fax: (01794) 519151 E-mail: info@whispaire.co.uk

BOAT HIRE

Avon Boating, Swans Nest Boathouse, Swans Nest Lane, Stratford-upon-Avon, Warwickshire, CV37 7LS Tel: (01789) 267073 Fax: (01789) 267073 E-mail: boat-hire@avon-boating.co.uk

Bridge Boats Ltd, Fry's Island, De Montfort Road, Reading, RG1 8DG Tel: 0118-959 0346 Fax: 0118-959 1114
E-mail: sales@bridgeboats.com

Broadland Passenger Craft, George Smith & Sons, The Rhond, Hoveton, Norwich, NR12 8UE Tel: (01603) 782527 Fax: (01603) 784124

Broads Tours Ltd, Faircroft Loynes, The Bridge, Wroxham, Norwich, NR12 8RX Tel: (01603) 782207 Fax: (01603) 784272
E-mail: info@broads.co.uk

Canal Cruising Co. Ltd, Crown Street, Stone, Staffordshire, ST15 8QN Tel: (01785) 813982 Fax: (01785) 819041
E-mail: kwyatt5745@aol.com

Chas Newens Marine Co. Ltd, The Boathouse, Embankment, London, SW15 1LB Tel: (020) 8788 4587 Fax: (020) 8780 2339
E-mail: sales@chastheboat.co.uk

▶ CRAIGCAT UK LIMITED, P.O. BOX 131, LYMINGTON, HAMPSHIRE, SO41 9UG
Tel: 07770 546250 Fax: 01590 610527
E-mail: enquiries@craigcat.co.uk

Daylock Marine Services, Banks End, Wyton, Huntingdon, Cambridgeshire, PE28 2AA
Tel: (01480) 455898 Fax: (01480) 455898

Gailey Marine Ltd, Gailey Wharf, Watling Street, Gailey, Stafford, ST19 5PR Tel: (01902) 790612 Fax: (01902) 791446
E-mail: jdboats@btinternet.com

George Wilson & Sons Ltd, Thames Street, Sunbury-on-Thames, Middlesex, TW16 6AQ
Tel: (01932) 782067 Fax: (01932) 782067

K & K Mouldings Ltd, Bridge Road, Ely, Cambridgeshire, CB7 4DY Tel: (01353) 663726 Fax: (01353) 668766
E-mail: sales@bridgeboatyard.com

Martham Boat Building & Development Co. Ltd, Cess Road, Martham, Great Yarmouth, Norfolk, NR29 4RF Tel: (01493) 740249 Fax: (01493) 740065
E-mail: info@marthamboats.com

Plymouth Boat Cruises Ltd, Millbrook, Torpoint, Cornwall, PL10 1EA Tel: (01752) 822797 Fax: (01752) 408590
E-mail: soundcruising@btinternet.com

Porter & Haylett Ltd, Viaduct Works, Wroxham, Norwich, NR12 8RX Tel: (01603) 782472 Fax: (01603) 783089
E-mail: sales@connoisseurafloat.com

Reading Marine Co. Ltd, Aldermaston Wharf, Wharf Side, Padworth, Reading, RG7 4JS
Tel: 0118-971 3666 Fax: 0118-971 4271
E-mail: sales@readingmarine.com

Sanderson Boat Hire, Riverside, Reedham, Norwich, NR13 3TE Tel: (01493) 700242 Fax: (01493) 701705
E-mail: sanderson_marine@amserve.com

▶ South West Yacht Brokers, Breakwater Road, Plymstock, Plymouth, PL9 7HJ Tel: (01752) 401421 Fax: (01752) 401421
E-mail: enquiries@south-west-rib-rides.co.uk

▶ Square Sail Ship Yard Ltd, Charlestown Harbour, St. Austell, Cornwall, PL25 3NJ
Tel: (01726) 70241 Fax: (01726) 61839
E-mail: info@square-sail.com

Turk Launches Ltd, Town End Pier, 68 High Street, Kingston Upon Thames, Surrey, KT1 1HN Tel: (020) 8546 2434 Fax: (020) 8546 5775 E-mail: operations@turks.co.uk

Herbert Woods, Broads Haven, Bridge Road, Potter Heigham, Great Yarmouth, Norfolk, NR29 5JD Tel: (01692) 670711 Fax: (01692) 670734 E-mail: mail@broads.co.uk

BOAT HULLS, GLASS FIBRE OR FIBREGLASS/GRP

A & I Composites Ltd, Mile End Road, Colwick, Nottingham, NG4 2DW Tel: 0115-940 2228 Fax: 0115-940 2228

Aquafibre Mouldings Ltd, Wendover Road, Rackheath Industrial Estate, Rackheath, Norwich, NR13 6LH Tel: (01603) 720651 Fax: (01603) 720654
E-mail: info@aquafibre.co.uk

Birchwood Marine Ltd, Fulwood Road North, Sutton-in-Ashfield, Nottinghamshire, NG17 2NB Tel: (01623) 515133 Fax: (01623) 440328 E-mail: info@birchwood.co.uk

▶ CRAIGCAT UK LIMITED, P.O. BOX 131, LYMINGTON, HAMPSHIRE, SO41 9UG
Tel: 07770 546250 Fax: 01590 610527
E-mail: enquiries@craigcat.co.uk

▶ Fibrotec Mouldings Ltd, Earls Colne Business Centre, Airfield, Earls Colne, Colchester, CO6 2NS Tel: (01787) 223912 Fax: (01787) 224444 E-mail: enquiry@fibrotec.co.uk

Sunseeker Exhibitions Ltd, 27-31 West Quay Road, Poole, Dorset, BH15 1HX Tel: (01202) 381111 Fax: (01202) 382222
E-mail: admin@sunseeker.com

VT Halmatic Ltd, Hamilton Road, Cosham, Portsmouth, PO6 4PX Tel: (023) 9253 9600 Fax: (023) 9253 9601
E-mail: info@halmatic.com

W A Simpson Marine Ltd, 1 Logie Avenue, Dundee, DD2 2AS Tel: (01382) 566670 Fax: (01382) 668661
E-mail: admin@wasimpsonmarine.com

BOAT LIFTING FRAMES

▶ Www.Boat-Stands.Co.Uk, Unit 3 Millview Barn, Off Grange Road, Bursledon, Southampton, SO31 8GD Tel: (023) 8045 2100
E-mail: info@boat-stands.com

BOAT REFURBISHMENT SERVICES

Aldeburgh Boatyard Co. Ltd, Fort Green, Aldeburgh, Suffolk, IP15 5DE Tel: (01728) 452019 Fax: (01728) 452019

Broom Boats Ltd, Brundall, Norwich, NR13 5PX
Tel: (01603) 712334 Fax: (01603) 714803
E-mail: enquiries@broomboats.com

Cambrian Marine Services Ltd, Ferry Road, Cardiff, CF11 0JL Tel: (029) 2034 3459 Fax: (029) 2034 5116
E-mail: cambrianmarine@aol.com

D P Marine Services, The Boat Yard, Hordern Road, Wolverhampton, WV6 0HT Tel: (01902) 755951

Dyer Bros Marine Ltd, 129 St. Denys Road, Southampton, SO17 2JY Tel: (023) 8055 5406

▶ Evans Boatwork, Unit 5 Havens Head Business Park, The Docks, Hakin, Milford Haven, Dyfed, SA73 3LD Tel: (07815) 075585 Fax: (07967) 303639
E-mail: info@evansboatwork.com

High Line Yachting Ltd, Mansion Lane, Iver, Buckinghamshire, SL0 9RG Tel: (01753) 651496 Fax: (01753) 630095
E-mail: sales@high-line.co.uk

Percuil Boat Yard, Portscatho, Truro, Cornwall, TR2 5ES Tel: (01872) 580564 Fax: (01872) 580044

Victory Boatbuilders, Lower Boat House North Pondside, The Historic Dockyard, Chatham, Kent, ME4 4TY Tel: (01634) 813057 Fax: (01634) 813057
E-mail: sales@havengore.com

BOAT TRAILERS

Eagle Trailers, 241A Blandford Road, Hamworthy, Poole, Dorset, BH15 4AZ Tel: (01202) 671057 Fax: (01202) 671057

S B S Ltd, Woden Road, Wolverhampton, WV10 0AS Tel: (01902) 455655 Fax: (01902) 453760 E-mail: sales@sbstrailers.co.uk

Severn Valley Trailers, Hanleaze Lodge, 73 Bristol Road, Keynsham, Bristol, BS31 2WD
Tel: 0117-986 3256 Fax: 0117-986 3256

T T C Engineering Ltd, Unit 13, Chalwyn Industrial Estate, Old Wareham Road, Poole, Dorset, BH12 4PE Tel: (01202) 738181

Wright Transport Services, 6 Council Houses, Sparham Hill, Sparham, Norwich, NR9 5QT
Tel: (01603) 872022 Fax: (01603) 872022

BOAT TRANSPORTATION

▶ ARGONAUTIC TRANSPORT, 77 Albany Road, Kensington, Liverpool, L7 8RQ Tel: (0845) 1307133 E-mail: aahbtrans@yahoo.co.uk

Kingsley Farrington, Whitlingham Lane, Trowse, Norwich, NR14 8TR Tel: (01603) 666545 Fax: (01603) 666545

S C D Ltd, Navigation House, 4 Wilford Bridge Road, Melton, Woodbridge, Suffolk, IP12 1RJ
Tel: (01394) 382600 Fax: (01394) 387672
E-mail: sales@scd-charts.co.uk

▶ Solent & Wight Line Cruises, Thetis Wharf, Medina Road, Cowes, Isle of Wight, PO31 7BP Tel: (01983) 289966

Yacht Shipping Ltd, Bowling Green House, 1 Orchard Place, Southampton, SO14 3PX
Tel: (023) 8022 3671 Fax: (023) 8033 0880
E-mail: info@ysl.wainwrightgroup.com

BOATS, ALUMINIUM

▶ Boats4fun, Averys Oak, Laughton, Lewes, East Sussex, BN8 6BY Tel: (07710) 000410
E-mail: sales@boats4fun.co.uk

▶ Bristol Yacht Brokerage Ltd, Junction Lock, Cumberland Basin, Bristol, BS1 6XL
Tel: 0117-930 4891 Fax: 0117-930 4882
E-mail: tim@bristolyachtbrokerage.com

BOATS, CABIN CRUISER, GLASS FIBRE OR FIBREGLASS

▶ Fibrotec Mouldings Ltd, Earls Colne Business Centre, Airfield, Earls Colne, Colchester, CO6 2NS Tel: (01787) 223912 Fax: (01787) 224444 E-mail: enquiry@fibrotec.co.uk

BOATS, CANAL/NARROW, STEEL HULLED

Branson Boats Design, Crease Drove, Crowland, Peterborough, PE6 0BN Tel: (01733) 211966 Fax: (01733) 211966
E-mail: bransonboats@btinternet.com

Colecraft Engineering Ltd, The Old Timber Yard, Southam Road, Long Itchington, Southam, Warwickshire, CV47 9QL Tel: (01926) 817070 Fax: (01926) 815124
E-mail: sales@colecraft.co.uk

Fernwood Craft Ltd, Unit 2C, Sewstern Industrial Estate, Sewstern, Grantham, Lincolnshire, NG33 5RD Tel: (01476) 860440 Fax: (01476) 861313 E-mail: info@fernwoodcraft.co.uk

H T Fabrications Ltd, 420 Thurmaston Boulevard, Leicester, LE4 9LE Tel: 0116-276 1814 Fax: 0116-246 0576
E-mail: ht@fabs.freeserve.co.uk

Lime Kiln Narrow Boats, 4 Bridgnorth Road, Wolverhampton, WV6 8AA Tel: (01902) 751147 Fax: (01902) 753853

Midland Canal Centre, Stenson, Barrow-On-Trent, Derby, DE73 1HL
Tel: (01283) 701933 Fax: (01283) 702818
E-mail: eddie@mccboats.co.uk

The New Boat Co., Hanbury Wharf, Hanbury Road, Droitwich, Worcestershire, WR9 7DU
Tel: (01905) 776646 Fax: (01905) 776750

S W Durham Steelcraft Ltd, Old Colliery Buildings, Trimdon Grange Industrial Estate, Trimdon Grange, Trimdon Station, County Durham, TS29 6PA Tel: (01429) 881300 Fax: (01429) 883184

John South (Boats) Ltd, 89 Condover Industrial Estate, near Shrewsbury, Dorrington, Shrewsbury, SY5 7NH Tel: (01743) 718415 Fax: (01743) 718415

BOATS, MOTOR/POWER

Birchwood Marine Ltd, Fulwood Road North, Sutton-in-Ashfield, Nottinghamshire, NG17 2NB Tel: (01623) 515133 Fax: (01623) 440328 E-mail: info@birchwood.co.uk

Fairline Boats plc, Barnwell Road, Oundle, Peterborough, PE8 5PA Tel: (01832) 273661 Fax: (01832) 273432
E-mail: sales@fairline.com

Gibbs, Sandhills Meadow, Shepperton, Middlesex, TW17 9HY Tel: (01932) 242977 Fax: (01932) 222817
E-mail: sales@gibbsmarine.co.uk

Offshore Powerboats Ltd, 1 Lymington Yacht Haven, Kings Saltern Road, Lymington, Hampshire, SO41 3QD Tel: (01590) 677955 Fax: (01590) 671890
E-mail: chris@offshorepowerboats.co.uk

Princess Yachts International plc, Newport Street, Plymouth, PL1 3QG Tel: (01752) 203888 Fax: (01752) 203777
E-mail: info@princess-yachts.com

Shepherds Windermere Ltd, Windermere Marina Village, The Marina, Bowness-on-Windermere, Windermere, Cumbria, LA23 3JQ Tel: (01539) 446004 Fax: (01539) 446005
E-mail: info@shepherdswindermere.co.uk

Sunseeker Exhibitions Ltd, 27-31 West Quay Road, Poole, Dorset, BH15 1HX Tel: (01202) 381111 Fax: (01202) 382222
E-mail: admin@sunseeker.com

BOATS, ROWING

Marine Trimming Service, Penton Hook Marina, Mixnams Lane, Chertsey, Surrey, KT16 8QR
Tel: (01932) 563779 Fax: (01932) 570540

BOATS, USED

▶ Asset Brokers (Int) Ltd, 123 Ashgrove Road West, Aberdeen, AB16 5FA Tel: (01224) 666308 Fax: (01224) 698154
E-mail: info@abil.org.uk

▶ Boats4fun, Averys Oak, Laughton, Lewes, East Sussex, BN8 6BY Tel: (07710) 000410
E-mail: sales@boats4fun.co.uk

▶ Network Conwy, Conwy Marina, Ellis Way, Conwy, Gwynedd, LL32 8GU Tel: (01492) 580001 Fax: (01492) 580004
E-mail: info@nybconwy.co.uk

BODY BUILDING/WEIGHT TRAINING/KEEP FIT EQUIPMENT

▶ Auction Fitness, Unit 10 Bakers Park, Cater Road, Bishopsworth, Bristol, BS13 7TW
Tel: (0870) 8519419 Fax: 0117-964 9679
E-mail: info@auctionfitness.com

Body Sculpture (International Europe) Ltd, Morley Carr Road, Low Moor, Bradford, West Yorkshire, BD12 0RW Tel: (01274) 693888 Fax: (01274) 693700
E-mail: hi-markgroup@btinternet.co.uk

▶ Custom Fitness LLP, 15 The New Poplars, Ash Street Ash, Aldershot, Hampshire, GU12 6LH
Tel: (01252) 328837 E-mail:

▶ Fitness Equipment Clearance, Boland House, Nottingham South & Wilford Industrial Estate, Nottingham, NG11 7EP Tel: 0115-982 2844 Fax: 0115-982 6775
E-mail: sales@fitness-equipment-clearance.co.uk

BODY BUILDING/WEIGHT TRAINING/ KEEP FIT EQUIPMENT – *continued*

▶ Fitness Warehouse, 2b Linton Street, Fulwood, Preston, PR2 3BJ Tel: (01772) 712888 Fax: (01772) 788938 E-mail: sales@gyms4home.com

▶ The Kettlebell Company Ltd, 4 Lockers Park Lane, Hemel Hempstead, Hertfordshire, HP1 1TH Tel: (01442) 247218 E-mail: sales@kettlebell.co.uk

Levenshulme Karate Club, Klondyke Club, Burnage Range, Levenshulme, Manchester, M19 2UG Tel: 0161-221 2676 E-mail: shukokaikarate2000@yahoo.co.uk

▶ Norlite Medical Ltd, 21-23 Justice Mill Lane, Aberdeen, AB11 6EQ Tel: (01224) 573582 Fax: (01224) 572436 E-mail: bob@norlite.co.uk

BODY CARE PRODUCTS

▶ Lotus Sales & Marketing Ltd, 35 Windsor Avenue, Sutton, Surrey, SM3 9RR Tel: (020) 8644 2717 Fax: (020) 8641 3082

▶ Organic & Natural Enterprise Group, Woodwind, The Avenue, Rowledge, Farnham, Surrey, GU10 4BD Tel: (01252) 793452 E-mail: myorganics@tiscali.co.uk

▶ Organic Towel Co., 108 Weston Street, London, SE1 3QB Tel: (0870) 0501261 Fax: (0870) 7622371 E-mail: contact@organictowel.co.uk

BODY PIERCING JEWELLERY

▶ Gemmedbellybars, 33 Westbury Close, Bransgore, Christchurch, Dorset, BH23 8AZ Tel: (01425) 672711 E-mail: hantsgirl2@hotmail.com

▶ Jewellery TV, Leeds, LS17 6WY Tel: (0870) 7447371 Fax: (0870) 1342096 E-mail: sales@jewellery.tv

BODYGUARD SECURITY SERVICES

Matrix Security UK, Ingles Manor, Castle Hill, Folkestone, Kent, CT20 RD Tel: 01304 207372 Fax: 01304 207395 E-mail: info@matrixsecurityuk.com

BOILER AND FURNACE FANS

Daniels Fans Ltd, Heol Gors, Dafen Indust Estate, Felinfoel, Llanelli, Dyfed, SA14 8QR Tel: (01554) 752148 Fax: (01554) 741109 E-mail: sales@danielsfans.ltd.uk

BOILER BLOWDOWN EQUIPMENT

Tyco Valves & Controls Distribution UK Ltd, White Moss Business Park, Moss Lane View, Skelmersdale, Lancashire, WN8 9TN Tel: (01695) 554800 Fax: (01695) 554835 E-mail: dny@tyco-valves.com

BOILER CONTROL SYSTEMS

Parts Centre, PO Box 48, Ripon, North Yorkshire, HG4 5NB Tel: (01765) 690690

Westbury Control Systems Ltd, Unit 5, Wylam Court, Telford Way, Stephenson Industrial Estate, Coalville, Leicestershire, LE67 3HE Tel: (01530) 510751 Fax: (01530) 510756 E-mail: sales@westbury-uk.com

BOILER ECONOMISER SYSTEM INSTALLATION

▶ Active Plumbing & Heating UK Ltd, 33 Thurloe Walk, Grays, Essex, RM17 5AN Tel: (01375) 369347 Fax: (01708) 349380

Bolton's Superheaters Ltd, Wellington Works, Wellington Road, Ashton-U-Lyne, Ashton-under-Lyne, Lancashire, OL6 7EF Tel: 0161-344 0208 Fax: 0161-343 3305 E-mail: sales@superheater.co.uk

Fuel Economy Ltd, 10 Whittle Road, Ferndown Industrial Estate, Wimborne, Dorset, BH21 7RU Tel: (01202) 895544 Fax: (01202) 897798 E-mail: sales@savastat.co.uk

Therm Tech Engineering Ltd, PO Box 30, Stockport, Cheshire, SK12 1BD Tel: (01625) 878831 Fax: (01625) 878832 E-mail: economisers@thermtech.fsnet.co.uk

Thermal Energy Construction Ltd, Trent Lane, Castle Donington, Derby, DE74 2NP Tel: (01332) 810999 Fax: (01332) 855175 E-mail: info@thermalenergy.co.uk

BOILER ECONOMISER SYSTEMS

Bolton's Superheaters Ltd, Wellington Works, Wellington Road, Ashton-U-Lyne, Ashton-under-Lyne, Lancashire, OL6 7EF Tel: 0161-344 0208 Fax: 0161-343 3305 E-mail: sales@superheater.co.uk

Fuel Economy Ltd, 10 Whittle Road, Ferndown Industrial Estate, Wimborne, Dorset, BH21 7RU Tel: (01202) 895544 Fax: (01202) 897798 E-mail: sales@savastat.co.uk

A.L. Starkie Ltd, Wellington Works, Wellington Rd, Ashton-under-Lyne, Lancs, OL6 7EF Tel: 0161-339 4549 Fax: 0161-343 3305 E-mail: sales@superheater.co.uk

Therm Tech Ltd, Unit 4a Kayley Industrial Estate, Richmond Street, Ashton-under-Lyne, Lancashire, OL7 0AU Tel: 0161 339 3049 Fax: 0161 343 3305 E-mail: thermtech@msn.com

Therm Tech Engineering Ltd, PO Box 30, Stockport, Cheshire, SK12 1BD Tel: (01625) 878831 Fax: (01625) 878832 E-mail: economisers@thermtech.fsnet.co.uk

Thorne International Boiler Services Ltd, Broad Lanes, Bilston, West Midlands, WV14 0RQ Tel: (01902) 404223 Fax: (01902) 404224 E-mail: info@tibsltd.com

BOILER ECONOMISER SYSTEMS MAINTENANCE OR REPAIR

▶ Active Plumbing & Heating UK Ltd, 33 Thurloe Walk, Grays, Essex, RM17 5AN Tel: (01375) 369347 Fax: (01708) 349380

BOILER EMISSION MONITORING EQUIPMENT

Energy Technology & Control Ltd, 25 North Street, Lewes, East Sussex, BN7 2PE Tel: (01273) 480667 Fax: (01273) 480652 E-mail: sales@energytechnologycontrol.com

BOILER ENGINEERING, *See also headings for particular types such as Installation etc; Repair etc*

▶ Active Plumbing & Heating UK Ltd, 33 Thurloe Walk, Grays, Essex, RM17 5AN Tel: (01375) 369347 Fax: (01708) 349380

BOILER FITTINGS

A & J Gummers Ltd, Unit H Redfern Park Way, Birmingham, B11 2DN Tel: 0121-706 2241 Fax: 0121-706 2960 E-mail: sales@gummers.co.uk

Allspares Heating Supplies, 60 Frances Street, Newtownards, County Down, BT23 7DY Tel: (028) 9181 7915 Fax: (028) 9181 7915

Aquamarine, 216 Fair Oak Road, Eastleigh, Hampshire, SO50 8HU Tel: (023) 8060 0473 Fax: (023) 8060 1381 E-mail: admin@aqua-marine.co.uk

Chanter Bio Med Ltd, 1 Hanworth Road, Low Moor, Bradford, West Yorkshire, BD12 0SG Tel: (01274) 414666 Fax: (01274) 414470 E-mail: info@chanterbiomed.co.uk

F M T Ltd, 606 Green Lane, Ilford, Essex, IG3 9SQ Tel: (020) 8590 3556 Fax: (020) 8599 1561

M T S (GB) Ltd, M T S Building, Hughenden Avenue, High Wycombe, Buckinghamshire, HP13 5FT Tel: (01494) 755600 Fax: (01494) 459775 E-mail: info@chaffoteaux.co.uk

Sabre Systems (Heating) Ltd, Unit 9, Ruxley Corner Industrial Estate, Edgington Way, Sidcup, Kent, DA14 5BL Tel: (020) 8308 0708 Fax: (020) 8309 6727 E-mail: sales@sabresystems.co.uk

▶ Somerset Gas Co. Ltd, 17 Knights Road, Chelston Business Park, Wellington, Somerset, TA21 9JH Tel: (01823) 661144 Fax: (01823) 661155 E-mail: info@somersetgas.eclipse.co.uk

BOILER GAS BURNERS

▶ Apex Domestic & Commercial Services Ltd, 43 Eastgate Street, Stafford, ST16 2LY Tel: (01785) 250699 Fax: (01785) 229616 E-mail: enquiries@apexservice.wanado.co.uk

▶ M R Gas Services, 6 Elm Grove, Plympton, Plymouth, PL7 2BW Tel: (01752) 346482 Fax:

BOILER HIRE

Associated Contract Energy Ltd, 73-75 Church Road, Redfield, Bristol, BS5 9JR Tel: 0117-939 4495 Fax: 0117-939 4496 E-mail: vivre21@hotmail.com

Bradlee Boilers Ltd, 3 Stambermill Industrial Estate, Timmis Road, Stourbridge, West Midlands, DY9 7BJ Tel: (01384) 423859 Fax: (01384) 895435 E-mail: sales@bradleeboilers.com

Rogan Heating Services, 4 Reach Road Industrial Estate, Reach Road, Burwell, Cambridge, CB5 0AH Tel: (01638) 743500 Fax: (01638) 743843 E-mail: roganhs@globalnet.co.uk

Watkins Hire, Churwell Vale, Shaw Cross Business Park, Dewsbury, West Yorkshire, WF12 7RD Tel: (01924) 439733 Fax: (01924) 439732 E-mail: hire@watkinshire.co.uk

BOILER INSPECTION SERVICES

J D Jackson (Electronics), Eastfield Labs, Danethorpe Hill, Newark, Nottinghamshire, NG24 2PD Tel: (01636) 705718 Fax: (01636) 610120 E-mail: sales@jacksonelectronics.co.uk

▶ Mark Payne, 53 South Coast Road, Peacehaven, East Sussex, BN10 8QW Tel: (01273) 583052

BOILER INSTALLATION OR ERECTION OR COMMISSIONING OR GENERAL ENGINEERING

▶ AM Electrical & Gas Installations, 41 Irlam Avenue, Eccles, Manchester, M30 0JR Tel: 0161 7079797

Atlantic Project Co., 828 Manchester Road, Rochdale, Lancashire, OL11 3AW Tel: (01706) 345661 Fax: (01706) 648243 E-mail: aslack@apcpower.com

Bemas Boiler Erectors Ltd, PO Box 28, Nottingham, NG10 2GA Tel: 0115-972 8954 Fax: 0115-946 1857 E-mail: paul@bemasboilers.co.uk

Boiler Tech Services, Unit 22 Demmings Road, Cheadle, Cheshire, SK8 2PE Tel: 0161-428 2967 Fax: 0161-428 6487 E-mail: peter@mead4656.fsnet.co.uk

Bolton's Superheaters Ltd, Wellington Works, Wellington Road, Ashton-U-Lyne, Ashton-under-Lyne, Lancashire, OL6 7EF Tel: 0161-344 0208 Fax: 0161-343 3305 E-mail: sales@superheater.co.uk

Bradlee Boilers Ltd, 3 Stambermill Industrial Estate, Timmis Road, Stourbridge, West Midlands, DY9 7BJ Tel: (01384) 423859 Fax: (01384) 895435 E-mail: sales@bradleeboilers.com

Donland Engineering Southern Ltd, Foundation House, Stoneylands Road, Egham, Surrey, TW20 9QR Tel: (01784) 436151 Fax: (01784) 436038 E-mail: e@donlandeng.co.uk

E-Tech Group (HVAC Div), The E-Tech Centre, Boundary Road, Great Yarmouth, Norfolk, NR31 0LY Tel: 01493 419800 Fax: 01493 419805 E-mail: etech-hvac@etechcentre.com

Flueclean Installations Services Ltd, Lytham Street Works, Stockport, Cheshire, SK3 8JB Tel: 0161-480 8551 Fax: 0161-477 7769 E-mail: sales@flueclean.com

G P Watson Ltd, Unit 5 Lancaster Port, Corintation Road, High Wycombe, Buckinghamshire, HP12 3TD Tel: (01494) 446515 Fax: (01494) 446615 E-mail: sales@gpwatson.co.uk

Giles D & B Ltd Service Engineers, 13 Ludgate Close, Waltham, Grimsby, South Humberside, DN37 0LX Tel: (01472) 822662 E-mail: manager@dbgilesltd.f9.co.uk

Bruce Hines, 50 Churchdale Road, Sheffield, S12 4XU Tel: 0114-239 5423

Holland Engineering, Victoria House, Paxton Street, Stoke-on-Trent, ST1 3SD Tel: (01782) 283364 Fax: (01782) 284241 E-mail: info@hollandengineering.co.uk

J B C Industrial Services Ltd, Howley Park Road East, Morley, Leeds, LS27 0SW Tel: 0113-220 3830 Fax: 0113-252 1407 E-mail: info@jbcindserv.co.uk

Northern Arc Electric Welding Co Leicester Ltd, 161 Scudamore Road, Leicester, LE3 1UQ Tel: 0116-287 4949 Fax: 0116-287 5153

▶ Mark Payne, 53 South Coast Road, Peacehaven, East Sussex, BN10 8QW Tel: (01273) 583052

Rogers Industrial Equipment Ltd, 97 Castle Road, Mumbles, Swansea, SA3 5TA Tel: (01792) 361018 Fax: (01792) 361019 E-mail: barry@rogersboilers.fsnet.co.uk

T B S Engineering, 11 Maylan Road, Earlstrees Industrial Estate, Corby, Northamptonshire, NN17 4DR Tel: (01536) 262697 Fax: (01536) 401053

Testbank Ship Repair & Boiler Co. Ltd, Western Avenue, Western Docks, Southampton, SO15 0HH Tel: (023) 8078 7878 Fax: (023) 8078 7826 E-mail: admin@testbank.co.uk

Thorne International Boiler Services Ltd, Broad Lanes, Bilston, West Midlands, WV14 0RQ Tel: (01902) 404223 Fax: (01902) 404224 E-mail: info@tibsltd.com

Westside Engineering Site Services Ltd, Westside House, Pontugwindy Industrial Estate, Caerphilly, Mid Glamorgan, CF83 3HU Tel: (029) 2086 0123 Fax: (029) 2085 1122

BOILER INSULATION, *See Insulating/Insulation etc*

BOILER LEVEL INDICATORS

Tyco Valves & Controls Distribution UK Ltd, White Moss Business Park, Moss Lane View, Skelmersdale, Lancashire, WN8 9TN Tel: (01695) 554800 Fax: (01695) 554835 E-mail: dny@tyco-valves.com

BOILER MAINTENANCE OR REPAIR

▶ 1st call aacronite, po box 16255, London, N19 5WF Tel: (07939) 484677 E-mail: mail@aacronite.com

A G S Environmental Maintenance, The Oaks, Boxhill Road, Tadworth, Surrey, KT20 7JT Tel: (01737) 843656 Fax: (01737) 842883 E-mail: sales@agsmaintenance.co.uk

▶ Alhco Sewer Rehabilitation Ltd, 114 Station Road, Westbury, Wiltshire, BA13 4TW Tel: (01373) 823814 E-mail: richard.jemmett@alhco.co.uk

Anglo-Swedish Engineering & Welding (Southern) Ltd, Unit 12, Lansdowne Workshops, Lansdowne Mews, Charlton, London, SE7 8AZ Tel: (020) 8858 2024 Fax: (020) 8858 7301 E-mail: info@metboilerrepairs.co.uk

Boiler Tech Services, Unit 22 Demmings Road, Cheadle, Cheshire, SK8 2PE Tel: 0161-428 2967 Fax: 0161-428 6487 E-mail: peter@mead4656.fsnet.co.uk

Chiller Rental Services, Wigan Road, Leyland, PR25 5XW Tel: (01772) 643040 Fax: (01772) 643041 E-mail: info@chiller-rental.com

Combserve Combustion Service Ltd, 1 Brookfield Works, Wood Street, Elland, West Yorkshire, HX5 9AP Tel: (01422) 370051 Fax: (01422) 377374 E-mail: combserve@hotmail.com

Economy Heating Services Ltd, Economy House, Hardley Industrial Estate, Hardley, Hythe, Southampton, SO45 3YQ Tel: (023) 8084 6646 Fax: (023) 8084 4479 E-mail: dick@economyservices.co.uk

Elyo Services, Apian House, Selinas Lane, Dagenham, Essex, RM8 1TB Tel: (020) 8252 2929 Fax: (020) 8270 7379

Evans Mechanical Services Ltd, Derby House, 29 Castle Street, Caergwrle, Wrexham, Clwyd, LL12 9AD Tel: (01978) 760000 Fax: (01978) 761082 E-mail: enquiries@evans-mech.co.uk

Flueclean Installations Services Ltd, Lytham Street Works, Stockport, Cheshire, SK3 8JB Tel: 0161-480 8551 Fax: 0161-477 7769 E-mail: sales@flueclean.com

Gibson Wight Ltd, 14-18 East Shaw Street, Kilmarnock, Ayrshire, KA1 4AN Tel: (01563) 523633 Fax: (01563) 536472 E-mail: charles.gibson@gibsonwight.co.uk

Giles D & B Ltd Service Engineers, 13 Ludgate Close, Waltham, Grimsby, South Humberside, DN37 0LX Tel: (01472) 822662 E-mail: manager@dbgilesltd.f9.co.uk

H A Mcewen Boiler Repairs Ltd, Farling Top Boilerworks, Farling Top, Cowling, Keighley, West Yorkshire, BD22 0NW Tel: (01535) 634674 Fax: (01535) 636802 E-mail: maria@mcewen82.fsnet.co.uk

H & I Engineering Ltd, Solway Works, Annan Road, Eastriggs, Annan, Dumfriesshire, DG12 6NJ Tel: (01461) 40500 Fax: (01461) 40801 E-mail: admin@hi-engineering.co.uk

Haggart Commercial Marine, 98-100 Vauxhall Street, Plymouth, PL4 0DD Tel: (01752) 660117 Fax: (01752) 660117

Harpers Weybridge, 135 Stubbington Lane, Fareham, Hampshire, PO14 2NF Tel: (01329) 662293 Fax: (01329) 665518

High-Fire Ltd, 37a Cyprus Rd, Leicester, LE2 8QP Tel: 0116-232 7980

Bruce Hines, 50 Churchdale Road, Sheffield, S12 4XU Tel: 0114-239 5423

Holland Engineering, Victoria House, Paxton Street, Stoke-on-Trent, ST1 3SD Tel: (01782) 283364 Fax: (01782) 284241 E-mail: info@hollandengineering.co.uk

James Ramsey Glasgow Ltd, 85 Dykehead Street, Queenslie Industrial Estate, Glasgow, G33 4AQ Tel: 0141-774 2602 Fax: 0141-774 4321 E-mail: jamesramseyltd@btconnect.com

Joseph H Wood & Son Ltd, 15 Hemmons Road, Manchester, M12 5ST Tel: 0161-248 9814 Fax: 0161-225 2044 E-mail: wood@steamforindustry.freeserve.co.uk

London Essential Maintenance Ltd, 62 Rainham Road, London, NW10 5DJ Tel: (0800) 0191363 Fax: (0870) 7621371 E-mail: sales@londonessential.co.uk

Multibasics Gas Service Engineers, 12 Thornton Road, Morecambe, Lancashire, LA4 5PE Tel: (01524) 415346 Fax: (01524) 412509 E-mail: sales@multibasics.com

OilanHeat (Maintenance) Ltd, 161 High Street, Aldershot, Hampshire, GU11 1TT Tel: (01252) 329789 Fax: (01252) 342804 E-mail: ac@lowbeck.com

Paine Manwaring Ltd, 7-11 Ardsheal Road, Worthing, West Sussex, BN14 7RW Tel: (01903) 237522 Fax: (01903) 236511 E-mail: enquires@painemanwearing.co.uk

R B B Refractory Engineers Ltd, 291 Watling Street, Dartford, DA2 6EP Tel: (01322) 394850 Fax: (01322) 394860 E-mail: enquiries@rbbrefractory.co.uk

BOILER MAINTENANCE OR REPAIR

– *continued*

S S Motors (Fuels) Ltd, 2 Honeysome Road, Chatteris, Cambridgeshire, PE16 6RZ Tel: (01354) 693181 Fax: (01354) 694181

Service Engineering Ltd, 45 Rosemary Terrace, Blyth, Northumberland, NE24 3DS Tel: (01670) 363309 Fax: (01670) 360528 E-mail: wldjrr@bun.com

Service Systems Ltd, 178 Oxford Road, Basford, Newcastle, Staffordshire, ST5 0QB Tel: (01782) 711077 Fax: (01782) 638538 E-mail: enquiries@servicesystemsltd.co.uk

▶ Somerset Gas Co. Ltd, 17 Knights Road, Chelston Business Park, Wellington, Somerset, TA21 9JH Tel: (01823) 661144 Fax: (01823) 661155 E-mail: info@somersetgas.eclipse.co.uk

SVR, Unit 1 35 Little London, Spalding, Lincolnshire, PE11 2UE Tel: (01775) 760999 Fax: (01775) 724547

Swift Maintenance Services, Unit 2 Albert Street, Wednesbury, West Midlands, WS10 7EW Tel: 0121-505 4001 Fax: 0121-502 2065

T J Foster Properties Ltd, Shear House, Petersfield Avenue, Slough, SL2 5DQ Tel: (01753) 531477 Fax: (01753) 526933 E-mail: foster@btconnect.com

▶ TBS Engineering (UK) Ltd, 63Market Street, Hollinsworth, Hyde, Cheshire, SK14 8HR Tel: (01457) 835585 Fax: (01457) 764627 E-mail: sales@tbsengineering.net

Thermsave Welding, 9 Wavertree Park Gardens, Low Moor, Bradford, West Yorkshire, BD12 0UY Tel: (01274) 424478 Fax: (01274) 424479 E-mail: thermsavewelding@blueyonder.co.uk

Thorne International Boiler Services Ltd, Broad Lanes, Bilston, West Midlands, WV14 0RQ Tel: (01902) 404223 Fax: (01902) 404224 E-mail: info@tibsltd.com

Truclass Ltd, Stallings Lane, Kingswinford, West Midlands, DY6 7HU Tel: (01384) 400919 Fax: (01384) 400719

Vokera Ltd, Stubs Beck Lane, West 26 Business Park, Cleckheaton, West Yorkshire, BD19 4TT Tel: (01274) 866112 Fax: (01274) 86655

W Bertram & Sons Ltd, Walpole Street, South Shields, Tyne & Wear, NE33 5EF Tel: 0191-455 6727 Fax: 0191-455 6727

BOILER MAINTENANCE OR REPAIR EQUIPMENT

▶ 1st call aacronite, po box 16255, London, N19 5WF Tel: (07939) 484677 E-mail: mail@aacronite.com

Engineering & Maintenance Services Ltd, Unit 12 St. Davids Industrial Estate, St. Davids Road, Swansea Enterprise Park, Swansea, SA6 8RX Tel: (01792) 797579 Fax: (01792) 772490 E-mail: ems@swanseauk.fsworld.co.uk

Vokera Ltd, Borderlake House, Unit 7 & 8, Riverside Industrial Estate, London Colney By Pass, London Colney, St. Albans, Hertfordshire, AL2 1HG Tel: (01442) 281400 Fax: (01442) 450565 E-mail: enquiries@vokera.co.uk

BOILER MAINTENANCE OR REPAIR EQUIPMENT HIRE

A R Adams & Son Ltd, Pill Bank Works, Coomassie Street, Newport, Gwent, NP20 2US Tel: (01633) 262060 Fax: (01633) 258295

Chiller Rental Services, Wigan Road, Leyland, PR25 5XW Tel: (01772) 643040 Fax: (01772) 643041 E-mail: info@chiller-rental.com

BOILER OR BOILER TUBE CLEANING EQUIPMENT

Airnesco Group Ltd, Unit 2, Bredgar Industrial Estate, Bredgar Road, Gillingham, Kent, ME8 6PL Tel: (01634) 267070 Fax: (01634) 267079 E-mail: info@airnesco.com

Goodway Service & Safety Ltd, 8 Foundry Court, Daventry, Northamptonshire, NN11 4RH Tel: (01327) 312468 Fax: (01327) 301404 E-mail: goodwaydist@msn.com

Multilink Resources Ltd, Suite 18, Vermont House, Bradley Lane, Standish, Wigan, Lancashire, WN6 0XF Tel: (01257) 427053 Fax: (01257) 427053 E-mail: enquire@multilink.co.uk

Rotatools UK Ltd, Brookfield Drive, Liverpool, L9 7EG Tel: 0151-525 8611 Fax: 0151-525 4868 E-mail: richard_dearn@hotmail.com

Skatoskalo International, 6 Morris Road, Royal Oak Industrial Estate, Daventry, Northamptonshire, NN11 8PD Tel: (01327) 312443 Fax: (01327) 314140 E-mail: sales@skatoskalo.com

BOILER REFRACTORIES

▶ Handsworth Refractories Ltd, Liverpool Street, Sheffield, S9 2PU Tel: 0114-244 2315 Fax: 0114-256 0559 E-mail: enquiries@hrluk.com

BOILER REMOVAL CONTRACTORS

Finch & Co., Homestead, Eastwick Road, Bookham, Leatherhead, Surrey, KT23 4BA Tel: (01372) 452711 Fax: (01372) 450957 E-mail: info@machinemovers.co.uk

▶ Sharpe Refinery Service Hydro Carbons Ltd, Arlington Works, Arlington Road, Twickenham, TW1 2BB Tel: (020) 8892 0502 Fax: (020) 8892 8193 E-mail: sales@sharpesoil.co.uk

BOILER SETTING OR LINING,

See Boiler Installation etc

BOILER SPARE PARTS

Monax Glass Ltd, 22 Charles Jarvis Court, Cupar, Fife, KY15 5EJ Tel: (01334) 657800 Fax: (01334) 657857 E-mail: monax@sol.co.uk

Parts Center Commercial, Unit 14, Harp Road, Off Guinness Road, Trafford Park, Manchester, M17 1SR Tel: 0161-848 0546 Fax: 0161-872 0265

BOILER SUPPLIES

Atag Heating UK Ltd, Unit 3 Beaver Trade Park, Quarry Lane, Chichester, West Sussex, PO19 8NY Tel: (01243) 815770 Fax: (01243) 839596 E-mail: info@atagheating.co.uk

BOILER TUBE OR BOILER CLEANING SERVICES, *See also Descaling Services*

Ace Industrial Boiler Cleaners, 10 Rollscourt Avenue, London, SE24 0EA Tel: (020) 7733 1676

Airnesco Group Ltd, Unit 2, Bredgar Industrial Estate, Bredgar Road, Gillingham, Kent, ME8 6PL Tel: (01634) 267070 Fax: (01634) 267079 E-mail: info@airnesco.com

Artisan Refractories Ltd, Hanley Road, Stoke-on-Trent, ST1 6BG Tel: (01782) 266563 Fax: (01782) 266563 E-mail: artisanref@aol.com

Beebys, The Depot, High Street, Stilton, Peterborough, PE7 3RA Tel: (01733) 244584 Fax: (01733) 244946 E-mail: info@beebys.co

Flueclean Installations Services Ltd, Lytham Street Works, Stockport, Cheshire, SK3 8JB Tel: 0161-480 8551 Fax: 0161-477 7769 E-mail: sales@flueclean.com

BOILER TUBES, *See also Copper Tube; Steel Tube etc*

Power Metal Supplies, 2-4 Winton Square, Basingstoke, Hampshire, RG21 8EN Tel: (01256) 811821 Fax: (01256) 811824 E-mail: powermetal@ukonline.co.uk

RTR Handelsgesellschaft, 8 Kingsway House, Kingsway, Team Valley Trading Estate, Gateshead, Tyne & Wear, NE11 0HW Tel: 0191-491 1292 Fax: 0191-491 1246 E-mail: sales@rtr.co.uk

Willingale Tubes Ltd, Chilton Industrial Estate, Windham Road, Sudbury, Suffolk, CO10 2XD Tel: (01787) 375300 Fax: (01787) 880108 E-mail: info@willingale-tubes.com

BOILERS

Clyde Energy Solutions Ltd, Unit 10, Lion Park Avenue, Chessington, Surrey, KT9 1ST Tel: (020) 8391 2020 Fax: (020) 8397 4598 E-mail: info@clyde-nrg.com

▶ Dash Energy Services, 32 Ash Lane, Hale, Altrincham, Cheshire, WA15 8PD Tel: 0161-980 0018 Fax: 0161-980 0018

Farm 2000 - Teisen Products Ltd, Bradley Green, Redditch, Worcestershire, B96 6RP Tel: (01527) 821621 Fax: (01527) 821665 E-mail: heat@farm2000.co.uk

Holland Engineering, Victoria House, Paxton Street, Stoke-on-Trent, ST1 3SD Tel: (01782) 283364 Fax: (01782) 284241 E-mail: info@hollandengineering.co.uk

Keston Boilers Ltd, 34 West Common Road, Bromley, BR2 7BX Tel: (020) 8462 0262 Fax: (020) 8462 4459 E-mail: info@keston.co.uk

BOLLARDS

Aremco Products, Foxoak Street, Cradley Heath, West Midlands, B64 5DQ Tel: (01384) 568566 Fax: (01384) 634601 E-mail: sales@aremco-products.co.uk

Associated Roto-Plastics Ltd, Green Grove Mill, Dyehouse Lane, Rochdale, Lancashire, OL16 2QN Tel: (0870) 8303900 Fax: (0870) 8303901 E-mail: sales@haywood-rotomoulding.co.uk

Broxap Mawrob, 121A-125A Sefton Street, Southport, Merseyside, PR8 5DR Tel: (01704) 513330 Fax: (01704) 500380 E-mail: sales@broxap.co.uk

Furnitubes International Ltd, Meridian House, Royal Hill, London, SE10 8RD Tel: (020) 8378 3200 Fax: (020) 8378 3250 E-mail: sales@furnitubes.com

Lyngrade Lancashire Ltd, Unit 23 Hardmans Business Centre, New Hall Hey Road, Rossendale, Lancashire, BB4 6HH Tel: (01706) 212780 Fax: (01706) 212816 E-mail: info@lyngrade.co.uk

Marshalls Mono Ltd, Landscape House, Premiere Way, Housefield Business Park, Elland, West Yorkshire, HX5 9HT Tel: (01422) 306400 Fax: (0870) 6002426

Orchard Street Furniture, 119 The Street, Crowmarsh Gifford, Wallingford, Oxfordshire, OX10 8EF Tel: (01491) 826100 Fax: (01491) 642126 E-mail: sales@orchardstreet.co.uk

Post & Column Company Ltd, Unit 1, Road Four, Winsford, Cheshire, CW7 2NU Tel: (01606) 550502 Fax: (01606) 550857 E-mail: info@postandcolumn.co.uk

Rotational Mouldings Ltd, Knowles Industrial Estate, Buxton Road, Furness Vale, High Peak, Derbyshire, SK23 7PH Tel: (01663) 742897 Fax: (01663) 747584 E-mail: sales@rotationalmouldings.co.uk

Signature Ltd, Signature House, Hainge Road, Tividale, Oldbury, West Midlands, B69 2NF Tel: 0121-557 0234 Fax: 0121-557 0995 E-mail: sales@signatureltd.com

Specialised Engineering Services, 129 Monk Street, Derby, DE22 3QE Tel: (01332) 370994 Fax: (01332) 294513 E-mail: sales@ukbollards.com

BOLT BOXES

Lemon Groundwork Supplies, Russell Gardens, Wickford, Essex, SS11 8BH Tel: (01268) 571571 Fax: (01268) 571555 E-mail: sales@lemon-gs.co.uk

Polycones Bolt Boxes Ltd, 9 Ashfold Avenue, Findon Valley, Worthing, West Sussex, BN14 0AP Tel: (01903) 526538 Fax: (01903) 526538

BOLT CUTTERS, HYDRAULIC

▶ MAN Hydraulics & Engineering Ltd, Unit 9, Thurnscoe Business Centre, Princess Drive, Thurnscoe, Rotherham, South Yorkshire, S63 0BL Tel: (01709) 880520 Fax: (05601) 165945 E-mail: manhydeng@yahoo.co.uk

BOLT LOOSENING/TIGHTENING SERVICES

Mott Macdonald UK Ltd, St Annes Wharf, 112 Quayside, Newcastle upon Tyne, NE1 3DX Tel: 0191-261 0866 Fax: 0191-261 1100 E-mail: marketing@mottmac.com

BOLT TORQUE AND TENSIONING, SUBSEA

▶ Boltight, Unit 2 Junction 10 Business Park, Bentley Mill Way, Walsall, WS2 0LE Tel: (01922) 631289 Fax: (01922) 633728 E-mail: sales@boltight.com

P S L Energy Services Ltd, Badentoy Avenue, Badentoy Industrial Estate, Portlethen, Aberdeen, AB12 4YB Tel: (01224) 783008 Fax: (01224) 783005E-mail: sales@psles.com

BOLT TORQUE/TENSIONING SERVICES

P S L Energy Services Ltd, Badentoy Avenue, Badentoy Industrial Estate, Portlethen, Aberdeen, AB12 4YB Tel: (01224) 783008 Fax: (01224) 783005E-mail: sales@psles.com

▶ Sparrows Offshore Services Ltd, Denmore Road, Bridge of Don, Aberdeen, AB23 8JW Tel: (01224) 704868 Fax: (01224) 825191 E-mail: sales@sparrows.co.uk

Torque Tension Systems Ltd, 5 Stephenson Court, Barrington Industrial Estate, Bedlington, Northumberland, NE22 7DQ Tel: (01670) 530411 Fax: (01670) 531991 E-mail: enquiries@tts-ltd.com

BOLTING CLOTH

Carrington Novare, Calder Works, Thornhill Road, Dewsbury, West Yorkshire, WF12 9QQ Tel: (01924) 465161 Fax: (01924) 457596 E-mail: enquiries@cpf.co.uk

BOLTS, *See also headings for particular types*

Basta Parsons Ltd, Alma Street, Wolverhampton, WV10 0EY Tel: (01902) 877770 Fax: (01902) 877771 E-mail: sjohnson@bastaparsonsqb.com

Buckinghamshire Fastener Co. Ltd, 14 Wilverley Road, Christchurch, Dorset, BH23 3RU Tel: (01202) 488202 Fax: (01202) 474442 E-mail: sales@buckfastener.co.uk

Builder Center Ltd, Finmere Road, Eastbourne, East Sussex, BN22 8QJ Tel: (01323) 725121 Fax: (01323) 738879

High Tensile Bolts Ltd, Imperial Works, 93 Lockfield Avenue, Enfield, Middlesex, EN3 7PY Tel: (020) 8805 8510 Fax: (020) 8805 1553 E-mail: kebrell@montal-internet.co.uk

I E Bolt & Nut Ltd, Unit 14 Alma Works, Alma Street, Cutler Heights, Bradford, West Yorkshire, BD4 9JE Tel: (01274) 686805 Fax: (01274) 680361 E-mail: sales@iebolt.co.uk

Kebrell Nuts & Bolts Ltd, Imperial Works, Lockfield Avenue, Enfield, Middlesex, EN3 7PY Tel: (020) 8805 8510 Fax: (020) 8805 1553 E-mail: kebrell@montal-internet.co.uk

Liebig Bolts Ltd, Silica Road, Amington Industrial Estate, Tamworth, Staffordshire, B77 4DT Tel: (01827) 50547 Fax: (01827) 310524 E-mail: sales@liebigbolts.co.uk

▶ Performance Alloys.com, Randalstown Road, Enkalon Industrial Estate, Antrim, BT41 4LD Tel: (028) 9446 5151 E-mail: sales@performancealloys.com

Pilgrim International Ltd, Southlink Business Park Unit 10, Oldham, OL4 1DE Tel: 0161-785 7700 E-mail: info@pilgrim-international.co.uk

Pugh & Sanders Ltd, Woods Lane, Derby, DE22 3UD Tel: (01332) 206770 Fax: (01332) 206771

▶ Swiftfix, 18 Newtown Road, Southampton, SO19 9HQ Tel: (023) 8044 8444 Fax: (023) 8044 8444 E-mail: sales@swiftfix.co.uk

TR Fastenings, Trifast House, Bolton Close, Bellbrook Industrial Estate, Uckfield, East Sussex, TN22 1QW Tel: (01825) 764711 Fax: (01256) 461281

BOLTS AND NUTS, *See headings for particular types*

See also headings for particular types

▶ A D A Fastfix Ltd, 5 Parkhouse Business Centre, Desborough Park Road, Parkhouse Business Centre, High Wycombe, Buckinghamshire, HP12 3DJ Tel: (0870) 7207100 Fax: (0870) 7207120 E-mail: alan@adafastfix.co.uk

A H C Camberley Ltd, 415-417 London Road, Camberley, Surrey, GU15 3HZ Tel: (01252) 735176 Fax: (01276) 709068 E-mail: oliver@ahc-camberley.co.uk

A & J Fasteners, 19 Manor Trading Estate, Brunel Road, Benfleet, Essex, SS7 4PS Tel: (01268) 566422 Fax: (01268) 566422

A T Engineering Supplies Ltd, Garstang Road, Claughton-on-Brock, Preston, PR3 0RB Tel: (01995) 640058 Fax: (01995) 640031

A&D, 3 44 Colville Road, London, W3 8BL Tel: (020) 8992 6721 Fax: (020) 8992 4677

A1 Fasteners Ltd, Unit 5/6, Brookwood Insutrial Estate, Eastleigh, Southampton, SO50 9EY Tel: (023) 8065 0666 Fax: (023) 8065 0601 E-mail: sales@a1-fasteners.co.uk

▶ A1 Supplies, The Acorns, Willisham Road, Barking, Ipswich, IP6 8HY Tel: (01473) 657227 Fax: (01473) 657229

Abco Industrial Fastners, Unit 5 The Gloucesters, Crompton Close, Basildon, Essex, SS14 3AY Tel: (01268) 520561 Fax: (01268) 534321

Abec Fixings Ltd, Unit 22 Small Heath Trading Estate, Armoury Road, Birmingham, B11 2RJ Tel: 0121-683 0061 Fax: 0121-683 0064 E-mail: sales@abecfixings.co.uk

Abel Fasteners, 25 Albion Street, Rugeley, Staffordshire, WS15 2BY Tel: (01889) 586675 Fax: (01889) 586676

Abell Fasteners, Unit 337 Rushock Trading Estate, Rushock, Droitwich, Worcestershire, WR9 0NR Tel: (01299) 251533 Fax: (01299) 251533

Acclaim Fasteners & Turned Parts, Unit 17 Premier Park Estate, Leys Road, Brierley Hill, West Midlands, DY5 3UP Tel: (01384) 76263 Fax: (01384) 76268

Aces Fans Ltd, 6 Ryefield Crescent, Northwood, Middlesex, HA6 1LR Tel: (01923) 827533 Fax: (01923) 835514 E-mail: sales@fixings-diy.co.uk

Acorn Fasteners Ltd, Unit W4 Lambs Business Park, Tilburstow Hill Road, South Godstone, Godstone, Surrey, RH9 8LJ Tel: (01342) 893500 Fax: (01342) 892820 E-mail: sales@acornfastenersltd.co.uk

Alfast Engineering Supplies Ltd, 2 Gloucester Road, Luton, LU1 3HX Tel: (01582) 418498 Fax: (01582) 418833 E-mail: sales@alfast.co.uk

Allcap Ltd, Unit 24c Morelands Trading Estate, Bristol Road, Gloucester, GL1 5RZ Tel: (01452) 525800 Fax: (01452) 331125 E-mail: sales@allcap.co.uk

Alpha Fasteners, Unit 13 Ffrwdgrech Industrial Estate, Ffrwdgrech Road, Brecon, Powys, LD3 8LA Tel: (01874) 625631 Fax: (01874) 625326 E-mail: sales@alphafasteners.co.uk

Andrews Fasteners Ltd, 8 Latchmore Industrial Park, Low Fields Road, Leeds, LS12 6DN Tel: 0113-246 9992 Fax: 0113-243 6463 E-mail: sales@andrewsfasteners.co.uk

Annalex Bute Ltd, Unit B6 Blaby Industrial Park, Winchester Avenue, Blaby, Leicester, LE8 4GZ Tel: 0116-277 9537 Fax: 0116-277 8623 E-mail: sales@annalexbyute.co.uk

BOLTS AND NUTS – *continued*

Antron Engineers Supplies, Unit 11 Broomers Hill Par, Broomers Hill Lane, Pulborough, West Sussex, RH20 2RY Tel: (01798) 872720 E-mail: sales@antroneng.co.uk

Archerdale Ltd, Hirstwood Works, Hirst Wood Road, Shipley, West Yorkshire, BD18 4BU Tel: (01274) 595783 Fax: (01274) 531263 E-mail: sales@archerdale.co.uk

Arkwell Fasteners Ltd, Unit 1, Chapel Street, Long Eaton, Nottingham, NG10 1EQ Tel: 0115-973 1181 Fax: 0115-946 1123 E-mail: sales@arkwell.co.uk

Astley Components, 623-625 High Road Leyton, London, E10 6RF Tel: (020) 8556 9711 Fax: (020) 8556 6641 E-mail: sales@astleycomp.co.uk

Avon Fastenings & Industrial Supplies Ltd, Unit 10, Western Road Industrial Estate, Stratford-Upon-Avon, Warwickshire, CV37 0AH Tel: (01789) 269661 Fax: (01789) 267051 E-mail: avonfastenings@aol.com

B & C Fixings Ltd, Archimedes House, 20 Cleveland Trading Estate, Darlington, County Durham, DL1 2PB Tel: (01325) 286842 Fax: (01325) 352563

B & D Bolts Ltd, Central Warehouse, Bradford Road, Batley, West Yorkshire, WF17 5LW Tel: (01924) 470331 Fax: (01924) 473749

B D M Fastenings, 10 Royce Road, Crawley, West Sussex, RH10 9NX Tel: (01293) 548186 Fax: (01293) 553274 E-mail: sales@bdm-fastenings.demon.co.uk

Bapp Industrial Supplies Castleford Ltd, Methley Road, Castleford, West Yorkshire, WF10 1PA Tel: (01977) 510640 Fax: (01977) 516514 E-mail: sales@bappcastleford.co.uk

Bapp Industrial Supplies Doncaster Ltd, Chappell Drive, Doncaster, South Yorkshire, DN1 2RW Tel: (01302) 364444 Fax: (01302) 321409

Bapp Industrial Supplies Lancs Ltd, Trafalgar Centre, Belfield Road, Rochdale, Lancashire, OL16 2UX Tel: (01706) 359500 Fax: (01706) 640270

Bapp Industrial Supplies Preston Ltd, 57 Roman Way Industrial Estate, Ribbleton, Preston, PR2 5BE Tel: (01772) 704700 Fax: (01772) 704701

Barnket Ltd, 128 Milton Road, Gravesend, Kent, DA12 2PG Tel: (01474) 327576 Fax: (01474) 567318

Basta Parsons Ltd, Alma Street, Wolverhampton, WV10 0EY Tel: (01902) 877770 Fax: (01902) 877771 E-mail: sjohnson@bastaparsonsqb.com

BBN Industrial Fasteners Ltd, Locksley, London End, Beaconsfield, Buckinghamshire, HP9 2JB Tel: (01494) 680078 Fax: (01494) 680093

Beardshaw Bolts & Fixings, Stalham Road, Hoveton, Norwich, NR12 8DU Tel: (01603) 783811 Fax: (01603) 783859 E-mail: sales@beardshaw.co.uk

Bee-Fast Fasteners Ltd, Montrose House, Lancaster Road, Cressex Business Park, High Wycombe, Buckinghamshire, HP12 3PY Tel: 0845 4940703 Fax: (01494) 436270 E-mail: sales@themontosegroup.com

▶ Blakes Of Farnham, 20 Caker Stream Road, Alton, Hampshire, GU34 2QA Tel: (01420) 86196 Fax: (01420) 86736 E-mail: sales@blakesoffarnham.com

Boka Bolt Supplies, 10 Cormorant Drive, Picow Farm Road, Runcorn, Cheshire, WA7 4UD Tel: (01928) 590440 Fax: (01928) 590400

Bolt & Bearing London, 21s Queensway, Enfield, Middlesex, EN3 4UL Tel: (020) 8805 7250 Fax: (020) 8804 0126 E-mail: sales@boltandbearing.co.uk

Bolt & Nut Manufacturing, White Lee Road, Swinton, Mexborough, South Yorkshire, S64 8BH Tel: (01709) 570212 Fax: (01709) 584125 E-mail: sales@tachart.com

Bolt & Nut Supplies Ltd, 35-37 Chapeltown, Pudsey, West Yorkshire, LS28 7RZ Tel: 0113-255 6336 Fax: 0113-256 9242

Boltworthy Ltd, Unit I1 Cowlairs, Nottingham, NG5 9RA Tel: 0115-977 0432 Fax: 0115-977 0424

Brandon Bolt Co., 4 Faraday Place, Thetford, Norfolk, IP24 3RG Tel: (01842) 766612 Fax: (01842) 755526 E-mail: sales@brandonbolt.fsnet.co.uk

Brian Walker & Son, 87 Garraways, Coffee Hall, Milton Keynes, MK6 5DU Tel: (01908) 666690 Fax: (01908) 233211

Bright Screw Co. Ltd, Bagley Lane, Rodley, Leeds, LS13 1JB Tel: 0113-256 4166 Fax: 0113-239 3480 E-mail: sales@brightscrew.co.uk

BRM, 1 Block 4, Cocker Avenue, Poulton Industrial Estate, Poulton-le-Fylde, Lancashire, FY6 8JU Tel: (01253) 885270 Fax: (01253) 884485 E-mail: enquiries@brmeng.co.uk

Brocol Engineers Supplies Ltd, 58 Hotchkiss Way, Binley Industrial Estate, Binley Industrial Estate, Coventry, CV3 2RL Tel: (024) 7644 1303 Fax: (024) 7644 1353 E-mail: sales@gtssltd.co.uk

Browns Fasteners Ltd, PO Box 13, Leeds, LS27 9QS Tel: 0113-252 2185 Fax: 0113-252 0826 E-mail: browns_fasteners@yahoo.com

Bunny's Bolts, The Depot The Mayford Centre, Mayford Green, Woking, Surrey, GU22 0PP Tel: (01483) 727227 Fax: (01483) 727995 E-mail: sales@bunnysbolt.com

▶ C Adams & Sons Midlands Ltd, Potters Lane, Wednesbury, West Midlands, WS10 7LH Tel: 0121-556 1774 Fax: 0121-556 5045 E-mail: sales@c-adams.co.uk

C W Fasteners, Unit 60 Sandy Way, Amington Industrial Estate, Tamworth, Staffordshire, B77 4DS Tel: (01827) 67091 Fax: (01827) 61552E-mail: cwdfasteners@btopenworld.com

C W W Engineers Supply Co. Ltd, 7 Stanlake Mews, London, W12 7HA Tel: (020) 8743 0651 Fax: (020) 8740 7731 E-mail: sales@cww.uk

Central Fasteners (Staffs) Ltd, Airfield Trading Estate, Hixon, Stafford, ST18 0PY Tel: (01889) 270163 Fax: (01889) 271270 E-mail: centralfasteners@aol.com

Challenge Europe Ltd, Shuttleworth Road, Elm Farm Industrial Estate, Bedford, MK41 0EP Tel: (01234) 346242 Fax: (01234) 327349 E-mail: sales@challenge-indfast.co.uk

Charnwood Fasteners Ltd, F27-30 Trading Estate, Cumberland Road, Loughborough, Leicestershire, LE11 5DF Tel: (01509) 237280 Fax: (01509) 262428

Clark Fixings Ltd, Unit 1, Crescent Works Industrial Estate, Willenhall Road, Darlaston, Wednesbury, West Midlands, WS10 8JJ Tel: 0121-568 6968 Fax: 0121-568 8719 E-mail: clarkfixings@btconnect.com

Clerkenwell Screws Ltd, 107-109 Clerkenwell Road, London, EC1R 5BY Tel: (020) 7405 1215 Fax: (020) 7831 3057

Coronhurst Ltd, Unit 16 Martindale Trading Estate, Martindale, Cannock, Staffordshire, WS11 7XL Tel: (01543) 577101 Fax: (01543) 571876 E-mail: info@coronhurst.co.uk

▶ Croft Impex Ltd, Unit 5 Henry Boot Way, Hull, HU4 7DY Tel: (01482) 351116 Fax: (01482) 351091 E-mail: sales@croftimpex.co.uk

Crossford Oil & Tool Supplies Ltd, Unit 94 Springvale Industrial Estate, Cwmbran, Gwent, NP44 5BH Tel: (01633) 873612 Fax: (01633) 864884 E-mail: sales@crossfords.co.uk

D B Industrial Fasteners Ltd, Q Gunnels Wood Road Industrial Estate, Gunnels Wood Road, Stevenage, Hertfordshire, SG1 2BH Tel: (01438) 728872 Fax: (01438) 740279 E-mail: salesdb@dbfasteners.com

Dave Vickers, Thame Station Industrial Estate, Thame, Oxon, OX9 3UH Tel: (01844) 260100 Fax: (01844) 260900

Dinstock Ltd, Unit C1, Hortonwood row 10, Telford, Shropshire, TF1 7ES Tel: (01952) 676700 Fax: (01952) 676800

Disc-Lock Europe Ltd, PO Box 134, Sittingbourne, Kent, ME9 7TF Tel: (01795) 844332 Fax: (01795) 843986 E-mail: info@disc-lock.com

East Midlands Fastener, 101 Sanders Road, Finedon Road Industrial Estate, Finedon Road Industrial Estate, Wellingborough, Northamptonshire, NN8 4NL Tel: (01933) 229110 Fax: (01933) 271600 E-mail: sales@emfast.co.uk

▶ Easy Fix, N Prospect Court, Nottingham Road, Ripley, Derbyshire, DE5 3AY Tel: (01773) 570400 Fax: (01773) 570400

Emkay Screw Supplies, 74 Pepys Way, Strood, Rochester, Kent, ME2 3LL Tel: (01634) 717256 Fax: (01634) 717256 E-mail: emkaysupplies@talktalk.net

Eurofast Petrochemical Supplies Ltd, Unit 30 Planetary Industrial Estate, Planetary Road, Willenhall, West Midlands, WV13 3TA Tel: (01902) 307788 Fax: (01902) 307744 E-mail: eps-sales@eurofast.co.uk

Everbright Stainless, Brimington Road North, Chesterfield, Derbyshire, S41 9BE Tel: (01246) 451600 Fax: (01246) 451611 E-mail: everbright.sales@infast.com

F R Scott Ltd, Canning Street, Hull, HU2 8QS Tel: (01482) 324731 Fax: (01482) 214290 E-mail: sales@frscott.co.uk

F R Smith & Co Newton Heath Ltd, Daisy Bank Mill, Terence Street, Manchester, M40 1GD Tel: 0161-681 1313 Fax: 0161-683 4763

F W B Cymru Co. Ltd, Five Crosses Industrial Estate, Ruthin Road, Minera, Wrexham, Clwyd, LL11 3RD Tel: (01978) 720720 Fax: (01978) 720721 E-mail: sales@fwbcymru.co.uk

Fabory UK Ltd, Block D Bay 9 Bescot Industrial Estate, Woden Road West, Wednesbury, West Midlands, WS10 7SG Tel: 0121-556 3474 Fax: 0121-556 7337E-mail: sales@fabory.com

Fairways Fasteners Ltd, Unit 6 Starvale Road Industrial Estate, Lye, Stourbridge, West Midlands, DY9 8PP Tel: (01384) 897535 Fax: (01384) 423611 E-mail: sales@screwsandbolts.co.uk

Fastener Warehouse Ltd, 5 Ambassador Industrial Estate, 9 Airfield Road, Christchurch, Dorset, BH23 3TG Tel: (01202) 479621 Fax: (01202) 477222 E-mail: sales@fastenerwarehouse.co.uk

Fasteners & Engineering Supplies Ltd, 5 Westgate, Cowbridge, South Glamorgan, CF71 7AQ Tel: (01446) 774888 Fax: (01446) 773778 E-mail: sales@f-e-s.co.uk

Fasteners Midlands Ltd, 16-17 Longford Industrial Estate, Longford Road, Cannock, Staffordshire, WS11 0DG Tel: (01543) 462416 Fax: (01543) 574308

Fitlock, 6 Vaughan St Industrial Estate, Manchester, M12 5BT Tel: 0161-231 3724 Fax: 0161-231 7392 E-mail: sales@fitlocksystems.com

Fixings Delivery, Unit 6 Catford Road, Roundthorn Industrial Estate, Roundthorn Industrial Estate, Manchester, M23 9LR Tel: 0161-945 0444 Fax: 0161-947 2710

Flintnine Fasteners Ltd, Highfield Road, Little Hulton, Manchester, M38 9ST Tel: 0161-790 7817 Fax: 0161-703 8314 E-mail: sales@flintnine.co.uk

Forward Industrial Products Group Ltd, Unit 2 Tyseley Park, Wharfedale Road Tyseley, Birmingham, B11 2DF Tel: 0121-707 2555 Fax: 0121-708 3081 E-mail: info@forwardindustrial.com

G I Fasteners Ltd, 8 Windmill Road Industrial Estate, Windmill Road, Loughborough, Leicestershire, LE11 1RA Tel: (01509) 260747 Fax: (01509) 217945

Galvanised Bolts & Nuts Ltd, 115 Lodgefield Road, Halesowen, West Midlands, B62 8AX Tel: 0121-602 3333 Fax: 0121-602 4040 E-mail: galvanised.boltsandnuts@btconnect.com

Garth T Wright Fasteners, Colwickwood Works, Colwick Road, Nottingham, NG2 4BG Tel: 0115-958 8360 Fax: 0115-948 4967 E-mail: wright@wright-engineers.co.uk

General Engineers Supply Co. Ltd, 555-557 High Road Leytonstone, London, E11 4PD Tel: (020) 8556 0201 Fax: (020) 8558 9305 E-mail: gens@engineers555.freeserve.co.uk

John George & Sons Ltd, 2-4 Deacon Way, Reading, RG30 6AZ Tel: 0118-941 1234 Fax: 0118-945 1059 E-mail: sales@johngeorge.co.uk

Glenwood Bolts, 2 Lintech Court, The Grip, Linton, Cambridge, CB21 4XN Tel: (01223) 893931 Fax: (01223) 894122 E-mail: glenwoodbolts@talk21.com

Habko Tools & Fastenings Ltd, Unit 1, Joseph Wilson Industrial Estate, South St, Whitstable, Kent, CT5 3PS Tel: (01227) 265444 Fax: (01227) 263517

Henry Halstead Ltd, 492 Holly Place, Walton Summit, Bamber Bridge, Preston, PR5 8AX Tel: (01772) 339521 Fax: (01772) 332233 E-mail: sales@henry-halstead.co.uk

Hampshire Bolt & Tool Supplies Ltd, Armstrong Road, Daneshill East, Basingstoke, Hampshire, RG24 8NU Tel: (01256) 329781 Fax: (01256) 817150 E-mail: jillcorreale@aol.com

▶ Hanson Auto Supplies, 9 Furze Road, Woodbury, Exeter, EX5 1PF Tel: (01395) 233747 Fax: (01395) 233434

Haroby Ltd, Unit 139 Bradley Hall Trading Estate, Bradley Lane, Standish, Wigan, Lancashire, WN6 0XQ Tel: (01257) 478100 Fax: (01257) 478109 E-mail: fasteners@haroby.co.uk

Harrison Matthews & Co. Ltd, 28 College Road, Sutton Coldfield, West Midlands, B73 5DJ Tel: 0121-355 4760 Fax: 0121-243 1104

Hereford Tool Hire, Sandark House, Netherwood Road, Rotherwas Industrial Estate, Hereford, HR2 6JU Tel: (01432) 353476 Fax: (01432) 352372

High Tensile Bolts Ltd, Imperial Works, 93 Lockfield Avenue, Enfield, Middlesex, EN3 7PY Tel: (020) 8805 8510 Fax: (020) 8805 1553 E-mail: kebrell@montal-internet.co.uk

Phil Holden Fasteners Ltd, 23 Swannington Road, Cottage Lane Industrial Estate, Broughton Astley, Leicester, LE9 6TU Tel: (01455) 285888 Fax: (01455) 285105 E-mail: enquiries@phs-ltd.com

I L S Ltd, Third Avenue, Pensnett Trading Estate, Kingswinford, West Midlands, DY6 7XX Tel: (01384) 402200 Fax: (01384) 402201 E-mail: marketing@ilsonline.com

IFI Scotland Ltd, Rennie Place, East Kilbride, Glasgow, G74 5HD Tel: (01355) 598440 Fax: (0800) 6520780 E-mail: sales@ifiltd.net

Industrial Trading Co. Ltd, PO Box 51, Worcester, WR1 1QE Tel: (01905) 20373 Fax: (01905) 27158

J D A Fixings, Unit 7 & 8 Indus Acre, Avro Way, Bowerhill, Melksham, Wiltshire, SN12 6TP Tel: (01225) 709970 Fax: (01225) 709995 E-mail: chris@jdafixings.com

J Hall & Son Fasteners Ltd, Bentley Mill Industrial Estate, Longmore Avenue, Walsall, WS2 0BW Tel: (01922) 626652 Fax: (01922) 649942 E-mail: jhallsales@btconnect.com

J R Webster, Unit 1 Prince William Avenue, Sandycroft, Deeside, Clwyd, CH5 2QZ Tel: (01244) 534747 Fax: (01244) 535866 E-mail: kwalker.jrw@cuk.com

J & T Group Ltd, Victoria Works, 153 Victoria Street, Hartshill, Stoke-on-Trent, ST4 6HA Tel: (01782) 349440 Fax: (01782) 349449 E-mail: sales@storagebins.co.uk

James Gill Ltd, 8 Donkin Road, 2 District Armstrong Industrial Estate, Armstrong, Washington, Tyne & Wear, NE37 1PF Tel: 0191-416 9357 Fax: 0191-415 5338

John Sylvester Fasteners & Plastics Ltd, Vulcan Street, Bradford, West Yorkshire, BD4 9QU Tel: (01274) 684040 Fax: (01274) 684240 E-mail: sales.fp@btconnect.com

William Johnston & Company Ltd, 9 Spiersbridge Terrace, Thornliebank Industrial Estate, Glasgow, G46 8JH Tel: 0141-620 1666 Fax: 0141-620 1888 E-mail: sales@williamjohnston.co.uk

K Engineering, Unit 29 Parkrose Industrial Estate, Middlemore Road, Smethwick, West Midlands, B66 2DZ Tel: 0121-558 4367 Fax: 0121-565 1129 E-mail: sales@k-engineering.co.uk

K Supplies Ltd, Unit 14 Harwood Street, Blackburn, BB1 3BS Tel: (01254) 679025 Fax: (01254) 677010 E-mail: salesblackburn@ksupplies.co.uk

Kebrell Nuts & Bolts Ltd, Imperial Works, Lockfield Avenue, Enfield, Middlesex, EN3 7PY Tel: (020) 8805 8510 Fax: (020) 8805 1553 E-mail: kebrell@montal-internet.co.uk

L & S Hardware, The Stabes, Victoria House, Banknock, Bonnybridge, Stirlingshire, FK4 1UE Tel: (01324) 849992 Fax: (01324) 849993

▶ L S S International Ltd, E 206 Manchester Road, Mossley, Ashton-under-Lyne, Lancashire, OL5 9AY Tel: (01457) 833170 Fax: (01457) 834087

Gilbert Laurence Ltd, 1 Union Buildings, Wallingford Road, Uxbridge, Middlesex, UB8 2FR Tel: (01895) 455980 Fax: (01895) 455999 E-mail: sales@gilbertlaurence.co.uk

Lawson Products Ltd, 300 Quadrant, Ash Ridge Road, Bradley Stoke, Bristol, BS32 4QA Tel: (01454) 202223 Fax: (01454) 618510

Lesmac Fasteners Ltd, 73 Dykehead Street, Glasgow, G33 4AQ Tel: 0141-774 0004 Fax: 0141-774 2229 E-mail: sales@lesmac.co.uk

Leyton Fasteners Ltd, 9-15 Cook Street, Ellesmere Port, CH65 4AU Tel: 0151-355 8045 Fax: 0151-356 1885 E-mail: sales@leytonfasteners.co.uk

James Lister & Sons Ltd, Spon La South, Smethwick, West Midlands, B66 1QJ Tel: 0121-553 2949 Fax: 0121-525 6116 E-mail: tools@lister.co.uk

Logistic Fasteners (UK) Ltd, Unit 2A Odell House, Summerleys Road, Princes Risborough, Buckinghamshire, HP27 9DT Tel: (01844) 275816 Fax: (01844) 342880 E-mail: logfast@aol.com

Lokfast Special Fasteners Ltd, Audley Street, Mossley, Ashton-under-Lyne, Lancashire, OL5 9NH Tel: (01457) 837514 Fax: (01457) 832213 E-mail: lockfast@aol.com

M C Mills & Co. Ltd, Lower Castlereagh St, Barnsley, South Yorkshire, S70 1AR Tel: (01226) 732566 Fax: (01226) 285446 E-mail: mc.mills@virgin.net

M D Fasteners Ltd, 129 Smiths Lane, Windsor, Berkshire, SL4 5PF Tel: (01753) 855773 Fax: (05600) 759015 E-mail: mdkfateners@yahoo.co.uk

M G H Industries Ltd, Lancaster House, Old Wellington Road, Eccles, Manchester, M30 9QG Tel: 0161-707 7690 Fax: 0161-707 7701 E-mail: sales@nultz-boltz.co.uk

Margnor Fasteners Ltd, 36 Stringers Avenue, Guildford, Surrey, GU4 7NW Tel: (01483) 536800 Fax: (01483) 536801

Martin Scott, 2 Hollies Industrial Estate, Graiseley Row, Wolverhampton, WV2 4HE Tel: (01902) 428381 Fax: (01902) 711222

Martyn Price Ltd, PO Box 48, Stourbridge, West Midlands, DY9 8QF Tel: (01384) 424767 Fax: (01384) 424833 E-mail: sales@martynprice.co.uk

C.J.D. Mayers & Co. Ltd, Unit 6, Speedwell Close Industrial Estate, Speedwell Road, Yardley, Birmingham, B25 8HT Tel: 0121-773 0101 Fax: 0121-773 0104 E-mail: mayers@madasafish.com

Mbe Fasteners, Unit D1 Bearsted Green Business Centre, The Green, Bearsted, Maidstone, Kent, ME14 4DF Tel: (01622) 736868 Fax: (01622) 730111

Merlin Accessories Ltd, Unit G, St. Martins Trade Park, Nickel Close, Winchester, Hampshire, SO23 7RJ Tel: (01962) 842002 Fax: (01962) 842420 E-mail: sales@merlinaccessories.com

Metal Work Supplies, Unit 15 Grandstand Business Centre, Westfields Trading Estate, Hereford, HR4 9NS Tel: (01432) 266621 Fax: (01432) 270323

Metalpoint Ltd, Factory D, Western Approach, South Shields, Tyne & Wear, NE33 5NN Tel: 0191-455 6086 Fax: 0191-455 2447 E-mail: sales@arndale.co.uk

Modern Screws Ltd, 5 Dartford Road, Bexley, Kent, DA5 2BH Tel: (01322) 553224 Fax: (01322) 555093 E-mail: sales@modern-screws.co.uk

Mofast Ltd, Unit D1 Peartree Industrial Park Crackley Way, Peartree Lane, Dudley, West Midlands, DY2 0UW Tel: (01384) 455440 Fax: (01384) 458595 E-mail: mfast-sales@morgalv.pus.com

▶ N E Fastenings Ltd, 175-179 Snowdon Road, Middlesbrough, Cleveland, TS2 1DB Tel: (01642) 244106 Fax: (01642) 244109

Namrick Ltd, 124 Portland Road, Hove, East Sussex, BN3 5QL Tel: (01273) 736963 Fax: (01273) 726708 E-mail: sales@namrick.co.uk

Newform Distribution Ltd, Unit B4-5 Dudley Central Trading Estate, Shaw Road, Dudley, West Midlands, DY2 8QX Tel: (01384) 230666 Fax: (01384) 235666 E-mail: sales@newformdistribution.co.uk

Non Standard Socket Screws Ltd, 358-364 Farm Street, Birmingham, B19 2TZ Tel: 0121-515 0121 Fax: 0121-523 4440 E-mail: sales@nssocketscrews.com

Norfolk Fasteners, Rash's Green, Dereham, Norfolk, NR19 1JG Tel: (01362) 696848 Fax: (01362) 695356

Norton, Works Road, Letchworth Garden City, Hertfordshire, SG6 1LP Tel: (01462) 676944 Fax: (01462) 677192 E-mail: nif-ltd@btconnect.com

Nu Screw & Nut, 311 Neasden La North, London, NW10 0AG Tel: (020) 8452 8633 Fax: (020) 8452 2987 E-mail: sales@nu-screw.co.uk

Nufast Ltd, 17 Hayward Industrial Estate, Vigo Place Aldridge, Walsall, WS9 8UG Tel: (01922) 740360 Fax: (01922) 453610 E-mail: sales@nufast.co.uk

Nuts, Cowling Brow Industrial Estate, Cowling Brow, Chorley, Lancashire, PR6 0QG Tel: (01257) 264040 Fax: (01257) 273782 E-mail: sales@nutsofchorley.co.uk

Nuts & Bolts, Unit 10, Longton Industrial Estate, Weston-super-Mare, Avon, BS23 3YB Tel: (01934) 416765 Fax: (01934) 418704 E-mail: enquires@nut-and-bolts.co.uk

▶ Nutty Bolt, 63 Old Lane, Openshaw, Manchester, M11 1DE Tel: (07760) 257132 E-mail: info@nuttybolt.com

▶ indicates data change since last edition

BOLTS AND NUTS – *continued*

Nylon & Alloys Ltd., 74 Half Acre Road, Hanwell, London, W7 3JJ Tel: (020) 8579 5166 Fax: (020) 8579 6986 E-mail: na@nylonalloys.co.uk

Olympus Distribution Ltd, Olympus Drive, Great Bridge, Tipton, West Midlands, DY4 7HY Tel: 0121-522 5600 Fax: 0121-522 5601 E-mail: sales@olympusdistribution.com

Orbital Fasteners, Olds Approach, Tolpits Lane, Watford, WD18 9XT Tel: (01923) 777777 Fax: (01923) 779169 E-mail: sales@orbitalfasteners.co.uk

Oxford Bearings Ltd, 41 Wedgewood Road, Bicester, Oxfordshire, OX26 4UL Tel: (01869) 249292 Fax: (01869) 241443

Oxford Bearings Ltd, 6 Chiltern Business Centre, Garsington Road, Oxford, OX4 6NG Tel: (01865) 718355 Fax: (01865) 747570 E-mail: oxford@oxfordbearings.co.uk

P C Supplies, 4 The Metro Centre, Peterborough, PE2 7UH Tel: (01733) 370000 Fax: (01733) 235528

P & D Fasteners Ltd, Mapplewell BSNS Park, Blacker Road, Staincross, Barnsley, South Yorkshire, S75 6BP Tel: (01226) 388899

P R D Fasteners Ltd, Unit 10 Monmer Close Industrial Estate, Willenhall, West Midlands, WV13 1JR Tel: (01902) 636246 Fax: (01902) 605759 E-mail: sales@prdfasteners.co.uk

P R D Holdings Ltd, Unit 13, Monmer Close, Willenhall, West Midlands, WV13 1JR Tel: (01902) 639360 Fax: (01902) 639365 E-mail: info@prdholdings.com

Peter Abbott, Unit 10 Keyford Court, Marston Trading Estate, Frome, Somerset, BA11 4BD Tel: (01373) 461261 Fax: (01373) 451513 E-mail: sales@peterabbott.co.uk

▶ Picador Engineering Co. Ltd, 103 Louth Road, Holton-le-Clay, Grimsby, South Humberside, DN36 5AD Tel: (01472) 824520 Fax: (01724) 280999 E-mail: picadoreng@aol.co.uk

Porta Tool Fixings Ltd, Units 6-8, Brunel Road, Leigh-on-Sea, Essex, SS9 5JL Tel: (01702) 510080 Fax: (01702) 510030 E-mail: portatools@btconnect.com

Power Tool Supplies Ltd, 379 Kingsway, Hove, East Sussex, BN3 4QD Tel: (01273) 420111 Fax: (01273) 422313

Precision Stainless Fasteners, Unit 5 Bilston Industrial Estate, Oxford Street, Bilston, West Midlands, WV14 7EG Tel: (01902) 408222 Fax: (01902) 409222 E-mail: apexbilston@btinternet.com

Pugh & Sanders Ltd, Unit 1 Moseley Business Park, Moseley Street, Burton-on-Trent, Staffordshire, DE14 1DW Tel: (01283) 510824 Fax: (01283) 511403 E-mail: pughsanders@aol.com

Pugh & Sanders Ltd, Woods Lane, Derby, DE22 3UD Tel: (01332) 206770 Fax: (01332) 206771

R A Poole, 5 Kingston Business Centre, Fullers Way South, Chessington, Surrey, KT9 1DQ Tel: (020) 8391 9140 Fax: (020) 8391 9150 E-mail: sales@rapoole.com

R C F Bolt & Nut Co. Ltd, Park Lane East, Tipton, West Midlands, DY4 8RF Tel: 0121-522 2353 Fax: 0121-522 2304 E-mail: rcf@dial.pipex.com

R H Bruce Co Ltd, 4 The Idas, Pontefract Road, Leeds, LS10 1SP Tel: 0113-271 5533 Fax: 0113-271 8833

R S Paskin & Co. Ltd, Mount Pleasant, Brierley Hill, West Midlands, DY5 2YR Tel: (01384) 78081 Fax: (01384) 76480 E-mail: sales@rspaskin.co.uk

Rapid Industrial Fasteners Ltd, 9 Gun Barrel Industrial Centre, Hayseech, Cradley Heath, West Midlands, B64 7JZ Tel: 0121-501 3903 Fax: 0121-585 5163 E-mail: sales@rapidfast.co.uk

Readyfix, Lodge Street, Preston, PR1 8XE Tel: (01772) 250060 Fax: (01772) 250075

Reid's, 1 51 Seafield Road, Inverness, IV1 1SG Tel: (01463) 717722 Fax: (01463) 717766 E-mail: admin@reidnutsandbolts-uk.com

M.D. Roe, Whitford Drive, Shirley, Solihull, West Midlands, B90 4YG Tel: 0121-246 3465 Fax: 0121-246 3466

Rosch Engineering, Units 1 2, Calibre Indust Park, Four Ashes, Wolverhampton, WV10 7DZ Tel: (01902) 798100 Fax: (01902) 798844 E-mail: info@rosch.co.uk

RSR Fasteners Ltd, 2 Pasadena Close, Hayes, Middlesex, UB3 3NQ Tel: (020) 8756 1818 Fax: (020) 8756 1819 E-mail: sales@rsrfasteners.co.uk

▶ Samac Fixings, Capitol Industrial Centre, Fulmar Way, Wickford, Essex, SS11 8YW Tel: (01268) 764488 Fax: (01268) 562085

Samuel Fields & Co., Croft Street, Willenhall, West Midlands, WV13 2NU Tel: (01902) 607177 Fax: (01902) 606582

Scottish Premier Fasteners, Unit 2 Block 2 Victoria Industrial Estate, Calderbank, Airdrie, Lanarkshire, ML6 9SE Tel: (01236) 751815 Fax: (01236) 751847 E-mail: scotspremfast@btconnect.com

Screwplan Ltd, Hazelwood St Works, Hazelwood Street, Todmorden, Lancashire, OL14 5BW Tel: (01706) 812299 Fax: (01706) 816258 E-mail: sales@screwplan.com

Secure Bolts, Unit 18 Blenheim Way, Liverpool, L24 1YH Tel: 0151-486 3154 Fax: 0151-486 3154

Sheffield Bolt & Nut Co. Ltd, Unit G Harrison Street, Rotherham, South Yorkshire, S61 1EE Tel: (01709) 550101 Fax: (01709) 550176 E-mail: sales.sbn@btconnect.com

Southwest Fasteners Ltd, Unit 7-8 306 Industrial Estate, 242-244 Broomhill Road, Bristol, BS4 5RG Tel: 0117-972 3242 Fax: 0117-971 7555 E-mail: southwestfastners@dial.pipex.com

Sovereign Fasteners Ltd, 70 Morgan Close, Willenhall, West Midlands, WV12 4LH Tel: (01902) 636191 Fax: (01902) 634508

Stainless Steel Centre Ltd, Renown Close, Chandler's Ford, Eastleigh, Hampshire, SO53 4HZ Tel: (023) 8027 1155 Fax: (023) 8027 1110 E-mail: sales@stainlesssteelcentre.co.uk

Stainless Threaded Fasteners Ltd, 7 Beldray Park, Beldray Road, Bilston, West Midlands, WV14 7NH Tel: (01902) 490490 Fax: (01902) 496583 E-mail: sales@stf.fasteners.co.uk

Staytite Ltd, Unit B Coronation Road, Cressex BSNS Park, High Wycombe, Buckinghamshire, HP12 4PR Tel: (01494) 462322 Fax: (01494) 464747 E-mail: fasteners@staytite.com

▶ Steadfast Engineering Co. Ltd, Broadway, Hyde, Cheshire, SK14 4QQ Tel: 0161 3683636

Steadfast Fastenings, 167 Junction Road, Burgess Hill, West Sussex, RH15 0JW Tel: (01444) 247755 Fax: (01444) 248022

Sterling Power Tools & Fixings, 103 Newland Road, Worthing, West Sussex, BN11 1LB Tel: (01903) 211543 Fax: (01903) 523066

Stones Bros, Garratt Street, Brierley Hill, West Midlands, DY5 1JU Tel: (01384) 79888 Fax: (01384) 77966

Swift Fasteners Ltd, Unit 20 Oldends Industrial Estate, Oldends, Stonehouse, Gloucestershire, GL10 3RQ Tel: (01453) 825222 Fax: (01453) 827824E-mail: sales@swift-fasteners-ltd.co.uk

T L M Construction Fasteners Ltd, 13 Davy Road, Astmoor Industrial Estate, Runcorn, Cheshire, WA7 1PZ Tel: (01928) 576193 Fax: (01928) 581308 E-mail: sales@tlmfasteners.co.uk

T Potter (1982) Ltd, 63 Whitehill Road, Glenrothes, Fife, KY6 2RP Tel: 0141-429 1500 Fax: (01592) 774666 E-mail: thos.potter@btinternet.com

T R Fastenings Ltd, Waterside Park, Golds Hill Way, Tipton, West Midlands, DY4 0WP Tel: (0800) 7315553 Fax: (0800) 525230 E-mail: sales@trfastenings.com

Target Fastenings Ltd, Holpur House, 5 Albert Road, Crowthorne, Berkshire, RG45 7LT Tel: (01344) 777189 Fax: (01344) 779038 E-mail: sales@targetfixings.com

Teesside Industrial Fasteners Ltd, 6 Douglas Close, Preston Farm Industrial Estate, Stockton-on-Tees, Cleveland, TS18 3SB Tel: 01642 675630

Thistle Bearings & Engineering Products Ltd, 38 Singer Road, Kelvin Industrial Estate, East Kilbride, Glasgow, G75 0XS Tel: (01355) 225491 Fax: (01355) 242502 E-mail: sales@thistlebearings.co.uk

Toolcom Supplies Ltd, Pitreavie Business Park, Pitreavie Business Park, Dunfermline, Fife, KY11 8UQ Tel: (01383) 728970 Fax: (01383) 620079 E-mail: sales@toolcom.co.uk

Toolmaster (Oxford) Ltd, 148 Oxford Road, Cowley, Oxford, OX4 2EA Tel: (01865) 712152 Fax: (01865) 747380 E-mail: sales@toolmaster.co.uk

TR Fastenings, Trifast House, Bolton Close, Bellbrook Industrial Estate, Uckfield, East Sussex, TN22 1QW Tel: (01825) 764711 Fax: (01256) 461281

Tregenza Richard, 72 Otley Road, Guiseley, Leeds, LS20 8BN Tel: 0113-270 2421 Fax: 0113-277 9868 E-mail: fasteners@tregenza.co.uk

Tri Ard Stainless Fasteners Ltd, 1 Manor Industrial Estate, Pleck Road, Walsall, WS2 9XX Tel: (01922) 612230 Fax: (01922) 614044

Triplefast International Ltd, Unit 13 Monmer Close Industrial Estate, Willenhall, West Midlands, WV13 1JR Tel: (01902) 636399 Fax: (01902) 609880 E-mail: sales@triplefast.co.uk

Unimaster Components, 9 Arnhem Road, Newbury, Berkshire, RG14 5RU Tel: (01635) 528692 E-mail: sales@unimaster.co.uk

Universal Manufacturing Supplies, 25 Whitehorse Street, Baldock, Hertfordshire, SG7 6QB Tel: (01462) 892277 Fax: (01462) 892277

Valley Fastners, 65 Hay Hall Road, Birmingham, B11 2AU Tel: 0121-693 0031 Fax: 0121-693 0032 E-mail: sales@siemensvdo.com

Vulcan Industrial Fasteners Ltd, Unit 6, Emerald Way, Stone Business Park, Stone, Staffordshire, ST15 0SR Tel: (01785) 818494 Fax: (01785) 818399 E-mail: sales@vulcanfasteners.co.uk

Bernard F. Wade Ltd, PO Box 1865, Sheffield, S36 8BY Tel: (01226) 370860 Fax: (01226) 370836 E-mail: berniebolt@talk21.com

▶ Walters Hexagon, 4 Grange Park, Newtownabbey, County Antrim, BT36 4LA Tel: (028) 9083 8924 Fax: (028) 9083 8924 E-mail: admin@waltershexagon.com

Welland Supplies, Blenheim Way, Northfields Industrial Estate, Market Deeping, Peterborough, PE6 8LD Tel: (01778) 380371 Fax: (01778) 346916 E-mail: sales@welland-supplies.co.uk

Wellfast Industrial Supplies Ltd, 157-159 New John Street, Halesowen, West Midlands, B62 8HT Tel: 0121-559 3805 Fax: 0121-559 9836E-mail: david@page6745.freeserve.co.uk

Westgate Fastenings, Gapton Hall Industrial Estate, Viking Road, Great Yarmouth, Norfolk, NR31 0NU Tel: (01493) 603207 Fax: (01493) 656284 E-mail: westgatefastenings@connectfree.co.uk

Westwood Bolt & Nut Co. Ltd, Claypit Lane, West Bromwich, West Midlands, B70 9UP Tel: 0121 5532405

D.P. White & Co., 58 Hackenden Cl, East Grinstead, West Sussex, RH19 3DS Fax: (01342) 335747

Wilfast Ltd, Masters House, 13 High Street, Clophill, Bedford, MK45 4AB Tel: (01525) 861999 Fax: (01525) 861919 E-mail: wilfast@kbnet.co.uk

Willenhall Fasteners Holdings Ltd, Frederick William Street, Willenhall, West Midlands, WV13 1NE Tel: (01902) 630760 Fax: (01902) 636447 E-mail: sales@willenfast.co.uk

Williams Fasteners Ltd, 8 Tees Court, Wallis Road, Skippers Lane Industrial Estate, Middlesbrough, Cleveland, TS6 6DX Tel: (01642) 460261 Fax: (01642) 440966

Williams Fasteners, Unit 4a, Shepcote Way, Tinsley Industrial Estate, Sheffield, S9 1TH Tel: 0114-256 5200 Fax: 0114-256 5210 E-mail: sales@williamsfasteners.com

▶ Woods & Hughes (Bolts & Screws) Ltd, Unit 9, Hill Top Industrial Estate, Shaw Street, West Bromwich, West Midlands, B70 0TX Tel: 0121-505 7551 Fax: 0121-505 7652 E-mail: sales@socketscrews.co.uk

Wurth (UK) Ltd, 1 Centurion Way, Erith, Kent, DA18 4AE Tel: (0870) 5987841 Fax: (0870) 5987842 E-mail: info@wurth.co.uk

BOLTS AND NUTS MAKING MACHINES

▶ Picador Engineering Co. Ltd, 103 Louth Road, Holton-le-Clay, Grimsby, South Humberside, DN36 5AD Tel: (01472) 824520 Fax: (01724) 280999 E-mail: picadoreng@aol.co.uk

Wafios-Metoma Ltd, 21 Colemeadow Road, North Moons Moat, Redditch, Worcestershire, B98 9PB Tel: (01527) 65396 Fax: (01527) 67570 E-mail: sales@wafios-metoma.com

BOLTS AND NUTS, ALLOY STEEL STUDBOLT

Midsteel Pipeline Ltd, Building 67 Third Avenue, Pensnett Trading Estate, Kingswinford, West Midlands, DY6 7FA Tel: (01384) 400321 Fax: (01384) 400461 E-mail: sales@midsteel.co.uk

Tapping Services, 18-19 Broad Lanes, Bilston, West Midlands, WV14 0RY Tel: (01902) 404882 Fax: (01902) 403692

BOLTS AND NUTS, SHERADIZED

I E Bolt & Nut Ltd, Unit 14 Alma Works, Alma Street, Cutler Heights, Bradford, West Yorkshire, BD4 9JE Tel: (01274) 686805 Fax: (01274) 680361 E-mail: sales@iebolt.co.uk

BOLTS AND NUTS, STAINLESS STEEL STUDBOLT

Precise Fastenings & Supplies Ltd, Ivanhoe Road, Finchampstead, Wokingham, Berkshire, RG40 4QQ Tel: 0118-932 8832 Fax: 0118-932 8519 E-mail: precisefastenings@fixings.fsworld.co.uk

▶ Sea Screw, 4 Churchdale Road, Eastbourne, East Sussex, BN22 8PS Tel: (01323) 430294 Fax: (01323) 411778

BOMB DETECTION EQUIPMENT

▶ UXB (UK) Ltd, Challacombe Close, Landkey, Barnstaple, Devon, EX32 0NG Tel: (01271) 831439 Fax: (01271) 831442 E-mail: pjh@uxb.com

BONDED INTERLININGS

Textile Bonding Ltd, Textile Bonding Limited, Midland Road, Higham Ferrers, Rushden, Northamptonshire, NN10 8ER Tel: (01933) 410100 Fax: (01933) 410200 E-mail: sales@textilebonding.co.uk

BONDED TEXTILE MATERIALS,

See Interlining etc; also other headings for particular types

BONDING FASTENERS

P S M International plc, Longacre, Willenhall, West Midlands, WV13 2JS Tel: (01902) 600000 Fax: (01902) 600073 E-mail: tlspsm@compuserve.com

Rotaloc Europe, 8 Wyvern Buildings, Grove Trading Estate, Dorchester, Dorset, DT1 1ST Tel: (01305) 257800 Fax: (01305) 259420 E-mail: sales@rotaloc.co.uk

BONDING WIRE, *See Bonding etc*

BONE CHINAWARE

Albany Fine China Ltd, 75 Water Works Road, Worcester, WR1 3EZ Tel: (01905) 726320 Fax: (01905) 726360

Ceramics Cafe, 6 Argyle Road, London, W13 8AB Tel: (020) 8810 4422 Fax: (020) 8810 5593

China Millers Ltd, 409 King Street, Stoke-on-Trent, ST4 3EF Tel: (01782) 313291 Fax: (01782) 599494

China Repairers, King Street Mews, London, N2 8DY Tel: (020) 8444 3030 E-mail: enquiries@chinarepairers.co.uk

Churchill Fine Bone China (Holdings) Ltd, Marlborough Works, High Street, Stoke-on-Trent, ST6 5NZ Tel: (01782) 577566 Fax: (01782) 810318 E-mail: churchill@churchillchina.plc.uk

Churchill Fine Bone China (Holdings) Ltd, Marlborough Works, High Street, Stoke-on-Trent, ST6 5NZ Tel: (01782) 577566 Fax: (01782) 810318 E-mail: churchill@churchillchina.com

▶ D J B Ceramics Ltd, Beaufort Mill, Beaufort Road, Stoke-on-Trent, ST3 1RH Tel: (01782) 312121 Fax: (01782) 312121 E-mail: djb.ceramics@btinternet.com

Dalton & Ditcham Agencies Ltd, Brent House, 3rd Floor Kenton Road, Harrow, Middlesex, HA3 8BT Tel: (020) 8909 3996 Fax: (020) 8909 2686 E-mail: dalton.ditcham@btinternet.com

Data Impex Ltd, 58 Beakes Road, Smethwick, West Midlands, B67 5RU Tel: (01902) 456619 Fax: 0121-533 0154 E-mail: sales@dataimpex.com

Fine China Restoration, 15 Heathfield Gardens, London, W4 4JU Tel: (020) 8994 8990

David Fryer Studios, Bracken Hill, Welsh Newton Common, Monmouth, Gwent, NP25 5RT Tel: (01989) 770402 Fax: (01989) 770807 E-mail: d.a.fryer@btopenworld.com

Heaton Catering Equipment Ltd, 160 Heaton Park Road, Newcastle Upon Tyne, NE6 5NR Tel: 0191-265 6709 Fax: 0191-265 6506 E-mail: sales@heatoncateringequipment.co.uk

Hudson & Middleton, Sutherland Works, Normacot Road, Stoke-on-Trent, ST3 1PP Tel: (01782) 319256 Fax: (01782) 343300 E-mail: enquiries@hudsonandmiddleton.co.uk

Ivyline, Unit 5, Seven Stars Industrial Estate Wheler Road, Coventry, CV3 4LB Tel: (024) 7621 7600 Fax: (024) 7630 6372

Mclaggan Smith Mugs Ltd, Jamestown, Alexandria, Dunbartonshire, G83 8BS Tel: (01389) 755655 Fax: (01389) 754260 E-mail: polly@msmugs.com

Noritake (UK) Ltd, 26 Heathfield, Stacey Bushes, Milton Keynes, MK12 6HR Tel: (01908) 318446 Fax: (01908) 320932 E-mail: china@noritake.co.uk

Royal Doulton, Sir Henry Doulton House, Forge Lane Etruria, Stoke-on-Trent, ST1 5NN Tel: (01782) 404040 Fax: (01782) 404000 E-mail: sales@royal-doulton.com

Royal Worcester, Royal Porcelain Works, Severn Street, Worcester, WR1 2NE Tel: (01905) 746000 Fax: (01905) 23601 E-mail: general@royal-worcester.co.uk

Staffordshire Porcelain & China, 70-72 Williamson Avenue, Stoke-on-Trent, ST6 8AU Tel: (01782) 536336 Fax: 01782 536336

Topaz China, Heaths Passage, Warren Street, Stoke-on-Trent, ST3 1QD Tel: (01782) 599827 Fax: (01782) 599827

Trader Tiles, Unit 2 Progress Business Park, Orders Lane, Kirkham, Preston, PR4 2TZ Tel: (01772) 681140 Fax: (01772) 681140

Waterford Wedgwood Australia Ltd, Barlaston, Stoke-on-Trent, ST12 9ES Tel: (01782) 204141 Fax: (01782) 204402 E-mail: sales@wedgwood.co.uk

Waterford Wedgwood UK P.L.C., Barlaston, Stoke-On-Trent, ST12 9ES Tel: (01782) 204141 Fax: (01782) 204402 E-mail: customer.care@wedgwood.com

BOOK COVER DESIGN

HallidayBooks, Hawthorn Cottage, 32 Rowsham Road, Hulcott, Aylesbury, Buckinghamshire, HP22 5DZ Tel: 01296 426671 E-mail: info@hallidaybooks.com

BOOK DEBT BUYERS, *See Factoring Services, Finance*

BOOK REBINDING

Cambray Bindery, 17 Warden Hill Road, Cheltenham, Gloucestershire, GL51 3AU Tel: (01242) 241216

Dunn & Wilson International Ltd, Glasgow Road, Camelon, Falkirk, FK1 4HP Tel: (01324) 621591 Fax: (01324) 611508 E-mail: info@rdw.co.uk

Kadocourt Ltd, The Gateway, Gatehouse Road, Aylesbury, Buckinghamshire, HP19 8ED Tel: (01296) 486192 Fax: (01296) 334655 E-mail: astron@kadocourt.co.uk

BOOK REBINDING – *continued*

Kensett Ltd, 196 Old Shoreham Road, Hove, East Sussex, BN3 7EX Tel: (01273) 725627 Fax: (01273) 724867

BOOK REPRINT PUBLISHING SERVICES

Dragon Rising Publishing, 18 Marlow Avenue, Eastbourne, East Sussex, BN22 8SJ Tel: (01323) 729666 Fax: E-mail: info@dragonrising.com

BOOKBINDING AND PRINTING BOARD

Griffin Print Ltd, 2-4 Belgic Square, Peterborough, PE1 5XF Tel: (01733) 553530 Fax: (01733) 555668 E-mail: info@griffinprint.co.uk

BOOKBINDING AND PRINTING MACHINERY BLADES

High Speed & Carbide Ltd, Freedom Works, John St, Sheffield, S2 4QT Tel: 0114-279 6197 Fax: 0114-279 7550 E-mail: sales@hscknives.co.uk

William Pinder & Sons Ltd, 4 Harling Road, Sharston Industrial Estate, Manchester, M22 4UZ Tel: 0161-998 1729 Fax: 0161-946 0734 E-mail: info@pinderblades.com

BOOKBINDING LEATHER

William Cowley, 97 Caldecote Street, Newport Pagnell, Buckinghamshire, MK16 0DB Tel: (01908) 610038 Fax: (01908) 611071

J Hewit & Sons Ltd, Kinauld Leather Works, 371 Lanark Road West, Currie, Midlothian, EH14 5RS Tel: 0131-449 2206 Fax: 0131-451 5081 E-mail: sales@hewit.com

J & T Beaven, The Midlands, Holt, Trowbridge, Wiltshire, BA14 6RJ Tel: (01225) 782245 Fax: (01225) 783155 E-mail: sales@beaven.com

▶ T & B Book Crafts, 2 Summer Place, Edinburgh, EH3 5NR Tel: 0131-556 7857

BOOKBINDING MACHINES

Joto Ltd, 1c North Cresent, London, E16 4TG Tel: (020) 7511 4411 Fax: (020) 7511 5266

Printing & Graphic Machinery Ltd, Millboard Road, Bourne End, Buckinghamshire, SL8 5XE Tel: (01628) 527372 Fax: (01628) 524466 E-mail: sales@pgm.co.uk

Renz UK Ltd, Hill End Farm, Hill End, Hatfield, Hertfordshire, AL9 5PQ Tel: (01707) 270001 Fax: (01707) 271769 E-mail: sales@renz.co.uk

BOOKBINDING MATERIALS

B N International, Metro Centre, Dwight Road, Watford, WD18 9YD Tel: (01923) 219132 Fax: (01923) 219134

Bookcraft Supplies, Kennedy Way, Green Lane, Stockport, Cheshire, SK4 2JX Tel: 0161-480 2118 Fax: 0161-480 3679 E-mail: info@fjratchford.co.uk

Cell Ltd, Hallsteads, Dove Holes, Buxton, Derbyshire, SK17 8BJ Tel: (01298) 816692 Fax: (01298) 816277 E-mail: sales@cell-limited.co.uk

Fibermark Red Bridge International Ltd, Ainsworth, Ainsworth, Bolton, BL2 5PD Tel: (01204) 522254 Fax: (01204) 384754 E-mail: sales@redbridge.co.uk

J Hewit & Sons Ltd, Kinauld Leather Works, 371 Lanark Road West, Currie, Midlothian, EH14 5RS Tel: 0131-449 2206 Fax: 0131-451 5081 E-mail: sales@hewit.com

Neschen UK Ltd, Emerald Way, Stone Business Park, Stone, Staffordshire, ST15 0SR Tel: (01785) 610110 Fax: (01785) 610111 E-mail: neschen@neschen.co.uk

Winter & Co UK Ltd, Stonehill, Stukeley Meadows Industrial Estate, Huntingdon, Cambridgeshire, PE29 6ED Tel: (01480) 377177 Fax: (01480) 377166 E-mail: sales@winteruk.com

BOOKBINDING MATERIALS, NON WOVEN/SYNTHETIC BASE

Fibermark Red Bridge International Ltd, Ainsworth, Ainsworth, Bolton, BL2 5PD Tel: (01204) 522254 Fax: (01204) 384754 E-mail: sales@redbridge.co.uk

Robinson & Mornin Bookbinders Ltd, Belfast Industrial Complex, Louden St, Belfast, BT13 2EZ Tel: (028) 9024 0942 Fax: (028) 9033 0687E-mail: trevor@rmbookbinders.com

BOOKBINDING TO THE TRADE

A1 Business Service Centre, 94 University Avenue, Belfast, BT7 1GY Tel: (028) 9032 3334 Fax: (028) 9023 8601 E-mail: a1businessservicecentre@hotmail.com

F.F. Allsopp, Union Road, Nottingham, NG3 1FH Tel: 0115-950 7631 Fax: 0115-950 1057 E-mail: info@allsopp.co.uk

Clays Ltd, St Ives House, Lavington Street, London, SE1 0NX Tel: (020) 7928 8844 Fax: (020) 7902 6436 E-mail: sales@st-ives.co.uk

Clifton & Son Ltd, Uplands Business Park, Blackhorse Lane, London, E17 5QJ Tel: (020) 8523 1133 Fax: (020) 8531 1341 E-mail: tim@clifton.org

William Clowes Ltd, Copland Way, Ellough, Beccles, Suffolk, NR34 7TL Tel: (01502) 712884 Fax: (01502) 717003 E-mail: william@clowes.co.uk

Deanprint Ltd, Cheadle Heath Works, Stockport Road, Stockport, Cheshire, SK3 0PR Tel: 0161-428 2236 Fax: 0161-428 0817 E-mail: sales@deanprint.co.uk

Encapsulating Co. Ltd, 3-11 Pensbury Place, London, SW8 4TP Tel: (020) 7498 6700 Fax: (020) 7498 6749 E-mail: admin@encapsulating.co.uk

F.J.Blissett & Company Ltd, Palmerston Works, Roslin Road Acton, London, W3 8DH Tel: (020) 8992 7183 Fax: (020) 8993 1815 E-mail: gary.blissett@blissets.com

Foil & Bookcraft, Unit 27 Baldock Industrial Estate, London Road, Baldock, Hertfordshire, SG7 6NG Tel: (01462) 490074 Fax: (01462) 490074

Henry Mills Ltd, 30 Chester Street, Aston, Birmingham, B6 4BE Tel: 0121-359 4671 Fax: 0121-333 3153 E-mail: binding@henrymills.co.uk

Kadocourt Ltd, The Gateway, Gatehouse Road, Aylesbury, Buckinghamshire, HP19 8ED Tel: (01296) 486192 Fax: (01296) 334655 E-mail: astron@kadocourt.co.uk

Kensett Ltd, 196 Old Shoreham Road, Hove, East Sussex, BN3 7EX Tel: (01273) 725627 Fax: (01273) 724867

M P G Books Ltd, Victoria Square, Bodmin, Cornwall, PL31 1EB Tel: (01208) 73266 Fax: (01208) 73603 E-mail: print@mpg-books.co.uk

Mackays Of Chatham Ltd, Badger Road, Chatham, Kent, ME5 8TD Tel: (01634) 864381 Fax: (01634) 867742 E-mail: macays@cpi-group.co.uk

James A. Marshall Ltd, 50 Crownpoint Road, Bridgeton, Glasgow, G40 2QE Tel: 0141-556 1626 Fax: 0141-556 4630 E-mail: enquiries@jamesamarshall.com

J. Muir Bookbinders Ltd, 64-68 Blackheath Road, London, SE10 8DA Tel: (020) 8692 7565 Fax: (020) 8692 2072 E-mail: jmuirbookbinders@yahoo.com

New Forest Binding Ltd, 1 25 Black Moor Road, Ebblake Industrial Estate, Verwood, Dorset, BH31 6BE Tel: (01202) 828877 Fax: (01202) 828844 E-mail: sales@newforestbinding.com

R G Scales, 92 Southwark Bridge Road, London, SE1 0EX Tel: (020) 7928 9738 Fax: (0845) 3459182 E-mail: info@document-centre.co.uk

Rothersthorpe Binders Ltd, Rothersthorpe Avenue, Rothersthorpe Avenue Industrial Estate, Northampton, NN4 8JH Tel: (01604) 762228 Fax: (01604) 768253

Roundabout Bookbinders Ltd, Vincent Lane, Dorking, Surrey, RH4 3HG Tel: (01306) 885336 Fax: (01306) 742604

Seven Corners Communications Group, Penmark House, Woodbridge Meadows, Guildford, Surrey, GU1 1BL Tel: (01483) 576777 Fax: (01483) 567876

▶ TJ International Ltd, Trecerus Industrial Estate, Padstow, Cornwall, PL28 8RW Tel: (01841) 532691 Fax: (01841) 532862

Walter Newbury Partners Ltd, Grangewood House, Grangewood Street, London, E6 1EZ Tel: (020) 8472 0526 Fax: (020) 8472 8875 E-mail: walternewbury@totalise.co.uk

West Country Binders Ltd, 35 Buckingham Road, Weston-super-Mare, Avon, BS24 9BG Tel: (01934) 630950 Fax: (01934) 636615 E-mail: alistair@westcountrybinders.co.uk

Winter & Co UK Ltd, Stonehill, Stukeley Meadows Industrial Estate, Huntingdon, Cambridgeshire, PE29 6ED Tel: (01480) 377177 Fax: (01480) 377166 E-mail: sales@winteruk.com

BOOKBINDING TRADE SUPPLIERS

Bookcraft Supplies, Kennedy Way, Green Lane, Stockport, Cheshire, SK4 2JX Tel: 0161-480 2118 Fax: 0161-480 3679 E-mail: info@fjratchford.co.uk

F J Ratchford Ltd, Kennedy Way, Green Lane, Stockport, Cheshire, SK4 2JX Tel: 0161-480 8484 Fax: 0161-480 3679 E-mail: sales@fjratchford.co.uk

Kolbus UK Ltd, 35 Heathfield, Stacey Bushes, Milton Keynes, MK12 6HR Tel: (01908) 317878 Fax: (01908) 310863 E-mail: sales@kolbus.co.uk

BOOKCASES

▶ Bourne & Son Ltd, Unit 23a Firsland Park Estate, Henfield Road, Albourne, Hassocks, West Sussex, BN6 9JJ Tel: (01273) 491554 Fax: (01273) 491554 E-mail: furniture@bourneandson.com

E F M A, 4 Northgate Close, Rottingdean, Brighton, BN2 7DZ Tel: (01273) 495002 Fax: (01273) 495022 E-mail: sales@efma.co.uk

Neil Smith Quality Home Improvements, 24 Hawthorn Hill, Trefechan, Merthyr Tydfil, Mid Glamorgan, CF48 2ES Tel: (01685) 723895 Fax: (01685) 723895

R E H Kennedy Ltd, Whitehouse Road, Ipswich, IP1 5LT Tel: (01473) 240044 Fax: (01473) 240098 E-mail: sales@rehkennedy.co.uk

BOOKKEEPING

▶ Access Services, 7 Renfrew Green, Strensall, York, YO32 5PF Tel: (01904) 490156 Fax: (01904) 490142 E-mail: nh@access-services.net

▶ Bookworm Services Ltd, Kingsnorth, Ashford, Kent, TN23 Tel: 07593 741917 Fax: 07593 741917 E-mail: sc9771@aol.com

▶ Debitz Book Keeping, 38 Charminster Avenue, Bournemouth, BH9 1SA Tel: 01202 523469 E-mail: debitz_bkeeper@yahoo.co.uk

▶ G C S Bookkeeping, 120 Blackhorse Road, Hawkesbury Village, Longford, Coventry, CV6 6DL Tel: (024) 7636 4282 Fax: (024) 7636 4282 E-mail: gailstevens@totalise.co.uk

Gemini Bookkeeping Services, 52 Popham Close, Tiverton, Devon, EX16 4GA Tel: 01884 252254 E-mail: hms40@btinternet.com

▶ Hanly Accounting Services, 59 Surbiton Hill Park, Surbiton, Surrey, KT5 8EH Tel: 020 83992074 E-mail: accounting@hanly.co.uk

J & S Horn Consultants Ltd, 24 Henderson Drive, Skene, Westhill, Aberdeenshire, AB32 6RA Tel: (01224) 744330 Fax: (01224) 744330 E-mail: training@peakperformance.tv

▶ Joy & Co., PO Box 1968, Ilford, Essex, IG2 6DU Tel: (020) 8554 2389 Fax: (0871) 6617776 E-mail: mail@joyandco.co.uk

▶ K3 Secretarial Services, Blenheim Court, 17 Beulah Hill, London, SE19 3LJ Tel: (07786) 923079 Fax: (020) 8771 3651 E-mail: info@kzvirtualassistant.com

▶ Loum Bookkeeping Services, Flat 2, 20 - 21 Richmond Place, Brighton, BN2 9NA Tel: 01273 570453 E-mail: salina.loum@ntlworld.com

▶ Sarah Philips Bookkeeping Ltd, 51 Cissbury Avenue, Peacehaven, East Sussex, BN10 8TW Tel: 01273 297294 Fax: 01273 575388 E-mail: info@sarahphilipsbookkeeping.co.uk

▶ UK Payroll, Gilbert Wakefield House, 67 Bewsey Street, Warrington, WA2 7JQ Tel: (01925) 631330 Fax: (01925) 638440 E-mail: info@uk-payroll.net

▶ Wise Owl Book Keepers, 15 Bridus Mead, Blewbury, Didcot, Oxfordshire, OX11 9PJ Tel: (01235) 850691 Fax: (0871) 7334308 E-mail: andrew@wiseowlbookkeepers.co.uk

BOOKKEEPING CONSULTANCY

▶ Bookworm Services Ltd, Kingsnorth, Ashford, Kent, TN23 Tel: 07593 741917 Fax: 07593 741917 E-mail: sc9771@aol.com

▶ G C S Bookkeeping, 120 Blackhorse Road, Hawkesbury Village, Longford, Coventry, CV6 6DL Tel: (024) 7636 4282 Fax: (024) 7636 4282 E-mail: gailstevens@totalise.co.uk

▶ Hanly Accounting Services, 59 Surbiton Hill Park, Surbiton, Surrey, KT5 8EH Tel: 020 83992074 E-mail: accounting@hanly.co.uk

▶ Sarah Philips Bookkeeping Ltd, 51 Cissbury Avenue, Peacehaven, East Sussex, BN10 8TW Tel: 01273 297294 Fax: 01273 575388 E-mail: info@sarahphilipsbookkeeping.co.uk

BOOKKEEPING SOFTWARE

Office Support Ltd, Old Farn House, Moreton-on-Lugg, Hereford, HR4 8DE Tel: (01432) 761884 Fax: (01432) 760866 E-mail: enquiries@office-support.co.uk

BOOKS, COMIC

▶ Big Al's, The Old Vicarage, 24 Zetland Street, Wakefield, West Yorkshire, WF1 1QT Tel: 07971 635051 E-mail: big_als_comics@hotmail.co.uk

BOOKS, MUSIC

▶ True Sounds, 14 Mason Road, Norwich, NR6 6RF Tel: 01603 483450 E-mail: info2@truesounds.net

▶ W R D Worldwide Music Ltd, 282 Camden Road, London, NW1 9AB Tel: (020) 7267 6762 Fax: (020) 7482 4029 E-mail: info@wrdmusic.com

BOOM ACCESS PLATFORM HIRE

▶ Already Hire Ltd, 469 Malton Avenue, Slough, SL1 4QU Tel: (01753) 512333 Fax: (01753) 533303

BOOTS, *See also other nearby headings for particular types*

▶ Blacks Shrewsbury, 27-28 Shoplatch, Shrewsbury, SY1 1HS Tel: (01743) 368272

Joseph Cheaney & Sons Ltd, PO Box 1 69 Rushton Road, Kettering, Northamptonshire, NN14 2RZ Tel: (01536) 760383 Fax: (01536) 761354 E-mail: info.cheaney@cheaney.co.uk

Davies Riding Boots, 6 Blaenant Industrial Estate, Blaenavon Road, Brynmawr, Ebbw Vale, Gwent, NP23 4BX Tel: (01495) 313045 Fax: (01495) 313045 E-mail: sales@daviesridingboots.co.uk

Edgar Bros, Heather Close, Lyme Green Business Park, Macclesfield, Cheshire, SK11 0LR Tel: (01625) 613177 Fax: (01625) 615276 E-mail: admin@edgar-brothers.co.uk

Edward Green & Co., Cliftonville Road, Northampton, NN1 5BU Tel: (01604) 626880 Fax: (01604) 626889 E-mail: enquiries@edwardgreen.com

Karrimor Ltd, Petre Road, Clayton Le Moors, Accrington, Lancashire, BB5 5JZ Tel: (01254) 893000 Fax: (01254) 893100 E-mail: webmaster@karrimor.co.uk

N P S Shoes, South St, Wollaston, Wellingborough, Northamptonshire, NN29 7RY Tel: (01933) 664207 Fax: (01933) 664699 E-mail: npsshoes@eurotellbroadband.com

▶ Plus in Boots Ltd, 150 Magna Road, Poole, Dorset, BH11 9NB Tel: 01202 581566

Samuel James Outdoor Centre, 75-77 Gisburn Road, Barrowford, Barrowford, Nelson, Lancashire, BB9 6DX Tel: (07939) 502602 Fax: (01282) 613415 E-mail: broomsticktrav@aol.com

Sanders & Sanders Ltd, Spencer Works, Spencer Road, Rushden, Northamptonshire, NN10 6AE Tel: (01933) 353066 Fax: (01933) 410355 E-mail: mail@sanders-uk.com

R.E. Tricker Ltd, St. Michaels Road, Northampton, NN1 3JX Tel: (01604) 630595 Fax: (01604) 624978 E-mail: sales@trickers.com

White & Co. Ltd, 50a Main Road, Hackleton, Northampton, NN7 2AB Tel: (01604) 870982 Fax: (01604) 870529 E-mail: shoes@whiteeb.co.uk

BOOTS, EQUESTRIAN, JODPHUR

▶ Horseswap.co.uk, East Lodge, Potterhanworth, Longhills, Branston, Lincoln, LN4 1HR Tel: (01522) 797131 Fax: (01522) 797131 E-mail: gaynor@horseswap.co.uk

BOOTS, FOOTBALL

▶ Football Equipment UK, 6 Bridge Garth, South Milford, LEEDS, LS25 5BJ Tel: 07949 145674 Fax: 0870 1342495 E-mail: markhalpin@ic24.net

▶ Pelican Trading UK Ltd, Galloway Lane, Pudsey, West Yorkshire, LS28 7UG Tel: 0113-257 2468 Fax: 0113-229 5834

RJM Sports Ltd, 54 Cow Wynd, Falkirk, FK1 1PU Tel: (01324) 873804 Fax: (01324) 873804 E-mail: sales@rjmsports.co.uk

BORE GAUGING INSTRUMENTS

Sangha Metrology, Blanche Street, Bradford, West Yorkshire, BD4 8DA Tel: (01274) 667785 Fax: (01274) 662523

BOREHOLE PUMPS

Caprari Pumps (UK) Ltd, Caprari House, Bakewell Road, Orton Southgate, Peterborough, PE2 6XU Tel: (01733) 371605 Fax: (01733) 371607 E-mail: info@caprari.co.uk

Midland Pumps Ltd, 25 Colemeadow Road, Moons Moat North Industrial Es, Redditch, Worcestershire, B98 9PB Tel: (01527) 598556 Fax: (01527) 598557 E-mail: sales@midlandpumps.co.uk

Sparrow Quality Water Solutions, The Abbey, Preston Road, Yeovil, Somerset, BA20 2EN Tel: (01935) 479395 Fax: (01935) 848523

BORESCOPE HIRE

Emmco Ltd, The Old Stables, Cork Lane, 19 West Bar Street, Banbury, Oxfordshire, OX16 9SA Tel: (01295) 262826 Fax: (01295) 709091 E-mail: info@emmcolimited.co.uk

Kerryredd Surveying Equipment Ltd, 1206 London Road, London, SW16 4DN Tel: (020) 8679 7233 Fax: (020) 8679 9147

BORESCOPES

Emmco Ltd, The Old Stables, Cork Lane, 19 West Bar Street, Banbury, Oxfordshire, OX16 9SA Tel: (01295) 262826 Fax: (01295) 709091 E-mail: info@emmcolimited.co.uk

Everest VIT (UK) Ltd, 18 Tannery Yard, Witney Street, Burford, Oxfordshire, OX18 4DW Tel: (01993) 822613 Fax: (01993) 822614 E-mail: sales.office-hswuk@btinternet.com

BORING BAR CUTTERS

Tapmatic Engineers' Merchants, 7d Millers Close, Fakenham, Norfolk, NR21 8NW Tel: (01328) 863676 Fax: (01328) 856118 E-mail: info@tapmatic.co.uk

BORING (DEEP HOLE) HONING SERVICES

Accura Holdings, Hickman Avenue, Wolverhampton, WV1 2DW Tel: (01902) 454460 Fax: (01902) 451840 E-mail: enquiries@accura.co.uk

Accure Geneva Ltd, 1-5 Goodwood Road, Pershore, Worcestershire, WR10 2JL Tel: (01386) 555335 Fax: (01386) 556739 E-mail: enquiries@geneva.accura.co.uk

Energy Alloys, Chesterfield Trading Estate, Carrwood Road, Sheepbridge, Chesterfield, Derbyshire, S41 9QB Tel: (01246) 264500 Fax: (01246) 264550 E-mail: imsuk.energy@ims-group.com

▶ Sheffield Deep Bore Ltd, Victoria Works, 31 Catley Road, Sheffield, S9 5JF Tel: 0114-261 9888 Fax: 0114-261 1181 E-mail: john.senior@esssteel.co.uk

Toolmasters Technical Ltd, Instanta Work, Charles Street, West Bromwich, West Midlands, B70 0AZ Tel: 0121-520 1889 Fax: 0121-520 1890 E-mail: sales@toolmasters.co.uk

Well Service, West Brent, Forties Road Industrial Estate, Hillside, Montrose, Angus, DD10 9ET Tel: (01674) 677177 Fax: (01674) 677277 E-mail: sales@wellservice.com

BORING HEADS

Tapmatic Engineers' Merchants, 7d Millers Close, Fakenham, Norfolk, NR21 8NW Tel: (01328) 863676 Fax: (01328) 856118 E-mail: info@tapmatic.co.uk

BOROSILICATE GLASS FABRICATION OR REPAIR

Stanfield Building Services Ltd, Imex Technology Park, Unit 7 Bellringer Road, Trentham, Stoke-on-Trent, ST4 8LJ Tel: (01782) 658877 Fax: (01782) 658899 E-mail: info@stanfieldbs.co.uk

BOTTLE CAP INDUCTION SEALING EQUIPMENT

Enercon Industries Ltd, 64 Edison Road, Rabans Lane Industrial Area, Aylesbury, Buckinghamshire, HP19 8UX Tel: (01296) 330542 Fax: (01296) 432098 E-mail: info@enerconind.co.uk

BOTTLE CAP LINERS/DISCS

Unipac, Greenock Road, Slough, SL1 4QQ Tel: (01753) 773000 Fax: (01753) 773111 E-mail: sales@unipac.biz

BOTTLE CAP TIGHTENING MACHINES

▶ Flocap Packaging Materials, 16d Coal Hill Lane, Farsley, Pudsey, West Yorkshire, LS28 5NA Tel: 0113-236 3026 Fax: 0113-236 3148 E-mail: sales@flocap.co.uk

BOTTLE CAPPING MACHINES

Alcoa C S I (UK) Ltd, Kelvin Way, West Bromwich, West Midlands, B70 7LB Tel: 0121-532 5000 Fax: 0121-553 3710 E-mail: ciaran.martin@alcoa.com

Croxson William & Son Ltd, Alpha Place, Garth Road, Morden, Surrey, SM4 4LX Tel: (020) 8337 2945 Fax: (020) 8337 6783 E-mail: exports@croxsons.com

Engelmann & Buckham Ltd, Buckham House, 25 Lenten Street, Alton, Hampshire, GU34 1HH Tel: (01420) 82421 Fax: (01420) 89193 E-mail: hrashleigh@buckham.co.uk

Eurofill Ltd, Unit 1 Old Allen Barn, Old Allen Road, Bradford, West Yorkshire, BD13 3RY Tel: (01535) 270590 Fax: (01535) 270590 E-mail: eurofill@btopenworld.com

▶ Flocap Packaging Materials, 16d Coal Hill Lane, Farsley, Pudsey, West Yorkshire, LS28 5NA Tel: 0113-236 3026 Fax: 0113-236 3148 E-mail: sales@flocap.co.uk

Masterfil Ltd, Olympus House, Mill Green Road, Haywards Heath, West Sussex, RH16 1XQ Tel: 01444 472300 Fax: 01444 472329 E-mail: sales@masterfil.com

Viscose Closures Ltd, Unit 1 Fleming Way, Crawley, West Sussex, RH10 9JY Tel: (01293) 519251 Fax: (01293) 540005 E-mail: sales@viscose.co.uk

BOTTLE CLEANING BRUSHES

Farrar James Brushes Ltd, 103 Northgate, Halifax, West Yorkshire, HX1 1XF Tel: (01422) 361072 Fax: (01422) 361072 E-mail: philip.reid5@btinternet.com

Progress Shaving Brush Ltd, 24 Spring Valley Industrial Estate, Douglas, Isle of Man, IM2 2QR Tel: (01624) 676030 Fax: (01624) 662056E-mail: enquiries@progress-vulfix.com

BOTTLE COLOURING CONTRACTORS/SERVICES

Colorlites, Unit 23 Lordswood Industrial Estate, Revenge Road, Chatham, Kent, ME5 8UD Tel: (01634) 862839 Fax: (01634) 865285 E-mail: salesdesk@colorlites.com

BOTTLE CRUSHERS

Balcan Engineering, Banovallum Court, Boston Road Industrial Estate, Horncastle, Lincolnshire, LN9 6JR Tel: (01507) 528500 Fax: (01507) 528528 E-mail: info@balcan.co.uk

Thetford International Limited, Rymer Point, Bury Road, Thetford, Norfolk, IP24 2PN Tel: (01842) 890500 Fax: (01842) 890077 E-mail: sales-serv@thetford-int.co.uk

BOTTLE FILLING MACHINES

Accuramatic Laboratory Equipment, 42 Windsor Road, King's Lynn, Norfolk, PE30 5PL Tel: (01553) 777253 Fax: (01553) 777253 E-mail: info@accuramatic.co.uk

Central Bottling International Ltd, Plumtree Farm Industrial Estate, Plumtree Road, Bircotes, Doncaster, South Yorkshire, DN11 8EW Tel: (01302) 711056 Fax: (01302) 710802 E-mail: sales@centralbottling.com

Dawsons, Unit 22 Victoria Spring Business Park, Wormald Street, Liversedge, West Yorkshire, WF15 6RA Tel: (01924) 414620 Fax: (01924) 414601 E-mail: customerservice@dawson-uk.com

Dinting Metric, 8 Hadfield Industrial Estate, Waterside, Hadfield, Glossop, Derbyshire, SK13 1BS Tel: (01457) 855510 Fax: (01457) 838609 E-mail: sales@dintingmetric.com

Eurofill Ltd, Unit 1 Old Allen Barn, Old Allen Road, Bradford, West Yorkshire, BD13 3RY Tel: (01535) 270590 Fax: (01535) 270590 E-mail: eurofill@btopenworld.com

Farason Ltd, Low Hall Road, Horsforth, Leeds, LS18 4EF Tel: 0113-258 6538 Fax: 0113-258 7149 E-mail: kdmcinnes@aol.com

H Erben Ltd, Lady Lane, Hadleigh, Ipswich, IP7 6AS Tel: (01473) 823011 Fax: (01473) 828252 E-mail: enquiries@urban.co.uk

Integrated Control Systems Ltd, Millars Business Centre, Fishponds Close, Wokingham, Berkshire, RG41 2TZ Tel: 0118-977 2226 Fax: 0118-977 4999 E-mail: sales@icsbms.co.uk

P L F International, Riverside House Iconfield Park, Freshfields Road, Parkeston, Harwich, Essex, CO12 4EN Tel: (01255) 552994 Fax: (01255) 552995 E-mail: sales@plfinternational.com

Propack Automation Machinery Ltd, Unit 8 Binns Close, Coventry, CV4 9TB Tel: (024) 7647 0074 Fax: (024) 7647 1190 E-mail: sales@propack.co.uk

BOTTLE FILLING SERVICES

▶ Primepac Solutions Ltd, Unit 36, Rassau Industrial Estate, Rassau, Ebbw Vale, Gwent, NP23 5SD Tel: (01495) 309367 Fax: (01495) 309367 E-mail: sales@primepacsolutions.co.uk

BOTTLE HANDLING EQUIPMENT

Conqueror Manufacturing Ltd, Unit 1 William Street, West Bromwich, West Midlands, B70 0BG Tel: 0121-522 2300 Fax: 0121-522 2400 E-mail: conquerormanuf@aol.com

Dassett Process Engineering Ltd, Daimler Close, Royal Oak Industrial Estate, Woodford Halse, Daventry, Northants, NN11 8QJ Tel: (01327) 312914 Fax: (01327) 314162 E-mail: info@dassett.com

Dawson, Stephenson Way, Thetford, Norfolk, IP24 3RU Tel: (01842) 753505 Fax: (01842) 753508 E-mail: sales@bwi-dawson.com

Noshe Engineering, Beech Farm, Coopers Green Lane, St. Albans, Hertfordshire, AL4 9HW Tel: (01727) 837146 Fax: (01727) 854144 E-mail: andrewauld@nosche.co.uk

BOTTLE INSPECTION MACHINERY AND EQUIPMENT

Aluminium Capping Services Ltd, 30-32 Singer Way, Kempston, Bedford, MK42 7AF Tel: (01234) 843301 Fax: (01234) 841820 E-mail: sales@aluminiumcapping.com

Iain Glass, Wrangham, Philips Lane, Darrington, Pontefract, West Yorkshire, WF8 3BH Tel: (01977) 795497 Fax: (01977) 790777 E-mail: iainglass@btclick.com

Inex Inspection System, Unit 14 First Avenue, Trafford Park, Manchester, M17 1JZ Tel: 0161-876 1700 Fax: 0161-876 1701

M & A Packaging Services Ltd, Spring Lane North, Malvern, Worcestershire, WR14 1BU Tel: (01684) 560099 Fax: (01684) 560095 E-mail: info@mapexinspection.co.uk

Peco Controls (Europe) Ltd, Kempton Road, Pershore, Worcestershire, WR10 2TA Tel: (01386) 556622 Fax: (01386) 552252 E-mail: office@peco-europe.com

BOTTLE MOULD TOOLS

R & D Tool & Engineering Ltd, Hamilton Road, Sutton-in-Ashfield, Nottinghamshire, NG17 5LD Tel: (01623) 556287 Fax: (01623) 552240 E-mail: sales@rdtool.co.uk

BOTTLE MOULDS, PLASTIC/ POLYETHYLENE TEREPHTHALATE (PET)

Nissei Asb Ltd, 2 Milnyard Square, Bakewell Road, Orton Southgate, Peterborough, PE2 6GX Tel: (01733) 233544 Fax: (01733) 235647 E-mail: capsales@nisseiasb.co.uk

R & D Tool & Engineering Ltd, Hamilton Road, Sutton-in-Ashfield, Nottinghamshire, NG17 5LD Tel: (01623) 556287 Fax: (01623) 552240 E-mail: sales@rdtool.co.uk

BOTTLE PRODUCTION PLANT

Maul Technology, 13 Bridge House, Bridge Street, Sunderland, SR1 1TE Tel: 0191-514 0611 Fax: 0191-565 5309 E-mail: sales@maultechnology.co.uk

Nissei Asb Ltd, 2 Milnyard Square, Bakewell Road, Orton Southgate, Peterborough, PE2 6GX Tel: (01733) 233544 Fax: (01733) 235647 E-mail: capsales@nisseiasb.co.uk

BOTTLE RINSER CONVEYOR SYSTEMS

Mec A Tec Services Ltd, Boleness Road, Wisbech, Cambridgeshire, PE13 2RB Tel: (01945) 474685 Fax: (01945) 474687 E-mail: mecatec@aol.com

BOTTLE WASHING MACHINES

Dawsons, Unit 22 Victoria Spring Business Park, Wormald Street, Liversedge, West Yorkshire, WF15 6RA Tel: (01924) 414620 Fax: (01924) 414601 E-mail: customerservice@dawson-uk.com

BOTTLED GASES

Andrew Gray & Co Fuels Ltd, Portland Depot, London Road, Kilmarnock, Ayrshire, KA3 7DD Tel: (01563) 525215 Fax: (01563) 541146 E-mail: andrew@graysfuels.freeserve.co.uk

Barry Sharman Caravans Ltd, The Caravan Centre, Colchester Road, Ipswich, IP4 4RU Tel: (01473) 713284 Fax: (01473) 273166 E-mail: sharmancaravans@supanet.com

Browns Of Burwell Ltd, 7 North Street, Burwell, Whittlesford, Cambridge, CB4 3QW Tel: (01638) 741306 Fax: (01638) 743497 E-mail: sales@brownsofburwell.co.uk

Calor Gas Ltd, Dockyard Road, Ellesmere Port, CH65 4EG Tel: 0151-355 3700 Fax: 0151-357 1944 E-mail: querynw@calor.co.uk

Calor Gas Ltd, Cambridge Works, Mornington Road, Smethwick, West Midlands, B66 2JE Tel: 0121-565 0703 Fax: 0121-558 5992

Calor Gas Ltd, Athena House, Athena Drive, Warwick, CV34 6RL Tel: (0800) 0224199 Fax: (0870) 4006904 E-mail: commercial@calor.co.uk

Calor Gas (Northern Ireland) Ltd, Airport Road West, Belfast, BT3 9EE Tel: (028) 9045 5588 Fax: (028) 9045 8072

Country & Mineral Supplies, 5 Beeches Industrial Estate, Coedcae Lane, Pontyclun, Mid Glamorgan, CF72 9DY Tel: (01443) 224239 Fax: (01443) 224239

Evans Bros, 6 High Street, Menai Bridge, Gwynedd, LL59 5ED Tel: (01248) 712388 Fax: (01248) 712388

Express Welding Supplies Ltd, Unit B3 Empress Park, Empress Road, Southampton, SO14 0JX Tel: (023) 8022 8668 Fax: (023) 8063 9697

Flogas UK Ltd, Unit W, Barton Industrial Estate, Faldo Road, Barton-Le-Clay, MK45 4RP Tel: (01582) 600858 Fax: (01582) 882256

Home Improvement Centre, 229-231 Dunstable Road, Luton, LU4 8BN Tel: (01582) 722189 Fax: (01582) 402789 E-mail: hic10@hotmail.com

Iwax Marketing Ltd, 8 Queen Street, Ballymoney, Co. Antrim, BT53 6JA Tel: (028) 2766 6455 Fax: (028) 2766 6549

John Stayte, Puddlesworth Lane, Eastington, Stonehouse, Gloucestershire, GL10 3AH Tel: (01453) 822859 Fax: (01453) 821298 E-mail: sales@johnstayteservices.co.uk

K P Thomas & Son, Templeton, Narberth, Dyfed, SA67 8SR Tel: (0800) 3286033 Fax: (01834) 861686 E-mail: kpthomas@templeton22.fsnet.co.uk

M K Services, 23 St Johns Way, Knowle, Solihull, West Midlands, B93 0LE Tel: (01564) 779976

Mount Caravans Ltd, Kingswood, London Apprentice, St. Austell, Cornwall, PL26 7AR Tel: (01726) 874100 Fax: (01726) 67448 E-mail: sales@mountcaravans.co.uk

Naylor Myers Ltd, Wakefield Road, Brighouse, West Yorkshire, HD6 1ZE Tel: (01484) 712531 Fax: (01484) 722365

Shawgas Gas Companies, 29 Aismunderby Road, Ripon, North Yorkshire, HG4 1SQ Tel: (01765) 602621 Fax: (01765) 602621

Walton Hire, Knowle Lane, Buckley, Clwyd, CH7 3JA Tel: (01244) 543365 Fax: (01244) 541200

Watt & Dewar, 62-68 New Row, Dunfermline, Fife, KY12 7EF Tel: (01383) 724146 Fax: (01383) 622966

Wyevale Garden Centres Ltd, Dunstable Road, Caddington, Luton, LU1 4AN Tel: (01582) 457313 Fax: (01582) 480716

BOTTLES, *See also headings for particular types under Bottles*

A E Chapman & Son Ltd, Timbermill Way, Gauden Road, London, SW4 6LY Tel: (020) 7622 4414 Fax: (020) 7720 0189 E-mail: aecsonltd@aol.com

Bettix Ltd, Lever Street, Bolton, BL3 6NZ Tel: (01204) 526241 Fax: (01204) 521958 E-mail: sales@bettix.co.uk

Howard Plastics Ltd, Unit 16 Alexandra Way, Ashchurch, Tewkesbury, Gloucestershire, GL20 8NB Tel: (01684) 298206 Fax: (01684) 850425 E-mail: sales@howardplastics.com

Involvement Packaging Ltd, Park Road, Stalybridge, Cheshire, SK15 1TA Tel: 0161-338 2807 Fax: 0161-338 2807 E-mail: salesstalybridge@involvementpkg.co.uk

Liquor Bottle Ltd, 7 Elsinore House, 77 Fulham Palace Road, London, W6 8JA Tel: (020) 8748 0008 Fax: (020) 8741 1701

Nekem Bottle Suppliers, Trinity Street, Hull, HU3 1JR Tel: (01482) 223424 Fax: (01482) 228811

Rawlings & Son (Bristol) Ltd, Cecil Road, Kingswood, Bristol, BS15 8NA Tel: 0117-960 4141 Fax: 0117-960 3989 E-mail: enq@rawlings-bristol.co.uk

Real Mackay Water Bottling Co., Penyffin, Nantgaredig, Carmarthen, Dyfed, SA32 7LJ Tel: (01267) 290655 Fax: (01267) 290960

▶ Swift Parts, 3 Rawfolds Industrial Estate, Bradford Road, Rawfolds, Cleckheaton, West Yorkshire, BD19 5LT Tel: (01274) 876777 Fax: (01274) 876505

BOTTLES, DRINK, PLASTIC

Bottlestore Ltd, Icknield Way Industrial Estate, Icknield Way, Tring, Hertfordshire, HP23 4JX Tel: (01442) 820920 Fax: (01442) 820939 E-mail: sales@bottlestore.co.uk

BOTTLES, DRINKING, PLASTIC

Bottlestore Ltd, Icknield Way Industrial Estate, Icknield Way, Tring, Hertfordshire, HP23 4JX Tel: (01442) 820920 Fax: (01442) 820939 E-mail: sales@bottlestore.co.uk

▶ Graham Packaging, Irton House, Warpsgrove Lane, Chalgrove, Oxford, OX44 7TH Tel: (01865) 400315 Fax: (01865) 893100

BOTTLES, ESSENTIAL OIL

▶ Bay House, Unit 1 New Rookery Farm, Little London, Silverstone, Towcester, Northamptonshire, NN12 8UP Tel: (01327) 856988 Fax: (01327) 856967 E-mail: sales@bay-house.co.uk

▶ Bushy Tail Ltd, Staveley Mill Yard, Back Lane, Staveley, Kendal, Cumbria, LA8 9LR Tel: (01539) 822244 Fax: 0870 8362158

Elixirs Of Life, PO Box 2085, Canvey Island, Essex, SS8 9WZ Tel: (01268) 680832 E-mail: elixirsoflife@blueyonder.co.uk

▶ Green Therapeutics, Pintail Close, Quedgeley, Gloucester, GL2 4LN Tel: (01452) 560429 E-mail: sales@green-t.info

▶ Herbalbrew, 7 Greenhill Road, Coleraine, County Londonderry, BT51 3JE Tel: (028) 7035 7225 E-mail: kat@herbalbrew.co.uk

BOTTLES, ESSENTIAL OIL – *continued*

▶ Quinessence Aromatherapy, 2 Forest Court, Linden Way, Coalville, Leicestershire, LE67 3JY Tel: (01530) 838358 Fax: (01530) 814171 E-mail: sales@quinessence.com

BOTTLES, GLASS, AMBER

▶ MGM Du Verre Ltd, London Road, Dorking, Surrey, RH5 6AA Tel: (01306) 886222 Fax: (01306) 886222 E-mail: info@mgm-duverre.co.uk

BOTTLES, OLIVE OIL

▶ French Flavour Ltd, PO Box 2192, Wrexham, Clwyd, LL14 2TB Tel: (01978) 844378 Fax: (01978) 844378 E-mail: info@frenchflavour.co.uk

▶ Mediterranean Pantry, PO Box 12465, Sutton Coldfield, West Midlands, B73 9BE Tel: 0121-351 4202 Fax: 0121-351 4202 E-mail: info@medpantry.co.uk

▶ MGM Du Verre Ltd, London Road, Dorking, Surrey, RH5 6AA Tel: (01306) 886222 Fax: (01306) 886222 E-mail: info@mgm-duverre.co.uk

BOTTLES, WINE, GLASS

▶ Devine Wines, Main Road, Gwaelod-y-Garth, Cardiff, CF15 9HJ Tel: (029) 2081 1200 Fax: (029) 2081 4080 E-mail: info@devinewine.co.uk

▶ MGM Du Verre Ltd, London Road, Dorking, Surrey, RH5 6AA Tel: (01306) 886222 Fax: (01306) 886222 E-mail: info@mgm-duverre.co.uk

BOTTLING PLANT

Central Bottling International Ltd, Plumtree Farm Industrial Estate, Plumtree Road, Bircotes, Doncaster, South Yorkshire, DN11 8EW Tel: (01302) 711056 Fax: (01302) 710802 E-mail: sales@centralbottling.com

Dawsons, Unit 22 Victoria Spring Business Park, Wormald Street, Liversedge, West Yorkshire, WF15 6RA Tel: (01924) 414620 Fax: (01924) 414601 E-mail: customerservice@dawson-uk.com

Diageo Global Supply, Banbeath Industrial Estate, Leven, Fife, KY8 5HD Tel: (01333) 424000 Fax: (01333) 425037 E-mail: marketing@diageo.com

Dinting Metric, 8 Hadfield Industrial Estate, Waterside, Hadfield, Glossop, Derbyshire, SK13 1BS Tel: (01457) 855510 Fax: (01457) 838609 E-mail: sales@dintingmetric.com

Findlay's Ltd, Pitcox, Dunbar, East Lothian, EH42 1RQ Tel: (01368) 850720 Fax: (01368) 850740 E-mail: sales@findlays-spring.com

Hunter Neil Packaging Ltd, Unit 5, Hilltop Meadows, Old London Road, Knockholt, Sevenoaks, Kent, TN14 7JW Tel: (01959) 532200 Fax: (01959) 534400 E-mail: info@hunterneil.co.uk

Moody plc, West Carr Road Industrial Estate, Retford, Nottinghamshire, DN22 7SN Tel: (01777) 701141 Fax: (01777) 709086 E-mail: info@moodyplc.com

Odescan Ltd, 37 Redhills Road, South Woodham Ferrers, Chelmsford, CM3 5UL Tel: (01245) 325135 Fax: (01245) 329035

▶ Scotserve Bottling Services Ltd, Unit 5, Lomond Industrial Estate, Alexandria, Dunbartonshire, G83 0TL Tel: 01389 756161

Willis European, Dock Meadow Drive, Wolverhampton, WV4 6LE Tel: (01902) 490895 Fax: (01902) 490896 E-mail: info@williseuropean.com

BOTTLING PLANT ENGINEERING

Anker Gasquet Ltd, Unit 40 Hollingworth Court, Ashford Road, Maidstone, Kent, ME14 5PP Tel: (01622) 664200 Fax: (01622) 750754 E-mail: anker-gasquet@email.msn.com

BOTTLING PLANT SPARE PARTS AND CONSUMABLES

Edghurst Ltd, Cowden Close, Horns Rd, Hawkhurst, Cranbrook, Kent, TN18 4QT Tel: (01580) 752330 Fax: (01580) 752892 E-mail: info@edghurst.demon.co.uk

▶ Scotserve Bottling Services Ltd, Unit 5, Lomond Industrial Estate, Alexandria, Dunbartonshire, G83 0TL Tel: 01389 756161

BOUNCY CASTLE HIRE

▶ 123 Bounce Croydon, 14 Waldorf Close, Croydon, CR2 6DY Tel: 0208 6456719 Fax: 07736 315888

▶ 1st Bounce Croydon, 60 Pawsons Road, Croydon, CR0 2QF Tel: (020) 8689 4997 Fax: 07932 999569 E-mail: info_1stbounce@hotmail.co.uk

▶ A B C Inflatables, 40 Parker Street, Barnsley, South Yorkshire, S70 6EG Tel: (01226) 241314 E-mail: carol@abc-inflatables.org.uk

▶ A1 Bouncy Castle, 13 Northfield Road, Princes Risborough, Buckinghamshire, HP27 0HY Tel: (01844) 274300 E-mail: farooqchappar@btconnect.com

▶ Abvleisure, 44 Satis Avenue, Sittingbourne, Kent, ME10 2LF Tel: (01795) 410459 E-mail: info@abvleisure.co.uk

▶ Awesome Bouncy Castles, 45 Woodlands Road, Stafford, ST16 1QP Tel: (01785) 600950 Fax: (07817) 128319

▶ Bags Of Fun, 9 Crofton Avenue, Corringham, Stanford-le-Hope, Essex, SS17 7TD Tel: (01375) 404716 E-mail: sales@rodeobullrides.co.uk

▶ Ben 'N' Jack's Bouncy Castles, 65 Bollington Road, Stockport, Cheshire, SK4 5ER Tel: 0161-432 1932 E-mail: michael.thompson93@ntlworld.com

▶ Big Bounce, 11a Venachar Avenue, Callander, Perthshire, FK17 8JQ Tel: (01877) 339952 E-mail: info@big-bounce-entertainment.co.uk

Big On Bouncing, 17 Wendover Road, Burnham, Slough, SL1 7ND Tel: (01628) 410736 E-mail: bigonbouncing@aol.com

▶ Billaboing Bouncy Castle, 9 Wilfrid Grove, West Bridgford, Nottingham, NG2 7AT Tel: (07875) 703971 E-mail: info@billaboing.co.uk

▶ Bonny Bouncy, 21 Morrison Avenue, Bonnybridge, Stirlingshire, FK4 1ET Tel: (07969) 995976 Fax: (01324) 878509 E-mail: bonnybig@blueyonder.co.uk

▶ BucksBouncers.Co.Uk, 258 Main Road, Naphill, High Wycombe, Buckinghamshire, HP14 4RX Tel: (01494) 566132 E-mail: info@bucksbouncers.co.uk

Catherines Castles, 11 Villa Way, Wootton, Northampton, NN4 6JH Tel: (01604) 877792 E-mail: info@catherinescastles.co.uk

▶ Clockworkz Leisure Ltd, 9 Phillips Chase, Off Bradford Street, Braintree, Essex, CM7 9BH Tel: (01376) 349542 E-mail: bookings@clockworkz.co.uk

▶ D & E Bouncy Castle Hire, 40 Winchelsea Road, Chatham, Kent, ME5 7LY Tel: (01634) 669880 Fax: (01634) 669880 E-mail: darren@d-and-e-bouncycastles.co.uk

▶ Fun4Kids, 1 Stuart Drive, Warrington, WA4 2BT Tel: (01925) 499688 E-mail: l.hardin@ntlworld.com

▶ Mike Gardiner, 2 Muirfield Way, Deans, Livingston, West Lothian, EH54 8DL Tel: (01506) 204188 E-mail: mike_gardiner2004@msn.com

▶ Hutch Hire Bouncy Castles, 11 Sunny Bank, Widmer End, High Wycombe, Buckinghamshire, HP15 6PA Tel: (01494) 716453 Fax: (0709) 2002053 E-mail: info@hutch-hire.co.uk

▶ Infl8 Bouncy Castle Hire, 4 Provender Walk, Belvedere Road, Faversham, Kent, ME13 7NF Tel: (01795) 537227

▶ Its A Bouncy Thing, 9 Knowle Avenue, Bexleyheath, Kent, DA7 5LP Tel: (020) 8312 0545 E-mail: info@itsabouncything.com

▶ Jammin Entertainments, Queen Street, Swaffham, Norfolk, PE37 7BZ Tel: (01760) 722247 E-mail: enquiry@jamminentertainments.co.uk

▶ JC Inflatables, 32 Lilac Avenue, Scunthorpe, South Humberside, DN16 1JG Tel: (01724) 862015 E-mail: info@jcinflatables.co.uk

▶ Jester Bounce, 83 Honeybourne, Bishop's Stortford, Hertfordshire, CM23 4ED Tel: (01279) 831559 E-mail: infojester@yahoo.co.uk

Kidds Stuff Ltd, 1 Danby Avenue, Old Whittington, Chesterfield, Derbyshire, S41 9NH Tel: (01246) 453055

▶ Little Monsters, 14 Fern Drive, Havant, Hampshire, PO9 2YH Tel: (023) 9278 8427 E-mail: littlemonsters@ntlworld.com

▶ Little Rascals Bouncy Castles, 55 Kingsway, Kingswood, Bristol, BS15 8AJ Tel: 0117-904 1801 E-mail: kerrybird@littlerascalsbouncycastles.co.uk

▶ Multi Madness, 1 Marsett Way, Whinmoor, Leeds, LS14 2DN Tel: 0113-216 4845

▶ Oh Bounce, 16 Gorse Cover Road, Severn Beach, Bristol, BS35 4NP Tel: (01454) 632440

▶ Rainbow Mini Gym Ltd, 152 Pitmore Road, Eastleigh, Hampshire, SO50 4LT Tel: (023) 8036 4956 E-mail: enquiries@rainbowminigym.co.uk

▶ Wigan Bouncy Castles, 75 Skull House Lane, Appley Bridge, Wigan, Lancashire, WN6 9DJ Tel: (01257) 251042 Fax: (01257) 251042 E-mail: hire@bouncey.co.uk

▶ www.bouncycastlerus.co.uk, Unit B7 Sanderson Center, Lees Lane, Gosport, Hampshire, PO12 3UL Tel: (07835) 767940 E-mail: info@bouncycastlerus.co.uk

BOUNCY CASTLE HIRE INSURANCE

▶ Abvleisure, 44 Satis Avenue, Sittingbourne, Kent, ME10 2LF Tel: (01795) 410459 E-mail: info@abvleisure.co.uk

▶ Little Monsters, 14 Fern Drive, Havant, Hampshire, PO9 2YH Tel: (023) 9278 8427 E-mail: littlemonsters@ntlworld.com

BOUNDARY SCAN SYSTEMS, JTAG

Jtag Technologies, Cople Road, Cardington, Bedford, MK44 3SN Tel: (01234) 831212 Fax: (01234) 831616 E-mail: sales@jtag.com

BOVINE SERUM ALBUMIN

Millipore UK Ltd, Fleming Road, Kirkton Campus, Livingston, West Lothian, EH54 7BN Tel: (01506) 404000 Fax: (01506) 404001 E-mail:

BOWLS, BOWLING ALLEY/ INDOOR

Bowling International UK Ltd, Bushacre Court, 14 Garrard Way, Kettering, Northamptonshire, NN16 8TD Tel: (01536) 412244 Fax: (01536) 410350

▶ Complete Leisure Ltd, 5 Spectrum Business Estate, Bircholt Road, Maidstone, Kent, ME15 9YP Tel: (01622) 683628 Fax: (01622) 683576 E-mail: sales@completebowling.co.uk

Vollmer UK Ltd, Orchard Park Industrial Estate, Town Street, Sandiacre, Nottingham, NG10 5BP Tel: 0115-949 1040 Fax: 0115-949 0042 E-mail: admin@vollmer-uk.com

BOWS, FASHION/DECORATIVE

▶ Balloons & Tunes, Bottom Lock Cottages, Glascote Road, Tamworth, Staffordshire, B77 2AE Tel: (01827) 316600 Fax: (01827) 311066 E-mail: us@balloonsandtunes.co.uk

Conservatory Supplies Ltd, The Conservatory Centre, Leighsinton Road, Malvern, Worcestershire, WR14 1JP Tel: (01684) 575588 Fax: (01684) 576077 E-mail: sales@csltd.net

Fashion Ribbon Ltd, Manners Avenue, Manners Industrial Estate, Ilkeston, Derbyshire, DE7 8EF Tel: 0115-930 8699 Fax: 0115-930 4555 E-mail: chris@fashionribbon.co.uk

Gift Design Co. Ltd, Old Griffin Field, Windsor Street, Pentre, Mid Glamorgan, CF41 7JJ Tel: (01443) 441616 Fax: (01443) 440419 E-mail: mail@gift-design.co.uk

▶ Mac Millan, 46A Wardo Avenue, Fulham, London, SW6 6RE Tel: 0207 731 8784 Fax: 0207 731 8622 E-mail: info@mac-millan.com

Stribbons Ltd, 99 Sanders Road, Finedon Road Industrial Estate, Wellingborough, Northamptonshire, NN8 4NL Tel: (01933) 443446 Fax: (01933) 443435 E-mail: info@stribbons.co.uk

BOX FITTINGS, *See Metal Fittings/Edgings/Accessories etc*

BOXBUILD, ELECTRICAL

Elite Electronic Systems Ltd, Lackaghboy Industrial Estate, Lackaghboy, Enniskillen, County Fermanagh, BT74 4RL Tel: (028) 6632 7172 Fax: (028) 6632 5668 E-mail: sales@elitees.com

BOXED BALLOONS

▶ Sky High Leisure Hot Air Balloon Team, Watery Lane Cottage, Wrexham, LL13 OSL Tel: (0845) 3302994 E-mail: info@skyhighleisure.com

BOXES, *See also headings for particular types such as Corrugated, Metal, Fancy etc*

▶ Avis Packaging Ltd, Grafton Works, Grafton Road, New Malden, Surrey, KT3 3AD Tel: (020) 8942 0415 E-mail: sales@avispack.co.uk

▶ Derek Barrott Packaging Ltd, Unit 1 B, Oak Business Park, Oaks Drive, Newmarket, Suffolk, CB8 7SX Tel: (01638) 660909 Fax: (01638) 666649 E-mail: admin@barrottpackaging.co.uk

▶ Bickerstaffe Containers Ltd, Grave Yard Lane, Bickerstaffe, Ormskirk, Lancashire, L39 9EG Tel: (01695) 424244 Fax: (01695) 424387

Boxes & Packaging Ltd, Dunbeath Road, Elgin Industrial Estate, Swindon, SN2 8EA Tel: (01793) 513233 Fax: (01793) 513225 E-mail: swindon@boxesandpackagingltd.co.uk

▶ Burscough Packaging Ltd, Unit 1a Abbey Lane Industrial Estate, Burscough, Ormskirk, Lancashire, L40 7RS Tel: (01704) 896216 Fax: (01704) 896659

Central Box Co. Ltd, 14-16 Lithgow Place, College Milton, East Kilbride, Glasgow, G74 1PW Tel: (01355) 233725 Fax: (01355) 265166

▶ Com Pak Design Ltd, Units 3-4 Kestral Close, Quarry Hill Road, Ilkeston, Derbyshire, DE7 4DA Tel: 0115-944 2224 Fax: 0115-944 1433

▶ Dusk Crafts, 6 Sherwood, Uplyme Road, Lyme Regis, Dorset, DT7 3LS Tel: 01297 445033 E-mail: info@duskcrafts.co.uk

▶ Eagle Corrugated Ltd, Kayley Industrial Estate, Richmond Street, Ashton-Under-Lyne, Lancashire, OL7 0AU Tel: 0161-343 1722

▶ East Kent Carton Manufacturers Ltd, Unit 8 Lysander Close, Pysons Road Industrial Estate, Broadstairs, Kent, CT10 2YJ Tel: (01843) 600033 Fax: (01843) 600055 E-mail: sales@ekcartons.co.uk

▶ Easypack Corrugated Cases Ltd, Finchley Avenue, Mildenhall, Bury St. Edmunds, Suffolk, IP28 7BG Tel: (01638) 715922 Fax: (01638) 712836 E-mail: sales@easypack.uk.com

▶ Emerald Packaging Ltd, Ravenhead Road, St. Helens, Merseyside, WA10 3LR Tel: (01744) 755352 Fax: (01744) 750120

▶ Encase Scotland Ltd, 9 Hawbank Road, East Kilbride, Glasgow, G74 5EG Tel: (01355) 246716 Fax: (01355) 264406

▶ Field Packaging, Bellhill North Industrial Estate, Bellshill, Lanarkshire, ML4 3EE Tel: (01698) 748384 Fax: (01698) 843946

▶ Flightcase Warehouse Ltd, Meltex House, 2 Mariner, Tamworth, Staffordshire, B79 7XE Tel: (01827) 60009 Fax: (01827) 313877 E-mail: sales@flightcasewarehouse.co.uk

▶ Jaxpal Ltd, Unit 37 Planetary Industrial Estate, Planetary Road, Willenhall, West Midlands, WV13 3XB Tel: (01902) 721066 Fax: (01902) 865839

▶ Kalas Gemini Ltd, 17a Redstone Industrial Estate, Redstone Road, Boston, Lincolnshire, PE21 8EA Tel: (01205) 311185 Fax: (01205) 366069

Lancashire Board & Paper Co. Ltd, Balderstone Lane, Heasandford Industrial Estate, Burnley, Lancashire, BB10 2AL Tel: (01282) 835033 Fax: (01282) 835044 E-mail: sales@lancsboard.co.uk

▶ Leighton Packaging Ltd, Leigh Commerce Park, Green Fold Way, Leigh, Lancashire, WN7 3XJ Tel: (01942) 601011 Fax: (01942) 601012E-mail: info@leighton-packaging.co.uk

Pollard Boxes, Feldspar Close, Enderby, Leicester, LE19 4SD Tel: 0116-275 2666 Fax: 0116-275 2888 E-mail: info@pollardboxes.co.uk

▶ Powell Packaging Ltd, Birkdale Road, Scunthorpe, South Humberside, DN17 2AU Tel: (01724) 853625 Fax: (01724) 280159 E-mail: powellpackaging@btconnect.com

Quantum Print & Packaging Ltd, Ashmore Lake Business Park, Spring Lane, Willenhall, West Midlands, WV12 4HN Tel: (01902) 367100 Fax: (01902) 367200 E-mail: sales@quantumppkg.co.uk

▶ Rose Wood Packaging Scotland, 9-15 Napier Place, Wardpark North, Cumbernauld, Glasgow, G68 0LL Tel: (01236) 782500 E-mail: enquires@rosewoodpackaging.co.uk

▶ Tecnovision, 33 Ashville Way, Whetstone, Leicester, LE8 6NU Tel: 0116-275 3262 Fax: 0116-275 3821

United Box, Airlie, Kirriemuir, Angus, DD8 5NY Tel: (01575) 530229 Fax: (01575) 530388

W Maccarthy & Sons Ltd, Unit 1 Block 1, Woolwich Dockyard Industrial Estate, Woolwich Church St, London, SE18 5PQ Tel: (020) 8316 4321 Fax: (020) 8316 5566 E-mail: box.maccarthy@virgin.net

BOXES, CARDBOARD, PRINTED

▶ Artefekz, 2 Parbrook Close, Tile Hill, Coventry, CV4 9XY Tel: (024) 7642 2000 Fax: (024) 7646 2694 E-mail: info@artefekz.com

Box & Seal, Unit 30 Whitehill Industrial Estate, Whitehill Lane, Wootton Bassett, Swindon, SN4 7DB Tel: (01793) 855855 Fax: (01793) 855853

▶ Indigoideas.Co.Uk, 3 Farm Road, Edgware, Middlesex, HA8 9LS Tel: (020) 8959 8337 E-mail: info@indigoideas.co.uk

▶ T L C Print Management Ltd, 4 Gadwey House, Leigh Street, High Wycombe, Buckinghamshire, HP11 2QU Tel: (01494) 522605 E-mail: lotte2005@btconnect.com

BOXES, FLAT PACK, CARDBOARD

▶ Cardboard Boxes, 1 Ivanhoe Street, Leicester, LE3 9GX Tel: 0116-275 2039

▶ Direct Cartons, Unit2, Mountain View, Holmfield, Halifax, West Yorkshire, HX2 9SL Tel: 0796 8070597 Fax: 01422 242347 E-mail: DIRECT.CARTONS@BTINTERNET.COM

Quickpak-UK Ltd, Office 2 Imex Business Centre, Oxleasow Road, Redditch, Worcestershire, B98 0RE Tel: (0845) 838 5979 Fax: (01527) 830 568 E-mail: sales@quickpak-uk.com

BOXES, GREETING CARDS

▶ Bag a Card, 2 Falmouth Way, London, E17 7NZ Tel: (0845) 6445787 E-mail: sales@bag-a-card.com

▶ indicates data change since last edition

BOXES, GREETING CARDS – *continued*

▶ Minty Designs, 1 New Buildings, Harbertonford, Totnes, Devon, TQ9 7SZ Tel: 01803 731077 Fax: (01803) 864649 E-mail: sales@mintydesigns.com
SendaCard, 19, Business Science Park, Nuns Corner, Grimsby, North East Lincolnshire, DN34 5FQ Tel: 01472 822554 E-mail: sales@sendacard.co.uk
▶ Toystat, 18 Gravelly Industrial Park, Birmingham, B24 8HZ Tel: 0121-327 9744 Fax: (0870) 0434484 E-mail: sales@toystat.co.uk

BOXES, STORAGE, PLASTIC

Access Storage, Shentonfield Road, Leestone Road Sharston Industrial Estate, Sharston Industrial Area, Manchester, M22 4RW Tel: 0161-428 1348 Fax: 0161-495 2100 E-mail: sharston@accessstorage.com
Guardian Self Storage Centre, Sherriff Street, Worcester, WR4 9AB Tel: (01905) 24700 Fax: (01905) 24764

BRACES AND SUSPENDERS, GARMENT, MEN'S/FASHION

Hunt & Holditch Ltd, Unit 12, 236-242 Lockwood Road, Huddersfield, HD1 3TG Tel: 01484 542148 Fax: 01484 549147 E-mail: hholditch@aol.com
Albert Thurston Ltd, 3 Frog Island, Leicester, LE3 5AG Tel: 0116-262 7515 Fax: 0116-251 3607 E-mail: sales@albertthurston.com
W Lees Walsall Ltd, Hatherton Works, Leamore Lane, Walsall, WS3 2BJ Tel: (01922) 476435 Fax: (01922) 407118 E-mail: sales@wlees.co.uk
Arnold Wills & Co. Ltd, Station Road, Uppingham, Oakham, Leicestershire, LE15 9TZ Tel: (01572) 822261 Fax: (01572) 821059 E-mail: enquiries@arnoldwills.co.uk

BRACKETS TO SPECIFICATION

A V F Group Ltd, Road 30, Hortonwood Industrial Estate, Telford, Shropshire, TF1 7YE Tel: (01952) 670009 Fax: (01952) 606205 E-mail: sales@avf.co.uk
Arvin Motion Control Ltd, 15 New Star Road, Leicester, LE4 9JD Tel: 0116-274 3600 Fax: 0116-274 3620 E-mail: info@camloc.com
Fablink UK Ltd, Arcwell Works, Stafford Road, Fordhouses, Wolverhampton, WV10 7EJ Tel: (01902) 397766 Fax: (01902) 788912 E-mail: sales@fablink.co.uk
Hawkesley Engineering Ltd, Unit 3, Avery Dell Industrial Estate, Birmingham, B30 3DZ Tel: 0121-433 4277 Fax: 0121-433 4280 E-mail: enquiries@hawkesley.co.uk
Zed Duct Systems Ltd, 5-5a Unit, Hill Street, Kidderminster, Worcestershire, DY11 6TD Tel: (01562) 824261 Fax: (01562) 746435

BRACKETS, SHELVING

Tebrax Ltd, International House, Cray Avenue, Orpington, Kent, BR5 3RY Tel: (01689) 897766 Fax: (01689) 896789 E-mail: brackets@tebrax.co.uk

BRAIDED HOSES

Hydraquip Hose, Head Office, 2 Raleigh Court, Crawley, West Sussex, RH10 9PD Tel: (01293) 615166 Fax: (01293) 614965 E-mail: sales@hydraquip.co.uk

BRAIDING MACHINE SPARE PARTS

▶ Oma UK Ltd, Unit 3-4 Greenfield Farm Industrial Estate, Hopkins Lane, Congleton, Cheshire, CW12 4TR Tel: (01260) 278585 Fax: (01260) 278590 E-mail: omauk@aol.com

BRAIDING MACHINES

Cobra Machinery, Riverdane Road, Eaton Bank Trading Estate, Congleton, Cheshire, CW12 1PL Tel: (01260) 279326 Fax: (01260) 299017 E-mail: sales@cobrabraids.co.uk

BRAIDS, *See also headings for particular types*

A Attenborough & Co Ltd, Nuart Road, Beeston, Nottingham, NG9 2NH Tel: 0115-925 8185 Fax: 0115-922 7445 E-mail: a.attenborough@btinternet.com
Barbra Coats Ltd, Hilden Mill, Lisburn, County Antrim, BT27 4RR Tel: (028) 9267 2231 Fax: (028) 9267 8048E-mail: mail@coats.com
Malmic Lace Ltd, Malmic House, Brookside Road, Ruddington, Nottingham, NG11 6AT Tel: 0115-940 5151 Fax: 0115-984 5706 E-mail: info@malmiclace.co.uk
Rykneld Tean Ltd, Hansard Gate, West Meadows Industrial Estate, Derby, DE21 6RR Tel: (01332) 542700 Fax: (01332) 542710 E-mail: sales@rykneldtean.co.uk
Twistlink Ltd, Stadon Road, Anstey, Leicester, LE7 7AY Tel: 0116-236 1860 Fax: 0116-236 6423 E-mail: sales@fabmania.com
W R Outhwaite & Son Ropemakers, Burtersett Road, Hawes, North Yorkshire, DL8 3NT Tel: (01969) 667487 Fax: (01969) 667576 E-mail: sales@ropemakers.com

BRAILLE BUSINESS CARDS

▶ Braille Translations, 9 Wadham Gardens, Greenford, Middlesex, UB6 0BP Tel: (07005) 860169 Fax: (020) 8422 2237 E-mail: ghow@brailletranslations.co.uk

BRAKE AND CLUTCH COMPONENTS

A J Parsons & Sons Ltd, Anglo Trading Estate, Commercial Road, Shepton Mallet, Somerset, BA4 5BY Tel: (01749) 346161 Fax: (01749) 346100 E-mail: sales@parsonsparts.co.uk
Automec Equipment & Parts Ltd, 36 Ballmoor, Buckingham, MK18 1RQ Tel: (01280) 822818 Fax: (01280) 823140 E-mail: info@automec.co.uk
The Automotive Friction Co. Ltd, Park Lane, Handsworth, Birmingham, B21 8LE Tel: 0121-553 1584 Fax: 0121-553 3275
B G Developments Ltd, Unit 9 West Court, Buntsford Park Road, Bromsgrove, Worcestershire, B60 3DX Tel: (01527) 832453 Fax: (01527) 575403 E-mail: info@bgdevelopments.co.uk
Bennett's, Chapel Pond Hill, Bury St. Edmunds, Suffolk, IP32 7HT Tel: (01284) 766166 Fax: (01284) 769634 E-mail: burystedmunds@bennetts.com
Brake Engineering, Redwither Road, Wrexham Industrial Estate, Wrexham, Clwyd, LL13 9RD Tel: (01978) 667803 Fax: (01978) 667801 E-mail: sales@brake-eng.com
Cohort Manufacturing, PO Box 6368, Kettering, Northamptonshire, NN14 4YZ Tel: (01933) 626062 Fax: (01933) 626562
E K Motor Factors Ltd, Lansil Way, Caton Road, Lancaster, LA1 3QY Tel: (01524) 32361 Fax: (01524) 64423 E-mail: ekslancs@globalnet.co.uk
Friction Linings Southampton Ltd, Unit 2 Easton La Business Park, Easton Lane, Winchester, Hampshire, SO23 7RQ Tel: (01962) 867666 E-mail: info@frictionlinings.co.uk
Groveley Engineering Ltd, Anchor Works, Groveley Road, Christchurch, Dorset, BH23 3HB Tel: (01202) 483497 Fax: (01202) 486658 E-mail: sales@groveley.co.uk
H Kimber Friction Ltd, Printing Trades House, Bond Street, Southampton, SO14 5QA Tel: (023) 8022 6577 Fax: (023) 8063 1154 E-mail: pscott.hkimber@auto-net.co.uk
I C A Motor Products, 146 University Street, Belfast, BT7 1HH Tel: (028) 9024 2191 Fax: (028) 9033 3866
J Motor Components Ltd, 1-5 Crimea Road Winton, Bournemouth, BH9 1AR Tel: (01202) 711177 Fax: (01202) 535777
Charles Johnson, 3 Beech Drive, Norwich, NR6 6RN Tel: (01603) 485429 Fax: (01603) 485459
Knorr Bremse Systems for Commercial Vehicles Ltd, Century House, Follybook Road, Emerald Park East, Emmersons Green, Bristol, BS16 7SE Tel: 0117-984 6100 Fax: 0117-984 6101
▶ Mansfield core supply, 53, Willowbridge lane, Sutton-in-ashfield, Nottinghamshire, NG17 1DW Tel: 01623 477583 E-mail: ianvardy@yahoo.com
Multitruck Components Ltd, 10 Clarke Road, Bletchley, Milton Keynes, MK1 1LG Tel: (01908) 644035 Fax: (01908) 379866 E-mail: multitruck@lineone.net
Pretech Engineering, Barrett Court, Cardiff Road, Reading, RG1 8ED Tel: 0118-957 3123 Fax: 0118-957 3123 E-mail: info@pretech.co.uk
Red Dot Ltd, 98 White Hart Lane, London, N22 5SG Tel: (020) 8888 2354 Fax: (020) 8881 0497 E-mail: sales@reddotracing.co.uk
Toyoda Gosei Fluid Systems UK Ltd, Rockingham Road, Market Harborough, Leicestershire, LE16 7QE Tel: (01858) 439800 Fax: (01858) 410191
Waveney Truck Parts Ltd, 172-174 Mile Cross Lane, Norwich, NR6 6RY Tel: (01603) 400774 Fax: (01603) 418427 E-mail: sales@waveneytruckparts.co.uk

BRAKE CLEANING

Safety-Kleen UK Ltd, 390 London Road, Isleworth, Middlesex, TW7 5AN Tel: (020) 8490 9084 Fax: (020) 8490 3859 E-mail: skuk@sk-europe.com

BRAKE DISCS, REAR

▶ The Brake Fit Centre, Unit 3, 171 New Road, Rainham, Essex, RM13 8SH Tel: (01708) 555552 Fax: (01708) 555552 E-mail: info@brakesessex.com

BRAKE DRUMS

Apec Ltd, Armstrong Way, Bristol, BS37 5NG Tel: (01454) 324644 Fax: (01454) 311414 E-mail: info@apecbraking.co.uk
Brake Engineering, Redwither Road, Wrexham Industrial Estate, Wrexham, Clwyd, LL13 9RD Tel: (01978) 667803 Fax: (01978) 667801 E-mail: sales@brake-eng.com
High Precision Machining Ltd, Unit 10 Washington Centre, Washington Street, Dudley, West Midlands, DY2 9RE Tel: (01384) 233133 Fax: (01384) 212755 E-mail: enquiries@eurac-group.com
J Spindler & Sons Ltd, Joma Roma, The Common, Metfield, Harleston, Norfolk, IP20 0LP Tel: (01986) 785335 Fax: (01986) 785472 E-mail: martin@srts.fsnet.co.uk
Thos Winnard & Sons Ltd, Sandbeck Way, Hellaby Industrial Estate, Rotherham, South Yorkshire, S66 8QL Tel: (01709) 542342 Fax: (01709) 701189

BRAKE FLUID

Alba Diagnostics Ltd, Unit 1 Bankhead Avenue, Glenrothes, Fife, KY7 6JG Tel: (01592) 774333 Fax: (01592) 774777 E-mail: marketing@brakefluidtester.com
Miswa Chemicals Ltd, Caswell Road, Brackmills Industrial Estate, Northampton, NN4 7PW Tel: (01604) 701111 Fax: (01604) 701120 E-mail: sales@miswa.com

BRAKE (INDUSTRIAL) MAINTENANCE/REPAIR SPECIALIST SERVICES

Burton Industrial Braking Co. Ltd, 1 Eton Park, Derby Road, Burton-On-Trent, Staffordshire, DE14 1RR Tel: (01283) 565118 Fax: (01283) 565118
Johnson Elevanja Ltd, Bath Road, Bridgwater, Somerset, TA6 4YQ Tel: (01278) 456411 Fax: (01278) 429949 E-mail: sales@jbrakes.com
Rotable Repairs Group Ltd, Unit 1/4, Britannia Business Park, Comet Way, Southend-on-Sea, SS2 6GE Tel: (01702) 529888 Fax: (01702) 523580 E-mail: info@rotablerepairs.com
Sabre Rail Services Ltd, Grindon Way, Heighington Lane Business Park, Newton Aycliffe, County Durham, DL5 6SH Tel: (01325) 300505 Fax: (01325) 300485 E-mail: info@sabre-rail.co.uk
Saftet Brakes, Unit D5 Halesfield 5, Telford, Shropshire, TF7 4QJ Tel: (01952) 581122 Fax: (01952) 585417 E-mail: sales@saftek.co.uk

BRAKE LININGS

Capel Mills Friction UK Ltd, Unit 6, Maple Works, Maple Road, Redhill, RH1 5HE Tel: (01737) 779090 Fax: (01737) 778040
E X B Ltd, Unit 15 Eldonwell Trading Estate, Eldon Way, Bristol, BS4 3QQ Tel: 0117-972 8380 Fax: 0117-972 3615
European Friction Industries, 6-7 Bonville Road, Bristol, BS4 5NZ Tel: 0117-977 7859 Fax: 0117-971 0573 E-mail: sales@efi.compulink.co.uk
Federal Mogul Friction Products Ltd, Hayfield Road, Chapel-en-le-Frith, High Peak, Derbyshire, SK23 0JP Tel: (01298) 811300 Fax: (01298) 811319 E-mail: info@ferodo.co.uk
Haldex Brake Products Ltd, Moons Moat Drive, Redditch, Worcestershire, B98 9HA Tel: (01527) 499499 Fax: (01527) 499500 E-mail: info@hbpuk.haldex.com
Roadlink International Ltd, Strawberry Lane, Willenhall, West Midlands, WV13 3RL Tel: (01902) 606210 Fax: (01902) 606604 E-mail: j.darwin@roadlink-international.co.uk
Saftek Brakes, 1 Rawfolds Industrial Estate, Bradford Road, Rawfolds, Cleckheaton, West Yorkshire, BD19 5LT Tel: (01274) 862666 Fax: (01274) 862444
Saftet Brakes, Unit D5 Halesfield 5, Telford, Shropshire, TF7 4QJ Tel: (01952) 581122 Fax: (01952) 585417 E-mail: sales@saftek.co.uk
Trimat Ltd, Narrowboat Way, Hurst Business Pk, Brierley Hill, W. Midlands, DY5 1UF Tel: (01384) 473400 Fax: (01384) 261010 E-mail: sales@trimat.co.uk
W R P Construction, Southway House, Southway Drive, Bristol, BS30 5LW Tel: 0117-961 9111 Fax: 0117-961 9222 E-mail: sales@frictionservices.co.uk

BRAKE SHOES

Apec Ltd, Armstrong Way, Bristol, BS37 5NG Tel: (01454) 324644 Fax: (01454) 311414 E-mail: info@apecbraking.co.uk
Brake Engineering, Redwither Road, Wrexham Industrial Estate, Wrexham, Clwyd, LL13 9RD Tel: (01978) 667803 Fax: (01978) 667801 E-mail: sales@brake-eng.com
Capel Mills Friction UK Ltd, Unit 6, Maple Works, Maple Road, Redhill, RH1 5HE Tel: (01737) 779090 Fax: (01737) 778040
J Spindler & Sons Ltd, Joma Roma, The Common, Metfield, Harleston, Norfolk, IP20 0LP Tel: (01986) 785335 Fax: (01986) 785472 E-mail: martin@srts.fsnet.co.uk

BRAKE TEST EQUIPMENT

Bowmonk Ltd, Diamond Road, St. Faiths Industrial Estate, Norwich, NR6 6AW Tel: (01603) 485153 Fax: (01603) 418150 E-mail: info@bowmonk.co.uk
Crypton Ltd, Bristol Road, Bridgwater, Somerset, TA6 4BX Tel: (01278) 436205 Fax: (01278) 450567 E-mail: sales@cryptontechnology.com
Hope Technical Developments Ltd, High Street, Ascot, Berkshire, SL5 7HP Tel: (01344) 624855 Fax: (01344) 626237 E-mail: info@hope-tecdev.com
U K Equipment Ltd, 48 Suttons Park Avenue, Reading, RG6 1AZ Tel: 0118-966 9121 Fax: 0118-966 4369

BRAKES, *See also headings for particular types*

Eurofriction Ltd, Cessnock Road, Hurlford, Kilmarnock, Ayrshire, KA1 5DD Tel: (01563) 546000 Fax: (01563) 546039
Haldex Brake Products Ltd, Moons Moat Drive, Redditch, Worcestershire, B98 9HA Tel: (01527) 499499 Fax: (01527) 499500 E-mail: info@hbpuk.haldex.com
J Motor Components Ltd, 1-5 Crimea Road Winton, Bournemouth, BH9 1AR Tel: (01202) 711177 Fax: (01202) 535777
Lucas Aftermarket Operations, Stratford Road, Shirley, Solihull, West Midlands, B90 4LA Tel: 0121-506 5000 Fax: 0121-506 5001 E-mail: enquiries@lucasestateagents.co.uk
Multi-Stroke Ltd, King Street, Old Hill, Cradley Heath, West Midlands, B64 6JJ Tel: (01384) 567481 Fax: (01384) 564382
T R W Automotive Ltd, New Road, New Inn, Pontypool, Gwent, NP4 0TL Tel: (01495) 754040 Fax: (01495) 752802

BRAKING RESISTORS

HVR International Ltd, Bede Trading Estate, Jarrow, Tyne & Wear, NE32 3EN Tel: 0191-489 7771 Fax: 0191-483 9501 E-mail: info@hvrint.com

BRANDING IRONS

Interbrand, 85 Strand, London, WC2R 0DW Tel: (020) 7554 1000 Fax: (020) 7554 1001 E-mail: ukinfo@interbrand.com

BRANDYSNAPS

Sharp & Nickless Ltd, 77 College Street, Long Eaton, Nottingham, NG10 4NN Tel: 0115-973 2169 Fax: 0115-973 2169 E-mail: sharp@brandysnap.co.uk
Wright & Co., Bramston Street, Brighouse, West Yorkshire, HD6 3AA Tel: (01484) 715166 Fax: (01484) 715166

BRASS ARCHITECTURAL FITTINGS

Armac Brassfounders Group Ltd, 60 Staniforth Street, Birmingham, B4 7DN Tel: 0121-359 4821 Fax: 0121-359 4698 E-mail: buyer@armac.co.uk

BRASS BARS AND SECTIONS

Righton Ltd, Units 5-6, The Nelson Centre, Portsmouth, PO3 5SE Tel: (023) 9262 3070 Fax: (023) 9267 7502 E-mail: portsmouthsales@righton.co.uk

BRASS BOLTS AND NUTS

Jaton, Patriot Drive, Rooksley, Milton Keynes, MK13 8PB Tel: (01908) 690055 Fax: (01908) 690401 E-mail: milton.keynes@outlet-jaton.com
Surrey Fastners, Course Road, Ascot, Berkshire, SL5 7HQ Tel: (01344) 876104 Fax: (01344) 620185 E-mail: surreyfast@aol.com

BRASS CASTINGS

Armac Brassfounders Group Ltd, 60 Staniforth Street, Birmingham, B4 7DN Tel: 0121-359 4821 Fax: 0121-359 4698 E-mail: buyer@armac.co.uk
Derbyshire Castings Ltd, Churchill Road, Altrincham, Cheshire, WA14 5LT Tel: 0161-928 1764 Fax: 0161-927 7623 E-mail: roger@derbyshirecastings.com
Devon Metalcrafts Ltd, 2 Victoria Way, Exmouth, Devon, EX8 1EW Tel: (01395) 272846 Fax: (01395) 276688 E-mail: info@devonmetalcrafts.co.uk

BRASS CASTINGS – *continued*

Samuel Heath & Sons P.L.C., Cobden Works, Leopold Street, Birmingham, B12 0UJ Tel: 0121-772 2303 Fax: 0121-772 3334 E-mail: info@samuel-heath.com
J T Barker & Sons Ltd, Leeds Foundries, Westland Square, Leeds, LS11 5SS Tel: 0113-271 6837 Fax: 0113-270 6901
Madeley Brass Castings, Unit B8 Court Works Industrial Estate, Bridgnorth Road, Madeley, Telford, Shropshire, TF7 4JB Tel: (01952) 583004 Fax: (01952) 583004
Monkman Brass Founders, 3 Broom Street, Bradford, West Yorkshire, BD4 7AP Tel: (01274) 732117 Fax: (01274) 732117
W Raybould & Sons Ltd, Croxstalls Close, Walsall, WS3 2XT Tel: (01922) 479196 Fax: (01922) 494616 E-mail: sales@raybould.co.uk

BRASS CIRCLES

KME UK Ltd, Severn House, Prescott Drive, Warndon Business Park, Worcester, WR4 9NE Tel: (01905) 751816 Fax: (01905) 751801 E-mail: info@kme.com

BRASS CURTAIN RAIL FITTINGS

▶ Curtain Traders, 123 High Street, Marlborough, Wiltshire, SN8 1LZ Tel: (01672) 516994 Fax: (01672) 512400
▶ In2interiors, 34 Aspen Gardens, Ashford, Middlesex, TW15 1ED Tel: (01784) 252900 Fax: (01784) 252900 E-mail: enquiries@in2interiors.co.uk

BRASS DATE CODING HOT FOIL MACHINES

Rotech Machines Ltd, Bridge Road East, Welwyn Garden City, Hertfordshire, AL7 1JU Tel: (01707) 393700 Fax: (01707) 392800

BRASS DECORATIVE FURNITURE FITTINGS

Armac Brassfounders Group Ltd, 60 Staniforth Street, Birmingham, B4 7DN Tel: 0121-359 4821 Fax: 0121-359 4698 E-mail: buyer@armac.co.uk
Martin Co. Ltd, 160 Dollman Street, Duddeston, Birmingham, B7 4RS Tel: 0121-359 2111 Fax: 0121-359 4698 E-mail: sales@martin.co.uk
Optium Brasses, 7 Castle Street, Bampton, Tiverton, Devon, EX16 9NS Tel: (01398) 331515 Fax: (01398) 331164 E-mail: brass@obida.com
Regis Reproduction Ltd, Unit 2 Station Road, Rowley Regis, Rowley Regis, West Midlands, B65 0JY Tel: 0121-561 5674 Fax: 0121-561 5680
Trueform Engineering Ltd, Unit 4 Pasadena Close, Pump Lane, Hayes, Middlesex, UB3 3NQ Tel: (020) 8561 4959 Fax: (020) 8848 1397 E-mail: sales@trueform.co.uk
Valli & Valli Ltd, Unit 8 Hedging Lane Industrial Estate, Hedging Lane, Wilnecote, Tamworth, Staffordshire, B77 5HH Tel: (01827) 283655 Fax: (01827) 280553 E-mail: sales@valiandvali.co.uk

BRASS DIES

Falcontec Ltd, Falcon House, Mucklow Hill, Halesowen, West Midlands, B62 8DT Tel: 0121-550 1076 Fax: 0121-585 5126 E-mail: info@falcontec.co.uk

BRASS DOOR FURNITURE

▶ Shiners Snobs Knobs, 81 Fern Avenue, Jesmond, Newcastle upon Tyne, NE2 2RA Tel: 0191-281 6474 Fax: 0191-281 9041 E-mail: onfo@snobsknobs.co.uk
▶ Webnet Ltd, 41 Tintern Avenue, Tyldesley, Manchester, M29 7WL Tel: (01942) 516162 Fax: (01942) 730484 E-mail: sales@yourhomedirect.co.uk

BRASS EXTRUSIONS

Metelec Ltd, Vulcan Industrial Estate, Walsall, WS2 7BZ Tel: (01922) 712665 Fax: (01922) 710919 E-mail: sales@metelec.co.uk

BRASS FABRICATORS

Brassworld Bar Equipment, Unit 22 Royal Industrial Estate, Jarrow, Tyne & Wear, NE32 3HR Tel: 0191-428 2233 Fax: 0191-483 8893 E-mail: lisa@ahlpipework.co.uk

BRASS FINISHING SERVICES

A P N Polishing, Unit 9, 54 Shernall Street, London, E17 9HP Tel: (020) 8520 3538 Fax: (020) 8520 3538
Beacon Metal Finishers Ltd, Unit 10 Sirhowy Industrial Estate, Thomas Ellis Way, Sirhowy, Tredegar, Gwent, NP22 4QZ Tel: (01495) 711383 Fax: (01495) 711383
Warley Polishing Ltd, James Scott Road, Halesowen, West Midlands, B63 2QT Tel: (01384) 634036 Fax: (01384) 411025 E-mail: sales@warleypolishing.co.uk

BRASS FOUNDRY TO ENGINEERS' SPECIFICATION FOUNDERS/FABRICATORS

Comap Westco, Unit C6 Moss Industrial Estate, St. Helens Road, Leigh, Lancashire, WN7 3PT Tel: (01942) 603351 Fax: (01942) 607780 E-mail: sales@comap.co.uk
Drysdale Brothers (Larbert) Ltd, 346 Main Street, Stenhousemuir, Larbert, Stirlingshire, FK5 3JR Tel: (01324) 562447 Fax: (01324) 556726 E-mail: enquiries@drysdalebrothers.com
Gray & Co. (Brassfounders) Ltd, Block 4, Cowlairs Industrial Estate, Glasgow, G22 5DQ Tel: 0141-558 7003 Fax: 0141-633 0950 E-mail: nismith@compuserve.com
Halifax Castings Brass Founders, Clarence House, Akeds Road, Halifax, West Yorkshire, HX1 2TR Tel: (01422) 365760
Heathcast Ltd, 66 Sydney Road, Watford, WD18 7QX Tel: (01923) 212628 Fax: (01923) 223427 E-mail: sales@heathcast.com
W Lane Ltd, Forty Foot Road, Middlesbrough, Cleveland, TS2 1HG Tel: (01642) 242871 Fax: (01642) 242046 E-mail: w.lane@parson-crossland.co.uk

BRASS GRAVITY DIE CASTINGS

Lenton Brook, Unit D Hawthorns Industrial Estate, Middlemore Road, Middlemore Road, Birmingham, B21 0BH Tel: 0121-523 9390 Fax: 0121-523 9390 E-mail: graham@lentonbrook.freeserve.co.uk

BRASS GRILLES

W J Gowar & Co. Ltd, Rheidol Mews, London, N1 8NU Tel: (020) 7226 3644 Fax: (020) 7226 2969

BRASS HIGH PRESSURE DIE CASTINGS

▶ Regon Ltd, Unit 21B, Avenue 2, Station Lane Industrial Estate, Witney, Oxfordshire, OX28 4YG Tel: (01993) 771441 Fax: (01993) 774105 E-mail: sales@regon.co.uk

BRASS INGOTS

Brookside Metal Co. Ltd, 28 Bilston Lane, Willenhall, West Midlands, WV13 2QE Tel: (01902) 365500 Fax: (01902) 636671 E-mail: richard.payne@brooksidemetal.com

BRASS PADLOCKS

B & G Lock & Tool Co. Ltd, Chapel Green, Willenhall, West Midlands, WV13 1RD Tel: (01902) 630290 Fax: (01902) 633794 E-mail: sales@bgpadlocks.co.uk
Dorplan Architectural Ironmongers, 434-436 Mutton Lane, Potters Bar, Hertfordshire, EN6 3AT Tel: (01707) 647647 Fax: (01707) 647378
Storage King, Orchard Works, Badsell Road, Orchard Business Centre, Five Oak Green, Tonbridge, Kent, TN12 6QU Tel: (01892) 832700 Fax: (01892) 838700 E-mail: fiveoak@storageking.co.uk

BRASS PIPELINE

▶ Waitings Drainage & Pipeline Contractors, Moss Road, Cliburn, Penrith, Cumbria, CA10 3AL Tel: (01931) 714270 Fax: (01931) 714508 E-mail: info@waitings.co.uk

BRASS PLATING SERVICES

D F King Electroplating, 5-7 Sandhurst Close, Kings Road, Canvey Island, Essex, SS8 0QY Tel: (01268) 695672 Fax: (01268) 511014
Midland Chromium Plating Co. Ltd, 116 Aldridge Road, Perry Barr, Birmingham, B42 2TP Tel: 0121-356 9431 Fax: 0121-356 5891 E-mail: info@midchrome.co.uk
Perfection Electro Plating Ltd, Unit 2 Brunswick Industrial Centre, Hertford Street, Birmingham, B12 8NJ Tel: 0121-440 3173 Fax: 0121-440 2661

BRASS POLISHING

▶ Briliant Products, PO Box 7956, Chelmsford, CM2 9WG Tel: (0870) 2403853 E-mail: info@briliant.biz

BRASS PRODUCTS, *See also other headings for particular products*

Brassart Ltd, 76 Attwood Street, Lye, Stourbridge, West Midlands, DY9 8RY Tel: (01922) 740512 Fax: (01384) 898705 E-mail: davidgregory@brassards.co.uk
Mcgrath Bros (Engineering) Ltd, Lisnagarvagh House, Lissue Road, Lisburn, County Antrim, BT28 2SU Tel: (028) 9262 1186 Fax: (028) 9262 1955 E-mail: cmccann@mcgrath-group.com
Regis Reproduction Ltd, Unit 2 Station Road, Rowley Regis, Rowley Regis, West Midlands, B65 0JY Tel: 0121-561 5674 Fax: 0121-561 5680

BRASS RODS

Diehl Sales UK, 2 West Street, Bradford, West Yorkshire, BD2 3BS Tel: (01274) 632227 Fax: (01274) 632059
W & S Allely Ltd, PO Box 58, Smethwick, West Midlands, B66 2RP Tel: 0121-558 3301 Fax: 0121-555 5194E-mail: sales@allely.co.uk

BRASS SHEET

Engravamet Engraving, Dock Meadow Drive, Wolverhampton, WV4 6LE Tel: (01902) 401666 Fax: (01902) 490129 E-mail: sales@engravamet.co.uk
Metelec Ltd, Vulcan Industrial Estate, Walsall, WS2 7BZ Tel: (01922) 712665 Fax: (01922) 710919 E-mail: sales@metelec.co.uk
W & S Allely Ltd, PO Box 58, Smethwick, West Midlands, B66 2RP Tel: 0121-558 3301 Fax: 0121-555 5194E-mail: sales@allely.co.uk

BRASS SPUR TEETH GROMMETS

Bodill Parker Group Ltd, Barnfield Industrial Estate, Speed Road, Tipton, West Midlands, DY4 9DY Tel: 0121-557 4164 Fax: 0121-557 4177 E-mail: sales@bodill-parker.co.uk

BRASS STOCKHOLDERS, *See also headings for particular products*

A S C Metals Ltd, Shaw Road, Bushbury, Wolverhampton, WV10 9LA Tel: (01902) 371700 Fax: (01902) 424324
Ace Metal, 10 Morgan Way, Bowthorpe Employment Area, Norwich, NR5 9JJ Tel: (01603) 731935 Fax: (01603) 748421 E-mail: acemetalsupplies@aol.com
Amari Copper Alloys, Unit 47, Eagle Rd, Moons Moat North Industrial Estate, Redditch, Worcestershire, B98 9HF Tel: (01527) 405600 Fax: (01527) 405605 E-mail: sales@amaricopperalloys.co.uk
Arrow Metals Ltd, 200 High Street, Boston Spa, Wetherby, West Yorkshire, LS23 6BT Tel: (01937) 845066 Fax: (01937) 845897 E-mail: arrowmetalsltd@aol.com
Berkshire Metals Ltd, 10-12 Armour Road, Tilehurst, Reading, RG31 6HS Tel: 0118-942 9476 Fax: 0118-942 4800
Engravamet Engraving, Dock Meadow Drive, Wolverhampton, WV4 6LE Tel: (01902) 401666 Fax: (01902) 490129 E-mail: sales@engravamet.co.uk
Maxim Industries Ltd, Bankfield Road, Tyldesley, Manchester, M29 8QH Tel: 0161-703 2244 Fax: 0161-702 6454 E-mail: info@themssgroup.co.uk
Metal Supermarket, 10 Madeley Road, Moons Moat North Industrial Estate, Redditch, Worcestershire, B98 9NB Tel: (01527) 68818 Fax: (01527) 68414 E-mail: mscredditch@aol.com
Metal Supermarkets, Unit 381a Jedburgh Court, Team Valley Trading Estate, Gateshead, Tyne & Wear, NE11 0BQ Tel: 0191-487 2144 Fax: 0191-487 2155 E-mail: gateshead@metalsupermarkets.org.uk
Metal Supermarkets Ltd, Trafford Park Way, Trafford Park, Trafford Park, Manchester, M17 1AN Tel: 0161-872 1199 Fax: 0161-872 8021 E-mail: mscmanchester@aol.com
Metal Supermarkets Coventry, Bayton Road, Exhall, Coventry, CV7 9EJ Tel: (024) 7636 6567 Fax: (024) 7636 6320 E-mail: msccoventry@aol.com
Metal Supermarkets Govan, Unit 8-9 Orton Place, Glasgow, G51 2HF Tel: 0141-440 1300 Fax: 0141-440 1308 E-mail: msgovan@aol.com
Metal Supermarkets Park Royal, Unit 11 Hanover Industrial Estate, Acton Lane, London, NW10 7NB Tel: (020) 8961 1414 Fax: (020) 8961 1419 E-mail: parkroyal@metalsupermarkets.org.uk
Metal Supermarkets Southampton, Unit 16 Mount Pleasant Industrial Estate, Mount Pleasant Road, Southampton, SO14 0SP Tel: (023) 8022 0999 Fax: (023) 8023 3449 E-mail: southampton@metalsupermarkets.org.uk
Multimetals (Scotland), Unit 1 Atlantic Way, Wednesbury, West Midlands, WS10 7WW Tel: 0121-505 2323 Fax: 0121-505 2324 E-mail: enquiries@multimetals.com
Nefco Multi Metals Ltd, Unit 19 Maun Valley Industrial Estate, Junction Road, Sutton-in-Ashfield, Nottinghamshire, NG17 5GS Tel: (01623) 551313 Fax: (01623) 551195 E-mail: nefco@btconnect.com
Nemco Metals International Ltd, 5 Pennard Close, Brackmills Indus Estate, Brackmills Industrial Estate, Northampton, NN4 7BE Tel: (01604) 666100 Fax: (01604) 768414 E-mail: sales@nemcometals.co.uk
Righton Ltd, Units 5-6, The Nelson Centre, Portsmouth, PO3 5SE Tel: (023) 9262 3070 Fax: (023) 9267 7502 E-mail: portsmouthsales@righton.co.uk
William Rowland Ltd, 7-23 Meadow Street, Sheffield, S3 7BL Tel: 0114-276 9421 Fax: 0114-275 9429 E-mail: e-mail@william-rowland.co.uk
Woodberry Chillcott & Co. Ltd, Unit 17 Court Road Industrial Estate, Cwmbran, Gwent, NP44 3AS Tel: (01633) 869311 Fax: (01633) 874676 E-mail: cwmbran@woodberrychillcott.co.uk
Woodberry Chillcott & Co. Ltd, 6 Spinnaker Road, Hempsted, Gloucester, GL2 5FD Tel: (01452) 418341 Fax: (01452) 300362 E-mail: sales@woodberrychillcott.co.uk
Woodberry Chillcott & Co. Ltd, Unit 6 Langage Industrial Estate, Eastern Wood Road, Plympton, Plymouth, PL7 5ET Tel: (01752) 343421 Fax: (01752) 346947 E-mail: plymouth@woodberrychillcott.co.uk
Woodberry Chillcott & Co. Ltd, 5 Mountbatten Business Park, Jackson Close, Portsmouth, PO6 1UR Tel: (023) 9238 8031 Fax: (023) 9237 3615 E-mail: portsmouth@woodberrychillcott.co.uk

BRASS STRIP MANUFRS

B Mason & Sons Ltd, Wharf Street, Aston, Birmingham, B6 5SA Tel: 0121-327 0181 Fax: 0121-322 8341 E-mail: sales@bmason.co.uk
Eip Metals, Rabone Lane, Smethwick, West Midlands, B66 3JH Tel: 0121-555 1199 Fax: 0121-555 1188 E-mail:
Nemco Metals International Ltd, 5 Pennard Close, Brackmills Indus Estate, Brackmills Industrial Estate, Northampton, NN4 7BE Tel: (01604) 666100 Fax: (01604) 768414 E-mail: sales@nemcometals.co.uk
▶ NINS Trading (UK) Ltd, Unit 6, Penllwyn Gwent Industrial Estate, Saville Road, Ogmore V, Bridgend, Mid Glamorgan, CF32 7AX Tel: (01656) 842400 Fax: (01656) 842888 E-mail: ndjokic@nins.co.uk

BRASS TUBES

Blackheath Tube Co Ltd, Castle Mill Works, Birmingham New Road, Dudley, West Midlands, DY1 4DA Tel: (01384) 255300 Fax: (01384) 255400 E-mail: sales@blackheathtube.co.uk
Marine Engineering Pipworks, Leechmere East Industrial Estate, Sunderland, SR2 9TE Tel: 0191-521 1941 Fax: 0191-523 6954 E-mail: info@mepsun.com

BRASS TURNED PARTS

Ardmore Construction Ltd, Bryne House, 54 Jeffreys Road, Enfield, Middlesex, EN3 7UB Tel: (020) 8805 0101 Fax: (020) 8364 7477 E-mail: millmarsh@mooregroup.co.uk
Autonic Engineering Co. Ltd, Salisbury Road, Hoddesdon, Hertfordshire, EN11 0HU Tel: (01992) 471101 Fax: (01992) 471102 E-mail: sales@autonic.co.uk
Brass Fittings & Supplies Ltd, Hawkshead Mill, Hope Street, Glossop, Derbyshire, SK13 7SS Tel: (01457) 854415 Fax: (01457) 855403 E-mail: b.f.s@btconnect.com
▶ Paramount Precision, Izons Indust Estate, Oldbury Road, West Bromwich, West Midlands, B70 9BS Tel: 0121-553 5553 Fax: 0121-532 0065 E-mail: allan@paramountprecision.fsnet.co.uk
Richard Kell, Blyth Valley Venture Workshops, Plessey Road, Blyth, Northumberland, NE24 4BN Tel: (01670) 363626 Fax: (01670) 363626

BRASS VALVES

Bemasan Ltd, Owen Road, Wolverhampton, WV3 0BB Tel: (01902) 772975 Fax: (01902) 424374 E-mail: nevasales@bemasan.com

BRASS WIRE

Chaplin Bros Birmingham Ltd, Unit 11a Reddicap Trading Estate, Sutton Coldfield, West Midlands, B75 7BU Tel: 0121-378 0565 Fax: 0121-378 0157

BRASS WIRE – *continued*

Eip Metals, Rabone Lane, Smethwick, West Midlands, B66 3JH Tel: 0121-555 1199 Fax: 0121-555 1188 E-mail:

W G H Wire Drawers Ltd, Imperial Works, 217 Oxford Street, Bilston, West Midlands, WV14 7HY Tel: (01902) 354142 Fax: (01902) 354250

BRASSIERES

Naturana Ltd, Eastern Avenue, Lichfield, Staffordshire, WS13 6RT Tel: (01543) 257333 Fax: (01543) 250230 E-mail: naturana.uk@btinternet.com

Playtex Ltd, Unit D Park Indust Estate, Gareloch Road, Port Glasgow, Renfrewshire, PA14 5XH Tel: (01475) 741631 Fax: (01475) 743119 E-mail: enquiries@playtex.co.uk

BRASSWARE

Ainsworth, Frenches Works, Chew Valley Road, Greenfield, Oldham, OL3 7AE Tel: (01457) 879000 Fax: (01457) 873279 E-mail: diyshop@ainsworthdiy.co.uk

The Brass Decorative Grille & Repolishing Co. Ltd, Unit B7 Phoenix Industrial Estate, Rosslyn Cresent, Harrow, Middlesex, HA1 2SP Tel: (020) 8863 8558 Fax: (020) 8863 5330 E-mail: sales@brassgrille.co.uk

Brass Reproductions, 226 Barr Street, Birmingham, B19 3AG Tel: 0121-554 8556 Fax: 0121-554 8556

Davies Bros (Metal Finishers), 123-127 Western Road, Hockley, Birmingham, B18 7QD Tel: 0121-554 3148 Fax: 0121-554 3148 E-mail: sales@british-fireside.co.uk

Dealpage Ltd, Station Road, Uppingham, Rutland, Leicestershire, LE15 9TX Tel: (01572) 823198 Fax: (01572) 823199

▶ Simonswerk UK Ltd, Burcot Works, Spring Street, Tipton, West Midlands, DY4 8TF Tel: 0121-522 2848 Fax: 0121-557 7042 E-mail: sales@simonswerk.co.uk

Valiant Trading Co., 63 Paxford Road, Wembley, Middlesex, HA0 3RJ Tel: (020) 8904 9999

W S Hardware, Stafford Road, Coven Heath, Wolverhampton, WV10 7PS Tel: (01902) 782200 Fax: (01902) 782500 E-mail: sales@ws-hardware.co.uk

BRAZED TOOLS

G M T C Tools Equipment Ltd, Berrington Road, Leamington Spa, Warwickshire, CV31 1NB Tel: (01926) 334655 Fax: (01926) 311811

Speedwell Tool Co, 62 Meadow Street, Preston, PR1 1SU Tel: (01772) 252951 Fax: (01772) 254861

BRAZING

Johnson Matthey Plc, York Way, Royston, Hertfordshire, SG8 5HJ Tel: (01763) 253200 Fax: (01763) 253168 E-mail: webbp@matthey.com

Mti Ltd, 8 Paramount Industrial Estate, Sandown Road, Watford, WD24 7XA Tel: (01923) 249844 Fax: (01923) 228951 E-mail: mti@dial.pipex.com

BRAZING ALLOYS

Grosvenor Electronic Supplies, Priory Tec Park Saxon Way, Priory Park, Hessle, North Humberside, HU13 9PB Tel: (01482) 627327 Fax: (01482) 627328 E-mail: sales@grosvenor-group.com

BRAZING EQUIPMENT OR MACHINERY

Cheltenham Induction Heating Ltd, Saxon Way, Cheltenham, Gloucestershire, GL52 6RU Tel: (01242) 222204 Fax: (01242) 224146 E-mail: sales@cihinduction.com

Fusion Automation Inc, Barrows Rd, The Pinnacles, Harlow, Essex, CM19 5FD Tel: (01279) 443122 Fax: (01279) 424057 E-mail: salesuk@fai-uk.com

Lamba Welding Systems, 31 Racecourse Road, Gallowfields Trading Estate, Richmond, North Yorkshire, DL10 4SU Tel: (01748) 850292 Fax: (01748) 850343

D.A. Ratchford, 6 Chester Hall Lane, Basildon, Essex, SS14 3BG Tel: (01245) 322720 Fax: (01268) 534828

BRAZING PASTES/POWDERS

Fusion Automation Inc, Barrows Rd, The Pinnacles, Harlow, Essex, CM19 5FD Tel: (01279) 443122 Fax: (01279) 424057 E-mail: salesuk@fai-uk.com

BREAD

British Bakeries Ltd, 783 Duke Street, Glasgow, G31 1LL Tel: 0141-556 5211 Fax: 0141-554 3508

Delice De France plc, Opal Way, Stone Business Park, Stone, Staffordshire, ST15 0SS Tel: (01785) 811200 Fax: (01785) 812233

▶ Le Moulin, Mill Walk, Wheathampstead, St. Albans, Hertfordshire, AL4 8DT Tel: (01582) 831988 Fax: (01582) 831988 E-mail: julie.bell@can-do.co.uk

BREAD ROLLS

▶ All Natural, 61e-61f Gorse Industrial Estate, Barnham, Thetford, Norfolk, IP24 2PH Tel: (01842) 890891 Fax: (01842) 890891 E-mail: michael@allnaturalbakery.co.uk

▶ Dorset Cake Co. Ltd, 50 Dorchester Road, Weymouth, Dorset, DT4 7JZ Tel: (01305) 786252 Fax: (01305) 777487 E-mail: office@dorsetcakeco.sagehost.co.uk

BREAD SLICING MACHINE BLADES

Con Mech Engineers, Hare Law Industrial Estate, Stanley, County Durham, DH9 8UR Tel: (01207) 230621 Fax: (01207) 290100 E-mail: sales@conmecheng.co.uk

BREADCRUMBS

Ripon Select Foods Ltd, Dallamires Way North, Ripon, North Yorkshire, HG4 1TL Tel: (01765) 601711 Fax: (01765) 607481 E-mail: ingredients@rsf.co.uk

BREADSTICKS

▶ All Natural, 61e-61f Gorse Industrial Estate, Barnham, Thetford, Norfolk, IP24 2PH Tel: (01842) 890891 Fax: (01842) 890891 E-mail: michael@allnaturalbakery.co.uk

BREAKFAST CEREALS

▶ Dailycer Chestergate, Unit 14, Fourth Avenue, Deeside Industrial Park, Deeside, Clwyd, CH5 2NR Tel: (01244) 289188

BREATHALYSERS

Intoximeters UK Ltd, The Alpha Centre, Babbage Road, Totnes, Devon, TQ9 5JA Tel: (01803) 868602 Fax: (01803) 868701

BREATHING AIR COMPRESSORS

Analox Sensor Technology Ltd, 15 Ellerbeck Court, Stokesley Business Park, Stokesley, Middlesbrough, Cleveland, TS9 5PT Tel: (01642) 711400 Fax: (01642) 713900 E-mail: admin@analox.net

Factair Ltd, 49 Boss Hall Road, Ipswich, IP1 5BN Tel: (01473) 746400 Fax: (01473) 747123 E-mail: sales@factair.co.uk

BREATHING APPARATUS

Airmed Medical Equipment Mnfrs, Southfield House, 99 Barry Road, London, SE22 0HR Tel: (020) 8693 0594 Fax: (020) 8693 0342 E-mail: info@airmedltd.com

Factair Ltd, 49 Boss Hall Road, Ipswich, IP1 5BN Tel: (01473) 746400 Fax: (01473) 747123 E-mail: sales@factair.co.uk

Interspiro Ltd, 7 Hawksworth Road, Central Park, Telford, Shropshire, TF2 9TU Tel: (01952) 200190 Fax: (01952) 299805 E-mail: enquiries@interspiro.com

Kiwi Products Dartford Ltd, 12 Dickens Court, Enterprise Close, Medway City Estate, Rochester, Kent, ME2 4LY Tel: (01634) 718484 Fax: (01634) 718484 E-mail: enquiries@kiwiproducts.co.uk

M S A Britain Ltd, Shawhead Industrial Estate, Coatbridge, Lanarkshire, ML5 4TD Tel: (01236) 424966 Fax: (01236) 440881 E-mail: sales@msabritain.co.uk

Resmar Ltd, 39 Dean Street, Winsford, Cheshire, CW7 1HG Tel: (01606) 863399 Fax: (01606) 558200 E-mail: wyn@resmar.co.uk

Scotsafe Testing Ltd, 17 Woodlands Drive, Kirkhill Industrial Estate, Aberdeen, AB21 0GW Tel: (01224) 771200 Fax: (01224) 725511 E-mail: adrian@scotsafe.co.uk

Scott Health & Safety Ltd, Pimbo Road, West Pimbo, Skelmersdale, Lancashire, WN8 9RA Tel: (01695) 727171 Fax: (01695) 711775 E-mail: plarge@tycoint.com

Wormald Lintott, Hewett Road, Great Yarmouth, Norfolk, NR31 0NN Tel: (01493) 440500 Fax: (01493) 442639 E-mail: wormaldsafetyandservice.uk@tycoint.com

BREATHING APPARATUS MAINTENANCE/REPAIR SERVICES

Interspiro Ltd, 7 Hawksworth Road, Central Park, Telford, Shropshire, TF2 9TU Tel: (01952) 200190 Fax: (01952) 299805 E-mail: enquiries@interspiro.com

Resmar Ltd, Adec House, Fitzherbert Road, Portsmouth, PO6 1RU Tel: (023) 9221 5700 Fax: (023) 9237 6744 E-mail: sales@resmar.co.uk

Scotsafe Testing Ltd, 17 Woodlands Drive, Kirkhill Industrial Estate, Aberdeen, AB21 0GW Tel: (01224) 771200 Fax: (01224) 725511 E-mail: adrian@scotsafe.co.uk

BREWERS YEAST

▶ Blindmans Brewery Ltd, Talbot Farm, Leighton, Frome, Somerset, BA11 4PN Tel: (01749) 880038 Fax: (01749) 880379 E-mail: info@blindmansbrewery.co.uk

BREWERY CASK TRACKING SYSTEMS

Control & Traceability Systems, The Mistal Hagg Farm, Haggs Road, Follifoot, Harrogate, North Yorkshire, HG3 1EQ Tel: (01423) 810820 Fax: (01423) 810288 E-mail: info@ctsol.co.uk

BREWERY CHEMICAL PRODUCTS

Murphy & Son Ltd, Alpine Street, Nottingham, NG6 0HQ Tel: 0115-978 5494 Fax: 0115-924 4654 E-mail: info@murphyandson.co.uk

Sutton & Phillips Ltd, 5 Stowupland Road, Stowmarket, Suffolk, IP14 5AQ Tel: (01449) 613205 Fax: (01449) 770350

BREWERY ENGINEERING SERVICES

Atlantic Ltd, K Chadwell Heath Industrial Park, Kemp Road, Dagenham, Essex, RM8 1SL Tel: (020) 8599 0600 Fax: (0870) 7774412 E-mail: atlantic@eidosnet.co.uk

Bibbys Of Halifax Ltd, Jasper Street Works, Queens Road, Halifax, West Yorkshire, HX1 4NT Tel: (01422) 366331 Fax: (01422) 330086 E-mail: bibbysofhalifax@aol.com

C & B Engineering Ltd, I Edison Courtyard, Brunel Road, Earlstrees Industrial Estate, Corby, Northamptonshire, NN17 4LS Tel: (01536) 202583 Fax: (01536) 269402 E-mail: ian.candbeng@btopenworld.com

Elson & Co. Ltd, Crown Industrial Estate, Anglesey Road, Burton-On-Trent, Staffordshire, DE14 3NX Tel: (01283) 500001 Fax: (01283) 517178 E-mail: elson@elson.co.uk

Meura (Brewery Equipment) Ltd, 1 Park Farm, Buntingford, Hertfordshire, SG9 9AZ Tel: (01763) 272680 Fax: (01763) 272321 E-mail: info@meura.co.uk

BREWERY PLANT AND EQUIPMENT

Aber Instruments Ltd, Unit 5, Science Park, Aberystwyth, Dyfed, SY23 3AH Tel: (01970) 636300 Fax: (01970) 615455 E-mail: sales@aberinstruments.co.uk

▶ Brewery Equipment Refurbishers, 3a Moorfield Road, Wolverhampton, WV2 4QT Tel: (01902) 421170 Fax: (01902) 421168

Brewing-Solutions Co UK Ltd, Unit 31, Osborne Mill Osborne Street, Oldham, OL9 6QQ Tel: 0161-622 1603 Fax: 0161-622 1662 E-mail: info@brewing-solutions.co.uk

Croston Engineering Ltd, Tarvin Mill Barrow Lane, Tarvin Sands, Tarvin, Chester, CH3 8JF Tel: (01829) 741119 Fax: (01829) 741169 E-mail: admin@croston-engineering.co.uk

Harry Mason Ltd, 217 Thimble Mill Lane, Birmingham, B7 5HS Tel: 0121-328 5900 Fax: 0121-327 7257 E-mail: gt@harrymason.co.uk

Meura (Brewery Equipment) Ltd, 1 Park Farm, Buntingford, Hertfordshire, SG9 9AZ Tel: (01763) 272680 Fax: (01763) 272321 E-mail: info@meura.co.uk

BREWERY SPRAYHEADS, CLEAN IN PLACE (CIP)

S B I Industries, Unit 10a Oakendene Industrial Estate, Bolney Road, Cowfold, Horsham, West Sussex, RH13 8AZ Tel: (01403) 864858 Fax: (01403) 864858 E-mail: richardball@sbindustries.co.uk

BREWERY VALVES AND FITTINGS

Chloroxy-Tech Ltd, Powke Lane Industrial Estate, Powke La, Blackheath, Birmingham, B65 0AH Tel: 0121-559 4141 Fax: 0121-559 2503 E-mail: chloroxy.tech@virgin.net

Trutorq Actuators, 1 The Anchorage, Gosport, Hampshire, PO12 1LY Tel: (023) 9251 1123 Fax: (023) 9250 2272 E-mail: leon@trutorq-actuators.com

Western Tooling Ltd, 55-57 Sterte Avenue, Poole, Dorset, BH15 2AJ Tel: (01202) 677654 Fax: (01202) 677876 E-mail: sales@westerntooling.co.uk

BREWING INDUSTRY DISPENSERS

Centek International, Unit 30 Lawson Hunt Industrial Park, Guildford Road, Broadbridge Heath, Horsham, West Sussex, RH12 3JR Tel: (01403) 263323 Fax: (01403) 270651 E-mail: info@nuplas.co.uk

BRICK CLADDING SYSTEMS

Almura Building Products, Cantay House, 62 St. Georges Place, Cheltenham, Gloucestershire, GL50 3PN Tel: (01242) 262900 Fax: (01242) 221333 E-mail: philipmarsh@almura.co.uk

Baggeridge Brick plc, Fir Street, Sedgley, Dudley, West Midlands, DY3 4AA Tel: (01902) 880555 Fax: (01902) 880432

Baggeridge Brick plc, Lynwick Street, Rudgwick, Horsham, West Sussex, RH12 3DH Tel: (01403) 822212 Fax: (01403) 823357 E-mail: info@baggeridge.co.uk

Roc Wales Ltd, Plas Yn Bonwm House, Holyhead Road, Corwen, Clwyd, LL21 9EG Tel: (01490) 413440 Fax: (01490) 413452 E-mail: panelsys@aol.com

BRICK CLEANING, *See Building Exterior Cleaning etc*

BRICK CUTTING OR SHAPING

Apex Block Cutters Ltd, 21 Murdock Road, Manton Industrial Estate, Bedford, MK41 7PE Tel: (01234) 355255 Fax: (01234) 352575 E-mail: sales@apexbuildingproducts.co.uk

Bulmer Brick Cutting Services, The Brickfields, Hedingham Road, Bulmer, Sudbury, Suffolk, CO10 7EF Tel: (01787) 269132 Fax: (01787) 269044 E-mail: info@brickcutter.com

Chelwood Group, Adswood Road, Cheadle Hulme, Cheadle, Cheshire, SK8 5QY Tel: 0161-485 8211 Fax: 0161-486 1968 E-mail: marketing@chelwood.co.uk

Cheneler Products Ltd, Bonehill Farm, Bonehill Road, Tamworth, Staffordshire, B78 3HP Tel: (01827) 65740 Fax: (01827) 59755

Dordon Brick Ltd, Unit 41 Fourways, Carlion Industrial Estate, Atherstone, Warwickshire, CV9 1LH Tel: (01827) 714123 Fax: (01827) 715343 E-mail: cutbricks@aol.com

E H Smith Builders Merchants Ltd, Mill Hill, Enderby, Leicester, LE19 4AJ Tel: 0116-275 0999 Fax: 0116-275 0135 E-mail: leicester@ehsmith.co.uk

Hednesford Brick Cutting Ltd, B Uxbridge Court, Littleworth Road, Cannock, Staffordshire, WS12 1NN Tel: (01543) 871244 Fax: (01543) 425946

Ibstock Brick Ltd, Lodge Lane Factory, Lodge Lane, Cannock, Staffordshire, WS11 0LT Tel: (01922) 708000 Fax: (01922) 417808

Kevington Building Products Ltd, Unit 7 Ludgershall Business Park, New Drove Road, Ludgershall, Andover, Hampshire, SP11 9RN Tel: (01264) 790400 Fax: (01264) 791762

Kevington Building Products Ltd, Rowfant Bus Centre, Wallage Lane, Turners Hill, Crawley, West Sussex, RH10 4NG Tel: (01342) 718899 Fax: (01342) 718528 E-mail: sales@kevingtonbrick.com

Kevington Building Products Ltd, Unit 27 Creeting Road, Stowmarket, Suffolk, IP14 5AY Tel: (01449) 770200 Fax: (01449) 771199

M C Brick Cutting Services Ltd, Unit 4 Sir Francis Ley Industrial Park, Derby, DE23 8XA Tel: (01332) 203332 Fax: (01332) 203335

Southern Brick Cutting Services Ltd, Kennel Lane, Reigate Road, Hookwood, Horley, Surrey, RH6 0AY Tel: (01293) 776888 Fax: (01293) 776598

Richard Stacey, The Workshop, Easthampnett Lane, Easthampnett, Chichester, West Sussex, PO18 0JY Tel: (01243) 533132 Fax: (01243) 538204 E-mail: sales@richardstacey.com

Walsall Brickcutting Ltd, 7 Field Gate, Walsall, WS1 3DJ Tel: (01922) 642499 Fax: (01922) 639135

Wienerberger Ltd, Smoke Jack Brickworks, Horsham Lane, Wallis Wood, Dorking, Surrey, RH5 5QH Tel: (01306) 627481 Fax: (01306) 627561

York Brick Cutting Co, Broad Oak Cottage, Dauby Lane, Kexby, York, YO41 5LJ Tel: (01904) 607123 Fax: (01904) 607500 E-mail: sales@yorkbrick.co.uk

▶ indicates data change since last edition

BRICK FACTORS OR MERCHANTS OR AGENTS

A E Spink Ltd, Kelham Street, Doncaster, South Yorkshire, DN1 3RA Tel: (01302) 321514 Fax: (01302) 327543

Builders Supply Co Leabrooks, 33 Greenhill Lane, Leabrooks, Alfreton, Derbyshire, DE55 4AS Tel: (01773) 602727 Fax: (01773) 540324

Charnwood Forest Brick Ltd, Old Station Close, Shepshed, Loughborough, Leicestershire, LE12 9NJ Tel: (01509) 503203 Fax: (01509) 507566 E-mail: sales@charnwoodforest.com

E. East & Son Ltd, 43-47 Chiltern Avenue, Amersham, Buckinghamshire, HP6 5AF Tel: (01494) 433936 Fax: (01494) 728366

Edward Henthorne & Co Ltd, 10-20 Chorley Road, Blackpool, FY3 7XQ Tel: (01253) 300006 Fax: (01253) 399969 E-mail: edwardhenthorne@aol.com

Ibstock Building Products Ltd, Ravenhead Factory, Chequer Lane, Upholland, Skelmersdale, Lancashire, WN8 0DD Tel: (01695) 625511 Fax: (01695) 624287 E-mail: w.lord@ibstock.co.uk

Keyline Brick & Builders Merchant, Beaufort Road, Plasmarl, Swansea, SA6 8HR Tel: (01792) 792264 Fax: (01792) 796279

W.T. Lamb & Sons Ltd, Nyewood Court, Brookers Road, Billingshurst, West Sussex, RH14 9RZ Tel: (01403) 785141 Fax: (01403) 784663 E-mail: sales@lambsbricks.com

Moore Scott & Co. Ltd, Knapp Lane, Cheltenham, Gloucestershire, GL50 3QJ Tel: (01242) 584400 Fax: (01242) 222388 E-mail: southern.sales@moorescott.co.uk

Northern Brick Specialists Ltd, Po Box 80, Corby, Northamptonshire, NN18 9ZA Tel: (01536) 460600 Fax: (01536) 460606

Pattison Brick & Cladding Merchants, 10 Batsford Close, Redditch, Worcestershire, B98 7TF Tel: (01527) 853163 Fax: (01527) 853163 E-mail: brikclad@suppanet.com

Taylor Maxwell Holdings Ltd, Taylor Maxwell House, The Promenade, Bristol, BS8 3NW Tel: 0117-973 7888 Fax: 0117-970 6652 E-mail: info@taylor.maxwell.co.uk

Taylor Maxwell South East, Brewery Court, 43-45 High Street, Theale, Reading, RG7 5AH Tel: 0118-930 6888 Fax: 0118-930 2888

BRICK PRODUCTION PLANT

Bennett & Sayer, Wetherby Road, Derby, DE24 8HN Tel: (01332) 345546 Fax: 01332 293215 E-mail: info@holdenengineering.co.uk

Consolidated Brick, Brindley Road, Cardiff, CF11 8TL Tel: (029) 2034 0168 Fax: (029) 2034 2466

Craven Fawcett Ltd, Elm Tree Street, Bellvue, Wakefield, West Yorkshire, WF1 5EQ Tel: (01924) 375444 Fax: (01924) 370928 E-mail: sales@cravenfawcett.com

Ibstock Brick Ltd, Chester Lane, St. Helens, Merseyside, WA9 4EN Tel: (01744) 831500 E-mail: parkhousesales@ibstock.co.uk

Mitchell Engineering Ltd, 10 Bridge Street, Cambuslang, Glasgow, G72 7ED Tel: 0141-641 2177 Fax: 0141-641 5185 E-mail: mail@mitchellengineering.co.uk

Phoenix Brick Co. Ltd, The Accounting House, Pottery Lane East, Whittington Moor, Chesterfield, Derbyshire, S41 9BH Tel: (01246) 233223 Fax: (01246) 230777 E-mail: erichall@phoenixbrick.freeserve.co.uk

Vico Engineering Services, Compstall Mills Estate, Andrew Street, Compstall, Stockport, Cheshire, SK6 5HN Tel: 0161-427 3644 Fax: 0161-426 0215 E-mail: info@vico-engineering.co.uk

BRICK REMEDIAL TREATMENT OR COLOURING SERVICES

▶ Brick & Stone Cosmetics Western Ltd, 56 Pinewood Road, Belper, Derbyshire, DE56 2TS Tel: (01773) 826160

▶ Colourite Building Services, The Leas, Minster on Sea, Sheerness, Kent, ME12 2NL Tel: (01795) 871077 E-mail: email@colourite.co.uk

Construction Cosmetics, Red Mill House Centurion Way Business Park, Alfreton Road, Derby, DE21 4AY Tel: (01332) 867740 Fax: (01332) 867741 E-mail: info@concos.co.uk

BRICK STAINS

▶ Brick & Stone Cosmetics Western Ltd, 56 Pinewood Road, Belper, Derbyshire, DE56 2TS Tel: (01773) 826160

Brick & Stone Doctors, 139 Newgate Lane, Mansfield, Nottinghamshire, NG18 2LG Tel: (01623) 402427 Fax: (01623) 402208 E-mail: brick.stonedoctors@ntlworld.com

Ferro Great Britain Ltd, Nile Street, Stoke-on-Trent, ST6 2BQ Tel: (01782) 820400 Fax: (01782) 820402

Lanxess Ltd, Lichfield Road, Branston, Burton-On-Trent, Staffordshire, DE14 3WH Tel: (01283) 714200 Fax: (01283) 714201 E-mail: info@hawley.edi.co.uk

BRICK SUPPORT OR RESTRAINT SYSTEMS

Alderdale Fixing Systems, New John Street, Halesowen, West Midlands, B62 8HT Tel: 0121-561 5500 Fax: 0121-561 3535 E-mail: sales@alderdale.com

Halfen Ltd, 31 Humphrys Road, Woodside Estate, Dunstable, Bedfordshire, LU5 4TP Tel: (01582) 470300 Fax: (0870) 5316304 E-mail: sales@halfen.co.uk

BRICKWORK OR CEMENT OR MASONRY OR STONEWORK PAINTS

▶ Renotex Ltd, Pollard Street, Lofthouse, Wakefield, West Yorkshire, WF3 3HG Tel: (01924) 820003 Fax: (01924) 829529 E-mail: sales@renotex.co.uk

S D Coatings, 1 Albion House, 9 Hexthorpe Business Park, Doncaster, South Yorkshire, DN4 0EJ Tel: (01302) 325758 Fax: (01302) 300522

BRIDAL TIARAS

▶ Caradan Designs, 13 Burrows Road, Kingswinford, West Midlands, DY6 8LS Tel: (01384) 273491

▶ Heavenly Halos (UK), Churston, Paignton, Devon, TQ4 Tel: 0845 833 0938 E-mail: sales@heavenlyhalos.co.uk

▶ Make Me A Princess Tiaras, 16 Quartz Avenue, Mansfield, Nottinghamshire, NG18 4XB Tel: (01623)627257 E-mail: enquiries@makemeaprincess.co.uk

Serenity Wedding Tiaras, 19 Eltham Road, West Bridgford, Nottingham, NG2 5JP Tel: 0115 8461148 E-mail: info@serenity-wedding-tiaras.com

BRIDAL VEILS

▶ John Frost Designer Bridalwear, 44 Smawthorne Lane, Castleford, West Yorkshire, WF10 4EW Tel: (01977) 552913 Fax: (01977) 604646

BRIDAL WEAR FABRIC

Carousel Bridal Veils Ltd, 174-176 Carlton Road, Nottingham, NG3 2BB Tel: 0115-947 6205 E-mail: info@carouselveils.com

▶ Dalston Mill Fabrics, 69-73 Ridley Road, London, E8 2NP Tel: (020) 7249 4129 E-mail: info@dalstonmillfabrics.co.uk

Fabric Place, 12 High Road, Chilwell, Beeston, Nottingham, NG9 4AE Tel: 0115-943 6636 Fax: 0115-943 1336 E-mail: info@fabricsinternational.com

Glenroyd Mills Ltd, Occupation Lane, Pudsey, West Yorkshire, LS28 8HW Tel: 0113-256 5667 Fax: 0113-257 6859 E-mail: sales@glenroyd.com

BRIDGE BEARINGS

A C M Bearings Ltd, 2 Wath West Industrial Estate, Derwent Way, Wath-upon-Dearne, Rotherham, South Yorkshire, S63 6EX Tel: (01709) 874951 Fax: (01709) 878818 E-mail: sales@acmbearings.co.uk

Maclellan Rubber, Neachells Lane, Wolverhampton, WV11 3QG Tel: (01902) 725515 Fax: (01902) 305201 E-mail: sales@maclellanrubber.com

BRIDGE CONSTRUCTION CONSULTANCY OR CONSULTING ENGINEERS

Amalgamated Construction Co. Ltd, Whaley Road, Barnsley, South Yorkshire, S75 1HT Tel: (01226) 243413 Fax: (01226) 320202 E-mail: info@amco-construction.co.uk

Costain Ltd, Costain House, 111 Westminster Bridge Road, London, SE1 7UE Tel: (020) 7705 8444 Fax: (020) 7705 8599

Fabermaunsell Ltd, Enterprise House, 160 Croydon Road, Beckenham, Kent, BR3 4DE Tel: (020) 8639 3515 Fax: (020) 8663 6723 E-mail: enquires@fabermaunsell.com

Hyder Consulting UK Ltd, 29 Pressenden Place, London, SW1E 5DZ Tel: (0870) 0003006 Fax: (0870) 0003906 E-mail: info@hyderconsulting.com

▶ Kenneth Grubb Associates Ltd, Wessex House, St Leonards Road, Bournemouth, BH8 8QS Tel: (01202) 311766 Fax: (01202) 318472 E-mail: email@kgal.co.uk

Kier Caribbean Ltd, Tempsford Hall, Sandy, Bedfordshire, SG19 2BD Tel: (01767) 640111 Fax: (01767) 641179 E-mail: david.parr@kier.co.uk

Mott Macdonald Ltd, Capital House, 48-52 Andover Road, Winchester, Hampshire, SO23 7BH Tel: (01962) 893100 Fax: (01962) 863224 E-mail: marketing@mottmac.com

Mott Macdonald UK Ltd, St Annes Wharf, 112 Quayside, Newcastle upon Tyne, NE1 3DX Tel: 0191-261 0866 Fax: 0191-261 1100 E-mail: marketing@mottmac.com

BRIDGE DEMOLITION

▶ W F Button & Son Ltd, Button House, Pix Farm Lane, Hemel Hempstead, Hertfordshire, HP1 2RY Tel: (01442) 879440 Fax: (01442) 879442 E-mail: sales@wfbutton.co.uk

BRIDGE INSPECTION BOOM ACCESS PLATFORMS

▶ Genie UK Ltd, The Maltings, Wharf Road, Grantham, Lincolnshire, NG31 6BH Tel: (01476) 584333 Fax: (01476) 584334 E-mail: infoeurope@genieind.com

BRIDGE MAINTENANCE CONTRACTORS

▶ Ashridge Construction Ltd, A A Workshop, Enterprise Way, Thatcham, Berkshire, RG19 4AE Tel: (01635) 879400 Fax: (01635) 879401 E-mail: enquiries@ashridge.co.uk

Fabermaunsell Ltd, Enterprise House, 160 Croydon Road, Beckenham, Kent, BR3 4DE Tel: (020) 8639 3515 Fax: (020) 8663 6723 E-mail: enquires@fabermaunsell.com

Universal Sealants UK Ltd, Kingston House, Pattinson North, Washington, Tyne & Wear, NE38 8QA Tel: 0191-416 1530 Fax: 0191-415 4377 E-mail: info@usluk.com

W H Kirkwood Ltd, 27 Hope Street, Greenock, Renfrewshire, PA15 4AW Tel: (01475) 721248 Fax: (01475) 888465 E-mail: info@whkirkwood.co.uk

BRIDGE MONITORING AND TESTING

Strainstall UK Ltd, 10 Mariners Way, Cowes, Isle of Wight, PO31 8PD Tel: (01983) 203600 Fax: (01983) 291335 E-mail: sales@strainstall.co.uk

BRIDGE MONITORING AND TESTING EQUIPMENT

▶ C N S Farnell, Elstree Business Centre, Elstree Way, Borehamwood, Hertfordshire, WD6 1RX Tel: (020) 8238 6900 Fax: (020) 8238 6901 E-mail: sales@cnsfarnell.com

Strainstall UK Ltd, 10 Mariners Way, Cowes, Isle of Wight, PO31 8PD Tel: (01983) 203600 Fax: (01983) 291335 E-mail: sales@strainstall.co.uk

BRIDGING LOAN FINANCE

▶ Credit Link U K, First Floor Nathaniel House, David Street, Bridgend Industrial Estate, Bridgend, Mid Glamorgan, CF31 3SA Tel: (01656) 767622 Fax: (01656) 669978 E-mail: enquiries@creditlink.co.uk

Shakespear Finance Ltd, International House, 223 Regent Street, London, W1B 2EB Tel: (0808) 1602576 E-mail: webmaster@adverse-credit-business-loans.co.uk

▶ Shakespeare finance ltd, 501 International House, 223 Regent Street, London, W1B 2EB Tel: (0808) 1602576 E-mail: webmaster@go4ukloans.co.uk

▶ Shakespeare Finance Ltd, 11 Parade House, 135 The Parade, High Street, Watford, WD17 1NA Tel: (020) 7097 3654 E-mail: m.wali@shakespearefinance.co.uk

▶ Western Standard Corporation, 49 Florence Road, Gedling, Nottingham, NG4 2QL Tel: 0115-940 3131 Fax: 0115-940 3134

BRIDLE BITS

Stanley Bros, Long Street, Premier Business Park, Walsall, WS2 9DX Tel: (01922) 621788 Fax: (01922) 723560 E-mail: info@stanley-brothers.com

BRIDLES

Butler Saddlery Ltd, 4 Fieldgate Works, New Street, Walsall, WS1 3DJ Tel: (01922) 627192 Fax: (01922) 627192

Equisport Saddlery & Riding Wear, 54 Walsall Street, Willenhall, West Midlands, WV13 2DU Tel: (01902) 630083 Fax: (01902) 609389 E-mail: pjequest@aol.com

Jabez Cliff & Co. Ltd, Globe Works, Lower Forster Street, Walsall, WS1 1XG Tel: (01922) 621676 Fax: (01922) 722575 E-mail: saddlery@barnsby.com

K M F Quality Bridles, 4a Ablewell Street, Walsall, WS1 2EQ Tel: (01922) 621773 Fax: (01922) 621773

Sabre Leather Co. Ltd, 19-21 Sandwell Street, Walsall, WS1 3DR Tel: (01922) 629925 Fax: (01922) 723463 E-mail: sales@sabreleather.co.uk

Shayler Saddlery, Short Street, Premier Business Park, Walsall, WS2 9EB Tel: (01922) 631926 Fax: (01922) 630019

Walsall Riding Saddle Co. Ltd, Crosby House, Garden Street, Walsall, WS2 8EF Tel: (01922) 624768 Fax: (01922) 641438 E-mail: sales@exsell.com

BRIEFCASES

Computer Luggage The Company, London Road, Unit 6, Marlborough, Wiltshire, SN8 2AP Tel: (01672) 519933 Fax: (01672) 519966 E-mail: sales@tehair.co.uk

BRIGHT ANNEALING SERVICES

P B A Heat Treating Ltd, Unit 7-8, Bevan Industrial Estate, Brierley Hill, West Midlands, DY5 3TF Tel: (01384) 480331 Fax: (01384) 78381 E-mail: sales@pbaheattreatment.co.uk

BRIGHT BARS, *See Steel Bar etc*

BRIGHT STEEL BARS

Acton Bright Steel Ltd, Gordon Road, Staines, Middlesex, TW18 3BG Tel: (01784) 463595 Fax: (01784) 451748 E-mail: sales@actonbrightsteel.co.uk

Bright Steels Ltd, Norton Works, Malton, North Yorkshire, YO17 9BD Tel: (01653) 694961 Fax: (01653) 695856 E-mail: info@bright-steels.com

C & S Steels Wolverhampton Ltd, Highfields Road, Bilston, West Midlands, WV14 0LQ Tel: (01902) 404771 Fax: (01902) 353348 E-mail: sales@prosol-electronics.co.uk

Corus Engineering Steels, PO Box 25, Wolverhampton, WV1 3DY Tel: (01902) 875000 Fax: (01902) 875011 E-mail: keith.grant@corusgroup.com

Eurosteel & Allied Ltd, 61 Washford Road, Sheffield, S9 3XW Tel: 0114-242 0066 Fax: 0114-242 0077 E-mail: frank@gsbaceroltd.co.uk

F T M Marketing Ltd, P O Box 163C, Esher, Surrey, KT10 0YH Tel: (020) 8286 6661 Fax: (020) 8286 2202 E-mail: info@sonneteer.co.uk

High Peak Steels Ltd, Thornfield House Brookfield Industrial Estate, Peakdale Road, Glossop, Derbyshire, SK13 6LQ Tel: (01457) 866911 Fax: (01457) 869178 E-mail: mark@highpeaksteels.com

John H Place Steels Ltd, 44 Black Park Road, Toomebridge, Antrim, BT41 3SL Tel: (028) 7965 0481 Fax: (028) 7965 0175 E-mail: sales@johnhplace.com

Kelvin Steels Ltd, Spiersbridge Lane, Thornliebank Industrial Estate, Thornliebank, Glasgow, G46 8JT Tel: 0141-638 7988 Fax: 0141-638 1097 E-mail: info@kelvinsteels.com

Kiveton Park Holdings Ltd, Kiveton Park, Sheffield, S26 6NQ Tel: (01909) 770252 Fax: (01909) 772949 E-mail: sales@kpsteel.co.uk

Macelloy Ltd, Hawke Street, Sheffield, S9 2LN Tel: 0114-242 6704 Fax: 0114-243 1324 E-mail: info@macalloy.com

Niagra Lasalle, Planetary Road, Willenhall, West Midlands, WV13 3SW Tel: (01902) 307007 Fax: (01902) 864269 E-mail: brightbar@niag.com

Abram Pulman & Sons Ltd, Walton Street, Sowerby Bridge, West Yorkshire, HX6 1AN Tel: (01422) 833993 Fax: (01422) 834100 E-mail: sales@pulmans.co.uk

Tatham Steels Ltd, Duke Avenue, Stamley Green Industrial Estate, Cheadle Hulme, Cheadle, Cheshire, SK8 6QZ Tel: 0161-485 8535 Fax: 0161-485 7804 E-mail: tathem@bmsteel.co.uk

United Bright Bar Co. Ltd, Station Road, Four Ashes, Wolverhampton, WV10 7DG Tel: (01902) 791010 Fax: (01902) 790044 E-mail: sales@unitedbrightbar.co.uk

Worcestershire Steels Co., Unit 20 Enfield Industrial Estate, Redditch, Worcestershire, B97 6BY Tel: (01527) 67777 Fax: (01527) 64225E-mail: worcestershire.steels@virgin.net

BRIGHT STEEL BOLTS AND NUTS

Bonut Engineering Ltd, Universal Works, Hibbert Street, Stockport, Cheshire, SK4 1NS Tel: 0161-480 1068 Fax: 0161-480 6173 E-mail: info@bonutengineering.co.uk

Ratae Engineers Ltd, Green Lane Works, George Street, Manchester, M30 0RG Tel: 0116-253 1721 Fax: 0161-787 7508 E-mail: sales@rataeengineers.com

BRIGHT TURNED STEEL BARS

Midland Engineering Steels, Units 6-8 Eagle Industrial Estate, Bagnall St, Great Bridge, Tipton, W. Midlands, DY4 7BS Tel: 0121-522 3535 Fax: 0121-522 3737 E-mail: mes@niag.com

Unsco, Manor Road, Kiveton Park Station, Sheffield, S26 6PB Tel: (01909) 770431 Fax: (01909) 772848 E-mail: galdrich@unsco.com

BRILLIANT GLASS CUTTING SERVICES

Glassart, Cross Bank Farm, Burnt Fen, Freckenham, Bury St. Edmunds, Suffolk, IP28 8EA Tel: (01353) 675285 Fax: (01353) 675285 E-mail: sales@glassartuk.com

McCollins, Boynton Hall, Boynton St, Hull, HU3 3BZ Tel: (01482) 329634 Fax: (01482) 329634

Price Glass Ltd, 414-414a Bath Road, Slough, SL1 6JA Tel: (01628) 664466 Fax: (01753) 733121 E-mail: sales@priceglass.co.uk

Wessex Crystal, Unit 4 Silver End Industrial Estate, Brierley Hill, West Midlands, DY5 3LA Tel: (01384) 481390 Fax: (01384) 481600

BRINELL METHOD HARDNESS TEST EQUIPMENT

Brooks Inspection Equipment Ltd, 1 Parsons Lane, Colchester, CO1 2NN Tel: (01206) 799170 Fax: (01206) 798238 E-mail: sales@brooksinspection.com

BRISTLES

Britain & Overseas Trading (Bristles) Ltd, 12 Willow St, London, EC2A 4BH Tel: (020) 7729 2487 Fax: (020) 7739 2795

Delbanco Meyer & Co. Ltd, Portland House, Ryland Road, London, NW5 3EB Tel: (020) 7468 3000 Fax: (020) 7468 3094

BRITISH STANDARD (BS) FLANGES

B D Profiles Ltd, PO Box 65, Cradley Heath, West Midlands, B64 5PP Tel: 0121-559 5136 Fax: 0121-561 4265 E-mail: syoung@bdprofiles.co.uk

BRITISH STANDARD (BS) INJECTION MOULDINGS, CLEAN ROOM ENVIRONMENT

Betts UK Ltd, 505 Ipswich Road, Colchester, CO4 9HE Tel: (01206) 753400 Fax: (01206) 844002 E-mail: simon.jones@betts-uk.com

Dubois Ltd, Arkwright Road, Willowbrook North Industrial Estate, Corby, Northamptonshire, NN17 5AE Tel: (01536) 274800 Fax: (01536) 274902 E-mail: huw.lewis@uk.ag.media.com

Medical & Cosmetic Mouldings Ltd, Gas Road, Sittingbourne, Kent, ME10 2QD Tel: (01795) 426452 Fax: (01795) 422790 E-mail: informationmcm@aol.com

BROACHES

Alcester Broach & Tool Co. Ltd, Pipers Road, Park Farm Industrial Estate, Redditch, Worcestershire, B98 0HU Tel: (01527) 523107 Fax: (01527) 526137 E-mail: sales@alcesterbroach.com

Forst UK Ltd, 14 Dartford Road, Leicester, LE2 7PR Tel: 0116-245 2000 Fax: 0116-245 2037 E-mail: sales@forst.co.uk

James D. Gibson & Co. Ltd, 399 Petre Street, Sheffield, S4 8LL Tel: 0114-243 0385 Fax: 0114-242 5490 E-mail: admin@jamesgibson.co.uk

Pharon S & R Ltd, 228 Lythalls Lane, Foleshill, Coventry, CV6 6GF Tel: (024) 7668 7235 Fax: (024) 7666 4397 E-mail: skelcher&rowe@pipemedia.co.uk

Pharos Redco Ltd, 228 Lythalls Lane, Foleshill, Coventry, CV6 6GF Tel: (024) 7668 7235 Fax: (024) 7666 6355 E-mail: mwinstone@pharosengineering.co.uk

BROACHING MACHINES

Forst UK Ltd, 14 Dartford Road, Leicester, LE2 7PR Tel: 0116-245 2000 Fax: 0116-245 2037 E-mail: sales@forst.co.uk

Odin Engineering Ltd, Unit 4, Fullwood Close, Aldermans Green Industrial Estate, Coventry, CV2 2SS Tel: (024) 7660 2622 Fax: (024) 7660 2649

BROACHING SERVICES

G W Atkins & Sons Ltd, 28 Wellington St, Syston, Leicester, LE7 2LG Tel: 0116-269 1240 Fax: 0116-269 3270

K. Preece Engineering, The Mill, Argyle Street, Glascote, Tamworth, Staffordshire, B77 3EG Tel: 01827 53391 Fax: (01827) 53391

Promac Precision Engineering Ltd, 49 Ivatt Way, Peterborough, PE3 7PN Tel: (01733) 333000 Fax: (01733) 333001 E-mail: management@promac.fsnet.co.uk

BROADBAND FAX SERVICES

▶ Adestra, Hollywell House, Osney Mead, Oxford, OX2 0EN Tel: (01865) 242425 Fax: (01865) 255241 E-mail: Sales@adestra.com

BROADBAND INTERNET ACCESS

CMS Broadband Ltd, Conchieton, Twynholm, Kirkcudbright, DG6 4TA Tel: (01557) 870256 Fax: (01557) 870400 E-mail: info@thinkcms.co.uk

▶ Reduce My Bills, 11 New River Green, Exning, Newmarket, Suffolk, CB8 7HS Tel: (0845) 3312673 E-mail: info@reducemybills.co.uk

▶ Telecomplus, Windmill Hill Drive, Bletchley, MK3 7RE Tel: 0800 0935854 E-mail: sales@telecomplus4u.co.uk

Telewest Communications Cable Ltd, 1 Genesis Business Park, Albert Drive, Woking, Surrey, GU21 5RW Tel: (01483) 750900 Fax: (01483) 750901 E-mail: info@ntl.co.uk

The Utility Warehouse, PO Box 407, Huntingdon, Cambridgeshire, PE29 2ZG Tel: (0845) 1242201 Fax: (0870) 7773753

▶ www.broadbandbuyer.co.uk, Unit 8, Cromwell Business Centre, Howard Way, Interchange Park, Newport Pagnell, Buckinghamshire, MK16 9QS Tel: (01908) 888327 Fax: (01908) 614521 E-mail: sales@broadbandbuyer.co.uk

BROADBAND WIRELESS NETWORK INSTALLATION SERVICES

Airbridge Networks Ltd, Blackburn Technology Management Centre, Blackburn, BB1 5QB Tel: (01254) 667900 Fax: (01254) 663907 E-mail: info@airbridge-networks.com

▶ Asj Itnet Com Ltd, 10 Morris Close, Croydon, CR0 7RD Tel: (07749) 446211 Fax: (07720) 270771 E-mail: info@asj-itnet.co.uk

B C C Ltd, PO Box 5875, Halesowen, West Midlands, B63 4RF Tel: 0121-501 2288 Fax: 0121-585 5757 E-mail: seb@bcclimited.co.uk

▶ Biject Ltd, 4 Kingston Close, Knott End-on-Sea, Poulton-le-Fylde, Lancashire, FY6 0DJ Tel: (01253) 812363

▶ Electronic Products Realisation, 6 Grant Street, Brighton, BN2 9UN Tel: (01273) 674757 E-mail: enqs@eprltd.co.uk

▶ It's Here, 3 Holgate Court, Western Road, Romford, RM1 3JS Tel: (01708) 737500 Fax: (01708) 737500 E-mail: info@itshere.uk.com

The Netpoint Project Ltd, Hove, East Sussex, BN3 3RZ Tel: (01273) 778122 Fax: (07092) 385043

▶ RAE Computing Ltd, Unit 8, Pennine Industrial Estate, Hangingroyd Lane, Hebden Bridge, West Yorkshire, HX7 7BZ Tel: (0845) 0048435 E-mail: info@raecomputing.com

Red-M Services Ltd, Graylands, Langhurstwood Road, Horsham, West Sussex, RH12 4QD Tel: (01403) 211100 Fax: (01403) 248597

▶ Tau Interactive, 65 The Parkway, Cottingham, Hull, HU12 9RE Tel: (08452) 600805 E-mail: info@tauinteractive.co.uk

▶ Tekksupport, 5 Kinghorn Court, Golspie, Sutherland, KW10 6SJ Tel: (01408) 633695 E-mail: info@tekksupport.co.uk

▶ Wales Telecom, Y Manor 6, Victoria Parade, South Beach, Pwllheli, Gwynedd, LL53 5AL Tel: (01758) 613078 E-mail: info@wales-telecom.co.uk

Westbrook Communications, Unit 9 Spectrum Industrial Estate, Bircholt Road, Maidstone, Kent, ME15 9YP Tel: (01622) 661860 Fax: (08700) 056902 E-mail: southeast@westbrookuk.com

BROADBAND WIRELESS NETWORK MAINTENANCE SERVICES

A S T Networks Ltd, Temple Court, Cathedral Road, Cardiff, CF11 9HA Tel: (0870) 1160110 Fax: (0870) 1160611 E-mail: enquiries@astnetworks.co.uk

▶ Asj Itnet Com Ltd, 10 Morris Close, Croydon, CR0 7RD Tel: (07749) 446211 Fax: (07720) 270771 E-mail: info@asj-itnet.co.uk

▶ Electronic Products Realisation, 6 Grant Street, Brighton, BN2 9UN Tel: (01273) 674757 E-mail: enqs@eprltd.co.uk

▶ Fwa Solutions, Springboard Innovation Centre, Llantarnam Park, Cwmbran, Gwent, NP44 3AW Tel: (01633) 488080 Fax: (01633) 647806 E-mail: sales@fwasolutions.com

▶ It's Here, 3 Holgate Court, Western Road, Romford, RM1 3JS Tel: (01708) 737500 Fax: (01708) 737500 E-mail: info@itshere.uk.com

The Netpoint Project Ltd, Hove, East Sussex, BN3 3RZ Tel: (01273) 778122 Fax: (07092) 385043

▶ Northern I T Consultancy, 5 Rishton Lane, Bolton, BL3 6QZ Tel: (0870) 7517444 Fax: 01204 456671 E-mail: Info@nitc.co.uk

Red-M Services Ltd, Graylands, Langhurstwood Road, Horsham, West Sussex, RH12 4QD Tel: (01403) 211100 Fax: (01403) 248597

▶ Steamrail IT Solutions, 57 Norburn Park, Witton Gilbert, Durham, DH7 6SG Tel: 0191-371 1011 E-mail: peter.russell@steamrail.co.uk

▶ Wales Telecom, Y Manor 6, Victoria Parade, South Beach, Pwllheli, Gwynedd, LL53 5AL Tel: (01758) 613078 E-mail: info@wales-telecom.co.uk

Westbrook Communications, Unit 9 Spectrum Industrial Estate, Bircholt Road, Maidstone, Kent, ME15 9YP Tel: (01622) 661860 Fax: (08700) 056902 E-mail: southeast@westbrookuk.com

▶ WP Internet Services, 14 Lovatt Close, Tilehurst, READING, RG31 5HG Tel: 07875 297424 E-mail: info@wpinternetservices.co.uk

BROADCASTING CABLES

Bryant Broadcast, 70b Stafford Road, Croydon, CR0 4NE Tel: (020) 8404 4050 Fax: (020) 8404 4080 E-mail: sales@bryant-broadcast.co.uk

BROADCASTING EQUIPMENT

A M S Neve Ltd, Billington Road, Burnley, Lancashire, BB11 5UB Tel: (01282) 457011 Fax: (01282) 417282 E-mail: info@ams-neve.com

Alice Soundtech Ltd, Unit 34d Hobbs Industrial Estate, Newchapel, Lingfield, Surrey, RH7 6HN Tel: (01342) 833500 Fax: (01342) 833350 E-mail: sales@alice.co.uk

Argosy Ltd, Units 6-7, Ridgeway, Drakes Drive, Long Crendon, Buckinghamshire, HP18 9BF Tel: (01844) 202101 Fax: (01844) 202025 E-mail: sales@argosycable.com

Audionics Ltd, 31 Jessops Riverside, Sheffield, S9 2RX Tel: 0114-242 2333 Fax: 0114-243 3913 E-mail: info@audionics.co.uk

B A L Broadcast, Unit 23 Croft Road Industrial Estate, Newcastle, Staffordshire, ST5 0TW Tel: (024) 7631 6500 Fax: (024) 7649 1117 E-mail: sales@bal.co.uk

Canford Audio, Crowther Road, Washington, Tyne & Wear, NE38 0BW Tel: 0191-418 1133 Fax: 0191-418 1001 E-mail: admin@canford.co.uk

Cintel International Ltd, Watton Road, Ware, Hertfordshire, SG12 0AE Tel: (01920) 463939 Fax: (01920) 460803 E-mail: sales@cintel.co.uk

Clyde Broadcast Products Ltd, 2 Rutherford Court, 15 North Avenue, Clydebank Business Park, Clydebank, Dunbartonshire, G81 2QP Tel: 0141-952 7950 Fax: 0141-941 1224 E-mail: mail@clydebroadcast.com

Conford Electronics, 1 Hillview, Conford, Liphook, Hampshire, GU30 7QW Tel: (01428) 751469 Fax: (01428) 751223 E-mail: contact@confordelec.co.uk

Courtyard Electronics Ltd, 13 Riverside Park, Dogflud Way, Farnham, Surrey, GU9 7UG Tel: (01252) 712030 Fax: (01252) 722060 E-mail: info@courtyard.co.uk

Dingle Star Ltd, Unit 27 Metro Centre, Britannia Way, Coronation Road, London, NW10 7PR Tel: (020) 8965 8060 Fax: (020) 8453 0885

Feltech Electronics Ltd, 7 Long Spring, Porters Wood, St. Albans, Hertfordshire, AL3 6PE Tel: (01727) 834888 Fax: (01727) 848704 E-mail: sales@feltech.co.uk

For-A (UK) Ltd, Unit C71, Barwell Business Park, Leatherhead Road, Chessington, Surrey, KT9 2NY Tel: (020) 8391 7979 Fax: (020) 8391 7978 E-mail: info@for-a.com

Holt Broadcast Services Ltd, Unit 13 Nimrod Industrial Estate, Nimrod Way, Reading, RG2 0EB Tel: 0118-931 0770 Fax: 0118-931 0696 E-mail: sales@holtbs.co.uk

Ikegami Electronics, Unit E1 Cologne Court, Brooklands Close, Sunbury-on-Thames, Middlesex, TW16 7EB Tel: (01932) 769700 Fax: (01932) 769710 E-mail: info@ikegami.co.uk

Integrated Broadcast Information Systems Ltd, The Maltings, Charlton Road, Shepton Mallet, Somerset, BA4 5QE Tel: (07002) 255424 Fax: (07002) 329424 E-mail: sales@ibistv.co.uk

Klark Teknik Group UK plc, Coppice Industrial Trading Estate, Walter Nash Road, Kidderminster, Worcestershire, DY11 7HJ Tel: (01562) 741515 Fax: (01562) 745371

Leitch Europe Ltd, Holland Park House, Oldbury, Bracknell, Berkshire, RG12 8TQ Tel: (01344) 446000 Fax: (01344) 446100 E-mail: sales.europe@leitch.com

Libec Europe Ltd, Priory House Industrial Estate, Pitsford Street, Birmingham, B18 6LX Tel: (01527) 596955 Fax: (01527) 596788 E-mail: sales@libeceurope.com

Libra Professional Broadcast, Chester House, 91-95 Alcester Road, Studley, Warwickshire, B80 7NJ Tel: (01527) 853305 Fax: (01527) 852086 E-mail: andy@libraproinfo.co.uk

M R G Systems Ltd, Willow Court, Beeches Green, Stroud, Gloucestershire, GL5 4BJ Tel: (01453) 751871 Fax: (01453) 753125 E-mail: sales@mrgsystems.co.uk

Melford Electronics Ltd, 14 Blenheim Road, Cresses Business Park, Cressex Business Park, High Wycombe, Buckinghamshire, HP12 3RS Tel: (01494) 638069 Fax: (01494) 463358 E-mail: sales@melford-elec.co.uk

Miranda Technologies Ltd, 1-2 Hithercroft Road, Wallingford, Oxfordshire, OX10 9DG Tel: (01491) 820000 Fax: (01491) 820001

Mosses & Mitchell Ltd, Unit 5, Bath Road Business Centre, Devizes, Wiltshire, SN10 1XA Tel: (01380) 722993 Fax: (01380) 728422 E-mail: sales@mosses-mitchel.com

▶ Multimedia Productions Ltd, Minster Chambers, Suite 1, 37 High St, Wimborne, Dorset, BH21 1HR Tel: (01202) 882059 Fax: (01202) 881091 E-mail: info@mmpuk.com

Paul K Sound & Vision, 16 Kings Lea, Adlington, Chorley, Lancashire, PR7 4EN Tel: (01257) 474233 Fax: (01257) 474233

▶ Pro Motion Hire, Unit 181, Hercules Road, London, SE1 7LD Tel: (020) 7735 9988 Fax: (020) 7735 6656 E-mail: info@promotionhire.co.uk

Quantel Ltd, 31 Turnpike Road, Newbury, Berkshire, RG14 2NX Tel: (01635) 48222 Fax: (01635) 815815 E-mail: quantel@quantel.com

Quasson Ltd, Quasson House, Rennie Gate, Andover, Hampshire, SP10 3TU Tel: (01264) 332132 Fax: (01264) 334470 E-mail: sales@quasson.co.uk

R T I (UK) Ltd, Unit 6 Swan Wharf, Waterloo Road, Uxbridge, Middlesex, UB8 2RA Tel: (01895) 252191 Fax: (01895) 274692 E-mail: email@rtiuk.co.uk

Softel Ltd, 7 Horseshoe Park, Pangbourne, Reading, RG8 7JW Tel: 0118-984 2151 Fax: 0118-984 3939 E-mail: sales@softel.co.uk

Sonifex Ltd, 61 Station Road, Irthlingborough, Wellingborough, Northamptonshire, NN9 5QE Tel: (01933) 650700 Fax: (01933) 650726 E-mail: sales@sonifex.co.uk

Sony Business Europe, Viables Industrial Estate, Jays Close, Basingstoke, Hampshire, RG22 4SB Tel: (01256) 355011 Fax: (01256) 474585

▶ Sound Broadcast Services, Lauriston House, Pitchill, Evesham, Worcestershire, WR11 8SN Tel: (01386) 871650 Fax: (01386) 871987 E-mail: sales@sbsfm.com

Soundcraft, Cranbourne House Cranborne Industrial Estate, Cranborne Road, Potters Bar, Hertfordshire, EN6 3JN Tel: (01707) 665000 Fax: (01707) 660482 E-mail: sales@soundcraft.com

Trilogy Broadcast, 26 Focus Way, Walworth Industrial Estate, Andover, Hampshire, SP10 5NY Tel: (01264) 384000 Fax: (01264) 334806 E-mail: sales@trilogycomms.com

▶ The UK Office Ltd, 11 Faulkners Way, Leighton Buzzard, Bedfordshire, LU7 2SS Tel: (01525) 382050 Fax: (0845) 299 1922 E-mail: tuko@theukoffice.com

Vinten Broadcast Ltd, Western Way, Bury St. Edmunds, Suffolk, IP33 3TB Tel: (01284) 752121 Fax: (01284) 750560 E-mail: contact@vinten.com

Vitec Group plc, 1 Wheatfield Way, Kingston upon Thames, Surrey, KT1 2TU Tel: (020) 8939 4650 Fax: (020) 8939 4680 E-mail: info@vitecgroup.com

Voco Systems Ltd, 75 The Grove, London, W5 5LL Tel: (020) 8579 8587 Fax: (020) 8840 0018

Vortex Communications Ltd, 75 The Grove, London, W5 5LL Tel: (020) 8579 2743 Fax: (020) 8840 0018 E-mail: info@vtx.co.uk

Westgate Developments, Derby House, 11 Rosebery Road, Langley Vale, Epsom, Surrey, KT18 6AF Tel: (01372) 800404 Fax: (01372) 800407 E-mail: west-gate@ntlworld.com

BROADCASTING EQUIPMENT HIRE

▶ Broadcast Services, The Coach House, Ruxbury Road, Chertsey, Surrey, KT16 9EP Tel: (01932) 570001 Fax: (01932) 570443 E-mail: hire@broadcast-services.co.uk

Dales Broadcast Ltd, Unit 4, Oaks Industrial Estate, Coventry Road, Narborough, LE19 2GF Tel: 0116-272 5190 Fax: 0116-272 5196 E-mail: sales@dalesbroadcast.co.uk

▶ Filmscape Media UK, 6 Stammerham Business Centre, Capel Road, Rusper, Horsham, West Sussex, RH12 4PZ Tel: (01306) 710144 E-mail: info@filmscapemedia.com

▶ Multimedia Productions Ltd, Minster Chambers, Suite 1, 37 High St, Wimborne, Dorset, BH21 1HR Tel: (01202) 882059 Fax: (01202) 881091 E-mail: info@mmpuk.com

▶ Pro Motion Hire, Unit 181, Hercules Road, London, SE1 7LD Tel: (020) 7735 9988 Fax: (020) 7735 6656 E-mail: info@promotionhire.co.uk

BROADCASTING MONITORING SERVICES

Durrants Press Cuttings Ltd, Discovery House, 28-42 Banner Street, London, EC1Y 8QE Tel: (020) 7674 0200 Fax: (020) 7674 0222 E-mail: contact@durrants.co.uk

BROADCASTING SEMICONDUCTORS

T D K Semi Conductor Co., 758-760 Great Cambridge Road, Enfield, Middlesex, EN1 3RN Tel: (020) 8443 7061 Fax: (020) 8443 7022 E-mail: neil.harrison@tsc.tdk.com

BROADCASTING SERVICES, ANALOGUE/DIGITAL

Camera Crewing Co., 2 Kingslea Road, Manchester, M20 4UA Tel: 0161-446 2666 Fax: 0161-448 2666 E-mail: ccc@cameracrewing.co.uk
Dales Broadcast Ltd, Unit 4, Oaks Industrial Estate, Coventry Road, Narborough, LE19 2GF Tel: 0116-272 5190 Fax: 0116-272 5196 E-mail: sales@dalesbroadcast.co.uk
Isis Media, PO Box 8209, Solihull, West Midlands, B93 0EN Tel: 0121-685 8225 Fax: 0121-685 8226 E-mail: sales@isismedia.co.uk
▶ Perryscope Productions, 3 Chapel Place, Arthur Street, Montgomery, Powys, SY15 6QZ Tel: (01686) 668114 Fax: (01686) 668537 E-mail: perrypro@globalnet.co.uk
S M G P.L.C., 200 Renfield Street, Glasgow, G2 3PR Tel: 0141-300 3000 Fax: 0141-300 3030
Snell & Wilcox Ltd, Durford Mill, Petersfield, Hants, GU31 5AZ Tel: (01730) 821188 Fax: (01730) 821199

BROADCASTING SOFTWARE

Integrated Broadcast Information Systems Ltd, The Maltings, Charlton Road, Shepton Mallet, Somerset, BA4 5QE Tel: (07002) 255424 Fax: (07002) 329424 E-mail: sales@ibistv.co.uk

BROADCASTING STUDIO INSTALLATIONS

Audio Agency Europe, PO Box 4601, Kiln Farm, Milton Keynes, MK19 7ZN Tel: (01908) 510123 Fax: (01908) 511123 E-mail: info@audioagencyeurope.com
▶ Berry Street Studio, 1 Berry Street, London, EC1V 0AA Tel: (020) 7253 5885 E-mail: info@berrystreetstudio.com
D E G A Broadcast Systems, 1 Newton Court, Rankine Road, Basingstoke, Hampshire, RG24 8GF Tel: (01256) 816220 Fax: (01256) 843952 E-mail: david@dega.co.uk

BROADCASTING VIDEO EQUIPMENT

Videofone Productions, 49 Wellington Road, Hampton, Middlesex, TW12 1JY Tel: (020) 8977 9112 Fax: (020) 8943 1147

BROADCASTING VISUAL DISPLAY (VDU) OR VIDEO MONITOR UNITS

Melford Electronics Ltd, 14 Blenheim Road, Cresses Business Park, Cressex Business Park, High Wycombe, Buckinghamshire, HP12 3RS Tel: (01494) 638069 Fax: (01494) 463358 E-mail: sales@melford-elec.co.uk

BROADLOOM CARPETS

▶ Automobile Trimmings Co., Stonebridge Works, Cumberland Road, Stanmore, Middlesex, HA7 1EL Tel: (020) 8204 8242 Fax: (020) 8204 0255 E-mail: sales@automobiletrim.com
Bodigian & Co. Ltd, Wenman Road, Industrial Estate, Thame, Oxfordshire, OX9 3SD Tel: (01844) 213555 Fax: (01844) 214120 E-mail: sales@bodigianofthame.co.uk
Brockway Carpets Ltd, Hoobrook, Kidderminster, Worcestershire, DY10 1XW Tel: (01562) 824737 Fax: (01562) 863598 E-mail: sales@brockway.co.uk
Checkmate Industries Ltd, Bridge House, 12 Bridge Street, Halstead, Essex, CO9 1HT Tel: (01787) 477272 Fax: (01787) 476334 E-mail: checkmatecarpets@btconnect.com
Crownham Ltd, Crownham House, Gladstone Street, Off Prospect Road, Cleckheaton, West Yorkshire, BD19 3DQ Tel: (01274) 855080 Fax: (01274) 855650
Howkel Carpets, 1 Taylor Mills, Fair Lea Road, Huddersfield, HD4 6HA Tel: (01484) 424919
William Pownall & Sons Ltd, Ensor Mill, Queensway, Rochdale, Lancashire, OL11 2NU Tel: (01706) 716000 Fax: (01706) 649002
Stalwart Commission Carpets, Primrose Works, Primrose Road, Clitheroe, Lancashire, BB7 1BT Tel: (01200) 423721 Fax: (01200) 420804 E-mail: sales@stalwartcarpets.co.uk
Weston Of Scandinavia (UK) Ltd, Fairfax House, Causton Road, Colchester, CO1 1RJ Tel: (01206) 542444 Fax: (01206) 761869

BROCHURE DESIGN AND PRINTING

▶ A P S, 50 Kings Road, Beith, Ayrshire, KA15 2BJ Tel: (01505) 500066 Fax: (01505) 500077 E-mail: brian@apsstationery.co.uk
▶ AAMdesign.co.uk, 80 Heath Road, Locks Heath, Southampton, SO31 6PJ Tel: 01489 605337E-mail: andy.moore@aamdesign.co.uk
Acorn Print (North Space), 60 Hampton Street, Birmingham, B19 3LU Tel: (01902) 630733 Fax: (01902) 608540 E-mail: sales@acornprint.uk.com
▶ Allforms Of Print Ltd, 25 Bridges Road, Norton Canes, Cannock, Staffordshire, WS11 9PB Tel: (01543) 276621 Fax: (01543) 450308 E-mail: sales@allforms.co.uk
Alpha Printing Services, 227b Withington Road, Manchester, M16 8LU Tel: 0161-862 9922 Fax: 0161-862 9944 E-mail: sales@alphaprint.com
Alphagraphics, 68 Darlington Street, Wolverhampton, WV1 4ND Tel: (01902) 711151 Fax: (01902) 710174 E-mail: wolves016@alphagraphics.co.uk
Alsager Printing Co. Ltd, Excalibur Industrial Estate, Fields Road, Alsager, Stoke-on-Trent, ST7 2LX Tel: (01270) 873897 Fax: (01270) 882804
Aquarius Press, Aquarius House, Montpelier Business Park, Leacon Road, Ashford, Kent, TN23 4FG Tel: (01233) 662544 Fax: (01233) 662577 E-mail: sales@aquarius.invictornet.co.uk
Armstrong Printing Ltd, Unit 4 Carsebridge Court, Alloa, Clackmannanshire, FK10 3LQ Tel: (01259) 722930 Fax: (01259) 721080 E-mail: sales@armstrongprinting.co.uk
Art Workshop NW Ltd, Unit 20 Kingston Mill, Chestergate, Stockport, Cheshire, SK3 0AL Tel: 0161-429 9445 Fax: 0161-480 0218
▶ Artwork Print Ltd, Unit 29, Wilmer Industrial Estate, Wilmer Place, London, N16 0LW Tel: (020) 7254 3993 E-mail: info@artworkprint.co.uk
B M Printers Ltd, Units 8-9, Queens Mill Road, Huddersfield, HD1 3PG Tel: (01484) 422593 Fax: (01484) 519399 E-mail: john@bmprinters.fsnet.co.uk
Bemrose Booth, PO Box 18, Derby, DE21 6XG Tel: (01332) 294242 Fax: (01332) 290366 E-mail: promote@bemrose.co.uk
Bezier Corporate Print, 145 Sterte Road, Poole, Dorset, BH15 2AF Tel: (01202) 681466 Fax: (01202) 670010 E-mail: sales@bezier.co.uk
Black Swan Printers, Unit 7 Shutterton Industrial Estate, Dawlish, Devon, EX7 0NH Tel: (01626) 865463 Fax: (01626) 888224 E-mail: sales@blackswanprinting.co.uk
▶ Bluprint Design & Copy, 79 Wellgate, Rotherham, South Yorkshire, S60 2LZ Tel: (01709) 838965 Fax: (01709) 365449 E-mail: info@bluprintdesign.co.uk
Buckland Press Ltd, Barwick Road, Dover, Kent, CT17 0LG Tel: (01304) 205900 Fax: (01304) 205619 E-mail: info@buckland.co.uk
▶ Buckleys, Welkin Mill, Welkin Road, Bredbury, Stockport, Cheshire, SK6 2BL Tel: 0161-430 4211 Fax: 0161-494 2837 E-mail: tony.stevens@buckleys-print.co.uk
Calderprint, 80 Manchester Road, Burnley, Lancashire, BB11 1QZ Tel: (01282) 831530 Fax: (01282) 831524 E-mail: enquiries@calderprint.co.uk
Capper Print, Lanelay Road Industrial Estate, Talbot Green, Pontyclun, Mid Glamorgan, CF72 8XX Tel: (01443) 225500 Fax: (01443) 235290 E-mail: sales@capperprint.co.uk
Caprin, Unit 2 Park Industrial Estate, Frogmore, St. Albans, Hertfordshire, AL2 2DR Tel: (01727) 872021 Fax: (01727) 875012 E-mail: office@caprin.co.uk
Carlton Press Group N W Ltd, 3-7 Britannia Road, Sale, Cheshire, M33 2AA Tel: 0161-962 8686 Fax: 0161-969 6300 E-mail: sales@carltonpressgroup.com
Cavalry Creative Services, 11 Bury Road, Hatfield, Hertfordshire, AL10 8BJ Tel: (01707) 274584 Fax: (01707) 321043 E-mail: cavalry@ntlworld.com
Central Print, 2 Swan Village Industrial Estate, Swan Lane, West Bromwich, West Midlands, B70 0NY Tel: 0121-500 6230 Fax: 0121-500 6230
Chase Design & Print, White Cottage Works, Rumer Hill Road, Cannock, Staffordshire, WS11 8EX Tel: (01543) 462334 Fax: (01543) 505707 E-mail: chasedesign2000@hotmail.com
Clearprint, 99 East Road, Sleaford, Lincolnshire, NG34 7EH Tel: (01529) 303176 Fax: (01529) 303172 E-mail: sales@clearaprint.com
Clifton Litho, 29-31 Richmond Road, Staines, Middlesex, TW18 2AA Tel: (01784) 458127 Fax: (01784) 465744
Columbian Press, 69 Lower Road, Kenley, Surrey, CR8 5NH Tel: (020) 8763 9088 Fax: (020) 8763 1053 E-mail: columbianpress@btinternet.com
Communique Print Services Ltd, 3-11 Little Peter Street, Manchester, M15 4PS Tel: 0161-274 0105 Fax: 0161-236 1251 E-mail: manchester@staniforth.co.uk
Cooper Printers, 43 Manse Street, Fraserburgh, Aberdeenshire, AB43 9JB Tel: (01346) 518831 Fax: (01346) 511311 E-mail: cooper.printers@virgin.net
Cottesmore Press, Baxters Yard, Stuart Street, Grantham, Lincolnshire, NG31 9AF Tel: (01476) 405959 Fax: (01476) 405959 E-mail: fastrack@cottersmorepressfsbusiness.co.uk
Creative Presentations, 5 The Square, Bagshot, Surrey, GU19 5AX Tel: (01276) 474182 Fax: (01276) 472982 E-mail: info@creative-presentations.com
Creative Store Ltd, Studio House, 142 Merton Hall Road, London, SW19 3PZ Tel: (020) 8543 3855 Fax: (020) 8540 7367 E-mail: sales@thecreativestore.co.uk
▶ CreatorArt, The Mega Centre, Bernard Road, Sheffield, S2 5BQ Tel: 0114-253 5996 Fax: 0114-269 5882 E-mail: design@creatorart.com
Darby Design & Print, 6 Kerry Close, Ancells Park, Fleet, Hampshire, GU51 2UF Tel: 01252 669948 E-mail: designandprint@ntlworld.com
▶ Decipher Design, 107, Boundary Rd, London, NW8 0RG Tel: (020) 7328 2545 E-mail: info@decipherdesign.co.uk
Delta Print, 19 Potters Lane, Kiln Farm, Milton Keynes, MK11 3HF Tel: (01908) 568020 Fax: (01908) 261383 E-mail: sales@deltaprint.fsworld.co.uk
Ltd Design Consultants, 54 Warwick Square, London, SW1V 2AJ Tel: (020) 7931 7607 Fax: (020) 7931 7608 E-mail: enquiries@ltddesign.co.uk
▶ Design Forte, Harewood Cottage, Main Street, Weeton, Leeds, LS17 0AY Tel: (01423) 734856 E-mail: chris@designforte.co.uk
Dudley Print, 2 The Sling, Dudley, West Midlands, DY2 9AJ Tel: (01384) 455316 Fax: (01384) 457519 E-mail: dudley.print@virgin.net
E G Brown Bristol Ltd, 63 Quarrington Road, Bristol, BS7 9PJ Tel: 0117-951 3215 Fax: 0117-935 4250
▶ Easy Tiger Creative Ltd, 25-27 Greenwich Market, Greenwich, London, SE10 9HZ Tel: (020) 8305 9292 E-mail: studio@easytigercreative.com
Econoprint UK Ltd, Cooper Drive, Springwood Industrial Estate, Braintree, Essex, CM7 2RF Tel: (01376) 349955 Fax: (01376) 346853 E-mail: sales@econoprint.co.uk
Efficiency Print Ltd, Engine Lane, Stourbridge, West Midlands, DY9 7AQ Tel: (01384) 891986 Fax: (01384) 893437 E-mail: colin@effprint.u-net.com
Elsam Cross & Co., 5-6 London Road, Spalding, Lincolnshire, PE11 2TA Tel: (01775) 723758 Fax: (01775) 768575 E-mail: geoff.hemsil@virgin.net
Entaprint Ltd, 1 Penfold Road Woodcote, Cranleigh, Surrey, GU6 8NZ Tel: (01483) 273173
W.H. Evans & Sons Ltd, Sealand Industrial Estate, 5 Knutsford Way, Chester, CH1 4NS Tel: (01244) 383456 Fax: (01244) 381822 E-mail: print@whevans.co.uk
▶ Exposure, Marketing and Design Services, 12 FieldFare, Billericay, Essex, CM11 2PA Tel: 01277 621474 E-mail: paula@exposureonline.co.uk
Ferguson Print Keswick Ltd, 24 St John Street, Keswick, Cumbria, CA12 5AT Tel: (01768) 772486 Fax: (01768) 771121 E-mail: fergusonbrosltd@btconnect.com
Finger Prints, Unit 3 Andrews Court, Andrews Way, Barrow-in-Furness, Cumbria, LA14 2UE Tel: (01229) 432959 Fax: (01229) 431955 E-mail: info@fingerprints.co.uk
▶ Footprints Solutions, Unit 1 Blakes Business Park Radcliffe Road, Huddersfield, HD3 4LX Tel: (01484) 648500
▶ Gem Stone Graphics Ltd, 4 Highdown Court, Forestfield, Crawley, West Sussex, RH10 6PR Tel: (01293) 524546E-mail: info@gsg-ltd.co.uk
Gilmour Print, Irvinehill Farm, Stewarton, Kilmarnock, Ayrshire, KA3 3EL Tel: (01294) 850217 Fax: (01294) 850444 E-mail: sales@gilmourprint.co.uk
Griffin Print Ltd, 2-4 Belgic Square, Peterborough, PE1 5XF Tel: (01733) 553530 Fax: (01733) 555668 E-mail: info@griffinprint.co.uk
Hill Shorter Group, 54 Roebuck Lane, West Bromwich, West Midlands, B70 6QP Tel: 0121-553 7011 Fax: 0121-500 5162 E-mail: sales@hillshorter.com
I D Design, 48 Broadway Avenue, Harlow, Essex, CM17 0AG Tel: (01279) 415548 Fax: (01279) 415548 E-mail: iddesign@dial.pipex.com
Company Image, 334 Selbourne Road, Luton, LU4 8NU Tel: (01582) 503010 Fax: (01582) 572069 E-mail: companyimage@btconnect.com
▶ Image + (Imageplus + plus), Unit 1 The Depot, Electric Wharf, Coventry, CV1 4JP Tel: (024) 7683 4780 Fax: (024) 7683 4781 E-mail: info@image-plus.co.uk
▶ imaginecolour.com, PO Box 814, Doncaster, South Yorkshire, DN1 9AG Tel: (0800) 1071860 Fax: (01302) 365850 E-mail: info@imaginecolour.com
Innervisions, Po Box 9, Retford, Nottinghamshire, DN22 7GZ Tel: (01777) 702913
▶ Kobu Ltd, 3 Manor Farm Offices, Northend Road, Fenny Compton, Southam, Warwickshire, CV47 2YY Tel: (01295) 771182 Fax: (01295) 771185 E-mail: info@kobu.co.uk
The Marvellous Media Company, Unit 1 GMS House, Boundary Road, Woking, Surrey, GU21 5BX Tel: 01483 740800 Fax: 01483 656810 E-mail: info@marvellousmedia.com
▶ Officeset Ltd, 450 Bath Road, London Heathrow Airport, Longford, West Drayton, Middlesex, UB7 0EB Tel: (0845) 3457035 Fax: (0845) 3457037 E-mail: info@officeset.co.uk
▶ Opt Complete Print Solutions Ltd, 58 Coulsdon Road, Coulsdon, Surrey, CR5 2LA Tel: (020) 8405 9386 Fax: (020) 8405 9386 E-mail: sales@optlimited.co.uk
▶ P J G Creative Design Ltd, 11 Mayer Gardens, Shenley Lodge, Milton Keynes, MK5 7EN Tel: (01908) 231175 E-mail: info@pjgcreative.com
Pentagon Press Ltd, Harriot Drive, Heathcote Industrial Estate, Warwick, CV34 6TJ Tel: (01926) 833481 Fax: (01926) 314017
▶ Print Search Ltd, Westinghouse Road, Trafford Park, Manchester, M17 1PJ Tel: 0161-872 8921 Fax: 0161-848 7323 E-mail: sales@princesearchpromotionalproducts.co.uk
Print4biz, PO Box 256, Bristol, BS16 5WW Tel: 0117-907 1907 Fax: 0117-907 1907 E-mail: enquiries@print4biz.org.uk
▶ Progressive Print Services, Firs Industrial Estate, Kidderminster, Worcestershire, DY11 7QN Tel: (01562) 747356 Fax: (01562) 747357 E-mail: sales@progressive-print.co.uk
Rap, Clowes Street, Hollinwood, Oldham, OL9 7LY Tel: 0161-947 3700 Fax: 0161-947 3729 E-mail: enquiries@rapspiderweb.com
▶ Sea Design, Lansdowne Road, Falmouth, Cornwall, TR11 4BE Tel: (01326) 311658 E-mail: info@sea-studio.com
Systima Technology Ltd, 7 Prospect Business Centre, Prospect Road, Cowes, Isle of Wight, PO31 7AD Tel: (01983) 248810 Fax: (01983) 248812 E-mail: Shane@systima-technology.co.uk
Taws Printers Ltd, 1 Hortonwood, Telford, Shropshire, TF1 7GN Tel: (01952) 281281 Fax: (01952) 281282 E-mail: info@taws.co.uk
▶ Topform Visual Communication Ltd, 2 The Courtyard, Lamdin Road, Bury St. Edmunds, Suffolk, IP32 6NU Tel: (01284) 747399 Fax: (01284) 747401 E-mail: sales@topformonline.co.uk
Turner Packaging Ltd, Horndon Business Park, West Horndon, Brentwood, Essex, CM13 3HW Tel: (01277) 810846 Fax: (01277) 810191 E-mail: service@turnerpack.co.uk
William Burrows Printers Ltd, Tansey Green Road, Brierley Hill, West Midlands, DY5 4TL Tel: (01384) 79678 Fax: (01384) 79678
Wombourne, Ounsdale Road, Wombourne, Wolverhampton, WV5 8EB Tel: (01902) 324222 Fax: (01902) 894081 E-mail: info@wombourne-printers.co.uk
Wyndeham Heron & Co. Ltd, The Bentalls Complex, Colchester Road, Heybridge, Maldon, Essex, CM9 4NW Tel: (01621) 877777 Fax: (01621) 877776

BROCHURE HOLDERS

Brochure Holders International Ltd, Victor Unit, Earls Colne Business Park, Earls Colne, Colchester, CO6 2NS Tel: (01787) 220700 Fax: (01787) 220701 E-mail: sales@brochureholders.co.uk
V K F Renzel, 20e Harris Business Park, Hanbury Road, Stoke Prior, Bromsgrove, Worcestershire, B60 4BD Tel: (01527) 878311 Fax: (01527) 878411 E-mail: sales@vkf-renzel.co.uk

BROCHURE PHOTOGRAPHERS

▶ Afan Digital Photography, 6A High Street, Cwmavon, Port Talbot, SA12 9LE Tel: (01639) 761025 E-mail: info@afandigital.co.uk
Artis Studios Ltd, The Studio 56a High Street, Sunninghill, Ascot, Berkshire, SL5 9NF Tel: (01344) 870033 E-mail: kat@artisstudios.com
▶ Aurora Imaging, Delfan, Cas-Mael, Haverfordwest, Pembrokeshire, SA62 5RJ Tel: 01348 881444 E-mail: info@photowales.com
▶ Campbell Gus, 23 Avondale Road, Rayleigh, Essex, SS6 8NJ Tel: (01268) 778519 E-mail: sales@justix.com
▶ Creative Photo Shop & Portrait Studio, Unit 16, 34 Gerard Street, Ashton-In-Makerfield, Wigan, Lancashire, WN4 9AE Tel: (01942) 725847 E-mail: info@creativephotoshop.co.uk
▶ Edwards Photography, 16 The Vale, London, W3 7SB Tel: (020) 8749 8887 E-mail: studio@edwardsphotography.co.uk
▶ Edwards Photography, 16 The Vale, London, W3 7SB Tel: (020) 8749 8887 Fax: E-mail: studio@edwardsphotography.co.uk
▶ EXPOSURE, 4, Spinney Cottage, Hardwick Lane, Studley, Warwickshire, B80 7AD Tel: 0845 2304530 E-mail: enquiries@exposure-photo.com
▶ Jo Grant Photographer, St. Davids Road, Southsea, Hampshire, PO5 1QJ Tel: (023) 9283 9139
Jacopo Pandolfi Photography, 145-157, St John Street, London, EC1V 4PY Tel: 07946 860678 E-mail: info@jacopopandolfi.com

BROCHURE PHOTOGRAPHERS – *continued*

▶ John Wilson, Ground Floor, 6 Madeira Road, London, SW16 2DF Tel: 020 8516 9582 E-mail: info@jcwilson.net

▶ Lewis Ronald, 5 Long Street, London, E2 8HN Tel: (020) 7033 9134 Fax:

▶ M&N Photography, Studio 25 @ Martello Street, London Fields, London, UK, E8 3PE Tel: (020) 7241 2816 E-mail: info@mn-photo.co.uk

▶ Ian Phillips-McLaren Photographers, Orchard End, Watling Lane, Thaxted, Essex, CM6 2QY Tel: (07889) 861654 E-mail: ian@ianphillips-mclaren.com

▶ Photo Dreams, 101 Burford, Brookside, Telford, Shropshire, TF3 1LJ Tel: (01952) 279110 E-mail: ian@photodreams.co.uk

▶ Photo Express, 7 Melville Terrace, Edinburgh, EH9 1ND Tel: 0131-667 2164 Fax: 0131-667 2164 E-mail: info@photo-express-edinburgh.co.uk

▶ Positive Pixels Photography, Stoneleigh, Bulford Road, Durrington, Salisbury, SP4 8DH Tel: (01980) 653138 E-mail: positive_pixels@tiscali.co.uk

R.P.L.Photography, Liverpool, L1 1EB Tel: (07947) 543764 E-mail: r.p.l.photography@mac.com

▶ Robert Irving Photography, 36 Parkway, Dorking, Surrey, RH4 1EU Tel: (01306) 879853 E-mail: info@robirvingphotography.com

Saban Photography, Charwell House, Wilsom Road, Alton, Hampshire, GU34 2PP Tel: (01420) 540227 E-mail: martin@saban.co.uk

▶ Sharp Photography, 14 Devonshire Place, Brighton, BN2 1QA Tel: (07775) 895477 E-mail: info@janesharp.com

Ken Shelton Photography, 10 New Walk Terrace, Fishergate, York, YO10 4BG Tel: (01904) 630112 E-mail: ken@nwt10.demon.co.uk

▶ Sky Eye Aerial Photography Ltd, PO Box 10, Reading, RG8 0EF Tel: (01491) 873277 Fax: (01491) 873430 E-mail: skyeyephoto@aol.com

▶ Terry Trott, The Studio, 24 School Lane, Bapchild, Sittingbourne, Kent, ME9 9NL Tel: (01795) 472833 Fax: (01795) 475941 E-mail: info@terrytrottphotography.co.uk

▶ Vision Photographic Ltd, Unit 1 Slader Business Park, Witney Road, Nuffield Industrial Estate, Poole, Dorset, BH17 0GP Tel: (01202) 667670 Fax: (01202) 668670 E-mail: info@visionphoto.co.uk

BROCHURE POLYWRAPPING

▶ Cavalier Mailing Services Ltd, Mackintosh Road, Rackheath Industrial Estate, Norwich, NR13 6LJ Tel: (01603) 720303 Fax: (01603) 721247 E-mail: a.kerridge@cavaliermailing.com

▶ Flostream Ltd, Springheath House, Kelpatrick Road, Slough, SL1 6BW Tel: 01628 669548 Fax: 01628 669256 E-mail: sales@flostream.co.uk

Washington Direct Mail Ltd, Fourth Avenue, Team Valley, Gateshead, Tyne & Wear, NE11 0JS Tel: 0191-482 4291 Fax: 0191-491 0109 E-mail: wdm@wdml.co.uk

BROKER DEALERS/ INTERNATIONAL SECURITIES DEALERS

S.P. Angel & Co., East India House, 109-117 Middlesex Street, London, E1 7JF Tel: (020) 7422 4300 Fax: (020) 7422 3401 E-mail: admin@spangel.co.uk

B N P Leasing Ltd, 10 Hareward Avenue, London, NW1 6AA Tel: (020) 7595 2000 Fax: (020) 7595 2555

Barclays Capital, 7th Floor, 5 North Colonnade, London, E14 4BB Tel: (020) 7623 2323 Fax: (020) 7621 5290

Bell Lawrie & Co., 7 Drumsheugh Gardens, Edinburgh, EH3 7QH Tel: 0131-225 2566 Fax: 0131-225 3134 E-mail: abj@blw.co.uk

Bell Lawrie White, 25 Albyn Place, Aberdeen, AB10 1YL Tel: (01224) 589345 Fax: (01224) 573199 E-mail: enquiries@blw.co.uk

Bell Lawrie White Ltd, 43 Buccleuch Street, Dumfries, DG1 2AB Tel: (01387) 252361 Fax: (01387) 257288 E-mail: gmckerrow@b/w.co.uk

Bmo Group, 95 Queen Victoria Street, London, EC4V 4HG Tel: (020) 7489 8844 Fax: (020) 7236 7041

Brewin Dolphin, Old Bank of England Court, Queen Street, Norwich, NR2 4SX Tel: (01603) 767776 Fax: (01603) 767476 E-mail: richardl@hillosborne.co.uk

Brewin Dolphin Securities Ltd, Edmund House, 12-22 Newhall Street, Birmingham, B3 3DB Tel: 0121-236 7000 Fax: 0121-212 0011 E-mail: martin.lord@brewin.co.uk

Brewin Dolphin Securities, Auburn House, Upper Piccadilly, Bradford, West Yorkshire, BD1 3NU Tel: (01274) 728866 Fax: (01274) 370483 E-mail: rupertf@hillosborne.co.uk

Brewin Dolphin Securities Ltd, Sutherland House, Cowbridge Road East, Cardiff, CF11 9BB Tel: (029) 2034 0100 Fax: (029) 2034 4999 E-mail: catherin.thomas@brewin.co.uk

Brewin Dolphin Securities, 50 South Street, Dorchester, Dorset, DT1 1DQ Tel: (01305) 259333 Fax: (01305) 269111 E-mail: david.evans@brewin.co.uk

Brewin Dolphin Securities, 1 Courthouse Square, Dundee, DD1 1NH Tel: (01382) 317200 Fax: (01382) 317201 E-mail: david.chalmers@blw.co.uk

Brewin Dolphin Securities Ltd, 2 Hyde Gardens, Eastbourne, East Sussex, BN21 4PN Tel: (08452) 131190 Fax: (01323) 644109

Brewin Dolphin Securities, 12-14 Fountain Street, Halifax, West Yorkshire, HX1 1LW Tel: (01422) 367707 Fax: (01422) 348362 E-mail: scott.cresswell@brewin.co.uk

Brewin Dolphin Securities, Kintail House, Beechwood Park, Inverness, IV2 3BW Tel: (01463) 225888 Fax: (01463) 226777 E-mail: john.clarkson@blw.co.uk

Brewin Dolphin Securities, 27 Charing Cross, St. Helier, Jersey, JE2 3RP Tel: (01534) 703000 Fax: (01534) 731910 E-mail: stuart.sangan@brewin.co.uk

Brewin Dolphin Securities Ltd, 34 Lisbon Street, Leeds, LS1 4LX Tel: 0113-245 9341 Fax: 0113-243 5666 E-mail: sales@brewin.co.uk

Brewin Dolphin Securities, Permanent House, Horsefair Street, Leicester, LE1 5BU Tel: 0116-242 0700 Fax: 0116-253 6585 E-mail: cjh@hillosborne.co.uk

Brewin Dolphin Securities, Wigford House, Brayford Wharf East, Lincoln, LN5 7AY Tel: (01522) 585100 Fax: (01522) 513965 E-mail: peters@hillosborne.co.uk

Brewin Dolphin Securities Ltd, 59 Madoc Street, Llandudno, Gwynedd, LL30 2TW Tel: (01492) 874391 Fax: (01492) 871990 E-mail: colin.wickens@brewin.co.uk

Brewin Dolphin Securities Ltd, 5 Giltspur Street, London, EC1A 9BD Tel: (020) 7248 4400 Fax: (020) 7236 2034 E-mail: info@brewin.co.uk

Brewin Dolphin Securities Ltd, 98 High St, Lymington, Hampshire, SO41 9AP Tel: (01590) 674288 Fax: (01590) 679039

Brewin Dolphin Securities Ltd, PO Box 512, Manchester, M2 7LE Tel: 0161-833 0961 Fax: 0161-839 1651 E-mail: neil.harding@brewin.co.uk

Brewin Dolphin Securities Ltd, Cross Keys House The Parade, Marlborough, Wiltshire, SN8 1NE Tel: (01672) 519600 Fax: (01672) 515550 E-mail: beverley.mcilvar@brewin.co.uk

Brewin Dolphin Securities, Pilgrim Street, Newcastle Upon Tyne, NE1 6RQ Tel: 0191-279 7300 Fax: 0191-279 7301

Brewin Dolphin Securities Ltd, Park House, 77-81 Bell Street, Reigate, Surrey, RH2 7AN Tel: (01737) 223722 Fax: (01737) 224848 E-mail: paul.cannons@brewin.co.uk

Brewin Dolphin Securities, 5 Alma Square, Scarborough, North Yorkshire, YO11 1JR Tel: (01723) 372478 Fax: (01723) 500116

Brewin Dolphin Securities, Progress House, Fudan Way, Thornaby, Stockton-On-Tees, Cleveland, TS17 6EN Tel: (01642) 608855 Fax: (01642) 604488 E-mail: william.bakerbaker@wise-speke.co.uk

Brewin Dolphin Securities Ltd, 2 Mendip House, High Street, Taunton, Somerset, TA1 3SX Tel: (01823) 332042 Fax: (01823) 335166 E-mail: terry.leach@brewin.co.uk

Brewin Dolphin Security Ltd, The Lypiatts, Lansdown Road, Cheltenham, Gloucestershire, GL50 2JA Tel: (01242) 577677 Fax: (01242) 520030 E-mail: edward.mawle@brewin.co.uk

Bridgewell Ltd, Old Change House, 128 Queen Victoria Street, London, EC4V 4BJ Tel: (020) 7003 3000 Fax: (020) 7369 0301

Brown Bros Harriman Ltd, Veritas House, 125 Finsbury Pavement, London, EC2A 1PN Tel: (020) 7588 6166 Fax: (020) 7614 2440

C I B C World Markets P.L.C., Cotton Centre, Cotton Lane, London, SE1 2QL Tel: (020) 7234 7100 Fax: (020) 7407 4127 E-mail: firstname.surname@cibc.co.uk

Calyon, Broadwalk House, 5 Appold Street, London, EC2A 2DA Tel: (020) 7214 5000 Fax: (020) 7588 0290

Carr Sheppards Crosthwaite, 25 Imperial Square, Cheltenham, Gloucestershire, GL50 1QZ Tel: (01242) 514756 Fax: (01242) 533000

Carr Sheppards Crosthwaite Ltd, 2 Gresham Street, London, EC2V 7QN Tel: (020) 7597 1234 Fax: (020) 7597 1000 E-mail: clientservices@carr-sheppards.co.uk

Charles Stanley & Co. Ltd, 25 Luke Street, London, EC2A 4AR Tel: (020) 7739 8200 Fax: (020) 7739 7798 E-mail: finance@charles-stanley.co.uk

Cunningham Coates Ltd, 19 Donegall Street, Belfast, BT1 2HA Tel: (028) 9032 3456 Fax: (028) 9023 1479 E-mail: info@cuncoates.com

D A B Carnegie, 2nd Floor 24 Chiswell Street, London, EC1Y 4UE Tel: (020) 7216 4000 Fax: (020) 7417 9424

Dolphin Bell Securities, PO Box 288, Guernsey, GY1 3RN Tel: (01481) 736682 Fax: (01481) 729910 E-mail: chris.brock@brewin.co.uk

Fox-Pitt Kelton Ltd, 25 Copthall Avenue, London, EC2R 7BP Tel: (020) 7933 4000

Gerrard, Temple Court, 35 Bull Street, Birmingham, B4 6ES Tel: 0121-200 2244 Fax: 0121-683 7300

J M Finn Nominees Ltd, Salisbury House, London Wall, London, EC2M 5TA Tel: (020) 7628 9688 Fax: (020) 7628 7314

J P Morgan Financial Investments Ltd, 60 Victoria Embkmt, London, EC4Y 0JP Tel: (020) 7600 2300

Kleinwort Benson Gilts Ltd, 20 Fenchurch St, London, EC3M 3BY Tel: (020) 7623 8000 Fax: (020) 7623 4069

MeesPierson Securities (UK) Ltd, 23 Camomile St, London, EC3A 7PP Tel: (020) 7444 8000 Fax: (020) 7444 8888

Mizuho International plc, Bracken House, 1 Friday Street, London, EC4M 9JA Tel: (020) 7236 1090

Morgan Stanley Bank International Ltd, 25 Cabot Square, Canary Wharf, London, E14 4QA Tel: (020) 7425 8000 Fax: (020) 7425 8990 E-mail: info@morganstanley.com

NatWest Stockbrokers Ltd, 55 Mansell Street, London, E1 8AN Tel: (0870) 6004080 Fax: (0870) 1288324

Paul E Schweder Miller, 46-50 Tabernacle Street, London, EC2A 4SJ Tel: (020) 7490 5000 Fax: (020) 7250 0802

Prebon Marshall Yamane Ltd, 155 Bishopsgate, London, EC2N 3DA Tel: (020) 7200 7000 Fax: (020) 7200 7177

Prudential-Bache International Ltd, 1-3 Strand, Trafalgar Sq, London, WC2N 5HE Tel: (020) 7439 4191 Fax: (020) 7437 9110

R B C Captial Markets, 71 Queen Victoria Street, London, EC4V 4AY Tel: (020) 7489 1133 Fax: (020) 7248 3940

Rathbone Neilson Cobbold Ltd, Port of Liverpool Building, Pier Head, Liverpool, L3 1NW Tel: 0151-236 9224 Fax: 0151-243 7001 E-mail: marketing@rathbones.com

Rowan Dartington Ltd, Colston Tower, Colston Street, Bristol, BS1 4RD Tel: 0117-933 0000 Fax: 0117-933 0009

Smith & Williamson Investment Management, 25 Moorgate, London, EC2R 6AY Tel: (020) 7776 8700 Fax: (020) 7131 4001 E-mail: info@smith.williamson.co.uk

W H Ireland Ltd, 11 St James's Square, Manchester, M2 6WH Tel: 0161-832 2174 Fax: 0161-833 0935 E-mail: laurie.beavers@wh-ireland.co.uk

Walker Crips Groups plc, Finsbury Tower, 103-105 Bunhill Row, London, EC1Y 8LZ Tel: (020) 7253 7502 Fax: (020) 7253 7500 E-mail: client.services@wbwcservices.co.uk

Williams De Broe plc, PO Box 515, London, EC2N 2HD Tel: (020) 7588 7511 Fax: (020) 7588 1702

Wise Speke, Commercial Union House, 39 Pilgrim Street, Newcastle upon Tyne, NE1 6RQ Tel: 0191-279 7300 Fax: 0191-279 7301 E-mail: gavin.martin@wise-speke.co.uk

BRONZE

Skymetals Non Ferrous Metals, Unit 3 Trillennium Highway Point, Gorsey Lane, Coleshill, Birmingham, B46 1JU Tel: (01675) 430140 Fax: (01675) 430346 E-mail: birmingham@allmetal.co.uk

Spectrum Alloys Ltd, Milton Road, Stoke-on-Trent, ST1 6LE Tel: (01782) 532800 Fax: (01782) 532809 E-mail: info@spectrumalloys.co.uk

BRONZE BEARINGS

Dyn Metal Ltd, 25-29 Chase Road, London, NW10 6TA Tel: (020) 8961 0656 Fax: (020) 8961 8820 E-mail: info@dynmetal.co.uk

BRONZE BUSHES

A W Precision Ltd, Cosford Lane, Rugby, Warwickshire, CV21 1QN Tel: (01788) 542271 Fax: (01788) 561256 E-mail: sales@awp-ltd.com

Sankyo Oilless Industry (U K) Ltd, Huffwood Trading Estate, Billingshurst, West Sussex, RH14 9UR Tel: (01403) 785378 Fax: (01403) 784634 E-mail: sales@sankyo-oilless.co.uk

BRONZE CASTINGS

Art Bronze Foundry Ltd, 1 Michael Road, London, SW6 2ER Tel: (020) 7736 7292 Fax: (020) 7731 5460 E-mail: service@artbronze.co.uk

Crowncast Ltd, Rushenden Road, Queenborough, Kent, ME11 5HD Tel: (01795) 662722 Fax: (01795) 666552 E-mail: crowncast@whsmithnet.co.uk

Dyn Metal Ltd, 25-29 Chase Road, London, NW10 6TA Tel: (020) 8961 0656 Fax: (020) 8961 8820 E-mail: info@dynmetal.co.uk

Lunt's Castings Ltd, Hawthorns Industrial Estate, Middlemore Road, Handsworth, Birmingham, B21 0BJ Tel: 0121-551 4301 Fax: 0121-523 7954 E-mail: info@luntscastings.co.uk

Morris Singer Ltd, Unit 10 Highfield Industrial Estate, Church Lane, Lasham, Alton, Hampshire, GU34 5SQ Tel: (01256) 381033 Fax: (01256) 381565 E-mail: info@morrissinger.co.uk

Star Metal Polishing Ltd, Hilton Trading Estate, Birmingham New Road, Wolverhampton, WV4 6BW Tel: (01902) 408455

Surecoat Powder Coatings, Unit 13 Bolton Textile Mill, Cawdor Street, Farnworth, Bolton, BL4 7EA Tel: (01204) 793339 Fax: (01204) 793339

Thurton Foundries Ltd, Loddon Rd, Thurton, Norwich, NR14 6AN Tel: (01508) 480301 Fax: (01508) 480303 E-mail: sales@thurtonfoundries.co.uk

Truscanian Ltd, St. Martins Industrial Estate, Engine Street, Oldbury, West Midlands, B69 4NL Tel: 0121-552 3011 Fax: 0121-552 4672

W Lane Ltd, Forty Foot Road, Middlesbrough, Cleveland, TS2 1HG Tel: (01642) 242871 Fax: (01642) 242046 E-mail: w.lane@parson-crossland.co.uk

White Eagle Foundry Ltd, 199 Cuckfield Road, Hurstpierpoint, Hassocks, West Sussex, BN6 9RT Tel: (01273) 832062 Fax: (01273) 833628 E-mail: wef@wef.co.uk

BRONZE FINISHING ABRASIVE MATERIALS

▶ Butterfly Bronze, 2 Bons Farm Cottages, Stapleford Road, Stapleford Tawney, Romford, RM4 1RP Tel: (020) 8500 3037 Fax: (01708) 687 488 E-mail: links@butterflybronze.com

BRONZE NAMEPLATES

Ellis Rees & Co., The Old Foundry, Grove Road, Northfleet, Gravesend, Kent, DA11 9AX Tel: (01474) 567861 Fax: (01474) 537056

Signet Signs Ltd, 45 West Town Road, Backwell, Bristol, BS48 3HG Tel: (01275) 463601 Fax: (01275) 462990 E-mail: mail@signetsigns.co.uk

BRONZE PLATING SERVICES

Bodycote Metallurgical Coatings Ltd, Harrison Way, Brunswick Business Park, Liverpool, L3 4BG Tel: 0151-709 8411 Fax: 0151-709 2622 E-mail: info@aerogistics.com

R. Wilson & Co. (Platers) Ltd, Zachrome Works, Sheffield Road, Whittington Moor, Chesterfield, Derbyshire, S41 8NH Tel: (01246) 450387 Fax: (01246) 455875 E-mail: office@zachrome.com

BRONZE POWDER

Ronald Britton & Co., Lower Eccleshill Road, Darwen, Lancashire, BB3 0RP Tel: (01254) 874750 Fax: (01254) 873009 E-mail: lara.thornhill@r-britton.com

Debdale Metal Powders Ltd, Waterhouse Road, Manchester, M18 7HZ Tel: 0161-231 1504 Fax: 0161-223 2763 E-mail: info@debdale.com

James Laird Gold Leaf Ltd, 18 Craig Road, Glasgow, G44 3DR Tel: 0141-637 8288 Fax: 0141-637 8288 E-mail: goldleaf@jameslaird.com

Services Supply Co., 26 Penybont Road, Pencoed, Bridgend, Mid Glamorgan, CF35 5RA Tel: (01656) 860344 Fax: (01656) 862555 E-mail: sales@goldleafsupplies.com

Wolstenholme Bidco Ltd, Springfield House, Lower Eccleshill Road, Darwen, Lancashire, BB3 0RP Tel: (01254) 873888 Fax: (01254) 703430 E-mail: sales@wolstenholme-int.com

BRONZE PREMIXES

Makin Metal Powers Ltd, Buckley Road, Rochdale, Lancashire, OL12 9DT Tel: (01706) 717317 Fax: (01706) 717303 E-mail: mmp@makin-metals.com

BROWN RICE

Eden Valley Wholefoods, 34 The Market, Scotch Street, Carlisle, CA3 8QX Tel: (01228) 546853

BRUSH (COSMETIC/MAKE-UP APPLICATION) IMPORT MERCHANTS OR AGENTS

S & M Products Ltd, Compstall Mills Estate, Andrew Street, Compstall, Stockport, Cheshire, SK6 5HN Tel: 0161-427 3864 Fax: 0161-426 0019 E-mail: info@brushclosures.com

BRUSH DESIGNERS OR CONSULTANTS

Accrington Brush Co. Ltd, Lower Grange Mill, Church Street, Accrington, Lancashire, BB5 2ES Tel: (01254) 871414 Fax: (01254) 872064 E-mail: info@a-brush.co.uk

Dawson & Son Ltd, Clayton Wood Rise, West Park Ring Road, Leeds, LS16 6RH Tel: 0113-275 9321 Fax: 0113-275 2761 E-mail: sales@dawsonbrush.co.uk

South Wales Brush Co Ltd, 1 Ely Distribution Centre, Argyle Way, Cardiff, CF5 5NJ Tel: (029) 2059 9199 Fax: (029) 2059 9299 E-mail: sales@brush.co.uk

▶ Sovereign Brush Co Ltd, 29-43 Sydney Road, Watford, WD18 7PZ Tel: (01923) 227301 Fax: (01923) 817121 E-mail: sales@sovereignbrush.com

BRUSH DESIGNERS OR CONSULTANTS – *continued*

Weston, Shipley & Weston Ltd, Premier Works, Samson Road, Hermitage Industrial Estate, Coalville, Leicestershire, LE67 3FP Tel: (01530) 814062 Fax: (01530) 814064 E-mail: eberryson@aol.com

Whitaker & Sawyer Ltd, Unit 17 Midas Business Centre, Wantz Road, Dagenham, Essex, RM10 8PS Tel: (020) 8593 7204 Fax: (020) 8595 7353 E-mail: info@wsbrushes.co.uk

BRUSH FILLINGS

Speciality Filaments Ltd, St. Helen Industrial Estate, Bishop Auckland, County Durham, DL14 9AD Tel: (01388) 661818 Fax: (01388) 450733

BRUSH PRODUCTION MACHINERY

Edward Jackson Ltd, Red Hall, Red Hall Lane, Southburgh, Thetford, Norfolk, IP25 7TG Tel: (01362) 820145 Fax: (01362) 820192 E-mail: info@edwardjacksonltd.com

BRUSH STRIPS

Dawson & Son Ltd, Clayton Wood Rise, West Park Ring Road, Leeds, LS16 6RH Tel: 0113-275 9321 Fax: 0113-275 2761 E-mail: sales@dawsonbrush.co.uk

Formseal South Ltd, 23 Snowdrop Close, Narborough, Leicester, LE19 3YB Tel: 0116-275 0052 Fax: 0116-286 5808 E-mail: sales@brushstrip.co.uk

Chris Naylor (SOMA) Ltd, The Bungalow, 6 West Shevin Road, Merston, Ilkley, West Yorkshire, LS29 6BG Tel: (01943) 876513 Fax: (01943) 878814 E-mail: chrisnaylor@chrisnaylorsoma.demon.co.uk

Osborn International Ltd, Dendix House, Lower Church Street, Chepstow, Gwent, NP16 5XT Tel: (01291) 634000 Fax: (01291) 634098 E-mail: uksales@osborn.co.uk

South Wales Brush Co Ltd, 1 Ely Distribution Centre, Argyle Way, Cardiff, CF5 5NJ Tel: (029) 2059 9199 Fax: (029) 2059 9299 E-mail: sales@brush.co.uk

BRUSHES

Edward W Mason Ltd, 14 Brownfields, Welwyn Garden City, Hertfordshire, AL7 1AN Tel: (01707) 331911 Fax: (01707) 331911 E-mail: craig@masonsbrushes.fsbusiness.co.uk

Munitech Ltd, Hoo Marina Industrial Estate, Vicarage Lane, Hoo, Rochester, Kent, ME3 9LB Tel: (01634) 250771 Fax: (01634) 250388 E-mail: info@munitech.co.uk

Osborn International Ltd, Dendix House, Lower Church Street, Chepstow, Gwent, NP16 5XT Tel: (01291) 634000 Fax: (01291) 634098 E-mail: uksales@osborn.co.uk

▶ R S D Supplies & Services Ltd, 2 Norton Centre, Poynernook Road, Aberdeen, AB11 5RW Tel: (01224) 213213

Rodo Ltd, Lumb Lane, Droylsden, Manchester, M43 7BU Tel: 0161-371 6400 Fax: 0161-371 6401 E-mail: sales@rodo.co.uk

Whitaker & Sawyer Ltd, Unit 17 Midas Business Centre, Wantz Road, Dagenham, Essex, RM10 8PS Tel: (020) 8593 7204 Fax: (020) 8595 7353 E-mail: info@wsbrushes.co.uk

BRUSHES TO SPECIFICATION

Accrington Brush Co. Ltd, Lower Grange Mill, Church Street, Accrington, Lancashire, BB5 2ES Tel: (01254) 871414 Fax: (01254) 872064 E-mail: info@a-brush.co.uk

BRUSHES, ARTISTS'

Colart Fine Art & Graphics Ltd, Whitefriars Avenue, Harrow, Middlesex, HA3 5RH Tel: (020) 8427 4343 Fax: (020) 8863 7177 E-mail: initial.surname@colart.co.uk

BRUSHES, BOILER/TUBE CLEANING

Farrar James Brushes Ltd, 103 Northgate, Halifax, West Yorkshire, HX1 1XF Tel: (01422) 361072 Fax: (01422) 361072 E-mail: philip.reid5@btinternet.com

BRUSHES, COSMETIC/MAKE-UP APPLICATION

Caressa Kahn, Wellfield Road, Hatfield, Hertfordshire, AL10 0BS Tel: (01707) 262287 Fax: (01707) 263297 E-mail: mail@i-kahn.co.uk

Gresco Brush Ltd, 16 Liberty Close, Woolsbridge Industrial Estate, Three Legged Cross, Wimborne, Dorset, BH21 6SY Tel: (01202) 826600 Fax: (01202) 826600 E-mail: paul@gresco.freeserve.co.uk

▶ Makeupworld, 5 Maes Street, St. Thomas, Swansea, SA1 8ES Tel: (07851) 734820 E-mail: customerservice@makeupworld.co.uk

▶ Professional Bridal Make-up, 29 Burnell Gate, Beaulieu Park, Chelmsford, CM1 6ED Tel: 01245 462200 E-mail: info@professionalbridalmakeup.co.uk

▶ The Virgin Cosmetics Company, 55 Drovers Way, Bradford, West Yorkshire, BD2 1JZ Tel: 01274 306430 E-mail: nicola@ashton2602.f2s.com

BRUSHES, GLASS FIBRE OR FIBREGLASS, HAND, PRECISION

▶ Koga, 323 Filton Avenue, Horfield, Bristol, BS7 0BB Tel: (0789) 1284705 E-mail: zinapromotion@o2.pl

BRUSHES, HYGIENE/FOOD INDUSTRY

Addis, Zone 3 Waterton Point, Brocastle Avenue, Waterton Industrial Estate, Bridgend, Mid Glamorgan, CF31 3US Tel: (01656) 664455 Fax: (01656) 664456 E-mail: e.marketing@addis.co.uk

R Russell, 45 Townsend Road, Chesham, Buckinghamshire, HP5 2AA Tel: (01494) 782837 Fax: (01494) 791598 E-mail: info@r-russellbrush.co.uk

W T Clark & Co (Brushes) Ltd, P O Box 2, Birmingham, B46 1HX Tel: (01675) 463085 Fax: (01675) 467455

BRUSHLESS DIRECT CURRENT (DC) ELECTRIC MOTOR DRIVES

Motech Control Ltd, Unit 14, Lloyds Court, Manor Royal, Crawley, West Sussex, RH10 9QX Tel: (01293) 440710 Fax: (01293) 440711 E-mail: sales@motech.co.uk

BRUSHWOOD OR UNDERGROWTH BRUSH CUTTERS

▶ Cambs Trading High Road Elm, Holly Cottage, Low Road, Wisbech, Cambridgeshire, PE14 0DD Tel: (01945) 474540 Fax: (01945) 474540 E-mail: admin@cambstrading.co.uk

Cullum Plant Hire & Sales Ltd, 11 Boleness Road, Wisbech, Cambridgeshire, PE13 2RB Tel: (01945) 463356 Fax: (01945) 463248 E-mail: cullumsales@btinternet.com

Davies Implements Ltd, Blaenteg, Llwynderi, Trevaughan, Carmarthen, Dyfed, SA31 3QN Tel: (01267) 237726 Fax: (01267) 238696 E-mail: davies@implements.preserve.co.uk

F & M Garden Machinery Ltd, The White House, Bentley Heath, Barnet, Hertfordshire, EN5 4RY Tel: (020) 8440 6165 Fax: (020) 8447 0670 E-mail: sales@fmgardenmachinery.com

Honda UK Ltd, 470 London Road, Slough, SL3 8QY Tel: (01753) 590500 Fax: (01753) 590000

Kawasaki Motors UK, 1 Dukes Meadow, Millboard Road, Bourne End, Buckinghamshire, SL8 5XF Tel: (01628) 856750 Fax: (01628) 856796 E-mail: customerservice@kawasaki.co.uk

Leigh Park Garden Machinery Ltd, Dunkirk Farm Estate, Frome Road, Southwick, Trowbridge, Wiltshire, BA14 9NJ Tel: (01225) 774202 Fax: (01225) 774303 E-mail: Enquiries@LeighParkGardenMachinery.co.uk

Makita UK Ltd, Vermont Place, Michigan Drive, Tongwell, Milton Keynes, MK15 8JD Tel: (01908) 211678 Fax: (01908) 211400 E-mail: info@makitauk.com

Andreas Stihl Ltd, Stihl House, Stanhope Road, Camberley, Surrey, GU15 3YT Tel: (01276) 20202 Fax: (01276) 670510 E-mail: postmaster@stihl.co.uk

BS 9000 SPECIFICATION CONNECTORS

Hub Electronics Ltd, Unit 1 Foundry Court, Foundry Lane, Horsham, West Sussex, RH13 5PY Tel: (01403) 255225 Fax: (01403) 263154 E-mail: tina@hubelectronics.co.uk

Hypertac Ltd, 36-38 Waterloo Road, London, NW2 7UH Tel: (020) 8450 8033 Fax: (020) 8208 4114 E-mail: info@hypertac.co.uk

I Q C International Ltd, PO Box 1024, Arundel, West Sussex, BN18 0LT Tel: (0870) 0130999 Fax: (0870) 0130888 E-mail: sales@iqc.co.uk

Itt Industries Ltd, Viables Industrial Estate, Jays Close, Basingstoke, Hampshire, RG22 4BA Tel: (01256) 311800 Fax: (01256) 811814

Lane Electronics, Slinfold Lodge, Stane Street, Slinfold, Horsham, West Sussex, RH13 0RN Tel: (01403) 790661 Fax: (01403) 790849 E-mail: sales@wealdelectronics.com

BUBBLE CAPS

J L Float Ltd, Westgate, Aldridge, Walsall, WS9 8UF Tel: (01922) 455677 Fax: (01922) 743193 E-mail: info@jlfloat.com

BUBBLE FILM

Adams Packaging Ltd, Timberlaine Estate, Quarry Lane, Chichester, West Sussex, PO19 8PP Tel: (01243) 783474 Fax: (01243) 815960 E-mail: adams-adams@cwcom.net

Allport Overland, Allport House, Thurrock Park Way, Tilbury, Essex, RM18 7HZ Tel: (01375) 487800 Fax: (01375) 487890 E-mail: info@allport.co.uk

Captain Packaging Ltd, 5 Clarence Wharf, Mumby Road, Gosport, Hampshire, PO12 1AJ Tel: (023) 9251 1125 Fax: (023) 9252 5844 E-mail: sales@captain.co.uk

Euro Supply & Trading Co., Canal Side, 3 Tattenhall Road, Tattenhall, Chester, CH3 9BD Tel: (01829) 771500 Fax: (01829) 771505

Nicholl Packaging Ltd, 4 Thackley Court, Thackley Old Road, Shipley, West Yorkshire, BD18 1BW Tel: (01274) 580563 Fax: (01274) 531675 E-mail: info@nichollpackaging.co.uk

Packaging Co., 195 Scudamore Road, Leicester, LE3 1UQ Tel: 0116-231 3444 Fax: 0116-231 3344 E-mail: sales@thepackagingcompany.co.uk

BUBBLE FILM AND FOAM CONVERTERS

The Bubble Factory Ltd, Grove Road, Preston, Canterbury, Kent, CT3 1EF Tel: (01227) 722228 Fax: (01227) 722399 E-mail: thebubble.factory@yahoo.co.uk

Locpac Suppliers, 2 Queensway Business Centre, Waterloo Road, Widnes, Cheshire, WA8 0FD Tel: 0151-423 2828 Fax: 0151-495 2630 E-mail: enquiries@locpac.co.uk

Marland Paper & Plastics Ltd, Whiteleather Square, Billingborough, Sleaford, Lincolnshire, NG34 0QP Tel: (01529) 240637 Fax: (01529) 240638 E-mail: sales@marland.co.uk

BUCHHOLZ RELAYS

P & B Weir, Unit 10 Leafield Industrial Estate, Leafield Way, Corsham, Wiltshire, SN13 9SW Tel: (01225) 811449 Fax: (01225) 810909 E-mail: sales@pbweir.com

BUCKET ELEVATORS

K M G Systems Ltd, Station Road, Gamlingay, Sandy, Bedfordshire, SG19 3HE Tel: (01767) 650760 Fax: (01767) 651622 E-mail: admin@kmgsystems.com

Stalum Engineering Ltd, 3 Darnall Works, Leathley Road, Leeds, LS10 1BG Tel: 0113-242 2289 Fax: 0113-234 7951 E-mail: sales@stalum.co.uk

BUCKETS AND PAILS, *See also headings for particular types*

Involvement Packaging Ltd, Park Road, Stalybridge, Cheshire, SK15 1TA Tel: 0161-338 2807 Fax: 0161-338 2807 E-mail: salesstalybridge@involvementpkg.co.uk

Main Line Products Richards, Attwood Street, Stourbridge, West Midlands, DY9 8SL Tel: (01384) 422661 Fax: (01384) 423163

Taylor Davis Ltd, Moat Road, West Wilts Trading Estate, Westbury, Wiltshire, BA13 4JF Tel: (01373) 864324 Fax: (01373) 858021 E-mail: sales@taylor-davis.co.uk

▶ Tomps Plaster Suppliers, 220 New Road, Sutton Bridge, Spalding, Lincolnshire, PE12 9QE Tel: (01406) 351001 Fax: (01406) 351513 E-mail: sales@tomps.com

BUCKLES, *See also headings for particular types*

A T H Alden Ltd, Sutherland Road, London, E17 6BU Tel: (020) 8531 3358 Fax: (020) 8527 9105 E-mail: simon@aldens.fsbusiness.co.uk

Butonia, 260-264 Kingsland Road, London, E8 4DG Tel: (020) 7249 5141 Fax: (020) 7249 8859 E-mail: bltd@butonia-group.com

Halicombe Trimmings Ltd, 15-16 Margaret Street, London, W1W 8RW Tel: (020) 7580 5423 Fax: (020) 7323 0245 E-mail: halicombe@aol.com

J T Batchelor Ltd, 9-10 Culford Mews, London, N1 4DZ Tel: (020) 7254 2962 Fax: (020) 7254 0357

Schwenk Ltd, 70-71 Wells Street, London, W1T 3HN Tel: (020) 7580 3674 Fax: (020) 7580 2342 E-mail: schwenk.ltd@virgin.net

Velcro Ltd, 1 Aston Way, Middlewich, Cheshire, CW10 0HS Tel: 01606 738806 Fax: 01606 738814 E-mail: uksales@velcro.co.uk

BUCKLES, PLASTIC

Dawk Trimmers, Crown Mill, 1 Crown Street, Salford, M3 7DH Tel: 0161-832 3262 Fax: 0161-834 4704E-mail: fpinetex@aol.com

BUILDERS HAND TOOLS

Ansell Handtools Sheffield Ltd, 72 Catley Road, Sheffield, S9 5JF Tel: 0114-244 8098 Fax: 0114-261 0252 E-mail: enquiries@ansell-handtools.com

Blakes Building Profiles Ltd, Unit 7 Jupiter House, Calleva Park, Reading, RG7 8NN Tel: 0118-981 2872 Fax: 0118-981 2872

Chesterman Marketing Ltd, 3 Kenworthy Road, Stafford, ST16 3DY Tel: (01785) 250341 Fax: (01785) 250345 E-mail: enquiries@chestermanmarketing.com

J.B.G. (Marketing) Ltd, Jay Bee House, 226a Whitehorse Road, Croydon, CR0 2LB Tel: (020) 8683 2610 Fax: (020) 8684 2523 E-mail: enquiries@jbgroves.freeserve.co.uk

BUILDERS' HARDWARE OR FITTINGS OR BRASS FOUNDRY

Avocet Hardware Taiwan Ltd, Brookfoot Mills, Elland Road, Brighouse, West Yorkshire, HD6 2RW Tel: (01484) 711700 Fax: (01484) 720124 E-mail: post@avocet-hardware.co.uk

Croft Architectural Hardware Ltd, 23 Lower Lichfield Street, Willenhall, West Midlands, WV13 1QQ Tel: (01902) 606493 Fax: (01902) 606933 E-mail: sales@croft-arch.co.uk

▶ Eurolink Hardware, 5 Halesowen Industrial Park, Chancel Way, Halesowen, West Midlands, B62 8SE Tel: 0121-501 2800 Fax: 0121-434 6989 E-mail: info@eurolinkhardware.co.uk

Harvey Steel Lintels Ltd, Commerce Way, Colchester, CO2 8HH Tel: (01206) 792001 Fax: (01206) 792022 E-mail: harvey@lintels.co.uk

Jorosa Ltd, 22 The Hive Industrial Estate, Hockley, Factory Road, Birmingham, B18 5JU Tel: 0121-507 1313 Fax: 0121-507 1440 E-mail: sales@jorosa.com

Nicholl & Wood Ltd, Netherton Works, Holmfield, Halifax, West Yorkshire, HX3 6ST Tel: (01422) 244484 Fax: (01422) 248777 E-mail: sales@niwood.co.uk

Paddock Fabrications Ltd, Fryers Road, Walsall, WS2 7LZ Tel: (01922) 470940 Fax: (01922) 476021 E-mail: sales@paddockfabrications.co.uk

S T B Construction, Low Field Farm Buildings, Ainderby Steeple, Northallerton, North Yorkshire, DL7 9SD Tel: 01609 776484 Fax: 01609 776484

Sperrin Metal Products Ltd, Cahore Road, Draperstown, Magherafelt, County Londonderry, BT45 7AP Tel: (028) 7962 8362 Fax: (028) 7962 8972 E-mail: sales@sperrin-metal.com

Till & Whitehead Ltd, Park House, 37 Ings Road, Osmondthorpe Lane, Leeds, LS9 9HG Tel: 0113-249 6641 Fax: 0113-248 8968 E-mail: leeds@tillwite.com

Willenhall Locks Ltd, Stringes Lane, Willenhall, West Midlands, WV13 1LF Tel: (01902) 636041 Fax: (01902) 636733 E-mail: sales@willenhall-locks.co.uk

BUILDERS' IRONMONGERY

▶ Alfred Ramsay, 299 Martindale Road, Hounslow, TW4 7HG Tel: (07951) 477347 Fax: (01932) 770943 E-mail: info@alfredramsay.co.uk

Avon Manufacturing Ltd, Viande House, Kineton Road, Southam, Warwickshire, CV47 0DR Tel: (01926) 817292 Fax: (01926) 814156 E-mail: sale@avonova.co.uk

B P C Building Products Ltd, Flanshaw Way, Wakefield, West Yorkshire, WF2 9LP Tel: (01924) 364794 Fax: (01924) 373846 E-mail: sales@bpcfixings.com

Berriman & Chapman, 41-43 Victoria Road, Scarborough, North Yorkshire, YO11 1SQ Tel: (01723) 360604 Fax: (01723) 378819

C B S (Midlands) Ltd, Kenilworth House, 118 Stourbridge Road, Dudley, West Midlands, DY1 2DP Tel: (01384) 254015 Fax: (01384) 456856

Calder Trade Supplies Ltd, Unit 11-12 Halifax Industrial Centre, Marshway, Halifax, West Yorkshire, HX1 5RW Tel: (01422) 330008 Fax: (01422) 349437 E-mail: sales@caldertrade.co.uk

Campbell & Mabbs Liverpool Ltd, 1 Regent Street, Liverpool, L3 7BN Tel: 0151-236 1555 Fax: 0151-236 1698 E-mail: camabbs@aol.com

Cartwright Hardware, Cartwright House, Springwell Road, Leeds, LS12 1AX Tel: 0113-243 6931 Fax: 0113-242 1716 E-mail: sales@cartwrighthardware.co.uk

Casswells Ltd, 6 High Street, Midsomer Norton, Radstock, BA3 2HR Tel: (01761) 413331 Fax: (01761) 410327

Fred Duncombe Ltd, Progress Drive, Cannock, Staffordshire, WS11 0JE Tel: (01543) 578661 Fax: (01543) 570050 E-mail: sales@fredduncombe.co.uk

BUILDERS' IRONMONGERY – *continued*

Fyfe & Mcgrouther, 218-254 Kennedy Street, Glasgow, G4 0BS Tel: 0141-552 4966 Fax: 0141-552 7917

John George & Sons Ltd, 2-4 Deacon Way, Reading, RG30 6AZ Tel: 0118-941 1234 Fax: 0118-945 1059 E-mail: sales@johngeorge.co.uk

Gibbs & Dandy plc, 462 Bath Road, Slough, SL1 6BQ Tel: (01628) 604343 Fax: (01628) 600744 E-mail: slough@gibbsanddandy.com

Hughes & Holmes, Unit F, Key Industrial Park, Fernside Road, Willenhall, West Midlands, WV13 3YA Tel: (01902) 728888 Fax: (01902) 727111 E-mail: willenhall@lister.co.uk

Ironmongery Direct Ltd, 2-4 Eldon Way Trading Estate, Eldon Way, Hockley, Essex, SS5 4AD Tel: (01702) 562770 Fax: (01702) 562799 E-mail: sales@ironmongerydirect.com

J P Corry N I Ltd, Unit 12a Pennybridge Industrial Estate, Ballymena, County Antrim, BT42 3HB Tel: (028) 2564 2261 Fax: (028) 2564 9175 E-mail: ballymena@jbcorry.co.uk

J T Atkinsons Ltd, Ullswater Road, Penrith, Cumbria, CA11 7EH Tel: (01768) 865561 Fax: (01768) 890111

Jewsons Ltd, Cefndy Road, Rhyl, Denbighshire, LL18 2EU Tel: (01745) 334402 Fax: (01745) 344483

Jorosa Ltd, 22 The Hive Industrial Estate, Hockley, Factory Road, Birmingham, B18 5JU Tel: 0121-507 1313 Fax: 0121-507 1440 E-mail: sales@jorosa.com

Kingdons Holdings Ltd, North Street, South Molton, Devon, EX36 3AP Tel: (01769) 573204 Fax: (01769) 573200 E-mail: sales@kingdons.co.uk

Kirkpatrick Ltd, PO Box 17, Walsall, WS2 9NF Tel: (01922) 620026 Fax: (01922) 722525 E-mail: sales@kirkpatrick.co.uk

Locks & Fittings Ltd, Unit 7-8 Rollingmill Business Park, Rollingmill Street, Walsall, WS2 9EQ Tel: (01922) 623200 Fax: (01922) 721086 E-mail: enquiries@locksandfittings.org.uk

M L Banfield & Sons Ltd, 1-2 Little Western Street, Brighton, BN1 2QH Tel: (01273) 737622 Fax: (01273) 720950 E-mail: philip@banfields.co.uk

Oak Engineering Ltd, Oak Street, Cradley Heath, West Midlands, B64 5JZ Tel: (01384) 569859 Fax: (01384) 410954 E-mail: oakhinges@woden.com

Pagets Builders Merchants Ltd, 94 Broadfield Road, Sheffield, S8 0XL Tel: 0114-292 3000 Fax: 0114-250 9350 E-mail: info@c-paget.co.uk

Phoenix International Ltd, Unit 2 Coronation Business Centre, Hard Ings Road, Keighley, West Yorkshire, BD21 3ND Tel: (01535) 691756 Fax: (01535) 611900

Rabo Merchants Ltd, 267 Bearwood Road, Smethwick, West Midlands, B66 4NA Tel: (01386) 700193 Fax: 0121-429 4993 E-mail: reception@rabo.co.uk

Royde & Tucker Ltd, Unit 15-16 The High Cross Centre, Fountayne Road, London, N15 4QN Tel: (020) 8801 7717 Fax: (020) 8801 5747 E-mail: sales@ratman.co.uk

Simpson Strong-Tie International Inc, Cardinal Point, Winchester Road, Tamworth, Staffordshire, B78 3HG Tel: (01827) 255600 Fax: (01827) 255616 E-mail: swilkes@strongtie.com

Till & Whitehead Ltd, Park House, 37 Ings Road, Osmondthorpe Lane, Leeds, LS9 9HG Tel: 0113-249 6641 Fax: 0113-248 8968 E-mail: leeds@tillwite.com

Till & Whitehead Ltd, Ellesmere Street, Manchester, M15 4JX Tel: 0161-827 3901 Fax: 0161-827 3915E-mail: sales@tillwite.com

Wessex Guild, 26-36 Horton Road, West Drayton, Middlesex, UB7 8JE Tel: (01895) 449595 Fax: (01895) 431665 E-mail: cmf@lineonewest.co.uk

Timothy Wood Ltd, Units 1-2, Bradley Mills Industrial Estate, Huddersfield, HD1 6PQ Tel: (01484) 440000 Fax: (01484) 440011

▶ The Wrington Vale Medical Practice, Ladymead Lane, Churchill, Winscombe, Avon, BS25 5NH Tel: (01934) 852362 E-mail: martin@wringtonvaleconstruction.co.uk

BUILDERS' LINES

▶ Stanton's brick cutting & bonding service, sunny avenue upton, pontefract west yorkshire, pontefract, west yorkshire, WF9 1DJ Tel: 01977 649760 E-mail: stanny2@tiscali.co.uk

BUILDERS' MERCHANTS

A Bertram Edwards Ltd, Old Coleham, Shrewsbury, SY3 7BU Tel: (01743) 357071 Fax: (01743) 357073 E-mail: info@bertram-edwards.co.uk

A E Procter Ltd, 22 Park Road, Feltham, Middlesex, TW13 6PU Tel: (020) 8898 0214 Fax: (020) 8898 4965E-mail: info@bmf.org.uk

A E Spink Ltd, Kelham Street, Doncaster, South Yorkshire, DN1 3RA Tel: (01302) 321514 Fax: (01302) 327543

A J Philpott & Sons Ltd, Fountain Street, Stoke-on-Trent, ST4 2HA Tel: (01782) 848603 Fax: (01782) 410726 E-mail: ajphilpott@email.com

A K Williams & Sons Ltd, Queen Street, Madeley, Telford, Shropshire, TF7 4BH Tel: (01952) 585740 Fax: (01952) 582021

A Warren & Sons Ltd, Stamford Works, Constantine Street, Oldham, OL4 3AD Tel: 0161-624 4621 Fax: 0161-627 5163 E-mail: warrens@zen.co.uk

Abbey Rose Buildbase, Blackpool Road, Peckham, London, SE15 3SU Tel: (020) 7639 0138 Fax: (020) 7732 5150 E-mail: peckham@buildbase.co.uk

Aerocrete Ltd, 1001 Shore Road, Belfast, BT36 7DE Tel: (028) 9078 2755 Fax: (028) 9078 2766 E-mail: info@jpcorry.co.uk

Ainscough Building Supplies Ltd, Mossy Lea Road, Wrightington, Wigan, Lancashire, WN6 9RS Tel: (01257) 421000 Fax: (01257) 426848 E-mail: ainscoughbuildingsupplies@hotmail.com

Aizlewoods Buildbase, Hermitage Mill, Hermitage Lane, Mansfield, Nottinghamshire, NG18 5HA Tel: (01623) 420121 Fax: (01623) 420384 E-mail: mansfield@buildbase.co.uk

Akehurst & Sons Ltd, 4 Railway Street, Gillingham, Kent, ME7 1YF Tel: (01634) 851526 Fax: (01634) 580996

Alco Builders World, Midhill Road, Sheffield, S2 3GW Tel: 0114-255 0021 Fax: 0114-255 6681 E-mail: email-sales@sheffield.timberworld.co.uk

Alex Morton, 43 Killysorrell Road, Dromore, County Down, BT25 1LB Tel: (028) 9269 3651 Fax: (028) 9269 3951 E-mail: amorton@domora43.fsnet.co.uk

Allmat East Surrey Ltd, The Kenley Waterworks, Godstone Road, Kenley, Surrey, CR8 5AE Tel: (020) 8668 6666 Fax: (020) 8763 2110 E-mail: info@allmat.co.uk

Andrews Of Wanstead, 10 Woodbine Place, London, E11 2RH Tel: (020) 8989 0377

Anglia Building Suppliers Ltd, Waltham Road, Boreham, Chelmsford, CM3 3AY Tel: (01245) 467505 Fax: (01245) 467506 E-mail: angliabs@btinternet.com

Antrim Builders Centre, Springfarm Industrial Estate, Antrim, BT41 4NT Tel: (028) 9446 5921 Fax: (028) 9446 1844 E-mail: collin.robinson@mcnoughton-blair.com

Ashmead Building Supplies Ltd, Portview Road, Avonmouth, Bristol, BS11 9LD Tel: 0117-982 8281 Fax: 0117-982 0135 E-mail: avon@ashmead.co.uk

▶ Avenue Supplies, 15 The Avenue, London, W13 8JR Tel: (020) 8997 5071 E-mail: sales@avenuesupplies.co.uk

Avery Truman DIY & Garden Centre, 13 The Arcade, Eltham High Street, London, SE9 1BE Tel: (020) 8850 9621 Fax: (020) 8850 9621

Axon Buildbase, Unit 1 McKenzie Industrial Park, Bird Hall Lane, Cheadle Heath, Stockport, Cheshire, SK3 0SB Tel: 0161-428 0314 Fax: 0161-491 0844 E-mail: stockport@buildbase.co.uk

B M B Ltd, 194 Newbold Road, Chesterfield, Derbyshire, S41 7AF Tel: (01246) 273500 Fax: (01246) 235252 E-mail: chesterfield@buildbase.co.uk

B S S Group plc, Fleet House, Lee Circle, Leicester, LE1 3QQ Tel: 0116-262 3232 Fax: 0116-253 1343 E-mail: sales@bssuk.co.uk

C.T. Baker Ltd, 133 High Street, Stalham, Norwich, NR12 9BB Tel: (01692) 580210 Fax: (01692) 581412

▶ Bakers & Larners Of Holt, 10 Market Place, Holt, Norfolk, NR25 6BW Tel: (01263) 712323 Fax: (01263) 712720 E-mail: sales@bakersandlarners.com

Bakers Of North Walsham, Midland Road, North Walsham, Norfolk, NR28 9JR Tel: (01692) 403718 Fax: (01692) 500545

Bathstore.com Ltd, Unit 2a Felnex Trading Estate, Wallington, Surrey, SM6 7EL Tel: (01923) 694740 Fax: (020) 8773 5004 E-mail: enquiries@bathstore.com

▶ Baudains Trade Supplies Ltd, Les Amballes, St. Peter Port, Guernsey, GY1 1WT Tel: (01481) 724642 Fax: (01481) 714399 E-mail: peter@btsgsy.com

Bearwood Builders Supply Co Smethwick Ltd, Three Shires Oak Road, Smethwick, West Midlands, B67 5BS Tel: 0121-429 2011 Fax: 0121-429 2226

Bell & Sime, Balunie Drive, Balunie Field Trading Estate, Dundee, DD4 8XE Tel: (01382) 730630 Fax: (01382) 739639 E-mail: dundee@buildbase.co.uk

Robert Bernard & Son Ltd, 26 Oxton Road, Birkenhead, Merseyside, CH41 2QJ Tel: 0151-652 3136 Fax: 0151-652 7552 E-mail: sales@bernards.co.uk

Best Building Supplies, 12-16 Platt Fold Street, Leigh, Lancashire, WN7 1JH Tel: (01942) 673876 Fax: (01942) 608038

Blandford Forum Timber Ltd, Holland Way, Blandford Forum, Dorset, DT11 7SX Tel: (01258) 452692 Fax: (01258) 459589 E-mail: talkwood@talk21.com

BMB Builderbase, Wakefield Road, Barnsley, South Yorkshire, S71 1NH Tel: (01226) 730400 Fax: (01226) 730600 E-mail: barnsley@buildbase.co.uk

Bolt Ltd, Bluebridge Industrial Estate, Colchester Road, Halstead, Essex, CO9 2EX Tel: (01787) 477261 Fax: (01787) 475680 E-mail: enquiries@boltbuildingsupplies.co.uk

Bond & White Buildbase, 40 Muswell Hill Road, Highgate, London, N6 5UN Tel: (020) 8883 9722 Fax: (020) 8444 5146 E-mail: highgate@buildbase.co.uk

Boys & Boden Ltd, Mill Lane, Welshpool, Powys, SY21 7BL Tel: (01938) 556677 Fax: (01938) 555773

Bradford & Sons Ltd, 98 Hendford Hill, Yeovil, Somerset, BA20 2QR Tel: (01935) 845245 Fax: (01935) 845242 E-mail: bradfords@bradfords.co.uk

Bradfords Building Supplies Ltd, 139 Bristol Road, Bridgwater, Somerset, TA6 4AQ Tel: (01278) 422654 Fax: (01278) 450574 E-mail: bbs.bridgwater@bradford.co.uk

Bradfords Underwood, Tolladine Road, Worcester, WR4 9EG Tel: (01935) 845245 Fax: (01905) 723743

Braintree Build Base, Manor Street, Braintree, Essex, CM7 3HS Tel: (01376) 322944 Fax: (01376) 550046 E-mail: briantree@buildbase.co.uk

T. Brewer & Co. Ltd, 110 Dunmow Road, Bishop's Stortford, Hertfordshire, CM23 5HN Tel: (01279) 658338 Fax: (01279) 757023 E-mail: stortford@tbrewer.co.uk

Brookers Builders Merchants Ltd, 43-53 Norman Road, St. Leonards-on-Sea, East Sussex, TN38 0EQ Tel: (01424) 423107 Fax: (01424) 718341

Brown & Kirby Ltd, Sidwell Street, Leicester, LE5 4GQ Tel: 0116-273 4613 Fax: 0116-273 3844 E-mail: brown.kirby@talk21.com

Build Center, Cambrian Works, Station Approach, Wrexham, Clwyd, LL11 2NY Tel: (01978) 354444 Fax: (01978) 351688

Build Centre, 555 South Street, Glasgow, G14 0QT Tel: 0141-954 5051 Fax: 0141-954 7322

Buildbase, Simpson Road, Bletchley, Milton Keynes, MK1 1BB Tel: (01908) 644222 Fax: (01908) 270243

Buildbase, Crinoline Commercial Area, Rawmarsh Road, Rotherham, South Yorkshire, S60 1SA Tel: (01709) 365686 Fax: (01709) 362365

Builder Center Ltd, Windsor Road, Bedford, MK42 9SU Tel: (01234) 272292 Fax: (01234) 365395 E-mail: peter.abbott@wolseley.co.uk

Builder Center Ltd, Dunmere Road, Bodmin, Cornwall, PL31 2QN Tel: (01208) 78211 Fax: (01208) 72934

Builder Center Ltd, Martin Street, Burnley, Lancashire, BB10 1SH Tel: (01282) 421811 Fax: (01282) 831723 E-mail: admin@buildercenter.co.uk

Builder Center Ltd, New Station Road, Dalbeattie, Kirkcudbrightshire, DG5 4AP Tel: (01556) 610208 Fax: (01556) 611514

Builder Center Ltd, Finmere Road, Eastbourne, East Sussex, BN22 8QJ Tel: (01323) 725121 Fax: (01323) 738879

Builder Center Ltd, 29 Wellside Place, Falkirk, FK1 5RL Tel: (01324) 632634 Fax: (01324) 670900

Builder Center Ltd, Conway Street, Hove, East Sussex, BN3 3LA Tel: (01273) 778778 Fax: (01273) 722413

Builder Center Ltd, 80 Low Hill, Liverpool, L6 1BT Tel: 0151-263 5544 Fax: 0151-263 1432

Builder Center, 1 Knowsley Street, Cheetham Hill Road, Manchester, M8 8QL Tel: 0161-834 9437 Fax: 0161-833 2706 E-mail: wolseley@center.co.uk

Builder Center Ltd, Cradle Hill Industrial Estate, Alfriston Road, Seaford, East Sussex, BN25 2AT Tel: (01323) 893243 Fax: (01323) 891072

Builder Center Ltd, 591 Sedlescombe Road North, St. Leonards-on-Sea, East Sussex, TN37 7PY Tel: (01424) 756946 Fax: (01424) 751481

Builder Centre, Clay Flatts Industrial Estate, Workington, Cumbria, CA14 2DB Tel: (01900) 62231 Fax: (01900) 67631

Builders Centre Sheffield Ltd, Nunnery Drive, Sheffield, S2 1TA Tel: 0114-272 4001 Fax: 0114-241 2840 E-mail: info@builderscentre.co.uk

Builders' Supply Co. Ltd, 8 Inglis Green Road, Edinburgh, EH14 2HX Tel: 0131-443 4474 Fax: 0131-455 7297

Builders Supply Co. (Kendal) Ltd, Ann Street, Kendal, Cumbria, LA9 6AA Tel: (01539) 721911 Fax: (01539) 740481 E-mail: info.kendal@builders-supply.co.uk

Builders Supply Co Leabrooks, 33 Greenhill Lane, Leabrooks, Alfreton, Derbyshire, DE55 4AS Tel: (01773) 602727 Fax: (01773) 540324

Builders Supply Stores Coventry Ltd, 45 Spon End, Coventry, CV1 3HG Tel: (024) 7671 2000 Fax: (024) 7671 4072 E-mail: info@bsscov.co.uk

Builders Supply (Wakefield) Ltd, 2 Thornes Lane, Wakefield, West Yorkshire, WF1 5QH Tel: (01924) 376821 Fax: (01924) 362018

Building Supplies (Holme Lane) Ltd, 115 Holme Lane, Sheffield, S6 4JR Tel: 0114-234 2501 Fax: 0114-285 2836

Bunce's Home Hardware, 112-114 Chapel Road, Worthing, West Sussex, BN11 1BX Tel: (01903) 235321 Fax: (01903) 823279 E-mail: enquiries@bunce-co.co.uk

Burnt Oak Builders Merchant Ltd, 41 Barnfield Road, Edgware, Middlesex, HA8 0AY Tel: (020) 8952 1257 Fax: (020) 8952 2538

James Burrell Ltd, Deptford Road, Gateshead, Tyne & Wear, NE8 2BR Tel: 0191-477 2249 Fax: 0191-490 0359 E-mail: jamesburrell@compuserve.com

James Burrell Ltd, Lockheed Close, Preston Farm Industrial Estate, Stockton-on-Tees, Cleveland, TS18 3SE Tel: (01642) 660820 Fax: (01642) 678616 E-mail: jamesburrell@compuserve.com

Burton Bell & Co. Ltd, 3 Kildonan Road, Liverpool, L17 0BU Tel: 0151-727 2231 Fax: 0151-727 2231

Buttle plc, 38-41 Castle Mews, London, NW1 8SY Tel: (020) 7485 8511 Fax: (020) 7482 3480 E-mail: bee@buttle.co.uk

C & A Supplies Ltd, Bidder Street, London, E16 4ST Tel: (020) 7474 0474 Fax: (020) 7474 5055 E-mail: info@cabp.co.uk

C F P Supplies, Unit 6-7 Building, 53b Third Avenue, Pensnett Trading Estate, Kingswinford, West Midlands, DY6 7XG Tel: (01384) 400220 Fax: (01384) 400160

C & S Builders Merchants Stamford Hill Ltd, 278-286 Stamford Hill, London, N16 6TY Tel: (020) 8809 5373 Fax: (020) 8800 3243

C & W Berry Ltd, Golden Hill Lane, Leyland, Leyland, PR25 2YH Tel: (01772) 431216 Fax: (01772) 622314 E-mail: enquiries@cwberry.com

Canvey Supply Co. Ltd, 101 Point Road, Canvey Island, Essex, SS8 7TJ Tel: (01268) 696666 Fax: (01268) 696724 E-mail: canveysupply@btconnect.com

Carver Gases Ltd, Littles Lane, Wolverhampton, WV1 1JY Tel: (01902) 577000 Fax: (01902) 712145 E-mail: mail@carvers.co.uk

Casswells Ltd, 6 High Street, Midsomer Norton, Radstock, BA3 2HR Tel: (01761) 413331 Fax: (01761) 410327

Centriforce Products Ltd, 14/16 Derby Road, Liverpool, L20 8EE Tel: 0151-207 8109 Fax: 0151-298 1319 E-mail: sales@centriforce.co.uk

Chaffey & Son, 10 Hollow Lane, Shinfield, Reading, RG2 9BT Tel: 0118-969 2424

Chandlers Building Supplies Ltd, The Broyle, Ringmer, Lewes, East Sussex, BN8 5NP Tel: (01273) 812721 Fax: (01273) 813958 E-mail: sales@chandlersbs.co.uk

Matthew Charlton Ltd, Station Road, Hexham, Northumberland, NE46 1HB Tel: (01434) 604911 Fax: (01434) 604147

Christies Ltd, Cloyfin Road, Coleraine, County Londonderry, BT52 2RA Tel: (028) 7035 4911 Fax: (028) 7035 1601 E-mail: christiesltd@btinternet.com

City Hardware Electrical Ltd, 6-10 Goswell Road, London, EC1M 7AA Tel: (020) 7253 4095 Fax: (020) 7490 2654 E-mail: sales@cityhardware.co.uk

City Plumbing Supplies Ltd, George Cayley Drive, York, YO30 4XE Tel: (01904) 690088 Fax: (01904) 692990

Noel Clay Buildbase, Gin Close Way, Awsworth, Nottingham, NG16 2TA Tel: 0115-938 2283 Fax: 0115-938 5229 E-mail: nottingham@buildbase.co.uk

Clower & Son Ltd, 48-52 Nottingham Road, Ripley, Derbyshire, DE5 3AT Tel: (01773) 742351 Fax: (01773) 744610

Collier & Catchpole Ltd, 11 London Road, Stanway, Colchester, CO3 0NT Tel: (01206) 715500 Fax: (01206) 715517 E-mail: mail@colliercatchpole.co.uk

Concrete Developments Great Barr Ltd, Baltimore Road, Great Barr, Birmingham, B42 1DD Tel: 0121-356 5575 Fax: 0121-344 3285 E-mail: james@concrete-developers.freeserve.co.uk

Cooper Clarke Civils & Lintels, Bloomfield Road, Farnworth, Bolton, BL4 9LP Tel: (01204) 862222 Fax: (01204) 795296 E-mail: farnworth@civilsandlintels.co.uk

Coopers Great Yarmouth Ltd, New Road, Fritton, Great Yarmouth, Norfolk, NR31 9HR Tel: (01493) 602204 Fax: (01493) 655620 E-mail: enquiries@supercoopers.co.uk

J.P. Corry Ltd, 648 Springfield Road, Belfast, BT12 7EH Tel: (028) 9024 3661 Fax: (028) 9026 2123 E-mail: info@jpcorry.co.uk

County Decorating, 134 Crossbrook Street, Cheshunt, Waltham Cross, Hertfordshire, EN8 8JH Tel: (01992) 628265 Fax: (01992) 628265 E-mail: countydecs_@cheshotmail.com

County Heating Centre Ltd, 6-18 Dunstall Street, Scunthorpe, South Humberside, DN15 6LF Tel: (01724) 844872 Fax: (01724) 871197

Coventry Building Supplies, 172a Holbrook Lane, Coventry, CV6 4BY Tel: (024) 7668 7172 Fax: (024) 7668 8172

David Cover & Son Ltd, Sussex House, Quarry Lane, Chichester, West Sussex, PO19 8PE Tel: (01243) 785141 Fax: (01243) 531151 E-mail: enquiries@covers-group.co.uk

Covers, Unit 1, Home Farm Business Centre Home Farm Road, Brighton, BN1 9HU Tel: (01273) 607044 Fax: (01273) 685208

Cunninghams, 564-566 Kingston Road, London, SW20 8DR Tel: (020) 8946 3352 Fax: (020) 8540 1626

D & M Builders Merchants, 73-81 Heath Road, Twickenham, TW1 4AW Tel: (020) 8892 3813 Fax: (020) 8744 1044

D Sutherland & Son Ltd, Union Street, Wick, Caithness, KW1 5ED Tel: (01955) 602101 Fax: (01955) 602917

David Cover & Son Ltd, Chatfields Yard, Cooksbridge, Lewes, East Sussex, BN8 4TJ Tel: (01273) 476133 Fax: (01273) 400164 E-mail: sales@covers-group.co.uk

Davroc Ltd, Ibroc House, Essex Road, Hoddesdon, Hertfordshire, EN11 0QS Tel: (01992) 441672 Fax: (01992) 708308 E-mail: info@davroc.co.uk

Days Buildbase, Burrfields Road, Portsmouth, PO3 5NA Tel: (023) 9266 2261 Fax: (023) 9266 6497 E-mail: portsmouth@buildbase.co.uk

Deben Buildbase, 15-17 Pickford Lane, Bexleyheath, Kent, DA7 4RD Tel: (020) 8304 3567 Fax: (020) 8298 0201 E-mail: bexleyheath@buildbase.co.uk

BUILDERS' MERCHANTS – *continued*

Deben Buildbase, 10/14 Crossway, Stoke Newington, London, N16 8HX Tel: (020) 7254 1117 Fax: (020) 7249 4535 E-mail: stokenewington@buildbase.co.uk

Derbyshire Building Supplies Ltd, Woodside Farm, Stanton Hill, Ticknall, Derby, DE73 7LA Tel: (01332) 865373 Fax: (01332) 865534 E-mail: sales@derbyshirebuildingsupplies.co.uk

Driffield Hardware Centre, Cranwell Road, Driffield, North Humberside, YO25 6UH Tel: (01377) 241399 Fax: (01377) 241252

E H Smith Builders Merchants Ltd, Leyhill Road, Bovingdon, Hemel Hempstead, Hertfordshire, HP3 0NW Tel: (01442) 833888 Fax: (01442) 834110 E-mail: sales@ehsmith.co.uk

E H Smith Builders Merchants Ltd, Mill Hill, Enderby, Leicester, LE19 4AJ Tel: 0116-275 0999 Fax: 0116-275 0135 E-mail: leicester@ehsmith.co.uk

Easiways Bermondsey Ltd, 138 Burnt Ash Road, Lee, London, SE12 8PU Tel: (020) 8852 2984 Fax: (020) 8852 2985

Eathornes Mica Hardware, 2 Drygate St, Larkhall, Lanarkshire, ML9 2AJ Tel: (01698) 881523 Fax: (01698) 882337

Edward Henthorne & Co Ltd, 10-20 Chorley Road, Blackpool, FY3 7XQ Tel: (01253) 300006 Fax: (01253) 399969 E-mail: edwardhenthorne@aol.com

Edwards Buildbase, 28 Elm Road, Wisbech, Cambridgeshire, PE13 2TB Tel: (01945) 584491 Fax: (01945) 475121 E-mail: wisbeck@billbase.co.uk

Edwards & Farndon, Lower Dartmouth Street, Birmingham, B9 4LG Tel: 0121-766 6255 Fax: 0121-766 8875

Eifionydd Farmers Association Ltd, Station Road, Tywyn, Gwynedd, LL36 9BG Tel: (01654) 710233 Fax: (01654) 712009

Embee Builders Merchants Ltd, 31-45 Mount Pleasant Road, Wallasey, Merseyside, CH45 5LA Tel: 0151-639 6127 Fax: 0151-630 2171 E-mail: sales@embeeltd.co.uk

Evans Bros, 6 High Street, Menai Bridge, Gwynedd, LL59 5ED Tel: (01248) 712388 Fax: (01248) 712388

F B M Group Services Ltd, 349-357 Ilderton Road, London, SE15 1NW Tel: (020) 7639 6991 Fax: (020) 7252 8017

F K Ellis & Sons Ltd, Unit 2 Lower Sydenham Industrial Estate, Kangley Bridge Road, London, SE26 5BA Tel: (020) 8676 9428 Fax: (020) 8676 9429 E-mail: sales@fkellis.com

F W Darby & Co. Ltd, Cannon Lane, Tonbridge, Kent, TN9 1PL Tel: (01732) 350286 Fax: (01732) 357857 E-mail: john.darby3@virgin.co.uk

Farmer Bros, 319 Fulham Road, London, SW10 9QL Tel: (020) 7351 0241 Fax: (020) 7351 4111

Firwood, Collingwood Avenue, Blackpool, FY3 8QH Tel: (01253) 392211 Fax: (01253) 392216

Firwood Timber & Building Supplies, 8 Greengate Lane, Prestwich, Manchester, M25 3HW Tel: 0161-798 8404 Fax: 0161-773 5386 E-mail: firwood@prestwichm25.wanadoo.co.uk

John Fleming & Co. Ltd, Silverburn Place, Bridge Of Don, Aberdeen, AB23 8EG Tel: (01224) 258200 Fax: (01224) 825377 E-mail: aberdeen@buildbase.co.uk

Ford, 2 Alexandria Trading Estate, Alexandria Road, Sidmouth, Devon, EX10 9HA Tel: (01395) 571020 Fax: (01395) 571005

Frank Key Nottingham Ltd, Portland Street, Daybrook, Nottingham, NG5 6BL Tel: 0115-920 8208 Fax: 0115-967 0393 E-mail: sales@frank-key.co.uk

Gibbon & Sons Ltd, Richmond Road, Cardiff, CF24 3XA Tel: (029) 2048 3331 Fax: (029) 2048 3333

Gibbs & Dandy plc, 462 Bath Road, Slough, SL1 6BQ Tel: (01628) 604343 Fax: (01628) 600744 E-mail: slough@gibbsanddandy.com

Graham Plumbing & Heating Merchants, Hillam Road, Bradford, West Yorkshire, BD2 1QN Tel: (01274) 735831 Fax: (01274) 720395

Grant & Stone Ltd, 54 Montem Lane, Slough, SL1 2QJ Tel: (01753) 520462 Fax: (01753) 511582 E-mail: sales@grant-stone.co.uk

Greenford Timber & Builders Merchants, 328 Uxbridge Road, London, W12 7LJ Tel: (020) 8743 6517 Fax: (020) 8743 6517

Thomas Griffiths & Son Ltd, 84 Chorlton Road, Manchester, M15 4AL Tel: 0161-226 1834 Fax: 0161-226 3773

H E Humphries Ltd, Monway House, Portway Road, Wednesbury, West Midlands, WS10 7DZ Tel: 0121-556 0097 Fax: 0121-556 9427

H E Olby & Co. Ltd, 299-313 Lewisham High Street, London, SE13 6NW Tel: (020) 8690 3401 Fax: (020) 8690 1408 E-mail: mail.heolby@virgin.net

H J Chard & Sons, Albert Rd, St Philips, Bristol, BS2 0XS Tel: 0117-977 7681 Fax: 0117-971 9802

H Morrell & Sons Ltd, 173-175 Kensington Lane, London, SE11 4HG Tel: (020) 7735 1681 Fax: (020) 7587 0533

H Skeels Leigh On Sea, 5 London Road, Leigh-on-Sea, Essex, SS9 3JJ Tel: (01702) 476295 Fax: (01702) 471324

Haldane Fisher, Castle Street, Portadown, Craigavon, County Armagh, BT62 1BD Tel: (028) 3833 7321 Fax: (028) 3833 0896 E-mail: sales.portadown@haldane-fisher.com

Haldane & Fisher Ltd, Isle Of Man Business Park, Douglas, Isle Of Man, IM2 2QY Tel: (01624) 624466 Fax: (01624) 661335 E-mail: wigan@enterprize.net

Hale & Co., Nailbridge, Drybrook, Gloucestershire, GL17 9JW Tel: (01594) 545300 Fax: (01594) 545301 E-mail: hale_companie@hotmail.com

Hall & Rogers Ltd, Hillkirk Street, Manchester, M11 3EZ Tel: 0161-273 8800 Fax: 0161-273 7279 E-mail: prigby@hallandrogers.co.uk

Halls Group Ltd, Riverside Road, Gorleston, Great Yarmouth, Norfolk, NR31 6PX Tel: (01493) 663144 Fax: (01493) 440225 E-mail: info@hallsgroup.uk.com

Harris, Charlotte Road, Stirchley, Birmingham, B30 2BT Tel: 0121-451 1664 Fax: 0121-433 3864 E-mail: sales@harrisofstirchley.co.uk

Harris & Bailey Ltd, 50 Hastings Road, Croydon, CR9 6BR Tel: (020) 8654 3181 Fax: (020) 8656 9369 E-mail: mail@harris-bailey.co.uk

Harris Group, 170 Cardigan Road, Leeds, LS6 1LL Tel: 0113-203 3129 Fax: 0113-203 3128 E-mail: pwcharrisaggs@aol.com

Harrison Jewitt Ltd, Flat, The Brickyard, Scotter Road South, Scunthorpe, South Humberside, DN17 2BT Tel: (01724) 281453 Fax: (01724) 281453 E-mail: sales@jewittonline.co.uk

Hawkesford Buildbase, Adderley Road, Market Drayton, Shropshire, TF9 3SW Tel: (01630) 652481 Fax: (01630) 655489 E-mail: marketdrayton@buildbase.co.uk

Hay & Co. Buildbase, Freefield Road, Lerwick, Shetland, ZE1 0NH Tel: (01595) 693057 Fax: (01595) 696037 E-mail: lerwick@buildbase.co.uk

Haywards Tewksbury Ltd, 126 High Street, Tewksbury, Tewkesbury, Gloucestershire, GL20 5JX Tel: (01684) 292282 Fax: (01684) 850634

Heathrow Buildbase, Longford House, Long Lane, Staines, Middlesex, TW19 7AT Tel: (01784) 253221 Fax: (01784) 241728 E-mail: heathrow@buildbase.co.uk

Herbert G Winfield, Winfields Yard, Hartspring Lane, Watford, WD25 8AQ Tel: (01923) 256133 Fax: (01923) 256133

Hill Bros Building Supplies Ltd, Well Lane, Wolverhampton, WV11 1XS Tel: (01902) 731253 Fax: (01902) 306424

Homepride Builders Merchants Ltd, Blackfen Road, Sidcup, Kent, DA15 8PW Tel: (020) 8850 1589 Fax: (020) 8850 4044

Hughes Forrest Ltd, Bolt Street, Newport, Gwent, NP20 2UP Tel: (01633) 250515 Fax: (01633) 843289

▶ Humberstone & Pulford Ltd, 113 Brackenborough Road, Louth, Lincolnshire, LN11 0AG Tel: (01507) 603001 Fax: (01507) 609646 E-mail: info@h-pbuilders.co.uk

Michael Hunter & Sons Ltd, Moorgate, Ormskirk, Lancashire, L39 4RX Tel: (01695) 576911 Fax: (01695) 570489

Hussey & Saunders Builders Merchants, Potkiln Lane, Jordans, Beaconsfield, Buckinghamshire, HP9 2XB Tel: (01494) 874116 Fax: (01494) 874685 E-mail: husseysaunders@aol.com

Interline Southwest Ltd, 18-19 Northfields Industrial Estate, Northfields Lane, Brixham, Devon, TQ5 8UA Tel: (01803) 853401 Fax: (01803) 856630

Iron Stores Jersey Ltd, 10-12 Commercial Buildings, St. Helier, Jersey, JE1 3UD Tel: (01534) 877755 Fax: (01534) 727449

J C Aldridge & Son Ltd, 10 Market Place, Berkeley, Gloucestershire, GL13 9BB Tel: (01453) 810223 Fax: (01453) 511205 E-mail: sales@jcaldridge.co.uk

J & G Archibald, Jagal House, Damson Way, Durham, DH1 2YD Tel: 0191-384 8484 Fax: 0191-386 2432 E-mail: sales@archibald.co.uk

J P Corry, 15 Moyola Road, Castledawson, Magherafelt, County Londonderry, BT45 8BH Tel: (028) 7946 8622 Fax: (028) 7946 8948 E-mail: info@ardstimber.com

J P Corry Lisburn Branch, Lisburn Business Park, 46 Hillsborough Old Road, Lisburn, County Antrim, BT27 5EW Tel: (028) 9266 2047 Fax: (028) 9266 6000 E-mail: lisburn@jpcory.co.uk

J P Corry Ni Ltd, 136-210 Tennent Street, Belfast, BT13 3GF Tel: (028) 9075 1756 Fax: (028) 9035 2807

J T Atkinsons Ltd, Ullswater Road, Penrith, Cumbria, CA11 7EH Tel: (01768) 865561 Fax: (01768) 890111

J T Dove Ltd, Orchard Street, Newcastle upon Tyne, NE1 3NB Tel: 0191-232 6151 Fax: 0191-222 1870 E-mail: newcastle@jtdove.co.uk

Jackson & Allen Ltd, 244 Chingford Mount Road, London, E4 8JP Tel: (020) 8529 7014 Fax: (020) 8520 8040

Jacksons Building Centres Ltd, Newbold Road, Chesterfield, Derbyshire, S41 7PB Tel: (01246) 203201 Fax: (01246) 208985 E-mail: paulbullivant@jacksonbc.co.uk

▶ James Maxwell Building Contractors Ltd, Midbrae, Kirkwynd, Langholm, Dumfriesshire, DG13 0JD Tel: (01387) 381352 E-mail: sales@maxwellthebuilders.co.uk

James Payne, 28-29 Vaughan Street, Llandudno, Gwynedd, LL30 1AB Tel: (01492) 876705 Fax: (01492) 860903 E-mail: jamespaynellandudno@hotmail.com.uk

B. Jenkins & Sons Ltd, Watton Saw Mills, Brecon, Powys, LD3 7EN Tel: (01874) 622853 Fax: (01874) 622750 E-mail: sales.bjenkins@btconnect.com

Jewson Ltd, 4 Beeching Road, Bexhill-on-Sea, East Sussex, TN39 3LG Tel: (01424) 731414 Fax: (01424) 731887

▶ Jewson Ltd, Nuttaberry Works, Bideford, Devon, EX39 4DU Tel: (01237) 473421 Fax: (01237) 474987

Jewson Ltd, Nelson Way, Boston, Lincolnshire, PE21 8UA Tel: (01205) 362451 Fax: (01205) 365898

Jewson Ltd, Merchant House Binley Business Park, Harry Weston Road, Coventry, CV3 2TT Tel: (024) 7643 8400 Fax: (024) 7643 8401

Jewson Ltd, 25 Bakewell Road, Loughborough, Leicestershire, LE11 5QY Tel: (01509) 212121 Fax: (01509) 610218

Jewson Ltd, 10 Mason Road, Norwich, NR6 6RR Tel: (01603) 410411 Fax: (01603) 789031

Jewson Ltd, 3 Lamarsh Road, Oxford, OX2 0HF Tel: (01865) 249821 Fax: (01865) 241831

Jewson Ltd, 89-105 High Street, Rowley Regis, West Midlands, B65 0EH Tel: 0121-559 1207 Fax: 0121-561 2461

Jewson Ltd, Orchard Road, Royston, Hertfordshire, SG8 5HA Tel: (01763) 241561 Fax: (01763) 247759

Jewsons, Unit 6, Priory Industrial Estate, Tetbury, Gloucestershire, GL8 8HZ Tel: (01666) 502405 Fax: (01666) 505655

John Mcmurtry & Co. Ltd, 42 Douglas Terrace, Ballymena, County Antrim, BT42 3AP Tel: (028) 2564 8116 Fax: (028) 2564 2519

Johnson & Co., Chapel Square, Deddington, Banbury, Oxfordshire, OX15 0SG Tel: (01869) 338275 Fax: (01869) 337014 E-mail: office@johnsonsofdeddington.co.uk

George Jones & Bros, 1-7 Lower Ashley Road, St. Agnes, Bristol, BS2 9QA Tel: 0117-955 6201 Fax: 0117-955 5503

Joseph Parr Alco Ltd, Higginshaw Lane, Royton, Oldham, OL2 6JD Tel: 0161-633 1264 Fax: 0161-620 0866 E-mail: aellis@josephparr.co.uk

Jueson Ltd, 318-326 Southbury Road, Enfield, Middlesex, EN1 1TT Tel: (020) 8804 8244 Fax: (020) 8804 2876 E-mail: email@cakebreads.co.uk

K A C Builders Merchants, 46 Stoke Newington Church Street, London, N16 0LU Tel: (020) 7254 0272 Fax: (020) 7254 0272

K F Supplies, York Road, Market Weighton, York, YO43 3EE Tel: (01430) 872017 Fax: (01430) 874195 E-mail: kfsupplies@aol.com

Kenrix Builders Merchants Ltd, 27 Wickham Lane, London, SE2 0XJ Tel: (020) 8265 4413 Fax: (020) 8265 4413

Kent Blaxill & Co. Ltd, 129-139 Layer Road, Colchester, CO2 9JY Tel: (01206) 216000 Fax: (01206) 762981 E-mail: sales@kentblaxill.co.uk

Keyline Ltd, Bentinck Street, Ashton-under-Lyne, Lancashire, OL7 0PT Tel: 0161-330 2214 Fax: 0161-343 2158

Keyline Brick & Builders Merchant, Beaufort Road, Plasmarl, Swansea, SA6 8HR Tel: (01792) 792264 Fax: (01792) 796279 E-mail: swanseavea@keyline.co.uk

Keyline Builders Merchants Ltd, Station Lane, Birtley, Chester le Street, County Durham, DH2 1AW Tel: 0191-410 2708 Fax: 0191-492 2104 E-mail: angela.mcrobbie@keyline.co.uk

Keyline Builders Merchants Ltd, 1 Bath Road, Edinburgh, EH6 7BB Tel: 0131-519 5000 Fax: 0131-519 5051

Keyline Builders Merchants Ltd, 1 Strathkelvin Place, Kirkintilloch, Glasgow, G66 1XH Tel: 0141-777 8979 Fax: 0141-775 1420 E-mail: welcome@keyline.co.uk

Keyline Builders Merchants Ltd, Moulton Park Industrial Estate, Northampton, NN3 6TE Tel: (01604) 643622 Fax: (01604) 790353 E-mail: welcome@keylineco.uk

Keys Mcmahon, 15 Bay Road, Londonderry, BT48 7SH Tel: (028) 7136 6321 Fax: (028) 7136 4388 E-mail: info@rkeys.com

Kingdons Holdings Ltd, North Street, South Molton, Devon, EX36 3AP Tel: (01769) 573204 Fax: (01769) 573200 E-mail: sales@kingdons.co.uk

L E W Diecastings Ltd, Trows Lane, Rochdale, Lancashire, OL11 2UF Tel: (01706) 632218 Fax: (01706) 643714 E-mail: alan@lew.co.uk

Labdon Building Supplies, Palmers Bridge, Station Road, Cullompton, Devon, EX15 1BQ Tel: (01884) 33405 Fax: (01884) 35405

Lafford Buildbase, Arrowhead Road, Theale, Reading, RG7 4AH Tel: 0118-932 3700 Fax: 0118-932 3202 E-mail: theale@buildbase.co.uk

Lakes Buildbase, Parcel Terrace, Derby, DE1 1LQ Tel: (01332) 349083 Fax: (01332) 290178E-mail: derbybuilding@buildbase.co.uk

Tom Langton & Son, Knowsthorpe Lane, Leeds, LS9 0AT Tel: 0113-249 9440 Fax: 0113-240 2287 E-mail: chris@tomlangtons.com

Larsens, 4 West Bank Road, Belfast, BT3 9JL Tel: (028) 9077 4000 Fax: (028) 9077 6945 E-mail: p.duffy@larsenbuildingproducts.com

Lawford & Sons Ltd, Graham Park Way, London, NW9 5PQ Tel: (020) 8200 6622 Fax: (020) 8905 9400

Lawsons Builders Merchants, 164 Collier Row Road, Romford, RM5 2BD Tel: (01708) 767716 Fax: (01708) 746354 E-mail: sales@lawsons.co.uk

Lazdan Builders Merchants Ltd, 218 Bow Common Lane, London, E3 4HH Tel: (020) 8980 2213 Fax: (020) 8980 5395

LBS Builders Merchants Ltd, Station Road, Llandeilo, Dyfed, SA19 6NL Tel: (01558) 822385 Fax: (01558) 822145 E-mail: mdavies@lbs-buildersmerchants.co.uk

Lee Brothers Construction Supplies, Spring Road, Ettingshall, Wolverhampton, WV4 6JT Tel: (01902) 491911 Fax: (01902) 353228 E-mail: sales@leebrothers.co.uk

Littlefairs Builders Merchants, Littlefairs, Hobson Lane, Kirkby Stephen, Cumbria, CA17 4RN Tel: (01768) 371216 Fax: (01768) 372234 E-mail: enquiries@littlefairs.co.uk

Local Building Supplies, 112 Richardshaw Lane, Stanningley, Pudsey, West Yorkshire, LS28 6BN Tel: 0113-255 6921 Fax: 0113-236 0358 E-mail: info@localbuildingsupplies.co.uk

Lomax Demolition & Timber Yard, Albion Street, Bury, Lancashire, BL8 2AD Tel: 0161-764 5845

Lowdens, 42 Duncrue Crescent, Belfast, BT3 9BW Tel: (028) 9037 0357 Fax: (028) 9037 1207

Chas Lowe & Sons (Builders' Merchants) Ltd, 156 London Road, Knebworth, Hertfordshire, SG3 6HA Tel: (01438) 812740 Fax: (01438) 814324 E-mail: peter@chaslowe.co.uk

M & H Builders Merchants Ltd, 72-74 Wood Street, Walthamstow, London, E17 3HT Tel: (020) 8521 5900 Fax: (020) 8509 1933

▶ M P Moran & Sons Ltd, Worthington House, 449-451 High Road, London, NW10 2JJ Tel: (020) 8459 9000 Fax: (020) 8451 4776 E-mail: sales@mpmoran.co.uk

Manchester Slate Ltd, 1119 Ashton Old Road, Manchester, M11 1AA Tel: 0161-223 5031 Fax: 0161-220 8925

Manjits Ltd, 304-310 Alcester Road, Birmingham, B13 8LJ Tel: 0121-449 5759 Fax: 0121-449 8925

Martin & Partners Ltd, 10-11 Regent Square, Northampton, NN1 2NQ Tel: (01604) 639466 Fax: (01604) 620552 E-mail: martin.partners@virgin.net

MBT Buildbase, 3 Dunnswood Road, Wardpark South, Cumbernauld, Glasgow, G67 3EN Tel: (01236) 454454 Fax: (01236) 454054 E-mail: cumbernauld@buildbase.co.uk

Merrick & Heath, Rolfe Street, Smethwick, West Midlands, B66 2AW Tel: 0121-558 1291 Fax: 0121-558 1291

Merritt & Fryers Ltd, Firth Street Works, Firth Street, Skipton, North Yorkshire, BD23 2PX Tel: (01756) 792485 Fax: (01756) 700391 E-mail: info@merrittandfryers.co.uk

Merton Timber Ltd, 65-71 Grove Vale, London, SE22 8EQ Tel: (020) 8299 4131 Fax: (020) 8693 4136 E-mail: sales@mertontimber.co.uk

Merton Timber, 28 Goat Road, Mitcham, Surrey, CR4 4HU Tel: (020) 8687 0055 Fax: (020) 8648 5663 E-mail: sales@merton-timber.co.uk

Merton Timber, Central House, Murray Road, Orpington, Kent, BR5 3QY Tel: (01689) 890044 Fax: (01689) 890066 E-mail: sales@merton-timber.co.uk

Milton Keynes Buildbase, Simpson Road, Bletchley, Milton Keynes, MK1 1BB Tel: (01908) 369801 Fax: (01908) 270243 E-mail: miltonkeynes@buildbase.co.uk

Monway Builders Supplies Ltd, Portway Road, Wednesbury, West Midlands, WS10 7EQ Tel: 0121-502 0911 Fax: 0121-556 9427

N & C Building Products Ltd, 41-51 Freshwater Road, Dagenham, Essex, RM8 1SP Tel: (020) 8586 4600 Fax: (020) 8586 4646 E-mail: head.office@nichollsandclarke.com

Naylor Myers Ltd, Wakefield Road, Brighouse, West Yorkshire, HD6 1ZE Tel: (01484) 712531 Fax: (01484) 722365

John Nicholls Trading Ltd, Overthorpe Road, Banbury, Oxfordshire, OX16 4TB Tel: (01295) 262294 Fax: (01295) 270895

Norbury Fencing & Building Supplies Ltd, 28 Marshgate Drive, Hertford, SG13 7AJ Tel: (01992) 554327 Fax: (01992) 505978 E-mail: sales@norburyfencing.co.uk

Norman Ltd, 19 Commercial Buildings, St. Helier, Jersey, JE1 1BU Tel: (01534) 883388 Fax: (01534) 883334 E-mail: sales@normans.je

Odds W J Ltd, Crown Quay Lane, Sittingbourne, Kent, ME10 3JB Tel: (01795) 470844 Fax: (01795) 420463

P A Seccombe & Son Ltd, Syon Lane, Isleworth, Middlesex, TW7 5PW Tel: (020) 8560 2246 Fax: (020) 8847 2849 E-mail: sales@seccombe.co.uk

P E Hines & Sons Ltd, Whitebridge Lane, Stone, Staffordshire, ST15 8LU Tel: (01785) 814921 Fax: (01785) 818808 E-mail: p.e.hines@iclwebkit.co.uk

P S L (Weir) Ltd, Ashcroft Road, Knowsley Industrial Estate North, Liverpool, L33 7TW Tel: 0151-547 2222 Fax: 0151-549 1060 E-mail: psllpool@hotmail.com

Parfix Equipment Company Ltd, Locksley House, Unit 4 Locksley Business Park, Belfast, BT6 9JD Tel: (028) 9070 6800 Fax: (028) 9070 6801 E-mail: dflood@parfixwholesaledirect.com

Parker Severn Builders Merchants Ltd, Lillington Road South, Bulwell, Nottingham, NG6 8NG Tel: 0115-927 7412 Fax: 0115-977 1382

Joseph Parr (Middlesbrough) Ltd, Blue House Point Road, Portrack Lane Trading Estate, Stockton-On-Tees, Cleveland, TS18 2PJ Tel: (01642) 679381 Fax: (01642) 617222 E-mail: jparrboro@aol.com

Pemberton Building Supplies Ltd, Richmond Hill, Wigan, Lancashire, WN5 8AA Tel: (01942) 218222 Fax: (01942) 225205

Plumb Center Ltd, 2 Clarks Industrial Estate, Newtown Road, Hove, East Sussex, BN3 7BA Tel: (01273) 324352 Fax: (01273) 208482

Pressco Components Ltd, Selborne Street, Walsall, WS1 2JN Tel: (01922) 620202 Fax: (01922) 726101 E-mail: press-sales@presco.co.uk

Price & Oliver Ltd, 254 Lozells Road, Birmingham, B19 1NR Tel: 0121-554 8491 Fax: 0121-554 8989

▶ indicates data change since last edition

BUILDERS' MERCHANTS – *continued*

PTS Plumbing Trade Supplies Ltd, Buccaneer Way, Magna Park, Lutterworth, Leicestershire, LE17 4YZ Tel: (01455) 551210 Fax: (01455) 550772
E-mail: magnareception@bssgroup.com

PTS Plumbing Trade Supplies Ltd, 24 Boleness Road, Wisbech, Cambridgeshire, PE13 2RB Tel: (01945) 589990 Fax: (01945) 474827

R J Pryce & Co. Ltd, Trinity Road, Lowestoft, Suffolk, NR32 1XJ Tel: (01502) 574141 Fax: (01502) 501213
E-mail: sales@rjpryce.co.uk

R W Almond & Co., R W Almond & Co Stephenson Way, Formby Business Park, Formby, Liverpool, L37 8EG Tel: (01704) 878651 Fax: (01704) 833821
E-mail: enquiries@rwalmond.co.uk

Radcliffe Building Supplies Ltd, Lord Street, Radcliffe, Manchester, M26 3BA Tel: 0161-724 6363 Fax: 0161-725 9128

Rawle Gammon & Baker Holdings Ltd, Gammon House, Riverside Road, Pottington Business Park, Barnstaple, Devon, EX31 1LX Tel: (01271) 375501 Fax: (01271) 329982
E-mail: barnstable@rgbltd.co.uk

A.F.G. Ray & Sons, The Old Coal Yard, Worcester Road, Kidderminster, Worcestershire, DY11 1HN Tel: (01562) 755585 Fax: (01562) 825218

Readymix Huddersfield Ltd, Red Doles Lane, Leeds Road, Huddersfield, HD2 1YD Tel: (01484) 535311 Fax: (01484) 558255
E-mail: sales@readymix-huddersfield.co.uk

Rhead Buildbase Ltd, Meir Road, Normacot, Stoke-On-Trent, ST3 7JD Tel: (01782) 599550 Fax: (01782) 599551
E-mail: stokeontrent@buildbase.co.uk

Ridgeons Ltd, Trinity Hall Industrial Estate, Nuffield Road, Cambridge, CB4 1TS Tel: (01223) 466000 Fax: (01223) 466079

Ridgeons Ltd, Ashdon Road Commercial Centre, Saffron Walden, Essex, CB10 2NQ Tel: (01799) 583000 Fax: (01799) 583039
E-mail: steven.sutton@ridgeons.co.uk

Ridgeons Ltd, Alexandra Road, Sudbury, Suffolk, CO10 2XH Tel: (01787) 881777 Fax: (01787) 881186 E-mail: sudburysales@ridgerns.net

William Roberts & Co. Ltd, Water Street, Menai Bridge, Gwynedd, LL59 5DE Tel: (01248) 712596 Fax: (01248) 717303
E-mail: dolgellau@williamroberts.co.uk

Robinson Buildbase Ltd, Green Street, Burton-On-Trent, Staffordshire, DE14 3RX Tel: (01283) 565021 Fax: (01283) 569240
E-mail: burton@buildbase.co.uk

Robinson Timber & Building Supplies, Dansom Lane North, Hull, HU8 7RS Tel: (01482) 320081 Fax: (01482) 586741

J. Rollings & Son Ltd, 15-21 Cannock Street, Leicester, LE4 9HR Tel: 0116-276 0275 Fax: 0116-246 0554

▶ RoofracksUK, Unit 12, Fountain Mill, Carluke Street, Blackburn, BB1 3JR Tel: (01254) 263558 Fax: (01254) 54776
E-mail: sales@roofracksuk.com

S P Brown & Co. Ltd, 31 Lockhart Street, London, E3 4BL Tel: (020) 8981 2747 Fax: (020) 8981 2747

S P Stow Ltd, Portland Street, Kirkby-in-Ashfield, Nottingham, NG17 7AD Tel: (01623) 752258 Fax: (01623) 752258

S S F Forthside Ltd, Merlin Way, Hillend, Dunfermline, Fife, KY11 9JY Tel: (01383) 824181 Fax: (01383) 824722

Saint Gobain Building Distribution Ltd, Merchant House, Binley Business Park, Harry Weston Road, Coventry, CV3 2TT Tel: (024) 7643 8400 Fax: (024) 7643 8505
E-mail: shelley.knowles@jewson.co.uk

Salisbury & Wood Ltd, Old Coach Road, Tansley, Matlock, Derbyshire, DE4 5FY Tel: (01629) 582272 Fax: (01629) 583989

Seccombe (Builders' Merchants) Ltd, 158-164 St. James Road, Croydon, CR9 2RT Tel: (020) 8689 4421 Fax: (020) 8684 7411

Selco, First Avenue, Minworth, Sutton Coldfield, West Midlands, B76 1BA Tel: 0121-313 2020 Fax: 0121-313 0523

Selco Trade Centres Ltd, 1 Charlote Road, Stirchley, Birmingham, B30 2BT Tel: 0121-433 3355 Fax: 0121-458 5996

Sexton Sales Ltd, D Wiggenhall Road Goods Yard, Wiggenhall Road, Watford, WD18 0EZ Tel: (01923) 240434 Fax: (01923) 818454
E-mail: enquiries@sextonsales.com

Shefford Building Supplies Ltd, 44 High Street, Shefford, Bedfordshire, SG17 5DG Tel: (01462) 813381 Fax: (01462) 811655

Shiner Ltd, 22 Church Road, Lawrence Hill, Bristol, BS5 9JB Tel: 0117-955 7432 Fax: 0117-955 4686
E-mail: admin@shiner.co.uk

Slocombe Buildbase, Searle Crescent, Winterstoke Commercial Centre, Weston-Super-Mare, Avon, BS23 3YX Tel: (01934) 626503 Fax: (01934) 635334
E-mail: westonsupermare@buildbase.co.uk

Southern Nail Supplies, Ikon House, 3 Arkwright Road, Reading, RG2 0LU Tel: 0118-987 3344

Spiller & Webber Ltd, Viney Court, Victoria Street, Taunton, Somerset, TA1 3JA Tel: (01823) 337333 Fax: (01823) 321364

Springfield Timber & Building Supplies, Broughton Works, Chester Road, Bretton, Chester, CH4 0DH Tel: (01244) 660351 Fax: (01244) 661276

John A. Stephens Ltd, 43 Radcliffe Road, West Bridgford, Nottingham, NG2 5FF Tel: 0115-981 4313

Sydenhams Ltd, 45-55 Ashley Road, Bournemouth, BH1 4LG Tel: (01202) 397454 Fax: (01202) 396465

T Bacon, Spink Hall Farm, Spink Hall Lane, Stocksbridge, Sheffield, S36 1FL Tel: 0114-288 2556 Fax: 0114-288 2556

T G Builders Merchants, Tattenhall Road, Tattenhall, Chester, CH3 9BD Tel: (01829) 770421 Fax: (01829) 770879
E-mail: admin@tggroup.co.uk

Taggart & Co. Ltd, 38-44 Main Street, Ballymoney, County Antrim, BT53 6AP Tel: (028) 2766 2130 Fax: (028) 2766 6129

Tamar Trading Co. Ltd, 15 Bodmin Street, Holsworthy, Devon, EX22 6BB Tel: (01409) 253555 Fax: (01409) 254496
E-mail: sales@tamartrading.com

Charles Tapp Builders' Merchants, 111 Southgate Road, London, N1 3JQ Tel: (020) 7359 9118 Fax: (020) 7359 9118

Thompson Builders Merchants Ltd, Bilton Road, Chelmsford, CM1 2UB Tel: (01245) 266754 Fax: (01245) 359070
E-mail: info@thompson-online.co.uk

Thompson & Parkes Ltd, Oldington Trading Estate, Kidderminster, Worcestershire, DY11 7QP Tel: (01562) 745881 Fax: (01562) 515578

Thompson Plumbase, 10 Chapel Street, Redruth, Cornwall, TR15 2DE Tel: (01209) 215676 Fax: (01209) 213222

Thornton Heath Dry Cleaners, 92 Brigstock Road, Thornton Heath, Surrey, CR7 7JA Tel: (020) 8683 2589 Fax: (020) 8240 0081
E-mail: thdiy-ltd@ukgateway.net

Tiger Timber Ltd, 36 Station Road, Chertsey, Surrey, KT16 8BE Tel: (01932) 560812 Fax: (01932) 570411

Walter Tipper Ltd, Dovefields, Uttoxeter, Staffordshire, ST14 8HR Tel: (01889) 565151 Fax: (01889) 567318
E-mail: info@tippersbm.co.uk

Towy Works Ltd, The Quay, Carmarthen, Dyfed, SA31 3JR Tel: (01267) 236601 Fax: (01267) 238189

Travis Perkins plc, Sydenham Wharf, Lower Bristol Road, Bath, BA2 3EE Tel: (01225) 446110 Fax: (01225) 442796
E-mail: bath@travisperkins.co.uk

Travis Perkins plc, The Quay, Fen Lane, Beccles, Suffolk, NR34 9BH Tel: (01502) 712421 Fax: (01502) 711110

Travis Perkins plc, 67 Shortmead Street, Biggleswade, Bedfordshire, SG18 0BD Tel: (01767) 313020 Fax: (01767) 601774
E-mail: biggswade@travisperkins.co.uk

Travis Perkins, 1 South Road, Hockley, Birmingham, B18 5LT Tel: 0121-554 3396 Fax: 0121-554 6811

Travis Perkins plc, Fairfield Street, Bradford, West Yorkshire, BD4 9QP Tel: (01274) 681065 Fax: (01274) 688843

Travis Perkins plc, New Road, Stoke Gifford, Bristol, BS34 8QW Tel: 0117-969 5811 Fax: 0117-923 6284

Travis Perkins plc, Kelston Road, Bristol, BS10 5EP Tel: 0117-950 4700 Fax: 0117-950 4500

Travis Perkins plc, Havyat Road Trading Estate, Havyat Road, Wrington, Bristol, BS40 5PA Tel: (01934) 862439 Fax: (01934) 863617

▶ Travis Perkins plc, Navigation Road, Chelmsford, CM2 6HX Tel: (01245) 490000 Fax: (01245) 359055

Travis Perkins plc, Gloucester Road, Cheltenham, Gloucestershire, GL51 8TP Tel: (01242) 521477 Fax: (01242) 584437

Travis Perkins plc, Mayors Avenue, Dartmouth, Devon, TQ6 9NG Tel: (01803) 832216 Fax: (01803) 835694

▶ Travis Perkins plc, Sandown Road, Derby, DE24 8SR Tel: (01332) 361377 Fax: (01332) 381597

Travis Perkins plc, Recreation Lane, Felixstowe, Suffolk, IP11 9DQ Tel: (01394) 278999 Fax: (01394) 273486

Travis Perkins plc, 24-42 Palmerston Road, Harrow, Middlesex, HA3 7RR Tel: (020) 8861 1750 Fax: (020) 8861 3556

Travis Perkins plc, Belle Vue Way, Hartlepool, Cleveland, TS25 1JZ Tel: (01429) 221133 Fax: (01429) 863357
E-mail: sales@travisperkings.co.uk

Travis Perkins plc, Thurman Street, Ilkeston, Derbyshire, DE7 4BY Tel: 0115-932 4278 Fax: 0115-944 1338

Travis Perkins plc, Shore St, Inverness, IV1 1NT Tel: (01463) 231171 Fax: (01463) 710315

Travis Perkins plc, Long Leys Road, Lincoln, LN1 1DU Tel: (01522) 527113 Fax: (01522) 567905

Travis Perkins plc, Chamberlayne Road, London, NW10 3NB Tel: (020) 8964 9000 Fax: (020) 8969 0702
E-mail: enquiries@travisperkins.com

Travis Perkins plc, 205 Balham High Road, London, SW17 7BQ Tel: (020) 8673 0181 Fax: (020) 8673 6818

Travis Perkins plc, 26 Sangley Road, London, SE6 2JN Tel: (020) 8698 1081 Fax: (020) 8461 1229

Travis Perkins plc, 61-63 Pimlico Road, London, SW1W 8NF Tel: (020) 7730 6622 Fax: (020) 7730 6012

Travis Perkins plc, Boyn Valley Road, Maidenhead, Berkshire, SL6 4EE Tel: (01628) 770577 Fax: (01628) 625919

Travis Perkins plc, 7 Seph Way, York Road Industrial Park, Malton, North Yorkshire, YO17 6YF Tel: (01653) 692444 Fax: (01653) 600453 E-mail: malton@travisperkins.co.uk

Travis Perkins plc, Bond Street, Malvern, Worcestershire, WR14 1TQ Tel: (01684) 568401 Fax: (01684) 892745
E-mail: malvern@travisperkins.co.uk

Travis Perkins plc, Liverpool Road, Eccles, Manchester, M30 0UG Tel: 0161-789 2631 Fax: 0161-787 7579
E-mail: andycorrigan@travisperkins.co.uk

Travis Perkins plc, Lodge Way House, Lodge Way, Northampton, NN5 7UG Tel: (01604) 752424 Fax: (01604) 758718
E-mail: careers@contemporary.co.uk

Travis Perkins plc, Livsey Street, Rochdale, Lancashire, OL16 1SS Tel: (01706) 657325 Fax: (01706) 648026
E-mail: rochdale@travisperkins.co.uk

Travis Perkins plc, Lissadel Street, Salford, M6 6BR Tel: 0161-736 8751 Fax: 0161-737 9744

Travis Perkins plc, Greenland Works, Coleford Road, Sheffield, S9 5NN Tel: 0114-244 1081 Fax: 0114-243 5276
E-mail: david.lee@travisperkins.co.uk

Travis Perkins plc, Manchester Road, Whitehill Industrial Estate, Whitehill Industrial Estate, Stockport, Cheshire, SK4 1NY Tel: 0161-480 0881 Fax: 0161-477 3658

Travis Perkins plc, 45 Stourbridge Road, Stourbridge, West Midlands, DY9 7DG Tel: (01384) 422314 Fax: (01384) 422860
E-mail: stourbridge@travisperkins.co.uk

Travis Perkins plc, Heathside House, Brighton Road, Tadworth, Surrey, KT20 6BE Tel: (01737) 362111 Fax: (01737) 370476
E-mail: burghheath@travisperkins.co.uk

Travis Perkins plc, 205 High Street, West Wickham, Kent, BR4 0LX Tel: (020) 8777 8326 Fax: (020) 8777 8567
E-mail: sean.patterson@travisperkins.co.uk

Travis Perkins plc, Pickerings Road, Halebank, Widnes, Cheshire, WA8 8XE Tel: 0151-424 1444 Fax: 0151-424 7770
E-mail: widnes@travisperkins.co.uk

Travis Perkins Trading Co. Ltd, Rowlandson Street, Grimsby, North East Lincolnshire, DN31 3LL Tel: (01472) 345471 Fax: (01472) 242760

Travis Perkins Trading Co. Ltd, Bluebridge Industrial Estate, 11 Second Avenue, Colchester Road, Halstead, Essex, CO9 2HA Tel: (01787) 477882 Fax: (01787) 473761

▶ Treviscoe Builders Merchants, The Old Cooperage, Little Treviscoe, St. Austell, Cornwall, PL26 7QP Tel: (01726) 822388 Fax: (01726) 823383
E-mail: sales@treviscoe.com

Turnbull & Co. Ltd, 95 Southgate, Sleaford, Lincolnshire, NG34 7RQ Tel: (01529) 303025 Fax: (01529) 413364

W Fayers & Sons Ltd, 76 Alfred Road, Buckhurst Hill, Essex, IG9 6DR Tel: (020) 8504 6625 Fax: (020) 8505 0626

W H Horton, West Street, Tamworth, Staffordshire, B79 7JE Tel: (01827) 52810 Fax: (01827) 66122
E-mail: info@whhorton.co.uk

W Hanson Timber & Builders Merchants Ltd, Uxbridge Road, Southall, Middlesex, UB1 3EQ Tel: (020) 8571 3161 Fax: (020) 8574 3816
E-mail: sales@w-hanson.co.uk

W M Kenyon Macclesfield Ltd, 73 Great King Street, Macclesfield, Cheshire, SK11 6PN Tel: (01625) 422074 Fax: (01625) 617712

W Madden Insulation, Swinnow View, Leeds, LS13 4TZ Tel: 0113-257 9818 Fax: 0113-257 7586 E-mail: sales@wmadden.demon.co.uk

W Young & Son Ltd, 6-8 Godstone Road, Purley, Surrey, CR8 2DA Tel: (020) 8660 1158 Fax: (020) 8763 2021

Warrington Civils & Lintels, Wilson Patten Street, Warrington, WA1 1HN Tel: (01925) 255700 Fax: (01925) 416520
E-mail: warrington@civilandlintels.co.uk

William Way (New Malden) Ltd, 74-76 Coombe Road, New Malden, Surrey, KT3 4QU Tel: (020) 8942 9498 Fax: (020) 8949 8712

Westcrete Pre-cast Concrete Ltd, Stoney Bridges, Membury Road, Axminster, Devon, EX13 5RL Tel: (01297) 32002
E-mail: sales@westcrete.fsnet.co.uk

Western Timber & Builders Merchants - Heston, 236a Heston Road, Hounslow, TW5 0RH Tel: (020) 8570 3218 Fax: (020) 8570 3794

Weston & Bolton Ltd, 118-126 Gipsy Lane, Leicester, LE4 6RL Tel: 0116-266 4441
E-mail: sales@weston-bolton.co.uk

Whitchurch Building Supplies, College Road, Cardiff, CF14 2NZ Tel: (029) 2062 5422 Fax: (029) 2061 6840

Whitten Timber Ltd, Eagle Wharf, Peckham Hill Street, London, SE15 5JT Tel: (020) 7732 3804 Fax: (020) 7635 3555

Wildman Transport (Bedford) Ltd, Postley Road, Kempston, Bedford, MK42 7BU Tel: (01234) 854244 Fax: (01234) 841362
E-mail: roy@wildmantransport.com

William Way Godstone Ltd, 38-42 High Street, Godstone, Surrey, RH9 8LW Tel: (01883) 742757 Fax: (01883) 742757

Wimbledon Builders Merchants Ltd, Gap Road, London, SW19 8JA Tel: (020) 8947 9933 Fax: (020) 8944 1622

Wollens Ltd, Wirrall Park Road, Glastonbury, Somerset, BA6 9XE Tel: (01458) 832244 Fax: (01458) 834926
E-mail: info@wollens.prestel.co.uk

Wolseley Build Centre Ltd, 12 Cross Lane, Wallasey, Merseyside, CH45 8RQ Tel: 0151-639 6031 Fax: 0151-639 0367
E-mail: s79-wallasey@wolseley.co.uk

Uriah Woodhead & Son Ltd, Valley House, Valley Road, Bradford, West Yorkshire, BD1 4RY Tel: (01274) 727528 Fax: (01274) 726574

Woodrows of Salisbury, Stephenson Road, Churchfields Industrial Estate, Salisbury, SP2 7NP Tel: (01722) 328401 Fax: (01722) 412782

BUILDERS' OR DIY TOOL HIRE

A R K S Tool Hire Ltd, Dawley Brook Road, Kingswinford, West Midlands, DY6 7BD Tel: (01384) 274050 Fax: (01384) 400459
E-mail: sales@arkstoolhire.co.uk

A1 Rentals Ltd, A1 House 22b Navigation Drive, Hurst Business Park, Brierley Hill, West Midlands, DY5 1UT Tel: (01384) 486200 Fax: (01384) 486204
E-mail: admin1@a1rentals.entadsl.com

▶ Abba Hire, Delbro House, Factory Road, Sealand, Deeside, Clwyd, CH5 2QJ Tel: (01244) 531986 Fax: (01244) 531986
E-mail: info@abbahire.co.uk

Action Hire Centres, 90 Cotmandene Crescent, St Pauls Cray, Orpington, Kent, BR5 2RG Tel: (020) 8300 2359 Fax: (020) 8302 7422

A-Plant Ltd, Mansfield Road, Derby, DE1 3RF Tel: (01332) 382275 Fax: (01332) 295504
E-mail: derbynorth@aplant.com

A-Plant Ltd, Nuthall Road, Nottingham, NG8 5BU Tel: 0115-942 0567 Fax: 0115-978 8868
E-mail: nottinghamwest@aplant.com

Arrowhead Hire, Unit 5 Kennet Weir Bussiness Park, Arrowhead Road, Theale, Reading, RG7 4AD Tel: 0118-930 3703 Fax: 0118-930 4160

Ashtead Plant Hire, 3 Dixon Way, Dixon Street, Lincoln, LN6 7DE Tel: (01522) 520688 Fax: (01522) 513577

Ashtead Plant Hire Co. Ltd, St Georges Road, Donnington, Telford, Shropshire, TF2 7RA Tel: (01952) 620320 Fax: (01952) 610708
E-mail: telford@aplant.com

Asles (Tool Hire & Sales) Ltd, 82 Broadway, Shifnal, Shropshire, TF11 8AZ Tel: (01952) 461266 Fax: (01952) 462337

Banson Tool Hire Ltd, 125 Pellon Lane, Halifax, West Yorkshire, HX1 5QN Tel: (01422) 254999 Fax: (01422) 254778

Beaver Tool Hire Ltd, 15-17 Kingston Road, Portsmouth, PO1 5RX Tel: (023) 9282 6632 Fax: (023) 9282 6639

Bells Tool Hire, Unit 337 Rushock Trading Estate, Rushock, Droitwich, Worcestershire, WR9 0NR Tel: (01299) 250578 Fax: (01299) 250578

Belmont Tool Hire Ltd, 310 Brighton Road, Belmont, Sutton, Surrey, SM2 5SU Tel: (020) 8770 9480 Fax: (020) 8770 9480

Brandon Hire plc, 151 Bute Street, Cardiff, CF10 5HQ Tel: (029) 2048 9898 Fax: (029) 2048 0772
E-mail: cardiff23@brandonhire.plc.uk

Brandon Hire plc, Llangunnor Road, Carmarthen, Dyfed, SA31 2PB Tel: (01267) 237405 Fax: (01267) 238299
E-mail: carmarthen@brandonhire.plc.uk

Build Center, Cambrian Works, Station Approach, Wrexham, Clwyd, LL11 2NY Tel: (01978) 354444 Fax: (01978) 351688

Champion Hire Ltd, 2 Roman Ridge Road, Sheffield, S9 1XG Tel: (0845) 3456900 Fax: 0114-249 4100
E-mail: sales@champion-hire.com

Charles Building Services Ltd, 6 Viewpoint, Hyatt Trading Estate, Stevenage, Hertfordshire, SG1 2EQ Tel: (01438) 750371

Chislett Hire, Enterprise Way, Pinchbeck, Spalding, Lincolnshire, PE11 3YR Tel: (01775) 725778 Fax: (01775) 767523
E-mail: sales@chislett.co.uk

M. Wallace Clelland & Co. Ltd, Burnside Industrial Estate, Kilsyth, Glasgow, G65 9JY Tel: (01236) 823015 Fax: (01236) 823256

▶ Dunloy Tool Hire & Sales, 3 Pulloxhill Business Park, Greenfield Road, Pulloxhill, Bedford, MK45 5EU Tel: (01525) 716715 Fax: (01525) 720795 E-mail: dunloy@btconnect.com

Fast Plant Swindon Ltd, Unit 2267, Dunbeath Road, Elgin Industrial Estate, Swindon, SN2 8EA Tel: (01793) 617854 Fax: (01793) 420809
E-mail: fastplantswindon@btconnect.com

H S S Ltd, 344 King Street, Hammersmith, Hammersmith, London, W6 0RX Tel: (020) 8748 6740 Fax: (020) 8563 2483

H S S Lift & Shift, Pryme Works, Silvercroft Street, Manchester, M15 4WG Tel: 0161-839 6122

▶ H S S Service Hire Group Ltd, 816 Oxford Road, Reading, RG30 1EL Tel: 0118-950 8882 Fax: 0118-975 0841

H T C Fastenings Ltd, Lyon Way, Hatfield Road, St. Albans, Hertfordshire, AL4 0LR Tel: (01727) 832131 Fax: (01727) 843234
E-mail: info@hertstools.co.uk

Heathfield Hire, Browning Road, Heathfield, East Sussex, TN21 8DB Tel: (01435) 864144 Fax: (01435) 866622
E-mail: sds-navron@line1.net

Hewden Hire Centres Ltd, 110 Commercial Road, Leeds, LS5 3AB Tel: 0113-230 4200 Fax: 0113-275 8830

▶ HSS Hire, Wakefield Road, Bradford, West Yorkshire, BD4 7LX Tel: (01274) 308055 Fax: (01274) 724773

▶ HSS Hire, 119 West Street, Glasgow, G5 8BA Tel: 0141-429 6141 Fax: 0141-429 1342

▶ HSS Hire, 151 Abbey Lane, Leicester, LE4 5NZ Tel: 0116-268 1441 Fax: 0116-268 1257

Junction News, 169 Conway Road, Llandudno Junction, Gwynedd, LL31 9EG Tel: (01492) 573266 Fax: (01492) 573266

M F Hire Ltd, 2-3 Colwick Road, Nottingham, NG2 4BG Tel: 0115-958 1505 Fax: 0115-950 3846 E-mail: eno@mfhgroup.co.uk

▶ indicates data change since last edition

BUILDERS' OR DIY TOOL HIRE - *continued*

J.G. Martin Plant Hire Ltd, 95 Orbiston Street, Motherwell, Lanarkshire, ML1 1PX Tel: (0870) 8536100 Fax: (0870) 8536099 E-mail: gail@martinplanthire.co.uk
North Eastern Plant & Fixings, 120 Londesborough Sreet, Hull, HU3 1DR Tel: (01482) 226140
A Plant P.L.C., Daleside Road, Nottingham, NG2 4DJ Tel: 0115-958 0085 Fax: 0115-948 3348 E-mail: garyhorton@aplant.com
Ree Even Hire, 186-188 Portland Road, Hove, East Sussex, BN3 5QN Tel: (01273) 778222 Fax: (01273) 778223 E-mail: sales@ree-even.co.uk
Seaton Heating & Engineering Services Ltd, Wilnecote Lane, Tamworth, Staffordshire, B77 2LE Tel: (01827) 286777 Fax: (01827) 288319
Shorts Group Ltd, Lyndhurst Road, Ascot, Berkshire, SL5 9ED Tel: (01344) 620316 Fax: (01344) 624572 E-mail: sales@shorts-services.co.uk
Smiths Equipment Hire Ltd, 245 Fleetwood Road, Thornton-Cleveleys, Lancashire, FY5 1NJ Tel: (01253) 862445 Fax: (01253) 853496
South Lincs Plant Hire & Sales Ltd, Enterprise Way, Pinchbeck, Spalding, Lincolnshire, PE11 3YR Tel: (01775) 766131 Fax: (01775) 711305
▶ Southampton Tools, 159-161 Obelisk Road, Southampton, SO19 9DN Tel: (023) 8043 5700 Fax: (023) 8044 7081
▶ Speedy Hire plc, Chase House, 16 The Parks, Newton-le-Willows, Merseyside, WA12 0JQ Tel: (01942) 720000 Fax: (01942) 720077 E-mail: customer.services@speedyhire.co.uk
Speedy Hire Centres Ltd, 56 Christchurch Road, Reading, RG2 7AZ Tel: 0118-931 2636 Fax: 0118-986 1555
Speedy Hire Centres Ltd, Hilton Industrial Estate, 1 Hepworth Road, Sunderland, SR5 3JT Tel: 0191-548 4114 Fax: 0191-516 0384
Speedy Hire Centres Ltd, Unit 3 Ironbridge Road, West Drayton, Middlesex, UB7 8DU Tel: (01895) 440046 Fax: (01895) 431417
Speedy Hire UK, 101 Blackhorse Lane, London, E17 6DJ Tel: (020) 8531 7621 Fax: (020) 8503 2599
Taylor Tool Hire & Garden Ware, Nailbridge, Drybrook, Gloucestershire, GL17 9JW Tel: (01594) 542853 Fax: (01594) 544773 E-mail: njt@taylortoolhire.co.uk
Tedbar Tinker Hire, 53 Carlisle Street, Sheffield, S4 7LJ Tel: 0114-275 3666 Fax: 0114-275 4183 E-mail: sales@tedbartinkerhire.co.uk
Telford Group Ltd, Enterprise House, Stafford Park 1, Telford, Shropshire, TF3 3BD Tel: (01952) 290800 Fax: (01952) 291303 E-mail: info@telfordgroup.co.uk
Tool Care Hire (Devon) Ltd, 19 Marsh Green Road, Marsh Barton Trading Estate, Exeter, EX2 8NY Tel: (01392) 250379 Fax: (01392) 274658
Traction Equipment (Stafford) Ltd, Glover Street, Stafford, ST16 2NY Tel: (01785) 223355 Fax: (01785) 211074 E-mail: call@tractionequipment.co.uk
Universal Access & Power Plants Ltd, 14 Pony Road, Cowley, Oxford, OX4 2RD Tel: (01865) 450000 Fax: (01865) 451111 E-mail: sales@universalhire.co.uk
Whittington Tool Hire, 73 Mason Road, Birmingham, B24 9EH Tel: 0121-382 5770 Fax: 0121-373 4542

BUILDING ACCESS DOOR ENTRY SYSTEMS

B C Technology Ltd, 3 Wallis Close, Park Farm Industrial Estate, Wellingborough, Northamptonshire, NN8 6AG Tel: (01933) 405050 Fax: (01933) 405454 E-mail: info@bctechnologyltd.co.uk
Bell System Telephones Ltd, Presley Way, Crownhill, Milton Keynes, MK8 0ET Tel: (01908) 261106 Fax: (01908) 261116 E-mail: sales@bellsystem.co.uk
Ellard Ltd, Dallimore Road, Roundthorn Industrial Estate, Manchester, M23 9NX Tel: 0161-945 4561 Fax: 0161-945 4566 E-mail: sales@ellard.co.uk
Fermax UK Ltd, Fermax House, Bebington Close, Billericay, Essex, CM12 0DT Tel: (01277) 634777 Fax: (01277) 634666 E-mail: sales@fermaxuk.com
Telenova Ltd, 144 Regina Road, Southall, Middlesex, UB2 5PP Tel: (020) 8571 5073
Telguard, 2 Ockley Court Farm Cottages, Coles Lane, Ockley, Dorking, Surrey, RH5 5LS Tel: (01306) 710120 Fax: (01306) 713769 E-mail: sales@telguard.co.uk

BUILDING ACCESS DOOR ENTRY SYSTEMS CONTRACTORS OR INSTALLATION OR SERVICE

▶ 24 7 CCTV Security Ltd, 33 Kingswood Road, Basildon, Essex, SS16 5UP Tel: (0870) 2242247 Fax: (0870) 4215949 E-mail: info@247cctv.co.uk
Delta Communications, 6 Knockbreda Park, Belfast, BT6 0HB Tel: (028) 9049 1212 Fax: (028) 9049 1833
Dorcom Ltd, Unit 3, St Joseph's Business Park, St Joseph's Close, Hove, East Sussex, BN3 7HG Tel: (01273) 202851 Fax: (01273) 220108 E-mail: info@dorcom.co.uk
Dorwingear, 107 Hospital Street, Birmingham, B19 3XA Tel: 0121-359 1744 Fax: 0121-333 3475 E-mail: dorwingearltd@btconnect.com
Interphone CCTV Ltd, Interphone House, P O Box 1, Harrow, Middlesex, HA3 5UH Tel: (020) 8621 6000 Fax: (020) 8621 6100 E-mail: security@interphone.co.uk
J D Groves Ltd, 7 Lenham Road East, Rottingdean, Brighton, BN2 7GP Tel: (01273) 306394 Fax: (01273) 300658
N A C D Ltd, 10 Avebury Court, Hemel Hempstead, Hertfordshire, HP2 7TA Tel: (01442) 211848 Fax: (01442) 212776 E-mail: sales@nacd.co.uk
Rentrifone Ltd, Premier House, 309 Ballards Lane, London, N12 8NE Tel: (020) 8455 3304 Fax: (020) 8609 0627 E-mail: rentrifone@hotmail.co.uk
Speak & Enter Services Ltd, 457 Alexandra Avenue, Rayners Lane, Harrow, Middlesex, HA2 9RY Tel: (020) 8429 2976 Fax: (020) 8429 3703 E-mail: derrick01@btconnect.com
T V A Installations Stockport Ltd, Waterloo House, Hopes Carr, Stockport, Cheshire, SK1 3BL Tel: 0161-480 2265 Fax: 0161-480 6720 E-mail: tva@btconnect.com

BUILDING ACCESS EQUIPMENT OR TOWER HIRE

Access Company Services Ltd, 103-106 Chadwick Road, Astmoor Industrial Estate, Runcorn, Cheshire, WA7 1PW Tel: (01928) 590880 Fax: (01928) 590877
Aerials For Industry, Diamond House, Thornes Moor Road, Wakefield, West Yorkshire, WF2 8PT Tel: (0870) 7871513 Fax: (01924) 374545 E-mail: info@afi-platforms.co.uk
Airborne Industrial Access Ltd, Pegasus House 15 Irwin Road, Guildford, Surrey, GU2 7PW Tel: (01483) 451610 Fax: (01483) 533009 E-mail: ringway@btinternet.com
Albion Tower Properties Ltd, 177 Greets Green Road, West Bromwich, West Midlands, B70 9ET Tel: 0121-557 4000 Fax: 0121-522 2703
Brandon Hire plc, 63 Lyde Green, Halesowen, West Midlands, B63 2PQ Tel: (01384) 566936 Fax: (01384) 410134 E-mail: info@brandonhire.plc.uk
Alan Drew Ltd, 8 Caxton Way, The Watford Bussiness Park, Watford, WD18 8JX Tel: (01923) 817933 Fax: (01923) 237824 E-mail: alandrew@onet.co.uk
F.L. Gamble & Sons Ltd, Meadow Road Industrial Estate, Dale Road, Worthing, West Sussex, BN11 2RY Tel: (01903) 230906 Fax: (01903) 210569 E-mail: sales@gamble-jarvis.co.uk
Go Hire Access Ltd, 6 Droicon Industrial Estate, Portway Road, Rowley Regis, West Midlands, B65 9BY Tel: 0121-559 0660 Fax: 0121-559 0770 E-mail: dudley@gohireaccess.co.uk
Hewden Instant Access Ltd, Staceys Yard, Station Road, Langley, Slough, SL3 6DB Tel: (01753) 548849 Fax: (01753) 540655
▶ Hireman (London) Ltd, Unit 4, Apex Industrial Estate, 22 Hythe Road, London, NW10 6RT Tel: (020) 8964 2464 Fax: (020) 8964 1343
J C Tool Hire, Valley St North, Darlington, County Durham, DL1 1QE Tel: (01325) 382038 Fax: (01325) 468539 E-mail: sales@joegreeners.co.uk
Kestrel Powered Access Ltd, 5 Victoria Terrace, St. Philips, Bristol, BS2 0TD Tel: 0117-958 8888 Fax: 0117-972 4125 E-mail: sales@kestrelaccess.co.uk
Mitie Generation Ltd, Meriton Street, Bristol, BS2 0SZ Tel: 0117-972 4550 Fax: 0117-972 4502 E-mail: bristol@generationuk.co.uk
▶ New Forest Hire, 146 - 148 Commercial Road, Totton, Southampton, SO40 3AA Tel: (023) 8086 2410 Fax: (023) 8087 0882 E-mail: admin@newforesthire.co.uk
North London Plant Hire, 4-16 Shacklewell Lane, London, E8 2EZ Tel: (020) 7254 3328 Fax: (020) 7923 4129 E-mail: sales@nlph.co.uk
Pinnacle Structures, Unit 7 Westwood Industrial Estate, Ewyas Harold, Hereford, HR2 0EL Tel: (01981) 241414 Fax: (01981) 241195 E-mail: mail@pinnaclestructures.co.uk
Platform, Lift House, Gloucester Road, Almondsbury, Bristol, BS32 4HY Tel: (01454) 270705 Fax: (01454) 312497 E-mail: info@platformcompany.co.uk
Power Tool Rentals Ltd, Halifax Road, Hipperholme, Halifax, West Yorkshire, HX3 8ER Tel: (01422) 205616 Fax: (01422) 206282 E-mail: enquiries@powertoolrentals.co.uk
Quinto Crane Hire, The Drift, Nacton Road, Ipswich, IP3 9QR Tel: (01473) 712041 Fax: (01473) 720386
Quinto Crane & Plant Ltd, Drakes Lane, Boreham, Chelmsford, CM3 3BE Tel: (01245) 360531 Fax: (01245) 362427
Quinto Crane & Plant Ltd, Admiralty Road, Great Yarmouth, Norfolk, NR30 3DY Tel: (01493) 331800 Fax: (01603) 407269
Quinto Crane & Plant Ltd, Wisbech Road, King's Lynn, Norfolk, PE30 5JL Tel: (01553) 764383 Fax: (01553) 768716
Quinto Crane & Plant Ltd, Markfield Road, Groby, Leicester, LE6 0FT Tel: (01530) 244181 Fax: (01530) 244808
Quinto Crane & Plant Ltd, Anson Road, Norwich Airport, Norwich, NR6 6EH Tel: (01603) 410881 Fax: (01603) 404565 E-mail: cranehire@quinto.co.uk
Quinto Crane & Plant Ltd, Royce Road, Peterborough, PE1 5YB Tel: (01733) 560338 Fax: (01733) 890829 E-mail: adrian@quinto.co.uk
S G B Rental & Sales, 104 Scrubs Lane, Willesden, London, NW10 6SF Tel: (020) 8969 3661 Fax: (020) 8960 6033
S R B E Ltd, Stewkley Road, Soulbury, Leighton Buzzard, Bedfordshire, LU7 0DF Tel: (01525) 270591 Fax: (01525) 270727 E-mail: sales@srbe.co.uk
Sangwin Concrete Products Ltd, Dansom Lane, Hull, HU8 7LN Tel: (01482) 329921 Fax: (01482) 215353 E-mail: info@sangwin.co.uk
Thames Crane Services Ltd, 327 Heyford Park, Camp Road, Upper Heyford, Bicester, Oxfordshire, OX25 5HA Tel: (01869) 232001 Fax: (01869) 232004
Geoff Till Electrical Contractors Ltd, 19 Sherwood Road, Aston Fields Industrial Estate, Bromsgrove, Worcestershire, B60 3DR Tel: (01527) 871123 Fax: (01527) 873075 E-mail: info@gtelec.co.uk

BUILDING ACCESS EQUIPMENT OR TOWERS

▶ Aid Building Company Ltd, 18 Camborne Avenue, Romford, RM3 8QP Tel: (07718) 757762 Fax: 01708 38442 E-mail: info@aidbuilding.com
Airborne Industrial Access Ltd, Pegasus House 15 Irwin Road, Guildford, Surrey, GU2 7PW Tel: (01483) 451610 Fax: (01483) 533009 E-mail: ringway@btinternet.com
Alimak Hek Ltd, Northampton Road, Rushden, Northamptonshire, NN10 6BW Tel: (01933) 354700 Fax: (01933) 410600 E-mail: ukinfo@alimakhek.com
Alto Tower Systems, 24 Walkers Road, North Moons, Moons Moat North Industrial Estate, Redditch, Worcestershire, B98 9HE Tel: (01527) 62946 Fax: (01527) 597444 E-mail: sales@alto-towers.co.uk
A-Plant Ltd, Mansfield Road, Derby, DE1 3RF Tel: (01332) 382275 Fax: (01332) 295504 E-mail: derbynorth@aplant.com
Ash Of Ancoats Ltd, 166-174 Great Ancoats Street, Manchester, M4 7AB Tel: 0161-273 6986 Fax: 0161-273 6986 E-mail: ashdiy@freenetname.co.uk
▶ Beaver Architectural Ironmongery, Unit D 18 Imperial Way, Croydon, CR0 4RR Tel: (020) 8681 3939 Fax: (020) 8649 8213 E-mail: gary@beaverai.co.uk
Cento Engineering Co. Ltd, Baddow Park, West Hanningfield Road, Great Baddow, Chelmsford, CM2 7SY Tel: (01245) 477708 Fax: (01245) 477748
Chislett Hire, Enterprise Way, Pinchbeck, Spalding, Lincolnshire, PE11 3YR Tel: (01775) 725778 Fax: (01775) 767523 E-mail: sales@chislett.co.uk
Cradle Access Services Ltd, PO Box 70, Erith, Kent, DA8 3WY Tel: (01322) 345999 Fax: (01322) 345999 E-mail: cradle.access@btconnect.com
Dragon, 72-74 Heol Tawe, Abercrave, Swansea, SA9 1XR Tel: (01639) 730031 Fax: (01639) 730020
Hill Top Fabrications Co 1998 Ltd, Unit 22 Siddons Factory Estate, Howard Street, West Bromwich, West Midlands, B70 0SU Tel: 0121-556 9666 Fax: 0121-556 3777 E-mail: hilltopfab@supanet.com
J A B Hire Services Ltd, J A B House, Delamare Road, Cheshunt, Waltham Cross, Hertfordshire, EN8 9SS Tel: (01992) 634666 Fax: (01992) 634777
Jackson Lifts Ltd, Unit 4-19, Ropery Business Park, London, SE7 7RX Tel: (020) 8293 4176 Fax: (020) 8305 0274 E-mail: sales@jacksonlifts.com
Kobi, Unit 19 Seax Court, Southfields Industrial Estate, Basildon, Essex, SS15 6SL Tel: (01268) 416335 Fax: (01268) 542148 E-mail: cradles@kobi.co.uk
London Tower Service Ltd, Unit 16 London Industrial Park, Eastbury Road, Beckton, London, E6 6LP Tel: (020) 7511 2090 Fax: (020) 7511 8060 E-mail: hire@londontowerservice.co.uk
Lyte Ladders & Towers, Wind Road, Ystradgynlais, Swansea, SA9 1AF Tel: (01639) 846816 Fax: (01639) 841541 E-mail: sales@lyteladders.co.uk
Mitie Generation Ltd, Meriton Street, Bristol, BS2 0SZ Tel: 0117-972 4550 Fax: 0117-972 4502 E-mail: bristol@generationuk.co.uk
On Site Supplies, Stephenson Way, Crawley, West Sussex, RH10 1TN Tel: (01293) 744444
P A S M A, PO Box 168, Leeds, LS11 9WW Tel: (0845) 2304041 Fax: (0845) 2304042 E-mail: pasma@portfolio-support.co.uk
▶ PMC Safety Netting Ltd, Unit 3, Appian Way, Europa Business Park, Grimsby, Lincolnshire, DN31 2UT Tel: (01472) 267733 Fax: (01472) 350921 E-mail: pmc.safetynetting@ntlworld.com
Ripco Sales, Bulldozer House, New Road, Sheerness, Kent, ME12 1AU Tel: (01795) 660666 Fax: (01795) 661559 E-mail: info@atecoaccess.com
Safe T Reach Ltd, Crucible Road, Corby, Northamptonshire, NN17 5TS Tel: (01536) 267686 Fax: (01536) 267686
▶ Standfast Access Equipement, Brendon Road, Bristol, BS3 4PX Tel: 0117-953 9533
Telford Tower & Scaffolding Ltd, Unit F7 Castle Trading Estate, Snedshill, Telford, Shropshire, TF2 9NP Tel: (01952) 612814 Fax: (01952) 613006
Youngman Group, The Causeway, Heybridge, Maldon, Essex, CM9 4LJ Tel: (01621) 745900 Fax: (01621) 745710 E-mail: youngmansales@youngmangroup.com

BUILDING ACCOMMODATION MODULES

Lydney Containers Ltd, Unit 14 Lydney Industrial Estate, Harbour Road, Lydney, Gloucestershire, GL15 4EJ Tel: (01594) 842378 Fax: (01594) 843213 E-mail: info@lydneycontainers.co.uk
Lydney Containers Ltd, Unit 29-30 Vulcan Works, Wargrave Road, Newton-le-Willows, Merseyside, WA12 8RN Tel: 01695 731890 Fax: 01925 229484 E-mail: info@lydneycontainers.co.uk
Grant Westfield Ltd, 3 Westfield Avenue, Edinburgh, EH11 2QH Tel: 0131-337 6262 Fax: 0131-337 2859 E-mail: sales@grantwestfield.co.uk

BUILDING AUTOMATION SYSTEMS

▶ RED Control Systems Otley Ltd, Wharfebank House, Wharfebank Business Centre, Ilkley Road, Otley, West Yorkshire, LS21 3JP Tel: (01943) 851000 Fax: (08714) 259742 E-mail: enquiries@redcontrolsystems.com

BUILDING BLOCKS

Anglosax Ltd, 3 Pomeroy Drive, Oadby Industrial Estate, Oadby, Leicester, LE2 5NE Tel: 0116-271 1005
Besblock Ltd, Halesfield 21, Telford, Shropshire, TF7 4NF Tel: (01952) 586778 Fax: (01952) 585224 E-mail: sales@besblock.com
Bolt Ltd, Bluebridge Industrial Estate, Colchester Road, Halstead, Essex, CO9 2EX Tel: (01787) 477261 Fax: (01787) 475680 E-mail: enquiries@boltbuildingsupplies.co.uk
Braces, South Cornelly, Bridgend, Mid Glamorgan, CF33 4RE Tel: (01656) 742830 Fax: (01656) 744463
Building Supplies (Holme Lane) Ltd, 115 Holme Lane, Sheffield, S6 4JR Tel: 0114-234 2501 Fax: 0114-285 2836
C & B Timbers/Custom Sheds, 12 Old Mill La Industrial Estate, Mansfield Woodhouse, Mansfield, Nottinghamshire, NG19 9BG Tel: (01623) 632872 Fax: (01623) 632872
Carter Concrete Ltd, Britons Lane, Beeston Regis, Sheringham, Norfolk, NR26 8TP Tel: (01263) 823434 Fax: (01263) 825678 E-mail: mail@carter-concrete.co.uk
Dog Lane Blockworks Ltd, Dog Lane, Horsford, Norwich, NR10 3DH Tel: (01603) 898676 Fax: (01603) 891649
Forticrete Ltd, Thornhill Works, Calder Road, Dewsbury, West Yorkshire, WF12 9HY Tel: (01924) 456416 Fax: (01924) 430697 E-mail: enquiries@forticrete.com
H & H Celcon Ltd, Heck Lane, Pollington, Goole, North Humberside, DN14 0BA Tel: (01405) 861212 Fax: (01405) 862168
▶ H Plus H Celcon Ltd, 3 Quartermaster Road, West Wilts Trading Estate, Westbury, Wiltshire, BA13 4JT Tel: (01732) 886333 Fax: (01373) 827631
Hampton Cast Stone, Unit 7, Merretts Mill, Woodchester, Stroud, Gloucestershire, GL5 5EU Tel: (01453) 836677 Fax: (01453) 835005E-mail: sales@hamptoncaststone.co.uk
Holbourne Engineering, Wem Engineering Centre, Church Lane, Wem, Shrewsbury, SY4 5HS Tel: (01939) 235124 Fax: (01939) 235126 E-mail: info@holborne-engineering.co.uk
Lignacite Ltd, Meadgate Works, Meadgate Road, Nazeing, Waltham Abbey, Essex, EN9 2PD Tel: (01992) 464441 Fax: (01992) 445713 E-mail: info@lignacite.co.uk
Lignacite Brandon Ltd, Norfolk House, High Street, Brandon, Suffolk, IP27 0AX Tel: (01842) 810678 Fax: (01842) 814602 E-mail: info@lignacite.co.uk
Masterblock, Nether Kellet, Carnforth, Lancashire, LA6 1EA Tel: (01524) 736636 Fax: (01524) 736635
Merton Timber, Rowfant Sawmills, Wallage Lane, Rowfant, Crawley, West Sussex, RH10 4NQ Tel: (01342) 716633 Fax: (01342) 716655 E-mail: sales@merton-timber.co.uk
Plasmor Ltd, Womersley Road, Knottingley, West Yorkshire, WF11 0DN Tel: (01977) 673221 Fax: (01977) 607071 E-mail: sales@plasmor.co.uk
Readyblock, 45 Craighulliar Road, Portrush, County Antrim, BT56 8NN Tel: (028) 7082 3374 Fax: (028) 7082 2682
Sellite Blocks Ltd, The Old Quarry, Long Lane, Great Heck, Goole, North Humberside, DN14 0BT Tel: (01977) 661631 Fax: (01977) 662155 E-mail: sales@sellite.co.uk
▶ Thin Joint Technology Ltd, 15 Manfred Street, Erskine Industrial Estate, Liverpool, L6 1AU Tel: 0151-260 2000 Fax: 0151-260 6745 E-mail: alan@clan.co.uk

BUILDING BLOCKS – *continued*

W Fayers & Sons, 15 Margaret Road, Barnet, Hertfordshire, EN4 9NR Tel: (020) 8370 6400 Fax: (020) 8370 6415

William Rainford, Leckwith Road, Bootle, Merseyside, L30 6YF Tel: 0151-525 5991 Fax: 0151-530 1676

BUILDING BOARD, *See Chipboard etc; also Wallboard etc*

BUILDING CHEMICAL PRODUCTS

Borregaard (UK) Ltd, Clayton Road, Risley Employment Area, Warrington, WA3 6QQ Tel: (01925) 285400 Fax: (01925) 285434 E-mail: marketing_europe@borregaard.com

Ideal Chemical Products, Unit D5 Taylor Business Park, Risley, Warrington, WA3 6BL Tel: (01925) 765934 Fax: (01925) 766220

Kingfisher Building Products Ltd, Cooper Lane, Bardsea, Ulverston, Cumbria, LA12 9RA Tel: (01229) 869100 Fax: (01229) 869101 E-mail: sales@kingfisherchem.com

M C Building Chemicals, Stechford Trading Estate Lyndon Road, Unit 17, Stechford, Birmingham, B33 8BU Tel: 0121-789 8333 Fax: 0121-789 8595 E-mail: sales@mc-bauchemie.de

Ronacrete Ltd, Ronac House, Selinas Lane, Dagenham, Essex, RM8 1QH Tel: (020) 8593 7621 Fax: (020) 8595 6969 E-mail: sosen@ronacrete.co.uk

Sealocrete PLA Ltd, Greenfield Lane, Rochdale, Lancashire, OL11 2LD Tel: (01706) 352255 Fax: (01706) 860880 E-mail: bestproduct@sealocrete.co.uk

Sika Ltd, Watchmead, Welwyn Garden City, Hertfordshire, AL7 1BQ Tel: (01707) 394444 Fax: (01707) 329129 E-mail: info@sika.com

Sovereign Chemical Ltd, Park Road, Barrow-In-Furness, Cumbria, LA14 4EQ Tel: (01229) 870800 Fax: (01229) 870850 E-mail: sales@sovchem.co.uk

▶ Syk Components, Unit 27 Commerce Court, Challenge Way, Bradford, West Yorkshire, BD4 8NW Tel: (01274) 662333 Fax: (01274) 664280 E-mail: sykcompsales@aol.com

Tetrosyl Ltd, Bevis Green Works, Mill Road, Walmersley, Bury, Lancashire, BL9 6RE Tel: 0161-764 5981 Fax: 0161-797 5899 E-mail: info@tetrosyl.com

BUILDING CONTRACTORS

1 T O 1 Lionheart, Trump House, 15 Edison Street, Hillington Industrial Estate, Glasgow, G52 4JW Tel: 0141-810 5353

▶ A A Contractors, 1 Somerton Green, Bognor Regis, West Sussex, PO22 8EZ Tel: (01243) 863209 Fax: (01243) 863025

A Adamson Ltd, Reeki House, Aberdeen Road, Laurencekirk, Kincardineshire, AB30 1AJ Tel: (01561) 377332 Fax: (01561) 378024

▶ A & B Builders, 8 York Road South, Wigan, Lancashire, WN4 9DT Tel: (01942) 720968 Fax: (01942) 272388 E-mail: abconstruction@abtec.net

▶ A Bradley Ltd, 213 Shore Road, Ballyronan, Magherafelt, County Londonderry, BT45 6LW Tel: (028) 7941 8421 Fax: (028) 7941 8383 E-mail: abradleyltd@tiscali.co.uk

▶ A C Site Construction Services Ltd, Construction House, Fourth Way, Wembley, Middlesex, HA9 0LH Tel: (020) 8900 2737

▶ A Carpenter & Son (Builders) Ltd, Landguard Manor, Landguard Manor Road, Shanklin, Isle Of Wight, PO37 7JB Tel: (01983) 862014 Fax: (01983) 864797

▶ A & D Builders Ltd, Thorne House, Eastville, Yeovil, Somerset, BA21 4JD Tel: (01935) 411334

▶ A & D Building Services Ltd, 106-108 Salamander Street, Edinburgh, EH6 7LA Tel: 0131-467 7170

A D Buildings Ltd, 2A Crown Street, Redbourn, St. Albans, Hertfordshire, AL3 7JU Tel: (01582) 794842 Fax: (01582) 793889 E-mail: adbuildings@connectfree.co.uk

▶ A D Hamilton Ltd, 1227-1235 Cumbernauld Road, Glasgow, G33 1AW Tel: 0141-770 5031

A E Griffin & Son, 10 North Street, Bere Regis, Wareham, Dorset, BH20 7LA Tel: (01929) 471253 Fax: (01929) 472208 E-mail: aegriffinandson@aol.com

▶ A E Howlett Ltd, Claybury Hall Farm, Roding Lane North, Woodford Green, Essex, IG8 8ND Tel: (020) 8550 2395 Fax: (020) 8551 6261

▶ A F McPherson & Co., 84-90 Holmscroft Street, Greenock, Renfrewshire, PA15 4DG Tel: (01475) 720881

▶ A G M Builders, 46 Headingley Road, Norton, Doncaster, South Yorkshire, DN6 9EN Tel: (01302) 708374 Fax: 01302 708374 E-mail: alan@agmbuilders.co.uk

▶ A Houghton & Co. Ltd, 630 Cranbrook Road, Ilford, Essex, IG6 1HJ Tel: (020) 8554 5716 Fax: (020) 8518 5327

▶ A J Clark Construction Ltd, 19 Bentinck Street, Kilmarnock, Ayrshire, KA1 4AW Tel: (01563) 539993

▶ A J Contracts Whitstable, Unit 181 John Wilson Business Park, Harvey Drive, Chestfield, Whitstable, Kent, CT5 3RB Tel: (01227) 280009 Fax: (01227) 275683 E-mail: sales@ajcontracts.co.uk

▶ A & J Glass & Glazing Ltd, 3 West Harbour Road, Edinburgh, EH5 1PH Tel: 0131-552 0001 Fax: 0131-552 0055

▶ A J Hawkridge & Sons, The Old Passenger Station, Milby, Boroughbridge, York, YO51 9BW Tel: (01423) 322506 Fax: (01423) 326752

▶ A J Rennie Ltd, Inverboyndie Industrial Estate, Banff, AB45 2JJ Tel: (01261) 818666 Fax: (01261) 818777

A J Roberts Ltd, 12 Methley Road, Castleford, West Yorkshire, WF10 1LX Tel: (01977) 553027 Fax: (01977) 513613

▶ A.K.S Ward, West Way, Botley, Oxford, OX2 0JJ Tel: (01865) 240071 Fax: (01865) 248006

▶ A O Roberts Ltd, Gaerwen Industrial Estate, Gaerwen, Gwynedd, LL60 6HR Tel: (01248) 422101 Fax: (01248) 422141 E-mail: enquiries@aoroberts.co.uk

A P E L Contractors, 1 Station Road, Methley, Leeds, LS26 9ER Tel: (01977) 603890 Fax: (01977) 603890

A P Lewis & Sons Ltd, Orion Way, Kettering Business Park, Kettering, Northamptonshire, NN15 6NL Tel: (01536) 525295 Fax: (01536) 525296

▶ A R Aspinall & Sons Ltd, 2 Station Road, Willingham, Cambridge, CB4 5HF Tel: (01954) 260391

▶ A Ross, Kendal Crescent Yard, Kendal Cresent, Alness, Ross-Shire, IV17 0UG Tel: (01349) 882250 Fax: (01349) 882266

▶ A Ryall & Son (Contractors) Ltd, 83 Victoria Road, Mexborough, South Yorkshire, S64 9BX Tel: (01709) 583248

▶ A S Wellington, 58-59 Village Farm Road, Village Farm Industrial Estate, Pyle, Bridgend, Mid Glamorgan, CF33 6BN Tel: (01656) 748020 Fax: (01656) 748029

▶ A Tait & Sons, Dounby, Orkney, KW17 2HT Tel: (01856) 771236 Fax: (01856) 771762

▶ A V Services, Unit 17 Avenue Industrial Estate, Southend Arterial Road, Harold Wood, Romford, RM3 0BY Tel: (01708) 376221 Fax: (01708) 376224

A.W. Construction Ltd, Old House, Gorsey Lane, Coleshill, Birmingham, B46 1JU Tel: (01675) 432102 Fax: (01675) 432112 E-mail: info@awconstruction.plc.uk

A W Hardy & Co. Ltd, Stock Road, Southend-on-Sea, SS2 5QG Tel: (01702) 462721 Fax: (01702) 469062 E-mail: enqs@hardygroup.demon.co.uk

▶ A W Lithgow Ltd, 2 Edinburgh Road, Cleghorn, Lanark, ML11 7RW Tel: (01555) 665066

▶ A&T, Fairview, Agraria Road, Guildford, Surrey, GU2 4LE Tel: (01483) 568181 Fax: (01483) 855187 E-mail: info@atbuilders.com

▶ Abacus Developments Ltd, 1 Abacus Park, Forth Avenue Industrial Estate, Kirkcaldy, Fife, KY2 5NZ Tel: (01592) 268408 Fax: (01592) 640740

▶ Abbey Contractors Ltd, Haydock Park Road, Derby, DE24 8HT Tel: (01332) 291646

Abbey Mews Builders Ltd, 618 Harrow Road, London, W10 4NJ Tel: (020) 8969 2449 Fax: (020) 8960 5090

▶ Abbeygate, 39 Shaftesbury Crescent, Staines, Middlesex, TW18 1QL Tel: (01784) 423405 Fax: (01784) 423405

▶ Abbeygrey Ltd, 331 Nottingham Road, Eastwood, Nottingham, NG16 2AP Tel: (01773) 769245 Fax: (01773) 533127

▶ Abbotshall Homes Ltd, 5 Oswald Road, Kirkcaldy, Fife, KY1 3JE Tel: (01592) 653653 Fax: (01592) 653353

Able (U K) Ltd, Able House, Billingham Reach Industrial Estate, Haverton Hill, Billingham, Cleveland, TS23 1PX Tel: (01642) 806080 Fax: (01642) 655655E-mail: info@ableuk.com

Absolutely Splashing Aquatic Consultants, 15 Salkeld Avenue, Ashton-in-Makerfield, Wigan, Lancashire, WN4 9NH Tel: (01942) 511947

Ackroyd & Abbott, 2 Rotherham Road, Sheffield, S13 9LL Tel: 0114-269 3201 Fax: 0114-254 0272

▶ Acorn Building Services Ltd, Sefton St, Leigh, Lancashire, WN7 1LX Tel: (01942) 609966 Fax: (01942) 262444 E-mail: reception@acornbuilders.com

Acorn Leisure, The Paddock, Tenby, Dyfed, SA70 8DJ Tel: (01834) 842931 Fax: (01834) 845174

▶ Acorn Services, 242 Portobello High Street, Edinburgh, EH15 2AT Tel: 0131-669 8444 Fax: 0131-669 8444

▶ Adept Building Contractors, 367-369 Croydon Road, Wallington, Surrey, SM6 7NY Tel: (020) 8254 9785 Fax: (020) 8254 9786

Agritask Construction Ltd, Tanhouse Farm, Rusper Road, Newdigate, Dorking, Surrey, RH5 5BX Tel: (01306) 631334 Fax: (01306) 631891 E-mail: info@agritask.co.uk

▶ Ailsa Building Ltd, 251 Dundyvan Road, Coatbridge, Lanarkshire, ML5 4AU Tel: (01236) 422615 Fax: (01236) 602623

▶ Aitken Building Contractors, 5 Wych Elm, Harlow, Essex, CM20 1QP Tel: (01279) 419422 Fax: (01279) 413199

▶ Aj Civil Engineering Ltd, Nantllan, Clarach, Aberystwyth, Dyfed, SY23 3DT Tel: (01970) 828316 Fax: (01970) 820446

▶ Akela Construction Contractors, 55 Hawbank Road, East Kilbride, Glasgow, G74 5EG Tel: (01355) 267744 Fax: (01355) 235656

Alan Grant Grampian Ltd, 59 Main Street, Alford, Aberdeenshire, AB33 8PX Tel: (01975) 562573 Fax: (01975) 563631

▶ Alan Megaw, 64 Mount Merrion Avenue, Belfast, BT6 0FR Tel: (028) 9058 2233

▶ Alderson Building Services, Whitehouse Lane, Ushaw Moor, Durham, DH7 7PG Tel: 0191-373 0393 Fax: 0191-373 6762

▶ Alex Lovie & Son, 41 Main Street, New Deer, Turriff, Aberdeenshire, AB53 6TA Tel: (01771) 644295 Fax: (01771) 644787

▶ Alexander Arthur & Sons (Scotland) Ltd, 4 Novar Drive, Glasgow, G12 9PU Tel: 0141-339 8595

▶ Alexander Morton Homes Scotland Ltd, Kilmaurs, Kilmarnock, Ayrshire, KA3 2PG Tel: (0845) 230 0204

▶ Alfred Cox & Sons Brighton Ltd, 28a Brigden Street, Brighton, BN1 5DP Tel: (01273) 552762 Fax: (01273) 552012

▶ Alfred Groves & Sons Ltd, Shipton Road, Milton-under-Wychwood, Chipping Norton, Oxfordshire, OX7 6JP Tel: (01993) 830302 Fax: (01993) 831752

▶ Allen Wilson Joinery Ltd, Unit 12, Trident Close, Rochester, Kent, ME2 4ER Tel: (01634) 290560 E-mail: all@allenwilson.co.uk

▶ Allenbuild Ltd, Unit 4b Interchange 25 Business Park, Bostocks Lane, Sandiacre, Nottingham, NG10 5QG Tel: 0115-921 0150 Fax: 0115-921 0199 E-mail: mailbox@allenbuild.co.uk

Allenbuild Ltd, Jubilee House, Waterside Drive, Wigan, Lancashire, WN3 5AZ Tel: (01942) 246265 Fax: (01942) 821573 E-mail: north.west@allenbuild.co.uk

▶ Allied Trades Ltd, 14-16 Highholm Street, Port Glasgow, Renfrewshire, PA14 5HJ Tel: (01475) 743666

Allworks Ltd, Unit 4 Dene Valley Business Centre, Brookhampton Lane, Kineton, Warwick, CV3 0JD Tel: (01926) 642544 Fax: (01926) 642512 E-mail: allworksltd@warwicks.fsnet.co.uk

▶ Amber Construction Services Ltd, Unit 62 Uplands Business Park, Blackhorse Lane, London, E17 5QJ Tel: (020) 8531 4553 Fax: (020) 8531 7553

▶ Amberwood Construction Contractors, 1088 Tollcross Road, Glasgow, G32 8UN Tel: 0141-778 6163 Fax: 0141-778 6163

▶ Amco Donelon, Unit 4a Birchwood One Business Park, Dewhurst Road, Birchwood, Warrington, WA3 7GB Tel: (01925) 838070 Fax: (01925) 816670

▶ Amec Construction (Scotland) Ltd, Lundholm Road, Stevenston, Ayrshire, KA20 3LJ Tel: (01294) 605562

Amec Process & Energy Ltd, 76-78 Old Street, London, EC1V 9RU Tel: (020) 7539 5800 Fax: (020) 7539 5900 E-mail: commercial@amec.com

D.S. & J. Anderson, Unit 4, Tayview Industrial Estate, Friarton Road, Perth, PH2 8DF Tel: (01738) 444885 Fax: (01738) 444885

▶ Anderson & Innes Ltd, 15 Nursery Avenue, Kilmarnock, Ayrshire, KA1 3DP Tel: (01563) 523188 Fax: (01563) 523516

▶ Anderson James Builders Ltd, 35a Kyle Road Irvine Indust Estate, Irvine, Ayrshire, KA12 8LE Tel: (01294) 279245

▶ Andrew Macphee Ltd, 8b Dochcarty Road, Dingwall, Ross-Shire, IV15 9UG Tel: (01349) 862862 Fax: (01349) 862863

▶ Andrew Thomas (Builders) Ltd, 7 New Street, Musselburgh, Midlothian, EH21 6JH Tel: 0131-665 2792

▶ Anglia Building & Decorating Contractors, Anglia House, Newmarket Road, Dyserth, Rhyl, Clwyd, LL18 6BS Tel: (01745) 572100 Fax: (01745) 571658 E-mail: info@angliabuilders.co.uk

Anglo-Holt Construction Ltd, 150 Birmingham Road, West Bromwich, West Midlands, B70 6QT Tel: 0121-525 6717 Fax: 0121-553 4701 E-mail: sales@anglo-holt.co.uk

▶ Angus Homes Ltd, Markethill Industrial Estate, Markethill Road, Turriff, Aberdeenshire, AB53 4AG Tel: (01888) 562639 Fax: (01888) 568953

▶ Ansell Builders, 7 New Road, Mytholmroyd, Hebden Bridge, West Yorkshire, HX7 5DZ Tel: (01422) 881991 E-mail: Caroline@ansellgroup.com

▶ Anvil Construction, Anvil House, Whittonstall, Consett, County Durham, DH8 9JN Tel: (01207) 560991 Fax: (01207) 563538

Anything in Wood Ltd, 44-46a Hamilton Street, Grimsby, North East Lincolnshire, DN32 7HL Tel: (01472) 344176 Fax: (01472) 344176

▶ Apex Tubulars, Cairnrobin Pipe Yard, Portlethen, Aberdeen, AB12 4SB Tel: (01224) 786900 Fax: (01224) 784258

▶ Apollo London Ltd, Conquest House, Church Street, Waltham Abbey, Essex, EN9 1DX Tel: (01992) 650333 Fax: (01992) 650999

▶ Approved Construction, Unit 5 Newcastle Enterprise Centre, High Street, Knutton, Newcastle, Staffordshire, ST5 6BX Tel: (01782) 799820 Fax: (01782) 799820

▶ Approved Services, 108 Calderglen Avenue, Blantyre, Glasgow, G72 9UN Tel: (0800) 0850295 Fax: (01698) 820444

▶ Aran Construction, Tarporley Road, Stretton, Warrington, WA4 4NB Tel: (01925) 860002 Fax: (01925) 860101

▶ Arc Construction Ltd, 14 Lower Green Road, Tunbridge Wells, Kent, TN4 8TE Tel: (01892) 514035 Fax: (01892) 616553

▶ Archibald Fergusson Ltd, Ardgowan, Strachur, Cairndow, Argyll, PA27 8DG Tel: (01369) 860231

▶ Archibald Mccorquodale & Son Ltd, 353-355 Langside Road, Glasgow, G42 8XT Tel: 0141-423 1187 Fax: 0141-423 0497

▶ Archibald Russell Of Denny Ltd, Drumbowie Farm, Denny, Stirlingshire, FK6 5LZ Tel: (01324) 822555

▶ Ardmore Construction Ltd, 3 Hollybrook Place, Glasgow, G42 7HB Tel: 0141-433 2588

▶ Argee Builders Ltd, 1 Rosendale Way, Blantyre, Glasgow, G72 0NJ Tel: (01698) 826824 Fax: (01698) 826828

Armfield, Heriot House, 88-90 Guildford Street, Chertsey, Surrey, KT16 9AD Tel: (01932) 566633 Fax: (01932) 566639

▶ Arran Construction Ltd, Cleveland Hall, Cleveland Street, Darlington, County Durham, DL1 2PE Tel: (01325) 267221 Fax: (01325) 369521

▶ Arthur Cooper Construction Ltd, 72 Church St, Greasbrough, Rotherham, South Yorkshire, S61 4DX Tel: (01709) 551086

▶ Arx Construction Ltd, The Bake House, 43 Bonnyrigg Road, Dalkeith, Midlothian, EH22 3HF Tel: 0131-663 0996

▶ Arx Construction Ltd, Arx House, 22 Cameron Knowe, Philpstoun, Linlithgow, West Lothian, EH49 6RL Tel: (01506) 830114

▶ Ascot Environmental, Astra House, Christy Way, Southfields Business Park, Basildon, Essex, SS15 6TQ Tel: (01268) 540480 Fax: (01268) 540850

Ashleigh Scotland Ltd, Lochar House, Dumfries, DG1 3NU Tel: (01387) 711500 Fax: (01387) 711501

▶ Ashvale Civil Engineering, Dallow Road, Luton, LU1 1TD Tel: (01582) 726650 Fax: (01582) 726652

▶ Ashwood Scotland, 159A West Main Street, Whitburn, Bathgate, West Lothian, EH47 0QQ Tel: (01501) 744988

▶ Ashworth Construction (North West) Ltd, 16a Boxer Place, Moss Side, Leyland, PR26 7QL Tel: (01772) 699800

▶ Associated Building Maintenance, 106 Whitworth Road, Rochdale, Lancashire, OL12 0JJ Tel: (01706) 654730 Fax: (01706) 648169

Atkin John Construction Ltd, Viking Place, Cardiff, CF10 4UU Tel: (029) 2044 2060 Fax: (029) 2044 2065 E-mail: atkintradespec@enterprise.net

▶ Atkinson D J Ltd Builders Contractors, 123 North Wingfield Road, Grassmoor, Chesterfield, Derbyshire, S42 5EB Tel: (01246) 855699 Fax: (01246) 854292

Atom Civil Engineering & Drainage, Carlinlees, Darvel, Ayrshire, KA17 0NG Tel: (0800) 3898986

▶ Aubrey Davidson & Co., 137 Barronstown Road, Banbridge, County Down, BT32 3SA Tel: (028) 4066 2379 Fax: (028) 4062 6769

▶ Audex Contracts, Block 3, 8 Causewayside Street, Glasgow, G32 8LP Tel: 0141-778 6448 Fax: 0141-764 1731

B A Shaw Contractors Ltd, 90 Mount Pleasant Road, Newtownabbey, County Antrim, BT37 0NQ Tel: (028) 9036 5706 Fax: (028) 9036 5570

▶ B A Williams, Unit 21, Top Barn Business Centre, Worcester Road, Holt Heath, Worcester, WR6 6NH Tel: (01905) 620791 Fax: (01905) 621751 E-mail: info@dawbulidingcontractors.co.uk

▶ B & B Builders Ltd, Tolver Farm Cottage, Tolver, Long Rock, Penzance, Cornwall, TR20 8YL Tel: (01736) 330996 Fax: (01736) 330996

B & B Construction Ltd, Baulker Farm, Baulker Lane, Farnsfield, Newark, Nottinghamshire, NG22 8HP Tel: (01623) 883771 Fax: (01623) 883771 E-mail: bernard@bbconstruction.freeserve.co.uk

B C L Construction Ltd, 263 Haydons Road, London, SW19 8TY Tel: (020) 8543 6221 Fax: (020) 8543 9725 E-mail: sales@bclltdconstruction.co.uk

▶ B H L Builders Oxford Ltd, Unit 5 Station Field Industrial Estate, Kidlington, Oxfordshire, OX5 1JD Tel: (01865) 378049 Fax: (01865) 378050

▶ B Jeffrey Construction Ltd, Control Tower, Rufforth Airfield, Wetherby Road, Rufforth, York, YO23 3QA Tel: (01904) 738326

B & K Building Services Ltd, Peveril House, Alfreton Road, Derby, DE21 4AG Tel: (01332) 331444 Fax: (01332) 291067 E-mail: bkbs@rwkhouse.co.uk

▶ B & M Contract Services Ltd, B & M House, Gordon Road, Southbourne, Emsworth, Hampshire, PO10 8AZ Tel: (01243) 377444 Fax: (01243) 377666

B M H Construction Co Clifton Ltd, 52 Clifton Road, Henlow, Bedfordshire, SG16 6BL Tel: (01462) 816555 E-mail: info@bmhconstruction.co.uk

▶ B McDougal Ltd, 7 Erskine Square, Hillington Industrial Estate, Glasgow, G52 4BJ Tel: 0141-882 4600

▶ B W Cook Construction, Rutland Farm, Wimblington Road, Manea, March, Cambridgeshire, PE15 0JR Tel: (01354) 688062 Fax: (01354) 680934

▶ B W May & Son Ltd, West La Trading Estate, West Lane, Sittingbourne, Kent, ME10 3TT Tel: (01795) 423021 Fax: (01795) 426974 E-mail: sales@bwmay.co.uk

▶ Baas Construction Ltd, The Old Chapel, Brooklandsroad, Burnley, Lancashire, BB11 3PR Tel: (01282) 437304 Fax: (01282) 452200

▶ Bagwell Ltd, Station Yard, Station Road, Sidmouth, Devon, EX10 9DN Tel: (01395) 577194 Fax: (01395) 577132

BUILDING CONTRACTORS – *continued*

Baines Herbert Ltd, No 2 Passage Chester Street, Stockport, Cheshire, SK3 0BR Tel: 0161-480 9796

Baker & Sons Danbury Ltd, Eves Corner, Danbury, Chelmsford, CM3 4QB Tel: (01245) 225876 Fax: (01245) 226821 E-mail: enq@bakersofdanbury.co.uk

▶ Baker & Sons Margate Ltd, 29 St. Augustines Avenue, Margate, Kent, CT9 4DN Tel: (01843) 220958 Fax: (01843) 292467

Baldwin Construction Ltd, The Old School, Arrow, Alcester, Warwickshire, B49 5PJ Tel: (01789) 762125 Fax: (01789) 400367 E-mail: bill.@baldwin-constr.fsnet.co.uk

Balfour Beatty plc, Fourth Floor, 130 Wilton Road, London, SW1V 1LQ Tel: (020) 7216 6800 Fax: (020) 7216 6950

Balfour Beatty Construction Ltd, Neville House, 42-46 Hagley Road, Birmingham, B16 8PE Tel: 0121-224 6600 Fax: 0121-224 6601 E-mail: reception.edgbaston@bbcl.co.uk

▶ Balfour Beatty Construction Ltd, Churchill House, 29 Mill Hill Road, Pontefract, West Yorkshire, WF8 4HY Tel: (01977) 602120 Fax: (01977) 602181

Balfour Beatty Construction Ltd, Balfour House, Churchfield Road, Walton-on-Thames, Surrey, KT12 2TD Tel: (020) 7922 0000 Fax: (01932) 229032

▶ Bamond Civil Engineering Ltd, The Maltings, East Tyndall Street, Cardiff, CF24 5EA Tel: (029) 2047 1189 Fax: (029) 2048 5053

Banchory Contractors Ltd, The Minklets, Crathes, Banchory, Kincardineshire, AB31 5QQ Tel: (01330) 844767 Fax: (01330) 844788 E-mail: info.bcl@bancon.co.uk

▶ Bankton Developments, 76 New Row, Tranent, East Lothian, EH33 2AA Tel: (01875) 616888 Fax: (01875) 616836

Banner Homes Group plc, Riverside House, Holtspur Lane, Wooburn Green, High Wycombe, Buckinghamshire, HP10 0TJ Tel: (01628) 536200 Fax: (01628) 536201 E-mail: info@banner-homes.co.uk

Barchem Construction Ltd, 3 Barton Court, 11-12 High Street, Highworth, Swindon, SN6 7AG Tel: (01793) 762380 Fax: (01793) 766005 E-mail: barchonpr@aol.com

▶ Barconn Ltd, Roostinghill Gravel Pit, Beetley, Dereham, Norfolk, NR20 4DH Tel: (01362) 869089 Fax: (01362) 860555

▶ Bardon Contracts Ltd, 45-47 River View, Chadwell St Mary, Grays, Essex, RM16 4BJ Tel: (01375) 841555

S.P. Bardwell Ltd, Mapledean Indl Estate, Maldon Rado, Latchingdon, Chelmsford, CM3 6LG Tel: (01621) 742742 Fax: (01621) 741723 E-mail: steve@spbardwell.co.uk

▶ Barfoot & Powell Ltd, Coal Park Lane, Swanwick, Southampton, SO31 7GW Tel: (01489) 576281 Fax: (01489) 576298

▶ Barhale Construction plc, Redburn Industrial Estate, Woodall Road, Enfield, Middlesex, EN3 4LE Tel: (020) 8443 0333 Fax: (020) 8804 9597 E-mail: info@barhale.co.uk

▶ Barker Building Ltd, Dormston Trading Estate, Burton Road, Dudley, West Midlands, DY1 2UF Tel: (01902) 885098

Barnes Group Ltd, 6 Bermuda Road, Ransoms Euro Park, Ipswich, IP3 9RU Tel: (01473) 272222 Fax: (01473) 272955 E-mail: cbruce@barnesconstruction.co.uk

▶ Barnes Webster & Sons Ltd, 29 Crown Street, Brentwood, Essex, CM14 4BA Tel: (01277) 233344 Fax: (01277) 200379 E-mail: post@barneswebster.co.uk

▶ Barnett Construction Ltd, Gannow Lane, Rose Grove, Burnley, Lancashire, BB12 6JJ Tel: (01706) 833900 Fax: (0845) 2268822

Barnwood Shopfitting Ltd, 203 Barnwood Road, Gloucester, GL4 3HS Tel: (01452) 614124 Fax: (01452) 371061 E-mail: email@barnwoodshopfitting.com

▶ Barr Ltd, Maybury House, Turnhouse Road, Edinburgh, EH12 8LX Tel: 0131-339 1000

▶ Barr Construction, Dunollie Road, Oban, Argyll, PA34 5PL Tel: (01631) 567362

Barr Holdings Ltd, 100 Inchinnan Road, Paisley, Renfrewshire, PA3 2RE Tel: 0141-848 8000 Fax: 0141-848 8001 E-mail: info@barr.co.uk

Barratt, Vico House, Ring Road, Lower Wortley, Leeds, LS12 6AN Tel: 0113-279 0099 Fax: 0113-279 0038

▶ Barratt East Midlands Ltd, 16 Regan Way, Chilwell, Beeston, Nottingham, NG9 6RZ Tel: 0115-907 8300 Fax: 0115-973 2329

Barratt East Midlands Ltd, 16 Regan Way, Chilwell, Beeston, Nottingham, NG9 6RZ Tel: 0115-907 8300 Fax: 0115-907 8301 E-mail: ianrose@barratt-eastmidlands.co.uk

▶ Barratt (East Scotland) Ltd, Craigcrook Castle, Craigcrook Road, Edinburgh, EH4 3PE Tel: 0131-336 3655

▶ Barratt Eastern Counties plc, Lorne Stewart House, 7 Springfield Lyons Approach, Springfield, Chelmsford, CM2 5EY Tel: (01245) 232200

Barratt Homes, 60 Whitehall Road, Halesowen, West Midlands, B63 3JS Tel: 0121-585 5303 Fax: 0121-585 5304

Barratt Newcastle Ltd, Barratt House, City West Business Park, Newcastle upon Tyne, NE4 7DF Tel: 0191-298 6100

Barratt (West Scotland) P.L.C., Mayfield House, 7 Maggie Woods Loan, Falkirk, FK1 5SJ Tel: (01324) 620011 Fax: (01324) 625916

▶ Barrett Homes Ltd, 1 Silver Street, Kettering, Northamptonshire, NN16 0BN Tel: (01536) 511711 Fax: (01536) 511042 E-mail: liz@johnbarratt.co.uk

▶ Barrett Homes, 900 Pavilion Drive, Northampton, NN4 7RG Tel: (01604) 664500 Fax: (01604) 664501

Batty & Dixon, Raymond Road, Doncaster, South Yorkshire, DN5 9PP Tel: (01302) 783130 Fax: (01302) 390440

Malcolm Baucher Ltd, Cavendish House, Brighton Road, Waterloo, Liverpool, L22 5NG Tel: 0151-920 8030 Fax: 0151-949 0527 E-mail: baucherbuild@aol.com

▶ Baxter Ltd, 8 Smith Street, Dundee, DD3 8AZ Tel: (01382) 832900

C.J. Bayliss (Hereford) Ltd, Albert House, Holmer, Hereford, HR1 1JN Tel: (01432) 265130 Fax: (01432) 274435 E-mail: cjbayliss@btconnect.com

▶ Beal Developments Ltd, Tower House Lane, Hedon Road, Hull, HU12 8EE Tel: (01482) 899114

▶ Beard & Tandy, Stenders Business Park, The Stenders, Mitcheldean, Gloucestershire, GL17 0JE Tel: (01594) 542997

Beavan & Hodges Ltd, 29-35 Portland Street, Hereford, HR4 9JF Tel: (01432) 272188 Fax: (01432) 351173

▶ Beechwood Developments, 70 Albion Road, Edinburgh, EH7 5QZ Tel: 0131-661 5999

▶ Bellway Homes Ltd, Bothwell House Hamilton Business Park, Caird Park, Hamilton, Lanarkshire, ML3 0QA Tel: (01698) 477440 Fax: (01698) 477441

▶ Ben Walton Contractors, Mill Pit, Houghton le Spring, Tyne & Wear, DH4 4RA Tel: 0191-385 2517 Fax: 0191-385 2517

▶ Benfield & Loxley Ltd, Old Bank House, 166 Oxford Road, Cowley, Oxford, OX4 2LA Tel: (01865) 717855 Fax: (01865) 715368 E-mail: mail@benfieldandloxley.co.uk

▶ Benjamin Armitage (Hyde) Ltd, 238 Stockport Road, Gee Cross, Hyde, Cheshire, SK14 5RG Tel: 0161-368 2319

Benson Bros Bristol Ltd, Carlton Lodge, 90 Gloucester Road, Patchway, Bristol, BS34 6PZ Tel: 0117-969 4241 Fax: 0117-931 2028

▶ Berkeley Homes, 3 Arsenal Way, London, SE18 6TF Tel: (020) 8319 5900

▶ Berkeley Homes (Southern) Ltd, Broadlands Business Campus, Langhurstwood Road, Horsham, West Sussex, RH12 4QP Tel: (01403) 211240

Berma Ltd, 31 Brooke Avenue, Harrow, Middlesex, HA2 0NB Tel: (020) 8423 6568 Fax: (020) 8864 6615

▶ Bermar Building Co. Ltd, 2 Bull Royd Industrial Estate, Bull Royd Lane, Bradford, West Yorkshire, BD8 0LH Tel: (01274) 493427 Fax: (01274) 483502

▶ Bernard Ward Ltd, Dean House Accent Park, Bakewell Road, Peterborough, PE2 6XS Tel: (01733) 390190

Bett Homes Ltd, Argyll Court, The Castle Business Park, Stirling, FK9 4TT Tel: (01786) 477777 Fax: (01786) 477666 E-mail: betthomes@bett.co.uk

▶ David Beveridge Ltd, 43-51 Jeanfield Road, Perth, PH1 1NZ Tel: (01738) 636736 Fax: (01738) 630100

▶ Bewick Homes Ltd, 40 Mill Street, Bedford, MK40 3HD Tel: (01234) 267459 Fax: (01234) 212864

▶ Bewley & Scott Ltd, Ellison Road, Gateshead, Tyne & Wear, NE11 9TS Tel: 0191-460 4219 Fax: 0191-460 1901

▶ Bexwell Construction Ltd, 27 Stamford Hill, London, N16 5TU Tel: (020) 8802 4109 Fax: (020) 8802 0523

▶ Biggs Building & Landscaping, 12 Westray Place, Bishopbriggs, Glasgow, G64 1UQ Tel: 0141-762 0004 Fax: 0141-762 0007

▶ Birch House Construction Ltd, 31 Icen Road, Weymouth, Dorset, DT3 5JL Tel: (01305) 785787 Fax: (01305) 781117

William Birch & Sons Ltd, 1 Link Road Court, Osbaldwick, York, YO10 3JQ Tel: (01904) 411411 Fax: (01904) 428428 E-mail: info@williambirch.co.uk

Birse Construction Ltd, Humber Road, Barton-upon-Humber, South Humberside, DN18 5BW Tel: (01652) 633222 Fax: (01652) 633360 E-mail: birseho@birse.co.uk

▶ Bishop Developments, 176 York Way, London, N1 0AZ Tel: (020) 7713 0455 Fax: (020) 7278 1594

▶ Biwater Leslie, PO Box 2, Glasgow, G78 1DU Tel: (01301) 703497

▶ Blackburn Marshall Construction Ltd, Wooler Street, Darlington, County Durham, DL1 1RQ Tel: (01325) 352109 Fax: (01325) 488146

▶ Blackburns Harleston Ltd, 37 Station Road, Harleston, Norfolk, IP20 9EW Tel: (01379) 852131 Fax: (01379) 853363 E-mail: mail@blackburns-harleston.co.uk

Blakeley Tonge & Partner Ltd, 3 Lever Bridge Mills, Radcliffe Road, Bolton, BL3 1RU Tel: (01204) 535580 Fax: (01204) 535581

▶ Blanchards Construction, 3 Newland Drive, Wallasey, Merseyside, CH44 2AX Tel: 0151-637 1222

▶ Blight & Scoble Ltd, Mardle Way, Buckfastleigh, Devon, TQ11 0JS Tel: (01364) 642253 Fax: (01364) 642074 E-mail: enquiries@blightandscoble.co.uk

▶ Bloor Homes, Rivermead Industrial Estate, Rivermead Drive, Westlea, Swindon, SN5 7EX Tel: (01793) 513938 Fax: (01793) 486953

▶ Bluestone plc, Waterside Centre, 4215 Solihull Parkway, Birmingham Business Park, Birmingham, B37 7YN Tel: 0121-329 1500 Fax: 0121-329 1501

Bluestone Ltd, Unit F3 Fareham Heights, Standard Way, Fareham, Hampshire, PO16 8XT Tel: (01329) 822888 Fax: (01329) 827272

▶ Bluestone Plc, Nations House, 103 Wigmore Street, London, W1U 1AQ Tel: (020) 7659 3333 Fax: (020) 7659 3300

Bluestone plc, 4 Phoenix Place, Nottingham, NG8 6BA Tel: 0115-964 7000 Fax: 0115-964 7001 E-mail: admin@bluestonesolutions.net

▶ Bluestone plc, The Meads Business Centre, Ashworth Road, Bridgemead, Swindon, SN5 7YJ Tel: (01793) 648000 Fax: (01793) 648001

▶ Bluestone plc, 3 Heron Gate Office Park, Hankridge Way, Taunton, Somerset, TA1 2LR Tel: (01823) 624100 Fax: (01823) 624101

▶ Bluu Group, Princess House, 50 Eastcastle Street, London, W1W 8EA Tel: (020) 7079 3400 Fax: (020) 7323 1723

Bonner & Cook Ltd, 14 South Road, Luton, LU1 3UD Tel: (01582) 732151 Fax: (01582) 480424

▶ Bonnington Contract Ltd, 58 Southcroft Road, Rutherglen, Glasgow, G73 1UG Tel: 0141-613 6132

▶ Bonser Building Contractors Ltd, Scotlands Industrial Estate, The Scotlands, Coalville, Leicestershire, LE67 3JJ Tel: (01530) 810336 Fax: (01530) 813409

Booker & Best, Windmill House, Windmill Road, St. Leonards-on-Sea, East Sussex, TN38 9BY Tel: (01424) 434391 Fax: (01424) 446833 E-mail: adrianstallworthy@bookerbest.co.uk

Border Construction Ltd, Marconi Road, Brough Road Industrial Estate, Carlisle, CA2 7NA Tel: (01228) 522296 Fax: (01228) 514928 E-mail: admin@border-construction.co.uk

▶ Border Construction Ltd, Rhymers Mill, Mill Road, Earlston, Berwickshire, TD4 6DG Tel: (01896) 849660 Fax: (01896) 848917

Bott Builders Ltd, Birmingham Road, Whitacre Heath Coleshill, Birmingham, B46 2ET Tel: (01675) 462214

▶ John Boult & Sons, 2a Farnell Street, Glasgow, G4 9SE Tel: 0141-333 1966 Fax: 0141-333 1456

Bourne Building Services, Builders Yard, Wool Road, Poole, Dorset, BH12 4NG Tel: (01202) 749105 Fax: (0870) 7707306

▶ Bovis Construction Contractors, 33 Bothwell Street, Glasgow, G2 6NL Tel: 0141-226 8500 Fax: 0141-226 8513

Bovis Lend Lease, 32 Cumberland Street, Bristol, BS2 8NL Tel: 0117-924 8094 Fax: 0117-924 7314

Bowden-Jackson (Construction) Ltd, PO Box Hk7, Leeds, LS11 7DY Tel: 0113-277 9539 Fax: 0113-277 9539

Bowey Construction Ltd, Albany Court, Newcastle Business Park, Newcastle upon Tyne, NE4 7YB Tel: 0191-273 3311 Fax: 0191-273 6620 E-mail: info@boweyconstruction.co.uk

Bowman E Sons Building Contractors, Cherryholt Road, Stamford, Lincolnshire, PE9 2EP Tel: (01780) 751015 Fax: (01780) 759051 E-mail: mail@ebowman.co.uk

Bowmer & Kirkland Ltd, High Edge Court, Church Street, Heage, Belper, Derbyshire, DE56 2BW Tel: (01773) 853131 Fax: (01773) 856710 E-mail: sales@bandk.co.uk

Bowmer & Kirkland Ltd, Aspect Gate, 166 College Road, Harrow, Middlesex, HA1 1BH Tel: (020) 8427 4322 Fax: (020) 8863 5627 E-mail: enquiries@bandk-harrow.co.uk

▶ Bracken Lea Homes Ltd, Unit 9 Main Street, Dunfermline, Fife, KY12 8QY Tel: (01383) 882882 Fax: (01383) 882244

▶ Bracken Lea Homes Planning Department Ltd, Culross, Dunfermline, Fife, KY12 8ET Tel: (01383) 880800

▶ Alexander Braidwood Ltd, Rosendale Way, Blantyre, Glasgow, G72 0NJ Tel: (01698) 822633

Bramall Construction, 3 Callflex Business Park, Golden Smithies Lane, Wath-upon-Dearne, Rotherham, South Yorkshire, S63 7ER Tel: (01709) 766000 Fax: (01709) 766001 E-mail: info@bramall.com

▶ Bramber Construction Ltd, 370 Brighton Road, Shoreham-by-Sea, West Sussex, BN43 6RE Tel: (01273) 465111 Fax: (01273) 440799 E-mail: info@bramber-construction.co.uk

▶ Brass Maintenance Ltd, Unit 8a G W S Trading Estate, Leabrook Road, Wednesbury, West Midlands, WS10 7NB Tel: 0121-556 2010 Fax: 0121-556 2040

▶ Braycot Construction Ltd, 56 Malt Mill Lane, Halesowen, West Midlands, B62 8JF Tel: 0121-559 2955 Fax: 0121-561 2324

W.W. Brazell Ltd, Raeburn Street, Hartlepool, Cleveland, TS26 8PT Tel: (01429) 272937 Fax: (01429) 274950

▶ Brian Brass, Kardale, Sandwick, Stromness, Orkney, KW16 3HY Tel: (01856) 841733

▶ Brick Peers, Milton Priory House, Gate Lane, Wells, Somerset, BA5 1UA Tel: (01749) 683110 Fax: (01749) 683117

▶ Brick & Steel Construction Co., 4-6 Boswell Square, Hillington Industrial Estate, Glasgow, G52 4BQ Tel: 0141-810 1919 Fax: 0141-810 1929

▶ Brier Construction Ltd, Upper Whittimere Cottage, Upper Whittimere, Bobbington, Stourbridge, West Midlands, DY7 5EP Tel: (01384) 221298 Fax: (01384) 221268

Bristlewand Ltd, 48 Ashton Vale Road, Bristol, BS3 2HQ Tel: 0117-963 6141 Fax: 0117-963 1954 E-mail: bristlewand@kennygroup.co.uk

Britannia Construction Ltd, Britannia House, Staverton Technology Park, Staverton, Cheltenham, Gloucestershire, GL51 6TQ Tel: (01452) 859880 Fax: (01452) 859881 E-mail: info@britanniaconstruction.co.uk

Britcon Ltd, Midland Road, Scunthorpe, South Humberside, DN16 1DQ Tel: (01724) 280022 Fax: (01724) 270616 E-mail: robinallen@britcon.co.uk

▶ Broadoak Construction Southeast Ltd, Triumph House, Guildford Road, Bookham, Leatherhead, Surrey, KT23 4HB Tel: (01372) 453111 Fax: (01372) 452193 E-mail: sales@broadoak-construction.co.uk

▶ Broadview Builders, Marshlands Lane, Heathfield, East Sussex, TN21 8EX Tel: (01435) 864924 Fax: (01435) 867544

Brock Brothers Builders Ltd, 20 Field Lane, Kessingland, Lowestoft, Suffolk, NR33 7QB Tel: (01502) 740617

▶ Brooks & Wood Ltd, 365 Foxhall Road, Ipswich, IP3 8LH Tel: (01473) 719191

▶ Brown & Armstrong Ltd, The Workshop, Glasson Industrial Estate, Maryport, Cumbria, CA15 8NT Tel: (01900) 812410

▶ Brown Bryan & Son, South Gable, Southsea Road, Flamborough, Bridlington, North Humberside, YO15 1AD Tel: (01262) 850477 Fax: (01262) 850477

L. Brown & Sons Ltd, St. Anns House, St. Anns Parade, Alderley Road, Wilmslow, Cheshire, SK9 1HG Tel: (01625) 522251 Fax: (01625) 533653 E-mail: mikemason@lbrowns.co.uk

▶ Browns Homes Ltd, St. Anns House, St. Anns Parade, Wilmslow, Cheshire, SK9 1HG Tel: (01625) 445606 Fax: (01625) 528527

▶ Bruce Collie Building Co. Ltd, 46 Silverknowes Road, Edinburgh, EH4 5LF Tel: 0131-336 5050

▶ Bruce Contracts, 72 Brand Street, Glasgow, G51 1DG Tel: 0141-427 5331 Fax: 0141-427 5639

Robert Bruce Construction Ltd, Unit 40 Thornleigh Trading Estate, Blowers Green Road, Dudley, West Midlands, DY2 8UB Tel: (01384) 457780 Fax: (01384) 259921

▶ Bryan C Cooper Ltd, 96 Newland, Sherborne, Dorset, DT9 3DT Tel: (01935) 814946 Fax: (01935) 816306

▶ Bryant & Towbridge Ltd, 47 Elizabeth Avenue, Christchurch, Dorset, BH23 2DN Tel: (01202) 484174

Bryen & Langley Ltd, 48-60 Footscray Road, London, SE9 2SU Tel: (020) 8850 7775 Fax: (020) 8850 6772 E-mail: info@bryen-langley.com

▶ Buchan Bros Ltd, Glenugie, Longside, Peterhead, Aberdeenshire, AB42 4XE Tel: (01779) 821419 Fax: (01779) 472737

▶ Building Craftsmen Dumfries Ltd, The Hollies, Lockerbie, Dumfriesshire, DG11 1BJ Tel: (01387) 263131 Fax: (01387) 263131

Building Design Patnership, 7 Hill Street, Bristol, BS1 5RW Tel: 0117-929 9861 Fax: 0117-922 5280 E-mail: bristol@bdp.co.uk

▶ Building Diagnostic & Assessment Services Ltd, Liberator House, Glasgow Prestwick International, Glasgow Prestwick Intnl Airpor, Prestwick, Ayrshire, KA9 2PL Tel: (0800) 7314364 Fax: (01292) 471146

▶ Building Services Ltd, Unit 2 Avon Court, Avon Close, Granby Industrial Estate, Weymouth, Dorset, DT4 9UX Tel: (01305) 770773

▶ Building Services Easton Ltd, Dereham Road, Easton, Norwich, NR9 5EH Tel: (01603) 742274 Fax: (01603) 741377

▶ Builth Building Services, Castle Road, Builth Wells, Powys, LD2 3EL Tel: (01982) 552746 Fax: (01982) 552746

Bullock Construction Ltd, Northgate, Aldridge, Walsall, WS9 8TU Tel: (01922) 458311 Fax: (01922) 459589 E-mail: admin@bullock.co.uk

▶ Burmor Construction Ltd, 23 Horsegate, Deeping St. James, Peterborough, PE6 8EN Tel: (01778) 342606 Fax: (01778) 344090

▶ Burns Construction Ltd, Midland Road, Barnsley, South Yorkshire, S71 4DR Tel: (01226) 726786

▶ Burns Construction (Aberdeen) Ltd, 34-36 St Peter Street, Aberdeen, AB24 3HU Tel: (01224) 562000

Burrell & Sons Ltd, Fair View, Belton Road, Epworth, Doncaster, South Yorkshire, DN9 1JL Tel: (01427) 874747 Fax: (01427) 875392 E-mail: burrell.construction@virgin.net

▶ Business Development Associates Ltd, 18 Rodney Street, Liverpool, L1 2TQ Tel: 0151-707 2308 Fax: 0151-709 9457 E-mail: bda_uk@hotmail.com

Byrne Bros Formwork Ltd, 13-15 White Hart Lane, London, SW13 0PX Tel: (020) 8878 9161 Fax: (020) 8878 3848 E-mail: info@byrne-bros.co.uk

▶ C B S Construction Ltd, Bunny Lane, Sherfield English, Romsey, Hampshire, SO51 6FT Tel: (01794) 884481 Fax: (01794) 884042

▶ C & C Contractors London Ltd, 123 Wennington Road, Rainham, Essex, RM13 9TH Tel: (01708) 550008 Fax: (01708) 551009

C E Bunch, 87 Chapel Street, Dudley, West Midlands, DY2 9PN Tel: (01384) 459241 Fax: (01384) 255166 E-mail: sales@cebunch.co.uk

C E Davidson Ltd, South View New Street, Fressingfield, Eye, Suffolk, IP21 5PJ Tel: (01379) 586606 Fax: (01379) 586511

C Fewster & Son Ltd, 2 Church Lane, Patrington, Hull, HU12 0RJ Tel: (01964) 630228 Fax: (01964) 631309 E-mail: enquiries@cfewster.co.uk

▶ C H B & W Ltd, Brickfield Cottages, 54 Kings Highway, London, SE18 2BG Tel: (020) 8855 8303 Fax: (020) 8855 5480

▶ C J Deighton & Co., 1 Main Street, West Wilts Trading Estate, Westbury, Wiltshire, BA13 4JU Tel: (01373) 824801 Fax: (01373) 824802

C J Ellmore & Co. Ltd, Henshaw Lane, Yeadon, Leeds, LS19 7RZ Tel: 0113-250 2881 Fax: 0113-239 1227 E-mail: mail@ellmore.co.uk

▶ indicates data change since last edition

BUILDING CONTRACTORS – *continued*

▶ C J Murfitt Ltd, 12a The Shade, Soham, Ely, Cambridgeshire, CB7 5DE Tel: (01353) 720002 Fax: (01353) 722931

▶ C L C Construction, Littlebrook Business Centre, Littlebrook Manorway, Dartford, DA1 5PS Tel: (01322) 292636

C M Services, 22 Lowbell Lane, London Colney, St. Albans, Hertfordshire, AL2 1AZ Tel: (01727) 825535 Fax: (01727) 825568 E-mail: info@cmbservices.co.uk

▶ C P Construction Gwent Ltd, Newtown Industrial Estate, Cross Keys, Newport, Gwent, NP11 7PZ Tel: (01495) 270804 Fax: (01495) 270728 E-mail: info@cpconstruction.co.uk

▶ C R Crane & Son Ltd, Manor Farm, Main Road, Nether Broughton, Melton Mowbray, Leicestershire, LE14 3HB Tel: (01664) 823366 Fax: (01664) 823534 E-mail: sales@crcrane.co.uk

C R Reynolds Construction Ltd, Gibson Lane, Melton, North Ferriby, North Humberside, HU14 3HH Tel: (01482) 637373 Fax: (01482) 637370 E-mail: crreynold@dial.hightec.com

C S C Construction Ltd, Stanley House, 15-17 Ladybridge Road, Cheadle Hulme, Cheadle, Cheshire, SK8 5BL Tel: 0161-486 9321 Fax: 0161-488 4399

▶ C S Gallagher Ltd, Deans Farm, 2 Phillips Lane, Stratford sub Castle, Salisbury, SP1 3YR Tel: (01722) 421988 Fax: (01722) 421421

▶ C Spencer, The Pentagon Centre, 310 Washington Street, Glasgow, G3 8AZ Tel: 0141-221 4859 Fax: 0141-221 8872

▶ C Spencer Ltd, Grainger House, Clayton St West, Newcastle upon Tyne, NE1 5EE Tel: 0191-261 1116 Fax: 0191-261 7829

C Syms & Sons Ltd, Systems Building, Bristol Road, Bumpers Farm, Chippenham, Wiltshire, SN14 6LH Tel: (01249) 654461 Fax: (01249) 443527

▶ C W Davis Ltd, Baxter Place, Seaton Delaval, Whitley Bay, Tyne & Wear, NE25 0AP Tel: 0191-237 2232 Fax: 0191-298 0036

▶ C Wren, 29 Woodchurch Road, Birkenhead, Merseyside, CH42 9LG Tel: 0151-653 4848 Fax: 0151-653 4425

▶ Caber Developments, 10-12 Pall Mall, Liverpool, L3 6AL Tel: 0151-255 0595 Fax: 0151-255 0601

▶ Cairney & Smith Construction Ltd, Unit 5, Murray Court, Hillhouse Industrial Estate, Hamilton, Lanarkshire, ML3 9SL Tel: (01698) 286888 Fax: (01698) 286888

Calder Building & Civil Engineering, 22 Tomich Industrial Estate, Muir Of Ord, Ross-Shire, IV6 7UA Tel: (01463) 870521

▶ Caledonia Homes, 81 Shore, Edinburgh, EH6 6RG Tel: 0131-454 3580

▶ Callaghan & Walker, 129 Washington Road, Sheffield, S11 8DP Tel: 0114-278 0876

▶ Cameron Homes Ltd, 53 High Street, Chasetown, Burntwood, Staffordshire, WS7 3XE Tel: (01543) 671818 Fax: (01543) 672367

A.R. Campbell (Construction) Ltd, Unit 86, Bandeuth Industrial Estate, Stirling, FK7 7ND Tel: (01786) 812900 Fax: (01786) 813388 E-mail: info@arcampbell.co.uk

▶ R.E. Campbell (Joinery) Ltd, Station Road, Spean Bridge, Inverness-Shire, PH34 4EP Tel: (01397) 712561

▶ Campbell & Smith Construction Group Ltd, Old Sawmill, Ormiston, Tranent, East Lothian, EH35 5NQ Tel: (01875) 610343

▶ Campion Homes, Pitreavie Drive, Pitreavie Business Park, Dunfermline, Fife, KY11 8UH Tel: (01383) 432600 Fax: (01383) 620467

▶ Camstruction Ltd, Cam House, 5 York Street, Aberdeen, AB11 5DL Tel: (01224) 593777 Fax: (01224) 594477 E-mail: sales@camstruction.com

▶ Capita Construction Ltd, Beech Court, 27 Summers Road, Burnham, Slough, SL1 7EP Tel: (01628) 665009 Fax: (01628) 559358

Capital Building Services, 123 High Street, Rainham, Gillingham, Kent, ME8 8AN Tel: (01634) 360210 Fax: (01634) 310724 E-mail: ray.capital@blueyonder.co.uk

Capital & Countys, 40 Broadway, London, SW1H 0BU Tel: (020) 7887 7000 Fax: (020) 7887 0004

Carillion plc, Green Park Road, Bath, BA1 1XH Tel: (01225) 428441 Fax: (01225) 422577

Carillion, 37 Stirling Road, Kilsyth, Glasgow, G65 0HW Tel: (01236) 823333 Fax: (01236) 825926 E-mail: solutions.scotland@mowlems.com

Carillion P.L.C., 24 Birch Street, Wolverhampton, WV1 4HY Tel: (01902) 422431 Fax: (01902) 316165 E-mail: n.simms@carillionplc.com

Carillion Building, 3 Abbots Key, Monks Ferry, Wirral, Merseyside, CH41 5LH Tel: 0151-666 5700 Fax: 0151-666 5777

▶ Carillion Construction, Hamilton House, Phoenix CR, Strathclyde Business Park, Bellshill, Lanarkshire, ML4 3NJ Tel: (01698) 738930 Fax: (01698) 738931

▶ Carlton Construction Ltd, 12 Oak Hill, Epsom, Surrey, KT18 7BT Tel: (01372) 749760 Fax: (01372) 745339

▶ Carnell Contruction, Carlbury Crossing Cottage, Durham Lane, Piercebridge, Darlington, County Durham, DL2 3TW Tel: (01325) 374575 Fax: (01325) 374578

▶ Carrwood Homes P.L.C., Carrwood House, 109 Shaw Heath, Stockport, Cheshire, SK2 6QH Tel: 0161-476 2255

Carter Construction Ltd, Richardson Street, Derby, DE22 3GR Tel: (01332) 381601 Fax: (01332) 290722 E-mail: sales@carterconstruction.co.uk

▶ Carter & Ward, Construction House, 82 Runwell Road, Wickford, Essex, SS11 7HJ Tel: (01268) 733421 Fax: (01268) 767686

▶ Casey Group Of Companies, Rydings Road, Rochdale, Lancashire, OL12 9PS Tel: (01706) 860032 Fax: (01706) 861156 E-mail: admin@casey.co.uk

CBM Construction Group Ltd, 44 Goodman Street, Leeds, LS10 1NY Tel: 0113-271 0200 Fax: 0113-271 2446 E-mail: info@cbm-construction.co.uk

▶ Cedar Building Services, 27 Sackville Road, Heaton, Newcastle upon Tyne, NE6 5SY Tel: 0191-265 3406 Fax: 0191-265 3406 E-mail: jon@cedarbs.wanadoo.co.uk

▶ Central Construction Norwich, 115 City Road, Norwich, NR1 2HL Tel: (01603) 762804 E-mail: info@centralconstruction.co.uk

▶ Century Builders Ltd, 217 Danes Drive, Glasgow, G14 9AQ Tel: 0141-954 3845

▶ Chamberlain Construction Ltd, Laurel House, Station Approach, Alresford, Hampshire, SO24 9JH Tel: (01962) 733056 Fax: (01962) 734841 E-mail: projects@chamberlainconstruction.co.uk

Chantry Builders Ltd, Bower Close, St. Johns Green, Rotherham, South Yorkshire, S61 3JL Tel: (01709) 550058 Fax: (01709) 555011

▶ Chappell & Dix Ltd, The Barns, Huntingford, Wotton-under-Edge, Gloucestershire, GL12 8EX Tel: (01453) 843504

Charles Building Services Ltd, 6 Viewpoint, Hyatt Trading Estate, Stevenage, Hertfordshire, SG1 2EQ Tel: (01438) 750371

Charles Church Western, Churchward House, Churchward Road, Yate, Bristol, BS37 5NN Tel: (01454) 333800 Fax: (01454) 327123

▶ Chas Lavery & Sons Ltd, 12 Kilmaine Street, Lurgan, Craigavon, County Armagh, BT67 9AL Tel: (028) 3832 6282

▶ Charles Sweetland & Sons Ltd, Cher, Minehead, Somerset, TA24 5EL Tel: (01643) 703085 Fax: (01643) 707256

▶ Chase Construction Group, 2 Camborne Mews, London, SW18 5ED Tel: (020) 8871 1828 Fax: (020) 8871 0108

Cheetham Hill Construction Ltd, Woodhill Road, Bury, Lancashire, BL8 1AR Tel: 0161-761 5109 Fax: 0161-761 1300 E-mail: enquiries@cheethamhillconstruction.co.uk

M.A. Cherrington Ltd, Haydown House, Wildhern, Andover, Hampshire, SP11 0JE Tel: (01264) 738224 Fax: (01264) 738382

▶ Cherry & Son Ltd, Crimea Yard, Great Tew, Chipping Norton, Oxfordshire, OX7 4AQ Tel: (01608) 683666 Fax: (01608) 683176

▶ Cheshire Brickworks, 150 Park Road, Timperley, Altrincham, Cheshire, WA15 6QE Tel: 0161-495 9121 E-mail: cheshire@cheshirebrickworks.co.uk

▶ City Construction Longcroft Ltd, Chislet Park, 12, Chislet, Canterbury, Kent, CT3 4BY Tel: (01227) 719559 Fax: (01227) 719558

▶ Clachan Construction Ltd, Ruthvenfield Road, Inveralmond Industrial Estate, Perth, PH1 3EE Tel: (01738) 620221 Fax: (01738) 630734

Clark Construction Ltd, Lancaster Approach, North Killingholme, Immingham, South Humberside, DN40 3JZ Tel: (01469) 540004 Fax: (01469) 540426 E-mail: info@clarkconstruction.co.uk

Clark Contracting, Brentford Grange Farm, Beaconsfield Road, Coleshill, Amersham, Buckinghamshire, HP7 0JU Tel: (01494) 431871 Fax: (01494) 431872 E-mail: sales@clark-contracting.co.uk

▶ Clark Contracts Ltd, Unit 2 East Main Industrial Estate, Broxburn, West Lothian, EH52 5AB Tel: 0131-551 3551 Fax: 0141-884 6211

▶ James Clark, 30 Glenlyon Place, Leven, Fife, KY8 4QY Tel: (01333) 426484 Fax: (01333) 426686

Claude Fenton, Arrowhead Road, Reading, RG7 4AE Tel: 0118-929 8900 Fax: 0118-930 6734 E-mail: reading@fentonplant.co.uk

Claydon Associates Ltd, Edison Road, Rabans Lane Industrial Area, Aylesbury, Buckinghamshire, HP19 8TE Tel: (01296) 434611 Fax: (01296) 436334 E-mail: associates@claydon-group.co.uk

▶ Cleanrock Civil Engineers, 46 Armitage Way, Cambridge, CB4 2UE Tel: (01223) 302921 Fax: (01223) 302927

▶ Cleckheaton Construction Ltd, Crossland House, Northgate, Cleckheaton, West Yorkshire, BD19 3NB Tel: (01274) 873344 Fax: (01274) 876850

▶ Cleland Construction Ltd, Greenside Depot, Biggar Road, Newarthill, Motherwell, Lanarkshire, ML1 5SS Tel: (01698) 860890

Clovemead, Stephenson House, Howley Lane, Warrington, WA1 2DN Tel: (01925) 411221 Fax: (01925) 418496 E-mail: clovemead@brunelhouse.u-net.com

▶ CMS Construction, 118 Longcauseway, Farnworth, Bolton, BL4 9BL Tel: (01204) 576558 Fax: (01204) 706116

▶ Cocksedge Building Contractors, 25 Hampstead Avenue, Mildenhall, Bury St. Edmunds, Suffolk, IP28 7AS Tel: (01638) 713694 Fax: (01638) 713588

Cofton Ltd, Firswood Road, Birmingham, B33 0ST Tel: 0121-628 4000 Fax: 0121-628 1398 E-mail: admin@cofton.co.uk

▶ Cole, 209 Upper Road, Carrickfergus, County Antrim, BT38 8PN Tel: (028) 9036 5650 Fax: (028) 9036 5660

▶ Coleman Construction & Utilities Rail Division, 2 Bridgeway, St. Leonards-on-Sea, East Sussex, TN38 8AP Tel: (01424) 715743 Fax: (01424) 714870 E-mail: accounts@colemanconstruction.net

▶ Collard Construction Ltd, 5 Belgrave Lane, Plymouth, PL4 7DA Tel: (01752) 309808 Fax: (01752) 309808

▶ Colley Construction Ltd, Watling Street, Cannock, Staffordshire, WS11 8LX Tel: (01922) 415407 Fax: (01922) 413938

▶ Collins (Construction) Ltd, 2A Carlton Grove, London, SE15 2UE Tel: (020) 7732 0241

Joseph Colman & Son Ltd, The Coachyard, Dowry Square, Bristol, BS8 4SJ Tel: 0117-926 5141 Fax: 0117-925 3881 E-mail: colmansoffice@cs.com

Colt Construction, Witty Street, Hull, HU3 4TT Tel: (01482) 581880 Fax: (01482) 215037 E-mail: info@colt-industrial.co.uk

▶ Combined Construction Ltd, 306 Glentanar Road, Balmore Industrial Estate, Glasgow, G22 7XS Tel: 0141-347 1800 Fax: 0141-347 1877

▶ Complete Property Maintenance Ltd, Broadcroft Business Centre, 24 Broadcroft, Kirkintilloch, Glasgow, G66 1HP Tel: 0141-775 2200 Fax: 0141-775 2063

▶ Concrete Contractors (Bristol) Ltd, Long Acres, Redfield Hill, Bitton, Bristol, BS30 6NX Tel: 0117-932 3847

Condale Construction Ltd, Millar Barn Lane, Rossendale, Lancashire, BB4 7AU Tel: (01706) 831100 Fax: (01706) 830990

▶ Conlon Construction, 20 Great Northern Way, Netherfield, Nottingham, NG4 2HD Tel: 0115-938 1800 Fax: 0115-938 1801 E-mail: office@conlonconstruction.co.uk

Conlon Construction Ltd, Charnley Fold Lane, Bamber Bridge, Preston, PR5 6BE Tel: (01772) 335268 Fax: (01772) 770200 E-mail: enquire@conlonconstruct.co.uk

▶ Constructall Ltd, The Old Granary, Thurley Farm, Pump Lane, Grazeley, Reading, RG7 1JN Tel: 0118-988 3322

D & J R Construction, 2 Farra Road, Portadown, Craigavon, County Armagh, BT62 1QZ Tel: (028) 3835 6450 Fax: (028) 3835 6450

▶ Constructive Approach, 6 Millside Industrial, Southmill Road, Bishop's Stortford, Hertfordshire, CM23 3DP Tel: (01279) 757225 Fax: (01279) 757427

▶ Contact Construction, 76 Riverside Drive, Radcliffe, Manchester, M26 1HY Tel: (01204) 701510 E-mail: costellosteve@hotmail.com

▶ Contract Services Ltd, 28 Church Road, Baglan, Port Talbot, West Glamorgan, SA12 8ST Tel: (01639) 823789 Fax: (01639) 823987 E-mail: info@contractservicesgroup.co.uk

Contract Services Renovation & Refurbishing Ltd, Lombardian House Liverpool Road, Cadishead, Manchester, M44 5DD Tel: 0161-777 8278 Fax: 0161-777 6298 E-mail: general@contracts-svcs.co.uk

▶ Control Plant Ltd, Lansbury Estate, 102 Lower Guildford Road, Knaphill, Woking, Surrey, GU21 2EP Tel: (01483) 472571 Fax: (01483) 475618

Coombe Valley Fabrications, Coombe Valley, Sandford, Crediton, Devon, EX17 4EN Tel: (01363) 774290

▶ Cooper Construction, 21 Commercial Road, Plymouth, PL4 0LE Tel: (01752) 665077 Fax: (01752) 225477 E-mail: office@cooperconstruction.uk.com

▶ John Cooper Construction Ltd, Cooper House, 25 Belmont Circle Kenton Lane, Harrow, Middlesex, HA3 8RF Tel: (020) 8907 8908 Fax: (020) 8907 8903 E-mail: info@johncooperconstruction.co.uk

▶ Corporate Business Contracts, 10 St Stephens Avenue, Rutherglen, Glasgow, G73 5LS Tel: 0141-634 0403 Fax: 0141-613 3479

▶ Costain Ltd, Cardiff Business Park, 18 Lambourne Crescent, Llanishen, Cardiff, CF14 5GF Tel: (029) 2075 7755

Costain Ltd, Costain House, 111 Westminster Bridge Road, London, SE1 7UE Tel: (020) 7705 8444 Fax: (020) 7705 8599

▶ Cottrell Brickwork Ceramics Ltd, 729 Woodbridge Road, Ipswich, IP4 4NB Tel: (01473) 724842 Fax: (01473) 717639

▶ Country Homes, 14-15 Axwell House, Westerton Road, East Mains Industrial Estate, Broxburn, West Lothian, EH52 5AU Tel: (01506) 852665

▶ Country Homes Anglia Ltd, Brome Industrial Park, Airfield Industrial Estate, Eye, Suffolk, IP23 7HN Tel: (01379) 871041 Fax: (01379) 870809

▶ County Constructions Ltd, New Barn Farm, Tadlow, Royston, Hertfordshire, SG8 0EL Tel: (01767) 631063 Fax: (01767) 631083

▶ Coupe Construction, Station Lane, Birtley, Chester le Street, County Durham, DH2 1AW Tel: 0191-410 2177 Fax: 0191-410 6583 E-mail: general@coupeconst.plus.com

▶ Cowan Construction Ltd, 144 Greaves Road, Lancaster, LA1 4UW Tel: (01524) 63954 Fax: (01524) 849118

▶ Cowan & Linn, 53 Morrison Street, Glasgow, G5 8LB Tel: 0141-429 2980

▶ Cowen Builders Ltd, 21 Benbow Drive, South Woodham Ferrers, Chelmsford, CM3 5FP Tel: (01245) 324276 Fax: (01245) 324174

Cowlin Construction Ltd, Stratton House, 39 Cater Road, Bristol, BS13 7UH Tel: 0117-983 2000 Fax: 0117-987 7758 E-mail: bristol@cowlin.co.uk

Cowlin Construction, 5 Armtech Row, Houndstone Business Park, Yeovil, Somerset, BA22 8RW Tel: (01935) 423131 Fax: (01935) 847680

▶ Cox & Allen (Kendal) Ltd, Unit 3, Shap Road, Shap Road Industrial Estate, Kendal, Cumbria, LA9 6NZ Tel: (01539) 733533

▶ Craigvar Construction, Langhaugh Mill, Langhaugh, Galashiels, Selkirkshire, TD1 2AJ Tel: (01896) 752828 Fax: (01896) 758040

▶ Cranford Builders, Cranford, Gollanfield, Inverness, IV2 7UR Tel: (01667) 462457

▶ Creative Conversions, 6 Bishop Street, Alfreton, Derbyshire, DE55 7EF Tel: (01773) 834508 Fax: (01773) 843508 E-mail: creativeconversions@hotmail.co.uk

▶ Crest Nicholson Residential (Eastern) Ltd, 1 The Progression Centre, Mark Road, Hemel Hempstead Industrial Estate, Hemel Hempstead, Hertfordshire, HP2 7DW Tel: (01442) 219921 Fax: (01442) 219829

▶ Crest Nicholson Residential South East Ltd, Crest House, 30 High Street, Westerham, Kent, TN16 1RG Tel: (01959) 564282 Fax: (01959) 564177

▶ Crest Nicholson Residential South East Ltd, Crest House, 30 High Street, Westerham, Kent, TN16 1RG Tel: (01959) 564282 Fax: (01959) 564177

▶ Crest Nicholson Residential SW Ltd, Crest House, Lime Kiln Close, Stoke Gifford, Bristol, BS34 8ST Tel: 0117-923 6600 Fax: 0117-969 5792

▶ Crosby Homes (Yorkshire) Ltd, Mortech Park, York Road, Leeds, LS15 4TA Tel: 0113-265 2000

Croudace Services Ltd, Croudace House, 97 Godstone Road, Caterham, Surrey, CR3 6XQ Tel: (01883) 346464 Fax: (01883) 349927 E-mail: info@croudacehomes.co.uk

▶ Crown Construction Contracting Ltd, 6 Benjamin Outram Business Centre, Whiteley Road, Ripley, Derbyshire, DE5 3QL Tel: (01773) 570044 Fax: (01773) 570121

▶ Cruden Building Ltd, 26 Orr Street, Glasgow, G40 2LQ Tel: 0141-551 0098

▶ Cruden Investments Ltd, Baberton House, Westburn Avenue, Edinburgh, EH14 3HN Tel: 0131-442 3862 Fax: 0131-442 4556

▶ Crupron Construction Ltd, PO Box 50, Dinas Powys, South Glamorgan, CF64 4HE Tel: (029) 2051 5562

Cumbrian Industrials Ltd, 3 Cowper Road, Gilwilly Industrial Estate, Penrith, Cumbria, CA11 9BN Tel: (01768) 865571 Fax: (01768) 862380 E-mail: enquiries@cumbrian-industrials.co.uk

▶ Cumming & Co. Ltd, 8 Whitefriars Street, Perth, PH1 1PP Tel: (01738) 567899 Fax: (01738) 567900

▶ Cummins & Pope Ltd, 10 London Road, Horndean, Waterlooville, Hampshire, PO8 0BZ Tel: (023) 9259 5199

Cunninghams, 564-566 Kingston Road, London, SW20 8DR Tel: (020) 8946 3352 Fax: (020) 8540 1626

Currall Lewis & Martin Construction Ltd, 89-93 Broadwell Road, Oldbury, West Midlands, B69 4BL Tel: 0121-552 9292 Fax: 0121-544 9899 E-mail: office@clmconstruction.com

▶ Currie Bros Ltd, Crowness Road, Hatston, Kirkwall, Orkney, KW15 1RG Tel: (01856) 877770 Fax: (01856) 876331

Currie & Brown, Osborne House, 1-5 Osborne Terrace, Edinburgh, EH12 5HG Tel: 0131-313 7020 Fax: 0131-313 7021

▶ Cyprus Construction Ltd, Leeds Road, Idle, Bradford, West Yorkshire, BD10 8JH Tel: (01274) 621820 Fax: (01274) 615919

▶ D A Kennedy Construction Ltd, North Muirton Industrial Estate, Inchcape Place, Perth, PH1 3DU Tel: (01738) 632700 Fax: (01738) 630214

▶ D B Consulting Ltd, 109 Blackthorn Road, Southampton, SO19 7LP Tel: (07717) 453409 E-mail: info@electricalconsultant.org

▶ D B M Engineering, Burnwood House, Rockley, Retford, Nottinghamshire, DN22 0QW Tel: (01777) 838100 Fax: (01777) 838710

▶ D B Russell (Construction) Ltd, Edward House, 18 Alexandra Road, Clevedon, Avon, BS21 7QE Tel: (01275) 876411 Fax: (01275) 875985

D C P M Manuals, Rock Drive, Gelli, Pentre, Rhondda Cynon Taff, CF41 7NX Tel: (01443) 442029 Fax: (01443) 442199 E-mail: info@dcpmmanuals.com

▶ D Cruikshanks & Son, 6A South Crescent Road, Ardrossan, Ayrshire, KA22 8DU Tel: (01294) 463410

▶ D D Porter Ltd, 1 Walnut Business Park, Walnut Street, Halifax, West Yorkshire, HX1 5JD Tel: (01422) 362374 Fax: (01422) 343467

D Devine, 20 Kimpton Road, Luton, LU2 0SX Tel: (01582) 450567

D Dunkerley & Son, High Street, Hogsthorpe, Skegness, Lincolnshire, PE24 5ND Tel: (01754) 872371 Fax: (01754) 872361 E-mail: gary@dunkerleyjoiners.freeserve.co.uk

▶ D E Clegg Ltd, Bishops House, 42 High Pavement, Nottingham, NG1 1HN Tel: 0115-841 3121 Fax: 0115-841 3122 E-mail: info@declegg.co.uk

▶ D F Blanchard Ltd, 12-14 Lower Road, Churchfields Industrial Estate, Salisbury, SP2 7QD Tel: (01722) 337331

▶ D G Esaias Ltd, 5 Castle Garage, Croft Road, Neath, West Glamorgan, SA11 1RW Tel: (01639) 641700 Fax: (01639) 641824

▶ D Geddes (Contractors) Ltd, Swillburne, Colliston, Arbroath, Angus, DD11 3SH Tel: (01241) 890237

▶ D H Potter & Co. Ltd, 9-11 Tower Street, Hartlepool, Cleveland, TS24 7HH Tel: (01429) 290800

▶ indicates data change since last edition

BUILDING CONTRACTORS - *continued*

▶ D I T T Construction Ltd, Holmsgarth Road, Lerwick, Shetland, ZE1 0PW Tel: (01595) 692733 Fax: (01595) 695110

▶ D J Bryant, 59 Queen Victoria Avenue, Hove, East Sussex, BN3 6XA Tel: (01273) 707300 Fax: (01273) 541005

D J Dickson Ltd, 127 Derryboy Road, Crossgar, Downpatrick, County Down, BT30 9DH Tel: (028) 4483 0434 Fax: (028) 4483 1492 E-mail: dickson.david@btconnect.com

▶ D M Construction Ltd, Marriott Way, Melton Constable, Norfolk, NR24 2BT Tel: (01263) 862512 Fax: (01263) 861512

▶ D M Homes Ltd, 37 Hartwood Road, Shotts, Lanarkshire, ML7 5BY Tel: (01698) 292321

▶ D Macdonald & Co, Balivanich, Isle of Benbecula, HS7 5LA Tel: (01870) 602396 Fax: (01870) 603298

▶ D Moffatt & Son Ltd, 3 Newbattle Road, Newtongrange, Dalkeith, Midlothian, EH22 4RA Tel: 0131-663 4732

▶ D & N Hall & Sons Ltd, 1a Retreat Place, London, E9 6RH Tel: (020) 8985 2877 Fax: (020) 8533 1574

▶ D P Builders Ltd, Coquet Enterprise Park, Amble, Morpeth, Northumberland, NE65 0PE Tel: (01665) 710315 Fax: (01665) 712385

▶ D S Watson, 19-21 Ravensmere, Beccles, Suffolk, NR34 9DX Tel: (01502) 470700 Fax: (01502) 470777

▶ Dalgarven Homes Ltd, Dalgarven House, 55 Maryborough Road, Prestwick, Ayrshire, KA9 1SW Tel: (01292) 478288 Fax: (01292) 478288

Dalton Joinery, Glendale Works, Dacre, Penrith, Cumbria, CA11 0HL Tel: (01768) 486684 Fax: (01768) 486684 E-mail: radjoinery@aol.com

▶ Damm Builders, 43 Watt Road, Hillington Industrial Estate, Glasgow, G52 4RY Tel: 0141-810 2460

Danaher & Rolls Ltd, Rufus Centre, Steppingley Road, Flitwick, Bedford, MK45 1AH Tel: (01525) 721900 Fax: (01525) 721800 E-mail: office@danaherandrolls.co.uk

▶ Dancourt Ltd, Davron Court, Whitehouse Place, Bristol, BS3 4BL Tel: 0117-953 9766 Fax: 0117-953 9767 E-mail: info@dancourt.co.uk

▶ Daniel Campbell & Son (Contractors) Ltd, 57-59 Kirk Street, Strathaven, Lanarkshire, ML10 6LB Tel: (01357) 520394

▶ Dave Upton, Walnut View, Brook Street, Moreton Pinkney, Daventry, Northamptonshire, NN11 3SL Tel: (01295) 760745 Fax: (01295) 760858

Davics Construction Ltd, 154 College Road, Liverpool, L23 3DP Tel: 0151-932 9007 Fax: 0151-931 2196

▶ David Avery Ltd, 34 Cheriton Road, Folkestone, Kent, CT20 1BZ Tel: (01303) 850288 Fax: (01303) 850289

▶ David Gregory Building & Roofing Contractors Ltd, Greaves Bakery, Townfoot, Rothbury, Morpeth, Northumberland, NE65 7SP Tel: (01669) 620064

▶ David Harrison, Stone Gables, 58 Langton Rd, Norton, Malton, North Yorkshire, YO17 9AE Tel: (01653) 693097

▶ David Morin Builders Ltd, 5 Saltcoats Road, Gullane, East Lothian, EH31 2AQ Tel: (01620) 843232 Fax: (01620) 844007

▶ David Patton & Sons (N I) Ltd, Woodside Road, Ballymena, County Antrim, BT42 4PT Tel: (028) 2564 2141

▶ David Wilson Homes Ltd, Barfield House, Britannia Road, Morley, Leeds, LS27 0DT Tel: 0113-252 9900

▶ Davies Edward Construction)Ltd, Tremorfa Foreshaw, Ocean Park, Cardiff, CF10 4LJ Tel: (029) 2049 8798 E-mail: admin@edav.co.uk

William Davis Ltd, Forest Field, Forest Road, Loughborough, Leicestershire, LE11 3NS Tel: (01509) 231181 Fax: (01509) 239773 E-mail: post@williamdavis.co.uk

▶ Dawn Group Ltd, 220 West George Street, Glasgow, G2 2PG Tel: 0141-285 6700

▶ Dazone Construction, 28 Creevagh Road, Londonderry, BT48 9XB Tel: (028) 7136 6292 Fax: (028) 7136 6293

Ernest Deacon Ltd, Victoria Road, Kington, Herefordshire, HR5 3BY Tel: (01544) 230403 Fax: (01544) 231740 E-mail: ernestdeacon@freeuk.com

▶ Dealmead Ltd, Knen Hall, Knenhall, Stone, Staffordshire, ST15 8TJ Tel: (01782) 373708 Fax: (01782) 373569

Charles Dean Partnership Ltd, Brasted Lodge, Westerham Road, Westerham, Kent, TN16 1QH Tel: (01959) 565909 Fax: (01959) 565606 E-mail: sales@charlesdean.co.uk

▶ Dean Edward, Unit C3 Horsted Keynes Industrial Park, Cinder Hill Lane, Horsted Keynes, Haywards Heath, West Sussex, RH17 7BA Tel: (01342) 811183 Fax: (01342) 811193

▶ Dearden Formwork & Steelfixing, Hunters Farm, Hunters Lane, Tarleton, Preston, PR4 6JL Tel: (01772) 811150 Fax: (01772) 811788

Debaff Developments Ltd, Unit 2a Forest Row Business Park, Station Road, Forest Row, East Sussex, RH18 5DW Tel: (01342) 822106 Fax: (01342) 824198

▶ Decorbuild & Co., Premier House, 50-52 Cross Lances Road, Hounslow, TW3 2AA Tel: (020) 8577 3773 Fax: (020) 8577 4547 E-mail: service@decorbuild.com

▶ Delson Contracts Ltd, Orchardbank Industrial Estate, Forfar, Angus, DD8 1TD Tel: (01307) 468666

▶ Dendale Ltd, New Street, Holbrook, Sheffield, S20 3GH Tel: 0114-248 0055 Fax: 0114-248 0460

▶ DENHAM BROTHERS LTD, 122 ANNS HILL RD, GOSPORT, HANTS, PO12 3JZ Tel: 07754 210523

▶ Denne Building Services Ltd, Bramling House, Bramling, Canterbury, Kent, CT3 1NB Tel: (01227) 723000 Fax: (01227) 723001

▶ Denne Group, Denne Court, Hengist Field, Borden, Sittingbourne, Kent, ME9 8FH Tel: (0870) 6001803 Fax: (01795) 434800 E-mail: info@denne.co.uk

Denne Group, Denne Court, Hengist Field, Borden, Sittingbourne, Kent, ME9 8FH Tel: (0870) 6001803 Fax: (01795) 434800

▶ John Dennis & Co. Ltd, 68 Lothian Street, Bonnyrigg, Midlothian, EH19 3AQ Tel: 0131-663 3275

▶ Depotbuild Ltd, The Old Sawmill, 105 Hague Lane, Renishaw, Sheffield, S21 3UR Tel: (01246) 436727

▶ Deveron Homes, Clashmach View, Huntly, Aberdeenshire, AB54 8PW Tel: (01466) 794300 Fax: (01466) 794600

Devon Contractors Ltd, Clyst Court, Hill Barton Business Park, Clyst St. Mary, Exeter, EX5 1SA Tel: (01395) 234280 Fax: (01395) 234281E-mail: office@devoncontractors.co.uk

▶ Dew Group, Carron Works, Stenhouse Road, Carron, Falkirk, FK2 8DR Tel: (01324) 627905 Fax: (01324) 633944

▶ Diack & Macaulay Ltd, 7 Gartferry Road, Chryston, Glasgow, G69 0LY Tel: (01236) 875166 Fax: (01236) 875488

▶ Dialog Global Trade, 655 North Circular Road, London, NW2 7AY Tel: (020) 8830 9555 Fax: (020) 8830 9800 E-mail: pyramidgroup@dg-trade.co.uk

▶ Direct Building Services, 502 Lickey Road, Rednal, Birmingham, B45 8UU Tel: 0121-460 1777 Fax: 0121-460 1555

▶ Direction International P.L.C., Hildenbrook House, The Slade, Tonbridge, Kent, TN9 1HR Tel: (01732) 366351

Division 5 Builders, 15-17 Arcola Street, London, E8 2DJ Tel: (020) 7241 1555

▶ Dixon Contractors, 143 Tullaghans Road, Dunloy, Ballymena, County Antrim, BT44 9EA Tel: (028) 2765 7310

▶ Docherty, 139 Stirling Road, Kilsyth, Glasgow, G65 0PT Tel: (01236) 826438 Fax: (01236) 826475

Donaghmore Construction Ltd, 3 Savings Bank Street, Dungannon, County Tyrone, BT70 1DT Tel: (028) 8772 6500 Fax: (028) 8772 4138

▶ Donaghy Civil Engineers, 42 Loanbank Quadrant, Glasgow, G51 3HZ Tel: 0141-440 1122 Fax: 0141-440 1133

▶ Donaldson Group Ltd, 2230 London Road, Glasgow, G32 8YG Tel: 0141-778 5533

▶ Dorelbury Ltd, 1 Crompton Way, Segensworth West, Fareham, Hampshire, PO15 5SS Tel: (01489) 885388 Fax: (01489) 885893

▶ Dovidio Brothers Ltd, Worth House Farm, Worth, Wookey, Wells, Somerset, BA5 1LW Tel: (01749) 673984

William Dowling Ltd, 71-73 Grand Street, Hilden, Lisburn, County Antrim, BT27 4TX Tel: (028) 9266 6444 Fax: (028) 9262 9678 E-mail: info@williamdowlingpreserve.co.uk

Downhill Enterprises Ltd, 62 Skegoneill Avenue, Belfast, BT15 3JQ Tel: (028) 9037 0165 Fax: (028) 9037 0204

John Doyle Construction Ltd, John Doyle House, 2-3 Little Burrow, Welwyn Garden City, Hertfordshire, AL7 4SP Tel: (01707) 329481 Fax: (01707) 328213 E-mail: admin@john-doyle.co.uk

▶ Drew & Sons, Venton Bungalow, Drewsteignton, Exeter, EX6 6PG Tel: (01647) 231306 Fax: (01647) 231306

▶ Drew Warren Building & Roofing Contractors, Coriander Cottage, Yelford, Witney, Oxfordshire, OX29 7QX Tel: (01865) 300977

▶ Droicon P.L.C, Trow Way, Diglis, Worcester, WR5 3BX Tel: (01905) 763445 Fax: (01905) 356423 E-mail: sales@droicon.co.uk

▶ Drumbow Homes Ltd, Drumbow Farm, Caldercruix, Airdrie, Lanarkshire, ML6 7RX Tel: (01236) 842296

▶ Duncan & Son Southwold Ltd, Unit 20 Southwold Business, Centre St Edmunds Road, Southwold, Suffolk, IP18 6JU Tel: (01502) 723636

▶ Dunne Building & Civil Engineering Ltd, Whitehill Industrial Estate, Bathgate, West Lothian, EH48 2EP Tel: (01506) 657777 Fax: (01506) 639810 E-mail: sales@dunne-group.com

Durkan Properties Ltd, Durkan House, 214-224 High Street, Waltham Cross, Hertfordshire, EN8 7DU Tel: (01992) 781400 Fax: (01992) 781500 E-mail: info@durkan.co.uk

▶ Duxbury Builders Ltd, Brook Street, Adlington, Chorley, Lancashire, PR6 9LE Tel: (01257) 481683 Fax: (01257) 474603

▶ E C Saines & Co. Ltd, 417 New Cross Road, London, SE14 6TA Tel: (020) 8692 4443

E G Carter & Co. Ltd, Bybrook House, Lower Tuffley Lane, Gloucester, GL2 5EE Tel: (01452) 529194

E Gillies, 21 Seafield Road, Inverness, IV1 1SG Tel: (01463) 233023 Fax: (01463) 712353

▶ E J Fleming Ltd, 19a Larkfield Road, Sevenoaks, Kent, TN13 2QH Tel: (01732) 453679 Fax: (01732) 740299

▶ E J Morgan & Son, School House, Sennybridge, Brecon, Powys, LD3 8TT Tel: (01874) 636766 Fax: (01874) 636766

▶ E N Suiter & Sons Ltd, 31 North Everard Street, King's Lynn, Norfolk, PE30 5HQ Tel: (01553) 763195 Fax: (01553) 767694

▶ E P Rothwell & Sons Ltd, Farnham Common Nurseries, Crown Lane, Farnham Royal, Slough, SL2 3SF Tel: (01753) 646012 Fax: (01753) 644087

▶ E R Jenkin & Sons, St. James Street, Penzance, Cornwall, TR18 2BT Tel: (01736) 361188 Fax: (01736) 361188

▶ E W Rayment & Co. Ltd, 3 Water End Road, Potten End, Berkhamsted, Hertfordshire, HP4 2SJ Tel: (01442) 864422 Fax: (01442) 877247

East Coast Construction, 78 Grange Ave, Filey, North Yorkshire, YO14 0AT Tel: 01723 516558 E-mail: posborne@ic24.net

Eastern Counties Contracting, Panton Groveange, Wirehill Lane, Wragby, Market Rasen, Lincolnshire, LN8 5LD Tel: (01673) 857755 Fax: (01673) 857766

Eastfield Joinery, Shavington House Farm, Crewe Road, Shavington, Crewe, CW2 5AH Tel: (01270) 664769 Fax: (01270) 665327 E-mail: sales@eastfieldjoinery.sagenet.co.uk

Eastwood Construction, Burns Lane, Warsop, Mansfield, Nottinghamshire, NG20 0QG Tel: (01623) 842581 Fax: (01623) 847955 E-mail: enquiries@adameastwood.co.uk

▶ Eco Build Developments Ltd, 17 Wyche Avenue, Kings Heath, Birmingham, B14 6LG Tel: 0121-441 4434 Fax: 0121-441 4434 E-mail: brettecobuild@aol.com

▶ Edmund Nuttall Ltd, Tenacre Court, Ashford Road, Harrietsham, Maidstone, Kent, ME17 1AH Tel: (01622) 852000 Fax: (01622) 851600

▶ Edmunds Webster Ltd, 2 Quarry Road, Treboeth, Swansea, SA5 9DJ Tel: (01792) 772475 Fax: (01792) 781652

▶ Edward Mackay Ltd, Rosslyn Yard, Rosslyn Street, Brora, Sutherland, KW9 6NY Tel: (01408) 621223

H.N. Edwards & Partners Ltd, Field House Barn, Chineham Lane, Sherborne St. John, Basingstoke, Hampshire, RG24 9LR Tel: (01256) 473601 Fax: (01256) 841402 E-mail: bdd@hnep.co.uk

Edwards S M Building Contractors, 77 Old Coach Road, Kelsall, Tarporley, Cheshire, CW6 0RA Tel: (01829) 752028 Fax: (01829) 751559

▶ Elder Homes Ltd, 10-16 Cluny Drive, Edinburgh, EH10 6DP Tel: 0131-447 3411

Eldwick Ltd, Bentley Buildings, Glaisdale, Whitby, North Yorkshire, YO21 2QY Tel: (01947) 897337 Fax: (01947) 897660

▶ Elite Homes North West, Redwood House Woodlands Park, Ashton Road, Newton-le-Willows, Merseyside, WA12 0ZW Tel: (0870) 3503535 Fax: (0870) 3503536 E-mail: reception@elitehomes.co.uk

▶ Ellenby Construction Co. Ltd, Stirling Industrial Estate, Chorley New Road, Horwich, Bolton, BL6 6DU Tel: (01204) 699316 Fax: (01204) 668431

▶ Ellis Timlin & Co. Ltd, Stubbins Lane, Ramsbottom, Bury, Lancashire, BL0 0PT Tel: (01706) 823176 Fax: (01706) 827711

Elliston Steady & Hawes (Aluminium) Ltd, Chapel Lane, Great Blakenham, Ipswich, IP6 0JT Tel: (01473) 830626 Fax: (01473) 832170 E-mail: esh@net.dii.co.uk

▶ Elphinstone & Howarth, Baillister, Tingwall Airport, Gott, Shetland, ZE2 9XJ Tel: (01595) 840222 Fax: (01595) 840505

Emanuel Whittaker Ltd, 400 Rochdale Road, Oldham, OL1 2LW Tel: 0161-624 6222 Fax: 0161-785 5510 E-mail: mail@emanuel-whittaker.co.uk

Emerson Developments Holdings Ltd, Emerson House, Heyes Lane, Alderley Edge, Cheshire, SK9 7LF Tel: (01625) 588400 Fax: (01625) 585791 E-mail: info@emerson.co.uk

▶ Emerson Willis Ltd, Romford Road, Aveley, South Ockendon, Essex, RM15 4XD Tel: (01708) 861044 Fax: (01708) 861066

Emes Building Services, 128-130 Grange Road, Ramsgate, Kent, CT11 9PT Tel: (01843) 850260

Enhurst Ltd, 65-69 County Street, London, SE1 4AD Tel: (020) 7403 0630 Fax: (020) 7407 5940 E-mail: office@enhurst.freeserve.co.uk

▶ Enilow Engineers Ltd, Astley Way, Astley Lane Industrial Estate, Swillington, Leeds, LS26 8XT Tel: 0113-286 8091 Fax: 0113-286 6560

▶ Epac, Unit 8, Burnmill Industrial Estate, Burnmill Road, Leven, Fife, KY8 4RA Tel: (01333) 428956

▶ Esendee Construction Ltd, 16 Enderby Road, Luton, LU3 2HQ Tel: (01582) 579812 Fax: (01582) 598783

F. Espley & Sons Ltd, Foregate House, 70A Foregate Street, Stafford, ST16 2PX Tel: (01785) 602040 Fax: (01785) 606566 E-mail: info@espleys.co.uk

▶ Euro Construction Corporation Ltd, 57 Crowhill Road, Waringstown, Craigavon, County Armagh, BT66 7SS Tel: (028) 3888 1867 Fax: (028) 3888 2262

Evans Bros (Southport) Ltd, 69 Upper Aughton Road, Southport, Merseyside, PR8 5ND Tel: (01704) 566155 Fax: (01704) 562088

▶ Express Pipe, 1 Tylers Road, Roydon, Harlow, Essex, CM19 5LJ Tel: (01279) 792233 Fax: (01279) 792334

▶ Extend A Home, Veitch Place, Lennoxtown, Glasgow, G66 7JL Tel: (01360) 312300

▶ F D Hutcheson, Unit 13 Clydebank Business Centre, 31 Clyde Street, Clydebank, Dunbartonshire, G81 1PF Tel: 0141-952 5868 Fax: 0141-952 5868

F E Peacock Construction Ltd, Southdown, South Road, Bourne, Lincolnshire, PE10 0DX Tel: (01778) 391520 Fax: (01778) 391539 E-mail: enquiries@fepeacock.co.uk

▶ F J Lane & Sons Ltd, 38 Temple Road, Windsor, Berkshire, SL4 1HW Tel: (01753) 866430 Fax: (01753) 850903 E-mail: sales@fjlane.co.uk

▶ F J Wookey & Co. Ltd, Lovell Mill, Sutton Hill Road, Bishop Sutton, Bristol, BS39 5UT Tel: (01275) 332377 Fax: (01275) 332377

▶ F N Rice Pirbright Ltd, Toad Hall, Vapery Lane, Pirbright, Woking, Surrey, GU24 0QD Tel: (01483) 472005 Fax: (01483) 797780

F Parkinson Ltd, Mowbray Drive, Blackpool, FY3 7UN Tel: (01253) 394411 Fax: (01253) 302088 E-mail: sales@fparkinson.co.uk

▶ F & R Jackson Ltd, Woodside House, Barnard Street, Staindrop, Darlington, County Durham, DL2 3ND Tel: (01833) 660367 Fax: (01833) 660882

▶ F W Burnett, Inchmarlo, Banchory, Kincardineshire, AB31 4BT Tel: (01330) 825660 Fax: (01330) 825339

F W Hawker & Sons Ltd, North End Joinery Works, Bath, BA1 7HN Tel: (01225) 858233 Fax: (01225) 852530 E-mail: joinery@hawker-bath.co.uk

▶ F W Leighton Construction Ltd, Station Yard, Station Lane, York, YO30 1BS Tel: (01904) 470838 Fax: (01904) 470432

▶ Factory Building Services Ltd, 76 St.Andrews Road, Birmingham, B9 4LN Tel: 0121-766 8705 Fax: 0121-753 1979

Harry Fairclough (Construction) Ltd, Howley Lane, Howley, Warrington, WA1 2DN Tel: (01925) 632214 Fax: (01925) 628301 E-mail: post@harryfairclough.co.uk

Fairhurst Ward Abbotts Ltd, 225 London Road, Greenhithe, Kent, DA9 9RR Tel: (01322) 387000 Fax: (01322) 370235 E-mail: works@fwa.dart.co.uk

▶ Fairley Homes Ltd, Fairfields, Moss Road, Dunmore, Falkirk, FK2 8RY Tel: (01324) 831999

Fairview Estates Housing Ltd, 50 Lancaster Road, Enfield, Middlesex, EN2 0BY Tel: (020) 8366 1271 Fax: (020) 8366 0189 E-mail: sales@fairview.co.uk

▶ Falla R F Ltd, Stony Lane, Christchurch, Dorset, BH23 1HD Tel: (01202) 499399 Fax: (01202) 470660

R.G. Falla Ltd, Bridge House, Rue De La Cache, St. Sampson, Guernsey, GY2 4AF Tel: (01481) 256585 Fax: (01481) 252318

Farebrother Group Ltd, Ridgeway House, Progress Way, Denton, Manchester, M34 2GP Tel: 0161-320 0056 Fax: 0161-320 5010 E-mail: farebrother@farebrother.co.uk

▶ Farnham Bros, Meavy Lane, Yelverton, Devon, PL20 6AJ Tel: (01822) 853176

Farrans Ltd, 99 Kingsway, Dunmurry, Belfast, BT17 9NU Tel: (028) 9061 1122 Fax: (028) 9062 9753 E-mail: construct@farrans.com

▶ Farrans Construction Ltd, Ely Road, Waterbeach, Cambridge, CB25 9PG Tel: (01223) 440000 Fax: (01223) 440469 E-mail: cambridge@farrans.com

▶ Farrans (Construction) Ltd, Oakbank, Mid Calder, Livingston, West Lothian, EH53 0JS Tel: (01506) 882588 Fax: (01506) 882688

▶ Fellows & Jones Builders)Ltd, Pinfold Street, Wednesbury, West Midlands, WS10 8SY Tel: 0121-526 4418

▶ Feltham Construction Ltd, Mandarin Court, Hambridge Road, Newbury, Berkshire, RG14 5SY Tel: (01635) 523526 E-mail: info@felthamconstruction.co.uk

▶ Fenbank Builders, Welbourne Lane East, Holbeach, Spalding, Lincolnshire, PE12 8AB Tel: (01406) 424071 Fax: (01406) 490871

▶ Fergal Contracting Co., The Downs Road, Stand Lake, Witney, Oxfordshire, OX29 7YP Tel: (01865) 300666 Fax: (01865) 300974

▶ J. & J. Ferguson, 33 Strathaven Road, Kirkmuirhill, Lanark, ML11 9RN Tel: (01555) 892695

▶ Fern Joinery, Cowie Road, Bannockburn, Stirling, FK7 8JW Tel: (01786) 816701

▶ Fion Construction Ltd, 30a Ben Nevis Industrial Estate, Ben Nevis Industrial Estate, Fort William, Inverness-Shire, PH33 6PR Tel: (01397) 702834 Fax: (01397) 706001

Firbeck Construction Ltd, 3 Lawn Court, Carlton-in-Lindrick, Worksop, Nottinghamshire, S81 9ED Tel: (01909) 733255 Fax: (01909) 733235 E-mail: info@firb.co.uk

Firmco Ltd, 127-129 Stanley Road, Ilford, Essex, IG1 1RQ Tel: (020) 8514 5544 Fax: (020) 8478 3133 E-mail: info@firmco.co.uk

▶ Fisher Construction Ltd, 2 Station Street, Wakefield, West Yorkshire, WF1 5AF Tel: (01924) 255662

Fisher & Sons Fakenham Ltd, 7 Dereham Road, Hempton, Fakenham, Norfolk, NR21 7LD Tel: (01328) 862781 Fax: (01328) 856229 E-mail: mail@fishers-fakenham.co.uk

Fitzpatrick Contractors Ltd, Hertford Road, Hoddesdon, Hertfordshire, EN11 9BX Tel: (01992) 305000 Fax: (01992) 305001 E-mail: enquiries@fitzpatrick.co.uk

▶ Fitzpatrick Contractors Ltd, Ryedale Court, London Road, Riverhead, Sevenoaks, Kent, TN13 2DN Tel: (01732) 455222 Fax: (01732) 452224

▶ Flack & Chapman, 12 Station Road, St. Ives, Cambridgeshire, PE27 5BH Tel: (01480) 494155

Fleming Buildings Ltd, 23 Auchinloch Road, Lenzie, Kirkintilloch, Glasgow, G66 5ET Tel: 0141-776 1267 Fax: 0141-775 1394 E-mail: office@fleming-buildings.co.uk

BUILDING CONTRACTORS – *continued*

Forbes West Ltd, 128 Tutbury Road, Burton-on-Trent, Staffordshire, DE13 0NU Tel: (01283) 564351 Fax: (01283) 535707

▶ Forbes & Whiteford Ltd, 5 New Mill Road, Kilmarnock, Ayrshire, KA1 3JG Tel: (01563) 522298 Fax: (01563) 524812

Forman Construction Ltd, 6 Donalds Lane, Dundee, DD2 4PF Tel: (01382) 610612 Fax: (01382) 400464 E-mail: enquiries@formanconstruction.co.uk

▶ Forsyth Building Ltd, 50 West Harbour Road, Edinburgh, EH5 1PP Tel: 0131-552 9393

▶ Fortesite Ltd, Flat 3, Weyhill Farm, Weyhill, Andover, Hampshire, SP11 8DE Tel: (01264) 771728

▶ Fosker & Lynn, Hawkins Road, Colchester, CO2 8JX Tel: (01206) 790027 Fax: (01206) 791583

Fosseway Homes, Coly House, Swan Hill Road, Colyford, Colyton, Devon, EX24 6HE Tel: (01297) 553562 Fax: (01297) 553563 E-mail: michael.gardener@totalise.co.uk

▶ Fosters Construction Ltd, Emmanuel, Trusthorpe Road, Sutton-on-Sea, Mablethorpe, Lincolnshire, LN12 2LL Tel: (01507) 443649 Fax: (01507) 443649 E-mail: neale.bloomfields@homecall.co.uk

▶ Fox Construction Ltd, Block 4, Chapelhall Industrial Estate, Chapelhall, Airdrie, Lanarkshire, ML6 8QH Tel: (01236) 754301 E-mail: mail@foxconstruction.co.uk

Francis Construction Ltd, Armour House, Colthrop Lane, Thatcham, Berkshire, RG19 4PD Tel: (01635) 862222 Fax: (01635) 876997 E-mail: info@francisconstruction.co.uk

Frank Haslam Milan, F H M House, Church Hill, Coleshill, Birmingham, B46 3AB Tel: (01675) 461661 Fax: (01675) 461662

▶ Frank Rogers (Building Contractors) Ltd, The Stables, Larkhill Lane, Liverpool, L13 9BR Tel: 0151-226 7172 Fax: 0151-270 2854

▶ Frank Wyatt & Son Builders Ltd, 70 Dorchester Road, Upton, Poole, Dorset, BH16 5NT Tel: (01202) 622207

▶ Fraser Langdon Southern Ltd, The Old Bakery, 17 Hyde Road, Paignton, Devon, TQ4 5BW Tel: (01803) 666619 Fax: (01803) 526622

▶ Fred Hall & Son Builders Ltd, Old School, Whittington, Carnforth, Lancashire, LA6 2NY Tel: (01524) 271322 Fax: (01524) 272460

▶ Friel Homes Ltd, Cross Keys Farm, 46 Hill Street, Hednesford, Cannock, Staffordshire, WS12 2DN Tel: (01543) 425544 Fax: (01543) 425205

▶ Friend Contracting, Miller Court, Millbay Road, Plymouth, PL1 3LQ Tel: (01752) 670555 Fax: (01752) 212303

Frisby Construction Ltd, 16 Glenfield Avenue, Weddington, Nuneaton, Warwickshire, CV10 0DZ Tel: (024) 7634 0958 Fax: (024) 7638 7173 E-mail: frisbyhomes@enta.net

▶ Front Line Construction Ltd, Burnside Road, Bathgate, West Lothian, EH48 4PX Tel: (01506) 632510

▶ Frudd Building Services Ltd, Byidon House, Rolleston Drive, Nottingham, NG5 7JP Tel: 0115-955 5888

▶ Fujitsu Telecommunications Europe Ltd, Unit 12 Honiton Business Park, Ottery Moor Lane, Honiton, Devon, EX14 1BG Tel: (01404) 45405 Fax: (01404) 45938

▶ Future Services Ltd, 26 Forth Street, Edinburgh, EH1 1LH Tel: 0131-550 3835 Fax: 0131-550 3834 E-mail: future_services_ltd@hotmail.co.uk

▶ Fwa West Ltd, 15 Warwick Road, West Drayton, Middlesex, UB7 9BT Tel: (01895) 449344

▶ G A Mell Ltd, Manor Farm Cottage, The Green, Finningley, Doncaster, South Yorkshire, DN9 3BP Tel: (01302) 770202

G Abbott & Co. Ltd, Brenda Road, Hartlepool, Cleveland, TS25 2BJ Tel: (01429) 234841 Fax: (01429) 234445

▶ G Armstrong, Woodbine Cottage, Myreton, Aberlady, Longniddry, East Lothian, EH32 0PZ Tel: (01875) 870229

▶ G B H Utilities, Church Street, Mexborough, South Yorkshire, S64 0HG Tel: (01709) 578578 Fax: (01709) 581589

G C N Plant Ltd, Foryd Bank, Green Avenue, Kinmel Bay, Rhyl, Clwyd, LL18 5ET Tel: (01745) 343089 Fax: (01745) 332115 E-mail: gari_hughes@hotmail.com

▶ G F Hill (Malvern) Ltd, Spring Lane, Malvern, Worcestershire, WR14 1AL Tel: (01684) 568456 Fax: (01684) 572401

▶ G Grigg & Sons, Inveresk Mills Industrial Park, Musselburgh, Midlothian, EH21 7UQ Tel: 0131-665 8052 Fax: 0131-665 4737

▶ G J Finch Ltd, 45 St Gabriels Avenue, Plymouth, PL3 4JQ Tel: (01752) 266093 Fax: (01752) 252015

▶ G L Quine Ltd, Great North Road, South Milford, Leeds, LS25 5LH Tel: (01977) 681999 Fax: (01977) 681888

G M I Construction Group plc, Middleton House, Westland Road, Leeds, LS11 5UH Tel: 0113-276 0505 Fax: 0113-276 0180 E-mail: build@gmicon.co.uk

G Mcveigh & Co. Ltd, Timothys Bridge Road, Stratford-upon-Avon, Warwickshire, CV37 9NQ Tel: (01789) 205803 Fax: (01789) 205828

G Middleton Ltd, Crosscroft Industrial Estate, Appleby-in-Westmorland, Cumbria, CA16 6HX Tel: (01768) 352067 Fax: (01768) 353228

▶ G P R Groundworks, 3A Baird Road, Kirkton Campus, Livingston, West Lothian, EH54 7AZ Tel: (01506) 464362

▶ G P Turner Builders Ltd, 4 Central Place, Haltwhistle, Northumberland, NE49 0DF Tel: (01434) 321000

▶ G & R Contracts, 15 Guthrie Place, Torrance, Glasgow, G64 4HJ Tel: (01360) 620559

▶ G S Brown Construction Ltd, Glencarse, Perth, PH2 7NF Tel: (01738) 860591 Fax: (01738) 860357 E-mail: office@gsbrown.co.uk

▶ G T Wall & Sons Ltd, 2 Hall Street, Stourbridge, West Midlands, DY8 2JE Tel: (01384) 394104 Fax: (01384) 371578

▶ G Towers & Son Ltd, Union Street, Blyth, Northumberland, NE24 2ED Tel: (01670) 352056

G W Deeley Ltd, George House, Herald Avenue, Coventry, CV5 6UB Tel: (024) 7671 8718 Fax: (024) 7660 6363 E-mail: info@deeley.co.uk

G W Deeley Ltd, Pond Wood Close, Moulton Park Industrial Estate, Northampton, NN3 6RT Tel: (01604) 642201 Fax: (01604) 492000 E-mail: enquiries@northampton.deeley.co.uk

▶ G & W Gardener Building Contractors, 67 Dane Road, Margate, Kent, CT9 2AE Tel: (01843) 229063 Fax: (01843) 293137

▶ G Wilkinson Construction Ltd, 65a Balby Road, Doncaster, South Yorkshire, DN4 0RE Tel: (01302) 342373

▶ G Woodland & Sons Ltd, Hatch Beauchamp, Taunton, Somerset, TA3 6TW Tel: (01823) 480248 Fax: (01823) 480239

▶ Gaj Construction Ltd, West Oak House, Westwood Way, Westwood Business Park, Coventry, CV4 8LB Tel: (024) 7642 2808 Fax: (024) 7642 2950

▶ Galldris Construction Ltd, Unit C, Mollison Avenue, Enfield, Middlesex, EN3 7UH Tel: (020) 8804 8569

▶ Galleywood Construction Ltd, Lodge Road, Hazeleigh, Chelmsford, CM3 6QX Tel: (01621) 828700 Fax: (01621) 826997

Galliers Ltd, Oxon Business Park, Bicton Heath, Shrewsbury, SY3 5DD Tel: (01743) 232040 Fax: (01743) 355669 E-mail: info@frankgalliers.co.uk

Galliford Try, Crab Lane, Fearnhead, Warrington, WA2 0XR Tel: (01925) 822821 Fax: (01925) 827924 E-mail: mail@galliford-northan.co.uk

Galliford Try Partnership Ltd, 50 Rainsford Road, Chelmsford, CM1 2XB Tel: (01245) 494849 Fax: (01245) 493494 E-mail: sales@gallifordtry.co.uk

Galliford Try Services Ltd, Cowley Business Park, Packet Boat Lane, Uxbridge, Middlesex, UB8 2AL Tel: (01895) 855001 Fax: (01895) 855298 E-mail: self@gallifordtry.co.uk

▶ Galtec Ltd, Bentham Lane, Witcombe, Gloucester, GL3 4UD Tel: (01452) 863666

▶ Gardiner & Faulkner Ltd, 21 Carlton Crescent, Southampton, SO15 2ET Tel: (023) 8023 8429

▶ Garland Contracts Ltd, 105 Sanderstead Road, South Croydon, Surrey, CR2 0PJ Tel: (020) 8667 0820 Fax: (020) 8667 9141

▶ Garside & Laycock, 4 Beeston Road, Lane End Place, Leeds, LS11 8JY Tel: 0113-244 0071 Fax: 0113-244 0075

▶ Gateway Homes, Learigg Road, Plains, Airdrie, Lanarkshire, ML6 7JL Tel: (01236) 843303

▶ Gazy Barns, M T Works, Gannow Lane, Burnley, Lancashire, BB12 6JJ Tel: (01282) 422442

▶ GBM Civils, Unit 19 Station Estate, Newbridge Hill, Louth, Lincolnshire, LN11 0JT Tel: (01507) 607944 Fax: (01507) 607900

Gee Construction Ltd, PO Box 14, Bridgend, Mid Glamorgan, CF31 3UD Tel: (01656) 653541 Fax: (01656) 657717

▶ Genesis Contractors Ltd, 32 Hillbrook Grove, Birmingham, B33 8DG Tel: 0121-628 2186 Fax: 0121-786 2367

▶ Genesis Medical Pre Installation Ltd, 3 Kingfisher House Crayfields Business Park, New Mill Road, Orpington, Kent, BR5 3QG Tel: (01689) 898978 Fax: (01689) 822777

▶ Geoffrey Osborne Civil Engineering Ltd, 4-5 Manor Courtyard, Sherington, Newport Pagnell, Buckinghamshire, MK16 9PR Tel: (01908) 614461 Fax: (01908) 614472

▶ George Bros Ltd, Holway Green, Taunton, Somerset, TA1 2YJ Tel: (01823) 331444 Fax: (01823) 335222

▶ George Hanson Building Contractors Ltd, 61 High Street, Rothesay, Isle of Bute, PA20 9AU Tel: (01700) 505005 Fax: (01700) 502795

▶ Geo Hanson & Sons (Hucknall) Ltd, 13 Watnall Road, Hucknall, Nottingham, NG15 7LD Tel: 0115-963 2013

▶ George Hardie & Son Ltd, 36-38 Potterrow, Edinburgh, EH8 9BT Tel: 0131-667 3911

Geo Houlton & Sons Holdings Ltd, Hyperion Street, Witham, Hull, HU9 1BD Tel: (01482) 320486 Fax: (01482) 228441 E-mail: sales@houlton.co.uk

▶ George M Bolton, 4 Harrison Lane, Edinburgh, EH11 1HG Tel: 0131-337 0000 Fax: 0131-337 0000

George Martin (Builders) Ltd, 5/9 Fairfield Road, Dundee, DD3 8HR Tel: (01382) 815415 Fax: (01382) 825199 E-mail: sales@vycon.co.uk

▶ George Morrison, Canal Road, Inverness, IV3 8NF Tel: (01463) 222246 Fax: (01463) 225511 E-mail: builders@george-morrison.co.uk

George Morrison Ltd, 22 High Street, Tain, Ross-Shire, IV19 1AE Tel: (01862) 892346 Fax: (01862) 894475 E-mail: kitchens@george-morrison.co.uk

George Sweeney Junior, 39 Whitehill Road, Glenrothes, Fife, KY6 2RW Tel: (01592) 774325 Fax: (01592) 774325

George Wilson Associates Ltd, PO Box 70, Whitstable, Kent, CT5 3RG Tel: (01227) 262707 Fax: (01227) 262707 E-mail: gwholdings@aol.com

▶ George Wimpey East Scotland Ltd, 28 Barnton Grove, Edinburgh, EH4 6BT Tel: 0131-338 4000

▶ George Wimpey West Midlands Ltd, Dominion Court, 39 Station Road, Solihull, West Midlands, B91 3RT Tel: 0121-703 3300 Fax: 0121-703 3380 E-mail: enquiries@georgewimpey.co.uk

George Wimpey West Scotland Ltd, Trident House, Renfrew Road, Paisley, Renfrewshire, PA3 4EF Tel: 0141-849 5500 Fax: 0141-849 5550

▶ Gilbert & Goode, The Old Workshops, Charlestown Road, St. Austell, Cornwall, PL25 3NJ Tel: (01726) 64800 Fax: (01726) 65159

Gilbert-Ash NI Ltd, 47 Boucher Road, Belfast, BT12 6HR Tel: (028) 9066 4334 Fax: (028) 4177 3488

▶ Gilchrist & Lynn Ltd, Hallcraig House, Hallcraig St, Airdrie, Lanarkshire, ML6 6AW Tel: (01236) 764879

▶ GKR Maintenance & Building Co. Ltd, Bedwas House Industrial Estate, Bedwas, Caerphilly, Mid Glamorgan, CF83 8DW Tel: (029) 2086 8585 Fax: (029) 2088 9040 E-mail: enquiries@gkrmaintenance.co.uk

▶ Gladstone, Dalhousie Business Park, 2 Carrington Road, Bonnyrigg, Midlothian, EH19 3HY Tel: 0131-660 6050 Fax: 0131-660 6650

M.J. Gleeson Group P.L.C., Haredon House, London Road, North Cheam, Sutton, Surrey, SM3 9BS Tel: (020) 8644 4321 Fax: (020) 8641 6110 E-mail: marketing@mjgleeson.com

▶ Glengarth Construction Ltd, Piercy Mill, Piercy Road, Rossendale, Lancashire, BB4 9JP Tel: (01706) 211999 Fax: (01706) 211888

▶ Glenside Recycling Ltd, Colliery, Coalpit Lane, Rugeley, Smethwick, West Midlands, B66 2JN Tel: (01889) 574045 Fax: 0121-565 0646 E-mail: mikekillett@glensiderecycling.com

▶ Godfrey & Hicks Builders Ltd, 109 Fordham Road, Snailwell, Newmarket, Suffolk, CB8 7NB Tel: (01638) 721900 Fax: (01638) 720010

Gold Star Construction Co. Ltd, Smithfield, Melton Road, Melton, Woodbridge, Suffolk, IP12 1NG Tel: (01394) 383056 Fax: (01394) 385898

Goodall Barnard, Kestrel Court Vyne Road, Sherborne St. John, Basingstoke, Hampshire, RG24 9HJ Tel: (01256) 851155 Fax: (01256) 851234 E-mail: buildit@goodall-barnard.co.uk

▶ Gordon Derry & Son, Derry Court, Polmorla Road, Wadebridge, Cornwall, PL27 7NE Tel: (01208) 812975 Fax: (01208) 815552

Gordon Durham & Co. Ltd, Moor Lane, East Boldon, Tyne & Wear, NE36 0AG Tel: 0191-536 7207 Fax: 0191-519 0097 E-mail: contracts@gordondurham.com

▶ Gordon Guthrie Contracts, 2 27 Beaverhall Road, Edinburgh, EH7 4JE Tel: 0131-556 9686 Fax: 0131-556 5774

▶ Gordon S Harding, Bousley End, Bousley Rise, Ottershaw, Chertsey, Surrey, KT16 0LB Tel: (01932) 873096 Fax: (01932) 873096

Henry Gough & Son Ltd, 530 Dudley Road, Wolverhampton, WV2 4DZ Tel: (01902) 351200 Fax: (01902) 454887

▶ Grange Building Services, Vogrie Grange, Gorebridge, Midlothian, EH23 4NT Tel: (01875) 823366 Fax: (01875) 823399 E-mail: gbs@vogrie.co.uk

▶ Grangefix Leeds Ltd, 107 Whitehall Road East, Birkenshaw, Bradford, West Yorkshire, BD11 2LQ Tel: (01274) 684684 Fax: (01274) 684684

▶ Grantchester Construction Ltd, 54 Broad Street, Ely, Cambridgeshire, CB7 4AH Tel: (01353) 667800 Fax: (01353) 667900

▶ Grantrial, New City Court, 20 St Thomas Street, London, SE1 9RS Tel: (020) 7939 3100

▶ Green Acres Homes (Exmouth) Ltd, Unit 2 Swifts Unit, Pound Lane, Exmouth, Devon, EX8 4NP Tel: (01395) 275304

▶ Green & Cameron Ltd, Canisbay, Wick, Caithness, KW1 4YB Tel: (01955) 611316 Fax: (01955) 611451

Tom Green Construction Ltd, Old Station Yard, The Limes, Ingatestone, Essex, CM4 0AZ Tel: (01277) 354141 Fax: (01277) 355505

Greenbooth Construction Co. Ltd, Hunt Lane, Chadderton, Oldham, OL9 0LR Tel: 0161-633 4815

▶ Greenhill Construction Derby Ltd, 611 Burton Road, Derby, DE23 6EJ Tel: (01332) 604055 Fax: (01332) 604058

▶ Greenways Construction (Midlands) Ltd, Weatherby Road, Osmaston Park Industrial Estate, Derby, DE24 8HL Tel: (01332) 370702

▶ Grehan Contractors Ltd, Grehan House, Molewood Road, Hertford, SG14 3AQ Tel: (01992) 500051 Fax: (01992) 500262

▶ Grelson Industries Ltd, Marlowe House, Stewkins, Stourbridge, West Midlands, DY8 4YW Tel: (01384) 444333

Gribbin Construction Co. Ltd, 140 Creagh Road, Castledawson, Magherafelt, County Londonderry, BT45 8EY Tel: (028) 7946 8636 Fax: (028) 7946 8949

▶ Grove Contractors, 16 Brookside Way, Kingswinford, West Midlands, DY6 9AW Tel: (01384) 277969 Fax: (01384) 277969 E-mail: mail@grovecontractors.co.uk

▶ Gullett & Sons Ltd, Unit 15 Saxway Business Centre, Chartridge Lane, Chartridge, Chesham, Buckinghamshire, HP5 2SH Tel: (01494) 778080 Fax: (01494) 776566

▶ John Gunn & Sons Ltd, Swiney Lybster, Lybster, Caithness, KW3 6BT Tel: (01593) 721236 E-mail: info@jgunn.co.uk

▶ Guthrie & Robertson (Builders) Ltd, Pittenzie Road, Crieff, Perthshire, PH7 3JN Tel: (01764) 653676 Fax: (01764) 655305 E-mail: info@guthrie-and-robertson.co.uk

Guy Property Developments Ltd, Pacioli House 9 Brookfield, Duncan Close, Moulton Park Industrial Estate, Northampton, NN3 6WL Tel: (01604) 496666 Fax: (01604) 499676

▶ H B G Construction, 32 Hailes Avenue, Edinburgh, EH13 0LZ Tel: 0131-441 7348

▶ H B G Construction Western Ltd, Millennium Gate, Gifford Court, Fox Den Road, Bristol, BS34 8TT Tel: 0117-944 8800

▶ H B Lewis & Sons Ltd, Langford Mill, Charfield Road, Kingswood, Wotton-under-Edge, Gloucestershire, GL12 8RL Tel: (01453) 845405 Fax: (01453) 521757 E-mail: admin@hblewis.co.uk

H B Pearce Contractors Ltd, Grey Gables, Pytchley Road, Kettering, Northamptonshire, NN15 6NE Tel: (01536) 310234 Fax: (01536) 310638

▶ H B Projects, 56 Commerce Court, Challenge Way, Bradford, West Yorkshire, BD4 8NW Tel: (01274) 269010 Fax: (01274) 669983

▶ H Bentley & Co., 4 Pool Street, Birkenhead, Merseyside, CH41 3NL Tel: 0151-647 8494 Fax: 0151-647 5497

H D Ebbutt & Son, 63 Jarvis Road, South Croydon, Surrey, CR2 6HW Tel: (020) 8688 1157

H. G. Construction (Holdings) Ltd, 4 Hunting Gate, Hitchin, Hertfordshire, SG4 0TJ Tel: (01462) 454444 Fax: (01462) 455924 E-mail: mail@hunting-gate.co.uk

▶ H & H Construction, 29 Tangley Lane, Guildford, Surrey, GU3 3JU Tel: (01483) 233885 Fax: (01483) 233885

H Hammond & Sons Ltd, D Little Moor Lane, Loughborough, Leicestershire, LE11 1SF Tel: (01509) 212095 Fax: (01509) 238849

▶ H Mcmurray & Son Ltd, Kilmacolm Road, Bridge of Weir, Renfrewshire, PA11 3PU Tel: (01505) 613289

H Morrell & Sons Ltd, 173-175 Kensington Lane, London, SE11 4HG Tel: (020) 7735 1681 Fax: (020) 7587 0533

▶ H Smith & Sons Ltd, Quarry Works, Honingham, Norwich, NR9 5AP Tel: (01603) 880258

▶ H Tomlinson & Son Ltd, Birchills Street, Walsall, WS2 8NG Tel: (01922) 623035 Fax: (01922) 623204 E-mail: sales@htomlinsonandson.co.uk

▶ H Tonge & Sons, 32 Parliament Street, Upholland, Skelmersdale, Lancashire, WN8 0LN Tel: (01695) 623063 Fax: (01695) 623341

H Turnbull & Co. Ltd, 226 Mulgrave Road, Sutton, Surrey, SM2 6JT Tel: (020) 8642 0513 Fax: (020) 8642 5246 E-mail: enquiries@turnbullgroup.co.uk

H W Fisher & Son Ltd, 22-24 Elms Road, Aldershot, Hampshire, GU11 1LJ Tel: (01252) 324008 Fax: (01252) 324498 E-mail: admin@hwfisherandson.co.uk

▶ H W Gaymer, 9 Old Water Yard, Curtis Road, Dorking, Surrey, RH4 1DY Tel: (01306) 875777 Fax: (01306) 876700

▶ H Watson & Son York, 9 Hawthorne Grove, York, YO31 7YA Tel: (01904) 424306

▶ H Wilson Alfriston Ltd, Yard & Office, 8 West Street, Alfriston, Polegate, East Sussex, BN26 5UX Tel: (01323) 870236 Fax: (01323) 870916

▶ Hadden Construction Ltd, 1 Maidenplain Place, Aberuthven, Auchterarder, Perthshire, PH3 1EL Tel: (01764) 660011 Fax: (01764) 660022 E-mail: sales@hadden.co.uk

▶ Hagan Homes Ltd, 183 Templepatrick Road, Doagh, Ballyclare, County Antrim, BT39 0RA Tel: (028) 9334 2234 Fax: (028) 9334 0674

▶ Haley Bros Builders Ltd, Burlees House, Hangingroyd Lane, Hebden Bridge, West Yorkshire, HX7 7DD Tel: (01422) 842858 Fax: (01422) 845896

Hall Construction Group, Clay Street, Hull, HU8 8HE Tel: (01482) 329204 Fax: (01482) 587722 E-mail: addressee@hallgroup.co.uk

Hamer Jack & Son Tottington Ltd, 200a Bury Road, Tottington, Bury, Lancashire, BL8 3DX Tel: (01204) 883867 Fax: (01204) 888592 E-mail: info@jackhamer-son.co.uk

▶ Hamilton Knight Development, 16 17 Canalside Industrial Park, Kinoulton Road, Cropwell Bishop, Nottingham, NG12 3BE Tel: 0115-989 4333 Fax: 0115-989 4333 E-mail: hkdevelopments@btconnect.com

▶ Hammond Builders, 9 Tyler Hill Road, Blean, Canterbury, Kent, CT2 9HP Tel: (01227) 470710 Fax: (01227) 470716

▶ Hanbury FP Ltd, 12 Wharfedale Road, Ipswich, IP1 4JP Tel: (01473) 241516 Fax: (01473) 241517 E-mail: enquiries@hanburyfp.co.uk

▶ Handyman Express, 19a Archel Road, London, W14 9QJ Tel: (020) 7385 7751 E-mail: info@handymanexpress.co.uk

▶ Hankinsons Cheshire Ltd, Middlewich Road, Northwich, Cheshire, CW9 7DW Tel: (01606) 338770 Fax: (01606) 48597 E-mail: mail@hankinsons.co.uk

▶ Hanson Quickfall Ltd, Enterprise Way, Ladysmith Road, Grimsby, South Humberside, DN32 9TW Tel: (01472) 341117 Fax: (01472) 250212 E-mail: info@hanserve.com

▶ Hantall Developments Ltd, Kingston Mill, Manchester Road, Hyde, Cheshire, SK14 2BZ Tel: 0161-368 5885 Fax: 0161-351 9082

BUILDING CONTRACTORS – *continued*

▶ Harcourts Civil Engineering, Cross Green Approach, Leeds, LS9 0SG Tel: 0113-391 8210 Fax: 0113-391 8219

▶ Hardman Construction Ltd, Brow Top, Quernmore, Lancaster, LA2 0QW Tel: (01524) 845456

Harlow & Milner Ltd, Milner Way, Ossett, West Yorkshire, WF5 9JN Tel: (01924) 277771 Fax: (01924) 280102 E-mail: info@harlow-milner.co.uk

▶ Harmony Construction Ltd, Old Rayne, Insch, Aberdeenshire, AB52 6TB Tel: (01464) 851581 Fax: (01464) 851581

▶ Harris & Harris Construction Ltd, Unit 1a, The Polden Business Centre, Bristol Road, Bridgwater, Somerset, TA6 4AW Tel: (01278) 431565

▶ Harron Homes, Chadwick House, Warrington Road, Birchwood Park, Warrington, WA3 6AE Tel: (01925) 823555

▶ Harry Armistead Ltd, Unit 2 Woodgate Park, Middlegate, White Lund Industrial Estate, Morecambe, Lancashire, LA3 3PS Tel: (01524) 848500 Fax: (01524) 848600

▶ Harry J Palmer (Broadstone) Ltd, Manor Works, 4 Dunyeats Road, Broadstone, Dorset, BH18 8AG Tel: (01202) 690701

▶ Hartfield Homes Ltd, Pentland House, Damhead, Edinburgh, EH10 7DP Tel: 0131-445 5855 Fax: 0131-445 2235 E-mail: sales@hartfieldhomes.com

▶ Harvest Homemaker, Unit 1, Elgin Works, Elgin Street, Dunfermline, Fife, KY12 7SD Tel: (01383) 736291

▶ Harvey & Clark, 9-11 Swadlincote Road, Woodville, Swadlincote, Derbyshire, DE11 8DE Tel: (01283) 221451 Fax: (01283) 550992

▶ Haslam Preservation Ltd, 49 Norbreck Road, Thornton-Cleveleys, Lancashire, FY5 1RR Tel: (01253) 503111 Fax: (01253) 503110

Jim Hastings Ltd, Seghill Industrial Estate, Seghill, Cramlington, Northumberland, NE23 7DR Tel: 0191-237 0633 Fax: 0191-237 2656

▶ Havenscroft Ltd, 3 Barn Close, Stone Cross, Pevensey, East Sussex, BN24 5EN Tel: (01323) 769260 Fax: (01323) 766351

Havering Building Specialists Ltd, 48 Brentwood Road, Romford, RM1 2EP Tel: (01708) 744574 Fax: (01708) 732722 E-mail: sales@hbsltd.uk.com

▶ Hawk Development Ltd, Charleston House, The Grange, Loppington, Shrewsbury, SY4 5SY Tel: (01939) 233153 Fax: (01939) 233510

▶ Hay Forres Ltd, Plasmon Yard, Fleurs Place, Forres, Morayshire, IV36 1LX Tel: (01309) 672400 Fax: (01309) 676403

Hayburn Wood Products, 299 Galgorm Road, Ahoghill, Ballymena, County Antrim, BT42 1JU Tel: (028) 2587 1442 Fax: (028) 2587 1177 E-mail: info@hayburn.co.uk

Hayes Control Systems, The Boathouse, Station Road, Henley-on-Thames, Oxfordshire, RG9 1AZ Tel: (01491) 410539 Fax: (01491) 577267 E-mail: sales@hayescontrol.co.uk

▶ Haymills Contractors Ltd, 32 St. Peters Road, Huntingdon, Cambridgeshire, PE29 7DA Tel: (01480) 414191 Fax: (01480) 414186

Haynes & Sons Daventry Ltd, 3 Badby Park, Heartlands Business Park, Daventry, Northamptonshire, NN11 8YT Tel: (01327) 703824

▶ Haywards Building Services, East Court Road, Worthing, West Sussex, BN14 7DB Tel: (01903) 600499 E-mail: darronhayward@hotmail.co.uk

▶ Hazelwood Development Ltd, 14 Wortley Road, High Green, Sheffield, S35 4LU Tel: 0114-286 9990 Fax: 0114-286 9991 E-mail: cupton@hazelwood-dev.co.uk

HBG Construction Ltd, Merit House, Edgware Road, London, NW9 5AF Tel: (020) 8200 7070 Fax: (020) 8200 3997

HBG Construction Scotland Ltd, Kelvin House, Buchanan Gate Business Park, Stepps, Glasgow, G33 6FB Tel: 0141-779 8888

Heart Of England Promotions, Old Hall, Wallhill Road, Fillongley, Coventry, CV7 8DX Tel: (01676) 540333 Fax: (01676) 540365 E-mail: sales@heartofengland.co.uk

Hearthstead Homes Ltd, 14 Station Rd., Crossgates, Leeds, LS15 7JX Tel: 0113-232 6634 Fax: 0113-232 6564 E-mail: sales@hearthstead.com

▶ Heather Developments Woking Ltd, Mayford Green, Woking, Surrey, GU22 0PN Tel: (01483) 765848 Fax: (01483) 762414

▶ Heddle Civil Engineers, Grainshore Road, Hatston, Kirkwall, Orkney, KW15 1FL Tel: (01856) 888666 Fax: (01856) 877666

Helme & Hallett Ltd, 42b High Street, Cuckfield, Haywards Heath, West Sussex, RH17 5EL Tel: (01444) 454776 Fax: (01444) 417716 E-mail: office@helme.co.uk

▶ Helmer & Dyer Ltd, High Wych, Sawbridgeworth, Hertfordshire, CM21 0JS Tel: (01279) 723441

Hendry & Sons Ltd, Station Road, Foulsham, Dereham, Norfolk, NR20 5RG Tel: (01362) 683249

Henry Boot Estates Ltd, Banner Cross Hall, Sheffield, S11 9PD Tel: 0114-255 5444 Fax: 0114-258 5548 E-mail: pr@henryboot.co.uk

Henry Boot Training Ltd, Callywhite Lane, Dronfield, Derbyshire, S18 2XN Tel: (01246) 410111 Fax: (01246) 410595

▶ Henry Bros Scotland Ltd, Claddoch House, Cardross, Dumbarton, G82 5HG Tel: (01389) 842210 Fax: (01389) 842220

▶ Henry Jones Criccieth Ltd, Maes Workshop, Criccieth, Gwynedd, LL52 0AB Tel: (01766) 522854 Fax: (01766) 523463

▶ Henry W Pollard & Sons Ltd, Monmouth Street, Bridgwater, Somerset, TA6 5EJ Tel: (01278) 422211 Fax: (01278) 445775 E-mail: info@pollard-ltd.com

▶ Heritage Building Co. Ltd, 1 Kinneil Road, Bo'ness, West Lothian, EH51 0AY Tel: (01506) 828202

Heritage Restoration Services Ltd, 18 Derby Road, Burton-on-Trent, Staffordshire, DE14 1RU Tel: (01283) 546266 Fax: (01283) 546266 E-mail: davekeytes@btopenworld.co.uk

▶ Hertel Services, Sellafield, Seascale, Cumbria, CA20 1PG Tel: (01946) 727417 Fax: (01946) 729126

Hewitt & Maughan Ltd, 11 Albion Close, Worksop, Nottinghamshire, S80 1RA Tel: (01909) 473581 Fax: (01909) 477960 E-mail: office@hewittandmaughan.sagehost.co.uk

▶ Hillfoot Homes Ltd, Hillfoots Farm, Dollar, Clackmannanshire, FK14 7PL Tel: (01259) 740000 Fax: (01259) 742090

Hills Construction, Wood Road, Kingswood, Bristol, BS15 8RA Tel: 0117-967 0014 Fax: 0117-961 8939 E-mail: sales@hillsconstruction.co.uk

▶ Hills Contractors Ltd, Unit 12 Holland Industrial Park, Bentley Road South, Wednesbury, West Midlands, WS10 8LN Tel: 0121-568 7432 Fax: 0121-568 6394 E-mail: sales@hillscontractors.co.uk

▶ Hobson & Porter Ltd, Malmo Road, Hull, HU7 0YF Tel: (01482) 823999 Fax: (01482) 823733

Geo Hodges & Son Ltd, 82 Horninglow Street, Burton-on-Trent, Staffordshire, DE14 1PN Tel: (01283) 565461 Fax: (01283) 510338 E-mail: contract@hodges.co.uk

▶ Hogg Robert Joiner, 36 Mount Stewart Street, Carluke, Lanarkshire, ML8 5EB Tel: (01555) 772627

▶ Holdsworth Contruction Ltd, 1210 Coventry Road, Yardley, Birmingham, B25 8DA Tel: 0121-772 1675 Fax: 0121-766 5262

▶ Hollingsworth Bros, St. Ives Way, Factory Road, Sandycroft, Deeside, Clwyd, CH5 2QS Tel: (01244) 539922 Fax: (01244) 538504

Holly Construction Ltd, Wellington Road, Dunston, Gateshead, Tyne & Wear, NE11 9JL Tel: 0191-460 0400

Holroyd Construction Ltd, Park Hill, Walton Road, Wetherby, West Yorkshire, LS22 5DZ Tel: (01937) 583131 Fax: (01937) 580034

▶ Holthurst Ltd, 2 The Crescent, Station Road, Woldingham, Caterham, Surrey, CR3 7DB Tel: (01883) 653366

▶ Homecare Contracts Ltd, 18 Dryden Vale, Bilston Glen Estate, Loanhead, Midlothian, EH20 9HN Tel: 0131-440 5550 Fax: 0131-440 3539

▶ Hometrader Ltd, 71-73 Long Street, Middleton, Manchester, M24 6UN Tel: 0161-643 9090

▶ Hopkins Bros, The Tythings Commercial Centre, Wincanton, Somerset, BA9 9RZ Tel: (01963) 32993 Fax: (01963) 34455 E-mail: les@hopkins.uk

Horsley Joinery, Manston Green Industrial Estate, Preston Road, Manston, Ramsgate, Kent, CT12 5BA Tel: (01843) 824002 Fax: (01843) 848354

▶ Horsnell Ltd, 190 Galleywood Road, Great Baddow, Chelmsford, CM2 8NB Tel: (01245) 471108 Fax: (01245) 471108 E-mail: chris@horsnellltd.fsnet.co.uk

▶ Housesmiths Ltd., 60 Hampstead House, 176 Finchley Road, London, NW3 6BT Tel: 020 7558 8693 E-mail: kellysearch@housesmiths.co.uk

▶ Howatson, Cae Bricks Brickfield Lane, Denbigh Road, Ruthin, Clwyd, LL15 1PE Tel: (01824) 703638 Fax: (01824) 707210

▶ Howden's Joinery Ltd, 4 Grange Road, Houstoun Industrial Estate, Livingston, West Lothian, EH54 5DE Tel: (01506) 444358

▶ Hugh Bourn Ltd, Louth Road, Wragby, Market Rasen, Lincolnshire, LN8 5PH Tel: (01673) 858831 Fax: (01673) 857006 E-mail: info@hughbourn.co.uk

Hugh J O'Boyle Ltd, 1 The Green, Irish Street, Downpatrick, County Down, BT30 6BE Tel: (028) 4461 2278 Fax: (028) 4461 3132 E-mail: info@hjob.co.uk

C. Hughes, 89 Station Rd, Flitwick, Bedford, MK45 1LA Tel: (01525) 717270 Fax: (01525) 717270 E-mail: clive.hughes1@ntlworld.com

▶ Hull Local Labour Initiative, 12-13 Bishop Lane, Hull, HU1 1PA Tel: (01482) 229986

▶ Hunter & Clark Ltd, Quay Road, Rutherglen, Glasgow, G73 1LD Tel: 0141-613 3500 Fax: 0141-613 3522

Hunter & Clark Ltd, 1173 Gallowgate, Glasgow, G31 4EG Tel: 0141-554 2327 Fax: 0141-554 4974 E-mail: enquires@hunterandclark.co.uk

▶ Hunter & Morrison, Precast Shed, Kirkhouse, Whiteness, Shetland, ZE2 9LL Tel: (01595) 840240

G. Hurst & Sons Contractors Ltd, Hallcroft Industrial Estate, Aurillac Way, Retford, Nottinghamshire, DN22 7PX Tel: (01777) 702208 Fax: (01777) 709889 E-mail: mail@ghurstcontractors.co.uk

Hutton Construction Ltd, Birch Business Centre, Maldon Road, Birch, Colchester, CO2 0LT Tel: (01206) 330386 Fax: (01206) 331177 E-mail: colchester@hutton-group.co.uk

Hutton Construction Ltd, Alsa Business Park, Alsa Street, Stansted, Essex, CM24 8SQ Tel: (01279) 647333 Fax: (01279) 647380

▶ Hydair, Unit 5, Morley Business Centre, Morley Road, Tonbridge, Kent, TN9 1RA Tel: (01732) 773844

▶ I G S Technical Services, 2239 London Road, Glasgow, G32 8XL Tel: 0141-764 0362

I. & H. I & H Brown Ltd, PO Box 51, Perth, PH1 3YD Tel: (01738) 637171 Fax: (01738) 637175 E-mail: enquiries@ihbrown.com

Ian Williams, Station Road, Warmley, Bristol, BS30 8XG Tel: 0117-960 9510 Fax: 0117-935 3772E-mail: lynne.westcott@ianwilliams.co.uk

▶ Illson Builders & Contractors Ltd, North Parade, Burley in Wharfedale, Ilkley, West Yorkshire, LS29 7JR Tel: (01943) 862022 Fax: (01943) 864191

▶ Imphouse Ltd, Merston Manor Farm, Chapel Lane, Merstone, Newport, Isle of Wight, PO30 3BZ Tel: (01983) 527855 Fax: (01983) 527877

▶ Inca Developments Ltd, 1 Totterdown Lane, Weston-super-Mare, Avon, BS24 9LU Tel: (0845) 2304622 Fax: (0845) 2304622

▶ Indigo Northern Ltd, 61 Saville Street, North Shields, Tyne & Wear, NE30 1AY Tel: 0191-258 2220

▶ Insurepair Glasgow Ltd, 24 Lochleven Road, Glasgow, G42 9JU Tel: 0141-649 6969 Fax: 0141-636 6748

▶ Integra Ltd, 16 Bloomsbury Street, Brighton, BN2 1HQ Tel: (01273) 606565 Fax: (01273) 608721

▶ Inter Dynamics, Friarton Bridge Park, 4 Friarton Road, Perth, PH2 8DD Tel: (01738) 626626

Interclass Holdings Ltd, Heathmill Road, Wombourne, Wolverhampton, WV5 8AP Tel: (01902) 324422 Fax: (01902) 324044 E-mail: wombourne@interclass.co.uk

Interserve, Consort House, Princes Road, Ferndown, Dorset, BH22 9JG Tel: (01202) 861702 Fax: (01202) 894325 E-mail: ferndown.office@interserveprojects.com

Interserve Holdings plc, Tilbury House, Ruscombe Park, Reading, RG10 9JU Tel: 0118-932 0123 Fax: 0118-932 0206 E-mail: info@interserveplc.co.uk

Interserve Project Services Ltd, 395 George Road, Erdington, Birmingham, B23 7RZ Tel: 0121-344 4888 Fax: 0121-344 4801 E-mail: information@interserveprojects.com

Interserve Project Services Ltd, Cambrian Buildings, Mount Stuart Square, Cardiff, CF10 5FL Tel: (029) 2048 1560 Fax: (029) 2048 3825 E-mail: cardiff.office@interserveprojects.com

Interserve Project Services Ltd, 1 Thunderhead Ridge, Glass Houghton, Castleford, West Yorkshire, WF10 4UA Tel: (01977) 522300 Fax: (01977) 522301 E-mail: leeds.office@interserveprojects.com

Interserve Project Services Ltd, Interserve House, Oberon Road, Exeter Business Park, Exeter, EX1 3QD Tel: (01392) 203350 Fax: (01392) 203347 E-mail: exeter.office@tilbury.co.uk

Interserve Project Services Ltd, Balmoral Suite Windsor House, Troon Way Business Centre, Humberstone Lane, Leicester, LE4 9HA Tel: 0116-276 3773 Fax: 0116-276 2992 E-mail: leicester.office@interserveprojects.com

Interserve Project Services Ltd, Clerk Street, Loanhead, Midlothian, EH20 9DP Tel: 0131-448 2800 Fax: 0131-448 2600 E-mail: edinburgh.office@interserveprojects.com

Interserve Project Services Ltd, Ross Road, Stockton-On-Tees, Cleveland, TS18 2NN Tel: (01642) 675125 Fax: (01642) 601970 E-mail: stockton.office@interserveprojects.com

Interserve Project Services Ltd, 138 Heol-Y-Gors, Cwmbwrla, Swansea, SA5 8LT Tel: (01792) 464001 Fax: (01792) 467499 E-mail: swansea.office@interserveprojects.com

Interserve Property Services, 35 Station Road North, Newcastle upon Tyne, NE12 7AR Tel: 0191-215 1434 Fax: 0191-215 1435 E-mail: newcastle.office@interserveprojects.com

Interserve Site Services, Woodhouse Drive, Wigan, Lancashire, WN6 7NT Tel: (01942) 236434 Fax: (01942) 824159 E-mail: wigan.office@interserveprojects.com

▶ Irvine Contractors, Unit 14B, Gremista Industrial Estate, Lerwick, Shetland, ZE1 0PX Tel: (01595) 692645

Irwins Ltd, Low Hall Road, Horsforth, Leeds, LS18 4EW Tel: 0113-250 6811 Fax: 0113-250 6933 E-mail: sales@irwins.co.uk

J A B Short Ltd, 214 Sheffield Road, Chesterfield, Derbyshire, S41 7JP Tel: (01246) 232109 Fax: (01246) 220304 E-mail: homes@jabshort.co.uk

▶ J A Kneen Developments Ltd, 3 Golden Hill, Leyland, PR25 3NN Tel: (01772) 621428 Fax: (01772) 621429

▶ J & A Mcdougall Ltd, 32 Combie Street, Oban, Argyll, PA34 4HT Tel: (01631) 562304 Fax: (01631) 564408 E-mail: enquiries@apartmentsoban.co.uk

▶ J Allan Osborne Preservations Ltd, 14 John Street, Helensburgh, Dunbartonshire, G84 8BA Tel: (01436) 676095 Fax: (01436) 679329

J B Bennett Contracts Ltd, Banton Mill Mill Road, Banton, Kilsyth, Glasgow, G65 0QG Tel: (01236) 823011 Fax: (01236) 821883

▶ J B Black, Bairdsmill, Crosshill, Maybole, Ayrshire, KA19 7PU Tel: (01655) 740331 Fax: (01655) 740322

▶ J & B Construction Co. Ltd, Unit 41-43 Cumberland Business Park, Cumberland Avenue, London, NW10 7RT Tel: (020) 8961 3847 Fax: (020) 8961 3816

▶ J B Roberts & Son, Abercwm Eiddaw Works, Upper Corris, Machynlleth, Powys, SY20 9BP Tel: (01654) 761208 Fax: (01654) 761718

J C Aldridge & Son Ltd, 10 Market Place, Berkeley, Gloucestershire, GL13 9BB Tel: (01453) 810223 Fax: (01453) 511205 E-mail: sales@jcaldridge.co.uk

▶ J C E George, Lamdin Road, Bury St. Edmunds, Suffolk, IP32 6NU Tel: (01284) 753631 Fax: (01284) 706151

▶ J C Morton, 4 Templehill, Troon, Ayrshire, KA10 6BE Tel: (01292) 315789 Fax: (01292) 318480 E-mail: info@jcmortonhomes.co.uk

J Charles & Son Ltd, Whitbygate, Thornton Dale, Pickering, North Yorkshire, YO18 7RY Tel: (01751) 474303

▶ J Craig Dykes Property Developments Ltd, 3 Brackenholme Cottages, Brackenholme, Selby, North Yorkshire, YO8 6EJ Tel: (01757) 630224 Fax: (01757) 630244

▶ J D C Builders (Devon) Ltd, Filham Park, Filham, Ivybridge, Devon, PL21 0LR Tel: (01752) 698699

▶ J & D Developments, 65 Well Street, Torrington, Devon, EX38 7BW Tel: (01805) 624701E-mail: info@jandddevelopments.co.uk

▶ J D Minto Ltd, Old Dronley Road, Backmuir of Liff, Dundee, DD2 5QT Tel: (01382) 580365 Fax: (01382) 580371 E-mail: sales@minto.webscot.net

▶ J E Hall & Co., Unit 2, Gower Street Trading Estate, St George, Telford, Shropshire, TF2 9HW Tel: (01952) 617637

▶ J E Nozedar Ltd, 10-12 Lorne Street, Middlesbrough, Cleveland, TS1 5QY Tel: (01642) 224193 Fax: (01642) 217457

▶ J & E Regan Builders & Contractors Ltd, Unit 4 Barncoose Industrial Estate, Barncoose, Redruth, Cornwall, TR15 3RQ Tel: (01209) 211616 Fax: (01209) 210175

▶ J & E Regan Builders & Contractors Ltd, Long Acre, Saltash, Cornwall, PL12 6LZ Tel: (01752) 841660 Fax: (01752) 841653

J E Stacey & Co. Ltd, Inceworth Building Works, Bodmin Street, Holsworthy, Devon, EX22 6BD Tel: (01409) 253555 Fax: (01409) 254496

J & E Woodworks, Barley Mow, Lampeter, Dyfed, SA48 7BY Tel: (01570) 422141 Fax: (01570) 422144 E-mail: sales@je-woodworks.co.uk

J G B Formwork Ltd, 182 Hyde End Road, Spencers Wood, Reading, RG7 1DG Tel: 0118-988 3424 Fax: 0118-988 6259

J Graham & Sons (Kilkeel)Ltd., 40 Greencastle Street, Kilkeel, Newry, County Down, BT34 4BH Tel: (028) 4176 2777 Fax: (028) 4176 4783E-mail: j.grahamsons@yahoo.co.uk

▶ J Guest Ltd, Knarsboro House, Bradley Road, Stourbridge, West Midlands, DY8 1XB Tel: (01384) 392444 Fax: (01384) 441875

▶ J H B Ltd, Greenhead, Lerwick, Shetland, ZE1 0PY Tel: (01595) 695577 Fax: (01595) 694709 E-mail: sales@jhbltd.co.uk

▶ J H B Ltd, Greenhead, Lerwick, Shetland, ZE1 0PY Tel: (01595) 695577 Fax: (01595) 694709 E-mail: sales@jhbltd.co.uk

▶ J H Civil Engineering Ltd, Carlisle Road, Airdrie, Lanarkshire, ML6 8RH Tel: (01236) 768174 Fax: (01236) 607155

▶ J Harley Building Services Ltd, 24 Fenella Street, Glasgow, G32 7JT Tel: 0141-778 6194 Fax: 0141-778 6194

J Harper & Sons Ltd, Southern Avenue, Leominster, Herefordshire, HR6 0QF Tel: (01568) 612925 Fax: (01568) 613615 E-mail: sales@harpergroup.com

▶ J Hawkins Ltd, Q Rocket Trading Centre, Bowring Park Road, Liverpool, L14 3NZ Tel: 0151-220 3767 Fax: 0151-220 7500

J J & A R Jackson Ltd, Bonemill Lane, Worksop, Nottinghamshire, S81 7BA Tel: (01909) 474233 Fax: (01909) 472688

J J Cavanagh Construction Ltd, Rowhurst Industrial Estate, Apedale Road, Newcastle, Staffordshire, ST5 6BH Tel: (01782) 565789 Fax: (01782) 564740 E-mail: sales@jjcav.co.uk

▶ J J Coughlan Ltd, 12 Walmgate Road, Greenford, Middlesex, UB6 7LH Tel: (020) 8991 5909 Fax: (020) 8991 2753

▶ J & J E Contractors Ltd, Borthwick View, Pentland Industrial Estate, Loanhead, Midlothian, EH20 9QH Tel: 0131-448 2220 Fax: 0131-448 2195

▶ J J L Artison, Nethermill, Netherton Road, Langbank, Port Glasgow, Port Of Glasgow, Renfrewshire, PA14 6YG Tel: (01475) 540060

J J Macmahon Ltd, 4 Loy Street, Cookstown, County Tyrone, BT80 8PE Tel: (028) 8676 3899 Fax: (028) 8676 7417 E-mail: jjmacmahon@hotmail.com

▶ J L Findlow & Sons Ltd, Ball Haye Road, Leek, Staffordshire, ST13 6AF Tel: (01538) 383174 Fax: (01538) 399997

▶ J & L Leonard, Hatston Industrial Estate, Kirkwall, Orkney, KW15 1RE Tel: (01856) 873482

J M Builders, Hallidays Mill, London Road, Chalford, Stroud, Gloucestershire, GL6 8NR Tel: (01453) 882207 Fax: (01453) 731076

▶ J M C Building Services Ltd, 1a Mount Street, Southport, Merseyside, PR9 0RG Tel: (01704) 543914 Fax: (01704) 353561

▶ J M S Construction, 28 Lawmoor Road, Dixon Blazes Industrial Estate, Glasgow, G5 0UG Tel: 0141-418 0902

▶ J Mcintyre & Son Ltd, 7 Ratcliffe Fold, Haslingden, Rossendale, Lancashire, BB4 5PZ Tel: (01706) 226180 Fax: (01706) 226180

▶ J Murphy Shaldon Ltd, 3 Bridge Road, Shaldon, Teignmouth, Devon, TQ14 0DD Tel: (01626) 873231 Fax: (01626) 873811

BUILDING CONTRACTORS – *continued*

J N Bentley Ltd, Keighley Road, Skipton, North Yorkshire, BD23 2QT Tel: (01756) 799425 Fax: (01756) 798068 E-mail: info@jnbentley.co.uk

▶ J N E Construction Ltd, Estover Close, Plymouth, PL6 7PL Tel: (01752) 696269 Fax: (01752) 696660

▶ J P Construction, Mill Lane, Normanton, West Yorkshire, WF6 1RE Tel: (01924) 220092 Fax: (01924) 223173

J P R Structural Remedy, 59 New Dock Road, Llanelli, Dyfed, SA15 2EH Tel: (01554) 757549

▶ J P Wild Ltd, 149 Dewsbury Road, Leeds, LS11 5NW Tel: 0113-277 4944

J Parkinson & Sons Ltd, 3 Hampson Lane, Hampson, Lancaster, LA2 0HY Tel: (01524) 753301 Fax: (01524) 753302 E-mail: bcampbell@askam.co.uk

J Pullan & Sons Ltd, Sunnyview Gardens, Leeds, LS11 8QT Tel: 0113-271 7221 Fax: 0113-271 9238 E-mail: general@pullans.com

▶ J R D Construction Ltd, Unit 2 65 South Street, Ilkeston, Derbyshire, DE7 5QQ Tel: 0115-944 7077 Fax: 0115-944 7859

▶ J & R Elliot Ltd, 30 Commercial Road, Hawick, Roxburghshire, TD9 7AD Tel: (01450) 372493 Fax: (01450) 377790

J & R M Richardson Construction Darlington Ltd, Trinity Hall, Portland Place, Darlington, County Durham, DL3 7BP Tel: (01325) 466688 Fax: (01325) 483311 E-mail: mail@richardson-construction.co.uk

▶ J Robertson, 1 Edinburgh Road, Cleghorn, Lanark, ML11 7RW Tel: (01555) 665084 Fax: (01555) 673819

▶ J S Crawford Contracts (Borders) Ltd, Priorwood, Melrose, Roxburghshire, TD6 9EG Tel: (01896) 822030 Fax: (01896) 823359 E-mail: sales@jscrawford.co.uk

▶ J Smart & Co. (Contractors) P.L.C., 46 Redbraes Place, Edinburgh, EH7 4LL Tel: 0131-554 6418

▶ J T Building Contractors, 12-14 Somerset House Suite 20 Hussar Court, Westside View, Waterlooville, Hampshire, PO7 7SG Tel: (023) 9225 9258 Fax: (023) 9225 9260 E-mail: info@jtbuilders.co.uk

▶ J T Skillicorn Ltd, Second Avenue, Onchan, Isle of Man, IM3 4LT Tel: (01624) 621110 Fax: (01624) 611015

J W Andrews Ltd, Derby Road, Swanwick, Alfreton, Derbyshire, DE55 1BG Tel: (01773) 602191 Fax: (01773) 541492

▶ J W Cannon Co. Ltd, William St, Carshalton, Surrey, SM5 2RB Tel: (020) 8647 5584

▶ J W Steele & Sons Ltd, 264 Baddow Road, Chelmsford, CM2 9QT Tel: (01245) 352487 Fax: (01245) 283617

Jack Lunn Construction Ltd, Progress House, 99 Bradford Road, Stanningley, Pudsey, West Yorkshire, LS28 6AT Tel: 0113-236 2777 Fax: 0113-236 2888 E-mail: admin@jacklunn.co.uk

▶ Jack Trathen Carpentry and Building Services, 52 Reeds Avenue, Earley, Reading, RG6 5SR Tel: 0118-954 7544 E-mail: jack@jacktrathen.co.uk

▶ Jackson Lloyd (D B M) Ltd, 2 Kilshaw Street, Wigan, Lancashire, WN5 8EA Tel: (01942) 620990

▶ James Brown Construction Ltd, 10 Eglinton Street, Irvine, Ayrshire, KA12 8AS Tel: (01924) 272780 Fax: (01563) 573370

▶ James Maxwell Building Contractors Ltd, Midbrae, Kirkwynd, Langholm, Dumfriesshire, DG13 0JD Tel: (01387) 381352 E-mail: sales@maxwellthebuilders.co.uk

▶ James Mearchent & Sons Ltd, 104 Pollokshaws Road, Glasgow, G41 1PZ Tel: 0141-644 3414

▶ James & Nicholas Ltd Liability Partnership, Grove House, Grove Place, Port Talbot, West Glamorgan, SA13 1XA Tel: (01639) 885431 Fax: (01639) 891687

▶ James Potter, Camps Industrial Estate, Kirknewton, Midlothian, EH27 8DF Tel: (01506) 881592 Fax: (01506) 884499

▶ James Swinton & Co., 11 Noble Place, Hawick, Roxburghshire, TD9 9QF Tel: (01450) 372470 Fax: (01450) 378967

▶ James West Ltd, 1 Office Block 1 Southlink Business Park, Hamilton Street, Oldham, OL4 1DE Tel: 0161-624 1956 Fax: 0161-628 4474

▶ James Wilson & Son Auchmillan Ltd, Auchmillan, Mauchline, Ayrshire, KA5 6HD Tel: (01290) 550253 Fax: (01290) 550253

Jamieson & Allan Construction, Unit 8, Bourtree Technology Park, Minto Drive, Altens Industrial Estate, Aberdeen, AB12 3LW Tel: (01224) 895333

▶ Jarvey Stone Ltd, 15a Edinburgh Road, Bathgate, West Lothian, EH48 1BA Tel: (01506) 632565 Fax: (01506) 634566

Jaywood Joineries Ltd, Andmar House, Tondu Road, Bridgend, Mid Glamorgan, CF31 4LJ Tel: (01656) 652831

▶ JBC Scotland, St. Ronans Drive, Kinross, KY13 8AF Tel: (01577) 864136 Fax: (01577) 864136

▶ Jeakins Weir Ltd, Unit 5, Lynch Road, Berkeley, Gloucestershire, GL13 9TA Tel: (01453) 810695

Jeakins Weir Ltd, Iceland House, Corporation Street, Corby, Northamptonshire, NN17 1NQ Tel: (01536) 265181 Fax: (01536) 400650

Jefco Services Ltd, Queens Road, Immingham, South Humberside, DN40 1QR Tel: (01469) 574888 Fax: (01469) 574224

▶ Jefco Services Ltd, 1 Colin Road, Scunthorpe, South Humberside, DN16 1TT Tel: (01724) 845626 Fax: (01724) 289784

▶ Jeffery & Pengelly, Unit 4 Fatherford Farm, Okehampton, Devon, EX20 1QQ Tel: (01837) 52277 Fax: (01837) 55379

▶ Jensen Construction Ltd, Portberry House, Portberry Street, South Shields, Tyne & Wear, NE33 1QX Tel: 0191-454 4083 Fax: 0191-454 7232

Jerram Developments Ltd, 14 Anning Street, London, EC2A 3LQ Tel: (020) 7729 2424 Fax: (020) 7739 9108 E-mail: hennessy@jerramfalkus.co.

▶ Jim Ennis Construction Ltd, Ennis House, Sorby Road, Irlam, Manchester, M44 5BA Tel: 0161-777 9977 Fax: 0161-777 9205 E-mail: sales@ogara.co.uk

▶ Joe Black Building Contractor, 11 Crannog Lane, Oban, Argyll, PA34 4HB Tel: (01631) 564623 Fax: (01631) 566799

▶ John Bain (Contractors) Ltd, Unit 1, 5 Kyle Road, Irvine Industrial Estate, Irvine, Ayrshire, KA12 8JF Tel: (01294) 277568

▶ John Brown (Strone) Ltd, Tyneshandon, Strone, Dunoon, Argyll, PA23 8TA Tel: (01369) 840387

▶ John Caven, Offerance Farm, Gartmore, Stirling, FK8 3RZ Tel: (01877) 382244 Fax: (01877) 389023

▶ John Corbett Construction Ltd, The Pier, Brodick, Isle of Arran, KA27 8AU Tel: (01770) 302537 Fax: (01770) 302748

John D Campbell, Jacks Cottage, Okewood Hill, Dorking, Surrey, RH5 5PU Tel: (01306) 627545 Fax: (01306) 628149

John Devlin & Son Dukinfield Ltd, 1 Platt Street, Dukinfield, Cheshire, SK16 4QZ Tel: 0161-330 5074 Fax: 0161-330 5074

▶ John Donaldson Builders, Abercorn Street, Paisley, Renfrewshire, PA3 4AY Tel: 0141-889 5190 Fax: 0141-848 6888

▶ John E Griggs & Sons Ltd, London Road, Shenley, Radlett, Hertfordshire, WD7 9EN Tel: (01923) 852322 Fax: (01923) 852324

▶ John Fyfe Ltd, 41 Westview Terrace, Stornoway, Isle of Lewis, HS1 2HP Tel: (01851) 702482

▶ John Gow & Sons, Graygoran House, Graygoran, Sauchie, Alloa, Clackmannanshire, FK10 3EH Tel: (01259) 722501

John Graham Dromore Ltd, Lagan Mills, Dromore, County Down, BT25 1AS Tel: (028) 9269 2291 Fax: (028) 9269 3412 E-mail: info@graham.co.uk

▶ John Johnstone Dalbeattie Ltd, Millisle, Dalbeattie, Kirkcudbrightshire, DG5 4AX Tel: (01556) 610226

▶ John Leitch Building Contractors, Midfield Road, Mitchelston Industrial Estate, Kirkcaldy, Fife, KY1 3NL Tel: (01592) 654306 Fax: (01592) 655545

John M Sykes & Sons, 98 Long Row, Horsforth, Leeds, LS18 5AT Tel: 0113-258 3881 Fax: 0113-258 0080 E-mail: jsykes@btconnect.com

▶ John Mackinnon Building Contractor, Torlundy, Fort William, Inverness-Shire, PH33 6SW Tel: (01397) 704802

▶ John Mowlem (Midlands) Ltd, Priory Court, 1 Derby Rd, Beeston, Nottingham, NG9 2SZ Tel: 0115-968 3400 Fax: 0115-943 6069

▶ John Nunn & Co (Builders), Retreat, Cliff Road, Waldringfield, Woodbridge, Suffolk, IP12 4QL Tel: (01473) 736383 Fax: (01473) 736427

▶ John Ruck Construction, Longmead, Elms Green, Leominster, Herefordshire, HR6 0NS Tel: (01568) 615807

▶ John Sisk & Sons Ltd, Unit 1740 1750, Solihull Parkway, Birmingham Business Park, Birmingham, B37 7YD Tel: 0121-329 0600 Fax: 0121-329 0606

John Smith & Son, The Abbey, 2 High Street, Auchterarder, Perthshire, PH3 1DF Tel: (01764) 662126 Fax: (01764) 662773

▶ John Thomson Construction Ltd, Park Terrace, Lamlash, Isle of Arran, KA27 8NB Tel: (01770) 600242 Fax: (01770) 600714 E-mail: office@thomsonconstruction.co.uk

▶ John Wylie Building Ltd, 9 Aitkenhead Road, Uddingston, Glasgow, G71 5RG Tel: (01698) 818480 Fax: (01698) 307001

▶ John Young Ltd, 2 Johnstone Street, Bellshill, Lanarkshire, ML4 1DE Tel: (01698) 748221

▶ Adam Johnson, 57 The Cross Way, Montagu Estate, Kenton, Newcastle upon Tyne, NE3 4SW Tel: (07709) 445676 E-mail: adamshotdogs@yahoo.co.uk

Johnson & Johnson, Glenthorne, Uxbridge Road, Uxbridge, Middlesex, UB10 0LF Tel: (01895) 270411 Fax: (01895) 270411

▶ Johnston Builders, Unit 17-18, Mayfield Industrial Estate, Dalkeith, Midlothian, EH22 4AD Tel: 0131-454 0796 Fax: 0131-454 0796 E-mail: sales@johnstonbuilders.co.uk

Joinery Construction & Maintenance Ltd, 14 Fullarton Drive, Glasgow East Investment Park, Glasgow, G32 8FA Tel: 0141-646 3800 Fax: 0141-646 3888

▶ Jones Bros (Henllan) Ltd, Unit 17, Cross Hands Business Centre, Heol Parc Mawr, Cross Hands Industrial Estate, Llanelli, Dyfed, SA14 6RE Tel: (01269) 844275

▶ Jones Bros Weston Rhyn Ltd, Garden Croft, Weston Rhyn, Oswestry, Shropshire, SY10 7SG Tel: (01691) 772091 Fax: (01691) 774325

▶ Jordan (Building & Joinery Contractors) Ltd, Lochlands Industrial Estate, Larbert, Stirlingshire, FK5 3NS Tel: (01324) 555844

Jovic Plant Ltd, Mayes Lane, Sandon, Chelmsford, CM2 7RP Tel: (01245) 224211 Fax: (01245) 224258 E-mail: sales@jovicplant.co.uk

▶ JRS, 47 Ridley Avenue, Howden, Wallsend, Tyne & Wear, NE28 0DY Tel: 0191-209 6565 E-mail: johnsansom00@hotmail.com

▶ JS Bloor Winslow Ltd, 85 Adlington Road, Wilmslow, Cheshire, SK9 2BT Tel: (01625) 539762 Fax: (01625) 546809 E-mail: wilm@bloorhomes.com

Jta Construction Huddersfield Ltd, 246 Lockwood Road, Huddersfield, HD1 3TG Tel: (01484) 303204 Fax: (01484) 303207

▶ Just Home Improvements Ltd, 181A Barrack Road, Christchurch, Dorset, BH23 2AR Tel: (01202) 479001

K & A Day Builders Ltd, The Builders Yard, Holtonwood Road, Stratford St. Mary, Colchester, CO7 6NE Tel: (01206) 231247 Fax: (01206) 231247

▶ K A Ingram, Quarry Ridge, Dallas, Forres, Morayshire, IV36 2RY Tel: (01343) 890369

▶ K & C Building Contractors Ltd, Enterprise House, Enterprise Park, Kinmel Bay, Rhyl, Clwyd, LL18 5JZ Tel: (01745) 334591

▶ K J Bryan Builders Ltd, 5 John Davies Workshops, Main Street, Huthwaite, Sutton-in-Ashfield, Nottinghamshire, NG17 2LQ Tel: (01623) 553997 Fax: (01623) 552815

▶ K J Samson Construction Kent Ltd, 1 Granville Cottages, The Crescent, Boughton-under-Blean, Faversham, Kent, ME13 9AY Tel: (01227) 750701 Fax: (01227) 752400

▶ K Martin Builders Ltd, 2a Sidney Road, Beckenham, Kent, BR3 4QA Tel: (020) 8650 4477 Fax: (020) 8650 5398

▶ K W Construction (Aberdeen) Ltd, 55 Constitution Street, Aberdeen, AB24 5ET Tel: (01224) 641190 Fax: (01224) 648329

▶ Kcp.Co.Uk, 159 Heathhall Industrial Estate, Heathhall, Dumfries, DG1 3PH Tel: (01387) 256532 Fax: (01387) 256532

▶ Keane Construction, 1 Springfield, Oxted, Surrey, RH8 9JL Tel: (01883) 722992 Fax: (01883) 722664

▶ Kelburne Construction Ltd, 8 Inkerman Place, Kilmarnock, Ayrshire, KA1 2LL Tel: (01563) 539116 Fax: (01563) 535911

▶ Kelly Mcevoy & Brown, 1-5 Castle Avenue, Castlewellan, County Down, BT31 9DX Tel: (028) 4377 0141 Fax: (028) 4377 0141

▶ Ken Barbour, Fitmacan, Boyndie, Banff, AB45 2LA Tel: (01261) 861455

Kendrick Homes Ltd, Tasker Street, Walsall, WS1 3QW Tel: (01922) 622263 Fax: (01922) 721632 E-mail: feedback@kendrick.co.uk

▶ Kenny Bros Civil Engineering Ltd, 8 Dales Lane, Whitefield, Manchester, M45 7RL Tel: 0161-766 7555

Kent Builders, 39 Ellingham, Hemel Hempstead, Herts, HP2 5LE Tel: (01442) 251425

▶ Kent Refurbishment, 216 Lower Twydall Lane, Gillingham, Kent, ME8 6QB Tel: (01634) 318626 E-mail: info@kent-refurbishment.co.uk

T. & A. Kernoghan Ltd, 5 Blackwater Road, Newtownabbey, County Antrim, BT36 4TZ Tel: (028) 9084 2311 Fax: (028) 9084 3107 E-mail: info@aol.com

Keycare Midlands Ltd, High Edge Court, Church Street, Heage, Belper, Derbyshire, DE56 2BW Tel: (01773) 854141 Fax: (01773) 856203 E-mail: enquiries@keycare-midlands.co.uk

Kidlington Joinery, The Old Builders Yard, High Street, Islip, Kidlington, Oxfordshire, OX5 2RX Tel: (01865) 374880 Fax: (01865) 379246

Kidman & Sons Ltd, 68 Victoria Road, Cambridge, CB4 3DY Tel: (01223) 352476 Fax: (01223) 351519

Kier North West, Yardley Road, Knowsley Industrial Park, Liverpool, L33 7ST Tel: 0151-546 3341 Fax: 0151-548 6039

Kier (Scotland), Buchanan Business Park, Cumbernauld Road, Stepps, Glasgow, G33 6HZ Tel: 0141-779 3020

Kier Southern, St. Andrews House, West Street, Havant, Hampshire, PO9 1LB Tel: (023) 9248 4343 Fax: (023) 9245 5414 E-mail: lisa.haywood@kier.co.uk

Kier Western, 27-37 Martin Street, Plymouth, PL1 3NQ Tel: (01752) 201123 Fax: (01392) 261789 E-mail: info.plymouth@kier.co.uk

▶ Kilbride Industrial Services, New Road, Cambuslang, Glasgow, G72 7PU Tel: 0141-646 1411 Fax: 0141-646 1422

▶ Killigrew King, 13 Calico Row, London, SW11 3YH Tel: (020) 7350 5900 Fax: (020) 7350 5909

▶ Kim Developments Ltd, Lower Farm, Warrington, Olney, Buckinghamshire, MK46 4HN Tel: (01234) 711797

King A & A Building Contractors, Brook Road Industrial Estate, Brook Road, Wimborne, Dorset, BH21 2BH Tel: (01202) 881819 Fax: (01202) 882514 E-mail: aaking@mpz.co.uk

▶ A. & L. King (Builders) Ltd, Hunter Street, Auchterarder, Perthshire, PH3 1PA Tel: (01764) 662688

King & Johnston Building Contractors Ltd, 380 New Hythe Lane, Larkfield, Aylesford, Kent, ME20 6RZ Tel: (01622) 792255 Fax: (01622) 792266

▶ Kingerlee Ltd, Langford Locks, Kidlington, Oxfordshire, OX5 1HR Tel: (01865) 840000 Fax: (01865) 840048

Kingsoak Homes, Eagle Close, Chandler's Ford, Eastleigh, Hampshire, SO53 4NF Tel: (023) 8046 1000 Fax: (023) 8046 1007

▶ Kingsoak South Midlands Ltd, Unit 4-5 Elm Court, Copse Drive, Coventry, CV5 9RG Tel: (01676) 525900 Fax: (01676) 525901

▶ Kirk Hallam Building Co. Ltd, 1 Langley Park Industrial Estate, North Street, Langley Mill, Nottingham, NG16 4BS Tel: (01773) 532000 Fax: (01773) 531010

Kirkman & Jourdain Holdings Ltd, 150 Brooker Road, Waltham Abbey, Essex, EN9 1JH Tel: (01992) 788588 Fax: (01992) 788643 E-mail: k.j@kirkmanandjourdain.com

▶ Kirkwood Homes Ltd, Woodside, Sauchen, Inverurie, Aberdeenshire, AB51 7LP Tel: (01330) 833595 Fax: (01330) 833625 E-mail: sales@kirkwoodhomes.co.uk

▶ Knapman & Sons Builders Ltd, 139 North Cray Road, Sidcup, Kent, DA14 5HE Tel: (020) 8302 2233 Fax: (020) 8302 6060

▶ Knight Projects Group Ltd, Station App, Atherton, Manchester, M46 9LJ Tel: (01942) 874171 Fax: (01942) 897482

KPK Building & Joinery Contractors, Burncoose Nursery, Burncoose, Gwennap, Redruth, Cornwall, TR16 6BJ Tel: (01209) 860472 Fax: (01209) 860213

▶ Kwikbuild, Peasiehill Road, Elliot Industrial Estate, Arbroath, Angus, DD11 2NJ Tel: (01241) 879751

▶ L J B Construction Ltd, 30 Southsea Road, Patchway, Bristol, BS34 5DY Tel: 0117-969 5777 Fax: 0117-969 5777

▶ Lad Construction Ltd, 16 Gorst Road, London, NW10 6LE Tel: (020) 8961 1342 Fax: (020) 8961 1649 E-mail: info@lad.co.uk

▶ Laidlaw Scott Ltd, 46 Queen Elizabeth Avenue, Hillington Industrial Estate, Glasgow, G52 4NQ Tel: 0141-848 6262 Fax: 0141-889 7800

▶ Laidrite Construction Ltd, Unit 4 Fynney Fields, Basford Lane Industrial Estate, Leek, Staffordshire, ST13 7QG Tel: (01538) 373648 Fax: (01538) 386210

▶ Laing Homes North Thames, Premiere House, Elstree Way, Borehamwood, Hertfordshire, WD6 1JH Tel: (020) 8236 3700 Fax: (020) 8236 3801

John Laing P.L.C., Allington House, 150 Victoria Street, London, SW1E 5LB Tel: (020) 7901 3200 Fax: (020) 7901 3520 E-mail: enquiries@equion.ltd.uk

▶ Laing O'Rourke Northern, Curtin House 6 Columbus Quay, Riverside Drive, Liverpool, L3 4DB Tel: 0151-726 2420 Fax: 0151-727 6748

▶ Laishley Ltd, B300 The Grange, Michelmersh, Romsey, Hampshire, SO51 0AE Tel: (01794) 368283 Fax: (01794) 367543

▶ Lakehouse Contracts Ltd, 1 King George Close, Romford, RM7 7LS Tel: (01708) 758800 Fax: (01708) 758888 E-mail: info@lakehouse.uk.com

Lak-Ler (Builders) Ltd, Aintree Close, Red Lane Industrial Estate, Coventry, CV6 5QB Tel: (024) 7668 1907 Fax: (024) 7663 8678

▶ Lampard & Partners, Little London, Albury, Guildford, Surrey, GU5 9DG Tel: (01483) 203741 Fax: (01483) 203445 E-mail: info@lampardandpartners.co.uk

▶ Landmark Builders Ltd, Unit 12 St Andrews Industrial Estate, Sydney Road, Birmingham, B9 4QB Tel: 0121-245 0575 Fax: 0121-245 0576

Langridge Homes Ltd, 17-21 Clumber Avenue, Sherwood Rise, Nottingham, NG5 1AG Tel: 0115-962 6626 Fax: 0115-969 1340

William Langshaw & Sons Ltd, Abbey Works, Back King Street, Whalley, Clitheroe, Lancashire, BB7 9SP Tel: (01254) 824518 Fax: (01254) 823830 E-mail: enquiries@wmlangshaw.co.uk

▶ Lanmarc Ltd, 5 Beechwood Business Park, Burdock Close, Cannock, Staffordshire, WS11 7GB Tel: (01543) 467477 Fax: (01543) 467699

▶ Laser Build, Findel House, Excelsior Road, Ashby-de-la-Zouch, Leicestershire, LE65 1NT Tel: (01530) 410280 Fax: (01530) 410281

▶ The Laurel Property Co. Ltd, The Laurels, Sling, Coleford, Gloucestershire, GL16 8JJ Tel: (01594) 833049

George Law Ltd, 35 Mill Street, Kidderminster, Worcestershire, DY11 6XB Tel: (01562) 820421 Fax: (01562) 829205

Lawlor Construction Ltd, Unit 12 Bentinck Street Industrial Estate, Manchester, M15 4LN Tel: 0161-839 3087 Fax: 0161-839 3010 E-mail: lawlorconstruct@btconnect.com

▶ Lay Construction Ltd, 1 Eastcott Hill, Swindon, SN1 3JG Tel: (01793) 616677 Fax: (01793) 488428 E-mail: post@whitehorse.co.uk

▶ Leacy Construction Contractors, 93 London Road, Sawbridgeworth, Hertfordshire, CM21 9JJ Tel: (01279) 723455

▶ Leadbitter Construction, Grange Court Abingdon Science Park, Barton Lane, Abingdon, Oxfordshire, OX14 3NB Tel: (01235) 544500 Fax: (01235) 544600

▶ Leadbitter Construction, 4 Ivanhoe Road, Finchampstead, Wokingham, Berkshire, RG40 4QQ Tel: 0118-973 7541 Fax: 0118-973 1901

▶ Leamore Contracts Ltd, 2-3 Walsall Road, Willenhall, West Midlands, WV13 2EH Tel: (01902) 601559 Fax: (01902) 637591

Leck Construction Ltd, Leck House, Ironworks Road, Barrow-in-Furness, Cumbria, LA14 2PQ Tel: (01229) 820394 Fax: (01229) 811414 E-mail: leckcon.bar@btinternet.com

▶ Lemmeleg, 3 West Parade, Wakefield, West Yorkshire, WF1 1LT Tel: (01924) 211300 Fax: (01924) 215161 E-mail: sales@lemmeleg.co.uk

BUILDING CONTRACTORS – *continued*

▶ Lemonpark Construction Ltd, Green Lane, Heywood, Lancashire, OL10 1NG Tel: (01706) 369008

▶ Les Taylor Group, Muir of Ord Industrial Estate, Great North Road, Muir Of Ord, Ross-Shire, IV6 7UA Tel: (01463) 870904 Fax: (01463) 870968

▶ Leven Crest Ltd, Suite 90, 38 Queen Street, Glasgow, G1 3DX Tel: 0141-204 7819

▶ Lewis Builders Ltd, Rigs Road, Stornoway, Isle of Lewis, HS1 2RF Tel: (01851) 705015 Fax: (01851) 703718 E-mail: sales@lewis-builders.com

▶ Lewis & Ross Contractors Ltd, Kings Head Yard, Kings Head Road, Gendros, Swansea, SA5 8DA Tel: (01792) 586664

Lexington Payne Homes Ltd, Longbeck Estate, Marske-by-the-Sea, Redcar, Cleveland, TS11 6HD Tel: (01642) 490808 Fax: (01642) 488520

▶ Linden Homes Ltd, 14 Bartram Road, Totton, Southampton, SO40 9PP Tel: (023) 8066 5100 Fax: (023) 8066 5155

Lindum BMS Grimsby, 1 Alexandra Road, Grimsby, South Humberside, DN31 1RD Tel: (01472) 355171 Fax: (01472) 236667 E-mail: ew@lindumgroup.co.uk

Lindum Group Ltd, Lindum House, Station Road, North Hykeham, Lincoln, LN6 3QX Tel: (01522) 500300 Fax: (01522) 500377

▶ Links Construction Services Ltd, 47C Bridge Street, Musselburgh, Midlothian, EH21 6AA Tel: 0131-665 2595

▶ Lloyd Construction, 10a 42 Bayton Road, Exhall, Coventry, CV7 9EJ Tel: (0870) 7590898 Fax: (0870) 7590899

▶ Lomond Homes Ltd, Unit 2 Strathenry Mill, Leslie, Glenrothes, Fife, KY6 3HU Tel: (01592) 742030

▶ Longbottom Wright, Mullany Business Park, Deanland Road, Golden Cross, Hailsham, East Sussex, BN27 3RP Tel: (01825) 872900 Fax: (01825) 873399

▶ Longrow Builders Ltd, 2D Edna Road, London, SW20 8BT Tel: (020) 8543 1227

▶ Lovell Ltd, Churchwood House, 116 Cockfosters Road, Barnet, Hertfordshire, EN4 0DR Tel: (020) 8370 6300 Fax: (020) 8370 6330

▶ Lovell Partnerships, Bell Heath Way, Birmingham, B32 3BZ Tel: 0121-421 8300 Fax: 0121-421 8210 E-mail: enquiries@lovellpartnerships.co.uk

Lovell Partnerships Ltd, Marston Park, Tamworth, Staffordshire, B78 3HN Tel: (01827) 305600 Fax: (01827) 305601 E-mail: enquiries@lovell.co.uk

▶ Lowrey Contractors Ltd, 200 South Liberty Lane, Bristol, BS3 2TY Tel: 0117-963 7111 Fax: 0117-963 7111

▶ Luddon Construction Ltd, Balmore House, 1497 Balmore Road, Glasgow, G23 5HD Tel: 0141-945 2233 Fax: 0141-946 5400 E-mail: enquiries@luddon.co.uk

▶ Luddon Construction Ltd, Bo'ness Road, Grangemouth, Stirlingshire, FK3 9UQ Tel: (01324) 485456

W.S. Lusher & Son Ltd, School Lane, Sprowston, Norwich, NR7 8TH Tel: (01603) 426363 Fax: (01603) 787669

Lynxcourt Ltd, Unit 9 Victoria Way, Newmarket, Suffolk, CB8 7SH Tel: (01638) 669214 Fax: (01638) 660209 E-mail: kiteley@lynxcourt.freeserve.co.uk

▶ M B Roche & Sons Ltd, 28 The Weir, Hessle, North Humberside, HU13 0RU Tel: (01482) 648731 Fax: (01482) 649273

▶ M C Clark Ltd, 3 Norwich Road, Hethersett, Norwich, NR9 3DD Tel: (01603) 501071 Fax: (01603) 811748 E-mail: mailbox@mcclarkbuilders.co.uk

▶ M Dunnigan, 44 Race Road, Bathgate, West Lothian, EH48 2AP Tel: (01506) 652751

▶ M E S L Group, Cordwallis House, Cordwallis Street, Maidenhead, Berkshire, SL6 7BG Tel: (01628) 771717 Fax: (01628) 770427

▶ M F J Homes, Red Craig Cottage, Burghead, Elgin, Morayshire, IV30 5XX Tel: (01343) 831100

M F Tofield & Sons, 14 Barton Road, Bletchley, Milton Keynes, MK2 3JG Tel: (01908) 274527 Fax: (01908) 371395 E-mail: enquiries@tofield.com

▶ M & G Construction Ltd, Gilbert House, Stanley Road, Ilford, Essex, IG1 1RB Tel: (020) 8514 2981 Fax: (020) 8553 0262

▶ M & J Ballantyne Ltd, 24 Shedden Park Road, Kelso, Roxburghshire, TD5 7AL Tel: (01573) 224255 Fax: (01573) 225603

▶ M J Berry, 1 Freeland Way, Erith, Kent, DA8 2LQ Tel: (01322) 351139 Fax: (01322) 351137

M J Gleeson Group plc, Unit 7-9 Callendar Business Park, Callendar Road, Falkirk, FK1 1XR Tel: (01324) 678460 Fax: (01324) 623741

▶ M J Green Navenby Ltd, Highfields, High Dyke, Navenby, Lincoln, LN5 0BQ Tel: (01522) 810295 Fax: (01522) 811263

▶ M J & K Speck, The Gables, Northside Road, Hollym, Withernsea, North Humberside, HU19 2RS Tel: (01964) 613356 Fax: (01964) 613354

▶ M J McCabe & Sons Ltd, Emerald House, Myrtle Lane, Billingshurst, West Sussex, RH14 9SG Tel: (01403) 785855

▶ M J Partridge Ltd, Builders Yard, Birdlip, Gloucester, GL4 8JH Tel: (01452) 862555 Fax: (01452) 864363

M J Taylor King Ltd, 1 Cowper Road, Harpenden, Hertfordshire, AL5 5NF Tel: (01582) 763430 Fax: (01582) 461156 E-mail: tailorking@ukonline.co.uk

▶ M & K Mcleod, Kilmory Industrial Estate, Kilmory, Lochgilphead, Argyll, PA31 8RR Tel: (01546) 602989 Fax: (01546) 603789 E-mail: sales@mkmacleod.co.uk

▶ M L Quinn Construction Ltd, 108 Carrickgallogly Road, Belleeks, Newry, County Down, BT35 7QS Tel: (028) 3087 9300

▶ M M R Ltd, Cash Feus, Strathmiglo, Cupar, Fife, KY14 7QT Tel: (01337) 860212 Fax: (01337) 860716

▶ M M R Ltd, Cash Feus, Strathmiglo, Cupar, Fife, KY14 7QT Tel: (01337) 860212 Fax: (01337) 860716

▶ M Miller, 55 Macrae Street, Wick, Caithness, KW1 5QW Tel: (01955) 602746 Fax: (01955) 605927

▶ M P Brothers Ltd, Unit 14 London Group Business Park, 715 North Circular Road, London, NW2 7AQ Tel: (020) 8208 1988 Fax: (020) 8208 0162

▶ M S P Construction, Northfield Road, Rotherham, South Yorkshire, S60 1RR Tel: (01709) 838472 Fax: (01709) 838586

▶ M W Crowe Ltd, Fen Road, Owmby-by-Spital, Market Rasen, Lincolnshire, LN8 2HP Tel: (01673) 878303 Fax: (01673) 878740

Mcaleer & Rushe Ltd, 24 Dungannon Road, Cookstown, County Tyrone, BT80 8TL Tel: (028) 8676 3741 Fax: (028) 8676 5265 E-mail: info@mcaleer-rushe.co.uk

Mcaleer & Teague, Camderry Road, Dromore, Omagh, County Tyrone, BT78 3AP Tel: (028) 8289 8535 Fax: (028) 8289 8244 E-mail: info@mactni.co.uk

▶ R. Macaskill Ltd, Ardhasaig, Isle Of Harris, HS3 3AJ Tel: (01859) 502066

▶ Mcburney Civils, Brittannia Indust Estate, Blackwood, Gwent, NP12 3SP Tel: (01443) 835305 Fax: (01443) 831055

▶ Mccallum & Craig Builders Ltd, 48 Strathmore Road, Glasgow, G22 7DW Tel: 0141-336 6300 Fax: 0141-336 5868

▶ Mccarthy & Stone Developments Ltd, Hartington House, Hartington Road, Altrincham, Cheshire, WA14 5LX Tel: 0161-941 6255 Fax: 0161-928 2803

▶ Mccarthy & Stone Developments Ltd, Emerald House, 30-38 High St, Byfleet, West Byfleet, Surrey, KT14 7QG Tel: (01932) 336099

Mccarthy & Stone Quest Trustees Ltd, 26-32 Oxford Road, Bournemouth, BH8 8EZ Tel: (01202) 292480 Fax: (01202) 557261 E-mail: info@mccarthyandstone.co.uk

▶ Macclesfield Joinery Ltd, R/O Artillery House, Heapy Street, Macclesfield, Cheshire, SK11 7JB Tel: (01625) 617428

Mccloskey & O'Kane Building Co. Ltd, 16 Windyhill Road, Limavady, County Londonderry, BT49 0RA Tel: (028) 7772 2711 Fax: (028) 7776 8505 E-mail: info@mccloskeyandokane.com

Mccombe Bros Antrim Ltd, Springfarm Industrial Estate, Antrim, BT41 4NT Tel: (028) 9446 2611 Fax: (028) 9446 2794 E-mail: info@mccombebros.co.uk

▶ Mccormack Developments Ltd, Main Street, Cowie, Stirling, FK7 7BN Tel: (01786) 813144 Fax: (01786) 813144

▶ Mcdougall Group, 3 Telford Court, 11 South Avenue, Clydebank Business Park, Clydebank, Dunbartonshire, G81 2NR Tel: 0141-951 1900 Fax: 0141-951 1900

▶ Mcdougall Group, Charlotte Dundas House, Dalgrain Road, Grangemouth, Stirlingshire, FK3 8EL Tel: (01324) 471797 Fax: (01324) 483544 E-mail: sales@themcdougallgroup.com

▶ McDowell Contractors Ltd, 5-6 Parkend Industrial Estate, Stornoway, Isle of Lewis, HS2 0AN Tel: (01851) 701558

▶ Mcfarlane, Ravenshill Drive, Cleland, Motherwell, Lanarkshire, ML1 5QL Tel: (01698) 862324

▶ Macform Ltd, Avalon, Wishaw, Lanarkshire, ML2 0RS Tel: (01698) 355585 Fax: (01698) 355585

▶ John McGeady Ltd, 17 South Annandale Street, Glasgow, G42 7LB Tel: 0141-422 1524

▶ Mcgougan & Co., The Roading, Campbeltown, Argyll, PA28 6LU Tel: (01586) 552531 Fax: (01586) 552531

▶ Mcgougan & Co., Glebe Street, Campbeltown, Argyll, PA28 6LR Tel: (07721) 753650 Fax: (01586) 552531

Mcgowan & Co (Contractors) Ltd, 28 Cramond Road South, Edinburgh, EH4 6AB Tel: 0131-336 2181 Fax: 0131-336 4037 E-mail: sales@jsmart.co.uk

▶ McGregor Construction Highlands Ltd, Seafield Road, Longman, Inverness, IV1 1SG Tel: (01463) 222791 Fax: (01463) 236657

▶ Mcguire Builing Maintenence Ltd, Unit 17 Dumbryden Industrial Estate, Dumbryden Road, Edinburgh, EH14 2AB Tel: 0131-467 7806 Fax: 0131-467 7808

▶ McGurran Construction, Main Street, Derrygonnelly, Enniskillen, County Fermanagh, BT93 6HW Tel: (028) 6864 1222 Fax: (028) 6864 1515 E-mail: info@mcgurranconstruction.com

McKean & Co. (Glasgow) Ltd, 48 Kelvingrove Street, Glasgow, G3 7RZ Tel: 0141-332 1822

▶ Mckean & Company (Glasgow) Ltd, 21/27 Woodville Street, Glasgow, G51 2RY Tel: 0141-445 0123 E-mail: enquiries@mckean-group.co.uk

Mckeand Smith Co. Ltd, Station Road, Albrighton, Wolverhampton, WV7 3EA Tel: (01902) 373426 Fax: (01902) 373469

▶ Mackintosh Joinery, 64 Haugh Road, Inverness, IV2 4SD Tel: (01463) 250160 Fax: (01463) 250180

▶ McLaughlan Construction Ltd, Burnside Cottage, Old Glasgow Road, Kilwinning, Ayrshire, KA13 7QJ Tel: (01294) 550533

Maclay Civil Engineering Ltd, 38 Stirling Road, Airdrie, Lanarkshire, ML6 7JA Tel: (01236) 768388 Fax: (01236) 748425

▶ Macleod & Mitchell (Contractors) Ltd, Unit 4, Cliffton, Poolewe, Achnasheen, Ross-Shire, IV22 2JU Tel: (01445) 781380

Macloch Construction, Unit 3 Zetland School, Middle St Lane, Grangemouth, Stirlingshire, FK3 8EH Tel: (01324) 486279 Fax: (01324) 473500

▶ Macloch Construction, Unit 3 Zetland School, Middle St Lane, Grangemouth, Stirlingshire, FK3 8EH Tel: (01324) 486279 Fax: (01324) 473500

Macmaster Garages, 55 Trent Road, Boughton, Newark, Nottinghamshire, NG22 9ZB Tel: (01623) 836230 Fax: (01623) 836230

▶ McNicholas P.L.C., Victoria Road, Ashford, Kent, TN23 7HE Tel: (01233) 666159

▶ Mcphillips Wellington Ltd, Horton House, Hortonwood 50, Telford, Shropshire, TF1 7FG Tel: (01952) 670440 Fax: (01952) 670388 E-mail: mcphilps@mcphilips.co.uk

▶ Macrae Bros, Laide, Achnasheen, Ross-Shire, IV22 2NB Tel: (01445) 731315 Fax: (01445) 731138

▶ Maden Design & Build, Old Schoolhouse, North Greenwich Road, Spittal, Berwick-Upon-Tweed, TD15 1RG Tel: (01289) 332204

▶ Mainline Construction, The Grove, Bognor Regis, West Sussex, PO22 7EY Tel: (01243) 863138 Fax: (01243) 870568

▶ Malcolm Smith Contracts Ltd, 6 Drumaline Ridge, Worcester Park, Surrey, KT4 7JT Tel: (020) 8337 4421 Fax: (020) 8337 4431

▶ Mandco Ltd, 50 Watson Road East, Nechells, Birmingham, B7 5SB Tel: 0121-327 5026 Fax: 0121-328 0610 E-mail: enquiries@mandco.co.uk

Manning Construction, Coychurch, Bridgend, Mid Glamorgan, CF35 5BU Tel: (01656) 862333 Fax: (01656) 861439

▶ Manor Builders (Yeovil) Ltd, Manor Road, Yeovil, Somerset, BA20 1UF Tel: (01935) 474429

Mansel Construction Services Ltd, Lawrence House, River Front, Enfield, Middlesex, EN1 3SY Tel: (020) 8367 2999 Fax: (020) 8370 2992 E-mail: mansellenfield@mansell.plc.uk

Mansell, Roman House, Granitehill Road, Aberdeen, AB16 7AW Tel: (01224) 717700 Fax: (01224) 698262 E-mail: info@mansell.plc.uk

▶ Mansell, Wards Road, Elgin, Morayshire, IV30 1NL Tel: (01343) 543974 Fax: (01343) 541045

Mansell Construction Services Ltd, 522 Derby Road, Nottingham, NG7 2GW Tel: 0115-978 0788 Fax: 0115-942 0808 E-mail: midlands@mansell.plc.co.uk

Mansell Construction Services Ltd, Roman House, Salisbury Road, Totton, Southampton, SO40 3XF Tel: (023) 8058 0400 Fax: (023) 8058 0401 E-mail: southampton@mansell.plc.uk

Mansell Construction Services Ltd, Wollaston Road, Stourbridge, West Midlands, DY8 4HP Tel: (01384) 440330 Fax: (01384) 440169 E-mail: stourbridge@mansell.plc.uk

Mansell Construction Services Ltd, Roman House, Turbine Way, Swaffham, Norfolk, PE37 7XD Tel: (01760) 721388 Fax: (01760) 724693 E-mail: swaffham@mansell.plc.uk

▶ Mansell Watson (Builders) Ltd, Willow Bank, Insch, Aberdeenshire, AB52 6XJ Tel: (01464) 820488 Fax: (01464) 820371 E-mail: info@mansellwatsonbuildersltd.co.uk

▶ Marbank Construction Ltd, Unit 3, Silver Court, Welwyn Garden, Welwyn Garden City, Hertfordshire, AL7 1TS Tel: (01707) 338844 Fax: (01707) 323322

▶ Marcus Worthington & Co. Ltd, Claughton Industrial Estate, Brockholes Way, Claughton-on-Brock, Preston, PR3 0PZ Tel: (01995) 640690 Fax: (01995) 640771 E-mail: enquiries@worthingtons.co.uk

▶ Mariners Building Contractors, 7 West Street, Selsey, Chichester, West Sussex, PO20 9AA Tel: (01243) 603468 Fax: (01243) 606405

▶ Mark Lee Construction Ltd, Unit 1-15 Greys Green Farm, Greys Green, Rotherfield Greys, Henley-on-Thames, Oxfordshire, RG9 4QG Tel: (01491) 629083 E-mail: info@tvpres.demon.co.uk

▶ Mark R Bennett, The Estate Office, 2a Bridge Street, Stourport-on-Severn, Worcestershire, DY13 8XD Tel: (01299) 871701

Mark Scott Construction Ltd, 434 Chartridge Lane, Chesham, Buckinghamshire, HP5 2SJ Tel: (01494) 794545

Marldon, Scout Lane, London, SW4 0LA Tel: (020) 7627 7600 Fax: (020) 7627 7601 E-mail: mdb@marldon.demon.co.uk

Marriott Construction, Marriott House, Brindley Close, Rushden, Northamptonshire, NN10 6EN Tel: (01933) 357511 Fax: (01933) 356746

Marshall Building Contractors Ltd, Huddersfield Road, Elland, West Yorkshire, HX5 9BW Tel: (01422) 375533 Fax: (01422) 310811

H. & J. Martin Ltd, Ulster Building Works, 163 Ormeau Road, Belfast, BT7 1SP Tel: (028) 9023 2622 Fax: (028) 9023 3104 E-mail: info@hjmartin.co.uk

▶ Master Houses Ltd, Newlands, Kirknewton, Midlothian, EH27 8LR Tel: (01506) 885588 Fax: (01506) 885588

▶ Material Resources, Kingstable Street, Eton, Windsor, Berkshire, SL4 6AB Tel: (01753) 624120 Fax: (01803) 732073

▶ Matthew Investments Ltd, 45-47 High Street, Potters Bar, Hertfordshire, EN6 5AW Tel: (01707) 655550 Fax: (01707) 664595 E-mail: sales@matthew-homes.co.uk

▶ Matthews, Home Farm, Hatfield Park, Hatfield, Hertfordshire, AL9 5NH Tel: (01707) 262351 Fax: (01707) 264813 E-mail: brian@buildingconservation.co.uk

▶ Maxi Construction Ltd, Firth Road, Houstoun Industrial Estate, Livingston, West Lothian, EH54 5DJ Tel: (01506) 442233 Fax: (01506) 442010

▶ Maythorn Construction Ltd, Compton Wharf, Bridgnorth Road, Wolverhampton, WV6 8AA Tel: (01902) 746181 Fax: (01902) 746388

▶ Mayway Construction Ltd, 2 Burbages Lane, Longford, Coventry, CV6 6AY Tel: (024) 7636 7714 Fax: (024) 7664 4462

Mbe Computer Systems, 3 Fair View Industrial Estate, Kingsbury Road, Curdworth, Sutton Coldfield, West Midlands, B76 9EE Tel: (01675) 470061 Fax: (01675) 470889 E-mail: phil.cowtan@morrisonplc.com

▶ MDM Specialist Trades Ltd, 36 Watt Road, Hillington, Glasgow, G52 4RY Tel: 0141-891 4981 Fax: 0141-891 4230 E-mail: info@mdmspecialisttrades.co.uk

▶ Mead Building Services Ltd, Tomo Industrial Estate, Packet Boat Lane, Uxbridge, Middlesex, UB8 2JP Tel: (01895) 460057 Fax: (01895) 460058

▶ Mearchent Sons Builders, Glenwood Business Park Block C, Glenwood Place, Glasgow, G45 9UH Tel: 0141-634 5731 Fax: 0141-634 5731

Medlock Construction Ltd, Greengate Street, Oldham, OL4 1FN Tel: 0161-621 5200

▶ Meikle Construction, 87 Coalburn Road, Coalburn, Lanark, ML11 0LU Tel: (01555) 820699 Fax: (01555) 820700

▶ Melavid Ltd, 39 Chesnut Grove, Birkenhead, Merseyside, CH42 0LB Tel: 0151-650 0074 Fax: 0151-647 3058

▶ Melcombe Regis Construction Ltd, The Old Forge, Wyke Square, Weymouth, Dorset, DT4 9XP Tel: (01305) 773239 Fax: (01305) 773239 E-mail: info@buildersdorset.co.uk

▶ Mercer Leyton (Building) Ltd, The Joinery Works, Ware Road, Tonwell, Ware, Hertfordshire, SG12 0HN Tel: (01920) 461972 Fax: (01920) 468889

▶ Michael Brady Ltd, Trinity House, Heather Park Drive, Wembley, Middlesex, HA0 1SU Tel: (020) 8900 2345 Fax: (020) 8903 2345

▶ Michael Healey & Son, Francis House, Talbot Way, Market Drayton, Shropshire, TF9 3SJ Tel: (01630) 653366 Fax: (01630) 653372

▶ Michael Jordan Ltd, Pittwood Road, Lillyhall, Workington, Cumbria, CA14 4JP Tel: (01900) 601675 Fax: (01900) 66006

Michael Thompson Ltd, Michael Thompsons Yard, St. Ninians Road, Carlisle, CA2 4LR Tel: (01228) 525314 Fax: (01228) 515022 E-mail: admin@michaelthompsonltd.co.uk

▶ Mid Cheshire Construction Ltd, 206 Chester Road, Hartford, Northwich, Cheshire, CW8 1LG Tel: (01606) 871349 Fax: (01606) 871350

▶ Milcon Construction & Property Services Ltd, Enterprise House Wistaston Road Business Centre, Wistaston Road, Crewe, CW2 7RP Tel: (01270) 580000 Fax: (01270) 500041

▶ Milford Homes Ltd, 850 Brighton Road, Purley, Surrey, CR8 2BH Tel: (020) 8763 3500 Fax: (020) 8763 8643

▶ Miller, 24 Carsegate Road, Inverness, IV3 8EX Tel: (01463) 241000 Fax: (01463) 230130

Miller Construction, Milllenim Way East, Pheonix Centre, Nottingham, NG8 6AR Tel: (0870) 3364900 Fax: 0115-927 1255 E-mail: nottingham@miller.co.uk

▶ Miller Construction (UK) Ltd, Unit 4 Pitreavie Court, Pitreavie Business Park, Queensferry Road, Dunfermline, Fife, KY11 8UF Tel: (01383) 627550

▶ Miller Homes, Unit 3630, Parkside, Birmingham Business Park, Birmingham, B37 7YG Tel: (0870) 3364800 Fax: 0121-779 5895 E-mail: sales@homes.miller.co.uk

▶ Millers Electrical & Building Services, 29 Portland Road, London, SE25 4UF Tel: (020) 8654 4440

▶ Mills & Douglas Builders Ltd, Barrington Road, Orwell, Royston, Hertfordshire, SG8 5QP Tel: (01223) 208123 E-mail: sales@millsanddouglas.co.uk

▶ Minerva Accord Ltd, City Gates, 2-4 Southgate, Chichester, West Sussex, PO19 8DJ Tel: (01243) 779257 Fax: (01243) 753102

Minortracts Builders Ltd, Sandown House, Auckland Road, Birmingham, B11 1RH Tel: 0121-772 2511 Fax: 0121-766 8243 E-mail: mail@minortracts.co.uk

Mitie Property Services London Ltd, Mitie House, Eskdale Road, Uxbridge, Middlesex, UB8 2RT Tel: (01895) 206850 Fax: (01895) 206851

Mitie Property Services North East Ltd, 1 Redesdale Court, Middlesbrough, Cleveland, TS2 1RL Tel: (01642) 247956 Fax: (01642) 223378 E-mail: prop@mitie.co.uk

▶ Mmaxx Underfloor Heating Ltd, 2 Lenziemill Road, Cumbernauld, Glasgow, G67 2RL Tel: (01236) 787000

▶ Molplant Ltd, 43 Castle Street, Dumfries, DG1 1DU Tel: (01387) 253030 Fax: (01387) 266158 E-mail: sales@molplant.co.uk

▶ indicates data change since last edition

BUILDING CONTRACTORS – *continued*

Monk & Silvester Developments Ltd, The Nook, Burton End, Stansted, Essex, CM24 8UQ Tel: (01279) 816542 Fax: (01279) 816104

Moore Bros, Unit 19 Midland Oak Trading Estate, Marlissa Drive, Coventry, CV6 6HQ Tel: (024) 7668 2888 Fax: (024) 7668 0888

Moore Construction, 2 Longfield Road, Eglinton, Londonderry, BT47 3PY Tel: (028) 7181 0147 Fax: (028) 7181 1018

▶ Moore & Mulheron Contracts Ltd, 36-38 Main Street, Stoneyburn, Bathgate, West Lothian, EH47 8AU Tel: (01501) 763099 Fax: (01501) 763150

▶ Moortown Construction, Clarall Cottage, Doncaster Road, Knottingley, West Yorkshire, WF11 8NY Tel: (01977) 676000 Fax: (01977) 679922

Morfitts Building Services, 16 St Michael's Lane, Leeds, LS6 3AJ Tel: 0113-275 8631 Fax: 0113-261 8701 E-mail: ajm@morfitts.co.uk

▶ Morgan Est Capital Projects, Harrier House, St. Albans Road East, Hatfield, Hertfordshire, AL10 0HE Tel: (01707) 272516 Fax: (01707) 272440 E-mail: sales@gleesonmcl.co.uk

▶ Morgan Utilities Ltd, Unit 14-17, Enterprise Centre, 1 Dryden Road, Loanhead, Midlothian, EH20 9LZ Tel: 0131-448 0900

▶ Morris Builders Ltd, Unit 6 Bondor Business Centre, London Road, Baldock, Hertfordshire, SG7 6HP Tel: (01462) 895540 Fax: (01462) 490081

▶ Morrison Building & Development Ltd, Atholl House, 49 Melville Street, Edinburgh, EH3 7HL Tel: 0131-226 4666

▶ Morrison Construction, Macadam Place, Dryburgh Industrial Estate, Dundee, DD2 3QR Tel: (01382) 833600 Fax: (01382) 833400

Morrison Construction Ltd, 37 Harbour Road, Longman Industrial Estate, Inverness, IV1 1UA Tel: (01463) 221016 Fax: (01463) 242245

▶ Morrison Construction Ltd, Singleton House Charter Court, Phoenix Way, Swansea Enterprise Park, Swansea, SA7 9DD Tel: (01792) 781450 Fax: (01792) 781435

▶ Morrison Construction Ltd, Shandwick House, Chapel St, Tain, Ross-Shire, IV19 1JF Tel: (01862) 892202

▶ Morven Construction Ltd, The Hedges, Camlon, Falkirk, FK1 4DZ Tel: (01324) 636165

▶ Moss Builders, 5 Central Depot, Forward Drive, Harrow, Middlesex, HA3 8NT Tel: (020) 8909 9936

▶ Moss Builders Ltd, 126-128 Uxbridge Road, London, W13 8QS Tel: (020) 8840 8877 Fax: (020) 8840 8899

Moss Joinery, 96 Leckhampton Road, Cheltenham, Gloucestershire, GL53 0BP Tel: (01242) 222622 Fax: (01242) 260265 E-mail: moss.cheltenham@kier.co.uk

Mossley Hill Building Service Ltd, Bridge Road, Mossley Hill, Liverpool, L18 5EG Tel: 0151-280 2868 Fax: 0151-280 2868 E-mail: mhbsltd@yahoo.co.uk

▶ Mouchel Parkman (South East) Ltd, 1st And 3rd Floor, Kingswood House, 47-51 Sidcup Hill, Sidcup, Kent, DA14 6HJ Tel: (020) 8308 0300

▶ Moulds Builders Ltd, Stoner Hill Road, Froxfield, Petersfield, Hampshire, GU32 1DY Tel: (01730) 264129 Fax: (01730) 260817

▶ Mountain Roofing, 4 Micklemoss Drive, Mountain, Queensbury, Bradford, West Yorkshire, BD13 1NF Tel: 07941 693963 E-mail: David158@btinternet.com

Mowbray & Son Ltd, North End Business Park, Station Road, Swineshead, Boston, Lincolnshire, PE20 3PW Tel: (01205) 820284 Fax: (01205) 820976 E-mail: mowbrayltd@tiscali.co.uk

▶ Mowlem P.L.C., Askern Road, Carcroft, Doncaster, South Yorkshire, DN6 8DH Tel: (01302) 330491

Mowlem Building, Pendennis Court, Salmouth Business Park, Bickland Water Road, Falmouth, Cornwall, TR11 4SY Tel: (0870) 7774468 Fax: (0870) 7774469 E-mail: buildingcornwall@mowlem.com

John Mowlem & Co. P.L.C., Port Causeway, Bromborough, Wirral, Merseyside, CH62 3PS Tel: 0151-482 3500 Fax: 0151-482 3585

▶ Mowlem Skill Base, Stone Place, Mayfield, Dalkeith, Midlothian, EH22 5PE Tel: 0131-663 3386

Muir Group Ltd, Muir House, Bellknowes Industrial Estate, Inverkeithing, Fife, KY11 1HF Tel: (01383) 416191 Fax: (01383) 410193 E-mail: muir@muir-group.co.uk

▶ Muirfield Contracts Ltd, Souter Head Road, Altens Industrial Estate, Aberdeen, AB12 3LF Tel: (01224) 893300 Fax: (01224) 893301 E-mail: sales@muirfieldcontracts.co.uk

▶ Muirfield (Contracts) Ltd, North Tay Works, 48 Loons Road, Dundee, DD3 6AP Tel: (01382) 668288 Fax: (01382) 642776 E-mail: enquiries@muirfieldcontracts.co.uk

▶ Mulalley & Co. Ltd, Teresa Gavin House, Southend Road, Woodford Green, Essex, IG8 8FA Tel: (020) 8551 9999 Fax: (020) 8550 7745

▶ Multiplex Construction, Elvin House, Stadium Way, Wembley, Middlesex, HA9 0DW Tel: (020) 8900 9111

▶ Munnelly Support Services Ltd, The Heights, 59-65 Lowlands Road, Harrow, Middlesex, HA1 3AW Tel: (020) 8515 0300 Fax: (020) 8861 5837

▶ Munro Builders Ltd, 45 Highfield Gardens, Westcliff-on-Sea, Essex, SS0 0SY Tel: (01702) 348319

William Munro Construction (Highland) Ltd, River Drive, Teaninich Industrial Estate, Alness, Ross-Shire, IV17 0PG Tel: (01349) 882373

▶ Murdoch Group Ltd, 23 Greenbank Industrial Estate, Ballyholland Road, Newry, County Down, BT34 2QN Tel: (028) 3025 0897 Fax: (028) 3025 1858

▶ Murdoch Mackenzie Construction Ltd, Coursington Road, Motherwell, Lanarkshire, ML1 1NR Tel: (01698) 265171 Fax: (01698) 276986

▶ Murdoch Smith & Co. Ltd, Crownest Loan, Stenhousemuir, Larbert, Stirlingshire, FK5 3BU Tel: (01324) 553167 Fax: (01324) 562194

▶ Murray & Burrell Ltd, Roxburgh Street, Galashiels, Selkirkshire, TD1 1PE Tel: (01896) 752364 Fax: (01896) 758189 E-mail: info@murrayandburrell.com

▶ Myersholm Construction Ltd, Station Yard, The Village, Strensall, York, YO32 5XD Tel: (01904) 490208 Fax: (01904) 491264

▶ N A Hamilton Contractors Ltd, Hamilton House, West Road, Stanley, County Durham, DH9 7XA Tel: (01207) 233444 Fax: (01207) 238222

▶ N E Cox Ltd, 190 Boldmere Road, Sutton Coldfield, West Midlands, B73 5UE Tel: 0121-355 8780 Fax: 0121-355 7436 E-mail: mail@necox.co.uk

▶ N Fairclough Builders Ltd, Bentley Road, Doncaster, South Yorkshire, DN5 9TG Tel: (01302) 783416 Fax: (01302) 783742

▶ N J B Contractors, Eastlands Industrial Estate, King George Avenue, Leiston, Suffolk, IP16 4LL Tel: (01728) 830924 Fax: (01728) 833675

▶ N Macdonald, Balliscate, Salen Road, Tobermory, Isle of Mull, PA75 6NS Tel: (01688) 302065 Fax: (01688) 302099

▶ N V C Construction Ltd, Bogenraith, Durris, Banchory, Kincardineshire, AB31 6DS Tel: (01330) 811788 Fax: (01330) 811780

▶ David Narro Associates Ltd, 36 Argyle Place, Edinburgh, EH9 1JT Tel: 0131-229 5553 Fax: 0131-229 5090 E-mail: sales@davidnarro.co.uk

Naylor & Walkden Ltd, Hatton Street, Adlington, Chorley, Lancashire, PR7 4HT Tel: (01257) 480222 Fax: (01257) 482696 E-mail: info@naylorwalkden.co.uk

▶ NDR Builders, Gainborough, Station Road, Tenterden, Kent, TN30 6HN Tel: (01580) 761222

▶ Nearly Construction Ltd, 19 Robertson Street, Glasgow, G78 1QW Tel: 0141-880 8720

▶ Necton Management Ltd, Oak Farm, North Pickenham Road, Necton, Swaffham, Norfolk, PE37 8DN Tel: (01760) 722183 Fax: (01760) 722342

▶ Needham, Florian House, 30 Wharfdale Road, Ipswich, IP1 4JP Tel: (01473) 220400 Fax: (01603) 891046

▶ Neil Grinnall, Galton Way, Hadzor, Droitwich, Worcestershire, WR9 7ER Tel: (01905) 827800 Fax: (01905) 827800 E-mail: enquiries@neilgrinnallhomes.co.uk

▶ Nelson Joinery & Building, Glen Way, Brierfield, Nelson, Lancashire, BB9 5NH Tel: (01282) 615550 Fax: (01282) 619055

New Quay Developments Ltd, 68 Armagh Road, Tandragee, Craigavon, County Armagh, BT62 2HS Tel: (028) 3884 0444 Fax: (028) 3884 1811 E-mail: info@newquayconstruction.com

▶ Newfield Jones Homes, Newfield House, 5 Fleet Street, Lytham St. Annes, Lancashire, FY8 2DQ Tel: (01253) 728760 Fax: (01253) 712204 E-mail: sales@newfieldjoneshomes.co.uk

▶ Newland Homes Ltd, 8 Lansdown Place, Cheltenham, Gloucestershire, GL50 2HU Tel: (01242) 513600 Fax: (01242) 514700

▶ Newman Moore Ltd, 42b Northgate, Sleaford, Lincolnshire, NG34 7AF Tel: (01529) 302430 Fax: (01529) 414476 E-mail: enquiries@newmanmoore.co.uk

▶ Newport Building Services Ltd, Units 3-4 Victoria Court, Hurricane Way, Wickford, Essex, SS11 8YY Tel: (01268) 575550 Fax: (01268) 575551

▶ Newton Contracting Services, Faraday House, Wolfreton Drive, Anlaby, Hull, HU10 7BY Tel: (01482) 655565 Fax: (01482) 654924

▶ Newtown Construction (Scotland) Ltd, Unit 3, Acorn Business Centre, Arran Road, Perth, PH1 3DZ Tel: (01738) 446226

▶ Niblock Builders Ltd, 135 Anerley Road, London, SE20 8AJ Tel: (020) 8778 3449 Fax: (020) 8659 0615

▶ Nicholls Countryside Construction Ltd, Wyvern House, Station Road, Billingshurst, West Sussex, RH14 9SE Tel: (01403) 782009 Fax: (01403) 786659

▶ Nicholls & Wilson Ltd, 44-45 Alston Drive, Bradwell Abbey, Milton Keynes, MK13 9HB Tel: (01908) 321123

▶ Nicholson Jones Partnership Ltd, 20 St. Andrews Crescent, Cardiff, CF10 3DD Tel: (029) 2072 9500 Fax: (029) 2072 9501

▶ Nike Construction Ltd, Phoenix Business Park, John Nike Way, Bracknell, Berkshire, RG12 8TN Tel: (01344) 789300 Fax: (01344) 789301

Nolan Davis Contracting Ltd, Devas House, 7A Browning Avenue, Thornhil, Southampton, SO19 6PW Tel: (023) 8046 5000 Fax: (023) 8047 7620 E-mail: info@nd-contracting.co.uk

▶ Norman Wright Portsmouth Ltd, 5 Warren Avenue Industrial Estate, Warren Avenue, Southsea, Hampshire, PO4 8PY Tel: (023) 9273 6340 Fax: (023) 9273 0066

North Manchester Joinery, Hulme St, Bury, Lancashire, BL8 1AN Tel: 0161-705 2960 Fax: 0161-764 0552

▶ Northern Construction Services (Engineering) Ltd, Silverburn Cresent, Bridge of Don Industrial Estate, Aberdeen, AB23 8EW Tel: (01224) 826012 Fax: (01224) 827292

▶ Northern Developments, Oakvale House, Thomas Lane, Burgh Road Industrial Estate, Carlisle, CA2 7ND Tel: (01228) 533315 Fax: (01228) 592244

▶ Northern Heritage Developments Ltd, 19 Haw Grove, Hellifield, Skipton, North Yorkshire, BD23 4JA Tel: (01729) 851065

▶ Norwest Holst Ltd, 6230 Bishops Court, Birmingham Business Court, Birmingham Business Park, Birmingham, B37 7YB Tel: 0121-788 7300 Fax: 0121-707 3438

▶ Norwest Holst Construction Ltd, Clair House, Sir Frank Whittle Road, Derby, DE21 4SS Tel: (01332) 387500 Fax: (01332) 384507

▶ Norwest Holst Services Ltd, Norwest House, Ditton Road, Widnes, Cheshire, WA8 0WE Tel: 0151-420 6520 Fax: 0151-423 3934

▶ Norwood Homes, Millbrae, Findhorn, Forres, Morayshire, IV36 3YY Tel: (01309) 691200 Fax: (01309) 691454

▶ Now Recruitment Ltd, 3 Chester Street, Newcastle upon Tyne, NE2 1AT Tel: 0191-209 1900 Fax: 0191-209 1911

▶ Nuttall Construction Ltd, Chadwick Road, Eccles, Manchester, M30 0WP Tel: 0161-787 7380 Fax: 0161-787 8505

▶ O X, Unit B, New Baltic Wharf, Evelyn Street, London, SE8 5RJ Tel: (020) 8469 3331

▶ Oakfield Construction, Dunsil Road Moorgreen Industrial Park, Engine Lane, Newthorpe, Nottingham, NG16 3QU Tel: (01773) 534000 Fax: (01773) 534222 E-mail: office@oakfieldconstruction.co.uk

Oakleaf Building Service, 1 Millside Park, Crouch Lane, Winkfield, Windsor, Berkshire, SL4 4PX Tel: (01344) 891277 Fax: (01344) 891299

▶ Oakwood Builders & Joinery Ltd, Oaklands, Old Icknield Way, Benson, Wallingford, Oxfordshire, OX10 6PW Tel: (01491) 836440 Fax: (01491) 826020

▶ O'Brien Construction Ltd, Park Lane, Thurso, Caithness, KW14 8JZ Tel: (01847) 893666 Fax: (01847) 893888

▶ Oddy Builders Ltd, Woodlands Factory, Stanks Lane South, Leeds, LS14 5LN Tel: 0113-264 3734 Fax: 0113-232 6672

O'Kane Bros Woodworking Ltd, 13 Hass Road, Dungiven, Londonderry, BT47 4QH Tel: (028) 7774 1705 Fax: (028) 7774 2343 E-mail: okanebros@aol.com

▶ Oliver Connell & Son Ltd, 35 Junction Road, London, W5 4XP Tel: (020) 8568 0001 Fax: (020) 8232 8151

▶ Oliveti Constructin Ltd, 2a Peatling Road, Countesthorpe, Leicester, LE8 5RD Tel: 0116-277 7771 Fax: 0116-277 7776

▶ Olli Construction Services, 21 Johnstone Road, London, E6 6JB Tel: (020) 8552 7122 Fax: (020) 8552 6263

▶ One 58 Associates Ltd, Unit 1 Grove Street, Cheltenham, Gloucestershire, GL50 3LZ Tel: (01242) 241158 Fax: (01242) 241580

▶ Onny Developments Ltd, 3 Corvedale Road, Craven Arms, Shropshire, SY7 9NE Tel: (01588) 672430 Fax: (01588) 672930 E-mail: sales@onnydevelop.co.uk

▶ Orbital Contractors Ltd, Gale Buildings, Gale Road, Knowsley Industrial Park, Liverpool, L33 7YB Tel: 0151-546 0830

▶ Oriole Constructors, 196 Fernbank Road, Ascot, Berkshire, SL5 8LA Tel: (01344) 885557

Geoffrey Osborne Ltd, Osborne House, Stockbridge Road, Chichester, West Sussex, PO19 8LL Tel: (01243) 787811 Fax: (01243) 531231 E-mail: andrew.smith@osborne.co.uk

▶ P A Sewell Ltd, Linchmere Place, Crawley, West Sussex, RH11 0EX Tel: (01293) 523790 Fax: (01293) 553849

▶ P & B Builders (Scotland) Ltd, 3-5 Rhannan Road, Glasgow, G44 3AZ Tel: 0141-633 2148

P B M Building Services Ltd, 70 Whalebone Lane South, Dagenham, Essex, RM8 1BB Tel: (020) 8595 5566

▶ P Brady Contractors Ltd, 48 Churchfield Road, London, W3 6DL Tel: (020) 8992 9861 Fax: (020) 8992 5597

▶ P C Mcqueenie, Carpet Lane, Edinburgh, EH6 6SP Tel: 0131-468 7061 Fax: 0131-467 0099

▶ P Hayward & Son Ltd, Broomhouses Industrial Estate, Lockerbie, Dumfriesshire, DG11 2RF Tel: (01576) 203982

▶ P J Allison Wirral Ltd, 4 May Road, Wirral, Merseyside, CH60 5RA Tel: 0151-342 7797 Fax: 0151-342 9244

▶ P J Carey Contractors Ltd, Chesney Wold, Bleak Hall, Milton Keynes, MK6 1NJ Tel: (01908) 668383 Fax: (01908) 667596

▶ P & J Hunter, Unit 4a Charlesfield Industrial Estate, St. Boswells, Melrose, Roxburghshire, TD6 0HH Tel: (01835) 824751 Fax: (01835) 824752

P M D Building Services Ltd, 32 Vilier Street, Sunderland, SR1 1EJ Tel: 0191-514 3444 Fax: 0191-514 3445

▶ P Moran Ltd, Smeaton, Dalkeith, Midlothian, EH22 2NN Tel: 0131-663 6246 Fax: 0131-663 9908

▶ P & R Materials, Clint Bank, Burnt Yates, Harrogate, North Yorkshire, HG3 3DW Tel: (01423) 770731 Fax: (01423) 771527

▶ P R S Building Contractors, Port Road, Palnackie, Castle Douglas, Kirkcudbrightshire, DG7 1PQ Tel: (01556) 600351 Fax: (01556) 600240

P S Construction Doncaster Ltd, Grange Farm, Mere Lane, Edenthorpe, Doncaster, South Yorkshire, DN3 2HS Tel: (01302) 300100 Fax: (01302) 300354 E-mail: sales@psconstruction.co.uk

▶ P S W Building Contractors Ltd, 163 A Donald Street, Cardiff, CF24 4TP Tel: (029) 2048 9648

▶ P T Smith Builders Ltd, Unit 18 Fysh House Farm, Cuckoo Hill, Bures, Suffolk, CO8 5LD Tel: (01787) 227786 Fax: (01787) 227287

▶ P Trant Guernsey Ltd, Fairfield, Forest Road, St. Martin, Guernsey, GY4 6UG Tel: (01481) 240471 Fax: (01481) 230468

▶ P & W Maintenance Contracting Ltd, Redwither Business Centre, Redwither Business Park, Wrexham, Clwyd, LL13 9XR Tel: (01978) 660040 Fax: (01978) 667110 E-mail: info@p-wcontracting.co.uk

▶ P W Reynolds Ltd, 50a Chatterton Road, Bromley, BR2 9QE Tel: (020) 8466 1001 Fax: (020) 8466 8555

▶ Pacy & Wheatley Ltd, 113 Thorne Road, Doncaster, South Yorkshire, DN2 5BQ Tel: (01302) 760843 Fax: (01302) 342992

▶ Palmac Contracting, 4 Adams Way, Springfield Business Park, Alcester, Warwickshire, B49 6PU Tel: (01789) 766022 Fax: (01789) 763662

▶ Palmers Of Oakham, 9 Penn Street, Oakham, Leicestershire, LE15 6BB Tel: (01572) 722096 Fax: (01572) 724653

▶ Pang Properties Ltd, Bleets Farm Buildings, Feltham, Frome, Somerset, BA11 5NA Tel: (01373) 453177 Fax: (01373) 453178

Parker Plant Hire Ltd, Glyncoed Terrace, Halfway, Llanelli, Dyfed, SA15 1HQ Tel: (01554) 772431 Fax: (01554) 775457 E-mail: sales@parker-hire.co.uk

▶ Parkway Yorkshire Ltd, South Park Industrial Estate, Wentworth Road, Scunthorpe, South Humberside, DN17 2SY Tel: (01724) 863135 Fax: (01724) 858161

▶ Pas (UK) Ltd, Willow Park Business Centre, 14 Upton Lane, Stoke Golding, Nuneaton, Warwickshire, CV13 6EU Tel: (01455) 213344

▶ Paul John Construction Leicester Ltd, Telford Way, Stephenson Industrial Estate, Coalville, Leicestershire, LE67 3HE Tel: (01530) 513400 Fax: (01530) 513445

▶ Paulcroft Ltd, 38 Norman Road, St. Leonards-on-Sea, East Sussex, TN38 0EJ Tel: (01424) 425796 Fax: (01424) 436412

Pearce Construction, Great Western House, Old Station Road, Barnstaple, Devon, EX32 8GW Tel: (01271) 345261 Fax: (01271) 322164 E-mail: buildit@pearcebarnstaple.co.uk

Pearl Building Services, Atlas House, 9 Wheatlands, Farsley, Pudsey, West Yorkshire, LS28 5HH Tel: 0113-255 2877 Fax: 0113-255 2877

Pectel Group, Pectel Court, Burnt Mills Road, Basildon, Essex, SS13 1DT Tel: (01268) 591222 Fax: (01268) 590998 E-mail: info@pectel-group.co.uk

▶ Pegasus Retirement Homes Ltd, Head Office, 105-107 Bath Road, Cheltenham, Gloucestershire, GL53 7LE Tel: (01242) 576610 Fax: (01242) 222723

▶ Pembroke Homes Ltd, Pembroke House, 3 Altrincham Road, Wilmslow, Cheshire, SK9 5ND Tel: (01625) 530330 Fax: (01625) 528221

▶ Pendragon Homes Ltd, Pendragon House, General Rees Square, Cwmbran, Gwent, NP44 1AJ Tel: (01633) 872406

▶ Penny Lane Builders, 88 Ash Grove, Wavertree, Liverpool, L15 1ET Tel: 0151-734 2171 Fax: 0151-733 9208 E-mail: office@pennylanebuilders.co.uk

Persimmon Homes Ltd, 10 Collingwood Road, Witham, Essex, CM8 2EA Tel: (01376) 518811 Fax: (01376) 514027

▶ Persimmon Homes East Yorkshire Ltd, Persimmon House, Morton Lane, Beverley, North Humberside, HU17 9DD Tel: (01482) 871885 Fax: (01482) 870080

▶ Persimmon Homes South West Ltd, Mallard Road, Sowton Trading Estate, Sowton Industrial Estate, Exeter, EX2 7LD Tel: (01392) 252541 Fax: (01392) 430195

▶ Persimmon Homes West Yorkshire Ltd, 3 Hepton Court, York Road, Leeds, LS9 6PW Tel: 0113-240 9726 Fax: 0113-240 8967

▶ Persimmon Partnerships (Scotland) Ltd, Bothwell Road, Hamilton, Lanarkshire, ML3 0DW Tel: (01698) 457117

▶ Peter Baines Ltd, Woods Lane, Derby, DE22 3UD Tel: (01332) 362465 Fax: (01332) 291981 E-mail: enquiries@peterbainesltd.fsnet.co.uk

▶ Peter Clegg & Son Builders Ltd, 54 Henry Road, West Bridgford, Nottingham, NG2 7NB Tel: 0115-982 5666 Fax: 0115-982 5777

The Pettifer Group Ltd, 50 Stratford Road, Shipston-On-Stour, Warwickshire, CV36 4BA Tel: (01608) 666600 Fax: (01608) 666611 E-mail: macpherson@pettifer.co.uk

▶ Philiam Construction, The Quadrant, Manor Park CR, Edgware, Middlesex, HA8 7LU Tel: (020) 8905 7995 Fax: (020) 8905 6777

▶ Phoenix Development & Construction Ltd, Manor Road, Horbury, Wakefield, West Yorkshire, WF4 6HH Tel: (01924) 260230

▶ Picter & Berry, Tetbury Road, Sherston, Malmesbury, Wiltshire, SN16 0LU Tel: (01666) 841485 Fax: (01666) 841485

Picton & Tree, The Bungalow, Edward Street, Milford Haven, Dyfed, SA73 2HY Tel: (01646) 692762 Fax: (01646) 692762

F.J. Pike (Ramsgate) Ltd, 111-115 Hardres Street, Ramsgate, Kent, CT11 8QU Tel: (01843) 593438 Fax: (01843) 595639 E-mail: contact@fjpike.co.uk

BUILDING CONTRACTORS – *continued*

▶ Pillar R C & Sons Ltd, 4 Anzac Street, Dartmouth, Devon, TQ6 9DL Tel: (01803) 832121 Fax: (01803) 834882 E-mail: sales@rcpillarandsonsltd.co.uk

Pitchmastic P M B Ltd, Royds Works, Attercliffe Road, Sheffield, S4 7WZ Tel: 0114-270 0100 Fax: 0114-276 8782 E-mail: info@pitchmasticpmb.co.uk

▶ PJP Southern Ltd, Unit 2 Wellington Park, Hedge End, Southampton, SO30 2QU Tel: (01489) 790545 Fax: (01489) 790492

▶ Ploughcroft Building Services, Unit 4 Bull Fold Garage, Owler Ings Road, Brighouse, West Yorkshire, HD6 1EJ Tel: (0800) 0344100 Fax: (01484) 723355

▶ Plumbing & Heating Services Ltd, Elphinstone Road, Tranent, East Lothian, EH33 2LG Tel: (01875) 610621 Fax: (01875) 613505 E-mail: mail@phs.org.uk

PMP Construction, 3 Devesky Road, Sixmilecross, Omagh, County Tyrone, BT79 9BU Tel: (028) 8076 1074 Fax: (028) 8076 0604

Pochin Contractors Ltd, Brooks Lane, Middlewich, Cheshire, CW10 0JQ Tel: (01606) 833333 Fax: (01606) 833331 E-mail: sales@pochins.plc.uk

Podmores Builders, Haydock Street, Warrington, WA2 7UW Tel: (01925) 582850 Fax: (01925) 582859 E-mail: admin@podmores.com

Pope Bros Building Contractors Swindon Ltd, 13 Cricklade Street, Swindon, SN1 3EZ Tel: (01793) 522113 Fax: (01793) 522517

Portal Contracting Ltd, Unit 1 Yeldon Court, Finedon Road Industrial Estate, Wellingborough, Northamptonshire, NN8 4SS Tel: (01933) 270970 Fax: (01933) 270760

Portview Fitout Ltd, 46 Florenceville Avenue, Belfast, BT7 3GZ Tel: (028) 9064 4765 Fax: (028) 9064 1330 E-mail: info@portview.co.uk

▶ Powerday plc, Crossan House, 28-31 Hythe Road, London, NW10 6RS Tel: (020) 8960 4646 Fax: (020) 8960 3110

▶ Powerstream Electrical & Building Services Ltd, Burbank Street, Hartlepool, Cleveland, TS24 7JW Tel: (01429) 277053 Fax: (01429) 865473 E-mail: sales@powerstream-ebs.com

▶ Premier Decking, 73 Leighton Street, Wishaw, Lanarkshire, ML2 8BQ Tel: (01698) 376965 Fax: (01698) 376965

▶ Premier Properties (Fife) Ltd, Unit 22 Elgin Street Industrial Estate, Dickson Street, Dunfermline, Fife, KY12 7SL Tel: (01383) 625250

▶ Press & Banks Ltd, The Street, Framfield, Uckfield, East Sussex, TN22 5NN Tel: (01825) 890255 Fax: (01825) 890102

Price Bros (Ascot) Ltd, Unit 1 Peter James Business Centre, Pump Lane, Hayes, Middlesex, UB3 3NT Tel: (020) 8569 2251 Fax: (020) 8569 2458 E-mail: info@pricebrothersascot.co.uk

▶ Primebuild Ltd, 5 Davieland Court, Broomloan Place, Glasgow, G51 2JR Tel: 0141-425 1902

▶ Propert Preservation & Building, Unit 2 Farset Enterprise Park, 638 Springfield Road, Belfast, BT12 7DY Tel: (028) 9031 0522 Fax: (028) 9023 8799

▶ Prosser Bros Contractors Ltd, Sunningdale, Worcester Road, Upton Warren, Bromsgrove, Worcestershire, B61 7EU Tel: (01527) 831476 Fax: (01527) 831643

Pyments Of Campden Ltd, Old Station Yard, Station Road, Chipping Campden, Gloucestershire, GL55 6LB Tel: (01386) 840233 Fax: (01386) 841057 E-mail: pymentsjoinery@btconnect.com

▶ Pyramid Construction UK Ltd, Unit 14 Fairway Industrial Centre, Golf Course Lane, Bristol, BS34 7QS Tel: 0117-969 2222 Fax: 0117-969 2299

▶ Queensbury Contractors, Plot 2 Units 1-3, Victoria Avenue Industrial Estate, Swanage, Dorset, BH19 1AU Tel: (01929) 424601

Quotecheckers, 55a Catherine St, St. Albans, Herts, AL3 5BN Tel: (07957) 951079 Fax: (07957) 234561 E-mail: sales@quotecheckers.co.uk

▶ R & A Builders, Laburnum House, Haymoor Green Road, Wybunbury, Nantwich, Cheshire, CW5 7HG Tel: (01270) 569817 Fax: (01270) 560527

▶ R A Wheeler, The Hollies, North Road, Middleham, Leyburn, North Yorkshire, DL8 4PJ Tel: (01969) 622144 Fax: (01969) 622144 E-mail: sales@raw-construction.com

R Baron Ltd, Peel Hall Street Works, Preston, PR1 6PU Tel: (01772) 795115 Fax: (01772) 204562

▶ R Blight Builders Ltd, Morton Works, Clovelly Road, Bideford, Devon, EX39 3QU Tel: (01237) 476927 Fax: (01237) 425407 E-mail: info@blightsbuilders.com

▶ R Brewer Construction Ltd, Bathurst House, Smythen St, Exeter, EX1 1BN Tel: (01392) 494424 E-mail: sales@rbrewer.co.uk

▶ R Brewer Construction Ltd, 87 Alexandra Road, St. Austell, Cornwall, PL25 4QW Tel: (01726) 69354

▶ R & C Poole, 7 Lyric Court, Rax Lane, Bridport, Dorset, DT6 3JS Tel: (01308) 427422 Fax: (01308) 421696

▶ R & C Williams Ltd, Salford Bridge Wharf, Tyburn Road, Birmingham, B24 8NP Tel: 0121-326 9696 Fax: 0121-328 3171

▶ R D J Builders (Rochdale) Ltd, 18A Bridge Street, Milnrow, Rochdale, Lancashire, OL16 3ND Tel: (01706) 632243

▶ R D K Construction Ltd, 52a Hamilton St, Saltcoats, Ayrshire, KA21 5DS Tel: (01294) 468365

▶ R Donnan, Commerce Road, Stranraer, Wigtownshire, DG9 7DD Tel: (01776) 706283 Fax: (01776) 706283

R Durtnell & Sons Ltd, Rectory Lane, Brasted, Westerham, Kent, TN16 1JR Tel: (01959) 564105 Fax: (01959) 564756 E-mail: rds@durtnell.co.uk

R E Lay Construction Ltd, 146 West Street, Dunstable, Bedfordshire, LU6 1NX Tel: (01582) 608571 Fax: (01582) 472092 E-mail: admin@r-e-lay.co.uk

▶ R E Pearce Properties Ltd, South Western Business Park, Sherborne, Dorset, DT9 3PS Tel: (01935) 816204 Fax: (01935) 816104

▶ R F Peachey & Sons Ltd, Orchard Place, London, N17 8BH Tel: (020) 8808 2461 Fax: (020) 8365 0437

▶ R G C General Builders, 35 Kingfisher Court, Newbury, Berkshire, RG14 5SJ Tel: (01635) 523321 Fax: (01635) 523679

R G Carter Building Ltd, Riverside Industrial Estate, Marsh Lane, Boston, Lincolnshire, PE21 7PJ Tel: (01205) 365557 Fax: (01205) 365515

▶ R G Carter (Cambridge) Ltd, Horizon Park, Barton Road, Comberton, Cambridge, CB3 7BN Tel: (01223) 265300

R G Carter Colchester Ltd, 5 Grange Way, Colchester, CO2 8HF Tel: (01206) 794455 Fax: (01206) 790872 E-mail: mail@rgcarter-colchester.co.uk

▶ R G Carter Ipswich Limited, 48 St. Nicholas Street, Ipswich, IP1 1TP Tel: 01473 233655 Fax: 01473 211097 E-mail: mail@rgcarter-ipswich.co.uk

R G Spiller Ltd, Millfield Close, Chard, Somerset, TA20 2DJ Tel: (01460) 62881 Fax: (01460) 65781

▶ R Gilmour & Son Ltd, 501 Crow Road, Glasgow, G11 7DN Tel: 0141-959 1961 Fax: 0141-569 1961

▶ R H Hammond Ltd, Unit 7, Northbrook Industrial Estate, Vincent Avenue, Southampton, SO16 6PB Tel: (023) 8077 2442

▶ R H White Ltd, 33 Burleigh Road, Enfield, Middlesex, EN1 1NY Tel: (020) 8367 4964 Fax: (020) 8364 4015

▶ R Harrison & Sons, Carr End, Glaisdale, Whitby, North Yorkshire, YO21 2QH Tel: (01947) 897249 Fax: (01947) 897007

▶ R.J. BUILDING SERVICES, 34 HIGH STREET, OAKFIELD, RYDE, ISLE OF WIGHT, PO33 1EL Tel: 01983 811196 E-mail: rjbuildingservices@ukbuilder.com

▶ R J Cadman Construction Ltd, Sixth Avenue, Flixborough, Scunthorpe, South Humberside, DN15 8SH Tel: (01724) 270033 Fax: (01724) 271160

▶ R J Mckelvey Building & Civil Engineering Contractors, 17 Carrickdartans Road, Castlederg, County Tyrone, BT81 7NQ Tel: (028) 8167 0586 Fax: (028) 8167 9449

▶ R J Mcleod Contractors Ltd, Atlantean House, Fodderty Way, Dingwall Business Park, Dingwall, Ross-Shire, IV15 9XB Tel: (01349) 860000 Fax: (01349) 860005

▶ R J Watkinson & Partners, 12 High Street, Lyndhurst, Hampshire, SO43 7BD Tel: (023) 8028 3794 Fax: (023) 8028 3655 E-mail: rjwptrs@rjwatkinsons.co.uk

▶ R J Winnicott Ltd, 11 The Green, Rowland's Castle, Hampshire, PO9 6BW Tel: (023) 9241 2741 Fax: (023) 9241 2212 E-mail: mail@winnicott.co.uk

▶ R & M Developments, Clifton Street, Miles Platting, Manchester, M40 8HF Tel: 0161-202 3030 Fax: 0161-202 2120

R Mansell (Developments) Ltd, Roman House, 13/27 Grant Road, Croydon, CR9 6BU Tel: (020) 8654 8191 Fax: (020) 8655 1286 E-mail: mailbox@mansell.plc.uk

▶ R Moulding & Co Salisbury Ltd, Ryeville, Warminster Road, South Newton, Salisbury, SP2 0QW Tel: (01722) 742228 Fax: (01722) 744502

▶ R N Thomson, West Sanquhar Road, Ayr, KA8 9HP Tel: (01292) 265533

▶ R Neck & Son Ltd, The Yard, St. Peters Road, Warley, Brentwood, Essex, CM14 5JF Tel: (01277) 232265 Fax: (01277) 261200

R O Donaghey Ltd, 8 Oldington Trading Estate, Kidderminster, Worcestershire, DY11 7QP Tel: (01562) 820351 Fax: (01562) 829825 E-mail: r.o.donagheyltd@tinyworld.co.uk

R P S Construction, Kingston Lodge Jekylls Gate, Holbeach Fen, Holbeach, Spalding, Lincolnshire, PE12 8QS Tel: (01406) 424406 Fax: (01406) 426260 E-mail: rps@rpsconstruction.co.uk

▶ R P Tyson Ltd, 1 Mitcham Road, Blackpool, FY4 4QN Tel: (01253) 696800 Fax: (01253) 696801

▶ R & R Trading Ltd, 76 Hollywood Lane, Wainscott, Rochester, Kent, ME3 8AR Tel: (01634) 714140 Fax: (01634) 712777

▶ R R Walls Ltd, Electric Parade, Seven Kings Road, Ilford, Essex, IG3 8BY Tel: (020) 8597 1126 Fax: (020) 8598 1707

R Roberts & Son, 260 Conway Road, Mochdre, Colwyn Bay, Clwyd, LL28 5DS Tel: (01492) 546917 Fax: (01492) 543600

▶ R Rollo & Sons, 51 High Street, Cockenzie, Prestonpans, East Lothian, EH32 0DG Tel: (01875) 811335 Fax: (01875) 814437

R T Little Brickwork Ltd, Orchard House, Commercial Road, Southampton, SO15 1GG Tel: (023) 8022 6262 Fax: (023) 8022 6266

R Thompson & Son, Parsons Lane, Alford, Lincolnshire, LN13 9HR Tel: (01507) 462292 Fax: (01507) 466576

▶ R & W Griffiths Ltd, 37 Ashton Road, Leeds, LS8 5JQ Tel: 0113-235 0020

▶ R W L Civil Engineering, 138 Nethergate, Dundee, DD1 4ED Tel: (01382) 204679

▶ R Whatmore Ltd, Brook Street, Oswaldtwistle, Accrington, Lancashire, BB5 3JH Tel: (01254) 233214 Fax: (01254) 385747

▶ R&P, 64 Greenhead Road, Dumbarton, G82 2PN Tel: (01389) 765367 Fax: (01389) 765368

▶ Radcliffe Contractors, Queens Square, Leeds Road, Huddersfield, HD2 1XN Tel: (01484) 420212 Fax: (01484) 540891

▶ Ralls Builders Ltd, Unit 3 Parklands Business Park, Forest Road, Waterlooville, Hampshire, PO7 6XP Tel: (023) 9225 3250 Fax: (023) 9225 3496 E-mail: paul.kelly@ralls-group.com

▶ Raymond Brown Building Ltd, 160 Christchurch Road, Ringwood, Hampshire, BH24 3AR Tel: (01425) 472241 Fax: (01425) 480625

▶ Raynesway Construction Services Ltd, Reema Road, Bellshill, Lanarkshire, ML4 1RT Tel: (01698) 503503 Fax: (01698) 503556

▶ Reaburn Developments, The Square, Blackness, Linlithgow, West Lothian, EH49 7NG Tel: (01506) 834833

▶ Read Construction Ltd, Station Road, Trevor, Llangollen, Clwyd, LL20 7TT Tel: (01978) 824288

▶ Readscroft Ltd, 33-35 Prince Albert Street, Birmingham, B9 5AG Tel: 0121-772 5664 Fax: 0121-771 0085

Red Rose Construction, Charter Street, Accrington, Lancashire, BB5 0SG Tel: (01254) 239300 Fax: (01254) 239300

▶ Redfern Building Services Ltd, Construction House, North Bondgate, Bishop Auckland, County Durham, DL14 7PG Tel: (01388) 661113 Fax: (01388) 607571

▶ Redrow Homes West Midlands Ltd, Steelpark Road, Halesowen, West Midlands, B62 8HD Tel: 0121-504 0280 Fax: 0121-504 0281

▶ Reeds Plant Ltd, New Tyne Iron House, Highrow, Newcastle Upon Tyne, NE15 8SE Tel: 0191-264 0404 Fax: (01912) 641889

▶ Reilly Civil Engineers, 21 Watt Road, Hillington Industrial Estate, Glasgow, G52 4RY Tel: 0141-882 9791

Relmfield Builders Ltd, Hammond Road, Elm Farm Industrial Estate, Bedford, MK41 0RJ Tel: (01234) 218101 Fax: (01234) 357892 E-mail: sonia@relmfield.co.uk

▶ Rendall Builders, 8 Grainshore Drive, Hatston, Kirkwall, Orkney, KW15 1FL Tel: (01856) 878338 Fax: (01856) 878338

Rescue Building & Plumbing Ltd, 126 Yardley Road, Acocks Green, Birmingham, B27 6LR Tel: 0121-708 1333 Fax: 0121-708 1933 E-mail: a1_rescue@hotmail.com

Reynolds & Bennett Contracts, 4 Kilbegs Road, Antrim, BT41 4NN Tel: (028) 9446 4385 Fax: (028) 9446 8664 E-mail: info@reynoldsandbennett.co.uk

▶ Rialto Homes P.L.C., Winterthur Way, Basingstoke, Hampshire, RG21 6SZ Tel: (01256) 474740

▶ Richard Henderson Ltd, Lancaster Road, Bishopbriggs, Glasgow, G64 2HU Tel: 0141-762 4645 Fax: 0141-762 4122

▶ Richard Ward Oxford Ltd, High Street, Islip, Kidlington, Oxfordshire, OX5 2RX Tel: (01865) 379244 Fax: (01865) 379246

▶ Richards Construction Ltd, 98 Cardiff Road, Llandaff, Cardiff, CF5 2DT Tel: (029) 2055 3440 Fax: (029) 2057 8219

Richards & Co. (Mansfield) Ltd, Matlock Mill, Sheepbridge Lane, Mansfield, Nottinghamshire, NG18 5DJ Tel: (01623) 621527 Fax: (01623) 622250

▶ Richmond Homes Scotland Ltd, Pitreavie Court Pitreavie Business Park, Queensferry Road, Dunfermline, Fife, KY11 8UU Tel: (01383) 622127 E-mail: sales@richmondhomes.co.uk

▶ Ridd Wood Partnership Ltd, Market House, 19-21 Market Place, Wokingham, Berkshire, RG40 1AP Tel: 0118-978 7930 Fax: 0118-977 4689

▶ Rigg Construction Southern Ltd, 21 Market Place, Melksham, Wiltshire, SN12 6ES Tel: (01225) 705668 Fax: (01225) 790069

▶ Ringland Construction Ltd, 3a High Street, Dronfield, Derbyshire, S18 1PX Tel: (01246) 290260 Fax: (01246) 290760

▶ Ringway Highway Services, St. Michaels Close, Aylesford, Kent, ME20 7TZ Tel: (01622) 882274 Fax: (01622) 790987

▶ Roach Bros Ltd, 129 Woodcote Road, Wallington, Surrey, SM6 0QD Tel: (020) 8647 1740 Fax: (020) 8669 8149

▶ Roadform Civil Engineering Co. Ltd, Roadform House, Milber Trading Estate, Newton Abbot, Devon, TQ12 4SG Tel: (01626) 331564 E-mail: sales@roadform.co.uk

▶ Roalco Building Services, 219 Holton Road, Barry, South Glamorgan, CF63 4HR Tel: (01446) 722241 Fax: (01446) 721774

▶ Robert Mason, 29 Provost Wynd, Cupar, Fife, KY15 5HE Tel: (01334) 655092 Fax: (01334) 655660

▶ Robert Norman Associates Ltd, Unit 20, Red House Farm, Marlborough Road, Saxtead, Woodbridge, Suffolk, IP13 9RD Tel: (01728) 685040

▶ Allan Robertson & Son, 1 Angus Road, Scone, Perth, PH2 6QU Tel: (01738) 551424 Fax: (01738) 553935

Robertson Group Construction Ltd, Whitemyres Avenue, Aberdeen, AB16 6NB Tel: (01224) 695498 Fax: (01224) 662264

▶ Robertson Residential, 10 Perimeter Road, Elgin, Morayshire, IV30 6AE Tel: (01343) 550000 Fax: (01343) 550100

Robinson & Sawdon Ltd, Alexandra House, English Street, Hull, HU3 2DJ Tel: (01482) 325577 Fax: (01482) 219341

▶ Robinsons Of Wigan Ltd, Kilshaw Street, Wigan, Lancashire, WN5 8EB Tel: (01942) 214511 Fax: (01942) 223935

▶ Robison & Davidson, Dalserf House, Linnet Way, Strathclyde Business Park, Bellshill, Lanarkshire, ML4 3RA Tel: (01698) 747000 Fax: (01698) 845459

Robison & Davidson Ltd, St. Catherine's, 35-39 Annan Road, Dumfries, DG1 3AF Tel: (01387) 267423 Fax: (01387) 264200 E-mail: mail@robisongroup.co.uk

Rock Building Ltd, Rok Centre, Wellington House, Falcon Court, Preston Farm Industrial Estate, Stockton-on-Tees, Cleveland, TS18 3TS Tel: (01642) 616616 Fax: (01642) 679526

▶ Rock Solutions Ltd, 4 Meverill Road, Tideswell, Buxton, Derbyshire, SK17 8PY Tel: (01298) 872368 Fax: (01298) 872868

▶ Rodgers Development Ltd, 33a Anthonys Road, Kilkeel, Newry, County Down, BT34 4PN Tel: (028) 4176 3146 Fax: (028) 4176 3146

Roger Eaves & Son Ltd, 13 London Street, Fleetwood, Lancashire, FY7 6JQ Tel: (01253) 874216 Fax: (01253) 773635 E-mail: rogereaves@btconnect.com

▶ Rogers Construction, 20 Berachah Road, Torquay, TQ1 3AX Tel: (01803) 200079 Fax: (01803) 291890

Rok P.L.C., Rok Centre, Castle House, Woodingdean Business Park, Brighton, BN2 6NA Tel: (01273) 391193 Fax: (01273) 391194 E-mail: rok@rokgroup.com

Rok plc, Rok Centre, Guardian Road Exeter Business, Exeter Business Park, Exeter, EX1 3PD Tel: (01392) 354000 Fax: (01392) 354031

▶ Rok, Stanley Harrison House, Norton Road, Malton, North Yorkshire, YO17 7PD Tel: (01392) 354000 Fax: (01653) 691111

▶ Rok Ltd, Suite B Hinksley Court, West Way, Oxford, OX2 9JU Tel: (01865) 305950 Fax: (01865) 724450

Rok Property Solutions, 68 Macrae Road, Pill, Bristol, BS20 0DD Tel: (01275) 378800 Fax: (01275) 376369 E-mail: wilkinsonandcoventry@rokgroup.com

Rokbuild, PO Box 4444, Yeovil, Somerset, BA20 2XX Tel: (01935) 424444 Fax: (01935) 420006 E-mail: rok@rokgroup.com

▶ Ronden Builders Ltd, Crawlaw Road Garage, Crawlaw Road, Peterlee, County Durham, SR8 3LR Tel: 0191-527 0764 Fax: 0191-527 1281

Roper Construction Ltd, 164-168 Powis Street, London, SE18 6NL Tel: (020) 8854 6622

▶ Rose Builders Ltd, Unit 3 Station Road, Mistley, Manningtree, Essex, CO11 1AA Tel: (01206) 392613 Fax: (01206) 392680 E-mail: info@rosebuilders.co.uk

▶ Ross, 3 Wellington Street, Millom, Cumbria, LA18 4DF Tel: (01229) 772551 Fax: (01229) 772510

Rotary Building Services, 53 Huntly Street, Aberdeen, AB10 1TH Tel: (01224) 633211 Fax: (01224) 633899

▶ Rothwell Robinson Ltd, Holyoake Road, Worsley, Manchester, M28 3DL Tel: 0161-790 9388 Fax: 0161-703 8863

Rowe Building Services Ltd, Unit 22 Challenge Centre, Sharps Close, Portsmouth, PO3 5RJ Tel: (023) 9265 2142 Fax: (023) 9265 2143

Rowlinson Holdings Ltd, London House, London Road South, Stockport, Cheshire, SK12 1YP Tel: (01625) 877177 Fax: (01625) 879995 E-mail: enquiries.@rowcon.co.uk

▶ Roxwell Ltd, 10-12 Stirling Road, London, E17 6BT Tel: (020) 8531 7778 Fax: (020) 8531 7761

▶ Roy Homes Ltd, 8 Lotland Street, Inverness, IV1 1PA Tel: (01463) 713838 Fax: (01463) 713161

▶ Rudridge Ltd, The Coxbridge Pit, Alton Road, Farnham, Surrey, GU10 5EH Tel: (01252) 711911 Fax: (01252) 718623

Russell Armer Ltd, Mintsfeet Place, Mintsfeet Road North, Kendal, Cumbria, LA9 6LL Tel: (01539) 722635 Fax: (01539) 740266 E-mail: sales@russell-armer.co.uk

▶ Rydon Construction, Poughcombe Barns, Ogbourne St. Andrew, Marlborough, Wiltshire, SN8 1SE Tel: (01672) 841034 Fax: (01672) 841038

▶ S A Developments, 5 Peel Street, Failsworth, Manchester, M35 0UF Tel: 0161-681 0511 Fax: 0161-682 3919

S A Parsons Building Contractors Ltd, Mansfield Road, Killamarsh, Sheffield, S21 2BW Tel: 0114-247 9100 Fax: 0114-247 9101 E-mail: parsonsgroup@parsonsgroup.co.uk

▶ S Brash, Eshiels, Peebles, EH45 8NA Tel: (01721) 723400 Fax: (01721) 723378

▶ S C Building Co., 207-209 Duckworth Street, Darwen, Lancashire, BB3 1AU Tel: (01254) 708338

S D C Builders, Limegrove House, Caxton Road, Elm Farm Industrial Estate, Bedford, MK41 0QQ Tel: (01234) 363155 Fax: (01234) 266385 E-mail: matt.clifford@sdc.co.uk

▶ S D M Building Contractors, 490 Calder Street, Glasgow, G42 0QD Tel: 0141-423 1444 Fax: 0141-423 7774 E-mail: sales@sdm-group.com

▶ S E H Holdings Ltd, Crowcroft Road, Nedging Tye, Ipswich, IP7 7HR Tel: (01449) 740971 Fax: (01449) 741403

▶ S G B Services Ltd, Unit 3000, Academy Park, Gower St, Glasgow, G51 1PR Tel: 0141-419440

▶ indicates data change since last edition

BUILDING CONTRACTORS – *continued*

▶ S I Evans & Son Ltd, 81 Lammas Street, Carmarthen, Dyfed, SA31 3AY Tel: (01267) 236253 Fax: (01267) 222727

▶ S J B Construction Ltd, Station Street, Treherbert, Treorchy, Mid Glamorgan, CF42 5HT Tel: (01443) 773570 Fax: (01443) 771739

▶ S J Quick & Sons, Heather Lane, Canonstown, Hayle, Cornwall, TR27 6NQ Tel: (01736) 740272 Fax: (01736) 741311

▶ S L M, 22 Albion Street, Syston, Leicester, LE7 2AA Tel: 0116-260 4638

▶ S T Clemens & Son Ltd, Providence Works, Lyndhurst Road, Chichester, West Sussex, PO19 7PF Tel: (01243) 782542 Fax: (01243) 773773

▶ S & T Fullers Builders Ltd, The Old Stables, Crescent Road, Faversham, Kent, ME13 7AS Tel: (01795) 532562 Fax: (01795) 531924

▶ Safety Barrier Erectors, Ballybrakes Indust Estate, Ballybrakes Road, Ballymoney, County Antrim, BT53 6LH Tel: (028) 2766 3164 Fax: (028) 2766 7815

Salt Riley Ltd, High Street, Tunstall, Stoke-On-Trent, ST6 5PD Tel: (01782) 837390 Fax: (01782) 577354

▶ Saltash Construction, 110-116 Ormside Street, London, SE15 1TF Tel: (020) 7277 5661 Fax: (020) 7277 5662

Frank Sandell & Sons (Worthing) Ltd, Sandell House, Railway Approach, Worthing, West Sussex, BN11 1UR Tel: (01903) 231774 Fax: (01903) 823128

Sanderson & Co, High Street, Leyburn, North Yorkshire, DL8 5AQ Tel: (01969) 623143 Fax: (01969) 623364

Sandy Company Builders, Greyfriars Place, Stafford, ST16 2SD Tel: (01785) 258164 Fax: (01785) 256526E-mail: info@sandy.co.uk

▶ Sanico Building Services Ltd, 17 George Street, Croydon, CR0 1LA Tel: (020) 84072032 E-mail: info@sanico.co.uk

William Sapcote & Sons Ltd, 87 Camden Street, Birmingham, B1 3DE Tel: 0121-233 1200 Fax: 0121-236 2731 E-mail: enquiries@sapcote.co.uk

▶ Scape Developments Ltd, Windsor House, 1270 London Road, London, SW16 4DH Tel: (020) 8679 7111 Fax: (020) 8679 0221

▶ SCC Construction, 83 Bell Lane, Broxbourne, Herts, EN10 7EX Tel: 01992 444588 Fax: 01992 444588 E-mail: shanieclark@hotmail.com

▶ Scotia Design Build Ltd, 175 Cocklaw Street, Kelty, Fife, KY4 0DH Tel: (01383) 831336 Fax: (01383) 831499

▶ Scotia Homes, Anderson Drive, Aberdeen, AB15 6BW Tel: (01224) 323954

▶ Scott Ferguson Building Co., Unit 38 Work West Enterprise Centre, 301 Glen Road, Andersonstown, Belfast, BT11 8BU Tel: (028) 9030 2900 Fax: (028) 9030 2900

▶ Scott Wilson Scotland Ltd, 23 Chester Street, Edinburgh, EH3 7ET Tel: 0131-225 1230 Fax: 0131-225 5582

Scriven Electrical Contractors Ltd, Unit 11, Brandon Way Industrial Estate, Brandon Way, West Bromwich, West Midlands, B70 9PW Tel: 0121-553 7243 Fax: 0121-553 7872 E-mail: building@scrivenelectric.demon.uk

Scruton & Co Builders Ltd, Redcliff House, Waterside Park, Hessle, North Humberside, HU13 0EG Tel: (01482) 644200 Fax: (01482) 647338 E-mail: annwelbourne@scruton.co.uk

▶ Sean Mcglone, 136 Lough Fea Road, Cookstown, County Tyrone, BT80 9ST Tel: (028) 8676 5116 Fax: (028) 8676 5057

▶ Sedac Construction Ltd, Triple House, Whitehill Road, Crowborough, East Sussex, TN6 1JP Tel: (01892) 669944

Seddon Stoke Ltd, PO Box 13, Stoke-on-Trent, ST4 3NN Tel: (01782) 599511 Fax: (01782) 599682 E-mail: transport@seddonstoke.co.uk

▶ Seearo Construction, Newmarket Road, Heydon, Royston, Hertfordshire, SG8 7PR Tel: (01763) 208332 Fax: (01763) 208880

▶ Seefin Construction Ltd, 12 Royal Terrace, Glasgow, G3 7NY Tel: 0141-333 1744

▶ Senator Homes Ltd, Hillcrest Avenue, Carlisle, CA1 2QJ Tel: (01228) 882200

▶ Sharkey Construction, The Paddocks, Ramsey Road, Laxey, Isle of Man, IM4 7PP Tel: (01624) 863113 Fax: (01624) 674131 E-mail: sharkey@manks.net

▶ Shaw Builders Ltd, Barnfield Road, Tipton, West Midlands, DY4 9DE Tel: 0121-520 5535 Fax: 0121-522 3485

▶ Shaylor Construction Ltd, Frederick James House Units 52 Wharf Approach, Anchor Brook I, Aldridge, Walsall, WS9 8BX Tel: (01922) 741570 Fax: (01922) 745604 E-mail: admin@shaylorconstruction.co.uk

Sheffield & Ford Builders Ltd, Mill Street, Duddington, Stamford, Lincolnshire, PE9 3QG Tel: (01780) 444666 Fax: (01780) 444567

Andrew Shepherd & Sons Ltd, Restenneth House, Old Brechin Road, Forfar, Angus, DD8 3DX Tel: (01307) 474510 Fax: (01307) 474530

Shepherd Construction Ltd, Frederick House, Fulford Road, York, YO10 4EA Tel: (01904) 634431 Fax: (01904) 610256 E-mail: admin@shepherdsolutions.com

▶ Shepherd General Builders Ltd, Restenneth House, Old Brechin Road, Forfar, Angus, DD8 3DX Tel: (01307) 474520 Fax: (01307) 474530

▶ Shepherd Homes Ltd, Huntington House, Jockey Lane, Huntington, York, YO32 9XW Tel: (01904) 650888 Fax: (01904) 650889 E-mail: sales@shepherd-homes.co.uk

▶ Sibbasbridge Ltd, 175a Evesham Road, Stratford-upon-Avon, Warwickshire, CV37 9BS Tel: (01789) 205253 Fax: (01789) 298101

Sidevale (Building Contractors) Ltd, 43-45 Acre Lane, London, SW2 5TN Tel: (020) 7274 4255 Fax: (020) 7274 9159

Sillars Holdings Ltd, Graythorp Industrial Estate, Hartlepool, Cleveland, TS25 2DF Tel: (01429) 268125 Fax: (01429) 860693 E-mail: sillhold@sillaraol.com

Simmonds Of Kensington, 4 Pembroke Place, London, W8 6ET Tel: (020) 7937 0122 Fax: (020) 7937 0322

Simons Construction Ltd, Outgang Lane, Osbaldwick, York, YO19 5GP Tel: (01904) 430200 Fax: (01904) 430210 E-mail: yorkhelpdesk@simonsgroup.com

Simons Group Ltd, 401 Monks Road, Lincoln, LN3 4NU Tel: (01522) 510000 Fax: (01522) 521812

Sinclair Decorators, Roscoe Street, Scarborough, North Yorkshire, YO12 7BY Tel: (01723) 367361 Fax: (01723) 370848 E-mail: admin@sinclair.co.uk

▶ Sir Robert Mcalpine Ltd, Yorkshire House, Grosvenor CR, London, SW1X 7EP Tel: (020) 7225 0064 Fax: (020) 7838 9157

▶ Sir Robert Mcalpine Ltd, Sellafield, Seascale, Cumbria, CA20 1PG Tel: (01946) 728080 Fax: (01946) 727295

▶ Skaino Ltd, West March Industrial Estate, West March, Daventry, Northamptonshire, NN11 4SA Tel: (01327) 871335 Fax: (01327) 706029

Skanska Construction, 8 Dysart Street, London, EC2A 2BX Tel: (020) 7377 1444 Fax: (020) 7377 1999

▶ Skanska Rashleigh Weatherfoil Ltd, 160 Blackswarth Road, Bristol, BS5 8AG Tel: 0117-954 1175 Fax: 0117-955 1672

▶ Skill Express Ltd, Unit 17, Enterprise Centre, 1 Dryden Road, Loanhead, Midlothian, EH20 9LZ Tel: 0131-440 9889

▶ Smart Construction, Inchinnan House, Inchinnan Road, Paisley, Renfrewshire, PA3 2RA Tel: 0141-840 4044

Smith, Inchbreck House, Drumlithie, Stonehaven, Kincardineshire, AB39 3YQ Tel: (01569) 740441

▶ Smith & Latimer Ltd, 1 Avebury Court Mark Road, Hemel Hempstead Industrial Estate, Hemel Hempstead, Hertfordshire, HP2 7TA Tel: (01442) 212966

T.A. Smith & Co. Ltd, 53-55 Scrutton Street, London, EC2A 4PJ Tel: (020) 7739 1702 Fax: (020) 8500 4634

▶ Smiths Building Contractors, 36 King Harald Street, Lerwick, Shetland, ZE1 0EQ Tel: (01595) 692251

▶ Sneyd Builders, 113-121 Garner Street, Stoke-on-Trent, ST4 7AX Tel: (01782) 272137 Fax: (01782) 201695

Sol Construction Ltd, Vale Road, Colwick, Nottingham, NG4 2EG Tel: 0115-961 3100 Fax: 0115-961 3400

Solihull Roofing & Building Co. Ltd, 236 Wharfdale Road, Tyseley, Birmingham, B11 2EG Tel: 0121-707 8600 Fax: 0121-706 4693 E-mail: sales@solihullroofing.co.uk

Sondom Development Co. Ltd, The Depot, Windsor Road, Bedford, MK42 9SU Tel: (01234) 350307 Fax: (01234) 262025 E-mail: buildright@sondom.demon.co.uk

▶ South Coast Construction, Ford House, 54 High Street, Fordingbridge, Hampshire, SP6 1AX Tel: (01425) 657272 Fax: (01425) 656788

▶ South Haven Construction Ltd, Stockwell Road, Pembroke Dock, Dyfed, SA72 6TQ Tel: (01646) 686838 Fax: (01646) 686296

▶ South Meadow Homes Ltd, 1 Gibbas Way, Upper Lamphey Road, Pembroke, Dyfed, SA71 5JA Tel: (01646) 682053 Fax: (01646) 682066

▶ South West Highways Ltd, Rydon Depo, Rydon Road, Kingsteignton, Newton Abbot, Devon, TQ12 3QG Tel: (01626) 351636 Fax: (01626) 332154

▶ Southborough Builders (2004) Ltd, Unit 1, Woodfalls Industrial Estate, Gravelly Ways, Laddingford, Maidstone, Kent, ME18 6DA Tel: (01622) 870167

▶ Southern Metropolitan, 2 Salisbury Road, Moseley, Birmingham, B13 8JS Tel: 0121-442 4200 Fax: 0121-442 4611

▶ Southwest Conservation, 15 Richmond Road, Taunton, Somerset, TA1 1EN Tel: (01823) 337447

▶ Space Solutions Ltd, 23 Ampthill Road, Shefford, Bedfordshire, SG17 5BD Tel: 01462 815206 Fax: 01462 641176 E-mail: space@space-solutions.co.uk

▶ Speakmans Ltd, Phoenix Way, Burnley, Lancashire, BB11 5SX Tel: (01282) 427529

▶ Speakmans Ltd, Phoenix House, 32 Broughton Street, Manchester, M8 8NN Tel: 0161-830 8300 Fax: 0161-839 3560

▶ Spectus Construction, Upton Snodsbury, Worcester, WR7 4NH Tel: (01905) 380056 Fax: (01905) 381933

▶ Spence, Audrey House, 16-20 Ely Place, London, EC1N 6SN Tel: (020) 7440 4670 Fax: (020) 7440 4671

Spicers Builders Ltd, Checketts Lane, Worcester, WR3 7JP Tel: (01905) 755744 Fax: (01905) 754005

▶ Springhill Ltd, 1 Main Street, Clarkston, Glasgow, G76 8DS Tel: 0141-644 2046 Fax: 0141-644 4062

Harry Spurr Ltd, Harvest Lane, Sheffield, S3 8EF Tel: 0114-272 4581 Fax: 0114-276 6246 E-mail: info@spurrs.co.uk

▶ Stacey Construction Ltd, Station Road, Wiveliscombe, Taunton, Somerset, TA4 2LX Tel: (01984) 623802 Fax: (01984) 624497

▶ Stafford Construction Ltd, 107 Bethania Street, Maesteg, Mid Glamorgan, CF34 9EX Tel: (01656) 735235 Fax: (01656) 735235

▶ Stall-Mech Engineering Services Ltd, 8 Anthony Way, Stallingborough, Grimsby, South Humberside, DN41 8BD Tel: (01472) 886030 Fax: (01472) 886020

Stamford Homes, Ashurst Southgate Park, Bakewell Road, Orton Southgate, Peterborough, PE2 6YS Tel: (01733) 396600 Fax: (01733) 396669 E-mail: sales@stamford-homes.co.uk

▶ Stan Randell & Co. Ltd, 71-73 Clarendon Road, Christchurch, Dorset, BH23 2AD Tel: (01202) 481871 Fax: (01202) 481874 E-mail: admin@stanrandellandco.co.uk

▶ Stanton's brick cutting & bonding service, sunny avenue upton, pontefract west yorkshire, pontefract, west yorkshire, WF9 1DJ Tel: 01977 649760 E-mail: stanny2@tiscali.co.uk

▶ Steadvale Air Systems Ltd, Boston Road, Glenrothes, Fife, KY6 2RE Tel: (01592) 771891 Fax: (01592) 772759 E-mail: sales@steadvale.co.uk

Steele & Bray Ltd, 59-67 Moore Street, Northampton, NN2 7HU Tel: (01604) 716808 Fax: (01604) 712434

Stepnell Estates Ltd, Lawford Road, Rugby, Warwickshire, CV21 2UU Tel: (01788) 574511 Fax: (01788) 541364 E-mail: gailb.@stepnell.co.uk

▶ Steve Hoskin Ltd, Pensilva Industrial Estate, St Ive Road, Pensilva, Liskeard, Cornwall, PL14 5RE Tel: (01579) 362630 Fax: (01579) 362644

▶ Stevens Bros Builders Ltd, St. Johns Road, Crowborough, East Sussex, TN6 1RP Tel: (01892) 653614 Fax: (01892) 667921

▶ Stevens Construction Ltd, Benover Road, Yalding, Maidstone, Kent, ME18 6AS Tel: (01892) 730634 Fax: (01892) 730540

▶ Stewart Homes (Scotland) Ltd, Atrium House, Callendar Business Park, Falkirk, FK1 1XR Tel: (01324) 670000

▶ Stewart McNee (Dunoon) Ltd, Sandbank Industrial Estate, Sandbank, Dunoon, Argyll, PA23 8PB Tel: (01369) 702578

▶ Stewart Milne Group, Kestrel House, 3 Kilmartin Place, Tannochside Business Park, Glasgow, G71 5PH Tel: (01698) 804804

▶ Stewart Property Services Ltd, 45 Polwarth CR, Edinburgh, EH11 1HS Tel: 0131-228 2867 Fax: 0131-228 2812

▶ Stewart Shaw Ltd, 10 Jane Street, Dunoon, Argyll, PA23 7HX Tel: (01369) 702085

▶ Stewart & Shields Ltd, 27 East King Street, Helensburgh, Dunbartonshire, G84 7QQ Tel: (01436) 672356 Fax: (01436) 679196

▶ Stirling Water Ltd, Hillside House, Laurelhill Business Park, Stirling, FK7 9JQ Tel: (01786) 445591

▶ Stitt Bros Ltd, Station Yard, Main Street, Killin, Perthshire, FK21 8UH Tel: (01567) 820344 Fax: (01567) 820944

George Stone Ltd, 10 Tower Road West, St. Leonards-On-Sea, East Sussex, TN38 0RG Tel: (01424) 436166 Fax: (01424) 420603 E-mail: info@georgestone.co.uk

Stoneham Construction Ltd, Station Road, Havenstreet, Ryde, Isle of Wight, PO33 4DT Tel: (01983) 883723 Fax: (01983) 883761 E-mail: info@stonehamconstruction.co.uk

▶ R.G. Stones (Buildings) Ltd, Rhoswiel Sawmills, Weston Rhyn, Oswestry, Shropshire, SY10 7TG Tel: (01691) 773391 Fax: (01691) 774316 E-mail: rgstones@btconnect.com

▶ Story Construction Ltd, Catherinefield Road, Dumfries, DG1 3PJ Tel: (01387) 249699 Fax: (01387) 249701 E-mail: admin@storyconstruction.co.uk

Strad Concrete, 125 Straid Road, Bushmills, County Antrim, BT57 8XU Tel: (028) 2073 1751 Fax: 028 20731751

▶ Stradform Ltd, The Conference Centre, East Moors Road, Cardiff, CF24 5SL Tel: (029) 2049 3989

▶ Strata Contracts Ltd, Copsham House, 53 Broad Street, Chesham, Buckinghamshire, HP5 3EA Tel: (01494) 778712 Fax: (01494) 778925 E-mail: stratacontracts@btconnect.com

▶ Stretton Bros Ltd, Hamilton Street, Oldham, OL4 1DA Tel: 0161-633 3990 Fax: 0161-627 4772

▶ Struer Consulting Engineers Ltd, 113 St. Georges Road, Glasgow, G3 6JA Tel: 0141-445 5621 Fax: 0141-331 1171

▶ Styan Builders Ltd, Builders Yard, Crabmill Lane, Easingwold, York, YO61 3DE Tel: (01423) 322711 Fax: (01423) 323985 E-mail: styanbuilders@btinternet.com

▶ Styles & Wood, Merlin Court, Atlantic Street, Altrincham, Cheshire, WA14 5NL Tel: 0161-924 1800

▶ Sub-K Civil Engineering/Building Contractors Ltd, 40 Mellerstain Road, Kirkcaldy, Fife, KY2 6UA Tel: (01592) 200245

▶ Sullivan Holdings Ltd, West Coppice Road, Walsall, WS8 7HB Tel: (01543) 377280 Fax: (01543) 373079 E-mail: sullivan.holdings@tiscali.co.uk

Surman Building Services, Queens Avenue, Factory Road, Birmingham, B18 5JX Tel: 0121-554 0390 Fax: 0121-554 3277

▶ Sutcliffe Properties Ltd, Hellifield, Skipton, North Yorkshire, BD23 4JR Tel: (01729) 850817 Fax: (01729) 850323

▶ Swan Hill Homes Ltd, Unit B, Gifford Court, Fox Den Road, Stoke Gifford, Bristol, BS34 8TT Tel: 0117-944 8700

▶ Swan Hill Homes Ltd, Swans Court, Watermans Business Park, Kingsbury C.R., Staines, Middlesex, TW18 3BA Tel: (01784) 464351

▶ Symark Builders Ltd, Dunleigh House, Butts Green, Lockerley, Romsey, Hampshire, SO51 0JG Tel: (01794) 341833

▶ Symonds Group Ltd, Unit 28-32 Concourse House 432, Dewsbury Road, Leeds, LS11 7DF Tel: 0113-385 7000 Fax: 0113-270 1597

▶ T A Brennan, Dreadnought, Hazel Road, Southampton, SO19 7GA Tel: (023) 8044 5908 Fax: (023) 8068 5704

▶ T A D Builders Ltd, Llwynhendy Farm, Llanelli, Dyfed, SA14 9SE Tel: (01554) 752884 Fax: (01554) 745005

T A Green, 73 High Street, Wincanton, Somerset, BA9 9JZ Tel: (01963) 34221 Fax: (01963) 31301

T & B Contractors Ltd, Place Farm, Wheathampstead, St. Albans, Hertfordshire, AL4 8SB Tel: (01582) 833633 Fax: (01582) 833899 E-mail: post@tandb-contractors.co.uk

T C Dolman Construction Ltd, Broad Street, Bilston, West Midlands, WV14 0BZ Tel: (01902) 492792 Fax: (01902) 403618

▶ T & C Williams (Builders) Ltd, 5-11 Norton Lees Lane, Sheffield, S8 9BA Tel: 0114-255 7387

▶ T D Mckane & Son, 15 Drumquin Road, Castlederg, County Tyrone, BT81 7PX Tel: (028) 8167 0870 Fax: (028) 8167 0870

T Denman & Sons Melton Mowbray Ltd, Cardigan House, Burton Street, Melton Mowbray, Leicestershire, LE13 1AW Tel: (01664) 569991 Fax: (01664) 410451 E-mail: enquiries@tdenman.co.uk

▶ T Donohoe Builders Ltd, 19-21 Chamberlain Street, Londonderry, BT48 6LR Tel: (028) 7126 7244 Fax: (028) 7137 1550

▶ T E Leece & Son Ltd, Main Road, Colby, Isle of Man, IM9 4LR Tel: (01624) 832051 Fax: (01624) 834111

T & E Neville Ltd, Neville House, 301 Marsh Road, Luton, LU3 2RZ Tel: (01582) 573496 Fax: (01582) 490216 E-mail: enquiries@nevilleconstruction.co.uk

▶ T G Cruse, Nettwood Farm, Nett Road, Shrewton, Salisbury, SP3 4HB Tel: (01980) 620369 Fax: (01980) 620821

T Gill & Son (Norwich) Ltd, Hall Road, Norwich, NR4 6DR Tel: (01603) 623161 Fax: (01603) 624397 E-mail: gills@tgillnorwich.freeserve.co.uk

▶ T H Kenyon Gatwick Ltd, 1 Building 583b, Perimeter Road South, London Gatwick Airport, Gatwick, West Sussex, RH6 0PQ Tel: (01293) 544300 Fax: (01293) 567786

▶ T & J Building Services Ltd, 144 Curzon Street, Long Eaton, Nottingham, NG10 4FS Tel: 0115-875 2317 E-mail: tandjbuilding@ntlworld.com

▶ T J Evers Ltd, New Road, Tiptree, Colchester, CO5 0HQ Tel: (01621) 815787 Fax: (01621) 818085

▶ T K Builders, Foundry Yard, Bellingham, Hexham, Northumberland, NE48 2DA Tel: (01434) 220800 Fax: (01434) 220800

▶ T Kane, 67 Strabane Road, Newtownstewart, Omagh, County Tyrone, BT78 4JZ Tel: (028) 8166 1600 Fax: (028) 8166 2711

▶ T Livingstone & Sons Builders Ltd, Hillwood, Cameron, St. Andrews, Fife, KY16 8PD Tel: (01334) 840268 Fax: (01334) 840288

▶ T Maguire & Co. (Contractors) Ltd, 3 Clarel Avenue, Birmingham, B8 1AF Tel: 0121-327 2726

▶ T Mann Ltd, 343 Eastwood Road North, Leigh-on-Sea, Essex, SS9 4LT Tel: (01702) 528437 Fax: (01702) 421344

▶ T Mannion & Co. Ltd, 26 Barrow Road, Cambridge, CB2 2AS Tel: (01223) 353372

▶ T N V Construction Ltd, Kingsbury Works, Kingsbury Road, London, NW9 8UP Tel: (020) 8200 9099

▶ T O Jones & Sons Ltd, Glenview, Llanybydder, Dyfed, SA40 9RL Tel: (01570) 480092 Fax: (01570) 481077

▶ T P Keville Construction Ltd, 83 Paget Road, Leicester, LE3 5HN Tel: 0116-251 4622 Fax: 0116-251 9081

▶ T P T Construction Ltd, Redstone Road, Narberth, Dyfed, SA67 7ES Tel: (01834) 861354 Fax: (01834) 861434

T R Smith & Sons Ltd, Station Road, Sutton-in-Ashfield, Nottinghamshire, NG17 5GB Tel: (01623) 555009 Fax: (01623) 442303

▶ T Sloyan & Sons (Builders), 19-21 Lightbody Street, Liverpool, L5 9UY Tel: 0151-207 2064

▶ T W Moore & Son, Criton Industrial Estate, Stanford Road, Orsett, Grays, Essex, RM16 3DH Tel: (01375) 892333 Fax: (01375) 892555

▶ T Wills & Son, Bridge Hill, Kirkbride, Wigton, Cumbria, CA7 5JB Tel: (01697) 351227 Fax: (01697) 351424

▶ K.J. Tait Engineers, 15 Woodside Terrace, Glasgow, G3 7XH Tel: 0141-332 9676 Fax: 0141-332 0995 E-mail: glasgow@kjtait.com

▶ Taylor Construction Ltd, 66C Hawthorn Road, Bognor Regis, West Sussex, PO21 2DD Tel: (01243) 829000 Fax: (01243) 829333

▶ Taylor Homes Scotland Ltd, 3 Woodhall Road, Wishaw, Lanarkshire, ML2 8PY Tel: (01698) 385777 Fax: (01698) 384275

Taylor Woodrow, 2 Princes Way, Solihull, West Midlands, B91 3ES Tel: 0121-600 8000 Fax: 0121-600 8001

BUILDING CONTRACTORS – *continued*

▶ Tayside Contracts, Contracts House, 1 Soutar Street, Dundee, DD3 8SS Tel: (01382) 812721 Fax: (01382) 889572

▶ Tayside Contracts, Kirriemuir Road, Forfar, Angus, DD8 3TH Tel: (01307) 462616 Fax: (01307) 466990

▶ Tayside Contracts, 4 Glenearn Road, Perth, PH2 0BE Tel: (01738) 624051 Fax: (01738) 444246

▶ Tefnut Builders Ltd, 3 Vale Grove, London, N4 1PY Tel: (020) 8802 3978 Fax: (020) 8809 1877

Templemead Ltd, 5 Ascot Road, Shotley Bridge, Consett, County Durham, DH8 0NU Tel: (01207) 581237 Fax: (01207) 581237

▶ Termrim Construction Ltd, 1 Pellon Place Dyson Wood Way, Bradley Business Park, Huddersfield, HD2 1GT Tel: (01484) 547525 E-mail: enquiries@termrim.co.uk

▶ Terry & Thomas Construction Ltd, 34 Redfern Road, Birmingham, B11 2BH Tel: 0121-707 7566 Fax: 0121-707 7566

▶ Thomas Armstrong Construction Ltd, 8 Foss Way, Walkerville Industrial Estate, Catterick Garrison, North Yorkshire, DL9 4SA Tel: (01748) 834849 Fax: (01748) 834297 E-mail: aggregates@thomasarmstrong.co.uk

Thomas Long & Sons Ltd, Park House, Mile End Road, Colwick, Nottingham, NG4 2DW Tel: 0115-961 8888 Fax: 0115-940 0118 E-mail: enquiries@thomaslonggroup.co.uk

▶ Thomas Menzies Builders Ltd, Hayfield Place, Hayfield Industrial Estate, Kirkcaldy, Fife, KY2 5DH Tel: (01592) 264712 Fax: (01592) 200498

▶ Thomas Muckle & Sons, Bridge Street, Cragside, Morpeth, Northumberland, NE65 7SG Tel: (01669) 620321 Fax: (01669) 620505 E-mail: enquiries@thomasmuckle.co.uk

▶ Thomas Sinden Construction Ltd, Unit 12, Brooke Trading Estate, Lyon Road, Romford, RM1 2AT Tel: (01708) 764111

▶ Thompson Bros Stockport, Riverside Works, 18a Crescent Road, Stockport, Cheshire, SK1 2QG Tel: 0161-480 2424 Fax: 0161-429 0924

▶ Thomson Construction, 3 Old Farm Road, Ayr, KA8 9ST Tel: (01292) 267477

Thomson & Douglas Ltd, Kingston Place, Kingsmuir, Forfar, Angus, DD8 2RG Tel: (01307) 466952 Fax: (01307) 462270 E-mail: tdj@freenetname.co.uk

▶ Ben Thow Ltd, Spires Business Units, Mugiemoss Road, Bucksburn, Aberdeen, AB21 9NY Tel: (01224) 699466 Fax: (01224) 699468

▶ Tinto Construction Ltd, 32 Main Street, Symington, Biggar, Lanarkshire, ML12 6LJ Tel: (01899) 308438

Toft-Johnston (Construction) Ltd, Kingsley House, Apedale Road, Chesterton, Newcastle, Staffordshire, ST5 6BH Tel: (01782) 566531 Fax: (01782) 564795 E-mail: admin@toftjohnson.co.uk

Tolent Construction Ltd, Ravensworth House, Fifth Avenue, Team Valley Trading Estate, Gateshead, Tyne & Wear, NE11 0HF Tel: 0191-487 0505 Fax: 0191-487 2990

▶ Tolent Construction Ltd, 5 Christie Way, Christie Fields, Manchester, M21 7QY Tel: 0161-445 1100 Fax: 0161-445 5623 E-mail: jthorpe@tolent.co.uk

▶ Tomlinson Building Ltd, 329 Tyburn Road, Birmingham, B24 8HJ Tel: 0121-327 2660 Fax: 0121-327 3110 E-mail: sales@tomlinsonbuilding.co.uk

G.F. Tomlinson Building Ltd, 14 City Road, Derby, DE1 3RQ Tel: (01332) 342202 Fax: (01332) 295936 E-mail: building@gftomlinson.co.uk

▶ Tompkins & May Partnership, Kingsmill Business Park, Chapel Mill Road, Kingston upon Thames, Surrey, KT1 3GZ Tel: (020) 8974 7270 E-mail: sales@tomkinsmay.com

▶ Tonwell Builders Ltd, 1 Union Street, Ramsbottom, Bury, Lancashire, BL0 9AN Tel: (01706) 821000 Fax: (01706) 821500 E-mail: sales@tonwell.com

▶ Topbond Ltd, Oyster Quey, Castle Road, Sittingbourne, Kent, ME10 3EU Tel: (01795) 414050 Fax: (01795) 472022 E-mail: user@topbond.co.uk

▶ Topmarx Ltd, Culverlands Business Park Chardland House, Winchester Road, Shedfield, Southampton, SO32 2JF Tel: (01329) 833400 Fax: (01329) 836789

▶ Torith Ltd, Macadam Place, Dundee, DD2 3QR Tel: (01382) 815731

▶ Torwood Timber Systems Ltd, Royston House, Royston Road, Deans Industrial Estate, Deans, Livingston, West Lothian, EH54 8AH Tel: (01506) 414105

Totty, Park House, Bradford Road, Chain Bar, Cleckheaton, West Yorkshire, BD19 6BW Tel: (01274) 866600 Fax: (01274) 866737

▶ Tough Security Systems Ltd, 60 Munro Place, Glasgow, G13 2UW Tel: 0141-434 1400

▶ Tower Conversions, 70 Espedair Street, Paisley, Renfrewshire, PA2 6RW Tel: 0141-887 1081

John Towle & Son Ltd, Cleveland Chambers, New Cleveland Street, Hull, HU8 7ER Tel: (01482) 223876 Fax: (01482) 224968

▶ Tradpin Construction Ltd, 14 Hemnall Street, Epping, Essex, CM16 4LW Tel: (01992) 561234

▶ Trak Construction Ltd, Seymour House, Whiteleaf Road, Hemel Hempstead, Hertfordshire, HP3 9DE Tel: (01442) 838500

▶ Transbuild Building Contractors Ltd, 37a Kenilworth Drive, Oadby, Leicester, LE2 5LT Tel: 0116-271 0897 Fax: 0116-272 0454

▶ Transform Building Services Ltd, 6 Lockyer House, Waterman St, London, SW15 1EE Tel: 020 8789 8780 Fax: 020 8789 8811 E-mail: contact@transformltd.co.uk

Treasure & Son Ltd, Temeside, Ludlow, Shropshire, SY8 1JW Tel: (01584) 872161 Fax: (01584) 874876 E-mail: mail@treasure&son.co.uk

▶ Trendgrey Construction Ltd, Coventry Bridge Meadow, Tomlow Road, Stockton, Southam, Warwickshire, CV47 8HX Tel: (01926) 814161

▶ Trent Valley Plumbing & Building Ltd, 113 Trent Boulevard, West Bridgford, Nottingham, NG2 5BN Tel: 0115-982 2332 Fax: 0115-982 0119

▶ Trenton Construction Co. Ltd, 2 Marychurch Road, Stoke-on-Trent, ST2 9BJ Tel: (01782) 264908 Fax: (01782) 205186

▶ Trinity Construction Services, Old Barn, Mountnessing Road, Blackmore, Ingatestone, Essex, CM4 0NX Tel: (01277) 822600 Fax: (01277) 822900 E-mail: sales@style2000.co.uk

▶ Tripstamp Ltd, 56 Pound Farm Road, Chichester, West Sussex, PO19 7PU Tel: (01243) 538912 Fax: (01243) 538910

Try Homes Southern Ltd, Bridge House, 27 Bridge Street, Leatherhead, Surrey, KT22 8HL Tel: (01372) 385170 Fax: (01372) 385199 E-mail: customerservice@tryhomes.co.uk

▶ Tuchan Tolmie, Avalon, Station Road, Conon Bridge, Dingwall, Ross-Shire, IV7 8BJ Tel: (01349) 861356 Fax: (01349) 865393

▶ Tulloch of Cummingston, Minulay, Cummingston, Elgin, Morayshire, IV30 5XY Tel: (01343) 835622

E. Turner Sons, 32 Cathedral Road, Cardiff, CF11 9UQ Tel: (029) 2022 1002 Fax: (029) 2038 8206

Turner Maintenance Ltd, Bessemer Road, Norwich, NR4 6DQ Tel: (01603) 626609 Fax: (01603) 626090

Turney Wylde Construction, Tyne View Terrace, Wallsend, Tyne & Wear, NE28 6SG Tel: 0191-295 8600 Fax: 0191-295 8601

▶ Turriff Contractors Ltd, Cornfield Road, Turriff, Aberdeenshire, AB53 4BP Tel: (01224) 494148

▶ Turton Construction Ltd, Sovereign Works, Gelderd Road, Birstall, Batley, West Yorkshire, WF17 9PY Tel: (01924) 477324

▶ Ucs Civils Ltd, Rand, Market Rasen, Lincolnshire, LN8 5NJ Tel: (01673) 859200 Fax: 01673 859201

▶ UK Gse, 8 Midland Court, Central Park, Lutterworth, Leicestershire, LE17 4PN Tel: (01455) 558847 Fax: (01455) 558424

▶ Ullapool Construction Ltd, North Road, Ullapool, Ross-Shire, IV26 2XL Tel: (01854) 612244 Fax: (01854) 612911

▶ Underground Moling Services Ltd, Units 2, Middlefield Industrial Estate, Falkirk, FK2 9HQ Tel: (01324) 625143 Fax: (01324) 624091 E-mail: sales@undergroundmoling.co.uk

▶ Underwood Construction Ltd, Commercial House, Fontwell Avenue, Eastergate, Chichester, West Sussex, PO20 3RY Tel: (01243) 545115 Fax: (01243) 545116

▶ Unilock Group, Unit 7 E, Enterprise Way, Vale Park, Evesham, Worcestershire, WR11 1GU Tel: (01386) 765155

▶ Unique Building Contractors, 20 Ivydale Road, Plymouth, PL4 7DF Tel: (01752) 228344 Fax: (01752) 250619

V A Marriott Ltd, Handford Road, Ipswich, IP1 2BA Tel: (01473) 255041 Fax: (01473) 232176 E-mail: info@marriottbuilders.co.uk

▶ V E Pinington & Sons Ltd, Aldrens Lane, Lancaster, LA1 2DE Tel: (01524) 65148

▶ V & M Day Ltd, 94 Water Road, Reading, RG30 2NN Tel: 0118-957 3117 Fax: 0118-950 3631

▶ Vale Building Services Ltd, Sundeala, Cardiff Road, Taffs Well, Cardiff, CF15 7PR Tel: (029) 2081 3183 Fax: (029) 2081 3512

Thomas Vale Construction Ltd, Foundation House, Paddock Road, Caversham, Reading, RG4 5BY Tel: 0118-947 8444 Fax: 0118-946 1086 E-mail: general@thomasvale.com

▶ Valentines Property Maintenance Ltd, 19 A Rock Street, Brighton, BN2 1NF Tel: (01273) 693522

▶ Valley Management & Maintenance Ltd, Eastern House, Porthcurno, Porthcurno, Penzance, Cornwall, TR19 6JT Tel: (01736) 810477 Fax: (01736) 810477

▶ Vasahus Ltd, Unit 4A, Wiston Business Park, London Road, Ashington, Pulborough, West Sussex, RH20 3DJ Tel: (01903) 891990 Fax: (01903) 892031E-mail: info@vasahus.biz

Veltshaw Builders Ltd, Pentney Road, Main Road, Narborough, King's Lynn, Norfolk, PE32 1TE Tel: (01760) 337424 Fax: (01760) 337511

W & A Baxter, 269 Gunters Bridge, Petworth, West Sussex, GU28 9JJ Tel: (01798) 342561 Fax: (01798) 342275

W A Deacon & Sons Ltd, 1 High Street, Lavenham, Sudbury, Suffolk, CO10 9PY Tel: (01787) 247389 Fax: (01787) 248581

W A Hare & Son Ltd, 94 Main Street, Kelfield, York, YO19 6RG Tel: (01757) 248188 Fax: (01757) 248999 E-mail: sales@wahare.com

▶ W A Willson Ltd, 24 Church Street, Hoo, Rochester, Kent, ME3 9AL Tel: (01634) 251096 Fax: (01634) 253845

▶ W B Bradford Measham Ltd, 45 High Street, Measham, Swadlincote, Derbyshire, DE12 7HR Tel: (01530) 272870 Fax: (01530) 271521

W Brown & Sons, Wreigh View, Thropton, Morpeth, Northumberland, NE65 7NA Tel: (01669) 620349 Fax: (01669) 621541

W D Stant Ltd, 37a Rivulet Road, Wrexham, Clwyd, LL13 8DY Tel: (01978) 266123 Fax: (01978) 361954 E-mail: sales@wdstant.co.uk

▶ W E Cox & Sons Ltd, 95 Stewart Road, Bournemouth, BH8 8PA Tel: (01202) 395863 Fax: (01202) 395863

▶ W F Clayton & Co., Sackville Road, Bangor, Gwynedd, LL57 1LE Tel: (01248) 353665 Fax: 01248 370958

▶ W F Giles & Sons Ltd, Dockham Road, Cinderford, Gloucestershire, GL14 2AL Tel: (01594) 823144

▶ W G Silverton & Co. Ltd, Meeting House Lane, Baldock, Hertfordshire, SG7 5BP Tel: (01462) 491800 Fax: (01462) 490740

▶ W H Catchpole Ltd, Bestwood Works, Drove Road, Portslade, Brighton, BN41 2PA Tel: (01273) 439227

W H Hodder & Sons, Forge Yard, Lymden Lane, Stonegate, Wadhurst, East Sussex, TN5 7EE Tel: (01580) 201501 Fax: (01580) 201502

W H Kirkwood Ltd, 27 Hope Street, Greenock, Renfrewshire, PA15 4AW Tel: (01475) 721248 Fax: (01475) 888465 E-mail: info@whkirkwood.co.uk

▶ W H Simmonds & Son Ltd, The Old House, West Street, Wrotham, Sevenoaks, Kent, TN15 7AR Tel: (01732) 883079 Fax: (01732) 884055 E-mail: info@whsimmonds.co.uk

▶ W H Snow Ltd, 17 Mansfield Street, Liverpool, L3 3EG Tel: 0151-207 0571

▶ W J Harte Construction Ltd, 1 Hamilton Road, Bothwell, Glasgow, G71 8AT Tel: (01698) 854033 Fax: (01698) 854667 E-mail: admin@wjharte.co.uk

▶ W J M & Co Builders Ipswich Ltd, 3a North Hill Road, Ipswich, IP4 2PW Tel: (01473) 212796 Fax: (01473) 287490

▶ W J Mclaughlin & Sons, 76 Sloughan Road, Drumquin, Drumquin, Omagh, County Tyrone, BT78 4QW Tel: (028) 8283 1270 Fax: (028) 8283 1623

▶ W J Olds Ltd, 365 Park Road, Birmingham, B18 5SR Tel: 0121-554 6068

▶ W Kelly & Co., 38 Derryleckagh Road, Newry, County Down, BT34 2NL Tel: (028) 3026 5461

▶ W M Black & Sons Building Contractors Ltd, 540 Gorgie Road, Edinburgh, EH11 3AL Tel: 0131-443 3400 Fax: 0131-443 7775

▶ W M Friel Ltd, Somervell Street, Cambuslang, Glasgow, G72 7EB Tel: 0141-646 1444 Fax: 0141-646 2200

▶ W R Newland & Sons Ltd, 129 Croydon Road, Caterham, Surrey, CR3 6PE Tel: (01883) 344622

▶ W Vallance, Hoddom Road, Ecclefechan, Lockerbie, Dumfriesshire, DG11 3BY Tel: (01576) 300279

W W Martin Thanet Ltd, Dane Park Road, Ramsgate, Kent, CT11 7LT Tel: (01843) 591584 Fax: (01843) 596333 E-mail: brian.pratt@wwmartin.co.uk

▶ W W Pert Construction Ltd, Broomfield Industrial Estate, Broomfield Road, Montrose, Angus, DD10 8SY Tel: (01674) 673883 Fax: (01674) 678533

▶ Wadey Builders, Leigh Road, Betchworth, Surrey, RH3 7AW Tel: (01306) 611467 Fax: (01306) 611519

▶ Wagg Jex & Co. Ltd, Harvest House, Wisbech Road, King's Lynn, Norfolk, PE30 5JL Tel: (01553) 772963 Fax: (01553) 769184

Wainhomes South West Ltd, Owlsfoot Business Centre, Sticklepath, Okehampton, Devon, EX20 2PA Tel: (01837) 841000

▶ Waite Property, St. Julians Avenue, St. Peter Port, Guernsey, GY1 1WB Tel: (01481) 722121 Fax: (01481) 722100

Walker Construction UK Ltd, Park Farm Road, Park Farm Industrial Estate, Folkestone, Kent, CT19 5DY Tel: (01303) 851111 Fax: (01303) 259439 E-mail: sales@walker-construction.co.uk

Walker Group Scotland Ltd, Westerwood House, Royston Road, Deans, Livingston, West Lothian, EH54 8AH Tel: (01506) 413101 Fax: (01506) 414843 E-mail: info@walkergroup.co.uk

▶ Walkers, 361 Argyll Street, Dunoon, Argyll, PA23 7RN Tel: (01369) 706003

▶ Walkplace Ltd, The Byre, Lower End Farm, Leafield, Witney, Oxfordshire, OX29 9QG Tel: (01993) 878550 Fax: (01993) 878036

▶ Waller Building Services, Pheasants Farm, Sheppey Way, Bobbing, Sittingbourne, Kent, ME9 8QX Tel: (01795) 424435 Fax: (01795) 424812 E-mail: info@wallerservices.com

Wallis Ltd, 47 Homesdale Road, Bromley, BR2 9TN Tel: (020) 8464 3377 Fax: (020) 8464 5847 E-mail: gen@wallisb.kier.co.uk

▶ Walsh Construction North West Ltd, 216 Belmont Road, Bolton, BL1 7AZ Tel: (01204) 303108

Walter Lilly & Co. Ltd, Waddon House, 283 Stafford Road, Croydon, CR0 4NN Tel: (020) 8730 6200 Fax: (020) 8730 6247 E-mail: info@walter-lilly.co.uk

▶ Walter Moss & Son Ltd, Market Street, Coalville, Leicestershire, LE67 3DX Tel: (01530) 831351 Fax: (01530) 832546 E-mail: construction@waltermoss.co.uk

▶ Ward Building Services Ltd, 223 Clepington Road, Dundee, DD3 7SZ Tel: (01382) 884123 Fax: (01382) 884248

▶ Warden Construction Ltd, Unit 4 Fishergate Court, Fishergate, Preston, PR1 8QF Tel: (01772) 270100 Fax: (01772) 270102 E-mail: info@warden.co.uk

Warings Construction Group Holdings Ltd, Gatcombe House, Hilsea, Portsmouth, PO2 0TU Tel: (023) 9269 4900 Fax: (023) 9269 4948

▶ Water Tech Systems 2000 Ltd, Unit 1, Lowesmoor Trading Estate, Worcester, WR1 2SF Tel: (01905) 22113

Waterhouse Building Refurbishment & Interiors, 98 Bradford Road, East Ardsley, Wakefield, West Yorkshire, WF3 2JL Tel: (01924) 822274 Fax: (01924) 823951 E-mail: info@waterhouse-ideas.co.uk

▶ Wates Construction Ltd, Network House, Basing View, Basingstoke, Hampshire, RG21 4HG Tel: (01256) 301750 Fax: (01256) 358166

▶ Wates Construction Ltd, Royds Hall Road, Leeds, LS12 6AJ Tel: 0113-231 1880 Fax: 0113-231 9994

Wates Construction Ltd, 1260 London Rd, Norbury, London, SW16 4EG Tel: (020) 8764 5000 Fax: (020) 8679 7611 E-mail: info@wates.co.uk

▶ George Watson (Construction) Ltd, Station Road, Hipperholme, Halifax, West Yorkshire, HX3 8HW Tel: (01422) 202695 Fax: (01422) 204469

▶ William Waugh & Sons (Builders) Ltd, Broadford, Auldgirth, Dumfries, DG2 0RT Tel: (01387) 740216 Fax: (01387) 740586

▶ WCL Ltd, 1 Oaks Drive, Newmarket, Suffolk, CB8 7SX Tel: (01638) 666006 Fax: (01638) 667245 E-mail: wcl.enquiries@uk.taylorwoodroe.com

Weaver plc, 86-92 Worcester Road, Bromsgrove, Worcestershire, B61 7AQ Tel: (01527) 575588 Fax: (01527) 575258 E-mail: info@weaver.plc.uk

▶ Web Construction Ltd, Bishops Court Gardens, Bishops Court Lane, Clyst St. Mary, Exeter, EX5 1DH Tel: (01392) 872100 Fax: (01392) 872101

Weber S B D, Old Paper Mill, Ballyclare, Co. Antrim, BT39 9EB Tel: (028) 9335 2999 Fax: (028) 9332 3232

▶ Webster Contracts Ltd, Kingsmuir, Forfar, Angus, DD8 2NS Tel: (01307) 466161

▶ Welch & Phillips Ltd, 17 New St, Wem, Shrewsbury, SY4 5AE Tel: (01939) 232762

Westbury Homes, Glanville House, Church Street, Bridgwater, Somerset, TA6 5AT Tel: (01278) 458645 Fax: (01278) 452274

▶ Westbury Homes, Anchor Boulevard, Crossways, Dartford, DA2 6QH Tel: (01322) 421800 Fax: (01322) 421900

▶ Westbury Homes, Bartley House, Station Road, Hook, Hampshire, RG27 9JF Tel: (01256) 744000 Fax: (01256) 769388

▶ Westpoint Homes Ltd, 3 Arthur Street, Clarkston, Glasgow, G76 8BQ Tel: 0141-644 2223 Fax: 0141-644 5059

▶ Westridge Construction Ltd, Junction Road, Bodiam, Robertsbridge, East Sussex, TN32 5UP Tel: (01580) 830600 Fax: (01580) 830700 E-mail: marketing@westridgeconstruction.co.uk

▶ Weybridge Construction, 1 Tristar Bus Centre, Star Road, Partridge Green, Horsham, West Sussex, RH13 8RY Tel: (01403) 713111

▶ Wharfebank Contract Associates, The Workshop, Wharfe Bank Terrace, Tadcaster, North Yorkshire, LS24 9AN Tel: (01937) 530048 Fax: (01937) 832676

▶ Wharfedale Construction Ltd, Moor Knoll Lane, East Ardsley, Wakefield, West Yorkshire, WF3 2DX Tel: (01924) 822185 Fax: (01924) 827832

▶ Wharton Construction Ltd, Kellaw Road, Darlington, County Durham, DL1 4YA Tel: (01325) 288742 E-mail: enquiries@whartonconstructionltd.co.uk

Wheatley & Sons Ltd, 25a Arnison Road, East Molesey, Surrey, KT8 9JQ Tel: (020) 8979 5762 Fax: (020) 8941 7388

P. Whelan Ltd, 113 New Bridge Street, Newcastle Upon Tyne, NE1 2SW Tel: 0191-261 2677 Fax: 0191-261 1248 E-mail: info@whelanconstruction.co.uk

White Building Services, 172 Southworth Road, Newton-le-Willows, Merseyside, WA12 0BT Tel: (01925) 225141 Fax: (01925) 226457 E-mail: mail@whitebuildingservices.co.uk

▶ White & Fensome Building Contractors, 2 Hewlett Road, Luton, LU3 2RP Tel: (01582) 594766 Fax: (01582) 594866

White Young Green Environmental Northern Ireland Ltd, 1 Locksley Business Park, Montgomery Road, Belfast, BT6 9UP Tel: (028) 9078 1090 Fax: (028) 9070 6050

▶ Whitelock & Co. Ltd, 308-310 Bournemouth Road, Poole, Dorset, BH14 9AR Tel: (01202) 763214 Fax: (01202) 752443 E-mail: enquiries@whitelock.co.uk

Whitestone Management Ltd, Whitestone House, Rover Way, Cardiff, CF24 2RX Tel: (029) 2045 1725 Fax: (029) 2045 1526

Wiggett Construction Group Ltd, Viking House, 449 Middleton Chadderton, Oldham, OL9 9LB Tel: 0161-626 3010 Fax: 0161-627 1373 E-mail: info@wiggett.co.uk

▶ Wilding Butler Construction Ltd, Wessex Way, Winchester, Hampshire, SO21 1WP Tel: (01962) 717850

▶ Wilf Noble, Sneaton Lane, Ruswarp, Whitby, North Yorkshire, YO22 5HL Tel: (01947) 824061 Fax: (01947) 820524

Willers & Sons, Centenary Works, Button End, Harston, Cambridge, CB22 7NX Tel: (01223) 870360 Fax: (01223) 870360

▶ William Black & Son Ltd, 7 Clerk Street, Brechin, Angus, DD9 6AF Tel: (01356) 623103 Fax: (01356) 623105

BUILDING CONTRACTORS – *continued*

▶ William Downer & lw, York Road, Totland Bay, Isle of Wight, PO39 0HB Tel: (01983) 752187 Fax: (01983) 754614

▶ William McClure & Sons, 49 Bank Street, Irvine, Ayrshire, KA12 0LL Tel: (01294) 279123

▶ WM Paton & Sons Ltd, Unit 1, 42 Waggon Road, Ayr, KA8 8BA Tel: (01292) 313311

▶ William Shanks Construction, 139 Greengairs Road, Greengairs, Airdrie, Lanarkshire, ML6 7SY Tel: (01236) 830417 Fax: (01236) 830742

▶ William Skinner & Son, Highfield, St. Quivox, Ayr, KA6 5HQ Tel: (0845) 0519060 Fax: (01292) 671133

William Tilston, 3a-3c The Borders Industrial Park, River Lane, Saltney, Chester, CH4 8RJ Tel: (01244) 678786 Fax: (01244) 683935

▶ William Woodsend Ltd, Palatine Street, Castle Boulevard, Lenton, Nottingham, NG7 1GH Tel: 0115-947 6792

▶ William Yuille, Grangeston, Girvan, Ayrshire, KA26 9PY Tel: (01465) 713527

▶ Williams, Cowlairs, Nottingham, NG5 9RA Tel: 0115-975 5888 Fax: 0115-974 4777

▶ Williams Associates (Southern) Ltd, Prospect House, Prospect Road, Cowes, Isle Of Wight, PO31 7AD Tel: (01983) 292000 Fax: (01983) 292550 E-mail: williamsassock@fsbdial.co.uk

Willmott Dixon Construction Ltd, Willmott Dixon House, Park Street, Hitchin, Hertfordshire, SG4 9AH Tel: (01462) 442200 Fax: (01462) 442204 E-mail: construction.hitchin@willmottdixon.co.uk

Willmott Dixon Construction Ltd, Unit 3 Cliffe Park, Bruntcliffe Road, Morley, Leeds, LS27 0RY Tel: 0113-238 3283 Fax: 0113-238 0268 E-mail: construction.leeds@willmottdixon.co.uk

Willmott Dixon Construction Ltd, Spirella Building, Bridge Road, Letchworth Garden City, Hertfordshire, SG6 4ET Tel: (01462) 671852 Fax: (01462) 681852 E-mail: head.office@willmottdixon.co.uk

▶ Willows Construction Services, 9 Ashton Road, Golborne, Warrington, WA3 3TS Tel: (01942) 528300

▶ Willstone Construction & Joinery Co. Ltd, Clowance Wood Farm, Clowance Wood, Praze-An-Beeble, Camborne, Cornwall, TR14 0NW Tel: (01209) 831001 Fax: (01209) 831001 E-mail: tracy@willstoneconstruction.co.uk

▶ Wilmac Construction, Woodhill Road, Sandon, Chelmsford, CM2 7SG Tel: (01245) 475082

Wilson Bowden Group Services Ltd, Wilson Bowden House, Leicester Road, Ibstock, Leicestershire, LE67 6WB Tel: (01530) 260777 Fax: (01532) 262805

Wilson Connolly Lancashire, Bradley Lane, Standish, Wigan, Lancashire, WN6 0XN Tel: (01257) 425511 Fax: (01257) 426674

Wilson Connolly Midlands, Century House, The Lakes, Northampton, NN4 7SJ Tel: (01604) 887220 Fax: (01604) 887221 E-mail: midlands@wilsonconnolly.co.uk

George Wimpey South West Ltd, Omicron Windmill Hill Business Park, Whitehill Way, Swindon, SN5 6PA Tel: (01793) 898200 Fax: (01793) 898207

George Wimpy West Yorkshire Ltd, Sandpiper House, Peel Avenue, Calder Park, Wakefield, West Yorkshire, WF2 7UA Tel: (01924) 241500 Fax: (01924) 241580

▶ Winfield Construction, Marshall House, Heanor Gate Road, Heanor, Derbyshire, DE75 7RG Tel: (01773) 762555 Fax: (01773) 762444

Wood Brothers Ltd, Unit 10 Fairways Business Centre, Airport Service Road, Portsmouth, PO3 5NU Tel: (023) 9266 4492 Fax: (023) 9267 9865 E-mail: sales@woodbrothers.co.uk

▶ Woodcote Building Services Ltd, Acton Street, Long Eaton, Nottingham, NG10 1FT Tel: 0115-946 5252 Fax: 0115-946 8262

▶ Woodland Commercial Ltd, 292 Worton Road, Isleworth, Middlesex, TW7 6EL Tel: (020) 8560 0010 Fax: (020) 8560 1470 E-mail: info@woodlandcommercial.co.uk

▶ Woodrow Construction Islay Ltd, Glenegedale, Isle of Islay, PA42 7AS Tel: (01496) 300003 Fax: (01496) 300111

▶ Wooldridge & Simpson Ltd, The Gables, Woodstock Road, Yarnton, Kidlington, Oxfordshire, OX5 1PH Tel: (01865) 370700 Fax: (01865) 370598

Wrekin Construction Co. Ltd, Enterprise Road, Raunds, Wellingborough, Northamptonshire, NN9 6JE Tel: (01933) 624404 Fax: (01933) 623496 E-mail: raunds@wrekin.co.uk

▶ Wrenco (Contractors)Limited, Sefton Lane Industrial Estate, Liverpool, L31 8DN Tel: 0151-520 2323 E-mail: ho@wrenco.co.uk

Wrencon Ltd, Baron House, Hillcommon, Taunton, Somerset, TA4 1DS Tel: (01823) 400021 Fax: (01823) 400051

▶ Wright Projects Ltd, 79 Back Sneddon Street, Paisley, Renfrewshire, PA3 2BT Tel: 0141-887 7597 Fax: 0141-887 7598

▶ Wright & Smith Ltd, 26 Whiston Road, Cogenhoe, Northampton, NN7 1NL Tel: (01604) 890277 Fax: (01604) 890641

▶ Wygar Construction Co. Ltd, 22 Broadway North, Walsall, WS1 2AJ Tel: (01922) 614535 Fax: (01922) 723405E-mail: info@wygar.co.uk

Y J L Construction Ltd, Lovell House, 616 Chiswick High Road, London, W4 5RX Tel: (020) 8982 4200 Fax: (020) 8994 9558

▶ Young Wilson & Cunningham Ltd, 40 Rogart Street, Glasgow, G40 2AA Tel: 0141-550 0984 Fax: 0141-554 4143

John Youngs Ltd, 24 City Road, Norwich, NR1 3AN Tel: (01603) 628421 Fax: (01603) 765742 E-mail: mail@john-young.co.uk

BUILDING DESIGN AND CONSTRUCTION, *See also headings for particular types*

▶ A R Plant Hire Ltd, Tanglewood Derritt Lane, Bransgore, Christchurch, Dorset, BH23 8AR Tel: (01425) 673388 Fax: (01425) 674485 E-mail: mail@ar-planthire.co.uk

Beighton Construction Ltd, 58 Dunston Road, Whittington Moor, Chesterfield, Derbyshire, S41 8XA Tel: (01246) 451098 Fax: (01246) 455421 E-mail: beightonconstruction@hotmail.com

▶ Builder Express co uk Ltd, 16 Rheidol Mews, Islington, London, N1 8NU Tel: (0800) 6191248

M.A. Carroll Engineers Ltd, Birkby, Huddersfield, HD1 5EY Tel: (01484) 510846 Fax: (01484) 425953 E-mail: macengs@cs.com

Complete Projects CDM Ltd, 25 Cadman Street, Mosborough, Sheffield, S20 5BU Tel: 0114-251 4106 Fax: 0114-251 4106 E-mail: info@completeprojectscdm.co.uk

Cowlin Construction Ltd, Stratton House, 39 Cater Road, Bristol, BS13 7UH Tel: 0117-983 2000 Fax: 0117-987 7758 E-mail: bristol@cowlin.co.uk

Cowlin Construction, 5 Armtech Row, Houndstone Business Park, Yeovil, Somerset, BA22 8RW Tel: (01935) 423131 Fax: (01935) 847680

D C P M Manuals, Rock Drive, Gelli, Pentre, Rhondda Cynon Taff, CF41 7NX Tel: (01443) 442029 Fax: (01443) 442199 E-mail: info@dcpmmanuals.com

Garenberg Garden Buildings, 99 Collingwood Road, Manchester, M19 2AW Tel: (01204) 593054 Fax: 01204 792736 E-mail: info@garenberg.co.uk

Hyder Consulting UK Ltd, 10 Medawar Road, Surrey Research Park, Guildford, Surrey, GU2 7AR Tel: (01483) 535000 Fax: (01483) 535051

Kingsoak Homes, Eagle Close, Chandler's Ford, Eastleigh, Hampshire, SO53 4NF Tel: (023) 8046 1000 Fax: (023) 8046 1007

MKA Projects Ltd, 15/20 Churchill Square, Kings Hill, West Malling, Kent, ME19 4YU Tel: (01732) 897917 Fax: (01732) 897927 E-mail: info@mka-projects.co.uk

Nel Construction Ltd, Unit 1 Hodge Back Business Park, Reedyford Road, Nelson, Lancashire, BB9 8TF Tel: (01282) 612258 Fax: (01282) 616951 E-mail: sales@nel-construction.co.uk

▶ R G Carter Ipswich Limited, 48 St. Nicholas Street, Ipswich, IP1 1TP Tel: 01473 233655 Fax: 01473 211097 E-mail: mail@rgcarter-ipswich.co.uk

Scruton & Co Builders Ltd, Redcliff House, Waterside Park, Hessle, North Humberside, HU13 0EG Tel: (01482) 644200 Fax: (01482) 647338 E-mail: annwelbourne@scruton.co.uk

Simons Group Ltd, 401 Monks Road, Lincoln, LN3 4NU Tel: (01522) 510000 Fax: (01522) 521812

▶ Stroma, Stroma Unit 4, Pioneer Way, Pioneer Business Park, Wakefield, West Yorkshire, WF10 5QU Tel: 0845 6211111 Fax: 0845 6211112 E-mail: info@stroma.com

▶ T & J Building Services Ltd, 144 Curzon Street, Long Eaton, Nottingham, NG10 4FS Tel: 0115-875 2317 E-mail: tandjbuilding@ntlworld.com

Totty, Park House, Bradford Road, Chain Bar, Cleckheaton, West Yorkshire, BD19 6BW Tel: (01274) 866600 Fax: (01274) 866737

W W P Consultants Ltd, 5-15 Cromer Street, London, WC1H 8LS Tel: (020) 7833 5767 Fax: (020) 7833 5766 E-mail: info@wwp-london.co.uk

BUILDING DESIGN AND CONSTRUCTION, TURNKEY PACKAGES

A M E C Design & Management Ltd, Amec House, Timothy's Bridge Road, Stratford-Upon-Avon, Warwickshire, CV37 9NJ Tel: (01789) 204288 Fax: (01789) 299135

Ascot Construction Services Ltd, 34 Albert Road, Heaton, Bolton, BL1 5HF Tel: (01204) 847700 Fax: (01204) 393950

▶ C C Contracting Ltd, Forge House, Dudley Road, Stourbridge, West Midlands, DY9 8EL Tel: (01384) 891891 Fax: (01384) 891831 E-mail: sales@cccontracting.co.uk

Fitzpatrick Contractors Ltd, Hertford Road, Hoddesdon, Hertfordshire, EN11 9BX Tel: (01992) 305000 Fax: (01992) 305001 E-mail: enquiries@fitzpatrick.co.uk

G M I Construction Group plc, Middleton House, Westland Road, Leeds, LS11 5UH Tel: 0113-276 0505 Fax: 0113-276 0180 E-mail: build@gmicon.co.uk

Guy Property Developments Ltd, Pacioli House 9 Brookfield, Duncan Close, Moulton Park Industrial Estate, Northampton, NN3 6WL Tel: (01604) 496666 Fax: (01604) 499676

▶ Insignia Consulting, Knights View, 104 The Street, Little Waltham, Chelmsford, CM3 3NT Tel: (01245) 360121 Fax: (01245) 360614 E-mail: cad@insignia-consulting.com

▶ Luddon Construction Ltd, Balmore House, 1497 Balmore Road, Glasgow, G23 5HD Tel: 0141-945 2233 Fax: 0141-946 5400 E-mail: enquiries@luddon.co.uk

Mansell, Roman House, Granitehill Road, Aberdeen, AB16 7AW Tel: (01224) 717700 Fax: (01224) 698262 E-mail: info@mansell.plc.uk

Mbe Computer Systems, 3 Fair View Industrial Estate, Kingsbury Road, Curdworth, Sutton Coldfield, West Midlands, B76 9EE Tel: (01675) 470061 Fax: (01675) 470889 E-mail: phil.cowtan@morrisonplc.com

SGB Rovacabin, 81 North Road, Yate, Bristol, BS37 7PS Tel: (01454) 325010 Fax: (01454) 322948

Shepherd Construction Ltd, Frederick House, Fulford Road, York, YO10 4EA Tel: (01904) 634431 Fax: (01904) 610256 E-mail: admin@shepherdsolutions.com

Terrapin Ltd, Bomnd Avenue, Bletchley, Milton Keynes, MK1 1JJ Tel: 0115-907 2700 Fax: 0115-972 2203 E-mail: sales@terrapin-ltd.co.uk

BUILDING ELECTRICAL ENGINEERING

Astelle Electrical Contractors Ltd, Mayflower House, 3 Chapel St, Billericay, Essex, CM12 9LT Tel: (01277) 651320 Fax: (01277) 630608

Centra Controls Ltd, 14 Landywood Lane, Cheslyn Hay, Walsall, WS6 7AH Tel: (01922) 415510 Fax: (01922) 415510 E-mail: centra@tiscala.co.uk

Clarke Engineering & Construction Co. Ltd, 13 Sydenham Road, Belfast, BT3 9DH Tel: (028) 9045 8337 Fax: (028) 9073 2382 E-mail: mail@ceccltd.co.uk

▶ Coleman Property Care Ltd, 29 Harley Street, London, W1G 9QR Tel: 0845 095 1280 Fax: 0845 095 1290 E-mail: info@colemanfm.com

D I S Group, Gainsborough House, 42-44 Bath Road, Cheltenham, Gloucestershire, GL53 7HJ Tel: (01242) 533120 Fax: (01242) 221187

Deandi Building Services Ltd, Crown House, Union Street, Willenhall, West Midlands, WV13 1UZ Tel: (01902) 609715 Fax: (01902) 634383

Hilton Building Services Ltd, Waterway St West, Nottingham, NG2 3AD Tel: 0115-986 1221 Fax: 0115-986 6870 E-mail: sales@hiltons.co.uk

I E I Ltd, Southern Cross, Basing View, Basingstoke, Hampshire, RG21 4HG Tel: (01256) 352361 Fax: (01256) 470259 E-mail: gen@iei-engineers.com

▶ K.T. Electrical Services, 26 Waverley Crescent, Grangemouth, Stirlingshire, FK3 8RB Tel: 07876 345366 Fax: 01324 875727

Kilby & Gayford Ltd, 30 Radford Way, Billericay, Essex, CM12 0DA Tel: (020) 7498 9898 Fax: (01277) 630193 E-mail: sales@killbygayford.com

Lorne Stewart plc, Phillips House, Sandgate Industrial Estate, Hartlepool, Cleveland, TS25 1UB Tel: (01429) 268116 Fax: (01429) 860244 E-mail: hartlepool@lornestewart.co.uk

▶ Reid Business Services Ltd, 333A Prince Regent Lane, Victoria Docks, London, E16 3JL Tel: (020) 7511 3745 Fax: (01234) 381112 E-mail: dr.reid@reidbusinessservices.co.uk

Sherwood Consulting Engineers, 26 Kings Meadow, Rainworth, Mansfield, Nottinghamshire, NG21 0FG Tel: (01623) 431128 Fax: (01623) 431129 E-mail: info@sherwoodce.com

BUILDING ENERGY MANAGEMENT SERVICES

Combined Services UK Ltd, 4 Marlborough Trading Estate, High Wycombe, Buckinghamshire, HP11 2LB Tel: (01494) 462262 Fax: (01494) 438707 E-mail: mailbox@combinedservices.co.uk

Cudd Bentley Consulting, Ashurst Manor, Church Lane, Ascot, Berkshire, SL5 7DD Tel: (01344) 628821 Fax: (01344) 623448 E-mail: reception@ascot.cbp.co.uk

▶ ENERG P.L.C., ENER-G House, Daniel Adamson Road, Salford, M50 1DT Tel: 0161-745 7450 Fax: 0161-745 7457 E-mail: info@energ.co.uk

Integrated Control Systems Ltd, Millars Business Centre, Fishponds Close, Wokingham, Berkshire, RG41 2TZ Tel: 0118-977 2226 Fax: 0118-977 4999 E-mail: sales@icsbms.co.uk

▶ JSH Energy Solutions Ltd, Ardennais House, 6 Sorrel Horse Mews, Grimwade Street, Ipswich, IP4 1LN Tel: 0845 050 5830 Fax: 01473 232137 E-mail: andrew.lashley@jshipswich.co.uk

BUILDING ENGINEERING

▶ Bace Ltd, Willoughby House, 439 Richmond Road, Twickenham, TW1 2AG Tel: (020) 7060 1620 Fax: (070) 0580 6646 E-mail: h.quinn@baceltd.com

▶ Eic Scotland Ltd, Dryden Road, Loanhead, Midlothian, EH20 9LZ Tel: 0131-440 0456 Fax: 0131-440 4546

▶ Templeman Associates Ltd, Unit 2, North Lynn Business Village, Bergen Way, North Lynn Industrial Estate, King's Lynn, Norfolk, PE30 2JG Tel: (01553) 776148 Fax: (01553) 778320 E-mail: templemanassociates@yahoo.co.uk

Thomas Komoly, 20 Hawthorn Grove, Wilmslow, Cheshire, SK9 5DE Tel: 01625 252804 E-mail: tomi@labconsultant.co.uk

BUILDING ENGINEERING PROJECT MANAGEMENT

▶ Capita Symonds Ltd, Edwinstowe House, High Street, Edwinstowe, Nottinghamshire, NG21 9PR Tel: (01623) 821506 Fax: (01623) 821507

BUILDING ENGINEERING SURVEY SERVICES

▶ Isis Surveyors Ltd, 7 Ashurst Close, Tadley, Hampshire, RG26 4AH Tel: 0118-981 4614 Fax: 0118-981 4614 E-mail: isissurveyors@ukonline.co.uk

BUILDING ESTIMATING

▶ Budget Estimate Ltd, 124 Cliff Road, Crigglestone, Wakefield, West Yorkshire, WF4 3EJ Tel: (01924) 250211 E-mail: info@budgetestimate.co.uk

Callworth Ltd, 294 High Street, Rochester, Kent, ME1 1HS Tel: (01634) 402381 Fax: (01634) 201770 E-mail: pj.crook@btinternet.com

Construction Management & Design, Ty Capel, Yr Henffordd, Nercwys, Mold, Clwyd, CH7 4DL Tel: (01352) 755522 Fax: (01352) 754656 E-mail: constmanagdesign@aol.com

▶ KS Associates, 3c Priory Business Park, Fraser Road, Bedford, MK44 3WH Tel: (01234) 838811 Fax: (01234) 838811 E-mail: admin@ks-associates.co.uk

▶ Principal Technical Services Ltd, Durham House, 39 Dale Road, Buxton, Derbyshire, SK17 6NJ Tel: 01298 767414 E-mail: enquiries@principalts.co.uk

UK Estimating Support Ltd, First Floor, 125-129 Witton Street, Northwich, Cheshire, CW9 5DY Tel: 0845 644 5327 Fax: 0845 644 5328 E-mail: office@estimatingsupport.co.uk

▶ Waterlock Business Development, The Studios, The Street, Stourmouth, Canterbury, Kent, CT3 1HZ Tel: (01227) 720007 Fax: (01227) 720001 E-mail: wbd@waterlock.co.uk

BUILDING EXTENSION DESIGN

▶ Aran Proplan, Aran House, Old Tarporley Road, Stretton, Warrington, WA4 4NB Tel: 01925 860002 Fax: 01925 860101 E-mail: a.newton@arangroup.com

BUILDING EXTERIOR CLEANING/WASHING CONTRACTORS

Building Restoration & Cleaning (Leeds) Ltd, Abbey Mills, Kirkstall, Leeds, LS5 3HP Tel: 0113-278 6472 Fax: 0113-275 4644 E-mail: brcleeds@btconnect.com

Highline Access Ltd, PO Box 2089, Bristol, BS99 7SZ Tel: (0870) 0435531 Fax: (0870) 0435532 E-mail: enquiries@highlineaccess.com

▶ I M B Cleaning & Maintenance, 29 Milton Road, Caterham, Surrey, CR3 5JG Tel: (01883) 334521 E-mail: imbcleaning@tiscali.co.uk

Just Developments, 4 Sunnybank, Holly Road, Wilmslow, Cheshire, SK9 1ND Tel: (01625) 530752 Fax: (01625) 530752 E-mail: jurgstaubli@hotmail.com

Masonry Cleaning Services, 1a Allpits Road, Calow, Chesterfield, Derbyshire, S44 5AU Tel: (01246) 209926 Fax: (01246) 211620 E-mail: mike@masonrycleaningservices.com

Programmed Environmental Maintenance Ltd, 135 Sandy Lane, Middlestown, Wakefield, West Yorkshire, WF4 4PR Tel: (01924) 270821 Fax: (01924) 264672 E-mail: inquiries@pem-ltd.co.uk

Remchem Ltd, Unit K Harlow House, Shelton Road, Willowbrook East Industrial Estate, Corby, Northamptonshire, NN17 5XH Tel: (01536) 205562 Fax: (01536) 401608 E-mail: sales@remchem.co.uk

Waterforce, Southport Delivery Office Southport Business Park, Wight Moss, Southport, Merseyside, PR8 4ZZ Tel: (0800) 0933267 E-mail: info@pressure-washing.me.uk

Wesco Access Ltd, 1 Struan Place, Douglas Water, Lanark, ML11 9LW Tel: (01555) 880808 Fax: (01555) 880901 E-mail: neil@wescoaccess.com

BUILDING EXTERIOR CLEANING/WASHING HIGH PRESSURE WATER EQUIPMENT, *See Water Jetting etc*

BUILDING EXTERIOR WATER JET HIGH PRESSURE CLEANING OR WASHING CONTRACTORS, *See Building Exterior etc*

BUILDING FLOOD PROTECTION SYSTEMS

▶ Affordable Flood Solutions Ltd, 16 Birch Green, Staines, Middlesex, TW18 4HA Tel: (01784) 460874 Fax: (01784) 460894 E-mail: info@a-f-s.biz

BUILDING FOUNDATION PILE DRIVING CONTRACTORS

AMEC Piling, Cold Meeth, Swynnton, Stone, Staffordshire, ST15 0UD Tel: (01785) 760022 Fax: (01785) 760762
Bachy Soletanche, Units 2 & 5 Prospect Place, Mill Lane, Alton, Hampshire, GU34 2SX Tel: (01420) 594700 Fax: (01420) 86971 E-mail: geotech@bacsol.co.uk
▶ Branlow Ltd, 8-9 St Peters Way, Warrington, WA2 7BT Tel: (01925) 639979 Fax: (01925) 411627 E-mail: info@branlow.co.uk
▶ Branlow Piling Solutions, Denzil, Main Road, Yapton, Arundel, West Sussex, BN18 0DX Tel: (01243) 555890 Fax: (01243) 555943 E-mail: info@branlow.co.uk
▶ Branlow Piling Solutions, 66 Waverley Crescent, Kirkintilloch, Glasgow, G66 2DA Tel: 0141-776 6659 Fax: 0141-776 6660 E-mail: admin@branlow.co.uk
Roger Bullivant Ltd, Walton Road, Drakelow, Burton-on-Trent, Staffordshire, DE15 9UA Tel: (01283) 511115 Fax: (01283) 540826 E-mail: marketing@roger-bullivant.co.uk
Colets Piling Ltd, Old Village Hall, The Street, Effingham, Leatherhead, Surrey, KT24 5JS Tel: (01372) 452506 Fax: (01372) 452427 E-mail: mail@coletspiling.com
Expanded Piling Co Ltd, Cheapside, Waltham, Grimsby, South Humberside, DN37 0JD Tel: (01472) 822552 Fax: (01472) 220675 E-mail: info@expandedpiling.com
Express Reinforcements Ltd, Unit 3A Denver Industrial Estate, Ferry Lane, Rainham, Essex, RM13 9BU Tel: (01708) 630767 Fax: (01708) 630787
Morcon Foundations Ltd, 2 Duffield Road Industrial Estate, Duffield Road, Little Eaton, Derby, DE21 5DR Tel: (01332) 834055 Fax: (01332) 834101 E-mail: post@morcon.demon.co.uk
R Withers Holdings Ltd, Beddington Farm Road, Croydon, CR0 4XB Tel: (020) 8684 7557 Fax: (020) 8689 2101 E-mail: enq@withers-group.co.uk
S & J Contractors, 81 Vicarage Hill, Benfleet, Essex, SS7 1PD Tel: (01268) 755761
Westpile Ltd, Dolphin Bridge House, Rockingham Road, Uxbridge, Middlesex, UB8 2UB Tel: (01895) 258266 Fax: (01895) 271805 E-mail: john.gedge@westpile.co.uk

BUILDING INFORMATION CENTRES OR SERVICES

Barbour ABI, Hinderton Piont, Lloyd Drive, Cheshire Oaks, Ellesmere Port, CH65 9HQ Tel: 0151 353 3512 Fax: 0151 353 3637 E-mail: info@barbour-abi.com
Builders Merchants Confederation Ltd, 15 Soho Square, London, W1D 3HL Tel: (020) 7439 1753 Fax: (020) 7734 2766 E-mail: info@bmf.org.uk
The Building Centre Bookshop, 26 Store Street, London, WC1E 7BT Tel: (020) 7692 4040 Fax: (020) 7636 3628 E-mail: bookshop@buildingcentre.co.uk
The Building Centre Bookshop, 26 Store Street, London, WC1E 7BT Tel: (020) 7692 4040 Fax: (020) 7636 3628 E-mail: agagliano@buildingcentre.co.uk
Building Products Index, 30 Gorst Road, London, NW10 6LE Tel: (020) 8838 1904 Fax: (020) 8838 1905 E-mail: bpindex@netscapeonline.co.uk
Cambridge Database Technologies Ltd, 102 Long Road, Cambridge, CB2 8HF Tel: (01223) 843840
Derbyshire Chamber Of Commerce & Industry, Commerce Centre, Canal Wharf, Chesterfield, Derbyshire, S41 7NA Tel: (01246) 211277 Fax: (01246) 203173 E-mail: chamber@derbyshire.org
Stramit International Ltd, Creeting Road, Stowmarket, Suffolk, IP14 5BA Tel: (01449) 613564 Fax: (01449) 678381 E-mail: sales@stramit-int.com

BUILDING INTERIOR STRIPPING OUT SERVICES

▶ Ceramics Channel Island Ceramics, Forest Road, Forest, Guernsey, GY8 0AB Tel: (01481) 234000 Fax: (01481) 234007

BUILDING MANAGEMENT COMPUTER SYSTEMS

▶ Ikonik Ltd, Unit 19, Victoria Way, Pride Park, Derby, DE24 8AN Tel: (01332) 224176

BUILDING MANAGEMENT CONTROL SYSTEMS

▶ Alpha Beta Controls Ltd, 14 Coles Lane, Sutton Coldfield, West Midlands, B72 1NE Tel: 0121-321 3844 Fax: 0121-321 3866 E-mail: sales@alphabetacontrols.co.uk
D D C Control Systems Ltd, Unit 1 Broadwyn Trading Estate, Waterfall Lane, Cradley Heath, West Midlands, B64 6PS Tel: 0121-561 3312 Fax: 0121-561 3541 E-mail: ian.biddle@ddccontrolsystems.co.uk
▶ Elesta UK Building Automation, PO Box 3418, Slough, SL1 0BR Tel: (01628) 664441 Fax: (01628) 664441 E-mail: info@elesta.co.uk
Franklin M & E Services Ltd, 6 Hoffmanns Way, Chelmsford, CM1 1GU Tel: (01245) 505050 Fax: (01245) 505051 E-mail: me@franklingroup.co.uk
Honeywell Control Systems Ltd, Honeywell House Arlington Business Park, Downshire Way, Bracknell, Berkshire, RG12 1EB Tel: (01344) 656000 Fax: (01344) 656240 E-mail: uk.infocentre@honeywell.com
Integrated Building Management Systems Ltd, Brunel Drive, Newark, Nottinghamshire, NG24 1SF Tel: (01636) 674875 Fax: (01636) 612228 E-mail: controls@integratedbms.co.uk
Siemens Technologies Ltd, Mersey House, 220-222 Stockport Road, Stockport, Cheshire, SK3 0LX Tel: 0161-428 3661 Fax: 0161-428 3662 E-mail: tom.wilkinson@siemens.com

BUILDING MANAGEMENT ENGINEERING

▶ B D T (uk) Ltd, Beaconsfield Lodge, Fore Street, Ashton Keynes, Swindon, SN6 6NP Tel: (01285) 862399 Fax: (01285) 862399 E-mail: richard.long@bdukltd.com
Cudd Bentley Consulting Ltd, Suite 1 Shelly Cresent Centre, 20 Farm House Way, Monkspath, Solihull, West Midlands, B90 4EH Tel: 0121-711 4343 Fax: 0121-711 3535
Mca Consulting Engineers Ltd, Newhouse Farm Business Centre, Horsham, West Sussex, RH12 4RU Tel: (01293) 851490 Fax: (01293) 852156 E-mail: sales@mcaltd.co.uk
Mbe Computer Systems, 3 Fair View Industrial Estate, Kingsbury Road, Curdworth, Sutton Coldfield, West Midlands, B76 9EE Tel: (01675) 470061 Fax: (01675) 470889 E-mail: phil.cowtan@morrisonplc.com
Sayvol Chemicals Ltd, 111 Laurence Leyland Complex, Irthlingborough Road, Wellingborough, Northamptonshire, NN8 1RT Tel: (01933) 442069 Fax: (01933) 442070 E-mail: enquiries@sayvol.com

BUILDING MANAGEMENT SYSTEM CONTROL PANELS

▶ E I S Axon Ltd, Unit 2, Crusader Industrial Estate, Stirling Road, Cressex Business Park, High Wycombe, Buckinghamshire, HP12 3ST Tel: (01494) 511558 Fax: (01494) 449351 E-mail: paul@eis-axon.co.uk

BUILDING MANAGEMENT SYSTEMS

▶ Aimteq Services Ltd, 9 Wilkinson Road, Love Lane Industrial Estate, Cirencester, Gloucestershire, GL7 1YT Tel: (01285) 655772 Fax: (01285) 655782 E-mail: info@aimteq.co.uk
Annicom Electronic Equipment Component, Highview, High Street, Bordon, Hampshire, GU35 0AX Tel: (01420) 487788 Fax: (01420) 487799 E-mail: sale@annicom.com
Cooling Heating Electrical Services, 18 Old Pawlett Road, West Huntspill, Highbridge, Somerset, TA9 3RH Tel: (07970) 565026 Fax: (01278) 795511 E-mail: sales@chesuk.com
▶ Eco Control Systems Ltd, Studio Centre, Wiston Road, Colchester, CO6 4LT Tel: (01206) 263390 Fax: (01206) 262899
▶ Elesta UK Building Automation, PO Box 3418, Slough, SL1 0BR Tel: (01628) 664441 Fax: (01628) 664441 E-mail: info@elesta.co.uk
Honeywell Control Systems Ltd, Honeywell House Arlington Business Park, Downshire Way, Bracknell, Berkshire, RG12 1EB Tel: (01344) 656000 Fax: (01344) 656240 E-mail: uk.infocentre@honeywell.com
Integrated Building Management Systems Ltd, Brunel Drive, Newark, Nottinghamshire, NG24 1SF Tel: (01636) 674875 Fax: (01636) 612228 E-mail: controls@integratedbms.co.uk
R E Building Services, Aspen House, Minster Drive, Minster on Sea, Sheerness, Kent, ME12 2ND Tel: (01795) 874479
Tac Satchwell, Europa House, 310 Europa Boulevard, Westbrook, Warrington, WA5 7XR Tel: (01925) 401000 Fax: (01925) 401166
Vickers Electronics Ltd, Alliance House, Westpoint Enterprise Park, Trafford Park, Manchester, M17 1QS Tel: (0870) 7420808 Fax: (0870) 7480808 E-mail: info@vickers-electronics.co.uk
▶ J. Wesley (Electrical Contractors) Ltd, Units 7-10 Station Approach, Hitchin, Hertfordshire, SG4 9UP Tel: (01462) 437677 Fax: (01462) 422738 E-mail: info@wesleyservices.co.uk

BUILDING MATERIAL IMPORT OR EXPORT

Apex Agencies International Ltd, Sportrite House, 155 Tame Road, Witton, Birmingham, B6 7DG Tel: 0121-328 9190 Fax: 0121-328 4175 E-mail: info@apex-world.com
Builders Equipment (Norwich) Ltd, 24 City Road, Norwich, NR1 3AN Tel: (01603) 616211 Fax: (01603) 630408 E-mail: mail@builders-equipment.co.uk
James Burrell Ltd, Lockheed Close, Preston Farm Industrial Estate, Stockton-on-Tees, Cleveland, TS18 3SE Tel: (01642) 660820 Fax: (01642) 678616 E-mail: jamesburrell@compuserve.com
China Trade Direct Ltd, 26b Sydney Road, Cradley Heath, West Midlands, B64 5BA Tel: (07909) 662093 Fax: 01384 565466 E-mail: chinatradedirect@btinternet.com
▶ Cornish Lime Co., Brims Park, Old Callywith Road, Bodmin, Cornwall, PL31 2DZ Tel: (01208) 77287 Fax: (01208) 73744 E-mail: sales@cornishlime.co.uk
Haldane Fisher, Carnbane Industrial Estate, Newry, County Down, BT35 6QQ Tel: (028) 3026 3201 Fax: (028) 3026 8101 E-mail: dgrayhaldanefisher@btinternet.com
Keble Light Ltd, Bourton Industrial Park, Bourton-on-the-Water, Cheltenham, Gloucestershire, GL54 2HQ Tel: (01451) 822442 Fax: (01451) 822412 E-mail: keblelight.export@virgin.net
▶ Luta Ltd, 106 Beecham Berry, Basingstoek, Basingstoke, Hampshire, RG22 4QN Tel: 0778 0993697 Fax: 01256 814135 E-mail: info@luta.co.uk
Masterbuild Plastics, Unit 8 Henley Business Park, Trident Close, Medway City Estate, Rochester, Kent, ME2 4FR Tel: (01634) 291277 Fax: (01634) 291278
Monomet Ltd, 14 Eton Grove, Dacre Park, London, SE13 5BY Tel: (020) 8463 9300 Fax: (020) 8318 3594
Pipe Centre, 18-22 Pages Walk, London, SE1 4SB Tel: (020) 7237 4421 Fax: (020) 7231 3223 E-mail: br.bermondey@wolseley.co.uk

BUILDING MATERIALS, *See also headings for particular types*

Builder Center Ltd, Conway Street, Hove, East Sussex, BN3 3LA Tel: (01273) 778778 Fax: (01273) 722413
Builder Center, 1 Knowsley Street, Cheetham Hill Road, Manchester, M8 8QL Tel: 0161-834 9437 Fax: 0161-833 2706 E-mail: wolseley@center.co.uk
C C L Stressing Systems Ltd, Unit 4, Park 2000, Millennium Way, Leeds, LS11 5AL Tel: 0113-270 1221 E-mail: sales@cclstressing.com
Cullen Engineering Ltd, 51 Naysmith Rd, Southfield Industrial Estate, Glenrothes, Fife, KY6 2SD Tel: (01592) 771132 Fax: (01383) 771182 E-mail: sales@cullen-bp.co.uk
Deebees Ltd, 4 Mayne Avenue, Bridge of Allan, Stirling, FK9 4RA Tel: (01786) 832014 Fax: (01786) 832825
Hanson Aggregates N W Area Office P.L.C., Edge Green Road, Ashton-In-Makerfield, Wigan, Lancashire, WN4 8YA Tel: (01942) 721776 Fax: (0870) 1207422
Keyline Builders Merchant, 2A Hospital Road, Haddington, East Lothian, EH41 3BH Tel: (01620) 822472 Fax: (01620) 825689
Knauf Drywall Ltd, Sittingbourne, Kent, ME10 3HW Tel: (01795) 424499 Fax: (01795) 428651 E-mail: info@knauf.co.uk
L M Products Ltd, Unit 10, Union Road, Oldbury, West Midlands, B69 3EX Tel: 0121-552 8622 Fax: 0121-544 4571 E-mail: sales@lmproducts.co.uk
Leigh Concrete Ltd, 30 Bridge Street, Heywood, Lancashire, OL10 1JF Tel: (01706) 366010 Fax: (01706) 366122
Mid Sussex Timber Co. Ltd, Station Road, Forest Row, East Sussex, RH18 5EL Tel: (01342) 822191 Fax: (01342) 823052 E-mail: sales@mstc.co.uk
John Mowlem & Co. P.L.C., White Lion Court, Swan Street, Isleworth, Middlesex, TW7 6RN Tel: (020) 8568 9111
R J Donaghy & Sons, 71b Lissan Road, Cookstown, County Tyrone, BT80 8QX Tel: (028) 8676 3202 Fax: (028) 8676 2835
R M C Group, Crown House, Evreux Way, Rugby, Warwickshire, CV21 2DT Tel: (01788) 542111 Fax: (01788) 540166 E-mail: enquiries@rugbycement.co.uk
S P Brown & Co. Ltd, 31 Lockhart Street, London, E3 4BL Tel: (020) 8981 2747 Fax: (020) 8981 2747
Timloc Building Products, Rawcliffe Road, Goole, North Humberside, DN14 6UQ Tel: (01405) 765567 Fax: (01405) 720479 E-mail: sales@timloc.co.uk
Vista Engineering Ltd, Carrbrook Works, Shallcross Mill Road, Whaley Bridge, High Peak, Derbyshire, SK23 7JL Tel: (01663) 736700 Fax: (01663) 736710
Western Blocks Ltd, 42 Upton Towans, Hayle, Cornwall, TR27 5BL Tel: (01736) 753128 Fax: (01736) 756857
R. Williamson, Brick Kiln Road, Hevingham, Norwich, NR10 5NN Tel: (01603) 754771

BUILDING MATERIALS SALES STAFF RECRUITMENT

▶ HR Personnel Ltd, Unit 5a Hogarth Court, Hogarth Crescent, Croydon, CR0 2JE Tel: 020 8683 7110 Fax: 0870 8903884 E-mail: rt_hrpersonnel@btconnect.com
▶ Manesis Search & Selection, 1 Lower Bar, Newport, Shropshire, TF10 7BE Tel: (01952) 811550 E-mail: recruit@manesis.co.uk

BUILDING MATERIALS TEST SERVICES

▶ Accelerated Weathering Laboratory Ltd, Berkeley House, Hunts Rise, South Marston Industrial Estat, Swindon, SN3 4TG Tel: (01793) 834211 Fax: (01793) 721212 E-mail: info@awlltd.co.uk
Quartz Scientific Computing Ltd, Dukes Yard, Acme Road, Watford, WD24 5AL Tel: (01923) 213983 Fax: (01923) 247732 E-mail: mail@quartz-scientific.co.uk

BUILDING MECHANICAL ENGINEERING

Armex Systems, 130 Park Road, Prestwich, Manchester, M25 0DU Tel: 0161-740 2178 Fax: 0161-740 8414
▶ Bentley Mechanical Services Ltd, 140 Barton Road, Comberton, Cambridge, CB23 7BT Tel: (01223) 264240 Fax: (01223) 264240 E-mail: office@bentleymechanicalservices.co.uk
Crown House Technologies, Peal House, 50 Waterloo Road, Wolverhampton, WV1 4RU Tel: (01902) 428666 Fax: (01902) 428774
Crown Steel Buildings, Green Park, Burnards House, Holsworthy, Devon, EX22 7JA Tel: (01409) 253315 Fax: (01409) 254224
D I S Group, Gainsborough House, 42-44 Bath Road, Cheltenham, Gloucestershire, GL53 7HJ Tel: (01242) 533120 Fax: (01242) 221187
Dave Dickinson & Associates Ltd, Ahed House, Sandbeds Trading Estate, Ossett, West Yorkshire, WF5 9ND Tel: (01924) 265757 Fax: (01924) 275117 E-mail: enquiries@ddaltd.co.uk
Electro Mech Industrial Services Ltd, Stanthope, Adsett, Westbury-on-Severn, Gloucestershire, GL14 1PH Tel: (01452) 760441 Fax: (01452) 760441
F P Hurley & Sons Ltd, Queens Road, Bridgend Industrial Estate, Bridgend, Mid Glamorgan, CF31 3UR Tel: (01656) 661151 Fax: (01656) 645477 E-mail: bridgend@fphurley.co.uk
G P Watson Ltd, Unit 5 Lancaster Port, Corintation Road, High Wycombe, Buckinghamshire, HP12 3TD Tel: (01494) 446515 Fax: (01494) 446615 E-mail: sales@gpwatson.co.uk
Gatwick Park Mechanical Services Ltd, P.O. Box 371, Caterham, Surrey, CR3 6UE Tel: (01883) 347133 Fax: (01883) 343813 E-mail: info@gatwickpark.com
Gemlog Controls Ltd, 22 Greenfield Way, Storrington, Pulborough, West Sussex, RH20 4PY Tel: (01903) 743835 Fax: (01903) 740071 E-mail: info@gemlog.co.uk
Haden Building Services Ltd, 44 Clarendon Road, Watford, WD17 1DR Tel: (01923) 232959 Fax: (01923) 295000 E-mail: headoffice@hadenyoung.co.uk
Hilton Building Services Ltd, Waterway St West, Nottingham, NG2 3AD Tel: 0115-986 1221 Fax: 0115-986 6870 E-mail: sales@hiltons.co.uk
I E I Ltd, Southern Cross, Basing View, Basingstoke, Hampshire, RG21 4HG Tel: (01256) 352361 Fax: (01256) 470259 E-mail: gen@iei-engineers.com
Integra Buildings Ltd, Main Street, Burstwick, Hull, HU12 9EA Tel: (01964) 626761 Fax: (01964) 626762 E-mail: sales@integrabuildings.co.uk
It Engineering, Kingsnorth Works, Hoo, Rochester, Kent, ME3 9NZ Tel: (01634) 253920

BUILDING MECHANICAL ENGINEERING – *continued*

▶ Kershaw Mechanical Services Ltd, Beadle Trading Estate, Ditton Walk, Cambridge, CB5 8PD Tel: (01223) 715800 Fax: (01223) 411061 E-mail: enquiries@kershaw-grp.co.uk
Killby & Gayford Ltd, 30 Radford Way, Billericay, Essex, CM12 0DA Tel: (020) 7498 9898 Fax: (01277) 630193 E-mail: sales@killbygayford.com
N S P Building Services Ltd, 24 Nova Lane, Birstall, Batley, West Yorkshire, WF17 9LE Tel: (01924) 445648 Fax: (01924) 445648
Oakwood Technology Group, Ill Road, Cheadle Hulme, Cheadle, Cheshire, SK8 6GN Tel: 0161-488 4343 Fax: 0161-488 4086 E-mail: sales@oakwoodair.co.uk
R A Beaver Ltd, Sheepbridge Works, Dunston Road, Chesterfield, Derbyshire, S41 9QD Tel: (01246) 261110 Fax: (01246) 261098 E-mail: office@rabeaver.com
Redbay Projects Ltd, 15 Dalton Court, Astmoor Industrial Estate, Runcorn, Cheshire, WA7 1PU Tel: (01928) 581782 Fax: (01928) 580619 E-mail: redbayprojects@aol.com
Sherwood Consulting Engineers, 26 Kings Meadow, Rainworth, Mansfield, Nottinghamshire, NG21 0FG Tel: (01623) 431128 Fax: (01623) 431129 E-mail: info@sherwoodce.com
T Sutcliffe & Co. Ltd, Weston Street, Bolton, BL3 2AL Tel: (01204) 535221 Fax: (01204) 380681
TS Direct, 473a King Street, Stoke-on-Trent, ST3 1EU Tel: (01782) 335962 Fax: (01782) 335962

BUILDING NOISE CONTROL SERVICES

Air Technology & Acoustics Ltd, 1451 Stratford Road, Hall Green, Birmingham, B28 9HT Tel: 0121-777 1847 Fax: 0121-777 3468

BUILDING OR CONSTRUCTION INDUSTRY PERSONNEL RECRUITMENT FROM EASTERN EUROPE

▶ Euroresource International Ltd, Kitchener House, Warwick Road, West Drayton, Middlesex, UB7 9BS Tel: (0845) 1562152 E-mail: enquiries@my-resource.co.uk

BUILDING OR DECORATING PLASTER

W. Allen, 176 Milton Road, Gillingham, Kent, ME7 5LR Tel: (07748) 474957
Artex Rawlplug Ltd, Pasture Lane, Ruddington, Nottingham, NG11 6AE Tel: 0115-984 9124 Fax: 0115-940 5240
British Gypsum Ltd, Gotham Road, East Leake, Loughborough, Leicestershire, LE12 6JQ Tel: 0115-945 1050 Fax: 0115-945 1154 E-mail: bgtechnical.enquiries@bpb.com
G D P Plastics, Unit 6, Empress Industrial Estate, Anderton Street, Ince, Wigan, Lancashire, WN2 2BG Tel: (01942) 820333
K C H Fibrous Plasters, Unit 13 Brickfields, Great Burches Road, Benfleet, Essex, SS7 3ND Tel: (01268) 741911 Fax: (01268) 414897
▶ Keelsupply Plaster Suppliers, 1 Tomlinson Business Park, Tomlinson Road, Leyland, PR25 2DY Tel: (01772) 641495 Fax: (01772) 641844
Knauf Drywall Ltd, Sittingbourne, Kent, ME10 3HW Tel: (01795) 424499 Fax: (01795) 428651 E-mail: info@knauf.co.uk
Plaster Elegance, Suite 1 Watling Chambers, 214 Watling Street, Bridgtown, Cannock, Staffordshire, WS11 0BD Tel: (01543) 466362 Fax: (01543) 466362
▶ Plaster Products, 319 Pleck Road, Walsall, WS2 9HA Tel: (01922) 633774
Simpson Strong-Tie International Inc, Cardinal Point, Winchester Road, Tamworth, Staffordshire, B78 3HG Tel: (01827) 255600 Fax: (01827) 255616 E-mail: swilkes@strongtie.com
South Western Industrial Plasters, 63 Netherstreet, Bromham, Chippenham, Wiltshire, SN15 2DP Tel: (01380) 850616
Whitchurch Building Supplies, College Road, Cardiff, CF14 2NZ Tel: (029) 2062 5422 Fax: (029) 2061 6840

BUILDING PRODUCT MANUFACTURERS ADVISORY SERVICES

▶ Booth Wire Products, Springvale Works, Elland Road, Brookfoot, Brighouse, West Yorkshire, HD6 2RN Tel: (01484) 714837 Fax: (01484) 710515 E-mail: sales@boothwire.co.uk

BUILDING PROJECT MANAGEMENT

Curtins Consulting Engineers plc, 26-29 St. Cross Street, London, EC1N 8UH Tel: (020) 7213 9000 Fax: (020) 7213 9001 E-mail: london@curtins.com
▶ TALKPROPERTY.NET Ltd T/A talkproperty, 89 Coningham Road, London, W12 8BS Tel: 07910 969619 E-mail: osp@talkproperty.net

BUILDING REFURBISHMENT CONTRACTORS

A D Buildings Ltd, 2A Crown Street, Redbourn, St. Albans, Hertfordshire, AL3 7JU Tel: (01582) 794842 Fax: (01582) 793889 E-mail: adbuildings@connectfree.co.uk
Aedean Chemical Industrial Ltd, 73A Old Woking Road, West Byfleet, Surrey, KT14 6LF Tel: (01932) 336171 Fax: (01932) 336758 E-mail: info@aedean.co.uk
▶ Affiliated Building Contracts, The Cottage, Draycote, Rugby, Warwickshire, CV23 9RB Tel: (01926) 634710 Fax: (01926) 632029
Beoley Building Services, 19 Druids Lane, Birmingham, B14 5SL Tel: 0121-436 5717 Fax: (01527) 597103
Bramall Construction, 3 Callflex Business Park, Golden Smithies Lane, Wath-upon-Dearne, Rotherham, South Yorkshire, S63 7ER Tel: (01709) 766000 Fax: (01709) 766001 E-mail: info@bramall.com
F. Brown P.L.C., 75 Moor Lane, Preston, PR1 1JQ Tel: (01772) 824141 Fax: (01772) 203383 E-mail: fbrownplc@btconnect.com
Bryen & Langley Ltd, 48-60 Footscray Road, London, SE9 2SU Tel: (020) 8850 7775 Fax: (020) 8850 6772 E-mail: info@bryen-langley.com
Bullock Construction Ltd, Northgate, Aldridge, Walsall, WS9 8TU Tel: (01922) 458311 Fax: (01922) 459589 E-mail: admin@bullock.co.uk
C J Ellmore & Co. Ltd, Henshaw Lane, Yeadon, Leeds, LS19 7RZ Tel: 0113-250 2881 Fax: 0113-239 1227 E-mail: mail@ellmore.co.uk
Cameron Industrial Services Ltd, 351 Hale Road, Widnes, Cheshire, WA8 8TS Tel: 0151-423 3892 Fax: 0151-423 3892 E-mail: enquiries@cameronltd.co.uk
Carillion P.L.C., 24 Birch Street, Wolverhampton, WV1 4HY Tel: (01902) 422431 Fax: (01902) 316165 E-mail: n.simms@carillionplc.com
Carillion Building, 3 Abbots Key, Monks Ferry, Wirral, Merseyside, CH41 5LH Tel: 0151-666 5700 Fax: 0151-666 5777
▶ Cedar Building Services, 27 Sackville Road, Heaton, Newcastle upon Tyne, NE6 5SY Tel: 0191-265 3406 Fax: 0191-265 3406 E-mail: jon@cedarbs.wanadoo.co.uk
City Response Ltd, 19 Cross Keys Street, Manchester, M4 5ET Tel: 0161-832 8325 Fax: 0161-834 2260
▶ Complete Technical Services Ltd, Hope Street, Rotherham, South Yorkshire, S60 1LH Tel: (01709) 821757 Fax: (01709) 385068 E-mail: gary.collinson@complete-tech.co.uk
Contract Services Renovation & Refurbishing Ltd, Lombardian House Liverpool Road, Cadishead, Manchester, M44 5DD Tel: 0161-777 8278 Fax: 0161-777 6298 E-mail: general@contracts-svcs.co.uk
Crips Ltd, 40 Oxford Drive, Berdmonsey Street, London, SE1 2FB Tel: (020) 7403 1190 Fax: (020) 7407 4734 E-mail: enquiries@crips.co.uk
D M L Contracting, 29-31 North Cross Road, London, SE22 9HZ Tel: (020) 8693 0416 Fax: (020) 8693 6221 E-mail: info@dml.co.uk
Durkan Properties Ltd, Durkan House, 214-224 High Street, Waltham Cross, Hertfordshire, EN8 7DU Tel: (01992) 781400 Fax: (01992) 781500 E-mail: info@durkan.co.uk
Hallford Refurbishments, A Silver End Business Park, Brettell Lane, Brierley Hill, West Midlands, DY5 3LG Tel: (01384) 573845 Fax: (01384) 573848
Hambridge Investments Newbury, 4 Vulcan Close, Sandhurst, Berkshire, GU47 9DD Tel: (01252) 860043 Fax: (01252) 890154
Hampshire Mezzanine Floors Ltd, Hawkeswood Road, Southampton, SO18 1AB Tel: (023) 8063 1888 Fax: (023) 8023 0033 E-mail: sales@hmf-uk.com
Harlow & Milner Ltd, Milner Way, Ossett, West Yorkshire, WF5 9JN Tel: (01924) 277771 Fax: (01924) 280102 E-mail: info@harlow-milner.co.uk
John C Lillywhite Ltd, Gravel Lane, Chichester, West Sussex, PO19 8PQ Tel: (01243) 781911 Fax: (01243) 780168 E-mail: jcl.builders@virgin.net
Lovell Partnerships Ltd, Marston Park, Tamworth, Staffordshire, B78 3HN Tel: (01827) 305600 Fax: (01827) 305601 E-mail: enquiries@lovell.co.uk
▶ M & D Wright Devlopment Ltd, 46 Park Lane, Bedhampton, Havant, Hampshire, PO9 3HL Tel: (023) 9247 5595 Fax: (023) 9247 6697 E-mail: dgolf@tiscali.co.uk
Omega Interiors, The Cavendish Centre, Winnall Close, Winchester, Hampshire, SO23 0LB Tel: (01962) 843542 Fax: (01962) 843062 E-mail: tony@omega-online.co.uk
R G Spiller Ltd, Millfield Close, Chard, Somerset, TA20 2DJ Tel: (01460) 62881 Fax: (01460) 65781
S D C Builders, Limegrove House, Caxton Road, Elm Farm Industrial Estate, Bedford, MK41 0QQ Tel: (01234) 363155 Fax: (01234) 266385 E-mail: matt.clifford@sdc.co.uk
Simons Group Ltd, 401 Monks Road, Lincoln, LN3 4NU Tel: (01522) 510000 Fax: (01522) 521812
Skanska Construction, 8 Dysart Street, London, EC2A 2BX Tel: (020) 7377 1444 Fax: (020) 7377 1999
Symm & Co. Ltd, Osney Mead, Oxford, OX2 0EQ Tel: (01865) 254900 Fax: (01865) 254935 E-mail: mailbox@symm.co.uk
T & E Neville Ltd, Neville House, 301 Marsh Road, Luton, LU3 2RZ Tel: (01582) 573496 Fax: (01582) 490216 E-mail: enquiries@nevilleconstruction.co.uk
T H Kenyon & Sons plc, Kenyon House, 14a Hockerill Street, Bishop's Stortford, Hertfordshire, CM23 2DW Tel: (01279) 858700 Fax: (01279) 653454
Wallis Ltd, 47 Homesdale Road, Bromley, BR2 9TN Tel: (020) 8464 3377 Fax: (020) 8464 5847 E-mail: gen@wallisb.kier.co.uk

BUILDING REGULATION CONSULTANCY

▶ R Walker, 41 The Pastures, Lower Bullingham, Hereford, HR2 6EU Tel: (01432) 341636 E-mail: enquires@rwalker-plans.co.uk

BUILDING RESTORATION OR CONSERVATION CONTRACTORS OR CONSULTANCY

Ballantine Engineering Ltd, Links Road, Bo'Ness, West Lothian, EH51 9PW Tel: (01506) 822721 Fax: (01506) 827326 E-mail: sales@ballantinebones.co.uk
Border Oak Ltd, Kingsland Sawmills, Kingsland, Leominster, Herefordshire, HR6 9SF Tel: (01568) 708752 Fax: (01568) 708295 E-mail: sales@borderoak.com
▶ Building Restoration Co., Kinbreac, Duror, Appin, Argyll, PA38 4DA Tel: (01631) 740300 Fax: (01631) 740216
Building Restoration & Cleaning (Leeds) Ltd, Abbey Mills, Kirkstall, Leeds, LS5 3HP Tel: 0113-278 6472 Fax: 0113-275 4644 E-mail: brcleeds@btconnect.com
Carillion plc, Green Park Road, Bath, BA1 1XH Tel: (01225) 428441 Fax: (01225) 422577
Carillion Building, 3 Abbots Key, Monks Ferry, Wirral, Merseyside, CH41 5LH Tel: 0151-666 5700 Fax: 0151-666 5777
Cathedral Works Organisation, Terminus Road, Chichester, West Sussex, PO19 8TX Tel: (01243) 784225 Fax: (01243) 813700 E-mail: info@cwo.uk.com
▶ Conran Homes Ltd, 25 King Street, Knutsford, Cheshire, WA16 6DW Tel: (01565) 650734 Fax: (01565) 650734
▶ Cornish Lime Co., Brims Park, Old Callywith Road, Bodmin, Cornwall, PL31 2DZ Tel: (01208) 77287 Fax: (01208) 73744 E-mail: sales@cornishlime.co.uk
▶ E M Treece, 42 South Road, Kirkby Stephen, Cumbria, CA17 4SN Tel: (01768) 371221 Fax: (01768) 371221 E-mail: edtreece@tiscali.co.uk
Faversham Joinery UK Ltd, Abbey Farm, Abbey Road, Faversham, Kent, ME13 7BL Tel: (01795) 537062 Fax: (01795) 597666 E-mail: enquiries@favershamjoinery.co.uk
Ferrosteel (Structures) Ltd, 60 Lichfield St, Walsall, WS4 2BX Tel: (01922) 637467 Fax: (01922) 720364
Hargreaves Construction Co. Ltd, Rustington House, Worthing Road, Rustington, Littlehampton, West Sussex, BN16 3PS Tel: (01903) 777777 Fax: (01903) 777700
▶ Ingram Consultancy Ltd, Manor Farm House, Chicklade Hindon, Hindon, Salisbury, SP3 5SU Tel: (01747) 820170 Fax: (01747) 820175 E-mail: enquiries@ingram-consultancy.co.uk
▶ Insurance Repair Solutions Ltd, Unit 6 Beta Terrace, Masterlord Business Park, West Road, Ransomes Europark, Ipswich, IP3 9SX Tel: (0870) 7607607 Fax: (0870) 7607607 E-mail: info@insurancerepairsolutions.co.uk
KSM Property Maintenance South East Ltd, PO Box 8002, Harlow, Essex, CM20 3XA Tel: (01279) 439777 Fax: (01279) 439750 E-mail: sales@ksm-maintenance.co.uk
Lewis Masonry, 14 The Barges, Tower Parade, Whitstable, Kent, CT5 2BF Tel: (01227) 280064 Fax: (01227) 280064 E-mail: lewismatanle@supanet.com
Linford-Bridgeman Ltd, Quonians, Lichfield, Staffordshire, WS13 7LB Tel: (01543) 414234 Fax: (01543) 258250 E-mail: clare.millington@linfordgroup.co.uk
Michael Barclay Partnership, 105 Strand, London, WC2R 0AB Tel: (020) 7240 1191 Fax: (020) 7240 2241
▶ N A Curtain Walling Ltd, Unit 1 Westfield Industrial Estate, Horndean, Waterlooville, Hampshire, PO8 9JX Tel: (023) 9259 5757 Fax: (023) 9259 5757 E-mail: robbiew@nacurtainwalling.com
Pavilion Estates Ltd, 7 Somerby Road, Pickwell, Melton Mowbray, Leicestershire, LE14 2RA Tel: (01664) 454869 Fax: (01664) 454869
Powa Pak Cleaners Ltd, Bletchley, Market Drayton, Shropshire, TF9 3RZ Tel: (01630) 638276 Fax: (01630) 638548 E-mail: sales@powapak.co.uk
Ropetech International Ltd, The Old School, Brynrefail, Caernarfon, Gwynedd, LL55 3NB Tel: 01286 685471 Fax: 01286 685473 E-mail: info@ropetech.com
Sandy Company Builders, Greyfriars Place, Stafford, ST16 2SD Tel: (01785) 258164 Fax: (01785) 256526E-mail: info@sandy.co.uk
Stonewest Holdings Ltd, Lamberts Place, St James's Road, Croydon, CR9 2HX Tel: (020) 8684 6646 Fax: (020) 8684 9323 E-mail: info@stonewest.co.uk
W T Rowley & Sons, 37 Canon Street, Shrewsbury, SY2 5HQ Tel: (01743) 356020
Weeks Restoration & Conservation, 7 Hurst Road, Eastbourne, East Sussex, BN21 2PJ Tel: (01323) 439899
Whitworth Co Partnership, 18 Hatter Street, Bury St. Edmunds, Suffolk, IP33 1NE Tel: (01284) 760421 Fax: (01284) 704734 E-mail: sales@wcp-architects.com
▶ Wiltshire Building Conservation, 33-35 Whistley Road, Potterne, Devizes, Wiltshire, SN10 5QY Tel: (01380) 729902 Fax: (0700) 5802576

BUILDING SEALANT APPLICATION CONTRACTORS

PJ Sealants Ltd, Barton House, 36 Ashby Road, Kegworth, Derby, DE74 2DH Tel: (01509) 670333 Fax: (01509) 670456 E-mail: pjsealants@aol.com
Sealant Techniques Ltd, Harvey Road, Basildon, Essex, SS13 1EP Tel: (01268) 726500 Fax: (01268) 590226
Sealtite Sealants Ltd, 66 Woodbrooke Way, Corringham, Stanford-le-Hope, Essex, SS17 9DW Tel: (01375) 641607 Fax: (01375) 361283
Square One Sealants Ltd, Elfords, Heightington, Bewdley, Worcestershire, DY12 2XW Tel: (01299) 878900 Fax: (01299) 871144 E-mail: sossealants@aol.com
Structural Sealant Services Ltd, Grove Farm, North Road, South Ockendon, Essex, RM15 6SR Tel: (01708) 853285 Fax: (01708) 851142E-mail: sales@structuralsealants.co.uk
Waterseal Waterbar & Sealant Ltd, 1 Weston Court, Stokesley Industrial Estate, Stokesley, Middlesbrough, Cleveland, TS9 5GA Tel: (01642) 717717 Fax: (01642) 717718
Walker Sealants, 14 Brown La West, Leeds, LS12 6BH Tel: 0113-242 1745 Fax: 0113-247 1745 E-mail: paulinecorbet@aol.com

BUILDING SERVICE COMPUTER AIDED DESIGN (CAD)

▶ Insignia Consulting, Knights View, 104 The Street, Little Waltham, Chelmsford, CM3 3NT Tel: (01245) 360121 Fax: (01245) 360614 E-mail: cad@insignia-consulting.com

BUILDING SERVICES

1 T O 1 Lionheart, Trump House, 15 Edison Street, Hillington Industrial Estate, Glasgow, G52 4JW Tel: 0141-810 5353
▶ 1st Call Changing Group, Monton House, Monton Green, Eccles, Manchester, M30 9LE Tel: 0161-281 7007 Fax: 0161-281 6006 E-mail: sales@1stcallbuildingservices.co.uk
▶ A & B Builders, 8 York Road South, Wigan, Lancashire, WN4 9DT Tel: (01942) 720968 Fax: (01942) 272388 E-mail: abconstruction@abtec.net
▶ A Bradley Ltd, 213 Shore Road, Ballyronan, Magherafelt, County Londonderry, BT45 6LW Tel: (028) 7941 8421 Fax: (028) 7941 8383 E-mail: abradleyltd@tiscali.co.uk
▶ A & D Builders Ltd, Thorne House, Eastville, Yeovil, Somerset, BA21 4JD Tel: (01935) 411334
▶ A & D Building Services Ltd, 106-108 Salamander Street, Edinburgh, EH6 7LA Tel: 0131-467 7170
▶ A O Roberts Ltd, Gaerwen Industrial Estate, Gaerwen, Gwynedd, LL60 6HR Tel: (01248) 422101 Fax: (01248) 422141 E-mail: enquiries@aoroberts.co.uk
▶ A S Wellington, 58-59 Village Farm Road, Village Farm Industrial Estate, Pyle, Bridgend, Mid Glamorgan, CF33 6BN Tel: (01656) 748020 Fax: (01656) 748029
▶ A Sharman & Sons Ltd, 22 Lynn Road, Southery, Downham Market, Norfolk, PE38 0HU Tel: (01366) 377571
▶ A Tait & Sons, Dounby, Orkney, KW17 2HT Tel: (01856) 771236 Fax: (01856) 771762
▶ A V Services, Unit 17 Avenue Industrial Estate, Southend Arterial Road, Harold Wood, Romford, RM3 0BY Tel: (01708) 376221 Fax: (01708) 376224
▶ Abacus Developments Ltd, 1 Abacus Park, Forth Avenue Industrial Estate, Kirkcaldy, Fife, KY2 5NZ Tel: (01592) 268408 Fax: (01592) 640740
▶ Abbotshall Homes Ltd, 5 Oswald Road, Kirkcaldy, Fife, KY1 3JE Tel: (01592) 653653 Fax: (01592) 653353

BUILDING SERVICES – *continued*

▶ Acorn Services, 242 Portobello High Street, Edinburgh, EH15 2AT Tel: 0131-669 8444 Fax: 0131-669 8444

▶ Ailsa Building Ltd, 251 Dundyvan Road, Coatbridge, Lanarkshire, ML5 4AU Tel: (01236) 422615 Fax: (01236) 602623

▶ Aitken Building Contractors, 5 Wych Elm, Harlow, Essex, CM20 1QP Tel: (01279) 419422 Fax: (01279) 413199

Alan Grant Grampian Ltd, 59 Main Street, Alford, Aberdeenshire, AB33 8PX Tel: (01975) 562573 Fax: (01975) 563631

▶ Alan Megaw, 64 Mount Merrion Avenue, Belfast, BT6 0FR Tel: (028) 9058 2233

▶ Alex Lovie & Son, 41 Main Street, New Deer, Turriff, Aberdeenshire, AB53 6TA Tel: (01771) 644295 Fax: (01771) 644787

▶ Allenbuild Ltd, Unit 4b Interchange 25 Business Park, Bostocks Lane, Sandiacre, Nottingham, NG10 5QG Tel: 0115-921 0150 Fax: 0115-921 0199 E-mail: mailbox@allenbuild.co.uk

▶ Allied Trades Ltd, 14-16 Highholm Street, Port Glasgow, Renfrewshire, PA14 5HJ Tel: (01475) 743666

▶ Andrew Macphee Ltd, 8b Dochcarty Road, Dingwall, Ross-Shire, IV15 9UG Tel: (01349) 862862 Fax: (01349) 862863

▶ Anglia Building & Decorating Contractors, Anglia House, Newmarket Road, Dyserth, Rhyl, Clwyd, LL18 6BS Tel: (01745) 572100 Fax: (01745) 571658 E-mail: info@angliabuilders.co.uk

▶ Angus Homes Ltd, Markethill Industrial Estate, Markethill Road, Turriff, Aberdeenshire, AB53 4AG Tel: (01888) 562639 Fax: (01888) 568953

▶ Ansell Builders, 7 New Road, Mytholmroyd, Hebden Bridge, West Yorkshire, HX7 5DZ Tel: (01422) 881991 E-mail: Caroline@ansellgroup.com

▶ Anvil Construction, Anvil House, Whittonstall, Consett, County Durham, DH8 9JN Tel: (01207) 560991 Fax: (01207) 563538

▶ Approved Services, 108 Calderglen Avenue, Blantyre, Glasgow, G72 9UN Tel: (0800) 0850295 Fax: (01698) 820444

▶ Aran Construction, Tarporley Road, Stretton, Warrington, WA4 4NB Tel: (01925) 860002 Fax: (01925) 860101

▶ Ardmore Construction Ltd, 3 Hollybrook Place, Glasgow, G42 7HB Tel: 0141-433 2588

▶ Argee Builders Ltd, 1 Rosendale Way, Blantyre, Glasgow, G72 0NJ Tel: (01698) 826824 Fax: (01698) 826828

▶ Arx Construction Ltd, The Bake House, 43 Bonnyrigg Road, Dalkeith, Midlothian, EH22 3HF Tel: 0131-663 0996

▶ Arx Construction Ltd, Arx House, 22 Cameron Knowe, Philpstoun, Linlithgow, West Lothian, EH49 6RL Tel: (01506) 830114

Ashleigh Scotland Ltd, Lochar House, Dumfries, DG1 3NU Tel: (01387) 711500 Fax: (01387) 711501

▶ Ashworth Construction (North West) Ltd, 16a Boxer Place, Moss Side, Leyland, PR26 7QL Tel: (01772) 699800

▶ Atkinson D J Ltd Builders Contractors, 123 North Wingfield Road, Grassmoor, Chesterfield, Derbyshire, S42 5EB Tel: (01246) 855699 Fax: (01246) 854292

▶ B A Williams, Unit 21, Top Barn Business Centre, Worcester Road, Holt Heath, Worcester, WR6 6NH Tel: (01905) 620791 Fax: (01905) 621751 E-mail: info@dawbulidingcontractors.co.uk

▶ B & B Builders Ltd, Tolver Farm Cottage, Tolver, Long Rock, Penzance, Cornwall, TR20 8YL Tel: (01736) 330996 Fax: (01736) 330996

▶ B & M Contract Services Ltd, B & M House, Gordon Road, Southbourne, Emsworth, Hampshire, PO10 8AZ Tel: (01243) 377444 Fax: (01243) 377666

▶ B McDougal Ltd, 7 Erskine Square, Hillington Industrial Estate, Glasgow, G52 4BJ Tel: 0141-882 4600

▶ Baas Construction Ltd, The Old Chapel, Brooklandsroad, Burnley, Lancashire, BB11 3PR Tel: (01282) 437304 Fax: (01282) 452200

▶ Bagwell Ltd, Station Yard, Station Road, Sidmouth, Devon, EX10 9DN Tel: (01395) 577194 Fax: (01395) 577132

▶ Balfour Beatty Construction Ltd, Churchill House, 29 Mill Hill Road, Pontefract, West Yorkshire, WF8 4HY Tel: (01977) 602120 Fax: (01977) 602181

▶ Bankton Developments, 76 New Row, Tranent, East Lothian, EH33 2AA Tel: (01875) 616888 Fax: (01875) 616836

▶ Barnett Construction Ltd, Gannow Lane, Rose Grove, Burnley, Lancashire, BB12 6JJ Tel: (01706) 833900 Fax: (0845) 2268822

▶ Barr Ltd, Maybury House, Turnhouse Road, Edinburgh, EH12 8LX Tel: 0131-339 1000

▶ Beard & Tandy, Stenders Business Park, The Stenders, Mitcheldean, Gloucestershire, GL17 0JE Tel: (01594) 542997

▶ Bexwell Construction Ltd, 27 Stamford Hill, London, N16 5TU Tel: (020) 8802 4109 Fax: (020) 8802 0523

▶ Biggs Building & Landscaping, 12 Westray Place, Bishopbriggs, Glasgow, G64 1UQ Tel: 0141-762 0004 Fax: 0141-762 0007

▶ Bishop Developments, 176 York Way, London, N1 0AZ Tel: (020) 7713 0455 Fax: (020) 7278 1594

▶ Blackburn Marshall Construction Ltd, Wooler Street, Darlington, County Durham, DL1 1RQ Tel: (01325) 352109 Fax: (01325) 488146

Blakeley Tonge & Partner Ltd, 3 Lever Bridge Mills, Radcliffe Road, Bolton, BL3 1RU Tel: (01204) 535580 Fax: (01204) 535581

▶ Blanchards Construction, 3 Newland Drive, Wallasey, Merseyside, CH44 2AX Tel: 0151-637 1222

▶ Bluestone plc, Waterside Centre, 4215 Solihull Parkway, Birmingham Business Park, Birmingham, B37 7YN Tel: 0121-329 1500 Fax: 0121-329 1501

Bluestone plc, 4 Phoenix Place, Nottingham, NG8 6BA Tel: 0115-964 7000 Fax: 0115-964 7001 E-mail: admin@bluestonesolutions.net

▶ Bluestone plc, The Meads Business Centre, Ashworth Road, Bridgemead, Swindon, SN5 7YJ Tel: (01793) 648000 Fax: (01793) 648001

▶ Bluestone plc, 3 Heron Gate Office Park, Hankridge Way, Taunton, Somerset, TA1 2LR Tel: (01823) 624100 Fax: (01823) 624101

▶ Bonnington Contract Ltd, 58 Southcroft Road, Rutherglen, Glasgow, G73 1UG Tel: 0141-613 6132

▶ Brick Peers, Milton Priory House, Gate Lane, Wells, Somerset, BA5 1UA Tel: (01749) 683110 Fax: (01749) 683117

▶ Brick & Steel Construction Co., 4-6 Boswell Square, Hillington Industrial Estate, Glasgow, G52 4BQ Tel: 0141-810 1919 Fax: 0141-810 1929

▶ Broadoak Construction Southeast Ltd, Triumph House, Guildford Road, Bookham, Leatherhead, Surrey, KT23 4HB Tel: (01372) 453111 Fax: (01372) 452193 E-mail: sales@broadoak-construction.co.uk

▶ Bruce Collie Building Co. Ltd, 46 Silverknowes Road, Edinburgh, EH4 5LF Tel: 0131-336 5050

▶ Bruce Contracts, 72 Brand Street, Glasgow, G51 1DG Tel: 0141-427 5331 Fax: 0141-427 5639

▶ Buchan Bros Ltd, Glenugie, Longside, Peterhead, Aberdeenshire, AB42 4XE Tel: (01779) 821419 Fax: (01779) 472737

▶ Building Services Scotland, Midlothian Inovation Centre, Roslin, Midlothian, EH25 9RE Tel: 0131-440 2020 Fax: 0131-448 0542

▶ Burmor Construction Ltd, 23 Horsegate, Deeping St. James, Peterborough, PE6 8EN Tel: (01778) 342606 Fax: (01778) 344090

▶ Burns Construction (Aberdeen) Ltd, 34-36 St Peter Street, Aberdeen, AB24 3HU Tel: (01224) 562000

▶ Business Development Associates Ltd, 18 Rodney Street, Liverpool, L1 2TQ Tel: 0151-707 2308 Fax: 0151-709 9457 E-mail: bda_uk@hotmail.com

▶ C & C Contractors London Ltd, 123 Wennington Road, Rainham, Essex, RM13 9TH Tel: (01708) 550008 Fax: (01708) 551009

▶ C H B & W Ltd, Brickfield Cottages, 54 Kings Highway, London, SE18 2BG Tel: (020) 8855 8303 Fax: (020) 8855 5480

▶ C J Deighton & Co., 1 Main Street, West Wilts Trading Estate, Westbury, Wiltshire, BA13 4JU Tel: (01373) 824801 Fax: (01373) 824802

▶ C P Construction Gwent Ltd, Newtown Industrial Estate, Cross Keys, Newport, Gwent, NP11 7PZ Tel: (01495) 270804 Fax: (01495) 270728 E-mail: info@cpconstruction.co.uk

▶ C R Crane & Son Ltd, Manor Farm, Main Road, Nether Broughton, Melton Mowbray, Leicestershire, LE14 3HB Tel: (01664) 823366 Fax: (01664) 823534 E-mail: sales@crcrane.co.uk

▶ C S Gallagher Ltd, Deans Farm, 2 Phillips Lane, Stratford sub Castle, Salisbury, SP1 3YR Tel: (01722) 421988 Fax: (01722) 421421

▶ C Spencer, The Pentagon Centre, 310 Washington Street, Glasgow, G3 8AZ Tel: 0141-221 4859 Fax: 0141-221 8872

▶ Caber Developments, 10-12 Pall Mall, Liverpool, L3 6AL Tel: 0151-255 0595 Fax: 0151-255 0601

▶ Cairney & Smith Construction Ltd, Unit 5, Murray Court, Hillhouse Industrial Estate, Hamilton, Lanarkshire, ML3 9SL Tel: (01698) 286888 Fax: (01698) 286888

Calder Building & Civil Engineering, 22 Tomich Industrial Estate, Muir Of Ord, Ross-Shire, IV6 7UA Tel: (01463) 870521

▶ Calder Building Services, 4 Keighley Road, Halifax, West Yorkshire, HX3 6QP Tel: (01422) 383113 Fax: (01422) 383117 E-mail: info@calderbuild.com

▶ R.E. Campbell (Joinery) Ltd, Station Road, Spean Bridge, Inverness-Shire, PH34 4EP Tel: (01397) 712561

▶ Camstruction Ltd, Cam House, 5 York Street, Aberdeen, AB11 5DL Tel: (01224) 593777 Fax: (01224) 594477 E-mail: sales@camstruction.com

Carlo Services, 71 Childwall Park Avenue, Liverpool, L16 0JE Tel: 0151-737 1030 Fax: 0151-737 2040

▶ Carlton Construction Ltd, 12 Oak Hill, Epsom, Surrey, KT18 7BT Tel: (01372) 749760 Fax: (01372) 745339

▶ Century Builders Ltd, 217 Danes Drive, Glasgow, G14 9AQ Tel: 0141-954 3845

▶ Chamberlain Construction Ltd, Laurel House, Station Approach, Alresford, Hampshire, SO24 9JH Tel: (01962) 733056 Fax: (01962) 734841 E-mail: projects@chamberlainconstruction.co.uk

Charles Building Services Ltd, 6 Viewpoint, Hyatt Trading Estate, Stevenage, Hertfordshire, SG1 2EQ Tel: (01438) 750371

▶ Charles Sweetland & Sons Ltd, Cher, Minehead, Somerset, TA24 5EL Tel: (01643) 703085 Fax: (01643) 707256

Chenko Kurtev, 21 Hastingwood Court, Pembroke Road, London, E17 9NQ Tel: (07810) 158794 Fax: (020) 8509 2955 E-mail: g_chenks@yahoo.co.uk

▶ James Clark, 30 Glenlyon Place, Leven, Fife, KY8 4QY Tel: (01333) 426484 Fax: (01333) 426686

▶ Cleland Construction Ltd, Greenside Depot, Biggar Road, Newarthill, Motherwell, Lanarkshire, ML1 5SS Tel: (01698) 860890

▶ CMS Construction, 118 Longcauseway, Farnworth, Bolton, BL4 9BL Tel: (01204) 576558 Fax: (01204) 706116

▶ Collard Construction Ltd, 5 Belgrave Lane, Plymouth, PL4 7DA Tel: (01752) 309808 Fax: (01752) 309808

▶ Constructall Ltd, The Old Granary, Thurley Farm, Pump Lane, Grazeley, Reading, RG7 1JN Tel: 0118-988 3322

▶ Constructive Approach, 6 Millside Industrial, Southmill Road, Bishop's Stortford, Hertfordshire, CM23 3DP Tel: (01279) 757225 Fax: (01279) 757427

▶ Contract Services Ltd, 28 Church Road, Baglan, Port Talbot, West Glamorgan, SA12 8ST Tel: (01639) 823789 Fax: (01639) 823987 E-mail: info@contractservicesgroup.co.uk

▶ Control Plant Ltd, Lansbury Estate, 102 Lower Guildford Road, Knaphill, Woking, Surrey, GU21 2EP Tel: (01483) 472571 Fax: (01483) 475618

▶ Cowen Builders Ltd, 21 Benbow Drive, South Woodham Ferrers, Chelmsford, CM3 5FP Tel: (01245) 324276 Fax: (01245) 324174

▶ Craigvar Construction, Langhaugh Mill, Langhaugh, Galashiels, Selkirkshire, TD1 2AJ Tel: (01896) 752828 Fax: (01896) 758040

▶ Cranford Builders, Cranford, Gollanfield, Inverness, IV2 7UR Tel: (01667) 462457

▶ Crest Plant Ltd, Portland House, 51 Colney Hatch Lane, London, N10 1LJ Tel: (020) 8444 4165 Fax: (020) 8444 1084

▶ Crown Construction Contracting Ltd, 6 Benjamin Outram Business Centre, Whiteley Road, Ripley, Derbyshire, DE5 3QL Tel: (01773) 570044 Fax: (01773) 570121

▶ Crupron Construction Ltd, PO Box 50, Dinas Powys, South Glamorgan, CF64 4HE Tel: (029) 2051 5562

▶ Cumming & Co. Ltd, 8 Whitefriars Street, Perth, PH1 1PP Tel: (01738) 567899 Fax: (01738) 567900

▶ Cummins & Pope Ltd, 10 London Road, Horndean, Waterlooville, Hampshire, PO8 0BZ Tel: (023) 9259 5199

▶ D D Porter Ltd, 1 Walnut Business Park, Walnut Street, Halifax, West Yorkshire, HX1 5JD Tel: (01422) 362374 Fax: (01422) 343467

▶ D G Esaias Ltd, 5 Castle Garage, Croft Road, Neath, West Glamorgan, SA11 1RW Tel: (01639) 641700 Fax: (01639) 641824

▶ D H Potter & Co. Ltd, 9-11 Tower Street, Hartlepool, Cleveland, TS24 7HH Tel: (01429) 290800

▶ D J Bryant, 59 Queen Victoria Avenue, Hove, East Sussex, BN3 6XA Tel: (01273) 707300 Fax: (01273) 541005

▶ D M Homes Ltd, 37 Hartwood Road, Shotts, Lanarkshire, ML7 5BY Tel: (01698) 292321

▶ D Moffatt & Son Ltd, 3 Newbattle Road, Newtongrange, Dalkeith, Midlothian, EH22 4RA Tel: 0131-663 4732

▶ Damm Builders, 43 Watt Road, Hillington Industrial Estate, Glasgow, G52 4RY Tel: 0141-810 2460

▶ Dave Upton, Walnut View, Brook Street, Moreton Pinkney, Daventry, Northamptonshire, NN11 3SL Tel: (01295) 760745 Fax: (01295) 760858

Davics Construction Ltd, 154 College Road, Liverpool, L23 3DP Tel: 0151-932 9007 Fax: 0151-931 2196

▶ David Gregory Building & Roofing Contractors Ltd, Greaves Bakery, Townfoot, Rothbury, Morpeth, Northumberland, NE65 7SP Tel: (01669) 620064

▶ David Harrison, Stone Gables, 58 Langton Rd, Norton, Malton, North Yorkshire, YO17 9AE Tel: (01653) 693097

▶ Davies Edward Construction)Ltd, Tremorfa Foreshaw, Ocean Park, Cardiff, CF10 4LJ Tel: (029) 2049 8798 E-mail: admin@edav.co.uk

▶ Deacon Construction, 2a Maritime Close, Medway City Estate, Medway City Estate, Rochester, Kent, ME2 4DJ Tel: (01634) 717445 Fax: (01634) 717445 E-mail: sales@deaconconstruction.co.uk

▶ Dean Edward, Unit C3 Horsted Keynes Industrial Park, Cinder Hill Lane, Horsted Keynes, Haywards Heath, West Sussex, RH17 7BA Tel: (01342) 811183 Fax: (01342) 811193

▶ Decorbuild & Co., Premier House, 50-52 Cross Lances Road, Hounslow, TW3 2AA Tel: (020) 8577 3773 Fax: (020) 8577 4547 E-mail: service@decorbuild.com

Denne Group, Denne Court, Hengist Field, Borden, Sittingbourne, Kent, ME9 8FH Tel: (0870) 6001803 Fax: (01795) 434800

▶ Direct Building Services, 502 Lickey Road, Rednal, Birmingham, B45 8UU Tel: 0121-460 1777 Fax: 0121-460 1555

▶ Direction International P.L.C., Hildenbrook House, The Slade, Tonbridge, Kent, TN9 1HR Tel: (01732) 366351

▶ Dixon Contractors, 143 Tullaghans Road, Dunloy, Ballymena, County Antrim, BT44 9EA Tel: (028) 2765 7310

▶ Donaldson Group Ltd, 2230 London Road, Glasgow, G32 8YG Tel: 0141-778 5533

▶ Dorelbury Ltd, 1 Crompton Way, Segensworth West, Fareham, Hampshire, PO15 5SS Tel: (01489) 885388 Fax: (01489) 885893

▶ Drew & Sons, Venton Bungalow, Drewsteignton, Exeter, EX6 6PG Tel: (01647) 231306 Fax: (01647) 231306

▶ Duncan & Son Southwold Ltd, Unit 20 Southwold Business, Centre St Edmunds Road, Southwold, Suffolk, IP18 6JU Tel: (01502) 723636

▶ Duxbury Builders Ltd, Brook Street, Adlington, Chorley, Lancashire, PR6 9LE Tel: (01257) 481683 Fax: (01257) 474603

▶ E C Saines & Co. Ltd, 417 New Cross Road, London, SE14 6TA Tel: (020) 8692 4443

▶ E J Morgan & Son, School House, Sennybridge, Brecon, Powys, LD3 8TT Tel: (01874) 636766 Fax: (01874) 636766

▶ Emerson Willis Ltd, Romford Road, Aveley, South Ockendon, Essex, RM15 4XD Tel: (01708) 861044 Fax: (01708) 861066

▶ Extend A Home, Veitch Place, Lennoxtown, Glasgow, G66 7JL Tel: (01360) 312300

▶ F D Hutcheson, Unit 13 Clydebank Business Centre, 31 Clyde Street, Clydebank, Dunbartonshire, G81 1PF Tel: 0141-952 5868 Fax: 0141-952 5868

▶ F W Burnett, Inchmarlo, Banchory, Kincardineshire, AB31 4BT Tel: (01330) 825660 Fax: (01330) 825339

▶ F W Leighton Construction Ltd, Station Yard, Station Lane, York, YO30 1BS Tel: (01904) 470838 Fax: (01904) 470432

▶ Factory Building Services Ltd, 76 St.Andrews Road, Birmingham, B9 4LN Tel: 0121-766 8705 Fax: 0121-753 1979

▶ Fairley Homes Ltd, Fairfields, Moss Road, Dunmore, Falkirk, FK2 8RY Tel: (01324) 831999

▶ Fenbank Builders, Welbourne Lane East, Holbeach, Spalding, Lincolnshire, PE12 8AB Tel: (01406) 424071 Fax: (01406) 490871

▶ Forsyth Building Ltd, 50 West Harbour Road, Edinburgh, EH5 1PP Tel: 0131-552 9393

▶ Fortesite Ltd, Flat 3, Weyhill Farm, Weyhill, Andover, Hampshire, SP11 8DE Tel: (01264) 771728

Frank Haslam Milan, F H M House, Church Hill, Coleshill, Birmingham, B46 3AB Tel: (01675) 461661 Fax: (01675) 461662

▶ Frank Rogers (Building Contractors) Ltd, The Stables, Larkhill Lane, Liverpool, L13 9BR Tel: 0151-226 7172 Fax: 0151-270 2854

▶ Fred Hall & Son Builders Ltd, Old School, Whittington, Carnforth, Lancashire, LA6 2NY Tel: (01524) 271322 Fax: (01524) 272460

▶ Friend Contracting, Miller Court, Millbay Road, Plymouth, PL1 3LQ Tel: (01752) 670555 Fax: (01752) 212303

▶ Frudd Building Services Ltd, Byidon House, Rolleston Drive, Nottingham, NG5 7JP Tel: 0115-955 5888

▶ G A Mell Ltd, Manor Farm Cottage, The Green, Finningley, Doncaster, South Yorkshire, DN9 3BP Tel: (01302) 770202

▶ G Armstrong, Woodbine Cottage, Myreton, Aberlady, Longniddry, East Lothian, EH32 0PZ Tel: (01875) 870229

▶ G P Turner Builders Ltd, 4 Central Place, Haltwhistle, Northumberland, NE49 0DF Tel: (01434) 321000

▶ G Woodland & Sons Ltd, Hatch Beauchamp, Taunton, Somerset, TA3 6TW Tel: (01823) 480248 Fax: (01823) 480239

▶ Galleywood Construction Ltd, Lodge Road, Hazeleigh, Chelmsford, CM3 6QX Tel: (01621) 828700 Fax: (01621) 826997

▶ Gardiner & Faulkner Ltd, 21 Carlton Crescent, Southampton, SO15 2ET Tel: (023) 8023 8429

▶ Garside & Laycock, 4 Beeston Road, Lane End Place, Leeds, LS11 8JY Tel: 0113-244 0071 Fax: 0113-244 0075

▶ Gazy Barns, M T Works, Gannow Lane, Burnley, Lancashire, BB12 6JJ Tel: (01282) 422442

▶ Genesis Contractors Ltd, 32 Hillbrook Grove, Birmingham, B33 8DG Tel: 0121-628 2186 Fax: 0121-786 2367

▶ George Hardie & Son Ltd, 36-38 Potterrow, Edinburgh, EH8 9BT Tel: 0131-667 3911

▶ George M Bolton, 4 Harrison Lane, Edinburgh, EH11 1HG Tel: 0131-337 0000 Fax: 0131-337 0000

▶ Glengarth Construction Ltd, Piercy Mill, Piercy Road, Rossendale, Lancashire, BB4 9JP Tel: (01706) 211999 Fax: (01706) 211888

▶ Gordon Guthrie Contracts, 2 27 Beaverhall Road, Edinburgh, EH7 4JE Tel: 0131-556 9686 Fax: 0131-556 5774

▶ Gordon S Harding, Bousley End, Bousley Rise, Ottershaw, Chertsey, Surrey, KT16 0LB Tel: (01932) 873096 Fax: (01932) 873096

▶ Greenhill Construction Derby Ltd, 611 Burton Road, Derby, DE23 6EJ Tel: (01332) 604055 Fax: (01332) 604058

▶ Grehan Contractors Ltd, Grehan House, Molewood Road, Hertford, SG14 3AQ Tel: (01992) 500051 Fax: (01992) 500262

▶ H B G Construction, 32 Hailes Avenue, Edinburgh, EH13 0LZ Tel: 0131-441 7348

▶ H B G Construction Western Ltd, Millennium Gate, Gifford Court, Fox Den Road, Bristol, BS34 8TT Tel: 0117-944 8800

▶ H B Projects, 56 Commerce Court, Challenge Way, Bradford, West Yorkshire, BD4 8NW Tel: (01274) 269010 Fax: (01274) 669983

▶ indicates data change since last edition

BUILDING SERVICES - *continued*

▶ Hadden Construction Ltd, 1 Maidenplain Place, Aberuthven, Auchterarder, Perthshire, PH3 1EL Tel: (01764) 660011 Fax: (01764) 660022 E-mail: sales@hadden.co.uk
▶ Haley Bros Builders Ltd, Burlees House, Hangingroyd Lane, Hebden Bridge, West Yorkshire, HX7 7DD Tel: (01422) 842858 Fax: (01422) 845896
Hallmark Concrete Crushing & Plant Hire, Units 1 & 2, 28 Hayes Road, Deanshanger, Milton Keynes, MK19 6HW Tel: (07970) 059927 Fax: (01908) 566527 E-mail: sales@hallmarkconstruction.co.uk
▶ Hamilton Knight Development, 16 17 Canalside Industrial Park, Kinoulton Road, Cropwell Bishop, Nottingham, NG12 3BE Tel: 0115-989 4333 Fax: 0115-989 4333 E-mail: hkdevelopments@btconnect.com
▶ Hantall Developments Ltd, Kingston Mill, Manchester Road, Hyde, Cheshire, SK14 2BZ Tel: 0161-368 5885 Fax: 0161-351 9082
▶ Harry Armistead Ltd, Unit 2 Woodgate Park, Middlegate, White Lund Industrial Estate, Morecambe, Lancashire, LA3 3PS Tel: (01524) 848500 Fax: (01524) 848600
▶ Harvest Homemaker, Unit 1, Elgin Works, Elgin Street, Dunfermline, Fife, KY12 7SD Tel: (01383) 736291
▶ Hazelwood Development Ltd, 14 Wortley Road, High Green, Sheffield, S35 4LU Tel: 0114-286 9990 Fax: 0114-286 9991 E-mail: cupton@hazelwood-dev.co.uk
▶ Heather Developments Woking Ltd, Mayford Green, Woking, Surrey, GU22 0PN Tel: (01483) 765848 Fax: (01483) 762414
▶ Heritage Building Co. Ltd, 1 Kinneil Road, Bo'ness, West Lothian, EH51 0AY Tel: (01506) 828202
Hillcrest Homes Ltd, Hillcrest, Knutsford Road, Grappenhall, Warrington, WA4 3LA Tel: (01925) 267314 Fax: (01925) 212171
▶ Homecare Contracts Ltd, 18 Dryden Vale, Bilston Glen Estate, Loanhead, Midlothian, EH20 9HN Tel: 0131-440 5550 Fax: 0131-440 3539
▶ Howden's Joinery Ltd, 4 Grange Road, Houstoun Industrial Estate, Livingston, West Lothian, EH54 5DE Tel: (01506) 444358
▶ Hydair, Unit 5, Morley Business Centre, Morley Road, Tonbridge, Kent, TN9 1RA Tel: (01732) 773844
▶ Inca Developments Ltd, 1 Totterdown Lane, Weston-super-Mare, Avon, BS24 9LU Tel: (0845) 2304622 Fax: (0845) 2304622
▶ Insurepair Glasgow Ltd, 24 Lochleven Road, Glasgow, G42 9JU Tel: 0141-649 6969 Fax: 0141-636 6748
▶ Inter Dynamics, Friarton Bridge Park, 4 Friarton Road, Perth, PH2 8DD Tel: (01738) 626626
▶ J A Kneen Developments Ltd, 3 Golden Hill, Leyland, PR25 3NN Tel: (01772) 621428 Fax: (01772) 621429
▶ J & B Construction Co. Ltd, Unit 41-43 Cumberland Business Park, Cumberland Avenue, London, NW10 7RT Tel: (020) 8961 3847 Fax: (020) 8961 3816
▶ J C Morton, 4 Templehill, Troon, Ayrshire, KA10 6BE Tel: (01292) 315789 Fax: (01292) 318480 E-mail: info@jcmortonhomes.co.uk
▶ J Craig Dykes Property Developments Ltd, 3 Brackenholme Cottages, Brackenholme, Selby, North Yorkshire, YO8 6EJ Tel: (01757) 630224 Fax: (01757) 630244
▶ J & E Regan Builders & Contractors Ltd, Long Acre, Saltash, Cornwall, PL12 6LZ Tel: (01752) 841660 Fax: (01752) 841653
J G B Formwork Ltd, 182 Hyde End Road, Spencers Wood, Reading, RG7 1DG Tel: 0118-988 3424 Fax: 0118-988 6259
▶ J Guest Ltd, Knarsboro House, Bradley Road, Stourbridge, West Midlands, DY8 1XB Tel: (01384) 392444 Fax: (01384) 441875
▶ J H B Ltd, Greenhead, Lerwick, Shetland, ZE1 0PY Tel: (01595) 695577 Fax: (01595) 694709 E-mail: sales@jhbltd.co.uk
▶ J H B Ltd, Greenhead, Lerwick, Shetland, ZE1 0PY Tel: (01595) 695577 Fax: (01595) 694709 E-mail: sales@jhbltd.co.uk
▶ J Harley Building Services Ltd, 24 Fenella Street, Glasgow, G32 7JT Tel: 0141-778 6194 Fax: 0141-778 6194
▶ J Hawkins Ltd, Q Rocket Trading Centre, Bowring Park Road, Liverpool, L14 3NZ Tel: 0151-220 3767 Fax: 0151-220 7500
▶ J J L Artison, Nethermill, Netherton Road, Langbank, Port Glasgow, Port Of Glasgow, Renfrewshire, PA14 6YG Tel: (01475) 540060
▶ J L Findlow & Sons Ltd, Ball Haye Road, Leek, Staffordshire, ST13 6AF Tel: (01538) 383174 Fax: (01538) 399997
J M Builders, Hallidays Mill, London Road, Chalford, Stroud, Gloucestershire, GL6 8NR Tel: (01453) 882207 Fax: (01453) 731076
▶ J N E Construction Ltd, Estover Close, Plymouth, PL6 7PL Tel: (01752) 696269 Fax: (01752) 696660
▶ J P Wild Ltd, 149 Dewsbury Road, Leeds, LS11 5NW Tel: 0113-277 4944
▶ J R D Construction Ltd, Unit 2 65 South Street, Ilkeston, Derbyshire, DE7 5QQ Tel: 0115-944 7077 Fax: 0115-944 7859
▶ J Robertson, 1 Edinburgh Road, Cleghorn, Lanark, ML11 7RW Tel: (01555) 665084 Fax: (01555) 673819
▶ J Smart & Co. (Contractors) P.L.C., 46 Redbraes Place, Edinburgh, EH7 4LL Tel: 0131-554 6418
▶ J T Building Contractors, 12-14 Somerset House Suite 20 Hussar Court, Westside View, Waterlooville, Hampshire, PO7 7SG Tel: (023) 9225 9258 Fax: (023) 9225 9260 E-mail: info@jtbuilders.co.uk
▶ James Brown Construction Ltd, 10 Eglinton Street, Irvine, Ayrshire, KA12 8AS Tel: (01924) 272780 Fax: (01563) 573370
▶ James Maxwell Building Contractors Ltd, Midbrae, Kirkwynd, Langholm, Dumfriesshire, DG13 0JD Tel: (01387) 381352 E-mail: sales@maxwellthebuilders.co.uk
▶ James West Ltd, 1 Office Block 1 Southlink Business Park, Hamilton Street, Oldham, OL4 1DE Tel: 0161-624 1956 Fax: 0161-628 4474
Jamieson & Allan Construction, Unit 8, Bourtree Technology Park, Minto Drive, Altens Industrial Estate, Aberdeen, AB12 3LW Tel: (01224) 895333
▶ Jarvey Stone Ltd, 15a Edinburgh Road, Bathgate, West Lothian, EH48 1BA Tel: (01506) 632565 Fax: (01506) 634566
▶ JBC Scotland, St. Ronans Drive, Kinross, KY13 8AF Tel: (01577) 864136 Fax: (01577) 864136
▶ Jeffery & Pengelly, Unit 4 Fatherford Farm, Okehampton, Devon, EX20 1QQ Tel: (01837) 52277 Fax: (01837) 55379
▶ Jensen Construction Ltd, Portberry House, Portberry Street, South Shields, Tyne & Wear, NE33 1QX Tel: 0191-454 4083 Fax: 0191-454 7232
▶ John Bain (Contractors) Ltd, Unit 1, 5 Kyle Road, Irvine Industrial Estate, Irvine, Ayrshire, KA12 8JF Tel: (01294) 277568
▶ John Caven, Offerance Farm, Gartmore, Stirling, FK8 3RZ Tel: (01877) 382244 Fax: (01877) 389023
▶ John Corbett Construction Ltd, The Pier, Brodick, Isle of Arran, KA27 8AU Tel: (01770) 302537 Fax: (01770) 302748
▶ John Johnstone Dalbeattie Ltd, Millisle, Dalbeattie, Kirkcudbrightshire, DG5 4AX Tel: (01556) 610226
▶ John Nunn & Co (Builders), Retreat, Cliff Road, Waldringfield, Woodbridge, Suffolk, IP12 4QL Tel: (01473) 736383 Fax: (01473) 736427
▶ John Sisk & Sons Ltd, Unit 1740 1750, Solihull Parkway, Birmingham Business Park, Birmingham, B37 7YD Tel: 0121-329 0600 Fax: 0121-329 0606
▶ John Wylie Building Ltd, 9 Aitkenhead Road, Uddingston, Glasgow, G71 5RG Tel: (01698) 818480 Fax: (01698) 307001
▶ Johnston Builders, Unit 17-18, Mayfield Industrial Estate, Dalkeith, Midlothian, EH22 4AD Tel: 0131-454 0796 Fax: 0131-454 0796 E-mail: sales@johnstonbuilders.co.uk
Joinery Construction & Maintenance Ltd, 14 Fullarton Drive, Glasgow East Investment Park, Glasgow, G32 8FA Tel: 0141-646 3800 Fax: 0141-646 3888
▶ Jordan (Building & Joinery Contractors) Ltd, Lochlands Industrial Estate, Larbert, Stirlingshire, FK5 3NS Tel: (01324) 555844
▶ K Morrison & Son Ltd, 1 Station Road, Braughing, Ware, Hertfordshire, SG11 2PB Tel: (01920) 822121
▶ K W Construction (Aberdeen) Ltd, 55 Constitution Street, Aberdeen, AB24 5ET Tel: (01224) 641190 Fax: (01224) 648329
▶ Ken Barbour, Fitmacan, Boyndie, Banff, AB45 2LA Tel: (01261) 861455
▶ Kilbride Industrial Services, New Road, Cambuslang, Glasgow, G72 7PU Tel: 0141-646 1411 Fax: 0141-646 1422
▶ Killigrew King, 13 Calico Row, London, SW11 3YH Tel: (020) 7350 5900 Fax: (020) 7350 5909
King & Johnston Building Contractors Ltd, 380 New Hythe Lane, Larkfield, Aylesford, Kent, ME20 6RZ Tel: (01622) 792255 Fax: (01622) 792266
Kingfisher Construction Services Ltd, Kempton Park Close, Derby, DE24 8QB Tel: (01332) 382088 Fax: (01332) 294902
▶ KMD, 109a Whippingham Road, Brighton, BN2 3PF Tel: (01273) 679700 Fax: (01273) 605057
▶ Knight Projects Group Ltd, Station App, Atherton, Manchester, M46 9LJ Tel: (01942) 874171 Fax: (01942) 897482
▶ Lad Construction Ltd, 16 Gorst Road, London, NW10 6LE Tel: (020) 8961 1342 Fax: (020) 8961 1649 E-mail: info@lad.co.uk
▶ Laidlaw Scott Ltd, 46 Queen Elizabeth Avenue, Hillington Industrial Estate, Glasgow, G52 4NQ Tel: 0141-848 6262 Fax: 0141-889 7800
▶ Laishley Ltd, B300 The Grange, Michelmersh, Romsey, Hampshire, SO51 0AE Tel: (01794) 368283 Fax: (01794) 367543
▶ Landmark Builders Ltd, Unit 12 St Andrews Industrial Estate, Sydney Road, Birmingham, B9 4QB Tel: 0121-245 0575 Fax: 0121-245 0576
▶ Leven Crest Ltd, Suite 90, 38 Queen Street, Glasgow, G1 3DX Tel: 0141-204 7819
▶ Lewis Builders Ltd, Rigs Road, Stornoway, Isle of Lewis, HS1 2RF Tel: (01851) 705015 Fax: (01851) 703718 E-mail: sales@lewis-builders.com
▶ Lloyd Construction, 10a 42 Bayton Road, Exhall, Coventry, CV7 9EJ Tel: (0870) 7590898 Fax: (0870) 7590899
▶ Longbottom Wright, Mullany Business Park, Deanland Road, Golden Cross, Hailsham, East Sussex, BN27 3RP Tel: (01825) 872900 Fax: (01825) 873399
▶ Longrow Builders Ltd, 2D Edna Road, London, SW20 8BT Tel: (020) 8543 1227
▶ M C Clark Ltd, 3 Norwich Road, Hethersett, Norwich, NR9 3DD Tel: (01603) 501071 Fax: (01603) 811748 E-mail: mailbox@mcclarkbuilders.co.uk
▶ M & G Construction Ltd, Gilbert House, Stanley Road, Ilford, Essex, IG1 1RB Tel: (020) 8514 2981 Fax: (020) 8553 0262
▶ M J Berry, 1 Freeland Way, Erith, Kent, DA8 2LQ Tel: (01322) 351139 Fax: (01322) 351137
M J Taylor King Ltd, 1 Cowper Road, Harpenden, Hertfordshire, AL5 5NF Tel: (01582) 763430 Fax: (01582) 461156 E-mail: tailorking@ukonline.co.uk
▶ M L Quinn Construction Ltd, 108 Carrickgallogly Road, Belleeks, Newry, County Down, BT35 7QS Tel: (028) 3087 9300
▶ M M R Ltd, Cash Feus, Strathmiglo, Cupar, Fife, KY14 7QT Tel: (01337) 860212 Fax: (01337) 860716
▶ M M R Ltd, Cash Feus, Strathmiglo, Cupar, Fife, KY14 7QT Tel: (01337) 860212 Fax: (01337) 860716
▶ M Miller, 55 Macrae Street, Wick, Caithness, KW1 5QW Tel: (01955) 602746 Fax: (01955) 605927
▶ M P Brothers Ltd, Unit 14 London Group Business Park, 715 North Circular Road, London, NW2 7AQ Tel: (020) 8208 1988 Fax: (020) 8208 0162
▶ Macclesfield Joinery Ltd, R/O Artillery House, Heapy Street, Macclesfield, Cheshire, SK11 7JB Tel: (01625) 617428
▶ Mcdougall Group, 3 Telford Court, 11 South Avenue, Clydebank Business Park, Clydebank, Dunbartonshire, G81 2NR Tel: 0141-951 1900 Fax: 0141-951 1900
▶ Mcdougall Group, Charlotte Dundas House, Dalgrain Road, Grangemouth, Stirlingshire, FK3 8EL Tel: (01324) 471797 Fax: (01324) 483544 E-mail: sales@themcdougallgroup.com
▶ Macform Ltd, Avalon, Wishaw, Lanarkshire, ML2 0RS Tel: (01698) 355585 Fax: (01698) 355585
▶ Mcguire Builing Maintenence Ltd, Unit 17 Dumbryden Industrial Estate, Dumbryden Road, Edinburgh, EH14 2AB Tel: 0131-467 7806 Fax: 0131-467 7808
▶ Mackintosh Joinery, 64 Haugh Road, Inverness, IV2 4SD Tel: (01463) 250160 Fax: (01463) 250180
▶ Mainline Construction, The Grove, Bognor Regis, West Sussex, PO22 7EY Tel: (01243) 863138 Fax: (01243) 870568
▶ Malcolm Smith Contracts Ltd, 6 Drumaline Ridge, Worcester Park, Surrey, KT4 7JT Tel: (020) 8337 4421 Fax: (020) 8337 4431
▶ Mark Lee Construction Ltd, Unit 1-15 Greys Green Farm, Greys Green, Rotherfield Greys, Henley-on-Thames, Oxfordshire, RG9 4QG Tel: (01491) 629083 E-mail: info@tvpres.demon.co.uk
▶ Mark R Bennett, The Estate Office, 2a Bridge Street, Stourport-on-Severn, Worcestershire, DY13 8XD Tel: (01299) 871701
▶ Master Houses Ltd, Newlands, Kirknewton, Midlothian, EH27 8LR Tel: (01506) 885588 Fax: (01506) 885588
▶ Matthews, Home Farm, Hatfield Park, Hatfield, Hertfordshire, AL9 5NH Tel: (01707) 262351 Fax: (01707) 264813 E-mail: brian@buildingconservation.co.uk
▶ Maxi Construction Ltd, Firth Road, Houstoun Industrial Estate, Livingston, West Lothian, EH54 5DJ Tel: (01506) 442233 Fax: (01506) 442010
▶ MDM Specialist Trades Ltd, 36 Watt Road, Hillington, Glasgow, G52 4RY Tel: 0141-891 4981 Fax: 0141-891 4230 E-mail: info@mdmspecialisttrades.co.uk
▶ Mearchent Sons Builders, Glenwood Business Park Block C, Glenwood Place, Glasgow, G45 9UH Tel: 0141-634 5731 Fax: 0141-634 5731
▶ Melavid Ltd, 39 Chesnut Grove, Birkenhead, Merseyside, CH42 0LB Tel: 0151-650 0074 Fax: 0151-647 3058
▶ Melcombe Regis Construction Ltd, The Old Forge, Wyke Square, Weymouth, Dorset, DT4 9XP Tel: (01305) 773239 Fax: (01305) 773239 E-mail: info@buildersdorset.co.uk
▶ Michael Healey & Son, Francis House, Talbot Way, Market Drayton, Shropshire, TF9 3SJ Tel: (01630) 653366 Fax: (01630) 653372
▶ Mid Cheshire Construction Ltd, 206 Chester Road, Hartford, Northwich, Cheshire, CW8 1LG Tel: (01606) 871349 Fax: (01606) 871350
▶ Milcon Construction & Property Services Ltd, Enterprise House Wistaston Road Business Centre, Wistaston Road, Crewe, CW2 7RP Tel: (01270) 580000 Fax: (01270) 500041
▶ Miller, 24 Carsegate Road, Inverness, IV3 8EX Tel: (01463) 241000 Fax: (01463) 230130
▶ Minerva Accord Ltd, City Gates, 2-4 Southgate, Chichester, West Sussex, PO19 8DJ Tel: (01243) 779257 Fax: (01243) 753102
▶ Mmaxx Underfloor Heating Ltd, 2 Lenziemill Road, Cumbernauld, Glasgow, G67 2RL Tel: (01236) 787000
▶ Morris Builders Ltd, Unit 6 Bondor Business Centre, London Road, Baldock, Hertfordshire, SG7 6HP Tel: (01462) 895540 Fax: (01462) 490081
▶ Morrison Building & Development Ltd, Atholl House, 49 Melville Street, Edinburgh, EH3 7HL Tel: 0131-226 4666
▶ Morrison Construction, Macadam Place, Dryburgh Industrial Estate, Dundee, DD2 3QR Tel: (01382) 833600 Fax: (01382) 833400
▶ Moss Builders Ltd, 126-128 Uxbridge Road, London, W13 8QS Tel: (020) 8840 8877 Fax: (020) 8840 8899
Mossley Hill Building Service Ltd, Bridge Road, Mossley Hill, Liverpool, L18 5EG Tel: 0151-280 2868 Fax: 0151-280 2868 E-mail: mhbsltd@yahoo.co.uk
▶ Munnelly Support Services Ltd, The Heights, 59-65 Lowlands Road, Harrow, Middlesex, HA1 3AW Tel: (020) 8515 0300 Fax: (020) 8861 5837
▶ Munro Builders Ltd, 45 Highfield Gardens, Westcliff-on-Sea, Essex, SS0 0SY Tel: (01702) 348319
William Munro Construction (Highland) Ltd, River Drive, Teaninich Industrial Estate, Alness, Ross-Shire, IV17 0PG Tel: (01349) 882373
▶ N A Hamilton Contractors Ltd, Hamilton House, West Road, Stanley, County Durham, DH9 7XA Tel: (01207) 233444 Fax: (01207) 238222
▶ N Macdonald, Balliscate, Salen Road, Tobermory, Isle of Mull, PA75 6NS Tel: (01688) 302065 Fax: (01688) 302099
▶ Natta Country Homes, Rose Court, Mill Lane, Crondall, Farnham, Surrey, GU10 5RP Tel: (01252) 851158 Fax: (01252) 851150
▶ NDR Builders, Gainborough, Station Road, Tenterden, Kent, TN30 6HN Tel: (01580) 761222
▶ Necton Management Ltd, Oak Farm, North Pickenham Road, Necton, Swaffham, Norfolk, PE37 8DN Tel: (01760) 722183 Fax: (01760) 722342
▶ Needham, Florian House, 30 Wharfdale Road, Ipswich, IP1 4JP Tel: (01473) 220400 Fax: (01603) 891046
▶ Newport Building Services Ltd, Units 3-4 Victoria Court, Hurricane Way, Wickford, Essex, SS11 8YY Tel: (01268) 575550 Fax: (01268) 575551
▶ Niblock Builders Ltd, 135 Anerley Road, London, SE20 8AJ Tel: (020) 8778 3449 Fax: (020) 8659 0615
▶ Nicholls & Wilson Ltd, 44-45 Alston Drive, Bradwell Abbey, Milton Keynes, MK13 9HB Tel: (01908) 321123
▶ Nike Construction Ltd, Phoenix Business Park, John Nike Way, Bracknell, Berkshire, RG12 8TN Tel: (01344) 789300 Fax: (01344) 789301
▶ Northern Developments, Oakvale House, Thomas Lane, Burgh Road Industrial Estate, Carlisle, CA2 7ND Tel: (01228) 533315 Fax: (01228) 592244
▶ Northern Heritage Developments Ltd, 19 Haw Grove, Hellifield, Skipton, North Yorkshire, BD23 4JA Tel: (01729) 851065
▶ Norwest Holst Ltd, 6230 Bishops Court, Birmingham Business Court, Birmingham Business Park, Birmingham, B37 7YB Tel: 0121-788 7300 Fax: 0121-707 3438
▶ Norwood Homes, Millbrae, Findhorn, Forres, Morayshire, IV36 3YY Tel: (01309) 691200 Fax: (01309) 691454
▶ O X, Unit B, New Baltic Wharf, Evelyn Street, London, SE8 5RJ Tel: (020) 8469 3331
▶ Oddy Builders Ltd, Woodlands Factory, Stanks Lane South, Leeds, LS14 5LN Tel: 0113-264 3734 Fax: 0113-232 6672
▶ Oliver Connell & Son Ltd, 35 Junction Road, London, W5 4XP Tel: (020) 8568 0001 Fax: (020) 8232 8151
▶ Olli Construction Services, 21 Johnstone Road, London, E6 6JB Tel: (020) 8552 7122 Fax: (020) 8552 6263
▶ One 58 Associates Ltd, Unit 1 Grove Street, Cheltenham, Gloucestershire, GL50 3LZ Tel: (01242) 241158 Fax: (01242) 241580
▶ Orbital Contractors Ltd, Gale Buildings, Gale Road, Knowsley Industrial Park, Liverpool, L33 7YB Tel: 0151-546 0830
▶ P & B Builders (Scotland) Ltd, 3-5 Rhannan Road, Glasgow, G44 3AZ Tel: 0141-633 2148
▶ P C Mcqueenie, Carpet Lane, Edinburgh, EH6 6SP Tel: 0131-468 7061 Fax: 0131-467 0099
▶ P J Allison Wirral Ltd, 4 May Road, Wirral, Merseyside, CH60 5RA Tel: 0151-342 7797 Fax: 0151-342 9244
▶ P & J Hunter, Unit 4a Charlesfield Industrial Estate, St. Boswells, Melrose, Roxburghshire, TD6 0HH Tel: (01835) 824751 Fax: (01835) 824752
P M D Building Services Ltd, 32 Vilier Street, Sunderland, SR1 1EJ Tel: 0191-514 3444 Fax: 0191-514 3445
▶ P Moran Ltd, Smeaton, Dalkeith, Midlothian, EH22 2NN Tel: 0131-663 6246 Fax: 0131-663 9908
▶ P R S Building Contractors, Port Road, Palnackie, Castle Douglas, Kirkcudbrightshire, DG7 1PQ Tel: (01556) 600351 Fax: (01556) 600240
▶ P T Smith Builders Ltd, Unit 18 Fysh House Farm, Cuckoo Hill, Bures, Suffolk, CO8 5LD Tel: (01787) 227786 Fax: (01787) 227287
▶ P Trant Guernsey Ltd, Fairfield, Forest Road, St. Martin, Guernsey, GY4 6UG Tel: (01481) 240471 Fax: (01481) 230468
▶ Palmac Contracting, 4 Adams Way, Springfield Business Park, Alcester, Warwickshire, B49 6PU Tel: (01789) 766022 Fax: (01789) 763662
▶ Pang Properties Ltd, Bleets Farm Buildings, Feltham, Frome, Somerset, BA11 5NA Tel: (01373) 453177 Fax: (01373) 453178
▶ Par Building Services, 1404 Pershore Road, Stirchley, Birmingham, B30 2PH Tel: 0121-459 9714 Fax: 0121-459 6403

BUILDING SERVICES – *continued*

▶ Pembroke Homes Ltd, Pembroke House, 3 Altrincham Road, Wilmslow, Cheshire, SK9 5ND Tel: (01625) 530330 Fax: (01625) 528221

▶ Penny Lane Builders, 88 Ash Grove, Wavertree, Liverpool, L15 1ET Tel: 0151-734 2171 Fax: 0151-733 9208 E-mail: office@pennylanebuilders.co.uk

▶ Peter Clegg & Son Builders Ltd, 54 Henry Road, West Bridgford, Nottingham, NG2 7NB Tel: 0115-982 5666 Fax: 0115-982 5777

▶ Philiam Construction, The Quadrant, Manor Park CR, Edgware, Middlesex, HA8 7LU Tel: (020) 8905 7995 Fax: (020) 8905 6777

▶ Picter & Berry, Tetbury Road, Sherston, Malmesbury, Wiltshire, SN16 0LU Tel: (01666) 841485 Fax: (01666) 841485

▶ PJP Southern Ltd, Unit 2 Wellington Park, Hedge End, Southampton, SO30 2QU Tel: (01489) 790545 Fax: (01489) 790492

▶ Ploughcroft Building Services, Unit 4 Bull Fold Garage, Owler Ings Road, Brighouse, West Yorkshire, HD6 1EJ Tel: (0800) 0344100 Fax: (01484) 723355

Podmores Builders, Haydock Street, Warrington, WA2 7UW Tel: (01925) 582850 Fax: (01925) 582859 E-mail: admin@podmores.com

▶ Powerday plc, Crossan House, 28-31 Hythe Road, London, NW10 6RS Tel: (020) 8960 4646 Fax: (020) 8960 3110

▶ Primebuild Ltd, 5 Davieland Court, Broomloan Place, Glasgow, G51 2JR Tel: 0141-425 1902

▶ Propert Preservation & Building, Unit 2 Farset Enterprise Park, 638 Springfield Road, Belfast, BT12 7DY Tel: (028) 9031 0522 Fax: (028) 9023 8799

▶ Pyramid Construction UK Ltd, Unit 14 Fairway Industrial Centre, Golf Course Lane, Bristol, BS34 7QS Tel: 0117-969 2222 Fax: 0117-969 2299

▶ R & A Builders, Laburnum House, Haymoor Green Road, Wybunbury, Nantwich, Cheshire, CW5 7HG Tel: (01270) 569817 Fax: (01270) 560527

▶ R Brewer Construction Ltd, Bathurst House, Smythen St, Exeter, EX1 1BN Tel: (01392) 494424 E-mail: sales@rbrewer.co.uk

▶ R Brewer Construction Ltd, 87 Alexandra Road, St. Austell, Cornwall, PL25 4QW Tel: (01726) 69354

▶ R D J Builders (Rochdale) Ltd, 18A Bridge Street, Milnrow, Rochdale, Lancashire, OL16 3ND Tel: (01706) 632243

▶ R Donnan, Commerce Road, Stranraer, Wigtownshire, DG9 7DD Tel: (01776) 706283 Fax: (01776) 706283

▶ R F Peachey & Sons Ltd, Orchard Place, London, N17 8BH Tel: (020) 8808 2461 Fax: (020) 8365 0437

▶ R G C General Builders, 35 Kingfisher Court, Newbury, Berkshire, RG14 5SJ Tel: (01635) 523321 Fax: (01635) 523679

R G Carter Building Ltd, Riverside Industrial Estate, Marsh Lane, Boston, Lincolnshire, PE21 7PJ Tel: (01205) 365557 Fax: (01205) 365515

▶ R G Carter (Cambridge) Ltd, Horizon Park, Barton Road, Comberton, Cambridge, CB3 7BN Tel: (01223) 265300

▶ R H Hammond Ltd, Unit 7, Northbrook Industrial Estate, Vincent Avenue, Southampton, SO16 6PB Tel: (023) 8077 2442

▶ R H White Ltd, 33 Burleigh Road, Enfield, Middlesex, EN1 1NY Tel: (020) 8367 4964 Fax: (020) 8364 4015

▶ R M B Maintenance Services Ltd, 1 Alcester Road, Birmingham, B13 8AR Tel: 0121-449 5777 Fax: 0121-449 4945

▶ R N Thomson, West Sanquhar Road, Ayr, KA8 9HP Tel: (01292) 265533

▶ R Neck & Son Ltd, The Yard, St. Peters Road, Warley, Brentwood, Essex, CM14 5JF Tel: (01277) 232265 Fax: (01277) 261200

▶ R P Tyson Ltd, 1 Mitcham Road, Blackpool, FY4 4QN Tel: (01253) 696800 Fax: (01253) 696801

▶ R & R Trading Ltd, 76 Hollywood Lane, Wainscott, Rochester, Kent, ME3 8AR Tel: (01634) 714140 Fax: (01634) 712777

R T Little Brickwork Ltd, Orchard House, Commercial Road, Southampton, SO15 1GG Tel: (023) 8022 6262 Fax: (023) 8022 6266

▶ R&P, 64 Greenhead Road, Dumbarton, G82 2PN Tel: (01389) 765367 Fax: (01389) 765368

▶ Raymond Brown Building Ltd, 160 Christchurch Road, Ringwood, Hampshire, BH24 3AR Tel: (01425) 472241 Fax: (01425) 480625

▶ Raynesway Construction Services Ltd, Reema Road, Bellshill, Lanarkshire, ML4 1RT Tel: (01698) 503503 Fax: (01698) 503556

▶ Reaburn Developments, The Square, Blackness, Linlithgow, West Lothian, EH49 7NG Tel: (01506) 834833

Red Rose Construction, Charter Street, Accrington, Lancashire, BB5 0SG Tel: (01254) 239300 Fax: (01254) 239300

▶ Rendall Builders, 8 Grainshore Drive, Hatston, Kirkwall, Orkney, KW15 1FL Tel: (01856) 878338 Fax: (01856) 878338

▶ Richard Ward Oxford Ltd, High Street, Islip, Kidlington, Oxfordshire, OX5 2RX Tel: (01865) 379244 Fax: (01865) 379246

▶ Roach Bros Ltd, 129 Woodcote Road, Wallington, Surrey, SM6 0QD Tel: (020) 8647 1740 Fax: (020) 8669 8149

▶ Robert Norman Associates Ltd, Unit 20, Red House Farm, Marlborough Road, Saxtead, Woodbridge, Suffolk, IP13 9RD Tel: (01728) 685040

▶ Allan Robertson & Son, 1 Angus Road, Scone, Perth, PH2 6QU Tel: (01738) 551424 Fax: (01738) 553935

▶ Rogers Construction, 20 Berachah Road, Torquay, TQ1 3AX Tel: (01803) 200079 Fax: (01803) 291890

▶ Rok, Stanley Harrison House, Norton Road, Malton, North Yorkshire, YO17 7PD Tel: (01392) 354000 Fax: (01653) 691111

▶ Rok Ltd, Suite B Hinksley Court, West Way, Oxford, OX2 9JU Tel: (01865) 305950 Fax: (01865) 724450

▶ Ronden Builders Ltd, Crawlaw Road Garage, Crawlaw Road, Peterlee, County Durham, SR8 3LR Tel: 0191-527 0764 Fax: 0191-527 1281

Roper Construction Ltd, 164-168 Powis Street, London, SE18 6NL Tel: (020) 8854 6622

▶ Ross, 3 Wellington Street, Millom, Cumbria, LA18 4DF Tel: (01229) 772551 Fax: (01229) 772510

Rowe Building Services Ltd, Unit 22 Challenge Centre, Sharps Close, Portsmouth, PO3 5RJ Tel: (023) 9265 2142 Fax: (023) 9265 2143

▶ Roxwell Ltd, 10-12 Stirling Road, London, E17 6BT Tel: (020) 8531 7778 Fax: (020) 8531 7761

▶ S A Developments, 5 Peel Street, Failsworth, Manchester, M35 0UF Tel: 0161-681 0511 Fax: 0161-682 3919

▶ S C Building Co., 207-209 Duckworth Street, Darwen, Lancashire, BB3 1AU Tel: (01254) 708338

▶ S D M Building Contractors, 490 Calder Street, Glasgow, G42 0QD Tel: 0141-423 1444 Fax: 0141-423 7774 E-mail: sales@sdm-group.com

▶ S J B Construction Ltd, Station Street, Treherbert, Treorchy, Mid Glamorgan, CF42 5HT Tel: (01443) 773570 Fax: (01443) 771739

▶ S J Quick & Sons, Heather Lane, Canonstown, Hayle, Cornwall, TR27 6NQ Tel: (01736) 740272 Fax: (01736) 741311

▶ S L M, 22 Albion Street, Syston, Leicester, LE7 2AA Tel: 0116-260 4638

▶ S & T Fullers Builders Ltd, The Old Stables, Crescent Road, Faversham, Kent, ME13 7AS Tel: (01795) 532562 Fax: (01795) 531924

▶ Saltash Construction, 110-116 Ormside Street, London, SE15 1TF Tel: (020) 7277 5661 Fax: (020) 7277 5662

▶ Scotia Homes, Anderson Drive, Aberdeen, AB15 6BW Tel: (01224) 323954

▶ Scott Ferguson Building Co., Unit 38 Work West Enterprise Centre, 301 Glen Road, Andersonstown, Belfast, BT11 8BU Tel: (028) 9030 2900 Fax: (028) 9030 2900

▶ Sean Mcglone, 136 Lough Fea Road, Cookstown, County Tyrone, BT80 9ST Tel: (028) 8676 5116 Fax: (028) 8676 5057

Sewell Group plc, Geneva Way, Leads Road, Hull, HU7 0DG Tel: (01482) 701251 Fax: (01482) 707568

▶ Shaw Builders Ltd, Barnfield Road, Tipton, West Midlands, DY4 9DE Tel: 0121-520 5535 Fax: 0121-522 3485

Andrew Shepherd & Sons Ltd, Restenneth House, Old Brechin Road, Forfar, Angus, DD8 3DX Tel: (01307) 474510 Fax: (01307) 474530

▶ Shepherd General Builders Ltd, Restenneth House, Old Brechin Road, Forfar, Angus, DD8 3DX Tel: (01307) 474520 Fax: (01307) 474530

▶ Skill Express Ltd, Unit 17, Enterprise Centre, 1 Dryden Road, Loanhead, Midlothian, EH20 9LZ Tel: 0131-440 9889

Smith, Inchbreck House, Drumlithie, Stonehaven, Kincardineshire, AB39 3YQ Tel: (01569) 740441

▶ Smiths Building Contractors, 36 King Harald Street, Lerwick, Shetland, ZE1 0EQ Tel: (01595) 692251

▶ Sneyd Builders, 113-121 Garner Street, Stoke-on-Trent, ST4 7AX Tel: (01782) 272137 Fax: (01782) 201695

Sol Construction Ltd, Vale Road, Colwick, Nottingham, NG4 2EG Tel: 0115-961 3100 Fax: 0115-961 3400

▶ South Coast Construction, Ford House, 54 High Street, Fordingbridge, Hampshire, SP6 1AX Tel: (01425) 657272 Fax: (01425) 656788

▶ South Haven Construction Ltd, Stockwell Road, Pembroke Dock, Dyfed, SA72 6TQ Tel: (01646) 686838 Fax: (01646) 686296

▶ Speakmans Ltd, Phoenix Way, Burnley, Lancashire, BB11 5SX Tel: (01282) 427529

▶ Speakmans Ltd, Phoenix House, 32 Broughton Street, Manchester, M8 8NN Tel: 0161-830 8300 Fax: 0161-839 3560

▶ Spectrum Services UK Ltd, 11 Sandown Road, Brislington, Bristol, BS4 3PL Tel: 0117-907 1644 Fax: 0117-907 1646

▶ Stacey Construction Ltd, Station Road, Wiveliscombe, Taunton, Somerset, TA4 2LX Tel: (01984) 623802 Fax: (01984) 624497

▶ Stafford Construction Ltd, 107 Bethania Street, Maesteg, Mid Glamorgan, CF34 9EX Tel: (01656) 735235 Fax: (01656) 735235

▶ Stewart McNee (Dunoon) Ltd, Sandbank Industrial Estate, Sandbank, Dunoon, Argyll, PA23 8PB Tel: (01369) 702578

▶ Stradform Ltd, The Conference Centre, East Moors Road, Cardiff, CF24 5SL Tel: (029) 2049 3989

▶ Styan Builders Ltd, Builders Yard, Crabmill Lane, Easingwold, York, YO61 3DE Tel: (01423) 322711 Fax: (01423) 323985 E-mail: styanbuilders@btinternet.com

▶ Styles & Wood, Merlin Court, Atlantic Street, Altrincham, Cheshire, WA14 5NL Tel: 0161-924 1800

▶ Sutcliffe Properties Ltd, Hellifield, Skipton, North Yorkshire, BD23 4JR Tel: (01729) 850817 Fax: (01729) 850323

▶ T A Brennan, Dreadnought, Hazel Road, Southampton, SO19 7GA Tel: (023) 8044 5908 Fax: (023) 8068 5704

▶ T B Williamson, Unit 39 Mayfield Industrial Estate, Dalkeith, Midlothian, EH22 4AD Tel: 0131-654 2900 Fax: 0131-654 2909

▶ T E Leece & Son Ltd, Main Road, Colby, Isle of Man, IM9 4LR Tel: (01624) 832051 Fax: (01624) 834111

▶ T G Cruse, Nettwood Farm, Nett Road, Shrewton, Salisbury, SP3 4HB Tel: (01980) 620369 Fax: (01980) 620821

▶ T Kane, 67 Strabane Road, Newtownstewart, Omagh, County Tyrone, BT78 4JZ Tel: (028) 8166 1600 Fax: (028) 8166 2711

▶ T Livingstone & Sons Builders Ltd, Hillwood, Cameron, St. Andrews, Fife, KY16 8PD Tel: (01334) 840268 Fax: (01334) 840288

▶ T N V Construction Ltd, Kingsbury Works, Kingsbury Road, London, NW9 8UP Tel: (020) 8200 9099

▶ T P Keville Construction Ltd, 83 Paget Road, Leicester, LE3 5HN Tel: 0116-251 4622 Fax: 0116-251 9081

▶ T W Moore & Son, Criton Industrial Estate, Stanford Road, Orsett, Grays, Essex, RM16 3DH Tel: (01375) 892333 Fax: (01375) 892555

▶ Taylor Construction Ltd, 66C Hawthorn Road, Bognor Regis, West Sussex, PO21 2DD Tel: (01243) 829000 Fax: (01243) 829333

▶ Taylor Homes Scotland Ltd, 3 Woodhall Road, Wishaw, Lanarkshire, ML2 8PY Tel: (01698) 385777 Fax: (01698) 384275

▶ Termrim Construction Ltd, 1 Pellon Place Dyson Wood Way, Bradley Business Park, Huddersfield, HD2 1GT Tel: (01484) 547525 E-mail: enquiries@termrim.co.uk

Tolent Construction Ltd, Ravensworth House, Fifth Avenue, Team Valley Trading Estate, Gateshead, Tyne & Wear, NE11 0HF Tel: 0191-487 0505 Fax: 0191-487 2990

▶ Tomlinson Building Ltd, 329 Tyburn Road, Birmingham, B24 8HJ Tel: 0121-327 2660 Fax: 0121-327 3110 E-mail: sales@tomlinsonbuilding.co.uk

▶ Tompkins & May Partnership, Kingsmill Business Park, Chapel Mill Road, Kingston upon Thames, Surrey, KT1 3GZ Tel: (020) 8974 7270 E-mail: sales@tomkinsmay.com

▶ Tonwell Builders Ltd, 1 Union Street, Ramsbottom, Bury, Lancashire, BL0 9AN Tel: (01706) 821000 Fax: (01706) 821500 E-mail: sales@tonwell.com

▶ Topbond Ltd, Oyster Quey, Castle Road, Sittingbourne, Kent, ME10 3EU Tel: (01795) 414050 Fax: (01795) 472022 E-mail: user@topbond.co.uk

▶ Topmarx Ltd, Culverlands Business Park Chardland House, Winchester Road, Shedfield, Southampton, SO32 2JF Tel: (01329) 834400 Fax: (01329) 836789

▶ Torwood Timber Systems Ltd, Royston House, Royston Road, Deans Industrial Estate, Deans, Livingston, West Lothian, EH54 8AH Tel: (01506) 414105

▶ Tradpin Construction Ltd, 14 Hemnall Street, Epping, Essex, CM16 4LW Tel: (01992) 561234

▶ Trent Valley Plumbing & Building Ltd, 113 Trent Boulevard, West Bridgford, Nottingham, NG2 5BN Tel: 0115-982 2332 Fax: 0115-982 0119

▶ Trinity Construction Services, Old Barn, Mountnessing Road, Blackmore, Ingatestone, Essex, CM4 0NX Tel: (01277) 822600 Fax: (01277) 822900 E-mail: sales@style2000.co.uk

▶ Tripstamp Ltd, 56 Pound Farm Road, Chichester, West Sussex, PO19 7PU Tel: (01243) 538912 Fax: (01243) 538910

▶ Tuchan Tolmie, Avalon, Station Road, Conon Bridge, Dingwall, Ross-Shire, IV7 8BJ Tel: (01349) 861356 Fax: (01349) 865393

▶ Turriff Contractors Ltd, Cornfield Road, Turriff, Aberdeenshire, AB53 4BP Tel: (01224) 494148

▶ Underwood Construction Ltd, Commercial House, Fontwell Avenue, Eastergate, Chichester, West Sussex, PO20 3RY Tel: (01243) 545115 Fax: (01243) 545116

▶ Unique Building Contractors, 20 Ivydale Road, Plymouth, PL4 7DF Tel: (01752) 228344 Fax: (01752) 250619

▶ Valley Management & Maintenance Ltd, Eastern House, Porthcurno, Porthcurno, Penzance, Cornwall, TR19 6JT Tel: (01736) 810477 Fax: (01736) 810477

▶ Visqueen Building Products, Albion House, 4 Compton Way, Witney, Oxfordshire, OX28 3AB Tel: (01993) 848800 Fax: (01993) 776233

▶ W A Willson Ltd, 24 Church Street, Hoo, Rochester, Kent, ME3 9AL Tel: (01634) 251096 Fax: (01634) 253845

▶ W B Bradford Measham Ltd, 45 High Street, Measham, Swadlincote, Derbyshire, DE12 7HR Tel: (01530) 272870 Fax: (01530) 271521

▶ W H Catchpole Ltd, Bestwood Works, Drove Road, Portslade, Brighton, BN41 2PA Tel: (01273) 439227

▶ W M Black & Sons Building Contractors Ltd, 540 Gorgie Road, Edinburgh, EH11 3AL Tel: 0131-443 3400 Fax: 0131-443 7775

▶ W M Friel Ltd, Somervell Street, Cambuslang, Glasgow, G72 7EB Tel: 0141-646 1444 Fax: 0141-646 2200

▶ W Vallance, Hoddom Road, Ecclefechan, Lockerbie, Dumfriesshire, DG11 3BY Tel: (01576) 300279

▶ W W Pert Construction Ltd, Broomfield Industrial Estate, Broomfield Road, Montrose, Angus, DD10 8SY Tel: (01674) 673883 Fax: (01674) 678533

▶ Waite Property, St. Julians Avenue, St. Peter Port, Guernsey, GY1 1WB Tel: (01481) 722121 Fax: (01481) 722100

Walker Group Scotland Ltd, Westerwood House, Royston Road, Deans, Livingston, West Lothian, EH54 8AH Tel: (01506) 413101 Fax: (01506) 414843 E-mail: info@walkergroup.co.uk

▶ Walkplace Ltd, The Byre, Lower End Farm, Leafield, Witney, Oxfordshire, OX29 9QG Tel: (01993) 878550 Fax: (01993) 878036

▶ Ward Building Services Ltd, 223 Clepington Road, Dundee, DD3 7SZ Tel: (01382) 884123 Fax: (01382) 884248

▶ Wates Construction Ltd, Royds Hall Road, Leeds, LS12 6AJ Tel: 0113-231 1880 Fax: 0113-231 9994

▶ WCL Ltd, 1 Oaks Drive, Newmarket, Suffolk, CB8 7SX Tel: (01638) 666006 Fax: (01638) 667245 E-mail: wcl.enquiries@uk.taylorwoodroe.com

▶ Wharton Construction Ltd, Kellaw Road, Darlington, County Durham, DL1 4YA Tel: (01325) 288742 E-mail: enquiries@whartonconstructionltd.co.uk

▶ White & Fensome Building Contractors, 2 Hewlett Road, Luton, LU3 2RP Tel: (01582) 594766 Fax: (01582) 594866

▶ William Shanks Construction, 139 Greengairs Road, Greengairs, Airdrie, Lanarkshire, ML6 7SY Tel: (01236) 830417 Fax: (01236) 830742

▶ William Skinner & Son, Highfield, St. Quivox, Ayr, KA6 5HQ Tel: (0845) 0519060 Fax: (01292) 671133

▶ Williams, Cowlairs, Nottingham, NG5 9RA Tel: 0115-975 5888 Fax: 0115-974 4777

▶ Wooldridge & Simpson Ltd, The Gables, Woodstock Road, Yarnton, Kidlington, Oxfordshire, OX5 1PH Tel: (01865) 370700 Fax: (01865) 370598

▶ Wright Projects Ltd, 79 Back Sneddon Street, Paisley, Renfrewshire, PA3 2BT Tel: 0141-887 7597 Fax: 0141-887 7598

▶ Young Wilson & Cunningham Ltd, 40 Rogart Street, Glasgow, G40 2AA Tel: 0141-550 0984 Fax: 0141-554 4143

BUILDING SERVICES (AUTOMATIC) CONTROL SYSTEM, *See Control Systems etc*

BUILDING SERVICES CONSULTANCY

▶ Crawt Simpkins Partnership, 71 Loudoun Road, London, NW8 0DQ Tel: (020) 7372 1881 Fax: (020) 7372 1991

▶ Grove Contractors, 16 Brookside Way, Kingswinford, West Midlands, DY6 9AW Tel: (01384) 277969 Fax: (01384) 277969 E-mail: mail@grovecontractors.co.uk

▶ Insignia Consulting, Knights View, 104 The Street, Little Waltham, Chelmsford, CM3 3NT Tel: (01245) 360121 Fax: (01245) 360614 E-mail: cad@insignia-consulting.com

BUILDING SERVICES CONTROL OR MONITORING EQUIPMENT

Honeywell Control Systems Ltd, Honeywell House Arlington Business Park, Downshire Way, Bracknell, Berkshire, RG12 1EB Tel: (01344) 656000 Fax: (01344) 656240 E-mail: uk.infocentre@honeywell.com

Serck Controls Ltd, Stonebridge Trading Estate, Rowley Drive, Coventry, CV3 4FH Tel: (024) 7651 1069 Fax: (024) 7630 2437 E-mail: sales@serck-controls.co.uk

BUILDING SERVICES ENGINEERS

Air Conditioning (Jersey), 9 New Street, St Helier, Jersey, JE2 3RA Tel: (01534) 870022 Fax: (01534) 870044

Argent F M Ltd, Unit 8, Penarth Centre, London, SE15 1TW Tel: (0870) 8900399 Fax: (0870) 8900398 E-mail: info@argent.fm.co.uk

M.E.C. Bird Associates Ltd, Horsleys Green, High Wycombe, Buckinghamshire, HP14 3UX Tel: (01494) 482348 Fax: (01494) 483348 E-mail: mecbird@aol.com

Borahurst Ltd, Devonshire House, 31 Holmesdale Road, Reigate, Surrey, RH2 0BJ Tel: (01737) 221733 Fax: (01737) 223512 E-mail: info@borahurst.com

Bower Fuller Ltd, 6 Bermuda Road, Ransomes Industrial Estate, Ipswich, IP3 9RU Tel: (01473) 272277 Fax: (01473) 270100 E-mail: services@bowerfuller.co.uk

C A Sothers Ltd, 156 Hockley Hill, Birmingham, B18 5AN Tel: 0121-554 2054 Fax: 0121-554 4090 E-mail: cas@sothers.com

BUILDING SERVICES ENGINEERS - *continued*

C D Stone Dunstable Ltd, Fairway Works, Southfields Road, Dunstable, Bedfordshire, LU6 3EP Tel: (01582) 605353 Fax: (01582) 660103

Capita Building Services, Salter House, 263-265 High Street, Berkhamsted, Hertfordshire, HP4 1AB Tel: (01442) 872121 Fax: (01442) 866565

Capon Computer Environmental Services Ltd, 149 Putnoe Street, Bedford, MK41 8JR Tel: (01234) 359791 Fax: (01234) 269995

Carter Fielding Associates Ltd, 19 Dryden Court, Parkleys, Richmond, Surrey, TW10 5LJ Tel: (020) 8546 7211 Fax: (020) 8546 7008 E-mail: surveyors@carterfielding.co.uk

Charter Building Services Ltd, Mayplace Road East, Bexleyheath, Kent, DA7 6EJ Tel: (01322) 558011 Fax: (01322) 520282 E-mail: mail@charter.uk.com

▶ CMB Fylde Engineering, 3 Skyways Commercial Campus, Amy Johnson Way, Blackpool, FY4 2RP Tel: (01253) 298366 Fax: (01253) 298377

Corinium Building Services, 25 Cotswold Avenue, Cirencester, Gloucestershire, GL7 1XW Tel: (01285) 641200 Fax: (01285) 641200 E-mail: cbsciren@fsbdial.co.uk

Cudd Bentley Consulting, Ashurst Manor, Church Lane, Ascot, Berkshire, SL5 7DD Tel: (01344) 628821 Fax: (01344) 623448 E-mail: reception@ascot.cbp.co.uk

Cudd Bentley Consulting Ltd, Suite 1 Shelly Cresent Centre, 20 Farm House Way, Monkspath, Solihull, West Midlands, B90 4EH Tel: 0121-711 4343 Fax: 0121-711 3535

▶ D B Consulting Ltd, 109 Blackthorn Road, Southampton, SO19 7LP Tel: (07717) 453409 E-mail: info@electricalconsultant.org

Dave Dickinson & Associates Ltd, Ahed House, Sandbeds Trading Estate, Ossett, West Yorkshire, WF5 9ND Tel: (01924) 265757 Fax: (01924) 275117 E-mail: enquiries@ddaltd.co.uk

Drake & Scull Engineering Ltd, Drake Scull Ho, 86 Talbot Rd, Old Trafford, Manchester, M16 0QD Tel: 0161-874 4800 Fax: 0161-874 4900

Emcor Facilities Services Ltd, 1 Thameside Centre, Kew Bridge Road, Brentford, Middlesex, TW8 0HF Tel: (020) 8380 6700 Fax: (020) 8380 6701

Evans Mechanical Services Ltd, Derby House, 29 Castle Street, Caergwrle, Wrexham, Clwyd, LL12 9AD Tel: (01978) 760000 Fax: (01978) 761082 E-mail: enquiries@evans-mech.co.uk

F P Hurley & Sons Ltd, Queens Road, Bridgend Industrial Estate, Bridgend, Mid Glamorgan, CF31 3UR Tel: (01656) 661151 Fax: (01656) 645477 E-mail: bridgend@fphurley.co.uk

Frasc Construction Ltd, Orchard House, Ellenbrook Road, Manchester, M28 1GB Tel: 0161-702 5500 Fax: 0161-702 5502

▶ Freeman Associates, 92 Church Street, Swinton, Mexborough, South Yorkshire, S64 8DQ Tel: (01709) 578078 Fax: (01709) 578153 E-mail: designs@freemanassociates.co.uk

William Freer Ltd, 350-360 Melton Road, Leicester, LE4 7SL Tel: 0116-268 9660 Fax: 0116-268 9650

▶ G P (M & E) Services Ltd, 1-3 Market Square, Bishop's Stortford, Hertfordshire, CM23 3UP Tel: (01279) 466738

Gallagher Tom Ltd, 156-158 Derby Street, Bolton, BL3 6JR Tel: (01204) 389792 Fax: (01204) 370929 E-mail: tomgallltd@aol.com

Gratte Brothers Ltd, 2 Regents Wharf, All Saints Street, London, N1 9RL Tel: (020) 7837 6433 Fax: (020) 7837 6779E-mail: info@gratte.com

▶ Guardian Environmental, 117 Clophill Road, Maulden, Bedford, MK45 2AE Tel: (01525) 862528 Fax: (01525) 862163 E-mail: val.barnes@guardian.uk.com

H & C Building Services, Group House, 52 Sutton Court Road, Sutton, Surrey, SM1 4SL Tel: (020) 8915 0909 Fax: (020) 8915 0734 E-mail: info@handcgroup.com

Haden Young Ltd, 11 Britannia Road, Patchway, Bristol, BS34 5TD Tel: 0117-969 3911 Fax: 0117-979 8711 E-mail: bristol@hadenyoung.co.uk

Hannaford Upright Building Services Consulting Engineers, Stuart House, 80-82 Maybury Road, Woking, Surrey, GU21 5JH Tel: (01483) 730221 Fax: (01483) 773970

Heap & Digby Ltd, 6a Park Road, Oxted, Surrey, RH8 0AL Tel: (01883) 717102 Fax: (01883) 381405 E-mail: sales@heapdigby.co.uk

I E I Ltd, Southern Cross, Basing View, Basingstoke, Hampshire, RG21 4HG Tel: (01256) 352361 Fax: (01256) 470259 E-mail: gen@iei-engineers.com

Interserve Engineering Services Ltd, Intersection House, 110-120 Birmingham Road, West Bromwich, West Midlands, B70 6RP Tel: 0121-500 5000 Fax: 0121-525 5574 E-mail: info@interserve-eng.com

Peter Jay & Partners, 176A Sutherland Ave, London, W9 1HR Tel: (020) 7286 6011 Fax: (020) 7286 6088

Jovic Plant Ltd, Mayes Lane, Sandon, Chelmsford, CM2 7RP Tel: (01245) 224211 Fax: (01245) 224258 E-mail: sales@jovicplant.co.uk

Kestrel Building Services Ltd, George Street, High Wycombe, Buckinghamshire, HP11 2RZ Tel: (01494) 474398 Fax: (01494) 472540 E-mail: info@kestreloffice.com

Knights Warner Kings Lynn Ltd, Austin Fields, King's Lynn, Norfolk, PE30 1PL Tel: (01553) 773929 Fax: (01553) 691532 E-mail: knights-warner@btconnect.com

Leivers Associates, 6 Clinton Avenue, Nottingham, NG5 1AW Tel: 0115-960 3548 Fax: 0115-969 1147 E-mail: sales@1eiversassociates.co.uk

M E H Group Services P.L.C., 1 Thornham Grove, Stratford, London, E15 1DN Tel: (020) 8534 4441 Fax: (020) 8519 1933 E-mail: mwood@mehltd.co.uk

Mca Consulting Engineers Ltd, Newhouse Farm Business Centre, Horsham, West Sussex, RH12 4RU Tel: (01293) 851490 Fax: (01293) 852156 E-mail: sales@mcaltd.co.uk

Mala Electrical Ltd, 126 Petherton Road, London, N5 2RT Tel: (020) 7359 3925 Fax: (020) 7359 4672 E-mail: mala@mala.co.uk

Martech Design Services, 109 London Road, Bagshot, Surrey, GU19 5DH Tel: (01276) 476922 Fax: (01276) 451622 E-mail: office@martechds.co.uk

Medtec Design Services Ltd, Unit 34, JS White Eastate, Cowes, Isle Of Wight, PO31 7LP Tel: (01983) 294974 Fax: (01983) 290255 E-mail: design@medtec.co.uk

N A Cullen & Co. Ltd, Hayhills Road, Silsden, Keighley, West Yorkshire, BD20 9NE Tel: (01535) 654968 Fax: (01535) 655590 E-mail: nacul@lineone.net

Norland Managed Services Ltd, 454-460 Old Kent Road, London, SE1 5AG Tel: (020) 7231 8888 Fax: (020) 7231 7547 E-mail: reception@norlandmanagedservices.co.uk

North Sea Ventilation Ltd, West Carr Lane, Hull, HU7 0BW Tel: (01482) 834050 Fax: (01482) 834060 E-mail: enquiries@nsv.co.uk

▶ Now Recruitment Ltd, 3 Chester Street, Newcastle upon Tyne, NE2 1AT Tel: 0191-209 1900 Fax: 0191-209 1911

Pedler Robin, Empire Buildings, 47-49 Church Street, Stoke-on-Trent, ST4 1DQ Tel: (01782) 749749 Fax: (01782) 747840 E-mail: sales@sgbworldservice.com

Project Co-Ordination Ltd, 34 Lower Addiscombe Road, Croydon, CR0 6AA Tel: (020) 8686 6844 Fax: (020) 8686 6815 E-mail: projectco@aol.com

R E Gore Building Services Ltd, Unit 1c Skillion Business Park, Thames Road, Barking, Essex, IG11 0JP Tel: (020) 8594 3700 Fax: (020) 8594 3704 E-mail: sales@regore.com

R E Green, Gubberford House, Gubberford Lane, Garstang, Preston, PR3 1PS Tel: (01995) 605318 E-mail: rigreen@talk21.com

R J Edwards, Unit 15 Ashcroft Road, Knowsley Industrial Park, Liverpool, L33 7TW Tel: 0151-545 1060 Fax: 0151-545 1061

R M J M Ltd, 83 Paul Street, London, EC2A 4UT Tel: (020) 7549 8900 Fax: (020) 7250 3131 E-mail: london@rmjm.com

Chris Reading Associates, 6 Charfield Close, Winchester, Hampshire, SO22 4PZ Tel: (07802) 618656 Fax: (01962) 861496 E-mail: consult@cvrassociates.freeserve.co.uk

Reycol Heating Co. Ltd, 15 Park Place, Newdigate Road, Harefield, Uxbridge, Middlesex, UB9 6EJ Tel: (01923) 720900 Fax: (01895) 824699

Shepherd Engineering Services Ltd, Mill Mount, York, YO24 1GH Tel: (01904) 629151 Fax: (01904) 610175

Sherwood Consulting Engineers, 26 Kings Meadow, Rainworth, Mansfield, Nottinghamshire, NG21 0FG Tel: (01623) 431128 Fax: (01623) 431129 E-mail: info@sherwoodce.com

Stiell Ltd, Cannock Side Park, Uddingston, Glasgow, G71 5PW Tel: (01698) 805100 Fax: (01698) 805111 E-mail: ho@stiell.co.uk

Townley Hughes & Co. Ltd, Unit 7 Meadow La Industrial Park, Ellesmere Port, CH65 4TY Tel: 0151-357 1800 Fax: 0151-357 2117 E-mail: townleyhughes@aol.com

Traditional Structures Contracts Ltd, Landywood Lane, Cheslyn Hay, Walsall, WS6 7AJ Tel: (01922) 414145 Fax: (01922) 416958

W S P Group P.L.C., Buchanan House, 24-30 Holborn, London, EC1N 2HS Tel: (020) 7314 5000 Fax: (020) 7314 5111 E-mail: info@wspgroup.com

BUILDING SERVICES ESTIMATING CONSULTANCY

Baker Wilkins & Smith, 57-63 Church Road, London, SW19 5DQ Tel: (020) 8406 4422 Fax: (020) 8944 6767 E-mail: dedwards@bakerwilkins.com

Callworth Ltd, 294 High Street, Rochester, Kent, ME1 1HS Tel: (01634) 402381 Fax: (01634) 201770 E-mail: pj.crook@btinternet.com

Cameron Durley Consulting, 110 Main Road, Sidcup, Kent, DA14 6NG Tel: (020) 8309 2400 Fax: (020) 8309 2401 E-mail: sidcup@camerondurley.co.uk

Ferrosteel (Structures) Ltd, 60 Lichfield St, Walsall, WS4 2BX Tel: (01922) 637467 Fax: (01922) 720364

Hannaford Upright Building Services Consulting Engineers, Stuart House, 80-82 Maybury Road, Woking, Surrey, GU21 5JH Tel: (01483) 730221 Fax: (01483) 773970

Peter Jay & Partners, 176A Sutherland Ave, London, W9 1HR Tel: (020) 7286 6011 Fax: (020) 7286 6088

▶ QSserv Ltd, 5 Joan Avenue, Greasby, Wirral, Merseyside, CH49 2PD Tel: (07747) 533644 Fax: (0871) 2424992 E-mail: i.lee@tiscali.co.uk

BUILDING SERVICES MAINTENANCE OR REPAIR

▶ AmG - Tony Ganchev, 50 Vulcan Close, London, UK, E6 5NY Tel: 07919 446843 Fax: 0207 4769123 E-mail: amgdirector@yahoo.co.uk

Arnold B Johnston, Dean Road, Yate, Bristol, BS37 5NR Tel: (01454) 316175 Fax: (01454) 884455 E-mail: mail@erh.co.uk

Bacogold (1965) Ltd, 18a Malyons Rd, London, SE13 7XG Tel: (020) 8690 4665

Beoley Building Services, 19 Druids Lane, Birmingham, B14 5SL Tel: 0121-436 5717 Fax: (01527) 597103

C L C Contractors Ltd, Northbrook Industrial Estate, Vincent Avenue, Southampton, SO16 6PQ Tel: (023) 8070 1111 Fax: (023) 8070 1171 E-mail: mail@clcgroup.com

Carter Fielding Associates Ltd, 19 Dryden Court, Parkleys, Richmond, Surrey, TW10 5LJ Tel: (020) 8546 7211 Fax: (020) 8546 7008 E-mail: surveyors@carterfielding.co.uk

CDT Response, Bourne Road Industrial Park, Bourne Road, Dartford, DA1 4BZ Tel: (01322) 555888 Fax: (01322) 555004 E-mail: helpdesk@responseuk.org

Citycare, Mile Cross Road, Norwich, NR3 2DY Tel: (01603) 484868 Fax: (01603) 496725

Comserve Ltd, Comserve House, 54 Watling Street, Radlett, Hertfordshire, WD7 7NN Tel: (01923) 853269 Fax: (01923) 857370 E-mail: service@comserve.co.uk

Dalkia, The Connect Centre, Kingston CR, Portsmouth, PO2 8AD Tel: (0800) 0853208 Fax: (023) 9262 9656 E-mail: enquiries@dalkia.co.uk

Essex & Anglia Preservation Ltd, 24 Church End Lane, Runwell, Wickford, Essex, SS11 7JQ Tel: (0800) 0851695 Fax: (0800) 0851695 E-mail: info@essexandanglia.co.uk

Grange Engineering, Trenholme Bar, Northallerton, North Yorkshire, DL6 3LE Tel: (01642) 706074 Fax: (01642) 701641

GSH Ltd, GSH House, Forge Lane, Stoke-on-Trent, ST1 5PZ Tel: (01782) 200400 Fax: (01782) 285552 E-mail: vacancies@gshgroup.com

▶ H & H Property Services, 3 Whittle Road, Ferndown Industrial Estate, Wimborne, Dorset, BH21 7RJ Tel: (07915) 086899 Fax: 01202 877064 E-mail: hhpropertyservices@tiscali.co.uk

Hambridge Investments Newbury, 4 Vulcan Close, Sandhurst, Berkshire, GU47 9DD Tel: (01252) 860043 Fax: (01252) 890154

Housing Direct, Sandwell Road, West Bromwich, West Midlands, B70 8TB Tel: 0121-569 6038 Fax: 0121-569 6041

Integral, Norris House, Crawhall Road, Newcastle upon Tyne, NE1 2BB Tel: 0191-261 1071 Fax: 0191-232 8069 E-mail: mnew@integral.co.uk

Interserve Engineering Services Ltd, Intersection House, 110-120 Birmingham Road, West Bromwich, West Midlands, B70 6RP Tel: 0121-500 5000 Fax: 0121-525 5574 E-mail: info@interserve-eng.com

Interserve Holdings plc, Tilbury House, Ruscombe Park, Reading, RG10 9JU Tel: 0118-932 0123 Fax: 0118-932 0206 E-mail: info@interserveplc.co.uk

John C Lillywhite Ltd, Gravel Lane, Chichester, West Sussex, PO19 8PQ Tel: (01243) 781911 Fax: (01243) 780168 E-mail: jcl.builders@virgin.net

Henry Jones & Sons Ltd, Wyvern, 1 Brynhedydd Road, Rhyl, Denbighshire, LL18 3UH Tel: (01745) 351314 Fax: (01745) 351314 E-mail: office@hjs1923.f9.co.uk

Kier Managed Services Ltd, Conway House, St. Mellons Business Park, Fortran Road, Cardiff, CF3 0EY Tel: (029) 2036 1616 Fax: (029) 2036 2303 E-mail: enquiries@kier.co.uk

▶ MEP ASSOCIATES, Pegasus, London Road, Crowborough, East Sussex, TN6 2TX Tel: 01892 669978 Fax: 08712 425325 E-mail: lbassett@mepa.co.uk

OilanHeat (Maintenance) Ltd, 161 High Street, Aldershot, Hampshire, GU11 1TT Tel: (01252) 329789 Fax: (01252) 342804 E-mail: ac@lowbeck.com

Project Co-Ordination Ltd, 34 Lower Addiscombe Road, Croydon, CR0 6AA Tel: (020) 8686 6844 Fax: (020) 8686 6815 E-mail: projectco@aol.com

S C Grover Ltd, Grover House Burntmill Industrial Estate, Elizabeth Way, Harlow, Essex, CM20 2JH Tel: (01279) 420763 Fax: (01279) 416535

▶ Smith Property Maintenance, 129 Albany Road, Hornchurch, Essex, RM12 4AQ Tel: (01708) 477764 Fax: (01708) 442100 E-mail: lg_smiths@hotmail.com

Swift Building Maintenance Services Ltd, 74 High St Colliers Wood, London, SW19 2BY Tel: (020) 8288 0919 Fax: (020) 8715 9963 E-mail: swift@collierswood98.freeserve.co.uk

T & E Neville Ltd, Neville House, 301 Marsh Road, Luton, LU3 2RZ Tel: (01582) 573496 Fax: (01582) 490216 E-mail: enquiries@nevilleconstruction.co.uk

Unicorn Building & Maintenance Ltd, Biltam Farm, Stan Hill, Charlwood, Horley, Surrey, RH6 0EP Tel: (01293) 862775 Fax: (01293) 863205

BUILDING SITE TEMPORARY ELECTRICAL EQUIPMENT

British Energy Ltd, 3 Redwood Crescent, East Kilbride, Glasgow, G74 5PR Tel: (01355) 262000 Fax: (01355) 262626

Electrosite UK Ltd, Easton Lane, Bozeat, Wellingborough, Northamptonshire, NN29 7NN Tel: (01933) 665022 Fax: (01933) 665520 E-mail: electrosite@kbnet.net

KES Power & Light Ltd, Stanton Road, Southampton, SO15 4HU Tel: (023) 8070 4703 Fax: (023) 8070 1430 E-mail: sakes@kes.co.uk

BUILDING STEAM CLEANING CONTRACTORS, *See Building Exterior Cleaning/Washing etc*

BUILDING STEEL FRAME CONSTRUCTORS OR FABRICATORS

A M P S Fabrications Ltd, Arch 36 Miles Street, London, SW8 1RY Tel: (020) 7587 1444 Fax: (020) 7587 5141 E-mail: ampsfabs@aol.com

Allerton Engineering Ltd, Allerton House, Thurston Road, Northallerton, North Yorkshire, DL6 2NA Tel: (01609) 774471 Fax: (01609) 780364 E-mail: sales@allertonengineering.co.uk

Barnet Metal Engineering Co. Ltd, Stirling Works, Tewin Road, Welwyn Garden City, Hertfordshire, AL7 1AG Tel: (01707) 324327 Fax: (01707) 371375

Caunton Engineering Ltd, Moorgreen Industrial Park, Engine Lane, Newthorpe, Nottingham, NG16 3QU Tel: (01773) 531111 Fax: (01773) 532020 E-mail: sales@caunton.co.uk

Cheshire Fabrications, Villa Farm, Sound Lane, Sound, Nantwich, Cheshire, CW5 8BE Tel: (01270) 780707 Fax: (01270) 780707

Corfix Structures Ltd, No 3 Hoobrook Industrial Estate, Kidderminster, Worcestershire, DY10 1HY Tel: (01562) 60226 Fax: (01562) 60227

Craufurd Engineering Services Ltd, Unit 4-5 Lower Mount Farm, Cookham, Maidenhead, Berkshire, SL6 9EE Tel: (01628) 532288 Fax: (01628) 532424

D A Green & Sons Ltd, High Road, Whaplode, Spalding, Lincolnshire, PE12 6TL Tel: (01406) 370585 Fax: (01406) 370766 E-mail: sales@dagreen.co.uk

DeVille & Lear Ltd, Mill Lane Works, Mill Lane, Roston, Ashbourne, Derbyshire, DE6 2EE Tel: (01335) 324302 Fax: (01335) 324568 E-mail: info@devilleandlear.co.uk

Fiscol Engineering, 85 Greenland CR, Southall, Middlesex, UB2 5ES Tel: (020) 8574 1065 Fax: (020) 8813 9780

Frank H Dale Ltd, Mill Street, Leominster, Herefordshire, HR6 8EF Tel: (01568) 612212 Fax: (01568) 619402 E-mail: sales@fhdale.co.uk

Haley Engineering Ltd, Bellcombe, Brent Road, East Brent, Highbridge, Somerset, TA9 4DB Tel: (01278) 760591 Fax: (01278) 760587 E-mail: sales@haleyengineering.co.uk

Henry Smith Constructional Engineer Ltd, Wharton Steel Works, Deakins Road, Winsford, Cheshire, CW7 3BW Tel: (01606) 592121 Fax: (01606) 559134 E-mail: admin@hs-steel.co.uk

Ivan J Cooper Moorside Ltd, Moorside Works, Ellastone Road, Cauldon Low, Stoke-on-Trent, ST10 3ET Tel: (01538) 702738 Fax: (01538) 702662E-mail: brenda-prince@btconnect.com

K & M Engineering Shropshire Ltd, Sarn Works, Westbury, Shrewsbury, SY5 9DA Tel: (01743) 884340 Fax: (01743) 884021 E-mail: kmeng@halfwayhse.fsnet.co.uk

Kitpac Buildings Ltd, Shares Hill, Great Saredon, Wolverhampton, WV10 7LN Tel: (01922) 415425 Fax: (01922) 414246 E-mail: lisa@kitpac.freeserve.co.uk

Leominster Construction Co. Ltd, Leominster Industrial Estate, Southern Avenue, Leominster, Herefordshire, HR6 0QF Tel: (01568) 612943 Fax: (01568) 612910

Maldon Marine Ltd, 16 West Station Yard, Spital Road, Maldon, Essex, CM9 6TW Tel: (01621) 859000 Fax: (01621) 858935 E-mail: info@maldon-marine.co.uk

Mecright Contractors Ltd, Unit 10 Prospect Business Park, Longford Road, Cannock, Staffordshire, WS11 0LG Tel: (01543) 469222 Fax: (01543) 469444 E-mail: patrick@mecright.co.uk

Newstyle Fabrications, Ifton Industrial Estate, St. Martins, Oswestry, Shropshire, SY11 3DA Tel: (01691) 773303 Fax: (01691) 773303

Oswestry Industrial Buildings Ltd, Maesbury Road, Oswestry, Shropshire, SY10 8HA Tel: (01691) 661596 Fax: (01691) 661597

Peter Hope Metals Ltd, 2 Grange Road Business Park, Grange Road, Batley, West Yorkshire, WF17 6LL Tel: (01924) 440055 Fax: (01924) 442200E-mail: peterhope.metalsltd@virgin.net

Proseal, 18 Terrace Row, Billington, Clitheroe, Lancashire, BB7 9NX Tel: (01254) 822699 Fax: (01254) 822699

BUILDING STEEL FRAME CONSTRUCTORS OR FABRICATORS – *continued*

Robinson Construction, Wincanton Close, Derby, DE24 8NJ Tel: (01332) 574711 Fax: (01332) 861401 E-mail: sales@robinsons.com

Robinsons Scotland Ltd, Broomhouses 2 Industrial Estate, Old Glasgow Road, Lockerbie, Dumfriesshire, DG11 2SD Tel: (01576) 205905 Fax: (01576) 204466 E-mail: sales@rbscotland.com

Shufflebottom Ltd, Heol Parc Mawr, Cross Hands Industrial Estate, Cross Hands, Llanelli, Dyfed, SA14 6RE Tel: (01269) 831831 Fax: (01269) 831031 E-mail: sales@shufflebottom.co.uk

South Lincs Construction Ltd, Bars Bridge, Bourne Road, Spalding, Lincolnshire, PE11 3NQ Tel: (01775) 640555 Fax: (01775) 640679 E-mail: info@aldesignandbuild.com

Stuart Building Services, Duncrub, Dunning, Perth, PH2 0QN Tel: (01764) 684840 Fax: (01764) 684841 E-mail: info@stuartbuildingservices.co.uk

Thircon Ltd, Hambleton Steel Works, York Road, Thirsk, North Yorkshire, YO7 3BT Tel: (01845) 522760 Fax: (01845) 524146

▶ Tom Lee, Unit 6 Littleton Trading Estate, Littleton Lane, Shepperton, Middlesex, TW17 0NF Tel: 01932 569939 Fax: 01932 569939E-mail: info@media-construction.co.uk

Valley Reinforcements Ltd, Endle Street, Southampton, SO14 5FZ Tel: (023) 8022 6126 Fax: (023) 8033 8832 E-mail: andy@vrconstruction.f2s.com

Wytkin Services, Waterswallows Industrial Park, Waterswallows Road, Buxton, Derbyshire, SK17 7JB Tel: (01298) 70069 Fax: (01298) 70069 E-mail: Wytkinservices@aol.com

BUILDING SURVEYORS

▶ Asset Construction Consultants, 1 Dittons Mews, St. Leonards-on-Sea, East Sussex, TN38 9TQ Tel: (01424) 853754 Fax: (01424) 851210 E-mail: matt@assetconstructionconsultants.co.uk

John Bell Surveyor & Valuer, The Corner House, Tuttington Road, Aylsham, Norwich, NR11 6TA Tel: (01263) 734403

C N P Ltd, Basilica, 2 King Charles Street, Leeds, LS1 6LS Tel: 0113-220 7330 Fax: 0113-266 0022

Cooke & Arkwright, 7-8 Windsor Place, Cardiff, CF10 3SX Tel: (029) 2034 6346 Fax: (029) 2034 6300 E-mail: sales@coark.com

▶ Future Inclusive Access Consultants, 90 Station Road, Kegworth, Derby, DE74 2FR Tel: (01509) 557848 Fax: (01509) 557848 E-mail: info@futureinclusive.co.uk

▶ Neil Harris, 3 Wethersfield Road, Oxton, Prenton, Merseyside, CH43 9UN Tel: (0800) 0838818 E-mail: neil@ricsonline.org

Henry Boot Construction, 71 Ardwick Green North, Manchester, M12 6FX Tel: 0161-272 6162 Fax: 0161-272 7334

Highline Access Ltd, PO Box 2089, Bristol, BS99 7SZ Tel: (0870) 0435531 Fax: (0870) 0435532 E-mail: enquiries@highlineaccess.com

I R T Surveys Ltd, Unit D, Software Media Centre, Prospect House, Technology Park, Dundee, DD2 1TY Tel: (01382) 598510 Fax: (01382) 598533 E-mail: info@irtsurveys.co.uk

King Sturge, 30 Warwick Street, London, W1B 5NH Tel: (020) 7493 4933 Fax: (020) 7409 0469 E-mail: firstname.surname@kingsturge.com

▶ Mag Surveys, Europa Business Park, 46 Bird Hall Lane Unit F-10, Stockport, Cheshire, SK3 0XA Tel: 0161-718 8213 Fax: 0161-718 8213 E-mail: greg@magsurveys.co.uk

▶ Martin Aitken Associates, Aspire Business Centre, 16 Farmeloan Road, Rutherglen, Glasgow, G73 1DL Tel: 0141-647 0101 Fax: 0141-647 0107 E-mail: martinaitkenassociates@btconnect.com

MKA Projects Ltd, 15/20 Churchill Square, Kings Hill, West Malling, Kent, ME19 4YU Tel: (01732) 897917 Fax: (01732) 897927 E-mail: info@mka-projects.co.uk

▶ Now Recruitment Ltd, 3 Chester Street, Newcastle upon Tyne, NE2 1AT Tel: 0191-209 1900 Fax: 0191-209 1911

▶ Si Property Consultants Ltd, 39 Hermitage Way, Stanmore, Middlesex, HA7 2AX Tel: (020) 8930 1684 Fax: 020 84242557 E-mail: office@siproperty.co.uk

Survey Supplies Ltd, 1-5 Bankfield Drive, Spondon, Derby, DE21 7QZ Tel: (01332) 675888 Fax: (01332) 661381 E-mail: info@surveysupplies.co.uk

▶ P.A. Taylor Plans, The Sand Quarry, Hougher Wall Road, Audley, Stoke-On-Trent, ST7 8JA Tel: (01782) 721111 Fax: (05600) 766363

Topcon Great Britain Ltd, Topcon House, Kennet Side, Newbury, Berkshire, RG14 5PX Tel: (01635) 551120 Fax: (01635) 551170

▶ Vector Surveys, 24 Edwin Street, London, E16 1QA Tel: (020) 7474 3991 Fax: (020) 7474 3991 E-mail: pjwarr@btopenwolrd.com

Watts & Partners, 2-12 Montgomery Street, Belfast, BT1 4NX Tel: (028) 9024 8222 Fax: (028) 9024 8007 E-mail: mail.belfast@watts.co.uk

▶ Watts & Partners, 60 Fountain Street, Manchester, M2 2FE Tel: 0161-831 6180 Fax: 0161-834 7750 E-mail: mail.manchester@watts.co.uk

BUILDING SYSTEM OR UNIT

▶ Alloway Timber Southern Ltd, Forval Close, Wandle Way, Mitcham, Surrey, CR4 4NE Tel: (020) 8640 5544 Fax: (020) 8640 5599 E-mail: sales@allowaytimber.com

Bellman Carter 2000 Ltd, Rear of, 358-374 Grand Drive, London, SW20 9NG Tel: (020) 8540 1372 Fax: (020) 8544 9424

▶ Cornish Lime Co., Brims Park, Old Callywith Road, Bodmin, Cornwall, PL31 2DZ Tel: (01208) 77287 Fax: (01208) 73744 E-mail: sales@cornishlime.co.uk

Design & Materials Ltd, Lawn Road, Carlton-In-Lindrick, Worksop, Nottinghamshire, S81 9LB Tel: (01909) 730333 Fax: (01909) 730605

Jorosa Ltd, 22 The Hive Industrial Estate, Hockley, Factory Road, Birmingham, B18 5JU Tel: 0121-507 1313 Fax: 0121-507 1440 E-mail: sales@jorosa.com

BUILDING SYSTEM OR UNIT COMPONENTS

Wolseley Centre, Willow Lane, Lune Industrial Estate, Lancaster, LA1 5NA Tel: (01524) 67227 Fax: (01524) 844101

BUILDING TO BUILDING WIRELESS INFRARED DATA LINKS

▶ WaveZone Ltd, 834 Stockport Rd, Manchester, M19 3AW Tel: (0845) 1668443 Fax: 0161-257 3248 E-mail: info@wavezone.co.uk

BUILDING WATER SYSTEM ENGINEERING

▶ Concrete Waterproofing, PO Box 864, Guildford, Surrey, GU2 9US Tel: (0870) 7621507 Fax: (0870) 7621507 E-mail: info@concretewaterproofing.co.uk

RPS Consulting Engineers, Elmwood House, 74 Boucher Road, Belfast, BT12 6RZ Tel: (028) 9066 7914 Fax: (028) 9066 8286 E-mail: belfast@rpsgroup.com

BUILDING WATERPROOFING CONTRACTORS

Cemplas Ltd, Holbrook House, 72 Lower Addiscombe Road, Croydon, CR9 6AD Tel: (020) 8654 3149 Fax: (020) 8656 6984 E-mail: info@cemplas.co.uk

▶ Impermia, 1 shaftesbury Gdns, London, NW10 6LP Tel: (020) 8961 5259 Fax: (020) 8961 5359 E-mail: info@impermia.co.uk

Lambert Contracts & Coatings Ltd, Hamilton House, Blackhall Lane, Paisley, Renfrewshire, PA1 1TA Tel: 0141-840 1444 Fax: 0141-848 9593 E-mail: sales@lambertcontracts.co.uk

Roofproof Ltd, The Reach, Remenham, Henley-on-Thames, Oxfordshire, RG9 3DD Tel: (01491) 572966 Fax: (01491) 572967 E-mail: sales@roofproof.co.uk

Stonbury Ltd, 4 Phoenix Enterprise Park, Grovehill Road, Beverley, North Humberside, HU17 0JG Tel: (01482) 881198 Fax: (01482) 868457 E-mail: admin@stonbury.co.uk

Structural Sealant Services Ltd, Grove Farm, North Road, South Ockendon, Essex, RM15 6SR Tel: (01708) 853285 Fax: (01708) 851142E-mail: sales@structuralsealants.co.uk

Waterseal Waterbar & Sealant Ltd, 1 Weston Court, Stokesley Industrial Estate, Stokesley, Middlesbrough, Cleveland, TS9 5GA Tel: (01642) 717717 Fax: (01642) 717718

BUILDING WATERPROOFING MATERIALS

Hexham Sealants & Coatings, Station Yard, Station Road, Corbridge, Northumberland, NE45 5AZ Tel: (01434) 633344 Fax: (01434) 633346 E-mail: sales@hexhamsealant.co.uk

Safeguard Chemicals Ltd, Redkiln Close, Horsham, West Sussex, RH13 5QL Tel: (01403) 210204 Fax: (01403) 217529 E-mail: info@safeguardchem.co.uk

BUILDING WATERPROOFING PREPARATIONS

Grangers International Ltd, Grange Close, Clover Nook Industrial Park, Somercotes, Alfreton, Derbyshire, DE55 4QT Tel: (01773) 521521 Fax: (01773) 521262 E-mail: grangers@grangers.co.uk

IKO Ltd, Appley Lane North, Appley Bridge, Wigan, Lancashire, WN6 9AB Tel: (01257) 255771 Fax: (01257) 252514

Remmers UK Ltd, Remmers House, 14 Victoria Way, Burgess Hill, West Sussex, RH15 9NF Tel: (01444) 244144 Fax: (01444) 243500 E-mail: sales@remmers.co.uk

Specialist Building Products, 24 Beaufort Drive, London, NW11 6BU Tel: (020) 8458 8212 Fax: (020) 8458 4116 E-mail: sbpchemicals@yahoo.com

Tremco Illbruck Production Ltd, 393 Edinburgh Avenue, Slough, SL1 4UF Tel: (01753) 691696 Fax: (01753) 822640

Uniroof International, Worth Corner, Turners Hill Road, Crawley, West Sussex, RH10 7SL Tel: (01293) 889888 Fax: (01293) 883369 E-mail: export@uniroof.com

Winn & Coales Denso Ltd, Denso House, 33-35 Chapel Road, London, SE27 0TR Tel: (020) 8670 7511 Fax: (020) 8761 2456 E-mail: mail@denso.net

BUILT IN FURNITURE

▶ A A Gliderobes, Stour Valley Industrial Estate, Ashford Road, Chartham, Canterbury, Kent, CT4 7HF Tel: (01227) 731746 Fax: (01227) 733745

Alan Johnson Cabinet Maker, Kingsgate Workshops, 110-116 Kingsgate Road, London, NW6 2JG Tel: (020) 7372 6736 Fax: (020) 7328 7878

Alpha Interiors, 1013b Finchley Road, London, NW11 7ES Tel: (020) 8455 6619 Fax: (020) 8951 0093

Baldwin & Moore Ltd, Unit 7 Elton Road Business Park, Derby, DE24 8EG Tel: (01332) 385356 Fax: (01332) 385377 E-mail: baldwinandmoore@derby22.fsnet.co.uk

▶ Barwoods Bedrooms Ltd, 34 Market Street, Mottram, Hyde, Cheshire, SK14 6JG Tel: (01457) 763355 Fax: (01457) 763355 E-mail: mbardsley@barwoods.com

Bedroom Options, 13 Wychwood Avenue, Edgware, Middlesex, HA8 6TL Tel: (020) 8952 3200 Fax: (020) 8952 3200

▶ Bespoke Timberworks, Unit 25, Brockley Cross Business Centre, Endwell Road, London, SE4 2PD Tel: (020) 7639 8060 Fax: (020) 7639 8060

Michael Bysouth & Son, The Barn Trueloves, Trueloves Lane, Ingatestone, Essex, CM4 0NQ Tel: (01277) 355315 Fax: (01277) 355315

▶ Capital Fit, 8 Tynewydd Terrace, Newbridge, Newport, Gwent, NP11 4LU Tel: (01495) 248082 Fax: (01495) 248082 E-mail: sales@capitalfit.com

Cole, 24 Station Parade, Hornchurch, Essex, RM12 5AB Tel: (01708) 444279 Fax: (01708) 705003

Colemans Kitchens & Bedrooms Ltd, 178 Victoria Road, Kirkby-in-Ashfield, Nottingham, NG17 8AT Tel: (01623) 751239 Fax: (01623) 754649

Country House Furniture Ltd, Inglenook, Sheep St, Stow on the Wold, Cheltenham, Glos, GL54 1AA Tel: (01451) 831525 Fax: (01451) 831527

Custom Connections, Unit 1, Green Lane, Romiley, Stockport, Cheshire, SK6 3JG Tel: 0161-406 8600 Fax: 0161-406 9846

D & M Design Bedrooms, 99 Neilston Road, Paisley, Renfrewshire, PA2 6ES Tel: 0141-889 0336 Fax: 0141-848 7908

▶ Dream Doors Glasgow Ltd, 25 New Endrick Road, Killearn, Glasgow, G63 9QT Tel: (0845) 6009232 Fax: (0845) 6009232

East Coast Fittings, Gaddesby Lane, Rearsby, Leicester, LE7 4YH Tel: (01664) 424288 Fax: (01664) 424243 E-mail: sales@eastcoastfittings.co.uk

▶ Fitted Furniture Supplies, Nash House, Pym Street, Leeds, LS10 1PG Tel: 0113-234 7676 Fax: 0113-234 7979

Furniture Technique Ltd, New Garden Street, Blackburn, BB2 3RE Tel: (01254) 581255 Fax: (01254) 694215

Guildford Fitted Furniture, 5 Elm Close, Ripley, Woking, Surrey, GU23 6LE Tel: (01483) 211722 Fax: (01483) 211722

Handmade Direct, 152-154 Merton Road, London, SW19 1EH Tel: (020) 8542 0321 Fax: (020) 8543 6521

Hanna Bros, 80 Moyad Road, Kilkeel, Newry, County Down, BT34 4HH Tel: (028) 4176 2358 Fax: (028) 4176 4909

▶ Harlequin Kitchens, 3 Chain Bar Mill, 809 Moston Lane, Manchester, M40 5RT Tel: 0161-684 9585 Fax: 0161-684 9585

▶ Harris Design Ltd, 19 Glenorrin Close Lambton, Washington, Tyne & Wear, NE38 0DZ Tel: 0191-417 6752

Harval Fitted Furniture, 4 Horbury Junction Industrial Estate, Calder Vale Road, Horbury, Wakefield, West Yorkshire, WF4 5ER Tel: (01924) 270121 Fax: (01924) 262115 E-mail: sales@harval.co.uk

Home Form Group, Unit 1, Renley Road Retail Park, Ipswich, IP2 0AQ Tel: (01473) 226009

▶ House Proud Installations, Courtyard 3, Wentworth Road, Mapplewell, Barnsley, South Yorkshire, S75 6DT Tel: (01226) 388220

▶ How Furniture, J Coronation Road, Ilkeston, Derbyshire, DE7 5UA Tel: 0115-932 0215 Fax: 0115-932 0216

▶ Integrated Cinema Experience, 11 Chatteris Close, Stoke-on-Trent, ST3 7TX Tel: 01782 399317 Fax: 01782 399317 E-mail: icexperience@yahoo.com

J J McCormack Fitted Furniture, 185 Main St, Uddingston, Glasgow, G71 7BP Tel: (01698) 818766 Fax: (01698) 818883

Karva Furniture, Widdrington, Morpeth, Northumberland, NE61 5DW Tel: (01670) 790325 Fax: (01670) 790325

▶ Kingswood Interiors, 26 Kingswood Drive, Walsall, WS6 6NX Tel: (01922) 417041

The Kitchen Accessory Company Ltd, Invicta House, 1 Claytonbrook Road, Openshaw, Manchester, M11 1AL Tel: 0161-223 5223 Fax: 0161-223 1149 E-mail: kitacco@aol.com

▶ Kitchens By Design, 41-43 Bell Street, Wigston, Leicestershire, LE18 1AD Tel: 0116-281 0440

▶ Kiwanda, Unit B4, Bolney Road, Cowfold, Horsham, West Sussex, RH13 8AZ Tel: (01403) 864848

Lamco Design, 35A Cardigan Road, Bournemouth, BH9 1BD Tel: (01202) 530724 Fax: (01202) 530724

L'Interieur Furniture, 4a Little Aston Lane, Sutton Coldfield, West Midlands, B74 3UF Tel: 0121-353 2525 Fax: 0121-353 4314 E-mail: info@linterieur.co.uk

Magnet Ltd, 78 Wigmore Street, London, W1U 2SL Tel: (020) 7486 8711 Fax: (020) 7486 3264 E-mail: wigmorestreet.branch@magnet.co.uk

▶ Meehan Handbuilt Furniture, Drumsillagh One, Springfield, Enniskillen, County Fermanagh, BT74 9DX Tel: (028) 6634 1111 Fax: (028) 6634 1100 E-mail: sales@meehanhandbuilt.com

Meibel Fitted, Unit 43 Elms Business Park, Cranfield Park Road, Wickford, Essex, SS12 9EP Tel: (01268) 561661 Fax: (01277) 650602 E-mail: sales@meibel.co.uk

▶ Merkaba, 17 Brook Street, Polegate, East Sussex, BN26 6BQ Tel: (01323) 848414 Fax: (01323) 848414

Millpond (UK) Ltd, The Factory, Boswithian Rd, Tolvaddon, Camborne, Cornwall, TR14 0EJ Tel: 01209 714222

N J Bennett, Norbury, Weston under Penyard, Ross-on-Wye, Herefordshire, HR9 7PG Tel: (01989) 564284 Fax: (01989) 564284

Oak Wood Furniture Manufacturers Ltd, Oakwood, Old Parish Road, Ynysybwl, Pontypridd, Mid Glamorgan, CF37 3EY Tel: (01443) 791701 Fax: (01443) 791821

Oakley Furniture, Unit 16 Oakley Wood, Benson, Wallingford, Oxfordshire, OX10 6QG Tel: (01491) 825880 Fax: (01491) 825880

Parker Furniture, 5 The Crown Centre, Bond Street, Macclesfield, Cheshire, SK11 6QS Tel: (01625) 614396 Fax: (01625) 263632 E-mail: sales@parkerfurniture.co.uk

The Pinery, 233 Oakbrook Road, Sheffield, S11 7EB Tel: 0114-230 2635 Fax: 0114-230 2635 E-mail: mail@pinery.co.uk

Princess Fitted Bedroom & Kitchen Furniture, 40 Whalebone Lane South, Dagenham, Essex, RM8 1BB Tel: (020) 8593 3884

R.D. Rawcliffe Ltd, Highfield House, Royds Lane, Leeds, LS12 6DU Tel: 0113-263 1535 Fax: 0113-289 0955

▶ Ridgewell Fitted Furniture, 1 Melton Road, Queniborough, Leicester, LE7 3FP Tel: 0116-269 6615 Fax: 0116-269 6615

▶ Robert Whitaker Ltd, Southview, Oxford Road, Long Compton, Shipston-on-Stour, Warwickshire, CV36 5LD Tel: (01608) 684982 E-mail: robwhitaker@onetel.com

Roundel Design UK Ltd, Flishinghurst Orchards, Chalk Lane, Cranbrook, Kent, TN17 2QA Tel: (01580) 712666 Fax: (01580) 713564 E-mail: sales@roundeldesign.co.uk

▶ S & L Ltd, Unit 13, Block 6, Old Mill Lane Industrial Estate, Mansfield Woodhouse, Mansfield, Nottinghamshire, NG19 9BG Tel: (01623) 652900 Fax: (01623) 652900

▶ Saddleworth Bedrooms & Kitchens, 18 Broadbent Road, Oldham, OL1 4HU Tel: 0161-620 2600

Select Kitchens & Bedrooms North East Ltd, 616 Durham Road, Gateshd, Gateshead, Tyne & Wear, NE9 6HY Tel: 0191-482 1889 Fax: 0191-482 1889 E-mail: info@selectkb.co.uk

Sharps Bedrooms Ltd, 44 Main Street, Milngavie, Glasgow, G62 6BU Tel: 0141-956 2242

▶ Sharps Bedrooms Ltd, 19 Haymarket, Leicester, LE1 3GD Tel: 0116-253 3099

Sharps Bedrooms Ltd, 38-40 Old Church Road, London, E4 8DB Tel: (020) 8529 0162

Sharps Bedrooms Ltd, Nene Valley Way, Northampton, NN3 5LU Tel: (01604) 408004

Sharps Bedrooms Ltd, 6 Thames Street, Staines, Middlesex, TW18 4SD Tel: (01784) 461791 Fax: (01784) 464073

▶ Sharps Bedrooms Ltd, 1 East Street, Taunton, Somerset, TA1 3LQ Tel: (01823) 423862

Sharps Bedrooms Ltd, 151-153 Montague Street, Worthing, West Sussex, BN11 3BZ Tel: (01903) 823438

Sliderobes, Unit 3C, Deacon Trrading Estate, Forstall Road, Aylesford, Maidstone, Kent, ME20 7SP Tel: (01622) 718987 Fax: (01622) 882114 E-mail: maystone@sliderobes.com

SMD, Merse Road, Moons Moat North Industrial Es, Redditch, Worcestershire, B98 9HL Tel: (01527) 69548 Fax: (01527) 584884

Specialist Services (South West) Ltd, Mardle Way, Buckfastleigh, Devon, TQ11 0JS Tel: (01364) 644101 Fax: (01364) 644080

Spectrum Fitted Furniture Ltd, Rosehill, Henley-On-Thames, Oxfordshire, RG9 3EB Tel: (01628) 820240 Fax: (01628) 820241

Staples Uk Ltd, Heights of Alma, Stanley, Crook, County Durham, DL15 9QW Tel: (01388) 768990

The Symphony Group plc, Gelderd Lane, Leeds, LS12 6AL Tel: 0113-230 8000 Fax: 0113-231 0138

BUILT IN FURNITURE – *continued*

Threeways Manufacturing, Unit 2a Larpool La Industrial Estate, Whitby, North Yorkshire, YO22 4LX Tel: (01947) 821831 Fax: (01947) 821831

Tony Green, 96 Nottingham Road, Gotham, Nottingham, NG11 0HH Tel: 0115-983 1414 Fax: 0115-983 1414

Traigo Kitchens & Furniture, Pasture Lane, Gaddesby, Leicester, LE7 4XD Tel: (01664) 840423 Fax: (01664) 840833

Steve Wicks Built-in Furniture, Unit 4, 133-139 Church Rd, Hadleigh, Essex, SS7 2EJ Tel: (020) 8980 8332 Fax: (020) 8980 8332

▶ Williamson Kitchens, 60 Union Street, Keith, Banffshire, AB55 5DP Tel: (01542) 888088 Fax: (01542) 888088

Woodstock Furniture Ltd, 4 William Street, London, SW1X 9HL Tel: (020) 7245 9989 Fax: (020) 7245 9981

BUILT IN VACUUM CLEANING SYSTEMS

Beam Vacuum Systems, 65 Deerpark Road, Castledawson, Magherafelt, County Londonderry, BT45 8BS Tel: (028) 7963 2424 Fax: (028) 7938 6869 E-mail: enquiries@beamvacuums.ie

BULK CONTAINERS

Feldbinder (UK) Ltd, Sutton Bridge, Spalding, Lincolnshire, PE12 9XE Tel: (01406) 353500 Fax: (01406) 353510 E-mail: sales@feldbinder.co.uk

G M P (Banbury) Ltd, Unit 2, Power Park, Station Approach, Banbury, Oxfordshire, OX16 5AB Tel: (01295) 275300 Fax: (01295) 275400 E-mail: gmpb@globalnet.co.uk

Industrial Bulk Containers Ltd, Newton Business Park, Talbot Road, Hyde, Cheshire, SK14 4UQ Tel: 0161-367 8695 Fax: 0161-367 8685 E-mail: ibc@industrialbulk.freeserve.co.uk

J M J Bulk Packaging Ltd, Earlstrees Road, Earlstrees Industrial Estate, Corby, Northamptonshire, NN17 4AZ Tel: (01536) 274400 Fax: (01536) 261180 E-mail: sales@packaging.uk.com

Lamb Commercials Ltd, 126 Tamnamore Road, Dungannon, County Tyrone, BT71 6HW Tel: (028) 8772 2111 Fax: (028) 8773 7393 E-mail: lambsales@erf.com

Mayfly Containers Ltd, Bridge St Industrial Estate, Bridge Street, Clay Cross, Chesterfield, Derbyshire, S45 9NU Tel: (01246) 862456 Fax: (01246) 862711

S C A Industrial, Dodwells Road, Hinckley, Leicestershire, LE10 3BX Tel: (01455) 251400 Fax: (01455) 251404 E-mail: info.industrial@sca.com

Sellers Engineering Ltd, Sellers Way, Chadderton, Oldham, OL9 8EY Tel: 0161-681 5846 Fax: 0161-683 5621

Storsack UK Ltd, Dalton Airfield, Dalton, Thirsk, North Yorkshire, YO7 3HE Tel: (01845) 577464 Fax: (01845) 578175 E-mail: info@storsack.co.uk

BULK LIQUID HANDLING SERVICES

Meller Flowtrans Ltd, 12 Millersdale Close, Euroway Industrial Estate, Bradford, West Yorkshire, BD4 6RX Tel: (01274) 687687 Fax: (01274) 687744 E-mail: info@mellerflowtrans.co.uk

BULK LIQUID STORAGE CONTRACTORS

A J S Group, Unit 8 Cairnhall Industrial Estate, Cairnhall Industrial Estate, Inverurie, Aberdeenshire, AB51 0YQ Tel: (01467) 633301 Fax: (01467) 633302

Asco Fuel & Lubricants, South Esplanade East, Aberdeen, AB11 3PB Tel: (01224) 890888 Fax: (01224) 890383

I B L Bulk Liquids, Lime Street, Hull, HU8 7AS Tel: (01482) 320736 Fax: (01482) 226162 E-mail: phil@intbl.co.uk

Kaneb Terminals Ltd, 3rd Floor Sierra House, St Marys Walk, Maidenhead, Berkshire, SL6 1QZ Tel: (01628) 687601 Fax: (01628) 771678 E-mail: mcloughlin@kneb.co.uk

BULK LIQUID VEHICLES, *See Tanker etc*

BULK MATERIAL CONVEYOR SYSTEMS

B. & W. Mechanical Handling Ltd, Gemini House Cambridgeshire, Business Park, Ely, Cambridgeshire, CB7 4EA Tel: (01353) 665001 Fax: (01353) 666734 E-mail: sales@bwmech.co.uk

C T M Root Crop Systems - Harpley Engineering Ltd, Cross Street, Harpley, King's Lynn, Norfolk, PE31 6TJ Tel: (01485) 520355 Fax: (01485) 520062 E-mail: sales@ctmharpley.co.uk

Collinson Ernest & Co. Ltd, Riverside Industrial Park, Tan Yard Road, Catterall, Preston, PR3 0HP Tel: (01995) 606451 Fax: (01995) 605503 E-mail: agri.sales@collinson.co.uk

Entecon UK Ltd, Stanhope Road, Yorktown Industrial Estate, Camberley, Surrey, GU15 3BW Tel: (01276) 414540 Fax: (01276) 414544 E-mail: enquiries@entecon.co.uk

Handling Techniques Ltd, Units 30-31, Upper Mills Estate, Stonehouse, Gloucestershire, GL10 2BJ Tel: (01453) 826016 Fax: (01453) 823994 E-mail: david@handlingtechniques.co.uk

▶ Robson Handling Technology Ltd, Coleford Road, Darnall, Sheffield, S9 5PA Tel: 0114-244 4221 Fax: 0114-243 3066 E-mail: info@robson.co.uk

BULK MATERIAL HANDLING EQUIPMENT

A S C Materials Handling Ltd, 67 Europa Business Park, Bird Hall Lane, Stockport, Cheshire, SK3 0XA Tel: 0161-428 8600 Fax: 0161-428 1112 E-mail: sales@as-c.co.uk

Bagfast Ltd, Unit 2, Morris Court, Colwick Industrial Estate, Nottingham, NG4 2JN Tel: 0115-940 1658 Fax: 0115-961 1714 E-mail: sales@bagfast.com

Brighouse Engineering Ltd, Martin House, 2 Martin Street, Brighouse, West Yorkshire, HD6 1DA Tel: (01484) 719999 Fax: (01484) 720422 E-mail: brigeng@compuserve.com

Centristic Ltd, 1 Cavalier Road, Heathfield Industrial Estate, Newton Abbot, Devon, TQ12 6TQ Tel: (01626) 834310 Fax: (01626) 834681 E-mail: centristic@btconnect.com

Clyde Process Solutions plc, Carolina Court, Lakeside, Doncaster, South Yorkshire, DN4 5RA Tel: (01302) 321313 Fax: (01302) 554400 E-mail: solutions@clydematerials.co.uk

Collinson Ernest & Co. Ltd, Riverside Industrial Park, Tan Yard Road, Catterall, Preston, PR3 0HP Tel: (01995) 606451 Fax: (01995) 605503 E-mail: agri.sales@collinson.co.uk

Croston Engineering Ltd, Tarvin Mill Barrow Lane, Tarvin Sands, Tarvin, Chester, CH3 8JF Tel: (01829) 741119 Fax: (01829) 741169 E-mail: admin@croston-engineering.co.uk

E M C Component Handling, Priors Mead, Alcester Road, Inkberrow, Worcester, WR7 4HN Tel: (01386) 793471 Fax: (01386) 793471 E-mail: EMCmail@componenthandling.co.uk

Eurpa Silos Ltd, Unit 15, Prydwen Road, Swansea West Industrial Estate, Swansea, SA5 4HN Tel: (01792) 410450 Fax: (01792) 410455

Feldbinder (UK) Ltd, Sutton Bridge, Spalding, Lincolnshire, PE12 9XE Tel: (01406) 353500 Fax: (01406) 353510 E-mail: sales@feldbinder.co.uk

General Bridge & Engineering Ltd, Fleming Road, Earlstrees Industrial Estate, Corby, Northamptonshire, NN17 4SW Tel: (01536) 205744 Fax: (01536) 402456 E-mail: email@genbridge.fsnet.co.uk

Handling Techniques Ltd, Units 30-31, Upper Mills Estate, Stonehouse, Gloucestershire, GL10 2BJ Tel: (01453) 826016 Fax: (01453) 823994 E-mail: david@handlingtechniques.co.uk

K F Alliance Engineering Ltd, Units 28-29, Enfield Industrial Estate, Redditch, Worcestershire, B97 6BY Tel: (01527) 63331 Fax: (01527) 591191 E-mail: kfa@btconnect.com

Law-Denis Engineering Ltd, Fengate, Peterborough, PE1 5PE Tel: (01733) 563000 Fax: (01733) 563300 E-mail: info@lawdenis.com

Matcon Group Ltd, Matcon House, London Road, Moreton-in-Marsh, Gloucestershire, GL56 0HJ Tel: (01608) 651666 Fax: (01608) 651635 E-mail: matcon@matcon.co.uk

Philman Engineering Ltd, Kingsnorth Works, Hoo, Rochester, Kent, ME3 9NZ Tel: (01634) 253968 Fax: (01634) 253968

Portasilo Ltd, New Lane, Huntington, York, YO32 9PR Tel: (01904) 624872 Fax: (01904) 611760 E-mail: bulk@portasilo.co.uk

Redler Ltd, Dudbridge Works, Dudbridge, Stroud, Gloucestershire, GL5 3EY Tel: (01453) 763611 Fax: (01453) 763582 E-mail: sales@redler.com

Rotolok Bulk Systems Ltd, 38 Woodham Lane, New Haw, Addlestone, Surrey, KT15 3NA Tel: (01932) 854756 Fax: (01932) 859427 E-mail: sales@blotch.co.uk

Solitec Engineering, Unit 8 Gilchrist Thomas Industrial Estate, Blaenavon, Pontypool, Gwent, NP4 9RL Tel: (01453) 828727 Fax: (01495) 790666 E-mail: solitec@aol.com

Taylor Woolhouse, Greasbrough Road, Rotherham, South Yorkshire, S61 4QQ Tel: (01709) 379500 Fax: (01709) 379600 E-mail: rotamill@aol.com

WAM Engineering Ltd, Unit 14, Alexandra Way, Ashchurch Business Centre, Tewkesbury, Gloucestershire, GL20 8NB Tel: (01684) 299100 Fax: (01684) 299104 E-mail: shev@wameng.com

BULK MATERIALS HANDLING EQUIPMENT CONSULTANTS OR DESIGNERS

A S C Materials Handling Ltd, 67 Europa Business Park, Bird Hall Lane, Stockport, Cheshire, SK3 0XA Tel: 0161-428 8600 Fax: 0161-428 1112 E-mail: sales@as-c.co.uk

BULK MATERIALS HANDLING EQUIPMENT HIRE

HSS Lift & Shift, Sotherby Road, Middlesbrough, Cleveland, TS3 8BS Tel: (01642) 246015 Fax: (01642) 251411

BULK MATERIALS HANDLING SERVICES

Bulk Storage & Process Systems Ltd, 1 Colekitchen Lane, Gomshall, Guildford, Surrey, GU5 9LH Tel: (01483) 202211 Fax: (01483) 205110 E-mail: sales@bulk-systems.co.uk

G T S Ltd, 85 Templepatrick Road, Ballyclare, County Antrim, BT39 9RQ Tel: (028) 9334 0510 Fax: (028) 9334 9339 E-mail: gts61242@aol.com

Teignmouth Quay Co Holdings Ltd, Old Quay, Teignmouth, Devon, TQ14 8ES Tel: (01626) 774044 Fax: (01626) 776240 E-mail: teignmouth@abports.co.uk

BULK STORAGE EQUIPMENT

Bulk Storage & Process Systems Ltd, 1 Colekitchen Lane, Gomshall, Guildford, Surrey, GU5 9LH Tel: (01483) 202211 Fax: (01483) 205110 E-mail: sales@bulk-systems.co.uk

BULKHEAD LIGHTING

Designplan Lighting Ltd, 6 Wealdstone Road, Sutton, Surrey, SM3 9RW Tel: (020) 8254 2000 Fax: (020) 8644 4253 E-mail: info@designplan.co.uk

J C C Lighting Products, Southern Cross Trading Estate, Lamplighter House, Bognor Regis, West Sussex, PO22 9TS Tel: (01243) 829040 Fax: (01243) 829051 E-mail: sales@jcc-lighting.co.uk

BULLION DEALERS

Gold Investments Ltd, 88 Gracechurch Street, London, EC3V 0DN Tel: (020) 7283 7752 Fax: (020) 7283 7754 E-mail: info@goldinvestments.co.uk

Goulding & Bird Ltd, 31 Hatton Wall, London, EC1N 8JJ Tel: (020) 7242 7525

Goulds Jewellers, 145 Highland Road, Southsea, Hampshire, PO4 9EY Tel: (023) 9273 1436 Fax: (023) 9278 8878 E-mail: sales@gouldjewllers.co.uk

Marple Laboratories Birmingham Ltd, 19 Northampton Street, Birmingham, B18 6DU Tel: 0121-233 1504 Fax: 0121-236 3287 E-mail: info@marplelabs.co.uk

Metalor Technologies (UK) Ltd, 74 Warstone Lane, Birmingham, B18 6NG Tel: 0121-236 3241 Fax: 0121-236 3568 E-mail: electrotechnics@metalor.com

Stephen Betts, 49-63 Spencer Street, Birmingham, B18 6DE Tel: 0121-233 9856 Fax: 0121-236 2265 E-mail: admin@bettsmetals.co.uk

BUNGS, COCK/FAUCET/TAP

British Bung Manufacturing Co. Ltd, Lowlands Works, Mirfield, West Yorkshire, WF14 8LY Tel: (01924) 493071 Fax: (01924) 480632 E-mail: brit.bung@telinco.co.uk

▶ SpeedPlumb.co.uk, Casemill, Temeside, Ludlow, Shropshire, SY8 1JW Tel: 0845 3732738

BUNK BEDS

Charterbrae Ltd, Unit 3 Coneygre Industrial Estate, Tipton, West Midlands, DY4 8XP Tel: 0121-520 5353 Fax: 0121-522 2018 E-mail: sales@cbbeds.u-net.com

Inpine Ltd, Anglia Way Industrial Estate, Anglia Way, Mansfield, Nottinghamshire, NG18 4LP Tel: (01623) 625468

BUNK BEDS, PINE

▶ Alpha Pine (Harrogate) Ltd, 55 Knaresborough Road, Harrogate, North Yorkshire, HG2 7LT Tel: (01423) 885196 Fax: (01423) 885196 E-mail: info@alphapine.co.uk

Childrens Bed Centres, Unit 3, Saltney Business Centre, High Street, Saltney, Chester, CH4 8SE Tel: (08448) 007772 Fax: (01244) 675637 E-mail: enquiries@childrensbedcentres.co.uk

Island Pine, 64 Union Place, Dungannon, County Tyrone, BT70 1DL Tel: (028) 8775 3545 Fax: (028) 8775 2747 E-mail: sales@islandpine.co.uk

BUNKERING/BUNKER AGENTS, DIESEL FUEL, ROAD VEHICLES

▶ Croft Fuels Ltd, PO BOX 0, LIVERPOOL, L38 0WY Tel: 0151 929 2900 Fax: 0151 929 3050 E-mail: sales@croft-fuels.co.uk

C.H. Jones Ltd, Premier Business Park, Queen Street, Walsall, WS2 9PB Tel: (01922) 615231 Fax: (01922) 704441 E-mail: info@keyfules.co.uk

BUNKERING/BUNKER AGENTS, MARINE FUEL

Bominflot Ltd, Ravensbourne Road, Bromley, BR1 1HN Tel: (020) 8315 5400 Fax: (020) 8315 5429 E-mail: mail@bominflot.co.uk

Bunkerfuels UK Ltd, 21-24 Mill Bank Tower, London, SW1P 4QP Tel: (020) 7828 3299 Fax: (020) 7834 4951 E-mail: bunkers@bunkerfuels.co.uk

E.A. Gibson Shipbrokers Ltd, PO Box 278, London, EC1P 1HP Tel: (020) 7667 1000 Fax: (020) 7831 8762 E-mail: tanker@eagibson.co.uk

Mctaggart Shipping & Management Co. Ltd, 1 Great Cumberland Place, London, W1H 7AL Tel: (020) 7468 8500 Fax: (020) 7468 8625 E-mail: chadring@macnav.com

BUNTING

Amazing Bunting Co., Units 1-7, 22 Pleydell Road, Northampton, NN4 8NL Tel: (01604) 675556 Fax: (01604) 675557 E-mail: sales@amazingbunting.co.uk

Banner Warehouse, Unit 4 & 5 Knowle Business Centre, Wadhurst Road, Frant, Tunbridge Wells, Kent, TN3 9EJ Tel: (0800) 0523659 Fax: (0800) 0523658 E-mail: regencysigns@btclick.com

Brook International, Flagship House, Riparian Way, Cross Hills, Keighley, West Yorkshire, BD20 7BW Tel: (01535) 639020 Fax: (01535) 639029 E-mail: info@brookinternational.com

Byte Systems, 50 Hoskyn Close, Rugby, Warwickshire, CV21 4LA Tel: (01788) 331495 Fax: (0870) 941027 E-mail: sales@byte-solutions.co.uk

Flag Services & Supply Co., 302 Westbourne Grove, Westcliff-on-Sea, Essex, SS0 0PT Tel: (01702) 333343 Fax: (01702) 343330

Flags & Banners Ltd, Springfield Industrial Estate, Burnham-on-Crouch, Essex, CM0 8TE Tel: (01621) 783221 Fax: (01621) 783532 E-mail: sales@flags-banners.co.uk

Halton Print & Promotional, High Street, Knutton, Newcastle, Staffordshire, ST5 6BX Tel: (01782) 712909 Fax: (01782) 713626 E-mail: info@haltonpromotional.co.uk

Heaton Paper Co. Ltd, Eldon Street, Gateshead, Tyne & Wear, NE8 3ND Tel: 0191-477 3783 Fax: 0191-490 0247 E-mail: sales@heatonpaper.co.uk

Kreative Bunting Ltd, 35 Charter Gate, Quarry Park Close, Moulton Park Industrial Estate, Northampton, NN3 6QB Tel: (01604) 790077 Fax: (01604) 643773 E-mail: sales@kreativebunting.com

SignRight, 157-161 West Road, Westcliff-On-Sea, Essex, SS0 9DH Tel: (01702) 308486 Fax: (0870) 7061711 E-mail: info@signright.co.uk

Trounce Ltd, New St Marks Works, St Marks Lane, Manchester, M8 4FW Tel: 0161-740 2159 Fax: 0161-721 4768 E-mail: sales@trounce.co.uk

BUOY (MARINE) MONITORING SYSTEMS

Strainstall UK Ltd, 10 Mariners Way, Cowes, Isle of Wight, PO31 8PD Tel: (01983) 203600 Fax: (01983) 291335 E-mail: sales@strainstall.co.uk

BUOYANCY AIDS

Cosalt International Ltd, Fish Dock Road, Grimsby, South Humberside, DN31 3NW Tel: (01472) 504300 Fax: (01472) 504200 E-mail: sales@cosaltlighting.co.uk

BUOYANCY PRODUCTS

Cosalt International Ltd, Fish Dock Road, Grimsby, South Humberside, DN31 3NW Tel: (01472) 504300 Fax: (01472) 504200 E-mail: sales@cosaltlighting.co.uk

BURGLAR ALARM COMPONENTS

Bazen & Page, 127 Whyke Lane, Chichester, West Sussex, PO19 8AU Tel: (01243) 782067 Fax: (01243) 869862 E-mail: bazen.page@tiscali.co.uk
Concept Smoke Screens, North End, Swineshead, Swineshead, Boston, Lincolnshire, PE20 3LR Tel: (01205) 821111 Fax: (01205) 820316 E-mail: info@smoke-screen.co.uk
Expo Link Alarms Ltd, 35 Knowley Road, Beach Hill, Wigan, Lancashire, WN6 7PZ Tel: (01942) 494004 Fax: (01942) 825991 E-mail: sales@linkalarms.co.uk
Pyronix Security Equipment Ltd, Pyronix House, Braithwell Way, Hellaby, Rotherham, South Yorkshire, S66 8QY Tel: (01709) 700100 Fax: (01709) 701042 E-mail: sales@pyronix.co.uk
Saffron Security, Stanstead House, Shire Hill, Saffron Walden, Essex, CB11 3AQ Tel: (01799) 529911 Fax: (01799) 529912

BURGLAR ALARM INSTALLATION OR SERVICING

A I S Alarms, Wharton House, 9 Wharton Avenue, Manchester, M21 7SQ Tel: 0161-881 4700 Fax: 0161-881 5203
Abacus Security Systems, 1a Bowdon Avenue, Barlborough, Chesterfield, Derbyshire, S43 4JE Tel: (01246) 813800 Fax: (01246) 813800
Abel Alarm Co. Ltd, 1a Albert Street, Oldham, OL8 3QP Tel: 0161-682 3689 Fax: 0161-684 8986 E-mail: info.manchester@abelalarm.co.uk
Abel Alarm Co. Ltd, 17 Slader Business Park, Witney Road, Nuffield Industrial Estate, Poole, Dorset, BH17 0GP Tel: (01202) 677144 Fax: (01202) 677944 E-mail: info.bournemouth@abelalarm.co.uk
Abel Alarm Co. Ltd, Unit 9 Woodside Road, South Marston Park, Swindon, SN3 4WA Tel: 01793 829312 Fax: 01793 825452 E-mail: info.swindon@abelalarm.co.uk
Active Alarms Plymouth Ltd, 42 Aylesbury Crescent, Whitleigh, Plymouth, PL5 4HX Tel: (01752) 774424 Fax: (01752) 774424
Active Security Group Ltd, Horsecroft Place, Harlow, Essex, CM19 5BT Tel: (01279) 420016 Fax: (01279) 444491
Advance Security Detection, 4 Falcon Road, Dewsbury, West Yorkshire, WF12 9NH Tel: (01924) 438844 Fax: (01924) 438844
Advanced Alarm Systems, 7 Fettercairn Gardens, Bishopbriggs, Glasgow, G64 1AY Tel: 0141-762 0040 Fax: 0141-563 9026
Alarmwise Burglar Alarm Systems, 37 Littlebeck Drive, Darlington, County Durham, DL1 2TN Tel: (01325) 480254 Fax: (01325) 266804
Asg Midlands, 2 Old Walsall Road, Birmingham, B42 1NN Tel: 0121-358 1524 Fax: 0121-358 1525
Atlas Fire & Security Ltd, Unit 8A Lansil Industrial Estate, Caton Road, Lancaster, LA1 3PQ Tel: (01524) 69488 Fax: (01524) 842972
Automatic Protection Equipment & Crown Security Se, 73 Lower High Street, Bristol, BS11 0AW Tel: 0117-982 5045 Fax: 0117-982 6046 E-mail: info@apealarms.co.uk
Avonbridge Alarms, 87 Bradley Crescent, Bristol, BS11 9SR Tel: 0117-982 2088 Fax: 0117-982 1292 E-mail: info@avonbridgealarms.co.uk
Aztek Services Ltd, Unit 8 Hall Barn Industrial Estate, Isleham, Ely, Cambridgeshire, CB7 5RB Tel: (01638) 781799 Fax: (01638) 781768 E-mail: sales@aztekservices.co.uk
B & D Electrical Security & Surveillance Ltd, Unit 12 Grinnall Business Centre, Sandy Lane, Stourport-on-Severn, Worcestershire, DY13 9QB Tel: (01299) 822758 Fax: (01299) 827995
Barb Security Systems, Reeds, Colliers End, Ware, Hertfordshire, SG11 1EH Tel: (0845) 2304248
Barry Bros Security, 121-123 Praed Street, London, W2 1RL Tel: (0800) 3168547 Fax: (020) 7262 5005 E-mail: info@barrybros.com
Baymont Alarms York, 137 Brecksfield, Skelton, York, YO30 1YE Tel: (01904) 471120 Fax: (01904) 471121 E-mail: sales@baymontalarms.uk
Best Security, 39b Moss Bank Road, St. Helens, Merseyside, WA11 7DD Tel: (01744) 757065 Fax: (01744) 600548
Beta Security Systems, Llandegai Industrial Estate, Llandygai, Bangor, Gwynedd, LL57 4YH Tel: (01248) 364967 Fax: (01248) 364967
Bharat Alarms, 32-34 Constitution Hill, Birmingham, B19 3JT Tel: 0121-236 7449 Fax: 0121-236 8996 E-mail: bharatuk@aol.com
C Q Alarms 1982 Ltd, 1a Dora Road, Birmingham, B10 9RF Tel: 0121-772 1566 Fax: 0121-766 8231
▶ C S I, 36 Luzley Brook Road, Royton, Oldham, OL2 6SQ Tel: (01706) 843249 E-mail: spencer.marsden1@btinternet.com
Castle Computers, 347 Barnsley Road, Wakefield, West Yorkshire, WF2 6AS Tel: (01924) 257291 Fax: (01924) 257291
Chris Lewis, Faraday House, 38 Poole Road, Bournemouth, BH4 9DW Tel: (01202) 751599 Fax: (01202) 759500 E-mail: sales@chrislewissecurity.co.uk
Cliftonville Intruder Alarms, 2 Alkali Row, Margate, Kent, CT9 1DB Tel: (01843) 297353 Fax: (01843) 297353 E-mail: cia.kent@btclick.com
Corstorphine Security Systems, 26 Saughton Road, Edinburgh, EH11 3PT Tel: 0131-444 0005 Fax: (0871) 4331212
Cress Security Co. Ltd, 6 Wolverhampton Road, Stafford, ST17 4BN Tel: (01785) 211014 Fax: (01785) 227711
Crown Security, 49a Cricklade Road, Swindon, SN2 1AA Tel: (01793) 433999 Fax: (01793) 434002
Crozet Alarms, PO Box 16, Oxted, Surrey, RH8 9YZ Tel: (01883) 723458 Fax: (01883) 730823 E-mail: sales@crozet.co.uk
Cumming Fire & Security, 10 Loch Way, Kemnay, Inverurie, Aberdeenshire, AB51 5QZ Tel: (01467) 643917 Fax: (01467) 643917 E-mail: sales@cummingfireandsecurity.co.uk
Darlington Alarm Centre, 78 Heathfield Park, Middleton St. George, Darlington, County Durham, DL2 1LW Tel: (01325) 354500 E-mail: sales@darlingtonalarmcentre.co.uk
David Blane, 66A Station Road, Petersfield, Hampshire, GU32 3ET Tel: (01730) 263202
Defiant Alarms Ltd, 45 Hornby Street, Wigan, Lancashire, WN1 2DR Tel: (01942) 248872 Fax: (01942) 248872
Diamond Alarm Systems, 106 Crwys Road, Cardiff, CF24 4NQ Tel: (029) 2045 1789 Fax: (029) 2037 2505
Digitec Installations Ltd, 2 Massey Walk, Manchester, M22 5JY Tel: 0161-437 9357 Fax: 0161-613 2769
▶ Eden Group, 43 Ellens Glen Road, Edinburgh, EH17 7QJ Tel: 0131-664 3906 Fax: 0131-658 1038 E-mail: Lynne@edengroup.co.uk
Elm Alarms, 14 St. Vincent Road, Clacton-on-Sea, Essex, CO15 1NA Tel: (01255) 475017 Fax: (01255) 475017
Empire Alarms, 38 Kenmore Road, Prenton, Merseyside, CH43 3AS Tel: 0151-608 9919 Fax: 0151-608 9919 E-mail: enquiries@empirealarms.co.uk
Etas, 1 Lancaster Close, Winsford, Cheshire, CW7 1PS Tel: (01606) 551555 Fax: (01606) 862733
Eurosecurity Alarms, 5 Harvine Walk, Stourbridge, West Midlands, DY8 3BQ Tel: (01384) 370717 Fax: (01384) 370717
Evesham Alarm Co., Summer Place, Blacksmiths Lane, Cropthorne, Pershore, Worcestershire, WR10 3LX Tel: (01386) 861386 E-mail: chris.tunstill@freenet.co.uk
Exco Fire & Safety Control Ltd, 46 St Gluvias Street, Penryn, Cornwall, TR10 8BJ Tel: (01326) 372878 Fax: (01326) 377135 E-mail: jack@excotec.co.uk
F R F Alarms Ltd, 136 Mackintosh Place, Cardiff, CF24 4RS Tel: (029) 2075 5799 Fax: (029) 2075 5799 E-mail: frfcardiff@aol.com
Falcon Security Systems South East Ltd, 64 Zealand Road, Canterbury, Kent, CT1 3QB Tel: (01227) 787017
Five Star Security Systems, 217 Manchester Road, Oldham, OL8 4QY Tel: 0161-682 9999 Fax: 0161-682 8787
G B Alarms Ltd, High St, Donington, Spalding, Lincolnshire, PE11 4TA Tel: (01775) 821100 Fax: (01775) 821395 E-mail: admin@gbalarms.com
G C Alarms, Emmslea, Highfield Road, Biggin Hill, Westerham, Kent, TN16 3UX Tel: (0500) 300984 Fax: (01959) 570374
G C S Alarms, Essex House, Stephenson Road, Clacton-on-Sea, Essex, CO15 4XA Tel: (01255) 220316 Fax: (01255) 479122 E-mail: sales@gcsalarms.co.uk
Gough & Kelly Ltd, 6 Hales Road, Leeds, LS12 4PL Tel: 0113-279 4801 Fax: 0113-279 8644 E-mail: sales@gough-kelly.co.uk
Grandrew Securities, 7 Linden Avenue, Wembley, Middlesex, HA9 8BB Tel: (020) 8902 5674 Fax: (020) 8900 9218
Guardian Security, Byre House, Cow Lane, Wincheap Industrial Estate, Canterbury, Kent, CT1 3RW Tel: (01227) 762128 Fax: (01227) 764638
H T Security Systems, 36 Loxwood Road, Waterlooville, Hampshire, PO8 9TU Tel: (023) 9259 9479 Fax: (023) 9259 9479
Hall & Rhodes Security Ltd, 138-140 Blackmoorfoot Road, Huddersfield, HD4 5RL Tel: (0800) 521271 Fax: (01484) 658897
Halliwell Electrical Contractors, 16 Hartington Road, Bramhall, Stockport, Cheshire, SK7 2DZ Tel: 0161-439 7694 Fax: (01625) 850117
Havelock Alarms, 6 Duncombe Avenue, Clydebank, Dunbartonshire, G81 6PP Tel: (01389) 873794 Fax: (01389) 876666
Himfen Alarms, 25 Station Road, Hockley, Essex, SS5 4BZ Tel: (01268) 750070
Holt Security Systems, 24a Royal George Road, Burgess Hill, West Sussex, RH15 9SE Tel: (01444) 241666 Fax: (01444) 243666 E-mail: holtsecurity@hotmail.com
Homeguard Security Systems, 4 Courtney Cl, Tewkesbury, Glos, GL20 5FB Tel: (01242) 676070 Fax: (01242) 676070
I D H Alarms Co. Ltd, 17 Edwin Street, Gravesend, Kent, DA12 1EH Tel: (01474) 363535 Fax: (01474) 535418
J & J Alarms, 171 Arbury Road, Nuneaton, Warwickshire, CV10 7NH Tel: (024) 7634 1508
J K Alarms, 9 Alexandria Street, Rossendale, Lancashire, BB4 8HP Tel: (01706) 218504 Fax: (01706) 218504
Kent Alarms Ltd, 37 Main Street, South Hiendley, Barnsley, South Yorkshire, S72 9BS Tel: (0800) 0854999 Fax: (01226) 717075 E-mail: sales@kentalarms.co.uk
Lancashire Security Systems, 90 Ings Lane, Rochdale, Lancashire, OL12 7DX Tel: (01706) 655253
Law Security Systems, 9 Deal Avenue, Burntwood, Staffordshire, WS7 2EU Tel: (01543) 683036 Fax: (01543) 683036
▶ Lincs Electrical Services, 6 Buttler Way, Sleaford, Lincolnshire, NG34 7PA Tel: (01529) 309505 E-mail: lincelectrical@tiscali.co.uk
M P Alarms, 21 Bailey Lane, Clenchwarton, King's Lynn, Norfolk, PE34 4AY Tel: (01553) 772991 Fax: (01553) 776587
M25 Security Systems Ltd, 276 New Road, Croxley Green, Rickmansworth, Hertfordshire, WD3 3HH Tel: (01923) 721222 Fax: (01923) 441118
Mca, 1 Millers Way, Wirral, Merseyside, CH46 6EH Tel: 0151-678 6663 Fax: 0151-678 6663
Master Alarms, Unit 1, The Arcade, Leagrave Road, Luton, LU4 8JE Tel: (01582) 484477 Fax: (01582) 413800
Mayfair Security Ltd, 62 Hillside Road, Southminster, Essex, CM0 7AL Tel: (01621) 772580 Fax: (01621) 774580
Millennium Security Systems, 6 Kirkland Way, Mile Oak, Tamworth, Staffordshire, B78 3PL Tel: (01827) 288727 Fax: (01827) 288727 E-mail: info@millennium-securitysystems.co.uk
Minster Alarms, Suncliffe House, 157 New Lane, Huntington, York, YO32 9NQ Tel: (01904) 466400 Fax: (01904) 466401 E-mail: sales@minsteralarms.co.uk
Morgan Alarm Systems, 20 Fir Tree Close, Tamworth, Staffordshire, B79 8NL Tel: (07973) 238772 Fax: (01827) 54698
Newark Alarm Systems, 2 Wetsyke Lane, Balderton, Newark, Nottinghamshire, NG24 3NY Tel: (01636) 674978 Fax: (01636) 640767
Nighthood Security Ltd, 209 The Heights, Northolt, Middlesex, UB5 4BX Tel: (020) 8423 5677 Fax: (020) 8426 9009
Nova Electronics Ltd, 18 Springclough Drive, Worsley, Manchester, M28 3HS Tel: 0161-702 8643 Fax: 0161-702 8643 E-mail: sales@nova-electronics.co.uk
Nu Tech Security, Station House, 1 Banstead Road, Banstead, Surrey, SM7 1PZ Tel: (01737) 551966 Fax: (01737) 379494
Ok G800, 43 Cannon Street, Preston, PR1 3NT Tel: (01772) 881800 Fax: (01772) 881800
Owl Security Services Ltd, 30C Cowbridge Road, Pontyclun, Mid Glamorgan, CF72 9EE Tel: (01443) 238600 Fax: (01443) 238600 E-mail: enquiries@owlsecurity.co.uk
Owl Security Systems, 4 Balmoral Road, Gidea Park, Romford, RM2 5XD Tel: (01708) 454043 Fax: (01708) 440886 E-mail: enquiries@owlsecuritysystems.co.uk
Oxlox Burglar Alarm Systems, 33 Field Avenue, Oxford, OX4 6PA Tel: (01865) 747445 Fax: (01865) 747445
Pacc Security Ltd, 90 Lots Road, London, SW10 0QD Tel: (020) 7376 3000 Fax: (020) 7376 3100 E-mail: security@paccsecurity.com
Pentagon Alarms, 27 The Gables, Dinas Powys, South Glamorgan, CF64 4DN Tel: (07767) 202397 Fax: 029 20515521
Pentland Security Scotland, 8 The Loan, Loanhead, Midlothian, EH20 9AF Tel: 0131-440 4466 Fax: 0131-440 4499
Phase 8 Electronics & Alarms Ltd, 189 Headstone Lane, Harrow, Middlesex, HA2 6ND Tel: (020) 8863 8792 Fax: (020) 8861 0478 E-mail: phase8alarms@aol.com
Phoenix Security Systems Ltd, 95 Park Road, Sale, Cheshire, M33 6JA Tel: 0161-976 6566 Fax: 0161-976 3869
▶ Phoenix Total Security, 297 Wood Lane, Dagenham, Essex, RM8 3NH Tel: (020) 8596 7920 Fax: (020) 8596 7921 E-mail: sales@phoenix-total-security.com
R S J Security Systems, 1 Sterry Drive, Epsom, Surrey, KT19 0TG Tel: (020) 8393 6269 Fax: (020) 8393 6304 E-mail: email@rsjsecurity.co.uk
Rapide Security Surveillance Ltd, 878-880 Alum Rock Road, Birmingham, B8 2TY Tel: 0121-327 3939 Fax: 0121-327 1088
Royal Security, Warrington Street, Lees, Oldham, OL4 5AE Tel: 0161-620 2303 Fax: 0161-665 3550
Safe Homes UK, 1 Anker Court, Bonehill Road, Tamworth, Staffordshire, B78 3HP Tel: 0870 8580112 Fax: 0870 8580113 E-mail: info@safehomes.co.uk
Safe & Sound, 2 Moorhead Street, Colne, Lancashire, BB8 9AU Tel: (01282) 867830
Saturn Security Installations Ltd, 678 Aigburth Road, Liverpool, L19 0NY Tel: 0151-427 5977 Fax: 0151-494 0766
Seaward Security Ltd, 40 Highwood Avenue, High Wycombe, Buckinghamshire, HP12 4LS Tel: (01494) 439886 Fax: (01494) 539269
Secure It All Ltd, 25 Howley Grange Road, Halesowen, West Midlands, B62 0HW Tel: 0121-423 1119 Fax: 0121-423 3393 E-mail: sales@secureitall.co.uk
Securexe Security Systems, 24 Park Lane, Exmouth, Devon, EX8 1TH Tel: (01395) 227337 Fax: (01395) 260260
Security 201, 332 Goring Road, Goring-by-Sea, Worthing, West Sussex, BN12 4PE Tel: (01903) 242902 Fax: (01903) 242618 E-mail: info@security201.co.uk
Security Design Centre Ltd, Falcon House, 10 Bloomfield Street West, Halesowen, West Midlands, B63 3RD Tel: 0121-550 8847 Fax: 0121-585 6142 E-mail: sales@securitydesigncentre.co.uk
Security First, 65 Bohemia Road, St. Leonards-on-Sea, East Sussex, TN37 6RG Tel: (01424) 427550 Fax: (01424) 427550
Sentinel Security Systems, 7 Southern Avenue, Leominster, Herefordshire, HR6 0QF Tel: (01568) 615500 Fax: (01568) 610555 E-mail: sentinelss@btinternet.com
Sesco Ltd, 3 Elm Road, Redhill, RH1 6AJ Tel: (01737) 763654 Fax: (01737) 772669 E-mail: enquiries@sesco.co.uk
Sheriff Alarms Alarm Company, 33 Ockerby Street, Nottingham, NG6 9GA Tel: 0115-916 7777
Spectrum Security Services Ltd, 111 Magdalen Street, Colchester, CO1 2LF Tel: (01206) 793915 Fax: (01206) 795974
Spy Alarms Ltd, 5 Sevenoaks Business Centre, Cramptons Road, Sevenoaks, Kent, TN14 5DQ Tel: (01732) 464649 Fax: (01732) 779568 E-mail: info@spyalarms.co.uk
Status Alarms Ltd, Holbrook Lane, Coventry, CV6 4AF Tel: (024) 7668 5523 Fax: (024) 7666 1127
Switchbox Vision Co., 6 Crown Court, Castle Street, Hinckley, Leicestershire, LE10 1DD Tel: (01455) 633505
T & D Security Systems, 103 Glasgow Road, Bathgate, West Lothian, EH48 2QN Tel: (0800) 3890219 Fax: (01506) 650611 E-mail: sales@tdsecurity.co.uk
Thorndon Security & Electrical Services, Cornerway 40a, Well Lane, Galleywood, Chelmsford, CM2 8QY Tel: (01245) 281880 Fax: (01245) 475233
Vision Security Consultants, 22 Radley Road, Wallasey, Merseyside, CH44 2BU Tel: 0151-630 1603
▶ Walker Security Systems Ltd, Unit 17 Anniesland Business Park, Netherton Road, Glasgow, G13 1EU Tel: 0141-959 7300 Fax: (0845) 2250700 E-mail: sales@walkersecurity.co.uk
Westronics Ltd, 11-12 Marcus Close, Tilehurst, Reading, RG30 4EA Tel: 0118-942 6726 Fax: 0118-945 1481 E-mail: sales@westronics.co.uk
Wilsecure Installations, 292 Dewsbury Road, Leeds, LS11 6JT Tel: 0113-271 6097 Fax: 0113-270 4259 E-mail: sales@tindsdaletv.co.uk
Wizard Systems, Lingley House, Commissioners Road, Rochester, Kent, ME2 4EE Tel: (01634) 718181 Fax: (01634) 715031
Wright Guard Security Systems & Electrical, 2 Columbia Avenue, Mansfield, Nottinghamshire, NG18 3LD Tel: (01623) 645808
Wyze Security Systems, 296 Stag Lane, London, NW9 0EG Tel: (020) 8998 3057 Fax: (020) 8998 1027
Xtal Security Systems Ltd, 191 Replingham Road, London, SW18 5LY Tel: (020) 8877 9802 Fax: (020) 8877 3427 E-mail: info@xtalsecurity.com
Yorkshire Alarms & Security Services, 63 Hawes Road, Harrogate, North Yorkshire, HG1 4SE Tel: (01423) 881294 Fax: (01423) 548058
Yorkshire Security Services, 38 Oaklands Avenue, Leeds, LS13 1LH Tel: 0113-257 3167

BURGLAR ALARM SYSTEMS

▶ A X L Security, 2 Nidd Valley Trading Estate, Market Flat Lane, Scotton, Knaresborough, North Yorkshire, HG5 9JA Tel: (01423) 860300 Fax: (01423) 869779 E-mail: sales@axlsecurity.co.uk
Alarm Line Security Systems, Bozon Hall, Wash Road, Kirton, Boston, Lincolnshire, PE20 1QJ Tel: (01205) 722838 Fax: (01205) 366755 E-mail: info@alarmline.co.uk
▶ Alerts Security/Installations Ltd, 1a Jubilee Terrace, Ryton, Tyne & Wear, NE40 4HL Tel: 0191-413 9090 Fax: 0191-413 9090
Asg Midlands, 2 Old Walsall Road, Birmingham, B42 1NN Tel: 0121-358 1524 Fax: 0121-358 1525
▶ Banbury Alarms, Unit 5 Thorpe Close, Banbury, Oxfordshire, OX16 4SW Tel: (01295) 263552
▶ BBC Security Systems, 11 Franklyn Avenue, Southampton, SO19 8AN Tel: (0845) 2306611 Fax: (0845) 2306622
C & H Alarm Systems, 12 Park Hill Gardens, Swallownest, Sheffield, S26 4WL Tel: 0114-293 9000 Fax: 0114-293 9000
▶ Catch Monitored Security, 38 Portrack Grange Road, Stockton-On-Tees, Cleveland, TS18 2PH Tel: (01642) 677747 Fax: (01642) 602517 E-mail: monitering@cgsl.org.uk
Coopers Security Ltd, Security House, Xerox Business Park, Mitcheldean, Gloucestershire, GL17 0SZ Tel: (01594) 543343 Fax: (01594) 545401 E-mail: marketing@menviersecurity.co.uk
▶ Craddock Security Systems, 11 Daisy Close, Corby, Northamptonshire, NN18 8LD Tel: (01536) 741361 Fax: (01536) 741644
Dean Head Services, 167 Cold Bath Road, Harrogate, North Yorkshire, HG2 0HN Tel: (01423) 564626 Fax: (01423) 564626
Dragon Fire & Security Ltd, Dragon House, Norwich Road, Cardiff, CF23 9AB Tel: (029) 2048 5555 Fax: (029) 2048 4400
▶ Eastern Security, 172 North Avenue, Southend-on-Sea, SS2 4EU Tel: (01702) 354836 Fax: (01702) 460178

BURGLAR ALARM SYSTEMS – *continued*

▶ Elite Security, 27 James Clements Close, Kilwinning, Ayrshire, KA13 6PW Tel: (01294) 550155 Fax: (01294) 550170

G D N Security & Home Maintenance Services, 4 Midgley Street, Colne, Lancashire, BB8 0HF Tel: (01282) 863195

▶ Global Fire Supplies, 2, Old Town Station Business Park, Bridgnorth Road, Cleobury Mortimer, Kidderminster, Worcs, DY14 8SY Tel: (01299) 271548 Fax: (01299) 405542

Guardall Ltd, Lochend Industrial Estate, Queen Anne Drive, Newbridge, Midlothian, EH28 8PL Tel: 0131-333 2900 Fax: 0131-333 4919 E-mail: sales@guardall.co.uk

Homeguard Security Systems Ltd, 3 Grimsdells Corner, Sycamore Road, Amersham, Buckinghamshire, HP6 5EL Tel: (01494) 728989 Fax: (01494) 728189 E-mail: sales@homeguardsecurity.co.uk

Hytek Alarms Ltd, 115 Fossdale Moss, Leyland, Leyland, PR26 7AS Tel: (01772) 436317 Fax: (01772) 467402

▶ Imp Security Systems Ltd, 14 Raynton Close Washingborough, Lincoln, LN4 1HD Tel: (01522) 793666 Fax: (01522) 797300 E-mail: info@impsecurity.co.uk

Intruder Security Services, Security House 6-7 The Downs, Great Dunmow, Dunmow, Essex, CM6 1DS Tel: (01279) 758870 Fax: (01371) 879201 E-mail: info@intruder.co.uk

Iti Security, Aylesford Business Centre, High Street, Aylesford, Kent, ME20 7AX Tel: (01732) 522090 E-mail: sales@itisecurity.co.uk

▶ Craig Jones, 2 Russell Avenue, High Lane, Stockport, Cheshire, SK6 8DT Tel: (01663) 762181

▶ M D A Security Systems Ltd, 10, Elm Lane, Tongham, Farnham, Surrey, GU10 1BX Tel: (01252) 342225

MG Micro, 41 Priest Meadow, Fleckney, Leicester, LE8 8TZ Tel: 0116-240 3157 Fax: 0116-240 3157

▶ Midland Security & Surveillance, 14 Clarry Drive, Sutton Coldfield, West Midlands, B74 2RA Tel: 0121-323 2126 Fax: 0121-323 2165

Moray Security, 7 Barwell Road, Forres, Morayshire, IV36 1FD Tel: (01309) 672117 E-mail: sales@moraysecurity.co.uk

MRP Alarms, The Forge Haggs Farm, Haggs Road, Follifoot, Harrogate, North Yorkshire, HG3 1EQ Tel: (01423) 873900 Fax: (01423) 872494 E-mail: sales@mrpalarms.com

▶ Pinnacle Telecommunications, 142N, St. Clair Street, Kirkcaldy, Fife, KY1 2BZ Tel: (01592) 654176 Fax: (01592) 654176

Rael Securities, 139 Rickerscote Road, Stafford, ST17 4HE Tel: (01785) 227632

▶ Rhino Security, 25 Willow Farm Way, Broomfield, Herne Bay, Kent, CT6 7PF Tel: (0870) 7491950 Fax: (0870) 0056833 E-mail: sale@rhinosecurityltd.co.uk

Riscr Group, Commerce House, Whitbrook Way, Stakehill Distribution Park, Middleton, Manchester, M24 2SS Tel: 0161-655 5555 Fax: 0161-655 5599 E-mail: sales@riscrgroup.co.uk

Texecom Ltd, 559A Wilbraham Road, Manchester, M21 0AE Tel: 0161-862 9482 Fax: 0161-881 5147 E-mail: enq@texe.com

Watchdogs Security Alarms, 47 Great Meadow, Shaw, Oldham, OL2 7PX Tel: (01706) 840077

Westcountry Security Ltd, 9 Orchard Court, Heron Road, Sowton Industrial Estate, Exeter, EX2 7LL Tel: (01392) 671561 Fax: (01392) 671562 E-mail: sales@westcountrysecurity.co.uk

BURGLAR ALARMS, *See also headings for particular types*

▶ 1st Security Concepts, 796 London Road, Larkfield, Aylesford, Kent, ME20 6HJ Tel: (01732) 321695 E-mail: thecoppings@msn.com

B Safe Security Systems, Security Buildings, Storforth Lane, Chesterfield, Derbyshire, S40 2TU Tel: (01246) 556400 Fax: (01246) 232050 E-mail: sales@bsafesecurity.co.uk

Besure Security Systems, Belcrest House, 114 Battle Road, St. Leonards-on-Sea, East Sussex, TN37 7EP Tel: (01424) 852343 Fax: (01424) 200999 E-mail: enquiries@besuresecurity.co.uk

Bharat Alarms, 32-34 Constitution Hill, Birmingham, B19 3JT Tel: 0121-236 7449 Fax: 0121-236 8996 E-mail: bharatuk@aol.com

C & H Alarm Systems, 12 Park Hill Gardens, Swallownest, Sheffield, S26 4WL Tel: 0114-293 9000 Fax: 0114-293 9000

▶ C S I, 36 Luzley Brook Road, Royton, Oldham, OL2 6SQ Tel: (01706) 843249 E-mail: spencer.marsden1@btinternet.com

Caretech Systems Ltd, 114 Cateran Way, Cramlington, Northumberland, NE23 6HG Tel: (01670) 739987 Fax: (0845) 2827347 E-mail: sales@caretechsystems.co.uk

Complete Home Security, 467 Liverpool Road, Southport, Merseyside, PR8 3BN Tel: (01704) 579844 Fax: (01704) 579844

Dawes Security Systems, 74 Hulme Hall Road, Cheadle Hulme, Cheadle, Cheshire, SK8 6LF Tel: 0161-485 8100 Fax: 0161-486 6500 E-mail: sales@dawessecurity.co.uk

Elm Alarms, 14 St. Vincent Road, Clacton-on-Sea, Essex, CO15 1NA Tel: (01255) 475017 Fax: (01255) 475017

Forest Alarms, Fetter Hill, Coleford, Gloucestershire, GL16 7LU Tel: (01594) 832739 Fax: (01594) 836464

Gardiner Security Ltd, Unit 2, Castleton Close, Leeds, LS12 2DS Tel: 0113-244 9031 Fax: 0113-244 9096

Guardian Electronic Security UK Ltd, Willow House, Mersey View, Liverpool, L22 6QA Tel: 0151-931 5511 Fax: 0151-284 5005

Houseguard Security Systems Ltd, 35 Peabody Road, Farnborough, Hampshire, GU14 6HA Tel: (01252) 377688 Fax: (01252) 375387

▶ J L G Security Services, Westmead House, 123 Westmead Road, Sutton, Surrey, SM1 4JH Tel: (020) 8642 8996 Fax: (020) 8643 6367 E-mail: sales@jlg.co.uk

▶ Lazer Security Ltd, DMB House, 2 Beckett Road, Doncaster, South Yorkshire, DN2 4AA Tel: (01302) 344773

Mainline Security Systems, 39 Wrawby Street, Brigg, South Humberside, DN20 9BS Tel: (01652) 650567 Fax: (01652) 658818

Oakpark Alarms, Hydra House, 26 North Street, Ashford, Kent, TN24 8JR Tel: (01233) 643851

▶ Oracle Security Systems Ltd, 19 Godric Square, Woodston Industrial Estate, peterborough, PE2 7JL Tel: 08700 801716 Fax: 01733 233323 E-mail: info@oraclesecurity.co.uk

Orion Security Systems, 39 Nursery Lane, Northampton, NN2 7QG Tel: (01604) 474016 Fax: (01604) 468846

▶ Progress Fire & Security Ltd, 54 Ashfield Road, Sale, Cheshire, M33 7DT Tel: 0161-976 4802 Fax: 0161-905 3948

▶ PRW Group Ltd, D Second Avenue, Westfield Industrial Estate, Midsomer Norton, Radstock, BA3 4BH Tel: (01761) 416885 Fax: (01761) 419381 E-mail: business@trwgroup.co.uk

Riscr Group, Commerce House, Whitbrook Way, Stakehill Distribution Park, Middleton, Manchester, M24 2SS Tel: 0161-655 5555 Fax: 0161-655 5599 E-mail: sales@riscrgroup.co.uk

Safeguard Security Systems, 17-19 Townhead, Kilmaurs, Kilmarnock, Ayrshire, KA3 2ST Tel: (01563) 523101 Fax: (01563) 523101

Security Group Distribution Ltd, 8 Oakenhill Road, Bristol, BS4 4LR Tel: 0117-914 1180 Fax: 0117-914 1181 E-mail: security@groupdistribution.fsnet.co.uk

Sound & Secure Ltd, 454-456 Thornton Road, Bradford, West Yorkshire, BD8 9BS Tel: (01274) 775005 Fax: (01274) 770051

Sovereign Security Services Ltd, 28 Station Road, Shirehampton, Bristol, BS11 9TX Tel: 0117-982 6618

Specialised Security Systems Ltd, Carmichael House, Village Green, Inkberrow, Worcester, WR7 4DZ Tel: (01386) 792522 Fax: (01386) 792729 E-mail: info@specialisedsecurity.co.uk

Spider Security Alarms, 8 Girtrell Road, Wirral, Merseyside, CH49 4LQ Tel: 0151-604 0344

▶ Ssed Ltd, 242 Trelawney Avenue, Langley, Slough, SL3 7UD Tel: (01753) 542727 Fax: (01753) 542727 E-mail: raj@gx-security.com

Steve Nunn Electrical Electric Contractors/Installers, 3 Forest End, Kennett, Newmarket, Suffolk, CB8 7RG Tel: (01638) 552110

Universal Locks, 894 Plymouth Road, Slough, SL1 4LP Tel: (01753) 696630 Fax: (01753) 568461 E-mail: info@universalsecurity.co.uk

BURGLARY PREVENTION ENGINEERS OR SERVICES

Profile Security Services, 2 Brittens Court, Clifton Reynes, Olney, Buckinghamshire, MK46 5LG Tel: (01234) 240500 Fax: (01234) 240460

Wireless Alarms, 17 Church Road, Great Bookham, Leatherhead, Surrey, KT23 3PG Tel: (01372) 450960 Fax: (01372) 450961

BURIED UTILITIES MAPPING

Aegis Survey Consultants Ltd, Ongar Road, Abridge, Romford, RM4 1AA Tel: (01708) 688050 Fax: (01708) 688045 E-mail: nt@aegissurveyconsultants.com

▶ Cornerstone Projects Ltd, PO Box 182, Wirral, Merseyside, CH29 9AU Tel: 0151-632 4555 Fax: (0870) 7626172 E-mail: enquiries@cornerstoneprojects.co.uk

Ekaw Projects Ltd, Link House, Church Street, Haxey, Doncaster, South Yorkshire, DN9 2HY Tel: (01427) 752006 Fax: (01427) 753581

Mason Land Surveys Ltd, Dickson Street, Dunfermline, Fife, KY12 7SL Tel: (01383) 727261 Fax: (01383) 739480 E-mail: sales@mason.co.uk

▶ UXB (UK) Ltd, Challacombe Close, Landkey, Barnstaple, Devon, EX32 0NG Tel: (01271) 831439 Fax: (01271) 831442 E-mail: pjh@uxb.com

BURIED UTILITIES SURVEYING

Aegis Survey Consultants Ltd, Ongar Road, Abridge, Romford, RM4 1AA Tel: (01708) 688050 Fax: (01708) 688045 E-mail: nt@aegissurveyconsultants.com

▶ Cornerstone Projects Ltd, PO Box 182, Wirral, Merseyside, CH29 9AU Tel: 0151-632 4555 Fax: (0870) 7626172 E-mail: enquiries@cornerstoneprojects.co.uk

F T Gearing Landscape Services Ltd, Crompton Road Depot, Stevenage, Hertfordshire, SG1 2EE Tel: (01438) 369321 Fax: (01438) 353039 E-mail: fred@ft-gearing.co.uk

BURIED VIA MULTILAYER PRINTED CIRCUITS

Huntrose UK Ltd, Jarman Way, Chard Business Park, Chard, Somerset, TA20 1FB Tel: (01460) 61895 Fax: (01460) 67088 E-mail: huntrose@lineone.net

BURNERS, DUAL FUEL, GAS/OIL

Eurograde Plant Ltd, 3 Viscount Industrial Estate, Horton Road, Colnbrook, Slough, SL3 0DF Tel: (020) 8606 0420 Fax: (01753) 681452 E-mail: david@eurograde.com

Maxon Combustion Systems Ltd, Chantry House, High Street, Coleshill, Birmingham, B46 3BP Tel: (01675) 464334 Fax: (01675) 467285 E-mail: kp@maxon.be

Metal Developments Ltd, The Workshop, Wheatcroft Farm, Cullompton, Devon, EX15 1RA Tel: (01884) 35806 Fax: (01884) 35505

N A Stordy Combustion Ltd, Heath Mill Road, Wombourne, Wolverhampton, WV5 8BD Tel: (01902) 891200 Fax: (01902) 895552 E-mail: sales@stordy.co.uk

S I T Bray Ltd, Education Road, Meanwood Road, Leeds, LS7 2AN Tel: 0113-281 6700 Fax: 0113-281 6702 E-mail: sit.uk@sitgroup.it

Saacke Ltd, Marshlands Spur, Portsmouth, PO6 1RX Tel: (023) 9238 3111 Fax: (023) 9232 7120 E-mail: info@saacke.co.uk

Weishaupt UK Ltd, Stoke Gardens, Slough, SL1 3QD Tel: (01753) 512345 Fax: (01753) 512585 E-mail: sales@weishaupt.idps.co.uk

BURNERS, OXY-FUEL

Maxon Combustion Systems Ltd, Chantry House, High Street, Coleshill, Birmingham, B46 3BP Tel: (01675) 464334 Fax: (01675) 467285 E-mail: kp@maxon.be

BURNISHED METALS

Barking Shopfronts Ltd, Unit 1 Barking Industrial Park, Alfreds Way, Barking, Essex, IG11 0TJ Tel: (020) 8591 0504 Fax: (020) 8594 3060

Trimetals Ltd, Sunrise Business Park, Higher Shaftesbury Road, Blandford Forum, Dorset, DT11 8ST Tel: (01258) 459441 Fax: (01258) 480408 E-mail: trimetals@btconnect.com

BURNISHING TOOLS

C L A Manufacturing Ltd, 10 Binns Close, Coventry, CV4 9TB Tel: (024) 7646 5535 Fax: (024) 7669 4543 E-mail: info@clatools.co.uk

BURSTING DISCS TO SPECIFICATION

Elfab Ltd, Alder Road, North Shields, Tyne & Wear, NE29 8SD Tel: 0191-293 1269 Fax: 0191-293 1200 E-mail: sales@elfab.com

BURSTING PANELS

Elfab Ltd, Alder Road, North Shields, Tyne & Wear, NE29 8SD Tel: 0191-293 1269 Fax: 0191-293 1200 E-mail: sales@elfab.com

BURSTING SAFETY DISCS

A F S Associates, 1 The Paddock, Much Wenlock, Shropshire, TF13 6LT Tel: (01952) 728188 Fax: (01952) 728174 E-mail: sales@afsassociates.co.uk

BUS BODY BUILDERS

Minibus Options Ltd, PO Box 1, High Peak, Derbyshire, SK23 7LY Tel: (01663) 735355 Fax: (01663) 735352 E-mail: sales@minibusoptions.co.uk

Optare Group Ltd, Manston Lane, Leeds, LS15 8SU Tel: 0113-264 5182 Fax: 0113-260 6635 E-mail: chris.wise@optare.com

BUS FITTINGS AND ACCESSORIES, *See Coach etc*

BUS HIRE

▶ Clydewide Taxis, 99 High Street, Lanark, ML11 7LN Tel: (01555) 663813 Fax: (01555) 678937 E-mail: taxis@clydewide.co.uk

▶ Metro Rentals Limited, Unit 2, Colne Way, Colne Way Court, Watford, WD24 7NE Tel: 01923 630630 Fax: 01923 639191 E-mail: enquiries@metrorentals.co.uk

▶ Timebus Travel, Boleyn Drive, St. Albans, Hertfordshire, AL1 2BP Tel: (01727) 866248

▶ Translinc Ltd, Jarvis House, 157 Sadler Road, Lincoln, LN6 3RS Tel: (01522) 503400 Fax: (01522) 552997 E-mail: sales@translinc.co.uk

BUS INTERIORS, GLASS FIBRE OR FIBREGLASS

Stuart Pease Fibreglass Ltd, Unit 1 Taylors Close, Parkgate, Rotherham, South Yorkshire, S62 6NW Tel: (01709) 527761 Fax: (01709) 522147 E-mail: stuartpeaseltd@btinternet.com

BUS SPARE PARTS/WEARING PARTS

Airlec Truck & Bus Parts, Unit 24 Tomlinson Business Park, Tomlinson Road, Leyland, PR25 2DY Tel: (01772) 433564 Fax: (01772) 433568 E-mail: sales@airlec.co.uk

▶ P S V Transport Systems Ltd, Unit 21 Impresa Park, Pindar Road, Hoddesdon, Hertfordshire, EN11 0DL Tel: (01992) 479950 Fax: (01992) 471676 E-mail: sales@psv-transport-systems.co.uk

▶ Ranell Ltd, Unit 7a Beckingham Business Park, Tolleshunt Major, Maldon, Essex, CM9 8LZ Tel: (01621) 869048 Fax: (01621) 868978 E-mail: info@ranell.com

BUSBAR ACCESSORIES

G K W Ltd, Merton Bank Road, St. Helens, Merseyside, WA9 1HP Tel: (01744) 762330 Fax: (01744) 754309 E-mail: kevin.jones@gordonkitto.co.uk

BUSBAR BENDING TOOLS

H.V. Wooding Ltd, Range Road Industrial Estate, Hythe, Kent, CT21 6HG Tel: (01303) 264471 Fax: (01303) 262408 E-mail: sales@hvwooding.co.uk

Instrument Transformers Ltd, 8 Lithgow Place, East Kilbride, Glasgow, G74 1PW Tel: (01355) 236057 Fax: (01355) 239259 E-mail: sales@itl-uk.com

BUSBAR CUTTING AND PUNCHING AND BENDING EQUIPMENT

S M L, 3 Little Common, Stanmore, Middlesex, HA7 3BZ Tel: (020) 8954 7302 Fax: (020) 8954 1703 E-mail: punches@sml.co.uk

BUSBAR DISTRIBUTION SYSTEMS

Eaton Electric Ltd, Reddings Lane, Tyseley, Birmingham, B11 3EZ Tel: 0121-685 2100 Fax: 0121-706 2012 E-mail: meminfo@eaton.com

Electrak Holdings Ltd, Number One Industrial Estate, Medomsley Road, Consett, County Durham, DH8 6SR Tel: (01207) 503400 Fax: (01207) 501799 E-mail: sales@electrak.co.uk

Eta-Com UK Ltd, Unit 15 City Business Centre, Brighton Road, Horsham, West Sussex, RH13 5BB Tel: (01403) 265767 Fax: (01403) 254131 E-mail: busduct@etacom-uk.com

Logstrup (UK) Ltd, Units 3H & 4H Lyntown Trading Estate, Lynwell Road, Manchester, M30 9QG Tel: 0161-788 9811 Fax: 0161-789 0063 E-mail: sales@logstrupuk.co.uk

M K Electric, The Arnold Centre, Paycocke Road, Basildon, Essex, SS14 3EA Tel: (01268) 563000 Fax: (01268) 563405 E-mail: mkorderingenquires@hornywell.com

Rolla Ltd, Atlas Mill Road, Brighouse, West Yorkshire, HD6 1ES Tel: (01484) 710226 Fax: (01484) 718608E-mail: sales@rolla.co.uk

Siemens P.L.C., Gatehouse Close, Aylesbury, Buckinghamshire, HP19 8DJ Tel: (01296) 339388 Fax: (01296) 339969 E-mail: marketing@moeller.co.uk

Staub Precision, 4 Vincients Road, Bumpers Farm, Chippenham, Wiltshire, SN14 6NQ Tel: (01249) 658197 Fax: (01249) 443408 E-mail: sales@staub.co.uk

BUSBAR FLEXIBLE EXPANSION JOINTS

Erico Europa GB Ltd, 52 Milford Road, Reading, RG1 8LJ Tel: 0118-958 8386 Fax: 0118-959 4856

BUSBAR INSULATION MATERIALS

▶ Electrical Insulators & Supports Ltd, Unit 3 Albert Street, Little Lever, Bolton, BL3 1JH Tel: (07092) 122440 E-mail: sales@electricalinsulators.co.uk

BUSBAR SECTIONS

Hydro Static Extrusions Ltd, Arran Road, North Muirton Industrial Estate, Perth, PH1 3DX Tel: (01738) 629381 Fax: (01738) 633933 E-mail: sales@hydrostatic.co.uk

BUSBAR SUPPORTS

▶ Electrical Insulators & Supports Ltd, Unit 3 Albert Street, Little Lever, Bolton, BL3 1JH Tel: (07092) 122440 E-mail: sales@electricalinsulators.co.uk

Termate Ltd, Leone Works, John Street, New Bassford, Nottingham, NG7 7HL Tel: 0115-978 4652 Fax: 0115-970 2106 E-mail: sales@termate.com

BUSBARS

▶ Electrical Insulators & Supports Ltd, Unit 3 Albert Street, Little Lever, Bolton, BL3 1JH Tel: (07092) 122440 E-mail: sales@electricalinsulators.co.uk

Hydro Static Extrusions Ltd, Arran Road, North Muirton Industrial Estate, Perth, PH1 3DX Tel: (01738) 629381 Fax: (01738) 633933 E-mail: sales@hydrostatic.co.uk

BUSINESS ADMINISTRATION SERVICES

▶ 1st Class Secretarial Services, 34 New Hunterfield, Gorebridge, Midlothian, EH23 4BD Tel: (01875) 823215 Fax: (01875) 823215 E-mail: dawn.lawson@1stclass.uk.com

▶ Adjayi Secretarial, 3 Maple Leaf Cottages, Blackboys, Uckfield, East Sussex, TN22 5LJ Tel: 01825 890955 Fax: 01825 890955 E-mail: sue@adjayi-secretarial.co.uk

▶ Downey & Co., Castle Street, Abergavenny, Gwent, NP7 5EE Tel: (01873) 859569 Fax: (01873) 855461 E-mail: huwdowney@btconnect.com

▶ Girl Friday Solutions, 13 Lower Icknield Way, Marsworth, Tring, Hertfordshire, HP23 4LW Tel: (07921) 770516 E-mail: girlfridaysolutions@hotmail.co.uk

J & S Horn Consultants Ltd, 24 Henderson Drive, Skene, Westhill, Aberdeenshire, AB32 6RA Tel: (01224) 744330 Fax: (01224) 744330 E-mail: training@peakperformance.tv

▶ K3 Secretarial Services, Blenheim Court, 17 Beulah Hill, London, SE19 3LJ Tel: (07786) 923079 Fax: (020) 8771 3651 E-mail: info@kzvirtualassistant.com

▶ MF Home Typists, 34 Devon Avenue, Twickenham, Twickenham, TW2 6PW Tel: (020) 8755 4450 E-mail: farrm001@rgfl.org.uk

▶ SpiderWeb Business Admin, 16 Allerton Close, Coventry, CV2 5DH Tel: (07981) 785717 Fax: E-mail: info@spideradmin.co.uk

▶ Symmetry Communication, Chalfont House, Hampden Road, Chalfont St. Peter, Gerrards Cross, Buckinghamshire, SL9 9RY Tel: (01753) 279200 Fax: (01753) 279301 E-mail: info@symmetryplc.com

The Trust Partnership, 6 Trull Farm Buildings, Trull, Tetbury, Gloucestershire, GL8 8SQ Tel: 01284 841900 Fax: 01285 841576 E-mail: Belinda@TheTrustPartnership.com

▶ Sandrine Vaillant, Old Vallis Cottage, Vallis Road, Frome, Somerset, BA11 3EN Tel: (0777) 9668707 Fax: (01373) 474945 E-mail: sandrine.vaillant@btinternet.co.uk

▶ Virtual Office Bureau Limited, 4 Twyfords, Crowborough, East Sussex, TN6 1YE Tel: 01892 653325 Fax: 01892 665861 E-mail: virtualofficebureau@yahoo.co.uk

▶ Willows Of London Ltd, 17 St. Johns Terrace, London, E7 8BX Tel: (020) 8345 6727 Fax: (020) 8257 7980 E-mail: peter@willowsoflondon.clara.co.uk

BUSINESS ADVICE

▶ 2-home-business.com Ltd, 501 International House, 223 Regent Street, London, UK, W1B 2QD Tel: 01743 284757 E-mail: enquiries@2-home-business.com

▶ 2XL: Business Solutions, 22 Lenten Grove, Heywood, Lancashire, OL10 2LR Tel: (01706) 620998E-mail: info@2xlbusinesssolutions.com

▶ Action International, 6 New James Street, Blaenavon, Pontypool, Torfaen, NP4 9JU Tel: (01495) 790008 Fax: (08701) 333796 E-mail: gitenkapdee@action-international.com

▶ Advanced Research Associates Ltd, 65 Mill Lane, Attleborough, Norfolk, NR17 2NW Tel: (01953) 452751 Fax: 01953 452751 E-mail: ARAltd@aol.com

▶ Agora Business Improvements Ltd, 5 Montgomery Mews, Leegomery, Telford, Shropshire, TF1 6YU Tel: 08454 089429 E-mail: neil.thomas@a-b-i.co.uk

▶ Amicable Mortgage Services, 32 Twyford Avenue, Southampton, SO15 5NP Tel: (0800) 7810414 Fax: (023) 8032 2832 E-mail: patrick@effectivebusiness.info

▶ Bizvizion Limited, Brighton Media Centre, 15-17 Middle Street, Brighton, BN1 1AL Tel: (01273) 275832 E-mail: info@bizvizion.co.uk

Bolton Business Ventures Ltd, 46 Lower Bridgeman Street, Bolton, BL2 1DG Tel: (01204) 391400 Fax: (01204) 380076 E-mail: sales@bbvonline.net

▶ Bosworth Business Management Limited, 37 Northumberland Avenue, Market Bosworth, Nuneaton, Warwickshire, CV13 0RJ Tel: 07050 369499 E-mail: contact@bbml.org

Business Centre, 132 Samlet Road, Swansea Enterprise Park, Swansea, SA7 9AF Tel: (01792) 310110 Fax: (0870) 4280925 E-mail: enquiries@thebusinesscentre.info

Business Link, Kingsgate House, 66-74 Victoria Street, London, SW1E 6SW Tel: (020) 7215 5000 Fax: (020) 7215 5001 E-mail: enquiries@businesslink.org

▶ Businessline, Wrexham Library, Rhosddu Road, Wrexham, Clwyd, LL11 1AU Tel: (01978) 292092 Fax: (01978) 292611 E-mail: businessline@wrexham.gov.uk

CMAssociates Limited, 23 Rhosleigh Avenue, Sharples Park, Bolton, BL1 6PP E-mail: enquires@cmassociates.co.uk

▶ Debt Aid, Chatton Mill, Chatton, Alnwick, Northumberland, NE66 5RA Tel: (01668) 215505 Fax: (01668) 215000 E-mail: marketing@debtaid.ltd.uk

▶ Direct Route Collections Ltd, Tong Hall, Tong Lane, Bradford, West Yorkshire, BD4 0RR Tel: 0113-287 9123 Fax: 0113-287 9153 E-mail: rdavy@directroute.co.uk

▶ Exceptional Thinking LLP, 10 Orchard Road, Alderton, Tewkesbury, Gloucestershire, GL20 8NS Tel: (0845) 6449371 Fax: 0870 751 8215 E-mail: info@exceptionalthinking.co.uk

Exportential, 13 Beccelm Drive, Crowland, Peterborough, PE6 0AG Tel: (01733) 211873 E-mail: info@exportential.co.uk

▶ The Fletcher Thompson Practice Limited, Mill House, 21 High Street, Ely, Cambs, CB7 5XR Tel: 0870 2323130 Fax: 0870 2323120 E-mail: info@fletcher-thompson.co.uk

▶ Garner Associates, 138 Bromham Road, Bedford, MK40 2QW Tel: (01234) 354508 Fax: (01234) 349588 E-mail: email@garnerassociates.co.uk

▶ Handscombe Financial Planning Ltd, Telford House, 102 Collingdon Street, Luton, LU1 1RX Tel: (01582) 400202 Fax: (01582) 400951 E-mail: advice@handscombes.com

▶ Helen Agutter, 1 Bedford Place, Brighton, BN1 2PT Tel: (01273) 231310 Fax: (01273) 231310 E-mail: helen.agutter@ntlworld.com

▶ Help 4 You Ltd, 6 Deal Castle Road, Deal, Kent, CT14 7BB Tel: (07773) 380133 E-mail: enquiries@help4you.ltd.uk

▶ KJW Resources Ltd, 12 Main Street, Scarcliffe, Chesterfield, Derbyshire, S44 6SZ Tel: (01246) 827703 E-mail: info@kjw-resources.com

▶ Manufacturing Executive Ltd, Ivy House 90 Town Street, Lound, Retford, Nottinghamshire, DN22 8RX Tel: (01777) 818280 E-mail: info@manufacturingexecutive.com

▶ Mba Businessense Ltd, Skiers Hall Farm, Elsecar, Barnsley, South Yorkshire, S74 8EU Tel: (01226) 748338 Fax: (01226) 748338 E-mail: info@mbabusinessense.co.uk

▶ Nationwide Telesales Co., 56 John O'Gaunt Road, Kenilworth, Warwickshire, CV8 1DZ Tel: (01926) 511651 Fax: (01926) 511651 E-mail: chris.bradford@nationwidetelesales.co.uk

▶ Nieman Walters, 7 Bourne Court Southend Road, Woodford Green, Essex, IG8 8HD Tel: (020) 8550 3131 Fax: (020) 8550 6020 E-mail: howard@nwnaccounts.com

Nukta Ltd, PO Box 31434, London, W4 4FQ Tel: (020) 8996 9043 Fax: (07092) 336473 E-mail: sales@nuktaltd.co.uk

▶ P & J Associates Ltd, Pulsar, Damask Green Road, Weston, Hitchin, Hertfordshire, SG4 7DA Tel: (01462) 790446 E-mail: info@pjassociates.co.uk

▶ Powerview Consulting Services, 44 Rectory Avenue, Corfe Mullen, Wimborne, Dorset, BH21 3EZ Tel: (01202) 699977 Fax: (01202) 699977 E-mail: business.growth@powerview-services.com

▶ Proficio Solutions Ltd, 2 Cleaver Cottages Appleshaw, Andover, Hampshire, SP11 9AD Tel: (01264) 772047 Fax: (01264) 772047 E-mail: info@proficiosolutions.co.uk

▶ Quality Matters Ltd, PO Box 5479, Maldon, Essex, CM9 8GG Tel: (01621) 868767 Fax: (01621) 868728 E-mail: sales@quality-matters.com

Real 60 Minute Money, 6A Bell Flats, 280-286 High Road, Willesden, London, NW10 2EX Tel: (0870) 896 4064 Fax: (0870) 762 3512 E-mail: info@real60minutemoney.co.uk

▶ Real Smart Hypnosis, Nova Lodge, Kenilworth Road, Leamington Spa, Warwickshire, CV32 6JJ Tel: (01926) 332935 E-mail: paulhastings@mac.com

▶ Redefining Financial Solutions Ltd, 9 Hardwicke Gardens, Amersham, Buckinghamshire, HP6 6AH Tel: (01494) 431739 E-mail: info@redefiningfinancialsolutions.com

▶ Solubus Ltd, Laggan, Sunnyside Road, Falkirk, FK1 4BG Tel: (01324) 871667 Fax: (01324) 871667 E-mail: stuart@solubus.co.uk

▶ Stewart & Partners, 6 Regent Gate, High Street, Waltham Cross, Hertfordshire, EN8 7AF Tel: (0870) 0508091 Fax: (0845) 2050033 E-mail: mail@stewartpartners.co.uk

Tancred Solutions, 32b High Causeway, Whittlesey, Peterborough, PE7 1AJ Tel: (01733) 350925 Fax: (01733) 350832 E-mail: info@tancredsolutions.com

▶ Unique Consulting Solutions Ltd, 32 New Road, Lymm, Cheshire, WA13 9DY Tel: (01925) 753899 Fax: (01925) 758815 E-mail: trevor@uniqueconsulting.co.uk

▶ V C Consulting, Suite 6, 146 Hagley Road, Birmingham, B16 9NX Tel: 0121-454 2334 Fax: 0121-454 5026 E-mail: info@vc-consulting.co.uk

Wellingborough Town Centre Patnership Ltd, 18-19 Spring Lane, Wellingborough, Northamptonshire, NN8 1EY Tel: (01933) 270795 Fax: (01933) 222202 E-mail: info@wellingboroughchamber.co.uk

Zemaitis Business Consultants, 278 City Way, Rochester, Kent, ME1 2BL Tel: (01634) 404903 Fax: (01634) 404903 E-mail: info@zemaitis-uk.com

BUSINESS ADVISERS, RATING/ RENT APPEAL

Adr International Ltd, 82 High Street, Wallingford, Oxfordshire, OX10 0BT Tel: (01491) 825666 Fax: (01491) 825688 E-mail: info@adr-international.com

Edinburgh Business Development, 27 Melville Street, Edinburgh, EH3 7JF Tel: 0131-477 7000 Fax: 0131-477 8051 E-mail: events@ecce.org

Ernst & Young Ltd, George House, 50 George Square, Glasgow, G2 1RR Tel: 0141-626 5000 Fax: 0141-626 5001

Future Machines Ltd, Unit 20 Fleetway Business Park, Wadsworth Road, Greenford, Middlesex, UB6 7LF Tel: (020) 8997 4488

Homestart Carrickfergus, 8 Meadowbank Road, Carrickfergus, County Antrim, BT38 8YF Tel: (028) 9332 8875 Fax: (028) 9336 9979 E-mail: info@ceal.co.uk

Leatherhead Food International Ltd, Randalls Road, Leatherhead, Surrey, KT22 7RY Tel: (01372) 376761 Fax: (01372) 386228 E-mail: enquiries@lfra.co.uk

North City Training, 275 Antrim Road, Belfast, BT15 2GZ Tel: (028) 9074 5408 Fax: (028) 9074 0329

Remote Technologies, West Greenbank, Hickmans la, Haywards Heath, W. Sussex, RH16 2DR Tel: (01273) 813869

Venture Wales, Venture House, Navigation Park, Abercynon, Mountain Ash, Mid Glamorgan, CF45 4SN Tel: (01443) 742888 Fax: (01443) 742444E-mail: abercynon@venturewales.com

West Of England Friends Housing Society Ltd, PO Box 164, Bristol, BS6 6BH Tel: 0117-989 2020 Fax: 0117-924 4615

BUSINESS ASSET FINANCE

▶ Golf Finance Ltd, 4 Church Road, North Berwick, East Lothian, EH39 4AD Tel: (01620) 890200 Fax: (01620) 895895 E-mail: sales@golffinance.co.uk

BUSINESS CARD DESIGN

▶ Accent Print & Design, 28-29 Maxwell Road, Woodston Industry, Peterborough, PE2 7JE Tel: (01733) 233238 Fax: (01733) 246519 E-mail: sales@accentprint.net

▶ The Design Initiative, Unit 2 Mowbray Street, Stockport, Cheshire, SK1 3EJ Tel: 0161-474 1314 Fax: 0161-474 1314 E-mail: info@designinitiative.co.uk

Graphic Core, 117 Gorseinon Road, Penllergaer, Swansea, SA4 9AA Tel: (01792) 895 100 Fax: (01792) 895 114 E-mail: studio@graphic-core.com

▶ Rude Goose Ltd, Balfron, Balfron, Glasgow, G63 0LF Tel: (01360) 551205 E-mail: zoe@rudegoose.com

▶ Teddington Photo Centre, 54 Broad Street, Teddington, Middlesex, TW11 8QY Tel: (020) 8943 5232 Fax: (020) 8943 5376

BUSINESS CARD PRINTING

Albion Printers, 3 Bearsted Green Business Centre, The Green, Bearsted, Maidstone, Kent, ME14 4DF Tel: (01622) 631666

Alphagraphics, 68 Darlington Street, Wolverhampton, WV1 4ND Tel: (01902) 711151 Fax: (01902) 710174 E-mail: wolves016@alphagraphics.co.uk

Biltmore Printers, 14 Manners View, Newport, Isle of Wight, PO30 5FA Tel: (01983) 529788 Fax: (01983) 825528 E-mail: info@biltmoreprinters.co.uk

C S F Print, 6 Hockliffe Brae, Walnut Tree, Milton Keynes, MK7 7BQ Tel: (01908) 550643 Fax: (01908) 550611 E-mail: sales@csfprint.com

Cardmaster UK, 2 Christopher Road, Leeds, LS6 2JX Tel: 0113-244 2265 Fax: 0113-244 2265 E-mail: bouncers@inname.com

Carfax Cards Ltd, 76 Glentham Road, London, SW13 9JJ Tel: (020) 8748 1122 Fax: (020) 8748 7110 E-mail: carfax@business-cards.co.uk

Cavalry Creative Services, 11 Bury Road, Hatfield, Hertfordshire, AL10 8BJ Tel: (01707) 274584 Fax: (01707) 321043 E-mail: cavalry@ntlworld.com

Clearprint, 99 East Road, Sleaford, Lincolnshire, NG34 7EH Tel: (01529) 303176 Fax: (01529) 303172 E-mail: sales@clearaprint.com

▶ Colourspec Ltd, 11 Cricketers Way, Chatteris, Cambridgeshire, PE16 6UR Tel: (01354) 696496 E-mail: sales@colourspec.co.uk

E G Brown Bristol Ltd, 63 Quarrington Road, Bristol, BS7 9PJ Tel: 0117-951 3215 Fax: 0117-935 4250

Efficiency Print Ltd, Engine Lane, Stourbridge, West Midlands, DY9 7AQ Tel: (01384) 891986 Fax: (01384) 893437 E-mail: colin@effprint.u-net.com

Entaprint Ltd, 1 Penfold Road Woodcote, Cranleigh, Surrey, GU6 8NZ Tel: (01483) 273173

Falcon Press (Stockton-on-Tees) Ltd, Task Industrial Estate, Portrack Lane, Stockton-On-Tees, Cleveland, TS18 2ES Tel: (01642) 674298 Fax: (01642) 612382 E-mail: enquiries@falconpress-printing.co.uk

Ferguson Print Keswick Ltd, 24 St John Street, Keswick, Cumbria, CA12 5AT Tel: (01768) 772486 Fax: (01768) 771121 E-mail: fergusonbrosltd@btconnect.com

Fine Print Stockport Ltd, Unit 6f Lowick Close, Hazel Grove, Stockport, Cheshire, SK7 5ED Tel: 0161-484 2244 Fax: 0161-484 2255 E-mail: info@fineprint-stockport.co.uk

G P S Document Management, Park House, 15-19 Greenhill Crescent, Watford, WD18 8PH Tel: (01923) 241272 Fax: (01923) 244475 E-mail: info@gpsdm.co.uk

H N Cooper, 353-355 High Street, West Bromwich, West Midlands, B70 9QG Tel: 0121-553 0836 Fax: 0121-553 0836

Company Image, 334 Selbourne Road, Luton, LU4 8NU Tel: (01582) 503010 Fax: (01582) 572069 E-mail: companyimage@btconnect.com

Kings Land Colour Ltd, Unit 2, Roslin Square, Roslin Road, Acton, London, W3 8DH Tel: (020) 8993 7111 Fax: (020) 8993 2243 E-mail: sales@kingslandcolour.co.uk

Kinmel Paper Supplies, 180 Wellington Road, Rhyl, Clwyd, LL18 1LL Tel: (01745) 354589 Fax: (01745) 354589

Limavady Printing Co. Ltd, 26C Catherine Street, Limavady, County Londonderry, BT49 9DB Tel: (028) 7776 2051 Fax: (028) 7776 2132 E-mail: print@limprint.com

Pennine Printing Services Ltd, Commercial Mills, Oldham Road, Sowerby Bridge, West Yorkshire, HX6 4EH Tel: (01422) 825333 Fax: (01422) 825444 E-mail: pennineprinting@btconnect.com

PMC Systems, Whitehill Industrial Estate, Whitehill Lane, Wootton Bassett, Swindon, SN4 7DB Tel: (01793) 848817 Fax: (01793) 848846 E-mail: pmccards@aol.com

▶ Print Innovative Technology Ltd, Camilla Court, The Street, Nacton, Ipswich, IP10 0EU Tel: (01473) 655141 Fax: (01473) 655148 E-mail: neil@print-it.tv

BUSINESS COACHING

Asset Business Coaching Ltd, 120 Narbeth Drive, Aylesbury, Buckinghamshire, HP20 1PZ Tel: 01296 394222 E-mail: info@assetbusinesscoaching.com

▶ CMS Partnership, MILRIG, 56 Prestwick Road, Ayr, KA8 8JR Tel: 01292 260393 Fax: 01292 281214 E-mail: rob@cms-partnership.com

▶ Crown Coaching, 11 Rookery Court, Marlow, Buckinghamshire, SL7 3HR Tel: (01628) 488042 E-mail: helen@crowncoaching.com

▶ Den Caney, 182 Stonehouse Lane, Quinton, Birmingham, B32 3AH Tel: 0121-427 2693 Fax: 0121-427 8905 E-mail: dencaneycoaches@blueyonder.co.uk

▶ Eskhill & Co., Eskhill House, 15 Inveresk Village, Musselburgh, Midlothian, EH21 7TD Tel: 0131-271 4000 Fax: 0131-271 7000

▶ Helen Redfern, 21 Vincent Road, Croydon, CR0 6ED Tel: (020) 8405 3392 E-mail: helen@helenredfern.co.uk

▶ Jigsaw Executive Ltd, Regus House, Herald Way, Pegasus Business Park, Castle Donington, DE74 2TZ Tel: 01332 638046 Fax: 01332 638001 E-mail: info@JigsawExecutive.com

▶ Leap Coaching Associates, 7 Hopewell Way, Crigglestone, Wakefield, West Yorkshire, WF4 3PU Tel: (01924) 254173

▶ Stephen Ward & Company, Warwick Corner, 42 Warwick Road, Kenilworth, Warwickshire, CV8 1HE Tel: 01926 866610 Fax: 01926 851534 E-mail: mail@stephen-ward.com

BUSINESS COACHING – *continued*

Unique Advantage Coaching, 11 Babylon Lane, Bishampton, Pershore, Worcestershire, WR10 2NN Tel: (0845) 6442424 Fax: (0870) 1328311
E-mail: enquiries@uniqueadvantage.co.uk

BUSINESS CONSULTANCY, INTERNATIONAL

▶ Andersen Offshore Company Formations, PO Box 8188, Colchester, CO3 3WW Tel: (020) 8123 1493 E-mail: idpnd@yahoo.co.uk

▶ Baxter (Consultants) Ltd, Floor 6, 456-458 The Strand, London, WC2R 0DZ Tel: 07092 090755
E-mail: enquiries@baxterconsultants.com

▶ Business Initiatives BDS Ltd, Hardhams Cottage Clay Lane, Fishbourne, Chichester, West Sussex, PO18 8BT Tel: (01243) 775785 Fax: (01243) 528923
E-mail: adrian@business-initiatives.com

▶ Camellia Universal Ltd, 3 Cornwall Road, Harpenden, Hertfordshire, AL5 4TQ Tel: (01582) 690442 Fax: 01582 690442
E-mail: camellia@camelliauniversal.com

▶ Pharmalink Consulting, Vandervell House, Vanwall Business Park, Maidenhead, Berkshire, SL6 4UB Tel: 01628 509090 Fax: 01628 509125
E-mail: info@pharmalinkconsulting.com

BUSINESS CONSULTANTS, MANAGEMENT/FINANCE

▶ A & C Management Consultants Ltd, 13a Harben Parade, Finchley Road, London, NW3 6LH Tel: (020) 7564 7050 Fax: (020) 7564 8764
E-mail: acmanagement@tiscali.co.uk

▶ The Accruals Bureau & Credithouse P.L.C., Spectrum House, Dunstable Road, Redbourn, St. Albans, Hertfordshire, AL3 7PR Tel: (0870) 4441753 Fax: (01582) 791203
E-mail: info@abandc.co.uk

Andersen, 4th Floor Forum Ho, Grenville St, St. Helier, Jersey, JE2 4UF Tel: (01534) 707100 Fax: (01534) 707101
E-mail: diane.l.porritt@uk.andersen.com

▶ Anpro Ltd, 1 Northumberland Avenue, London, WC2N 5BW Tel: (020) 7872 5658 Fax: (020) 7872 5611 E-mail: change@anpro.co.uk

Arno GB Ltd, Discovery House, 125 Redcliff Street, Bristol, BS1 6HU Tel: 0117-929 2541 Fax: 0117-929 4684
E-mail: display@arno-online.co.uk

▶ Auto Business Solutions Ltd, Ivy Road Industrial Estate, Chippenham, Wiltshire, SN15 1SB Tel: (0870) 7779116 Fax: (0870) 7779115 E-mail: john_mitchell@absol.co.uk

▶ Better Strategy Ltd, 22 The Grove, Farnborough, Hampshire, GU14 6QR Tel: (01252) 682167

▶ BKB-Consultancy, Firtree Cottage, Oakenshaw, Crook, County Durham, DL15 0TH Tel: (01388) 745182
E-mail: bryan.burke@bkb-consultancy.co.uk

Bolton Business Ventures Ltd, 46 Lower Bridgeman Street, Bolton, BL2 1DG Tel: (01204) 391400 Fax: (01204) 380076
E-mail: sales@bbvonline.net

▶ Bowers & Co, York House, 4 Sheepscar Way, Leeds, LS7 3JB Tel: 0113 2379500 Fax: 0113 2379550 E-mail: ajb@companydoctor.co.uk

▶ Business Development International, Business House, Higher Wych, Malpas, Cheshire, SY14 7JT Tel: (01948) 780515
E-mail: info@bdinternational.co.uk

▶ Business Information Systems, 11 Upper Church Park, Mumbles, Swansea, SA3 4DD Tel: (01792) 361121 Fax: (01792) 361421
E-mail: peter@bizis.co.uk

Business Link East, 4 Bishops Square Business Park, Hatfield, Hertfordshire, AL10 9NE Tel: (0845) 7171615 Fax: (0845) 6076117
E-mail: info@businesslinkeast.org.uk

Cambridge Venture Management Ltd, Unit 54, St. Johns Innovation Centre, Cowley Road, Cambridge, CB4 0WS Tel: (01223) 423828 Fax: (01223) 420418
E-mail: cvm@dial.pipex.com

Cap Gemini, 1 Forge End, Woking, Surrey, GU21 6DB Tel: (01483) 764764 Fax: (01483) 786161 E-mail: sales@uk.ggey.com

Champ Consultants Ltd, 13 Deacon Place, Caterham, Surrey, CR3 5FN Tel: (01883) 330580 Fax: (0870) 4215242
E-mail: chantal@champconsultants.co.uk

▶ Chandler & Co., Red Hill, Wateringbury, Maidstone, Kent, ME18 5NN Tel: (01622) 817484 Fax: (01622) 817152
E-mail: info@chandlerandco.co.uk

▶ Complete Telecoms Ltd, 132 Henwick Road, Worcester, WR2 5PB Tel: (0845) 4564110 Fax: (0870) 0528973
E-mail: enquiries@completetelecoms.co.uk

Croft plc, 74 Hounds Gate, Nottingham, NG1 6BA Tel: 0115-952 7551 Fax: 0115-952 7553 E-mail: sales@croftplc.com

Dwyers Business Management Services, Belton Ho, 15 Belton Drive, West Bridgford, Nottingham, NG2 7SJ Tel: 0115-984 2642 Fax: 0115-984 2642

▶ Eastwood Anglo European Investments Ltd, Burnell Arms, Winkburn, Newark, Nottinghamshire, NG22 8PQ Tel: (01636) 636132 Fax: (01636) 636643
E-mail: tom@eastwoodanglo.com

▶ ECITechnical Services, Unit 1, Poole Hall Industrial Estate, Ellesmere Port, CH66 1ST Tel: 0151-357 2200 Fax: 0151-357 2235
E-mail: sales@ecitec.co.uk

▶ Emea International Consulting, 500 Chiswick High Road, Chiswick, London, W4 5RG Tel: (020) 8995 8903
E-mail: info@praeda.co.uk

▶ Equinox Financial Search & Selection, Unity House, Clive Street, Bolton, BL1 1ET Tel: (0870) 9192457 Fax: (0870) 9192458
E-mail: iwright@equinox-financial.co.uk

Ethos Partnership Limited, Suite E8, Business & Innovation Centre, Wearfield, Sunderland, SR5 2TP Tel: 0191-516 6251 Fax: (01892) 528433
E-mail: kym@ethospartnershipltd.co.uk

Futurestech, Garden House, Frogmore Park, Watton at Stone, Hertford, SG14 3RU Tel: 0+33 388 236671 Fax: 0+33 369 208047
E-mail: info@futurestech.com

Glenfield Associates, 2b Mossop Drive, Langtoft, Peterborough, PE6 9LY Tel: (01778) 343567 Fax: (01778) 347382
E-mail: sales@glenfieldbs.co.uk

High Point Rendel, Suite 3 Bowling Hill Business Park, Quarry Road, Chipping Sodbury, Bristol, BS37 6JL Tel: (01454) 312266 Fax: (01454) 312666 E-mail: bris-hpr@netcomuk.co.uk

Infotrends Ltd, Sceptre House, 7-9 Castle Street, Luton, LU1 3AJ Tel: (01582) 400120 Fax: (01582) 411001 E-mail: info@capv.com

Intec Telecom Systems plc, 2 Wells Court, Albert Drive, Woking, Surrey, GU21 5UB Tel: (01483) 745800 Fax: (01483) 745860
E-mail: sales@intec-telecom-systems.com

▶ Jigsaw Training & Consultancy Services Ltd, Premier House, 50-52 Cross Lances Road, Hounslow, TW3 2AA Tel: (020) 8572 6388
E-mail: enquiries@outcomes4u.com

Simon Kelly Partnership, 12 Argyle Road, Clevedon, Avon, BS21 7BP Tel: (01275) 875569 Fax: (01275) 875509
E-mail: simon_kelly@btinternet.com

Kramba Associates Ltd, 6 Lynwood Close, Darwen, Lancashire, BB3 0JY Tel: (01254) 776616 Fax: (01254) 776616
E-mail: kramba@tiscali.co.uk

▶ Marchaven Consulting Ltd, 8 Daisy Lane, Overseal, Swadlincote, Derbyshire, DE12 6JH Tel: (01283) 761813
E-mail: jarvis.whitehead@marchaven.co.uk

Mott Macdonald UK Ltd, St Annes Wharf, 112 Quayside, Newcastle upon Tyne, NE1 3DX Tel: 0191-261 0866 Fax: 0191-261 1100
E-mail: marketing@mottmac.com

Northern Financial Solutions, 68 Bradford Road, Clayton, Bradford, West Yorkshire, BD14 6DN Tel: 01274 815999 Fax: 01274 883833
E-mail: enquiries@nfsonline.plus.com

Ogl Computer Services Group, Worcester Road, Stourport-on-Severn, Worcestershire, DY13 9AT Tel: (01299) 873873 Fax: (01299) 873700 E-mail: enquiries@ogl.co.uk

▶ Ops Partnership, 22 Walkern Road, Stevenage, Hertfordshire, SG1 3RD Tel: (01707) 328660 Fax: (01707) 328661
E-mail: info@theopspartnership.com

▶ Optima Partnership, 1 Howarth Court, Vicarage Lane, Water Orton, Birmingham, B46 1RF Tel: (0870) 9041188 Fax: (0871) 4337050E-mail: info@optimapartnership.co.uk

Panoptic Solutions Ltd, 43 Temple Row, Birmingham, B2 5LS Tel: (0121) 2376057 Fax: (0121) 2376100
E-mail: info@panopt.co.uk

▶ People and Performance Consulting, 400 Thames Valley Park Drive, Thames Valley Park, Reading, RG6 1PT Tel: 0118 9653440 Fax: 0118 9653441
E-mail: contact@papcl.com

Pi Ally Ltd, 24 Merton Road, Benfleet, Essex, SS7 5QJ Tel: (01268) 569190 Fax: (01268) 565517 E-mail: johnhall@pially.com

▶ PI Consulting, Beech House, Melbourn Science Park, Cambridge Road, Melbourn, Royston, Hertfordshire, SG8 6HB Tel: (01763) 226242
E-mail: vincent.bryant@piconsulting.org.uk

▶ Purchasing Assistance Ltd, The Spinney 2 Park Road, Norton, Malton, North Yorkshire, YO17 9EA Tel: (01653) 696226 Fax: 01653 696226
E-mail: info@purchasing-assistance.co.uk

R I C S, Surveyor Court, Westwood Business Park, Westwood Way, Coventry, CV4 8JE Tel: (024) 7669 4757 Fax: (020) 7334 3800
E-mail: contact@rics.org

Redleaf Vehicle Leasing, 28-29 Westhampnett Road, Chichester, West Sussex, PO19 7HH Tel: (08457) 669988 Fax: (01243) 780750

▶ Rely Consulting Ltd, 76 Valley Drive, Brighton, BN1 5FD Tel: (01273) 822082 Fax: (0870) 1383454 E-mail: darren.trussell@relycon.com

Reynolds & Associates, Mendota, Stonehouse Lane, Cookham, Maidenhead, Berkshire, SL6 9TP Tel: (01628) 471680 Fax: (01628) 471680 E-mail: br@reynoldsconsult.co.uk

Rural Solutions, The Stable Courtyard, Broughton Hall Business Park, Skipton, North Yorkshire, BD23 3AE Tel: (01756) 799955 Fax: (01756) 799988 E-mail: info@ruralsolutions.co.uk

Sapphire One Consulting Ltd, 5 Wordsworth Road, Addlestone, Surrey, KT15 2SW Tel: (01932) 857109 Fax: (0870) 0562324
E-mail: info@sapphireone.co.uk

Scottish Enterprise Renfrewshire, 25 Causeyside Street, Paisley, Renfrewshire, PA1 1UL Tel: 0141-848 0101 Fax: 0141-848 6930
E-mail: network.helpline@scotent.co.uk

Skillframe Ltd, 138 Walton Road, East Molesey, Surrey, KT8 0HP Tel: (020) 8941 7733 Fax: (020) 8941 3301
E-mail: info@skillframe.co.uk

▶ Talking Chalk Ltd, Eastwood House, Chalk Lane, East Horsley, Leatherhead, Surrey, KT24 6TH Tel: (0845) 6586914 Fax: (020) 7681 1332
E-mail: information@talkingchalk.co.uk

The Trust Partnership, 6 Trull Farm Buildings, Trull, Tetbury, Gloucestershire, GL8 8SQ Tel: 01284 841900 Fax: 01285 841576
E-mail: Belinda@TheTrustPartnership.com

Tsana Ltd, 41 Baldwin Way, Swindon, Dudley, West Midlands, DY3 4PF Tel: (01384) 400566
E-mail: sales@tsana.com

▶ Unique Consulting Solutions Ltd, 32 New Road, Lymm, Cheshire, WA13 9DY Tel: (01925) 753899 Fax: (01925) 758815
E-mail: trevor@uniqueconsulting.co.uk

▶ Versyns Ventures Ltd, Versyns House, Vale Road, Mayfield, East Sussex, TN20 6BD Tel: (01435) 874800 Fax: (01435) 873631
E-mail: chrislilly@versynsventures.com

BUSINESS COST REDUCTION CONSULTANCY

Cost Index Ltd, 48 Meadow Rise, Barton under Needwood, Burton-on-Trent, Staffordshire, DE13 8DT Tel: 01283 716426 Fax: 01283 716426 E-mail: chris@costindex.co.uk

▶ Purchasing Assistance Ltd, The Spinney 2 Park Road, Norton, Malton, North Yorkshire, YO17 9EA Tel: (01653) 696226 Fax: 01653 696226
E-mail: info@purchasing-assistance.co.uk

BUSINESS DEVELOPMENT CONSULTANTS/SERVICES

▶ 5th of 4th Business Development, 57 Kennedy Way, Airth, Falkirk, FK2 8GB Tel: 01324 831789 E-mail: enquiries@5th-of-4th.com

Advantage Business Group Ltd, East St, Farnham, Surrey, GU9 7TB Tel: (01252) 738500 Fax: (01252) 717065
E-mail: enquiries@advantage-business.co.uk

▶ Aerostructures Business Consultancy Ltd, 2 Hornchurch Court, Heritage Place, Heywood, Lancashire, OL10 2WL Tel: (01706) 360548 Fax: 01706 360548
E-mail: rob.lundy@virgin.net

Asset Business Coaching Ltd, 120 Narbeth Drive, Aylesbury, Buckinghamshire, HP20 1PZ Tel: 01296 394222
E-mail: info@assetbusinesscoaching.com

Bicel Industries Ltd, 64 Sandown Avenue, Swindon, SN3 1QQ Tel: (01793) 491988 Fax: (01793) 692462

▶ Bizvizion Limited, Brighton Media Centre, 15-17 Middle Street, Brighton, BN1 1AL Tel: (01273) 275832
E-mail: info@bizvizion.co.uk

Black Country Chamber & Business Link, Dudley Court South The Waterfront, Level Street, Brierley Hill, West Midlands, DY5 1XN Tel: (0845) 1131234 Fax: (01384) 360560
E-mail: sales@blackcountrybusinesslink.com

Black Country Chamber & Business Link, Dudley Court South The Waterfront, Level Street, Brierley Hill, West Midlands, DY5 1XN Tel: (0845) 1131234 Fax: (01384) 360560
E-mail: sales@blackcountrybusinesslink.com

▶ Brookfield, Kent Street, Wigan, Lancashire, WN1 3BB Tel: (07971) 484695

▶ Business Advisor Partnership, Hamlet House, 63 High Street, Eccleshall, Stafford, ST21 6BW Tel: (01785) 851536 Fax: (01785) 859437 E-mail: pat@thebusinessadvisor.org

Business In Focus Ltd, Enterprise Centre, Bryn Road, Aberkenfig, Bridgend, Mid Glamorgan, CF32 9BS Tel: (01656) 724414 Fax: (01656) 721163 E-mail: opt@businessinfocus.co.uk

Business Link, Pity Me Business Centre, Abbey Road Business Park, Pity Me, Durham, DH1 5JZ Tel: 0191-374 4000 Fax: 0191-374 4010 E-mail: customerservices@blcd.co.uk

Business Link, Kingsgate House, 66-74 Victoria Street, London, SW1E 6SW Tel: (020) 7215 5000 Fax: (020) 7215 5001
E-mail: enquiries@businesslink.org

Business Link, Tees Valley Business Centre, 2 Queens Square, Middlesbrough, Cleveland, TS2 1AA Tel: (01642) 806666 Fax: (01642) 341425
E-mail: enquiries@businesslinknortheast.co.uk

Business Link, 5 Phoenix Place, Nottingham, NG8 6BA Tel: (0845) 7586644 Fax: 0115-977 7399 E-mail: info@blnotts.com

Business Link, Merck House, Seldown Lane, Poole, Dorset, BH15 1TD Tel: (01202) 785400 Fax: (01202) 448838

Business Link, 45a Newdown Road, Scunthorpe, South Humberside, DN17 2TX Tel: (01724) 291510 Fax: (01724) 291511
E-mail: info@blhumber.co.uk

Business Link, Bus & Innovation Centre, Sunderland Enterprise Park, Wearfield, Sunderland, SR5 2TA Tel: 0191-516 6700 Fax: 0191-516 6777
E-mail: enquiries@businesslinktw.co.uk

Business Link, Emlyn Square, Swindon, SN1 5BP Tel: (0845) 6004141 Fax: (01722) 415447 E-mail: info@blbw.co.uk

Business Link, Creech Castle, Bathpool, Taunton, Somerset, TA1 2DX Tel: (0845) 7211112 Fax: (01823) 274862
E-mail: sales@somerset.businesslink.co.uk

Business Link, 34 Tower View Kings Hill, Kings Hill, West Malling, Kent, ME19 4ED Tel: (01732) 878000 Fax: (01732) 841109
E-mail: info@businesslinkkent.co.uk

Business Link, Arabesque House, Monks Cross Drive, Huntington, York, YO32 9WU Tel: (01904) 686000 Fax: (01904) 686020
E-mail: info.centre@blyny.co.uk

Business Link Berkshire & Wiltshire, Thames Tower, 37-41 Station Road, Reading, RG1 1LX Tel: (0845) 6004141

Business Link For Cambridgeshire, Centenary House, St. Marys Street, Huntingdon, Cambridgeshire, PE29 3PE Tel: (0845) 6097979

Business Link Cheshire & Warrington Ltd, International Business Centre, Delta Crescent, Westbrook, Warrington, WA5 7WQ Tel: (01925) 715200 Fax: (01925) 715005
E-mail: info@blinkcw.co.uk

Business Link For Cumbria, Capital Buildings Hilltop Heights, London Road, Carlisle, CA1 2NS Tel: (0870) 7571177 Fax: (01228) 613233

Business Link Derbyshire, Canal Wharf, Chesterfield, Derbyshire, S41 7NA Tel: (0845) 6011038 Fax: (01246) 233228

Business Link Derbyshire, Innovation Ho, Riverside Pk, Raynesway, Derby, DE21 7BF Tel: (0845) 6011038 Fax: (01332) 548088

Business Link Devon & Cornwall Ltd, Prosper House, Buddshead Road, Plymouth, PL6 5XR Tel: (01752) 785785 Fax: (01752) 770925

Business Link East Midlands, Innovation House, East Service Road, Raynesway, Spondon, Derby, DE21 7BF Tel: (0845) 0586644 Fax: (01332) 280792
E-mail: info@businesslinkem.co.uk

Business Link For Greater Merseyside, Halton Business Forum, Victoria Sq, Widnes, Cheshire, WA8 7QZ Tel: (0845) 3300151 Fax: 0151-420 9424
E-mail: questions@halton-businesslink.co.uk

Business Link Hertfordshire, 45 Grosvenor Road, St. Albans, Hertfordshire, AL1 3AW Tel: (01727) 813813 Fax: (01727) 813776
E-mail: stevem@exemplas.com

Business Link Humber, 1B Osborne Street, Grimsby, North East Lincolnshire, DN31 1EY Tel: (01472) 362868 Fax: (01472) 356052

Business Link Humber, Owen Avenue, Priory Park, Hessle, North Humberside, HU13 9PD Tel: (0845) 1243333 Fax: (01482) 641044

Business Link London Ltd, Link, 298-308 Southbury Road, Enfield, Middlesex, EN1 1TS Tel: (0845) 6000787 Fax: (020) 7111 0301
E-mail: info@bllondon.com

Business Link For Norfolk, PO Box 36, Swaffham, Norfolk, PE37 7WZ Tel: (0845) 7218218 Fax: (01760) 726727
E-mail: success@businesslinknorfolk.co.uk

Business Link North & Western Lancashire, Lancashire Enterprises Business Park, Centurion Way, Leyland, PR26 6TY Tel: (01772) 790200 Fax: (01772) 443002
E-mail: info@nwl.businesslink.co.uk

Business Link Shropshire Ltd, Trevithick House, Unit B1 Stafford Park 4, Telford, Shropshire, TF3 3BA Tel: (0845) 7543210
E-mail: enquiries@blwm.com

Business Link Solutions Ltd, Eastern By Pass, Thame, Oxfordshire, OX9 3FF Tel: (01844) 210400 Fax: (01235) 468200

Business Link South Yorkshire, Reresby House, Bow Bridge Close, Rotherham, South Yorkshire, S60 1BY Tel: (01709) 386300 Fax: (01709) 386330
E-mail: enquiries@blsy.com

Business Link South Yorkshire, Albion House, Savile Street, Sheffield, S4 7UQ Tel: (0800) 0737474 Fax: 0114-201 2525
E-mail: enquiries@blsy.com

Business Link Suffolk Ltd, Felaw Maltings, 42 Felaw Street, Ipswich, IP2 8PN Tel: (01473) 417000 Fax: (01473) 417070
E-mail: admin@bls.org.uk

Business Link Surrey, 5th Floor Hollywood House, Church St East, Woking, Surrey, GU21 6HJ Tel: (0845) 7494949 Fax: (01483) 771507
E-mail: sales@businesslinksurrey.co.uk

Business Link Sussex, Sussex Enterprise Greenacre Court, Station Rd, Burgess Hill, W. Sussex, RH15 9DS Tel: (0845) 0360144 Fax: (01444) 259255
E-mail: marketing@sussexenterprise.co.uk

Business Link Wessex, Wates House, Wallington Hill, Fareham, Hampshire, PO16 7BJ Tel: (0845) 4588558 Fax: (01329) 223223
E-mail: info@businesslink.co.uk

Business Link Wessex, Suite 1 Slade Bldgs, The Square, Gillingham, Dorset, SP8 4AY Tel: (0845) 4588558 Fax: (01747) 821613

Business Link Wessex, Mill Court, Furrlongs, Newport, Isle of Wight, PO30 2AA Tel: (08454) 588558 Fax: (01983) 533508
E-mail: tbutler@iwpartnership.com

Business Link West Yorkshire, Unit 4 Meadow Court, Millshaw Business Pk, Millshaw, Leeds, LS11 8LZ Tel: 0871 220 5000 Fax: 0113-383 7700 E-mail: info@blinkleeds.co.uk

Business Links For Northumberland, Wansbeck Business Centre, Rotary Parkway, Ashington, Northumberland, NE63 8QZ Tel: (01670) 528000 Fax: (01670) 813355

Business West, Leigh Court Business Centre, Pill Road, Abbots Leigh, Bristol, BS8 3RA Tel: (01275) 373373 Fax: (01275) 370706
E-mail: info@businesslinksw.co.uk

C A C I Anadata Ltd, Thomas Yeoman House, Coventry Canal Basin, St. Nicholas Street, Coventry, CV1 4LY Tel: (024) 7684 6846 Fax: (024) 7683 7099
E-mail: marketing@caci.co.uk

C M A Solutions Ltd, Fleet Mill, Minley Road, Fleet, Hampshire, GU51 2RD Tel: (01252) 861500 Fax: (01252) 861550
E-mail: cma@cma-sol.co.uk

BUSINESS DEVELOPMENT CONSULTANTS/SERVICES – *continued*

C S L Recruitment & Consulting Ltd, Hurst House, 157-169 Walton Road, East Molesey, Surrey, KT8 0DX Tel: (020) 8224 9840 Fax: (020) 8941 4095 E-mail: sales@imesconsulting.com

The Chamber Business, Kimpton Road, Luton, LU2 0SX Tel: (01582) 522448 Fax: (01582) 522450 E-mail: info@chamber-business.com

Chamber Business Enterprise, Churchgate House, 56 Oxford Street, Manchester, M60 7HJ Tel: 0161-237 4070 Fax: 0161-236 9945 E-mail: mgore@blnm.co.uk

Clear Cube Consulting Ltd, 145-157 St. John Street, London, EC1V 4PY Tel: (020) 8776 8788 Fax: (020) 7253 9040 E-mail: info@asimex-consulting.co.uk

The Countryside Agency, John Dower House, Crescent Place, Cheltenham, Gloucestershire, GL50 3RA Tel: (01242) 521381 Fax: (01242) 584270 E-mail: info@countryside.gov.uk

Coupland Bell Ltd, Barclays Venture Centre University of Warwick, Science Park, Coventry, CV4 7EZ Tel: (01926) 777566 E-mail: info@couplandbell.com

Crisp Marketing Associates Ltd, 45 Queen Street, Exeter, EX4 3SR Tel: (01392) 412582 Fax: (01392) 421942 E-mail: office@crisp-uk.com

Croft plc, 74 Hounds Gate, Nottingham, NG1 6BA Tel: 0115-952 7551 Fax: 0115-952 7553 E-mail: sales@croftplc.com

▶ Crown Coaching, 11 Rookery Court, Marlow, Buckinghamshire, SL7 3HR Tel: (01628) 488042 E-mail: helen@crowncoaching.com

D T I (Department of Trade and Industry), 1 Victoria Street, London, SW1H 0ET Tel: (020) 7215 5000 Fax: (020) 7215 3529 E-mail: dti.enquiries@dti.gsi.gov.uk

Deloitte, Stonecutter Court, 1 Stonecutter Street, London, EC4A 4TR Tel: (020) 7936 3000 Fax: (020) 7583 1198

E A Technology Ltd, Capenhurst Lane, Capenhurst, Chester, CH1 6ES Tel: 0151-339 4181 Fax: 0151-347 2404 E-mail: john.hutchinson@eatechnology.com

▶ E B A Consulting Ltd, PO Box 14, Kidwelly, Dyfed, SA17 4YH Tel: (01554) 890300 Fax: (01554) 891508 E-mail: info@ebassociates.co.uk

East Durham Business Service, 1 Palmer Road, South West Industrial Estate, Peterlee, County Durham, SR8 2HU Tel: 0191-586 3366 Fax: 0191-518 0332E-mail: sales@edbs.co.uk

▶ Esys Plc, 1 Occam Court, Occam Road, Surrey Research Park, Guildford, Surrey, GU2 7HJ Tel: (01483) 304545 Fax: (01483) 303878 E-mail: info@esys.co.uk

▶ First Concepts Ltd, Concept House, 7 Holly Grove, Tabley, Knutsford, Cheshire, WA16 0HR Tel: (0845) 4567684 Fax: (0845) 4567694 E-mail: info@firstconcepts.co.uk

G P W Consultancy, 3 Redcourt, Woking, Surrey, GU22 8RA Tel: (01932) 355770 Fax: (01932) 336454 E-mail: information@gpw.co.uk

R.S. Garrow Ltd, 4 Mosspark Avenue, Milngavie, Glasgow, G62 8NL Tel: 0141-956 2732 Fax: 0141-570 2732 E-mail: bobgarrow@rsgarrow.co.uk

Glenfield Associates, 2b Mossop Drive, Langtoft, Peterborough, PE6 9LY Tel: (01778) 343567 Fax: (01778) 347382 E-mail: sales@glenfieldbs.co.uk

Greater Merseyside Enterprise Ltd, Egerton Housetower Road, Birkenhead, Merseyside, CH41 1FN Tel: (0845) 3300151 Fax: (08453) 300150 E-mail: information@gme.org.uk

▶ Griffiths & James Ltd, Brecon House, William Brown Close, Llantarnam Industrial Park, Cwmbran, Gwent, NP44 3AB Tel: (01633) 877900 Fax: (01633) 877733 E-mail: office@4growth.biz

Highlands & Islands Enterprise, Cowan House, Highlander Way, Inverness Business & Retail Pa, Inverness, IV2 7GF Tel: (01463) 234171 Fax: (01463) 244469 E-mail: hie.general@hient.co.uk

P.R. Hornsby & Co. Business Sales Ltd, 72 East Hill, Colchester, CO1 2QW Tel: (01206) 793790 Fax: (01206) 793791 E-mail: hornsbysales@btconnect.com

HR Insight Ltd, Reeves Way, South Woodham Ferrers, Chelmsford, CM3 5XF Tel: (01245) 324824 Fax: (01245) 324103 E-mail: support@hrinsight.co.uk

Imperial Business Systems, 7 Hill Street, Bristol, BS1 5PU Tel: 0117-925 1700 Fax: 0117-925 2515 E-mail: ibs@imperial.co.uk

▶ Insourcing Business Support Ltd, 16 Saddlers Close, Glenfield, Leicester, LE3 8QU Tel: (07968) 865285 E-mail: info@ibs-ltd.co.uk

▶ Invigorative Ltd, 3 26-28 Finchley Road, London, NW8 6ES Tel: (020) 7722 7673 E-mail: office@invigorative.com

Malcolm Joynes Consultancy, 7 Bracken Hall, Bracken Place, Chilworth, Southampton, SO16 3ET Tel: (023) 8076 7442 Fax: (0870) 7051038 E-mail: malcolm@malcolm-joynes.co.uk

Simon Kelly Partnership, 12 Argyle Road, Clevedon, Avon, BS21 7BP Tel: (01275) 875569 Fax: (01275) 875509 E-mail: simon_kelly@btinternet.com

Kiddy & Partners 2007 Ltd, 74a Charlotte Street, London, W1T 4QH Tel: (020) 7486 6867 Fax: (020) 7486 6863 E-mail: info@kpl.co.uk

Learning & Skills Council Co Durham, Allergate House, Belmont Business Park, Durham, DH1 1TW Tel: (0845) 0194174 Fax: 0191-376 2302 E-mail: ask@lsc.gov.uk

Macey & Macey Ltd, 50 Cutlers Place Colehill, Wimborne, Dorset, BH21 2HU Tel: (01202) 882400 E-mail: enquiries@maceyandmacey.co.uk

Mott Macdonald, 1 Atlantic Quay, Broomielaw, Glasgow, G2 8GB Tel: 0141-222 4500 Fax: 0141-221 2048 E-mail: marketing@mottmac.com

Newry & Mourne Enterprise Agency, Win Business Park, Canal Quay, Newry, County Down, BT35 6PH Tel: (028) 3026 7011 Fax: (028) 3026 1316 E-mail: info@nmea.net

North West Business Link Ltd, Lee House, 90 Great Bridgewater Street, Manchester, M1 5JW Tel: 0161-236 4114 Fax: 0161-228 3043 E-mail: info@business-support-solutions.co.uk

Open Logistics Ltd, PO Box 147, Harrogate, North Yorkshire, HG2 8AH Tel: (01423) 569642

▶ Parkes Office & Event Solutions, The Priors, Bedworth, Warwickshire, CV12 9NZ Tel: (024) 7631 6995 Fax: (024) 7675 8822 E-mail: info@parkesoes.com

Regan Consulting Practice Ltd, Choni Cottage, Manor Road, South Wingfield, Alfreton, Derbyshire, DE55 7NH Tel: (01773) 521528 Fax: (01773) 830688 E-mail: helpdesk@reganconsulting.co.uk

Research Associates UK Ltd, 99 Oulton Road, Stone, Staffordshire, ST15 8DX Tel: (01785) 813164 Fax: (01785) 813268 E-mail: sales@research-associates.co.uk

St. James Property Development Ltd, 180 Brompton Road, London, SW3 1HQ Tel: (020) 7565 8000 Fax: (020) 7565 8008

The Salamander Organisation Ltd, 5 Innovation Close, York Science Park, York, YO10 5ZF Tel: (0870) 1611700 Fax: (0870) 1611701 E-mail: matthew.bosson@tsorg.com

Scottish Enterprise Dunbartonshire, Spectrum House, 1a North Avenue, Clydebank Business Park, Clydebank, Dunbartonshire, G81 2DR Tel: 0141-951 2121 Fax: 0141-951 1907 E-mail: dunbartonshire@scotent.co.uk

Scottish Enterprise Forth Valley, Laurel House, Laurelhill Business Park, Stirling, FK7 9JQ Tel: (01786) 451919 Fax: (01786) 478123 E-mail: forthvalley@scotent.co.uk

▶ Scottish Enterprise Lanarkshire, Dove Wynd, Strathcyde Business Park, Strathclyde Business Park, Bellshill, Lanarkshire, ML4 3AD Tel: (01698) 745454 Fax: (01698) 842211 E-mail: paul.mccarthy@scotent.co.uk

Tenon, Salisbury House, 31 Finsbury Circus, London, EC2M 5SQ Tel: (020) 7628 2040 Fax: (020) 7638 0217 E-mail: info@tenongroup.com

▶ Unique Consulting Solutions Ltd, 32 New Road, Lymm, Cheshire, WA13 9DY Tel: (01925) 753899 Fax: (01925) 758815 E-mail: trevor@uniqueconsulting.co.uk

Value In Approach, Imex Busines Centre, Shobnall Road, Burton-On-Trent, Staffordshire, DE14 2AU Tel: (01283) 567505 Fax: (01283) 505805

▶ Versyns Ventures Ltd, Versyns House, Vale Road, Mayfield, East Sussex, TN20 6BD Tel: (01435) 874800 Fax: (01435) 873631 E-mail: chrislilly@versynsventures.com

▶ Waterlock Business Development, The Studios, The Street, Stourmouth, Canterbury, Kent, CT3 1HZ Tel: (01227) 720007 Fax: (01227) 720001 E-mail: wbd@waterlock.co.uk

Whitewedge Systems Ltd, 42 Jacklyns Lane, Alresford, Hampshire, SO24 9LG Tel: (01962) 734165 Fax: (01962) 734214 E-mail: nick.stone@www.sys.co.uk

BUSINESS DISASTER RECOVERY

▶ Poppleton & Appleby, 32 High Street, Manchester, M4 1QD Tel: 0161-834 7025 Fax: 0161-833 1548 E-mail: enquires@pandamanchester.co.uk

BUSINESS ECONOMIC SURVEY CONSULTANCY, *See also Economic Consultants*

Anite Mobile Working Solutions, 353 Buckingham Avenue, Slough, Slough, SL1 4PF Tel: (01753) 804000 Fax: (01753) 735735

Aware Marketing Consultants, 16 Craigweil Close, Stanmore, Middlesex, HA7 4TR Tel: (020) 8954 9121 Fax: (020) 8954 2102 E-mail: aweiss@marketing-intelligence.co.uk

▶ Business Engineering Ltd, 15 The Maples, Banstead, Surrey, SM7 3QZ Tel: (01737) 373121 Fax: (01737) 211837 E-mail: peter@business-engineering.co.uk

C A C I Anadata Ltd, Thomas Yeoman House, Coventry Canal Basin, St. Nicholas Street, Coventry, CV1 4LY Tel: (024) 7684 6846 Fax: (024) 7683 7099 E-mail: marketing@caci.co.uk

Economic Development Service, Gloucester City Council, 75-81 Eastgate Street, Gloucester, GL1 1PN Tel: (01452) 544911 Fax: (01452) 396994

BUSINESS EDUCATION RESOURCES

▶ Terry Allen Education, Lower Bramblewood, Mill Hill Lane, Brockham, Betchworth, Surrey, RH3 7LR Tel: (01737) 843212 Fax: (01737) 843212 E-mail: contacts@terryalleneducation.co.uk

▶ t3money Ltdd, 27 Hadley Way, Winchmore Hill, London, N21 1AL Tel: (07984) 467103

▶ Touch The Sky Ltd, Mulberry Business Centre, 323 Goring Road, Goring-by-Sea, Worthing, West Sussex, BN12 4NX Tel: 01903 507744 E-mail: lucienne.sharpe@touchthesky.uk.com

BUSINESS EDUCATION RESOURCES FOR PROFIT

▶ Terry Allen Education, Lower Bramblewood, Mill Hill Lane, Brockham, Betchworth, Surrey, RH3 7LR Tel: (01737) 843212 Fax: (01737) 843212 E-mail: contacts@terryalleneducation.co.uk

▶ t3money Ltdd, 27 Hadley Way, Winchmore Hill, London, N21 1AL Tel: (07984) 467103

▶ Twenty Four Seven, 1 Marsel House, Stephensons Way, Ilkley, West Yorkshire, LS29 8DD Tel: (01943) 604777 Fax: (01943) 604800 E-mail: education@247recruitment.org.uk

▶ Wintur Project Services Ltd, 9 Selborne Gardens, Perivale, Greenford, Middlesex, UB6 7PD Tel: (0845) 0450920 Fax: (0845) 0450921 E-mail: sales@fortunes-forever.com

BUSINESS EDUCATION SERVICES

▶ Wintur Project Services Ltd, 9 Selborne Gardens, Perivale, Greenford, Middlesex, UB6 7PD Tel: (0845) 0450920 Fax: (0845) 0450921 E-mail: sales@fortunes-forever.com

BUSINESS ENTERTAINMENT/ INCENTIVE ORGANISERS/ SERVICES

Air Displays (International) Ltd, Building 509, Churchill Way, Biggin Hill Airport, Westerham, Kent, TN16 3BN Tel: (01959) 572277 Fax: (01959) 575969 E-mail: sales@airdisplaysint.co.uk

Arena Events, Unit 1 Perimeter Road, The N.E.C., Birmingham, B40 1PJ Tel: (0870) 7203010 Fax: (0870) 7201101 E-mail: info@arenaevents.com

Bisley Shooting Ground Ltd, Bisley Camp, Brookwood, Woking, Surrey, GU24 0NY Tel: (01483) 797017 Fax: (01483) 476953 E-mail: office@bisleyshooting.co.uk

▶ Classic Motoring Ltd, Smilers Cottage, Brimpsfield, Gloucester, GL4 8LD Tel: (01452) 864050 E-mail: info@classicmotoring.co.uk

Conference Search Ltd, 92 Church Lane, Marple, Stockport, Cheshire, SK6 7AR Tel: 0161-427 7057 Fax: 0161-427 2415 E-mail: sales@conferencesearch.co.uk

▶ Countywide Entertainments, 63 Normandy Close, Exmouth, Devon, EX8 4PB Tel: (01395) 268263 E-mail: steve@countywideentertainments.co.uk

▶ David Lancaster, 23 Borrowdale Road, Lancaster, LA1 3HF Tel: (01524) 66913 Fax: 01524 66913 E-mail: david@davidlancaster.co.uk

▶ Encore Entertainment Ltd, 44 Churchfield Road, Walton-on-Thames, Surrey, KT12 2SY Tel: 01932 253273 E-mail: Encore_info@yahoo.co.uk

▶ Entents Ltd, 1 Sycamore Close, Ross-on-Wye, Herefordshire, HR9 5UA Tel: (01989) 563783

Impress Event Management Ltd, The Annex, 8 Kelsey Way, Beckenham, Kent, BR3 3LL Tel: (020) 8663 6647 Fax: (020) 8663 3195 E-mail: matthew@impressevents.co.uk

▶ Knights Templar Events, PO Box 740, Warrington, WA4 2WT Tel: (01925) 267658 Fax: (01925) 267658 E-mail: info@knightstemplarevents.co.uk

▶ Master Blaster Disco's, 20 Pinewood, Forest Hill, Skelmersdale, Lancashire, WN8 6UZ Tel: (07769) 734126 E-mail: masterblasterdiscos@hotmail.co.uk

Mimicks Face Painting, 5 Corinthian Road, Chandler's Ford, Eastleigh, Hampshire, SO53 2BA Tel: (023) 8025 5894 E-mail: mimicks@ntlworld.com

Mithril Racing Ltd, Goodwood Airfield, Goodwood, Chichester, West Sussex, PO18 0PH Tel: (01243) 528815 Fax: (01243) 771522 E-mail: chris@mithril.co.uk

▶ Moor Leisure, Fingle Cottage, Moretonhampstead Road, Lustleigh, Newton Abbot, Devon, TQ13 9SN Tel: (01647) 277528 Fax: (01647) 277549

▶ Projector Hire, 36 Parrock Avenue, Gravesend, Kent, DA12 1QQ Tel: 0798 454 3625

Soundswright Entertainers, 66 Church Street, Hartlepool, Cleveland, TS24 7DN Tel: (01429) 221133 E-mail: enquiries@soundswrightday.com

Theme Traders Ltd, The Stadium, Oaklands Road, London, NW2 6DL Tel: (020) 8452 8518 Fax: (020) 8450 7322 E-mail: mailroom@themetraders.com

BUSINESS EVENT MARKETING

▶ ARCH Marketing Solutions Ltd, Kildare House, 102-104 Sheen Road, Richmond, Surrey, TW9 1UF Tel: (020) 8334 1137 Fax: E-mail: info@archmarketing.co.uk

▶ Marketing Outsourced, 15 Heaven Tree Close, London, N1 2PW Tel: (020) 7354 5657

The Zest Collective Ltd, 14 Birchwood Drive, Hambleton, Poulton-le-Fylde, Lancashire, FY6 9AQ Tel: (01253) 702035 E-mail: invest@zestisbest.net

BUSINESS EVENT SERVICES

▶ 20five eight Lifestyle Management, 8 Rubislaw Terrace, Aberdeen, AB10 1XE Tel: 01224 611555 E-mail: sherida@20five8.co.uk

▶ Adjayi Secretarial, 3 Maple Leaf Cottages, Blackboys, Uckfield, East Sussex, TN22 5LJ Tel: 01825 890955 Fax: 01825 890955 E-mail: sue@adjayi-secretarial.co.uk

▶ Ashton Billige Property Marketing Ltd, 71 Doods Road, Reigate, Surrey, RH2 0NT Tel: 01737 225752 Fax: 01737 225752 E-mail: enquiries@abpropertymarketing.co.uk

▶ Aztec Innovations, Burnhouse Industrial Estate, Whitburn, Bathgate, West Lothian, EH47 0LQ Tel: (01506) 204188

▶ The Bus Business, The Coach House, Spofforth Hall, Nickols Lane, Spofforth, Harrogate, North Yorkshire, HG3 1WE Tel: (0845) 2250320 Fax: (0845) 2802461 E-mail: info@thebusbusiness.com

▶ Edinburgh Event Production Services, 5/6 Broughton Place Lane, Edinburgh, EH1 3RS Tel: 0131-558 3824 E-mail: eeps@warpro.co.uk

▶ Exmoor Manor Hotel, Barbrook, Lynton, Devon, EX35 6LD Tel: (01598) 752404 Fax: (01598) 753636 E-mail: info@exmoormanorhotel.co.uk

▶ Parkes Office & Event Solutions, The Priors, Bedworth, Warwickshire, CV12 9NZ Tel: (024) 7631 6995 Fax: (024) 7675 8822 E-mail: info@parkesoes.com

▶ Pendleton Events Ltd, Pendleton House 37 Horseshoe, Close Pound Hill, Crawley, West Sussex, RH10 7YS Tel: (07984) 510856 Fax: 0845 330 7263 E-mail: info@pendletonevents.co.uk

▶ Projector Hire, 36 Parrock Avenue, Gravesend, Kent, DA12 1QQ Tel: 0798 454 3625

BUSINESS FORECASTING CONSULTANCY

▶ Business Engineering Ltd, 15 The Maples, Banstead, Surrey, SM7 3QZ Tel: (01737) 373121 Fax: (01737) 211837 E-mail: peter@business-engineering.co.uk

Business Link East, 4 Bishops Square Business Park, Hatfield, Hertfordshire, AL10 9NE Tel: (0845) 7171615 Fax: (0845) 6076117 E-mail: info@businesslinkeast.org.uk

C A C I Anadata Ltd, Thomas Yeoman House, Coventry Canal Basin, St. Nicholas Street, Coventry, CV1 4LY Tel: (024) 7684 6846 Fax: (024) 7683 7099 E-mail: marketing@caci.co.uk

Cap Gemini, 1 Forge End, Woking, Surrey, GU21 6DB Tel: (01483) 764764 Fax: (01483) 786161 E-mail: sales@uk.ggey.com

The Henley Centre, 9 Bridewell Place, Bridewell Gate, London, EC4V 6AW Tel: (020) 7955 1800 Fax: (020) 7353 2899 E-mail: future@henleycentre.com

BUSINESS FORM STATIONERY PRINTING, *See Form, Business/Office etc*

BUSINESS GIFTS, *See Advertising Gift/Business Incentive etc*

BUSINESS INFORMATION ADVISORY SERVICES

Andersen, 4th Floor Forum Ho, Grenville St, St. Helier, Jersey, JE2 4UF Tel: (01534) 707100 Fax: (01534) 707101 E-mail: diane.l.porritt@uk.andersen.com

Atradius, 3 Harbour Drive, Cardiff, CF10 4WZ Tel: (029) 2082 4000 Fax: (029) 2082 4003 E-mail: reception@atradius.com

Black Country Chamber & Business Link, Dudley Court South The Waterfront, Level Street, Brierley Hill, West Midlands, DY5 1XN Tel: (0845) 1131234 Fax: (01384) 360560 E-mail: sales@blackcountrybusinesslink.com

Black Country Chamber & Business Link, Dudley Court South The Waterfront, Level Street, Brierley Hill, West Midlands, DY5 1XN Tel: (0845) 1131234 Fax: (01384) 360560 E-mail: sales@blackcountrybusinesslink.com

BUSINESS INFORMATION ADVISORY SERVICES – *continued*

Bolton Business Ventures Ltd, 46 Lower Bridgeman Street, Bolton, BL2 1DG Tel: (01204) 391400 Fax: (01204) 380076 E-mail: sales@bbvonline.net

Bradford Chamber Of Commerce & Industry, Devere House Vicar Lane, Little Germany, Bradford, West Yorkshire, BD1 5AH Tel: (01274) 772777 Fax: (01274) 771081 E-mail: sales@bradfordchamber.co.uk

The British Library, The British Library STB, London, NW1 2DB Tel: (020) 7412 7000 Fax: (020) 7412 7609 E-mail: business-information@bl.uk

British Market Research Association, Devonshire House, 60 Goswell Road, London, EC1M 7AD Tel: (020) 7566 3636 Fax: (020) 7689 6220 E-mail: admin@bmra.org.uk

Business Database Production Ltd, 19 Hatherley Road, Sidcup, Kent, DA14 4BH Tel: (020) 8300 3661 Fax: (020) 8300 7367 E-mail: marilynbdp@aol.com

Business Link, Pity Me Business Centre, Abbey Road Business Park, Pity Me, Durham, DH1 5JZ Tel: 0191-374 4000 Fax: 0191-374 4010 E-mail: customerservices@blcd.co.uk

Business Link, Tees Valley Business Centre, 2 Queens Square, Middlesbrough, Cleveland, TS2 1AA Tel: (01642) 806666 Fax: (01642) 341425 E-mail: enquiries@businesslinknortheast.co.uk

Business Link, 5 Phoenix Place, Nottingham, NG8 6BA Tel: (0845) 7586644 Fax: 0115-977 7399 E-mail: info@blnotts.com

Business Link, Merck House, Seldown Lane, Poole, Dorset, BH15 1TD Tel: (01202) 785400 Fax: (01202) 448838

Business Link, 45a Newdown Road, Scunthorpe, South Humberside, DN17 2TX Tel: (01724) 291510 Fax: (01724) 291511 E-mail: info@blhumber.co.uk

Business Link, Bus & Innovation Centre, Sunderland Enterprise Park, Wearfield, Sunderland, SR5 2TA Tel: 0191-516 6700 Fax: 0191-516 6777 E-mail: enquiries@businesslinktw.co.uk

Business Link, Emlyn Square, Swindon, SN1 5BP Tel: (0845) 6004141 Fax: (01722) 415447 E-mail: info@blbw.co.uk

Business Link, Creech Castle, Bathpool, Taunton, Somerset, TA1 2DX Tel: (0845) 7211112 Fax: (01823) 274862 E-mail: sales@somerset.businesslink.co.uk

Business Link, 34 Tower View Kings Hill, Kings Hill, West Malling, Kent, ME19 4ED Tel: (01732) 878000 Fax: (01732) 841109 E-mail: info@businesslinkkent.co.uk

Business Link, Arabesque House, Monks Cross Drive, Huntington, York, YO32 9WU Tel: (01904) 686000 Fax: (01904) 686020 E-mail: info.centre@blyny.co.uk

Business Link Berkshire & Wiltshire, Thames Tower, 37-41 Station Road, Reading, RG1 1LX Tel: (0845) 6004141

Business Link For Cambridgeshire, Centenary House, St. Marys Street, Huntingdon, Cambridgeshire, PE29 3PE Tel: (0845) 6097979

Business Link Cheshire & Warrington Ltd, International Business Centre, Delta Crescent, Westbrook, Warrington, WA5 7WQ Tel: (01925) 715200 Fax: (01925) 715005 E-mail: info@blinkcw.co.uk

Business Link For Cumbria, Capital Buildings Hilltop Heights, London Road, Carlisle, CA1 2NS Tel: (0870) 7571177 Fax: (01228) 613233

Business Link Derbyshire, Canal Wharf, Chesterfield, Derbyshire, S41 7NA Tel: (0845) 6011038 Fax: (01246) 233228

Business Link Derbyshire, Innovation Ho, Riverside Pk, Raynesway, Derby, DE21 7BF Tel: (0845) 6011038 Fax: (01332) 548088

Business Link Devon & Cornwall Ltd, Prosper House, Buddshead Road, Plymouth, PL6 5XR Tel: (01752) 785785 Fax: (01752) 770925

Business Link East Midlands, Innovation House, East Service Road, Raynesway, Spondon, Derby, DE21 7BF Tel: (0845) 0586644 Fax: (01332) 280792 E-mail: info@businesslinkem.co.uk

Business Link For Greater Merseyside, Halton Business Forum, Victoria Sq, Widnes, Cheshire, WA8 7QZ Tel: (0845) 3300151 Fax: 0151-420 9424 E-mail: questions@halton-businesslink.co.uk

Business Link Hertfordshire, 45 Grosvenor Road, St. Albans, Hertfordshire, AL1 3AW Tel: (01727) 813813 Fax: (01727) 813776 E-mail: stevem@exemplas.com

Business Link Humber, 1B Osborne Street, Grimsby, North East Lincolnshire, DN31 1EY Tel: (01472) 362868 Fax: (01472) 356052

Business Link Humber, Owen Avenue, Priory Park, Hessle, North Humberside, HU13 9PD Tel: (0845) 1243333 Fax: (01482) 641044

Business Link London Ltd, Link, 298-308 Southbury Road, Enfield, Middlesex, EN1 1TS Tel: (0845) 6000787 Fax: (020) 7111 0301 E-mail: info@bllondon.com

Business Link For Norfolk, PO Box 36, Swaffham, Norfolk, PE37 7WZ Tel: (0845) 7218218 Fax: (01760) 726727 E-mail: success@businesslinknorfolk.co.uk

Business Link North West, St. Nicholas House, Old Church Yard, Liverpool, L2 8TY Tel: (0845) 0066888 Fax: (01772) 790140 E-mail: info@businesslinknw.co.uk

Business Link North & Western Lancashire, Lancashire Enterprises Business Park, Centurion Way, Leyland, PR26 6TY Tel: (01772) 790200 Fax: (01772) 443002 E-mail: info@nwl.businesslink.co.uk

Business Link Shropshire Ltd, Trevithick House, Unit B1 Stafford Park 4, Telford, Shropshire, TF3 3BA Tel: (01645) 7543210 E-mail: enquiries@blwm.com

Business Link Solutions Ltd, Eastern By Pass, Thame, Oxfordshire, OX9 3FF Tel: (01844) 210400 Fax: (01235) 468200

Business Link South Yorkshire, Reresby House, Bow Bridge Close, Rotherham, South Yorkshire, S60 1BY Tel: (01709) 386300 Fax: (01709) 386330 E-mail: enquiries@blsy.com

Business Link South Yorkshire, Albion House, Savile Street, Sheffield, S4 7UQ Tel: (0800) 0737474 Fax: 0114-201 2525 E-mail: enquiries@blsy.com

Business Link Suffolk Ltd, Felaw Maltings, 42 Felaw Street, Ipswich, IP2 8PN Tel: (01473) 417000 Fax: (01473) 417070 E-mail: admin@bls.org.uk

Business Link Surrey, 5th Floor Hollywood House, Church St East, Woking, Surrey, GU21 6HJ Tel: (0845) 7494949 Fax: (01483) 771507 E-mail: sales@businesslinksurrey.co.uk

Business Link Sussex, Sussex Enterprise Greenacre Court, Station Rd, Burgess Hill, W. Sussex, RH15 9DS Tel: (0845) 0360144 Fax: (01444) 259255 E-mail: marketing@sussexenterprise.co.uk

Business Link Wessex, Wates House, Wallington Hill, Fareham, Hampshire, PO16 7BJ Tel: (0845) 4588558 Fax: (01329) 223223 E-mail: info@businesslink.co.uk

Business Link Wessex, Suite 1 Slade Bldgs, The Square, Gillingham, Dorset, SP8 4AY Tel: (0845) 4588558 Fax: (01747) 821613

Business Link Wessex, Mill Court, Furrlongs, Newport, Isle of Wight, PO30 2AA Tel: (08454) 588558 Fax: (01983) 533508 E-mail: tbutler@iwpartnership.com

Business Link West Yorkshire, Unit 4 Meadow Court, Millshaw Business Pk, Millshaw, Leeds, LS11 8LZ Tel: 0871 220 5000 Fax: 0113-383 7700 E-mail: info@blinkleeds.co.uk

Business Links For Northumberland, Wansbeck Business Centre, Rotary Parkway, Ashington, Northumberland, NE63 8QZ Tel: (01670) 528000 Fax: (01670) 813355

▶ Business West, Trimbridge House, Trim Street, Bath, BA1 2DP Tel: (01225) 338383 Fax: (01225) 321971 E-mail: katherine_jenner@bathnes.gov.uk

Business West, Leigh Court Business Centre, Pill Road, Abbots Leigh, Bristol, BS8 3RA Tel: (01275) 373373 Fax: (01275) 370706 E-mail: info@businesslinksw.co.uk

P W Callaghan, Emerys, 2 Bucks Lane, Little Eversden, Cambridge, CB3 7HL Tel: (01223) 262444 Fax: (01223) 263241 E-mail: callaghanpw@aol.com

Cardiff Chamber of Commerce, Suite 1, 2nd Floor, St. Davids House, Wood Street, Cardiff, CF10 5AS Tel: (029) 2034 8280 Fax: (029) 2048 9785 E-mail: enquiries@cardiffchamber.co.uk

Central & West Lancashire Chamber Of Commerce & Industry, Unit 9-10 Eastway Business Village, Olivers Place, Fulwood, Preston, PR2 9WT Tel: (01772) 653000 Fax: (01772) 655544 E-mail: info@lancschamber.co.uk

The Chamber Business, Kimpton Road, Luton, LU2 0SX Tel: (01582) 522448 Fax: (01582) 522450 E-mail: info@chamber-business.com

Chamber Business Connections, Commerce House, Bridgeman Place, Bolton, BL2 1DW Tel: (01204) 363212 Fax: (01204) 363212 E-mail: enquiries@chamberhelp.co.uk

Chamber Business Enterprise, Churchgate House, 56 Oxford Street, Manchester, M60 7HJ Tel: 0161-237 4070 Fax: 0161-236 9945 E-mail: mgore@blnm.co.uk

Chamber Of Commerce, 2 Berkley Crescent, Gravesend, Kent, DA12 2AD Tel: (01474) 320805 Fax: (01474) 537152 E-mail: sales@gravesham.co.uk

Chamber Of Commerce & Business Link West Mercia, Severn House, Prescott Drive, Worcester, WR4 9NE Tel: (0845) 6414641 Fax: (0845) 6414641 E-mail: enquiries@hwchamber.co.uk

Chappell Associates, Westfield House, Bratton Road, Westbury, Wiltshire, BA13 3EP Tel: (01373) 826506 Fax: (01373) 824952 E-mail: sales@chappellassociates.co.uk

▶ China Company Research Services Ltd, Catherinefield House, Catherinefield Business Park, Dumfries, DG1 3PQ Tel: (01387) 247588 Fax: (01387) 257143 E-mail: info@ccrs.info

Chinese Marketing & Communications, 16 Nicholas Street, Manchester, M1 4EJ Tel: (0870) 0181298 Fax: (0870) 0181299 E-mail: support@chinese-marketing.com

▶ Clearwater Business Consulting Ltd, 28 Clearwater, Londonderry, BT47 6BE Tel: (028) 7131 3660 E-mail: peter@clearwaterconsulting.org

Computer Performance International Ltd, Outwoods, Oxford Road, Gerrards Cross, Buckinghamshire, SL9 7PU Tel: (01753) 890808 Fax: (01753) 890918 E-mail: mail@cpiuk.co.uk

Cumbria Chamber Of Commerce, Carlisle Enterprise Centre, James Street, Carlisle, CA2 5DA Tel: (01228) 534120 Fax: (01228) 515602 E-mail: sales@cumbriachamberofcommerce.co.uk

Derbyshire Chamber Of Commerce & Industry, Commerce Centre, Canal Wharf, Chesterfield, Derbyshire, S41 7NA Tel: (01246) 211277 Fax: (01246) 203173 E-mail: chamber@derbyshire.org

Dover District Chamber Of Commerce, White Cliffs BSNS Park, Honeywood Road, Whitfield, Dover, Kent, CT16 3EH Tel: (01304) 824955 Fax: (01304) 822354 E-mail: mail@doverchamber.co.uk

East Durham Business Service, 1 Palmer Road, South West Industrial Estate, Peterlee, County Durham, SR8 2HU Tel: 0191-586 3366 Fax: 0191-518 0332E-mail: sales@edbs.co.uk

Emap Glenigan, 41-47 Seabourne Road, Bournemouth, BH5 2HU Tel: (0800) 373771 Fax: (01202) 431204 E-mail: info@glenigan.emap.com

Esmerk, Thames Tower, Station Road, Reading, RG1 1LX Tel: 0118-956 5820 Fax: 0118-956 5850 E-mail: response@esmerk.com

Experian, Talbot House, Talbot Street, Nottingham, NG80 1TH Tel: (0870) 0121111 Fax: (01753) 594001

Federation Of Crafts & Commerce, 4-5 The Briars, Waterberry Drive, Waterlooville, Hampshire, PO7 7YH Tel: (023) 9223 7010 Fax: (023) 9223 2120 E-mail: info@fcc.org.uk

Fife Chamber of Commerce & Enterprise, Wemyssfield House, Wemyssfield, Kirkcaldy, Fife, KY1 1XN Tel: (01592) 201932 Fax: (01592) 641187 E-mail: enquiries@fifechamber.co.uk

Frost & Sullivan Ltd, Sullivan House, 4 Grosvenor Gardens, London, SW1W 0DH Tel: (020) 7730 3438 Fax: (020) 7730 3343

Greater Merseyside Enterprise Ltd, Egerton Housetower Road, Birkenhead, Merseyside, CH41 1FN Tel: (0845) 3300151 Fax: (08453) 300150 E-mail: information@gme.org.uk

Institute of Chartered Accountants-England & Wales, PO Box 433, London, EC2P 2BJ Tel: (020) 7920 8100 Fax: (020) 7920 0547 E-mail: feedback@icaew.co.uk

J B Computer Management, 39 Luckley Road, Wokingham, Berkshire, RG41 2ES Tel: 0118-978 5161 Fax: 0118-977 4108 E-mail: sales@cdc-jbcm.com

Lambert Roper & Horsefield, The Old Woolcombers Mill, 12-14 Union St South, Halifax, West Yorkshire, HX1 2LE Tel: (01422) 360788 Fax: (01422) 380201 E-mail: mail@lrh.co.uk

Larne Enterprise Development Co. Ltd, Ledcom Industrial Estate, Bank Road, Larne, County Antrim, BT40 3AW Tel: (028) 2827 0742 Fax: (028) 2827 5653 E-mail: davidgillespie@ledcom.org

The Lennox Partnership Ltd, Unit 1a Erskine House, North Avenue, Clydebank Business Park, Clydebank, Dunbartonshire, G81 2DR Tel: 0141-951 1131 Fax: 0141-952 0312 E-mail: info@thelennoxpartnership.org

Market Research Society, 15 Northburgh Street, London, EC1V 0JR Tel: (020) 7490 4911 Fax: (020) 7490 0608 E-mail: sales@mrs.org.uk

Modulex Systems Ltd, 9a North Portway Close, Round Spinney Industrial Estate, Northampton, NN3 8RQ Tel: (01604) 672100 Fax: (01604) 672161 E-mail: mxuk@modulex.co.uk

Norfolk & Waveney Enterprise Services, Queens Road, Great Yarmouth, Norfolk, NR30 3HT Tel: (01493) 850204 Fax: (01493) 330754 E-mail: enquiries@business-advice.co.uk

North East Chamber Of Commerce, Aykley Heads Business Centre, Aykley Heads, Durham, DH1 5TS Tel: 0191-386 1133 Fax: 0191-386 1144 E-mail: information@ne-cc.com

North West Business Link Ltd, Lee House, 90 Great Bridgewater Street, Manchester, M1 5JW Tel: 0161-236 4114 Fax: 0161-228 3043 E-mail: info@business-support-solutions.co.uk

Scottish Enterprise Network, 150 Broomielaw, Atlantic Quay, Glasgow, G2 8LU Tel: 0141-248 2700 Fax: 0141-221 3217 E-mail: network.helpline@scotent.co.uk

Scottish Executive, Meridian Court, 5 Cadogan Street, Glasgow, G2 6AT Tel: 0141-248 4774 Fax: 0141-242 5589 E-mail: ceu@scotland.gsi.gov.uk

Sirsi, Unicorn House, Station Close, Potters Bar, Hertfordshire, EN6 3JW Tel: (01707) 646848 Fax: (01707) 858111 E-mail: sirsi@sirsi.co.uk

Stevenage Business Initiative, The Business & Technology Centre, Bessemer Drive, Stevenage, Hertfordshire, SG1 2DX Tel: (01438) 315733 Fax: (01438) 313001 E-mail: sbienq@stevbtc.demon.co.uk

Surrey Chamber Of Commerce Ltd, 5th Floor Hollywood House, Church Street East, Woking, Surrey, GU21 6HJ Tel: (01483) 726655 Fax: (01483) 740217 E-mail: info@surrey_chambers.co.uk

Taylor Nelson Sofres plc, 66 Wilson Street, London, EC2A 2JX Tel: (020) 7868 6500 Fax: (020) 7868 6501 E-mail: christine.davidson@tnsofres.com

BUSINESS INFORMATION SERVICES

▶ Business West, Trimbridge House, Trim Street, Bath, BA1 2DP Tel: (01225) 338383 Fax: (01225) 321971 E-mail: katherine_jenner@bathnes.gov.uk

▶ Business24, Welton House, Lime Kiln Way, Lincoln, LN2 4WH Tel: (01522) 574204 Fax: 01522 574035 E-mail: enquiries@business24.co.uk

▶ Consultancy People Ltd, Nelson House, 1a Church Street, Epsom, Surrey, KT17 4PF Tel: (0845) 0504657 E-mail: mail@consultpeople.com

▶ Port Strategy, The Old Mill, Lower Quay, Fareham, Hampshire, PO16 0RA Tel: 01329 825335 Fax: 01329 825330 E-mail: info@portstrategy.com

▶ Wintur Project Services Ltd, 9 Selborne Gardens, Perivale, Greenford, Middlesex, UB6 7PD Tel: (0845) 0450920 Fax: (0845) 0450921 E-mail: sales@fortunes-forever.com

BUSINESS INFORMATION SERVICES, EU, DAILY TENDER ALERTING SERVICE

▶ SDF-ASSIST, Daisyfield Business Centre, Appleby Street, Blackburn, BB1 3BL Tel: 01234 246396 Fax: 01234 246884 E-mail: info@sdfassist.com

BUSINESS INFORMATION SERVICES, MAILING LISTS

▶ Whichlist.com, Tapton Park Innovation Centre, Brimington Road, Chesterfield, Derbyshire, S41 0TZ Tel: (01246) 297179 Fax: (01246) 297180 E-mail: sales@whichlist.com

BUSINESS INTELLIGENCE SOFTWARE

▶ ASTRAC Ltd, Innovation Centre, Warwick Technology Park, Warwick, CV34 6UW Tel: (01926) 623060 Fax: (01926) 623061 E-mail: info@astrac.com

BUSINESS INTERNET SERVICES

▶ 2f3 Internet, 103 Malbet Park, Edinburgh, EH16 6WB Tel: 0131-666 2555 E-mail: info@2f3.com

▶ 2-home-business.com Ltd, 501 International House, 223 Regent Street, London, UK, W1B 2QD Tel: 01743 284757 E-mail: enquiries@2-home-business.com

▶ 3B Designs, 32 Eaglewood Close, Torquay, TQ2 7SS Tel: (01803) 615903

4 Web UK Ltd, 12 Maycroft Avenue, Withington, Manchester, M20 4XX Tel: 0161-291 8082 E-mail: ross@4webuk.com

▶ Accountancy & Business Cartoons, 4 Auckland Way, Hartburn, Stockton-on-Tees, Cleveland, TS18 5LG Tel: (01642) 581847 Fax: (01642) 581847 E-mail: vh2@businesscartoons.co.uk

▶ Alternative Focus Media, 68 Castle Gate, Newark, Nottinghamshire, NG24 1BG Tel: (01636) 706106 Fax: (01636) 611149 E-mail: mike@alternativefocusmedia.com

▶ Amber Green, 135 George Street, Edinburgh, EH2 4JS Tel: 0131-514 4000 Fax: 0131-514 4001 E-mail: info@ambergreen.co.uk

▶ Angel Solutions, 30 Faraday Road, Wavertree Technology Park, Liverpool, L13 1EH Tel: (0845) 8330933 Fax: (0845) 8338561 E-mail: info@angelsolutions.co.uk

▶ Axess, 1 Orchard Close, Pinchbeck, Spalding, Lincolnshire, PE11 3RL Tel: (01775) 724066 Fax: (01775) 712812 E-mail: lowe.john@btconnect.com

▶ B I Worldwide Ltd, 1 Vantage Court, Tickford Street, Newport Pagnell, Buckinghamshire, MK16 9EZ Tel: (01908) 214700 Fax: (01908) 214777 E-mail: enquires@eu.biworldwide.com

▶ Better 4 Business, 11 Brook Hey Avenue, Bolton, BL3 2EQ Tel: (0870) 8749500 E-mail: enquiries@better4business.co.uk

BITS Ltd, 45 Manor Fields, Bratton, Westbury, Wiltshire, BA13 4ST Tel: (0845) 0940458 E-mail: info@bits-solutions.co.uk

▶ Box Clever Solutions Ltd, PO Box 427, Southport, Merseyside, PR8 2WG Tel: (0845) 1235730 Fax: (0845) 1235736 E-mail: info@business-made-simple.co.uk

Bridgewater Software Development, Audley House, Northbridge Road, Berkhamsted, Hertfordshire, HP4 1EH Tel: (01442) 870244 Fax: (01442) 879993 E-mail: info@bridgewater.it

▶ Broxden Ltd, 8 Algo Business Centre, Glenearn Road, Perth, PH2 0NJ Tel: (01738) 450422 Fax: (01738) 783685 E-mail: sales@broxden.co.uk

Bull Group Ltd, Unit D Henfield Business Park, Sussex, Henfield, West Sussex, BN5 9SL Tel: (01273) 491490 Fax: (01273) 490813 E-mail: sales@bullnet.co.uk

▶ Byrne Consultancy Ltd, 34 Ashburnham Loan, South Queensferry, West Lothian, EH30 9LE Tel: 0131-331 3694 Fax: 0131-331 3694

C P I, Concorde House, 56 Station Road, Finchley Central, London, N3 2SA Tel: (020) 8235 3535 Fax: (020) 8235 3555 E-mail: info@cpilondon.com

▶ Campbell Pryde, 10 Hampton Gardens, Sawbridgeworth, Hertfordshire, CM21 0AN Tel: (01279) 425283 E-mail: sales@campbellpryde.com

BUSINESS INTERNET SERVICES - *continued*

▶ Carola.Co.Uk :Web Development & Consultancy, 45 Queens Drive, London, N4 2SZ Tel: (020) 8802 5570 E-mail: caterina@carola.co.uk

▶ CD Web Design, Forester's Cottage, Kilmaron Estate, Cupar, Fife, KY15 4NE Tel: (07715) 707953 Fax: (01334) 650908

Centrical Solutions, 20a West Park, Harrogate, North Yorkshire, HG1 1BJ Tel: (01423) 817555 Fax: (01423) 817999 E-mail: karen@centricalsolutions.com

Cobweb Solutions Ltd, Delme Place, Cams Hall Estate, Fareham, Hampshire, PO16 8UX Tel: (0845) 2239000 Fax: (0845) 2493310 E-mail: sales@cobweb.co.uk

▶ Coleman Taylor Graphic Design, Haven House, 10 Haven Close, Grasscroft, Saddleworth, Oldham, OL4 4DU Tel: (01457) 872666 E-mail: info@colemantaylor.co.uk

Computer Doctor Services Ltd, 20a Portland Road, Kilmarnock, Ayrshire, KA1 2BS Tel: (01563) 537733 Fax: (01563) 537733 E-mail: kellyenquiry@computerdoctorservice.co.uk

Connaught Lithoservices Ltd, 129 Munster Road, London, SW6 6DD Tel: (020) 7731 0900 Fax: (020) 7731 0066 E-mail: info@connaught.net

▶ Connexions 4 London, 22 St. Peters Road, Bournemouth, BH1 2LE Tel: (01202) 299799 Fax: (0870) 7061094 E-mail: matt@c4l.co.uk

▶ Cyberience Internet Solutions, 56 Willow Grove, Livingston, West Lothian, EH54 5NA Tel: 07764 494889 Fax: 07764 494889 E-mail: contact@cyberience.co.uk

▶ D C A Data Solutions, 17 Gayfield Square, Edinburgh, EH1 3NX Tel: 0131-556 7787 Fax: 0131-556 2856

▶ DA Internet, 128 Peckover Drive, Pudsey, Leeds, LS28 8EG Tel: 078216 11939 E-mail: sales@dainternet.net

▶ Daneswood Solutions Ltd, The Studio, 40/41 Monmouth Street, Topsham, Exeter, EX3 3AJ Tel: 0845 257 1102 Fax: 0871 994 3169 E-mail: info@daneswood.co.uk

▶ Deepbluemedia, Flat 3, 375 Union Street, Aberdeen, AB11 6BT Tel: (01224) 592572 E-mail: info@deepbluemedia.co.uk

▶ Disco Dog, 23 Spittal Street, Edinburgh, EH3 9DZ Tel: 0131-622 0556 E-mail: info@discodog.co.uk

▶ Dispirito Design Ltd, Tump House Studio, Dingestow, Monmouth, Gwent, NP25 4DX Tel: (01600) 740432 E-mail: info@dispirito.co.uk

Ecentric Media Ltd, PO Box 473, Horsham, West Sussex, RH12 5YL Tel: (01403) 253022 Fax: 01403 253022 E-mail: enquiries@ecentricmedia.co.uk

▶ ECRE8, 4 Highlands Drive, Daventry, Northamptonshire, NN11 8ST Tel: (01327) 310808 Fax: (01327) 310808 E-mail: stuart@ecre8.co.uk

▶ Electronic Business Services Ltd, Cavalry Park, Peebles, EH45 9BU Tel: (01721) 724881 Fax: (01721) 724882 E-mail: info@ebs-europe.com

▶ Electronic Products Realisation, 6 Grant Street, Brighton, BN2 9UN Tel: (01273) 674757 E-mail: enqs@eprltd.co.uk

▶ Enhanced Business Solutions Ltd, Wrest Park, Silsoe, Bedford, MK45 4HR Tel: (01525) 862555 Fax: (01525) 862500 E-mail: enquiries@retail-services.co.uk

▶ Evaluation Centre, 15 Chiltern Business Centre, 63-65 Woodside Road, Amersham, Buckinghamshire, HP6 6AA Tel: (0870) 9088767 Fax: (0870) 1340931 E-mail: info@pmp.co.uk

▶ Exa Networks, 27-29 Mill Field Road, Cottingley Business Park, Cottingley, Bingley, West Yorkshire, BD16 1PY Tel: (0845) 1451234 Fax: (01274) 567646 E-mail: sales@exa-networks.co.uk

▶ Fire Without Smoke Software Ltd, Queens Road, Bridgend Industrial Estate, Bridgend, Mid Glamorgan, CF31 3UT Tel: (01656) 669119 Fax: (01656) 890723 E-mail: sales@fwoss.com

▶ Fresh Biz Marketing, 1 Oban Close, Wakefield, West Yorkshire, WF3 1JU Tel: 0870 284 6180 Fax: 0870 284 6181 E-mail: info@freshbizmarketing.com

▶ Gary Crook Ltd, Regus House, Southampton International Business Park, George Curl Way, Southampton, SO18 2RZ Tel: (023) 8030 2005 Fax: (023) 8030 2225 E-mail: gary@wsi-internet4business.com

▶ H & M Consulting Ltd, 61 George Street, Perth, PH1 5LB Tel: (0870) 7606897

▶ hostukdomain.com, Flat 1, 23 Acock Grove, Northolt, Middlesex, UB5 4RT Tel: (0800) 0409695 E-mail: sales@hostukdomain.com

▶ Ideka Ltd, 57 Barleyfields Road, Wetherby, West Yorkshire, LS22 7PT Tel: (01937) 582942 Fax: (01937) 582942 E-mail: sales@ideka.co.uk

▶ Impact Computing & Consulting, Oak Mount, Blackpool Road, Newton, Preston, PR4 3RE Tel: (01772) 684282 Fax: (01772) 681597 E-mail: sales@impactcomputing.co.uk

▶ inCharge.co.uk, 49 Kingston Street, Cambridge, CB1 2NU Tel: (01223) 579600

▶ Integral Solutions, Rhumhor, Carrick Castle, Lochgoilhead, Cairndow, Argyll, PA24 8AF Tel: (0845) 6444990 Fax: (07092) 117060 E-mail: info@integral-solutions.net

▶ Iweave Ltd, 4 Brentham Crescent, Stirling, FK8 2AZ Tel: (01786) 450606 Fax: (01786) 462876

▶ K-Point Internet Solutions Ltd, 1 Osborne Promenade, Warrenpoint, Newry, County Down, BT34 3NQ Tel: (028) 4175 4836 E-mail: info@kpoint.co.uk

▶ L & M Hosting, Internet House, 64 Haig Street, Grangemouth, Stirlingshire, FK3 8QF Tel: (0845) 3312898 Fax: (0845) 6443809

▶ LittleFish Web Design, 79 King George Avenue, Horsforth, Leeds, LS18 5ND Tel: 0113 2170419 E-mail: contact@littlefishwebdesign.com

▶ Loud-N-Clear Com Ltd, 29 Castle Crescent, Reading, RG1 6AQ Tel: 0118-967 7693 Fax: 0118-954 2756 E-mail: enquiries@loud-n-clear.com

▶ Loyal E, 39 Stonewell Park Road, Congresbury, Bristol, BS49 5DP Tel: (01934) 832143 Fax: (01934) 832143 E-mail: enquiries@loyal-e.com

▶ M8 Design, 102 Bath Street, Glasgow, G2 2EN Tel: (0870) 7460424 Fax: (0870) 7420745

▶ MitraWorks, Church Street, Monmouth, NP25 6BU Tel: (01600) 775576 E-mail: info@mitraworks.co.uk

▶ MMS Almac Print Ltd, Unit 4 Tyock Industrial Estate, Elgin, Morayshire, IV30 1XY Tel: (01343) 551353 Fax: (01343) 551962 E-mail: sales@mms-almac.co.uk

MyVideoTalk, 163 Winchester Road, Highams Park, Waltham Forest, London, E4 9JN Tel: 020 85235278 E-mail: myvideotalk@uwclub.net

▶ Net Commerce Solutions Ltd, 6 Bramble Close, Harpenden, Hertfordshire, AL5 4AN Tel: (0870) 2467642 Fax: (0871) 4337349 E-mail: info@net-commerce-solutions.co.uk

▶ Netpresto Ltd, Wellington Street, Gateshead, Tyne & Wear, NE8 2AJ Tel: 0191-478 2233 Fax: 0191-477 7929 E-mail: sales@netpresto.co.uk

▶ North Square, Hardwick, Wellingborough, Northamptonshire, NN9 5AL Tel: (01933) 401501 Fax: (01933) 402403 E-mail: info@north-square.com

Ocean Road, Unit 43, Kersey Road, Flushing, Falmouth, Cornwall, TR11 5TR Tel: (0845) 0034220 Fax: (0870) 9159418 E-mail: enquiries@oceanroad.co.uk

▶ Oceanic Design, Highview, Little Staughton, Bedford, MK44 2BH Tel: (01234) 378171 E-mail: sales@oceanicdesign.com

Office Overload, Peelers End, May Lane, Pilley, Lymington, Hampshire, SO41 5QR Tel: (01590) 688476 Fax: (01590) 675133 E-mail: sue@officeoverload.com

▶ Open Creation, Fermoy House, Shepley Road, Barnt Green, Birmingham, B45 8JN Tel: 0121 2882205 E-mail: mail@opencreation.co.uk

▶ Oxford Internet Marketing, 10 Manor Farm Close, Kingham, Chipping Norton, Oxfordshire, OX7 6YX Tel: (01608) 658803 Fax: (0870) 1275668 E-mail: stephen@oxfordinternetmarketing.co.uk

Paradigm Redshift Ltd, Lion Gate Barn, Petworth Road, Witley, Godalming, Surrey, GU8 5QW Tel: (01428) 684710 E-mail: enquiries@paradigm-redshift.com

▶ Pipemedia Ltd, Unit 1 Warren Park Way, Enderby, Leicester, LE19 4SA Tel: (0871) 5757575 Fax: (0871) 4250008 E-mail: sales@pipemedia.com

▶ Principal Image, Cherry Tree Lane, Rostherne, Altrincham, Cheshire, WA14 3RZ Tel: (01565) 830213 Fax: (01565) 830214 E-mail: info@principalimage.com

Real 60 Minute Money, 6A Bell Flats, 280-286 High Road, Willesden, London, NW10 2EX Tel: (0870) 896 4064 Fax: (0870) 762 3512 E-mail: info@real60minutemoney.co.uk

▶ Retail Answers, Surrey House, 196 Barnett Wood Lane, Ashtead, Surrey, KT21 2LW Tel: 01372 272800 E-mail: info@retailanswers.co.uk

▶ The Right Service, Bradford Road, Birmingham, B36 9AA Tel: 0121-246 8490 Fax: 0121-246 8490 E-mail: questions@therightservice.com

▶ SF Consultants, 31 Austins Mead, Bovingdon, Hertfordshire, HP3 0JU Tel: 01442 380120 Fax: 01442 380334 E-mail: stephanie.farrer@ntlworld.com

▶ Simplified Solutions, 80 Gathurst Road, Orrell, Wigan, Lancashire, WN5 8QH Tel: (0792) 1040857

▶ Smartways Technology Ltd, 1 Scirocco Close, Northampton, NN3 6AP Tel: (01604) 670500 Fax: (01604) 670567 E-mail: admin@a-i-t.co.uk

▶ South Coast Web Solutions, 5 County Gardens, Fareham, Hampshire, PO14 3JA Tel: 01329 314226 E-mail: scws-uk@ntlworld.com

▶ Steelworks It, C23 Houghton Enterprise Centre, Lake Road, Houghton le Spring, Tyne & Wear, DH5 8BJ Tel: 0191-584 8811 Fax: 0191-584 7856 E-mail: sales@switcms.com

▶ Stockfolder.com, 1 North Avenue, Ealing, London, London, W13 8AP Tel: 0208 998 3445 E-mail: info@stockfolder.com

Systima Technology Ltd, 7 Prospect Business Centre, Prospect Road, Cowes, Isle of Wight, PO31 7AD Tel: (01983) 248810 Fax: (01983) 248812 E-mail: Shane@systima-technology.co.uk

▶ T H UK Online Marketing, Bedford Heights, Brickhill Drive, Bedford, MK41 7PH Tel: (01234) 219119 Fax: (01234) 271862 E-mail: resources@thuk.co.uk

▶ Thelwell Consultants Ltd, The Innovation Centre, Brunswick Street, Nelson, Lancashire, BB9 0PQ Tel: (01282) 877097 Fax: (01282) 877098 E-mail: info@tcreative.co.uk

▶ Tiger Digital Ltd, 31 Merchants House, Collington Street, Greenwich, London, SE10 9LX Tel: (0870) 1909745 Fax: (0870) 1909745 E-mail: helpme@tigerdigital.net

▶ Toltech Internet Solutions, Mansion House, 1 Ardgowan Square, Greenock, Renfrewshire, PA16 8NG Tel: (01475) 716726 Fax: (01475) 727854 E-mail: info@toltech.co.uk

▶ Toucan Graphics, 20 Calderhall Avenue, East Calder, Livingston, West Lothian, EH53 0DJ Tel: (01506) 204700 Fax: (01506) 204700 E-mail: info@toucangraphics.com

▶ UK Dynamo, The Innovation Centre, Epinal Way, Loughborough, Leicestershire, LE11 3EH Tel: (01509) 228864 E-mail: mc@ukdynamo.com

▶ The Utility Warehouse Discount Club, 110 Crossways Road, Knowle Park, Bristol, BS4 2SU Tel: 0117-977 9275

▶ V H S Holdings Ltd, 7 College Park Drive, Westbury-On-Trym, Bristol, BS10 7AN Tel: 0117- 950 0202 Fax: 0117- 377 7842 E-mail: vgr@vhsholdings.com

▶ Vnet Web Solutions, 46 Clensmore Street, Kidderminster, Worcestershire, DY10 2JS Tel: (01562) 66610 Fax: 01562) 829026 E-mail: vnet@veldonn.co.uk

▶ Web Alive (UK) Ltd, 25 Chalk Farm Road, London, NW1 8AG Tel: (0871) 4346400 Fax: (0871) 4346401 E-mail: fraser.henderson@webalive.co.uk

▶ Webcredible Ltd, 99 Mansell Street, London, E1 8AX Tel: (020) 7423 6320 Fax: 0207 481 2569 E-mail: info@webcredible.co.uk

▶ WSI Core Solutions, 65 Hendon Way, London, NW2 2LX Tel: (020) 8458 2928 Fax: (0871) 6616581 E-mail: sally@wsicoresolutions.com

WSI Smart Web Systems, 2 Naunton Way, Leckhampton, Cheltenham, Gloucestershire, GL53 7BQ Tel: (01242) 570330 Fax: (01242) 570330 E-mail: tony@hodderonline.com

BUSINESS MAGAZINES

▶ The Ashford Advertiser, PO Box 1, Ashford, Kent, TN23 4ZU Tel: (01233) 624538 Fax: (01233) 641900 E-mail: theadvertiser@aol.com

National Bartender Magazine, PO Box 9667, Nottingham, NG10 9BZ Tel: 0115-925 5227 E-mail: sb@freerbutler-gds.co.uk

▶ Port Strategy, The Old Mill, Lower Quay, Fareham, Hampshire, PO16 0RA Tel: 01329 825335 Fax: 01329 825330 E-mail: info@portstrategy.com

▶ Sign Update, 1 Allens Orchard, Chipping Warden, Banbury, Oxfordshire, OX17 1LX Tel: (01295) 660666 Fax: (0560) 1162164 E-mail: sb@freerbutler-gds.co.uk

BUSINESS NUMBER TELEPHONE CALL SERVICE PROVIDERS

▶ Alphatalk Ltd, 109 Digbeth, Birmingham, B5 6DT Tel: 0121-633 5200 Fax: (0870) 2005200 E-mail: info@alphatalk.com

Callsure Business Telephone Numbers, 36 Duncroft, Windsor, Berkshire, SL4 4HH Tel: (0844) 4780121 E-mail: sales@callsure07050.co.uk

▶ Charles Stuart Phone Services, 18 Harewood Avenue, Newark, Nottinghamshire, NG24 4BE Tel: (01636) 705313 Fax: (08714) 335235 E-mail: sales@charles-stuart.com

▶ Zimo Communications, 26 York Street, London, W1U 6PZ Tel: (0800) 3213000 E-mail: sales@ewcoms.com

BUSINESS OPPORTUNITY NETWORKING CONSULTANTS

▶ Everyday Essentials, 2 Cranford Crescent, Kilfennan, Londonderry, BT47 5QN Tel: (028) 7129 1478 E-mail: everyday_essentials@hotmail.com

▶ Kleeneze Ltd, 21 Bridle Close, Bradville, Milton Keynes, MK13 7EW Tel: (01908) 226025 Fax: (01908) 226025 E-mail: peacheybigbucks@aol.com

▶ Put Your Family First, 5 Hastings Close, Ysbytty Fields, Abergavenny, Monmouthshire, NP7 9JD Tel: (01873) 851046 Fax: (01873) 851046 E-mail: barrie@putyourfamilyfirst.biz

BUSINESS OPPORTUNITY PROMOTION

▶ Blueblossom Ltd, 61 St. Albans Hill, Hemel Hempstead, Hertfordshire, HP3 9NQ Tel: (01442) 219795 Fax: (01442) 219795 E-mail: info@blueblossom.co.uk

▶ Everyday Essentials, 2 Cranford Crescent, Kilfennan, Londonderry, BT47 5QN Tel: (028) 7129 1478 E-mail: everyday_essentials@hotmail.com

▶ ExtraMoneyTime, Byecroft, Bircher, Leominster, Herefordshire, HR6 0BP Tel: (01568) 780848

▶ Kleeneze Ltd, 80 Conniburrow Boulevard, Conniburrow, Milton Keynes, MK14 7DA Tel: (01908) 664153 E-mail: britishbiz@yahoo.co.uk

▶ Kleeneze Ltd, 21 Bridle Close, Bradville, Milton Keynes, MK13 7EW Tel: (01908) 226025 Fax: (01908) 226025 E-mail: peacheybigbucks@aol.com

▶ Put Your Family First, 5 Hastings Close, Ysbytty Fields, Abergavenny, Monmouthshire, NP7 9JD Tel: (01873) 851046 Fax: (01873) 851046 E-mail: barrie@putyourfamilyfirst.biz

▶ Lawrence Stones, 30 Lucerne Close, Worcester, WR3 7NA Tel: (01905) 456906 E-mail: lawrence@stone1012.freeserve.co.uk

BUSINESS PERFORMANCE IMPROVEMENT SERVICES

▶ Blue Osprey Ltd, 9 Gala Avenue, Deanpark, Renfrew, PA4 0UH Tel: 0141-885 0715 E-mail: alastairm@blueosprey.com

Cost Index Ltd, 48 Meadow Rise, Barton under Needwood, Burton-on-Trent, Staffordshire, DE13 8DT Tel: 01283 716426 Fax: 01283 716426 E-mail: chris@costindex.co.uk

▶ Scotscraig BUSINESS SOLUTIONS, The Clock House, 87 Paines Lane, PINNER, Middlesex, HA5 3BZ Tel: 020 8933-9962 E-mail: reception@scotscraigsolutions.co.uk

▶ Scott-Grant Technical Services, Portland Tower, Portland Street, Manchester, M1 3LD Tel: 0161-234 2121 Fax: 0161-234 2125 E-mail: training@scott-grant.co.uk

BUSINESS PLANNING SERVICES, FINANCIAL

▶ Redarch Associates Ltd, Unit 1 42 Feering Hill, Feering, Colchester, CO5 9NH Tel: (01376) 573767 Fax: (01376) 573900 E-mail: enquiry@redarch.co.uk

▶ Tichler & Co, The Office at TIMBERS, Hatching Green, Harpenden, Herts, AL5 2JP Tel: 01582 768072

BUSINESS PROCESS MANAGEMENT (BPM) SOFTWARE

▶ Business Initiatives BDS Ltd, Hardhams Cottage Clay Lane, Fishbourne, Chichester, West Sussex, PO18 8BT Tel: (01243) 775785 Fax: (01243) 528923 E-mail: adrian@business-initiatives.com

▶ C Sam, Bridge House, 1-2 Riverside Drive, Aberdeen, AB11 7LH Tel: (01224) 586855 Fax: (01244) 586866 E-mail: sales@c-sam.co.uk

Compete IT Ltd, 5 Watling Court, Attleborough Fields Industrial Estate, Nuneaton, Warwickshire, CV11 6GX Tel: (0870) 2202644 Fax: (0870) 2202643 E-mail: info@compete-it.co.uk

CW Concepts Ltd, Concept House, 6 Richard Lewis Close, Llandaff, Cardiff, CF5 2TB Tel: (0845) 0715056 Fax: (0845) 0715065 E-mail: info@cwconcepts.co.uk

▶ Cyclone Holdings Ltd, PO Box 29, Tenbury Wells, Worcestershire, WR15 8HT Tel: (01584) 811467 Fax: E-mail: admin@cyclone-chieftain.co.uk

▶ Dexter-IT, 11 Babylon Lane, Bishampton, Pershore, Worcestershire, WR10 2NN Tel: 0845 6442414 Fax: 0870 1328311 E-mail: enquiries@Dexter-IT.co.uk

▶ Dko Consulting Ltd, Caladh, Rock Road, Storrington, Pulborough, West Sussex, RH20 3AH Tel: (01903) 891528 Fax: (01903) 891528 E-mail: sales@dko-consulting.com

▶ Infographics UK Ltd, Leslie House, Allen Road, Livingston, West Lothian, EH54 6TQ Tel: (01592) 750677 Fax: (01592) 610534

Outsourced H R Solutions, 54 Clarendon Road, Watford, WD17 1DU Tel: (01923) 431675 Fax: (01923) 431875 E-mail: info@invosoftsolutions.com

▶ Smartdata, Abertechnium, Y Lanfa, Trefechan, Aberystwyth, Dyfed, SY23 1AS Tel: (0845) 6128061 Fax: (01970) 613480 E-mail: enquiries@smartdata.co.uk

BUSINESS PROCESS OUTSOURCING, CREDIT CONTROL

▶ Crescent Credit Control, PO Box 459, Walton-on-Thames, Surrey, KT12 2WE Tel: (01932) 706590 Fax: (01932) 706590 E-mail: info@credit-specialists.co.uk

▶ Sterling Financial Ltd, Church Farm, Little Sodbury, Chipping Sodbury, Bristol, BS37 6QA Tel: (01454) 317272 Fax: (07884) 500629 E-mail: mail@sterlingfinancial.ltd.uk

BUSINESS PSYCHOLOGY CONSULTANTS

▶ ThinkWell, 78 Laitwood Road, London, SW12 9QJ Tel: (020) 8675 6454

BUSINESS SALES CONSULTANTS OR NEGOTIATORS

1 Solutions, 15 Royston Road, St. Albans, Hertfordshire, AL1 5NF Tel: (01727) 869020 E-mail: 101@another.com

▶ Hall Management Consultants Ltd, Unit 3, Brookend Business Park, Brookend Lane, Kempsey, Worcester, WR5 3LF Tel: 01905 769086 E-mail: enquiry@hmc-online.co.uk

▶ Market Synergies Ltd, 65 Cannon Court Road, Maidenhead, Berkshire, SL6 7QP Tel: (0790) 9993682 E-mail: enquiries@marketsynergies.co.uk

BUSINESS SCHOOLS

▶ Learning Partnership, Unit 8 The Old Power Station, 121 Mortlake High Street, London, SW14 8SN Tel: (020) 8876 9322 Fax: (020) 8876 9322 E-mail: info@tlp.org

▶ Oxford Management College, Eynsham Hall, North Leigh, Witney, Oxfordshire, OX29 6PN Tel: (01865) 514106 Fax: (01993) 883986 E-mail: info@oxfordmanagementcollege.com

BUSINESS SPEAKERS

▶ RS-Events Ltd, 72 Overcliff Road, Lewisham, London, SE13 7UA Tel: (020) 8473 5529 E-mail: info@rs-events.co.uk

BUSINESS STRATEGY CONSULTANTS

Applabs Ltd, Preston Technology Centre, Marsh Lane, Preston, PR1 8UQ Tel: (01772) 885850 Fax: (01772) 558881 E-mail: info@isintegration.com

▶ Better Strategy Ltd, 22 The Grove, Farnborough, Hampshire, GU14 6QR Tel: (01252) 682167

BISC, 10 Park Lane, Reigate, Surrey, RH2 8JX Tel: (01737) 222119 Fax: (01737) 222119 E-mail: bs@bisconsultants.co.uk

▶ Bluefin Solutions Ltd, Utell House, 2 Kew Bridge Road, Brentford, Middlesex, TW8 0JF Tel: (0870) 2330404 Fax: (0870) 2330405 E-mail: enquiries@bluefinsolutions.com

▶ Bluetree Specific Skills, 18 Croftfield Road, Godmanchester, Huntingdon, Cambridgeshire, PE29 2ED Tel: (0845) 4534500 Fax: (0870) 8681610 E-mail: graham@bluetreeuk.com

▶ Box Clever Solutions Ltd, PO Box 427, Southport, Merseyside, PR8 2WG Tel: (0845) 1235730 Fax: (0845) 1235736 E-mail: info@business-made-simple.co.uk

Business Insights Group Ltd, Brandiston House, 98 High Street, Ingatestone, Essex, CM4 0BA Tel: (01277) 355755 Fax: (01277) 355753 E-mail: info@digroup.co.uk

Careybrook Ltd, PO Box 205, Southam, Warwickshire, CV47 0ZL Tel: (01926) 813619 Fax: (01926) 814898 E-mail: cb.ltd@btinternet.com

Chamber Business Connections, Commerce House, Bridgeman Place, Bolton, BL2 1DW Tel: (01204) 363212 Fax: (01204) 363212 E-mail: enquiries@chamberhelp.co.uk

Computer Consultants Ltd, Guild Street, Stratford-upon-Avon, Warwickshire, CV37 6RP Tel: (01789) 261200 Fax: (01789) 262525 E-mail: sales@cclnet.co.uk

▶ E B A Consulting Ltd, PO Box 14, Kidwelly, Dyfed, SA17 4YH Tel: (01554) 890300 Fax: (01554) 891508 E-mail: info@ebassociates.co.uk

Effective Solutions For Business, Acquest Ho, 183 Kingston Rd, London, SW19 1LH Tel: (020) 8395 6472 Fax: (020) 8241 2502 E-mail: sales@effects.co.uk

G P W Consultancy, 3 Redcourt, Woking, Surrey, GU22 8RA Tel: (01932) 355770 Fax: (01932) 336454 E-mail: information@gpw.co.uk

I B M (UK) Ltd, 1 New Square, Feltham, Middlesex, TW14 8HB Tel: (020) 8818 6060 Fax: (020) 8818 5499

▶ Independent Buyers Ltd, Station Road, Hatton, Derby, DE65 5YX Tel: (01283) 516517 Fax: (01283) 512481 E-mail: info@independentbuyers.com

Infogain Ltd, 18 Forlease Road, Maidenhead, Berkshire, SL6 1RU Tel: (01628) 580600 Fax: (01628) 580610 E-mail: info@infogain.com

Insight Consulting, Churchfield House, 3 & 5 The Quintet, Churchfield Road, Walton-On-Thames, Surrey, KT12 2TZ Tel: (01932) 241000 Fax: (01932) 244590 E-mail: insight@insight.co.uk

▶ Integer Research, 55 Farringdon Road, London, EC1M 3JB Tel: (020) 7092 8100 Fax: (020) 7503 1266 E-mail: sales@integer-research.com

Simon Kelly Partnership, 12 Argyle Road, Clevedon, Avon, BS21 7BP Tel: (01275) 875569 Fax: (01275) 875509 E-mail: simon_kelly@btinternet.com

▶ NOV8 Ltd, Hartham Park, Corsham, Wiltshire, SN13 0RP Tel: (01249) 700009 E-mail: kellysearch@nov8.biz

▶ Pactum Partium Ltd, 24 Nursery Gardens, Bedford, MK41 8DU Tel: (07890) 267779 E-mail: info@pactern-partium.com

▶ Papertex Ltd, PO Box 11, Skipton, North Yorkshire, BD23 9AF Tel: (01756) 649033 Fax: (0870) 8362330 E-mail: info@papertex.co.uk

▶ PI Consulting, Beech House, Melbourn Science Park, Cambridge Road, Melbourn, Royston, Hertfordshire, SG8 6HB Tel: (01763) 226242 E-mail: vincent.bryant@piconsulting.org.uk

▶ Quadrant Consultants Ltd, 35 Endell Street, Covert Garden, London, WC2H 9BA Tel: (020) 7240 7200 Fax: 0207 240 7201 E-mail: huw.watkins@qcl.co.uk

▶ Robb Fordyce, Greenburn Tornaveen, Torphins, Banchory, Kincardineshire, AB31 4LL Tel: (01339) 883832 E-mail: john@robb-fordyce.co.uk

▶ Scotscraig BUSINESS SOLUTIONS, The Clock House, 87 Paines Lane, PINNER, Middlesex, HA5 3BZ Tel: 020 8933-9962 E-mail: reception@scotscraigsolutions.co.uk

Taylor Nelson Sofres plc, 66 Wilson Street, London, EC2A 2JX Tel: (020) 7868 6500 Fax: (020) 7868 6501 E-mail: christine.davidson@tnsofres.com

▶ Transform ebusiness Ltd, Fortissat House, Newmill-Canthill Road, Shotts, Lanarkshire, ML7 4NS Tel: (07793) 973873 E-mail: imacg@transform-ebusiness.com

BUSINESS SUPPORT SERVICES

Alternet, 5 Cardiff Road, Luton, LU1 1PP Tel: (0870) 6009968 Fax: (0870) 6009969 E-mail: jimrudd@alternetuk.com

Amcort Ltd, Field House, McMichaels Way, Hurst Green, Etchingham, East Sussex, TN19 7HJ Tel: (01580) 860500 Fax: (01580) 860171 E-mail: info@amcort.com

Black Country Chamber & Business Link, Dudley Court South The Waterfront, Level Street, Brierley Hill, West Midlands, DY5 1XN Tel: (0845) 1131234 Fax: (01384) 360560 E-mail: sales@blackcountrybusinesslink.com

Black Country Chamber & Business Link, Dudley Court South The Waterfront, Level Street, Brierley Hill, West Midlands, DY5 1XN Tel: (0845) 1131234 Fax: (01384) 360560 E-mail: sales@blackcountrybusinesslink.com

▶ Box Clever Solutions Ltd, PO Box 427, Southport, Merseyside, PR8 2WG Tel: (0845) 1235730 Fax: (0845) 1235736 E-mail: info@business-made-simple.co.uk

▶ Jo Branagan Business Support Services, 188 Danube Road, Hull, HU5 5UX Tel: (07973) 511026 E-mail: info@jo-branagan.co.uk

▶ BROWNWARRIORSOURCING, 112 Findhorn Street, Fintry, Dundee, DD4 9PN Tel: 01382 506814 E-mail: duncanscott@brownwarriorsourcing.co.uk

Burton & District/Tamworth Chamber of Commerce & Industry, Greton House, Waterside Court, Third Avenue, Centrum 100, Burton-On-Trent, Staffordshire, DE14 2WQ Tel: (01283) 563761 Fax: (01283) 510753 E-mail: services@burtonchamber.co.uk

Business Link, Pity Me Business Centre, Abbey Road Business Park, Pity Me, Durham, DH1 5JZ Tel: 0191-374 4000 Fax: 0191-374 4010 E-mail: customerservices@blcd.co.uk

Business Link, Kingsgate House, 66-74 Victoria Street, London, SW1E 6SW Tel: (020) 7215 5000 Fax: (020) 7215 5001 E-mail: enquiries@businesslink.org

Business Link, Tees Valley Business Centre, 2 Queens Square, Middlesbrough, Cleveland, TS2 1AA Tel: (01642) 806666 Fax: (01642) 341425 E-mail: enquiries@businesslinknortheast.co.uk

Business Link, 5 Phoenix Place, Nottingham, NG8 6BA Tel: (0845) 7586644 Fax: 0115-977 7399 E-mail: info@blnotts.com

Business Link, Merck House, Seldown Lane, Poole, Dorset, BH15 1TD Tel: (01202) 785400 Fax: (01202) 448838

Business Link, 45a Newdown Road, Scunthorpe, South Humberside, DN17 2TX Tel: (01724) 291510 Fax: (01724) 291511 E-mail: info@blhumber.co.uk

Business Link, Bus & Innovation Centre, Sunderland Enterprise Park, Wearfield, Sunderland, SR5 2TA Tel: 0191-516 6700 Fax: 0191-516 6777 E-mail: enquiries@businesslinktw.co.uk

Business Link, Emlyn Square, Swindon, SN1 5BP Tel: (0845) 6004141 Fax: (01722) 415447 E-mail: info@blbw.co.uk

Business Link, Creech Castle, Bathpool, Taunton, Somerset, TA1 2DX Tel: (0845) 7211112 Fax: (01823) 274862 E-mail: sales@somerset.businesslink.co.uk

Business Link, 34 Tower View Kings Hill, Kings Hill, West Malling, Kent, ME19 4ED Tel: (01732) 878000 Fax: (01732) 841109 E-mail: info@businesslinkkent.co.uk

Business Link, Arabesque House, Monks Cross Drive, Huntington, York, YO32 9WU Tel: (01904) 686000 Fax: (01904) 686020 E-mail: info.centre@blyny.co.uk

Business Link Berkshire & Wiltshire, Thames Tower, 37-41 Station Road, Reading, RG1 1LX Tel: (0845) 6004141

Business Link For Cambridgeshire, Centenary House, St. Marys Street, Huntingdon, Cambridgeshire, PE29 3PE Tel: (0845) 6097979

Business Link Cheshire & Warrington Ltd, International Business Centre, Delta Crescent, Westbrook, Warrington, WA5 7WQ Tel: (01925) 715200 Fax: (01925) 715005 E-mail: info@blinkcw.co.uk

Business Link For Cumbria, Capital Buildings Hilltop Heights, London Road, Carlisle, CA1 2NS Tel: (0870) 7571177 Fax: (01228) 613233

Business Link Derbyshire, Canal Wharf, Chesterfield, Derbyshire, S41 7NA Tel: (0845) 6011038 Fax: (01246) 233228

Business Link Derbyshire, Innovation Ho, Riverside Pk, Raynesway, Derby, DE21 7BF Tel: (0845) 6011038 Fax: (01332) 548088

Business Link Devon & Cornwall Ltd, Prosper House, Buddshead Road, Plymouth, PL6 5XR Tel: (01752) 785785 Fax: (01752) 770925

Business Link East Midlands, Innovation House, East Service Road, Raynesway, Spondon, Derby, DE21 7BF Tel: (0845) 0586644 Fax: (01332) 280792 E-mail: info@businesslinkem.co.uk

Business Link For Greater Merseyside, Halton Business Forum, Victoria Sq, Widnes, Cheshire, WA8 7QZ Tel: (0845) 3300151 Fax: 0151-420 9424 E-mail: questions@halton-businesslink.co.uk

Business Link Hertfordshire, 45 Grosvenor Road, St. Albans, Hertfordshire, AL1 3AW Tel: (01727) 813813 Fax: (01727) 813776 E-mail: stevem@exemplas.com

Business Link Humber, 1B Osborne Street, Grimsby, North East Lincolnshire, DN31 1EY Tel: (01472) 362868 Fax: (01472) 356052

Business Link Humber, Owen Avenue, Priory Park, Hessle, North Humberside, HU13 9PD Tel: (0845) 1243333 Fax: (01482) 641044

Business Link London Ltd, Link, 298-308 Southbury Road, Enfield, Middlesex, EN1 1TS Tel: (0845) 6000787 Fax: (020) 7111 0301 E-mail: info@bllondon.com

Business Link For Norfolk, PO Box 36, Swaffham, Norfolk, PE37 7WZ Tel: (0845) 7218218 Fax: (01760) 726727 E-mail: success@businesslinknorfolk.co.uk

Business Link North West, St. Nicholas House, Old Church Yard, Liverpool, L2 8TY Tel: (0845) 0066888 Fax: (01772) 790140 E-mail: info@businesslinknw.co.uk

Business Link North & Western Lancashire, Lancashire Enterprises Business Park, Centurion Way, Leyland, PR26 6TY Tel: (01772) 790200 Fax: (01772) 443002 E-mail: info@nwl.businesslink.co.uk

Business Link Shropshire Ltd, Trevithick House, Unit B1 Stafford Park 4, Telford, Shropshire, TF3 3BA Tel: (0845) 7543210 E-mail: enquiries@blwm.com

Business Link Solutions Ltd, Eastern By Pass, Thame, Oxfordshire, OX9 3FF Tel: (01844) 210400 Fax: (01235) 468200

Business Link South Yorkshire, Reresby House, Bow Bridge Close, Rotherham, South Yorkshire, S60 1BY Tel: (01709) 386300 Fax: (01709) 386330 E-mail: enquiries@blsy.com

Business Link South Yorkshire, Albion House, Savile Street, Sheffield, S4 7UQ Tel: (0800) 0737474 Fax: 0114-201 2525 E-mail: enquiries@blsy.com

Business Link Suffolk Ltd, Felaw Maltings, 42 Felaw Street, Ipswich, IP2 8PN Tel: (01473) 417000 Fax: (01473) 417070 E-mail: admin@bls.org.uk

Business Link Surrey, 5th Floor Hollywood House, Church St East, Woking, Surrey, GU21 6HJ Tel: (0845) 7494949 Fax: (01483) 771507 E-mail: sales@businesslinksurrey.co.uk

Business Link Sussex, Sussex Enterprise Greenacre Court, Station Rd, Burgess Hill, W. Sussex, RH15 9DS Tel: (0845) 0360144 Fax: (01444) 259255 E-mail: marketing@sussexenterprise.co.uk

Business Link Wessex, Wates House, Wallington Hill, Fareham, Hampshire, PO16 7BJ Tel: (0845) 4588558 Fax: (01329) 223223 E-mail: info@businesslink.co.uk

Business Link Wessex, Suite 1 Slade Bldgs, The Square, Gillingham, Dorset, SP8 4AY Tel: (0845) 4588558 Fax: (01747) 821613

Business Link Wessex, Mill Court, Furrlongs, Newport, Isle of Wight, PO30 2AA Tel: (08454) 588558 Fax: (01983) 533508 E-mail: tbutler@iwpartnership.com

Business Link West Yorkshire, Unit 4 Meadow Court, Millshaw Business Pk, Millshaw, Leeds, LS11 8LZ Tel: 0871 220 5000 Fax: 0113-383 7700 E-mail: info@blinkleeds.co.uk

Business Links For Northumberland, Wansbeck Business Centre, Rotary Parkway, Ashington, Northumberland, NE63 8QZ Tel: (01670) 528000 Fax: (01670) 813355

Business West, Leigh Court Business Centre, Pill Road, Abbots Leigh, Bristol, BS8 3RA Tel: (01275) 373373 Fax: (01275) 370706 E-mail: info@businesslinksw.co.uk

Capita Business Services Ltd, Manvers House, Manvers Street, Trowbridge, Wiltshire, BA14 8YX Tel: (01225) 773000 Fax: (01225) 777625

Cardiff Chamber of Commerce, Suite 1, 2nd Floor, St. Davids House, Wood Street, Cardiff, CF10 5AS Tel: (029) 2034 8280 Fax: (029) 2048 9785 E-mail: enquiries@cardiffchamber.co.uk

The Chamber Business, Kimpton Road, Luton, LU2 0SX Tel: (01582) 522448 Fax: (01582) 522450 E-mail: info@chamber-business.com

Chamber Business Enterprise, Churchgate House, 56 Oxford Street, Manchester, M60 7HJ Tel: 0161-237 4070 Fax: 0161-236 9945 E-mail: mgore@blnm.co.uk

Chamber Of Commerce Trade & Industry, Commerce House, Fenton Street, Lancaster, LA1 1AB Tel: (01524) 381331 Fax: (01524) 389505 E-mail: sales@lancaster-chamber.org.uk

Chase Business Service, 14 Elton Avenue, Greenford, Middlesex, UB6 0PW Tel: (020) 8864 0701 Fax: (0870) 0518485 E-mail: chase@greenford.demon.co.uk

▶ Chiene & Taite CA, 61 Dublin Street, Edinburgh, EH3 6NL Tel: 0131-558 5800 Fax: 0131-558 5899

▶ Consultancy People Ltd, Nelson House, 1a Church Street, Epsom, Surrey, KT17 4PF Tel: (0845) 0504657 E-mail: mail@consultpeople.com

D H M Marketing Services, Orchard House, Westbury Road, Warminster, Wiltshire, BA12 0AW Tel: (01985) 217950 Fax: (01985) 217950 E-mail: enquiries@dohelpme.co.uk

▶ Direct Route Collections Ltd, Tong Hall, Tong Lane, Bradford, West Yorkshire, BD4 0RR Tel: 0113-287 9123 Fax: 0113-287 9153 E-mail: rdavy@directroute.co.uk

Dover District Chamber Of Commerce, White Cliffs BSNS Park, Honeywood Road, Whitfield, Dover, Kent, CT16 3EH Tel: (01304) 824955 Fax: (01304) 822354 E-mail: mail@doverchamber.co.uk

▶ Eastside Consulting, 91 Brick Lane, London, E1 6QL Tel: 020 77706144 E-mail: trevor@eastsideconsulting.co.uk

Economic Development Service, Gloucester City Council, 75-81 Eastgate Street, Gloucester, GL1 1PN Tel: (01452) 544911 Fax: (01452) 396994

▶ Edivorp Ltd, 4 Bowland Rise, Chandlers Ford, Chandler's Ford, Eastleigh, Hampshire, SO53 4QW Tel: (023) 8025 2600 E-mail: enquiries@edivorp.co.uk

▶ Escutcheon Limited, Suite 20, The Cavendish Centre, Winchester, Hampshire, SO23 0LB Tel: 0870 2250995 Fax: 0870 2250996 E-mail: answers@helpmybusiness.co.uk

▶ Fitzpatrick Wilkes & Co. Ltd, The Old Forge Cottages, The Green, Beeston, Sandy, Bedfordshire, SG19 1PF Tel: (01767) 692473 E-mail: info@fitzpatrick-wilkes.co.uk

▶ Glue2 Ltd, Greystones, Front Street, Chedzoy, Bridgwater, Somerset, TA7 8RE Tel: (01278) 439152 Fax: (01278) 439152

Greater Merseyside Enterprise Ltd, Egerton Housetower Road, Birkenhead, Merseyside, CH41 1FN Tel: (0845) 3300151 Fax: (08453) 300150 E-mail: information@gme.org.uk

Haden Building Management Ltd, Summit House, Glebe Way, West Wickham, Kent, BR4 0RJ Tel: (020) 8918 4200 Fax: (020) 8918 4391

I S S UK Ltd, Wells House, 65 Boundary Road, Woking, Surrey, GU21 5BS Tel: (01483) 754960 Fax: (01483) 745999 E-mail: iss@uk.issworld.com

▶ Insourcing Business Support Ltd, 16 Saddlers Close, Glenfield, Leicester, LE3 8QU Tel: (07968) 865285 E-mail: info@ibs-ltd.co.uk

JHP Training Sheffield, 40 Castle Square, Sheffield, S1 2GF Tel: 0114-275 7286 Fax: 0114-279 7503 E-mail: sheffield.business.centre@jhp-group.com

▶ Katalyst Learning Ltd, Butterthwaite House, Jumble Lane, Ecclesfield, Sheffield, S35 9XJ Tel: 0114 257 6722 Fax: 0114 257 6733 E-mail: info@katalystlearning.co.uk

Learning & Skills Council Co Durham, Allergate House, Belmont Business Park, Durham, DH1 1TW Tel: (0845) 0194174 Fax: 0191-376 2302 E-mail: ask@lsc.gov.uk

The Lennox Partnership Ltd, Unit 1a Erskine House, North Avenue, Clydebank Business Park, Clydebank, Dunbartonshire, G81 2DR Tel: 0141-951 1131 Fax: 0141-952 0312 E-mail: info@thelennoxpartnership.org

Liverpool Chamber Of Commerce & Industry, 1 Old Hall Street, Liverpool, L3 9HG Tel: 0151-227 1233 Fax: 0151-236 0121 E-mail: info@liverpoolchamber.org.uk

London North Learning & Skills Council, Dumayne House, 1 Fox Lane, London, N13 4AB Tel: (0845) 0194158 Fax: (020) 8882 5931 E-mail: post@nltec.co.uk

▶ Lucid Innovation Group, PO Box 180, Manchester, M21 9XW Tel: 0161-860 0058 E-mail: ideas@lucidinnovation.com

▶ M & R Facilities Management Ltd, Unit 11, 13 Telford Road Thornton, Ellesmere Port, CH65 5EU Tel: 0151-357 1901 Fax: 0151-357 1902 E-mail: sales@mrfm.co.uk

Magpies Nest, 58 Tong Lane, Whitworth, Rochdale, Lancashire, OL12 8BE Tel: (01706) 853081

Mailboxes Etc (UK) Ltd, 19-21 Crawford Street, London, W1H 1PJ Tel: (020) 7224 2666 Fax: (020) 7224 2777 E-mail: peter@mailboxes-etc.co.uk

▶ The Company Merchant Ltd, Redditch, Worcestershire, B98 0NU Tel: (0870) 4323232 Fax: (0870) 4323295 E-mail: mail@thecompanymerchant.co.uk

▶ myHotDesk, 27 John Player Building, Stirling Enterprise Park, Stirling, Stirling, FK7 7RP Tel: 01786 450022 E-mail: advice@www.myhotdesk.com

North West Business Link Ltd, Lee House, 90 Great Bridgewater Street, Manchester, M1 5JW Tel: 0161-236 4114 Fax: 0161-228 3043 E-mail: info@business-support-solutions.co.uk

▶ OnLine Office Services, 15 Knocklands Court, Ballymoney, County Antrim, BT53 6LN Tel: (028) 2766 9566 Fax: (028) 2766 9566 E-mail: info@onlineofficeservices.co.uk

▶ Poppleton & Appleby, 32 High Street, Manchester, M4 1QD Tel: 0161-834 7025 Fax: 0161-833 1548 E-mail: enquires@pandamanchester.co.uk

BUSINESS SUPPORT SERVICES – *continued*

Productivity Solutions Ltd, PO Box 2133, Stoke-on-Trent, ST3 4WP Tel: (01782) 855739 Fax: (01782) 855739 E-mail: headoffice@psleurope.com

Productivity Solutions Ltd, PO Box 3272, Stourbridge, West Midlands, DY8 2ZA Tel: (01562) 720630 Fax: (01562) 720630 E-mail: info@psleurope.com

Rolls-Royce Aircraft Management Ltd, PO Box 31, Derby, DE24 8BJ Tel: (01332) 242424 Fax: (01332) 249936

▶ Rotherham Investment and Development Office, Reresbey House, Bowbridge Close, Rotherham, South Yorkshire, S60 1YR Tel: (01709) 372099 Fax: (01709) 837953 E-mail: info@rido.org.uk

Saracen's House Business Centre, Saracens House, 25 ST. Margarets Green, Ipswich, IP4 2BN Tel: (01473) 225951 Fax: (01473) 211508 E-mail: reception@saracens.co.uk

Scottish Enterprise Dunbartonshire, Spectrum House, 1a North Avenue, Clydebank Business Park, Clydebank, Dunbartonshire, G81 2DR Tel: 0141-951 2121 Fax: 0141-951 1907 E-mail: dunbartonshire@scotent.co.uk

Serco Group P.L.C., Serco House, 16 Bartley Wood, Business Park, Hook, Hampshire, RG27 9UY Tel: (01256) 745900 Fax: (01256) 744111

▶ SF Consultants, 31 Austins Mead, Bovingdon, Hertfordshire, HP3 0JU Tel: 01442 380120 Fax: 01442 380334 E-mail: stephanie.farrer@ntlworld.com

Solidbase (UK) Ltd, Egerton Court, Haig Road, Knutsford, Cheshire, WA16 8FB Tel: (01565) 621150 Fax: (01565) 653950 E-mail: info@solidbase.co.uk

▶ Steve Parker ICD International Company Development, 24 Shearwater Drive, Amblecote, Brierley Hill, West Midlands, DY5 2RD Tel: 01384 893346 Fax: 01384 893346 E-mail: steveparker1@ukonline.co.uk

Stevenage Business Initiative, The Business & Technology Centre, Bessemer Drive, Stevenage, Hertfordshire, SG1 2DX Tel: (01438) 315733 Fax: (01438) 313001 E-mail: sbienq@stevbtc.demon.co.uk

Stuart Edwards Fullermoon, 102-104 High Street, Croydon, CR9 1TN Tel: (020) 8686 4771 Fax: (020) 8688 7121 E-mail: sales@stuart-edwards.com

Thames Cleaning Co. Ltd, 14 Hatherley Road, Sidcup, Kent, DA14 4BG Tel: (020) 8302 6633 Fax: (020) 8300 7779 E-mail: jenny.mclaren@thamescleaning.co.uk

Torfaen County Borough Council Children's Information Service Edu, County Hall, Croesyceiliog, Cwmbran, Gwent, NP44 2WN Tel: (01633) 648305 Fax: (01633) 648088 E-mail: info@invest-in-torfaen.org

▶ Sandrine Vaillant, Old Vallis Cottage, Vallis Road, Frome, Somerset, BA11 3EN Tel: (0777) 9668707 Fax: (01373) 474945 E-mail: sandrine.vaillant@btinternet.co.uk

▶ Versyns Ventures Ltd, Versyns House, Vale Road, Mayfield, East Sussex, TN20 6BD Tel: (01435) 874800 Fax: (01435) 873631 E-mail: chrislilly@versynsventures.com

Wellingborough Town Centre Patnership Ltd, 18-19 Spring Lane, Wellingborough, Northamptonshire, NN8 1EY Tel: (01933) 270795 Fax: (01933) 222202 E-mail: info@wellingboroughchamber.co.uk

▶ Whitegold Taxis, 4 Inglenook Court, Maltby, Rotherham, South Yorkshire, S66 7NZ Tel: (01709) 812222 Fax: 01709 769560 E-mail: larjimoh@yahoo.com

BUSINESS SUPPORT SERVICES, TRAINING

▶ Accountancy & Business Cartoons, 4 Auckland Way, Hartburn, Stockton-on-Tees, Cleveland, TS18 5LG Tel: (01642) 581847 Fax: (01642) 581847 E-mail: vh2@businesscartoons.co.uk

▶ Barrimon Solutions, Jersey Crescent, Stoke-on-Trent, ST3 4TJ Tel: (01384) 823828

▶ Business24, Welton House, Lime Kiln Way, Lincoln, LN2 4WH Tel: (01522) 574204 Fax: 01522 574035 E-mail: enquiries@business24.co.uk

▶ Dynamic Customer Solutions Ltd, 92 Sandgate Road, Hall Green, Birmingham, B28 0UL Tel: 0121-733 6672 E-mail: liz@dynamiccs.co.uk

▶ Excelerated Performance Consulting, 6 Romani Close, Warwick, CV34 4TY Tel: 01926 402667 Fax: 01926 402667 E-mail: info@excelerated-performance.co.uk

▶ Fitzpatrick Wilkes & Co. Ltd, The Old Forge Cottages, The Green, Beeston, Sandy, Bedfordshire, SG19 1PF Tel: (01767) 692473 E-mail: info@fitzpatrick-wilkes.co.uk

▶ Libra Management Consultants, Suite 14-15 Axwel House, Westerton Road, East Mains Industrial Estate, Broxburn, West Lothian, EH52 5AU Tel: 0845 1249342 Fax: 0707 5024394 E-mail: admin@libramanagement.com

Manufacturing Excellence Ltd, Round Foundry Media Centre, Foundry Street, Leeds, LS11 5QP Tel: (0870) 4202460 E-mail: Roger.lees@manufacturingexcellence.co.uk

▶ Motivating Moves, 3 Cotswold Gardens, Downswood, Maidstone, Kent, ME15 8TB Tel: (07968) 947999 Fax: (01622) 863199 E-mail: enquires@motivatingmoves.co.uk

▶ Pyramid Training (UK) Ltd, Beechwood House, 34 Beechwood Avenue, Bradford, West Yorkshire, BD6 3AF Tel: (01274) 677776 E-mail: info@pyramid2000.fsnet.co.uk

QCS International Ltd, 13 The Wynd, Cumbernauld, Glasgow, G67 2ST Tel: (01236) 734447 Fax: (01236) 725070 E-mail: sales@qcsl.co.uk

▶ Rubus Consultants Ltd, Llanvair Discoed, Chepstow, Monmouthshire, NP16 6LY Tel: (01633) 400 051 E-mail: andrew.miller@rubus-consultants.co.uk

▶ Sense-Ability, Felin Brithdir, Rhydlewis, Llandysul, Dyfed, SA44 5SN Tel: 0151-652 1053 E-mail: post@sense-ability.co.uk

▶ Solubus Ltd, Laggan, Sunnyside Road, Falkirk, FK1 4BG Tel: (01324) 871667 Fax: (01324) 871667 E-mail: stuart@solubus.co.uk

▶ Steve Parker ICD International Company Development, 24 Shearwater Drive, Amblecote, Brierley Hill, West Midlands, DY5 2RD Tel: 01384 893346 Fax: 01384 893346 E-mail: steveparker1@ukonline.co.uk

BUSINESS SYSTEM COMPONENTS

Computer Performance International Ltd, Outwoods, Oxford Road, Gerrards Cross, Buckinghamshire, SL9 7PU Tel: (01753) 890808 Fax: (01753) 890918 E-mail: mail@cpiuk.co.uk

Link Systems, The Farmhouse, Steeple View Farm, Dunton Road, Basildon, Essex, SS15 4DB Tel: (0845) 2302940 Fax: (01268) 496029 E-mail: sales@link-systems.co.uk

BUSINESS SYSTEMS

Apogee Corporation Ltd, Unit 8 Willow Lane Business Park, Nyton Road, Mitcham, Surrey, CR4 4NA Tel: (0845) 3009955 Fax: (0845) 3009944 E-mail: reception@apogeecorp.com

Cable Print, Unit 1, Black Ven Farm, Hartgrove, Shaftesbury, Dorset, SP7 0AS Tel: (0845) 2267012 Fax: (0845) 2267012 E-mail: cableprint@tiscali.com

City Office Ni Ltd, 67 Boucher Cresent, Belfast, BT12 6HU Tel: (028) 9038 1838 Fax: (028) 9038 1954 E-mail: info@cityofficni.com

▶ D. Collis, 51 Harehill Road, Grangewood, Chesterfield, Derbyshire, S40 2NG Tel: (01246) 540180 Fax: (01246) 540180 E-mail: david@dcollis.wanadoo.co.uk

Hamlet Computer Group Ltd, 5 Oriel Court, Omega Park, Alton, Hampshire, GU34 2YT Tel: (01420) 83550 Fax: (01420) 541364 E-mail: sales@hamletcg.co.uk

Inpace Ltd, 100 Brize Norton Road, Minster Lovell, Witney, Oxfordshire, OX29 0SG Tel: (01993) 706303 Fax: (01993) 706305 E-mail: info@inpace.com

Insider Technologies Ltd, Spinnaker Court Chandlers Point, 37 Broadway, Salford, M50 2YR Tel: 0161-876 6606 Fax: 0161-868 6666 E-mail: sales@insidertech.co.uk

London Communications plc, 134 Gloucester Avenue, Regents Park, London, NW1 8JA Tel: (020) 7586 9851 Fax: (020) 7483 6401 E-mail: clive.waylett@londoncomms.com

Lynbrook Reprographic Ltd, Unit 15A, Boxer Place, Leyland, PR26 7QL Tel: (01772) 452125 Fax: (01772) 622304 E-mail: sales@lynbrookreprographic.co.uk

N C R UK Group Ltd, 206 Marylebone Road, London, NW1 6LY Tel: (020) 7723 7070 Fax: (020) 7725 8224

Ogl Computer Services Group, Worcester Road, Stourport-on-Severn, Worcestershire, DY13 9AT Tel: (01299) 873873 Fax: (01299) 873700 E-mail: enquiries@ogl.co.uk

P & I Design Ltd, 2 Reed Street, Thornaby, Stockton-on-Tees, Cleveland, TS17 7AF Tel: (01642) 617444 Fax: (01642) 616447 E-mail: drr@pidesign.co.uk

▶ Quenvhas, 253 Dysart Road, Grantham, Lincolnshire, NG31 7LP Tel: (01476) 409929 E-mail: enquire@quenvas.co.uk

Rembrand Ltd, 51 Angel Road, Norwich, NR3 3HR Tel: (01603) 788477 Fax: (01603) 788466

▶ Sirius Concepts Ltd, Oswald Hall, Auchincruive, Ayr, KA6 5HW Tel: (01292) 521376 Fax: (01292) 525939 E-mail: enquiries@sircon.co.uk

Triangular Business Systems, 1 Marlston Court, Rough Hill, Marlston-cum-Lache, Chester, CH4 9JT Tel: (01244) 683450 Fax: (01244) 674949 E-mail: enquiries@triangularsystems.co.uk

BUSINESS TO BUSINESS (B2B) ELECTRONIC MAIL (EMAIL) MARKETING

▶ Marketing Outsourced, 15 Heaven Tree Close, London, N1 2PW Tel: (020) 7354 5657

▶ Pinpointworld, 24 Orton Enterprise Centre, Bakewell Road, Orton Southgate, Peterborough, PE2 6XU Tel: (01733) 233550 Fax: (01733) 233650 E-mail: contact@pinpointworld.com

▶ Redbark, Badger House, Desborough, Kettering, Northamptonshire, NN14 2NS Tel: 01604 648773 Fax: 0871 242 5181 E-mail: redbark@tiscali.co.uk

▶ The Rooster Ltd, 37 Sandelswood End, Beaconsfield, Buckinghamshire, HP9 2AA Tel: (01494) 672966 E-mail: adevillard@therooster.co.uk

▶ Sence Valley Consulting, 14 Nethercote, Newton Burgoland, Coalville, Leicestershire, LE67 2ST Tel: 01530 272561 E-mail: results@sencevalley.co.uk

▶ stream:20, Southbank house, Blackprince Road, London, SE1 7SJ Tel: 0207 7932450

▶ Tactical MarComms, 16 Blythe Road, Corfe Mullen, Wimborne, Dorset, BH21 3LR Tel: (01202) 699967 Fax: (01202) 699967 E-mail: eddie.palmer@tacticalmarcomms.com

▶ Whichlist.com, Tapton Park Innovation Centre, Brimington Road, Chesterfield, Derbyshire, S41 0TZ Tel: (01246) 297179 Fax: (01246) 297180 E-mail: sales@whichlist.com

The Zest Collective Ltd, 14 Birchwood Drive, Hambleton, Poulton-le-Fylde, Lancashire, FY6 9AQ Tel: (01253) 702035 E-mail: invest@zestisbest.net

BUSINESS TRAINING SERVICES

J & S Horn Consultants Ltd, 24 Henderson Drive, Skene, Westhill, Aberdeenshire, AB32 6RA Tel: (01224) 744330 Fax: (01224) 744330 E-mail: training@peakperformance.tv

▶ Power Partners Development, 4 Blackthorn Close, Biddisham, Axbridge, Somerset, BS26 2RN Tel: 01934 750364

BUSINESS TRAINING SOFTWARE

Andrew Charles Associates, 119 Mulberry Road, Northfleet, Gravesend, Kent, DA11 8QA Tel: (01474) 532865 Fax: (01474) 320442 E-mail: enquires@andrewcharles.co.uk

▶ Bristol Computer Training, 92 Egerton Road, Bishopston, Bristol, BS7 8HP Tel: 0117 9247567 E-mail: mail@bristolcomputertraining.co.uk

▶ Business It Central, Sussex College, College Road, Crawley, West Sussex, RH10 1NR Tel: (01293) 442326 Fax: (01293) 453421 E-mail: business1@centralsussex.ac.uk

▶ C S D Training Partnership, 33 Grange Drive, Castle Donington, Derby, DE74 2QU Tel: (01332) 810117 E-mail: admin@csd-training.co.uk

Check Tek Ltd, 38-42 Newport Street, Swindon, SN1 3DR Tel: (01793) 480022 Fax: (01793) 480066 E-mail: sales@check-tek.co.uk

Clearwater Consultancy Ltd, 18 St Georges Street, Chorley, Lancashire, PR7 2AA Tel: (01257) 272730 Fax: (01257) 272731 E-mail: info@clearwater-consultancy.co.uk

Clover Consultancy, 21 The Crescent, Taunton, Somerset, TA1 4EB Tel: (01823) 336220 Fax: (01823) 270105 E-mail: info@cloveruk.net

▶ Computersolutions-online, PO Box 24, Cardiff, CF23 0AA Tel: (08701) 999 630 Fax: (07092) 860228 E-mail: enquiries@cs-o.co.uk

LEARN>DO London0" pno ="0020925" corp ="00222477" new="N" rule=" " type="NORM"> Do>Learn>do, 21 Cantelowes Road, London, NW1 9XR Tel: 020 7267 8228 Fax: 020 7267 8228 E-mail: info@do-learn-do.com

▶ Energema Ltd, 77 Nicholas Gardens, High Wycombe, Buckinghamshire, HP13 6JG Tel: (01494) 465394 E-mail: info@energema.co.uk

Enterprise International UK Ltd, Whitbourne Lodge, 137 Church Street, Malvern, Worcestershire, WR14 2AN Tel: (01684) 566953 Fax: (01684) 560018 E-mail: info@ei-europe.com

Information Transfer, Burleigh House, 15 Newmarket Road, Cambridge, CB5 8EG Tel: (01223) 312227 Fax: (01223) 310200

Invensys Systems (UK) Ltd, Highbank House, Exchange Street, Stockport, Cheshire, SK3 0ET Tel: 0161-429 6744 Fax: 0161-480 9063

▶ JayrConsulting Ltd Freelance Training Consultants, 33 Ixworth Close, Watermeadow Estate, Northampton, NN3 8TW Tel: 01604 642041 Fax: 01604 642041 E-mail: john.roberts@jayrconsulting.co.uk

▶ JK Assist, Lingley House, Commissioners Road, Rochester, Kent, ME2 4EE Tel: 01634 712171 E-mail: info@jk-assist.co.uk

▶ Learn 247 online, 1 Dawney Drive, Four Oaks, Birmingham, B75 5JA Tel: 0121-323 2224 Fax: 0121-323 2224 E-mail: sales@learn247online.com

▶ Macuncle.Com, 2a Blakeney Road, Beckenham, Kent, BR3 1HA Tel: (07740) 796183 Fax: E-mail: eamon@macuncle.com

▶ Maxtar Ltd, 14 Chanctonbury View, Henfield, West Sussex, BN5 9TW Tel: (07714) 850950 Fax: (01273) 491848 E-mail: juergen.brinner@maxtar.co.uk

Midas Computer Systems, Gilnockie Station Ho, Canonbie, Dumfriesshire, DG14 0SG Tel: (01387) 371526 Fax: (01387) 371526

▶ MK Training, Sunningdale Avenue, Feltham, Middlesex, TW13 5JU Tel: (07976) 515095 E-mail: mk.training@virgin.net

N-Tire Systems Ltd, P O Box 215, Brentford, Middlesex, TW8 8RT Tel: (0845) 658 1505 Fax: (0845) 658 1505 E-mail: office@n-tiresystems.co.uk

Parity Solutions Ltd, Wimbledon Bridge House, 1 Hartfield Road, London, SW19 3RU Tel: (020) 8543 5353 Fax: (020) 8545 6456 E-mail: marketing@parity.co.uk

▶ Pitman Training, Bishops Stortford, Suite 3, 15 Market Square, Bishop's Stortford, Hertfordshire, CM23 3UT Tel: (01279) 466200 Fax: (01279) 466220 E-mail: bishopsstortford@pitman-training.net

Pyramid Consultancy, Murlain House, Union Street, Chester, CH1 1QP Tel: (01244) 357277 Fax: (01244) 357278 E-mail: sales@pyramidconsultancy.co.uk

▶ Rescue From Technology, 17 Linley Court, Thicket Road, Sutton, Surrey, SM1 4QA Tel: 0870 3831519 Fax: 07092 309964 E-mail: enquiries@rescuefrom.com

▶ The Software Practice, Bullbeck Mill, Mill Lane, Barrington, Cambridge, CB2 5QY Tel: (01223) 872874 Fax: (01223) 872876 E-mail: enquiries@softwarepractice.co.uk

▶ SUS IT, PO Box 114, Cheadle, Cheshire, SK8 7WQ Tel: 0161-439 0783 Fax: 0161-439 0783 E-mail: enquiries@sus-it.uk.com

The Training Foundry, City Campus, Pond Street, Sheffield, S1 1WB Tel: 0114-225 5888 Fax: 0114-225 5889 E-mail: itfoundry@shu.ac.uk

Tutorpro Ltd, 10 High Street, Wellington, Somerset, TA21 8RA Tel: (01823) 661669 Fax: (01823) 661668 E-mail: general@tutorpro.com

BUSINESS TRANSFER AGENTS

▶ Aconsultingmk Business Transfer Agents, 24 Iron Duke Close, Daventry, Northamptonshire, NN11 9LN Tel: (01327) 705100 Fax: (01327) 705100 E-mail: brian@amicia.co.uk

Beacon Computer Technology Ltd, 43 Clifton Road, Cambridge, CB1 7ED Tel: (01223) 506616 Fax: (01223) 506620 E-mail: sales@beacon-ct.co.uk

Colchester Business Transfer Agents, Suite 3 Hadleigh Business Centre, 351 London Road, Hadleigh, Benfleet, Essex, SS7 2BT Tel: (01206) 767147 Fax: (01702) 554253 E-mail: sales@cbta.co.uk

Crowndale Associates Ltd, 3 St Marys Street, Worcester, WR1 1HA Tel: (01905) 452570 Fax: (01905) 21044 E-mail: pauld@crowndaleassociates.com

▶ Haughtons Business Sales, Gladstone Street, Kibworth, Leicester, LE8 0HL Tel: 0116-279 2509 Fax: 0116-279 2509 E-mail: alan@hbsales.co.uk

Lakey & Co., Saxon House, Crown Road, Old Buckenham, Attleborough, Norfolk, NR17 1SD Tel: (01953) 861180 Fax: (01953) 861060

▶ Lakey & Co Yorkshire, Barugh Close, Melmerby, Ripon, North Yorkshire, HG4 5NB Tel: 01765 640064 E-mail: sales@lakey-yorkshire.co.uk

R M S Commercial, 48A Osborne Road, Newcastle Upon Tyne, NE2 2AL Tel: 0191-212 0000 Fax: 0191-281 9074 E-mail: info@ellisonrms.co.uk

BUSINESS TRAVEL MANAGEMENT

▶ Amc Solutions UK Ltd, 16 St. James Avenue, Sutton, Surrey, SM1 2TH Tel: (020) 8642 7214 Fax: 0870 766 9675 E-mail: info@amc-solutions.com

▶ Direct Passport & Visa Company Ltd, 12 Chepstow Road, London, W2 5BD Tel: (029) 1412 2072E-mail: directvisas@e3internet.com

Omega World Travel Ltd, 11 York Road, London, SE1 7NX Tel: (020) 7922 0770 Fax: (020) 7922 0799 E-mail: sales@owt.net

BUSINESS TURNAROUND MANAGEMENT

▶ Manufacturing Executive Ltd, Ivy House 90 Town Street, Lound, Retford, Nottinghamshire, DN22 8RX Tel: (01777) 818280 E-mail: info@manufacturingexecutive.com

BUSINESS WEBSITE CONSULTANCY

Bridgewater Software Development, Audley House, Northbridge Road, Berkhamsted, Hertfordshire, HP4 1EH Tel: (01442) 870244 Fax: (01442) 879993 E-mail: info@bridgewater.it

▶ Chapter Eight Ltd, Medius House, 2 Sheraton Street, Soho, London, W1F 8BH Tel: (020) 7788 9861 Fax: (020) 7788 9862

▶ Club Together Ltd, 31 Strathmore Road, Teddington, Middlesex, TW11 8UJ Tel: (020) 8943 2682 E-mail: dave.weston@teddingtontennis.org

▶ ECRE8, 4 Highlands Drive, Daventry, Northamptonshire, NN11 8ST Tel: (01327) 310808 Fax: (01327) 310808 E-mail: stuart@ecre8.co.uk

Leicester Office Solutions, Optec House, Wigston, Leicestershire, LE18 1HY Tel: 0845 0940363 E-mail: info@losdesign.co.uk

▶ indicates data change since last edition

BUSINESS WEBSITE CONSULTANCY – *continued*

▶ LittleFish Web Design, 79 King George Avenue, Horsforth, Leeds, LS18 5ND Tel: 0113 2170419 E-mail: contact@littlefishwebdesign.com
▶ PELICAN Solutions Ltd, 5 Westbrook Court, Sharrow Vale Road, SHEFFIELD, S11 8YZ Tel: 0114 233 5200

BUSINESS WEBSITE MAINTENANCE

Bridgewater Software Development, Audley House, Northbridge Road, Berkhamsted, Hertfordshire, HP4 1EH Tel: (01442) 870244 Fax: (01442) 879993 E-mail: info@bridgewater.it
▶ Chapter Eight Ltd, Medius House, 2 Sheraton Street, Soho, London, W1F 8BH Tel: (020) 7788 9861 Fax: (020) 7788 9862
▶ Club Together Ltd, 31 Strathmore Road, Teddington, Middlesex, TW11 8UJ Tel: (020) 8943 2682 E-mail: dave.weston@teddingtontennis.org
▶ ECRE8, 4 Highlands Drive, Daventry, Northamptonshire, NN11 8ST Tel: (01327) 310808 Fax: (01327) 310808 E-mail: stuart@ecre8.co.uk
▶ LittleFish Web Design, 79 King George Avenue, Horsforth, Leeds, LS18 5ND Tel: 0113 2170419 E-mail: contact@littlefishwebdesign.com

BUSINESS/OFFICE CONTRACT SERVICES

▶ Alternative Direct Marketing, 20 Fletcher Gate, Nottingham, NG1 2FZ Tel: (0871) 2202520 Fax: (0871) 2200141
Business In Focus Ltd, Enterprise Centre, Bryn Road, Aberkenfig, Bridgend, Mid Glamorgan, CF32 9BS Tel: (01656) 724414 Fax: (01656) 721163 E-mail: opt@businessinfocus.co.uk
Dunelm Office Interiors, 149 Kells Lane, Gateshead, Tyne & Wear, NE9 5HR Tel: 0191-491 5080 Fax: 0191-420 0197
▶ Star Business Support, 6 Werner Court, Aylesbury, Buckinghamshire, HP21 9QS Tel: (01296) 483352
Webber Office Solutions Inc Blare It Out Biographi, 117 Marsh Road, Rhyl, Clwyd, LL18 2AB Tel: (01745) 337066 Fax: (01745) 337072 E-mail: sales@officerus.com
Woodrow Business Centre, 65-66 Woodrow, London, SE18 5DH Tel: (020) 8854 1194 Fax: (020) 8317 0394 E-mail: info@woodrowbusinesscentre.com

BUTANE GAS

Budget Gas Ltd, Halesfield 21, Telford, Shropshire, TF7 4NX Tel: (01952) 583908 Fax: (01952) 586692
Flogas UK Ltd, Unit W, Barton Industrial Estate, Faldo Road, Barton-Le-Clay, MK45 4RP Tel: (01582) 600858 Fax: (01582) 882256
J Harrison & Sons Coal Merchants Ltd, The Coal Yard, Milton Road, Stoke-on-Trent, ST1 6LE Tel: (01782) 534110 Fax: (01782) 535039 E-mail: sales@jharrison-fuel.co.uk
Labro Tools & Gas Supply Co., 42-42a Nunhead Lane, London, SE15 3TU Tel: (020) 7639 9739 Fax: (020) 7252 8943
Spoors Ltd, Railway Street, Bishop Auckland, County Durham, DL14 7LR Tel: (01388) 603865 Fax: (01388) 608029 E-mail: spoors@onyxnet.co.uk

BUTCHERS' BLOCKS

Capstan Food Equipment, 1 Wyndham House, High Street, Kentisbeare, Cullompton, Devon, EX15 2AA Tel: (01884) 266750 Fax: (01884) 266750
G & T Packaging Ltd, Unit 10A, Factory Lane, Warminster, Wiltshire, BA12 8LT Tel: (01985) 216441 Fax: (01985) 216491 E-mail: enquiries@gtpack.btopenworld.com
P G Gibbins & Son, 19 Forknell Avenue, Coventry, CV2 3EN Tel: (024) 7644 5229 Fax: (024) 7644 5229
W G Pinsent Ltd, Unit B5 Star Business Centre, Marsh Way, Rainham, Essex, RM13 8UP Tel: (01708) 552943 Fax: (01708) 630890

BUTCHERS' CUTLERY

Amefa (UK) Ltd, Lion Works, 15 Orgreave Drive, Handsworth, Sheffield, S13 9NR Tel: (0844) 5553234 Fax: (0844) 5553435 E-mail: sales@amefa.co.uk
Capstan Food Equipment, 1 Wyndham House, High Street, Kentisbeare, Cullompton, Devon, EX15 2AA Tel: (01884) 266750 Fax: (01884) 266750
F. Heinemann Ltd, PO Box 76, Northwood, Middlesex, HA6 3AJ Tel: (01923) 829993 Fax: (01923) 825519 E-mail: heinecas@btinternet.com
Herbert M. Slater Ltd, 332 Coleford Road, Sheffield, S9 5PH Tel: 0114-261 2308 Fax: 0114-261 2305 E-mail: info@slaterknives.co.uk
Stone Food Equipment, 40 High Street, Stone, Staffordshire, ST15 8AU Tel: (01785) 817258 Fax: (01785) 817258

BUTCHERS' CUTLERY GRINDING MACHINES

Autool Grinders Ltd, Padiham Road, Sabden, Clitheroe, Lancashire, BB7 9EW Tel: (01282) 775000 Fax: (01282) 773486 E-mail: sales@autool.co.uk
Capstan Food Equipment, 1 Wyndham House, High Street, Kentisbeare, Cullompton, Devon, EX15 2AA Tel: (01884) 266750 Fax: (01884) 266750

BUTCHERS' STEELS

Egginton Bros Ltd, 25-31 Allen Street, Sheffield, S3 7AW Tel: 0114-276 6123 Fax: 0114-273 8465 E-mail: steve@eggintongroup.co.uk

BUTCHERS' SUPPLY SERVICES, EQUIPMENT/SUNDRIES

Amko Foods Ltd, Shiffnall Street, Bolton, BL2 1BZ Tel: (01204) 388801 E-mail: sales@amko.fsnet.co.uk
Atlantic Service Co. (UK) Ltd, Pen-Y-Fan Industrial Estate, Croespenmaen, Crumlin, Newport, Gwent, NP11 4EG Tel: (01495) 246012 Fax: (01495) 248113 E-mail: sales@atlantic-service.co.uk
Brolyn Butchers Supplies, New Street, Bridgend Industrial Estate, Bridgend, Mid Glamorgan, CF31 3UD Tel: (01656) 668614 Fax: (01656) 668614
C H Sundries, Willows, Langford Lane, Pen Elm, Taunton, Somerset, TA2 6NZ Tel: (01823) 253441 Fax: (01823) 321410
Castle Meats Burnham Ltd, 11 Harrison Way, Slough, SL1 5LG Tel: (01628) 666034 Fax: (01628) 660768
Dalziel Ltd, Belgowan St, Bellshill North Ind Estate, Bellshill, Lanarkshire, ML4 3NS Tel: (01698) 749595 Fax: (01698) 740503
Dixons Of Darlington, North Road, Middlesbrough, Cleveland, TS2 1DD Tel: (01642) 244995 Fax: (01642) 249336
G L Calvert, Phoenix Works, Willows Lane, Accrington, Lancashire, BB5 0RT Tel: (01254) 235184 Fax: (01254) 235184
Glenco Food Trade Supplies, 30 Pancake Lane, Hemel Hempstead, Hertfordshire, HP2 4NQ Tel: (01442) 267172 Fax: (01442) 267172 E-mail: graeme.north@ntlworld.com
H M Dunlop, 35 Barnish Road, Kells, Ballymena, County Antrim, BT42 3PA Tel: (028) 2589 2194 Fax: (028) 2589 2194
Mcnaughton & Watson Ltd, 423 Gallowgate, Glasgow, G40 2EA Tel: 0141-554 2757 Fax: 0141-551 9809
Otley Casing & By-Products Ltd, Millshaw, Beeston, Leeds, LS11 8DB Tel: 0113-271 0039
P G Gibbins & Son, 19 Forknell Avenue, Coventry, CV2 3EN Tel: (024) 7644 5229 Fax: (024) 7644 5229
Pioneer Food Service, PO Box 30, Carlisle, CA1 2RR Tel: (01228) 523474 Fax: (01228) 512906 E-mail: sales@pioneerfoodservice.co.uk
Ribdeal Ltd, 15 Walton Park La, Walton-on-Thames, Surrey, KT12 3HF Tel: (01932) 246337 Fax: (01932) 225678
Smithfield Casings & Sundries, Unit 6 West Burrowfield, Welwyn Garden City, Hertfordshire, AL7 4TW Tel: (01707) 328557 Fax: (01707) 335801
Spring Field Catering Butchers Ltd, 182 Herbert Avenue, Poole, Dorset, BH12 4HU Tel: (01202) 744910 Fax: (01202) 716588
Stanley Butchers Supply Co., 364 Prescot Road, Old Swan, Liverpool, L13 3AP Tel: 0151-228 1209 Fax: 0151-475 2343 E-mail: sbssupply@hotmail.com
Thomas Ford Smithfield, Hereford House, 23 Smithfield Street, London, EC1A 9LF Tel: (020) 7248 5868 Fax: (020) 7248 6330 E-mail: sales@thomasford.biz
Viscount Butchers Products Ltd, 10-30 Robinson Street East, Grimsby, South Humberside, DN32 9AE Tel: (01472) 345847 Fax: (01472) 354787 E-mail: sales@visprod.co.uk
W F Chinn Ltd, Marsh Lane, Crediton, Devon, EX17 1ES Tel: (01363) 772639 Fax: (01363) 772639 E-mail: wfchinn@lineone.net
W R Wright & Sons Ltd, 110-118 Cherry Lane, Liverpool, L4 8SF Tel: 0151-270 2904 Fax: 0151-226 8833 E-mail: sales@wrwright.co.uk

BUTT CONNECTORS

▶ DogEgg Ltd, Network House, Bolton Road, Pendlebury, Swinton, Manchester, M27 8BB Tel: 0161-728 4666 Fax: (07869) 078013 E-mail: sales@dogegg.net

BUTT FUSION WELDING EQUIPMENT

H F Northan Ltd, High Street, Haxey, Doncaster, South Yorkshire, DN9 2HH Tel: (01427) 752708 Fax: (01427) 752173

BUTT HINGES

Basta Parsons Ltd, Alma Street, Wolverhampton, WV10 0EY Tel: (01902) 877770 Fax: (01902) 877771 E-mail: sjohnson@bastaparsonsqb.com

BUTT WELD PIPELINE FITTINGS

Accura Pipe Fitting Ltd, Hickman Avenue, Wolverhampton, WV1 2DW Tel: (01902) 453322 Fax: (01902) 453314 E-mail: pipefittings@accura.co.uk

BUTT WELDING EQUIPMENT

Britannia Welding Supplies Ltd, 7 Rotunda Estate, Aldershot, Hampshire, GU11 1TG Tel: (01252) 350866 Fax: (01252) 330938 E-mail: debbie@britweld.co.uk
H P F Energy Services, 1 Links Place, Aberdeen, AB11 5DY Tel: (01224) 584588 Fax: (01224) 211938 E-mail: sales@hpf-energy.com

BUTTER

▶ Fior D I Latte, Unit 22, Jubilee Drive, Loughborough, Leicestershire, LE11 5XS Tel: (01509) 211310
▶ Mclelland Cheese Packaging, Commerce Road, Stranraer, Wigtownshire, DG9 7DA Tel: (01776) 706790 Fax: (01776) 707629
▶ Voyager Foods, B Sunrise Enterprise Park, Ferryboat Lane, Sunderland, SR5 3RX Tel: 0191-549 5700 Fax: 0191-549 3418

BUTTERFLY VALVES

Clesse (UK) Ltd, Unit 8, Planetary Industrial Estate, Wednesfield, Wolverhampton, WV13 3XQ Tel: (01902) 383233 Fax: (01902) 383234 E-mail: sales@clesse.co.uk
Cotswold Valves Ltd, Upper Mills Trading Estate, Stonehouse, Gloucestershire, GL10 2BJ Tel: (01453) 826612 Fax: (01453) 827505 E-mail: info@cotswoldvalves.co.uk
Curtis Wright, Gore Cross Business Park, Corbin Way, Bradpole, Bridport, Dorset, DT6 3UX Tel: (01308) 422256 Fax: (01308) 427760 E-mail: sales@sp.curtisswright.com
Danfoss Ltd, Capswood Business Centre, Oxford Road, Denham, Uxbridge, Middlesex, UB9 4LH Tel: (0870) 6080008 Fax: (0870) 6080009
Erhard Valves Ltd, Unit 4, Buckingham Close, Bermuda Industrial Estate, Nuneaton, Warwickshire, CV10 7JT Tel: (024) 7635 4470 Fax: (024) 7635 0225 E-mail: sales@erhardvalves.co.uk
Frenstar, Unit 240 Ordinance Business Park, Aerodrome Road, Gosport, Hampshire, PO13 0FG Tel: (01329) 233445 Fax: (01329) 233450 E-mail: info@frenstar.co.uk
G R Controls, 19 109 Sydenham Road, Birmingham, B11 1DG Tel: 0121-773 8007 Fax: 0121-773 8007 E-mail: grcontrols1@yahoo.co.uk
GBH Technical Ltd, Blackness Avenue, Altens Industrial Estate, Altens Industrial Estate, Aberdeen, AB12 3PG Tel: (01224) 879000 Fax: (01224) 899898 E-mail: sales@gbhtechnical.com
Induchem, Unit 1 Greenfield Farm Industrial Estate, Congleton, Cheshire, CW12 4TR Tel: (01260) 277234 Fax: (01260) 277649 E-mail: sales@induchem.ie
Kee Valves, The Old School, Outclough Road, Brindley Ford, Stoke-on-Trent, ST8 7QD Tel: (01782) 523388 Fax: (01782) 523399 E-mail: sales@keevalves.co.uk
Leeds Valve Co. Ltd, Caledonia Road, Batley, West Yorkshire, WF17 5NH Tel: (01924) 428000 Fax: (01924) 428001 E-mail: sales@leedsvalve.com
Metso Automation Ltd, 2 Lindenwood, Crockford Lane, Chineham, Basingstoke, Hampshire, RG24 8QY Tel: (0870) 6061478 Fax: (01256) 707661 E-mail: sales@metso.com
Midland Industrial Designers Ltd, Common Lane, Watnall, Nottingham, NG16 1HD Tel: 0115-938 2154 Fax: 0115-938 6315 E-mail: sales@mid.uk.com
Oppenheimer Engineering Services, 20 Vanguard Way, Shoeburyness, Southend-on-Sea, SS3 9RA Tel: (0870) 8722752 Fax: (0870) 8722750 E-mail: oes@oppenheimers.co.uk
Pipeline Products Ltd, Units 15-16 Five C Business Centre, Concorde Drive, Clevedon, Avon, BS21 6UH Tel: (01275) 873103 Fax: (01275) 873801 E-mail: info@pipelineproducts.ltd.uk
Tomoe Valve Ltd, Estuary Road, Queensway Meadows Industrial Estate, Newport, Gwent, NP19 4SP Tel: (01633) 636800 Fax: (01633) 636801
Tyco Valves & Controls Distribution (UK) Ltd, Crosby Road, Market Harborough, Leicestershire, LE16 9EE Tel: (01858) 467281 Fax: (01858) 434728 E-mail: uk_sales@tyco-valves.com
Wolstenholmes Valves, Ainsworth Vale Mill, Vale Street, Bolton, BL2 6QF Tel: (01204) 528609 Fax: (01204) 361964 E-mail: sales@wolstenholmes-valves.co.uk

BUTTON CARDING/ MERCHANDISING SYSTEMS SUPPLIERS/SERVICES TO THE TRADE

Jason Buttons Ltd, Unit 40 Mgi Estate, Milkwood Road, London, SE24 0JF Tel: (020) 7274 0724 Fax: (020) 7737 0022

BUTTON COVERERS/COVERING SERVICES

Baratix, 15b Regency Mews High Road, London, NW10 2TE Tel: (020) 8459 0832 Fax: (020) 8459 0832

BUTTON COVERING MOULDS

A M J Engineering, 38 Towerfield Road, Shoeburyness, Southend-on-Sea, SS3 9QT Tel: (01702) 295331 Fax: (01702) 296862 E-mail: info@amjbuttons.com

BUTTONHOLE MACHINES

A M F Reece (UK), Clayton Wood Close, West Park Ring Road, Leeds, LS16 6QE Tel: 0113-275 9131 Fax: 0113-275 4116 E-mail: amfreece@amfreece.co.uk

BUTTONS, *See also headings for particular types*

A Brown & Co., 2a Everton Road, Croydon, CR0 6LA Tel: (020) 8654 7310 Fax: (020) 8654 7316 E-mail: buttons@buttonhouse.fsnet.co.uk
A & N Trimmings Ltd, 5-7 Cyril Road, Birmingham, B10 0SS Tel: 0121-771 4040 Fax: 0121-766 6878 E-mail: sales@antrimm.co.uk
Butonia, 260-264 Kingsland Road, London, E8 4DG Tel: (020) 7249 5141 Fax: (020) 7249 8859 E-mail: bltd@butonia-group.com
Jason Buttons Ltd, Unit 40 Mgi Estate, Milkwood Road, London, SE24 0JF Tel: (020) 7274 0724 Fax: (020) 7737 0022
C A Sperati The Special Agency plc, 54 Westcombe Hill, London, SE10 0LR Tel: (020) 8858 7069 Fax: (020) 8853 5349 E-mail: enquires@casperatiplc.com
Europa Trimmings Ltd, 13-15 Lever Street, London, EC1V 3QU Tel: (020) 7250 1663 Fax: (020) 7253 4309
James Grove & Sons Ltd, PO Box 5, Halesowen, West Midlands, B63 3UW Tel: 0121-550 4015 Fax: 0121-501 3905 E-mail: sales@jamesgroveandsons.co.uk
W.N. Gutteridge Ltd, 11-13 Wellington Street, Leicester, LE1 6HH Tel: 0116-254 3825 Fax: 0116-247 0276 E-mail: buttons@gutteridge.co.uk
Halicombe Trimmings Ltd, 15-16 Margaret Street, London, W1W 8RW Tel: (020) 7580 5423 Fax: (020) 7323 0245 E-mail: halicombe@aol.com
London Trimmings Wholesale Ltd, 26-28 Cambridge Heath Road, London, E1 5QH Tel: (020) 7790 2233 Fax: (020) 7265 8946 E-mail: ykk@aol.com
M Courts Ltd, 31 Commercial Road, London, N18 1TP Tel: (020) 8884 0999 Fax: (020) 8884 4666 E-mail: mcourtsltd@btconnect.com
Northern Trimmings, 4 Dale House, Vickers Street, Manchester, M40 8EF Tel: 0161-205 6845 Fax: 0161-205 6845
Wm. & A.M. Robb Ltd, 84 Cheapside Street, Glasgow, G3 8BE Tel: 0141-221 4631 Fax: 0141-221 2377 E-mail: sales@wmrobb.co.uk
Schwenk Ltd, 70-71 Wells Street, London, W1T 3HN Tel: (020) 7580 3674 Fax: (020) 7580 2342 E-mail: schwenk.ltd@virgin.net
J. & J. Stern Glass, Hanway House, 306-308 West Hendon Broadway, Edgware Road, London, NW9 6AE Tel: (020) 8202 2177 Fax: (020) 8202 2719 E-mail: sales@jj-stern.co.uk
Universal Button Co. Ltd, 10-12 Witan Street, London, E2 6JX Tel: (020) 7739 5750 Fax: (020) 7739 1961

BUTYL POND LINERS

Pond Liners Direct Ltd, 8 Millbrook Business Park, Hoe Lane, Nazeing, Waltham Abbey, Essex, EN9 2RJ Tel: (01992) 890901 Fax: (01992) 893393 E-mail: info@e-pond.co.uk

BUTYL RUBBER (IIR) SHEET

D B T Medical Ltd, 14 The Crofts, Witney, Oxfordshire, OX28 4DJ Tel: (01993) 773673 Fax: (01993) 778267 E-mail: office@dbtmedical.co.uk
Russetts Developments Ltd, 27 Burners Lane, Kiln Farm, Milton Keynes, MK11 3HA Tel: (0870) 7702800 Fax: (0870) 7702801 E-mail: info@russetts.co.uk

BUYING/PURCHASING AGENTS,

See also headings for Sourcing and Procurement etc

Associated Independent Stores Ltd, Cranmore Avenue, Shirley, Solihull, West Midlands, B90 4LF Tel: 0121-711 2200 Fax: 0121-711 1334 E-mail: mail@aistores.co.uk
B J Supplies, Merlin Way, Quarry Hill Industrial Park, Quarry Hill Industrial Estate, Ilkeston, Derbyshire, DE7 4RA Tel: 0115-944 1949 Fax: 0115-944 1945 E-mail: bjsupplies@hotmail.com
Bedford Timber Supplies Ltd, Cauldwell Walk, Bedford, MK42 9DT Tel: (01234) 272171 Fax: (01234) 269235 E-mail: matt@batfordtimbersupplies.co.uk
Cedabond Catering Equipment Ltd, 42 Brook Lane, Warash, Southampton, SO31 9FG Tel: (01489) 576 779 E-mail: pnewman@cedabond.co.uk
CH Field Services Ltd, 3A Albert Court, Prince Consort Road, London, SW7 2BJ Tel: (020) 7589 1256 Fax: (020) 7591 4994 E-mail: tlovekin@charleskendall.com
Commercial Out Sourcing Ltd, 46 Starrs Mead, Battle, East Sussex, TN33 0UH Tel: (01424) 774287 Fax: (01424) 775876 E-mail: mail@cos-uk.com
Consortium For Purchasing & Distribution Ltd, Hammond Way, Trowbridge, Wiltshire, BA14 8RR Tel: (01225) 777333 Fax: (01225) 775921 E-mail: sales@theconsortium.co.uk
▶ Independent Buyers Ltd, Station Road, Hatton, Derby, DE65 5YX Tel: (01283) 516517 Fax: (01283) 512481 E-mail: info@independentbuyers.com
Interim Resolutions Ltd, 4 Crowtrees Park, Rastrick, Brighouse, West Yorkshire, HD6 3XQ Tel: (01484) 710354 E-mail: b.hemingway@ukonline.co.uk
M I D A International Ltd, Bordesley Hall, The Holloway, Alvechurch, Birmingham, B48 7QA Tel: (01527) 585505 Fax: (01527) 585575 E-mail: enquiries@mida.co.uk
Matalan Ltd, Gillibrands Road, Skelmersdale, Lancashire, WN8 9TB Tel: (01695) 552400 Fax: (01695) 552401
The Nuance Group UK Ltd, 84-98 Southampton Road, Eastleigh, Hampshire, SO50 5ZF Tel: (023) 8067 3000 Fax: (023) 8067 3199
▶ Panaf Car Accessories, 174 Enterprise Court, Eastways, Witham, Essex, CM8 3YS Tel: (01376) 511550 Fax: (01376) 515131 E-mail: panaf@btclick.com
San & Sons Ltd, Argonaut House, 369 Burnt Oak, Broadway, Edgware, Middlesex, HA8 5XZ Tel: (020) 8951 6070 Fax: (020) 8951 6050 E-mail: pault@argonaut.com
Yorkshire Purchasing Organisation, 41 Kenmore Road, Wakefield 41 Industrial Estate, Wakefield, West Yorkshire, WF2 0XE Tel: (01924) 824477 Fax: (01924) 834805 E-mail: sales@wpo.co.uk

BUYING/PURCHASING AGENTS, ELECTRICAL/ELECTRONICS INDUSTRY

Electrical Wholesale Specialists, Unit12a Marshfield Avenue Village Farm Indust Estate, Pyle, Bridgend, Mid Glamorgan, CF33 6BJ Tel: (01656) 741133 Fax: (01656) 749957 E-mail: ewssalesteam@btconnect.com

BUYING/PURCHASING AGENTS, OVERSEAS

A F Blakemore & Son Ltd, Arden Industrial Estate, Arden Road, Saltley, Birmingham, B8 1DL Tel: 0121-328 2111 Fax: 0121-327 7366
Ace International, Wedge Street, Walsall, WS1 2HQ Tel: (01922) 746454 Fax: (01922) 638484 E-mail: ace@aceinternationaluk.com
Amc, 45 Great Portland Street, London, W1W 7LD Tel: (020) 7468 0130 Fax: (020) 7468 0131
Ardvick Trading & Supply Co., 37-39 Peckham Road, Camberwell, London, SE5 8UH Tel: (020) 7703 9135 Fax: (020) 7708 0844
Bond Trading GB Ltd, 2 Gillingham Green, Gillingham, Kent, ME7 1SS Tel: (01634) 580670 Fax: (01634) 855455 E-mail: bondtradingltd@aol.com
Bridgewater Europe Ltd, 132 Windmill Rd, Gillingham, Kent, ME7 5PD Tel: (01634) 311717 Fax: (01634) 310632 E-mail: riaz@zoom.co.uk
Busi & Stephenson Ltd, 101 Bold Street, Liverpool, L1 4HL Tel: 0151-709 8998 Fax: 0151-709 8919 E-mail: busico@boldst.demon.co.uk
Cedar Supplies Ltd, PO Box 59, Crowborough, East Sussex, TN6 3NQ Tel: (01892) 853389 Fax: (01892) 853411 E-mail: sales@cedarsupplies.com
Ceva Logistics, Tunnel Estate, Easton Avenue, Grays, Essex, RM20 3LW Tel: (01708) 258200 Fax: (01708) 258299
Dawcul Ltd, 42 West St, Marlow, Buckinghamshire, SL7 2NB Tel: (01628) 472737 Fax: (01628) 890055 E-mail: sales@dawcul.co.uk
Diak Technical Export Ltd, Diak House, Romsey, Hampshire, SO51 6AE Tel: (01794) 518808 Fax: (01794) 519960 E-mail: sales@diak.com
Falkland Islands Trading Co. Ltd, 1ST Floor, Charrington House, The Causeway, Bishop's Stortford, Hertfordshire, CM23 2ER Tel: (01279) 461630 Fax: (01279) 461631 E-mail: admin@fihplc.com
Ger & Co. (UK) Ltd, 3rd Floor St. Thomas House, 3 Gees Court, London, W1U 1JD Tel: (020) 7491 4636 Fax: (020) 7408 0078 E-mail: geruk@btinternet.com
Gulf Helicopters Co., 1 Stockwell Works, Stephenson Way, Crawley, West Sussex, RH10 1TN Tel: (01293) 401333 Fax: (01293) 611566 E-mail: mgr_uk@gulfhelicopters.com
Harvey Scruton, North Lane, Huntington, York, YO32 9SU Tel: (01904) 400878 Fax: (01904) 400120
Interspace Communications Ltd, Fourth Floor Trafalgar House, 11 Waterloo Place, London, SW1Y 4AU Tel: (020) 7930 8001 Fax: (020) 7930 0465 E-mail: isclon@msn.com
Longulf Ltd, Prince Albert House, 2 Kingsmill Terrace, London, NW8 6BN Tel: (020) 7722 7733 Fax: (020) 7722 9028 E-mail: info@longulf.com
Sealand General Exporters, 78 New Oxford Street, London, WC1A 1HB Tel: (020) 7580 8663 Fax: (020) 7580 8662 E-mail: sales@sealand.co.uk
Swann Technology Ltd, 3 The Quadrant, Newark Close, Royston, Hertfordshire, SG8 5HL Tel: (01763) 249967 Fax: (01763) 249626 E-mail: swancygnet@cs.com
Transglobal Distribution Ltd, PO Box 26, Radlett, Hertfordshire, WD7 9ZY Tel: (01923) 853319 Fax: (01923) 853319 E-mail: transglobaldistribut@lycos.com
▶ Transworld Properties Ltd, 10 Eastern Avenue, Peterborough, PE1 4PJ Tel: (01733) 709807 Fax: (01733) 752548 E-mail: sales@overseas-properties.uk.com
View Pulse, 6 Tarranbrae, Willesden Lane, London, NW6 7PL Tel: (020) 7372 7595 Fax: (020) 7372 4067
Windmill Buying Services Ltd, 4 Derby Street, Norwich, NR2 4PU Tel: (01603) 632008 Fax: (01603) 612236 E-mail: wwindmill@compuserve.com
Yanco Ltd, Monks Ferry, Birkenhead, Merseyside, CH41 5LH Tel: 0151-650 8600 Fax: 0151-650 2277 E-mail: buyers@yanco.co.uk

CAB DEFLECTORS, COMMERCIAL VEHICLE, GRP

Hilton Docker Mouldings Ltd, Freedo Mill, Foxcroft Street, Littleborough, Lancashire, OL15 8LB Tel: (01706) 379358 Fax: (01706) 378546 E-mail: sales@hiltondoc.co.uk

CABIN FILTERS

Andrew Page Ltd, Apson House, Colton Mill, Bullerthorpe Lane, Leeds, LS15 9JL Tel: 0113-397 0200 Fax: 0113-397 0295 E-mail: accounts@andrewpage.com

CABIN TRANSPORTATION OR INSTALLATION

▶ Milbank Trucks Ltd, Airfield, Earls Colne, Colchester, CO6 2NS Tel: (01787) 224226 Fax: (01787) 220533

CABINET ENCLOSURES

D P Fabrications Ltd, Chantry Road, Woburn Road Industrial Estate, Kempston, Bedford, MK42 7HU Tel: (01234) 840166 Fax: (01234) 840177 E-mail: sales@dpfabs.co.uk
Dataracks, Stagwood House, Beach Road, Cottenham, Cambridge, CB4 8FP Tel: (01954) 252229 Fax: (01954) 251461 E-mail: sales@dataracks.co.uk

CABINET HARDWARE, PLASTIC

Extra Trade UK Ltd, 22 Sherwell Rise, Allerton, Bradford, West Yorkshire, BD15 7AP Tel: 01274 481994 Fax: 01274 547989 E-mail: extratradeuk@btinternet.com

CABINET MAKERS, *See also Furniture, Wooden etc*

▶ A La Maison, 119 Norman Road, West Malling, Kent, ME19 6RW Tel: (01732) 844129
A M R Cabinet Makers & French Polishers, Unit 3 Millie Street, Kirkcaldy, Fife, KY1 2NL Tel: (01592) 640941 Fax: 0159 2640 941
▶ Abbey Trading Co., 252 Seven Mile Straight, Nutts Corner, Crumlin, County Antrim, BT29 4YT Tel: (028) 9082 5000
▶ Acanthus, Unit 2-4 Sandon Industrial Estate, Sandon Way, Liverpool, L5 9YN Tel: 0151-207 1057 Fax: 0151-207 3537 E-mail: sales@acanthusfurniture.co.uk
Alan Englefield, Owl Cottage, High Street, Netheravon, Salisbury, SP4 9PJ Tel: (01980) 670396 Fax: (01980) 670396
Alden Cabinet Designs, 6 Marlborough Business Centre, Marlborough Road, Lancing, West Sussex, BN15 8TP Tel: (01903) 765521 Fax: (01903) 851087
▶ Alexander's Woodworks, Whitebridge Garage, Old Bath Road, Charvil, Reading, RG10 9QJ Tel: 0118-932 1966 Fax: 0118-944 0517 E-mail: alexwoodltd@onetel.com
All Seasons, The Hermitage, Alders Avenue, Baldwins Hill, East Grinstead, West Sussex, RH19 2BX Tel: (0844) 8005827 Fax: (01342) 321162
▶ Allen & Youngs, Marsh Farm, Marsh Road, Hilperton Marsh, Trowbridge, Wiltshire, BA14 7PJ Tel: (01225) 776858 Fax: (01225) 776858
Anthony Nixon Furniture, Birch Road, Barnard Castle, County Durham, DL12 8JR Tel: (01833) 690666 Fax: (01833) 690777
Antique Furniture Designs Ltd, The Warehouse, Sandy Bank Road, New York, Lincoln, LN4 4YE Tel: (01526) 342821 Fax: (01526) 344186 E-mail: sales@antiquefurnituredesigns.com
Arcana, Cheeks Farm, Farnham, Surrey, GU10 5HD Tel: (01420) 22813 Fax: (01420) 22813 E-mail: sales@cabinetmakers.co.uk
Arch 18, Kingsdown Cl, London, W10 6SW Tel: 020 72295391 E-mail: michaelreed@arch18.co.uk
Arctek Carpentry, 44 The Croft, Marlow, Buckinghamshire, SL7 1UP Tel: (01628) 475624
Ashcroft Woodworking, Thompsons Yard, Chipping Hill, Witham, Essex, CM8 2DE Tel: (01376) 514771 Fax: (01376) 514771
B & J Signs, 14 Farrington Court, Burnley, Lancashire, BB11 5SS Tel: (01282) 454807 Fax: (01282) 831781 E-mail: sales@bjsigns.co.uk
Barn Studios, The Old Barn Manor Farm, Woodstock Lane South, Claygate, Esher, Surrey, KT10 0TA Tel: (01372) 467755
David Bartram, The Raveningham Centre, Beccles Rd, Raveningham, Norwich, NR14 6NU Tel: (01508) 548721 Fax: (01508) 548721
Benchmark Interiors Ltd, Unit 2, Trading Estate, Kelvin Way, West Bromwich, West Midlands, B70 7TN Tel: 0121-553 0023 Fax: 0121-553 0024
Bespoke Furniture, 63A Road A, Boughton Industrial Estate, Boughton, Newark, Nottinghamshire, NG22 9LE Tel: (07768) 847737 E-mail: enquiries@bespokefurn.co.uk
▶ Bespoke Interiors Of Cheshire Ltd, Tameside Works, Dukinfield, Cheshire, SK16 5PT Tel: 0161-343 7972 Fax: 0161-343 7973
Bishopton Joinery, Burton Farm, Bishopton, Stratford-upon-Avon, Warwickshire, CV37 0RW Tel: (01789) 298448 Fax: (01789) 298448
Blakes Woodcrafts, Holme Pierrepont Hall, Holme Lane, Holme Pierrepont, Nottingham, NG12 2LD Tel: 0115-933 6106
▶ The Boddington Collection, Castle Farm, Cholmondeley, Malpas, Cheshire, SY14 8AQ Tel: (0870) 2406135 Fax: (01948) 822151 E-mail: info@theboddington collection.co.uk
Bott Ltd, Bude-Stratton Business Park, Bude, Cornwall, EX23 8LY Tel: (01288) 357788 Fax: (01288) 352692 E-mail: info@bottltd.co.uk
The Bradshaw Pattern Company Ltd, Rowland House Lion Mill, Fitton Street, Royton, Oldham, OL2 5JX Tel: 0161-624 5043 Fax: 0161-628 3245
A.C. Buckoke & Sons Ltd, Factory 11-25 Chatfield Road, London, SW11 3SE Tel: (020) 7223 3746 Fax: (020) 7223 3746 E-mail: acbuckoke@yahoo.co.uk
▶ C & C Cabinet Makers, Unit F5 The Brickyards, Steep Marsh, Petersfield, Hampshire, GU32 2BN Tel: (01730) 891400 Fax: (01730) 891403 E-mail: glyn@candccabinetmakers.co.uk
C J Trethewy, Waverley Farm, Waverley Lane, Farnham, Surrey, GU9 8EP Tel: (01252) 783008
C M Joinery, Coggeshall Road, Bradwell, Braintree, Essex, CM77 8EU Tel: (01376) 331666 Fax: (01376) 331444 E-mail: info@wood-work.demon.co.uk
▶ The Cabinet Makers, Unit 12 Brighton Road Industrial Estate, Heaton Mersey, Stockport, Cheshire, SK4 2BQ Tel: 0161-432 4455 E-mail: duncan@thecabinetmakers.net
D. Cass, 1 Park Road, Hull, HU3 1TH Tel: (01482) 225866
Christopher Dyer & Co., 36 School Road, Finstock, Chipping Norton, Oxfordshire, OX7 3DJ Tel: (01993) 705001 Fax: (01993) 705741 E-mail: info@cabinetmaker.co.uk
Classic Images Ltd, Oakcroft Works, Oakcroft Road, Chessington, Surrey, KT9 1RH Tel: (020) 8391 1133 Fax: (020) 8397 5040 E-mail: classicimages@ukonline.co.uk
Coryndon Ltd, Rainscombe Farm Buildings, Oare, Marlborough, Wiltshire, SN8 4HZ Tel: (01672) 562581 Fax: (01672) 563995
Cove Workshop, 61 Gobbins Road, Islandmagee, Larne, County Antrim, BT40 3TY Tel: (028) 9335 3403 Fax: (028) 9335 3404 E-mail: sales@thechairmaker.com
Craigie & Scott, 3 Riverside, Station Road, Bruton, Somerset, BA10 0EH Tel: (01749) 812867 Fax: (01749) 812867 E-mail: craigiewoodworks@waitrose.com
Alan Cross Ltd, 15 Ludlow Hill Road, West Bridgford, Nottingham, NG2 6HF Tel: 0115-923 2223 Fax: 0115-923 2223 E-mail: enquiries@alancrossuk.com
D G Booth, Scandinavia, Ash Terrace, Ashmore Green, Thatcham, Berkshire, RG18 9EU Tel: (01635) 862572
D G Clifton & Son, High Street, Loxwood, Billingshurst, West Sussex, RH14 0RE Tel: (01403) 753337 E-mail: enquiries@dgclifton.com
D Shackleton, 19 High Street, Snainton, Scarborough, North Yorkshire, YO13 9AE Tel: (01723) 859577
David J Haddock, Rope Farm, Mapperton Hill, Milton on Stour, Gillingham, Dorset, SP8 5QG Tel: (01747) 860016 Fax: (01747) 860221
Dawson Reproductions, 74 Church Street, Leatherhead, Surrey, KT22 8ER Tel: (01372) 375383 Fax: (01372) 362975
Dawson's Pattern Works Ltd, Westland Square, Leeds, LS11 5SS Tel: 0113-270 5142 Fax: 0113-276 1335
Design Cabinet Makers, Unit 1 Clapham North Business Centre, 26-32 Voltaire Road, London, SW4 6DH Tel: (020) 7627 1440 Fax: (020) 7627 1440
Ian Dickson Ltd, 22a Kemball Street, Ipswich, IP4 5EE Tel: (01473) 714750 Fax: (01473) 727923
Dovetail Woodcraft, The Old Bakery, 8 Edward Street, Bridgwater, Somerset, TA6 5ET Tel: (01278) 424021 Fax: (01278) 424021
▶ Dovetails, Shay Lane Works, Shay Lane, Ovenden, Halifax, W. Yorkshire, HX3 6SF Tel: (01422) 329988
Dovetails, Browns Marsh, North Molton, South Molton, Devon, EX36 3HQ Tel: (01769) 574027 Fax: 01769 574027
Graham Dutnall, Unit 5 Shawbarn, Whitesmith, Lewes, East Sussex, BN8 6JD Tel: (01825) 872181
E E Moss, 3 26 Maryland Road, London, E15 1JJ Tel: (020) 8519 4227 Fax: (020) 8502 7087
▶ Edmonds Cabinet Makers, Edmonds Cabinet Makers, Buscott Farm, Ashcott, Bridgwater, Somerset, TA7 9QP Tel: 01458 210359 Fax: 01458 211005 E-mail: info@edmondscabinetmakers.co.uk
John Edmunds, Buscott Farm, 23 Station Road, Ashcott, Bridgwater, Somerset, TA7 9QP Tel: (01458) 210359
Ian Edwards, The Old Chapel, 282 Skipton Road, Harrogate, North Yorkshire, HG1 3HE Tel: (01423) 500442 Fax: (01423) 705200 E-mail: enquiries@iansbespokefurniture.co.uk
Enright Cabinets, Botany Bay Lane, Chislehurst, Kent, BR7 5PT Tel: (020) 8295 0539
▶ Fine Furniture Design, Unit 2e Honeybourne Airfield Trading Estate, Honeybourne, Evesham, Worcestershire, WR11 7QF Tel: (01386) 833452 Fax: (01386) 833878
Forest Hall Joinery, The Dovecotts, Ryes Lane, Hatfield Heath, Bishop's Stortford, Hertfordshire, CM22 7BS Tel: (01279) 730021 Fax: (01279) 730021
Furniture Maker Furniture Maker, Unit 19, Hoobrook Enterprise Centre, Worcester Road, Kidderminster, Worcestershire, DY10 1HB Tel: (01562) 825995
Future Signs, 2a Bedford Court, Bedford Street, Leighton Buzzard, Bedfordshire, LU7 1JE Tel: (01525) 373733 Fax: (01525) 850211 E-mail: futuresign@btinternet.com
Gavin Robertson Furniture, Easter Altourie, Inverness, IV3 8LB Tel: (01463) 861261 Fax: (01463) 861436
▶ Graceful Reproductions, The Pantile Building, Rendlesham, Woodbridge, Suffolk, IP12 2RJ Tel: (01394) 460014 Fax: (01394) 460014
David Groom Joinery, 5-8 Eastfield Road, Wollaston, Wellingborough, Northamptonshire, NN29 7RU Tel: (01933) 664494 Fax: (01933) 663085
H W Designs, 3 Hod Drive, Stourpaine, Blandford Forum, Dorset, DT11 8TJ Tel: (01258) 452114
Halstead & Fowler, 4 Park Road, Holbeach, Spalding, Lincolnshire, PE12 7EE Tel: (01406) 425173 Fax: (01406) 425173 E-mail: sales@halsteadandfowler.co.uk
Harlock Joinery Ltd, Brook Street, Redditch, Worcestershire, B98 8NG Tel: (01527) 68541 Fax: (01527) 68541 E-mail: harlockjoinery@btconnect.com
Harris Custom Woodworking, 3 New Firms Centre, Fairground Way, Walsall, WS1 4NU Tel: (01922) 611122 Fax: (01922) 611122
▶ Hart Interiors Midlands Ltd, Unit 10 The Mushroom Farm, Bottesford Lane, Orston, Nottingham, NG13 9NX Tel: (01949) 851800 Fax: (01949) 851800
Haselbech Oak & Country Furniture, Haselbech Hill, Haselbech, Northampton, NN6 9LL Tel: (01604) 686360 Fax: (01604) 686360 E-mail: enquiries@haselbechoak.co.uk
Heritage Cabinet Makers, 1 Mushroom Farm, Bottesford Lane, Orston, Nottingham, NG13 9NX Tel: (01949) 851505
Heritage Furniture, Springbank Farm, Monument Farm Lane, Foxhall, Ipswich, IP10 0AQ Tel: (01473) 611522 Fax: (01473) 635803
Higgs Designs, 5 Woodgates Farm, Woodgates End, Dunmow, Essex, CM6 2BN Tel: (01279) 851115
▶ Ikon Designs, Ridge House, Clay Street, Penkridge, Stafford, ST19 5AF Tel: (01785) 716116 Fax: (01785) 716702

CABINET MAKERS – *continued*

Ivor Newton & Son Fuel & Car Sales, Aston Road, Haddenham, Aylesbury, Buckinghamshire, HP17 8AF Tel: (01844) 291461

▶ John Beavan, Kyre, Tenbury Wells, Worcestershire, WR15 8RW Tel: (01885) 410549 Fax: (01885) 410563 E-mail: info@johnbeavan.com

Joshua Jones, White Mill Farm, Sturminster Marshall, Wimborne, Dorset, BH21 4BX Tel: (01258) 858470

▶ JPM Manufacturing, 4 Admin Road, Knowsley Industrial Park, Liverpool, L33 7TZ Tel: 0151-549 1123 Fax: 0151-549 1124

▶ K Lumsden, Little Kings Ash Farm, Kings Ash, Great Missenden, Buckinghamshire, HP16 9NP Tel: (01494) 837666

▶ Kaywood Cabinet Makers, Unit 2b Westthorpe Fields Road, Killamarsh, Sheffield, S21 1TZ Tel: 0114-247 7700 Fax: 0114-247 7700 E-mail: kaywoodsfurniture@hotmail.com

▶ Kingswood Cabinets, HCS Workshops, Binders Industrial Estate, Cryers Hill, High Wycombe, Buckinghamshire, HP15 6LJ Tel: 07966 263491 E-mail: Mat@KingswoodCabinets.com

Kitchens & Bedrooms Ltd, Whitehall Industrial Estate, Whitehall Road, Leeds, LS12 5JB Tel: 0113-263 9888 Fax: 0113-203 8917

▶ Kontur Cabinet Makers, 13 Rectory Lane, Radcliffe, Manchester, M26 2QU Tel: 0161-723 2603 Fax: 0161-723 3373 E-mail: kontur@btconnect.com

L Hardy, Timeside, Salisbury Street, Mere, Warminster, Wiltshire, BA12 6HF Tel: (01747) 860125

Lancaster & Tomkinson, Unit 10, Brock Way, Newcastle, Staffordshire, ST5 6AZ Tel: (01782) 614156 Fax: (01782) 622334 E-mail: contact@lancaster-tomkinson.com

Leslie J Plail, Unit 1+2 Furlongs Farm, Riverside, Eynsford, Dartford, DA4 0AE Tel: (01322) 865688

▶ M Denyer & R Tribble, Unit 2 New Mill End, Luton, LU1 3TS Tel: (01582) 460035 Fax: (01582) 460035

Alf McKay, Manor Barn, Crewkerne, Somerset, TA18 8QT Tel: (01460) 78916 Fax: (01460) 78916

Martin Leighfield, Main Street, Checkendon, Reading, RG8 0SP Tel: (01491) 681444 Fax: (01491) 681155

Michael W Hart, Inveresk Village, Musselburgh, Midlothian, EH21 7TD Tel: 0131-665 0764 Fax: 0131-665 0764

Millstore Fine Furniture, 12 Fysh House Farm, Cuckoo Hill, Bures, Suffolk, CO8 5LD Tel: (01787) 227770 Fax: (01787) 227007

Minister Joinery, Riverside Barn, Bridport, Dorset, DT6 4PQ Tel: (01308) 485740 Fax: (01308) 485752

N Gilks, Hailes Farm, Hailes, Cheltenham, Gloucestershire, GL54 5PB Tel: (01242) 604662 Fax: (01242) 604663

Noble Russell Furniture Ltd, Station Road, Uppingham, Rutland, Leicestershire, LE15 9TX Tel: (01572) 821591 Fax: (01572) 823434 E-mail: sales@noblerussell.co.uk

Norfolk Cabinet Makers Ltd, Park Farm Workshops, Beeston Lane, Beeston St. Andrew, Norwich, NR12 7BP Tel: (01603) 408904 Fax: (01603) 488718 E-mail: info@norfolkcabinetmakers.co.uk

Oakleaf Cabinet Makers, 20 Fieldside, Crowle, Scunthorpe, South Humberside, DN17 4HL Tel: (01724) 711027 Fax: (01724) 710018 E-mail: enquiries@oakleafcabinetmakers.co.uk

Old Forge Woodturners, Rear of, 126 London Road, Boston, Lincolnshire, PE21 7HB Tel: (01205) 353283 Fax: (01205) 353283

Old School Furniture, 10 Headbrook, Kington, Herefordshire, HR5 3DZ Tel: (01544) 239000

Out Of The Woods, Mill Lane, Halton, Lancaster, LA2 6ND Tel: (01524) 811968

Overton Cabinet Makers, 85 Milestone Road, Carterton, Oxfordshire, OX18 3RL Tel: (01993) 843376 E-mail: info@thecraftsman.co.uk

P J & M E Norris & Son, Units 7-8 The Old Creamery, Station Road, Wrenbury, Nantwich, Cheshire, CW5 8EX Tel: (01270) 780003 Fax: (01270) 780003

P & P Joinery, 157 Hornsey Park Road, London, N8 0JX Tel: (020) 8881 1111 Fax: (020) 8881 0027

Pannell Cabinet Makers, Maytham Works Maytham Farm, Hatters Hill, Rolvenden, Cranbrook, Kent, TN17 4QA Tel: (01797) 270927

Parkside Cabinets & Interiors Ltd, The Old Goods Yard, West Wycombe Road, High Wycombe, Buckinghamshire, HP12 4AH Tel: (01494) 530301 Fax: (01494) 472440 E-mail: worktop@globalnet.co.uk

▶ Parlett & Cordell, Creeches Lane, Walton, Street, Somerset, BA16 9RR Tel: (01458) 446820

Petra, 1 Moat Lane Crossing, Moat Lane, Caersws, Powys, SY17 5SE Tel: (01686) 688131 Fax: (01686) 688283 E-mail: sales@cardtables.co.uk

Pinewood Joiners, Unit 3-4, Pickwick Industrial Estate Tintern Road, St. Helen Auckland, Bishop Auckland, County Durham, DL14 9EL Tel: (01388) 450749 Fax: (01388) 450749

Plain Tree Furniture, Main Street, Kirkby Malzeard, Ripon, North Yorkshire, HG4 3SD Tel: (01765) 658955

▶ Quercus Rex Ltd, The Workshop, Crocker Hill Farm, Trotton, Petersfield, Hampshire, GU31 5EL Tel: (01730) 814814 Fax: (01730) 814814

R E Woods Cabinet Makers, Mountain Ash, Dereham Road, Thuxton, Norwich, NR9 4QH Tel: (01362) 850460 Fax: (01362) 858360 E-mail: rewoods@cabinertmaker76.freeserve.co.uk

Regent House Manufacturing, Harveys Warehouse, Newport Road, Gnosall, Stafford, ST20 0BL Tel: (01785) 823544 Fax: (01785) 822953 E-mail: sales@regentbespokecabinets.co.uk

Richard J Reading, Westwood Cottage, Trolliloes, Hailsham, East Sussex, BN27 4QR Tel: (01435) 830249 Fax: (01435) 830249

Robins Cabinet Makers, Lodge Farm Bungalow, Kineton, Warwick, CV35 0JH Tel: (01926) 640151 Fax: (01926) 640151

Robinson Gay Cabinet Makers Ltd, Shieldhall, Wallington, Morpeth, Northumberland, NE61 4AQ Tel: (01830) 540387 Fax: (01830) 540490

Roger Baughan, Wayland Farm, Wharf Road, Fenny Compton, Southam, Warwickshire, CV47 2XD Tel: (01295) 770647 Fax: (01295) 770647

Rooksmoor Timber Co. Ltd, Vatch Lane, Eastcombe, Stroud, Gloucestershire, GL6 7DY Tel: (01453) 882240 Fax: (01453) 731112 E-mail: enquiries@rooksmoor.com

Rowandale Cabinet Makers, Speedwell Mill, Millers Green, Wirksworth, Matlock, Derbyshire, DE4 4BL Tel: (01629) 824041 Fax: (01629) 824041

Sambell Engineering Ltd, Winston Avenue, Croft, Leicester, LE9 3GQ Tel: (01455) 283251 Fax: (01455) 283908 E-mail: post@atacama-audio.co.uk

Schimmer Child, 31 Westward Road, Stroud, Gloucestershire, GL5 4JA Tel: (01453) 757333 Fax: (01453) 757333 E-mail: mail@schimmerchild.co.uk

▶ Scott Woyka Furniture, Falmouth Wharves, North Parade, Falmouth, Cornwall, TR11 2TF Tel: (01326) 311777 Fax: 01326 311777

Sean Feeney Furniture, The Old School House, Preston on Stour, Stratford-upon-Avon, Warwickshire, CV37 8NG Tel: (01789) 450519 E-mail: sales@seanfeeneyfurniture.co.uk

Sheridans, 213 Humberstone Lane, Leicester, LE4 9JR Tel: 0116-269 6198 Fax: 0116-269 6198

▶ Robert Sleven, Butlers Farm Buildings, Butlers Lane, Saffron Walden, Essex, CB10 2ND Tel: (01799) 529440 E-mail: info@robertsleven.co.uk

Solectron Systems UK, Arisdale Avenue, South Ockendon, Essex, RM15 5TT Tel: (01708) 852223 Fax: (01708) 850217

South Devon Craft & Furniture Centre, New Road, Modbury, Ivybridge, Devon, PL21 0QH Tel: (01548) 830405

▶ Stuart Harris Cabinet Maker, Ilex Farm Workshop, Waterhouse Lane, Ardleigh, Colchester, CO7 7NE Tel: (01206) 230078 Fax: (01206) 231177 E-mail: info@harriscabinetmaker.co.uk

Sui Generis, Redbanks, Eday, Orkney, KW17 2AA Tel: (01857) 622219 Fax: (01857) 622219

T M Gibson, Jorrocks Works, Hamsterley Hall, Hamsterley Mill, Rowlands Gill, Tyne & Wear, NE39 1NJ Tel: (01207) 542369 Fax: (01207) 544013 E-mail: admin@tmgibson.co.uk

T S Barrows & Son, Hamlyn Lodge, Station Road, Ollerton, Newark, Nottinghamshire, NG22 9BN Tel: (01623) 823600 E-mail: info@hamlynlodge.com

Temperature Applied Sciences Ltd, Unit 15 Martlets Way, Goring-by-Sea, Worthing, West Sussex, BN12 4HF Tel: (01903) 506903 Fax: (01903) 506911

▶ Treetop Design, Lisnaskea, Enniskillen, County Fermanagh, BT92 0FS Tel: (028) 6772 4285 Fax: (028) 6772 4285

▶ Tyrone Fabrication Ltd, 87 Goland Road, Ballygawley, Dungannon, County Tyrone, BT70 2LA Tel: (028) 8556 7200 Fax: (028) 8556 7089

Vincent Rickards, Unit 22 Blackworth Industrial Estate, Highworth, Swindon, SN6 7NA Tel: (01793) 765251 Fax: (01793) 765251 E-mail: vincerickards@onetel.com

W J Gresham & Son, Commonside, Old Leake, Boston, Lincolnshire, PE22 9PR Tel: (01205) 870279 Fax: (01205) 870954

Brian Walker, Westwood, Fovant, Salisbury, SP3 5JW Tel: (01722) 714370 Fax: (01722) 714853

Walnut Tree Workshop, The Old Dairy, Woodgreen Road, Breamore, Fordingbridge, Hampshire, SP6 2AB Tel: (01725) 512165

Jamie Ward Furniture, 7 Combroke Grove, Hatton Park, Warwick, CV35 7TG Tel: (07970) 422867 E-mail: jamie@jamieward.com

John Warren Furniture Ltd, 4-6 New Inn, Broadway, London, EC2A 3PZ Tel: (020) 8986 3366 Fax: (020) 7729 8770 E-mail: sales@jwfltd.co.uk

Westwood Furniture, Sugworth Farm Unit 12, Borde Hill Lane, Haywards Heath, West Sussex, RH16 1XP Tel: (01444) 410211 Fax: (01444) 410211 E-mail: sales@westwoodfurniture.co.uk

Whale & Martin, 156 Broadgate, Weston Hills, Spalding, Lincolnshire, PE12 6DQ Tel: (01406) 380731 Fax: (01406) 380984

Witheridge Post Office & Stores, 17 West Street, Witheridge, Tiverton, Devon, EX16 8AA Tel: (01884) 861684 Fax: (01884) 860329

▶ Wood N Things, 5 James Street, Brigg, South Humberside, DN20 8LS Tel: (01652) 650054 Fax: (01652) 650054

CABINET MOUNTED AIR CONDITIONING (AC) EQUIPMENT

▶ Dalair Ltd, Southern Way, Wednesbury, West Midlands, WS10 7BU Tel: 0121-556 9944 Fax: 0121-502 3124 E-mail: sales@dalair.co.uk

CABINETS, COMPUTER DATA NETWORK, WALLMOUNTED

Data Room Supplies, Conbar House, Mead Lane, Hertford, SG13 7AP Tel: (01992) 558737 Fax: (01992) 558714 E-mail: sales@dataroomsupplies.co.uk

CABINETS, GLASS FIBRE/GRP

Intertec, Unit 5, Verwood Industrial Estate, Black Hill, Verwood, Dorset, BH31 6HA Tel: (01202) 822277 Fax: (01202) 821188 E-mail: sales@intertec-inst.co.uk

N F S Fire Protection Ltd, Morton Street, Middleton, Manchester, M24 6AN Tel: 0161-643 9338 Fax: 0161-655 3878

Stuart Pease Fibreglass Ltd, Unit 1 Taylors Close, Parkgate, Rotherham, South Yorkshire, S62 6NW Tel: (01709) 527761 Fax: (01709) 522147 E-mail: stuartpeaseltd@btinternet.com

CABINETS, STORAGE, DRAWER, MODULAR

▶ Conservation By Design Ltd, 5 Singer Way, Woburn Road Industrial Estate, Kempston, Bedford, MK42 7AW Tel: (01234) 853555 Fax: (01234) 852334 E-mail: info@conservation-by-design.co.uk

CABINETS, WOODEN/ FURNITURE

101 Furniture Solutions Ltd, 59 Burton Road, Carlton, Nottingham, NG4 3DQ Tel: 0115-987 9631 Fax: 0115-940 0931 E-mail: info@101fs.co.uk

Alstons Upholstery Ltd, Albro Works, Gosbecks Road, Colchester, CO2 9JU Tel: (01206) 765343 Fax: (01206) 763401 E-mail: enquiries@alstons.co.uk

Andrena Direct Furniture, Auction House, Geddings Road, Hoddesdon, Hertfordshire, EN11 0NT Tel: (01992) 451722 Fax: (01992) 466024 E-mail: enquiries@anrenda.co.uk

Badman & Badman Ltd, The Drill Hall, Langford Road, Weston-super-Mare, Avon, BS23 3PQ Tel: (01934) 644122 Fax: (01934) 628189 E-mail: sales@badman.co.uk

William Bartlett & Son Ltd, Grafton Street, High Wycombe, Buckinghamshire, HP12 3AJ Tel: (01494) 526491 Fax: (01494) 451021 E-mail: sales@williambartlett.co.uk

Belvedere Manufacturing Co. Ltd, The Old Printing Works, Waterloo Road, Radstock, BA3 3EP Tel: (01761) 437621 Fax: (01761) 436616 E-mail: belvederemfg@aol.com

▶ Bourne & Son Ltd, Unit 23a Firsland Park Estate, Henfield Road, Albourne, Hassocks, West Sussex, BN6 9JJ Tel: (01273) 491554 Fax: (01273) 491554 E-mail: furniture@bourneandson.com

Simon Butler, Unit 10E, Wincombe Park Business Centre, Shaftesbury, Dorset, SP7 9QJ Tel: (01747) 850150 Fax: (01747) 850250 E-mail: info@comptonsmith.co.uk

Michael Bysouth & Son, The Barn Trueloves, Trueloves Lane, Ingatestone, Essex, CM4 0NQ Tel: (01277) 355315 Fax: (01277) 355315

C Watts, Rear of, 27-29 Buller Street, Grimsby, South Humberside, DN32 8BL Tel: (01472) 359547 Fax: (01472) 359547 E-mail: sales@companyhospitality.com

Chillington Wolverhampton Ltd, Chillington Fields, Wolverhampton, WV1 2BY Tel: (01902) 451326 Fax: (01902) 452010

Cita Furniture, 36 Seein Road, Sion Mills, Strabane, County Tyrone, BT82 9NJ Tel: (028) 8165 9744 Fax: (028) 8165 9744

Classic Fireplaces & Furniture, Unit F Weddington Industrial Estate, Nuneaton, Warwickshire, CV10 0AP Tel: (024) 7634 3407 Fax: (07070) 711475

Corwell Cabinet Makers, Unit 6 Amners Farm, Burghfield, Reading, RG30 3UE Tel: 0118-983 3404 Fax: 0118-983 3404 E-mail: info@corwell.co.uk

Dalewood Designs, Greenhill Lane, Riddings, Alfreton, Derbyshire, DE55 4EX Tel: (01773) 604384 Fax: (01773) 604384

Dictacliff Ltd, Burywater Barn, Burywater Lane, Newport, Saffron Walden, Essex, CB11 3TZ Tel: (01799) 542242 Fax: (01799) 542322 E-mail: john@dictacliff.co.uk

Eight By Four Ltd, Eight By Four, 6A Kings Yard, Carpenters Road, London, E15 2HD Tel: (020) 8985 6001 Fax: (020) 8533 5372 E-mail: sales@eightbyfour.co.uk

Elevation, 66 Patcham Terrace, London, SW8 4BP Tel: (020) 7622 5433

Elliott & Co, Sherborne, Cheltenham, Gloucestershire, GL54 3DW Tel: (01451) 844448 Fax: (01451) 844695 E-mail: info@outofthewood.co.uk

F B Design Cabinet Makers, The Old Granary Workshop, Herriard Park, Herriard, Basingstoke, Hampshire, RG25 2PL Tel: (01256) 381855 Fax: (01256) 381856 E-mail: david@fbdesign.co.uk

Furniture Fusion, Bedford Road, Apsley Guise, Milton Keynes, MK17 8DJ Tel: (01908) 586334 Fax: (01908) 586332 E-mail: info@furniturefusion.co.uk

Furniture Maker Furniture Maker, Unit 19, Hoobrook Enterprise Centre, Worcester Road, Kidderminster, Worcestershire, DY10 1HB Tel: (01562) 825995

G B J Cabinet Makers, 40b Worcester Road, Titton, Stourport-on-Severn, Worcestershire, DY13 9PD Tel: (01299) 823740 Fax: (01299) 823740

E & S Gott, Priestley Butts, Whitby Road, Pickering, North Yorkshire, YO18 7HL Tel: (01751) 472009

Modus Furniture Ltd, Unit 12-14, Rose Mills Industrial Estate, Hort Bridge, Ilminster, Somerset, TA19 9PS Tel: (01460) 57465 Fax: (01460) 57004 E-mail: sales@modusfurniture.co.uk

Peter Mullins Cabinet Makers, 2 St. Marys Road, Hayling Island, Hampshire, PO11 9BY Tel: (023) 9246 7141 Fax: (023) 9246 9626 E-mail: p.mullins@btconnect.com

P Bastow, Silver Street, Reeth, Richmond, North Yorkshire, DL11 6SP Tel: (01748) 884555 Fax: (01748) 884181

Praxis Farm Ltd, Hoe Lane, Flansham, Bognor Regis, West Sussex, PO22 8NN Tel: (01243) 587354 Fax: (01243) 587353

Scullion Bruce & Co., 8 Littlejohn Street, Aberdeen, AB10 1FF Tel: (01224) 624954 Fax: (01224) 624954

Chris Sharp Cabinets Ltd, Tillbridge Lane, Scampton, Lincoln, LN1 2SX Tel: (01522) 504505 Fax: (01522) 514958

J.E. Spence Ltd, Church Lane, Adel, Leeds, LS16 8DE Tel: 0113-267 4110

Timber Technicians, Salterford Farm, Whinbush Lane, Calverton, Nottingham, NG14 6PE Tel: 0115-965 3399

Veneer Workshop Ltd, 37a South Street, Portslade, Brighton, BN41 2LE Tel: (01273) 422332 Fax: (01273) 418220 E-mail: mail@veneerworkshop.co.uk

W Kelly & Sons, 2 Islington Square, Liverpool, L3 8DD Tel: 0151-207 3050 Fax: 0151-207 3050

Waring & Woodfellows, Esgriar Saw Mills, Llanfair Clydogau, Lampeter, Dyfed, SA48 8LL Tel: (01570) 493450 Fax: (0870) 1254632 E-mail: info@woodfellows.com

Whiteleaf Ltd, Po Box 2, Princes Risborough, Buckinghamshire, HP27 9DP Tel: (01844) 261199 Fax: (01844) 342337 E-mail: sales@whiteleaffurniture.co.uk

The Woodworks, 5 Landscape Road, Weston-On-The-Grn, Bicester, Oxfordshire, OX25 3SX Tel: (01869) 343010 Fax: (01869) 343797 E-mail: info@woodworksweb.co.uk

CABLE ACCESSORIES DISTRIBUTORS OR AGENTS

2 E (UK) Ltd, Heyes Farm House, Grimshaw Road, Skelmersdale, Lancashire, WN8 6BH Tel: (01695) 50300 Fax: (01695) 50338 E-mail: sales@2euk.com

A C A Cable Distributors, Unit 7 Coegnant Close, Brackla Industrial Estate, Bridgend, Mid Glamorgan, CF31 2AY Tel: (01656) 766060 Fax: (01656) 664123 E-mail: sales@acacables.co.uk

▶ Active Communications, 10 Unicorn Avenue, Eastern Green, Coventry, CV5 7GH Tel: (024) 7647 4124 E-mail: sales@activecomms.com

Allied Cables Ltd, Liverpool Road, Warrington, WA5 1AP Tel: (01925) 445764 Fax: (01925) 232880 E-mail: alliedcables@absonline.net

Birch Valley Plastics Ltd, Darklake View, Estover, Plymouth, PL6 7TL Tel: (01752) 696515 Fax: (01752) 696724 E-mail: admin@birchvalley.co.uk

▶ Birkett Electric Ltd, Bridge House, Longwick Road, Princes Risborough, Buckinghamshire, HP27 9RS Tel: (01844) 274480 Fax: (01844) 274470 E-mail: info@birkett-electric.com

Clipper Components Ltd, 3 Ministry Wharf, Wycombe Road, Saunderton, High Wycombe, Buckinghamshire, HP14 4HW Tel: (01296) 432067 Fax: (01296) 487272 E-mail: ccompo6494@aol.com

Comtec Cables, Unit 3 Cardinal Way, Godmanchester, Huntingdon, Cambridgeshire, PE29 2XN Tel: (01480) 415400 Fax: (01480) 454724 E-mail: sales@comtec-comms.com

▶ Eclipse Presentations Ltd, 5 Chaffinch Business Park, Croydon Road, Beckenham, Kent, BR3 4AA Tel: (020) 8662 6444 Fax: (020) 8650 4635 E-mail: info@eclipse-presentations.co.uk

▶ Eland Cables Ltd, 120 Highgate Studios, 53-79 Highgate Road, London, NW5 1TL Tel: (020) 7241 8787 Fax: (020) 7241 8700 E-mail: sales@eland.co.uk

Express Electrical & Engineering Supplies, 37 Cable Depot Road, Clydebank, Dunbartonshire, G81 1UY Tel: 0141-941 3689 Fax: 0141-952 8155 E-mail: sales@expresselectrical.co.uk

CABLE ACCESSORIES DISTRIBUTORS OR AGENTS – *continued*

Grove Electronic Sales, 1 Grange Road Business Centre, Grange Road, Christchurch, Dorset, BH23 4JD Tel: (01425) 275060 Fax: (01425) 275070 E-mail: sales@grovesales.co.uk
Hellermanntyton, Wharf Approach, Aldridge, Walsall, WS9 8BX Tel: (01922) 458151 Fax: (01922) 743237 E-mail: sales@hellermantyton.co.uk
Hylec Components Ltd, 6 Stanton Close, Finedon Road Industrial Estate, Wellingborough, Northamptonshire, NN8 4HN Tel: (01933) 234400 Fax: (01933) 234411 E-mail: sales@hylec.co.uk
I S P Industrial Support Products Ltd, Unit H2 Lambs Farm Business Park, Basingstoke Road, Swallowfield, Reading, RG7 1PQ Tel: 0118-988 6873 Fax: 0118-988 6576 E-mail: info@isp-cablejointing.co.uk
Industrial Control Distributors, 8-9 Bridle Close, Finedon Road Industrial Estate, Wellingborough, Northamptonshire, NN8 4RN Tel: (01933) 446464 Fax: (01933) 442244 E-mail: sales@i-c-d.com
K S S Ltd, 122 Redriff Rd, London, SE16 6QD Tel: (020) 7232 2260 Fax: (020) 7232 2288 E-mail: kabletie@btinternet.com
▶ Kompress Holdings Ltd, 34 Dalziel Road, Hillington Industrial Estate, Glasgow, G52 4NN Tel: 0141-883 0228 Fax: 0141-883 6123 E-mail: sales@kompress.com
Kompress Holdings Ltd, Unit 5 Little Tennis Street, Nottingham, NG2 4EL Tel: 0115-958 1029 Fax: 0115-958 4180 E-mail: info@kompress.com
Legrand Electric Ltd, Great King Street North, Birmingham, B19 2LF Tel: 0121-515 0515 Fax: 0121-515 0516 E-mail: legrand.sales@legrand.co.uk
Northern Electrical Connectors, Unit 8 Glover Centre, Egmont Street, Mossley, Ashton-Under-Lyne, Lancashire, OL5 9PY Tel: (01457) 837511 Fax: (01457) 835216 E-mail: martin@nec-ltd.net
P C S Cables & Connectors Ltd, 14-16 Kingfisher Park, Three Cross Road, West Moors, Wimborne, Dorset, BH21 6US Tel: (01202) 871924 Fax: (01202) 895661 E-mail: enquiries@pcscables.com
Panduit Europe Ltd, West World, Westgate, London, W5 1UD Tel: (020) 8601 7200 Fax: (020) 8601 7319
▶ PolyOil Ltd, Unit A2, Wellheads Crescent, Wellheads Industrial Estate, Dyce, Aberdeen, AB21 7GA Tel: (01224) 799950 Fax: (01224) 799951 E-mail: info@polyoil.com
Rex Electrical Wholesale, 231 London Road, Staines, Middlesex, TW18 4HR Tel: (01784) 463366 Fax: (01784) 449781
Rotronic Distribution Services, Unit 1a Crompton Fields, Crompton Way, Crawley, West Sussex, RH10 9EE Tel: (01293) 565556 Fax: (01293) 843710 E-mail: sales@rotronic.co.uk
S E S Sterling Ltd, Halesfield 17, Harcourt Business Park, Telford, Shropshire, TF7 4PW Tel: (01952) 684196 Fax: (01952) 684286 E-mail: sales@ses-sterling.com
Seacon Europe Ltd, Seacon House, Hewett Road, Great Yarmouth, Norfolk, NR31 0RB Tel: (01493) 652733 Fax: (01493) 652840 E-mail: sales@seaconeurope.com
Servicepower Ltd, Rosse Works, Moorhead Lane, Shipley, West Yorkshire, BD18 4JH Tel: (01274) 785500 Fax: (01274) 785544 E-mail: sales@servicepower.ltd.uk
Sicame Electrical Developments Ltd, Riverholme Works, Huddersfield Road, Holmfirth, HD9 3TN Tel: (01484) 681115 Fax: (01484) 687352 E-mail: sales@sicame.co.uk
Sicane Electrical Distribution Ltd, Amington Industrial Estate, Tamworth, Staffordshire, B77 4DS Tel: (01827) 68333 Fax: (01827) 65700 E-mail: barbara.shewan@sicame.co.uk
Source, 1 Oak Court, Pennant Way, Lee Mill Industrial Estate, Ivybridge, Devon, PL21 9GP Tel: (01752) 698698 Fax: (01752) 698001 E-mail: sales@cable-accessories.com
Takbro Ltd, 59 Church Street, Walshaw, Bury, Lancashire, BL8 3BN Tel: (01204) 887001 Fax: (01204) 545400 E-mail: sales@takbro.co.uk
Thorne & Derrick, Units 9-10 Birchills Trading Estate, Emery Road, Bristol, BS4 5PF Tel: 0117-977 4647 Fax: 0117-977 5582 E-mail: southernsales@thorneandderrick.co.uk
Thorne & Derrick, Units 5 & 6 Gear House, Saltmeadows Road, Gateshead, Tyne & Wear, NE8 3AH Tel: 0191-490 1547 Fax: 0191-477 5371 E-mail: sales@thorneandderrick.co.uk
Tyco Electronics, Head Office, Faraday Road, Swindon, SN3 5HH Tel: (01793) 528171 Fax: (01793) 572516 E-mail: PICUK@tycoelectronics.com
W F Electrical Distributors, 313-333 Rainham Road South, Dagenham, Essex, RM10 8SX Tel: (020) 8517 7000 Fax: (020) 8595 0519 E-mail: peter.warsap@hagemeyer.co.uk

CABLE ASSEMBLY/HARNESS,

See also headings for particular types

Tony James Component Wiring Ltd, Unit E10 Speedwell Way, Harleston Industrial Estate, Harleston, Norfolk, IP20 9EH Tel: (01379) 854485 Fax: (01379) 852718 E-mail: enquires@tonyjames.co.uk
T F C Cable Assemblies Ltd, Excelsior Park, Wishaw, Lanarkshire, ML2 0ER Tel: (01698) 355017 Fax: (01698) 350559 E-mail: info@tfcasm.co.uk

CABLE ASSEMBLY/HARNESS BRAIDING MACHINES

Jacarem Ltd, 78 Asheridge Road, Chesham, Buckinghamshire, HP5 2PY Tel: (01494) 791336 Fax: (01494) 792336 E-mail: sales@jacarem.co.uk

CABLE ASSEMBLY/HARNESS CUTTING/STRIPPING MACHINES

Connect 2 Technology Ltd, Longbeck Road, Marske-by-the-Sea, Redcar, Cleveland, TS11 6HQ Tel: (01642) 492220 Fax: (01642) 492223 E-mail: sales@connect2t.co.uk
Orchard Technologies Ltd, Unit F5 Market Overton Industrial Estate, Thistleton Road, Market Overton, Oakham, Leicestershire, LE15 7PP Tel: (01572) 768489 Fax: (01572) 768181 E-mail: richard@orchard56.freeserve.co.uk
▶ Pirelli Cables & Components, Hall Lane, Prescot, Merseyside, L34 5UR Tel: 0151-430 3655 Fax: 0151-430 3636 E-mail: energysales@pirelli.com
Precision Cableforms & Terminations, Thetford Road, Ingham, Bury St. Edmunds, Suffolk, IP31 1NR Tel: (01284) 729514 Fax: (01284) 729515 E-mail: mark_pctltd@hotmail.com
Swale Components Ltd, Unit 88 John Wilson Business Park, Chestfield, Whitstable, Kent, CT5 3QT Tel: (01227) 771100 Fax: (01227) 771117 E-mail: sales@swalecomponents.com

CABLE ASSEMBLY/HARNESS TEST EQUIPMENT

Gemini Connections Ltd, 487 Holden Road, Leigh, Lancashire, WN7 2JJ Tel: (01942) 674929 Fax: (01942) 707516 E-mail: gemini.connections@virgin.net
M K Test Systems Ltd, Orchard Court, West Buckland, Wellington, Somerset, TA21 9LE Tel: (01823) 661100 Fax: (01823) 661160 E-mail: sales@mktest.com

CABLE ASSEMBLY/HARNESS, AIRCRAFT INDUSTRY

▶ A & I Accessory Ltd, 19 Macadam Place, South Newmoor Industrial Estate, Irvine, Ayrshire, KA11 4HP Tel: (01294) 211555 Fax: (01294) 211114 E-mail: sales@aiaccessory.com
▶ Brucom Distribution Ltd, Unit 7 & 13 Jupiter Business Park, Airfield Industrial Estate, Hixon, Stafford, ST18 0PF Tel: (01889) 272645 Fax: (01889) 271737 E-mail: sales@brucom.co.uk

CABLE ASSEMBLY/HARNESS, AUTOMOTIVE INDUSTRY

Airspace Avionics Ltd, 7-8 New Road Avenue, Chatham, Kent, ME4 6BB Tel: (01634) 843878 Fax: (01634) 401361 E-mail: peterfarrer@airspaceavionics.co.uk
Auto Europe Parts Ltd, Unit 11 Betchworth Works, Ifield Road, Charlwood, Horley, Surrey, RH6 0DX Tel: (01293) 863777 Fax: (01293) 863888 E-mail: info@autoeurope.co.uk
▶ Brucom Distribution Ltd, Unit 7 & 13 Jupiter Business Park, Airfield Industrial Estate, Hixon, Stafford, ST18 0PF Tel: (01889) 272645 Fax: (01889) 271737 E-mail: sales@brucom.co.uk
Cable Harnesses, Unit 16, Trostre Industrial Park, Llanelli, Dyfed, SA14 9UU Tel: (01554) 777200 Fax: (01554) 777224 E-mail: reception@cableharnessesuk.com
J K Control Systems Ltd, Unit 14 Kernick Industrial Estate, Penryn, Cornwall, TR10 9EP Tel: (01326) 378432 Fax: (01326) 378423 E-mail: info@jkcontrolsystems.co.uk
Nippon Antenna Europe, Venture House, Bone Lane, Newbury, Berkshire, RG14 5SH Tel: (01635) 30001 Fax: (01635) 35406 E-mail: nae@nippon-antenna.co.uk
▶ Pirelli Cables & Components, Hall Lane, Prescot, Merseyside, L34 5UR Tel: 0151-430 3655 Fax: 0151-430 3636 E-mail: energysales@pirelli.com
Redileads Anglesey Ltd, Industrial Estate Road, Llangefni, Gwynedd, LL77 7JA Tel: (01248) 750280 Fax: (01248) 722031 E-mail: enquiries@redileads.co.uk
Schort Industries Ltd, Trent Valley Industrial Estate, Rugeley, Staffordshire, WS15 3HA Tel: (01889) 583929 Fax: (01889) 583969 E-mail: sales@schort.co.uk
Westwire Harnessing Ltd, Unit 10 Headlands Trading Estate, Headlands Grove, Swindon, SN2 7JQ Tel: (01793) 537217 Fax: (01793) 421039 E-mail: graham@westwire.demon.co.uk

CABLE ASSEMBLY/HARNESS, COAXIAL

Cablelink UK Ltd, Lisle Road, High Wycombe, Buckinghamshire, HP13 5SH Tel: (01494) 525224 Fax: (01494) 525224 E-mail: sales@cablelink.co.uk
Connect 2 Technology Ltd, Longbeck Road, Marske-by-the-Sea, Redcar, Cleveland, TS11 6HQ Tel: (01642) 492220 Fax: (01642) 492223 E-mail: sales@connect2t.co.uk
Instrumentation & Control Services, Unit 3 The Old Forge, Peterchurch, Hereford, HR2 0SD Tel: (01981) 550011 Fax: (01981) 550955 E-mail: ics@ics-hereford.co.uk
▶ Parkfield Electronics, 4 Parkfield Avenue, Rose Green, Bognor Regis, West Sussex, PO21 3BW Tel: 01243 261990 Fax: 01243 261990E-mail: info@parkfieldelectronics.co.uk
Select Cables Ltd, Painter Close, Portsmouth, PO3 5RS Tel: (023) 9265 2552 Fax: (023) 9265 5277 E-mail: sales@selectcables.com
Vitelec Electronics Ltd, Station Road, Bordon, Hampshire, GU35 0LG Tel: (01420) 488661 Fax: (01420) 488014 E-mail: sales@vitelec.co.uk

CABLE ASSEMBLY/HARNESS, DEFENCE STANDARDS

Airspace Avionics Ltd, 7-8 New Road Avenue, Chatham, Kent, ME4 6BB Tel: (01634) 843878 Fax: (01634) 401361 E-mail: peterfarrer@airspaceavionics.co.uk
▶ Brucom Distribution Ltd, Unit 7 & 13 Jupiter Business Park, Airfield Industrial Estate, Hixon, Stafford, ST18 0PF Tel: (01889) 272645 Fax: (01889) 271737 E-mail: sales@brucom.co.uk
▶ Pirelli Cables & Components, Hall Lane, Prescot, Merseyside, L34 5UR Tel: 0151-430 3655 Fax: 0151-430 3636 E-mail: energysales@pirelli.com
Tekdata Distribution Ltd, Technology House, Crown Road, Stoke-on-Trent, ST1 5NJ Tel: (01782) 274255 Fax: (01782) 665511 E-mail: sales@tekdata.co.uk
Tyco Electronics, Head Office, Faraday Road, Swindon, SN3 5HH Tel: (01793) 528171 Fax: (01793) 572516 E-mail: PICUK@tycoelectronics.com
Ultra Electronics Electrics, Kingsditch Lane, Cheltenham, Gloucestershire, GL51 9PG Tel: (01242) 221166 Fax: (01242) 221167 E-mail: admin@ultra-electronics.com
Weststar Industries, 77 Cricklade Road, Swindon, SN2 1AB Tel: (01793) 512686 Fax: (01793) 512686
Westwire Harnessing Ltd, Unit 10 Headlands Trading Estate, Headlands Grove, Swindon, SN2 7JQ Tel: (01793) 537217 Fax: (01793) 421039 E-mail: graham@westwire.demon.co.uk

CABLE ASSEMBLY/HARNESS, ELECTRICAL/ELECTRONIC

A S T Distribution Ltd, Unit 16, Berkshire House, Swindon, SN1 2NR Tel: (01793) 541890 Fax: (01793) 541891 E-mail: sales@astcables.co.uk
Airfawn Consultants Ltd, New Haden Works, Draycott Cross Road, Cheadle, Stoke-on-Trent, ST10 2NW Tel: (01538) 750788 Fax: (01538) 751511 E-mail: aiirfawnltd@btconnect.com
Airspace Avionics Ltd, 7-8 New Road Avenue, Chatham, Kent, ME4 6BB Tel: (01634) 843878 Fax: (01634) 401361 E-mail: peterfarrer@airspaceavionics.co.uk
Ambitron Components Ltd, 4 Station Road, Hungerford, Berkshire, RG17 0DY Tel: (01488) 685404 Fax: (01488) 685406 E-mail: sales@ambitron.co.uk
Amos Electronics, 4 Little Balmer, Buckingham Industrial Estate, Buckingham, MK18 1TF Tel: (01280) 817877 Fax: (01280) 814140 E-mail: purchasing@paramountelectronics.co.uk
Asmec Electronics Solutions Ltd, 64-68 Wilbury Way, Hitchin, Hertfordshire, SG4 0TP Tel: (01462) 441155 Fax: (01462) 441150 E-mail: nashr@asmec.com
Axis Electronics, Manton Lane, Bedford, MK41 7NY Tel: (01234) 342932 Fax: (01234) 364941 E-mail: sales@axis-electronics.com
Black Box Network Services (Nottingham) Ltd, 464 Basingstoke Road, Reading, RG2 0BG Tel: 0115-900 3333 Fax: 0115-900 3390
Brockhill Enterprises Ltd, Hobson Lane, Kirkby Stephen, Cumbria, CA17 4RN Tel: (01768) 372027 Fax: (01768) 372049 E-mail: sales@brockhill.sagehost.co.uk
Cable First Ltd, 32-40 Harwell Road, Poole, Dorset, BH17 0GE Tel: (01202) 687337 Fax: (01202) 672501 E-mail: sales@cablefirst.co.uk
Cable Harnesses, Unit 16, Trostre Industrial Park, Llanelli, Dyfed, SA14 9UU Tel: (01554) 777200 Fax: (01554) 777224 E-mail: reception@cableharnessesuk.com
▶ Cable Solutions Worldwide Ltd, Unit A1, Wellheads Crescent, Wellheads Industrial Estate, Aberdeen, AB21 7GA Tel: (01224) 727910 Fax: (01224) 725360 E-mail: ricky.gill@1st4cables.com
Cablenet Cable & Wire Suppliers, Cablenet House, Lightwater Road, Lightwater, Surrey, GU18 5XQ Tel: (01276) 851900 Fax: (01276) 851909 E-mail: sales@cablenet.uk.com
Cambridge Electronic Industries Ltd, Denny Industrial Centre, Denny End Road, Waterbeach, Cambridge, CB25 9PB Tel: (01223) 860041 Fax: (01223) 863625 E-mail: sales@cambridgeconnectors.com
Cinch Connectors Ltd, Shireoaks Road, Worksop, Nottinghamshire, S80 3HA Tel: (01909) 474131 Fax: (01909) 478321 E-mail: sales@cinchuk.com
Copper & Optic Terminations Ltd, 90 Town Road, Stoke-on-Trent, ST1 2LD Tel: (01782) 275810 Fax: (01782) 287820 E-mail: sales@copperandoptic.com
Cranfield Electrical Ltd, 2 Adams Close, Kempston, Bedford, MK42 7JE Tel: (01234) 853044 Fax: (01234) 853054 E-mail: sales@cranfieldelectrical.com
D & K Wiring Services Ltd, Unit 1 Urban Hive, Sundon Park Road, Luton, LU3 3QU Tel: (01582) 492033 Fax: (01582) 565944 E-mail: sales@dkwiring.co.uk
D L Electrical Supplies (Mitcham) Ltd, 1A Totterdown Street, London, SW17 8TB Tel: (020) 8672 0064 Fax: (020) 8767 6372 E-mail: sales@dlelectrical.co.uk
Deval Ltd, Unit 6 Hamilton Way, New Milton, Hampshire, BH25 6TQ Tel: (01425) 620772 Fax: (01425) 638431 E-mail: sales@deval-ltd.co.uk
Edo MBM Technology Ltd, Emblem House, Home Farm Business Park, Brighton, BN1 9HU Tel: (01273) 810500 Fax: (01273) 810565 E-mail: info@edombmtech.co.uk
Electro Technik Ltd, 10-12 Shaw Lane, Stoke Prior, Bromsgrove, Worcestershire, B60 4DT Tel: (01527) 831794 Fax: (01527) 574470 E-mail: electro.technik@virgin.net
Elite Electronic Systems Ltd, Lackaghboy Industrial Estate, Lackaghboy, Enniskillen, County Fermanagh, BT74 4RL Tel: (028) 6632 7172 Fax: (028) 6632 5668 E-mail: sales@elitees.com
Enham Garden Centre, Enham Alamein, Andover, Hampshire, SP11 6JS Tel: (01264) 345800 Fax: (01264) 333638 E-mail: info@enham.co.uk
D. Evans Electrical Ltd, Stretton Way, Wilson Road, Huyton Industrial Estate, Liverpool, L36 6JF Tel: 0151-489 1232 Fax: 0151-480 1496 E-mail: drowley@d-evans.co.uk
Heart Electronics Ltd, 2 King Edward Road, Nuneaton, Warwickshire, CV11 4BB Tel: (024) 7635 3615 Fax: (024) 7635 3616 E-mail: info@heartelectronics.com
Honda Connectors Ltd, Unit B1, Marston Gates, South Marston Park, Swindon, SN3 4DE Tel: (01793) 836250 Fax: (01793) 836255 E-mail: sales@hondaconnectors.co.uk
Hunter Electronic Components Ltd, Unit 9 Ely Road, Theale Estate, Reading, RG7 4BQ Tel: (01628) 675911 Fax: 01189 325136 E-mail: sales@hcal.co.uk
Industrial Electronic Wiring, 10 Birch, Kembrey Park, Swindon, SN2 8UU Tel: (01793) 694033 Fax: (01793) 496295 E-mail: info@iew.co.uk
Instrumentation & Control Services, Unit 3 The Old Forge, Peterchurch, Hereford, HR2 0SD Tel: (01981) 550011 Fax: (01981) 550955 E-mail: ics@ics-hereford.co.uk
▶ Iubeo Europe Ltd, 82 Tenter Road, Moulton Park, Northampton, NN3 6AX Tel: +44 (01604) 646433 Fax: +44 (01604) 643737 E-mail: david@iubeo-europe.com
Jacarem Ltd, 78 Asheridge Road, Chesham, Buckinghamshire, HP5 2PY Tel: (01494) 791336 Fax: (01494) 792336 E-mail: sales@jacarem.co.uk
Tony James Component Wiring Ltd, Unit E10 Speedwell Way, Harleston Industrial Estate, Harleston, Norfolk, IP20 9EH Tel: (01379) 854485 Fax: (01379) 852718 E-mail: enquires@tonyjames.co.uk
Kembrey Wiring Systems Ltd, Garrard Way, Greenbridge, Swindon, SN3 3HY Tel: (01793) 693361 Fax: (01793) 614298 E-mail: sales@kembrey.co.uk
Kezvale Ltd, 5 Johnsons Industrial Estate, Silverdale Road, Hayes, Middlesex, UB3 3BA Tel: (020) 8569 2731 Fax: (020) 8569 2790 E-mail: info@kezvale.co.uk
Leaders 89 Ltd, Cable Harnesses, 6 Union Road, Chippenham, Wiltshire, SN15 1HW Tel: (01249) 651180 Fax: (01249) 651180
Lear Corporation UK Ltd, Glaisdale Parkway, Nottingham, NG8 4GP Tel: 0115-901 2200 Fax: 0115-928 9688
Lema Electronics, 1 Talisman Business Centre, Duncan Road, Park Gate, Southampton, SO31 7GA Tel: (01489) 572230 Fax: (01489) 578741 E-mail: sales@lemaelectronics.co.uk
M S S L Systems, Albany Road, Gateshead, Tyne & Wear, NE8 3AT Tel: 0191-477 3518 Fax: 0191-490 0264 E-mail: info@mssl.com
Magna Electronics Ltd, 9 Harrow Road, Hereford, HR4 0EH Tel: (01432) 353434 Fax: (01432) 278749 E-mail: mark@magna-electronics.co.uk
Manjet Electronics, Longmeadow Works, Ringwood Road, Three Legged Cross, Wimborne, Dorset, BH21 6RD Tel: (01202) 823013 Fax: (01202) 823013
Nova Electronic Developments Co Ltd, 49 Florence Road, Gedling, Nottingham, NG4 2QL Tel: 0115-910 9910 Fax: 0115-910 9900 E-mail: sales@novadev.co.uk
Ohmega Ltd, Wick Industrial Estate, Gore Road, New Milton, Hampshire, BH25 6SJ Tel: (01425) 619709 Fax: (01425) 638905 E-mail: ohmega@ohmega.freeserve.co.uk

CABLE ASSEMBLY/HARNESS, ELECTRICAL/ELECTRONIC – *continued*

Pallas Connections Ltd, Unit 1 Field Farm Business Centre, Launton, Bicester, Oxfordshire, OX26 5EL Tel: (01869) 277053 Fax: (01869) 277058 E-mail: hornby@pallasconnections.co.uk

▶ Parkfield Electronics, 4 Parkfield Avenue, Rose Green, Bognor Regis, West Sussex, PO21 3BW Tel: 01243 261990 Fax: 01243 261990E-mail: info@parkfieldelectronics.co.uk

Precision Cableforms & Terminations, Thetford Road, Ingham, Bury St. Edmunds, Suffolk, IP31 1NR Tel: (01284) 729514 Fax: (01284) 729515 E-mail: mark_pctltd@hotmail.com

R G Cables & Crimps, Unit 10 Fleckney Industrial Estate, Churchill Way, Fleckney, Leicester, LE8 8UD Tel: 0116-240 4500 Fax: 0116-240 4501

R & J Harnesses Ltd, Unit 6-7 The Courtyard Deeside Enterprise Centre, Rowleys Drive, Shotton, Deeside, Clwyd, CH5 1PP Tel: (01244) 812282 Fax: (01244) 818100

Raven Electronic Services Ltd, Unit 13, Little End Road, Eaton Socon, St. Neots, Cambridgeshire, PE19 8JH Tel: (01480) 407744 Fax: (01480) 470382 E-mail: dave@ravenelectronics.co.uk

Redileads Anglesey Ltd, Industrial Estate Road, Llangefni, Gwynedd, LL77 7JA Tel: (01248) 750280 Fax: (01248) 722031 E-mail: enquiries@redileads.co.uk

▶ Remploy Ltd, Stone Court, Siskin Drive, Middlemarch Business Park, Coventry, CV3 4FJ Tel: (024) 7651 5800 Fax: (024) 7651 5860 E-mail: info@remploy.co.uk

Rockford Group Ltd, Rockford House, Renalsham, Woodbridge, Suffolk, IP12 2GJ Tel: (01394) 420800 Fax: (01394) 420820 E-mail: sales@rockford.co.uk

St Cross Electronics Ltd, 14 Mount Pleasant Industrial Estate, Mount Pleasant Road, Southampton, SO14 0SP Tel: (023) 8022 7636 Fax: (023) 8033 1769 E-mail: sales@st-cross-electronics.co.uk

Schort Industries Ltd, Trent Valley Industrial Estate, Rugeley, Staffordshire, WS15 3HA Tel: (01889) 583929 Fax: (01889) 583969 E-mail: sales@schort.co.uk

Seacon Europe Ltd, Seacon House, Hewett Road, Great Yarmouth, Norfolk, NR31 0RB Tel: (01493) 652733 Fax: (01493) 652840 E-mail: sales@seaconeurope.com

Selwyn Electronics Ltd, Unit B8 Chaucer Business Park, Watery Lane, Kemsing, Sevenoaks, Kent, TN15 6QY Tel: (01732) 765100 Fax: (01732) 765190 E-mail: connect@selwyn.co.uk

Servicepower Ltd, Rosse Works, Moorhead Lane, Shipley, West Yorkshire, BD18 4JH Tel: (01274) 785500 Fax: (01274) 785544 E-mail: sales@servicepower.ltd.uk

Sicame Electrical Developments Ltd, Riverholme Works, Huddersfield Road, Holmfirth, HD9 3TN Tel: (01484) 681115 Fax: (01484) 687352 E-mail: sales@sicame.co.uk

Simclar International Ltd, Pitreavie Business Park, Queensferry Road, Dunfermline, Fife, KY11 8UN Tel: (01383) 735161 Fax: (01383) 739986 E-mail: sales@simclar.com

Surgecam Ltd, Cold Hesledon Industrial Estate, Cold Hesledon, Seaham, County Durham, SR7 8ST Tel: 0191-513 0666 Fax: 0191-513 0862 E-mail: david.watson@surgecam.co.uk

Swansea Industrial Components Ltd, 66-70 Morfa Road, Swansea, SA1 2EF Tel: (01792) 458777 Fax: (01792) 456252

T F C Cable Assemblies Ltd, Excelsior Park, Wishaw, Lanarkshire, ML2 0ER Tel: (01698) 355017 Fax: (01698) 350559 E-mail: info@tfcasm.co.uk

Tekdata Distribution Ltd, Technology House, Crown Road, Stoke-on-Trent, ST1 5NJ Tel: (01782) 274255 Fax: (01782) 665511 E-mail: sales@tekdata.co.uk

Tele Connect Ltd, 12 Rosevale Road, Parkhouse Industrial Estate West, Newcastle, Staffordshire, ST5 7EF Tel: (01782) 563443 Fax: (01782) 566227

Tenkay Electronics Ltd, Lancing Business Park, Marlborough Road, Lancing, West Sussex, BN15 8TN Tel: (01903) 855455 Fax: (01903) 761942 E-mail: sue.brown@tenkay.co.uk

Time 24 Ltd, Robimatic House, 19 Victoria Gardens, Burgess Hill, West Sussex, RH15 9NB Tel: (01444) 257655 Fax: (01444) 259000 E-mail: sales@time24.co.uk

Trowtronics UK Ltd, Unit 41 South Hampshire Industrial Park, Totton, Southampton, SO40 3SA Tel: (023) 8066 0055 Fax: (023) 8066 0012 E-mail: trowtronics.@aol.conf.au

Volex, Butts Mill, Butts Street, Leigh, Lancashire, WN7 3AD Tel: (01942) 672393 Fax: (01942) 677395 E-mail: sales@volexwiring.com

W H Kemp, Cory Way, West Wilts Trading Estate, Westbury, Wiltshire, BA13 4QT Tel: (01373) 823322 Fax: (01373) 824411 E-mail: sales@whkemp.co.uk

Weststar Industries, 77 Cricklade Road, Swindon, SN2 1AB Tel: (01793) 512686 Fax: (01793) 512686

Westwire Harnessing Ltd, Unit 10 Headlands Trading Estate, Headlands Grove, Swindon, SN2 7JQ Tel: (01793) 537217 Fax: (01793) 421039 E-mail: graham@westwire.demon.co.uk

Wire All Products, 42 New Road, Rochester, Kent, ME1 1DX Tel: (01634) 812984 Fax: 01634 409636 E-mail: sales@wireall.co.uk

Woven Electronics Componants Ltd, Burcombe Lane, Wilton, Salisbury, SP2 0ES Tel: (01722) 744242 Fax: (01722) 744079 E-mail: woven@wovenelectronics.co.uk

CABLE ASSEMBLY/HARNESS, OVER MOULDED AND DISCRETE

Interconnect Products Ltd, Marlborough Road, Wootton Bassett, Swindon, SN4 7SA Tel: (01793) 849811 Fax: (01793) 849809 E-mail: sales@interconnect.demon.co.uk

CABLE ASSEMBLY/HARNESS, RAILWAY LOCOMOTIVE

Leaders 89 Ltd, Cable Harnesses, 6 Union Road, Chippenham, Wiltshire, SN15 1HW Tel: (01249) 651180 Fax: (01249) 651180

Weststar Industries, 77 Cricklade Road, Swindon, SN2 1AB Tel: (01793) 512686 Fax: (01793) 512686

CABLE ASSEMBLY/HARNESS, SMALL COMPUTER SYSTEM INTERFACE (SCSI)

C & M Corporation, Dunfermline, Fife, KY12 9YX Tel: (01383) 621225 Fax: (01383) 623455 E-mail: sales@cmcorporation.co.uk

Cablelink UK Ltd, Lisle Road, High Wycombe, Buckinghamshire, HP13 5SH Tel: (01494) 525224 Fax: (01494) 525224 E-mail: sales@cablelink.co.uk

CABLE ASSEMBLY/HARNESS, TO SPECIFICATION

Cable Harnesses, Unit 16, Trostre Industrial Park, Llanelli, Dyfed, SA14 9UU Tel: (01554) 777200 Fax: (01554) 777224 E-mail: reception@cableharnessesuk.com

Connector & Terminal Supplies Ltd, Unit A3 Mountbatten Business Park, Jackson Close, Portsmouth, PO6 1US Tel: (023) 9237 5966 Fax: (023) 9237 5904 E-mail: sales@connectors-uk.com

▶ Davies Bros, 5 Holborn Square, Birkenhead, Merseyside, CH41 9HQ Tel: 0151-647 3002 Fax: 0151-647 3002 E-mail: dvsbrn@aol.com

Farcroft Electronic Services Ltd, Tanglewood 88 Jobs Lane, Coventry, CV4 9ED Tel: (024) 7646 0087 Fax: (024) 7647 0369 E-mail: enquires@farcroft-uk.com

CABLE BOXES, JOINT/ JUNCTION

Kembrey Wiring Systems Ltd, Garrard Way, Greenbridge, Swindon, SN3 3HY Tel: (01793) 693361 Fax: (01793) 614298 E-mail: sales@kembrey.co.uk

CABLE CATENARY SYSTEMS

Irvine Martin Ltd, Kenton Road, Debenham, Stowmarket, Suffolk, IP14 6LA Tel: (01728) 860909 Fax: (01728) 861056 E-mail: info@irvine-martin.co.uk

CABLE CLAMPS

Atlantic Supports Engineering, 3 Llandough Trading Estate, Penarth Road, Cardiff, CF11 8RR Tel: (029) 2070 8461 Fax: (029) 2035 0437 E-mail: sales@atlantic-supports.co.uk

K S S Ltd, 122 Redriff Rd, London, SE16 6QD Tel: (020) 7232 2260 Fax: (020) 7232 2288 E-mail: kabletie@btinternet.com

CABLE CLIPS

Albion Manufacturing Ltd, The Granary, Silfield Road, Wymondham, Norfolk, NR18 9AU Tel: (01953) 605983 Fax: (01953) 606764 E-mail: sales@albionmanufacturing.com

Fischer Group Of Companies, Whiteley Road, Hithercroft Industrial Estate, Wallingford, Oxfordshire, OX10 9AT Tel: (01491) 827919 Fax: (01491) 827953 E-mail: sales@fischer.co.uk

Jegs Electrical Ltd, 20 Progress Road, Eastwood, Leigh-On-Sea, Essex, SS9 5LW Tel: (01702) 421555 Fax: (01702) 420363 E-mail: mail@jegs.co.uk

CABLE COLOURING SERVICES

P C S Cables & Connectors Ltd, 14-16 Kingfisher Park, Three Cross Road, West Moors, Wimborne, Dorset, BH21 6US Tel: (01202) 871924 Fax: (01202) 895661 E-mail: enquiries@pcscables.com

CABLE CONTRACTORS

Cable Jointing Services Ltd, Cedric Works, Cedric CR, Sunderland, SR2 7QP Tel: 0191-514 1165 Fax: 0191-564 0005 E-mail: sales@cablejointingservices.com

Cooper Armer International Co. Ltd, Unit 2C Fernfield Farm, Whaddon Road, Milton Keynes, MK17 0PR Tel: (01908) 503018 Fax: (01908) 503811 E-mail: info@caidata.co.uk

Engineered Systems (Electrical) Ltd, Systems House, Unit 1, Waterside Industrial Park, Waterside Road, Leeds, LS10 1RW Tel: 0113-272 1222 Fax: 0113-272 1333 E-mail: mick@eselimited.co.uk

First Projects Ltd, City Business Centre, Station Rise, York, YO1 6GA Tel: (01904) 613361 Fax: (01904) 612936

Lineartron Cabling Systems Ltd, Unit 5 Slader Business Park, Witney Road, Nuffield Industerial Estate, Poole, Dorset, BH17 0GP Tel: (01202) 672689 Fax: (01202) 672457 E-mail: sales@lineartron.co.uk

Melandra Cable Installation & Maintenance Co. Ltd, Unit 2-3, Dinting Trading Estate, Dinting Lane, Glossop, Derbyshire, SK13 7NU Tel: (01457) 855200 Fax: (01457) 863391 E-mail: melandracables@btopenworld.com

Murphy Ltd, Ashley House, Ashley Road, London, N17 9LZ Tel: (020) 8885 3545 Fax: (020) 8801 1126 E-mail: emq@murphy-ltd-.uk

Powersystems UK Ltd, Badminton Road Trading Estate, Badminton Road, Yate, Bristol, BS37 5GG Tel: (01454) 318000 Fax: (01454) 318111 E-mail: sales@powersystemsuk.co.uk

Rochester Corporation, 2nd Floor Taylor Building, 62-64 Bromham Road, Bedford, MK40 2QG Tel: (01234) 327013 Fax: (01234) 327062 E-mail: djharris@rochester-cables.com

Rystan Installations Ltd, Rystan House, The Opening, Codicote, Hitchin, Hertfordshire, SG4 8UF Tel: (01438) 820651 Fax: (01438) 821493

I.S.G. Webb Ltd, Unit 2 Progress Estate, Bircholt Road, Maidstone, Kent, ME15 9YH Tel: (01622) 670281 Fax: (01622) 683528 E-mail: project.office@isgwebb.com

CABLE CROPPERS

Insulated Tools Ltd, Charlwoods Road, East Grinstead, West Sussex, RH19 2HR Tel: (01342) 324255 Fax: (01342) 327115 E-mail: enquiries@insulatedtools.co.uk

Sheffield Shears Co. Ltd, 28 Trinity Street, Sheffield, S3 7AJ Tel: 0114-272 2644 Fax: 0114-272 2644

CABLE CUTTING AND CRIMPING

Orchard Technologies Ltd, Unit F5 Market Overton Industrial Estate, Thistleton Road, Market Overton, Oakham, Leicestershire, LE15 7PP Tel: (01572) 768489 Fax: (01572) 768181 E-mail: richard@orchard56.freeserve.co.uk

CABLE DESIGN

Raven Electronic Services Ltd, Unit 13, Little End Road, Eaton Socon, St. Neots, Cambridgeshire, PE19 8JH Tel: (01480) 407744 Fax: (01480) 470382 E-mail: dave@ravenelectronics.co.uk

CABLE DISTRIBUTION CABINETS

▶ Active Communications, 10 Unicorn Avenue, Eastern Green, Coventry, CV5 7GH Tel: (024) 7647 4124 E-mail: sales@activecomms.com

CABLE DISTRIBUTORS OR AGENTS

A C A Cable Distributors, Unit 7 Coegnant Close, Brackla Industrial Estate, Bridgend, Mid Glamorgan, CF31 2AY Tel: (01656) 766060 Fax: (01656) 664123 E-mail: sales@acacables.co.uk

A C Electrical Wholesale Ltd, 2 Royal Buildings, Marlborough Road, Lancing, West Sussex, BN15 8SJ Tel: (01903) 765813 Fax: (01903) 753467 E-mail: lancing@ac-electrical.co.uk

A1 Cable Express Ltd, Unit 27 Hailey Road Business Park, Hailey Road, Erith, Kent, DA18 4AA Tel: (020) 8312 4006 Fax: (020) 8312 4883

Anixter, A The Beacons Warrington Road, Birchwood Park, Birchwood, Warrington, WA3 6GP Tel: (01925) 850808 Fax: (01925) 418166 E-mail: jackie.fisher@anixter.com

Anixter, A The Beacons Warrington Road, Birchwood Park, Birchwood, Warrington, WA3 6GP Tel: (01925) 850808 Fax: (01925) 418166

Apex Cables Ltd, St Johns Road, Meadowfield Industrial Estate, Durham, DH7 8RJ Tel: 0191-378 7900 Fax: 0191-378 7909 E-mail: apex@apexcables.co.uk

BCD Cables Ltd, The E-Tech Centre, Boundary Road, Great Yarmouth, Norfolk, NR31 0LY Tel: (01493) 604604 Fax: (01493) 604606 E-mail: john.milne@etechcentre.com

Cable Services Liverpool, 43 St.Johns Road, Bootle, Merseyside, L20 8BH Tel: 0151-933 9022 Fax: 0151-933 9765 E-mail: lpool@cableservices.co.uk

Cable Services UK Ltd, Rhosddu Industrial Estate, Main Road, Rhosrobin, Wrexham, Clwyd, LL11 4YZ Tel: (01978) 340450 Fax: (01978) 311315 E-mail: uk@cableservices.co.uk

Capital Cables, D 20 Frogmore Industrial Estate, Motherwell Way, Grays, Essex, RM20 3XD Tel: (01708) 864464 Fax: (01708) 865385

City Electrical Factors Ltd, Unit 6 Dunbeath Court, Elgin Industrial Estate, Swindon, SN2 8QF Tel: (01793) 535256 Fax: (01793) 513287 E-mail: sales.swindon@cef.co.uk

Commtech Trading Co. (Lancashire) Ltd, 5 Petre Road, Clayton Park Industrial Estate, Accrington, Lancashire, BB5 5JB Tel: (01254) 232638 Fax: (01254) 301197 E-mail: sales@commtechcomm.com

Denray Cables & Controls, Edwards House, 327 Whapload Road, Lowestoft, Suffolk, NR32 1UL Tel: (01502) 516971 Fax: (01502) 537045

Deta Electrical Co. Ltd, Kingsway House, Laporte Way, Luton, LU4 8RJ Tel: (01582) 544544 Fax: (01582) 544501 E-mail: sales@detaelectrical.co.uk

E C Cables Ltd, Unit 4B, Waymills Industrial Estate, Waymills, Whitchurch, Shropshire, SY13 1TT Tel: (01948) 660950 Fax: (01948) 660959 E-mail: ec.cables@virgin.net

Eldis Electrical Distributors, 239-242 Great Lister Street, Birmingham, B7 4BS Tel: 0121-359 4521 Fax: 0121-333 1432 E-mail: eldis@eldis.co.uk

Elite Cables & Components Ltd, 5 Smiths Forge, North End Road, Yatton, Bristol, BS49 4AU Tel: (01934) 876661 Fax: (01934) 876646 E-mail: sales@elitecables.co.uk

Erf Electrical Wholesalers Ltd, Salop Street, Daybrook, Nottingham, NG5 6HD Tel: 0115-920 3960 Fax: 0115-967 3866 E-mail: sales.nottingham@erfelectrical.co.uk

G E T, Key Point, 3-17 High Street, Potters Bar, Hertfordshire, EN6 5AJ Tel: (01707) 601601 Fax: (01707) 601708 E-mail: sales@getplc.com

H T Cables, 40 Lancaster Gardens, Penn, Wolverhampton, WV4 4DN Tel: (01902) 339926 Fax: (01902) 659426 E-mail: seona_macrae@lineone.net

J E Wildbore Ltd, Waddington Street, Oldham, OL9 6QU Tel: 0161-624 4475 Fax: 0161-627 0930 E-mail: sales@jwildbore.co.uk

Maplin Electronics P.L.C., National Distribution Centre, Valley Road, Wombwell, Barnsley, South Yorkshire, S73 0BS Tel: (0870) 4296000 Fax: (0870) 4296001 E-mail: sales@maplin.co.uk

Nationwide Cables, Unit 34, Minworth Industrial Park, Forge Lane, Minworth, Sutton Coldfield, West Midlands, B76 1AH Tel: 0121-313 1001 Fax: 0121-351 4851

Nexans Logistics, Llewellyn House, Chesney Wold, Bleak Hall, Milton Keynes, MK6 1NE Tel: (01908) 250850 Fax: (01908) 250851 E-mail: info@nexans.co.uk

P X Manufacturing & Distribution Co. Ltd, Unit 1A, Lyon Way Industrial Estate, Lyon Way, Rockware Avenue, Greenford, Middlesex, UB6 0BN Tel: (020) 8575 0407 Fax: (020) 8578 2887 E-mail: sales@pxcables.com

▶ Sellec Special Cables Ltd, Dukeries Way, Worksop, Nottinghamshire, S81 7DW Tel: (01909) 483539 Fax: (01909) 500181 E-mail: sales@sellec.com

UK Cables Ltd, London Distribution Centre, Westlands Industrial Estate, Millington Road, Hayes, Middlesex, UB3 4AZ Tel: (020) 8561 9111 Fax: (020) 8561 6777

Webb & Wells Ltd, 9 Chilford Court, Rayne Road, Braintree, Essex, CM7 2QS Tel: (01376) 550044 Fax: (01376) 550022 E-mail: sales@webbwells.co.uk

Wessex Belden CDT, Unit 8 Crow Arch Lane Industrial Estate, Crow Arch Lane, Ringwood, Hampshire, BH24 1PE Tel: (01425) 480804 Fax: (01425) 480805 E-mail: sales@wessexcdt.co.uk

Wilson Electrical Distributors, Unit 6 Waterside, Hamm Moor Lane, Addlestone, Surrey, KT15 2SN Tel: (01932) 848020 Fax: (01932) 820600 E-mail: sales@wilsonelectrical.com

CABLE DRAIN CLEANING MACHINES

▶ associated drain cleaning services, 80 hawthorn way, shepperton, middlesex, TW17 8QD Tel: 01932 765892 Fax: 01932 765892 E-mail: info@associated-services.co.uk

▶ K M R Pipelines Ltd, 7 mount view Gardens, Norton Lees, Sheffield, S8 8PY Tel: 0114 2551447 Fax: 0114 2551447 E-mail: lawrence@kmrpipelines.co.uk

CABLE DRUM HANDLING EQUIPMENT

A Williamson & Son, 34 Main Street, Milton of Balgonie, Glenrothes, Fife, KY7 6PX Tel: (01592) 758307 Fax: (01592) 610570

CABLE DRUM HANDLING EQUIPMENT – *continued*

Clydesdale Ltd, 3 Sunbeam Road, Woburn Road Industrial Estate, Kempston, Bedford, MK42 7BZ Tel: (01234) 855855 Fax: (01234) 856845 E-mail: david@clydesdale.ltd.uk
S E B International Ltd, Unity Road, Lowmoor Industrial Estate, Kirkby-in-Ashfield, Nottingham, NG17 7LE Tel: (01623) 754490 Fax: (01623) 753477 E-mail: contact@sebinternational.com

CABLE DRUM JACKS

Autoreel Ltd, Palmer Drive, Stapleford, Nottingham, NG9 7BW Tel: 0115-939 0200 Fax: 0115-939 0201 E-mail: autoreel@autoreel.co.uk
S E B International Ltd, Unity Road, Lowmoor Industrial Estate, Kirkby-in-Ashfield, Nottingham, NG17 7LE Tel: (01623) 754490 Fax: (01623) 753477 E-mail: contact@sebinternational.com

CABLE DRUM TRAILERS

Avonride Ltd, Spelter Site, Caerau, Maesteg, Mid Glamorgan, CF34 0AQ Tel: (01656) 739111 Fax: (01656) 737677 E-mail: salesmaesteg@knottuk.com
King Highway Products Ltd, Riverside, Market Harborough, Leicestershire, LE16 7PX Tel: (01858) 467361 Fax: (01858) 467161 E-mail: sales@skyking.co.uk
J.M. Loveridge P.L.C., Higher Merley Lane, Corfe Mullen, Wimborne, Dorset, BH21 3EQ Tel: (01202) 882306 Fax: (01202) 880059
S E B International Ltd, Unity Road, Lowmoor Industrial Estate, Kirkby-in-Ashfield, Nottingham, NG17 7LE Tel: (01623) 754490 Fax: (01623) 753477 E-mail: contact@sebinternational.com

CABLE DRUM/REEL, CARDBOARD

Pentre Reels Ltd, Unit 2 Moss Industrial Estate, Off St Helens Road, Leigh, Lancashire, WN7 3PF Tel: (01942) 607080 Fax: (01942) 261878 E-mail: sales@pentrereels.co.uk

CABLE DRUM/REEL, METAL

Jo-El Electric Ltd, Stafford Park 5, Telford, Shropshire, TF3 3AS Tel: (01952) 209001 Fax: (01952) 238090 E-mail: info@jo-el.com

CABLE DRUM/REEL, WOOD

Askern UK Ltd, High Street, Askern, Doncaster, South Yorkshire, DN6 0AA Tel: (01302) 703065 Fax: (01302) 701992 E-mail: info@askern.com
Pentre Reels Ltd, Unit 2 Moss Industrial Estate, Off St Helens Road, Leigh, Lancashire, WN7 3PF Tel: (01942) 607080 Fax: (01942) 261878 E-mail: sales@pentrereels.co.uk

CABLE DUCTING AND PANEL TRUNKING

▶ Medaes Ltd, Telford Cresent, Speedwell Industrial Estate, Staveley, Chesterfield, Derbyshire, S43 3PF Tel: (01246) 474242 Fax: (01246) 472982 E-mail: sales@medaes.co.uk
Unitrunk Cable Systems, Unit 2 Orbital Way, Denton, Manchester, M34 3QA Tel: 0161-336 1177 Fax: 0161-336 1188

CABLE FAULT LOCATORS

Antec Instrumentation, Unit 1, 59 Queensway North, Team Valley Trading Estate, Gateshead, Tyne & Wear, NE11 0NX Tel: 0191-482 4241 Fax: 0191-487 8835
Cable Check Systems, Unit 18 Quay Lane, Hardway, Gosport, Hampshire, PO12 4LJ Tel: (023) 9252 8396 Fax: (023) 9258 9748 E-mail: info@greenpersonnel.co.uk
Drallim Industries, Drury Lane, St. Leonards-on-Sea, East Sussex, TN38 9BA Tel: (01424) 205140 Fax: (01424) 202140 E-mail: sales@drallim.com
High Voltage Maintenance Services, Littlebrook Business Centre, Littlebrook Manorway, Dartford, DA1 5PZ Tel: (01322) 273100 Fax: (01322) 294413 E-mail: enquiries@hvms.co.uk
K & S Engineering & Scientific Ltd, 18 Clifton Gardens, London, NW11 7EL Tel: (020) 8731 7461 Fax: (020) 8731 8604 E-mail: seedetails@www.kse-sci.com
Qualitrol Hathaway Instruments Division, Brewery Road, Hoddesdon, Hertfordshire, EN11 8HF Tel: (01992) 463502 Fax: (01992) 463507 E-mail: sales@hathaway-systems.com
Radiodetection Ltd, Western Drive, Bristol, BS14 0AF Tel: 0117-988 6232 Fax: (01275) 550004 E-mail: sales@radiodetection.com

Zumbach Electronics, Unit 22 Cromwell Business Centre, Howard Way, Interchange Park, Newport Pagnell, Buckinghamshire, MK16 9QS Tel: (0870) 7743301 Fax: (0870) 7743302 E-mail: sales@zumbach.com

CABLE FORMS

M J P Electronics Ltd, Unit 1, Gore Cross Business Park, Corbin Way, Bradpole, Bridport, Dorset, DT6 3UX Tel: (01308) 425800 Fax: (01308) 455770 E-mail: murry@mjpelectronics.com
Tabelek (Control Systems) Ltd, Jubilee Road, Waterlooville, Hampshire, PO7 7RE Tel: (023) 9261 0016 Fax: 023 9261 0016

CABLE GLANDS

G.H. Lucas & Co. Ltd, 249 Ordsall Lane, Salford, M5 3WH Tel: 0161-872 7468 Fax: 0161-926 8810 E-mail: info@ghlucas.co.uk
Hylec Components Ltd, 6 Stanton Close, Finedon Road Industrial Estate, Wellingborough, Northamptonshire, NN8 4HN Tel: (01933) 234400 Fax: (01933) 234411 E-mail: sales@hylec.co.uk
Wellhead Electrical Supplies Ltd, Unit 4d Wellheads CR, Wellheads Industrial Estate, Aberdeen, AB21 7GA Tel: (01224) 723606 Fax: (01224) 723606 E-mail: sales@wellheads.co.uk

CABLE GRIPS

Cable Grips (Minehead) Ltd, Ponsford Road, Minehead, Somerset, TA24 5DX Tel: (01643) 702177 Fax: (01643) 704012 E-mail: rodgerwood@cablegripsltd.co.uk

CABLE HANDLING EQUIPMENT

Autoreel Ltd, Palmer Drive, Stapleford, Nottingham, NG9 7BW Tel: 0115-939 0200 Fax: 0115-939 0201 E-mail: autoreel@autoreel.co.uk
Bewa (UK) Ltd, Noble Square Industrial Estate, Brynmawr, Ebbw Vale, Gwent, NP23 4BS Tel: (01495) 310170 Fax: (01495) 311816 E-mail: bewauk@yahoo.co.uk
Hubbell Ltd, Brunel Drive, Stretton, Burton-On-Trent, Staffordshire, DE13 0BZ Tel: (01283) 500500 Fax: (01283) 500400
Lifting Gear Hire plc, Unit D4 South Orbital Trading Park, Hedon Road, Hull, HU9 1NJ Tel: (01482) 223737 Fax: (01482) 219491 E-mail: hull-lifting@speedydepots.co.uk
Metool Products Ltd, Unit 1 Mercian Park, Mercian Close, Ilkeston, Derbyshire, DE7 8HG Tel: 0115-922 5931 Fax: 0115-925 8183 E-mail: postmaster@metool.com
Speedy LGH, West Thamesmead Business Park, 7 Kellner Road, London, SE28 0AX Tel: (020) 8854 6248 Fax: (020) 8316 0501 E-mail: south-thames@lgh.co.uk
Speedy/LGH, Unit 1C, Walney Road Industrial Estate, Barrow-In-Furness, Cumbria, LA14 5UG Tel: (01229) 835407 Fax: (01229) 811236 E-mail: cumbria@lgh.co.uk
Wampfler Co Ltd, Unit B4, Altrincham Business Park, Stuart Road, Broadheath, Altrincham, Cheshire, WA14 5GJ Tel: 0161-929 6032 Fax: 0161-928 9126 E-mail: wampfler.uk@wampfler.com

CABLE HARNESSES, *See also Cable Assembly etc*

Crawford Hansford & Kimber Ltd, 18 Farnborough Road, Farnborough, Hampshire, GU14 6AY Tel: (01252) 377077 Fax: (01252) 377228 E-mail: admin@crawfordhk.com

CABLE IDENTIFICATION SYSTEMS

Bridgelock Engineering & Marketing Ltd, 137 Slough Road, Datchet, Slough, SL3 9AE Tel: (01753) 549373 Fax: (01753) 580269 E-mail: sales@bridgelock.com

CABLE INSTALLATION

A P C Solutions (UK) Ltd, Unit 18 The Old Cinema, Allshots Industrial Estate, Kelvedon, Colchester, CO5 9DF Tel: (01376) 585554 Fax: (01376) 585727 E-mail: info@apcsolutionuk.com
Ashby Computer Services, Sywell Airport Business Park, Wellingborough Road, Sywell, Northampton, NN6 0BN Tel: (01604) 790979 Fax: (01604) 491859 E-mail: enquiries@ashbycomputers.co.uk
First Projects Ltd, City Business Centre, Station Rise, York, YO1 6GA Tel: (01904) 613361 Fax: (01904) 612936

CABLE INSTALLATION EQUIPMENT

Cowell Export, Marsh Green, Edenbridge, Kent, TN8 5QL Tel: (01732) 864211 Fax: (01732) 863106 E-mail: mail@bobcowell.co.uk
Polysleeve Products Ltd, Groby Lodge Farm, Groby, Leicester, LE6 0GN Tel: (01530) 249719 Fax: (01530) 249729

CABLE JOINTING

▶ Birkett Electric Ltd, Bridge House, Longwick Road, Princes Risborough, Buckinghamshire, HP27 9RS Tel: (01844) 274480 Fax: (01844) 274470 E-mail: info@birkett-electric.com
Cable Jointing Services Ltd, Cedric Works, Cedric CR, Sunderland, SR2 7QP Tel: 0191-514 1165 Fax: 0191-564 0005 E-mail: sales@cablejointingservices.com
D S G Canusa GmbH & Co., Sales Bergstrand House, Parkwood Close, Roborough, Plymouth, PL6 7SG Tel: (01752) 209880 Fax: (01752) 209850 E-mail: info@dsgcanusa.com
▶ Global Jointing Systems, Unit 7, Park Lane Industrial Estate, Corsham, Wiltshire, SN13 9LG Tel: (01249) 715566 Fax: (01249) 715533 E-mail: office@globalresins.co.uk

CABLE JOINTING ACCESSORIES

B & H (Nottingham) Ltd, Middlemore Lane West, Aldridge, WS9 8EB Tel: (01922) 744144 Fax: (01922) 744150

CABLE JOINTING COMPOUNDS

Scapa, Manchester Road, Ashton-under-Lyne, Lancashire, OL7 0ED Tel: 0161-301 7400 Fax: 0161-301 7445E-mail: sales@scapa.com

CABLE JOINTING KITS

I S P Industrial Support Products Ltd, Unit H2 Lambs Farm Business Park, Basingstoke Road, Swallowfield, Reading, RG7 1PQ Tel: 0118-988 6873 Fax: 0118-988 6576 E-mail: info@isp-cablejointing.co.uk

CABLE JOINTING/CRIMPING SYSTEMS, *See Crimping etc*

CABLE LADDER SUPPORT SYSTEMS

Cable Services Liverpool, 43 St.Johns Road, Bootle, Merseyside, L20 8BH Tel: 0151-933 9022 Fax: 0151-933 9765 E-mail: lpool@cableservices.co.uk
▶ Metstrut, Unit 3 Granada Trading Estate, Off Park Street, Oldbury, West Midlands, B69 4LH Tel: 0121-601 6085 Fax: 0121-601 6177 E-mail: nsmith@metsec.com
Unistrut Holdings Ltd, Unistrut House, Edison Road, Bedford, MK41 0HU Tel: (01234) 220400 Fax: (01234) 216004 E-mail: cmathews@tyco-bspd.com
Vantrunk Building Services Ltd, Goddard Road, Astmoor Industrial Estate, Runcorn, Cheshire, WA7 1QF Tel: (01928) 564211 Fax: (01928) 580157 E-mail: sales@vantrunk.co.uk

CABLE LAYING EQUIPMENT

Cable Grips (Minehead) Ltd, Ponsford Road, Minehead, Somerset, TA24 5DX Tel: (01643) 702177 Fax: (01643) 704012 E-mail: rodgerwood@cablegripsltd.co.uk
CBS Products Ltd, Pillings Road, Oakham, Leicestershire, LE15 6QF Tel: (01572) 723665 Fax: (01572) 756009 E-mail: sales@cbsproducts.com
Clydesdale Ltd, 3 Sunbeam Road, Woburn Road Industrial Estate, Kempston, Bedford, MK42 7BZ Tel: (01234) 855855 Fax: (01234) 856845 E-mail: david@clydesdale.ltd.uk
Sheen Equipment, Greasley Street, Nottingham, NG6 8NH Tel: 0115-927 2321 Fax: 0115-977 0671

CABLE LOCATING EQUIPMENT HIRE

Laser Plane Ltd, 6 Devonshire Business Park, Knights Park Road, Basingstoke, Hampshire, RG21 6XE Tel: (01256) 460161 Fax: (01256) 363283 E-mail: laserplaneltd@tiscali.co.uk

CABLE LOCATING SERVICES

Cable Detection Ltd, 16 Alderflat Drive, Newstead Indsustrial Trading Estate, Trentam, Stoke-On-Trent, ST4 8HX Tel: (01782) 654450 Fax: (01782) 642584
Leica Geosystems Ltd, Davy Avenue, Knowlhill, Milton Keynes, MK5 8LB Tel: (01908) 256500 Fax: (01908) 609992 E-mail: uk.construction@leica-geosystems.com

CABLE LOCATORS

Leica Geosystems Ltd, Davy Avenue, Knowlhill, Milton Keynes, MK5 8LB Tel: (01908) 256500 Fax: (01908) 609992 E-mail: uk.construction@leica-geosystems.com

CABLE MANAGEMENT SYSTEMS

Ada Computer Systems Ltd, Network House House, Albert Drive, Burgess Hill, West Sussex, RH15 9TN Tel: (01444) 232000 Fax: (01444) 247754E-mail: sales@ada.co.uk
Barton Engineering, Birchills, Walsall, WS2 8QE Tel: (01922) 433100 Fax: (01922) 646675
Cable Management Centre Ltd, 3 C M T Industrial Estate, Broadwell Road, Oldbury, West Midlands, B69 4BQ Tel: 0121-544 0077 Fax: 0121-544 0088
Cableflow International Ltd, Windsor House, Abbey Barn Road, High Wycombe, Buckinghamshire, HP11 1NN Tel: (01494) 528811 Fax: (01494) 531188 E-mail: sales@cableflow.com
Centaur Manufacturing Ltd, Pipers Road, Park Farm Industrial Estate, Redditch, Worcestershire, B98 0HU Tel: (01527) 528049 Fax: (01527) 500882 E-mail: sales@centaurmfg.co.uk
Electrak Holdings Ltd, Number One Industrial Estate, Medomsley Road, Consett, County Durham, DH8 6SR Tel: (01207) 503400 Fax: (01207) 501799 E-mail: sales@electrak.co.uk
Electrix International Ltd, 1a-1b Dovecot Hill, South Church Enterprise Park, Bishop Auckland, County Durham, DL14 6XP Tel: (01388) 774455 Fax: (01388) 777359 E-mail: enquiries@electrix.co.uk
Electropatent International Ltd, 30-32 Blyth Road, Hayes, Middlesex, UB3 1BY Tel: (020) 8867 3500 Fax: (020) 8573 9090 E-mail: sales@electropatent.co.uk
Hager Engineering Ltd, 50 Horton Wood, Telford, Shropshire, TF1 7FT Tel: (0870) 2402400 Fax: (0870) 2400400E-mail: info@hager.co.uk
Kensal Handling Systems Ltd, Kensal House, President Way, Luton, LU2 9NR Tel: (01582) 425777 Fax: (01582) 425776 E-mail: sales@kensal.com
Lenson Select UK Ltd, Brandon Way, West Bromwich, West Midlands, B70 8JA Tel: 0121-553 6699 Fax: 0121-553 6622 E-mail: sales@lenson-select.co.uk
M K Electric, The Arnold Centre, Paycocke Road, Basildon, Essex, SS14 3EA Tel: (01268) 563000 Fax: (01268) 563405 E-mail: mkorderingenquires@hornywell.com
Metool Products Ltd, Unit 1 Mercian Park, Mercian Close, Ilkeston, Derbyshire, DE7 8HG Tel: 0115-922 5931 Fax: 0115-925 8183 E-mail: postmaster@metool.com
Mita (U K) Ltd, Manor Farm Industrial Estate, Flint, Clwyd, CH6 5UY Tel: (01352) 792200 Fax: (01252) 792314 E-mail: info@mita.co.uk
▶ Office Electrics Ltd, 1 Calder Point, Monckton Road Industrial Estate, Wakefield, West Yorkshire, WF2 7AL Tel: (01924) 367255 Fax: (01924) 290652 E-mail: sales@office-electrics.co.uk
Office Interiors, 1-2 Trevilson, St. Newlyn East, Newquay, Cornwall, TR8 5JF Tel: (01872) 510953 Fax: (01872) 510954 E-mail: sales@officeinteriors.co.uk
Osmor Products Ltd, Unit 12 Ditchling Common, Ditchling, Hassocks, West Sussex, BN6 8SG Tel: (01444) 236900 Fax: (01444) 230770 E-mail: sales@osmor.co.uk
Powerplan, Brockholes Way, Claughton On Brock, Preston, PR3 0PZ Tel: (01995) 640844 Fax: (01995) 640798 E-mail: enquiries@powerplan.co.uk
Siemens P.L.C., Gatehouse Close, Aylesbury, Buckinghamshire, HP19 8DJ Tel: (01296) 339388 Fax: (01296) 339969 E-mail: marketing@moeller.co.uk
Stephen Glover & Co. Ltd, Long Street, Walsall, WS2 9DU Tel: (01922) 611311 Fax: (01922) 721824 E-mail: verglo@btconnect.com
Stuttaford Ltd, Unit 31, East Lane, Wembley Commercial Centre, Wembley, Middlesex, HA9 7UR Tel: (020) 8904 2300
Tyco Electronics, Kinmel Park, Bodelwyddan, Rhyl, Clwyd, LL18 5TZ Tel: (01745) 584545 Fax: (01745) 584780 E-mail: admin@pinacl.com
Uni Trunk Ltd, Altona Road, Lisburn, County Antrim, BT27 5QB Tel: (028) 9262 5100 Fax: (028) 9262 5101 E-mail: lisburn@unitrunk.co.uk
Unistrut Holdings Ltd, Unistrut House, Edison Road, Bedford, MK41 0HU Tel: (01234) 220400 Fax: (01234) 216004 E-mail: cmathews@tyco-bspd.com

CABLE MANAGEMENT SYSTEMS – *continued*

Universal Fixings Ltd, Unit 1 2 Balds Lane, Jubilee Business Park, Lye, Stourbridge, West Midlands, DY9 8SH Tel: (01384) 422284

Vantrunk Building Services Ltd, Goddard Road, Astmoor Industrial Estate, Runcorn, Cheshire, WA7 1QF Tel: (01928) 564211 Fax: (01928) 580157 E-mail: sales@vantrunk.co.uk

Voltex Electronics Ltd, Octagon House, Bradford Road, Sandbeds, Keighley, West Yorkshire, BD20 5LY Tel: (01274) 510668 Fax: (01274) 510669 E-mail: sales@voltexelectronics.com

CABLE MARKERS

B M K Industrial I D Systems, 1 Claremont Street, Aberdeen, AB10 6QP Tel: (01224) 213325 Fax: (01224) 213377 E-mail: bmk.id@talk21.com

Grafoplast, PO Box 159, Stevenage, Hertfordshire, SG2 7QA Tel: (01438) 861166 Fax: (01438) 861123 E-mail: sales@grafoplasteurope.com

Silver Fox Ltd, Swallow Court, Swallowfields, Welwyn Garden City, Hertfordshire, AL7 1SA Tel: (01707) 373727 Fax: (01707) 372193 E-mail: sales@silfox.co.uk

CABLE MARKING EQUIPMENT

Bridgelock Engineering & Marketing Ltd, 137 Slough Road, Datchet, Slough, SL3 9AE Tel: (01753) 549373 Fax: (01753) 580269 E-mail: sales@bridgelock.com

White & Street International Ltd, Unit 17-18, Enfield Industrial Estate, Redditch, Worcestershire, B97 6BN Tel: (01527) 67881 Fax: (01527) 69966 E-mail: enquiries@whiteandstreet.com

CABLE MARKING SERVICES

P C S Cables & Connectors Ltd, 14-16 Kingfisher Park, Three Cross Road, West Moors, Wimborne, Dorset, BH21 6US Tel: (01202) 871924 Fax: (01202) 895661 E-mail: enquiries@pcscables.com

CABLE MECHANICAL CONTROLS

Century Cables & Controls Ltd, Century House, 8 South Street, Crowland, Peterborough, PE6 0AJ Tel: (01733) 211600 Fax: (01733) 211082 E-mail: kwhincup@yahoo.com

Elmill Products Ltd, 139a Engineer Road, West Wilts Trading Estate, Westbury, Wiltshire, BA13 4JW Tel: (01373) 864267 Fax: (01373) 858266 E-mail: sales@elmill.co.uk

Wicks & Martin Ltd, Bromyard Industrial Estate, Bromyard, Herefordshire, HR7 4HT Tel: (01885) 483636 Fax: (01885) 483692 E-mail: mike@wicksandmartin.co.uk

CABLE MOUNT CONNECTORS

Cambridge Electronic Industries Ltd, Denny Industrial Centre, Denny End Road, Waterbeach, Cambridge, CB25 9PB Tel: (01223) 860041 Fax: (01223) 863625 E-mail: sales@cambridgeconnectors.com

CABLE NETWORK INSTALLATION

A P C Solutions (UK) Ltd, Unit 18 The Old Cinema, Allshots Industrial Estate, Kelvedon, Colchester, CO5 9DF Tel: (01376) 585554 Fax: (01376) 585727 E-mail: info@apcsolutionuk.com

Advanced Network, 12 Primrose Gdns, London, NW3 4TN Tel: (020) 7586 3232

BDJR Computers Ltd, 6 St Albans Square, Bootle, Merseyside, L20 7BA Tel: 0151-922 0430 Fax: 0151-474 0703 E-mail: kevin@bdjr.com

▶ Computer Services & Engineers, Unit 4a Stag Industrial Estate, Atlantic Street, Broadheath, Altrincham, Cheshire, WA14 5DW Tel: 0161-941 4555 Fax: 0161-941 6182 E-mail: sales@cselimited.co.uk

Durkin & Sons Ltd, Amex House, North End Road, Wembley, Middlesex, HA9 0UU Tel: (020) 8900 0203 Fax: (020) 8903 4754 E-mail: michaeldurkin@ndirect.co.uk

Elan Support Services, Allerton Bywater Business Park, Newton Lane, Allerton Bywater, Castleford, West Yorkshire, WF10 2AL Tel: (01977) 604384 Fax: (01977) 604021 E-mail: evahorbury@elansupports.co.uk

Eric Johnson Of Northwich Ltd, Ash House, Ash House Lane, Little Leigh, Northwich, Cheshire, CW8 4RG Tel: (01606) 892244 Fax: (01606) 892442 E-mail: irj@johnson42.fsnet.co.uk

▶ I T Installations Ltd, Aizlewoods Mill, Nursery Street, Sheffield, S3 8GG Tel: 0114-282 3301 Fax: 0114-282 3302 E-mail: sales@it-installations.co.uk

Information Technology Services, 4 Ashley Road, Epsom, Surrey, KT18 5AX Tel: (01372) 800466 Fax: (01372) 740544 E-mail: sales@it-services.co.uk

▶ Lateral Blue Ltd, 9 Columba Road, Edinburgh, EH4 3QZ Tel: 0131-332 5152 Fax: 0870 1329471 E-mail: info@lateralblue.co.uk

Lima Networks, 5-6 Carolina Way, Quays Reach, Salford, M50 2ZY Tel: 0161-743 3000 Fax: (0845) 3451220 E-mail: sales@lima.com

Lineartron Maintenance Ltd, Lineartron House, 7 Black Moor Road, Ebblake Industrial Estate, Verwood, Dorset, BH31 6AX Tel: (01202) 828001 Fax: (01202) 828089 E-mail: sales@lineartron.co.uk

Microcraft Ltd, PO Box 3252, Tamworth, Staffs, B79 0BF Tel: (01827) 373551 Fax: (01827) 284667 E-mail: harryke@microcraft.ltd.uk

Molex Premise Networks Ltd, Network House, Concorde Way, Fareham, Hampshire, PO15 5RL Tel: (01489) 572111 Fax: (01489) 559106 E-mail: sales@molexpn.co.uk

P M P Micros, Rock Cottage, Hawber Lane, Silsden, Keighley, West Yorkshire, BD20 0LE Tel: (07967) 173739 Fax: (01535) 653006 E-mail: peter@pmp-micros.co.uk

Performance Computers North East Ltd, 10-11 Post House Wynd, Darlington, County Durham, DL3 7LU Tel: (01325) 267333 Fax: (01325) 489093 E-mail: sales@performancecomputers.co.uk

▶ RAE Computing Ltd, Unit 8, Pennine Industrial Estate, Hangingroyd Lane, Hebden Bridge, West Yorkshire, HX7 7BZ Tel: (0845) 0048435 E-mail: info@raecomputing.com

S P Web Connections, Hazelwood House, Hazelwood Close, Crawley Down, Crawley, West Sussex, RH10 4HE Tel: (01342) 716971 E-mail: info@spwebco.com

▶ Structured Lan, The Garage, Crag Lane, Beckwithshaw, Harrogate, North Yorkshire, HG3 1QA Tel: (01423) 508011 Fax: (01423) 508011 E-mail: structuredlan@btconnect.com

▶ Suna Supplies Ltd, B 91 Ewell Road, Surbiton, Surrey, KT6 6AH Tel: (020) 8390 8811 Fax: (020) 8390 4331 E-mail: sales@suna.co.uk

Suna Supplies Ltd, B 91 Ewell Road, Surbiton, Surrey, KT6 6AH Tel: (020) 8390 8811 Fax: (020) 8390 4331 E-mail: sales@suna.co.uk

CABLE OR HOSE DRAG CHAIN SYSTEMS

Metool Products Ltd, Unit 1 Mercian Park, Mercian Close, Ilkeston, Derbyshire, DE7 8HG Tel: 0115-922 5931 Fax: 0115-925 8183 E-mail: postmaster@metool.com

CABLE OR PIPE PENETRATION FIRE SEALS

C S D Sealing Systems Ltd, Offshore House, Albert Street, Blyth, Northumberland, NE24 1LZ Tel: (01670) 353300 Fax: (01670) 369503E-mail: info@csdsealingsystems.co.uk

Pyricon Ltd, PO Box 4641, London, SE11 4XE Tel: (020) 7735 8777

Quelfire Ltd, PO Box 35, Altrincham, Cheshire, WA14 5QA Tel: 0161-928 7308 Fax: 0161-924 1340

S P C, Unit 1, Chalford Industrial Estate, Chalford, Stroud, Glos, GL6 8NT Tel: (01453) 885929 Fax: (01453) 731044

CABLE OR PIPE SERVICE SYSTEM FLOOR DUCTING

Screeduct Ltd, Unit 8, Northcot Business Park, Blockley, Moreton-In-Marsh, Gloucestershire, GL56 9LH Tel: (01386) 701372 Fax: (01386) 701571 E-mail: sales@screeduct.com

CABLE OR WIRE CRIMPING MACHINES

OTG Ltd, Maidstone Road, Platt, Sevenoaks, Kent, TN15 8JE Tel: (01732) 780780 Fax: (01732) 780835 E-mail: info@otg-ltd.com

CABLE OR WIRE CRIMPING TOOLS

Cembre Ltd, Fair View Industrial Estate, Kingsbury Road, Curdworth, Sutton Coldfield, West Midlands, B76 9EE Tel: (01675) 470440 Fax: (01675) 470220 E-mail: sales@cembre.co.uk

Instrument Transformers Ltd, 8 Lithgow Place, East Kilbride, Glasgow, G74 1PW Tel: (01355) 236057 Fax: (01355) 239259 E-mail: sales@itl-uk.com

Jackson Engineering Stoke On Trent Ltd, Scott Lidgett Road, Stoke-on-Trent, ST6 4LX Tel: (01782) 812139 Fax: (01782) 824374 E-mail: sales@jacksonengineering.co.uk

Maun Industries Ltd, Moor Lane, Mansfield, Nottinghamshire, NG18 5SE Tel: (01623) 624525 Fax: (01623) 659969 E-mail: maun.industries@btinternet.com

OTG Ltd, Maidstone Road, Platt, Sevenoaks, Kent, TN15 8JE Tel: (01732) 780780 Fax: (01732) 780835 E-mail: info@otg-ltd.com

Sicame Electrical Developments Ltd, Riverholme Works, Huddersfield Road, Holmfirth, HD9 3TN Tel: (01484) 681115 Fax: (01484) 687352 E-mail: sales@sicame.co.uk

CABLE PREPARATION

Brockhill Enterprises Ltd, Hobson Lane, Kirkby Stephen, Cumbria, CA17 4RN Tel: (01768) 372027 Fax: (01768) 372049 E-mail: sales@brockhill.sagehost.co.uk

Orchard Technologies Ltd, Unit F5 Market Overton Industrial Estate, Thistleton Road, Market Overton, Oakham, Leicestershire, LE15 7PP Tel: (01572) 768489 Fax: (01572) 768181 E-mail: richard@orchard56.freeserve.co.uk

CABLE PREPARATION EQUIPMENT

Brockhill Enterprises Ltd, Hobson Lane, Kirkby Stephen, Cumbria, CA17 4RN Tel: (01768) 372027 Fax: (01768) 372049 E-mail: sales@brockhill.sagehost.co.uk

CABLE PRESSURE MONITORING EQUIPMENT

Drallim Industries, Drury Lane, St. Leonards-on-Sea, East Sussex, TN38 9BA Tel: (01424) 205140 Fax: (01424) 202140 E-mail: sales@drallim.com

CABLE PRODUCTION MACHINERY

Autoreel Ltd, Palmer Drive, Stapleford, Nottingham, NG9 7BW Tel: 0115-939 0200 Fax: 0115-939 0201 E-mail: autoreel@autoreel.co.uk

B A Thorne Ltd, Eagle Road, Moons Moat North Industrial Es, Redditch, Worcestershire, B98 9HF Tel: (01527) 584714 Fax: (01527) 584784 E-mail: bat@bathorne.co.uk

Cable & Wire Technical Services Ltd, 12 Tudor Grove, Gillingham, Kent, ME8 9AF Tel: (01634) 234786 Fax: (01634) 370980

Edscha (U K) Manufacturing Ltd, Middlemarch Business Park, Coventry, CV3 4FJ Tel: (024) 7651 6900 Fax: (024) 7630 2299 E-mail: enquiries@edscha.co.uk

Metaltech, Bonsall Street, Mill Hill, Blackburn, BB2 4DD Tel: (01254) 691488

Northampton Machinery Co., 7 Deer Park Road, Moulton Park Industrial Estate, Northampton, NN3 6RX Tel: (01604) 782220 Fax: (01604) 782230 E-mail: sales@mgshall.com

Techna International, Unit 1 Metro Centre, Dwight Road, Watford, WD18 9HG Tel: (01923) 222227 Fax: (01923) 219700 E-mail: sales@techna.co.uk

CABLE PROTECTION COVERS

▶ PPL Marine Products, Tufthane Building, Falkland Close, Coventry, CV4 8AU Tel: 02476 464509 Fax: 02476 694313 E-mail: sales@ppl-marine.com

CABLE PROTECTION PRODUCTS

Schlumberger, Harlaw Road, Inverurie, Aberdeenshire, AB51 4TE Tel: (01467) 623059 Fax: (01467) 623062

CABLE PULLING EQUIPMENT

Thornbush Components & Tooling, 156 Woodland Drive, Hove, East Sussex, BN3 6DE Tel: (01273) 383972 Fax: (01273) 881771 E-mail: greenlee@thornbush.co.uk

CABLE PULLING WINCHES

Cowell Export, Marsh Green, Edenbridge, Kent, TN8 5QL Tel: (01732) 864211 Fax: (01732) 863106 E-mail: mail@bobcowell.co.uk

▶ Fellows Stringer Ltd, 83-84 Cinder Bank, Dudley, West Midlands, DY2 9BH Tel: (01384) 459978 Fax: (01384) 458963 E-mail: dan@fellows-stringer.co.uk

Tele Radio Limited, Beechfield House, Lyme Green Business Park, Winterton Way, Macclesfield, Cheshire, SK11 0LP Tel: 01625 509125 Fax: 01625 440022 E-mail: sales@teleradiouk.com

Winchmaster Lifting Equipment, 6 South Orbital Trading Park, Hedon Road, Hull, HU9 1NJ Tel: (01482) 223663 Fax: (01482) 218285 E-mail: sales@winchmaster.co.uk

CABLE REELS

Conductix Ltd, 1 Michigan Avenue, Salford, M50 2GY Tel: 0161-848 0161 Fax: 0161-873 7017 E-mail: info@conductix.co.uk

Redashe Ltd, Unit 8 The Brook Trading Estate, Deadbrook Lane, Aldershot, Hampshire, GU12 4XB Tel: (01252) 785010 Fax: (01252) 329328 E-mail: info@redashe.co.uk

W F Electrical, Unit 6 Westerton Road, East Mains Industrial Estate, Broxburn, West Lothian, EH52 5AU Tel: (01506) 858833 Fax: (01506) 855257 E-mail: edinbugh.industrial@hagemeyerservicecentre.co.uk

Youldon, 7 West Road, Harlow, Essex, CM20 2BU Tel: (01279) 774300 Fax: (01279) 774310 E-mail: sales@collins-youldon.com

CABLE REPAIR

Lineartron Maintenance Ltd, Lineartron House, 7 Black Moor Road, Ebblake Industrial Estate, Verwood, Dorset, BH31 6AX Tel: (01202) 828001 Fax: (01202) 828089 E-mail: sales@lineartron.co.uk

CABLE REWINDING/COILING/ MEASURING EQUIPMENT, COMBINED

Metaltech, Bonsall Street, Mill Hill, Blackburn, BB2 4DD Tel: (01254) 691488

CABLE SCRAP/WASTE RECYCLING/DISPOSAL/ RECOVERY MERCHANTS OR PROCESSORS

H. Gothard & Sons Hiab Services, 19 Fairfield Mount, Ossett, West Yorkshire, WF5 0TE Tel: (01924) 260116 E-mail: hiabservices@msn.com

Mountstar Cable, Hobson Industrial Estate, Hobson, Newcastle upon Tyne, NE16 6EA Tel: (01207) 270731 Fax: (01207) 271004 E-mail: sales@mountstar.com

Springvale Metals, 55 Springvale Street, Willenhall, West Midlands, WV13 1EJ Tel: (01902) 606562 Fax: (01902) 606619

Telecom Green Ltd, Highfield Drive, Eaglescliffe, Stockton-on-Tees, Cleveland, TS16 0DL Tel: (0870) 7200028 Fax: (0870) 7200029 E-mail: rob.govier@telecomgreen.co.uk

Wallhurst Metals Ltd, 97 Holborn Hill, Birmingham, B6 7QX Tel: 0121-327 3597 Fax: 0121-327 3597

Weymouth Scrap Co., 20 Cambridge Road, Granby Industrial Estate, Weymouth, Dorset, DT4 9TJ Tel: (01305) 785538 Fax: (01305) 777595

CABLE SLEEVING

Jones Stroud Insulations, Queen Street, Longridge, Preston, PR3 3BS Tel: (01772) 783011 Fax: (01772) 784200 E-mail: info@krempel-group.com

CABLE SOCKETS

Cable First Ltd, 32-40 Harwell Road, Poole, Dorset, BH17 0GE Tel: (01202) 687337 Fax: (01202) 672501 E-mail: sales@cablefirst.co.uk

CABLE STRIPPING MACHINES

Cablespeed, 447 Oakshott Place, Bamber Bridge, Preston, PR5 8AT Tel: (0870) 6098025 Fax: (0870) 6098026 E-mail: sales@cablespeed.co.uk

CABLE SUPPORT SYSTEMS

Fairclough & Wood Ltd, Unit 10b Carcroft Enterprise Park, Carcroft, Doncaster, South Yorkshire, DN6 8DD Tel: (01302) 726027 Fax: (01302) 330221 E-mail: sales@faircloughwood.co.uk

Philip Grahame International Ltd, Dukes Park Industrial Estate, Montrose Road, Chelmsford, CM2 6TE Tel: (01245) 451717 Fax: (01245) 451870 E-mail: sales@pgrahame.com

Hubbell Ltd, Brunel Drive, Stretton, Burton-On-Trent, Staffordshire, DE13 0BZ Tel: (01283) 500500 Fax: (01283) 500400

L P A Niphan Ltd, P O Box 15, Saffron Walden, Essex, CB11 4AN Tel: (01799) 512800 Fax: (01799) 512828 E-mail: sales@lpa-niphan.com

Mita (U K) Ltd, Manor Farm Industrial Estate, Flint, Clwyd, CH6 5UY Tel: (01352) 792200 Fax: (01252) 792314 E-mail: info@mita.co.uk

CABLE SUPPORT SYSTEMS – *continued*

Orbital Fasteners, Olds Approach, Tolpits Lane, Watford, WD18 9XT Tel: (01923) 777777 Fax: (01923) 779169 E-mail: sales@orbitalfasteners.co.uk

CABLE SUPPORT SYSTEMS INSTALLATION SERVICES

Electrical Power Specialists Reading Ltd, 1 Blenheim Road, Reading, RG1 5NG Tel: 0118-935 1933 Fax: 0118-935 2373 E-mail: info@epsdirect.co.uk

CABLE SYSTEMS, FIBRE OPTIC

Orostream Applied Contracting Ltd, Park Road, Crowborough, East Sussex, TN6 2QT Tel: (01892) 665888 Fax: (01892) 663218 E-mail: oracl@aol.com

CABLE TENSION TEST EQUIPMENT

Integrated Display Systems Ltd, Unit 15, Muarice Road, Wallsend, Tyne & Wear, NE28 6BY Tel: 0191-262 0091 Fax: 0191-262 0091 E-mail: sales@clavis.co.uk

CABLE TERMINATIONS

Seacon Europe Ltd, Seacon House, Hewett Road, Great Yarmouth, Norfolk, NR31 0RB Tel: (01493) 652733 Fax: (01493) 652840 E-mail: sales@seaconeurope.com

▶ Thomas & Betts Holdings UK, Wilford Road, Nottingham, NG2 1EB Tel: 0115-964 3837 Fax: 0115-986 0538 E-mail: martin.critchley@tnb.com

CABLE TEST EQUIPMENT

Cable Check Systems, Unit 18 Quay Lane, Hardway, Gosport, Hampshire, PO12 4LJ Tel: (023) 9252 8396 Fax: (023) 9258 9748 E-mail: info@greenpersonnel.co.uk

▶ Cirris Solutions Ltd, 4 Commerce Way, Stanbridge Road, Leighton Buzzard, Bedfordshire, LU7 4RW Tel: (01525) 374466 Fax: (01525) 374468 E-mail: sales@cirris.co.uk

Integrated Engineering Solutions Ltd, Millbrook Road West, Southampton, SO15 0HW Tel: (023) 8090 5020 Fax: (023) 8070 4073 E-mail: mail@iesl.co.uk

M K Test Systems Ltd, Orchard Court, West Buckland, Wellington, Somerset, TA21 9LE Tel: (01823) 661100 Fax: (01823) 661160 E-mail: sales@mktest.com

Megar Ltd, Archcliffe Road, Dover, Kent, CT17 9EN Tel: (01304) 502100 Fax: (01304) 241491 E-mail: uksales@megger.com

CABLE TIES

Active Electronics Plc, Albion House, Gordon Road, High Wycombe, Buckinghamshire, HP13 6ET Tel: (01494) 441414 Fax: (01494) 524674 E-mail: pool@active-electronics.co.uk

Alexander Industrial Supplies Essex Ltd, Unit D Eastways, Witham, Essex, CM8 3YQ Tel: (01376) 500303 Fax: (01376) 502090 E-mail: sales@alexander-industrial.co.uk

Avery Dennison UK Ltd, Business Media Division Thomas Road, Wooburn Industrial Park, Wooburn Green, High Wycombe, Buckinghamshire, HP10 0PE Tel: (01628) 859500 Fax: (01628) 859599 E-mail: sales@averydennison.com

Donner Oswald & Co, 11-15 Jarrom Street, Leicester, LE2 7DH Tel: 0116-254 8210 Fax: 0116-247 0338 E-mail: sales@oswalddonner.com

▶ Elpress UK, Unit 4 Carraway Road, Gillmoss Ind Est, Liverpool, L11 0EE Tel: 0151-547 2666 Fax: 0151-547 1444 E-mail: sales@e-tech-components.co.uk

Eurolok Ltd, Tame Park, Vanguard, Wilnecote, Tamworth, Staffordshire, B77 5DY Tel: (01827) 287439 Fax: (01827) 287485 E-mail: sales@eurolok.com

G T Products Europe Ltd, Unit 14 Ford La Business Park, Ford, Arundel, West Sussex, BN18 0UZ Tel: (01243) 555303 Fax: (01243) 555304 E-mail: enquiries@gtproductseurope.com

Hellermann Tyton, 1 Robeson Way, Manchester, M22 4TY Tel: 0161-945 4181 Fax: 0161-947 2233 E-mail: enquiries@hellermantyton.co.uk

I L S Ltd, Third Avenue, Pensnett Trading Estate, Kingswinford, West Midlands, DY6 7XX Tel: (01384) 402200 Fax: (01384) 402201 E-mail: marketing@ilsonline.com

Legrand Electric Ltd, Great King Street North, Birmingham, B19 2LF Tel: 0121-515 0515 Fax: 0121-515 0516 E-mail: legrand.sales@legrand.co.uk

Morells, 99 Mabgate, Leeds, LS9 7DR Tel: 0113-245 0371 Fax: (0845) 4501717 E-mail: leeds@morrells-woodfinishes.com

R E Knight Ltd, Fishers Way, Belvedere, Kent, DA17 6BS Tel: (020) 8310 8900 Fax: (020) 8311 4530 E-mail: enquiries@reknight.co.uk

S D Products, The Broadway, Mansfield, Nottinghamshire, NG18 2RL Tel: (01623) 655265 Fax: (01623) 420689 E-mail: sales@sdproducts.co.uk

Saren Engineering Ltd, Unit 10 Premier Trading Estate, 118 Dartmouth Middleway, Birmingham, B7 4AT Tel: 0121-359 4890 Fax: 0121-359 6951 E-mail: info@saren.co.uk

▶ Thomas & Betts Holdings UK, Wilford Road, Nottingham, NG2 1EB Tel: 0115-964 3837 Fax: 0115-986 0538 E-mail: martin.critchley@tnb.com

Thornbush Components & Tooling, 156 Woodland Drive, Hove, East Sussex, BN3 6DE Tel: (01273) 383972 Fax: (01273) 881771 E-mail: greenlee@thornbush.co.uk

Velcro Ltd, 1 Aston Way, Middlewich, Cheshire, CW10 0HS Tel: 01606 738806 Fax: 01606 738814 E-mail: uksales@velcro.co.uk

CABLE TRAYS, *See also headings for particular types*

Edmundson Export Services, Unit 1 Skyport Drive, Harmondsworth, West Drayton, Middlesex, UB7 0LB Tel: (020) 8283 0820 Fax: (020) 8283 0821 E-mail: enquiries@edmundsonexport.com

Fairclough & Wood Ltd, Unit 10b Carcroft Enterprise Park, Carcroft, Doncaster, South Yorkshire, DN6 8DD Tel: (01302) 726027 Fax: (01302) 330221 E-mail: sales@faircloughwood.co.uk

CABLE TRUNKING SYSTEMS

Alumasc Interior Building Products Ltd, Unit C1 Halesfield 19, Telford, Shropshire, TF7 4QT Tel: (01952) 580590 Fax: (01952) 587805 E-mail: sales@alumascinteriors.com

Bex Contracts plc, Bex House, Crabtree Manorway South, Belvedere, Kent, DA17 6BJ Tel: (020) 8311 2992 Fax: (020) 8311 2303

Cable Management Centre Ltd, 3 C M T Industrial Estate, Broadwell Road, Oldbury, West Midlands, B69 4BQ Tel: 0121-544 0077 Fax: 0121-544 0088

Cableflow International Ltd, Windsor House, Abbey Barn Road, High Wycombe, Buckinghamshire, HP11 1NN Tel: (01494) 528811 Fax: (01494) 531188 E-mail: sales@cableflow.com

Centaur Manufacturing Ltd, Pipers Road, Park Farm Industrial Estate, Redditch, Worcestershire, B98 0HU Tel: (01527) 528049 Fax: (01527) 500882 E-mail: sales@centaurmfg.co.uk

Philip Grahame International Ltd, Dukes Park Industrial Estate, Montrose Road, Chelmsford, CM2 6TE Tel: (01245) 451717 Fax: (01245) 451870 E-mail: sales@pgrahame.com

Screeduct Ltd, Unit 8, Northcot Business Park, Blockley, Moreton-In-Marsh, Gloucestershire, GL56 9LH Tel: (01386) 701372 Fax: (01386) 701571 E-mail: sales@screeduct.com

Zed Duct Systems Ltd, 5-5a Unit, Hill Street, Kidderminster, Worcestershire, DY11 6TD Tel: (01562) 824261 Fax: (01562) 746435

CABLES, *See also headings under Cables etc*

Autac Products Ltd, Bollin Cable Works, London Road, Macclesfield, Cheshire, SK11 7RN Tel: (01625) 619277 Fax: (01625) 619366 E-mail: info@autac.co.uk

Axon Cable Ltd, 22 Ridge Way, Donibristle Industrial Park, Hillend, Dunfermline, Fife, KY11 9JN Tel: (01383) 821081 Fax: (01383) 821080 E-mail: sales@axon-cable.co.uk

B I Communications, 7 Buckwins Square, Burnt Mills Industrial Estate, Basildon, Essex, SS13 1BJ Tel: (01268) 729393 Fax: (01268) 727987 E-mail: bicomms@dircon.co.uk

Belden C D T Ltd, Littleborough, Lancashire, OL15 8YJ Tel: (01706) 374015 Fax: (01706) 370576

Brand Rex Ltd, Viewfield Industrial Estate, Glenrothes, Fife, KY6 2RS Tel: (01592) 772124 Fax: (01592) 775314 E-mail: loswald@brand-rex.com

Cablepoint Ltd, Phoenix House, Amsterdam Road, Sutton Fields Industrial Estate, Hull, HU7 0XP Tel: (01482) 837400 Fax: (01482) 839651 E-mail: sales@cablepoint.co.uk

Concordia Co. Ltd, Derwent Street, Long Eaton, Nottingham, NG10 3LP Tel: 0115-946 7400 Fax: 0115-946 1026

Coronation Cables Ltd, Abbey Industrial Estate, Mount Pleasant, Wembley, Middlesex, HA0 1NR Tel: (020) 8900 1383 Fax: (020) 8903 7089 E-mail: details@coronationcables.co.uk

Custom Design Cables, Unit 4 Westwood Farm, Highcross Road, Southfleet, Gravesend, Kent, DA13 9PH Tel: (01474) 834893 Fax: (01474) 834595E-mail: info@customdesigncables.com

Draka Comteq Cables Ltd, Crowther Road, Washington, Tyne & Wear, NE38 0AQ Tel: 0191-415 5000 Fax: 0191-415 8278

Edmundson Export Services, Unit 1 Skyport Drive, Harmondsworth, West Drayton, Middlesex, UB7 0LB Tel: (020) 8283 0820 Fax: (020) 8283 0821 E-mail: enquiries@edmundsonexport.com

Haani Cables Ltd, Tofts Farm Industrial Estate East, Brenda Road, Hartlepool, Cleveland, TS25 2BS Tel: (01429) 221184 Fax: (01429) 272714 E-mail: info@haanicables.co.uk

J D Cables Ltd, Park House, Greenhill Cresent, Watford, WD18 8PH Tel: (01923) 222600 Fax: (01923) 222608 E-mail: sales@jdcables.com

J D R Cable Systems Ltd, 175 Wisbech Road, Littleport, Ely, Cambridgeshire, CB6 1RA Tel: (01353) 865800 Fax: (01353) 861388 E-mail: uk@jdrcables.com

J N R Electronics Assemblies, 158 Wheatfield Road, Luton, LU4 0TD Tel: (01582) 471278 Fax: (01582) 600703E-mail: admin@jnr.org.uk

Lapp Ltd, 3 Perivale Park, Horsenden La South, Greenford, Middlesex, UB6 7RL Tel: (020) 8758 7800 Fax: (020) 8758 7880 E-mail: sales@lappgroup.com

North West Cables Ltd, School Lane, Knowsley Business Park, Prescot, Merseyside, L34 9HD Tel: 0151-548 3888 Fax: 0151-549 1169 E-mail: sales@northwestcables.co.uk

Permanoid Ltd, Hulme Hall Lane, Miles Platting, Manchester, M40 8HH Tel: 0161-205 6161 Fax: 0161-205 9325 E-mail: sales@permanoid.co.uk

Ripca (UK) Ltd, First Fl, Unit 5 Capricorn Centre, Craines Farm Road, Basildon, Essex, SS14 3JJ Tel: (01268) 293020 Fax: (01268) 571852

S E I Interconnect Products Ltd, 10 Axis Court, Mallard Way, Riverside Business Park, Swansea, SA7 0AJ Tel: (01639) 822806 Fax: (01792) 794357 E-mail: nperkins@sumi-electric.com

Suhner Electronics Ltd, Telford Road, Bicester, Oxfordshire, OX26 4LA Tel: (01869) 364100 Fax: (01869) 249046 E-mail: info.uk@hubersuhner.co.uk

▶ Test Devices, 21 Sedling Road, Wear Industrial Estate, Washington, Tyne & Wear, NE38 9BZ Tel: 0191-419 2345 Fax: 0191-419 2345 E-mail: sales@trnlcd.co.uk

Venhill Engineering Ltd, 21 Ranmore Road, Dorking, Surrey, RH4 1HE Tel: (01306) 885111 Fax: (01306) 740535 E-mail: info@venhill.co.uk

Wessel Energy Cables, Aghafad, Longford, County Longford, Tel: 0161-763 7474 Fax: 0161-763 7373 E-mail: abbcablesales.ie@abb.com

Wrexham Mineral Cables Ltd, Plot 4 Wynnstay Technology Park, Ruabon, Wrexham, Clwyd, LL14 6EN Tel: (01978) 810789 Fax: (01978) 821502 E-mail: sales@wrexhammineralcable.com

CABLES TO SPECIFICATION

Belcom Cable & Wire Suppliers, Warish Hall, Warish Hall Road, Takeley, Bishop's Stortford, Hertfordshire, CM22 6NZ Tel: (01279) 871150 Fax: (01279) 871129 E-mail: dave@belcom.co.uk

Flexform Ltd, 34 Montgomery Road, Belfast, BT6 9HL Tel: (028) 9079 2155 Fax: (028) 9079 9031E-mail: info@cablespecialists.co.uk

Teledyne Reynolds Industries Ltd, Navigation House, Canal View Road, Newbury, Berkshire, RG14 5UR Tel: (01635) 262200 Fax: (01635) 30920 E-mail: trlsales@teledyne.com

CABLES, AMERICAN STANDARDS

Electro Cables Ltd, Unit 2 Alliance Close, Attleborough Fields Industrial Estate, Nuneaton, Warwickshire, CV11 6SD Tel: (024) 7632 0066 Fax: (024) 7632 0122 E-mail: sales@electrocables.co.uk

CABLES, AUDIO SPEAKER/ INSTRUMENT

Nova Electronic Developments Co Ltd, 49 Florence Road, Gedling, Nottingham, NG4 2QL Tel: 0115-910 9910 Fax: 0115-910 9900 E-mail: sales@novadev.co.uk

▶ Reef Inc, P.O.Box 185, Manchester, M41 6XG Tel: 0870 211 9888

CABLES, HARSH ENVIRONMENT, FIBRE OPTIC

N F I Ltd, 259 York Town Road, College Town, Sandhurst, Berkshire, GU47 0RT Tel: (01276) 600200 Fax: (01276) 600161 E-mail: info@nfi.uk.com

CABLES, HYDRAULIC, SUBSEA/ UNDERWATER

Cortland Fibron B X Ltd, Unitc R D Park, Stephenson Close, Hoddesdon, Hertfordshire, EN11 0BW Tel: (01992) 471444 Fax: (01992) 471555

Exeeco Ltd, Regina House, Ring Road, Bramley, Leeds, LS13 4ET Tel: 0113-256 7922 Fax: 0113-236 3310 E-mail: sales@exeeco.co.uk

J D R Cable Systems Ltd, 175 Wisbech Road, Littleport, Ely, Cambridgeshire, CB6 1RA Tel: (01353) 865800 Fax: (01353) 861388 E-mail: uk@jdrcables.com

Oceaneering Multiflex, Dundas Road, Rosyth, Dunfermline, Fife, KY11 2XS Tel: (01383) 643400 Fax: (01383) 643590 E-mail: enquiries@oceaneering.com

CABLES, MICROPHONE, EXTENSION

▶ GC Sound and Light, Unit 5, Premier Business Park, Huntspill Road, Highbridge, Somerset, TA9 3DE Tel: (01278) 794414 E-mail: gcwebsite@aol.com

CABLES, RADIO FREQUENCY (RF)/COAXIAL

Anixter UK Ltd, Anixter House, 1 York Road, Uxbridge, Middlesex, UB8 1RN Tel: (0845) 6041301 Fax: (01895) 818182

▶ Cobra Electronics Ltd, 1 Greenacres, Bordon, Hampshire, GU35 0EX Tel: (01420) 479830 Fax: (01420) 479860 E-mail: sales@cobra4coax.com

R F S UK Ltd, 9 Haddenham Business Park, Thame Road, Haddenham, Aylesbury, Buckinghamshire, HP17 8LJ Tel: (01844) 294900 Fax: (01844) 294944 E-mail: sales@rfsworld.com

Radiall Ltd, Ground Floor, 6 The Ground Union Office Park, Packet Boat Lane, Uxbridge, Middlesex, UB8 2GH Tel: (01895) 425000 Fax: (01895) 425010 E-mail: info@radiall.com

Wessex Belden CDT, Unit 8 Crow Arch Lane Industrial Estate, Crow Arch Lane, Ringwood, Hampshire, BH24 1PE Tel: (01425) 480804 Fax: (01425) 480805 E-mail: sales@wessexcdt.co.uk

CABLES, SECURITY, FIRE ALARM

Crosland Ltd, 502 Bradford Road, Batley, West Yorkshire, WF17 5JX Tel: (01924) 474625 Fax: (01924) 443554 E-mail: sales@crosland-electrical.com

CABLES, UNIVERSAL SERIAL BUS (USB), NETWORK LINK

Maxspeed Engineering Ltd, Foxoak Street, Cradley Heath, West Midlands, B64 5DE Tel: (01384) 564999 Fax: (01384) 564888

CABLES, X-RAY EQUIPMENT

Thermo Fisher Sceientific, Unit A2, Swift Park, Old Leicester Road, Rugby, Warwickshire, CV21 1DZ Tel: (01788) 820319 Fax: (01788) 820301 E-mail: saleswiuk@thermofisher.com

CABLING INSTALLATION

▶ Mr Cable.co.uk, 79, Waldeck Street, Reading, RG1 2RF Tel: 07910 491212 E-mail: info@mrcable.co.uk

CADMIUM PLATING SERVICES

Lyndhurst Precision Engineering Ltd, Weir Mill, Crosse Hall Street, Chorley, Lancashire, PR6 0UH Tel: (01257) 267876 Fax: (01257) 260724 E-mail: sales@lyndhurst-precision.co.uk

CAFE FURNITURE

Grosvenor Fabrications, Limes House, Silver Street, Stansted, Essex, CM24 8HE Tel: (01279) 814146 Fax: (01279) 814179 E-mail: sales@grosvenorfabrications.co.uk

CAFETIERES

▶ The London Tiffin Co, Unit Cu533 St Martins Square Middle Mall, Bullring, Birmingham, B5 4BE Tel: 0121-616 2407 Fax: 0121-616 1448 E-mail: bullring@tiffinbite.com

▶ Tasty Bites, 116 St. Marys Road, Garston, Liverpool, L19 2JG Tel: 0151-494 3145 Fax: 0151-494 3145

CAKE BOARDS/CARDS/DRUMS

Cakeboards Ltd, George Street, Burnley, Lancashire, BB11 1LX Tel: (01282) 423142 Fax: (01282) 477048 E-mail: sales@cakeboards.co.uk

Culpitt Ltd, Jubilee Industrial Estate, Ashington, Northumberland, NE63 8UQ Tel: (01670) 814545 Fax: (01670) 815248 E-mail: reception@culpitt.com

CAKE BOARDS/CARDS/DRUMS – *continued*

Sugar Shack, 87 Burnt Oak Broadway, Edgware, Middlesex, HA8 5EP Tel: (0800) 5975097 Fax: (020) 8951 4888 E-mail: sales@sugarshack.co.uk

CAKE DECORATIONS/FRILLS/NOVELTIES

▶ Blue Ribbons, 29 Walton Road, East Molesey, Surrey, KT8 0DH Tel: (020) 8941 1591 E-mail: sales@blueribbons.co.uk

Cake Corner, 33 Orchard Street, Weston-super-Mare, Avon, BS23 1RH Tel: (01934) 626587

Cake Dec Centre, 59 Victoria Terrace, Whitley Bay, Tyne & Wear, NE26 2QN Tel: 0191-251 0663 Fax: 0191-251 0663

Caketops Cake Decorating Equipment, 7 The Pantiles, Bexleyheath, Kent, DA7 5HH Tel: (01322) 448602

Confectionery Supplies, 31 Lower Cathedral Road, Cardiff, CF11 6LU Tel: (029) 2037 2161 Fax: (029) 2039 6632

▶ Creative Celebration Cakes, 12 Church Close, East Huntspill, Highbridge, Somerset, TA9 3QF Tel: 01278 793216 E-mail: Elaine@creativecelebrationcakes.co.uk

Culpitt Ltd, Jubilee Industrial Estate, Ashington, Northumberland, NE63 8UQ Tel: (01670) 814545 Fax: (01670) 815248 E-mail: reception@culpitt.com

Dibro Ltd, Unit 2, Bechers Drive, Aintree Racecourse Retail & Business Park, Liverpool, L9 5AY Tel: 0151-525 0365 Fax: 0151-525 0342 E-mail: tom@dibro.com

Paul Guy & Co. Ltd, Unit 10, The Busiiness Centre, Corinium Industrial Estate, Raans Road, Amersham, Buckinghamshire, HP6 6FB Tel: (01494) 432121 Fax: (01494) 432727 E-mail: guypauluk@aol.com

The Handmade Cake Co., 55 St Marks Road, Maidenhead, Berkshire, SL6 6DP Tel: (01628) 770908 Fax: (01628) 639248 E-mail: sales@handmadecake.co.uk

Hero UK LLP, Bishop Dyke Road, Sherburn In Elmet, Leeds, LS25 6JA Tel: (01977) 684937 Fax: (01977) 683654 E-mail: info@supercook.co.uk

Ice 'N' Easy, 25 High Street, Chipping Sodbury, Bristol, BS37 6BA Tel: (01454) 312205

Icing On The Cake, 19 South Walk, Basildon, Essex, SS14 1BZ Tel: (01268) 286970 Fax: (01268) 530839

The Sugarcraft Centre, 106 Lower Road, Hullbridge, Hockley, Essex, SS5 6DD Tel: (01702) 231967 Fax: (01702) 231967

▶ Sugarfayre Cake Decorating Equipment, 11 Wrexham Street, Mold, Clwyd, CH7 1ET Tel: (01352) 757305

▶ V Celebrate, 181 Streatfield Road, Harrow, Middlesex, HA3 9DA Tel: (020) 8204 7807 Fax: (020) 8204 7807

▶ Wendy's Cakes, 285 Sheldon Heath Road, Birmingham, B26 2TY Tel: 0121-243 7341 E-mail: wendyscakes@yahoo.co.uk

CAKE ICING EQUIPMENT

B & D Manufacturing Ltd, 15 Albert Road, Aldershot, Hampshire, GU11 1SZ Tel: (01252) 341553 Fax: (01252) 328824

Bekenal, PO Box 8494, Solihull, W. Midlands, B91 2BS Tel: 0121-705 2478 Fax: 0121-705 2478

Cakeboards Ltd, George Street, Burnley, Lancashire, BB11 1LX Tel: (01282) 423142 Fax: (01282) 477048 E-mail: sales@cakeboards.co.uk

Confectionery Supplies, 31 Lower Cathedral Road, Cardiff, CF11 6LU Tel: (029) 2037 2161 Fax: (029) 2039 6632

Fireside Brews, 22 Commercial Street, Shipley, West Yorkshire, BD18 3SP Tel: (01274) 599592

P M E Sugar Craft, Chadwell Heath Lane, Romford, RM6 4NP Tel: (020) 8590 5959 Fax: (020) 8590 7373 E-mail: admin@cakedecoration.co.uk

Sugar Shack, 87 Burnt Oak Broadway, Edgware, Middlesex, HA8 5EP Tel: (0800) 5975097 Fax: (020) 8951 4888 E-mail: sales@sugarshack.co.uk

CAKE MIXES

▶ Wendy's Cakes, 285 Sheldon Heath Road, Birmingham, B26 2TY Tel: 0121-243 7341 E-mail: wendyscakes@yahoo.co.uk

CAKE PLATE FITTINGS

J E S Manufacturing Co. Ltd, 53 Wharf Road, Tyseley, Birmingham, B11 2DX Tel: 0121-706 1425 Fax: 0121-707 3988 E-mail: sales@jesmanufacturing.co.uk

CAKES

▶ Cappuccino & Gateau Ltd, 173 Crickelwood Broadway, London, NW2 3HT Tel: (020) 8208 4668 E-mail: cappucinogateau@ukcom.com

Delice De France plc, Opal Way, Stone Business Park, Stone, Staffordshire, ST15 0SS Tel: (01785) 811200 Fax: (01785) 812233

Doughty Cakes, 3 Greetwell Hollow, Crofton Drive, Lincoln, LN3 4NR Tel: (01522) 543434 Fax: (01522) 543434 E-mail: doughtycakes@btconnect.com

▶ Ekhaya Foods Ltd, 66 Potters Lane, Send, Woking, Surrey, GU23 7AL Tel: (01483) 773534 E-mail: info@ekhayafoods.co.uk

Knowlsons Of Blackpool, 20 Boome Street, Blackpool, FY4 2JX Tel: (01253) 406555 Fax: (01253) 406606

La Galinette Ltd, Legacy Centre, Hanworth Trading Estate, Hampton Road West, Hanworth, Feltham, Middlesex, TW13 6DH Tel: (020) 8755 5858 Fax: (020) 8755 5878 E-mail: sales@lagalinette.co.uk

CALCIUM CARBONATE

Imerys Minerals Ltd, Par Moor Centre, Par Moor Road, Par, Cornwall, PL24 2SQ Tel: (01726) 818000 Fax: (01726) 811200 E-mail: perfmins@imerys.com

Lehvoss UK Ltd, 20 West Road, Congleton, Cheshire, CW12 4ER Tel: (01260) 291000 Fax: (01260) 291111 E-mail: contact@lehvoss.co.uk

Pumex (UK) Ltd, Hall Road, Aylesford, Maidstone, Kent, ME20 7QZ Tel: (01622) 882022 Fax: (01622) 882441 E-mail: info@pumex.co.uk

CALCIUM CHLORIDE

Brunner Mond Group Ltd, PO Box 4, Northwich, Cheshire, CW8 4DT Tel: (01606) 724000 Fax: (01606) 781353 E-mail: sales.enquiries@brunnermond.com

Molecular Products Group plc, Mill End, Thaxted, Dunmow, Essex, CM6 2LT Tel: (01371) 830676 Fax: (01371) 830998 E-mail: sales@molprod.com

CALCULATOR MANUFRS

Bennett, 1 Iremonger Road, Off London Road, Nottingham, NG2 3BL Tel: 0115-955 8000 Fax: 0115-955 8008 E-mail: sales@bennittsykes.co.uk

Bingo Office Supplies Ltd, PO Box 845, Halifax, West Yorkshire, HX3 6YR Tel: (0800) 0424646 Fax: (0800) 0424329 E-mail: sales@bingo-office.co.uk

Broughton & Co Bristol Ltd, 4 Axis, Hawkfield Way, Hawkfield Business Park, Bristol, BS14 0BY Tel: 0117-964 1300 Fax: 0117-964 1003 E-mail: broughtons1bristol@btinternet.com

Casio Electronics Co. Ltd, 6 1000 North Circular Road, London, NW2 7JD Tel: (020) 8450 9131 Fax: (020) 8452 6323

M.H. Mear & Co. Ltd, 56 Nettleton Road, Huddersfield, HD5 9TB Tel: (01484) 648181 Fax: (01484) 485408 E-mail: kath@mhmear.com

Research Micro Systems Ltd, Radclyffe House, 66-68 Hagley Road, Birmingham, B16 8PF Tel: 0121-410 5860

Sci-Net, Unit 5, Lakeside Farm, Middle Aston, Bicester, Oxfordshire, OX25 5PP Tel: (01869) 349949 Fax: (01869) 340063 E-mail: solutions@sci-net.co.uk

Sharp Electronics (UK) Ltd, Sharp House, Thorp Road, Manchester, M40 5BE Tel: 0161-205 2333 Fax: 0161-205 7076

Tab Business Machines & Equipment Ltd, 2-3 London Road, London, SE1 6JZ Tel: (020) 7620 3366 Fax: (020) 7633 0206 E-mail: sales@tab.uk.com

Typewriter & Equipment Co. Ltd, Teco House, High Street, Lye, Stourbridge, West Midlands, DY9 8LU Tel: (01384) 424416 Fax: (01384) 423423 E-mail: info@tecoltd.co.uk

CALCULATORS, ADVERTISING/PROMOTIONAL

Blundell Harling Ltd, 9 Albany Road, Granby Industrial Estate, Weymouth, Dorset, DT4 9TH Tel: (01305) 206000 Fax: (01305) 760598 E-mail: sales@blundellharling.co.uk

CALENDAR METAL FITTINGS/RIMS/CLIPS

Joto Ltd, 1c North Cresent, London, E16 4TG Tel: (020) 7511 4411 Fax: (020) 7511 5266

CALENDAR PADS

Lowe Aston Partnership, Moorlands Lane, Saltash, Cornwall, PL12 4HL Tel: (01752) 842233 Fax: (01752) 848060 E-mail: info@loweaston.co.uk

CALENDARS

▶ Calendar Lady Promotions Ltd, 2 Barnfield Cottages, Upton Bishop, Ross-on-Wye, Herefordshire, HR9 7TZ Tel: (01989) 780727 Fax: (01989) 780276 E-mail: info@calendarlady.co.uk

Calendar Sales, 192 Oritor Road, Cookstown, County Tyrone, BT80 9RF Tel: (028) 8676 3377 Fax: (028) 8676 3706 E-mail: info@calendarsales.co.uk

Direct Diary Planner, 111 Brecon Road, Hirwaun, Aberdare, Mid Glamorgan, CF44 9NS Tel: (01685) 810217 Fax: (01685) 810217

G H Enterprises, 10 Coope Road, Bollington, Kerridge, Macclesfield, Cheshire, SK10 5AE Tel: (01625) 574336 Fax: (01625) 573727 E-mail: ghe@breathemail.net

John Hinde UK Ltd, Unit 12b-D, Cardrew Industrial Estate, Redruth, Cornwall, TR15 1SS Tel: (01209) 211111 Fax: (01209) 210088 E-mail: sales@johnhinde.co.uk

Kenbe Reproductions Ltd, 25 City Industrial Park, Southern Road, Southampton, SO15 1HG Tel: (023) 8022 5020 Fax: (023) 8022 2491 E-mail: calenders@kenbe.co.uk

Lowe Aston Partnership, Moorlands Lane, Saltash, Cornwall, PL12 4HL Tel: (01752) 842233 Fax: (01752) 848060 E-mail: info@loweaston.co.uk

▶ Magicboxgifts, Optec House, Westfield Avenue, Wigston, Leicester, LE18 1HY Tel: 0116-229 0232 Fax: 0116-229 0232 E-mail: sales@magicboxgifts.com

Moments Calendars, Wayzgoose Drive, Derby, DE21 6ST Tel: (01332) 285911 Fax: (01332) 285912 E-mail: sales@moments.co.uk

Rose Colchester Ltd, Clough Road, Severalls Industrial Park, Colchester, CO4 9QT Tel: (01206) 844500 Fax: (01206) 845872 E-mail: sales@rosecalendars.co.uk

CALENDARS, GIFT

▶ Captive Calendars, 12 Fairway*, Sawbridgeworth, Hertfordshire, CM21 9NJ Tel: 01279 319769

▶ Sedgemoor Publicity, The Barn, 1 Sedgemoor Road, Weston-super-Mare, Avon, BS23 2TA Tel: (01934) 417352 Fax: (01934) 417352 E-mail: sales@sedgemoorpublicity.co.uk

CALENDERED RUBBER SHEET

D B T Medical Ltd, 14 The Crofts, Witney, Oxfordshire, OX28 4DJ Tel: (01993) 773673 Fax: (01993) 778267 E-mail: office@dbtmedical.co.uk

Hose Components, Enterprise Works, 2 Hunsley Street, Sheffield, S4 8DY Tel: 0114-261 9766 Fax: 0114-261 7464 E-mail: richard.garlick@hosecomponents.co.uk

CALENDERS

Glendale Print & Finishing Ltd, 8 Orchard Business Centre, North Farm Road, Tunbridge Wells, Kent, TN2 3XF Tel: (01892) 544988 Fax: (01892) 548181 E-mail: info@glendaleprintandfinishing.co.uk

Impact Calendars, 1 Redwood Park, Capel, Tonbridge, Kent, TN12 6WB Tel: (01892) 838811 Fax: (01892) 836699 E-mail: impactcal@dial.pipex.com

CALIBRATING AND TESTING ASSESSMENT SERVICES

Charnwood Instrumentation Services, 81 Park Road, Coalville, Leicestershire, LE67 3AF Tel: (01530) 510615 Fax: (01530) 510950 E-mail: graham@instrumentationservices.net

M P Calibration Services Ltd, A1 Romany Centre, Wareham Road, Holton Heath, Poole, Dorset, BH16 6JL Tel: (01202) 624468 Fax: (01202) 625132 E-mail: info@mpcalibration.co.uk

North West Inspex, Caddick Road, Knowsley Business Park, Prescot, Merseyside, L34 9HP Tel: 0151-548 9908 Fax: 0151-549 1182 E-mail: inspexuk@aol.com

Oldham Metropolitan Borough Trading Standards, North House, 130 Rochdale Road, Oldham, OL1 2JA Tel: 0161-911 4474 Fax: 0161-911 3481 E-mail: env.tradingstandard@oldham.gov.uk

Procal Ltd, Communications House, Woodfield Lane, Ashtead, Surrey, KT21 2BT Tel: (01372) 271313 Fax: (01372) 270100 E-mail: enquiries@procal.co.uk

Quality Instrument Services, Unit 7, Walkers Road, Moons Moat North, Redditch, Worcestershire, B98 9HE Tel: (01527) 596704 Fax: (01527) 596705

CALIBRATING EQUIPMENT

Haven Automation Ltd, Kingsway, Fforestfach, Swansea, SA5 4EX Tel: (01792) 588722 Fax: (01792) 582624 E-mail: sales@haven.co.uk

I A M Engineering Services, Fornighty Schoolhouse, Nairn, IV12 5JB Tel: (01667) 453509 Fax: (01667) 453066 E-mail: iameng@btinternet.com

Integrated Display Systems Ltd, Unit 15, Muarice Road, Wallsend, Tyne & Wear, NE28 6BY Tel: 0191-262 0091 Fax: 0191-262 0091 E-mail: sales@clavis.co.uk

Micron Metrology 2000 Ltd, Eurolab House, Unit 10, Valepits Road, Garretts Green Industrial Estate, Birmingham, B33 0TD Tel: 0121-784 7498 Fax: 0121-783 6031 E-mail: alansmith@micron-metrology.co.uk

Renishaw Plc, New Mills, Wotton-under-Edge, Gloucestershire, GL12 8JR Tel: (01453) 524126 Fax: (01453) 524201 E-mail: uk@renishaw.com

Spline Gauges, Piccadilly, Tamworth, Staffordshire, B78 2ER Tel: (01827) 872771 Fax: (01827) 874128 E-mail: sales@splinegauges.co.uk

Time Electronics Ltd, Unit 11, Sovereign Way, Tonbridge, Kent, TN9 1RH Tel: (01732) 355993 Fax: (01732) 770312 E-mail: mail@timeelectronics.co.uk

Verus Instruments Ltd, Clare House, Pinewood Road, High Wycombe, Buckinghamshire, HP12 4DA Tel: (01494) 558206 Fax: (01494) 558383 E-mail: sales@verus.co.uk

CALIBRATING EQUIPMENT INSTALLATION/COMMISSIONING/MAINTENANCE SERVICES

C M M Services Ltd, Butlers Leap, Rugby, Warwickshire, CV21 3RQ Tel: (01788) 570357 Fax: (01788) 567991 E-mail: cmm@itpgroup.co.uk

D P Instrumentation Ltd, 2 Ainslie Street, West Pitkerro Industrial Estate, Broughty Ferry, Dundee, DD5 3RR Tel: (01382) 731200 Fax: (01382) 731201 E-mail: sales@dpil.co.uk

Haven Automation Ltd, Kingsway, Fforestfach, Swansea, SA5 4EX Tel: (01792) 588722 Fax: (01792) 582624 E-mail: sales@haven.co.uk

Zwick Ltd, Main Enquiries, Southern Avenue, Leominster, Herefordshire, HR6 0QH Tel: (01568) 615201 Fax: (01568) 616626 E-mail: sales.info@zwick.co.uk

CALIBRATING EQUIPMENT, CURRENT

Haven Automation Ltd, Kingsway, Fforestfach, Swansea, SA5 4EX Tel: (01792) 588722 Fax: (01792) 582624 E-mail: sales@haven.co.uk

CALIBRATING EQUIPMENT, FLOW

▶ Ipc Services UK Ltd, Unit A3 Springhead Enterprise Park, Springhead Road, Northfleet, Gravesend, Kent, DA11 8HB Tel: (01474) 356551 Fax: (01474) 369283 E-mail: sales@ipcservices.co.uk

CALIBRATING EQUIPMENT, LEAK DETECTOR

Ateq UK Ltd, Unit 71 Heming Road, The Washford Industrial Estate, Redditch, Worcestershire, B98 0EA Tel: (01527) 520011 Fax: (01527) 520022 E-mail: info@ateq.co.uk

CALIBRATING EQUIPMENT, PRESSURE/TEMPERATURE/ELECTRICAL

Caltest Instruments Ltd, PO Box 7717, Lockerbie, Dumfriesshire, DG11 1YF Tel: (01387) 811910 Fax: (01387) 810195 E-mail: sales@caltest.co.uk

Furness Controls Ltd, Beeching Road, Bexhill-on-Sea, East Sussex, TN39 3LJ Tel: (01424) 730316 Fax: (01424) 730317 E-mail: sales@furness-controls.com

G E Sensing, Fir Tree Lane, Groby, Leicester, LE6 0FH Tel: 0116-231 7100 Fax: 0116-231 7101

Hawco Refridgeration, The Wharf, Abbey Mill Business Park, Lower Eashing, Godalming, Surrey, GU7 2QN Tel: (01483) 869070 Fax: (01483) 869001 E-mail: sales@hawco.co.uk

CALIBRATING EQUIPMENT, TEMPERATURE

F G H Controls Ltd, Openshaw Way, Letchworth Garden City, Hertfordshire, SG6 3ER Tel: (01462) 686677 Fax: (01462) 480633 E-mail: sales@fgh.co.uk

Isothermal Technology Ltd, 42a Pine Grove, Southport, Merseyside, PR9 9AG Tel: (01704) 544611 Fax: (01704) 544799 E-mail: info@isotech.co.uk

CALIBRATING SERVICES, *See also headings for particular applications*

Abbey Gauge Co. Ltd, 139-141 Becontree Avenue, Dagenham, Essex, RM8 2UL Tel: (020) 8590 3233 Fax: (020) 8590 5082 E-mail: sales@abbeygauge.co.uk
Chelmsford Precision Services, 29 The Westerings, Great Baddow, Chelmsford, CM3 3UY Tel: (01245) 474901
Dowding & Mills Calibration, The Service Centre Watchmoor Point, Watchmoor Road, Camberley, Surrey, GU15 3AD Tel: (01276) 701717 Fax: (01276) 700245 E-mail: calibration.camberley@dowdingandmills.com
Procal Ltd, Communications House, Woodfield Lane, Ashtead, Surrey, KT21 2BT Tel: (01372) 271313 Fax: (01372) 270100 E-mail: enquiries@procal.co.uk
Sercal NDT Equipment Ltd, 1 Littleton Business Park, Littleton Drive, Cannock, Staffordshire, WS12 4TR Tel: (01543) 570074 Fax: (01543) 465090 E-mail: sales@sercal.co.uk
T J Williams, Wimbourne Road, Barry, South Glamorgan, CF63 3DH Tel: (01446) 729200 Fax: (01446) 739281 E-mail: sales@tjwelectrical.co.uk
Validation Centre, Unit 9 Sinclair Court, Great Yarmouth, Norfolk, NR31 0NH Tel: (01493) 443800 Fax: (01493) 443900 E-mail: sales@tvcalx.co.uk
Veeco Instruments Ltd, Nanotech House Buckingway Business Park, Anderson Road, Swavesey, Cambridge, CB24 4UQ Tel: (01954) 233900 Fax: (01954) 231300 E-mail: info@veeco.co.uk
WBM, 34-35 Whitburn Street, Bridgnorth, Shropshire, WV16 4QN Tel: (01746) 761358 Fax: (01746) 764163 E-mail: wbm.calibration@tiscali.co.uk
York Metrology Ltd, 6 Highmeres Road, Leicester, LE4 9LZ Tel: 0116-246 0250

CALIBRATING SERVICES, ACCELEROMETERS

▶ C V M S L, Millside, The Moor, Melbourn, Royston, Hertfordshire, SG8 6ED Tel: (01763) 262112 Fax: (01763) 263335 E-mail: service@cvmsl.co.uk

CALIBRATING SERVICES, ELECTRO OPTICAL EQUIPMENT

Micron Techniques Ltd, 22 Ashley Walk, Mill Hill, London, NW7 1DU Tel: (020) 8343 4836 Fax: (020) 8343 4286 E-mail: micron@micronlondon.demon.co.uk

CALIBRATING SERVICES, ELECTRONIC EQUIPMENT

A J Mare Instruments, 110 Church Road, Perry Barr, Birmingham, B42 2LF Tel: 0121-356 8511 Fax: 0121-344 3644 E-mail: pimmy-21@hotmail.com
Absolute Calibration Ltd, 14 Murrills Estate, Portchester, Fareham, Hampshire, PO16 9RD Tel: (023) 9232 1712 Fax: (023) 9221 0034 E-mail: calit@absolute-cal.co.uk
C M M Services Ltd, Butlers Leap, Rugby, Warwickshire, CV21 3RQ Tel: (01788) 570357 Fax: (01788) 567991 E-mail: cmm@itpgroup.co.uk
C R I Ltd, 8 Langley Court, Langley Road, Burscough Industrial Estate, Ormskirk, Lancashire, L40 8JR Tel: (01704) 895950 Fax: (01704) 896260E-mail: cri@cybase.co.uk
Calibration Services Ltd, 29 Tennant Avenue, East Kilbride, Glasgow, G74 5NA Tel: (01355) 248102 Fax: (01355) 248102 E-mail: calibriation@dial.pipex.com
Calpar Electronics, Calpar House, 1 Windermere Road, Beeston, Nottingham, NG9 3AS Tel: 0115-925 8335 Fax: 0115-925 8335 E-mail: keith@calpar-electronics
Dowding & Mills Engineering Services Ltd, 71b Whitecraigs Road, Glenrothes, Fife, KY6 2RX Tel: (01592) 773008 Fax: (01592) 772877 E-mail: calibration.glenrothes@dowdingandmills.com
Essex Calabration Services, Five Tree Works Industrial Estate, Bakers Lane, West Hanningfield, Chelmsford, CM2 8LD Tel: (01277) 841410 Fax: (01277) 841418 E-mail: info@essexcal.demon.co.uk
Fire Instrumentation & Research Equipment Ltd, Holmesfield Road, Warrington, WA1 2DS Tel: (01925) 646643 Fax: (01925) 646622 E-mail: info@fire-uk.com
First Option Ltd, Signal House, Jacklyns Lane, Alresford, Hampshire, SO24 9JJ Tel: (01962) 738200 Fax: (01962) 738201 E-mail: mail@firstoption.net
Foxwell Instruments, Unit 19 Bond Indust Estate, Wickhamford, Evesham, Worcestershire, WR11 7RJ Tel: (01386) 833522 Fax: (01386) 833544 E-mail: info@foxwellinstruments.com
Industrial Calibration Ltd, Sunbeam Road, Kempston, Bedford, MK42 7BZ Tel: (01234) 857171 Fax: (01234) 840371 E-mail: clive@industrialcalibration.com
Inmar Automation Ltd, Test House, 118 Ringwood Road, Totton, Southampton, SO40 8DS Tel: (023) 8086 4179 Fax: (023) 8086 1613 E-mail: sales@inmar.co.uk
Micron Metrology 2000 Ltd, Eurolab House, Unit 10, Valepits Road, Garretts Green Industrial Estate, Birmingham, B33 0TD Tel: 0121-784 7498 Fax: 0121-783 6031 E-mail: alansmith@micron-metrology.co.uk
Q A Calibration Systems Ltd, Cressett Lane, Brierley Hill, West Midlands, DY5 3XT Tel: (01384) 70062 Fax: (01384) 261377 E-mail: qacs2000@aol.com
Quasartronics Ltd, 3 Watt House Dudley Innovation Centre, Second Avenue, Pensnett Trading Estate, Kingswinford, West Midlands, DY6 7YD Tel: (01384) 401132 Fax: (01384) 400754 E-mail: sales@quasartronics.com
Southern Calibration Laboratories Ltd, 7 Solent Industrial Estate, Shamblehurst Lane, Hedge End, Southampton, SO30 2FX Tel: (01489) 790296 Fax: (01489) 790294 E-mail: info@southcal.co.uk
T E R Instruments Ltd, 2-6 Peel Lane, Astley, Tyldesley, Manchester, M29 7QX Tel: (01942) 882275 Fax: (01942) 897958 E-mail: info@ter.co.uk
Universal Instrument Services Ltd, Cambridge Road, Whetstone, Leicester, LE8 6PA Tel: 0116-275 0123 Fax: 0116-275 0262 E-mail: sales@uiscal.co.uk

CALIBRATING SERVICES, ELECTRONIC INSTRUMENTATION

▶ Calco Instruments, 2 Leonard Street, Beverley Road, Hull, HU3 1SA Tel: (01482) 339300 Fax: (01482) 339301 E-mail: enquiries@calco-instruments.com

CALIBRATING SERVICES, FLOW MEASUREMENT EQUIPMENT

Apph Aviation Services Ltd, Unit 1 Rokeby Court, Manor Park, Runcorn, Cheshire, WA7 1RW Tel: (01928) 579791 Fax: (01928) 579811
Bulk Meter Services, 3 Faversham Road, Challock, Ashford, Kent, TN25 4BQ Tel: (0845) 2307887 Fax: (01233) 740943 E-mail: sales@bms-ltd.com
Dantec Dynamics Ltd, Unit 16 Garonor Way, Portbury, Bristol, BS20 7XE Tel: (01275) 375333 Fax: (01275) 375336 E-mail: scientific@dantecdynamics.com
GB Engineering Services, 6 Town House Farm, Alsager Road, Audley, Stoke-on-Trent, ST7 8JQ Tel: (01782) 723666 Fax: (01782) 723777
Its Testing Services UK Ltd, Wellheads Crescent, Wellheads Industrial Estate, Aberdeen, AB21 7GA Tel: (01224) 723242 Fax: (01224) 722894
Poole Instrument Calibration Ltd, 6 Cabot Business Village, Holyrood Close, Poole, Dorset, BH17 7BA Tel: (01202) 658333 Fax: (01202) 659966 E-mail: sales@pooleinstruments.com

CALIBRATING SERVICES, GAS DETECTION EQUIPMENT

Specialty Gases Ltd, Buiding 940 Kent Science Park, Sittingbourne, Kent, ME9 8PS Tel: (01795) 599099 Fax: (01795) 411525 E-mail: sales@specialty-gases.com
Survequip.com, Centrix House, Ash 05, 26 Crow Lane East, Newton-le-Willows, Merseyside, WA12 9UY Tel: (0800) 13 13 435 Fax: (01925) 273001 E-mail: sales@survequip.com

CALIBRATING SERVICES, GAUGES

Broomfield Carbide Gauges Ltd, Unit 7 Crossley Mills, New Mill Road Honley, Honley, Holmfirth, HD9 6PL Tel: (01484) 664982 Fax: (01484) 664982 E-mail: info@broomfieldgauges.com

CALIBRATING SERVICES, HIGH VOLTAGE EQUIPMENT

Essex Calabration Services, Five Tree Works Industrial Estate, Bakers Lane, West Hanningfield, Chelmsford, CM2 8LD Tel: (01277) 841410 Fax: (01277) 841418 E-mail: info@essexcal.demon.co.uk

CALIBRATING SERVICES, HUMIDITY EQUIPMENT

Poole Instrument Calibration Ltd, 6 Cabot Business Village, Holyrood Close, Poole, Dorset, BH17 7BA Tel: (01202) 658333 Fax: (01202) 659966 E-mail: sales@pooleinstruments.com

CALIBRATING SERVICES, INSTRUMENT

Northern Design Electronics Ltd, 228 Bolton Road, Bradford, West Yorkshire, BD3 0QW Tel: (01274) 729533 Fax: (01274) 721074 E-mail: sales@ndmeter.co.uk
Optical Services, 15 Barkestone Close, Emerson Valley, Milton Keynes, MK4 2AT Tel: (01908) 526100 Fax:
W F Ltd, Upper Gallery, Station Approach Industrial Estate, Pulborough, West Sussex, RH20 1AQ Tel: (01798) 875312 Fax: (01798) 875570 E-mail: wf@wf-online.com
W F Electrical, Unit 6 Westerton Road, East Mains Industrial Estate, Broxburn, West Lothian, EH52 5AU Tel: (01506) 858833 Fax: (01506) 855257 E-mail: edinbugh.industrial@hagemeyerservicecentre.co.uk
Weirgrove Automation Ltd, Lords Mill, Oakridge Road, High Wycombe, Buckinghamshire, HP11 2PA Tel: (01494) 448387 Fax: (01494) 530734 E-mail: weirgrove@weirgrove.co.uk
York Metrology Ltd, 6 Highmeres Road, Leicester, LE4 9LZ Tel: 0116-246 0250

CALIBRATING SERVICES, MAGNETIC

Hirst Magnetic Instruments Ltd, Pesla House, Tregoniggie Industrial Estate, Falmouth, Cornwall, TR11 4SN Tel: (01326) 372734 Fax: (01326) 378069 E-mail: dudding@hirst-magnetics.com

CALIBRATING SERVICES, MECHANICAL EQUIPMENT/ MACHINE TOOL

Aspland Gauge Co Ltd, Broadway, Hyde, Cheshire, SK14 4QF Tel: 0161-368 3432 Fax: 0161-367 8426 E-mail: sales@aspland.co.uk
Broadleaf Engineering, 1 Craven Street, Leicester, LE1 4BX Tel: 0116-253 9200 Fax: 0116-253 0598
Broomfield Carbide Gauges Ltd, Unit 7 Crossley Mills, New Mill Road Honley, Honley, Holmfirth, HD9 6PL Tel: (01484) 664982 Fax: (01484) 664982 E-mail: info@broomfieldgauges.com
Alan Browne Gauges Ltd, Blackdown Mill, Blackdown, Leamington Spa, Warwickshire, CV32 6QT Tel: (01926) 424278 Fax: (01926) 451865 E-mail: sales@alanbrowne.co.uk
C D Measurements Ltd, Chomlea, Hadfield Road, Hadfield, Glossop, Derbyshire, SK13 2ER Tel: (01457) 852929 Fax: (01457) 860619
C M M Services Ltd, Butlers Leap, Rugby, Warwickshire, CV21 3RQ Tel: (01788) 570357 Fax: (01788) 567991 E-mail: cmm@itpgroup.co.uk
Disking International, 5 South Street, Farnham, Surrey, GU9 7QU Tel: (01252) 719719 Fax: (01252) 719819 E-mail: farnhamshop@disking.co.uk
Dowding & Mills Engineering Services Ltd, 71b Whitecraigs Road, Glenrothes, Fife, KY6 2RX Tel: (01592) 773008 Fax: (01592) 772877 E-mail: calibration.glenrothes@dowdingandmills.com
Fire Instrumentation & Research Equipment Ltd, Holmesfield Road, Warrington, WA1 2DS Tel: (01925) 646643 Fax: (01925) 646622 E-mail: info@fire-uk.com
G B Quality Assurance Ltd, 9 Moor Lane Industrial Estate, Chancel Way, Birmingham, B6 7AU Tel: 0121-356 7430 Fax: 0121-344 3837 E-mail: info@gbquality.com
M P Calibration Services Ltd, A1 Romany Centre, Wareham Road, Holton Heath, Poole, Dorset, BH16 6JL Tel: (01202) 624468 Fax: (01202) 625132 E-mail: info@mpcalibration.co.uk
Measure-Rite Ltd, Great Central Way Industrial Estate, Great Central Way, Rugby, Warwickshire, CV21 3XH Tel: (01788) 577512 Fax: (01788) 560864 E-mail: sales@measure-rite.com
Metrology Instrument Solutions, 94 Repton Road, Hartshorne, Swadlincote, Derbyshire, DE11 7AE Tel: (01283) 223800 E-mail: metrology@mcmail.com
Micron Metrology 2000 Ltd, Eurolab House, Unit 10, Valepits Road, Garretts Green Industrial Estate, Birmingham, B33 0TD Tel: 0121-784 7498 Fax: 0121-783 6031 E-mail: alansmith@micron-metrology.co.uk
Premier Calibration Ltd, Unit 3l Lake Enterprise Park, Sandall Stones Road, Kirk Sandall Industrial Estate, Doncaster, South Yorkshire, DN3 1QR Tel: (01302) 888448 Fax: (01302) 881197 E-mail: premcal@btconnect.com
Quality Control Metrology Services Ltd, Unit 10 Holly Park Industrial Estate, Spitfire Road, Birmingham, B24 9PB Tel: 0121-377 8989 Fax: 0121-377 8976 E-mail: qcms@qcms.fsnet.co.uk
▶ Total Maintenance Solutions, Unit 94 Silverbriar, Business & Innovation Centre, Sunderland Enterprise Park, Sunderland, SR5 2TQ Tel: 0191-516 6489 Fax: 0191-516 6499 E-mail: sales@online-tms.com
W B J Ltd, Metrology House, Dukinfield Road, Hyde, Cheshire, SK14 4SD Tel: 0161-367 9898 Fax: 0161-367 9700 E-mail: admin@wbj.co.uk
Wortley Standards Ltd, Forge Lane, Wortley, Sheffield, S35 7DN Tel: 0114-288 2423 Fax: 0114-288 2423 E-mail: wortley@globalnet.co.uk

CALIBRATING SERVICES, ON SITE

▶ Ever Cal, Citadel Trading Park, Citadel Way, Hull, HU9 1TQ Tel: (01482) 610601 Fax: (01482) 610602 E-mail: sales@ever-cal.com
Procal Ltd, Communications House, Woodfield Lane, Ashtead, Surrey, KT21 2BT Tel: (01372) 271313 Fax: (01372) 270100 E-mail: enquiries@procal.co.uk

CALIBRATING SERVICES, OPTICAL PROJECTORS

Optical Services, 15 Barkestone Close, Emerson Valley, Milton Keynes, MK4 2AT Tel: (01908) 526100 Fax:

CALIBRATING SERVICES, PIPETTE

European Instruments, Shotover Kilns, Headington, Oxford, OX3 8ST Tel: (01865) 750375 Fax: (01865) 769985 E-mail: balances@euroinst.co.uk

CALIBRATING SERVICES, PRESSURE EQUIPMENT

E & I Hire Ltd, Newspaper House, Tannery Lane, Penketh, Warrington, WA5 2UD Tel: (01925) 726677 Fax: (01925) 725544 E-mail: sales@eihire.co.uk
Electrical Mechanical Instrument Services (UK) Ltd, Central Equipment Base, Greenwell Road, East Tullos Industrial Estate, Aberdeen, AB12 3AX Tel: (01224) 894494 Fax: (01224) 894929 E-mail: info@emis-uk.com
Foxwell Instruments, Unit 19 Bond Indust Estate, Wickhamford, Evesham, Worcestershire, WR11 7RJ Tel: (01386) 833522 Fax: (01386) 833544 E-mail: info@foxwellinstruments.com
Gauge Developments Ltd, Langham Street, Ashton-under-Lyne, Lancashire, OL7 9AX Tel: 0161-343 3020 Fax: 0161-343 2969 E-mail: gdev@btconnect.com
Premier Calibration Ltd, Unit 3l Lake Enterprise Park, Sandall Stones Road, Kirk Sandall Industrial Estate, Doncaster, South Yorkshire, DN3 1QR Tel: (01302) 888448 Fax: (01302) 881197 E-mail: premcal@btconnect.com
Zygal Controls Ltd, 149 Stanwell Road, Ashford, Middlesex, TW15 3QN Tel: (01784) 251134 Fax: (01784) 243688 E-mail: saleszygal@aol.com

CALIBRATING SERVICES, TEMPERATURE EQUIPMENT

Absolute Calibration Ltd, 14 Murrills Estate, Portchester, Fareham, Hampshire, PO16 9RD Tel: (023) 9232 1712 Fax: (023) 9221 0034 E-mail: calit@absolute-cal.co.uk
Essex Calabration Services, Five Tree Works Industrial Estate, Bakers Lane, West Hanningfield, Chelmsford, CM2 8LD Tel: (01277) 841410 Fax: (01277) 841418 E-mail: info@essexcal.demon.co.uk
Foxwell Instruments, Unit 19 Bond Indust Estate, Wickhamford, Evesham, Worcestershire, WR11 7RJ Tel: (01386) 833522 Fax: (01386) 833544 E-mail: info@foxwellinstruments.com
G B Quality Assurance Ltd, 9 Moor Lane Industrial Estate, Chancel Way, Birmingham, B6 7AU Tel: 0121-356 7430 Fax: 0121-344 3837 E-mail: info@gbquality.com
Isothermal Technology Ltd, 42a Pine Grove, Southport, Merseyside, PR9 9AG Tel: (01704) 544611 Fax: (01704) 544799 E-mail: info@isotech.co.uk
Littlebrook Power Services Ltd, Littlebrook Complex, Manor Way, Dartford, DA1 5PU Tel: (01322) 280038 Fax: (01322) 284835 E-mail: general@littlebrookservices.co.uk

CALIBRATING SERVICES, TEST EQUIPMENT

Air Flow Measurements Ltd, 72 Manchester Road, Kearsley, Bolton, BL4 8NZ Tel: (01204) 571499 Fax: (01204) 571734 E-mail: info@airflowmeasurements.com
Anritsu Ltd, 200 Capability Green, Luton, LU1 3LU Tel: (01582) 433200 Fax: (01582) 731303 E-mail: sales@anritsu.co.uk
Fluke UK Ltd, 52 Hurricane Way, Norwich, NR6 6JB Tel: (01603) 256600 Fax: (01603) 483670 E-mail: sales@flukeprecision.co.uk
Humberside Instruments Ltd, 13-15 Barkhouse Lane, Cleethorpes, South Humberside, DN35 8RA Tel: (01472) 691157 Fax: (01472) 692585 E-mail: sales@humbrsideinstruments.co.uk

CALIBRATING SERVICES, TEST EQUIPMENT – *continued*

Littlebrook Power Services Ltd, Littlebrook Complex, Manor Way, Dartford, DA1 5PU Tel: (01322) 280038 Fax: (01322) 284835 E-mail: general@littlebrookservices.co.uk
M T I Instruments & Calibration, Littleburn Industrial Estate, Langley Moor, Durham, DH7 8HJ Tel: 0191-378 3990 Fax: 0191-378 3973
Pullman Instruments (UK) Ltd, Chatsworth House, Chatsworth Terrace, Harrogate, North Yorkshire, HG1 5HT Tel: (01423) 720360 Fax: (01423) 720361 E-mail: info@pullman.co.uk
Q A Calibration Systems Ltd, Cressett Lane, Brierley Hill, West Midlands, DY5 3XT Tel: (01384) 70062 Fax: (01384) 261377 E-mail: qacs2000@aol.com
R D P Howden Ltd, Southam, Warwickshire, CV47 0ZD Tel: (01926) 813141 Fax: (01926) 810007 E-mail: info@rdphowden.co.uk
R & H Testing Services Ltd, Cannel Road, Burntwood Business Park, Burntwood, Staffordshire, WS7 3FU Tel: (01543) 677400 Fax: (01543) 677477 E-mail: sales@randhtesting.com
Sheffield Testing Laboratories Ltd, 56 Nursery Street, Sheffield, S3 8GP Tel: 0114-272 6581 Fax: 0114-272 3248 E-mail: hq@sheffieldtesting.com
Terotest Ltd, 33 Station Road, Ashwell, Baldock, Hertfordshire, SG7 5LG Tel: (01462) 742499 Fax: (01462) 742497 E-mail: info@terotest.com

CALIBRATING SERVICES, TORQUE EQUIPMENT

E & I Hire Ltd, Newspaper House, Tannery Lane, Penketh, Warrington, WA5 2UD Tel: (01925) 726677 Fax: (01925) 725544 E-mail: sales@eihire.co.uk
▶ Ever Cal, Citadel Trading Park, Citadel Way, Hull, HU9 1TQ Tel: (01482) 610601 Fax: (01482) 610602 E-mail: sales@ever-cal.com
Sensor Technology Ltd, PO Box 36, Banbury, Oxfordshire, OX15 6JB Tel: (01295) 730746 Fax: (01295) 738966 E-mail: info@sensors.co.uk

CALIBRATING SERVICES, WEIGHING EQUIPMENT

A D F Scale Co., Unit 6 Key Point, Keys Park Road, Hednesford, Cannock, Staffordshire, WS12 2FN Tel: (01543) 572165 Fax: (01543) 459005 E-mail: enquiries@adfscale.co.uk
Darenth Weighing Services Ltd, 75 Campbell Road, Maidstone, Kent, ME15 6PS Tel: (0870) 4436670 Fax: (0870) 4436671
European Instruments, Shotover Kilns, Headington, Oxford, OX3 8ST Tel: (01865) 750375 Fax: (01865) 769985 E-mail: balances@euroinst.co.uk
Halifax Scale Co., Brighouse Road, Hipperholme, Halifax, West Yorkshire, HX3 8EF Tel: (01422) 201016 Fax: (01422) 203775 E-mail: info@halifaxscale.co.uk
Oldham Metropolitan Borough Trading Standards, North House, 130 Rochdale Road, Oldham, OL1 2JA Tel: 0161-911 4474 Fax: 0161-911 3481 E-mail: env.tradingstandard@oldham.gov.uk
Stevens Group Ltd, Challenge Way, Blackburn, BB1 5QB Tel: (01254) 685200 Fax: (01254) 685202 E-mail: sales@stevensgroup.com
John White & Son (Weighing Machines) Ltd, 6 Back Dykes, Auchtermuchty, Cupar, Fife, KY14 7DW Tel: (01337) 827600 Fax: (01337) 827444 E-mail: enquiries@johnwhiteandson.com

CALIBRATING TEST EQUIPMENT

Micro Technology Consultants, Unit 32 Business Centre, Main Street, Coatbridge, Lanarkshire, ML5 3RB Tel: (01236) 432205 Fax: (01236) 421933

CALIBRATING TEST EQUIPMENT HIRE

E & I Hire Ltd, Newspaper House, Tannery Lane, Penketh, Warrington, WA5 2UD Tel: (01925) 726677 Fax: (01925) 725544 E-mail: sales@eihire.co.uk
Mobile Communications Solutions Ltd, Unit 5-6, Station Yard, Llanrwst, Gwynedd, LL26 0EH Tel: (0845) 3626365 Fax: (0845) 3623616 E-mail: kevin.jones@mcs-cymru.co.uk

CALIBRATION EQUIPMENT

Cal-Com Systems Ltd, Calibration House, Moorefield Grove, Bolton, BL2 2LQ Tel: (01204) 383311 Fax: (01204) 382556

CALIBRATION LABORATORIES

▶ Ballistic Research Ltd, PO Box 263, Romsey, Hampshire, SO51 7WY Tel: (01794) 521113 Fax: (01794) 521623 E-mail: info@ballisticresearch.co.uk
▶ Calco Instruments, 2 Leonard Street, Beverley Road, Hull, HU3 1SA Tel: (01482) 339300 Fax: (01482) 339301 E-mail: enquiries@calco-instruments.com
Instruments & Controls Hull, Faraday Works, Crowle Street, Hull, HU9 1RH Tel: (01482) 225607 Fax: (01482) 217122 E-mail: sales@instco.co.uk
National Physical Laboratory, Hampton Road, Teddington, Middlesex, TW11 0LW Tel: (020) 8977 3222 Fax: (020) 8943 6458 E-mail: enquiry@npl.co.uk
Poole Instrument Calibration Ltd, 6 Cabot Business Village, Holyrood Close, Poole, Dorset, BH17 7BA Tel: (01202) 658333 Fax: (01202) 659966 E-mail: sales@pooleinstruments.com
Portable Appliance Safety Services Ltd, 1 Hunters Buildings, Bowesfield Lane, Stockton-on-Tees, Cleveland, TS18 3QZ Tel: (01642) 603039 Fax: (0870) 1431869 E-mail: info@pat-services.co.uk
Servicecal Ltd, 19 Green Lane, Eccles, Manchester, M30 0RP Tel: 0161-789 8990 Fax: 0161-789 8991 E-mail: info@servicecal.co.uk
Westco Bilanciai Ltd, Broadgauge House, Westridge Way, Bishops Lydeard, Taunton, Somerset, TA4 3RU Tel: (01823) 433411 Fax: (01823) 433334 E-mail: sales@westcoweigh.co.uk

CALICO

A. Holt & Sons Ltd, 115 Whitecross Street, London, EC1Y 8JQ Tel: (020) 7256 2222 Fax: (020) 7638 3578 E-mail: sales@aholt.co.uk

CALL CENTRE CONTINUITY SERVICES

▶ Ansaback, Melford Court 2 The Havens, Ransomes Europark, Ipswich, IP3 9SJ Tel: (01473) 322900 Fax: (01473) 321801 E-mail: mtaylor@ansaback.co.uk

CALL HANDLING SERVICES

▶ Enclosed Solutions Ltd, 7a The Mall, Ealing Broadway, London, W5 2PJ Tel: 0208 7990900 Fax: 0208 799 0910 E-mail: paul@enclosed.co.uk

CALORIFIERS

H R S Heat Exchangers Ltd, 10-12 Caxton Way, Watford Business Park, Watford, WD18 8TX Tel: (01923) 232335 Fax: (01923) 230266 E-mail: mail@hrs.co.uk
Manchester Calorifiers Ltd, Lund Street, Manchester, M16 9EJ Tel: 0161-872 3613 Fax: 0161-872 3027
Ormandy Rycroft, Duncombe Road, Bradford, West Yorkshire, BD8 9TB Tel: (01274) 490911 Fax: (01274) 498580 E-mail: sales@rycroft.com
Strebel Ltd, Unit 1f Albany Park, Camberley, Surrey, GU16 7PB Tel: (01276) 685422 Fax: (01276) 685405 E-mail: andy.parker@strebel.co.uk
Telford Copper Cylinders, Haybridge Road, Wellington, Telford, Shropshire, TF1 2NW Tel: (01952) 262300 Fax: (01952) 253452 E-mail: sales@telford-group.com
Thermo Logistics, 3 21-23 Emery Road, Bristol, BS4 5PF Tel: 0117-971 7001 Fax: 0117-971 7113 E-mail: thermologistics@btconnect.com

CAM BLANKS

Midland Cam & Tool (1982) Co., 21 Nursery Road, Hockley, Birmingham, B19 2XN Tel: 0121-551 9922 Fax: 0121-551 9929 E-mail: tooling@centreless.com

CAM BUCKLE FASTENERS WITH WEBBING

▶ D B C M Web Design, 14 Wallacebrae Drive, Danestone, Aberdeen, AB22 8YB Tel: (01224) 825401 E-mail: info@dbcmtest.co.uk

CAM SWITCHES

Davron, 21 Beechfield Road, Davenport, Stockport, Cheshire, SK3 8SF Tel: 0161-483 5678 Fax: 0161-483 5678 E-mail: sales@davron.co.uk
Salzer UK Ltd, 44 Edison Road, Aylesbury, Buckinghamshire, HP19 8TE Tel: (01296) 399992 Fax: (01296) 392229 E-mail: info@salzeruk.co.uk

CAMCORDER BATTERIES

Absolute Battery UK Ltd, Darrell House, Darrell Road, Felixstowe, Suffolk, IP11 3UU Tel: (01394) 674949 Fax: (01394) 279005
▶ Battech International Ltd, 83 Shropshire Street, Market Drayton, Shropshire, TF9 3DQ Tel: (0871) 5500051 E-mail: sales@bat-tech.co.uk
▶ Budget, 13 865 Ringwood Road, Bournemouth, BH11 8LW Tel: (01202) 582700 Fax: (01202) 573200 E-mail: info@budgetbatteries.co.uk
▶ Mr.Amin, 3 Galen Place, London, WC1A 2JR Tel: (020) 7240 6774 Fax: (020) 7419 4729 E-mail: sales@microglobe.co.uk
▶ Tantronics Ltd, Goyt Mill, Upper Hibbert Lane, Marple, Stockport, Cheshire, SK6 7HX Tel: 0161-427 1100 Fax: 0161-427 5100 E-mail: info@tantronics.co.uk

CAMERA ACCESSORIES/SPARE PARTS

Intec, 35 Trelowarren Street, Camborne, Cornwall, TR14 8AD Tel: (01209) 716717 Fax: (01209) 610580
Kood International Ltd, 6 Wellington Road, London Colney, St. Albans, Hertfordshire, AL2 1EY Tel: (01727) 823812 Fax: (01727) 827338 E-mail: info@koodinternational.com

CAMERA AND PHOTOGRAPHIC MAGAZINES

▶ Beverley Foster Wedding Photographer, 14 Moorfields, Leek, Staffordshire, ST13 5LU Tel: (01538) 386403 E-mail: admin@weddingstorybook.co.uk
▶ Chris Williams Photography, 31 Manor House Road, Glastonbury, Somerset, BA6 9DF Tel: 01458 835946
▶ Hughescrafts, Hughescrafts, 33 Thorntondale Drive, Marton Lodge, Bridlington, East Riding of Yorkshire, YO16 6GW Tel: (01262) 602180 E-mail: john@hughescrafts.com
▶ Louis James-Parker, Cedars East, Chapel Road, West Row, Bury St. Edmunds, Suffolk, IP28 8PA Tel: (01638) 713350 E-mail: Louisjp@gmail.com
▶ Pixelate Imaging, 8 Flitcroft Street, London, WC2H 8DL Tel: (020) 7240 9808 Fax: (020) 7240 9188 E-mail: studio@pixelate.biz
▶ Red Dog Photography, 31 Cheadle Road, Uttoxeter, Staffordshire, ST14 7BX Tel: (01889) 569232 E-mail: duncan@reddogphoto.co.uk
▶ TravellingPhotos.com, 1 Station Road, Lewes, East Sussex, BN7 2YY Tel: (07880) 730096

CAMERA BATTERIES

▶ Newton Ellis & Co, 29 Cheapside, Liverpool, L2 2DY Tel: 0151-236 1391 E-mail: info@newtonellis.co.uk
▶ The Small Battery Co., 70 Cromford Road, London, SW18 1NY Tel: (020) 8871 3730 Fax: (020) 8871 3686 E-mail: info@smallbattery.company.org.uk

CAMERA CASES

Sino West Business Consultancy Ltd, 32 William Bristow Road, Coventry, CV3 5LQ Tel: (024) 7650 2465 Fax: (024) 7650 3215 E-mail: enquiry@sinowest.co.uk

CAMERA CONTROL SYSTEMS

▶ Oliver Control Systems Ltd, Units 4 - 6 Sun Valley Business Park, Winall Close, Winchester, Hants, SO23 0LB Tel: (01962) 859306 Fax: (01962) 859304 E-mail: sales@oliver-control.com
Pearpoint Holdings Ltd, 47 Woolmer Trading Estate, Bordon, Hampshire, GU35 9QE Tel: (01420) 489901 Fax: (01420) 477597
Vicon Industries Ltd, 17 Brunel Way, Fareham, Hampshire, PO15 5TX Tel: (01489) 566300 Fax: (01489) 566322 E-mail: sales@vicon.co.uk

CAMERA FILTERS

Lee Filters, Unit 1-2 Kingsway, Andover, Hampshire, SP10 5LQ Tel: (01264) 364112 Fax: (01264) 355058 E-mail: sales@leefilters.com
▶ Vision Light Plastics Ltd, 2-7 Decoy Road, Worthing, West Sussex, BN14 8ND Tel: (01903) 823339 Fax: (01903) 206868 E-mail: sales@visionlight.co.uk

CAMERA FLASHGUNS

Intro 2020 Ltd, Unit 1, Priors Way, Maidenhead, Berkshire, SL6 2HP Tel: (01628) 674411 Fax: (01628) 771055 E-mail: jane@intro2020.co.uk

CAMERA HIRE

▶ 400 Co. Ltd, Unit A1-A2 Askew Crescent Workshops, 2 Askew Cresent, London, W12 9DP Tel: (020) 8746 1400 Fax: (020) 8746 0847 E-mail: christian@the400.co.uk
▶ Filmscape Media UK, 6 Stammerham Business Centre, Capel Road, Rusper, Horsham, West Sussex, RH12 4PZ Tel: (01306) 710144 E-mail: info@filmscapemedia.com

CAMERA LENSES

Intro 2020 Ltd, Unit 1, Priors Way, Maidenhead, Berkshire, SL6 2HP Tel: (01628) 674411 Fax: (01628) 771055 E-mail: jane@intro2020.co.uk

CAMERAS, INDUSTRIAL/ SPECIAL PURPOSE

AGFA-Gevaert Ltd, 27 Great West Road, Brentford, Middlesex, TW8 9AX Tel: (020) 8231 4301 Fax: (020) 8231 4315 E-mail: agfauk@agfa.com
Hamamatsu Photonics UK Ltd, 10 Tewin Road, Welwyn Garden City, Hertfordshire, AL7 1BW Tel: (01707) 294888 Fax: (01707) 325777 E-mail: info@hamamatsu.co.uk
Kodak Ltd, Hemel One, Boundary Way, Hemel Hempstead, Hertfordshire, HP2 7YU Tel: (01442) 261122 E-mail: gb-ei-orders@kodak.com
Pearpoint Holdings Ltd, 47 Woolmer Trading Estate, Bordon, Hampshire, GU35 9QE Tel: (01420) 489901 Fax: (01420) 477597
Photek Ltd, 26 Castleham Road, St. Leonards-On-Sea, East Sussex, TN38 9NS Tel: (01424) 850555 Fax: (01424) 850051 E-mail: sales@photek.co.uk

CAMERAS, SUBSEA/ UNDERWATER

▶ Bennex (Aquaculture), Bennex House, The Enterprise Park, Forres, Morayshire, IV36 2AB Tel: (01309) 678270 Fax: (01309) 673215 E-mail: aquaculture@bennex.co.uk
C S I P Ltd, Unit 11 Granby Court, Surrey Close, Granby Industrial Estate, Weymouth, Dorset, DT4 9XB Tel: (01305) 779020 Fax: (01305) 778095 E-mail: sales@csip.co.uk

CAMOUFLAGE NETS

▶ The Sporting Experience, 4 Meadow La, Lapworth, Solihull, W. Midlands, B94 6LS Tel: (01564) 782234 Fax: (01564) 782234 E-mail: info@thesportingexperience.co.uk

CAMPER VAN HIRE

Trucks R Us, Sovereign House, Farthing Road, Ipswich, IP1 5AP Tel: (01473) 744117 Fax: (01473) 748850 E-mail: sales@trucks-are-us.co.uk
▶ Vanandman.com, 33 Shaldon Drive, Morden, Surrey, SM4 4BE Tel: (0870) 8505282 E-mail: garyij@hotmail.com

CAMPER VANS

Trucks R Us, Sovereign House, Farthing Road, Ipswich, IP1 5AP Tel: (01473) 744117 Fax: (01473) 748850 E-mail: sales@trucks-are-us.co.uk

CAMPING EQUIPMENT

A M G Outdoor Ltd, Kelburn Business Park, Port Glasgow, Renfrewshire, PA14 6TD Tel: (01475) 744122 Fax: (01475) 742333 E-mail: info@amg-outdoor.co.uk
Army & Navy, Lockwood Way, London, E17 5RB Tel: (020) 8527 3735 Fax: (020) 8527 6639
Attleborough Camping Hire, 31 Besthorpe Road, Attleborough, Norfolk, NR17 2AN Tel: (01953) 452825
Oswald Bailey Ltd, 72-74 Palmerston Road, Bournemouth, BH1 4JT Tel: (01202) 397273 Fax: (01202) 397274
Oswald Bailey Ltd, 317 Ashley Road, Poole, Dorset, BH14 0AP Tel: (01202) 740724
Barretts Of Feckenham, Astwood Lane, Feckenham, Redditch, Worcestershire, B96 6HQ Tel: (01527) 892935 Fax: (01527) 892455
Base Camp, 1a Clifton Road, Littlehampton, West Sussex, BN17 5AS Tel: (01903) 723853 Fax: (01903) 723853 E-mail: sales@base-camp.co.uk
BEE, Yardes Cott, Dewlish, Dorchester, Dorset, DT2 7LT Tel: 01258 837234
Blacks Ltd, 38-39 Long Causeway, Peterborough, PE1 1YJ Tel: (01733) 340674 Fax: (01733) 347683

CAMPING EQUIPMENT – *continued*

Blacks Leisure Group plc, 74 Bull Street, Birmingham, B4 6AD Tel: 0121-233 1678 Fax: 0121-236 8209
Blacks Leisure Group plc, Unit 11 254-284 Sauchiehall Street, Glasgow, G2 3EQ Tel: 0141-353 2344 Fax: 0141-331 0614
Blacks Leisure Group plc, 10 Phoenix Court, Guildford, Surrey, GU1 3EG Tel: (01483) 506432
Blacks Leisure Group plc, Shopping Centre, Brent Cross, London, NW4 3FP Tel: (020) 8203 9895
Blacks Leisure Group plc, 8 The Arcadia Centre, The Broadway, London, W5 2ND Tel: (020) 8840 1514
Blacks Leisure Group plc, 8-10 Old Hall Street, Stoke-on-Trent, ST1 1QT Tel: (01782) 212870
Blacks Outdoor Group, 61b Friargate Walk, St. Georges Shopping Centre, Preston, PR1 2NQ Tel: (01772) 252669
▶ Blacks Shrewsbury, 27-28 Shoplatch, Shrewsbury, SY1 1HS Tel: (01743) 368272
▶ Blacktoe Ltd, 53 The Slough, Redditch, Worcestershire, B97 5JR Tel: (01527) 458954
Braithwaite Paul Outdoor Sports, Rhodes Bank, Oldham, OL1 1TA Tel: 0161-620 3900 Fax: 0161-620 2863 E-mail: sales@paulbraithwaites.co.uk
Brenig Outdoor Clothing, Greenfield Road, Greenfield, Holywell, Clwyd, CH8 7GR Tel: (01352) 718025 Fax: (01352) 718025 E-mail: sales@brenig.co.uk
Broad Lane Caravans Ltd, 1 Somers Road, Rugby, Warwickshire, CV22 7DB Tel: (01788) 542672 Fax: (01788) 546109 E-mail: rugby@broadlane.co.uk
Joe Brown, Capel Curig, Betws-y-Coed, Gwynedd, LL24 0EN Tel: (01690) 720205 Fax: (01690) 720224
▶ C C Outdoor Ltd, Exhibition Centre, Hostingley Lane, Middlestown, Wakefield, West Yorkshire, WF4 4PZ Tel: (01924) 272877 Fax: (01924) 261927
C W Tents, Unit 9a Backworth Workshops, Station Road, Backworth, Newcastle upon Tyne, NE27 0RT Tel: 0191-268 0110 Fax: 0191-268 9943
Camping & General, 126 Arterial Road, Leigh-on-Sea, Essex, SS9 4DG Tel: (01702) 525536 Fax: (01702) 420230
▶ Camping & Surplus, 53-59 Woodhouse Road, London, N12 9ET Tel: (020) 8445 4747
Carrimor Outdoor Clothing, Red Lion Square, Grasmere, Ambleside, Cumbria, LA22 9SP Tel: (01539) 435614 Fax: (01539) 435122
Caseys Camping, Pool Road, Otley, West Yorkshire, LS21 1DY Tel: (01943) 465462 Fax: (01943) 850825 E-mail: sales@caseyscamping.com
Cotswold Outdoor Ltd, 13 Lower Northam Road, Hedge End, Southampton, SO30 4FN Tel: (01489) 799555 Fax: (01489) 790010
Craven Rambler, 19 Coach Street, Skipton, North Yorkshire, BD23 1LH Tel: (01756) 796166 Fax: (01756) 700213 E-mail: sales@penninecruises.com
Don Valley Sports, Littleworth Lane, Rossington, Doncaster, South Yorkshire, DN11 0HJ Tel: (01302) 868408 Fax: (01302) 868286 E-mail: sales@donvalleysports.co.uk
Downshire Camping & Caravan Centre, 12 Newry Road, Banbridge, County Down, BT32 3HN Tel: (028) 4062 3378 Fax: (028) 4062 9295 E-mail: sales@downshirecaravans.net
Escape, 29 Emscote Road, Warwick, CV34 5QH Tel: (01926) 493929 Fax: (01926) 492626 E-mail: shop@escape2.co.uk
Field & Trek plc, Market Cross, Ambleside, Cumbria, LA22 9BT Tel: (01539) 434350 Fax: (01539) 431067 E-mail: info@fieldandtrack.com
Field & Trek plc, 3 Palace Street, Canterbury, Kent, CT1 2DY Tel: (01227) 470023 Fax: (01227) 477072
Field & Trek UK Ltd, Langdale House, Sable Way, Southfields Business Park, Basildon, Essex, SS15 6SR Tel: (0870) 7771071 Fax: (01268) 494432 E-mail: sales@fieldandtrek.co.uk
G R & R D Taylor, 15 Market Street, Kirkby Lonsdale, Carnforth, Lancashire, LA6 2AU Tel: (01524) 271170 Fax: (01524) 271170 E-mail: sales@gr-rdtaylor.co.uk
Globetrekker, 25 High Street, Heritage Close, St. Albans, Hertfordshire, AL3 4EH Tel: (01727) 835999 Fax: (01727) 835777 E-mail: m.tearle@fsmail.net
▶ Handell Outdoor, Ware, Hertfordshire, SG12 9WX Tel: (01920) 871228 E-mail: info@handy.uk.com
J R Camping Ltd, Egginton Road, Hilton, Derby, DE65 5FJ Tel: (01283) 733525 Fax: (01283) 734812 E-mail: derby@jrleisure.com
J R Leisure, 50 Oswin Road, Leicester, LE3 1HR Tel: 0116-247 0740 Fax: 0116-247 0865
J & R Stores Ltd, Catfoot Lane, Lambley, Nottingham, NG4 4QG Tel: 0115-920 4152 Fax: 0115-920 4152 E-mail: lanley@grleisure.com
Katz & Co. (Folkestone) Ltd, 331-333 Cheriton Road, Folkestone, Kent, CT19 4BQ Tel: (01303) 271001 Fax: (01303) 279959 E-mail: sales@katzltd.com
Killin Outdoor Centre, Dreadnought Place, Main Street, Killin, Perthshire, FK21 8UJ Tel: (01567) 820652 Fax: (01567) 820116 E-mail: shop@killinoutdoor.co.uk
Kountry Kit Ltd, 22-23 West Street, Tavistock, Devon, PL19 8AN Tel: (01822) 613089 Fax: (01822) 615798 E-mail: enquires@kountrykit.fsnet.co.uk
LPC Caravan Dealers, 7 South Circular Business Park, Newtownards Road, Bangor, County Down, BT19 7AG Tel: (028) 9146 5551 Fax: (028) 9146 8815
Millets, 33 Bridge Street, Evesham, Worcestershire, WR11 4SQ Tel: (01386) 446759
Millets (Camping & Countrywear) Ltd, 119 Broadway, Bexleyheath, Kent, DA6 7HF Tel: (020) 8303 5089 Fax: (020) 8301 4603
Millets (Camping & Countrywear) Ltd, 65 High Street, Bromley, BR1 1JY Tel: (020) 8460 0418
Millets (Camping & Countrywear) Ltd, Unit 2b Sauchiehall Centre, Sauchiehall Street, Glasgow, G2 3ER Tel: 0141-332 5617 Fax: 0141-332 5617
Millets (Camping & Countrywear) Ltd, 68 Northbrook Street, Newbury, Berkshire, RG14 1AE Tel: (01635) 40070 Fax: (01635) 40070
Millets (Camping & Countrywear) Ltd, 4-5 St Marys Butts, Reading, RG1 2LN Tel: 0118-959 5228
Millets (Camping & Countrywear) Ltd, 42-44 South Street, Romford, RM1 1RB Tel: (01708) 743751 Fax: (01708) 743751
Millets (Camping & Countrywear) Ltd, 13 Gaolgate Street, Stafford, ST16 2BQ Tel: (01785) 251912 Fax: (01785) 259250
Millets (Camping & Countrywear) Ltd, 24 Queen Street, Wrexham, Clwyd, LL11 1AL Tel: (01978) 261267
Mountain Trail, The Lynch Building, 49 High Street, Holywood, County Down, BT18 9AB Tel: (028) 9042 8529
▶ Mountain Warehouse Ltd, 35a Stonegate, York, YO1 8AW Tel: (01904) 658458 Fax: (01904) 658458
Nomad Travellers Store & Medical Centre, 3-4 Wellington Terrace, Turnpike Lane, London, N8 0PX Tel: (0845) 3104470 Fax: (020) 8889 9529
North West Supplies, Llwyn Onn Industrial Estate, Amlwch, Gwynedd, LL68 9BQ Tel: (01407) 832020 Fax: (01407) 832200 E-mail: support@northwestsupplies.co.uk
Oswald Bailey Ltd, 106 Commercial Road, Bournemouth, BH2 5LR Tel: (01202) 552742
Oswald Bailey Ltd, 61 The Horsefair, Bristol, BS1 3JP Tel: 0117-929 3523 Fax: (01202) 397274
Oswald Bailey Ltd, 2 Saxon Square, Christchurch, Dorset, BH23 1QA Tel: (01202) 483043
Out & About, 18 Bower Road, Harrogate, North Yorkshire, HG1 5BW Tel: (01423) 561592 Fax: (01423) 560668 E-mail: sales@outandabout-online.co.uk
Out & About, 2 Elcho Street Brae, Peebles, EH45 8HU Tel: (01721) 723590 Fax: (01721) 723590
Out & About, 88 Brighton Road, Worthing, West Sussex, BN11 2EN Tel: (01903) 234915 Fax: (01903) 234915 E-mail: enquiries@outandabout-online.co.uk
Outdoor Choice, High Street, Glan Y Traeth, Barmouth, Gwynedd, LL42 1DS Tel: (01341) 280948
Outdoor Group Ltd, Mansard Close, Westgate Industrial Estate, Northampton, NN5 5DL Tel: (01604) 441111 Fax: (01604) 441164 E-mail: enquiries@blacks.co.uk
Outdoor Scene, 40-44 Carrington Street, Nottingham, NG1 7GD Tel: 0115-950 4998 Fax: 0115-948 3305 E-mail: carrington@outdoorscene.co.uk
Outdoor World, Mersey Buildings, 304 Winwick Road, Warrington, WA2 8JG Tel: (01925) 634794 Fax: (01925) 232717 E-mail: info@outdoorworld.org
Outdoors, 40-44 St. Georges Walk, Croydon, CR0 1YJ Tel: (020) 8688 1730 Fax: (020) 8688 1730
Quay Outdoor Activity Centre, 23 Victoria Parade, Torquay, TQ1 2BD Tel: (01803) 292080 Fax: (01803) 214635
Regatta Great Outdoors Factory Outlet, Freeport Village, Anchorage Road, Fleetwood, Lancashire, FY7 6AE Tel: (01253) 777705 Fax: (01253) 777705 E-mail: enquiries@regatta.co.uk
Romeo Trading Company Ltd, Romeo House, 160 Bridport Road, London, N18 1SY Tel: (020) 8803 0066 Fax: (020) 8803 0008 E-mail: admin@romeotrading.com
Safari, 44 Cascades, Portsmouth, PO1 4RR Tel: (023) 9282 9410 Fax: (023) 9281 6070
Samuel James Outdoor Centre, 75-77 Gisburn Road, Barrowford, Barrowford, Nelson, Lancashire, BB9 6DX Tel: (07939) 502602 Fax: (01282) 613415 E-mail: broomsticktrav@aol.com
W. Slack & Sons, 38 Rosemary Street, Mansfield, Nottinghamshire, NG18 1QL Tel: (01623) 624449
Soldier Of Fortune Adventure, 8-10 Lower Bridge Street, Chester, CH1 1RS Tel: (01244) 328205 Fax: (01244) 328205
Springfield Camping, Denholme Mill, Burnley Road, Luddendenfoot, Halifax, West Yorkshire, HX2 6AR Tel: (01422) 883164 Fax: (01422) 886698 E-mail: sales@springfield-camping.co.uk
Stafford Outdoor Leisure, 38 Mill Street, Stafford, ST16 2AJ Tel: (01785) 240594 Fax: (01785) 213420 E-mail: sales@staffordoutdoor.com
▶ Sunflair Camping Equipment Suppliers, Parham Airfield, Parham, Woodbridge, Suffolk, IP13 9AF Tel: (01728) 720773 Fax: (01728) 720774
Sutterton Camping Equipment, Post Office Lane, Sutterton, Boston, Lincolnshire, PE20 2EB Tel: (01205) 460485 Fax: (01205) 460162 E-mail: sales@sutterton-camping.com
Sutton-In-Ashfield Supply Stores Ltd, 9 Market Street, Huthwaite, Sutton-in-Ashfield, Nottinghamshire, NG17 2LB Tel: (01623) 554238 Fax: (01623) 550464 E-mail: sss-ltd@tiscali.co.uk
T A M Leisure Ltd, 180 Kingston Road, New Malden, Surrey, KT3 3RD Tel: (020) 8949 5435 Fax: (020) 8336 1418 E-mail: sales@tamleisure.co.uk
Taunton Leisure, 110 Fore Street, Exeter, EX4 3JF Tel: (01392) 498793 Fax: (01392) 496965
Tent Hire, 105a Pargeter Street, Walsall, WS2 8QR Tel: (01922) 634808 Fax: (01922) 647788
Tyf Adventure Ltd, 1 High Street, St. Davids, Haverfordwest, Dyfed, SA62 6SA Tel: (01437) 721611 Fax: (01437) 721692 E-mail: sales@tyf.com
W M Camping Ltd, Herne Road, Herne Bay, Kent, CT6 7LH Tel: (01227) 712222 Fax: (01227) 712222 E-mail: sales@wmcamping.co.uk
W Yeomans Ltd, 11 Midland Way, Barlborough, Chesterfield, Derbyshire, S43 4XA Tel: (01246) 571270 Fax: (01246) 571271 E-mail: mailbox@wyeomans.com
Wearhouse Ltd, 32 North Street, Taunton, Somerset, TA1 1LW Tel: (01823) 333291 Fax: (01823) 334699
Work & Weather Wear, 44 High Street, Biggar, Lanarkshire, ML12 6BJ Tel: (01899) 221076 Fax: (01899) 221450
Yeomans Army Stores, 5-7 Rodgers Lane, Alfreton, Derbyshire, DE55 7FF Tel: (01773) 831486 Fax: (01246) 551024 E-mail: mailbox@yeomansoutdoors.co.uk
▶ Yeomans Army Stores, 146 Parade, Leamington Spa, Warwickshire, CV32 4AG Tel: (01926) 451276
Yeomans Army Stores, 6 Jubilee Buildings, Sutton-in-Ashfield, Nottinghamshire, NG17 1DE Tel: (01623) 511339
Yeomans Outdoor Centre, 5 Keighley Road, Skipton, North Yorkshire, BD23 2LP Tel: (01756) 797733
Yeomans Outdoors, 3 Victoria Square, Ashbourne, Derbyshire, DE6 1GG Tel: (01335) 342468
Yeomans Outdoors, 84-86 St. Peters Street, Derby, DE1 1SR Tel: (01332) 384684 E-mail: enquiries@yeomansoutdoors.co.uk
Yeomans Outdoors, 1b Oxford Street, Ripley, Derbyshire, DE5 3AG Tel: (01773) 748044
Yha Adventure Shops P.L.C., 90-98 Corporation Street, Birmingham, B4 6XS Tel: 0121-236 7799 Fax: 0121-236 4118 E-mail: birmingham@yhaadventure.com

CAMPING EQUIPMENT, WATER BOTTLES

▶ The Army Store, 11 - Wyndham Arcade, St Mary's Street, Cardiff, CF10 1FH Tel: 02920 343141 E-mail: info@thearmystore.co.uk

CAMS

Camco UK Ltd, 432 Perth Avenue, Slough, SL1 4TS Tel: (01753) 786100 Fax: (01753) 786101 E-mail: sales@camcoindex.com
David Newman Camshafts & Co., Farnborough Way, Orpington, Kent, BR6 7DH Tel: (01689) 857109 Fax: (01689) 855498 E-mail: info@newman-cams.com
Engine Developments, Leigh Road, Swift Valley Industrial Estate, Rugby, Warwickshire, CV21 1DS Tel: (01788) 541114 Fax: (01788) 546303 E-mail: sales@engdev.com
Inchlines Ltd, 11 Hilltop Road, Hamilton Industrial Park, Leicester, LE5 1TT Tel: 0116-276 5111 Fax: 0116-276 6596 E-mail: info@inchlines.com
Midland Cam & Tool (1982) Co., 21 Nursery Road, Hockley, Birmingham, B19 2XN Tel: 0121-551 9922 Fax: 0121-551 9929 E-mail: tooling@centreless.com
Provincial Engineers Colne Ltd, 2 Waterside Industrial Estate, Mill Green, Colne, Lancashire, BB8 0TA Tel: (01282) 863893 Fax: (01282) 868704

CAMSHAFT GRINDING MACHINES

▶ S I M Machine Tools Ltd, 5-6a Unit, London Terrace, Darwen, Lancashire, BB3 3DF Tel: (01254) 777117 Fax: (01254) 774841 E-mail: sales@simmachinetools.com

CAMSHAFTS

David Newman Camshafts & Co., Farnborough Way, Orpington, Kent, BR6 7DH Tel: (01689) 857109 Fax: (01689) 855498 E-mail: info@newman-cams.com
Federal-Mogul Camshaft Castings Ltd, Tutnalls, Lydney, Gloucestershire, GL15 5PX Tel: (01594) 842112 Fax: (01594) 841037
Wescombe Maurice B, Silverdale Road, Hayes, Middlesex, UB3 3BN Tel: (020) 8561 0862 Fax: (020) 8561 7007

CAN CRUSHERS

G C Equipment Ltd, Unit 6, St Margarets Business Park, Moor Mead Road, Twickenham, TW1 1JN Tel: (020) 8891 1500 Fax: (020) 8891 6735 E-mail: sales@gcequipment.co.uk
▶ Home Recycling Ltd, Bulton Brow, Sowerbry, Ingleby Barwick, Sowerby Bridge, West Yorkshire, HX6 2AG Tel: (0845) 6123191 Fax: (0845) 6123292 E-mail: sales@homerecycling.co.uk

CAN FILLING MACHINES

Angelus Machine Corporation International, De Salis Drive, Hampton Lovett, Droitwich, Worcestershire, WR9 0QE Tel: (01905) 779602 Fax: (01905) 771882 E-mail: admin@angelus-machine.co.uk
M & P (Engineering) Ltd, Wharfside Way, Trafford Park, Manchester, M17 1AN Tel: 0161-872 8378 Fax: 0161-872 9250 E-mail: info@mp-engineering.co.uk

CAN HANDLING EQUIPMENT

Angelus Machine Corporation International, De Salis Drive, Hampton Lovett, Droitwich, Worcestershire, WR9 0QE Tel: (01905) 779602 Fax: (01905) 771882 E-mail: admin@angelus-machine.co.uk

CAN INSPECTION EQUIPMENT

Peco Controls (Europe) Ltd, Kempton Road, Pershore, Worcestershire, WR10 2TA Tel: (01386) 556622 Fax: (01386) 552252 E-mail: office@peco-europe.com

CAN PRODUCTION MACHINERY

Angelus Machine Corporation International, De Salis Drive, Hampton Lovett, Droitwich, Worcestershire, WR9 0QE Tel: (01905) 779602 Fax: (01905) 771882 E-mail: admin@angelus-machine.co.uk
Carnaud Metal Box Engineering, Dockfield Road, Shipley, West Yorkshire, BD17 7AY Tel: (01274) 846200 Fax: (01274) 846201 E-mail: william.jowitt@eur.crowncorrk.com
T & S Overseas Ltd, PO Box 248, Rochdale, Lancashire, OL11 4YA Tel: (01706) 350406 Fax: (01706) 526809

CANAL HEARING AIDS

Puretone plc, Unit 9-10 Henley Business Park, Trident Close, Medway City Estate, Rochester, Kent, ME2 4FR Tel: (01634) 719427 Fax: (01634) 719450 E-mail: sales@puretone.net

CANDLE FILTERS

Howard Filter Systems, East Skirdle, Waterrow, Taunton, Somerset, TA4 2AY Tel: (01984) 623112 Fax: (01984) 624770 E-mail: hfsl@btconnect.co.uk

CANDLE HOLDERS

▶ Hocus Pocus, 38 Gardner Street, Brighton, BN1 1UN Tel: (01273) 572212 Fax: (01273) 572207 E-mail: info@hocuspocus.co.uk

CANDLE HOLDERS, GLASS

▶ Yankee Candles Europe, 1 Bristol Distribution Park, Hawkley Drive, Bradley Stoke, Bristol, BS32 0BF Tel: (01454) 454500 Fax: (01454) 454510

CANDLE LAMPS

A B S (Electrical Engineering & Supplies) Ltd, Unit F, Northbrook Trading Estate, Northbrook Road, Worthing, West Sussex, BN14 8PN Tel: (01903) 235636 Fax: (01903) 232512 E-mail: sales@abs-electrical.co.uk
Decorlight, B 68 Pier Avenue, Clacton-on-Sea, Essex, CO15 1NH Tel: (01255) 421818 Fax: (01255) 474147

CANDLE MAKING REQUISITES

E.H. Thorne (Beehives) Ltd, Beehive Works, Louth Road, Wragby, Market Rasen, Lincolnshire, LN8 5LA Tel: (01673) 858555 Fax: (01673) 857004 E-mail: sales@thorne.co.uk

CANDLE WICKS

Hayes & Finch Ltd, Hanson Road, Liverpool, L9 7BP Tel: 0151-523 6303 Fax: 0151-523 4537 E-mail: sales@hfltd.com

CANDLES

▶ easyonlineshop, 68 Monument Road, Talke Pits, Stoke-on-Trent, ST7 1SJ Tel: (01782) 771592 E-mail: lisahughesann@yahoo.co.uk

▶ The Felbrigg Design Co, 51 Long Street, Tetbury, Gloucestershire, GL8 8AA Tel: (01666) 505026 Fax: (01666) 505026 E-mail: tetbury@felbriggdesign.com

▶ Functional Art, 127 Homesdale Road, Bromley, BR2 9LE Tel: (0796) 7077808 E-mail: rosanna@functional-art.co.uk

▶ Gamrie's Candle World, Main Street, Garmond, Turriff, Aberdeenshire, AB53 5TQ Tel: (01888) 544170 Fax: (01888) 544415 E-mail: sales@gamriescandles.co.uk

▶ Gifts & Gold, 8 Chipstead Valley Road, Coulsdon, Surrey, CR5 2RA Tel: (020) 8763 2520 Fax: (020) 8763 2520 E-mail: giftsandgold@aol.com

▶ Herbalbrew, 7 Greenhill Road, Coleraine, County Londonderry, BT51 3JE Tel: (028) 7035 7225 E-mail: kat@herbalbrew.co.uk

▶ Hocus Pocus, 38 Gardner Street, Brighton, BN1 1UN Tel: (01273) 572212 Fax: (01273) 572207 E-mail: info@hocuspocus.co.uk

Jeyes Group Ltd, Brunel Way, Thetford, Norfolk, IP24 1HF Tel: (01842) 757575 Fax: (01842) 757812

Shearer Candles Ltd, 23 Robert Street, Glasgow, G51 3HB Tel: 0141-445 1066 Fax: 0141-445 1061 E-mail: sales@shearer-candles.com

▶ Yankee Candles Europe, 1 Bristol Distribution Park, Hawkley Drive, Bradley Stoke, Bristol, BS32 0BF Tel: (01454) 454500 Fax: (01454) 454510

CANDLESTICKS

▶ easyonlineshop, 68 Monument Road, Talke Pits, Stoke-on-Trent, ST7 1SJ Tel: (01782) 771592 E-mail: lisahughesann@yahoo.co.uk

CANDY BARS

Sweets For U, Unit 9, Bradley Hall Trading Estate, Bradley Lane, Standish, Wigan, Lancashire, WN6 0XQ Tel: (01257) 400780 E-mail: julierose_4@hotmail.com

CANE GOODS AND FURNITURE

▶ Bracken Wood Furniture, Unit 8 Headway Business Park, Denby Dale Road, Wakefield, West Yorkshire, WF2 7AZ Tel: (01924) 381580 Fax: (01924) 290811 E-mail: sales@brackenwoodfurniture.co.uk

Cane Collection Ltd, 70 Fred Dannatt Road, Mildenhall, Bury St. Edmunds, Suffolk, IP28 7RD Tel: (01638) 714832 Fax: (01638) 510840 E-mail: sales@canecollection.co.uk

Cane Direct, Goyt Mill, Upper Hibbert Lane, Marple, Stockport, Cheshire, SK6 7HX Tel: 0161-427 7774 Fax: 0161-427 7225 E-mail: admin@cane-direct.co.uk

Canterbury Cane, 358 Abergele Road, Old Colwyn, Colwyn Bay, Clwyd, LL29 9LS Tel: (01492) 514448 Fax: (01492) 514448

Christine's Cane Furniture, 2a Watson Road, Worksop, Nottinghamshire, S80 2BB Tel: (01909) 483790 Fax: (01909) 483790 E-mail: christinestevens30@virgin.com

Diamond Windows, 25 The Fairways, New River Trading Estate, Cheshunt, Waltham Cross, Hertfordshire, EN8 0NL Tel: (01992) 635162 Fax: (01992) 623300

▶ Eurocush Cane Goods, 1 Dereham Road, Norwich, NR2 4HX Tel: (01603) 663686 Fax: (01603) 664604

Habasco International Ltd, Stafford Mills, George Street, Milnsbridge, Huddersfield, HD3 4JD Tel: (01484) 642115 Fax: (01484) 640058 E-mail: sales@habasco.net

J W Taylor & Son, Les-Osiers, Ings Road, Ulleskelf, Tadcaster, North Yorkshire, LS24 9SS Tel: (01937) 832138

Kingsway Cane Furniture Ltd, 119 Parker Drive, Leicester, LE4 0JP Tel: 0116-235 0419 Fax: 0116-236 6724 E-mail: sales@kingswaycane.co.uk

Kingsworthy Foundry Co. Ltd, London Road, Kingsworthy, Winchester, Hampshire, SO23 7QG Tel: (01962) 883776 Fax: (01962) 882925 E-mail: kwf@fsbdial.co.uk

▶ Natural Comforts, Unit 10-11 Orde Wingate Way, Stockton-on-Tees, Cleveland, TS19 0GA Tel: (01642) 611172 Fax: (01642) 611173 E-mail: naturalcomfortsuk@btinternet.com

Product Express Ltd, Hartley Business Centre, 272-284 Monkmoor Road, Shrewsbury, SY2 5ST Tel: (01743) 359459 Fax: (01743) 359123 E-mail: sales@productexpress.co.uk

Raynesway Interiors, 5 227 Derby Road, Chaddesden, Derby, DE21 6SY Tel: (01332) 280585 Fax: (01332) 280585

Supercrafts Cane Goods, Harlestone Road, Northampton, NN5 6NU Tel: (01604) 581757 Fax: (01604) 581554 E-mail: supercrafts@btinternet.co.uk

CANE MERCHANTS OR AGENTS

Centre Cane Co., 16 Shakletons, Ongar, Essex, CM5 9AT Tel: (01277) 363285 Fax: (01277) 366682 E-mail: centrcane@aol.com

Jacobs Young & Westbury, Bridge Road, Haywards Heath, West Sussex, RH16 1UA Tel: (01444) 412411 Fax: (01444) 457662 E-mail: sales@jyw-uk.com

CANISTERS

D K S Packaging Ltd, 62-70 Litherland Road, Bootle, Merseyside, L20 3HZ Tel: 0151-922 2656 Fax: 0151-933 0547 E-mail: reception@dkspackaging.co.uk

CANNERS/CANNING SERVICES, CONTRACT

Ham Packers Ltd, Saltash Industrial Estate, Saltash, Cornwall, PL12 6LF Tel: (01752) 845235 Fax: (01752) 842333

CANOE PADDLES

The Dinghy Store, Sea Wall, Whitstable, Kent, CT5 1BX Tel: (01227) 274168 Fax: (01227) 772750 E-mail: sales@thedinghystore.co.uk

Rocon Plastics Ltd, Unit 9e Dukesway, Prudhoe, Northumberland, NE42 6PQ Tel: (01661) 836938 Fax: (01661) 836939 E-mail: harry@rocon.demon.co.uk

▶ Storm Kayaks and Equipment, Unit 8 Harbour House, Harbour Way, Shoreham-by-Sea, West Sussex, BN43 5HZ Tel: (01273) 465406 E-mail: tony@stormkayaks.co.uk

CANOES

▶ The Outdoor Pursuits Co-operative, 22-24 Radford Street, Stone, Staffordshire, ST15 8DA Tel: (01785) 818500

▶ Seawing Boats, 18 Darrowby Close, Thirsk, North Yorkshire, YO7 1FJ Tel: (01845) 527397 E-mail: info@seawingboats.co.uk

▶ Storm Kayaks and Equipment, Unit 8 Harbour House, Harbour Way, Shoreham-by-Sea, West Sussex, BN43 5HZ Tel: (01273) 465406 E-mail: tony@stormkayaks.co.uk

CANS

Carnaudmetalbox, Golf Course Lane, Leicester, LE3 1TX Tel: 0116-291 3300 Fax: 0116-291 3312

Impress Metal Packaging, Salhouse Road, Norwich, NR7 9AT Tel: (01603) 427313 Fax: (01603) 408571

CANS, BEER/BEVERAGE

Ball Packaging Europe UK Ltd, Lakeside, Chester Business Park, Chester, CH4 9QT Tel: (01244) 681155 Fax: (01244) 680320 E-mail: chester_reception@ball-europe.com

Carnaud Metalbox P.L.C., Perry Wood Walk, Worcester, WR5 1EG Tel: (01905) 762000 Fax: (01905) 762357

Crown Packaging (U K) Plc, Borland Avenue, Borland Avenue, Botcherby, Carlisle, CA1 2TL Tel: (01228) 811200 Fax: (01228) 811290

CANTEEN CUTLERY CASES

Chimo Holdings, White Rose Works, 61 Eyre Lane, Sheffield, S1 3GF Tel: 0114-272 4656 Fax: 0114-249 0922 E-mail: sales@chimoholdings.co.uk

Charles Kirkby & Sons Ltd, 84 Sidney Street, Sheffield, S1 4RH Tel: 0114-272 1327 Fax: 0114-275 6506

CANTEEN TABLES

Gopak Ltd, Range Road, Hythe, Kent, CT21 6HG Tel: (01303) 265751 Fax: (01303) 268282 E-mail: sales@gopak.co.uk

CANTILEVER RACKING

▶ Dyfed Industrial Developments, Graig, Burry Port, Dyfed, SA16 0BJ Tel: (01554) 832777 Fax: (01554) 832777 E-mail: did@draenog.freeserve.co.uk

Rack Stor Ltd, Suite 14 South West Centre, Archer Rd, Sheffield, S8 0JR Tel: 0114-296 0066 Fax: 0114-296 0055 E-mail: contactus@rackstor.co.uk

Trade Systems, 48-56 Hawks Road, Kingston Upon Thames, Surrey, KT1 3EE Tel: (020) 8549 5281 Fax: (020) 8541 5637 E-mail: sales@tradesystems.co.uk

CANVAS FINE ART PRINTS

▶ contemporaryart4all.co.uk, 14 West Park Crescent, Inverbervie, Montrose, Angus, DD10 0TX Tel: 01561 362902 E-mail: ros@contemporaryart4all.co.uk

▶ Digital Design Canvas UK, 10, churchbury rd, enfield, middx, EN1 3HR Tel: 0208 3646205 E-mail: enquiries@digitaldesignuk.co.uk

▶ Digitata Ltd, Old Academy, Back Road, Stromness, Orkney, KW16 3AW Tel: (01856) 851740 Fax: (0870) 0518821 E-mail: info@digitatadesign.co.uk

▶ DPS Fine Art, 14 Hermes Way, Sleaford, Lincolnshire, NG34 7WH Tel: 01529 300452 Fax: 01529 300452 E-mail: matt@dpsfineart.co.uk

▶ Iconic Imaging Ltd, 18 Squirrel Lane, Ashford, Kent, TN25 4GG Tel: (01233) 663866 E-mail: sales@iconicimaging.co.uk

▶ Neil Hipkiss Fine Art Studio, PO Box 781, Worcester, WR4 4BQ Tel: (01886) 888658 E-mail: neil.hipkiss@blueyonder.co.uk

▶ Ubermagic, 78 Western Road, Leigh-on-Sea, Essex, SS9 2PW Tel: (01702) 470573 E-mail: support@ubermagic.co.uk

▶ www.emmalove.com, Bridle Lane, Streetly, Sutton Coldfield, West Midlands, B74 3PT Tel: (0797) 1425195 E-mail: design@interiorlove.co.uk

CANVAS GOODS, MADE-UP

A Shores & Co Leather & Canvas Products Ltd, Byron St Mills, Millwright Street, Leeds, LS2 7QG Tel: 0113-245 6062

B & H Canvas Products Ltd, 33a Chester Street, Cardiff, CF11 6PY Tel: (029) 2034 3610 Fax: (029) 2056 3753

Custom Covers 1984 Ltd, Quayside Road, Southampton, SO18 1AD Tel: (023) 8033 5744 Fax: (023) 8022 5581 E-mail: sales@customcovers.co.uk

Emlyn Canvas & Cordage Co. Ltd, George Street Conservatory Centre, Granville Square, Newport, Gwent, NP20 2AB Tel: (01633) 262262 Fax: (01633) 222420

Fine Group Son Ltd, 93 Manor Farm Road, London, Wembley, Middlesex, HA0 1XB Tel: (020) 8214 8600 Fax: (020) 8997 8410 E-mail: sales@finegoup.co.uk

Fisher Tarpaulins, Unit 5-6 The Maltings, Navigation Drive, Hurst Business Park, Brierley Hill, West Midlands, DY5 1UT Tel: (01384) 571313 Fax: (01384) 261666

Garland Sails, 246a Soundwell Road, Bristol, BS15 1PN Tel: 0117-935 3233 Fax: 0117-935 3233 E-mail: garlandsails@ukonline.co.uk

Gostelow Advertising Ltd, 21-22 Francis Street, Hull, HU2 8DT Tel: (01482) 323459 Fax: (01482) 586325 E-mail: alec@gostelow.karoo.co.uk

Jacon Ltd, 1 Brickfield Industrial Estate, New Road, Gillingham, Dorset, SP8 4LT Tel: (01747) 825858 Fax: (01747) 825634 E-mail: info@jacon.co.uk

Jarvis Manufacturing Ltd, 22b Hawthorn Road, Eastbourne, East Sussex, BN23 6QA Tel: (01323) 411993 Fax: (01323) 649662 E-mail: info@jarvismanufacturing.co.uk

Kingswood Canvas Ltd, Unit 8-9 Douglas Road Industrial Park, Douglas Road, Kingswood, Bristol, BS15 8PD Tel: 0117-960 1281 Fax: 0117-935 2632 E-mail: kingswoodcanvas@btconnect.com

Lawson Bros, 7 Snoll Hatch Road, East Peckham, Tonbridge, Kent, TN12 5EE Tel: (01622) 872816

M B Products Ltd, Parkgate Works, Coleman Street, Parkgate, Rotherham, South Yorkshire, S62 6EL Tel: (01709) 528215 Fax: (01709) 710796 E-mail: roger@mbpgroup.freeserve.co.uk

M & N Canvas Services Ltd, Butterthwaite Lane, Ecclesfield, Sheffield, S35 9WA Tel: 0114-246 1293 Fax: 0114-257 0311

Andrew Mitchell & Co. Ltd, 15 Dunivaig Road, Glasgow, G33 4TT Tel: 0141-773 5454 Fax: 0141-773 5455E-mail: info1@mitco.co.uk

Sail Loft, Port Edgar Marina, Port Edgar, South Queensferry, West Lothian, EH30 9SQ Tel: 0131-331 4949 Fax: 0131-331 4848 E-mail: info@sail-loft.co.uk

Stuart Brumby Cover Makers, 18 Park Farm Road, Foxhills Industrial Estate, Scunthorpe, South Humberside, DN15 8QP Tel: (01724) 280440 Fax: (01724) 280440

▶ Tocco Photos on Canvas, PO Box 67, York, YO61 1WU Tel: (0845) 6426526 E-mail: info@toccoinside.co.uk

Truro Canvas, Malpas Road, Truro, Cornwall, TR1 1QH Tel: (01209) 820945 Fax: (01872) 240011

George Woodall & Sons Ltd, 35 & 37 Market Place, Malton, North Yorkshire, YO17 7LP Tel: (01653) 692086 Fax: (01653) 691488 E-mail: shop@gwoodall.com

CANVAS WIND BREAKS OR WINDSHIELDS

Cornish Windbreaks, Treleigh Avenue, Redruth, Cornwall, TR15 1DB Tel: (01209) 214944 Fax: (01209) 214944

CAP AND CLOSURE CONTAINER SEALING COMPOUNDS

Metal Closures Huddersfield Ltd, Tandem Industrial Estate, Wakefield Road, Tandem, Huddersfield, HD5 0BL Tel: (01484) 533216 Fax: (01484) 543203 E-mail: sales@metal-closures.co.uk

CAPACITIVE SENSORS

Rechner UK Ltd, Unit 6, The Old Mill, Reading Road, Pangbourne, Reading, RG8 7HY Tel: 0118-976 6450 Fax: 0118-976 6451 E-mail: info@rechner-sensors.co.uk

CAPACITOR CLIPS

F T Pressings Ltd, Eagle Works, New Road, Studley, Warwickshire, B80 7LY Tel: (01527) 854925 Fax: (01527) 854925

CAPACITORS, *See also headings for particular types*

A D I American Distributors Inc, Units 3-4 Peckworth Industrial Estate, Bedford Road, Lower Standon, Henlow, Bedfordshire, SG16 6EE Tel: (01462) 850804 Fax: (01462) 819596 E-mail: sales@americandistr.com

Adex Technical Ltd, Unit 4 Canal Ironworks, Hope Mill Lane, London Road, Stroud, Gloucestershire, GL5 2SH Tel: (01453) 889202 Fax: (01453) 889203 E-mail: sales@adexltd.co.uk

Advanced Power Components plc, Unit 47 Riverside Estate, Sir Thomas Longley Road, Medway City Estate, Rochester, Kent, ME2 4DP Tel: (01634) 290588 Fax: (01634) 290591 E-mail: sales@apc-plc.co.uk

Anglia, Sandall Road, Wisbech, Cambridgeshire, PE13 2PS Tel: (01945) 474747 Fax: (01945) 474849 E-mail: sales@angliac.com

Campbell Collins Ltd, 162 High St, Stevenage, Hertfordshire, SG1 3LL Tel: (01438) 369466 Fax: (01438) 316465 E-mail: sales@camcol.co.uk

D N A UK Ltd, Bighton Hill, Ropley, Alresford, Hampshire, SO24 9SQ Tel: (01962) 772666 Fax: (01962) 772660 E-mail: info@dnacap.com

Dubilier Electronic Component Distributors, Station House Station Yard Industrial Park, Station Road, Dunmow, Essex, CM6 1XD Tel: (01371) 875758 Fax: (01371) 875075 E-mail: sales@dubilier.co.uk

Easby Electronics Ltd, Mercury Road, Gallowfields Trading Estate, Richmond, North Yorkshire, DL10 4TQ Tel: (01748) 850555 Fax: (01748) 850556 E-mail: sales@easby.co.uk

▶ Enspec Power Ltd, Stanfield Business Centre, Addison Street, Sunderland, SR2 8BL Tel: 0191-514 2090 Fax: 0191-514 2151 E-mail: info@enspecpower.com

Eton M E M Low Voltage Products Ltd, Grimshaw Lane, Middleton Farm, Manchester, M24 1GQ Tel: 0161-655 8900 Fax: (0870) 0507525 E-mail: ukresiorders@eton.com

Globec UK, Unit 15 Shrivenham Hundred Business Park, Majors Road, Watchfield, Swindon, SN6 8TZ Tel: (01793) 780790 Fax: (01793) 780776 E-mail: info@globec.co.uk

Induction Services Ltd, 16 Wharfedale Cresent, Droitwich, Worcestershire, WR9 8TU Tel: (01905) 771669 Fax: (01905) 797609 E-mail: sales@inductionservices.co.uk

L C R Capacitors Eu Ltd, Unit 18 Rassau Industrial Estate, Rassau, Ebbw Vale, Gwent, NP23 5SD Tel: (01495) 307070 Fax: (01495) 306965 E-mail: sales@lcrcapacitors.co.uk

N I C Components Europe, 14 Top Angel, Buckingham Industrial Estate, Buckingham, MK18 1TH Tel: (01280) 813737 Fax: (01280) 814737 E-mail: niesales@niccomp.com

Nichicon Europe Ltd, Riverside Way, Camberley, Surrey, GU15 3YL Tel: (01276) 405500 Fax: (01276) 686531

Northcott Electronics Ltd, 1 Marquis Business Centre, Royston Road, Baldock, Hertfordshire, SG7 6XL Tel: (01462) 490999 Fax: (01462) 490990 E-mail: info@northcott.co.uk

Power Capacitors Ltd, 30 Redfern Road, Birmingham, B11 2BH Tel: 0121-708 2811 Fax: 0121-765 4054 E-mail: sales@powercapacitors.co.uk

Ridgeway Components Ltd, Unit 5, Prosperity Way, Middlewich, Cheshire, CW10 0GD Tel: (01606) 841010 Fax: (01606) 841011 E-mail: sales@ridgeway-components.co.uk

T T I, 2 Cliveden Office Village, Lancaster Road, Cressex Business Park, High Wycombe, Buckinghamshire, HP12 3YZ Tel: (01494) 460000 Fax: (01494) 460090 E-mail: sales.london@uk.ttiinc.com

CAPACITORS, ELECTRIC/ ELECTRONIC

A B B Power Ltd, Stonefield Works, Oulton Road, Stone, Staffordshire, ST15 0RS Tel: (01785) 825050 Fax: (01785) 819019
Ampohm Wound Products, Unit 1d Treburley Industrial Estate, Treburley, Launceston, Cornwall, PL15 9PU Tel: (01579) 370025 Fax: (01579) 370051 E-mail: ampcaps15@btconnect.com
Cambridge Capacitors Ltd, Budds Lane, Romsey, Hampshire, SO51 0ZQ Tel: (01794) 513481 Fax: (01794) 523940 E-mail: sales@camcap.co.uk
D N A UK Ltd, Bighton Hill, Ropley, Alresford, Hampshire, SO24 9SQ Tel: (01962) 772666 Fax: (01962) 772660 E-mail: info@dnacap.com
Evox Rifa Uk, 20-21 Cumberland Drive, Granby Industrial Estate, Weymouth, Dorset, DT4 9TE Tel: (01305) 830737 Fax: (01305) 760670
Industrial Capacitors Wrexham Ltd, Miners Road, Llay Industrial Estate, Llay, Wrexham, Clwyd, LL12 0PJ Tel: (01978) 853805 Fax: (01978) 853785 E-mail: sales@icwltd.co.uk
Iskra UK Ltd, Redlands, Coulsdon, Surrey, CR5 2HT Tel: (020) 8668 7141 Fax: (020) 8668 3108
J B Electrical Ltd, 5-6 Lion Industrial Park, Northgate Way, Walsall, WS9 8RL Tel: (01922) 459351 Fax: (01922) 743506 E-mail: jeff.bird@fsmail.net
L C R Capacitors Eu Ltd, Unit 18 Rassau Industrial Estate, Rassau, Ebbw Vale, Gwent, NP23 5SD Tel: (01495) 307070 Fax: (01495) 306965 E-mail: sales@lcrcapacitors.co.uk
M F D Capacitors (1991) Ltd, Lion Lane, Penley, Wrexham, LL13 0LY Tel: (01978) 710551 Fax: (01978) 710501 E-mail: sales@mfdcapacitors.co.uk
N C S Inc, 49 Parc-y-Felin, Creigiau, Cardiff, CF15 9PB Tel: (029) 2089 1515 Fax: (029) 2089 1694
Rush Industrial Sales, 126 Station Road, Tempsford, Sandy, Bedfordshire, SG19 2AY Tel: (01767) 640779 Fax: (01767) 640617 E-mail: sales@rushind.com

CAPPING MACHINES

Engelmann & Buckham Ltd, Buckham House, 25 Lenten Street, Alton, Hampshire, GU34 1HH Tel: (01420) 82421 Fax: (01420) 89193 E-mail: hrashleigh@buckham.co.uk

CAPPUCCINO COFFEE

▶ C JS Coffee Bar, 55 High Street, East Grinstead, West Sussex, RH19 3DD Tel: (01342) 301910
▶ Cappuccino & Gateau Ltd, 173 Crickelwood Broadway, London, NW2 3HT Tel: (020) 8208 4668 E-mail: cappucinogateau@ukcom.com

CAPS

Castell Iso Lok, The Castell Building, 217 Kingsbury Road, London, NW9 9PQ Tel: (020) 8511 1858 Fax: (020) 8205 0055 E-mail: sales@castell.com
▶ Keith Crafter Agencies, 8 Cause End Road, Wootton, Bedford, MK43 9DA Tel: (01234) 766014 Fax: (01234) 766014 E-mail: jim@kcaclosures.co.uk
Engelmann & Buckham Ltd, Buckham House, 25 Lenten Street, Alton, Hampshire, GU34 1HH Tel: (01420) 82421 Fax: (01420) 89193 E-mail: hrashleigh@buckham.co.uk

CAPS, RAIN, EXHAUST

▶ GenCat Ltd, Unit 16, The Edge Business Centre, Humber Road, London, NW2 6EW Tel: 0208 450 6160 Fax: 0208 452 2822 E-mail: info@gencat.co.uk

CAPSTAN LATHES

Emi-Mec, Unit E2 Doulton Road Trading Estate, Doulton Road, Rowley Regis, West Midlands, B65 8JQ Tel: (01384) 633968 Fax: (01384) 633946 E-mail: sales@emi-mec.eu
Reardon Engineering Co., Unit 6 9, 35 River Road, Barking, Essex, IG11 0DA Tel: (01708) 748253 Fax: (020) 8594 7398

CAPSTAN MACHINISTS/ AUTOMATIC MACHINE PRODUCTS

Alexican Ltd, 177 King Street, Dukinfield, Cheshire, SK16 4LG Tel: 0161-339 1999 Fax: 0161-330 1555 E-mail: info@alexican.co.uk
Ashtead Engineering Co. Ltd, Unit 2 3 Camphill Industrial Estate, Camphill Road, West Byfleet, Surrey, KT14 6EW Tel: (01932) 353121 Fax: (01932) 342968 E-mail: ashteadeng@byfleet.net
B G T Automatics Ltd, 2 Paragon Court, Tongham Road, Aldershot, Hampshire, GU12 4AA Tel: (01252) 318111 Fax: (01252) 311831 E-mail: carol@bgtcnc.freeserve.co.uk
Brass Turned Parts Ltd, 160 Dollman Street, Birmingham, B7 4RS Tel: 0121-359 1234 Fax: 0121-359 4698 E-mail: enquiries@brassturnedparts.co.uk
C N Smart (UK) Ltd, Unit 3, Baltimore Trading Estate, Baltimore Road, Great Barr, Birmingham, B42 1DD Tel: 0121-356 2920 Fax: 0121-356 6129 E-mail: cnsmart@hotmail.com
Camlit Precision Engineering Ltd, Sand Road Industrial Estate, Sand Road, Great Gransden, Sandy, Bedfordshire, SG19 3AH Tel: (01767) 677263 Fax: (01767) 677720
Clarkwood Engineering Ltd, 7 Blackenhall Industrial Estate, Sunbeam Street, Wolverhampton, WV2 4PF Tel: (01902) 710868 Fax: (01902) 712840 E-mail: enquiries@clarkwood.co.uk
Cobra Engineering, 34 Tenby Street, Birmingham, B1 3ES Tel: 0121-233 1724 Fax: 0121-236 3731
F & C Automatic Production Ltd, Quarry Road, Newhaven, East Sussex, BN9 9DG Tel: (01273) 515485 Fax: (01273) 517827
L J Dennison, 94 Leopold Street, Birmingham, B12 0UD Tel: 0121-772 8871 Fax: 0121-772 8871
Mellorsons Manufacturing Ltd, George Street, West Bromwich, West Midlands, B70 6NH Tel: 0121-580 0520 Fax: 0121-580 0521
Northwood Engineering Birmingham Co. Ltd, 122 Emily Street, Birmingham, B12 0XJ Tel: 0121-440 6731 Fax: 0121-440 3549 E-mail: northwoodengltd@aol.com
Park Engineering Wolverhampton Co. Ltd, Portersfield Industrial Estate, Portersfield Road, Cradley Heath, West Midlands, B64 7BW Tel: (01384) 566263 Fax: (01384) 564700 E-mail: neil_roberts@btconnect.com
Precision Services Of Redditch, 59 Padgets Lane, Redditch, Worcestershire, B98 0RD Tel: (01527) 528000 Fax: (01527) 517174
R P L Productions Ltd, Northcote Road, Birmingham, B33 9BE Tel: 0121-624 5000 Fax: 0121-784 5400 E-mail: info@rplproductions.co.uk
S Z N Pendle Automatics Ltd, 1 Stanhope Street, Birmingham, B12 0UZ Tel: 0121-772 2516 Fax: 0121-766 6310
Taylorfab Precision Engineers, Unit 5 Greenwood Court, Ramridge Road, Luton, LU2 0TN Tel: (01582) 737279 Fax: (01582) 735616
Warwick Brassfounders & Engineering Co. Ltd, 14-16 Haden Street, Birmingham, B12 9BH Tel: 0121-440 0901 Fax: 0121-440 6725
West Midlands Precision Engineering Ltd, Unit 10/14, Gainsborough Trad Estate, Rufford Road, Stourbridge, West Midlands, DY9 7ND Tel: (01384) 397071 Fax: (01384) 378628 E-mail: info@westmidlandstpreg.co.uk

CAR ACCIDENT REPAIRS

▶ Auto Smart Repairs Ltd, 8 Riverway, Staines, Middlesex, TW18 2SJ Tel: (01784) 442000 E-mail: michael@autosmartrepairsltd.com
▶ Dentastic Paintless Dent Repairs, 1 Delamere Road, Urmston, Manchester, M41 5GL Tel: (07958) 573 234 E-mail: richard@dentastic.co.uk
▶ Dents UK Car Body Repairs, 490 High Road, Ilford, Essex, IG1 1UE Tel: (020) 8478 7356 Fax: (020) 8478 7356 E-mail: sales@dentsuk.com
▶ The Hitman, Cheltenham Street, Bath, BA2 3EX Tel: (0808) 1000881
P D Stevens & Sons Ltd, Greenfields Lane, Market Drayton, Shropshire, TF9 3SL Tel: (01630) 652396 Fax: (01630) 652141
▶ Platinum Accident Repair Centre, Cheltenham Street, Bath, BA2 3EX Tel: (01225) 448590 Fax: (01225) 443098
▶ Platinum Motor Group, 16-17 The Causeway, Chippenham, Wiltshire, SN15 3DA Tel: (01249) 654321 Fax: (01249) 462683 E-mail: platinum.chippenham.sales@net.vauxhall.co.uk
▶ Platinum Vauxhall, 8 Meridian Business Park, North Bradley, Trowbridge, Wiltshire, BA14 0BJ Tel: (01225) 759585 Fax: (01225) 759576
▶ Platinum Vauxhall Frome, Manor Road, Marston Trading Estate, Warminster, Wiltshire, BA12 6HR Tel: (01373) 463351 Fax: (01373) 462001 E-mail: platinum.frome.sales@net.vauxhall.co.uk
▶ S R Williams, 691-693 Warrington Road, Risley, Warrington, WA3 6AY Tel: (01925) 816700 Fax: (01925) 852961 E-mail: srwgarage@csemail.co.uk
▶ Scratch Wizard Bumper Repairs Service, Andover Green, Bovington, Wareham, Dorset, BH20 6LN Tel: (0800) 0076829 E-mail: michael.lane01@tiscali.co.uk
▶ Smart Refinishers (Aberdeen) Ltd, Kirkhill Indust Estate, Aberdeen, AB21 0HP Tel: (01224) 772999 Fax: (01224) 772007 E-mail: sales@smartrefinishers.co.uk
▶ Smart Wise UK Ltd, 5 Ashwyn Business Centre, Marchants Way, Burgess Hill, West Sussex, RH15 8QY Tel: (01444) 257342 Fax: (01444) 257673 E-mail: sales@smartwise.com
▶ Wiltshire Accident Repair Centre, Hopton Estate, London Road, DEVIZES, Wiltshire, SN10 2EY Tel: 01380 735035 Fax: 01380 728532 E-mail: info@wiltshireaccident.com
▶ ZNR paintwork Ltd, 12 Burgess Road, Ivyhouse Lane Industrial Estate, Hastings, East Sussex, TN35 4NR Tel: 01424 432465

CAR AUDIO REPAIR

▶ Advanced Car Audio & Security, Unit 36 Vulcan Road South, Norwich, NR6 6AF Tel: (01603) 789896 Fax: (01603) 789467
▶ Autoelectronix, PO Box 588, Warrington, WA4 6XT Tel: (07811) 944824 E-mail: enquiries@autoelectronix.co.uk
▶ Autoinstalls UK Ltd, Unit 11B Lincoln Way, Salthill Industrial Estate, Clitheroe, Clitheroe, Lancashire, BB7 1QD Tel: (01200) 420750 Fax: (01200) 420751 E-mail: sales@autoinstallsuk.com
▶ Toyota & Lexus Specialists Ltd, 63 Connaught Road, Sutton, Surrey, SM1 3PJ Tel: (020) 8286 2201 E-mail: info@toyotalexusspecialists.co.uk

CAR CARE PRODUCTS, *See also headings for particular types*

Alarm It Northern UK, Lamport Street, Middlesbrough, Cleveland, TS1 5QL Tel: (01642) 244634 Fax: (01642) 242033 E-mail: autotune@btconnect.com
Arasco Auto Products Corp, 185 Sunningvale Ave, Biggin Hill, Westerham, Kent, TN16 3TL Tel: (01959) 565535 Fax: (01959) 573131
Auto Audio Leeds Ltd, 35 Wakefield Road, Swillington, Leeds, LS26 8DT Tel: 0113-286 2970 Fax: 0113-287 0222 E-mail: autoaudiosales@aol.com
Auto Style, Unit 16 Little Balmer, Buckingham Industrial Park, Buckingham, MK18 1TF Tel: (01280) 817962 Fax: (01280) 817963
B S B, 28 Heathfield Road, Bexleyheath, Kent, DA6 8NP Tel: (020) 8303 0196 Fax: (020) 8303 6466
B S S Trading Co. Ltd, Worton Hall Worton Hall Industrial Estate, Worton Road, Isleworth, Middlesex, TW7 6ER Tel: (020) 8569 7007 Fax: (020) 8569 8008 E-mail: bss@freenetname.co.uk
Car Wash Consultants Ltd, The Platt, Amersham, Buckinghamshire, HP7 0HX Tel: (01494) 723819 Fax: (01494) 723796 E-mail: carwashc@aol.com
Car Wash UK Ltd, 9-11 Hikers Way, Drakes Drive, Long Crendon, Aylesbury, Buckinghamshire, HP18 9RW Tel: (01844) 202123 Fax: (01844) 202831 E-mail: carwashuk@btconnect.com
Carlton Automotive Refinishing Supplies, Mirravale Trading Estate, Selinas Lane, Dagenham, Essex, RM8 1YY Tel: (020) 8592 6300 Fax: (020) 8595 9550 E-mail: c-a-r-s@supanet.com
E T B Instruments Ltd, Unit 15 Brookside, Sumpters Way Temple Farm, Temple Farm Industrial Estate, Southend-on-Sea, SS2 5RR Tel: (01702) 601055 Fax: (01702) 601056 E-mail: info@etbinstruments.com
Ford Motor Co. Ltd, Trafford House, Station Way, Basildon, Essex, SS16 5XX Tel: (01268) 703000 Fax: (01268) 703000 E-mail: enquiries@ford.co.uk
▶ Haines Brothers, No1 Dawsons Lane, Barwell, Leicester, LE9 8BE Tel: (01455) 845855 Fax: (01455) 840168
Holt Lloyd (International) Ltd, Oakhurst Drive, Lawnhurst Industrial Estate, Cheadle Heath, Stockport, Cheshire, SK3 0RZ Tel: 0161-491 7391 Fax: 0161-491 7393 E-mail: info@holtsauto.com
In Car Connection Ltd, 3 Stirling Road, Dunblane, Perthshire, FK15 9EP Tel: (01786) 825581 Fax: (01786) 825581
Johnson Controls Ltd, Tachbrook Park Drive, Tachbrook Park, Warwick, CV34 6RH Tel: (01926) 885288 Fax: (01926) 426119
Johnson Controls UK Automotive Ltd, 10 Hedera Road, Redditch, Worcestershire, B98 9EY Tel: (01527) 507100 Fax: (01527) 507101
M B Carwash, The Mardy, Llandenny, Usk, Gwent, NP15 1DN Tel: (01291) 690404 Fax: (01291) 639503 E-mail: mb'carwash@onet.co.uk
McIntosh Enterprises, 227 Kilsyth Road, Banknock, Bonnybridge, Stirlingshire, FK4 1UF Tel: (01324) 841674 Fax: (01324) 841674
Monaghans Vinyl & Sunroof Services, 142 North Road, Darlington, County Durham, DL1 2EJ Tel: (01325) 357028
Moorfield Industries Ltd, Dover Mill, Chunal Lane, Glossop, Derbyshire, SK13 6LA Tel: (01457) 891520 Fax: (01457) 855157 E-mail: rodben@moorfieldin.co.uk
Norwood Supplies, 28 Foulds Close, Gillingham, Kent, ME8 0QF Tel: (01634) 362670 Fax: (01634) 370042
Pentagon Auto Tints, Freeth Street, Unit 14-15, Birmingham, B16 0QZ Tel: 0121-456 1516 Fax: 0121 456 2826
Performance Products Ltd, Cleaver House, Sarus Court, Manor Park, Runcorn, Cheshire, WA7 1UL Tel: (01928) 579579 Fax: (0870) 7871700
R A M Mobile Electronics, 1 Therm Road, Hull, HU8 7BF Tel: (01482) 589522 Fax: (01482) 589546 E-mail: enquiries@rammobile.com
R J S Kennedy, 46 Drumfad Road, Millisle, Newtownards, County Down, BT22 2JA Tel: (028) 9186 2000 Fax: (028) 9186 2077
Richbrook International Ltd, 18 York Road, London, SW19 8TP Tel: (020) 8543 7111 Fax: (020) 8543 9111 E-mail: sales@richbrook.co.uk
R-Tek Ltd, Stephenson Road, Washington, Tyne & Wear, NE37 3HR Tel: 0191-415 7000 Fax: 0191-415 7070
Sebring International, Lotts Bridge, Threeholes, Wisbech, Cambridgeshire, PE14 9JG Tel: (01354) 638678 Fax: (01354) 638640 E-mail: sales@sebringcars.co.uk
South London Auto Paints, 40 Deptford Broadway, London, SE8 4PQ Tel: (020) 8692 6940 Fax: (020) 8692 7862
Specialised Car Covers Ltd, Concourse House, Main Street, Burley in Wharfedale, Ilkley, West Yorkshire, LS29 7JP Tel: (01943) 864646 Fax: (01943) 864365 E-mail: sales@carcoversuk.com
Sterling Products Ltd, Richmond Street, West Bromwich, West Midlands, B70 0DD Tel: 0121-557 0022 Fax: 0121-557 0222
▶ Stirling, 7 Cunningham Road, Stirling, FK7 7SW Tel: (01786) 445349 Fax: (01786) 445349 E-mail: sales@fergusons450222.com
Strathclyde Auto Supplies Ltd, Townholm Kilmarnock, Kilmarnock, Ayrshire, KA3 1BB Tel: (01563) 534440 Fax: (01563) 534361 E-mail: info@acs-auto.co.uk
Summit Accessories, 1 Lombard Way, Banbury, Oxfordshire, OX16 4TJ Tel: (01295) 275469 Fax: (01295) 270249 E-mail: sales@summit-auto.com
Supagard Ltd, 23-25 Gavinton Street, Glasgow, G44 3EF Tel: 0141-633 5933 Fax: 0141-637 7219 E-mail: info@supagard.co.uk
Thoroughbred Covers, 20 East Causeway Vale, Leeds, LS16 8LG Tel: 0113-261 0695 Fax: 0113 2310835
Thyssen & Krupp Automotive, 2200 Talbot Road, Fareham, Hampshire, PO15 5RY Tel: (01329) 844231 Fax: (01329) 844218
Treves (U K) Ltd, Farnham Lane, Farnham, Knaresborough, North Yorkshire, HG5 9JR Tel: (01423) 798800 Fax: (01423) 798827 E-mail: enquiries@treves.co.uk
Vehicle Cleaning Products, Unit 1997 Lea Valley Business Centre, 1 Hawley Road, London, N18 3SB Tel: (020) 8367 4609 E-mail: sales@vcp.gbr.cc
Visscher Caravelle UK Ltd, 5-9 Erica Road, Stacey Bushes, Milton Keynes, MK12 6HS Tel: (01908) 220101 Fax: (01908) 220911
Alan Ward UK, Unit 9, Brookfield Drive, Bridgtown, Cannock, Staffordshire, WS11 0JN Tel: (01543) 506509 Fax: (01543) 573800
Ware Motorama Ltd, Silverhook House, Bates Road, Romford, RM3 0JH Tel: (01708) 330500 Fax: (01708) 330504 E-mail: 520@wipers.co.uk

CAR HIRE

▶ 1car1.com, 15 / Walter Street, Kirkstall, Leeds, LS4 2BB Tel: 0113 387 5559 Fax: 0113 387 5561 E-mail: sales@1car1.com
▶ Arriva Vehicle Rental, Cattle Market Road, Nottingham, NG2 3GY Tel: 0115-968 2900
▶ Classic Carrieage Co., Risdon Farm, Boasley Cross, Okehampton, Devon, EX20 4JQ Tel: (0845) 6441581 Fax:
▶ Handyhire Ltd, Trinity Road, Chelmsford, CM2 6HS Tel: (01245) 353555 Fax: (01245) 493380 E-mail: handyhire@btconnect.com
▶ Leeds Car Hire, Sheepscar St South, Leeds, LS7 1AD Tel: 0113-244 5244 Fax: 0113 399 3281 E-mail: amjid@leedscarhire.com
▶ VehicleOptions (Wales), Redwither Business Centre, Redwither Business Park, Wrexham, LL13 9XR Tel: (01978) 664516 Fax: (01978) 661494E-mail: nickcarlton@vehicleoptions.biz

CAR HIRE, CHAUFFEUR DRIVEN

▶ 1st Airports Express Cars, 104 Gloucester Road, London, SW7 4RH Tel: (020) 7244 6556
▶ Abbey Chauffeur Services, 299 Southwell Road East, Rainworth, Mansfield, Nottinghamshire, NG21 0BL Tel: (01623) 794406 Fax: E-mail: sales@abbey-chauffeurs.co.uk
▶ Airport Cars, Synegis House, Crockhamwell Road, Woodley, Reading, RG5 3LE Tel: 0118-967 0252 Fax: E-mail: sales@airportcarswokingham.co.uk
▶ Aylesbury Limousines, 279 Tring Road, Aylesbury, Buckinghamshire, HP20 1PH Tel: (01296) 484051 Fax: (01296) 420791 E-mail: lisa@aylesburylimousines.co.uk
▶ Big Limo Co. Ltd, 13 Waterloo Road, Wolverhampton, WV1 4DJ Tel: (0845) 6442290 Fax: (0845) 6442290 E-mail: ask@thebiglimo.co.uk
Carey Camelot Chauffeur Drive Ltd, Headfort Place Garage, 11-15 Headfort Place, London, SW1X 7DE Tel: (020) 7201 1706 Fax: (020) 7823 1278 E-mail: res@careyuk.com
▶ Cars For Stars, Great Northern Warehouse, 275 Deansgate, Manchester, M3 4EL Tel: (0845) 2264195 Fax: (01942) 701521 E-mail: nigel@carsforstars-manchester.co.uk
▶ Cars For Stars Ltd, 105 London Street, Reading, RG1 4QD Tel: (0845) 2264205 Fax: 0118-951 7989 E-mail: info@carsforstars-reading.co.uk
▶ Cars for Stars (Cambridge), The Old Brickworks, Little Fen Drove, Burwell, Cambridge, CB5 0BN Tel: 0845 2264202 Fax: 01638 743244 E-mail: info@carsforstars-cambridge.co.uk

CAR HIRE, CHAUFFEUR DRIVEN –

continued

▶ Cars for Stars (Lincoln), Yew Tree House, Summergates Lane, Batoft, Skegness, Lincolnshire, PE24 5BZ Tel: 0845 2264216 Fax: 0845 1235238 E-mail: info@carsforstars-lincoln.co.uk

▶ Cars for Stars (Preston), Unit 22, Sycamore Trading Estate, Squires Gate Lane, Blackpool, FY4 3RL Tel: 0845 2264207 Fax: 01253 349111

▶ Charter Self Drive Ltd, Charter House, Forge Way Cleveland Street, Darlington, County Durham, DL1 2PB Tel: (01325) 481814 Fax: (01325) 484636 E-mail: Info@charterselfdrive.co.uk

▶ Chauffeur Driven, 68 High Street, Witney, Oxon, OX28 6HJ Tel: 0800 5876646 E-mail: info@chauffeurdriven.net

▶ Classic Carrieage Co., Risdon Farm, Boasley Cross, Okehampton, Devon, EX20 4JQ Tel: (0845) 6441581 Fax:

▶ Grosvenor Executive Travel, 7 Pencoed Lane, Llanmartin, Newport, Gwent, NP18 2ED Tel: (0800) 4583874 E-mail: sales@grosvenorexecutivetravel.co.uk

▶ Heathrow Chauffeurs Ltd, 13 Victoria Road, Slough, SL2 5ND Tel: (01753) 511430 Fax: (01753) 511530 E-mail: steve@heathrowchauffeurs.com

▶ Niall Johnston, 22 Berens Road, Shrivenham, Swindon, SN6 8EG Tel: (08709) 502012 Fax: (01793) 783769 E-mail: info@stretched4u.com

▶ Les Podraza, PO Box 93, Redditch, Worcestershire, B96 6EN Tel: 01527 465117 E-mail: capricorndriverservices@yahoo.co.uk

▶ Low Cost Airport Transfers, 36 Walters Road, Ogmore Vale, Bridgend, Mid Glamorgan, CF32 7DN Tel: (01656) 841353 E-mail: info@low-cost-airport-transfers.co.uk

▶ Mark One Limousines, 75 Merrivale Road, Portsmouth, PO2 0TH Tel: (023) 9266 9062 Fax: (023) 9267 7755 E-mail: markone.limousines@ntlworld.com

▶ My-Limo.Co.Uk, 140 Meadow Way, Norwich, NR6 6XU Tel: (0870) 2426958 Fax: (01603) 415077 E-mail: info@my-limo.co.uk

▶ Platinum Chauffeurs, 42 Church Street, Needingworth, St. Ives, Cambridgeshire, PE27 4TB Tel: (01480) 463777 E-mail: info@platinumdrive.co.uk

▶ Premier Limousines, 1 Briarwood Gardens, Sunnyside, Rotherham, South Yorkshire, S66 3XR Tel: (0800) 4584966 Fax: (01709) 533735E-mail: info@premier-limousines.co.uk

▶ Private Hire, Laurel House, 2 Chapel Road, Langham, Colchester, CO4 5NZ Tel: 01206 271255 Fax: 01206 272277 E-mail: info@privatecarhire.co.uk

▶ Topclass Executive Private Hire, 1st Floor Co-op Stores, The Street, Woolpit, Bury St. Edmunds, Suffolk, IP30 9RU Tel: (07949) 372949 E-mail: info@topclass-executive.co.uk

CAR LEASING

▶ Deal Detective, Knavesmire House, 4 Campleshon Road, York, YO23 1PE Tel: (01904) 632615 Fax: (01904) 629825 E-mail: deals@thedealdetectives.com

▶ EasyLeaseTrader Ltd, Walton Lodge, Hill Cliffe Rd, Walton, Warrington, WA4 6NU Tel: 01925 217250 Fax: 01925 217251 E-mail: allan.bromley@easyleasetrader.com

▶ Hackfield Leasing Ltd, 121 High Street, Cranfield, Bedford, MK43 0BS Tel: (01234) 756152 Fax: (01234) 750850 E-mail: rex.holton@hacfield.com

▶ Hiltingbury Motors Ltd, 72 Hiltingbury Road, Chandlers Ford, Eastleigh, Hampshire, SO53 5SS Tel: (023) 8026 6688 Fax: (023) 8026 6680 E-mail: sales@hiltingburymazda.com

L 4 Lease Ltd, Keystone House, 30 Exeter Road, Bournemouth, BH2 5AR Tel: (0870) 4462407 Fax: (07005) 804365 E-mail: info@myfleet.co.uk

▶ Leasing Quote, c/o Able It, Atlantic Business Centre, 111 Marlowes, Hemel Hempstead, Hertfordshire, HP1 1BB Tel: (0800) 0198836 E-mail: inbox@leasingquote.co.uk

▶ Nationwide Vehicles Direct Ltd, Dalriada Crescent, Motherwell, Lanarkshire, ML1 3XS Tel: 0141-587 8898 E-mail: joannecrawford03@yahoo.co.uk

▶ Southampton Mazda, Bursledon Road, Southampton, SO19 7LW Tel: (023) 8042 2777 Fax: (023) 8044 3320 E-mail: sales@southamptonmazda.co.uk

CAR MECHANICAL SERVICING

▶ Alanco Motor Services Ltd, Goldmartin Garage, Sampys Mill, Mawnan Smith, Falmouth, Cornwall, TR11 5EW Tel: (01326) 250394 Fax: (01326) 250394 E-mail: info@alanco.co.uk

JS Auto Repairs, 137 Picasso Way, Shoeburyness, Southend-on-Sea, SS3 9UY Tel: (07779) 799027 Fax: (01702) 316137 E-mail: cs@jsautorepairs.co.uk

▶ Lowhall Motors, Woodbottom Mills, Low Hall Road, Horsforth, Leeds, LS18 4EF Tel: 0113-250 4411

▶ Station Garage, Wilbraham Road, Fulbourn, Cambridge, CB21 5ET Tel: (01223) 880747 Fax: (01223) 880885 E-mail: mail@stationgaragefulbourn.co.uk

▶ Totally 2cv, Pucknell Farm, Dores Lane, Braishfield, Romsey, Hampshire, SO51 0QJ Tel: (023) 8067 6002 E-mail: Newportcv@btinternet.com

▶ Wyatt Engineering, Darrow Wood Farm, Shelfanger Road, Diss, Norfolk, IP22 4XY Tel: (01379) 640200 Fax: (01379) 640200

▶ XJ Services, Heritage Way, Corby, Northamptonshire, NN17 5XW Tel: (01536) 201888 E-mail: tim@xjservices.co.uk

CAR PARK ENTRY AND EXIT CONTROL SYSTEMS

A Markham & Sons Ltd, London Road, Bowers Gifford, Basildon, Essex, SS13 2DT Tel: (01268) 553748 Fax: (01268) 584502 E-mail: info@markhams.co.uk

Aremco Products, Foxoak Street, Cradley Heath, West Midlands, B64 5DQ Tel: (01384) 568566 Fax: (01384) 634601 E-mail: sales@aremco-products.co.uk

National Car Parks Ltd (N C P), 21 Bryanston Street, London, W1H 7AB Tel: (0870) 6067050 Fax: (020) 7491 3577 E-mail: marketing@ncp.co.uk

CAR PARK EQUIPMENT INSTALLATION OR MAINTENANCE OR SERVICING

National Car Parks Ltd (N C P), 21 Bryanston Street, London, W1H 7AB Tel: (0870) 6067050 Fax: (020) 7491 3577 E-mail: marketing@ncp.co.uk

CAR PARK MARKING

▶ Parking Protection Services Ltd, PO Box 489, Edgware, Middlesex, HA8 9ZR Tel: (0870) 3450310 E-mail: info@parkingprotectionservices.co.uk

CAR PARKING/STORAGE SYSTEMS

▶ ANOTHER LEVEL CAR PARKS LTD, Tweedale Way, Chadderton, Oldham, OL9 7LD Tel: 0845 345 3835 Fax: 0845 345 3836 E-mail: INFO@ANOTHERLEVELCARPARKS.COM

Compex Development & Marketing Ltd, Century House, The Lake, Northampton, NN4 7HD Tel: (01604) 233333 Fax: (01604) 233334 E-mail: sales@compexdm.co.uk

CAR TELEPHONES, *See headings for Cellular Radio Telephone*

CAR TRANSPORTER COVERS

Terapin Curtain Systems, 2 Glenavy Road, Upper Ballinderry, Lisburn, County Antrim, BT28 2EU Tel: (028) 9265 1007 Fax: (028) 9265 2019 E-mail: info@terapin.com

CARAVAN AWNINGS

Davan Caravans & Motor Homes Ltd, Goosey Lane, St. Georges, Weston-super-Mare, Avon, BS22 7XA Tel: (01934) 510606 Fax: (01934) 516025 E-mail: info@davan.co.uk

Michael Jordan Caravans Ltd, Station Approach, Gomshall, Guildford, Surrey, GU5 9NX Tel: (01483) 203335 Fax: (01483) 202780 E-mail: sales@michaeljordancaravans.co.uk

Mcintyre Caravans, Hempsted Bridge, Bristol Road, Gloucester, GL2 5DH Tel: (01452) 520737 Fax: (01452) 309970 E-mail: info@goldencastle.co.uk

N R Components Ltd, Der Street, Todmorden, Lancashire, OL14 5QY Tel: (01706) 815821 Fax: (01706) 818505 E-mail: info@nrawnings.com

CARAVAN FITTINGS AND ACCESSORIES

Barry Sharman Caravans Ltd, The Caravan Centre, Colchester Road, Ipswich, IP4 4RU Tel: (01473) 713284 Fax: (01473) 273166 E-mail: sharmancaravans@supanet.com

Caravan Accessories Kenilworth Ltd, Unit 10 Princes Drive Industrial Estate, Coventry Road, Kenilworth, Warwickshire, CV8 2FD Tel: (01926) 854271 Fax: (01926) 853954 E-mail: sales@caktanks.co.uk

Chichester Caravans, Worcester Road, Upton Warren, Bromsgrove, Worcestershire, B61 7EX Tel: (01527) 831515 Fax: (01527) 870315 E-mail: chichester123@yahoo.co.uk

Chichester Caravans, Main Road, Nutbourne, Chichester, West Sussex, PO18 8RL Tel: (01243) 377441 Fax: (01243) 377442

Colin's Caravans of Berkshire Ltd, Bath Road, Aldermaston, Reading, RG7 5JD Tel: 0118-971 2424 Fax: 0118-971 3010 E-mail: sales@colinscaravans.com

D L S Plastics Ltd, Occupation Lane, Gonrby Moor, Grantham, Lincolnshire, NG32 2BP Tel: (01476) 564549 Fax: (01476) 567538 E-mail: sales@dlsplastics.co.uk

Davan Caravans & Motor Homes Ltd, Goosey Lane, St. Georges, Weston-super-Mare, Avon, BS22 7XA Tel: (01934) 510606 Fax: (01934) 516025 E-mail: info@davan.co.uk

J A Kinnersley & Co. Ltd, Copenhagen Road, Hull, HU7 0XQ Tel: (01482) 826020 Fax: (01482) 878447 E-mail: sales@j-kinnersley.co.uk

J & J Engineering (Walsall) Ltd, Fryers Road, Leamore Enterprise Park, Bloxwich, Walsall, WS2 7LZ Tel: (01922) 710204 Fax: (01922) 710191 E-mail: jwoodall@btconnect.com

Mcintyre Caravans, Hempsted Bridge, Bristol Road, Gloucester, GL2 5DH Tel: (01452) 520737 Fax: (01452) 309970 E-mail: info@goldencastle.co.uk

Mayfield Leisure Ltd, 26-32 Cobham Road, Wimborne, Dorset, BH21 7NP Tel: (01202) 855222 Fax: (01202) 732853 E-mail: enquiries@themayfieldgroup.co.uk

Maypole Ltd, 54 Kettles Wood Drive, Birmingham, B32 3DB Tel: 0121-423 3011 Fax: 0121-423 3020 E-mail: maypole@maypole.ltd.uk

Morco Products Ltd, Morco House, 59 Beverley Road, Hull, HU3 1XW Tel: (01482) 325456 Fax: (01482) 212869

Nimbus Products (Sheffield) Ltd, Julian Way, Tyler Street Industrial Estate, Sheffield, S9 1GD Tel: 0114-243 2362 Fax: 0114-243 5046 E-mail: sales@nimbusproducts.co.uk

Plastics Manchester Ltd, Plasman Industrial Centre, Peter Moss Way, Manchester, M19 3PX Tel: 0161-257 2929 Fax: 0161-257 3203 E-mail: info@thompson-plastics-group.co.uk

Pyramid Products Ltd, Unit 1 Victoria Street, Mansfield, Nottinghamshire, NG18 5RR Tel: (01623) 421277 Fax: (01623) 421288 E-mail: sales@pyramid-products.co.uk

E.T. Riddiough Sales Ltd, Lodge Mill, Barden Lane, Burnley, Lancashire, BB12 0DY Tel: (01282) 434678 Fax: (01282) 412524 E-mail: etriddiough@onetel.net.uk

Russell Sales Ltd, Truma House, Beechers Park, Eastern Avenue, Burton-On-Trent, Staffordshire, DE13 0BB Tel: (01283) 511883 Fax: (01283) 511329 E-mail: sales@miriadproducts.com

Spinflo Ltd, Unit 19, Oakham Drive, Sheffield, S3 9QX Tel: 0114-273 8157 E-mail: sales@spinflo-group.co.uk

T A M Leisure Ltd, 180 Kingston Road, New Malden, Surrey, KT3 3RD Tel: (020) 8949 5435 Fax: (020) 8336 1418 E-mail: sales@tamleisure.co.uk

Thompson Plastics Group Ltd, Bridge Works, Hessle, North Humberside, HU13 0TP Tel: (01482) 646464 Fax: (01482) 644446 E-mail: info@thompson-plastics.co.uk

W4 Ltd, Unit B, Ford Lane Industrial Estate, Arundel, West Sussex, BN18 0DF Tel: (01243) 553355 Fax: (01243) 553540 E-mail: enquiries@w4limited.com

West Alloy Ltd, Garth Road, Morden, Surrey, SM4 4LN Tel: (020) 8337 2211 Fax: (020) 8330 7640 E-mail: sales@westalloy.com

CARAVAN FLUES

Bankside Patterson Ltd, Catwick Lane, Brandesburton, Driffield, East Yorkshire, YO25 8RW Tel: (01964) 545454 Fax: (01964) 545459 E-mail: sales@bankside-patterson.co.uk

CARAVAN HIRE

▶ Caravan Hire Butlins, Minehead, Somerset, TA24 5SH Tel: (01793) 339832 E-mail: gina.traynor1@ntlworld.com

▶ Ian Howard Caravans, 1 Didcot Drive, Nottingham, NG8 5EQ Tel: 0845 838 7570 Fax: 08719 895259 E-mail: ian@howardcaravans.co.uk

CARAVAN MAGAZINES

National Caravan Council Ltd, Catherine House, Victoria Road, Aldershot, Hampshire, GU11 1SS Tel: (01252) 318251 Fax: (01252) 322596 E-mail: info@nationalcaravan.co.uk

CARAVAN MAINTENANCE/ REPAIR SERVICES

Broad Lane Caravans Ltd, 1 Somers Road, Rugby, Warwickshire, CV22 7DB Tel: (01788) 542672 Fax: (01788) 546109 E-mail: rugby@broadlane.co.uk

Carlight Caravans Ltd, Unit 5-7 Tamson Way, Church Lane, Sleaford, Lincolnshire, NG34 7DE Tel: (01529) 302120 Fax: (01529) 302240 E-mail: mail@carlight.co.uk

Chichester Caravans, Worcester Road, Upton Warren, Bromsgrove, Worcestershire, B61 7EX Tel: (01527) 831515 Fax: (01527) 870315 E-mail: chichester123@yahoo.co.uk

Chichester Caravans, Main Road, Nutbourne, Chichester, West Sussex, PO18 8RL Tel: (01243) 377441 Fax: (01243) 377442

P.S. Higgins Electrical Services, Clarence House, 30 Queen Street, Market Drayton, Shropshire, TF9 1PS Tel: (01630) 655416 Fax: (01630) 658415 E-mail: info@pshiggins.co.uk

Mount Caravans Ltd, Kingswood, London Apprentice, St. Austell, Cornwall, PL26 7AR Tel: (01726) 874100 Fax: (01726) 67448 E-mail: sales@mountcaravans.co.uk

Yorkshire Caravans of Bawtry Ltd, Doncaster Road, Bawtry, Doncaster, South Yorkshire, DN10 6DG Tel: (01302) 710366 Fax: (01302) 710910 E-mail: info@yorkshirecaravans.com

CARAVAN SECURITY LOCKS

Lock Assist, 139 Royal George Road, Burgess Hill, West Sussex, RH15 9TD Tel: (01444) 244344 Fax: (01444) 241324 E-mail: info@lockassist.co.uk

CARAVANS, *See also headings for particular types*

Anderson Cars, Alington Road, Little Barford, St. Neots, Cambridgeshire, PE19 6YH Tel: (01480) 212845 Fax: (01480) 213007 E-mail: jason@petercandersoncars.com

Barry Sharman Caravans Ltd, The Caravan Centre, Colchester Road, Ipswich, IP4 4RU Tel: (01473) 713284 Fax: (01473) 273166 E-mail: sharmancaravans@supanet.com

Broad Lane Caravans Ltd, 1 Somers Road, Rugby, Warwickshire, CV22 7DB Tel: (01788) 542672 Fax: (01788) 546109 E-mail: rugby@broadlane.co.uk

Carlight Caravans Ltd, Unit 5-7 Tamson Way, Church Lane, Sleaford, Lincolnshire, NG34 7DE Tel: (01529) 302120 Fax: (01529) 302240 E-mail: mail@carlight.co.uk

Chichester Caravans, Worcester Road, Upton Warren, Bromsgrove, Worcestershire, B61 7EX Tel: (01527) 831515 Fax: (01527) 870315 E-mail: chichester123@yahoo.co.uk

Chichester Caravans, Main Road, Nutbourne, Chichester, West Sussex, PO18 8RL Tel: (01243) 377441 Fax: (01243) 377442

Colin's Caravans of Berkshire Ltd, Bath Road, Aldermaston, Reading, RG7 5JD Tel: 0118-971 2424 Fax: 0118-971 3010 E-mail: sales@colinscaravans.com

D L S Plastics Ltd, Occupation Lane, Gonrby Moor, Grantham, Lincolnshire, NG32 2BP Tel: (01476) 564549 Fax: (01476) 567538 E-mail: sales@dlsplastics.co.uk

Davan Caravans & Motor Homes Ltd, Goosey Lane, St. Georges, Weston-super-Mare, Avon, BS22 7XA Tel: (01934) 510606 Fax: (01934) 516025 E-mail: info@davan.co.uk

Downshire Camping & Caravan Centre, 12 Newry Road, Banbridge, County Down, BT32 3HN Tel: (028) 4062 3378 Fax: (028) 4062 9295 E-mail: sales@downshirecaravans.net

Elite Caravans Ltd, 7 Signet Court, Swans Road, Cambridge, CB5 8LA Tel: (01223) 361433 Fax: (01223) 312010

Gobur Caravans Ltd, Peacock Way, Melton Constable, Norfolk, NR24 2BY Tel: (01263) 860031 Fax: (01263) 861494 E-mail: sales@goburcaravans.co.uk

Golden Castle Caravans Ltd, Cheltenham Road East, Gloucester, GL2 9QL Tel: (01452) 713311 Fax: (01452) 856538 E-mail: info@goldencastle.co.uk

Harringtons Caravans Ltd, Chester Road, Oakmere, Northwich, Cheshire, CW8 2HB Tel: (01606) 882032 Fax: (01606) 889213 E-mail: sales@harringtonscaravans.co.uk

Michael Jordan Caravans Ltd, Station Approach, Gomshall, Guildford, Surrey, GU5 9NX Tel: (01483) 203335 Fax: (01483) 202780 E-mail: sales@michaeljordancaravans.co.uk

Mcintyre Caravans, Hempsted Bridge, Bristol Road, Gloucester, GL2 5DH Tel: (01452) 520737 Fax: (01452) 309970 E-mail: info@goldencastle.co.uk

Mount Caravans Ltd, Kingswood, London Apprentice, St. Austell, Cornwall, PL26 7AR Tel: (01726) 874100 Fax: (01726) 67448 E-mail: sales@mountcaravans.co.uk

Somerset Camping Ltd, Walford Cross, Taunton, Somerset, TA2 8QR Tel: (01823) 413333 Fax: (01823) 413344 E-mail: enquiries@somersetcaravans.co.uk

Tanfield Towbars, Blatchford Road, Horsham, West Sussex, RH13 5QR Tel: (01403) 269100 Fax: (01403) 251199

Vehicletrademaster, PO Box 5347, Northampton, NN3 7YT Tel: (08702) 405445 Fax: (08702) 405445 E-mail: vtmoffice@btinternet.com

Yorkshire Caravans of Bawtry Ltd, Doncaster Road, Bawtry, Doncaster, South Yorkshire, DN10 6DG Tel: (01302) 710366 Fax: (01302) 710910 E-mail: info@yorkshirecaravans.com

CARBIDE CUTTERS

Maydown International Tours Ltd, Mercury Park, Amber Close, Tamworth, Staffordshire, B77 4RP Tel: (01827) 309700 Fax: (01827) 309719

CARBIDE TIPPED DRILL BITS

Armeg Ltd, Callywhite Lane, Dronfield, Derbyshire, S18 2XJ Tel: (01246) 411081 Fax: (01246) 411882 E-mail: j.mowthorpe@armeg.co.uk
Cirbo Ltd, 16 Normandy Way, Bodmin, Cornwall, PL31 1EX Tel: (01208) 74174 Fax: (01208) 76801
Harthill Developments Ltd, Mansfield Road, Aston, Sheffield, S26 5PQ Tel: 0114-287 4522 Fax: 0114-287 6397 E-mail: sales@harthill.com
Irwin Industrial Tool Co. Ltd, Parkway Works, Kettlebridge Road, Sheffield, S9 3BL Tel: 0114-244 9066 Fax: 0114-256 1788 E-mail: sales@record.co.uk
Pen Cutting Tools Ltd, Bold Street, Sheffield, S9 2LR Tel: 0114-243 0055 Fax: 0114-243 0066 E-mail: sales@pencuttingtools.co.uk
Tekron Hard Metals Ltd, 6 Marsh Green Close, Biddulph, Stoke-on-Trent, ST8 6TA Tel: (01782) 522563 Fax: (01782) 516452 E-mail: tekrontool@madasafish.com
Titman Tip Tools Ltd, Valley Road, Clacton-on-Sea, Essex, CO15 6PP Tel: (01255) 220123 Fax: (01255) 221422 E-mail: sales@titman.co.uk

CARBIDE TIPPED REAMERS

Brunswick Tooling Ltd, Unit 3, The Tiding Industrial Park, Birds Royd Lane, Brighouse, West Yorkshire, HD6 1LQ Tel: (01484) 719900 Fax: (01484) 404727 E-mail: sales@brunswicktooling.co.uk
Tungscarb Products Ltd, 5 Bodmin Road, Coventry, CV2 5DB Tel: (024) 7661 4498 Fax: (024) 7660 2173 E-mail: sales@tungscarbproduct.co.uk

CARBIDE TIPPED TOOLS

Albe (England) Ltd, 51 Bideford Avenue, Perivale, Greenford, Middlesex, UB6 7PR Tel: (020) 8997 7282 Fax: (020) 8998 2932 E-mail: sales@albe.com

CARBIDE TOOL GRINDING MACHINES

Autool Grinders Ltd, Padiham Road, Sabden, Clitheroe, Lancashire, BB7 9EW Tel: (01282) 775000 Fax: (01282) 773486 E-mail: sales@autool.co.uk
Coborn Engineering Co. Ltd, Chesham Close, Romford, RM7 7PJ Tel: (01708) 744666 Fax: (01708) 725187 E-mail: coborneng@aol.com

CARBON BLACK

Cabot Carbon Ltd, Lees Lane, Stanlow, Ellesmere Port, CH65 4HT Tel: 0151-355 3677 Fax: 0151-356 0712
Hubron Sales, Albion Street, Failsworth, Manchester, M35 0WW Tel: 0161-681 2691 Fax: 0161-683 4045 E-mail: sales@hubron.com

CARBON BRUSH HOLDERS

Morganite Electro Carbon, Stanhope Street, Birmingham, B12 0UZ Tel: 0121-773 3738 Fax: 0121-771 4473E-mail: sales@mecl.co.uk
Schunk UK Ltd, Richardshaw Drive, Pudsey, West Yorkshire, LS28 6QR Tel: 0113-256 7238 Fax: 0113-255 2017 E-mail: schunk.uk.sales@schunk-group.com

CARBON BRUSHES

Carlingwood Ltd, 1 Bridge Green, Prestbury, Macclesfield, Cheshire, SK10 4HR Tel: (01625) 828342 Fax: (01625) 827471
Gledco Engineered Materials, Bankfield Terrace, Leeds, LS4 2JR Tel: 0113-275 1144 Fax: 0113-230 4724 E-mail: sales@usggledco.co.uk
Le Carbone Great Britain Ltd, South Street, Portslade, Brighton, BN41 2LX Tel: (01273) 415701 Fax: (01273) 415673
Morganite Electrical Carbon Ltd, Upper Fforest Way, Swansea Enterprise Park, Swansea, SA6 8PP Tel: (01792) 763000 Fax: (01792) 763191 E-mail: sales@mecl.co.uk
Morganite Electro Carbon, Stanhope Street, Birmingham, B12 0UZ Tel: 0121-773 3738 Fax: 0121-771 4473E-mail: sales@mecl.co.uk
Oilite Bowman, 10 Isis Court, Wyndyke Furlong, Abingdon Business Park, Abingdon, Oxfordshire, OX14 1DZ Tel: (01235) 815816 Fax: (01235) 811234 E-mail: steve@bowman.co.uk
Schunk UK Ltd, Richardshaw Drive, Pudsey, West Yorkshire, LS28 6QR Tel: 0113-256 7238 Fax: 0113-255 2017 E-mail: schunk.uk.sales@schunk-group.com
SGL Carbon, 4 Arden Court, Arden Road, Alcester, Warwickshire, B49 6HN Tel: (01789) 400221 Fax: (01789) 400822 E-mail: enquiries@sglcarbon.co.uk

CARBON COMPONENTS

Aztec Composites, Unit 9 Queens Park Industrial Estate, Studland Road, Northampton, NN2 6NA Tel: (01604) 721727 Fax: (01604) 720420 E-mail: rgoodman@azteccomposites.co.uk
Gledco Engineered Materials, Bankfield Terrace, Leeds, LS4 2JR Tel: 0113-275 1144 Fax: 0113-230 4724 E-mail: sales@usggledco.co.uk
Le Carbone Great Britain Ltd, South Street, Portslade, Brighton, BN41 2LX Tel: (01273) 415701 Fax: (01273) 415673
Morgan Advanced Materials & Technology, Unit 13, Madeley Road, North Moons Moat, Redditch, Worcestershire, B98 9NB Tel: (01527) 69205 Fax: (01527) 62195
Morganite Electrical Carbon Ltd, Upper Fforest Way, Swansea Enterprise Park, Swansea, SA6 8PP Tel: (01792) 763000 Fax: (01792) 763191 E-mail: sales@mecl.co.uk
Schunk UK Ltd, Richardshaw Drive, Pudsey, West Yorkshire, LS28 6QR Tel: 0113-256 7238 Fax: 0113-255 2017 E-mail: schunk.uk.sales@schunk-group.com
SGL Carbon, 4 Arden Court, Arden Road, Alcester, Warwickshire, B49 6HN Tel: (01789) 400221 Fax: (01789) 400822 E-mail: enquiries@sglcarbon.co.uk

CARBON DIOXIDE (CO2)

Air Liquide UK Ltd, Cedar House, 39 London Road, Reigate, Surrey, RH2 9QE Tel: (01737) 241133 Fax: (01737) 241842 E-mail: genenq.aluk@airliquide.com
▶ Scientific & Technical Gases Ltd, 1 Speedwell Road, Parkhouse Industrial Estate East, Newcastle, Staffordshire, ST5 7RG Tel: (01782) 564906 Fax: (01782) 564906 E-mail: info@stgas.eu

CARBON DIOXIDE (CO2) ANALYSERS

Analox Sensor Technology Ltd, 15 Ellerbeck Court, Stokesley Business Park, Stokesley, Middlesbrough, Cleveland, TS9 5PT Tel: (01642) 711400 Fax: (01642) 713900 E-mail: admin@analox.net

CARBON DIOXIDE (CO2) EMERGENCY DOOR SAFETY INTERLOCK SYSTEMS

Boewood Prevention Ltd, PO Box 44, Newtown, Powys, SY16 1WD Tel: (01686) 622228 Fax: (01686) 622451 E-mail: sales@doorsafety.co.uk

CARBON DIOXIDE (CO2) STORAGE AND DISTRIBUTION SYSTEMS

Air Liquide UK Ltd, Cedar House, 39 London Road, Reigate, Surrey, RH2 9QE Tel: (01737) 241133 Fax: (01737) 241842 E-mail: genenq.aluk@airliquide.com

CARBON FIBRE AIRCRAFT COMPONENTS

AIM Composites Ltd, Pembroke Avenue, Waterbeach, Cambridge, CB5 9QR Tel: (01223) 441000 Fax: (01223) 862336 E-mail: sales@aimcomposites.com
Aztec Composites, Unit 9 Queens Park Industrial Estate, Studland Road, Northampton, NN2 6NA Tel: (01604) 721727 Fax: (01604) 720420 E-mail: rgoodman@azteccomposites.co.uk
Insys Services Ltd, Reddings Wood, Ampthill, Bedford, MK45 2HD Tel: (01525) 843661 Fax: (01525) 843766
Jet Blades & Engineering, Maguire Industrial Estate, 219 Torrington Avenue, Coventry, CV4 9HN Tel: (024) 7646 6841 Fax: (024) 7647 4215 E-mail: info@jetblades.com
Racing Developments, 48-50 Tanners Drive, Blakelands, Milton Keynes, MK14 5BW Tel: (01908) 210775 E-mail: info@racingdevelopments.com
Southdown Composites Ltd, Lasham Airfield, Lasham, Alton, Hampshire, GU34 5SR Tel: (01256) 381359 Fax: (01256) 381359 E-mail: sales@southdowncomposites.com

CARBON FIBRE COMPONENTS TO SPECIFICATION

Attwater Group, PO Box 39, Preston, PR1 1TA Tel: (01772) 258245 Fax: (01772) 203361 E-mail: info@attwater.co.uk
Aztec Composites, Unit 9 Queens Park Industrial Estate, Studland Road, Northampton, NN2 6NA Tel: (01604) 721727 Fax: (01604) 720420 E-mail: rgoodman@azteccomposites.co.uk
Southdown Composites Ltd, Lasham Airfield, Lasham, Alton, Hampshire, GU34 5SR Tel: (01256) 381359 Fax: (01256) 381359 E-mail: sales@southdowncomposites.com

CARBON FIBRE FABRICATORS

Attwater Group, PO Box 39, Preston, PR1 1TA Tel: (01772) 258245 Fax: (01772) 203361 E-mail: info@attwater.co.uk
Calcarb Ltd, 12 North Road, Bellshill, Lanarkshire, ML4 1EN Tel: (01698) 740818 Fax: (01698) 841979 E-mail: sales@calcarb.com
▶ Smart Fibres Ltd, 12 The Court Yard, Eastern Road, Bracknell, Berkshire, RG12 2XB Tel: (01344) 484111 Fax: (01344) 423241 E-mail: info@smartfibres.com

CARBON FIBRE FABRICS/TAPES

Carr Reinforcements, Carr House, Brighton Road, Stockport, Cheshire, SK4 2BE Tel: 0161-443 3377 Fax: 0161-443 3388 E-mail: erictaylor@btconnect.com
Gurit, St. Cross Business Park, Newport, Isle of Wight, PO30 5WU Tel: (01983) 828000 Fax: (01983) 828100 E-mail: info@gurit.com
▶ Smart Fibres Ltd, 12 The Court Yard, Eastern Road, Bracknell, Berkshire, RG12 2XB Tel: (01344) 484111 Fax: (01344) 423241 E-mail: info@smartfibres.com

CARBON FIBRE PROFILES

Exel P.L.C., 23 Hall Rd, Hebburn, Tyne & Wear, NE31 2UG Tel: 0191-483 2671 Fax: 0191-489 0422 E-mail: jim.edmunds@btinternet.com
▶ Smart Fibres Ltd, 12 The Court Yard, Eastern Road, Bracknell, Berkshire, RG12 2XB Tel: (01344) 484111 Fax: (01344) 423241 E-mail: info@smartfibres.com

CARBON FIBRE RAW MATERIALS

A. Martin Bunzl Ltd, 27 London Road, Bromley, BR1 1DF Tel: (020) 8464 4141 Fax: (020) 8460 2035 E-mail: sales@martinbunzl.co.uk
SGL Technic Ltd, Muir of Ord Industrial Estate, Great North Road, Muir of Ord, Ross-Shire, IV6 7UA Tel: (01463) 870000 Fax: (01463) 871402
Toray Europe Ltd, 7 Old Park Lane, London, W1K 1AD Tel: (020) 7663 7700 Fax: (020) 7872 8071

CARBON FIBRE REINFORCED PLASTIC PRODUCTS

▶ Performance Plastics, Brock House, Grigg Lane, Brockenhurst, Hampshire, SO42 7RE Tel: (01590) 622666 Fax: (01590) 622629 E-mail: info@performance-plastics.co.uk
PRF Composite Materials, 3 Upton Road, Poole, Dorset, BH17 7AA Tel: (01202) 680022 Fax: (01202) 680077 E-mail: mail@prfcomposites.com

CARBON FIBRE TUBES

Century Composites Ltd, 58-59 Hutton Close, Crowther, Washington, Tyne & Wear, NE38 0AH Tel: 0191-416 8200 Fax: 0191-415 5962
Custom Composites Ltd, Hugo Street, Rochdale, Lancashire, OL11 2PH Tel: (01706) 526255 Fax: (01706) 350187 E-mail: mail@customcom.co.uk
Exel P.L.C., 23 Hall Rd, Hebburn, Tyne & Wear, NE31 2UG Tel: 0191-483 2671 Fax: 0191-489 0422 E-mail: jim.edmunds@btinternet.com
Performance Composites Ltd, Unit 13a The Old Sawmills, Halves Lane, East Coker, Yeovil, Somerset, BA22 9JJ Tel: (01935) 864098 Fax: (01935) 863807 E-mail: sms@performance-composites.com
St. Bernard Composites Ltd, 21 Invincible Road, Farnborough, Hampshire, GU14 7QU Tel: (01252) 304000 Fax: (01252) 304001 E-mail: info@stbernard.co.uk
URENCO (Capenhurst) Ltd, Capenhurst, Chester, CH1 6ER Tel: 0151-473 4000 Fax: 0151-473 4384 E-mail: cad@cap.urenco.co.uk

CARBON FIBRE, WOVEN

▶ Integra Composites, Unit 8 The Sidings, Wilford Bridge Road, Melton, Woodbridge, Suffolk, IP12 1RB Tel: (01394) 385838 Fax: (01394) 380919 E-mail: sg@integracomposites.co.uk

CARBON FILTER COMPONENTS

Jacobi Carbons, 3 Moss Industrial Estate, St. Helens Road, Leigh, Lancashire, WN7 3PT Tel: (01942) 670600 Fax: (01942) 670605 E-mail: infouk@jacobi.net
Purification Products Ltd, Reliance Works, Saltaire Road, Shipley, West Yorkshire, BD18 3HL Tel: (01274) 530155 Fax: (01274) 580453 E-mail: sales@purification.co.uk

CARBON FILTERS

Eastfield Engineering Ltd, PO Box 232, Stafford, ST19 5QY Tel: (01785) 714794 Fax: (01785) 711373 E-mail: sales@eastfield-engineering.com
Emcel Filters Ltd, Blatchford Road, Horsham, West Sussex, RH13 5RA Tel: (01403) 253215 Fax: (01403) 259881 E-mail: filtration@emcelfilters.co.uk
Fenchurch Environmental Group Ltd, Dennow Farm, Firs Lane, Appleton, Warrington, WA4 5LF Tel: (01925) 269111 Fax: (01925) 269444 E-mail: sales@fengroup.com
Jasun Filtration plc, Riverside House, Parrett Way, Bridgwater, Somerset, TA6 5LB Tel: (01278) 452277 Fax: (01278) 450873 E-mail: info@jfilters.com
Sutcliffe Speakman Ltd, Edgar House, Lockett Road, Ashton-In-Makerfield, Wigan, Lancashire, WN4 8DE Tel: (01942) 275400 Fax: (01942) 275600 E-mail: immisioncontrols@waterlink.com

CARBON GOUGING RODS

Ralph Coidan Ltd, 2 Boltby Way, Eaglescliffe, Stockton-on-Tees, Cleveland, TS16 0RH Tel: (01642) 790100 Fax: (01642) 790488 E-mail: sales@coidan.co.uk

CARBON PAPER PRODUCTS

Aero-Print Securities Ltd, Gatehouse Way, Aylesbury, Buckinghamshire, HP19 8DD Tel: (01296) 485131 Fax: (01296) 485097 E-mail: sales@aero-print.co.uk
Crusoe Paper Ltd, D Banovallum Court, Holmes Way, Horncastle, Lincolnshire, LN9 6JW Tel: (01507) 524545 Fax: (01507) 524580
K M P Crusader Manufacturing Co. Ltd, Oldmedow Road, King's Lynn, Norfolk, PE30 4LD Tel: (01553) 817200 Fax: (01553) 691909 E-mail: sales@kmp-uk.co.uk
Keymax International Ltd, West Road, Templefields, Harlow, Essex, CM20 2AL Tel: (01279) 454455 Fax: (01279) 445550 E-mail: ttrsales@keymax.co.uk
Yorkhaven Ltd, Unit 4 Lye Valley Industrial Estate, Stourbridge, West Midlands, DY9 8HX Tel: (01384) 892075 Fax: (01384) 897416 E-mail: sales@yorkhaven.co.uk

CARBON SEALS

Gledco Engineered Materials, Bankfield Terrace, Leeds, LS4 2JR Tel: 0113-275 1144 Fax: 0113-230 4724 E-mail: sales@usggledco.co.uk

CARBON STEEL CASTINGS

Ampo UK, Holly Tree Cottage, Stocks Lane, Welshampton, Ellesmere, Shropshire, SY12 0NT Tel: (01948) 710764 Fax: (01948) 710914 E-mail: ampouk@aol.com
Brafe Engineering Ltd, Grundisburgh Road, Woodbridge, Suffolk, IP13 6HX Tel: (01394) 380000 Fax: (01394) 380300 E-mail: sclarke@brafe.com

CARBON STEEL COILS

Phoenix Steel Services Ltd, Units 3-4, Charlotte Street, Dudley, West Midlands, DY1 1TD Tel: (01384) 458866 Fax: (01384) 455576 E-mail: sales@phoenixsteelservices.co.uk

CARBON STEEL DUCTING

C S Struthers, Valletta Street, Hull, HU9 5NU Tel: (01482) 707766 Fax: (01482) 787479 E-mail: sales@csstruthers.co.uk

CARBON STEEL FLANGES

B D Profiles Ltd, PO Box 65, Cradley Heath, West Midlands, B64 5PP Tel: 0121-559 5136 Fax: 0121-561 4265 E-mail: syoung@bdprofiles.co.uk
Formula One Pipelines Ltd, Unit 20, Delph Road, Delph Road Industrial Estate, Brierley Hill, West Midlands, DY5 2TW Tel: (01384) 482211 Fax: (01384) 482223
Glamal Engineering Ltd, Pegasus House, Wynyard Avenue, Wynyard, Billingham, Cleveland, TS22 5TB Tel: (01740) 645040 Fax: (01642) 565831 E-mail: sales@glamal.co.uk

CARBON STEEL FLANGES – *continued*

T P S Technitube UK Ltd, T P S Building, Blatchford Road, Horsham, West Sussex, RH13 5QR Tel: (01403) 269471 Fax: (01403) 265443 E-mail: sales@tpsuk.co.uk

CARBON STEEL HEXAGONS

Corus, Unit 2 Pullman Court, Bolton, BL2 1HL Tel: (01204) 370999 Fax: (01204) 396684 E-mail: chris.deacon@corusgroup.com
Corus, Hetton Lyons Industrial Estate, Hetton-le-Hole, Houghton le Spring, Tyne & Wear, DH5 0RD Tel: 0191-526 3288 Fax: 0191-517 0138 E-mail: paul.brown@corusgroup.com
Corus Engineering Steels, Coleford Road, Sheffield, S9 3QE Tel: 0114-244 7264 Fax: 0114-243 0941 E-mail: chris.deacon@corusgroup.com
Corus Engineering Steels, PO Box 25, Wolverhampton, WV1 3DY Tel: (01902) 875000 Fax: (01902) 875011 E-mail: keith.grant@corusgroup.com

CARBON STEEL PIPEWORK FABRICATORS

▶ Broplant Fabrications Ltd, Moorfield Industrial Estate, Cotes Heath, Stafford, ST21 6QY Tel: (01782) 791232 Fax: (01782) 791611 E-mail: broplantfabs@ukonline.co.uk
Fiscol Engineering, 85 Greenland CR, Southall, Middlesex, UB2 5ES Tel: (020) 8574 1065 Fax: (020) 8813 9780
Furniss & White Foundries Ltd, Unit 17 Abbey Way, North Anston Trading Estate, North Anston, Sheffield, S25 4JL Tel: (01909) 568831 Fax: (01909) 569322 E-mail: upgrading@f-w-f.co.uk
Malcolm Robertson and Sons Ltd, Unit 2 Church Street, Caldewgate, Carlisle, CA2 5TJ Tel: (01228) 521018 Fax: (01228) 542458
Steel Technic Ltd, Mells, Frome, Somerset, BA11 3RH Tel: (01373) 813323 Fax: (01373) 813325

CARBON STEEL PROCESS LINE PLANT

Vai UK Ltd, 7 Fudan Way, Thornaby, Stockton-on-Tees, Cleveland, TS17 6ER Tel: (01642) 662100 Fax: (01642) 606569 E-mail: contact@vai.co.uk

CARBON TIP TOOLS

Acemaster Products Ltd, 1 Julius Way, Lydfield Green, Lydney, Gloucestershire, GL15 5QS Tel: (01594) 842442 Fax: (01594) 843033

CARBONATED MINERAL WATER

Barrett's, Tivoli Road, Margate, Kent, CT9 5TA Tel: (01843) 228581 Fax: (01843) 228878
Blue Keld Springs Ltd, Fossil Nest Cranswick, Cranswick, Driffield, North Humberside, YO25 9RE Tel: (01377) 275302 Fax: (01377) 271360 E-mail: sales@bluekeld.co.uk
Britannia Soft Drinks Ltd, Britvic House, Broomfield Road, Chelmsford, CM1 1TU Tel: (01245) 261871 Fax: (01245) 267147 E-mail: forename.surname@britvic.co.uk
Buxton Mineral Water, Station Road, Buxton, Derbyshire, SK17 6AQ Tel: (01298) 766000 Fax: (01298) 72088
Coca-Cola Enterprises Europe Ltd, Charter Place, Vine Street, Uxbridge, Middlesex, UB8 1EZ Tel: (01895) 231313
Davies Brook & Co Ltd, Moreton-on-Lugg, Hereford, HR4 8DY Tel: (01432) 760666 Fax: (01432) 761477
Decantae Mineral Water Ltd, Trofarth Farm, Llangernyw, Abergele, Clwyd, LL22 8RF Tel: (01745) 860340 Fax: (01745) 860552
Lakeland Spring Soft Drinks Ltd, Red Lonning Industrial Estate, Whitehaven, Cumbria, CA28 6SJ Tel: (01946) 690777 Fax: (01946) 690888 E-mail: lakelandspring@aol.com
Nestle Waters Pow Wow, Unit 6 Circle South, Wharside Way, Trafford, Manchester, M17 1NS Tel: (0845) 6013030 Fax: 0161-877 5258
Nestle Waters Powwow, St Georges Well, Long Hanborough, Witney, Oxfordshire, OX29 8BT Tel: (01993) 882802 Fax: (01993) 883872
Nestle Waters UK Ltd, Trinity Court, Church Street, Rickmansworth, Hertfordshire, WD3 1LD Tel: (01923) 897700 Fax: (01923) 897608 E-mail: enquiries@waters.nestle.com
Purely Scottish Ltd, Woollands, Cockburnspath, Berwickshire, TD13 5XW Tel: (01368) 860600 Fax: (01368) 861960 E-mail: sales@purelyscottish.com
Sangs Banff Ltd, Macduff Industrial Estate, Old Gamrie Road, Macduff, Banffshire, AB44 1GD Tel: (01261) 832911 Fax: (01261) 833637 E-mail: sales@sangs.co.uk
Strathmore Mineral Water Co. Ltd, 126 West High St, Forfar, Angus, DD8 1BP Tel: (01307) 466147 Fax: (01307) 466072 E-mail: bobwatson@matthewclark.co.uk
Streten Hills Mineral Water Co., Shrewsbury Road, Church Stretton, Shropshire, SY6 6HD Tel: (01694) 722935 Fax: (01694) 724318
W Hall & Son Holywell Ltd, Greenfield Road, Greenfield, Holywell, Clwyd, CH8 7QB Tel: (01352) 711444 Fax: (01352) 714793
Waters & Robson Abbeywell Ltd, Abbey Well, 12 Coopies Lane, Morpeth, Northumberland, NE61 6JF Tel: (01670) 513113 Fax: (01670) 515821 E-mail: enquiries@abbey-well.co.uk

CARBONATED SOFT DRINKS

▶ Rush Drinks, Ashpool House, Sandy Lane, Lowton, Warrington, WA3 1BG Tel: (01942) 680006 Fax: (01942) 607412 E-mail: enquiries@rushdrink.com

CARBONISED FORM MULTIPART STATIONERY

▶ Coates & Parker Ltd, 36 Market Place, Warminster, Wiltshire, BA12 9AN Tel: (01985) 213030 Fax: (01985) 217680 E-mail: sales@coatesandparker.co.uk

CARBURETTORS

Broadway Electrical Services, 36 The Broadway, Grays, Essex, RM17 6EW Tel: (01375) 372782 Fax: (01375) 381457 E-mail: broadwayelectrical@lycos.co.uk
Burlen Fuel Systems Ltd, Spitfire Hous, Castle Road, Salisbury, SP1 3SA Tel: (01722) 412500 Fax: (01722) 334221 E-mail: info@burlen.co.uk
Euro Carb Ltd, 256 Kentwood Hill, Tilehurst, Reading, RG31 6DR Tel: 0118-943 1180 Fax: 0118-943 1190 E-mail: sales@dellorto.co.uk

CARD BLANKS, CARDBOARD/ PAPERBOARD

▶ Creative Detail, 32 Thorncliffe Drive, Darwen, Lancashire, BB3 3QA Tel: 01254 773391 E-mail: val@creative-detail.co.uk
Daneside Boxes, 5 Albany Mill, Canal Street, Congleton, Cheshire, CW12 3AE Tel: (01260) 273959 Fax: (01260) 273959
Impress Cards, Slough Farm, Westhall, Halesworth, Suffolk, IP19 8RN Tel: (01986) 781422 Fax: (01986) 781677 E-mail: sales@impresscards.com
Fred Johnson, Unit D2, Impirial Business Centre, West Mill, Gravesend, Kent, DA11 0DL Tel: (01474) 569919 Fax: (01474) 533261 E-mail: info@fjpaper.co.uk

CARD MAKING KITS, PORTABLE, IDENTITY (ID)/ SECURITY

Databac Group, 1 The Ashway Centre, Elm CR, Kingston upon Thames, Surrey, KT2 6HH Tel: (020) 8546 9826 Fax: (020) 8547 1026 E-mail: info@databac.com
Xcard Printers, 8 Cowley Mill Trading Estate, Longbridge Way, Cowley, Uxbridge, Middlesex, UB8 2YG Tel: (01895) 256332 Fax: (01895) 230902 E-mail: info@xcardtechnology.com

CARDBOARD BOX/CASE/ CONTAINER MACHINERY

Crosland V K Ltd, Unit 4, Lyons Road, Trafford Park, Manchester, M17 1RN Tel: 0161-877 8668 Fax: 0161-876 5234 E-mail: sales@croslandvk.com
I D Machinery Ltd, 78 Alston Drive, Bradwell Abbey, Milton Keynes, MK13 9HG Tel: (01908) 321778 Fax: (01908) 322707 E-mail: sales@idmachinery.com
Rodwell H T B, Bentalls, Basildon, Essex, SS14 3SD Tel: (01268) 286646 Fax: (01268) 287799 E-mail: sales@rodwell-autoclave.com
Sandland Packaging Ltd, 5 Phoenix Industrial Estate, Loxdale Street, Bilston, West Midlands, WV14 0PR Tel: (01902) 496925 Fax: (01902) 354760 E-mail: sales@sandlandpackaging.co.uk
Springpack, New Road, Pershore, Worcestershire, WR10 1BY Tel: (01386) 552550 Fax: (0870) 7747402

CARDBOARD BOX/CASE/ CONTAINERS

A S C Cartons Ltd, Hillside Works, Leeds Road, Shipley, West Yorkshire, BD18 1DZ Tel: (01274) 599842 Fax: (01274) 592225 E-mail: sales@asc-cartons.co.uk
Alexander Trading Co., Oakmere Training Centre, Cherry Lane, Liverpool, L4 6UG Tel: 0151-286 0061 Fax: 0151-284 4380
Alexir Packaging Ltd, Faraday Road, Crawley, West Sussex, RH10 9UR Tel: (01293) 544644 Fax: (01293) 544744 E-mail: enquiries@alexir.co.uk
Allens Removals, 161 Jackmans Place, Letchworth Garden City, Hertfordshire, SG6 1RG Tel: (07850) 872308 Fax: (01462) 621701
Doric Anderton Ltd, King Edward Street, Grimsby, South Humberside, DN31 3JP Tel: (01472) 362429 Fax: (01472) 343300 E-mail: mandy.pratt@doricandertonltd.com
▶ Avis Packaging Ltd, Grafton Works, Grafton Road, New Malden, Surrey, KT3 3AD Tel: (020) 8942 0415 E-mail: sales@avispack.co.uk
▶ Derek Barrott Packaging Ltd, Unit 1 B, Oak Business Park, Oaks Drive, Newmarket, Suffolk, CB8 7SX Tel: (01638) 660909 Fax: (01638) 666649 E-mail: admin@barrottpackaging.co.uk
Barrows Cartons Ltd, Unit 1a Squires Mill, Micklehurst Road, Mossley, Ashton-under-Lyne, Lancashire, OL5 9JL Tel: (01457) 835253 Fax: (01457) 835898 E-mail: kel.b@btinternet.com
Beamglow Ltd, Somersham Road, St. Ives, Cambridgeshire, PE27 3LP Tel: (01480) 465012 Fax: (01480) 494826 E-mail: cartons@beamglow.co.uk
▶ Bickerstaffe Containers Ltd, Grave Yard Lane, Bickerstaffe, Ormskirk, Lancashire, L39 9EG Tel: (01695) 424244 Fax: (01695) 424387
Birmingham Packaging Co., 40 Rushey Lane, Tyseley, Birmingham, B11 2BL Tel: 0121-706 9171 Fax: 0121-708 2565 E-mail: sales@birminghampackaging.co.uk
Box Factory Ltd, 2 Caswell Road, Leamington Spa, Warwickshire, CV31 1QD Tel: (01926) 430510 Fax: (01926) 430505
Boxes & Packaging, Unit 10 Southside, Bredbury Park Industrial Estate, Bredbury, Stockport, Cheshire, SK6 2SP Tel: 0161-406 4200 Fax: 0161-406 7217 E-mail: manchester@boxesandpackaging.co.uk
Boxes & Packaging Ltd, Dunbeath Road, Elgin Industrial Estate, Swindon, SN2 8EA Tel: (01793) 513233 Fax: (01793) 513225 E-mail: swindon@boxesandpackagingltd.co.uk
Boxline Ltd, Bradgate Street, Leicester, LE4 0AW Tel: 0116-262 7571 Fax: 0116-251 5090 E-mail: sales@boxline.co.uk
Breamfold Packaging Ltd, 129 Richmond Road, London, E8 3NJ Tel: (020) 7249 6735 Fax: (020) 7249 6737 E-mail: sales@breamfoldpackaging.co.uk
Bridgeshire Packaging Ltd, 1 Wimsey Way, Alfreton Trading Estate, Somercotes, Alfreton, Derbyshire, DE55 4LS Tel: (01773) 601000 Fax: (01773) 606075 E-mail: sales@bridgeshire.co.uk
▶ Burscough Packaging Ltd, Unit 1a Abbey Lane Industrial Estate, Burscough, Ormskirk, Lancashire, L40 7RS Tel: (01704) 896216 Fax: (01704) 896659
Burton Box Co. Ltd, Burton Road Works, Burton-On-Trent, Staffordshire, DE14 3DH Tel: (01283) 540023 Fax: (01283) 565985
Caps Cases Ltd, Studlands Park Industrial Estate, Newmarket, Suffolk, CB8 7AU Tel: (01638) 667326 Fax: (01638) 667407 E-mail: info@capscases.co.uk
Captain Packaging Ltd, 5 Clarence Wharf, Mumby Road, Gosport, Hampshire, PO12 1AJ Tel: (023) 9251 1125 Fax: (023) 9252 5844 E-mail: sales@captain.co.uk
Carton Packaging Supplies Ltd, Unit 5F, Nobel Road, Eley Estate, London, N18 3BH Tel: (020) 8807 7244 Fax: (020) 8807 7327 E-mail: cartonpack93@msn.com
Cavendish Packaging Ltd, Manor Royal, Faraday Road, Crawley, West Sussex, RH10 9UR Tel: (01293) 525556 Fax: (01293) 528886
Central Box Co. Ltd, 14-16 Lithgow Place, College Milton, East Kilbride, Glasgow, G74 1PW Tel: (01355) 233725 Fax: (01355) 265166
Charapak Ltd, Meadow Lane, Alfreton, Derbyshire, DE55 7EZ Tel: (01773) 835735 Fax: (01773) 520148 E-mail: sales@charapak.co.uk
Clarke Rubicon Ltd, Telford Way, Stephenson Industrial Estate, Coalville, Leicestershire, LE67 3HE Tel: (01530) 513700 Fax: (01530) 513701 E-mail: info@clarke-rubicon.co.uk
Clifford Packaging Ltd, Bradbourne Drive, Tilbrook, Milton Keynes, MK7 8AQ Tel: (0870) 1226333 Fax: (01908) 270429 E-mail: enquiries@cliffordpackaging.com
▶ Com Pak Design Ltd, Units 3-4 Kestral Close, Quarry Hill Road, Ilkeston, Derbyshire, DE7 4DA Tel: 0115-944 2224 Fax: 0115-944 1433
Compack Ltd, 1 Letham Road, Houstoun Industrial Estate, Livingston, West Lothian, EH54 5BY Tel: (01506) 438654 Fax: (01506) 433815
T. Cooper & Co. (Macclesfield) Ltd, Hobson Street, Macclesfield, Cheshire, SK11 8BB Tel: 01625 422953
Coutts Retail Communications Ltd, Golden House, Great Pulteney Street, London, W1F 9NN Tel: (020) 7534 8800 Fax: (020) 7534 8805
E.B. Crowhurst & Co. Ltd, Building 50, Pensnett Trading Estate, Kingswinford, West Midlands, DY6 7XD Tel: (01384) 400100 Fax: (01384) 400455 E-mail: sales@crowhurst.cio.uk
Cutts Box Co. Ltd, Lion Works, Mowbray Street, Sheffield, S3 8EZ Tel: 0114-272 8673 Fax: 0114-276 5757
D S Smith, Scarne Industrial Estate, Launceston, Cornwall, PL15 9HN Tel: (01566) 777700 Fax: (01566) 774489 E-mail: sales@launceston.dssp.com
D S Smith, Muir Road, Houstoun Industrial Estate, Livingston, West Lothian, EH54 5DP Tel: (01506) 432841 Fax: (01506) 438347
D S Smith, Fordham Road, Newmarket, Suffolk, CB8 7TX Tel: (01638) 722100 Fax: (01638) 722101
Dairi Pak, Platt Bridge, Ruyton XI Towns, Shrewsbury, SY4 1LS Tel: (01939) 260342 Fax: (01939) 260275 E-mail: sales@dairi-pak.co.uk
David S Smith, Prickwillow Road, Queen Adelaide, Ely, Cambridgeshire, CB7 4TZ Tel: (01353) 660000 Fax: (01353) 660011 E-mail: steve.wills@ely.dssp.com
▶ Dial a Box Ltd, 35 Riverside Close, Warrington, WA1 2JD Tel: (01925) 650964 Fax: (0800) 7316769 E-mail: sales@dial-a-box.co.uk
▶ Direct Cartons, Unit2, Mountain View, Holmfield, Halifax, West Yorkshire, HX2 9SL Tel: 0796 8070597 Fax: 01422 242347 E-mail: DIRECT.CARTONS@BTINTERNET.COM
Doncaster Packaging Ltd, Units 4/5 Shaw Lane Indust Estate Ogden Road, Long Sandall, Doncaster, South Yorkshire, DN2 4SQ Tel: (01302) 365334 Fax: (01302) 329012
▶ Eagle Corrugated Ltd, Kayley Industrial Estate, Richmond Street, Ashton-Under-Lyne, Lancashire, OL7 0AU Tel: 0161-343 1722
▶ Easypack Corrugated Cases Ltd, Finchley Avenue, Mildenhall, Bury St. Edmunds, Suffolk, IP28 7BG Tel: (01638) 715922 Fax: (01638) 712836 E-mail: sales@easypack.uk.com
Edward J Wood & Co Printers Ltd, 31-37 Rosslyn Cresent, Harrow, Middlesex, HA1 2SA Tel: (020) 8427 6418 Fax: (020) 8861 2126 E-mail: jonengland@compuserve.com
▶ Emerald Packaging Ltd, Ravenhead Road, St. Helens, Merseyside, WA10 3LR Tel: (01744) 755352 Fax: (01744) 750120
Encase Ltd, Beaumont Road, Banbury, Oxfordshire, OX16 1RE Tel: (01295) 250971 Fax: (01295) 752910
Encase Northern Ltd, 2 Yeadon Airport Industrial Estate, Harrogate Road, Yeadon, Leeds, LS19 7WP Tel: 0113-250 5616 Fax: 0113-239 1145 E-mail: operations.northern@encase.co.uk
▶ Encase Scotland Ltd, 9 Hawbank Road, East Kilbride, Glasgow, G74 5EG Tel: (01355) 246716 Fax: (01355) 264406
F G Curtis & Co Plc, Crownhall House, Elm Grove, London, SW19 4HE Tel: (020) 8947 8178 Fax: (020) 8944 1530 E-mail: info@fgcurtis.co.uk
Fairmile Cardboard Containers Ltd, Willow Tree Buisness Park, Pattenden Lane, Marden, Tonbridge, Kent, TN12 9QJ Tel: (01622) 832110 Fax: (01622) 833285 E-mail: judylorne@aol.com
▶ Farish Associates, 94 Sutton Court, Chiswick, London, W4 3JF Tel: (020) 8742 3223 Fax: (020) 8742 3226 E-mail: sales@farish.com
Field Group Ltd, Misbourne House Badminton Court, Church Street, Amersham, Buckinghamshire, HP7 0DD Tel: (01494) 720200 Fax: (01494) 431138 E-mail: marketing@fieldgroup.com
▶ Field Packaging, Bellhill North Industrial Estate, Bellshill, Lanarkshire, ML4 3EE Tel: (01698) 748384 Fax: (01698) 843946
▶ Flightcase Warehouse Ltd, Meltex House, 2 Mariner, Tamworth, Staffordshire, B79 7XE Tel: (01827) 60009 Fax: (01827) 313877 E-mail: sales@flightcasewarehouse.co.uk
L.P. Foreman & Sons Ltd, Farrow Road, Wigford Industrial Estate, Chelmsford, CM1 3TH Tel: (01245) 264521 Fax: (01245) 495232 E-mail: sales@lpforeman.co.uk
Forton Packaging Ltd, 11 Brookgate, Bristol, BS3 2UN Tel: 0117-953 7222 Fax: 0117-953 7456 E-mail: sales@fortonpack.com
Fyne Packaging Ltd, PO Box 443, Leighton Buzzard, Bedfordshire, LU7 4WG Tel: (01525) 370765 Fax: (01525) 376010 E-mail: sales@fynepac.co.uk
Garthwest Ltd, Rotterdam Road, Hull, HU7 0XA Tel: (01482) 825121 Fax: (01482) 825229 E-mail: info@garthwest.freeserve.co.uk
Leonard Gould & Co. Ltd, Union Park, Bircholt Road, Maidstone, Kent, ME15 9XT Tel: (01622) 623400 Fax: (01622) 686695 E-mail: sales@leonardgould.co.uk
H S G Packing Cases Ltd, Long Row, New Works Road, Low Moor, Bradford, West Yorkshire, BD12 0QN Tel: (01274) 601137 Fax: (01274) 678597 E-mail: sales@hsg-packing-cases.co.uk
Heritage Packaging, 3 Whitebridge Industrial Estate, Whitebridge Lane, Stone, Staffordshire, ST15 8LQ Tel: (01785) 819189 Fax: (01785) 819089 E-mail: heripak@hotmail.com
George Howard Packaging Ltd, Unit 5-6, Power Industrial Estate, Slade Green Road, Erith, Kent, DA8 2HU Tel: (01322) 338855 Fax: (01322) 349922
Howarth Packaging Ltd, Units 7-11, Hugh Business Park, Waterfoot, Rossendale, Lancashire, BB4 7BT Tel: (01706) 214531 Fax: (01706) 224060 E-mail: server@howarthpackaging.demon.co.uk
I Palmer & Son Ltd, 106 Lower Parliament Street, Nottingham, NG1 1EH Tel: 0115-950 3458 Fax: 0115-941 3458

CARDBOARD BOX/CASE/ CONTAINERS – *continued*

▶ Jaxpal Ltd, Unit 37 Planetary Industrial Estate, Planetary Road, Willenhall, West Midlands, WV13 3XB Tel: (01902) 721066 Fax: (01902) 865839
Jaycee Packaging Ltd, 8 Fairefield Crescent, Glenfield, Leicester, LE3 8EH Tel: 0116-231 4994 Fax: 0116-231 4989
Jelmead Ltd, Units 1 & 4 Francis Works, Geddings Road, Hoddesdon, Hertfordshire, EN11 0NT Tel: (01992) 442751 Fax: (01992) 463739
Justinor Products Ltd, St. Johns Business Park, St. Johns Grove, Hull, HU9 3RL Tel: (01482) 799321 Fax: (01482) 799470 E-mail: sales@justinor.co.uk
K C M Packaging Ltd, Units 17-18 Etherow Industrial Estate, Woolley Bridge Road, Hadfield, Glossop, Derbyshire, SK13 2GA Tel: (01457) 862617 Fax: (01457) 861540 E-mail: sales@kcmpackaging.co.uk
Kappa Corby Corlon Packaging, Arnsley Road, Weldon North Industrial Estate, Corby, Northamptonshire, NN17 5QW Tel: (01536) 406784 Fax: (01536) 400320 E-mail: sales@kappa-corby.co.uk
Kappa Corrugated UK Ltd, Knowl Street, Stalybridge, Cheshire, SK15 3AR Tel: 0161-338 3711 Fax: 0161-303 2647
Langlands & Mcainsh (Packaging) Ltd, 133 Seagate, Dundee, DD1 2HP Tel: (01382) 224657 Fax: (01382) 201969
Lea Boxes Ltd, 38 Camford Way, Luton, LU3 3AN Tel: (01582) 505561 Fax: (01582) 490352 E-mail: maria@leaboxes.co.uk
▶ Leighton Packaging Ltd, Leigh Commerce Park, Green Fold Way, Leigh, Lancashire, WN7 3XJ Tel: (01942) 601011 Fax: (01942) 601012E-mail: info@leighton-packaging.co.uk
Link Packaging Ltd, Tingley Bar Industrial Estate, Tingley Mills, Morley, Leeds, LS27 0HE Tel: 0113-252 7011 Fax: 0113-238 0069 E-mail: linkltd@aol.com
Lionkent Ltd, Unit 18 Serl Industrial Estate, London Road, Baldock, Hertfordshire, SG7 6NG Tel: (01462) 892870 Fax: (01462) 893981
The London Fancy Box Company Ltd, Poulton Close, Coombe Valley, Dover, Kent, CT17 0XB Tel: (01304) 242001 Fax: (01304) 240229 E-mail: a.darrall@londonfancybox.co.uk
Makkipak Ltd, Mallard Close, Earls Barton, Northampton, NN6 0JF Tel: (01604) 812755 Fax: (01604) 812413 E-mail: sales@makkipak.com
Manuel Lloyd Ltd, 20 Bull Lane, London, N18 1SX Tel: (020) 8807 4303 Fax: (020) 8807 3839
▶ Marshall Langston Ltd, Marlan House, Lower Tuffley Lane, Gloucester, GL2 5DT Tel: (01452) 529717 Fax: (01452) 309994 E-mail: sales@marshalllangston.co.uk
▶ Meridian, Spring La North, Malvern, Worcestershire, WR14 1BU Tel: (01684) 578441 Fax: (01684) 578442
Mondi Packaging, Harfreys Road, Harfreys Industrial Estate, Great Yarmouth, Norfolk, NR31 0LS Tel: (01493) 656431 Fax: (01493) 440235
Mondi Packaging UK Ltd, Mold Business Park, Mold, Clwyd, CH7 1XZ Tel: (01352) 750655 Fax: (01352) 750677 E-mail: mark.mccleery@mondipackaging.com
Mondiboard, Carlisle Road, Larkhall, Lanarkshire, ML9 3PX Tel: (01698) 885848 Fax: (01698) 882421
N Smith & Co. Ltd, Leopold Works, 28 Hainge Road, Tividale, Oldbury, West Midlands, B69 2NZ Tel: 0121-557 1891 Fax: 0121-521 5700 E-mail: sales@nsmithbox.co.uk
Nelsons For Cartons & Packaging Ltd, Auster Industrial Estate, Silverdale Drive, Thurmaston, Leicester, LE4 8NG Tel: 0116-264 1050 Fax: 0116-264 1051
Nicholl Packaging Ltd, 4 Thackley Court, Thackley Old Road, Shipley, West Yorkshire, BD18 1BW Tel: (01274) 580563 Fax: (01274) 531675 E-mail: info@nichollpackaging.co.uk
North West Fire Ltd, Ross Road, Ellesmere Port, CH65 3DB Tel: 0151-355 6822 Fax: (01978) 751646
Northern Box & Packaging Co. Ltd, Moss Bridge Mill, Blackburn Road, Darwen, Lancashire, BB3 0AJ Tel: (01254) 702375 Fax: (01254) 873709
Northumbrian Packaging, Gear House, Saltmeadows Road, Gateshead, Tyne & Wear, NE8 3AH Tel: 0191-490 3372 Fax: 0191-490 3372 E-mail: northpackaging@fsbdial.co.uk
Ozbox, Herald Way, Binley Industrial Estate, Binley Industrial Estate, Coventry, CV3 2RQ Tel: (024) 7656 1561 Fax: (024) 7656 1555 E-mail: tena.snell@ozbox.co.uk
P J Packaging Ltd, 20 High Street, Wem, Shrewsbury, SY4 5DL Tel: (01939) 235073 Fax: (01939) 235074 E-mail: sales@pjpackaging.ltd.uk
Packaging Supplies Ltd, Unit 2-3 Thorney Lane North, Iver, Buckinghamshire, SL0 9HF Tel: (01753) 653303 Fax: (01753) 655276 E-mail: sales@pack-supplies.co.uk
▶ Pack-Online Ltd, Chestnut House Spetisbury, Blandford, Spetisbury, Blandford Forum, Dorset, DT11 9DF Tel: (01258) 450389 Fax: (01258) 459252 E-mail: boxoffice@pack-online.co.uk
Peak Box Designs Ltd, Unit 1, Ensor Way, New Mills, High Peak, Derbyshire, SK22 4NQ Tel: (01663) 747889 Fax: (01663) 743979
Porter Packaging Co. Ltd, Hardwick Grange, Woolston, Warrington, WA1 4RT Tel: (01925) 822828 Fax: (01925) 837593
▶ Powell Packaging Ltd, Birkdale Road, Scunthorpe, South Humberside, DN17 2AU Tel: (01724) 853625 Fax: (01724) 280159 E-mail: powellpackaging@btconnect.com
Printcut Boxfast Ltd, 144 Charles Henry Street, Birmingham, B12 0SD Tel: 0121-622 4353 Fax: 0121-622 1254 E-mail: sales@pcbf.co.uk
Propak, Tything Road West, Kinwarton, Alcester, Warwickshire, B49 6EP Tel: (01789) 765111 Fax: (01789) 765720 E-mail: sales@propakbox.com
Quality Control Laboratory Ltd, 13a Newbury Road, London, E4 9JH Tel: (020) 8523 3003 Fax: (020) 8523 3003 E-mail: sales@qc2000.freeserve.co.uk
Quickcase Boxes, 2 Brimscombe Mills Estate, London Road, Brimscombe, Stroud, Gloucestershire, GL5 2SA Tel: (01453) 884572 Fax: (01453) 885552
R S B Services, 16a Verney Rd, London, SE16 3DH Tel: (020) 7277 5161 Fax: (020) 7277 5115
Reedbut Ltd, Bond Avenue, Bletchley, Milton Keynes, MK1 1JJ Tel: (01908) 630200 Fax: (01908) 630210 E-mail: sales@reedbut.com
Ribble Packaging Ltd, Greengate Street, Oldham, OL4 1DF Tel: 0161-284 9000 Fax: 0161-627 5049 E-mail: ribble@ribble-pack.co.uk
▶ Rose Wood Packaging Scotland, 9-15 Napier Place, Wardpark North, Cumbernauld, Glasgow, G68 0LL Tel: (01236) 782500 E-mail: enquires@rosewoodpackaging.co.uk
S C A Containerboard UK, East Mill, Aylesford, Kent, ME20 7PA Tel: (01622) 883661 Fax: (01622) 883660 E-mail: scacontainerboard.uk@sca.com
S C A Packaging Ltd, 95a James Street, York, YO10 3WW Tel: (01904) 430915 Fax: (01904) 430921
S C A Packaging Bingham, Moorbridge Road, Bingham, Nottingham, NG13 8GG Tel: (01949) 838667 Fax: (01949) 838993
S C A Packaging Darlington Ltd, Faverdale Industrial Estate, Darlington, County Durham, DL3 0PE Tel: (01325) 284284 Fax: (01325) 460704E-mail: enquiries@scapackaging.co.uk
S.Cohen(Boxes)Limited, Unit 1b St Marks, Industrial Estate, London, E16 2BS Tel: (020) 7055 5330 Fax: (020) 7055 5331 E-mail: sales@scohenboxes.co.uk
S E A Packaging, Lavenham Road, Yate, Bristol, BS37 5QY Tel: (01454) 314509 Fax: (01454) 325711
Saica Packaging UK Ltd, Road Three, Winsford Industrial Estate, Winsford, Cheshire, CW7 3RJ Tel: (01606) 562700 Fax: (01606) 562762 E-mail: reception@saica-packaging.co.uk
J.T. Sawyer & Co. Ltd, Mottram Street, Stockport, Cheshire, SK1 3PA Tel: 0161-480 3366 Fax: 0161-480 9201 E-mail: boxes@sawyers.boxes.co.uk
Sca Packaging Ltd, UK Central Office, Papyrus Way, Larkfield, Aylesford, Kent, ME20 7TW Tel: (01622) 883000 Fax: (01622) 716308
Scottish Sea Food Processing Federation, South Esplanade West, Food Resource Centre, Aberdeen, AB1 1AA Tel: (01224) 897744 Fax: (01224) 871405 E-mail: rhona@aberdeenfish.co.uk
Sealtight Gaskets Ltd, Unit 15 Calow Brook Drive, Hasland, Chesterfield, Derbyshire, S41 0DR Tel: (01246) 221400 Fax: (01246) 222401 E-mail: harveyslack@supernet.com
Seddon Packaging & Print Ltd, Orient House, Field Street, Kettering, Northamptonshire, NN16 8BD Tel: (01536) 517303 Fax: (01536) 410674 E-mail: info@seddon.co.uk
Simpkin & Icke Holdings Ltd, Glaisdale Works, Glaisdale Drive, Nottingham, NG8 4JU Tel: 0115-929 2106 Fax: 0115-929 0446 E-mail: boxes@simpkin-and-icke.co.uk
Smithpack Ltd, 1 Pegasus Way, Bowerhill, Melksham, Wiltshire, SN12 6TR Tel: (01225) 709628 Fax: (01225) 709884
Smurfit Kappa, 24-26 Robjohns Road, Chelmsford, CM1 3BB Tel: (01245) 493777 Fax: (01245) 353427
Stevens A & Co Yeovil Ltd, Woodland Grove, Yeovil, Somerset, BA20 1NZ Tel: (01935) 476151 Fax: (01935) 422648 E-mail: peter@stevensboxes.com
Suttons Performance Packaging, 16 Albert Way, Chatteris, Cambridgeshire, PE16 6US Tel: (01354) 693171 Fax: (01354) 695430 E-mail: info@suttonspp.co.uk
Talbots Birmingham Ltd, 56-60 Princip Street, Birmingham, B4 6LN Tel: 0121-333 3544 Fax: 0121-333 3520 E-mail: sales@talbotsbirm.co.uk
Tams Packaging Ltd, Sopers Road, Cuffley, Potters Bar, Hertfordshire, EN6 4TP Tel: (01707) 876777 Fax: (01707) 872233 E-mail: tams.packaging@talk21.com
▶ Tecnovision, 33 Ashville Way, Whetstone, Leicester, LE8 6NU Tel: 0116-275 3262 Fax: 0116-275 3821
Tee-Kay Packaging, Fengate, Peterborough, PE1 5XG Tel: (01733) 311867 Fax: (01733) 311017 E-mail: robert@tee-kay.co.uk
TRM Packaging Ltd, Red Cat Lane, Burscough, Ormskirk, Lancashire, L40 0SY Tel: (01704) 892811 Fax: (01704) 895546 E-mail: sales@trmpack.co.uk
Tylex Bropad Ltd, Ballingdon Hill Industrial Estate, Ballingdon Hill, Sudbury, Suffolk, CO10 2DX Tel: (01787) 371158 Fax: (01787) 311044 E-mail: tylex.polystyrene@btinternet.com
W Maccarthy & Sons Ltd, Unit 1 Block 1, Woolwich Dockyard Industrial Estate, Woolwich Church St, London, SE18 5PQ Tel: (020) 8316 4321 Fax: (020) 8316 5566 E-mail: box.maccarthy@virgin.net
The Walsall Box Co. Ltd, Bank Street, Walsall, WS1 2ER Tel: (01922) 628118 Fax: (01922) 723395 E-mail: mail@thewalsallbox.co.uk
Welsh Boxes of Swansea Ltd, Bruce Road, Swansea Industrial Estate, Fforestfach, Swansea, SA5 4HX Tel: (01792) 586527 Fax: (01792) 585410 E-mail: sales@welshboxes.co.uk
Wevax Ltd, Prospect Close, Lowmoor Business Park, Kirkby-in-Ashfield, Nottingham, NG17 7LF Tel: (01623) 754268 Fax: (01623) 723447
Richard Wood Packaging Ltd, Guys Industrial Estate Tollgate Road, Burscough, Ormskirk, Lancashire, L40 8TG Tel: (01704) 893073 Fax: (01704) 895276 E-mail: woodpackaging@aol.co.uk
York Box, 31 Auster Road, Clifton Moor, York, YO30 4XA Tel: (01904) 610651 Fax: (01904) 691458

CARDBOARD BOXES OR CASES OR CONTAINERS, HEAVY DUTY

▶ Canford Magna Storage, Unit 11, Canford Business Park, Magna Road, Wimborne, Dorset, BH21 3BT Tel: (01202) 570970 Fax: (01202) 577971 E-mail: storage@1stchoiceremovals.net
▶ Direct Cartons, Unit2, Mountain View, Holmfield, Halifax, West Yorkshire, HX2 9SL Tel: 0796 8070597 Fax: 01422 242347 E-mail: DIRECT.CARTONS@BTINTERNET.COM

CARDBOARD BOXES/CASES/ CONTAINERS, HEAVY DUTY, TO SPECIFICATION

Beulah Packaging Cards Ltd, 25 Scotts Road, Bromley, BR1 3QD Tel: (020) 8466 8610 Fax: (020) 8466 8612 E-mail: info@beulahpackaging.co.uk
Box Factory Ltd, 2 Caswell Road, Leamington Spa, Warwickshire, CV31 1QD Tel: (01926) 430510 Fax: (01926) 430505
Bripak UK Ltd, Delta Works, Devonshire Road, Eccles, Manchester, M30 0WX Tel: 0161-787 8770 Fax: 0161-707 0009
Carton Packaging Supplies Ltd, Unit 5F, Nobel Road, Eley Estate, London, N18 3BH Tel: (020) 8807 7244 Fax: (020) 8807 7327 E-mail: cartonpack93@msn.com
Castle Corrugated Cases Ltd, Hadnock Road, Monmouth, Gwent, NP25 3NQ Tel: (01600) 715727 Fax: (01600) 714942
CRP Print & Packaging Ltd, Cooks Road, Weldon North Industrial Estate, Corby, Northamptonshire, NN17 5JT Tel: (01536) 200333 Fax: (01536) 403329 E-mail: sales@crpprint.co.uk
Encase Ltd, Beaumont Road, Banbury, Oxfordshire, OX16 1RE Tel: (01295) 250971 Fax: (01295) 752910
G Ryder & Co. Ltd, Denbigh Road, Bletchley, Milton Keynes, MK1 1DG Tel: (01908) 375524 Fax: (01908) 373658 E-mail: john.discombe@ryderbox.co.uk
Jerrards, Marks Farm, Frating Road, Great Bromley, Colchester, CO7 7JN Tel: (0870) 7304050 Fax: (01206) 257524 E-mail: jerrards@btinternet.com
Marish Packaging Ltd, Riverside Way, Cowley, Uxbridge, Middlesex, UB8 2YF Tel: (01895) 256885 Fax: (01895) 256905 E-mail: sales@marishpackaging.co.uk
Pudelko Corrugated Cases Ltd, Unit 20 Goldicote Business Park, Banbury Road, Goldicote, Stratford-upon-Avon, Warwickshire, CV37 7NB Tel: (01789) 740973 Fax: (01789) 740395 E-mail: pudelkoccl@aol.com
Quadwall (Heavy Duty Corrugated) Ltd, Unit B5 (1 & 2) Moss Industrial Estate, St. Helens Road, Leigh, Lancashire, WN7 3PT Tel: (01942) 674012 Fax: (01942) 260167 E-mail: sales@quadwall.co.uk
Tylex Bropad Ltd, Ballingdon Hill Industrial Estate, Ballingdon Hill, Sudbury, Suffolk, CO10 2DX Tel: (01787) 371158 Fax: (01787) 311044 E-mail: tylex.polystyrene@btinternet.com
Zetland Boxes, 70 Heworth Village, York, YO31 1AL Tel: (01904) 424000 Fax: (01904) 422408 E-mail: ken@zetlandboxes.co.uk

CARDBOARD CORES

Birmingham Mailing Cases Ltd, Machin Road, Birmingham, B23 6DR Tel: 0121-373 0401 Fax: 0121-377 7671 E-mail: birmingham.mailingcases@virgin.net
Crayford Tubes Ltd, Unit 33 Acorn Industrial Park, Crayford Road, Dartford, DA1 4AL Tel: (01322) 526614 Fax: (01322) 559462 E-mail: info@crayford-tubes.co.uk
Just Paper, Foxlea House, Cliffe-Cum-Lund, Selby, North Yorkshire, YO8 6PE Tel: (01757) 630226 Fax: (01757) 630227 E-mail: sales@justpapertubes.co.uk

CARDBOARD CYLINDRICAL CONTAINERS

Birmingham Mailing Cases Ltd, Machin Road, Birmingham, B23 6DR Tel: 0121-373 0401 Fax: 0121-377 7671 E-mail: birmingham.mailingcases@virgin.net
Crayford Tubes Ltd, Unit 33 Acorn Industrial Park, Crayford Road, Dartford, DA1 4AL Tel: (01322) 526614 Fax: (01322) 559462 E-mail: info@crayford-tubes.co.uk

CARDBOARD ENGINEERING

▶ G D Designs, 14 Smallford Lane, Smallford, St. Albans, Hertfordshire, AL4 0SA Tel: (01727) 828183 Fax: (01727) 828183 E-mail: g.donovan@virgin.net

CARDBOARD FOOD PACKAGING

Appledore Packaging, Rose Dene, Green Farm Lane, Shorne, Gravesend, Kent, DA12 3HL Tel: (01474) 770018 Fax: (01474) 770019 E-mail: enquiries@appledore-packaging.co.uk
Firstan Ltd, Trafalgar Way, Bar Hill, Cambridge, CB3 8SQ Tel: (01954) 201010 Fax: (01954) 782923 E-mail: sales@firstan.co.uk
G Alderson, 11a Clarke Road, Bletchley, Milton Keynes, MK1 1UA Tel: (01908) 641680 Fax: (01908) 643517
Garthwest Ltd, Rotterdam Road, Hull, HU7 0XA Tel: (01482) 825121 Fax: (01482) 825229 E-mail: info@garthwest.freeserve.co.uk
Ice Cream Container Co. Ltd, 6 Beresford Avenue, Wembley, Middlesex, HA0 1SA Tel: (020) 8903 9021 Fax: (020) 8900 2472 E-mail: sales@icecream-cont.co.uk
W K Thomas & Co. Ltd, Mount House, Mount Road, Chessington, Surrey, KT9 1HY Tel: (020) 8391 2211 Fax: (020) 8391 2980 E-mail: info@wkthomas.com

CARDBOARD PACKAGING

Allpoint Packaging Ltd, Witch Lane Industrial Estate, Charter Alley, Basingstoke, Hampshire, RG26 5PY Tel: (01256) 851081 Fax: (01256) 851305 E-mail: allpointp@aol.com
Fiskeby Board Ltd, Lloyd Berkeley Place, Pebble Lane, Aylesbury, Buckinghamshire, HP20 2JH Tel: (01296) 426219 Fax: (01296) 482682 E-mail: pat.bannerman@fiskeby.com
Horne Robert Paper Company Ltd, Huntsman House, 40 Tameside Drive, Birmingham, B35 7BD Tel: 0121-776 7777 Fax: 0121-749 2670 E-mail: rh.birmingham@roberthorne.co.uk
Kite Packaging, PO Box 50, Blackwood, Gwent, NP12 2XF Tel: (01495) 230976 Fax: (01495) 230080 E-mail: southwales@packwithkite.com
Kite Packaging, 186 Torrington Avenue, Coventry, CV4 9AJ Tel: (024) 7642 0088 Fax: (024) 7642 0062 E-mail: sales@packwithkite.com
Kite Packaging, H Park 34, Collett, Didcot, Oxfordshire, OX11 7WB Tel: (01235) 815615 Fax: (01235) 750760 E-mail: thamesvalley@packwithkite.com
Kite Packaging, Unit 24-28, Stakehill Industrial Estate, Middleton, Manchester, M24 2RW Tel: 0161-643 1001 Fax: 0161-643 1122 E-mail: manchester@packwithkite.com
Kite Packaging, Portfield Road, Portsmouth, PO3 5SF Tel: (023) 9265 2676 Fax: (023) 9265 2677 E-mail: southcoast@packwithkite.com
Kite Packaging Ltd (Sheffield), Unit 3, Grange Mill Lane, Sheffield, S9 1HW Tel: (01709) 565010 Fax: (01709) 565011 E-mail: sheffield@packwithkite.com
Longulf Ltd, Prince Albert House, 2 Kingsmill Terrace, London, NW8 6BN Tel: (020) 7722 7733 Fax: (020) 7722 9028 E-mail: info@longulf.com
Turner Packaging Ltd, Horndon Business Park, West Horndon, Brentwood, Essex, CM13 3HW Tel: (01277) 810846 Fax: (01277) 810191 E-mail: service@turnerpack.co.uk

CARDBOARD PACKAGING BALERS

Creative Packaging South Wales, 47a Millers Avenue, Brynmenyn, Bridgend, CF32 9TD Tel: (01656) 720444 Fax: (01656) 720769 E-mail: enquiries@creative-packaging.co.uk

CARDBOARD POSTAL TUBULAR CONTAINERS

Kennet Plastics, Unit A, Aerial Business Park, Lambourn Woodlands, Hungerford, Berkshire, RG17 7RZ Tel: (01488) 72055 Fax: (01488) 71122 E-mail: sales@kennet-pack.co.uk

▶ indicates data change since last edition

CARDBOARD SHOP DISPLAYS

Corrugated Case Co. Ltd, Unit 1, Pilsley Road, Danesmoor, Chesterfield, Derbyshire, S45 9BU Tel: (01246) 860990 Fax: (01246) 860991 E-mail: info@corrugatedcase.com

CARDBOARD TUBE MAKING MACHINERY

C Perkin Ltd, 6 Shaw Cross Court, Horace Waller V C Parade, Shaw Cross Business Park, Dewsbury, West Yorkshire, WF12 7RF Tel: (01924) 439449 Fax: (01924) 438908 E-mail: info@cperkin.com

CARDBOARD TUBES

Birmingham Mailing Cases Ltd, Machin Road, Birmingham, B23 6DR Tel: 0121-373 0401 Fax: 0121-377 7671 E-mail: birmingham.mailingcases@virgin.net

Braythorn Ltd, Phillips Street, Birmingham, B6 4PT Tel: 0121-359 8800 Fax: 0121-359 8412 E-mail: sales@braythorn.co.uk

Caraustar Industrial & Consumer Products Group Ltd, 86 Bison Place, Moss Side, Leyland, PR26 7QR Tel: (01772) 621562 Fax: (01772) 622263 E-mail: david.dredge@caraustar.com

Cardboard Tubes Ltd, Unit D2 Zenith, Paycocke Road, Basildon, Essex, SS14 3DW Tel: (01268) 247380 Fax: (01268) 271979 E-mail: sales@cardboardtubes.co.uk

Corenso (UK) Ltd, North Tyne Industrial Estate, Whitley Road, Longbenton, Newcastle Upon Tyne, NE12 9SZ Tel: 0191-266 0222 Fax: 0191-270 1663

Cores & Tubes Ltd, 42 Vulcan Way, New Addington, Croydon, CR0 9UG Tel: (01689) 848586 Fax: (01689) 841468 E-mail: info@coresandtubes.co.uk

Crayford Tubes Ltd, Unit 33 Acorn Industrial Park, Crayford Road, Dartford, DA1 4AL Tel: (01322) 526614 Fax: (01322) 559462 E-mail: info@crayford-tubes.co.uk

Curran Packaging Co. Ltd, Thames Industrial Park, Princess Margaret Road, East Tilbury, Tilbury, Essex, RM18 8RH Tel: (01375) 857131 Fax: (01375) 856884 E-mail: sales@curran.co.uk

Deva Cores Ltd, Stephen Gray Road, Bromfield Industrial Estate, Mold, Clwyd, CH7 1HE Tel: (01352) 751777 Fax: (01352) 700066 E-mail: info@devacores.com

J F B Cores Ltd, 7 Boleyn Court, Manor Park, Runcorn, Cheshire, WA7 1SR Tel: (01928) 571812 Fax: (01928) 571813 E-mail: sales@cores.co.uk

Just Paper, Foxlea House, Cliffe-Cum-Lund, Selby, North Yorkshire, YO8 6PE Tel: (01757) 630226 Fax: (01757) 630227 E-mail: sales@justpapertubes.co.uk

Kennet Plastics, Unit A, Aerial Business Park, Lambourn Woodlands, Hungerford, Berkshire, RG17 7RZ Tel: (01488) 72055 Fax: (01488) 71122 E-mail: sales@kennet-pack.co.uk

▶ Pack-Online Ltd, Chestnut House Spetisbury, Blandford, Spetisbury, Blandford Forum, Dorset, DT11 9DF Tel: (01258) 450389 Fax: (01258) 459252 E-mail: boxoffice@pack-online.co.uk

▶ Prima Board, 4-5 The Circuit Babbage Road, Engineer Park, Sandycroft, Deeside, Clwyd, CH5 2QD Tel: (01244) 535421 Fax: (01244) 538963 E-mail: sales@primaconverters.co.uk

E. Revell & Sons Ltd, Unit 1C Joesph Wilson Industrial Estate, Mill Strood Road, Whitstable, Kent, CT5 3PS Tel: (01227) 277020 Fax: (01227) 770839

Smurfit Composites, Richmond Works, Moresby Road, Hensingham, Whitehaven, Cumbria, CA28 8TS Tel: (01946) 61671 Fax: (01946) 592281

CARDS, MEMBERSHIP/ PRIVILEGE

Cardex Facilities, Essex Technology & Innovation Centre, The Gables, Ongar, Essex, CM5 0GA Tel: (01277) 364455 Fax: (01277) 366330 E-mail: lillian.hill@cardex.co.uk

Databac Group, 1 The Ashway Centre, Elm CR, Kingston upon Thames, Surrey, KT2 6HH Tel: (020) 8546 9826 Fax: (020) 8547 1026 E-mail: info@databac.com

I D Data Ltd, The New Mint House, Bedford Road, Petersfield, Hampshire, GU32 3AL Tel: (01730) 235700 Fax: (01730) 235711 E-mail: enquiry@iddata.com

Impressions, 31 Shannon Way, Canvey Island, Essex, SS8 0PD Tel: (01268) 694175 Fax: (01268) 682000

Liberty Printers Ltd, Willett Road, Thornton Heath, Surrey, CR7 6AA Tel: (020) 8684 1486 Fax: (020) 8689 3202 E-mail: service@libertyprinters.co.uk

The Plastic Card Shop, Kemps Place, Selborne Road, Greatham, Liss, Hampshire, GU33 6HG Tel: (0845) 6448171 Fax: (0845) 2260814 E-mail: sales@theplasticcardshop.co.uk

Thames Card Technology Ltd, Thames House, Arterial Road, Rayleigh, Essex, SS6 7UQ Tel: (01268) 775555 Fax: (01268) 777660 E-mail: info@thamesgroup.co.uk

CARDS, PERIPHERAL COMPONENT INTERCONNECT (PCI), UNIVERSAL SERIAL BUS (USB) PORTS

▶ J Tech Suffolk Computer Systems Ltd, 27-29 Orwell Road, Felixstowe, Suffolk, IP11 7DD Tel: (01394) 271555 Fax: 05600 766700 E-mail: sales@jtechsuffolk.com

CARE HOME RESOURCES

▶ Independence Homes Ltd, Airport House, Purley Way, Croydon, CR0 0DZ Tel: (020) 8668 4947 Fax: 0208 288 3614

CAREER GUIDANCE

▶ Aspire Beyond, 2nd Floor 145-157 St John Street, London, EC1V 4PY Tel: 0870-490 4296 Fax: 0870-706 4880 E-mail: info@aspirebeyond.co.uk

▶ CVwriting.net, 29 Great George Street, Bristol, BS1 5QT Tel: 0870 766 9896 E-mail: enquiries@CVwriting.net

▶ Elspeth Reid Coaching, 102 Clarence Road, London, SW19 8QD Tel: (020) 8879 7676 E-mail: coach@elspethreid.com

CAREERS DEVELOPMENT

▶ Aspire Beyond, 2nd Floor 145-157 St John Street, London, EC1V 4PY Tel: 0870-490 4296 Fax: 0870-706 4880 E-mail: info@aspirebeyond.co.uk

▶ Career Energy, 4 Staple Inn, London, WC1V 7QH Tel: (020) 7831 2015 E-mail: info@careerenergy.co.uk

▶ CVwriting.net, 29 Great George Street, Bristol, BS1 5QT Tel: 0870 766 9896 E-mail: enquiries@CVwriting.net

▶ Fort Chapard Ltd, Prospect House, 32 Sovereign Street, Leeds, LS1 4BJ Tel: 0113-389 1085 Fax: 0113-389 1190 E-mail: info@fortchapard.com

CAREERS MANAGEMENT SERVICES

1st Choice, 6 St. Ives Crescent, Sale, Cheshire, M33 3RU Tel: (07840) 344464 E-mail: firstchoicecvservices@ntlworld.com

Andrew Sidebottom, 8 Overland Road, Cottingham, North Humberside, HU16 4PZ Tel: (01482) 847491 Fax: (01482) 847491 E-mail: info@psydebottom.co.uk

▶ Aspire Beyond, 2nd Floor 145-157 St John Street, London, EC1V 4PY Tel: 0870-490 4296 Fax: 0870-706 4880 E-mail: info@aspirebeyond.co.uk

▶ Career Energy, 4 Staple Inn, London, WC1V 7QH Tel: (020) 7831 2015 E-mail: info@careerenergy.co.uk

Charm Managaement Specialists Ltd, 13 High Street, Ruddington, Nottingham, NG11 6DT Tel: 0115-984 7760 Fax: 0115-921 1887 E-mail: resources@charmhrm.co.uk

▶ CVwriting.net, 29 Great George Street, Bristol, BS1 5QT Tel: 0870 766 9896 E-mail: enquiries@CVwriting.net

FOCUS Eap, 1st Floor The Podium, Metropolitan House Darkes Lane, Potters Bar, Hertfordshire, EN6 1AG Tel: (01707) 661300 Fax: (01707) 661242 E-mail: info@focuseap.co.uk

▶ Fort Chapard Ltd, Prospect House, 32 Sovereign Street, Leeds, LS1 4BJ Tel: 0113-389 1085 Fax: 0113-389 1190 E-mail: info@fortchapard.com

H D A International, 4 Park Place, 12 Lawn Lane, Vauxhall, London, SW8 1UD Tel: (020) 7820 9199 Fax: (020) 7735 8175 E-mail: admin@hda.co.uk

▶ Millnet Financial Ltd, Stapleton House, 29-33 Scrutton Street, London, EC2A 4HU Tel: (020) 7375 2300 Fax: (020) 7422 8888 E-mail: help@efinancialcareers.com

CARGO CARRYING NETS

Am Safe Ltd, Tamian Way, Hounslow, TW4 6BL Tel: (020) 8572 0321 Fax: (020) 8572 2096 E-mail: sales@am-safe.co.uk

CARGO CARRYING UNITS

C T C Container Trading (U.K.) Ltd, Hillview Base, Hillview Rd, East Tullos, Aberdeen, AB12 3HB Tel: (01224) 879111 Fax: (01224) 879015 E-mail: information@ctccontainers.com

CARGO CONTAINER SECURING EQUIPMENT

Contec & Co., Sub-Station Road, Felixstowe, Suffolk, IP11 3JB Tel: (01394) 674574 Fax: (01394) 674574

CARGO EXPEDITING SERVICES

▶ Ryburn Associates, 23-25 Hob Lane, Soyland, Sowerby Bridge, Halifax, West Yorkshire, HX6 4LU Tel: 01422 823473 Fax: 01422 823473 E-mail: info@ryburnassociates.co.uk

CARGO HANDLING SERVICES, *See also Stevedoring Services*

Aeroflot Russian International Airlines, 70 Piccadilly, London, W1J 8SB Tel: (020) 7355 2233 Fax: (020) 7355 2323 E-mail: infres@aeroflot.co.uk

B E Moors Ltd, Kemp House, 152-160 City Road, London, EC1V 2NP Tel: (020) 7855 5300 Fax: (020) 7454 9090 E-mail: admin@bemoors.co.uk

Continental Airlines, Beulah Court, Albert Road, Horley, Surrey, RH6 7HP Tel: (0845) 6076760 Fax: (01293) 773726

DHL Global Forwarding Ltd, Danzas House, Dawley Park, Kestrel Way, Hayes, Middlesex, UB3 1HJ Tel: (020) 8754 5000 Fax: (020) 8754 5154 E-mail: penny.darnbrook@dhl.com

Forest Freight Ltd, Fairview Indust Park, Barlow Way, Rainham, Essex, RM13 8BT Tel: (01708) 552222 Fax: (01708) 553330 E-mail: sales@forestfreight.co.uk

Maersk Sealand (UK), Silkhouse Court, Tithebarn Street, Liverpool, L2 2LZ Tel: (08703) 330804 Fax: 0151-236 4199 E-mail: lplmng@maersk.com

The Maersk Company UK Ltd, Maersk House, Brayham Street, London, E1 8EP Tel: (020) 7441 1439 Fax: (020) 7712 5100 E-mail: gbrmkt@maersk.com

Mersey Forwarding Co Shipping Services Ltd, Mersey House, 1 Church Street, Bootle, Merseyside, L20 1AF Tel: 0151-933 2000 Fax: 0151-933 0883 E-mail: tlennonmfss@btconnect.com

North East Contract Services Ltd, Howdon Terminal, Willington Quay, Wallsend, Tyne & Wear, NE28 6UL Tel: 0191-234 5511 Fax: 0191-234 0888 E-mail: newcastle@ofsprayltd.com

Roadways Container Logistics, Box Lane, Renwick Road, Barking, Essex, IG11 0SQ Tel: (020) 8700 4932 Fax: (020) 8700 2163 E-mail: rcl@roadways.co.uk

Teignmouth Quay Co Holdings Ltd, Old Quay, Teignmouth, Devon, TQ14 8ES Tel: (01626) 774044 Fax: (01626) 776240 E-mail: teignmouth@abports.co.uk

CARGO OR LIFTING SLINGS

A P Lifting Gear, Northfield Road, Dudley, West Midlands, DY2 9JQ Tel: (01384) 250552 Fax: (01384) 250282 E-mail: apliftingsales@btconnect.com

Tony Beal Ltd, 18 Station Road, Baillieston, Glasgow, G69 7UF Tel: 0141-773 2166 Fax: 0141-773 2904 E-mail: tbl@bealgroup.com

Checkmate Designs, New Road, Sheerness, Kent, ME12 1PZ Tel: (01795) 580333 Fax: (01795) 668280 E-mail: sales@checkmateuk.com

Polystrop Ltd, Bridge Road, Kingswood, Bristol, BS15 4FW Tel: 0117-970 1196 Fax: 0117-970 1205

RSS Group, Unit 32A/32B Village Farm Industrial Estate, Pyle, Bridgend, Mid Glamorgan, CF33 6BL Tel: (01656) 740074 Fax: (01656) 747057 E-mail: steve@rssgroup.co.uk

CARGO SECURING EQUIPMENT

Andrew Mitchell Co. Ltd, Bates Business Centre, Church Road, Harold Wood, Romford, RM3 0JF Tel: (01708) 370800 Fax: (01708) 377190 E-mail: info@mitco.co.uk

Beaconsfield Products Halesowen Ltd, Foxoak Street, Cradley Heath, West Midlands, B64 5DE Tel: (01384) 569571 Fax: (01384) 566328 E-mail: sales@beacoproducts.co.uk

N M I Safety Systems Ltd, 17 Lake Business Centre, Tariff Road, London, N17 0YX Tel: (020) 8801 5339 Fax: (020) 8801 3491 E-mail: sales@nmisafty.com

Pritchard Tyrite, Crockford Lane, Chineham, Basingstoke, Hampshire, RG24 8NA Tel: (01256) 400600 Fax: (01256) 400622 E-mail: martin@calhoun.co.uk

Spanset Ltd, Telford Way, Middlewich Bus Industrial, Park, Middlewich, Cheshire, CW10 0HX Tel: (01606) 737494 Fax: (01606) 737502 E-mail: sales@spanset.com

CARGO SECURING NETS

Tony Beal Ltd, 18 Station Road, Baillieston, Glasgow, G69 7UF Tel: 0141-773 2166 Fax: 0141-773 2904 E-mail: tbl@bealgroup.com

P G S Supplies Ltd, Worthing Road, Sheffield, S9 3JB Tel: 0114-276 5566 Fax: 0114-276 5265 E-mail: sales@pgs-supplies.co.uk

CARGO SURVEYORS/ INSPECTION SERVICES

A. Adamson, 81 Iona Way, Tiraintilloch, Glasgow, G66 3PU Tel: (0141) 552 5749 Fax: (0141) 552 4917

BMT Murray Fenton Ltd, 70 Newcomen Street, London, SE1 1YT Tel: (020) 7234 9160 Fax: (020) 7234 9161 E-mail: enquiries@bmtmarcon.com

Inchcape Shipping Services UK Ltd, East Side Locks, Immingham Dock, Immingham, South Humberside, DN40 2LZ Tel: (01469) 571400 Fax: (01469) 571309

L G S A Marine, The White House, Clifton Marine Parade, Gravesend, Kent, DA11 0DY Tel: (01474) 357181 Fax: (01474) 569037 E-mail: gravesned@lgsamarine.co.uk

L G S A Marine, 67-83 Mariners House Queens Dock Commercial Centre, Norfolk S, Liverpool, L1 0BG Tel: 0151-707 2233 Fax: 0151-707 2170 E-mail: liverpool@lgsamarine.co.uk

R Brumwell & Co., Compton House, Walnut Tree Close, Guildford, Surrey, GU1 4TX Tel: (01483) 302276 Fax: (01483) 302292 E-mail: brumwell@btinternet.com

Saybolt UK Ltd, Oliver Close, Grays, Essex, RM20 3EE Tel: (01708) 862611 Fax: (01708) 867401

CARNIVAL NOVELTIES

Candy Floss Machine Manufacturers Ltd, Gables West, Barrow Hill, Sellindge, Ashford, Kent, TN25 6JG Tel: (01303) 813171 Fax: (01303) 813171 E-mail: malcolm.frazer@virgin.net

Cheadle Royal (Industries) Ltd, Wilmslow Road, Cheadle, Cheshire, SK8 3US Tel: 0161-428 4101 Fax: 0161-428 1764 E-mail: sales@cri-ltd.net

D & F Party Ltd, Units 25-26 Walthamstow Business Centre, Clifford Road, London, E17 4SX Tel: (020) 8523 5555 Fax: (020) 8523 5554 E-mail: sales@dfparty.co.uk

Draper Party Products, 30 Comberton Hill, Kidderminster, Worcestershire, DY10 1QN Tel: (01562) 754973

Fun Busters, PO Box 7148, Redditch, Worcestershire, B98 7WW Tel: (01527) 578200 Fax: (01527) 517473

Gaffney Party Products, 215 Shrub End Road, Colchester, CO3 4PZ Tel: (01206) 766688 Fax: (01206) 766688 E-mail: sales@gaffneypartyproducts.co.uk

Heaton Paper Co. Ltd, Eldon Street, Gateshead, Tyne & Wear, NE8 3ND Tel: 0191-477 3783 Fax: 0191-490 0247 E-mail: sales@heatonpaper.co.uk

Jarroy Importers Ltd, Unit 8 Heron Industrial Estate, Barbers Road, London, E15 2PE Tel: (020) 8519 7780 Fax: (020) 8519 7265 E-mail: info@jarroy.com

Pencil House Ltd, 16 Brunel Road, Earlstrees Industrial Estate, Corby, Northamptonshire, NN17 4JW Tel: (01536) 400107 Fax: (01536) 265694

Smiffy's, Heapham Road South, Caldicott Drive, Heapham Road Industrial Estate, Gainsborough, Lincolnshire, DN21 1FJ Tel: (01427) 616831 Fax: (01427) 617190 E-mail: info@smiffys.com

Swinnertons Of Walsall, 1 Holtshill Lane, Walsall, WS1 2JA Tel: (01922) 626081 Fax: (01922) 626082

CARPENTRY SERVICES, *See also Joinery etc*

Ashford Woodturners, Old Saw Mill, Hothfield, Ashford, Kent, TN26 1EN Tel: (01233) 623090 Fax: (01233) 643423 E-mail: ashford.woodturners@btinternet.com

▶ Avandale Maintenance, 6 Roebuck Close, Hertford, SG13 7TE Tel: (01992) 581899 E-mail: alandunnage@ntlworld.com

▶ Beefast Contractors Ltd, 85 Highlands Close, Kidderminster, Worcestershire, DY11 6JU Tel: (01562) 630861 Fax: (01562) 630861 E-mail: beefast85@aol.com

▶ BookShelving, 40 Marlborough Road, Romford, RM7 8AJ Tel: 01708 736305

C L C Contractors Ltd, 21 Oswin Road, Leicester, LE3 1HR Tel: 0116-254 4105 Fax: 0116-254 2784 E-mail: leicester@clcgroup.com

C M Services, 22 Lowbell Lane, London Colney, St. Albans, Hertfordshire, AL2 1AZ Tel: (01727) 825535 Fax: (01727) 825568 E-mail: info@cmbservices.co.uk

Carpenter Oak & Woodland Co. Ltd, Lintrathen, Kirriemuir, Angus, DD8 5JA Tel: (01575) 560393 Fax: (01575) 560295

Chenko Kurtev, 21 Hastingwood Court, Pembroke Road, London, E17 9NQ Tel: (07810) 158794 Fax: (020) 8509 2955 E-mail: g_chenks@yahoo.co.uk

CARPENTRY SERVICES – *continued*

▶ Chiltern Handiman Services, Forest Lodge, Christmas Common, Watlington, Oxfordshire, OX49 5HN Tel: (01491) 613074 E-mail: enquiries@chilternhandiman.co.uk

▶ D.H. Carpentry, 3 Tytherley Road, Southampton, SO18 5DW Tel: (023) 8034 4299 Fax: (023) 8034 0954 E-mail: d.hawkins50@ntlworld.com

D H Keys & Sons Ltd, 45 Belvedere Road, Ipswich, IP4 4AB Tel: (01473) 728117 Fax: (01473) 729729

Davis, Old Wesley Hall, Bridge Street, Newbridge, Newport, Gwent, NP11 5FE Tel: (01495) 243619 Fax: (01495) 243619

Featherbow Woodcraft, Unit 1 Hillfields Farm, Lighthorne, Warwick, CV35 0BQ Tel: (01926) 651133 Fax: (01926) 651133

Georgian Medal Joinery Ltd, Unit 1, Meadow St, Treforest, Pontypridd, Mid Glamorgan, CF37 1UD Tel: (01443) 493288 Fax: (01443) 493288 E-mail: sales@hitec-cathodic.co.uk

Helme & Hallett Ltd, 42b High Street, Cuckfield, Haywards Heath, West Sussex, RH17 5EL Tel: (01444) 454776 Fax: (01444) 417716 E-mail: office@helme.co.uk

Highland Wood Windows Ltd, 46 Station Road, Worthing, West Sussex, BN11 1JP Tel: (01903) 237613 Fax: (01903) 820253 E-mail: sales@parker-joinery.com

J C D Contracts Ltd, 49 Kenilworth Drive, Oadby, Leicester, LE2 5LT Tel: 0116-271 6671 Fax: 0116-271 6672

J Pitchford & Son, Bolventure, Betley Lane, Bayston Hill, Shrewsbury, SY3 0HB Tel: (01743) 872155

K C & Son Construction Ltd, Amberley Way, Hounslow, TW4 6BH Tel: (020) 8577 2222 Fax: (020) 8577 2323

▶ KMD, 109a Whippingham Road, Brighton, BN2 3PF Tel: (01273) 679700 Fax: (01273) 605057

N Stephenson & Son Kettering Ltd, 49 Grafton Street, Kettering, Northamptonshire, NN16 9DF Tel: (01536) 512625 Fax: (01536) 522869 E-mail: nstephenson@realemail.co.uk

Nicholas Soper & Co, 225 Citadel Road East, Plymouth, PL1 2NG Tel: (01752) 695748 Fax: (01752) 696740

Palgrave Brown UK Ltd, Canterbury Industrial Park, Island Road, Hersden, Canterbury, Kent, CT3 4HQ Tel: (01227) 712322 Fax: (01227) 712852

Reading Carpentry Services Ltd, 1a Eaton Place, Reading, RG1 7LP Tel: 0118-950 0971 Fax: 0118-950 0971

Rodgers Paul Joinery, Unit 13, Ellerbeck Way, Middlesbrough, Cleveland, TS9 5JZ Tel: (01642) 714417 Fax: (01642) 714417

▶ Scott and Sons, 14 School Road, Faversham, Kent, ME13 8QZ Tel: (01795) 537221 E-mail: slarty@bardfast.wanadoo.co.uk

Steve Church Carpentry & Interior Contractors, 15 Lampits Hill Avenue, Corringham, Stanford-le-Hope, Essex, SS17 7NY Tel: (07960) 140338 Fax: (01375) 678513 E-mail: enquiries@steve-church.com

T R Price & Son, Unit F3 Dudley Central Trading Estate, Hope Street, Dudley, West Midlands, DY2 8RS Tel: (01384) 237629

Taylor & Son (Joinery) Ltd, 42 A Vicarage Road, Halesowen, West Midlands, B62 8HU Tel: 0121-559 3955 Fax: 0121-559 5412

Theale Fireplaces Reading Ltd, Bath Road, Sulhamstead, Reading, RG7 5HJ Tel: 0118-930 2232 Fax: 0118-932 3344 E-mail: sales@thealefireplaces.com

Tithe Joinery, Upper Hammonds Farm, Ripley Lane, West Horsley, Leatherhead, Surrey, KT24 6JL Tel: (01483) 283689 Fax: (01483) 282365

▶ Windsor Kitchens, 39 Martley Gardens, Hedge End, Southampton, SO30 2XB Tel: 01489 795489 E-mail: sales@windsorkitchens.com

CARPET CLEANING EQUIPMENT

Adam Cleaning Service, 29 Somersby Close, Gregg Hall, Lincoln, LN6 8AF Tel: (01522) 530467

Bissell Homecare, The Boatyard, 105 Straight Road, Old Windsor, Windsor, Berkshire, SL4 2SE Tel: (0870) 2250109 Fax: (01753) 867684

Carpet Cleaners London UK, 37 Muswell Avenue, London, N10 2EB Tel: (0800) 0436001 E-mail: info@carpet-cleaner.co.uk

▶ Carpet Cleaning London UK, Colton House, Princes Avenue, London, N3 2EB Tel: (0870) 0052895 E-mail: clients@professional-carpet-cleaning-london.co.uk

Caterclean Supplies, Meadow Street, Townhill, Swansea, SA1 6RZ Tel: (01792) 582000

▶ Cleansmart Carpet Cleaning Machines & Equipment, W12 Lenton Business Centre, Lenton Boulevard, Lenton, Nottingham, NG7 2BY Tel: (0845) 8620209

Extracta Products Ltd, Third Avenue, Team Valley Trading Estate, Gateshead, Tyne & Wear, NE11 0PR Tel: 0191-482 5005 Fax: 0191-491 0462 E-mail: extracta@extracta.co.uk

Hydramaster, The Chapel, Treskillard, Redruth, Cornwall, TR16 6JY Tel: 01209 710335 Fax: 01209 714050

Rug Doctor Ltd, 29 Decoy Road, Worthing, West Sussex, BN14 8ND Tel: (01903) 235558 Fax: (01903) 209671 E-mail: enquiries@rugdoctor.com

CARPET CLEANING MACHINE OR EQUIPMENT HIRE

Arrow Cleaning Services, 17 The Hudson, Wyke, Bradford, West Yorkshire, BD12 8HZ Tel: (01274) 690805 Fax: (01274) 690805 E-mail: sales@cleaningservicesleeds.co.uk

Carpet Cleaners London UK, 37 Muswell Avenue, London, N10 2EB Tel: (0800) 0436001 E-mail: info@carpet-cleaner.co.uk

▶ Carpet Cleaning London UK, Colton House, Princes Avenue, London, N3 2EB Tel: (0870) 0052895 E-mail: clients@professional-carpet-cleaning-london.co.uk

▶ Companyclean Ltd, Unit 2A 83 Prestbury Road, Cheltenham, Gloucestershire, GL52 2DR Tel: (01242) 572918 E-mail: sales@companyclean.co.uk

I.N. Evans & Son, Tegfan Garage, 30 Carmarthen Road, Llandeilo, Dyfed, SA19 6RS Tel: (01558) 822542 Fax: (01558) 822337

P Copping Ltd, Harvey Road, Basildon, Essex, SS13 1EP Tel: (01268) 590105 Fax: (01268) 591265 E-mail: sales@pcopping.com

Rug Doctor Ltd, 29 Decoy Road, Worthing, West Sussex, BN14 8ND Tel: (01903) 235558 Fax: (01903) 209671 E-mail: enquiries@rugdoctor.com

CARPET CLEANING MACHINES

Active Chemical Products Ltd, Butts Business Centre, Fowlmere, Royston, Hertfordshire, SG8 7SL Tel: (01763) 208222 Fax: (01763) 208906 E-mail: sales@alltec.co.uk

▶ Cleansmart Carpet Cleaning Machines & Equipment, W12 Lenton Business Centre, Lenton Boulevard, Lenton, Nottingham, NG7 2BY Tel: (0845) 8620209

Craftex Cleaning Supplies, 66-68 Priory Bridge Road, Taunton, Somerset, TA1 1QB Tel: (01823) 332696

Express Cleaning Supplies, Unit 14 190 Malvern Common, Malvern, Worcestershire, WR14 3JZ Tel: (01684) 565552 Fax: (01684) 577707 E-mail: sales@express-cleaning-supplies.co.uk

Extracta Products Ltd, Third Avenue, Team Valley Trading Estate, Gateshead, Tyne & Wear, NE11 0PR Tel: 0191-482 5005 Fax: 0191-491 0462 E-mail: extracta@extracta.co.uk

Host Von Schrader, Unit 6 Capenhurst Technology Park, Capenhurst, Chester, CH1 6EH Tel: 0151-347 1900 Fax: 0151-347 1901 E-mail: host@hostvs.co.uk

P Copping Ltd, Harvey Road, Basildon, Essex, SS13 1EP Tel: (01268) 590105 Fax: (01268) 591265 E-mail: sales@pcopping.com

CARPET CLEANING PREPARATIONS

▶ A Fleming, 19 Laurel Braes, Bridge of Don, Aberdeen, AB22 8XY Tel: (01224) 820333 E-mail: info@aflemingcarpetclean.com

Active Chemical Products Ltd, Butts Business Centre, Fowlmere, Royston, Hertfordshire, SG8 7SL Tel: (01763) 208222 Fax: (01763) 208906 E-mail: sales@alltec.co.uk

▶ Angel Chemdry, 53 Goodwood Avenue, Hutton, Brentwood, Essex, CM13 1QD Tel: (01277) 217776 Fax: (01277) 217776 E-mail: angelchemdry@talktalk.net

Craftex Cleaning Supplies, 66-68 Priory Bridge Road, Taunton, Somerset, TA1 1QB Tel: (01823) 332696

▶ Dirt Master Services, 37 Hillside Crescent, Edinburgh, EH6 8NP Tel: (07835) 627741 E-mail: info@dirtmaster.co.uk

▶ MCS Flooring & Fabric Cleaning, Rundells, Harlow, Essex, CM18 7HB Tel: (01279) 866838 E-mail: chamois.leathers@ntlworld.com

P Copping Ltd, Harvey Road, Basildon, Essex, SS13 1EP Tel: (01268) 590105 Fax: (01268) 591265 E-mail: sales@pcopping.com

▶ Servicemaster Ltd, The Cleaning & Restoration Centre, Lime Avenue, Torquay, TQ2 5JL Tel: (01803) 200985 Fax: (01803) 200985 E-mail: office@cleanandrestore.co.uk

CARPET CLEANING SERVICES OR CONTRACTORS

▶ A Fleming, 19 Laurel Braes, Bridge of Don, Aberdeen, AB22 8XY Tel: (01224) 820333 E-mail: info@aflemingcarpetclean.com

A M Cleaning Services, West Lodge, Beckenham Place Park, Beckenham, Kent, BR3 5BP Tel: (020) 8658 8181 E-mail: info@amcleaning.info

Aadvark, 242 Gosport Road, Fareham, Hampshire, PO16 0SS Tel: (01329) 822515 Fax: (01329) 823630

Access Cleaning Solutions, 321 Blythswood Court, Glasgow, G2 7PH Tel: 0141-221 7355 E-mail: info@accesscleaningsolutions.co.uk

Acclaim Carpet Cleaners, 20 Graydon Avenue, Chichester, West Sussex, PO19 8RF Tel: (01243) 780381 Fax: (01243) 780381 E-mail: info@1aacclaim.co.uk

Adam Cleaning Service, 29 Somersby Close, Gregg Hall, Lincoln, LN6 8AF Tel: (01522) 530467

All Care Cleaning Services, 16 Brondesbury Villas, London, NW6 6AA Tel: (020) 7625 2225

Ambassador Cleaning Services Company, 18 Ashwin Street, London, E8 3DL Tel: (020) 7241 0937 Fax: (020) 7249 9583

▶ Angel Chemdry, 53 Goodwood Avenue, Hutton, Brentwood, Essex, CM13 1QD Tel: (01277) 217776 Fax: (01277) 217776 E-mail: angelchemdry@talktalk.net

▶ Aquamagic, 30 Cambridge Crescent, Rotherham, South Yorkshire, S65 2RB Tel: (01709) 376222 Fax: 07092 877608 E-mail: dene@aquamagicuk.co.uk

Arrow Cleaning Services, 17 The Hudson, Wyke, Bradford, West Yorkshire, BD12 8HZ Tel: (01274) 690805 Fax: (01274) 690805 E-mail: sales@cleaningservicesleeds.co.uk

Ashburne, 16-20 Penallta Road, Ystrad Mynach, Hengoed, Mid Glamorgan, CF82 7AP Tel: (01443) 816618 Fax: (01443) 816880

▶ Atlas Carpetcare, 93 Heath End Road, Flackwell Heath, High Wycombe, Buckinghamshire, HP10 9ES Tel: (01628) 533329 Fax: E-mail: paul@wiseman250.fsnet.co.uk

▶ Aurora Services, 58 Kinnaird Close, Slough, SL1 6AS Tel: (0870) 9504617 Fax: 07732 103565 E-mail: aurora.services@tiscali.co.uk

▶ Benchmark Cleaning Services Ltd, 59 Grantock Road, Walthamstow, London, E17 4DF Tel: (020) 8297 9136 Fax: (020) 8418 5866 E-mail: info@benchmarkcleaning.co.uk

▶ Carpet Cleaning, 30 Kipling Close, Llanrumney, Cardiff, CF3 5JZ Tel: (029) 2021 2599 E-mail: enquiries@carpetcleaningwales.com

Carpet Cleaning Co., 40 Scotstoun Street, Glasgow, G14 0UN Tel: 0141-958 0759

▶ Carpet Cleaning In Hampshire, 7 Buttermere Drive, Camberley, Surrey, GU15 1QU Tel: (01276) 66217 Fax: (01276) 66217 E-mail: muz15@hotmail.com

▶ Clean Tech, 35 Church Close, Grimston, King's Lynn, Norfolk, PE32 1BN Tel: (01485) 609223 Fax: (01485) 600475 E-mail: mikebarrett@genie.co.uk

Cleaning Contractors Services Group Ltd, 253 Alcester Road South, Kings Heath, Birmingham, B14 6DT Tel: 0121-444 4232 Fax: 0121-443 1117 E-mail: contractcleaning@kingsheathb14.wannadoo.co.uk

Courtesy Cleaning Services Ltd, Courtesy House 35 Redburn Industrial Estate, Woodall Road, Enfield, Middlesex, EN3 4LQ Tel: (020) 8805 8586 Fax: (020) 8805 5868

▶ Crown Cleaning Management, 1 Silver Street, Lincoln, LN2 1DY Tel: (01522) 545400 Fax: (01522) 545403 E-mail: info@crown-cleaning.com

▶ D B Services, 194 West Street, Fareham, Hampshire, PO16 0HF Tel: (01329) 288464 Fax: (01329) 825815 E-mail: southern@dbservices.co.uk

Derriclean, 12 Lakeside Close, St Johns, Woking, Surrey, GU21 8UN Tel: (01483) 824010 Fax: (01483) 824010 E-mail: gr.derrick@ntlworld.com

▶ Dirt Master Services, 37 Hillside Crescent, Edinburgh, EH6 8NP Tel: (07835) 627741 E-mail: info@dirtmaster.co.uk

▶ Ecoknowlogy International Ltd, 26 York Street, London, W1U 6PZ Tel: (0870) 7777420 Fax: (0870) 7777421 E-mail: info@ecoknowlogy-intl.com

▶ Edinburgh Cleaning Services Ltd, Unit 5A, Whitehill Industrial Estate, Dalkeith, Midlothian, EH22 2QB Tel: 0131-660 0220 E-mail: sales@cleanse.uk.com

English Cleaning Co., 272 Latimer Industrial Estate, Latimer Road, London, W10 6RQ Tel: (020) 8960 0000 Fax: (020) 8969 7077 E-mail: info@english-cleaning.co.uk

Enviroclean Services Ltd, Unit A 5 Colville Road, London, W3 8BL Tel: (020) 8896 0088 Fax: (020) 8896 2676

▶ Fabtec Upholstery Cleaners, Plevna Place, Alton, Hampshire, GU34 2DS Tel: (01420) 87199 E-mail: michael@fabteccleaning.co.uk

▶ Greenserve Cleaning Services, 63 Tenter Road, Moulton Park Industrial Estate, Moulton Park Industrial Estate, Northampton, NN3 6AX Tel: (01604) 494605 Fax: (01604) 645786 E-mail: enquiries@greenservecleaning.co.uk

▶ Gunns Upholstery Cleaners, 65 Mitchell Gardens, South Shields, Tyne & Wear, NE34 6EF Tel: 0191-454 2819 E-mail: stevegunn@gunnscleaning.co.uk

▶ Hydro Dynamix, 46 Langham Road, Standish, Wigan, Lancashire, WN6 0TF Tel: (01257) 424555 E-mail: info@hydro-dynamix.com

▶ I M B Cleaning & Maintenance, 29 Milton Road, Caterham, Surrey, CR3 5JG Tel: (01883) 334521 E-mail: imbcleaning@tiscali.co.uk

▶ M & Dee, 34 Farley Hill, Luton, LU1 5HQ Tel: 07768 626141 E-mail: m.and.dee@lycos.co.uk

▶ Master Clean, 41 Willows Lane, Rochdale, Lancashire, OL16 4BQ Tel: (01706) 710426 Fax: (01706) 710426 E-mail: master_clean@walla.com

▶ MCS Flooring & Fabric Cleaning, Rundells, Harlow, Essex, CM18 7HB Tel: (01279) 866838 E-mail: chamois.leathers@ntlworld.com

▶ Mr H Carpets, 1 Bevois Hill, Southampton, SO14 0SJ Tel: (0800) 8087654 Fax: (023) 8022 6182 E-mail: info@mrhcarpets.co.uk

▶ Outright Cleaning, 52 Edderston Ridge, Peebles, EH45 9NA Tel: (01721) 729066 E-mail: neil@outrightcleaning.co.uk

▶ P.Dee Cleaning Services, 1 Woodlea Gardens, Sauchie, Alloa, Clackmannanshire, FK10 3BD Tel: (01259) 218097 E-mail: peter_docherty@hotmail.co.uk

Pilgrim Payne & Co. Ltd, Units 12-14 Wharfeside, Rosemont Road, Wembley, Middlesex, HA0 4PE Tel: (020) 8453 5350 Fax: (020) 8453 5604 E-mail: info@pilgrimpayne.co.uk

▶ Pinnacle Cleaning, 41 Bramble Court, Ferndown, Bournemouth, BH22 0HL Tel: 0870 345 5757 E-mail: webenquiries@pinnacle-cleaning.co.uk

▶ Quick Response, 101 Commercial Road, London, E1 1RD Tel: (020) 7247 5555 Fax: (020) 7247 9477 E-mail: cs@quickcleaning.co.uk

R P C Cleaning Services Ltd, 201 Acton Lane, London, W4 5DA Tel: (020) 8994 4778 Fax: (020) 8994 4178

▶ The Red Carpet, 21 Morris Court, Waltham Abbey, Essex, EN9 3DX Tel: 01992 619469 E-mail: theredcarpet@hotmail.co.uk

▶ Servicemaster Ltd, The Cleaning & Restoration Centre, Lime Avenue, Torquay, TQ2 5JL Tel: (01803) 200985 Fax: (01803) 200985 E-mail: office@cleanandrestore.co.uk

▶ Smart Cleanings UK Ltd, 66 Queen''s Park, Aylesbury, Buckinghamshire, HP21 7RT Tel: 08448 442548 Fax: 01296 580632 E-mail: admin@smart-cleanings.co.uk

▶ Smith's Cleaning, 17 Lytchett Way, Poole, Dorset, BH16 5LS Tel: (01202) 620895 E-mail: smithscleaning@ntlworld.com

▶ Straker Cleaning, 41 Abbotts Road, Sutton, Surrey, SM3 9SJ Tel: (020) 8644 8892 E-mail: chris@strakercleaning.co.uk

▶ Turner Specialist Cleaning, Stopford Road, St. Helier, Jersey, JE2 4LZ Tel: (07797) 733183

▶ Twinkle Clean, Bexleyheath, Kent, DA7 9DH Tel: (0870) 0669919 E-mail: clean@twinkleclean.com

Ultra Clean, Hillside Cottage, Croesau Bach, Oswestry, Shropshire, SY10 9AY Tel: (01691) 670837 Fax: (01691) 670837 E-mail: philevo@btinternet.com

CARPET CUTTING SERVICES

Gaskells Logistics, Unit 13, Churchfields Business Park, Clensmore Street, Kidderminster, Worcestershire, DY10 2JY Tel: (01562) 820006 Fax: (01562) 820016

CARPET EXPORT MERCHANTS OR AGENTS

Azizollahoff & Co., Building A Oriental Carpet Centre, 105 Eade Road, London, N4 1TJ Tel: (020) 8802 3107 Fax: (020) 8442 8949 E-mail: azizcocarpets@mserve.com

Brockway Carpets Ltd, Hoobrook, Kidderminster, Worcestershire, DY10 1XW Tel: (01562) 824737 Fax: (01562) 863598 E-mail: sales@brockway.co.uk

Chinese Carpet Co. Ltd, 1st Floor Building C, 105 Eade Rd, London, N4 1TJ Tel: (020) 8802 2323 Fax: (020) 8802 0560

Essie Carpets, 62 Piccadilly, London, W1J 0DZ Tel: (020) 7493 7766 Fax: (020) 7495 3456 E-mail: essiesakhai@compuserve.com

I Nemetnejad Ltd, 403-405 Edgware Road, London, NW2 6LN Tel: (020) 8830 5511 Fax: (020) 8530 5522 E-mail: info@inemetnejad.com

M A Samad, 105 Eade Road, London, N4 1TJ Tel: (020) 8802 2929 Fax: (020) 8802 2777

▶ Yashar Bish, 96 Gloucester Road, Brighton, BN1 4AP Tel: (01273) 671900 Fax: (01273) 671900 E-mail: kim@yashar-bish.com

CARPET FELT

P. & R. Ratcliffe Ltd, Stanley Mill, Shackleton Street, Burnley, Lancashire, BB10 3BH Tel: (01282) 421026 Fax: (01282) 412321 E-mail: underlays@tiscaly.co.uk

▶ Yashar Bish, 96 Gloucester Road, Brighton, BN1 4AP Tel: (01273) 671900 Fax: (01273) 671900 E-mail: kim@yashar-bish.com

CARPET FINISHING MACHINES

Cobble Blackburn Ltd, Gate Street, Blackburn, BB1 3AH Tel: (01254) 55121 Fax: (01254) 671125 E-mail: info@cobble.co.uk

CARPET FITTING ACCESSORIES, *See also headings for particular types*

Cadonmain Ltd, 3 Aspen Court, Lancing, West Sussex, BN15 8UN Tel: (01903) 750522 Fax: (01903) 851111

Evermore Carpets, 148 Westpole Avenue, Cockfosters, Barnet, Hertfordshire, EN4 0AR Tel: (020) 8449 7362

Henry's Blind & Carpet Centre, 77-79b Mid Street, Fraserburgh, Aberdeenshire, AB43 9JD Tel: (01346) 514357 Fax: (01346) 514357

Salesmark Ltd, Howard Road, Eaton Socon, St. Neots, Cambridgeshire, PE19 8ET Tel: (01480) 212888 Fax: (01480) 218585 E-mail: sales@salesmark.co.uk

▶ indicates data change since last edition

CARPET FITTING ACCESSORIES – *continued*

Neil Smith Ltd, 370 Gallowgate, Glasgow, G4 0TX Tel: 0141-552 1141 Fax: 0141-552 0623

CARPET GRIPPERS

Cadonmain Ltd, 3 Aspen Court, Lancing, West Sussex, BN15 8UN Tel: (01903) 750522 Fax: (01903) 851111

CARPET HANDLING MACHINES

T & E Fabrications Ltd, Mucklow Hill, Halesowen, West Midlands, B62 8DL Tel: 0121-585 7600 Fax: 0121-585 7601 E-mail: teltd@btconnect.com

CARPET IMPORT

Azizollahoff & Co., Building A Oriental Carpet Centre, 105 Eade Road, London, N4 1TJ Tel: (020) 8802 3107 Fax: (020) 8442 8949 E-mail: azizcocarpets@mserve.com

Nathan Azizollahoff, Top Floor Building A, 105 Eade Road, London, N4 1TJ Tel: (020) 8802 0077 Fax: (020) 8802 1144 E-mail: joseph@jazico.com

Chinese Carpet Co. Ltd, 1st Floor Building C, 105 Eade Rd, London, N4 1TJ Tel: (020) 8802 2323 Fax: (020) 8802 0560

Essie Carpets, 62 Piccadilly, London, W1J 0DZ Tel: (020) 7493 7766 Fax: (020) 7495 3456 E-mail: essiesakhai@compuserve.com

I Nemetnejad Ltd, 403-405 Edgware Road, London, NW2 6LN Tel: (020) 8830 5511 Fax: (020) 8530 5522 E-mail: info@inemetnejad.com

M A Samad, 105 Eade Road, London, N4 1TJ Tel: (020) 8802 2929 Fax: (020) 8802 2777

Telenzo Carpets Ltd, 2-4 Southgate, Elland, West Yorkshire, HX5 0BW Tel: (01422) 371226 Fax: (01422) 377452

CARPET LININGS OR ACCESSORIES

Roger Fell Ltd, Northside Industrial Park, Whitley Bridge, Goole, North Humberside, DN14 0GH Tel: (01977) 662211 Fax: (01977) 662334 E-mail: fellscarpets@aol.com

▶ M & L Carpets Ltd, 54 Crouch End Hill, London, N8 8AA Tel: (020) 8341 0914 Fax: (020) 8341 0914 E-mail: info@mlcarpets.com

Saxon Carpets, Wilden Lane, Stourport-on-Severn, Worcestershire, DY13 9LW Tel: (01299) 827477 Fax: (01299) 827052 E-mail: sales@carpetsofkidderminster.com

CARPET LOOMS

Crabtree Textile Machines Ltd, Norman Road, Oswaldtwistle, Accrington, Lancashire, BB5 4NF Tel: (01254) 304410 Fax: (01254) 304415 E-mail: info@crabtreelooms.com

CARPET MATERIALS

▶ Quadrant Modular Ltd, Unit 3d Priory Park, Mills Road, Aylesford, Kent, ME20 7PP Tel: (01622) 719090 Fax: (01622) 719191

CARPET PLANNING OR FITTING SERVICES

▶ All Floors 'N' Rugs, 14 Limes Walk, Oakengates, Telford, Shropshire, TF2 6EP Tel: (01952) 618191 Fax: (01952) 222151 E-mail: sales@floorsnrugs.co.uk

Allans, Chapel Walk, Rotherham, South Yorkshire, S60 1EP Tel: (01709) 377530 Fax: (01709) 837672 E-mail: allanscarpets@btinternet.com

Aylesbury Flooring, 3 Jansel Square, Aylesbury, Buckinghamshire, HP21 7ES Tel: (01296) 415038 Fax: (01296) 393891 E-mail: carpets@aylesburyflooring.co.uk

▶ Easiclear, Atlas Transport Estate, Lombard Road, London, SW11 3RE Tel: (02077) 389555 E-mail: info@easiclear.co.uk

Gerratts Carpet Planning, 22 Southolm Street, London, SW11 5EZ Tel: (020) 7498 2622 Fax: (020) 7498 6429

His Contracts, 24-28 Pritchards Road, London, E2 9AP Tel: (020) 7739 1455 Fax: (020) 7729 9438 E-mail: info@hiscontracts.co.uk

K C Carpets Ltd, 2 High Street, Moreton-in-Marsh, Gloucestershire, GL56 0AP Tel: (01608) 650331 Fax: (01608) 650829

L & S Carpet Co. Ltd, 48 Central Road, Morden, Surrey, SM4 5RU Tel: (020) 8648 6131 Fax: (020) 8648 6193

▶ M & L Carpets Ltd, 54 Crouch End Hill, London, N8 8AA Tel: (020) 8341 0914 Fax: (020) 8341 0914 E-mail: info@mlcarpets.com

▶ Mr H Carpets, 1 Bevois Hill, Southampton, SO14 0SJ Tel: (0800) 8087654 Fax: (023) 8022 6182 E-mail: info@mrhcarpets.co.uk

Practical Upholsterers Ltd, 35a Pound Farm Road, Chichester, West Sussex, PO19 7PU Tel: (01243) 786090 Fax: (01243) 786090

A.E. Scott Ltd, 65 Sienna, White Hart Avenue, London, SE28 0GU Tel: (020) 7232 1903 Fax: (020) 8301 8221 E-mail: info@scottscarpets.com

Wittons Carpets Ltd, Olive Mill, Olive Lane, Darwen, Lancashire, BB3 3DJ Tel: (01254) 702211

Woods Dorchester, 34-35 High East Street, Dorchester, Dorset, DT1 1HN Tel: (01305) 262666 Fax: (01305) 250073 E-mail: woodsdor@globalnet.co.uk

CARPET PROTECTION FILM

Coverguard, 8 Flanders Park, Hedge End, Southampton, SO30 2FZ Tel: 01489 776 022 Fax: 01489 775 015 E-mail: info@coverguard.com

CARPET REPAIR/RESTORATION SERVICES

Evermore Carpets, 148 Westpole Avenue, Cockfosters, Barnet, Hertfordshire, EN4 0AR Tel: (020) 8449 7362

CARPET SERVICES

Allans, Chapel Walk, Rotherham, South Yorkshire, S60 1EP Tel: (01709) 377530 Fax: (01709) 837672 E-mail: allanscarpets@btinternet.com

Avena Carpets Ltd, Bankfield Mills, Haley Hill, Halifax, West Yorkshire, HX3 6ED Tel: (01422) 330261 Fax: (01422) 348399 E-mail: avena@btconnect.com

Aylesbury Flooring, 3 Jansel Square, Aylesbury, Buckinghamshire, HP21 7ES Tel: (01296) 415038 Fax: (01296) 393891 E-mail: carpets@aylesburyflooring.co.uk

C W Jones Flooring Ltd, 10 Vale Lane, Bristol, BS3 5RU Tel: 0117-966 1454 Fax: 0117-963 9733 E-mail: info@cwjfloorings.co.uk

Carpet Services London Ltd, 79a Russell Road, London, SW19 1QN Tel: (020) 8543 9131 Fax: (020) 8540 2911 E-mail: csll@btconnect.com

Carpetronic Flooring Services, 15 Scotts Road, Paisley, Renfrewshire, PA2 7AN Tel: 0141-887 7733 Fax: 0141-887 1771 E-mail: carpetronic@horncroft.co.uk

Cavalier Carpets Ltd, Thompson St Industrial Estate, Blackburn, BB2 1TX Tel: (01254) 268000 Fax: (01254) 268001 E-mail: info@cavalier-carpets.co.uk

Climpson & Co Ltd, 8 St. Albans Place, London, N1 0NX Tel: (020) 7226 4414 Fax: (020) 7226 4414

D Donovan & Sons Carpet Services Ltd, 112 Blythe Road, London, W14 0HD Tel: (020) 7603 4161 Fax: (020) 7602 9929

Dorgrove Floors Ltd, 9 Causeway Green Road, Oldbury, West Midlands, B68 8LA Tel: 0121-544 7877 Fax: 0121-511 1386 E-mail: dorgrove@aol.com

Easifloor Ltd, Cranes Close, Basildon, Essex, SS14 3JB Tel: (01268) 288744 Fax: (01268) 532305 E-mail: tiles@easifloor.fsnet.co.uk

Evermore Carpets, 148 Westpole Avenue, Cockfosters, Barnet, Hertfordshire, EN4 0AR Tel: (020) 8449 7362

Floorings Of Frome, Textile House, Manor Furlong, Frome, Somerset, BA11 4RJ Tel: (01373) 462666 Fax: (01373) 466651 E-mail: fromecarpetsandflooring@btconnect.com

Gateway Ceramics Ltd, School Lane, Chandler's Ford, Eastleigh, Hampshire, SO53 4DG Tel: (023) 8026 0290 Fax: (023) 8025 1049

H B D Floors Ltd, 6 Falcon Units, Bradley Lane, Newton Abbot, Devon, TQ12 1NB Tel: (01626) 366333 Fax: (01626) 366444

▶ Hutton Premises Solutions, Station Road, Bagshot, Surrey, GU19 5AS Tel: (01276) 472400 Fax: (01276) 470996 E-mail: ben.hutton@virgin.net

J & J Floorings (Watford) Ltd, 18 Caxton Way, Watford Business Park, Watford, WD18 8UA Tel: (01923) 231644 Fax: (01923) 818946

John Abbott Flooring Contractors Ltd, Wallshaw House, Wallshaw Street, Oldham, OL1 3XD Tel: 0161-624 8246 Fax: 0161-627 1779 E-mail: sales@johnabbottflooring.co.uk

L G M Ltd, Coppice Trading Estate, Kidderminster, Worcestershire, DY11 7QY Tel: (01562) 823700 Fax: (01562) 68237 E-mail: acook@lgm-ltd.co.uk

Peter Newman Flooring Ltd, Unit 27 Newtown Business Park, Albion Close, Parkstone, Poole, Dorset, BH12 3LL Tel: (01202) 747175 Fax: (01202) 723421 E-mail: info@peternewmanflooring.com

North Wales Floorings Ltd, 117-119 Conway Road, Colwyn Bay, Clwyd, LL29 7LT Tel: (01492) 530448 Fax: (01492) 532800

Pelican Flooring, 178 Stoke Newington Road, London, N16 7UY Tel: (020) 7254 7955 Fax: (020) 7254 7955

Rees Flooring Ltd, Unit 12 Sovereign Park, Cleveland Way, Hemel Hempstead Industrial Estate, Hemel Hempstead, Hertfordshire, HP2 7DA Tel: (01442) 283250 Fax: (01442) 283263

S & M Myers Ltd, 100-106 Mackenzie Road, London, N7 8RG Tel: (020) 7609 0091 Fax: (020) 7609 2457

A.E. Scott Ltd, 65 Sienna, White Hart Avenue, London, SE28 0GU Tel: (020) 7232 1903 Fax: (020) 8301 8221 E-mail: info@scottscarpets.com

▶ T1 Commercial, PO Box 5783, Westcliff-on-Sea, Essex, SS1 9BX Tel: (01702) 305856 E-mail: enquiries@t1-commercial.com

CARPET TILES

C. Abbott Ltd, Dane Place, 470-480 Roman Road, Bow, London, E3 5LU Tel: (020) 8980 4158 Fax: (020) 8981 3852 E-mail: info@abbottscarpets.co.uk

Armstrong Floor Products UK Ltd, Hitching Court, Abingdon Business Park, Abingdon, Oxfordshire, OX14 1RB Tel: (01235) 554848 Fax: (01235) 553583 E-mail: uk-info@armstrong.com

Bonar Floors, 92 Seedlee Road, Walton Summit Centre, Bamber Bridge, Preston, PR5 8AE Tel: (01772) 646900 Fax: (01772) 646912

Bondworth Ltd, Townshend Works, Puxton Lane, Kidderminster, Worcestershire, DY11 5DF Tel: (01562) 745000 Fax: (01562) 732827 E-mail: sales@bondworth.co.uk

Burmatex Ltd, Victoria Mills, The Green, Ossett, West Yorkshire, WF5 0AN Tel: (01924) 262525 Fax: (01924) 280033 E-mail: info@burmatex.co.uk

▶ Decorative Flooring Services, 1501 Nitshill Road, Thornliebank, Glasgow, G46 8QG Tel: 0141-621 2990 Fax: 0141-621 2991 E-mail: sales@decorativeflooringservices.co.uk

Dorgrove Floors Ltd, 9 Causeway Green Road, Oldbury, West Midlands, B68 8LA Tel: 0121-544 7877 Fax: 0121-511 1386 E-mail: dorgrove@aol.com

G W Brooks Flooring Ltd, Unit 19 Waterside Industrial Estate, Ettingshall Road, Wolverhampton, WV2 2RH Tel: (01902) 498213 Fax: (01902) 495707 E-mail: sales@brooksflooring.co.uk

Heckmondwike F B Ltd, PO Box 7, Liversedge, West Yorkshire, WF15 7XA Tel: (01924) 406161 Fax: (01924) 413613 E-mail: sales@heckmondwike-fb.co.uk

▶ Interface Europe Ltd, Shelf Mills, Halifax, West Yorkshire, HX3 7PA Tel: (01274) 690690 Fax: (01274) 694095 E-mail: info@interface.com

Milliken Industrials Ltd, Wellington Street, Bury, Lancashire, BL8 2AY Tel: 0161-764 2244 Fax: 0161-705 2148 E-mail: john.lancashire@milliken.com

Paragon By Heckmondwike, Farfield Park, Manvers, Rotherham, South Yorkshire, S63 5DB Tel: (01709) 763800 Fax: (0800) 7314521

Rawson Carpets Ltd, Castlebank Mills, Portobello Road, Wakefield, West Yorkshire, WF1 5PS Tel: (01924) 382860 Fax: (01924) 290334 E-mail: sales@rawsoncarpets.co.uk

Sanquhar Tile Services Ltd, Blackaddie Road, The Industrial Estate, Sanquhar, Dumfriesshire, DG4 6DB Tel: (01659) 50497 Fax: (01659) 58384

▶ T1 Commercial, PO Box 5783, Westcliff-on-Sea, Essex, SS1 9BX Tel: (01702) 305856 E-mail: enquiries@t1-commercial.com

▶ Tetras Interiors Ltd, 55 Lincoln Road, Poole, Dorset, BH12 2HT Tel: (01202) 566480 Fax: (01202) 386403 E-mail: tetrasinteriors@aol.com

Westco Group Ltd, Penarth Road, Cardiff, CF11 8YN Tel: (029) 2037 6700 Fax: (029) 2038 3573 E-mail: westco@westcodiy.co.uk

CARPET TUFTING MACHINES

David Almond Ltd, Union Works, Bacup Road, Rossendale, Lancashire, BB4 7LN Tel: (01706) 214817 Fax: (01706) 214819 E-mail: venor@davidalmond.freeserve.uk

CARPET UNDERLAY, *See also headings for particular types*

LCW, 56 Norfolk Street, Liverpool, L1 0BE Tel: 0151-709 7034 Fax: 0151-708 6022

CARPET YARN

Joseph Barraclough Ltd, Bankfield Mills, Mirfield, West Yorkshire, WF14 9DD Tel: (01924) 493147 Fax: (01924) 490702 E-mail: info@barrayarn.co.uk

Beaumont Blending Co. Ltd, Ings Dyeworks, Wakefield Road, Scissett, Huddersfield, HD8 9JL Tel: (01484) 863526 Fax: (01484) 865479

Bonar Yards & Fabrics Ltd, St Salvador Street, Dundee, DD3 7EU Tel: (01382) 227346 Fax: (01382) 202378 E-mail: ascott@bonaryarns.com

Calder Textiles Ltd, Anchor House Dewsbury Mills, Thornhill Road, Dewsbury, West Yorkshire, WF12 9QE Tel: (01924) 456411 Fax: (01924) 457387 E-mail: info@caldertextilex.co.uk

Fred Lawton & Son Ltd, Meltham Mills, Meltham, Holmfirth, HD9 4AY Tel: (01484) 852573 Fax: (01484) 852737 E-mail: enquiries@fredlawton.com

S Lyles & Sons Co, Calder Bank Mills, Calder Bank Road, Dewsbury, West Yorkshire, WF12 9QW Tel: (01924) 436500 Fax: (01924) 436511

Saxon Carpets, Wilden Lane, Stourport-on-Severn, Worcestershire, DY13 9LW Tel: (01299) 827477 Fax: (01299) 827052 E-mail: sales@carpetsofkidderminster.com

Sillaford Ltd, Martin House, 2 Martin Street, Brighouse, West Yorkshire, HD6 1DA Tel: (01484) 710231 Fax: (01484) 714607 E-mail: sales@sillaford.com

William S Graham & Sons Dewsbury Ltd, Ravens Ing Mills, Ravensthorpe, Dewsbury, West Yorkshire, WF13 3JF Tel: (01924) 462456 Fax: (01924) 457985

Woollen Spinners (Huddersfield) Ltd, Wellington Mills, Lindley, Huddersfield, HD3 3HR Tel: (01484) 322200 Fax: (01484) 644829 E-mail: wshuddes@aol.com

CARPETS, *See also headings for particular types*

C. Abbott Ltd, Dane Place, 470-480 Roman Road, Bow, London, E3 5LU Tel: (020) 8980 4158 Fax: (020) 8981 3852 E-mail: info@abbottscarpets.co.uk

Acaster Carpets, Brockett Industrial Estate, The Airfield, Acaster Malbis, York, YO23 2PT Tel: (01904) 702343 Fax: (01904) 702343

Armstrong Floor Products UK Ltd, Hitching Court, Abingdon Business Park, Abingdon, Oxfordshire, OX14 1RB Tel: (01235) 554848 Fax: (01235) 553583 E-mail: uk-info@armstrong.com

▶ Automobile Trimmings Co., Stonebridge Works, Cumberland Road, Stanmore, Middlesex, HA7 1EL Tel: (020) 8204 8242 Fax: (020) 8204 0255 E-mail: sales@automobiletrim.com

Avena Carpets Ltd, Bankfield Mills, Haley Hill, Halifax, West Yorkshire, HX3 6ED Tel: (01422) 330261 Fax: (01422) 348399 E-mail: avena@btconnect.com

Axminster Carpets Ltd, Woodmead Road, Axminster, Devon, EX13 5PQ Tel: (01297) 33533 Fax: (01297) 35241 E-mail: sales@axminster-carpets.co.uk

Azizollahoff & Co., Building A Oriental Carpet Centre, 105 Eade Road, London, N4 1TJ Tel: (020) 8802 3107 Fax: (020) 8442 8949 E-mail: azizcocarpets@mserve.com

B H Carpets, Unit 24 Oakwood Place, Oakwood Road, Croydon, CR0 3QS Tel: (020) 8665 9110 Fax: (020) 8665 6611

Beds Flooring Distributors, Cambridge Road, Bedford, MK42 0LH Tel: (01234) 342444 Fax: (01234) 364925 E-mail: sales@bedsflooring.co.uk

Best Buy Carpet & Divan Centre, 2 Arksey Lane, Bentley, Doncaster, South Yorkshire, DN5 0RR Tel: (01302) 873586 Fax: (01302) 873586

Bodigian & Co. Ltd, Wenman Road, Industrial Estate, Thame, Oxfordshire, OX9 3SD Tel: (01844) 213555 Fax: (01844) 214120 E-mail: sales@bodigianofthame.co.uk

Bonar Floors, 92 Seedlee Road, Walton Summit Centre, Bamber Bridge, Preston, PR5 8AE Tel: (01772) 646900 Fax: (01772) 646912

Bondworth Ltd, Townshend Works, Puxton Lane, Kidderminster, Worcestershire, DY11 5DF Tel: (01562) 745000 Fax: (01562) 732827 E-mail: sales@bondworth.co.uk

Brighton Carpet Centre, 102 Preston Drove, Brighton, BN1 6EW Tel: (01273) 564037 Fax: (01273) 561622 E-mail: sales@brightoncarpetcentre.co.uk

Brintons Carpets (U S A) Ltd, PO Box 16, Kidderminster, Worcestershire, DY10 1AG Tel: (01562) 820000 Fax: (01562) 634540 E-mail: solutions@brintons.co.uk

Brockway Carpets Ltd, Hoobrook, Kidderminster, Worcestershire, DY10 1XW Tel: (01562) 824737 Fax: (01562) 863598 E-mail: sales@brockway.co.uk

Burmatex Ltd, Victoria Mills, The Green, Ossett, West Yorkshire, WF5 0AN Tel: (01924) 262525 Fax: (01924) 280033 E-mail: info@burmatex.co.uk

▶ Carpet Clearance Corner, 41 Whitby Road, Ellesmere Port, CH65 8AB Tel: 0151-355 7733

▶ Carpet It, 517 Leeds Road, Huddersfield, HD2 1YJ Tel: (01484) 519840 Fax: (01484) 519835

Carpet Services London Ltd, 79a Russell Road, London, SW19 1QN Tel: (020) 8543 9131 Fax: (020) 8540 2911 E-mail: csll@btconnect.com

▶ Carpet Shop, New Road, Sheerness, Kent, ME12 1BW Tel: (01795) 661060 Fax: (01795) 661060

▶ Carpet Style, Unit 1 Great Northern Way, Netherfield, Nottingham, NG4 2HD Tel: 0115-940 4110 Fax: 0115-940 4611

▶ Carpet Whipping & Fringing Services, Unit H Union Drive, Sutton Coldfield, West Midlands, B73 5TE Tel: 0121-321 3830 Fax: 0121-321 3569

CARPETS – *continued*

▶ Carpetright plc, Unit 2c Northwich Retail Park, Manchester Road, Northwich, Cheshire, CW9 5LY Tel: (01606) 47585 Fax: (01606) 47285

Carpetright plc, Amberley House, New Road, Rainham, Essex, RM13 8QN Tel: (01708) 525522 Fax: (01708) 559361 E-mail: enquiries@carpetright.co.uk

▶ Carpets 4 Less, Carleton New Road, Skipton, North Yorkshire, BD23 2DE Tel: (01756) 795432 E-mail: sales@carpets4less.com

▶ Carpets Direct, 1 Dominion Works, Denholme Gate Road, Hipperholme, Halifax, West Yorkshire, HX3 8JG Tel: (01422) 202220 Fax: (01422) 202220

Causeway Carpets, Roe Lee Mill, Whalley New Road, Blackburn, BB1 9SU Tel: (01254) 676996 Fax: (01254) 680510 E-mail: info@causewaycarpets.com

Cavalier Carpets Ltd, Thompson St Industrial Estate, Blackburn, BB2 1TX Tel: (01254) 268000 Fax: (01254) 268001 E-mail: info@cavalier-carpets.co.uk

Checkmate Industries Ltd, Bridge House, 12 Bridge Street, Halstead, Essex, CO9 1HT Tel: (01787) 477272 Fax: (01787) 476334 E-mail: checkmatecarpets@btconnect.com

Cheshires Of Nottingham, Concorde House, Dabell Avenue, Nottingham, NG6 8WA Tel: 0115-977 0278 Fax: 0115-979 4085 E-mail: cheshires@mcd.co.uk

▶ CJ Carpets & Lighting, 53 Scotgate, Stamford, Lincolnshire, PE9 2YQ Tel: (01780) 754825 Fax: (01780) 754825

Clarendon Southern, 4-5 Toll Gate Estate, Stanbridge Earls, Romsey, Hampshire, SO51 0HE Tel: (01794) 517649 Fax: (01794) 515968

Classic Interiors Malvern Ltd, 47 Worcester Road, Malvern, Worcestershire, WR14 4AD Tel: (01684) 573734 Fax: (01684) 892519 E-mail: classicinteriors@btopenworld.com

Claymore Carpets, 48 Brown Street, Dundee, DD1 5DT Tel: (01382) 229414 Fax: (01382) 229414 E-mail: claymorecarpetscts.co.uk

Coraff Ltd, 51 Market Place, London, NW11 6JT Tel: (020) 8731 7766 Fax: (020) 8209 0098 E-mail: sales@coraffcarpets.co.uk

▶ Deans Carpets, 28c Sherwood Street, Warsop, Mansfield, Nottinghamshire, NG20 0JW Tel: (01623) 846655 Fax: (01623) 846655

Designer Carpets, 2 Ham Street, Richmond, Surrey, TW10 7HT Tel: (020) 8332 6006 Fax: (020) 8332 0660 E-mail: info@designercarpets.co.uk

E G Rackham & Co. Ltd, 6 Jubilee Avenue, London, E4 9JD Tel: (020) 8531 9225 Fax: (020) 8531 0426 E-mail: sales@rackhams.co.uk

▶ Elba Flooring & Bed Centre, 23-24 Mill Street, Gowerton, Swansea, SA4 3ED Tel: (01792) 879555 Fax: (01792) 879555

Essie Carpets, 62 Piccadilly, London, W1J 0DZ Tel: (020) 7493 7766 Fax: (020) 7495 3456 E-mail: essiesakhai@compuserve.com

Roger Fell Ltd, Northside Industrial Park, Whitley Bridge, Goole, North Humberside, DN14 0GH Tel: (01977) 662211 Fax: (01977) 662334 E-mail: fellscarpets@aol.com

▶ Fleetwood Fox, 96 Springfield Road, Wellington, Somerset, TA21 8LH Tel: (01823) 667337

▶ The Flooring Firm Ltd, 131 Station Road, Bamber Bridge, Preston, PR5 6QS Tel: (01772) 316688 Fax: (01772) 624111

Floorings Of Frome, Textile House, Manor Furlong, Frome, Somerset, BA11 4RJ Tel: (01373) 462666 Fax: (01373) 466651 E-mail: fromecarpetsandflooring@btconnect.com

Florco, Aylesford Way, Thatcham, Berkshire, RG19 4NW Tel: (01635) 863456 Fax: (01635) 871024 E-mail: info@florco-sales.co.uk

▶ Fringes, Strode Road, Newnham Industrial Estate, Plympton, Plymouth, PL7 4AY Tel: (01752) 345464 Fax: (01752) 345464

Gardiner & Collis Ltd, 4-5 Crofton Close, Allenby Industrial Estate, Lincoln, LN3 4NT Tel: (01522) 533416 Fax: (01522) 514642

Gaskells Logistics, Unit 13, Churchfields Business Park, Clensmore Street, Kidderminster, Worcestershire, DY10 2JY Tel: (01562) 820006 Fax: (01562) 820016

Greenwood & Coope Ltd, Holme Mill, Railway Street, Ramsbottom, Bury, Lancashire, BL0 9AU Tel: (01706) 825211 Fax: (01706) 821633 E-mail: info@cormarcarpets.co.uk

Greenwood & Coope Ltd, Brookhouse Mill, Holcombe Road, Greenmount, Bury, Lancashire, BL8 4HR Tel: (01204) 881234 Fax: (01204) 887722 E-mail: info@cormarcarpets.co.uk

▶ Hagston Carpets, Skiff Lane, Holme-On-Spalding-Moor, York, YO43 4AZ Tel: (01430) 427820 Fax: (01430) 427820

Hancock & Lant, 164-170 Queens Road, Sheffield, S2 4DH Tel: 0114-272 2176 Fax: 0114-270 0289

Heckmondwike F B Ltd, PO Box 7, Liversedge, West Yorkshire, WF15 7XA Tel: (01924) 406161 Fax: (01924) 413613 E-mail: sales@heckmondwike-fb.co.uk

John Henman Ltd, 81 High Street, West Wickham, Kent, BR4 0LS Tel: (020) 8777 4853

▶ Heritage Carpets, 47 Formans Road, Sparkhill, Birmingham, B11 3AR Tel: 0121-778 6444 Fax: 0121-778 6444 E-mail: sales@heritagecarpets.co.uk

Howkell Rugs Ltd, Lower Viaduct Street, Huddersfield, HD1 6BN Tel: (01484) 425422 Fax: (01484) 425422

▶ Interface Europe Ltd, Shelf Mills, Halifax, West Yorkshire, HX3 7PA Tel: (01274) 690690 Fax: (01274) 694095 E-mail: info@interface.com

Joseph Lavian, Oriental Carpet Centre, 105 Eade Road, London, N4 1TJ Tel: (020) 8800 0707 Fax: (020) 8800 0404 E-mail: lavian@lavian.com

▶ Joyce V'Soske UK Ltd, 168 Lavender Hill, London, SW11 5TF Tel: (020) 7801 6221 Fax: (020) 7801 6201 E-mail: chris@csdc.co.uk

Kellars Ltd, Unit 14, Rugby Park, Bletchley Road, Stockport, Cheshire, SK4 3EJ Tel: 0161-443 0970 Fax: 0161-432 7453 E-mail: tonybates@aol.com

Kingsmead Carpets Ltd, Caponacre Industrial Estate, Cumnock, Ayrshire, KA18 1SH Tel: (01290) 421511 Fax: (01290) 424211

Kustom Sport, 1 2 & 3 Carlton Industrial Estate, Albion Road, Carlton, Barnsley, South Yorkshire, S71 3HW Tel: (01226) 203347 Fax: (01226) 203357 E-mail: Kustomsport@tiscali.co.uk

▶ L & P Flooring, Victoria Road, Bradford, West Yorkshire, BD2 2BH Tel: (01274) 634455 Fax: (01274) 634455

Littner Hampton Ltd, Unit 30 Forest Business Park, South Access Road, London, E17 8AD Tel: (020) 8520 8474 Fax: (020) 8520 4464 E-mail: littnerhampton@aol.com

▶ M A Carpets, 401 Kenton Lane, Harrow, Middlesex, HA3 8RZ Tel: (020) 8909 1373

M Lord & Sons, Florence Mill, Whalley New Road, Blackburn, BB1 9SR Tel: (01254) 661002 Fax: (01254) 661002

M S Contract Carpets, Carr House Lane, Shelf, Halifax, West Yorkshire, HX3 7RB Tel: (01274) 691511 Fax: (01274) 693474

▶ Marine Decor, Castle Street, Trowbridge, Wiltshire, BA14 8AY Tel: (01225) 768802 Fax: (01225) 768822 E-mail: kerryjohns@aol.com

Marlows Carpet, 67 East Hill, London, SW18 2QE Tel: (020) 8871 1169 Fax: (020) 8877 9425 E-mail: marlows@dsl.pipex.com

▶ Matrix Flooring Solutions Ltd, 471 Ranglet Road, Walton Summit Centre, Bamber Bridge, Preston, PR5 8AR Tel: (01772) 330033 Fax: (01772) 330053 E-mail: sales@matrixflooring.net

Mercado Belfast, 101B Airport Road West, Belfast, BT3 9ED Tel: (028) 9046 7680 Fax: (028) 9046 7699 E-mail: sales@merbelfast.co.uk

▶ National Carpet Group, Eclipse Centre, Buckley Road, Rochdale, Lancashire, OL12 9BH Tel: (01706) 714455 Fax: (01706) 714454 E-mail: info@nationalcarpets.co.uk

Newton Abbot Flooring, 129 Winner Street, Paignton, Devon, TQ3 3BP Tel: (01803) 525177 Fax: (01803) 520359 E-mail: classic.floors@virgin.net

Opus Carpets Ltd, 106 North End Road, London, W14 9PP Tel: (020) 7385 3151 Fax: (020) 7386 8252

Phoenox Home Furnishings Ltd, Spring Grove Mills, Clayton West, Huddersfield, HD8 9HH Tel: (01484) 863227 Fax: (01484) 865352 E-mail: info@phoenox.co.uk

William Pownall & Sons Ltd, Ensor Mill, Queensway, Rochdale, Lancashire, OL11 2NU Tel: (01706) 716000 Fax: (01706) 649002

R P S Flooring Ltd, Old Mill Lane Industrial Estate, Mansfield Woodhouse, Mansfield, Nottinghamshire, NG19 9BG Tel: (01623) 624198 Fax: (01623) 620931

Roberts & Chick (Timber Lines) Ltd, 95 St James Mill Road, St James Business Park, Northampton, NN5 5JP Tel: (01604) 753223 Fax: (01604) 586100 E-mail: sales@roberts-chick.co.uk

▶ A. Robertson & Son, 6 Argyle Street, Rothesay, Isle Of Bute, PA20 0AT Tel: (01700) 503575 Fax: (01700) 503834 E-mail: service@robertsonsfurniture.co.uk

Ruislip Carpets, 22 Long Drive, Ruislip, Middlesex, HA4 0HG Tel: (020) 8845 7603 Fax: (020) 8845 7603

S & M Myers Ltd, 100-106 Mackenzie Road, London, N7 8RG Tel: (020) 7609 0091 Fax: (020) 7609 2457

Saxon Carpets, Wilden Lane, Stourport-on-Severn, Worcestershire, DY13 9LW Tel: (01299) 827477 Fax: (01299) 827052 E-mail: sales@carpetsofkidderminster.com

Thomas Scatchard & Sons Ltd, Croft Mills, Batley Road, Heckmondwike, West Yorkshire, WF16 0EQ Tel: (01924) 402051 Fax: (01924) 406515

▶ Select Carpets, Unit F5 Hilton Main Industrial Estate, Bognop Road, Essington, Wolverhampton, WV11 2BE Tel: (01902) 737722 Fax: (01902) 737725

Stoddard International P.L.C., Barbados Road, Kilmarnock, Ayrshire, KA1 1SX Tel: (01563) 578000 Fax: (01563) 578015 E-mail: enquires@stoddardintl.co.uk

T T Carpets & Ceilings, The Red Barn, Harmony Hill, Milnthorpe, Cumbria, LA7 7QA Tel: (01539) 562898 Fax: (01539) 564404 E-mail: enquires@ttcarpets.fsnet.co.uk

▶ Tankard Of Bradford, 758 Aireworth Road, Keighley, West Yorkshire, BD21 4DH Tel: (01535) 663566 Fax: (01535) 663544

Telenzo Carpets Ltd, 2-4 Southgate, Elland, West Yorkshire, HX5 0BW Tel: (01422) 371226 Fax: (01422) 377452

▶ Town & Country Carpets, 20 Mostyn Avenue, Llandudno, Gwynedd, LL30 1YY Tel: (01492) 872400 E-mail: siliven@aol.com

Ulster Carpet Mills Ltd, Castleisland Factory, Garvaghy Road, Portadown, Craigavon, County Armagh, BT62 1EE Tel: (028) 3833 4433 Fax: (028) 3833 3142

▶ Veitchi Scotland Ltd, 15 Bouverie Street, Rutherglen, Glasgow, G73 2RY Tel: 0141-647 0661 Fax: 0141-613 1575

Victoria P.L.C., Worcester Road, Kidderminster, Worcestershire, DY10 1HL Tel: (01562) 749300 Fax: (01562) 749649

Vigo Carpet Gallery Ltd, 6A Vigo Street, London, W1S 3HF Tel: (020) 7439 6971 Fax: (020) 7439 2353 E-mail: vigo@btinternet.com

Westex Carpets Ltd, Castle Mills, Northgate, Cleckheaton, West Yorkshire, BD19 3JB Tel: (01274) 861334 Fax: (01274) 873266 E-mail: info@westexcarpets.co.uk

Woodward Grosvenor & Co. Ltd, Green Street, Kidderminster, Worcestershire, DY10 1HR Tel: (01562) 820020 Fax: (01562) 820042 E-mail: sales@woodward.com

Young & Cunningham (Liverpool) Ltd, Lees Road, Knowsley Industrial Park, Liverpool, L33 7SE Tel: 0151-546 2324 Fax: 0151-548 6428

CARRIER BAG PRINTING SPECIALISTS/SERVICES

Adam Adams Ltd, 1 Chapel Road, Portslade, Brighton, BN41 1PF Tel: (01273) 431100 Fax: (01273) 431110 E-mail: adam-adams@cwcom.net

Bunzl Cleaning & Hygiene Supplies, Unit 4c Swallowfield Way, Hayes, Middlesex, UB3 1DQ Tel: (020) 8581 2345 Fax: (020) 8581 3344 E-mail: admin@bunzlcleaningsupplies.co.uk

Classic Printed Bag Co. Ltd, Unit 5, Silver Business Park, Airfield Way, Christchurch, Dorset, BH23 3TA Tel: (01202) 488144 Fax: (01202) 481341 E-mail: bags@classicbag.co.uk

V.C. Crow & Co. Ltd, Unit F, Halesfield 19, Telford, Shropshire, TF7 4QT Tel: (01952) 686888 Fax: (01952) 686889 E-mail: info@cropac.co.uk

Donington Plastics Ltd, Unit 1 Spiral Tube Works, Derby, DE24 8BT Tel: (01332) 363313 Fax: (01332) 361355 E-mail: sales@doningtongroup.co.uk

Durasak, Stansfeld Street, Blackburn, BB2 2NG Tel: (01254) 51733 Fax: (01254) 51833 E-mail: sales@durasat.co.uk

Fobbed Off, 3 The Mews, Breadcroft Lane, Harpenden, Hertfordshire, AL5 4TF Tel: (01582) 768295 Fax: (01582) 768295 E-mail: nick@ncooper45.freeserve.co.uk

Hearngrange Trading Ltd, Suite 202 Banderway House, 156-162 Kilburn High Road, London, NW6 4JQ Tel: (020) 7372 2010 Fax: (020) 7328 4996

Markapac, 37-41 Finchley Park, London, N12 9JY Tel: (0800) 2300301 Fax: (0800) 2300302 E-mail: info@detsafe.co.uk

CARRIER BAG PRODUCTION MACHINERY

Jenton International Ltd, Unit 9 10 Evingar Industrial Estate, Ardglen Road, Whitchurch, Hampshire, RG28 7BB Tel: (01256) 892194 Fax: (01256) 896486 E-mail: sales@jenton.co.uk

CARRIER BAGS, *See also headings for particular types*

Creation Carriers, Vista Business Centre, 50 Salisbury Road, Hounslow, TW4 6JQ Tel: (020) 8538 0204 Fax: (020) 8538 0207 E-mail: creationcarriers@btconnect.com

Danda UK Packaging Ltd, 8 Drury Way Industrial Estate, Laxcon Close, London, NW10 0TG Tel: (020) 8459 5500 Fax: (020) 8459 2351

Downes & Duncan, Unit 2, Ashley Drive, Bothwell, Glasgow, G71 8BS Tel: (01698) 803088 Fax: (01698) 803087 E-mail: sales@downsduncan.co.uk

Nottingham Paper Bag Co. Ltd, Mundella Works, Mundella Road, Nottingham, NG2 2EQ Tel: 0115-986 1376 Fax: 0115-986 2018 E-mail: sales@thepaperman.net

Park Packaging Ltd, 2 Ashley Drive, Bothwell, Glasgow, G71 8BS Tel: (01698) 801943 Fax: (01698) 801925 E-mail: info@parkpackaging.co.uk

Progressive Supplies Paper Ltd, 18 Crawford Place, London, W1H 5AY Tel: (020) 7563 7330 Fax: (020) 7706 3058 E-mail: sales@progressivesupplies.com

Sai Pac UK Ltd, Poly House, 88 Park Road, Ilford, Essex, IG1 1SF Tel: (020) 8553 4050 Fax: (020) 8553 5151

Taurus Packaging, Meadow Lane, Little Houghton, Northampton, NN7 1AH Tel: (01604) 891707 Fax: (01604) 891708 E-mail: tauruspackaging@hotmail.com

Thompson Packaging, Unit 5, Kenyons Farm, Gough Lane, Walton Summit, Preston, PR5 6AR Tel: (01772) 620768 Fax: (01772) 620764 E-mail: info@arranmarketing.co.uk

W F Denny, F Tudor Road, Broadheath, Altrincham, Cheshire, WA14 5RZ Tel: 0161-927 4949 Fax: 0161-927 4940 E-mail: wfdennyenquiries@btconnect.com

Weald Ltd, High Street, Buxted, Uckfield, East Sussex, TN22 4LA Tel: (01825) 732000 Fax: (01825) 732722 E-mail: tony@wealdpackaging.freeserve.uk

CARRIER BAGS, POLYETHYLENE (PE)

Adam Adams Ltd, 1 Chapel Road, Portslade, Brighton, BN41 1PF Tel: (01273) 431100 Fax: (01273) 431110 E-mail: adam-adams@cwcom.net

Airborne Packaging Ltd, Pegasus House, Beatrice Road, Leicester, LE3 9FH Tel: 0116-253 6136 Fax: 0116-251 4485 E-mail: sales@airbornebags.co.uk

Alphawrap Printers, 13 Miners Road, Llay Industrial Estate, Llay, Wrexham, Clwyd, LL12 0PJ Tel: (01978) 856109 Fax: (01978) 852077 E-mail: admin@alphawrap.co.uk

Anglo Packaging Ltd, 10 Silverdale, Meadow Road, Worthing, West Sussex, BN11 2RZ Tel: (01903) 202333 Fax: (01903) 232333 E-mail: info@anglopackaging.com

Applewade Packaging Ltd, Park House, 15-19 Greenhill CR, Watford, WD18 8PH Tel: (01923) 250202 Fax: (01923) 251101 E-mail: sales@applewade.co.uk

Bailey Packaging Ltd, Unit 26 Garden Estate, Lowtherville Road, Ventnor, Isle of Wight, PO38 1YD Tel: (01983) 855535 Fax: (01983) 853358

▶ Bpi Packaging, Brook Road, Buckhurst Hill, Essex, IG9 5TU Tel: (020) 8504 9151 Fax: (020) 8506 1892 E-mail: salesessex@bpipoly.com

Cardinal Packaging Ltd, Unit 29, Rassau Industrial Estate, Ebbw Vale, Gwent, NP23 5SD Tel: (01495) 308800 Fax: (01495) 301776 E-mail: sales@cardinal-pkg.co.uk

Classic Printed Bag Co. Ltd, Unit 5, Silver Business Park, Airfield Way, Christchurch, Dorset, BH23 3TA Tel: (01202) 488144 Fax: (01202) 481341 E-mail: bags@classicbag.co.uk

Creation Carriers, Vista Business Centre, 50 Salisbury Road, Hounslow, TW4 6JQ Tel: (020) 8538 0204 Fax: (020) 8538 0207 E-mail: creationcarriers@btconnect.com

V.C. Crow & Co. Ltd, Unit F, Halesfield 19, Telford, Shropshire, TF7 4QT Tel: (01952) 686888 Fax: (01952) 686889 E-mail: info@cropac.co.uk

Decomatic, Unit 6, Robins Drive, Bridgwater, Somerset, TA6 4DL Tel: (01278) 444151 Fax: (01278) 422411 E-mail: sales@decomatic.com

Express Polythene Ltd, Barford Street, Birmingham, B5 6AH Tel: 0121-622 2319 Fax: 0121-622 1179 E-mail: sales@expresspolythene.co.uk

Fobbed Off, 3 The Mews, Breadcroft Lane, Harpenden, Hertfordshire, AL5 4TF Tel: (01582) 768295 Fax: (01582) 768295 E-mail: nick@ncooper45.freeserve.co.uk

Hado Polythene, Spring Lane, Malvern, Worcestershire, WR14 1AJ Tel: (01684) 574800 Fax: (01684) 892450 E-mail: sales@hadopolythene.co.uk

▶ Harris & Spilsbury Ltd, 131 St Margarets Road, Ward End, Birmingham, B8 2BD Tel: 0121-327 1095 Fax: 0121-326 0818 E-mail: sales@harris-and-spilsbury.co.uk

Hills Poly Print Ltd, Alma Park Road, Grantham, Lincolnshire, NG31 9SE Tel: (01476) 577132 Fax: (01476) 590368 E-mail: sales@hillspoly-print.com

Keenpac Ltd, Centurion Way, Meridian Business Park, Leicester, LE19 1WH Tel: 0116-289 0900 Fax: 0116-289 3757 E-mail: info@keenpac.co.uk

Kyme Packaging Ltd, The Dairy, 2, Culverthorpe, Grantham, Lincolnshire, NG32 3NQ Tel: (01529) 455777 Fax: (01529) 455787 E-mail: kyme.packaging@virgin.net

Nelson Packaging, Waidshouse Mill, Townsley Street, Nelson, Lancashire, BB9 0RY Tel: (01282) 690215 Fax: (01282) 699976

Nottingham Paper Bag Co. Ltd, Mundella Works, Mundella Road, Nottingham, NG2 2EQ Tel: 0115-986 1376 Fax: 0115-986 2018 E-mail: sales@thepaperman.net

Polyan Covers, 5 Bainbridge Wharf, Farnhill, Keighley, West Yorkshire, BD20 9BX Tel: (01535) 631212 Fax: (01535) 631313

Progressive Supplies Paper Ltd, 18 Crawford Place, London, W1H 5AY Tel: (020) 7563 7330 Fax: (020) 7706 3058 E-mail: sales@progressivesupplies.com

Saklok, Roughway Mill, Dunks Green, Tonbridge, Kent, TN11 9SG Tel: (01732) 810813 Fax: (01732) 810838 E-mail: roughway@btconnect.com

Sapphire Packaging, 28 Eldon Way, Hockley, Essex, SS5 4AD Tel: (01702) 205999 Fax: (01702) 562107 E-mail: sales@sapphirepackaging.com

Thomas Norman, Unit 1 Moreton Industrial Estate, London Road, Swanley, Kent, BR8 8DE Tel: (01322) 611600 Fax: (01322) 611609 E-mail: info@thomasnorman.co.uk

Tpi Plastic Sheeting Supplies, Scott Lidgett Road, Stoke-on-Trent, ST6 4NQ Tel: (01782) 837141 Fax: (01782) 575154 E-mail: info@tpi-polythene.co.uk

Wessex Polybags, Unit 1 Ashville Trading Estate, Royston Road, Baldock, Hertfordshire, SG7 6NN Tel: (01462) 490600 Fax: (01462) 490800 E-mail: sales@wessexpolybags.co.uk

CARRIER BAGS, POLYETHYLENE (PE) – *continued*

Westside Polythene Ltd, Ribble Works, Wakefield Road, Bispham, Blackpool, FY2 0DL Tel: (01253) 358742 Fax: (01253) 500120 E-mail: info@westsidepolythene.co.uk

William Jones Packaging, Unit B5 South Point, Foreshore Road, Cardiff, CF10 4SP Tel: (029) 2048 6262 Fax: (029) 2048 1230 E-mail: sales@wjpackaging.co.uk

CARS

▶ Abbey Group Motors, 32 Abbey Foregate, Shrewsbury, SY2 6BT Tel: 01743 242888

▶ Bluroc Leasing4u, 4 Mallard Way, Crewe, CW1 6ZQ Tel: (01270) 617540 Fax: (0870) 0941442 E-mail: info@leasing4u.co.uk

▶ J. Charles (Auto Advantage) Ltd, 1 Shallcross Mill Road, Whaley Bridge, High Peak, Derbyshire, SK23 7JQ Tel: (0845) 3303545 Fax: (0845) 3303543 E-mail: virgin.surfer@virgin.net

▶ Deal Detective, Knavesmire House, 4 Campleshon Road, York, YO23 1PE Tel: (01904) 632615 Fax: (01904) 629825 E-mail: deals@thedealdetectives.com

▶ GT4 Drivers Club, 21 Glenesha Gardens, Fareham, Hampshire, PO15 6QH Tel: 01202 772695 E-mail: contactus@gt4dc.co.uk

▶ Hiltingbury Motors Ltd, 72 Hiltingbury Road, Chandlers Ford, Eastleigh, Hampshire, SO53 5SS Tel: (023) 8026 6688 Fax: (023) 8026 6680 E-mail: sales@hiltingburymazda.com

▶ Independent Cars Ltd, Hydra Business Park, Nether Lane, Ecclesfield, Sheffield, S35 9ZX Tel: (0845) 4303020 Fax: 0114-232 9130 E-mail: info@independentcars.co.uk

J C Campbell Ni Ltd, Shore Road, Rostrevor, Newry, County Down, BT34 3AA Tel: (028) 4173 8691 Fax: (028) 4173 8949 E-mail: sales@jccampbell.co.uk

▶ L C V Leasing & Finance Ltd, Unit 1a Basepoint Enterprise Centre, Stroudley Road, Basingstoke, Hampshire, RG24 8UP Tel: (0845) 4665599 Fax: (01256) 406739 E-mail: info@lcvleasing.co.uk

▶ Platinum Motor Group, 16-17 The Causeway, Chippenham, Wiltshire, SN15 3DA Tel: (01249) 654321 Fax: (01249) 462683 E-mail: platinum.chippenham.sales@net.vauxhall.co.uk

▶ Platinum Nissan, Meridian Motor Park, North Bradley, Trowbridge, Wiltshire, BA14 0BJ Tel: (01225) 759510 Fax: (01225) 759501 E-mail: d17115man@uk.nissan.biz

▶ Platinum Nissan Box, St Martins Garage, Bath Road, Box, Corsham, Wiltshire, SN13 8AE Tel: (01225) 744444 Fax: (01225) 744477 E-mail: sales@platinumnissan.co.uk

▶ Platinum Renault, Meridian Business Park, North Bradley, Trowbridge, Wiltshire, BA14 0BJ Tel: (01225) 759525 Fax: (01225) 759526

▶ Platinum Renault Bath, Lower Bristol Road, Bath, BA2 3DN Tel: (01225) 485410 Fax: (01225) 338653

▶ Platinum Renault Chippenham, London Road, Chippenham, Wiltshire, SN15 3BB Tel: (01249) 651131 Fax: (01249) 658813

▶ Platinum Skoda, Lower Bristol Road, Bath, BA2 3DR Tel: (01225) 324910 Fax: (01225) 324919 E-mail: enquiries@platinumskoda.co.uk

▶ Platinum Toyota, Meridian Motor Park, North Bradley, Trowbridge, Wiltshire, BA14 0BJ Tel: (01225) 759560 Fax: (01225) 759551

▶ Platinum Toyota Bath, Lower Bristol Road, Bath, BA2 3DN Tel: (01225) 486200 Fax: (01225) 420815 E-mail: im-pb@platinum.toyota.co.uk

▶ Platinum Vauxhall, 8 Meridian Business Park, North Bradley, Trowbridge, Wiltshire, BA14 0BJ Tel: (01225) 759585 Fax: (01225) 759576

▶ Platinum Vauxhall Frome, Manor Road, Marston Trading Estate, Warminster, Wiltshire, BA12 6HR Tel: (01373) 463351 Fax: (01373) 462001 E-mail: platinum.frome.sales@net.vauxhall.co.uk

Renault, 1 Crofton Road, Orpington, Kent, BR6 8AB Tel: (01689) 897897 Fax: (01689) 877188

▶ Renrod Ltd, Union House, Union Street, Trowbridge, Wiltshire, BA14 8RY Tel: (01225) 756100 Fax: (01225) 756149 E-mail: enquiries@renrodmg.co.uk

▶ Southampton Mazda, Bursledon Road, Southampton, SO19 7LW Tel: (023) 8042 2777 Fax: (023) 8044 3320 E-mail: sales@southamptonmazda.co.uk

▶ Wellsway BMW, Lower Bristol Road, Bath, BA2 3DR Tel: (01225) 448145 Fax: (01225) 420794

▶ Wellsway Mini, Lower Bristol Road, Bath, BA2 3DR Tel: (01225) 448555 Fax: (01225) 420794 E-mail: sales@wellswaymini.co.uk

CARTON FILLING AND PACKING MACHINES

R.A. Jones Europak, Unit 30 Concourse House, Leeds, LS11 7DF Tel: 0113 2765842

Soudal Ltd, Telford Way, Stephenson Industrial Estate, Coalville, Leicestershire, LE67 3HE Tel: (01530) 510502 Fax: (01530) 510970 E-mail: sales@soudal.co.uk

CARTON FORMING/FILLING/ CLOSING MACHINES

The Dabarr Group Ltd, The Packhouse, Parsonage Farm Heath Road, Boughton Monchelsea, Maidstone, Kent, ME17 4JB Tel: (01622) 747450 Fax: (01622) 746812 E-mail: info@dabarr.co.uk

Jacob White Packaging Ltd, Riverside Industrial Estate, Dartford, DA1 5BY Tel: (01322) 272531 Fax: (01322) 270692 E-mail: jwhiteuk@aol.com

Norden UK Ltd, Church Street, Baldock, Hertfordshire, SG7 5AF Tel: (01462) 895245 Fax: (01462) 895683 E-mail: enquiries@norden.co.uk

CARTON GLUEING SERVICES, TO THE TRADE

Carton Creations Ltd, Unit 17, Waterside Industrial Park, Waterside Road, Leeds, LS10 1RW Tel: 0113-270 1333

CARTON INSPECTION EQUIPMENT

Peco Controls (Europe) Ltd, Kempton Road, Pershore, Worcestershire, WR10 2TA Tel: (01386) 556622 Fax: (01386) 552252 E-mail: office@peco-europe.com

CARTON PRINTING

Boxpak Ltd, 65 Church Road, Newtownabbey, County Antrim, BT36 7LR Tel: (028) 9036 5421 Fax: (028) 9086 6731 E-mail: sales@boxpak.co.uk

M.S.O. Cleland Ltd, The Linenhall Press, 399 Castlereagh Road, Belfast, BT5 6QP Tel: (028) 9040 0200 Fax: (028) 9070 5446 E-mail: info@mso.com

Contact Print & Packaging Ltd, Haigh Avenue, Stockport, Cheshire, SK4 1NU Tel: 0161-480 3568 Fax: 0161-480 8185

▶ East Kent Carton Manufacturers Ltd, Unit 8 Lysander Close, Pysons Road Industrial Estate, Broadstairs, Kent, CT10 2YJ Tel: (01843) 600033 Fax: (01843) 600055 E-mail: sales@ekcartons.co.uk

Edward J Wood & Co Printers Ltd, 31-37 Rosslyn Cresent, Harrow, Middlesex, HA1 2SA Tel: (020) 8427 6418 Fax: (020) 8861 2126 E-mail: jonengland@compuserve.com

Landor Cartons Ltd, Church Manorway, Erith, Kent, DA8 1NP Tel: (01322) 435426 Fax: (01322) 445830 E-mail: erithsales@landorcartons.co.uk

M R Designs, 6 Lower Farm, 130 High Street, Irchester, Wellingborough, Northamptonshire, NN29 7AB Tel: (01933) 410016 Fax: (01933) 419929 E-mail: mr-designs@btconnect.com

Glen Pack Ltd, 36 Kelvinhaugh Street, Glasgow, G3 8PB Tel: 0141-221 5012 Fax: 0141-248 2555 E-mail: glenpackltd@tiscali.co.uk

Q C Cartons Ltd, Unit 1, 1 Sargon Way, Great Gimsby Business Park, Grimsby, South Humberside, DN37 9PH Tel: (01472) 268525 Fax: (01472) 268526

Waddingtons Cartons Ltd, Cockburn Fields, Middleton Grove, Leeds, LS11 5LX Tel: 0113-276 0730 Fax: 0113-276 0165 E-mail: enquiries@myholdings.co.uk

CARTON SEALING MACHINES

Endoline Machinery Ltd, Stratton Business Park, London Road, Biggleswade, Bedfordshire, SG18 8QB Tel: (01767) 316422 Fax: (01767) 318033 E-mail: info@endoline.co.uk

Pakprint Tapes Ltd, Woodlands, Dale Street, Longwood, Huddersfield, HD3 4TG Tel: (01484) 644884 Fax: (01484) 460094 E-mail: gat@pakprint.co.uk

Soco System UK Ltd, Unit 18 Palmerston Street, Joiners Square Industrial Estate, Stoke-on-Trent, ST1 3EU Tel: (01782) 274100 Fax: (01782) 272696 E-mail: paul.bangs@socosystem.co.uk

Trident Group UK Ltd, 14-15 Yeldon Court, Finedon Road Industrial Estate, Wellingborough, Northamptonshire, NN8 4SS Tel: (01933) 228228 Fax: (01933) 229922 E-mail: sales@tridentgroupuk.com

Watershed Packaging Ltd, Westpoint, Westland Square, Leeds, LS11 5SS Tel: 0113-277 0606 Fax: 0113-277 7174 E-mail: sales@watershed-packaging.co.uk

CARTON WINDOW PATCHING

Carton Creations Ltd, Unit 17, Waterside Industrial Park, Waterside Road, Leeds, LS10 1RW Tel: 0113-270 1333

CARTONS, *See also headings for particular types*

Acacia, 37 Shoebury Avenue, Shoeburyness, Southend-on-Sea, SS3 9BH Tel: (01702) 297555 Fax: (01702) 298015

Advanced Protective Packaging Ltd, Unit 58 Pioneer Mill, Milltown Street, Radcliffe, Manchester, M26 1WN Tel: 0161-724 8080 Fax: 0161-725 9074 E-mail: brian@advanced-pp.co.uk

Alcan Packaging, 83 Tower Road North, Warmley, Bristol, BS30 8XP Tel: 0117-958 2200 Fax: 0117-958 2206 E-mail: sarah.harriman@alcan.com

Allens Removals, 161 Jackmans Place, Letchworth Garden City, Hertfordshire, SG6 1RG Tel: (07850) 872308 Fax: (01462) 621701

B B F Services Ltd, 49 Saxon Road, Whitby, North Yorkshire, YO21 3NU Tel: (01947) 601173 Fax: (0870) 7598439 E-mail: bbfservicesltd@aol.com

Barrows Cartons Ltd, Unit 1a Squires Mill, Micklehurst Road, Mossley, Ashton-under-Lyne, Lancashire, OL5 9JL Tel: (01457) 835253 Fax: (01457) 835898 E-mail: kel.b@btinternet.com

Beamglow Ltd, Somersham Road, St. Ives, Cambridgeshire, PE27 3LP Tel: (01480) 465012 Fax: (01480) 494826 E-mail: cartons@beamglow.co.uk

Bloomfield Supplies, Naas Lane, Gloucester, GL2 5RG Tel: (01452) 883354 Fax: (01452) 725115 E-mail: info@bloomfieldsupplies.co.uk

Bosworth Wright, Express Works, Hollow Road, Anstey, Leicester, LE7 7FP Tel: 0116-236 2231 Fax: 0116-235 2230 E-mail: bosworthwright@hotmail.com

Box & Seal, Unit 30 Whitehill Industrial Estate, Whitehill Lane, Wootton Bassett, Swindon, SN4 7DB Tel: (01793) 855855 Fax: (01793) 855853

Boxes G H Ltd, Palatine Mill, Meadow Street, Great Harwood, Blackburn, BB6 7EJ Tel: (01254) 888151 Fax: (01254) 889569 E-mail: carton@boxesgh.co.uk

Bridger Packaging, Avenue One, Letchworth Garden City, Hertfordshire, SG6 2WP Tel: (01462) 636465 Fax: (01462) 636433 E-mail: postmaster@bridger.co.uk

Brimur Packaging Ltd, 1-3 Hostmoor Avenue, March Industrial Estate, March, Cambridgeshire, PE15 0AX Tel: (01354) 658585 Fax: (01354) 653780

Brookley Case Co. Ltd, Shaw Road, Dudley, West Midlands, DY2 8TP Tel: (01384) 259908 Fax: (01384) 241624 E-mail: brookley.case@btinternet.com

Bruce Boxes Ltd, Timothys Bridge Road, Stratford-Upon-Avon, Warwickshire, CV37 9NQ Tel: (01789) 269811 Fax: (01789) 414489 E-mail: sales@brucebox.co.uk

C & D Cartons Ltd, Third Cross Road, Twickenham, TW2 5DU Tel: (020) 8894 1181 Fax: (020) 8898 1608

C P C Kings Lynn, Oldmedow Road, Hardwick Industrial Estate, King's Lynn, Norfolk, PE30 4LL Tel: (01553) 761481 Fax: (01553) 766203

Cameron Linn Ltd, Belgrave Street, Bellshill Industrial Estate, Bellshill, Lanarkshire, ML4 3NP Tel: (01698) 300400 Fax: (01698) 300900 E-mail: info@cameronlinn.co.uk

Cardboard Box Co. Ltd, Clayton Park Enterpsise Centre, Petre Road, Clayton Le Moors, Accrington, Lancashire, BB5 5JB Tel: (01254) 232223 Fax: (01254) 232636 E-mail: info@thecardboardbox.co.uk

Carton Packaging Supplies Ltd, Unit 5F, Nobel Road, Eley Estate, London, N18 3BH Tel: (020) 8807 7244 Fax: (020) 8807 7327 E-mail: cartonpack93@msn.com

Case & Container Supply Co Ltd, 11 Wilson Road, Wigston, Leicestershire, LE18 4TP Tel: 0116-277 0000 Fax: 0116-277 0072 E-mail: sales@casecontainer.co.uk

Cavendish Packaging Ltd, Manor Royal, Faraday Road, Crawley, West Sussex, RH10 9UR Tel: (01293) 525556 Fax: (01293) 528886

Cell Ltd, Hallsteads, Dove Holes, Buxton, Derbyshire, SK17 8BJ Tel: (01298) 816692 Fax: (01298) 816277 E-mail: sales@cell-limited.co.uk

Cheshire Packaging Ltd, Unit B2 Talbot Road, Newton Business Park, Hyde, Cheshire, SK14 4UQ Tel: 0161-367 8331 Fax: 0161-367 8417

Cohen Packaging Ltd, Unit 15 Clayton Court, Castle Avenue Industrial Estate, Invergordon, Ross-Shire, IV18 0SB Tel: (01349) 853880 Fax: (01349) 853964

Colourpass Cartons Ltd, 52 Cressex Enterprise Centre, Lincoln Road, Cressex Business Park, High Wycombe, Buckinghamshire, HP12 3RL Tel: (01494) 452527 Fax: (01494) 463815 E-mail: mikewillard2211@aol.com

Colton Packaging Ltd, 60-65 The Warren, East Goscote, Leicester, LE7 3XA Tel: 0116-264 1060 Fax: 0116-264 1066

Compack Ltd, 1 Letham Road, Houstoun Industrial Estate, Livingston, West Lothian, EH54 5BY Tel: (01506) 438654 Fax: (01506) 433815

▶ Complete Packaging Solutions, 52-54 Hayhill Industrial Estate, Barrow upon Soar, Loughborough, Leicestershire, LE12 8LD Tel: (01509) 816262 Fax: (01509) 816488 E-mail: sales@completepackagingsolutions.com

Contact Print & Packaging Ltd, Haigh Avenue, Stockport, Cheshire, SK4 1NU Tel: 0161-480 3568 Fax: 0161-480 8185

▶ Corrugated Box Supplies Ltd, Kelvin Way, West Bromwich, West Midlands, B70 7LG Tel: 0121-525 5555 Fax: 0121-553 2501

Crawford's Packaging, 1 Barton Street, North Tawton, Devon, EX20 2HN Tel: (01837) 82388 Fax: (01837) 82388

Croftbench Ltd, Pindar Road, Hoddesdon, Hertfordshire, EN11 0DA Tel: (01992) 444133 Fax: (01992) 445296

Cut Above, 7 Langham Road, Leicester, LE4 9WF Tel: 0116-246 1376 Fax: 0116-276 5275 E-mail: sales@cutaboveuk.com

D E Montfort Packaging, De Montfort Place, 18 Slater St, Leicester, LE3 5ASY Tel: 0116-242 3900 Fax: 0116-253 9055 E-mail: raithbylawrence@btconnect.com

D S Smith, Paper Mill Road, Rawcliffe Bridge, Goole, North Humberside, DN14 8SL Tel: (01405) 837400 Fax: (01405) 837192

David S Smith, Prickwillow Road, Queen Adelaide, Ely, Cambridgeshire, CB7 4TZ Tel: (01353) 660000 Fax: (01353) 660011

Dayworth Packaging, Unit Q1, Trecenydd Industrial Estate, Caerphilly, Mid Glamorgan, CF83 2RZ Tel: (029) 2085 4860 Fax: (029) 2085 4861 E-mail: enquiries@dayworthpackaging.co.uk

Delta Print & Packaging Ltd, Factory No. 10, Kennedy Way Industrial Estate, Belfast, BT11 9DT Tel: (028) 9062 8626 Fax: (028) 9030 1505 E-mail: info@deltapack.com

Dunmar Packaging Ltd, Kus Industrial Estate, Manor Lane, Hawarden, Deeside, Clwyd, CH5 3PJ Tel: (01244) 526872 Fax: (01244) 537396

Edward J Wood & Co Printers Ltd, 31-37 Rosslyn Cresent, Harrow, Middlesex, HA1 2SA Tel: (020) 8427 6418 Fax: (020) 8861 2126 E-mail: jonengland@compuserve.com

Elite Office Supplies, 74 Bookerhill Road, High Wycombe, Buckinghamshire, HP12 4EX Tel: (01494) 473632 Fax: (01494) 440937

Elopak UK, Meadway, Hertfordshire, Rutherford Close, Stevenage, Hertfordshire, SG1 2PR Tel: (01438) 847400 Fax: (01438) 741324 E-mail: elopak.hq@elopak.com

Elopak UK, Meadway, Rutherford Close, Stevenage, Hertfordshire, SG1 2PR Tel: (01438) 847400 Fax: (01438) 741324 E-mail: elopak.hq@elopak.no

Elsa Waste Paper Ltd, Unit 1 Station Road, Reddish, Stockport, Cheshire, SK5 6YZ Tel: 0161-432 3984 Fax: 0161-442 3105

Encase Ltd, Beaumont Road, Banbury, Oxfordshire, OX16 1RE Tel: (01295) 250971 Fax: (01295) 752910

English Corrugating Paper Co. Ltd, Wilson Place, Bristol, BS2 9HL Tel: 0117-955 2002 Fax: 0117-955 4004 E-mail: sales@english-corrugating.co.uk

F G Curtis & Co Plc, Crownhall House, Elm Grove, London, SW19 4HE Tel: (020) 8947 8178 Fax: (020) 8944 1530 E-mail: info@fgcurtis.co.uk

F P Cartons Ltd, Ironmould Lane, Bristol, BS4 5SA Tel: 0117-972 3233 Fax: 0117-971 0381 E-mail: fpcartonltd@freeuk.com

Fairmile Cardboard Containers Ltd, Willow Tree Buisness Park, Pattenden Lane, Marden, Tonbridge, Kent, TN12 9QJ Tel: (01622) 832110 Fax: (01622) 833285 E-mail: judylorne@aol.com

Fast-Pak Packaging Ltd, Unit 1 Kayley Industrial Estate, Richmond Street, Ashton-under-Lyne, Lancashire, OL7 0AU Tel: 0161-339 0697 Fax: 0161-339 4700 E-mail: fastpak@talk21.com

Field Boxmore, Millennium Way West, Nottingham, NG8 6AW Tel: 0115-979 6300 Fax: 0115-979 6333

Firstan Ltd, Trafalgar Way, Bar Hill, Cambridge, CB3 8SQ Tel: (01954) 201010 Fax: (01954) 782923 E-mail: sales@firstan.co.uk

Flexible Packagings Ltd, Unit B Kingsbridge Industrial Estate, Kingsbridge Road, Barking, Essex, IG11 0BD Tel: (020) 8507 1200 Fax: (020) 8507 8979 E-mail: flexiblepackagings@talk21.com

Graham's Cartons, Garston Quays, Blackburn Street, Liverpool, L19 8EL Tel: 0151-427 6565 Fax: 0151-427 5123 E-mail: colin.graham@grahams-cartons.co.uk

H & S Partners Ltd, Forstal Road, Aylesford, Kent, ME20 7AD Tel: (01622) 717387 Fax: (01622) 710211 E-mail: hspartners@btconnect.com

Harrison Packaging, Easter Park, Teesside Industrial Estate, Stockton-on-Tees, Cleveland, TS17 9NT Tel: (01642) 754600 Fax: (01642) 769900 E-mail: sales@harrisonpack.com

Hart Boulton & Co. Ltd, Hampton Street, Joiners Square Industrial Estate, Stoke-on-Trent, ST1 3EX Tel: (01782) 260723 Fax: (01782) 263466

Heritage Packaging, 3 Whitebridge Industrial Estate, Whitebridge Lane, Stone, Staffordshire, ST15 8LQ Tel: (01785) 819189 Fax: (01785) 819089 E-mail: heripak@hotmail.com

Howarth Packaging Ltd, Units 7-11, Hugh Business Park, Waterfoot, Rossendale, Lancashire, BB4 7BT Tel: (01706) 214531 Fax: (01706) 224060 E-mail: server@howarthpackaging.demon.co.uk

Ideal Packaging Co, Unit 49, Queens Court Trading Estate Greets Green Road, West Bromwich, West Midlands, B70 9EL Tel: 0121-557 3624 Fax: 0121-520 5316 E-mail: sales@idealpackaging.co.uk

CARTONS – *continued*

Jaffabox Ltd, Starley Way, Birmingham, B37 7HB Tel: 0121-250 2000 Fax: 0121-250 2001 E-mail: sales@jaffabox.com

Jaycee Packaging Ltd, 8 Fairefield Crescent, Glenfield, Leicester, LE3 8EH Tel: 0116-231 4994 Fax: 0116-231 4989

Jaymar Packaging Ltd, Jaymar House First Avenue, Crew Gates Industrial Estate, Crewe, CW1 6XS Tel: (01270) 500711 Fax: (01270) 580837 E-mail: sales@jaymar.co.uk

Jelmead Ltd, Units 1 & 4 Francis Works, Geddings Road, Hoddesdon, Hertfordshire, EN11 0NT Tel: (01992) 442751 Fax: (01992) 463739

Johnsons Cartons, West Morland House, 160 Clifton Dr South, Lytham St. Annes, Lancashire, FY8 1HG Tel: (01253) 721766 Fax: (01253) 780200 E-mail: sales@johnsons-cartons.co.uk

Justinor Products Ltd, St. Johns Business Park, St. Johns Grove, Hull, HU9 3RL Tel: (01482) 799321 Fax: (01482) 799470 E-mail: sales@justinor.co.uk

Lancashire Board & Paper Co. Ltd, Balderstone Lane, Heasandford Industrial Estate, Burnley, Lancashire, BB10 2AL Tel: (01282) 835033 Fax: (01282) 835044 E-mail: sales@lancsboard.co.uk

Landor Cartons Ltd, Church Manorway, Erith, Kent, DA8 1NP Tel: (01322) 435426 Fax: (01322) 445830 E-mail: erithsales@landorcartons.co.uk

Leyprint Ltd, Leyland Lane, Leyland, PR25 1UT Tel: (01772) 425000 Fax: (01772) 425001 E-mail: info@leyprint.co.uk

Link Packaging Ltd, Tingley Bar Industrial Estate, Tingley Mills, Morley, Leeds, LS27 0HE Tel: 0113-252 7011 Fax: 0113-238 0069 E-mail: linkltd@aol.com

M Y Cartons Ltd, Grosvenor Road, Gillingham Business Park, Gillingham, Kent, ME8 0SA Tel: (01634) 388777 Fax: (01634) 377733 E-mail: sales@mypackaging.com

▶ Majestic Corrugated Cases Ltd, Unit 30 Parkrose Industrial Estate, Middlemore Road, Smethwick, West Midlands, B66 2DZ Tel: (01902) 733330 Fax: 0121-558 7000 E-mail: kavi.jundu@majesticbox.com

Manuel Lloyd Ltd, 20 Bull Lane, London, N18 1SX Tel: (020) 8807 4303 Fax: (020) 8807 3839

Mayr Melnhof Packaging UK Ltd, Fourth Avenue, Deeside Industrial Park, Deeside, Clwyd, CH5 2NR Tel: (01244) 289885 Fax: (01244) 281223 E-mail: sales@mm-packaging.com

Middlesex Packaging Ltd, Middlesex House, Crown Trading Centre, Clayton Road, Hayes, Middlesex, UB3 1DU Tel: (020) 8756 0808 Fax: (020) 8848 1991

Millvale Ltd, Briar Close, Evesham, Worcestershire, WR11 4JT Tel: (01386) 446661 Fax: (01386) 442931 E-mail: sales@millvaleltd.co.uk

MMP UK Ltd, Dunnings Bridge Road, Bootle, Merseyside, L30 6TR Tel: 0151-522 2700 Fax: 0151-522 2747

N Smith & Co. Ltd, Leopold Works, 28 Hainge Road, Tividale, Oldbury, West Midlands, B69 2NZ Tel: 0121-557 1891 Fax: 0121-521 5700 E-mail: sales@nsmithbox.co.uk

New Town Printers Redditch Ltd, Brickyard Lane, Studley, Warwickshire, B80 7EE Tel: (01527) 850011 Fax: (01527) 850055 E-mail: info@newtownprinters.co.uk

▶ Newcel Paper Converters, 4 Milltown Industrial Estate, Greenan Road, Warrenpoint, Newry, County Down, BT34 3FN Tel: (028) 4175 3864 Fax: (028) 3026 0028

North West Fire Ltd, Ross Road, Ellesmere Port, CH65 3DB Tel: 0151-355 6822 Fax: (01978) 751646

Northampton Carton Service, 1 Orchard Cottage, Clifford Hill, Little Houghton, Northampton, NN7 1AL Tel: (01604) 899498 Fax: (01604) 899324

Northdown Packaging, 13c Quarry Wood Industrial Estate, Mills Road, Aylesford, Kent, ME20 7NA Tel: (01622) 710695 Fax: (01622) 790889 E-mail: sales@northdownpackaging.co.uk

Northern Box & Packaging Co. Ltd, Moss Bridge Mill, Blackburn Road, Darwen, Lancashire, BB3 0AJ Tel: (01254) 702375 Fax: (01254) 873709

Offset Holdings Ltd, 188 Forstal Road, Aylesford, Kent, ME20 7DB Tel: (01622) 710759 Fax: (01622) 717486

Glen Pack Ltd, 36 Kelvinhaugh Street, Glasgow, G3 8PB Tel: 0141-221 5012 Fax: 0141-248 2555 E-mail: glenpackltd@tiscali.co.uk

Packaging Co., 195 Scudamore Road, Leicester, LE3 1UQ Tel: 0116-231 3444 Fax: 0116-231 3344 E-mail: sales@thepackagingcompany.co.uk

Packaging Supplies Ltd, Unit 2-3 Thorney Lane North, Iver, Buckinghamshire, SL0 9HF Tel: (01753) 653303 Fax: (01753) 655276 E-mail: sales@pack-supplies.co.uk

▶ Pack-Online Ltd, Chestnut House Spetisbury, Blandford, Spetisbury, Blandford Forum, Dorset, DT11 9DF Tel: (01258) 450389 Fax: (01258) 459252 E-mail: boxoffice@pack-online.co.uk

Peak Box Designs Ltd, Unit 1, Ensor Way, New Mills, High Peak, Derbyshire, SK22 4NQ Tel: (01663) 747889 Fax: (01663) 743979

▶ Plaistere & Hanger Cartons, Pilot Road, Corby, Northamptonshire, NN17 5YH Tel: (01536) 443896 Fax: (01536) 443894 E-mail: pnh60@btconnect.com

Potters Packaging, Govan Road, Fenton Industrial Estate, Stoke-On-Trent, ST4 2RS Tel: (01782) 848888 Fax: (01782) 848900

Printcut Boxfast Ltd, 144 Charles Henry Street, Birmingham, B12 0SD Tel: 0121-622 4353 Fax: 0121-622 1254 E-mail: sales@pcbf.co.uk

Professional Packaging Services Ltd, 1 The Barn, Hawksworth Lane, Guiseley, Leeds, LS20 8HD Tel: (01943) 882400 Fax: (01943) 878191 E-mail: sales@p-p-s-ltd.com

Propak, Tything Road West, Kinwarton, Alcester, Warwickshire, B49 6EP Tel: (01789) 765111 Fax: (01789) 765720 E-mail: sales@propakbox.com

PSW Packaging Ltd, 1 Creslands, Oldmixon CR, Weston-super-Mare, Avon, BS24 9AX Tel: (01934) 418183 Fax: (01934) 626953 E-mail: pswpackagingltd@fsbdial.co.uk

Quality Control Laboratory Ltd, 13a Newbury Road, London, E4 9JH Tel: (020) 8523 3003 Fax: (020) 8523 3003 E-mail: sales@qc2000.freeserve.co.uk

Qualvis Litho Ltd, 854 Melton Road, Thurmaston, Leicester, LE4 8BT Tel: 0116-260 2220 Fax: 0116-260 1066 E-mail: jason@qualvis.co.uk

R D S Cartons Ltd, 3 Schoolfield Road, Grays, Essex, RM20 3HR Tel: (01708) 861355 Fax: (01708) 863913 E-mail: rdscartons@btconnect.com

R Howard Ltd, Croft Bank, Skegness, Lincolnshire, PE24 4AW Tel: (01754) 880226 Fax: (01754) 881263

Reedbut Ltd, Bond Avenue, Bletchley, Milton Keynes, MK1 1JJ Tel: (01908) 630200 Fax: (01908) 630210 E-mail: sales@reedbut.com

Ribble Packaging Ltd, Greengate Street, Oldham, OL4 1DF Tel: 0161-284 9000 Fax: 0161-627 5049 E-mail: ribble@ribble-pack.co.uk

Robor Cartons Ltd, Chartwell Road, Lancing, West Sussex, BN15 8TX Tel: (01903) 750428 Fax: (01903) 766151 E-mail: sales@robor.co.uk

S C A Packaging Bingham, Moorbridge Road, Bingham, Nottingham, NG13 8GG Tel: (01949) 838667 Fax: (01949) 838993

S.Cohen(Boxes)Limited, Unit 1b St Marks, Industrial Estate, London, E16 2BS Tel: (020) 7055 5330 Fax: (020) 7055 5331 E-mail: sales@scohenboxes.co.uk

Sadlers Carton Stockholders Ltd, 10 Tilton Road, Small Heath, Birmingham, B9 4PE Tel: 0121-772 5200 Fax: 0121-771 4368 E-mail: sales@sadlers.co.uk

Smurfit Cartons UK, Freebournes Road, Witham, Essex, CM8 3DA Tel: (01376) 512501 Fax: (01376) 520442

South Coast Cartons, Unit 36, Bailey Gate Industrial Estate, Sturminster Marshall, Wimborne, Dorset, BH21 4DB Tel: (01258) 858445 Fax: (01258) 858223

Springfield Cartons Ltd, Cottenham Lane, Salford, M7 1TW Tel: 0161-833 9857 Fax: 0161-832 1831

Stevens A & Co Yeovil Ltd, Woodland Grove, Yeovil, Somerset, BA20 1NZ Tel: (01935) 476151 Fax: (01935) 422648 E-mail: peter@stevensboxes.com

Stott O'Connell, 1 Nesfield Street, Bradford, West Yorkshire, BD1 3ET Tel: (01274) 722549 Fax: (01274) 724524

T & B Containers Ltd, Broadgate, Wrangle, Boston, Lincolnshire, PE22 9DY Tel: (01205) 270200 Fax: (01205) 270594

T Leighton & Sons, Unit 1a Albion Trading Estate, Mossley Road, Ashton-under-Lyne, Lancashire, OL6 6NQ Tel: 0161-330 4933 Fax: 0161-343 7025 E-mail: tlsbox@aol.com

Tee-Kay Packaging, Fengate, Peterborough, PE1 5XG Tel: (01733) 311867 Fax: (01733) 311017 E-mail: robert@tee-kay.co.uk

Trenton Millway Holdings Ltd, Marston Road, St Neots, St. Neots, Cambridgeshire, PE19 2HF Tel: (01480) 473693 Fax: (01480) 406225 E-mail: sales@trentonbox.co.uk

Venture Packaging Inovations Ltd, Sketchley La Industrial Estate, 14 Waterfield Way, Burbage, Hinckley, Leicestershire, LE10 3ER Tel: (01455) 251457 Fax: (01455) 613645 E-mail: sales@vpi.org.uk

W & M Watson, Unit 1a Clyde Industrial Estate, Glasgow, G73 1PP Tel: (01506) 852324 Fax: (01506) 855210

Waddingtons Cartons Ltd, Cockburn Fields, Middleton Grove, Leeds, LS11 5LX Tel: 0113-276 0730 Fax: 0113-276 0165 E-mail: enquiries@myholdings.co.uk

The Walsall Box Co. Ltd, Bank Street, Walsall, WS1 2ER Tel: (01922) 628118 Fax: (01922) 723395 E-mail: mail@thewalsallbox.co.uk

West Coast Corrugated Ltd, Tokenspire Park, Moorgate Road, Knowsley Industrial Park, Liverpool, L33 7RX Tel: 0151-549 1002 Fax: 0151-549 1185

Richard Wood Packaging Ltd, Guys Industrial Estate Tollgate Road, Burscough, Ormskirk, Lancashire, L40 8TG Tel: (01704) 893073 Fax: (01704) 895276 E-mail: woodpackaging@aol.co.uk

York Box, 31 Auster Road, Clifton Moor, York, YO30 4XA Tel: (01904) 610651 Fax: (01904) 691458

Zetland Boxes, 70 Heworth Village, York, YO31 1AL Tel: (01904) 424000 Fax: (01904) 422408 E-mail: ken@zetlandboxes.co.uk

CARTONS, FEFCO STANDARDS

▶ Mondi Packaging Bux, Airfield Works, Pulham St. Mary, Diss, Norfolk, IP21 4QH Tel: (01379) 676531 Fax: (01379) 676275 E-mail: sales.bux@mondipackaging.com

CARTRIDGE FILLING SERVICES, SINGLE/TWO COMPONENT, ADHESIVE/SEALANT ETC

Cartridge World Ltd, 506 Stafford Road, Wolverhampton, WV10 6AN Tel: (01902) 788240 Fax: (01902) 789283 E-mail: cwoxley@cartridgeworld.org

Mac Cartridges, Unit 11 Pinfold Lane, Llay Industrial Estate, Llay, Wrexham, Clwyd, LL12 0PX Tel: (01978) 853669 Fax: (01978) 853500

CARTRIDGE FILTERS

Amazon Filters Ltd, Albany Park, Frimley Road, Camberley, Surrey, GU15 2RA Tel: (01276) 670600 Fax: (01276) 670101 E-mail: sales@amazonfilters.co.uk

▶ Facet Industrial UK Ltd, Unit G4, Treforest Industrial Estate, Pontypridd, Mid Glamorgan, CF37 5YL Tel: (01443) 844141 Fax: (01443) 844282E-mail: uksales@facetinternational.net

Incamesh Filtration Ltd, Dingle Lane, Appleton, Warrington, WA4 3HR Tel: (01925) 261900 Fax: (01925) 860568 E-mail: sales@incamesh.co.uk

M F & T, 22 Dawkins Road Industrial Estate, Hamworthy, Poole, Dorset, BH15 4JY Tel: (01202) 666456 Fax: (01202) 685545 E-mail: steve.hunt@porvairfilteration.com

Microelectronics, Europa House, Havant Street, Portsmouth, PO1 3PD Tel: (023) 9230 3303 Fax: (023) 9230 2506 E-mail: processuk@pall.com

Power Utilities Ltd, Queen Street, Premier Business Park, Walsall, WS2 9QE Tel: (01922) 720561 Fax: (01922) 720461 E-mail: filters@power-utilities.com

Vee Bee Ltd, Old Wharf Road, Stourbridge, West Midlands, DY8 4LS Tel: (01384) 378884 Fax: (01384) 374179 E-mail: veebee-filtration@veebee.co.uk

Wolf Filtration Ltd, 81 Burlington Street, Ashton-under-Lyne, Lancashire, OL6 7HJ Tel: 0161-339 1604 Fax: 0161-343 1434 E-mail: sales@wolffiltration.co.uk

CARTRIDGES, INDUSTRIAL/ TOOL

Mac Cartridges, Unit 11 Pinfold Lane, Llay Industrial Estate, Llay, Wrexham, Clwyd, LL12 0PX Tel: (01978) 853669 Fax: (01978) 853500

CASE ERECTING/FORMING MACHINES

Cermex UK Ltd, PO Box 12, Huntingdon, Cambridgeshire, PE29 6EF Tel: (01480) 455919 Fax: (01480) 451520 E-mail: sales@cermexuk.com

O K International Europe Ltd, Shepherds Grove Industrial Estate, Stanton, Bury St. Edmunds, Suffolk, IP31 2AR Tel: (01359) 250705 Fax: (01359) 250165 E-mail: sales@okinteurope.co.uk

Soco System UK Ltd, Unit 18 Palmerston Street, Joiners Square Industrial Estate, Stoke-on-Trent, ST1 3EU Tel: (01782) 274100 Fax: (01782) 272696 E-mail: paul.bangs@socosystem.co.uk

CASE FITTINGS, *See Metal Fittings/Edgings/Accessories etc*

CASE HARDENING

P B A Heat Treating Ltd, Unit 7-8, Bevan Industrial Estate, Brierley Hill, West Midlands, DY5 3TF Tel: (01384) 480331 Fax: (01384) 78381 E-mail: sales@pbaheattreatment.co.uk

Servis Heat Treatment Co. Ltd, 258b Ipswich Road, Trading Estate, Slough, SL1 4EP Tel: (01753) 521823 Fax: (01753) 531094 E-mail: sales@servisheattreatment.com

Tti Group Ltd, 39-43 Bilton Way, Luton, LU1 1UU Tel: (01582) 486644 Fax: (01582) 481148 E-mail: sales@ttigroup.co.uk

Zotic Ltd, 26-30 Highgate Square, Highgate, Birmingham, B12 0DU Tel: 0121-440 3130 Fax: 0121-440 6646

CASE NOTE FOLDERS

Croftons Manufacturers, Unit A001-2 Faircharm Trading Estate, 8-12 Creekside, London, SE8 3DX Tel: (020) 8320 2083 Fax: (020) 8320 2084 E-mail: enquiries@croftonltd.com

CASEMENT TYPE WINDOW FASTENERS OR STAYS

Caldwell Hardware Ltd, Herald Way, Binley Industrial Estate, Binley Industrial Estate, Coventry, CV3 2RQ Tel: (024) 7643 7900 Fax: (024) 7643 7969 E-mail: sales@caldwell.co.uk

Cavendish Hardware, 8 242 Tithe Street, Leicester, LE5 4BN Tel: 0116-274 1746 Fax: 0116-246 1545 E-mail: sales@cavendish-hardware.co.uk

Lightfoot Windows Ltd, 31 Crouch Hill, London, N4 4AS Tel: (020) 7272 1622 Fax: (020) 7281 1404

LSH Ltd, Western Road, Silver End, Witham, Essex, CM8 3QB Tel: (01376) 507507 Fax: (01376) 584687 E-mail: sales@lairdsecurity.co.uk

Paddock Fabrications Ltd, Fryers Road, Walsall, WS2 7LZ Tel: (01922) 470940 Fax: (01922) 476021 E-mail: sales@paddockfabrications.co.uk

Regent Lock Co. Ltd, Bath Road Industrial Estate, Chippenham, Wiltshire, SN14 0AB Tel: (01249) 650416 Fax: (01249) 443014

CASES, *See also headings for particular types: Box, Case, Container etc; also material used*

Allpac Exports, PO Box 46, Barnsley, South Yorkshire, S75 2BL Tel: (01226) 280033 Fax: (01226) 280044 E-mail: allpacexports@aol.com

▶ Armour Systems Ltd, Unit D, Lyon Road, Denbigh West, Milton Keynes, MK1 1EX Tel: (01908) 370345 Fax: (01908) 366659 E-mail: info@armoursystems.co.uk

▶ Bourne Fibre Manufacturing Ltd, The Chapel, The Street, Brockdish, Diss, Norfolk, IP21 4JY Tel: (01379) 668743 Fax: (01379) 669032 E-mail: hopeatthechapel@aol.com

A.C. Buckoke & Sons Ltd, Factory 11-25 Chatfield Road, London, SW11 3SE Tel: (020) 7223 3746 Fax: (020) 7223 3746 E-mail: acbuckoke@yahoo.co.uk

C F Cases Ltd, 13 Consul Road, Rugby, Warwickshire, CV21 1PB Tel: (01788) 535484 Fax: (01788) 570933 E-mail: sales@cfcases.co.uk

Capital Case Co, 55 Lonsdale Road, London, NW6 6RA Tel: (020) 7624 3333 Fax: (020) 7624 2533

Case Co., Leighton Court, Lower Eggleton, Ledbury, Herefordshire, HR8 2UN Tel: (01531) 640543 Fax: (01531) 640759 E-mail: julie@thecasecompany.co.uk

Commercial Trading, Bridge Road, Kingswood, Bristol, BS15 4PT Tel: 0117-961 0710 Fax: 0117-960 2933 E-mail: commercial.trading@btinternet.com

Computer Luggage The Company, London Road, Unit 6, Marlborough, Wiltshire, SN8 2AP Tel: (01672) 519933 Fax: (01672) 519966 E-mail: sales@tehair.co.uk

Excelsior Rotational Moulding Ltd, Ferngrove Mills, Rochdale Old Road, Bury, Lancashire, BL9 7LS Tel: 0161-797 0855 Fax: 0161-763 1614 E-mail: sales@excelsior-ltd.co.uk

Fibre Box Co. Ltd, Victoria Works, Barton Road, Dukinfield, Cheshire, SK16 4US Tel: 0161-308 4856 Fax: 0161-339 1666 E-mail: dalesmanu@hotmail.co.uk

▶ Gard Plasticases Ltd, 2 Arnolds Business Park, Branbridges Road, East Peckham, Tonbridge, Kent, TN12 5LG Tel: (01622) 871887 Fax: (01622) 871895 E-mail: sales@gardplasticases.com

Jit Pak, Unit 14 Pages Industrial Park, Eden Way, Leighton Buzzard, Bedfordshire, LU7 4TZ Tel: (01525) 374412 Fax: (01525) 374416 E-mail: info@jitpak.co.uk

King Bros (Burnham) Ltd, 53 Huntercombe Lane North, Slough, SL1 6DX Tel: 01628 661481 Fax: 01628 667466

Lightwood plc, Hangar 2, North Weald Airfield, North Weald, Epping, Essex, CM16 6AA Tel: (01992) 524237 Fax: (01992) 524501 E-mail: store@lightwoodplc.demon.co.uk

Marber Promotions & Marketing Ltd, 30b Park Road, Hale, Altrincham, Cheshire, WA15 9NN Tel: 0161-927 9085 Fax: 0161-927 9087 E-mail: enquiries@marber.co.uk

▶ Marshall Langston Ltd, Marlan House, Lower Tuffley Lane, Gloucester, GL2 5DT Tel: (01452) 529717 Fax: (01452) 309994 E-mail: sales@marshalllangston.co.uk

Nomad plc, Rockingham Road, Market Harborough, Leicestershire, LE16 7QE Tel: (01858) 464878 Fax: (01858) 410175 E-mail: nomadsolutions@aol.com

Oakleigh Cases Ltd, 10 The Summit Centre, Summit Road, Potters Bar, Hertfordshire, EN6 3JN Tel: (01707) 655011 Fax: (01707) 646447 E-mail: sales@oakleighcases.com

Peter Jones Ilg Ltd, Lower Monk Street, Abergavenny, Gwent, NP7 5NA Tel: (01873) 852742 Fax: (01873) 857573 E-mail: sales@peterjonesilg.co.uk

Protechnic Ltd, Unit 109 Central Park, Petherton Road, Bristol, BS14 9BZ Tel: (01275) 833779 Fax: (01275) 835560 E-mail: sales@protechnic.com

Quentor Ltd, 10 Fitzmaurice Court, Rackheath, Norwich, NR13 6PY Tel: (01603) 721604 Fax: (01603) 721992 E-mail: sales@quentor.com

CASES – *continued*

Record Dimensions Co., Kelvedon House, Hall Lane, Knutsford, Cheshire, WA16 7AE Tel: (01565) 873300 Fax: (01565) 873000 E-mail: sales@rdco.co.uk

S Ashby & Co, 59 Sibson Road, Birstall, Leicester, LE4 4DX Tel: 0116-267 1122 Fax: 0116-267 1122

S C A Packaging Oldbury, Rood End Road, Oldbury, West Midlands, B69 4HT Tel: 0121-552 0696 Fax: 0121-552 0623

Topper Cases Ltd, St. Peter's Hill, Huntingdon, Cambridgeshire, PE29 7DX Tel: (01480) 457251 Fax: (01480) 452107 E-mail: sales@toppercases.co.uk

Trifibre Containers International, Mill Road, Newbourne, Woodbridge, Suffolk, IP12 4NP Tel: (01473) 811865 Fax: (01473) 811873 E-mail: mukesh@trifibre.co.uk

▶ White Rose Packaging, Unit 23-24 Latchmore Industrial Park, Low Fields Road, Leeds, LS12 6DN Tel: 0113-246 0410 Fax: 0113-234 3136E-mail: sales@whiterosepackaging.co.uk

CASES, COMPUTER SERVER

▶ BG IT Services, 3, Glen Court, Grasmere Road, Bromley, BR1 4BD Tel: 070 9223 1080 Fax: 070 9223 1080 E-mail: us@bg-it.com

▶ C H C Solutions, Thorley Health Centre, Villiers-Sur-Marne, Bishop's Stortford, Hertfordshire, CM23 4EG Tel: (01279) 210088 Fax: (0870) 1417242 E-mail: contactus@chcsolutions.co.uk

Ctech 2000 Ltd, Royle Road, Rochdale, Lancashire, OL11 3ES Tel: (0870) 2004786 Fax: (0870) 9507755 E-mail: sales@ctech2000.co.uk

▶ Infinity Business Solutions, Shinfield Grange, Cutbush Lane, Shinfield, Reading, RG2 9AF Tel: 0118-988 2777 E-mail: sales@infinity-bf.com

▶ J C Technology, Suite 6,, Lyon House, 10 West Park, Harrogate, North Yorkshire, HG1 1BL Tel: (01423) 530040 E-mail: info@jctechnology.org

▶ Sapath Systems, 145 Vaughan Road, Harrow, Middlesex, HA1 4EG Tel: (0870) 9502936 Fax: (0870) 1281422E-mail: info@sapath.com

CASES, COMPUTER SOFTWARE

▶ Brit Software Ltd, Unit 6, Quayside Business Centre, Lowestoft Enterprise Park, School Road, Lowestoft, Suffolk, NR33 9NW Tel: (0870) 7664965 Fax: (0870) 0117596 E-mail: info@britsoftware.com

▶ Genstar Trading, Unit 2, Colne Way Court, Watford, WD24 7NE Tel: (01923) 806806 Fax: (01923) 805805 E-mail: sales@genstar.co.uk

▶ J C Technology, Suite 6,, Lyon House, 10 West Park, Harrogate, North Yorkshire, HG1 1BL Tel: (01423) 530040 E-mail: info@jctechnology.org

CASES, CORRUGATED

James Packaging Ltd, Unit 24A, Park Avenue Industrial Estate, Sundon Park, Luton, LU3 3BP Tel: (01582) 561333 Fax: (01582) 561444

CASES, MUSIC/DJ EQUIPMENT

Abracadabra Discotheques, 314 Nelson Road, Twickenham, TW2 7AH Tel: (020) 8893 3313 Fax: (020) 8893 8813 E-mail: sales@abra.co.uk

DJ & Music Shop, Dyffryn Orion, Saron Road, Pentrecwrt, Llandysul, Carmarthenshire, SA44 5DL Tel: (01559) 362957 E-mail: info@djandmusicshop.co.uk

Qmusic Ltd, 23a Airport Industrial Estate, Newcastle upon Tyne, NE3 2EF Tel: 0191-286 2039 Fax: 0191-286 0177 E-mail: info@qmusic.co.uk

▶ Top Class Disco's, 1 Salisbury Terrace, Stockton-on-Tees, Cleveland, TS20 2DS Tel: (01642) 863851

CASES, NOTEBOOK COMPUTER

▶ A J Computing, 12 Church Lane, Little Bytham, Grantham, Lincolnshire, NG33 4QP Tel: (01780) 410998 E-mail: alex@aj-computing.co.uk

▶ Caseonline, Unit 13, Roman Way Business Park, Godmanchester, Huntingdon, Cambridgeshire, PE29 2LN Tel: (01480) 453288 Fax: (01480) 451088 E-mail: sales@caseonline.co.uk

▶ Cream Computers UK Ltd, The Red House, Kingswood Park, Bonsor Drive, Tadworth, Surrey, KT20 6AY Tel: (01737) 377220 Fax: (01737) 377221 E-mail: ray@creamcomputers.com

Ctech 2000 Ltd, Royle Road, Rochdale, Lancashire, OL11 3ES Tel: (0870) 2004786 Fax: (0870) 9507755 E-mail: sales@ctech2000.co.uk

▶ J C Technology, Suite 6,, Lyon House, 10 West Park, Harrogate, North Yorkshire, HG1 1BL Tel: (01423) 530040 E-mail: info@jctechnology.org

▶ Laptopshop IT Ltd, 12-14 Valley Bridge Road, Clacton-on-Sea, Essex, CO15 4AD Tel: (01255) 422033 Fax: (01255) 470300 E-mail: sales@laptopshop.co.uk

Protec Metal Work Ltd, 7 H T H Complex, Blackwater Way, Aldershot, Hampshire, GU12 4DN Tel: (01252) 310443 Fax: (01252) 341787 E-mail: protecmetal@btconnect.com

▶ Retrolutions Ltd, 85 Lincoln Road, Stevenage, Herts, SG1 4PL Tel: 01438 743346 E-mail: richard.thatcher@retrolutions.com

CASES, RACKMOUNTED, COMPUTER SERVER

Kingsworthy Foundry Co. Ltd, London Road, Kingsworthy, Winchester, Hampshire, SO23 7QG Tel: (01962) 883776 Fax: (01962) 882925 E-mail: kwf@fsbdial.co.uk

CASES, SHOTGUN, LEATHER

▶ Wighill Park Guns, Wighill Park Nurseries, Wighill Park, Tadcaster, North Yorkshire, LS24 8BW Tel: (01937) 833757 Fax: (01937) 530563 E-mail: info@wighillparkguns.co.uk

CASES, TO SPECIFICATION/ CUSTOM BUILT

Clubsafe Case Mnfrs, 1 Spinners End Industrial Estate Oldfields, Corngreaves, Cradley Heath, West Midlands, B64 6BS Tel: (01384) 411311 Fax: (01384) 411311 E-mail: enquiries@cslclubsafe.co.uk

E P S Logistics Technology Ltd, Staplehurst Road, Sittingbourne, Kent, ME10 1XS Tel: (01795) 424433 Fax: (01795) 426970 E-mail: sales@epslt.co.uk

Fibre Box Co. Ltd, Victoria Works, Barton Road, Dukinfield, Cheshire, SK16 4US Tel: 0161-308 4856 Fax: 0161-339 1666 E-mail: dalesmanu@hotmail.co.uk

Mec Com Ltd, St. Leonards Works, St. Leonards Avenue, Stafford, ST17 4LT Tel: (01785) 273708 Fax: (01785) 273777 E-mail: sales@mec-com.ltd.uk

CASES, WOODEN

Brookley Case Co. Ltd, Shaw Road, Dudley, West Midlands, DY2 8TP Tel: (01384) 259908 Fax: (01384) 241624 E-mail: brookley.case@btinternet.com

E E Olley & Sons Ltd, Dartford Trade Park, Dartford, DA1 1PE Tel: (01322) 227681 Fax: (01322) 289724 E-mail: sales@eeolley.co.uk

▶ Raymond Mcleod Farms Ltd, Longham Hall, Longham, Dereham, Norfolk, NR19 2RJ Tel: (01362) 687240 Fax: 0870 7626195 E-mail: mcleod@mcleodfarms.co.uk

CASH ACCEPTOR VENDING DEVICES, BANKNOTE/COIN

Banking Automation Ltd, Unit 2 Woodley Park Estate, Reading Road, Reading, RG5 3AW Tel: 0118-969 2224 Fax: 0118-944 1191 E-mail: robinguest@bankingautomation.co.uk

Essex Engineering Works Wanstead Ltd, 12 Nelson Road, London, E11 2AX Tel: (020) 8989 2012 Fax: (020) 8530 1117 E-mail: enquiries@essexengineering.co.uk

M E I, Eskdale Road, Winnersh Triangle, Wokingham, Berkshire, RG41 5AQ Tel: 0118-969 7700 Fax: 0118-944 6412

CASH BOXES

Checkmate Devices Ltd, Gore Cross Business Park, Corbin Way, Bradpole, Bridport, Dorset, DT6 3UX Tel: (01308) 423871 Fax: (01308) 458276 E-mail: checkmate@ackerman-eng.com

CASH CHANGE VENDING MACHINES

▶ Note Machine, Humphries House, Elvicta Estates, Crickhowell, Powys, NP8 1DF Tel: (01873) 811634 Fax: (01873) 811552

CASH COLLECTION VEHICLE SAFES

Checkmate Devices Ltd, Gore Cross Business Park, Corbin Way, Bradpole, Bridport, Dorset, DT6 3UX Tel: (01308) 423871 Fax: (01308) 458276 E-mail: checkmate@ackerman-eng.com

CASH CONVEYING SYSTEMS

Air Tube Carrier Systems, 79 Turnberry, Bracknell, Berkshire, RG12 8ZH Tel: (01344) 423659 Fax: (01344) 423659

Quirepace Ltd, Cleveland Place, Cleveland Road, Gosport, Hampshire, PO12 2JG Tel: (023) 9251 1008 Fax: (023) 9251 3244 E-mail: info@quirepace.co.uk

CASH DISPENSERS, BANK

▶ Complete Technical Services Ltd, Hope Street, Rotherham, South Yorkshire, S60 1LH Tel: (01709) 821757 Fax: (01709) 385068 E-mail: gary.collinson@complete-tech.co.uk

▶ Note Machine, Humphries House, Elvicta Estates, Crickhowell, Powys, NP8 1DF Tel: (01873) 811634 Fax: (01873) 811552

CASH DRAWERS

Cash Bases Ltd, The Drove, Newhaven, East Sussex, BN9 0LA Tel: (01273) 616300 Fax: (01273) 512010 E-mail: info@cashbases.co.uk

CASH HANDLING SOFTWARE

Retail System Services Ltd, Reave Cottage, Long Stratton, Norwich, NR15 2RP Tel: (07771) 724450 Fax: (0870) 70599471

CASH HANDLING SYSTEMS

De La Rue Cash Systems, 7-8 Wolfe Close, Parkgate Industrial Estate, Knutsford, Cheshire, WA16 8XJ Tel: (01565) 654662 Fax: (01565) 658657 E-mail: robert.clark@uk.delarue.com

Orbital Epos Systems Ltd, Canada House Business Centre, 272 Field End Road, Eastcote, Ruislip, Middlesex, HA4 9NA Tel: (020) 8582 0331 Fax: (020) 8582 0335 E-mail: sales@epossystems.co.uk

CASH REGISTER DRAWERS

Cornwall Scale & Equipment Co., 29 Mount Ambrose, Redruth, Cornwall, TR15 1NX Tel: (01209) 213413 Fax: (01209) 872902 E-mail: martin.jsanders@virgin.net

▶ S&S, 69 Cross Lane, Mountsorrel, Loughborough, Leicestershire, LE12 7BU Tel: 0116-210 6007 Fax: 0116-210 6779 E-mail: glensmith002@ntlworld.com

CASH REGISTER MAINTENANCE/REPAIR SERVICES

Anglia Epos, Hall Lodges, Gateley, Dereham, Norfolk, NR20 5EF Tel: (01328) 829607 Fax: (01328) 829607

Argyll Cash Register Systems, Unit 25a Anniesland Industrial Estate, Glasgow, G13 1EU Tel: 0141-950 6766 Fax: 0141-950 6750 E-mail: sales@argyllsystems.co.uk

Birmingham Cash Registers Ltd, 135 Quinton Road West, Birmingham, B32 2RE Tel: 0121-565 3131 Fax: 0121-565 3213 E-mail: lesley@birminghamcash.co.uk

▶ BizEquip Ltd, 6 Kingscroft Road, Hucclecote, Gloucester, GL3 3RF Tel: (01452) 618888 Fax: (01452) 542621 E-mail: sales@bize-mail.info

▶ CNS Systems, 29 Fen Road, Watlington, King's Lynn, Norfolk, PE33 0JA Tel: (01553) 811838 Fax: (01553) 810363 E-mail: sales@cns-systems.co.uk

C R S Cash Registers, Low Sell, Gateshead, Tyne & Wear, NE9 5WY Tel: 0191-491 3530 Fax: 0191-491 3530 E-mail: terence.cullen@talk21.com

CCR Services Ltd, 128 Vale Road, Rhyl, Clwyd, LL18 2PD Tel: (01745) 360788 Fax: (01745) 360788 E-mail: info@ccrservices.co.uk

Citadel Retail Systems, 62 Portman Road, Reading, RG30 1EA Tel: 0118-959 8020

City Cash Registers, 35 Leachfield Road, Galgate, Lancaster, LA2 0NX Tel: (01524) 751051 Fax: (01524) 752672

Cornwall Scale & Equipment Co., Wallasey, 29 Mount Ambrose, Redruth, Cornwall, TR15 1NX Tel: (01209) 213413 Fax: (01209) 213413 E-mail: martin.jsanders@virgin.net

Epos Cash Registers, 38 Prince Charles Road, Exeter, EX4 7EF Tel: (01392) 276688 Fax: (01392) 276688 E-mail: dave@eposcashregister.co.uk

Fisher Scales, 11-11a Unit, Station Road Industrial Estate, Attleborough, Norfolk, NR17 2NP Tel: (01953) 450310 Fax: (01953) 456391 E-mail: fisher.scales@virgin.net

Freelance Cash Register Services, 31 Wood Green Road, Oldbury, West Midlands, B68 0DE Tel: 0121-421 3973 Fax: 0121-421 3973

G A Wedderburn & Co. Ltd, 44a Kinson Road, Bournemouth, BH10 4AN Tel: (01202) 523996 Fax: (01202) 523994 E-mail: team@gawedderburnbmth.fsnet.co.uk

L C R Ltd, 197 Church Street, Blackpool, FY1 3NY Tel: (01253) 628020 Fax: (01253) 621718 E-mail: sales@lcrbpl.co.uk

Langley Business Systems Ltd, 29 Junction Street South, Oldbury, West Midlands, B69 4TA Tel: 0121-552 2570 Fax: 0121-511 1317E-mail: sales@lbswholesale.demon.co.uk

LBS South West Ltd, 29 Amberley Way, Wickwar, Wotton-under-Edge, Gloucestershire, GL12 8LW Tel: 0117-956 3004 Fax: (01454) 299209 E-mail: sales@lbscashregisters.co.uk

▶ Merlin Office Equipment, 1-7 Glasgow Street, Dumfries, DG2 9AF Tel: (01387) 257027 Fax: (01387) 250037 E-mail: service@merlinofficeequipment.co.uk

Micro-Till Systems, 172 Baddow Road, Chelmsford, CM2 9QW Tel: (01245) 347094 Fax: (01245) 347094

Mid Glam Cash Registers, Croftmore, Gelliwion Woods, Maesycoed, Pontypridd, Mid Glamorgan, CF37 1QB Tel: 07957 566120 Fax: 01443 407738 E-mail: Paul.Suminski@midglamcashregisters.co.uk

Orbital Epos Systems Ltd, Canada House Business Centre, 272 Field End Road, Eastcote, Ruislip, Middlesex, HA4 9NA Tel: (020) 8582 0331 Fax: (020) 8582 0335 E-mail: sales@epossystems.co.uk

Professional Retail Systems, Bridgewater Close, Hapton, Burnley, Lancashire, BB11 5TT Tel: (01282) 425566 Fax: (01282) 423831 E-mail: gt.prs-epos@btconnect.com

Retail Equipment Sales & Services Ltd, 12 Everite Road Industrial Estate, Westgate, Widnes, Cheshire, WA8 8RA Tel: 0151-420 2147 Fax: 0151-420 2147 E-mail: sales@retailequipment.co.uk

South Ribble Cash Registers, Middleforth, Penwortham, Preston, PR1 9QR Tel: (01772) 740588 Fax: 01772 740588 E-mail: info@srcr.co.uk

Wakefield Cash Registers, 250 Bradford Road, Wakefield, West Yorkshire, WF1 2BA Tel: (01924) 366753

WCR, 169 Irvine Road, Kilmarnock, Ayrshire, KA1 2LA Tel: (01563) 535962 Fax: (01563) 511337

Wiltshire & Avon Cash Registers Ltd, 80 West Street, Old Market, St. Philips, Bristol, BS2 0BW Tel: 0117-955 5708 Fax: 0117-954 0904

CASH REGISTER PAPER ROLLS

▶ All Role Solutions, Unit 1 Bridge Farm, Holme Drove, Wyton, Huntingdon, Cambridgeshire, PE28 2AD Tel: (01487) 843255 Fax: (01487) 843003 E-mail: sales@allrol.co.uk

▶ CNS Systems, 29 Fen Road, Watlington, King's Lynn, Norfolk, PE33 0JA Tel: (01553) 811838 Fax: (01553) 810363 E-mail: sales@cns-systems.co.uk

Meriden Paper Ltd, 38 Meriden Street, Digbeth, Birmingham, B5 5LS Tel: 0121-643 2168 Fax: 0121-631 3378 E-mail: admin@meridenpaper.co.uk

▶ Merlin Office Equipment, 1-7 Glasgow Street, Dumfries, DG2 9AF Tel: (01387) 257027 Fax: (01387) 250037 E-mail: service@merlinofficeequipment.co.uk

Mid Glam Cash Registers, Croftmore, Gelliwion Woods, Maesycoed, Pontypridd, Mid Glamorgan, CF37 1QB Tel: 07957 566120 Fax: 01443 407738 E-mail: Paul.Suminski@midglamcashregisters.co.uk

Multidata Europe, Hunts Hill, Blunsdon, Swindon, SN26 7BN Tel: (01793) 706161 Fax: (01793) 706150 E-mail: nigel@multidata.co.uk

CASH REGISTER SYSTEMS CONSULTANTS OR SERVICES

▶ BizEquip Ltd, 6 Kingscroft Road, Hucclecote, Gloucester, GL3 3RF Tel: (01452) 618888 Fax: (01452) 542621 E-mail: sales@bize-mail.info

▶ E M F Electronics, 146 Portsmouth Road, Lee-on-the-Solent, Hampshire, PO13 9AE Tel: (023) 9255 6225 E-mail: sales@emf-electronics.co.uk

▶ Merlin Office Equipment, 1-7 Glasgow Street, Dumfries, DG2 9AF Tel: (01387) 257027 Fax: (01387) 250037 E-mail: service@merlinofficeequipment.co.uk

Monarch Business Systems, 121 Allington Drive, Birstall, Leicester, LE4 4FF Tel: 0116-267 5956 Fax: 0116-267 5956 E-mail: info@monarch-ecr.co.uk

▶ S&S, 69 Cross Lane, Mountsorrel, Loughborough, Leicestershire, LE12 7BU Tel: 0116-210 6007 Fax: 0116-210 6779 E-mail: glensmith002@ntlworld.com

WCR, 169 Irvine Road, Kilmarnock, Ayrshire, KA1 2LA Tel: (01563) 535962 Fax: (01563) 511337

CASH REGISTERS

▶ A B E Solutions, Mile-End Avenue, Aberdeen, AB15 5LR Tel: (01224) 622239 Fax: (01224) 622240 E-mail: sales@abesolutions.co.uk

CASH REGISTERS – *continued*

A C R Cash Register Systems, 570 Pollokshaws Road, Glasgow, G41 2PF Tel: 0141-424 0558 Fax: 0141-424 0655

Abbey Business Machines, 13-15 Oakford, Kingsteignton, Newton Abbot, Devon, TQ12 3EQ Tel: (01626) 202502 Fax: (01626) 202503 E-mail: sales@abbeybusinessmachines.co.uk

Ace Business Machines, 1 Lacre Way, Letchworth Garden City, Hertfordshire, SG6 1NR Tel: (01462) 676002 Fax: (01462) 484315 E-mail: sales@acetills.co.uk

Ace Scale & Cash Systems, Whisperdale Farm, Silpho, Scarborough, North Yorkshire, YO13 0JT Tel: 01723 381579 Fax: 01723 381579

Advance Cash Registers Ltd, 9 Ashbourne Parade, London, W5 3QS Tel: (020) 8997 8070 Fax: (020) 8997 2265 E-mail: advancedcr@aol.com

Anchor Data Systems Ltd, Unit 36 North City Business Centre, 2 Duncairn Gardens, Belfast, BT15 2GG Tel: (028) 9074 0315 Fax: (028) 9035 1531 E-mail: info@anchordata.co.uk

B J Lashbrook & Son, Red Lion Street, Redcar, Cleveland, TS10 3HF Tel: (01642) 482629 Fax: (01642) 489720 E-mail: bj@bjlashbrook.freeserve.co.uk

B & M Business Machines Ltd, 30 Military Road, Colchester, CO1 2AJ Tel: (01206) 576872 Fax: (01206) 576873

Barnsley Cash Registers, 2the Parade, Clough Fields Road, Hoyland, Barnsley, South Yorkshire, S74 0HR Tel: (01226) 744003 Fax: (01226) 744003 E-mail: barnsleytills@aol.com

Birmingham Cash Registers Ltd, 135 Quinton Road West, Birmingham, B32 2RE Tel: 0121-565 3131 Fax: 0121-565 3213 E-mail: lesley@birminghamcash.co.uk

▶ BizEquip Ltd, 6 Kingscroft Road, Hucclecote, Gloucester, GL3 3RF Tel: (01452) 618888 Fax: (01452) 542621 E-mail: sales@bize-mail.info

Bleep (UK) P.L.C., Rown House, 9-31 Victoria Road, Park Royal, London, NW10 6DP Tel: (020) 7724 2000 Fax: (020) 7706 1935 E-mail: info@bleepplc.com

British & American Retail Systems Ltd, 151b Dentons Green Lane, Dentons Green, St. Helens, Merseyside, WA10 6RG Tel: (01744) 750221 Fax: (01744) 750222 E-mail: britishamerican@btopenworld.com

Broughton & Co Bristol Ltd, 4 Axis, Hawkfield Way, Hawkfield Business Park, Bristol, BS14 0BY Tel: 0117-964 1300 Fax: 0117-964 1003 E-mail: broughtons1bristol@btinternet.com

Buchanan Business Systems Ltd, 14 Barrow Close, Sweet Briar Road Industrial Estate, Norwich, NR3 2AT Tel: (01603) 400550 Fax: (01603) 400770 E-mail: sales@buchananforce9.co.uk

C C M Flintex Ltd, Linden Lea House, High Pitfold, Hindhead, Surrey, GU26 6BN Tel: (01483) 426980 Fax: (01428) 608608 E-mail: tony@flintex.freeserve.co.uk

▶ CNS Systems, 29 Fen Road, Watlington, King's Lynn, Norfolk, PE33 0JA Tel: (01553) 811838 Fax: (01553) 810363 E-mail: sales@cns-systems.co.uk

C R S Cash Registers, Low Sell, Gateshead, Tyne & Wear, NE9 5WY Tel: 0191-491 3530 Fax: 0191-491 3530 E-mail: terence.cullen@talk21.com

Cash Register Services, Eastwood Court, Manor Lane, Hawarden, Deeside, Clwyd, CH5 3QB Tel: (01244) 528998 Fax: (01244) 528998

Cash Register Services London Ltd, Hertford Rdedmonton, London, N9 7ES Tel: (0800) 3580593 Fax: (020) 8443 0446 E-mail: crs5143@aol.com

Cash Register Supply Co., 94-96 Rushmere Road, Ipswich, IP4 4JY Tel: (01473) 723515 Fax: (01473) 405631 E-mail: sales@crs-ipswich.co.uk

Casio Electronics Co. Ltd, 6 1000 North Circular Road, London, NW2 7JD Tel: (020) 8450 9131 Fax: (020) 8452 6323

CCM, 452 Holdenhurst Road, Bournemouth, BH8 9AF Tel: (01202) 302666 Fax: (01202) 302999 E-mail: sales@rakretail.co.uk

▶ CCR, 4 Woodend Street, Stoke-on-Trent, ST4 3JS Tel: (01782) 323601 Fax: (01782) 323626 E-mail: mail@ccrsales.co.uk

▶ Chester Cash Registers, Unit 6 Eastwood Court, Manor Lane, Hawarden, Deeside, Clwyd, CH5 3QB Tel: (01244) 528999 Fax: (01244) 528998 E-mail: cashregisters@fsbdial.co.uk

Classic Cash Register Finance Ltd, Victory Works, Northam Road, Stoke-on-Trent, ST1 6DA Tel: (01782) 283333 Fax: (01782) 204261 E-mail: info@classic-retail.co.uk

Clyde Cash Registers Ltd, 909 Dumbarton Road, Glasgow, G11 6NB Tel: 0141-337 6199 Fax: 0141-337 6199 E-mail: clydecashregisters@hotmail.com

▶ Common Sense Solutions, 12 Mark Road, Hemel Hempstead Industrial Estate, Hemel Hempstead, Hertfordshire, HP2 7BN Tel: (01442) 260586 Fax: (01442) 397884

Consolidated Cash Systems, 28 Springfield Road, Luton, LU3 2HF Tel: (01582) 494946 Fax: (01582) 494946

Database Workshop Ltd, 11b Church Street, Tamworth, Staffordshire, B79 7DH Tel: (01827) 52233 Fax: (01827) 52234 E-mail: alison@dbw.net

Dragon Cash Registers Wales Ltd, 110 High Street, Swansea, SA1 1LZ Tel: (01792) 460168 Fax: (01792) 460493 E-mail: sales@dragon-cashregisters.co.uk

E B Service, 45 Bennett Road, Ipswich, IP1 5HU Tel: (01473) 421370 Fax: (01473) 421370 E-mail: eb.service@ntlworld.com

▶ E C R Concepts, Unit 28, Hirwaun Industrial Estate, Hirwaun, Aberdare, Mid Glamorgan, CF44 9UP Tel: (01685) 810222 Fax: (01685) 810333

E C R Retail Systems Ltd, 297-303 Edgware Road, London, NW9 6NB Tel: (020) 8205 7766 Fax: (020) 8205 1493 E-mail: sales@ecr-systems.co.uk

Exeter Scale & Equipment Co., Grace Road Central, Marsh Barton Trading Estate, Exeter, EX2 8QA Tel: (01392) 275324

Fisher Scales, 11-11a Unit, Station Road Industrial Estate, Attleborough, Norfolk, NR17 2NP Tel: (01953) 450310 Fax: (01953) 456391 E-mail: fisher.scales@virgin.net

Fleet Cash Registers, 3 Henage Cottage, Henage Street, Queensbury, Bradford, West Yorkshire, BD13 2EX Tel: (01274) 880804

Freelance Cash Register Services, 31 Wood Green Road, Oldbury, West Midlands, B68 0DE Tel: 0121-421 3973 Fax: 0121-421 3973

Geller Business Equipment, Unit 14-15, Fairway Drive, Greenford, Middlesex, UB6 8PW Tel: (020) 8839 1000 Fax: (020) 8839 1030 E-mail: info@geller.co.uk

Gold (UK) Scanning Systems Ltd, 12a Pimlico Road, Runcorn, Cheshire, WA7 4US Tel: (01928) 500505 Fax: (01928) 500242 E-mail: golduk@btconnect.com

I K A Retail Solutions Ltd, 2 Hazelwood Lane, London, N13 5EX Tel: (020) 8447 9164 Fax: (020) 8292 9009 E-mail: sales@ikaepos.com

Invicta Retail Systems Ltd, 18-20 Newington Road, Ramsgate, Kent, CT12 6EE Tel: (01843) 586955 Fax: (01843) 850543 E-mail: sales@eposgroup.co.uk

L C R Ltd, 197 Church Street, Blackpool, FY1 3NY Tel: (01253) 628020 Fax: (01253) 621718 E-mail: sales@lcrbpl.co.uk

Lancashire Cash Registers T P Data, 30 The Crescent, Maghull, Liverpool, L31 7BL Tel: 0151-531 6667 Fax: 0151-531 0066

Langley Business Systems Ltd, 29 Junction Street South, Oldbury, West Midlands, B69 4TA Tel: 0121-552 2570 Fax: 0121-511 1317E-mail: sales@lbswholesale.demon.co.uk

Lincoln Equipment Ltd, Cash Register Centre, Moorland Way, Lincoln, LN6 7JW Tel: (01522) 814555 Fax: (01522) 814556 E-mail: enquiries@lsepos.co.uk

Micro-Till Systems, 172 Baddow Road, Chelmsford, CM2 9QW Tel: (01245) 347094 Fax: (01245) 347094

Nationwide Retail Systems Ltd, Lamesley House, Durham Road, Birtley, Chester le Street, County Durham, DH3 1HU Tel: 0191-410 5167 Fax: 0191-410 3833

P C Cash Control Systems, 176 Tynemouth Road, North Shields, Tyne & Wear, NE30 1EG Tel: 0191-257 3738 E-mail: sales@pccash.co.uk

Pennant P B M Ltd, 8 Locarno Avenue, Luton, LU4 9EJ Tel: (01582) 576422 Fax: (01582) 581792 E-mail: pennant@email.com

Positive Solutions Ltd, Solutions House, School Lane, Brinscall, Chorley, Lancashire, PR6 8QP Tel: (01254) 833300 Fax: (01254) 833333

Premier Cash Registers, 20 Orchy Gardens, Clarkston, Glasgow, G76 8ND Tel: 0141-633 1440 Fax: 0141-577 0058

Q-Tron Ltd, The Ross Wing, Redhill Court, Doncaster, South Yorkshire, DN11 9ED Tel: (01302) 311066 Fax: (01302) 311774 E-mail: q-tron@btconnect.com

Rentequip Check Out Services, 8 Popple Way, Stevenage, Hertfordshire, SG1 3TG Tel: (01438) 359852 Fax: (01438) 361910

▶ Retail Asset Management Ltd, Unit 3, 223-225 High St, Epping, Essex, CM16 4BL Tel: (01992) 561101 Fax: (01992) 561050 E-mail: retailasset@aol.com

Romar Cash Registers, 140 Portway, London, E15 3QW Tel: (020) 8472 4157 Fax: (020) 8552 5748 E-mail: info@romar.co.uk

S C R Retail Systems, 2 Kendal Road, Shrewsbury, SY1 4ER Tel: (01743) 441591 Fax: (01743) 468697 E-mail: paperway@tiscali.co.uk

▶ S&S, 69 Cross Lane, Mountsorrel, Loughborough, Leicestershire, LE12 7BU Tel: 0116-210 6007 Fax: 0116-210 6779 E-mail: glensmith002@ntlworld.com

SAL Supplies, 40 Regent Quay, Aberdeen, AB11 5BE Tel: (01224) 574405 Fax: (01224) 212444

Sharp Electronics (UK) Ltd, Sharp House, Thorp Road, Manchester, M40 5BE Tel: 0161-205 2333 Fax: 0161-205 7076

▶ South Yorkshire Cash Registers & Scales, Unit 2 Longacre Way, Holbrook Industrial Estate, Holbrook, Sheffield, S20 3FS Tel: 0114-288 0854 Fax: 0114-247 8777 E-mail: sycr@btconnect.com

Sovereign Business Equipment, Unit 3 Leigh Park, Fulflood Road, Havant, Hampshire, PO9 5AX Tel: (023) 9247 4272 E-mail: sovbus.equip@ntlworld.com

Tiger Information Sytems, Unit 4E, Newton Court, Wavertree Technology Park, Liverpool, L13 1EJ Tel: 0151-252 0600 Fax: 0151-252 0900 E-mail: mail@tiger-sys.com

Till Track, 14 Laughton Avenue, West Bridgford, Nottingham, NG2 7GJ Tel: 0115-923 1065 Fax: 0115-914 7376

▶ Total Epos Solutions, Woodstock Road, Belfast, BT6 9DL Tel: (028) 9046 1166 Fax: (028) 9046 1166

▶ W R S, Systems House, St. Cross Lane, Newport, Isle Of Wight, PO30 5BZ Tel: (01983) 533888 Fax: (01983) 530163 E-mail: sales@wrssystems.co.uk

WCR, 169 Irvine Road, Kilmarnock, Ayrshire, KA1 2LA Tel: (01563) 535962 Fax: (01563) 511337

West Country Cash Registers, 31 Merrivale Road, Beacon Park, Plymouth, PL2 2QG Tel: (01752) 210011 Fax: (01752) 210012

Western Office Equipment, 53 Omaha Road, Walker Lines Industrial Estate, Bodmin, Cornwall, PL31 1ES Tel: (01208) 72042 Fax: (01208) 79642 E-mail: western@office54.fsbusiness.co.uk

Wiltshire & Avon Cash Registers Ltd, 80 West Street, Old Market, St. Philips, Bristol, BS2 0BW Tel: 0117-955 5708 Fax: 0117-954 0904

Y C R Cash Registers, 100 Embankment Road, Plymouth, PL4 9HY Tel: (01752) 251901 Fax: (01752) 600880

CASH SECURITY BAGS

Bond R S C Associates Ltd, Unit 3 Mercy Terrace, Ladywell, London, SE13 7UX Tel: (020) 8314 1188 Fax: (020) 8314 1221 E-mail: info@bondmailrooms.com

Johnson Security Ltd, Orchard Industrial Estate, Toddington, Cheltenham, Gloucestershire, GL54 5EB Tel: (01242) 621362 Fax: (01242) 621554 E-mail: sales@johnson-security.co.uk

Lewis Security Group Ltd, 1 Hanlon Court, Royal Industrial Estate, Jarrow, Tyne & Wear, NE32 3HR Tel: 0191-496 2400 Fax: 0191-496 2401 E-mail: sales@lsgroup.com

CASHMERE

Berk, 46-49 Burlington Arcade, London, W1J 0ET Tel: (020) 7493 0028 Fax: (020) 7499 4312

Bulmer & Lumb Group Ltd, Albert Street, Lockwood, Huddersfield, HD1 3PE Tel: (01484) 423231 Fax: (01484) 435313 E-mail: headoffice@taylor-and-lodge.co.uk

H Dawson Sons & Co (Wool) Ltd, Mercury House, Essex St, Bradford, West Yorkshire, BD4 7PG Tel: (01274) 727464 Fax: (01274) 723326 E-mail: info@h-dawson-wool.com

Harper- Little Ltd, 50 Brunswick Square, Hove, East Sussex, BN3 1EF Tel: (020) 7993 4087 Fax: (0870) 6220607

▶ Paint Box Textiles, 16 Valley Road, Liversedge, West Yorkshire, WF15 6JY Tel: (01924) 235123 Fax: (01924) 235223 E-mail: sales@paintboxtextiles.co.uk

▶ Wool Duvets, Jasmine House, Saxlingham Road, Blakeney, Holt, Norfolk, NR25 7PB Tel: (01263) 741799 E-mail: enquiries@woolduvets.co.uk

Woolexpo Ltd, 19 Bruton Place, London, W1J 6LZ Tel: (020) 8274 0565 Fax: (020) 7629 2513 E-mail: chris@woolexpo.biz

CASING AND TUBING SERVICES

B J Tubular Services, Hareness Circle, Altens Industrial Estate, Aberdeen, AB12 3LY Tel: (01224) 249678 Fax: (01224) 249106 E-mail: jbaglee@bjservices.co.uk

Franks International Ltd, Unit 1 Bessemer Way, Great Yarmouth, Norfolk, NR31 0LX Tel: (01493) 443044 Fax: (01493) 443055 E-mail: email.barrywoodhouse@franks.co.uk

Vallourec Mannesmann Oil & Gas UK Ltd, 4 Prospect Place, Westhill, Aberdeenshire, AB32 6SY Tel: (01224) 279340 Fax: (01224) 279341 E-mail: info@vmog.co.uk

CASING CONNECTORS

Franks International Ltd, Unit 1 Bessemer Way, Great Yarmouth, Norfolk, NR31 0LX Tel: (01493) 443044 Fax: (01493) 443055 E-mail: email.barrywoodhouse@franks.co.uk

CASING PROTECTORS

M S I Oilfield Products, Units 5-6 Murcar Industrial Estate, Denmore Road, Bridge of Don, Aberdeen, AB23 8JW Tel: (01224) 708011 Fax: (01224) 708022 E-mail: bherd@msiproducts.com

CASINO GAME TABLES

▶ Galaxy Casino, Highfield Road, Kettering, Northamptonshire, NN15 6HT Tel: (01536) 000000 E-mail: caleb158@hotmail.co.uk

CASSETTE AIR CONDITIONING (AC) EQUIPMENT

Panasonic Air Conditioning, Panasonic House, Willoughby Road, Bracknell, Berkshire, RG12 8FP Tel: (01344) 853186 Fax: (01344) 853217 E-mail: nicky.dopson@panasonic.co.uk

CASSETTE CASES, TYPEWRITER RIBBON ETC

KO-REC-TYPE, Unit 4, Beta House, Orchard Industrial Estate, Toddington, Cheltenham, Gloucestershire, GL54 5EB E-mail: sales@korectype.co.uk

CASSETTE CASES, VIDEO

De Luxe Media Services Ltd, Phoenix Park, Great West Road, Brentford, Middlesex, TW8 9PL Tel: (020) 8232 7600 Fax: (020) 8232 7601

Piper Media Products, Unit G Bastre Enterprise Park, Newtown, Powys, SY16 1DZ Tel: (01686) 610640 Fax: (01686) 610660

Quality Plastics Supplies Ltd, Unit C 2 Endeavour Way, London, SW19 8UH Tel: (020) 8946 8388 Fax: (020) 8947 8909 E-mail: sales@qualityplastics.co.uk

▶ Vision Warehouse, Unit 35 Stadium Business Centre, North End Road, Wembley, Middlesex, HA9 0AT Tel: (020) 8903 8185 Fax: (020) 8903 8566 E-mail: info@visionuk.co.uk

CASSETTE DIGITAL RECORDERS

Avalon Electronics Ltd, Langhorne Park House, High Street, Shepton Mallet, Somerset, BA4 5AQ Tel: (01749) 345266 Fax: (01749) 345267 E-mail: info@avalon-electronics.com

CASSETTES, AUDIO/ CAMCORDER/VIDEO

Protech Ltd, 4 Nuffield Road, St. Ives, Cambridgeshire, PE27 3LX Tel: (01325) 310520 Fax: (01480) 300670 E-mail: sales@pro-tech-ltd.co.uk

CAST IRON

Ambassador Marketing, 6 G Belgic Square, Peterborough, PE1 5XF Tel: (01733) 563275 Fax: (01733) 63275

Penclawdd Forge, Station Square, Penclawdd, Swansea, SA4 3XT Tel: (01792) 850124 Fax: (01792) 416267

CAST IRON ACCESS COVERS OR GRATING

ElkinTatic, Hammond House, Holmestone Road, Poulton Close, Dover, Kent, CT17 0UF Tel: (01304) 203545 Fax: (01304) 215001 E-mail: acp@gaticdover.co.uk

Slinden Services, 3 Riverside Court, Westminster Industrial Estate, Measham, Swadlincote, Derbyshire, DE12 7DS Tel: (01530) 274646 Fax: (01530) 274647 E-mail: info@slindenservices.co.uk

CAST IRON BAR MANUFRS

Arrow Butler Castings Ltd, Station Road, Whittington Moor, Chesterfield, Derbyshire, S41 9ES Tel: (01246) 450027 Fax: (01246) 261913 E-mail: sales@arrowbutlercastings.co.uk

Corus Service Centre, Unit 4 Symondscliffe Way, Portskewett, Caldicot, Gwent, NP26 5PW Tel: (01291) 421732 Fax: (01291) 425085

Hydraulic Supplies Ltd, Unit 5-6 Block 2, Wednesbury Trading Estate, Wednesbury, West Midlands, WS10 7JN Tel: 0121-505 3663 Fax: 0121-505 3375 E-mail: sales@hydraulicsupplies.co.uk

U C B Starkeys Technicast Ltd, 45 Kingston Way, Stockholm Road, Hull, HU7 0XW Tel: (01482) 825203 Fax: (01482) 878094 E-mail: enquiries@bi-group.com

CAST IRON DRAIN OR SANITARY PIPES

Alumasc Exterior Building Products, White House Works, Bold Road, Sutton, St. Helens, Merseyside, WA9 4JG Tel: 01744 648400 Fax: 01744 648401 E-mail: info@alumasc-exteriors.co.uk

Hargreaves Foundry Drainage Ltd, Carr House, Water Lane, Halifax, West Yorkshire, HX3 9HG Tel: (01422) 330607 Fax: (01422) 320349 E-mail: sales@hargreavesfoundry.co.uk

CAST IRON FIRE GRATES

Davies Bros (Metal Finishers), 123-127 Western Road, Hockley, Birmingham, B18 7QD Tel: 0121-554 3148 Fax: 0121-554 3148 E-mail: sales@british-fireside.co.uk

▶ indicates data change since last edition

CAST IRON GUTTERS

▶ The Salvage Doctor, Rowhurst Forge, Oxshott Road, Leatherhead, Surrey, KT22 0EN Tel: (01372) 360 191 Fax: (01372) 360 171 E-mail: info@salvagedoctor.com

CAST IRON MANHOLE COVERS OR FRAMES

Durey Castings Ltd, Shell Garage, Hawley Road, Dartford, DA1 1PU Tel: (01322) 272424 Fax: (01322) 288073 E-mail: sales@dureycastings.co.uk
Salmor Group Ltd, 150 Valley Money Rd, Banbridge, Co. Down, BT32 4HW Tel: (028) 4066 2999 Fax: (028) 4066 2298
Peter Savage Ltd, Liberty House, Liberty Way, Attleborough Fields Ind Estate, Nuneaton, Warwickshire, CV11 6RZ Tel: (024) 7664 1777 Fax: (024) 7637 5250 E-mail: sales@peter-savage.co.uk

CAST IRON PIPE AND TUBE FITTINGS

The Cast Iron Company Ltd, 8 Old Lodge Place, Twickenham, TW1 1RQ Tel: (020) 8744 9992 Fax: (020) 8744 1121 E-mail: info@castiron.co.uk

CAST IRON PLATING SERVICES

Alban Engineering Services Ltd, Wood Street Passage, Wood Street, Kettering, Northamptonshire, NN16 9SQ Tel: (01536) 513225 Fax: (01536) 513225
Miller Plating Co., Unit 15 All Saints Industrial Estate, All Saints Street, Birmingham, B18 7RJ Tel: 0121-523 3348 Fax: 0121-515 3187

CAST IRON RAINWATER GOODS

J.W.D. Rainwater Systems Ltd, Captain Clarke Road, Broadway Industrial Estate, Hyde, Stockport, Cheshire, SK1 4QG Tel: 0161-351 9990 Fax: 0161-351 9992 E-mail: info@rainwatergoods.co.uk
N R S Ltd, 14 Lysander Road, Bowerhill, Melksham, Wiltshire, SN12 6SP Tel: (01225) 709408 Fax: (01225) 708719 E-mail: info@n-rs.co.uk

CAST IRON STOVES

▶ Cast Iron Fires.Com, Grove Mill, Commerce Street, Carrs Industrial Estate, Haslingden, Lancashire, BB4 5JT Tel: 0845 230 1991 E-mail: enquiries@castironfires.com
▶ Ecoflue Ltd, Copperfields, Beach Road, Kessingland, Lowestoft, Suffolk, NR33 7RW Tel: (01502) 741388 Fax: 07900 606241 E-mail: blojus@aol.com
▶ Stovesonline Ltd, Box and Rose Cottage, Capton, Dartmouth, Devon, TQ6 0JE Tel: 0845 226 5754 Fax: 0870 220 0920 E-mail: info@stovesonline.co.uk

CAST IRON WELDING

Ace Welding (Edensbridge), Merle Common Road, Oxted, Surrey, RH8 0RP Tel: (01883) 712668 Fax: (01883) 717524
Anvil Iron Crafts, The Forge, Gittisham, Honiton, Devon, EX14 3AR Tel: (01404) 42510 Fax: (01404) 42510
Hart Brothers Engineering Ltd, Sothall Works, Sothall, Oldham, OL4 2AD Tel: 0161-737 6791 Fax: 0161-633 5316 E-mail: xk220@aol.com

CAST IRON, GREY

College Engineering Supply, 2 Sandy Lane, Codsall, Wolverhampton, WV8 1EJ Tel: (01902) 842284 Fax: (01902) 842284 E-mail: enquiries@collegeengineering.co.uk

CAST METAL NAMEPLATES

Leander Architectural, Hallsteads Close, Dove Holes, Buxton, Derbyshire, SK17 8BP Tel: (01298) 814941 Fax: (01298) 814970 E-mail: sales@1eanderarch.demon.co.uk

CAST METAL SIGNS

Leander Architectural, Hallsteads Close, Dove Holes, Buxton, Derbyshire, SK17 8BP Tel: (01298) 814941 Fax: (01298) 814970 E-mail: sales@1eanderarch.demon.co.uk
R C H Signs, Unit 18 Marian Mawr Industrial Estate, Dolgellau, Gwynedd, LL40 1UU Tel: (01341) 423577 Fax: (01341) 422646 E-mail: sales@rchsigns.com
Sign-Maker.Net, Little Knowle Farm, High Bickington, Umberleigh, Devon, EX37 9BJ Tel: (01769) 560675 Fax: (01769) 560819 E-mail: enquiries@sign-maker.net

CAST NYLON PRODUCTS

Devol Engineering Ltd, 13 Clarence Street, Greenock, Renfrewshire, PA15 1LR Tel: (01475) 720934 Fax: (01475) 787873 E-mail: sales@devol.com
Westley Plastics Ltd, Gawne Lane, Cradley Heath, West Midlands, B64 5QY Tel: (01384) 414840 Fax: (01384) 414849 E-mail: sales@plastics.co.uk

CAST RESIN TRANSFORMERS

A F Switchgear & Control Panels Ltd, Nunn Brook Road, Huthwaite, Sutton-in-Ashfield, Nottinghamshire, NG17 2HU Tel: (01623) 555600 Fax: (01623) 555800 E-mail: e-mail@afswitchgear.co.uk
Hawker Siddeley Switchgear Ltd, Newport Road, Pontllanfraith, Blackwood, Gwent, NP12 2XH Tel: (01495) 223001 Fax: (01495) 225674 E-mail: sales@hss-ltd.com

CAST STEEL ROLLMAKERS

Akers UK Ltd, Suite 14, Shire Hall Complex, Pentonville, Newport, Gwent, NP20 5HB Tel: (01633) 265544 E-mail: sales@akersuk.com
The Davy Roll Co. Ltd, P O Box 21, Gateshead, Tyne & Wear, NE8 3DX Tel: 0191-477 1261 Fax: 0191-477 8096 E-mail: enquiries@davyroll.co.uk
Rola Cylinder Manufacturers Ltd, Porritt Street, Bury, Lancashire, BL9 6HJ Tel: 0161-761 3913 Fax: 0161-762 9281
Tomah Engineers Ltd, 104 Fitzwalter Rd., Sheffield, S2 2SP Tel: 0114-272 1199 Fax: 0114-276 8675 E-mail: tomaheng@aol.com

CAST STEEL VALVES

Bells Engineering Products Ltd, 874 Plymouth Road, Slough, SL1 4LP Tel: (01753) 567788 Fax: (01753) 567799 E-mail: bells.engineering@virgin.net
Capital Valves Ltd, Wembley Point, Harrow Road, Wembley, Middlesex, HA9 6DE Tel: (020) 8900 0471 Fax: (020) 8900 0808 E-mail: sales@capitalvalves.co.uk
Valvelink UK Ltd, 17 Cotswold Green, Stonehouse, Gloucestershire, GL10 2ES Tel: (01453) 822222 Fax: (01453) 821111

CASTING CONSULTANTS/ RESEARCH

Castings Technology International, Waverley Advance Manufacturing Park, Brunel Way, Rotherham, South Yorkshire, S60 5WG Tel: 0114-272 8647 Fax: 0114-273 0852 E-mail: info@castingstechnology.com
Engineering & Developments Lymington Ltd, Gosport Street, Lymington, Hampshire, SO41 9BB Tel: (01590) 673729 Fax: (01590) 675778 E-mail: sales@engdev.co.uk
J. & D. Hunt, Whitegate House, 77 Scott Street, Burnley, Lancashire, BB12 6NJ Tel: (01282) 772745 Fax: (01282) 772745 E-mail: huntcast@btconnect.com

CASTING EQUIPMENT, INVESTMENT/LOST FOAM PROCESS

Vulcan Europe, 9 New Star Road, Leicester, LE4 9JD Tel: 0116-246 0055 Fax: 0116-246 1142 E-mail: sales@vulcaneurope.com

CASTING HEAT TREATMENT

Alloy Heat Treatment, Block 6 Grazebrook Industrial Park, Peartree Lane, Dudley, West Midlands, DY2 0XW Tel: (01384) 456777 Fax: (01384) 453900 E-mail: sales@alloyheat.co.uk

CASTING (INVESTMENT) TOOLING

D G T Precision Engineering, 9C, Corbin Way, Gore Cross Business Park, Bridpole, Bridport, Dorset, DT6 3UX Tel: (01308) 420024 Fax: (01308) 424007 E-mail: info@dgtpreceng.co.uk
Investment Castings Congleton Ltd, Greenfield Farm Industrial Estate, Congleton, Cheshire, CW12 4TR Tel: (01260) 280181 Fax: (01260) 298208 E-mail: info@investment-castings.co.uk
Tarpey-Harris Ltd, Flamstead House, Denby Hall Business Park, Denby, Ripley, Derbyshire, DE5 8NN Tel: (01332) 883950 Fax: (01332) 883951 E-mail: steve.jones@tarpey-harris.co.uk

CASTING MACHINISTS

Bowater Cordell Ltd, Dukesway, Teesside Industrial Estate, Thornaby, Stockton-On-Tees, Cleveland, TS17 9LT Tel: (01642) 750303 Fax: (01642) 750164 E-mail: bowater@cordellgroup.com
Brockmoor Foundry, The Leys, Brierley Hill, West Midlands, DY5 3UJ Tel: (01384) 480026 Fax: (01384) 480032 E-mail: sales@brockmoor.co.uk
Castech (UK) Ltd, Unit 10 Manor Farm, Main Road, Newport Pagnell, Buckinghamshire, MK16 9JS Tel: 01234 391973 Fax: 01234 391185 E-mail: info@castech.co.uk
George Taylor & Co (Hamilton) Ltd, Kemp St, Hamilton, Lanarkshire, ML3 6PQ Tel: (01698) 284949 Fax: (01698) 891285 E-mail: office@gtham.co.uk
Slater Yendall Ltd, Howard Road, Park Farm North, Redditch, Worcestershire, B98 7SE Tel: (01527) 529069 Fax: (01527) 510359

CASTING (PRECISION) SOLUTION

Morrison Hydraulics Ltd, 331-337 Derby Road, Bootle, Merseyside, L20 8LQ Tel: 0151-933 0044 Fax: 0151-944 1302 E-mail: chemicals@morrisonsgrp.co.uk

CASTING REPAIR/ RECLAMATION/RESTORATION SERVICES

Barr & Grosvenor Ltd, Jenner Street, Wolverhampton, WV2 2AE Tel: (01902) 352390 Fax: (01902) 871342 E-mail: sales@bargrosvenorwannado.co.uk
Cast Iron Welding Service Ltd, 2 Samson Road, Hermitage Industrial Estate, Coalville, Leicestershire, LE67 3FP Tel: (01530) 811308 Fax: (01530) 835724 E-mail: sales@castironwelding.co.uk
Cast Metal Repairs Ltd, High Street Mills, High St, Heckmondwike, W. Yorkshire, WF16 0DL Tel: (01924) 403444 Fax: (01924) 410164 E-mail: tranter@rhodesengineering.co.uk
Casting Repairs Ltd, Hipper St South, Chesterfield, Derbyshire, S40 1SS Tel: (01246) 246700 Fax: (01246) 206519 E-mail: andrea.peck@casting-repairs.co.uk
Dukerswell Engineers Ltd, 52 Buckland Road, Maidstone, Kent, ME16 0SH Tel: (01622) 757710 Fax: (01622) 755516 E-mail: dukerswell@skynow.net
Furniss & White Foundries Ltd, Unit 17 Abbey Way, North Anston Trading Estate, North Anston, Sheffield, S25 4JL Tel: (01909) 568831 Fax: (01909) 569322 E-mail: upgrading@f-w-f.co.uk
GNT Engineering, Golden Triangle Industrial Estate, Harrison Street, Widnes, Cheshire, WA8 8TN Tel: 0151-420 3420 Fax: 0151-423 1579 E-mail: geoff@gntfab.fsnet.co.uk
Hallcalm UK, Redworth Street, Hartlepool, Cleveland, TS24 7LG Tel: (01429) 891011 Fax: (01429) 236746 E-mail: engineering@hallcalm.co.uk
Hart Brothers Engineering Ltd, Sothall Works, Sothall, Oldham, OL4 2AD Tel: 0161-737 6791 Fax: 0161-633 5316 E-mail: xk220@aol.com
Metal Stitching Services Ltd, The Old Court Yard, Warwick Street, Prestwich, Manchester, M25 3HN Tel: 0161-773 6919 Fax: 0161-798 7352
Metalock Engineering, Hamilton, Glasgow, Tel: 0141-641 3368 E-mail: sales@metalock.co.uk
Metalock Engineering UK Ltd, Paragon Way, Bayton Road Industrial Estate, Coventry, CV7 9QS Tel: (01322) 290090 Fax: (01322) 290088 E-mail: sales@metalock.co.uk
Surelock Casting Repairs, Unit 3, Pillings Road Industrial Estate, Oakham, Leicestershire, LE15 6QF Tel: (01572) 722051 Fax: (01572) 722051 E-mail: surelock@onetel.com

CASTINGS, *See also headings for particular types under Castings*

Aeromet International plc, Eurolink Industrial Centre, Castle Road, Sittingbourne, Kent, ME10 3RN Tel: (01795) 415000 Fax: (01795) 415015 E-mail: andrew.king@aeromet.co.uk
Alpha Pattern Co., Grove Road, Northfleet, Gravesend, Kent, DA11 9AX Tel: (01474) 568669 Fax: (01474) 568669
▶ B A S Castings Ltd, Wharf Road Industrial Estate, Pinxton, Nottingham, NG16 6LE Tel: (01773) 812028 Fax: (01773) 861948 E-mail: sales@bascastings.com
Brockmoor Foundry, The Leys, Brierley Hill, West Midlands, DY5 3UJ Tel: (01384) 480026 Fax: (01384) 480032 E-mail: sales@brockmoor.co.uk
Chamberlin & Hill plc, Chuckery Foundary, Chuckery Road, Walsall, WS1 2DU Tel: (01922) 492000 Fax: (01922) 638370 E-mail: plc@chamberlin.co.uk
Ecu Castings, Claytons Meadow, Bourne End, Buckinghamshire, SL8 5DQ Tel: (01628) 524672 Fax: (01628) 850914 E-mail: robinecu@aol.com
George Taylor & Co (Hamilton) Ltd, Kemp St, Hamilton, Lanarkshire, ML3 6PQ Tel: (01698) 284949 Fax: (01698) 891285 E-mail: office@gtham.co.uk
Intergrated Casting Technology, 5 Portersfield Road, Cradley Heath, West Midlands, B64 7BN Tel: (01384) 413678 Fax: (01384) 413660 E-mail: sales@wood-loines.com
▶ Investment Castings Ltd, 130 Great North Road, Birchwood Industrial Estate, Hatfield, Hertfordshire, AL9 5JN Tel: (01707) 262871 Fax: (01707) 271565 E-mail: investmentcastings130@yahoo.co.uk
Lakeland Mouldings, Soulby, Penrith, Cumbria, CA11 0JE Tel: (01768) 486989 Fax: (01768) 486989 E-mail: ann@lakelandmouldings.co.uk
M F C Patterns & Castings, Unit 6 Broomhouse Lane, Edlington, Doncaster, South Yorkshire, DN12 1ET Tel: (01709) 864305
Robinson Pattern Equipment Ltd, Rabone Lane, Smethwick, West Midlands, B66 3JH Tel: 0121-558 4576 Fax: 0121-555 5295 E-mail: sales@robpatequip.demon.co.uk
S.J.S. Engineering, 114-116 Newhall Street, Willenhall, West Midlands, WV13 1LQ Tel: (01902) 606602 Fax: (01902) 606011
▶ Sabar UK Ltd, 17 Duckworth Street, Darwen, Lancashire, BB3 1AR Tel: (01254) 702456 Fax: (01254) 702456 E-mail: sabaruk@ntlworld.com
Vanguard Foundry Ltd, Bott Lane, Lye, Stourbridge, West Midlands, DY9 7AW Tel: (01384) 422557 Fax: (01384) 423338 E-mail: jwilletts@vanguargfoundry.co.uk
▶ William Cook Holbrook Precision Ltd, Station Road, Halfway, Sheffield, S20 3GD Tel: 0114-251 0410 Fax: 0114-251 0096 E-mail: admin@william-cook.co.uk
William Hunter & Sons (Ironfounders) Ltd, Halton House, Millrigg Road, Wiston, Biggar, Lanarkshire, ML12 6HT Tel: (01899) 850500 Fax: (01899) 850566

CASTINGS TO SPECIFICATION

Hampton Cast Stone, Unit 7, Merretts Mill, Woodchester, Stroud, Gloucestershire, GL5 5EU Tel: (01453) 836677 Fax: (01453) 835005E-mail: sales@hamptoncastsone.co.uk
▶ William Cook Holbrook Precision Ltd, Station Road, Halfway, Sheffield, S20 3GD Tel: 0114-251 0410 Fax: 0114-251 0096 E-mail: admin@william-cook.co.uk

CASTINGS, ABRASION/ CORROSION/WEAR RESISTING ALLOY

Brafe Engineering Ltd, Grundisburgh Road, Woodbridge, Suffolk, IP13 6HX Tel: (01394) 380000 Fax: (01394) 380300 E-mail: sclarke@brafe.com
T H Dick & Co Ltd, Church Row, Cleveland St, Hull, HU8 7BD Tel: (01482) 329652 Fax: (01482) 589986E-mail: info@thdick.co.uk
Wearparts UK Ltd, Oaks Industrial Estate, Gilmorton Road, Lutterworth, Leicestershire, LE17 4HA Tel: (01455) 553551 Fax: (01455) 550907 E-mail: sales@wearparts.com

CASTINGS, ALUMINIUM/ALLOY

A D & C Ltd, 80 Wrentham Street, Birmingham, B5 6QL Tel: 0121-666 6070 Fax: 0121-666 7585 E-mail: davidaustin@btconnect.com
Alpac Alloys Holdings Ltd, Dale Street, Burton-on-Trent, Staffordshire, DE14 3TE Tel: (01283) 567737 Fax: (01283) 512359 E-mail: peter@alpacgroup.com
Alucast Ltd, Western Way, Wednesbury, West Midlands, WS10 7BW Tel: 0121-556 6111 Fax: 0121-505 1302 E-mail: sales@alucast.co.uk
The Alumasc Group Plc, Station Road, Burton Latimer, Kettering, Northamptonshire, NN15 5JP Tel: (01536) 383848 Fax: (01536) 723835 E-mail: info@alumascprecision.co.uk
Aluminium Products Ltd, Alpro Foundry, Haines Street, West Bromwich, West Midlands, B70 7DA Tel: 0121-553 1911 Fax: 0121-500 5796 E-mail: alpro@compuserve.com
Aluminium Service Co. (Warwick) Ltd, Millers Road, Warwick, CV34 5AE Tel: (01926) 491824 Fax: (01926) 410072
Archway Brown Ltd, 43 Bury Mead Road, Hitchin, Hertfordshire, SG5 1RT Tel: (01462) 432139 Fax: (01462) 420102
Arrow Butler Castings Ltd, Station Road, Whittington Moor, Chesterfield, Derbyshire, S41 9ES Tel: (01246) 450027 Fax: (01246) 261913 E-mail: sales@arrowbutlercastings.co.uk
Barton Aluminium Foundries, Rayboulds Bridge Rd, Walsall, WS2 8PG Tel: (01922) 637551 Fax: (01922) 644481 E-mail: sales@barton-aluminium.co.uk
Brad Ken Uk Ltd, Heath Road, Wednesbury, West Midlands, WS10 8JL Tel: 0121-526 4111 Fax: 0121-526 4174

CASTINGS, ALUMINIUM/ALLOY – continued

British Engines Ltd, St Peters, Newcastle upon Tyne, NE6 1BS Tel: 0191-265 9091 Fax: 0191-276 3244 E-mail: sales@bel.co.uk

Brooks Crownhill Patternmakers Ltd, North Way, Andover, Hampshire, SP10 5AZ Tel: (01264) 355136 Fax: (01264) 332145 E-mail: info@bcplimited.co.uk

C & J Castings, 42 Bayton Road, Exhall, Coventry, CV7 9EJ Tel: (024) 7636 3031 Fax: (024) 7636 3556 E-mail: clive@42baytonroad.freeserve.co.uk

Caddy Castings Ltd, Springfield Road, Grantham, Lincolnshire, NG31 7BQ Tel: (01476) 566667 Fax: (01476) 570220 E-mail: caddycastings@btinternet.com

Cannop Foundry 1981 Ltd, Forest Vale Indust Estate, Crabtree Road, Forest Vale Industrial Estate, Cinderford, Gloucestershire, GL14 2YQ Tel: (01594) 822143 Fax: (01594) 824200 E-mail: sales@cannop.co.uk

Charter Castings Ltd, Bagnall Street, Great Bridge, Tipton, West Midlands, DY4 7BS Tel: 0121-557 9831 Fax: 0121-520 4761 E-mail: mail@chartercastings.co.uk

Darlaston Diecast Alloys Ltd, Ashmore Lake Way, Willenhall, West Midlands, WV12 4LF Tel: (01902) 606436 Fax: (01902) 609405 E-mail: darlastondiecast@btconnect.com

David Hunt Castings, Romsey Industrial Estate, Budds La, Romsey, Hants, SO51 0HA Tel: (01794) 511259 Fax: (01794) 518325 E-mail: davidhunt.castings@btopenworld.com

Derbyshire Castings Ltd, Churchill Road, Altrincham, Cheshire, WA14 5LT Tel: 0161-928 1764 Fax: 0161-927 7623 E-mail: roger@derbyshirecastings.com

Draycast Foundries Ltd, Bellingdon Road, Chesham, Buckinghamshire, HP5 2NR Tel: (01494) 786077 Fax: (01494) 791337 E-mail: sales@draycast.co.uk

Ecu Castings, Claytons Meadow, Bourne End, Buckinghamshire, SL8 5DQ Tel: (01628) 524672 Fax: (01628) 850914 E-mail: robinecu@aol.com

Feldaroll Foundry Ltd, Units 14-21A, Bailie Gate Industrial Estate, Sturminster Marshall, Wimborne, Dorset, BH21 4DB Tel: (01258) 857754 Fax: (01258) 857353

Glen Castings Ltd, Meadows Mill, Burnley Road, Bacup, Lancashire, OL13 8BZ Tel: (01706) 873967 Fax: (01706) 879234 E-mail: glencas@lancs.co.uk

Grainger & Worrall Ltd, Unit 1-4 Stanmore Industrial Estate, Bridgnorth, Shropshire, WV15 5HP Tel: (01746) 768250 Fax: (01746) 768251 E-mail: sales@gwcast.co.uk

Harrison Castings Ltd, Gough Road, Leicester, LE5 4AP Tel: 0116-276 9351 Fax: 0116-246 0199 E-mail: contacts@harrisoncastings.com

Hemphill Castings Ltd, 273 Bromford Lane, Washwood Heath, Birmingham, B8 2SG Tel: 0121-327 5459 Fax: 0121-322 2040

Hockley Pattern & Tool Company Ltd, Lodgefield Road, Halesowen, West Midlands, B62 8AR Tel: 0121-561 4665 Fax: 0121-525 0595 E-mail: sales@hockleypattern.co.uk

I S C Ltd, Deiniolen, Caernarfon, Gwynedd, LL55 3DE Tel: (01286) 871999 Fax: (01286) 870127 E-mail: sales@iscwales.com

Ideal Sand & Die Casting Co., Unit 5, New Field Industrial Estate, High St, Stoke-on-Trent, ST6 5PB Tel: (01782) 818866 Fax: (01782) 836750 E-mail: sales@idealcasting.co.uk

J I Blackburn Foundry Ltd, Grove Works, West Road, Bridport, Dorset, DT6 5JT Tel: (01308) 459040 Fax: (01308) 459040

J T Hickinbottom Dudley Ltd, Unit 22 Thornleigh, Trading Estate, Dudley, West Midlands, DY2 8UB Tel: (01384) 234468 Fax: (01384) 254075 E-mail: jthickinbottom.dudley@zoom.co.uk

Keith Prosser, Unit 22 Victoria Business Centre, Victoria Street, Accrington, Lancashire, BB5 0PJ Tel: (01254) 384898 Fax: (01254) 384898 E-mail: kpcast@prosser.fslife.co.uk

L E W Diecastings Ltd, Trows Lane, Rochdale, Lancashire, OL11 2UF Tel: (01706) 632218 Fax: (01706) 638473 E-mail: alan@lew.co.uk

Lectroheat Industrial Heating Ltd, Unit 16 Pantglas Industrial Estate, Bedwas, Caerphilly, Mid Glamorgan, CF83 8DR Tel: (029) 2088 9300 Fax: (029) 2086 1872 E-mail: info@lectroheat.com

Lestercast Ltd, 14-16 Ireton Avenue, Leicester, LE4 9EU Tel: 0116-276 7284 Fax: 0116-246 0401 E-mail: sales@lestercast.co.uk

Longton Light Alloys Ltd, Foxley Lane, Stoke-on-Trent, ST2 7EH Tel: (01782) 536615 Fax: (01782) 533415 E-mail: info@aluminium-castings.com

Maybrey Reliance, Worsley Bridge Road, Lower Sydenham, London, SE26 5BE Tel: (01322) 315370 Fax: (01322) 550724 E-mail: sales@maybrey.co.uk

Maycast Nokes Precision Engineering Ltd, Factory La West, Halstead, Essex, CO9 1EX Tel: (01787) 472500 Fax: (01787) 474264 E-mail: enquiries@maycast.co.uk

Metal Castings Ltd, Droitwich Road, Worcester, WR3 7JX Tel: (01905) 754400 Fax: (01905) 754347 E-mail: sales@metalcastingsltd.com

Monkman Brass Founders, 3 Broom Street, Bradford, West Yorkshire, BD4 7AP Tel: (01274) 732117 Fax: (01274) 732117

Penhall Ltd, 9 Enterprise Court, Newton Close, Park Farm Industrial Estate, Wellingborough, Northamptonshire, NN8 6UW Tel: (01933) 678851 Fax: (01933) 674204

Perry Castings, Bank Street, Wolverhampton, WV10 9DU Tel: (01902) 732910 Fax: (01902) 721046

Polycast Ltd, Clocktower Buildings, Shore Road, Warsash, Southampton, SO31 9GQ Tel: (01489) 885560 Fax: (01489) 885608 E-mail: sales@polycast.ltd.uk

Premiere Castings Ltd, The Old Foundry, Green Street, Oldham, OL8 1TA Tel: 0161-620 6605 Fax: 0161-678 6552 E-mail: premier.castings@btconnect.com

Procast Components Ltd, Unit 3 Cadwell Lane, Hitchin, Hertfordshire, SG4 0SA Tel: (01462) 441442 Fax: (01462) 436265 E-mail: procast@btclick.com

Pump International Ltd, Trevool, Praze, Camborne, Cornwall, TR14 0PJ Tel: (01209) 831937 Fax: (01209) 831939 E-mail: sales@pumpinternational.com

Quality Castings Slough Ltd, Northern Way, Bury St. Edmunds, Suffolk, IP32 6NW Tel: (01284) 755941 Fax: (01284) 761770 E-mail: sales@qualitycastings.co.uk

R M J Alloys Ltd, 48 Bayton Road, Exhall, Coventry, CV7 9EJ Tel: (024) 7636 7508 Fax: (024) 7636 0280 E-mail: sales@rmjalloys.co.uk

Rolls-Royce P.L.C., PO Box 31, Derby, DE24 8BJ Tel: (01332) 240642 Fax: (01332) 240604

Roston Castings, Mill Lane, Ellastone, Ashbourne, Derbyshire, DE6 2HF Tel: (01335) 324368 Fax: (01335) 324544 E-mail: sales@rostoncastings.co.uk

Sant Products Ltd, Unit 42 Coneygre Industrial Estate, Tipton, West Midlands, DY4 8XP Tel: 0121-557 7066 Fax: 0121-557 2007

Surecoat Powder Coatings, Unit 13 Bolton Textile Mill, Cawdor Street, Farnworth, Bolton, BL4 7EA Tel: (01204) 793339 Fax: (01204) 793339

Thurton Foundries Ltd, Loddon Rd, Thurton, Norwich, NR14 6AN Tel: (01508) 480301 Fax: (01508) 480303 E-mail: sales@thurtonfoundries.co.uk

Tritech Alkast, Castle Park Road, Whiddon Valley Industrial Esta, Barnstaple, Devon, EX32 8PA Tel: (01271) 376521 Fax: (01271) 326155 E-mail:

Truscanian Ltd, St. Martins Industrial Estate, Engine Street, Oldbury, West Midlands, B69 4NL Tel: 0121-552 3011 Fax: 0121-552 4672

▶ Ulster Castings Ltd, 2-4 Bridge St, Comber, Newtownards, County Down, BT23 5AT Tel: (028) 9187 2372 Fax: (028) 9187 0088 E-mail: jneedham@ulstercastings.com

W H Rowe & Son Ltd, Quayside Road, Southampton, SO18 1DH Tel: (023) 8022 5636 Fax: (023) 8022 5146 E-mail: sales@whrowe.com

West Midlands Foundry Co. Ltd, Blakemore Road, West Bromwich, West Midlands, B70 8JF Tel: 0121-553 1515 Fax: 0121-500 5839

Westland Casting Co. Ltd, 4-5 Vaux Road, Finedon Road Industrial Estate, Wellingborough, Northamptonshire, NN8 4TG Tel: (01933) 276718 Fax: (01933) 442185 E-mail: info@westlandcastings.co.uk

White Eagle Foundry Ltd, 199 Cuckfield Road, Hurstpierpoint, Hassocks, West Sussex, BN6 9RT Tel: (01273) 832062 Fax: (01273) 833628 E-mail: wef@wef.co.uk

Zeus Pattern & Tool Co. Ltd, Sunrise Business Park, High Street Wooliston, Stourbridge, West Midlands, DY8 4ZZ Tel: (01384) 482222 Fax: (01384) 446446

CASTINGS, ALUMINIUM/ALLOY, PRESSURE

The Alumasc Group Plc, Station Road, Burton Latimer, Kettering, Northamptonshire, NN15 5JP Tel: (01536) 383848 Fax: (01536) 723835 E-mail: info@alumascprecision.co.uk

CASTINGS, BRONZE, FINE ART

▶ Sarah Bardsley Contemporary Artist, Church Fields, Nutley, Uckfield, East Sussex, TN22 3NA Tel: (07884) 495007 E-mail: info@artbyslb.co.uk

▶ Callaghan Fine Paintings, 22 St. Marys Street, Shrewsbury, SY1 1ED Tel: (01743) 343452 E-mail: art@callaghan-finepaintings.com

▶ Evergreen Gallery, 12 Sheaf Street, Daventry, Northamptonshire, NN11 4AB Tel: (01327) 878117 E-mail: info@evergreengallery.co.uk

CASTINGS, COPPER/ALLOY

Arrow Butler Castings Ltd, Station Road, Whittington Moor, Chesterfield, Derbyshire, S41 9ES Tel: (01246) 450027 Fax: (01246) 261913 E-mail: sales@arrowbutlercastings.co.uk

Corus Process Engineering, Old Frame RM, Derwent Howe, Workington, Cumbria, CA14 3YZ Tel: (01900) 68000 Fax: (01900) 601111 E-mail: cpe@corusgroup.com

Davis & Hill, 56 Pritchett Street, Birmingham, B6 4EY Tel: 0121-359 4091 Fax: 0121-333 3163 E-mail: sales@davisandhill.co.uk

Draycast Foundries Ltd, Bellingdon Road, Chesham, Buckinghamshire, HP5 2NR Tel: (01494) 786077 Fax: (01494) 791337 E-mail: sales@draycast.co.uk

Ecu Castings, Claytons Meadow, Bourne End, Buckinghamshire, SL8 5DQ Tel: (01628) 524672 Fax: (01628) 850914 E-mail: robinecu@aol.com

Technicast Moulds, Unit 1 Garnett Close, Watford, WD24 7GN Tel: (01923) 246530 Fax: (01923) 255983 E-mail: isoo4e2893@blueyonder.co.uk

CASTINGS, INVESTMENT/LOST WAX PROCESS

Alfa, Rockwood, Keldholme, York, YO62 6NB Tel: (01751) 432953 Fax: (01751) 432518

Anderson Stewart Castings Ltd, Block 1 Lochshore Industrial Estate, Caledonia Road, Glengarnock, Beith, Ayrshire, KA14 3DB Tel: (01505) 683368 Fax: (01505) 683771 E-mail: mail@ascast.co.uk

Ceramicast Precision Investment Castings Ltd, Castings House, Boundary Road, Woking, Surrey, GU21 5BX Tel: (01483) 751666 Fax: (01483) 751888 E-mail: sales@ceramicast.com

Cronite Precision Castings Ltd, Blacknell Lane, Crewkerne, Somerset, TA18 7YA Tel: (01460) 270300 Fax: (01460) 72643 E-mail: cpc@cronite.co.uk

Devon Metalcrafts Ltd, 2 Victoria Way, Exmouth, Devon, EX8 1EW Tel: (01395) 272846 Fax: (01395) 276688 E-mail: info@devonmetalcrafts.co.uk

F P Castings Ltd, 40 Glenburn Road, East Kilbride, Glasgow, G74 5BA Tel: (01355) 900020 Fax: (01355) 900021 E-mail: fpcastings@aol.com

Hooker Group Ltd, Waterside, Brightlingsea, Colchester, CO7 0AU Tel: (01206) 302611 Fax: (01206) 305014 E-mail: sales@hooker.co.uk

Howmet Ltd, Kestrel Way, Sowton Industrial Estate, Exeter, EX2 7LG Tel: (01392) 429700 Fax: (01392) 429701 E-mail: info@howmet.com

Incamet Ltd, Springhill Industrial Estate, Douglas, Lanark, ML11 0RE Tel: (01555) 851280 Fax: (01555) 851127 E-mail: info@incametltd.co.uk

Investment Castings Congleton Ltd, Greenfield Farm Industrial Estate, Congleton, Cheshire, CW12 4TR Tel: (01260) 280181 Fax: (01260) 298208 E-mail: info@investment-castings.co.uk

Lestercast Ltd, 14-16 Ireton Avenue, Leicester, LE4 9EU Tel: 0116-276 7284 Fax: 0116-246 0401 E-mail: sales@lestercast.co.uk

Lost Wax Castings Ltd, 23 Tithe Cl, Codicote, Hitchin, Herts, SG4 8UX Tel: (01438) 820822 Fax: (01438) 820822 E-mail: sjm3753735@gsk.com

Lost Wax Development, Firs Industrial Estate Ricketts Close, Off Oldington Lane, Kidderminster, Worcestershire, DY11 7QN Tel: (01562) 822100 Fax: (01299) 877352 E-mail: sales@lwd.co.uk

Lunt's Castings Ltd, Hawthorns Industrial Estate, Middlemore Road, Handsworth, Birmingham, B21 0BJ Tel: 0121-551 4301 Fax: 0121-523 7954 E-mail: info@luntscastings.co.uk

Maybrey Reliance, Worsley Bridge Road, Lower Sydenham, London, SE26 5BE Tel: (01322) 315370 Fax: (01322) 550724 E-mail: sales@maybrey.co.uk

Maycast Nokes Precision Engineering Ltd, Factory La West, Halstead, Essex, CO9 1EX Tel: (01787) 472500 Fax: (01787) 474264 E-mail: enquiries@maycast.co.uk

Medical Technology Ltd, Parkway Close, Parkway Industrial Estate, Sheffield, S9 4WH Tel: 0114-273 8764 Fax: 0114-273 8764

▶ Micro Metalsmiths Ltd, Kirkdale Road, Kirkbymoorside, York, YO62 6PX Tel: 0845 2139030 Fax: (01751) 432061 E-mail: info@micrometalsmiths.co.uk

Niagara Falls Castings UK Ltd, Budbrooke Road, Warwick, CV34 5XH Tel: (01926) 496258 Fax: (01926) 496250 E-mail: sales@nf-castings.co.uk

Rolls-Royce P.L.C., PO Box 31, Derby, DE24 8BJ Tel: (01332) 247018 Fax: (01332) 246970

Stone Foundries Ltd, Woolwich Road, London, SE7 8SL Tel: (020) 8853 4648 Fax: (020) 8305 1934 E-mail: enquiries@stone-foundries-limited.com

Tritech Alkast, Castle Park Road, Whiddon Valley Industrial Esta, Barnstaple, Devon, EX32 8PA Tel: (01271) 376521 Fax: (01271) 326155 E-mail:

Tritech Precision Products Ltd, Bridge Road North, Wrexham Industrial Estate, Wrexham, Clwyd, LL13 9PS Tel: (01978) 661111 Fax: (01978) 661392 E-mail: info@tritech-precision-products.co.uk

Trucast Ltd, Marlborough Road, Ryde, Isle of Wight, PO33 1AD Tel: (01983) 567611 Fax: (01983) 567618 E-mail: info@doncasters.com

CASTINGS, SAND

Aluminium Products Ltd, Alpro Foundry, Haines Street, West Bromwich, West Midlands, B70 7DA Tel: 0121-553 1911 Fax: 0121-500 5796 E-mail: alpro@compuserve.com

Archway Brown Ltd, 43 Bury Mead Road, Hitchin, Hertfordshire, SG5 1RT Tel: (01462) 432139 Fax: (01462) 420102

Art Founders, 11 Springwood Industrial Estate, Braintree, Essex, CM7 2YP Tel: (01376) 343222 Fax: (01376) 341793 E-mail: info@msaf.co.uk

C & J Castings, 42 Bayton Road, Exhall, Coventry, CV7 9EJ Tel: (024) 7636 3031 Fax: (024) 7636 3556 E-mail: clive@42baytonroad.freeserve.co.uk

Madeley Brass Castings, Unit B8 Court Works Industrial Estate, Bridgnorth Road, Madeley, Telford, Shropshire, TF7 4JB Tel: (01952) 583004 Fax: (01952) 583004

Painter & Son Ltd, Pope Iron Road, Worcester, WR1 3HB Tel: (01905) 22787 Fax: (01905) 24181

Sarginsons Industries Ltd, Torrington Avenue, Coventry, CV4 9AG Tel: (024) 7646 6291 Fax: (024) 7646 8135 E-mail: keithb@sarginsons.co.uk

Surecoat Powder Coatings, Unit 13 Bolton Textile Mill, Cawdor Street, Farnworth, Bolton, BL4 7EA Tel: (01204) 793339 Fax: (01204) 793339

Thurton Foundries Ltd, Loddon Rd, Thurton, Norwich, NR14 6AN Tel: (01508) 480301 Fax: (01508) 480303 E-mail: sales@thurtonfoundries.co.uk

Vald Birn (UK) Ltd, Cambois, Blyth, Northumberland, NE24 1SW Tel: (01670) 818111 Fax: (01670) 855511 E-mail: sales@valdbirn.co.uk

W H Rowe & Son Ltd, Quayside Road, Southampton, SO18 1DH Tel: (023) 8022 5636 Fax: (023) 8022 5146 E-mail: sales@whrowe.com

William Cook, Cross Green Approach, Leeds, LS9 0SG Tel: 0113-249 6363 Fax: 0113-249 1376 E-mail: sales@william-cook.co.uk

CASTINGS, SAND, PRECISION

Barton Aluminium Foundries, Rayboulds Bridge Rd, Walsall, WS2 8PG Tel: (01922) 637551 Fax: (01922) 644481 E-mail: sales@barton-aluminium.co.uk

CASTINGS, STAINLESS STEEL

Ampo UK, Holly Tree Cottage, Stocks Lane, Welshampton, Ellesmere, Shropshire, SY12 0NT Tel: (01948) 710764 Fax: (01948) 710914 E-mail: ampouk@aol.com

British Engines Ltd, St Peters, Newcastle upon Tyne, NE6 1BS Tel: 0191-265 9091 Fax: 0191-276 3244 E-mail: sales@bel.co.uk

Darwins Holdings Ltd, Fitzwilliam Works, Sheffield Road, Sheffield, S9 1RL Tel: 0114-244 8421 Fax: 0114-256 1775

Gabriel & Co. Ltd, Abro Works, 10 Hay Hall Road, Tyseley, Birmingham, B11 2AU Tel: 0121-248 3333 Fax: 0121-248 3330 E-mail: sales@gabrielco.com

▶ H I Quality Steel Castings Ltd, Foundry Street, Wittington Moor, Chesterfield, Derbyshire, S41 9AX Tel: (01246) 260303 Fax: (01246) 260245 E-mail: steven@hiqsc.com

Hooker Group Ltd, Waterside, Brightlingsea, Colchester, CO7 0AU Tel: (01206) 302611 Fax: (01206) 305014 E-mail: sales@hooker.co.uk

Lost Wax Castings Ltd, 23 Tithe Cl, Codicote, Hitchin, Herts, SG4 8UX Tel: (01438) 820822 Fax: (01438) 820822 E-mail: sjm3753735@gsk.com

Norton Cast Products Ltd, Capital Steel Works, Tinsley Park Road, Sheffield, S9 5DL Tel: 0114-244 8722 Fax: 0114-242 5523 E-mail: info@nortoncast.com

▶ Precision Products (Cumberland) Ltd, Highmill, Alston, Cumbria, CA9 3HT Tel: (01434) 381228 Fax: (01434) 381038 E-mail: sales@shawprocess.co.uk

Terrill Bros (Founders) Ltd, 2 Guildford Road Industrial Estate, Hayle, Cornwall, TR27 4QZ Tel: (01736) 752168 Fax: (01736) 756215 E-mail: sales@terrill-bros.co.uk

Trefoil Steel Co. Ltd, Rotherfield Works, Deadmans Hole Lane, Sheffield, S9 1QQ Tel: (01709) 830701 Fax: (01709) 830737 E-mail: sales@trefoilsteel.com

Tritech Precision Products Ltd, Bridge Road North, Wrexham Industrial Estate, Wrexham, Clwyd, LL13 9PS Tel: (01978) 661111 Fax: (01978) 661392 E-mail: info@tritech-precision-products.co.uk

CASTOR FITTINGS OR SOCKETS

Page Castor Ltd, Blakemore Road, West Bromwich, West Midlands, B70 8JF Tel: 0121-553 1710 Fax: 0121-525 0631

CASTOR OIL IMPORT MERCHANTS OR AGENTS

Augustus Oils Ltd, 64 Woolmer Way, Bordon, Hampshire, GU35 9QF Tel: (01420) 488555 Fax: (01420) 476777 E-mail: sales@augustus-oils.ltd.uk

William Hodgson & Co., 73A London Road, Alderley Edge, Cheshire, SK9 7DY Tel: (01625) 599111 Fax: (01625) 599222

W.S. Lloyd Ltd, 7 Redgrove House, Stonards Hill, Epping, Essex, CM16 4QQ Tel: (01992) 572670 Fax: E-mail: jhogg@wslloyd.com

CASTORS, *See also headings for particulor types*

A U T (Wheels & Castors) Co. Ltd, The Wheel House, Egmont Street, Mossley, Ashton-under-Lyne, Lancashire, OL5 9NB Tel: (01457) 837772 Fax: (01457) 832472 E-mail: sales@aut.co.uk

Alexander Industrial Supplies Essex Ltd, Unit D Eastways, Witham, Essex, CM8 3YQ Tel: (01376) 500303 Fax: (01376) 502090 E-mail: sales@alexander-industrial.co.uk

Baz Roll Products Ltd, Portemarsh Road, Calne, Wiltshire, SN11 9BW Tel: (01249) 822222 Fax: (01249) 822300 E-mail: sales@bazroll.co.uk

Blickle Castors & Wheels Ltd, 30 Vincent Avenue, Crownhill, Milton Keynes, MK8 0AB Tel: (01908) 560904 Fax: (01908) 260510 E-mail: sales@blickle.co.uk

Carrington Bearings & Engineering Ltd, 8 Torridge Close, Telford Way Industrial Estate, Kettering, Northamptonshire, NN16 8PY Tel: (01536) 518666 Fax: (01536) 412131 E-mail: sales@carringtonbearings.co.uk

▶ Castor Services Ltd, The Wheel House, Egmont Street, Mossley, Ashton-under-Lyne, Lancashire, OL5 9NB Tel: (01457) 838001 Fax: (01457) 838998 E-mail: sales@castorserviceslimited.co.uk

CMS Industries, Downsview Road, Wantage, Oxfordshire, OX12 9FF Tel: (01235) 773370 Fax: (01235) 773371 E-mail: sales@cmsindustries.com

Crofts & Assinder, Standard Brass Works, Lombard Street, Deritend, Birmingham, B12 0QX Tel: 0121-622 1074 Fax: 0121-622 1074 E-mail: general@crofts.co.uk

Drive Design Ltd, Clayton Lodge, Clayton Lane, Clayton, Bradford, West Yorkshire, BD14 6RF Tel: (01274) 883070 Fax: (01274) 883061 E-mail: sales@drivedesignltd.co.uk

▶ Eurowire Containers Ltd, Maypole Fields, Cradley, Halesowen, West Midlands, B63 2QB Tel: (01384) 561786 Fax: (01384) 564044 E-mail: support@eurowirecontainers.com

H C Slingsby plc, Otley Road, Shipley, West Yorkshire, BD17 7LW Tel: (01274) 535030 Fax: (01274) 535033 E-mail: sales@slingsby.com

H Varley Ltd, Unit 5, Century Park, Unit 5, Pacific Road, Altrincham, Cheshire, WA14 5BJ Tel: 0161-928 9617 Fax: 0161-928 7824 E-mail: sales@varley.co.uk

Long Technology Ltd, 1 Richmond Lane, Huntly, Aberdeenshire, AB54 8FJ Tel: (01466) 794646 Fax: (01466) 794111 E-mail: sales@longtechnology.com

M S A Wheels & Casters Ltd, 10 Maclure Road, Rochdale, Lancashire, OL11 1DN Tel: (01706) 516640 Fax: (0870) 7590160 E-mail: sales@msawhhelsandcasters.co.uk

Manner UK Ltd, 13 Station Road, Cam, Dursley, Gloucestershire, GL11 5NS Tel: (01453) 546333 Fax: (01453) 549222 E-mail: sales@manner.co.uk

Motion Industries UK Ltd, Unit 2 Bracken Trade Park, Duners Lane, Bury, Lancashire, BL9 9QP Tel: 0161-705 1237 Fax: 0161-705 1239E-mail: enquires@bearingsuppliers.co.uk

P & L Industrial Equipment Ltd, Lind Street, Manchester, M40 7ES Tel: 0161-273 2626 Fax: 0161-274 3633 E-mail: sales@plcastors.co.uk

Revvo Castor Co., Somerford Road, Christchurch, Dorset, BH23 3PZ Tel: (01202) 484211 Fax: (01202) 477896 E-mail: sales@revvo.co.uk

Satoris Products Ltd, 25 Bradfield Close, Finedon Road Industrial Estate, Wellingborough, Northamptonshire, NN8 4RQ Tel: (01933) 274323 Fax: (01933) 274313 E-mail: edaids@aol.com

▶ Tellure Rota, PO Box 29, Ashton-under-Lyne, Lancashire, OL5 9NB Tel: (01457) 832556 Fax: (01457) 838406 E-mail: sales@aut.co.uk

Thistle Bearings & Engineering Products Ltd, 38 Singer Road, Kelvin Industrial Estate, East Kilbride, Glasgow, G75 0XS Tel: (01355) 225491 Fax: (01355) 242502 E-mail: sales@thistlebearings.co.uk

Transmission & Engineering Services, Unit 17 Springfield Road, Grantham, Lincolnshire, NG31 7BL Tel: (01476) 591500 Fax: (01476) 590336

H. Varley Ltd, Unit 82, The Wenta Business Centre, Colne Way, Watford, WD24 7ND Tel: (01923) 249334 Fax: (01923) 245513 E-mail: sales@varley.co.uk

Western Castors & Wheels Ltd, Mardle Way, Bucksfastleigh, Buckfastleigh, Devon, TQ11 0NR Tel: (01364) 43235 Fax: (01364) 643405 E-mail: sales@western-uk.com

▶ Wolds Engineering Services Ltd, Unit 1d Pocklington Industrial Estate, Pocklington, York, YO42 1NR Tel: (01759) 303877 Fax: (01759) 306952 E-mail: johnoxley@btconnect.com

CASUAL DENIM SHIRTS

▶ Savu UK Ltd, 1 Green View Park, 1 Colin Crescent, Colindale, London, NW9 6EU Tel: (020) 8205 0890 Fax: (020) 8205 0890 E-mail: info@savu.co.uk

CASUAL WEAR

A & S Clothing Manufacturers Ltd, 7 Mott Street, Birmingham, B19 3HD Tel: 0121-233 3625 Fax: 0121-236 2730

A S Garments Ltd, 16 Sycamore Road, Handsworth, Birmingham, B21 0QL Tel: 0121-551 6158 Fax: 0121-551 6158

Albert Martin & Co. Ltd, Kirkby Road, Sutton-in-Ashfield, Nottinghamshire, NG17 1GP Tel: (01623) 441122 Fax: (01623) 551037

Barana P.L.C., 2-3 Charter Street, Leicester, LE1 3UD Tel: 0116-253 9380 Fax: 0116-262 7023 E-mail: enquiries@barana.co.uk

Brenson Fashions Ltd, 32 Fortesque Avenue, London, E8 3QB Tel: (020) 8533 1525 Fax: (020) 8533 4427

Burberry Ltd, Abergorki Industrial Estate, Ynyswen Road, Treorchy, Mid Glamorgan, CF42 6EF Tel: (01443) 772020 Fax: (01443) 775956 E-mail: info@burberry.com

Chana Garments Ltd, 169 Booth Street, Birmingham, B21 0NU Tel: 0121-551 1601 Fax: 0121-507 0471

F. Chand & Co. Ltd, 81 Rabone Lane, Smethwick, West Midlands, B66 3JH Tel: 0121-565 3959 Fax: 0121-565 3959

Doon Trading Co., 55 Westfield Road, Smethwick, West Midlands, B67 6AW Tel: 0121-555 5398 Fax: 0121-555 5398

Dubb Bros Ltd, 121 Soho Hill, Birmingham, B19 1AX Tel: 0121-554 6492 Fax: 0121-554 6759

Dubb Fashions, 1-3 Rawlings Road, Smethwick, West Midlands, B67 5AD Tel: 0121-420 2707 Fax: 0121-434 4050

Eurstyle Ltd, Park House, 19-20 Bright Street, Wednesbury, West Midlands, WS10 9HX Tel: 0121-526 2973 Fax: 0121-526 2061 E-mail: sales@vtex.co.uk

F & W Manufacturing Co., 95-97 Wigmore Street, London, W1U 1QW Tel: (020) 7224 4882 Fax: (020) 7224 4032

Falcon Jeanswear, Argyle Works, Alma Street, Smethwick, Warley, West Midlands, B66 2RL Tel: 0121-565 1533 Fax: 0121-565 1533 E-mail: falcon@euroshops.co.uk

Fashion Wear Manufacturers Ltd, 135 Gipsy Lane, Leicester, LE4 6RH Tel: 0116-261 1122 Fax: 0116-261 1133 E-mail: enquiries@jeanmaker.co.uk

Fingerprint Embroiderers, 19 Bank Street, Kirriemuir, Angus, DD8 4BE Tel: (01575) 572373 Fax: (01575) 540371

Gill & Co., 94 Owen Road, Wolverhampton, WV3 0AL Tel: (01902) 420707 Fax: (01902) 420707

Hebden Cord Co Ltd, 17 Old Gate, Hebden Bridge, West Yorkshire, HX7 6EW Tel: (01422) 843152 Fax: (01422) 846354 E-mail: hebcord@aol.com

Jogo Associates Ltd, Marlsbro House, 52 Newton St, Manchester, M1 1ED Tel: 0161-236 7132 Fax: 0161-236 1616

Kewal Brothers Textiles Ltd, Unit 51/52 Bridge Trading Estate, Bridge Street North, Smethwick, West Midlands, B66 2BZ Tel: 0121-555 8080 Fax: 0121-555 8081

Laxmi Investments Ltd, 123 Barkby Road, Leicester, LE4 9LG Tel: 0116-276 6625 Fax: 0116-246 0787

Lee Cooper Group Ltd, Lee Cooper House, 17 Bath Road, Slough, SL1 3UF Tel: (01753) 771908 Fax: (01753) 779299 E-mail: lcuk@aol.com

Levi Strauss UK Ltd, Swan Valley, Northampton, NN4 9BA Tel: (01604) 581501 Fax: (01604) 599815

Loyal & Sons Ltd, 50 Kenilworth Drive, Oadby, Leicester, LE2 5LG Tel: 0116-271 8235 Fax: 0116-271 8235 E-mail: ajitloyal@aol.com

M B M Clothing Ltd, 90 Freer Road, Aston, Birmingham, B6 6NB Tel: 0121-554 7522 Fax: 0121-554 7522

Malhi Trimmings Ltd, Excelda Works, 36 Rookery Road, Handsworth, Birmingham, B21 9NB Tel: (0121) 554 5731 Fax: (0121) 554 5733 E-mail: sales@mahligroup.co.uk

Mann Bros Ltd, 142 High Street, West Bromwich, West Midlands, B70 6JJ Tel: 0121-553 7156 Fax: 0121-553 1961 E-mail: info@mannbros.co.uk

P R Textiles, 31-32 Cliveland Street, Birmingham, B19 3SH Tel: 0121-359 2741 Fax: 0121-333 3600

P S Gill & Sons, 261-277 Rookery Road, Handsworth, Birmingham, B21 9PT Tel: 0121-554 7521 Fax: 0121-554 9033 E-mail: ssgill@psgill.com

Pinstripe Clothing Co. Ltd, 49-51 Dale Street, Manchester, M1 2HF Tel: 0161-236 5640 Fax: 0161-236 8863

Premier World Trading Ltd, Raintex House, Smethwick, West Midlands, B66 2AA Tel: 0121-555 6479 Fax: 0121-555 6532 E-mail: sales@pwtltd.co.uk

R K Clothing Manufacturers Ltd, 300-306 Park Road, Hockley, Birmingham, B18 5HE Tel: 0121-551 1379 Fax: 0121-551 1379

R S Leisurewear, House of Rs, 26 Smith Dorien Road, Leicester, LE5 4BF Tel: 0116-274 0234 Fax: 0116-246 1259 E-mail: rsgroup@webleicester.co.uk

Ralawise Ltd, Cornbrook Park Road, Manchester, M15 4EE Tel: 0161-872 8112 Fax: 0161-872 2554 E-mail: sales@ralawise.com

Rana Textiles Ltd, 914-918 Stratford Road, Sparkhill, Birmingham, B11 4BT Tel: 0121-777 3986 Fax: 0121-247 2255

Romeo Trading Company Ltd, Romeo House, 160 Bridport Road, London, N18 1SY Tel: (020) 8803 0066 Fax: (020) 8803 0008 E-mail: admin@romeotrading.com

S & J Knitwear Ltd, Payne Street, Leicester, LE4 7RD Tel: 0116-261 1701 Fax: 0116-266 6965

S L K Kentex Fashions Ltd, 90-104 Constitution Hill, Hockley, Birmingham, B19 3JT Tel: 0121-236 6653 Fax: 0121-212 3530 E-mail: kentex@btinternet.com

Saul Trading, 427-431 Moseley Road, Balsall Heath, Birmingham, B12 9BX Tel: 0121-440 3276 Fax: 0121-440 3276

Tankson Textiles, 173 Rolfe Street, Smethwick, West Midlands, B66 2AS Tel: 0121-558 1733

▶ TEP UK Ltd, 8 King Edward Street, Oxford, OX1 4HS Tel: (07921) 706641 E-mail: info@tepuk.com

Thornbury Clothing Co., 25 Thornbury Road, Birmingham, B20 3DE Tel: 0121-356 6777 Fax: 0121-344 4050

Tiki International (Plastics) Ltd, Velator Industrial Estate, Braunton, Devon, EX33 2DX Tel: (01271) 812442 Fax: (01271) 816570 E-mail: tiki@tikisurf.force9.co.uk

Tradewinds Merchandising Co. Ltd, Lynton Road, London, N8 8SL Tel: (020) 8341 9700 Fax: (0845) 2309006 E-mail: sales@tradewinds.eu.com

Wealth Of Nations World-Wide Ltd, Crouches Farm, Furnace Lane, Horsmonden, Tonbridge, Kent, TN12 8LX Tel: (01892) 724724 Fax: (01892) 724726 E-mail: info@wealthofnations.co.uk

Wilsport, 5 Fleming Close, Wellingborough, Northamptonshire, NN8 6UF Tel: (01933) 403404 Fax: (01933) 405070 E-mail: edw@wilsport.freeserve.co.uk

CASUAL WEAR IMPORT MERCHANTS OR AGENTS

Pinstripe Clothing Co. Ltd, 49-51 Dale Street, Manchester, M1 2HF Tel: 0161-236 5640 Fax: 0161-236 8863

Rajan Trading International Ltd, Rajan House, 61 Great Ducie Street, Manchester, M3 1RR Tel: 0161-834 2147 Fax: 0161-835 2435 E-mail: sales@rajan-group.co.uk

Regatta Ltd, Risol House Mercury Park, Mercury Way, Urmston, Manchester, M41 7RR Tel: 0161-749 1313 Fax: 0161-749 1210 E-mail: sales@regatta.com

CASUALTY STRETCHERS

▶ Bell Stretchers, Unit 1B, Boundary Bank, Underbarrow Road, Kendal, Cumbria, LA9 5RR Tel: (01539) 732281 E-mail: info@bellstretchers.co.uk

Hill-Rom UK Ltd, Clinitron House, Ashby Park, Ashby-de-la-Zouch, Leicestershire, LE65 1JG Tel: (01530) 411000 Fax: (01530) 411555 E-mail: name@hill-rom.co.uk

CATALOGUE PARCEL DELIVERY SERVICES

▶ Tuffnells Parcels Express Ltd, Azalea Road, Rogerstone, Newport, Gwent, NP10 9SA Tel: (01633) 891010 Fax: (01633) 891044 E-mail: nick.walters@tuffnells.co.uk

CATALOGUES, OFFICE FURNITURE

▶ Blandford Office Furniture, 20a Sunrise Business Park, Higher Shaftesbury Road, Blandford Forum, Dorset, DT11 8ST Tel: (01258) 450006 Fax: (01258) 459933 E-mail: ian@officefurniture.demon.co.uk

▶ C I S Office Furniture Ltd, Furniture House, Potters Lane, Wednesbury, West Midlands, WS10 7LP Tel: 0121-556 8741 Fax: 0121-556 9588 E-mail: sales@cisoffice.co.uk

Ideal Business Supplies Ltd, Marsh Lanelords Meadow Industrial Estate, Lords Meadow Industrial Estate, Crediton, Devon, EX17 1ES Tel: (01363) 775999 Fax: (01363) 775996 E-mail: info@idealbusinesssupplies.co.uk

▶ Levant Office Interiors, Tedco Business Works, Henry Robson Way, South Shields, Tyne & Wear, NE33 1RF Tel: 0191-427 4692 Fax: 0191-427 4694 E-mail: enquiries@levantofficeinteriors.com

Office 21 Projects Ltd, Whitby Oliver, 31 Hospital Fields Road, Fulford Industrial Estate, Fulford Road, York, YO10 4FS Tel: (01904) 655106 E-mail: info@office21.co.uk

▶ Rouge Interiors Ltd, 19 Hoblands, Haywards Heath, West Sussex, RH16 3SB Tel: (01444) 415695 Fax: (01444) 416823 E-mail: info@rougeinteriors.co.uk

▶ Scorpio Business Solutions, 86 Mozart Close, Basingstoke, Hampshire, RG22 4HZ Tel: (07861) 215091 Fax: (01256) 410789 E-mail: scorpiosupplies@hotmail.com

▶ UK Seating Direct, 47 Albert Street, Aberdeen, AB25 1XT Tel: 0870 6092106 Fax: 0870 6092105 E-mail: info@ukseatingdirect.co.uk

CATALYST HANDLING EQUIPMENT

GWS Engineers Ltd, First Avenue, Flixborough Industrial Estate, Flixborough, Scunthorpe, South Humberside, DN15 8SE Tel: (01724) 856665 Fax: (01724) 280805 E-mail: mail@gws-engineers.co.uk

CATALYTIC CONVERTER DEVELOPMENT ENGINEERS/ MANUFACTURING SERVICES, VEHICLE EXHAUST

Benson Components Ltd, Saxon Works, South St, Openshaw, Manchester, M11 2FY Tel: (0845) 1300000 Fax: 0161-231 6866 E-mail: sales@bensonexhausts.com

▶ Blackthorn Enviromental Ltd, Forum House, Stirling Road, Chichester, West Sussex, PO19 7DN Tel: (0870) 0101800 Fax: (0870) 0101811 E-mail: contact@blackthorn.eu.com

▶ London Stainless Steel Exhaust Centre Ltd, Coopers Place, Combe Lane, Wormley, Godalming, Surrey, GU8 5SZ Tel: (01428) 687722 Fax: (01428) 687790 E-mail: info@quicksilverexhausts.com

CATALYTIC CONVERTERS, VEHICLE EXHAUST

Agrie Mach Ltd, Wayfarers, Domewood, Copthorne, Crawley, West Sussex, RH10 3HD Tel: (01342) 713743 Fax: (01342) 719181 E-mail: info@agriemach.com

Benson Components Ltd, Saxon Works, South St, Openshaw, Manchester, M11 2FY Tel: (0845) 1300000 Fax: 0161-231 6866 E-mail: sales@bensonexhausts.com

▶ Blackthorn Enviromental Ltd, Forum House, Stirling Road, Chichester, West Sussex, PO19 7DN Tel: (0870) 0101800 Fax: (0870) 0101811 E-mail: contact@blackthorn.eu.com

C E S UK Ltd, Knutsford Way, Sealand Industrial Estate, Chester, CH1 4NS Tel: (01244) 372555 Fax: (01244) 371248 E-mail: sales@cesuk.com

▶ Cats Direct, 70-72 Acton Road, Long Eaton, Nottingham, NG10 1FR Tel: 0115-983 5280 Fax: 0115-972 1112 E-mail: mail@cats-direct.com

Servais Silencers, 409 Harlestone Road, Northampton, NN5 6PB Tel: (01604) 754888 Fax: (01604) 759548

▶ Viking International, 26-32 Millbrae Road, Langside, Glasgow, G42 9TU Tel: 0141-632 3222

CATEGORY FIVE (CAT5) CABLES, DATA COMMUNICATION

▶ A C T Comms Ltd, Hexagon House, 71 Lower Road, Kenley, Caterham, Surrey, CR8 5NH Tel: (0870) 7747576 Fax: (0870) 1600094 E-mail: sales@actcomms.co.uk

▶ Cablecomm Voice & Data Solutions Ltd, Aztec House, 187-189 Kings Road, Reading, RG1 4EX Tel: (0800) 0582662 Fax: 0118-988 3716 E-mail: sales@cablecomm.co.uk

Complete Connections, 75 Milford Road, Reading, RG1 8LG Tel: 0118-959 4286 Fax: 0118-950 5263 E-mail: sales@cableshop.co.uk

Data Cabling Ltd, 6 Farrier Road, Lincoln, LN6 3RU Tel: (01522) 500699 Fax: (01522) 500882 E-mail: sales@data-cabling.co.uk

Noble Computer Services, 9 Newton Road, Ipswich, IP3 8HE Tel: (01473) 424342 Fax: (01473) 424466 E-mail: info@noble-online.co.uk

CATERERS' CLOTHING

Punch Bowl, 214 Porchester Road, Nottingham, NG3 6HG Tel: 0115-958 9961 Fax: 0115-958 9962

Tibard Limited, Tibard House, Broadway, Dukinfield, Cheshire, SK16 4UU Tel: 0161-342-1000 Fax: 0161-343 2016 E-mail: sales@tibard.co.uk

CATERERS' FORKS

M & G Catering, 69/79 Hadfield Street, Old Trafford, Manchester, M16 9FE Tel: 0161-848 0959 Fax: 0161-848 0959 E-mail: mg-catering@ntlworld.com

Plastic Development Techniques Ltd, Unit 4, Block 2 Wednesbury Trading Estate, Darlaston Road, Wednesbury, West Midlands, WS10 7JN Tel: 0121-556 9966 Fax: 0121-556 0208 E-mail: charles@pdt-ltd.freeserve.co.uk

CATERING

▶ A J Catering, Concorde House, Concorde Way, Preston Farm Industrial Estate, Stockton-on-Tees, Cleveland, TS18 3RB Tel: (01642) 617948 Fax: (01642) 607906

Chef De La Maison Ltd, Winslow Road, Netherton, Peterborough, PE3 9RE Tel: (01733) 332122 Fax: (01733) 332122 E-mail: charis@chefdelamaison.co.uk

The Cook & The Butler Event Company Ltd, Blackfriars Foundry Annexe, 65 Glasshill Street, London, SE1 0QR Tel: (020) 7620 1818 Fax: (020) 7620 1820 E-mail: cookandbutler@btconnect.com

K2 Catering Ltd, PO Box 49808, London, NW5 2YA Tel: (07970) 425285 Fax: (020) 7284 1325 E-mail: ian@k2catering.com

▶ MRI Catering, 45 Bishops Way, Andover, Hampshire, SP10 3EH Tel: (01264) 339006 Fax: (01264) 363487 E-mail: kieran@mricatering.co.uk

Topline Catering, Old Mills Indust Estate, Old Mills, Paulton, Bristol, BS39 7SU Tel: (01761) 415154 Fax: (01275) 333308 E-mail: mail@toplinecatering.co.uk

CATERING CHEF TEMPORARY STAFF RECRUITMENT AGENCIES

Orb Recruitment Ltd, PO Box 50, Manchester, M3 4EL Tel: 0161-244 5526 Fax: 0161-244 5526 E-mail: richard@premier-recruit.com

▶ Premier Recruitment International Ltd, PO Box 250, London, W1T 6DU Tel: (020) 7631 0050 Fax: 0870 288 4990 E-mail: info@premier-recruit.com

▶ Robochef Freelance Catering Services, 40 Hamill drive, Kilsyth, Glasgow, G65 0EQ Tel: (0785) 4400849 E-mail: mark@robochef.co.uk

▶ theCATERINGjob.com, PO Box 2448, Slough, SL1 1ZB Tel: 0870 8701193 Fax: 0870 8701194 E-mail: coz.dauncey@thecateringjob.com

CATERING CONSULTANCY

▶ Catering Systems Ltd, 9 Compton Road, Brighton, BN1 5AL Tel: (01273) 508626 Fax: (01273) 505852 E-mail: info@cateringsystems.co.uk

▶ Complete Catering Advice, 7 Market Street, Kettering, Northants, NN16 0AH Tel: (01536) 481973 E-mail: Info@completecateringadvice.co.uk

▶ Consuming Passion, Arundel House, 22 The Drive, Hove, East Sussex, BN3 3JD Tel: (01273) 719160 E-mail: saragsanders@hotmail.com

Dining in Style Group Limited, 18 High Street, Pinner, Middlesex, HA5 5PW Tel: (020) 8866 7856 Fax: (020) 8866 1033 E-mail: paul@dininginstyle.co.uk

Executive Catering Services, 107a High Street, Carrville, Durham, DH1 1BQ Tel: 0191-386 3682 Fax: 0191-383 0280 E-mail: eccs107a@aol.com

▶ Fatstrippa Clearflow, Ainsley Grove, Faverdale, Darlington, County Durham, DL3 0GD Tel: (01325) 460040 E-mail: fatstrippa@fsmail.net

Review Consultancy, Beechcroft, 138 London Road, Waterlooville, Hampshire, PO7 5ST Tel: (023) 9223 2647 Fax: (023) 9223 2647 E-mail: info@reviewconsultancy.co.uk

Alexander Jon Richardson & Associates, Severals House, Church Lane, Doddington, March, Cambridgeshire, PE15 0TA Tel: 01354 740076

Sterling Foodservice Design Ltd, 2 Wheeley Ridge, Wheeley Road, Alvechurch, Birmingham, B48 7DD Tel: 0121-445 0900 Fax: 0121-445 0901 E-mail: info@sterlingfoodservice.com

Supply Direct Ltd, 8 Priory House, Cloisters Business Park, 8 Battersea Park Road, London, SW8 4BH Tel: (020) 7622 9119 Fax: (020) 7622 0567 E-mail: info@supplydirect.com

Turpin Smale Foodservice Consultancy, Blackfriars Foundry, 156 Blackfriars Road, London, SE1 8EN Tel: (020) 7620 0011 Fax: (0870) 141 0397 E-mail: chris.brown@turpinsmale.co.uk

CATERING CONVECTION STEAMERS

Collins Walker Ltd, Unit 7a Nottingham South & Wilford Industrial Estate, Ruddington Lane, Nottingham, NG11 7EP Tel: 0115-981 8044 Fax: 0115-945 5376 E-mail: sales@collins-walker.co.uk

CATERING COUNTER EQUIPMENT

▶ Just Catering Ltd, Jessop Avenue, Norwood Green, Southall, Middlesex, UB2 5UY Tel: (0845) 0034271 Fax: (0845) 0034271 E-mail: sales@justcatering.com

CATERING COUNTER TOP STEAMERS

Collins Walker Ltd, Unit 7a Nottingham South & Wilford Industrial Estate, Ruddington Lane, Nottingham, NG11 7EP Tel: 0115-981 8044 Fax: 0115-945 5376 E-mail: sales@collins-walker.co.uk

CATERING DISHWASHERS

Active Appliances, 13 Orchard Road, South Croydon, Surrey, CR2 9LY Tel: (020) 8657 0493

Cabbola Food Service Equipment, 47 New Street, Hinckley, Leicestershire, LE10 1QY Tel: (01455) 612020 Fax: (01455) 636364 E-mail: sales@cabbola.com

Catering Kitchen Sheffield, 100 Lyons Street, Sheffield, S4 7QS Tel: 0114-276 3550 Fax: 0114-270 6128

Claremont Catering Engineers, 69-71 Lower Bents Lane, Bredbury, Stockport, Cheshire, SK6 2NL Tel: 0161-406 6464 Fax: 0161-406 6383 E-mail: info@claremontengineers.co.uk

D E A Design, Suite 4 143-145 Yorkshire St, Oldham, OL1 3TH Tel: 0161-627 0724 Fax: 0161-622 1311

J F K Installations, PO Box 1587, Stafford, ST16 3HR Tel: (01785) 212280

Lenrich Labs, 7 Shefton Rise, Northwood, Middlesex, HA6 3RE Tel: (01923) 826590 Fax: (01923) 841575 E-mail: bud@sheftonfreeserve.co.uk

▶ M & A City Kitchen Equipment, 214 Century Building, Tower Street, Brunswick Business Park, Liverpool, L3 4BJ Tel: 0151-709 6303 Fax: 0151-709 6324 E-mail: salesliverpool@ma-enviro.co.uk

CATERING (ELECTRICAL/ ELECTRONIC CONTROL UNIT) SPARE PARTS

Bishop's Express, 8-9 Flexi Units, Budlake Road, Marsh Barton Trading Estate, Exeter, EX2 8PY Tel: (01392) 271237 Fax: (01392) 272171

▶ Fatstrippa Clearflow, Ainsley Grove, Faverdale, Darlington, County Durham, DL3 0GD Tel: (01325) 460040 E-mail: fatstrippa@fsmail.net

CATERING EQUIPMENT DISTRIBUTORS

CCE Group Ltd, Bentley Farm, Unit 1, Old Church Hill, Langdon Hills, Basildon, Essex, SS16 6HZ Tel: (01268) 412121 Fax: (01268) 412600 E-mail: sales@contractcateringequipment.co.uk

Cemak Catering Equipment Ltd, The Atrium, Curtis Road, Dorking, Surrey, RH4 1XA Tel: (01306) 646860 Fax: (01306) 646363 E-mail: sales@cemak.co.uk

Direct Catering Supplies, Unit 16, Mornington Road, Smethwick, Birmingham, B66 2JE Tel: 0121-558 4200 Fax: 0121-565 3132 E-mail: sales@directcateringsupplies.co.uk

GS Group, Aspen Way, Yalberton Industrial Estate, Paignton, Devon, TQ4 7QR Tel: (01803) 528586 Fax: (01803) 554338 E-mail: info@gsgroup.co.uk

Sweetheat Technology Ltd, 16 Millwater Avenue, Dewsbury, West Yorkshire, WF12 9QN Tel: (01924) 488619 Fax: (01924) 488619 E-mail: nazim@sweetheat.co.uk

CATERING EQUIPMENT ENGINEERS, INSTALLATION/ MAINTENANCE/REPAIR

A B H Services, 11 Ash Court, Maltby, Rotherham, South Yorkshire, S66 8RQ Tel: (01709) 819621 Fax: (01709) 769825

Abraxas Catering Ltd, Ricketts Place, Firs Lane Industrial Estate, Kidderminster, Worcestershire, DY11 7QN Tel: (01562) 863222 Fax: (01562) 863133 E-mail: info@abraxascatering.co.uk

Acorn Catering Equipment Co., George Baylis Road, Berry Hill Industrial Estate, Droitwich, Worcestershire, WR9 9RB Tel: (01905) 798080 Fax: (01905) 797745 E-mail: sales@acorncateringequipment.co.uk

▶ Allied Catering Equipment, 33 Mayfield Place, Newcastle, Staffordshire, ST5 9LZ Tel: (01782) 711551 Fax: (01782) 711551

Alray Catering Equipment, 30 Prince Andrew Close, Maidenhead, Berkshire, SL6 8QH Tel: (01628) 676099 Fax: (01628) 676099

Ascot Heath, Brockhill Farm, Mathon Rd, Colwall, Malvern, Worcs, WR13 6EP Tel: (01684) 541100 Fax: (01684) 541455 E-mail: sales@ascotheath.co.uk

Border Food Machinery, 39 Kingstown Broadway, Kingstown Industrial Estate, Carlisle, CA3 0HA Tel: (01228) 534996 Fax: (01228) 514260

C L S Laundry Equipment, Unit A17-19, Holmer Trading Estate, Hereford, HR1 1JS Tel: (01432) 275712 Fax: (01432) 275712 E-mail: intercountyservices@orange.net

Capri Catering Equipment Services, 55 Great Tindal Street, Birmingham, B16 8DR Tel: 0121-236 5015 Fax: 0121-454 4011 E-mail: capricatering@blueyonder.co.uk

Catercall Ltd, 1 Facet Road, Birmingham, B38 9PT Tel: 0121-433 5444 Fax: 0121-433 4876 E-mail: admin@catercalltechservices.co.uk

Catering Engineers NW Ltd, 3 Ketlan Court, River Lane, Saltney, Chester, CH4 8SB Tel: (01244) 676999 Fax: (01244) 676886 E-mail: info@cenw.fsnet.co.uk

Catering Installation & Service Ltd, 536-537 Ipswich Road, Slough, SL1 4EQ Tel: (01753) 820166 Fax: (01753) 824885 E-mail: sales@orangeflame.co.uk

Catering Supplies & Repair Co. Ltd, 122 Muirhall Road, Larbert, Stirlingshire, FK5 4AP Tel: (01324) 552601 Fax: (01324) 563329 E-mail: info@csr-ltd.co.uk

Caterlec Services Ltd, 1 Charles Watling Way, Norwich, NR5 9JH Tel: (01603) 742888 Fax: (01603) 742711

Caterline, 20 John Newington Close, Kennington, Ashford, Kent, TN24 9SG Tel: (01622) 661696 Fax: (01233) 663144

▶ Caterline Commercial Kitchens Ltd, Unit 16 Primrose Trading Estate, Cradley Road, Dudley, West Midlands, DY2 9SA Tel: (01384) 459111 Fax: (01384) 456986

Caterlink, 20 Newton Rd, Great Barr, Birmingham, B43 6BN Tel: 0121-358 5844 Fax: 0121 358 6914

Catertech, 4e Haverscroft Industrial Estate, New Road, Attleborough, Norfolk, NR17 1YE Tel: (01953) 454200 Fax: (01953) 454207

Catertech, 18 Brynards Hill, Wootton Bassett, Swindon, SN4 7ER Tel: (01793) 848002 Fax: (01793) 848002 E-mail: enquires@catertech.net

Chefmate Ltd, Sunnydale Road, Bakers Field, Nottingham, NG3 7GG Tel: (07770) 663314 Fax: 01623 797997

Chiller Box Ltd, Unit 6, Carbery Enterprise Park, 36 White Hart Lane, Tottenham, London, N17 8DP Tel: (0800) 8491188 E-mail: mail@chillerbox.com

Commercial Catering Centre, 46b Grasmere Road, Blackpool, FY1 5HT Tel: (01253) 292976 Fax: (01253) 292977 E-mail: markconstantine@aol.com

Commercial Catering Engineers Ltd, 13 Clarkson Road, Lingwood, Norwich, NR13 4BA Tel: (01603) 713679

Commercial Catering Services, Station Business Park, Pensarn, Abergele, Clwyd, LL22 7PX Tel: (01745) 822166 Fax: (01745) 832656 E-mail: comcatering@btconnect.com

Commercial Trade Services Group Ltd, Lea Park Trading Estate, Warley Close, London, E10 7LF Tel: (020) 8558 9988 Fax: (020) 8558 1155 E-mail: services@comtrad.co.uk

Complete Catering & Engineering Services Ltd, 29-30 Milk Street, Birmingham, B5 5TR Tel: 0121-633 0110 Fax: 0121-633 0399

Cosmo Services Ltd, 5 Rudolf Place, London, SW8 1RP Tel: (020) 7582 1144 Fax: (020) 7735 2400 E-mail: office@cosmogroup.co.uk

Court Catering Equipment Limited, Units 1 & 2 Acton Vale Industrial Park, Cowley Road, London, W3 7QE Tel: (020) 8746 0808 Fax: (020) 8746 1116 E-mail: sales@courtcatering.co.uk

Crane Catering Services, 6 The Crescent, Station Road, Woldingham, Caterham, Surrey, CR3 7DB Tel: (01883) 652045 Fax: (01883) 652097

D Tipton, Kinston Elms, Church Road, North Leigh, Witney, Oxfordshire, OX29 6TX Tel: (01993) 881651 Fax: (01993) 883424

Daly Catering & Bakery Maintenance, Unit 4 Lennox Industrial Mall, Lennox Road, Basingstoke, Hampshire, RG22 4AP Tel: (01256) 364500 Fax: (01256) 814069 E-mail: sarah.daly@daly-electrical.co.uk

Devons Catering Equipment, 1589-1593 London Road, London, SW16 4AA Tel: (020) 8679 8585 Fax: (020) 86796633 E-mail: info@devonscatering.co.uk

Dickinson Catering Equipment, 7 Stalbridge Road, Crewe, CW2 7LR Tel: 0800-977 5325 Fax: (01270) 215213 E-mail: menderman@aol.com

E F R Refrigeration, 695 High Road, Ilford, Essex, IG3 8RH Tel: (020) 8590 0022 Fax: (020) 8599 2870 E-mail: danney535@fsmail.net

Edwards Of Oldham Ltd, Shaw Road, Royton, Oldham, OL2 6EF Tel: 0161-665 2001 Fax: 0161-624 9300

Enodis (UK) Food Service Ltd, Unit 5E, Langley Business Centre, Station Road, Langley, Slough, SL3 8DS Tel: (01753) 485900 E-mail: enodis.uk.sales@enodis.com

First In Service Ltd, Windsor Industrial Estate, Rupert Street, Birmingham, B7 4PR Tel: 0121-333 3301 Fax: 0121-333 3302 E-mail: sellis@firstinservice.co.uk

Food Service Engineers Ltd Ltd, Ilkley Road, Wharfedenk Business Centre, Otley, W. Yorkshire, LS21 3JP Tel: (01943) 467467 Fax: (01943) 467565 E-mail: beamhouse@aol.com

▶ Gas Catering Services, 18 Robert Cort Industrial Estate, Britten Road, Reading, RG2 0AU Tel: 0118-975 6500 Fax: 0118-975 1222 E-mail: info@gascatering.co.uk

Grampian Catering Equipment Ltd, Unit 2, New Inn Buildings, Market Street, Ellon, Aberdeenshire, AB41 9JD Tel: (01358) 729500 Fax: (01358) 729501 E-mail: sales@grampiancateringequipment.co.uk

Hatfield Catering Equipment, Foundry Street, Chesterfield, Derbyshire, S41 9AU Tel: (01246) 454533 Fax: (01246) 455316 E-mail: sales@hatfieldcatering.co.uk

Hobart UK, 51 The Bourne, Southgate, London, N14 6RT Tel: (0844) 8887777 Fax: (020) 8886 0450 E-mail: info@hobartuk.com

Independent Catering Engineers Ltd, Crossley New Road, Todmorden, Lancashire, OL14 8RP Tel: (01706) 819901 Fax: (01706) 819902

K B Catering Ltd, Unit 15, Craven Way, Newmarket, Suffolk, CB8 0BW Tel: (01638) 667994 Fax: (01638) 665970 E-mail: sales@kb-catering.co.uk

Kitcheneers Ltd, Monarch House, Honeywell Lane, Oldham, OL8 2LY Tel: 0161-665 5800 Fax: 0161-627 4507 E-mail: sales@kitcheneers.co.uk

L C Kittow Ltd, 34 Spear Road, Southampton, SO14 6UH Tel: (023) 8032 2650 Fax: (023) 8032 2651 E-mail: info@lckittow.com

Linkgain Services, 14 Larksfield Close, Carterton, Oxfordshire, OX18 3SY Tel: (01993) 844589 Fax: (01993) 212801 E-mail: linkgain@ntlworld.com

M & D Commerical Kitchens, 1A Union Street, Royton, Oldham, OL2 5JD Tel: 0161-620 5556 Fax: 0161-620 5556

M S A Ltd, Wassalls Hall, Bishops Wood Road, Wickham, Hampshire, PO17 5AT Tel: (01329) 835440 Fax: (01329) 835430 E-mail: sales@msaltd.com

J.C. McCollom, 2 Carew Street, London, SE5 9DF Tel: (020) 7733 7025 Fax: (020) 7733 7025

▶ Magnetron Catering Equipment, 5-21 Carrock Road, Croft Business Park, Bromborough, Wirral, Merseyside, CH62 3RA Tel: (0870) 8400720 Fax: (08708) 740721 E-mail: sales@catmag.fsnet.co.uk

Mayday Commercial Catering Services, 21 Walmley Ash Road, Sutton Coldfield, West Midlands, B76 1HY Tel: 0121-313 0301

Mend-All Catering Services Ltd, 24 Cromwell Road, Hove, East Sussex, BN3 3EB Tel: 01273 777200

Millers Catering Equipment, Unit 2 College Fields Business Centre, Prince Georges Road, Merton, London, SW19 2PT Tel: (020) 8687 5390 Fax: (020) 8687 5399 E-mail: sales@millerscatering.co.uk

Nene Catering Equipment, 19 Upper Priory Street, Grafton Street Industrial Estate, Northampton, NN1 2PT Tel: (01604) 621555 Fax: (01604) 621383 E-mail: sales@nenecateringequipment.co.uk

Normanton Catering, Normanton Works, 2 Crompton Street, Shaw, Oldham, OL2 8AG Tel: (01706) 291783 Fax: (01706) 291783 E-mail: office@normantonltd.com

P & A Services Ltd, Pepper Road, Hazel Grove, Stockport, Cheshire, SK7 5BW Tel: 0161-483 8060 Fax: 0161-483 8066 E-mail: sales@paservice.co.uk

▶ Select Fabrications Ltd, Unit 3 2-3 King Edward Close, Worthing, West Sussex, BN14 8DJ Tel: (01903) 238225 Fax: (01903) 238225

Severn Catering Services Ltd, Rivendel House, Saul, Gloucester, GL2 7LG Tel: 01452 740033

Walter Sharp & Sons, 498 Calder Street, Glasgow, G42 0QD Tel: 0141-423 8300 Fax: 0141-423 9200

Sherwood Enterprise, Unit 5a, Bailey Gate Industrial Estate, Sturminster Marshall, Wimborne, Dorset, BH21 4DB Tel: (01258) 857703 Fax: (01258) 858383 E-mail: yonkos@aol.com

Slicer Maintenance Services, PO Box 152, Macclesfield, Cheshire, SK10 4LX Tel: (01625) 827827 Fax: 01625 820011 E-mail: enquiries@smsfoodequip.com

Swift Maintenance Services, Unit 2 Albert Street, Wednesbury, West Midlands, WS10 7EW Tel: 0121-505 4001 Fax: 0121-502 2065

▶ T T Catering Solutions Ltd, Unit 3-4 Swan Park, Kettlebrook Road, Tamworth, Staffordshire, B77 1AG Tel: (01827) 54400 Fax: (01827) 315016 E-mail: tedblake@ttcatsol.co.uk

Tates, 4 Knightwood Court, Shuttleworth Close, Gapton Hall Industrial Estate, Great Yarmouth, Norfolk, NR31 0NQ Tel: (01493) 604197 Fax: (01493) 652816 E-mail: enquiries@tatesengineering.com

Technifix Catering Equipment, Nigg Station, Arabella, Tain, Ross-Shire, IV19 1QH Tel: (01862) 863231 Fax: (01862) 863343 E-mail: sales@technifix.com

▶ Tecs Catering Equipment, 329 Alder Road, Poole, Dorset, BH12 5BH Tel: (01202) 536322

Truscott Catering Equipment Ltd, 54c South Nelson Road, South Nelson Industrial Estate, Cramlington, Northumberland, NE23 1WF Tel: (01670) 714440 Fax: (01670) 715585

Tyrrell Services, 29 Cavendish Road, Woking, Surrey, GU22 0EP Tel: (01483) 776684 Fax: (01483) 776684

▶ Walker Catering Supplies Ltd, Sherwood House, Bloomsgrove Industrial Estate, Nottingham, NG7 3JG Tel: 0115-979 0110 Fax: 0115-979 1393 E-mail: info@walkercateringsupplies.com

Yorkshire Glass & Dishwashers, Unit 1 Wood Street, Brighouse, West Yorkshire, HD6 1PW Tel: (01484) 712270 Fax: (01484) 712369

CATERING EQUIPMENT HIRE

1st Class Catering Equipment Hire, 29 Flash Lane, Mirfield, West Yorkshire, WF14 0PJ Tel: (01924) 496592 Fax: (01924) 496592

5 Star Catering Equipment Hire, 20 Greys Court, Kingsland Grange, Woolston, Warrington, WA1 4SH Tel: 0161-835 4040 Fax: (01925) 820179 E-mail: sales@5starhire.co.uk

Abba Party Land, 1a Greenford Avenue, Southall, Middlesex, UB1 2AA Tel: (020) 8574 8275 Fax: (020) 8574 6036

Ace Catering Hire, 115 Nursery Gardens, Staines, Middlesex, TW18 1EL Tel: (01784) 455243 Fax: (01784) 455243 E-mail: jmansell_507@hotmail.com

▶ Allens Catering Hire, Middlesex Business Centre, Bridge Road, Southall, Middlesex, UB2 4AB Tel: (020) 8574 9600 Fax: (020) 8574 1385 E-mail: sales@allenshire.co.uk

▶ Awesome Catering, Crome Cottage, Coxford, King's Lynn, Norfolk, PE31 6TB Tel: (01485) 528816 E-mail: peter@theawesomechef.com

B & B Catering, 5 Cross Lane West, Gravesend, Kent, DA11 7PZ Tel: (01474) 535427 Fax: (01474) 322500 E-mail: sally@bandbcatering.co.uk

Barbara Caterers Hire, 20 Almond Crescent, Swanpool, Swanpool, Lincoln, LN6 0HN Tel: (01522) 859457

Butterflies Catering Equipment Hire, 4 Elm Tree Farm, Sheepway, Portbury, Bristol, BS20 7TF Tel: (01275) 375545 Fax: (01275) 374425

Camden Hire Ltd, Unit C, 125 Brantwood Road, Tottenham, London, N17 0DX Tel: (020) 8961 6161 Fax: (020) 8961 6162 E-mail: contact@thorns.co.uk

Cater Hire Ltd, Bray House, Pottersheath Road, Welwyn, Hertfordshire, AL6 9TA Tel: (01438) 815428 Fax: (01438) 815428 E-mail: caterhireagd@aol.com

Cater Hire Ltd, Unit J Gregorys Bank, Worcester, WR3 8AB Tel: (01905) 23260 Fax: (01905) 23152 E-mail: info@cater-hire.co.uk

Caterfreeze Products Ltd, 59 Main Street, Castlederg, County Tyrone, BT81 7AN Tel: (028) 8167 1247 Fax: (028) 8167 9863 E-mail: caterfreeze@btopenworld.com

Catering Concepts Ltd, Duck Pool Farm, Duck Pool Lane, Beckington, Frome, Somerset, BA11 6TX Tel: (01373) 831180 Fax: (01373) 831170 E-mail: info@cateringconceptsltd.com

Catering Equipment Engineers Ltd, Kildrum Indust Estate, Kildrum Road, Shankbridge, Ballymena, County Antrim, BT42 3EY Tel: (028) 2589 2122 Fax: (028) 2589 8208 E-mail: info@cee-group.com

Catering Linen Hire, Unit E7 Aladdin Centre, Long Drive, Greenford, Middlesex, UB6 8UH Tel: (020) 8575 1844 Fax: (020) 8575 9025 E-mail: maureen.cooper@ukonline.co.uk

Charters Ltd, 6 Centre Way, Claverings Industrial Estate, London, N9 0AP Tel: (020) 8345 6999 Fax: (020) 8345 5837 E-mail: sales@chartershire.com

Chelsea Hire, 54-58 Bunting Road, Northampton, NN2 6EE Tel: (01604) 722255 E-mail: enquiries@chelseahire.co.uk

China Trading Co., 42 Winchgrove Road, Bracknell, Berkshire, RG42 2EL Tel: (01344) 428866 Fax: (01344) 428866

Clarks Catering Hire, Tatchbury Lane, Winsor, Southampton, SO40 2GZ Tel: (023) 8081 3219

Container Kitchen Systems Ltd, Henley Park, Normandy, Guildford, Surrey, GU3 2BL Tel: (0845) 812 0800 Fax: (0845) 812 0801 E-mail: mark.kingston@ckssltd.co.uk

Co-ordination Catering Hire Ltd, Unit 4 Wallis Court, Fleming Way, Crawley, West Sussex, RH10 9NY Tel: (01293) 553040 Fax: (01293) 553020 E-mail: info@co-ordination.net

Coronet Hire Services, Parles Farm, Bank Lane, Warton, Preston, PR4 1TB Tel: (01772) 634771 Fax: (01772) 631092 E-mail: nikki.nye@tiscali.co.uk

Cotswold Crockery Hire, Well Cottage, Ewen, Cirencester, Gloucestershire, GL7 6BU Tel: (01285) 770212 Fax: (01285) 770212 E-mail: cotswoldcrockery@btopenworld.com

Cottage Catering Hire Services, Redriff, Ethelbert Road, Rochford, Essex, SS4 3JS Tel: (01702) 204472 Fax: (01702) 204521

Crystal Supplies, 4 Bessemer Road, Cardiff, CF11 8BA Tel: (029) 2022 4227 Fax: (029) 2039 0724

Davies & Davies, 22 Lower Street, Rode, Frome, Somerset, BA11 6PU Tel: (01373) 831331 Fax: (01373) 831331

Dining in Style Group Limited, 18 High Street, Pinner, Middlesex, HA5 5PW Tel: (020) 8866 7856 Fax: (020) 8866 1033 E-mail: paul@dininginstyle.co.uk

Elliott Gamble Kitchen Rental Ltd, St. Georges House, Gaddesby Lane, Rearsby, Leicester, LE7 4YH Tel: (01664) 424888 Fax: (01664) 424955 E-mail: enquiries@gamble-kr.co.uk

Fiesta, Farley Farms Bridge Farm, Reading Road, Arborfield, Reading, RG2 9HT Tel: 0118-976 2310 Fax: 0118-976 2311 E-mail: enquiries@fiestamarqueehire.co.uk

Geneen's Catering Service, Bridgebrook Shop, The Village, Great Waltham, Chelmsford, CM3 1AT Tel: (01245) 362352 Fax: (01245) 362999

▶ Green Fig Catering Ltd, 47 Station Road, Alresford, Colchester, CO7 8BU Tel: 01206 826682 E-mail: enquiries@greenfigcatering.com

Harveys Catering, Unit 4 King James Court, London, SE1 0DH Tel: (0800) 214719 Fax: (020) 7401 7794 E-mail: enquiries@harveys-catering.co.uk

Heritage Linen Hire Service Ltd, Market Place, Tetney, Grimsby, South Humberside, DN36 5NN Tel: (01472) 812161 Fax: (01472) 812161 E-mail: heritage.linen@hotmail.com

Hobart UK, 51 The Bourne, Southgate, London, N14 6RT Tel: (0844) 8887777 Fax: (020) 8886 0450 E-mail: info@hobartuk.com

▶ HSS Hire, 25 Willow Lane, Mitcham, Surrey, CR4 4TS Tel: (020) 8260 3100 Fax: (020) 8687 5005 E-mail: hire@hss.co.uk

Ian & Janet Downer Ltd, 2 Orient Road, Paignton, Devon, TQ3 2PB Tel: (01803) 527068 Fax: (01803) 527068

J B Cater Hire, Unit 10 Nursteed Road Trading Estate, Wallis Road, Devizes, Wiltshire, SN10 3EW Tel: (01380) 729192 Fax: (01380) 729192 E-mail: info@wallismarquees.co.uk

Johnson Hospitality Services Ltd, Unit 5, Martinbridge Trading Estate, Lincoln Road, Enfield, Middlesex, EN1 1QL Tel: (020) 8443 3333 Fax: (020) 8805 8710

Jongor Hampshire & Dorset Ltd, Copnor Road, Portsmouth, PO3 5LA Tel: (01202) 536306 Fax: (023) 9267 7417 E-mail: sales@jongor.com

▶ Keemlaw Ltd, Super Abbey Estate, Beddow Way, Aylesford, Kent, ME20 7BH Tel: (01732) 870078 Fax: (01732) 870068 E-mail: info@keemlaw.co.uk

Lace Hire Altrincham Ltd, 203 Woodhouse La East, Timperley, Altrincham, Cheshire, WA15 6AS Tel: 0161-905 1652 Fax: 0161-905 1652 E-mail: altcaterhire@tisacali.co.uk

Leach Glass & Catering Equipment Hire Service, Unit 3, Switch Hill, School Yard, Horbury, Wakefield, West Yorkshire, WF4 6NA Tel: (01924) 278516 Fax: (01924) 274399

Mid Somerset Catering Hire, 8 Wireworks Estate, Bristol Road, Bridgwater, Somerset, TA6 4AP Tel: (01278) 422666 Fax: (01278) 420325

Occasions Catering Hire, 12 Oak Industrial Park, Chelmsford Road, Dunmow, Essex, CM6 1XN Tel: (01371) 872183 Fax: (01371) 872838 E-mail: petersimpson@occasionscateringhire.co.uk

Old Barn Catering Hire Ltd The, The Old Barn, The Bridge, Lower Eashing, Godalming, Surrey, GU7 2QF

K.A. Owen, 3 St. John Street, Low Town, Bridgnorth, Shropshire, WV15 6AG Tel: (01746) 765476 Fax: (01746) 767344

P C H Supplies, 47 Washway Road, Sale, Cheshire, M33 7AB Tel: 0161-976 4136 Fax: 0161-439 9435

PKL Group (UK) Ltd, Stella Way, Bishops Cleeve, Cheltenham, Glos, GL52 7DQ Tel: (01242) 663000 Fax: (01242) 677819 E-mail: postbox@pkl.co.uk

Plates A Plenty, 78 Glebe Road, Minchinhampton, Stroud, Gloucestershire, GL6 9LQ Tel: (01453) 882051 Fax: (01453) 882051

▶ R & R Catering Hire Ltd, 9 Coln Park, Andoversford Industrial Estate, Andoversford, Cheltenham, Gloucestershire, GL54 4HJ Tel: (01242) 820100 Fax: (01242) 820050 E-mail: enquiries@rrhire.co.uk

Gerald Rutherford Ltd, Unit 2 Rutherford House, Upton Street, Hull, HU8 7DA Tel: (01482) 323419 Fax: (01482) 214880 E-mail: sales@rutherfordvending.co.uk

▶ Shaker UK Ltd, Unit 213 Jubilee Trade Centre, 130 Pershore Street, Birmingham, B5 6ND Tel: 0121-622 2055

South Western Equipment Catering Services, Southlands Farm, Cockers Hill, Compton Dando, Bristol, BS39 4JX Tel: (01761) 490167 Fax: (01761) 490167

▶ Stead Experience, 1 Nicholas Street, Barnsley, South Yorkshire, S70 6DU Tel: (07717) 004065E-mail: steadexperience@hotmail.com

Table Toppers, 34 Highview Gardens, Upminster, Essex, RM14 2YZ Tel: (01708) 640495

▶ Thorns Catering Hire Equipment, 1 Newhaven Business Park, Barton Lane, Eccles, Manchester, M30 0HH Tel: 0161-788 9064 Fax: 0161-788 9103

Thorns Furniture & Catering Hire plc, C 125 Brantwood Road, London, N17 0DX Tel: (020) 8801 4444 Fax: (020) 8801 4445 E-mail: contact@thorns.co.uk

Tiger Hire, Crossing Gate Farm, Thorpe Lane, Eagle, Lincoln, LN6 9DY Tel: (01522) 869641 Fax: (01522) 869641 E-mail: tigerhire@fsbdial.co.uk

Top Table, 31 Whiteley Village, Whiteley Way, Whiteley, Fareham, Hampshire, PO15 7LJ Tel: (01489) 580258 Fax: (01489) 580258 E-mail: whitley@lifstyle.co.uk

Top Table Ltd, White Woods, Brasted Chart, Westerham, Kent, TN16 1LS Tel: (01959) 561363 Fax: (01959) 561363

Top Table Catering Hire, 13 Bessemer Close, Cardiff, CF11 8DL Tel: (029) 2023 2408 E-mail: toptable@cf11.fsnet.co.uk

Top Table Catering Hire, 6 Yeoman Close, Kidderminster, Worcestershire, DY10 1NU Tel: (01562) 637557 Fax: (01562) 743028

Top Table Hire, Dairy Farm, Eydon Road, Woodford Halse, Daventry, Northamptonshire, NN11 3RG Tel: (01327) 260575 Fax: (01327) 261843 E-mail: sales@toptablehire.com

Trent Pottery A Funiture Ltd, Regent Street, Narborough, Leicester, LE19 2DS Tel: 0116-286 4911 Fax: 0116-286 7286 E-mail: sales@pubfurnitureuk.co.uk

Well Laid Table, Green Acres, Whaplode Drove, Spalding, Lincolnshire, PE12 0SP Tel: (01406) 330206 Fax: (01406) 330206

Wessex Cater Hire, 17 St. James Road, Southampton, SO15 5FB Tel: (023) 8077 5497 Fax: (023) 8077 5548 E-mail: info@wessexcaterhire.co.uk

▶ Western Event Hire, C Clarke Centre, Hennock Road North, Marsh Barton Trading Estate, Exeter, EX2 8NJ Tel: (0845) 6061062 Fax: (01392) 411952

Whittlesey Catering Hire Ltd, Unit 15 Springwater Business Park, Station Road, Whittlesey, Peterborough, PE7 2EU Tel: (01733) 203491 Fax: (01733) 203491 E-mail: sales@cateringhireuk.com

CATERING EQUIPMENT MAINTENANCE

AGGORA (Technical) Ltd, Centech House, Centech Park, Fringe Meadow Road, Redditch, Worcestershire, B98 9NR Tel: (0845) 1177999 Fax: (0845) 1177222 E-mail: solutions@aggora.co.uk

CATERING EQUIPMENT MANUFACTURERS

▶ RSC Services, 74 Wrexham Avenue, Walsall, WS2 0DQ Tel: (07855) 302995 E-mail: richard@rstowe.wanadoo.co.uk

CATERING EQUIPMENT MANUFRS, *See also headings for particular items or usage*

A M A Fabrications Ltd, Low Mill Lane, Ravensthorpe Industrial Estate, Dewsbury, West Yorkshire, WF13 3LN Tel: (01924) 507217 Fax: (01924) 507216 E-mail: sales@ama-fabs.co.uk

Ace General Engineering Cornwall Ltd, Quarry Park Road, Newquay, Cornwall, TR7 2NY Tel: (01637) 873324 Fax: (01637) 876904

Airedale Catering Equipment Ltd, Airedale House, Victoria Road, Eccleshill, Bradford, West Yorkshire, BD2 2BN Tel: (01274) 626666 Fax: (01274) 626750 E-mail: design@airedale-group.co.uk

Aluline T/A Olympic, 59-62 Brindley Road, Astmoor Industrial Estate, Runcorn, Cheshire, WA7 1PF Tel: (01928) 563532 Fax: (01928) 580224 E-mail: accounts@barolympics.co.uk

Anchor Food Service Equipment Ltd, 4 Capital Industrial Estate, Crabtree Manorway South, Belvedere, Kent, DA17 6BJ Tel: (020) 8311 1313 Fax: (020) 8311 4431 E-mail: anchor.food@btclick.com

Asmex Ltd, Unit 43 Gemini Business Estate, Landmann Way, London, SE14 5RL Tel: (020) 7394 9090 Fax: (020) 7394 9191

B E K Engineering Ltd, Unit C1, New St, Charfield, Wotton-under-Edge, Gloucestershire, GL12 8ES Tel: (01453) 844372 Fax: (01453) 842050 E-mail: bek@harris-pye.com

Bentsfield Engineering Ltd, Holme Mills, West Slaithwaite Road, Huddersfield, HD7 6LS Tel: (01484) 841100 Fax: (01484) 841919 E-mail: enqurles@bentsfield.com

Bishop's Express, 8-9 Flexi Units, Budlake Road, Marsh Barton Trading Estate, Exeter, EX2 8PY Tel: (01392) 271237 Fax: (01392) 272171

E.A. Bitterling Ltd, Poulton Drive, Daleside Road Industrial Estate, Nottingham, NG2 4BN Tel: 0115-986 2934 Fax: 0115-986 3027 E-mail: info@bitterling.co.uk

CCE Group Ltd, Bentley Farm, Unit 1, Old Church Hill, Langdon Hills, Basildon, Essex, SS16 6HZ Tel: (01268) 412121 Fax: (01268) 412600 E-mail: sales@contractcateringequipment.co.uk

Calomax Ltd, Lupton Avenue, Leeds, LS9 7DD Tel: 0113-249 6681 Fax: 0113-235 0358 E-mail: sales@calomax.co.uk

Caterers Equipment World, 121 Avenue Street, Parkhead, Glasgow, G40 3SA Tel: 0141 5565740 Fax: 0141 5565740 E-mail: enquiries@cew-soltan.co.uk

Catering-Suppliers.com, PO Box 12976, Witton, B6 7AP Tel: 0121-331 4200 E-mail: cateringsuppliers@gmail.com

Catershop Catering Equipment, 3 Robberds Way, Bowthorpe Employment Area, Norwich, NR5 9JF Tel: (01603) 741133 Fax: (01603) 744255 E-mail: sales@catershop.co.uk

Commercial Catering Centre, 46b Grasmere Road, Blackpool, FY1 5HT Tel: (01253) 292976 Fax: (01253) 292977 E-mail: markconstantine@aol.com

County Engineering (Lincoln) Ltd, 23 Crofton Road, Allenby Industrial Estate, Lincoln, LN3 4NL Tel: (01522) 510753 Fax: (01522) 560497 E-mail: sales@county-engineering.co.uk

Crolla Ice Cream Co. Ltd, 48 Jessie Street, Glasgow, G42 0PG Tel: 0141-423 1161 Fax: 0141-423 2596 E-mail: sales@crollaicecream.co.uk

Custom Stainless Fabrication Ltd, Unit 20 Leyton Business Centre, Etloe Rd, London, E10 7BT Tel: (020) 8558 2596 Fax: (020) 8558 7650 E-mail: csfltd@talk21.com

Dame Catering, 49 Milton Road, Westcliff-on-Sea, Essex, SS0 7JP Tel: (01702) 354541 Fax: (01702) 431775 E-mail: catering@uktraders.com

Denton's Catering Equipment Ltd, 2-4 Clapham High Street, London, SW4 7UT Tel: (020) 7622 7157 Fax: (020) 7622 5546 E-mail: sales@dentons.co.uk

Disposables & Catering Supplies, Haltwhistle House, Haltwhistle Road, South Woodham Ferrers, Chelmsford, CM3 5ZA Tel: (01245) 320839 Fax: (01245) 322256 E-mail: sales@dcs-swf.co.uk

Dtech Catering Ltd, Wedgwood Works, Ravensdale, Stoke-On-Trent, ST6 4NU Tel: (01782) 817521 Fax: (01782) 817520

Dualit Ltd, County Oak Way, Crawley, West Sussex, RH11 7ST Tel: (01293) 652500 Fax: (01293) 652555E-mail: sales@dualit.com

Edwards Of Oldham Ltd, Shaw Road, Royton, Oldham, OL2 6EF Tel: 0161-665 2001 Fax: 0161-624 9300

Ellidge Ltd, Henderson Street, Littleborough, Lancashire, OL15 8DT Tel: (01706) 378400 Fax: (01706) 378400

Ellidge & Fairley, New Line Industrial Estate, The Sidings, Bacup, Lancashire, OL13 9RW Tel: (01706) 875175 Fax: (01706) 875120 E-mail: info@ellidgefairley.co.uk

Enodis Ltd, Provincial Park, Nether Lane, Ecclesfield, Sheffield, S35 9ZX Tel: 0114-257 0100 Fax: 0114-257 0251 E-mail: geremy.hobbs@enodis.co.uk

Ensign Associates, 75 Bourn Lea, Houghton le Spring, Tyne & Wear, DH4 4PF Tel: 0191-385 5188 Fax: 0191-385 5188

Fairfax Display Co. Ltd, 137A Cowick Street, St. Thomas, Exeter, EX4 1HS Tel: (01392) 273324 Fax: (01392) 410808

Falcon Food Service Equipment, PO Box 37, Stirling, FK9 5PY Tel: (01786) 455200 Fax: (01786) 469454 E-mail: info@afefalcon.com

Fast Food Essentials Direct, PO Box 1, Halesowen, W. Midlands, B63 2RB Tel: (0845) 6014713 Fax: (0845) 6014201 E-mail: sales@fastfoodessentials.com

Frymaster Catering Equipment, 9 North Street, Rugby, Warwickshire, CV21 2AB Tel: (01788) 537111 Fax: (01788) 541199

G S K Fabrications, 3 Capel Road, Clydach, Swansea, SA6 5PZ Tel: (01792) 849494 Fax: (01792) 849494 E-mail: stephen@gsk-fabrications.co.uk

Goldstar Fabrication & Ventilation, Haven Road, Colchester, CO2 8HT Tel: (01206) 867770 Fax: (01206) 867771 E-mail: enquiries@goldstatfabs.demom.co.uk

Grayshott Stoneware Ltd, School Road, Grayshott, Hindhead, Surrey, GU26 6LR Tel: (01428) 604404 Fax: (01428) 604944 E-mail: sales@grayshottpottery.com

H M Stainless Fabrications Ltd, 227 Bradford Road, Batley, West Yorkshire, WF17 6JL Tel: (01924) 266422 Fax: (01924) 266423 E-mail: david.keylorson@btconnect.com

J. Reuben Hobson & Co. Ltd, Albany House, 6 Wicker Lane, Sheffield, S3 8HQ Tel: 0114-272 1604 Fax: 0114-275 5567

Hopkins X L Ltd, 151 Kent Road, Pudsey, West Yorkshire, LS28 9NF Tel: 0113-257 7934 Fax: 0113-257 6759 E-mail: sales@hopkins.biz

Instanta Ltd, Canning Road, Southport, Merseyside, PR9 7SN Tel: (01704) 501114 Fax: (01704) 501115 E-mail: info@instanta.com

J & J Products Ashford Ltd, 3 River Gardens Business Centre, Spur Road, Feltham, Middlesex, TW14 0SN Tel: (020) 8890 5085 Fax: (020) 8751 1896 E-mail: jj.products@cwcom.net

J W F (UK) Ltd, 2 Stevenson Road, Sheffield, S9 3XG Tel: 0114-244 8821 Fax: 0114-244 4084

Jackson & Kelly Ltd, Wernolau Fawr, Llanboidy, Whitland, Dyfed, SA34 0EN Tel: (01994) 448245 Fax: (01994) 448752

Leon Jaeggi & Sons, Helcetia House, Austin Road, Ashford, Kent, TN23 6JR Tel: (01233) 634635 Fax: (01233) 633311 E-mail: leon@jaeggi.com

James Whiteside & Co., 141 Church Lane, East Peckham, Tonbridge, Kent, TN12 5JJ Tel: (01622) 871513 Fax: (01622) 871992 E-mail: jameswhitesideco@btopenworld.com

Jetpacks, 39 Stockport Road, Marple, Stockport, Cheshire, SK6 6BD Tel: 0161-449 5657 Fax: 0161-484 5420 E-mail: info@jetpacks.com

▶ Just Catering Ltd, Jessop Avenue, Norwood Green, Southall, Middlesex, UB2 5UY Tel: (0845) 0034271 Fax: (0845) 0034271 E-mail: sales@justcatering.com

Klaremont Foods Service Products Ltd, 67 Weir Road, London, SW19 8UG Tel: (020) 8971 2012 Fax: (020) 8971 2005 E-mail: sales@klaremont.com

Ling Marketing, Stones House, Lower Broad Oak Road, West Hill, Ottery St. Mary, Devon, EX11 1XH Tel: (01404) 811111 Fax: (01404) 811345

London Catering Disposables, 43 Southfields Road, London, SW18 1QW Tel: (020) 8874 7951 Fax: (020) 8877 1806 E-mail: lcd43@btinternet.com

M B M UK, Eurotec Building, New Road, Newhaven, E. Sussex, BN9 0DR Tel: (01273) 472554 Fax: (01273) 476100

Mainland Catering Equipment Ltd, Unit 1a Fountain Mill, Rakefoot, Haslingden, Rossendale, Lancashire, BB4 5RE Tel: (01706) 244810 Fax: (01706) 244811 E-mail: sales@mainlandcatering.co.uk

Max Appliances Ltd, Kingfisher House, Wheel Park, Westfield, Hastings, East Sussex, TN35 4SE Tel: (01424) 751666 Fax: (01424) 751444 E-mail: sales@max-appliances.co.uk

E & R Moffat Ltd, Bonnymuir Works, Seabegs Road, Bonnybridge, Stirlingshire, FK4 2BS Tel: (01324) 812272 Fax: (01324) 814107 E-mail: sales@ermoffat.co.uk

CATERING EQUIPMENT MANUFRS

– continued

R.H. Morton & Co. Ltd, 22 Crownpoint Road, Glasgow, G40 2BS Tel: 0141 5518136
New Concept (Scotland) Ltd, 588 Glasgow Road, Clydebank, Dunbartonshire, G81 1NH Tel: 0141-952 7901 Fax: 0141-941 1006 E-mail: sales@newconcept-ltd.com
Northern Refrigeration & Catering Equipment Ltd, Rotherside Road, Eckington, Sheffield, S21 4HL Tel: (01246) 434340 Fax: (01246) 434341
Promart Manufacturing Ltd, Caddick Road, Knowsley Industrial Park South, Knowsley Business Park, Prescot, Merseyside, L34 9HP Tel: 0151-547 4666 Fax: 0151-546 6152 E-mail: sales@promart.co.uk
The Rank Co. Ltd, Isaacs Place, Port Talbot, West Glamorgan, SA12 6NP Tel: (01639) 882540 Fax: (01639) 892483
Reed Fabrications, Station Road, North Hykeham, Lincoln, LN6 3QY Tel: (01522) 693974 Fax: (01522) 501731
Reward Manufacturing Company Ltd, Sackville Mills, Sackville Street, Skipton, North Yorkshire, BD23 2PR Tel: (01756) 797755 Fax: (01756) 796644 E-mail: info@rewardtrolleys.com
Samuel Groves & Co. Ltd, Norton Street, Birmingham, B18 5RQ Tel: 0121-554 2001 Fax: 0121-523 2924 E-mail: sales@samuelgroves.co.uk
Severn Catering Equipment, 9 Suffolk Parade, Cheltenham, Gloucestershire, GL50 2AB Tel: (01242) 234307 Fax: (01242) 262656
Alan Silverwood Ltd, Ledsam House, Ledsam Street, Birmingham, B16 8DN Tel: 0121-454 3571 Fax: 0121-454 6749 E-mail: sales@alan-silverwood.co.uk
South Coast Catering, 43 Seaside, Eastbourne, East Sussex, BN22 7NB Tel: (01323) 444530 Fax: (01323) 641176 E-mail: info@sccuk.com
Southcroft Engineering Co. Ltd, Thurcroft Industrial Estate, New Orchard Road, Thurcroft, Rotherham, South Yorkshire, S66 9HY Tel: (01709) 545147 Fax: (01709) 700259
Stainless Design Services Ltd, C The Old Bakery, Kiln Lane, Swindon, SN2 2NP Tel: (01793) 692666 Fax: (01793) 487242 E-mail: sds@stainlessdesign.co.uk
Samuel Staniforth Ltd, Old Lane, Halfway, Sheffield, S20 3GZ Tel: 0114-248 8250 Fax: 0114-258 6066 E-mail: info@s-stainiforth.co.uk
Stigwood & Sons, Grafton Street, Oldham, OL1 4SD Tel: 0161-633 3398 Fax: 0161-633 3398
Stirling Steelcraft (Liverpool) Ltd, 11-13 Cheapside, Liverpool, L2 2DY Tel: 0151-236 4752 Fax: 0151-236 5466
T S E (Catering Equipment) Ltd, Valmar Trading Estate, Valmar Road, Camberwell Green, London, SE5 9NP Tel: (020) 7274 4577 Fax: (020) 7978 8141
Techbake Ltd, Ham Farm, Southwick, Fareham, Hants, PO17 6AU Tel: 023 92215521 Fax: 023 92214521
Teejay Workwear Ltd, Dy2 Dean Clough Office Park, Halifax, West Yorkshire, HX3 5AX Tel: (01422) 369754 Fax: (01422) 383223 E-mail: sales@teejayworkwear.co.uk
Thames Valley Catering Equipment, 11 Strawberry Hill, Bloxham, Banbury, Oxfordshire, OX15 4NW Tel: 01295 677058 E-mail: simonwratten@btinternet.com
Timmick Precision Engineering, 17 Arkwright Court, Astmoor, Runcorn, Cheshire, WA7 1NX Tel: (01928) 563009 Fax: (01928) 563009
Unitech Engineering Ltd, Prospect Road, Burntwood, Staffordshire, WS7 0AL Tel: (01543) 675800 Fax: (01543) 687070 E-mail: info@unitech.uk.com
R.S. Vent, 28 Swan Road, Washington, Tyne & Wear, NE38 8JJ Tel: 0191 4165737
West 9 Coffee Ltd, Arabica House, The Pines, Broad Street, Guildford, Surrey, GU3 3VH Tel: (01483) 303641 Fax: (01483) 303615
Weston Catering Products, Unit B3, Oldmixon Cresent, Weston-Super-Mare, Avon, BS24 9AY Tel: (01934) 642477 Fax: (01934) 624484
Wilman Universal Industries, Green Lane, Hounslow, TW4 6DF Tel: (020) 8570 4455 Fax: (020) 8572 2389 E-mail: sales@universaldispensesystems.com

CATERING EQUIPMENT SERVICING

AGGORA (Technical) Ltd, Centech House, Centech Park, Fringe Meadow Road, Redditch, Worcestershire, B98 9NR Tel: (0845) 1177999 Fax: (0845) 1177222 E-mail: solutions@aggora.co.uk

CATERING EQUIPMENT WHOLESALERS

Anglia Glassware & Bar Supplies, 6 Oakfield, Stebbing, Dunmow, Essex, CM6 3SX Tel: (01371) 856857 Fax: (01371) 874040 E-mail: angliaglassware@btclick.com
Catering World, Millcroft Road, Rutherglen, Glasgow, G73 1EN Tel: 0141-613 2075 Fax: 0141-613 2085 E-mail: enquiries@catering-world.co.uk
▶ Cutting Edge Food Equipment, 4C Station Yard, Thame, Oxfordshire, OX9 3UH Tel: (01844) 212120 Fax: (01844) 212550 E-mail: dhazel@aol.com
▶ Forthcare, Unit 7, Hardengreen Industrial Estate, Dalkeith, Midlothian, EH22 3NX Tel: 0131-663 7175 Fax: 0131-663 7175
G S Catering, 36-38 Castleton Boulevard, Skegness, Lincolnshire, PE25 2TS Tel: (01754) 764933 Fax: (01754) 764933
▶ The London Tiffin Co, Unit Cu533 St Martins Square Middle Mall, Bullring, Birmingham, B5 4BE Tel: 0121-616 2407 Fax: 0121-616 1448 E-mail: bullring@tiffinbite.com
▶ Watco Refrigeration Ltd, Unit 1 Hardengreen Industrial Estate, Dalkeith, Midlothian, EH22 3NX Tel: 0131-561 9502 Fax: 0131-561 9503

CATERING EQUIPMENT, ADJUSTABLE FOOT INSERTS

▶ Grease Guardian Products, Unit 1 Wareley Road, Woodston, Peterborough, PE2 9PF Tel: 01733 755500 Fax: 01733 704795 E-mail: sales@greaseguardian.info

CATERING EQUIPMENT, CARVING KNIVES, WOODEN HANDLE

Eurocater, Suite 201 - 205 Grosvenor Gardens House, 35 - 37 Grosvenor Gardens, Victoria, London, UK, SW1W 0BS Tel: 0207 630 4880 Fax: 0207 630 4890 E-mail: info@eurocater.co.uk

CATERING EQUIPMENT, COLD ROOMS

CMR Catering Equipment, 27 Queen Street, Ashford, Kent, TN23 1RF Tel: (07773) 885556
CMR Catering Equipment, 27 Queen Street, Ashford, Kent, TN23 1RF Tel: (07773) 885556 Fax: (0871) 2301318 E-mail: info@cmr-catering-equipment.co.uk
▶ Coldhold Systems Ltd, Albright Road, Widnes, Cheshire, WA8 8FY Tel: 0151-423 0023 Fax: 0151-423 0043 E-mail: info@coldhold.com
Eurocater, Suite 201 - 205 Grosvenor Gardens House, 35 - 37 Grosvenor Gardens, Victoria, London, UK, SW1W 0BS Tel: 0207 630 4880 Fax: 0207 630 4890 E-mail: info@eurocater.co.uk
Brian Greslow, 6-8 lime grove, Seaforth, liverpool, L21 3TT Tel: (0800) 458 1920 Fax: 0151-474 5353

CATERING EQUIPMENT, COOKING EQUIPMENT

CMR Catering Equipment, 27 Queen Street, Ashford, Kent, TN23 1RF Tel: (07773) 885556
CMR Catering Equipment, 27 Queen Street, Ashford, Kent, TN23 1RF Tel: (07773) 885556 Fax: (0871) 2301318 E-mail: info@cmr-catering-equipment.co.uk
Eurocater, Suite 201 - 205 Grosvenor Gardens House, 35 - 37 Grosvenor Gardens, Victoria, London, UK, SW1W 0BS Tel: 0207 630 4880 Fax: 0207 630 4890 E-mail: info@eurocater.co.uk
Galgrom Group, 81-87 Academy Street, Belfast, BT1 2LS Tel: (028) 9032 2042 Fax: (028) 9023 3119 E-mail: sales@galgormgroup.com
Brian Greslow, 6-8 lime grove, Seaforth, liverpool, L21 3TT Tel: (0800) 458 1920 Fax: 0151-474 5353
Unox UK, Unit 3 Marsh Farm Business Centre, Bowling Alley, Crondall, Farnham, Surrey, GU10 5RJ Tel: (01252) 851522 Fax: (01252) 851492 E-mail: info@unoxuk.com

CATERING EQUIPMENT, FRYERS, HOT AIR

Buyers Mate, 218F Sackville Place, 44-48 Magdalen Street, Norwich, NR23 1JU Tel: (01603) 611642 Fax: (01603) 115792 E-mail: sales@buyersmate.net
Dorset Food Machinery, 29c St. Catherines Road, Bournemouth, BH6 4AE Tel: (01202) 423754 Fax: (01202) 434583

CATERING EQUIPMENT, JUICERS, BAR

Naked Orange, Fresh Produce Unit, Ballingry, Lochgelly, Fife, KY5 8LR Tel: (01592) 860490 E-mail: mwood869@btinternet.com

CATERING EQUIPMENT, PEPPER MILL AND SALT SHAKER SETS

Cookequip Ltd, Unit 4, Sumner Place, Addlestone, Surrey, KT15 1QD Tel: (01932) 841171 E-mail: sales@cookequip.co.uk

CATERING EQUIPMENT, PIZZA OVENS, USED

Brian Greslow, 6-8 lime grove, Seaforth, liverpool, L21 3TT Tel: (0800) 458 1920 Fax: 0151-474 5353

CATERING EQUIPMENT, WATER FILTRATION SYSTEMS, COMBINATION OVEN

Old Ford Ltd, 381 Old Ford Road, London, E3 2LU Tel: (020) 8981 7373 Fax: (020) 8981 2784 E-mail: catering@oldford.co.uk
▶ T T Catering Solutions Ltd, Unit 3-4 Swan Park, Kettlebrook Road, Tamworth, Staffordshire, B77 1AG Tel: (01827) 54400 Fax: (01827) 315016 E-mail: tedblake@ttcatsol.co.uk

CATERING ESPRESSO MACHINES

▶ Espressocare, 12 Gordon Street, Colne, Lancashire, BB8 0NE Tel: 01282 710651 Fax: 01282 710651 E-mail: sales@espressocare.co.uk

CATERING GLASSWARE HIRE

Lace Hire Altrincham Ltd, 203 Woodhouse La East, Timperley, Altrincham, Cheshire, WA15 6AS Tel: 0161-905 1652 Fax: 0161-905 1652 E-mail: altcaterhire@tisacali.co.uk

CATERING HEATED TROLLEYS

Jones Bros & Warriss Ltd, 104 Mary St, Sheffield, S1 4RU Tel: 0114-272 0820 Fax: 0114-272 9011 E-mail: warriss@gxn.co.uk
Reward Manufacturing Company Ltd, Sackville Mills, Sackville Street, Skipton, North Yorkshire, BD23 2PR Tel: (01756) 797755 Fax: (01756) 796644 E-mail: info@rewardtrolleys.com
Stellex Ltd, Hadston Industrial Estate, Hadston, Morpeth, Northumberland, NE65 9YG Tel: (01670) 760082 Fax: (01670) 761404 E-mail: sales@stellex.co.uk

CATERING HEATING ELEMENTS

T P Fay (Kirkby) Ltd, 1 Spinney Close, Kirkby, Liverpool, L33 7XZ Tel: 0151-546 6232 Fax: 0151-549 1477E-mail: sales@tpfay.co.uk

CATERING HYGIENE SERVICES

Davenport House, Worfield, Bridgnorth, Shropshire, WV15 5LE Tel: (01746) 716221 Fax: (01746) 716021
Instock Disposables Ltd, Howe Moss Drive, Kirkhill Industrial Estate, Dyce, Aberdeen, AB21 0GL Tel: (01224) 723823 Fax: (01224) 725586
Moveable Feasts, 60 Albany Road, Broughty Ferry, Dundee, DD5 1NW Tel: (01382) 480811

CATERING INDUSTRY ADVISORY SERVICES

British Hospitality Association, Queens House, 55-56 Lincolns Inn Fields, London, WC2A 3BH Tel: (020) 7404 7744 Fax: (020) 7404 7799 E-mail: bha@bha.org.uk

CATERING KITCHEN PLANNERS/DESIGNERS/ CONSULTANTS

A A Interior Design Ltd, 187 Downs Road, Walmer, Deal, Kent, CT14 7TL Tel: (01304) 373205 Fax: (01304) 373205 E-mail: info@aadesign.uk.com
Architectural & Industrial Group, 29 High Street, Hampton Wick, Kingston upon Thames, Surrey, KT1 4DA Tel: (020) 8977 8203 Fax: (01932) 829706 E-mail: sales@boschkitchens.com
▶ Catering Systems Ltd, 9 Compton Road, Brighton, BN1 5AL Tel: (01273) 508626 Fax: (01273) 505852 E-mail: info@cateringsystems.co.uk
▶ Higham Furniture, Flint Barn, New Barns Farm, Drove Road, Southwick, Fareham, Hampshire, PO17 6EW Tel: (0845) 8684477 Fax: (0870) 0681067 E-mail: tim@higham.co.uk
John Strand MK Ltd, 12-22 Herga Road, Harrow, Middlesex, HA3 5AS Tel: (020) 8930 6006 Fax: (020) 8930 6008 E-mail: enquirey@johnstrand-mk.co.uk
Lockhart Catering Equipment, 8 Fountain Court, New Leaze, Bradley Stoke, Bristol, BS32 4LA Tel: (01454) 202500 Fax: (01454) 202266
Traditional Design, Unit 7 Waterside Mill, Waterside, Macclesfield, Cheshire, SK11 7HG Tel: (01625) 425292

CATERING KITCHEN VENTILATION CONTRACTORS

Audnam Metalworkers, 6 Platts Road, Stourbridge, West Midlands, DY8 4YR Tel: (01384) 374468 Fax: (01384) 440947
D M C Ltd, 7 Sherwood Court, Thurston Road, Lewisham, London, SE13 7SD Tel: (020) 8297 1001 Fax: (020) 8297 1002

CATERING PAPERBOARD DISPOSABLE CARTONS

Colpac Ltd, Enterprise Way, Maulden Road, Bedford, MK45 5BW Tel: (01525) 712261 Fax: (01525) 718205 E-mail: sales@colpac.co.uk
Edsol Ltd, Edsol House, Meanwood Road, Buslingthorpe Green, Leeds, LS7 2HG Tel: 0113-262 1122 Fax: 0113-262 3957 E-mail: info@edwardsofleeds.com

CATERING SERVICES, PERSONAL CHEF

Dining 4 You, 8 Saunders Street, Gillingham, Kent, ME7 1ET Tel: 07804 325697 E-mail: info@dining4you.co.uk
▶ your private chef, 48 cornmow Drive, London, NW10 1BA Tel: 0208 4386554 E-mail: info@yourprivatechef.co.uk

CATERING SIZE CHEESE

▶ David South Ltd, Southdale House Holloway Drive, Wardley Industrial Estate, Worsley, Manchester, M28 2LA Tel: 0161-279 8020 Fax: 0161-279 8021

CATERING STAFF RECRUITMENT AGENCIES/ CONSULTANTS/SERVICES

Blue Arrow, 5 Colston Centre, Colston Avenue, Bristol, BS1 4UB Tel: 0117-929 8435 Fax: 0117-925 0231 E-mail: info@bluearrow.co.uk
▶ D T L Training & Recruitment, Unit 1, Dunstall Hill Industrial Estate, Gorsebrook Road, Wolverhampton, WV6 0PJ Tel: (01902) 422722 Fax: (01902) 422711 E-mail: info@d-t-l.co.uk
Eden Catering Services Ltd, Ferndown Middle School, Peter Grant Way, Church Road, Ferndown, Dorset, BH22 9UP Tel: (01202) 876216
Eurest, 47-51 Kingston Crescent, Portsmouth, PO2 8AA Tel: (023) 9266 0088 Fax: (023) 9266 5590
▶ Global Choices, Barkat House, 116-118 Finchley Road, London, NW3 5HT Tel: 0207 433 2501 Fax: 0207 435 1397 E-mail: info@globalchoices.co.uk
H Careers.Company Co .Uk, Iverson Road, London, NW6 2QT Tel: (0800) 0851335 Fax: (020) 7372 4466 E-mail: mike@hcareers.co.uk
▶ Halcyon Recruitment UK Ltd, Direct House, 38-39 Centurion Way, Farington, Leyland, PR25 4GU Tel: (01772) 641268 E-mail: admin@halcyonrecruitment.co.uk
▶ The Harris Lord Group Ltd, 45a Carfax, Horsham, West Sussex, RH12 1EQ Tel: (01403) 273370 Fax: (01403) 273364
Hill Top, 36-38 Breeze Hill, Bootle, Merseyside, L20 9NZ Tel: 0151-922 5487 Fax: 0151-933 6818
▶ HR Personnel Ltd, Unit 5a Hogarth Court, Hogarth Crescent, Croydon, CR0 2JE Tel: 020 8683 7110 Fax: 0870 8903884 E-mail: rt_hrpersonnel@btconnect.com
▶ Hudsons Pantry, Hudsons Pantry, Towcester, Northamptonshire, NN12 7HT Tel: (01327) 352443 E-mail: Info@hudsonspantry.co.uk
▶ Mavero Recruitment, 145-157 St John Street, London, EC1V 4PY Tel: 0207 8710727 Fax: 0207 7882992 E-mail: info@mavero.co.uk
Orb Recruitment Ltd, PO Box 50, Manchester, M3 4EL Tel: 0161-244 5526 Fax: 0161-244 5526 E-mail: richard@premier-recruit.com
▶ Outsource 2 Solutions, Talbot House, 204-226 Imperial Drive, Rayners Lane, Harrow, Middlesex, HA2 7HH Tel: (020) 8426 1088 Fax: (020) 8426 1145 E-mail: enos@outsource2solutions.co.uk

CATERING STAFF RECRUITMENT AGENCIES/CONSULTANTS/ SERVICES – *continued*

Personnel Selection, 46 West Street, Brighton, BN1 2RA Tel: (01273) 205281 Fax: (01273) 204091 E-mail: brit@persel.co.uk

▶ Premier Recruitment International Ltd, PO Box 250, London, W1T 6DU Tel: (020) 7631 0050 Fax: 0870 288 4990 E-mail: info@premier-recruit.com

▶ Red Eagle, 38 Bouverie Square, Folkestone, Kent, CT20 1BA Tel: (01303) 851133 Fax: (01303) 851134 E-mail: jobs@red-eagle.co.uk

Redgoldfish Jobs, Cornelius House, Whitehouse Court, Cannock, Staffordshire, WS11 3DA Tel: (01543) 468800 Fax: (01543) 468900 E-mail: info@redgoldfish.co.uk

▶ Robochef Freelance Catering Services, 40 Hamill drive, Kilsyth, Glasgow, G65 0EQ Tel: (0785) 4400849 E-mail: mark@robochef.co.uk

Stafflink (UK) Ltd, 138 Lower Road, London, SE16 2UG Tel: (020) 7252 2212 Fax: (020) 7252 2901 E-mail: info@staff-link.co.uk

▶ theCATERINGjob.com, PO Box 2448, Slough, SL1 1ZB Tel: 0870 8701193 Fax: 0870 8701194 E-mail: coz.dauncey@thecateringjob.com

CATERING VENDING MACHINE SPARE PARTS

▶ Midland Vending Supplies, Unit 46 Willan Industrial Estate, West Ashton Street, Salford, M50 2XS Tel: 0161-745 9966 E-mail: midlandvendingsupplys@yahoo.co.uk

CATERING WAREWASHING EQUIPMENT

Electrolux Professional, Crystal Court, Aston Cross Business Park, Rocky Lane, Aston, Birmingham, B6 5RQ Tel: 0121-220 2800 Fax: 0121-220 2801 E-mail: foodservice@electrolux.co.uk

Hobart UK, 51 The Bourne, Southgate, London, N14 6RT Tel: (0844) 8887777 Fax: (020) 8886 0450 E-mail: info@hobartuk.com

CATERING WASTE DISPOSAL

▶ Pelican Fine Foods, 6 St. Johns Lane, Bewdley, Worcestershire, DY12 2QZ Tel: (01299) 400598 Fax: (01299) 404090 E-mail: pelican@wasteoil.co.uk

CATERING WATER COOLERS

▶ Forest Edge Water, Mill Cottage, Beaulieu, Hampshire, SO42 7YG Tel: (01590) 611227 Fax: (01590) 611487

▶ Simply Pure Water, 4 Common Road, Skelmanthorpe, Huddersfield, HD1 5EU Tel: (01484) 868226 Fax: (01484) 866677 E-mail: sales@simplypurewater.co.uk

▶ Water Smart (NW) Ltd, Unit 5 Imex Spaces, Glenfield Business Park, Philips Road, Blackburn, BB1 5PF Tel: (0845) 4506984 Fax: (01257) 793366 E-mail: watersmart@btinterent.com

CATERING WHOLESALERS

Kirby's Produce, Unit B56-B59, Fruit & Vegetable Market, New Covent Garden, Nine Elms Lane, London, SW8 5JB Tel: (020) 7622 4494 Fax: (020) 7720 5352 E-mail: info@kirbysproduce.com

CATHODE RAY TUBE CHASSIS

Video Display Europe, Unit 5 Old Forge Trading Estate, Dudley Rd, Stourbridge, W. Midlands, DY9 8EL Tel: (01384) 894777 Fax: (01384) 895788 E-mail: sales@vdceuro.com

CATHODE RAY TUBE COMPONENTS

Video Display Europe, Unit 5 Old Forge Trading Estate, Dudley Rd, Stourbridge, W. Midlands, DY9 8EL Tel: (01384) 894777 Fax: (01384) 895788 E-mail: sales@vdceuro.com

CATHODE RAY TUBES, *See also headings under Electronic Tube*

Active Electronics Plc, Albion House, Gordon Road, High Wycombe, Buckinghamshire, HP13 6ET Tel: (01494) 441414 Fax: (01494) 524674 E-mail: pool@active-electronics.co.uk

Billington Export Ltd, Units 1e-2e, Gilmans Industrial Estate, Billingshurst, West Sussex, RH14 9EZ Tel: (01403) 784961 Fax: (01403) 783519 E-mail: sales@bel-tubes.co.uk

Brimar Ltd, Greenside Way, Middleton, Manchester, M24 1SN Tel: 0161-681 7072 Fax: 0161-683 5978 E-mail: dave.eldridge@brimar.ltd.uk

C M L Innovative Technologies Ltd, Beetons Way, Bury St. Edmunds, Suffolk, IP32 6RA Tel: (01284) 762411 Fax: (01284) 754406 E-mail: sales@cml-it.com

Ginsbury Electronics Ltd, 1 Exeter House, Boufort Court, Rochester, Kent, ME2 4FE Tel: (01634) 298900 Fax: (01634) 290904 E-mail: sales@ginsbury.co.uk

M B Electronics, Clayfield Industrial Estate, Tickhill Road, Doncaster, South Yorkshire, DN4 8QG Tel: (01302) 855229 Fax: (01302) 855229

Video Display Europe, Unit 5 Old Forge Trading Estate, Dudley Rd, Stourbridge, W. Midlands, DY9 8EL Tel: (01384) 894777 Fax: (01384) 895788 E-mail: sales@vdceuro.com

CATHODIC PROTECTION DESIGN

▶ Iicorr Ltd, Greenbank Place, East Tullos, Aberdeen, AB12 3BT Tel: (01224) 898282 Fax: (01224) 898202 E-mail: dennis.parr@iicorr.co.uk

▶ MCPS Ltd, Tedco BSNS Works, Tedco Business Works, Henry Robson Way, South Shields, Tyne & Wear, NE33 1RF Tel: 0191-454 4444 Fax: 0191-427 4607 E-mail: sales@mcpsltd.com

CATHODIC PROTECTION SERVICES

B A C Corrosion Control Ltd, Stafford Park 11, Telford, Shropshire, TF3 3AY Tel: (01952) 290321 Fax: (01952) 290325 E-mail: sales@bacgroup.com

Cathelco Ltd, 18 Hipper St South, Chesterfield, Derbyshire, S40 1SS Tel: (01246) 277656 Fax: (01246) 206519 E-mail: sales@cathelco.co.uk

Cathodic Protection Co. Ltd, Venture Way, Grantham, Lincolnshire, NG31 7XS Tel: (01476) 590666 Fax: (01476) 570605 E-mail: cpc@cathodic.co.uk

Concrete Repairs Ltd, Cathite House, 23a Willow Lane, Mitcham, Surrey, CR4 4TU Tel: (020) 8288 4848 Fax: (020) 8288 4847 E-mail: sales@concrete-repairs.co.uk

Corrintec Ltd, Marine House, 18 Hipper Street South, Chesterfield, Derbyshire, S40 1SS Tel: (01246) 246700 Fax: (01246) 246701 E-mail: sales@corrintec.co.uk

Corrpro Companies Europe, 4 Mill Court, The Sawmills, Durley, Southampton, SO32 2EJ Tel: (01489) 861980 Fax: (01489) 861981 E-mail: ccel@onyxnet.co.uk

▶ Cumberland Cathodic Protection, 4 Strand View, Liverpool Intermodal Freeport Terminal, Bootle, Merseyside, L20 1HA Tel: 0151-922 3041 Fax: 0151-922 4605 E-mail: sales@cumberlandcp.com

Pipeline Maintenance Ltd, Unit 12 Merlin Park, Fred Dannatt Road, Mildenhall, Bury St. Edmunds, Suffolk, IP28 7RD Tel: (01638) 711955 Fax: (01638) 711953

Subspection Ltd, Shelf House, New Farm Road, Alresford, Hampshire, SO24 9QE Tel: (01962) 734977 Fax: (01962) 735277 E-mail: sales@subspection.com

CATHODIC PROTECTION SYSTEMS

B A C Corrosion Control Ltd, Stafford Park 11, Telford, Shropshire, TF3 3AY Tel: (01952) 290321 Fax: (01952) 290325 E-mail: sales@bacgroup.com

Cathelco Ltd, 18 Hipper St South, Chesterfield, Derbyshire, S40 1SS Tel: (01246) 277656 Fax: (01246) 206519 E-mail: sales@cathelco.co.uk

Cathodic Protection Co. Ltd, Venture Way, Grantham, Lincolnshire, NG31 7XS Tel: (01476) 590666 Fax: (01476) 570605 E-mail: cpc@cathodic.co.uk

Corrpro Companies Europe Ltd, 2 Adam Street, Stockton-on-Tees, Cleveland, TS18 3HQ Tel: (01642) 614106 Fax: (01642) 614100 E-mail: ccel@corrpro.co.uk

▶ Cumberland Cathodic Protection, 4 Strand View, Liverpool Intermodal Freeport Terminal, Bootle, Merseyside, L20 1HA Tel: 0151-922 3041 Fax: 0151-922 4605 E-mail: sales@cumberlandcp.com

M.G. Duff International Ltd, Unit 1 Timberlane Industrial Estate, Gravel Lane, Chichester, West Sussex, PO19 8PP Tel: (01243) 533336 Fax: (01243) 533422 E-mail: sales@mgduff.co.uk

Dynamics (Bristol) Ltd, 1 Evercreech Way, Walrow Industrial Estate, Highbridge, Somerset, TA9 4AN Tel: (01278) 780222 Fax: (01278) 781824 E-mail: info@dynamicsbristol.co.uk

A.H. Latham Marine, Highfield Business Centre, 1 Simmonds Road, Wincheap Industrial Estate, Canterbury, Kent, CT1 3RA Tel: (01227) 472822 Fax: (01227) 768597 E-mail: sales@zincsmart.com

Permarock Products Ltd, Jubilee Drive, Loughborough, Leicestershire, LE11 5TW Tel: (01509) 262924 Fax: (01509) 230063 E-mail: sales@permarock.com

Pipeline Maintenance Ltd, Unit 12 Merlin Park, Fred Dannatt Road, Mildenhall, Bury St. Edmunds, Suffolk, IP28 7RD Tel: (01638) 711955 Fax: (01638) 711953

Proconics Ltd, 43 Hipper St South, Chesterfield, Derbyshire, S40 1SS Tel: (01246) 221210 Fax: (01246) 563923 E-mail: petel@cathelco.co.uk

Subspection Ltd, Shelf House, New Farm Road, Alresford, Hampshire, SO24 9QE Tel: (01962) 734977 Fax: (01962) 735277 E-mail: sales@subspection.com

U S Filters Electrocatalytic Products, 9 Norman Way, Severn Bridge Industrial Estate, Portskewett, Caldicot, Gwent, NP26 5YN Tel: (01291) 426500 Fax: (01291) 426501 E-mail: sales@elcat.co.uk

▶ Z-Guard Zinc Anodes, Unit 203 Tedco Business Works, Henry Robson Way, South Shields, Tyne & Wear, NE33 1RF Tel: (0870) 2421973 Fax: (0870) 2421974 E-mail: sales@z-guard.co.uk

CATHODIC PROTECTION SYSTEMS MAINTENANCE/ REPAIR SERVICES

Corrintec Ltd, Marine House, 18 Hipper Street South, Chesterfield, Derbyshire, S40 1SS Tel: (01246) 246700 Fax: (01246) 246701 E-mail: sales@corrintec.co.uk

▶ Cumberland Cathodic Protection, 4 Strand View, Liverpool Intermodal Freeport Terminal, Bootle, Merseyside, L20 1HA Tel: 0151-922 3041 Fax: 0151-922 4605 E-mail: sales@cumberlandcp.com

Pipeline Maintenance Ltd, Unit 12 Merlin Park, Fred Dannatt Road, Mildenhall, Bury St. Edmunds, Suffolk, IP28 7RD Tel: (01638) 711955 Fax: (01638) 711953

CATTERY ANIMAL CAGES

Poltec Ltd, 1 Old Stafford Road, Slade Heath, Wolverhampton, WV10 7PH Tel: (01902) 790238 E-mail: sales@poltec.co.uk

CATTLE FEEDING FENCES

Mcveigh-Parker & Co. Ltd, Six Acre Farm, Stane Street, Adversane, Billingshurst, West Sussex, RH14 9JR Tel: (01403) 784250 Fax: (01403) 786394 E-mail: sales@mcveighparker.co.uk

CATTLE FEEDS

Clynderwen & Cardiganshire Farmers Ltd, Glanrhyd Stores, Glanrhyd, Cardigan, Dyfed, SA43 3NX Tel: (01239) 612057 Fax: (01239) 615295

Portequip Ltd, Penninghame Home Farm, Penninghame, Newton Stewart, Wigtownshire, DG8 6RD Tel: (01671) 402775 Fax: (01671) 403791

CAULKING COMPOUNDS

Kalon Pension Trustees Ltd, Huddersfield Road, Birstall, Batley, West Yorkshire, WF17 9XA Tel: (01924) 354000 Fax: (01924) 354001 E-mail: sales@kalon.co.uk

Lloyds Mastics Ltd, Lloyds House, 19-21 Kents Hill Road, Benfleet, Essex, SS7 5PN Tel: (01268) 792626 Fax: (01268) 792646 E-mail: info@lloydsmastics.co.uk

M W Polymer Products Ltd, The Old Brewery, Duffield Road, Little Eaton, Derby, DE21 5DS Tel: (01332) 835001 Fax: (01332) 835051

Orion Paints Ltd, Unit 22 Manor Complex, Kirkby Bank Road, Knowsley Industrial Park, Liverpool, L33 7SY Tel: 0151-548 6756 Fax: 0151-549 1572 E-mail: sales@orionpaints.co.uk

CAVITY OR ACCESS FLOORING

Bathgate Flooring Ltd, 1 Fir Tree Lane, Rotherwas, Hereford, HR2 6LA Tel: (01432) 353003 Fax: (01432) 353004

Kingspan Access Floors Ltd, Marfleet Lane, Hull, HU9 5SG Tel: (01482) 781701 Fax: (01482) 799272 E-mail: enquiries@kingspanaccessfloors.co.uk

Raised Floor Systems, Peak House, Works Road, Letchworth Garden City, Hertfordshire, SG6 1GB Tel: (01582) 734161 Fax: (01582) 400946 E-mail: sales@raisedfloorsystems.co.uk

CAVITY WALL CLEANING

▶ Insuheat Ltd, Bay 2 Tractor Spares Industrial Estate, Strawberry Lane, Willenhall, West Midlands, WV13 3RN Tel: (01902) 603334 Fax: (01902) 604442 E-mail: admin@insuheat.co.uk

CAVITY WALL CLOSURES

Cavity Trays Ltd, Boundary Avenue, Lufton Trading Estate, Lufton, Yeovil, Somerset, BA22 8HU Tel: (01935) 474769 Fax: (01935) 428223 E-mail: sales@cavitytrays.co.uk

Quantum Profile Systems, Salmon Fields, Royton, Oldham, OL2 6JG Tel: 0161-627 4222 Fax: 0161-627 4333 E-mail: sales@quantum-ps.co.uk

CAVITY WALL INSULATION CONTRACTORS

A A Z Aluminium & uPVC Centre, Satya-Niwas, 53 Hencroft Street South, Slough, SL1 1RF Tel: (01753) 539248 Fax: (01753) 539248

Coulson, William James House, Cowley Road, Cambridge, CB4 0WX Tel: (01223) 423800 Fax: (01223) 420550 E-mail: group@coulson.co.uk

Dyson Insulations Ltd, Unit 16H, Sollingsby Park, Gateshead, Tyne & Wear, NE10 8YF Tel: 0191-416 5969 Fax: 0191-417 3817

▶ Global Insulation Ltd, Unit 12 Monksbridge Trading Estate, Outgang Lane, Dinnington, Sheffield, S25 3QZ Tel: (01909) 550850 Fax: (01909) 550974 E-mail: martyn@globalinsulate.co.uk

▶ Insu-Build Direct Ltd, Unit 17, Symondscliffe Way, Portskewett, Caldicot, Gwent, NP26 5PW Tel: (01291) 420007 Fax: (01291) 430548 E-mail: wales@insubuild.co.uk

Mark Insulation Ltd, 4 Ravenhurst Court, Birchwood, Warrington, WA3 6PN Tel: (01925) 822882 Fax: (01925) 819292

Miller Pattison Ltd, 3 Park Square, Thorncliffe Park, Chapeltown, Sheffield, S35 2PH Tel: 0114-240 4370 Fax: 0114-240 4380 E-mail: sheffield@miller-pattison.co.uk

Quantum Profile Systems, Salmon Fields, Royton, Oldham, OL2 6JG Tel: 0161-627 4222 Fax: 0161-627 4333 E-mail: sales@quantum-ps.co.uk

CD CASE DESIGN

▶ Totally Ratted Productions, 95 Ewart Road*Forest Fields, Forest Fields, Nottingham, NG7 6HG Tel: 0115 8330457 E-mail: productions@totallyratted.com

CD CASES, PLASTIC

▶ Amps International Ltd, 11 Lime Hill Road, Tunbridge Wells, Kent, TN1 1LJ Tel: (01892) 538862 Fax: (01892) 513992 E-mail: sales@ampsl.com

▶ JKME, Cromer House, B5/3 Caxton Way, Stevenage, Hertfordshire, SG1 2DF Tel: (0845) 1080660

CD DUPLICATING

▶ A19 Duplication, PO Box 428, Middlesbrough, Cleveland, TS1 9AF Tel: (01642) 225283 E-mail: sales@a19duplication.co.uk

Allstar Services Ltd, 25 Forward Drive, Harrow, Middlesex, HA3 8NT Tel: (020) 8861 6440 Fax: (020) 8861 3134 E-mail: sales@allstar.co.uk

▶ Artside Barnsley, 23 Gerald Place, Kendray, Barnsley, South Yorkshire, S70 3BW Tel: 07947 339658 E-mail: youngbritishartist@hotmail.com

▶ Atticoustic, 56a Lansdown, Stroud, Gloucestershire, GL5 1BN Tel: (01453) 755592 E-mail: pete@atticoustic.com

▶ C D Duplicator, 51 New Chester Road, New Ferry, Wirral, Merseyside, CH62 1AA Tel: (0845) 0940947 E-mail: info@cdduplicator.co.uk

Copymaster International Ltd, 14 Lombard Road, Merton, London, SW19 3TZ Tel: (020) 8543 9223 Fax: (020) 8543 9299 E-mail: sales@copymaster.co.uk

▶ Cordialav, 55 The Oaks, Abbeymead, Gloucester, GL4 5WP Tel: (01452) 616785 Fax: (01452) 616785 E-mail: enquiries@cordialav.co.uk

D W Group Ltd, Unit 7 Peverel Drive, Milton Keynes, MK1 1NL Tel: (01908) 642323 Fax: (01908) 640164 E-mail: sales@dw-view.com

Davis Rubin Associates Ltd, PO Box 15, Towcester, Northamptonshire, NN12 8DJ Tel: (01327) 830999 Fax: (01327) 831000 E-mail: btrubin@davisrubin.com

Disc Wizards, 33-35 Daws Lane, Mill Hill, London, NW7 4SD Tel: (020) 8931 0001 Fax: (020) 8931 0001 E-mail: info@discwizards.com

▶ Discburner CD Duplication, 11 Sunnyhill, Witley, Godalming, Surrey, GU8 4UH Tel: 0800 0508449 E-mail: info@discburner.co.uk

▶ East Anglian Radio Services, 4 High Beech, Lowestoft, Suffolk, NR32 2RY Tel: (01502) 568021 Fax: (01502) 600176 E-mail: office@eastanglianradio.com

Humphries Video Services Ltd, Unit 2 Willow Business Centre, 17 Willow Lane, Mitcham, Surrey, CR4 4NX Tel: (020) 8648 6111 Fax: (020) 8648 5261E-mail: sales@hvs.co.uk

CD DUPLICATING – *continued*

▶ Media Heaven Ltd, 12 Castleton Close, Leeds, LS12 2DS Tel: 0113-244 3550 Fax: 0113-244 3994 E-mail: info@mediaheaven.co.uk

West Street Studios, West Street Studios, 3 West Street, Buckingham, MK18 1HL Tel: (01280) 822814 Fax: E-mail: jamie@weststreetstudios.co.uk

▶ Xpresscds Tape & CD Manufacturers, The Converted Barn, Thorn Road, Marden, Tonbridge, Kent, TN12 9LN Tel: (01622) 832302 E-mail: info@xpresscds.co.uk

CD ENVELOPES, PAPER

▶ Eurostationers, Talbot House, 204-226 Imperial Drive, Harrow, Middlesex, HA2 7HH Tel: (0845) 2020051 Fax: (0845) 2020052 E-mail: sales@eurostationers.com

▶ Poly Postal Packaging, Unit 2 Carlton Grove, Ermine Estate, Lincoln, LN2 2EA Tel: 07986 373236 Fax: 07075 020627 E-mail: enquiries@polypostalpackaging.co.uk

▶ Quires Ltd, Unit 14, CR Bates Industrial Estate, Wycombe Road, Stokenchurch, Buckinghamshire, HP14 3PD Tel: (01494) 485229 Fax: (01494) 485293 E-mail: sales@quires.co.uk

CD INSERT PRINTING

▶ Ab CD Solutions, 7 Bower Road, Wrecclesham, Farnham, Surrey, GU10 4ST Tel: (01252) 793577 Fax: (01252) 795146 E-mail: sales@ab-cd.co.uk

CD OR DVD GLASS MASTERING REPLICATING

▶ Xpresscds Tape & CD Manufacturers, The Converted Barn, Thorn Road, Marden, Tonbridge, Kent, TN12 9LN Tel: (01622) 832302 E-mail: info@xpresscds.co.uk

CD PLAYERS, DISC JOCKEY (DJ)

▶ Abysss Audio & Lighting Sales, 24 Burton Road, Overseal, Swadlincote, Derbyshire, DE12 6LQ Tel: (07960) 953489 E-mail: sales@abyssaudiolighting.co.uk

▶ Discos Occasions, 12 Park Meadow, Westhoughton, Bolton, BL5 3UZ Tel: (01942) 817292 Fax: E-mail: info@occasionsdiscos.co.uk

▶ Phase One DJ Solutions, Station Road, Darlington, County Durham, DL3 6TA Tel: (01325) 480507 E-mail: mike@djanddiscostuff.com

CD REPLICATING

Davis Rubin Associates Ltd, PO Box 15, Towcester, Northamptonshire, NN12 8DJ Tel: (01327) 830999 Fax: (01327) 831000 E-mail: btrubin@davisrubin.com

Thamesdown SDC, Frankland Road, Blagrove, Swindon, SN5 8YU Tel: (01793) 428700 Fax: (01793) 511125 E-mail: sales@tsfltd.co.uk

CD ROM BUSINESS CARDS

▶ Media Heaven Ltd, 12 Castleton Close, Leeds, LS12 2DS Tel: 0113-244 3550 Fax: 0113-244 3994 E-mail: info@mediaheaven.co.uk

CD ROM DESIGN AND DEVELOPMENT SERVICES

▶ Citrus Media Ltd, Trivarden House, Milton Road, Shipton-under-Wychwood, Chipping Norton, Oxfordshire, OX7 6BD Tel: (01993) 830955 Fax: (01993) 831906 E-mail: info@citrus-media.co.uk

Iceni Productions Ltd, The Studio, Long Lane, Fradley, Lichfield, Staffordshire, WS13 8NX Tel: (01283) 792990 Fax: (01283) 792993 E-mail: sales@iceni.tv

Infologistix Ltd, 4 Wesleyan Chapel Walk, Stapleford, Nottingham, NG9 8BQ Tel: 0115-939 9907 Fax: 0115-939 9117 E-mail: info@infologistix.co.uk

The Marvellous Media Company, Unit 1 GMS House, Boundary Road, Woking, Surrey, GU21 5BX Tel: 01483 740800 Fax: 01483 656810 E-mail: info@marvellousmedia.com

Oakleaf Graphics, Portland House, Bolsover Business Park, Woodhouse Lane, Bolsover, Chesterfield, Derbyshire, S44 6BD Tel: (01246) 828228 E-mail: sales@oakleafgraphics.co.uk

CD ROM DUPLICATING

Allstar Services Ltd, 25 Forward Drive, Harrow, Middlesex, HA3 8NT Tel: (020) 8861 6440 Fax: (020) 8861 3134 E-mail: sales@allstar.co.uk

▶ Atticoustic, 56a Lansdown, Stroud, Gloucestershire, GL5 1BN Tel: (01453) 755592 E-mail: pete@atticoustic.com

▶ C D Duplicator, 51 New Chester Road, New Ferry, Wirral, Merseyside, CH62 1AA Tel: (0845) 0940947 E-mail: info@cdduplicator.co.uk

Copymaster International Ltd, 14 Lombard Road, Merton, London, SW19 3TZ Tel: (020) 8543 9223 Fax: (020) 8543 9299 E-mail: sales@copymaster.co.uk

Data Business, 1-4 Bankside, Kidlington, Oxfordshire, OX5 1JE Tel: (01865) 848574 Fax: (0870) 766 5210 E-mail: sales@databiz.com

Disc Wizards, 33-35 Daws Lane, Mill Hill, London, NW7 4SD Tel: (020) 8931 0001 Fax: (020) 8931 0001 E-mail: info@discwizards.com

▶ Discburner CD Duplication, 11 Sunnyhill, Witley, Godalming, Surrey, GU8 4UH Tel: 0800 0508449 E-mail: info@discburner.co.uk

Ram Peripherals, 14 Lombard Road, Merton, London, SW19 3TZ Tel: (020) 8543 9696 Fax: (020) 8543 3419 E-mail: sales@ram-peripherals.co.uk

West Street Studios, West Street Studios, 3 West Street, Buckingham, MK18 1HL Tel: (01280) 822814 Fax: E-mail: jamie@weststreetstudios.co.uk

▶ Xpresscds Tape & CD Manufacturers, The Converted Barn, Thorn Road, Marden, Tonbridge, Kent, TN12 9LN Tel: (01622) 832302 E-mail: info@xpresscds.co.uk

CD ROM PRESENTATIONS

▶ Dickfisher Ltd, 5 Harland Close, Little Haywood, Stafford, ST18 0JY Tel: (01889) 881159 E-mail: dick@dickfisher.com

▶ Merlin Corporate Services, 34 Hatton Lane, Stretton, Warrington, WA4 4NG Tel: (01925) 730077 Fax: (01925) 730659 E-mail: info@merlin.uk.net

▶ Metallic Mango CD Duplication, 30 Water Street, Birmingham, B3 1HL Tel: 0121-604 0302 Fax: E-mail: info@metallicmango.co.uk

▶ Summit Seven Ltd, 5 Vine Street, King Charles Court, Evesham, Worcestershire, WR11 4RF Tel: (01386) 765488 E-mail: info@summit7.co.uk

▶ Type In Motion Ltd, 169 High Street, Boston Spa, Wetherby, West Yorkshire, LS23 6BH Tel: (01937) 844815 Fax: (01937) 845327 E-mail: enquiries@typeinmotion.co.uk

CD ROM PUBLISHERS

Dorling Kindersley Holdings P.L.C., 80 The Strand, London, WC2R 0LR Tel: (020) 7010 3000 Fax: (020) 7010 6060

Jane's Information Group, 163 Brighton Road, Coulsdon, Surrey, CR5 2YH Tel: (020) 8700 3700 Fax: (020) 8763 1005 E-mail: info@janes.com

Kompass Publishers, Windsor Court, East Grinstead House, East Grinstead, West Sussex, RH19 1XA Tel: (0800) 0185882 Fax: (01342) 335747 E-mail: sales@kompass.co.uk

Lexisnexis UK, 2 Addiscombe Road, Croydon, CR9 5AF Tel: (020) 8662 2000 Fax: (020) 8662 2012 E-mail: sales@lexisnexis.co.uk

Ovid Technologies Ltd, 250 Waterloo Road, London, SE1 8RD Tel: (020) 7981 0600 Fax: (020) 7981 0601 E-mail: europe@ovid.com

Water Active Ltd, PO Box 627, Watford, WD23 2JW Tel: 01923 235050 Fax: 01923 252220 E-mail: info@wateractive.co.uk

CD ROMS

Arrow Imaging Ltd, 34 Pebble Close, Tamworth Business Park, Amington, Tamworth, Staffordshire, B77 4RP Tel: (01827) 310350 Fax: (01827) 313880 E-mail: sales@arrow-imaging.co.uk

CD SCANNING

C A Design Services Ltd, The Design Centre, Hewett Road, Gapton Hall, Great Yarmouth, Norfolk, NR31 0NN Tel: 01493 440444 Fax: 01493 442480 E-mail: sales@cadesignservices.co.uk

Docscan Ltd, 23 Cater Road, Bishopsworth, Bristol, BS13 7TW Tel: 0117-935 9818 Fax: 0117-935 9828 E-mail: docscan@servicepointuk.com

▶ Timezone Digital Storage Ltd, Rivacre Business Centre, Mill Lane, Ellesmere Port, CH66 3TH Tel: 0151-339 2070 E-mail: info@timezonedigital.com

CDR DUPLICATING

▶ C D Duplicator, 51 New Chester Road, New Ferry, Wirral, Merseyside, CH62 1AA Tel: (0845) 0940947 E-mail: info@cdduplicator.co.uk

▶ Media Heaven Ltd, 12 Castleton Close, Leeds, LS12 2DS Tel: 0113-244 3550 Fax: 0113-244 3994 E-mail: info@mediaheaven.co.uk

CDRWS

Golding Products Ltd, Unit 24 Hortonwood 33, Telford, Shropshire, TF1 7YQ Tel: (01952) 606667 Fax: (01952) 670267 E-mail: sales@goldingproducts.com

CDS

Ar Computing, 8 Friday Street, Minehead, Somerset, TA24 5UA Tel: (01643) 707381 Fax: (01643) 707431 E-mail: enquiries@arcomputing.co.uk

▶ Discovery Media Direct, 1 Brookhampton Lane, Kineton, CV35 0JA Tel: 0871 474 2724

Ergo Computer Accessories Ltd, 5 Pipers Industrial Estate, Pipers Lane, Thatcham, Berkshire, RG19 4NA Tel: (01635) 877979 Fax: (01635) 877676 E-mail: sales@ergo-consumables.co.uk

▶ Sensual Reading.com Limited, 47 Manchester Road, Denton, Manchester, M34 2AF Tel: 07723 060498 E-mail: sensualreading@sensualreading.com

Sounds Good Ltd, Chiltern Enterprise Centre, 12 Station Road, Theale, Reading, RG7 4AA Tel: 0118-930 1700 Fax: 0118-930 1709 E-mail: info@sounds-good.co.uk

Techpoint Services, 133 Mains Lane, Poulton-le-Fylde, Lancashire, FY6 7LD Tel: (01253) 895999 Fax: (01253) 895999 E-mail: sales@diplidata.co.uk

Westlakes, 440 High Road, Wembley, Middlesex, HA9 6AH Tel: (020) 8902 2392 Fax: (020) 8902 1780 E-mail: enquiries@westlakes.uk.com

CDS, RECORDABLE (CDR)

▶ Disccity Ltd, Unit 12, Westbrook Road, Westbrook Trading Estate, Trafford Park, Manchester, M17 1AY Tel: 0870 166 0757 Fax: 0870 166 0759 E-mail: enqs@disccity.co.uk

CE MARKING SERVICES

Southwood quality and regulatory solutions, 1 Hall Cottages, Freethorpe road, Southwood, Norwich, NR13 3LR Tel: (01493) 701452 Fax: (01493) 701452 E-mail: mark.read@southwood-qrs.co.uk

▶ WolfsonEMC, Cardiff University, Queens Building, Newport Road, Cardiff, CF24 3AA Tel: (029) 2087 5936 Fax: (07898) 199422 E-mail: richard@WolfsonEMC.co.uk

CEDAR DECKING

▶ Decking Style, 19 Manor Road, East Grinstead, West Sussex, RH19 1LP Tel: (01342) 303120 E-mail: info@deckingstyle.co.uk

CEILING CONSTRUCTION

A C S, 33 Vernon Walk, Tadworth, Surrey, KT20 5QP Tel: (01737) 371286

CEILING CONTRACTORS

A C S, 33 Vernon Walk, Tadworth, Surrey, KT20 5QP Tel: (01737) 371286

Allwood Ceiling Services, Shaws Farm, Horsell Common, Woking, Surrey, GU21 4XZ Tel: (01483) 724180 Fax: (01483) 724316 E-mail: acs4you@aol.com

CEILING FANS

Astra Distribution Manchester Ltd, Unit 6, Lowercroft Business Park, Lowercroft Road, Bury, Lancashire, BL8 3PA Tel: 0161-797 3222 Fax: 0161-797 3444 E-mail: support@astra247.com

Nuaire Group, Western Indust Estate, Caerphilly, Mid Glamorgan, CF83 1BQ Tel: (029) 2088 5911 Fax: (029) 2088 7033 E-mail: info@nuaire.co.uk

CEILING FINISHES OR COATINGS

Cheltenham Ceiling Co. Ltd, 81-85 Calton Road, Gloucester, GL1 5DT Tel: (01452) 411740 Fax: (01452) 527368

CEILING OR WALL ACCESS PANELS

Lazer Partitions & Ceilings, 119a Tarring Road, Worthing, West Sussex, BN11 4HE Tel: (01903) 205719 Fax: (01903) 204041 E-mail: lazer@mistral.co.uk

CEILINGS

A C S, 33 Vernon Walk, Tadworth, Surrey, KT20 5QP Tel: (01737) 371286

▶ J Holdsworth Associates, Alexander House, Robinson Terrace, Washington, Tyne & Wear, NE38 7BD Tel: 0191-417 2543 Fax: 0191-417 1486 E-mail: jhassociates1@aol.com

▶ Reflective Ceilings, 6 Moorhead Road, Horsham, West Sussex, RH12 4ND Tel: (07961) 863678 Fax: (01403) 270337 E-mail: james@reflective-ceilings.co.uk

CELLULAR BATTERIES

Absolute Battery UK Ltd, Darrell House, Darrell Road, Felixstowe, Suffolk, IP11 3UU Tel: (01394) 674949 Fax: (01394) 279005

▶ TMD-UK Ltd, 28B High Street, Sunninghill, Ascot, Berkshire, SL5 9NE Tel: (0870) 9906001 Fax: (0870) 9906002 E-mail: service@tmd-uk.co.uk

CELLULAR COMMUNICATIONS NETWORK INSTALLATION CONTRACTORS

Edi Telecommunications Equipment, 2 Church Road, Cholsey, Wallingford, Oxfordshire, OX10 9PP Tel: (01491) 652145 Fax: (01491) 652214

M C I, Reading International Business Park, Reading, RG2 6DA Tel: 0118-905 5000 Fax: 0118-905 5711

Murphy Telecommunications, 293 Salisbury Road, Totton, Southampton, SO40 3LZ Tel: (023) 8086 1479 Fax: (023) 8086 8483 E-mail: murtel@talktalk.net

▶ Shire Consulting, 8 Spicer Street, St. Albans, Hertfordshire, AL3 4PQ Tel: (01727) 838455 Fax: (01727) 835047 E-mail: enquiries@shire-uk.com

CELLULOSE ACETATE

Clarifoil, PO Box 5, Derby, DE21 7BP Tel: (01332) 661422 Fax: (01332) 660178 E-mail: info@clarifoil.com

CELLULOSE FIBRES

Thornhill Fibres Ltd, North Street, Rotherham, South Yorkshire, S60 1LG Tel: (01709) 370707 Fax: (01709) 830300

CELLULOSE FILM

▶ Innovia Films Ltd, Station Rd, Wigton, Cumbria, CA7 9BG Tel: (01697) 342281 Fax: (01697) 341452 E-mail: filmsinfo@innoviafilms.com

Wilson Packaging Products, 38 Hatherley Road, Manchester, M20 4RU Tel: 0161-434 0454 Fax: 0161-448 1070 E-mail: wilsonpackaging@btconnect.com

CELLULOSE FILM PACKAGING

Shredhouse Gift Packaging, Salisbury Road Business Park, Salisbury Road, Pewsey, Wiltshire, SN9 5PZ Tel: (01672) 564333 Fax: (01672) 564301

CELLULOSE FINISHES OR LACQUERS OR ENAMELS OR PAINTS

Ici Paints plc T/As Dulux, Wexham Road, Slough, SL2 5DS Tel: (01753) 550000 Fax: (01753) 578218 E-mail: sales@dulux.com

Key Paint Ltd, 1 Eldon Road, Luton, LU4 0AZ Tel: (01582) 572627 Fax: (01582) 593489

L E Went Ltd, 52-56 Burlington Road, New Malden, Surrey, KT3 4NU Tel: (020) 8949 0626 Fax: (020) 8715 1116 E-mail: iew.paint@virgin.net

Sanderson, Sanderson House, Oxford Road, Denham, Uxbridge, Middlesex, UB9 4DX Tel: (01895) 830000 Fax: (01895) 830055

Sonneborn & Rieck Ltd, 91-95 Peregrine Road, Ilford, Essex, IG6 3XH Tel: (020) 8500 0251 Fax: (020) 8500 3696 E-mail: export@sonneborn-rieck.co.uk

Technical Paint Services, 27 Southcote Road, Bournemouth, BH1 3SH Tel: (01202) 295570 Fax: (0845) 2301255 E-mail: sales@technicalpaintservices.com

CELLULOSE SPONGES

M A P A Spontex UK Ltd, Berkeley Business Park Berkeley Business Park, Wainwright Road, Worcester, WR4 9ZS Tel: (01905) 450300 Fax: (01905) 450350

CELLULOSE WOOD FINISHES

Fairleys Paint Stripping, Unit 14 Byron House, Hall Dene Way, Seaham Grange Industrial Estat, Seaham, County Durham, SR7 0PY Tel: 0191-510 0051 Fax: 0191-510 0051

CEMENT, *See also headings for particular types*

Civil & Marine Slag Cement Ltd, Llanwern Works, Llanwern, Newport, Gwent, NP19 4QX Tel: (01633) 278708 Fax: (01633) 277017

Dragon Alfa Cement Ltd, The Docks, Sharpness, Berkeley, Gloucestershire, GL13 9UX Tel: (01453) 819098 Fax: (01453) 811953

Hanson Cement Ltd, 3160 Solihull Parkway, Birmingham Business Park, Birmingham, B37 7YN Tel: (0845) 6001616 Fax: 0121-606 1436 E-mail: customer.services@castlecement.co.uk

Lafarge Cement Ltd, New Edinburgh Road, Uddingston, Glasgow, G71 6NE Tel: (01698) 812261 Fax: (01698) 814980

Lagan Cement Co., Mccaughey Road, Belfast, BT3 9AG Tel: (028) 9074 3293 Fax: (028) 9074 9340

Modern Mix Concrete Supplies Ltd, Unit 1 Empson Street, London, E3 3LT Tel: (020) 7538 2266 Fax: (020) 7537 3256

N I C Ltd, Mariners Street, Goole, North Humberside, DN14 5BW Tel: (01405) 782600 Fax: (01405) 782612 E-mail: nic@damacgroup.co.uk

▶ Paragon Materials Ltd, Maritime House, Southside 3, Chatham Docks, Chatham, Kent, ME4 4SR Tel: (01634) 890744 Fax: (01634) 890745

CEMENT APPLICATION EQUIPMENT

Power-Sprays Ltd, Avonmouth Way, Bristol, BS11 9YA Tel: 0117-982 0067 Fax: 0117-982 0060

CEMENT BASED FLOORING

Stanford Design & Construct Ltd, 5 Richmond St South, West Bromwich, West Midlands, B70 0DG Tel: 0121-522 2220 Fax: 0121-522 2020 E-mail: sales@stanford-flooring.co.uk

CEMENT COLOURS

Blue Circle Industries UK P.L.C., West Medina Wharf, Stag Lane, Newport, Isle Of Wight, PO30 5TS Tel: (01983) 522271 Fax: (01983) 524972

Calder Colours Ashby Ltd, Dents Road, Nottingham Road Indust Estate, Ashby DeLa Zouch, Ashby-de-la-Zouch, Leicestershire, LE65 1JS Tel: (01530) 412885 Fax: (01530) 417315 E-mail: office@caldercolours.co.uk

Cement UK, Lappel Bank, Sheerness Docks, Sheerness, Kent, ME12 1RS Tel: (01795) 669023 Fax: (01795) 669510

Lanxess Ltd, Lichfield Road, Branston, Burton-On-Trent, Staffordshire, DE14 3WH Tel: (01283) 714200 Fax: (01283) 714201 E-mail: info@hawley.edi.co.uk

Natural Cement Distribution, Unit 12 Redbrook Business Park, Wilthorpe Road, Barnsley, South Yorkshire, S75 1JN Tel: (01226) 299333 Fax: (01226) 299777

P J Colours Ltd, Excelsior Works, Castle Park, Flint, Clwyd, CH6 5NT Tel: (01352) 732157 Fax: (01352) 735530 E-mail: info@pjcolours.com

CEMENT PRODUCTION PLANT

Blue Circle Industries UK P.L.C., West Medina Wharf, Stag Lane, Newport, Isle Of Wight, PO30 5TS Tel: (01983) 522271 Fax: (01983) 524972

Cemex UK Ltd, Crown House, Evreux Way, Rugby, Warwickshire, CV21 2DT Tel: 0114-242 6050 Fax: (01788) 517220

F L Smidth Ltd, 17 Lansdowne Road, Croydon, CR9 2JT Tel: (020) 8603 1500 Fax: (020) 8681 7229 E-mail: fls@flsmidth.co.uk

CEMENT PRODUCTION PLANT INSTALLATION OR MAINTENANCE OR SERVICING

Westside Welding and Engineering Ltd, 9 Broadfield Place, Welwyn Garden City, Hertfordshire, AL8 6LJ Tel: 01707 332872 Fax: 01707 332872 E-mail: westsideweld@hotmail.co.uk

CEMENT PUMPS

Denhaolm Oilfield Services, Greenbank Place, East Tullos Industrial Estate, Aberdeen, AB12 3BT Tel: (01224) 249424 Fax: (01224) 249496

Power-Sprays Ltd, Avonmouth Way, Bristol, BS11 9YA Tel: 0117-982 0067 Fax: 0117-982 0060

CEMENT TEST EQUIPMENT, *See Concrete Test etc*

CEMENT WATERPROOFERS

David Ball Group plc, Huntingdon Road, Cambridge, CB23 8HN Tel: (01954) 780687 Fax: (01954) 782912 E-mail: sales@davidballgroup.com

Vandex (UK) Ltd, PO Box 200, Guildford, Surrey, GU2 4WD Tel: (0870) 2416264 Fax: (0870) 2416274 E-mail: info@vandex.co.uk

CEMENT WATERPROOFING CONTRACTORS

▶ Substructure Protection Ltd, Warth Mill, Huddersfield Road, Diggle, Oldham, OL3 5PJ Tel: (01457) 878200 Fax: (01457) 879132 E-mail: sales@spsltd.co.uk

CEMENTED CARBIDE ROLLMAKERS

Akers UK Ltd, Suite 14, Shire Hall Complex, Pentonville, Newport, Gwent, NP20 5HB Tel: (01633) 265544 E-mail: sales@akersuk.com

CENTRAL HEATERS

Adept Heating & Mechanical Services Ltd, Raidons, Nutbourne Lane, Nutbourne, Pulborough, West Sussex, RH20 2HS Tel: (01798) 875239 Fax: (01798) 875239 E-mail: daveblaber@aol.com

▶ Curtis Plumbing & Heating, 2 Pollard Court, Pollard Road, Morden, Surrey, SM4 6EH Tel: (07020) 930940 Fax: 020 81506313 E-mail: sales@cphs.co.uk

▶ Elliott Environmental, Unit 10, Brympton Way, Lynx West Trading Estate, Yeovil, Somerset, BA20 2HP Tel: (01935) 413700 Fax: (01935) 413722 E-mail: jim@e-e-s.co.uk

The Heating People Ltd, 1 Brooklands, Filey, North Yorkshire, YO14 9BA Tel: (0845) 8382732 Fax: (01723) 513981 E-mail: enquiries@theheatingpeople.co.uk

▶ UK-CentralHeating.com, Unit 29, Humphries Court, Whitley Road, Manchester, M40 7GB Tel: 0871 4744351 Fax: 0871 2360251 E-mail: sales@uk-centralheating.com

CENTRAL HEATING BOILERS

▶ M H Cragg & Sons Ltd, Ingleside, 11 Lee Lane, Horwich, Bolton, BL6 7BP Tel: (01204) 697157 Fax: (01204) 699113

CENTRAL HEATING INSTALLATION OR SERVICING

Air Quality Control Ltd, Ground Floor, 339 Hollinwood Avenue, Manchester, M40 0JA Tel: 0161-688 6880 Fax: 0161-682 6864 E-mail: admin@aqc-ltd.co.uk

▶ Alhco Sewer Rehabilitation Ltd, 114 Station Road, Westbury, Wiltshire, BA13 4TW Tel: (01373) 823814 E-mail: richard.jemmett@alhco.co.uk

▶ Aqua Attention, 16 Orchard Way, North Bradley, Trowbridge, Wiltshire, BA14 0SU Tel: (01225) 754599 Fax: (01225) 777878 E-mail: sales@aquaattention.co.uk

▶ Armstrong, 6 James Carter Road, Mildenhall, Bury St. Edmunds, Suffolk, IP28 7DE Tel: (01638) 715713 Fax: (01638) 713007

B A Halston Heating, Stoney Croft, The Lynch, Kensworth, Dunstable, Bedfordshire, LU6 3QZ Tel: (01582) 872445 Fax: (01582) 872445

B T U Pool Services Ltd, 38 Weyside Road, Guildford, Surrey, GU1 1JB Tel: (01483) 727444 Fax: (01483) 766254 E-mail: sales@btu-group.com

▶ Berry's Plumbing & Heating Ltd, 141 Manchester Road East, Little Hulton, Manchester, M38 9AN Tel: 0161-790 9933 Fax: 0161-790 9944

▶ Boiler Diagnostics Ltd, 127 Simpson Road, Snodland, Kent, ME6 5QH Tel: (01634) 244120 Fax: (01634) 245305 E-mail: matt@boilerdiagnostics.co.uk

Bower & Child Ltd, 91 Wakefield Road, Huddersfield, HD5 9AB Tel: (01484) 425416 Fax: (01484) 517353

Bradley Industrial Services, Thornleigh, Summerhill, Kingswinford, West Midlands, DY6 9JF Tel: (01384) 271911 Fax: (01384) 273104

Colin Bullot & Sons Ltd, 7 Glendale Walk, Cheshunt, Waltham Cross, Hertfordshire, EN8 9RJ Tel: (01992) 627407 Fax: (01992) 633198 E-mail: colin@bullut.co.uk

▶ C L I Heating Ltd, Unit 56, Bowen Industrial Estate, Aberbargoed, Bargoed, Mid Glamorgan, CF81 9EP Tel: (01443) 828100

▶ C & L Plumbing Services, Bridge Works, Wood Lane, Rothwell, Leeds, LS26 0RS Tel: 0113-282 3728 Fax: 0113-282 2105

▶ Capital Plumbing & Heating, 20 Mylo Griffiths Close, Cardiff, CF5 2RQ Tel: (029) 2057 8268 E-mail: rmr.roberts@virgin.net

CHAS Appliance Spares, 36 Tynewydd Road, Rhyl, Clwyd, LL18 3SP Tel: (01745) 355066 Fax: (01745) 355077

Controls Center, 112a Warner Road, London, SE5 9HQ Tel: (020) 7733 0951 Fax: (020) 7370 7312

▶ Cook & Harris Ltd, Unit 36 Barnack Trading Centre, Novers Hill, Bedminster, Bristol, BS3 5QE Tel: 0117-966 4792 Fax: 0117-963 9007

Countrylife Stoves, Coopers Orchard, Brook Street, North Newton, Bridgwater, Somerset, TA7 0BL Tel: (01278) 662449 Fax: (01278) 662449

▶ D S I Heating Installations Ltd, Olde Byre, Stoke Street, Rodney Stoke, Cheddar, Somerset, BS27 3UP Tel: (01749) 870192 Fax: (01749) 870811 E-mail: sfoster@dsiheating.freeserve.co.uk

D Train, 43-45 Fisher Street, Stranraer, Wigtownshire, DG9 7LH Tel: (01776) 702357 Fax: (01776) 702357

David G Alker, The Quern, Chapel Lawn, Bucknell, Shropshire, SY7 0BW Tel: (01547) 530344 Fax: (01547) 530844 E-mail: davequern@aol.com

▶ Dimor Plumbing Ltd, 15 Acorn Business Centre, Livingstone Way, Taunton, Somerset, TA2 6BD Tel: (01823) 331405 Fax: (01823) 352911

Dove Heating Ltd, 227 Kingston Road, New Malden, Surrey, KT3 3SZ Tel: (020) 8241 0141 Fax: (020) 8942 9992

J.A. Evans, 10 Underdale Avenue, Shrewsbury, SY2 5DY Tel: (01743) 236598

▶ EXBG, 16 Altamont, Westview Road, Warlingham, Surrey, CR6 9JD Tel: (01883) 620070 E-mail: info@exbg.co.uk

▶ Fenhams Contracts, 2-6 Ivy Road, Gosforth, Newcastle Upon Tyne, NE3 1DB Tel: 0191-223 0600

▶ Gas Connect Heating Ltd, Leigh House, Broadway West, Leigh-on-Sea, Essex, SS9 2DD Tel: (01702) 474792 Fax: (01702) 471647

▶ Gas Master, 36 Plover Crescent, Anstey Heights, Leicester, LE4 1EB Tel: 0116-236 7705 E-mail: platform40@hotmail.com

▶ Gaswise Services Ltd, Horsleys Fields, King's Lynn, Norfolk, PE30 5DD Tel: (01553) 769404 Fax: (01553) 774033

▶ George Thompson Heating Ltd, Thornton Road, Carlisle, CA3 9HZ Tel: (01228) 527390 Fax: (01228) 512627

Grail & Preece Ltd, 44 Hamstead Road, Hockley, Birmingham, B19 1DB Tel: 0121-554 6667 Fax: 0121-554 6992 E-mail: info@grailandpreece.co.uk

▶ Charles Grey, 27 Alton Road, Richmond, Surrey, TW9 1UJ Tel: (07703) 533703 E-mail: charles@greyuk.net

▶ H I Services Ltd, Unit 2a Woodfalls Business Centre, Gravelly Ways, Laddingford, Maidstone, Kent, ME18 6DA Tel: (01622) 873004 Fax: (01622) 873005

Heath Technical Services, 83 Corsletts Avenue, Broadbridge Heath, Horsham, West Sussex, RH12 3NY Tel: (01403) 249152 Fax: (01403) 265093

Hodgkinson Bennis Ltd, Highfield Road, Little Hulton, Manchester, M38 9SS Tel: 0161-790 4411 Fax: 0161-703 8505 E-mail: enquiries@hbcombustion.com

Homeserve Servowarm, 3 Clarke Industrial Estate, Wetmore Road, Burton-on-Trent, Staffordshire, DE14 1QT Tel: (01283) 511244 Fax: (01283) 569162 E-mail: admin@servowarm.co.uk

▶ J E Nixon & Son, Northern Works, Bellingham, Hexham, Northumberland, NE48 2BS Tel: (01434) 220268 Fax: (01434) 220372

J F Heppelthwaite Ltd, Sherwood House 6 Marlborough Parade, Uxbridge Road, Uxbridge, Middlesex, UB10 0LR Tel: (01895) 460002 Fax: (01895) 460004

▶ J V Geer & Sons Ltd, 51 London Road, Sevenoaks, Kent, TN13 1AU Tel: (01732) 454082 Fax: (01732) 454728

▶ Jonathan Mayers Services Ltd, 11 Newman Road, Trevethin, Pontypool, Gwent, NP4 8HQ Tel: (08701) 160821 Fax: (08701) 160821 E-mail: sales@j-m-s.co.uk

Lans & Addison, 3 Rose Cottage, Wappenshall, Telford, Shropshire, TF6 6DE Tel: (01952) 255109 Fax: (01952) 255109

Llewellyn Heating Ltd, Station Approach, Hereford, HR1 1BB Tel: (01432) 266413 Fax: (01432) 271493

▶ M B Plumbing & Heating, 189 Ashgate Road, Chesterfield, Derbyshire, S40 4AP Tel: (01246) 555161

▶ Manley Hill Plumbing & Heating Contractors, Unit 7, 8-10 Marlborough Hill, Harrow, Middlesex, HA1 1UX Tel: (020) 8863 0373 Fax: (020) 8424 8500 E-mail: enquiries@manleyhill.co.uk

Oil Services South West, Chimsworthy, Bratton Clovelly, Okehampton, Devon, EX20 4JE Tel: (01837) 871444 Fax: (01837) 871525

▶ Mark Payne, 53 South Coast Road, Peacehaven, East Sussex, BN10 8QW Tel: (01273) 583052

▶ PHG Services, 6 Hartshead Avenue, Stalybridge, Cheshire, SK15 1BY Tel: (07976) 325482 E-mail: phgservices@btconnect.com

▶ Premier, The Commercial Centre, 2 Commercial Brow, Hyde, Cheshire, SK14 2JW Tel: 0161-351 1212 Fax: 0161-351 1001 E-mail: sales@premierelectricalsupplies.com

▶ R J S Heating Plumbing & Mechanical Services Ltd, 26 Chipstead Station Parade, Chipstead, Coulsdon, Surrey, CR5 3TF Tel: (01737) 550110 Fax: (01737) 556770

▶ R Park & Sons Ltd, Unit 1 Aldwych Court, 586A Blackpool Road, Ashton-On-Ribble, Preston, PR2 1JA Tel: (01772) 720007

Ravensbourne Heating, Unit 4, 102 Tindal St, Moseley, Birmingham, B12 9QL Tel: 0121 4499633 Fax: 0121 4499633

▶ Reactfast, Unit 1 Jubilee Trade Centre, 130 Pershore Street, Birmingham, B5 6ND Tel: 0800 195 1269 E-mail: enquiries@reactfast.co.uk

▶ Redcar Plumbing & Heating, The Innovation Centre, Vienna Court, Kirkleatham Business Park, Redcar, Cleveland, TS10 5SH Tel: (01642) 777800 Fax: (01642) 777850

▶ Robert J Dutton, 2 Springfield Road, Shepshed, Loughborough, Leicestershire, LE12 7EE Tel: (01509) 502402 Fax: (01509) 600327

▶ Roland Amey, Unit B, Copley Hill Farm, Cambridge Road, Babraham, Cambridge, CB2 4AF Tel: (01223) 835725

Rudd Engineering Ltd, 18 Sebergham Grove, London, NW7 2AU Tel: (020) 8959 8181

▶ Russell C Soper, 57 Farringdon Road, Plymouth, PL4 9ER Tel: (01752) 268666

▶ Scotiathermel, 2B Craiglockhart Drive South, Edinburgh, EH14 1HZ Tel: 0131-455 7805 Fax: 0131-443 6190

Servoto Warm Ltd, Coronation Road, High Wycombe, Buckinghamshire, HP12 3SU Tel: (01494) 474474 Fax: (01494) 492321 E-mail: sales@servowarm.co.uk

Sidney Cubbage Heating & Ventilating Ltd, 37-43 Green Street, High Wycombe, Buckinghamshire, HP11 2RF Tel: (01494) 523661 Fax: (01494) 462707 E-mail: scl@sidneycubbage.com

▶ T E Mears Ltd, Feltham Hill Road, Feltham, Middlesex, TW13 7ND Tel: (020) 8890 2853

▶ T G Services, Unit 5a Vicarage Farm Business Park, Winchester Road, Fair Oak, Eastleigh, Hampshire, SO50 7HD Tel: (023) 8069 5554 Fax: (01489) 860103 E-mail: enquiries@hotandcool.co.uk

T W Steam & Heating Services Ltd, Unit 7-8 Rennys Lane, Durham, DH1 2RS Tel: 0191-384 1400 Fax: 0191-386 4251

▶ Thames Gas Maintenance, 56 Gloucester Road, London, SW7 4UB Tel: (020) 8870 8500

Thermodiffusion Ltd, Hill Place, London Road, Southborough, Tunbridge Wells, Kent, TN4 0PY Tel: (01892) 511533 Fax: (01892) 515140 E-mail: thermodiffusion@btconnect.com

Total Gas Services, 199 Station Road, Kingsheath, Birmingham, B14 7TB Tel: 0121-269 7980 Fax: 0121-251 2920 E-mail: info@gasservices.co.uk

U E S Ltd, Newark Road South, Glenrothes, Fife, KY7 4NS Tel: (01592) 773275 Fax: (01952) 773753

▶ Viking Heating, 119 Brompton Park, Brompton on Swale, Richmond, North Yorkshire, DL10 7JR Tel: (01748) 818622 E-mail: enquiries@vikingheating.co.uk

▶ Walmotts Gas Service Engineers, D L O Stores, Alexandra Road, Grantham, Lincolnshire, NG31 7AS Tel: (01476) 594451 Fax: (01476) 591349

▶ Wheldon Contracts & Services Ltd, 127 High Street, Newport Pagnell, Buckinghamshire, MK16 8SE Tel: (01908) 211127 Fax: (01908) 612008 E-mail: sales@wheldons.co.uk

CENTRAL HEATING SYSTEM COMPONENTS

▶ Blaze Heating, 75 Milborough Crescent, London, SE12 0RP Tel: (020) 3149 3488 E-mail: info@blazeheating.co.uk

▶ The Gasworks Company UK Ltd, 24 Baycliff Drive, Dalton-in-Furness, Cumbria, LA15 8XE Tel: (07841) 342298 Fax: (01229) 768266 E-mail: support@thegasworkscompany.co.uk

The Heating People Ltd, 1 Brooklands, Filey, North Yorkshire, YO14 9BA Tel: (0845) 8382732 Fax: (01723) 513981 E-mail: enquiries@theheatingpeople.co.uk

▶ J H S Plumbing & Heating Ltd, Tamsui, Sevenoaks Road, Ightham, Sevenoaks, Kent, TN15 9DS Tel: (01732) 884949 Fax: (01322) 860922 E-mail: korina@draindoctors.biz

▶ UK-CentralHeating.com, Unit 29, Humphries Court, Whitley Road, Manchester, M40 7GB Tel: 0871 4744351 Fax: 0871 2360251 E-mail: sales@uk-centralheating.com

CENTRAL IMPRESSION ENVELOPE PRINTING SYSTEMS

Pamarco Europe Ltd, New Cut Lane, Woolston, Warrington, WA1 4AQ Tel: (01925) 456789 Fax: (01925) 456778 E-mail: sales-roll@pamarco.co.uk
T & A Envelopes Ltd, 10 Moray Court, Kimberley, Nottingham, NG16 2TL Tel: 0115-938 4674 Fax: 0115-945 8348 E-mail: t_a.envelopes@mac.com
Toplink Envelopes Ltd, Marsh Lane, Temple Cloud, Bristol, BS39 5AZ Tel: (01761) 453865 Fax: (01761) 453866 E-mail: mail@toplink.co.uk

CENTRAL PROCESSING UNIT (CPU) COOLING FANS

Highridge Computers Ltd, 275 Tutbury Road, Burton-on-Trent, Staffordshire, DE13 0NZ Tel: (01283) 500530 Fax: (01283) 500540 E-mail: karl@highridge.net

CENTRALISED CLEANING AND HYGIENE SYSTEMS

Haskel Energy Systems Ltd, North Hylton Road, Sunderland, SR5 3JD Tel: 0191-549 1212 Fax: 0191-549 0911 E-mail: sales@haskel.co.uk

CENTRALISERS

▶ PolyOil Ltd, Unit A2, Wellheads Crescent, Wellheads Industrial Estate, Dyce, Aberdeen, AB21 7GA Tel: (01224) 799950 Fax: (01224) 799951 E-mail: info@polyoil.com
Ray Oil Tool Co. Ltd, Unit 48 Howe Moss Avenue, Dyce, Aberdeen, AB21 0GP Tel: (01224) 773313 Fax: (01224) 773304 E-mail: sales@rayoiltool.co.uk

CENTRE BOLTS

Greenaway & Co. Ltd, Penybont Bryncrug, Tywyn, Gwynedd, LL36 9PT Tel: (01654) 710073 Fax: (01654) 711846 E-mail: mail@greenawayuk.fsnet.co.uk

CENTRE LATHE TURNING

Alford Engineering, Fen Lane, Maltby le Marsh, Alford, Lincolnshire, LN13 0JT Tel: (01507) 450566 Fax: (01507) 450327
Bowden Precision Engineering Co. Ltd, Riverside, Market Harborough, Leicestershire, LE16 7PU Tel: (01858) 467508 Fax: (01858) 431656 E-mail: enquiries@bowdenprecision.co.uk
Contract Turning Ltd, Unit 27 Ventura Place, Poole, Dorset, BH16 5SW Tel: (01202) 625502 Fax: (01202) 625502 E-mail: info@contractturning.co.uk
Dowling & Fransen (Engineers) Ltd, North End Road, Wembley, Middlesex, HA9 0AN Tel: (020) 8903 2155 Fax: (020) 8903 2158 E-mail: dowling@fransen.fsbusiness.co.uk
Excel Precision Engineering Services Ltd, Unit 16, Trostra Industrial Estate, Llanelli, Dyfed, SA14 9UU Tel: (01554) 751935 Fax: (01554) 778804 E-mail: debbie@excel-eng.co.uk
G S W Haswell, The Workshop, Winchester Street, Botley, Southampton, SO30 2AA Tel: (01489) 785293
G W Lambert Engineers Ltd, 10 Queens Road, High Wycombe, Buckinghamshire, HP13 6AQ Tel: (01494) 525977 Fax: (01494) 528238
George Bros Engineers Ltd, Dyffryn Close, Swansea Enterprise Park, Swansea, SA6 8QG Tel: (01792) 790550 Fax: (01792) 701608
Green Engineering, Cheethams Mill, Park Street, Stalybridge, Cheshire, SK15 2BT Tel: 0161-303 7129 Fax: 0161-303 7129
H.C Turk Engineering Services Ltd, 4a The Mews, Bentley Street, Gravesend, Kent, DA12 2DH Tel: (01474) 325331 Fax: (01474) 353140
John Bradley Engineering Ltd, 5 Broadfield Road, Seymour St, Heywood, Lancashire, OL10 3AJ Tel: (01706) 366794 Fax: (01706) 620270 E-mail: jbe@johnbradleygroup.co.uk
Lecol Engineering Ltd, 123 Barr Street, Birmingham, B19 3DE Tel: 0121-523 0404 Fax: 0121-523 2372
P.S. Marsden (Precision Engineers) Ltd, Private Road No 8, Colwick Industrial Estate, Nottingham, NG4 2JX Tel: 0115-987 9026 Fax: 0115-940 0805 E-mail: precision@psmarsden.co.uk
Media Resources, Church Croft House, Station Road, Rugeley, Staffordshire, WS15 2HE Tel: (01889) 503100 Fax: (01889) 503100 E-mail: info@media-resources.co.uk
▶ One Off Engineering Ltd, Simpson Street, Hyde, Cheshire, SK14 1BJ Tel: 0161-366 7276 Fax: 0161-366 7276 E-mail: oneoffeng@fsmail.net
▶ QRS Precision Engineering, Unit 4 Hartlepool Workshops, Usworth Road, Hartlepool, Cleveland, TS25 1PD Tel: (01429) 891300 Fax: (01429) 295933 E-mail: qrsengineering@aol.com
Ram Machining Ltd, Providence Street, Stourbridge, West Midlands, DY9 8HS Tel: (01384) 424144 Fax: (01384) 892396
▶ S W S Machining Ltd, Progress Drive, Cannock, Staffordshire, WS11 0JE Tel: (01543) 504181 Fax: (01543) 573834 E-mail: sales@swsmachining.co.uk
Warren Engineering Ltd, Birkbeck Road, Sidcup, Kent, DA14 4DB Tel: (020) 8300 5111 Fax: (020) 8308 9977 E-mail: warrenengineering@supanet.com
Whitmarley Engineering Co. Ltd, Ivy Road, Stirchley, Birmingham, B30 2NX Tel: 0121-458 7491 Fax: 0121-433 4137 E-mail: enquiries@whitmarley.fsnet.co.uk

CENTRE LATHE TURNING MILLING AND BORING

Malt Mill Engineering Co. Ltd, 4 Kinwarton Workshops, Kinwarton Farm Road, Kinwarton, Alcester, Warwickshire, B49 6EH Tel: (01789) 764497 Fax: (01789) 400161 E-mail: maltmill@aol.com
Whiteland Engineering Ltd, Torrington Lane, Bideford, Devon, EX39 4BH Tel: (01237) 472203 Fax: (01237) 472205 E-mail: info@whitelandengineering.co.uk

CENTRELESS GRINDING

Accles & Shelvoke Ltd, Selco Way Off First Avenue, Minworth Industrial Estate, Minworth, Sutton Coldfield, West Midlands, B76 1BA Tel: 0121-313 4567 Fax: 0121-313 4569 E-mail: sales@eley.co.uk
Alexican Ltd, 177 King Street, Dukinfield, Cheshire, SK16 4LG Tel: 0161-339 1999 Fax: 0161-330 1555 E-mail: info@alexican.co.uk
Argent Steel Ltd, 1 Matthew Street, Sheffield, S3 7BE Tel: 0114-270 1428 Fax: 0114-272 3717 E-mail: enquiries@argentsteel.co.uk
Ashtead Engineering Co. Ltd, Unit 2 3 Camphill Industrial Estate, Camphill Road, West Byfleet, Surrey, KT14 6EW Tel: (01932) 353121 Fax: (01932) 342968 E-mail: ashteadeng@byfleet.net
A.J. Baker (Grinding) Ltd, Middlemore Lane West, Redhouse Industrial Estate, Aldridge, Walsall, WS9 8BG Tel: (01922) 745075 Fax: 0121-378 3291 E-mail: enquiries@ajbaker.com
Bond Precision Grinding Ltd, Trafalgar Works, Effingham Road, Sheffield, S9 3QA Tel: 0114-273 1212 Fax: 0114-276 5387 E-mail: bondpreci@aol.com
Bosworth Tools (Cutters) Ltd, Unit 19 20, Sketchley Meadows Industrial Estate, Hinckley, Leicestershire, LE10 3ES Tel: (01455) 250066 Fax: (01455) 250077
George Burdekin Ltd, 9-11 Holbrook Lane, Coventry, CV6 4AD Tel: (024) 7666 7272 Fax: (024) 7666 8050 E-mail: sales@gburdekin.co.uk
Burnac Ltd, Ohio Grove, Hot Lane Industrial Estate, Stoke-on-Trent, ST6 2BL Tel: (01782) 837599 Fax: (01782) 837149 E-mail: burnac@burnac.co.uk
C R I Grinding Ltd, 2a Goodridge Avenue, Gloucester, GL2 5EA Tel: (01452) 529475 Fax: (01452) 306362 E-mail: cri.grinding@virgin.net
Central Grinding Services, 3a Pomeroy Drive, Oadby, Leicester, LE2 5NE Tel: 0116-271 8188 Fax: 0116-271 8199 E-mail: central@grinding.fsnet.co.uk
Centreless Precision Grinding Ltd, Unit 19b Tyseley Industrial Estate, Seeleys Road, Birmingham, B11 2LQ Tel: 0121-772 1616 Fax: 0121-772 7099
Contract Engineering Ltd, Meadow Mill, Water Street, Stockport, Cheshire, SK1 2BY Tel: 0161-480 5673 Fax: 0161-477 2687
Dobson & Beaumont Ltd, Appleby Street, Blackburn, BB1 3BH Tel: (01254) 53297 Fax: (01254) 676121 E-mail: philip@dobsonandbeaumont.co.uk
Dynasurf, Millbuck Way, Sandbach, Cheshire, CW11 3HT Tel: (01270) 763091 Fax: (01270) 766564 E-mail: dynasurf@btconnect.com
Green & Preece Grinding Ltd, Rufford Road, Stourbridge, West Midlands, DY9 7NE Tel: (01384) 397040 Fax: (01384) 440267 E-mail: green-preece-grinding.co.uk@zetnet.co.uk
K M A Grinding, Unit 62 Western Business Park, Great Western Close, Birmingham, B18 4QF Tel: 0121-554 5537 Fax: 0121-554 1933
Leigh Precision Grinding, 132 Blyth Road, Hayes, Middlesex, UB3 1TD Tel: (020) 8573 0451 Fax: (020) 8561 6399 E-mail: leighgrinding@btinternet.co.uk
▶ Microplus Engineering Ltd, Unit 12 Gainsborough Trad Estate, Rufford Road, Stourbridge, West Midlands, DY9 7ND Tel: (01384) 442991 Fax: (01384) 441164
Multi-Grind Services Ltd, Unit 10, Harefield Road Industrial Estate, Rickmansworth, Hertfordshire, WD3 1PQ Tel: (01923) 725230 Fax: (01923) 777915 E-mail: steve@multigrind.co.uk
P L Grinding, Unit B8 Guy Motors Industrial Park, Park Lane, Wolverhampton, WV10 9QF Tel: (01902) 723597 Fax: (01902) 723597 E-mail: thegrindingway@blueyonder.co.uk
Poole Grinders Ltd, 81 Sterte Avenue West, Poole, Dorset, BH15 2AL Tel: (01202) 675650 Fax: (01202) 666388
Scorpion Tooling Services, Unit 7 & 9, Libbys Drive, Stroud, Gloucestershire, GL5 1RN Tel: (01453) 751511 Fax: (01453) 766676
West Midland Grinding Ltd, 1 Brookvale Trading Estate, Moor Lane, Birmingham, B6 7AQ Tel: 0121-356 3356 Fax: 0121-344 3770

CENTRELESS GRINDING MACHINES

A.J. Baker (Grinding) Ltd, Middlemore Lane West, Redhouse Industrial Estate, Aldridge, Walsall, WS9 8BG Tel: (01922) 745075 Fax: 0121-378 3291 E-mail: enquiries@ajbaker.com
Centreless Precision Grinding Ltd, Unit 19b Tyseley Industrial Estate, Seeleys Road, Birmingham, B11 2LQ Tel: 0121-772 1616 Fax: 0121-772 7099

CENTRELESS TURNING

Copeland & Craddock Ltd, Radnor Park Trading Estate, Back Lane, Congleton, Cheshire, CW12 4PX Tel: (01260) 279641 Fax: (01260) 276987 E-mail: mail@copelandandcraddock.co.uk

CENTRIFUGAL BLOWERS

▶ Howden Process Compressors Donkin Division, Holmewood Industrial Park, Park Road, Holmewood, Chesterfield, Derbyshire, S42 5UY Tel: (01246) 859053 Fax: (01246) 859054 E-mail: hdb.sales@howden.com

CENTRIFUGAL CASTING EQUIPMENT

Gibson Centri-Tech Ltd, Hilltop Works, Eastern Avenue, Lichfield, Staffordshire, WS13 6UY Tel: (01543) 418701 Fax: (01543) 418703 E-mail: sales@gibsoncentritech.co.uk

CENTRIFUGAL CASTINGS

G K N Ltd, Sheepbridge Works, Sheepbridge Lane, Chesterfield, Derbyshire, S41 9QD Tel: (01246) 260026 Fax: (01246) 260022
Gibson Centri-Tech Ltd, Hilltop Works, Eastern Avenue, Lichfield, Staffordshire, WS13 6UY Tel: (01543) 418701 Fax: (01543) 418703 E-mail: sales@gibsoncentritech.co.uk

CENTRIFUGAL CLUTCHES

Broadbent Drives, Britannia Mills, Portland Street, Bradford, West Yorkshire, BD5 0DW Tel: (01274) 783434 Fax: (01274) 390527 E-mail: sales@broadbent-drives.co.uk
Lancereal Ltd, Springfield Mills, Springfield Lane, Kirkburton, Huddersfield, HD8 0NZ Tel: (01484) 606040 Fax: (01484) 609911 E-mail: sales@lancereal.com

CENTRIFUGAL FANS

Air Vent Technology Ltd, Unit 1 Regents Court, Walworth Industrial Estate, Andover, Hampshire, SP10 5NX Tel: (01264) 356415 Fax: (01264) 337854 E-mail: avtltd@btopenworld.com
Alfa Fans Ltd, Unit 7, Green Lane, Bridgtown, Cannock, Staffordshire, WS11 0JJ Tel: (01543) 466420 Fax: (01543) 462393 E-mail: sales@alfafans.co.uk
B.O.B Stevenson Ltd, Coleman Street, Derby, DE24 8NL Tel: (01332) 574112 Fax: (01332) 757286 E-mail: sales@bobstevenson.co.uk
Birmingham Fan UK Ltd, Old Walsall Road, Hampstead Industrial Estate, Birmingham, B42 1EA Tel: 0121-357 2941 Fax: 0121-357 5805 E-mail: birmfansales@aol.com
Central Fans Colasit Ltd, Unit 19 Lakeside Industrial Estate, New Meadow Road, Redditch, Worcestershire, B98 8YW Tel: (01527) 517200 Fax: (01527) 517195 E-mail: nt@central-fans.co.uk
Daniels Fans Ltd, Heol Gors, Dafen Indust Estate, Felinfoel, Llanelli, Dyfed, SA14 8QR Tel: (01554) 752148 Fax: (01554) 741109 E-mail: sales@danielsfans.ltd.uk
Fan Engineering (Midlands) Ltd, 19B Sandy Way, Amington Industrial Estate, Tamworth, Staffordshire, B77 4DS Tel: (01827) 57000 Fax: (01827) 64641 E-mail: fanengineering@aol.co.uk
Fan Systems Group, Witt House, Brookwoods Industrial Estate, Halifax, West Yorkshire, HX4 9BH Tel: (01422) 378120 Fax: (01422) 378672 E-mail: sales@fansystems.co.uk
Fans & Spares Ltd, 6 Brookmead Industrial Estate, Beddington Lane, Croydon, CR0 4TB Tel: (020) 8683 1241 Fax: (020) 8689 0043 E-mail: croydon@fansandspares.co.uk
Fans & Spares Ltd, Unit 2 Rosevale Road, Parkhouse Industrial Estate We, Newcastle, Staffordshire, ST5 7EF Tel: (01782) 579076 Fax: (01782) 563592 E-mail: stoke@fansandspares.co.uk
Finna Fans, Unit 2 Hill Street, Kidderminster, Worcestershire, DY11 6TD Tel: (01562) 60035 Fax: (01562) 753188
Flextraction Ltd, 10 Digby Drive, Leicester Road Industrial Estate, Melton Mowbray, Leicestershire, LE13 0RQ Tel: (01664) 410641 Fax: (01664) 480244 E-mail: sales@flextraction.co.uk
G T Fan Services & Repairs Ltd, Unit D Leona Industrial Estate, Nimmings Road, Halesowen, West Midlands, B62 9JQ Tel: 0121-559 1824 Fax: 0121-561 2153
Kennedy Transmission Ltd, Station Road, Facit Whitworth, Rochdale, Lancashire, OL12 8LJ Tel: (01706) 853021 Fax: (01706) 852217 E-mail: kennedytransmissions@hotmail.com
M Y Fans Ltd, Westend Street, Oldham, OL9 6AJ Tel: 0161-628 3337 Fax: 0161-627 4153 E-mail: m.y.fans@mmp-ltd.co.uk
P M G Technical Services Ltd, Unit 9, Walton Industrial Estate, Beacon Road, Stone, Staffordshire, ST15 0NN Tel: (01785) 818857 Fax: (01785) 816587 E-mail: info@pmgtech.co.uk
R H F Fans Ltd, 2 Ferrous Way, Irlam, Manchester, M44 5FS Tel: 0161-776 6400 Fax: 0161-775 6566 E-mail: sales@rhf-fans.co.uk
Stockbridge Airco Ltd, Blossom Street Works, Ancoats, Manchester, M4 6AE Tel: 0161-236 9314 Fax: 0161-228 0009 E-mail: mark@stockbridge-airco.com
Torin Ltd, Drakes Way, Swindon, SN3 3JB Tel: (01793) 524291 Fax: (01793) 486570 E-mail: sales@torin-sifan.com
Victoria Fan & Engineering Supplies Ltd, Audley Street Works, Audley Street, Mossley, Ashton-under-Lyne, Lancashire, OL5 9HW Tel: (01457) 835391 Fax: (01457) 833378 E-mail: sales@victoriafans.co.uk

CENTRIFUGAL POLISHING MACHINES

Finishing Techniques Ltd, Halter Inn Works, Holcombe Brook, Ramsbottom, Bury, Lancashire, BL0 9SA Tel: (01706) 825819 Fax: (01706) 825748 E-mail: sales@fintek.co.uk

CENTRIFUGAL PUMP PROTECTION CONSULTANTS/ SPECIALISTS

Tyco Valves & Controls Distribution UK Ltd, White Moss Business Park, Moss Lane View, Skelmersdale, Lancashire, WN8 9TN Tel: (01695) 554800 Fax: (01695) 554835 E-mail: dny@tyco-valves.com

CENTRIFUGAL PUMPS

Apex Fluid Engineering Ltd, 4 Morley Road, Staple Hill, Bristol, BS16 4QT Tel: 0117-907 7555 Fax: 0117-907 7556 E-mail: enquiries@apexpumps.com
Armstrong Holden Brooke Pullen, Ormside House, 21 Ormside Way, Redhill, RH1 2JG Tel: (01737) 378100 Fax: (01737) 378140 E-mail: sales@holdenbrookpullen.com
Barber Pumps Ltd, Jacksons Yard, Douglas Road North, Fulwood, Preston, PR2 3QH Tel: (01772) 715502 Fax: (01772) 712716 E-mail: barberpumps@aol.com
Bedford Pump Ltd, Brooklands, Woburn Road Industrial Estate, Kempston, Bedford, MK42 7UH Tel: (01234) 852071 Fax: (01234) 856620 E-mail: sales@bedfordpumps.co.uk
Beresford Pumps Ltd, Unit 7, Network Park, Duddeston Mill Road, Saltley, Birmingham, B8 1AU Tel: 0121-503 3001 Fax: 0121-503 3002 E-mail: info@beresfordpumps.co.uk
Calpeda Ltd, Wedgwood Road Industrial Estate, Bicester, Oxfordshire, OX26 4UL Tel: (01869) 241441 Fax: (01869) 240681 E-mail: pumps@calpeda.co.uk
Caprari Pumps (UK) Ltd, Caprari House, Bakewell Road, Orton Southgate, Peterborough, PE2 6XU Tel: (01733) 371605 Fax: (01733) 371607 E-mail: info@caprari.co.uk
Desktop Security Solutions, 14 Penrose Avenue, Watford, WD19 5AD Tel: (020) 8386 1624 Fax: (020) 8386 1624 E-mail: sales@desktopsecuritysolutions.co.uk
Elmbridge Pump Co., 6a Shepherd Road, Gloucester, GL2 5EQ Tel: (01452) 501102 Fax: (01452) 303691 E-mail: sales@elmbridgepump.com
Euro Industrial Engineering, 161 Fog Lane, Manchester, M20 6FJ Tel: 0161-438 0438 Fax: 0161-438 2538 E-mail: info@eieuk.com
Fluid Equipment International Ltd, 10 Blandford Heights Industrial Estate, Blandford Forum, Dorset, DT11 7TE Tel: (01258) 459401 Fax: (01258) 459068 E-mail: sales.feil@btconnect.com
G.V.E. Ltd, Ashburton House, Trafford Park Road, Trafford Park, Manchester, M17 1BN Tel: 0161-872 0777 Fax: 0161-872 9324 E-mail: info@gvepumps.co.uk

▶ indicates data change since last edition

CENTRIFUGAL PUMPS – *continued*

Godwin Pumps Ltd, Quenington, Cirencester, Gloucestershire, GL7 5BX Tel: (01285) 750271 Fax: (01285) 750352 E-mail: sales@godwinpumps.co.uk

Grundfos Pumps Ltd, Grovebury Road, Leighton Buzzard, Bedfordshire, LU7 4TL Tel: (01525) 850000 Fax: (01525) 850011 E-mail: ukindustry@grundfos.com

Hamworthy P.L.C., Fleets Corner, Poole, Dorset, BH17 0JT Tel: (01202) 662600 Fax: (01202) 662636 E-mail: info@hamworthy.com

Holden & Brooke Ltd, Wenlock Way, Manchester, M12 5JL Tel: 0161-223 2223 Fax: 0161-220 9660 E-mail: marketing@holdenbrooke.com

Hydromarque Ltd, 21 Stapledon Road, Orton Southgate, Peterborough, PE2 6TD Tel: (01733) 370545 Fax: (01733) 361249 E-mail: mail@hydromarque.com

J P Pumps Ltd, Meadow Brook Industrial Centre, Maxwell Way, Crawley, West Sussex, RH10 9SA Tel: (01293) 553495 Fax: (01293) 524635 E-mail: mailbox.uk@johnson-pump.com

Mid Kent Electrical Engineering Co., The Street, Detling, Maidstone, Kent, ME14 3JT Tel: (01622) 735702 Fax: (01622) 734844 E-mail: pumpsales@mke.co.uk

▶ Pump Supply & Repair Group, Armstrong Hall, Wharton Rd, Winsford, Cheshire, CW7 3AD Tel: 0161-794 8038 Fax: 0161-794 8052 E-mail: salesc@pumpgroup.co.uk

Pumps & Equipment Warwick Ltd, 6 Collins Road, Heathcote Industrial Estate, Warwick, CV34 6TF Tel: (01926) 451744 Fax: (01926) 451284 E-mail: sales@pumps-equip.co.uk

Richard Hill Pumps Ltd, Brooke Road, Ridlington, Oakham, Leicestershire, LE15 9AJ Tel: (01572) 823385 Fax: (01572) 821660

Selwood Pump Co. Ltd, 188 Robin Hood Lane, Birmingham, B28 0LG Tel: 0121-777 5631 Fax: 0121-702 2195 E-mail: graham.gallon@selwood-pumps.com

Stuart Turner Ltd, Market Place, Henley-on-Thames, Oxfordshire, RG9 2AD Tel: (01491) 572655 Fax: (01491) 573704 E-mail: sales@stuart-turner.co.uk

Union Pumps Union Pumps, Green Road, Penistone, Sheffield, S36 6BJ Tel: (01226) 763311 Fax: (01226) 766535 E-mail: bkearsley@unionpump.textron.com

Weir Minerals Europe Ltd, Halifax Road, Todmorden, Lancashire, OL14 5RT Tel: (01706) 814251 Fax: (01706) 815350 E-mail: sales.uk@weirminerals.com

CENTRIFUGAL WATER PUMPS

Beresford Pumps Ltd, Unit 7, Network Park, Duddeston Mill Road, Saltley, Birmingham, B8 1AU Tel: 0121-503 3001 Fax: 0121-503 3002 E-mail: info@beresfordpumps.co.uk

Flowserve Pumps Ltd, PO Box 17, Newark, Nottinghamshire, NG24 3EN Tel: (01636) 705151 Fax: (01636) 705991 E-mail: newark@flowserve.com

P F S (Helston) Ltd, Unit 9, Water-Ma-Trout Industrial Estate, Helston, Cornwall, TR13 0LW Tel: (01326) 565454 Fax: (01326) 565505 E-mail: sales@pfs-uk.co.uk

CENTRIFUGE MAINTENANCE/ REPAIR SERVICES

Ashbrook Simon-Hartley Ltd, Derby Road, Clay Cross, Chesterfield, Derbyshire, S45 9AG Tel: (01246) 252600 Fax: (01246) 252601 E-mail: enquiries@as-h.com

CENTRIFUGES, *See also headings for particular types*

Ashbrook Simon-Hartley Ltd, Derby Road, Clay Cross, Chesterfield, Derbyshire, S45 9AG Tel: (01246) 252600 Fax: (01246) 252601 E-mail: enquiries@as-h.com

Dirk European Holdings Ltd, Dirk House, 29-31 Woodchurch Lane, Prenton, Birkenhead, Merseyside, CH42 9PJ Tel: 0151-608 8552 Fax: 0151-608 7579 E-mail: gdirk@dirkgroup.com

Hawksley & Sons Ltd, Marlborough Road, Lancing, West Sussex, BN15 8TN Tel: (01903) 752815 Fax: (01903) 766050 E-mail: enquiries@hawksley.co.uk

CERAMIC ARMOUR

▶ John Marshall Armour Systems Ltd, 578 Coldhams Lane, Cambridge, CB1 3JR Tel: (01223) 516814 Fax: (01223) 516813 E-mail: sales@marshallarmour.com

CERAMIC BALL BEARINGS

Spheric Trafalgar Ltd, Bentley House Wiston Business Park, London Road, Ashington, Pulborough, West Sussex, RH20 3DJ Tel: (01903) 891200 Fax: (01903) 891220 E-mail: sales@ballbiz.co.uk

CERAMIC BEADS

▶ BeadVoodoo!, 134 Sicily Park, Belfast, BT10 0AP Tel: (020) 8123 0703 E-mail: admin@beadvoodoo.com

Ceramic Substrates & Components Ltd, Lukely Works, 180 Carisbrooke Road, Newport, Isle of Wight, PO30 1DH Tel: (01983) 528697 Fax: (01983) 822252 E-mail: sales@ceramic-subtrates.co.uk

P E Hines & Sons Ltd, Whitebridge Lane, Stone, Staffordshire, ST15 8LU Tel: (01785) 814921 Fax: (01785) 818808 E-mail: p.e.hines@iclwebkit.co.uk

CERAMIC BEARINGS

Koyo (UK) Ltd, Whitehall Avenue, Kingston, Milton Keynes, MK10 0AX Tel: (01908) 289300 Fax: (01908) 289333 E-mail: info@koyo.co.uk

N S K Ltd, Northern Road, Newark, Nottinghamshire, NG24 2JF Tel: (01636) 705298 Fax: (01636) 605000 E-mail: info-uk@nsk.com

Snfa Bearings Ltd, Wotton Road, Charfield, Wotton-under-Edge, Gloucestershire, GL12 8SP Tel: (01453) 843501 Fax: (01453) 842577 E-mail: sales@snfa-bearings.co.uk

CERAMIC CANDLE FILTERS

N G K Spark Plugs UK Ltd, Maylands Avenue, Hemel Hempstead, Hertfordshire, HP2 4SD Tel: (01442) 281000 Fax: (01442) 281001 E-mail: enquiries@ngk.co.uk

CERAMIC CAPACITORS

Charcroft Electronics Ltd, Pump House Dol Y Coed, Llanwrtyd Wells, Powys, LD5 4TH Tel: (01591) 610408 Fax: (01591) 610385 E-mail: sales@charcroft.com

Murata Electronics Ltd, Oak House, Ancells Road, Fleet, Hampshire, GU51 2QW Tel: (01252) 811666 Fax: (01252) 811777 E-mail: enquiry@murata.co.uk

Nichicon Europe Ltd, Riverside Way, Camberley, Surrey, GU15 3YL Tel: (01276) 405500 Fax: (01276) 686531

T D K Electronics Europe Ltd, Confort House, 5-7 Queensway, Redhill, RH1 1YB Tel: (01737) 781372 Fax: (01737) 773810

Vishay Ltd, Units 6-7, Marshall Road, Hillmead, Swindon, SN5 5FZ Tel: (01793) 521351 Fax: (01793) 525163

CERAMIC CLAY

Manor Signs, 62 Knighton Lane, Leicester, LE2 8BE Tel: (0116) 283 5007 Fax: (0116) 283 8946

CERAMIC COLOURS

A T C Colours Ltd, Vale Works, New Haden Road, Cheadle, Stoke-on-Trent, ST10 1UF Tel: (01538) 754400 Fax: (01538) 751212 E-mail: mail@atccolours.co.uk

Ferro Great Britain Ltd, Westgate, Aldridge, Walsall, WS9 8YH Tel: (01922) 458300 Fax: (01922) 741399

Heraeus Silica & Metals Ltd, Cinderhill Industrial Estate, Stoke-on-Trent, ST3 5LB Tel: (01782) 599423 Fax: (01782) 599802 E-mail: enquiries@4cmd.com

Johnson Matthey P.L.C., King Street, Fenton, Stoke-On-Trent, ST3 4DF Tel: (01782) 590000 Fax: (01782) 339955

Milton Bridge Ceramic Colour Ltd, Unit 9 Trent Trading Park, Botteslow Street, Stoke-on-Trent, ST1 3NA Tel: (01782) 274229 Fax: (01782) 281591

Sneyd Oxides Ltd, Sneyd Mills, Leonora Street, Stoke-On-Trent, ST6 3BZ Tel: (01782) 577600 Fax: (01782) 835742 E-mail: ceramics@sneydoxides.co.uk

W G Ball Ltd, Longton Mill, Anchor Road, Stoke-on-Trent, ST3 1JW Tel: (01782) 312286 Fax: (01782) 598148 E-mail: sales@wgball.com

CERAMIC COMPONENTS

A G Rutter Ltd, Fitzherbert Road, Portsmouth, PO6 1RU Tel: (023) 9278 9300 Fax: (023) 9278 9500 E-mail: sales@dtw-tiles.co.uk

Omegaslate UK Ltd, 2 Chirk Close, Kidderminster, Worcestershire, DY10 1YG Tel: (01562) 755824 Fax: (01562) 742979 E-mail: info@omegaslate.com

Potters Potclais Group, Pelsall Road, Walsall, WS8 7DL Tel: (01543) 377015 Fax: (01543) 372301

Potterycrafts Ltd, Winton House, Winton Approach, Croxley Green, Rickmansworth, Hertfordshire, WD3 3TL Tel: (01923) 800006 Fax: (01923) 245544

CERAMIC CONSULTANTS

Cactus Ceramics & Crafts, 4 Merville Garden Village, Newtownabbey, County Antrim, BT37 9TF Tel: (028) 9085 9869 Fax: (028) 9084 0113

Ceramic Research Ltd, Queens Road, Stoke-on-Trent, ST4 7LQ Tel: (01782) 764444 Fax: (01782) 412331 E-mail: sales@ceram.co.uk

H & H Ceramics, 85 South Street, Pennington, Lymington, Hampshire, SO41 8DY Tel: (01590) 679026 Fax: (01590) 679026

Santech Design Ltd, The Mount, Church Lane, Endon, Stoke-On-Trent, ST9 9HF Tel: (01782) 503388 Fax: (01782) 505234 E-mail: dm@santechdesign.co.uk

CERAMIC COOKWARE

Beagle Cookware, 72-78 Stour Street, Birmingham, B18 7AJ Tel: 0121-454 3323 Fax: 0121-454 3342

Chomette Ltd, 307 Merton Road, London, SW18 5JS Tel: (020) 8877 7000 Fax: (020) 8874 8627 E-mail: paulb@chomettedornberger.co.uk

Churchill Fine Bone China (Holdings) Ltd, Marlborough Works, High Street, Stoke-on-Trent, ST6 5NZ Tel: (01782) 577566 Fax: (01782) 810318 E-mail: churchill@churchillchina.com

The Tabletop Group, Pool Potteries, Pool Street, Church Gresley, Swadlincote, Derbyshire, DE11 8EQ Tel: (01283) 213800 Fax: (01283) 817969 E-mail:

Taylor Tunnicliff Ltd, Normacot Road, Stoke-on-Trent, ST3 1PA Tel: (01782) 501174 Fax: (01782) 328807

CERAMIC ENGINEERING

Ascotex Ltd, Calder Works, Simonstone, Burnley, Lancashire, BB12 7NL Tel: (01282) 772011 Fax: (01282) 773600 E-mail: sales@ascotex.com

Britech Industries Ltd, Cinderhill Trading Estate, Weston Coyney Road, Longton, ST3 5JU Tel: (01782) 388280 Fax: (01782) 392441 E-mail: sales@britech.co.uk

Ceramics & Crystal Ltd, 7 Montpelier Gardens, London, E6 3JB Tel: (020) 8552 3122 Fax: (020) 8552 3122

▶ The Potters Friend, 6 Rawle Close, Cheadle, Stoke-On-Trent, ST10 1UX Tel: (01538) 751200 E-mail: thepottersfriend@aol.com

Staffordshire Property Development, Spot Service Stations, Sutherland Road, Stoke-on-Trent, ST3 1HZ Tel: (01782) 311562 Fax: (01782) 598316

Technical & Maintenance Services Ltd, 18 Pepper Road, Calverton, Nottingham, NG14 6LH Tel: 0115-965 3036 Fax: 0115-965 5274 E-mail: brian.burbidge@talk21.com

Walther Trowal Ltd, Spedding Road, Fenton Industrial Estate, Fenton, Stoke-on-Trent, ST4 2SN Tel: (01782) 412111 Fax: (01782) 744267 E-mail: enquires@metaret.co.uk

CERAMIC ENGINEERING COMPONENTS

VZS Seagoe Advanced Ceramics, 35-38 Cavendish Way, Glenrothes, Fife, KY6 2SB Tel: (01592) 630505 Fax: (01592) 773192 E-mail: sales@vzs-seagoe.com

CERAMIC FIBRE

MacGregor & Moir, Unit 4, 95 Westburn Drive, Cambuslang, Glasgow, G72 7NA Tel: 0141-643 3636 Fax: 0141-641 8505 E-mail: info@macgregorandmoir.com

Jesse Shirley & Son Ltd, Etruria, Lower Bedford Street, Stoke-on-Trent, ST4 7AF Tel: (01782) 212473 Fax: (01782) 287308 E-mail: enquiries@jesseshirley.com

CERAMIC FIBRE PRODUCTS

▶ Kiln Maintenance Ltd, 4 Florida Close, Hot Lane Industrial Estate, Stoke-on-Trent, ST6 2DJ Tel: (01782) 816383 Fax: (01782) 575651 E-mail: sales@kilnmaintenance.co.uk

CERAMIC FLOOR TILES

▶ Art Plus Function Ltd, Macknade, Selling Road, Faversham, Kent, ME13 8XF Tel: (01795) 530400 Fax: (0870) 7627707 E-mail: info@artplusfunction.co.uk

Bon Accord Glass, Bon Accord House, Riverside Drive, Aberdeen, AB11 7SL Tel: (01224) 588944 Fax: (01224) 582731

C B Horne, 1a Coteroyd Avenue, Churwell/Morley, Leeds, LS27 7TU Tel: (07748) 086633 E-mail: info@tilersuk.com

▶ Galloway Windows, Creebridge Mill, Creebridge, Newton Stewart, Wigtownshire, DG8 6NP Tel: (01671) 404848 Fax: (01671) 404969

CERAMIC GLAZES

Johnson Matthey P.L.C., King Street, Fenton, Stoke-On-Trent, ST3 4DF Tel: (01782) 590000 Fax: (01782) 339955

Potclays Ltd, Brick Kiln Lane, Stoke-on-Trent, ST4 7BP Tel: (01782) 219816 Fax: (01782) 286506 E-mail: sales@potclays.co.uk

Sneyd Oxides Ltd, Sneyd Mills, Leonora Street, Stoke-On-Trent, ST6 3BZ Tel: (01782) 577600 Fax: (01782) 835742 E-mail: ceramics@sneydoxides.co.uk

W G Ball Ltd, Longton Mill, Anchor Road, Stoke-on-Trent, ST3 1JW Tel: (01782) 312286 Fax: (01782) 598148 E-mail: sales@wgball.com

CERAMIC HAIR STRAIGHTENERS

▶ Capital Hair & Beauty Ltd, 3 Burton Road, Norwich, NR6 6AX Tel: (01603) 788778 Fax: (01603) 788856 E-mail: norwich@capitalhairandbeauty.co.uk

▶ Ceramic Hair Straighteners, 3 Pye Road, Heswall, Wirral, Merseyside, CH60 0DB Tel: 0151-342 4591 Fax: 0151-342 1130 E-mail: sales@ceramicstraighteners.com

CERAMIC HEATING ELEMENTS

▶ Bomac Electric Ltd, Randles Road, Knowsley Business Park, Prescot, Merseyside, L34 9HX Tel: 0151-546 4401 Fax: 0151-549 1661 E-mail: sales@bomac-elec.co.uk

CERAMIC INVESTMENT CASTING CORES

Carpenter Certech, 92b Brunel Road, Earlstrees Industrial Estate, Corby, Northamptonshire, NN17 4JW Tel: (01536) 202282 Fax: (01536) 202261

Ceramic Core Systems Ltd, Unit F Sawtry Business Park, Sawtry, Huntingdon, Cambridgeshire, PE28 5GQ Tel: (01487) 832283 Fax: (01487) 832887

Ross Ceramics Ltd, Derby Road, Denby, Ripley, Derbyshire, DE5 8NA Tel: (01773) 570800 Fax: (01773) 570152 E-mail: sales@rossceramics.co.uk

CERAMIC LABORATORY EQUIPMENT

E J Payne Ltd, 1-3 Belgrave Road, Stoke-on-Trent, ST3 4PR Tel: (01782) 312534 Fax: (01782) 599868 E-mail: sales@ejpayne.com

CERAMIC MACHINING

Coorstek, 64-66 Cavendish Way, Glenrothes, Fife, KY6 2SB Tel: (01592) 773743 Fax: (01592) 774925 E-mail: sales@coorstek.co.uk

Custom Grind Ltd, Unit 1c Brown Lees Road Industrial Estate, Forge Way, Knypersley, Stoke-on-Trent, ST8 7DN Tel: (01782) 518503 Fax: (01782) 522110 E-mail: sales@customgrind.com

D M Hughes Ltd, 31 Weardale Lane, Glasgow, G33 4JJ Tel: 0141-774 2898 Fax: 0141-774 2251

Morgan Advanced Materials & Technology, Unit 13, Madeley Road, North Moons Moat, Redditch, Worcestershire, B98 9NB Tel: (01527) 69205 Fax: (01527) 62195

Shanoc Precision Engineering, Unit 11 Bondor Business Centre, London Road, Baldock, Hertfordshire, SG7 6HP Tel: (01462) 895936 Fax: (01462) 895936

CERAMIC MAGNETS

Cermag Ltd, 94 Holywell Road, Sheffield, S4 8AS Tel: 0114-244 6136 Fax: 0114-256 1769 E-mail: sales@cermag.co.uk

▶ Guys Magnets, 12 Barbel Close, Calne, Wiltshire, SN11 9QP Tel: (01249) 811372 Fax: (01249) 812778 E-mail: guy@guysmagnets.com

Magnetic Component Engineering (U K) Ltd, 1 Union Street, Luton, LU1 3AN Tel: (01582) 735226 Fax: (01582) 734226 E-mail: eurosales@mceproducts.com

CERAMIC MATERIAL PROCESSING PLANT

Britech Industries Ltd, Cinderhill Trading Estate, Weston Coyney Road, Longton, ST3 5JU Tel: (01782) 388280 Fax: (01782) 392441 E-mail: sales@britech.co.uk

▶ indicates data change since last edition

CERAMIC MATERIALS, PIEZOELECTRIC

▶ Alba Ultrasound Ltd, Unit 3, Todd Campus, 45 Acre Road, Glasgow, G20 0XA Tel: 0141-946 5000 Fax: 0141-946 5111 E-mail: bwooldridge@albaultrasound.com

CERAMIC MODELS

C Hemstock, The Old Malt Kiln, Main Street, Carlton-on-Trent, Newark, Nottinghamshire, NG23 6NW Tel: (01636) 822326 Fax: (01636) 821556

CERAMIC MOSAIC TILES

▶ Art Plus Function Ltd, Macknade, Selling Road, Faversham, Kent, ME13 8XF Tel: (01795) 530400 Fax: (0870) 7627707 E-mail: info@artplusfunction.co.uk
C B Horne, 1a Coteroyd Avenue, Churwell/Morley, Leeds, LS27 7TU Tel: (07748) 086633 E-mail: info@tilersuk.com
▶ Mosaic Co., Mosaic House, Phoenix Park, Eaton Socon, St. Neots, Cambridgeshire, PE19 8EP Tel: (01480) 474714 Fax: (01480) 474715 E-mail: sales@mosaiccompany.co.uk

CERAMIC OR FANCY OR GLAZED OR WALL TILES

A Bleakley & Co., Winters Bridge, Portsmouth Road, Thames Ditton, Surrey, KT7 0ST Tel: (020) 8398 8137 Fax: (020) 8398 7877 E-mail: peter@ableakley.freeserve.co.uk
A World Of Ceramics, 82 Priory Road, Kenilworth, Warwickshire, CV8 1LQ Tel: (01926) 854500 Fax: (01926) 856660
▶ Castyle Ltd, Sandbach Road, Stoke-on-Trent, ST6 2DR Tel: (01782) 838333 Fax: (01782) 838306
Central Flooring & Tile Co., 51 Mullaghboy Heights, Magherafelt, County Londonderry, BT45 5NU Tel: (028) 7963 3076
Ceramiks, Hadfield Road, Cardiff, CF11 8AQ Tel: (0808) 1555629 Fax: (029) 2022 0559 E-mail: ceramiks@comptongroup.com
City Ceramics, Quarry Lane, Chichester, West Sussex, PO19 8NY Tel: (01243) 775613 Fax: (01243) 776863
City Tiles Contracts Ltd, 73 Dean Court Road, Rottingdean, Brighton, BN2 7DL Tel: (01273) 390777 Fax: (01273) 390888
Kenneth Clark Ceramics, The North Wing, Southover Grange, Southover Road, Lewes, East Sussex, BN7 1TP Tel: (01273) 476761 Fax: (01273) 479565
Eastern Glazed Ceramics Ltd, Tile House, Eversley Road, Norwich, NR6 6TA Tel: (01603) 423391 Fax: (01603) 789040 E-mail: enquiries@egctiles.co.uk
Eastern Glazed Ceramics Ltd, 1270 Lincoln Road, Peterborough, PE4 6LE Tel: (01733) 324074 Fax: (01733) 321909 E-mail: peterborough@egctiles.co.uk
Fired Earth Ltd, 1-3 Twyford Mill, Oxford Road, Adderbury, Banbury, Oxfordshire, OX17 3SX Tel: (01295) 812088 Fax: (01295) 810832 E-mail: info@firedearth.com
▶ GoodSource Global Trading Ltd, Unit 26, Cavans Way, Binley Industrial Estate, Coventry, CV3 2SF Tel: (08456) 448148 Fax: (08706) 622166 E-mail: contact@goodsource.co.uk
H & E Smith Ltd, Brittanic Works, Broom Street, Stoke-on-Trent, ST1 2ER Tel: (01782) 281617 Fax: (01782) 269882 E-mail: sales@hesmith.co.uk
H & R Johnson Tiles Ltd, Harewood Street, Tunstall, Stoke-on-Trent, ST6 5JZ Tel: (01782) 575575 Fax: (01782) 577377 E-mail: sales@johnson-tiles.com
▶ Leafcutter Design, 119 Penn Hill Avenue, Poole, Dorset, BH14 9LY Tel: (01202) 716969 Fax: (01202) 716969 E-mail: sales@leafcutterdesign.co.uk
Original Style Ltd, Falcon Road, Sowton Industrial Estate, Exeter, EX2 7LF Tel: (01392) 474011 Fax: (01392) 219932 E-mail: info@stovax.com
Perry Street Tile Centre, 38 Perry Street, Dungannon, County Tyrone, BT71 6AJ Tel: (028) 8772 9316 Fax: (028) 8772 4939
Phoenix Tile Studio, Winkhill Mill, Swan Street, Stoke-on-Trent, ST4 7RH Tel: (01782) 745599 Fax: (01782) 745599 E-mail: office@phoenixtilestudio.fsbusiness.co.uk
Pilkington's Tiles Ltd, Blandford Road, Poole, Dorset, BH15 4AR Tel: (01202) 672741 Fax: (01202) 671866
Pilkingtons Tiles Group Plc, P O Box 4, Manchester, M27 8LP Tel: 0161-727 1000 Fax: 0161-727 1122 E-mail: info@pilkingtontiles.com
Quiligotti Terrazzo Ltd, PO Box 4, Manchester, M27 8LP Tel: 0161-727 1189 Fax: 0161-793 1173 E-mail: sales@pilkingtons.com
Rogers Ceramics, Unit 3 Metcalf Way, Crawley, West Sussex, RH11 7SU Tel: (01293) 612057 Fax: (01293) 612047 E-mail: info@rogers-ceramics.com
S F C Ceramics Ltd, 4-6 Bethel Street, Brighouse, West Yorkshire, HD6 1JN Tel: (01484) 400377 Fax: (01484)400677
Simmy Ceramics, Sayer House, Oxgate Lane, London, NW2 7JN Tel: (020) 8208 0416 Fax: (020) 8450 1140 E-mail: sales@simmyceramics.com
Studio Ceramics Ltd, 72 Fosse Road, Farndon, Newark, Nottinghamshire, NG24 4ST Tel: (01636) 673527 Fax: (01636) 612871 E-mail: sales@studioceramics.com
Swedecor Ltd, Manchester Street, Hull, HU3 4TX Tel: (01482) 329691 Fax: (01482) 212988 E-mail: info@swedecor.com
Terrafirma Ceramica Ltd, 119 Northfield Avenue, London, W13 9QR Tel: (020) 8840 2844 Fax: (020) 8840 2054
Thames Valley Tiles, Bagshot Road, Bracknell, Berkshire, RG12 9SE Tel: (01344) 420585 Fax: (01344) 420585
Tile & Bath Select Ltd, 73 Park Street, Aylesbury, Buckinghamshire, HP20 1DU Tel: (01296) 336181 Fax: (01296) 336191
Tranasco Co. Ltd, Unit 28 Greenhill Industrial Estate, Coatbridge, Lanarkshire, ML5 2AG Tel: (01236) 424400 Fax: (01236) 424477
Welbeck Tiles Ltd, Workshop, 2-3 Trereife Park, Penzance, Cornwall, TR20 8TB Tel: (01736) 333106 Fax: (01736) 762000 E-mail: info@welbecktiles.com
▶ Wudo Ltd, 2 Stanley Road, Hertford, SG13 7LQ Tel: (01992) 504014 Fax: (01992 537388 E-mail: rachelwu@lineone.net

CERAMIC PRECIOUS METALS, *See Precious Metals*

CERAMIC PRODUCT PUNCHES

Boden Engineers, Unit 9 Moorfields Industrial Estate, Cotes Heath, Stafford, ST21 6QY Tel: (01782) 791777 Fax: (01782) 791777

CERAMIC PRODUCTION PLANT AND MACHINERY

Firestool, Auckland Street, Stoke-on-Trent, ST6 2AY Tel: (01782) 819164 Fax: (01782) 835642
Hulse Engineering, Duke Street, Stoke-on-Trent, ST4 3NR Tel: (01782) 316589 Fax: (01782) 598504 E-mail: hulsefabricationsltd@hotmail.com

CERAMIC PRODUCTION PLANT CONTRACTORS OR DESIGNERS

Britech Industries Ltd, Cinderhill Trading Estate, Weston Coyney Road, Longton, ST3 5JU Tel: (01782) 388280 Fax: (01782) 392441 E-mail: sales@britech.co.uk
Rimington-Vian, 1 Emtres Mews, Camblewell, London, SE5 9BT Tel: (020) 7733 4441 Fax: (020) 7733 4441 E-mail: post@rimingtonvian.co.uk

CERAMIC PRODUCTS (INDUSTRIAL) MANUFRS

Advanced Ceramics Ltd, Castle Works, Stafford, ST16 2ET Tel: (01785) 241000 Fax: (01785) 214073 E-mail: mail@aclstafford.co.uk
Almurad DIY Bradford Ltd, Bell House, Southfield Lane, Bradford, West Yorkshire, BD7 3NN Tel: (01274) 522375 Fax: (01274) 656333
BAB Industrial & Commercial, 7 Stainburn Avenue, Leeds, LS17 6PQ Tel: 0113-269 5936 Fax: 0113-269 5936 E-mail: brian@boardman-online.co.uk
Carpenter Certech, 92b Brunel Road, Earlstrees Industrial Estate, Corby, Northamptonshire, NN17 4JW Tel: (01536) 202282 Fax: (01536) 202261
Casting Supplies Ltd, Unit 19 Trent Trading Park, Botteslow Street, Joiners Square, Stoke-on-Trent, ST1 3LY Tel: (01782) 289574 Fax: (01782) 279272
Ceramic Gas Products Ltd, Albion Works, Uttoxeter Road, Stoke-on-Trent, ST3 1PH Tel: (01782) 599922 Fax: (01782) 598037 E-mail: joan@ceramicgasproducts.co.uk
Ceramic Substrates & Components Ltd, Lukely Works, 180 Carisbrooke Road, Newport, Isle of Wight, PO30 1DH Tel: (01983) 528697 Fax: (01983) 822252 E-mail: sales@ceramic-subtrates.co.uk
Ceramtec UK Ltd, Sidmouth Road, Colyton, Devon, EX24 6JP Tel: (01297) 552707 Fax: (01297) 553325 E-mail: sales@ceramtec.co.uk
East Midlands Ceramics Ltd, Unit 1 Cowlairs, Nottingham, NG5 9RA Tel: 0115-977 0155 Fax: 0115-977 0710 E-mail: sales@east-midlands-ceramics.co.uk
Foxwood Ceramics, 729 Woodbridge Road, Ipswich, IP4 4NB Tel: (01473) 717717 Fax: (01473) 717639 E-mail: info@foxwoodceramics.co.uk
H V Skan Ltd, 425-433 Stratford Road, Shirley, Solihull, West Midlands, B90 4AE Tel: 0121-733 3003 Fax: 0121-733 1030 E-mail: info@skan.co.uk
Highland Stoneware Scotland Ltd, Baddidarroch, Lochinver, Lairg, Sutherland, IV27 4LP Tel: (01571) 844376 Fax: (01571) 844626 E-mail: potters@highlandstoneware.co.uk
Horizon Technology, Units 1-2, Dacre Castle, Dacre, Penrith, Cumbria, CA11 0HL Tel: (01768) 486711 Fax: (01768) 486770
Jamies Tiles, Wear Street, Sunderland, SR5 2BH Tel: 0191-548 5678 Fax: 0191-548 2906 E-mail: sales@jamiestiles.co.uk
Just Mugs Ltd, Unit 5, Hanley Business Park, Cooper Street, Stoke-On-Trent, ST1 4DW Tel: (01782) 274888 Fax: (01782) 202181 E-mail: info@justmugs.com
Morgan Advanced Ceramics, Bewdley Road, Stourport-on-Severn, Worcestershire, DY13 8QR Tel: (01299) 827000 Fax: (01299) 827872 E-mail: webleads@morganadvancedceramics.com
Nicobond International Ltd, 26 Colquhoun Avenue, Hillington Industrial Estate, Glasgow, G52 4BN Tel: 0141-880 1200 Fax: 0141-880 1212 E-mail: nicobond.glasgow@nichollsandclarke.com
Pyrotek Engineering Materials Ltd, Garamonde Drive, Wymbush, Milton Keynes, MK8 8LN Tel: (01908) 561155 Fax: (01908) 560473 E-mail: petwin@pyrotek-inc.com
Sheerlyte Aggregates, Adelaide Street, Stoke-on-Trent, ST6 2BD Tel: (01782) 835369 Fax: (01782) 834496 E-mail: mark@timberandtile.com
SKM Products Ltd, Unit N3 Troon Way Business Centre, Humberstone Lane, Leicester, LE4 9HA Tel: 0116-246 1727 Fax: 0116-246 0313
Taylor Tiles Holdings Ltd, Plasmarl Industrial Estate, Beaufort Road, Swansea Enterprise Park, Swansea, SA6 8JG Tel: (01792) 797712 Fax: (01792) 791103 E-mail: info@taylortiles.co.uk
VZS Seagoe Advanced Ceramics, 35-38 Cavendish Way, Glenrothes, Fife, KY6 2SB Tel: (01592) 630505 Fax: (01592) 773192 E-mail: sales@vzs-seagoe.com
Wade Ceramics Ltd, Royal Victoria Pottery, Westport Road, Burslem, Stoke-On-Trent, ST6 4AG Tel: (01782) 577321 Fax: (01782) 575195 E-mail: alan.keenan@wade.co.uk
Walther Trowal Ltd, Spedding Road, Fenton Industrial Estate, Fenton, Stoke-on-Trent, ST4 2SN Tel: (01782) 412111 Fax: (01782) 744267 E-mail: enquires@metaret.co.uk
Whitfield & Son Ltd, Marsh Trees House, Marsh Parade, Newcastle, Staffordshire, ST5 1BT Tel: (01782) 622666 Fax: (01782) 622655 E-mail: sales@whitson.co.uk
Zodiac Automotive UK Ltd, Wansbeck Bus Park, Rotary Parkway, Ashington, Northumberland, NE63 8QZ Tel: (01670) 562000 Fax: (01670) 855590

CERAMIC PRODUCTS, DECORATIVE

▶ Mello Ltd, 86 Church Lane, Arlesey, Bedfordshire, SG15 6UX Tel: 01462 733993 Fax: 01462 733993 E-mail: mello@hmlc.fsnet.co.uk

CERAMIC RAW MATERIALS

A.B.S. International Ltd, Persia House, 27 Aughton Road, Southport, Merseyside, PR8 2AG Tel: (01704) 564386 Fax: (01704) 550091 E-mail: abs@provider.co.uk
C P Ceramics, 150 Columbia Road, London, E2 7RG Tel: (020) 7366 9570 Fax: (020) 7366 9715 E-mail: sales@cpceramics.com
Cermatco Ltd, Aylesham Industrial Estate, Aylesham, Canterbury, Kent, CT3 3EP Tel: (01304) 842222 Fax: (01304) 842434 E-mail: info@cermatco.co.uk
China Millers Ltd, 409 King Street, Stoke-on-Trent, ST4 3EF Tel: (01782) 313291 Fax: (01782) 599494
Global Ceramic Materials Ltd, Milton Works, Leek New Road, Stoke-on-Trent, ST2 7EF Tel: (01782) 537297 Fax: (01782) 537867 E-mail: sales@gsb.net
Johnson Matthey P.L.C., King Street, Fenton, Stoke-On-Trent, ST3 4DF Tel: (01782) 590000 Fax: (01782) 339955
Keith Ceramic Materials Ltd, Fishers Way, Belvedere, Kent, DA17 6BS Tel: (020) 8311 8299 Fax: (020) 8311 8238
R A Watts Ltd, 36-38 Woodcote Road, Wallington, Surrey, SM6 0NN Tel: (020) 8647 1074 Fax: (020) 8773 3595 E-mail: sales@rawatts.fsbusiness.co.uk

CERAMIC RESONATORS

Eurosource Electronics Ltd, Parkway House, Sheen Lane, London, SW14 8LS Tel: (020) 8878 5355 Fax: (020) 8878 5733 E-mail: sales@eurosource.co.uk

CERAMIC SANITARY WARE, *See headings under Sanitary Ware*

CERAMIC SINKS

Astracast P.L.C., PO Box 20, Birstall, West Yorkshire, WF17 9XD Tel: (01924) 477466 Fax: (01924) 475801 E-mail: marketing@astracast.co.uk
Ideal Standard Social Club, County Road North, Hull, HU5 4HS Tel: (01482) 343852 Fax: (01482) 445886 E-mail: ideal-standard@asvr.com
Rangemaster, Meadow Lane, Long Eaton, Nottingham, NG10 2AT Tel: 0115-946 4000 Fax: 0115-946 0374 E-mail: sales@rangemaster.co.uk
Shaws Of Darwen, Waterside, Darwen, Lancashire, BB3 3NX Tel: (01254) 771086 Fax: (01254) 873462 E-mail: sales@shaws-of-darwen.co.uk

CERAMIC SPRAYING/COATING MATERIALS

Ferro Great Britain Ltd, Nile Street, Stoke-on-Trent, ST6 2BQ Tel: (01782) 820400 Fax: (01782) 820402
Ferro Great Britain Ltd, Westgate, Aldridge, Walsall, WS9 8YH Tel: (01922) 458300 Fax: (01922) 741399
Park Cross Engineering, 33 Moss Lane, Worsley, Manchester, M28 3WD Tel: 0161-799 0660 Fax: 0161-703 8006 E-mail: mail@park-cross.co.uk

CERAMIC SPRAYING/COATING SERVICES

Celcoat Ltd, 3 Crown Works, Rotherham Road, Beighton, Sheffield, S20 1AH Tel: 0114-269 0771 Fax: 0114-254 0495 E-mail: celcoatltd@tiscali.co.uk
Ceramet Plasma Coatings Ltd, Ryeford Industrial Estate, Ryeford, Stonehouse, Gloucestershire, GL10 2LA Tel: (01453) 828416 Fax: (01453) 823068 E-mail: sales@ceramet.co.uk
Exel Industrial UK Ltd, Unit 4 Lockflight Buildings, Wheatlea Industrial Estate, Wigan, Lancashire, WN3 6XR Tel: (01942) 829111 Fax: (01942) 820491 E-mail: enquiries@exel-uk.com
Metallizers (Heckmondwike) Ltd, Old White Lee Colliery, Leeds Road, Heckmondwike, West Yorkshire, WF16 9BH Tel: (01924) 473840 Fax: (01924) 473794

CERAMIC TEST EQUIPMENT

▶ C N S Farnell, Elstree Business Centre, Elstree Way, Borehamwood, Hertfordshire, WD6 1RX Tel: (020) 8238 6900 Fax: (020) 8238 6901 E-mail: sales@cnsfarnell.com
Ceramicos, The Warehouse, Whitehill Cottage, Oxhill, Warwick, CV35 0RH Tel: 01295 680176 Fax: 01295 680174 E-mail: sales@ceramicos.co.uk
E J Payne Ltd, 1-3 Belgrave Road, Stoke-on-Trent, ST3 4PR Tel: (01782) 312534 Fax: (01782) 599868 E-mail: sales@ejpayne.com

CERAMIC TEXTILES

D M Hughes Ltd, 31 Weardale Lane, Glasgow, G33 4JJ Tel: 0141-774 2898 Fax: 0141-774 2251
Edward Keirby & Co. Ltd, Vine Works, Chichester Street, Rochdale, Lancashire, OL16 2BG Tel: (01706) 645330 Fax: (01706) 352882 E-mail: info@edwardkeirby.co.uk
Nicobond (South West) Ltd, 325-327 Penarth Road, Cardiff, CF11 7TT Tel: (029) 2039 0146 Fax: (029) 2022 4356
Spectile Ltd, 2 Poplar Grove, Crewe, CW1 4AZ Tel: (01270) 587222 Fax: (01270) 250888 E-mail: sales@spectile.co.uk

CERAMIC THREAD GUIDES

Sharkie & Huntbatch Ltd, Riverdane Road, Eaton Bank Trading Estate, Congleton, Cheshire, CW12 1PL Tel: (01260) 274747 Fax: (01260) 299017 E-mail: office@sharkies.co.uk

CERAMIC TILE CONTRACTORS

▶ Atlantis Ceramics, 3 Wilton Way, Exeter, EX1 3UH Tel: (07919) 575300 E-mail: atlantis.ceramics@mail.com

CERAMIC TIPPED CUTTING TOOLS

Central Tools & Consumables, 18-19 Haverscroft Industrial Estate, New Road, Attleborough, Norfolk, NR17 1YE Tel: (01953) 453919 Fax: (01953) 456410 E-mail: carlwcentral@aol.com
N G K Spark Plugs UK Ltd, Maylands Avenue, Hemel Hempstead, Hertfordshire, HP2 4SD Tel: (01442) 281000 Fax: (01442) 281001 E-mail: enquiries@ngk.co.uk

CERAMIC TRANSFERS

Tudor, 2 Kirkwall Grove, Stoke-on-Trent, ST2 7PH Tel: (01782) 538777 Fax: (01782) 538777

▶ indicates data change since last edition

CERAMIC WALL TILES

C B Horne, 1a Coteroyd Avenue, Churwell/Morley, Leeds, LS27 7TU Tel: (07748) 086633 E-mail: info@tilersuk.com

▶ Galloway Windows, Creebridge Mill, Creebridge, Newton Stewart, Wigtownshire, DG8 6NP Tel: (01671) 404848 Fax: (01671) 404969

CERAMICS, ADVANCED

▶ Ceram-Tech, 52 Crossgreen Drive, Uphall, Broxburn, West Lothian, EH52 6DR Tel: (01506) 857805

CEREAL BARS

▶ Baking Solutions Ltd, Avenue Two, Witney, Oxfordshire, OX28 4YQ Tel: (01993) 864777 Fax: (01993) 777440 E-mail: info@bakingsolutions.co.uk

CEREAL FOOD PROCESSING PLANT AND MACHINERY

▶ Jex Engineering Co. Ltd, Adam Smith Street, Grimsby, South Humberside, DN31 1SJ Tel: (01472) 361311 Fax: (01472) 240218 E-mail: phill.bodsworth@jexengineering.com

Nestle Cereal Partners, Bridge Road East, Welwyn Garden City, Hertfordshire, AL7 1RR Tel: (01707) 824400 Fax: (01707) 824401

▶ Wolverine Proctor & Schwartz, 3 Langlands Avenue, East Kilbride, Glasgow, G75 0YG Tel: (01355) 575350 Fax: (01355) 575351

CEREAL FOOD PRODUCTS

▶ A D M Millings Ltd, Seaforth Flour Mill, Seaforth Dock, Seaforth, Liverpool, L21 4PG Tel: 0151-922 8911

▶ Adm, South End Mills, Mill Street, Liverpool, L8 6QZ Tel: 0151-552 5100 Fax: 0151-552 5150

Belso's Cereals Research & Development, 45-46 Stapledon Road, Orton Southgate, Peterborough, PE2 6TD Tel: (01733) 234076 Fax: (01733) 235799E-mail: info@belso.co.uk

British Diamalt, Maltkiln Lane, Newark, Nottinghamshire, NG24 1HN Tel: (01636) 614730 Fax: (01636) 614740 E-mail: sales@diamalt.co.uk

Canterbury Wholefoods, Jewry Lane, Canterbury, Kent, CT1 2JB Tel: (01227) 464623 Fax: (01227) 764838 E-mail: enquiries@canterbury-wholefoods.co.uk

Cereal Partners UK, Port Causeway, Bromborough, Wirral, Merseyside, CH62 4TH Tel: 0151-512 4700 Fax: 0151-512 4702

▶ Clarks (Wantage) Ltd, Town Mills, Wantage, Oxfordshire, OX12 9AB Tel: (01235) 768991

Dalziel Ltd, Unit 11 Hunslet Trading Estate, Low Road, Leeds, LS10 1QR Tel: 0113-277 7662 Fax: 0113-271 4954

▶ Dasca Cornmill Ingredients, Crosby Road South, Seaforth, Liverpool, L21 4PF Tel: 0151-922 6261 Fax: 0151-933 8208

European Oat Millers Ltd, Mile Road, Bedford, MK42 9TB Tel: (01234) 327922 Fax: (01234) 353892 E-mail: sales@oatmillers.com

F Stoker & Son, Bishopdyke Road, Sherburn in Elmet, Leeds, LS25 6HP Tel: (01977) 683788 Fax: (01977) 682318

Grangestone Grain Co., Girvan Distillery, Grangestone Industrial Estate, Girvan, Ayrshire, KA26 9PT Tel: (01465) 713531 Fax: (01465) 713533

▶ Heygates Ltd, Eagle Roller Mills, Downham Market, Norfolk, PE38 9EP Tel: (01366) 383361 Fax: (01366) 384687

J & V Dalton Ltd, Dalmark House, Eye, Peterborough, PE6 7UD Tel: (01733) 222391 Fax: (01733) 223246 E-mail: sales@dalmark.co.uk

Nestle Cereal Partners, Bridge Road East, Welwyn Garden City, Hertfordshire, AL7 1RR Tel: (01707) 824400 Fax: (01707) 824401

▶ Quaker Oats Ltd, Uthrogle Mills, Cupar, Fife, KY15 4PD Tel: (01334) 652961

▶ Rank Hovis Ltd, Scottstoun Mill, Partick Bridge Street, Glasgow, G11 6PH Tel: (0870) 7281111 Fax: 0141-303 5550

▶ Rank Hovis Ltd, Canklow Road, Rotherham, South Yorkshire, S60 2JG Tel: (01709) 726800 Fax: (01709) 360513

Ryecroft Foods Ltd, Tudno Mill, Smith Street, Ashton-under-Lyne, Lancashire, OL7 0DB Tel: 0161-342 1600 Fax: 0161-342 1605

Weetabix Food Co Ltd, Weetabix Mills, Burton Latimer, Kettering, Northamptonshire, NN15 5JR Tel: (01536) 722181 Fax: (01536) 725361 E-mail: foodservice@weetabix.com

▶ Westmill Foods Ltd, The Quay, Selby, North Yorkshire, YO8 4EG Tel: (01757) 293200 Fax: (01757) 293208 E-mail: sales@allinsonbaking.com

Wholebake Ltd, Tyn Llidiart Industrial Estate, Corwen, Clwyd, LL21 9RR Tel: (01490) 412297 Fax: (01490) 412053 E-mail: wholebake@aol.co.uk

CEREAL SYRUP PRODUCERS OR SUPPLIERS

British Diamalt, Maltkiln Lane, Newark, Nottinghamshire, NG24 1HN Tel: (01636) 614730 Fax: (01636) 614740 E-mail: sales@diamalt.co.uk

CERTIFICATION ENGINEERS OR SERVICES

Gas Tec At C R E Ltd, P O Box 279, Cheltenham, Gloucestershire, GL52 7ZJ Tel: (01242) 677877 Fax: (01242) 676506 E-mail: enquiries@gastecuk.com

I C S, 178 Reddicap Heath Road, Sutton Coldfield, West Midlands, B75 7ET Tel: 0121-241 2299 Fax: 0121-241 4623 E-mail: wayne@ics-mail.com

T U V Rheinland Group UK, 24 Bennetts Hill, Birmingham, B2 5QP Tel: 0121-634 8000 Fax: 0121-634 8080 E-mail: safety@uk.tuv.com

CERTIFIED REFERENCE MATERIALS, METALS BASED

Bureau Of Analysed Samples Ltd, Newham Hall, Stokesley Road, Newby, Middlesbrough, Cleveland, TS8 9EA Tel: (01642) 300500 Fax: (01642) 315209 E-mail: enquiries@basrid.co.uk

CERTIFYING AUTHORITIES

I C S, 178 Reddicap Heath Road, Sutton Coldfield, West Midlands, B75 7ET Tel: 0121-241 2299 Fax: 0121-241 4623 E-mail: wayne@ics-mail.com

Moduspec Engineering UK Ltd, 2 Craigshaw Road, West Tullos Industrial Estate, Aberdeen, AB12 3AQ Tel: (01224) 248144 Fax: (01224) 284125 E-mail: sales@moduspec.com

National Security Inspectorate, Orchard House, 2 Victoria Square, Droitwich, Worcestershire, WR9 8DS Tel: (01905) 773131 Fax: (01905) 773102 E-mail: admin@nsi.org.uk

Quality Scheme for Ready Mixed Concrete, 1 Mount Miews, High Street, Hampton, Middlesex, TW12 2SH Tel: (020) 8941 0273 Fax: (020) 8979 4558 E-mail: qsrmc@qsrmc.co.uk

UK Accreditation Service Ltd, 21-47 High Street, Feltham, Middlesex, TW13 4UN Tel: (020) 8917 8400 Fax: (020) 8917 8500 E-mail: info@ukas.com

CHAIN ASSEMBLIES

B & S Chains (Midlands) Ltd, 29 Toys Lane, Halesowen, West Midlands, B63 2JX Tel: (01384) 413088 Fax: (01384) 413066 E-mail: enquiries@bandschains.co.uk

Chain Products Ltd, 49 Ward Street, Birmingham, B19 3TD Tel: 0121-359 0697 Fax: 0121-359 3672 E-mail: chainproducts@aol.com

Deacon Products Ltd, Unit 1, Penn Industrial Estate, Providence Street, Cradley Heath, West Midlands, B64 5DJ Tel: (01384) 416931 Fax: (01384) 635172 E-mail: info@chain-fittings.co.uk

▶ English Chain Co Ltd, Chain House, Brighton Road, Godalming, Surrey, GU7 1NS Tel: (01483) 428383 Fax: (01483) 861931 E-mail: sales@englishchain.co.uk

TMC, Crease Drove, Crowland, Peterborough, PE6 0BN Tel: (01733) 211339 Fax: (01733) 211444 E-mail: tmc@crowlandcranes.co.uk

William Hackett Chains Ltd, Maypole Fields, Halesowen, West Midlands, B63 2QE Tel: (01384) 569431 Fax: (01384) 639157 E-mail: info@williamhackett.co.uk

CHAIN BLOCKS

Lifting Gear Hire plc, 120 Bolton Road, Atherton, Manchester, M46 9YZ Tel: (01942) 878081 Fax: (01942) 895018 E-mail: info@lgh.co.uk

TMC, Crease Drove, Crowland, Peterborough, PE6 0BN Tel: (01733) 211339 Fax: (01733) 211444 E-mail: tmc@crowlandcranes.co.uk

William Hackett Chains Ltd, Maypole Fields, Halesowen, West Midlands, B63 2QE Tel: (01384) 569431 Fax: (01384) 639157 E-mail: info@williamhackett.co.uk

CHAIN CABLES

Griffin Woodhouse, Greenfields, Romsley Lane, Shatterford, Bewdley, Worcestershire, DY12 1RS Tel: (01299) 861829 Fax: (01299) 861830E-mail: sales@griffin-woodhouse.co.uk

CHAIN CONVEYOR SYSTEMS

Amber Industries Ltd, Brook House, Brook Street, Tipton, West Midlands, DY4 9DD Tel: 0121-530 8664 Fax: 0121-530 8665 E-mail: info@amber-industries.ltd.uk

Challenger Handling Ltd, 1 Warwick Street, Hull, HU9 1ET Tel: (01482) 224404 Fax: (01482) 210808 E-mail: sales@challenger-group.co.uk

Crescent-Webb Ltd, 14-15 Weller Street, London, SE1 1LQ Tel: (020) 7407 0085 Fax: (020) 7403 0889

Excel Automation Ltd, Gregorys Bank, Worcester, WR3 8AB Tel: (01905) 721500 Fax: (01905) 613024 E-mail: information@excel-automation.co.uk

Jervis B Webb Co. Ltd, Swan Valley Way, Northampton, NN4 8BD Tel: (0845) 1270222 Fax: (0845) 1270221 E-mail: sales@jervisbwebb.co.uk

John Morgan Conveyors Ltd, 1 Purbrook Road, Wolverhampton, WV1 2EJ Tel: (01902) 455755 Fax: (01902) 452245 E-mail: jmconveyors@btinternet.com

Mercia Mechanical Handling Ltd, Unit C4-C6, Guy Motors Industrial Park, Park Lane, Wolverhampton, WV10 9QF Tel: (01902) 739852 Fax: (01902) 739547 E-mail: merciamech@btconnect.com

Midland Handling Equipment Ltd, Stretton Road, Great Glen, Leicester, LE8 9GN Tel: 0116-259 3175 Fax: 0116-259 2820 E-mail: sales@mhel.co.uk

MK Profile Systems, 9 Cowling Business Park, Canal Side, Chorley, Lancashire, PR6 0QL Tel: (01257) 263937 Fax: (01257) 271409 E-mail: info@mkprofiles.co.uk

R J T Conveyors (International) Ltd, Unit 20 Beven Industrial Estate, Beven Road, Brierley Hill, West Midlands, DY5 3TF Tel: (01384) 864458 Fax: (01384) 827777 E-mail: sales@rjtconveyors.com

Redler Ltd, Dudbridge Works, Dudbridge, Stroud, Gloucestershire, GL5 3EY Tel: (01453) 763611 Fax: (01453) 763582 E-mail: sales@redler.com

CHAIN DRIVES

Diamond Chain Co., Unit 7-9 Blaydon Industrial Park, Chainbridge Road, Blaydon-on-Tyne, Tyne & Wear, NE21 5AB Tel: 0191-414 8822 Fax: 0191-414 8877 E-mail: sales@diamondchain.co.uk

Ewart Chain Ltd, Colombo Street, Derby, DE23 8LX Tel: (01332) 345451 Fax: (01332) 371753 E-mail: sales@ewartchain.co.uk

Longford Bearings Engineering Sales Ltd, Transmission House, 10a Lady Lane, Longford, Coventry, CV6 6AZ Tel: (024) 7636 0666 Fax: (024) 7636 0759

Toogood Industrial Ltd, Unit H7, Haysbridge Business Centre, Brickhouse Lane, South Godstone, Godstone, Surrey, RH9 8JW Tel: (01342) 844188 Fax: (01342) 844220 E-mail: office@toogood.co.uk

Transmission Development Co GB Ltd, 26 Dawkins Road, Poole, Dorset, BH15 4HF Tel: (01202) 675555 Fax: (01202) 677466 E-mail: sales@transdev.co.uk

CHAIN GRATE BOILERS

Bib Cochran Ltd, Newbie Works, Annan, Dumfriesshire, DG12 5QU Tel: (01522) 510510 Fax: (01461) 205511 E-mail: enquiries@bibcochran.com

CHAIN LINK FENCING

F J Campion Ltd, Thames View, Upper Sunbury Road, Hampton, Middlesex, TW12 2DL Tel: (020) 8979 2351 Fax: (020) 8979 2351

Fencing Products Ltd, 10 King Street Lane, Winnersh, Wokingham, Berkshire, RG41 5AS Tel: 0118-978 5162 Fax: 0118-977 6422 E-mail: j.a.o.@btinternet.com

Richards & Hewitt Sales Ltd, Dorset Way, Byfleet, West Byfleet, Surrey, KT14 7LB Tel: (01932) 346025 Fax: (01932) 348517

CHAIN LINK FENCING CONTRACTORS

Boundary Fencing Supplies, Unit 1, Vale View Business Park, Crown Lane South, Ardleigh, Colchester, CO7 7PL Tel: (01206) 230231

▶ First Fencing, 585, Southleigh Road, Emsworth, Hampshire, PO10 7TE Tel: 01243 430502 E-mail: info@firstfencing.co.uk

G A Collinson Fencing Co Ltd, Stannetts, Laindon, Basildon, Essex, SS15 6DN Tel: (01268) 411671 Fax: (01268) 541134 E-mail: info@collinsonfencing.co.uk

▶ Id Fencing, 24 Hayle Avenue, Warwick, CV34 5TW Tel: (01926) 496753 Fax: (01926) 496753 E-mail: info@idfencing.co.uk

▶ Kirkaldy Fencing & Dyking, 64 Feus, Auchterarder, Perthshire, PH3 1DG Tel: (01764) 663115 E-mail: kirkaldyfencinganddyking@msn.com

▶ Landscapes Of Bath, York Buildings, Bath, BA1 2EB Tel: (07739) 462855 Fax: (01225) 462358E-mail: sales@landscapesofbath.co.uk

Trentham Fencing & Contractors Ltd, 17-19 Church Lane, Stoke-on-Trent, ST4 4QB Tel: (01782) 644165 Fax: (01782) 644490 E-mail: sales@trenthamfencing.co.uk

CHAIN LUBRICANTS

Hughes & Holmes, Unit F, Key Industrial Park, Fernside Road, Willenhall, West Midlands, WV13 3YA Tel: (01902) 728888 Fax: (01902) 727111 E-mail: willenhall@lister.co.uk

Hydralube Ltd, 72A Parker Road, Hastings, East Sussex, TN34 3TT Tel: (01424) 465527 Fax: (01424) 201363 E-mail: sales@hydralube.co.uk

CHAIN MANUFRS, *See also headings for particular types under Chains*

Bearing & Transmission Supplies Ltd, Watling House, Sutherland Street, Stoke-on-Trent, ST4 4HS Tel: (01782) 846216 Fax: (01782) 749080 E-mail: sales@btslimited.freeserve.co.uk

Binson Bearing Co., 335 A Round Hay Road, Leeds, LS8 4HT Tel: 0113-249 0251 Fax: 0113-235 0375 E-mail: sales@binsonbearings.ssnet.co.uk

Carfax Bearings Ltd, 30-34 Birmingham New Road, Wolverhampton, WV4 6RY Tel: (01902) 338111 Fax: (01902) 341334 E-mail: sale@mainlinebearings.com

Central Bearings & Transmissions Ltd, 43 Padgets Lane, Redditch, Worcestershire, B98 0RD Tel: (01527) 500803 Fax: (01527) 510462 E-mail: sales@centralbearings.com

Chains Ltd, Winterbottom Lane, Mere, Knutsford, Cheshire, WA16 0QQ Tel: (01565) 830747 Fax: (01565) 830331 E-mail: sales@chainandconveyor.com

▶ Chaintech Northern Ltd, 22 Ganners Lane, Leeds, LS13 2NX Tel: (07767) 307497 Fax: 0113-256 2379 E-mail: keith@chaintech.fsbusiness.co.uk

Curteis Ltd, Pant Lane, Dudleston, Ellesmere, Shropshire, SY12 9EG Tel: (01691) 690505 Fax: (01691) 690556E-mail: info@curteis.com

Link Controls Ltd, Stuart Road, Manor Park, Runcorn, Cheshire, WA7 1TS Tel: (01925) 222436 Fax: (01928) 579259 E-mail: sales@linkcontrols.co.uk

▶ Pewag Contiweiss Deutschland GmbH, 39 Beechwood Park Road, Solihull, West Midlands, B91 1ES Tel: 0121 2405527

R & C Glen Scotland Ltd, Glen House, 29 Orleans Avenue, Glasgow, G14 9NF Tel: 0141-959 9988 Fax: 0141-959 9666 E-mail: sales@rcglen.co.uk

Sanmar Ltd, 29 Orleans Avenue, Glasgow, G14 9NF Tel: 0141-954 2944 Fax: 0141-959 9666 E-mail: sales@sanmar-chain.com

Shropshire Bearing Services, 6 Beveley Road, Oakengates, Telford, Shropshire, TF2 6AT Tel: (01952) 610157 Fax: (01952) 619669 E-mail: shropshirebearings@hotmail.com

South Wales Marine, Unit 4, Vale Court Alamein Road Morfa Industrial Estate, Landore, Swansea, SA1 2HY Tel: (01792) 463000 E-mail: info@sw-marine.co.uk

Stalum Engineering Ltd, 3 Darnall Works, Leathley Road, Leeds, LS10 1BG Tel: 0113-242 2289 Fax: 0113-234 7951 E-mail: sales@stalum.co.uk

Eliza Tinsley & Co. Ltd, Unit 12, Cinder Road, Chasetown Industrial Estate, Burntwood, Staffordshire, WS7 8XD Tel: (01543) 683595 Fax: (01543) 674620

Zinco Midlands, Midland House, 52 Lower Forster Street, Walsall, WS1 1XB Tel: (01922) 625586 Fax: (0800) 0286370 E-mail: info@zincomids.co.uk

CHAIN SLINGS

Barnes Lifting Services Ltd, Station Works, Main Road, Unstone, Dronfield, Derbyshire, S18 4AQ Tel: (01246) 417941 Fax: (01246) 410244

Blackburn Bailey Ltd, Wantz Road, Dagenham, Essex, RM10 8PS Tel: (020) 8593 7346 Fax: (020) 8984 0813 E-mail: info@blackburngroup.co.uk

Griffin Woodhouse, Greenfields, Romsley Lane, Shatterford, Bewdley, Worcestershire, DY12 1RS Tel: (01299) 861829 Fax: (01299) 861830E-mail: sales@griffin-woodhouse.co.uk

Onecall, 50 Avenue Road, Aston, Birmingham, B6 4DY Tel: (0800) 6524646 Fax: 0121-333 3996

CHAIN SPROCKETS

▶ Automotion (International) Ltd, Alexia House Dunley Hill Court, Ranmore, Dorking, Surrey, RH5 6SX Tel: (01483) 286674 Fax: (01483) 286675 E-mail: info@automotion.co.uk

Flexon plc, Upper Church Lane, Tipton, West Midlands, DY4 9PA Tel: 0121-521 3600 Fax: 0121-520 0822 E-mail: sales@flexon.co.uk

Force Seven Bearings, First Avenue, Team Valley Trading Estate, Gateshead, Tyne & Wear, NE11 0NU Tel: 0191-487 2421 Fax: 0191-491 0842 E-mail: force7@nbcgroup.com

James Hesketh & Co. Ltd, New Works, Sion Street, Radcliffe, Manchester, M26 3SB Tel: 0161-723 2789 Fax: 0161-725 9072

CHAIN SPROCKETS – *continued*

Humberside Gear Co. Ltd, Thrunscoe House, Thrunscoe Road, Cleethorpes, South Humberside, DN35 8TA Tel: (01472) 601111 Fax: (01472) 602143 E-mail: humberside.gears@virgin.net
Kobo (UK) Ltd, Ketten House, Leestone Road, Sharston Industrial Area, Manchester, M22 4RH Tel: 0161-491 9840 Fax: 0161-428 1999 E-mail: info@kobo.co.uk
Roger Maughfling Engineering Ltd, Station Works, Knucklas, Knighton, Powys, LD7 1PN Tel: (01547) 528201 Fax: (01547) 520392 E-mail: supersprox@supersprox.demon.co.uk
Metalite Ltd, 121 Barkby Road, Leicester, LE4 9LU Tel: 0116-276 7874 Fax: 0116-233 0337
Sigma Industries Ltd, 19 Dunlop Road, Redditch, Worcestershire, B97 5XP Tel: (01527) 547771 Fax: (01527) 547772 E-mail: sales.sigmaind@btopenworld.com
Super Gear Co. Ltd, Unit 2 Nine Trees Trading Estate, Morthen Road, Thurcroft, Rotherham, South Yorkshire, S66 9JG Tel: (01709) 702320 Fax: (01709) 700733

CHAIN TEST/MAINTENANCE/ REPAIR SERVICES

Abel Foxall Lifting Gear Ltd, Wood Street, Liverpool, L1 4LA Tel: 0151-709 6882 Fax: 0151-707 0723 E-mail: allanmolloy@rossendalegroup.co.uk
Balmoral Group Ltd, Balmoral Park, Aberdeen, AB12 3GY Tel: (01224) 859000 Fax: (01224) 859059 E-mail: group@balmoral.co.uk
Barnes Lifting Services Ltd, Station Works, Main Road, Unstone, Dronfield, Derbyshire, S18 4AQ Tel: (01246) 417941 Fax: (01246) 410244
Bootham Engineers Mechanical Services, Amy Johnson Way, Clifton Moor, York, YO30 4WT Tel: (01904) 477670 Fax: (01904) 691826 E-mail: engineering.location@dowdingandmills.com
Chains & Lifting Tackle Midlands Ltd, Dewsbury Road, Fenton Industrial Estate, Stoke-on-Trent, ST4 2TD Tel: (01782) 747400 Fax: (01782) 744508 E-mail: info@chainsandlifting.co.uk
Charles Pearson (Hull) Ltd, New Works, Spyvee Street, Hull, HU8 7JU Tel: (01482) 329602 Fax: (01482) 325860 E-mail: keith@cpgltd.com
I & P Lifting Gear Ltd, 237 Scotia Road, Stoke-on-Trent, ST6 4PS Tel: (01782) 814411 Fax: (01782) 575510 E-mail: info@iandplifting.co.uk

CHAIN WHEELS

Industrial Chains & Gears, 45 Copeland Avenue, Tittensor, Stoke-on-Trent, ST12 9JA Tel: (01782) 374300 Fax: (01782) 373804 E-mail: peter@i-c-g.fsnet.co.uk

CHAINS, SMALL/LIGHTWEIGHT

Deva Dog Ware Ltd, 320 Witton Road, Birmingham, B6 6PA Tel: 0121-327 1108 Fax: 0121-328 2699 E-mail: info@devadogware.com
Fencing Supplies Holdings Ltd, Bond 36 Mellors Road, Trafford Park, Manchester, M17 1PB Tel: 0161-872 8813 Fax: 0161-872 3221

CHAINSAWS

Terry Bass Garden Machinery Services, Mortimer Trading Estate, Hereford, HR4 9SP Tel: (01432) 357933 Fax: (01432) 357933 E-mail: tcbass@freenetname.co.uk
▶ Cambs Trading High Road Elm, Holly Cottage, Low Road, Wisbech, Cambridgeshire, PE14 0DD Tel: (01945) 474540 Fax: (01945) 474540 E-mail: admin@cambstrading.co.uk
Chain Saw Services, 16 Pinfold Lane, North Luffenham, Oakham, Leicestershire, LE15 8LE Tel: (01780) 721070 Fax: (01780) 729455
Countrywide Farmers plc, Church Street, Melksham, Wiltshire, SN12 6LS Tel: (01225) 701470 Fax: (01225) 702318 E-mail: info@countrywidefarmers.co.uk
Curtis & Shaw, Cowbeech, Hailsham, East Sussex, BN27 4JE Tel: (01323) 833441 Fax: (01323) 833072 E-mail: sales@curtisandshaw.co.uk
Emak UK Ltd, Unit A1 Chasewater Industrial Estate, Burntwood Business Park, Burntwood, Staffordshire, WS7 3XD Tel: (01543) 687660 Fax: (01543) 670721 E-mail: sales@emak.co.uk
F & M Garden Machinery Ltd, The White House, Bentley Heath, Barnet, Hertfordshire, EN5 4RY Tel: (020) 8440 6165 Fax: (020) 8447 0670 E-mail: sales@fmgardenmachinery.com
Honey Bros, New Pond Road, Peasmarsh, Guildford, Surrey, GU3 1JR Tel: (01483) 575098 Fax: (01483) 535608 E-mail: sales@honeybros.co.uk
Husqvarna Outdoor Products Ltd, Oldends Lane Industrial Estate, Stonedale Road, Stonehouse, Gloucestershire, GL10 3SY Tel: (01453) 820300 Fax: (01453) 826936 E-mail: info.husqvarna@husqvarna.co.uk
Lanark Chainsaw Service, 13 Westbank Holdings, Ravenstruther, Lanark, ML11 8NL Tel: (01555) 870259 Fax: (01555) 870259
Meadhams Lawnmowers Sales & Service, 12 Bankside, Kidlington, Oxfordshire, OX5 1JE Tel: (01865) 378010 Fax: (01865) 378010 E-mail: meadhams@btinternet.com
Powells Forest & Gardens, Cap View, Llangua, Abergavenny, Gwent, NP7 8HD Tel: (01981) 240403 Fax: (01981) 240403
Power Rewind Ltd, 1 Conder Way, Colchester, CO2 8JN Tel: (01206) 791316 Fax: (01206) 792689
R A & M D Butler, Murrays Service Station, Ashford Hill, Thatcham, Berkshire, RG19 8BQ Tel: 0118-981 3646 Fax: 0118-981 9139 E-mail: info@butlersgarage.co.uk
Stanton Hope Ltd, 11 Seax Court, Southfields, Laindon, Basildon, Essex, SS15 6LY Tel: (01268) 419141 Fax: (01268) 545992 E-mail: sales@stantonhope.co.uk
Andreas Stihl Ltd, Stihl House, Stanhope Road, Camberley, Surrey, GU15 3YT Tel: (01276) 20202 Fax: (01276) 670510 E-mail: postmaster@stihl.co.uk
Taylor Tool Hire & Garden Ware, Nailbridge, Drybrook, Gloucestershire, GL17 9JW Tel: (01594) 542853 Fax: (01594) 544773 E-mail: njt@taylortoolhire.co.uk

CHAIR COVER HIRE

▶ Cinderella Elegance Chair Covers, Apartment 8, 5 Bewley Street, Wimbledon, London, SW19 1XF Tel: (020) 8540 8161 E-mail: info@cinderellaelegance.co.uk
▶ Just Weddings Ltd, Buck Farm Willington, near Malpas, Willington, Malpas, Cheshire, SY14 7LX Tel: (08707) 577227 E-mail: info@just-wed.com
▶ Pretty Chairs, 32 St. Matthews Close, Renishaw, Sheffield, S21 3WT Tel: (01246) 430883 E-mail: sales@prettychairs.co.uk
▶ Tie The Knot, 4 Albert Road, London, N4 3RW Tel: (07956) 245585

CHAIRS, DINING, LEATHER

The Furniture Warehouse, The Seed House, Bell Walk, Bell Lane, Uckfield, East Sussex, TN22 1AB Tel: (01825) 769202 E-mail: sales@sofasandfurniture.co.uk
▶ Imperial World Ltd, 40 Station Road, London, SW19 2LP Tel: (020) 8542 0883 Fax: (020) 8542 0992 E-mail: mail@imperial-world.com
▶ M R F, 40 St Judes Road West, Wolverhampton, WV6 0DA Tel: (01902) 568037 Fax: (01902) 650410 E-mail: sales@mrfdesign.co.uk

CHAIRS, UPHOLSTERED/ FIRESIDE

A J Way & Co. Ltd, Sunters End, Hillbottom Road, Sands Industrial Estate, High Wycombe, Buckinghamshire, HP12 4HS Tel: (01494) 471821 Fax: (01494) 450597 E-mail: sales@ajway.co.uk
Davison Highley Ltd, Old Oxford Road, Piddington, High Wycombe, Buckinghamshire, HP14 3BE Tel: (01494) 883862 Fax: (01494) 881572 E-mail: magic@davisonhighley.co.uk
DFS Trading Ltd, 1 Rockingham Way, Adwick-le-Street, Doncaster, South Yorkshire, DN6 7NA Tel: (01302) 330365 Fax: (01302) 330880
▶ ImagineHowe, Rennadal House, Firth, Orkney, KW17 2NY Tel: (07786) 578000
M A S Furniture Contracts Ltd, Welham House, Travellers Lane, North Mymms, Hatfield, Hertfordshire, AL9 7HF Tel: (01707) 272737 Fax: (01707) 260124 E-mail: sales@masfurniture.co.uk
Sauvagnat UK Ltd, Unit 12 Weights Farm Business Park, Weights Lane, Redditch, Worcestershire, B97 6RG Tel: (0845) 0536000 Fax: (0845) 0536001 E-mail: sales@edencontractfurniture.co.uk
Sherborne Upholstery Ltd, Pasture Lane, Clayton, Bradford, West Yorkshire, BD14 6LT Tel: (01274) 882633 Fax: (01274) 815129 E-mail: mail@sherbourne-uph.co.uk

CHALK

Needham Chalks Ltd, Ipswich Road, Needham Market, Ipswich, IP6 8EL Tel: (01449) 720227 Fax: (01449) 720520 E-mail: needhamchalks@btinternet.com
Totternhoe Lime & Stone Co. Ltd, Lower End, Totternhoe, Dunstable, Bedfordshire, LU6 2BU Tel: (01525) 220300 Fax: (01525) 221895 E-mail: tottenhoelime@btclick.com

CHAMBER OF COMMERCE AND INDUSTRY ASSOCIATIONS

Business Link Shropshire Ltd, Trevithick House, Unit B1 Stafford Park 4, Telford, Shropshire, TF3 3BA Tel: (0845) 7543210 Fax: (01952) 208208 E-mail: enquiries@bl-shropshire.co.uk
Jersey Chamber of Commerce & Industry Inc., Chamber House, 25 Pier Road, St. Helier, Jersey, JE1 4HF Tel: (01534) 724536 Fax: (01534) 734942 E-mail: admin@jerseychamber.com
Maidstone & Mid Kent Chamber Of Commerce Industry Training, Westree Road, Maidstone, Kent, ME16 8HB Tel: (01622) 695544 Fax: (01622) 682513 E-mail: sales@inmaidstone.com
Northamptonshire Chamber, Opus House, Anglia Way, Moulton Park Industrial Estate, Northampton, NN3 6JA Tel: (01604) 490490 Fax: (01604) 670362 E-mail: info@businesslinknorthants.org
Scottish Executive, Meridian Court, 5 Cadogan Street, Glasgow, G2 6AT Tel: 0141-248 4774 Fax: 0141-242 5589 E-mail: ceu@scotland.gsi.gov.uk
Southampton & Fareham Chamber Of Commerce & Industry Ltd, 53 Bugle Street, Southampton, SO14 2LF Tel: (023) 8022 3541 Fax: (023) 8022 7426 E-mail: info@soton-chamber.co.uk
Thames Valley Chamber Of Commerce, 121 Clare Road, Stanwell, Staines, Middlesex, TW19 7QP Tel: (01784) 242478 Fax: (01784) 242472 E-mail: heathrow@thamesvalleychamber.co.uk
Thames Valley Chamber Of Commerce & Industry, Foyer Building, Crest Road, High Wycombe, Buckinghamshire, HP11 1UD Tel: (01494) 445909 Fax: (01494) 440156 E-mail: wycombe@thamesvalleychamber.co.uk
Thames Valley Chamber Of Commerce & Industry Ltd, 467 Malton Avenue, Slough, SL1 4QU Tel: (01753) 870500 Fax: (01753) 870515 E-mail: sales@thamesvalleychamber.co.uk
Turkish Chamber Of Commerce & Industry, Bury House, 33 Bury Street, London, SW1Y 6AU Tel: (020) 7321 0999 Fax: (020) 7321 0989 E-mail: info@tbcci.org
Wigan Borough Partnership Ltd, Wigan Investment Centre, Waterside Drive, Wigan, Lancashire, WN3 5BA Tel: (01942) 705705 Fax: (01942) 705272 E-mail: kmulligan@wbp.org.uk

CHAMBERMAID TROLLEYS

Obtain-Wise Ltd, Captiva House, 34 Heathfield, Stacey Bushes, Milton Keynes, MK12 6HR Tel: (01604) 758999 Fax: (01908) 310555 E-mail: info@obtainwise.com

CHAMBERS OF COMMERCE

Chamber Business Enterprise, Churchgate House, 56 Oxford Street, Manchester, M60 7HJ Tel: 0161-237 4070 Fax: 0161-236 9945 E-mail: info@chamber-link.co.uk

CHAMBERS OF COMMERCE AND INDUSTRY (BRITISH) OPERATING IN THE BRITISH ISLES (RESTRICTED USAGE)

▶ Aberdeen & Grampian Chamber Of Commerce, 213 George Street, Aberdeen, AB25 1HY Tel: (01224) 620621 Fax: (01224) 645777 E-mail: info@agcc.co.uk
Ashford (Kent) Chamber Of Commerce Industry & Enterprise Ltd, Ashford Business Pointwaterbrook Avenuesevington, Sevington, Ashford, Kent, TN24 0LH Tel: (01233) 503838 Fax: (01233) 503687 E-mail: sales@ashford-chamber.co.uk
Ayrshire Chamber Of Commerce & Industry, Suite 1005 Terminal Building, Prestwick Airport, Glasgow Prestwick Intnl Airport, Prestwick, Ayrshire, KA9 2PL Tel: (01292) 678666 Fax: (01292) 678667 E-mail: enquiries@ayrshire-chamber.org
Barking & Dagenham Chamber Of Commerce, Suite A Roycraft House, 15 Linton Road, Barking, Essex, IG11 8HE Tel: (020) 8591 6966 Fax: (020) 8594 1576 E-mail: info@bdchamber.co.uk
Bath Chamber Of Commerce, Trimbridge House, Trim Street, Bath, BA1 2DP Tel: (01225) 460655 Fax: (01225) 462612 E-mail: info@bathchamber.co.uk
Birmingham Chamber Training Ltd, 75 Harbourne Road, Edgbaston, Birmingham, B15 3DH Tel: 0121-454 1999 Fax: 0121-455 8700 E-mail: enquiries@birminghamchamber.org.uk
Boston Chamber Of Commerce & Industry, Boston Business Centre, Norfolk Street, Boston, Lincolnshire, PE21 9HH Tel: (01205) 358800 Fax: (01205) 359388 E-mail: bcci@btclick.com
Bournemouth Chamber Of Trade & Commerce, 15 Alum Chine Road, Bournemouth, BH4 8DT Tel: (01202) 540870 Fax: (01202) 751997 E-mail: sales@bournemouthchamber.org.uk
Bradford Chamber Of Commerce & Industry, Devere House Vicar Lane, Little Germany, Bradford, West Yorkshire, BD1 5AH Tel: (01274) 772777 Fax: (01274) 771081 E-mail: sales@bradfordchamber.co.uk
Burton & District/Tamworth Chamber of Commerce & Industry, Greton House, Waterside Court, Third Avenue, Centrum 100, Burton-On-Trent, Staffordshire, DE14 2WQ Tel: (01283) 563761 Fax: (01283) 510753 E-mail: services@burtonchamber.co.uk
Business West, Leigh Court Business Centre, Pill Road, Abbots Leigh, Bristol, BS8 3RA Tel: (01275) 373373 Fax: (01275) 370706 E-mail: info@businesswest.co.uk
Canada-Uk Chamber Of Commerce, 38 Grosvenor Street, London, W1K 4DP Tel: (020) 7258 6572 Fax: (020) 7258 6594 E-mail: info@canada-uk.org
Cardiff Chamber of Commerce, Suite 1, 2nd Floor, St. Davids House, Wood Street, Cardiff, CF10 5AS Tel: (029) 2034 8280 Fax: (029) 2048 9785 E-mail: enquiries@cardiffchamber.co.uk
Central & West Lancashire Chamber Of Commerce & Industry, Unit 9-10 Eastway Business Village, Olivers Place, Fulwood, Preston, PR2 9WT Tel: (01772) 653000 Fax: (01772) 655544 E-mail: info@lancschamber.co.uk
Chamber Business Connections, Commerce House, Bridgeman Place, Bolton, BL2 1DW Tel: (01204) 363212 Fax: (01204) 363212 E-mail: enquiries@chamberhelp.co.uk
Chamber Of Commerce, 2 Berkley Crescent, Gravesend, Kent, DA12 2AD Tel: (01474) 320805 Fax: (01474) 537152 E-mail: sales@gravesham.co.uk
Chamber Of Commerce, Charles House, 5-11 Regent Street, London, SW1Y 4LR Tel: (020) 7930 0219 Fax: (020) 7930 7946 E-mail: info@norwegian-chamber.co.uk
Chamber Of Commerce (Barnsley & Rotherham) Ltd, Barnsley Business Innovation Centre, Innovation Way, Barnsley, South Yorkshire, S75 1JL Tel: (01226) 217770 Fax: (01226) 784464
Chamber Of Commerce & Business Link West Mercia, Severn House, Prescott Drive, Worcester, WR4 9NE Tel: (0845) 6414641 Fax: (0845) 6414641 E-mail: enquiries@hwchamber.co.uk
Chamber of Commerce (Medway), Medway Business Point, Stirling House, Sunderland Quay, Culpeper Close, Medway City Estate, Rochester, Kent, ME2 4HN Tel: (01634) 311411 Fax: (01634) 311440 E-mail: chamber@medway.co.uk
Chamber Of Commerce Trade & Industry, Commerce House, Fenton Street, Lancaster, LA1 1AB Tel: (01524) 381331 Fax: (01524) 389505 E-mail: sales@lancaster-chamber.org.uk
Conference & Events Derbyshire, Innovation House East Service Road, Raynesway, Spondon, Derby, DE21 7BF Tel: (01332) 548000 Fax: (01332) 548088
Derbyshire Chamber Of Commerce & Industry, Commerce Centre, Canal Wharf, Chesterfield, Derbyshire, S41 7NA Tel: (01246) 211277 Fax: (01246) 203173 E-mail: chamber@derbyshire.org
Doncaster Chamber, Enterprise House, White Rose Way, Hyde Park 45, Doncaster, South Yorkshire, DN4 5ND Tel: (01302) 341000 Fax: (01302) 328382 E-mail: chamber@doncaster-chamber.co.uk
Dorking & District Chamber of Commerce, 156 High Street, Dorking, Surrey, RH4 1BQ Tel: (01306) 880110 Fax: (01306) 502283
Dover District Chamber Of Commerce, White Cliffs BSNS Park, Honeywood Road, Whitfield, Dover, Kent, CT16 3EH Tel: (01304) 824955 Fax: (01304) 822354 E-mail: mail@doverchamber.co.uk
East Lancashire Chamber Of Commerce & Industry, Red Rose Court, Clayton Business Park, Clayton le Moors, Accrington, Lancashire, BB5 5JR Tel: (01254) 356400 Fax: (01254) 388900 E-mail: info@chamberelancs.co.uk
Fife Chamber of Commerce & Enterprise, Wemyssfield House, Wemyssfield, Kirkcaldy, Fife, KY1 1XN Tel: (01592) 201932 Fax: (01592) 641187 E-mail: enquiries@fifechamber.co.uk
Greater (Altrincham) Chamber of Commerce, Trade & Industry, 6B Old Market Place, Altrincham, Cheshire, WA14 4NP Tel: 0161-941 3250 Fax: 0161-941 1909
Halton Chamber Of Commerce & Enterprise, Halton Business Forum, Victoria Square, Widnes, Cheshire, WA8 7QZ Tel: 0151-420 9400 Fax: 0151-420 9424 E-mail: sales@exporters-alliance.org.uk
Hull & Humber Chamber Of Commerce, 34-38 Beverley Road, Hull, HU3 1YE Tel: (01482) 324976 Fax: (01482) 213962 E-mail: b.massie@hull-humber-chamber.co.uk
Islington Chamber of Commerce & Trade Ltd, 64 Essex Road, London, N1 8LR Tel: (020) 7226 1593 Fax: (020) 7226 5437 E-mail: admin@islchamber.org.uk
Italian Chamber Of Commerce For U K, 1 Princes Street, London, W1B 2AY Tel: (020) 7495 8191 Fax: (020) 7495 8194 E-mail: info@italchamind.org.uk
Joint Arab British Chamber Of Commerce, 43 Upper Grosvenor Street, London, W1K 2NJ Tel: (020) 7235 4363 Fax: (020) 7245 6688 E-mail: bims@abcc.org.uk
Leicestershire Chamber Of Commerce & Industry, 5 New Walk, Leicester, LE1 6TE Tel: 0116-247 1800 Fax: 0116-247 0430 E-mail: info@chamberofcommerce.co.uk
Lincolnshire Chamber Of Commerce & Industry, Outer Circle Road, Lincoln, LN2 4HY Tel: (01522) 523333 Fax: (01522) 546667 E-mail: enquiries@lincs-chamber.co.uk
Liverpool Chamber Of Commerce & Industry, 1 Old Hall Street, Liverpool, L3 9HG Tel: 0151-227 1233 Fax: 0151-236 0121 E-mail: info@liverpoolchamber.org.uk

CHAMBERS OF COMMERCE AND INDUSTRY (BRITISH) OPERATING IN THE BRITISH ISLES (RESTRICTED USAGE) – *continued*

London Money Market Association, 2 Gresham Street, London, EC2V 7QP Tel: (020) 7597 4485 Fax: (020) 7597 4491 E-mail: richard.vardy@investec.co.uk

Londonderry Chamber Of Commerce, 1 St Columbs Court, Londonderry, BT48 6PT Tel: (028) 7126 2379 Fax: (028) 7128 6789 E-mail: info@londonderrychamber.co.uk

The Mid Yorkshire Chamber Of Commerce & Industry Ltd, Commerce House, Wakefield Road, Huddersfield, HD5 9AA Tel: (01484) 438800 Fax: (01484) 514199 E-mail: post@chambercom6.bdx.co.uk

Newport & Gwent Chamber of Commerce & Industry, Unit 30, Enterprise Way, Newport, Gwent, NP20 2AQ Tel: (01633) 222664 Fax: (01633) 222301 E-mail: info@ngb2b.co.uk

Norfolk Chamber Of Commerce, 9 Norwich Business Park, Whiting Road, Norwich, NR4 6DJ Tel: (01603) 625977 Fax: (01603) 633032 E-mail: info@norfolkchamber.co.uk

North East Chamber Of Commerce, Aykley Heads Business Centre, Aykley Heads, Durham, DH1 5TS Tel: 0191-386 1133 Fax: 0191-386 1144 E-mail: information@ne-cc.com

North Kent Chamber Of Commerce, Upper Rose Gallery, Bluewater, Greenhithe, Kent, DA9 9SP Tel: (01322) 381333 Fax: (01322) 381555 E-mail: enquiries@northkentchamber.org

North London Chamber Of Commerce Ltd, Enfield Business Centre, 201 Hertford Road, Enfield, Middlesex, EN3 5JH Tel: (020) 8443 4464 Fax: (020) 8443 3822 E-mail: nlcc@bl4london.com

Northern Ireland Chamber of Commerce & Industry, 22 Great Victoria Street, Belfast, BT2 7BJ Tel: (028) 9024 4113 Fax: (028) 9024 7024 E-mail: mail@northernirelandchamber.com

Nottinghamshire Chamber Of Commerce & Industry, 309 Haydn Road, Nottingham, NG5 1DG Tel: 0115-962 4624 Fax: 0115-985 6612 E-mail: info@nottschamber.co.uk

Plymouth Chamber Of Commerce, 22 Lockyer Street, Plymouth, PL1 2QW Tel: (01752) 220471 Fax: (01752) 600333 E-mail: chamber@plymouth-chamber.co.uk

Portsmouth & South East Hampshire Chamber of Commerce & Industry, Regional Business Centre, Harts Farm Way, Havant, Hampshire, PO9 1HR Tel: (023) 9244 9449 Fax: (023) 9244 9444 E-mail: sehants@chamber.org.uk

Rochdale Borough Chamber, Old Post Office, The Esplanade, Rochdale, Lancashire, OL16 1AE Tel: (01706) 644664 Fax: (01706) 713211

St Albans Chamber Of Commerce, 3 Soothouse Spring, St. Albans, Hertfordshire, AL3 6PF Tel: (01727) 863054 Fax: (01727) 851200 E-mail: office@stalbans-chamber.co.uk

Sefton Chamber of Commerce & Industry, 22 Hoghton Street, Southport, Merseyside, PR9 0PA Tel: (01704) 531710 Fax: (01704) 539255 E-mail: office@seftonchamber.org.uk

Southampton & Fareham Chamber Of Commerce & Industry Ltd, 53 Bugle Street, Southampton, SO14 2LF Tel: (023) 8022 3541 Fax: (023) 8022 7426 E-mail: info@soton-chamber.co.uk

Southwark Chamber Of Commerce, 21 Potier Street, London, SE1 4UX Tel: (020) 7403 5500 Fax: (020) 7403 5500 E-mail: admin@southwarkcommerce.com

Stockport Chamber of Commerce & Industry, Stockport Business Centre, 1 St. Peters Square, Stockport, Cheshire, SK1 1NN Tel: 0161-474 3780 Fax: 0161-476 0138

Suffolk Chamber Of Commerce, Felaw Maltings, 42 Felaw Street, Ipswich, IP2 8SQ Tel: (01473) 694807 Fax: (01473) 603888 E-mail: info@suffolkchamber.co.uk

Surrey Chamber Of Commerce Ltd, 5th Floor Hollywood House, Church Street East, Woking, Surrey, GU21 6HJ Tel: (01483) 726655 Fax: (01483) 740217 E-mail: info@surrey_chambers.co.uk

Thames Valley Chamber Of Commerce, 121 Clare Road, Stanwell, Staines, Middlesex, TW19 7QP Tel: (01784) 242478 Fax: (01784) 242472 E-mail: heathrow@thamesvalleychamber.co.uk

Thames Valley Chamber Of Commerce & Industry Ltd, 467 Malton Avenue, Slough, SL1 4QU Tel: (01753) 870500 Fax: (01753) 870515 E-mail: sales@thamesvalleychamber.co.uk

Thames Valley Chamber Of Commerce & Industry Ltd, 467 Malton Avenue, Slough, SL1 4QU Tel: (01753) 870500 Fax: (01753) 870515 E-mail: sales@thamesvalleychamber.co.uk

Warrington Chamber Of Commerce, International Business Centre, Delta CR, Westbrook, Warrington, WA5 7WQ Tel: (01925) 715150 Fax: (01925) 715159 E-mail: info@warrington-chamber.co.uk

Watford & West Herts Chamber Of Commerce, The Business Centre, Colne Way, Watford, WD24 7AA Tel: (01923) 442442 Fax: (01923) 445050 E-mail: sales@watford-chamber.co.uk

West Wales Chamber of Commerce, Creswell Buildings, 1 Burrows Place, Swansea, SA1 1SW Tel: (01792) 653297 Fax: (01792) 648345 E-mail: info@wwcc.co.uk

Wirral Chamber Of Commerce & Industry Ltd, 16 Grange Road West, Birkenhead, Merseyside, CH41 4DA Tel: 0151-647 8899 Fax: 0151-650 0440 E-mail: mail@wirralchamber.u-net.com

Worthing Chamber of Commerce & Industry Ltd, 7 Richmond Road, Worthing, West Sussex, BN11 1PN Tel: (01903) 203484 Fax: (01903) 203289 E-mail: mail@worthingchamber.co.uk

CHAMFERING TOOLS, BAR/ TUBE

Hillcliff Tools Ltd, 11 Catley Road, Sheffield, S9 5JF Tel: 0114-244 3665 Fax: 0114-242 3319 E-mail: jj@hillcliff-tools.com

CHAMOIS LEATHER

A L Maugham & Co. Ltd, 5-9 Fazakerley Street, Liverpool, L3 9DN Tel: 0151-236 1872 Fax: 0151-236 1872

Hanlin Export & Import Agents, 167a Wood Lane, Earlswood, Solihull, West Midlands, B94 5JL Tel: (01564) 702116 Fax: (01564) 703978 E-mail: hanlin.uk@btinternet.com

Holbros Ltd, Morvil House Maypole CR, Darent Industrial Park, Erith, Kent, DA8 2JZ Tel: (01322) 335424 Fax: (01322) 333703 E-mail: info@holbros.co.uk

Hutchings & Harding Group Ltd, 163 High Street, Sawston, Cambridge, CB22 3HN Tel: (01223) 832281 Fax: (01223) 836401 E-mail: sales@chamois.com

J & T Beaven, The Midlands, Holt, Trowbridge, Wiltshire, BA14 6RJ Tel: (01225) 782245 Fax: (01225) 783155 E-mail: sales@beaven.com

Martin Cox, Jacksons Lane, Wellingborough, Northamptonshire, NN8 4LB Tel: (01933) 276935 Fax: (01933) 277127 E-mail: sales@martincoxchamois.com

CHANDELIER LIGHTING

▶ Coconut House Ltd, Hall Street, Long Melford, Sudbury, Suffolk, CO10 9JQ Tel: (01787) 312922 E-mail: chrisandgina@coconuthouse.co.uk

David Hunt Lighting Ltd, Tilemans Lane, Shipston-on-Stour, Warwickshire, CV36 4HP Tel: (01608) 661590 Fax: (01608) 662951

Davis Cash & Co. Ltd, Alexandra Road, Enfield, Middlesex, EN3 7EN Tel: (020) 8804 4028 Fax: (020) 8805 2896 E-mail: sales@daviscash.co.uk

Fantastic Lighting Ltd, 4 Kennet Road, Dartford, DA1 4QN Tel: (01322) 558649 Fax: (01322) 521117 E-mail: sales@fantastic-lighting.co.uk

CHANGE GIVING MACHINES

Coinage (Bristol) Ltd, 91 Mayflower Street, Plymouth, PL1 1SB Tel: (0870) 1600992 Fax: (01364) 73799 E-mail: sales@coinage.co.uk

Scan Coin Ltd, Dutch House, 110 Broadway, Salford, M50 2UW Tel: 0161-873 0500 Fax: 0161-873 0501 E-mail: sales@scancoin.co.uk

Thomas Automatics Co. Ltd, Bishop Meadow Road, Loughborough, Leicestershire, LE11 5RE Tel: (01509) 267611 Fax: (01509) 266836 E-mail: sales@thomas-a.co.uk

CHANGE MANAGEMENT CONSULTANTS

A S K Europe plc, Trent House University Way, Cranfield Technology Park, Cranfield, Bedford, MK43 0AN Tel: (01234) 757575 Fax: (01234) 757576 E-mail: mail@askeurope.com

BISC, 10 Park Lane, Reigate, Surrey, RH2 8JX Tel: (01737) 222119 Fax: (01737) 222119 E-mail: bs@bisconsultants.co.uk

▶ Bluetree Specific Skills, 18 Croftfield Road, Godmanchester, Huntingdon, Cambridgeshire, PE29 2ED Tel: (0845) 4534500 Fax: (0870) 8681610 E-mail: graham@bluetreeuk.com

▶ Jo Branagan Business Support Services, 188 Danube Road, Hull, HU5 5UX Tel: (07973) 511026 E-mail: info@jo-branagan.co.uk

Cabrio Management Services, 6 Ash Meadow, Willesborough, Ashford, Kent, TN24 0LW Tel: (01233) 623230 E-mail: enquiries@cabrio.co.uk

P W Callaghan, Emerys, 2 Bucks Lane, Little Eversden, Cambridge, CB3 7HL Tel: (01223) 262444 Fax: (01223) 263241 E-mail: callaghanpw@aol.com

Charm Managaement Specialists Ltd, 13 High Street, Ruddington, Nottingham, NG11 6DT Tel: 0115-984 7760 Fax: 0115-921 1887 E-mail: resources@charmhrm.co.uk

▶ Complete Telecoms Ltd, 132 Henwick Road, Worcester, WR2 5PB Tel: (0845) 4564110 Fax: (0870) 0528973 E-mail: enquiries@completetelecoms.co.uk

Datasmith Ltd, 30 Helen Street, Golborne, Warrington, WA3 3QR Tel: (01942) 700828 Fax: (01942) 516572 E-mail: tony@datasmith.co.uk

FOCUS Eap, 1st Floor The Podium, Metropolitan House Darkes Lane, Potters Bar, Hertfordshire, EN6 1AG Tel: (01707) 661300 Fax: (01707) 661242 E-mail: info@focuseap.co.uk

▶ I Change Ltd, Birchwood, South Munstead Lane, Godalming, Surrey, GU8 4AG Tel: (01483) 208505 Fax: (01483) 208505 E-mail: info@i-change.biz

Innovise Software Ltd, Hellier House, Wychbury Court, Brierley Hill, West Midlands, DY5 1TA Tel: (01384) 484032 Fax: (01277) 822566 E-mail: info@innovise.com

Intec Telecom Systems plc, 2 Wells Court, Albert Drive, Woking, Surrey, GU21 5UB Tel: (01483) 745800 Fax: (01483) 745860 E-mail: sales@intec-telecom-systems.com

▶ Lasa Development UK Ltd, Little Manor, Itlay, Daglingworth, Cirencester, Gloucestershire, GL7 7HZ Tel: (01285) 643469 E-mail: info@lasadev.com

▶ Lifescales, Spectrum House, Dunstable Road, Redbourn, St. Albans, Hertfordshire, AL3 7PR Tel: (0845) 6381330 E-mail: info@workscales.co.uk

▶ People and Performance Consulting, 400 Thames Valley Park Drive, Thames Valley Park, Reading, RG6 1PT Tel: 0118 9653440 Fax: 0118 9653441 E-mail: contact@papcl.com

Pi Ally Ltd, 24 Merton Road, Benfleet, Essex, SS7 5QJ Tel: (01268) 569190 Fax: (01268) 565517 E-mail: johnhall@pially.com

▶ PI Consulting, Beech House, Melbourn Science Park, Cambridge Road, Melbourn, Royston, Hertfordshire, SG8 6HB Tel: (01763) 226242 E-mail: vincent.bryant@piconsulting.org.uk

▶ PITHON Limited, Ground Floor, 74 Markland Avenue, Uckfield, East Sussex, TN22 2DG Tel: 01825 767669 E-mail: info@pithon.co.uk

Serco Solutions, P O Box 57 Laburnum House, Birmingham, B30 2BD Tel: 0121-459 1155 Fax: 0121-459 2199 E-mail: mediaanddesign@serco.com

Tancred Solutions, 32b High Causeway, Whittlesey, Peterborough, PE7 1AJ Tel: (01733) 350925 Fax: (01733) 350832 E-mail: info@tancredsolutions.com

Tmi, 50 High Street, Henley-in-Arden, West Midlands, B95 5AN Tel: (01527) 851741 Fax: (01527) 851777 E-mail: sales@tmi.co.uk

▶ Trinem Consulting, 10 Montrose Terrace, Edinburgh, EH7 5DL Tel: 0131-652 8190 Fax: 0131-652 3512 E-mail: info@trinem.com

CHANGING ROOM FURNITURE

Davian Systems, 46 Bank Road, Dawley Bank, Telford, Shropshire, TF4 2BB Tel: (01952) 507377 Fax: (01952) 507377 E-mail: info@daviansystemsltd.co.uk

CHARCOAL

Big K Charcoal Merchants, Whittington Hill, Whittington, King's Lynn, Norfolk, PE33 9TE Tel: (01366) 500252 Fax: (01366) 500395 E-mail: sales@bigk.co.uk

J Harrison & Sons Coal Merchants Ltd, The Coal Yard, Milton Road, Stoke-on-Trent, ST1 6LE Tel: (01782) 534110 Fax: (01782) 535039 E-mail: sales@jharrison-fuel.co.uk

▶ Labtos Ltd, Unit 3, Abbey Park Industrial Estate, Abbey Road, Barking, Essex, IG11 7BT Tel: (0870 2407269 Fax: 01268 693600 E-mail: info@labtos.co.uk

Rectella International Ltd, Queensway House, Queensway, Clitheroe, Lancashire, BB7 1AU Tel: (01200) 442299 Fax: (01200) 452015 E-mail: sales@flexr.co.uk

Swiftlight Charcoal, Marley Lane, Battle, East Sussex, TN33 0RE Tel: (01424) 870333 Fax: (01424) 870527 E-mail: steve@swift-lite.com

CHARCOAL PREPARATIONS

J L Bragg Ipswich Ltd, 34 Boss Hall Road, Ipswich, IP1 5BN Tel: (01473) 748345 Fax: (01473) 749889 E-mail: bragg@charcoal.uk.com

Rectella International Ltd, Queensway House, Queensway, Clitheroe, Lancashire, BB7 1AU Tel: (01200) 442299 Fax: (01200) 452015 E-mail: sales@flexr.co.uk

CHARGED COUPLED DEVICE (CCD) CAMERAS

Kodak Ltd, Hemel One, Boundary Way, Hemel Hempstead, Hertfordshire, HP2 7YU Tel: (01442) 261122 E-mail: gb-ei-orders@kodak.com

Vicon Industries Ltd, 17 Brunel Way, Fareham, Hampshire, PO15 5TX Tel: (01489) 566300 Fax: (01489) 566322 E-mail: sales@vicon.co.uk

CHARITIES

▶ Bradford Community Enviroment Project, Unit 14 Carlisle Business Centre, Carlisle Road, Bradford, West Yorkshire, BD8 8BD Tel: (01274) 223236 Fax: (01274) 223353 E-mail: info@bcep.org.uk

CHARPY IMPACT PREPARATION TEST EQUIPMENT

Blacks Equipment Ltd, Barton La, Armthorpe, Doncaster, S. Yorkshire, DN3 3AA Tel: (01302) 834444 Fax: (01302) 831834 E-mail: sales@blacksequipment.com

CHARPY IMPACT TEST EQUIPMENT

Brooks Inspection Equipment Ltd, 1 Parsons Lane, Colchester, CO1 2NN Tel: (01206) 799170 Fax: (01206) 798238 E-mail: sales@brooksinspection.com

CHART RECORDER CONSUMABLES

Eurotherm, Faraday Close, Durrington, Worthing, West Sussex, BN13 3PL Tel: (01903) 268500 Fax: (01903) 265982 E-mail: info@eurotherm.com

Sensitised Coatings Ltd, Bergen Way, North Lynn Industrial Estate, King's Lynn, Norfolk, PE30 2JL Tel: (01553) 764836 Fax: (01553) 760377 E-mail: sales@senco.co.uk

CHART RECORDERS, *See also headings for particular types*

Dia-Nielsen UK Ltd, Enfield Lock, South Ordnance Road, Enfield, Middlesex, EN3 6JG Tel: (01992) 787110

Eurotherm, Faraday Close, Durrington, Worthing, West Sussex, BN13 3PL Tel: (01903) 268500 Fax: (01903) 265982 E-mail: info@eurotherm.com

Record Electrical Associates Ltd, Unit C1, Longford Industrial Trading Estate, Thomas Street, Stretford, Manchester, M32 0JT Tel: (0845) 5314117 Fax: (0845) 2571054 E-mail: info@reauk.com

CHASSIS RUNNERS

Accuride International Ltd, Liliput Road, Brackmills Industrial Estate, Northampton, NN4 7AS Tel: (01604) 761111 Fax: (01604) 767190 E-mail: saleseurope@accuride-europe.com

CHASSIS, CARAVAN

Bankside Patterson Ltd, Catwick Lane, Brandesburton, Driffield, East Yorkshire, YO25 8RW Tel: (01964) 545454 Fax: (01964) 545459 E-mail: sales@bankside-patterson.co.uk

Bell Trailers Ltd, Finedon Sidings, Finedon, Wellingborough, Northamptonshire, NN9 5NY Tel: (01536) 723695 Fax: (01536) 724054 E-mail: belltrailers@lineone.net

Gateway Fabrications Ltd, Broad Lane, Gilberdyke, Brough, North Humberside, HU15 2TS Tel: (01430) 440185 Fax: (01430) 441850 E-mail: sales@bathroompods.com

CHASSIS, PASSENGER VEHICLE/BUS/COACH

Scania (Great Britain) Ltd, Delaware Drive, Tongwell, Milton Keynes, MK15 8HB Tel: (01908) 210210 Fax: (01908) 215040

Volvo Group UK Ltd, Wedgnock Lane, Warwick, CV34 5YA Tel: (01926) 401777 Fax: (01926) 490991 E-mail: recruitment@newskies.com

CHECK VALVES

Barnes & Gannon Ltd, Charles House, Royle Barn Road, Rochdale, Lancashire, OL11 3DT Tel: (01706) 344997 Fax: (01706) 641653 E-mail: sales@aqua-check.co.uk

Capital Valves Ltd, Wembley Point, Harrow Road, Wembley, Middlesex, HA9 6DE Tel: (020) 8900 0471 Fax: (020) 8900 0808 E-mail: sales@capitalvalves.co.uk

Cottam & Preedy Ltd, 68 Lower City Road, Tividale, Oldbury, West Midlands, B69 2HF Tel: 0121-552 5281 Fax: 0121-552 6895 E-mail: enquiries@cottampreedy.co.uk

Danfoss Ltd, Capswood Business Centre, Oxford Road, Denham, Uxbridge, Middlesex, UB9 4LH Tel: (0870) 6080008 Fax: (0870) 6080009

CHECK VALVES – *continued*

Goodwin International Ltd, Ivy House Foundry, Hanley, Stoke-on-Trent, ST1 3NR Tel: (01782) 220000 Fax: (01782) 208060 E-mail: goodwinplc@goodwin.co.uk
Hattersley Newman Hender Ltd, 2 Burscough Road, Ormskirk, Lancashire, L39 2XG Tel: (01695) 577199 Fax: (01695) 578775 E-mail: uksales@hattersley.com
Hoerbiger UK Ltd, 1649 Pershore Road, Stirchley, Birmingham, B30 3DR Tel: 0121-433 3636 Fax: 0121-433 3854 E-mail: info.huk@hoerbiger.com
K Controls Ltd, Stone Close, West Drayton, Middlesex, UB7 8JU Tel: (01895) 449601 Fax: (01895) 448586 E-mail: sales@k-controls.co.uk
Kee Valves, The Old School, Outclough Road, Brindley Ford, Stoke-on-Trent, ST8 7QD Tel: (01782) 523388 Fax: (01782) 523399 E-mail: sales@keevalves.co.uk
Mokveld, Unit 2 Butts Courtyard, The Butts, Poulton, Cirencester, Gloucestershire, GL7 5HY Tel: (01285) 851225 Fax: (01285) 851342 E-mail: uk@mokveld.com
Northvale Korting Ltd, Uxbridge Road, Leicester, LE4 7ST Tel: 0116-266 5911 Fax: 0116-261 0050 E-mail: sales@northvalekorting.co.uk
Reliance Water Controls Ltd, Worcester Road, Evesham, Worcestershire, WR11 4RA Tel: (01386) 47148 Fax: (01386) 47028 E-mail: sales@rwc.co.uk
Tamo Ltd, 195 Horton Road, West Drayton, Middlesex, UB7 8HP Tel: (01895) 859700 Fax: (01895) 859888 E-mail: info@tamo.co.uk
Unilathe Ltd, Ford Green Business Park, Ford Green Road Smallthorne, Stoke-on-Trent, ST6 1NG Tel: (01782) 533300 Fax: (01782) 532013 E-mail: sales@unilathe.co.uk
Wolstenholmes Valves, Ainsworth Vale Mill, Vale Street, Bolton, BL2 6QF Tel: (01204) 528609 Fax: (01204) 361964 E-mail: sales@wolstenholmes-valves.co.uk

CHECK WEIGHER/WEIGHING SYSTEMS

▶ ABBEY MANUFACTURING, UNIT 2 TATES, AVIS WAY, NEWHAVEN, EAST SUSSEX, BN9 0DH Tel: 01273 513000 Fax: 01273 513100 E-mail: info.abbey@btconnect.com
County Scales Ltd, Langley Business Park, Station Road, Langley Mill, NG16 4DG Tel: (0800) 7311774 Fax: (01773) 763222
A.E.W. Delford, Main Road, Dovercourt, Harwich, Essex, CO12 4LP Tel: (01255) 241000 Fax: (01255) 241155 E-mail: sales@delford.co.uk
DEM Industrial Weighing Systems, 3 Hill Rise, Measham, Swadlincote, Derbyshire, DE12 7NZ Tel: (01530) 272704 Fax: (01530) 272704 E-mail: sales@demmachines.co.uk
Digi Europe Ltd, Digi House, Rookwood Way, Haverhill, Suffolk, CB9 8DG Tel: (01440) 712176 Fax: (01440) 712173
Driver Southall Ltd, Unit 18 Maybrook Industrial Estate, Maybrook Road, Walsall, WS8 7DG Tel: (01543) 375566 Fax: (01543) 375979 E-mail: email@driversouthall.co.uk
Estera Scales Ltd, Europa House, Dorking Business Park, Dorking, Surrey, RH4 1HJ Tel: (01306) 740785 Fax: (01306) 740786
Harford Cost Control, 35 Harford Street, Flat 2, Trowbridge, Wiltshire, BA14 7HL Tel: (01225) 764461 Fax: (01225) 769733 E-mail: admin@harfordcontrol.com
Lock Inspection Group Ltd, Lock House, Neville Street, Oldham, OL9 6LF Tel: 0161-624 0333 Fax: 0161-624 5181 E-mail: marketing@lockinspection.co.uk
Metal Detection Ltd, Burntmeadow Road, Redditch, Worcestershire, B98 9PA Tel: (01527) 65858 Fax: 0121-522 2013 E-mail: info@mastermagnets.co.uk
P C L Machinery, 5 Elan Court, Norris Way, Rushden, Northants, NN10 6BP Tel: (01933) 410707 Fax: (01933) 410807 E-mail: sales@pclmachinery.co.uk
Thermo Electron, 2a Swift Park, Old Leicester Road, Rugby, Warwickshire, CV21 1DZ Tel: (01788) 820300 Fax: (01788) 820419 E-mail: sales.wi.uk@dermofisher.com
Waymatic Ltd, 15 Bridgewater Way, Windsor, Berkshire, SL4 1RD Tel: (01753) 869218 Fax: (01753) 830519 E-mail: waymatic@btconnect.com

CHEESE COATING WAXES

▶ Ascott Smallholding Supplies Ltd, Unit 9/10, The Old Creamery, Four Crosses, Llanymynech, Powys, SY22 6LP Tel: (0845) 1306285 Fax: (0870) 7740140 E-mail: phil@ascott.biz
Dairyborn Foods Ltd, Eaton Green Road, Luton, LU2 9XF Tel: (01582) 457979 Fax: (01582) 400957
Saputo Cheese UK Ltd, The Creamery, Aberarad, Newcastle Emlyn, Carmarthenshire, SA38 9DQ Tel: (01239) 710424 Fax: (01239) 710175

CHEESE CUTTING EQUIPMENT

Arcall plc, Westminster Road, Wareham, Dorset, BH20 4SR Tel: (01929) 554884 Fax: (01929) 554466 E-mail: email@arcall.co.uk
Digby & Nelson Ltd, 8 Deer Park Road, London, SW19 3UU Tel: (020) 8543 1141 Fax: (020) 8543 5408
Dunelm Supplies Ltd, Netherset Lane, Madeley, Crewe, CW3 9PF Tel: (01782) 750884 Fax: (01782) 751305 E-mail: dunelmpete@aol.co.uk
Real Cheese Shop, 62 Barnes High Street, London, SW13 9LF Tel: (020) 8878 6676

CHEESE GIFT PACKS

Ashley Chase Estate Ltd, Parks Farm, Litton Cheney, Dorchester, Dorset, DT2 9AZ Tel: (01308) 482580 Fax: (01308) 482662 E-mail: cheese@fordfarm.com

CHEFS UNIFORMS

Jay-Pee Workwear, Unit 1, Thomas Street, Congleton, Cheshire, CW12 1QU Tel: (01260) 299706 Fax: (01260) 299757 E-mail: sales@jaypeeworkwear.co.uk

CHEFS, RELIEF

Chef Call Ltd, 44 Barr Common Road, Walsall, WS9 0SY Tel: (01922) 452508 Fax: (01922) 452543 E-mail: chefcall@aol.com

CHEMICAL ABSORBENTS

Advanced Admixtures Ltd, 147 Park Road, Timperley, Altrincham, Cheshire, WA15 6QQ Tel: 0161-962 6267 Fax: 0161-962 6267
Barton Chemicals Ltd, Greendykes Industrial Estate, Broxburn, West Lothian, EH52 6PG Tel: (01506) 862299 Fax: (01506) 862288 E-mail: barton.chemicals@virgin.net
C.P. Burns & Associates Ltd, Peter's Farm, Helmdon, Brackley, Northants, NN13 5QH Tel: (01295) 768271 Fax: (01295) 768298 E-mail: enquiries@burnsassociates.demon.co.uk
Chesham Speciality Ingredients Ltd, Cunnigham House, Westfield Lane, Kenton, Harrow, Middlesex, HA3 9ED Tel: (020) 8907 7779 Fax: (020) 8927 0686 E-mail: sales@cheshamchemicals.co.uk
Degussa Knottingley Ltd, Common Lane, Knottingley, West Yorkshire, WF11 8BN Tel: (01977) 673321 Fax: (01977) 607032
Elcef Fibre, 9 Oundle Road, Chesterton, Peterborough, PE7 3UA Tel: (01733) 233293 Fax: (01733) 235351 E-mail: info@spillshop.co.uk
Kingdom Agribusiness, 7 Douglas Cresent, Kinross, KY13 8TJ Tel: (01577) 863396
Alex Shanks, 2 Hagmill Crescent, East Shawhead Enterprise Park, Coatbridge, Lanarkshire, ML5 4NS Tel: (01236) 436017 Fax: (01236) 436017 E-mail: sales@alexshanks.com
▶ Syntec Manufacturing Ltd, 6 Mid Road, Blairlinn Industrial Estate, Cumbernauld, Glasgow, G67 2TT Tel: (01236) 739696 Fax: (01236) 727955 E-mail: sales@syntecchemicals.com

CHEMICAL ACCELERATORS

Apollo Scientific Ltd, Bredbury, Stockport, Cheshire, SK6 2QR Tel: (01256) 336097 Fax: (01256) 336097 E-mail: johncaparn@fsmail.net

CHEMICAL ADDITIVES

▶ Britmilk, Ballantrae House, Collin, Dumfries, DG1 4PT Tel: (01387) 750459 Fax: (01387) 750243 E-mail: info@britmilk.co.uk
Elementis UK Ltd, Nettlehill Road, Houston Industrial Estate, Livingston, West Lothian, EH54 5DL Tel: (01506) 430331 Fax: (020) 7398 1401 E-mail: info@elementis.com
Nalco, Pembroke Refinery, Pembroke, Dyfed, SA71 5SJ Tel: (01646) 641369 Fax: 01646 641369

CHEMICAL ANALYSERS

Core Laboratories, 17 Howe Moss Drive, Kirkhill Industrial Estate, Dyce, Aberdeen, AB21 0GL Tel: (01224) 421000 Fax: (01224) 421003 E-mail: sales@corelab.co.uk
Metrohm UK Ltd, 2 Buckingham Industrial Park, Top Angel, Buckingham Industrial Estate, Buckingham, MK18 1TH Tel: (01280) 824824 Fax: (01280) 824800 E-mail: enquiry@metrohm.co.uk
Quartz Scientific Computing Ltd, Dukes Yard, Acme Road, Watford, WD24 5AL Tel: (01923) 213983 Fax: (01923) 247732 E-mail: mail@quartz-scientific.co.uk
Sartec, Century Farmhouse, Reading Street, Tenterden, Kent, TN30 7HS Tel: (01233) 758157 Fax: (01233) 758158 E-mail: sales@sartec.co.uk
Spectro Analytical UK Ltd, Fountain House, Great Cornbow, Halesowen, West Midlands, B63 3BL Tel: 0121-550 8997 Fax: 0121-550 5165 E-mail: sales@spectro.co.uk

CHEMICAL ANALYSTS/ ANALYSING SERVICES

Analytical Technologies Ltd, Lynchford House Lynchford Lane, Farnborough, Hampshire, GU14 6JB Tel: (01252) 514711 Fax: (01252) 511855 E-mail: analyticaltechnologies@aol.com
Bodycote Materials Testing, 12 High March, High March Industrial Estate, Daventry, Northamptonshire, NN11 4HB Tel: (01327) 702964 Fax: (01327) 871119 E-mail: daventry@bodycote.com
Commercial Testing Services Ltd, Blackmore Street, Sheffield, S4 7TZ Tel: 0114-276 8758 Fax: 0114-272 0449 E-mail: cts@allvac.com
Harwell Scientifics, 551 South Becquerel Avenue, Didcot, Oxfordshire, OX11 0TB Tel: (01235) 841970 Fax: (01235) 832287 E-mail: sales@scientifics.com
Metaltech Ltd, Hownsgill Drive, Consett, County Durham, DH8 9HU Tel: (01207) 501085 Fax: (01207) 580743 E-mail: gf@metaltech.co.uk
Romil Ltd, The Source, Convent Drive, Waterbeach, Cambridge, CB5 9QT Tel: (01223) 863873 Fax: (01223) 862700 E-mail: sales@romil.com
Scientifics Ltd, 2-6 Langlands Place, Kelvin South Business Park, East Kilbride, Glasgow, G75 0YF Tel: (01355) 225488 Fax: (01355) 249669 E-mail: east.kilbride@scientifics.com

CHEMICAL ANCHORING SYSTEMS

SSR Stainless Steel Reinforcement Ltd, Units B & C Burnt Common, London Road, Send, Woking, Surrey, GU23 7LN Tel: (01483) 226426 Fax: (01483) 226427 E-mail: ssr@btconnect.com

CHEMICAL BASED DECORATORS SUPPLIES OR SUNDRIES

Decor Centre, North Quay, Pwllheli, Gwynedd, LL53 5YR Tel: (01758) 612562 Fax: (01758) 704999 E-mail: sales@decorcentrewales.com
Hobstar Ltd, Palace Chemicals Ltd, Speke Hall Industrial Estate, Liverpool, L24 4AB Tel: 0151-486 6101 Fax: 0151-448 1982 E-mail: sales@palacechemicals.co.uk

CHEMICAL BLACK

Precise Electro Plating Works Ltd, Pitt Road, Southampton, SO15 3FQ Tel: (023) 8022 8014 Fax: (023) 8022 8114

CHEMICAL BLACK OXIDATION

Barton Forge & Ironwork Ltd, 48 Alexandra Road, Enfield, Middlesex, EN3 7EH Tel: (020) 8804 1752
Collins, Unit 5-6 Aultone Yard Industrial Estate, Aultone Way, Carshalton, Surrey, SM5 2LH Tel: (020) 8647 3123 Fax: (020) 8647 3123
En Mach Services, Unit 11 Lythalls Lane Industrial Estate, Lythalls Lane, Coventry, CV6 6FJ Tel: (024) 7668 1403 Fax: (024) 7668 1403 E-mail: yanhunt@tiscali.co.uk
Heer Platers Ltd, 9 Auster Industrial Estate, Silverdale Drive, Thurmaston, Leicester, LE4 8NG Tel: 0116-264 0931 Fax: 0116-264 0931

CHEMICAL BLENDING SERVICES

▶ Mcintyre UK Ltd, Holywell Green, Holywell Green, Halifax, West Yorkshire, HX4 9HZ Tel: (01422) 312200 Fax: (01422) 312214

CHEMICAL BLENDING/MIXING SERVICES

▶ Almetron Ltd, Unit 24 Abenbury Way, Wrexham Industrial Estate, Wrexham, Clwyd, LL13 9UZ Tel: (01978) 660297 Fax: (01978) 661104 E-mail: info@almetron.co.uk
Bio-Productions, 72 Victoria Road, Burgess Hill, West Sussex, RH15 9LH Tel: (01444) 244000 Fax: (01444) 244999 E-mail: info@bio-productions.co.uk
Booth & Openshaw Blackburn Ltd, 17-19 St. Peter Street, Blackburn, BB2 2HH Tel: (01254) 52828
Citrikem Ltd, 2 Cameron Court, Winwick Quay, Warrington, WA2 8RE Tel: (01925) 234707 Fax: (01925) 234693 E-mail: info@klenzan.co.uk
Contract Blending & Packing Ltd, Heys Lane, Great Harwood, Blackburn, BB6 7UA Tel: (01254) 877870 Fax: (01254) 877871
East Lancashire Chemical Co. Ltd, Edge Lane, Droylsden, Manchester, M43 6AU Tel: 0161-371 5585 Fax: 0161-301 1990 E-mail: info@eastlancschemical.com
Mold Hygiene Chemicals Co. Ltd, Unit 3 Antelope Industrial Park, Rhydymwyn, Mold, Clwyd, CH7 5JH Tel: (01352) 741000 Fax: (01352) 740074 E-mail: sales@mirjhygiene.co.uk
Raw Chemical Distribution, Morton Peto Road, Harfreys Industrial Estate, Great Yarmouth, Norfolk, NR31 0LT Tel: (01493) 443223 Fax: (01493) 443177 E-mail: sales@rawchem.co.uk
Rutpen Ltd, Lambourn Woodlands, Hungerford, Berkshire, RG17 7TJ Tel: (01488) 71926 Fax: (01488) 71947E-mail: mail@rutpen.co.uk
The White Sea & Baltic Company Ltd, Arndale House, Otley Road, Leeds, LS6 2UU Tel: 0113-230 4774 Fax: 0113-230 4770 E-mail: sales@whitesea.co.uk

CHEMICAL CATALYSTS

Albemarle UK Ltd, Teesport, Middlesbrough, Cleveland, TS6 7SA Tel: (01642) 463314 Fax: (01642) 463315
Uniqema, Pool Lane, Bromborough Pool, Wirral, Merseyside, CH62 4UF Tel: 0151-643 3200 Fax: 0151-645 9197

CHEMICAL CHIMNEY CLEANERS

Brapack Ltd, Brapack Moreton Avenue, Hithercroft Industrial Estate, Wallingford, Oxfordshire, OX10 9DE Tel: (01491) 833131 Fax: (01491) 825409 E-mail: sales@brapack.com

CHEMICAL CLEANING EQUIPMENT ACCESSORIES

Centurywise Chemicals, Oaker Mount, 175 Stockport Road West, Bredbury, Stockport, Cheshire, SK6 2AP Tel: 0161-430 8773 Fax: 0161-430 8773 E-mail: centurywise@aol.com
▶ E C M Fleet Wash, 148 Station Road, Whittlesey, Peterborough, PE7 2HA Tel: (01733) 206749 Fax: (01733) 206992
▶ Neotex Services Ltd, 176 Hitchin Road, Arlesey, Bedfordshire, SG15 6SD Tel: (0870) 890 0086 Fax: 0870 033 9219 E-mail: info@neotex.co.uk

CHEMICAL CLEANING SERVICES

▶ Bolton Stone Restoration Ltd, Winter House, Winter Street, Bolton, BL1 8AZ Tel: (01204) 843853 Fax: (01204) 849841 E-mail: enquiries@boltonstone.co.uk
▶ S C Pointing Services, 6 Beswick Street, Draldsden, Manchester, M43 7FL Tel: 0161-370 2710 Fax: 0161-370 2710

CHEMICAL CLOSURES

Cope Allman Plastic Packaging Ltd, Railway Triangle, Walton Road, Portsmouth, PO6 1TS Tel: (023) 9237 0102 Fax: (023) 9238 0314 E-mail: bridget.lambert@copeallman.com
Greif UK Ltd, Merseyside Works, Oil Sites Road, Ellesmere Port, CH65 4EZ Tel: 0151-373 2000 Fax: 0151-373 2072 E-mail: kathy.turton@tri-sure.com
United Closures And Plastics Ltd, Salhouse Road, Norwich, NR7 9AL Tel: (01603) 423131 Fax: (01603) 407942

CHEMICAL CONSULTANTS

▶ Access consulting, 5 Errwood Crescent, Burnage, Manchester, M19 2NX Tel: 0161 2257342 Fax: 07896 344014 E-mail: jimthomas007@ntlworld.com
DKSH Great Britain, Wimbledon Hill Road, London, SW19 7PA Tel: (020) 8879 5500 Fax: (020) 8879 5501 E-mail: info.lon@dksh.com
Griffin Europe Marketing, 1 Peterborough Business Pk, Lynch Wood, Peterborough, PE2 6FZ Tel: 01733 361144 Fax: 01733 361189
▶ Integer Research, 55 Farringdon Road, London, EC1M 3JB Tel: (020) 7092 8100 Fax: (020) 7503 1266 E-mail: sales@integer-research.com
Mckinsey & Co. (UK), 1 Jermyn Street, London, SW1Y 4UH Tel: (020) 7839 8040 Fax: (020) 7339 5000
Quartz Scientific Computing Ltd, Dukes Yard, Acme Road, Watford, WD24 5AL Tel: (01923) 213983 Fax: (01923) 247732 E-mail: mail@quartz-scientific.co.uk
S T A S Ltd, Ryland Grange Farm, Fulbeck Heath, Grantham, Lincolnshire, NG32 3HJ Tel: (01400) 261745 Fax: (01400) 262287 E-mail: stasltd@aol.com

CHEMICAL CONTRACT MANUFACTURING

Direct Chemicals & Detergents Ltd, Unit 17 Eagle Trading Estate, 29 Willow Lane, Mitcham, Surrey, CR4 4UY Tel: (020) 8687 6679

▶ Impala Business Solutions, Unit 7, Gurnos Industrial Estate, Bethel Road, Ystalyfera, Swansea, SA9 2HW Tel: (01639) 841256

Mold Hygiene Chemicals Co. Ltd, Unit 3 Antelope Industrial Park, Rhydymwyn, Mold, Clwyd, CH7 5JH Tel: (01352) 741000 Fax: (01352) 740074 E-mail: sales@mirjhygiene.co.uk

Pentagon Chemicals, Dock Road, Northside, Workington, Cumbria, CA14 1JJ Tel: (01900) 604371 Fax: (01900) 66943 E-mail: sales@pentagonchemicals.co.uk

Phoenix (Wirral) Ltd, Unit 28-34, Thursby Road, Bromborough, Wirral, Merseyside, CH62 3PW Tel: 0151-334 9044 Fax: 0151-334 9045 E-mail: chris@phoenixchem.com

Rhodia Pharma Solutions, Dudley Lane, Dudley, Cramlington, Northumberland, NE23 7QG Tel: 0191-250 0471 Fax: 0191-250 1514 E-mail: john.lindley@eu.rhodia.com

Rutpen Ltd, Lambourn Woodlands, Hungerford, Berkshire, RG17 7TJ Tel: (01488) 71926 Fax: (01488) 71947E-mail: mail@rutpen.co.uk

Synprotec Ltd, 303 Clayton Lane, Clayton, Manchester, M11 4SX Tel: 0161-223 3344 Fax: 0161-220 8778 E-mail: sales@synprotec.com

CHEMICAL DISPENSING CONTROL SYSTEMS

▶ Green Valet, 59 Valentine Crescent, Sheffield, S5 0NX Tel: 0114-245 9909 Fax: 0114-245 9909

CHEMICAL DISPERSING AGENTS

Town End Leeds plc, Silver Court, Intercity Way, Leeds, LS13 4LY Tel: 0113-256 4251 Fax: 0113-239 3315E-mail: sales@dyes.co.uk

CHEMICAL DOSING EFFLUENT TREATMENT PLANT

Gee & Co Effluent Control & Recovery Ltd, Gee House, Holbourn Hill, Birmingham, B7 5JR Tel: 0121-326 1700 Fax: 0121-326 1779 E-mail: info@geeco.co.uk

Goodwater Ltd, 23-24 Ivanhoe Road, Hogwood Industrial Estate, Finchampstead, Wokingham, Berkshire, RG40 4QQ Tel: 0118-973 5003 Fax: 0118-973 5004 E-mail: info@goodwater.co.uk

CHEMICAL DOSING EQUIPMENT

CSS Ltd, Road Three, Winsford Industrial Estate, Winsford, Cheshire, CW7 3PD Tel: (01606) 861809 Fax: (01606) 559337 E-mail: sales@chemicalsupport.co.uk

Fabricated Products, 4 Foundry House, Sheffield Road, Rotherham, South Yorkshire, S60 1BN Tel: (01709) 720842 Fax: (01709) 720846 E-mail: info@fabricatedproducts.co.uk

Fire Systems Ltd, Station House, 5 Ridsdale Road, London, SE20 8AG Tel: (020) 8659 7235 Fax: (020) 8659 7237 E-mail: enquiries@firesystems.co.uk

Haskel Energy Systems Ltd, North Hylton Road, Sunderland, SR5 3JD Tel: 0191-549 1212 Fax: 0191-549 0911 E-mail: sales@haskel.co.uk

CHEMICAL DRYERS

▶ Wolverine Proctor & Schwartz, 3 Langlands Avenue, East Kilbride, Glasgow, G75 0YG Tel: (01355) 575350 Fax: (01355) 575351

CHEMICAL ENGINEERING

Atkins Consultants Ltd, Bank Chambers, Faulkner Street, Manchester, M1 4EH Tel: 0161-245 3400 Fax: 0161-245 3500 E-mail: jon.baker@atkinsglobal.com

British Chemical Engineering Contractors Association, 1 Regent Street, London, SW1Y 4NR Tel: (020) 7839 6514 Fax: (020) 7930 3466 E-mail: ian.corbidge@bceca.org.uk

Calculated Solutions UK Ltd, 69 Ivy Road, Maclesfield, Macclesfield, Cheshire, SK11 8QN Tel: (01625) 269198 Fax: (01625) 265512 E-mail: calsol@ntlworld.com

Davy Process Technology, The Technology Centre, Princeton Drive, Thornaby, Stockton-On-Tees, Cleveland, TS17 6PY Tel: (01642) 853800 Fax: (01642) 853801 E-mail: davy@davyprotech.com

▶ Manrochem Ltd, 18 New North Parade, Huddersfield, HD1 5JP Tel: (01484) 453868 Fax: (01484) 453884 E-mail: rih@manrochem.co.uk

Process Manufacturing Ltd, Well Spring Close, Atherstone, Warwickshire, CV9 1LQ Tel: (0121) 553 7772 Fax: (0121) 553 4746 E-mail: enquies@surfacedynamics.co.uk

Purvin & Gertz Inc, Stratton House, Stratton Street, London, W1J 8LA Tel: (020) 7499 0115 Fax: (020) 7499 1985 E-mail: prwiley@purvingertz.com

Ronacrete Ltd, Ronac House, Selinas Lane, Dagenham, Essex, RM8 1QH Tel: (020) 8593 7621 Fax: (020) 8595 6969 E-mail: sosen@ronacrete.co.uk

Peter Sandham Associates, 2 Wesley Street, Castleford, West Yorkshire, WF10 1AE Tel: (01977) 519600 Fax: (01977) 555290 E-mail: paulsandham@totalise.co.uk

▶ T P Aspinall & Sons Ltd, Middleton Business Park, Middleton Road, Middleton, Morecambe, Lancashire, LA3 3PW Tel: (01524) 852883 Fax: (01524) 853303 E-mail: enquiries@aspinall.co.uk

CHEMICAL ENGINEERING CONSULTANTS

C & G Industrial Chemicals Ltd, Sovereign Works, Deep Dale Lane, Lower Gornal, Dudley, West Midlands, DY3 2AF Tel: (01384) 455225 E-mail: angiegroves@tiscali.co.uk

Calculated Solutions UK Ltd, 69 Ivy Road, Maclesfield, Macclesfield, Cheshire, SK11 8QN Tel: (01625) 269198 Fax: (01625) 265512 E-mail: calsol@ntlworld.com

Chemical Corporation UK Ltd, Atlas House Unit 9, Bedwas Business Centre, Bedwas, Caerphilly, Mid Glamorgan, CF83 8DU Tel: (029) 2088 0222 Fax: (029) 2088 0676 E-mail: sales@chemicalcorporation.co.uk

Hunter & Associates, 161 Henrietta St, Ashton-under-Lyne, Lancs, OL6 8PH Tel: 0161-330 8460 Fax: 0161-339 7858 E-mail: hunters@moggs.demon.co.uk

Information Search & Analysis Consultants, 89 Chandos Avenue, London, N20 9EG Tel: (020) 8446 2776 Fax: (020) 8343 9471 E-mail: dr.g.munday@issaconsult.co.uk

List Design Group Ltd, Manby Road By Passage, Immingham, South Humberside, DN40 2DW Tel: (01469) 571888 Fax: (01469) 571450 E-mail: ldgltd@aol.com

Peter Sandham Associates, 2 Wesley Street, Castleford, West Yorkshire, WF10 1AE Tel: (01977) 519600 Fax: (01977) 555290 E-mail: paulsandham@totalise.co.uk

CHEMICAL ENGRAVERS

Etch Components, Unit 3 58 Caroline Street, Birmingham, B3 1UF Tel: 0121-233 4409 Fax: 0121-233 9282

Exel Engraving Ltd, 19 Brickfields Industrial Estate, Finway Road, Hemel Hempstead, Hertfordshire, HP2 7QA Tel: (01442) 270510 Fax: (01442) 270520 E-mail: exelsales@aol.com

Gravutex Eschmann International Ltd, Unit 10 Peakdale Road, Brookfield Industrial Estate, Glossop, Derbyshire, SK13 6LQ Tel: (01457) 867627 Fax: (01457) 855536 E-mail: aharrison@gravutexeshman.co.uk

Hockerill Engraving, 2d Willis Vean Industrial Estate, Mullion, Helston, Cornwall, TR12 7DF Tel: (01326) 240400 Fax: (01326) 240620 E-mail: hockerill@dial.pipex.com

Sign Industries Ltd, Mains of Gardyne, Forfar, Angus, DD8 2SQ Tel: (01241) 828694 Fax: (01241) 828331 E-mail: info@signindustries.com

CHEMICAL ETCHING

Avon Engraving Services, 15 Barratt Street, Bristol, BS5 6DE Tel: 0117-951 0234 Fax: 0117-952 0234

CHEMICAL EXPORT MERCHANTS OR AGENTS

Albion Chemicals, Pensnett House, Second Avenue, Pensnett Trading Estate, Kingswinford, West Midlands, DY6 7PP Tel: (01384) 400222 Fax: (01384) 400020 E-mail: sales@brenntag.co.uk

BCS Uk Ltd, Marle Place, Brenchley, Tonbridge, Kent, TN12 7HS Tel: (01892) 724534 Fax: (01892) 724099

C P International Chemical Ltd, New Town Road, Bishop's Stortford, Hertfordshire, CM23 3SA Tel: (01279) 506330 Fax: (01279) 755873 E-mail: chemicals@cpgroup.co.uk

Cayley Chemical Corporation Ltd, 10 Manor Park Business Centre, Mackenzie Way, Swindon Village, Cheltenham, Gloucestershire, GL51 9TX Tel: (01242) 222971 Fax: (01242) 227634 E-mail: cayley@btinternet.com

China Industrial Materials Ltd, Unit 29 Phoenix International Industrial Estate, Charles Street, West Bromwich, West Midlands, B70 0AY Tel: 0121-520 3050 Fax: 0121-601 8039 E-mail: marketing@cimukltd.com

Monroe Exports (UK) Ltd, 39 Hartland Drive, Edgware, Middlesex, HA8 8RJ Tel: (020) 8958 9673 Fax: (020) 8357 2810 E-mail: jdhruve@btclick.com

Pacegrove Ltd, Unit 13 Courtyard Workshops, Bath Street, Market Harborough, Leicestershire, LE16 9EW Tel: (01858) 431381 Fax: (01858) 432426 E-mail: winlab@pacegrove.co.uk

R A Watts Ltd, 36-38 Woodcote Road, Wallington, Surrey, SM6 0NN Tel: (020) 8647 1074 Fax: (020) 8773 3595 E-mail: sales@rawatts.fsbusiness.co.uk

Thor Overseas Ltd, Ramsgate Road, Margate, Kent, CT9 4JY Tel: (01843) 227681 Fax: (01843) 298813 E-mail: mailbox@thor-int.co.uk

Trading House International Ltd, 80 South Audley Street, London, W1K 1JH Tel: (020) 7491 9002 Fax: (020) 7491 9005 E-mail: tradinghouse@freenet.co.uk

CHEMICAL FILLING AND PACKING

Mold Hygiene Chemicals Co. Ltd, Unit 3 Antelope Industrial Park, Rhydymwyn, Mold, Clwyd, CH7 5JH Tel: (01352) 741000 Fax: (01352) 740074 E-mail: sales@mirjhygiene.co.uk

P E M Plant & Chemicals International Ltd, 6 Brindley Road, Clacton-on-Sea, Essex, CO15 4XL Tel: (01255) 426366 Fax: (01255) 426046 E-mail: rklueter@pemchemicals.co.uk

Woodman Hill Ltd, Imperial Way, Watford, WD24 4YX Tel: (01923) 233977 Fax: (01923) 235941 E-mail: sales@woodmanhill.co.uk

CHEMICAL IMPORT MERCHANTS OR AGENTS

BCS Uk Ltd, Marle Place, Brenchley, Tonbridge, Kent, TN12 7HS Tel: (01892) 724534 Fax: (01892) 724099

C C P Gransden Bi-Chem, 17 Moss Road, Ballygowan, Newtownards, County Down, BT23 6JQ Tel: (028) 9752 8501 Fax: (028) 9752 1024 E-mail: info@ccp-gransden.com

C P International Chemical Ltd, New Town Road, Bishop's Stortford, Hertfordshire, CM23 3SA Tel: (01279) 506330 Fax: (01279) 755873 E-mail: chemicals@cpgroup.co.uk

Chemox Ltd, Sussex House 11 The Pines Trading Estate, Broad Street, Guildford, Surrey, GU3 3BH Tel: (01483) 450660 Fax: (01483) 450770 E-mail: chemox@tbase.co.uk

China Industrial Materials Ltd, Unit 29 Phoenix International Industrial Estate, Charles Street, West Bromwich, West Midlands, B70 0AY Tel: 0121-520 3050 Fax: 0121-601 8039 E-mail: marketing@cimukltd.com

D B M Chemicals Ltd, 73 Ferry Lane South, Rainham, Essex, RM13 9YH Tel: (01708) 522151 Fax: (01708) 557546 E-mail: jrhornett@aol.com

Maprac (UK) Ltd, 57-59 High Street, Hoddesdon, Hertfordshire, EN11 8TQ Tel: (01992) 440880 Fax: (01992) 442422 E-mail: info@mapracuk.co.uk

Sigma-Aldrich Co. Ltd, Fancy Road, Poole, Dorset, BH12 4QH Tel: (01202) 712300 Fax: (01202) 712350 E-mail: ukcustsv@europe.sial.com

The White Sea & Baltic Company Ltd, Arndale House, Otley Road, Leeds, LS6 2UU Tel: 0113-230 4774 Fax: 0113-230 4770 E-mail: sales@whitesea.co.uk

CHEMICAL INDUSTRY HOSES

Amnitec Ltd, Abercanaid, Merthyr Tydfil, Mid Glamorgan, CF48 1UX Tel: (01685) 385641 Fax: (01685) 389683 E-mail: sales@amnitec.co.uk

C M T Flexibles, Unit 14D Two Locks, Hurst Business Park, Brierley Hill, West Midlands, DY5 1UU Tel: (01384) 480197 Fax: (01384) 74840 E-mail: sales@cmtflexibles.com

Goodyear Great Britain Ltd, Bushbury Lane, Bushbury, Wolverhampton, WV10 6DH Tel: (01902) 327000 Fax: (01902) 327060

CHEMICAL INJECTION EQUIPMENT

Alldos Ltd, 82 Gravelly Industrial Park, Birmingham, B24 8TL Tel: 0121-328 3336 Fax: 0121-328 4332 E-mail: alldos.uk@alldos.com

B & G Cleaning Systems Ltd, Abeles Way, Holly Lane Industrial Estate, Atherstone, Warwickshire, CV9 2QZ Tel: (01827) 717028 Fax: (01827) 714041 E-mail: sales@bgclean.co.uk

Caproco plc, 31 Davey House, St Neots Road, Eaton Ford, St. Neots, Cambridgeshire, PE19 7BA Tel: (01480) 407600 Fax: (01480) 407619 E-mail: caproco@btconnect.com

G M Engineering Ltd, 12 Greenbank Place, East Tullos Industrial Estate, Aberdeen, AB12 3BT Tel: (01224) 895431 Fax: (01224) 871027 E-mail: info@gm-engineering.com

Haskel Energy Systems Ltd, North Hylton Road, Sunderland, SR5 3JD Tel: 0191-549 1212 Fax: 0191-549 0911 E-mail: sales@haskel.co.uk

Hingerose Ltd, 5 Ryder Court, Corby, Northamptonshire, NN18 9NX Tel: (01536) 461441 Fax: (01536) 461600 E-mail: info@hingerose.co.uk

Positive Metering Systems, Suite 5, The Cloisters, Broyle Place Farm, Laughton Road, Ringmer, East Sussex, BN8 5SD Tel: (01273) 815990 Fax: (01273) 815999 E-mail: projects@positivesystems.co.uk

Rose Corrosion Services Ltd, 1 The Galloway Centre, Hambridge Lane, Newbury, Berkshire, RG14 5TL Tel: (01635) 552225 Fax: (01635) 568690 E-mail: rcsl@rosecorrosionservices.co.uk

Tube Tec, Spurryhillock Industrial Estate, Broomhill Road, Stonehaven, Kincardineshire, AB39 2NH Tel: (01569) 762211 Fax: (01569) 768065 E-mail: sales@tubetec.co.uk

CHEMICAL INJECTION PUMPS

▶ Achromatic Limited, Grangemouth Enterprise & Technology Centre, Falkirk Road, Grangemouth, Stirlingshire, FK3 8XS Tel: (01324) 619360 Fax: (01324) 622399 E-mail: info@achromatic.co.uk

G M Engineering Ltd, 12 Greenbank Place, East Tullos Industrial Estate, Aberdeen, AB12 3BT Tel: (01224) 895431 Fax: (01224) 871027 E-mail: info@gm-engineering.com

Morgans Products, 7 Myreside Drive, Inverkeilor, Arbroath, Angus, DD11 5PZ Tel: (01241) 830267 Fax: (01241) 830435 E-mail: dosher@inverkeilor.rapiddial.co.uk

Sera Dosing UK Ltd, 7 Woodland Drive, Alma Park Road, Grantham, Lincolnshire, NG31 9SR Tel: (01476) 565512 Fax: (01476) 590171 E-mail: enquiries@liquiddosing.co.uk

CHEMICAL LABORATORY EQUIPMENT

Associated Laboratories Services UK Ltd, Unit 55 Lakes Industrial Park, Lower Chapel Hill, Braintree, Essex, CM7 3RU Tel: (01376) 322938 Fax: (01376) 552106 E-mail: info@als-uk-ltd.com

CHEMICAL MANUFRS, *See also headings under Chemicals; & other headings for particular types*

A H Marks & Co. Ltd, Wyke Lane, Wyke, Bradford, West Yorkshire, BD12 9EJ Tel: (01274) 691234 Fax: (01274) 691176 E-mail: info@ahmarks.com

A P C (Scotland) Ltd, Po Box 14554, Kinross, KY13 9ZJ Tel: (01577) 864231 Fax: (01577) 865677

▶ Acorn Chemical Services, Unit 16-17, Milland Road Industrial Estate, Neath, West Glamorgan, SA11 1NJ Tel: (01639) 641222 Fax: (01639) 632255 E-mail: admin@equilibrium.net

▶ Actikem Ltd, Ravensdale, Stoke-on-Trent, ST6 4NU Tel: (01782) 577002 Fax: (01782) 577008E-mail: andrew.mooney@actikem.com

R.P. Adam Ltd, Arpal Works, Riverside Road, Selkirk, TD7 5DU Tel: (01750) 21586 Fax: (01750) 21506 E-mail: salesinfo@rpadam.co.uk

▶ Aggregate Industries Ltd, Old Station Yard, Beauly, Inverness-Shire, IV4 7BG Tel: (01463) 782868 Fax: (01463) 782873

Aggregate Industries Ltd, Toms Forest Quarry, Kintore, Inverurie, Aberdeenshire, AB51 0YU Tel: (01467) 644200 Fax: (01467) 644250 E-mail: enquiries@aggregates.com

Agma Ltd, Gemini Works, Haltwhistle, Northumberland, NE49 9HA Tel: (01434) 320598 Fax: (01434) 321650 E-mail: enquiries@agma.co.uk

Albemarle UK Ltd, Teesport, Middlesbrough, Cleveland, TS6 7SA Tel: (01642) 463314 Fax: (01642) 463315

Albion Chemicals Ltd, Bristol Road, Portishead, Bristol, BS20 6QG Tel: (01275) 844518 Fax: (01275) 818041

▶ Albion Chemicals Ltd, Union Mills, Oxford Road, Gomersal, Cleckheaton, West Yorkshire, BD19 4JW Tel: (01274) 850300 Fax: (01274) 851252 E-mail: enquiries@albionchemicals.co.uk

Albion Chemicals, Pensnett House, Second Avenue, Pensnett Trading Estate, Kingswinford, West Midlands, DY6 7PP Tel: (01384) 400222 Fax: (01384) 400020 E-mail: sales@brenntag.co.uk

▶ Albion Chemicals Ltd, Albion House Warden Park, Green Lane, Yeadon, Leeds, LS19 7XX Tel: 0113-387 9200 Fax: 0113-387 9280 E-mail: enquiries@albionchemicals.co.uk

Albion Chemicals Ltd, Albion House Warden Park, Green Lane, Yeadon, Leeds, LS19 7XX Tel: 0113-387 9200 E-mail: comm@hayschem.co.uk

Albion Colours Ltd, High Level Way, Halifax, West Yorkshire, HX1 4PN Tel: (01422) 358431 Fax: (01422) 330867 E-mail: colours.sales@albionchemicals.co.uk

▶ Alex Ross & Sons Ltd, 21 Henderson Drive, Inverness, IV1 1TR Tel: (01463) 232061 Fax: (01463) 713740

▶ Alfa Chemicals Ltd, Arc House, Terrace Road South, Binfield, Bracknell, Berkshire, RG42 4PZ Tel: (01344) 861800 Fax: (01344) 451400 E-mail: info@alfa-chemicals.co.uk

J. Allcock & Sons Ltd, Textile Street, West Gorton, Manchester, M12 5DL Tel: 0161-223 7181 Fax: 0161-223 0173 E-mail: ja@allcocks.co.uk

CHEMICAL MANUFRS – *continued*

Alpha Chemicals Ltd, 29 Winchester Avenue, Denny, Stirlingshire, FK6 6QE Tel: (01324) 824181 Fax: (01324) 822101 E-mail: alphachem@winning.sol.co.uk

Amatar Ltd, Amatar House, Manor Road, Woodley, Stockport, Cheshire, SK6 1RT Tel: 0161-494 6692 Fax: 0161-406 6752 E-mail: djo171135@aol.com

Anderson Gibb & Wilson, 543 Gorgie Road, Edinburgh, EH11 3AR Tel: 0131-443 4556 Fax: 0131-455 7608 E-mail: tennants.edinburgh@dial.pipex.com

Anglesey Aluminium Metal Ltd, Penrhos Works, Holyhead, Gwynedd, LL65 2UJ Tel: (01407) 725000 Fax: (01407) 725001

Apaseal Ltd, Unit 32 The Willow Estate, Avis Way, Newhaven, East Sussex, BN9 0DD Tel: (01273) 517995 Fax: (01273) 611061

Apex Industrial Chemicals Ltd, Peterseat Drive, Altens Industrial Estate, Aberdeen, AB12 3HT Tel: (01224) 878420 Fax: (01224) 871195 E-mail: sales@apex-chemical.co.uk

Atotech UK Ltd, William Street, West Bromwich, West Midlands, B70 0BE Tel: 0121-606 7777 Fax: 0121-606 7200 E-mail: sales.uk@atotech.com

B I P Organics Ltd, Brooks Lane Industrial Estate, Middlewich, Cheshire, CW10 0JG Tel: (01606) 835271 Fax: (01606) 835274

B O C Group P.L.C., Chertsey Road, Windlesham, Surrey, GU20 6HJ Tel: (01276) 477222 Fax: (01276) 471333

▶ B P, Saltend, Hull, HU12 8DS Tel: (01482) 896251

Banner Chemicals Ltd, Unit B, Hampton Court, Manor Park, Runcorn, Cheshire, WA7 1TU Tel: (01928) 597000 Fax: (01928) 597001 E-mail: reception@bannerchemicals.co.uk

▶ Bardon Aggregate, Fledmyre Quarry, Forfar, Angus, DD8 2HX Tel: (01307) 464728

Basf Public Ltd Company, Earl Road, Cheadle Hulme, Cheadle, Cheshire, SK8 6QG Tel: 0161-485 6222 Fax: 0161-486 0891 E-mail: info.service@basf-plc.co.uk

Baxenden Chemicals Ltd, Paragon Works, Rising Bridge, Accrington, Lancashire, BB5 2SL Tel: (01254) 872278 Fax: (01254) 871247

Bayer, 230 Science Park, Milton Road, Cambridge, CB4 0WB Tel: (01223) 226500 Fax: (01223) 426240

Bayer UK plc, Bayer House, Strawberry Hill, Newbury, Berkshire, RG14 1JA Tel: (01635) 563000 Fax: (01635) 563393 E-mail: corporate.communications@bayer.co.uk

▶ Beauty Tech International Ltd, Golf House, Horsham Road, Pease Pottage, Crawley, West Sussex, RH11 9SG Tel: (01293) 530300

Best-Chem Ltd, Barracks Road, Sandy Lane, Stourport-On-Severn, Worcestershire, DY13 9QB Tel: (01299) 827232 Fax: (01299) 827608

Biachem Ltd, Boundary House, 91-93 Charterhouse Street, London, EC1M 6HR Tel: (020) 7250 1905 Fax: (020) 7250 1913 E-mail: info@biachem.com

Bio Crop Science Ltd, Sweet Briar Road, Norwich, NR6 5AP Tel: (01603) 242424 Fax: (01603) 242331

Bio Natura Ltd, PO Box 2, Ilkley, West Yorkshire, LS29 8AS Tel: (01943) 816816 Fax: (01943) 816818 E-mail: sales@bionutura.co.uk

Bio-Productions, 72 Victoria Road, Burgess Hill, West Sussex, RH15 9LH Tel: (01444) 244000 Fax: (01444) 244999 E-mail: info@bio-productions.co.uk

Blackburn Chemicals Ltd, Cunliffe Road, Whitebirk Industrial Estate, Blackburn, BB1 5SX Tel: (01254) 52222 Fax: (01254) 664224 E-mail: info@bbchem.co.uk

William Blythe Ltd, Bridge Street, Church, Accrington, Lancashire, BB5 4PD Tel: (01254) 320000 Fax: (01254) 320001 E-mail: ian.pearce@wm-blythe.co.uk

William Blythe Ltd, Hapton Works, Manchester Road, Hapton, Burnley, Lancashire, BB12 7LF Tel: (01254) 320000 Fax: (01254) 320001

▶ Bonnar Sand & Gravel Co. Ltd, Clachan Gravel Pit, Cairndow, Argyll, PA26 8BL Tel: (01499) 600269

▶ Border Fine Arts, Townfoot, Langholm, Dumfriesshire, DG15 0ET Tel: (01387) 383027 Fax: (01387) 383020 E-mail: norman.maxwell@enesco.co.uk

Borregaard (UK) Ltd, Clayton Road, Risley Employment Area, Warrington, WA3 6QQ Tel: (01925) 285400 Fax: (01925) 285434 E-mail: marketing_europe@borregaard.com

Brotherton Speciality Products Ltd, Calder Vale Road, Wakefield, West Yorkshire, WF1 5PH Tel: (01924) 371919 Fax: (01924) 290408 E-mail: info@brotherton.co.uk

Brunner Mond Group Ltd, PO Box 4, Northwich, Cheshire, CW8 4DT Tel: (01606) 724000 Fax: (01606) 781353 E-mail: sales.enquiries@brunnermond.com

Butler Wentwood Ltd, Units 2-4, New Road, New Inn, Pontypool, Gwent, NP4 0TL Tel: (01495) 763040 Fax: (01495) 763505 E-mail: inquiries@butlerwentwood.sagehost.co.uk

C T Supplies Ltd, Unit 94 Northwick Business Centre, Blockley, Moreton-in-Marsh, Gloucestershire, GL56 9RF Tel: (01386) 700884 Fax: (01386) 700126 E-mail: sales@ct-supplies.co.uk

Caldic UK Ltd, Stainsby Close, Holmewood Industrial Estate, Holmewood, Chesterfield, Derbyshire, S42 5UG Tel: (01246) 854111 Fax: (01246) 856222 E-mail: info@caldic.com

Champion Technolgies Ltd, W Sam White Building, Peter Seat Drive, Altens, Aberdeen, AB12 3HT Tel: (01224) 879022 Fax: (01224) 876022 E-mail: champion@champion-servo.com

Chance & Hunt Ltd, Alexander House, Crown Gate, Runcorn, Cheshire, WA7 2UP Tel: (01928) 793000 Fax: (01928) 714351 E-mail: passport@chance-hunt.com

Stan Chem International Ltd, Gapton Hall Industrial Estate, Viking Road, Great Yarmouth, Norfolk, NR31 0NU Tel: (01493) 419904 Fax: (01493) 442241 E-mail: yarmouth@stanchem.co.uk

Chemaide Ltd, Unit 8 Gilmans Industrial Estate, Billingshurst, West Sussex, RH14 9EZ Tel: (01403) 780638 Fax: (01403) 780639 E-mail: info@chemaide.co.uk

Chemi-Kal Ltd, Powerforce House, Rowland Way, Hoo Farm Industrial Estate, Kidderminster, Worcestershire, DY11 7RA Tel: (01562) 755884 Fax: (01562) 825319 E-mail: chemi-kal@globalnet.co.uk

Chemox Ltd, Sussex House 11 The Pines Trading Estate, Broad Street, Guildford, Surrey, GU3 3BH Tel: (01483) 450660 Fax: (01483) 450770 E-mail: chemox@tbase.co.uk

Chemquest Ltd, Springfield House, Water Lane, Wilmslow, Cheshire, SK9 5BG Tel: (01625) 528808 Fax: (01625) 527557 E-mail: enquiries@chemquest.co.uk

Chemtechno Ltd, 49 Queens Gardens, London, W2 3AA Tel: (020) 7723 2323 Fax: (020) 7724 9297 E-mail: chemtechno@dial.pipex.com

Chesham Speciality Ingrediants Ltd, Cunnigham House, Westfield Lane, Kenton, Harrow, Middlesex, HA3 9ED Tel: (020) 8907 7779 Fax: (020) 8927 0686 E-mail: sales@cheshamchemicals.co.uk

Chevron Oronite Sa, St. Marks House, St. Marks Road, Windsor, Berkshire, SL4 3BD Tel: (01753) 844301 Fax: (01753) 844300

▶ Ciba Speciality Chemicals Colours plc, Hawkhead Road, Paisley, Renfrewshire, PA2 7BG Tel: 0141-887 1144 Fax: 0141-840 2283

Ciba Specialty Chemicals plc, Charter Road, Macclesfield, Cheshire, SK10 2NX Tel: (01625) 665000 Fax: (01625) 619637

Cle-Pol Manufacturing Co Ltd, PO Box 5, Barking, Essex, IG11 0TL Tel: (020) 8532 6900 Fax: (020) 8532 6940

▶ Cloburn Quarry Co Ltd, Pettinain, Lanark, ML11 8SR Tel: (01555) 663444 Fax: (01555) 664111

Cole & Wilson Ltd, Nabbs Lane Chemical Works, Slaithwaite, Huddersfield, HD7 5AT Tel: (01484) 842353 Fax: (01484) 843598 E-mail: sales@colewilson.co.uk

Complete Solution, 12 High Street, Newhall, Swadlincote, Derbyshire, DE11 0HX Tel: (01283) 229466 Fax: (01283) 229466

Contract Chemicals Properties Ltd, Penrhyn Road, Knowsley Business Park, Prescot, Merseyside, L34 9HY Tel: 0151-548 8840 Fax: 0151-548 6548 E-mail: info@contract-chemicals.com

Cornelius Group plc, Woodside, Dunmow Road, Birchanger, Bishop's Stortford, Hertfordshire, CM23 5RG Tel: (01279) 714300 Fax: (01279) 714320 E-mail: sales.dept@cornelius.co.uk

▶ Hugh Crane Cleaning Equipment Ltd, Fishley Lane, South Walsham Road, Acle, Norwich, NR13 3ES Tel: (01493) 750072 Fax: (01493) 751854 E-mail: sales@hughcrane.co.uk

CSL, Caxton Road, Newton Industrial Estate, Carlisle, CA2 7NS Tel: (01228) 544422 Fax: (01228) 544464

D B M Chemicals Ltd, 73 Ferry Lane South, Rainham, Essex, RM13 9YH Tel: (01708) 522151 Fax: (01708) 557546 E-mail: jrhornett@aol.com

Degussa Ltd, Winterton House, Winterton Way, Lyme Green Business Park, Macclesfield, Cheshire, SK11 0LP Tel: (01625) 503050 Fax: (01625) 502096

▶ Doosanbabcock, Porterfield Road, Renfrew, PA4 8DJ Tel: 0141-886 4141

Dow Chemical, 2 Heathrow Boulevard, 284 Bath Road, West Drayton, Middlesex, UB7 0DQ Tel: (020) 8917 5000 Fax: (020) 8917 5400

Dow Chemicals Ltd, PO Box 54, Middlesbrough, Cleveland, TS90 8JA Tel: (01642) 543000 Fax: (01642) 374192

Du Pont UK Ltd, Wedgewood Way, Stevenage, Hertfordshire, SG1 4QN Tel: (01438) 734000 Fax: (01438) 734836 E-mail: enquiries@dupontpharma.com

E C Gulbrandsen Ltd, Water Lane, Ancaster, Grantham, Lincolnshire, NG32 3QS Tel: (01400) 230700 Fax: (01400) 230601

Echem Ltd, 147 Kirkstall Road, Leeds, LS3 1JN Tel: 0113-245 7471 Fax: 0113-244 5082 E-mail: info@echem.co.uk

▶ Edmund Nuttall Ltd, Glasgow Road, Kilsyth, Glasgow, G65 9BL Tel: (01236) 467050 Fax: (01236) 467072

Elementis Specialties, Birtley, Chester le Street, County Durham, DH3 1QX Tel: 0191-410 5522 Fax: 0191-410 6005 E-mail: specinfo.uk@elemantis.com

Elementis UK Ltd, Nettlehill Road, Houston Industrial Estate, Livingston, West Lothian, EH54 5DL Tel: (01506) 430331 Fax: (020) 7398 1401 E-mail: info@elementis.com

Elixair International Ltd, Unit F2, Roman Hill Trading Estate, Broadmayne, Dorchester, Dorset, DT2 8LY Tel: (01305) 854735 Fax: (01305) 852060 E-mail: elixair.int@virgin.net

▶ Ennstone Thistle Ltd, Cloddach Quarry, Elgin, Morayshire, IV30 8TW Tel: (01343) 559830

▶ Ennstone Thistle Ltd, Craigenlow Quarry, Dunecht Westhill, Skene, Aberdeenshire, AB32 7ED Tel: (01330) 833361

▶ Enstil & Thistle, Banavie Quarry, Banavie, Fort William, Inverness-Shire, PH33 7LX Tel: (01397) 772267 Fax: (01397) 772389

Euram Chemicals Ltd, PO Box 346, Marlow, Buckinghamshire, SL7 1WH Tel: (01628) 472848 Fax: (01628) 890095 E-mail: sales@euramchemicals.co.uk

Evotec UK Ltd, 151 Milton Park, Milton, Abingdon, Oxfordshire, OX14 4SD Tel: (01235) 441200 Fax: (01235) 863139 E-mail: sales@evotecoai.com

F2 Chemicals Ltd, Lea Lane, Lea Town, Preston, PR4 0RZ Tel: (01772) 775802 Fax: (01772) 775808 E-mail: gerry.may@fluoros.co.uk

Ferro Metal & Chemical Corporation Ltd, 179 Kings Road, Reading, RG1 4EX Tel: 0118-960 4700 Fax: 0118-950 9216 E-mail: sales@phibrochem.com

Fisher Scientific Holding UK Ltd, Bishop Meadow Road, Loughborough, Leicestershire, LE11 5RG Tel: (01509) 231166 Fax: (01509) 231893 E-mail: info@fisher.co.uk

Fleming Technical Ltd, Brunel Road, Croft Business Park, Wirral, Merseyside, CH62 3NY Tel: 0151-343 1800 Fax: 0151-343 1801 E-mail: gil@fleming-tech.co.uk

▶ Fluid Technology Generation Ltd, Drum Industrial Estate, Drum Industrial Estate, Chester le Street, County Durham, DH2 1SR Tel: 0191-411 1777 Fax: 0191-411 1888 E-mail: flutechnolgy@btconnect.com

Gainland International Ltd, Factory Road, Sandycroft, Deeside, Clwyd, CH5 2QJ Tel: (01244) 536326 Fax: (01244) 531254 E-mail: sandralewis@gccdiagnostics.com

▶ Glenside, Block 2 Unit 4 Bandeath Industrial Estate, Throsk, Stirling, FK7 7NP Tel: (01786) 816655 Fax: (01786) 816100

Goldschmidt UK Ltd, Tego House, Chippenham Drive, Kingston, Milton Keynes, MK10 0AF Tel: (01908) 582250 Fax: (01908) 582254 E-mail: angus.smith@degussa.com

Gower Chemicals Ltd, Crymlyn Burrows, Swansea, SA1 8PT Tel: (01792) 473344 Fax: (01792) 456578 E-mail: stewarth@gowerchemicals.ltd.uk

H Schreiber, Stadium Industrial Estate, 8 Cradock Road, Luton, LU4 0JF Tel: (01582) 575727 Fax: (01582) 575733 E-mail: laraine@techscrew.com

Helm Great Britain Ltd, Wimbledon Bridge House, 1 Hartfield Road, London, SW19 3RU Tel: (020) 8544 9000 Fax: (020) 8544 1011 E-mail: chemicals@helmgreatbritain.co.uk

Henkel, Technologies House, Wood La End, Hemel Hempstead, Hertfordshire, HP2 4RQ Tel: (01442) 278000 Fax: (01442) 278071

▶ Heraeus Quartz Ltd, 5 Langlands Place, Kelvin South Business Park, East Kilbride, Glasgow, G75 0YF Tel: (01355) 244456

Trevor Holley Associates, Little London, Combs, Stowmarket, Suffolk, IP14 2ES Tel: (01449) 612084 Fax: (01449) 771027 E-mail: t.holley@btinternet.com

▶ Homecare Technology, Unit 9a Marshfield Bank, Crewe, CW2 8UY Tel: (01270) 508989 Fax: (01270) 215753 E-mail: sales@homecareproducts.co.uk

Honeywill & Stein Ltd, Times House, Throwley Way, Sutton, Surrey, SM1 4AF Tel: (020) 8770 3455 Fax: (020) 8770 3464 E-mail: schuelerm@honeywill.co.uk

▶ Hunting Oilfield Services International Ltd, Badentoy Avenue, Badentoy Industrial Estate Portlethen, Aberdeen, AB12 4SQ Tel: (01224) 787000

Huntsman, Hitchen Lane, Shepton Mallet, Somerset, BA4 5TZ Tel: (01749) 335200 Fax: (01749) 344221

▶ Hydra Technologies Ltd, Unit 3 Queensway Business Centre, 4 The Queensway, Fforestfach, Swansea, SA5 4DT Tel: (01792) 586800 Fax: (01792) 561606

Industrial Chemicals & Equipment Ltd, 59 Cranes Park, Surbiton, Surrey, KT5 8AS Tel: (020) 8399 9333 Fax: (020) 8399 9555 E-mail: ice.ltd@virgin.net

Innospec Ltd, Innospec Manufacturing Park, Oil Sites Road, Ellesmere Port, CH65 4EY Tel: 0151 3553611 Fax: 0151 3562349 E-mail: corporatecommunications@innospecinc.com

Innovo Chemicals Ltd, The Common, Cranleigh, Surrey, GU6 8RY Tel: (01483) 277219 Fax: (01483) 268030 E-mail: sales@innovochem.co.uk

J Storey & Co. Ltd, Heron Chemical Works, Moor Lane, Lancaster, LA1 1QQ Tel: (01524) 63252 Fax: (01524) 381805 E-mail: sales@samuelbanner.co.uk

J & W Whewell Ltd, Newbridge Chemical Works, York Street, Radcliffe, Manchester, M26 2GL Tel: 0161-796 6333 Fax: 0161-766 3017 E-mail: sales@jwwhewell.co.uk

Jacobson Chemicals Ltd, Unit 4, Newman Lane, Alton, Hampshire, GU34 2QR Tel: (01420) 86934 Fax: (01420) 549574 E-mail: sales@jacobsonchemicals.co.uk

Jennychem, Jennychem House, Sort Mill Road, Mid Kent Business Park, Snodland, Kent, ME6 5UA Tel: (01634) 290770 Fax: (01634) 245777 E-mail: jenny@jennychem.com

Kanor Chemicals, 12-14 Wharf Street, Warrington, WA1 2HT Tel: (01925) 639509 Fax: (01925) 445914

Keeling & Walker Ltd, Whieldon Road, Stoke-on-Trent, ST4 4JA Tel: (01782) 744136 Fax: (01782) 744126 E-mail: sales@keelingwalker.co.uk

Kelher Supplies, 46 Fairfax Road, Birkenhead, Merseyside, CH41 9EJ Tel: 0151-647 9595 Fax: 0151-647 4077 E-mail: info@kelhersupplies.co.uk

▶ Kemira Growhow UK Ltd, Ince, Chester, CH2 4LB Tel: 0151-357 2777 Fax: 0151-357 1755 E-mail: kemira-growhow.uk@kemira-growhow.com

Kinder Marketing, Unit D Roe Cross Indust Park, Old Road, Mottram, Hyde, Cheshire, SK14 6LG Tel: (01457) 762758 Fax: (01457) 776547

Klenzan Ltd, 2 Cameron Court, Winwick Quay, Warrington, WA2 8RE Tel: (01925) 234696 Fax: (01925) 234693 E-mail: info@klenzan.co.uk

Kuehne + Nagel Ltd, Hays House, Sunrise Parkway, Linford Wood, Milton Keynes, MK14 6BW Tel: (01908) 255000 Fax: (01908) 255200

▶ Laird Bros Forfar Ltd, Old Brechin Road, Lunanhead, Forfar, Angus, DD8 3NQ Tel: (01307) 466577 Fax: (01307) 468642

Lambson Ltd, Avenue D, 603 Thorp Arch Estate, Wetherby, Leeds, LS23 7FS Tel: (01937) 840150 Fax: (01937) 840171 E-mail: sales@lambson.com

Langley-Smith & Co. Ltd, 36 Spital Square, London, E1 6DY Tel: (020) 7247 7473 Fax: (020) 7375 1470 E-mail: sales@langley-smith.co.uk

Larsens, 4 West Bank Road, Belfast, BT3 9JL Tel: (028) 9077 4000 Fax: (028) 9077 6945 E-mail: p.duffy@larsenbuildingproducts.com

Lawrence Industries Ltd, Lawrence House, Apollo, Tamworth, Staffordshire, B79 7TA Tel: (01827) 314151 Fax: (01827) 314152 E-mail: sales@l-i.co.uk

Libra Speciality Chemicals Ltd, Brinell Drive, Northbank Industrial Park, Irlam, Manchester, M44 5LF Tel: 0161-775 1888 Fax: 0161-777 9109 E-mail: sales@librachem.co.uk

Link Contract Supplies Ltd, Unit 1, 172-174 Mile Cross Lane, Norwich, NR6 6RY Tel: (01603) 415355 Fax: (01603) 401921

▶ London Chemicals & Resources Ltd, Studio V, Trinity Buoy Wharf, 64 Orchard Place, London, E14 0JY Tel: (020) 7183 0651 Fax: (020) 7987 7980 E-mail: info@lcrl.net

The Lyndann Group, Broadmeadows, Padstow Road, St. Breock, Wadebridge, Cornwall, PL27 7LS Tel: (01208) 815040 Fax: E-mail: daveharring@btconnect.com

M J M Engineering Ltd, 14 Rydal Avenue, Droylsden, Manchester, M43 6HH Tel: 0161 3717902

M S L Ltd, 101 Smithycroft Road, Glasgow, G33 2RH Tel: 0141-770 4366 Fax: 0141-770 4084 E-mail: msl.quality@virgin.net

Maprac (UK) Ltd, 57-59 High Street, Hoddesdon, Hertfordshire, EN11 8TQ Tel: (01992) 440880 Fax: (01992) 442422 E-mail: info@mapracuk.co.uk

Melbray Chemicals Ltd, Chemical House, Durham Lane Industrial Park, Stockton-on-Tees, Cleveland, TS16 0RG Tel: (01642) 790483 Fax: (01642) 790486 E-mail: melbraychemicals@btconnect.com

Merlin Chemicals Ltd, Passfield Mill Business Park, Mill Lane, Passfield, Liphook, Hampshire, GU30 7QU Tel: (01428) 751122 Fax: (01428) 751133 E-mail: sales@merlinchemicals.co.uk

MSH Chemical Manufacturing Ltd, Unit 2 Oak Lane, Kingswinford, West Midlands, DY6 7JD Tel: (01384) 402991 Fax: (01384) 402989

Multex Chemicals, Multex House, Cannon Street, Hull, HU2 0AB Tel: (01482) 320432 Fax: (01482) 321777 E-mail: sales@multexchemicals.co.uk

Nayler Chemicals Ltd, Unit 34b Kirkless Industrial Estate, Cale Lane, Aspull, Wigan, Lancashire, WN2 1HF Tel: (01942) 829955 Fax: (01942) 233400 E-mail: k.pover@naychem.freeserve.co.uk

Nielson Chemicals Ltd, Rawdon Road, Moira, Swadlincote, Derbyshire, DE12 6DA Tel: (01283) 222277 Fax: (01283) 225731 E-mail: info@nielsenchemicals.com

▶ Nippon Gohsei UK, Saltend, Hull, HU12 8DS Tel: (01482) 333320 Fax: (01482) 309332

▶ Nobel Enterprises, P O Box 2, Stevenston, Ayrshire, KA20 3LN Tel: (01294) 487000 Fax: (01294) 487111

Oakmere Technical Services Ltd, Unit 9, Pool Bank Business Park, High St, Chester, CH3 8JH Tel: (01829) 742100 Fax: (01829) 742109 E-mail: sales@oakmerets.com

Oleotec Ltd, Rossfield Road, Ellesmere Port, CH65 3BS Tel: 0151-357 1778 Fax: 0151-357 1857 E-mail: sales@oleotec.com

Omnichem Ltd, Mill Street East, Dewsbury, West Yorkshire, WF12 9BQ Tel: (01924) 461341 Fax: (01924) 458995 E-mail: info@nickersons.co.uk

Oxford Chemicals Ltd, Zinc Works Road, Seaton Carew, Hartlepool, Cleveland, TS25 2DT Tel: (01429) 863222 Fax: (01429) 867567 E-mail: sales@oxfordchemicals.com

P E M Plant & Chemicals International Ltd, 6 Brindley Road, Clacton-on-Sea, Essex, CO15 4XL Tel: (01255) 426366 Fax: (01255) 426046 E-mail: rklueter@pemchemicals.co.uk

P J S Chemicals, 8 Station Estate, Station Road, Tadcaster, North Yorkshire, LS24 9SG Tel: (01937) 832928 Fax: (01937) 834852 E-mail: pjschemicals@aol.com

Pearl Chemicals Ltd, The White House, Darlaston Park, Stone, Staffordshire, ST15 0ND Tel: (01785) 819747 Fax: (01785) 811567 E-mail: g.dee@pearlchem.co.uk

▶ indicates data change since last edition

CHEMICAL MANUFRS – *continued*

Pentagon Chemicals, Dock Road, Northside, Workington, Cumbria, CA14 1JJ Tel: (01900) 604371 Fax: (01900) 66943 E-mail: sales@pentagonchemicals.co.uk

Pentol Enviro UK Ltd, Belasis Business Centre, Coxwold Way, Belasis Hall Technology Park, Billingham, Cleveland, TS23 4EA Tel: (01642) 566086 Fax: (01642) 560087 E-mail: office.gb@pentol.co.uk

Peter Whiting Chemicals Ltd, 8 Barb Mews, London, W6 7PA Tel: (020) 8741 4025 Fax: (020) 8741 1737 E-mail: sales@whiting-cemicals.co.uk

Pfizer Ltd, Walton Oaks, Dorking Road, Tadworth, Surrey, KT20 7NS Tel: (01304) 616161 Fax: (01304) 656221

Prayon Speciality Products Ltd, River Lodge, West Common, Harpenden, Hertfordshire, AL5 2JD Tel: (01582) 765228 Fax: (01582) 769989 E-mail: info@prayon.co.uk

Process Measurement & Analysis Ltd, Brockmill House, Carr Lane, Huddersfield, HD7 5BG Tel: 0151-649 8477 Fax: (01484) 843689 E-mail: sales@processmeasurement.uk.com

Provan Maintenance Ltd, 29 Winchester Avenue, Denny, Stirlingshire, FK6 6QE Tel: (01324) 826600 Fax: (01324) 822101 E-mail: provanmain@winning.sol.co.uk

R & J Garroway Ltd, 6 The Docks, Grangemouth, Stirlingshire, FK3 8UB Tel: (01324) 665455 Fax: (01324) 474754

Raught Ltd, 117 The Drive, Ilford, Essex, IG1 3JE Tel: (020) 8554 9921 Fax: (020) 8554 8337 E-mail: raughtltd@aol.com

▶ Resolution UK Performance Products, The Business Centre Oaklands Office Park, Hooton Road, Hooton, Ellesmere Port, CH66 7NZ Tel: 0151-326 2521 Fax: 0151-326 2541

▶ Rexodan International, PO Box 24, Widnes, Cheshire, WA8 0RB Tel: 0151-422 1100 Fax: 0151-422 1111 E-mail: export@rexodan.com

▶ RHI Refractories UK, PO Box 3, Clydebank, Dunbartonshire, G81 1RW Tel: 0141-952 1990 E-mail: firstname.secondname@rhi-ag.com

Rhodia Organique Fine Ltd, St. Andrews Road, Avonmouth, Bristol, BS11 9YF Tel: 0117-948 4242 Fax: 0117-948 4256 E-mail: mike.inscew@rhodia.uk

Rhodia Pharma Solutions, Three Trees Road, Newbie, Annan, Dumfriesshire, DG12 5QH Tel: (01461) 203661

Rhodia Pharma Solutions, Dudley Lane, Dudley, Cramlington, Northumberland, NE23 7QG Tel: 0191-250 0471 Fax: 0191-250 1514 E-mail: john.lindley@eu.rhodia.com

▶ R-M C Power Recovery Ltd, Unit 6, Stamford Business Park, Ryhall Road, Stamford, Lincolnshire, PE9 1XT Tel: (01780) 762555 Fax: (01780) 762599

▶ Roderick Macaskill Contractor, Ardhasaig, Isle of Harris, HS3 3AJ Tel: (01859) 502066

Rohm & Haas UK Ltd, Tyneside Works, Jarrow, Tyne & Wear, NE32 3DJ Tel: 0191-489 8181 Fax: 0191-489 8520

▶ Rom Ltd, Murraysgate Industrial Estate, Whitburn, Bathgate, West Lothian, EH47 0LE Tel: (01501) 740661 E-mail: sales@rom.co.uk

Romil Ltd, The Source, Convent Drive, Waterbeach, Cambridge, CB5 9QT Tel: (01223) 863873 Fax: (01223) 862700 E-mail: sales@romil.com

Rudolf Chemicals Ltd, Keys Road, Nixs Hill Industrial Estate, Alfreton, Derbyshire, DE55 7FQ Tel: (01773) 832703 Fax: (01773) 520092 E-mail: rudolf@rudolfchemicals.freeserve.co.uk

S I S Chemicals Ltd, 1 The Square, Pennington, Lymington, Hampshire, SO41 8GN Tel: (01590) 674202 Fax: (01590) 679505 E-mail: info@sischem.co.uk

S W C Health & Hygiene Ltd, Ripley Drive, Normanton Industrial Estate, Wakefield, West Yorkshire, WF6 1QT Tel: (01924) 891738 Fax: (01924) 220213 E-mail: mail@swc-online.co.uk

Safeguard Solutions Ltd, 16 Larcombe Avenue, Wirral, Merseyside, CH49 6NB Tel: 0151-606 0457 Fax: 0151-604 0810 E-mail: safeguard-@btclick.com

▶ Sanchem Ltd, Orchard Works, Webber Road, Knowsley Industrial Park, Liverpool, L33 7SW Tel: 0151-546 1555 Fax: 0151-546 1666

Sasol UK Ltd, 1 Hockley Court, 2401 Stratford Road, Hockley Heath, Solihull, West Midlands, B94 6NW Tel: (01564) 783060 Fax: (01564) 784088 E-mail: sales@sasol.com

Scott Bader Co. Ltd, Wollaston Hall, Wollaston, Wellingborough, Northamptonshire, NN29 7RL Tel: (01933) 663100 Fax: (01933) 663028 E-mail: sales@scottbader.com

Seal Sands Chemicals Ltd, Seal Sands Road, Seal Sands, Middlesbrough, Cleveland, TS2 1UB Tel: (01642) 546546 Fax: (01642) 546068 E-mail: george.christopherson@cambrex.com

Seppic UK Ltd, PO Box 338, Hounslow, TW4 6JQ Tel: (020) 8577 8800 Fax: (020) 8570 2106 E-mail: sales@seppic.com

Servo Chem Ltd, PO Box 221, Weston-super-Mare, Avon, BS22 9ZA Tel: (01934) 713999 Fax: (01934) 713990 E-mail: info@servo-chem.co.uk

Shepherd Widnes Ltd, Moss Bank Road, Widnes, Cheshire, WA8 0RU Tel: 0151-424 9156 Fax: 0151-495 1446 E-mail: sales@shepwidnes.co.uk

Sherman Chemicals plc, Brickfields Business Park, Gillingham, Dorset, SP8 4PX Tel: (01747) 823293 Fax: (01747) 825383 E-mail: info@sherchem.co.uk

Sigma-Aldrich Co. Ltd, Fancy Road, Poole, Dorset, BH12 4QH Tel: (01202) 712300 Fax: (01202) 712350 E-mail: ukcustsv@europe.sial.com

Sintec Keramik Ltd, Lake Road, Leeway Industrial Estate, Newport, Gwent, NP19 4SR Tel: (01633) 636500 Fax: (01633) 636501 E-mail: info.uk@sintec-keramik.com

Solvay Interox Ltd, PO Box 7, Warrington, WA4 6HA Tel: (01925) 651277 Fax: (01925) 655856 E-mail: peroxide.warrington@solvay.com

Solvent Resource Management Ltd, Middleton Road, Middleton, Morecambe, Lancashire, LA3 3JW Tel: (01524) 853053 Fax: (01524) 851284 E-mail: sales@srm-ltd.com

Solvent Resource Management Ltd, Rye Harbour Road, Rye, East Sussex, TN31 7TE Tel: (01797) 223936 Fax: (01797) 223017 E-mail: sales@srm-ltd.com

Sparkford Chemicals Ltd, Sparkfrod House, 58 The Avenue, Southampton, SO17 1XS Tel: (023) 8022 8747 Fax: (023) 8021 0240 E-mail: info@sparkford.co.uk

Stag Chem Ltd, 6b Mid Road, Cumbernauld, Glasgow, G67 2TT Tel: (01236) 457900 Fax: (01236) 727955 E-mail: sales@stagchem.co.uk

Stepan UK Ltd, Bridge House, Bridge Street, Stalybridge, Cheshire, SK15 1PH Tel: 0161-338 5511 Fax: 0161-338 4245 E-mail: sales@stepanuk.com

Sud Chemie UK Ltd, 3 Drake Mews, Gadbrook Park, Rudheath, Northwich, Cheshire, CW9 7XF Tel: (01606) 813060 Fax: (01606) 813061 E-mail: info.uk@sud-chemie.com

▶ Syntec Manufacturing Ltd, 6 Mid Road, Blairlinn Industrial Estate, Cumbernauld, Glasgow, G67 2TT Tel: (01236) 739696 Fax: (01236) 727955 E-mail: sales@syntecchemicals.com

Synthite Ltd, Alyn Works, Denbigh Road, Mold, Clwyd, CH7 1BT Tel: (01352) 752521 Fax: (01352) 700182

Tank Storage & Services Ltd, Unit 9 Spring Rise, Falconer Road, Haverhill, Suffolk, CB9 7XU Tel: (01440) 712614 Fax: (01440) 712615 E-mail: admin@tankstorage.co.uk

▶ Tarmac Ltd, Upper Cruiks, Inverkeithing, Fife, KY11 1HH Tel: (01383) 413241 Fax: (01383) 413244

▶ Tarmac Ltd, New Bigging Quarry, Carnwath, Lanark, ML11 8NE Tel: (01555) 840361

▶ Tayside Contracts, Collace Quarry, Collace, Perth, PH2 6JB Tel: (01821) 650222 Fax: (01821) 650440

Tecnon Orbichem Ltd, 12 Calico House, Clove Hitch Quay, London, SW11 3TN Tel: (020) 7924 3955 Fax: (020) 7978 5307 E-mail: sales@orbichem.com

Tennants Consolidated Ltd, 69 Grosvenor Street, London, W1K 3JW Tel: (020) 7493 5451 Fax: (020) 7495 6736

Tennants Distribution, Gelderd Road, Birstall, Batley, West Yorkshire, WF17 9LY Tel: (01924) 474447 Fax: (01924) 477842 E-mail: sales.leeds@tennantsdistribution.com

Tennants Distribution, Ryders Green Road, West Bromwich, West Midlands, B70 0AX Tel: 0121-557 9751 Fax: 0121-557 8144 E-mail: sales.westbromwich@tennantsdistribution.com

Terry Chemicals Ltd, Beckside Road, Dalton-in-Furness, Cumbria, LA15 8DZ Tel: (01229) 466373 Fax: (01229) 466604

Tessenderlo Fine Chemicals Ltd, Macclesfield Road, Leek, Staffordshire, ST13 8LD Tel: (01538) 399100 Fax: (01538) 399025 E-mail: sales@tessenderlofinechemicals.com

Tessenderlow UK Ltd, West Bank Dock Estate, Widnes, Cheshire, WA8 0NY Tel: 0151-424 4281 Fax: 0151-423 6757

Thaumaturgy UK Ltd, PO Box 37, Nelson, Lancashire, BB9 4BE Tel: (01254) 680223 Fax: (01254) 682378 E-mail: thaumaturgy@dial.pipex.com

Thomas Swan & Co., Crookhall, Consett, County Durham, DH8 7ND Tel: (01207) 505131 Fax: (01207) 590467 E-mail: sales@thomas-swan.co.uk

Thor Overseas Ltd, Ramsgate Road, Margate, Kent, CT9 4JY Tel: (01843) 227681 Fax: (01843) 298813 E-mail: mailbox@thor-int.co.uk

Thor Specialities UK Ltd, Wincham Avenue, Wincham, Northwich, Cheshire, CW9 6GB Tel: (01606) 818800 Fax: (01606) 818801 E-mail: info@thor.com

Timstar Laboratory Supplies Ltd, Linea House Marshfield Bank Employment Park, Marshfield Bank, Crewe, CW2 8UY Tel: (01270) 250459 Fax: (01270) 250601 E-mail: sales@timstar.co.uk

Tioxide Europe Ltd, Moortown Road, Nettleton, Market Rasen, Lincolnshire, LN7 6AA Tel: (01472) 852037 Fax: (01472) 852037

Tower Chemicals Ltd, First Avenue, Grangefield Industrial Estate, Pudsey, West Yorkshire, LS28 6QN Tel: 0113-256 8111 Fax: 0113-256 9111 E-mail: sales@towerchemicals.co.uk

▶ William Tracey Ltd, Dunniflats Depot, Lugton, Kilmarnock, Ayrshire, KA3 4EA Tel: (01505) 850343 Fax: (01505) 850102 E-mail: dunniflats@wmtracey.co.uk

Trafalgar Chemicals Ltd, Wylds Road, Bridgewater, Bridgwater, Somerset, TA6 4BH Tel: (01278) 431330 Fax: (01278) 431323 E-mail: trafalgersales@ambersil.co.uk

Travik Chemicals Ltd, Grindon Way, Heighington Lane Business Park, Newton Aycliffe, County Durham, DL5 6SH Tel: (01325) 307000 Fax: (01325) 307070E-mail: info@travik.co.uk

Twinstar Chemicals Ltd, Cunningham House, Westfield Lane, Harrow, Middlesex, HA3 9ED Tel: (020) 8907 2944 Fax: (020) 8927 0683 E-mail:

United Agri Products, 23-24 Ilton Business Park, Ilton, Ilminster, Somerset, TA19 9DU Tel: (01460) 55129 Fax: (01460) 55171

Univar Northern Ireland Ltd, 2 Malone Road, Belfast, BT9 5BN Tel: (028) 9068 1434 Fax: (028) 9038 1880

▶ Universal Chemicals, Yardley Road, Knowsley Industrial Park, Liverpool, L33 7SS Tel: 0151-549 1071 Fax: 0151-546 8803

V W R International Ltd, Hunter Boulevard, Magna Park, Lutterworth, Leicestershire, LE17 4XN Tel: (01455) 558600 Fax: (01455) 558586 E-mail: uk.sales@uk.vwr.com

Varichem Co. Ltd, Blaenant Industrial Estate, Blaenavon Road, Brynmawr, Ebbw Vale, Gwent, NP23 4BX Tel: (01495) 312388 Fax: (01495) 312167 E-mail: info@varichem.co.uk

Venchem Ltd, Knotts Lane, Colne, Lancashire, BB8 8AA Tel: (01282) 861198 Fax: (01282) 860020 E-mail: sales@venchem.co.uk

Vickers Laboratories Ltd, Grangefield Industrial Estate, Richardshaw Road, Pudsey, West Yorkshire, LS28 6QW Tel: 0113-236 2811 Fax: 0113-236 2703 E-mail: info@vicklabs.co.uk

Wallace Of Kelso Ltd, Bowmont Street, Kelso, Roxburghshire, TD5 7EA Tel: (01573) 224131 Fax: (01573) 226145 E-mail: info@wallaceofkelso.co.uk

Wedge Chemicals Ltd, 34 Selsdon Road, South Croydon, Surrey, CR2 6PB Tel: (020) 8680 6960 Fax: (020) 8688 4053 E-mail: sales@wedgechemicals.co.uk

Wengain, Lisle Lane, Ely, Cambridgeshire, CB7 4AS Tel: (01353) 668181 Fax: (01353) 668102 E-mail: sales.enquiries@wengain.co.uk

The White Sea & Baltic Company Ltd, Arndale House, Otley Road, Leeds, LS6 2UU Tel: 0113-230 4774 Fax: 0113-230 4770 E-mail: sales@whitesea.co.uk

Whyte Group Ltd, Marlborough House, 298 Regents Park Road, London, N3 2UA Tel: (020) 8346 5946 Fax: (020) 8349 4589 E-mail: sales@whytechem.co.uk

Wickham Industries Ltd, Ledston Luck Enterprise Park, Leeds, LS25 7BF Tel: 0113-287 2002 Fax: 0113-287 3020 E-mail: info@wickhamindustries.co.uk

Ian Wilson, 11 East Main Street, Harthill, Shotts, Lanarkshire, ML7 5QW Tel: (01501) 753206 Fax: (01501) 752580 E-mail: nielsenscotland@compuserve.com

▶ Wirral Fospray Ltd, Hawarden Business Park, Clwyd Close Manor Lane, Hawarden, Deeside, Clwyd, CH5 3NS Tel: (01244) 520202 Fax: (01244) 520363 E-mail: sales@wirralfospray.co.uk

Woburn Chemicals Ltd, Chesney Wold, Bleak Hall, Milton Keynes, MK6 1LQ Tel: (01908) 670081 Fax: (01908) 670084 E-mail: sales@woburnchemicals.co.uk

Wychem Ltd, Bury Road, Stradishall, Newmarket, Suffolk, CB8 8YN Tel: (01440) 820338 Fax: (01440) 820399

▶ Tom Young Ltd, Wishaw Low Road, Cleland, Motherwell, Lanarkshire, ML1 5QU Tel: (01698) 860516 Fax: (01698) 861529

Zok International Group, Airworthy House, Elsted, Midhurst, West Sussex, GU29 0JT Tel: (01730) 811920 Fax: (01730) 811930 E-mail: zok@zok.com

CHEMICAL MIXERS

Advanced Engineering Middleton Ltd, Unit 5D, Transpennine Trading Estate, Gorells way, Rochdale, Lancashire, OL11 2PX Tel: (01706) 759003 Fax: (01706) 759004 E-mail: info@aemixers.com

Chemineer Ltd, 7 Cranmer Road, West Meadows Industrial Estate, Derby, DE21 6XT Tel: (01332) 363175 Fax: (01332) 290323 E-mail: sales@chemineer.com

Fillworth (UK) Ltd, Unit 2, Baltic Road, Felling, Gateshead, Tyne & Wear, NE10 0SB Tel: 0191-500 0230 Fax: 0191-500 0231 E-mail: mail@fillworth.com

John R Boone Ltd, 18 Silk Street, Congleton, Cheshire, CW12 4DH Tel: (01260) 272894 Fax: (01260) 281128 E-mail: sales@jrboone.com

Mixing Solutions Ltd, Unit G Venture House, Bone Lane, Newbury, Berkshire, RG14 5SH Tel: (01635) 275300 Fax: (01635) 275375 E-mail: sales@mixingsolutions.com

Statiflo International Ltd, Crown Centre, Bond Street, Macclesfield, Cheshire, SK11 6QS Tel: (01625) 433100 Fax: (01625) 511376 E-mail: sales@statiflo.co.uk

Warbrick International, Cranford Court, King Street, Knutsford, Cheshire, WA16 8BW Tel: (01565) 652616 Fax: (01565) 633159 E-mail: sales@warbrick.co.uk

Ytron Quadro (UK) Ltd, Unit D Chiltern Commerce Centre, 43 Asheridge Road, Chesham, Buckinghamshire, HP5 2PY Tel: (01494) 792898 Fax: (01494) 792699 E-mail: sales@ytron-quadro.co.uk

CHEMICAL MIXING/DILUTION EQUIPMENT

Champion Photochemistry S.L., 23 Robjohns Road, Chelmsford, CM1 3AG Tel: (01245) 214940 Fax: (01245) 214957 E-mail: sales@championphotochemistry.co.uk

CHEMICAL OR HAZARDOUS SUBSTANCE WARNING LABELS

Eurosoft (Leeds) Ltd, Howcroft House, 919 Bradford Road, Birstall, Batley, West Yorkshire, WF17 9JX Tel: (01924) 474732 Fax: (01924) 475729 E-mail: sales@eurosoft-leeds.co.uk

Hibiscus plc, Hudswell Road, Leeds, LS10 1AG Tel: 0113-242 4272 Fax: 0113-242 4230 E-mail: info@hibiscus-plc.com

Sherwood Transfer Co., 28 Victoria Road, Nottingham, NG5 2NB Tel: 0115-960 3995 Fax: 0115-969 1948

CHEMICAL PLANT AND EQUIPMENT, *See also other nearby headings for particular types*

Aqua Marine Chemicals Ltd, Unit 6 Strensham Business Park, Strensham, Worcester, WR8 9JZ Tel: (01684) 290077 Fax: (01684) 290608 E-mail: laura@bayer-wood.co.uk

Ayton Equipment Ltd, Station Yard, Station Road, Stokesley, Middlesbrough, Cleveland, TS9 7AB Tel: (01642) 711455 Fax: (01642) 710100 E-mail: marketing@ayton.com

C D R Pumps UK Ltd, 28 Trojan Centre, Finedon Road Industrial Estate, Wellingborough, Northamptonshire, NN8 4ST Tel: (0870) 7561428 Fax: (01933) 226225 E-mail: sales@cdrpumps.com

Delkor Ltd, Unit C, First Avenue, Midsomer Norton, Radstock, BA3 4BS Tel: (01761) 417079 Fax: (01761) 414435

Hiley Engineering (Halifax) Co. Ltd, Station Road, Shay Lane, Holmfield, Halifax, West Yorkshire, HX2 9AY Tel: (01422) 248327 Fax: (01422) 240610 E-mail: hileyeng@hileyeng.co.uk

Hyundai Heavy Industries Co. Ltd, Second Floor The Triangle, 5-17 Hammersmith Grove, London, W6 9LT Tel: (020) 8741 0501 Fax: (020) 8741 5620

▶ Icam Engineering Ltd, Dock Road Industrial Estate, Connah's Quay, Deeside, Clwyd, CH5 4DS Tel: (01244) 831143 Fax: (01244) 831338 E-mail: icam@daisyconnect.com

Melbray Chemicals Ltd, Chemical House, Durham Lane Industrial Park, Stockton-on-Tees, Cleveland, TS16 0RG Tel: (01642) 790483 Fax: (01642) 790486 E-mail: melbraychemicals@btconnect.com

Netzsch-Mastermix, 23 Lombard Street, Lichfield, Staffordshire, WS13 6DP Tel: (01543) 418938 Fax: (01543) 418926 E-mail: info@nmx.netzsch.com

Perry Process Equipment Ltd, Station Road, Aycliffe Industrial Park, Newton Aycliffe, County Durham, DL5 6EQ Tel: (01325) 315111 Fax: (01325) 301496 E-mail: info@perryprocess.co.uk

Pfaudler Balfour, Riverside Road, Leven, Fife, KY8 4RW Tel: (01333) 423020 Fax: (01333) 427432 E-mail: sales@pfaudlerbalfour.co.uk

R E D S Services, 5 Spires Business Units, Mugiemoss Road, Bucksburn, Aberdeen, AB21 9NY Tel: (01224) 693284 Fax: (01224) 699687

Rigal Chemical & Process Plant Ltd, Gravelhill Lane, Whitley, Goole, North Humberside, DN14 0JJ Tel: (01977) 661095 Fax: (01977) 662165 E-mail: sales@rigal-luton.co.uk

Tomlander Ltd, Paston Road, Sharston, Manchester, M22 4TF Tel: 0161-902 0226 Fax: 0161-945 5203 E-mail: tomlander@msn.com

CHEMICAL PLANT CONTRACTORS OR DESIGNERS

K Home International Ltd, Ingram House, Allensway, Stockton-on-Tees, Cleveland, TS17 9HA Tel: (01642) 765421 Fax: (01642) 760721 E-mail: enquiry@khomeint.co.uk

▶ Manrochem Ltd, 18 New North Parade, Huddersfield, HD1 5JP Tel: (01484) 453868 Fax: (01484) 453884 E-mail: rih@manrochem.co.uk

Projen plc, Winnington Avenue, Northwich, Cheshire, CW8 4EE Tel: (01606) 871111 Fax: (01606) 871133 E-mail: mailbox@projen.co.uk

Simon-Carves Ltd, PO Box 17, Cheadle, Cheshire, SK8 5BR Tel: 0161-486 4000 Fax: 0161-486 1302 E-mail: simon.carves@simoncarves.com

Worleyparsons Europe Ltd, Parkview, Great West Road, Brentford, Middlesex, TW8 9AZ Tel: (020) 8758 9477 Fax: (020) 8710 0220 E-mail: info@worleyparsons.com

CHEMICAL PLANT GLASSWARE SUPPLIES OR ERECTION OR INSTALLATION CONTRACTORS

D M K Chemical Process Plant Ltd, Unit 7B, Riverside Industrial Estate, Fiddlers Ferry, Warrington, WA5 2UL Tel: (01925) 727227 Fax: (01925) 652075 E-mail: dmk@netcentral.co.uk

CHEMICAL PLANT LINING SERVICES OR CONTRACTORS

Edlon, Riverside, Leven, Fife, KY8 4RT Tel: (01333) 426222 Fax: (01333) 426314 E-mail: sales@edlon.co.uk

CHEMICAL PRESERVATIVES

Stonham Hedgerow Ltd, Hemingstone Fruit Farm, Main Road, Hemingstone, Ipswich, IP6 9RJ Tel: (01449) 760330 Fax: (01449) 760330 E-mail: enquiries@stonhamhedgerow.co.uk

CHEMICAL PROCESS INVESTIGATION SERVICES

Chemical Solutions, 474 Reigate Road, Epsom, Surrey, KT18 5XA Tel: (01737) 351777 Fax: (01737) 371606

CHEMICAL PROCESS PLANT, *See Process Plant etc*

CHEMICAL PROCESSING SERVICES

Industrial Chemicals Ltd, Titan Works, Hogg Lane, Grays, Essex, RM17 5DU Tel: (01375) 389000 Fax: (01375) 389110

Stephenson Group Ltd, PO Box 305, Bradford, West Yorkshire, BD7 1HY Tel: (01274) 723811 Fax: (01274) 370108 E-mail: src@stephensongroup.co.uk

CHEMICAL PUMPS

Anglo Pumps Ltd, 4a-B Aston Road, Cambridge Road Industrial Estate, Bedford, MK42 0LJ Tel: (01234) 353525 Fax: (01234) 211655 E-mail: sales@anglo-pumps.co.uk

Beresford Pumps Ltd, Unit 7, Network Park, Duddeston Mill Road, Saltley, Birmingham, B8 1AU Tel: 0121-503 3001 Fax: 0121-503 3002 E-mail: info@beresfordpumps.co.uk

Centrifugal Pump Services Ltd, Pump House, Bird Hall Lane, Cheadle Heath, Stockport, Cheshire, SK3 0XX Tel: 0161 4280133 Fax: 0161 4280188 E-mail: sales@centrifugalpumps.co.uk

David Bedlington Ltd, Flemingate Works, Flemingate, Beverley, North Humberside, HU17 0NZ Tel: (01482) 867590 Fax: (01482) 866472

I T T Water & Waste Water, Colwick Indust Estate, Colwick Industrial Estate, Nottingham, NG4 2AN Tel: 0115-940 0111 Fax: (01202) 631008 E-mail: admin@allweiler-pumps.demon.co.uk

Knight UK Ltd, Unit 15 The Brunel Centre, Newton Road, Crawley, West Sussex, RH10 9TU Tel: (01293) 615570 Fax: (01293) 615585

Lutz (UK) Ltd, Gateway Estate, West Midlands Freeport, Birmingham, B26 3QD Tel: 0121-782 2662 Fax: 0121-782 2680 E-mail: lutzpump@aol.com

▶ Pump Supply & Repair Group, Armstrong Hall, Wharton Rd, Winsford, Cheshire, CW7 3AD Tel: 0161-794 8038 Fax: 0161-794 8052 E-mail: salesc@pumpgroup.co.uk

▶ Sel Tek, 31 Dellburn Street, Motherwell, Lanarkshire, ML1 1SE Tel: (01698) 262569 Fax: (01698) 259799 E-mail: enquiry@sel-tek.co.uk

Serfilco Europe Ltd, Broadoak Business Park, Ashburton Road West, Trafford Park, Manchester, M17 1RW Tel: 0161-872 1317 Fax: 0161-873 8027 E-mail: sales@serfilco-europe.com

Sterling Fluid Systems UK Ltd, Atlantic Street, Broadheath, Altrincham, Cheshire, WA14 5DH Tel: 0161-928 6371 Fax: 0161-925 2129 E-mail: sales@sterlingfluid.com

Totton Pumps, Rushington Business Park, Chaple Lane, Totton, Southampton, SO40 9AH Tel: (023) 8066 6685 Fax: (023) 8066 6880 E-mail: info@totton-pumps.com

Williamson Pumps, Aviation House, The Street, Poynings, Brighton, BN45 7AQ Tel: (01273) 857752 Fax: (0845) 2263639 E-mail: info@williamsonpumps.co.uk

CHEMICAL REAGENTS

▶ Aquakem Technology Ltd, 6 The Elms, Tallarn Green, Malpas, Cheshire, SY14 7HY Tel: (0870) 0887051 Fax: (0870) 0887052 E-mail: aquakem@btinternet.com

Echem Ltd, 147 Kirkstall Road, Leeds, LS3 1JN Tel: 0113-245 7471 Fax: 0113-244 5082 E-mail: info@echem.co.uk

Elemental Microanalysis Ltd, Okehampton Business Park, Okehampton, Devon, EX20 1UB Tel: (01837) 54446 Fax: (01837) 54544 E-mail: info@microanalysis.co.uk

CHEMICAL REPACKING

Sherman Chemicals plc, Brickfields Business Park, Gillingham, Dorset, SP8 4PX Tel: (01747) 823293 Fax: (01747) 825383 E-mail: info@sherchem.co.uk

Trafford Rubber Additives Ltd, Alma Works, Station Street, Dukinfield, Cheshire, SK16 4SE Tel: 0161-339 8693 Fax: 0161-343 2965 E-mail: info@trafford-rubber-additives.co.uk

CHEMICAL RESEARCH

Centec, Brooks Lane, Middlewich, Cheshire, CW10 0JG Tel: (01606) 737720 Fax: (01606) 737511 E-mail: enquiry@centec.uk.com

Elixair International Ltd, Unit F2, Roman Hill Trading Estate, Broadmayne, Dorchester, Dorset, DT2 8LY Tel: (01305) 854735 Fax: (01305) 852060 E-mail: elixair.int@virgin.net

Huntingdon Life Sciences, Occold, Eye, Suffolk, IP23 7PX Tel: (01480) 892000 Fax: (01379) 651165 E-mail: sales@ukorg.huntingdon.com

Synprotec Ltd, 303 Clayton Lane, Clayton, Manchester, M11 4SX Tel: 0161-223 3344 Fax: 0161-220 8778 E-mail: sales@synprotec.com

U F C Ltd, Synergy House, Guildhall Close, Manchester Science Park, Manchester, M15 6SY Tel: 0161-232 5500 Fax: 0161-232 5501 E-mail: info@ultrafine.co.uk

CHEMICAL STORAGE CONTRACTORS

Oikos Storage Ltd, Hole Haven Wharf, Canvey Island, Essex, SS8 0NR Tel: (01268) 682206 Fax: (01268) 510095E-mail: info@oikos.co.uk

Simon Storage Immingham West Ltd, West Riverside, Immingham Dock, Immingham, North East Lincolnshire, DN40 2QU Tel: (01469) 572615 Fax: (01469) 577019

T D G European Chemicals, Euro Terminal, Westinghouse Road, Trafford Park, Manchester, M17 1PY Tel: 0161-932 6900 Fax: 0161-932 6990 E-mail: businessenquiries@tdg.co.uk

Vopak Terminal Teeside Ltd, Seal Sands, Middlesbrough, Cleveland, TS2 1UA Tel: (01642) 546767 Fax: (01642) 543600

CHEMICAL STORAGE CYLINDERS

▶ Icam Engineering Ltd, Dock Road Industrial Estate, Connah's Quay, Deeside, Clwyd, CH5 4DS Tel: (01244) 831143 Fax: (01244) 831338 E-mail: icam@daisyconnect.com

CHEMICAL TANKS

Brooks Composites Ltd, Percival Lane, Runcorn, Cheshire, WA7 4DS Tel: (01928) 574776 Fax: (01928) 577067 E-mail: sales@brooks-composites.co.uk

Cookson & Zinn PTL Ltd, Station Road Works, Station Road, Hadleigh, Ipswich, IP7 5PN Tel: (01473) 825200 Fax: (01473) 828446 E-mail: info@czltd.com

Hes Engineering Services Ltd, Bingswood Trading Estate, Whaley Bridge, High Peak, Derbyshire, SK23 7LY Tel: (01663) 735333 Fax: (01663) 735377

Jay Rubber Linings Ltd, 132 Queen Street, Crewe, CW1 4AU Tel: (01270) 254655 Fax: (01270) 254526 E-mail: sales@jayrubberlinings.co.uk

Liquid Metering Instruments Ltd, L M I House, West Dudley Street, Winsford, Cheshire, CW7 3AG Tel: (01606) 550583 Fax: (01606) 550485 E-mail: sales@llmipumps.co.uk

Mottram Industrial Plastics, 99a North Street, Cannock, Staffordshire, WS11 0AZ Tel: (01543) 573735 Fax: (01543) 574925 E-mail: andy@mottramindustrialplastics.co.uk

Premier Plastics Ltd, Unit 43 St. Helens Court, St. Helens Way, Thetford, Norfolk, IP24 1HG Tel: (01842) 750461 Fax: (01842) 754743 E-mail: enquiries@premierplastics.org.uk

Thornton International, Unit 1-3 Denver Industrial Estate, 44 Ferry Lane, Rainham, Essex, RM13 9YH Tel: (01233) 740009 Fax: (01708) 557353 E-mail: thornton.international@btinternet.com

CHEMICAL TEST KITS

▶ Aquakem Technology Ltd, 6 The Elms, Tallarn Green, Malpas, Cheshire, SY14 7HY Tel: (0870) 0887051 Fax: (0870) 0887052 E-mail: aquakem@btinternet.com

CHEMICAL TOILETS

Jobec UK Ltd, Stonnall House Farm, Mill Lane Lower Stonnall, Stonnall, Walsall, WS9 9HN Tel: (01543) 483172 Fax: (01543) 483173 E-mail: jobec@tinyworld.co.uk

CHEMICAL TREATMENT OF METAL, *See Metal Pretreatment etc*

CHEMICAL VALVES

Progressive Engineers Ltd, Groby Road, Audenshaw, Manchester, M34 5HT Tel: 0161-371 0440 Fax: 0161-371 0444 E-mail: info@progressive-eng.com

Western Automation Ivac, 5 Colemans Bridge, Witham, Essex, CM8 3HP Tel: (01376) 511808 Fax: (01376) 500862 E-mail: sales@waivac.co.uk

Whittle Valve Repairs Ltd, Unit 3 Tower Enterprise Park, Great George Street, Wigan, Lancashire, WN3 4DP Tel: (01942) 493495 E-mail: sales@whittle-valves.co.uk

CHEMICAL VAPOUR DEPOSITION SERVICES

Ionbond Ltd, Factory 36 Number One Industrial Estate, Medomsley Road, Consett, County Durham, DH8 6TS Tel: (01207) 500823 Fax: (01207) 590254 E-mail: info@ionbond.com

CHEMICAL WASTE RECYCLING OR DISPOSAL OR RECOVERY OR MERCHANTS OR PROCESSORS

Beolia Enviromental Services plc, 154a Pentonville Road, London, N1 9PE Tel: (020) 7812 5000 Fax: (020) 7812 5026 E-mail: edward.demaslatrie@veolia.co.uk

Cleaning Supplies UK, Lovet House, Lovet Road, The Pinnacles, Harlow, Essex, CM19 5TB Tel: (01279) 459345 Fax: (01279) 772376 E-mail: websupport@cleaningsuppliesuk.com

Cleansing Service Group Ltd, Botley Road, Hedge End, Southampton, SO30 2HE Tel: (01489) 785856 Fax: (01489) 789821 E-mail: enquiries@csgwasteman.co.uk

Collier Industrial Waste Ltd, Nash Road, Trafford Park, Manchester, M17 1SX Tel: 0161-848 7722 Fax: 0161-872 9906

▶ Envirogreen Special Waste Services, 765 Henley Road, Slough, SL1 4JW Tel: (0845) 7125398 Fax: (01753) 537314 E-mail: info@envirogreen.co.uk

Eurotech Environmental Ltd, Northern Road, Newark, Nottinghamshire, NG24 2EU Tel: (0800) 0281786 Fax: (01636) 611727 E-mail: sales@eurotechenvironmental.com

Gordons Environmental Ltd, 66-68 Back Sneddon Street, Paisley, Renfrewshire, PA3 2BY Tel: 0141-842 1189 Fax: 0141-842 1139 E-mail: gordonsltd@aol.com

Industrial Suppliers (Wimborne) Ltd, Higher Merley Lane, Corfe Mullen, Wimborne, Dorset, BH21 3EG Tel: (01202) 882331 Fax: (01202) 841282 E-mail: enquiries@iswgroup.co.uk

▶ Konrad Chemicals, Manchester Road, Wilmslow, Cheshire, SK9 2JW Tel: (01625) 531581 Fax: (01625) 529906 E-mail: konradchemicals@ntlworld.com

Kurion Technologies Ltd, 43 Brunel Close, Drayton Fields Industrial Estate, Daventry, Northamptonshire, NN11 8RB Tel: (01327) 876600 Fax: (01327) 705131 E-mail: sales@kurion.co.uk

Lab 3 Ltd, 1 The Business Centre, Ross Road, Weedon Road Industrial Estate, Northampton, NN5 5AX Tel: (0870) 4445553 Fax: (0870) 1260350 E-mail: sales@lab3.co.uk

P & R Disposal Services, 117 Clydesdale Place, Leyland, PR26 7QS Tel: (01772) 454129 Fax: (01772) 622258 E-mail: sales@distillex.xo.uk

P & R Labpak Ltd, 6 Ketterer Court, St. Helens, Merseyside, WA9 3AH Tel: 0870 0342055 Fax: 0870 0342056 E-mail: sales@prlabs.co.uk

Remondis UK Ltd, A Scot La Industrial Estate, Scot Lane, Blackrod, Bolton, BL6 5SL Tel: (01942) 831362 Fax: (01942) 833051 E-mail: sales@remondisuk.co.uk

Solvent Resource Management Ltd, Rye Harbour Road, Rye, East Sussex, TN31 7TE Tel: (01797) 223936 Fax: (01797) 223017 E-mail: sales@srm-ltd.com

Southern Refining Services Ltd, Membury Airfield, Lambourn Woodlands, Hungerford, Berkshire, RG17 7TJ Tel: (01488) 72898 Fax: (01488) 72762 E-mail: richard.srs@btconnect.com

CHEMICALS, CUSTOM SYNTHESIS

Fluorochem Ltd, Wesley Street, Glossop, Derbyshire, SK13 7RY Tel: (01457) 865698 Fax: (01457) 869360 E-mail: enquiries@fluorochem.co.uk

CHEMICALS, HAIR DYE

▶ Academy Hair & Beauty UK Ltd, 4 Kent Street Industrial Estate, 26 Kent Street, Leicester, LE5 3BD Tel: 0116-262 4946 Fax: 0116-251 6489 E-mail: mail@academy-beauty.com

CHEMICALS, METALLURGICAL/ METAL TREATMENT

Ashland Foundry Products, Vale Industrial Estate, Kidderminster, Worcestershire, DY11 7QU Tel: (01562) 821300 Fax: (01562) 740785

Foseco FS Ltd, Coleshill Road, Tamworth, Staffordshire, B78 3TL Tel: (01827) 289999 Fax: (01827) 250806 E-mail: enquiries@foseco.com

CHEMICALS, PHARMACEUTICAL INDUSTRY

Albemarle UK Ltd, Teesport, Middlesbrough, Cleveland, TS6 7SA Tel: (01642) 463314 Fax: (01642) 463315

Allchem (International) Ltd, Broadway House, 21 Broadway, Maidenhead, Berkshire, SL6 1NJ Tel: (01753) 443331 Fax: (01753) 443323 E-mail: info@allchem.co.uk

Bayer UK plc, Bayer House, Strawberry Hill, Newbury, Berkshire, RG14 1JA Tel: (01635) 563000 E-mail: corporate.communications@bayer.co.uk

Chemquest Ltd, Springfield House, Water Lane, Wilmslow, Cheshire, SK9 5BG Tel: (01625) 528808 Fax: (01625) 527557 E-mail: enquiries@chemquest.co.uk

Contract Chemicals Properties Ltd, Penrhyn Road, Knowsley Business Park, Prescot, Merseyside, L34 9HY Tel: 0151-548 8840 Fax: 0151-548 6548 E-mail: info@contract-chemicals.com

Dow Mirfield, Steanard Lane, Mirfield, West Yorkshire, WF14 8HZ Tel: (01924) 493861 Fax: (01924) 490972 E-mail: enquiries@dow.com

Genzyme Vehicle Leasing Ltd, Hollands Road, Haverhill, Suffolk, CB9 8PU Tel: (01440) 703522 Fax: (01440) 716269

Glaxosmithkline, Harmire Road, Barnard Castle, County Durham, DL12 8DT Tel: (01833) 690600 Fax: (01833) 692300

Macfarlan Smith Ltd, Wheatfield Road, Edinburgh, EH11 2QA Tel: 0131-337 2434 Fax: 0131-337 9813 E-mail: msl@macsmith.com

Phoenix (Wirral) Ltd, Unit 28-34, Thursby Road, Bromborough, Wirral, Merseyside, CH62 3PW Tel: 0151-334 9044 Fax: 0151-334 9045 E-mail: chris@phoenixchem.com

Prom Chem Ltd, 89 High Street, Caterham, Surrey, CR3 5UH Tel: (01883) 341444 Fax: (01883) 341666 E-mail: promchem@prom.co.uk

Purac Biochem UK Ltd, 50-54 St. Pauls Square, Birmingham, B3 1QS Tel: 0121-236 1828 Fax: 0121-236 1401 E-mail: puk@purac.com

CHEMICALS, RUBBER PRODUCTION INDUSTRY

Aquaspersions Ltd, Beacon Hill Road, Halifax, West Yorkshire, HX3 6AQ Tel: (01422) 386200 Fax: (01422) 386239 E-mail: info@aquaspersions.co.uk

Chemical Release Co. Ltd, 5 Cheltenham Mount, Harrogate, North Yorkshire, HG1 1DW Tel: (01423) 569715 Fax: (01423) 563384 E-mail: crc@releaseagents.co.uk

Elastomerics Ltd, Summit House, 48a Bramhall Lane South, Bramhall, Stockport, Cheshire, SK7 1AH Tel: 0161-439 9119 Fax: 0161-440 8035 E-mail: info@elastomerics.com

Rhodia UK Ltd, Oak House, Reeds Crescent, Watford, WD24 4QP Tel: (01923) 485868 Fax: (01923) 211580 E-mail: info@rhodia.com

Robinson Brothers Ltd, Phoenix Street, West Bromwich, West Midlands, B70 0AH Tel: 0121-553 2451 Fax: 0121-500 5183 E-mail: sales@robinsonbrothers.ltd.uk

Stephenson Group Ltd, PO Box 305, Bradford, West Yorkshire, BD7 1HY Tel: (01274) 723811 Fax: (01274) 370108 E-mail: group@stephensongroup.co.uk

Trafford Rubber Additives Ltd, Alma Works, Station Street, Dukinfield, Cheshire, SK16 4SE Tel: 0161-339 8693 Fax: 0161-343 2965 E-mail: info@trafford-rubber-additives.co.uk

CHEMICALS, TEXTILE PRODUCTION INDUSTRY

Aquaspersions Ltd, Beacon Hill Road, Halifax, West Yorkshire, HX3 6AQ Tel: (01422) 386200 Fax: (01422) 386239 E-mail: info@aquaspersions.co.uk

CHEMISTS' SUNDRIES, *See also headings for particular types*

Boots, 32 The Broadway, Joel Street, Northwood, Middlesex, HA6 1PF Tel: (01923) 820841 Fax: (01923) 825555

Bray Group Ltd, Olive House, Regal Way, Faringdon, Oxfordshire, SN7 7BX Tel: (01367) 240736 Fax: (01367) 242625 E-mail: info@bray.co.uk

▶ Smartways Pharmaceuticals Pharmaceutical Suppliers, 130 Northcote Road, London, SW11 6QZ Tel: (020) 7924 7475 Fax: (020) 7564 8890 E-mail: Info@Smartway-pw.co.uk

CHEMISTS, WHOLESALE

Albert Harrison Company Ltd, Queens Road, Accrington, Lancashire, BB5 6DS Tel: (01254) 306840 Fax: (01254) 872174 E-mail: sales@albert-harrison.co.uk

Bayer P.L.C., 47 Deerdykes View, Westfield, Glasgow, G68 9HN Tel: (01236) 458909 Fax: (01236) 458828

Booth & Openshaw Blackburn Ltd, 17-19 St. Peter Street, Blackburn, BB2 2HH Tel: (01254) 52828

Boots Chemists P.L.C., Unit 23-24, Buttercrane Shopping Centre, Buttercrane Quay, Newry, County Down, BT35 8HJ Tel: (028) 3026 8234 Fax: (028) 3026 7902

Chandis Ltd, 5 Great Union Road, St. Helier, Jersey, JE2 3YA Tel: (01534) 736401 Fax: (01534) 768442 E-mail: admin@chandis.com

Durbin (U.K.) Ltd, 180 Northolt Road, South Harrow, Harrow, Middlesex, HA2 0LT Tel: (020) 8869 6500 Fax: (020) 8869 6565 E-mail: durbin@durbin.co.uk

E M T Healhcare Ltd, 4 Padge Road, Boulevard Industrial Park, Beeston, Nottingham, NG9 2JR Tel: 0115-849 7700 Fax: 0115-849 7701 E-mail: info@emthealthcare.com

East Anglian Pharmaceuticals Ltd, Pinetrees Business Park, Pinetrees Road, Norwich, NR7 9BB Tel: (01603) 300336 Fax: (01603) 433274

Interchem (Chemist Wholesale) Ltd, 2-26 Anthony Road, Saltley, Birmingham, B8 3AA Tel: 0121-328 3479 Fax: 0121-328 3479 E-mail: dispharma@aol.com

▶ Makeupworld, 5 Maes Street, St. Thomas, Swansea, SA1 8ES Tel: (07851) 734820 E-mail: customerservice@makeupworld.co.uk

Mawdsley Yorkshire Ltd, 7 Parkway One, Parkway Drive, Sheffield, S9 4WU Tel: 0114-244 0321 Fax: 0114-243 6054

P I F Medical Supplies Ltd, Standard House, Prospect Place, Nottingham, NG7 1RX Tel: 0115-947 4531 Fax: 0115-941 7097 E-mail: sales@pif-medical.co.uk

Phoenix Healthcare Distribution Ltd, South Elgin Street, Clydebank, Dunbartonshire, G81 1PL Tel: 0141-952 3261 Fax: 0141-951 1708

Phoenix Healthcare Distrubtions Ltd, Farrington Place, Rossendale Road, Burnley, Lancashire, BB11 5TZ Tel: (01282) 426363 Fax: (01282) 477630E-mail: burnley@pheonixmedical.co.uk

Skot Chemist, 139 Victoria Road, London, N9 9BA Tel: (020) 8803 3221 Fax: (020) 8807 2946

▶ Smartways Pharmaceuticals Pharmaceutical Suppliers, 130 Northcote Road, London, SW11 6QZ Tel: (020) 7924 7475 Fax: (020) 7564 8890 E-mail: Info@Smartway-pw.co.uk

CHENILLE/BUMP CHENILLE

Hewitt & Booth Ltd, St Andrews Road, Huddersfield, HD1 6RZ Tel: (01484) 546621 Fax: (01484) 450580 E-mail: sales@hewittandbooth.com

▶ Paint Box Textiles, 16 Valley Road, Liversedge, West Yorkshire, WF15 6JY Tel: (01924) 235123 Fax: (01924) 235223 E-mail: sales@paintboxtextiles.co.uk

CHESTNUT FENCING

J E Homewood & Son, 20 Weyhill, Haslemere, Surrey, GU27 1BX Tel: (01428) 643819 Fax: (01428) 645419 E-mail: steve@homewoodfencing.co.uk

The Scotia Fencing Company Ltd, Howe Road, Kilsyth, Glasgow, G65 0TA Tel: (01236) 823339 Fax: (01236) 826434

CHICKEN

▶ Southmead Poultry, Southmead, Leatherhead, Surrey, KT22 Tel: 01372 458320 E-mail: southmead@dsl.pipex.com

▶ Verseveld P.L.C., Coningsby House, 24 St. Andrews Street, Droitwich, Worcestershire, WR9 8DY Tel: (01905) 797999 Fax: (01905) 798958 E-mail: marc@verseveldplc.com

CHICKEN BURGERS

R A Robinson & Son, Unit 7 Turnpike Industrial Estate, Newbury, Berkshire, RG14 2LR Tel: (01635) 41045 Fax: (01635) 41045

▶ Verseveld P.L.C., Coningsby House, 24 St. Andrews Street, Droitwich, Worcestershire, WR9 8DY Tel: (01905) 797999 Fax: (01905) 798958 E-mail: marc@verseveldplc.com

CHICKENS

▶ Southmead Poultry, Southmead, Leatherhead, Surrey, KT22 Tel: 01372 458320 E-mail: southmead@dsl.pipex.com

▶ Verseveld P.L.C., Coningsby House, 24 St. Andrews Street, Droitwich, Worcestershire, WR9 8DY Tel: (01905) 797999 Fax: (01905) 798958 E-mail: marc@verseveldplc.com

CHILDREN PHOTOGRAPHERS

▶ ALPS Mobile & Studio photography, Lee Lane, Pinkneys Green, Maidenhead, Berkshire, SL6 Tel: 07779 572360 E-mail: apage@e-work.co.uk

▶ Chris Hanley, 2 Wellfield Road, Stockport, Cheshire, SK2 6AS Tel: 0161-487 1217 E-mail: info@chrishanleyphotography.co.uk

▶ Colorfoto Lifestyle Portrait Studio, Image House, East Tyndall St, Cardiff Bay, Cardiff, CF24 5EF Tel: 029 20448222 E-mail: info@colorfotolifestyle.co.uk

▶ GMB Photography, 127a High Street, Barkingside, Ilford, Essex, IG6 2AR Tel: 020 8551 6885 E-mail: info@gmbphotography.co.uk

▶ Inspired Photography Ltd, 27 Kirkdale Mount, Leeds, LS12 6AZ Tel: 0113 2109653 E-mail: timlawton1981@yahoo.co.uk

▶ Russell-Stoneham Photography, Suite 35, 2 Old Brompton Road, London, SW7 3DQ Tel: (020) 7413 9988 Fax: (020) 7581 4445 E-mail: puz.rs@btinternet.com

▶ S D M Images, 16 Blenheim Close, Chandler's Ford, Eastleigh, Hampshire, SO53 4LD Tel: (023) 8027 6828 E-mail: info@sdmimages.co.uk

▶ Shaun Edwards, Unit 9 171 Evendons Lane, Wokingham, Berkshire, RG41 4EH Tel: 0118-979 2226 E-mail: info@shaunedwards.com

▶ Stone Studio, 45 High Street, Petersfield, Hampshire, GU32 3JR Tel: (01730) 269966 Fax: (01730) 269966 E-mail: mail@thestonestudio.co.uk

▶ Suzanne Grala Photography, PO Box 458, Epsom, Surrey, KT17 4WY E-mail: suzi@suzanne.grala.co.uk

CHILDREN'S NURSERY EQUIPMENT

▶ Active Learning Ltd, Hartley Business Centre, 28 Hucknall Road, Nottingham, NG5 1FD Tel: 0115-960 6111 Fax: 0115-960 6111 E-mail: sales@activelearning-uk.com

▶ Au Pair Professional, Lacewing Close, Plaistow, London, E13 8AD Tel: 079 30540127 E-mail: info@aupairprofessional.com

▶ Beeswitched, PO Box 413, Horsham, West Sussex, RH12 2YD Tel: (01403) 242003 E-mail: info@beeswitched.com

▶ Bumps Maternity Wear, 19 Frederick Street, Sunderland, SR1 1LT Tel: 0191-565 3232 Fax: 0191 5520988 E-mail: info@bumpsmaternity.com

▶ Camelot Kids, 117 Aysgarth, Bracknell, Berkshire, RG12 8SF Tel: (01344) 301726

Eibe Play Ltd, Eibe House, Home Farm, A3 By-Pass Road, Hurtmore, Godalming, Surrey, GU8 6AD Tel: (01483) 813834 Fax: (01483) 813851 E-mail: eibe@eibe.co.uk

▶ First Class Leisure, 1e Darlaston Lane, Bilston, West Midlands, WV14 7BW Tel: (01902) 635003 Fax: (01902) 609783 E-mail: info@1stclassleisure.co.uk

Kiddies World, Roseville House, Grant Avenue, Leeds, LS7 1QB Tel: 0113-243 5003 Fax: 0113-243 5004

▶ Kidz Bedroom Depot Ltd, Apt 6 Littlemere Court, 42 Ashley Road, Altrincham, Cheshire, WA14 2LZ Tel: 0161-929 1103 Fax: 0161-929 9488 E-mail: info@kidzbedroomdepot.com

▶ Nanny Tax, 28 Minchenden Crescent, London, N14 7EL Tel: 020 8882 6847 Fax: 020 8886 1624 E-mail: post@taxingnannies.co.uk

▶ Office Star Group, Crucible Close, Mushet Industrial Park, Coleford, Gloucestershire, GL16 8RE Tel: (01594) 810081 Fax: (01594) 810111E-mail: 4schools@officestar-group.com

▶ Step By Step Nursery, Watford College Site, Park Avenue, Bushey, WD23 2DD Tel: (01923) 639333 Fax: (01923) 639334 E-mail: enquiries@sbsnursery.com

CHILDREN'S WEAR

Amar Textiles, 105 Grange Street, Derby, DE23 8HD Tel: (01332) 365527 Fax: (01332) 731771

▶ Ambidex Fashions, 82-90 Mile End Road, London, E1 4UN Tel: (020) 7790 7170 Fax: (020) 7790 7178

Ashton Seals Ltd, PO Box 1030, Barnsley, South Yorkshire, S73 0YP Tel: (01226) 273700 Fax: (01226) 756774 E-mail: sales@ashtonseals.com

Banner Ltd, Banner House, Greg Street, Stockport, Cheshire, SK5 7BT Tel: 0161-474 8000 Fax: 0161-474 7655 E-mail: admin@bannergroup.co.uk

Bedewear Manufacturing Co. Ltd, Bede Street, Leicester, LE3 5LD Tel: 0116-254 9031

Bush Baby Ltd, PO Box 61, Stockport, Cheshire, SK3 0AP Tel: 0161-474 7097 Fax: 0161-476 2647 E-mail: sales@bushbaby.com

▶ Cage Clothing, 43-68 Lower Villiers Street, Wolverhampton, WV2 4NA Tel: (01902) 717396

Carfax Gowns Ltd, 1st Floor, 15 Poland Street, London, W1F 8QE Tel: (020) 7287 3300 Fax: (020) 7287 6542

Chantelle Originals Ltd, 70 Elm Grove, Southsea, Hampshire, PO5 1LN Tel: (023) 9283 0273 Fax: (023) 9283 0273

Cooneen Textiles Ltd, 23 Cooneen Road, Fivemiletown, County Tyrone, BT75 0NE Tel: (028) 8952 1401 Fax: (028) 8952 1488 E-mail: info@cooneen.co.uk

Corgi Hosiery Ltd, New Road, Ammanford, Dyfed, SA18 3DS Tel: (01269) 592104 Fax: (01269) 593220 E-mail: sales@corgihosiery.co.uk

▶ David Luke Ltd, 4 Midland Street, Manchester, M12 6LB Tel: 0161-272 7474 Fax: 0161-272 6363 E-mail: sales@davidluke.com

Dewhirst Childrenswear Ltd, Amsterdam Road, Hull, HU7 0XF Tel: (01482) 835373 Fax: (01482) 824377

Eurotex Children & Babywear, 105 Warren Street, Dewsbury, West Yorkshire, WF12 9AS Tel: (01924) 461293 Fax: (01924) 460707 E-mail: enquirie@eurotexltd.com

Fashion Craft Ltd, 11 Dolphin Street, Ardwick, Manchester, M12 6BG Tel: 0161-273 3947 Fax: 0161-273 3947

Fashion Fair Ltd, Unit 2 Benson Street, Leicester, LE5 4HB Tel: 0116-273 0107 Fax: 0116-273 3837 E-mail: fashionfairltd@yahoo.co.uk

Fashionstop Ltd, Unit 1 Redcross Mill, Redcross Street, Rochdale, Lancashire, OL12 0NZ Tel: (01706) 525304 Fax: (01706) 658983

GHD Manufacture, Park Lane, Wolverhampton, WV10 9QE Tel: (01902) 726442 Fax: (01902) 726442

Gill & Co., 94 Owen Road, Wolverhampton, WV3 0AL Tel: (01902) 420707 Fax: (01902) 420707

Halle Models Leek Ltd, Belle Vue Road, Leek, Staffordshire, ST13 8EP Tel: (01538) 399731 Fax: (01538) 399354

J. & N. Herz Ltd, Broadstone House, Broadstone Road, Reddish, Stockport, Cheshire, SK5 7DL Tel: 0161-443 3030 Fax: 0161-443 0345 E-mail: jherz@herz.co.uk

Jaswal Fashions, Gas Street, Back of Kempton Building, Leicester, LE1 3XL Tel: 0116-253 1625 Fax: 0116-251 2204

Kabooki (UK), Old Engine Shed, Westfield Road, Wells, Somerset, BA5 2HS Tel: (01749) 677044 Fax: (01749) 677055

Kasmani Enterprises, Unit 6 43 Lancaster Street, Leicester, LE5 4GD Tel: 0116-274 2804

Laura Ashley Ltd, Design Centre, 27 Bagleys Lane, London, SW6 2QA Tel: (020) 7880 5100 Fax: (020) 7880 5200

Marco Trading Co. Ltd, Marco House, Tariff Street, Manchester, M1 2FF Tel: 0161-228 6765 Fax: 0161-236 3611 E-mail: info@marco-uk.com

Stephen Marks (London) Ltd, Unit B, Dolphin Way, Purfleet, Essex, RM19 1NZ Tel: (020) 7036 7000 Fax: (020) 7036 7001

Marwaha Textiles Ltd, 7 Brays Lane, Coventry, CV2 4DT Tel: (024) 7644 1216

Moon Star Garments, S M B Ho, Gipsy La, Leicester, LE4 6RE Tel: 0116-268 2322 Fax: 0116-268 2322

Mothercare plc, 16 High Street, Falkirk, FK1 1EX Tel: (01324) 629722

Oaktarget Ltd, 33 Kitchener Road, Leicester, LE5 4AU Tel: 0116-274 0304 Fax: 0116-276 7782 E-mail: sales@oaktarget.com

Jeffrey Ohrenstein Ltd, 35 Brunel Road, East Acton, London, W3 7XR Tel: (020) 8740 1100 Fax: (020) 8749 9889 E-mail: jeffrey@jogroup.co.uk

R N D Clothing Manufacturers Ltd, 998 Foleshill Road, Coventry, CV6 6EN Tel: (024) 7663 8989 Fax: (024) 7666 6214 E-mail: rdhami@rndclothing.co.uk

Rockgreen Ltd, 128 Whitechapel Road, London, E1 1JE Tel: (020) 7377 9552 Fax: (020) 7375 0549 E-mail: rockgreenltd@btinternet.com

Rosemarie Tayler Ltd, The Chase, Purdis Farm Lane, Ipswich, IP3 8UF Tel: (01473) 272041 Fax: (01473) 272041

S M Bros Ltd, 1st Floor Union Mill, Cambrian St, Manchester, M40 7EG Tel: 0161-274 3112 Fax: 0161-274 3312

Shah Trading, 146a Vine Place, Rochdale, Lancashire, OL11 1QZ Tel: (01706) 659774

▶ Sleepythings, 1 Wood Farm Cottages, Bramdean, Alresford, Hampshire, SO24 0JL Tel: 01962 771784 Fax: 01962 771784 E-mail: info@sleepythings.co.uk

Strom International Ltd, Unit B3 Connaught Business Centre, Edgware Road, London, NW9 6JL Tel: (020) 8205 9697 Fax: (020) 8905 8189 E-mail: sales@strom.co.uk

▶ Sylvia Jeffreys, Queensway, Wrexham, Clwyd, LL13 8YR Tel: (01978) 360390 Fax: (01978) 361684

▶ Team Tots Clothing Ltd, Unit 3 Oak House Moorgreen Industrial Park, Engine Lane, Newthorpe, Nottingham, NG16 3QU Tel: (01773) 717653 Fax: (01773) 717653

▶ Tec Clothing Manufacturers, 534 Stoney Stanton Road, Coventry, CV6 5FS Tel: (024) 7666 8310

▶ Three Bears Babywear, Cartwright Street, Wolverhampton, WV2 3BT Tel: (01902) 870838 Fax: (01902) 352005

Top Gear Clothing, 69 Waterloo Road, Smethwick, West Midlands, B66 4JS Tel: 0121-555 8765 Fax: 0121-555 8765

Tots & Teens Ltd, Unit B Cumberland Business Park, 17 Cumberland Avenue, London, NW10 7RT Tel: (020) 8965 8158 Fax: (020) 8961 6184 E-mail: contex@babybright.co.uk

Tots Tunnel, 89 Commerce Street, Glasgow, G5 8EP Tel: 0141-418 0494 Fax: 0141-418 0494

Verona Originals Ltd, 89-91 New Road, Whitechapel, London, E1 1HH Tel: (020) 7375 1666 Fax: (020) 7274 3025 E-mail: ray@raifashions.com

Vijay Fashions Ltd, 120 Broughton Street, Manchester, M8 8AN Tel: 0161-834 7711 Fax: 0161-833 0933 E-mail: ianq@vijayfashions.co.uk

Wick's Ltd, Unit 18L Ring Road, Burntwood Business Park, Burntwood, Staffordshire, WS7 3JQ Tel: (01543) 672488 Fax: (01543) 685211

CHILDRENS BIBS

▶ Elizabeth-Anne Childrens Wear, Unit 21 D Vale Business Park, Llandow, Cowbridge, South Glamorgan, CF71 7PF Tel: (01446) 776877 Fax: (01446) 776877 E-mail: info@elizabeth-anne.co.uk

▶ Flyers Group P.L.C., 1 Windsor Industrial Estate, 424 Ware Road, Hertford, SG13 7EW Tel: (01992) 538003 Fax: (01992) 507109 E-mail: sales@flyers-clothing.co.uk

Stuart Niman Ltd, Units 1-3 Mushroom Street, Leeds, LS9 7NB Tel: 0113-246 7575 Fax: 0113-246 7669 E-mail: sales@stuartniman.co.uk

CHILDRENS BOOKS

▶ dae illustrations, 31 westby avenue, Blackpool, FY4 3QL Tel: 07900 532083 E-mail: abyllez@yahoo.com

CHILDRENS CLOTHING

▶ Baystream, Unit 4 Metro Trading Centre, Second Way, Wembley, Middlesex, HA9 0YJ Tel: (020) 8903 5552 Fax: (020) 8903 9595

▶ Cooneen Textiles Ltd, Unit 1, Dark Lane, Manchester, M12 6FA Tel: 0161-273 5213 Fax: 0161-274 3713

▶ Harris & Harris, 5 New Street, Barnsley, South Yorkshire, S70 1RX Tel: (01226) 280280 Fax: (01226) 280280

▶ Loopy, 10 Jacob's Yard, Middle Barton, Chipping Norton, Oxfordshire, OX7 7BY Tel: (01869) 347726 Fax: (01869) 347726 E-mail: loopydesign@aol.com

▶ Snout Ltd, 9 The Lime Kilns, Barrow upon Soar, Loughborough, Leicestershire, LE12 8YF Tel: (01509) 415643 E-mail: info@snoutthings.co.uk

CHILDRENS EVENTS ENTERTAINMENT AGENTS

▶ A1 Bouncy Castles, Green Leys, Downley, High Wycombe, Buckinghamshire, HP13 5UH Tel: (01494) 464902

▶ The Booking Agency, 152 Malpas Road, Newport, NP20 5PN Tel: (01633) 671498 Fax: (0871) 6612184 E-mail: info@thebookingagency.co.uk

▶ Changing Faces.Biz, 1 Courtney Road, Rushden, Northamptonshire, NN10 9FL Tel: (01933) 419910 E-mail: info@changingfaces.biz

▶ Funkie World Entertainments Ltd, 7 Trevarrick Court, Horwich, Bolton, BL6 6TF Tel: (07005) 981782 E-mail: aquatane@aquatane.co.uk

Gekko Entertainments, 42 Theobalds Road, London, WC1X 8NW Tel: (020) 7404 1252 Fax: (020) 7242 1691 E-mail: info@gekkoentertainments.com

Jen's Face Painting, 123 Repton Road, Bristol, BS4 3LY Tel: 0117-985 9258 E-mail: crackerjacks@blueyonder.co.uk

▶ Mosaic Parties for Children, 404 Richmond Road, Twickenham, TW1 2EB Tel: 020 8977 4526 E-mail: sarahj.perkins1@virgin.net

▶ Professor Paradox, 42 St. James Street, St. James, South Petherton, Somerset, TA13 5BN Tel: 01460 242549 E-mail: mike@wisefool.co.uk

▶ Star Quality Entertainment Agency UK, 10 Park Meadow Avenue, Bilston, West Midlands, WV14 6HA Tel: (01902) 578959 E-mail: info@starqualityentertainment.net

▶ indicates data change since last edition

CHILDRENS EVENTS ENTERTAINMENT AGENTS – *continued*

▶ Tea Korrs Event Planning And Management, 159 Mellish Street, London, E14 8PJ Tel: 078 65054464 E-mail: teakorrs@gmail.com

▶ WonderWorks, Redemption House, 53 Theobald Street, Borehamwood, Herts, WD6 4RT Tel: 020 8953 7733 Fax: 020 8953 3388 E-mail: info@wworks.co.uk

CHILDRENS FOOTWEAR, *See Shoe, Children's etc; also other headings for particular types*

CHILDRENS JACKETS

▶ Flyers Group P.L.C., 1 Windsor Industrial Estate, 424 Ware Road, Hertford, SG13 7EW Tel: (01992) 538003 Fax: (01992) 507109 E-mail: sales@flyers-clothing.co.uk

CHILDRENS PADDED JACKETS

▶ Flyers Group P.L.C., 1 Windsor Industrial Estate, 424 Ware Road, Hertford, SG13 7EW Tel: (01992) 538003 Fax: (01992) 507109 E-mail: sales@flyers-clothing.co.uk

CHILDRENS PARTY GIFTS

PartyTimeKids, 2 Apollo Close, Oakhurst, Swindon, SN25 2JB Tel: 07719 570976 E-mail: info@partytimekids.co.uk

CHILDRENS ROOM MURALS

▶ John Crawford Artist/Signwriter, 120 Hundred Acre Road, Streetly, Sutton Coldfield, West Midlands, B74 2BJ Tel: 0121-353 1772 E-mail: john@jcrawford.fsnet.co.uk

▶ Imaginative Interiors, 11 Burnside Close, Harrogate, North Yorkshire, HG1 2BQ Tel: (01423) 565959

CHILDRENS SHOES

Bacup Shoe Co. Ltd, Atherton Holme Mill, Railway Street, Bacup, Lancashire, OL13 0UF Tel: (01706) 873304 Fax: (01706) 873216 E-mail: admin@bacupshoe.co.uk

Chuckle Shoes, 3 New Bridge Street, Exeter, EX4 3JW Tel: (01392) 270321 Fax: (01392) 207003

C. & J. Clark International Ltd, 40 High Street, Street, Somerset, BA16 0YA Tel: (01458) 443131 Fax: (01458) 447547 E-mail: john.keery@clarks.com

E Sutton & Son Ltd, Riverside, Bacup, Lancashire, OL13 0DT Tel: (01706) 874961 Fax: (01706) 879268 E-mail: firstname@esutton.co.uk

Early Days, 15B Mandervell Road, Oadby, Leicester, LE2 5LQ Tel: 0116-271 6944 Fax: 0116-271 9869 E-mail: sales@earlydays.ltd.uk

Florentine Shoes, European Cargo Centre, Motherwell Way, Grays, Essex, RM20 3XD Tel: (01708) 867111 Fax: (01708) 862110 E-mail: mikeluff@florentineshoes.freeserve.co.uk

Lambert Howarth Group P.L.C., Healeywood Road, Burnley, Lancashire, BB11 2HL Tel: (01282) 471200 Fax: (01282) 471279

▶ Piggy's Childrens Footwear Ltd, 14 St. Marys Hill, Stamford, Lincolnshire, PE9 2DP Tel: (01780) 763758 Fax: (01780) 763758 E-mail: sales@piggys-shoes.co.uk

Shoe Zone Ltd, Haramead Business Centre, Humberstone Road, Leicester, LE1 2LH Tel: 0116-222 3000 Fax: 0116-222 3001 E-mail: info@shoezone.net

CHILDRENS SLEEP SUITS

▶ Elizabeth-Anne Childrens Wear, Unit 21 D Vale Business Park, Llandow, Cowbridge, South Glamorgan, CF71 7PF Tel: (01446) 776877 Fax: (01446) 776877 E-mail: info@elizabeth-anne.co.uk

Stuart Niman Ltd, Units 1-3 Mushroom Street, Leeds, LS9 7NB Tel: 0113-246 7575 Fax: 0113-246 7669 E-mail: sales@stuartniman.co.uk

CHILDRENS T SHIRTS

Stuart Niman Ltd, Units 1-3 Mushroom Street, Leeds, LS9 7NB Tel: 0113-246 7575 Fax: 0113-246 7669 E-mail: sales@stuartniman.co.uk

▶ P J Heaven, PO Box 164, Beverley, North Humberside, HU17 7AP Tel: (01482) 860777 Fax: (01482) 860777 E-mail: sales@pjheaven.co.uk

CHILLED FOOD PACKING SERVICES

Cavaghan & Gray Group Ltd, Brunel House, Brunel Way, Durranhill Industrial Estate, Carlisle, CA1 3NQ Tel: (01228) 518200 Fax: (01228) 518215 E-mail: enquiries@northern-foods.co.uk

▶ Rich Complements, Barker Business Park, Melmerby Green Lane, Melmerby, Ripon, North Yorkshire, HG4 5NB Tel: (01765) 640077 Fax: (01765) 640077 E-mail: info@richcomplements.co.uk

CHILLED WAREHOUSING

▶ Norish Ltd, P O Box 255, Dartford, DA1 9AL Tel: (0870) 7351318 Fax: (01322) 303470 E-mail: sales@norish.com

CHILLED WATER PUMPS

P F S (Helston) Ltd, Unit 9, Water-Ma-Trout Industrial Estate, Helston, Cornwall, TR13 0LW Tel: (01326) 565454 Fax: (01326) 565505 E-mail: sales@pfs-uk.co.uk

CHILLERS, *See also headings for particular types*

Clivet UK, Unit 4 Kingdom Close, Segenworth East, Fareham, Hampshire, PO15 5TJ Tel: (01489) 550621 Fax: (01489) 573033 E-mail: info@clivet-uk.co.uk

I C S Group, Gore Road Industrial Estate, New Milton, Hampshire, BH25 6SA Tel: (01425) 625900 Fax: (01425) 639041 E-mail: info@industrialcooling.co.uk

Real Mackay Water Bottling Co., Penyffin, Nantgaredig, Carmarthen, Dyfed, SA32 7LJ Tel: (01267) 290655 Fax: (01267) 290960

CHIMNEY BUILDERS

▶ Chimney Co., 39 Crescent Road, Warley, Brentwood, Essex, CM14 5JR Tel: (0800) 7319570 Fax: (01277) 204322

▶ getabuilder.co.uk, Offices 343, 14 Clifton Down Road, Clifton Village, Clifton, Bristol, BS8 4BF Tel: 0117 9390418 E-mail: theteam@getabuilder.co.uk

M M F Ltd, 55 Woodburn Road, Smethwick, West Midlands, B66 2PU Tel: 0121-555 6555 Fax: 0121-555 6816 E-mail: sales@fluepipes.com

CHIMNEY COWLS

▶ Apex Cowls, Lyncombe, Didcot Road, Harwell, Didcot, Oxfordshire, OX11 0DP Tel: (01235) 820876 E-mail: enquiries@apexcowls.co.uk

Ascott Clark, 42 Western Lane, Buxworth, High Peak, Derbyshire, SK23 7NS Tel: (01663) 734221 Fax: (01663) 734318 E-mail: info@ascottclark.com

Flues & Flashings Ltd, Unit 246 Ikon Industrial Estate, Droitwich Road, Hartlebury, Kidderminster, Worcestershire, DY10 4EU Tel: (01299) 250049 Fax: (01299) 250947 E-mail: info@fluesandflashings.co.uk

H Docherty Ltd, Red Shute Hill Industrial Estate, Red Shute Hill, Hermitage, Thatcham, Berkshire, RG18 9QL Tel: (01635) 200145 Fax: (01635) 201737 E-mail: info@docherty.co.uk

▶ Zero 3 Chimney Engineering, 7 Eaton Road, Southsea, Hampshire, PO5 1SQ Tel: (07796) 424041 E-mail: zero3ceng@yahoo.co.uk

CHIMNEY SHAFT BUILDING OR REPAIR

Bierrum Structural Services Ltd, 105 High Street, Houghton Regis, Dunstable, Bedfordshire, LU5 5BJ Tel: (01582) 845745 Fax: (01582) 845746 E-mail: admin@bierrum.co.uk

David G Alker, The Quern, Chapel Lawn, Bucknell, Shropshire, SY7 0BW Tel: (01547) 530344 Fax: (01547) 530844 E-mail: davequern@aol.com

CHIMNEY SWEEPING SYSTEMS OR EQUIPMENT

Tamar Specialist Brushes, Exeter, EX2 8WW Tel: (01392) 491818 Fax: (01392) 491818 E-mail: enquiries@tamarbrushes.co.uk

CHIMNEY SYSTEMS

▶ John Cameron Ltd, Unit 5 & 6, 55 Maclellan Street, Glasgow, G41 1RR Tel: 0141-427 5353 Fax: 0141-427 4422 E-mail: sales@jcpbm.co.uk

Red Bank Manufacturing Co. Ltd, Atherstone Road, Measham, Swadlincote, Derbyshire, DE12 7EL Tel: (01530) 270333 Fax: (01530) 270542 E-mail: info@redbank-manufacturing.co.uk

CHINA CLAY

Global Ceramic Materials Ltd, Milton Works, Leek New Road, Stoke-on-Trent, ST2 7EF Tel: (01782) 537297 Fax: (01782) 537867 E-mail: sales@gsb.net

Goonvean Ltd, St. Stephen, St. Austell, Cornwall, PL26 7QF Tel: (01726) 822381 Fax: (01726) 822341 E-mail: g@goonvean.co.uk

Imerys Minerals Ltd, Par Moor Centre, Par Moor Road, Par, Cornwall, PL24 2SQ Tel: (01726) 818000 Fax: (01726) 811200 E-mail: perfmins@imerys.com

CHINAWARE

▶ Alexander Johnston Plasterers Ltd, 4 Urquhart Lane, Aberdeen, AB24 5LQ Tel: (01224) 626838

Broadhurst Bros Burslem Ltd, Waterloo Road, Burslem, Stoke-on-Trent, ST6 2EL Tel: (01782) 834561 Fax: (01782) 832102

C & S Catering Supplies Ltd, Whitehouse Farm, Littlefield Green, White Waltham, Maidenhead, Berkshire, SL6 3JL Tel: 0118-934 1300 Fax: 0118-932 0304 E-mail: candscatering@candscatering.freeserve.co.uk

Churchill Fine Bone China (Holdings) Ltd, Marlborough Works, High Street, Stoke-on-Trent, ST6 5NZ Tel: (01782) 577566 Fax: (01782) 810318 E-mail: churchill@churchillchina.plc.uk

Cinque Ports Pottery, The Monastery, Conduit Hill, Rye, East Sussex, TN31 7LE Tel: (01797) 222033 Fax: (01797) 222400 E-mail: cppottery@aol.com

City Catering Equipment (London) Ltd, Railway Arch, 7-8 Commercial Street, London, E1 6NU Tel: (020) 7247 4620

CPS Supply Co. Ltd, 5 Riverside Road, London, SW17 0BA Tel: (020) 8944 9016 Fax: (020) 8944 9018

▶ Crown Trent China Ltd, Spring Garden Road, Longton, Stoke-On-Trent, ST3 2TE Tel: (01782) 332623 E-mail: sam@crowntrent.com

Dalton & Ditcham Agencies Ltd, Brent House, 3rd Floor Kenton Road, Harrow, Middlesex, HA3 8BT Tel: (020) 8909 3996 Fax: (020) 8909 2686 E-mail: dalton.ditcham@btinternet.com

▶ Drymen Pottery, Main Street, Drymen, Glasgow, G63 0BJ Tel: (01360) 660458 Fax: (01360) 660211

▶ Duchess China Ltd, Uttoxeter Road, Stoke-on-Trent, ST3 1NX Tel: (01782) 313061 Fax: (01782) 314589

Dunoon Ceramics Ltd, 5 Walton Industrial Estate, Beacon Road, Stone, Staffordshire, ST15 0RY Tel: (01785) 817414 Fax: (01785) 812322 E-mail: sales@dunoonmugs.co.uk

F. Eardley (Potteries) Ltd, Foley Works, Brocksford Street, Fenton, Stoke-on-Trent, ST4 3HF Tel: (01782) 313871 Fax: (01782) 325057

Emma Bridgewater, 739 Fulham Road, London, SW6 5UL Tel: (020) 7371 5264 Fax: (020) 7384 2457

▶ English Country Pottery Ltd, Wickwar Trading Estate, 61 Station Road, Wickwar, Wotton-under-Edge, Gloucestershire, GL12 8NB Tel: (01454) 299100 Fax: (01454) 294053 E-mail: sales@ecpdesign.co.uk

Febland Group Ltd, Ashworth Road, Marton, Blackpool, FY4 4UN Tel: (01253) 600600 Fax: (01253) 792211 E-mail: info@febland.co.uk

Fegg Hayes Pottery Ltd, 2-4 Beaumont Road, Stoke-on-Trent, ST6 6BE Tel: (01782) 838328 Fax: (01782) 826378 E-mail: info@fegghayespottery.co.uk

▶ Fosters Pottery Ltd, Wilson Way, Pool, Redruth, Cornwall, TR15 3RX Tel: (01209) 314410 Fax: (01209) 210246

David Fryer Studios, Bracken Hill, Welsh Newton Common, Monmouth, Gwent, NP25 5RT Tel: (01989) 770402 Fax: (01989) 770807 E-mail: d.a.fryer@btopenworld.com

▶ G W P UK Ltd, 3 Old Port Road, Nurston, Barry, South Glamorgan, CF62 3BH Tel: (01446) 711260 Fax: (01446) 711978 E-mail: gwpukltd@btconnect.com

Thomas Goode & Co. Ltd, 19 South Audley Street, London, W1K 2BN Tel: (020) 7499 2823 Fax: (020) 7629 4230 E-mail: info@thomasgoode.com

▶ Griselda Hill Pottery, Kirkbrae, Ceres, Cupar, Fife, KY15 5ND Tel: (01334) 828273 Fax: (01334) 828008 E-mail: info@wemyss-ware.co.uk

Hargreaves & Son Ltd, 16-18 Spring Gardens, Buxton, Derbyshire, SK17 6DE Tel: (01298) 23083 Fax: (01298) 25323 E-mail: hargreaves.son@freeuk.com

Harry Hancock Bar & Caterering Equipment, 12c Scott Lidgett Industrial Estate, Scott Lidgett Road, Stoke-on-Trent, ST6 4NQ Tel: (01782) 837303 Fax: (01782) 838612 E-mail: sales@hancocks-catering.co.uk

Hudson & Middleton, Sutherland Works, Normacot Road, Stoke-on-Trent, ST3 1PP Tel: (01782) 319256 Fax: (01782) 343300 E-mail: enquiries@hudsonandmiddleton.co.uk

Impressions Design Ltd, Sutherland Works, Beaufort Road, Stoke-on-Trent, ST3 1RH Tel: (01782) 329535 Fax: (01782) 329535 E-mail: info@impressionsdesignltd.co.uk

K B Design & Promotion Ltd, City Business Centre, Brighton Road, Horsham, West Sussex, RH13 5BA Tel: (01403) 262499 Fax: (01403) 261932 E-mail: sales@kb-design.com

Lesser & Pavey Ltd, Leonardo House Fawkes Avenue, Dartford Trade Park, Dartford, DA1 1JQ Tel: (01322) 279225 Fax: (01322) 279586 E-mail: sales@leonardo.co.uk

The London Pottery Company Ltd, 54 Weir Road, London, SW19 8UG Tel: (020) 8944 9738 Fax: (020) 8944 0400 E-mail: info@london-pottery.co.uk

Lubkowski Saunders & Associates Designs & Exports Ltd, E Dolphin Estate, Windmill Road West, Sunbury-on-Thames, Middlesex, TW16 7HE Tel: (01932) 789721 Fax: (01932) 789793 E-mail: sales@lsa-international.co.uk

Pottery & Porcelain Restoration, 3 Whessoe Road, Darlington, County Durham, DL3 0QP Tel: (01325) 460319 Fax: (01325) 460319

Prestons (Cash & Carry) Ltd, 110 Oldham Road, Manchester, M4 6AG Tel: 0161-236 9258 Fax: 0161-236 7760

Reject Pot Shop, 56 Chalk Farm Road, London, NW1 8AN Tel: (020) 7485 2326 Fax: (020) 7485 2326 E-mail: sales@rejectpotshop.co.uk

Ray Sanders Ltd, 550 Edge Lane, Old Swan, Liverpool, L13 1AJ Tel: 0151-259 1221 Fax: 0151-220 6856 E-mail: pottypots@aol.com

▶ Scotia Ceramics Ltd, Coll Pottery, Coll, Isle Of Lewis, HS2 0JP Tel: (01851) 820219

Staffordshire Figure Co., 70-72 Hospital St, Nantwich, Cheshire, CW5 5RP Tel: 01270 625006 Fax: 01270 629603

▶ Tams Group Ltd, Blyth Pottery, Uttoxeter Road, Longton, Stoke-On-Trent, ST3 1QQ Tel: (01782) 339199 Fax: (01782) 339194 E-mail: uksales@tams.co.uk

Trauffler, Unit 1, 307 Merton Road, London, SW18 5JS Tel: (020) 7251 0240 Fax: (020) 8874 8627 E-mail: sales@trauffler.com

Trelowarren Pottery Ltd, Mawgan, Helston, Cornwall, TR12 6AF Tel: (01326) 221366 E-mail: trelowarren.pottery@virgin.net

CHINESE GOODS IMPORT MERCHANTS OR AGENTS

Catenate Consulting Ltd, Beech Leigh, Rectory Hill, Berrynarbor, Ilfracombe, Devon, EX34 9SE Tel: (01271) 882460 Fax: (01271) 882460 E-mail: sales@catenate-consulting.co.uk

▶ Effectual Storage Services, 5 Benfield Way, Braintree, Essex, CM7 3YS Tel: (01376) 551234 Fax: (01376) 551515 E-mail: sales@effectualstorage.co.uk

CHIPBOARD

Adlington Paper & Board Supplies Ltd, Unit 1 Adlington Industrial Estate, Adlington, Macclesfield, Cheshire, SK10 4NL Tel: (01625) 850885 Fax: (01625) 850882 E-mail: adlingtonpaper@btconnect.com

Barlows Boards Ltd, 8 Rushey Lane, Birmingham, B11 2BL Tel: 0121-706 2067 Fax: 0121-707 9550 E-mail: bugbashbar@yahoo.co.uk

C F Anderson & Son Ltd, 228 Old London Road, Marks Tey, Colchester, CO6 1HD Tel: (020) 7226 1212 Fax: (020) 7359 1112 E-mail: cfanderson@cfanderson.co.uk

Egger UK Holdings Ltd, Anick Grange Road, Hexham, Northumberland, NE46 4JS Tel: (01434) 602191 Fax: (01434) 605103 E-mail: info@egger.co.uk

Gower Timber Ltd, Crofty Indust Estate, Crofty, Swansea, SA4 3SW Tel: (01792) 851140 Fax: (01792) 850128 E-mail: classact@gowertimberltd.fsnet.co.uk

Ipswich Plastics Ltd, Foxtail Road, Ransomes Industrial Estate, Ipswich, IP3 9RX Tel: (01473) 270101 Fax: (01473) 721446

▶ L F P (UK) Ltd, LFP House, 1 Grange Meadows, Elmswell, Bury St. Edmunds, Suffolk, IP30 9GE Tel: (01359) 242900 Fax: (01359) 242121 E-mail: info@lfpuk.co.uk

Lafford & Moore, Power House, Powerscroft Road, Sidcup, Kent, DA14 5EA Tel: (020) 8309 4224 Fax: (020) 8309 4222 E-mail: sales@laffordandmoore.co.uk

R P Panels Ltd, Pindar Road, Hoddesdon, Hertfordshire, EN11 0BZ Tel: (01992) 444221 Fax: (01992) 466656

Spanboard Products Ltd, Hillmans Way, Coleraine, County Londonderry, BT52 2ED Tel: (028) 7035 5126 Fax: (028) 7035 8670 E-mail: faels@stanboard.co.uk

Stellafoam Ltd, Manor Way, Rainham, Essex, RM13 8RH Tel: (01708) 522551 Fax: (01708) 522162 E-mail: sales@stellafoam.ltd.uk

CHIROPODY EQUIPMENT MACHINERY

C P L, 2 St. James Road, Brackley, Northamptonshire, NN13 7XY Tel: (01280) 706661 Fax: (01280) 706671 E-mail: canonbury@canonbury.com

CHIROPODY EQUIPMENT MACHINERY – *continued*

Chiromart, Suite 3, 36 Sea Road, Bexhill-on-Sea, East Sussex, TN40 1ED Tel: (01424) 731432 Fax: (01424) 225836
E-mail: chiromart@tiscali.co.uk

CHIROPODY REQUISITES

Cuxson Gerrard & Co., 125 Broadwell Road, Oldbury, West Midlands, B69 4BF
Tel: 0121-544 7117 Fax: 0121-544 8616
E-mail: sales@cuxsongerrard.com

CHISELS

Austin Mcgillivray & Co., 124 Scotland Street, Sheffield, S3 7DE Tel: 0114-273 8041 Fax: 0114-275 0290
E-mail: enquiries@sheffieldknives.co.uk

Crown Hand Tools Ltd, Excelsior Works, Burnt Tree Lane, Hoyle Street, Sheffield, S3 7EX Tel: 0114-272 3366 Fax: 0114-272 5252
E-mail: info@crowntools.com

Metal-Woods Ltd, 14 Church Street, Market Harborough, Leicestershire, LE16 7AB Tel: (01858) 462641 Fax: (01858) 431616
E-mail: sales@metal-woods.co.uk

James Sime & Co. Ltd, 29 Cow Wynd, Falkirk, FK1 1PT Tel: (01324) 622592 Fax: (01324) 612522

Alan Wasden Ltd, Niloc Works, Penistone Road, Sheffield, S6 2FW Tel: 0114-234 8824 Fax: 0114-232 1246

CHLORINATION PLANT

Active Water Systems, 122 Newport Road, Caldicot, Monmouthshire, NP26 4BT Tel: (01291) 420012 Fax: (0870) 4294048
E-mail: us@ActiveWater.co.uk

Alldos Ltd, 82 Gravelly Industrial Park, Birmingham, B24 8TL Tel: 0121-328 3336 Fax: 0121-328 4332
E-mail: alldos.uk@alldos.com

ProMinent Fluid Controls (UK) Ltd, Resolution Road, Ashby-de-la-Zouch, Leicestershire, LE65 1DW Tel: (01530) 560555 Fax: (01530) 560777 E-mail: sales@prominent.co.uk

Severn Trent Water Ltd, Park Lane, Minworth, Sutton Coldfield, West Midlands, B76 9BL Tel: 0121-722 4000 Fax: 0121-313 1938
E-mail: salesenq@severntrentservices.co.uk

U S Filters Electrocatalytic Products, 9 Norman Way, Severn Bridge Industrial Estate, Portskewett, Caldicot, Gwent, NP26 5YN Tel: (01291) 426500 Fax: (01291) 426501
E-mail: sales@elcat.co.uk

CHLOROFLUOROCARBON (CFC) FREE CLEANING MATERIALS

Jack Dusty's Stores, 400 Sandwell Road, Kingswood, Bristol, BS15 1JJ Tel: 0117-949 6686 Fax: 0117-949 6495
E-mail: enquiries@jackdusty.co.uk

Enviroclean Ltd, Spratton Grange Farm, Welford Road, Spratton, Northampton, NN6 8LA Tel: (01604) 846378

Janitorial Express, 3 Brewery Road, London, N7 9QJ Tel: (020) 7700 3322 Fax: (020) 7700 2299 E-mail: info@janitorialexpress.co.uk

CHOCOLATE

▶ Hand Made Chocolate Co. Ltd, Unit 10 Pitt Street, Denton, Manchester, M34 6PT Tel: 0161-320 0660 Fax: 0161-320 0770
E-mail: sales@handmadechocolate.co.uk

CHOCOLATE BARS

Charvo Finishing Ltd, Snaygill Industrial Estate, Keighley Road, Skipton, North Yorkshire, BD23 2QR Tel: (01756) 795028 Fax: (01756) 798473 E-mail: sales@charvo.co.uk

▶ Cocoda, 61 London Road, Woolmer Green, Knebworth, Herts, SG3 6JE Tel: 01438 810999 Fax: 01438 817193
E-mail: mail@cocoda.biz

Fine Confectionery Co. Ltd, Unit 20 The Mead Business Centre, Mead Lane, Hertford, SG13 7BJ Tel: (01992) 551075 Fax: (01992) 581780 E-mail: info@fineconfectionery.co.uk

▶ halalsweeties.com, Unit 1, London, NW9 Tel: 020 82389877 Fax: 020 82389877
E-mail: customerservices@halalsweeties.com

▶ The Marmalade Cat Co., Ingles Meadow, Castle Hill Avenue, Folkestone, Kent, CT20 2RD Tel: (0870) 0634868 Fax: (0870) 0634869 E-mail: info@marmaladecat.com

▶ Simon Dunn, 2 Commercial Road, Hazel Grove, Hazel Grove, Stockport, Cheshire, SK7 4AA Tel: 0161-483 2228 Fax: 0161-483 2228
E-mail: info@simondunnschocolates.co.uk

CHOCOLATE FLAVOURED BREAD

▶ Chocolate Paradise, 122 Station Road, Shotts, Lanarkshire, ML7 4BQ Tel: 01501 821958
E-mail: bookings@chocolate-paradise.co.uk

CHOCOLATE FLAVOURED MILK

▶ Chocolate Paradise, 122 Station Road, Shotts, Lanarkshire, ML7 4BQ Tel: 01501 821958
E-mail: bookings@chocolate-paradise.co.uk

CHOCOLATE FOUNTAINS

▶ Chocolate Fountains from Hot Chocolate Lunch Ltd, St Hilda Close, Deepcar, Sheffield, S36 2TH Tel: 0784 0685595
E-mail: info@hotchocolatelunch.com

'Just Jax' Dinner Parties & Buffets, 27 Birch Street, Fleetwood, Lancashire, FY7 6TW Tel: 01253 772336 E-mail: info@justjax.co.uk

CHOCOLATE LIQUORS

▶ Simon Dunn, 2 Commercial Road, Hazel Grove, Hazel Grove, Stockport, Cheshire, SK7 4AA Tel: 0161-483 2228 Fax: 0161-483 2228
E-mail: info@simondunnschocolates.co.uk

CHOCOLATE PRODUCTION MACHINERY

Bramigk & Co. Ltd, Chelmsford, CM2 7WG Tel: (01245) 477616 Fax: (01245) 477498
E-mail: info@bramigk.co.uk

Cadbury Ltd, Somerdale, Keynsham, Bristol, BS31 2AU Tel: 0117-986 1789 Fax: 0117-937 6590

Lloyds International Ltd, Station Road, Reddish, Stockport, Cheshire, SK5 6ND Tel: 0161-219 0909 Fax: 0161-431 5780
E-mail: vicky@thos-storey.co.uk

Premier Bartleet Ltd, Mountbatten House Fairacres Industrial Estate, Dedworth Road, Windsor, Berkshire, SL4 4LE Tel: (01753) 754850 Fax: (01753) 754851
E-mail: info@prembar.com

Raymond Travel, 192 High Street, Dorking, Surrey, RH4 1QR Tel: (01306) 743780 Fax: (01306) 743764
E-mail: info@raymondtravel.co.uk

CHOCOLATES

Big Bear Ltd, Fox'S Confectionery, Sunningdale Road, Braunstone, Leicester, LE3 1UE Tel: 0116-287 3561 Fax: 0116-232 0117
E-mail: info@foxs.co.uk

Cadbury Ltd, Somerdale, Keynsham, Bristol, BS31 2AU Tel: 0117-986 1789 Fax: 0117-937 6590

Casemir Chocolates UK Ltd, 5a Tetherdown, London, N10 1ND Tel: (020) 8365 2132
E-mail: info@casemirchocolates.co.uk

Charvo Finishing Ltd, Snaygill Industrial Estate, Keighley Road, Skipton, North Yorkshire, BD23 2QR Tel: (01756) 795028 Fax: (01756) 798473 E-mail: sales@charvo.co.uk

Dining in Style Group Limited, 18 High Street, Pinner, Middlesex, HA5 5PW Tel: (020) 8866 7856 Fax: (020) 8866 1033
E-mail: paul@dininginstyle.co.uk

▶ halalsweeties.com, Unit 1, London, NW9 Tel: 020 82389877 Fax: 020 82389877
E-mail: customerservices@halalsweeties.com

▶ Simon Dunn, 2 Commercial Road, Hazel Grove, Hazel Grove, Stockport, Cheshire, SK7 4AA Tel: 0161-483 2228 Fax: 0161-483 2228
E-mail: info@simondunnschocolates.co.uk

CHOKE CONTROL VALVES

Circor Instrumentation Ltd, Frays Mill Works, Cowley Road, Uxbridge, Middlesex, UB8 2AF Tel: (01895) 206780 Fax: (020) 8423 5933
E-mail: aratna@circor.co.uk

CHOKE VALVES

Masterflo Valve Co (U K) Ltd, Blackness Road, Altens Industrial Estate, Altens, Aberdeen, AB12 3LH Tel: (01224) 878999 Fax: (01224) 878989 E-mail: info@masterflo.co.uk

Mokveld, Unit 2 Butts Courtyard, The Butts, Poulton, Cirencester, Gloucestershire, GL7 5HY Tel: (01285) 851225 Fax: (01285) 851342 E-mail: uk@mokveld.com

CHOPPING BOARDS

Global Foodservice Equipment Ltd, Global House, 104-108 School Road, Tilehurst, Reading, RG31 5AX Tel: (0870) 6004333 Fax: (0870) 2434334
E-mail: sales@global-fse.co.uk

Nisbets plc, Fourth Way, Bristol, BS11 8TB Tel: (0845) 1405555 Fax: (0845) 1435555
E-mail: sales@nisbets.co.uk

Prima Catering Supplies, 2 Whitworth Industrial Estate, Tilton Road, Birmingham, B9 4PP Tel: 0121-771 3116 Fax: 0121-772 2616
E-mail: primacatering@hotmail.com

▶ Thewoodcarver.Co.Uk, Firthview, Culbo, Culbokie, Dingwall, Ross-Shire, IV7 8JX Tel: (01349) 877546
E-mail: info@thewoodcarver.co.uk

Tradestock Ltd, Poole Works, Poole, Wellington, Somerset, TA21 9HW Tel: (01823) 661717 Fax: (01823) 666543
E-mail: sales@tradestockltd.co.uk

CHRISTENING GIFTWARE

heirlooms.uk.com, 11 Fontaine Road, London, SW16 3PB Tel: 02086 792196 Fax: 020 7738 9787 E-mail: info@heirlooms.uk.com

▶ Special Treasures, 193 Hylton Road, Millfield, Sunderland, SR4 7YE Tel: (07931) 756051
E-mail: emahoward@yahoo.co.uk

CHRISTENING ROBES

▶ K Mayhew Publishing Ltd, Buxhall, Stowmarket, Suffolk, IP14 3BW Tel: (01449) 737978 Fax: (01449) 737834
E-mail: info@kevinmayhewltd.com

▶ Sleepythings, 1 Wood Farm Cottages, Bramdean, Alresford, Hampshire, SO24 0JL Tel: 01962 771784 Fax: 01962 771784
E-mail: info@sleepythings.co.uk

CHRISTMAS CARDS

▶ Compass Business Promotions Ltd, 16 Crosslee Gardens, Crosslee, Johnstone, Renfrewshire, PA6 7AF Tel: (01505) 613569 Fax: (01505) 612603

▶ K Mayhew Publishing Ltd, Buxhall, Stowmarket, Suffolk, IP14 3BW Tel: (01449) 737978 Fax: (01449) 737834
E-mail: info@kevinmayhewltd.com

▶ Santa Letters UK, Unit 80, Speke Hall Industrial Estate, Liverpool, L24 1YA Tel: 0151-428 0638
E-mail: kmorrisroe@gmail.com

Nigel Tooley Ltd, PO Box 91, Ashtead, Surrey, KT21 1YX Tel: (01372) 278620
E-mail: coincabinet@btconnect.com

▶ www.greetingcards-online.co.uk, Barley Sheaf School House, Holland Fen, Lincoln, LN4 4QH Tel: (01205) 280469 Fax: (01205) 280469
E-mail: enquiries@greetingcards-online.co.uk

CHRISTMAS CRACKERS

Bonnett Maintenance Chemicals, Unit 44 Corringham Industrial Estate, Corringham Road, Gainsborough, Lincolnshire, DN21 1QB Tel: (01427) 613240 Fax: (01427) 617308
E-mail: enquiries@bonnetts.f9.co.uk

Robin Reed Ltd, Oldbury One, Brades Road, Oldbury, West Midlands, B69 1XX Tel: 0121-552 1001 Fax: 0121-544 5009
E-mail: crackers@robinreed.com

CHRISTMAS SUPPLIES

▶ K Mayhew Publishing Ltd, Buxhall, Stowmarket, Suffolk, IP14 3BW Tel: (01449) 737978 Fax: (01449) 737834
E-mail: info@kevinmayhewltd.com

CHRISTMAS TABLEWARE

The Poole Pottery, 48 Wyatts Lane, Corfe Mullen, Wimborne, Dorset, BH21 3SQ Tel: (01202) 600838 E-mail: chris@mrpottery.co.uk

CHRISTMAS TREES

▶ Ashridge Trees, Grove Cross Barn, Castle Cary, Somerset, BA7 7NJ Tel: (01963) 359444 Fax: (01963) 359445
E-mail: julian@ashridgetrees.co.uk

Creative Works UK Ltd, Unit 1 The Stable Block, Brewer Street Bletchingley, Bletchingley, Redhill, RH1 4QP Tel: (01883) 742999
E-mail: info@ckworks.net

▶ Mercaston Tree Co., Ednaston, Ednaston, Ashbourne, Derbyshire, DE6 3AE Tel: (01335) 360947 Fax: (01335) 360394
E-mail: enquiries@mercastontreecompany.com

Stockeld Farms Ltd, Kingbarrow Farm, Harrogate Road, Wetherby, West Yorkshire, LS22 4AL Tel: (01937) 586101 Fax: (01937) 580084
E-mail: peterstockeld@bigfastweb.net

CHROMATE CONVERSION PROCESSING

Fowlers Specialist Treatments Ltd, 126 129 Pritchett Street, Aston, Birmingham, B6 4EH Tel: 0121-359 8571 Fax: 0121-359 4037
E-mail: enquiries@fowlersindustrial.co.uk

Surface Technology plc, Godiva Place, Coventry, CV1 5PN Tel: (024) 7625 8444 Fax: (024) 7655 1402 E-mail: sales@ultraseal.co.uk

CHROMATOGRAPHIC ACCESSORIES

Biotoge Ltd, Duffryn Business Park, Ystrad Mynach, Hengoed, Mid Glamorgan, CF82 7RJ Tel: (01443) 811811 Fax: (01443) 816552
E-mail: sales@jones-chrom.co.uk

Cambridge Scientific Instruments Ltd, 12-15 Sedgway Business Park, Common Road, Witchford, Ely, Cambridgeshire, CB6 2HY Tel: (01353) 669916 Fax: (01353) 669917
E-mail: camsci@btconnect.com

Chromacol Ltd, Unit 3, Little Mundells, Mundells Industrial Estate, Welwyn Garden City, Hertfordshire, AL7 1EW Tel: (01707) 394949 Fax: (01707) 391311
E-mail: chromacol@easynet.co.uk

Jasco UK Ltd, 18 Oak Industrial Park, Chelmsford Road, Dunmow, Essex, CM6 1XN Tel: (01371) 876988 Fax: (01371) 875597
E-mail: inbox@jasco.co.uk

New Vision Associates Ltd, Vision Worksventnor Street, Bradford, West Yorkshire, BD3 9JP Tel: (01274) 728831 Fax: (01274) 308702
E-mail: sales@new-vision.co.uk

CHROMATOGRAPHY COLUMN PACKING MATERIALS

Alltech Assoicates Applied Science Ltd, 6 Kellet Road Industrial Estate, Kellet Road, Carnforth, Lancashire, LA5 9XP Tel: (01524) 734451 Fax: (01524) 733599
E-mail: sales@alltechweb.com

▶ Fortis Technologies Ltd, 34 Coalbrookdale Road, Clayhill Industrial Park, Neston, CH64 3UG Tel: 0151-336 2266 Fax: 0151-336 2669 E-mail: info@fortis-technologies.com

CHROMATOGRAPHY COLUMNS

Biotoge Ltd, Duffryn Business Park, Ystrad Mynach, Hengoed, Mid Glamorgan, CF82 7RJ Tel: (01443) 811811 Fax: (01443) 816552
E-mail: sales@jones-chrom.co.uk

▶ Fortis Technologies Ltd, 34 Coalbrookdale Road, Clayhill Industrial Park, Neston, CH64 3UG Tel: 0151-336 2266 Fax: 0151-336 2669 E-mail: info@fortis-technologies.com

CHROMATOGRAPHY EQUIPMENT

ATAC Ltd, 6 Redlands Centre, Redlands, Coulsdon, Surrey, CR5 2HT Tel: (020) 8763 9494 Fax: (020) 8763 9540
E-mail: atac@atacuk.com

Bio-chem Fluidics Ltd, Unit 2, College Park, Coldhams Lane, Cambridge, CB1 3HD Tel: (01223) 416642 Fax: (01223) 416787
E-mail: sales@omnifit.com

Biotoge Ltd, Duffryn Business Park, Ystrad Mynach, Hengoed, Mid Glamorgan, CF82 7RJ Tel: (01443) 811811 Fax: (01443) 816552
E-mail: sales@jones-chrom.co.uk

Cecil Instruments Ltd, Cambridge Road Industrial Estate, Milton, Cambridge, CB24 6AZ Tel: (01223) 420821 Fax: (01223) 420475
E-mail: info@cecilinstruments.com

Chromacol Ltd, Unit 3, Little Mundells, Mundells Industrial Estate, Welwyn Garden City, Hertfordshire, AL7 1EW Tel: (01707) 394949 Fax: (01707) 391311
E-mail: chromacol@easynet.co.uk

Metrohm UK Ltd, 2 Buckingham Industrial Park, Top Angel, Buckingham Industrial Estate, Buckingham, MK18 1TH Tel: (01280) 824824 Fax: (01280) 824800
E-mail: enquiry@metrohm.co.uk

Owens Polyscience Ltd, 34 Chester Road, Macclesfield, Cheshire, SK11 8DG Tel: (01625) 610118 Fax: (01625) 423850

▶ Polymer Laboratories Ltd, Essex Road, Church Stretton, Shropshire, SY6 6AX Tel: (01694) 723581 Fax: (01694) 722171
E-mail: sales@polymerlabs.com

S G E (Europe) Ltd, 1 Potters Lane, Kiln Farm, Milton Keynes, MK11 3LA Tel: (01908) 568844 Fax: (01908) 566790 E-mail: uk@sge.com

▶ Spectro Service Ltd, Top Station Road, Top Station Road Industrial Estate, Brackley, Northamptonshire, NN13 7UG Tel: (01280) 705577 Fax: (01280) 705510
E-mail: sales@spectroservice.co.uk

▶ Uson Ltd, Western Way, Bury St. Edmunds, Suffolk, IP33 3SP Tel: (01284) 760606 Fax: (01284) 763049 E-mail: info@uson.co.uk

Varian Ltd, 28 Manor Road, Walton-On-Thames, Surrey, KT12 2QF Tel: (01932) 898000 Fax: (01932) 228769

CHROME HARD PLATED CYLINDERS/PISTONS/RODDING

C A Honemaster Ltd, Unit 14 Malmesbury Road, Kingsditch Trading Estate, Cheltenham, Gloucestershire, GL51 9PL Tel: (01242) 584326 Fax: (01242) 226158
E-mail: kieran.reel@btconnect.com

CHROME HARD PLATED CYLINDERS/PISTONS/RODDING – *continued*

Hydraulic Supplies Ltd, Unit 5-6 Block 2, Wednesbury Trading Estate, Wednesbury, West Midlands, WS10 7JN Tel: 0121-505 3663 Fax: 0121-505 3375
E-mail: sales@hydraulicsupplies.co.uk

Neville Roe Industries Ltd, Euro Works, Liverpool Street, Sheffield, S9 2PU Tel: 0114-243 0395 Fax: 0114-243 3310
E-mail: enquiries@nevroeind.com

CHROME HARD PLATING SERVICES

Armoloy UK Ltd, Mammoth Drive, Wolverhampton Science Park, Wolverhampton, WV10 9TF Tel: (01902) 310375 Fax: (01902) 310075
E-mail: armoloyuk@aol.com

Dynasurf, Millbuck Way, Sandbach, Cheshire, CW11 3HT Tel: (01270) 763091 Fax: (01270) 766564 E-mail: dynasurf@dynasurf.com

G.B. Hard Chrome Ltd, 23-25 Nobel Square, Burnt Mills, Basildon, Essex, SS13 1LP Tel: 0845 8550608 Fax: (01268) 727524
E-mail: dan.griffiths@gbhard-chrome.co.uk

H D Simpson & Co Polishers Ltd, Downing Street Industrial Estate, Smethwick, West Midlands, B66 2JH Tel: 0121-558 3469 Fax: 0121-558 3469

H Reis Ltd, Powke Lane, Cradley Heath, West Midlands, B64 5QF Tel: (01384) 567727 Fax: (01384) 410317
E-mail: terry.reis@chromebar.co.uk

Healey & Sprowson Ltd, Stuart Road, Bredbury Park Industrial Estate, Bredbury, Stockport, Cheshire, SK6 2SR Tel: 0161-494 1126 Fax: 0161-406 6162E-mail: hs@absonline.net

▶ Hi Chrome (Europe) Ltd, Heathenford Industrial Estate, Widowhill Road, Burnley, Lancashire, BB10 2TT Tel: (01282) 418300 Fax: (01282) 418310
E-mail: sales@hycrome.com

I H C Plating (Nelson) Ltd, Unit 2 Valley Trading Estate, Southfield Street, Nelson, Lancashire, BB9 0LD Tel: (01282) 693195 Fax: (01282) 696117

John Stokes Ltd, 60 High Street, Princes End, Tipton, West Midlands, DY4 9HP Tel: 0121-520 6301 Fax: 0121-557 7191
E-mail: stokeschrome@hotmail.com

Metallizers (Heckmondwike) Ltd, Old White Lee Colliery, Leeds Road, Heckmondwike, West Yorkshire, WF16 9BH Tel: (01924) 473840 Fax: (01924) 473794

Michrome Electro Plating Ltd, Harrowbrook Road, Hinckley, Leicestershire, LE10 3DJ Tel: (01455) 637156 Fax: (01455) 637131

Neville Roe Industries Ltd, Euro Works, Liverpool Street, Sheffield, S9 2PU Tel: 0114-243 0395 Fax: 0114-243 3310
E-mail: enquiries@nevroeind.com

New Tech Finishing, Commercial Road, Walsall, WS2 7NQ Tel: (01922) 404604 Fax: (01922) 711083 E-mail: enquiries@ntfltd.co.uk

Niphos Metal Finishing Co. Ltd, 25 Hope Street, Crewe, CW2 7DR Tel: (01270) 214081 Fax: (01270) 214089

Poeton Cardiff Ltd, Penarth Road, Cardiff, CF11 8UL Tel: (029) 2038 8182 Fax: (029) 2038 8185 E-mail: cardiff@poeton.co.uk

Poeton Industries Ltd, Eastern Avenue, Gloucester, GL4 3DN Tel: (01452) 300500 Fax: (01452) 500400
E-mail: sales@poeton.co.uk

Poli Chrome Engineers Moulds Ltd, Adswood Road, Stockport, Cheshire, SK3 8HR Tel: 0161-477 7370 Fax: 0161-477 1020
E-mail: ianlusby1@hotmail.com

Polish Craft Ltd, 68g Sapcote Trading Centre, Wyrley Road, Birmingham, B6 7BN Tel: 0121-322 2344 Fax: 0121-322 2344

Reddish Electroplating, Mersey Street, Stockport, Cheshire, SK1 2HX Tel: 0161-480 7890 Fax: 0161-480 4383
E-mail: rep-sales@btconnect.com

Rockrome, 156 Sandy Road, Liverpool, L21 1AQ Tel: 0151-928 0080 Fax: 0151-928 8388

S W S Metal Treatments Ltd, Second Avenue, Trafford Park, Manchester, M17 1EE Tel: 0161-872 3569 Fax: 0161-848 7356
E-mail: enquiries@swsmetaltreatments.co.uk

Sharrod Hardchrome Co. Ltd, Hose Street, Tunstall, Stoke-on-Trent, ST6 5AL Tel: (01782) 815941

Walton Plating Ltd, 118 Ashley Road, Walton-on-Thames, Surrey, KT12 1HN Tel: (01932) 221206 Fax: (01932) 246699
E-mail: enquiries@waltonplating.co.uk

XL Plating Co, 99-103 Ryecroft Street, Gloucester, GL1 4NB Tel: (01452) 525400

CHROME PLATED STEEL TUBES

Kirkby Steel Tubes Ltd, Abbotsfield Road, Reginald Road Industrial Estat, St. Helens, Merseyside, WA9 4HU Tel: (01744) 830600 Fax: (01744) 830609E-mail: mail@kst.uk.com

Rothley Ltd, Macrome Road, Wolverhampton, WV6 9HG Tel: (01902) 756461 Fax: (01902) 745554 E-mail: sales@rothley.com

CHROME PLATING, DECORATIVE

Reeve Metal Finishing Co. Ltd, 40 Anne Road, Smethwick, West Midlands, B66 2NZ Tel: 0121-558 0692 Fax: 0121-558 4708
E-mail: cw@reevemetalfinishing.co.uk

CHROMIUM ELECTROPLATING

LWD Precision Engineering Co Ltd, 169 Elland Road, Leeds, LS11 8BY Tel: 0113-271 3097 Fax: 0113-271 8655
E-mail: sales@lwdeng.com

CHROMIUM PLATED GOODS

Liberty Plc, 210-220 Regent St, London, W1B 5AH Tel: (020) 7734 1234 Fax: (020) 7573 9876 E-mail: info@liberty.co.uk

CHROMIUM PLATING, *See also Chrome Hard Plating Services*

Armoloy UK Ltd, Mammoth Drive, Wolverhampton Science Park, Wolverhampton, WV10 9TF Tel: (01902) 310375 Fax: (01902) 310075
E-mail: armoloyuk@aol.com

D F King Electroplating, 5-7 Sandhurst Close, Kings Road, Canvey Island, Essex, SS8 0QY Tel: (01268) 695672 Fax: (01268) 511014

Derby Plating Services Ltd, 148 Abbey Street, Derby, DE22 3SS Tel: (01332) 382408 Fax: (01332) 382408

I H C Plating (Nelson) Ltd, Unit 2 Valley Trading Estate, Southfield Street, Nelson, Lancashire, BB9 0LD Tel: (01282) 693195 Fax: (01282) 696117

M A J Hi Spec Ltd, 1 Scott St, Keighley, West Yorkshire, BD21 2JJ Tel: (01535) 606524 Fax: (01535) 610255

Midland Chromium Plating Co. Ltd, 116 Aldridge Road, Perry Barr, Birmingham, B42 2TP Tel: 0121-356 9431 Fax: 0121-356 5891
E-mail: info@midchrome.co.uk

Nottingham Platers Ltd, Southwark Street, Nottingham, NG6 0DB Tel: 0115-978 4637 Fax: 0115-978 9754
E-mail: martin@chrome-platers.com

Nuneaton Fine Finishers, Maguire Industrial Estate, Unit 3 Torrington Avenue, Coventry, CV4 9HN Tel: (024) 7642 2002 Fax: (024) 7647 1460

Premier Plating Ltd, Lancaster Road, Cressex Business Park, High Wycombe, Buckinghamshire, HP12 3PY Tel: (01494) 533650 Fax: (01494) 473726
E-mail: gregmurray@premier-plating.co.uk

RCJ Metal Finishers Ltd, 3 Pindar Road, Hoddesdon, Hertfordshire, EN11 0BZ Tel: (01992) 467931 Fax: (01992) 471547
E-mail: john@rcjmf.co.uk

Reliable Stamping, 38 New John St West, Birmingham, B19 3NB Tel: 0121-359 6918 Fax: 0121-333 4691
E-mail: sales@reliable-stamping.co.uk

Satchrome Ltd, Unit 19 Birchills House Industrial Estate, Green Lane, Walsall, WS2 8LF Tel: (01922) 622721 Fax: (01922) 625353
E-mail: satchrome@yahoo.co.uk

Thomas H Gee & Co. Ltd, 271 Summer Lane, Birmingham, B19 2PX Tel: 0121-359 1279 Fax: 0121-359 7686
E-mail: sales@thomashgee.co.uk

Thomas HG & Co. Ltd, 78 Steward Street, Birmingham, B18 7AF Tel: 0121-454 0677 Fax: 0121-454 0677
E-mail: markf@thomashgee.co.uk

Tregunna's Metal Finishing Services, Hatton Row, London, NW8 8PP Tel: (020) 7262 5678 Fax: (020) 7724 2354
E-mail: sales@hattanmetalcraft.co.uk

West Bromwich Central Plating Co. Ltd, Great Bridge St, West Bromwich, West Midlands, B70 0DA Tel: 0121-557 5352

Willochrome Ltd, Westside, Jackson Street, St. Helens, Merseyside, WA9 3AT Tel: (01744) 738488 Fax: (01744) 23039

R. Wilson & Co. (Platers) Ltd, Zachrome Works, Sheffield Road, Whittington Moor, Chesterfield, Derbyshire, S41 8NH Tel: (01246) 450387 Fax: (01246) 455875
E-mail: office@zachrome.com

CHUCK JAWS

▶ Arbury Tools & Equipment Ltd, Whitacre Road, Industrial Estate, Nuneaton, Warwickshire, CV11 6BY Tel: (024) 7638 4896 Fax: (024) 7638 4896 E-mail: ronsinfo1@yahoo.co.uk

Thame Engineering Co. Ltd, Field End, Thame Road, Long Crendon, Aylesbury, Buckinghamshire, HP18 9EJ Tel: (01844) 208050 Fax: (01844) 201699
E-mail: sales@thame-eng.com

Universal Engineering Workholding Ltd, New Street, Netherton, Huddersfield, HD4 7EZ Tel: (01484) 663018 Fax: (01484) 663758
E-mail: sales@uew.co.uk

CHUCKS, *See also headings for particular types*

600 Group Plc, 600 House, Landmark Court, Revie Road, Leeds, LS11 8JT Tel: 0113-277 6100 Fax: 0113-276 5600
E-mail: sales@600group.com

S M W Autoblok, 8 The Metro Centre, Peterborough, PE2 7UH Tel: (01733) 394394 Fax: (01733) 394395
E-mail: sales@smwautoblok.co.uk

Thame Engineering Co. Ltd, Field End, Thame Road, Long Crendon, Aylesbury, Buckinghamshire, HP18 9EJ Tel: (01844) 208050 Fax: (01844) 201699
E-mail: sales@thame-eng.com

John Walton Machine Tools Ltd, Smithy Carr Lane, Brighouse, West Yorkshire, HD6 2HL Tel: (01484) 712507 Fax: (01484) 710549
E-mail: cyoung@chucks.co.uk

CHUCKS TO SPECIFICATION

Precision Products, 2a Penner Road, Havant, Hampshire, PO9 1QH Tel: (023) 9248 1848 Fax: (023) 9245 5024
E-mail: salesppp@aol.com

CHURCH CANDLES

Custom Candles Ltd, 12 Cross Lane, Coal Aston, Dronfield, Derbyshire, S18 3AL Tel: (01246) 414740 Fax: (01246) 290012
E-mail: sales@customcandles.co.uk

Ethos Candles Ltd, Quarry Fields, Mere, Warminster, Wiltshire, BA12 6LA Tel: (01747) 860960 Fax: (01747) 860934
E-mail: sales@charlesfarris.co.uk

Shearer Candles Ltd, 23 Robert Street, Glasgow, G51 3HB Tel: 0141-445 1066 Fax: 0141-445 1061 E-mail: sales@shearer-candles.com

CHURCH RESTORATION CONTRACTORS

A J Restoration Co Ltd, Restoration House, Second Avenue, Greasley St, Nottingham, NG6 8NE Tel: 0115-927 7044 Fax: 0115-976 3476 E-mail: ajrestoration.co@btconnect.com

Bowman E Sons Building Contractors, Cherryholt Road, Stamford, Lincolnshire, PE9 2EP Tel: (01780) 751015 Fax: (01780) 759051
E-mail: mail@ebowman.co.uk

W.S. Lusher & Son Ltd, School Lane, Sprowston, Norwich, NR7 8TH Tel: (01603) 426363 Fax: (01603) 787669

W Clarke, 98 Cardiff Road, Llandaff, Cardiff, CF5 2DT Tel: (029) 2056 2058 Fax: (029) 2056 2180 E-mail: wmcllandaff@aol.com

Weeks Restoration & Conservation, 7 Hurst Road, Eastbourne, East Sussex, BN21 2PJ Tel: (01323) 439899

CHURCH ROBES

J & M Sewing Services, 1 Charlotte Square, Newcastle upon Tyne, NE1 4XF Tel: 0191-232 9589 Fax: 0191-230 1215
E-mail: jandmsewing@btconnect.com

CHURCH WOODWORKERS OR WOODWORKING

J R Spalding, 55 Mill Street, Kingston upon Thames, Surrey, KT1 2RG Tel: (020) 8546 0363 Fax: (020) 8546 0363
E-mail: jrspalding.joinery@amserve.net

W Clarke, 98 Cardiff Road, Llandaff, Cardiff, CF5 2DT Tel: (029) 2056 2058 Fax: (029) 2056 2180 E-mail: wmcllandaff@aol.com

CHUTNEYS

▶ Gillies Fine Foods Ltd, Inchrory Drive, Dingwall, Ross-Shire, IV15 9XH Tel: (01349) 861100 Fax: (01349) 864400
E-mail: info@gilliesfinefoods.co.uk

CIDER

▶ Ralph D J Owen, Old Badland, New Radnor, Presteigne, Powys, LD8 2TG Tel: (01544) 350304 Fax: (01544) 350304
E-mail: james@ralphscider.fsnet.co.uk

CIDER VINEGAR

Aspall, The Cider House, Aspall Hall, Debenham, Stowmarket, Suffolk, IP14 6PD Tel: (01728) 860510 Fax: (01728) 861031
E-mail: barry@aspall.co.uk

CIGARETTE BUTT BINS WITH CIGARETTE EXTINGUISHER

▶ Bins and Things Ltd, 30 High Warren Close, Appleton, Warrington, WA4 5SB Tel: 07771 638413

CIGARETTE LIGHTERS

A1 Promotional Pens, 2-4 Mount Pleasant Road, Aldershot, Hampshire, GU12 4NL Tel: (01252) 320571 Fax: (01252) 403635
E-mail: sales@pens.co.uk

Accutec Design Ltd, Unit C3 Haysbridge Business Centre, Brickhouse Lane, South Godstone, Godstone, Surrey, RH9 8JW Tel: (01342) 842129 Fax: (01342) 844027

Alfred Dunhill Ltd, 27 Knightsbridge, London, SW1X 7YB Tel: (020) 7838 8000 Fax: (020) 7838 8333

▶ Savage No.1, 89 Delphi Way, Crookhorn, Waterlooville, Hampshire, PO7 8AY Tel: (07745) 119063
E-mail: savageno1@ntlworld.com

▶ Swedish Match UK Ltd, Sword House, Totteridge Road, High Wycombe, Buckinghamshire, HP13 6DG Tel: (01494) 533300 Fax: (01494) 437459
E-mail: gareth.newton@swedishmatch.co.uk

▶ Wholesale Movie TV Music Gifts Ltd, 1St Floor, 1 Chapel Street, Bridlington, North Humberside, YO15 2DR Tel: (01262) 677730 Fax: (01262) 675702

CIGARETTE MACHINERY/PLANT

Focke & Co. UK Ltd, Courtenay Works, Monument Way East, Woking, Surrey, GU21 5LY Tel: (01483) 756094 Fax: (01483) 765099 E-mail: fockeuk@btconnect.com

Hauni London Ltd, Hope House, 45 Great Peter Street, London, SW1P 3LT Tel: (020) 7222 3956 Fax: (020) 7222 8648

▶ W. Salsbury Ltd, 22a-24 Newnham Street, Bedford, MK40 3JR Tel: (01234) 354286

CIGARETTE PACKING MACHINE MAINTENANCE/REPAIR SERVICES

Focke & Co. UK Ltd, Courtenay Works, Monument Way East, Woking, Surrey, GU21 5LY Tel: (01483) 756094 Fax: (01483) 765099 E-mail: fockeuk@btconnect.com

CIGARETTE PACKING MACHINES

Focke & Co. UK Ltd, Courtenay Works, Monument Way East, Woking, Surrey, GU21 5LY Tel: (01483) 756094 Fax: (01483) 765099 E-mail: fockeuk@btconnect.com

Colin Mear Engineering Ltd, Combe Wood, Combe St Nicholas, Chard, Somerset, TA20 3NL Tel: (01460) 67351 Fax: (01460) 65661 E-mail: cme@cme-ltd.com

CIGARETTE PAPERS

Sinclair Collis Ltd, Unit 4 & 5, Laches Close, Four Ashes, Wolverhampton, WV10 7DZ Tel: (01902) 797272 Fax: (01902) 797270

Rizla UK Ltd, Severn Road, Treforest Industrial Estate, Pontypridd, Mid Glamorgan, CF37 5SP Tel: (01443) 841641 Fax: (01443) 841138

CIGARETTE VENDING MACHINE OPERATING SERVICES

Sinclair Collis Ltd, Unit 4 & 5, Laches Close, Four Ashes, Wolverhampton, WV10 7DZ Tel: (01902) 797272 Fax: (01902) 797270

Cranes Ltd, 14 Valley Side Parade, London, E4 8AJ Tel: (020) 8524 3928 Fax: (020) 8559 4459
E-mail: sales@cranescigarettevending.co.uk

▶ Forbidden Fruits, Telford Way, Severalls Industrial Park, Colchester, CO4 9QP Tel: (01206) 514049 Fax: (0870) 1693473
E-mail: enquiry@forbiddenfruits.net

W E Rudd Ltd, Unit 23 Louis Pearlman Centre, Goulton Street, Hull, HU3 4DL Tel: (01482) 327792

▶ W. Salsbury Ltd, 22a-24 Newnham Street, Bedford, MK40 3JR Tel: (01234) 354286

CIGARETTE VENDING MACHINES

Sinclair Collis Ltd, Unit 4 & 5, Laches Close, Four Ashes, Wolverhampton, WV10 7DZ Tel: (01902) 797272 Fax: (01902) 797270

▶ Forbidden Fruits, Telford Way, Severalls Industrial Park, Colchester, CO4 9QP Tel: (01206) 514049 Fax: (0870) 1693473
E-mail: enquiry@forbiddenfruits.net

CIGARETTE VENDING MACHINES – *continued*

Precision Vending Machines Ltd, Unit 2, Avonside Industrial Estate, Feeder Road, St. Philips, Bristol, BS2 0UB Tel: 0117-972 3232 Fax: 0117-972 3887

▶ W. Salsbury Ltd, 22a-24 Newnham Street, Bedford, MK40 3JR Tel: (01234) 354286

CIGARETTES

Gallaher Group plc, Members Hill, Brooklands Road, Weybridge, Surrey, KT13 0QU Tel: (01932) 859777 Fax: (01932) 832792 E-mail: info@gallaherltd.com

Imperial Tobacco Ltd, PO Box 244, Bristol, BS99 7UJ Tel: 0117-966 7957 Fax: 0117-966 7405 E-mail: keith.tatham@uk.imptob.com

CIGARS

Donatel Freres Ltd, The Vintage House, 42 Old Compton Street, London, W1D 4LR Tel: (020) 7437 2592 Fax: (020) 7734 1174 E-mail: vintagehouse.co@virgin.net

James J. Fox & Robert Lewis, 19 St. James Street, London, SW1A 1ES Tel: (020) 7493 9009 Fax: (020) 7495 0097 E-mail: brady@jjfox.co.uk

Imperial Tobacco Ltd, PO Box 244, Bristol, BS99 7UJ Tel: 0117-966 7957 Fax: 0117-966 7405 E-mail: keith.tatham@uk.imptob.com

▶ Swedish Match UK Ltd, Sword House, Totteridge Road, High Wycombe, Buckinghamshire, HP13 6DG Tel: (01494) 533300 Fax: (01494) 437459 E-mail: gareth.newton@swedishmatch.co.uk

CINE EQUIPMENT, *See also headings for particular types*

P E C Video Ltd, 65-66 Dean Street, London, W1D 4PL Tel: (020) 7437 4633 Fax: (020) 7025 1320 E-mail: sales@pec.co.uk

CINE FILM EDITING EQUIPMENT

Cintel International Ltd, Watton Road, Ware, Hertfordshire, SG12 0AE Tel: (01920) 463939 Fax: (01920) 460803 E-mail: sales@cintel.co.uk

CINE FILM PROCESSING SYSTEMS/EQUIPMENT

Cintel International Ltd, Watton Road, Ware, Hertfordshire, SG12 0AE Tel: (01920) 463939 Fax: (01920) 460803 E-mail: sales@cintel.co.uk

Photomec (London) Ltd, Porters Wood, Valley Road Industrial Estate, St. Albans, Hertfordshire, AL3 6NU Tel: (01727) 850711 Fax: (01727) 843991 E-mail: photomec@photomec.co.uk

CINEMA FILM DISTRIBUTION

▶ Final Events, PO Box 41, Derby, DE1 9ZR Tel: 0870 027 3656 Fax: 0870 027 3656 E-mail: info@finalevents.co.uk

CINEMA PROJECTION ROOM EQUIPMENT

Border Television Ltd, The Television Centre, Carlisle, CA1 3NT Tel: (01228) 525101 Fax: (01228) 541384 E-mail: ian@border-tv.com

CINEMA SUPPLY SERVICES

▶ Renovation Seating Service, 96 Stone Cross La North, Lowton, Warrington, WA3 2SG Tel: (07766) 727811 Fax: (01942) 723033 E-mail: renovation.seating@fsmail.net

Jack Roe (CS) Ltd, Poplar House, Peterstow, Ross-On-Wye, Herefordshire, HR9 6JR Tel: (01989) 567474 Fax: (01989) 762206 E-mail: sales@jack-roe.co.uk

Trailers Distribution Services, Unit 2 Charnley Fold Lane, Bamber Bridge, Preston, PR5 6AA Tel: (01772) 315557 Fax: (01772) 315939 E-mail: trailers.ltd@btinternet.com

Watershed Media Centre, 1 Canons Road, Bristol, BS1 5TX Tel: 0117-927 6444 Fax: 0117-921 3958 E-mail: admin@watershed.co.uk

CIRCLIP MANUFRS

Cirteq Ltd, Hayfield, Colne Road, Keighley, West Yorkshire, BD20 8QP Tel: (01535) 633333 Fax: (01535) 632966 E-mail: sales@cirteq.com

Clarendon Engineering Ltd, 30 High Street, Earl Shilton, Leicester, LE9 7DG Tel: (01455) 841200 Fax: (01455) 841110 E-mail: sales@clarendoneng.co.uk

Seager Bearings Ltd, 52 Goldsmith Road, Birmingham, B14 7EL Tel: 0121-444 5391 Fax: 0121-443 5229 E-mail: sales@seager-bearings.co.uk

Springmasters Ltd, Arthur Street, Redditch, Worcestershire, B98 8LF Tel: (01527) 521000 Fax: (01527) 528866 E-mail: sales@springmasters.com

Supaseal (U K) Ltd, PO Box 5329, Market Harborough, Leicestershire, LE16 7PT Tel: (01858) 434141 Fax: (01858) 434717 E-mail: admin@supaseal.co.uk

UK Spring Supplies, 7 Elmwood, Sawbridgeworth, Hertfordshire, CM21 9NL Tel: (01279) 723666 Fax: (01279) 723729 E-mail: larryelmwood@aol.com

Universal Seals & Bearings Ltd, Waterloo Indust Park, Upper Brook Street, Stockport, Cheshire, SK1 3BP Tel: 0161-429 0287 Fax: 0161-477 2940

CIRCUIT BREAKER (CB) MONITORING EQUIPMENT

▶ Spares-Direct-2-U, 20 Allerton Grange Gardens, Moortown, Leeds, LS17 6LL Tel: 0113 2263384 Fax: 0113 2955753 E-mail: info@sparesdirect2u.com

CIRCUIT BREAKERS (CB), *See also headings for particular types*

Albol Electronic & Mechanical Products Ltd, Crown Buildings, Crown Street, London, SE5 0UR Tel: (020) 7703 2311 Fax: (020) 7703 3282 E-mail: sales@albol.co.uk

Arrow Components, Unit 5 Mill Court, Spindle Way, Crawley, West Sussex, RH10 1TT Tel: (01293) 558900 Fax: (01293) 558901

Barnbrook Systems Ltd, 25 Fareham Park Road, Fareham, Hampshire, PO15 6LD Tel: (01329) 847722 Fax: (01329) 844132 E-mail: barnbrook@aol.co.uk

C M T S, 7 Churchfield Road, Sudbury, Suffolk, CO10 2YA Tel: (01787) 468685 Fax: (01787) 466887 E-mail: sales@cmts.co.uk

Contactum Ltd, Victoria Works, Edgware Road, London, NW2 6LF Tel: (020) 8452 6366 Fax: (020) 8208 3340 E-mail: general@contactum.co.uk

D V R Electrical Wholesale Ltd, Unit 1 Dawson Road, Bletchley, Milton Keynes, MK1 1LH Tel: (01908) 271555 Fax: (01908) 271367 E-mail: info@dvr.co.uk

Electrium Sales Ltd, Walkmill Business Park, Walkmill Way, Cannock, Staffordshire, WS11 0XE Tel: (01543) 455000 Fax: (01543) 455001 E-mail: darren.garbett@electrium.co.uk

Electrium Sales Ltd, Sharston Road, Wythenshawe, Manchester, M22 4RA Tel: 0161-998 5454 Fax: 0161-945 1587

Induction Services Ltd, 16 Wharfedale Cresent, Droitwich, Worcestershire, WR9 8TU Tel: (01905) 771669 Fax: (01905) 797609 E-mail: sales@inductionservices.co.uk

National Semiconductor UK Ltd, Larkfield Industrial Estate, Greenock, Renfrewshire, PA16 0EQ Tel: (01475) 633733 Fax: (01475) 638515

Novar ED&S, The Arnold Centre, Paycocke Road, Basildon, Essex, SS14 3EA Tel: (01268) 563000 Fax: (01268) 563538 E-mail: mk_reception@nova.com

Schneider Electric Ltd, 120 New Cavendish Street, London, W1W 6XX Tel: (0870) 6088608 Fax: (0870) 6088606

Terasaki Europe Ltd, 80 Beardmore Way, Clydebank, Dunbartonshire, G81 4HT Tel: 0141-565 1600 Fax: 0141-952 9246 E-mail: marketing@terasaki.com

CIRCULAR BASE DRUM LINERS

Chiltern Plastics Ltd, Unit 31, Jubilee Trade Centre, Jubilee Road, Letchworth Garden City, Hertfordshire, SG6 1SP Tel: (01462) 676262 Fax: (01462) 481075 E-mail: carrol@chilternplastics.co.uk

CIRCULAR CUTTERS

Blade & Cutter Ltd, Unit 5 Hattersley Industrial Estate, Stockport Road, Hyde, Cheshire, SK14 3QT Tel: 0161-367 8240 Fax: 0161-367 8785

City Press Knives, 101 Weymouth Street, Leicester, LE4 6FR Tel: 0116-266 0709 Fax: 0116-266 0711

CIRCULAR DICHROISM SPECTROMETERS

Applied Photophysics, 203 Kingston Road, Leatherhead, Surrey, KT22 7PB Tel: (01372) 386537 Fax: (01372) 386477 E-mail: sales@photophysics.com

CIRCULAR DIE THREAD ROLLS

Wexco Ltd, Earlswood Trading Estate, Poolhead Lane, Earlswood, Solihull, West Midlands, B94 5EW Tel: (01564) 703624 Fax: (01564) 703066 E-mail: sales@wexco.co.uk

CIRCULAR DISTRIBUTION

C W T Advertising, 121 Becontree Avenue, Dagenham, Essex, RM8 2UJ Tel: (020) 8590 0083

Holborn Direct Mail, Capacity House, 2-6 Rothsay Street, London, SE1 4UD Tel: (020) 7407 6444 Fax: (020) 7357 6065 E-mail: peter@holborndirectmail.co.uk

Mail Marketing (Scotland) Ltd, 42 Methil Street, Glasgow, G14 0SZ Tel: 0141-950 2222 Fax: 0141-950 2726 E-mail: glasgow@mailmarkscot.com

▶ Marketing Direct, Northfield Road, Princes Risborough, Buckinghamshire, HP27 0HY Tel: (07734) 951179

TNT Post UK Ltd, 1 Globeside Business Park, Fieldhouse Lane, Marlow, Buckinghamshire, SL7 1HY Tel: (01628) 771232 Fax: (01628) 816600

CIRCULAR MULTIPIN CONNECTORS

Dialight B L P Ltd, Exning Road, Newmarket, Suffolk, CB8 0AX Tel: (01638) 665161 Fax: (01638) 660718 E-mail: sales@blpcomp.com

Lemo U K Ltd, 12 North Street, Worthing, West Sussex, BN11 1DU Tel: (01903) 234543 Fax: (01903) 206231 E-mail: uk.office.services@lemo.com

Radiall Ltd, Ground Floor, 6 The Ground Union Office Park, Packet Boat Lane, Uxbridge, Middlesex, UB8 2GH Tel: (01895) 425000 Fax: (01895) 425010 E-mail: info@radiall.com

CIRCULAR SAW BLADES

Burton Saw International Ltd, Trading Estate, Valmar Road, London, SE5 9NW Tel: (020) 7737 3577 Fax: (020) 7733 2368 E-mail: blades@burtonsaw.co.uk

CIRCULAR SAWING MACHINERY

Brunner Machine Tools Ltd, 6 Colville Road, London, W3 8BL Tel: (020) 8992 6011 Fax: (020) 8992 7559 E-mail: sales@brunnermachine.co.uk

CIRCULAR SAWS

Atkins Saws, 53 Richmond Road, Solihull, West Midlands, B92 7RR Tel: 0121-707 1600

Atkinson Walker Saws Ltd, Bower Street, Sheffield, S3 8RU Tel: 0114-272 4748 Fax: 0114-272 5065 E-mail: sales@atkinson-walker-saws.co.uk

Birmingham Saw Blades Ltd, 117 Station Road, Cradley Heath, West Midlands, B64 6PL Tel: 0121-559 5931 Fax: 0121-561 5121 E-mail: sales@dynashape.co.uk

F S W Tooling, Brewery Road, Hoddesdon, Hertfordshire, EN11 8HF Tel: (01992) 469538 Fax: (01992) 468996

Hitachi Power Tools (UK) Ltd, Precedent Drive, Rooksley, Milton Keynes, MK13 8PJ Tel: (01908) 354700 Fax: (01908) 606642 E-mail: info@hitachi-powertools.co.uk

Martin & Partners Ltd, 10-11 Regent Square, Northampton, NN1 2NQ Tel: (01604) 639466 Fax: (01604) 620552 E-mail: martin.partners@virgin.net

S C M Group UK Ltd, Dabell Avenue, Nottingham, NG6 8WA Tel: 0115-977 0044 Fax: 0115-977 0946

Sharpening & Supply (Midlands) & Co., 1 Queen Street, Darlaston, Wednesbury, West Midlands, WS10 8JF Tel: 0121-526 6800 Fax: 0121-526 2256 E-mail: sharpsupplytool@westmids.fsbusiness.co.uk

South Midland Saws Ltd, Lincoln Road, Cressex Business Park, High Wycombe, Buckinghamshire, HP12 3RQ Tel: (01494) 520612 Fax: (01494) 465373 E-mail: sales@scsaws.co.uk

Thames Valley Saw Services Ltd, Gravel Lane, Drayton, Abingdon, Oxfordshire, OX14 4HY Tel: (01235) 550088 Fax: (01235) 553150 E-mail: sales@tvss.co.uk

CIRCULAR SLITTING KNIVES

B B S Cutter, 282 Upper Balsall Heath Road, Birmingham, B12 9DR Tel: 0121-440 4034 Fax: 0121-446 4090 E-mail: info@bbscutters.co.uk

CIRCULATING PUMPS

A B S Pumps Ltd, Astral Towers, 5TH Floor, Betts Way, Crawley, West Sussex, RH10 9UY Tel: (01293) 558140 Fax: (01293) 527972

Sandycott Pump Mnfrs, Manor House, Church Street, Eckington, Sheffield, S21 4BH Tel: (01246) 436632 Fax: (01246) 433372 E-mail: sales@hydron-pumps.com

CIRCULATORS

Melcom Electronics, Elliott House, Gogmore Lane, Chertsey, Surrey, KT16 9AP Tel: (01932) 565544 Fax: (01932) 569988 E-mail: melcomsales@melcom.co.uk

RF & Noise Components Ltd, 10 Crouchmans Yd, Poynters Lane, Shoeburyness, Southend-on-Sea, SS3 9TS Tel: (01702) 535298 Fax: (01702) 535299 E-mail: sales@rfandnoisecomponents.co.uk

CIRCUS PROPS/SPECIAL EQUIPMENT, CUSTOM BUILT

▶ Eve Lowrie Props, 12 Aaron Lodge, 144 Burnt Ash Hill, London, SE12 0HU Tel: (07919) 411872 E-mail: evelowrie@hotmail.com

S P Engineering, M Hawthorns Industrial Estate, Middlemore Road, Handsworth, Birmingham, B21 0BH Tel: 0121-554 1404 Fax: 0121-523 5834

CITRATES

R A Watts Ltd, 36-38 Woodcote Road, Wallington, Surrey, SM6 0NN Tel: (020) 8647 1074 Fax: (020) 8773 3595 E-mail: sales@rawatts.fsbusiness.co.uk

Tate & Lyle Citric Acid, Denison Road, Selby, North Yorkshire, YO8 8EF Tel: (01757) 703691 Fax: (01757) 701468

CITRIC ACID

▶ Koenig & Wiegand, 45 Sarisbury Close, Tadley, Hampshire, RG26 3SZ Tel: 0118-981 9481 Fax: (020) 7117 3273 E-mail: s.hewett@koenig-wiegand.de

Tate & Lyle Citric Acid, Denison Road, Selby, North Yorkshire, YO8 8EF Tel: (01757) 703691 Fax: (01757) 701468

CIVIL ENGINEERING AND PUBLIC WORKS CONTRACTORS

▶ A Coupland Surfacing Ltd, Pudding Lane, Off Warden Tree Lane, Pinchbeck, Spalding, Lincolnshire, PE11 3TJ Tel: (01775) 767110 Fax: (01775) 711246

▶ A H Lewis Contractors, 50 Cradge Bank, Spalding, Lincolnshire, PE11 3AB Tel: (01775) 411570

▶ A T Knott & Sons, Cornelian Cottages, 76a Manor Road, Wallington, Surrey, SM6 0AB Tel: (020) 8669 5208 Fax: (020) 8669 5150

A.W. Construction Ltd, Old House, Gorsey Lane, Coleshill, Birmingham, B46 1JU Tel: (01675) 432102 Fax: (01675) 432112 E-mail: info@awconstruction.plc.uk

A W Hardy & Co. Ltd, Stock Road, Southend-on-Sea, SS2 5QG Tel: (01702) 462721 Fax: (01702) 469062 E-mail: enqs@hardygroup.demon.co.uk

▶ Adana Construction Ltd, Europa Business Park, Bird Hall Lane, Stockport, Cheshire, SK3 0XA Tel: 0161-428 1613

Aftercrete Constructional Engineering Co. Ltd, 5 Nursery Road, Luton, LU3 2RG Tel: (01582) 507270 Fax: (01582) 493878 E-mail: neill@aftercrete.co.uk

▶ Agetur Ltd, St. Davids Court, Top Station Road, Brackley, Northamptonshire, NN13 7UG Tel: (01280) 702121 Fax: (01280) 703088

▶ Martin Alan Construction Ltd, Limemount, 5 Dudhope Terrace, Dundee, DD3 6HG Tel: (01382) 206330 Fax: (01382) 206331

Alfred Mcalpine plc, Kinnaird House, 1 Pall Mall East, London, SW1Y 5AZ Tel: (020) 7930 6255 Fax: (020) 7839 6902

▶ Alfred Mcalpine plc, Trafford Park, Manchester, M17 1JJ Tel: 0161-848 7666 Fax: 0161-872 6887

Alfred Mcalpine plc, West Carr Road, Retford, Nottinghamshire, DN22 7SW Tel: (01777) 714200 Fax: (01777) 714233 E-mail: sales@alfred-mcalpine.com

▶ Alfred Mcalpine Infrastructure Servicess, 1 Lilybank Street, Hamilton, Lanarkshire, ML3 6NN Tel: (01698) 281319 Fax: (01698) 286547

▶ All Way Surfacing & Construction Ltd, 1 Fermoy, Frome, Somerset, BA11 2EP Tel: (01373) 473641 Fax: (01373) 452532

▶ Alltgoch Construction, Cwrtnewydd, Llanybyder, Dyfed, SA40 9YJ Tel: (01570) 434337 Fax: (01437) 899353

Allton Contractors Ltd, PO Box 4, Ripon, North Yorkshire, HG4 1JD Tel: (01765) 604351 Fax: (01765) 600669 E-mail: alton@eborconcrete.co.uk

CIVIL ENGINEERING AND PUBLIC WORKS CONTRACTORS – *continued*

Alston Lime Stone Co. Ltd, PO Box 8, Chester le Street, County Durham, DH3 2SS Tel: 0191-410 9611 Fax: 0191-492 0729

Amec Process & Energy Ltd, 76-78 Old Street, London, EC1V 9RU Tel: (020) 7539 5800 Fax: (020) 7539 5900 E-mail: commercial@amec.com

▶ Amec Utilities Design & Build Ltd, 65 Bonnington Road, Edinburgh, EH6 5JQ Tel: 0131-553 7300 Fax: 0131-553 6956

▶ Amey Infer- Structure Services Ltd, Second Floor, 1 Redcliff Street, Bristol, BS1 6QZ Tel: 0117-934 8836

Anderton Kitchen Ltd, Braconash Road, Leyland, PR25 3ZE Tel: (01772) 433577 Fax: (01772) 622402 E-mail: anderton-kitchen@btclick.com

Anglo-Holt Construction Ltd, 150 Birmingham Road, West Bromwich, West Midlands, B70 6QT Tel: 0121-525 6717 Fax: 0121-553 4701 E-mail: sales@anglo-holt.co.uk

Armagh Construction Ltd, 14 Ennislare Road, Armagh, BT60 2AX Tel: (028) 3752 3047 Fax: (028) 3752 3166 E-mail: acl_scc@ireland.com

Armfield, Heriot House, 88-90 Guildford Street, Chertsey, Surrey, KT16 9AD Tel: (01932) 566633 Fax: (01932) 566639

Arnold B Johnston, Dean Road, Yate, Bristol, BS37 5NR Tel: (01454) 316175 Fax: (01454) 884455 E-mail: mail@erh.co.uk

Arqiva Ltd, Unit 13, Garonor Way, Portbury, Bristol, BS20 7XE Tel: (01275) 371371 Fax: (01275) 371269

▶ Ashworth Norman Ltd, Mellor Street, Rochdale, Lancashire, OL11 5BT Tel: (01706) 648501 Fax: (01706) 345721

Atkin John Construction Ltd, Viking Place, Cardiff, CF10 4UU Tel: (029) 2044 2060 Fax: (029) 2044 2065 E-mail: atkintradespec@enterprise.net

Austick Construction Ltd, West Park View, Dudley, Cramlington, Northumberland, NE23 7AA Tel: 0191-250 2425 Fax: 0191-250 2450 E-mail: austickconstruction@hotmail.co.uk

B C D Marine Ltd, Vanguard House, Vanguard Road, Gapton Hall Industrial Estate, Great Yarmouth, Norfolk, NR31 0NT Tel: (01493) 444002 Fax: (01493) 652576

B C Dyson & Co., Prescott Lodge, Prescott Street, Halifax, West Yorkshire, HX1 2QW Tel: (01422) 360934 Fax: (01422) 320379 E-mail: b.c.dyson@bt.openworld.com

▶ B J Process & Pipeline Service, Suffolk Road, Great Yarmouth, Norfolk, NR31 0ER Tel: (01493) 442398 Fax: (01493) 656258

B & K Building Services Ltd, Peveril House, Alfreton Road, Derby, DE21 4AG Tel: (01332) 331444 Fax: (01332) 291067 E-mail: bkbs@rwkhouse.co.uk

B L Refrigeration & Air Conditioning Ltd, Unit 3, Channel Commercial Park, Queens Island, Belfast, BT3 9DT Tel: (028) 9045 3325 Fax: (028) 9045 0073 E-mail: info@blgroup.co.uk

Balfour Beatty, Chaddock Lane, Worsley, Manchester, M28 1XW Tel: 0161-790 3000 Fax: 0161-703 5307

Balfour Beatty Construction Ltd, 23 Ravelston Terrace, Edinburgh, EH4 3TW Tel: 0131-332 9411 Fax: 0131-332 5937 E-mail: info@bbcl.co.uk

Balfour Beatty Construction International Ltd, 7 Mayday Road, Thornton Heath, Surrey, CR7 7XA Tel: (020) 8684 6922 Fax: (020) 8710 5222

BAM Ritchies, Nailsea Wall, Kenn Pier, Clevedon, North West Somerset, BS21 6UE Tel: 01275 875338 Fax: 01275 870076 E-mail: ritchies@bamritchies.co.uk

Baram Ltd, Unit 1 Station Hill, Curdridge, Southampton, SO30 2DN Tel: (01489) 785086 Fax: (01489) 785929 E-mail: baramltd@aol.com

S.P. Bardwell Ltd, Mapledean Indi Estate, Maldon Rado, Latchingdon, Chelmsford, CM3 6LG Tel: (01621) 742742 Fax: (01621) 741723 E-mail: steve@spbardwell.co.uk

▶ Barhale Construction plc, Bushey & Oxhey Railway Yard, Pinner Road, Watford, WD19 4EA Tel: (01923) 800864 Fax: 01923 655656 E-mail: info@barhale.co.uk

Barnes Group Ltd, 6 Bermuda Road, Ransoms Euro Park, Ipswich, IP3 9RU Tel: (01473) 272222 Fax: (01473) 272955 E-mail: cbruce@barnesconstruction.co.uk

▶ Barr Ltd, Killoch Depot, Ochiltree, Cumnock, Ayrshire, KA18 2RL Tel: (01290) 700681

Barr Holdings Ltd, 100 Inchinnan Road, Paisley, Renfrewshire, PA3 2RE Tel: 0141-848 8000 Fax: 0141-848 8001 E-mail: info@barr.co.uk

Barton Plant Ltd, Cranford Road, Burton Latimer, Kettering, Northamptonshire, NN15 5TB Tel: (01536) 722100 Fax: (01536) 722714 E-mail: enquiries@barton-plant.co.uk

Beaver International, Station Road, Plumtree, Plumtree, Nottingham, NG12 5NA Tel: 0115-937 5900 Fax: 0115-937 4074

Bechtel Holdings Ltd, 245 Hammersmith Road, London, W6 8DP Tel: (020) 8846 5111 Fax: (020) 8846 6940

▶ Bedrock Crushing & Recycled Materials Ltd, Bow Depot, Marshgate Sidings, London, E15 2PB Tel: (020) 8503 0006

▶ Bellstan Ltd, Old Post House, Wood Lane, Beech Hill, Reading, RG7 2BE Tel: 0118-988 3413 Fax: 0118-988 2820

Benson Bros Bristol Ltd, Carlton Lodge, 90 Gloucester Road, Patchway, Bristol, BS34 6PZ Tel: 0117-969 4241 Fax: 0117-931 2028

Bethell Group plc, Dane House Europa Trading Estate, Stoneclough Road, Radcliffe, Manchester, M26 1GE Tel: (01204) 439100 Fax: (01204) 439101 E-mail: mail@bethell.co.uk

Bierrum Structural Services Ltd, 105 High Street, Houghton Regis, Dunstable, Bedfordshire, LU5 5BJ Tel: (01582) 845745 Fax: (01582) 845746 E-mail: admin@bierrum.co.uk

Birch Bros Kidderminster Ltd, Barracks Road, Sandy Lane Industrial Estate, Stourport-On-Severn, Worcestershire, DY13 9QB Tel: (01299) 826227 Fax: (01299) 826229 E-mail: civils@birch-brothers.co.uk

Birse Construction Ltd, Humber Road, Barton-upon-Humber, South Humberside, DN18 5BW Tel: (01652) 633222 Fax: (01652) 633360 E-mail: birseho@birse.co.uk

C.A. Blackwell (Contracts) Ltd, Coggeshall Road, Earls Colne, Colchester, CO6 2JX Tel: (01787) 223131 Fax: (01787) 224391 E-mail: enquires@cablackwell.co.uk

Blueboar Farm Contracts Ltd, London Road, Dunchurch, Rugby, Warwickshire, CV23 9LH Tel: (01788) 810854 Fax: (01788) 817100 E-mail: enquiries@blueboarcontracts.co.uk

Border Construction Ltd, Marconi Road, Brough Road Industrial Estate, Carlisle, CA2 7NA Tel: (01228) 522296 Fax: (01228) 514928 E-mail: admin@border-construction.co.uk

▶ Border Paving Ltd, Maltkiln Farm, Chapel Lane, Bronington, Whitchurch, Shropshire, SY13 3HR Tel: (01948) 780902 Fax: (01948) 780630

Bowsprit Contracting Ltd, J The Henfield Business Park, Shoreham Road, Henfield, West Sussex, BN5 9SL Tel: (01273) 491499 Fax: (01273) 491982 E-mail: enquiries@bowspritltd.co.uk

Bristlewand Ltd, 48 Ashton Vale Road, Bristol, BS3 2HQ Tel: 0117-963 6141 Fax: 0117-963 1954 E-mail: bristlewand@kennygroup.co.uk

Brock plc, New Hey, Chester Road, Great Sutton, Ellesmere Port, CH66 2LS Tel: 0151-339 8113 Fax: 0151-347 1254

▶ Brookside Construction, 19a Church Street, Oadby, Leicester, LE2 5DB Tel: 0116-271 0680 Fax: 0116-271 0991 E-mail: caroline@brooksideconstruction.co.uk

Buckle & Davies Construction Ltd, 4 Little Langlands, East Hagbourne, Didcot, Oxfordshire, OX11 9TA Tel: (01235) 819586 Fax: (01235) 819586

▶ Burdens, Whitehall Industrial Estate, Whitehall Road, Leeds, LS12 5JB Tel: 0113-231 1339 Fax: 0113-231 1889

Butterley Ltd, Langthwaite Grange Industrial Estate, South Kirkby, Pontefract, West Yorkshire, WF9 3AP Tel: (01977) 643461 Fax: (01977) 655353

▶ C & D Facilities & Ground Maintenance, 38 Wendover Way, Tilehurst, Reading, RG30 4RU Tel: 0118-942 3999 Fax: 0118-942 6682

C D L Construction Co Egham Ltd, Lynchford Lane, Farnborough, Hampshire, GU14 6JD Tel: (01252) 513388 Fax: (01252) 518791

C J Thorne & Co. Ltd, Union Point, Ridgewood, Uckfield, East Sussex, TN22 5SS Tel: (01825) 764123 Fax: (01825) 764126 E-mail: info@thornegroupuk.com

C R Reynolds Construction Ltd, Gibson Lane, Melton, North Ferriby, North Humberside, HU14 3HH Tel: (01482) 637373 Fax: (01482) 637370 E-mail: crreynold@dial.hightec.com

Cameron Brook & Associates, 1 Royal Oak Passage, High Street, Huntingdon, Cambridgeshire, PE29 3EA Tel: (01480) 436236 Fax: (01480) 436336 E-mail: sales@cameronbrook.co.uk

▶ Campbell Construction (Liverpool) Ltd, Westport Business Complex, Bankhall Lane, Liverpool, L20 8EW Tel: 0151-922 2244

Can Geotechnical Ltd, Smeckley Wood Close, Chesterfield Trading Estate, Chesterfield, Derbyshire, S41 9PZ Tel: (01246) 261111 Fax: (01246) 261626 E-mail: info@can.ltd.uk

▶ Cane Contractors, 14 Wadhurst Close, Bognor Regis, West Sussex, PO21 5LD Tel: (01243) 825139 Fax: (01243) 825139 E-mail: elieencane@btconnect.com

Capell Construction Ltd, Tollemache Road North, Spittlegate Level, Grantham, Lincolnshire, NG31 7UH Tel: (01476) 592000 Fax: (01476) 592100 E-mail: janem@capellconstruction.co.uk

▶ Cappagh Contractors Construction London Ltd, 8 Waterside Way, London, SW17 0HB Tel: (020) 8947 4000 Fax: (020) 8944 9447

Carillion P.L.C., 24 Birch Street, Wolverhampton, WV1 4HY Tel: (01902) 422431 Fax: (01902) 316165 E-mail: n.simms@carillionplc.com

Carillion Mowlems, Foundation House, Eastern Road, Bracknell, Berkshire, RG12 2UZ Tel: (01344) 720001

▶ Carlier Asphalt, Factory Lane, Croydon, CR0 3RL Tel: (020) 8688 4351

Carmac, Burton Road, Finedon, Wellingborough, Northamptonshire, NN9 5HX Tel: (01933) 682345 Fax: (01933) 682555 E-mail: admin@carmac.co.uk

▶ Cemex UK Construction Services Ltd, Smithfold Lane, Little Hulton, Worsley, Manchester, M28 0GP Tel: 0161-702 6366 Fax: 0161-702 6422

Charles L Warren Ltd, Station Approach, Pasture Road, Wirral, Merseyside, CH46 8SF Tel: 0151-677 2368 Fax: 0151-677 1910 E-mail: clwarrenltd@aol.com

▶ Charles Lawrence Surfaces plc, Newbridge Industrial Estate, Newbridge, Midlothian, EH28 8PJ Tel: 0131-333 3030 Fax: 0131-333 4154

Cheetham Hill Construction Ltd, Woodhill Road, Bury, Lancashire, BL8 1AR Tel: 0161-761 5109 Fax: 0161-761 1300 E-mail: enquiries@cheethamhillconstruction.co.uk

Chiltern Thrust Bore Ltd, Unit 1 The Barn, Firs Farm, Stagsden, West End, Bedford, MK43 8TB Tel: (01234) 825948 Fax: (01234) 824147 E-mail: chiltern@onweb.co.uk

Cirencester Civil Engineering Ltd, 4 Esland Place, Love Lane, Cirencester, Gloucestershire, GL7 1YG Tel: (01285) 652020 Fax: (01285) 651007 E-mail: sales@cirencestercivilengineering.co.uk

Clark Construction Ltd, Lancaster Approach, North Killingholme, Immingham, South Humberside, DN40 3JZ Tel: (01469) 540004 Fax: (01469) 540426 E-mail: info@clarkconstruction.co.uk

▶ Clehonger Plant Hire Ltd, Unit 4-5 Beech Business Park, Tillington Road, Hereford, HR4 9QJ Tel: (01432) 277366 Fax: (01432) 277366

Clovemead, Stephenson House, Howley Lane, Warrington, WA1 2DN Tel: (01925) 411221 Fax: (01925) 418496 E-mail: clovemead@brunelhouse.u-net.com

Cofton Ltd, Firswood Road, Birmingham, B33 0ST Tel: 0121-628 4000 Fax: 0121-628 1398 E-mail: admin@cofton.co.uk

Colas Ltd, Wallage Lane, Rowfant, Crawley, West Sussex, RH10 4NF Tel: (01342) 711000 Fax: (01342) 711198 E-mail: info@colas.co.uk

Colas (I O M) Ltd, Balthane Industrial Estate, Ballasalla, Isle Of Man, IM9 2AQ Tel: (01624) 823360 Fax: (01624) 825604

▶ Component Erectors Ltd, Levenmouth Business Centre, Hawkslaw Trading Estate, Riverside, Leven, Fife, KY8 4LT Tel: (01333) 429300

▶ John Cooper Construction Ltd, Cooper House, 25 Belmont Circle Kenton Lane, Harrow, Middlesex, HA3 8RF Tel: (020) 8907 8908 Fax: (020) 8907 8903 E-mail: info@johncooperconstruction.co.uk

▶ Coulson Construction Ltd, Woodbine Cottage Birtley, Birtley, Hexham, Northumberland, NE48 3HL Tel: (01434) 230612

▶ Court Paving Ltd, 20 Princess Drive, Knaresborough, North Yorkshire, HG5 0AG Tel: (01423) 860641

Cristom Construction Ltd, Plot 10 Ryeford Indust Estate, Ryeford, Stonehouse, Gloucestershire, GL10 2LQ Tel: (01453) 823847 Fax: (01453) 823847

▶ Crummock Scotland Ltd, Butlerfield Industrial Estate, Bonnyrigg, Midlothian, EH19 3JQ Tel: (01875) 823222 Fax: (01875) 823444

▶ Cuchulain Construction, 124 Kings Park Avenue, Glasgow, G44 4HS Tel: 0141-632 3020

▶ Cumbrian Industrials Ltd, 150 Preston Road, Lytham St. Annes, Lancashire, FY8 5AT Tel: (01253) 741730 Fax: (01253) 796532

Currall Lewis & Martin Construction Ltd, 89-93 Broadwell Road, Oldbury, West Midlands, B69 4BL Tel: 0121-552 9292 Fax: 0121-544 9899 E-mail: office@clmconstruction.com

D A Cant Ltd, Unit 23 Lodge Lane, Langham, Colchester, CO4 5NE Tel: (01206) 231500 Fax: (01206) 231599 E-mail: d.a.cant@virgin.net

D C T Civil Engineering Ltd, Prospect House, George Street, Shaw, Oldham, OL2 8DX Tel: (01706) 842929 Fax: (01706) 882158 E-mail: info@dct-civils.co.uk

▶ D & E Mackay Contractors Ltd, Craigearn Business Park, Midmills, Kintore, Inverurie, Aberdeenshire, AB51 0TH Tel: (01467) 633388 Fax: (01467) 633454

▶ D G Pool & Leisure, Bines Green, Partridge Green, Horsham, West Sussex, RH13 8EH Tel: (01403) 711581 Fax: (01403) 713581

▶ Dales Sports Surfaces Ltd, Sharpes Lane, Sheepgate, Leverton, Boston, Lincolnshire, PE22 0AR Tel: (01205) 761066 Fax: (01205) 760856

Darby Groundworks, Salamons Way, Rainham, Essex, RM13 9UL Tel: (01708) 521100 Fax: (01708) 525533 E-mail: admin@emerald-hse.com

Gerald Davies Ltd, Kenfig Industrial Estate, Margam, Port Talbot, West Glamorgan, SA13 2PE Tel: (01656) 745525 Fax: (01656) 746270 E-mail: enquiries@geralddavies.co.uk

Dean & Dyball Developments Ltd, Endeavour House, Crow Arch Lane, Ringwood, Hampshire, BH24 1PN Tel: (01425) 470000 Fax: (01425) 472724 E-mail: enquiries@deandyball.co.uk

Deane Public Works Ltd, Irvinestown, Enniskillen, County Fermanagh, BT94 1RE Tel: (028) 6862 1555 Fax: (028) 6862 8523 E-mail: sales@deanepublicworks.co.uk

▶ Delta Pipelines, Redwither Road, Wrexham Industrial Estate, Wrexham, Clwyd, LL13 9RD Tel: (01978) 661221

▶ Dince Hill Property Ltd, Manor Mill, South Brent, Devon, TQ10 9JD Tel: (01364) 72779

Dixon Hurst Kemp Ltd, Station House, Bepton Road, Midhurst, West Sussex, GU29 9RE Tel: (01243) 787888 Fax: (01243) 787180 E-mail: chichester@dhk.co.uk

I.G. Doran & Partners, Malone Exchange, 226 Lisbon Road, Belfast, BT9 6GE Tel: (028) 9038 1321 Fax: (028) 9066 3255

▶ Dowhigh Ltd, Park La West, Bootle, Merseyside, L30 3SU Tel: 0151-523 4372 Fax: 0151-525 6074

John Doyle Construction Ltd, John Doyle House, 2-3 Little Burrow, Welwyn Garden City, Hertfordshire, AL7 4SP Tel: (01707) 329481 Fax: (01707) 328213 E-mail: admin@john-doyle.co.uk

▶ Driveway Design, 2 Randolph Court, Randolph Industrial Estate, Kirkcaldy, Fife, KY1 2YY Tel: (01592) 654300 Fax: (01592) 654390

▶ Driveway Co Scotland Ltd, 69 Buchanan Street, Glasgow, G1 3HL Tel: 0141-314 3839 Fax: 0141-314 3738

▶ Droicon P.L.C, Trow Way, Diglis, Worcester, WR5 3BX Tel: (01905) 763445 Fax: (01905) 356423 E-mail: sales@droicon.co.uk

DSD Construction Ltd, Robert Street, Carlisle, CA2 5AN Tel: (01228) 594969 Fax: (01228) 598588 E-mail: admin@dsdconstruction.com

▶ Duncan Pryde, Cartmore Industrial Estate, Lochgelly, Fife, KY5 8LL Tel: (01592) 783130

Dundee Plant Co. Ltd, Longtown Street, Dundee, DD4 8LF Tel: (01382) 507506 Fax: (01382) 507550

Durkin & Sons Ltd, Amex House, North End Road, Wembley, Middlesex, HA9 0UU Tel: (020) 8900 0203 Fax: (020) 8903 4754 E-mail: michaeldurkin@ndirect.co.uk

E R D C Group Ltd, 20 Harvest Road, Newbridge, Midlothian, EH28 8LW Tel: 0131-333 1100 Fax: 0131-335 4300 E-mail: info@erdc.co.uk

Earney Contracts, 221 Comber Road, Lisburn, County Antrim, BT27 6XY Tel: (028) 9263 8269 Fax: (028) 9263 9009 E-mail: s.earney@btconnect.com

▶ Earthworks & Contracting Ltd, The Walfe, Main Street, Hickling, Melton Mowbray, Leicestershire, LE14 3AH Tel: (01664) 823789 Fax: (01664) 823382

Easy Excavations Ltd, PO Box 33, Bolton, BL1 2QS Tel: (01204) 383838 Fax: (01204) 364002

Eaton Tractors Ltd, High Street, Little Paxton, St. Neots, Cambridgeshire, PE19 6HD Tel: (01480) 473121 Fax: (01480) 404585

▶ Eco European Ltd, Unit 1, Langlands Gate, East Kilbride, Glasgow, G75 0ZY Tel: (01355) 900159

▶ Edmund Nuttall Ltd, Cambrian Buildings, Mount Stuart Square, Cardiff, CF10 5FL Tel: (029) 2046 2838 Fax: (029) 2048 9946

▶ Edmund Nuttall Ltd, Allbrook Depot, Allbrook Hill, Eastleigh, Hampshire, SO50 4LY Tel: (023) 8061 1333 Fax: (023) 8062 9186

▶ Edmund Nuttall Ltd, 1 Eagle House, Asama Court, Newcastle Business Park, Newcastle upon Tyne, NE4 7LN Tel: 0191-273 7000 Fax: 0191-273 7002

Eldwick Ltd, Bentley Buildings, Glaisdale, Whitby, North Yorkshire, YO21 2QY Tel: (01947) 897337 Fax: (01947) 897660

F. Espley & Sons Ltd, Foregate House, 70A Foregate Street, Stafford, ST16 2PX Tel: (01785) 602040 Fax: (01785) 606566 E-mail: info@espleys.co.uk

▶ European Site Services Ltd, Unit 5, Harbour Industrial Estate, Ardrossan, Ayrshire, KA22 8EG Tel: (01294) 467360

F G Whitley & Sons Co. Ltd, Padeswood Road, Buckley, Clwyd, CH7 2JJ Tel: (01244) 550792 Fax: (01244) 549397

F M Conway, Conway House, Rochester Way, Dartford, DA1 3QY Tel: (020) 8636 8822 Fax: (020) 8636 8827 E-mail: enquires@fmconway.co.uk

F Parkinson Ltd, Mowbray Drive, Blackpool, FY3 7UN Tel: (01253) 394411 Fax: (01253) 302088 E-mail: sales@fparkinson.co.uk

Harry Fairclough (Construction) Ltd, Howley Lane, Howley, Warrington, WA1 2DN Tel: (01925) 632214 Fax: (01925) 628301 E-mail: post@harryfairclough.co.uk

Farrans Ltd, 99 Kingsway, Dunmurry, Belfast, BT17 9NU Tel: (028) 9061 1122 Fax: (028) 9062 9753 E-mail: construct@farrans.com

Firbeck Construction Ltd, 3 Lawn Court, Carlton-in-Lindrick, Worksop, Nottinghamshire, S81 9ED Tel: (01909) 733255 Fax: (01909) 733235 E-mail: info@firb.co.uk

▶ First Engineering Ltd, Station Road, Crianlarich, Perthshire, FK20 8QN Tel: (01838) 300255

Fitzgerald Contractors Ltd, 125 Cheston Road, Birmingham, B7 5EA Tel: 0121-326 0402 Fax: 0121-328 1963 E-mail: sales@fitzgerald-uk.com

Fitzpatrick Contractors Ltd, Hertford Road, Hoddesdon, Hertfordshire, EN11 9BX Tel: (01992) 305000 Fax: (01992) 305001 E-mail: enquiries@fitzpatrick.co.uk

Flowline Civil Engineering Ltd, Merthyr Tydfil Industrial Park, Pentrebach, Merthyr Tydfil, Mid Glamorgan, CF48 4DR Tel: (01443) 691452 Fax: (01443) 692397

▶ Flynn Surfacing Ltd, Sandfold Lane, Manchester, M19 3BJ Tel: 0161-248 8842 Fax: 0161-248 8805

▶ Forthstream Ltd, Locks Street, Coatbridge, Lanarkshire, ML5 3RT Tel: (01236) 424333

▶ Fox Plant (Owmby) Ltd, Caenby Hall, Caenby Corner, Market Rasen, Lincolnshire, LN8 2BU Tel: (01673) 878444 Fax: (01673) 878644 E-mail: office@foxowmby.com

▶ Fradley Patio & Landscape Centre Ltd, Hungry Horse Craft Centre, Weeford Road, Sutton Coldfield, West Midlands, B75 6NA Tel: 0121-323 4555

Frank Tucker Ltd, Victoria Works, Rook Lane, Bradford, West Yorkshire, BD4 9NL Tel: (01274) 681221 Fax: (01274) 688902 E-mail: franktuker@franktuker.co.uk

▶ Fullwood Holdings Ltd, 10 Jerviston Street, New Stevenston, Motherwell, Lanarkshire, ML1 4LY Tel: (01698) 733351

CIVIL ENGINEERING AND PUBLIC WORKS CONTRACTORS – *continued*

▶ G A Duncan & Sons Ltd, Gordon Castle Farm, Fochabers, Morayshire, IV32 7PQ Tel: (01343) 821609 Fax: (01343) 821413

▶ G B J Environmental Systems Ltd, 4 Gatewarth Industrial Estate, Barnard Street, Warrington, WA5 1DD Tel: (01925) 635568 Fax: (01925) 242667

▶ G & B Roadmarkings, Cairnhill Trading Estate, Unit 9, Cairnhill Rd, Airdrie, Lanarkshire, ML6 9HA Tel: (01236) 764867 Fax: (01236) 767336

▶ G B Site Services, 21 Bonnyside Road, Bonnybridge, Stirlingshire, FK4 2AD Tel: (01324) 882503 Fax: (01324) 882504

G & D Joinery, 1 Chater Street, Belfast, BT4 1BL Tel: (028) 9045 1375 Fax: (028) 9073 8414

▶ G F Tomlinson, Navigation Complex, Navigation Road, Worcester, WR5 3DE Tel: (01905) 764421 Fax: (01905) 769918

▶ G Lund Ltd, The Ashes, Cliburn, Penrith, Cumbria, CA10 3AL Tel: (01931) 714515 Fax: (01931) 714545

G Mcveigh & Co. Ltd, Timothys Bridge Road, Stratford-upon-Avon, Warwickshire, CV37 9NQ Tel: (01789) 205803 Fax: (01789) 205828

▶ G Thornton (Contracts) Ltd, Metcalf Drive, Altham Industrial Estate, Accrington, Lancashire, BB5 5TU Tel: (01282) 777345

Gabriel Contractors Ltd, Jeffreys Road, Enfield, Middlesex, EN3 7UA Tel: (020) 8804 5444 Fax: (020) 8805 0813 E-mail: enquiries@gabrielceng.co.uk

Galboola Ltd, 23 Blenheim Road, St. Dials, Cwmbran, Gwent, NP44 4NA Tel: (01633) 862853 Fax: (01633) 877524

Galliford Try, Crab Lane, Fearnhead, Warrington, WA2 0XR Tel: (01925) 822821 Fax: (01925) 827924 E-mail: mail@galliford-northan.co.uk

Gee Construction Ltd, PO Box 14, Bridgend, Mid Glamorgan, CF31 3UD Tel: (01656) 653541 Fax: (01656) 657717

Geo Houlton & Sons Holdings Ltd, Hyperion Street, Witham, Hull, HU9 1BD Tel: (01482) 320486 Fax: (01482) 228441 E-mail: sales@houlton.co.uk

▶ Gilvar Lining Ltd, Old Station Yard, Walton Lane, Barton under Needwood, Burton-on-Trent, Staffordshire, DE13 8EJ Tel: (01283) 712450 Fax: (01283) 716525

▶ Glamorgan Engineering Consultancy, The Old Bakery, Moy Road Industrial Estate, Taffs Well, Cardiff, CF15 7GE Tel: (029) 2082 0600 Fax: (029) 2082 0601 E-mail: enquiries@glamorgan-engineering-consultancy.gov.uk

M.J. Gleeson Group P.L.C., Haredon House, London Road, North Cheam, Sutton, Surrey, SM3 9BS Tel: (020) 8644 4321 Fax: (020) 8641 6110 E-mail: marketing@mjgleeson.com

▶ Glendale Grounds Management Ltd, 401 Walsall Road, Perry Barr, Birmingham, B42 1BT Tel: 0121-356 4226 Fax: 0121-331 1871

M. Gould (Scunthorpe) Ltd, Midland Road, Scunthorpe, South Humberside, DN16 1DQ Tel: (01724) 866772 Fax: (01724) 855708 E-mail: m.gouldscunthorpeltd@btconnect.com

▶ Govin & Clarke Ltd, 11 Greendale Crescent, Leigh, Lancashire, WN7 2LQ Tel: (01942) 604018

Gracelands Ltd, Unit 3 Queensway, New Milton, Hampshire, BH25 5NN Tel: (01425) 621200 Fax: (01425) 638637 E-mail: theoffice@gracelandsltd.freeserve.co.uk

▶ Graham Construction Division, Peppercorn House, 8 Huntingdon Street, St. Neots, Cambridgeshire, PE19 1BH Tel: (01480) 404404 Fax: (01480) 403377

Granville Steel Contracting plc, Steel Close, Eaton Socon, St. Neots, Cambridgeshire, PE19 8TT Tel: (01480) 213513 Fax: (01480) 405994 E-mail: jane.taylor@aggregate.co.uk

Greenbooth Construction Co. Ltd, Hunt Lane, Chadderton, Oldham, OL9 0LR Tel: 0161-633 4815

▶ Greenways Construction (Midlands) Ltd, Weatherby Road, Osmaston Park Industrial Estate, Derby, DE24 8HL Tel: (01332) 370702

Grimshaw Kinnear Ltd, St. Peters Works, Tewkesbury Road, Cheltenham, Gloucestershire, GL51 9AL Tel: (01242) 513251 Fax: (01242) 226396 E-mail: sales@grimshawgroup.co.uk

▶ H M S Highway Maintenance Specialists Ltd, Bruntingthorpe Industrial Estate, Lutterworth, Leicestershire, LE17 5QZ Tel: 0116-279 9099 E-mail: sales@hmslimited.co.uk

Hadfield Cawkwell Davidson, 17 Broomgrove Road, Sheffield, S10 2LZ Tel: 0114-266 8181 Fax: 0114-266 6246 E-mail: sales@hcd.co.uk

Hall Construction Group, Clay Street, Hull, HU8 8HE Tel: (01482) 329204 Fax: (01482) 587722 E-mail: addressee@hallgroup.co.uk

▶ Hanson Quarry Products Europe Ltd, The Ridge, Chipping Sodbury, Bristol, BS37 6AY Tel: (01454) 316000 Fax: (01454) 325161

▶ Harfield Bros Contracting Ltd, Unit C4, Premiere Bus Centre, Speedfield Industrial Estate, Fareham, Hampshire, PO14 1TY Tel: (01329) 827567 Fax: (01329) 828639 E-mail: office@harfieldbros.com

▶ Harlequin Swimming Pools Ltd, Innersdown Farm, Micheldever, Winchester, Hampshire, SO21 3BW Tel: (01962) 774004 Fax: (01962) 774008

Jim Hastings Ltd, Seghill Industrial Estate, Seghill, Cramlington, Northumberland, NE23 7DR Tel: 0191-237 0633 Fax: 0191-237 2656

Hayes Control Systems, The Boathouse, Station Road, Henley-on-Thames, Oxfordshire, RG9 1AZ Tel: (01491) 410539 Fax: (01491) 577267 E-mail: sales@hayescontrol.co.uk

▶ Hecket Multiserve Steelphalt Ltd, Sheffield Road, Rotherham, South Yorkshire, S60 1DR Tel: (01709) 300500 Fax: (01709) 300599

Henry Boot Estates Ltd, Banner Cross Hall, Sheffield, S11 9PD Tel: 0114-255 5444 Fax: 0114-258 5548 E-mail: pr@henryboot.co.uk

Henry Boot Training Ltd, Callywhite Lane, Dronfield, Derbyshire, S18 2XN Tel: (01246) 410111 Fax: (01246) 410595

▶ Henry Kemp (Road Maintenance) Ltd, Century House, Century Road, Retford, Nottinghamshire, DN22 7TD Tel: (01777) 703643

▶ Hewlett Civil Engineering Ltd, Prestige Court, Beza Road, Leeds, LS10 2BD Tel: 0113-277 6677 Fax: 0113-270 9537

Geo Hodges & Son Ltd, 82 Horninglow Street, Burton-on-Trent, Staffordshire, DE14 1PN Tel: (01283) 565461 Fax: (01283) 510338 E-mail: contract@hodges.co.uk

Holroyd Construction Ltd, Park Hill, Walton Road, Wetherby, West Yorkshire, LS22 5DZ Tel: (01937) 583131 Fax: (01937) 580034

▶ Howatson, Cae Bricks Brickfield Lane, Denbigh Road, Ruthin, Clwyd, LL15 1PE Tel: (01824) 703638 Fax: (01824) 707210 E-mail: dave.burke@tarmac.co.uk

Humber Workboats Ltd, North Killingholme, Immingham, South Humberside, DN40 3LX Tel: (01469) 540156 Fax: (01469) 540303 E-mail: elliotmorton@humberworkboats.co.uk

Hurst Pierce & Malcolm, Celtic House, 33 Johns Mews, London, WC1N 2QL Tel: (020) 7242 3593 Fax: (020) 7405 5274 E-mail: hurstpm@globalnet.co.uk

Hutchings & Carter Ltd, The Avenue, Lasham, Alton, Hampshire, GU34 5SU Tel: (01256) 381338 Fax: (01256) 381876 E-mail: robert.white@hncltd.com

George Hutchison Associates Ltd, 51 Brookfield Road, Cheadle, Cheshire, SK8 1ES Tel: 0161-491 4600 Fax: 0161-491 4700 E-mail: enquiries@stressstrain.com

Hutton Construction Ltd, Birch Business Centre, Maldon Road, Birch, Colchester, CO2 0LT Tel: (01206) 330386 Fax: (01206) 331177 E-mail: colchester@hutton-group.co.uk

I. & H. I & H Brown Ltd, PO Box 51, Perth, PH1 3YD Tel: (01738) 637171 Fax: (01738) 637175 E-mail: enquiries@ihbrown.com

Ikm Network Communications Ltd, Intec House, St.Nicholas Close, Fleet, Hampshire, GU51 4JA Tel: (01252) 365700 Fax: (01252) 622131 E-mail: sales@ikm.co.uk

▶ Inbowles & Leisure, Sportsman Farm, Hollywood Road, Mellor, Stockport, Cheshire, SK6 5LR Tel: 0161-484 5488 Fax: 0161-484 5486

▶ Incaforce Civil, The Coach House, Rectory Road, Cliffe, Rochester, Kent, ME3 7RP Tel: (01634) 222061

Interclass Holdings Ltd, Heathmill Road, Wombourne, Wolverhampton, WV5 8AP Tel: (01902) 324422 Fax: (01902) 324044 E-mail: wombourne@interclass.co.uk

Interserve Project Service Ltd, Crabtree Manorway South, Belvedere, Kent, DA17 6BH Tel: (020) 8311 5500 Fax: (020) 8311 1701 E-mail: belvedere.office@interserveprojects.com

Interserve Project Services Ltd, 395 George Road, Erdington, Birmingham, B23 7RZ Tel: 0121-344 4888 Fax: 0121-344 4801 E-mail: information@interserveprojects.com

Interserve Project Services Ltd, Cambrian Buildings, Mount Stuart Square, Cardiff, CF10 5FL Tel: (029) 2048 1560 Fax: (029) 2048 3825 E-mail: cardiff.office@interserveprojects.com

Interserve Project Services Ltd, Tilbury House, Hermitage Lane, Mansfield, Nottinghamshire, NG18 5HE Tel: (01623) 633216 Fax: (01623) 659438 E-mail: mansfield.office@interserveprojects.com

Interserve Project Services Ltd, 138 Heol-Y-Gors, Cwmbwrla, Swansea, SA5 8LT Tel: (01792) 464001 Fax: (01792) 467499 E-mail: swansea.office@interserveprojects.com

▶ Inverness Caledonian Thistle Football Club, Caledonian Stadium, Stadium Road, Inverness, IV1 1FF Tel: (01463) 222880

J Browne Construction Co. Ltd, Beacon House, North Circular Road, London, NW10 0HF Tel: (020) 8451 4111 Fax: (020) 8459 6879 E-mail: info@jbconstruction.co.uk

J C Edwardson Ltd, Unit 13 Wigan Enterprise Park, Seaman Way, Ince, Wigan, Lancashire, WN2 2LE Tel: (01942) 820943 Fax: (01942) 829185

▶ J Chaplow & Sons Ltd, Helsington Mills, Helsington, Kendal, Cumbria, LA9 5RL Tel: (01539) 720358 Fax: (01539) 735593 E-mail: enquiries@jchaplow.co.uk

J E Stacey & Co. Ltd, Inceworth Building Works, Bodmin Street, Holsworthy, Devon, EX22 6BD Tel: (01409) 253555 Fax: (01409) 254496

▶ J H Connon Ltd, Harlaw Road, Inverurie, Aberdeenshire, AB51 4FH Tel: (01467) 621406 Fax: (01467) 620806 E-mail: sales@jhconnon.co.uk

▶ J Hendry Ashphalt Contractors, Clippens Yard, Loanhead, Midlothian, EH20 9NS Tel: 0131-440 1109 Fax: 0131-440 4231

J J Cavanagh Construction Ltd, Rowhurst Industrial Estate, Apedale Road, Newcastle, Staffordshire, ST5 6BH Tel: (01782) 565789 Fax: (01782) 564740 E-mail: sales@jjcav.co.uk

▶ J Murphy & Sons Ltd, 5 Finedon Sidings Industrial E, Furnace Lane, Finedon, Wellingborough, Northamptonshire, NN9 5NY Tel: (01536) 420638

J N Bentley Ltd, Keighley Road, Skipton, North Yorkshire, BD23 2QT Tel: (01756) 799425 Fax: (01756) 798068 E-mail: info@jnbentley.co.uk

▶ J P C S Ltd, The Sidings, Hampton Heath Industrial Estate, Hampton, Malpas, Cheshire, SY14 8LU Tel: (01948) 820696 Fax: (01948) 820252

▶ J P Kennedy Construction Co. Ltd, Unit 5 Watling Gate, 297-303 Edgware Road, London, NW9 6NB Tel: (020) 8905 8942 Fax: (020) 8200 6124

J Parkinson & Sons Ltd, 3 Hampson Lane, Hampson, Lancaster, LA2 0HY Tel: (01524) 753301 Fax: (01524) 753302 E-mail: bcampbell@askam.co.uk

Jackson Group Properties 11 Ltd, Jackson House, 86 Sandyhill Lane, Ipswich, IP3 0NA Tel: (01473) 335000 Fax: (01473) 219939 E-mail: enquiries@jackson-building.co.uk

▶ James Tobin & Son Ltd, Martland Industrial Estate, Smarts Heath Lane, Woking, Surrey, GU22 0RQ Tel: (01483) 233084

▶ Jayen Ltd, Goose Green Marsh, St Peter, Jersey, JE3 7BU Tel: (01534) 871086

Jefco Services Ltd, Queens Road, Immingham, South Humberside, DN40 1QR Tel: (01469) 574888 Fax: (01469) 574224

Jim Mccoll Associates, 6a Mill Lane, Edinburgh, EH6 6TJ Tel: 0131-555 0721 Fax: 0131-555 0723 E-mail: enquiries@mccollassoc.co.uk

▶ John A Bates Contractors Ltd, Chance House, Crystal Drive, Smethwick, West Midlands, B66 1RD Tel: 0121-558 3823 Fax: 0121-555 5942

John Graham Dromore Ltd, Lagan Mills, Dromore, County Down, BT25 1AS Tel: (028) 9269 2291 Fax: (028) 9269 3412 E-mail: info@graham.co.uk

John Jones Excavation Ltd, Norjon House, Newby Road, Stockport, Cheshire, SK7 5DU Tel: 0161-483 9316 Fax: 0161-483 8006

John Williams & Co Crwbin Quarries Ltd, Pantyrathro Manor, Llangain, Carmarthen, Dyfed, SA33 5AJ Tel: (01267) 241226 Fax: (01267) 241630

Joyce, Speedwell Road, Yardley, Birmingham, B25 8HH Tel: 0121-773 6821 Fax: 0121-772 4941 E-mail: joycecomputers@btconnet.com

K M Construction North Wales Ltd, Lower Denbigh Road, St. Asaph, Clwyd, LL17 0EL Tel: (01745) 583752 Fax: (01745) 584705

▶ K Stewart (Strathpeffer) Ltd, Blairninich, Strathpeffer, Ross-Shire, IV14 9AB Tel: (01997) 421333

Karl Construction Ltd, 92 Old Ballyrobin Road, Muckamore, Antrim, BT41 4TJ Tel: (028) 9442 5600 Fax: (028) 9442 5605 E-mail: sales@kar1.co.uk

▶ Kearns & Co. Ltd, 8 Hamilton Road, St. Albans, Hertfordshire, AL1 4PZ Tel: (01727) 865981

▶ Kehoe Contractors Ltd, Rear of, 102 Vandyke Road, Leighton Buzzard, Bedfordshire, LU7 3HA Tel: (01525) 852588 Fax: (01525) 852570

Kelly Bros Road Markings Ltd, 15 Station Road, Yate, Bristol, BS37 5HT Tel: (01454) 312675 Fax: (01454) 320425

▶ Kelly Communications Ltd, Kelly House, 8 Headstone Road, Harrow, Middlesex, HA1 1PD Tel: (020) 8424 0909 Fax: (020) 8424 0509

Kennedy Asphalt, Downs Road, Willenhall, West Midlands, WV13 2PF Tel: 0121-568 7903 Fax: 0121-526 7265

▶ KG Contractors Ltd, 184 Avenue Farm, Sutton Bridge, Spalding, Lincolnshire, PE12 9QF Tel: (01406) 359115 Fax: (01406) 359114

Kier Caribbean Ltd, Tempsford Hall, Sandy, Bedfordshire, SG19 2BD Tel: (01767) 640111 Fax: (01767) 641179 E-mail: david.parr@kier.co.uk

Kier Southern, St. Andrews House, West Street, Havant, Hampshire, PO9 1LB Tel: (023) 9248 4343 Fax: (023) 9245 5414 E-mail: lisa.haywood@kier.co.uk

▶ Kyle Tarmacadam Ltd, 2 Murdoch Place, Oldhall West Industrial Estate, Irvine, Ayrshire, KA11 5DG Tel: (01294) 279206

▶ L & R Roadlines Ltd, 24-32 Forth Street, Liverpool, L20 8JW Tel: 0151-933 6293

Lagan Construction Ltd, Rosemount House, 21-23 Sydenham Road, Belfast, BT3 9HA Tel: (028) 9045 5531 Fax: (028) 9045 8940 E-mail: charles.brand@lagan-group.com

Land & Marine, Lawrence House, Lower Bristol Road, Bath, BA2 9ET Tel: (01225) 331116 Fax: (01225) 445057 E-mail: steveholton@landandmarine.co.uk

Laser Civil Engineering Ltd, Bredon House, Worcester, WR2 4SQ Tel: (01905) 832900 Fax: (01905) 832901

George Law Ltd, 35 Mill Street, Kidderminster, Worcestershire, DY11 6XB Tel: (01562) 820421 Fax: (01562) 829205

Lawlor Construction Ltd, Unit 12 Bentinck Street Industrial Estate, Manchester, M15 4LN Tel: 0161-839 3087 Fax: 0161-839 3010 E-mail: lawlorconstruct@btconnect.com

Leck Construction Ltd, Leck House, Ironworks Road, Barrow-in-Furness, Cumbria, LA14 2PQ Tel: (01229) 820394 Fax: (01229) 811414 E-mail: leckcon.bar@btinternet.com

▶ Lewis Buxton Groundworks, Unit 2, Thurnscoe Business Park, Phoenix Lane, Rotherham, South Yorkshire, S63 0BH Tel: (01709) 890600

Lightways (Contractors) Ltd, Lochlands Industrial Estate, Larbert, Stirlingshire, FK5 3NS Tel: (01324) 553025 Fax: (01324) 557870 E-mail: head.office@lightways.co.uk

Lincs Pumps & Pipeline, Water Gate, Quadring, Spalding, Lincolnshire, PE11 4PY Tel: (01775) 821163 Fax: (01775) 821613

Lindum Group Ltd, Lindum House, Station Road, North Hykeham, Lincoln, LN6 3QX Tel: (01522) 500300 Fax: (01522) 500377

▶ Line Markings Ltd, Brownsburn Industrial Estate, Airdrie, Lanarkshire, ML6 9SE Tel: (01236) 755114 Fax: (01236) 751880

▶ Luddon Construction Ltd, Balmore House, 1497 Balmore Road, Glasgow, G23 5HD Tel: 0141-945 2233 Fax: 0141-946 5400 E-mail: enquiries@luddon.co.uk

▶ Lymburn Contractors Ltd, Macmanniston Cottage, Dalrymple, Ayr, KA6 6BT Tel: (01292) 560369 Fax: (01292) 560643 E-mail: enquiries@lynburn.co.uk

▶ Lynch Ltd, 45 Neptune Street, London, SE16 7JP Tel: (020) 7394 8811 Fax: (020) 7394 8844

▶ M D Clarke (Contractors) Ltd, Midland House, Brent, Ninian Way, Tame Valley Industrial Estate, Tamworth, Staffordshire, B77 5DF Tel: (01827) 282323

▶ M & D Foundations & Building Services, 6 Holmeroyd Road, Adwick-le-Street, Doncaster, South Yorkshire, DN6 7BH Tel: (01302) 337711 Fax: (01302) 330335 E-mail: sales@mdfoundations.com

▶ M & E Civil Engineering & Groundwork Ltd, Unit 2 Evegate Park Barn, Ashford, Kent, TN25 6SX Tel: (01303) 814444 E-mail: sales@mecivilengineering.co.uk

M J Gleeson Group plc, Unit 7-9 Callendar Business Park, Callendar Road, Falkirk, FK1 1XR Tel: (01324) 678460 Fax: (01324) 623741

▶ M & M Road Surfacing, 9A Bankhead Medway, Edinburgh, EH11 4BY Tel: (07860) 388272

M T M Construction Ltd, Blackburn Industrial Estate, Kinellar, Aberdeen, AB21 0RX Tel: (01224) 790888 Fax: (01224) 790922 E-mail: info@mtmconstructionltd.co.uk

M Walsh & Sons Ltd, 190 Malvern Com, Poolbrook, Malvern, Worcestershire, WR14 3JZ Tel: (01684) 572247 Fax: (01684) 574465

▶ Mabey Hire Ltd, Travellers Lane, North Mymms, Hatfield, Hertfordshire, AL9 7HN Tel: (01707) 267171 Fax: (01707) 268971

▶ Mabey Hire Ltd, Oakwood Grange, Robbinetts Lane, Cossall, Nottingham, NG16 2RX Tel: 0115-930 1154 Fax: 0115-944 0195

Mcaleer & Teague, Camderry Road, Dromore, Omagh, County Tyrone, BT78 3AP Tel: (028) 8289 8535 Fax: (028) 8289 8244 E-mail: info@mactni.co.uk

▶ McCarthy Surfacing Ltd, Beckton Works, Jenkins Lane, Barking, Essex, IG11 0AD Tel: (020) 8594 1966 Fax: (020) 8594 7244

Mcgowan & Co (Contractors) Ltd, 28 Cramond Road South, Edinburgh, EH4 6AB Tel: 0131-336 2181 Fax: 0131-336 4037 E-mail: sales@jsmart.co.uk

F.B. McKee & Co. Ltd, 62-66 Duncrue Street, Belfast, BT3 9AY Tel: (028) 9035 1071 Fax: (028) 9035 4103 E-mail: fbmckee@btconnect.com

▶ Mackellar Ltd, Strathspey Industrial Estate, Woodlands Terrace, Grantown-on-Spey, Morayshire, PH26 3NB Tel: (01479) 872577 Fax: (01479) 872436 E-mail: enquiries@mackellars.co.uk

J.T. Mackley & Co. Ltd, Bankside House, Henfield Road, Small Dole, Henfield, West Sussex, BN5 9XQ Tel: (01273) 492212 Fax: (01273) 494328 E-mail: construct@mackley.co.uk

Mcmahon Contractors Services Ltd, Old Station Yard, Station Road, Stratford-upon-Avon, Warwickshire, CV37 8RP Tel: (01789) 720836 Fax: (01789) 721048 E-mail: sales@mcmahon-holdings.co.uk

Mcnicholas Construction Holdings Ltd, Lismirrane Industrial Park, Elstree Road, Borehamwood, Hertfordshire, WD6 3EA Tel: (020) 8953 4144 Fax: (020) 8953 1860 E-mail: sales@mcnicholas.co.uk

Mcquillan Civil Engineers, 11 Ballinderry Road, Lisburn, County Antrim, BT28 2SA Tel: (028) 9266 8831 Fax: (028) 9266 8832 E-mail: john@johnmcquillan.com

Maltaward Ltd, Wellingham House Holmbush Potteries, Crawley Road, Faygate, Horsham, West Sussex, RH12 4SE Tel: (01293) 854930 Fax: (01293) 854939 E-mail: gtreacy@maltaward.co.uk

▶ Maltby Engineering Co. Ltd, Denaby Industrial Estate, Old Denaby, Doncaster, South Yorkshire, DN12 4JJ Tel: (01709) 862076

Manning Construction, Coychurch, Bridgend, Mid Glamorgan, CF35 5BU Tel: (01656) 862333 Fax: (01656) 861439

▶ Markon Ltd, Marcon, Inchneuk Road, Glenboig, Coatbridge, Lanarkshire, ML5 2QX Tel: (01236) 875134 Fax: (01236) 875525 E-mail: enquiries@markon.co.uk

▶ Marshall Surfacing Contracts Ltd, 249 Godstone Road, Whyteleafe, Surrey, CR3 0EN Tel: (01883) 622241 Fax: (01883) 627265

Martello Plant Hire Ltd, Potts Marsh Industrial Estate, Westham, Pevensey, East Sussex, BN24 5NA Tel: (01323) 761887 Fax: (01323) 461933

CIVIL ENGINEERING AND PUBLIC WORKS CONTRACTORS – *continued*

H. & J. Martin Ltd, Ulster Building Works, 163 Ormeau Road, Belfast, BT7 1SP Tel: (028) 9023 2622 Fax: (028) 9023 3104 E-mail: info@hjmartin.co.uk

Matthews Sussex Ltd, Stephenson Place, Stephenson Way, Crawley, West Sussex, RH10 1TN Tel: (01293) 617014 Fax: (01293) 617018

May Gurney Construction Ltd, Haden House, Argyle Way, Stevenage, Hertfordshire, SG1 2AD Tel: (01438) 363900 Fax: (01438) 363945

May Gurney (Highways), Chalk Lane, Snetterton, Norwich, NR16 2LB Tel: (01953) 888828 Fax: (01953) 888846

▶ MCB Roads, 54 Ronaldstone Road, Sidcup, Kent, DA15 8QU Tel: (020) 8850 6428

▶ Mead Construction (Cambridge) Ltd, Liberty Barns, Heath Road, Swaffham Prior, Cambridge, CB5 0LA Tel: (01638) 742463

Melliss & Partners, Boundary House The Pines Business Park, Broad Street, Guildford, Surrey, GU3 3BH Tel: (01483) 567879 Fax: (01483) 574616 E-mail: mail@melliss.com

Modern Plant Hire, 6 Somers Road, Rugby, Warwickshire, CV22 7DE Tel: (01788) 565186 Fax: (01788) 579878

Monk Of Colne Ltd, 5 Sun Street, Newtown, Colne, Lancashire, BB8 0JJ Tel: (01282) 863122 Fax: (01282) 871121 E-mail: sales@monkofcolne.co.uk

Chris Moore Transport Co. Ltd, Mill Court Barns, Binsted, Alton, Hampshire, GU34 4JF Tel: (01420) 23555 E-mail: chris_moore2000@hotmail.com

▶ Mooreland Construction Ltd, Leabrook Road, Wednesbury, West Midlands, WS10 7LZ Tel: 0121-505 6248

▶ Moorhead Excavations, Westfield Court, Lower Wortley Road, Leeds, LS12 4PX Tel: 0113-279 6556 Fax: 0113-231 0096

▶ Morricom Ltd, Fiboard House, 5 Oakleigh Gardens, London, N20 9AB Tel: (020) 8343 8663

Morrison Construction Ltd, 37 Harbour Road, Longman Industrial Estate, Inverness, IV1 1UA Tel: (01463) 221016 Fax: (01463) 242245

Mott Macdonald, 1 Atlantic Quay, Broomielaw, Glasgow, G2 8GB Tel: 0141-222 4500 Fax: 0141-221 2048 E-mail: marketing@mottmac.com

Mott Macdonald Ltd, Capital House, 48-52 Andover Road, Winchester, Hampshire, SO23 7BH Tel: (01962) 893100 Fax: (01962) 863224 E-mail: marketing@mottmac.com

▶ Mowlem P.L.C., Tilbury Docks, Tilbury, Essex, RM18 7EF Tel: (01375) 850840 Fax: (01375) 856954

John Mowlem & Co. P.L.C., Port Causeway, Bromborough, Wirral, Merseyside, CH62 3PS Tel: 0151-482 3500 Fax: 0151-482 3585

▶ Mowlem Utilities Services Ltd, 10 Woodhall Millbrae, Juniper Green, Midlothian, EH14 5BH Tel: 0131-453 6000

▶ Mulholland Contracts Ltd, Polbeth Industrial Estate, Polbeth, West Calder, West Lothian, EH55 8TJ Tel: (01506) 871376 Fax: (01506) 871156

Murphy Ltd, Ashley House, Ashley Road, London, N17 9LZ Tel: (020) 8885 3545 Fax: (020) 8801 1126 E-mail: emq@murphy-ltd-.uk

N Coppard Groundworks, 13 Ghyll Road, Heathfield, East Sussex, TN21 0AQ Tel: (01892) 669163

N O'Dwyer & Partners, 15 Downshire Road, Newry, County Down, BT34 1EE Tel: (028) 3026 6915 Fax: (028) 3026 4810 E-mail: info@nicholasodwyer.co.uk

▶ N R A Roofing & Flooring Services Ltd, Rock House, Belfield Street, Ilkeston, Derbyshire, DE7 8DU Tel: 0115-930 4019 Fax: 0115-944 1728

Nash Mynard Design Ltd, Dodford Mill, Dodford, Northampton, NN7 4SS Tel: (01327) 341643 Fax: (01327) 341801

▶ National Road Planning, School Road, Bulkington, Bedworth, Warwickshire, CV12 9JB Tel: (024) 7664 0664 Fax: (024) 7664 0663

▶ New County Road Surfacing Ltd, Penshaw Way, Birtley, Chester Le Street, County Durham, DH3 2SA Tel: 0191-410 9061

New Quay Developments Ltd, 68 Armagh Road, Tandragee, Craigavon, County Armagh, BT62 2HS Tel: (028) 3884 0444 Fax: (028) 3884 1811 E-mail: info@newquayconstruction.com

▶ Newmac Asphalt Services Ltd, Hunter Street, Paisley, Renfrewshire, PA1 1DN Tel: 0141-889 3174 Fax: 0141-889 3175

▶ North Yorkshire County Contractors Ltd, Grimbald Park, Wetherby Road, Knaresborough, North Yorkshire, HG5 8LJ Tel: (01423) 865584 Fax: (01423) 861162

▶ Northern Highways Ltd, Charnock Road, Liverpool, L9 7ET Tel: 0151-521 8400 Fax: 0151-521 8500

Norwest Holst Construction Ltd, Astral House, Imperial Way, Watford, WD24 4YX Tel: (01923) 233433 Fax: (01923) 256481

Nu Weld Engineering Services Ltd, 36 Oxford Street, Birmingham, B5 5NR Tel: 0121-633 0909 Fax: 0121-633 3124 E-mail: enquiries@nu-weld.co.uk

Edmund Nuttall Ltd, St James House, Knoll Road, Camberley, Surrey, GU15 3XW Tel: (01276) 63484 Fax: (01276) 66060 E-mail: headoffice@edmund-nuttall.co.uk

O'Hare & McGovern Ltd, Carnbane House, Shepherds Way, Newry, County Down, BT35 6EE Tel: (028) 3026 4662 Fax: (028) 3026 2747 E-mail: carnbanehouse@ohareandmcgovern.com

O'Keeffe Groundworks Ltd, The Brickfields, Oxhey Lane, Watford, WD19 5RF Tel: (01923) 818603 Fax: (01923) 242311 E-mail: sandra@okeeffegroundworks.com

▶ O'Rourke Construction Ltd, 154-158 Sydenham Road, London, SE26 5JZ Tel: (020) 8659 6559 Fax: (020) 8778 7224 E-mail: info@orouke-uk.com

Geoffrey Osborne Ltd, Osborne House, Stockbridge Road, Chichester, West Sussex, PO19 8LL Tel: (01243) 787811 Fax: (01243) 531231 E-mail: andrew.smith@osborne.co.uk

▶ Ottley & Sons, Downham Road, Ramsden Heath, Billericay, Essex, CM11 1PZ Tel: (01268) 711347 Fax: (01268) 711867

▶ P M Harris Ltd, Coton-in-the-Clay, Ashbourne, Derbyshire, DE6 5GY Tel: (01283) 821222 Fax: (01283) 821211

P S Construction Doncaster Ltd, Grange Farm, Mere Lane, Edenthorpe, Doncaster, South Yorkshire, DN3 2HS Tel: (01302) 300100 Fax: (01302) 300354 E-mail: sales@psconstruction.co.uk

▶ P S M Builders, Orchard, Birdham Road, Chichester, West Sussex, PO20 7EQ Tel: (01243) 774605

▶ P T Saunders, Southleigh Farm, Southleigh Road, Havant, Hampshire, PO9 2NX Tel: (023) 9248 0878

▶ Pave Aways Ltd, Avenue Mill, Knockin, Oswestry, Shropshire, SY10 8HQ Tel: (01691) 682111 Fax: (01691) 682123

Pell Frischmann Group Ltd, 4 Manchester Square, London, W1A 1AU Tel: (020) 7486 3661 Fax: (020) 7487 4153 E-mail: pflondon@pellfrischmann.com

Penfold Public Works (Sussex) Ltd, The Chalk Pit, Mile Oak Road, Portslade, Brighton, BN41 2RB Tel: (01273) 412224 Fax: (01273) 412563E-mail: info@penfoldpublicworks.co.uk

The Pettifer Group Ltd, 50 Stratford Road, Shipston-On-Stour, Warwickshire, CV36 4BA Tel: (01608) 666600 Fax: (01608) 666611 E-mail: macpherson@pettifer.co.uk

▶ Pike W L & Son Ltd, Tarvonga, Hill Brow Road, Liss, Hampshire, GU33 7LH Tel: (01730) 892884 Fax: (01730) 895647

▶ Power Lines Pipes & Cables Ltd, Roadmeetings, Carluke, Lanarkshire, ML8 4QE Tel: (01555) 772572 Fax: (01555) 772976 E-mail: info@plpc.co.uk

▶ PP Construction, Deepwater Yard, Part Lane, Swallowfield, Reading, RG7 1TB Tel: 0118-988 7211 Fax: 0118-988 7266

▶ Prangle & Carey Ltd, Bath Road, Chippenham, Wiltshire, SN14 0AB Tel: (01249) 653705 Fax: (01249) 447438

▶ Prestigue Civil Engineering Westbury Ltd, Duncote, Towcester, Northamptonshire, NN12 8AL Tel: (01327) 358653 Fax: (01327) 358753 E-mail: info@prestigecivil.co.uk

Priory Plant Ltd, Norman House, Wattons Lane, Southam, Warwickshire, CV47 0HX Tel: (01926) 812343 Fax: (01926) 813942 E-mail: vicky.t@prioryplant.co.uk

▶ Propipe Ltd, Park View West Industrial Estate, Hartlepool, Cleveland, TS25 1UD Tel: (01429) 890190 Fax: (01429) 890198

▶ Q E Paving, Unit 45, Tumulus Way, Llandow Trading Estate, Cowbridge, South Glamorgan, CF71 7PB Tel: (01446) 794793

R B Allfree & Co Ltd, Unit 2a Turnoaks Lane, Chesterfield, Derbyshire, S40 2HA Tel: (01246) 554050 Fax: (01246) 554060 E-mail: info@rballfree.freeserve.co.uk

R C Murray, 17 Woodland Gardens, North Wootton, King's Lynn, Norfolk, PE30 3PX Tel: (01553) 631770 Fax: (01553) 631770 E-mail: rcmkl@freeuk.com

▶ R Elliott & Sons Ltd, Sandford Farm, Newhouse, Motherwell, Lanarkshire, ML1 5SX Tel: (01698) 870222

R G Spiller Ltd, Millfield Close, Chard, Somerset, TA20 2DJ Tel: (01460) 62881 Fax: (01460) 65781

R J Canning Ltd, Highbank House, Pear Tree Lane, Newbury, Berkshire, RG14 2LU Tel: (01635) 33606 Fax: (01635) 33607 E-mail: highbanks@supanet.com

▶ R J Dance Contractors Ltd, 310 Brighton Road, Sutton, Surrey, SM2 5SU Tel: (020) 8288 1840 Fax: (020) 8288 1841

▶ R J Mcleod Contractors Ltd, 2411 London Road, Glasgow, G32 8XT Tel: 0141-764 2411

▶ R L Davies, 25 Raven Road, Walsall, WS5 3PZ Tel: (01922) 645443 Fax: (01922) 645443

▶ R Lindsay & Co. Ltd, Hayfield Place, Hayfield Industrial Estate, Kirkcaldy, Fife, KY2 5DH Tel: (01592) 260154 Fax: (01592) 641813 E-mail: sales@rlindsay.com

R M B Contractors Ltd, Ripley Road, Ambergate, Belper, Derbyshire, DE56 2EP Tel: (01773) 853151 Fax: (01773) 857306

R M Mogridge, Henbury Farm, East Orchard, Shaftesbury, Dorset, SP7 0LG Tel: (01747) 811718 Fax: (01747) 812113

R O Donaghey Ltd, 8 Oldington Trading Estate, Kidderminster, Worcestershire, DY11 7QP Tel: (01562) 820351 Fax: (01562) 829825 E-mail: r.o.donagheyltd@tinyworld.co.uk

R & S Whiting, Oak Lodge, North Walsham Road, Norwich, NR6 7JG Tel: (01603) 425832 Fax: (01603) 787900

R Z Construction Ltd, Pembroke Centre, 3 Cheney Manor Estate, Swindon, SN2 2PQ Tel: (01793) 614441 Fax: (01793) 420251

R&R, 79 Mortimers Lane, Fair Oak, Eastleigh, Hampshire, SO50 7BT Tel: (023) 8069 2476 Fax: (023) 8069 2720

▶ Rail Ability Ltd, Unit B Tilcon Avenue, Stafford, ST18 0YJ Tel: (01785) 214747 Fax: (01785) 214717 E-mail: mail@railability.co.uk

▶ Raynesway Construction (Southern) Ltd, 260 Aztec West, Almondsbury, Bristol, BS32 4SY Tel: (01454) 617620

Redrow Homes, Redrow House, St David's Park, Ewloe, Deeside, Clwyd, CH5 3RX Tel: (01244) 520044 Fax: (01244) 520580 E-mail: heather@redrow.demon.co.uk

Rees Pipeline Services Ltd, Clare House, Coppermill Lane, Harefield, Middlesex, UB9 6HZ Tel: (01895) 823711 Fax: (01895) 825263 E-mail: dave.fitzgerald@clancygroup.co.uk

Regal Construction, La Grande Route De St. Laurent, St. Lawrence, Jersey, JE3 1NN Tel: (01534) 865333 Fax: (01534) 861431 E-mail: regal-con@jerseymail.co.uk

John Reilly Civil Engineering Ltd, 103 Desborough Road, Eastleigh, Hampshire, SO50 5NT Tel: (023) 8062 9900 Fax: (023) 8061 3571 E-mail: info@johnreilly.co.uk

Richards & Co. (Mansfield) Ltd, Matlock Mill, Sheepbridge Lane, Mansfield, Nottinghamshire, NG18 5DJ Tel: (01623) 621527 Fax: (01623) 622250

Ridings Construction Co. Ltd, The Ropewalk, Hallfield Road, York, YO31 7XG Tel: (01904) 625269 Fax: (01904) 642280 E-mail: info@ridingsconstruction.co.uk

▶ Riggott & Co. Ltd, Station Lodge, Lodge Lane, Tuxford, Newark, Nottinghamshire, NG22 0NL Tel: (01777) 872525 Fax: (01777) 872626 E-mail: info@riggott.co.uk

▶ Ringway Highway Services, Stanton House, Stanton Way, Huntingdon, Cambridgeshire, PE29 6PY Tel: (01480) 434365 Fax: (01480) 433282

▶ Ringway Signs Ltd, Twenty Twenty Industrial Estate, St. Laurence Avenue, Allington, Maidstone, Kent, ME16 0LL Tel: (01622) 692277 Fax: (01622) 685992

Roadways & Car Parks Ltd, 174 Twickenham Road, Isleworth, Middlesex, TW7 7DW Tel: (020) 8560 7211 Fax: (020) 8560 1894 E-mail: reg.havard@roadways.demon.co.uk

▶ Roberts (C G T) Ltd, Lunn Lane, Beal, Goole, North Humberside, DN14 0SE Tel: (01977) 670082

Rock Building Ltd, Rok Centre, Wellington House, Falcon Court, Preston Farm Industrial Estate, Stockton-on-Tees, Cleveland, TS18 3TS Tel: (01642) 616616 Fax: (01642) 679526

▶ Roger Bullivant Ltd, Cleadon Lane, East Boldon, Tyne & Wear, NE36 0AJ Tel: 0191-537 2542 Fax: 0191-536 0404

S D C Builders, Limegrove House, Caxton Road, Elm Farm Industrial Estate, Bedford, MK41 0QQ Tel: (01234) 363155 Fax: (01234) 266385 E-mail: matt.clifford@sdc.co.uk

▶ S E H Holdings Ltd, Crowcroft Road, Nedging Tye, Ipswich, IP7 7HR Tel: (01449) 740971 Fax: (01449) 741403

▶ S H S Overton Airfields Ltd, Grantham Road, Wellingore, Lincoln, LN5 0HH Tel: (01522) 810351

▶ S S Engineering, Cleveland House, Cleveland Street, Darlington, County Durham, DL1 2NU Tel: (01325) 357465 Fax: (01325) 380327

▶ Sac Heartland Environmental, Ferguson Building, Craibstone Estate, Bucksburn, Aberdeen, AB21 9YA Tel: (01224) 711095 Fax: (01224) 711268 E-mail: info@sac.ac.uk

Charles Scott & Partners (London) Ltd, 23 Skylines, Limeharbour, London, E14 9TS Tel: (020) 7538 1333 Fax: (020) 7538 3747 E-mail: cspll@aol.com

▶ Seymour, 6 Mousebank Lane, Lanark, ML11 7PP Tel: (01555) 666123 Fax: (01555) 661302

Shairwood Contracts Ltd, Colchester Road, Tendring, Clacton-on-Sea, Essex, CO16 9AA Tel: (01255) 830704 Fax: (01255) 831047 E-mail: Office@sherwood.Co.uk

Sillars Holdings Ltd, Graythorp Industrial Estate, Hartlepool, Cleveland, TS25 2DF Tel: (01429) 268125 Fax: (01429) 860693 E-mail: sillhold@sillaraol.com

▶ Sim Building Group Ltd, Whitegates, Lenzie Road, Kirkintilloch, Glasgow, G66 3BL Tel: 0141-776 5151 Fax: 0141-777 8103

Simmons plc, Simmons House Townsend Farm Road, Townsend Industrial Estate, Houghton Regis, Dunstable, Bedfordshire, LU5 5BQ Tel: (01582) 606163 Fax: (01582) 662175 E-mail: info@simmonsplc.com

▶ Smith Construction Heckington Ltd, Station Road, Heckington, Sleaford, Lincolnshire, NG34 9NF Tel: (01529) 461500 Fax: (01529) 461463 E-mail: info@smithsportscivils.co.uk

Smyth Steel Ltd, 15 Gorran Road, Garvagh, Coleraine, County Londonderry, BT51 4HA Tel: (028) 7086 8544 Fax: (028) 7086 8102 E-mail: mail@smyth-steel.co.uk

▶ Souters Sports Ltd, Unit 80, Bandeath Industrial Estate, Stirling, FK7 7NP Tel: (01786) 480720

▶ South Yorks Tarmacadam Contractors Ltd, Wentworth Industrial Estate, Wentworth Way, Tankersley, Barnsley, South Yorkshire, S75 3DH Tel: (01226) 748748

▶ Sports Turf Services, Bellfield Park, Kinross, KY13 0NL Tel: (01577) 863864

▶ Sportsground Drainage Contractors, Backhill Farm, Carberry, Musselburgh, Midlothian, EH21 8QD Tel: 0131-654 2882 Fax: 0131-654 0466

Stamford Homes, Ashurst Southgate Park, Bakewell Road, Orton Southgate, Peterborough, PE2 6YS Tel: (01733) 396600 Fax: (01733) 396669 E-mail: sales@stamford-homes.co.uk

Star Civil Engineering Ltd, Templar Indust Park, Torrington Avenue, Coventry, CV4 9AP Tel: (024) 7642 1122 Fax: (024) 7645 4973 E-mail: info@starcivil.co.uk

Stargrade Constuction, 2 Morrison Court, Crownhill, Milton Keynes, MK8 0DA Tel: (01908) 560774 Fax: (01908) 567136

Stave-Con Ltd, 6-7 Spring Road Industrial Estate, Lanesfield, Wolverhampton, WV4 6JT Tel: (01902) 493749 Fax: (01902) 401466

Stepnell Estates Ltd, Lawford Road, Rugby, Warwickshire, CV21 2UU Tel: (01788) 574511 Fax: (01788) 541364 E-mail: gailb.@stepnell.co.uk

▶ Strandhill Civil Engineering Ltd, 3 Dukes Road, Southampton, SO14 0SQ Tel: (023) 8055 9121 Fax: (023) 8055 9660

Stuart Building Services, Duncrub, Dunning, Perth, PH2 0QN Tel: (01764) 684840 Fax: (01764) 684841 E-mail: info@stuartbuildingservices.co.uk

▶ Suffolk Fleet Maintenance, Blyth Road, Halesworth, Suffolk, IP19 8EN Tel: (01986) 874427 Fax: (01986) 873279

▶ Swatman Groundworks Ltd, Fairfield, North Cove, Beccles, Suffolk, NR34 7QG Tel: (01502) 476208 Fax: (01502) 476580

T & B Contractors Ltd, Place Farm, Wheathampstead, St. Albans, Hertfordshire, AL4 8SB Tel: (01582) 833633 Fax: (01582) 833899 E-mail: post@tandb-contractors.co.uk

T G Contractors Holbeach Ltd, 21 Western Avenue, Holbeach, Spalding, Lincolnshire, PE12 7QD Tel: (01406) 422500 Fax: (01406) 422784

T H Kenyon & Sons plc, Kenyon House, 14a Hockerill Street, Bishop's Stortford, Hertfordshire, CM23 2DW Tel: (01279) 858700 Fax: (01279) 653454

▶ T J Riley (Plant & Transport) Ltd, Beveridge Lane Industrial Esta, Ellistown, Coalville, Leicestershire, LE67 1FB Tel: (01530) 264050

▶ T K P Surfacing Ltd, Unit 5, Argyle Commercial Centre, Argyle Street, Swindon, SN2 8AR Tel: (01793) 430014

▶ T McKie, Deans Park, Irongray Road, Dumfries, DG2 0HS Tel: (01387) 720826

T R L Ltd, Crowthorne House, Nine Mile Ride, Wokingham, Berkshire, RG40 3GA Tel: (01344) 773131 Fax: (01344) 770356 E-mail: info@tr1.co.uk

▶ T Robertson & Sons, Whinpark Quarry, Mount Pleasant, Newburgh, Cupar, Fife, KY14 6DG Tel: (01337) 840212 Fax: (01337) 841078

Taisei Europe Ltd, 19 Hanover Sq, London, W1S 1HY Tel: (020) 7316 4000 Fax: (020) 7316 4001

Tarmac Southern Ltd, Holborough Road, Snodland, Kent, ME6 5PJ Tel: (0845) 6007888 Fax: (01634) 248295 E-mail: info@tarmac-southern.co.uk

▶ Tayside Contracts, Brioch Road, Crieff, Perthshire, PH7 3SG Tel: (01764) 652115 Fax: (01764) 655418

▶ Tayside Contracts, Feus Road, Perth, PH1 2UQ Tel: (01738) 630044 Fax: (01738) 630515

▶ Tercon Ltd, 6 Barnack Trading Centre, Novers Hill, Bedminster, Bristol, BS3 5QE Tel: 0117-963 9039 Fax: 0117-966 7074

▶ Terracarbon Ltd, The Garage, Hingham Road, Hackford, Wymondham, Norfolk, NR18 9HF Tel: (01953) 851535 Fax: (01953) 851328

▶ Tidey & Webb Ltd, Broomers Corner, Shipley, Horsham, West Sussex, RH13 8PX Tel: (01403) 741673 Fax: (01403) 741674

Tithegrove Ltd, Fairview House, 43 Bath Road, Swindon, SN1 4AS Tel: 0870 4282822 Fax: 0871 2267808 E-mail: admin@tithegrove.co.uk

Toft-Johnston (Construction) Ltd, Kingsley House, Apedale Road, Chesterton, Newcastle, Staffordshire, ST5 6BH Tel: (01782) 566531 Fax: (01782) 564795 E-mail: admin@toftjohnson.co.uk

Tomlinson & White (Contracts) Ltd, Smithy Avenue, Clay Cross, Chesterfield, Derbyshire, S45 9NX Tel: (01246) 250060 Fax: (01246) 250004

▶ Tonic Construction Ltd, The Coach House, Queen Court, West Tockenham, Swindon, SN4 7PJ Tel: (01793) 741234

Toty Building Services Ltd, Park House, Woodland Park, Bradford Road, Chain Bar, Cleckheaton, West Yorkshire, BD19 6BW Tel: (01274) 866700 Fax: (01274) 866737 E-mail: info@toty-building.co.uk

Train & Kemp, 10 Kennington Park Place, London, SE11 4AS Tel: (020) 7582 1276 Fax: (020) 7582 5728 E-mail: mail@trainandkemp.co.uk

Trant Construction Ltd, Rushington Business Park, Rushington Lane, Totton, Southampton, SO40 9LT Tel: (023) 8066 5544 Fax: (023) 8066 5500 E-mail: construction@trant.co.uk

Treasure & Son Ltd, Temeside, Ludlow, Shropshire, SY8 1JW Tel: (01584) 872161 Fax: (01584) 874876 E-mail: mail@treasure&son.co.uk

Tullyraine Quarries Ltd, 122 Dromore Road, Banbridge, County Down, BT32 4EG Tel: (028) 4066 2481 Fax: (028) 4066 2748 E-mail: enquiries@tullyrainequarries.co.uk

Underpin & Makegood (Contracting) Ltd, 37 Millmarsh Lane, Enfield, Middx, EN3 7UY Tel: (020) 8805 4000 Fax: (020) 8805 4222 E-mail: david@underpin.com

CIVIL ENGINEERING AND PUBLIC WORKS CONTRACTORS – *continued*

▶ Underwater Pool Repair Services Ltd, 448-450 Manchester Road East, Little Hulton, Manchester, M38 9NS Tel: 0161-799 1222 Fax: 0161-702 9958

Vale Contractors (South Wales) Ltd, Unit 45 Tumulus Way, Llandow Trading Estate, Llandow, Cowbridge, South Glamorgan, CF71 7PB Tel: (01446) 793562 Fax: (01446) 795231 E-mail: sale@valecontractors.co.uk

▶ Versotech Ltd, 81D Main Street, Calderbank, Airdrie, Lanarkshire, ML6 9SG Tel: (01236) 753875 Fax: (01236) 754497 E-mail: info@versotech.co.uk

VKHP, 5 Newcomen Road, Tunbridge Wells, Kent, TN4 9PA Tel: (01892) 521841 Fax: (01892) 533149 E-mail: tw@vkhp.co.uk

W D L (Contracting) Ltd, Stuart Quarry, Penderyn, Aberdare, Mid Glamorgan, CF44 9JY Tel: (01685) 811525 Fax: (01685) 814326 E-mail: accounts@wdlewisaberdare.co.uk

W H Kirkwood Ltd, 27 Hope Street, Greenock, Renfrewshire, PA15 4AW Tel: (01475) 721248 Fax: (01475) 888465 E-mail: info@whkirkwood.co.uk

▶ W I & A Gilbert Road Contractors, Easter Kersland, Dalry, Ayrshire, KA24 4JA Tel: (01294) 834433 Fax: (01294) 833343

▶ W K Engineering Services, Tweed Road, Clevedon, Avon, BS21 6RR Tel: (01275) 349700 Fax: (01275) 349722 E-mail: info@wk.com

W Knight & Co Roadworks Ltd, Lissett Road, Maidenhead, Berkshire, SL6 1AZ Tel: (01628) 673014

▶ W M Donald Ltd, Marlaine, Netherley, Stonehaven, Kincardineshire, AB39 3QN Tel: (01569) 730590 Fax: (01569) 731315

▶ W T Construction Poole Ltd, Selbys Yard, Huntick Road, Lytchett Matravers, Poole, Dorset, BH16 6BB Tel: (01202) 620541 Fax: (01202) 620543

Walcon Ltd, Cockerell Close, Segensworth West, Fareham, Hampshire, PO15 5SR Tel: (01489) 579977 Fax: (01489) 579988 E-mail: sales@walconmarine.com

Walgrave Electrical Services Ltd, 13 North Portway Close, Round Spinney, Northampton, NN3 8RQ Tel: (01604) 490100 Fax: (01604) 490101 E-mail: walgrave@skynet.co.uk

Warings Construction Group Holdings Ltd, Gatcombe House, Hilsea, Portsmouth, PO2 0TU Tel: (023) 9269 4900 Fax: (023) 9269 4948

Watson Hallam, Burlington House, 369 Wellingborough Road, Northampton, NN1 4EU Tel: (01604) 230823 Fax: (01604) 230923

▶ Weldon Plant Ltd, Lammas Road, Weldon North, Corby, Northamptonshire, NN17 5JF Tel: (01536) 260833 Fax: (01536) 261880 E-mail: sales@weldonplant.co.uk

Wheal Jane Enterprises Ltd, Old Mine Offices, Wheal Jane, Baldhu, Truro, Cornwall, TR3 6EE Tel: (01872) 560200 Fax: (01872) 562020 E-mail: carnon@wheal-jane.co.uk

▶ Whitnell Plant, School Farm Buildings, School Road, Langham, Colchester, CO4 5PB Tel: (01206) 272834 Fax: (01206) 272104 E-mail: sales@whitnell.co.uk

▶ William Hughes Civil Engineering Ltd, Bodffordd, Llangefni, Gwynedd, LL77 7DZ Tel: (01248) 750193 Fax: (01248) 723709 E-mail: admin@williamhughes.com

Owen Williams Ltd, 41 Whitcomb Street, London, WC2H 7DT Tel: (020) 7839 1072 Fax: (020) 7827 2439

Ken Wilson Associates, 52 Union Road, Inverness, IV2 3JY Tel: (01463) 237375 Fax: (01463) 237666 E-mail: enquiries@kwa.uk.net

▶ Witham Valley Civil Engineering Ltd, Slippery Gowt Lane, Wyberton, Boston, Lincolnshire, PE21 7AA Tel: (01205) 311021 Fax: (01205) 359376

Wrekin Construction Co Ltd, Lamledge Lane, Shifnal, Shropshire, TF11 8BE Tel: (01952) 468000 Fax: (01952) 468001 E-mail: info@wrekin.co.uk

Wrekin Construction Co. Ltd, Enterprise Road, Raunds, Wellingborough, Northamptonshire, NN9 6JE Tel: (01933) 624404 Fax: (01933) 623496 E-mail: raunds@wrekin.co.uk

CIVIL ENGINEERING AND PUBLIC WORKS MATERIALS

A M E C Group Ltd, Church Street, Adlington, Chorley, Lancashire, PR7 4LB Tel: (01257) 484400 Fax: (01257) 484405

Cirencester Civil Engineering Ltd, 4 Esland Place, Love Lane, Cirencester, Gloucestershire, GL7 1YG Tel: (01285) 652020 Fax: (01285) 651007 E-mail: sales@cirencestercivilengineering.co.uk

Collier & Catchpole Ltd, 11 London Road, Stanway, Colchester, CO3 0NT Tel: (01206) 715500 Fax: (01206) 715517 E-mail: mail@colliercatchpole.co.uk

ElkinTatic, Hammond House, Holmestone Road, Poulton Close, Dover, Kent, CT17 0UF Tel: (01304) 203545 Fax: (01304) 215001 E-mail: acp@gaticdover.co.uk

M Lambe Construction Ltd, Newton House, Newton Place, Birmingham, B18 5JY Tel: 0121-523 0666 Fax: 0121-554 8896

William McDowell & Partners, Aldersgate House, 13-19 University Road, Belfast, BT7 1NA Tel: (028) 9024 5444 Fax: (028) 9024 5916

Moulding Contracts Ltd, Block 3 St. Cuthberts House, Durham Way North, Aycliffe Industrial Park, Newton Aycliffe, County Durham, DL5 6DN Tel: (01325) 311422 Fax: (01325) 310725E-mail: south@mouldingcontracts.com

Parker Merchanting Ltd, John O Gaunts Trading Estate, Leeds Road, Rothwell, Leeds, LS26 0DU Tel: 0113-282 2933 Fax: 0113-282 2620 E-mail: info.parker@hagemeyer.co.uk

Sandy Company Builders, Greyfriars Place, Stafford, ST16 2SD Tel: (01785) 258164 Fax: (01785) 256526E-mail: info@sandy.co.uk

CIVIL ENGINEERING AND PUBLIC WORKS PLANT AND EQUIPMENT

Cirencester Civil Engineering Ltd, 4 Esland Place, Love Lane, Cirencester, Gloucestershire, GL7 1YG Tel: (01285) 652020 Fax: (01285) 651007 E-mail: sales@cirencestercivilengineering.co.uk

Electro Services Ltd, 14 Pulloxhill Business Park, Greenfield Road, Pulloxhill, Bedford, MK45 5EU Tel: (01525) 719994 Fax: (01525) 719995 E-mail: electrogbr@aol.com

W.J. Farvis & Sons Ltd, Temple Works, Morley Road, Southville, Bristol, BS3 1DT Tel: 0117-966 6677 Fax: 0117-966 9893 E-mail: sales@favis.co.uk

John Howe, Gardeners Cottage, Leek Old Road, Sutton, Macclesfield, Cheshire, SK11 0HZ Tel: (01625) 610943 Fax: (01625) 610943

CIVIL ENGINEERING JACKING SYSTEMS

Doorman Long Tech, The Charles Parker Building, Midland Road, Higham Ferrers, Rushden, Northamptonshire, NN10 8DN Tel: (01933) 319133 Fax: (01933) 319135 E-mail: dlt@dormanlong.com

CIVIL ENGINEERING RECRUITMENT

Aalpha Solutions (North West) Ltd, 169 Cross Green Lane, Cross Green, Leeds, LS9 0BD Tel: 0113-249 6900 Fax: 0113-249 6906 E-mail: info@aalphasolutions.co.uk

▶ Ably Resources Ltd, 1 Cumbernauld Road, Buchanan Business Park, Stepps, Glasgow, G33 6HZ Tel: 0141-565 1270 Fax: 0141-779 1616 E-mail: enquiries@ablyresource.com

▶ Appoint Direct Ltd, PO Box 8828, Chelmsford, CM1 7WP Tel: (01245) 442777 Fax: (08456) 443005 E-mail: info@appointdirect.com

▶ ARV Solutions, 27 Southmead Road, Westbury-On-Trym, Bristol, BS10 5DL Tel: 0117 9083173 Fax: 0871 661 3669 E-mail: mail@arvsolutions.co.uk

▶ Blue Silicon, 214 Kings Ash Road, Paignton, Devon, TQ3 3XL Tel: (0870) 7070005 E-mail: kellysearch@bluesilicon.co.uk

▶ Calibre Recruitment, Unit 10 River Court Brighouse Business Village, Brighouse Road, Middlesbrough, Cleveland, TS2 1RT Tel: (01642) 244020 Fax: (01642) 243480 E-mail: careers@calibre-recruitment.co.uk

▶ Can London Ltd, Unit A Springhead Enterprise Park, Springhead Road, Northfleet, Gravesend, Kent, DA11 8HB Tel: (01474) 538100 Fax: (01474) 538101 E-mail: info@canlondon.co.uk

▶ Construction Consultancy Services Ltd, 3 Wellington Park, Belfast, BT9 6DJ Tel: (028) 9092 3360 Fax: (028) 9038 2451 E-mail: info@ccsni.com

DTC Surfacing, Birchmere, Balmedie, Aberdeen, AB23 8YS Tel: (01358) 742368 Fax: (01358) 742020 E-mail: info@dtcsurfacing.co.uk

▶ E T S Technical Sales, Phoenix House, Phoenix Way, Cirencester, Gloucestershire, GL7 1QG Tel: (0870) 0702246 E-mail: mark@ets-technical-sales.co.uk

▶ Ecruit UK Ltd, 41 Convent Road, Ashford, Middlesex, TW15 2HJ Tel: (08718) 714605 Fax: (08712) 773138 E-mail: admin@ecruit-direct.co.uk

▶ Human Resources Consultancy, 50 Keedwell Hill, Long Ashton, Bristol, BS41 9DR Tel: (01275) 540510 Fax: (01275) 540510 E-mail: melaniehall@hrc-bristol.co.uk

▶ I T S Western, 1 Apex Court, Woodlands, Bradley Stoke, Bristol, BS32 4JT Tel: (01454) 619928 Fax: (01454) 619391 E-mail: spencertownsley@itswestern.co.uk

▶ International Recruitment Bureau Ltd., Address 274 Hither green lane, London, SE13 6T Tel: 07776 472126 Fax: 02086 959200

▶ I-volv Recruitment Solutions, 8 Clifton Road, High Brooms, Tunbridge Wells, Kent, TN2 3AR Tel: 01892 689301 E-mail: recruitment@i-volv.co.uk

▶ Jobsearch Northern Ireland, PO Box 05, Ballymena, County Antrim, BT44 9YF Tel: 028276 41743

▶ Lechley Recruitment, The Rural Business Centre, Bilsborrow, Preston, PR3 0RY Tel: 01995 642260 Fax: 01995 642258 E-mail: scott@lechley.com

▶ Linx Recruitment, Archway House, Norton Way North, Letchworth Garden City, Hertfordshire, SG6 1BH Tel: (01462) 677669 E-mail: keith@linxrecruitment.co.uk

▶ Monterey Recruitment, Suite 8 Merlin House, Mossland Road, Hillington Park, Glasgow, G52 4XZ Tel: (0845) 4332211 Fax: (0845) 4332217

▶ Now Recruitment Ltd, 5 The Square, Broad Street, Birmingham, B15 1AS Tel: 0121-693 9408 E-mail: info@nowrecruitment.com

▶ Orr Simpson, Morsel House, Moss Hill Lane, York, YO26 9SY Tel: (01423) 339569 Fax: (01423) 330724 E-mail: info@orrsimpson.co.uk

▶ Prestige Recruitment Services Ltd, Saddlers Court, 650 Warwick Road, Solihull, West Midlands, B91 3DX Tel: 0121-244 4484 Fax: 0121-244 4494

Prime50plus, PO Box 5050, Huddersfield, HD1 4WB Tel: (0845) 4562201 E-mail: paul.kern@prime50plus.co.uk

▶ Professional Management Resources Ltd, P O Box 23, Wadhurst, East Sussex, TN5 6XL Tel: (01892) 784226 Fax: (01892) 784228 E-mail: info@pmr-worldjobs.co.uk

▶ RecruitEU Ltd, PO Box 43574, London, UK, SW15 1XA Tel: 0207 8708824 Fax: 0870 7051298 E-mail: nigelholmes@recruiteu.com

▶ Salestarget.co.uk, Holden House, 57 Rathbone Place, London, W1T 1LD Tel: 020 7769 9200 Fax: 020 7769 9008 E-mail: info@salestarget.co.uk

Staffhunt, 30 Birch Grove, Menstrie, Clackmannanshire, FK11 7DW Tel: (01786) 834776 E-mail: info@staffhunt.org

▶ Tim Cowell, Clayhill Farm, Marden Rd, Cranbrook, Kent, TN17 2LP Tel: (01580) 715111 Fax: (01580) 714718 E-mail: webmaster@manufacturingjobs.co.uk

UJOB - UK Employment Vacancies, PO Box 139, Thornton-Cleveleys, Lancashire, FY5 4WU Tel: (0870) 7668565 E-mail: ujob@ujob.co.uk

▶ Will Recruit, Kingswood House, The Avenue, Cliftonville, Northampton, NN1 5BT Tel: (0870) 0468686 E-mail: info@willrecruit.com

CIVIL ENGINEERING TEST EQUIPMENT

Arqiva Ltd, Unit 13, Garonor Way, Portbury, Bristol, BS20 7XE Tel: (01275) 371371 Fax: (01275) 371269

Materials Testing Equipment Ltd, Gilwilly Industrial Estate, Penrith, Cumbria, CA11 9BQ Tel: (01768) 865302 Fax: (01768) 890954 E-mail: mte@materialstestingequip.com

CIVIL ENGINEERING WATER PIPE MAINTENANCE OR REPAIR

▶ Cane Contractors, 14 Wadhurst Close, Bognor Regis, West Sussex, PO21 5LD Tel: (01243) 825139 Fax: (01243) 825139 E-mail: elieencane@btconnect.com

▶ DAL Utilities Ltd, 2 Westcliff Park Drive, Westcliff-on-sea, Essex, SS0 9LP Tel: 01702 304849 Fax: 01702 304849 E-mail: dal_ltd@btinternet.com

CIVIL ENGINEERING, SERVICE WATER PIPE LAYING

▶ Cane Contractors, 14 Wadhurst Close, Bognor Regis, West Sussex, PO21 5LD Tel: (01243) 825139 Fax: (01243) 825139 E-mail: elieencane@btconnect.com

CLAD STEEL STRIPS

Corus Ltd, PO Box 69, Rotherham, South Yorkshire, S60 1BN Tel: (01709) 377113 Fax: (01709) 375250 E-mail: bsmsales@corusgroup.com

CLADDING MATERIALS

▶ Dundas UPVC, 1D Payne Street, Port Dundas Trading Estate, Glasgow, G4 0LE Tel: 0141 353 1996

CLADDING PANEL REPAIR AND RESPRAY

Coating Repair Specialists, 2 Somerset Road, Springwell Estate, Sunderland, SR3 4EB Tel: 0191- 522 9577 Fax: 0191- 522 9577 E-mail: j.collier40@ntlworld.com

CLADDING SYSTEMS

A M E, 5 Glebe Road, Skelmersdale, Lancashire, WN8 9JP Tel: (01695) 50658 Fax: (01695) 50652 E-mail: info@amefacades.com

Altro Ltd, Works Road, Letchworth Garden City, Hertfordshire, SG6 1NW Tel: (01462) 707604 Fax: (01462) 707504 E-mail: leisure@altro.co.uk

Colorgroup Ltd, Whitehead Estate, Docks Way, Newport, Gwent, NP20 2NW Tel: (01633) 223854 Fax: (01633) 253992 E-mail: dave.burston@colorgroup.co.uk

Corus Building Systems, Units 1-3 Fishwicks Industrial Estate, Kilbuck Lane, St. Helens, Merseyside, WA11 9SZ Tel: (01942) 295500 Fax: (01942) 272136E-mail: info@kalzip.co.uk

M.G. Duff International Ltd, Unit 1 Timberlane Industrial Estate, Gravel Lane, Chichester, West Sussex, PO19 8PP Tel: (01243) 533336 Fax: (01243) 533422 E-mail: sales@mgduff.co.uk

Maple Leaf Insulations Conservatories, Maple Leaf House, Canterbury Road, Worthing, West Sussex, BN13 1AW Tel: (01903) 692122 Fax: (01903) 831570

▶ Nelson Associates, 186 Seacliff Road, Bangor, County Down, BT20 5HA Tel: (028) 9145 6109 Fax: (028) 9145 6109 E-mail: clivenelson@btinternet.com

Plastestrip Profiles Ltd, Trenance Mill, St. Austell, Cornwall, PL25 5LZ Tel: (01726) 74771 Fax: (01726) 69238 E-mail: sales@plaspro.force9.co.uk

Rooftech, RoofTech House, Four Seasons Crescent, Kimpton Road, Sutton, Surrey, SM3 9QR Tel: (020) 8641 7077 Fax: (020) 8641 7006 E-mail: mail@rooftech.info

Southern Sheeting Supplies (Roofing and Cladding), Hill Place Farm, Turners Hill Road (B2110), East Grinstead, West Sussex, RH19 4LX Tel: (01342) 315300 Fax: (01342) 410560E-mail: sales@southernsheeting.co.uk

CLAMP METERS

▶ Richmond Electronic Services Ltd, 42 Hurricane Way, Norwich Airport Industrial, Estate Norfolk, Norwich, NR6 6JB Tel: (020) 7942 0700 Fax: (020) 7942 0701

CLAMPING SYSTEMS

▶ PPL Marine Products, Tufthane Building, Falkland Close, Coventry, CV4 8AU Tel: 02476 464509 Fax: 02476 694313 E-mail: sales@ppl-marine.com

CLAMPS, *See also headings for particular types under Clamps*

Hillcliff Tools Ltd, 11 Catley Road, Sheffield, S9 5JF Tel: 0114-244 3665 Fax: 0114-242 3319 E-mail: jj@hillcliff-tools.com

Lenzkes Clamping Tools, Universal House, Farfield Park, Manvers, Rotherham, South Yorkshire, S63 5DB Tel: (01709) 870000 Fax: (01709) 870010

Swindens Revolving Head Vices Ltd, Suite 401 Langham Ho, 302 Regent St, London, W1B 3AT Tel: (020) 7580 6491 Fax: (020) 7580 4729 E-mail: am@swindens-vices.co.uk

CLASSIC CAR REPAIR

▶ Auto Smart Repairs Ltd, 8 Riverway, Staines, Middlesex, TW18 2SJ Tel: (01784) 442000 E-mail: michael@autosmartrepairsltd.com

▶ Dents UK Car Body Repairs, 490 High Road, Ilford, Essex, IG1 1UE Tel: (020) 8478 7356 Fax: (020) 8478 7356 E-mail: sales@dentsuk.com

▶ Scratch Wizard Bumper Repairs Service, Andover Green, Bovington, Wareham, Dorset, BH20 6LN Tel: (0800) 0076829 E-mail: michael.lane01@tiscali.co.uk

▶ Smart Wise UK Ltd, 5 Ashwyn Business Centre, Marchants Way, Burgess Hill, West Sussex, RH15 8QY Tel: (01444) 257342 Fax: (01444) 257673 E-mail: sales@smartwise.com

CLASSIC DESIGN BOATS

▶ Bristol Yacht Brokerage Ltd, Junction Lock, Cumberland Basin, Bristol, BS1 6XL Tel: 0117-930 4891 Fax: 0117-930 4882 E-mail: tim@bristolyachtbrokerage.com

Moss David Boat Builders, Wyre Road, Skippool Creek, Thornton-Cleveleys, Lancashire, FY5 5LF Tel: (01253) 893830 Fax: (01253) 893830 E-mail: mr.davidmoss@virgin.net

CLASSICAL MUSIC SOUND RECORDING

▶ Digital Media Music, 61 Birkbeck Road, Mill Hill, London, NW7 4BP Tel: 020881 67775 E-mail: info@digitalmediamusic.co.uk

▶ Riverside Studios, Four Horse Shoes Yard, Milnsbridge, Huddersfield, HD3 4NE Tel: (01484) 642131 E-mail: contact@riversidestudios.info

▶ Schtum Ltd, 11 Osram Road, East Lane Business Park, Wembley, Middlesex, HA9 7NG Tel: (020) 8904 4422 Fax: (020) 8904 3777 E-mail: info@schtum.co.uk

▶ Totally Ratted Productions, 95 Ewart Road*Forest Fields, Nottingham, NG7 6HG Tel: 0115 8330457 E-mail: productions@totallyratted.com

CLAY

Castle Clay Sales, Podmore Street, Stoke-on-Trent, ST6 2EZ Tel: (01782) 575992 Fax: (01782) 575995 E-mail: claysales@ukonline.co.uk

Gothers Moor Fabrications, Gothers Road, Gothers Moor Cottage, St Dennis, St. Austell, Cornwall, PL26 8DF Tel: (01726) 822185 Fax: (01726) 823825

Hepworth Building Products Ltd, 47 Coppice Side, Swadlincote, Derbyshire, DE11 9AA Tel: (01283) 552467 Fax: (01283) 221034

Hepworths Building Products Ltd, Woodville Works, Woodville, Swadlincote, Derbyshire, DE11 8BQ Tel: (01283) 216111 Fax: (01283) 522009

Imerys Minerals Ltd, Furzebrook Road, Wareham, Dorset, BH20 5AR Tel: (01626) 333797 Fax: (01929) 552845

Marshalls Clay Products Ltd, Quarry Lane, Dewsbury, West Yorkshire, WF12 7JJ Tel: 0113-220 3500 Fax: 0113-220 3555

Moore & Sons Ltd, PO Box 407, Newcastle, Staffordshire, ST5 7EE Tel: (01782) 563470 Fax: (01782) 561796

Potclays Ltd, Brick Kiln Lane, Stoke-on-Trent, ST4 7BP Tel: (01782) 219816 Fax: (01782) 286506 E-mail: sales@potclays.co.uk

▶ Your Party By Post, 82 Copthorne Road, Felbridge, East Grinstead, West Sussex, RH19 2NU Tel: (0845) 4084512 E-mail: shop@yourpartybypost.co.uk

CLAY PAVING BRICKS

Ashmead Building Supplies Ltd, Portview Road, Avonmouth, Bristol, BS11 9LD Tel: 0117-982 8281 Fax: 0117-982 0135 E-mail: avon@ashmead.co.uk

Dunton Bros Ltd, Blackwell Hall Lane, Chesham, Buckinghamshire, HP5 1TN Tel: (01494) 783730 Fax: (01494) 791255 E-mail: sales@duntons.com

Marshalls Clay Products Ltd, Quarry Lane, Dewsbury, West Yorkshire, WF12 7JJ Tel: 0113-220 3500 Fax: 0113-220 3555

CLAY PLASTER

Lime Green Products Ltd, The Coates Kiln, Stretton Road, Much Wenlock, Shropshire, TF13 6DG Tel: (01952) 728611 Fax: (01952) 728361 E-mail: enquire@lime-green.co.uk

CLAY PRODUCT MOULDS

G M Ceramic Mould Making Services, 108 Trentham Road, Dresden, Stoke-on-Trent, ST3 4ED Tel: (01782) 324359

Leonard Hall Patterns Ltd, 352 Loxley Road, Sheffield, S6 4TJ Tel: 0114-234 3571 Fax: 0114-234 3571

CLEAN AIR EQUIPMENT

Airfeso Ltd, 16-18 Main Street, Bolton by Bowland, Clitheroe, Lancashire, BB7 4NW Tel: (01200) 447206 Fax: (01200) 447443 E-mail: airfeso@aol.com

Alert Products, Hollins Lane, Tilstock, Whitchurch, Shropshire, SY13 3NU Tel: (01948) 880627 Fax: (01948) 880339 E-mail: graham.dewson@ukonline.co.uk

Bassaire Ltd, Duncan Road, Park Gate, Southampton, SO31 1ZS Tel: (01489) 885111 Fax: (01489) 885211 E-mail: sales@bassaire.co.uk

Baxi Heating Ltd, Brook House, Coventry Road, Warwick, CV34 4LL Tel: (01772) 693700 Fax: (01926) 410006 E-mail: service@heatteam.co.uk

Clean Modules Ltd, Unit 3, Hawthorne Road, Castle Donington, Derby, DE74 2QR Tel: (01332) 696970 Fax: 01332 696963 E-mail: enquiries@cleanmodules.co.uk

Envair Ltd, Envair House, York Avenue, Haslingden, Rossendale, Lancashire, BB4 4HX Tel: (01706) 228416 Fax: (01706) 229577 E-mail: sales@envair.co.uk

Howorth Airtech Ltd, Victoria Works, Lorne Street, Farnworth, Bolton, BL4 7LZ Tel: (01204) 700900 Fax: (01204) 862378 E-mail: info@howorthairtech.co.uk

Medical Air Technology, Mars Street, Oldham, OL9 6LY Tel: 0161-621 6200 Fax: 0161-624 7547E-mail: sales@medicalairtechnology.com

Puraflow Ltd, 44a St James Street, Burnley, Lancashire, BB11 1NQ Tel: (01282) 831094 Fax: (01282) 455938

CLEAN IN PLACE (CIP) SYSTEMS

▶ L H Stainless Ltd, Towieburn, Keith, Banffshire, AB55 5JA Tel: (01466) 792222 Fax: (01466) 795329 E-mail: sales@l-h-s.co.uk

CLEAN ROOM AEROSOL GENERATING EQUIPMENT

Concept Engineering Ltd, 7 Woodlands Business Park, Woodlands Park Avenue, Maidenhead, Berkshire, SL6 3UA Tel: (01628) 825555 Fax: (01628) 826261 E-mail: info@concept-smoke.co.uk

CLEAN ROOM AIR CONDITIONING (AC) SYSTEMS

Airology Systems Ltd, Brickyard Lane, Studley, Warwickshire, B80 7EE Tel: (01527) 850717 Fax: (01527) 850737 E-mail: aircon@airology.freeserve.co.uk

Batchelor Air Conditioning, 3 Stilebrook Road, Olney, Buckinghamshire, MK46 5EA Tel: (01234) 241781 Fax: (01234) 241781

Tecomak Ltd, Valley Industries, Tonbridge Road, Hadlow, Tonbridge, Kent, TN11 0AH Tel: (01732) 852250 Fax: (01732) 852251 E-mail: sales@tecomak.co.uk

CLEAN ROOM AUTOMATIC LOCKING/INTERLOCK SYSTEMS

Cleanroom Supplies Ltd, Violet House, Cumrew, Carlisle, CA8 9DD Tel: (01768) 896800 Fax: 01228 830100

CLEAN ROOM CLOTHING/ CONSUMABLES, ENVIRONMENTAL

A I S Countdown Ltd, Unit 33 Riverside, Medway City Estate, Sir Thomas Longley Road, Rochester, Kent, ME2 4DP Tel: (01634) 719422 Fax: (01634) 290269 E-mail: sales@aiscountdown.com

Contamination Control Apparel Ltd, Northolt Drive, Bolton, BL3 6RE Tel: (01204) 528019 Fax: (01204) 361549E-mail: cca@mikar.co.uk

Countdown Clean Systems Ltd, Unit 2276, Dunbeath Road, Elgin Industrial Estate, Swindon, SN2 8EA Tel: (01793) 512505 Fax: (01793) 541884 E-mail: ais@countdown.com

Lynbond 2000 Ltd, St. Davids House, 8 Blenheim Court Brownfields, Welwyn Garden City, Hertfordshire, AL7 1AD Tel: (01707) 259996 Fax: (01707) 259997 E-mail: solutions@lynbond2000.com

Micronclean (Newbury) Ltd, Faraday Road, Newbury, Berkshire, RG14 2AD Tel: (01635) 37901 Fax: (01635) 31528 E-mail: sales@micronclean-newbury.co.uk

CLEAN ROOM CONSTRUCTORS/ ASSEMBLY SERVICES

Clean Modules Ltd, Unit 3, Hawthorne Road, Castle Donington, Derby, DE74 2QR Tel: (01332) 696970 Fax: 01332 696963 E-mail: enquiries@cleanmodules.co.uk

Clean Room Installation Services Ltd, 9 The Metro Centre, Ronsons Way, St. Albans, Hertfordshire, AL4 9QT Tel: (01727) 840594 Fax: (01727) 843368 E-mail: cleanrooms@stodec.co.uk

Clestra Cleanrooms, Hamilton House, 3 North Street, Carshalton, Surrey, SM5 2HZ Tel: (020) 8773 2121 Fax: (020) 8260 6814

Colsec Ltd, Wassage Way, Hampton Lovett, Droitwich, Worcestershire, WR9 0NX Tel: (01905) 795070 Fax: (01905) 794013 E-mail: sales@colsec.co.uk

CLEAN ROOM DESIGN SERVICES

Clean Room Installation Services Ltd, 9 The Metro Centre, Ronsons Way, St. Albans, Hertfordshire, AL4 9QT Tel: (01727) 840594 Fax: (01727) 843368 E-mail: cleanrooms@stodec.co.uk

▶ IRIS Engineering & Technology Ltd, 2 Gill Burn, Sherburn Towers, Rowlands Gill, Tyne & Wear, NE39 2PT Tel: 01207 543914 E-mail: bob.preston@iriset.co.uk

Pert Building Services Ltd, 31 Bunbury Road, Northfield, Birmingham, B31 2DR Tel: 0121-411 2333 Fax: 0121-411 2600 E-mail: barrieroberts@pert-aircon.co.uk

Scientific Lesser Ltd, Hanworth Lane, Chertsey, Surrey, KT16 9JX Tel: (01932) 568122 Fax: (01932) 560818 E-mail: sllairskil@aol.com

CLEAN ROOM DOOR EQUIPMENT

P B S C Ltd, Bradley Junction Industrial Estate, Leeds Road, Huddersfield, HD2 1UR Tel: (01484) 354500 Fax: (01484) 354504 E-mail: info@pbsc.co.uk

CLEAN ROOM DOOR/WINDOW

▶ A & J Window Cleaners, 33 Auckland Avenue, Ramsgate, Kent, CT12 6HZ Tel: (01843) 597808 E-mail: ukgb_net@yahoo.co.uk

▶ ClearView Ladderless Window Cleaning, 21 Lightfoot Road, Uttoxeter, Staffordshire, ST14 7HA Tel: 01889 560119

▶ DSB Cleaning Services, Park Court Offices, 43-45 Rhosddu Road, Wrexham, Clwyd, LL11 2NS Tel: (01978) 352900 Fax: (01978) 355027 E-mail: info@dsbcleaningservices.co.uk

▶ Martin, 8 Walnut Tree Avenue, Martham, Great Yarmouth, Norfolk, NR29 4QS Tel: (01493) 740746 E-mail: martin@procleaning-office.co.uk

CLEAN ROOM EQUIPMENT

A I S Countdown Ltd, Unit 33 Riverside, Medway City Estate, Sir Thomas Longley Road, Rochester, Kent, ME2 4DP Tel: (01634) 719422 Fax: (01634) 290269 E-mail: sales@aiscountdown.com

Aerogo UK Ltd, 11a Orchard Road, Royston, Hertfordshire, SG8 6HL Tel: (01763) 249349 Fax: (0870) 4014546 E-mail: sales@aerogo-uk.co.uk

Almond Engineering Ltd, 3A Fleming Road, Kirkton Campus, Livingston, West Lothian, EH54 7BN Tel: (01506) 412647 Fax: (01506) 412647 E-mail: info@almond.co.uk

Apreco Ltd, Bruff Works, Suckley, Worcester, WR6 5DR Tel: (01886) 884090 Fax: (01886) 884099 E-mail: info@apreco.co.uk

Branchsound Ltd, Unit 9, Springfield Road Industrial Estate, Burnham-on-Crouch, Essex, CM0 8TE Tel: (01621) 782964 Fax: (01621) 783314 E-mail: tecnauticwindow@btclick.com

Clean Air Technologies, Unit B11 Laser Quay, Culpeper Close, Medway City Estate, Rochester, Kent, ME2 4HU Tel: (01634) 725295 Fax: (01634) 713929 E-mail: sales@catltd.com

Clean Modules Ltd, Unit 3, Hawthorne Road, Castle Donington, Derby, DE74 2QR Tel: (01332) 696970 Fax: 01332 696963 E-mail: enquiries@cleanmodules.co.uk

Guardline Technology Ltd, 5 Brunel Way, Thetford, Norfolk, IP24 1HP Tel: (01842) 822150 Fax: (01842) 820300 E-mail: sales@guardline.co.uk

Medical Air Technology, Mars Street, Oldham, OL9 6LY Tel: 0161-621 6200 Fax: 0161-624 7547E-mail: sales@medicalairtechnology.com

P B S C Ltd, Bradley Junction Industrial Estate, Leeds Road, Huddersfield, HD2 1UR Tel: (01484) 354500 Fax: (01484) 354504 E-mail: info@pbsc.co.uk

Stekko Co Ltd, 4 Avocet Trading Estate, Richardson Street, High Wycombe, Buckinghamshire, HP11 2SB Tel: (01494) 459332 Fax: (01494) 459313 E-mail: sales@stekko.co.uk

Trox UK Ltd, Caxton Way, Thetford, Norfolk, IP24 3SQ Tel: (01842) 754545 Fax: (01842) 763051 E-mail: sales@troxuk.co.uk

CLEAN ROOM EQUIPMENT MAINTENANCE, REPAIR AND VALIDATION

Clean Air Technologies, Unit B11 Laser Quay, Culpeper Close, Medway City Estate, Rochester, Kent, ME2 4HU Tel: (01634) 725295 Fax: (01634) 713929 E-mail: sales@catltd.com

CLEAN ROOM INSTALLATION OR SERVICE CONTRACTORS

Blandford Engineering, Unit 7 Littletowns Estate, Blandford Heights, Blandford Forum, Dorset, DT11 7UR Tel: (01258) 454222 Fax: (01258) 480433 E-mail: blandfordpumps@btinternet.com

Clean Air Technologies, Unit B11 Laser Quay, Culpeper Close, Medway City Estate, Rochester, Kent, ME2 4HU Tel: (01634) 725295 Fax: (01634) 713929 E-mail: sales@catltd.com

Clean Room Installation Services Ltd, 9 The Metro Centre, Ronsons Way, St. Albans, Hertfordshire, AL4 9QT Tel: (01727) 840594 Fax: (01727) 843368 E-mail: cleanrooms@stodec.co.uk

Colsec Ltd, Wassage Way, Hampton Lovett, Droitwich, Worcestershire, WR9 0NX Tel: (01905) 795070 Fax: (01905) 794013 E-mail: sales@colsec.co.uk

P H Services Ltd, 37 Limberline Spur, Portsmouth, PO3 5DX Tel: (023) 9269 3448 Fax: (023) 9263 9094 E-mail: huntphill@aol.com

Scientific Lesser Ltd, Hanworth Lane, Chertsey, Surrey, KT16 9JX Tel: (01932) 568122 Fax: (01932) 560818 E-mail: sllairskil@aol.com

Tecomak Ltd, Valley Industries, Tonbridge Road, Hadlow, Tonbridge, Kent, TN11 0AH Tel: (01732) 852250 Fax: (01732) 852251 E-mail: sales@tecomak.co.uk

CLEAN ROOM MONITORING EQUIPMENT

Keller UK Ltd, Winfrith Technology Centre, Winfrith Newburgh, Dorchester, Dorset, DT2 8ZB Tel: (01929) 401200 Fax: (07000) 329535 E-mail: sales@keller-pressure.co.uk

CLEAN ROOM OVENS

▶ Cookerburra Oven Cleaning Services, 18 Monterey Street, Manselton, Swansea, SA5 9PE Tel: 01792 475551 Fax: 01792 467765 E-mail: neil.cox@cookerburra.co.uk

▶ Oven Butler, 17 Sheffield Road, Anston, Sheffield, S25 5DT Tel: (01909) 564411 E-mail: paul.allen15@btinternet.com

CLEAN ROOM PAINTING SERVICES

Harlow Spraytech, St. James Centre, 7 East Road, Harlow, Essex, CM20 2BJ Tel: (01279) 414665 Fax: (01279) 416828

CLEAN ROOM TEST AND VALIDATION SERVICES

▶ High Edge Consulting Ltd, 115 Musters Road, Ruddington, Nottingham, NG11 6JA Tel: 0115-921 6200 E-mail: info@highedge.co.uk

Isotron Plc, Moray Road, Elgin Industrial Estate, Swindon, SN2 8XS Tel: (01793) 601000 Fax: (01793) 601010 E-mail: sales@isotron.co.uk

▶ Omega Projects, 67 Buckstone Avenue, Alwoodley, Leeds, LS17 5EZ Tel: 0845 686 0099 E-mail: info@omega-projects.com

CLEAN ROOM WALL SYSTEMS

Clestra Cleanrooms, Hamilton House, 3 North Street, Carshalton, Surrey, SM5 2HZ Tel: (020) 8773 2121 Fax: (020) 8260 6814

Montage Design, 3 2 Sycamore House, Vantage Point Business Village, Mitcheldean, Gloucestershire, GL17 0DD Tel: (01594) 546100 Fax: (01594) 546200 E-mail: sales@montagedesigns.co.uk

Plascore (UK), PO Box 2, Cheltenham, Gloucestershire, GL54 5YR Tel: (0871) 918 1525 Fax: (0871) 918 1525 E-mail: info@coretexgroup.co.uk

CLEAN ROOM WIPES

▶ Saraco Industries, PO Box 190, Bolton, BL1 8AH Tel: (01204) 381990 Fax: (01204) 525190 E-mail: info@saraco-industries.com

CLEAN ROOMS

▶ HartfordPharma, 4 Kingsley Close, Hartford, Northwich, Cheshire, CW8 1SD Tel: (01606) 79230 Fax: (07092) 150518 E-mail: admin@hartfordpharma.com

CLEANERS, DOMESTIC

▶ Arleys Angels Ltd, 2 Old Farm, Arley Road, Appleton, Warrington, WA4 4RP Tel: (01925) 266834 Fax: (01925) 266895 E-mail: info@arleysangels.co.uk

▶ Brighters, 20 Spring Lane, Cambridge, CB5 9BL Tel: 01223 812549 E-mail: info@brighters.co.uk

▶ Competitive Cleaning, 4 Haselden Crescent, Wakefield, West Yorkshire, WF2 8NW Tel: (01924) 382716 Fax: 07849 343175 E-mail: competitiveclean@yahoo.co.uk

▶ Kremena Krumova Ltd, 1 Percy Road, North Finchley, London, N12 8BY Tel: (020) 8445 2267 E-mail: keme@abv.bg

▶ R & A Home Services, 139 Huyton House Road, Liverpool, L36 2PF Tel: 0151-289 4217 Fax: 0151-480 2688 E-mail: enquiries@rahomeservices.co.uk

CLEANING CHEMICAL PREPARATIONS, *See headings for particular types such as Cleanser; or Detergent*

CLEANING CHEMICAL PRODUCTS AND RAW MATERIALS

A K Supplies, 5 Regent Road, Handsworth, Birmingham, B21 8AB Tel: 0121-554 7107 Fax: 0121-682 3958

CLEANING CHEMICAL PRODUCTS AND RAW MATERIALS – *continued*

Acorn Maintenance Systems, 33 Brayford Avenue, Brierley Hill, West Midlands, DY5 3PW Tel: (01384) 423351 Fax: (01384) 423351

Air Services, Redgate Road South Lancashire Industrial Estate, South Lancashire Industrial Es, Ashton-in-Makerfield, Wigan, Lancashire, WN4 8DT Tel: (01942) 722333 Fax: (01942) 725716 E-mail: sales@air-serv.co.uk

American Marketing Systems, 13b Palmer Avenue, Blackpool, FY1 5JP Tel: (01253) 401872

Anglian Chemicals Ltd, Fakenham Industrial Estae, Millers Close, Fakenham, Norfolk, NR21 8NW Tel: (01328) 851407 Fax: (01328) 855701 E-mail: sales@anglianchemicals.com

Atlas Industrial Services Ltd, Tofts Farm Industrial Estate East, Brenda Road, Hartlepool, Cleveland, TS25 2BS Tel: (01429) 233018 Fax: (01429) 863316 E-mail: m.gcoop@tiscali.co.uk

Besglos Polish Co Ltd, George Street, Burnley, Lancashire, BB11 1ND Tel: (01282) 432351 Fax: (01282) 421558 E-mail: sales@besglos.co.uk

Bissell Homecare, The Boatyard, 105 Straight Road, Old Windsor, Windsor, Berkshire, SL4 2SE Tel: (0870) 2250109 Fax: (01753) 867684

Brapack Ltd, Brapack Moreton Avenue, Hithercroft Industrial Estate, Wallingford, Oxfordshire, OX10 9DE Tel: (01491) 833131 Fax: (01491) 825409 E-mail: sales@brapack.com

Chemical Corporation UK Ltd, Atlas House Unit 9, Bedwas Business Centre, Bedwas, Caerphilly, Mid Glamorgan, CF83 8DU Tel: (029) 2088 0222 Fax: (029) 2088 0676 E-mail: sales@chemicalcorporation.co.uk

Cleaning & Hygiene Distributors, Sandbach Road, Stoke-on-Trent, ST6 2DU Tel: (01782) 825222 Fax: (01782) 825200

Cle-Pol Manufacturing Co. Ltd, PO Box 5, Barking, Essex, IG11 0TL Tel: (020) 8532 6900 Fax: (020) 8532 6940

Coventry Chemicals Ltd, Woodhams Road, Siskin Drive, Coventry, CV3 4FX Tel: (024) 7663 9739 Fax: (024) 7663 9717

Crystal Cleaning Supplies, 82 St James Way, Sidcup, Kent, DA14 5HF Tel: (020) 8309 0237 Fax: (020) 8308 0825 E-mail: sales@crystalcleaningsupplies.co.uk

Decon Laboratories Ltd, Conway Street, Hove, East Sussex, BN3 3LY Tel: (01273) 739241 Fax: (01273) 722088 E-mail: sales@decon.co.uk

Delta Hygiene Supplies, P O Box 126, Rotherham, South Yorkshire, S66 2TP Tel: (01709) 533040 Fax: (01709) 540425

Devway Marketing Ltd, 86 Oatlands Drive, Weybridge, Surrey, KT13 9HS Tel: (01932) 252699 Fax: (01932) 220972

Douglas Supplies, Brunton Quarry, North Gosforth, Newcastle upon Tyne, NE13 6PH Tel: 0191-236 5196 Fax: 0191-236 2777

E K C Technology Ltd, 19 Law Place, Nerston, East Kilbride, Glasgow, G74 4QL Tel: (01355) 244652 Fax: (01355) 595444 E-mail: sales@ekctech.co.uk

Esk Hygeine Supplies Ltd, Saffron Way, Leicester, LE2 6UP Tel: 0116-283 9362 E-mail: sales@eskgroup.co.uk

Ferry Chem Ltd, Unit 3c Pentre Industrial Estate, Pentre Queensferry, Pentre, Deeside, Clwyd, CH5 2DQ Tel: (01244) 533033 Fax: (01244) 533033

Field International UK, Unit 5 Gordleton Farm, Silver Street, Sway, Lymington, Hampshire, SO41 6DJ Tel: (01425) 628075 Fax: (01425) 628570 E-mail: peter@fieldsupplies.demon.co.uk

Fisher Research Ltd, Roval Works, 78 Bilton Way, Enfield, Middlesex, EN3 7LW Tel: (020) 8804 1891 Fax: (020) 8443 1868 E-mail: mail@fisherresearch.com

Fleetfield Chemical Co. Ltd, Norfolk Barocks, 76-136 Edmund Road(Clough Road Entrance), Sheffield, S2 4EE Tel: 0114-273 8999 Fax: 0114-243 3739

Green of Lincoln, Pyke Road, Lincoln, LN6 3QS Tel: (01522) 500006

Greyland Ltd, Greg Street, Stockport, Cheshire, SK5 7BX Tel: 0161-476 3607 Fax: 0161-477 1870 E-mail: greyland@cwcom.net

Hayes Hygiene, Paddock Barn Farm, Woldingham, Caterham, Surrey, CR3 7JD Tel: (01883) 330173 Fax: (01883) 330174

Hygienique Cleaning Materials, Unit C1 Broadway Industrial Estate, King William Street, Salford, M50 3UQ Tel: 0161-872 3666 Fax: 0161-873 7474 E-mail: hygienique@btopenworld.com

I M C C O Ltd, 1 Ashleigh Close, Barby, Rugby, Warwickshire, CV23 8UG Tel: (01788) 891866 Fax: (01788) 891953 E-mail: imcco_2000@yahoo.com

Kemtec Manufacturing, 1a Caddick Road, Knowsley Business Park, Prescot, Merseyside, L34 9HP Tel: 0151-549 1559 Fax: 0151-549 1729 E-mail: enquiries@kemtec.co.uk

Kitchen Master, Unit 8 Ashurst Drive, Stockport, Cheshire, SK3 0RY Tel: 0161-428 7777 Fax: 0161-428 7755

Kleen Tex Industries Ltd, Causeway Mill Express Trading Estate, Stone Hill Road, Farnworth, Bolton, BL4 9TP Tel: (01204) 863000 Fax: (01204) 863001 E-mail: sales@kleentexuk.com

L A Brook Ltd, Royds Mill, Leeds Road, Ossett, West Yorkshire, WF5 9YA Tel: (01924) 277026 Fax: (01924) 262074 E-mail: sales@labrook.com

London Oil Refining Co., Richardshaw Road, Grangefield Industrial Estate, Stanningley, Pudsey, West Yorkshire, LS28 6QZ Tel: 0113-236 0036 Fax: 0113-236 0038 E-mail: info@astonish.co.uk

Lower Swell Chemicals Ltd, Sunnydale, Naunton, Cheltenham, Gloucestershire, GL54 3AD Tel: (01451) 850456 Fax: (01451) 810707 E-mail: enquiries@lscltd.fsnet.co.uk

Maintenance Supply Co. Ltd, Codham Hall, Codham Hall Lane, Great Warley, Brentwood, Essex, CM13 3JT Tel: (01277) 200520 Fax: (01277) 225378 E-mail: maintenancesupply@jangro.net

Mel Cleaning Chemicals, Bank Top Industrial Estate, St. Martins, Oswestry, Shropshire, SY10 7HB Tel: (01691) 774300 Fax: (01691) 770001 E-mail: gemma@laws3311.fsbusiness.co.uk

Mid Warwickshire Cleaning Supplies Ltd, Budbrooke Road Industrial Estate, Budbrooke Road, Budbrooke Industrial Estate, Warwick, CV34 5WQ Tel: (01926) 497272 Fax: (01926) 408407 E-mail: sales@mwcleaningsupplies.co.uk

Mirj Hygiene Products Ltd, Unit 3, Antelope Industrial Park, Rhydymwyn, Mold, Clwyd, CH7 5JH Tel: (01352) 741919 Fax: (01352) 741920 E-mail: sales@mirjhygiene.co.uk

Peter Moss Ltd, Unit 36 Greenfield Business Park, Bagillt Road, Greenfield, Holywell, Clwyd, CH8 7HJ Tel: (01352) 714361 Fax: (01352) 711946 E-mail: petermoss.ltd@ei.dosnet.co.uk

Multex Chemicals, Multex House, Cannon Street, Hull, HU2 0AB Tel: (01482) 320432 Fax: (01482) 321777 E-mail: sales@multexchemicals.co.uk

Nielson Chemicals Ltd, Rawdon Road, Moira, Swadlincote, Derbyshire, DE12 6DA Tel: (01283) 222277 Fax: (01283) 225731 E-mail: sales@arrowchem.co.uk

Paper Hygiene Services, Sandleas Way, Leeds, LS15 8AW Tel: 0113-232 6777 Fax: 0113-232 6730

Phillips Payne Products Ltd, Crabtree Farm, Church Street, Newnham, Daventry, Northamptonshire, NN11 3ET Tel: (01327) 879100 Fax: (01327) 871633 E-mail: mh@icm-cambs.co.uk

Polytek Chemical Mnfrs, 7 Beech Court, Doune, Perthshire, FK16 6HT Tel: (01786) 841541 Fax: (01786) 841537

Precedent Industrial Products UK Ltd, PO Box 2668, Poole, Dorset, BH17 0RT Tel: (01202) 673339 Fax: (01202) 673339 E-mail: sales@galvtech.com

Quatchem Chemicals Ltd, 1 Victoria Trading Estate, Drury Lane, Chadderton, Oldham, OL9 7PJ Tel: 0161-947 0177 Fax: 0161-947 0180 E-mail: sales@quatchem.co.uk

R B Polishes Ltd, 579 London Road, Isleworth, Middlesex, TW7 4EJ Tel: (020) 8560 6348 Fax: (020) 8568 1253

Regent Distributors Ltd, 3 Regent Road, Handsworth, Birmingham, B21 8AB Tel: 0121-554 7107 Fax: 0121-682 3958 E-mail: info@regent-uk.com

▶ Rexodan International, PO Box 24, Widnes, Cheshire, WA8 0RB Tel: 0151-422 1100 Fax: 0151-422 1111 E-mail: export@rexodan.com

Sherwood Services UK Ltd, Parkway House, Wakefield Road, Ossett, West Yorkshire, WF5 9JA Tel: (01924) 267077 Fax: (01924) 261911

Unico Ltd, North Main Street, Carronshore, Falkirk, FK2 8HT Tel: (01324) 573410 Fax: (01324) 573401 E-mail: sales@unicodirect.com

▶ Uniteg Overseas Solvents Ltd, Business & Technology Centre, Bessemer Drive, Stevenage, Hertfordshire, SG1 2DX Tel: (01438) 310037 Fax: (01438) 310001 E-mail: uniteg@btopenworld.com

Van Zelm Chem, 82 Williams St, Grays, Essex, RM17 6DZ Tel: (01375) 374612 Fax: (01375) 404007 E-mail: sales@vanzelm.co.uk

Walker Bros Services, Hurst Street, Bury, Lancashire, BL9 7ES Tel: 0161-761 7776 Fax: 0161-761 1666

CLEANING CHEMICALS

British Association for Chemical Specialities, The Gatehouse, White Cross, Lancaster, LA1 4XQ Tel: (01524) 849606 Fax: (01524) 849194 E-mail: enquiries@bacsnet.org

Firkser Chemicals Ltd, 24 Willow Court, Abbey Road, Macclesfield, Cheshire, SK10 3PD Tel: (01625) 612900 Fax: (01625) 503763

▶ Jandle Supplies, 87 White Horse Lane, London Colney, St. Albans, Hertfordshire, AL2 1JW Tel: (01727) 824518 Fax: (01727) 824518 E-mail: desmondodonnell@hotmail.com

▶ Mid Somerset Cleaning Supplies, Rear of Crest Home Improvement, Crown Trading Estate, Shepton Mallet, Somerset, BA4 5QQ Tel: (01749) 343243 E-mail: evmcs@aol.com

Nielson Chemicals Ltd, Rawdon Road, Moira, Swadlincote, Derbyshire, DE12 6DA Tel: (01283) 222277 Fax: (01283) 225731 E-mail: sales@arrowchem.com

Safechem Ltd, Drum Industrial Estate, Drum Industrial Estate, Chester le Street, County Durham, DH2 1SR Tel: 0191-410 8668 Fax: 0191-410 2934 E-mail: enquiries@safechem.co.uk

CLEANING CLOTH FABRICS

▶ Haines Brothers, No1 Dawsons Lane, Barwell, Leicester, LE9 8BE Tel: (01455) 845855 Fax: (01455) 840168

Jack Oldman Textiles, Station Approach, Whaley Lane, Whaley Bridge, High Peak, Derbyshire, SK23 7AF Tel: (01663) 734334 Fax: (01663) 734334 E-mail: jill@jackoldhamtextiles.co.uk

Texon Nonwoven Ltd, Skelton Industrial Estate, Skelton-in-Cleveland, Saltburn-by-the-Sea, Cleveland, TS12 2LH Tel: (01287) 650551 Fax: (01287) 650788 E-mail: enquiries@texon.com

CLEANING CLOTHS

▶ Advance Products Ltd, Meadow Mills, Carlton Road, Dewsbury, West Yorkshire, WF13 2BA Tel: (01924) 486000 Fax: (01924) 486001 E-mail: sales@advance-products.co.uk

Brencliffe Ltd, Rossendale Road, Burnley, Lancashire, BB11 5HD Tel: (01282) 435226 Fax: (01282) 436147 E-mail: sales@brencliffe.com

Cleaning Rag Supply Co. Ltd, 28 Brearley Street, Hockley, Birmingham, B19 3NR Tel: 0121-333 4446 Fax: 0121-333 4442 E-mail: enquiries@cleaningragsupply.co.uk

Cleaning Supplies Direct, 424 Portswood Road, Southampton, SO17 3SD Tel: (023) 8043 4139 Fax: (023) 8090 0556 E-mail: sales@cleaningsuppliesltd.co.uk

Coppermill, 118-122 Cheshire Street, London, E2 6EJ Tel: (020) 7739 6102 Fax: (020) 7739 9400 E-mail: info@coppermill.ltd.uk

D W Begal & Son, Vulcan Works, Malta Street, Manchester, M4 7AP Tel: 0161-273 3296 Fax: 0161-273 3293

Davis & Moore, 5 Bute Street, Salford, M50 1DU Tel: 0161-737 1166 Fax: 0161-736 4038

Donelan Trading Ltd, Tower Road, Darwen, Lancashire, BB3 2DU Tel: (01254) 873873 Fax: (01254) 873065 E-mail: sales@donelan-trading.co.uk

Easiclean Products, 10 East House Farm, Atherstone Lane, Merevale, Atherstone, Warwickshire, CV9 2HT Tel: (01827) 874787 Fax: (01827) 874745 E-mail: info@easicleanwipersl.com

Environment Saving Supplies Ltd, 25-27 Dugdale Street, Nuneaton, Warwickshire, CV11 5QJ Tel: (024) 7638 6544 Fax: (024) 7664 1865 E-mail: info@envirocleanse.co.uk

FISHWICK INDUSTRIAL SUPPLY COMPANY, Caxton Road, Fulwood, Preston, PR2 9ZT Tel: (01772) 705005

Flavells, 4 Peasehill Road, Ripley, Derbyshire, DE5 3JG Tel: (01773) 741502 Fax: (01773) 741502

▶ Haines Brothers, No1 Dawsons Lane, Barwell, Leicester, LE9 8BE Tel: (01455) 845855 Fax: (01455) 840168

James Hargreaves (Bacup) Ltd, Irwell Mill, Lee Street, Bacup, Lancashire, OL13 0AG Tel: (01706) 874701 Fax: (01706) 877005 E-mail: info@jameshargreaves.co.uk

Harris & Co., Farrs Lane, Bristol, BS1 4PZ Tel: 0117-927 7434 Fax: 0117-925 2354

Howard Wipers Ltd, Unit 13 Winchester Avenue, Denny, Stirlingshire, FK6 6QE Tel: (01324) 822599 Fax: (01324) 826555

Jack Oldman Textiles, Station Approach, Whaley Lane, Whaley Bridge, High Peak, Derbyshire, SK23 7AF Tel: (01663) 734334 Fax: (01663) 734334 E-mail: jill@jackoldhamtextiles.co.uk

Kingsley, Tregoniggie Industrial Estate, Falmouth, Cornwall, TR11 4SN Tel: (01326) 373531 Fax: (01326) 372965 E-mail: kingsley_falmouth@hotmail.com

Kitchen Master, Unit 8 Ashurst Drive, Stockport, Cheshire, SK3 0RY Tel: 0161-428 7777 Fax: 0161-428 7755

Lees Newsome Ltd, Ashley Mill, Ashley Street, Oldham, OL9 6LS Tel: 0161-652 1321 Fax: 0161-627 3362 E-mail: sales@leesnewsome.co.uk

Leetex Wipers & Disposables Ltd, Unit 4, Hollis Road, Earlesfield Lane Industrial Estate, Grantham, Lincolnshire, NG31 7QH Tel: (01476) 577777 Fax: (01476) 577774

M A P A Spontex UK Ltd, Berkeley Business Park Berkeley Business Park, Wainwright Road, Worcester, WR4 9ZS Tel: (01905) 450300 Fax: (01905) 450350

Midland Wiper Manufacturing Co. Ltd, Fletcher Street, Long Eaton, Nottingham, NG10 1JU Tel: 0115-973 5187 Fax: 0115-946 2012 E-mail: office@midlandwiper.co.uk

North West Wiper Co., 6 Acorn Business Centre, Lees Road, Knowsley Industrial Park, Liverpool, L33 7SL Tel: 0151-546 4005 Fax: 0151-546 4005

▶ P C Textiles, 1 Glasgow Road, Denny, Stirlingshire, FK6 5DN Tel: (01324) 826993 Fax: (01324) 826442

Robert Scott & Sons, Oakview Mills, Manchester Road, Greenfield, Oldham, OL3 7HG Tel: (01457) 873931 Fax: (01457) 819490 E-mail: admin@robert-scott.co.uk

Rossendale Wipers, 19 Waingate Close, Rossendale, Lancashire, BB4 7SQ Tel: (01706) 221922 Fax: (01706) 221922

Saul D Harrison & Sons plc, 4 Langley Close, Romford, RM3 8XB Tel: (01708) 377330 Fax: (01708) 377220 E-mail: info@sauldharrison.com

Warner Textile Machinery, Magna Road, Wigston, Leicestershire, LE18 4ZH Tel: 0116-278 7578 Fax: 0116-278 7588 E-mail: wtm@warnertextilemachinery.co.uk

CLEANING EQUIPMENT, JET WASH, GARAGE FORECOURT

▶ Go (UK) Ltd, 28a The Market Place, Melbourne, Derby, DE73 1DS Tel: 0870 7562542 Fax: 0870 7562544 E-mail: freightspeed2@hotmail.com

CLEANING SERVICES, COMPUTER HARDWARE ETC

▶ 2-Inspire, 8 Old School Close, Netheravon, Salisbury, SP4 9QJ Tel: (01980) 671182

▶ Clean I.T. Services Ltd., 70, Brookfield Avenue, Glasgow, G33 1SX Tel: 0141 558 5496 E-mail: info@cleanitservices.co.uk

▶ Cleaner Systems Ltd, 108 Preston Road, Birmingham, B26 1TQ Tel: (0800) 7561331 Fax: (0800) 7569821 E-mail: info@cleaner-systems.co.uk

▶ Kizza Business Consultants Ltd, Seaton Close, Plaistow, London, E13 8JJ Tel: (020) 7511 8187 E-mail: pollykidza@yahoo.com

The Total Package Ltd, The Granary, Birling, West Malling, Kent, ME19 5JF Tel: (01732) 526910 Fax: (01732) 526939 E-mail: info@thetotalpackage.co.uk

CLEANING SERVICES, FOOD OR CATERING INDUSTRY

Alpha Plus, 10 Caputhall Road, Deans Industrial Estate, Livingston, West Lothian, EH54 8AS Tel: (01506) 401401 E-mail: service@alphascot.co.uk

F & G Cleaners Ltd, 31 Engleheart Road, London, SE6 2HN Tel: (020) 8698 1337 Fax: (020) 8697 0391 E-mail: mainoffice@fandgcleaners.co.uk

Filta Group Ltd, The Locks, Hillmorton, Rugby, Warwickshire, CV21 4PP Tel: (01788) 550100 Fax: (01788) 551839 E-mail: sales@filtagroup.com

Hygiene Group Ltd, 409-412 Montrose Avenue, Slough, SL1 4TJ Tel: (01753) 820991 Fax: (01753) 578189 E-mail: sales@hygiene.co.uk

Kitchen Deep Cleaning, 9 High Street, Orpington, Kent, BR6 0JE Tel: (01689) 828233 Fax: (01689) 828233

Trustclean Ltd, Queens Court, Doncaster, South Yorkshire, DN5 9QH Tel: (01302) 783193 Fax: (01302) 781556 E-mail: info@trustclean.co.uk

CLEANING SERVICES, PHARMACEUTICAL INDUSTRY

Hygiene Group Ltd, 409-412 Montrose Avenue, Slough, SL1 4TJ Tel: (01753) 820991 Fax: (01753) 578189 E-mail: sales@hygiene.co.uk

CLEANING SERVICES, PVCU BUILDING PRODUCTS, HIGH LEVEL

▶ Stonecraft Weston, Unit 21 Kewstoke Quarry, Kewstoke Road, Worle, Weston-super-Mare, Somerset, BS23 4QA Tel: (07778) 302672 Fax: (01934) 413295 E-mail: nickstonecraft@aol.com

CLEANING STAFF RECRUITMENT AGENCIES

Direct Specialist Recruitment, 8-10 North Street, Barking, Essex, IG11 8AW Tel: (020) 8591 6787 Fax: (020) 8591 6787 E-mail: info@dsrecruitment.com

▶ Hudsons Pantry, Hudsons Pantry, Towcester, Northamptonshire, NN12 7HT Tel: (01327) 352443 E-mail: Info@hudsonspantry.co.uk

CLEANING (VEHICLE) MATERIALS/PRODUCTS, CHEMICAL

Apex General Supplies Ltd, Unit 14 Apex House, Radford Crescent, Radford Way, Billericay, Essex, CM12 0DG Tel: (01277) 623269 Fax: (01277) 630739

Autoglym, Works Road, Letchworth Garden City, Hertfordshire, SG6 1LU Tel: (01462) 677766 Fax: (01462) 677712 E-mail: sales@autoglym.com

Autosmart International Ltd, Lynn Lane, Shenstone, Lichfield, Staffordshire, WS14 0DH Tel: (01543) 481616 Fax: (01543) 481549 E-mail: info@autosmart.co.uk

CLEANING (VEHICLE) MATERIALS/PRODUCTS, CHEMICAL – *continued*

Brapack Ltd, Brapack Moreton Avenue, Hithercroft Industrial Estate, Wallingford, Oxfordshire, OX10 9DE Tel: (01491) 833131 Fax: (01491) 825409 E-mail: sales@brapack.com

Car Wash Consultants Ltd, The Platt, Amersham, Buckinghamshire, HP7 0HX Tel: (01494) 723819 Fax: (01494) 723796 E-mail: carwashc@aol.com

Ferry Chem Ltd, Unit 3c Pentre Industrial Estate, Pentre Queensferry, Pentre, Deeside, Clwyd, CH5 2DQ Tel: (01244) 533033 Fax: (01244) 533033

Industrial Chemicals & Equipment Ltd, 59 Cranes Park, Surbiton, Surrey, KT5 8AS Tel: (020) 8399 9333 Fax: (020) 8399 9555 E-mail: ice.ltd@virgin.net

Kautex Textron CVS Ltd, Dyffryn Business Park, Ystrad Mynach, Hengoed, Mid Glamorgan, CF82 7RJ Tel: (01443) 621800 Fax: (01443) 621940

Proficio Cleaning Services, 52 Crossgates, Bellshill, Lanarkshire, ML4 2EE Tel: (01698) 740840 Fax: (01698) 740008 E-mail: sales@proficio.co.uk

Quadralene Ltd, Bateman Street, Derby, DE23 8JL Tel: (01332) 292500 Fax: (01332) 295941 E-mail: info@quadralene.co.uk

Solvitol Ltd, Shadon Way, Birtley, Chester Le Street, County Durham, DH3 2RE Tel: 0191-410 9131 Fax: 0191-492 0503

▶ Tec UK, Royal Oak Way North Unit A, Daventry Distribution Centre, Royal Oak Industrial Estate, Daventry, Northamptonshire, NN11 8LR Tel: (01327) 300400 Fax: (01327) 879679 E-mail: tecuk@aol.com

Under Pressure, Unit 8 Eastlands, Coal Park Lane, Southampton, SO31 7GW Tel: (01489) 589891 Fax: (01489) 589785 E-mail: info@underpressure.uk.com

▶ Uniteg Overseas Solvents Ltd, Business & Technology Centre, Bessemer Drive, Stevenage, Hertfordshire, SG1 2DX Tel: (01438) 310037 Fax: (01438) 310001 E-mail: uniteg@btopenworld.com

CLEANING, COMMERCIAL, WOODEN FLOORS

▶ Allwood Floors, 28 Faraday Road, Rugby, Warwickshire, CV22 5ND Tel: (01788) 569980 Fax: (01788) 569978 E-mail: info@allwood-floors.co.uk

▶ Arrow Cleaning Services, 17 The Hudson, Wyke, Bradford, West Yorkshire, BD12 8HZ Tel: (01274) 690805 Fax: (01274) 690805 E-mail: sales@arrow-cleaning.co.uk

▶ C & M Flooring & Maintenance, 9 Hammonds Lane, Great Warley, Brentwood, Essex, CM13 3AH Tel: (07950) 933025 Fax: (01277) 228414 E-mail: nigel.magee@virgin.net

▶ Kinv Property Maintenance, 6 High Street, Princes Risborough, Buckinghamshire, HP27 0AX Tel: (01844) 274876 Fax: (01844) 274876 E-mail: info@kinv.co.uk

▶ Naked Floors, 2 / 18 Stone Street, Brighton, BN1 2HB Tel: (01273) 208951 E-mail: enquiries@nakedfloors.com

Nilfisk Northern Ireland Ltd, Unit 9, 48 Duncrue Street, Belfast, BT3 9AR Tel: (028) 9074 1444 Fax: (028) 9075 4555 E-mail: sales@nilfix.co.uk

Sanding Wooden Floors, 127 Tarnwood Park, Eltham, London, SE9 5NX Tel: (020) 8859 4063 E-mail: simon.killgallon@btconnect.com

CLEANSERS, *See also headings for particular types*

A & M Cleaning Supplies, 3-7 Orbital Crescent, Watford, WD25 0HB Tel: (01923) 671587 Fax: (01923) 671889 E-mail: sales@aandmcs.co.uk

Colin Burton Supplies Ltd, 9 George Avenue, Mile Oak, Tamworth, Staffordshire, B78 3PN Tel: (01827) 289091

Deb Ltd, 108 Spencer Road, Belper, Derbyshire, DE56 1JX Tel: (01773) 596700 Fax: (01773) 822548 E-mail: enquiry@deb.co.uk

London Oil Refining Co., Richardshaw Road, Grangefield Industrial Estate, Stanningley, Pudsey, West Yorkshire, LS28 6QZ Tel: 0113-236 0036 Fax: 0113-236 0038 E-mail: info@astonish.co.uk

P B Beauty, Aintree Avenue, White Horse Business Park, Trowbridge, Wiltshire, BA14 0XB Tel: (01225) 768491 Fax: (01225) 716100

Sanmex (International) Plc, 5-9 Dalmarnock Road, Rutherglen, Glasgow, G73 1NY Tel: 0141-647 2244 Fax: 0141-613 1228 E-mail: info@sanmex.com

CLEANSERS, HOUSEHOLD-USE

Dri Pak Ltd, Furnace Road, Ilkeston, Derbyshire, DE7 5EP Tel: 0115-932 5165 Fax: 0115-944 0297 E-mail: sales@dripak.co.uk

Jeyes Group Ltd, Brunel Way, Thetford, Norfolk, IP24 1HF Tel: (01842) 757575 Fax: (01842) 757812

Powder & Liquid Products Ltd, Factory 37, No 1 Industrial Estate, Consett, County Durham, DH8 6TW Tel: (01207) 591217 Fax: (01207) 592119 E-mail: sales@plp.co.uk

Unilvever, Coal Road, Seacroft, Leeds, LS14 2AR Tel: 0113-222 5000 Fax: 0113-222 5362

CLEAR ON CLEAR LABELS

Labelsco, 29 Moat Way, Barwell, Leicester, LE9 8EY Tel: (01455) 852400 Fax: (01455) 841444 E-mail: sales@labelsco.co.uk

CLEARANCE GAUGES

Plastigauge, Unit 2, Gaugemaster Way, Ford, Arundel, West Sussex, BN18 0RX Tel: (01903) 882822 Fax: (01903) 884962 E-mail: sales@plastigauge.co.uk

CLEVIS ASSEMBLIES

Arvin Motion Control Ltd, 15 New Star Road, Leicester, LE4 9JD Tel: 0116-274 3600 Fax: 0116-274 3620 E-mail: info@camloc.com

CLEVIS PINS

Automotive Cable Products Ltd, Copperworks Road, Llanelli, Dyfed, SA15 2NE Tel: (01554) 752207 Fax: (01554) 749600 E-mail: info@automotivecableproducts.co.uk

CLIMATIC CHAMBERS

▶ Cambridge Glass House Co. Ltd, 236 Main Road, Newport, Brough, North Humberside, HU15 2RH Tel: (01430) 449440 Fax: (01430) 449331 E-mail: info@cambridgeglasshouse.co.uk

Climatec Ltd, Unit 23 Empire Centre Imperial Way, Watford, WD24 4YH Tel: (01923) 237178 Fax: (01923) 237403 E-mail: robert_livingstone@talk21.com

Priorclave Ltd, 129-131 Nathan Way, Woolwich, London, SE28 0AB Tel: (020) 8316 6620 Fax: (020) 8855 0616 E-mail: sales@priorclave.co.uk

Temperature Applied Sciences Ltd, Unit 15 Martlets Way, Goring-by-Sea, Worthing, West Sussex, BN12 4HF Tel: (01903) 506903 Fax: (01903) 506911

CLING FILM CUTTING EDGES

▶ Linpac Filmco, Salters Lane, Sedgefield, Stockton-on-Tees, Cleveland, TS21 3EE Tel: (01740) 620751 Fax: (01740) 625825 E-mail: gary.trotter@linpak-filmco.co.uk

CLINICAL REAGENTS

Abtek (Biologicals) Ltd, Unit 4, Taylor Street, Liverpool, L5 5AD Tel: 0151-298 1501 Fax: 0151-298 1758 E-mail: info@abtekbio.com

Cellpath plc, Unit 66 Mochdre Industrial Estate, Mochdre, Newtown, Powys, SY16 4LE Tel: (01686) 611333 Fax: (01686) 622946 E-mail: sales@cellpath.co.uk

Clin-Tech Ltd, Unit G Perram Works, Merrow Lane, Guildford, Surrey, GU4 7BN Tel: (01483) 301902 Fax: (01483) 301907 E-mail: info@clin-tech.co.uk

Euro DPC Ltd, Glyn Rhonwy, Llanberis, Caernarfon, Gwynedd, LL55 4EL Tel: (01286) 871871 Fax: (01286) 871802 E-mail: euro@dpconline.com

Gainland International Ltd, Factory Road, Sandycroft, Deeside, Clwyd, CH5 2QJ Tel: (01244) 536326 Fax: (01244) 531254 E-mail: sandralewis@gccdiagnostics.com

Helena Laboratories UK Ltd, Colima Avenue, Sunderland Enterprise Park, Sunderland, SR5 3XB Tel: 0191-549 6064 Fax: 0191-549 6271 E-mail: info@helena.co.uk

Hypoguard Ltd, Dock Lane, Melton, Woodbridge, Suffolk, IP12 1PE Tel: (01394) 387333 Fax: (01394) 380152 E-mail: enquiries@hypoguard.co.uk

Serotec Ltd, Unit 22 Bankside, Station Approach, Kidlington, Oxfordshire, OX5 1JE Tel: (01865) 852700 Fax: (01865) 373899 E-mail: sales@serotec.co.uk

CLINICAL WASTE COLLECTION

SRCL, The Incinerator Building, Kennington Road, Willesborough, Ashford, Kent, TN24 0LZ Tel: (0845) 1242020 Fax: 0113-235 1286 E-mail: mwardle@srcl.com

SRCL, Bolton Incinerator, Incinerator Building, Bolton General Hospital, Minerva Road, Bolton, BL4 0JR Tel: (0845) 1242020 Fax: 0113-235 1286 E-mail: mwardle@srcl.com

CLINICAL WASTE CONTAINERS

Chemsafe Containers Ltd, Higher Merley Lane, Corfe Mullen, Wimborne, Dorset, BH21 3EG Tel: (01202) 881502 Fax: (01202) 841282 E-mail: chemsafe@iswgroup.co.uk

CLINICAL WASTE DISPOSAL/RECOVERY/RECYCLING CONTRACTORS OR MERCHANTS

Cleaning Supplies UK, Lovet House, Lovet Road, The Pinnacles, Harlow, Essex, CM19 5TB Tel: (01279) 459345 Fax: (01279) 772376 E-mail: websupport@cleaningsuppliesuk.com

Grundon Waste Ltd, Lakeside Industrial Estate, Colnbrook By Passage, Colnbrook, Slough, SL3 0EG Tel: (01753) 686777 Fax: (01753) 686002

Tom Hamilton Transport, Burnside, Kinglassie, Lochgelly, Fife, KY5 0UP Tel: (01592) 882307 E-mail: tom@tht.co.uk

▶ Mountain, Summit House, Northfield Road, Quarrington, Sleaford, Lincolnshire, NG34 8RT Tel: (0800) 0266936 Fax: (01529) 413857 E-mail: sales@greenmountains.co.uk

O C S Group Uk, 78 Gatwick Road, Crawley, West Sussex, RH10 9YB Tel: (01293) 553121 Fax: (01293) 663385 E-mail: info@catering.ocs.co.uk

CLINKER BLOCKS OR SLABS

H+H Celcon Ltd, Celcon House, Ightham, Sevenoaks, Kent, TN15 9HZ Tel: (01732) 886333 Fax: (01732) 886810 E-mail: marketing@celcon.co.uk

CLIP JOINTED SHEET METAL DUCTING

Abtek Ltd, Unit 10, Camperdown Industrial Estate, Newcastle upon Tyne, NE12 5UJ Tel: 0191-268 8555 Fax: 0191-268 8777 E-mail: sales@abtekltd.co.uk

Boxer Designs & Manufacturing, Unit 2 Boundary Court, Heaton Chapel, Stockport, Cheshire, SK4 5GA Tel: 0161-975 1830 Fax: 0161-431 3364 E-mail: sales@boxer-design.co.uk

Boyd & Co (Metalworkers) Ltd, Chainbridge Road, Blaydon-on-Tyne, Tyne & Wear, NE21 5SW Tel: 0191-414 3331 Fax: 0191-414 0340 E-mail: info@boydduct.co.uk

Hopefield Fabrications Ltd, Windacre Works, Mather Road, Bury, Lancashire, BL9 6RA Tel: 0161-797 1991 Fax: 0161-764 1461 E-mail: gary@hopefieldfab.fsnet.co.uk

CLIP ON SPECTACLE MAGNIFIERS

▶ Retrospecs.co.uk, 20 George Street, St. Albans, Hertfordshire, AL3 4ES Tel: (01727) 761048 E-mail: admin@retrospecs.co.uk

CLIPS

Defence Fasteners Ltd, Brighton Road, Pease Pottage, Crawley, West Sussex, RH11 9AD Tel: (01293) 525811 Fax: (01293) 525814 E-mail: sales@defencefasteners.com

Dene Spring UK Ltd, Bridge Works, Allum Lane, Borehamwood, Hertfordshire, WD6 3LT Tel: (020) 8953 6888 Fax: (020) 8207 5872 E-mail: deor@denespringuk.co.uk

F T Pressings Ltd, Eagle Works, New Road, Studley, Warwickshire, B80 7LY Tel: (01527) 854925 Fax: (01527) 854925

CLOAKROOM EQUIPMENT

Abacus Building Components, Manor House, Rise Road, Sigglesthorne, Hull, HU11 5QH Tel: (01964) 533720 Fax: (01964) 535958 E-mail: abacuscomp@aol.com

Arkinstall Ltd, 6 Buntsford Park Road, Bromsgrove, Worcestershire, B60 3DX Tel: (01527) 872962 Fax: (01527) 837127 E-mail: info@arkinstall.co.uk

Boyco Co., Europa Way, Stockport, Cheshire, SK3 0XE Tel: 0161-428 7077

Welco, 2 Parklands, Rednal, Birmingham, B45 9PZ Tel: (0800) 9549001 Fax: (0845) 6888900 E-mail: sales@welco.co.uk

▶ Younger Enterprizes, Newton Bank, St. Andrews, Fife, KY16 9TY Tel: (07903) 841590 Fax: (01334) 478905 E-mail: jmdy@sol.co.uk

CLOCK BELLS

▶ Gifts & Gold, 8 Chipstead Valley Road, Coulsdon, Surrey, CR5 2RA Tel: (020) 8763 2520 Fax: (020) 8763 2520 E-mail: giftsandgold@aol.com

Gillett & Johnston Croydon Ltd, Unit 9a Twin Bridges Business Park, 232 Selsdon Road, South Croydon, Surrey, CR2 6PL Tel: (020) 8686 2694 Fax: (020) 8681 4028 E-mail: any@gillettjohnston.co.uk

Good Directions Ltd, 1D Ravenstor Road, Wirksworth, Derby, DE4 4FY Tel: (01629) 824282 Fax: (01629) 824333 E-mail: info@good-directions.co.uk

Taylors Eyre & Smith Ltd, The Bell Foundry, Freehold Street, Loughborough, Leicestershire, LE11 1AR Tel: (01509) 212241 Fax: (01509) 263305 E-mail: office@taylorbells.co.uk

Time & Frequency Solutions Ltd, 25 Eastways, Witham, Essex, CM8 3AL Tel: (01376) 514114 Fax: (01376) 516116 E-mail: sales@timefreq.com

Whitechapel Bell Foundry Ltd, 34 Whitechapel Road, London, E1 1DY Tel: (020) 7247 2599 Fax: (020) 7375 1979 E-mail: sales@whitechapelbellfoundry.co.uk

CLOCK CASES

Fenclocks Suffolk Ltd, 85 Gregory Road, Mildenhall, Bury St. Edmunds, Suffolk, IP28 7DF Tel: (01638) 712981 Fax: (01638) 712956 E-mail: time@fenclocks.freeserve.co.uk

Knight & Gibbins Ltd, Windham Road, Chilton Industrial Estate, Sudbury, Suffolk, CO10 2XD Tel: (01787) 377264 Fax: (01787) 378258 E-mail: sales@knightandgibbins.co.uk

Mills & Sons Longcases, 15 Townsend Lane, Long Lawford, Rugby, Warwickshire, CV23 9DQ Tel: (01788) 565268

Time & Frequency Solutions Ltd, 25 Eastways, Witham, Essex, CM8 3AL Tel: (01376) 514114 Fax: (01376) 516116 E-mail: sales@timefreq.com

CLOCK COMPONENTS

Accutec Design Ltd, Unit C3 Haysbridge Business Centre, Brickhouse Lane, South Godstone, Godstone, Surrey, RH9 8JW Tel: (01342) 842129 Fax: (01342) 844027

Bedford Dials Ltd, Corn Exchange, Teme Street, Tenbury Wells, Worcestershire, WR15 8BB Tel: (01584) 810345 Fax: (01584) 810683 E-mail: info@bedforddials.co.uk

▶ Horological Repair Service, 37 Green End, Denton, Manchester, M34 7PT Tel: 0161-336 5215 Fax: 0161-336 5215 E-mail: info@hrs-clocks.co.uk

Mahoney Associates Ltd, Stapleton Road, Bristol, BS5 0RB Tel: 0117-955 6800 Fax: 0117-935 0556

Mega-Quartz UK Ltd, 25 Boshers Gardens, Egham, Surrey, TW20 9NZ Tel: (01784) 437072 Fax: (01784) 435793 E-mail: megaquartzuk@aol.com

Time & Frequency Solutions Ltd, 25 Eastways, Witham, Essex, CM8 3AL Tel: (01376) 514114 Fax: (01376) 516116 E-mail: sales@timefreq.com

CLOCK DIALS/FACE

Good Acre Engraving, 120 Main Street, Sutton Bonington, Loughborough, Leicestershire, LE12 5PF Tel: (01509) 673082 Fax: (01509) 673082 E-mail: goodacre@ndirect.co.uk

Good Directions Ltd, 1D Ravenstor Road, Wirksworth, Derby, DE4 4FY Tel: (01629) 824282 Fax: (01629) 824333 E-mail: info@good-directions.co.uk

▶ Horological Repair Service, 37 Green End, Denton, Manchester, M34 7PT Tel: 0161-336 5215 Fax: 0161-336 5215 E-mail: info@hrs-clocks.co.uk

CLOCK HANDS

Everglades International Ltd, The Old Station, Station Road, Cheddar, Somerset, BS27 3AH Tel: (01934) 744051 Fax: (01934) 743184

CLOCK IMPORT/EXPORT MERCHANTS OR AGENTS

Accutec Design Ltd, Unit C3 Haysbridge Business Centre, Brickhouse Lane, South Godstone, Godstone, Surrey, RH9 8JW Tel: (01342) 842129 Fax: (01342) 844027

L C Designs Co. Ltd, Sheldon Way, Larkfield, Aylesford, Kent, ME20 6SE Tel: (01622) 716000 Fax: (01622) 791119 E-mail: enquiries@londonclock.co.uk

Peers Hardy (U K) Ltd, Tompion House, 25 Birmingham Road, West Bromwich, West Midlands, B70 6RR Tel: 0121-525 8577 Fax: 0121-500 5276 E-mail: nbaker@peershardy.co.uk

M.A. Rapport & Co. Ltd, Ivor House, Bridge Street, Cardiff, CF10 2TH Tel: (029) 2037 3737 Fax: (029) 2022 0121 E-mail: info@rapportlondon.com

Widdop Bingham & Co. Ltd, Broadgate, Broadway Business Park, Chadderton, Oldham, OL9 9XE Tel: 0161-688 1200 Fax: 0161-682 6808 E-mail: sales@widdop.co.uk

CLOCK SPRINGS

Baron Springs, Unit 3 70 Strathclyde Street, Glasgow, G40 4JR Tel: 0141-550 3477 Fax: 0141-554 7240

▶ indicates data change since last edition

CLOCK SPRINGS – *continued*

Don Springs (Sheffield) Ltd, 340 Coleford Road, Sheffield, S9 5PH Tel: 0114-244 1545 Fax: 0114-243 5291 E-mail: tony@donsprings.co.uk

Kern-Liebers Ltd, Corringham Road Industrial Estate, Gainsborough, Lincolnshire, DN21 1QB Tel: (01427) 612085 Fax: (01427) 610301 E-mail: kl-uk@kern-liebers.com

CLOCK SYSTEMS

Contarnex Europe Ltd, 252 Martin Way, Morden, Surrey, SM4 4AW Tel: (020) 8540 1034 Fax: (020) 8543 3058 E-mail: enquiries@contarnex.com

CLOCKS, *See also headings under particular types*

A & A Time Ltd, 13 Rutherford Road, Maghull, Liverpool, L31 3DD Tel: 0151-531 6913 Fax: 0151-531 7353 E-mail: sales@aandatime.co.uk

Canavan Clockmakers, Unit 24, 24 Ulster Street, Lurgan, Craigavon, County Armagh, BT67 9AN Tel: (028) 3832 1100 E-mail: sales@canavanclockmakers.com

E A Combs Ltd, Quantum House Station Estate, Eastwood Close, London, E18 1BY Tel: (020) 8530 4216 Fax: (020) 8530 1310 E-mail: sales@eacombs.com

Ellison Bros, 24 Donegall Street, Belfast, BT1 2GP Tel: (028) 9032 5320 Fax: (028) 9032 8143E-mail: sales@ellisonbrothers.co.uk

Fenclocks Suffolk Ltd, 85 Gregory Road, Mildenhall, Bury St. Edmunds, Suffolk, IP28 7DF Tel: (01638) 712981 Fax: (01638) 712956 E-mail: time@fenclocks.freeserve.co.uk

Georgian Crystal Tutbury Ltd, 1 Silk Mill Lane, Tutbury, Burton-on-Trent, Staffordshire, DE13 9LE Tel: (01283) 814534 Fax: (01283) 520186

Grayshott Stoneware Ltd, School Road, Grayshott, Hindhead, Surrey, GU26 6LR Tel: (01428) 604404 Fax: (01428) 604944 E-mail: sales@grayshottpottery.com

H M Temple & Co. Ltd, 111 Broughton Street, Edinburgh, EH1 3RZ Tel: 0131-556 4791 Fax: 0131-556 3609

Hawkins Clock Co. Ltd, PO Box 39, Peterborough, PE6 8XQ Tel: (01733) 330222 Fax: (01733) 333700 E-mail: sales@hawkinsclocks.co.uk

Initial Monogram Co. Ltd, 18 Capel Road, Watford, WD19 4AE Tel: (01923) 255540 Fax: (01923) 819003 E-mail: initialmonogram@ntlworld.com

Kitney & Co., Unit 12 Crystal Business Centre, Sandwich, Kent, CT13 9QX Tel: (01304) 611968 Fax: (01304) 614642 E-mail: sales@kitneyandco.com

Knight & Gibbins Ltd, Windham Road, Chilton Industrial Estate, Sudbury, Suffolk, CO10 2XD Tel: (01787) 377264 Fax: (01787) 378258 E-mail: sales@knightandgibbins.co.uk

L C Designs Co. Ltd, Sheldon Way, Larkfield, Aylesford, Kent, ME20 6SE Tel: (01622) 716000 Fax: (01622) 791119 E-mail: enquiries@londonclock.co.uk

F.W. Needham Ltd, 84 Great Hampton Street, Birmingham, B18 6EP Tel: 0121-554 5453 Fax: 0121-554 9859 E-mail: fw-needham@btconnect.com

Newgate Clocks Ltd, 5 Maesbury Road Industrial Estate, Oswestry, Shropshire, SY10 8HA Tel: (01691) 679994 Fax: (01691) 679995

William Potts & Sons Ltd, 112 Alfreton Road, Derby, DE21 4AU Tel: (01332) 345569 Fax: (01332) 290642 E-mail: sales@pottsofleeds.com

Prince Electronics, 7 Leyden Street, London, E1 7LE Tel: (020) 7377 8871 Fax: (020) 7247 7986 E-mail: ali.budhwani@btconnect.com

M.A. Rapport & Co. Ltd, Ivor House, Bridge Street, Cardiff, CF10 2TH Tel: (029) 2037 3737 Fax: (029) 2022 0121 E-mail: info@rapportlondon.com

Roger Lascelles Clocks Ltd, Unit 11 Wimbledon Stadium Business Centre, Riverside Road, London, SW17 0BA Tel: (020) 8879 6011 Fax: (020) 8879 1818 E-mail: info@rogerlascelles.com

▶ Storm Of London, 53a Neal Street, London, WC2H 9PJ Tel: (020) 7240 0888 Fax: (020) 7240 8586

Time & Motion, 1 Beckside, Beverley, North Humberside, HU17 0PB Tel: (01482) 881574

Topical Time Ltd, 5 Bleeding Heart Yard, London, EC1N 8SJ Tel: (020) 7405 2439 Fax: (020) 7831 4254E-mail: topicaltime@btconnect.com

Tommy Tucker Ltd, Barnham House, Aurillac Way, Hallcroft Industrial Estate, Retford, Nottinghamshire, DN22 7PX Tel: (01777) 705141 Fax: (01777) 860859 E-mail: sales@mgagency.demon.co.uk

W Haycock, Leys Bank, North Leys, Ashbourne, Derbyshire, DE6 1DQ Tel: (01335) 342395 Fax: (01335) 342395

▶ Watchesuk Com, Atlantic Square, 24 Station Road, Witham, Essex, CM8 2TL Tel: (01376) 500501 Fax: (01376) 500777

Wharton Electronics, Unit 15 Thame Park Business Centre, Wenman Road, Thame, Oxfordshire, OX9 3XA Tel: (01844) 260567 Fax: (01844) 218855 E-mail: info@wharton.co.uk

Yorkshire Clock Builders, 654 Chesterfield Road, Sheffield, S8 0SB Tel: 0114-255 0786 Fax: 0114-255 0786 E-mail: tictoc@ycbclocks.co.uk

CLOCKS, QUARTZ/CRYSTAL CONTROLLED

Bude Time Enterprises Ltd, Higher Wharf, Bude, Cornwall, EX23 8LW Tel: (01288) 353832 Fax: (01288) 355562 E-mail: sales@budetime.co.uk

Tradestock Ltd, Poole Works, Poole, Wellington, Somerset, TA21 9HW Tel: (01823) 661717 Fax: (01823) 666543 E-mail: sales@tradestockltd.co.uk

CLOSED CIRCUIT TELEVISION (CCTV) ACCESS CONTROL SYSTEMS

▶ Ace Security Systems Ltd, 12 Triumph Way, Kempston, Bedford, MK42 7QB Tel: (01234) 854455 Fax: (01234) 855345 E-mail: sales@acesecurity.co.uk

▶ Active Alarms Ltd, 3 Fayland Avenue, London, SW16 1TB Tel: (020) 8769 5003 E-mail: sales@active-alarms.com

▶ Advanced Perimeter Systems, 16 Cunningham Road, Springkerse Industrial Estate, Stirling, FK7 7TP Tel: (01786) 479862 Fax: (01786) 470331 E-mail: sales@aps-perimeter-security.com

▶ B B S Security Systems Ltd, Vision House, 25 Dick O' The Banks Road, Crossways, Dorchester, Dorset, DT2 8BJ Tel: (01305) 851516 Fax: (01305) 851517 E-mail: mail@bbssecurity.co.uk

▶ Band Systems, Unit 3, Twyford Business Park, Station Road, Twyford, Reading, RG10 9TU Tel: 0118-377 9000 Fax: 0118-970 6804

Barrier Surveillance Services, 77 Main Street, Shildon, County Durham, DL4 1AN Tel: (01388) 776833 Fax: (01388) 775886

▶ Better Environment & Security Technologies B E S T Ltd, Glen Rose, The Hollow, West Hoathly, East Grinstead, West Sussex, RH19 4QE Tel: (01342) 811990 Fax: 01342 811990 E-mail: britsectec@aol.com

▶ Big Brother Security (UK) Ltd, Harmer Street, Gravesend, Kent, DA12 2AX Tel: (01474) 354086 Fax: (01474) 354086 E-mail: info@bigbrothersecurity.org.uk

▶ Bluerock Security Ltd, St. James Road, Brackley, Northamptonshire, NN13 7XY Tel: (01280) 706969 Fax: (01280) 706969 E-mail: sales@bluerocksecurity.com

▶ Camtek Surveillance Systems Ltd, Bagshot, Surrey, GU19 5XX Tel: (01276) 470999 Fax: (01276) 850679 E-mail: ks@camteksurveillance.co.uk

▶ Check Your Security Ltd, Grange, Cottage Road, West Somerton, Great Yarmouth, Norfolk, NR29 4DL Tel: (01493) 393333 Fax: (0870) 4797149 E-mail: info@checkyoursecurity.co.uk

▶ Combined Security, 79 Pickford Lane, Bexleyheath, Kent, DA7 4RW Tel: (020) 8304 6111 Fax: (020) 8304 6555 E-mail: info@combinedsecurity.co.uk

▶ Cook Facilities Ltd, Technology Centre, 20 Westgate, Morecambe, Lancashire, LA3 3LN Tel: (01524) 402090 Fax: (01524) 418269 E-mail: sales@cookfire.co.uk

▶ Covert Surveillance & Investigations, 107 Brookdale Road, Liverpool, L15 3JF Tel: 0151-222 1188 Fax: 0151-222 1188 E-mail: enquries@csilimited.co.uk

▶ D M G Security Systems, Knowler Hill, Liversedge, West Yorkshire, WF15 6DY Tel: (01924) 400927 E-mail: sales@dmgsecuritysystems.co.uk

▶ Demopad Software Ltd, Midwest House, Canal Road, Timperley, Cheshire, WA14 1TF Tel: 08700 551100 Fax: 08707 062171 E-mail: sales@sentrypad.com

▶ Elektrek Services Ltd, 19 Manning Road, Felixstowe, Suffolk, IP11 2AY Tel: (01394) 270777 Fax: 01394 670189 E-mail: mail@elektrek.com

▶ Epis Services, Mexborough Business Centre, College Road, Mexborough, South Yorkshire, S64 9JP Tel: (01709) 577736 Fax: (01709) 577764 E-mail: enquiries@epis-services.co.uk

Fa Solutions, 9 Beckford Way, Maidenbower, Crawley, West Sussex, RH10 7LT Tel: (01293) 886643 E-mail: sales@faselectrical.co.uk

Future Access Technologies, 18 Cherry Lane, Pond Park, Lisburn, County Antrim, BT28 3JT Tel: (028) 9262 9689 Fax: (028) 9267 6573 E-mail: info@futureaccess.co.uk

▶ Hartford Security, 16,Nelson Street, Dewsbury, West Yorkshire, WF13 1NA Tel: (01924) 467269 Fax: (01924) 430800 E-mail: info@harfordssecurity.co.uk

▶ Hilton Security Systems, Rose Cottage, Pailton Fields, Pailton, Rugby, Warwickshire, CV23 0QJ Tel: 01788 551966 Fax: 01788 338989 E-mail: info@hiltonsecurity.co.uk

▶ I F S Electronic Security Division, 20 St. Johns Road, Bootle, Merseyside, L20 8NJ Tel: 0151-955 4200 Fax: 0151-955 4240 E-mail: phill.ashton@ifscontractors.com

▶ Intruder Protection Services Ltd, 2 Wenban Road, Worthing, West Sussex, BN11 1HY Tel: (01903) 204845

▶ Marco Electrical, 22 Tresillian Street, Cattedown, Plymouth, PL4 0QW Tel: (01752) 256243 Fax: (01752) 256249

▶ Peel Electrical & Security Systems Ltd, 34 Henfield Close, Clayton le Moors, Accrington, Lancashire, BB5 5WP Tel: (01254) 398181 Fax: 01254 398181 E-mail: SALES@PEELSECURITY.CO.UK

▶ Secure Solutions, 37 New Road, Burton Lazars, Melton Mowbray, Leicestershire, LE14 2UU Tel: 01664 568155 Fax: 01664 561990

▶ Stafford Uniprint, 2 Willoughby Court, Bramshall, Uttoxeter, Staffordshire, ST14 5NH Tel: (01889) 567532 Fax: (01782) 395801 E-mail: uniprint@tesco.net

▶ Swift, Matthew Elliott House, 64 Broadway, Salford, M50 2TS Tel: 0161-872 6262 Fax: 0161-877 2424 E-mail: info@swiftsecurity.com

CLOSED CIRCUIT TELEVISION (CCTV) CABINETS

▶ 24 7 CCTV Security Ltd, 33 Kingswood Road, Basildon, Essex, SS16 5UP Tel: (0870) 2242247 Fax: (0870) 4215949 E-mail: info@247cctv.co.uk

Enclosure Systems Ltd, Platt Industrial Estate, Maidstone Road, Borough Green, Sevenoaks, Kent, TN15 8JA Tel: (01732) 886552 Fax: (01732) 886443 E-mail: sales@enclosures.co.uk

CLOSED CIRCUIT TELEVISION (CCTV) CAMERA TOWERS OR MASTS

Altron Communications Equipment Ltd, Tower House, Parc Hendre, Capel Hendre, Ammanford, Dyfed, SA18 3SJ Tel: (01269) 831431 Fax: (01269) 845348 E-mail: comms@altron.co.uk

Andromica Video Systems Ltd, Victory House, 54 Wallingford Road, Uxbridge, Middlesex, UB8 2RW Tel: (01895) 257971 Fax: (01895) 273483 E-mail: admin@andromica.co.uk

CLOSED CIRCUIT TELEVISION (CCTV) COMPONENTS

C C T V Installations, 47 Sussex Road, Southport, Merseyside, PR9 0SP Tel: (01704) 884244 Fax: (01704) 884243 E-mail: sales@cctvinstallations.gbr.cc

Cricklewood Electronics Ltd, 40-42 Cricklewood Broadway, London, NW2 3ET Tel: (020) 8452 0161 Fax: (020) 8208 1441 E-mail: sales@cricklewoodelectronics.com

Norbain SD Ltd, Eskdale Road, Winnersh, Wokingham, Berkshire, RG41 5TS Tel: 0118-944 0123 Fax: 0118-9440999 E-mail: james.smith@norbain.co.uk

Richardson Electronics, Inspring House, Searby Road, Lincoln, LN2 4DT Tel: (01522) 542631 Fax: (01522) 545453 E-mail: info@rell.com

Zoom CCTV, Mono Lodge, Bridge Street, Golborne, Warrington, WA3 3QA Tel: (01942) 276699 Fax: (01942) 272590 E-mail: zoom@zoomcctv.com

CLOSED CIRCUIT TELEVISION (CCTV) CONTRACTORS

Access Control Automation Ltd, Arun Business Park, Bognor Regis, West Sussex, PO22 9SX Tel: (01243) 830641 Fax: (01243) 830738 E-mail: sales@accesscontrolautomation.com

Access Controls UK Ltd, 62 Ocean Close, Fareham, Hampshire, PO15 6QP Tel: (01329) 513222 Fax: (01329) 513221 E-mail: enquiries@accesscontrols.co.uk

Automatic Protection Systems, 156 The Bluebells, Bradley Stoke, Bristol, BS32 8DW Tel: 0117-979 8330 Fax: 0117-979 8330

C C T V Installations, 47 Sussex Road, Southport, Merseyside, PR9 0SP Tel: (01704) 884244 Fax: (01704) 884243 E-mail: sales@cctvinstallations.gbr.cc

Camrascan Ltd, Clarence House, Minerva Business Park, Lynch Wood, Peterborough, PE2 6FT Tel: (01733) 239633 Fax: (01733) 362706 E-mail: sales@camrascan.co.uk

Civic Security Ltd, Vision House, 182 Landells Road, London, SE22 9PP Tel: (020) 8299 5150 Fax: (020) 8299 5160 E-mail: sales@civicsecurity.com

Connectic Synx Ltd, The Flarepath, Elsham Wolds Industrial Estate, Brigg, South Humberside, DN20 0SP Tel: (01652) 688908 Fax: (01652) 688928 E-mail: sales@synx.ltd.uk

D P Security, Ryecroft House, Green St Green Road, Dartford, DA2 8DX Tel: (01474) 707030 Fax: (01474) 707313 E-mail: info@dpsecurity.co.uk

Electrical & Alarm Services, Colebrook Road, Plympton, Plymouth, PL7 4AA Tel: (01752) 337271 Fax: (01752) 337271 E-mail: easdale@eurobell.co.uk

▶ Europa Security, 68 Privett Road, Fareham, Hampshire, PO15 6SP Tel: (0709) 2111588 Fax: (0709) 2376783 E-mail: admin@europasecurity.co.uk

G B Alarms Ltd, High St, Donington, Spalding, Lincolnshire, PE11 4TA Tel: (01775) 821100 Fax: (01775) 821069 E-mail: admin@gbalarms.com

GFH SOUND AND VISION LTD, 39 SHERRARDS WAY, BARNET, HERTS, EN5 2BW Tel: 07815 735607 Fax: (020) 8449 6531 E-mail: garretthenderson345@hotmail.com

Greens Water Systems, Longacre Business Park, Westminster Road, North Hykeham, Lincoln, LN6 3QH Tel: (01522) 697785 Fax: (01522) 823899 E-mail: info@water-systems.co.uk

Hall & Rhodes Security Ltd, 138-140 Blackmoorfoot Road, Huddersfield, HD4 5RL Tel: (0800) 521271 Fax: (01484) 658897

Higgins Electronics, 116-120 High Street, Aberlour, Banffshire, AB38 9PA Tel: (01340) 871275 Fax: (01340) 871275

I D Installations, 202 Nuthurst Road, Manchester, M40 3PP Tel: 0161-682 4595 Fax: 0161-682 4595 E-mail: david@idinstallations.freeserve.co.uk

Kezvale Ltd, 5 Johnsons Industrial Estate, Silverdale Road, Hayes, Middlesex, UB3 3BA Tel: (020) 8569 2731 Fax: (020) 8569 2790 E-mail: info@kezvale.co.uk

King Communication Services, 19 Coatbank Street, Coatbridge, Lanarkshire, ML5 3SP Tel: (01236) 429445 Fax: (01236) 429445 E-mail: info@kingcoms.com

LB Ford Ltd, Park Lane, Nottingham, NG6 0DT Tel: 0115-927 2821 Fax: 0115-976 1041 E-mail: lb@ford.co.uk

▶ Lion Watch Security Services Ltd, 143 High Street, Chesterton, Cambridge, CB4 1NL Tel: (07903) 960665 E-mail: info@lionwatch.co.uk

Lisburn Security Services Ltd, Security House, Lissea Industrial Estate East, Lisburn, County Antrim, BT28 2RD Tel: (028) 9260 5859 Fax: (028) 9262 2423 E-mail: gsmith@lisburnsecurityservices.co.uk

Mison Security Ltd, 5 Skyline, Lime Harbour, London, E14 9TS Tel: (020) 7093 1177 Fax: (020) 7923 0493 E-mail: mail@misonsecurity.com

Quadrant Research & Development Ltd, 3a Attenborough Lane, Beeston, Nottingham, NG9 5JN Tel: 0115-925 2521 Fax: 0115-943 1561 E-mail: sales@quadrantcctv.com

Secure Engineering Ltd, Friday Street Barn, East Sutton, Maidstone, Kent, ME17 3DD Tel: (01622) 844244 Fax: (01622) 844567 E-mail: sales@secureeng.co.uk

A.J. Sibthorpe & Co. Ltd, 22-42 Freshwater Road, Dagenham, Essex, RM8 1RY Tel: (020) 8597 7000 Fax: (020) 8597 7300

Squirealarms Ltd, 165-171 Humberstone Road, Leicester, LE5 3AF Tel: 0116-262 3916 E-mail: info@squirealarms.co.uk

Surveillance Solutions Ltd, 127 Ouzlewell Green, Lofthouse, Wakefield, West Yorkshire, WF3 3QW Tel: (0845) 1304631 Fax: (0870) 1333608 E-mail: chris@ssl-cctv.co.uk

UK Fire International Ltd, The Safety Centre, Mountergate, Norwich, NR1 1PY Tel: (01603) 727000 Fax: (01603) 727073 E-mail: norwich@ukfire.co.uk

Vue, 187 Cross Street, Sale, Cheshire, M33 7JG Tel: 0161-962 4356 Fax: 0161-973 5060 E-mail: sales@vue-cctv.co.uk

Zoom CCTV, Mono Lodge, Bridge Street, Golborne, Warrington, WA3 3QA Tel: (01942) 276699 Fax: (01942) 272590 E-mail: zoom@zoomcctv.com

CLOSED CIRCUIT TELEVISION (CCTV) DESIGN OR CONSULTANCY OR INSTALLATION

A G S Security Systems Ltd, Field Way, Denbigh Road, Mold, Flintshire, CH7 1BP Tel: (01244) 812222 Fax: (01352) 707889 E-mail: info@ags-security.co.uk

A1 T S Security Systems, 65 Woodchurch Lane, Birkenhead, Merseyside, CH42 9PL Tel: 0151-608 0935 Fax: 0151-608 9741

Access Fire & Security Ltd, Henley House, 1293-1295 Warick Road, Acocks Green, Birmingham, B27 6PU Tel: 0121-765 4900 Fax: 0121-765 4901 E-mail: michael@accessfire.co.uk

Acorn Security Alarms Ltd, Swan House, Bonds Mill, Stonehouse, Gloucestershire, GL10 3RF Tel: (01453) 794050 Fax: (01453) 794051 E-mail: info@acornsecurityalarms.co.uk

ADT Fire & Security plc, Adt House, Kilmartin Place, Uddingston, Glasgow, G71 5PH Tel: (01698) 486000 Fax: (01698) 486100 E-mail: info@adtfireandsecurity.co.uk

Advanced Network, 12 Primrose Gdns, London, NW3 4TN Tel: (020) 7586 3232

Alarm Communication Ltd, 1 Westfield Road, Woking, Surrey, GU22 9LZ Tel: (01483) 771186 Fax: (01483) 771861 E-mail: office@alarmcommunication.co.uk

Alert Alarms, 16 Church Parade, Canvey Island, Essex, SS8 9RQ Tel: (01268) 696534 Fax: (01268) 680785 E-mail: alertalarms@blueyonder.co.uk

Automatic Protection Systems, 156 The Bluebells, Bradley Stoke, Bristol, BS32 8DW Tel: 0117-979 8330 Fax: 0117-979 8330

B T B, Supreme House, 1 Pitt Lane, Bideford, Devon, EX39 3JA Tel: (01237) 424046 Fax: (01237) 423376

▶ indicates data change since last edition

CLOSED CIRCUIT TELEVISION (CCTV) DESIGN OR CONSULTANCY OR INSTALLATION – *continued*

Ble Ltd, Church Street, Eckington, Sheffield, S21 4BH Tel: (01246) 436361 Fax: (01246) 436726 E-mail: sales@blegroup.co.uk

C C T V People Ltd, PO Box 89, Cleckheaton, West Yorkshire, BD19 6YL Tel: (0800) 318748 Fax: (01274) 852188

C J Security Systems Ltd, Unit 3 Fence Avenue, Macclesfield, Cheshire, SK10 1LT Tel: (01625) 613707 Fax: (01625) 617898 E-mail: sales@cheshirelock.co.uk

Cameras Stop Crime, Hillcrest, Roucan Road, Collin, Dumfries, DG1 4JF Tel: (01387) 750689 Fax: (01387) 750689

Camrascan Ltd, Clarence House, Minerva Business Park, Lynch Wood, Peterborough, PE2 6FT Tel: (01733) 239633 Fax: (01733) 362706 E-mail: sales@camrascan.co.uk

Castle Alarms, Millennium House, Boundary Bank, Kendal, Cumbria, LA9 5RR Tel: (01539) 731394 Fax: (01539) 735367 E-mail: sales@fp.castlealarms.f9.co.uk

▶ The CCTV Co., Crows Nest, Ashton Road, Billinge, Wigan, Lancashire, WN5 7XY Tel: (01744) 891702 Fax: (01744) 891710 E-mail: john@thecctvcompany.com

CCTV Systems Manchester Ltd, 31a Astley Street, Tyldesley, Manchester, M29 8HG Tel: (01942) 894008 Fax: (01942) 893339 E-mail: info@cctv.tv

Chroma Visual, 61 Leyland Trading Estate, Wellingborough, Northamptonshire, NN8 1RS Tel: (01933) 443737 Fax: (01933) 271770 E-mail: cvl@globalnet.co.uk

▶ Chromavision CCTV & Video Equipment, 88 Judd Road, Tonbridge, Kent, TN9 2NJ Tel: (01732) 771999 Fax: (01732) 771888 E-mail: john@chroma-vision.co.uk

Daemon Fire & Security Ltd, 41-42 Albert Road, Tamworth, Staffordshire, B79 7JS Tel: (01827) 69266 Fax: (01827) 53584 E-mail: sales@daemonfire.co.uk

Dorcom Ltd, Unit 3, St Joseph's Business Park, St Joseph's Close, Hove, East Sussex, BN3 7HG Tel: 01273 202851 Fax: 01273 220108 E-mail: info@dorcom.co.uk

G C S Alarms, Essex House, Stephenson Road, Clacton-on-Sea, Essex, CO15 4XA Tel: (01255) 220316 Fax: (01255) 479122 E-mail: sales@gcsalarms.co.uk

Golding Audio, 8 Peartree Business Centre, Peartree Road, Stanway, Colchester, CO3 0JN Tel: (01206) 762462 Fax: (01206) 762633 E-mail: enquiries@goldingaudio.co.uk

▶ Home Security Services UK Ltd, 3 Campbell Street, Roe Lee, Blackburn, BB1 9AF Tel: (0800) 6520642 Fax: (01254) 698064 E-mail: sales@homesecurityservicesuk.co.uk

Hunter Security Ltd, Walnut Tree Farm, Cockmannings Lane, Orpington, Kent, BR5 4HF Tel: (01689) 870951 Fax: (01689) 822363 E-mail: enquiries@huntersecurity.com

Ics Installations Ltd, 5 Bates Close, Larkfield, Aylesford, Kent, ME20 6TG Tel: (01732) 848550 Fax: (01732) 848550 E-mail: lloyd.porter@ics-installations.com

Initial Electronic Security Systems Ltd, 1 Orbit Centre, Ashworth Road, Bridgemead, Swindon, SN5 7YG Tel: (01793) 531955 Fax: (01793) 488850 E-mail: swindon@ies.uk.com

Internal T V Contracts, Brooklands Approach, Romford, RM1 1DX Tel: (01708) 725511 Fax: (01708) 730507 E-mail: itcuksales@aol.com

▶ ISEC Solutions, Meadowcroft, Nottingham Road, Ravenshead, Nottingham, NG15 9HP Tel: 01623 792200 Fax: 01623 792293 E-mail: mark@isec-solutions.co.uk

▶ Lincs Electrical Services, 6 Buttler Way, Sleaford, Lincolnshire, NG34 7PA Tel: (01529) 309505 E-mail: lincelectrical@tiscali.co.uk

M G Visual C C T V Ltd, 1 3 Wigan Road, Skelmersdale, Lancashire, WN8 8NB Tel: (01695) 558591 Fax: (01695) 558591 E-mail: sales@mgvisual.co.uk

Metro Security, 5 Ashton Road, Harold Hill, Romford, RM3 8UJ Tel: (0870) 6090095 Fax: (0870) 6090096 E-mail: info@metrosecurity.co.uk

Octagon Security, 87 High Road, Ickenham, Uxbridge, Middlesex, UB10 8LH Tel: (01895) 624545 Fax: (01895) 624546 E-mail: sales@octogan.ltc.co.uk

▶ Optimum Security Services, Unit 3, Manor Business Park, Witney Road, Finstock, Chipping Norton, Oxfordshire, OX7 3DG Tel: (0870) 3502171 Fax: (0870) 3502172 E-mail: info@optimum.me.uk

▶ Optyma Security Systems, 6 Harcourt Road, Bexleyheath, Kent, DA6 8AQ Tel: (020) 8304 8635 Fax: (020) 8304 4633

▶ P & R Security Systems Ltd, 119 Lees Road, Oldham, OL4 1JW Tel: 0161-652 9984 Fax: 0161-620 8111 E-mail: sales@pandrsecurities.co.uk

Programmed Communications, Unit 9 Bluebird House, Povey Cross Road, Horley, Surrey, RH6 0AF Tel: (01293) 822033 Fax: (01293) 821958

Rentrifone Ltd, Premier House, 309 Ballards Lane, London, N12 8NE Tel: (020) 8455 3304 Fax: (020) 8609 0627 E-mail: rentrifone@hotmail.co.uk

Secure Engineering Ltd, Friday Street Barn, East Sutton, Maidstone, Kent, ME17 3DD Tel: (01622) 844244 Fax: (01622) 844567 E-mail: sales@secureeng.co.uk

Secure It All Ltd, 25 Howley Grange Road, Halesowen, West Midlands, B62 0HW Tel: 0121-423 1119 Fax: 0121-423 3393 E-mail: sales@secureitall.co.uk

Sentinel Security Systems, 7 Southern Avenue, Leominster, Herefordshire, HR6 0QF Tel: (01568) 615500 Fax: (01568) 610555 E-mail: sentinelss@btinternet.com

Shire Security Ltd, 2 Henson Park, Henson Way, Telford Way Industrial Estate, Kettering, Northamptonshire, NN16 8PX Tel: (01536) 410483 Fax: (01536) 412631 E-mail: info@shiresecurity.co.uk

Solent Audio Visual, Meadowsweet Cottage, Hambledon Road, Denmead, Waterlooville, Hampshire, PO7 6QA Tel: (023) 9223 0999 Fax: (023) 9223 0555 E-mail: colin@solentav.demon.co.uk

Status Alarms Ltd, Holbrook Lane, Coventry, CV6 4AF Tel: (024) 7668 5523 Fax: (024) 7666 1127

T H White Installation Ltd, 3 Nursteed Road Trading Estate, William Road, Devizes, Wiltshire, SN10 3EW Tel: (01380) 726656 Fax: (01380) 725707 E-mail: thwhite@bigwig.net

Television Installation Services (Mansfield) Ltd, Old Mill Lane Industrial Estate, Mansfield Woodhouse, Mansfield, Nottinghamshire, NG19 9BG Tel: (01623) 425800 Fax: (01623) 650767 E-mail: sales@tisnet.co.uk

Videoquest 2004 Ltd, 27 Masson Avenue, Ruislip, Middlesex, HA4 6QT Tel: (020) 8842 2783 Fax: (020) 8842 2784 E-mail: videoquestltd@btconnect.com

Zoom CCTV, Mono Lodge, Bridge Street, Golborne, Warrington, WA3 3QA Tel: (01942) 276699 Fax: (01942) 272590 E-mail: zoom@zoomcctv.com

CLOSED CIRCUIT TELEVISION (CCTV) EQUIPMENT

21st Century Security, PO Box 60, Heathfield, East Sussex, TN21 8ZJ Tel: (01435) 868245 Fax: (01435) 868245

▶ 2CTV.co.uk, PO Box 2011, Preston, PR5 8WU Tel: 07929 610498 E-mail: sales@2ctv.co.uk

A C E Security Ltd, Hole Farm, Lye Garden, Crowborough, East Sussex, TN6 1UU Tel: (01892) 603800 Fax: (01892) 603808 E-mail: onwatch@onwatch.com

A C L Camcom Ltd, Unit 1 The Hamiltons, Torquay Road, Shaldon, Teignmouth, Devon, TQ14 0AY Tel: (01626) 871043

A D T Fire & Security P.L.C., Security House, The Summit, Hanworth Road, Sunbury-on-Thames, Middlesex, TW16 5DB Tel: (0800) 0111111

A R P Electrical, 31 Edwards Road, Halifax, West Yorkshire, HX2 7DG Tel: (01422) 353778 Fax: (01422) 353778

Abel Alarm Co. Ltd, 98 Addington Road, Reading, RG1 5PX Tel: 0118-935 2218 Fax: 0118-966 7277 E-mail: info.reading@abelalarm.co.uk

▶ Access CCTV & Securities, 119 Hoyle Street, Warrington, WA5 0LP Tel: (01925) 632000 Fax: (01925) 632777 E-mail: accesscctvsec@yahoo.co.uk

Addlestone Electronics, Kistadan, Church Lane, Bisley, Woking, Surrey, GU24 9EA Tel: (01483) 480969 Fax: (01483) 797268 E-mail: sales@addlestone-electronics.co.uk

▶ Advanced Cctv Mounting Equipment, Philips Road, Whitebirk Industrial Estate, Blackburn, BB1 5PG Tel: (01254) 676632 Fax: (01254) 677627

▶ Aegis Security Solutions, 7 Allenby Business Park, Crofton Road, Lincoln, LN3 4NL Tel: (01522) 529321 Fax: (01522) 539039

Alarm Tech 2000, 42 Edinburgh Drive, Holton-le-Clay, Grimsby, South Humberside, DN36 5DF Tel: (01472) 825555 Fax: (01472) 595044 E-mail: alarm_tech_2000@yahoo.com

Allen & Feldhaus Ltd, Hathaway House, Fermor Road, Crowborough, East Sussex, TN6 3AN Tel: (0800) 781 9885 Fax: (0870) 762 3882 E-mail: dan.f@orange.net

Alpha Cam, 68 Wilson Street, Alexandria, Dunbartonshire, G83 0EE Tel: (01389) 729333 Fax: (01389) 729444

Andromica Video Systems Ltd, Victory House, 54 Wallingford Road, Uxbridge, Middlesex, UB8 2RW Tel: (01895) 257971 Fax: (01895) 273483 E-mail: admin@andromica.co.uk

▶ Anglesey Scanner Security, Cae Cali, Brynteg, Gwynedd, LL78 8JJ Tel: (01248) 853353 Fax: (01248) 853666

Atlas Alarms, 2-8 Blackburn Road, Darwen, Lancashire, BB3 1QJ Tel: (01254) 873232 Fax: (01254) 761277 E-mail: admin@atlasalarms.co.uk

Automate UK, 9 Hill La Industrial Estate, Markfield, Leicestershire, LE67 9PN Tel: (01530) 249444 Fax: (01530) 249444 E-mail: sales@automateuk.co.uk

Automatic Protection Systems, 156 The Bluebells, Bradley Stoke, Bristol, BS32 8DW Tel: 0117-979 8330 Fax: 0117-979 8330

▶ B L T V Security Systems, 20 Broad Acres, Haxby, York, YO32 3WL Tel: (01904) 758555

B & M Business Machines Ltd, 30 Military Road, Colchester, CO1 2AJ Tel: (01206) 576872 Fax: (01206) 576873

Bayline Systems Ltd, 76 Abergele Road, Colwyn Bay, Clwyd, LL29 7PP Tel: (01492) 535445 Fax: (01492) 535443 E-mail: sales@bayline.co.uk

C C T V Installations, 47 Sussex Road, Southport, Merseyside, PR9 0SP Tel: (01704) 884244 Fax: (01704) 884243 E-mail: sales@cctvinstallations.gbr.cc

C C T V Systems, 18 Avondale Road, Waterlooville, Hampshire, PO7 7ST Tel: (023) 9226 7999 Fax: (023) 9223 3664 E-mail: cctvsystems@btinternet.com

Camera Technical Services, 1b St Lawrences Rd, Coventry, CV6 7AE Tel: 024 76661133

Cameras Stop Crime, Hillcrest, Roucan Road, Collin, Dumfries, DG1 4JF Tel: (01387) 750689 Fax: (01387) 750689

▶ Camplex Ltd, 6 Albemarle Link, Springfield, Chelmsford, CM2 5AG Tel: (0870) 2422462 Fax: (0870) 2422463

Cam-Tec Surveillance Systems, 190 Uttoxeter Road, Blythe Bridge, Stoke-on-Trent, ST11 9JR Tel: (01782) 396619 Fax: (01782) 388549 E-mail: sales@cam-tec.com

Camwatch Ltd, 128 Maltravers Road, Sheffield, S2 5AZ Tel: 0114-281 9999 Fax: 0114-241 2864 E-mail: enquiries@camwatch.co.uk

▶ Captive Systems UK Ltd, 82 Caunce Street, Blackpool, FY1 3ND Tel: (01253) 627600 Fax: (01253) 627560 E-mail: info@captivesystems.co.uk

CCTV 4U Ltd, Unit A5, Maritime Park, Pembroke Dock, Pembrokeshire, SA72 6UL Tel: 0 845 226 31 91 Fax: 0 845 226 31 94 E-mail: info@cctv4u.co.uk

▶ CCTV Services Ltd, Unit 11, Plot 27, Llandegai Industrial Estate, Bangor, Gwynedd, LL57 4YH Tel: (08703) 770100 Fax: (08703) 770108 E-mail: mike@cctvserviceslimited.com

Christie Intruder Alarms Ltd, Security House, 212-218 London Road, Waterlooville, Hampshire, PO7 7AJ Tel: (023) 9226 5111 Fax: (023) 9226 5112 E-mail: enquiries@ciaalarms.co.uk

Cobra Security Systems Ltd, 155 Station Road, London, E4 6AG Tel: (020) 8529 0179 Fax: (020) 8529 0091 E-mail: keith@cobra-security.fsnet.co.uk

Connectic Synx Ltd, The Flarepath, Elsham Wolds Industrial Estate, Brigg, South Humberside, DN20 0SP Tel: (01652) 688908 Fax: (01652) 688928 E-mail: sales@synx.ltd.uk

Conway Security Products Ltd, Seymour House, Copyground Lane, High Wycombe, Buckinghamshire, HP12 3HE Tel: (01494) 461373 Fax: (01494) 531685 E-mail: sales@conway-cctv.co.uk

Cov Tek Security County Systems Ltd, 10 Captain Street, Coleraine, County Londonderry, BT52 2NJ Tel: (028) 7032 6166 Fax: (028) 7032 7225 E-mail: cctv@covtec.com

▶ Crimewatch Video International, 89-91 Wellington Road North, Stockport, Cheshire, SK4 2LP Tel: 0161-480 5003 E-mail: sales@crimewatchcctv.com

▶ Crossover Group Ltd, High Street, Ashwell, Baldock, Hertfordshire, SG7 5NT Tel: (01462) 742948 Fax: (01462) 743619 E-mail: sales@crossovergroup.com

▶ Cyber-Eye, 45, Altom Street, Blackburn, BB1 7LJ Tel: (01254) 678879 Fax: (01254) 678558

▶ D & G Short, 19 Station Road, Flitwick, Bedford, MK45 1JT Tel: (01525) 753819 Fax: (01525) 716687 E-mail: info@dandgshort.com

Dedicated Micros Ltd, Aegon House, Daresbury Park, Daresbury, Warrington, WA4 4HS Tel: (01928) 706400 Fax: (01928) 706350 E-mail: customerservice@dmicros.com

Dennard Ltd, 55 Fleet Road, Fleet, Hampshire, GU51 3PN Tel: (01252) 614884 Fax: (01252) 626013 E-mail: sales@dennard-cctv.com

▶ Digi Tech Ltd, Unit 7 Plantation Business Park, Stadium Road, Wirral, Merseyside, CH62 3RN Tel: 0151-343 9595 Fax: 0151-343 9575

Duoguard Burglar Alarm Systems, 15 Llandaff Road, Beaufort, Ebbw Vale, Gwent, NP23 5RL Tel: (01495) 304931

Eagle Security Solutions Ltd, 162 Trafalgar Road, London, SE10 9TZ Tel: (0845) 9002950 E-mail: info@eaglesecuritysolutions.co.uk

Electro-Flow Controls Ltd, Unit 3 Souter Head Industrial Centre, Souter Head Road, Altens, Aberdeen, AB12 3LF Tel: (01224) 249355 Fax: (01224) 249339 E-mail: efcltd@attglobal.net

▶ G1, 280 Western Road, London, SW19 2QA Tel: (020) 8687 3140 Fax: (020) 8687 3141 E-mail: mail@g1.tv

▶ Gestalt Technology Ltd, 11, The Sawyers House, 113 London Road, Horndean, Waterlooville, Hampshire, PO8 0BJ Tel: (023) 9259 4270 Fax: (023) 9259 4271E-mail: info@gtg.uk.com

Globewatch Securities Ltd, 74 Bewsey Street, Warrington, WA2 7JE Tel: (01925) 232022 Fax: (01925) 232024

Gough & Kelly Ltd, 6 Hales Road, Leeds, LS12 4PL Tel: 0113-279 4801 Fax: 0113-279 8644 E-mail: sales@gough-kelly.co.uk

Guardian Alarms Ltd, 20-22 Sydenham Road, Croydon, CR0 2EF Tel: (020) 8686 8777 Fax: (020) 8686 9777 E-mail: sales@guardianalarms.co.uk

▶ David Hall Communications, 19 Taylor Avenue, Cringleford, Norwich, NR4 6XY Tel: (01603) 506602 E-mail: david@davidhallcomms.co.uk

Hartburn Security Alarms, 8 Spalding Rd, Hartlepool, Cleveland, TS25 2LD Tel: (01429) 871111

Heuston Technologies, 39 Princetown Road, Bangor, County Down, BT20 3TA Tel: (028) 9147 8054 Fax: (028) 9147 8054 E-mail: richardheuston@utvinternet.co.uk

Hitachi Denshi UK, Windsor House, Britannia Road, Waltham Cross, Hertfordshire, EN8 7NX Tel: (01992) 704595 Fax: (0845) 1212180 E-mail: sales@hitachi-ke-eu.com

▶ Home Security Services UK Ltd, 51 Highbank, Blackburn, BB1 9SX Tel: (0800) 6520642 Fax: (01254) 698064 E-mail: Info@hssukltd.co.uk

Internal T V Contracts, Brooklands Approach, Romford, RM1 1DX Tel: (01708) 725511 Fax: (01708) 730507 E-mail: itcuksales@aol.com

I-Scan Security Systems, 3 Hazel Rd, Berkhamsted, Hertfordshire, HP4 2JN Tel: 01442 866907

J M F Vision Systems Ltd, The Lindens, Friern Park, London, N12 9DJ Tel: (020) 8445 0452

▶ Den Jackson Solutions Ltd, 5 Ames Court, Cawston, Norwich, NR10 4QD Tel: (01603) 879999

Kinetic Products Ltd, Unit B1, Brookside Business Park, Greengate Middleton, Manchester, M24 1GS Tel: 0161-654 9595 Fax: 0161-654 9596 E-mail: sales@kinetic-security.co.uk

Kultronic Security Systems Ltd, 28 Ennerdale Avenue, Liverpool, L31 9BU Tel: 0151-531 6429 Fax: 0151-531 6429

Link CCTV Systems, Unit 2, Campus 5, Letchworth Garden City, Hertfordshire, SG6 2JF Tel: (01462) 682300 Fax: (01462) 678382 E-mail: service@linkcctv.co.uk

Look C, Unit 3c The Waterfront, Goldcrest Way, Newcastle upon Tyne, NE15 8NY Tel: 0191-229 5720 Fax: 0191-229 5730

Look CCTV Ltd, Aldon Road, Poulton Industrial Estate, Poulton-le-Fylde, Lancashire, FY6 8JL Tel: (01253) 891222 Fax: (01253) 891221 E-mail: enquiries@lookcctv.com

M & E Alarms Ltd, Lower Charlecott, Tawstock, Barnstaple, Devon, EX31 3JY Tel: (01271) 858550 Fax: (01271) 858423 E-mail: sales@m-and-e.co.uk

Marriott Security Ltd, 18 Ridgeway, Peterborough, PE2 8HQ Tel: (01733) 894334

Minder Alarm Co., 1 Market Place, Penistone, Sheffield, S36 6DA Tel: (01226) 370100 Fax: (01226) 764994 E-mail: minderalarmsltd@btconnect.com

Moreton Alarm Supplies, Unit 1, Soveriegn Way, Maritime Business Park, Dock Road, Birkenhead, Merseyside, CH41 1DG Tel: 0151-630 0000 Fax: 0151-670 9888 E-mail: save@mas-uk.co.uk

N J M Trading, 32 Temple St, Wolverhampton, WV2 4AN Tel: 01902 429022 Fax: 01902 429052

Nortek Electronic Circuits Ltd, Bridge Mill, Royle Street, Congleton, Cheshire, CW12 1HR Tel: (01260) 276409 Fax: (01260) 299399 E-mail: mail@nortek.co.uk

Oaks CCTV Ltd, 6 St. Helens Way, Thetford, Norfolk, IP24 1HG Tel: (01842) 820627 Fax: (01842) 820624

Ogier Electronics Ltd, Sandridge Park, Porters Wood, St. Albans, Hertfordshire, AL3 6PH Tel: (01727) 853521 Fax: (01727) 852186

▶ Omega Red Group Ltd, Dabell Avenue, Blenheim Industrial Estate, Bulwell, Nottingham, NG6 8WA Tel: 0115-877 6666 Fax: 0115-876 7766 E-mail: aimiga@redgroup.co.uk

▶ P & R Security Systems Ltd, 119 Lees Road, Oldham, OL4 1JW Tel: 0161-652 9984 Fax: 0161-620 8111 E-mail: sales@pandrsecurities.co.uk

Pacc Security Ltd, 90 Lots Road, London, SW10 0QD Tel: (020) 7376 3000 Fax: (020) 7376 3100 E-mail: security@paccsecurity.com

Paul K Sound & Vision, 16 Kings Lea, Adlington, Chorley, Lancashire, PR7 4EN Tel: (01257) 474233 Fax: (01257) 474233

Peca Electronics, 1 Parnell Court, Andover, Hampshire, SP10 3LX Tel: (01264) 355975 Fax: (01264) 366536 E-mail: sales@peca-electronics.co.uk

Pentax UK Ltd, Pentax House, Heron Drive, Slough, SL3 8PN Tel: (01753) 792792 Fax: (01753) 792794 E-mail: contactus@.pentax.co.uk

Petards Ltd, 8 Windmill Business Village, Brooklands Close, Sunbury-on-Thames, Middlesex, TW16 7DY Tel: (01932) 788288 Fax: (01932) 788322 E-mail: sales@petards.com

▶ Powersafe Communications Ltd, Tangiers, Haverfordwest, Dyfed, SA62 4BU Tel: (01437) 779977 Fax: (01437) 779639 E-mail: enquiries@powersafe.co.uk

Premier Security Services, 42 Second Avenue, Stafford, ST16 1PR Tel: (01785) 225951 Fax: (01785) 225951 E-mail: sales@premiersecurityservices.co.uk

Proline Ltd, 530 Commercial Road, London, E1 0HY Tel: (020) 7702 1983 Fax: (020) 7791 2288

▶ Property Protection Systems, Old Tithe Barn, Witcombe, Martock, Somerset, TA12 6AJ Tel: (01935) 825892 Fax: (01935) 825892 E-mail: sales@property-protection-systems.co.uk

Quantum, Unit 5, Herbert Walker Avenue, Southampton, SO15 1HJ Tel: (023) 8033 3372 Fax: (023) 8033 3372

▶ Rovtech Systems Ltd, 7 The Old Brewery, Shore Street, Barrow-in-Furness, Cumbria, LA14 2UB Tel: (01229) 822121 Fax: (01229) 870208 E-mail: info@rovtechsystems.co.uk

S G D Security Ltd, 26-28 Dalcross Street, Cardiff, CF24 4SD Tel: (029) 2046 4120 Fax: (029) 2047 0843 E-mail: info@sgdsecurity.com

Safe & Sound Security Systems Security Alarms, 9 Devonshire Road, Gravesend, Kent, DA12 5AA Tel: (01474) 350613 Fax: (01474) 350613

CLOSED CIRCUIT TELEVISION (CCTV) EQUIPMENT – *continued*

Scot-Tech Surveillance Ltd, 6 Mead Avenue, Chryston, Glasgow, G69 0EZ Tel: (01236) 874870 Fax: (01236) 874870

Secure Engineering Ltd, Friday Street Barn, East Sutton, Maidstone, Kent, ME17 3DD Tel: (01622) 844244 Fax: (01622) 844567 E-mail: sales@secureeng.co.uk

▶ Security Direct, 1 River Road Business Park, 33 River Road, Barking, Essex, IG11 0DA Tel: (020) 8522 0251 Fax: (020) 8507 9900

▶ Security Electronics Industries Ltd, Unit 19, Anniesland Business Park, Glasgow, G13 1EU Tel: 0141-959 5999 E-mail: sales@securityelectronicsonline.com

▶ Semper Vigil Security Ltd, Unit 9 Hardengreen Business Centre, Dalkeith, Midlothian, EH22 3NX Tel: 0131-660 9481 E-mail: semper.vigil@btconnect.com

Shawley Ltd, Suflex Estate, Newport Road, Risca, Newport, Gwent, NP11 6YD Tel: (01633) 619999 Fax: (01633) 619977 E-mail: sales@shawley.com

Solent Audio Visual, Meadowsweet Cottage, Hambledon Road, Denmead, Waterlooville, Hampshire, PO7 6QA Tel: (023) 9223 0999 Fax: (023) 9223 0555 E-mail: colin@solentav.demon.co.uk

Sonalux Systems, Tanglewood, Hophurst Hill, Crawley Down, Crawley, West Sussex, RH10 4LP Tel: (01342) 717691 Fax: (01342) 717094 E-mail: rob@sonalux.tv

▶ South Wales Cameras Ltd, Unit 2, Bessemer Workshop, Bessemer Close, Cardiff, CF11 8CL Tel: (029) 2034 2681 Fax: (029) 2034 2486 E-mail: southwalescamera@btconnect.com

Sovereign International Ltd, 86 Church Road, Formby, Liverpool, L37 3NG Tel: (01704) 832800 Fax: (01704) 832700 E-mail: sales@sovereign-cctv.co.uk

▶ Step Forward, 3 Langdon Hills Business Park, Florence Way, Basildon, Essex, SS16 6AJ Tel: (01268) 544044 Fax: (01268) 544045 E-mail: sales@sfruk.com

Still Frame, Knight House, Farren Court, Cowfold, Horsham, West Sussex, RH13 8BT Tel: (01403) 865268 Fax: (01403) 865269 E-mail: info@stillframe.co.uk

Successful Security Ltd, 73 Rowantree Road, Dromore, County Down, BT25 1NW Tel: (028) 9269 8090 Fax: (028) 9269 8241 E-mail: sales@successfulsecurity.com

Technical Services Shropshire Ltd, Unit 8, Bicton Business Park, Isle Lane, Bicton Heath, Shrewsbury, SY3 8DY Tel: (01743) 851313 Fax: (01743) 851211 E-mail: info@tsshropshire.co.uk

▶ Tel C Ltd, 109-111 Pope Street, Birmingham, B1 3AG Tel: 0121-200 1031 E-mail: sales@thecctvshop.com

▶ Universal Security UK Ltd, Unit 120 City Business Park, Somerset Place, Plymouth, PL3 4BB Tel: (01752) 511222 Fax: (01752) 202426 E-mail: sales@unisecltd.co.uk

▶ Universal Technologies, Stanton Lane, Potters Marston, Leicester, LE9 3JR Tel: (01455) 273663 Fax: (01455) 273993 E-mail: sales@universaltechno-cctv.com

Vicon Industries Ltd, 17 Brunel Way, Fareham, Hampshire, PO15 5TX Tel: (01489) 566300 Fax: (01489) 566322 E-mail: sales@vicon.co.uk

▶ Vicon Industries Ltd, Whitworth Court, Manor Park, Runcorn, Cheshire, WA7 1TA Tel: (01928) 530420 Fax: (01928) 530421

Video Tec Ltd, Unit 132 Bradley Hall Trading Estate, Standish, Wigan, Lancashire, WN6 0XQ Tel: (01257) 428601 Fax: (01257) 428606 E-mail: admin@vtecltd.co.uk

Videor Technical GmbH, 14 Campbell Court, Bramley, Tadley, Hampshire, RG26 5EG Tel: (0870) 7749944 Fax: (0870) 7749955 E-mail: info@videortechnical.com

Vision Aids Ltd, PO Box 4370, Epping, Essex, CM16 5FA Tel: (01992) 573550 Fax: (01992) 573580

Visual Information Systems, Unit 8 Canal Business Park, Dumballs Road, Cardiff, CF10 5FE Tel: (029) 2025 2020 Fax: (07967) 057997

▶ Visual Security Solutions, 16, Ilton Business Park, Ilton, Ilminster, Somerset, TA19 9DU Tel: (01460) 259573 Fax: (01460) 259574

Voltek Automation, Churchill Way, Nelson, Lancashire, BB9 6RT Tel: (0870) 7454971 Fax: (0870) 7454972 E-mail: sales@voltek.co.uk

Waterfront Systems Ltd, Thornhill Lodge, Thornhill, Stalbridge, Sturminster Newton, Dorset, DT10 2SH Tel: (01963) 364307 Fax: (01963) 364306

▶ Wireless CCTV, Mitchell Hey Mills, College Road, Rochdale, Lancashire, OL12 6AE Tel: (01706) 631166 Fax: (01706) 631122 E-mail: sales@wcctv.com

CLOSED CIRCUIT TELEVISION (CCTV) EQUIPMENT HIRE

Dee Communications, 453 Brook Lane, Birmingham, B13 0BT Tel: 0121-702 2552 Fax: 0121-778 3633 E-mail: sales@deecomms.co.uk

Internal T V Contracts, Brooklands Approach, Romford, RM1 1DX Tel: (01708) 725511 Fax: (01708) 730507 E-mail: itcuksales@aol.com

CLOSED CIRCUIT TELEVISION (CCTV) INSPECTION ENGINEERING SERVICES

▶ Essex Security Services Ltd, 154 Church Hill, Loughton, Essex, IG10 1LJ Tel: (020) 8502 1360 Fax: (020) 8502 2700 E-mail: all@essexsecurity.co.uk

J D Jackson (Electronics), Eastfield Labs, Danethorpe Hill, Newark, Nottinghamshire, NG24 2PD Tel: (01636) 705718 Fax: (01636) 610120 E-mail: sales@jacksonelectronics.co.uk

CLOSED CIRCUIT TELEVISION (CCTV) PIPELINE INSPECTION

Shire Security Ltd, 2 Henson Park, Henson Way, Telford Way Industrial Estate, Kettering, Northamptonshire, NN16 8PX Tel: (01536) 410483 Fax: (01536) 412631 E-mail: info@shiresecurity.co.uk

CLOSERS TO THE FOOTWEAR TRADE

Apex Closing (Footwear), Radiant Works, Burnley Road, Rossendale, Lancashire, BB4 8EW Tel: (01706) 218981 Fax: (01706) 218981

CLOSET AUGERS

1st Choice Plumbing Services Nw, 2 Buxton Street, Accrington, Lancashire, BB5 0SF Tel: (07947) 355964 E-mail: john23zx@aol.com

CLOTH CUTTING MACHINES

Scan Relation, 2 The Mews, 15a Liverpool Road, Southport, Merseyside, PR8 4AS Tel: (01704) 550500 Fax: (01704) 566958 E-mail: smithage@btinternet.com

CLOTH CUTTING SERVICES

T G Lewis Ltd, 15 Staveley Way, Brixworth Industrial Estate, Brixworth, Northampton, NN6 9EU Tel: (01604) 881966 Fax: (01604) 882318

CLOTH SAMPLE PINKING MACHINES

Allertex Ltd, Paradise Street, Bradford, West Yorkshire, BD1 2HP Tel: (01274) 723783 Fax: (01274) 728267 E-mail: info@allertex.co.uk

CLOTHES AIRER/DRYING EQUIPMENT

Hills Industries Ltd, Pontygwindy Industrial Estate, Caerphilly, Mid Glamorgan, CF83 3HU Tel: (029) 2088 3951 Fax: (029) 2088 6102 E-mail: info@hills-industries.co.uk

CLOTHES HANGERS

▶ Fashion Hangers Ltd, 15-19 Garman Road, London, N17 0UR Tel: (020) 8885 3055 Fax: (020) 8885 4426

CLOTHES LINES

Hills Industries Ltd, Pontygwindy Industrial Estate, Caerphilly, Mid Glamorgan, CF83 3HU Tel: (029) 2088 3951 Fax: (029) 2088 6102 E-mail: info@hills-industries.co.uk

James Lever & Sons Ltd, Unit 26 Orient Works Morris Green, Business Park Prescott, Bolton, BL3 3PE Tel: (01204) 658154 Fax: (01204) 658154 E-mail: sales@jameslever.co.uk

Spinnaker Products Ltd, Unit 15, Rylands Farm Industrial Estate, Bagley Road, Rockwell Grove, Wellington, Somerset, TA21 9PZ Tel: (01823) 400969 Fax: (01823) 665268

CLOTHING, *See also headings for particular types*

▶ A B Clothing Ltd, 63 Britannia Street, Leicester, LE1 3LE Tel: 0116-251 2518 Fax: 0116-251 2518

A & K Clothing (Derby) Ltd, 110A Porter Road, Derby, DE23 6RA Tel: (01332) 772795 Fax: (01332) 772794 E-mail: info@akclothing.com

A & K Fashions, 1 Stonehouse Street, Middlesbrough, Cleveland, TS5 6HR Tel: (01642) 850574 Fax: (01642) 850584

▶ A L M Ltd, Enterprise Unit 1 Maes Y Clawdd, Maesbury Road Industrial Estate, Oswestry, Shropshire, SY10 8NN Tel: (01691) 655940 Fax: (01691) 655940

A & M Mclellan Ltd, 94-96 Moorside Road, Swinton, Manchester, M27 0HJ Tel: 0161-794 1169 Fax: 0161-794 3733 E-mail: sales@mclellan-sport.co.uk

A M S Fabric Ltd, 53 Rolleston Street, Leicester, LE5 3SD Tel: 0116-274 0253 Fax: 0116-251 6865

A R F Trading Co., 104A Durham St, Rochdale, Lancashire, OL11 1LS Tel: (01706) 352144 Fax: (01706) 352144

A S Clothing, 3 Bayswater Crescent, Leeds, LS8 5QG Tel: 0113-240 4085

A & S GB Ltd, 130-132 Taunton Road, Ashton-under-Lyne, Lancashire, OL7 9EE Tel: 0161-330 9131 Fax: 0161-330 9131 E-mail: amjud@aol.com

Ace Sports & Ladyline, 49 Duke Street, Staveley, Staveley, Chesterfield, Derbyshire, S43 3PD Tel: (01246) 470650 Fax: (01246) 280473 E-mail: malc@ace-sports.freeserve.co.uk

Action Apparal Ltd, 62-63 Hemming Road, Washford, Redditch, Worcestershire, B98 0EA Tel: (01527) 510545 Fax: (01527) 510678 E-mail: alans@actionapparal.co.uk

Active Asian Suits, 420 Katherine Road, London, E7 8NP Tel: (020) 8471 1894 Fax: (020) 8470 0022 E-mail: activeasianssuits@aol.com

Advanced Clothing Co., Vantel House, Parkway South, Wheatley, Doncaster, South Yorkshire, DN2 4JR Tel: (01302) 320200

Afay Ltd, 6 Stoddart Street, South Shields, Tyne & Wear, NE34 0JT Tel: 0191-456 1253 Fax: 0191-454 2808

▶ Alex Scott & Co Kiltmakers Ltd, 43 Schoolhill, Aberdeen, AB10 1JT Tel: (01224) 643924 Fax: (01224) 626061 E-mail: sales@kiltmakers.co.uk

Alterlist Ltd, 32 Mason Street, Manchester, M4 5EY Tel: 0161-833 2723 Fax: 0161-833 2723

▶ Alternates Clothing Mnfrs, 80 Mary Street, Laurieston, Falkirk, FK2 9PS Tel: (01324) 633606 Fax: (01324) 633606

Amar Textiles, 105 Grange Street, Derby, DE23 8HD Tel: (01332) 365527 Fax: (01332) 731771

Amarenda Ltd, Unit 1A Green End Farm Business Unit, 93A Church Lane, Sarratt, Rickmansworth, Hertfordshire, WD3 6HH Tel: (01923) 291550 Fax: (01923) 291660 E-mail: enquiries@amarenda.co.uk

▶ Ambertex Ltd, 11 Parkhall Road, Walsall, WS5 3HF Tel: (01922) 620908 Fax: (01922) 620403 E-mail: sales@ambertex.com

▶ Ample Clothing Mnfrs, 15 Yorkshire Road, Leicester, LE4 6PH Tel: 0116-261 3052 Fax: 0116-261 3053

Analan Supplies Ltd, 62 High Street, Beighton, Sheffield, S20 1ED Tel: 0114-269 7060 Fax: 0114-254 8445 E-mail: analan@talk21.com

Anderson Apparel Ltd, Unit 4-5 Village Workshops, Pandy Road, Llanbrynmair, Powys, SY19 7AA Tel: (01650) 521880 Fax: (01650) 521880

▶ Anglo Sphere Ltd, 97 Commercial Road, London, E1 1RD Tel: (020) 7377 2111 Fax: (020) 7377 2999

Apri Ltd, 8-12 Orpheus Street, London, SE5 8RR Tel: (020) 7701 5494 Fax: (020) 7703 4223

Aquascutum International Ltd, Ibex House, 42-47 Minories, London, EC3N 1DY Tel: (020) 7675 9050 Fax: (020) 7675 9099 E-mail: john.harper@aquascutum.co.uk

Arcadia Group Ltd, Hudson Road, Leeds, LS9 7DN Tel: 0113-249 4949 Fax: 0113-380 6282

Aristec Ltd, 97 Hildyard Road, Leicester, LE4 5GG Tel: 0116-266 1707 Fax: 0116-266 1995 E-mail: aristec@fsnet.co.uk

▶ Arjun International, 36 Cobden Street, Leicester, LE1 2LB Tel: 0116-251 4100 Fax: 0116-251 8789 E-mail: sales@arjuninternational.co.uk

Arkay Clothing Ltd, 5 Easter Langlee Industrial Estate, Melrose Road, Galashiels, Selkirkshire, TD1 2UH Tel: (01896) 754933 Fax: (01896) 754932

Atlas Manufacturers, 61 High Street, West Bromwich, West Midlands, B70 6NZ Tel: 0121-553 7744 Fax: 0121-553 4774

Austin Reed Ltd, Station Road, Thirsk, North Yorkshire, YO7 1QH Tel: (01845) 573000 Fax: (01845) 525536 E-mail: sales@austinreed.co.uk

Aytans Manufacturing Co., 107-115 Whitechapel Road, London, E1 1DT Tel: (020) 7247 0089 Fax: (020) 7375 1837 E-mail: sales@aytans.com

B & B Knitwear Ltd, Westgate, Long Eaton, Nottingham, NG10 1EF Tel: 0115-972 2471 Fax: 0115-946 3815

B M B Menswear Ltd, Granary Buildings, Canal Wharf, Holbeck, Leeds, LS11 5BB Tel: 0113-259 5500 Fax: 0113-259 5512

Back To Fashion, 78 Katherine Rd, London, E6 1EN Tel: (020) 8470 0054 Fax: (020) 8470 0054

Bahadur Garments, 29 Wood Hill, Leicester, LE5 3SP Tel: 0116-251 3538 Fax: 0116-262 3423 E-mail: bahadurgarments@yahoo.com

Bains Fashions, 104 Bridge Road, Leicester, LE5 3LD Tel: 0116-276 1525 Fax: 0116-210 0562 E-mail: admin@ambni.co.uk

Be Textiles Ltd, 5 London Street, Leicester, LE5 3RL Tel: 0116-221 3300

Be That Body, Christs Hospital Sports Centre, Christs Hospital, Horsham, West Sussex, RH13 0YP Tel: (023) 8025 1125 E-mail: enquiries@bethatbody.com

Bella Moda, 48-66 Queensland Road, London, N7 7AS Tel: (020) 7609 2123 Fax: (020) 7609 1144

Ben Nevis Clothing, 237 Royal College Street, London, NW1 9LT Tel: (020) 7485 9989 Fax: (020) 7916 2324 E-mail: info@bennevisclothing.com

Big Boss (London) Ltd, 201 Whitechapel Road, London, E1 1DE Tel: (020) 7377 6068 Fax: (020) 7377 6068

Blind Date, 58 East Main Street, Whitburn, Bathgate, West Lothian, EH47 0RD Tel: (01501) 740166 Fax: (01501) 740166

▶ Blue Star Jeans Ltd, Chesterfield Road, Leicester, LE5 5LF Tel: 0116-273 3533

Body Casual UK Ltd, 76 Dorothy Road, Leicester, LE5 5DQ Tel: 0116-273 6776 Fax: 0116-273 6776

Breeze UK Ltd, 18 St. Pancras Way, London, NW1 0QG Tel: (020) 7383 2288 Fax: (020) 7383 2288 E-mail: reception@breezeuk.com

▶ Brennand Clothing Ltd, Halliwell Industrial Estate, Rossini Street, Bolton, BL1 8DL Tel: (01204) 493160 Fax: (01204) 493190

Brightwell Warehouse, 11 Barr Street, Birmingham, B19 3EH Tel: 0121-236 2112 Fax: 0121-236 2112 E-mail: manj97@hotmail.com

Brioni UK Ltd, 32 Britton Street, London, EC1M 5UH Tel: (020) 7491 7701 Fax: (020) 7491 7701

Oliver Brown, 75 Lower Sloane Street, London, SW1W 8DA Tel: (020) 7259 9494 Fax: (020) 7259 9444 E-mail: info@oliverbrown.org.uk

Burberry Ltd, Abergorki Industrial Estate, Ynyswen Road, Treorchy, Mid Glamorgan, CF42 6EF Tel: (01443) 772020 Fax: (01443) 775956 E-mail: info@burberry.com

Bush Baby Ltd, PO Box 61, Stockport, Cheshire, SK3 0AP Tel: 0161-474 7097 Fax: 0161-476 2647 E-mail: sales@bushbaby.com

C & L Products, Tall Trees, Lazenbys Estate, Walliswood, Dorking, Surrey, RH5 5RE Tel: (01306) 627721 Fax: (01306) 627721 E-mail: sales@c-lproducts.co.uk

J. Cainer & Sons (Bolton) Ltd, Knavebrook House, Morris Street, Radcliffe, Manchester, M26 2HF Tel: 0161-796 8444 Fax: 0161-796 1444

▶ Caledonia Textiles, Bridgeton Business Centre, 285 Abercromby Street, Glasgow, G40 2DD Tel: 0141-556 2705 Fax: 0141-564 5123

Captive Clothing Ltd, Great Titchfield House, 14-18 Great Titchfield Street, London, W1W 8BD Tel: (020) 7436 7744 Fax: (020) 7436 8500

Carryon Clothing Mnfrs, Ravenscroft, Stoney Lane, Urpeth, Stanley, County Durham, DH9 0SJ Tel: 0191-370 0250 Fax: 0191-370 1226 E-mail: sales@carryonclothing.co.uk

Catwalk Ltd, 69 St Barnabas Rd, Leicester, LE5 4BE Tel: 0116-246 1909 Fax: 0116-276 6403 E-mail: Office@catwalk.ltd.uk

Century Clothing, Swinburne Street, Nottingham, NG3 2GD Tel: 0115-950 4744 Fax: 0115-924 1896 E-mail: paul@centuryclothing.co.uk

Chana Garments Ltd, 169 Booth Street, Birmingham, B21 0NU Tel: 0121-551 1601 Fax: 0121-507 0471

F. Chand & Co. Ltd, 81 Rabone Lane, Smethwick, West Midlands, B66 3JH Tel: 0121-565 3959 Fax: 0121-565 3959

Chantelle Originals Ltd, 70 Elm Grove, Southsea, Hampshire, PO5 1LN Tel: (023) 9283 0273 Fax: (023) 9283 0273

Cheshire Bespoke, 1-2 Lancaster Fields, Crewe, CW1 6FF Tel: (01270) 587002 Fax: (01270) 216952

Chicago Clothing Co., 77 London Street, Leicester, LE5 3RW Tel: 0116-276 4004 Fax: 0116-276 4004

Chrisym Leisure Wear, Ferndale House, Mill Hill Road, Arnesby, Leicester, LE8 5WG Tel: 0116-247 8303 Fax: 0116-247 8303

Chrysalis Clothes Ltd, L Harlow House Shelton Road, Willowbrook East Industrial Estate, Corby, Northamptonshire, NN17 5XH Tel: (01536) 269034 Fax: (01536) 269034 E-mail: blackmor@btconnect.com

City Styles Leicester Ltd, 150 St Nicholas Circle, Leicester, LE1 4JJ Tel: 0116-251 5411

City Tayloring, 219 Bow Road, London, E3 2SJ Tel: (020) 8981 1450 Fax: (020) 8983 1728

Claire International Ltd, 29 The Bank, Barnard Castle, County Durham, DL12 8PL Tel: (01833) 637325 Fax: (01833) 690880

▶ Clan Albanach Kiltmakers, 24 High Street, South Queensferry, West Lothian, EH30 9PP Tel: 0131-331 2221 Fax: 0131-319 2221

Cliffridge Ltd, 83 Kempston Street, Liverpool, L3 8HE Tel: 0151-207 2770 Fax: 0151-207 2770

Club First Ltd, Unit 51, Milmead Industrial Centre, Mill Mead Road, London, N17 9QU Tel: (020) 8493 9611

Club Ties, Brook Street Studios, 60 Brook Street, Glasgow, G40 2AB Tel: 0141-554 3066 Fax: 0141-554 4581 E-mail: clubties@hotmail.com

Conquest Clothing Ltd, The Old Farm House, Amport, Andover, Hampshire, SP11 8JB Tel: (01264) 889566 Fax: (01264) 889371 E-mail: bob@conquestclothing.co.uk

Constitution Warehouse, 39-45 Constitution Hill, Birmingham, B19 3LE Tel: 0121-236 1910 Fax: 0121-236 6897

CLOTHING - *continued*

Corporate CMT Ltd, 59 Featherstone Lane, Featherstone, Pontefract, West Yorkshire, WF7 6LS Tel: (01977) 792226 Fax: (01977) 795536

▶ Corporate Image, 41-45 Richmond Terrace, Carmarthen, Dyfed, SA31 1HG Tel: (01267) 233737

Cotswold Collections, 15 King Street, Ludlow, Shropshire, SY8 1AQ Tel: (01584) 875612 Fax: (01584) 875998

Cover Up Clothing Ltd, 122-128 Arlington Road, London, NW1 7HP Tel: (020) 7267 9222 Fax: (020) 7267 8868

Crystal Ltd, Unit D Leswin Pl, London, N16 7NJ Tel: 020 72758322 Fax: 020 79231172

Culm Industrial Clothing, Saunders Way, Cullompton, Devon, EX15 1BS Tel: (01884) 32302 Fax: (01884) 38482

▶ Cyci Clothing Mnfrs, Southwick Place, London, W2 2TN Tel: (020) 7706 1020 Fax: (020) 7706 1040

D B Thomas & Son Ltd, 219 Bow Road, London, E3 2SJ Tel: (020) 8980 9743 Fax: (020) 8981 4979

D Gurteen & Sons Ltd, Chauntry Mills, Haverhill, Suffolk, CB9 8AZ Tel: (01440) 702601 Fax: (01440) 703394 E-mail: sales@gurteen.co.uk

D & M Fashions Scotland Ltd, Block 3 Units 1 & 2 Riverbank Industrial Estate, Ward Street, Alloa, Clackmannanshire, FK10 1ET Tel: (01259) 721400 Fax: (01259) 720170

D P S Birmingham Ltd, 46 Hallam Street, Birmingham, B12 9PS Tel: 0121-440 3203 Fax: 0121-440 5220

▶ D R Clothing, 17 Parkburn Court, Parkburn Industrial Estate, Hamilton, Lanarkshire, ML3 0QQ Tel: (01698) 712693 Fax: (01698) 712693

D R Garments Ltd, 39 Spalding Street, Leicester, LE5 4PH Tel: 0116-276 3550 Fax: 0116-276 3570 E-mail: dr@drgarments.com

D S Fashions, Units 8-9, Albert Road, Darlington, County Durham, DL1 2PD Tel: (01325) 357144 Fax: (01325) 357144

Daks Simpson Ltd, 10 Old Bond Street, London, W1S 4PL Tel: (020) 7409 4000 Fax: (020) 7499 4494

Daleswear, Dales Business Park, New Road, Ingleton, Carnforth, Lancashire, LA6 3HL Tel: (01524) 241477 Fax: (01524) 241047 E-mail: sales@daleswear.co.uk

Dallas Wear, 11 Vallance Road, London, E1 5HS Tel: (020) 7247 6435 Fax: (020) 7247 8824 E-mail: sales@dallsawear.com

T. Deas & Sons Ltd, 27-29 Wilder Street, Bristol, BS2 8QA Tel: 0117-924 6967

Dee Kay Knitwear, 227-229 Belgrave Gate, Leicester, LE1 3HT Tel: 0116-253 7560 Fax: 0116-253 7852

Deeny Manufacturing, 4 Arcadia Avenue, Sale, Cheshire, M33 3SA Tel: 0161-976 3976 Fax: (0161) 976397

Delta Textiles London Ltd, 4-10 North Road, London, N7 9EY Tel: (020) 7316 7200 Fax: (020) 7316 7276

▶ Desire, Whitehedge Road, Liverpool, L19 1RZ Tel: 0151-427 4002

Dewhirst Childrenswear Ltd, Amsterdam Road, Hull, HU7 0XF Tel: (01482) 835373 Fax: (01482) 824377

Dewhirst Group Ltd, Dewhirst House, Westgate, Driffield, North Humberside, YO25 6TH Tel: (01377) 252561 Fax: (01377) 253814 E-mail: technical.support@dewhirst.com

Dewhirst Group Ltd, Road Five, Winsford Industrial Estate, Winsford, Cheshire, CW7 3PN Tel: (01606) 555600 Fax: (01606) 555601 E-mail: linda.bradbury@dewhirst.com

DGS, 7 New Albion Estate, Halley Street, Glasgow, G13 4DJ Tel: 0141-941 3553 Fax: 0141-941 3777

▶ Diadora (UK) Ltd, Sovereign Court, King Edward Street, Macclesfield, Cheshire, SK10 1AA Tel: (01625) 421212

Diamond Styles, 13 Melton Street, Leicester, LE1 3NB Tel: 0116-251 2745 Fax: 0116-251 2745

▶ Dili, 2-4 Tottenham Road, London, N1 4BZ Tel: (020) 7923 4888

▶ Direct Fabrics, Rolleston Road, Skeffington, Leicester, LE7 9YD Tel: 0116-259 9700

Double K J Textiles Ltd, Cameron Road, Derby, DE23 8RT Tel: (01332) 773699 Fax: (01332) 773699

Douglas & Grahame UK Ltd, Shenstone Business Park, Lynn Lane, Shenstone, Lichfield, Staffordshire, WS14 0SB Tel: (0870) 8507777 Fax: (0870) 2077700

Dub Clothing Mnfrs, Thurland Chambers, 4-6 Thurland Street, Nottingham, NG1 3DR Tel: 0115-924 3166 Fax: 0115-924 3166 E-mail: sales@dubclothing.com

Dubb Bros Ltd, 121 Soho Hill, Birmingham, B19 1AX Tel: 0121-554 6492 Fax: 0121-554 6759

Dubb Fashions, 1-3 Rawlings Road, Smethwick, West Midlands, B67 5AD Tel: 0121-420 2707 Fax: 0121-434 4050

Duvatex Mytholmroyd Ltd, 8 Sunderland Street, Halifax, West Yorkshire, HX1 5AF Tel: (01422) 363534 Fax: (01422) 320335

Dynamic Fashion World, 2A Marlborough Road, Nuneaton, Warwickshire, CV11 5PG Tel: (024) 7664 2003 Fax: (024) 7664 2003 E-mail: razwan-amin@hotmail.com

E Felman Ltd, Barking Industrial Park, Alfreds Way, Barking, Essex, IG11 0TJ Tel: (020) 8594 0643 Fax: (020) 8594 0659

▶ E P Ltd, 86-88 Lower Lichfield Street, Willenhall, West Midlands, WV13 1QE Tel: (01902) 366533 Fax: (01902) 366550

E T H Ltd, 17 Pilrig Street, Edinburgh, EH6 5AN Tel: 0131-553 2721

Easyfeel Clothing Co., 7-9 Sebert Road, London, E7 0NG Tel: (020) 8522 0100 Fax: (020) 8522 1500 E-mail: easyfeel@mtlworld.com

Echo Ltd, 85 Greenwood Rd, London, E8 1NT Tel: 020 724 94796

▶ Ede & Ravenscoft, 9 Henry Crabb Road, Littleport, Ely, Cambridgeshire, CB6 1SE Tel: (01353) 862973 Fax: (01353) 863590

Elif Fashions Ltd, 2 Leswin Place, London, N16 7NJ Tel: (020) 7923 7469 Fax: (020) 7923 7469E-mail: enquiries@eliffashions.com

▶ Elljay Clothing Mnfrs, Unit 18 Enterprise Centre, Ray Street, Huddersfield, HD1 6BL Tel: (01484) 518488 Fax: (01484) 545422

▶ Equi Brief Ltd, Pinmore Mains, Pinmore, Girvan, Ayrshire, KA26 0TD Tel: (01465) 841161 Fax: (01465) 841161

▶ ETC Embroidery, Enterprise House, 94 David Street, Bridgeton, Glasgow, G40 2UH Tel: 0141-550 1188 Fax: 0141-550 2999

Eternal Clothing Ltd, 275a Ley Street, Ilford, Essex, IG1 4BN Tel: (020) 8514 3544 Fax: (020) 8514 1786 E-mail: ecuk@aol.com

Excalibur Textiles, Unit 3, 71-77 Stoney Stanton Road, Coventry, CV1 4FW Tel: (024) 7655 5330 Fax: (024) 7655 5360

Excel London, 6-16 Arbutus Street, London, E8 4DT Tel: (020) 7241 2100 Fax: (020) 7923 0098 E-mail: info@excellondon.co.uk

Expectations, 75 Great Eastern Street, London, EC2A 3RY Tel: (020) 7739 0292 Fax: (020) 7256 0910

F H Fashion, 2-6 Shaftesbury Rd, London, E7 8PD Tel: 020 84707215

F & W Manufacturing Co., 95-97 Wigmore Street, London, W1U 1QW Tel: (020) 7224 4882 Fax: (020) 7224 4032

▶ Fabricville Ltd, 83 Mortimer Street, London, W1W 7SL Tel: (020) 7636 2201 Fax: (020) 7631 5399

Faisaltex Ltd, Faisal House, 107-109 Fletcher Road, Preston, PR1 5JG Tel: (01772) 704440 Fax: (01772) 794837

Farfeild Clothing, Farfield Mill, Sedbergh, Cumbria, LA10 5LW Tel: (01539) 620169 Fax: (01539) 621716 E-mail: info@farfield.co.uk

Fashion Fair Ltd, Unit 2 Benson Street, Leicester, LE5 4HB Tel: 0116-273 0107 Fax: 0116-273 3837 E-mail: fashionfairltd@yahoo.co.uk

Fashion Rate Int Ltd, 1 Salisbury St, Wolverhampton, WV3 0BG Tel: (01902) 313679 Fax: (01902) 713877

▶ Fashion Trend Wolverhampton Ltd, Kalair Court, Marston Road, Wolverhampton, WV2 4NJ Tel: (01902) 426900 Fax: (01902) 426900

Fashion Warehouse, 64 Whitechapel High Street, London, E1 7PL Tel: (020) 7247 4595 Fax: (020) 7247 4596

Fashion Wear Manufacturers Ltd, 135 Gipsy Lane, Leicester, LE4 6RH Tel: 0116-261 1122 Fax: 0116-261 1133 E-mail: enquiries@jeanmaker.co.uk

Fashionstop Ltd, Unit 1 Redcross Mill, Redcross Street, Rochdale, Lancashire, OL12 0NZ Tel: (01706) 525304 Fax: (01706) 658983

Feline Ltd, 48 Lord Street, Cheetham, Manchester, M3 1HN Tel: 0161-819 2717 Fax: 0161-819 2695

Femme Top Dezigne, 117 Asfordby Street, Leicester, LE5 3QF Tel: 0116-253 0130 Fax: 0116-253 0130

Findhorn Supplies, 106 Findhorn Street, Dundee, DD4 9PN Tel: (01382) 509381 Fax: (01382) 509381

▶ Finesse Ltd, 7 St. Pancras Commercial Centre, Pratt Street, London, NW1 0BY Tel: (020) 7485 7766 Fax: (020) 7485 7799

Firstneat Ltd, 99 Mabgate, Leeds, LS9 7DR Tel: 0113-245 4039 Fax: 0113-245 4039

▶ The Five Star Knitwear (UK) Ltd, Majid House, 49 Devonshire St North, Manchester, M12 6JR Tel: 0161-273 6009

▶ Flaxstyle Factory Outlet, Tariff Road, London, N17 0DY Tel: (020) 8808 4088 Fax: (020) 8885 3319 E-mail: info@flaxstyle.co.uk

Flint Casual Wear, Amundsen House, Hinckley, Leicestershire, LE10 0DP Tel: (01455) 633937 Fax: (01455) 890464

Forest Countrywear, 3 High Street, Fordingbridge, Hampshire, SP6 1AS Tel: (01425) 655393 Fax: (01425) 655393 E-mail: sue@forestsaddlery.freeserve.co.uk

Frillies Ltd, First Floor Shell Leyland, Wigan Road, Leyland, PR25 5UD Tel: (01772) 621037 Fax: (01772) 621037

Fudge Jeans Ltd, Queens Mill, Queen Street, Ossett, West Yorkshire, WF5 8AW Tel: (01924) 263391 Fax: (01924) 278419

Future Leisure, Napier Works Spencer Park, Greasbrough Street, Rotherham, South Yorkshire, S60 1RF Tel: (01709) 360359 Fax: (01709) 360359

▶ Fyfe & Allan, 90-96 Dykehead Street, Glasgow, G33 4AQ Tel: 0141-774 5900 Fax: 0141-774 7360

G D S Shirts, 4 Barrock Street, Thurso, Caithness, KW14 7DB Tel: (01847) 893197 Fax: (01847) 893197

G G S Fashions Ltd, 50 Lamb Lane, London, E8 3PJ Tel: (020) 7923 1911 Fax: (020) 7254 3052

G K Fashions, Bingley Street, Wolverhampton, WV3 0HS Tel: (01902) 426255 Fax: (01902) 426281

▶ G N Clothing Ltd, 27, Eldon Street, Walsall, WS1 2JP Tel: (01922) 644748 Fax: (01922) 720702

Galaxy Manufacturing Co., 59 Mere Lane, Rochdale, Lancashire, OL11 3TD Tel: (01706) 642575 Fax: (01706) 642517

▶ The Gap, 167-201 Argyle Street, Glasgow, G2 8DJ Tel: 0141-221 0629

▶ Gateline Clothing Mnfrs, 6 2 Overbury Road, London, N15 6RH Tel: (020) 8809 2065 Fax: (020) 8809 7786 E-mail: gateline@hotmail.com

Gee, 138 Richmond Road, Kingston upon Thames, Surrey, KT2 5EZ Tel: (020) 8546 4453 Fax: (020) 8546 2057 E-mail: drewgoater@hotmail.co.uk

Jay Gee Clothing, Melbourne Works, Melbourne Street, Hebden Bridge, West Yorkshire, HX7 6AS Tel: (01422) 845292

Geminique Children & Babywear, 1 Small Business Centre, Penmaen Road, Pontllanfraith, Blackwood, Gwent, NP12 2DZ Tel: (01495) 229969 Fax: (01495) 229969

Gems, 51 Spring Rd, Kempston, Bedford, MK42 8LS Tel: 01234 351186 Fax: 01234 351186

▶ Gilbey Fashions Ltd, 19-21 Great Portland Street, London, W1W 8QB Tel: (020) 7436 3677 Fax: (020) 7436 7006

Glengarnock Garments Ltd, Unit 1-4 Block 3, River Place, Kilbirnie, Ayrshire, KA25 7EN Tel: (01505) 682759 Fax: (01505) 683105 E-mail: sales@glengarnock.com

Glenshane Fashions, 6 Victoria Road, Londonderry, BT47 2AB Tel: (028) 7131 2343 Fax: (028) 7131 2307 E-mail: info@glenshanefashions.com

Go Beyond, Oxford Street, Castleford, West Yorkshire, WF10 5RQ Tel: (01977) 710222 Fax: (01977) 710255 E-mail: sales@gobeyond.co.uk

G.D. Golding Ltd, 220 Hatfield Road, St. Albans, Hertfordshire, AL1 4LW Tel: (01727) 841321 Fax: (01727) 831462 E-mail: tailors@goldings.co.uk

Gradel Line, 39 Bavaria Road, London, N19 4EU Tel: (020) 7281 7674 E-mail: gradeline@btclick.com

H F Creation International Ltd, B6 Bordesley Green Road, Birmingham, B9 4TA Tel: 0121-766 8288 Fax: 0121-773 2944 E-mail: info@paul-andrew.com

H M Clothing Co., Sycamore House, Crawford Street, Rochdale, Lancashire, OL16 5RS Tel: (01706) 715512 Fax: (01706) 715512

Harrison Direct Ltd, 152 Castleford Road, Normanton, West Yorkshire, WF6 2EP Tel: (01924) 895598 Fax: (01924) 895077

Harrison-field Ltd, Martyn Street, Airdrie, Lanarkshire, ML6 9AU Tel: (01236) 747771 Fax: (01236) 766880

Harry G Smith Ltd, PO Box 89, Aberdeen, AB12 3DA Tel: (01224) 897044 Fax: (01224) 894648 E-mail: office@harrygsmith.co.uk

▶ Hebei Light (UK) Ltd, 38 Appledore Avenue, South Ruislip, Ruislip, Middlesex, HA4 0UU Tel: (020) 8841 8291 Fax: (020) 8831 4615 E-mail: heli.uk@btinternet.com

J. & N. Herz Ltd, Broadstone House, Broadstone Road, Reddish, Stockport, Cheshire, SK5 7DL Tel: 0161-443 3030 Fax: 0161-443 0345 E-mail: jherz@herz.co.uk

▶ Highland Dress Hire, 39, Scotland Way,, Horsforth, Leeds, LS18 5SQ Tel: 0113 2280146 Fax: 0113 3682650 E-mail: john@highlandhire.co.uk

▶ Highlandwear Direct, 4-9 Huntly Street, Inverness, IV3 5PR Tel: (01463) 229200 Fax: (01463) 229201 E-mail: sales@highlandweardirect.com

Adam Hill Ltd, Union St, Lurgan, Craigavon, Co. Armagh, BT66 8EG Tel: (028) 3831 6158 Fax: (028) 3832 1354

▶ Hobby Casuals, The Sanderson Centre, Lees Lane, Gosport, Hampshire, PO12 3UL Tel: (023) 9258 3826 Fax: (023) 9251 0287

Brian Holden Ltd, 14 Racca Green, Knottingley, West Yorkshire, WF11 8AT Tel: (01977) 672791 Fax: (01977) 672791

▶ Hollyoak Clothing Ltd, Abbey Park Street, Leicester, LE4 5AF Tel: 0116-251 2410 Fax: 0116-233 2225

▶ Kerry Hope, 3 Amhurst Terrace, London, E8 2BT Tel: (020) 7254 3322 Fax: (020) 7254 3354 E-mail: sales@kerryhope.co.uk

▶ House Of Creation, 97 Hildyard Road, Leicester, LE4 5GG Tel: 0116-261 2805

▶ Hucke Ltd, Berners House, 47-48 Berners Street, London, W1T 3NF Tel: (020) 7580 7890 Fax: (020) 7580 7442 E-mail: sales@hucke.com

Humphreys & Sons Ltd, Newton Lane, Wigston, Leicestershire, LE18 3SG Tel: 0116-288 1105 Fax: 0116-288 0661 E-mail: ian@europasports.co.uk

I C E Sportswear, 145 Ryhope Road, Sunderland, SR2 7UG Tel: 0191-565 8387 Fax: 0191-565 8387

I J Textiles (Clothing Manufacturers), 229 Westminster Road, Handsworth, Birmingham, B20 3NB Tel: 0121-356 3860 Fax: 0121-356 4864

I & S Fashions Ltd, 5 Vine Court, London, E1 1JH Tel: (020) 7247 9526 Fax: (020) 7377 8853

Ibrahim & Sons Ltd, 313-319 Katherine Road, London, E7 8PJ Tel: (020) 8471 4051 Fax: (020) 8552 4375

▶ Ice Fashions Ltd, 32-34 Great Titchfield Street, London, W1W 8BG Tel: (020) 7436 1022 Fax: (020) 7436 1077

Ilasco Ltd, 52-53 Nasmyth Road, Southfield Industrial Estate, Glenrothes, Fife, KY6 2SD Tel: (01592) 771241 Fax: (01592) 771071 E-mail: sales@ardmel-group.co.uk

Imani Clothing Ltd, 15 Chatley Street, Manchester, M3 1HU Tel: 0161-834 3367 Fax: 0161-833 0490

Imperial Garments, 22 Victoria Road, Aston, Birmingham, B6 5HA Tel: 0121-554 0416 Fax: 0121-554 3691 E-mail: sschowlia@aol.com

Indialinks Fashion Shops, 317 Regent Street, London, W1B 2HT Tel: (020) 7637 1070

Innocence Clothing Ltd, 103 Wantz Road, Dagenham, Essex, RM10 8PS Tel: (020) 8593 0593 Fax: (020) 8593 0587 E-mail: info@innocenceclothing.com

Island Clothing, 41-43 Western Boulevard, Leicester, LE2 7HN Tel: 0116-275 6444 Fax: 0116-275 6333

J & B Theatrical UK Ltd, Unit 26, Kansas Ave, Salford, M50 2GL Tel: (07765) 108857 E-mail: jamesjandb@aol.com

▶ J J Clothing Ltd, 219 Western Road, Leicester, LE3 0EA Tel: 0116-275 6252

J & J Screen Printing, 16 High Street, Stanstead Abbotts, Ware, Hertfordshire, SG12 8AE Tel: (01920) 872284

J & M Sewing Services, 1 Charlotte Square, Newcastle upon Tyne, NE1 4XF Tel: 0191-232 9589 Fax: 0191-230 1215 E-mail: jandmsewing@btconnect.com

J P Casuals, 1 Singers Yard, Torquay Road, Paignton, Devon, TQ3 2AH Tel: (01803) 666662 Fax: (01803) 666662

J P L Clothing Ltd, Victoria Street, Darwen, Lancashire, BB3 3HB Tel: (01254) 873922 Fax: (01254) 762362

J Stott & Son Ltd, 56 Tontine Street, Blackburn, BB1 7ED Tel: (01254) 56616 Fax: (01254) 662780 E-mail: tony@stotts.fsbusiness.co.uk

▶ Jacques Vert (Retail) Ltd, Webber Pavilion, Seaham Grange Industrial Estat, Seaham, County Durham, SR7 0PZ Tel: 0191-521 3555

Jammy Kids, Roseville House, Roseville Road, Leeds, LS7 1BQ Tel: 0113-244 6780 Fax: 0113-244 6780

Janal Bindings, Unit 11 Mahal Business Centre, 270 St. Saviours Road, Leicester, LE5 4HG Tel: 0116-273 1155

K E M Fashions, 71-73 Powerscroft Road, London, E5 0PT Tel: (020) 8985 9387 Fax: (020) 8985 9387

Kandel & Jacobs Ltd, Water Street, Northwich, Cheshire, CW9 5HP Tel: (01606) 43105 Fax: (01606) 40063 E-mail: kandel.jacobs@btopenworld.com

Katz & Co. (Folkestone) Ltd, 331-333 Cheriton Road, Folkestone, Kent, CT19 4BQ Tel: (01303) 271001 Fax: (01303) 279959 E-mail: sales@katzltd.com

▶ Keela (International) Ltd, 53 Nasmyth Road, Glenrothes, Fife, KY6 2SD Tel: (01592) 771241

▶ Khan Fashion Studio, Unit 4, 344-346 St. Saviours Road, Leicester, LE5 4HJ Tel: 0116-273 6882 Fax: 0116-273 6882

Kilgour, 7-8 Savile Row, London, W1S 3PE Tel: (020) 7734 6905 Fax: (020) 7287 8147 E-mail: kilgour@8savilerow.com

Kiltex Fashions Ltd, Rear Of 72 Queen St, Maidenhead, Berks, SL6 1HY Tel: (01628) 673367 Fax: (01753) 868608

Kindplace Ltd, 45 Fitzroy Street, London, W1T 6DY Tel: (020) 7383 7277 Fax: (020) 7388 7227

Kinloch Anderson Ltd, 4 Dock Street, Leith, Edinburgh, EH6 6EY Tel: 0131-555 1355 Fax: 0131-555 1392 E-mail: enquiries@kinlochanderson.com

▶ Klew Gets Wed, Unit 3, Millbrook Business Park Hoe Lane, Nazeing, Waltham Abbey, Essex, EN9 2RJ Tel: (01992) 890378 Fax: 01992 890378 E-mail: info@klew.co.uk

Kruger Tissue Industrial Division, Penygroes Industrial Estate, Penygroes, Caernarfon, Gwynedd, LL54 6DB Tel: (01286) 880969 Fax: (01286) 880026

Lady 1, 154 West Green Road, London, N15 5AE Tel: (020) 8802 3201 E-mail: sales@try1clothing.co.uk

▶ Lager, Holywell House, Parsons Lane, Hinckley, Leicestershire, LE10 1XT Tel: (01455) 238725

Lal & Co. (Glasgow), Laltex House, 12-18 Coburg Street, Glasgow, G5 9JF Tel: 0141-429 0935 Fax: 0141-429 8036

▶ Lambton Tailoring, Unit 25g Springfield Commercial Centre, Bagley Lane, Farsley, Pudsey, West Yorkshire, LS28 5LY Tel: 0113-257 0841 Fax: 0113-239 4472

▶ lastseason.com, 12 Myton Crescent, Warwick, CV34 6QA Tel: (01926) 313175 E-mail: info@lastseason.com

Lawrayne Clothing Mnfrs, 13 Lockett Street, Manchester, M8 8EE Tel: 0161-839 1084 Fax: 0161-839 1084

Leading Labels Ltd, 1 Main Street, Alexandria, Dunbartonshire, G83 0UG Tel: (01389) 607101 Fax: (01389) 607104

Leaf Clothing, 1 Niphon Works, 43-68 Lower Villiers Street, Wolverhampton, WV2 4NA Tel: (01902) 427946

Linkhill Marketing Ltd, 4 The Linen House, 253 Kilburn Lane, London, W10 4BQ Tel: (020) 8964 3990 Fax: (020) 8964 3910 E-mail: sales@uniformsjohnmarks.com

Little Miss Clothing, Unit 1 Church Street, Moxley, Wednesbury, West Midlands, WS10 8RD Tel: 0121-556 4870 Fax: 0121-556 2259

Lovell Sport Ltd, Unit 3 Alvis Court, Billingham, Cleveland, TS23 4JG Tel: (01642) 566444 Fax: (01642) 651022

CLOTHING - *continued*

Lynton Clothes (1997) Ltd, Unit 1, Camart House, 15-19 Cowper Road, Leeds, LS9 7HR Tel: 0113-248 2111 Fax: 0113-248 1137

M B M Clothing Ltd, 90 Freer Road, Aston, Birmingham, B6 6NB Tel: 0121-554 7522 Fax: 0121-554 7522

M I G Pattern Cutting Services Ltd, 3 D Mackenzie Road, London, N7 8QZ Tel: (020) 7700 6164 Fax: (020) 7700 6687 E-mail: sales@migpatterncutting.com

▶ M W T International Ltd, Great North Way, York, YO26 6RB Tel: (01904) 789880 Fax: (01904) 693192 E-mail: sales@mwtsafestyle.co.uk

▶ Mcgregor International Ltd, 12 Oakfield House, Oakfield Road, Altrincham, Cheshire, WA15 8EW Tel: 0161-942 4800 Fax: 0161-942 4808 E-mail: office@mcgregor-mc.co.uk

Magee Clothing Ltd, Unit 5-25 Woodside Road Industrial Estate, Woodside Road, Ballymena, County Antrim, BT42 4QJ Tel: (028) 2564 6211 Fax: (028) 2564 5111 E-mail: mageesales@aol.com

▶ Maggie Carol Ltd, Unit 1 & 2, Fallbarn Road, Rossendale, Lancashire, BB4 7NT Tel: (01706) 228879

Magill Menswear, 45 Ashgrove Road, Newry, County Down, BT34 1QN Tel: (028) 3026 1311 Fax: (028) 3026 2930 E-mail: magillgroup@btconnect.com

Malhi Trimmings Ltd, Excelda Works, 36 Rookery Road, Handsworth, Birmingham, B21 9NB Tel: (0121) 554 5731 Fax: (0121) 554 5733 E-mail: sales@mahligroup.co.uk

Manhattan Design Studio, 25a Harrington Street, Pear Tree, Derby, DE23 8PE Tel: (01332) 776464 Fax: (01332) 776464

Maple Leaf Design Ltd, 4 Queen Street, Leicester, LE1 1QW Tel: 0116-262 6326 Fax: 0116-222 8919

▶ Mardale Clothing Ltd, Unit 101 Oystons Mill, Strand Road, Preston, PR1 8UR Tel: (01772) 722513 Fax: (01772) 726715 E-mail: sales@mardale.com

▶ Mary Ann, Acton Place Industrial Estate, Melford Road, Acton, Sudbury, Suffolk, CO10 0BB Tel: (01787) 377978

Matglobe Ltd, 7-9 Davenant Street, London, E1 5NB Tel: (020) 7375 2877 Fax: (020) 7479 9414

Matric Services & Supplies Ltd, Unit 25-26 Essington Light Industrial Estate, Bognop Road, Essington, Wolverhampton, WV11 2BJ Tel: (01922) 479132 Fax: (01922) 494450 E-mail: matric@amserve.com

▶ Mayor's Sportswear & Menswear, 1606 Dumbarton Road, Glasgow, G14 9DB Tel: 0141-959 0959 Fax: 0141-959 0959

Melson And Co, 125 High St, West Bromwich, W. Midlands, B70 6NY Tel: 0121-525 2226 Fax: 0121-525 2226

Mem Saab World Of Fabric, 89 Erleigh Road, Reading, RG1 5NN Tel: 0118-966 6037

Mileta Sports Ltd, Spen Vale Mills, Spen Vale Street, Heckmondwike, West Yorkshire, WF16 0NQ Tel: (01924) 409311 Fax: (01924) 409839 E-mail: email@tog24.com

Mill Shop Ltd, Tynwald Mills, St. Johns, Isle of Man, IM4 3AD Tel: (01624) 801213 Fax: (01624) 801893 E-mail: bobjeavons@manx.net

Mizzy's Sports, 10 Hall Road West, Liverpool, L23 8SY Tel: 0151-931 4955 Fax: 0151-931 5818 E-mail: mizzyssports2002@yahoo.co.uk

▶ Moette Leisurewear Ltd, The Old Chapel, Quebec Street, Langley Park, Durham, DH7 9XA Tel: 0191-373 5995 Fax: 0191-373 6318 E-mail: mail@moette.co.uk

Moneymore Manufacturing Co. Ltd, 7 Smith Street, Moneymore, Magherafelt, County Londonderry, BT45 7PF Tel: (028) 8674 7177 Fax: (028) 8674 7077

Morglam Ltd, Burley Mills, 3 Navigation Street, Leicester, LE1 3UR Tel: 0116-299 2209 E-mail: alexmaher@morglam.com

Muddy Puddles Ltd, Hingston Farm, Bigbury, Kingsbridge, Devon, TQ7 4BE Tel: (0870) 4204950 Fax: (0870) 4204943 E-mail: help@muddypuddles.com

Murray, Castle Court, Bodmin Road, Coventry, CV2 5DB Tel: (024) 7658 7980 Fax: (024) 7658 7981 E-mail: jheadley@jheadley.co.uk

Myers & Myers Imports Ltd, 35 Ringley Road, Whitefield, Manchester, M45 7LD Tel: 0161-798 9004 Fax: 0161-773 9700

N A K Trading Co. Ltd, 153 Dukes Rd, Western Ave, Park Royal, London, W3 0SL Tel: (020) 8752 1815 Fax: (020) 8752 1878

N F R Racewear, 15 Water Street, Radcliffe, Manchester, M26 3DE Tel: 0161-723 4012 Fax: 0161-280 9949 E-mail: sales@nfrlivethedream.co.uk

Nagra Bros, 149 Harrison Road, Leicester, LE4 6NP Tel: 0116-261 0511 Fax: 0116-261 1697

▶ Nalli Ltd, 281 Kings Road, London, SW3 5EW Tel: (020) 7351 5292

Nater Leisurewear, Goodsmoor Road, Littleover, Derby, DE23 1NH Tel: (01332) 770554 Fax: (01332) 271201 E-mail: info@nater.co.uk

Naughty Holdings Ltd, 5th Floor, 19-20 Berners Street, London, W1T 3LW Tel: (020) 7323 2222 Fax: (020) 7436 8835 E-mail: fashion@naughty.co.uk

▶ New Meuro Design, 99 Bridge Road, Leicester, LE5 3LD Tel: 0116-276 8988 Fax: 0116-276 8988

Newrooss Impex Ltd, New Skopes House, 2 Cross Green Garth, Cross Green Industrial Estate, Leeds, LS9 0SF Tel: 0113-240 2211 Fax: 0113-248 9544 E-mail: sales@skopes.com

▶ Newstar Clothing Services, Newstar House, Salmon Street, Preston, PR1 4BQ Tel: (01772) 558862 Fax: (01772) 558879 E-mail: sales@newstarjeans.co.uk

Newton Sports Ltd, Hill St Works, Hill Street, Hyde, Cheshire, SK14 5RL Tel: 0161-368 0707 Fax: 0161-368 4222 E-mail: sales@newtonsports.co.uk

Northern Mens & Boyswear Ltd, 52 Lower Oxford Street, Castleford, West Yorkshire, WF10 4AF Tel: (01977) 556203 Fax: (01977) 556203

▶ Nurse Care Uniform Co. Ltd, Lime Street, Southampton, SO14 3DA Tel: (023) 8022 5335 Fax: (023) 8032 2169

Oaktarget Ltd, 33 Kitchener Road, Leicester, LE5 4AU Tel: 0116-274 0304 Fax: 0116-276 7782 E-mail: sales@oaktarget.com

▶ Offshoot Clothing Ltd, Offshoot House, 68 The Grove, Ilkley, West Yorkshire, LS29 9PA Tel: (01943) 817650 Fax: (01943) 817660 E-mail: info@offshoot.co.uk

Omar Trading Co., West Street, Rochdale, Lancashire, OL16 2EN Tel: (01706) 344273 Fax: (01706) 715136

Orbit International P.L.C., Orbit House, 5 Dugdale Street, Birmingham, B18 4JA Tel: 0121-558 8444 Fax: 0121-565 0385 E-mail: sales@orbit-int.co.uk

▶ Orchid Bridals, Britannia Buildings, Coventry Road, Burbage, Hinckley, Leicestershire, LE10 2HL Tel: (01455) 230033 Fax: (01455) 230035 E-mail: sales@orchidbrides.com

Original Blues Clothing Co. Ltd, Enterprise House, 133 Blyth Road, Hayes, Middlesex, UB3 1DD Tel: (020) 8813 7766 Fax: (020) 8813 7811 E-mail: sales@original-blues.com

Orions Fashions, 1 Castlefield Street, Stoke-on-Trent, ST4 7AQ Tel: (01782) 287779 Fax: (01782) 201850

Outdoor Group Ltd, Mansard Close, Westgate Industrial Estate, Northampton, NN5 5DL Tel: (01604) 441111 Fax: (01604) 441164 E-mail: enquiries@blacks.co.uk

Oxford Fashions, 143 Oxford Street, Glasgow, G5 9JE Tel: 0141-429 4291 Fax: 0141-429 4291

P + B Gora Ltd, 119 Oak Road, West Bromwich, West Midlands, B70 8HP Tel: 0121-580 4984 Fax: 0121-525 8742

P D P Associates Ltd, 23 Darlington Rd, Stockton-on-Tees, Cleveland, TS18 5BL Tel: (01642) 657010

P & P Clothing, Old Mill La Industrial Estate, Mansfield Woodhouse, Mansfield, Nottinghamshire, NG19 9BG Tel: (01623) 422044 Fax: (01623) 424557 E-mail: sales@pandp.force9.co.uk

P R Textiles, 31-32 Cliveland Street, Birmingham, B19 3SH Tel: 0121-359 2741 Fax: 0121-333 3600

P S Gill & Sons, 261-277 Rookery Road, Handsworth, Birmingham, B21 9PT Tel: 0121-554 7521 Fax: 0121-554 9033 E-mail: ssgill@psgill.com

▶ Paramo Ltd, Durgates Industrial Estate, Durgates, Wadhurst, East Sussex, TN5 6DF Tel: (01892) 786444 Fax: (01892) 784961

▶ Parmar Clothing, 9 Wanlip Street, Leicester, LE1 2JS Tel: 0116-251 5820

Patrol Jeanswear Ltd, Unit 4, Campbell St, Preston, PR1 5LX Tel: (01772) 653523 Fax: (01772) 655377

Permess UK Ltd, Low Prudhoe Industrial Estate, Prudhoe, Northumberland, NE42 6HD Tel: (01661) 832774 Fax: (01661) 832633 E-mail: sales@tencate.co.uk

Perry Ellis Europe Ltd, Crittall Road, Witham, Essex, CM8 3DJ Tel: (01376) 502345 Fax: (01376) 500733 E-mail: custserv@farah.co.uk

Petra Style Ltd, 10a Gourley St, London, N15 5NG Tel: 020 88026665 Fax: 020 88021999

▶ Pheonix Clothing, Unit E Lower Parliament Street, Nottingham, NG1 3BB Tel: 0115-959 9944 Fax: 0115-911 5345 E-mail: pheonixclothing@hotmail.com

Phoenix Casuals Ltd, Deltex, Flathouse Rd, Portsmouth, PO1 4QS Tel: 023 92877715 Fax: 023 92877715

Planet Processing Ltd, 24 Fairfax Road, Heathfield Industrial Estate, Newton Abbot, Devon, TQ12 6UD Tel: (01626) 832229 Fax: (01626) 835559 E-mail: sales@planetprocessing.com

▶ Polaris Apparel Ltd, Business Park, Station Road, Bolsover, Chesterfield, Derbyshire, S44 6BH Tel: (01246) 240218 Fax: (01246) 241560

Portwest Clothing Ltd, Fields End Business Park, Thurnscoe, Rotherham, South Yorkshire, S63 0JF Tel: (01709) 894575 Fax: (01709) 880830 E-mail: orders@portwest.com

▶ Positive Clothing London Ltd, 20 Wells Mews, London, W1T 3HQ Tel: (020) 7299 3500 Fax: (020) 7299 3518

▶ Premier Drapers, 28 Linden Street, Leicester, LE5 5EE Tel: 0116-249 0043 Fax: 0116-249 0070

Premier World Trading Ltd, Raintex House, Smethwick, West Midlands, B66 2AA Tel: 0121-555 6479 Fax: 0121-555 6532 E-mail: sales@pwtltd.co.uk

Prince Manufacturing Co., Pool Street, Wolverhampton, WV2 4HN Tel: (01902) 714895 Fax: (01902) 714895

Qmec Ltd, Quarry Road, Bolsover, Chesterfield, Derbyshire, S44 6NT Tel: (01246) 822228 Fax: (01246) 827907

Quality Clothing Industry, Threadsneedel House, 27 Copdale Road, Leicester, LE5 4FG Tel: 0116-273 0194 Fax: 0116-273 0199 E-mail: sales@quality-clothing.co.uk

Quantum Clothing, North Street, Huthwaite, Sutton-in-Ashfield, Nottinghamshire, NG17 2PE Tel: (01623) 447200 Fax: (01623) 447201 E-mail: K.Orward@quantumclothing.com

Quara Sportswear, The Old Smithy, Bethel, Caernarfon, Gwynedd, LL55 1UW Tel: (01248) 671114 Fax: (01248) 671049

▶ R Cundle, 12 Whinbrook Crescent, Leeds, LS17 5PN Tel: 0113-288 8390 Fax: 0113-288 8390

R JS, 134 High Street, Sheerness, Kent, ME12 1UB Tel: (01795) 660134 Fax: (01795) 427348

▶ R & O Textiles, Unit 1 Frederick Street, Walsall, WS2 9NJ Tel: (01922) 613183 Fax: (01922) 613183

Rab Down Equipment, 32 Edward Street, Sheffield, S3 7GB Tel: 0114-275 7544 Fax: 0114-278 0584E-mail: sales@rab.uk.com

J.T. Raca International Ltd, 92-100 Earl Street, Northampton, NN1 3AX Tel: (01604) 230808 Fax: (01604) 620866 E-mail: info@jtraca.com

▶ Rair International Ltd, 2 Brougham Street, Leicester, LE1 2BA Tel: 0116-253 3078 Fax: 0116-253 3078

▶ Rawhide Corsets, Unit 209 The Custard Factory, Gibb Street, Birmingham, B9 4AA Tel: 0121-608 1220 E-mail: sales@rawhidecorsets.co.uk

▶ Real Clothing Co. Ltd, Unit 19 Lockwood Industrial Park, Mill Mead Road, London, N17 9QP Tel: (020) 8885 9500 Fax: (020) 8365 1926

Redgold Fashions Ltd, 219-221 Bow Road, London, E3 2SJ Tel: (020) 8980 9745 Fax: (020) 8980 4979

J.M. Reed & Co. Ltd, Kingsbury Episcopi, Martock, Somerset, TA12 6BD Tel: (01935) 822505 Fax: (01935) 823971 E-mail: dms@southcombe.com

▶ Reflex International Ltd, 1 Butchers Road, London, E16 1PH Tel: (020) 7511 4541 Fax: (020) 7474 6861 E-mail: ian@reflexinternational.com

Reliance Fashions, Duncrue Cresent, Belfast, BT3 9BW Tel: (028) 9077 6848 Fax: (028) 9077 6848

Rella Ltd, Unit 2 Silver Indust Est, Reform Row, London, N17 9SZ Tel: 020 88855517 Fax: 020 88852037

Resources Computer Support Ltd, Norwich Road, Attleborough, Norfolk, NR17 2JX Tel: (01953) 457977 Fax: (01953) 457978

Rhodi plc, 1 Fishwick Park, Mercer Street, Preston, PR1 4LZ Tel: (01772) 562288 Fax: (01772) 562277 E-mail: fp@rhodiplc.co.uk

▶ Rikz International, Kierbeck Business Complex, North Woolwich Road, London, E16 2BG Tel: (020) 7474 7526 Fax: (020) 7474 7526

▶ Rimtex Ltd, 8-9 Lawson Street, North Shields, Tyne & Wear, NE29 6TF Tel: 0191-257 6400 Fax: 0191-259 5006 E-mail: scottmack@btconnect.com

Ringtag International, 50 Whitehall Street, Rochdale, Lancashire, OL12 0LN Tel: (01706) 354854 Fax: (01706) 712181 E-mail: ring_tag@onetel.com

River Stone Clothing, 44 River St, Birmingham, B5 5SA Tel: 0121-766 8921

▶ Rmuk Ltd, 100 Morgan Close, Willenhall, West Midlands, WV12 4LH Tel: (01902) 602333 Fax: (01902) 602335

Roberto Group, Limestone Road, Nantyglo, Ebbw Vale, Gwent, NP23 4ND Tel: (01495) 310798 Fax: (01495) 313320 E-mail: keri.davis@robertogroup.co.uk

Richard Roberts Fashion Ltd, 59 Clarke Road, Northampton, NN1 4PL Tel: (01604) 627126 Fax: (01604) 259831

Robin Hood Clothing Ltd, 9 Riverside Business Park, Lyon Road, London, SW19 2RL Tel: (020) 8544 9977 Fax: (020) 8544 9979 E-mail: ssk@dircon.co.uk

Romantica Of Devon Ltd, 37 West St, Witheridge, Tiverton, Devon, EX16 8AA Tel: (01884) 860728 Fax: (01884) 860458 E-mail: enquiries@romanticaofdevon.co.uk

Romeo Trading Company Ltd, Romeo House, 160 Bridport Road, London, N18 1SY Tel: (020) 8803 0066 Fax: (020) 8803 0008 E-mail: admin@romeotrading.com

▶ Rostrum Sportswear Ltd, Princes Street, Lochmaben, Lockerbie, Dumfriesshire, DG11 1PQ Tel: (01387) 811315 Fax: (01387) 811990 E-mail: info@rostrumsportswear.co.uk

S M Bros Ltd, 1st Floor Union Mill, Cambrian St, Manchester, M40 7EG Tel: 0161-274 3112 Fax: 0161-274 3312

Saira Of Manchester Ltd, 4 Addington Street, Manchester, M4 5FQ Tel: 0161-839 9839 Fax: 0161-839 9839

Samina Fashions, 75 Tweedale Street, Rochdale, Lancashire, OL11 3TZ Tel: (01706) 644459 Fax: (01706) 644459

Sangson Ltd, 221 Lozells Rd, Birmingham, B19 1RJ Tel: 0121-551 6530 Fax: 0121-551 6107

Sapphire Knitwear, 445 St Saviours Road, Leicester, LE5 4HH Tel: 0116-273 3803 Fax: 0116-273 3803

Sardar & Sons London Ltd, 31 New Road, London, E1 1HE Tel: (020) 7375 0246 Fax: (020) 7247 5239

Saul Trading, 427-431 Moseley Road, Balsall Heath, Birmingham, B12 9BX Tel: 0121-440 3276 Fax: 0121-440 3276

▶ Scot Crest, Concept House, Old Monkland Road, Coatbridge, Lanarkshire, ML5 5EU Tel: (01236) 606560 Fax: (01236) 627711

Season Link Ltd, 15 Summer Lane, Birmingham, B19 3RZ Tel: 0121-236 7330 Fax: 0121-236 7370 E-mail: sales@seasonlink.co.uk

Semore Classic Clothing, 104 Smawthorne Grove, Castleford, West Yorkshire, WF10 5AT Tel: (01977) 556307 E-mail: pamatsemoreclas6@aol.com

Seven Stars Manufacturers, 2 Trafalgar Street, Rochdale, Lancashire, OL16 2EB Tel: (01706) 641628 Fax: (01706) 641628

▶ Severnside Safety Supplies Ltd, Malmesbury Road, Kingsditch Trading Estate, Cheltenham, Gloucestershire, GL51 9PL Tel: (01242) 525811 Fax: (01242) 224184 E-mail: sales@sevsafe.co.uk

Sharif Fashion, 15a Clark Street, London, E1 2HD Tel: (020) 7790 0546 Fax: (020) 7790 0546

Sidhu Fashions Ltd, Bentley Lane, Walsall, WS2 8SP Tel: (01922) 720854 Fax: (01992) 616314 E-mail: admin@sidhufashions.co.uk

Silver Dollar, Units 30-31 Byker Business Development Centre, Albion Row, Newcastle upon Tyne, NE6 1LQ Tel: 0191-224 3005 Fax: 0191-224 3005

▶ Sky Fashion Garments, 36 Cyprus Road, Leicester, LE2 8QS Tel: 0116-283 7755 Fax: 0116-283 8322 E-mail: dazzle.europe@totaliser.co.uk

Slimma plc, PO Box 30, Leek, Staffordshire, ST13 8AR Tel: (01538) 399141 Fax: (01538) 385438 E-mail: admin@slimma.com

Slioch Outdoor Equipment Ltd, Cliffton Place, Poolewe, Achnasheen, Ross-Shire, IV22 2JU Tel: (01445) 781412 Fax: (01445) 781412

Sloan Molyneaux & Co. Ltd, Maldon Street, Belfast, BT12 6HE Tel: (028) 9032 6868 Fax: (028) 9043 8107 E-mail: office@sloanmolyneaux.co.uk

▶ Snout Ltd, 9 The Lime Kilns, Barrow upon Soar, Loughborough, Leicestershire, LE12 8YF Tel: (01509) 415643 E-mail: info@snoutthings.co.uk

▶ Soft Touch Clothing Ltd, Unit 4, Lancaster Street, Leicester, LE5 4GA Tel: 0116-276 0548 Fax: 0116-276 9038

Sogi Clothing Co, 24 Heathfield Road, Handsworth, Birmingham, B19 1HB Tel: 0121-515 1225 Fax: 0121-515 1225

Sohal Trading UK Co., 132 Tew Park Road, Birmingham, B21 0TR Tel: 0121-523 0622 Fax: 0121-523 0622

Sos Derby Ltd, 21 Noel Street, London, W1F 8GP Tel: (020) 7734 2882 Fax: (020) 7734 1441

Spa Fabrics Ltd, Unit 4c, 40 Sawday Street, Leicester, LE2 7JW Tel: 0116-285 8637 Fax: 0116-254 6931 E-mail: spafabrics@aol.com

Spencer Manufacturing Co Ltd, Wilson Street, Oldham, OL8 1HN Tel: 0161-627 2918 Fax: 0161-627 2137

Sperrin Knitwear Ltd, 57 Oldtown Street, Cookstown, County Tyrone, BT80 8EE Tel: (028) 8676 1634

Star Garments Co. Ltd, Caressa House, Cemetery Road, Pudsey, West Yorkshire, LS28 7XD Tel: 0113-257 8234 Fax: 0113-239 3421 E-mail: wwg@wwgroup.co.uk

Starlight Garments, Jubilee Centre, Gate Street, Blackburn, BB1 3AQ Tel: (01254) 690227 Fax: (01254) 690227

Starlit, 2 Dutton Street, Manchester, M3 1LE Tel: 0161-832 0112 Fax: 0161-832 0112

Stewardsons, Main Street, Hawkshead, Ambleside, Cumbria, LA22 0NT Tel: (01539) 436741 Fax: (01539) 436675 E-mail: sales@stewardsons.co.uk

▶ Stewart Christie & Co. Ltd, 63 Queen Street, Edinburgh, EH2 4NA Tel: 0131-225 6639 Fax: 0131-220 2397

G. Stockman, 137 Stoke Newington Road, London, N16 8BP Tel: (020) 7249 6017 Fax: (020) 7254 8895

J. Stott & Sons Ltd, 7 Richmond Hill, Blackburn, BB1 7LB Tel: (01254) 51567 Fax: (01254) 682780 E-mail: tony@jstott.com

Sundernote Ltd, HRS House, Garrets Green Lane, Birmingham, B33 0UE Tel: 0121-783 3896 Fax: 0121-783 5801 E-mail: info@trogenltd.com

Sunhill Fashion, 342 Main Street, Glasgow, G40 1LN Tel: 0141-556 4040 Fax: 0141-556 4040

Sunny Textiles Ltd, 115 Soho Hill, Hockley, Birmingham, B19 1AY Tel: 0121-523 9921

Sutcliffe Farrar & Co. Ltd, Banksfield Works, Mytholmroyd, Hebden Bridge, West Yorkshire, HX7 5LT Tel: (01422) 883363 Fax: (01422) 885479 E-mail: sales@fieldclassics.com

Swantex Ltd, Bromley Ho, Spindle St, Congleton, Cheshire, CW12 1QN Tel: (01260) 291110 Fax: (01260) 291112 E-mail: dave@swantex1.fsnet.co.uk

T J Fashion, 10-14 Bridge St, Oldbury, W. Midlands, B69 4BT Tel: 0121-565 5785 Fax: 0121-565 5785

T. R. Y. Ltd, 94 Halstead Street, Leicester, LE5 3RD Tel: 0116-262 9504 Fax: 0116-262 3421 E-mail: try147@hotmail.com

T S K Manufacturers Ltd, 27 Whitechapel Road, London, E1 1DU Tel: (020) 7247 6701 Fax: (020) 7377 6897

T S K Manufacturers Ltd, 27 Whitechapel Road, London, E1 1DU Tel: (020) 7247 6701 Fax: (020) 7377 6897

Tamla Of Dearne Valley Ltd, 77A Kilnhurst Road, Rawmarsh, Rotherham, South Yorkshire, S62 5QQ Tel: (01709) 527600 Fax: (01709) 527600

Tankson Textiles, 173 Rolfe Street, Smethwick, West Midlands, B66 2AS Tel: 0121-558 1733

CLOTHING – *continued*

Tartan Hose, 44 Newry Road, Kilkeel, Newry, County Down, BT34 4DU Tel: (028) 4176 5717 Fax: (028) 4176 3241 E-mail: tartanhose@btconnect.com

▶ Tec Clothing Manufacturers, 534 Stoney Stanton Road, Coventry, CV6 5FS Tel: (024) 7666 8310

Tepe Fashions, 126 Stratford Road, Sparkhill, Birmingham, B11 1AJ Tel: 0121-766 5635 Fax: 0121-753 5635

▶ Terfware All Terrain Mountain Boarding Apparel, 4 Lopes Road, Dousland, Yelverton, Devon, PL20 6NX Tel: (01822) 854354

▶ Tex Styles, 41 Northfield Park, Hayes, Middlesex, UB3 4NU Tel: (020) 8384 2036 Fax: (020) 8384 1088

Thornbury Clothing Co., 25 Thornbury Road, Birmingham, B20 3DE Tel: 0121-356 6777 Fax: 0121-344 4050

Tie Rack Corporate Neckwear Ltd, Capital Interchange Way, Brentford, Middlesex, TW8 0EX Tel: (020) 8230 2300 Fax: (020) 8230 2301

▶ Tom James Of London Ltd, 15-17 Christopher Street, London, EC2A 2BS Tel: (020) 7247 5246 Fax: (020) 7247 6153

Topaz Blue Ltd, Middlesex Building, Elstree Aerodrome, Elstree, Borehamwood, Hertfordshire, WD6 3AW Tel: (020) 8207 1007 Fax: (020) 8207 0307 E-mail: sales@topazblue.com

▶ Tradelane Limited, 1 Victoria Avenue, Birmingham, B1 1BD Tel: 0121 6322240 Fax: 0121 6322241 E-mail: info@tradelane.co.uk

Trimtex Clothing Co. Ltd, Unit 63 Ada Street Workshops, 8 Andrews Road, London, E8 4QN Tel: (020) 7254 8888 Fax: (020) 7254 8889 E-mail: pauljmay@onetel.com

▶ Trust Deal, 295 Haggerston Road, London, E8 4EN Tel: (020) 7254 3567 Fax: (020) 7254 3567

▶ Tunics 2 U, 1076 Tollcross Road, Glasgow, G32 8UN Tel: 0141-764 0055 Fax: 0141-764 0055 E-mail: tunic.makers@ntlworld.com

Turnip House Knitwear, 24 Trassey Road, Newcastle, County Down, BT33 0QB Tel: (028) 4372 6754 Fax: (028) 4372 6754 E-mail: info@turniphouse.com

Udare Ltd, Unit 2 Hampstead West, 224 Iverson Road, London, NW6 2HL Tel: (020) 7372 2220 Fax: (020) 7328 8803

The Uniform Co., Unit 2 Imperial Works, Fountayne Road, London, N15 4QL Tel: (020) 8801 5011

Uniform Express Ltd, Unit C7 South Way, Bounds Green Industrial Estate, Bounds Green Road, London, N11 2UL Tel: (020) 8368 0114 Fax: (020) 8361 0624 E-mail: mail@uniformexpress.co.uk

Unisport, D1-D2, 3-19 Victorian Grove, London, N16 8EN Tel: (020) 7241 6104

United Fashions Ltd, Irvinebank Rd, Darvel, Ayrshire, KA17 0HS Tel: 01560 321717 Fax: 01560 323323

▶ United Safety, Unit 25b Station Lane Industrial Estate, Station Lane, Old Whittington, Chesterfield, Derbyshire, S41 9QX Tel: (01246) 268990 Fax: (01246) 268889 E-mail: unitedsafety@tiscali.co.uk

Venus Fashions, Unit 5, 5 Tavistock Road, London, W11 1AT Tel: (020) 8880 2929

Venus Fashions, Roundthorn Rd, Oldham, OL4 1AX Tel: 0161-627 2057 Fax: 0161-626 0241

▶ VI Sigma, 60 White Lion Street, London, N1 9PH Tel: (020) 7837 7830 Fax: (020) 7837 7840

Vishal Fashions Ltd, 137 Harrison Road, Leicester, LE4 6NP Tel: 0116-268 2944 Fax: 0116-268 2944

W Yeomans Ltd, 11 Midland Way, Barlborough, Chesterfield, Derbyshire, S43 4XA Tel: (01246) 571270 Fax: (01246) 571271 E-mail: mailbox@wyeomans.com

P. & S. Warwick, Unit 48 Sapcote Trading Centre, 374 High Road, London, NW10 2DJ Tel: (020) 8451 2385 Fax: (020) 8830 1161

Watts & Stone, Castle Balfour Demesne, Lisnaskea, Enniskillen, County Fermanagh, BT92 0LT Tel: (028) 6772 1282 Fax: (028) 6772 1106E-mail: sales@wattsandstone.co.uk

Wealth Of Nations World-Wide Ltd, Crouches Farm, Furnace Lane, Horsmonden, Tonbridge, Kent, TN12 8LX Tel: (01892) 724724 Fax: (01892) 724726 E-mail: info@wealthofnations.co.uk

Wear Fine, School Street, Rochdale, Lancashire, OL12 0NY Tel: (01706) 650545 Fax: (01706) 359774

Winstons Sport & Casual Wear, 2-4 Bridge Road, Orpington, Kent, BR5 2BH Tel: (01689) 837975 Fax: (01689) 603512 E-mail: stevewinstons@aol.com

Workware Protective Equipment, Tannery House, Tannery Road, Harraby Green Business Park, Carlisle, CA1 2SS Tel: (01228) 591091 Fax: (01228) 590026 E-mail: sales@workware.co.uk

▶ Workwear World, 445 Honeypot Lane, Stanmore, Middlesex, HA7 1JJ Tel: (020) 8206 2004 Fax: (020) 8206 2005 E-mail: sales@workwearworld.co.uk

World Leisurewear Ltd, 46 High Street, Cowes, Isle Of Wight, PO31 7RR Tel: (01983) 291744 Fax: (01983) 297252 E-mail: sales@worldleisurewear.com

▶ Ben Worsley, 14 Foster Avenue, Beaumont Park, Huddersfield, HD4 5LN Tel: (01484) 326669 Fax: (01484) 326669 E-mail: info@ben-worsley.com

▶ Z 2 Clothing, Conduit Lane, Bridgnorth, Shropshire, WV16 5BW Tel: 01746 762467 Fax: 01746 762467 E-mail: info@z2clothing.com

▶ Zips & Rips, 2B Whitewell Road, Newtownabbey, County Antrim, BT36 7ES Tel: (028) 9037 1555

CLOTHING ACCESSORIES, SCOTTISH HIGHLAND DRESS

Kinloch Anderson Ltd, 4 Dock Street, Leith, Edinburgh, EH6 6EY Tel: 0131-555 1355 Fax: 0131-555 1392 E-mail: enquiries@kinlochanderson.com

▶ Taycraft, 6 Strathmore Avenue, Coupar Angus, Perthshire, PH13 9ED Tel: (01828) 628477 E-mail: lachie_mackintosh@yahoo.com

CLOTHING ARMBANDS

▶ IM-Press Promotions Ayr Ltd, 3 Barclaugh Drive, Coylton, Ayr, KA6 6HS Tel: (01292) 570495 Fax: (01292) 570495 E-mail: im-pressayr@btconnect.com

CLOTHING BELTS

Tie Rack Ltd, 49 Regent Arcade, Regent Street, Cheltenham, Gloucestershire, GL50 1JZ Tel: (01242) 574228

▶ Z 2 Clothing, Conduit Lane, Bridgnorth, Shropshire, WV16 5BW Tel: 01746 762467 Fax: 01746 762467 E-mail: info@z2clothing.com

▶ Zodiac Industries Ltd, Kingswear Drive, Vallets Lane, Bolton, BL1 6DU Tel: (01204) 842211

CLOTHING CARDBOARD PACKAGING INSERTS

▶ Supply Co. Ltd, Brookfield Industrial Estate, Peakdale Road, Glossop, Derbyshire, SK13 6LQ Tel: (01457) 869875 Fax: (01457) 855852E-mail: service@supplycompany.co.uk

CLOTHING DESIGN

▶ freis fresche ltd, Acklam Road, Middlesbrough, Cleveland, TS5 7HA Tel: 0870 8965715

Planet Kids, 8 Actons Walk, Wood Street, Wigan, Lancashire, WN3 4HN Tel: (01942) 403910 Fax: (01942) 231188 E-mail: sales@planetkids.org.uk

CLOTHING IMPORT/EXPORT MERCHANTS OR AGENTS

A & S GB Ltd, 130-132 Taunton Road, Ashton-under-Lyne, Lancashire, OL7 9EE Tel: 0161-330 9131 Fax: 0161-330 9131 E-mail: amjud@aol.com

Action Apparal Ltd, 62-63 Hemming Road, Washford, Redditch, Worcestershire, B98 0EA Tel: (01527) 510545 Fax: (01527) 510678 E-mail: alans@actionapparal.co.uk

Breeze UK Ltd, 18 St. Pancras Way, London, NW1 0QG Tel: (020) 7383 2288 Fax: (020) 7383 2288 E-mail: reception@breezeuk.com

Carmel, 287 Haggerston Road, London, E8 4EN Tel: (020) 7275 7037 Fax: (020) 7275 7038

Chadha & Son, 112-116 Whitechapel Rd, London, E1 1JE Tel: 020 72470348

Cohen & Wilks International Ltd, Aquatite House, Mabgate, Leeds, LS9 7DR Tel: 0113-245 0804 Fax: 0113-391 7858 E-mail: reception@cwil.co.uk

D Cutler International Ltd, 148-150 Commercial Street, London, E1 6NU Tel: (020) 7377 8738 Fax: (020) 7377 2624 E-mail: d.cutler@hotmail.co.uk

D R Warehouse Ltd, 60-64 Great Hampton Street, Birmingham, B18 6EL Tel: 0121-551 4920 Fax: 0121-551 6504

Duke Street Textiles, 65 St Marys Road, Garston, Liverpool, L19 2NL Tel: 0151-427 4080 Fax: 0151-427 5000 E-mail: dukestreettextiles@virginnet.com

Escada UK Ltd, 6 Cavendish Place, London, W1G 9NB Tel: (020) 7580 6066 Fax: (020) 7637 8749

Fabrianne Collection Ltd, Danielle House, Southmoor Road, Wythenshawe, Manchester, M23 9GP Tel: 0161-945 8001 Fax: 0161-947 8843

Fiction Clothing Co. (UK) Ltd, 112-114 North Acton Road, London, NW10 6QH Tel: (020) 8961 9202 Fax: (020) 8961 9051

Fielding Group Ltd, 18 Eynecourt Road, Woodside Estate, Dunstable, Bedfordshire, LU5 4TS Tel: (01582) 632300 Fax: (01582) 632500 E-mail: beth@fieldinggroup.co.uk

Karrimor Ltd, Petre Road, Clayton Le Moors, Accrington, Lancashire, BB5 5JZ Tel: (01254) 893000 Fax: (01254) 893100 E-mail: webmaster@karrimor.co.uk

Laltex & Co. Ltd, Leigh Commerce Park, Green Fold Way, Leigh, Lancashire, WN7 3XH Tel: (01942) 687000 Fax: (01942) 687070 E-mail: mail@laltex.com

Norman Linton Ltd, Linton House, 39-51 Highgate Road, London, NW5 1RS Tel: (020) 7267 0921 Fax: (020) 7267 0928 E-mail: email@normanlinton.co.uk

Lotus Fashions, Matlock Road, Coventry, CV1 4JR Tel: (024) 7668 0091 Fax: (024) 7663 7084 E-mail: sales@lotusfashions.com

▶ Luta Ltd, 106 Beecham Berry, Basingstoek, Basingstoke, Hampshire, RG22 4QN Tel: 0778 0993697 Fax: 01256 814135 E-mail: info@luta.co.uk

Mirage Fashions Ltd, 313 Saffron Lane, Leicester, LE2 6UE Tel: 0116-283 7259 Fax: 0116-283 1523 E-mail: enquiries@mirage-fashions.co.uk

Myers & Myers Imports Ltd, 35 Ringley Road, Whitefield, Manchester, M45 7LD Tel: 0161-798 9004 Fax: 0161-773 9700

Nathan's Wastesavers Ltd, Unit 13 Winchester Avenue, Denny, Stirlingshire, FK6 6QE Tel: (01324) 826828 Fax: (01324) 826555

Paul Smith Foundation, Riverside Buildings, Riverside Way, Nottingham, NG2 1DP Tel: 0115-986 8877 Fax: 0115-986 2649

Salvatex Holdings Ltd, 1 St. Marks Road, St. James Industrial Estate, Corby, Northamptonshire, NN18 8AN Tel: (01536) 400002 Fax: (01536) 400169

Sanger Textile & Co., 74A Middlesex Street, London, E1 7EZ Tel: (020) 7247 8949 Fax: (020) 7247 8949

Scotts Clothing Corp. Ltd, 15-19 Manor Street, Ardwick Green, Manchester, M12 6HE Tel: 0161-273 7677 Fax: 0161-273 7699

Sheridan Knitwear, Ground Floor, 371 Oldham Road, Manchester, M40 8EA Tel: 0161-203 5444 Fax: 0161-203 5557

Surin Fashions Ltd, 4 Belgrave Commercial Centre, 160 Belgrave Road, Leicester, LE4 5AU Tel: 0116-266 6191 Fax: 0116-261 1699

Sykes & East Ltd, Cleeve Court, 1 Cleeve Road, Leatherhead, Surrey, KT22 7UD Tel: (01372) 363054 Fax: (01372) 362920

Trutex plc, Jubilee Mill, Taylor Street, Clitheroe, Lancashire, BB7 1NL Tel: (01200) 421202 Fax: (01200) 421209 E-mail: info@trutex.com

VF Northern Europe Ltd, Park Road East, Calverton, Nottingham, NG14 6GD Tel: 0115-965 6565 Fax: 0115-965 7742

Visionstyle Leisure, Houldsworth Mill, Houldsworth Street, Reddish, Stockport, Cheshire, SK5 6DA Tel: 0161-442 7082 Fax: 0161-442 1939 E-mail: sales@visionstyle.co.uk

CLOTHING IRONING PRESSES

▶ The Ironing Maiden Service, 34 The Mews, Trafalgar Street, Brighton, BN34 2DD Tel: 01273 50 70 41 E-mail: e.mokeeva@e3internet.com

CLOTHING LABELS

Adare Label Converters Ltd, Falconer Road, Haverhill, Suffolk, CB9 7XU Tel: (01440) 714996 Fax: (01440) 766501 E-mail: sales@labelconverters.co.uk

Braitrim Group Ltd, Braitrim House, 98 Victoria Road, London, NW10 6NB Tel: (020) 8723 3000 Fax: (020) 8723 3001 E-mail: service@braitrim.com

Fastabs Ltd, Unit 3 Oswin Road, Brailsford Industrial Estate, Leicester, LE3 1HR Tel: 0116-291 6660 Fax: 0116-291 6661 E-mail: fastabs@virgin.net

Hutton Textiles Supplies, Julian House, 32 Warkworth Drive, Chester le Street, County Durham, DH2 3JR Tel: 0191-388 7657 Fax: 0191-387 1450

Labelon Sales Ltd, Unit 10 Chilford Court, Rayne Road, Braintree, Essex, CM7 2QS Tel: (01376) 553030 Fax: (01376) 349437 E-mail: sales@labelon.co.uk

▶ Namemark Ltd, PO Box 1792, Christchurch, Dorset, BH23 4YR Tel: (01425) 278070 Fax: (01425) 278070

Thomas Walker Pensions Trust Ltd, 39 St Paul's Square, Birmingham, B3 1QY Tel: 0121-236 5565 Fax: 0121-236 6725 E-mail: sales@thomaswalker.co.uk

CLOTHING MACHINERY

Dewshurst Mensware Ltd, 3 Stephenson Road, North East Industrial Estate, Peterlee, County Durham, SR8 5AA Tel: 0191-518 6699 Fax: 0191-518 0445

CLOTHING METAL DETECTORS

Lock Inspection Group Ltd, Lock House, Neville Street, Oldham, OL9 6LF Tel: 0161-624 0333 Fax: 0161-624 5181 E-mail: marketing@lockinspection.co.uk

CLOTHING PACKAGING

Garment Related Services Ltd, 2a Westbury Road, London, E7 8BU Tel: (020) 8555 6555 Fax: (020) 8221 1355

▶ Supply Co. Ltd, Brookfield Industrial Estate, Peakdale Road, Glossop, Derbyshire, SK13 6LQ Tel: (01457) 869875 Fax: (01457) 855852E-mail: service@supplycompany.co.uk

CLOTHING TRADE LEATHER

Leathertex Ltd, 143 Bethnal Green Road, London, E2 7DG Tel: (020) 7613 4251 Fax: (020) 7613 4252 E-mail: leathertexltd@aol.com

CLOTHING, FASHION

European Army Surplus, 14 Nobel Square, Burnt Mills Industrial Estate, Burnt Mills Industrial Estate, Basildon, Essex, SS13 1LS Tel: (01268) 591552 Fax: (01268) 591553 E-mail: email@europeanarmysurplus.co.uk

▶ Ice Clothing Co. Ltd, 13 Hessel Street, London, E1 2LR Tel: (020) 7488 3234 Fax: (020) 7488 2808 E-mail: info@ice-clothing.co.uk

CLOTHS, ANTISTATIC

▶ Direct2workwear, Limlow House, Royston Road, Litlington, Royston, Hertfordshire, SG8 0RS Tel: (0845) 3454550 Fax: (0800) 174137 E-mail: martin@direct2workwear.com

CLUB/COMPANY NECKTIES OR SCARVES

Club Ties, Brook Street Studios, 60 Brook Street, Glasgow, G40 2AB Tel: 0141-554 3066 Fax: 0141-554 4581 E-mail: clubties@hotmail.com

Leisurelines Embroiderers, Unit 10 Staunton Court Business Park, Ledbury Road, Staunton, Gloucester, GL19 3QS Tel: (0800) 7318410

Munday C H Ltd, 8 St. Johns Road, Woking, Surrey, GU21 7SE Tel: (01483) 771588 Fax: (01483) 756627 E-mail: enquiries@chmunday.co.uk

Network Promotions, 5 Braehead Business Units, Braehead Road, Linlithgow, West Lothian, EH49 6EP Tel: (01506) 845797 Fax: (01506) 845149

O H Hewett Ltd, 21 Farncombe Street, Godalming, Surrey, GU7 3AY Tel: (01483) 426917 Fax: (01483) 424810 E-mail: enquiries@ohhewett.co.uk

Personal Touch, Stag House, Western Way, Exeter, EX1 2DE Tel: (01392) 410260 Fax: (01392) 421235 E-mail: sales@personaltouch-emb.co.uk

Woodstock Neckwear Ltd, Telford Road, Glenrothes, Fife, KY7 4NX Tel: (01592) 771777 Fax: (01592) 631717

CLUTCH AND BRAKE UNITS

B G Developments Ltd, Unit 9 West Court, Buntsford Park Road, Bromsgrove, Worcestershire, B60 3DX Tel: (01527) 832453 Fax: (01527) 575403 E-mail: info@bgdevelopments.co.uk

Nigel Bray Ltd, 3 Grandstand Business Centre, Westfields Trading Estate, Hereford, HR4 9NS Tel: (01432) 351400 Fax: (01432) 351888 E-mail: sales@nigelbrayltd.fsbusiness.co.uk

Bushey Hall Garage, Bushey Hall Drive, Bushey, WD23 2QE Tel: (01923) 237135 Fax: (01923) 235372 E-mail: bushey.hall@virgin.net

Clarke Bros Auto Factors Ltd, 161/163 Cromac Street, Belfast, BT2 8JE Tel: (028) 9024 8444 Fax: (028) 9023 8094

Heavy Vehicle Brakes Ltd, 3 Sampson Business Park, Berwick Lane, Hallen, Bristol, BS10 7RS Tel: 0117-959 3582 Fax: 0117-959 3588

Industrial Clutch Parts Ltd, Unit 11 Bingswood Trading Estate, Whaley Bridge, High Peak, Derbyshire, SK23 7LY Tel: (01663) 734627 Fax: (01663) 733023 E-mail: sales@icpltd.co.uk

▶ Mansfield core supply, 53, Willowbridge lane, Sutton-in-ashfield, Nottinghamshire, NG17 1DW Tel: 01623 477583 E-mail: ianvardy@yahoo.com

CLUTCH BONDING AND RELINING

Saftet Brakes, Unit D5 Halesfield 5, Telford, Shropshire, TF7 4QJ Tel: (01952) 581122 Fax: (01952) 585417 E-mail: sales@saftek.co.uk

CLUTCH COILS

Premier Rewinds, 566-568 Attercliffe Road, Sheffield, S9 3QP Tel: 0114-261 9104 Fax: 0114-244 9111

Springmakers Redditch, Doward Crest, The Doward, Whitchurch, Ross-on-Wye, Herefordshire, HR9 6DZ Tel: (01600) 890325 Fax: (01600) 890325

CLUTCH COMPONENTS, *See also Brake/Clutch etc*

Hatcham Motor Services, 1 Hatcham Park Road, London, SE14 5QE Tel: (020) 7732 7942 Fax: (020) 7732 7942

Quinton Hazell Automotive Ltd, Conway Road, Colwyn Bay, Clwyd, LL28 5BS Tel: (01492) 544201 Fax: (01492) 542202

Toyoda Gosei Fluid Systems UK Ltd, Rockingham Road, Market Harborough, Leicestershire, LE16 7QE Tel: (01858) 439800 Fax: (01858) 410191

CLUTCH LININGS/FACINGS

Raybestos G B F Ltd, Unit 1 Preserve Works, Jubilee Way, Thackley Old Rd, Shipley, W. Yorkshire, BD18 1QB Tel: (01274) 597332 Fax: (01274) 597357 E-mail: info@raybestosgbf.freeserve.co.uk

Saftek Brakes, 1 Rawfolds Industrial Estate, Bradford Road, Rawfolds, Cleckheaton, West Yorkshire, BD19 5LT Tel: (01274) 862666 Fax: (01274) 862444

CLUTCH PLATES

L U K A S (Hereford) Ltd, Holme Lacy Road, Rotherwas, Hereford, HR2 6LA Tel: (01432) 265265 Fax: (01432) 275146

Luk Aftermarket Service Ltd, Holme Lacy Road, Hereford, HR2 6BQ Tel: (01432) 264264 Fax: (01432) 275146 E-mail: sales@luk.co.uk

Vee Clutch Plates, Mill Lane, Brighouse, West Yorkshire, HD6 1PN Tel: (01484) 721409 Fax: (01484) 400203 E-mail: vee@clutch.fsbusiness.co.uk

CLUTCHES, *See also headings for particular types under Clutches*

Alcon Components Ltd, Concentric Park, Apollo, Tamworth, Staffordshire, B79 7TN Tel: (01827) 723700 Fax: (01827) 723701 E-mail: info@alcon.co.uk

Charles Johnson, 3 Beech Drive, Norwich, NR6 6RN Tel: (01603) 485429 Fax: (01603) 485459

Setco Automotive UK Ltd, Lipe Clutch Division, York Avenue Haslingden, Haslingden, Rossendale, Lancashire, BB4 4HU Tel: (01706) 237200 Fax: (01706) 229585

Z F Trading, Eldon Way, Crick, Northampton, NN6 7SL Tel: (01788) 822353 Fax: (01788) 823829 E-mail: sales@zf.com

CNC COMPUTER SYSTEMS

A C I Europe Ltd, 16 Plover Close, Interchange Park, Newport Pagnell, Buckinghamshire, MK16 9PS Tel: (01908) 514500 Fax: (01908) 610111 E-mail: sales@aciuk.co.uk

Amtech Industrial Computer Solutions, Ramage House, Samson Close, Newcastle upon Tyne, NE12 6DX Tel: 0191-268 2022 Fax: 0191-268 2092 E-mail: sales@amtechltd.co.uk

CNC CONTROL SYSTEMS

A C I Europe Ltd, 16 Plover Close, Interchange Park, Newport Pagnell, Buckinghamshire, MK16 9PS Tel: (01908) 514500 Fax: (01908) 610111 E-mail: sales@aciuk.co.uk

Nee Controls, 19b White Rose Way, Gateshead, Tyne & Wear, NE10 8YX Tel: 0191-415 9751 Fax: 0191-416 1603 E-mail: sales@nee-controls.com

NUM (UK) Ltd, Unit 3, Fairfield Court, Seven Stars Industrial Estate, Coventry, CV3 4LJ Tel: (0871) 7504020 Fax: (0871) 7504021 E-mail: solutions@schneider-num.co.uk

R S Micro, 129 Brookfield Place, Walton Summit Centre, Bamber Bridge, Preston, PR5 8BF Tel: (01772) 628000 Fax: (01772) 628888 E-mail: rs_micro@compuserve.com

CNC CUTTING SYSTEMS

Cromwell Ltd, Station Road, North Hykeham, Lincoln, LN6 9AL Tel: (01522) 500888 Fax: (01522) 500857 E-mail: sales@cromwell.co.uk

Homag UK Ltd, 10c Sills Road, Castle Donington, Derby, DE74 2US Tel: (0870) 2433244 Fax: (01332) 856400 E-mail: sales@homag-uk.co.uk

MTC Software Ltd, 7 Clarendon Place, Leamington Spa, Warwickshire, CV32 5QL Tel: (0870) 8031297 Fax: (0870) 8031298 E-mail: mtc@mtc-europe.co.uk

CNC ENGINEERING SERVICES OR MACHINISTS

A D X Precision Engineering, The Sanderson Centre, Lees Lane, Gosport, Hampshire, PO12 3UL Tel: (023) 9252 0027 Fax: (023) 9252 0027 E-mail: dave@adxprecision.freeserve.co.uk

A & G Precision Engineers Ltd, 1 Hythe Works, Diplocks Way, Hailsham, East Sussex, BN27 3JF Tel: (01323) 847718 Fax: (01323) 440138

Accure Geneva Ltd, 1-5 Goodwood Road, Pershore, Worcestershire, WR10 2JL Tel: (01386) 555335 Fax: (01386) 556739 E-mail: enquiries@geneva.accura.co.uk

Acrona Engineering, Unit 1, Woodview Estate, Church Hanborough, Witney, Oxfordshire, OX29 8AA Tel: (01993) 880588 Fax: (01993) 880590 E-mail: sales@acrona-engineering.co.uk

Adelphi Precision Ltd, Sawpit Industrial Estate, Tibshelf, Derbyshire, DE55 5NH Tel: (01773) 872351 Fax: (01773) 875067 E-mail: adelphiprecision@ic24.net

Advance Metal Components Ltd, Units 12-14, Minters Industrial Estate, Southwall Road, Deal, Kent, CT14 9PZ Tel: (01304) 380574 Fax: (01304) 380619 E-mail: sales@amc-uk.com

Advanced Engineering Techniques Ltd, 9-15 Holbrook Avenue, Holbrook Industrial Estate, Holbrook, Sheffield, S20 3FF Tel: 0114-247 5725 Fax: 0114-247 5726 E-mail: sales@aetuk.com

Aim Engineering Ltd, Melandra Road, Brookfield, Glossop, Derbyshire, SK13 6JE Tel: (01457) 862505 Fax: (01457) 861753 E-mail: sdada@aimeng.co.uk

Alan Gordon, George Street, Chorley, Lancashire, PR7 2BE Tel: (01257) 274723 Fax: (01257) 241342 E-mail: sales@alangordoneng.co.uk

Aldersbrook Engineering, B Ajax Works, Hertford Road, Barking, Essex, IG11 8DY Tel: (020) 8591 0685 Fax: (020) 8591 9388 E-mail: enquiries@aldersbrook-engineering.com

Allendale Components, 28 Allendale Tee, New Marske, Redcar, Cleveland, TS11 8HN Tel: (01642) 478738 Fax: (01642) 272683 E-mail: p.wall@ntlworld.com

Alstone Engineering, Unit 1 Towers Business Park, Wheelhouse Road, Rugeley, Staffordshire, WS15 1UZ Tel: (01889) 577775 Fax: (01889) 575111

Alton Precision Engineering Ltd, Unit 27a Chemical Lane, Stoke-on-Trent, ST6 4PB Tel: (01782) 813735 Fax: (01782) 813752 E-mail: altonpre@clara.co.uk

Ambery Metalform Components, Unit F6 Newton Business Park, Talbot Road, Hyde, Cheshire, SK14 4UQ Tel: 0161-367 9616 Fax: 0161-368 0689 E-mail: sales@ambery-metalform.co.uk

Amdale Ltd, 6-7 Culverin Square, Limberline Road, Hilsea, Portsmouth, PO3 5BU Tel: (023) 9266 0726 Fax: (023) 9265 5177 E-mail: sales@amdale.co.uk

Anglo Precision Engineering Co. Ltd, Deans Yard, 15 South Road, Baldock, Hertfordshire, SG7 6BZ Tel: (01462) 491105 Fax: (01462) 491106 E-mail: sales@anglo-precision.co.uk

Apb Precision Engineers, Lakeside Business Park, Swan Lane, Sandhurst, Berkshire, GU47 9DN Tel: (01252) 890061 Fax: (01252) 890062

APPH Nottingham Ltd, Urban Road, Kirkby-In-Ashfield, Nottingham, NG17 8AP Tel: (01623) 754355 Fax: (01623) 723904 E-mail: sales@beauforteng.co.uk

Archfact Ltd, 10 Pipers Wood Industrial Park, Waterberry Drive, Waterlooville, Hampshire, PO7 7XU Tel: (023) 9224 0700 Fax: (023) 9223 0157 E-mail: info@archfact.com

Argo Products Ltd, Viola Street, Bolton, BL1 8NG Tel: (01204) 595224 Fax: (01204) 307729

Arrow Precision Engineering Ltd, 12 Barley Field, Hinckley Fields Industrial Estate, Hinckley, Leicestershire, LE10 1YE Tel: (01455) 234200 Fax: (01455) 233545 E-mail: sales@arrowprecision.co.uk

Ashford Engineering Services, Unit 3 New Street Farm, Great Chart, Ashford, Kent, TN23 3DL Tel: (01233) 668883 Fax: (01233) 668883 E-mail: clive@asheng.freeserve.co.uk

Ashtead Engineering Co. Ltd, Unit 2 3 Camphill Industrial Estate, Camphill Road, West Byfleet, Surrey, KT14 6EW Tel: (01932) 353121 Fax: (01932) 342968 E-mail: ashteadeng@byfleet.net

Aspec Precision Engineers, Unit P1 Dales Manor Business Park, Grove Road, Sawston, Cambridge, CB22 3TJ Tel: (01223) 836710 Fax: (01223) 836294 E-mail: info@aspec.co.uk

▶ Asset Protection Administration, The Terminal Building, Union Wharf, Leicester Road, Market Harborough, Leicestershire, LE16 7UW Tel: (01858) 469955 Fax: (01858) 466460 E-mail: apa@apa-admin.co.uk

Atlantic Auto Engineering, Unit 7b Fernfield Farm, Little Horwood Road, Little Horwood, Milton Keynes, MK17 0PS Tel: (01908) 501904 Fax: (01908) 501904

Automatic Engineers (Hinckley) Ltd, Burbage Road, Burbage, Hinckley, Leicestershire, LE10 2TP Tel: (01455) 238033 Fax: (01455) 615101 E-mail: roger@automaticengineers.com

▶ Av-Tech Manufacturing Co. Ltd, Unit 33 London Road Industrial Estate, Baldock, Hertfordshire, SG7 6NG Tel: (01462) 893336 Fax: (01462) 893336

▶ AXYZ Engineering Ltd, 34 Rotherford Road, Southfield Industrial Estate, Glenrothes, Fife, KY6 2RT Tel: (01592) 772500 Fax: (01592) 771170

B A E Systems Land Systems (Bridging) Ltd, P O Box 37, Wolverhampton, WV4 6YN Tel: (01902) 405050 Fax: (01902) 355354 E-mail: kathryn.fisher@baesystems.com

B B F CNC Machining, 31 Knowl Piece, Hitchin, Hertfordshire, SG4 0TY Tel: (01462) 432700 Fax: (01462) 431414 E-mail: bbf.cnc@btinternet.com

▶ B D Cravens, Rossfield Road, Ellesmere Port, CH65 3AW Tel: 0151-356 5654 Fax: 0151-356 7822 E-mail: bdcraveneng@tiscali.co.uk

B D R Micro Instruments Ltd, The Bringey, Church Street, Great Baddow, Chelmsford, CM2 7JW Tel: (01245) 476777 Fax: (01245) 475761 E-mail: info@bdr-micro.co.uk

B L Precision Ltd, Unit 6-7 Focal Point, Lacerta Court, Letchworth Garden City, Hertfordshire, SG6 1FJ Tel: (01462) 670800 Fax: (01462) 816865 E-mail: info@blprecision.co.uk

B O M Light Engineering Ltd, B O M Engineering Tools, Station Road, Morley, Leeds, LS27 8JT Tel: 0113-253 7544 Fax: 0113-252 7851 E-mail: sales@bomeng.co.uk

B P Engineering Ltd, John Harper Street, Willenhall, West Midlands, WV13 1RE Tel: (01902) 609167 Fax: (01902) 605766

B R M Precision Engineers & Toolmakers Ltd, Unit 3, Brooks Street Business Centre, Brook Street, Colchester, CO1 2UZ Tel: (01206) 794617 Fax: (01206) 793839

B S P Engineering Ltd, Maitland Road, Lion Barn Industrial Estate, Needham Market, Ipswich, IP6 8NZ Tel: (01449) 722222 Fax: (01449) 721989 E-mail: sales@bspengineering.co.uk

Baker Blower Engineering Co. Ltd, 39 Stanley Street, Sheffield, S3 8HH Tel: 0114-272 5527 Fax: 0114-272 7533 E-mail: bakerblower@aol.com

Balco Prescision Engineering, 24 Benfield Way, Braintree, Essex, CM7 3YS Tel: (01376) 347767 Fax: (01376) 347767

Bar Engineering, 20 West Dock Avenue, Hull, HU3 4JR Tel: (01482) 224966 Fax: (01482) 211443

Bedford Transmissions Ltd, Unit 26-27, Raynham Road, Bishop's Stortford, Hertfordshire, CM23 5PE Tel: (01279) 461397 Fax: (01279) 659017 E-mail: enquires@btlgears.co.uk

Bennett & Sayer, Wetherby Road, Derby, DE24 8HN Tel: (01332) 345546 Fax: 01332 293215 E-mail: info@holdenengineering.co.uk

Billcar Engineering Ltd, Unit 1a March Way, Battlefield Enterprise Park, Shrewsbury, SY1 3JE Tel: (01743) 469398 Fax: (01743) 450084 E-mail: billcarengine@hotmail.com

Birmingham Machine Tool Services Ltd, 312-314 Bradford Street, Birmingham, B5 6ET Tel: 0121-622 6339 Fax: 0121-666 6406 E-mail: bhammctool@aol.com

Boiler Management Systems (International) Ltd, 189-191 Rutland Road, Sheffield, S3 9PT Tel: 0114-275 5500 Fax: 0114-275 5533 E-mail: isd@bmsint.com

Bollin Dale Engineering Ltd, Pownall Square, Macclesfield, Cheshire, SK11 8DT Tel: (01625) 422620 Fax: (01625) 614322 E-mail: sales@bollineng.co.uk

Brandon Precision, Holmewall Road, Leeds, LS10 4TQ Tel: 0113-277 5671 Fax: 0113-271 2161 E-mail: enquiries@brandon-medical.com

Bridgeforth Engineering, Unit 13-14, Belleknowes Industrial Estate, Inverkeithing, Fife, KY11 1HZ Tel: (01383) 413441 Fax: (01383) 418391 E-mail: sales@bridgeforthl.co.uk

Bromyard Engineering Company Ltd, 23 Rowberry Street, Bromyard, Herefordshire, HR7 4DT Tel: (01885) 483257 Fax: (01885) 488028 E-mail: linda@bromyard.com

Brookes Engineers Ltd, Hope Street, Rotherham, South Yorkshire, S60 1LH Tel: (01709) 365418 Fax: (01709) 828453 E-mail: sales@brookeseng.co.uk

Burtech Precision Ltd, First Avenue, Flixborough Industrial Estate, Flixborough, Scunthorpe, South Humberside, DN15 8SE Tel: (01724) 866406 Fax: (01724) 280614

Burton & Smith Ltd, Unit 32p The Washford Industrial Estate, Heming Road, Redditch, Worcestershire, B98 0DH Tel: (01527) 516925 Fax: (01527) 514900 E-mail: burtonandsmith@lycos.co.uk

C H W (Metal Components) Ltd, Unit 1A, Abercromby Industrial Estate, Abercromby Avenue, High Wycombe, Buckinghamshire, HP12 3AX Tel: (01494) 530883 Fax: (01494) 463581

C J Engineering Ltd, 2 Faraday Place, Thetford, Norfolk, IP24 3RG Tel: (01842) 761726 Fax: (01842) 761119 E-mail: kevin@cjeng.co.uk

C P E Precision Engineering Co. Ltd, Sutherland House, Arlington Way, Sundorne Retail Park, Shrewsbury, SY1 4YA Tel: (01743) 444250 Fax: (01743) 462563

C S D Controls (U K), Britannia Way, Malvern, Worcestershire, WR14 1GZ Tel: (01684) 567044 Fax: (01604) 567017 E-mail: retrofit@csdcontrols.co.uk

C S Milne Engineering, Unit 2 Peckleton Lane Business Park, Peckleton Common, Elmesthorpe, Leicester, LE9 7SH Tel: (01455) 822569 Fax: (01455) 824012 E-mail: sales@cs-milne.co.uk

C T L Engineering Co. Ltd, Cromwell Road, Bredbury, Stockport, Cheshire, SK6 2RH Tel: 0161-430 3173 Fax: 0161-430 8643 E-mail: sales@ctl-eng.com

Cambmac Ltd, 4 Commercial Road, March, Cambridgeshire, PE15 8QP Tel: (01354) 655270 Fax: (01354) 657447 E-mail: info@cambmac.fsnet.co.uk

Camlit Precision Engineering Ltd, Sand Road Industrial Estate, Sand Road, Great Gransden, Sandy, Bedfordshire, SG19 3AH Tel: (01767) 677263 Fax: (01767) 677720

Canwire Services Ltd, 14 Gospel End Street, Dudley, West Midlands, DY3 3LS Tel: (01902) 881460 Fax: (01902) 881393 E-mail: canwireservices1@aol.com

Capalex, Cleator Moor, Cumbria, CA25 5QB Tel: (01946) 811771 Fax: (01946) 813681 E-mail: sales@capalex.com

Chad Engineering (UK) Ltd, Unit 2, Business Village, Wexham Road, Slough, SL2 5HF Tel: (01753) 537980 Fax: (01753) 553472 E-mail: enquiries@chad-engineering.co.uk

Chase Precision Engineering Ltd, 10 7 Blackmoor Road, Ebblake Industrial Estate, Verwood, Dorset, BH31 6AX Tel: (01202) 813237 Fax: (01202) 813734

Chelburn Precision Ltd, 2 Plot 7-9 Trans Pennine Trading Estate, Gorrells Way, Rochdale, Lancashire, OL11 2PX Tel: (01706) 644538 Fax: (01706) 861733 E-mail: chelburn@zen.co.uk

Cheltape Engineering Company Ltd, Stoneville Street, Cheltenham, Gloucestershire, GL51 8PH Tel: (01242) 245121 Fax: (01242) 224345 E-mail: sales@cheltape.co.uk

Chequers UK Ltd, 78 Ponders End Industrial Estate, East Duck Lees Lane, Enfield, Middlesex, EN3 7SR Tel: (020) 8805 8855 Fax: (020) 8805 9318

CNC Support Ltd, Advance Factory Site, Skipton Road, Trawden Colne, Colne, Lancashire, BB8 8BJ Tel: (01282) 859122 Fax: (01282) 859144 E-mail: sales@cncsupport.co.uk

Colbree Precision Ltd, Units 10-12 Beacon Court, Pitstone Green Business Park, Quarry Road, Pitstone, Leighton Buzzard, Bedfordshire, LU7 9GY Tel: (01296) 664200 Fax: (01296) 664201 E-mail: sales@colbree.com

Colson Engineering, 8 Headlands Trading Estate, Swindon, SN2 7JQ Tel: (01793) 526660 Fax: (01793) 513294 E-mail: sales@colsonengineering.com

Comet-Pramesco Services, 30 Holywell Avenue, Folkestone, Kent, CT19 6JZ Tel: (01303) 255585 Fax: (01303) 243122 E-mail: steve_baxter@lineone.net

Computerised Engineering Co., Unit 2a High Pastures, Stortford Road, Hatfield Heath, Bishop's Stortford, Hertfordshire, CM22 7DL Tel: (01279) 739455 Fax: (01279) 739454 E-mail: james@computerisedengineering.com

Computerised Engineering Services Ltd, 11 Alverton Close, Great Hampton, Malton, North Yorkshire, YO17 6RR Tel: (07767) 834329 Fax: (01653) 669083 E-mail: info@ces-ltd.co.uk

Constant Precision, 5 Triumph Way, Woburn Road Industrial Estate, Kempston, Bedford, MK42 7QB Tel: (01234) 851131 Fax: (01234) 841265 E-mail: sales@constant-precision.co.uk

Cordelle Precision Engineers, 76 Wharfdale Road, Birmingham, B11 2DE Tel: 0121-706 0525 Fax: 0121-706 3551

Cousins Engineering, 23 Bunting Road, Northampton, NN2 6EE Tel: (01604) 712456 Fax: (01604) 719578 E-mail: sales@counsinsengineering.co.uk

Cowfold Precision Engineering, Oakendene Industrial Estate, Bolney Road, Cowfold, Horsham, West Sussex, RH13 8AZ Tel: (01403) 864945 Fax: (01403) 864945 E-mail: cowfold.precision@blueyonder.co.uk

Creaton Engineering Ltd, 6 Merse Road, Moons Moat North Industrial Es, Redditch, Worcestershire, B98 9HL Tel: (01527) 582900 Fax: (01527) 582909 E-mail: enquiries@creaton-engineering.co.uk

Crowthorne Numerical Control Ltd, 13 St Georges Industrial Estate, Wilton Road, Camberley, Surrey, GU15 2QW Tel: (01276) 20076 Fax: (01276) 685344 E-mail: info@crowthornenc.com

Currock Engineering Co. Ltd, Industrial Buildings, Beehive Lane, Chelmsford, CM2 9TE Tel: (01245) 257785 Fax: (01245) 283287 E-mail: currock@compuserve.com

Cutter Grinding Services, 22b Guildford Street, Luton, LU1 2NR Tel: (01582) 735626 Fax: (01582) 404164 E-mail: john.malia@tesco.net

Cwmbran Engineering Services, Unit 38 John Baker Close, Llantarnam Industrial Park, Cwmbran, Gwent, NP44 3AX Tel: (01633) 871616 Fax: (01633) 861052 E-mail: sales@cesmoulds.co.uk

D C E Holne Ltd, Mardle Way Industrial Estate, Buckfastleigh, Devon, TQ11 0NS Tel: (01364) 643862 Fax: (01364) 643025 E-mail: enquiries@dce-holne.co.uk

D C Engineering, Steel Close, Eaton Socon, St. Neots, Cambridgeshire, PE19 8TT Tel: (01480) 216598 Fax: (01480) 473857 E-mail: melvyn@dcengineering.fsnet.co.uk

D & G Engineering, Unit 18 Lynx Cresent, Weston-super-Mare, Avon, BS24 9DJ Tel: (01934) 628476 Fax: (01934) 418410

D J B Precision Engineering, 24 Chantry Road, Woburn Road Industrial Estate, Kempston, Bedford, MK42 7JF Tel: (01234) 840174 Fax: (01234) 855566 E-mail: djbeng@btconnect.com

▶ D M E U K, Carrwood Road, Chesterfield Trading Estate, Chesterfield, Derbyshire, S41 9QB Tel: (020) 7133 0037 Fax: (020) 7133 0036 E-mail: dme_uk@dmeeu.com

D P R Engineering, Unit 11 Prospect Business Park, Longford Road, Cannock, Staffordshire, WS11 0LG Tel: (01543) 577910 Fax: (01543) 572306

Daniels Precision Engineering, Queens Road, Southall, Middlesex, UB2 5AY Tel: (020) 8574 3037

▶ indicates data change since last edition

CNC ENGINEERING SERVICES OR MACHINISTS – *continued*

Dart Precision Engineering, 41 Eton Wick Road, Eton Wick, Windsor, Berkshire, SL4 6LU Tel: (01753) 831110 Fax: (01753) 831110

Deans Engineering Livingston Ltd, Royston Road, Deans Industrial Estate, Deans, Livingston, West Lothian, EH54 8AH Tel: (01506) 419797 Fax: (01506) 413849 E-mail: enquiries@deansengineering.com

Graham Debling Precision Engineering Ltd, 3A-4 Booth Place, Margate, Kent, CT9 1QN Tel: (01843) 298804 Fax: (01843) 298858 E-mail: gdebling@gdpe.co.uk

Denford Ltd, Birds Royd, Brighouse, Brighouse, West Yorkshire, HD6 1NB Tel: (01484) 712264 Fax: (01484) 722160 E-mail: sales@denford.co.uk

Desman Engineering Ltd, Burma Road, Blidworth, Mansfield, Nottinghamshire, NG21 0RT Tel: (01623) 490086 Fax: (01623) 490087 E-mail: sales@desman-engineering.com

Detek Ltd, 27 Granby Street, Loughborough, Leicestershire, LE11 3DU Tel: 0116-235 0244 Fax: 0116-235 8750 E-mail: detek@lineone.net

Drey Precision Ltd, 11-12 Priestley Way, Crawley, West Sussex, RH10 9NT Tel: (01293) 542695 Fax: (01293) 553703 E-mail: sales@drey.net

Drysdale Brothers (Larbert) Ltd, 346 Main Street, Stenhousemuir, Larbert, Stirlingshire, FK5 3JR Tel: (01324) 562447 Fax: (01324) 556726 E-mail: enquiries@drysdalebrothers.com

Duckworth & Kent Reading Ltd, 113 Armour Road, Tilehurst, Reading, RG31 6HB Tel: 0118-942 9828 Fax: 0118-945 1191 E-mail: duckworth.kent@btconnect.com

Dyglen Engineering Ltd, 68 Cavendish Way, Glenrothes, Fife, KY6 2SB Tel: (01592) 774881 Fax: (01592) 774871 E-mail: admin@dyglen.co.uk

Dynamic Die & Steel (Sheffield) Ltd, 136 Savile Street East, Sheffield, S4 7UQ Tel: 0114-276 1100 Fax: 0114-275 0752

E & E Engineering Ltd, Unit 74 Blackpole Trading Estate West, Worcester, WR3 8TJ Tel: (01905) 453527 Fax: (01905) 457395 E-mail: enquiries@e-and-e.co.uk

E G L Vaughan Ltd, Brook St, Glossop, Derbyshire, SK13 8BG Tel: (01457) 866614 Fax: (01457) 869364 E-mail: egl.vaughan@virgin.net

E J M Engineering Ltd, Regent Road, Countesthorpe, Leicester, LE8 5RF Tel: 0116-278 7020 Fax: 0116-278 7020 E-mail: eric@ejm-engineering.co.uk

Edwards Bros, Unit J1 Dominion Way, Rustington, Littlehampton, West Sussex, BN16 3HQ Tel: (01903) 787184 Fax: (01903) 787184

Ees Engineering Ltd, Sheddingdean Industrial Estate, Marchants Way, Burgess Hill, West Sussex, RH15 8QY Tel: (01444) 244733 Fax: (01444) 236939

Eljays Spark Erosion Services Ltd, 6 Kirby Estate, Trout Road, West Drayton, Middlesex, UB7 7RU Tel: (01895) 448380 Fax: (01895) 420977 E-mail: sales@eljays.co.uk

P.M.J. Engineering Co. Ltd, 5 & 6 Brunswick Road, Birmingham, B12 8NP Tel: 0121 4406760

Euro Moulds Ltd, Units 5 & 10 Borers Yard, Borers Arms Road, Copthorne, Crawley, West Sussex, RH10 3LH Tel: (01342) 712113 Fax: (01342) 717571 E-mail: euromoulds@btinternet.com

European CNC Turned Parts Ltd, Unit 101 Telsen Industrial Centre, Thomas Street, Birmingham, B6 4TN Tel: 0121-359 2812 Fax: 0121-359 3520 E-mail: mick@europeancnc.com

Ewen Engineering, Roscoe Road, Sheffield, S3 7DZ Tel: 0114-273 0327 Fax: 0114-275 1955 E-mail: sales@ewenengineering.co.uk

Express Engineering Thompson Ltd, Kingsway North, Team Valley Trading Estate, Gateshead, Tyne & Wear, NE11 0EG Tel: 0191-487 2021 Fax: 0191-487 3172 E-mail: sales@express-group.co.uk

Fairfield Tool & Die Co Maesteg Ltd, Cwmdu Institute, Bridgend Road, Maesteg, Mid Glamorgan, CF34 0NW Tel: (01656) 733455 Fax: (01656) 738710 E-mail: ftdtony@btconnect.com

Fairwood Engineering Ltd, Dock Road, The Docks, Port Talbot, West Glamorgan, SA13 1RA Tel: (01639) 892117 Fax: (01639) 899238 E-mail: karen@fairwoodengineering.com

Falcon Engineering Ltd, 28 Wash Road, Hutton, Brentwood, Essex, CM13 1TB Tel: (01277) 226861 Fax: (01277) 230091 E-mail: neil@faleng.demon.co.uk

Farge Engineering Stockport Ltd, 4 Greyhound Industrial Estate, Melford Road, Hazel Grove, Stockport, Cheshire, SK7 6DD Tel: 0161-456 8209 Fax: 0161-483 9738

Fastec Engineering Services Ltd, Unit 8 Studlands Park Avenue, Studlands Park Industrial Estate, Newmarket, Suffolk, CB8 7AU Tel: (01638) 660186 Fax: (01638) 667374E-mail: danny@fastecengineeing.co.uk

Flexible Machining Systems Ltd, 2-3 Blatchford Road, Horsham, West Sussex, RH13 5QR Tel: (01403) 270466 Fax: (01403) 270458 E-mail: sales@fmsltd.co.uk

Ford Component Manufacturing Ltd, East Side, Tyne Dock, South Shields, Tyne & Wear, NE33 5ST Tel: 0191-454 0141 Fax: 0191-456 0028 E-mail: sales@fordcomps.co.uk

G A Engineering, Unit 12, Ash Industrial Estate, Flex Meadow, Harlow, Essex, CM19 5TJ Tel: (01279) 414972 Fax: (01279) 416029

G B M Engineering, Unit 4 Inngae Park, Holly Lane Industrial Estate, Atherstone, Warwickshire, CV9 2NA Tel: (01827) 712213 Fax: (01827) 718503

G B Precision Engineering Co., 1 Port Hope Road, Birmingham, B11 1JS Tel: 0121-766 7008 Fax: 0121-773 2824 E-mail: info@gbprecision.co.uk

► G D K Engineering Co. Ltd, Unit 65 Blackpole Trading Estate West, Worcester, WR3 8TJ Tel: (01905) 454261 Fax: (01905) 454231 E-mail: sales@gdk-engineering.co.uk

G & R Engineering (Nantwich) Ltd, Tricketts Lane, Willaston, Nantwich, Cheshire, CW5 6PY Tel: (01270) 661033 Fax: (01270) 664524 E-mail: brian@gr-eng.fsnet.co.uk

Gemweld Fabrications & Engineering Co. Ltd, Lancaster Way, Market Deeping, Peterborough, PE6 8LA Tel: (01778) 344733 Fax: (01778) 343988 E-mail: cam@gemweld.co.uk

Genhart Ltd, 3 Malmesbury Road, Kingsditch Trading Estate, Cheltenham, Gloucestershire, GL51 9PL Tel: (01242) 241734 Fax: (01242) 227500 E-mail: frank@genhart.co.uk

Glenhead Engineering Ltd, 60 Beardmore Way, Clydebank, Dunbartonshire, G81 4HT Tel: 0141-952 9945 Fax: 0141-951 1731 E-mail: info@glenheadengineering.co.uk

Goodturn Engineering Ltd, Unit 2 Brook Street, Redditch, Worcestershire, B98 8NG Tel: (01527) 596325 Fax: (01527) 597325 E-mail: mail@goodturn-engineering.co.uk

Goodwin Technology Ltd, B2 Prenton Way, North Cheshire Trading Estate, Prenton, Merseyside, CH43 3DU Tel: 0151-608 8666 Fax: 0151-638 2456 E-mail: sales@gtprecision.co.uk

GP Precision Engineering Ltd, Unit 19 Nineteen Morses Lane, Industrial Estate, Brightlingsea, Colchester, CO7 0SF Tel: (01206) 303668 Fax: (01206) 303668 E-mail: Enquiries@GPPrecisionEngineering.co.uk

Grange Square Ltd, Halloughton Grange Whitacre Heath, Nether Whitacre, Coleshill, Birmingham, B46 2HP Tel: (01675) 481661 Fax: (01675) 481615

Greenfield Engineering Titanium Ltd, 44 Hockley Street, Hockley, Birmingham, B18 6BH Tel: 0121-507 0994 E-mail: getiuk@aol.com

Griff Chains Ltd, Quarry Road, Dudley Wood, Dudley, West Midlands, DY2 0ED Tel: (01384) 569415 Fax: (01384) 410580 E-mail: sales@griffchains.co.uk

Group 4 Engineering, Pontardawe Industrial Estate, Pontardawe, Swansea, SA8 4EN Tel: (01792) 865000 Fax: (01792) 865099 E-mail: mail@group4engineering.co.uk

H C Holifield Oxford Ltd, Nuffield Way, Abingdon, Oxfordshire, OX14 1RX Tel: (01235) 520284 Fax: (01235) 559001 E-mail: sales@holifields.co.uk

H C M Engineering Ltd, Pedmore Road, Stourbridge, West Midlands, DY9 7DZ Tel: (01384) 422643 Fax: (01384) 899210 E-mail: simonh@hcmeng.co.uk

► H K V Engineering, 16 Crawford House, West Avenue, Wigston, Leicestershire, LE18 2FB Tel: 0116-288 7751 Fax: 0116-288 7751 E-mail: carolrobinson@aol.com

H P C Engineering Plc, Victoria Gardens, Victoria Gardens Industrial Estate, Burgess Hill, West Sussex, RH15 9RQ Tel: (01444) 241671 Fax: (01444) 247587 E-mail: peterhowell@hpcplc.co.uk

H P C Services Ltd, Unit 14 Solomon Road, Ilkeston, Derbyshire, DE7 5UA Tel: 0115-932 3773 Fax: 0115-932 2857 E-mail: sales@slidinghead.com

H T S Precision Engineering Co. Ltd, Unit 3, Shamrock Quay, William Street, Northam, Southampton, SO14 5QL Tel: (023) 8033 3668 Fax: (023) 8063 7216

Halesowen Components Ltd, 126 Coombs Road, Halesowen, West Midlands, B62 8AF Tel: 0121-559 3771 Fax: 0121-561 5323 E-mail: sales@halesowencnc.co.uk

Harcol Ltd, 5 Croxstalls Road, Walsall, WS3 2XU Tel: (01922) 494951 Fax: (01922) 710370 E-mail: harcol@engs.fslife.co.uk

Hart Automation Ltd, Icknield Road, Luton, LU3 2NY Tel: (01582) 599545 Fax: (01582) 579818

Thomas Hatchard & Sons Ltd, Wellington Road, Brighton, BN41 1DN Tel: (01273) 430740 Fax: (01273) 410734 E-mail: sales@ths-eng.com

Hawk Engineering, Bessemer Road, Sheffield, S9 3XN Tel: 0114-281 7111 Fax: 0114-281 7222 E-mail: sales@hawkengineering.co.uk

Helmrick Engineers Ltd, Ossett Lane, Dewsbury, West Yorkshire, WF12 8LS Tel: (01924) 462743 Fax: (01924) 430229 E-mail: helmrickuk@aol.com

Herts & Essex Precision Engineers, Unit 10 Zone B Chelmsford Road Industrial Estate, Chelmsford Road, Dunmow, Essex, CM6 1HD Tel: (01371) 875459 Fax: (01371) 872270 E-mail: hertsessex@aol.com

Hewmor Products Ltd, Unit D4 Hilton Trading Estate, Hilton Road, Lanesfield, Wolverhampton, WV4 6DW Tel: (01902) 491144 Fax: (01902) 401952 E-mail: hewmor.products@btconnect.com

Higar Engineering Ltd, Gore Road Industrial Estate, New Milton, Hampshire, BH25 6TH Tel: (01425) 617511 Fax: (01425) 629463 E-mail: sales@higar.com

Highfield CNC Engineering Ltd, 39 Knowl Piece, Wilbury Way, Hitchin, Hertfordshire, SG4 0TY Tel: (01462) 442252 Fax: (01462) 442257 E-mail: highfieldcnc@aol.com

► Hilmax Precision Engineering Ltd, Unit 31, Sedgewick Road, Luton, LU4 9DT Tel: (01582) 573384 Fax: (01582) 508868 E-mail: info@hilmax.co.uk

Hollinwood Wood Precision Engineering Ltd, 8 Victoria Trading Estate, Drury Lane, Chadderton, Oldham, OL9 7PJ Tel: 0161-682 7900 Fax: 0161-681 4900 E-mail: sales@hollinwood.com

Stanley Horne & Sons Ltd, Bentley Mill Close, Walsall, WS2 0BN Tel: (01922) 611451 Fax: (01922) 726070 E-mail: sales@stanleyhorne.co.uk

Hudson's, Unit 33-35 Nailsea Trading Estate, Southfield Road, Nailsea, Bristol, BS48 1JE Tel: (01275) 857335 Fax: (01275) 810587 E-mail: hudsoneng@btconnect.com

Humark Engineering, Cavendish Bridge, Shardlow, Derby, DE72 2HL Tel: (01332) 799999 Fax: (01332) 799999

Hunprenco Group of Companies Ltd., Hunmanby Industrial Estate, Bridlington Road, Hunmanby, Filey, North Yorkshire, YO14 0PH Tel: (01723) 890105 Fax: (01723) 890018 E-mail: hunprenco@btinternet.com

Hyde Precision Components Ltd, Oldham Street, Denton, Manchester, M34 3SA Tel: 0161-337 9242 Fax: 0161-335 0787 E-mail: sales@hyde-precision.co.uk

I S C Ltd, Deiniolen, Caernarfon, Gwynedd, LL55 3DE Tel: (01286) 871999 Fax: (01286) 870127 E-mail: sales@iscwales.com

Industrial Plant Development Ltd, 4 Gloucester Road, Luton, LU1 3HX Tel: (01582) 731925 Fax: (01582) 480448 E-mail: ipdltd@btinternet.com

International Engine Services, 6 Moss Road, Witham, Essex, CM8 3UQ Tel: (01376) 503115 Fax: (01376) 503118 E-mail: graham@iesracing.co.uk

Intime Engineering Ledbury Ltd, 7c Lower Road, Ledbury, Herefordshire, HR8 2DH Tel: (01531) 633450 Fax: (01531) 635197 E-mail: colin@intime-eng.com

J & B Limmax, 22 Horsecroft Place, Harlow, Essex, CM19 5BX Tel: (01279) 444243 Fax: (01279) 450571 E-mail: sales@marksmanpaintball.com

J C Engineering Ltd, St. Ivel Way, Bristol, BS30 8TY Tel: 0117-961 6535 Fax: 0117-960 5657 E-mail: enquiries@jc-engineering.co.uk

J J Hardy & Sons Ltd, Brenda Road, Hartlepool, Cleveland, TS25 2BL Tel: (01429) 279837 Fax: (01429) 860182 E-mail: sales@jjhardy.co.uk

J M Lane, 121 Harecroft Road, Wisbech, Cambridgeshire, PE13 1RS Tel: (01945) 583292 Fax: (01945) 461435

J S G Engineering, Unit 3/4, Wren Centre, Westbourne Road, Emsworth, Hampshire, PO10 7SU Tel: (01243) 379698 Fax: (01243) 379857 E-mail: jim@jsgeng.fsnet.co.uk

James Engineering Ltd, Prenton Way, North Cheshire Trading Estate, Prenton, Merseyside, CH43 3DU Tel: 0151-609 1000 Fax: 0151-609 0741 E-mail: sales@jameseng.com

Jaybee Engineering Co Brighton Ltd, Avis Way, Newhaven, East Sussex, BN9 0DS Tel: (01273) 514623 Fax: (01273) 513702 E-mail: sales@jaybee-eng.co.uk

Jencol Engineering Ltd, 1 Somersham Road, St. Ives, Cambridgeshire, PE27 3LN Tel: (01480) 492922 Fax: (01480) 492926 E-mail: sales@jencolengineering.co.uk

K M Industrial Products Ltd, Unit 23, Mackintosh Road, Rackheath Industrial Estate, Rackheath, Norwich, NR13 6LJ Tel: (01603) 720792 Fax: (01603) 721192 E-mail: kmindustrial@fsmail.net

Kalstan Engineering Ltd, Cavendish Road, Stevenage, Hertfordshire, SG1 2ET Tel: (01438) 745588 Fax: (01438) 360579 E-mail: sjkalmar@kalstanengineering.co.uk

Kenard Engineering Co. Ltd, Green Street Green Road, Dartford, DA1 1QE Tel: (01322) 421200 Fax: (01322) 421220 E-mail: info@kenard.co.uk

William S Kenyon Ltd, 131 Town Street, Sandiacre, Nottingham, NG10 5DS Tel: 0115-939 8800 Fax: 0115-939 1404 E-mail: info@turnedparts.co.uk

Kerndale Ltd, Pontygwindy Industrial Estate, Caerphilly, Mid Glamorgan, CF83 3HU Tel: (029) 2086 5152 Fax: (029) 2088 7742 E-mail: tonydoel@kerndale.demon.co.uk

Kiwi Products Dartford Ltd, 12 Dickens Court, Enterprise Close, Medway City Estate, Rochester, Kent, ME2 4LY Tel: (01634) 718484 Fax: (01634) 718484 E-mail: enquiries@kiwiproducts.co.uk

Knightsridge Engineering Services Ltd, 10 Nettlehill Road, Houstoun Industrial Estate, Livingston, West Lothian, EH54 5DL Tel: (01506) 430605 Fax: (01506) 440380 E-mail: kesl@btconnect.com

Krouse Precision Engineering Ltd, Carterton Industrial Estate, Black Bourton Road, Carterton, Oxfordshire, OX18 3EZ Tel: (01993) 843683 Fax: (01993) 840539 E-mail: sales@jdkrouse.co.uk

L Person & Son Ltd, 33 Hollands Road, Haverhill, Suffolk, CB9 8PU Tel: (01440) 702811 Fax: (01440) 702711 E-mail: david@personhaverhill.freeserve.co.uk

Laig Engineering Ltd, 1 Bunting Road, Bury St. Edmunds, Suffolk, IP32 7BX Tel: (01284) 763852 Fax: (01284) 706866 E-mail: info@laig.uk.com

Lamberton Ltd, Block G, West Way, Porterfield Road, Renfrew, PA4 8DJ Tel: 0141-889 1660 Fax: 0141-887 4829

Langton Engineering, Denmark Street, Maidenhead, Berkshire, SL6 7BN Tel: (01628) 632764 Fax: (01628) 776183

Lantern Engineering Ltd, Hamilton Road, Maltby, Rotherham, South Yorkshire, S66 7NE Tel: (01709) 813636 Fax: (01709) 817130 E-mail: sales@lantern.co.uk

Lecol Engineering Ltd, 123 Barr Street, Birmingham, B19 3DE Tel: 0121-523 0404 Fax: 0121-523 2372

Lesk Engineers Ltd, Carden Street, Worcester, WR1 2AX Tel: (01905) 23187 Fax: (01905) 612536E-mail: company@leskengineers.co.uk

Lister Precision Components Ltd, 27 Benedict Square, Werrington, Peterborough, PE4 6GD Tel: (01733) 573700 Fax: (01733) 326224 E-mail: keith@listerprecision.co.uk

Logica Engineering Ltd, 2 Firbank Court, Firbank Way, Leighton Buzzard, Bedfordshire, LU7 4YJ Tel: (01525) 373377 Fax: (01525) 853377

Lymington Precision Engineers, Gosport Street, Lymington, Hampshire, SO41 9EE Tel: (01590) 677944 Fax: (01590) 647000

M & D Tooling, 12a Carvers Trading Estate, Southampton Road, Ringwood, Hampshire, BH24 1JS Tel: (01425) 489945 Fax: (01425) 489946

M G Sanders Co. Ltd, Newcastle Street, Stone, Staffordshire, ST15 8JU Tel: (01785) 815544 Fax: (01785) 815642 E-mail: sales@mgsanders.co.uk

M J B Engineering Ltd, 133 Barkers Lane, Bedford, MK41 9RX Tel: (01234) 358454 Fax: (01234) 273423 E-mail: sales@mjbengineering.co.uk

M J Raven & Son Ltd, Unit 22 Patricia Way, Pysons Road Industrial Estate, Broadstairs, Kent, CT10 2LF Tel: (01843) 866676 Fax: (01843) 866070 E-mail: sales@mjraven.co.uk

M P M Presstools, 1 Chancel Way Industrial Estate, Chancel Way, Birmingham, B6 7AU Tel: 0121-356 7600 Fax: 0121-356 9766 E-mail: mpm.presstools@btconnect.com

M&B, Blaby Industrial Park, Winchester Avenue, Blaby, Leicester, LE8 4GZ Tel: 0116-277 6363 Fax: 0116-278 7871 E-mail: enquiries@mbgears.co.uk

Machined Fabrications Ltd, 20 Blowers Green Road, Dudley, West Midlands, DY2 8UP Tel: (01384) 257681 Fax: (01384) 241571 E-mail: machfabs@aol.com

Malcolm Engineering Co. Ltd, Banks Road, McMullen Industrial Estate, Darlington, County Durham, DL1 1YF Tel: (01325) 461549 Fax: (01325) 381196 E-mail: malco@malcolm-eng.co.uk

Marnol Precision Engineering, Unit 9 Bee-Hive Trading Estate, 72-78 Crews Hole Road, St. George, Bristol, BS5 8AY Tel: (01275) 50095

Marrill Engineering Co. Ltd, Waterman Road, Coventry, CV6 5TP Tel: (024) 7668 9221 Fax: (024) 7666 8114 E-mail: sales@marrill.co.uk

Melborha Engineering Co. Ltd, Unit B, Cradock Road, Luton, LU4 0JF Tel: (01582) 494387

Mercantile Met-Tech Ltd, Plumpton House, Plumpton Road, Hoddesdon, Hertfordshire, EN11 0LB Tel: (01992) 445709 Fax: (01992) 467217 E-mail: info@mercantilemettech.co.uk

Metfab Design Ltd, Unit 220 Foley Industrial Estate, Kidderminster, Worcestershire, DY11 7DH Tel: (01562) 864129 Fax: (01562) 864129

Micra Pattern Co. Ltd, 91 Sorby Street, Sheffield, S4 7LA Tel: 0114 2720724

Microtec CNC Ltd, 370 Thurmaston Boulevard, Troon Industrial Area, Leicester, LE4 9LE Tel: 0116-246 0020 Fax: 0116-246 1006 E-mail: postmaster@microtec.uk.com

Microtech Precision Ltd, Unit D1 Bersham Enterprise Centre, Colliery Road, Rhostyllen, Wrexham, Clwyd, LL14 4EG Tel: (01978) 362295 Fax: (01978) 352043 E-mail: sales@microtechprecision.co.uk

Millturn Engineering, 17 Burrel Road, St. Ives, Cambridgeshire, PE27 3LE Tel: (01480) 469644 Fax: (01480) 469342

Mogul Engineers Ltd, Chesterton Road, Eastwood Trading Estate, Rotherham, South Yorkshire, S65 1SU Tel: (01709) 379293 Fax: (01709) 378869 E-mail: enquires@mogul-engineers.co.uk

Mold Systems, Millennium Way, Heighington Lane Business Park, Newton Aycliffe, County Durham, DL5 6JW Tel: (01325) 328700 Fax: (01325) 328707 E-mail: sales@moldsystems.com

MTS, Greenside Way, Middleton, Manchester, M24 1SW Tel: 0161-345 4760 Fax: 0161-345 4766 E-mail: sales@mtsprecision.co.uk

Muller Redditch Ltd, Bartleet Road, Washford Industrial Estate, Redditch, Worcestershire, B98 0DG Tel: (01527) 526920 Fax: (01527) 502166 E-mail: sales@muller-redditch.co.uk

N R Automatics Ltd, Duckworth Mill, Skipton Road, Colne, Lancashire, BB8 0RH Tel: (01282) 868500 Fax: (01282) 869885

Neida Products Engineering Ltd, Trentham Lakes South, Stoke-on-Trent, ST4 8GQ Tel: (01782) 643643 Fax: (01782) 644220 E-mail: sales@neida.co.uk

Newburgh Engineering Co. Ltd, Newburgh Works, Bradwell, Hope Valley, Derbyshire, S33 9NT Tel: (01709) 724260 E-mail: sales@newburgh.co.uk

Newcom Precision Engineering Ltd, 1 Earith Business Park, Meadow Drove, Earith, Huntingdon, Cambridgeshire, PE28 3QF Tel: (01487) 840870 Fax: (01487) 740046 E-mail: info@newcom-engineering.co.uk

Newcut Precision, Northern Mill Industrial Estate, Field Road, Ramsey, Huntingdon, Cambridgeshire, PE26 1JD Tel: (01487) 813131 Fax: (01487) 812400

CNC ENGINEERING SERVICES OR MACHINISTS – *continued*

Newman Stallard Precision Engineers Ltd, 2 Westwood Court, Brunel Road, Totton, Southampton, SO40 3WX Tel: (023) 8086 4291 Fax: (023) 8042 8146

Newport Spark Erosion Services, 18-19 South Road, Harlow, Essex, CM20 2AR Tel: (01279) 415900 Fax: (01279) 454753 E-mail: sales@newport-eng.co.uk

Normec (Manchester) Ltd, Westwood Industrial Estate, Arkwright Street, Oldham, OL9 9LZ Tel: 0161-627 2367 Fax: 0161-627 2378 E-mail: admin@normecmanchester.co.uk

Nusell Engineering Co, 484 Penistone Road, Sheffield, S6 2FU Tel: 0114-233 0244 Fax: 0114-232 6998

Nutter Aircrafts Ltd, New Works, Chadwick Street, Blackburn, BB2 4AA Tel: (01254) 505200 Fax: (01254) 505205

O E S Ltd, Unit S1 Didcot Enterprise Centre, Southmead Industrial Pk, Hawksworth, Didcot, Oxon, OX11 7PH Tel: (01235) 511922 Fax: (01235) 511822

Olympic Engineering, Unit F5 Charles House, Bridge Road, Southall, Middlesex, UB2 4BD Tel: (020) 8574 4406 Fax: (020) 8571 1556 E-mail: oloieng@aol.com

Ottaway Engineering Ltd, Renown Close, Chandlers Ford Industrial Estate, Chandler's Ford, Eastleigh, Hampshire, SO53 4HZ Tel: (023) 8026 9977 Fax: (023) 8027 0270 E-mail: info@otteng.co.uk

Oxford Network Support, 6 Colwell Drive, Abingdon, Oxfordshire, OX14 1AU Tel: (01235) 468530 Fax: (01235) 555581 E-mail: sales@oxfordnetworksupport.com

Oxford Precision Components, Unit 1-5 Osney Mead, Oxford, OX2 0ES Tel: (01865) 798338 Fax: (01865) 798555

P M P L Telford Ltd, Unit 25 Heath Hill Industrial Estate, Dawley, Telford, Shropshire, TF4 2RH Tel: (01952) 507978 Fax: (01952) 507978 E-mail: daviespmp@aol.com

P M Precision Engineering, Unit 2A, Bridge Works, Bridge Road, Camberley, Surrey, GU15 2QR Tel: (01276) 691285 Fax: (01276) 27193 E-mail: hillary@pmeng.co.uk

▶ P R Smith Engineering, Station Works, Lyndhurst Road, Ascot, Berkshire, SL5 9ED Tel: (01344) 874763 Fax: (01344) 875433 E-mail: topmut@themutznutz.com

Padmode Ltd, Unit 9 Denvers Yard, Ware, Hertfordshire, SG11 1AL Tel: (01279) 843035

Paragon Toolmaking & Precision Engineering Co. Ltd, 321 National Avenue, Hull, HU5 4JB Tel: (01482) 343439 Fax: (01482) 448623 E-mail: sales@paragon-tools.co.uk

Partex Engineering, 7a Hicks Road, Markyate, St. Albans, Hertfordshire, AL3 8LJ Tel: (01582) 840188 Fax: (01582) 840188

PDL Engineering Ltd, 5 Whittle Road, Ferndown Industrial Estate, Wimborne, Dorset, BH21 7RJ Tel: (01202) 871188 Fax: (01202) 892499

PDQ Engineering Ltd, Industrial Road, Hertburn, Washington, Tyne & Wear, NE37 2SA Tel: 0191-417 2343 Fax: 0191-416 5518 E-mail: john@pdqengineering.com

Pegmount Ltd, Unit 1 Apex Centre, Lovell, Lichfield Road Industrial Estate, Tamworth, Staffordshire, B79 7TA Tel: (01827) 68804 Fax: (01827) 69929 E-mail: sales@phoenixmanufacturing.co.uk

Phoenix Precision Ltd, Crompton Road, Southfield Industrial Estate, Glenrothes, Fife, KY6 2SF Tel: (01592) 772077 Fax: (01592) 773535 E-mail: sales@phoenixprecision.com

Phoenix Turned Parts, 4-5 Mica Close, Tamworth, Staffordshire, B77 4DR Tel: (01827) 59441 Fax: (01827) 54750 E-mail: mike.pegg@btbusinessconnect.co.uk

PJP Precision Engineering Ltd, 5 Berkshire Business Centre, Berkshire Drive, Thatcham, Berkshire, RG19 4EW Tel: (01635) 872792 Fax: (01635) 864390 E-mail: pjpm@msn.com

Plastic Machining Services, Halesfield 23, Telford, Shropshire, TF7 4NY Tel: (01952) 680369 Fax: (01952) 680371E-mail: info@p-m-s.co.uk

Portsmouth Aviation Ltd, Airport Service Road, Portsmouth, PO3 5PF Tel: (023) 9266 2251 Fax: (023) 9267 3690 E-mail: info@portav.co.uk

Precision Services Of Redditch, 59 Padgets Lane, Redditch, Worcestershire, B98 0RD Tel: (01527) 528000 Fax: (01527) 517174

Premax Engineering Ltd, 56 Porchester Street, Birmingham, B19 2LA Tel: 0121-359 5380 Fax: 0121-333 3097 E-mail: info@premax.co.uk

Pretech Engineering, Barrett Court, Cardiff Road, Reading, RG1 8ED Tel: 0118-957 3123 Fax: 0118-957 3123 E-mail: info@pretech.co.uk

Pro-Tech Precision Ltd, Station Road West, Ash Vale, Aldershot, Hampshire, GU12 5QD Tel: (01252) 516242 Fax: (01252) 524025 E-mail: sales@pro-techprecision.com

Qualicut Engineering Ltd, Wharf Street, Chadderton, Oldham, OL9 7PF Tel: 0161-633 1633 Fax: 0161-633 1660 E-mail: info@qualicut.co.uk

Qualiturn Products Ltd, 18 Merchant Drive, Mead Lane, Hertford, SG13 7AY Tel: (01992) 584499 Fax: (01992) 551726 E-mail: kssales@qualiturn.co.uk

▶ Quayside Precision Engineering, Unit 14-15 Vancouver Wharf, Hazel Road, Southampton, SO19 7BN Tel: (023) 8043 9700 Fax: (023) 8043 9701

Quelch Engineering Ltd, Threaf House, Wallingford Road, Uxbridge, Middlesex, UB8 2RW Tel: (01895) 233225 Fax: (01895) 811047 E-mail: doug@quelcheng.co.uk

R D Precision Ltd, Golden Hill Park, Freshwater, Isle Of Wight, PO40 9UJ Tel: (01983) 754811 Fax: (01983) 754186 E-mail: info@rdprecisions.co.uk

R J B Engineering Ltd, Unit 5 Oak Industrial Park, Chelmsford Road, Dunmow, Essex, CM6 1XN Tel: (01371) 876377 Fax: (01371) 876378 E-mail: rbrown7571@aol.com

R & K Metal Components, Unit 37 Claro Court Business Centre, Claro Road, Harrogate, North Yorkshire, HG1 4BA Tel: (01423) 523139 Fax: (01423) 523139

R M W Witney Ltd, Unit 10br Bromag Industrial Estate, Burford Road, Minster Lovell, Witney, Oxfordshire, OX29 0SR Tel: (01993) 702505 Fax: (01993) 774103 E-mail: sales@rmwwitneyltd.co.uk

R Mcmahon Engineering Ltd, Unit 5 Oldends Industrial Estate, Oldends, Stonehouse, Gloucestershire, GL10 3RQ Tel: (01453) 828666 Fax: (01453) 828360 E-mail: howard@mcmahon-engineering.com

R P A International Ltd, P.O. Box 441, Tonbridge, Kent, TN9 9DZ Tel: (0845) 8803222 E-mail: info@rpainternational.co.uk

Rayburn Plastics Ltd, Whitehouse Street, Walsall, WS2 8HR Tel: (01922) 625572 Fax: (01922) 723333 E-mail: sales@rayburn.co.uk

C. Rayment (Precision Engineering) Ltd, Addison Road, Chilton Industrial Estate, Sudbury, Suffolk, CO10 2YW Tel: (01787) 372697 Fax: (01787) 881448 E-mail: sales@c-rayment.demon.co.uk

Rayne Precision Engineering Ltd, Unit 5 Far Lane Industrial Estat, Froghall Road, Ipstones, Stoke-on-Trent, ST10 2NA Tel: (01538) 266100 Fax: (01538) 266800 E-mail: rayne_precision@yahoo.co.uk

Read Precision Engineering Ltd, 10 William Street, Northampton, NN1 3EW Tel: (01604) 601372 Fax: (01604) 601373 E-mail: sales@readengineering.co.uk

Redline C N C, Units 4-5, 15 Balcombe Road, Horley, Surrey, RH6 7JR Tel: (01293) 820090 Fax: (01293) 820091 E-mail: sales@redline-cnc.co.uk

Reldale Ltd, 60 Dunster Street, Northampton, NN1 3JY Tel: (01604) 632438 Fax: (01604) 632438 E-mail: enquiries@reldaleltd.co.uk

Richard A Fores Ltd, Dagmar Road, Southall, Middlesex, UB2 5NX Tel: (020) 8574 5287 Fax: (020) 8574 3105 E-mail: r.a.fores@btinternet.com

Robinson Pattern Equipment Ltd, Rabone Lane, Smethwick, West Midlands, B66 3JH Tel: 0121-558 4576 Fax: 0121-555 5295 E-mail: sales@robpatequip.demon.co.uk

Rojak Tool & Die Co. Ltd, Falkland Close, Coventry, CV4 8AU Tel: (024) 7646 7969 Fax: (024) 7669 4458 E-mail: rojak@ukf.net

Roton Precision Engineering Ltd, The Old Ambulance, Stansfield Road, Todmorden, Lancashire, OL14 5DL Tel: (01706) 813399 Fax: (01706) 813399

Rousant Sherwood Ltd, Van Alloys Indust Estate, Busgrove Lane, Stoke Row, Henley-on-Thames, Oxfordshire, RG9 5QW Tel: (01491) 680767 Fax: (01491) 682290 E-mail: rousant@msn.com

S E S Precision Engineers Ltd, 206 Bromley Road, Catford, London, SE6 2XA Tel: (020) 8461 4240 Fax: (020) 8695 6561

S J Clifford & Co. Ltd, B 19 Bayton Road Industrial Estate, Bayton Road, Exhall, Coventry, CV7 9EL Tel: (024) 7636 3961 Fax: (024) 7664 4097 E-mail: sales@sjclifford.co.uk

S & S Precision Engineering Ltd, 23 Rainhill Close, East Stephenson Industrial Estate, Washington, Tyne & Wear, NE37 3HN Tel: 0191-416 2184 Fax: 0191-419 1586 E-mail: bob@ssprecision.com

Saygrove System & Technology, Units 9-10 Catheralls Industrial Estate, Brookhill Way, Buckley, Clwyd, CH7 3PS Tel: (01244) 550022 Fax: (01244) 549843 E-mail: info@saygrove.co.uk

Scrutton Engineering Ltd, Duck Lees Lane Industrial Estate, 73 East Duck Lees Lane, Enfield, Middlesex, EN3 7SR Tel: (020) 8443 4010 Fax: (020) 8609 0050 E-mail: info@selfab.com

Servex Ltd, Bellingdon Road, Chesham, Buckinghamshire, HP5 2NN Tel: (01494) 784501 Fax: (01494) 784086 E-mail: engineering@servexltd.co.uk

Shanick Engineering Co. Ltd, Byfield Place, Bognor Regis, West Sussex, PO22 9QY Tel: (01243) 863666 Fax: (01243) 827629 E-mail: shannick.eng@surfree.co.uk

▶ SJA UK Ltd, 5 Lupton Road, Thame Industrial Estate, Thame, Oxfordshire, OX9 3SE Tel: (01844) 218275 E-mail: steve@sjalimited.co.uk

▶ Slater & Crabtree Ltd, Thornes Lane, Wakefield, West Yorkshire, WF1 5RW Tel: (01924) 374874 Fax: (01924) 378288 E-mail: precision@slatercrabtree.co.uk

Sprite Engineering Ltd, 10 Lenziemill Road, Cumbernauld, Glasgow, G67 2RL Tel: (01236) 457970 Fax: (01236) 457970

Squires Gear & Engineering Ltd, 98 Swan Lane, Coventry, CV2 4GB Tel: (024) 7623 1110 Fax: (024) 7623 1112 E-mail: djs@squires-gear.co.uk

Streamline Precision Ltd, Spedding Road, Fenton Industrial Estate, Fenton, Stoke-On-Trent, ST4 2ST Tel: (01782) 847408 Fax: (01782) 749261

Survirn Engineering Ltd, 1581 Bristol Road South, Rednal, Birmingham, B45 9UA Tel: 0121-453 7718 Fax: 0121-453 6915 E-mail: sales@survirn.co.uk

P.B. Sutton Engineering Co, 3 Hedley Road, St. Albans, Hertfordshire, AL1 5JL Tel: (01727) 858731 Fax: (01727) 847064 E-mail: hazel@pbsuttonsagehost.co.uk

Swefco Ltd, 188 Corporation Road, Newport, Gwent, NP19 0DQ Tel: (01633) 250170 Fax: (01633) 250171E-mail: swefco@aol.com

Swift, Unit 13 Glover Centre, Egmont Street, Mossley, Ashton-under-Lyne, Lancashire, OL5 9PY Tel: (01457) 834005 Fax: (01457) 836617 E-mail: enquiries@swiftengineering.co.uk

T M Engineers Midlands Ltd, Oak Lane, Kingswinford, West Midlands, DY6 7JW Tel: (01384) 400212 Fax: (01384) 296019 E-mail: sales@tmengineers.co.uk

T P Cooke, 1 Kym Road, Bicton Industrial Park, Kimbolton, Huntingdon, Cambridgeshire, PE28 0LW Tel: (01480) 860138 Fax: (01480) 860138 E-mail: tpcookeengineering@btinternet.com

T R Precision Engineering Co. Ltd, 1 Wattville Road, Smethwick, West Midlands, B66 2NT Tel: 0121-565 1384 Fax: 0121-565 2946 E-mail: trprecision@btconnect.com

Taylor & Whiteley Ltd, Riverside House,, Queen Square Business Park, Huddersfield Road, Honley, Holmfirth, HD9 6QZ Tel: (01484) 662059 Fax: (01484) 665373

Tenable Screw Company Ltd, 16 Deer Park Road, London, SW19 3UB Tel: (020) 8542 6225 Fax: (020) 8543 5789 E-mail: sales@tenable.co.uk

E.H. Thompson & Son (London) Ltd, Hallsford Bridge Industrial Estate, Stondon Road, Ongar, Essex, CM5 9RB Tel: (01277) 365500 Fax: (01277) 365550 E-mail: ehthompsons@btconnects.com

Thornpark Ltd, B1-B2 Pegasus Court, Ardglen Road, Whitchurch, Hampshire, RG28 7BP Tel: (01256) 896161 Fax: (01256) 896162 E-mail: sales@thornpark.co.uk

Thunder Engineering, 1 Garfield Street, Leicester, LE4 5GF Tel: 0116-253 1105 Fax: 0116-253 1105

Trident Microsystems Ltd, Perrywood Business Park, Honeycrock Lane, Redhill, RH1 5JQ Tel: (01737) 780790 Fax: (01737) 771908 E-mail: sales@trident-uk.co.uk

Tryang Jig & Gauge Co., Unit 3-4 Wynford Industrial Estate, Wynford Road, Birmingham, B27 6JP Tel: 0121-706 8050 Fax: 0121-765 4294 E-mail: mikedavis@tryang.fsbusiness.co.uk

Turnbridge Engineering Ltd, Hanworth Court, Hanworth Road, Low Moor, Bradford, West Yorkshire, BD12 0SG Tel: (01274) 693699 Fax: (01274) 693944 E-mail: admin@turnbridge.co.uk

Turnell & Odell Ltd, 61-65 Sanders Road, Finedon Road Industrial Estate, Wellingborough, Northamptonshire, NN8 4NL Tel: (01933) 222061 Fax: (01933) 440073 E-mail: sales@toengineering.co.uk

Turner Aluminium Castings Ltd, 1 Robinson Close, Telford Way Industrial Estate, Kettering, Northamptonshire, NN16 8PU Tel: (01536) 525270 Fax: (01536) 412367

V L B Products Ltd, 12 Birch Road East Industrial Estate, Birch Road East, Birmingham, B6 7DB Tel: 0121-328 4575

Vetraform Ltd, Unit 19-20, Halesfield 18, Telford, Shropshire, TF7 4PP Tel: (01952) 587631 Fax: (01952) 582596 E-mail: alex@vetraform.co.uk

W A Engineering (Nuneaton) Ltd, Carlyon Road, Carlyon Road Industrial Estate, Atherstone, Warwickshire, CV9 1LQ Tel: (01827) 715188 Fax: (01827) 717168 E-mail: sales@waengineering.co.uk

W E C S Precision Ltd, Blenheim Road, Longmead Industrial Estate, Epsom, Surrey, KT19 9BE Tel: (01372) 741633 Fax: (01372) 740539 E-mail: npooles@wecsprecision.com

Warman CNC, 214 Moseley Street, Birmingham, B5 6LE Tel: 0121-622 4045 Fax: 0121-666 6539 E-mail: warmancnc@aol.com

Wellvil Engineering Company Ltd, Spring Place, New Street, Luton, LU1 5DF Tel: (01582) 727171

Wenda Electronics & Engineering, 47 Cobham Road, Ferndown Industrial Estate, Wimborne, Dorset, BH21 7QZ Tel: (01202) 874961 Fax: (01202) 861260 E-mail: wendasheetmetal@cwcom.net

Westcom Engineers, Global Park, East Gates Industrial Estate, Colchester, CO1 2TW Tel: (01206) 794114 Fax: (01206) 792749 E-mail: admin@westcomeng.fsnet.co.uk

Westway Precision Engineering Ltd, Henty Road, Southampton, SO16 4GF Tel: (023) 8078 9229 Fax: (023) 8070 2967

Widdowson-Dalebrook Engineers Ltd, Basford Road, Crewe, CW2 6ES Tel: 01270 661111

Williams & Co Southampton Ltd, Victoria Street, Southampton, SO14 5QZ Tel: (023) 8022 0490 Fax: (023) 8063 8930 E-mail: sales@williams-eng.co.uk

Wrekin Shell Mouldings Ltd, Unit D1 & D2, Halesfield 21, Telford, Shropshire, TF7 4NX Tel: (01952) 580946 Fax: (01952) 582546 E-mail: wsm@dynafluid.com

York Assemblies Ltd, 374 Thurmaston BLVD, Leicester, LE4 9LE Tel: 0116-246 3240

CNC ENGINEERING SERVICES OR MACHINISTS, HIGH SPEED

Allendale Components, 28 Allendale Tee, New Marske, Redcar, Cleveland, TS11 8HN Tel: (01642) 478738 Fax: (01642) 272683 E-mail: p.wall@ntlworld.com

Creaton Engineering Ltd, 6 Merse Road, Moons Moat North Industrial Es, Redditch, Worcestershire, B98 9HL Tel: (01527) 582900 Fax: (01527) 582909 E-mail: enquiries@creaton-engineering.co.uk

Crowthorne Numerical Control Ltd, 13 St Georges Industrial Estate, Wilton Road, Camberley, Surrey, GU15 2QW Tel: (01276) 20076 Fax: (01276) 685344 E-mail: info@crowthornenc.com

D C Engineering, Steel Close, Eaton Socon, St. Neots, Cambridgeshire, PE19 8TT Tel: (01480) 216598 Fax: (01480) 473857 E-mail: melvyn@dcengineering.fsnet.co.uk

H C Holifield Oxford Ltd, Nuffield Way, Abingdon, Oxfordshire, OX14 1RX Tel: (01235) 520284 Fax: (01235) 559001 E-mail: sales@holifields.co.uk

J&B, 7 Cambridge Road, Granby Industrial Estate, Weymouth, Dorset, DT4 9TJ Tel: (01305) 775377 Fax: (01305) 780443

CNC ENGINEERING SERVICES OR MACHINISTS, THREE DIMENSIONAL (3D)

Dimmock Engineering, Unit 6 Westbury Close, Houghton Regis, Dunstable, Bedfordshire, LU5 5BL Tel: (01582) 602588 Fax: (01582) 602588 E-mail: sjdimmock1@aol.com

Jbi Technology Ltd, Unit 2-3 Bond Street, West Bromwich, West Midlands, B70 7DQ Tel: 0121-553 0500 Fax: 0121-553 5333 E-mail: info@jbitech.co.uk

Robinson Pattern Equipment Ltd, Rabone Lane, Smethwick, West Midlands, B66 3JH Tel: 0121-558 4576 Fax: 0121-555 5295 E-mail: sales@robpatequip.demon.co.uk

▶ Sentripod Survey Company Ltd, The Lodge, 13 The Hamlet, Chippenham, Wiltshire, SN15 1BY Tel: (01249) 462039 Fax: (01249) 462039 E-mail: info@sentripod.co.uk

▶ SJA UK Ltd, 5 Lupton Road, Thame Industrial Estate, Thame, Oxfordshire, OX9 3SE Tel: (01844) 218275 E-mail: steve@sjalimited.co.uk

CNC GRINDING

Bedestone Ltd, Boulton Ho, 41 Icknield St, Hockley, Birmingham, B18 5AY Tel: 0121-554 3283 Fax: 0121-507 0140 E-mail: bedestone@aol.com

C & G Cutters & Grinding Ltd, Clarendon Road, Blackburn, BB1 9SS Tel: (01254) 663193 Fax: (01254) 665139 E-mail: sales@cg-grind-eng-serv.co.uk

Davies Precision Grinding Ltd, 282 Upper Balsall Heath Road, Birmingham, B12 9DR Tel: 0121-440 4400 Fax: 0121-440 1414

Kepston Holdings Ltd, Unit 2 Coppice Lane, Walsall, WS9 9AA Tel: (01922) 743133 Fax: (01922) 743130 E-mail: sales@kepston.co.uk

Multi-Grind Services Ltd, Unit 10, Harefield Road Industrial Estate, Rickmansworth, Hertfordshire, WD3 1PQ Tel: (01923) 725230 Fax: (01923) 777915 E-mail: steve@multigrind.co.uk

N C Geary (Precision Engineering), 10 Mill Road, Christchurch, Dorset, BH23 2JY Tel: (01202) 483585 Fax: (01202) 471163 E-mail: nick@geary-engineering.co.uk

CNC GRINDING MACHINES

Aaron Manufacturing Ltd, Unit K-L Waterside, 25-27 Willis Way, Poole, Dorset, BH15 3TD Tel: (01202) 670071 Fax: (01202) 682952 E-mail: enquiries@aaronmanufacturing.co.uk

CNC LASER CUTTING SERVICES

Dyer Engineering Ltd, Unit 3-5 Morrison Industrial Estate North, Stanley, County Durham, DH9 7RU Tel: (01207) 234355 Fax: (01207) 282834 E-mail: sales@dyer-engineering.ltd.uk

Prima Industrie UK Ltd, Unit 1 Phoenix Park, Bayton Road Industrial Estate, Coventry, CV7 9QN Tel: (024) 7664 5588 Fax: (024) 7664 5115 E-mail: info@primauk.com

Standard & Pochin Ltd, 94 Lyde Road, Yeovil, Somerset, BA21 5DS Tel: (01935) 421481 Fax: (01935) 428030 E-mail: info@ijmcgilltransport.com

CNC LASER CUTTING SOFTWARE

MTC Software Ltd, 7 Clarendon Place, Leamington Spa, Warwickshire, CV32 5QL Tel: (0870) 8031297 Fax: (0870) 8031298 E-mail: mtc@mtc-europe.co.uk

CNC LATHE CUTTING TOOLS

Brooke Cutting Tools (UK) Ltd, Denby Way, Hellaby, Rotherham, South Yorkshire, S66 8HU Tel: (01709) 314500 Fax: (01709) 314501 E-mail: info@brooke.co.uk

Emi-Mec, Unit E2 Doulton Road Trading Estate, Doulton Road, Rowley Regis, West Midlands, B65 8JQ Tel: (01384) 633968 Fax: (01384) 633946 E-mail: sales@emi-mec.eu

F & C Automatic Production Ltd, Quarry Road, Newhaven, East Sussex, BN9 9DG Tel: (01273) 515485 Fax: (01273) 517827

High Speed & Carbide Ltd, Freedom Works, John St, Sheffield, S2 4QT Tel: 0114-279 6197 Fax: 0114-279 7550 E-mail: sales@hscknives.co.uk

CNC LATHES

Charter Engineering Services, 6 Sycamore Centre, Sycamore Road, Eastwood Trading Estate, Rotherham, South Yorkshire, S65 1EN Tel: (01709) 836822 Fax: (01709) 836955 E-mail: sales@chartmach.co.uk

Clovelly Engineering Ltd, Unit 59, Lunsford Road, Leicester, LE5 0HW Tel: 0116-246 1831 Fax: 0116-246 1474E-mail: clovellyt@aol.com

Colchester Lathe Co. Ltd, P O Box 20, Heckmondwike, West Yorkshire, WF16 0HN Tel: (01924) 412603 Fax: (01924) 412604 E-mail: sales@colchester.co.uk

Crawford-Swift, Rosemount Works, Huddersfield Road, Elland, West Yorkshire, HX5 0EE Tel: (01422) 379222 Fax: (01422) 379122 E-mail: mail@crawfordswift.co.uk

Datamach Ltd, Falkland Close, Charter Avenue Industrial Estate, Coventry, CV4 8AU Tel: (024) 7647 0707 Fax: (024) 7646 4059 E-mail: enquiries@datamach.co.uk

Dean Smith & Grace Ltd, PO Box 15, Keighley, West Yorkshire, BD21 4PG Tel: (01535) 605261 Fax: (01535) 680921 E-mail: mail@deansmithandgrace.co.uk

Fairbank Brearley International Ltd, Crown Works, Grantham Road, Halifax, West Yorkshire, HX3 6PL Tel: (01422) 360231 Fax: (01422) 355157 E-mail: mail@smarttecgroup.com

Global Machine Tools, Sudmeadow Road, Gloucester, GL2 5HG Tel: (01452) 526089 Fax: (01452) 307157 E-mail: mail@globalmachinetools.com

Hillcrest Machinery Engineering Portchester Ltd, 1 Pennant Park, Standard Way, Fareham, Hampshire, PO16 8XU Tel: (01329) 231245 Fax: (01329) 822753 E-mail: office@hillcresteng.co.uk

Hullmatic Engineering Ltd, 1 Lancaster Way Earls Colne Business Park, Airfield, Earls Colne, Colchester, CO6 2NS Tel: (01787) 222099 Fax: (01787) 224317 E-mail: hullmatic@aol.com

M H C Industrials Ltd, Wetmore Road, Burton-On-Trent, Staffordshire, DE14 1QN Tel: (01283) 564651 Fax: (01283) 511526 E-mail: sales@mhcind.co.uk

Mills Manufacturing Technology, Tachbrook Park Drive, Warwick, CV34 6RH Tel: (01926) 736736 Fax: (01926) 736737 E-mail: sales@millscnc.co.uk

MS Pollard Ltd, St. Saviours Rd, Leicester, LE5 4HP Tel: 0116-276 7534 Fax: 0116-274 1547 E-mail: finn@mspollard.com

Somerset Machine Tools, 29 Brimbleworth Lane, St. Georges, Weston-super-Mare, Avon, BS22 7XS Tel: (01934) 510686 Fax: (01934) 522279 E-mail: smtcnc@aol.com

▶ Takisawa Ltd, Meir Road, Redditch, Worcestershire, B98 7SY Tel: (01527) 522211 Fax: (01527) 510728 E-mail: sales@takisawa.com

Tenga Engineering Co. Ltd, Britannia House, Queensway, New Milton, Hampshire, BH25 5NN Tel: (01425) 622567 Fax: (01425) 622789

CNC MACHINE TOOL COMMUNICATION SYSTEMS

MyVideoTalk, 163 Winchester Road, Highams Park, Waltham Forest, London, E4 9JN Tel: 020 85235278 E-mail: myvideotalk@uwclub.net

CNC MACHINE TOOL MAINTENANCE OR REPAIR

A E S Enterprises Ltd, Nuffield Industrial Estate, 40 Banbury Road, Poole, Dorset, BH17 0GA Tel: (01202) 683875 Fax: (01202) 683875

Action Hire Centres, 90 Cotmandene Crescent, St Pauls Cray, Orpington, Kent, BR5 2RG Tel: (020) 8300 2359 Fax: (020) 8302 7422

Boost Machine Co., Diamond Road, Whitstable, Kent, CT5 1LN Tel: (01227) 272947 Fax: (01227) 272947

▶ Dpge Rebuilds, Unit 11 Martor Industrial Estate, Tormarton Road, Chippenham, Wiltshire, SN14 8LJ Tel: (01225) 892226 Fax: (01225) 892129 E-mail: sales@dpge-rebuilds.co.uk

▶ Engineering Solutions 2000 Ltd, 32 Butterton Road, Rhyl, Denbighshire, LL18 1RF Tel: 07850 511707 Fax: (01745) 353184 E-mail: machinerepairs@yahoo.co.uk

T W Ward CNC Machinery Ltd, Savile Street, Sheffield, S4 7UD Tel: 0114-276 5411 Fax: 0114-270 0786 E-mail: sales@wardcnc.com

Taktec Ltd, 158 Kristiansand Way, Letchworth Garden City, Hertfordshire, SG6 1TY Tel: (01462) 486985 Fax: (01462) 486985

CNC MACHINE TOOL RETROFITTING

Asquith Butler, Huddersfield Road, Brighouse, West Yorkshire, HD6 3RA Tel: (01484) 726620 Fax: (01484) 718708 E-mail: info@asquithbutler.com

▶ Flamtek Ltd, Unit 21, Midway Business Centre, Bridge Street, Clay Cross, Derbyshire, S45 9NU Tel: 01246 273925 Fax: 01246 277452 E-mail: kevin@flamtek.com

▶ Fortron UK Ltd, 307 Ecroyd Suite, Turner Road, Lomeshaye Business Village, Nelson, Lancashire, BB9 7DR Tel: (01282) 607893 Fax: (01282) 607894 E-mail: service@fortron.uk.com

▶ Servotek CNC, 16 Padgate, Thorpe End, Norwich, NR13 5DG Tel: 07860 408629 Fax: 01603 431992 E-mail: mail@servotek.co.uk

▶ Seymour Engineering Ltd, Phoebe Lane, Halifax, West Yorkshire, HX3 9AS Tel: (01422) 362135 Fax: (01422) 322511 E-mail: info@seymourengineering.co.uk

CNC MACHINE TOOL SOFTWARE SYSTEMS

Amar Engineering Consultants, Unit 70 Station Road Workshops, Station Road, Kingswood, Bristol, BS15 4PJ Tel: 0117-956 5522 Fax: 0117-956 5573 E-mail: webe-amar@demon.co.uk

Eagland Machine Tools Ltd, The Studio, Hill Road, Lyme Regis, Dorset, DT7 3PG Tel: (01297) 446000 Fax: (01297) 446001 E-mail: info@eagland.co.uk

Gridmaster Ltd, Weekley, Kettering, Northamptonshire, NN16 9UP Tel: (01536) 484948 Fax: (01536) 484948 E-mail: sales@gridmaster.co.uk

▶ GS Productivity Solutions, 37 Baileys Mead Road, Stapleton, Bristol, BS16 1AE Tel: 0117-965 0300E-mail: info@gspsltd.co.uk

▶ Red Rock Controls, 36 Sunnyside Lane, Balsall Common, Coventry, CV7 7FY Tel: (07968) 217494 E-mail: roger@redrockcontrols.co.uk

Tech Cadcam, Minster House, Western Way, Bury St. Edmunds, Suffolk, IP33 3SP Tel: (01284) 754781 Fax: (01284) 750344 E-mail: sales@techcadcam.net

CNC MACHINE TOOL SPINDLE TOOLING

Advanced Technology Machines Ltd, 4 Molly Millars Bridge, Wokingham, Berkshire, RG41 2WY Tel: 0118-977 0099 Fax: 0118-989 2288 E-mail: sales@atmmt.com

▶ Quality Tooling North East Ltd, 5 Back Norfolk Street, Sunderland, SR1 1EA Tel: 0191-514 5153 Fax: 0191-510 8485 E-mail: sales@quality-tooling.co.uk

CNC MACHINE TOOLS

600 Centre, Unit 18-19 Loughborough Motorway Trading Estate, Gelders Hall Road, Shepshed, Loughborough, Leicestershire, LE12 9NH Tel: (01509) 600600 Fax: (01509) 600159 E-mail: sales@600centre.co.uk

Brookes Machine Tools Ltd, Derby Road, Kegworth, Derby, DE74 2EN Tel: (01509) 672256 Fax: (01509) 674502 E-mail: bmtlimited@aol.com

▶ C N C Check Machine Tools Ltd, Kitchener Road, Leicester, LE5 4AT Tel: 0116-274 1044 Fax: 0116-274 1046 E-mail: mail@cnccheckmachinetools.co.uk

Cincinnati Machine Ltd, PO Box 505, Birmingham, B24 0QU Tel: 0121-351 3821 Fax: 0121-313 5379 E-mail: info@cinmach.co.uk

George Kingsbury, Quay Lane, Hardway, Gosport, Hampshire, PO12 4LB Tel: (023) 9258 0371 Fax: (023) 9250 1741 E-mail: mtools@gkholdings.com

Heller Machine Tools, Acanthus Road, Ravensbank Business Park, Redditch, Worcestershire, B98 9EX Tel: 0121-275 3300 Fax: 0121-275 3340 E-mail: sales@heller.co.uk

Hurco Europe Ltd, Halifax Road, Cressex Business Park, High Wycombe, Buckinghamshire, HP12 3SN Tel: (01494) 442222 Fax: (01494) 443350 E-mail: sales@hurco.co.uk

IndustrialMachines.Net Ltd, Ipsley Street, Redditch, Worcestershire, B98 7AA Tel: (0870) 8890270 Fax: (0870) 8890271 E-mail: sales@industrialmachines.net

John Leighton C N C Services Ltd, 13 Valley Road, Keighley, West Yorkshire, BD21 4LZ Tel: (01535) 607941 Fax: (01535) 691177 E-mail: johnleightoncnc@aol.com

Larchwood Machine Tools Ltd, 61 Blue Lake Road, Dorridge, Solihull, West Midlands, B93 8BH Tel: (01564) 776234 Fax: (01564) 779270 E-mail: sales@larchwoodltd.co.uk

Lead Precision Machine Tools Ltd, Calamine House, Calamine Street, Macclesfield, Cheshire, SK11 7HU Tel: (01625) 434990 Fax: (01625) 434996 E-mail: sales@leadmachinetools.co.uk

M Tech UK Ltd, 913a Uppingham Road, Bushby, Leicester, LE7 9RR Tel: 0116-241 5791

Percy Martin Ltd, Church Hill Road, Thurmaston, Leicester, LE4 8DJ Tel: 0116-260 5582 Fax: 0116-264 0227 E-mail: info@percymartin.co.uk

Matchmaker CNC, 8 Woodland Studios, Brook Willow Farm, Woodlands Road, Leatherhead, Surrey, KT22 0AN Tel: (01372) 844999 Fax: (01372) 844998 E-mail: sales@matchmakermc.co.uk

Mills Manufacturing Technology, Tachbrook Park Drive, Warwick, CV34 6RH Tel: (01926) 736736 Fax: (01926) 736737 E-mail: sales@millscnc.co.uk

Miyano Machinery UK Ltd, 9A Navigation Drive, Hurst Business Park, Brierley Hill, West Midlands, DY5 1UT Tel: (01384) 489500 Fax: (01384) 489501 E-mail: sales@macrocnc.co.uk

N C Engineering Ltd, 1 Park Avenue, Bushey, WD23 2DA Tel: (01923) 691500 Fax: (01923) 691599 E-mail: sales@ncengineering.co.uk

NCMT Ltd, Ferry Works, Summer Road, Thames Ditton, Surrey, KT7 0QJ Tel: (020) 8398 4277 Fax: (020) 8398 3631

Somerset Machine Tools, 29 Brimbleworth Lane, St. Georges, Weston-super-Mare, Avon, BS22 7XS Tel: (01934) 510686 Fax: (01934) 522279 E-mail: smtcnc@aol.com

Stirchley Machine Tool Co. Ltd, 401-407 Tyburn Road, Birmingham, B24 8HJ Tel: 0121-328 2424 Fax: 0121-327 6200

Victor Europe Ltd, Victor House, Eagle Technology Park, Queensway, Rochdale, Lancashire, OL11 1TQ Tel: (01706) 648485 Fax: (01706) 648483 E-mail: sales@victoreurope.com

Whitehouse Machine Tools Ltd, 7 Princes Drive Industrial Estate, Coventry Road, Kenilworth, Warwickshire, CV8 2FD Tel: (01926) 852725 Fax: (01926) 850620 E-mail: sales@wmtcnc.com

Wightman Stewart Ltd, Oldham Road, Sowerby Bridge, West Yorkshire, HX6 4EH Tel: (01422) 823801 Fax: (01422) 824031 E-mail: info@wightmanstewart.co.uk

CNC MACHINERY OR SYSTEM INSTALLATION

▶ L M T S, 36 Ocean Street, Plymouth, PL2 2DJ Tel: (07968) 113070 Fax: (01752) 597 69 E-mail: daveking@cncengineers.com

CNC MACHINERY OR SYSTEM REMOVAL OR RELOCATION

▶ CML Group, Bluebell Farm, Hewitts Road, Orpington, Kent, BR6 7QR Tel: (01959) 533833 Fax: (01689) 821893 E-mail: alyson@ah-design.co.uk

CNC MACHINERY WORKHOLDING FIXTURES

Bartling Designs Ltd, Staplehurst Road, Sittingbourne, Kent, ME10 1TA Tel: (01795) 476424 Fax: (01795) 475751 E-mail: bartlingdesigns@bartlingdesigns.com

Craftsman Tools Ltd, Side Copse, Otley, West Yorkshire, LS21 1JE Tel: (01943) 466788 Fax: (01943) 850144 E-mail: r.johnson@craftsmantools.com

Denebank Engineering UK Ltd, 108 Windmill Road, Sunbury-on-Thames, Middlesex, TW16 7HB Tel: (01932) 788180 Fax: (01932) 788150 E-mail: paulgoldthorpe@denebank.co.uk

Sam Tooling Ltd, 60 Newland Street, Coleford, Gloucestershire, GL16 8AL Tel: (01594) 835542 Fax: (01594) 837293

CNC MACHINERY/MACHINE TOOLS, USED

Anglo-African Machinery Co. Ltd, Clent House, Bromsgrove Road, Clent, Stourbridge, West Midlands, DY9 9PY Tel: (01562) 883067 Fax: (01562) 885335 E-mail: angloafrican@btconnect.com

▶ Dpge Rebuilds, Unit 11 Martor Industrial Estate, Tormarton Road, Chippenham, Wiltshire, SN14 8LJ Tel: (01225) 892226 Fax: (01225) 892129 E-mail: sales@dpge-rebuilds.co.uk

▶ Ems Ltd, Grimshaw Street, Burnley, Lancashire, BB11 2AZ Tel: (07986) 782978 Fax: (01282) 860638 E-mail: mtools@btinternet.com

▶ G M Machinery, 13 Den Hill Drive, Springhead, Oldham, OL4 4NR Tel: 0161-633 8880 Fax: 0161-633 7323 E-mail: info@gmmachinery.com

IndustrialMachines.Net Ltd, Ipsley Street, Redditch, Worcestershire, B98 7AA Tel: (0870) 8890270 Fax: (0870) 8890271 E-mail: sales@industrialmachines.net

M & B Engineering, 62-63 John Wilson Business Park, Thanet Way, Whitstable, Kent, CT5 3QT Tel: (01227) 261917 Fax: (01227) 770809 E-mail: robertacors@tiscali.co.uk

Stevens Machine Tools, 37-41 Anne Road, Smethwick, West Midlands, B66 2NZ Tel: 0121-555 6392 Fax: 0121-565 2438 E-mail: info@stevensmachinetools.co.uk

CNC MACHINERY/SYSTEMS CONSULTANTS OR DESIGNERS

Control Applications Ltd, Unit 12, Steeton Grove, Steeton, West Yorkshire, BD20 6TT Tel: (01535) 650890 Fax: (01535) 658824 E-mail: info@controlapplications.co.uk

Hadfield CNC & Electronics Co. Ltd, 15 Retford Road, Worksop, Nottinghamshire, S80 2PT Tel: (01909) 500760 Fax: (01909) 542800 E-mail: service@hcnc.co.uk

▶ Red Rock Controls, 36 Sunnyside Lane, Balsall Common, Coventry, CV7 7FY Tel: (07968) 217494 E-mail: roger@redrockcontrols.co.uk

CNC MACHINERY/SYSTEMS MAINTENANCE/REPAIR SERVICES

▶ CB CNC UK Ltd, Apartment 113, Whitfield Mill, Meadow Road, Apperley Bridge, Bradford, West Yorkshire, BD10 0LP Tel: (07881) 922680 Fax: (01274) 612808 E-mail: cc.silv-birch@fsmail.net

CNC Support Ltd, Advance Factory Site, Skipton Road, Trawden Colne, Colne, Lancashire, BB8 8BJ Tel: (01282) 859122 Fax: (01282) 859144 E-mail: sales@cncsupport.co.uk

▶ Dpge Rebuilds, Unit 11 Martor Industrial Estate, Tormarton Road, Chippenham, Wiltshire, SN14 8LJ Tel: (01225) 892226 Fax: (01225) 892129 E-mail: sales@dpge-rebuilds.co.uk

Engineering Equipment Centre Ltd, 27 St Margarets Road, Bournemouth, BH10 4BG Tel: (01202) 528249 Fax: (01202) 528979

▶ L M T S, 36 Ocean Street, Plymouth, PL2 2DJ Tel: (07968) 113070 Fax: (01752) 597 69 E-mail: daveking@cncengineers.com

F S R Maintenance, 8 Arnside Road, Waterlooville, Hants, PO7 7UP Tel: (023) 9226 3222 Fax: (023) 9223 0946 E-mail: fsr@shaftfield.co.uk

Piper Developments Ltd, Townsend House, Townsend Way, Birmingham, B1 2RT Tel: 0121-242 1194 Fax: 0121-242 1194

Saxon Engineering, Unit 1, Bredgar Road, Gillingham, Kent, ME8 6PL Tel: (01634) 370023 Fax: (01634) 263250 E-mail: saxoneng@aol.com

Skippy's Machine Tools, 12 Queens Road, Erdington, Birmingham, B23 7JP Tel: 0121-386 3622 Fax: 0121-386 3623 E-mail: service@skippysmt.com

CNC MACHINERY/SYSTEMS SALES/SUPPORT SERVICES

B R E Europe Ltd, London Road, Feering, Colchester, CO5 9ED Tel: (01376) 572500 Fax: (01376) 572600 E-mail: sales@breltd.com

MAKA Machinery UK Ltd, Unit 19 Queensway Link Industrial Estate, Stafford Park 17, Telford, Shropshire, TF3 3DN Tel: (01952) 270006 Fax: (01952) 270007 E-mail: info@makauk.com

Osai UK Ltd, Mount House, Bond Avenue, Bletchley, Milton Keynes, MK1 1SF Tel: (01908) 642687 Fax: (01908) 642688 E-mail: sales@osai.co.uk

CNC MACHINING CENTRES

Daws Engineering Ltd, Curtis Road, Dorking, Surrey, RH4 1XD Tel: (01306) 881546 Fax: (01306) 740407 E-mail: rob.collinson@dawseng.co.uk

Evridge Precison Engineering Ltd, Holmesdale Works, Holmesdale Road, South Darenth, Dartford, DA4 9JP Tel: (01322) 868961 Fax: (01322) 868962 E-mail: mailbox@evridgeengineering.com

Haas Automation Ltd, Bradgate House, 13 Unthank Road, Norwich, NR2 2PA Tel: (01603) 760539 Fax: (01603) 760542

Padmode Ltd, Unit 9 Denvers Yard, Ware, Hertfordshire, SG11 1AL Tel: (01279) 843035

Smeaton Hanscomb & Co. Ltd, Lisle Road, Hughenden Avenue, High Wycombe, Buckinghamshire, HP13 5SQ Tel: (01494) 521051 Fax: (01494) 461176 E-mail: sales@smeathans.plus.com

▶ Takisawa Ltd, Meir Road, Redditch, Worcestershire, B98 7SY Tel: (01527) 522211 Fax: (01527) 510728 E-mail: sales@takisawa.com

CNC METAL SPINNERS

Craft Metal Products, Unit 18 Birksland Industrial Estate, Bradford, West Yorkshire, BD4 8TY Tel: (01274) 731531 Fax: (01274) 731531

CNC MILLING

B B F CNC Machining, 31 Knowl Piece, Hitchin, Hertfordshire, SG4 0TY Tel: (01462) 432700 Fax: (01462) 431414 E-mail: bbf.cnc@btinternet.com
Detek Ltd, 27 Granby Street, Loughborough, Leicestershire, LE11 3DU Tel: 0116-235 0244 Fax: 0116-235 8750 E-mail: detek@lineone.net
▶ E C Tooling Systems Ltd, 1 Havant Business Centre, Harts Farm Way, Havant, Hampshire, PO9 1HU Tel: (023) 9248 0481 Fax: (023) 9248 0482 E-mail: info@ectooling.com
H P C Services Ltd, Unit 14 Solomon Road, Ilkeston, Derbyshire, DE7 5UA Tel: 0115-932 3773 Fax: 0115-932 2857 E-mail: sales@slidinghead.com
Holman Engineering Co. Ltd, 6 Kings Road Works, Kings Road, New Haw, Addlestone, Surrey, KT15 3BG Tel: (01932) 353555 Fax: (01932) 353666 E-mail: enquiries@holman-engineering.co.uk
MRW Engineering Ltd, Unit 23a Hoo Farm Industrial Estate, Worcester Road, Kidderminster, Worcestershire, DY11 7RA Tel: (01562) 745042 Fax: (01562) 746472 E-mail: sales@mrwe.co.uk
N S J Engineering, 231 Handsworth Road, Handsworth, Sheffield, S13 9BL Tel: 0114-243 1769 Fax: 0114-243 1408 E-mail: neil@nsjengineering.co.uk

CNC MILLING ENGINEERING

Acrona Engineering, Unit 1, Woodview Estate, Church Hanborough, Witney, Oxfordshire, OX29 8AA Tel: (01993) 880588 Fax: (01993) 880590 E-mail: sales@acrona-engineering.co.uk
Aldersbrook Engineering, B Ajax Works, Hertford Road, Barking, Essex, IG11 8DY Tel: (020) 8591 0685 Fax: (020) 8591 9388 E-mail: enquiries@aldersbrook-engineering.com
Amdale Ltd, 6-7 Culverin Square, Limberline Road, Hilsea, Portsmouth, PO3 5BU Tel: (023) 9266 0726 Fax: (023) 9265 5177 E-mail: sales@amdale.co.uk
Bo Mic Engineering, 1 Brickyard Lane, New Road, Gillingham, Dorset, SP8 4JL Tel: (01747) 824216 Fax: (01747) 821726 E-mail: sale@bomic.co.uk
Clovelly Engineering Ltd, Unit 59, Lunsford Road, Leicester, LE5 0HW Tel: 0116-246 1831 Fax: 0116-246 1474E-mail: clovellyt@aol.com
Cousins Engineering, 23 Bunting Road, Northampton, NN2 6EE Tel: (01604) 712456 Fax: (01604) 719578 E-mail: sales@counsinsengineering.co.uk
Deckel Grinders Ltd, Pasture Lane Business Centre, Pasture Lane, Rainford, St. Helens, Merseyside, WA11 8PU Tel: (01744) 886651 Fax: (01744) 885201 E-mail: sales@deckel-grinders.com
E J M Engineering Ltd, Regent Road, Countesthorpe, Leicester, LE8 5RF Tel: 0116-278 7020 Fax: 0116-278 7020 E-mail: eric@ejm-engineering.co.uk
E J Tools (Press Toolmakers) Ltd, 112 Middlemore Industrial Estate, Smethwick, Warley, West Midlands, B66 2EP Tel: 0121-558 4154 Fax: 0121-558 4154 E-mail: richard_webb@btconnect.com
Earhtech Engineering Ltd, Unit 1, Grovebury Place Estate, Grovebury Road, Leighton Buzzard, Bedfordshire, LU7 4SH Tel: (01525) 374362 Fax: (01525) 377304
European CNC Turned Parts Ltd, Unit 101 Telsen Industrial Centre, Thomas Street, Birmingham, B6 4TN Tel: 0121-359 2812 Fax: 0121-359 3520 E-mail: mick@europeancnc.com
▶ Isosure Ltd, 18 Spring Terrace, Goodshawfold, Rossendale, Lancashire, BB4 8QR Tel: (01706) 225419 Fax: (01706) 230784 E-mail: info@isosure.com
Kenworth Engineering Ltd, Jackson Place, Wilton Road Industrial Estate, Humberston, Grimsby, North East Lincolnshire, DN36 4AS Tel: (01472) 210678 Fax: (01472) 210912 E-mail: rob@kenworthengineering.co.uk
Merriefield Engineering Ltd, 7 Willis Way, Poole, Dorset, BH15 3SS Tel: (01202) 680644 Fax: (01202) 684389 E-mail: sales@merriefield.co.uk
Monard Precision Engineering Ltd, Avon Industrial Estate, Butlers Leap, Rugby, Warwickshire, CV21 3UY Tel: (01788) 569998 Fax: (01788) 568434 E-mail: monard@avonrugby.freeserve.co.uk
Progress N C, Unit 14 Progress Business Park, Orders Lane, Kirkham, Preston, PR4 2TZ Tel: (01772) 687879 Fax: (01772) 687879
Qstar Precision Ltd, 2 Shortsands Yard, Cambridge Street, St. Neots, Cambridgeshire, PE19 1PQ Tel: (01480) 210915 Fax: (01480) 210927 E-mail: info@qstarprecision.co.uk
Ringwood Precision, 2 Millstream Trading Estate, Christchurch Road, Ringwood, Hampshire, BH24 3SA Tel: (01425) 476296 Fax: (01425) 476296 E-mail: ukroy@freenetname.co.uk
Tryax Ltd, 10 Jubilee Trading Centre, Jubilee Road, Letchworth Garden City, Hertfordshire, SG6 1NE Tel: (01462) 481295 Fax: (01462) 685275 E-mail: sales@tryax.com
Turntech Precision Engineers, Unit 33 Liberty Close, Woolsbridge Industrial Estate, Three Legged Cross, Wimborne, Dorset, BH21 6SY Tel: (01202) 822040 Fax: (01202) 829146 E-mail: sales@turntech-precision.co.uk
Wimborne Engineering, 58 Cobham Road, Ferndown Industrial Estate, Wimborne, Dorset, BH21 7QH Tel: (01202) 893043 E-mail: knud@moldtecknik.co.uk

CNC MILLING MACHINES

Eurospark Cutting Tools, Ashby Road, Stapleton, Leicester, LE9 8JE Tel: (01455) 292002 Fax: (01455) 293002 E-mail: sales@eurospark.co.uk
Holland & Harrison Ltd, 46 Vale Road, Bushey, WD23 2HQ Tel: (01923) 220752 Fax: (01923) 234011E-mail: cnc@hollandandharrison.co.uk
Pinnacle C N C Ltd, 5 Kirby Road, Nelson, Lancashire, BB9 6RS Tel: 01282 695222

CNC PRECISION ENGINEERING

MRW Engineering Ltd, Unit 23a Hoo Farm Industrial Estate, Worcester Road, Kidderminster, Worcestershire, DY11 7RA Tel: (01562) 745042 Fax: (01562) 746472 E-mail: sales@mrwe.co.uk
Protocol Engineering, Unit 17 Tanfield Lea Industrial Estate South, Tanfield Lea, Stanley, County Durham, DH9 9XB Tel: (01207) 290052 Fax: (01207) 290142 E-mail: protocol_engineering@yahoo.co.uk
▶ Rockingham Manufacturing, M Harlow House, Shelton Road, Willowbrook East Industrial Estate, Corby, Northamptonshire, NN17 5XH Tel: (01536) 266953 Fax: (01226) 400493

CNC PRECISION TURNED COMPONENTS TO SPECIFICATION

G W Atkins & Sons Ltd, 28 Wellington St, Syston, Leicester, LE7 2LG Tel: 0116-269 1240 Fax: 0116-269 3270
Hyspeed CNC Ltd, Clovelly Road, Southbourne, Emsworth, Hampshire, PO10 8PE Tel: (01243) 377751 Fax: (01243) 377754 E-mail: sales@hyspeed.co.uk
Normec (Manchester) Ltd, Westwood Industrial Estate, Arkwright Street, Oldham, OL9 9LZ Tel: 0161-627 2367 Fax: 0161-627 2378 E-mail: admin@normecmanchester.co.uk

CNC PRECISION TURNED PARTS

Abtech Precision Ltd, 95 Alston Drive, Bradwell Abbey, Milton Keynes, MK13 9HF Tel: (01908) 318218 Fax: (01908) 318308 E-mail: enquiries@abtech-precision.co.uk
Addmore Engineering, Unit 18 Broadmead Business Park, Broadmead Road, Stewartby, Bedford, MK43 9NX Tel: (01234) 766957 Fax: (01234) 766951 E-mail: sales@addmoreengineering.co.uk
Anglia Precision Engineering, 32 Stapledon Road, Orton Southgate, Peterborough, PE2 6TD Tel: (01733) 703230 Fax: (01733) 703231 E-mail: sales@angliaprecision.com
▶ B D Cravens, Rossfield Road, Ellesmere Port, CH65 3AW Tel: 0151-356 5654 Fax: 0151-356 7822 E-mail: bdcraveneng@tiscali.co.uk
Bo Mic Engineering, 1 Brickyard Lane, New Road, Gillingham, Dorset, SP8 4JL Tel: (01747) 824216 Fax: (01747) 821726 E-mail: sale@bomic.co.uk
Cousins Engineering, 23 Bunting Road, Northampton, NN2 6EE Tel: (01604) 712456 Fax: (01604) 719578 E-mail: sales@counsinsengineering.co.uk
D P R Engineering, Unit 11 Prospect Business Park, Longford Road, Cannock, Staffordshire, WS11 0LG Tel: (01543) 577910 Fax: (01543) 572306
Dean Smith & Grace Ltd, PO Box 15, Keighley, West Yorkshire, BD21 4PG Tel: (01535) 605261 Fax: (01535) 680921 E-mail: mail@deansmithandgrace.co.uk
Exact Engineering Thompson Ltd, Kingsway South, Team Valley Trading Estate, Gateshead, Tyne & Wear, NE11 0JS Tel: 0191-482 6622 Fax: 0191-482 1602 E-mail: john.martin@exact-engineering.com
G & R Pollard Engineering Ltd, Alexandra Way, Ashchurch, Tewkesbury, Gloucestershire, GL20 8NB Tel: (01684) 274847 Fax: (01684) 851960 E-mail: grpoll@globalnet.co.uk
Gibbs Gears Precision Engineers Ltd, 58 B Western Road, Tring, Hertfordshire, HP23 4BB Tel: (01442) 828898 Fax: (01422) 828020 E-mail: sales@gibbsgears.com
H C Holifield Oxford Ltd, Nuffield Way, Abingdon, Oxfordshire, OX14 1RX Tel: (01235) 520284 Fax: (01235) 559001 E-mail: sales@holifields.co.uk
Harris Repair Consultancy Service Ltd, Unit 3, Crondal Road, Exhall, Coventry, CV7 9NH Tel: (024) 7636 4848 Fax: (024) 7664 4411 E-mail: g.harris@harrisrcs.com
Holman Engineering Co. Ltd, 6 Kings Road Works, Kings Road, New Haw, Addlestone, Surrey, KT15 3BG Tel: (01932) 353555 Fax: (01932) 353666 E-mail: enquiries@holman-engineering.co.uk
Kalstan Engineering Ltd, Cavendish Road, Stevenage, Hertfordshire, SG1 2ET Tel: (01438) 745588 Fax: (01438) 360579 E-mail: sjkalmar@kalstanengineering.co.uk
Logica Engineering Ltd, 2 Firbank Court, Firbank Way, Leighton Buzzard, Bedfordshire, LU7 4YJ Tel: (01525) 373377 Fax: (01525) 853377
M & B Engineering, 62-63 John Wilson Business Park, Thanet Way, Whitstable, Kent, CT5 3QT Tel: (01227) 261917 Fax: (01227) 770809 E-mail: robertacors@tiscali.co.uk
M S P Ltd, Roman Way, Coleshill, Birmingham, B46 1HG Tel: (01675) 469100 Fax: (01675) 463699 E-mail: sales@msp.ltd.uk
Metfab Design Ltd, Unit 220 Foley Industrial Estate, Kidderminster, Worcestershire, DY11 7DH Tel: (01562) 864129 Fax: (01562) 864129
N R Automatics Ltd, Duckworth Mill, Skipton Road, Colne, Lancashire, BB8 0RH Tel: (01282) 868500 Fax: (01282) 869885
Neida Products Engineering Ltd, Trentham Lakes South, Stoke-on-Trent, ST4 8GQ Tel: (01782) 643643 Fax: (01782) 644220 E-mail: sales@neida.co.uk
Normec (Manchester) Ltd, Westwood Industrial Estate, Arkwright Street, Oldham, OL9 9LZ Tel: 0161-627 2367 Fax: 0161-627 2378 E-mail: admin@normecmanchester.co.uk
Northern Cam Company Ltd, Unit 127 Whitehall Indust Estate, Whitehall Road, Leeds, LS12 5JB Tel: 0113-279 2733 Fax: 0113-279 4547 E-mail: info@northerncam.co.uk
P M P L Telford Ltd, Unit 25 Heath Hill Industrial Estate, Dawley, Telford, Shropshire, TF4 2RH Tel: (01952) 507978 Fax: (01952) 507978 E-mail: daviespmp@aol.com
Pegmount Ltd, Unit 1 Apex Centre, Lovell, Lichfield Road Industrial Estate, Tamworth, Staffordshire, B79 7TA Tel: (01827) 68804 Fax: (01827) 69929 E-mail: sales@phoenixmanufacturing.co.uk
Phoenix Turned Parts, 4-5 Mica Close, Tamworth, Staffordshire, B77 4DR Tel: (01827) 59441 Fax: (01827) 54750 E-mail: mike.pegg@btbusinessconnect.co.uk
Qualiturn Products Ltd, 18 Merchant Drive, Mead Lane, Hertford, SG13 7AY Tel: (01992) 584499 Fax: (01992) 551726 E-mail: kssales@qualiturn.co.uk
R M Mallen C N C Machinery Ltd, 15 Hainge Road, Tividale, Oldbury, West Midlands, B69 2NR Tel: 0121-557 3141 Fax: 0121-557 3814
Reldale Ltd, 60 Dunster Street, Northampton, NN1 3JY Tel: (01604) 632438 Fax: (01604) 632438 E-mail: enquiries@reldaleltd.co.uk
▶ Rotherham CNC Ltd, Unit 30 Orgreave Close, Sheffield, S13 9NP Tel: 0114-269 9800 Fax: 0114-269 9800
F.W. Russell (Gauges) Ltd, 2-3 Avenue Industrial Estate, Gallows Corner, Romford, RM3 0HS Tel: (01708) 376888 Fax: (01708) 374050
▶ Sassen Engineering Ltd, 19 Aston Road North, Birmingham, B6 4DS Tel: 0121-359 7411 Fax: 0121-359 2404 E-mail: sales@sassenengineering.co.uk
Truturn Precision Engineering (Charfield) Ltd, Units L2-L3, Bath Road Trading Estate, Lightpill, Stroud, Gloucestershire, GL5 3QF Tel: (01453) 752888 Fax: (01453) 753888 E-mail: truturn@truturn.co.uk
Unicut, 6 Tewin Court, Welwyn Garden City, Hertfordshire, AL7 1AU Tel: (01707) 331227 Fax: (01707) 390382 E-mail: sales@unicutprecision.com
Westcombe Industries Ltd, Royce Road, Peterborough, PE1 5YB Tel: (01733) 746300 Fax: (01733) 746310
Whiteland Engineering Ltd, Torrington Lane, Bideford, Devon, EX39 4BH Tel: (01237) 472203 Fax: (01237) 472205 E-mail: info@whitelandengineering.co.uk
Xavier Engineering Ltd, Fleetwood Road, Lune Street, Padiham, Burnley, Lancashire, BB12 8DG Tel: (01282) 680000 Fax: (01282) 680888 E-mail: sales@xavier-eng.co.uk

CNC PRESS TOOLS

Mills & Coombs, 95A Chaplin Road, Easton, Bristol, BS5 3JE Tel: 0117-961 3882 Fax: 0117-961 3887
▶ Tek Neek, Unit 10, Glenfield Park, Philips Rd, Blackburn, BB1 5PS Tel: (01254) 583008 Fax: (01254) 682965

CNC PUNCH PRESSES

Shaw Sheet Metal Rugby Ltd, 13 Paynes Lane, Rugby, Warwickshire, CV21 2UH Tel: (01788) 536033 Fax: (01788) 536922 E-mail: sales@shawsheetmetal.co.uk

CNC PUNCHING

Binns Security Fencing Ltd, Pressmetal House St. Augustines Business Park, Estuary Close, Whitstable, Kent, CT5 2QJ Tel: (01227) 794490 Fax: (01227) 794488
Bowson Engineering Ltd, Oak House, Dewsbury Road, Fenton Industrial Estate, Stoke-on-Trent, ST4 2TE Tel: (01782) 749000 Fax: (01782) 749299 E-mail: sales@bowson.co.uk
F.W. Frost (Engineers) Ltd, Bidewell Close, Drayton High Road, Norwich, NR8 6AP Tel: (01603) 867301 Fax: (01603) 261586 E-mail: sales@fwfrost-engineers.co.uk
High Speed Piercing Ltd, Pindar Road, Hoddesdon, Hertfordshire, EN11 0DE Tel: (01992) 445123 Fax: (01992) 466541 E-mail: admin@highspeedpiercing.co.uk
J S J Precision, Milburn Road, Stoke-on-Trent, ST6 2QF Tel: (01782) 269694 Fax: (01782) 279138
John Dent Engineering Co. Ltd, 1432a Clock Tower Road, Isleworth, Middlesex, TW7 6DT Tel: (020) 8560 4414 Fax: (020) 8847 4582 E-mail: info@johndentengineering.com
K M Pressings Ltd, 37B Copenhagen Road, Sutton Field Industrial Estate, Hull, HU7 0XQ Tel: (01482) 877900 Fax: (01482) 877909 E-mail: jonathon@kmpressing.karew.co.uk
Leeds Welding Co. Ltd, Westland Square, Leeds, LS11 5SS Tel: 0113-271 1000 Fax: 0113-271 1023 E-mail: sales@leedswelding.co.uk
Llandaff Engineering Co. Ltd, Paper Mill Road, Canton, Cardiff, CF11 8PH Tel: (029) 2083 8300 Fax: (029) 2056 5125 E-mail: majenkins@llandaffeng.com
Paragon Pressings, 3b Harpings Road, Hull, HU5 4JF Tel: (01482) 462822 Fax: (01482) 462833
Wrightform Ltd, Church Road, Redgrave, Diss, Norfolk, IP22 1RJ Tel: (01379) 898400 Fax: (01379) 898405 E-mail: sales@wrightform.com

CNC PUNCHING MACHINES

Kingsland Engineering Co. Ltd, Weybourne Road, Sheringham, Norfolk, NR26 8HE Tel: (01263) 822153 Fax: (01263) 825667 E-mail: info@kingsland.com

CNC ROUTING

Autograph, The Malthouse, 139-141 Eastgate, Worksop, Nottinghamshire, S80 1QS Tel: (01909) 488500 Fax: (01909) 482687 E-mail: autographsigns.uk@btconnect.com
Lydwood Ltd, Lower Lydbrook, Lydbrook, Gloucestershire, GL17 9NB Tel: (01594) 860374 Fax: (01594) 861312 E-mail: nick@lydwood.co.uk
Mansells Ltd, 20 Vanguard Way, Shoeburyness, Southend-on-Sea, SS3 9RA Tel: (01702) 294222 Fax: (08708) 722750 E-mail: man@oppenheimers.co.uk
Sprint Graphics, Station Road, Irthlingborough, Wellingborough, Northamptonshire, NN9 5QE Tel: (01933) 651908 Fax: (01933) 655688 E-mail: sales@sprintgraphics.co.uk

CNC SLIDING HEADS

Addmore Engineering, Unit 18 Broadmead Business Park, Broadmead Road, Stewartby, Bedford, MK43 9NX Tel: (01234) 766957 Fax: (01234) 766951 E-mail: sales@addmoreengineering.co.uk
Hullmatic Engineering Ltd, 1 Lancaster Way Earls Colne Business Park, Airfield, Earls Colne, Colchester, CO6 2NS Tel: (01787) 222099 Fax: (01787) 224317 E-mail: hullmatic@aol.com

CNC TOOL HOLDERS

Abtech Precision Ltd, 95 Alston Drive, Bradwell Abbey, Milton Keynes, MK13 9HF Tel: (01908) 318218 Fax: (01908) 318308 E-mail: enquiries@abtech-precision.co.uk

CNC TRIMMING MACHINES

G A Engineering, Unit 12, Ash Industrial Estate, Flex Meadow, Harlow, Essex, CM19 5TJ Tel: (01279) 414972 Fax: (01279) 416029
MAKA Machinery UK Ltd, Unit 19 Queensway Link Industrial Estate, Stafford Park 17, Telford, Shropshire, TF3 3DN Tel: (01952) 270006 Fax: (01952) 270007 E-mail: info@makauk.com
▶ Shelley Thermoformers International Ltd, Stonehill, Stukeley Meadows Industrial Es, Huntingdon, Cambridgeshire, PE29 6DR Tel: (01480) 453651 Fax: (01480) 52113 E-mail: sales@cannon-shelley.co.uk
Thermwood Europe Ltd, Unit 3, Evans Business Centre, Belmont Industrial Estate, Durham, DH1 1SE Tel: 0191-383 2883 Fax: 0191-383 2884 E-mail: sales@thermwood.co.uk

CNC TUBE BENDING MACHINES

▶ B E W O (UK) Ltd, Unit 3 Bay 2, Eastacre, The Willenhall Estate, Willenhall, West Midlands, WV13 2JZ Tel: (01902) 635027 Fax: (01902) 635843E-mail: info@bewo.co.uk

CNC TUBE MANIPULATION

Projax Tools (1989) Ltd, Arthur St, Redditch, Worcestershire, B98 8DZ Tel: 01527 523734

CNC TURNING SERVICES

Aaron Manufacturing Ltd, Unit K-L Waterside, 25-27 Willis Way, Poole, Dorset, BH15 3TD Tel: (01202) 670071 Fax: (01202) 682952 E-mail: enquiries@aaronmanufacturing.co.uk

Bedrock Engineering, Unit 7, Palmers Road Industrial Estate, Emsworth, Hampshire, PO10 7DH Tel: (01243) 377435 Fax: (01243) 377443 E-mail: info@bedrockengineering.co.uk

Bowden Precision Engineering Co. Ltd, Riverside, Market Harborough, Leicestershire, LE16 7PU Tel: (01858) 467508 Fax: (01858) 431656 E-mail: enquiries@bowdenprecision.co.uk

Clovelly Engineering Ltd, Unit 59, Lunsford Road, Leicester, LE5 0HW Tel: 0116-246 1831 Fax: 0116-246 1474E-mail: clovellyt@aol.com

Copper Mill Engineering, The Mill, Bath Road, Bitton, Bristol, BS30 6LW Tel: 0117-932 2614 Fax: 0117-932 9388 E-mail: rusell@coppermillengineering.com

Denholm Rees & O'Donnell Ltd, 116 Albany Road, Walton, Liverpool, L9 0HB Tel: 0151-525 1663 Fax: 0151-525 1618 E-mail: sales@denholms.co.uk

Detek Ltd, 27 Granby Street, Loughborough, Leicestershire, LE11 3DU Tel: 0116-235 0244 Fax: 0116-235 8750 E-mail: detek@lineone.net

E J Tools (Press Toolmakers) Ltd, 112 Middlemore Industrial Estate, Smethwick, Warley, West Midlands, B66 2EP Tel: 0121-558 4154 Fax: 0121-558 4154 E-mail: richard_webb@btconnect.com

Erodex UK Ltd, 42 Station Street, Wednesbury, West Midlands, WS10 8BW Tel: 0121-526 7368 Fax: 0121-526 6582 E-mail: sales@afshaw.com

G D S Design, 15 Avon Business Park, Lodge Causeway, Fishponds, Bristol, BS16 3JP Tel: 0117-958 6606 Fax: 0117-958 6605 E-mail: info@gds-design.freeserve.co.uk

Halesowen Components Ltd, 126 Coombs Road, Halesowen, West Midlands, B62 8AF Tel: 0121-559 3771 Fax: 0121-561 5323 E-mail: sales@halesowencnc.co.uk

Kenworth Engineering Ltd, Jackson Place, Wilton Road Industrial Estate, Humberston, Grimsby, North East Lincolnshire, DN36 4AS Tel: (01472) 210678 Fax: (01472) 210912 E-mail: rob@kenworthengineering.co.uk

Lattimer Engineering Ltd, 79-83 Shakespeare Street, Southport, Merseyside, PR8 5AP Tel: (01704) 535040 Fax: (01704) 541046 E-mail: sales@lattimer.com

Machining Centre Ltd, Pembroke Lane, Milton, Abingdon, Oxfordshire, OX14 4EA Tel: (01235) 831343 Fax: (01235) 834708 E-mail: info@machiningcentre.co.uk

Merriefield Engineering Ltd, 7 Willis Way, Poole, Dorset, BH15 3SS Tel: (01202) 680644 Fax: (01202) 684389 E-mail: sales@merriefield.co.uk

MTS, Greenside Way, Middleton, Manchester, M24 1SW Tel: 0161-345 4760 Fax: 0161-345 4766 E-mail: sales@mtsprecision.co.uk

Padmode Ltd, Unit 9 Denvers Yard, Ware, Hertfordshire, SG11 1AL Tel: (01279) 843035

Qstar Precision Ltd, 2 Shortsands Yard, Cambridge Street, St. Neots, Cambridgeshire, PE19 1PQ Tel: (01480) 210915 Fax: (01480) 210927 E-mail: info@qstarprecision.co.uk

Skeens Precision Engineering Ltd, 55-55a Jubilee Road, Waterlooville, Hampshire, PO7 7RE Tel: (023) 9226 2191 Fax: (023) 9225 4219 E-mail: skeens@deans.freeserve.co.uk

T & G Engineering Co. Ltd, Unit 14 Camphill Industrial Estate, Camphill Road, West Byfleet, Surrey, KT14 6EW Tel: (01932) 353228 Fax: (01932) 349692 E-mail: sales@tgengineering.co.uk

T Halliday Engineering Ltd, Orchard Road, Hamworth Road Industrial Estate, Sunbury-on-Thames, Middlesex, TW16 5BZ Tel: (01932) 787862 Fax: (01932) 787839 E-mail: keng@btclick.com

Tryax Ltd, 10 Jubilee Trading Centre, Jubilee Road, Letchworth Garden City, Hertfordshire, SG6 1NE Tel: (01462) 481295 Fax: (01462) 685275 E-mail: sales@tryax.com

Turntech Precision Engineers, Unit 33 Liberty Close, Woolsbridge Industrial Estate, Three Legged Cross, Wimborne, Dorset, BH21 6SY Tel: (01202) 822040 Fax: (01202) 829146 E-mail: sales@turntech-precision.co.uk

Unijet Products Ltd, Unit 4 The Ham, Brentford, Middlesex, TW8 8EZ Tel: 020 85608978

CNC WATER JET CUTTING MACHINES

MTC Software Ltd, 7 Clarendon Place, Leamington Spa, Warwickshire, CV32 5QL Tel: (0870) 8031297 Fax: (0870) 8031298 E-mail: mtc@mtc-europe.co.uk

CNC WIRE BENDING MACHINES

▶ Ultimation Machines Ltd, Laundry Way, Capel, Dorking, Surrey, RH5 5LG Tel: (01306) 712205 Fax: (01306) 713182

CNC WIRE EROSION MACHINING

Delen Tooling, Lansbury Estate, 102 Lower Guildford Road, Knaphill, Woking, Surrey, GU21 2EP Tel: (01483) 487033 Fax: (01483) 487033 E-mail: info@delentooling.co.uk

Edwards Precision Engineering Ltd, 173-179 Tyburn Road, Erdington, Birmingham, B24 8NQ Tel: 0121-327 7828 Fax: 0121-327 7987 E-mail: enquiries@edwards-precision.co.uk

Exact Engineering Thompson Ltd, Kingsway South, Team Valley Trading Estate, Gateshead, Tyne & Wear, NE11 0JS Tel: 0191-482 6622 Fax: 0191-482 1602 E-mail: john.martin@exact-engineering.com

Harper & Simmons Ltd, 19 Howard Road, Park Farm, Redditch, Worcestershire, B98 7SE Tel: (01527) 518121 Fax: (01527) 518123 E-mail: robertsimmons@harperandsimmons.co.uk

M G M Precision Engineering Ltd, M G M House, Newburn Bridge Road, Newburn, Newcastle upon Tyne, NE15 8NR Tel: 0191-499 0005 Fax: 0191-499 0007 E-mail: mgm@mgmplc.com

Tarpey-Harris Ltd, Flamstead House, Denby Hall Business Park, Denby, Ripley, Derbyshire, DE5 8NN Tel: (01332) 883950 Fax: (01332) 883951 E-mail: steve.jones@tarpey-harris.co.uk

Wire Erosion Co. Ltd, Units 8-9, Springfield Business Centre, Oldends Lane, Stonehouse, Gloucestershire, GL10 3SX Tel: (01453) 827771 Fax: (01453) 827761

CNC WOODWORK

▶ The Routing & Packaging Company Ltd, Unit 1 Walk Mill Green Road, Colne, Lancashire, BB8 8AL Tel: (01282) 864629 Fax: (01282) 864661 E-mail: nigel@trppackaging.co.uk

CNC WOODWORKING MACHINES

Central c.n.c. Machinery Ltd, Unit 12B, Scar La, Milnsbridge, Huddersfield, HD3 4PE Tel: 0845 4941645 Fax: (01484) 460101 E-mail: enquiries@centralcnc.co.uk

J M J Ltd, Main Street, Skidby, Cottingham, North Humberside, HU16 5TX Tel: (01482) 840103 Fax: (01482) 875052 E-mail: info@jmjwood.co.uk

Pinnacle C N C Ltd, 5 Kirby Road, Nelson, Lancashire, BB9 6RS Tel: 01282 695222

Reichenbacher-Hamuel, Unit 2 The Moorlands, Lee Lane, Millhouse Green, Sheffield, S36 9NN Tel: (01226) 761799 Fax: (01226) 761589 E-mail: denise@r.co.uk

COACH BODY BUILDERS

Advanced Systems UK Ltd, Smarden BSNS Estate, Monks Hill, Smarden, Ashford, Kent, TN27 8QJ Tel: (01233) 770000 Fax: (01233) 770000 E-mail: admin@advancedsystemsltd.co.uk

Aztec Garage, 6-8 Emery Road, Bristol, BS4 5PF Tel: 0117-977 0314 Fax: 0117-977 4431 E-mail: myrtletree@holding4337.freeserve.co.uk

B H C Coach Builders, The Stables, Stanwell New Road, Staines, Middlesex, TW18 4HZ Tel: (01784) 453148

Chambers Engineering Ltd, Warmstone Lane, Waddesdon, Aylesbury, Buckinghamshire, HP18 0NQ Tel: (01296) 651380 Fax: (01296) 651063 E-mail: chameng@btconnect.com

Coleman Milne, Wigan Road, Westhoughton, Bolton, BL5 2EE Tel: (01942) 815600 Fax: (01942) 815115 E-mail: sales@woodall-nicholson.co.uk

Eagle Specialist Vehicles Ltd, 105 Manchester Road, West Houghton, Bolton, BL5 3QH Tel: (01942) 850200 Fax: (01942) 819745 E-mail: eaglespecial@aol.com

A.M. Ede Technical Services Ltd, Conger Cottage, Market Square, Dunstable, Bedfordshire, LU5 6BP Tel: (01525) 873890 Fax: (01525) 873890

Emanuel Bros Ltd, Wexham Road, Slough, SL1 1RW Tel: (01753) 524153 Fax: (01753) 530775 E-mail: sales@emanuelbrothers.co.uk

George Newberry Coachbuilders, 3 Northburn Road, Coatbridge, Lanarkshire, ML5 2HY Tel: (01236) 710900 Fax: (01236) 710900 E-mail: andy@gnewberrycoachbiulders.com

▶ M & H Coachworks Ltd, New Princess Street, Leeds, LS11 9BA Tel: 0113-244 1671 Fax: 0113-243 8959 E-mail: paul@mhcoachworks.wanadoo.co.uk

Onyx Conversions, Mitchell Main Industrial Estate, Mitchell Road, Wombwell, Barnsley, South Yorkshire, S73 8HA Tel: (01226) 752121 Fax: (01226) 270084

P M H Coachbuilders Ltd, Longcroft House, Glasgow Road, Dennyloanhead, Bonnybridge, Stirlingshire, FK4 1QW Tel: (01324) 841702 Fax: (01324) 849458

Truck Tac Ireland, 32 Camaghy Road, Galbally, Dungannon, County Tyrone, BT70 2NT Tel: (028) 8775 8736 Fax: (028) 8775 8926

Westmorland Truck Bodies Ltd, 19 Cumberland St, Hull, HU2 0QB Tel: (01482) 329062 Fax: (01482) 329062

COACH BODY MAINTENANCE/ REPAIR SERVICES

Alexandrer, Unit B, Barrows Road, Harlow, Essex, CM19 5FD Tel: (01920) 462383 Fax: (01279) 419744

Aztec Garage, 6-8 Emery Road, Bristol, BS4 5PF Tel: 0117-977 0314 Fax: 0117-977 4431 E-mail: myrtletree@holding4337.freeserve.co.uk

Carrier Sutrak, Unit 6, The IO Centre, Lodge Farm Industrial Estate, Northampton, NN5 7UW Tel: (01604) 581468 Fax: (01604) 758132

Evobush UK Ltd, Ashcroft Way, Crosspoint Business Park, Coventry, CV2 2TU Tel: (024) 7662 6000 Fax: (024) 7662 6010

M. Hayward & Daughter (South Wales) Ltd, Cwmau Bach, St. Peters, Carmarthen, Dyfed, SA31 3RR Tel: (01267) 235467 Fax: (01267) 220641

Hunt & Keal, 53-57 Minerva Road, London, NW10 6HJ Tel: (020) 8838 2332 Fax: (020) 8838 2800

▶ M & H Coachworks Ltd, New Princess Street, Leeds, LS11 9BA Tel: 0113-244 1671 Fax: 0113-243 8959 E-mail: paul@mhcoachworks.wanadoo.co.uk

Maybole Coachworks, 3 Barns Terrace, Maybole, Ayrshire, KA19 7EP Tel: (01655) 883911 Fax: (01655) 740458

Newcote Coachworks Ltd, Unit 4, Bessborough Works, Molesey Road, West Molesey, Surrey, KT8 2QS Tel: (020) 8979 0563 Fax: (020) 8941 7251

P M H Coachbuilders Ltd, Longcroft House, Glasgow Road, Dennyloanhead, Bonnybridge, Stirlingshire, FK4 1QW Tel: (01324) 841702 Fax: (01324) 849458

Westmorland Truck Bodies Ltd, 19 Cumberland St, Hull, HU2 0QB Tel: (01482) 329062 Fax: (01482) 329062

COACH FITTINGS AND ACCESSORIES

B M A C Ltd, Units 13 14, Shepley Industrial Estate South, Shepley Road, Audenshaw, M34 5DW Tel: 0161-367 3070 Fax: 0161-336 5691 E-mail: enquiries@bmac.ltd.uk

Duoflex Ltd, Trimmingham House, 2 Shires Road, Buckingham Road Industrial Estate, Brackley, Northamptonshire, NN13 7EZ Tel: (01280) 701366 Fax: (01280) 704799 E-mail: sales@duoflex.co.uk

▶ John Adams Ltd, Atlas Industrial Estate, Edgefauld Avenue, Glasgow, G21 4UR Tel: 0141-557 0007 Fax: 0141-558 9564 E-mail: sales@jadams.ibcos.net

▶ M & H Coachworks Ltd, New Princess Street, Leeds, LS11 9BA Tel: 0113-244 1671 Fax: 0113-243 8959 E-mail: paul@mhcoachworks.wanadoo.co.uk

Moseley Distributors Ltd, Rydenmains Road, Glenmavis, Airdrie, Lanarkshire, ML6 0PP Tel: (01236) 750501 Fax: (01236) 750503

Rex Bousfield Ltd, Fairview Industrial Estate, Holland Road, Oxted, Surrey, RH8 9BD Tel: (01883) 717033 Fax: (01883) 717890 E-mail: john.medcraft@bousfield.com

Shades Technics, 3 Marshgate Drive, Hertford, SG13 7AQ Tel: (01992) 501683 Fax: (01992) 501669 E-mail: sales@shades-technics.com

Smyth's Equipment Supply Co., Tamar Commercial Centre, Chater Street, Belfast, BT4 1BL Tel: (028) 9045 1355 Fax: (028) 9045 4838 E-mail: sescobelfast@aol.com

COACH HIRE

▶ B.J.Travel, 9, Woodview, Paulton, Bristol, BS39 7XQ Tel: 01761 412822 Fax: 01761 412822 E-mail: quotes@bj-travel.co.uk

▶ Clydewide Taxis, 99 High Street, Lanark, ML11 7LN Tel: (01555) 663813 Fax: (01555) 678937 E-mail: taxis@clydewide.co.uk

▶ Den Caney, 182 Stonehouse Lane, Quinton, Birmingham, B32 3AH Tel: 0121-427 2693 Fax: 0121-427 8905 E-mail: dencaneycoaches@blueyonder.co.uk

▶ Elite Services Ltd, Unit 3 & 6 Adswood Industrial Estate, Adswood Road, Stockport, Cheshire, SK3 8LF Tel: 0161-480 0617 Fax: 0161-480 3099 E-mail: sam_nickson@hotmail.com

Eltham Executive Charter, Crown Woods Way, London, SE9 2NL Tel: (020) 8850 2011 Fax: (020) 8850 5210E-mail: eec@cwcom.net

▶ Excel Chauffeur Services, Warrington Business Park, Long Lane, Warrington, WA2 8TX Tel: (0871) 2881433 Fax: (0871) 2881433 E-mail: enquiries@xl-cars.co.uk

Executive Catering Services, 107a High Street, Carrville, Durham, DH1 1BQ Tel: 0191-386 3682 Fax: 0191-383 0280 E-mail: eccs107a@aol.com

▶ Luxtravel Ltd, Tenterden Road, Biddenden, Ashford, Kent, TN27 8BH Tel: (01580) 292970 Fax: (01622) 750751 E-mail: enquiries@luxtravel.co.uk

▶ Pauls Mini Bus, 14 Cross Walk, Bristol, BS14 0RX Tel: (01275) 542422 Fax: (01275) 831476 E-mail: info@paulsminibus.co.uk

▶ T W Bell Belsay Ltd, Burnside Garage, Grange Road, Stamfordham, Newcastle upon Tyne, NE18 0PF Tel: (01661) 886207

▶ Translinc Ltd, Jarvis House, 157 Sadler Road, Lincoln, LN6 3RS Tel: (01522) 503400 Fax: (01522) 552997 E-mail: sales@translinc.co.uk

COAL EFFECT GAS FIRES

▶ Embers Fireplaces, 221 Frimley Green Road, Frimley Green, Camberley, Surrey, GU16 6LA Tel: (01252) 837837 Fax: (01252) 837837 E-mail: steve@fireplaces.co.uk

COAL PREPARATION PLANT

Don Valley Engineering Co. Ltd, Sandall Stones Road, Kirk Sandall Industrial Estate, Doncaster, South Yorkshire, DN3 1QR Tel: (01302) 881188 E-mail: info@donvalleyeng.com

Parnaby Cyclones International Ltd, Avenue One, Chilton, Ferryhill, County Durham, DL17 0SH Tel: (01388) 720849 Fax: (01388) 721415 E-mail: enquiries@parnaby.co.uk

COAL/COKE/SMOKELESS/SOLID FUEL PRODUCERS/ WHOLESALERS

A & H Ashby, Wakes Colne Mills, Colchester Road, Wakes Colne, Colchester, CO6 2BY Tel: (01787) 222259

Andrew Gray & Co Fuels Ltd, Portland Depot, London Road, Kilmarnock, Ayrshire, KA3 7DD Tel: (01563) 525215 Fax: (01563) 541146 E-mail: andrew@graysfuels.freeserve.co.uk

▶ Bakers Of Oakley, Bakers Yard, Pardown, Oakley, Basingstoke, Hampshire, RG23 7DY Tel: (01256) 780266

C P L Industries Ltd, Mill Lane, Chesterfield, Derbyshire, S42 6NG Tel: (01246) 277001 Fax: (01246) 212212 E-mail: corporate@cplindustries.co.uk

Charles Swan Walsall Ltd, Old Landywood Lane, Essington, Wolverhampton, WV11 2AP Tel: (01922) 408152 Fax: (01922) 711350

Frank Chivers & Son, 1 Estcourt Street, Devizes, Wiltshire, SN10 1LQ Tel: (01380) 723411 Fax: (01380) 728078

Coalite Smokeless Fuels, PO Box 21, Chesterfield, Derbyshire, S44 6AB Tel: (01246) 822281 Fax: (01246) 240044 E-mail: enquiries@coalite.co.uk

Country & Mineral Supplies, 5 Beeches Industrial Estate, Coedcae Lane, Pontyclun, Mid Glamorgan, CF72 9DY Tel: (01443) 224239 Fax: (01443) 224239

CPL Distibution, Holly House, Fen Road, Donington, Spalding, Lincolnshire, PE11 4XE Tel: (01775) 820403 Fax: (01775) 822396

Evans & Reid Coal Co. Ltd, Empire House, Cardiff, CF10 5QZ Tel: (029) 2048 8111 Fax: (029) 2049 1130 E-mail: evansandreid@btinternet.com

▶ Fergusson Group, Castlecraig Business Park, Players Road, Stirling, FK7 7SH Tel: (01786) 477222 Fax: (01786) 463522

J A Smallshaw, 22a Castle Street, Shrewsbury, SY1 2BJ Tel: (01743) 362482 Fax: (01743) 367668

J Brierley Macclesfield Ltd, Bakestonedale Road, Pott Shrigley, Macclesfield, Cheshire, SK10 5RX Tel: (01625) 573837

J Harrison & Sons Coal Merchants Ltd, The Coal Yard, Milton Road, Stoke-on-Trent, ST1 6LE Tel: (01782) 534110 Fax: (01782) 535039 E-mail: sales@jharrison-fuel.co.uk

J Wilmer, Signal Way, Swindon, SN3 1PD Tel: (01793) 522535

Kelly Fuels, Brownstown Business Centre, Brownstown Road, Portadown, Craigavon, County Armagh, BT62 4EA Tel: (028) 3835 0360 Fax: (028) 3835 0356

Lochmaben Coal Co., Crofts Vennel, Queen Street, Lochmaben, Lockerbie, Dumfriesshire, DG11 1PP Tel: (01387) 810466 Fax: (01387) 810497

Maxibrite Ltd, Mwyndy Industrial Estate, Mwyndy, Pontyclun, Mid Glamorgan, CF72 8PN Tel: (01443) 224283 Fax: (01443) 227085 E-mail: sales@maxibrite.co.uk

Pryce Bateman & Son, Prince William Avenue, Sandycroft, Deeside, Clwyd, CH5 2QZ Tel: (01352) 753056 Fax: (01244) 533775 E-mail: pbateman@callnetuk.com

Chas B. Pugh (Walsall) Ltd, Heath Road, Darlaston, Wednesbury, West Midlands, WS10 8LU Tel: 0121-568 7568 Fax: 0121-568 8666 E-mail: pughmail@supanet.com

Rackhams, Deben Mills, Wickham Market, Woodbridge, Suffolk, IP13 0RG Tel: (01728) 746207 Fax: (01728) 747772

T R Rickard, Corminnow, High Street, St. Austell, Cornwall, PL26 7TE Tel: (01726) 72675

W M Mcewen Miller, George Street, Wick, Caithness, KW1 4DG Tel: (01955) 603188 Fax: (01955) 602479

COAL/COKE/SMOKELESS/SOLID FUEL PRODUCERS/WHOLESALERS

– continued

Walter Bailey Par Ltd, St Andrews Road, Par, Cornwall, PL24 2LX Tel: (01726) 812245 Fax: (01726) 812246
Walter Woodthorpe Ltd, Manifirs House, London Road, Kirton, Boston, Lincolnshire, PE20 1JE Tel: (01205) 722050 Fax: (01205) 722818
Wulfruna Col Co., Minerva Wharf, Horseley Field, Wolverhampton, WV1 3DT Tel: (01902) 453517

COALESCER AND SEPARATOR FILTERS

Aljac Fuelling Components, Pitfield House, Station Approach, Shepperton, Middlesex, TW17 8AN Tel: (01932) 269869 Fax: (01932) 269230 E-mail: sales@aljac.com
Amafiltergroup Ltd, Navigation Road, Stoke-on-Trent, ST6 3RU Tel: (01782) 575611 Fax: (01782) 577001 E-mail: salesuk@amafilter.com
▶ Avery Hardoll, Holland Way, Blandford Forum, Dorset, DT11 7BJ Tel: (01258) 486600 Fax: (01258) 486601 E-mail: sales@meggittfuelling.com
▶ Facet Industrial UK Ltd, Unit G4, Treforest Industrial Estate, Pontypridd, Mid Glamorgan, CF37 5YL Tel: (01443) 844141 Fax: (01443) 844282E-mail: uksales@facetinternational.net
Hydro Pneumatic Services, Bastion House, Harlequin Avenue, Brentford, Middlesex, TW8 9EW Tel: (020) 8560 4968 Fax: (020) 8560 4958
Power Utilities Ltd, Queen Street, Premier Business Park, Walsall, WS2 9QE Tel: (01922) 720561 Fax: (01922) 720461 E-mail: filters@power-utilities.com
R A Driair Ltd, 9 Maguire Industrial Estate, Torrington Avenue, Coventry, CV4 9HN Tel: (024) 7646 6061 Fax: (024) 7669 4516 E-mail: sales@driair.co.uk
Separ Distribution, 428 Whippendell Road, Watford, WD18 7QU Tel: (01923) 819041 Fax: (01923) 255052 E-mail: filtration@separ.co.uk

COASTERS, PROMOTIONAL

H Conduit, 4 King William Enterprise Park, King William Street, Salford, M50 3ZP Tel: 0161-877 0877 Fax: 0161-877 3434 E-mail: hconduit@btconnect.com

COASTERS/DRINK MATS

Burton Beer Mats Ltd, Moor St Works, Burton-on-Trent, Staffordshire, DE14 3TA Tel: (01283) 564769 Fax: (01283) 535492 E-mail: sales@burtonbeermatsltd.co.uk
Georgian Crystal Tutbury Ltd, 1 Silk Mill Lane, Tutbury, Burton-on-Trent, Staffordshire, DE13 9LE Tel: (01283) 814534 Fax: (01283) 520186
H Conduit, 4 King William Enterprise Park, King William Street, Salford, M50 3ZP Tel: 0161-877 0877 Fax: 0161-877 3434 E-mail: hconduit@btconnect.com
Impressions, J1 Dunkerswell Business Park, Dunkerswell Airfield, Honiton, Devon, EX14 4LE Tel: (01404) 891850 Fax: (01404) 891850 E-mail: rob@impressions1990.co.uk
Judges Postcards Ltd, 176 Bexhill Road, St. Leonards-on-Sea, East Sussex, TN38 8BN Tel: (01424) 420919 Fax: (01424) 438538 E-mail: sales@judges.co.uk
Keswick Trays, Forest View Farm, Peckleton Lane, Desford, Leicester, LE9 9JU Tel: (01455) 828990 Fax: (01455) 828999 E-mail: david@keswicktrays.f9.co.uk
▶ Magic Touch, 63 Barnton Street, Stirling, FK8 1HH Tel: (01786) 445992 Fax: (01786) 434922
Pimpernel (Holdings) Ltd, 26-32 Derwent Street, Consett, County Durham, DH8 8LY Tel: 01207 588402 Fax: (01207) 507873 E-mail: sales@pimpernelinternational.com
Tradestock Ltd, Poole Works, Poole, Wellington, Somerset, TA21 9HW Tel: (01823) 661717 Fax: (01823) 666543 E-mail: sales@tradestockltd.co.uk

COAT HANGERS

Braitrim Group Ltd, Braitrim House, 98 Victoria Road, London, NW10 6NB Tel: (020) 8723 3000 Fax: (020) 8723 3001 E-mail: service@braitrim.com
John Dron Ltd, 43 Blundells Road, Bradville, Milton Keynes, MK13 7HD Tel: (01908) 311388 Fax: (01908) 222200 E-mail: sales@johndron.co.uk
▶ Hangersnest Ltd, PO Box 2403, Woodford Green, Essex, IG8 1AL Tel: (07921) 245058
Indaux UK Ltd, Mga House, Ray Mill Road East, Maidenhead, Berkshire, SL6 8ST Tel: (01628) 780250 Fax: (01628) 780251 E-mail: sales@indaux.com
L P Hangers, Units 5-9, Parker Paul Trading Estate, Sunbeam Street, Wolverhampton, WV2 4PF Tel: (01902) 420653 Fax: (01902) 714716 E-mail: info@lphangers.co.uk

Laundry Supplies Ltd, Vulcan Road, Lode Lane Industrial Estate, Solihull, West Midlands, B91 2JY Tel: 0121-705 4645 Fax: 0121-711 2051 E-mail: sales@slmarketing.co.uk
Wm. & A.M. Robb Ltd, 84 Cheapside Street, Glasgow, G3 8BE Tel: 0141-221 4631 Fax: 0141-221 2377 E-mail: sales@wmrobb.co.uk
H.& L. Russel Ltd, Russel House, Hornsby Way, Southfields Business Park, Basildon, Essex, SS15 6TF Tel: (01268) 889000 Fax: (01268) 889100 E-mail: sales@russel.co.uk

COATED AND LAMINATED PAPER BAGS

▶ Keep Me Promotions, 2 New Concordia Wharf, Mill Street, London, SE1 2BB Tel: (020) 7231 0001 Fax: (0870) 7605511 E-mail: steve@keepmepromotions.com

COATED COLD DRAWN SEAMLESS TUBES

Mueller Europe Ltd, Oxford Street, Bilston, West Midlands, WV14 7DS Tel: (01902) 499700 Fax: (01902) 405838 E-mail: sales@muellereurope.com

COATED COPPER TUBES

Mueller Europe Ltd, Oxford Street, Bilston, West Midlands, WV14 7DS Tel: (01902) 499700 Fax: (01902) 405838 E-mail: sales@muellereurope.com

COATED FABRIC PRODUCTS, TO CUSTOMERS SPECIFICATION

Plasticotta, Union Road, Bolton, BL2 2HL Tel: (01204) 381991 Fax: (01204) 528863

COATED FABRICS

C M I Plastics Ltd, Wood Street Works, Wood Street, Burnley, Lancashire, BB10 1QH Tel: (01282) 420021 Fax: (01282) 831387 E-mail: sales@cmi-ltd.com
Coating Applications Group, Newhouse Road, Huncoat Business Park, Accrington, Lancashire, BB5 6NT Tel: (01254) 391769 Fax: (01254) 393519 E-mail: sales@coatingapplications.co.uk
Cooper Tyre & Rubber Co UK Ltd, Bath Road, Melksham, Wiltshire, SN12 8AA Tel: (01225) 703101 Fax: (01225) 707880
H D K Industries Ltd, 13 Whalley Avenue, Sale, Cheshire, M33 2BP Tel: 0161-905 1869 Fax: 0161-905 1879
I Q Textiles, Mid Road, Prestonpans, East Lothian, EH32 9ER Tel: (01875) 811200 Fax: (01875) 811452
J B Broadley, Reeds Holme Works, Burnley Road, Rossendale, Lancashire, BB4 8LN Tel: (01706) 213661 Fax: (01706) 227786 E-mail: info@jbbroadley.co.uk
John Heathcoat & Co Holdings Ltd, Westexe, Tiverton, Devon, EX16 5LL Tel: (01884) 254949 Fax: (01884) 252897 E-mail: email@heathcoat.co.uk
▶ Kindon Textiles Ltd, 31 Belmont Way, Rochdale, Lancashire, OL12 6HR Tel: (01706) 656951 Fax: (01706) 345496 E-mail: g-kindon@msn.com
Frank Pine Ltd, Crown Mill, 1 Crown Street, Salford, M3 7DH Tel: 0161-834 0456 Fax: 0161-832 0385E-mail: fpinetex@aol.com
Plasticotta, Union Road, Bolton, BL2 2HL Tel: (01204) 381991 Fax: (01204) 528863
Polyone Acrol, Unit G 3, Newton Business Park, Talbot Road, Hyde, Cheshire, SK14 4UQ Tel: 0161-367 8773 Fax: 0161-367 8281
Proofings Technology Ltd, Hare Hill Road, Littleborough, Lancashire, OL15 9HE Tel: (01706) 372314 Fax: (01706) 370473 E-mail:

COATED GLASS

W H Constable & Co. Ltd, 16 Barnwell Business Park, Barnwell Drive, Cambridge, CB5 8UZ Tel: (01223) 211888 Fax: (01223) 416888

COATED PAPER/BOARD PROCESSORS OR SERVICES

Arjo Wiggins Fine Papers Ltd, Chineham, Basingstoke, Hampshire, RG24 8BA Tel: (01256) 728728 Fax: (01256) 728889
E. Becker Ltd, 2 Hazlemere View, Hazlemere, High Wycombe, Buckinghamshire, HP15 7BY Tel: (01494) 713777 Fax: (01494) 713888 E-mail: e.becker@breathemail.net
Brown Brothers Group Ltd, 168/170 South Street, Dorking, Surrey, RH4 2ES Tel: (01306) 742611 Fax: (01306) 742601 E-mail: duncan@brownbros.co.uk

C M C Products, Cuxham, Watlington, Oxfordshire, OX49 5NH Tel: (01491) 612676 Fax: (01491) 613771 E-mail: johncarr.cmc@myopal.net
Caledonian Paper plc, Meadowhead Road, Irvine, Ayrshire, KA11 5AT Tel: (01294) 312020 Fax: (01294) 314400 E-mail: sales@upn-kymmene.com
G S Smith Ltd, Lockwood Street, Hull, HU2 0HL Tel: (01482) 323503 Fax: (01482) 223174 E-mail: sales@gssmith.com
Horne Robert Paper Company Ltd, Huntsman House, 40 Tameside Drive, Birmingham, B35 7BD Tel: 0121-776 7777 Fax: 0121-749 2670 E-mail: rh.birmingham@roberthorne.co.uk
International Paper Ltd, Inverurie Mills, Inverurie, Aberdeenshire, AB51 5NR Tel: (01467) 627000 Fax: (01467) 627102 E-mail: bill.conn@ipaper.com
Slater Harrison & Co. Ltd, Lowerhouse Mills, Bollington, Macclesfield, Cheshire, SK10 5HW Tel: (01625) 578900 Fax: (01625) 578972 E-mail: l.preston@slater-harrison.co.uk
Smurfit Townsend Hook, Paper Mills, Mill Street, Snodland, Kent, ME6 5AX Tel: (01634) 240205 Fax: (01634) 243458 E-mail: sales@smurfit-europe.com
Torras Paper Ltd, Creator House, Maidstone Road, Kingston, Milton Keynes, MK10 0BD Tel: (01908) 288000 Fax: (01908) 288001 E-mail: info@torraspapel.es
Tullis Russell Coaters Ltd, Church Street, Bollington, Macclesfield, Cheshire, SK10 5QF Tel: (01625) 573051 Fax: (01625) 575525 E-mail: enquiries@trcoaters.co.uk
Tullis Russell Coaters Ltd, Brittains Paper Mills, Commercial Road, Hanley, Stoke-on-Trent, ST1 3QS Tel: (01782) 202567 Fax: (01782) 202157 E-mail: enquiries@trcoaters.co.uk

COATED PLASTIC PROCESSORS OR SERVICES

▶ Cox Plastics Technologies Ltd, Weedon Road Industrial Estae, Northampton, NN5 5AX Tel: (01604) 752200 Fax: (01604) 752266 E-mail: info@arkplastics.co.uk

COATED RUBBER, *See Rubber Coated etc; also Rubber Dipped etc*

COATED SPECIALIST PROCESSORS OR SERVICES

Dispec Anodizing Ltd, Unit 4 Sough Bridge Mill, Colne Road, Barnoldswick, Lancashire, BB18 6UH Tel: (01282) 841341 Fax: (01282) 841341 E-mail: dispec@ic24.net
Fast Line Coatings Ltd, 9 Wellfield Business Park, Wellfield Road, Preston, PR1 8SZ Tel: (01772) 563550 Fax: (01772) 563551 E-mail: sales@fastlinecoatings.com
Intumescent Protective Coatings Ltd, 1 Jupiter Court Orion Business Park, Tyne Tunnel Trading Estate, North Shields, Tyne & Wear, NE29 7SE Tel: 0191-272 8225 Fax: 0191-272 8226

COATED TABLE LINEN

Petra, 1 Moat Lane Crossing, Moat Lane, Caersws, Powys, SY17 5SE Tel: (01686) 688131 Fax: (01686) 688283 E-mail: sales@cardtables.co.uk

COATING FILTERS

▶ Airpel Filtration, Hambridge Road, Newbury, Berkshire, RG14 5TR Tel: +44 (0) 1635 263915 Fax: +44 (0) 1635 36006 E-mail: airpel@spx.com

COATING THICKNESS CONTROL SYSTEMS

Elcometer Instruments Ltd, Edge Lane, Droylsden, Manchester, M43 6BU Tel: 0161-371 6000 Fax: 0161-371 6010 E-mail: sales@elcometer.com

COATINGS

Kirtek Industries Ltd, Thorney Road, Crowland, Peterborough, PE6 0AL Tel: (01733) 211290 Fax: (01733) 212331 E-mail: gkerk01@fsmail.net

COATS

Kesta At David Barry Ltd, 7-9 Solebay Street, London, E1 4PW Tel: (020) 7790 2525 Fax: (020) 7790 5656 E-mail: sales@kesta.co.uk
Noble Furs Regent Street Ltd, 3 New Burlington Place, London, W1S 2HR Tel: (020) 8734 6394 Fax: (020) 7734 6396 E-mail: enquiries@noblefurs.com

Silverts Ltd, 116-120 Goswell Road, London, EC1V 7DP Tel: (020) 7253 5766 Fax: (020) 7608 2230 E-mail: sales@silverts.co.uk

COAXIAL CABLES

▶ Cobra Electronics Ltd, 1 Greenacres, Bordon, Hampshire, GU35 0EX Tel: (01420) 479830 Fax: (01420) 479860 E-mail: sales@cobra4coax.com
Electro Cables Ltd, Unit 2 Alliance Close, Attleborough Fields Industrial Estate, Nuneaton, Warwickshire, CV11 6SD Tel: (024) 7632 0066 Fax: (024) 7632 0122 E-mail: sales@electrocables.co.uk
Nova Electronic Developments Co Ltd, 49 Florence Road, Gedling, Nottingham, NG4 2QL Tel: 0115-910 9910 Fax: 0115-910 9900 E-mail: sales@novadev.co.uk

COAXIAL CONNECTORS

A E R C O Ltd, Units 16-17 Lawson Hunt Industrial Park, Broadbridge Heath, Horsham, West Sussex, RH12 3JR Tel: (01403) 260206 Fax: (01403) 259760 E-mail: sales@aerco.co.uk
▶ Cobra Electronics Ltd, 1 Greenacres, Bordon, Hampshire, GU35 0EX Tel: (01420) 479830 Fax: (01420) 479860 E-mail: sales@cobra4coax.com
Probus Electronics Ltd, Findon, Southill Lane, Pinner, Middlesex, HA5 2EQ Tel: (020) 8866 7272 Fax: (020) 8866 2999 E-mail: sales@probus.freeserve.co.uk
R F S UK Ltd, 9 Haddenham Business Park, Thame Road, Haddenham, Aylesbury, Buckinghamshire, HP17 8LJ Tel: (01844) 294900 Fax: (01844) 294944 E-mail: sales@rfsworld.com
Radiall Ltd, Ground Floor, 6 The Grand Union Office Park, Packet Boat Lane, Uxbridge, Middlesex, UB8 2GH Tel: (01895) 425000 Fax: (01895) 425010 E-mail: info@radiall.com
Rhophase Microwaves Ltd, Earlstrees Court, Earlstrees Industrial Estate, Corby, Northamptonshire, NN17 4RH Tel: (01536) 263440 Fax: (01536) 260764 E-mail: sales@rhophase.co.uk
Rosenberger Micro-Coax Ltd, 2 Mercury House, Calleva Park, Aldermaston, RG7 8PN Tel: 0118-981 0023 Fax: 0118-981 6180 E-mail: sales@rmcoax.com
Suhner Electronics Ltd, Telford Road, Bicester, Oxfordshire, OX26 4LA Tel: (01869) 364100 Fax: (01869) 249046 E-mail: info.uk@hubersuhner.co.uk
Vitelec Electronics Ltd, Station Road, Bordon, Hampshire, GU35 0LG Tel: (01420) 488661 Fax: (01420) 488014 E-mail: sales@vitelec.co.uk

COAXIAL MATRIX SYSTEMS

Signal Management Ltd, Plumpton House, Plumpton Road, Hoddesdon, Hertfordshire, EN11 0LB Tel: (01992) 463603 Fax: (01992) 443824 E-mail: enquiries@signalman.co.uk

COAXIAL RELAYS

Pickering Electronics Ltd, Stephenson Road, Clacton-on-Sea, Essex, CO15 4NL Tel: (01255) 428141 Fax: (01255) 475058 E-mail: sales@pickeringrelay.com
Signal Management Ltd, Plumpton House, Plumpton Road, Hoddesdon, Hertfordshire, EN11 0LB Tel: (01992) 463603 Fax: (01992) 443824 E-mail: enquiries@signalman.co.uk

COBALT ALLOY CASTINGS

Hooker Group Ltd, Waterside, Brightlingsea, Colchester, CO7 0AU Tel: (01206) 302611 Fax: (01206) 305014 E-mail: sales@hooker.co.uk
Norton Cast Products Ltd, Capital Steel Works, Tinsley Park Road, Sheffield, S9 5DL Tel: 0114-244 8722 Fax: 0114-242 5523 E-mail: info@nortoncast.com
Polycast Ltd, Clocktower Buildings, Shore Road, Warsash, Southampton, SO31 9GQ Tel: (01489) 885560 Fax: (01489) 885608 E-mail: sales@polycast.ltd.uk

COBALT METAL

Jack Sharkey & Co. Ltd, 2 Middlemore Road, Smethwick, West Midlands, B66 2DR Tel: 0121-558 7444 Fax: 0121-558 9810
Luvata Sales Oy (UK), Regency Chambers Regency Arcade, 154-156 Parade, Leamington Spa, Warwickshire, CV32 4BQ Tel: (01689) 825677 Fax: (01926) 459149 E-mail: enquiries@outokumpu.com
Special Alloys Northern Ltd, Greasbrough Road, Rotherham, South Yorkshire, S60 1RW Tel: (01709) 828333 Fax: (01709) 829915 E-mail: nickeightyatspecialalloys@fsmail.net

COCKROACH PEST CONTROL MATERIALS

▶ Pestcontrolpro .Co.Uk, 37 Lyndon Road, Bramham, Wetherby, West Yorkshire, LS23 6RH Tel: (07725) 317112

COCONUT OIL, ORGANIC

▶ Coconut Island, 43 Enys Road, Eastbourne, East Sussex, BN21 2DH Tel: (01323) 641757 E-mail: smaas@btinternet.com
▶ fresh-coconut organic virgin coconut oil, 145A Wembley Park Drive, Wembley, Middx, HA9 8HQ Tel: 07950 606390

CODED WELDING

Fabrication & Installation Ltd, Units 6-9 Enterprise Way, Ladysmith Road, Grimsby, South Humberside, DN32 9TW Tel: (01472) 240409 Fax: (01472) 240408
Ryeford Engineering, 14 Ebley Road, Stonehouse, Gloucestershire, GL10 2LH Tel: (01453) 825841 Fax: (01453) 827732 E-mail: nick@ryefordeng.co.uk
Thermsave Welding, 9 Wavertree Park Gardens, Low Moor, Bradford, West Yorkshire, BD12 0UY Tel: (01274) 424478 Fax: (01274) 424479 E-mail: thermsavewelding@blueyonder.co.uk

CODING MACHINES

Overprint Packaging plc, 1 Thame Road Industrial Estate, Thame Road, Haddenham, Aylesbury, Buckinghamshire, HP17 8BY Tel: (01844) 292959 Fax: (01844) 292979 E-mail: info@overprint.co.uk
Rotech Machines Ltd, Bridge Road East, Welwyn Garden City, Hertfordshire, AL7 1JU Tel: (01707) 393700 Fax: (01707) 392800

CODING PRINTER COMPONENTS

M & A Packaging Services Ltd, Spring Lane North, Malvern, Worcestershire, WR14 1BU Tel: (01684) 560099 Fax: (01684) 560095 E-mail: info@mapexinspection.co.uk
Overprint Packaging plc, 1 Thame Road Industrial Estate, Thame Road, Haddenham, Aylesbury, Buckinghamshire, HP17 8BY Tel: (01844) 292959 Fax: (01844) 292979 E-mail: info@overprint.co.uk
Zebra Technologies (Europe) Ltd, Zebra House, The Valley Centre, Gordon Road, High Wycombe, Buckinghamshire, HP13 6EQ Tel: (01494) 472872 Fax: (01494) 450103

CODING, BAR CODE, *See Bar Code etc*

CODING/MARKING SERVICES

Crown Gold Blocking Co. Ltd, 63 Camden Street, Birmingham, B1 3DD Tel: 0121-233 1670 Fax: 0121-233 1670
Overprint Packaging plc, 1 Thame Road Industrial Estate, Thame Road, Haddenham, Aylesbury, Buckinghamshire, HP17 8BY Tel: (01844) 292959 Fax: (01844) 292979 E-mail: info@overprint.co.uk
Scan Logic Ltd, Shenstone Drive, Walsall, WS9 8TP Tel: (01922) 458158 Fax: (01922) 745110 E-mail: sales@scanlogic.co.uk

COEXTRUDED POLYETHYLENE (PE) FILM

Cirrus Plastics, Esky Drive, Carn Industrial Area, Portadown, Craigavon, County Armagh, BT63 5WD Tel: (028) 3835 0001 Fax: (028) 3835 0002 E-mail: sales@cirrusplastics.co.uk

COFFEE

Cafédirect plc, City Cloisters Suite B2, 196 Old Street, London, EC1V 9FR Tel: (020) 7490 9520 Fax: (020) 7490 9521 E-mail: info@cafedirect.co.uk
Metropolitan Coffee Co. Ltd, 28-30 Telford Way, London, W3 7XS Tel: (020) 8743 8959 Fax: (020) 8743 4929 E-mail: sales@metropolitancoffee.co.uk
Pennine Tea & Coffee Limited, 6-8 Hall Street, Halifax, West Yorkshire, HX1 5AY Tel: (01422) 347734 Fax: (01422) 347734 E-mail: aespresso@aol.com
Smith's Coffee Co. and The Natural Coffee Co., Arabica House, Ebberns Road, Apsley, Hemel Hempstead, Herts, HP3 9RD Tel: (01442) 234239 Fax: (01442) 248614 E-mail: sales@smiths-coffee.demon.co.uk

COFFEE BEAN PROCESSING EQUIPMENT

▶ Miko.co.uk, Unit 2, Tweed Road, Clevedon, Somerset, BS21 6RR Tel: (01275) 874416 Fax: (01275) 342027 E-mail: info@mikocoffee.co.uk

COFFEE CONCEPT DEVELOPMENT

Mantaya Beverages Systems (MBS) Ltd, Unit 3 Blakenhall Farm, Linton Road, Caldwell, Swadlincote, Derbyshire, DE12 6RU Tel: (01283) 762867 Fax: (01283) 763859 E-mail: sales@mantaya.com

COFFEE FILTER PANS

Thomas & Green Ltd/Konos Gmbh, 81 Orchard Way, Burmell, Cambridge, CB25 0EQ Tel: 07768 682210 Fax: 01638 605146 E-mail: richard.start@ntlworld.com

COFFEE FLAVOURS

▶ Buccaneer Trading, Spire Hill Farm, Thornhill, Stalbridge, Dorset, DT10 2SG Tel: 01258 821389

COFFEE MACHINE MAINTENANCE OR REPAIR

dorset rancilio espresso machine engineer repairs, Espressocity, 9 Chettle Village, Blandford Forum, Dorset, DT11 8DB Tel: (01258) 830624 E-mail: sales@espressocity.co.uk

COFFEE MACHINE WATER SOFTENERS

▶ J. Randalls of Dunstable, 38 Downs Road, Dunstable, Bedfordshire, LU5 4DD Tel: (07967) 247788 E-mail: jim.randall@btinternet.com

COFFEE MACHINES

▶ Allied Drinks System, Mexborough Business Centre, College Road, Mexborough, South Yorkshire, S64 9JP Tel: (0800) 442299 Fax: (01709) 781818 E-mail: sales@allied-drinks.co.uk
Apex Coffee Co. Ltd, Unit 4 Langdon Hills Business, Florence Way, Basildon, Essex, SS16 6AJ Tel: (01268) 411940 Fax: (01268) 491688 E-mail: roytaylor@apexcoffee.co.uk
Arcadia Coffee Services, 65 Mayflower Road, Park Street, St. Albans, Hertfordshire, AL2 2QN Tel: (01727) 873202 Fax: (01727) 873202
Argosy Coffee Services, 44 Rownhams Lane, North Baddesley, Southampton, SO52 9HQ Tel: (023) 8073 2345 Fax: (023) 8073 2234
Betttavend Ltd, 5 Speedwell Close, Chandlers Ford Industrial Estate, Eastleigh, Hampshire, SO53 4BT Tel: (023) 8025 5222 Fax: (023) 8027 6644 E-mail: enquiries@bettavend.co.uk
Blue Spring, Hanney Road, Steventon, Abingdon, Oxfordshire, OX13 6DJ Tel: (01235) 861000 Fax: (01235) 861999
▶ Cafe Espress First Service, Regent Park, Booth Drive, Park Farm Industrial Estate, Wellingborough, Northamptonshire, NN8 6GR Tel: (01933) 670999 Fax: (01933) 670998
Coffee Craft, 30 Industrial Estate, Old Church Road, East Hanningfield, Chelmsford, CM3 8AB Tel: (01245) 403301 Fax: (01245) 403306 E-mail: mail@coffeecraft.co.uk
▶ Coffee Merchants, Rathdown Road, Lissue Industrial Estate, Lisburn, County Antrim, BT28 2RE Tel: (028) 9262 2733 Fax: (028) 9262 2734 E-mail: stuart@coffeemerchantsltd.com
▶ Coffee Point plc, Henfield Road, Small Dole, Henfield, West Sussex, BN5 9XH Tel: (01903) 879102 Fax: (01903) 879642
▶ Coffee Warehouse, Reform Street, Hull, HU2 8EF Tel: (01482) 216061 Fax: (01482) 221225
Devons Catering Equipment, 1589-1593 London Road, London, SW16 4AA Tel: (020) 8679 8585 Fax: (020) 86796633 E-mail: info@devonscatering.co.uk
Eurosmart Ltd, 192 Clarendon Pk Rd, Leicester, LE2 3AF Tel: 0116-270 7440 Fax: 0116-270 7440
Express Cappuccino Servicing, 4 Addison Gardens, Grays, Essex, RM17 5QU Tel: (01375) 385634 Fax: (01375) 396944
▶ Havana Coffee Co., Unit 11 Gratton Court, Gratton Way, Roundswell Business Park, Barnstaple, Devon, EX31 3NL Tel: (01271) 374376 Fax: (01271) 374376
Melitta System Service, Unit 21 Grove Park Industrial Estate, Waltham Road, White Waltham, Maidenhead, Berkshire, SL6 3LW Tel: (01628) 829888 Fax: (01628) 825111
Midwest Market Force Ltd, 46 Raddens Road, Halesowen, West Midlands, B62 0AN Tel: 0121-421 2333 Fax: 0121-421 3555 E-mail: mwmf@btconnect.com
Peros Ltd, 8 Century Point, Halifax Road, Cressex Business Park, High Wycombe, Buckinghamshire, HP12 3SL Tel: (01494) 436426 Fax: (01494) 769545 E-mail: coffee@peros.co.uk
Prima Coffee Service Ltd, Tewkesbury Business Park, Tewkesbury, Gloucestershire, GL20 8PF Tel: (01684) 854410 Fax: 01684 854410 E-mail: prima.coffee@btinternet.com
Strong Vend Ltd, 8 St Marks Industrial Estate, 439 North Woolwich Road, London, E16 2BS Tel: (020) 7511 3511 Fax: (020) 7473 0573 E-mail: info@strongvend.co.uk
Style Cafe Ltd, Vivary Mill, Vivary Way, Colne, Lancashire, BB8 9NW Tel: (01282) 869641 Fax: (01282) 869616 E-mail: sales@stylecafe.co.uk
Traders Coffee Ltd - Traders of Surbiton, 274 Ewell Road, Surbiton, Surrey, KT6 7AG Tel: (020) 8390 0311 Fax: (020) 8390 8280 E-mail: admin@coffeebay.co.uk

COFFEE MACHINES, LARGE SCALE/CATERING

▶ Axon Enterprises Ltd, 8a & 8b St. Martins Street, Hereford, HR2 7RE Tel: (01432) 359906 Fax: (01432) 352436 E-mail: sales@axon-enterprises.co.uk
Coffee People, Unit 9 Watford Enterprise Centre, 25 Greenhill Crescent, Watford, WD18 8XU Tel: (01923) 242022 Fax: (01923) 242044 E-mail: coffe.people@hotmail.co.uk
Instanta Ltd, Canning Road, Southport, Merseyside, PR9 7SN Tel: (01704) 501114 Fax: (01704) 501115 E-mail: info@instanta.com
M S A Ltd, Wassalls Hall, Bishops Wood Road, Wickham, Hampshire, PO17 5AT Tel: (01329) 835440 Fax: (01329) 835430 E-mail: sales@msaltd.com
Melitta System Service, Unit 21 Grove Park Industrial Estate, Waltham Road, White Waltham, Maidenhead, Berkshire, SL6 3LW Tel: (01628) 829888 Fax: (01628) 825111

COFFEE ROASTER SERVICES

▶ James's Gourmet Coffee Co. Ltd, Cropper Row, Haigh Industrial Estate, Ross-on-Wye, Herefordshire, HR9 5LA Tel: (0870) 7870233 Fax: (01989) 566244 E-mail: peter@jamesgourmetcoffee.com

COFFEE ROASTING MACHINES

Argosy Coffee Services, 44 Rownhams Lane, North Baddesley, Southampton, SO52 9HQ Tel: (023) 8073 2345 Fax: (023) 8073 2234
Fracino Catering Equipment, Unit 17-19 Birch Road East Industrial Estate, Birch Road East, Birmingham, B6 7DA Tel: 0121-328 5757 Fax: 0121-327 3333 E-mail: sales@fracino.com
West 9 Coffee Ltd, Arabica House, The Pines, Broad Street, Guildford, Surrey, GU3 3VH Tel: (01483) 303641 Fax: (01483) 303615

COFFEE SPOONS

▶ Buccaneer Trading, Spire Hill Farm, Thornhill, Stalbridge, Dorset, DT10 2SG Tel: 01258 821389

COFFEE TABLE LEGS

▶ Imperial World Ltd, 40 Station Road, London, SW19 2LP Tel: (020) 8542 0883 Fax: (020) 8542 0992 E-mail: mail@imperial-world.com
▶ SPP Folding Tables, 8 Castle Street, Castle Gate, Hertford, SG14 1HD Tel: (01992) 410333 E-mail: enquiries@tables4sale.com

COFFEE VENDING MACHINES

▶ Coffee Point plc, Henfield Road, Small Dole, Henfield, West Sussex, BN5 9XH Tel: (01903) 879102 Fax: (01903) 879642

COFFIN FURNITURE

▶ pet2rest, Frizley House, 8 Radford Bank, Stafford, ST17 4PL Tel: 01785 211052 Fax: 01785 227649 E-mail: sales@pet2rest.com
John Wilde & Co. Ltd, 66-72 Devon Street, Birmingham, B7 4SL Tel: 0121-380 0300 Fax: 0121-359 5438 E-mail: enquiries@johnwilde.co.uk

COFFINS

F E Harris Ltd, Barn Close, Plympton, Plymouth, PL7 5HQ Tel: (01752) 338311 Fax: (01752) 340748 E-mail: feharris@btconnect.com
John Sheridan & Sons, 72 Old Rossorry Road, Enniskillen, County Fermanagh, BT74 7LF Tel: (028) 6632 2510 Fax: (028) 6632 3895 E-mail: shaunsheridan@email.com
▶ pet2rest, Frizley House, 8 Radford Bank, Stafford, ST17 4PL Tel: 01785 211052 Fax: 01785 227649 E-mail: sales@pet2rest.com
T & I Stockman Ltd, 19 Holwell Road, Brixham, Devon, TQ5 9NE Tel: (01803) 882385 E-mail: info@stockmanfuneralservice.co.uk
▶ Traditional Print, Chapel Road, Ridgewell, Halstead, Essex, CO9 4RU Tel: (01440) 788866 Fax: (01440) 788877

COIL COATING EQUIPMENT

KCS Herr-Voss UK Ltd, Glassworks House, Park Lane, Halesowen, West Midlands, B63 2QS Tel: (01384) 568114 Fax: (01384) 568115 E-mail: ukdrawingoffice@kcsherrvossuk.com

COIL FINISHING/POLISHING SERVICES, METAL

Warley Polishing Ltd, James Scott Road, Halesowen, West Midlands, B63 2QT Tel: (01384) 634036 Fax: (01384) 411025 E-mail: sales@warleypolishing.co.uk

COIL HANDLING EQUIPMENT

M I Engineering Ltd, Bromley Street, Stourbridge, West Midlands, DY9 8HU Tel: (01384) 894156 Fax: (01384) 894151
Wilmat Handling Company Ltd, 43 Steward Street, Birmingham, B18 7AE Tel: 0121-454 7514 Fax: 0121-456 1792 E-mail: info@wilmat-handling.co.uk

COIL PROCESSING EQUIPMENT

Bromley Car Audio, 50 Homesdale Road, Bromley, BR2 9LD Tel: (020) 8460 8704 Fax: (020) 8460 8704 E-mail: sales@caraudioonline.co.uk

COIL SKEINING MACHINERY

Pillerhouse International Ltd, Rodney Way, Chelmsford, CM1 3BY Tel: (01245) 491333 Fax: (01245) 491331 E-mail: sales@pillarhouse.co.uk

COIL SPRINGS

Allevard Springs Ltd, Cambrian Industrial Park, Clydach Vale, Rhondda, Tonypandy, Mid Glamorgan, CF40 2XX Tel: (01443) 424700 Fax: (01443) 424736
Alliance Spring Co Ltd, 44-46 Queensland Road, London, N7 7AR Tel: (020) 7607 3767 Fax: (020) 7609 2994 E-mail: sales@tascuk.co.uk
Ashfield Springs Ltd, Nunn Brook Rise, Huthwaite, Sutton-in-Ashfield, Nottinghamshire, NG17 2PD Tel: 0845 4941745 Fax: (01623) 455502 E-mail: bryan.smith@ashfield-springs.com
Baumann Springs & Pressings UK Ltd, East Mill Lane, Sherborne, Dorset, DT9 3DR Tel: (01935) 818100 Fax: (01935) 814141 E-mail: info@baumann-springs.com
Claridge Presswork Co. Ltd, 11 Bolton Road, Reading, RG2 0NH Tel: 0118-986 0114 Fax: 0118-931 3842 E-mail: sales@springsandwireforms.co.uk
Don Springs (Sheffield) Ltd, 340 Coleford Road, Sheffield, S9 5PH Tel: 0114-244 1545 Fax: 0114-243 5291 E-mail: tony@donsprings.co.uk
Firth Rixson Superalloys Ltd, Shepley Street, Glossop, Derbyshire, SK13 7SA Tel: (01457) 854351 Fax: (01457) 855529 E-mail: lbrierley@firthrixson.com
Flexo Springs Ltd, Hill Street, Kingswood, Bristol, BS15 4HB Tel: 0845 4941786 Fax: 0117-935 2597 E-mail: sales@flexosprings.com
Lancashire Spring Company, Meadowhead Spring Works, Off Dale Street, Milnrow, Rochdale, Lancashire, OL16 4HG Tel: (01706) 715800 Fax: (01706) 715801 E-mail: info@lancashire-spring.co.uk
C. Norris (Spring Specialists) Ltd, Ladyhouse Spring Works, Newhey Road, Milnrow, Rochdale, Lancashire, OL16 4JD Tel: (01706) 642555 Fax: (01706) 648347 E-mail: andrewward@btconnect.com
Penning Springs, Bolton Road North, Ramsbottom, Bury, Lancashire, BL0 0LY Tel: (01706) 824614 Fax: (01706) 821636
Performance Springs Ltd, Queensway Industrial Estate, Scafell Road, St Annes, Lytham St. Annes, Lancashire, FY8 3HE Tel: (01253) 716900 Fax: (01253) 716911 E-mail: sales@performance-springs.com
Reliable Spring & Manufacturing Co. Ltd, Unit 4a Princes End Industrial Estate, Nicholls Road, Tipton, West Midlands, DY4 9LG Tel: 0121-557 4999 Fax: 0121-557 6959 E-mail: sales@reliablespring.co.uk
Richfield Springs, 73 Other Road, Redditch, Worcestershire, B98 8DP Tel: (01527) 595882 Fax: (01527) 595883

COIL SPRINGS – *continued*

Skegness Springs Ltd, Hassall Road, Skegness, Lincolnshire, PE25 3TB Tel: (0845) 4305000 Fax: (01754) 610584 E-mail: sales@skegsprings.co.uk
Frederick Spring Co., Princes End Industrial Park, Nicholls Road, Tipton, West Midlands, DY4 9LG Tel: 0121-557 4080 Fax: 0121-557 6959 E-mail: robjenkins@btclick.com
Springcoil Spring Distributors, 2 Woodbourn Hill, Sheffield, S9 3NE Tel: 0114-273 1111 Fax: 0114-273 0222 E-mail: enquiries@springcoil.co.uk

COIL TAPING MACHINES

▶ Ridgway Machines Ltd, Bridge Works Leicester Road, Anstey, Leicester, LE7 7AT Tel: 0116-235 3055 Fax: 0116-235 3057 E-mail: sales@ridgwayeng.com

COIL WINDERS/COILS, ELECTRICAL

Aden Electronics Holdings Ltd, Unit 3 Montpelier Business Park, Dencora Way, Ashford, Kent, TN23 4FG Tel: (01233) 664445 Fax: (01233) 664626 E-mail: info@adenelectronics.co.uk
Best Windings Ltd, Viking Works, Bucklesham Road, Kirton, Ipswich, IP10 0NX Tel: (01394) 448424 Fax: (01394) 448430 E-mail: kevin@bestwindings.co.uk
Delton Central Services Ltd, 62-70 Camden Street, Birmingham, B1 3DP Tel: 0121-233 1051 Fax: 0121-236 6178 E-mail: sales@deltongroup.co.uk
The Deritend Group Ltd, Armstrong Street, West Marsh Industrial Estate, Grimsby, North East Lincolnshire, DN31 1XD Tel: (01472) 242870 Fax: (01472) 242863 E-mail: grimsby@deritend.co.uk
Electrex World Ltd, Units 44-45 Vanalloys Business Park, Stoke Row, Henley-On-Thames, Oxfordshire, RG9 5QW Tel: (01491) 682369 Fax: (01491) 682286 E-mail: electrex@btinternet.com
Fyfe Wilson & Co. Ltd, Raynham Road, Bishop's Stortford, Hertfordshire, CM23 5PF Tel: (01279) 653333 Fax: (01279) 504941 E-mail: sales@fyfewilson.co.uk
Hayward Holdings Ltd, 5 Howard Industrial Estate, Chilton Road, Chesham, Buckinghamshire, HP5 2AS Tel: (01494) 775075 Fax: (01494) 784861 E-mail: enquiries@hayward-holdings.demon.co.uk
Inphase Transformers Ltd, Kenyon Business Centre, 21 Kenyon Road, Brierfield, Nelson, Lancashire, BB9 5SP Tel: (01282) 614684 Fax: (01282) 695588 E-mail: inphase-tf-ltd@tiscali.co.uk
Interactive Components, 2A Patrick Way, Aylesbury, Buckinghamshire, HP21 9XH Tel: (01296) 425656 Fax: (01296) 395332 E-mail: interactive@bucksnet.co.uk
M B K Motor Rewinds Ltd, 10a Lythalls Lane, Coventry, CV6 6FG Tel: (024) 7668 9510 Fax: (024) 7666 2944 E-mail: sales@mbk-rewinds.co.uk
McKinlay Electrical Manufacturing Co. Ltd, 62 Weir Rd, Wimbledon, London, SW19 8UG Tel: (020) 8879 1141 Fax: (020) 8946 3047 E-mail: mckinlayelec@aol.com
Midland Electrical Holdings Ltd, 14 Abbotsinch Road, Grangemouth, Stirlingshire, FK3 9UX Tel: (01324) 486817 Fax: (01324) 474834 E-mail: info@midlandgroup.co.uk
N E L UK Ltd, 75 Burton Road, Carlton, Nottingham, NG4 3FP Tel: 0115-940 1894 Fax: 0115-987 0878E-mail: tony@nel-uk.co.uk
Northern Coil Services, Unit 6 Aston Court, Kingsland Grange, Woolston, Warrington, WA1 4SG Tel: (01925) 819642 Fax: (01925) 825865 E-mail: ncsdeakin@aol.com
Pontiac Coil Europe Ltd, PO Box 246, Nottingham, NG2 1NQ Tel: 0115-986 1126 Fax: 0115-986 0563 E-mail: info@pontiaccoil.co.uk
Recoil Ltd, 162-164 Ravenscroft Road, Beckenham, Kent, BR3 4TW Tel: (020) 8659 6977 Fax: (020) 8659 2973 E-mail: info@recoilltd.com
Telerelay Sales Ltd, Park Drive Industrial Estate, Braintree, Essex, CM7 1AW Tel: (01376) 321216 Fax: (01376) 347910 E-mail: sales@telerelay.sagehost.co.uk
Trans Tronic, Whitting Valley Road, Old Whittington, Chesterfield, Derbyshire, S41 9EY Tel: (01246) 264260 Fax: (01246) 455281 E-mail: sales@trans-tronic.co.uk
Transmag Power Transformers Ltd, 66-72 Lower Essex Street, Birmingham, B5 6SU Tel: 0121-622 3217 Fax: 0121-622 3217 E-mail: sales@transmag-transformers.co.uk

COIL WINDERS/CUSTOM BUILT COILS

Airtronics Ltd, Victoria Works, 14A Albert Road, Belvedere, Kent, DA17 5LJ Tel: (01322) 431638 Fax: (01322) 430413 E-mail: sales@airtronics.co.uk
Coilmech Transformer Mnfrs, 1 Barratt Industrial Park, Whittle Avenue, Fareham, Hampshire, PO15 5SL Tel: (01489) 885309 Fax: (01489) 885309
Electro Inductors, 19-25 Neville Road, Croydon, CR0 2DS Tel: (020) 8684 6100 Fax: (020) 8684 6109 E-mail: sales@aluminium-inductors.co.uk
Midvale Electrical Engineering Co. Ltd, 20 Butlers Leap, Rugby, Warwickshire, CV21 3RQ Tel: (01788) 543216 Fax: (01788) 540899 E-mail: sales@midvale-electrical.com
North Devon Electronics Ltd, Velator, Braunton, Devon, EX33 2DX Tel: (01271) 813553 Fax: (01271) 816171E-mail: sales@nde.co.uk
Recoil Ltd, 162-164 Ravenscroft Road, Beckenham, Kent, BR3 4TW Tel: (020) 8659 6977 Fax: (020) 8659 2973 E-mail: info@recoilltd.com

COIL WINDING MACHINES

Edson Machinery Co. Ltd, Unit 5 Snowhill Business Centre, Snow Hill, Copthorne, Crawley, West Sussex, RH10 3EZ Tel: (01342) 719719 Fax: (01342) 719718 E-mail: sales@edson.co.uk
Ingrid West Machinery Ltd, Unit 5L, Delta Drive, Tewkesbury Business Park, Tewkesbury, Gloucestershire, GL20 8HB Tel: (01684) 273164 Fax: (01684) 273171 E-mail: enquiries@ingridwest.co.uk
Stator Systems, 7 Potton Road, Abbotsley, St. Neots, Cambridgeshire, PE19 6TX Tel: (01767) 679076 Fax: (01767) 679162
Tanaka Seiki Europe Ltd, 18 Ptarmigan Place, Townsend Drive, Nuneaton, Warwickshire, CV11 6RX Tel: (024) 7635 1153 Fax: (024) 7632 8717 E-mail: tanaka@freezone.co.uk
UK Worldwide Engineering Ltd, 21 Westhall Park, Warlingham, Surrey, CR6 9HS Tel: (01883) 624137 Fax: (01883) 624137 E-mail: brigil@compuserve.com
Whitelegg Machines Ltd, Horsham Road, Beare Green, Dorking, Surrey, RH5 4LQ Tel: (01306) 713200 Fax: (01306) 711865 E-mail: sales@whitelegg.com
Winding Technology, Moorland House, Midway, South Crosland, Huddersfield, HD4 7DA Tel: (01484) 663389 Fax: (01484) 666783 E-mail: coil@winding.demon.co.uk

COIL WINDING MACHINES, AUTOMATIC

▶ Ridgway Machines Ltd, Bridge Works Leicester Road, Anstey, Leicester, LE7 7AT Tel: 0116-235 3055 Fax: 0116-235 3057 E-mail: sales@ridgwayeng.com

COIL WINDINGS/COILS

Recoil Ltd, 162-164 Ravenscroft Road, Beckenham, Kent, BR3 4TW Tel: (020) 8659 6977 Fax: (020) 8659 2973 E-mail: info@recoilltd.com
S & S Windings Ltd, 5 Focus 303 Business Centre, South Way, Andover, Hampshire, SP10 5NY Tel: (01264) 334095 Fax: (01264) 334095 E-mail: sswindings@btclick.com
▶ Toroidal Engineering Co., Queach Holdings, Leys Hill, Walford, Ross-on-Wye, Herefordshire, HR9 5QU Tel: (01989) 566710 E-mail: paul@tec.uk.com

COILED CABLES

Kalestead Ltd, Network House, 300-302 Cressing Road, Braintree, Essex, CM7 3PG Tel: (01376) 349036 Fax: (01376) 348976 E-mail: sales@kalestead.co.uk

COILED TUBING SERVICES

B J Completion Services, Blackness Avenue, Altens Industrial Estate, Aberdeen, AB12 3PG Tel: (01224) 897929 Fax: (01224) 896118 E-mail: sales@bjservices.com
▶ Morrison & Macdonald Holdings Ltd, 63 Murray Street, Paisley, Renfrewshire, PA3 1QW Tel: 0141-889 8787 Fax: 0141-889 9760 E-mail: almacdonald@btconnect.com

COIN ACCEPTOR MECHANISMS

Coin Acceptors Europe Ltd, 4 The Felbridge Centre, Imberhorne Lane, East Grinstead, West Sussex, RH19 1XP Tel: (01342) 315724 Fax: (01342) 313850 E-mail: sales@coinco.com
Essex Engineering Works Wanstead Ltd, 12 Nelson Road, London, E11 2AX Tel: (020) 8989 2012 Fax: (020) 8530 1117 E-mail: enquiries@essexengineering.co.uk
M E I, Eskdale Road, Winnersh Triangle, Wokingham, Berkshire, RG41 5AQ Tel: 0118-969 7700 Fax: 0118-944 6412
Money Controls Ltd, New Coin Street, Royton, Oldham, OL2 6JZ Tel: 0161-678 0111 Fax: 0161-626 7674 E-mail: sales@moneycontrols.com
Photo Me (International) plc, Church Road, Bookham, Leatherhead, Surrey, KT23 3EU Tel: (01372) 453399 Fax: (01372) 459064 E-mail: christianname.surname@photo-me.co.uk
Revolution Entertainment Systems Ltd, Showell Road, Wolverhampton, WV10 9NL Tel: (01902) 713000 Fax: (01902) 711555
Selecta UK Ltd, Unit 7 Stockton Close, Minworth Industrial Park, Minworth, Sutton Coldfield, West Midlands, B76 1DH Tel: 0121-313 2442 Fax: 0121-313 5037

COIN COUNTING MACHINES

Scan Coin Ltd, Dutch House, 110 Broadway, Salford, M50 2UW Tel: 0161-873 0500 Fax: 0161-873 0501 E-mail: sales@scancoin.co.uk

COIN HANDLING COMPONENTS

M E I, Eskdale Road, Winnersh Triangle, Wokingham, Berkshire, RG41 5AQ Tel: 0118-969 7700 Fax: 0118-944 6412
Money Controls Ltd, New Coin Street, Royton, Oldham, OL2 6JZ Tel: 0161-678 0111 Fax: 0161-626 7674 E-mail: sales@moneycontrols.com

COIN HANDLING EQUIPMENT

Money Controls Ltd, New Coin Street, Royton, Oldham, OL2 6JZ Tel: 0161-678 0111 Fax: 0161-626 7674 E-mail: sales@moneycontrols.com
Starpoint Electrics Ltd, Units 1-5 King George's Trading Estate, Davis Road, Chessington, Surrey, KT9 1TT Tel: (020) 8391 7700 Fax: (020) 8391 7760 E-mail: sales@starpoint.uk.com
Sterling Plastics, 5 Crocus Place, Crocus Street, Nottingham, NG2 3DE Tel: 0115-985 1101 Fax: 0115-985 1101

COIN METERS

Essex Engineering Works Wanstead Ltd, 12 Nelson Road, London, E11 2AX Tel: (020) 8989 2012 Fax: (020) 8530 1117 E-mail: enquiries@essexengineering.co.uk

COIN OPERATED LIGHT METERS

B & W Billiards & Snooker Services Ltd, Unit 3 Sapcote Trading Centre, Powke Lane, Old Hill, Cradley Heath, West Midlands, B64 5QR Tel: (01384) 638191 Fax: (01384) 638195 E-mail: sales@bandwbilliards.co.uk

COIN OPERATED LOCKERS

Astor-Rack, 579 Gale Street, Dagenham, Essex, RM9 4TS Tel: (020) 8984 8499 Fax: (020) 8984 8412 E-mail: sales@astor-rack.co.uk
Helmsman, Northern Way, Bury St. Edmunds, Suffolk, IP32 6NH Tel: (01284) 727600 Fax: (01284) 727601 E-mail: sales@helmsman.co.uk

COIN OPERATED LOCKS

Baton Lock Ltd, Baton House, 4TH Avenue The Village, Trafford Park, Manchester, M17 1DB Tel: 0161-877 4444 Fax: 0161-877 4545 E-mail: kevin.bratt@batonlockuk.com
Ison Ltd, Victoria St, High Wycombe, Buckinghamshire, HP11 2LT Tel: (01494) 437020 Fax: (01494) 526615 E-mail: fred@isonuk.net

COIN OPERATED PERSONAL WEIGHING MACHINE OPERATING SERVICES

Brash Industrial Scales, 3 I Anchor Bridge Way, Dewsbury, West Yorkshire, WF12 9QS Tel: (01924) 465169
H K Process Measurement Ltd, Princess Works, Birds Royd Lane, Brighouse, West Yorkshire, HD6 1LQ Tel: (01484) 400334 Fax: (01484) 400779E-mail: martin.hindle@hkprocess.co.uk
W S G Operating Co. Ltd, New Walton Pier Co Ltd, Walton on the Naze, Essex, CO14 8ES Tel: (01255) 670970 Fax: (01255) 850383 E-mail: sales@wsgscales.com

COIN OPERATED TIMERS/ CONTROLLERS

Leisure Control Systems, Clump Farm Industrial Estate, Shaftesbury Lane, Blandford Forum, Dorset, DT11 7TD Tel: (01258) 489075 Fax: (01258) 488526 E-mail: sales@wyvern-innleisure.co.uk

COIN PACKAGING EQUIPMENT

De La Rue Cash Systems, 7-8 Wolfe Close, Parkgate Industrial Estate, Knutsford, Cheshire, WA16 8XJ Tel: (01565) 654662 Fax: (01565) 658657 E-mail: robert.clark@uk.delarue.com

COINS

▶ Anglo Saxon Coins, PO Box 38444, London, SE16 2WF Tel: (020) 7232 1885 E-mail: info@anglosaxoncoins.com
Michael Beaumont, PO Box 8, Nottingham, NG4 4QZ Tel: 0115-987 8361 Fax: 0115-987 8361 E-mail: michael.beaumont1@ntlworld.com
Coincraft Coins, PO Box 112, London, WC1B 3PH Tel: (020) 7636 1188 Fax: (020) 7323 2860 E-mail: info@coincraft.com
Gannochy Coins & Medals, 46 Burleigh Street, Cambridge, CB1 1DJ Tel: (01223) 461505 Fax: (01223) 461505 E-mail: gannothycoins@aol.com
J Bridgeman, 129a Blackburn Road, Accrington, Lancashire, BB5 0AA Tel: (01254) 384757
Lindner Publications, Unit3a, Hayle Industrial Park, Hayle, Cornwall, TR27 5JR Tel: (01736) 751914 Fax: (01736) 751911 E-mail: info@prinz.co.uk
Nigel Tooley Ltd, PO Box 91, Ashtead, Surrey, KT21 1YX Tel: (01372) 278620 E-mail: coincabinet@btconnect.com
Vista Ward Banknotes, 5 Greenfields Way, Burley in Wharfedale, Ilkley, West Yorkshire, LS29 7RB Tel: (01943) 865709 Fax: (01943) 865609

COINS, GOLD

▶ Anglo Saxon Coins, PO Box 38444, London, SE16 2WF Tel: (020) 7232 1885 E-mail: info@anglosaxoncoins.com

COIR YARNS/FIBRES

▶ Money For Old Rope, PO Box 332, Bushey, WD23 3XZ Tel: 07050 686012 Fax: 07050 686013 E-mail: john@solditonline.net

COKE

Glendale Forge, Monk Street, Thaxted, Dunmow, Essex, CM6 2NR Tel: (01371) 830466 Fax: (01371) 831419 E-mail: sales@glendaleforge.co.uk
Monckton Coke & Chemical Company Ltd, PO Box 25, Barnsley, South Yorkshire, S71 4BE Tel: (01226) 722601 Fax: (01226) 700307

COKE OVEN MACHINERY

John M Henderson & Co. Ltd, Kings Works, Sir William Smith Road, Kirkton Industrial Estate, Arbroath, Angus, DD11 3RD Tel: (01241) 870774 Fax: (01241) 875559 E-mail: contracts@johnmhenderson.co.uk

COLA SOFT DRINKS

ABCO-Anderson Beverage Co. Ltd, Unit 6B, Chevychase Court, Seaham Grange Estate, Seaham, County Durham, SR7 0PR Tel: 0191-521 3366 Fax: 0191-521 3377 E-mail: info@abcosoftdrinks.co.uk

COLD CATHODE LIGHTING

A C D C Lighting Systems Ltd, Pasture Lane Works, Pasture Lane, Barrowford, Nelson, Lancashire, BB9 6ES Tel: (01282) 608400 Fax: (01282) 608401 E-mail: sales@acdclighting.co.uk
Acme Neon, Fitzroy Terrace, Grafton Street, Northampton, NN1 2NU Tel: (01604) 631068 Fax: (01604) 631068 E-mail: sales@acmeneon.co.uk
Masonlite Ltd, 36 Second Avenue, Chatham, Kent, ME4 5AX Tel: (01634) 812751 Fax: (01634) 811883 E-mail: neon@masonlite.com

COLD CHISELS

Ansell Handtools Sheffield Ltd, 72 Catley Road, Sheffield, S9 5JF Tel: 0114-244 8098 Fax: 0114-261 0252 E-mail: enquiries@ansell-handtools.com
Paramo Tools Group Ltd, Bailey St, Sheffield, S1 3BS Tel: 0114-249 0880 Fax: 0114-249 0881

COLD CUTTING EQUIPMENT

Circle Technical Services Ltd, Turulus Way, Midmill Business Park, Kintore, Aberdeenshire, AB51 0TG Tel: (01467) 632020 Fax: (01467) 632022 E-mail: info@circletechnical.co.uk

COLD CUTTING EQUIPMENT – *continued*

Colt Industrial Services Ltd, Colt Business Park, Witty Street, Hull, HU3 4TT Tel: (01482) 214244 Fax: (01482) 215037 E-mail: sales@colt.co.uk
M O S Cold Cutting Systems Ltd, Acorn Park Industrial Estate, Charlestown, Shipley, W. Yorkshire, BD17 7SW Tel: (01274) 588066 Fax: (01274) 588077 E-mail: stm@constructionplus.net

COLD DRAWN SEAMLESS STEEL TUBES

Corus Ltd, West Wing Midland House, New Road, Halesowen, West Midlands, B63 3HY Tel: 0121-585 5522 Fax: 0121-585 5241 E-mail: cdtl@corusgroup.com
Kirkby Steel Tubes Ltd, Abbotsfield Road, Reginald Road Industrial Estat, St. Helens, Merseyside, WA9 4HU Tel: (01744) 830600 Fax: (01744) 830609E-mail: mail@kst.uk.com
M K Wheeler Ltd, Nine Lock Works, Mill Street, Brierley Hill, West Midlands, DY5 2SX Tel: (01384) 487600 Fax: (01384) 487619 E-mail: sales@vanleeuwenwheeler.co.uk
Pipe & Tube Group Ltd, Armstrong Road, Basingstoke, Hampshire, RG24 8NU Tel: (01256) 811121 Fax: (01256) 842310 E-mail: info@pipeandtubegroup.co.uk

COLD DRAWN STEEL SECTIONS

Asd Metal Services, Thames Wharf, Dock Road, London, E16 1AF Tel: (020) 7476 0444 Fax: (020) 7476 0239 E-mail: customer.care@asdmetalservices.co.uk

COLD DRAWN WELDED SEAM STEEL TUBES

Newman-Phoenix Drawn Tube Ltd, Phoenix Street, West Bromwich, West Midlands, B70 0AS Tel: 0121-543 5700 Fax: 0121-500 3030

COLD DRAWN WELDED TUBES

Newman-Phoenix Drawn Tube Ltd, Phoenix Street, West Bromwich, West Midlands, B70 0AS Tel: 0121-543 5700 Fax: 0121-500 3030

COLD FORGING EQUIPMENT

HCH Engineering Ltd, Unit 4 Charlton Drive, Corngreaves Trading Estate, Cradley Heath, West Midlands, B64 7BJ Tel: (01384) 413233 Fax: (01384) 633637 E-mail: hch@ntlbusiness.com

COLD FORGING TECHNOLOGY KNOW HOW

Carbide Dies (Birmingham) Ltd, 7 Port Hope Road, Birmingham, B11 1JS Tel: 0121-772 0817 Fax: 0121-773 9342 E-mail: jim@ctr-uk.com

COLD FORGINGS, *See Cold Forging etc*

COLD FORMED PRECISION PRODUCTS, *See also headings for particular products*

Floform Ltd, Henfaes Lane, Welshpool, Powys, SY21 7BJ Tel: (01938) 552611 Fax: (01938) 555339 E-mail: sales@floform.co.uk
H E P Rolled Sections, Bayton Road, Exhall, Coventry, CV7 9EJ Tel: (024) 7658 5600 Fax: (024) 7658 5649 E-mail: info@metsec.com
S F S Intect, Unit 13 Welshpool Enterprise Centre, Welshpool, Powys, SY21 7SL Tel: (01938) 556035 Fax: (01938) 556036 E-mail: hbob@sfsintec.biz

COLD HEADED PRODUCTS

A W S, Nelsons Wharf, Sandy Lane Industrial Estate, Stourport-on-Severn, Worcestershire, DY13 9QB Tel: (01299) 829202 Fax: (01299) 829203 E-mail: sales@aws-services.co.uk
Bradleys Rivets Ltd, Unit 8b Reddicap Trading Estate, Sutton Coldfield, West Midlands, B75 7BU Tel: 0121-326 7468 Fax: 0121-327 1092 E-mail: enquiries@bradleysrivets.com
Components & Technology, Unit M Valley Way, Market Harborough, Leicestershire, LE16 7PS Tel: (01858) 439503 Fax: (01858) 466536 E-mail: sales@coldform.co.uk
Cutform Holdings Ltd, 6 Phoenix Industrial Estate, North Street, Lewes, East Sussex, BN7 2PQ Tel: (01273) 480420 Fax: (01273) 483089 E-mail: sales@cutform.co.uk
Fisco Fasteners Ltd, Sirdar Road, Rayleigh, Essex, SS6 7XF Tel: (01268) 745421 Fax: (01268) 745467 E-mail: sales@fisco-fasteners.co.uk
S F S Intect, Unit 13 Welshpool Enterprise Centre, Welshpool, Powys, SY21 7SL Tel: (01938) 556035 Fax: (01938) 556036 E-mail: hbob@sfsintec.biz
Sapphire Products Ltd, 4 Dunton Trading Estate, Mount Street, Birmingham, B7 5QL Tel: 0121-326 6000 Fax: 0121-328 5518 E-mail: sapphireproducts@boltblue.com

COLD HEADING MACHINES

Johnson Machine & Tool, Westbourne Road, Wednesbury, West Midlands, WS10 8BJ Tel: 0121-568 8013 Fax: 0121-526 4984 E-mail: jmt@johnson-group.co.uk

COLD HEADING TOOLS

Carbide Dies (Birmingham) Ltd, 7 Port Hope Road, Birmingham, B11 1JS Tel: 0121-772 0817 Fax: 0121-773 9342 E-mail: jim@ctr-uk.com
Johnson Machine & Tool, Westbourne Road, Wednesbury, West Midlands, WS10 8BJ Tel: 0121-568 8013 Fax: 0121-526 4984 E-mail: jmt@johnson-group.co.uk
Rectory Tool Company Ltd, 7 Port Hope Road, Camp Hill, Birmingham, B11 1JS Tel: 0121-773 9135 Fax: 0121-773 9342 E-mail: dianne@ctr.uk.com

COLD HEADING WIRE

▶ Carrington Wire, P O Box 56, Cardiff, CF24 2WR Tel: (029) 2025 6100 Fax: (029) 2025 6101 E-mail: sales@carringtonwiregroup.co.uk

COLD PRESS RESIN INJECTION TOOLS

Design Pattern & Tool Co. Ltd, Unit 31A, Central Industrial Estate, Cable Street, Wolverhampton, WV2 2RL Tel: (01902) 872777 Fax: (01902) 872778 E-mail: sales@designpattern.co.uk

COLD REDUCED STEEL SHEET

C J Upton & Sons Ltd, 7 Stamford Square, Ashton-under-Lyne, Lancashire, OL6 6QU Tel: 0161-339 3330 Fax: 0161-339 3304 E-mail: sales@cjupton.com
Clifton Steel Ltd, 122 Fazeley Industrial Estate, Fazeley Street, Birmingham, B5 5RS Tel: 0121-603 4000 Fax: 0121-603 4001 E-mail: sales@cliftonsteel.co.uk

COLD ROLL FORMING

Boxer Designs & Manufacturing, Unit 2 Boundary Court, Heaton Chapel, Stockport, Cheshire, SK4 5GA Tel: 0161-975 1830 Fax: 0161-431 3364 E-mail: sales@boxer-design.co.uk

COLD ROLLED ALUMINIUM SECTIONS

D J Stanton Engineering Ltd, Station Road, Hook Norton, Banbury, Oxfordshire, OX15 5LS Tel: (01608) 737452 Fax: (01608) 737051
M J Sections Ltd, Unit 5 Marriott Road Industrial Estate, Netherton, Dudley, West Midlands, DY2 0JZ Tel: (01384) 230444 Fax: (01384) 456086 E-mail: sales@mjsections.co.uk

COLD ROLLED PRODUCTION/ SERVICES, *See headings for particular products*

COLD ROLLED PRODUCTS

Roll Form Technology Ltd, Unit 19 Spring Road Industrial Estate, Lanesfield Drive, Wolverhampton, WV4 6UB Tel: (01902) 491972 Fax: (01902) 491432 E-mail: marina@rollformtech.com

COLD ROLLED SEAMLESS STEEL TUBES

▶ Gatehill Trading Ltd, 18 Gatehill Road, Northwood, Middlesex, HA6 3QD Tel: (01923) 820206 Fax: (01923) 450999 E-mail: gatehill@gtrad.co.uk

COLD ROLLED SECTION ROLL FORMING MACHINES

Bulldog Industrial Holdings Ltd, Carrington Road, Stockport, Cheshire, SK1 2JT Tel: 0161-477 0775 Fax: 0161-480 0133 E-mail: sales@bulldogprocess.com
P.W. Forming Ltd, Highgrove Close, Willenhall, West Midlands, WV12 5SZ Tel: (01922) 401615 Fax: (01922) 409517
Roll Form Technology Ltd, Unit 19 Spring Road Industrial Estate, Lanesfield Drive, Wolverhampton, WV4 6UB Tel: (01902) 491972 Fax: (01902) 491432 E-mail: marina@rollformtech.com

COLD ROLLED SECTIONS

Doby Ltd, Doby Ltd, Hare Law Industrial Estate, Stanley, County Durham, DH9 8UJ Tel: (01207) 299861 Fax: (01207) 283563 E-mail: sales@dobyverrolec.com
Elwell Sections Ltd, Phoenix Street, West Bromwich, West Midlands, B70 0AQ Tel: 0121-553 4274 Fax: 0121-553 4272 E-mail: sales@elwellsections.com
Roll Form Technology Ltd, Unit 19 Spring Road Industrial Estate, Lanesfield Drive, Wolverhampton, WV4 6UB Tel: (01902) 491972 Fax: (01902) 491432 E-mail: marina@rollformtech.com

COLD ROLLED STEEL SECTIONS

Albion Section Ltd, Albion Road, West Bromwich, West Midlands, B70 8BD Tel: 0121-553 1877 Fax: 0121-553 5507 E-mail: albionsections@enterprise.net
Ayrshire Metal Products, Royal Oak Way North, Royal Oak Industrial Estate, Daventry, Northamptonshire, NN11 8NR Tel: (01327) 300990 Fax: (01327) 300885 E-mail: sales@ayrshire.co.uk
Bridge Steel Sections, PO Box 92, Smethwick, West Midlands, B66 2PA Tel: 0121-555 1460 Fax: 0121-555 1461 E-mail: sales.ssl@hadleygroup.co.uk
Bridge Steel Sections Ltd, Ridgeacre Road, West Bromwich, West Midlands, B71 1BB Tel: 0121-553 6771 Fax: 0121-556 6325 E-mail: sales.bss@hadleygroup.co.uk
Compound Sections Ltd, Bond Avenue, Bletchley, Milton Keynes, MK1 1JS Tel: (01908) 622400 Fax: (01908) 622421
Detrra Fabrications Ltd, Unit 12 Droicon Industrial Estate, Portway Road, Rowley Regis, West Midlands, B65 9BY Tel: 0121-559 1152 Fax: 0121-559 6909 E-mail: derekk@btconnect.com
Hill Top, Ridgacre Road, West Bromwich, West Midlands, B71 1BB Tel: 0121-555 1470 Fax: 0121-555 1471 E-mail: sales.hts@hadleygroup.co.uk
Hi-Span Ltd, Ayton Road, Wymondham, Norfolk, NR18 0RD Tel: (01953) 603081 Fax: (01953) 607842 E-mail: sales@hi-span.com
Niagara Lasalle UK, Victoria Steelworks, Bull Lane, Wednesbury, West Midlands, WS10 8RS Tel: 0121-506 7500 Fax: 0121-506 7501 E-mail: hotrolled@niag.com
Rollform Sections Ltd, PO Box 92, Smethwick, West Midlands, B66 2PA Tel: 0121-555 1310 Fax: 0121-555 1311 E-mail: sales.rs@hadleygroup.co.uk
Sections & Tubes Ltd, Hall Street, West Bromwich, West Midlands, B70 7DW Tel: 0121-553 2721 Fax: 0121-500 5002 E-mail: admin@sectionsandtubes.co.uk
Spice Hawk Steel Sections Ltd, Gupta Trading Estate, West Bromwich Street, Oldbury, West Midlands, B69 3AP Tel: 0121-552 5151 Fax: 0121-544 4994
Superior Sections Ltd, 32 Regal Drive, Walsall Enterprise Park, Walsall, WS2 9HQ Tel: (01922) 620333 Fax: (01922) 610555 E-mail: sales@superiorsections.co.uk
West Mercia Sections Ltd, Nicholls Road, Tipton, West Midlands, DY4 9LG Tel: 0121-557 9927 Fax: 0121-520 3133 E-mail: sales@westmerciasections.freeserve.co.uk

COLD ROLLED STEEL STRIPS

BSS Steelstrip Ltd, 42 Gatcombe Way, Priorslee, Telford, Shropshire, TF2 9GZ Tel: (01952) 290313 E-mail: bss@steelstrip.co.uk
Corus Ltd, PO Box 69, Rotherham, South Yorkshire, S60 1BN Tel: (01709) 377113 Fax: (01709) 375250 E-mail: info@corusgroup.com
Corus Ltd, PO Box 69, Rotherham, South Yorkshire, S60 1BN Tel: (01709) 377113 Fax: (01709) 375250 E-mail: bsmsales@corusgroup.com
Ductile Stourbridge Cold Mills Ltd, PO Box 13, Willenhall, West Midlands, WV13 1HQ Tel: (01902) 365400 Fax: (01902) 365444 E-mail: info@dscm.co.uk
Graham Perry Steels Ltd, Units 1-3 Dock Meadow Drive Industrial Estate, Lanesfield Drive, Spring Road, Ettingshall, Wolverhampton, WV4 6LE Tel: (01902) 490450 Fax: (01902) 490217 E-mail: sales@grahamperrysteels.co.uk
Pinnstrip Steel Services Ltd, Portway Road, Wednesbury, West Midlands, WS10 7DZ Tel: 0121-556 4493 Fax: 0121-556 6526 E-mail: sales@pinnstrip.co.uk

COLD ROOM DOORS

▶ Coldhold Systems Ltd, Albright Road, Widnes, Cheshire, WA8 8FY Tel: 0151-423 0023 Fax: 0151-423 0043 E-mail: info@coldhold.com
Storer Refrigeration & Catering Manufacturers Ltd, Newstead Industrial Estate, Brookfield Road, Arnold, Nottingham, NG5 7ER Tel: 0115-920 0329 Fax: 0115-967 0676 E-mail: tedblake@supanet.com

COLD ROOM FITTINGS

Celltherm Coldrooms Ltd, Unit 4, Acan Way, Narborough, Leicester, LE19 2GW Tel: 0116-275 1331 Fax: 0116-275 1304 E-mail: sales@celltherm.co.uk
Hemsec Developments Ltd, Stoney Lane, Rainhill, Prescot, Merseyside, L35 9LL Tel: 0151-426 7171 Fax: 0151-493 1331 E-mail: sales@hemsec.com
Linde Refrigeration & Retail Systems Ltd, Meridian House, Peter's Way, Oxford, OX4 6HQ Tel: (01865) 337700 Fax: (01865) 337799
▶ MTC Insulation Solutions Ltd, Royston House, 267 Cranmore Boulevard Shirley, Shirley, Solihull, West Midlands, B90 4QT Tel: (0845) 2300082 Fax: (01564) 820083 E-mail: info@mtcltd.co.uk
Polysec Cold Rooms Ltd, Blackpole Trading Estate West, Hindlip Lane, Blackpole, Worcester, WR3 8TJ Tel: (01905) 458551 Fax: (01905) 754137 E-mail: mail@polysec.co.uk
▶ T T Catering Solutions Ltd, Unit 3-4 Swan Park, Kettlebrook Road, Tamworth, Staffordshire, B77 1AG Tel: (01827) 54400 Fax: (01827) 315016 E-mail: tedblake@ttcatsol.co.uk

COLD ROOMS

Adcock Refrigeration & Air Conditioning Ltd, 152 London Road, Copford, Colchester, CO6 1BQ Tel: (01206) 212502 Fax: (01206) 212080 E-mail: mail20@adcock.co.uk
Batchelor Air Conditioning, 3 Stilebrook Road, Olney, Buckinghamshire, MK46 5EA Tel: (01234) 241781 Fax: (01234) 241781
Border Holdings Coldstore (UK) Ltd, Avonmouth Way, Avonmouth, Bristol, BS11 9LX Tel: 0117-982 8589 Fax: 0117-982 4565
Colsec Ltd, Wassage Way, Hampton Lovett, Droitwich, Worcestershire, WR9 0NX Tel: (01905) 795070 Fax: (01905) 794013 E-mail: sales@colsec.co.uk
Elan Industries, Unit 1 Townfield Industrial Estate, Townfield Street, Oldham, OL4 1XF Tel: 0161-627 2300 Fax: 0161-627 1899 E-mail: elanind@aol.com
Eurocold, Unit 7, Blackmoor Farm, New Road, Maulden, Bedford, MK45 2BG Tel: (01525) 406666 Fax: (01525) 403838 E-mail: sales@eurocold.co.uk
Frimatec UK Ltd, 5 Townsend Centre Blackburn Road, Townsend Industrial Estate, Houghton Regis, Dunstable, Bedfordshire, LU5 5BQ Tel: (01582) 471600 Fax: (01582) 472050 E-mail: frimatec@nildram.co.uk
Hurstway Insulation Co. Ltd, Lawrence House, Transfesa Road, Paddock Wood, Tonbridge, Kent, TN12 6UT Tel: (01892) 838444 Fax: (01892) 833111 E-mail: hurstway@totalise.co.uk
Isd Cold Stores Ltd, 125 Business Park, Llanthony Road, Gloucester, GL2 5JQ Tel: (01452) 520649 Fax: (01452) 301910 E-mail: sales@isdcoldstores.co.uk
Lightfoot Refrigeration Co. Ltd, Unit D2, Premier Business Centre, Newgate Lane, Fareham, Hampshire, PO14 1TY Tel: (01329) 237272 Fax: (01329) 237276 E-mail: office@lightfootrefrigeration.com
Paneltex Ltd, Kingston International Park, Somerden Road, Hull, HU9 5PE Tel: (01482) 787236 Fax: (01482) 787238 E-mail: sales@paneltex.co.uk
Polarcold Refrigeration Ltd, 2 The Parade, Tattenham Way, Burgh Heath, Tadworth, Surrey, KT20 5NG Tel: 01737 373367 Fax: 01737 373387 E-mail: info@polarcold.co.uk
Polysec Cold Rooms Ltd, Blackpole Trading Estate West, Hindlip Lane, Blackpole, Worcester, WR3 8TJ Tel: (01905) 458551 Fax: (01905) 754137 E-mail: mail@polysec.co.uk
Scandia Coldrooms, Brunel Road, Gorse Lane Industrial Estate, Clacton-on-Sea, Essex, CO15 4LU Tel: (01255) 433595 Fax: (01255) 222691 E-mail: enquiries@scandia-coldrooms.co.uk
Stancold, Portview Road, Bristol, BS11 9LQ Tel: 0117-316 7000 Fax: 0117-316 7001 E-mail: sales@stancold.co.uk

COLD STORAGE FACILITIES/ SERVICES/COLD STORES

A C S & T Wolverhampton Ltd, Park Lane, Wolverhampton, WV10 9QD Tel: (01902) 731611 Fax: (01902) 862947 E-mail: adodd@acst.co.uk

▶ A H C (Warehousing) Ltd, Foundry Lane, Widnes, Cheshire, WA8 8UF Tel: 0151-424 7100 Fax: 0151-495 1990

A H Hiller & Son Ltd, Dunnington Heath Farm, Alcester, Warwickshire, B49 5PD Tel: (01789) 772771 Fax: (01789) 490439

▶ Aberdeen Self Storage, PO Box 10114, Aberdeen, AB21 9YB Tel: (01224) 774682

Andrew Johnson Knudtzon, Boulevard, Hull, HU3 4DY Tel: (01482) 326873 Fax: (01482) 327934 E-mail: info@ajkltd.co.uk

Associated Cold Stores & Transport Ltd, South Humberside Industrial Estate, Grimsby, South Humberside, DN31 2WR Tel: (01472) 240269 Fax: (01472) 240269 E-mail: acoldnsn@acst.co.uk

▶ Austin Wilkinson Ltd, Coal Pit Lane, Atherton, Manchester, M46 0RY Tel: (01942) 887000 Fax: (01942) 888222

Ballymena Meats, Pennybridge Industrial Estate, Ballymena, County Antrim, BT42 3HB Tel: (028) 2565 3710 Fax: (028) 2564 7593 E-mail: ballymena.meats@nireland.com

▶ Banburys Ltd, Castle Park Road, Whiddon Valley Industrial Estate, Barnstaple, Devon, EX32 8PA Tel: (01271) 326200 Fax: (01271) 327880 E-mail: removals@banburys.com

▶ Booker Cash & Carry Ltd, Lacy Street, Paisley, Renfrewshire, PA1 1QP Tel: 0141-889 7997 Fax: 0141-848 5279

Braehead (S F O Enterprises) Ltd, West Shore Road Industrial Estate, Fraserburgh, Aberdeenshire, AB43 9LG Tel: (01346) 513777 Fax: (01346) 514123 E-mail: gwatt@scottishfisherman.co.uk

▶ Brandford, Majestic Mill, Greenacres Road, Lees, Oldham, OL4 3NT Tel: 0161-345 4858 E-mail: info@storagecompany.co.uk

▶ Burn Stewart Distillers Ltd, 101 Carlisle Road, Airdrie, Lanarkshire, ML6 8AG Tel: (01236) 764838 Fax: (01236) 768141

▶ Cannington Coldstores, Swang Farm, Cannington, Bridgwater, Somerset, TA5 2NJ Tel: (01278) 671347 Fax: (01278) 671841 E-mail: tim.roe@canningtoncoldstores.co.uk

▶ Capell's Building Stores, Les Petites Capelles Road, St. Sampson, Guernsey, GY2 4GR Tel: (01481) 245897 Fax: (01481) 247399

▶ Cardiff Archives, Unit 7-8 Curran Buildings, Curran Road, Cardiff, CF10 5NE Tel: (029) 2066 8915 Fax: (029) 2034 3158

Celsius First Ltd, Scania House, Annwell St, Hoddesdon, Hertfordshire, EN11 8TT Tel: 01992 449600 Fax: (01992) 467148 E-mail: information@celsiusfirst.com

Central Cold Storage Co., Leamore Lane, Walsall, WS2 7DQ Tel: (01922) 401307 Fax: (01922) 710033 E-mail: johncoxcoldstoresltd@btinternet.com

▶ Christian Salvesen plc, Pilsworth Road, Bury, Lancashire, BL9 8RD Tel: 0161-796 5900 Fax: 0161-796 5007

▶ Christian Salvesen plc, Easton, Grantham, Lincolnshire, NG33 5AU Tel: (01476) 515000 Fax: (01476) 515011

Christian Salvesen plc, Salvesen Buildings, Ladysmith Road, Grimsby, South Humberside, DN32 9SL Tel: (01472) 327200 Fax: (01472) 327210

▶ Cold Move Ltd, Glovers Meadow, Maesbury Road Industrial Estate, Oswestry, Shropshire, SY10 8JN Tel: (01691) 677404 Fax: (01691) 677404

Coldstore, Coldstore Road, Felixstowe, Suffolk, IP11 8SF Tel: (01394) 604786

▶ Copeland Industrial Park, 133 Copeland Road, London, SE15 3SN Tel: (020) 7635 0000 Fax: (020) 7635 0100

▶ Corkill Datasafe, 39 Finch Road, Douglas, Isle of Man, IM1 2PW Tel: (01624) 666575 Fax: (01624) 661095

▶ Costco UK Ltd, Costkea Way, Loanhead, Midlothian, EH20 9BY Tel: 0131-440 4518 Fax: 0131-440 0390

▶ Costco Wholesale UK Ltd, Arnhall Business Park, Westhill, Aberdeenshire, AB32 6UF Tel: (01224) 745560 Fax: (01224) 745563

Cumbrian Sea Foods, Whelpside, Whitehaven, Cumbria, CA28 8XX Tel: (01946) 63131 Fax: (01946) 63232

▶ D F Warehouses Ltd, Old Brighton Road South, Pease Pottage, Crawley, West Sussex, RH11 9NQ Tel: (01293) 540686 Fax: (01293) 536260

▶ D J M Logistics UK Ltd, Road One, Winsford, Cheshire, CW7 3YZ Tel: (01606) 861972 Fax: (01606) 550540

▶ Dams Of Craigie Farm Ltd, Dams of Craigie, Whitecairns, Aberdeen, AB23 8XE Tel: (01651) 862274 Fax: (01651) 862078

▶ E G Hicks, Monks Hall Hanger, Bowsers Lane, Little Walden, Saffron Walden, Essex, CB10 1XQ Tel: (01799) 521559 Fax: (01799) 528339

▶ E H D London Number 1 Bond, Unit 1-2 Twickenham Trading Estate, Rugby Road, Twickenham, TW1 1DQ Tel: (020) 8744 3856 Fax: (020) 8744 2647

▶ Easons Ice Cream, Freckleton Road, Kirkham, Preston, PR4 3RB Tel: (01772) 684446 Fax: (01772) 683535

▶ East Kent Storage, Bysing Wood Road, Faversham, Kent, ME13 7UE Tel: (01795) 532227 Fax: (01795) 590056

▶ Ellis, 5 Macdougall Street, Greenock, Renfrewshire, PA15 2TG Tel: (01475) 888561

▶ EXL Coughlin, 4 Renaissance Way, Liverpool, L24 9PY Tel: 0151-448 2100 Fax: 0151-448 2139

Fenland Coolbox, Commercial Corner Barn, Mouth Lane, North Brink, Wisbech, Cambridgeshire, PE13 4UG Tel: 01945 450800

▶ Firmin Coates Ltd, Earls Road, Grangemouth, Stirlingshire, FK3 8XG Tel: (01324) 471356 Fax: (01324) 489260

▶ Flexistore Storage Services, Pomathorn Road, Penicuik, Midlothian, EH26 8PJ Tel: (01968) 670246 Fax: (01968) 676010 E-mail: sales@flexistore.co.uk

Fylde Ice & Cold Storage Co., Wyre Dock, Fleetwood, Lancashire, FY7 6SU Tel: (01253) 873249 Fax: (01253) 777752 E-mail: kelly@flyde-ice.co.uk

▶ Glasgow Removals, 192 Swanston Street, Glasgow, G40 4HH Tel: 0141-550 8333

Tom Granby Liverpool, Caddick Road, Knowsley Business Park, Prescot, Merseyside, L34 9HP Tel: 0151-548 8768 Fax: 0151-549 1979 E-mail: a.smith@dbcfoodservice.co.uk

Granville Cold Storage Co., Granville Road, Dungannon, County Tyrone, BT70 1NJ Tel: (028) 8772 6336 Fax: (028) 8772 7187

▶ Green Tree, Tudworth Road, Hatfield, Doncaster, South Yorkshire, DN7 6NL Tel: (01302) 840305 Fax: (01302) 840592

▶ H S H Coldstores, Birchin Way, Grimsby, South Humberside, DN31 2SG Tel: (01472) 264900 Fax: (01472) 347984

▶ Houston Warehousing Ltd, Wright Street, Renfrew, PA4 8AN Tel: 0141-848 5511

Ibl, Acornfield Road, Knowsley Industrial Park, Liverpool, L33 7YX Tel: 0151-549 1082 Fax: 0151-549 1246

▶ Immingham Storage Co. Ltd, East Riverside, Immingham Dock, Immingham, South Humberside, DN40 2LZ Tel: (01469) 578889 Fax: (01469) 572001

▶ Import Services, Tollbar Way, Hedge End, Southampton, SO30 2UH Tel: (01489) 799500

Innovate Logistics, 1 Willow Drive, Annesley, Nottingham, NG15 0DP Tel: (01623) 727300

▶ Iron Mountain Ltd, Unit 25 Wellheads Terrace, Wellheads Industrial Estate, Aberdeen, AB21 7GF Tel: (01224) 796600 Fax: (01224) 729095

▶ Iron Mountain Ltd, 320 Western Road, London, SW19 2QA Tel: (020) 8685 5370 Fax: (020) 8685 5380

Isd Cold Stores Ltd, 125 Business Park, Llanthony Road, Gloucester, GL2 5JQ Tel: (01452) 520649 Fax: (01452) 301910 E-mail: sales@isdcoldstores.co.uk

▶ John G Russell Ltd, Deanside Road, Glasgow, G52 4XB Tel: 0141-810 8200

▶ John G Russell Transport, 6-7 Salamander Street, Edinburgh, EH6 7JZ Tel: 0131-553 1225

Jolly's Transport, Irongate Arches, Copeland Rd, London, SE15 3SH Tel: 020 76394450

Kingdom Storage, 14 Faraday Road, Glenrothes, Fife, KY6 2RU Tel: (01592) 630882 Fax: (01592) 630892

Langdon Group Ltd, Wallfird Cross, Taunton, Somerset, TA2 8QP Tel: (01823) 412800 Fax: (01823) 412678 E-mail: sales@langdons.co.uk

▶ Langdons Industry Ltd, Skimpot Road, Luton, LU4 0JB Tel: (0870) 0008363 Fax: (0870) 0008365

▶ Laurmar Storage & Distribution, Units 1-3, Heathhall Industrial Estate, Heathhall, Dumfries, DG1 3PH Tel: (01387) 250738 Fax: (01387) 259464

Levington Cold Store Co., Levington Street, Grimsby, South Humberside, DN31 3HY Tel: (01472) 359140 Fax: (01472) 355523

Lowe Paddock Wood Paddock Wood Cold Storage Ltd, Transfesa Road, Paddock Wood, Tonbridge, Kent, TN12 6UT Tel: (01892) 832436 Fax: (01892) 835028 E-mail: lowepaddockwood@btconnect.com

Lowestoft Ice Co. Ltd, Battery Green Road, Lowestoft, Suffolk, NR32 1DQ Tel: (01502) 565565 Fax: (01502) 514382

Lunar Freezing & Cold Storage Co. Ltd, East Quay, The Harbour, Peterhead, Aberdeenshire, AB42 1JF Tel: (01779) 477446 Fax: (01779) 476599

▶ Malcolm Plant, PO Box 1, Irvine, Ayrshire, KA12 8JA Tel: (01294) 272314 Fax: (01294) 222288

▶ Mitech Storage Services, Vicarage Farmbrington Rdflore, Flore, Northampton, NN7 4NQ Tel: (01327) 341822 Fax: (01327) 341844

▶ Nippon Express UK Ltd, Unit 5110, Hunter Boulevard, Magna Park, Lutterworth, Leicestershire, LE17 4XN Tel: (01455) 205031 Fax: (01455) 558473

▶ Norish Food Care, 1 Benfield Way, Braintree, Essex, CM7 3YS Tel: (01376) 347311 Fax: (01376) 550887 E-mail: sales@norish.com

▶ Norish Food Care, Pedmore Road, Brierley Hill, West Midlands, DY5 1LJ Tel: (01384) 480858 Fax: (01384) 480425 E-mail: sales@norish.com

Norish Food Care Ltd, Northern Way, Bury St. Edmunds, Suffolk, IP32 6NL Tel: (01284) 763464 Fax: (01284) 768241 E-mail: enquiries@norish.com

▶ Norish Food Care, Lympne Industrial Estate, Lympne, Hythe, Kent, CT21 4LR Tel: (01303) 233930 Fax: (01303) 233939 E-mail: sales@norish.com

▶ Norish Food Care Ltd, Ash Road South, Wrexham Industrial Estate, Wrexham, Clwyd, LL13 9UG Tel: (01978) 660033 Fax: (01978) 660099 E-mail: sales@norish.com

▶ The North British Distillery Co. Ltd, Addiewell, West Calder, West Lothian, EH55 8NP Tel: (01506) 872666

Northern Refrigeration & Catering Equipment Ltd, Rotherside Road, Eckington, Sheffield, S21 4HL Tel: (01246) 434340 Fax: (01246) 434341

▶ Oriel Transport, Ferrard Road, Kirkcaldy, Fife, KY2 5SA Tel: (01592) 201810

P M L (Cold Store) Ltd, Brighton Road, Pease Pottage, Old Brighton Road South, Crawley, West Sussex, RH11 9NG Tel: (01293) 517260 Fax: (01293) 613970

▶ Pollock (Scotrans) Ltd, Unit 1-6 Royal Elizabeth Yard, Kirkliston, West Lothian, EH29 9EN Tel: 0131-319 2200 Fax: 0131-319 2233

▶ Portrack Severnsides Ltd, Grange BSNS Centre, The Grange Business Centre, Belasis Avenue, Billingham, Cleveland, TS23 1LG Tel: (01642) 554063 Fax: (01642) 554063 E-mail: phandling@aol.com

▶ R C S UK Ltd, Brunel Road, Wakefield 41 Industrial Estate, Wakefield, West Yorkshire, WF2 0XG Tel: (01924) 870888 Fax: (01924) 871888

▶ R & H Ltd, Unit18 Equity Trading Centre, Hobley Drive, Swindon, SN3 4NS Tel: (01793) 616891

R J Phillips & Sons Removers & Storage, Harlescott Lane, Shrewsbury, SY1 3AH Tel: (01743) 442230 Fax: (01743) 446739 E-mail: wayt@tdg.co.uk

▶ Raxel Storage Systems Ltd, Southern Barn Farm, The Heath, Leadenham, Lincoln, LN5 0QG Tel: (01400) 275000 Fax: (01400) 275110 E-mail: sales@raxel.co.uk

▶ Rayleigh Coldstore Ltd, Stadium Trading Estate, Stadium Way, Benfleet, Essex, SS7 3NZ Tel: (01268) 741131 Fax: (01268) 745030E-mail: admin@rayleighcoldstore.co.uk

▶ Rygor Warehousing Ltd, 172-174 Chemical Road, West Wilts Trading Estate, Westbury, Wiltshire, BA13 4JN Tel: (01373) 826118 Fax: (01373) 823090

▶ Safestore Ltd, Stirling Way, Borehamwood, Hertfordshire, WD6 2BT Tel: (020) 8732 1500 Fax: (020) 8732 1510 E-mail: borehamwood@safestoretrading.co.uk

▶ SBS Logistics Ltd, Inglesmaldie, Luthermuir, Laurencekirk, Kincardineshire, AB30 1QD Tel: (01674) 840007 Fax: (01674) 840009

Selectricks Ltd, 98 Reginald Rd, Southsea, Hants, PO4 9HW Tel: 023 92738214

▶ Simon Storage (Seal Sands) Ltd, Seal Sands, Middlesbrough, Cleveland, TS2 1UB Tel: (01642) 546775

▶ Snowie Logistics (Scotland), Grange Lane, Grangemouth, Stirlingshire, FK3 8EG Tel: (01324) 483774

South Darenth Farms & Coldstores Co. Ltd, St. Margarets Farm, St. Margarets Road, South Darenth, Dartford, DA4 9LB Tel: (01322) 863267 Fax: (01322) 861200 E-mail: sdfarms@btconnect.com

▶ Southern File & Data Management, 1 Elgar Estate, Preston Road, Reading, RG2 0BE Tel: 0118-975 9200 Fax: 0118-975 9300

▶ Space Station, Brewery Lane, Gateshead, Tyne & Wear, NE10 0EY Tel: 0191-438 1616 Fax: 0191-438 2626 E-mail: sales@spacestationstorage.co.uk

Storefast Ltd, North End Park Corner Road, Betsham, Southfleet, Gravesend, Kent, DA13 9LJ Tel: (01474) 833824 Fax: (01474) 833236 E-mail: sales@storefast.co.uk

▶ Swift FM Ltd, Swift Park, Old Leicester Road, Rugby, Warwickshire, CV21 1DZ Tel: (01788) 820200 Fax: (01788) 820222

T D G Storage UK, Chancel Lane, Pinhoe, Exeter, EX4 8JS Tel: (01392) 467135 Fax: (01392) 466233 E-mail: joneske@tdg.co.uk

T D G Storage UK Ltd, Wisbech Road, King's Lynn, Norfolk, PE30 5LQ Tel: (01553) 761166 Fax: (01553) 767447 E-mail: wayt@tdg.co.uk

▶ T D G Storage UK, 339&361 Prescot Road, Old Swan, Liverpool, L13 3BS Tel: 0151-259 4505 Fax: 0151-228 3634 E-mail: breenk@tdg.co.uk

▶ T D G UK Storage, 350 Renfrew Road, Glasgow, G51 4SP Tel: 0141-445 2933 Fax: 0141-445 1038

T D G UK Storage, Stock Office, Portland Road, Retford, Nottinghamshire, DN22 7NR Tel: (01777) 702616 Fax: (01777) 860521 E-mail: wayt@tdg.co.uk

▶ T Guy Ltd, Guys Industrial Estate, Tollgate Road, Burscough, Ormskirk, Lancashire, L40 8TG Tel: (01704) 893304 Fax: (01704) 893603

TDG UK Ltd, New Market Green, Leeds, LS9 0RW Tel: 0113-249 5604 Fax: 0113-249 1832 E-mail: greenwoodf@tdg.co.uk

▶ TDG UK Ltd, Skimpot Road, Luton, LU4 0JD Tel: (01582) 572387 Fax: (01582) 847235 E-mail: wayt@tdg.co.uk

▶ TDG UK Ltd, 29-30 Berth, Tilbury Docks, Tilbury, Essex, RM18 7DU Tel: (01375) 844266 Fax: (01375) 844335

▶ Terry Milner Proccesing Ltd, Unit 4-5, Bath Lane, Leeds, LS13 3BD Tel: 0113-236 3686 Fax: 0113-236 3391

▶ Tesam Distribution Ltd, Pinnacle House, Shrewsbury Avenue, Peterborough, PE2 7BJ Tel: (01733) 236277 Fax: (01733) 236278

Thornton International, Unit 1-3 Denver Industrial Estate, 44 Ferry Lane, Rainham, Essex, RM13 9YH Tel: (01233) 740009 Fax: (01708) 557353 E-mail: thornton.international@btinternet.com

Turners Soham Ltd, Fordham Road, Newmarket, Suffolk, CB8 7NR Tel: (01638) 720335 Fax: (01638) 720940 E-mail: carol.chapman@turners-distribution.com

▶ W H Malcolm Ltd, Newhouse Industrial Estate, Motherwell, Lanarkshire, ML1 5RY Tel: (01698) 834007 Fax: (01698) 832133

West Kent Cold Storage Co Ltd, Arctic House, Rye Lane, Dunton Green, Sevenoaks, Kent, TN14 5HB Tel: (01732) 748200 Fax: (01732) 740667 E-mail: gordon.fuller@wkcs.co.uk

▶ Woodward Food Service, Carsegate Road North, Inverness, IV3 8EA Tel: (01463) 236521 Fax: (01463) 243720

Woodwards Food Service, Craigshaw Drive, West Tullos Industrial Estate, Aberdeen, AB12 3AN Tel: (01224) 291744 Fax: (01224) 291765

COLD STORE CLOTHING

Delf Freezer Wear Ltd, Delf House, Pool Close, West Molesey, Surrey, KT8 2HW Tel: 020 89412802 Fax: (020) 89417201 E-mail: david.barker@delf.co.uk

COLD STORE GLOVES

C A C Industrial Products Ltd, Thornton Industrial Trading Estate, Milford Haven, Dyfed, SA73 2RU Tel: (01646) 692626 Fax: (01646) 690144 E-mail: sales@cac-industrial.co.uk

Scilabub Ltd, Unit 9 Huntingdon Court, Huntingdon Way, Measham, Swadlincote, Derbyshire, DE12 7NQ Tel: (01530) 279996 Fax: (01530) 270759 E-mail: sales@scilabub.com

COLD STORE HIGH DENSITY RACKING SYSTEMS

Dugard Logistics Ltd, 2 Sherwood Road, Bromsgrove, Worcestershire, B60 3DU Tel: (01527) 575947 Fax: (01527) 576100 E-mail: richardshowell@msn.com

COLD STORE INSULATION CONTRACTORS

▶ Carter Retail Equipment, 90 Lea Ford Road, Birmingham, B33 9TX Tel: 0121-250 1111 Fax: 0121-250 1122E-mail: info@cre-ltd.co.uk

Easy Cool Refrigeration Ltd, 30 Eleanor Crescent, Newcastle, Staffordshire, ST5 3SA Tel: (01782) 628750 Fax: (01782) 628750 E-mail: info@rsm-reallycool.co.uk

Kingspan Contoled Environments, Hanger 1A, Wrights Lane, Burtonwood, Warrington, WA5 4DB Tel: (01925) 711157 Fax: (01925) 711158

Polysec Cold Rooms Ltd, Blackpole Trading Estate West, Hindlip Lane, Blackpole, Worcester, WR3 8TJ Tel: (01905) 458551 Fax: (01905) 754137 E-mail: mail@polysec.co.uk

COLD WATER TANKS

▶ Brice-Baker Group, Rookery Road, The Lane, Wyboston, Bedford, MK44 3AX Tel: (01480) 216618 Fax: (01480) 406226 E-mail: info@bricebaker.co.uk

COLLABORATION PARTNER SEARCHES, CONSTRUCTION INDUSTRY

▶ SDF-ASSIST, Daisyfield Business Centre, Appleby Street, Blackburn, BB1 3BL Tel: 01234 246396 Fax: 01234 246884 E-mail: info@sdfassist.com

COLLAPSIBLE ALUMINIUM TUBES

Pharmatube Ltd, Units 1-2, Shield Drive, Wardley Business Park, Manchester, M28 2QB Tel: 0161-794 7391 Fax: 0161-727 8318 E-mail: sales@pharmatube.com

COLLAPSIBLE METAL TUBES

J K J Manufacturing Ltd, Amsterdam Road, Hull, HU7 0XF Tel: (01482) 825868 Fax: (01482) 878659 E-mail: mail@e-pac.co.uk

Mirum Products Ltd, Station Road, Ardleigh, Colchester, CO7 7RT Tel: (01206) 230230 Fax: (01206) 231764 E-mail: mirum@talk21.com

COLLAPSIBLE OR FOLDING GATES

Craig & Buchanan Ltd, 23 Lochburn Road, Glasgow, G20 9AE Tel: 0141-946 2007 Fax: 0141-945 2100 E-mail: shona@craigbuchanan.co.uk

COLLAPSIBLE PLASTIC TUBES

Depicton Ltd, Units 3-5 Maer Lane Industrial Estate, Market Drayton, Shropshire, TF9 1QX Tel: (01630) 655800 Fax: (01630) 653258 E-mail: sales@depicton.com

COLLAPSIBLE TUBE FILLING CONTRACT SERVICES

C B Baggs Ltd, 1 Claremont Industrial Estate, London, NW2 1AL Tel: (020) 8905 5111 Fax: (020) 8905 5222 E-mail: info@cbbaggs.co.uk

COLLAR STUDS

Exmoor Plastics, Unit 2 4 Trinity Business Centre, South Street, Taunton, Somerset, TA1 3AQ Tel: (01823) 276837 Fax: (01823) 334154 E-mail: sales@exmoorplastics.co.uk

COLLATED COIL OR STRIP NAILS

Bea Fastening Systems Ltd, Waterside Road, Beverley, North Humberside, HU17 0ST Tel: (01482) 889911 Fax: (01482) 871804 E-mail: sales@uk.bea-group.com

Pneutek (International) Ltd, Unit 1, Sovereign Way, Trafalgar Industrial Estate, Downham Market, Norfolk, PE38 9SW Tel: (01366) 388866 E-mail: airfasteners@thesmallbusinessclinique.com

COLLATED STRIP STAPLES

Pakmark, Units 1-2 Benson Industrial Estate, Benson Rd, Birmingham, B18 5TS Tel: 0121-523 0665 Fax: 0121-523 5343 E-mail: pakmark@btconnect.com

COLLATING MACHINES

K A S Paper Systems Ltd, Brewers Hill Road, Dunstable, Bedfordshire, LU6 1AD Tel: (01582) 662211 Fax: (01582) 664222 E-mail: mail@kaspapersystems.com

Setmasters Ltd, Lymington Saleroom, Emsworth Road, Lymington, Hampshire, SO41 9BL Tel: (01590) 675555 Fax: (01590) 682659 E-mail: collating@setmasters.co.uk

Watkiss Automation Sales Ltd, Watkiss House, 1 Blaydon Road, Sandy, Bedfordshire, SG19 1RZ Tel: (01767) 681800 Fax: (01767) 691769 E-mail: sales@watkiss.com

COLLECTING MAGAZINES

▶ 4mags, 30B Grosvenor Road, Caversham, Reading, RG4 5EN Tel: 07939 084481 E-mail: sales@4mags.co.uk

COLLEGES, CATERING

Thames Valley University, St Mary's Road, London, W5 5RF Tel: (020) 8231 2221 Fax: (020) 8231 2360 E-mail: learning.advice@tvu.ac.uk

University of Derby Buxton, Devonshire Campus, 1 Devonshire Road, Buxton, Derbyshire, SK17 6RY Tel: (01298) 71100 Fax: (01298) 27261 E-mail: enquiriesudb@derby.ac.uk

COLLET CHUCKS

Brunner Machine Tools Ltd, 6 Colville Road, London, W3 8BL Tel: (020) 8992 6011 Fax: (020) 8992 7559 E-mail: sales@brunnermachine.co.uk

Holmes UK Ltd, 5 Monarch Industrial Park, Kings Road, Tyseley, Birmingham, B11 2AP Tel: 0121-706 6936 Fax: 0121-707 9913 E-mail: sales@holmesmachines.co.uk

I Q T Ltd, 42-44 The Street, Appledore, Ashford, Kent, TN26 2BX Tel: (01233) 758772 Fax: (01233) 758773 E-mail: iqtltd@aol.com

COLLETS

600 Group Plc, 600 House, Landmark Court, Revie Road, Leeds, LS11 8JT Tel: 0113-277 6100 Fax: 0113-276 5600 E-mail: sales@600group.com

Herbert Tooling Ltd, Roseme, Sandy Lane, Fillongley, Coventry, CV7 8DD Tel: (01676) 540040 Fax: (01676) 540040 E-mail: info@herbert-tooling.com

Holmes UK Ltd, 5 Monarch Industrial Park, Kings Road, Tyseley, Birmingham, B11 2AP Tel: 0121-706 6936 Fax: 0121-707 9913 E-mail: sales@holmesmachines.co.uk

P T G Work Holding, 7 Eclipse Office Park, High Street, Staple Hill, Bristol, BS16 5EL Tel: 0117-970 1101 Fax: 0117-970 1181

Thermwood Europe Ltd, Unit 3, Evans Business Centre, Belmont Industrial Estate, Durham, DH1 1SE Tel: 0191-383 2883 Fax: 0191-383 2884 E-mail: sales@thermwood.co.uk

COLOUR ASSESSMENT EQUIPMENT

The Tintometer Ltd, Lovibond House, Solar Way, Solstice Park, Amesbury, Salisbury, SP4 7SZ Tel: (01980) 664800 Fax: (01980) 625412 E-mail: sales@tintometer.com

Verivide, Quartz Close, Enderby, Leicester, LE19 4SG Tel: 0116-284 7790 Fax: 0116-284 7799 E-mail: enquiries@verivide.com

COLOUR CARDS

Multicolor UK Ltd, The Drift, Nacton Road, Ipswich, IP3 9QP Tel: 01473 723443 Fax: (01473) 270671 E-mail: info@multicolor.co.uk

COLOUR FORMERS

Univar Ltd, International House, Zenith, Paycocke Road, Basildon, Essex, SS14 3DW Tel: (01268) 594400 Fax: (01268) 594482 E-mail: exports@univareurope.com

COLOUR LASER COPYING

Advanced Security Systems, 932 Ashton Road, Oldham, OL8 3JS Tel: 0161-785 8000 Fax: 0161-785 8888

▶ Copy Shop Newbury Ltd, Unit 1, Mill Lane, Newbury, Berkshire, RG14 5RE Tel: (01635) 49959 E-mail: sales@copyshopnewbury.co.uk

COLOUR MANAGEMENT EQUIPMENT

▶ Colour Management by ColourPhil, White Hill Court, Berkhamsted, Hertfordshire, HP4 2PS Tel: (01442) 874937

Verivide, Quartz Close, Enderby, Leicester, LE19 4SG Tel: 0116-284 7790 Fax: 0116-284 7799 E-mail: enquiries@verivide.com

COLOUR MANAGEMENT SYSTEMS

▶ Colour Management by ColourPhil, White Hill Court, Berkhamsted, Hertfordshire, HP4 2PS Tel: (01442) 874937

▶ Northlight Images, 86 Harrow Road, Leicester, LE3 0JW Tel: 0116-291 9092 E-mail: sales@northlight-it.com

COLOUR MATCHED PLASTIC INJECTION MOULDINGS

▶ Rite Systems, 43 The Stripe, Stokesley, Middlesbrough, Cleveland, TS9 5PX Tel: (01642) 713140 E-mail: jgreen@ritesystems.com

COLOUR MEASURING INSTRUMENTS

Astranet Systems Ltd, PO Box 734, Cambridge, CB2 5PE Tel: (01223) 872197 Fax: (01223) 872197 E-mail: info@astranetsystems.com

QC Lighting Systems, 83 Mercia Avenue, Charlton, Andover, Hampshire, SP10 4EJ Tel: (01264) 332892 Fax: (01264) 332892 E-mail: sales@qclightingsystems.co.uk

X-Rite Ltd, The Acumen Centre, First Avenue, Poynton, Stockport, Cheshire, SK12 1FJ Tel: (01625) 871100 Fax: (01625) 871444

COLOUR METERS

The Tintometer Ltd, Lovibond House, Solar Way, Solstice Park, Amesbury, Salisbury, SP4 7SZ Tel: (01980) 664800 Fax: (01980) 625412 E-mail: sales@tintometer.com

COLOUR PRINTING

A F Litho Ltd, Grenaby Works, Grenaby Road, Croydon, CR0 2EJ Tel: (020) 8689 7849 Fax: (020) 8689 0479 E-mail: sales@aflitho.co.uk

A R Facer Ltd, Kerry St, Horsforth, Leeds, LS18 4AW Tel: 0113-258 2551 Fax: 0113-259 0868E-mail: sales@facerprinters.demon.co.uk

A Romanes & Son Ltd, Pitreavie Business Park, Dunfermline, Fife, KY11 8QS Tel: (01383) 728201 Fax: (01383) 737040 E-mail: advertising@dunfermlinepress.co.uk

Abbotsgate Printers, Lincoln Street, Hull, HU2 0PB Tel: (01482) 225257 Fax: (01482) 225559 E-mail: abbotsgateprint@aol.com

Adare Pillings Ltd, Elland Lane, Elland, West Yorkshire, HX5 9DZ Tel: (01422) 379711 Fax: (01422) 377503 E-mail: info@adarepillings.com

▶ Ambassador Litho Ltd, 25 Hockeys Lane, Bristol, BS16 3HH Tel: 0117-965 5252 Fax: 0117-965 3275 E-mail: info@ambassador.co.uk

B A F Printers Ltd, Portland House, Cross Chancellor Street, Leeds, LS6 2TG Tel: 0113-243 9788 Fax: 0113-243 8741 E-mail: office@bafprinters.co.uk

B J T Print Services Ltd, Common La, Kenilworth, Warwickshire, CV8 2EL Tel: (01926) 852085 Fax: (01926) 859591

B S C Print, B S C House, 48 Weir Road, Wimbledon, London, SW19 8UG Tel: (020) 8947 8571 Fax: (020) 8947 3319 E-mail: sales@bscprint..co.uk

Barden Print Ltd, Bay Hall Print Works, Common Road, Huddersfield, HD1 5EU Tel: (01484) 422522 Fax: (01484) 435158 E-mail: design@bardenprint.com

Beith Printing Co. Ltd, 1-7 Earl Haig Road, Hillington Industrial Estate, Glasgow, G52 4JU Tel: 0141-882 9088 Fax: 0141-882 3204 E-mail: mail@beith-printing.co.uk

Berrico Ltd, 57 Churchfield Road, London, W3 6AU Tel: (020) 8992 6454 Fax: (020) 8752 0670 E-mail: berrico@berrico.co.uk

Blackmore Ltd, Longmead, Shaftesbury, Dorset, SP7 8PX Tel: (01747) 853034 Fax: (01747) 854500 E-mail: sales@.blackmore.co.uk

Boxpak Ltd, 65 Church Road, Newtownabbey, County Antrim, BT36 7LR Tel: (028) 9036 5421 Fax: (028) 9086 6731 E-mail: sales@boxpak.co.uk

Brown & Son, Crow Arch Lane, Ringwood, Hampshire, BH24 1PD Tel: (01425) 476133 Fax: (01425) 477063 E-mail: sales@vanboorn.co.uk

Buccleuch Printers Ltd, Carnarvon Street, Hawick, Roxburghshire, TD9 7EB Tel: (01450) 372566 Fax: (01450) 375146 E-mail: info@buccleuchprinters.co.uk

Buckland Press Ltd, Barwick Road, Dover, Kent, CT17 0LG Tel: (01304) 205900 Fax: (01304) 205619 E-mail: info@buckland.co.uk

▶ Buckleys, Welkin Mill, Welkin Road, Bredbury, Stockport, Cheshire, SK6 2BL Tel: 0161-430 4211 Fax: 0161-494 2837 E-mail: tony.stevens@buckleys-print.co.uk

Buzzard Screen Print Ltd, 17 Wing Road, Leighton Buzzard, Bedfordshire, LU7 2NG Tel: (01525) 373527 Fax: (01525) 851260 E-mail: sales@buzzardscreenprint.co.uk

Carlton Press Group N W Ltd, 3-7 Britannia Road, Sale, Cheshire, M33 2AA Tel: 0161-962 8686 Fax: 0161-969 6300 E-mail: sales@carltonpressgroup.com

Castle Colour Press Ltd, 3 Morgan Way, Bowthorpe Employment Area, Norwich, NR5 9JJ Tel: (01603) 741278 Fax: (01603) 749227 E-mail: reception@castlecolour.co.uk

Chapel Press Ltd, Parkgate Close, Bredbury, Stockport, Cheshire, SK6 2SZ Tel: 0161-406 9495 Fax: 0161-292 0200 E-mail: info@chapelpress.com

Clanpress (Kings Lynn) Ltd, 1 Dundee Court, Hamburg Way, King's Lynn, Norfolk, PE30 2ND Tel: (01553) 772737 Fax: (01553) 768403 E-mail: clanpress@aol.com

Colorscope Printers Ltd, Charlwoods Road, East Grinstead, West Sussex, RH19 2HF Tel: (01342) 311821 Fax: (01342) 315358 E-mail: sales@colorscope.co.uk

Colourfast, 2 The Arcade, Cwmbran, Gwent, NP44 1PQ Tel: (01633) 865586 Fax: (01633) 869434E-mail: arcadecolour1@btconnect.com

Colourplus Print & Design, Unit 28 Monument Business Park, Warpsgrove Lane, Chalgrove, Oxford, OX44 7RW Tel: (01865) 400040 Fax: (01865) 400040 E-mail: design@colourplus.co.uk

Compass Print Ltd, Hareness Road, Altens Industrial Estate, Aberdeen, AB12 3LE Tel: (01224) 875987 Fax: (01224) 896137 E-mail: info@compassprint.co.uk

Connaught Lithoservices Ltd, 129 Munster Road, London, SW6 6DD Tel: (020) 7731 0900 Fax: (020) 7731 0066 E-mail: info@connaught.net

The Cos Group Ltd, Unit 6 Ty Verlon Industrial Estate, Cardiff Road, Barry, South Glamorgan, CF63 2BE Tel: (01446) 418000 Fax: (01446) 418009 E-mail: sales@cosgroup.co.uk

Cotterill Cook Printers Ltd, 40 St Clements Road, Nechells, Birmingham, B7 5AF Tel: 0121-327 1156 Fax: 0121-327 5203 E-mail: print@cotterillcook.fsnet.co.uk

County Offset, North Quays Business Park, Atlantic Street, Broadheath, Altrincham, Cheshire, WA14 5BF Tel: 0161-928 5333 Fax: 0161-927 7069 E-mail: sales@countyprint.com

Crewe Colour Printers Ltd, Millbuck Way, Sandbach, Cheshire, CW11 3SH Tel: (01270) 761113 Fax: (01270) 766386

Data Print, 11A West Way, Oxford, OX2 0JB Tel: (01865) 243624 Fax: (01865) 243624 E-mail: info@dataprintoxford.co.uk

Dax Printing Co. Ltd, Free Street, Bishops Waltham, Southampton, SO32 1EE Tel: (01489) 891006 Fax: (01489) 891699 E-mail: general@daxprinting.co.uk

Deanprint Ltd, Cheadle Heath Works, Stockport Road, Stockport, Cheshire, SK3 0PR Tel: 0161-428 2236 Fax: 0161-428 0817 E-mail: sales@deanprint.co.uk

Dorling Print Ltd, Dorling House, 44 Wates Way, Mitcham, Surrey, CR4 4HR Tel: (020) 8685 9399 Fax: (020) 8685 9140 E-mail: info@dorling.co.uk

Edward Dudfield Ltd, 4 Whilems Works, Forest Road, Ilford, Essex, IG6 3HJ Tel: (020) 8500 4455 Fax: (020) 8500 4488 E-mail: sales@dudfields.co.uk

Dudley Print, 2 The Sling, Dudley, West Midlands, DY2 9AJ Tel: (01384) 455316 Fax: (01384) 457519 E-mail: dudley.print@virgin.net

Duffield Printers Ltd, 421 Kirkstall Road, Leeds, LS4 2HA Tel: 0113-279 3011 Fax: 0113-231 0098 E-mail: info@duffieldprinters.co.uk

Engravings Services Ltd, 21 Radnor Street, Hulme, Manchester, M15 5RD Tel: 0161-226 1197 Fax: 0161-227 9554 E-mail: studio@engraving.pennine.net

▶ Ernest Cummins Ltd, 385 Canal Road, Bradford, West Yorkshire, BD2 1AW Tel: (01274) 582555 Fax: (01274) 582666

Etrinsic, 473 Stratford Road, Shirley, Solihull, West Midlands, B90 4AD Tel: (0870) 4646131 Fax: (0870) 4646040

Falcon Press (Stockton-on-Tees) Ltd, Task Industrial Estate, Portrack Lane, Stockton-On-Tees, Cleveland, TS18 2ES Tel: (01642) 674298 Fax: (01642) 612382 E-mail: enquiries@falconpress-printing.co.uk

Falder Matthews Ltd, 6 Seax Way, Basildon, Essex, SS15 6SW Tel: (01268) 413611 Fax: (01268) 541637 E-mail: enquiries@fmprint.co.uk

Francis Anthony, Blowing House Hill, St. Austell, Cornwall, PL25 5AH Tel: (01726) 61264 Fax: (01726) 69533 E-mail: info@francis-antony.co.uk

G G Stevenson Printers, 2 Lower Pleasance, Dundee, DD1 5QU Tel: (01382) 225768 E-mail: stevensonprinters@lineone.net

Gemini Press Ltd, Unit A1 Dolphin Way, Shoreham-by-Sea, West Sussex, BN43 6NZ Tel: (01273) 464884 Fax: (01273) 464744 E-mail: info@gemini-group.co.uk

Glenwood Printing, 4 Peter Baines Industrial Estate, Woods Lane, Derby, DE22 3UD Tel: (01332) 368674 Fax: (01332) 381444 E-mail: sales@glenwood-printing.co.uk

Gorman Shorrock & Davies Ltd, 52 Heyrod Street, Manchester, M1 2WW Tel: 0161-273 3909 Fax: 0161-273 6690

Handley Printers Ltd, 125 Stockport Road West, Bredbury, Stockport, Cheshire, SK6 2AN Tel: 0161-430 8188 Fax: 0161-406 6032 E-mail: puzzhand@aol.com

Headley Brothers Ltd, The Invicta Press, Queens Road, Ashford, Kent, TN24 8HH Tel: (01233) 623131 Fax: (01233) 612345 E-mail: printing@headley.co.uk

Heronsgate Ltd, Unit 18-20 Herons Gate Trading Estate, Paycocke Road, Basildon, Essex, SS14 3EU Tel: (01268) 288637 Fax: (01268) 272585 E-mail: sales@heronsgateprint.com

Hi Tec Print, 9-10 Houghton Road, North Anston Trading Estate, North Anston, Sheffield, S25 4JJ Tel: (01909) 568533 Fax: (01909) 568206 E-mail: sales@hitecprint.co.uk

Hill Shorter Group, 54 Roebuck Lane, West Bromwich, West Midlands, B70 6QP Tel: 0121-553 7011 Fax: 0121-500 5162 E-mail: sales@hillshorter.com

Howies Ltd, 10 Kings Haugh, Peffermill Industrial Estate, Edinburgh, EH16 5UY Tel: 0131-661 7302 Fax: 0131-661 7479

Image X P S Ltd, 11 North Street, Portslade, Brighton, BN41 1DH Tel: (01273) 421242 Fax: (01273) 421210

Ivanhoe Printing Co. Ltd, Station Road, Musselburgh, Midlothian, EH21 7PE Tel: 0131-665 8444 Fax: 0131-653 2691

J H Greene, Netherton Business Centre, West Netherton Street, Kilmarnock, Ayrshire, KA1 4BT Tel: (01563) 539006 Fax: (01563) 571941

J Thomson Colour Printers Ltd, 14-16 Carnoustie Place, Glasgow, G5 8PB Tel: 0141-429 1094 Fax: 0141-429 5638

Jade Press Ltd, Eagle House, Torre Road, Leeds, LS9 7QL Tel: 0113-248 0929 Fax: 0113-248 4609 E-mail: sales@jadepress.co.uk

John Good Ltd Trading As Cantate, Building B Parkfield Industrial Estate, Culvert Place, Battersey, London, SW11 5DZ Tel: (020) 7622 3401 Fax: (020) 7498 1497 E-mail: enquiries@cantate.biz

Jones & Palmer Ltd, 95 Carver Street, Birmingham, B1 3AR Tel: 0121-236 9007 Fax: 0121-236 5513 E-mail: info@jonesandpalmer.co.uk

Judges Postcards Ltd, 176 Bexhill Road, St. Leonards-on-Sea, East Sussex, TN38 8BN Tel: (01424) 420919 Fax: (01424) 438538 E-mail: sales@judges.co.uk

Keene Printing Co. Ltd, 33-41 Dallington St, London, EC1V 0BB Tel: (020) 7251 2722 Fax: (020) 7490 8736 E-mail: info@keenes.co.uk

COLOUR PRINTING – *continued*

Kings Land Colour Ltd, Unit 2, Roslin Square, Roslin Road, Acton, London, W3 8DH Tel: (020) 8993 7111 Fax: (020) 8993 2243 E-mail: sales@kingslandcolour.co.uk

L & S Litho Printers & Designers Ltd, 15-27 Arrol Place, Glasgow, G40 3NY Tel: 0141-556 2837 Fax: 0141-554 2590 E-mail: bill.livingstone@btslitho.com

Labute Colour Printers Ltd, Cambridge Printing Park, Milton, Cambridge, CB4 6AZ Tel: (01223) 420000 Fax: (01223) 420860 E-mail: info@labute.co.uk

▶ Lanceni Press Ltd, 1 Garrood Drive, Fakenham, Norfolk, NR21 8NN Tel: (01328) 851578 Fax: (01328) 851298 E-mail: lanceni@clara.net

Leyprint Ltd, Leyland Lane, Leyland, PR25 1UT Tel: (01772) 425000 Fax: (01772) 425001 E-mail: info@leyprint.co.uk

Lithographics Ltd, Bromyard Road, Worcester, WR2 5HN Tel: (01905) 429011 Fax: (01905) 748257 E-mail: info@lithographics.co.uk

Lithograve (Birmingham) Ltd, 8-10 Lawford Close, Birmingham, B7 4HJ Tel: 0121-359 3350 Fax: 0121-359 3119 E-mail: dave@lithograve.com

Lithoprint Ltd, 4 Earl Haig Road, Hillington Park, Glasgow, G52 4RP Tel: 0141-891 8000 Fax: 0141-810 5496

▶ Loudmouth Postcards, 5 Hendon Street, Sheffield, S13 9AX Tel: (0845) 2309805 Fax: 0114-288 0044 E-mail: chet@loudworld.co.uk

LPC Printing Co. Ltd, Hardley Industrial Estate, Hardley Hythe, Southampton, SO45 3ZX Tel: (023) 8084 6334 Fax: (023) 8084 0389 E-mail: enquiries@lpcprinting.com

M J Millward Printing Ltd, 21 Nottingham South & Wilford Industrial Estate, Nottingham, NG11 7EP Tel: 0115-981 3378 Fax: 0115-981 2386 E-mail: mgmprint@compuserve.com

McCorquodale Confidential Print Ltd, South Portway Close, Round Spinney, Northampton, NN3 8RH Tel: (01604) 790234 Fax: (01604) 790880 E-mail: sales@theprintfactory.co.uk

Maldon Printing Co. Ltd, Unit 2-14 Wycke Hill Business Park, Wycke Hill, Maldon, Essex, CM9 6UZ Tel: (01621) 853904 Fax: (01621) 859565

Malvern Press Ltd, 71 Dalston Lane, London, E8 2NG Tel: (020) 7249 2991 Fax: (020) 7254 1720 E-mail: admin@malvernpress.com

Mason Albums Two Trees Press Ltd, Grey Street, Denton, Manchester, M34 3RU Tel: 0161-336 2002 Fax: 0161-335 0346 E-mail: print@twotreespress.co.uk

Midas Press, 3 Columbus Drive, Southwood Business Park, Farnborough, Hampshire, GU14 0NZ Tel: (01252) 517221 Fax: (01252) 516455 E-mail: sales@midaspress.co.uk

Mooncie Printing Services, 62 Evington Valley Road, Leicester, LE5 5LJ Tel: 0116-273 8882 E-mail: moonicieprinting@aol.com

Nayler Group Ltd, Aero Mill, Kershaw Street, Church, Accrington, Lancashire, BB5 4JS Tel: (01254) 234247 Fax: (01254) 383996 E-mail: info@naylorgroup.co.uk

New Goswell Printing Co., Unit 4 100 The Highway, London, E1W 2BX Tel: (020) 7481 1775 Fax: (020) 7488 9130

Newnorth Print, College Street, Kempston, Bedford, MK42 8NA Tel: (01234) 341111 Fax: (01234) 271112 E-mail: newnorth@newnorth.co.uk

▶ One Stop Print Shop Ltd, 2 Black Swan Walk, Leominster, Herefordshire, HR6 8HU Tel: (01568) 613888 Fax: (01568) 613402 E-mail: sales@theonestopprintshop.co.uk

P B F Press Ltd, 12 Little Ridge, Welwyn Garden City, Hertfordshire, AL7 2BH Tel: (01707) 372185 Fax: (01707) 375580 E-mail: pbf-press@btconnect.com

Park Communications Ltd, Lea Mill, Eastway, London, E9 5NU Tel: (020) 8525 6200 Fax: (020) 8525 6201 E-mail: heath.mason@btinternet.com

Parkdale Press, 11-12 Tilley Road, Crowther, Washington, Tyne & Wear, NE38 0AE Tel: 0191-417 8927 Fax: 0191-419 2459 E-mail: parkdale.press@virgin.net

Paton Brown Ltd, Calico House, Printwork Lane, Manchester, M19 3JP Tel: (0870) 4445501 Fax: (0870) 4445502 E-mail: info@patonbrown.co.uk

Pennine Printing Services Ltd, Commercial Mills, Oldham Road, Sowerby Bridge, West Yorkshire, HX6 4EH Tel: (01422) 825333 Fax: (01422) 825444 E-mail: pennineprinting@btconnect.com

Pepberry Ltd, Marwain House, Clarke Road, Bletchley, Milton Keynes, MK1 1LG Tel: (01908) 643022 Fax: (01908) 648132

Philip Myers Press Holdings Ltd, 9 Clayton Road, Birchwood, Warrington, WA3 6PH Tel: (01925) 819021 Fax: (01925) 828147 E-mail: print@myerspress.com

Polar Print Group Ltd, Venturi House, 9-17 Tuxford Road, Hamilton Industrial Park, Leicester, LE4 9WE Tel: 0116-274 4700 Fax: 0116-274 4799

Polestar Chromoworks Ltd, Wigman Road, Nottingham, NG8 3JA Tel: 0115-900 8300 Fax: 0115-900 8320

▶ Portland Print, Telford Way, Telford Way Industrial Estate, Kettering, Northamptonshire, NN16 8UN Tel: (01536) 511555 Fax: (01536) 310136

H. Portsmouth & Son, 1033-1043 London Road, Leigh-On-Sea, Essex, SS9 3JY Tel: (01702) 478255 Fax: (01702) 473640 E-mail: print@hportsmouth.freeserve.co.uk

Premier Print & Design Services Ltd, Unit 33 Park Farm Industrial Estate, Ermine Street, Buntingford, Hertfordshire, SG9 9AZ Tel: (01763) 272461 Fax: (01763) 272955

Price John & Sons Ltd, Brook Street, Bilston, West Midlands, WV14 0NW Tel: (01902) 353441 Fax: (01902) 404728 E-mail: sales@john-price.co.uk

▶ Print-Craft, Mortimer-Reid House, 2 Herald Way, Binley Industrial Estate, Coventry, CV3 2NY Tel: (024) 7656 0920 Fax: (024) 7656 0930

Printline Ltd, Unit 12, Grosvenor Way, London, E5 9ND Tel: (020) 8806 9090 Fax: (020) 8806 9434 E-mail: sales@printline.co.uk

Printselect Ltd, 46 Watts Grove, London, E3 3RE Tel: (020) 7538 3448 Fax: (020) 7538 0222 E-mail: printselect.uk@virgin.net

Prism Digital Colour Ltd, 4 Moreton Park Industrial Estate, Moreton Road South, Luton, LU2 0TL Tel: (01582) 456144 Fax: (01582) 453396 E-mail: sales@prismdigital.co.uk

Provincial Printing & Publishing Co. Ltd, Sanatorium Road, Cardiff, CF11 8DG Tel: (029) 2022 8729 Fax: (029) 2037 3494 E-mail: sales@printppp.co.uk

Prudential Printers, Unit 71 Birch Road East Industrial Estate, Birch Road East, Birmingham, B6 7DA Tel: 0121-328 1454 Fax: 0121-327 7073 E-mail: prudential_printers@yahoo.co.uk

R A H Advertising Ltd, 320 Palatine Road, Northenden, Manchester, M22 4HF Tel: 0161-902 0555 Fax: 0161-902 0777 E-mail: info@rahadvertising.com

Radford Press Ltd, Miller House, 30 Wilmot Road, London, E10 5LU Tel: (020) 8558 4814 Fax: (020) 8558 0345 E-mail: sales@radfordpress.co.uk

Raithby Lawrence & Co. Ltd, 18 Slater Street, Leicester, LE3 5AS Tel: 0116-251 0961 Fax: 0116-253 2581E-mail: sales@rlprint.com

Rap, Clowes Street, Hollinwood, Oldham, OL9 7LY Tel: 0161-947 3700 Fax: 0161-947 3729 E-mail: enquiries@rapspiderweb.com

Rapidocolor UK Ltd, Unit 15 Waverley Industrial Estate, Hailsham Drive, Harrow, Middlesex, HA1 4TR Tel: (020) 8863 6404 Fax: (020) 8863 1434 E-mail: sales@rapidocolor.co.uk

Rebourn Ltd, 14 The Green, Chipping Norton, Oxfordshire, OX7 5NH Tel: (01608) 642020 Fax: (01608) 642031

Reid Printers, 79-109 Glasgow Road, Blantyre, Glasgow, G72 0LY Tel: (01698) 826000 Fax: (01698) 824944 E-mail: sales@reid-print-group.co.uk

Renault Printing Co. Ltd, 54 Factory Estate, College Road, Perry Barr, Birmingham, B44 8BS Tel: 0121-356 0331 Fax: 0121-356 0153 E-mail: sales@renaultprint.co.uk

Renfor Four Colour, Paper Mill End Industrial Estate, Birmingham, B44 8NH Tel: 0121-356 9555 Fax: 0121-356 3555 E-mail: info@renfor.co.uk

Richaprint Ltd, Priory Road, Freiston, Boston, Lincolnshire, PE22 0JZ Tel: (01205) 760774 Fax: (01205) 761084 E-mail: roger.young@richprint.co.uk

Robor Cartons Ltd, Chartwell Road, Lancing, West Sussex, BN15 8TX Tel: (01903) 750428 Fax: (01903) 766151 E-mail: sales@robor.co.uk

Rustin Clark, 45 Waterloo Road, London, NW2 7TX Tel: (020) 8452 1091 Fax: (020) 8452 2008 E-mail: rustinclark@rustinclark.co.uk

S F Taylor & Co. Ltd, Whitehill Industrial Estate, Haigh Avenue, Stockport, Cheshire, SK4 1NU Tel: 0161-429 7200 Fax: 0161-429 5720 E-mail: gilltress@sftaylor.com

S G Print Ltd, PO Box 6068, Basildon, Essex, SS14 3WJ Tel: (01621) 773610 Fax: (01621) 773271 E-mail: sales@sgprint.ltd.uk

Seven Corners Communications Group, Penmark House, Woodbridge Meadows, Guildford, Surrey, GU1 1BL Tel: (01483) 576777 Fax: (01483) 567876

Shanks Printers & Finishers Ltd, Unit 6/7 Martello Enterprise Centre, Courtwick Lane, Wick, Littlehampton, West Sussex, BN17 7PA Tel: (01903) 716442 Fax: (01903) 733019 E-mail: terri@shanksprinters.co.uk

Shere Print, 8 West Street, Dorking, Surrey, RH4 1BL Tel: (01306) 888050 Fax: (01306) 888180 E-mail: info@shere.com

Stephenson & Johnson Ltd, Malaga House, Pink Bank Lane, Manchester, M12 5GH Tel: 0161-223 0011 Fax: 0161-223 0404

T W G Packaging, King Edward Industrial Estate, Gibraltar Row, Liverpool, L3 7HJ Tel: 0151-227 1045 Fax: 0151-236 2114 E-mail: mygpackaging@compuserve.com

Technart Ltd, Unit 45 City Industrial Park, Southern Road, Southampton, SO15 1HG Tel: (023) 8022 2409 Fax: (023) 8021 1403 E-mail: prepress@technart.co.uk

Tresises, Stanley Street, Burton-on-Trent, Staffordshire, DE14 1DY Tel: (01283) 568276 Fax: (01283) 511207

View Point Internet Ltd, Venture House Arlington Square, Downshire Way, Bracknell, Berkshire, RG12 1WA Tel: (01344) 300100 Fax: (01344) 742950 E-mail: sales@viewpoint.net.uk

Wass Quadrant Printers Ltd, 2 Rodney Street, London, N1 9JH Tel: (020) 7278 7897 Fax: (020) 7837 1119 E-mail: print@wassquadrant.com

West Yorkshire Printing Co. Ltd, Wyprint House, Smith Way, Wakefield Road, Ossett, West Yorkshire, WF5 9JZ Tel: (01924) 280522 Fax: (01924) 280145 E-mail: sales@westyor.co.uk

Wood Mitchell Printers Ltd, Festival Way, Stoke-on-Trent, ST1 5TH Tel: (01782) 202440 Fax: (01782) 202402 E-mail: rmitchell@wood-mitchell.co.uk

Wood & Richardson Ltd, Royden House, 156 Haxby Road, York, YO31 8JN Tel: (01904) 622712 Fax: (01904) 620352 E-mail: sales@woodrichardson.co.uk

Wright's Sandbach Ltd, 9 Old Middlewich Road, Sandbach, Cheshire, CW11 1DP Tel: (01270) 762416 Fax: (01270) 760278 E-mail: sales@wrightsprinters.com

Wye Valley Printers, Units 8 & 9, Foley Trading Estate, Hereford, HR1 2SF Tel: (01432) 268286 Fax: (01432) 356322 E-mail: sales@wyevalleyprinters.co.uk

Zedi Signs, Connaught House, 32 Connaught Street, Northampton, NN1 3BP Tel: (01604) 231525 Fax: (01604) 231527 E-mail: zedisigns@aol.com

COLOUR RECOGNITION EQUIPMENT

Powelectrics Ltd, 46 Kepler, Tamworth, Staffordshire, B79 7XE Tel: (01827) 310666 Fax: (01827) 310999 E-mail: sales@powelectrics.co.uk

COLOUR REPRODUCTION/ MAKE-UP SERVICES, ELECTRONICS

C3 Imaging Ltd, Severalls Business Park, Telford Way, Colchester, CO4 9QP Tel: (01206) 845544 Fax: (01206) 845856 E-mail: jacqueline@hilocolour.co.uk

Grasmere (Digital) Imaging Ltd, Bramley Business Centre, Stanningley Road, Leeds, LS13 4EN Tel: 0113-224 8600 Fax: 0113-239 3166 E-mail: admin@grasmeredigital.co.uk

Hartham Press Ltd, 5a Marshgate Trading Estate, Hertford, SG13 7AB Tel: (01992) 589334 Fax: (01992) 554826 E-mail: sales@harthampress.com

▶ Professional Bridal Make-up, 29 Burnell Gate, Beaulieu Park, Chelmsford, CM1 6ED Tel: 01245 462200 E-mail: info@professionalbridalmakeup.co.uk

COLOUR SCHEME INTERIOR DESIGN CONSULTANCY

▶ 1:50, 15 Silver Birch Close, Sholing, Southampton, SO19 8FY Tel: (0845) 2262817 E-mail: info@1-50.co.uk

▶ Amber Radiator Covers, 14 Freemans Way, Harrogate, North Yorkshire, HG3 1DH Tel: (01423) 883386 Fax: (01423) 883386 E-mail: sales@amberradiatorcovers.co.uk

Apiffany Interior Design Ltd, Yandell Publishing Ltd, 9 Vermont Place, Tongwell, Milton Keynes, MK15 8JA Tel: (0870) 1212617 Fax: (0870) 1212618 E-mail: info@apiffany.co.uk

▶ Chantilly, Reading Road, Cholsey, Wallingford, Oxon, OX10 9HL Tel: 01491 652848 Fax: 07889 644848 E-mail: susiegsmith@btinernet.com

▶ Cheshire Interiors, 75 Shepperton Close, Appleton, Warrington, WA4 5JZ Tel: 01925 213339 E-mail: tamara@cheshireinteriors.com

Clear Water Interiors, 69 Anglesmede Crescent, Pinner, Middlesex, HA5 5ST Tel: (020) 8863 1732

▶ Design4business, Design 4 Business, Prestwick Hall Farm, Ponteland, Newcastle upon Tyne, NE20 9TU Tel: 01661 820769

▶ Emma Pettifer Richardson, Cavenagh House, The Square, Sheriff Hutton, York, YO60 6QX Tel: (01347) 878173 Fax: (01347) 878176 E-mail: info@abouthouse.co.uk

▶ Imaginative Interiors, 11 Burnside Close, Harrogate, North Yorkshire, HG1 2BQ Tel: (01423) 565959

▶ in2style Ltd, 143 Richmond Road, London, E8 3NJ Tel: (020) 7249 4286 E-mail: info@in2style.org

▶ Inspirit Interiors, Repton Road, Nottingham, NG6 9GE Tel: 0115-877 6959 Fax: 0115-877 6959 E-mail: enquiries@inspirit-interiors.co.uk

▶ Interior Solutions, 57 Comiston View, Edinburgh, EH10 6LT Tel: 0131-445 2200 Fax: 0131-466 1516 E-mail: mail@interiorsolutionsedinburgh.com

Interiors By Design, 37 The Spinney, Pulborough, West Sussex, RH20 2AP Tel: (01798) 874969 E-mail: interiorsbydesign@ukonline.co.uk

▶ Kelson Interiors, Topcliffe Lane, Morley, Leeds, LS27 0HW Tel: 0113-252 7900 Fax: 0113-252 7977 E-mail: info@kelson.co.uk

▶ Ladesigns.Co.Uk, 20 Hartfield Road, Eastbourne, East Sussex, BN21 2AR Tel: (07801) 421368 E-mail: info@ladesigns.co.uk

▶ Christina Lees, Cocoa Court, 21a Pillory Street, Nantwich, Cheshire, CW5 5BZ Tel: (01270) 611142 Fax: (01270) 842822

▶ Lemon Tree Interiors, 5 Cambridge Road, Ely, Cambridgeshire, CB7 4HJ Tel: (01353) 610585 Fax: (01353) 610466 E-mail: Design@LemonTreeInteriors.Co.Uk

▶ Sally Treloar, Southview, Whiteoak Green, Hailey, Witney, Oxfordshire, OX29 9XP Tel: 01993 869119 E-mail: support@firstideas.co.uk

▶ Zemira Designs, 26 Fairwood Park, Marton-in-Cleveland, Middlesbrough, Cleveland, TS8 9XP Tel: (01642) 271440 E-mail: zemiradesigns@hotmail.com

COLOUR SEPARATION/ SCANNING/SCREENING SERVICES

Centreprint Graphics Ltd, Units 1-2, Lanesfield Drive, Ettingshall, Wolverhampton, WV4 6UA Tel: (01902) 402693 Fax: (01902) 491794 E-mail: sales@centreprint.co.uk

Colourscans Ltd, Unit 89 The Washford Industrial Estate, Heming Road, Redditch, Worcestershire, B98 0EA Tel: (01527) 500048 Fax: (01527) 526673 E-mail: info@lemonpress.co.uk

Design & Media Solutions, Tovil Hill, Maidstone, Kent, ME15 6QS Tel: (01622) 681366 Fax: (01622) 688928 E-mail: craftsmencolour@craftsmencolour.co.uk

Document Imaging Services Ltd, Image House, Radford Way, Billericay, Essex, CM12 0BT Tel: (01277) 625000 Fax: (01277) 624999 E-mail: sales@document-imaging.co.uk

Swaingrove Ltd, Unit 3-4 Fourwheel Drive, Rougham Industrial Estate, Rougham, Bury St. Edmunds, Suffolk, IP30 9ND Tel: (01359) 271385 Fax: (01359) 271327 E-mail: systems@swaingrove.co.uk

COLOUR TONERS

▶ Speedbird Supplies, 15 Thistledown Drive, Ixworth, Bury St. Edmunds, Suffolk, IP31 2NH Tel: (01359) 235170 Fax: (01359) 232015 E-mail: sales@speedbird-supplies.co.uk

COLOURED COATINGS FOR PVCU FASCIAS

▶ Dundas UPVC, 1D Payne Street, Port Dundas Trading Estate, Glasgow, G4 0LE Tel: 0141 353 1996

COLOURED FLUORESCENT LAMPS OR TUBES

EncapSulite International Ltd, 17 Chartwell Business Park, Chartmoor Road, Leighton Buzzard, Bedfordshire, LU7 4WG Tel: (01525) 376974 Fax: (01525) 850306 E-mail: reply@encapsulite.co.uk

COLOURED LAMPS

G C Designs Ltd, Mansion House Buildings, Market Place, Crich, Matlock, Derbyshire, DE4 5DD Tel: (01773) 857388 Fax: (01773) 857388E-mail: gwyncarless@gcdesigns.co.uk

COLOURED SILICONE RUBBER PRODUCTS

Primasil Silicones Ltd, Kington Rd, Weobley, Hereford, HR4 8QU Tel: (01544) 312600 Fax: (01544) 312601 E-mail: sales@primasil.com

COLOURING PRODUCTS

▶ Doodlebugz, Marton, Marton cum Grafton, York, YO51 9QE Tel: (01347) 830100 Fax: (01347) 830100 E-mail: info@doodlebugz.co.uk

COLOURS, *See also headings for particular types*

A T C Colours Ltd, Vale Works, New Haden Road, Cheadle, Stoke-on-Trent, ST10 1UF Tel: (01538) 754400 Fax: (01538) 751212 E-mail: mail@atccolours.co.uk

E.P. Bray & Co. Ltd, Coombes Lane Works, Charlesworth, Glossop, Derbyshire, SK13 5DQ Tel: (01457) 853277 Fax: (01457) 856114 E-mail: epbray@charlesworth81.fsnet.co.uk

BTC Speciality Chemical Distribution Ltd, PO Box 4, Cheadle, Cheshire, SK8 6QG Tel: 0161-488 5223 Fax: 0161-486 6184 E-mail: sales@btc-uk.com

Calder Colours Ashby Ltd, Dents Road, Nottingham Road Indust Estate, Ashby DeLa Zouch, Ashby-de-la-Zouch, Leicestershire, LE65 1JS Tel: (01530) 412885 Fax: (01530) 417315 E-mail: office@caldercolours.co.uk

▶ Cathay Pigments, Norman House, Friar Gate, Derby, DE1 1NU Tel: (01332) 371759

D G Colour Ltd, 15 Shrrington, Warminster, Wiltshire, BA12 0SN Tel: 01985 878185 Fax: 0207 149 9826 E-mail: info@dgcolour.co.uk

Ferro Great Britain Ltd, Nile Street, Stoke-on-Trent, ST6 2BQ Tel: (01782) 820400 Fax: (01782) 820402

COLOURS – *continued*

Holliday Pigments Ltd, Morley Street, Hull, HU8 8DN Tel: (01482) 329875 Fax: (01484) 329791 E-mail: sales@holliday-pigments.com

▶ Imperial Colours & Chemicals, Admiral House, Blakeridge Lane, Batley, West Yorkshire, WF17 8PD Tel: (01924) 477433

Lanxess Ltd, Lichfield Road, Branston, Burton-On-Trent, Staffordshire, DE14 3WH Tel: (01283) 714200 Fax: (01283) 714201 E-mail: info@hawley.edi.co.uk

Llewellyn Ryland Ltd, Haden Street, Birmingham, B12 9DB Tel: 0121-440 2284 Fax: 0121-440 0281 E-mail: sales@llewellyn-ryland.co.uk

Oxkem Chemical Mnfrs, 117 Loverock Road, Reading, RG30 1DZ Tel: 0118-952 2929 Fax: 0118-952 2959 E-mail: sales@oxkem.com

P J Colours Ltd, Excelsior Works, Castle Park, Flint, Clwyd, CH6 5NT Tel: (01352) 732157 Fax: (01352) 735530 E-mail: info@pjcolours.com

Unicolour Ltd, Tandem Works, Wakefield Road, Waterloo, Huddersfield, HD5 0AN Tel: (01484) 516974 Fax: (01484) 510667 E-mail: dyes@unicolour.co.uk

Univar Ltd, International House, Zenith, Paycocke Road, Basildon, Essex, SS14 3DW Tel: (01268) 594400 Fax: (01268) 594482 E-mail: exports@univareurope.com

W G Ball Ltd, Longton Mill, Anchor Road, Stoke-on-Trent, ST3 1JW Tel: (01782) 312286 Fax: (01782) 598148 E-mail: sales@wgball.com

COMBAT SYSTEM SOFTWARE

Cash Control Equipment, 390 Cathcart Road, Glasgow, G42 7DF Tel: 0141-423 9999 Fax: 0141-423 0690 E-mail: epos@cashcontrol.co.uk

COMBINATION ACCESS LOCKS,

See Digital Combination etc

COMBINE HARVESTERS

Mark Hellier Tractors Se Ltd, Thousand Acre Farm, Biddenden, Ashford, Kent, TN27 8BF Tel: (01580) 291271 Fax: (01580) 292432 E-mail: mail@markhellier.co.uk

COMBINED HEAT AND POWER SYSTEMS

Aircogen CHP Solutions, Werrington Parkway, Peterborough, PE4 5HG Tel: (01733) 292450 Fax: (01733) 292460 E-mail: info@aircogen.co.uk

Dalkia Utilities plc, Oakenshaw Lane, Crofton, Wakefield, West Yorkshire, WF4 1SE Tel: (01924) 258331 Fax: (01924) 259585

Finning UK Ltd, 688-689 Stirling Road, Slough, SL1 4ST Tel: (01753) 497300 Fax: (01753) 497333 E-mail: mbarnes@finning.co.uk

Integrated Energy Systems Ltd, 11a Lune Street, Preston, PR1 2NL Tel: (01772) 250707 Fax: (01772) 258322 E-mail: admin@intergratedenergy.co.uk

KKK Limited, 7 Regent Park, Park Farm Industrial Estate, Off Booth Drive, Wellingborough, Northants, NN8 6GR Tel: (01933) 671480 Fax: (01933) 671470 E-mail: kkk.limited@agkkk.de

Peter Brotherhood Holdings Ltd, Werrington Park Way, Peterborough, PE4 5HG Tel: (01733) 292200 Fax: (01733) 292300 E-mail: sales@peterbrotherhood.co.uk

COMBINED HEAT AND POWER TURNKEY SERVICES

A B B Power Ltd, Stonefield Works, Oulton Road, Stone, Staffordshire, ST15 0RS Tel: (01785) 825050 Fax: (01785) 819019

COMBINED WEIGHING AND TIPPING WEIGHBRIDGES

▶ Avery Weigh Tronix Ltd, 13-14 Monckton Road Industrial Estate, Wakefield, West Yorkshire, WF2 7BP Tel: (0870) 9050041 Fax: (0870) 9050042 E-mail: hiredivisionuk@awtxglobal.com

COMBUSTION CONSULTANCY OR CONSULTING ENGINEERS

Abbeville Instrument Control Ltd, Bridge Street, Derby, DE1 3LA Tel: (01332) 371138 Fax: (01332) 291668 E-mail: sales@aicderby.co.uk

▶ BMT Combustion Systems Ltd, Foxbourne Business Center, Heathmill Close, Wombourne, Wolverhampton, WV5 8EX Tel: (01902) 896183 Fax: (01902) 897372 E-mail: trevor@bmtcombustion.co.uk

Boden Clark Ltd, George Henry Rd, Greatbridge, Tipton, W. Midlands, DY4 7BZ Tel: 0121-557 1700 Fax: 0121-557 3788

Eemech Ltd, Unit 1 Kenn Court Business Park, Roman Farm Road, Bristol, BS4 1UL Tel: 0117-964 4497 Fax: 0117-964 4487 E-mail: eemech@hotmail.com

Flare Products Ltd, 14 Broadmead Business Park, Broadmead Road, Stewartby, Bedford, MK43 9NX Tel: (01234) 767755 Fax: (01234) 768624 E-mail: stuartalansimpson@btopenworld.com

Hodgkinson Bennis Ltd, Highfield Road, Little Hulton, Manchester, M38 9SS Tel: 0161-790 4411 Fax: 0161-703 8505 E-mail: enquiries@hbcombustion.com

Meridian Azimuth, 51 Watson Crescent, Edinburgh, EH11 1EW Tel: (07876) 127164 E-mail: alain.grangeret@meridianaz.co.uk

N A Stordy Combustion Ltd, Heath Mill Road, Wombourne, Wolverhampton, WV5 8BD Tel: (01902) 891200 Fax: (01902) 895552 E-mail: sales@stordy.co.uk

Saacke Ltd, Marshlands Spur, Portsmouth, PO6 1RX Tel: (023) 9238 3111 Fax: (023) 9232 7120 E-mail: info@saacke.co.uk

COMBUSTION CONTROL SYSTEMS

Elcontrol Ltd, 5 Regulus Works, 79 Lynch Lane, Weymouth, Dorset, DT4 9DW Tel: (01305) 773426 Fax: (01305) 760539 E-mail: sales@elcontrol.co.uk

Energy Technology & Control Ltd, 25 North Street, Lewes, East Sussex, BN7 2PE Tel: (01273) 480667 Fax: (01273) 480652 E-mail: sales@energytechnologycontrol.com

Igniters Combustion Engineering Ltd, Unit 6 Prospect Drive, Britannia Enterprise Park, Lichfield, Staffordshire, WS14 9UX Tel: (01543) 251478 Fax: (01543) 257850 E-mail: renglish@igniters.co.uk

Saacke Ltd, Marshlands Spur, Portsmouth, PO6 1RX Tel: (023) 9238 3111 Fax: (023) 9232 7120 E-mail: info@saacke.co.uk

COMBUSTION ENGINEERING SERVICES

Central Diesel, Unit 18 Erdington Industrial Park, Chester Road, Birmingham, B24 0RD Tel: 0121-386 1700 Fax: 0121-386 1744

Combserve Combustion Service Ltd, 1 Brookfield Works, Wood Street, Elland, West Yorkshire, HX5 9AP Tel: (01422) 370051 Fax: (01422) 377374 E-mail: combserve@hotmail.com

Eemech Ltd, Unit 1 Kenn Court Business Park, Roman Farm Road, Bristol, BS4 1UL Tel: 0117-964 4497 Fax: 0117-964 4487 E-mail: eemech@hotmail.com

Flare Products Ltd, 14 Broadmead Business Park, Broadmead Road, Stewartby, Bedford, MK43 9NX Tel: (01234) 767755 Fax: (01234) 768624 E-mail: stuartalansimpson@btopenworld.com

John Zink Division KCTG Ltd, 140 Windmill Road, Dolphin House, Sunbury-on-Thames, Middlesex, TW16 7HT Tel: (01932) 769830 Fax: (01932) 787471

Meridian Azimuth, 51 Watson Crescent, Edinburgh, EH11 1EW Tel: (07876) 127164 E-mail: alain.grangeret@meridianaz.co.uk

Time Engineers Ltd, Unit 3, Manor Way, Rainham, Essex, RM13 8RH Tel: (01708) 555464 Fax: (01708) 555765

Whites Burners Ltd, 9 Ilfracombe Gardens, Whitley Bay, Tyne & Wear, NE26 3ND Tel: 0191-252 9933 Fax: 0191-252 9955

COMBUSTION SYSTEM AIR PREHEATERS

▶ BMT Combustion Systems Ltd, Foxbourne Business Center, Heathmill Close, Wombourne, Wolverhampton, WV5 8EX Tel: (01902) 896183 Fax: (01902) 897372 E-mail: trevor@bmtcombustion.co.uk

COMBUSTION SYSTEMS

Hamworthy Combustion Engineering Ltd, Fleets Corner, Poole, Dorset, BH17 0LA Tel: (01202) 662700 Fax: (01202) 669875 E-mail: info@hamworthy-combustion.com

Hengelmolen Engineering Ltd, Great Bridge Industrial Estate, Tipton, West Midlands, DY4 0HR Tel: 0121-520 1181 Fax: 0121-557 5201 E-mail: hengelmolen@btconnect.com

Hirt Combustion Engineers Ltd, Woodford Green Works, Leslie Road, Woodford Park Industrial Estate, Winsford, Cheshire, CW7 2RB Tel: (01606) 861366 Fax: (01606) 861408 E-mail: sales@hirt.co.uk

Igniters Combustion Engineering Ltd, Unit 6 Prospect Drive, Britannia Enterprise Park, Lichfield, Staffordshire, WS14 9UX Tel: (01543) 251478 Fax: (01543) 257850 E-mail: renglish@igniters.co.uk

Maxon Combustion Systems Ltd, Chantry House, High Street, Coleshill, Birmingham, B46 3BP Tel: (01675) 464334 Fax: (01675) 467285 E-mail: kp@maxon.be

▶ James Proctor Ltd, PO Box 19, Burnley, Lancashire, BB11 1NN Tel: (01282) 453816 Fax: (01282) 416178 E-mail: sales@jamesproctor.com

COMBUSTION SYSTEMS, BIO-FUEL

▶ James Proctor Ltd, PO Box 19, Burnley, Lancashire, BB11 1NN Tel: (01282) 453816 Fax: (01282) 416178 E-mail: sales@jamesproctor.com

COMMERCIAL AIR CONDITIONING (AC) EQUIPMENT

Bostel Brothers Ltd, 1-3 The Compound, Northease Close, Hove, East Sussex, BN3 8LJ Tel: (01273) 430264 Fax: (01273) 422605

Macqueen Air Conditioning Ltd, 39-41 Carrholm Road, Leeds, LS7 2NQ Tel: 0113-393 0287 Fax: 0113-393 0284 E-mail: sales@macqueen-ac.co.uk

Riseborough Refrigeration Service Ltd, 164 Glenroy Street, Roath, Cardiff, CF24 3LA Tel: (029) 2049 6007 Fax: (029) 2049 2409

Thermofrost Cryo plc, Ernest Avenue, London, SE27 0DA Tel: (020) 8670 3663 Fax: (020) 8761 8081E-mail: info@thermofrostcryo.co.uk

COMMERCIAL AIR CONDITIONING (AC) SYSTEMS

A C J Industrial Ltd, Longbeck Trading Estate, Marske-By-The-Sea, Redcar, Cleveland, TS11 6HB Tel: (01642) 483045 Fax: (01642) 487588 E-mail: garbut@globalnet.co.uk

Max Fordham & Partners, 42-43 Gloucester Cresent, London, NW1 7PE Tel: (020) 7267 5161 Fax: (020) 7482 0329 E-mail: post@maxfordham.com

Shepherd Engineering Services Ltd, Mill Mount, York, YO24 1GH Tel: (01904) 629151 Fax: (01904) 610175

COMMERCIAL AIR CONDITIONING (AC) UNITS

Coverite Air Conditioning Services Ltd, Unit 17 Coldart Business Centre, Dartford, DA1 2HZ Tel: (01322) 270989 Fax: (01322) 278203 E-mail: info@coverite-ac.co.uk

COMMERCIAL ART DIRECTION

▶ Eyestorm, Units G & H, The Network Centre, Berkley Way, Hebburn, Tyne & Wear, NE31 1SF Tel: 0191-424 2242 E-mail: michael.davison@eyestorm.com

COMMERCIAL CARPETS

▶ Carpets Direct, 1 Dominion Works, Denholme Gate Road, Hipperholme, Halifax, West Yorkshire, HX3 8JG Tel: (01422) 202220 Fax: (01422) 202220

COMMERCIAL CLEANING

Aadvark, 242 Gosport Road, Fareham, Hampshire, PO16 0SS Tel: (01329) 822515 Fax: (01329) 823630

▶ Ablib, 1 Foresters Cottages, Mead Road, Edenbridge, Kent, TN8 5DE Tel: (01732) 867879 E-mail: ablibcleaners@hotmail.co.uk

Ace Cleaning Service, Corner Road, Pillowell, Lydney, Gloucestershire, GL15 4QU Tel: (01594) 562688 Fax: (01594) 563722 E-mail: acecleaning@lydney24.fsbusiness.co.uk

Adept Cleaning Services Ltd, 5 Gainsborough Drive, Mile Oak, Tamworth, Staffordshire, B78 3PJ Tel: (01827) 287100 Fax: (01827) 287666

Anglian Cleaning Services Ltd, 8 Magdalen St, Colchester, CO1 2JT Tel: (01206) 763501 Fax: (01206) 571794 E-mail: info@angliancleaning.com

Aramark Ltd, Caledonia House Lawnswood Business Park, Redvers Close, Leeds, LS16 6QY Tel: 0113-230 5300 Fax: (0870) 1118199 E-mail: client-care@aramark.co.uk

▶ Aroma Cleaning Ltd, 4b Coventry Road, Burbage, Hinckley, Leicestershire, LE10 2HL Tel: (0845) 3706106 Fax: (01455) 238480 E-mail: sales@aromacleaning.co.uk

Care Group Ltd, Unit 7 Hartham Lane, Hertford, SG14 1QN Tel: (01992) 505100 Fax: (01992) 509599 E-mail: caregroup@btconnect.com

▶ Cassini, 141 Shirley Road, Southampton, SO15 3FH Tel: (023) 8022 1740 Fax: (023) 8033 9220 E-mail: enquiry@cassinigroup.co.uk

▶ CHR Commercial Cleaning Services Ltd, Unit 12 Union Bridge Mills, Roker Lane, Pudsey, West Yorkshire, LS28 9LE Tel: 0113-257 7893 Fax: 0113-236 0916 E-mail: brendan@chrservices.co.uk

▶ cibsfacilities.com, Unit 1, 20-22 Union Road, London, SW4 6JP Tel: (0800) 0757515 Fax: (0870) 3452428E-mail: sales@ci-bs.com

Clean It All, Keepers Cottage, Alston Lane, Churston Ferrers, Brixham, Devon, TQ5 0HT Tel: (01803) 842249 Fax: (01803) 842249

Cleanrite Property Services Ltd, 10 Nab Hill Avenue, Leek, Staffordshire, ST13 8EE Tel: (01538) 386857 E-mail: clean.rite@btopenworld.com

▶ Coleman F M Ltd, PO Box 2088, Rayleigh, Essex, SS6 8WB Tel: (0845) 2261756 Fax: (0845) 2261757

D & G Sullivan, 6 Sextant Park, Neptune Close, Medway City Estate, Rochester, Kent, ME2 4LU Tel: (01634) 730011 Fax: (01634) 730022

Dougland Holdings Ltd, Little Park Farm, Segensworth West Industrial Estate, Fareham, Hampshire, PO15 5SN Tel: (01489) 574234 Fax: (01489) 576104 E-mail: margaret@dougland.co.uk

EDSCO, 118 Featherbed Lane, Hillmorton, Rugby, Warwickshire, CV21 4LQ Tel: 01788 331530 Fax: 01788 336858 E-mail: e.scholey@ntlworld.com

▶ Gemini Cleaning, Trewilyn, Ruddlemoor, St. Austell, Cornwall, PL26 8XF Tel: (0845) 2260974 Fax: (0845) 2260974 E-mail: gemini_cleaners@hotmail.com

Hydra Myst Services, 166 Clifton Road, Aberdeen, AB24 4HA Tel: (01224) 491825 Fax: (01224) 488616

▶ I M B Cleaning & Maintenance, 29 Milton Road, Caterham, Surrey, CR3 5JG Tel: (01883) 334521 E-mail: imbcleaning@tiscali.co.uk

I S S Support Services, Strathdon Drive, London, SW17 0PS Tel: (020) 8947 9045 Fax: (020) 8947 9732

Imperial Cleaning, Unit 7 Springwood, Cheshunt, Waltham Cross, Hertfordshire, EN7 6AZ Tel: (01992) 628342 Fax: (01992) 628342 E-mail: imperialenquiries@btinternet.com

Inflight Cleaning Services, Room 295 Ground Floor, International Pier Terminal Buiding, Glasgow Airport, Abbotsinch, Paisley, Renfrewshire, PA3 2TD Tel: 0141-848 7118 Fax: 0141-848 7112

Initial Cleaning Services, Unit 2, Rhymney River Bridge Road, Cardiff, CF3 7AF Tel: (029) 2046 4243 Fax: (029) 2048 7248 E-mail: initialcleaning@rentokilinitial.com

Jannock Cleaning Services, Captiva House, Queensway, Banbury, Oxfordshire, OX16 9NF Tel: (01295) 277737 Fax: (01295) 277732

Kier Managed Services Ltd, Conway House, St. Mellons Business Park, Fortran Road, Cardiff, CF3 0EY Tel: (029) 2036 1616 Fax: (029) 2036 2303 E-mail: enquiries@kier.co.uk

The Lyndann Group, Broadmeadows, Padstow Road, St. Breock, Wadebridge, Cornwall, PL27 7LS Tel: (01208) 815040 Fax: E-mail: daveharring@btconnect.com

▶ Magic Bean & Cow Ltd., 93-97 Gowe Street, London, WC1E 6AD Tel: (07841) 841319 Fax: 0207 9169686 E-mail: info@magicbeanandcow.co.uk

▶ Mattvac Carpet & Upholstery Cleaning, 45 Hallidale Crescent, Renfrew, PA4 0YA Tel: 0141-562 3873 E-mail: sales@mattvac.co.uk

Mike O'Leary Cleaning Services, 181 Scribers Lane, Birmingham, B28 0PN Tel: 0121-745 4662 Fax: 0121-745 4662

Minster Cleaning Services, 1 Priors Gate, Priory Street, Ware, Hertfordshire, SG12 0DA Tel: (01920) 462261 Fax: (01920) 462265 E-mail: hertfordshire@minstergroup.co.uk

N J M Cleaning Ltd, 137 Essex Road, Romford, RM7 8BD Tel: (01708) 742127 E-mail: sales@njmcleaning.co.uk

▶ Pinnacle Cleaning, 41 Bramble Court, Ferndown, Bournemouth, BH22 0HL Tel: 0870 345 5757 E-mail: webenquiries@pinnacle-cleaning.co.uk

Premier Cleaning Solutions Ltd, 6 Carrock Road, Croft Business Park, Bromborough, Wirral, Merseyside, CH62 3RA Tel: 0151-201 6767 Fax: 0151-201 6767 E-mail: phil_morris@tinyworld.co.uk

Shadow Sales & Service, 6 Lyttleton Court, Droitwich, Worcestershire, WR9 7BG Tel: (01905) 797898 Fax: (01905) 798399 E-mail: mike.ssslimited@btconnect.com

Spic 'N' Span, 20 Edith Avenue, Plymouth, PL4 8TH Tel: (01752) 666707 Fax: (01752) 666707

Square 1 Cleaning Services, Botany Bay Ii, Playhatch, Reading, RG4 9QU Tel: 0118-946 1503 E-mail: square1@botanybayii.freeserve.co.uk

▶ Thoroughclean Services, 4 Deemouth Business Centre, South Esplanade East, Aberdeen, AB11 9PB Tel: (01224) 891570 Fax: (01224) 891540 E-mail: sales@thoroughclean.co.uk

WGC Ltd, 7 Academy Buildings, Fanshaw Street, London, N1 6LQ Tel: (020) 7729 2980 Fax: (020) 7729 5828 E-mail: sales@wgc-group.co.uk

▶ Yorkshire Cottage Services, Heathfield, Ugthorpe, Whitby, North Yorkshire, YO21 2BG Tel: (01947) 841114 Fax: (01947) 841189 E-mail: ugthorpe@btinternet.com

COMMERCIAL COFFEE MACHINES

Teknomat UK Ltd, Unit 27, Wornal Park, Menmarsh Road, Worminghall, Aylesbury, Buckinghamshire, HP18 9PH Tel: (01844) 339828 Fax: (01844) 339829

COMMERCIAL ENQUIRY AGENTS, *See also Trade Protection Associations*

Graydon UK Ltd, 66 College Road, 2nd Floor Hygeia Building, Harrow, Middlesex, HA1 1BE Tel: (020) 8515 1400 Fax: (020) 8515 1499 E-mail: mail@graydon.co.uk

Highcrest Accident Repair Centre Ltd, James Street, Markham, Blackwood, Gwent, NP12 0QN Tel: (01495) 221767 Fax: (01495) 220486

▶ Investigator Direct (Operations) Limited, Floor Six, 456 - 458 Strand, London, WC2R 0DZ Tel: 0870 9903211 Fax: 0870 9903212 E-mail: admin@id-net.co.uk

James Spinks & Sons Ltd, Bramshot House, Clemence Lane, Tamworth, Staffordshire, B79 9DH Tel: (01827) 382850 Fax: (01827) 382855 E-mail: data.resource@virgin.net

Star Credit Services Ltd, 10-12 Lombard Road, London, SW19 3TZ Tel: (020) 8540 9691 Fax: (020) 8540 6021 E-mail: info@star-serv.com

COMMERCIAL ESTATE AGENTS

▶ 4 Homes Abroad, 6 Henley Close, Chardstock, Axminster, Devon, EX13 7SX Tel: (01454) 777686 E-mail: sales@4homesabroad.com

Bantel Investments Ltd, 45-47 North Bridge Street, Hawick, Roxburghshire, TD9 9PX Tel: (01450) 373352 Fax: (01450) 377531

Brecker Grossmith & Co., 63 Wigmore Street, London, W1U 1BQ Tel: (020) 7486 3531 Fax: (020) 7935 3074 E-mail: enquiries@breckergrossmith.co.uk

Colliers Cre, Broad Quay House, Broad Quay, Bristol, BS1 4DJ Tel: 0117-917 2000 Fax: 0117-917 2099 E-mail: sales@colliers.com

Colliers Cre, 9 Marylebone Lane, London, W1U 1HL Tel: (020) 7935 4499 Fax: (020) 7487 1894 E-mail: property@colliersCre.co.uk

Conway Relf, 7 Apple Tree Yard, London, SW1Y 6LD Tel: (020) 7629 9100 Fax: (020) 7484 9250 E-mail: property@conwayrelf.com

Create Real Estate, PO Box 48533, London, NW4 2XW Tel: (020) 8457 3200 Fax: (020) 8457 3202 E-mail: info@create-re.com

Cresswell Morgan Associates, 41 Chobham Road, Woking, Surrey, GU21 6JD Tel: (01483) 776686 Fax: (01483) 730199

▶ Daniel Sims, 2 Cheriton High Street, Folkestone, Kent, CT19 4ER Tel: (01303) 277211 Fax: (01303) 270370 E-mail: sales@danielsims.co.uk

David Lewis & Co., 21 Gloucester Place, London, W1U 8HR Tel: (020) 7486 2277 Fax: (020) 7224 5173

Dixon Webb, Palmyra Square Chambers, 15 Springfield Street, Warrington, WA1 1BJ Tel: (01925) 577577 Fax: (01925) 579679 E-mail: warrington@dixonwebb.com

Dovey Estates Ltd, Suffolk House, Trade Street, Cardiff, CF10 5DQ Tel: (029) 2034 4150 Fax: (029) 2034 4170 E-mail: dovey@estatesltd.fsnet.co.uk

Finders-Seekers, Mill Cotts, Lamerton, Tavistock, Devon, PL19 8RJ Tel: (01822) 618717 Fax: (01822) 618717 E-mail: enquire@finders-seekers.co.uk

Flexioffices, 46 Manchester Street, London, W1U 7LS Tel: (020) 7831 2201 Fax: (020) 7831 1753 E-mail: search@flexioffices.com

Fred A Lodge & Sons Ltd, Stonebridge Mills, Stonebridge Lane, Leeds, LS12 4QL Tel: 0113-263 7341 Fax: 0113-263 7341

George Moss & Son Ltd, Unit C4, 1 Centre Court, Moss Industrial Estate, Leigh, Lancashire, WN7 3PT Tel: (01942) 671231 Fax: (01942) 683768 E-mail: sales@georgemoss.co.uk

▶ GO HAVEN LTD, 72A WESTBOURNE RD, HUDDERSFIELD, HD1 4LE Tel: 01484 544300 E-mail: enquire@gohaven.com

Campbell Gordon, 50 Queens Road, Reading, RG1 4HU Tel: 0118-959 7555 Fax: 0118-959 7550 E-mail: info@campbellgordon.co.uk

▶ Go-to-Spain, Amberley, Cotswold Close, Tredington, Shipston-on-Stour, Warwickshire, CV36 4NR Tel: (01608) 661801 E-mail: sales@go-to-spain.com

Houghton Grear, 7 Harley Street, London, W1G 9QD Tel: (020) 7580 9357 Fax: (020) 7580 4716

Hurst Warne Ltd, 323 Kingston Road, Leatherhead, Surrey, KT22 7TU Tel: (01372) 360190 Fax: (01372) 360211 E-mail: enquiries@hurstwarne.co.uk

▶ Isherwoods, 12 Imperial Square, Cheltenham, Gloucestershire, GL50 1QB Tel: (01242) 226999 Fax: (01242) 227444

J P C Commercial Services Ltd, Elm Tree Farm, Cedar Street, Chesterfield, Derbyshire, S43 2LF Tel: (01246) 280123 Fax: (01246) 477421 E-mail: acom1jpc@aol.com

John De Stefano & Co. Ltd, 13 Stratford Place, London, W1C 1BD Tel: (020) 7493 9999 Fax: (020) 7493 1200

▶ Kingsley Commercial, Chenil House, 181-183 Kings Road, London, SW3 5EB Tel: (020) 7352 3130 Fax: (020) 7352 5111 E-mail: sales@kingsleycommercial.co.uk

Kitchen La Frenais Morgan, 1 Tenterden Street, London, W1S 1TA Tel: (020) 7317 3700 Fax: (020) 7317 3701 E-mail: info@klmproperty.co.uk

Knight Frank Property Company, Knight Frank 20 Hanover Square, London, W1S 1HZ Tel: (020) 7408 1100 Fax: (020) 7493 4114 E-mail: farms.estates@knightfrank.com

Koopmans Surveyors, 34 Watling Street, Radlett, Hertfordshire, WD7 7NN Tel: (01923) 853749 Fax: (01923) 854493 E-mail: property@koopmans.co.uk

Lambert Smith Hampton, 79 Mosley Street, Manchester, M2 3LQ Tel: 0161-228 6411 Fax: 0161-228 7354 E-mail: manchester@lsh.co.uk

Lambert Smith Hampton Group Ltd, Regent Arcade House, 19-25 Argyle Street, London, W1F 7TS Tel: (020) 7494 4000 Fax: (020) 7414 0866 E-mail: westend@lsh.co.uk

Maconochies of Kilmarnock Ltd, 22-26 Campbell Street, Riccarton, Kilmarnock, Ayrshire, KA1 4HW Tel: (01563) 522681 Fax: (01563) 541297

▶ National Homebuyers, Stirling House, 1 20 Victoria Way, Burgess Hill, West Sussex, RH15 9NF Tel: (01444) 257111 Fax: (01444) 257333 E-mail: info@nationalhomebuyers.co.uk

Page & Wells, 52-54 Kings Street, Maidstone, Kent, ME14 1DB Tel: (01622) 756703 Fax: (01622) 671351 E-mail: sales@page-wells.co.uk

Penn Studios, Penn Farm Studios, Harston Road, Haslingfield, Cambridge, CB23 1JZ Tel: (01487) 773282

▶ Propertystorm, The Coach House, Edstone, Wootton Wawen, Henley-in-Arden, West Midlands, B95 6DD Tel: (07971) 095664 E-mail: propertystorm@btinternet.com

▶ Read Maurice Residential, 48 Andover Road, Cheltenham, Gloucestershire, GL50 2TL Tel: (01242) 241122 Fax: (01242) 243377 E-mail: post@readmorris.co.uk

Michael Rogers, 2 Friars Lane, Richmond, Surrey, TW9 1NL Tel: (020) 8332 7788 Fax: (020) 8332 7799 E-mail: niall.christian@michaelrogers.co.uk

▶ Royston Estate Agents, 118-120 Glenthorne Road, London, W6 0LP Tel: (020) 8563 7100 Fax: (020) 8563 7045 E-mail: kellysearch.com@roystonw6.co.uk

Scott Burridge Chick, Daniell House, 26 Falmouth Road, Truro, Cornwall, TR1 2HX Tel: (01872) 277397 Fax: (01872) 223342 E-mail: enq@sbcproperty.com

▶ South West Tourism, Tourism House Pynes Hill, Rydon Lane, Exeter, EX2 5WT Tel: (01392) 360050 Fax: (01392) 445112 E-mail: info@swtourism.co.uk

Tallett Charter Surveyors, 18 Long Ashton Road, Long Ashton, Bristol, BS41 9LD Tel: (01275) 540200 Fax: (01275) 540203 E-mail: tallett@tallett.co.uk

Clive Willoughby & Associates, 4 New Burlington Place, London, W1S 2HS Tel: (020) 7437 6171 Fax: (020) 7437 0846 E-mail: clive.willoughby@fifieldglyn.com

▶ www.hotelstobuy.co.uk, 46 Trefusis Road, Falmouth, Cornwall, TR11 4QQ Tel: 01326 313295 E-mail: admin@hotelstobuy.co.uk

COMMERCIAL FUEL DISPENSING PUMPS

C I Automation Ltd, Shaftesbury Centre, Percy Street, Swindon, SN2 2AZ Tel: (01793) 530063 Fax: (01793) 530064

COMMERCIAL GARAGE DOORS

▶ Kay Garage Doors, Unit 1, Phoenix Industrial Estate, Kerse Road, Stirling, FK7 7SG Tel: (01786) 474709 Fax: (01786) 451540 E-mail: info@kaygaragedoors.co.uk

COMMERCIAL GAS SUPPLIERS

Powergen plc, Westwood Way, Westwood Business Park, Coventry, CV4 8LG Tel: (024) 7642 4000 Fax: (024) 7642 5432 E-mail: domestic@powergen.co.uk

Powergen plc, Colliers Way, Nottingham, NG8 6AL Tel: (0870) 4191539 Fax: 0115-995 6738 E-mail: sales@eme.co.uk

▶ Switch2save.Co.Uk, 171 Robin Hood Lane, Birmingham, B28 0JE Tel: 0121-778 2722 Fax: (0871) 2427376 E-mail: savemoney@switch2save.co.uk

▶ T M S Gas Services, 18 Marshall Close, Spixworth, Norwich, NR10 3NX Tel: (01603) 710500

COMMERCIAL GREENHOUSE ESTATE AGENTS

▶ Angel Property Services, Silton Road, Bourton, Gillingham, Dorset, SP8 5DD Tel: (08712) 715128 E-mail: rennie@angelpropertyservices.net

COMMERCIAL HEATERS

Johnson & Starley Ltd, Brackmills Indust Estate, Brackmills Industrial Estate, Northampton, NN4 7HR Tel: (01604) 762881 Fax: (01604) 767408 E-mail: sales@johnsonandstarley.co.uk

Wickes Building Supplies Ltd, Newcraighall Road, Edinburgh, EH15 3HS Tel: 0131-669 6161 Fax: 0131-669 4366

COMMERCIAL MUSIC COMPOSING

▶ Beat Suite, Studio 1, 5-7 Pink Lane, Newcastle upon Tyne, NE1 5DW Tel: 0191-221 2400 Fax: 0191-261 5746 E-mail: info@beatsuite.com

▶ Digital Media Music, 61 Birkbeck Road, Mill Hill, London, NW7 4BP Tel: 020881 67775 E-mail: info@digitalmediamusic.co.uk

Elite, Forest Row, East Sussex, RH18 5ES Tel: (01342) 822292 E-mail: info@elitespage.co.uk

▶ Gospel Frontiers Ltd, 8 Balgowan Road, Beckenham, Kent, BR3 4HJ Tel: (020) 8650 9607 E-mail: ian@gospelfrontiers.co.uk

▶ Orbital Productions, 38 Burnfoot Road, Hawick, Roxburghshire, TD9 8EN Tel: (01450) 378212 E-mail: sg1@orbital-productions.com

▶ SinCity Records UK, Polaris Studio's, Milestone Cottage, 61 London Road, Calne, Wiltshire, SN11 0AA Tel: 01249 816026 Fax: 01249 816026 E-mail: sincity@pobox.com

▶ Sunrise Music Group, 11 Redstock Close, Westhoughton, Bolton, BL5 3UX Tel: 01942-810 820 E-mail: sales@sunrisemusicgroup.co.uk

▶ The Theme Team Production Music, The Theme Team, 1 Leigh Rd, Gravesend, Kent, DA11 7PS Tel: (01474) 320460 E-mail: info@thethemeteam.biz

COMMERCIAL OR INDUSTRIAL FLUE SYSTEMS

Hamworthy Heating Ltd, Shady Lane, Birmingham, B44 9ER Tel: 0121-360 7000 Fax: 0121-325 2309 E-mail: hayley.miller@hamworthy-heating.com

Hamworthy Heating Ltd, Fleets Corner, Poole, Dorset, BH17 0HH Tel: (01202) 662500 Fax: (01202) 662550 E-mail: sales@hamworthy-heating.com

Sigram Flue Systems, Unit 8 Shepley Industrial Estate South, Audenshaw, Manchester, M34 5DW Tel: 0161-320 6515 Fax: 0161-320 6515 E-mail: sales@sigram.co.uk

COMMERCIAL OR INDUSTRIAL PHOTOGRAPHERS

A M Photographic, St. Johns Innovation Centre, Cowley Road, Cambridge, CB4 0WS Tel: (0870) 1635192 E-mail: tony@amphotographic.co.uk

A P R Photography Ltd, Robeson Way, Gatley, Manchester, M22 4SX Tel: (01625) 610999 Fax: (01625) 610055 E-mail: tim@aprphoto.co.uk

Accolade Photography, Cannybrow Barn, Gatebeck, Kendal, Cumbria, LA8 0HS Tel: (01539) 567030 Fax: (01539) 567030 E-mail: sales@thebestphotography.co.uk

Advertising Design & Photography, 16-20 Little Patrick Street, Belfast, BT15 1BA Tel: (028) 9032 2605 Fax: (028) 9023 1235 E-mail: adesphot@yahoo.co.uk

Aerial Close-Up Ltd, 70 Northampton Road, Denton, Northampton, NN7 1DL Tel: (01604) 899499 Fax: (08708) 318491 E-mail: info@aerialcloseup.com

Airfotos Ltd, 37 Belsay Gardens, Newcastle upon Tyne, NE3 2AU Tel: 0191-285 4625 Fax: 0191-285 4625

▶ Alba Photography, 54 Milndavie Crescent, Strathblane, Glasgow, G63 9DF Tel: (01360) 770349

▶ Alex Tomlinson Photography, Alington House, Ledbury Road, Ross-on-Wye, Herefordshire, HR9 7BG Tel: 01989 563430 E-mail: enquiry@the-photographer.eclipse.co.uk

▶ ALPS Mobile & Studio photography, Lee Lane, Pinkneys Green, Maidenhead, Berkshire, SL6 Tel: 07779 572360 E-mail: apage@e-work.co.uk

Alvey & Towers, Unit 9, Enterprise House, Coalville, Leicestershire, LE67 3LA Tel: (01530) 450011 Fax: (01530) 450011 E-mail: office@alveyandtowers.com

John Ash Photography Ltd, Church Farm, Ashchurch Road, Ashchurch, Tewkesbury, Gloucestershire, GL20 8JU Tel: (01684) 291200 Fax: (01684) 291201 E-mail: sales@ash-photography.com

Baileys Of Bromsgrove Ltd, 12a St. John Street, Bromsgrove, Worcestershire, B61 8QY Tel: (01527) 873128 Fax: (01527) 873128 E-mail: sales@baileyphotographic.com

Beedle & Cooper Photograpy, Orchard Studio, 8 Beech Lane, Kislingbury, Northampton, NN7 4AL Tel: (01604) 832555 E-mail: beedle.cooper@btinternet.com

Blackwater Photographic Co., 69 Fleet Road, Fleet, Hampshire, GU51 3PJ Tel: (01252) 613243 Fax: (01252) 811223 E-mail: keithe@patrol.i-way.co.uk

Burton Photography, 19 Britton Street, Clerkenwell, London, EC1M 5NQ Tel: (020) 7253 6111 Fax: (020) 7253 6444 E-mail: info@burtonphoto.co.uk

C G S Photographers, 102 Ewell By-Pass, Epsom, Surrey, KT17 2PP Tel: (020) 8394 0010 Fax: (020) 8393 0372 E-mail: info@cgs-photographers.co.uk

▶ Captured Image Photography, 7 Dunstans Croft, Mayfield, East Sussex, TN20 6UH Tel: 01435 874894 E-mail: andy@capturedimagephotography.co.uk

Ceejay Photographic, 290 Ashby High Street, Scunthorpe, South Humberside, DN16 2RX Tel: (01724) 280510 Fax: (01724) 289966 E-mail: sales@ceejaysystems.com

Centremark Design Ltd, 143 New London Road, Chelmsford, CM2 0QT Tel: (01245) 345143 Fax: (01245) 345144 E-mail: info@centremark-design.co.uk

Charlesworth & Valentine, 34 Bridgnorth Road, Aqueduct Village, Telford, Shropshire, TF3 1BZ Tel: (01952) 592012 Fax: (01952) 270121

Clarrie Jackson Photography, 18 Whites Road, Cleethorpes, South Humberside, DN35 8RP Tel: (01472) 696979

Paul Cordwell Photography Ltd, Unit 3 Century Park, Garrison Lane, Birmingham, B9 4NZ Tel: (07831) 416477 E-mail: paul@paulcordwell.com

Countrywide Photographic, 116 Ellingham Industrial Centre, Ellingham Way, Ashford, Kent, TN23 6LZ Tel: (01233) 666868 Fax: E-mail: info@countrywidephotographic.co.uk

Alan Curtis Photography, 34 Church Hill, Belbroughton, Stourbridge, West Midlands, DY9 0DT Tel: (01562) 731222 Fax: (01299) 250122 E-mail: alancurtinphoto@btconnect.com

David John Houlston, 62 Haygate Drive, Wellington, Telford, Shropshire, TF1 2BZ Tel: (01952) 244905 Fax: (01952) 244905 E-mail: enquiries@houlstonphotography.co.uk

David Lee Photography, George Street, Barton-upon-Humber, South Humberside, DN18 5ES Tel: (01652) 632451 Fax: (01652) 637481 E-mail: enquiries@davidleephotography.co.uk

Alan Dench Photography, Carringtons, Pond Hall Road, Ipswich, IP7 5PQ Tel: (01473) 828343 Fax: (01473) 828864

Ebdon Studios, 276 Broadway, Bexleyheath, Kent, DA6 8BE Tel: (020) 8303 1052 E-mail: sales@ebdon.co.uk

▶ Elvele Images Ltd, 13 Westland Road, Kirk Ella, Hull, HU10 7PH Tel: (01482) 650674 E-mail: info@elvele.com

▶ Emphasis Photography, 517 Hagley Road, Birmingham, B66 4AX Tel: 0121-558 8733 Fax: 0121-558 8755 E-mail: richard@emphasis.biz

▶ Ewing & Reeson, 38 Broadway, St. Ives, Cambridgeshire, PE27 5BN Tel: (01480) 469295 Fax: (01480) 495367 E-mail: sales@commercial-photography.co.uk

Five Valleys Photography, Unit 4 Salmon Springs TDG Estate, Cheltenham Road, Stroud, Gloucestershire, GL6 6NU Tel: (01453) 766660 Fax: (01453) 766388 E-mail: info@fivevalleys.co.uk

Foto Theme Digital, 70 Wells Street, London, W1T 3QD Tel: (020) 7436 7998 Fax: (020) 7255 1213E-mail: info@fotothemedigital.co.uk

G Hooper, 6 Sunnyside Gardens, Kidderminster, Worcestershire, DY11 5JW Tel: (01562) 752290 E-mail: sales@garryhooper.com

Geoffrey Photographers, 58 St. Augustine Avenue, Grimsby, South Humberside, DN32 0LD Tel: (01472) 750033 Fax: (01472) 593829E-mail: stephen.almond@ntlworld.com

▶ Glen Pitt-Pladdy, Photographer, The Penthouse, 11 Alexandra Road, Reading, RG1 5PE Tel: 0789 9915864

▶ GMB Photography, 127a High Street, Barkingside, Ilford, Essex, IG6 2AR Tel: 020 8551 6885 E-mail: info@gmbphotography.co.uk

▶ Gordon Fozard, 3 Knowsley Terrace, Woodside Road, Chiddingfold, Godalming, Surrey, GU8 4QU Tel: 01428 682911 E-mail: studio@southphotography.co.uk

Gregson Studio, 42 Bury Close, Gosport, Hampshire, PO12 3TU Tel: (023) 9252 0808 E-mail: m.sowdon@fsbdial.co.uk

Grosvenor Northampton Ltd, Unit D Stonecircle Road, Round Spinney, Northampton, NN3 8RF Tel: (01604) 670673 Fax: (01604) 648438

H Tempest Ltd, The Colour Laboratory, Lelant, St. Ives, Cornwall, TR26 3HU Tel: (01736) 752411 Fax: (01736) 751463

Mark Harwood Photographic Studio, 12 Waterside, 44-48 Wharf Rd, London, N1 7SF Tel: (020) 7490 8787 Fax: (020) 7490 1009 E-mail: mark.harwood@appleonline.net

COMMERCIAL OR INDUSTRIAL PHOTOGRAPHERS – *continued*

Hovercam Ltd, White House Drakes View, Staddon Heights, Plymouth, PL9 9SP Tel: (01752) 482711 Fax: (01752) 482744 E-mail: info@hovercam.com

▶ Image 2 Ltd, 68 Nightingale Road, Rickmansworth, Hertfordshire, WD3 7BT Tel: (01923) 775098 Fax: (01923) 896679 E-mail: prrk@image2photo.co.uk

The Image Depot Ltd, The Old Exchange, Wellington Court, Belper, Derbyshire, DE56 1UP Tel: (01773) 827610 Fax: (01773) 826630 E-mail: adrianheapy@adrianheapy.co.uk

▶ In Camera Photography, 11 Hambleton Terrace, Knaresborough, North Yorkshire, HG5 0DD Tel: (01423) 546322 E-mail: enquiries@incameraphotography.com

Indusfoto Ltd, 39-41 Margravine Road, London, W6 8LL Tel: (020) 7385 7618 Fax: (020) 7381 0047 E-mail: mark@indusfoto.co.uk

Tony Isbitt Photography, 107 Burnt Ash Lane, Bromley, BR1 5AB Tel: (020) 8460 5710 Fax: (020) 8460 5710 E-mail: info@tonyisbittphotography.co.uk

J L Allwork Ltd, 177 High Street, Tonbridge, Kent, TN9 1BX Tel: (01732) 352160 Fax: (01732) 352160 E-mail: allwork@lineone.net

Jacopo Pandolfi Photography, 145-157, St John Street, London, EC1V 4PY Tel: 07946 860678 E-mail: info@jacopopandolfi.com

▶ Jeremy Rendell Photography, Florin Court, 8 Dock Street, London, E1 8JR Tel: 07860 277411 E-mail: jeremy.rendell@btbconnect.com

John Benton Harris, 25 Morland Avenue, Croydon, CR0 6EA Tel: (020) 8656 0055 Fax: (020) 8656 0055

The John Mills Group, 11 Hope Street, Liverpool, L1 9BJ Tel: 0151-709 9822 Fax: 0151-709 6585 E-mail: sales@johnmillsgroup.com

Knights Photographers, 51 Bear Street, Barnstaple, Devon, EX32 7DB Tel: (01271) 371776

Paul Lapsley Photography Ltd, 3-4 25 Somers Road, Rugby, Warwickshire, CV22 7DG Tel: (01788) 561511 Fax: (01788) 540781 E-mail: plpphoto@btconnect.com

J.C. Lawrence & Sons, 44 Elmhurst Road, Gosport, Hampshire, PO12 1PQ Tel: (023) 9258 1445

Leonard E Goode Ltd, 594 College Road, Kingstanding, Birmingham, B44 0HU Tel: 0121-373 7581 Fax: 0121-373 7585 E-mail: sales@legoode.co.uk

Lighthouse Images, 2 Fords Court Cottages, Budlake, Exeter, EX5 3JS Tel: (01392) 882345 Fax: (01392) 882858

Linear Photographics Ltd, Unit 17 Magreal Industrial Estate, Freeth Street, Ladywood, Birmingham, B16 0QZ Tel: (0121) 454 5864

Locker Philip Photographic Design Studios Ltd, 132 Bradford Street, Farnworth, Bolton, BL4 9JY Tel: (01204) 707725 Fax: (01204) 792575 E-mail: info@photographicdesign.com

M G P Photography Ltd, 36-37 Featherstone St, London, EC1Y 8QZ Tel: (020) 7608 1066 Fax: (020) 7336 8338

M & M Studios, Millers Yard, Hayseech Road, Halesowen, West Midlands, B63 3PD Tel: 0121-501 3868 Fax: 0121-585 5377

M Michaels, 69 St. Marks Road, London, W10 6JG Tel: (020) 8964 5555 Fax: (020) 8964 5929

▶ M&N Photography, Studio 25 @ Martello Street, London Fields, London, UK, E8 3PE Tel: (020) 7241 2816 E-mail: info@mn-photo.co.uk

Steve Macare Photography, 59 Dragon Avenue, Harrogate, North Yorkshire, HG1 5DS Tel: (01423) 561809 Fax: (01423) 561809 E-mail: stevemacare@ntlworld.com

Memory Lane Productions, Shalford, Ricksons Lane, West Horsley, Leatherhead, Surrey, KT24 6HU Tel: (01483) 284409 E-mail: maclanep56@btinternet.com

Mid Cornwall Photographic, 11 Victoria Road, St. Austell, Cornwall, PL25 4QF Tel: (01726) 72695 Fax: (01726) 72695 E-mail: mc.photographic@btconnect.com

Robert Montgomery & Partners, 3 Junction Mews, London, W2 1PN Tel: (020) 7439 1877 Fax: (020) 7434 1144 E-mail: info@creativetalentlimited.com

Moore David Photography, Missions House, Biddulph Common Road, Biddulph, Stoke-on-Trent, ST8 7SR Tel: (01782) 515588 E-mail: david@moorephoto.co.uk

Noble Paul Photographic, Victoria Road, Unit 4, Burgess Hill, West Sussex, RH15 9LH Tel: (01444) 232367 E-mail: info@pnoblephoto.net

Octopus Insight, 5 Windsor Works, Windsor Street, Beeston, Nottingham, NG9 2BW Tel: 0115-917 2222 Fax: 0115-917 2211 E-mail: photography@octopusinsight.com

P I C Photos, 9 Park Lane, Harefield, Uxbridge, Middlesex, UB9 6BJ Tel: (01895) 822100 Fax: (01895) 822500 E-mail: scott_picphotos@yahoo.com

▶ Peter Cousins, 14 Dryden Court, Clinton Park, Tattershall, Lincoln, LN4 4PR Tel: 01526 345174 E-mail: portraitsrusltd@aol.com

▶ Philip Chambers, 17 Brockenhurst Close, Woking, Surrey, GU21 4DS Tel: (01483) 765618 Fax: (01483) 765618 E-mail: philpchambers@philipchambers.f9.co.uk

Photo Centre, Bridge Street, Berwick-upon-Tweed, TD15 1ES Tel: (01289) 306434 Fax: (01289) 303400

Photo Shot Holding, 29-31 Saffron Hill, London, EC1N 8SW Tel: (020) 7421 6004 Fax: (020) 7421 6006 E-mail: colin@uppa.co.uk

Photoflex Ltd, 36 Spindus Road, Liverpool, L24 1YA Tel: (07860) 836145 Fax: 0151-207 2783 E-mail: mail@photoflex.co.uk

▶ Photopia Photography, 4, Halifax Road,, Hove Edge, Brighouse, West Yorkshire, HD6 2EN Tel: 07795 313032 E-mail: becca@photopiaphotography.co.uk

Photovisual, 315 London Road, Westcliff-On-Sea, Essex, SS0 7BX Tel: (01702) 348296 Fax: (01702) 346991 E-mail: photography@photo-visual.com

Picture Workshop, 45 Highgate Place, Highgate, Birmingham, B12 0DD Tel: 0121-440 2342 Fax: 0121-440 2844 E-mail: sales@pictureworkshop.co.uk

▶ Pixeleyes Photography, 3rd floor, 21 perseverance works, 38 kingsland road, London, London, E2 8DA Tel: 020 7739 7239 Fax: 020 7739 7377 E-mail: studio@pixeleyesphotography.co.uk

Professional Images, 12 Swindon Road, Highworth, Swindon, SN6 7SL Tel: (01793) 766379 Fax: (01793) 763335 E-mail: info@professional-images.com

Profile Photography, 27 Palmerston Boulevard, Leicester, LE2 3YS Tel: 0116-288 3506

Quick Print Photographic Services Ltd, The Studios, Chartham Rd, South Norwood, London, SE25 4HW Tel: (020) 8654 7068 Fax: (020) 8655 3640

Realistic Digital Graphics, Stafford Studios, 129a Stafford Road, Wallington, Surrey, SM6 9BN Tel: (020) 8669 4900 Fax: (020) 8773 0129 E-mail: info@realistic-digital.com

Reeve Photography, Rectory Farm, 1 Brewery Road, Pampisford, Cambridge, CB22 3EN Tel: (01223) 832200 Fax: (01223) 832242 E-mail: pix@reevephotography.co.uk

▶ Roger Askew, 14 Winterborne Road, Abingdon, Oxfordshire, OX14 1AJ Tel: (07971) 404571 E-mail: roger@rogeraskewphotography.co.uk

▶ Shannon Fine Art Photography, Norseman Studio Unit 8, Tedco Business Centre, Viking Industrial Park, Jarrow, Tyne & Wear, NE32 3DT Tel: 0191-428 3517

Ken Shelton Photography, 10 New Walk Terrace, Fishergate, York, YO10 4BG Tel: (01904) 630112 E-mail: ken@nwt10.demon.co.uk

Sidney Darby, 4 Garman Close, Birmingham, B43 6NB Tel: 0121-357 2001 Fax: 0121-358 3011 E-mail: tony@sidneydarbyphotography.co.uk

Sidney Harris Photography, 4 Brookland Close, London, NW11 6DJ Tel: (020) 8458 0137 Fax: (020) 8455 6220

Skyscene, Flat 5 Napier Court, Gefle Close, Bristol, BS1 6XY Tel: 0117-929 0735 Fax: 0117-914 3775 E-mail: info@skyscene.co.uk

Peter Smith Photography, George House, Derwent Road, York Road Business Park, Malton, North Yorkshire, YO17 6YB Tel: (0870) 2201249 Fax: (01653) 600314 E-mail: peter@petersmith.com

Spectrum Photos, Belgrave Gate, Leicester, LE1 3GQ Tel: 0116-251 9478 Fax: 0116-251 9478 E-mail: spectrumphoto@virginnet.co.uk

Stephenson & Johnson Ltd, Malaga House, Pink Bank Lane, Manchester, M12 5GH Tel: 0161-223 0011 Fax: 0161-223 0404

Steve Downer Photography & Video, The Gatehouse, High Street, Ratley, Banbury, Oxfordshire, OX15 6DT Tel: (01295) 670836 Fax: (01295) 670836 E-mail: downerfilm@aol.com

Stewart Downie Sutton Coldfield, 87 Jockey Road, Sutton Coldfield, West Midlands, B73 5PH Tel: 0121-354 8610 Fax: 0121-681 2235E-mail: stewartdownie@blueyonder.co.uk

Studio Argent Ltd, School Lane, Knowsley, Prescot, Merseyside, L34 9EN Tel: 0151-548 7722 Fax: 0151-549 1713 E-mail: sales@studioargent.co.uk

Studio North, 41 Cecil Street, Carlisle, CA1 1NS Tel: (01228) 533344 E-mail: sales@studionorthphotographers.co.uk

Sue & John Jorgensen, 9 Canham Road, London, W3 7SR Tel: (020) 8749 6306 Fax: (020) 8749 6754

Swaine Photographic, 139 Pinks Hill, Swanley, Kent, BR8 8NP Tel: (0800) 9567310 Fax: (01474) 872154 E-mail: alanswaine@aol.com

Ron Taylor Studio, 152 North High Street, Musselburgh, Midlothian, EH21 6AR Tel: 0131-653 2700 Fax: 0131-653 2700 E-mail: rontaylor@easynet.co.uk

Time Ltd, 6 Brook St Mill, Brook Street, Macclesfield, Cheshire, SK11 7AW Tel: (01625) 615768 Fax: (01625) 614605 E-mail: ron@timescctv.co.uk

▶ Total Photography, 38 High Street, Brandon, Suffolk, IP27 0AQ Tel: (01842) 819570 Fax: (01842) 819570 E-mail: totalrobmcdonald@yahoo.co.uk

Visual Impact, Wakes End Farm, Wakes End, Eversholt, Milton Keynes, MK17 9FB Tel: (01525) 280518 E-mail: info@visualimpact.uk

Viva Imaging Ltd, Photographic House, Northgate, Nottingham, NG7 7BE Tel: 0115-978 4527 Fax: 0115-978 3791 E-mail: sales@vivaimaging.co.uk

W.G. Photo, Southdownview Road, Worthing, West Sussex, BN14 8NJ Tel: (01903) 200528 Fax: (01903) 200528 E-mail: mike@wgphoto.co.uk

Winpenny Photography, 3 Wesley Street, Otley, West Yorkshire, LS21 1AZ Tel: (01943) 462597 Fax: (01943) 850861 E-mail: webmaster@winpennyphoto.co.uk

Working Images, The Old Stables, Kingston House Estate, Kingston Bagpuize, Abingdon, Oxfordshire, OX13 5AX Tel: (07831) 843338 Fax: (01865) 375855 E-mail: chris@working-images.co.uk

David Yates Studio, 409 Hempshaw Lane, Offerton, Stockport, Cheshire, SK1 4QA Tel: 0161-476 0464 E-mail: davidyates409@aol.com

COMMERCIAL OR OFFICE ACOUSTIC TREATMENT

C E P Cladding Ltd, Wainwright Close, St. Leonards-On-Sea, East Sussex, TN38 9PP Tel: (01424) 852641 Fax: (01424) 852797 E-mail: claddings@cepgroup.co.uk

Trim Acoustics, Unit 38 Redburn Industrial Estate, Woodall Road, Enfield, Middlesex, EN3 4LE Tel: (020) 8443 0099 Fax: (020) 8443 1919 E-mail: sales@trimacoustics.co.uk

COMMERCIAL PAINTING CONTRACTORS

Chidlow Decorators, Unit 33 Business Resource Centre, Admin Road, Knowsley Industrial Park, Liverpool, L33 7TX Tel: 0151-546 7754 Fax: 0151-546 7754 E-mail: admin@chidlowdecorators.co.uk

▶ D N Decorations, 22 Germander Way, Bicester, Oxfordshire, OX26 3WB Tel: (0800) 0192733 Fax: (0870) 7575045 E-mail: sales@dndltd.co.uk

▶ DK Property Maintenance, 28 Springbourne Court, Beckenham, Kent, BR3 5ED Tel: 020 84606857 Fax: 0845 3309318 E-mail: dkpm@btconnect.com

▶ Fairway Decorating Services Limited, Wilson Business Park, Monsall Road, Newton Heath, Manchester, M40 8WN Tel: 0161 205 8000 Fax: 0160 205 8010 E-mail: admin@fairway-decorating.com

▶ George Jones & Son Ltd, 9 Sheil Road, Liverpool, L6 3AA Tel: 0151-263 2348 Fax: 0151-264 0100 E-mail: mail@georgejones.org.uk

▶ John Hill Building Contractor, 11 Goslipgate, Pickering, North Yorkshire, YO18 8DQ Tel: (07890) 942046 Fax: (01751) 477975 E-mail: info@countrywidedecorators.co.uk

▶ Michael Nutt, 80 College Road, Sittingbourne, Kent, ME10 1LD Tel: (07970) 956264 E-mail: michaelks@michaelnutt.com

COMMERCIAL PROPERTY INSURANCE

Axa Insurance, 1 Aldgate, London, EC3N 1RE Tel: (020) 7702 3109 Fax: (020) 7369 3909

Blue Moon Insurance, Church Street, Wellingborough, Northamptonshire, NN8 4PD Tel: (01933) 303020 Fax: (01933) 303021 E-mail: sales@bluemooninsurance.co.uk

▶ Bruce Stevenson Risk Management, 38-40 New City Road, Glasgow, G4 9JT Tel: 0141 353 3539 Fax: 0141 353 3888 E-mail: mark.costello@brucestevenson.co.uk

Chapman Stevens, 21 Wintersells Road, Byfleet, West Byfleet, Surrey, KT14 7LF Tel: (01932) 334140 Fax: (01932) 351238

Collier Insurance, 146 Bellegrove Road, Welling, Kent, DA16 3QR Tel: (020) 8303 4761 Fax: (020) 8301 6021 E-mail: info@collierinsurance.co.uk

▶ Eqi Insurance, 11a The Cross, Lymm, Cheshire, WA13 0HR Tel: 01925 751758 Fax: 01925 751538 E-mail: greg@eqi-insurance.co.uk

Friends Provident, UK House, Castle Street, Salisbury, SP1 3SH Tel: (0870) 6071352 Fax: (0870) 5314151

Low Quote Limited, 2a Alton House Office Park, Gatehouse Way, Gatehouse Industrial Area, Aylesbury, Bucks, HP19 8YF Tel: (07834) 542976 E-mail: admin@low-quote.net

M M A Insurance plc, 2 Norman Place, Reading, RG1 8DA Tel: 0118-955 2222 Fax: 0118-955 2211 E-mail: info@mma-insurance.com

Milne Friend & Partners, Suite 2-5 Renslade House, Bonhay Road, Exeter, EX4 3AY Tel: (01392) 430097 Fax: (01392) 218696 E-mail: rodmilne@milnefriend.co.uk

N I G, Crown House, 145 City Road, London, EC1V 1LP Tel: (020) 7656 6000 Fax: (020) 7251 0345 E-mail: marion.chan@nig-uk.com

▶ Property Repair Ltd, 52 Montrose Terrace, Edinburgh, EH7 5DL Tel: 0131-478 3391 Fax: 0131 4777553 E-mail: info@propertyrepairltd.co.uk

Royal & Sun Alliance Insurance P.L.C., Leadenhall Court, 1 Leadenhall St, London, EC3V 1PP Tel: (020) 7283 9000 Fax: (020) 7337 5200 E-mail: piumail@uk.royalsun.com

▶ Stride Ltd, The Briars, Waterberry Drive, Waterlooville, Hampshire, PO7 7YH Tel: (023) 9224 8790 Fax: (023) 9224 8799 E-mail: info@stride.co.uk

T & R Direct, 275 Ashley Road, Poole, Dorset, BH14 9DS Tel: (01202) 712800 Fax: (01202) 739347 E-mail: Lee@trdirect.co.uk

COMMERCIAL PROPERTY MAINTENANCE

▶ 50plus Handyman, 11 Sycamore Dene, Chesham, Buckinghamshire, HP5 3JT Tel: (0845) 2250495 Fax: (01494) 791609 E-mail: enquiries@the50plus.co.uk

▶ Anscombe Property Maintenance, 8 Leybourne Parade, Brighton, BN2 4LW Tel: (01273) 693844 Fax: 01273 693844 E-mail: info@anscombepropertymaintenance.co.uk

▶ Associated Securities, Unit 14 15, Cam Square, Wilbury Way, Hitchin, Hertfordshire, SG4 0TZ Tel: (01462) 421188 Fax: 01462 421188 E-mail: associatedsecurities@btconnect.com

▶ B & R Maintenance, 140 Harport Road, Redditch, Worcestershire, B98 7PD Tel: (01527) 460344 E-mail: brmaintenance@hotmail.co.uk

▶ Blundeston Property Maintenance, 61 Lakeside Rise, Blundeston, Lowestoft, Suffolk, NR32 5BD Tel: (07887) 604133 E-mail: philip.hannant@btinternet.com

P.F. Burridge & Sons Ltd, Units 8 & 9, Wesley Way, Benton Square Industrial Estate, Newcastle Upon Tyne, NE12 9TA Tel: 0191-266 5332 Fax: 0191-266 9250 E-mail: info@pfburridge.co.uk

C & C Property Consultants, 145-157 St. John Street, London, EC1V 4PY Tel: (0845) 0538867 Fax: (0707) 5209515 E-mail: pmsgwentltd@yahoo.com

▶ Chiltern Handyman Service, 123 Waterside,, Chesham, Buckinghamshire, HP5 1PE Tel: 07958 967549 E-mail: mike@chilternhandyman.com

▶ Complete Cladding Co., 13 Roundmoor Drive, Cheshunt, Waltham Cross, Hertfordshire, EN8 9HZ Tel: (01992) 622299 Fax: 01992 622299 E-mail: wayne@thecompletecladdingcompany.com

▶ Inside Out Property Maintenance & Landscaping, 25 Roundhill Way, Guildford, Surrey, GU2 8HJ Tel: 01483 459344 E-mail: insideoutpml@btinternet.com

▶ Kingsmede Ltd, 18 Warbreck Drive Bispham, Blackpool, FY2 9RZ Tel: (01253) 358827 E-mail: handymen@kingsmede.co.uk

Mitie Property Services North West Ltd, 1-3 Rough Hey Road, Grimsargh, Preston, PR2 5AR Tel: (01772) 703328 Fax: (01772) 793257 E-mail: propertyservices@mitie.co.uk

▶ Olimax Property Care Ltd, Olimax Property Care Limited,, Olimax House, 17 Donald Aldred Drive, Burley In Wharfedale, Ilkley, West Yorkshire, LS29 7SG Tel: 01943 865721 E-mail: info@olimax.net

▶ Paragon Professional Handyman, Unit 142, 22 Notting Hill Gate, London, W11 3JE Tel: 07835 478129 E-mail: freequote@paragonhandyman.co.uk

▶ Pipe Flow (Worthing) Ltd, 14 Third Avenue, Worthing, West Sussex, BN14 9NZ Tel: 01903 236714 E-mail: pipeflow@aol.com

▶ Three Counties Property Maintenance, Aylward Drive, Stevenage, Hertfordshire, SG2 8UR Tel: (01438) 748208 Fax: (01438) 759299 E-mail: info@threecountiespropertymaintenance.co.uk

▶ Toolbox Buddy, Regus House, George Curl Way, Southampton, SO18 2RZ Tel: 0800 023 4948 E-mail: enquiries@toolboxbuddy.co.uk

COMMERCIAL PROPERTY MANAGEMENT

▶ Anthony J Lewis & Co., 63 Leigh Hill Road, Cobham, Surrey, KT11 2HY Tel: (01932) 700063 Fax: (0870) 0940804 E-mail: service@anthonyjlewis.com

▶ Bache Treharne, Cornwall House, 31 Lionel Street, Birmingham, B3 1AP Tel: 0121-212 0005 Fax: 0121-212 0009 E-mail: sales@bachellp.com

Humphrey Bradley Ltd, Tingley Bar Industrial Estate, Tingley Mills, Morley, Leeds, LS27 0HE Tel: 0113-253 2581 Fax: 0113-238 0069

▶ Corniche Estates, Campbell Park, Fernhurst Road, Liphook, Hampshire, GU30 7LU Tel: (01428) 741999 Fax: (01428) 741005

▶ Grovelands Investments, Business Centre, 120 West Heath Road, London, NW3 7TU Tel: (020) 8731 9777 Fax: (020) 8731 9773 E-mail: info@grovelands.net

▶ MTEK Technical Services Ltd, 97 Charlton Road, Keynsham, Bristol, BS31 2JW Tel: 0117 330 6880 Fax: 0117 330 6142 E-mail: info@mtek-ts.co.uk

▶ Pearl & Coutts Ltd, 116 Clarence Road, London, E5 8JA Tel: (020) 7843 3788 Fax: (020) 7843 3799 E-mail: enquiries@pearl-coutts.co.uk

▶ RDA Building Solutions, 16 Enterprise Close, Warsash, Southampton, SO31 9BD Tel: 01489 572295 Fax: 01489 557634 E-mail: buildingsolutions@uk2.net

▶ Richard Perkins & Associates, The Barn, 2 Gunton Church Lane, Lowestoft, Suffolk, NR32 4LE Tel: (01502) 514738 Fax: (01502) 568674 E-mail: sales@richard-perkins.co.uk

▶ Steggles Larner, 25 Charing Cross, Norwich, NR2 4AX Tel: (01603) 724724 Fax: (01603) 724700

COMMERCIAL PROPERTY MORTGAGE BROKERS

▶ Personal Touch Leicester, 111 Belvior Road, Coalville, Leicestershire, LE67 3PH Tel: 0871 750 4330 Fax: 0871 750 4327 E-mail: enquires@ptimortgages.co.uk

COMMERCIAL REFRIGERATION MAINTENANCE

▶ Catex Catering Equipment (2002) Ltd, Unit 2 La Rue Le Gros, La Rue Des Pres Trading Estate, St. Saviour, Jersey, JE2 7QP Tel: (01534) 725582 Fax: (01534) 734314 E-mail: catex@jerseymail.co.uk

Centigrade Ltd, 9 Beverley Road, Tilehurst, Reading, RG31 5PT Tel: 0118-942 4939 Fax: 0118-942 4939

Chelmer Food Machinery, Stone Cottage Farm, Ipswich Road, Dedham, Colchester, CO7 6HS Tel: (01206) 321222 Fax: (01206) 321221 E-mail: sales@cfmsupplies.com

Curaim (UK) Ltd, Units 11-12 Cockridden Farm Industrial Estate, Brentwood Road, Herongate, Brentwood, Essex, CM13 3LH Tel: (01277) 811003 Fax: (01277) 811522 E-mail: curaim@aol.com

E J M Engineered Systems Ltd, Unit 1 Thornley Station Industrial Estate, Shotton Colliery, Durham, DH6 2QA Tel: (01429) 836161 Fax: (01429) 838034 E-mail: sales@ejmrefrigeration.co.uk

Ransome Group Services Ltd, Unit 5-6 Clopton Commercial Park, Clopton, Woodbridge, Suffolk, IP13 6QT Tel: (01473) 737731 Fax: (01473) 737398 E-mail: info@ransomeengineering.co.uk

COMMERCIAL RELOCATABLE BUILDINGS

Churchtown Ltd, 18A London Street, Southport, Merseyside, PR9 0UE Tel: (01704) 227826 Fax: (01704) 220247 E-mail: cabins@churchtown.co.uk

Derbybeech Ltd, Swinemoor Industrial Estate, Barmston Road, Beverley, North Humberside, HU17 0LA Tel: (01482) 868993 Fax: (01482) 872109 E-mail: info@derbybeech.com

G E Capital Modular Space, Langford Bridge, Cambridge Road, Langford, Biggleswade, Bedfordshire, SG18 9PL Tel: (01462) 701711 Fax: (01462) 701355

COMMERCIAL SECURITY SERVICES

▶ Alamo Security Services, Channelsea House, Canning Road, Stratford, London, E15 3ND Tel: (020) 8519 8866 Fax: (020) 8519 1191 E-mail: info@alamosecurity.co.uk

▶ Censor Security, Unit 342 Camberwell Business Centre, 99-103 Lomond Grove, London, SE5 7HN Tel: (0845) 2309816 Fax: (020) 7703 7243 E-mail: admin@censorgroup.co.uk

▶ Metro Security Services, Liverpool, L28 1YX Tel: (0845) 2269185 E-mail: metrosecurity@lycos.co.uk

COMMERCIAL SIGNS

Advasign, Gelli Industrial Estate, Gelli, Pentre, Mid Glamorgan, CF41 7UW Tel: (01443) 441112 E-mail: info@advasign.co.uk

Aldermaston Signs, Unit 24 Youngs Industrial Estate, Paices Hill, Aldermaston, Reading, RG7 4PW Tel: 0118-981 1170 Fax: 0118-981 7690 E-mail: info@aldermastonsigns.co.uk

Boston Signs & Displays, Unit 1, Spalding Road, Boston, Lincolnshire, PE21 8XL Tel: (01205) 363849 Fax: (01205) 367725 E-mail: boston_signs@yahoo.co.uk

Brighton Sign Co., Foredown House, 2-4 Foredown Drive, Portslade, Brighton, BN41 2BB Tel: (01273) 424900 Fax: (01273) 412006 E-mail: sales@brightonsigns.co.uk

City Signs, Darley Abbey Mills, Darley Abbey, Derby, DE22 1DZ Tel: (01332) 349772 Fax: (01332) 341164

City Signs Midlands Ltd, 34 Jasper Street, Stoke-on-Trent, ST1 3DA Tel: (01782) 281069 Fax: (01782) 281609 E-mail: citysignuk@netscapeonline.co.uk

Studio 127, 127 East Parade, Keighley, West Yorkshire, BD21 5HX Tel: (01535) 605148 Fax: (01535) 691521 E-mail: enquiries@studio127.co.uk

COMMERCIAL SPLIT SYSTEM PORTABLE AIR CONDITIONING (AC) UNITS

Airconaire Ltd, Unit 6 Deacon Trading Centre, Knight Road, Rochester, Kent, ME2 2AU Tel: (01634) 711264 Fax: (01634) 717100 E-mail: info@airconaire.co.uk

COMMERCIAL TURNKEY COMPUTER SYSTEMS

A Bet A Technology Ltd, Suite 9, 5 Lenten Street, Alton, Hampshire, GU34 1HG Tel: (01420) 549988 Fax: (01420) 546710 E-mail: info@abeta.co.uk

Coniston Computers Ltd, Hylton Park, Wessington Way, Sunderland, SR5 3NR Tel: 0191-516 0088 Fax: 0191-516 0476

Cube Conversions Ltd, 10 Ravenswood Road, Bristol, BS6 6BN Tel: 0117-946 7036 Fax: 0117-946 7036

COMMERCIAL VEHICLE BODY BUILDERS

A & A Bodies, Morbec Farm, Arterial Road, Wickford, Essex, SS12 9JF Tel: (01268) 590446 Fax: (01268) 414416

▶ A C Body Repairs, Unit 2 Yattendon Road, Upper Basildon, Reading, RG8 8NW Tel: (01491) 671800

A Lloyd & Son, Urban Road, Kirkby-in-Ashfield, Nottingham, NG17 8AP Tel: (01623) 752965 Fax: (01623) 752965

A Pile & Son Ltd, St Vincents Road, Dartford, DA1 1UU Tel: (01322) 224346 Fax: (01322) 277321

Abron Refinishers, Berryleys, Grange, Keith, Banffshire, AB55 6LN Tel: (01542) 870354 Fax: (01542) 870354 E-mail: info@abronrefinishers.co.uk

Ace Body Builders Ltd, Albert Road, Leeds, LS27 8LD Tel: 0113-253 2562 Fax: 0113-252 8673 E-mail: info@acebodybuilders.fsbusiness.co.uk

Adcliffe Drawdeal Ltd, Rempstone Road, Coleorton, Coalville, Leicestershire, LE67 8HR Tel: (01530) 222010 Fax: (01530) 222589 E-mail: sales@adcliffe.co.uk

▶ Advanced Body Repairs Ltd, Willow Road, Yaxley, Peterborough, PE7 3HT Tel: (01733) 246970 Fax: (01733) 246979 E-mail: matt.lynn@lawrencedavid.co.uk

Advanced Vehicle Builders Ltd, Bridge Street Industrial Estate, Bridge Street, Clay Cross, Chesterfield, Derbyshire, S45 9NU Tel: (01246) 250022 Fax: (01246) 250016 E-mail: info@minibus.co.uk

Agenda Vehicle Specialists, Drayton Garage, Barton Stacey, Winchester, Hampshire, SO21 3NF Tel: (01264) 720612 Fax: (01264) 720612

Aire Truck Bodies Ltd, Lennerton Lane, Sherburn in Elmet, Leeds, LS25 6JE Tel: (01977) 684541 Fax: (01977) 683351 E-mail: post@aire-trucks.com

Aire Truck Bodies Ltd Shipley, Wharncliffe Road, Shipley, West Yorkshire, BD18 2AW Tel: (01274) 585250 Fax: (01274) 532398 E-mail: shipley@aire-trucks.com

▶ Aldercote Ltd, The Embankment, Woodhouse Street, Hull, HU9 1RJ Tel: (01482) 222377 Fax: (020) 7681 3117 E-mail: sales@aldercote.com

Alloy Bodies Ltd, Jubilee Works, Clifton Street, Miles Platting, Manchester, M40 8HN Tel: 0161-205 7612 Fax: 0161-202 1917 E-mail: info@alloybodies.co.uk

Anglian Developments Ltd, School Lane, Neatishead, Norwich, NR12 8BU Tel: (01692) 630808 Fax: (01692) 631591 E-mail: angdev@paston.co.uk

Aztec Garage, 6-8 Emery Road, Bristol, BS4 5PF Tel: 0117-977 0314 Fax: 0117-977 4431 E-mail: myrtletree@holding4337.freeserve.co.uk

Batley Body Builders Ltd, Thomas St, Bradford Road, Batley, West Yorkshire, WF17 8PR Tel: (01924) 473602 Fax: (01924) 471161

▶ Bell Truck Sales, Macklin Avenue, Cowpen Lane Industrial Estate, Billingham, Cleveland, TS23 4BY Tel: (01642) 561333 Fax: (01642) 561999

Belle Coach Works, 26-28 Pinbush Road, Lowestoft, Suffolk, NR33 7NL Tel: (01502) 514001 Fax: (01502) 562217 E-mail: marton@shreevem.freeserve.co.uk

Bevan Motor Bodies Ltd, Blakeley Hall Road, Oldbury, West Midlands, B69 4ET Tel: 0121-533 2000 Fax: 0121-544 7783

Bexley Vehicle Bodies, Unit 14, Belvedere Industrial Estate, Fishers Way, Belvedere, Kent, DA17 6BS Tel: (020) 8311 6100 Fax: (020) 8311 6101

▶ Blackmore Hurrell, Rear of, 103 Wolseley Road, Plymouth, PL2 3BL Tel: (01752) 567056

Boalloy Ltd, Radnor Park Trading Estate, West Heath, Congleton, Cheshire, CW12 4QA Tel: (01260) 275155 Fax: (01260) 279696 E-mail: buying@boalloy.org

Bodycraft 2004, Unit A4, Worcester Trading Estate, Worcester, WR3 8HR Tel: (01905) 753631 Fax: (01905) 756790 E-mail: bobbycraft@tiscali.co.uk

▶ Bodyline, 18 Park Farm Industrial Estate, Evesham Road, Greet, Cheltenham, Gloucestershire, GL54 5BX Tel: (01242) 621257 Fax: (01242) 603781

Bowdery & Wilkinson, 7 Powke Lane Industrial Estate, Powke Lane, Rowley Regis, West Midlands, B65 0AH Tel: 0121-561 3448 Fax: 0121-561 3448

Boweld Engineering, Pentre Halkyn, Rhes-y-Cae, Holywell, Clwyd, CH8 8JP Tel: (01352) 781566 Fax: (01352) 781141

R. Boyle Motor Engineering Ltd, Blackwall Way, London, E14 9QG Tel: (020) 7987 2683 Fax: (020) 7987 2683

Brade-Leigh Bodies Ltd, Albion Industrial Estate, Oldbury Road, West Bromwich, West Midlands, B70 9EH Tel: 0121-553 4361 Fax: 0121-500 6139 E-mail: sales@brade-leigh.co.uk

Brown & Cayton Coachworks Ltd, Unit 8 The Airfield, Little Staughton, Bedford, MK44 2BN Tel: (01234) 376591 Fax: (01234) 376202 E-mail: brown.cayton@btopenworld.com

Build-A-Van, Riverside Mill, Brunswick Street, Nelson, Lancashire, BB9 0HZ Tel: (01282) 693025 Fax: (01282) 603921 E-mail: graham.hardman@btconnect.com

Bulkrite Commercial Vehicle Bodybuilders, Dorrington, Shrewsbury, SY5 7EB Tel: (01743) 718232 Fax: (01743) 718293 E-mail: bulkrite_1@lineone.net

Cabus Garage, Lancaster New Road, Cabus, Preston, PR3 1AD Tel: (01524) 791417 Fax: (01524) 791417

S. Cartwright & Sons, Atlantic Street, Broadheath, Altrincham, Cheshire, WA14 5DH Tel: 0161-928 0966 Fax: 0161-926 8410 E-mail: sales@cartwright-group.co.uk

Cebotec Ltd, 26 Castle Road, Bankside Industrial Estate, Falkirk, FK2 7UY Tel: (01324) 877778 Fax: (01324) 882525 E-mail: sales@cebotec.co.uk

Central Welding, 50 Creagh Road, Toomebridge, Antrim, BT41 3SE Tel: (028) 7965 0841 Fax: (028) 7965 9772 E-mail: info@centralwelding.co.uk

Colliers Truck Builders Ltd, Blackwater Trading Estate, The Causeway, Maldon, Essex, CM9 4GG Tel: (01621) 843109 Fax: (01621) 843047 E-mail: mainoffice@collierstruckbuilders.co.uk

▶ Commercial Bodies East Anglia, 9 Hurricane Way, Norwich, NR6 6EZ Tel: (01603) 484047 Fax: (01603) 417834 E-mail: mwcbea@freenet.co.uk

Commercial Body Specialists, 2 Beresford Trading Estate, High Street, Stoke-on-Trent, ST6 5EU Tel: (01782) 832554 Fax: (01782) 832426

Commercial Colours Ltd, Zone 3 Link 56, Weighbridge Road, Deeside Industrial Park, Deeside, Clwyd, CH5 2LL Tel: (01244) 281352 Fax: (01244) 280936 E-mail: admin@commercialcolours.co.uk

Commercial Vehicle Bodies, Lady Pitt Farm, Fosse Road, Syerston, Newark, Nottinghamshire, NG23 5NQ Tel: (01636) 525874 Fax: (01636) 525874

Coote Lane Garage, Coote Lane, Whitestake, Preston, PR4 4LJ Tel: (01772) 335385 Fax: (01772) 335385

Cumberland Commercial Bodies, Unit 3 Peart Road, Derwent Howe Industrial Estate, Workington, Cumbria, CA14 3YT Tel: (01900) 606000 Fax: (01900) 606001 E-mail: ss@ccbodies.freeserve.co.uk

▶ D E M Transport, 30 Plume Street, Birmingham, B6 7RT Tel: 0121-328 2422 Fax: 0121-328 2422

Lawrence David Ltd, Maxwell Road, Peterborough, PE2 7JR Tel: (01733) 397600 Fax: (01733) 397601 E-mail: sales@lawrencedavid.co.uk

Derbyshire Commercial Bodybuilders Ltd, 8 Derby Road, Denby, Ripley, Derbyshire, DE5 8RA Tel: (01332) 781498 Fax: (01332) 781498

Alan Dunbar, Old Hall, Tough, Alford, Aberdeenshire, AB33 8ES Tel: (01975) 562664 Fax: (01975) 562741

E R F Strathclyde Ltd, Dalgrain Industrial Estate, Grangemouth, Stirlingshire, FK3 8EB Tel: (01324) 473700 Fax: (01324) 665323

Eftee Metal Bodies Ltd, Glencraig Street, Airdrie, Lanarkshire, ML6 9AS Tel: (01236) 765975 Fax: (01236) 747415 E-mail: mail@efteetmetals.co.uk

▶ Ellis & Sons Vehicle Builders Ltd, Hawkbrand House, Longbrooks Farm, Knowle Road, Brenchley, Tonbridge, Kent, TN12 7DJ Tel: (01892) 725720 Fax: (01892) 725728 E-mail: sales@ellisandson.com

Essex Bodybuilders Ltd, Arterial House, Claydons Lane, Rayleigh, Essex, SS6 7UP Tel: (01268) 778326 Fax: (01268) 774988

▶ Field Vehicle Maintenance, Sundon Road, Harlington, Dunstable, Bedfordshire, LU5 6LN Tel: (01525) 876240 Fax: (01525) 876240

FM Engineering Services Ltd, Burtonhead Road, St. Helens, Merseyside, WA9 5EA Tel: (01744) 746800 Fax: (01744) 746810 E-mail: markowens@fmengineering.co.uk

Fowler Sheldon Ltd, Argyle Street, Birmingham, B7 5TJ Tel: 0121-328 5434 Fax: 0121-322 2014 E-mail: fowlersheldon@aol.com

Frank Guy, Bidston House, Astwith Close, Holmewood, Chesterfield, Derbyshire, S42 5UR Tel: (01246) 851222 Fax: (01246) 851225 E-mail: sales@frank-guy.co.uk

G M Panels, Units 1 & 2, Milvale Street, Stoke-on-Trent, ST6 3NT Tel: (01782) 834600 Fax: (01782) 834602 E-mail: enquiries@gmpanels.co.uk

Gablesea Glassfibre Ltd, Howley Park Industrial Estate, Howley Park Road East, Morley, Leeds, LS27 0BN Tel: 0113-252 6511 Fax: 0113-253 1548 E-mail: sales@truckroofs.co.uk

▶ Gardiner Bodies, Kingswood Farm, Tandridge Lane, Lingfield, Surrey, RH7 6LP Tel: 01342 893535 E-mail: lee@gardinerbodies.com

GB Transport Engineering, 22 Algores Way, Wisbech, Cambridgeshire, PE13 2TQ Tel: (01945) 461780 Fax: (01945) 587107 E-mail: sales@gb-truckworld.co.uk

▶ Grants Coachworks, Stable Road, Shotts, Lanarkshire, ML7 5BH Tel: (01501) 826888

Gray & Adams Doncaster Ltd, Pipering Lane, Doncaster, South Yorkshire, DN5 9EL Tel: (01302) 787755 Fax: (01302) 783675 E-mail: sales@gray-adams-donc.co.uk

H & H Commercial Refinishers, 8 Marsh Lane, Henstridge, Templecombe, Somerset, BA8 0TG Tel: (01963) 363651 Fax: (01963) 363651

▶ Harris Truck & Van, 5 Wheaton Road, Witham, Essex, CM8 3UJ Tel: (01376) 533680

Highway Commercial Engineers, Tywardreath Highway, St Blazey, Par, Cornwall, PL24 2RN Tel: (01726) 814580 Fax: (01726) 817845

▶ Holmes & Jones, 3 St. Johns Road, Saxmundham, Suffolk, IP17 1BE Tel: (01728) 603504 Fax: (01728) 604825

Horton Commercial Ltd, 63 Haviland Road, Ferndown Industrial Estate, Wimborne, Dorset, BH21 7PY Tel: (01202) 877704 Fax: (01202) 870261 E-mail: info@abacuscarhire.co.uk

Thomas Hosking & Sons Ltd, Dumballs Road, Cardiff, CF10 5FE Tel: (029) 2048 0324 Fax: (029) 2049 2075 E-mail: thomashosking@btconnect.com

Houghton-Parkhouse Ltd, Grisleymire Lane, Milnthorpe, Cumbria, LA7 7RF Tel: (01539) 563347 Fax: (01539) 562472 E-mail: sales@houghtons.com

J.T. Hutchinson, Baileywood Farm, Baileywood Lane, Holme-On-Spalding-Moor, York, YO43 4HH Tel: (01430) 860161

Ice Lite Ltd, Pendle House, Mead Way, Shuttleworth Mead, Padiham, Lancashire, BB12 7NG Tel: (0870) 770 7458 Fax: (0870) 770 7459 E-mail: sales@icelite.co.uk

J Little, Norfolk Street, Nelson, Lancashire, BB9 7SY Tel: (01282) 698777

J S Fraser (Oxford) Ltd, Cotswold Dene, Standlake, Witney, Oxfordshire, OX29 7PL Tel: (01865) 303014 Fax: (01865) 303015 E-mail: sales@jsfraser.com

J W Blake & Son, 159 Brooker Road, Waltham Abbey, Essex, EN9 1JH Tel: (01992) 713756 Fax: (01992) 713756

L.E. Jackson (Coachworks) Ltd, Vehicle Body Centre, Queens Road, Loughborough, Leicestershire, LE11 1HD Tel: (01509) 230811 Fax: (01509) 230812

▶ Jany, St. James Buildings, 79 Oxford Street, Manchester, M1 6FQ Tel: 0161-228 2798 Fax: 0161-237 9429 E-mail: sales@jany.co.uk

Kemp Commercial Bodybuilders Ltd, 30 Brunel Road, Manor Trading Estate, Benfleet, Essex, SS7 4PS Tel: (01268) 792491 Fax: (01268) 795121 E-mail: kempbodybuilders@tesco.net

Kent & Sussex Truck Centre Ltd, Longfield Road, Tunbridge Wells, Kent, TN2 3EY Tel: (01892) 515333 Fax: (01892) 531813 E-mail: vehicles@kst.co.uk

Kinetic Special Vehicles Ltd, Kings Cross Centre, Weel Road, Tickton, Beverley, North Humberside, HU17 9RY Tel: (01964) 543398 Fax: (01964) 543845 E-mail: sales@kinetic.uk.com

Lancashire Tippers, Kirkhall Workshops, Bilbao Street, Bolton, BL1 4HH Tel: (01204) 493750 Fax: (01204) 847966 E-mail: lanctip@masseytruckengineering.co.uk

▶ LD Trailer Sales Ltd, Munroe House, Ringtail Court, Burscough Industrial Estate, Burscough, Lancashire, L40 8LB Tel: 01704 893009 Fax: 01704 896660 E-mail: sales@ldtrailersales.co.uk

▶ Leeward Coachbuilders Ltd, Richards Street, Wednesbury, West Midlands, WS10 8AJ Tel: 0121-526 4709 Fax: 0121-526 4718 E-mail: sales@leewardcoachbuilders.co.uk

▶ Linktip, Rainbow Business Park, Stringes Lane, Willenhall, West Midlands, WV13 1HH Tel: (01902) 365880 Fax: (01902) 365889

Lonsdale Commercial Body Builders Ltd, Unit2, Gulf Works, Off Penarth Road, Cardiff, CF11 8TW Tel: (029) 2034 3077 Fax: (029) 2023 7506 E-mail: lee@lonsdalej.fsnet.co.uk

M & P Carriage Works (Coventry) Ltd, Torrington Avenue, Coventry, CV4 9BL Tel: (024) 7642 1515 Fax: (024) 7642 1818

M S Bodies (Bristol) Ltd, 152a Soundwell Rd, Bristol, BS16 4RT Tel: 0117-940 6886 Fax: 0117-976 0910

Manchester Vehicle Painters, Unit 2 Reliance Trading Estate, Manchester, M40 3AG Tel: 0161-682 2556 Fax: 0161-682 0090

Marsh Barton Coachworks Ltd, Grace Road, Marsh Barton, Exeter, EX2 8PU Tel: (01392) 202224 Fax: (01392) 423576 E-mail: admin@marshbartoncoachworks.co.uk

Marshall Specialist Vehicles Ltd, The Airport, Cambridge, CB5 8RX Tel: (01223) 373900 Fax: (01223) 373064 E-mail: info@marshallsv.com

▶ Martrans Bodies Ltd, Blyborough, Gainsborough, Lincolnshire, DN21 4EY Tel: (01427) 667600 Fax: (01427) 667612 E-mail: martronstrailers@btconnect.com

Neath Coachbuilders Ltd, Cilfrew, Neath, West Glamorgan, SA10 8LF Tel: (01639) 643629 Fax: (01639) 646566 E-mail: enquiries@neathcoachbuilders.co.uk

Osborne Motor Bodies, Roothers Industries, Debden Green, Debden Green, Saffron Walden, Essex, CB11 3LX Tel: (01371) 831313 Fax: (01371) 831194 E-mail: sales@osborne.ltd.uk

P D Stevens & Sons Ltd, Greenfields Lane, Market Drayton, Shropshire, TF9 3SL Tel: (01630) 652396 Fax: (01630) 652141

P P S Commercials Ltd, Cemetery Road, Radcliffe, Manchester, M26 4FT Tel: 0161-724 5022 Fax: 0161-723 5918 E-mail: enquiries@ppscommercials.co.uk

▶ indicates data change since last edition

COMMERCIAL VEHICLE BODY BUILDERS – *continued*

Panema Trailer Engineering Ltd, Chalk Lane, Snetterton, Norwich, NR16 2JZ Tel: (01953) 887622 Fax: (01953) 888515 E-mail: info@panematrailers.co.uk

Park Sheet Metal Co. Ltd, Bayton Road, Exhall, Coventry, CV7 9DJ Tel: (024) 7636 1606 Fax: (024) 7664 4078 E-mail: office@parksheetmetal.co.uk

Parkway Coach Building, 7 Ballycreely Road, Comber, Newtownards, County Down, BT23 5PX Tel: (07713) 489506 Fax: (028) 9752 8918

Penman Engineering Ltd, Heathhall Industrial Estate, Heathhall, Dumfries, DG1 3NY Tel: (01387) 252784 Fax: (01387) 267332 E-mail: info@penman.co.uk

Pickerings Transport Services Ltd, 852 Melton Road, Thurmaston, Leicester, LE4 8BT Tel: 0116-269 6111 Fax: 0116-260 7436

Plaxton, Ryton Road, North Anston, Sheffield, S25 4DL Tel: (01909) 551166 Fax: (01909) 567994

Portland Commercial Bodies Ltd, Unit 2 Portland Street, Birmingham, B6 5RX Tel: 0121-327 2713 Fax: 0121-328 0302 E-mail: portlandbodies@btconnect.com

▶ Purely Paintworks, 4 Collec Depot, Billington Road, Leighton Buzzard, Bedfordshire, LU7 9HH Tel: (01525) 371122

▶ Quaylink Transport, 1 Richmond Road, Manchester, M14 6YW Tel: 0161-873 8500 Fax: 0161-873 8500 E-mail: lisacquaylink@tiscali.co.uk

R Hind, Durranhill Trading Estate, Carlisle, CA1 3NQ Tel: (01228) 523647 Fax: (01228) 512712

Randolph Coachworks Ltd, Evenwood, Bishop Auckland, County Durham, DL14 9QL Tel: (01388) 832560 Fax: (01388) 834504

Peter G. Reeves & Co. Ltd, Haden Works, Haden Street, Birmingham, B12 9HN Tel: 0121-440 4225 Fax: 0121-446 4252

▶ Rettendon Trucks & Bodies, Tile Works Lane, Rettendon Common, Chelmsford, CM3 8HB Tel: (01245) 400465

Richard Parry, Yockleton, Shrewsbury, SY5 9QQ Tel: (01743) 821333 Fax: (01743) 873604

Richardsons Commercials Oldham Ltd, Glen Trading Estate, Wellyhole Street, Oldham, OL4 3BF Tel: 0161-652 4241 Fax: 0161-628 4070

Roco Truck Bodies Ltd, Roscoe House, Brighouse Road, Bradford, West Yorkshire, BD12 0QF Tel: (01274) 606056 Fax: (01274) 690057 E-mail: info@rocotruckbodies.co.uk

S F Vehicle Builders Ltd, Crossways, Church Stretton, Shropshire, SY6 6PG Tel: (01694) 722804 Fax: (01694) 723583

Scania (Great Britain) Ltd, Avonmouth Way, Bristol, BS11 8DB Tel: 0117-937 9800 Fax: 0117-982 4103

SDC Trailers Ltd, Bradder Way, Mansfield, Nottinghamshire, NG18 5DQ Tel: (01623) 625354 Fax: (01623) 626946 E-mail: admin@sdctrailers.com

Silverline Coachworks, Unit 4 Harrimans Lane, Lenton La Industrial Estate, Lenton Lane Industrial Estate, Nottingham, NG7 2SD Tel: 0115-970 3210 Fax: 0115-970 3210

Solent Body Builders Ltd, 4 Cockerell Close, Fareham, Hampshire, PO15 5SR Tel: (01489) 575611 Fax: (01489) 578780 E-mail: kevin@solentbodybuilders.co.uk

▶ Spraytek, Frith Farm, Frith Lane, Wickham, Fareham, Hampshire, PO17 5AW Tel: (01329) 836300 Fax: (01329) 836301

Stables Garage, Stone Street, Cleckheaton, West Yorkshire, BD19 5EE Tel: (01274) 869601 Fax: (01274) 869601

Stag Commercial Body Manufacturers Ltd, Unit 1a Cockshute Industrial Estate, Shelton New Road, Stoke-on-Trent, ST4 7AW Tel: (01782) 287528 Fax: (01782) 283504 E-mail: stagcommercial@yahoo.co.uk

Stambermill Autocraft, Building 80, First Avenue, Pensnett Trading Estate, Kingswinford, West Midlands, DY6 7FQ Tel: (01384) 298682 Fax: (01384) 866003

Sterling Coach Works, Ellerbeck Way, Stokesley Industrial Park, Stokesley, Middlesborough, Cleveland, TS9 5JZ Tel: (01642) 713333 Fax: (01642) 713805 E-mail: info@worldwidetrots.co.uk

▶ Sunningvale Coach Works, 274 Davidson Road, Croydon, CR0 6DF Tel: (020) 8663 8800 Fax: (020) 8663 8829

Super Trucks Ltd, Beaufort Street, St. Helens, Merseyside, WA9 3BQ Tel: (01744) 25348 Fax: (01744) 27772 E-mail: supertrucks@btinternet.com

Supreme Bodies Midlands Ltd, Ablow Street, Wolverhampton, WV2 4ER Tel: (01902) 426244 Fax: (01902) 710669

▶ T C L Transport Engineers Ltd, Elmfield Business Park, Lotherton Way, Garforth, Leeds, LS25 2JY Tel: 0113-286 3322 Fax: 0113-286 4422

T G S Coach Works, Balaclava Industrial Estate, Balaclava Road, Bristol, BS16 3LJ Tel: 0117-965 9965

T P S Automotives, Hoobrook Trading Estate, Worcester Road, Kidderminster, Worcestershire, DY10 1HY Tel: (01562) 744492 Fax: (01562) 746442 E-mail: tps.auto@lineone.net

T V Kenealy, The Yard, Harthall Lane, Pimlico, Hemel Hempstead, Hertfordshire, HP3 8SE Tel: (01923) 266341 Fax: (01923) 291107

Terbergmatec UK Ltd, Highgrounds Way, Rhodesia, Worksop, Nottinghamshire, S80 3AF Tel: (01909) 484000 Fax: (01909) 489000

Welford Thomas Ltd, Unit 35 Thornleigh Trading Estate, Dudley, West Midlands, DY2 8UB Tel: (01384) 451340 Fax: (01384) 451345 E-mail: wellford.bodies@btinternet.co.uk

▶ Trafford Trailer Repairs, Stretford Motorway Estate, Stretford, Manchester, M32 0ZH Tel: 0161-865 6225 Fax: 0161-865 6226

Transport Enterprises Ltd, Unit 11, Swannington Road, Broughton Astley, Leicester, LE9 6TU Tel: (01455) 285295 Fax: (01455) 285283

Truck Care, 3 Holmer Road, Hereford, HR4 9SD Tel: (01432) 342679 Fax: (01432) 265414 E-mail: truckcaregl@aol.com

Truck Tec, 1 Clark Way, Bellshill Industrial Estate, Bellshill, Lanarkshire, ML4 3NX Tel: (01698) 339090 Fax: (01698) 339080 E-mail: sales@trucktecltd.co.uk

▶ Truckcraft Bodies Ltd, Cooper Street Works, Cooper Street, Dukinfield, Cheshire, SK16 4JB Tel: 0161-830 0011 Fax: 0161-830 0022

Trumac Groups Ltd, Brook Lane, The Ham, Westbury, Wiltshire, BA13 4HB Tel: (01373) 821600 Fax: (01373) 826808

Turner Vehicle Bodies Ltd, Carseview Road, Forfar, Angus, DD8 3BT Tel: (01307) 462142 Fax: (01307) 466070

Van Bodies Lancs Ltd, East Gate, White Lund Trading Estate, White Lund Industrial Estate, Morecambe, Lancashire, LA3 3DY Tel: (01524) 34422 Fax: (01524) 381432 E-mail: vanbodies@btconnect.com

Vehicle Build, 4 George Baylis Road, Berry Hill Industrial Estate, Droitwich, Worcestershire, WR9 9RB Tel: (01905) 826083 Fax: (01905) 826093

Webb Truck Equipment, Acton Place, Melford Road, Acton, Sudbury, Suffolk, CO10 0BB Tel: (01787) 377368 Fax: (01787) 880618 E-mail: sales@web-extrareach.co.uk

Weightlifter Bodies Ltd, Grange Lane North, Scunthorpe, South Humberside, DN16 1BN Tel: (01724) 872444 Fax: (01724) 853647

▶ West Thurrock Coachworks Ltd Grays, 2 Manor Way Industrial Estate, Curzon Drive, Grays, Essex, RM17 6BG Tel: (01375) 397989 Fax: (01375) 398282

Whitby Morrison Ltd, Fourth Avenue, Western Road Industrial Estate, Crewe, CW1 6TT Tel: (01270) 581318 Fax: (01270) 250220

▶ Z S Bodies Ltd, Moat Way, Barwell, Leicester, LE9 8EY Tel: (01455) 844901 Fax: (01455) 840262

COMMERCIAL VEHICLE BODY FITTINGS

Boalloy Ltd, Radnor Park Trading Estate, West Heath, Congleton, Cheshire, CW12 4QA Tel: (01260) 275155 Fax: (01260) 279696 E-mail: buying@boalloy.org

Colliers Truck Builders Ltd, Blackwater Trading Estate, The Causeway, Maldon, Essex, CM9 4GG Tel: (01621) 843109 Fax: (01621) 843047 E-mail: mainoffice@collierstruckbuilders.co.uk

Daniel Lewis & Son Ltd, 493-495 Hackney Road, London, E2 9ED Tel: (020) 7739 8881 Fax: (020) 7739 2136 E-mail: daniellewis@ad.com

Derbyshire Commercial Bodybuilders Ltd, 8 Derby Road, Denby, Ripley, Derbyshire, DE5 8RA Tel: (01332) 781498 Fax: (01332) 781498

Alan Dunbar, Old Hall, Tough, Alford, Aberdeenshire, AB33 8ES Tel: (01975) 562664 Fax: (01975) 562741

Essex Bodybuilders Ltd, Arterial House, Claydons Lane, Rayleigh, Essex, SS6 7UP Tel: (01268) 778326 Fax: (01268) 774988

GB Transport Engineering, 22 Algores Way, Wisbech, Cambridgeshire, PE13 2TQ Tel: (01945) 461780 Fax: (01945) 587107 E-mail: sales@gb-truckworld.co.uk

M S Engineering, PO Box 255, Bedford, MK41 9BH Tel: (01234) 772255 Fax: (01234) 772266 E-mail: info@msengineering.co.uk

▶ McPhee Bros (Blantyre) Ltd, 58 John Street, Blantyre, Glasgow, G72 0JF Tel: (01698) 823422 Fax: (01698) 823853 E-mail: lorna@mcfeemixers.co.uk

Merritt Plastics Ltd, 5 Winster Buildings, Manners Avenue, Manners Industrial Estate, Ilkeston, Derbyshire, DE7 8EF Tel: 0115-944 7661 Fax: 0115-944 1864 E-mail: simon@merrittplastics.fsnet.co.uk

Parlok UK Ltd, Cornwall Street, Parr Industrial Estate, St. Helens, Merseyside, WA9 1PT Tel: (01744) 639191 Fax: (01744) 612870 E-mail: sales@parlok.co.uk

Powertec, Spa Lane, Linthwaite, Huddersfield, HD7 5QB Tel: (01484) 842293 Fax: (01484) 842293

COMMERCIAL VEHICLE BRAKE POWER SYSTEMS

Commercial Replacements, Unit L1 Blackpole Trading Estate East, Blackpole Road, Worcester, WR3 8SG Tel: (01905) 458052 Fax: (01905) 756078

COMMERCIAL VEHICLE CHASSIS

▶ B P Rolls Ltd, West Portway, Andover, Hampshire, SP10 3LF Tel: (01264) 361516 Fax: (01264) 333473 E-mail: sales@bprolls.co.uk

Chassis Developments Ltd, Grovebury Road, Leighton Buzzard, Bedfordshire, LU7 4SL Tel: (01525) 374151 Fax: (01525) 370127 E-mail: david.brain@chassisdevelopments.co.uk

Heskin Fabrications Ltd, Whalley Works, Whalley Road, Heskin, Chorley, Lancashire, PR7 5NY Tel: (01257) 451483 Fax: (01257) 453242 E-mail: heskinfabs@btconnect.co.uk

▶ TATA - Phoenix Distribution Ltd, PO Box 41, Birmingham, B31 2TN Tel: 0121-472 4862 Fax: 0121-482 4158 E-mail: anthony.miles@pheonixdist.com

Wheelbase Engineering Ltd, Lower Eccleshill Road, Darwen, Lancashire, BB3 0RP Tel: (01254) 819399 Fax: (01254) 776920 E-mail: sales@wheelbase.net

COMMERCIAL VEHICLE COMPONENT/SPARE PARTS EXPORT MERCHANTS OR AGENTS

Aerodyne Services, 10 Hydepark Close, Newtownabbey, County Antrim, BT36 4WS Tel: (028) 9083 6333 Fax: (028) 9084 1525

C H B Engineering, Mantra House, South Street, Keighley, West Yorkshire, BD21 1SX Tel: (01535) 607741 Fax: (01535) 690539

▶ Centaur Van & Truck, 20-22 Kenyon Lane, Manchester, M40 9JQ Tel: 0161-205 3885 E-mail: parts@cvtmercaid.co.uk

▶ Croft Bros UK Ltd, Unit D1 Riverside Way, Cowley, Uxbridge, Middlesex, UB8 2YF Tel: (01895) 850700 Fax: (01895) 270584 E-mail: info@croftbrothers.co.uk

▶ Engine Spares, 82 Mitcham Road, London, SW17 9NG Tel: (020) 8767 5990 Fax: (020) 8767 5991 E-mail: smithaustin01@btconnect.com

Eurotruck (Truck Trailer Spares) Ltd, 263 Derby Road, Bramcote, Nottingham, NG9 3JA Tel: 0115-939 7660 Fax: 0115-939 6428

Export Africa, 1 Terminus Industrial Estate, Durham Street, Portsmouth, PO1 1NR Tel: (023) 9282 3590 Fax: (023) 9281 2038 E-mail: sales@rundleholdings.co.uk

Motor Parts Direct Ltd, Unit 4 The Cobden Centre, Hawksworth, Didcot, Oxfordshire, OX11 7HL Tel: (01235) 817890 Fax: (01235) 813897

Western Truck Ltd, 123 Clydesdale Place, Moss Side Industrial Estate, Leyland, PR26 7QS Tel: (01772) 454124 Fax: (01772) 456075 E-mail: rr@westerntruck.co.uk

COMMERCIAL VEHICLE COMPONENTS AND SPARE PARTS

A J Parsons & Sons Ltd, Anglo Trading Estate, Commercial Road, Shepton Mallet, Somerset, BA4 5BY Tel: (01749) 346161 Fax: (01749) 346100 E-mail: sales@parsonsparts.co.uk

▶ Air-Weigh Inc Ltd, Fleet Villa, Godnow Road, Crowle, Scunthorpe, East Yorkshire, DN17 4DU Tel: (01724) 712000 Fax: (01724) 712111 E-mail: airweighinc@hotmail.com

Allen Industrial, Phoenix House, Kinmel Park Industrial Estate, Bodelwyddan, Rhyl, Clwyd, LL18 5TY Tel: (01745) 586300 Fax: (01745) 586301 E-mail: mail@allen-industrial.co.uk

Allmakes Ltd, 176 Milton Park, Milton, Abingdon, Oxfordshire, OX14 4SW Tel: (01235) 821122 Fax: (01235) 821133 E-mail: allmakes@allmakes.co.uk

Ashtree Glass Ltd, Ashtree Works, Brownroyd Street, Bradford, West Yorkshire, BD8 9AF Tel: (01274) 546732 Fax: (01274) 548525 E-mail: sales@ashtree.yorks.com

B S Commercial Repairs Ltd, 3 Clothier Road, Bristol, BS4 5PS Tel: 0117-977 2608 Fax: 0117-972 1967 E-mail: sales@bs-commercial.co.uk

▶ Baer Cargolift, Birch Lane Business Park, Unit 9, Aldridge, Walsall, WS9 0NF Tel: (01922) 456700 Fax: (01922) 455551

Bloxwich Engineering Ltd, Fryers Road, Walsall, WS2 7LZ Tel: (01922) 710510 Fax: (01922) 713510 E-mail: bloxwich@bloxwich.u-net.com

Bond Engineering Ltd, Harrowbrook Road, Hinckley, Leicestershire, LE10 3DJ Tel: (01455) 632775 Fax: (01455) 632738 E-mail: bondeng31@aol.com

Boydell & Jacks Ltd, Marlborough Street, Burnley, Lancashire, BB11 2HW Tel: (01282) 456411 Fax: (01282) 437496 E-mail: sales@featherwing.com

Brian Currie, 3 Brunel Road, Bedford, MK41 9TG Tel: (01234) 325737 Fax: (01234) 360804

C D A R T Engineering, 1-2 Willow Road, Castle Donington, Derby, DE74 2NP Tel: (01332) 811150 Fax: (01332) 811306

C H B Engineering, Mantra House, South Street, Keighley, West Yorkshire, BD21 1SX Tel: (01535) 607741 Fax: (01535) 690539

▶ Centaur Van & Truck, 20-22 Kenyon Lane, Manchester, M40 9JQ Tel: 0161-205 3885 E-mail: parts@cvtmercaid.co.uk

Colliers Truck Builders Ltd, Blackwater Trading Estate, The Causeway, Maldon, Essex, CM9 4GG Tel: (01621) 843109 Fax: (01621) 843047 E-mail: mainoffice@collierstruckbuilders.co.uk

Commercial Body Fittings, 80 Bridge Road East, Welwyn Garden City, Hertfordshire, AL7 1JY Tel: (01707) 371161 Fax: (01707) 372603 E-mail: sales@cbf.uk.com

Commercial Replacements, Unit L1 Blackpole Trading Estate East, Blackpole Road, Worcester, WR3 8SG Tel: (01905) 458052 Fax: (01905) 756078

D B Wilson & Co. Ltd, 1 Alleysbank Road, Rutherglen, Glasgow, G73 1AL Tel: 0141-647 0161 Fax: 0141-613 1795 E-mail: dbwilsonjr@aol.com

D Martindale Ltd, Crosse Hall Street, Chorley, Lancashire, PR6 0QQ Tel: (01257) 263504 Fax: (01257) 263504 E-mail: info@donaldmartindale.co.uk

David Huggett Commercial Motor Factors Ltd, D Brittania Road, Waltham Cross, Hertfordshire, EN8 7NH Tel: (01992) 762519 Fax: (01992) 718472

E X B Ltd, Unit 15 Eldonwell Trading Estate, Eldon Way, Bristol, BS4 3QQ Tel: 0117-972 8380 Fax: 0117-972 3615

European Truck Parts Ltd, Junction Two Industrial Estate, Demuth Way, Oldbury, West Midlands, B69 4LT Tel: 0121-544 1222 Fax: 0121-544 9500 E-mail: rob@etp-uk.com

Fleet Parts Ltd, New Cut Industrial Estate, New Cut Lane, Woolston, Warrington, WA1 4AG Tel: (01925) 824019 Fax: (01925) 838496 E-mail: sales@fleetparts.com

Foxwood Boring & Grinding Ltd, 17 Whitting Valley Road, Old Whittington, Chesterfield, Derbyshire, S41 9EY Tel: (01246) 260199 Fax: (01246) 455274 E-mail: ken@foxwooddiesel.com

Greenhous, March Way, Battlefield Enterprise Park, Shrewsbury, SY1 3JE Tel: (01743) 467904 Fax: (01743) 457500 E-mail: enquiries@greenhous.co.uk

Griptone Ltd, A Link 580, 188 Moorside Road, Swinton, Manchester, M27 9LB Tel: 0161-727 9011 Fax: 0161-727 9021 E-mail: sales@griptone.co.uk

Groeneveld UK Ltd, Unit 29a Loughborough Motorway Trading Estate, Gelders Hall Road, Shepshed, Loughborough, Leicestershire, LE12 9NH Tel: (01509) 600033 Fax: (01509) 602000 E-mail: groenevel.uk@talk21.com

H G H Components Ltd, 77 River Road, Barking, Essex, IG11 0DS Tel: (020) 8594 7500 Fax: (020) 8594 7533

H G V Truck & Trailer Parts, Marsh Lane, Boston, Lincolnshire, PE21 7SJ Tel: (01205) 365258 Fax: (01205) 355225 E-mail: info@hgvtruckparts.com

▶ Interfit, 14 Station Road, Reddish, Stockport, Cheshire, SK5 6ND Tel: 0161-431 4626 Fax: 0161-431 4626 E-mail: info@inter-fit.co.uk

James & Bloom Ltd, Blenheim Place, Gateshead, Tyne & Wear, NE11 9HF Tel: 0191-461 0088 Fax: 0191-461 0146

Jones Springs Engineering Ltd, Gladstone Street, Wednesbury, West Midlands, WS10 8BE Tel: 0121-568 7575 Fax: 0121-568 7692 E-mail: sales@jones-springs.co.uk

Kent & Sussex Truck Centre Ltd, Longfield Road, Tunbridge Wells, Kent, TN2 3EY Tel: (01892) 515333 Fax: (01892) 531813 E-mail: vehicles@kst.co.uk

Ketlon Ltd, Paddock Wood Distribution Centre, Paddock Wood, Tonbridge, Kent, TN12 6UU Tel: (01892) 835555 Fax: (01892) 832389 E-mail: sales@ketlon.co.uk

Kingsdown, Brook Street, Snodland, Kent, ME6 5BB Tel: (01634) 249555 Fax: (01634) 249550 E-mail: sales@kingsdownuk.com

L C Davis & Sons Ltd, 6 Prince Georges Road, London, SW19 2PX Tel: (020) 8648 3113 Fax: (020) 8640 8282 E-mail: info@lcdavis.com

Lampion & Co. Ltd, Unit 36 Hortonwood 33, Telford, Shropshire, TF1 7EX Tel: (01952) 608600 Fax: (01952) 608700 E-mail: sales@lampion.co.uk

M A N E R F UK Ltd, Frankland Road, Blagrove, Swindon, SN5 8YU Tel: (01793) 448000 Fax: (01793) 448260

M L C Monsoon Ltd, Northfield Business Park, London Road, Lower Dicker, Hailsham, East Sussex, BN27 4BZ Tel: (01323) 440422 Fax: (01323) 845705

M S Engineering, PO Box 255, Bedford, MK41 9BH Tel: (01234) 772255 Fax: (01234) 772266 E-mail: info@msengineering.co.uk

Mann & Overton Ltd, 39-41 Brewery Road, London, N7 9QH Tel: (020) 7700 0888 Fax: (020) 7700 6676 E-mail: info@mannandoverton.com

Multipart Universal, 8 Stevenson Way, Sheffield, S9 3WZ Tel: 0114-261 1122 Fax: 0800 834500 E-mail: uksales@ucukltd.com

Parlok UK Ltd, Cornwall Street, Parr Industrial Estate, St. Helens, Merseyside, WA9 1PT Tel: (01744) 639191 Fax: (01744) 612870 E-mail: sales@parlok.co.uk

Poolec Automotive Products Ltd, Fourth Way, Bristol, BS11 8DL Tel: 0117-982 9109 Fax: 0117-982 7690 E-mail: poolec.bristol@btconnect.com

R C S Hose & Hydraulics Ltd, Crucible Road, Corby, Northamptonshire, NN17 5TS Tel: 0800 3893132

COMMERCIAL VEHICLE COMPONENTS AND SPARE PARTS

– *continued*

▶ Ranell Ltd, Unit 7a Beckingham Business Park, Tolleshunt Major, Maldon, Essex, CM9 8LZ Tel: (01621) 869048 Fax: (01621) 868978 E-mail: info@ranell.com

Smyth's Equipment Supply Co., Tamar Commercial Centre, Chater Street, Belfast, BT4 1BL Tel: (028) 9045 1355 Fax: (028) 9045 4838 E-mail: sescobelfast@aol.com

Sperry Springs (Sussex) Ltd, Unit 4 Kingston Industrial Estate, Easton Road, Aldershot, Hampshire, GU12 4YA Tel: (01903) 762272 Fax: (01252) 327773

Stedall Vehicle Fittings Ltd, Unit 1a Badminton Road Trading Estate, Yate, Bristol, BS37 5JS Tel: (01454) 314646 Fax: (01454) 312077 E-mail: info@stedall.co.uk

Truck & Trailer Components Ltd, Unipart House, Garsington Road, Cowley, Oxford, OX4 2PG Tel: (01865) 383999 Fax: (0800) 361677 E-mail: ttc@unipart.co.uk

Truck & Trailer Equipment Ltd, 37-39 Hawes Lane, Rowley Regis, Warley, West Midlands, B65 9AL Tel: 0121-559 7711 Fax: 0121-559 5637 E-mail: sales@trucktrailerequip.co.uk

Vernon Developments, Unit B, Mucklow Hill Trading Estate, Phase 2, Halesowen, West Midlands, B62 8DQ Tel: 0121-501 1171 Fax: 0121-550 6181

Walsall Brake Services Ltd, Middlemore Lane West, Aldridge, Walsall, WS9 8BG Tel: (01922) 744625 Fax: (01922) 744626

Waveney Truck Parts Ltd, 172-174 Mile Cross Lane, Norwich, NR6 6RY Tel: (01603) 400774 Fax: (01603) 418427 E-mail: sales@waveneytruckparts.co.uk

Z F Trading, Eldon Way, Crick, Northampton, NN6 7SL Tel: (01788) 822353 Fax: (01788) 823829 E-mail: sales@zf.com

COMMERCIAL VEHICLE CONTRACT HIRE

Active Signs Maintenance, 24 Leigh Road, Ramsgate, Kent, CT12 5EU Tel: (01843) 580801 Fax: (01843) 852830 E-mail: sales@activevehicles.co.uk

Addscan Hire Centre, 221 Edleston Road, Crewe, CW2 7HT Tel: (01270) 211061 Fax: (01270) 211353 E-mail: lynne_smith@btconnect.com

Auto Rentals Ltd, Fleming Road, Skippers Lane Industrial Estate, Middlesbrough, Cleveland, TS6 6TT Tel: (01642) 469000 Fax: (01642) 464475 E-mail: info@autorentalscleveland.co.uk

C A Trott Plant Hire Ltd, 21 Hurricane Way, Airport Industrial Estate, Norwich, NR6 6EZ Tel: (01603) 426487 Fax: (01603) 417837 E-mail: enquiries@trott-rentals.com

Cartek Vehicle Solutions, Craven House Lansbury Estate, 102 Lower Guildford Road, Knaphill, Woking, Surrey, GU21 2EP Tel: (01483) 799499 Fax: (01483) 487400 E-mail: sales@cartek.co.uk

Citroen Birmingham, Small Heath Highway, Birmingham, B10 0BT Tel: 0121-766 7060 Fax: 0121-766 7042 E-mail: sisav@supanet.com

Clayton Contracts, 6 Beverley Close, Penkridge, Stafford, ST19 5SS Tel: (01785) 716133 Fax: (01785) 716166 E-mail: kelly@claytoncarcontracts.co.uk

D P H, Whitburn Road, Bathgate, West Lothian, EH48 2HR Tel: (01506) 630887 Fax: (01506) 634835

Dawsongroup P.L.C., Delaware Drive, Tongwell, Milton Keynes, MK15 8JH Tel: (01908) 218111 Fax: (01908) 218444 E-mail: contactus@dawsongroup.co.uk

Economy Hire (Dorset) Ltd, 10 Parkside Industrial Estate, Ringwood, Hampshire, BH24 3SQ Tel: (01425) 474593 Fax: (01425) 479964 E-mail: jclark@economyhire.co.uk

▶ Hertz Rent A Car Ltd, 34-62 Staines Road, Hounslow, TW3 3LZ Tel: (020) 8570 5000 Fax: (020) 8750 3978

Hill Hire plc, Wharfedale Road, Euroway Industrial Estate, Bradford, West Yorkshire, BD4 6SG Tel: (0870) 5133423 Fax: (01274) 651347 E-mail: sales@hillhire.co.uk

Howarth Bros Haulage Ltd, Unit 3 Moss Lane, Royton, Oldham, OL2 6HR Tel: (01706) 847514 Fax: (01706) 882607 E-mail: howarth.bros@btinternet.com

Hudson, Doncaster Road, Bawtry, Doncaster, South Yorkshire, DN10 6NX Tel: (01302) 710711 Fax: (01302) 710782 E-mail: info@johnhudson.co.uk

J W Barrow & Co., Griffiths Road, Lostock Gralam, Northwich, Cheshire, CW9 7NU Tel: (01606) 331222 Fax: (01606) 331333 E-mail: jwbarrow@btinternet.com

K T Ivory plc, Harper Lodge Farm, Harper Lane, Radlett, Hertfordshire, WD7 7HU Tel: (01923) 856081 Fax: (01923) 852470 E-mail: ivorys1@btconnect.com

L & F Plant Hire Company Ltd, 36-44 London Lane, London, E8 3PR Tel: (020) 8985 1472 Fax: (020) 8986 3518

Lex Transfleet Ltd, 17 Western Road, London, NW10 7LT Tel: (020) 8961 5225 Fax: (020) 8965 9214

Lex Vehicle Leasing Ltd, Heathside Park, Heathside Park Road, Stockport, Cheshire, SK3 0RB Tel: (0870) 1124000 Fax: (0870) 1124400

▶ Lightwood Contracts Ltd, Lightwood Road, Longton, Stoke-on-Trent, ST3 4JG Tel: (01782) 599600 Fax: (01782) 330753 E-mail: stevehill@plattsgarage.com

▶ Luxtravel Ltd, Tenterden Road, Biddenden, Ashford, Kent, TN27 8BH Tel: (01580) 292970 Fax: (01622) 750751 E-mail: enquiries@luxtravel.co.uk

▶ Nationwide Vehicles Direct Ltd, Dalriada Crescent, Motherwell, Lanarkshire, ML1 3XS Tel: 0141-587 8898 E-mail: joannecrawford03@yahoo.co.uk

Neva Consultants Leeds, Unit 41, Unity Business Centre, 26 Roundhay Road, Leeds, LS7 1AB Tel: (0845) 2062277 Fax: (0845) 2072277 E-mail: howard.mostyn@nevaplc.co.uk

▶ Paige Hire Fleet Management, Phoenix House, River Gardens, Feltham, Middlesex, TW14 0RD Tel: 0208 8900334 Fax: 0208 8906992 E-mail: info@paigerental.com

▶ Practical Car & Van Rental, Unit 6 Willow Road, Trent Lane Indust Estate, Derby, DE74 2NP Tel: (01332) 812151 Fax: (01332) 853530 E-mail: andrewsherwood1@hotmail.com

RH Rentals, Lenton Lane, Nottingham, NG7 2NR Tel: 0115-943 8030 Fax: 0115-943 8045 E-mail: daniel.stevenson@rh-freight.co.uk

▶ Ryder plc, 26-29 Morris Road, Nuffield Industrial Estate, Poole, Dorset, BH17 0GG Tel: (01202) 685181 Fax: (01202) 240841 E-mail: andrew_ellis@ryder.com

Southern Motor Group Van Centre, 22 Lansdowne Road, Croydon, CR0 2BD Tel: (020) 8680 5533 Fax: (020) 8688 3840 E-mail: sales@smguk.co.uk

▶ TATA - Phoenix Distribution Ltd, PO Box 41, Birmingham, B31 2TN Tel: 0121-472 4862 Fax: 0121-482 4158 E-mail: anthony.miles@pheonixdist.com

Tipper Hire, 36-44 London Lane, London, E8 3PR Tel: (020) 8985 6758 Fax: (020) 8986 3518 E-mail: tipperhireuk@btconnect.com

▶ Translinc Ltd, Jarvis House, 157 Sadler Road, Lincoln, LN6 3RS Tel: (01522) 503400 Fax: (01522) 552997 E-mail: sales@translinc.co.uk

▶ VehicleOptions (Wales), Redwither Business Centre, Redwither Business Park, Wrexham, LL13 9XR Tel: (01978) 664516 Fax: (01978) 661494E-mail: nickcarlton@vehicleoptions.biz

▶ Vipul Dave, 72 Portswood Road, Southampton, SO17 2FW Tel: 0845 8382737 Fax: 0845 8382736 E-mail: info@motordriven.co.uk

▶ Walsall Van Hire, 305-317 Wednesbury Road, Pleck, Walsall, WS2 9QJ Tel: 01922 639652 E-mail: andrew@walsallvanhire.co.uk

Wheels Van & Truck Rentals, 7 St. Albans Road, Barnet, Hertfordshire, EN5 4LN Tel: (020) 8441 1818 Fax: (020) 8440 1921

COMMERCIAL VEHICLE CONVERSION

▶ LD Trailer Sales Ltd, Munroe House, Ringtail Court, Burscough Industrial Estate, Burscough, Lancashire, L40 8LB Tel: 01704 893009 Fax: 01704 896660 E-mail: sales@ldtrailersales.co.uk

COMMERCIAL VEHICLE DELIVERY SERVICES

▶ Alan-Peters Group, 38 Newton Road, Isleworth, Middlesex, TW7 6QD Tel: 020 8569 9006 Fax: 020 8569 7789 E-mail: info@alan-petersgroup.co.uk

C P S Oxford Ltd, Partridge Yard, Eynsham Road, Cassington, Witney, Oxfordshire, OX29 4EU Tel: (01865) 881204 Fax: (01865) 880617

▶ Hyway Logistics, Lincoln Court, Washington Street, Bolton, BL3 5EZ Tel: (01204) 365403 Fax: (01204) 365418 E-mail: delivery@hywaylogistics.co.uk

Mainland Car Deliveries Ltd, Mainland House, Bootle, Merseyside, L20 3EF Tel: 0151-933 9612 Fax: 0151-933 4751 E-mail: contactus@mcd-ltd.co.uk

▶ TATA - Phoenix Distribution Ltd, PO Box 41, Birmingham, B31 2TN Tel: 0121-472 4862 Fax: 0121-482 4158 E-mail: anthony.miles@pheonixdist.com

COMMERCIAL VEHICLE DRIVER RECRUITMENT AGENCIES OR CONSULTANCY OR SERVICES

Ace Appointments, 4 Market Square, Northampton, NN1 2DL Tel: (01604) 630781 Fax: (01604) 620495 E-mail: recruit@aceappsnorth.co.uk

Blue Arrow, 32 Friar Lane, Nottingham, NG1 6DQ Tel: 0115-947 2252 Fax: 0115-950 3766 E-mail: nottingham@bluearrow.co.uk

Crown Personnel Ltd, 2 St. Giles Square, Northampton, NN1 1DA Tel: (01604) 622244 Fax: (01604) 230825 E-mail: branch@crownjobs.com

Direct Specialist Recruitment, 8-10 North Street, Barking, Essex, IG11 8AW Tel: (020) 8591 6787 Fax: (020) 8591 6787 E-mail: info@dsrecruitment.com

Driver Hire, Swan Street, Leicester, LE3 5AW Tel: 0116-251 6700 E-mail: leicester@driverhire.co.uk

Driver Hire, Unit 16 Enterprise House, Dalziel Street, Motherwell, Lanarkshire, ML1 1PJ Tel: (01698) 275444 Fax: (01698) 276555 E-mail: southampton@driver-hire.co.uk

Driver Hire, 476 Broadway, Chadderton, Oldham, OL9 9NS Tel: 0161-683 4333 Fax: 0161-683 8888

Driver Hire, 108 Town Street, Stanningley, Pudsey, West Yorkshire, LS28 6EZ Tel: 0113-229 9400 Fax: 0113-229 9500

Driver Hire Group Services, Progress House, Castlefields Lane, Bingley, West Yorkshire, BD16 2AB Tel: (01274) 551166 Fax: (01274) 551165 E-mail: info@driver-hire.co.uk

Driver Hire Nationwide, Moulton Park Business Centre, Redhouse Road, Moulton Park Industrial Estate, Northampton, NN3 6AQ Tel: (01604) 670199 Fax: (01604) 644872 E-mail: enquiries@driver-hire.co.uk

Kelly Services, 22 Hanover Buildings, Southampton, SO14 1JU Tel: (023) 8023 5835 Fax: (023) 8023 6519 E-mail: southampton@kellyservices.co.uk

▶ Linc's 2 Drivers, Unit 2, Earlesfield Lane, Grantham, Lincolnshire, NG31 7NT Tel: (01476) 570601 Fax: (01476) 570268 E-mail: info@links2drivers.co.uk

Manpower UK Ltd, Capital Court, 30 Windsor Street, Uxbridge, Middlesex, UB8 1AB Tel: (01895) 205200 Fax: (01895) 205201

▶ Red Eagle, 38 Bouverie Square, Folkestone, Kent, CT20 1BA Tel: (01303) 851133 Fax: (01303) 851134 E-mail: jobs@red-eagle.co.uk

Stafflink (UK) Ltd, 138 Lower Road, London, SE16 2UG Tel: (020) 7252 2212 Fax: (020) 7252 2901 E-mail: info@staff-link.co.uk

COMMERCIAL VEHICLE DRIVING TRAINING

A P T T Ltd, Ty-Bach, Mount Bradford, St. Martins, Oswestry, Shropshire, SY11 3EY Tel: (01691) 773732 Fax: (01691) 773732 E-mail: enquiries@rmbtrainingsevices.co.uk

▶ Accidon'T, 20 East Argyle Street, Helensburgh, Dunbartonshire, G84 7RR Tel: (01436) 678018 Fax: (01436) 678808 E-mail: simon.johnston@accidont.co.uk

D & B Training Ltd, Sandy Court Moss Industrial Estate, St. Helens Road, Leigh, Lancashire, WN7 3PT Tel: (01942) 678986 Fax: (01942) 602566 E-mail: sales@db-training.net

D S C Associates, Chester Court Chester Park, Alfreton Road, Derby, DE21 4AB Tel: (01332) 204144 Fax: (01332) 200344 E-mail: info@derwentsafetycentre.co.uk

Hiremech Ltd, 1 Triumph Trading Estate, Tariff Road, London, N17 0EB Tel: (020) 8880 3322 Fax: (020) 8880 3355 E-mail: paul@hiremech.co.uk

Manchester Training Ltd, Greengate, Middleton, Manchester, M24 1RU Tel: (0800) 3895283 Fax: 0161-653 3536 E-mail: mail@manchestertraining.com

▶ Nationwide Instructor Training College, 441 Dudley Road, Wolverhampton, WV2 3AQ Tel: (0845) 1304035 Fax: (0845) 1304507 E-mail: info@drivinginstructorcollege.co.uk

Nightfreight GB Ltd, Europa House, 122 Conway Street, Birkenhead, Merseyside, CH41 6RY Tel: 0151-649 0123 Fax: 0151-649 0101 E-mail: itdepartment@nightfreight.co.uk

COMMERCIAL VEHICLE DRIVING TRAINING, HEAVY GOODS VEHICLE (HGV)

▶ Truck Training UK (Warrington) Ltd, The Old Barn, Bellhouse Lane, Moore, Warrington, WA4 6TR Tel: (01925) 740404 Fax: (01925) 740404 E-mail: info@trukwarrington.com

COMMERCIAL VEHICLE DRIVING TRAINING, LIGHT GOODS VEHICLE (LGV)

▶ Big Rigs LGV Driver Training, Hereford, Hereford, HR4 7SG Tel: 01432 761004 Fax: 01432 769305 E-mail: info@bigrigstraining.com

COMMERCIAL VEHICLE ELECTRONIC REVERSING AIDS

Croft Backstop Ltd, Winston Avenue, Croft, Leicester, LE9 3GQ Tel: (01455) 285600 Fax: (01455) 285909 E-mail: sales@croftbackstop.com

COMMERCIAL VEHICLE ENGINEERING

Adams Morey, Unit A 1-2 River Way Industrial Estate, Newport, Isle of Wight, PO30 5UY Tel: (01983) 522552 Fax: (01983) 821169

Alco Waste Management Ltd, Joseph Noble Road, Lillyhall Industrial Estate, Lillyhall, Workington, Cumbria, CA14 4JH Tel: (01900) 602205 Fax: (01900) 601886

Appleton Commercial Engineering, Unit 3c Lyncastle Way, Barleycastle Lane, Appleton, Warrington, WA4 4ST Tel: (01925) 601855 Fax: (01925) 860478 E-mail: email@ace-commercials.com

B S Commercial Repairs Ltd, 3 Clothier Road, Bristol, BS4 5PS Tel: 0117-977 2608 Fax: 0117-972 1967 E-mail: sales@bs-commercial.co.uk

Boalloy Ltd, Radnor Park Trading Estate, West Heath, Congleton, Cheshire, CW12 4QA Tel: (01260) 275155 Fax: (01260) 279696 E-mail: buying@boalloy.org

C D A R T Engineering, 1-2 Willow Road, Castle Donington, Derby, DE74 2NP Tel: (01332) 811150 Fax: (01332) 811306

Carkeek Engineers, 15 Valley Road, Plympton, Plymouth, PL7 1RS Tel: (01752) 517460 Fax: (01752) 347470

Chambers Engineering Ltd, Warmstone Lane, Waddesdon, Aylesbury, Buckinghamshire, HP18 0NQ Tel: (01296) 651380 Fax: (01296) 651063 E-mail: chameng@btconnect.com

Crossroads Commercials Group Ltd, Pheasant Drive, Birstall, Batley, West Yorkshire, WF17 9LR Tel: (01924) 425000 Fax: (01924) 441111 E-mail: info@crossroads.co.uk

A.W.D. Dwight & Sons (Engineers) Ltd, Delamare Road, Cheshunt, Waltham Cross, Hertfordshire, EN8 9UD Tel: (01992) 634255 Fax: (01992) 626672 E-mail: sales@imperialengineering.co.uk

F.J. Fildes, Stourbridge Road, Lye, Stourbridge, West Midlands, DY9 7BU Tel: (01384) 892939 Fax: (01384) 892903 E-mail: postmaster@rmgroup.co.uk

Ford & Slater Of Peterborough, America House, Newark Road, Peterborough, PE1 5YD Tel: (01733) 295000 Fax: (01733) 295010 E-mail: enquiries@fordandslater.co.uk

Gary Holmes Engineering, Unit B, Smiths Yard, Stone Lane, Axford, Marlborough, Wiltshire, SN8 2EY Tel: (01672) 516041 Fax: (01672) 515893

▶ McPhee Bros (Blantyre) Ltd, 58 John Street, Blantyre, Glasgow, G72 0JF Tel: (01698) 823422 Fax: (01698) 823853 E-mail: lorna@mcfeemixers.co.uk

Marlborough Four Wheel Drive, Unit B, Smiths Yard, Axford, Marlborough, Wiltshire, SN8 2EY Tel: (01672) 516041 Fax: (01672) 519189

Mauville Servicing Ltd, Baird Way, Thetford, Norfolk, IP24 1JA Tel: (01842) 755363 Fax: (01842) 765085

Mittens Vehicle Servicing, The Council Depot, Swindon Road, Cheltenham, Gloucestershire, GL51 9JZ Tel: (01242) 526445 Fax: (01242) 526445

Panema Trailer Engineering Ltd, Chalk Lane, Snetterton, Norwich, NR16 2JZ Tel: (01953) 887622 Fax: (01953) 888515 E-mail: info@panematrailers.co.uk

Pullman Fleet Services, Rotherham Road, Maltby, Rotherham, South Yorkshire, S66 8EL Tel: (01709) 810230 Fax: (01709) 790174 E-mail: richard.austwick@pullmanfleet.co.uk

R W Boyles Transport Ltd, Shires Road, Buckingham Road Industrial Estate, Brackley, Northamptonshire, NN13 7EZ Tel: (01280) 702690 Fax: (01280) 701619 E-mail: ron@boyles.fslife.co.uk

Ratcliff Care Ltd, Unit 19, Saddleback Road, Westgate Industrial Estate, Northampton, NN5 5HL Tel: (01604) 591359

▶ Tec UK, Royal Oak Way North Unit A, Daventry Distribution Centre, Royal Oak Industrial Estate, Daventry, Northamptonshire, NN11 8LR Tel: (01327) 300400 Fax: (01327) 879679 E-mail: tecuk@aol.com

COMMERCIAL VEHICLE FUELLING SYSTEMS INSTALLATION CONTRACTORS

▶ Car & Van Hire, Unit 6-7 Harlaw Way, Harlaw Road Industrial Estate, Inverurie, Aberdeenshire, AB51 4SG Tel: (01467) 629999 Fax: (01467) 622211 E-mail: info@carandvanhire.net

Centaur Fuel Management, 251 Manchester Road, Walkden, Manchester, M28 3HE Tel: (0870) 7576323 Fax: 0161-794 8031 E-mail: mc@centauronline.co.uk

COMMERCIAL VEHICLE HANDBRAKES

Commercial Replacements, Unit L1 Blackpole Trading Estate East, Blackpole Road, Worcester, WR3 8SG Tel: (01905) 458052 Fax: (01905) 756078

Vernon Developments, Unit B, Mucklow Hill Trading Estate, Phase 2, Halesowen, West Midlands, B62 8DQ Tel: 0121-501 1171 Fax: 0121-550 6181

COMMERCIAL VEHICLE INTERNAL STORAGE KITS

Quality Industries Ltd, Unit C 18 Stafford Park, Telford, Shropshire, TF3 3BN Tel: (01952) 292166 Fax: (01952) 292167 E-mail: sales@qivansystems.co.uk

COMMERCIAL VEHICLE LIVERY/ ADVERTISING GRAPHICS SERVICES

A W S Metal Finishers, 79 Baltimore Road, Birmingham, B42 1DG Tel: 0121-357 3127 Fax: 0121-357 3127 E-mail: airbrush12@aol.com
Allen Signs Ltd, Waddington House, Whisby Way, Lincoln, LN6 3LQ Tel: (01522) 501500 Fax: (01522) 501600 E-mail: enquiries@allensigns.co.uk
A.J. Darling & Sons Ltd, Unit 1, Mereway Road, Twickenham, TW2 6RF Tel: (020) 8898 5555 Fax: (020) 8898 9874 E-mail: darlingsigns@aol.com
Designs, 53 Middleton Road, Banbury, Oxfordshire, OX16 3QR Tel: (01295) 254777 Fax: (01295) 254541 E-mail: david@designs-uk.com
England Signs, The Malthouse, Main St, Offenham, Evesham, Worcs, WR11 8QD Tel: (01386) 442712 Fax: (01386) 442977
F.J. Fildes, Stourbridge Road, Lye, Stourbridge, West Midlands, DY9 7BU Tel: (01384) 892939 Fax: (01384) 892903 E-mail: postmaster@rmgroup.co.uk
Imagination Signs, 43 Birdham Road, Chichester, West Sussex, PO19 8TB Tel: (01243) 783569 Fax: (01243) 785011 E-mail: sales@imaginationsigns.co.uk
John Eley, 17-18 Leofric Square, Peterborough, PE1 5TU Tel: (01733) 344293 Fax: (01733) 344293 E-mail: eleysigns@johneleysigns.com
Kiosk, No. 2, 43 High Street, Leamington Spa, Warwickshire, CV31 1LN Tel: (01926) 776282
System Signs Ltd, Unit 6a Canons Yard Industrial Estate, Station Road, Wootton Bassett, Swindon, SN4 7SP Tel: (01793) 852996 Fax: (01793) 852455 E-mail: info@system-signs.com
▶ Ti-Visual Ltd, 4 Greenfields, Upton, Chester, CH2 1LN Tel: (01244) 382287 Fax: 0870 1357161 E-mail: info@ti-visual.co.uk
▶ UK Sign Co., Unit 9a Beauchamp Industrial Park, Watling Street, Wilnecote, Tamworth, Staffordshire, B77 5BZ Tel: (01827) 262277 E-mail: sales@uksigncompany.com

COMMERCIAL VEHICLE MANUAL GEARBOXES

P & R Gearboxes, Woodside Service Station, Copthorne Road, Crawley, West Sussex, RH10 3PD Tel: (01293) 888141

COMMERCIAL VEHICLE PAINTING/FINISHING SERVICES

Abm Trucks, 16 Roudham Park Industrial Estate, Harling Road, Norwich, NR16 2SN Tel: (01953) 718572 Fax: (01953) 718572
Alloy Bodies Ltd, Jubilee Works, Clifton Street, Miles Platting, Manchester, M40 8HN Tel: 0161-205 7612 Fax: 0161-202 1917 E-mail: info@alloybodies.co.uk
▶ B P Rolls Ltd, West Portway, Andover, Hampshire, SP10 3LF Tel: (01264) 361516 Fax: (01264) 333473 E-mail: sales@bprolls.co.uk
C P S Oxford Ltd, Partridge Yard, Eynsham Road, Cassington, Witney, Oxfordshire, OX29 4EU Tel: (01865) 881204 Fax: (01865) 880617
C V P, Neales Yard, Queen Victoria Street, Blackburn, BB2 2QG Tel: 01254 679028
Essex Bodybuilders Ltd, Arterial House, Claydons Lane, Rayleigh, Essex, SS6 7UP Tel: (01268) 778326 Fax: (01268) 774988
Fleet Finish Ltd, Carseview Road, Forfar, Angus, DD8 3BT Tel: (01307) 468616 Fax: (01307) 468618
GB Transport Engineering, 22 Algores Way, Wisbech, Cambridgeshire, PE13 2TQ Tel: (01945) 461780 Fax: (01945) 587107 E-mail: sales@gb-truckworld.co.uk
Gladwins Ltd, Church Road, Warboys, Huntingdon, Cambridgeshire, PE28 2RJ Tel: (01487) 822427 Fax: (01487) 823142 E-mail: gladwinsbodyshop@aol.com
J K Commercials, Stopes Road, Little Lever, Bolton, BL3 1NP Tel: 0161-724 5579 Fax: 0161-724 5579
Marcroft Engineering Ltd, Whieldon Road, Stoke-on-Trent, ST4 4HP Tel: (01782) 844075 Fax: (01782) 843579
▶ North Ayrshire Commercials, 5 Irvine Road, Lugton, Kilmarnock, Ayrshire, KA3 4ED Tel: (01294) 850049 E-mail: enquiries@northayrshirecommercials.co.uk
▶ Permagard Car Washing Supplies, 1u-1v Unit Standard Industrial Estate, Factory Road, London, E16 2EJ Tel: (020) 7473 0099 Fax: (020) 7474 0771 E-mail: sales@permagard.info
R W Evans Transport Ltd, Hilton Bank, Shifnal, Shropshire, TF11 8RH Tel: (01952) 691666 Fax: (01952) 691466
S Macneillie & Son Ltd, Stockton Close, Walsall, WS2 8LD Tel: (01922) 725560 Fax: (01922) 720916
Transpaint UK Ltd, 114 B M K Industrial Estate, Wakefield Road, Liversedge, West Yorkshire, WF15 6BS Tel: (01924) 503200 Fax: (01924) 500912 E-mail: transpaint@ltlbusiness.com

COMMERCIAL VEHICLE PAINTS

Broomstick Car & Commercials Ltd, Willow Farm, Ivinghoe Aston, Leighton Buzzard, Bedfordshire, LU7 9DF Tel: (01525) 220123 Fax: (01525) 221351
Granville Supplies Peterborough Ltd, Fengate, Peterborough, PE1 5XB Tel: (01733) 340100 Fax: (01733) 898370 E-mail: sales@granvillesupplies.co.uk
T & R Williamson Ltd, 36 Stonebridgegate, Ripon, North Yorkshire, HG4 1TP Tel: (01765) 607711 Fax: (01765) 607908 E-mail: sales@trwilliamson.co.uk
Unity Coach Painters, Unit 16 Sandybridge La Industrial Estate, Shafton, Barnsley, South Yorkshire, S72 8PH Tel: (01226) 781800

COMMERCIAL VEHICLE PROTECTION EQUIPMENT, NUDGE BARS ETC

▶ Stanwell Trailers, 3 Bedfont Road, Stanwell, Staines, Middlesex, TW19 7LR Tel: (01784) 252145 Fax: (01784) 244217 E-mail: mick@stanwelltrailers.co.uk

COMMERCIAL VEHICLE REPAIR

A Chard & Son Ltd, Unit 1 Small Street, St. Philips, Bristol, BS2 0SQ Tel: 0117-977 7876 Fax: 0117-977 7876
A M Transport (Liverpool) Ltd, Unit 12 B, Candy Park, Plantation Road, Bromborough, Wirral, Merseyside, CH62 3QS Tel: 0151-346 1780 Fax: 0151-346 1781
A & R Vehicle Services Ltd, Darlaston Road, Wednesbury, West Midlands, WS10 7TZ Tel: 0121-526 6611 Fax: 0121-526 2848 E-mail: admin@aandrvehicleservices.co.uk
A T F Services, 60 Brick Kiln Lane, Parkhouse Industrial Estate West, Newcastle, Staffordshire, ST5 7AS Tel: (01782) 561095 Fax: (01782) 566444
Appleton Commercial Engineering, Unit 3c Lyncastle Way, Barleycastle Lane, Appleton, Warrington, WA4 4ST Tel: (01925) 601855 Fax: (01925) 860478 E-mail: email@ace-commercials.com
Application Specific Computers Ltd, Chapel Lane, Emley, Huddersfield, HD8 9ST Tel: (01924) 844600 Fax: (01924) 844606
Austin Bros Ltd, 413 London Road, Slough, SL3 8PS Tel: (01753) 593007 Fax: (01753) 593329 E-mail: info@austinbrothers.co.uk
B M Commercials, Firbank Industrial Estate, Dallow Road, Luton, LU1 1TW Tel: (01582) 400262 Fax: (01525) 406089
▶ B P Rolls Ltd, West Portway, Andover, Hampshire, SP10 3LF Tel: (01264) 361516 Fax: (01264) 333473 E-mail: sales@bprolls.co.uk
Baker Auto Care, 18 Bankside, Station Approach, Kidlington, Oxfordshire, OX5 1JE Tel: (01865) 376008 Fax: (01865) 841511
Barwick Commercials, Rennesley Works, Anchor Lane, Wadesmill, Ware, Hertfordshire, SG12 0TE Tel: (01920) 462370
Blackmore Commercials, Little Tennis Street, Nottingham, NG2 4EL Tel: 0115-958 6696 Fax: 0115-979 9698
Bodycraft 2004, Unit A4, Worcester Trading Estate, Worcester, WR3 8HR Tel: (01905) 753631 Fax: (01905) 756790 E-mail: bobbycraft@tiscali.co.uk
Broomstick Car & Commercials Ltd, Willow Farm, Ivinghoe Aston, Leighton Buzzard, Bedfordshire, LU7 9DF Tel: (01525) 220123 Fax: (01525) 221351
Brown & Cayton Coachworks Ltd, Unit 8 The Airfield, Little Staughton, Bedford, MK44 2BN Tel: (01234) 376591 Fax: (01234) 376202 E-mail: brown.cayton@btopenworld.com
Brownlow Way Garage, Topping Street, Off Brownlow Way, Bolton, BL1 3UB Tel: (01204) 533300 Fax: (01204) 533300
C D A R T Engineering, 1-2 Willow Road, Castle Donington, Derby, DE74 2NP Tel: (01332) 811150 Fax: (01332) 811306
C & J Commercials, Falcon Garage, Sparth Bottoms Road, Rochdale, Lancashire, OL11 4HT Tel: (01706) 632680 Fax: (01706) 632680
Car Comm Aid Ltd, 47-49 Henshall Road, Parkhouse Industrial Estate, Parkhouse Industrial Estate West, Newcastle, Staffordshire, ST5 7RY Tel: (01782) 563474 Fax: (01782) 563550 E-mail: mail@carcommaid.co.uk
▶ Centaur Van & Truck, 20-22 Kenyon Lane, Manchester, M40 9JQ Tel: 0161-205 3885 E-mail: parts@cvtmercaid.co.uk
Frank Chivers & Son, 1 Estcourt Street, Devizes, Wiltshire, SN10 1LQ Tel: (01380) 723411 Fax: (01380) 728078
▶ Commercial Bodies East Anglia, 9 Hurricane Way, Norwich, NR6 6EZ Tel: (01603) 484047 Fax: (01603) 417834 E-mail: mwcbea@freenet.co.uk
Commercial Body Works, Toseland Road, Graveley, St. Neots, Cambridgeshire, PE19 6PS Tel: (01480) 831821 Fax: (01480) 831322
Commercial Colours Ltd, Zone 3 Link 56, Weighbridge Road, Deeside Industrial Park, Deeside, Clwyd, CH5 2LL Tel: (01244) 281352 Fax: (01244) 280936 E-mail: admin@commercialcolours.co.uk
Commercial Refurb Ltd, Unit 6 Orton Industrial Estate, London Road, Coalville, Leicestershire, LE67 3JA Tel: (01530) 810982
Cordwallis Commercials (Maidenhead) Ltd, Cordwallis Street, Maidenhead, Berkshire, SL6 7BE Tel: (01628) 622264 Fax: (01628) 770446
D C W Accided Repairs Ltd, Cornhill Close, Lodge Farm Industrial Estate, Harlestone Road, Northampton, NN5 7UQ Tel: (01604) 753208 Fax: (01604) 759718
▶ Dashtech Services (UK), Delta Street, New Basford, Nottingham, NG7 7GJ Tel: (07980) 213377 E-mail: m_ali1972@hotmail.com
David B Harries, Maesyronnen, Llangeitho, Tregaron, Dyfed, SY25 6TT Tel: (01974) 821682 Fax: (01974) 821682 E-mail: enquiries@dbhtranspoters.co./uk
Lawrence David Ltd, Maxwell Road, Peterborough, PE2 7JR Tel: (01733) 397600 Fax: (01733) 397601 E-mail: sales@lawrencedavid.co.uk
Dennison Commercials Ltd, 16 Carewamean Road, Killeavy, Newry, County Down, BT35 8JQ Tel: (028) 3026 5425 Fax: (028) 3026 3807 E-mail: sales@dennisons.co.uk
Don Bur Service Ltd, Boothen Old Road, Stoke-on-Trent, ST4 4EE Tel: (01782) 749333 Fax: (01782) 749191 E-mail: sales@donbur.co.uk
▶ Ellis Motors, 6 Sheddingdean Business Centre, Marchants Way, Burgess Hill, West Sussex, RH15 8QY Tel: (01444) 480606 Fax: (01444) 480606 E-mail: fixit@ellismotors.co.uk
Fleet Speed Coachworks Ltd, Unit 7-11 Plot 6 Fairfields, Free Prae Road, Chertsey, Surrey, KT16 8EA Tel: (01932) 568848 Fax: (01932) 568840
Forge Engineering, Tarran Way Industrial Estate, Pasture Road, Tarran Industrial Estate, Wirral, Merseyside, CH46 4TP Tel: 0151-678 7777 Fax: 0151-677 0006
G B Truck Service, Cross Keys Works, Cross Keys Lane, Hoyland, Barnsley, South Yorkshire, S74 0QA Tel: (01226) 744114 Fax: (01226) 749999 E-mail: sales@gbtrucks.co.uk
Greenhous, March Way, Battlefield Enterprise Park, Shrewsbury, SY1 3JE Tel: (01743) 467904 Fax: (01743) 457500 E-mail: enquiries@greenhous.co.uk
Hallen Motor Bodies, Collins Street, Bristol, BS11 9JJ Tel: 0117-982 3314 Fax: 0117-982 3314
Handley Plant & Vehicle Repairs, Ashmead, 62 Petersfield Road, Midhurst, West Sussex, GU29 9JR Tel: (01730) 816785 Fax: (01730) 816785
▶ Hartlebury Plant & Motor Services, Unit 7 Oldington Trading Estate, Kidderminster, Worcestershire, DY11 7QP Tel: (01562) 824300 Fax: (01562) 827500
▶ Heathrow Truck Centre, Lakeside Industrial Estate, Bath Road, Colnbrook, Slough, SL3 0ED Tel: (01753) 681818 Fax: (01753) 680270
Houghton-Parkhouse Ltd, Grisleymire Lane, Milnthorpe, Cumbria, LA7 7RF Tel: (01539) 563347 Fax: (01539) 562472 E-mail: sales@houghtons.com
J Mccartney Ltd, 168 Park View Road, London, N17 9BL Tel: (020) 8808 0582 Fax: (020) 8365 1884 E-mail: jmccartneylimited@parkviewroad.fsnet.co.uk
J W Barrow & Co., Griffiths Road, Lostock Gralam, Northwich, Cheshire, CW9 7NU Tel: (01606) 331222 Fax: (01606) 331333 E-mail: jwbarrow@btinternet.com
J W Blake & Son, 159 Brooker Road, Waltham Abbey, Essex, EN9 1JH Tel: (01992) 713756 Fax: (01992) 713756
J W J Car & Commercial Repairs, 113-115 Codicote Road, Welwyn, Hertfordshire, AL6 9TY Tel: (01438) 820351
Jempsons Ltd, Slade Yard, Rye, East Sussex, TN31 7DG Tel: (01797) 228500 Fax: (01797) 225080 E-mail: commercials@jempsons.co.uk
Kent & Sussex Truck Centre Ltd, Longfield Road, Tunbridge Wells, Kent, TN2 3EY Tel: (01892) 515333 Fax: (01892) 531813 E-mail: vehicles@kst.co.uk
Kumarlo Bodyworks Ltd, 22 Ivanhoe Road, Finchampstead, Wokingham, Berkshire, RG40 4QQ Tel: 0118-973 3077 Fax: 0118-973 4787 E-mail: enquiries@kumarlobodyworks.co.uk
Lambourne's Ltd, White Post Hill, Farningham, Dartford, DA4 0LB Tel: (08700) 362436 Fax: (01322) 865491 E-mail: sales@lambournes.co.uk
Alan Richard Lock, Pathfields Industrial Estate, South Molton, Devon, EX36 3LH Tel: (01769) 572220 Fax: (01769) 574777
M S A Engineering Services Ltd, Sub-Station Road, Felixstowe, Suffolk, IP11 3JB Tel: (01394) 675108 Fax: (01394) 673311
M & S Commercials Ltd, Bealey Industrial Estate, Dumers Lane, Radcliffe, Manchester, M26 2BD Tel: 0161-724 1311 Fax: 0161-724 1322 E-mail: mandscommercials@aol.com
Merlin Motor Co. Ltd, 3 Lodge Estate, Withybush Road, Haverfordwest, Dyfed, SA62 4BW Tel: (01437) 764928 Fax: (01437) 769628
Milton Keynes Vehicle Services, Unit 27 Harmill Industrial Estate, Grovebury Road, Leighton Buzzard, Bedfordshire, LU7 4FF Tel: (01525) 374633 Fax: (01525) 374633
Mossley, Unit 89 Earls Road, Grangemouth, Stirlingshire, FK3 8XE Tel: (01324) 474555 Fax: (01324) 474555 E-mail: mossleyautos@aol.com
Neath Coachbuilders Ltd, Cilfrew, Neath, West Glamorgan, SA10 8LF Tel: (01639) 643629 Fax: (01639) 646566 E-mail: enquiries@neathcoachbuilders.co.uk
Nicholls Commercials, 95a Mitcham Lane, London, SW16 6LY Tel: (020) 8677 0873 Fax: (020) 8769 0443
North Yorkshire Commercials Ltd, Dalton Airfield, Dalton, Thirsk, North Yorkshire, YO7 3HE Tel: (01845) 578123 Fax: (01845) 578144
Ooops! Net, 4 K & B Estate, Holyrood Close, Poole, Dorset, BH17 7BP Tel: (01202) 695999 Fax: (01202) 696333 E-mail: mail@ooops.net
▶ P D Commercials, 5c Kingswood Douglas Estate, Kingswood, Bristol, BS15 8HJ Tel: 0117-960 8757 Fax: 0117-960 8758
P H Antell & Sons Ltd, Blandford Road, Shillingstone, Blandford Forum, Dorset, DT11 0SF Tel: (01258) 860233 Fax: (01258) 860266
Pullman Fleet Services, Timber Works, Whiteball, Wellington, Somerset, TA21 0LY Tel: (01823) 672909 Fax: (01823) 672978
R C S Hose & Hydraulics Ltd, Crucible Road, Corby, Northamptonshire, NN17 5TS Tel: 0800 3893132
R W Evans Transport Ltd, Hilton Bank, Shifnal, Shropshire, TF11 8RH Tel: (01952) 691666 Fax: (01952) 691466
Ratcliff Care Ltd, Unit 19, Saddleback Road, Westgate Industrial Estate, Northampton, NN5 5HL Tel: (01604) 591359
S & W Garages Commercial Ltd, Printshop Lane, Atherton, Manchester, M46 9BJ Tel: (01942) 878961 Fax: (01942) 897955
Spectrum, 540 London Road, Grays, Essex, RM20 3BJ Tel: (01708) 868306 Fax: (01708) 860118 E-mail: spectrumvr@aol.com
Sterlings D F C Ltd, Ynys Bridge, Hoel-Yr-Ynys, Tongwynlais, Cardiff, CF15 7NT Tel: (029) 2081 3131 Fax: (029) 2081 3598 E-mail: rvs@easynet.co.uk
Stiller Group Ltd, Vulcan Road, Bilston, West Midlands, WV14 7LB Tel: (01902) 491151 Fax: (01902) 402613
▶ Stone Hardy, 1 Aubrey Street, Salford, M50 3UT Tel: 0161-868 2880 Fax: 0161-868 2899
T Baden Hardstaff Ltd, Hillside, Gotham Road, Kingston-on-Soar, Nottingham, NG11 0DF Tel: 0115-983 1234 Fax: 0115-983 1225
T J Commercials, 10 Doons Road, Cookstown, County Tyrone, BT80 9LL Tel: (028) 8675 1760 Fax: (028) 8675 1760
T J Penny, Hammondstreet Road, Cheshunt, Waltham Cross, Hertfordshire, EN7 6PQ Tel: (01707) 875878
E.D. Thomas Ltd, 113 Fordwater Road, Chertsey, Surrey, KT16 8HB Tel: (01932) 566963
Thomas Transport Ltd, Coppards Lane, Northiam, Rye, East Sussex, TN31 6QR Tel: (01797) 252387 Fax: (01797) 252625
Transport Fabrications Ltd, Appleton Road, Acaster Malbis, York, YO23 2UZ Tel: (01904) 744622 Fax: (01904) 744633 E-mail: stuarttransfab1@aol.com
Trident Commercials, Hermitage Lane, Aylesford, Kent, ME20 7PX Tel: (01622) 720020 Fax: (01622) 720082
Truck-Alignment Ltd, Anchor & Hope Lane, London, SE7 7RY Tel: (020) 8858 3781 Fax: (020) 8858 5663 E-mail: admin@vipgroupltd.co.uk
Truckfix Leeds, Harper Farm, Whitehall Road, Leeds, LS12 6JU Tel: 0113-231 1788 Fax: 0113-279 6874
Woodford Engineering, Unit 1A, The Bridge, Narberth, Dyfed, SA67 8QA Tel: (01834) 861368 Fax: (01834) 861368
Wornald Auto Refinishers, Units 9-10 Park Drive Business Center, Wakefield, West Yorkshire, WF3 3ET Tel: (01924) 822444

COMMERCIAL VEHICLE ROOF RACKS OR BARS

▶ Demar Ltd, Era House, Weir Lane, Worcester, WR2 4AY Tel: (01905) 422688 Fax: (01905) 422610 E-mail: sales@demarvan.co.uk
▶ Ski Rack Surfboard Car Roof Rack Cheap Car Roof Rack, 15 Ambridge Close, Northampton, NN4 9RW Tel: (01604) 710106 E-mail: sales@rackinabag.co.uk

COMMERCIAL VEHICLE SIDE CURTAINS

Andrew Mitchell Co. Ltd, Bates Business Centre, Church Road, Harold Wood, Romford, RM3 0JF Tel: (01708) 370800 Fax: (01708) 377190 E-mail: info@mitco.co.uk
J & J Carter Ltd, 8 Lion Court, Basingstoke, Hampshire, RG24 8QU Tel: (01256) 811455 Fax: (01256) 811458 E-mail: sales@jjcarter.com
K & T Tilts, Readmans Industrial Estate, Station Road, East Tilbury, Tilbury, Essex, RM18 8QR Tel: (01375) 840880 Fax: (01375) 840740 E-mail: info@kandttilts.co.uk
W. J. Leech & Sons Ltd, 275 Derby Road, Bootle, Merseyside, L20 8PL Tel: 0151-933 9334 Fax: 0151-933 5005 E-mail: david@wjleech.com

COMMERCIAL VEHICLE SIDE CURTAINS – *continued*

Roland Tilts UK Ltd, Unit 1 Usher Street, Bradford, West Yorkshire, BD4 7DS Tel: (01274) 391645 Fax: (01274) 305156

Simark Engineering Co., Griffin Industrial Estate, Rowley Regis, West Midlands, B65 0SN Tel: 0121-559 1351 Fax: 0121-559 3205 E-mail: simark.engineering@virgin.net

Stronghold International, Nicholson Court, Geddings Road, Hoddesdon, Hertfordshire, EN11 0NE Tel: (01992) 460274 Fax: (01992) 479471 E-mail: sales@stronghold.co.uk

Terapin Curtain Systems, 2 Glenavy Road, Upper Ballinderry, Lisburn, County Antrim, BT28 2EU Tel: (028) 9265 1007 Fax: (028) 9265 2019 E-mail: info@terapin.com

Volvo Truck South Ltd, Station Road, Stoney Stanton, Leicester, LE9 4LU Tel: (01455) 273260 Fax: (01455) 272092

COMMERCIAL VEHICLE SUSPENSION COMPONENTS

Ferrabyrne Ltd, Fort Road Industrial Estate, Wick, Littlehampton, West Sussex, BN17 7QU Tel: (01903) 721317 Fax: (01903) 730452 E-mail: sales@ferrabyrne.co.uk

COMMERCIAL VEHICLE VALETING

▶ 1st Dirt Busters, 20 Clarendon Road, Southsea, Hampshire, PO5 2EE Tel: (023) 9282 9429 E-mail: dirt.busters@virgin.net

▶ Aautoclean Car Valet Services, 30 Oakdale Road, Oldbury, West Midlands, B68 8AY Tel: (07776) 194420 Fax: 0121-544 3276 E-mail: aautoclean@blueyonder.co.uk

▶ ACS Mobile Valeting, Wilthorpe, Barnsley, South Yorkshire, S75 1JW Tel: 07913 504999 E-mail: valeting@acsmobile.co.uk

▶ Autogleam Mobile Valeting, 76 Birkdale, Warmley, Bristol, BS30 8GH Tel: 0117-961 8666 Fax: 0117-914 0777 E-mail: info@autogleam.net

Car Care, 153 St. Johns Road, Kettering, Northamptonshire, NN15 5AZ Tel: (01536) 524512 E-mail: sales@carcare-mvs.co.uk

▶ Car Treat (Mobile Car Valeting), 135 Rylands Road, Kennington, Kennington, Ashford, Kent, TN24 9LU Tel: (01233) 629247 E-mail: jonathan4reeves@uk2.net

▶ G R Valeting, 35 Rutland Close, Catterick Garrison, North Yorkshire, DL9 3HJ Tel: (01748) 833434 E-mail: gordon@grvaleting.com

▶ K G B Car Valeting, 12 Stuchbury Close, Aylesbury, Buckinghamshire, HP19 8GD Tel: (01296) 436444 Fax: (01296) 436444 E-mail: info@kgbcarvaleting.co.uk

▶ LBVALETING, 55 Walnut Crescent, Kettering, Northamptonshire, NN16 9PX Tel: (01536) 501217 E-mail: lbvaleting@hotmail.com

▶ Lellers Valeting Centres Ltd, 159 Turners Hill, Cheshunt, Waltham Cross, Hertfordshire, EN8 9BH Tel: (01992) 641383 Fax: E-mail: valet@lellers.co.uk

Posh Wosh - Mobile Car Valeting Ashford Kent, Unit 19, Dunnock Road, Kennington, Ashford, Kent, TN25 4QJ Tel: (07811) 547041 Fax: (01233) 630537 E-mail: posh_wosh2003@hotmail.com

Professional Mobile Valet Service, 31 Brimbleworth Lane, St. Georges, Weston-super-Mare, Avon, BS22 7XS Tel: (07811) 158953 E-mail: professionalmobilevaletservice@hotmail.co.uk

▶ Squeaky Clean, 34 Dean Road, Wrexham, Clwyd, LL13 9EH Tel: (07713) 922158 E-mail: info@squeaky-clean.me.uk

▶ Valet Magic, 6 High Street, Stanwell, Staines, Middlesex, TW19 7JS Tel: (01753) 680395 Fax: (01753) 680395 E-mail: info@valetmagic.com

▶ Waterless Detailers (Derby) Ltd, 20 Victoria Drive, Woodville, Swadlincote, Derbyshire, DE11 8DY Tel: (07970) 607166 E-mail: derby@waterlessdetailers.co.uk

COMMERCIAL VEHICLE WASHING SYSTEMS

Kautex Textron CVS Ltd, Dyffryn Business Park, Ystrad Mynach, Hengoed, Mid Glamorgan, CF82 7RJ Tel: (01443) 621800 Fax: (01443) 621940

▶ Washtec UK Ltd, 14a Oak Industrial Park, Chelmsford Road, Dunmow, Essex, CM6 1XN Tel: (01371) 878800 Fax: (01371) 878810 E-mail: sales@washtec-uk.com

Wheelwash Ltd, Leslie Road, Woodford Park Industrial Estate, Winsford, Cheshire, CW7 2RB Tel: (01606) 592044 Fax: (01606) 592045 E-mail: sales@wheelwash.com

COMMERCIAL VEHICLES

A L Musselwhite Ltd, Budds Lane, Romsey, Hampshire, SO51 0HA Tel: (01794) 516222 Fax: (01794) 830224 E-mail: almusselwhite@virgin.net

A M Phillip Trucktech, Muiryfaulds, Forfar, Angus, DD8 1XP Tel: (01307) 820255 Fax: (01307) 820417 E-mail: agritech@amphillip.co.uk

▶ Abbey Group Motors, 32 Abbey Foregate, Shrewsbury, SY2 6BT Tel: 01743 242888

Adams Morey Ltd, Yeomans Industrial Park, Yeomans Way, Bournemouth, BH8 0BJ Tel: (01202) 524422 Fax: (01202) 524448 E-mail: enquiries@adamsmorey.com

B M Commercials, Firbank Industrial Estate, Dallow Road, Luton, LU1 1TW Tel: (01582) 400262 Fax: (01525) 406089

Billet Auto Sales Ltd, Archers Fields, Basildon, Essex, SS13 1DN Tel: (01268) 286764 Fax: (01268) 532349

Bridges of Minworth, Kingsbury Road, Minworth, Sutton Coldfield, West Midlands, B76 9DD Tel: 0121-351 1965 Fax: 0121-351 7793 E-mail: sales@bridges-bridmin.co.uk

C D Bramall Plc, Etherstone Avenue, Newcastle upon Tyne, NE7 7LQ Tel: 0191-266 3311 Fax: 0191-215 0762 E-mail: newcastlehyundaisales@evanshalshaw.com

C J Leonard, Clevestone Works, Whitby Road, Guisborough, Cleveland, TS14 7DA Tel: (01287) 633842 Fax: (01287) 633871 E-mail: sales@cjleonard.co.uk

Carecross Wood Craftsmen, Higher Lake Farm, Woodland, Ashburton, Newton Abbot, Devon, TQ13 7JR Tel: (01364) 652638 Fax: (01364) 652638 E-mail: sales@quizecall.com

▶ Channel Commercials plc, Cobbswood Industrial Estate, Brunswick Road, Ashford, Kent, TN23 1EH Tel: (01233) 629272 Fax: (01233) 636322 E-mail: louisedodds@channelcommercials.co.uk

Citroen Birmingham, Small Heath Highway, Birmingham, B10 0BT Tel: 0121-766 7060 Fax: 0121-766 7042 E-mail: sisav@supanet.com

Clark Commercials (Aberdeen) Ltd, Wellheads Drive, Wellheads Industrial Estate, Dyce, Aberdeen, AB21 7GQ Tel: (01224) 725412 Fax: (01224) 793319 E-mail: sales@clarkcommercials.co.uk

▶ Clark Motor Engineering, 1 & 2 Charlwood Park Cottages, Charlwood Road, Horley, Surrey, RH6 0AJ Tel: 01293 772202 E-mail: recovery@clarkmotorengineering.co.uk

▶ Clean Air Power, 1 Aston Way, Moss Side, Leyland, PR26 7UX Tel: (01772) 624499 Fax: (01772) 436495

Cordwallis Commercials (Maidenhead) Ltd, Cordwallis Street, Maidenhead, Berkshire, SL6 7BE Tel: (01628) 622264 Fax: (01628) 770446

Crossroads Commercials Group Ltd, Pheasant Drive, Birstall, Batley, West Yorkshire, WF17 9LR Tel: (01924) 425000 Fax: (01924) 441111 E-mail: info@crossroads.co.uk

Daf Trucks Ltd, Eastern By Passage, Thame, Oxfordshire, OX9 3FB Tel: (01844) 261111 Fax: (01844) 217111 E-mail: info@daftrucks.com

Dunstonian Holdings Ltd, 28a Station Square, Petts Wood, Orpington, Kent, BR5 1LS Tel: (01689) 832545 Fax: (01689) 878258 E-mail: enquiries@dunstonian.co.uk

Evobush UK Ltd, Ashcroft Way, Crosspoint Business Park, Coventry, CV2 2TU Tel: (024) 7662 6000 Fax: (024) 7662 6010

Ford Motor Co. Ltd, Central Head Office, Eagle Way, Brentwood, Essex, CM13 3BW Tel: (023) 8058 7300

GK Group, Wakefield Road, Carlisle, CA3 0HE Tel: (01228) 517200 Fax: (01228) 517349 E-mail: info@gk-ford.co.uk

H & L Garages Ltd, Grange Lane North, Scunthorpe, South Humberside, DN16 1BT Tel: (01724) 856655 Fax: (01724) 868493 E-mail: info@handlgarages.co.uk

Hartwell Truck, London Road, Dunstable, Bedfordshire, LU6 3DT Tel: (01582) 597575 Fax: (01582) 582650

▶ Hertz Car Sales, Unit 2 Aire Place Mills, Kirkstall Road, Chipping Warden, Banbury, Oxfordshire, OX17 1LL Tel: (01295) 667000 Fax: (01295) 667017

▶ Irisbus UK Ltd, Iveco House, Station Road, Watford, WD17 1SR Tel: (01923) 259660 Fax: (01923) 259623 E-mail: sales@irisbus.co.uk

J T Commercials, Wareham Road, Holton Heath, Poole, Dorset, BH16 6JW Tel: (01202) 632122 Fax: (01202) 621099

John R Weir Ltd, Hareness Road, Altens Industrial Estate, Aberdeen, AB12 3LE Tel: (01224) 871234 Fax: (01224) 894848 E-mail: sales@commercials.johnrweir.co.uk

L C Davis & Sons Ltd, 6 Prince Georges Road, London, SW19 2PX Tel: (020) 8648 3113 Fax: (020) 8640 8282 E-mail: info@lcdavis.com

L W Vass Holdings Ltd, Station Road, Ampthill, Bedford, MK45 2RB Tel: (01525) 403255 Fax: (01525) 404194 E-mail: sales@vass.co.uk

Leyland Trucks Ltd, Croston Road, Leyland, PR26 6LZ Tel: (01772) 621400 Fax: (01772) 625910 E-mail: sales@packar.com

▶ Lightwood Contracts Ltd, Lightwood Road, Longton, Stoke-on-Trent, ST3 4JG Tel: (01782) 599600 Fax: (01782) 330753 E-mail: stevehill@plattsgarage.com

M A N E R F UK Ltd, Frankland Road, Blagrove, Swindon, SN5 8YU Tel: (01793) 448000 Fax: (01793) 448260

M C Truck & Bus Ltd, Maymac House Unit 2 Yeoman Industrial Park, Test Lane, Southampton, SO16 9JX Tel: (023) 8066 3500 Fax: (023) 8087 3160

Mann & Overton Ltd, 39-41 Brewery Road, London, N7 9QH Tel: (020) 7700 0888 Fax: (020) 7700 6676 E-mail: info@mannandoverton.com

Marshall Specialist Vehicles Ltd, The Airport, Cambridge, CB5 8RX Tel: (01223) 373900 Fax: (01223) 373064 E-mail: info@marshallsv.com

Mercedes Benz (UK) Ltd, Tongwell, Delaware Drive, Milton Keynes, MK15 8BA Tel: (01908) 245000

Mudie Bond Ltd, Newtown Trading Estate, Northway Lane, Tewkesbury, Gloucestershire, GL20 8JG Tel: (01684) 295090 Fax: (01684) 850616 E-mail: sales@mudie-bond.co.uk

Norfolk Truck Enfield Ltd, Mollison Avenue, Enfield, Middlesex, EN3 7NE Tel: (020) 8804 1266 Fax: (020) 8443 2590

▶ North Ayrshire Commercials, 5 Irvine Road, Lugton, Kilmarnock, Ayrshire, KA3 4ED Tel: (01294) 850049 E-mail: enquiries@northayrshirecommercials.co.uk

Oakland Coachbuilders Ltd, Unit 3, KDO Business Centre, Little Witley, Worcester, WR6 6LR Tel: (01299) 896754 Fax: (01299) 896885 E-mail: oakland.horsebox@btconnect.com

Oakley Coachbuilders, High Cross, Ware, Hertfordshire, SG11 1AD Tel: (01920) 466781 Fax: (01920) 467895 E-mail: sales@oakleyhorseboxes.co.uk

Park Road Commercials, Manchester Road Garage, Blackrod, Bolton, BL6 5RU Tel: (01942) 811017 Fax: (01942) 811017

Polar Ford Barnsley, 223 Dodworth Road, Barnsley, South Yorkshire, S70 6PA Tel: (01226) 732732 Fax: (01226) 732867 E-mail: ford@barnsley.polar-motor.co.uk

Polar Ford York, Jockey Lane, Huntington, York, YO32 9GY Tel: (01904) 625371 Fax: (01904) 622238 E-mail: ford@york.polar-motor.co.uk

R K Trucks Centre Ltd, Edgar Road, Comber Road, Carryduff, Belfast, BT8 8NB Tel: (028) 9081 3600 Fax: (028) 9081 4115 E-mail: donna@rktrucks.com

R W Evans Transport Ltd, Hilton Bank, Shifnal, Shropshire, TF11 8RH Tel: (01952) 691666 Fax: (01952) 691466

Razorback Vehicles Corporation Ltd, Regus Building, Central Boulevard, Shirley, Solihull, West Midlands, B90 8AG Tel: (01564) 711051 Fax: (01564) 711451 E-mail: sales@razorback-vehicles.com

Richardson Ford, Westgate, Driffield, North Humberside, YO25 6SY Tel: (01377) 255294 Fax: (01377) 252887 E-mail: info@richardson-ford.co.uk

S Jones Transport Ltd, Anglian Road, Walsall, WS9 8ET Tel: (01922) 450000 Fax: (01922) 455920 E-mail: info@sjonestransport.com

Scania (Great Britain) Ltd, Delaware Drive, Tongwell, Milton Keynes, MK15 8HB Tel: (01908) 210210 Fax: (01908) 215040

Sherwood Truck & Van Ltd, Berristow Lane, Blackwell, Alfreton, Derbyshire, DE55 5HP Tel: (01773) 863311 Fax: (01773) 580271 E-mail: enquiries@sherwoodtruckandvan.com

Shinehill Ltd, 127 Ettingshall Road, Wolverhampton, WV2 2JP Tel: (01902) 451322 Fax: (01902) 870621 E-mail: shinehill@fsnet.co.uk

Sterling Coach Works, Ellerbeck Way, Stokesley Industrial Park, Stokesley, Middlesborough, Cleveland, TS9 5JZ Tel: (01642) 713333 Fax: (01642) 713805 E-mail: info@worldwidetrots.co.uk

Swansea Truck Centre Ltd, Unit 43 Cwmdu Industrial Estate, Carmarthen Road, Gendros, Swansea, SA5 8LG Tel: (01792) 582255 Fax: (01792) 579895 E-mail: sgc@swanseatrucks.co.uk

Taggart Motor Group, 528-540 Windmillhill Street, Motherwell, Lanarkshire, ML1 2AQ Tel: (01698) 266133 Fax: (01698) 262693 E-mail: enquiries@taggarts.co.uk

TC Harrison, Oxney Road, Peterborough, PE1 5YN Tel: (01733) 425555 Fax: (01733) 425556

▶ Trailertech Services Ltd, Unit 7 Plaxton Park, Cayton Low Road, Eastfield, Scarborough, North Yorkshire, YO11 3BQ Tel: (01723) 584897 Fax: (01723) 585235

Tregoning Ford, Tollgate, St. Breock, Wadebridge, Cornwall, PL27 7HT Tel: (01208) 893000 Fax: (01208) 815320 E-mail: sales@tregoningford.co.uk

Trio Hire Direct Ltd, 1 Summerson Court, Summerson Road, Bleak Hall, Milton Keynes, MK6 1LE Tel: (01908) 222700 Fax: (01908) 222842 E-mail: info@trio-waste.co.uk

Vehicletrademaster, PO Box 5347, Northampton, NN3 7YT Tel: (08702) 405445 Fax: (08702) 405445 E-mail: vtmoffice@btinternet.com

Visual Impact Signs, Breach Road, West Thurrock, Grays, Essex, RM20 3NR Tel: (01708) 865566 Fax: (01708) 865566

Volvo Group UK Ltd, Wedgnock Lane, Warwick, CV34 5YA Tel: (01926) 401777 Fax: (01926) 490991 E-mail: recruitment@newskies.com

Volvo Truck, Pytchley Lodge Road Industrial Estate, Pytchley Lodge Road, Kettering, Northamptonshire, NN15 6JJ Tel: (01536) 516311 Fax: (01536) 412386

Volvo Truck & Bus Scotland Ltd, 9 Fifty Pitches Place, Glasgow, G51 4GA Tel: 0141-810 2777 Fax: 0141-810 2788 E-mail: enquiries@volvoscot.co.uk

▶ W & J Allardyce Commercials Ltd, Hillside Garage, Longridge, Bathgate, West Lothian, EH47 8AN Tel: (01501) 770218 Fax: (01501) 771425 E-mail: william.allardyce@btopenworld.com

Western Truck Ltd, 123 Clydesdale Place, Moss Side Industrial Estate, Leyland, PR26 7QS Tel: (01772) 454124 Fax: (01772) 456075 E-mail: rr@westerntruck.co.uk

Whitby Morrison Ltd, Fourth Avenue, Western Road Industrial Estate, Crewe, CW1 6TT Tel: (01270) 581318 Fax: (01270) 250220

York, Ward & Rowlatt Ltd, St. Johns Street, Wellingborough, Northamptonshire, NN8 4LG Tel: (01933) 443403 Fax: (01933) 445044 E-mail: info@yorkward.co.uk

COMMINUTING MILLS

Bowsey Hill Sawmill, Bear Lane, Wargrave, Reading, RG10 8QJ Tel: 0118-940 2240

Ytron Quadro (UK) Ltd, Unit D Chiltern Commerce Centre, 43 Asheridge Road, Chesham, Buckinghamshire, HP5 2PY Tel: (01494) 792898 Fax: (01494) 792699 E-mail: sales@ytron-quadro.co.uk

COMMISSION WEAVING

Gainsborough Silk Weaving Co. Ltd, Alexandra Road, Sudbury, Suffolk, CO10 2XH Tel: (01787) 372081 Fax: (01787) 881785 E-mail: sales@gainsborough.co.uk

COMMISSION WOOL SCOURING

Thomas Chadwick & Sons, Eastfield Mills, Goods Lane, Dewsbury, West Yorkshire, WF12 8EH Tel: (01924) 465023 Fax: (01924) 465279 E-mail: tchadwick@standard-wool.co.uk

Haworth Scouring Co., Cashmere Works, Birksland Street, Bradford, West Yorkshire, BD3 9SX Tel: (01274) 846500 Fax: (01274) 846501

COMMODE CHAIRS

A J Way & Co. Ltd, Sunters End, Hillbottom Road, Sands Industrial Estate, High Wycombe, Buckinghamshire, HP12 4HS Tel: (01494) 471821 Fax: (01494) 450597 E-mail: sales@ajway.co.uk

COMMODITY BROKERS/ DEALERS

Bysel Ltd, Selby House, 27a Batley Road, Heckmondwike, West Yorkshire, WF16 9ND Tel: (01924) 403857 Fax: (01924) 405368 E-mail: export@byselcandy.com

Cargill Finance Ltd, Knowle Hill Park, Fairmile Lane, Cobham, Surrey, KT11 2PD Tel: (01932) 861000 Fax: (01932) 861200

C. Czarnikow Sugar Ltd, 24 Chiswell Street, London, EC1Y 4SG Tel: (020) 7972 6600 Fax: (020) 7972 6699 E-mail: czarnikow@czarnikow.com

East End Foods (Midlands) Ltd, P S W Buildings, 58-66 Darwin Street, Birmingham, B12 0TY Tel: 0121-772 5201 Fax: 0121-772 4079

Itl Impex Ltd, Commercial House, 19 Station Road, Bognor Regis, West Sussex, PO21 1QD Tel: (01243) 841734 Fax: (01243) 841734 E-mail: itl@hopcbroadband.com

Landauer Ltd, 25 Beaufort Court, Admirals Way, London, E14 9XL Tel: (020) 7538 5383 Fax: (020) 7538 2007 E-mail: trading@landauerseafood.com

Louis Dreyfus Investment Co. Ltd, Queensbury House, 3 Old Burlington Street, London, W1S 3LD Tel: (020) 7596 1000 Fax: (020) 7529 9000 E-mail: ldbeijing@louisdreyfus.com

Marex Carlton Ltd, Gossard House, Savile Row, London, W1S 3PE Tel: (020) 7491 6700 Fax: (020) 7491 6799

Marex Financial Ltd, Ground & 1St Floor Trinity Tower, Thomas Moore Square, London, E1W 1YH Tel: (020) 7488 3232 Fax: (020) 7265 3959

Sethia (London) Ltd, Sethia House, 105 St John St, London, EC1M 4AS Tel: (020) 7814 9014 Fax: (020) 7814 9016 E-mail: info@sethia-london.com

Simportex, 452a Finchley Road, London, NW11 8DG Tel: (020) 8457 8770 Fax: (020) 8457 7484 E-mail: sales@simportex.com

Sucden UK Ltd, 5 London Bridge Street, London, SE1 9SG Tel: (020) 7940 9400 Fax: (020) 7940 9500 E-mail: info@sucden.co.uk

Sucre Export London Ltd, Greencoat House, Francis Street, London, SW1P 1DH Tel: (020) 7873 0088 Fax: (020) 7873 0100 E-mail: sucre@sopex.co.uk

John Wyatt Ltd, Braithwaite Street, Leeds, LS11 9XE Tel: 0113-244 4151 Fax: 0113-242 3186 E-mail: enquiries@johnwyattltd.co.uk

COMMODITY EXCHANGES

Baltic Exchange Ltd, 24 St.Mary Axe, London, EC3A 8EX Tel: (020) 7623 5501 Fax: (020) 7369 1622 E-mail: admin@balticexchange.com

London Metal Exchange Ltd, 56 Leadenhall Street, London, EC3A 2DX Tel: (020) 7264 5555 Fax: (020) 7680 0505 E-mail: info@lme.co.uk

COMMUNICATION AERIALS

A N D & Group, Tanners Bank, North Shields, Tyne & Wear, NE30 1JH Tel: (01233) 635278 Fax: (0870) 4449680 E-mail: info@and-group.net
Active Aerials & Systems, 53 Rugeley Road, Armitage, Rugeley, Staffordshire, WS15 4AR Tel: 01543 307072 E-mail: active.systems@ntlworld.com
▶ DML International Limited, 6 Grebe Close, Poynton, Stockport, Cheshire, SK12 1HU Tel: 01625 850055 Fax: 01625 850055 E-mail: enquiries@dml.uk.com
Lintec Antennas, Unit 22 Woods Way, Goring-by-Sea, Worthing, West Sussex, BN12 4QY Tel: (01903) 242243 Fax: (01903) 242588 E-mail: sales@lintec-antennas.co.uk
▶ Oxford Strategic Ltd, The Maggalen Centre, Oxford Science Park, Oxford, OX4 4GA Tel: (01865) 784110 Fax: (01865) 748111 E-mail: info@oxfordstrategic.com
Scannest Ltd, 1 Horsewell Court, Moulton, Northampton, NN3 7XB Tel: (01604) 670064 Fax: (01604) 492767
Swindon Aerials, 31 Newport Street, Swindon, SN1 3DP Tel: (01793) 531400 Fax: (01793) 431831 E-mail: roysas777@yahoo.com
Wilsecure Installations, 292 Dewsbury Road, Leeds, LS11 6JT Tel: 0113-271 6097 Fax: 0113-270 4259 E-mail: sales@tindsdaletv.co.uk

COMMUNICATION DATA ENCODING SYSTEMS

Sound Concepts, 56 St. Saviours Crescent, Luton, LU1 5HG Tel: (01582) 416964 Fax: (01582) 480841

COMMUNICATION HEADSETS

Adodo, Howitt Buildings, Lenton Boulevard, Nottingham, NG7 2BG Tel: 0115-970 1471 Fax: 0115-970 1671 E-mail: solutions@adodo.co.uk
Audio Mouldings Ltd, Unit 4 Langley Terrace, Latimer Road, Luton, LU1 3XA Tel: (01582) 424606 Fax: (01582) 459891 E-mail: audiomouldings@aol.com
Clement Clarke International Ltd, Unit A Cartel Business Estate, Edinburgh Way, Harlow, Essex, CM20 2TT Tel: (01279) 414969 Fax: (01279) 456339 E-mail: info@c3headsets.com
Commscare, 20 Norbury Crescent, Hazel Grove, Stockport, Cheshire, SK7 5PD Tel: 0161-482 4433 Fax: 0161-482 4777 E-mail: sales@headsetsolutions.co.uk
Comtec Cables, Unit 3 Cardinal Way, Godmanchester, Huntingdon, Cambridgeshire, PE29 2XN Tel: (01480) 415400 Fax: (01480) 454724 E-mail: sales@comtec-comms.com
Direct Telecommunications Systems Ltd, Direct House, 16 Commercial Road, Skelmanthorpe, Huddersfield, HD8 9DA Tel: (01484) 867867 Fax: (01484) 867860 E-mail: info@direct-telecom.co.uk
Fulcrum Headsets, Unit 19, Apex Business Centre, Boscombe Road, Dunstable, Bedfordshire, LU5 4SB Tel: (0845) 4304070 Fax: (0845) 4304061 E-mail: sales@fulcrum-headsets.co.uk
GN Great Nordic UK Ltd, Runnymede House, 96-97 High Street, Egham, Surrey, TW20 9HQ Tel: (01784) 220140 Fax: (01784) 220144
Racal Acoustics, Waverley Industrial Park, Hailsham Drive, Harrow, Middlesex, HA1 4TR Tel: (020) 8515 6200 Fax: (020) 8427 0350 E-mail: email@racalacoustic.com
SELEX Communications, Green Park Business Centre, Sutton-On-Forest, York, YO61 1ET Tel: (01347) 811881 Fax: (01347) 811991 E-mail: davies.sales@selex-comms.com
Sitelink Communications, 14 Collingwood Court, Riverside Park Industrial Esta, Middlesbrough, Cleveland, TS2 1RP Tel: (01642) 232468 Fax: (01642) 226155 E-mail: teeside@sitelink.co.uk
Talking Headsets Ltd, Woodlands, The Bridle Lane, Hambrook, Chichester, West Sussex, PO18 8UG Tel: (01243) 573226 Fax: (01243) 574318 E-mail: info@talkingheadsets.co.uk

COMMUNICATION SYSTEMS,

See also headings for particular types

Auriga Communications Ltd, Auriga House, Thompson Close, Harpenden, Hertfordshire, AL5 4ES Tel: (01582) 466800 Fax: (01582) 466839 E-mail: sales@auriga.co.uk
Business Communications, Units 2 Bramshot Barns, Bramshot Lane, Fleet, Hampshire, GU51 2RU Tel: (01252) 617116 Fax: (01252) 626216 E-mail: info@businesscomms.co.uk
Controlware Communications Systems Ltd, 2 The Vo-Tec Centre, Hambridge Lane, Newbury, Berkshire, RG14 5TN Tel: (01635) 584500 Fax: (01635) 584599 E-mail: info@controlware.co.uk
Dee Communications Ltd, Dutton Green, Stanney Mill, Chester, CH2 4SA Tel: 0151-356 5955 Fax: 0151-356 5944 E-mail: sales@deecommunications.co.uk
Delta Point Computers Ltd, Oakley House, Pinfold Lane, Ashampstead, Reading, RG8 8SH Tel: (01635) 579059 Fax: (020) 7691 9601
Hermes Datacommunications International Ltd, Hermes House, Oxon Business Park, Bicton Heath, Shrewsbury, SY3 5DD Tel: (01743) 235555 Fax: (01743) 271717 E-mail: info@hermes.com
Jotron (UK) Ltd, Crossland Park, Cramlington, Northumberland, NE23 1LA Tel: (01670) 712000 Fax: (01670) 590265 E-mail: salesair@jotron.com
Mitier Communications, 2 Rudgard Avenue, Cherry Willingham, Lincoln, LN3 4JG Tel: (01522) 754279 Fax: (01522) 751942 E-mail: info@radiolinc.co.uk
Optilan, Common Lane Industrial Estate, Kenilworth, Warwickshire, CV8 2EL Tel: (01926) 864999 Fax: (01926) 851818
S O T Mobile Link, 1 Tanners Road, Stoke-on-Trent, ST2 8DP Tel: (01782) 541271 Fax: (01782) 541346 E-mail: gary@mobile-link.co.uk
Saturn Sales & Services Ltd, Unit 11 Morland Industrial Park, Morland Road, Highbridge, Somerset, TA9 3ET Tel: (01278) 794798 Fax: (01278) 788704
Simrad Ltd, Star Lane, Margate, Kent, CT9 4NP Tel: (01843) 290290 Fax: (01843) 290471

COMMUNICATION SYSTEMS CONSULTANTS OR DESIGNERS

Accutest Ltd, Wren Nest Road, Glossop, Derbyshire, SK13 8HB Tel: (01457) 866613 Fax: (01457) 856789 E-mail: sales@accutest.co.uk
Albion Computers P.L.C., 112 Strand, London, WC2R 0AG Tel: (020) 7212 9090 Fax: (020) 7212 9091 E-mail: sales@albion.co.uk
Altis Consulting Ltd, 11 Thatcham Business Village, Colthrop Way, Thatcham, Berkshire, RG19 4LW Tel: (01635) 867575 Fax: (01635) 867576 E-mail: sales@altisltd.com
Bluebell Associates Ltd, Cresta House, 42 Water Lane, Wilmslow, Cheshire, SK9 5AL Tel: (01625) 539288 Fax: (01625) 539211
Business Communications, Units 2 Bramshot Barns, Bramshot Lane, Fleet, Hampshire, GU51 2RU Tel: (01252) 617116 Fax: (01252) 626216 E-mail: info@businesscomms.co.uk
Communisis Security Products Ltd, Trafford Wharf Road, Trafford Park, Manchester, M17 1HE Tel: 0161-869 1000 Fax: 0161-869 1010
Contacta Ltd, 11 Tower View, Kings Hill, West Malling, Kent, ME19 4UY Tel: (01732) 223900 Fax: (01732) 223909 E-mail: sales@contacta.co.uk
Dataflex Design Communications Ltd, 2Nd Floor Chancery House, St. Nicholas Way, Sutton, Surrey, SM1 1JB Tel: (020) 8710 1700 Fax: (020) 8710 1705
Edinburgh Solutions, 6 York Place, Basement Flat 2, Edinburgh, EH1 3EP Tel: 0131-557 1001E-mail: graeme.thomas-green@virgin.net
Improcom Ltd, Management House, Cottingham Road, Corby, Northamptonshire, NN17 1TD Tel: (01536) 207107 Fax: (01536) 265699 E-mail: admin@improcom.co.uk
Information Transfer, Burleigh House, 15 Newmarket Road, Cambridge, CB5 8EG Tel: (01223) 312227 Fax: (01223) 310200
Lord Communications Ltd, 2 Thelby Cl, Luton, LU3 2UF Tel: 01582 494600 Fax: 01582-583383
Optilan, Common Lane Industrial Estate, Kenilworth, Warwickshire, CV8 2EL Tel: (01926) 864999 Fax: (01926) 851818
▶ Roke Manor Research, Roke Manor, Old Salisbury Lane, Romsey, Hampshire, SO51 0ZN Tel: (01794) 833000 Fax: (01794) 833433 E-mail: info@roke.co.uk
Wolff Olins Brand Consultants, 10 Regents Wharf, All Saints Street, London, N1 9RL Tel: (020) 7713 7733 Fax: (020) 7713 0217 E-mail: enquiries@wolff-olins.com

COMMUNICATION SYSTEMS MAINTENANCE OR REPAIR

Business Communications, Units 2 Bramshot Barns, Bramshot Lane, Fleet, Hampshire, GU51 2RU Tel: (01252) 617116 Fax: (01252) 626216 E-mail: info@businesscomms.co.uk
Liric Associates, Jericho Farm House, Worton, Witney, Oxfordshire, OX29 4SZ Tel: (01865) 880366 Fax: (01865) 882054 E-mail: sales@1iric.co.uk

COMMUNICATION SYSTEMS TO MAIN FRAME COMPUTER

Christchurch Computer Centre, 2-4 Fairmile Parade, Fairmile Road, Christchurch, Dorset, BH23 2LP Tel: (01202) 486338 Fax: (0845) 8622661 E-mail: sales@c-c-c.co.uk
Comtek Computers Manchester, 12 Silver Street, Bury, Lancashire, BL9 0EX Tel: 0161-761 2200 Fax: 0161-761 2211 E-mail: kazpenash@comtekcomputersmanchester.co.uk

COMMUNICATION SYSTEMS, MOBILE, INSTALLATION CONTRACTORS

▶ Hands 3 Communications UK Ltd, The Lodge, Darenth Hill, Dartford, DA2 7QR Tel: (07900) 511526 E-mail: mick@hands3communications.com
Lyster & Associates, The Coach House, Ashford Lodge, Sudbury Road, Halstead, Essex, CO9 2RR Tel: (01787) 477777 Fax: (01787) 477377E-mail: postmaster@lyster-assoc.co.uk

COMMUNICATION SYSTEMS, SUBSEA/UNDERWATER

Thales Underwater Systems, Ocean House, Throop Road, Templecombe, Somerset, BA8 0DH Tel: (01963) 370551 Fax: (01963) 372200 E-mail: sales@tms-ltd.com

COMMUNICATION SYSTEMS, TO CUSTOMER SPECIFICATION

Avc Europe Ltd, Bessemer Drive, Stevenage, Hertfordshire, SG1 2DT Tel: (01438) 341300 Fax: (01438) 341301 E-mail: info@avcgroup.co.uk
Azzuri Connection Ltd, Haleworth House, Tite Hill, Egham, Surrey, TW20 0LT Tel: (01784) 486550 Fax: (01784) 486587
Contacta Ltd, 11 Tower View, Kings Hill, West Malling, Kent, ME19 4UY Tel: (01732) 223900 Fax: (01732) 223909 E-mail: sales@contacta.co.uk
DS Developments, Unit 41a Hobbs Industrial Estate, Newchapel, Lingfield, Surrey, RH7 6HN Tel: (01342) 835444 Fax: (01342) 832277 E-mail: sales@dsdevelopments.co.uk
Joyce-Loebl Ltd, 390 Princesway, Team Valley Trading Estate, Gateshead, Tyne & Wear, NE11 0TU Tel: 0191-420 3000 Fax: 0191-420 3030 E-mail: andy.kevins@joyce-loebel.com
L M W Electronics Ltd, L M W House Merrylees Industrial Estate, Lee Side, Desford, Leicester, LE9 9FS Tel: (01530) 231141 Fax: (01530) 231143 E-mail: sales@lmw.co.uk
Lyster & Associates, The Coach House, Ashford Lodge, Sudbury Road, Halstead, Essex, CO9 2RR Tel: (01787) 477777 Fax: (01787) 477377E-mail: postmaster@lyster-assoc.co.uk
R.F. Technology Ltd, Unit 15d Compton Pl, Surrey Ave, Camberley, Surrey, GU15 1HL Tel: (01276) 686889 Fax: (01276) 686244
Windcrest (HSP Electronics) Ltd, Unit 8 Abbey Manufacturing Estate, Mount Pleasant, Wembley, Middlesex, HA0 1NR Tel: (020) 8795 0333 Fax: (020) 8795 0444 E-mail: windcrest@aol.com

COMMUNICATIONS SOFTWARE

Create Form International Ltd, Instone House, Instone Road, Dartford, DA1 2AG Tel: (01322) 279797 Fax: (01322) 279779 E-mail: info@createform.com
Dacoll Ltd, Gardners Lane, Bathgate, West Lothian, EH48 1TP Tel: (01506) 815000 Fax: (01506) 656012 E-mail: sales@dacoll.co.uk
Equanet Ltd, Red Lion Road, Surbiton, Surrey, KT6 7RG Tel: (020) 8974 2321 Fax: (020) 8974 2982
Forum Softwear Ltd, Rock House, Sandy Haven, St. Ishmaels, Haverfordwest, Dyfed, SA62 3DN Tel: (01646) 636363 Fax: (01646) 636737 E-mail: sales@forumboats.com
Infomatrix Ltd, The Old School, High Street, Fen Drayton, Cambridge, CB4 4SJ Tel: (01954) 232010 Fax: (01954) 230031 E-mail: chris.jones@infomatrix.com
KK Systems Ltd, PO Box 2770, Brighton, BN45 7ED Tel: (01273) 857185 Fax: (01273) 857186 E-mail: sales@kksystems.com
Maxima, 2 Bell Business Park, Smeaton Close, Aylesbury, Buckinghamshire, HP19 8JR Tel: (01296) 318060 Fax: (01296) 318089
Teligent Ltd, Mark House, Mark Road, Hemel Hempstead, Hertfordshire, HP2 7UE Tel: (01442) 283800 Fax: (01442) 283806 E-mail: info@teligent.co.uk
Ubiquity Software Corporation, Suite B Building 3 The Eastern Business Park, Wern Fawr Lane, St. Mellons, Cardiff, CF3 5EA Tel: (029) 2081 7500 Fax: (029) 2081 7501

COMMUNITY PSYCHOLOGY CONSULTANTS

Box 42 Ltd, PO Box 42, St. Helens, Merseyside, WA10 3BF Tel: (0845) 3700442 Fax: (0845) 3700542 E-mail: welcome@box42.com

COMPACT DISC READ ONLY MEMORY (CD ROM) DESIGN AND DEVELOPMENT SERVICES, CATALOGUES AND BROCHURES

▶ A & H Commercial Printers, 153-155 Ley Street, Ilford, Essex, IG1 4BL Tel: (020) 8478 2558 Fax: (020) 8514 5366 E-mail: info@ahprinters.com
▶ Beat Creative Design & Print Management, Cedar House, Vine Lane, Hillingdon, Uxbridge, Middlesex, UB10 0BX Tel: (01895) 252152 Fax: (01895) 230233 E-mail: enquiries@beat-creative.co.uk
▶ Citrus Media Ltd, Trivarden House, Milton Road, Shipton-under-Wychwood, Chipping Norton, Oxfordshire, OX7 6BD Tel: (01993) 830955 Fax: (01993) 831906 E-mail: info@citrus-media.co.uk
▶ Design Extreme Ltd, Wood Hill, Squirrel's Jump, Alderley Edge, Cheshire, SK9 7DR Tel: (01625) 586522 Fax: (01625) 586533 E-mail: info@designextremelimited.co.uk
▶ The Design Initiative, Unit 2 Mowbray Street, Stockport, Cheshire, SK1 3EJ Tel: 0161-474 1314 Fax: 0161-474 1314 E-mail: info@designinitiative.co.uk
▶ Dickfisher Ltd, 5 Harland Close, Little Haywood, Stafford, ST18 0JY Tel: (01889) 881159 E-mail: dick@dickfisher.com
▶ Fabre, 54 Ryde Avenue, Hull, HU5 1QA Tel: (07958) 346249E-mail: hello@fabre.co.uk
▶ Fresh Lemon, Unit 17 Wrotham Business Park, Wrotham Park, Barnet, Hertfordshire, EN5 4SZ Tel: (020) 8275 8585 Fax: (020) 8275 8586 E-mail: info@freshlemon.co.uk
Iceni Productions Ltd, The Studio, Long Lane, Fradley, Lichfield, Staffordshire, WS13 8NX Tel: (01283) 792990 Fax: (01283) 792993 E-mail: sales@iceni.tv
Lawrence Creative Ltd, 1 Newton Place, Glasgow, G3 7PR Tel: 0141-333 9009 Fax: 0141-333 9495 E-mail: design@lawrencecreative.com
The Marvellous Media Company, Unit 1 GMS House, Boundary Road, Woking, Surrey, GU21 5BX Tel: 01483 740800 Fax: 01483 656810 E-mail: info@marvellousmedia.com
▶ Multicreative Media, 261 Kingston Road, Epsom, Surrey, KT19 0BN Tel: (020) 8393 4200 E-mail: mail@multicreativemedia.co.uk

COMPACT FLASH (CF) MEMORY CARDS

Lexicon Distribution, 11 Ackroyd St, Morley, Leeds, LS27 8QX Tel: 0113-252 2727 Fax: 0113-252 3177 E-mail: rob@xic.co.uk

COMPACT HYDRAULIC DUMPER TRUCKS

▶ RMC Services Ltd, Cornerways House, School Lane, Ringwood, Hampshire, BH24 1LG Tel: (01425) 654467

COMPACTION BAGS, REFUSE/ SCRAP/WASTE

Controlled Waste Ltd, Highview Works, New Years Green Lane, Harefield, Uxbridge, Middlesex, UB9 6LX Tel: (01895) 673069 Fax: (01895) 636068
Donington Plastics Ltd, Unit 1 Spiral Tube Works, Derby, DE24 8BT Tel: (01332) 363313 Fax: (01332) 361355 E-mail: sales@doningtongroup.co.uk
▶ Environmental Waste Controls P.L.C., Laurel House, Kitling Road, Knowsley Business Park, Prescot, Merseyside, L34 9JA Tel: (0845) 4562456 Fax: (0845) 4563998 E-mail: enquiry@ewc.eu.com
North Sea Compactors, 7 Logman Centre, Greenbank Cresent, East Tullos Industrial Estate, Aberdeen, AB12 3BG Tel: (01224) 248455 Fax: (01224) 248454 E-mail: nscompac@netcomuk.co.uk
Sellers Engineering Ltd, Sellers Way, Chadderton, Oldham, OL9 8EY Tel: 0161-681 5846 Fax: 0161-683 5621

COMPACTION EQUIPMENT

Bomag Great Britain Ltd, Sheldon Way, Larkfield, Aylesford, Kent, ME20 6SE Tel: (01622) 715252 Fax: (01622) 710233 E-mail: sales@bomag.com
▶ Clee Hill Plant Ltd, 41 Downiebrae Road, Rutherglen, Glasgow, G73 1PW Tel: 0141-647 0067 Fax: 0141-647 7600 E-mail: glasgow@cleehill.co.uk
Clee Hill Plants, Mansfield Road, Corbriggs, Chesterfield, Derbyshire, S41 0JW Tel: (01246) 551637 Fax: (01246) 551639 E-mail: sales@cleehill.co.uk
Controlled Waste Ltd, Highview Works, New Years Green Lane, Harefield, Uxbridge, Middlesex, UB9 6LX Tel: (01895) 673069 Fax: (01895) 636068

COMPACTION EQUIPMENT – *continued*

Fenton Plant Hire, A Culverlands Industrial Estate, Winchester Road, Shedfield, Southampton, SO32 2JF Tel: (01329) 830011 Fax: (01329) 833683 E-mail: sales@fentonplant.co.uk

▶ Hill Engineering Ltd, 1 Sandy Road, Newry, County Down, BT34 2LB Tel: (028) 3025 2555 Fax: (028) 3026 4020 E-mail: sales@hillengineeringltd.com

Kenburn Waste Management, Kenburn House, Porters Wood, St. Albans, Hertfordshire, AL3 6HX Tel: (01727) 844988 Fax: (01727) 844778 E-mail: info@kenburn.co.uk

▶ Kindunique Ltd, Grieves Buildings, Front Street, New Herrington, Houghton le Spring, Tyne & Wear, DH4 7AU Tel: 0191-512 0052 Fax: 0191-512 0543 E-mail: holtkindunique@dsi.pipex.com

▶ Spec Check Europe Ltd, Lion Buildings, 8 Market Place, Uttoxeter, Staffordshire, ST14 8HP Tel: (01889) 569666 Fax: (01889) 569777E-mail: sales@spec-checkeurope.com

Taylor Construction Plant Ltd, Unit 2, Broadmeadows, Harburn, West Calder, West Lothian, EH55 8RT Tel: (01621) 850777 Fax: (01621) 843330 E-mail: mail@tcp.eu

COMPACTION SYSTEMS, REFUSE/SCRAP/WASTE

Bomag Great Britain Ltd, Sheldon Way, Larkfield, Aylesford, Kent, ME20 6SE Tel: (01622) 715252 Fax: (01622) 710233 E-mail: sales@bomag.com

Controlled Waste Ltd, Highview Works, New Years Green Lane, Harefield, Uxbridge, Middlesex, UB9 6LX Tel: (01895) 673069 Fax: (01895) 636068

Marshall Cooke Ltd, Burrell Way, Thetford, Norfolk, IP24 3RW Tel: (01842) 764312 Fax: (01842) 761033 E-mail: sales@marshallcooke.com

Dicom Ltd, Lydford Road, Alfreton, Derbyshire, DE55 7RQ Tel: (01773) 520565 Fax: (01773) 520881 E-mail: sales@dicom.ltd.uk

▶ Environmental Waste Controls P.L.C., Laurel House, Kitling Road, Knowsley Business Park, Prescot, Merseyside, L34 9JA Tel: (0845) 4562456 Fax: (0845) 4563998 E-mail: enquiry@ewc.eu.com

▶ Hardall International Ltd, Fairway Works, Southfields Road, Dunstable, Bedfordshire, LU6 3EP Tel: (01582) 500860 Fax: (01582) 690975 E-mail: sales@hardall.co.uk

Lennox House Holdings Ltd, Beeding Close, Southern Cross Trading Estate, Bognor Regis, West Sussex, PO22 9TS Tel: (01243) 866565 Fax: (01243) 868301 E-mail: enquiries@ggcompacters.co.uk

Miltek, Rectory Farm, Brandon Road, Stubton, Newark, Nottinghamshire, NG23 5BY Tel: (01636) 626796 Fax: (01636) 626905 E-mail: sales@miltekbalers.com

R & H Tomlinson Ltd, The Recycling Centre, Hackworth Industrial Park, Shildon, County Durham, DL4 1HF Tel: (01388) 778222 Fax: (01388) 778333 E-mail: nicktomlinson007@aol.com

Randalls Fabrications Ltd, Randall Fabrication, Hoyle Mill Road, Kinsley, Pontefract, West Yorkshire, WF9 5JB Tel: (01977) 615132 Fax: (01977) 610059 E-mail: sales@randallsfabrications.co.uk

Thetford International Limited, Rymer Point, Bury Road, Thetford, Norfolk, IP24 2PN Tel: (01842) 890500 Fax: (01842) 890077 E-mail: sales-serv@thetford-int.co.uk

COMPANY FORMING CONSULTANTS/SERVICES

Access Company Formations Ltd, 31 Church Rd, Hendon, London, NW4 4EB Tel: (020) 8202 2220 Fax: (020) 8202 2202 E-mail: graham@offshorecos.freeserve.com

Credit Solutions Ltd, Barlow House, 3 Butter Hill, Carshalton, Surrey, SM5 2TW Tel: (020) 8773 7111 Fax: (020) 8773 9919 E-mail: credsol@globalnet.co.uk

▶ London Law Agency Ltd, 67-69 Southampton Row, London, WC1B 4ET Tel: (020) 7436 5880 Fax: (020) 7583 1531 E-mail: info@londonlaw.co.uk

▶ The Company Merchant Ltd, Redditch, Worcestershire, B98 0NU Tel: (0870) 4323232 Fax: (0870) 4323295 E-mail: mail@thecompanymerchant.co.uk

COMPANY LITERATURE PRINTING TO SPECIFICATION

▶ Regarder Limited, 0-6-2 Omnia One, 125 Queen Street, Sheffield, S1 2DG Tel: 0114 279 2828 Fax: 0114 279 2829 E-mail: regarder1@aol.com

COMPANY REGISTRATION AGENTS OR CONSULTANTS

▶ @UK PLC, 5 Jupiter House, Calleva Park, Aldermaston, RG7 8NN Tel: (0870) 4866006 E-mail: info@ukplc.net

1st Contact, Clydesdale Bank House, 33 Regent Street, London, SW1Y 4ZT Tel: (0800) 0393082 Fax: (020) 7494 4334 E-mail: info@1st-contact.co.uk

Chettleburgh International Ltd, Temple House, 20 Holywell Row, London, EC2A 4XH Tel: (020) 7377 0381 Fax: (020) 7377 0381 E-mail: info@chettleburghs.co.uk

Stanley Davis Group Ltd, 41 Chalton Street, London, NW1 1JD Tel: (020) 7554 2222 E-mail: info@stanleydavis.co.uk

Douglas Co Services Ltd, Regent House, 316 Beulah Hill, London, SE19 3HF Tel: (020) 8761 1176 Fax: (020) 8761 7486 E-mail: enquiries@douglas-cs.co.uk

Law & Accountancy Agency Services Ltd, 31 Corsham Street, London, N1 6DR Tel: (020) 7250 1410 Fax: (020) 7250 1973 E-mail: searches@landa.ltd.uk

Raymond Morris Group Ltd, Invision House, Wilbury Way, Hitchin, Hertfordshire, SG4 0TW Tel: (020) 7729 1234 Fax: (020) 7251 0965 E-mail: infodesk@rmonline.com

Nationwide Trademarks, Somerset House, 40-49 Price Street, Birmingham, B4 6LZ Tel: 0121-678 9005 Fax: 0121-678 9001 E-mail: sales@anewbusiness.co.uk

Paramount Co. Formations Ltd, 35 Firs Avenue, London, N11 3NE Tel: (020) 8883 6161 Fax: (020) 8883 1269 E-mail: pcfltd@aol.com

Rapid Co. Services Ltd, 209A Station Lane, Hornchurch, Essex, RM12 6LL Tel: (01708) 478690 Fax: (01708) 478680

Same Day Company Services, 9 Perseverance Works, Kingsland Road, London, E2 8DD Tel: (020) 7613 8161 Fax: (020) 7613 8162 E-mail: jw@samedaycompany.co.uk

▶ Secretariat Business Services, Suite 16, Folkestone Enterprise Centre, Shearway Business Park, Folkestone, Kent, CT19 4RH Tel: (0870) 3300615 E-mail: info@secretariatservices.net

Temple's Ltd, Kemp House, 152-160 City Road, London, EC1V 2NX Tel: (020) 7566 3939 Fax: (020) 7566 3935 E-mail: info@templesltd.co.uk

Vickers Co Formations, 1 High St Mews, London, SW19 7RG Tel: (020) 8944 2067 Fax: (020) 8241 9879 E-mail: enquiries@vickersinformation.co.uk

White Rose Formations, Sovereign House, 7 Station Road, Kettering, Northamptonshire, NN15 7HH Tel: (01536) 414088 Fax: (01536) 481278 E-mail: office@wrfinternational.demon.co.uk

York Place Co Services Ltd, 12 York Place, Leeds, LS1 2DS Tel: 0113-242 0222 Fax: 0113-242 5904 E-mail: yorkplace@yorkplace.co.uk

COMPANY RELOCATION CONSULTANCY

▶ Morrell Homefinders, 97 Birchwood Way, Park Street, St. Albans, Hertfordshire, AL2 2SF Tel: (01727) 874622 Fax: (01727) 874611 E-mail: info@morrellhomefinders.co.uk

▶ Relocation Relocation, 35A Ludgate, Alloa, Clackmannanshire, FK10 1DS Tel: (01259) 212478 Fax: (01259) 212478 E-mail: lisa@relocationrelocation.net

▶ Sands Home Search, PO Box 5561, Ringwood, Hampshire, BH24 1EN Tel: (01425) 462549 Fax: (0871) 6612892 E-mail: info@sandshomesearch.com

COMPANY SEALS

Bolsons Ltd, The Gatehouse, Cooks Road, London, E15 2PW Tel: (020) 8555 7137 Fax: (020) 8519 6641 E-mail: info@bolsons.co.uk

P R O Marketing Co. Ltd, Unit 10 Jubilee Trade Centre, Jubilee Road, Letchworth Garden City, Hertfordshire, SG6 1SP Tel: (01462) 677188 Fax: (01462) 685275 E-mail: sales@proengraving.com

Vickers Co Formations, 1 High St Mews, London, SW19 7RG Tel: (020) 8944 2067 Fax: (020) 8241 9879 E-mail: enquiries@vickersinformation.co.uk

COMPANY SEARCH/TRACING SERVICES

Access Company Formations Ltd, 31 Church Rd, Hendon, London, NW4 4EB Tel: (020) 8202 2220 Fax: (020) 8202 2202 E-mail: graham@offshorecos.freeserve.com

C A R E S GB Ltd, Suite, 8 Stoke Road, Stoke-on-Trent, ST4 2DP Tel: (01782) 212613 Fax: (01782) 212046

Chettleburgh International Ltd, Temple House, 20 Holywell Row, London, EC2A 4XH Tel: (020) 7377 0381 Fax: (020) 7377 0381 E-mail: info@chettleburghs.co.uk

Stanley Davis Group Ltd, 41 Chalton Street, London, NW1 1JD Tel: (020) 7554 2222 E-mail: info@stanleydavis.co.uk

Debtsave, Palmerston House, 814 Brighton Road, Purley, Surrey, CR8 2BR Tel: (020) 8655 8484 Fax: (020) 8655 8501 E-mail: debtsave@palmerston.co.uk

▶ Icc Information Ltd, Field House, 72 Old Field Road, Hampton, Middlesex, TW12 2HQ Tel: (020) 7426 8510 Fax: (020) 7426 8551 E-mail: sales@icc-credit.co.uk

Jack Russell Collections & Investigations, Bayleaf House, 10 York Road, Northampton, NN1 5QG Tel: (01604) 634170 Fax: (01604) 635507 E-mail: jrnorth@debtcollect.co.uk

Jordan Publishing Ltd, 21 St Thomas Street, Bristol, BS1 6JS Tel: 0117-923 0600 Fax: 0117-925 0486 E-mail: customersupport@jordans.co.uk

L & A Personal Searches Ltd, 31 Corsham Street, London, N1 6DR Tel: (020) 7250 1410 Fax: (020) 7250 1973 E-mail: searches@landa.ltd.uk

Law & Accountancy Agency Services Ltd, 31 Corsham Street, London, N1 6DR Tel: (020) 7250 1410 Fax: (020) 7250 1973 E-mail: searches@landa.ltd.uk

▶ London Law Agency Ltd, 67-69 Southampton Row, London, WC1B 4ET Tel: (020) 7436 5880 Fax: (020) 7583 1531 E-mail: info@londonlaw.co.uk

Paramount Co. Formations Ltd, 35 Firs Avenue, London, N11 3NE Tel: (020) 8883 6161 Fax: (020) 8883 1269 E-mail: pcfltd@aol.com

Research Associates, 282 Latimer Road, London, W10 6QW Tel: (020) 7854 9000 Fax: (020) 7854 9090 E-mail: paulhawkes@investigationservices.co.uk

Same Day Company Services, 9 Perseverance Works, Kingsland Road, London, E2 8DD Tel: (020) 7613 8161 Fax: (020) 7613 8162 E-mail: jw@samedaycompany.co.uk

Spectrum Investigations, 1 The Arches, Park Street, Wellington, Telford, Shropshire, TF1 3PE Tel: (01952) 276493 Fax: (01952) 412674 E-mail: specrumpi@blueyonder.co.uk

Status Credit Reports Ltd, 21 Whitchurch Road, Cardiff, CF14 3JN Tel: (029) 2054 4333 Fax: (029) 2054 4300 E-mail: orders@statuscredit.com

Temple's Ltd, Kemp House, 152-160 City Road, London, EC1V 2NX Tel: (020) 7566 3939 Fax: (020) 7566 3935 E-mail: info@templesltd.co.uk

Thomson Financial Ltd, Aldgate House, 33 Aldgate High Street, London, EC3N 1DL Tel: (020) 7369 7000 Fax: (020) 7369 7240

▶ UK Locate and Trace Group, P O Box 76, Bolton, BL1 4WQ Tel: 08701 624961

Vickers Co Formations, 1 High St Mews, London, SW19 7RG Tel: (020) 8944 2067 Fax: (020) 8241 9879 E-mail: enquiries@vickersinformation.co.uk

Waterlow Secretaries Ltd, 6-8 Underwood Street, London, N1 7JQ Tel: (020) 7250 3350 Fax: (020) 7608 0867 E-mail: companyservices@waterlow.com

York Place Co Services Ltd, 12 York Place, Leeds, LS1 2DS Tel: 0113-242 0222 Fax: 0113-242 5904 E-mail: yorkplace@yorkplace.co.uk

COMPASSES, *See also headings for particular types*

Parker Diving Ltd, A P Valves Building, Water Ma Trout Industrial Estate, Nancegollan, Helston, Cornwall, TR13 0BN Tel: (01326) 561040 Fax: (01326) 573605 E-mail: sales@apvalves.com

Viking Optical Ltd, Blyth Road, Halesworth, Suffolk, IP19 8EN Tel: (01986) 875315 Fax: (01986) 874788 E-mail: viking@vikingoptical.co.uk

COMPASSES, MARINE/ NAVIGATIONAL

John Lilley & Gillie Ltd, Clive Street, North Shields, Tyne & Wear, NE29 6LF Tel: 0191-257 2217 Fax: 0191-257 1521 E-mail: sales@lilleyandgillie.co.uk

COMPETITIVE ANALYSIS MARKET RESEARCH

Aware Marketing Consultants, 16 Craigweil Close, Stanmore, Middlesex, HA7 4TR Tel: (020) 8954 9121 Fax: (020) 8954 2102 E-mail: aweiss@marketing-intelligence.co.uk

COMPETITIVE SPORTS CLOTHING, *See also headings for particular types*

Accused, Ark Lane, Deal, Kent, CT14 6PU Tel: (01304) 360626 Fax: (01304) 364600 E-mail: accused@accused.co.uk

Ace Sports & Ladyline, 49 Duke Street, Staveley, Staveley, Chesterfield, Derbyshire, S43 3PD Tel: (01246) 470650 Fax: (01246) 280473 E-mail: malc@ace-sports.freeserve.co.uk

Amazon Promotions, Unit 126 Oystons Mill, Strand Road, Preston, PR1 8UR Tel: (01772) 722800 Fax: (01772) 722800 E-mail: maria.atherton@rediffmail.com

Bindra Bros Ltd, 6-8 Hazel Street, Leicester, LE2 7JN Tel: 0116-247 0116 Fax: 0116-247 0126 E-mail: hazelfashion@hotmail.com

City Styles Leicester Ltd, 150 St Nicholas Circle, Leicester, LE1 4JJ Tel: 0116-251 5411

Direct Sports Leisurewear Ltd, 6 Chartmoor Road, Leighton Buzzard, Bedfordshire, LU7 4WG Tel: (01525) 853344 Fax: (01525) 858600 E-mail: sales@directsportswear.co.uk

Dixons Clothing Co., Berwick Street Mills, Berwick Street, Halifax, West Yorkshire, HX1 1QL Tel: (01422) 322284 Fax: (01422) 364068 E-mail: sales@dixons-clothing.fsnet.co.uk

Drakes Pride Bowls Co., 128 Richmond Row, Liverpool, L3 3BL Tel: 0151-298 1355 Fax: 0151-298 2988 E-mail: drakespride@eaclare.co.uk

Football Kits Direct Ltd, Bridge Trading Estate, Bridge St North, Smethwick, West Midlands, B66 2BZ Tel: 0121-558 5846 Fax: 0121-555 7109 E-mail: salesunderscorefootballkitsdirect@nsn.com

Freedom, Gate Lane, Sutton Coldfield, West Midlands, B73 5TX Tel: 0121-355 8668 Fax: 0121-355 2113 E-mail: sales@swimcap.com

Gymphlex Ltd, Boston Road, Horncastle, Lincolnshire, LN9 6HU Tel: (01507) 523243 Fax: (01507) 524421 E-mail: sales@gymphlex.co.uk

Halbro Sportswear Ltd, Chorley New Road, Horwich, Bolton, BL6 7JG Tel: (01204) 696476 Fax: (01204) 699479 E-mail: sales@halbro.com

Harrison Sportswear, 95-97 Market Street, Little Lever, Bolton, BL3 1HH Tel: (01204) 791356 Fax: (01204) 791356 E-mail: johnachild5@hotmail.com

Hossacks Clothing Mnfrs, 106 Park Street Lane, Park Street, St. Albans, Hertfordshire, AL2 2JQ Tel: (01727) 875586 Fax: (01727) 875581 E-mail: info@hossacks.com

Humphreys & Sons Ltd, Newton Lane, Wigston, Leicestershire, LE18 3SG Tel: 0116-288 1105 Fax: 0116-288 0661 E-mail: ian@europasports.co.uk

J Milom Ltd, Springfield Mills, Sherborne Street, Manchester, M3 1ND Tel: 0161-832 6155 Fax: 0161-833 0663 E-mail: sales@milom.co.uk

T.H. Knightall, Hawksley Avenue, Sheffield, S6 2BG Tel: 0114-234 8886 Fax: 0114-285 4753 E-mail: thkltd@aol.com

Laxmi Investments Ltd, 123 Barkby Road, Leicester, LE4 9LG Tel: 0116-276 6625 Fax: 0116-246 0787

R.A. Laxton Ltd, Unit 3k The Stormall Industrial Estate, Liddicoat Road, Lostwithiel, Cornwall, PL22 0HE Tel: (01208) 872224 Fax: (01208) 871070

▶ Leisurewear-actecs, 6 Penhill Industrail Park, Beaumont Road, Banbury, Oxon, OX16 1RW Tel: (01295) 703165 Fax: (01295) 255059 E-mail: sales@actecs.co.uk

Lusso Sportswear, 1 Withins Street, Radcliffe, Manchester, M26 2RX Tel: 0161-724 5222 Fax: 0161-724 9393 E-mail: sales@lusso.co.uk

Nater Leisurewear, Goodsmoor Road, Littleover, Derby, DE23 1NH Tel: (01332) 770554 Fax: (01332) 271201 E-mail: info@nater.co.uk

J. Nuttall & Co. Ltd, Cox Buxton Road, Newtown, New Mills, High Peak, Derbyshire, SK22 3JT Tel: (01663) 746041 Fax: (01663) 749046

P P Fashions, 45 Forest Road, Leicester, LE5 0DW Tel: 0116-253 9226 Fax: 0116-251 2948

Pretty Ponies Ltd, Unit 9 The Sidings, Whalley, Clitheroe, Lancashire, BB7 9SE Tel: (01254) 822044 Fax: (01254) 822034 E-mail: sales@prettyponies.co.uk

▶ Primo Teamwear, Factory Street, Bradford, West Yorkshire, BD4 9NW Tel: (01274) 682682 Fax: (01274) 652265

Pro Star, PO Box 20, Wakefield, West Yorkshire, WF2 7AY Tel: (01924) 291441 Fax: (01924) 364411 E-mail: info@prostar.co.uk

Protec, 52 Liscard Road, Wallasey, Merseyside, CH44 9AF Tel: 0151-639 1390 Fax: 0151-639 1390

Rochford Sports Knitwear, Summerleigh, Quaperlake Street, Bruton, Somerset, BA10 0HG Tel: (01749) 813240 Fax: (01749) 813240

Romus Sportswear, Dixies, High Street, Ashwell, Hertfordshire, SG7 5NT Tel: (01462) 742101 Fax: (01462) 742088 E-mail: johnrbonnett@aol.com

Rossi Sports & Leisurewear, 24 Blackhills Road, Peterlee, County Durham, SR8 4DW Tel: 0191-518 2228 Fax: 0191-518 2228

Rugby Clothing Co. Ltd, 101 Old Westgate, Dewsbury, West Yorkshire, WF13 1NB Tel: (01924) 460130 Fax: (01924) 457960 E-mail: enquiries@rugby-clothing.co.uk

S T M Force Ltd, Rear of, 145-147 Northfield Road, Coventry, CV1 2BQ Tel: (024) 7652 0631 Fax: (024) 7663 3303 E-mail: sales@stmforce.co.uk

Sallis Healthcare Ltd, Waterford Street, Nottingham, NG6 0DH Tel: 0115-978 7841 Fax: 0115-942 2272 E-mail: info@sallis.co.uk

Sharpe Master Sportswear Shop, 49 St Helens Road, Swansea, SA1 4BD Tel: (01792) 414300 Fax: (01792) 414300 E-mail: enquiries@sharpemaster.co.uk

Speedo International Ltd, Ascot Road, Nottingham, NG8 5AJ Tel: 0115-916 7000 Fax: 0115-910 5005 E-mail: speedoinfo@pentland.com

Teritex Sportswear, Teritex Factory, Boughton, Newark, Nottinghamshire, NG22 9ZD Tel: (01623) 861381 Fax: (01623) 835301 E-mail: info@teritex.com

Thin Air, Griffin Farm House, Bowden Hill, Lacock, Chippenham, Wiltshire, SN15 2PP Tel: (01249) 730099 Fax: (01249) 730066 E-mail: sales@racewear.co.uk

▶ indicates data change since last edition

COMPETITIVE SPORTS CLOTHING
– continued

Total Restraint Systems Ltd, Unit 4 Hurricane Close, Old Sarum, Salisbury, SP4 6LG Tel: (01722) 326080 Fax: (01722) 334437 E-mail: post@totalrestarint.com
Umbro International Ltd, Umbro House, 5400 Lakeside, Cheadle, Cheshire, SK8 3GQ Tel: 0161-492 2000 Fax: 0161-492 2001 E-mail: sales@umbro.com
Wilsport, 5 Fleming Close, Wellingborough, Northamptonshire, NN8 6UF Tel: (01933) 403404 Fax: (01933) 405070 E-mail: edw@wilsport.freeserve.co.uk
Winterton Leisurewear Ltd, Regent Road, Countesthorpe, Leicester, LE8 5RF Tel: 0116-277 9789 Fax: 0116-278 4395 E-mail: info@magicfit.co.uk
Yansport Safety Wear Ltd, Frederick Street, Walsall, WS2 9NE Tel: (01922) 721721 Fax: (01922) 723710

COMPLETE ACOUSTIC CEILINGS

▶ Cleanceil, 46 Owen Road, Kirkdale, Liverpool, L4 1RW Tel: 0870 910 1602 E-mail: enquiries@cleanceil.co.uk
Sas International, Murray Gardens, Maybole, Ayrshire, KA19 7AZ Tel: (01655) 882555 Fax: (01655) 883781

COMPLETE AIRCRAFT GALLEYS

A I M Group plc, 16 Carlton Cresent, Southampton, SO15 2ES Tel: (023) 8033 5111 Fax: (023) 8022 9733
Aim Aviation Henshalls Ltd, Abbot Close, Byfleet, West Byfleet, Surrey, KT14 7JT Tel: (01932) 351011 Fax: (01932) 352792 E-mail: c.herrington@aim-henshalls.co.uk

COMPLETE BUILDING SYSTEM OR UNIT

Britspace Modular Buildings, Unicorn House, Broad Lane, Gilberdyke, Brough, East Yorkshire, HU15 2TS Tel: (01430) 444400 Fax: (01430) 444401 E-mail: info@britspace.com
Bullock & Driffill Ltd, Staunton Works, Newark Road, Staunton in the Vale, Nottingham, NG13 9PF Tel: (01400) 280000 Fax: (01400) 280010 E-mail: bullock.driffill@btopenworld.com
Caledonian Building Systems Ltd, Carlton Works, Ossington Road, Carlton-on-Trent, Newark, Nottinghamshire, NG23 6NT Tel: (01636) 821645 Fax: (01636) 821261
Elliott Group Ltd, Manor Drive, Peterborough, PE4 7AP Tel: (01733) 298700 Fax: (01733) 573543 E-mail: hirediv@elliott-group.co.uk
Elliott Redispace, Valletta Street, Hull, HU9 5NP Tel: (01482) 781202 Fax: (01482) 712157 E-mail: hirediv@elliott-group.co.uk
G E Capital Modular Space, Langford Bridge, Cambridge Road, Langford, Biggleswade, Bedfordshire, SG18 9PL Tel: (01462) 701711 Fax: (01462) 701355
Greens Of Mepal, 1 Brangehill Lane, Mepal, Ely, Cambridgeshire, CB6 2AL Tel: (01353) 778450
Keystone Computers, 17 Perry Vale, London, SE23 2NE Tel: (020) 8699 4546 Fax: (020) 8473 8361
Pasuda Buildings Ltd, Highfield Lane, Sheffield, S13 9NA Tel: 0114-254 0188 Fax: 0114-254 0705 E-mail: sales@pasuda.co.uk
S G B Rovacabin, B Peterley Road, Cowley, Oxford, OX4 2TZ Tel: (01865) 337200 Fax: (01865) 337201 E-mail: rovasales@sgb.co.uk
Tabs Technicom UK P.L.C., Stockholm Road, Suttonfields Industrial Estate, Hull, HU7 0XW Tel: (01482) 825558 Fax: (01482) 825557
Terrapin Ltd, Bomnd Avenue, Bletchley, Milton Keynes, MK1 1JJ Tel: 0115-907 2700 Fax: 0115-972 2203 E-mail: sales@terrapin-ltd.co.uk
Thurston Building Systems, Quarry Hill Industrial Estate, Hawking Croft Road, Horbury, Wakefield, West Yorkshire, WF4 6AJ Tel: (01924) 265461 Fax: (01924) 280246 E-mail: sales@thurstongroup.co.uk
Wernick Group Holdings Ltd, Molineux House, Russell Gardens, Wickford, Essex, SS11 8BL Tel: (01268) 735544 E-mail: simon.doran@wernickwickford.co.uk
Wernick Hire Ltd, Wellington Road, Gateshead, Tyne & Wear, NE11 9JL Tel: 0191-461 1000 Fax: 0191-461 1001
Westframe Investments Ltd, 162-164 Teignmouth Road, Torquay, TQ1 4RY Tel: (01803) 313861 Fax: (01803) 312063 E-mail: westframe@construction-ltd.fsnet.co.uk
Wingham Engineering Co. Ltd, Unit 8 Building 2, Sandwich Industrial Estate, Sandwich, Kent, CT13 9LY Tel: (01304) 612284 Fax: (01304) 620012 E-mail: sales@quickway-wingham.co.uk
Yorkon Ltd, New Lane, Huntington, York, YO32 9PT Tel: (01904) 610990 Fax: (01904) 610880 E-mail: contact@yorkon.com

COMPLETE BUSES

Alexander Dennis Ltd, 91 Glasgow Road, Camelon, Falkirk, FK1 4JB Tel: (01324) 621672 Fax: (01324) 632469 E-mail: enquiries@alexander-dennis.com
S C Bus & Coach Builders, Hambledon Road, Waterlooville, Hampshire, PO7 7UB Tel: (023) 9225 8211 Fax: (023) 9225 5611 E-mail: sales@caetano.co.uk

COMPLETE CENTRAL HEATING SYSTEMS

▶ Aqua Force Plumbing Installations, 35 Highfield CR, Barlby, Selby, North Yorkshire, YO8 5HD Tel: (01757) 210136 E-mail: afpi@shoppers-pantry.com
▶ Classic Heating Services, 103 Station Road, Sutton Coldfield, West Midlands, B73 5LA Tel: 0121-355 1782 E-mail: ian@walklett.freeserve.co.uk
▶ East Kent Plumbing & Heating Sevices, 5 Pinewood Close, Ramsgate, Kent, CT12 6DH Tel: (01843) 586864 Fax: (01843) 586864 E-mail: Eastkent@msn.com
▶ Charles Grey, 27 Alton Road, Richmond, Surrey, TW9 1UJ Tel: (07703) 533703 E-mail: charles@greyuk.net

COMPLETE COACHES

Browns Coachworks Ltd, 282 Moira Road, Lisburn, County Antrim, BT28 2TU Tel: (028) 9262 1711 Fax: (028) 9262 1962 E-mail: info@brownscoachworks.com
Cebotec Ltd, 26 Castle Road, Bankside Industrial Estate, Falkirk, FK2 7UY Tel: (01324) 877778 Fax: (01324) 882525 E-mail: sales@cebotec.co.uk
Evobush UK Ltd, Ashcroft Way, Crosspoint Business Park, Coventry, CV2 2TU Tel: (024) 7662 6000 Fax: (024) 7662 6010
Harding's International Coaches, Oxleasow Road, Redditch, Worcestershire, B98 0RE Tel: (01527) 525200
▶ L S Patterns, Unit 2 Stonebroom Industrial Estate, Stonebroom, Alfreton, Derbyshire, DE55 6LQ Tel: (01773) 591777 Fax: (01773) 875777 E-mail: len@lspatterns.com
W H Bence Coachworks Ltd, Great Western Business Park, Armstrong Way, Yate, Bristol, BS37 5NG Tel: (01454) 310909 Fax: (01454) 321665
Wright Bus Ltd, Galgorm Industrial Estate, Fenaghy Road, Galgorm, Ballymena, County Antrim, BT42 1PY Tel: (028) 2564 1212 Fax: (028) 2564 9703 E-mail: sales@wright-bus.com

COMPLETE COMPUTER CABLES

Cablelines (Nottingham) Ltd, Unit 4 Orchard Park Industrial Estate, Sandiacre, Nottingham, NG10 5BP Tel: 0115-949 1010 Fax: 0115-949 1019 E-mail: sales@cablelines.com
Cablenet Cable & Wire Suppliers, Cablenet House, Lightwater Road, Lightwater, Surrey, GU18 5XQ Tel: (01276) 851900 Fax: (01276) 851909 E-mail: sales@cablenet.uk.com
Dunasfern Cable & Wire Suppliers, 24 Peverel Drive, Bletchley, Milton Keynes, MK1 1NW Tel: (01908) 647144 Fax: (01908) 270106 E-mail: dunasfern.sales@virgin.net
End Design Ltd, Unit 37, Bookham Industrial Park, Church Road, Leatherhead, Surrey, KT23 3EU Tel: (01372) 458080 Fax: (01372) 450592 E-mail: sales@end-design.co.uk
Lindy Electronics Ltd, Sadler Foster Way, Teesside Industrial Estate, Stockton-on-Tees, Cleveland, TS17 9JY Tel: (01642) 754000 Fax: (01642) 754027 E-mail: postmaster@lindy.co.uk
Protus Electronics Ltd, Bosworth, Sulhamstead Road, Ufton Nervet, Reading, RG7 4DH Tel: 0118-973 0255 Fax: 0118-973 0070 E-mail: pandmhoward@aol.ccom.com
Wadsworth Electronics Ltd, Central Avenue, West Molesey, Surrey, KT8 2QB Tel: (020) 8268 7000 Fax: (020) 8268 6565 E-mail: info@wadsworth.co.uk
I.S.G. Webb Ltd, Unit 2 Progress Estate, Bircholt Road, Maidstone, Kent, ME15 9YH Tel: (01622) 670281 Fax: (01622) 683528 E-mail: project.office@isgwebb.com
York Distribution Ltd, 23-24 Auster Road, York, YO30 4XA Tel: (01904) 693969 Fax: (01904) 693255 E-mail: sales@ydl.co.uk

COMPLETE GAS FIRED CENTRAL HEATING SYSTEMS

▶ Capital Plumbing & Heating, 20 Mylo Griffiths Close, Cardiff, CF5 2RQ Tel: (029) 2057 8268 E-mail: rmr.roberts@virgin.net
Colbear Ltd, 45 Lady Lane Industrial Estate, Hadleigh, Ipswich, IP7 6BQ Tel: (01473) 823722 Fax: (01473) 827466 E-mail: info@colbearuk.com
Compac Services Ne Ltd, Compac House, 173 Victoria Road, South Shields, Tyne & Wear, NE33 4NW Tel: 0191-454 9090 Fax: 0191-454 1212 E-mail: sales@compac.co.uk
▶ Heat Plant Services, 4 Lauradale, Bracknell, Berkshire, RG12 7DT Tel: (01344) 427861 Fax: (01344) 427861 E-mail: heatplant5@aol.com
▶ I C Rushton, 16 Rostherne Avenue, High Lane, Stockport, Cheshire, SK6 8AR Tel: (01663) 762540 E-mail: IanCRushton@aol.com
Archie Kidd (Thermal) Ltd, Pullshot, Devizes, Wiltshire, SN10 1RT Tel: (01380) 828490 Fax: (01380) 828186

COMPLETE NON FERROUS METAL PRODUCTION PLANT

R Wright & Son Marine Engineers Ltd, Church Broughton Road, Foston, Derby, DE65 5PW Tel: (01283) 812177 Fax: (01283) 812052

COMPLETE OIL FIRED CENTRAL HEATING SYSTEMS

Colbear Ltd, 45 Lady Lane Industrial Estate, Hadleigh, Ipswich, IP7 6BQ Tel: (01473) 823722 Fax: (01473) 827466 E-mail: info@colbearuk.com
▶ Heat Plant Services, 4 Lauradale, Bracknell, Berkshire, RG12 7DT Tel: (01344) 427861 Fax: (01344) 427861 E-mail: heatplant5@aol.com

COMPLETE PACKAGE WORKSHOP EQUIPMENT

Clarks Garage (Walkern) Ltd, 107 High Street, Walkern, Stevenage, Hertfordshire, SG2 7NU Tel: (01438) 861634 E-mail: clarksgarage@hotmail.com
P Keable, 12 Avenue Clamart, Scunthorpe, South Humberside, DN15 8EQ Tel: (01724) 855989 Fax: (01724) 855989
Stow Agricultural Services, Lower Swell Road, Stow on the Wold, Cheltenham, Gloucestershire, GL54 1LD Tel: (01451) 830400

COMPLETE TELEPHONE EXCHANGE INSTALLATIONS

Ericsson Ltd, Midleton Gate, Guildford Business Park, Guildford, Surrey, GU2 8SG Tel: (01483) 303666 Fax: (01483) 303537

COMPONENT HANDLING TROLLEYS

Connor Innovations, 23a Pensilva Industrial Estate, St Ive Road, Pensilva, Liskeard, Cornwall, PL14 5RE Tel: (01579) 363067 Fax: (01579) 363581

COMPONENT PREFORMING TOOLS

NSK Steering Systems Europe Ltd, Silverstone Drive, Gallagher Business Park, Coventry, CV6 6PA Tel: (024) 7658 8588 Fax: (024) 7658 8599 E-mail: surman@nsk.com

COMPONENT RECLAMATION/ RECYCLING SERVICES, OBSOLETE COMPONENTS

Nottingham Sleeper Co. Ltd, Alpine Industrial Park, Jockey Lane, Elkesley, Retford, Nottinghamshire, DN22 8BN Tel: (01777) 838097 Fax: (01777) 838098 E-mail: enquiries@nottssleeper.co.uk

COMPONENTS TO SPECIFICATION

Cronation Ltd, Carlton Business Centre, 104 Nechells Place, Birmingham, B7 5AB Tel: 0121-359 7567 Fax: 0121-359 5339 E-mail: sales@cronation.co.uk
Switchcraft Incorporated, Robinson Way, Portsmouth, PO3 5TD Tel: (023) 9266 1579 Fax: (023) 9227 4731 E-mail: intsales@switchcraft.com
U M E C UK Ltd, Business Centre, Barham Court, Teston, Maidstone, Kent, ME18 5BZ Tel: (01622) 618780 Fax: (01622) 618782 E-mail: sales@umec.co.uk

COMPONENTS, OPTICAL, INFRARED

S D I Displays Ltd, Ratcliffe Road, Sileby, Loughborough, Leicestershire, LE12 7PZ Tel: (01509) 813166 Fax: (01509) 816369
T D K Electronics, T D K House, 5-7 Queensway, Redhill, RH1 1YB Tel: (01737) 773773 Fax: (01737) 781360

COMPONENTS, OPTICAL, ULTRAVIOLET (UV)

T D K Electronics, T D K House, 5-7 Queensway, Redhill, RH1 1YB Tel: (01737) 773773 Fax: (01737) 781360

COMPOSITE CABLES

J D Cables Ltd, Park House, Greenhill Cresent, Watford, WD18 8PH Tel: (01923) 222600 Fax: (01923) 222608 E-mail: sales@jdcables.com

COMPOSITE COMPONENT AUTOCLAVE MOULDS

Composite Tooling & Structures Ltd, Lola House, Clebe Road, Huntingdon, Cambridgeshire, PE29 7DS Tel: (01480) 459378 Fax: (01480) 455585

COMPOSITE COMPONENT MACHINING EQUIPMENT/ MACHINERY

Magnum Venus Platech Ltd, MTC, Chilsworthy Beam, Gunnislake, Cornwall, PL18 9AT Tel: (01822) 832621 Fax: (01822) 833999 E-mail: rtm@plastech.co.uk

COMPOSITE COMPONENT MOULDING SYSTEMS

▶ Aeroform Ltd, Dawkins Road Industrial Estate, Hamworthy, Poole, Dorset, BH15 4JW Tel: (01202) 683496 Fax: (01202) 622033 E-mail: sales@aeroform.co.uk
J R Technology Ltd, 81 North End, Meldreth, Royston, Hertfordshire, SG8 6NU Tel: (01763) 260721 Fax: (01763) 260809 E-mail: enquiries@jrtech.co.uk
N P Aerospace Ltd, 473 Foleshill Road, Coventry, CV6 5AQ Tel: (024) 7663 8464 Fax: (024) 7668 7313 E-mail: info@np-aerospace.co.uk
Rolls-Royce P.L.C., PO Box 31, Derby, DE24 8BJ Tel: (01332) 349077 Fax: (01332) 291118

COMPOSITE COMPONENT MOULDINGS

Aavf Co. Ltd, Clovelly Road, Bideford, Devon, EX39 3EX Tel: (01237) 475501 Fax: (01237) 479879 E-mail: sales@aavf.co.uk
▶ Composite Integration, Unit 21f Saltash Industrial Estate, Saltash, Cornwall, PL12 6LF Tel: (01752) 849998 Fax: (01752) 849808 E-mail: info@composite-integration.co.uk
H Q Fibre Products, Blofield Road, Lingwood, Norwich, NR13 4AJ Tel: (01603) 713972 Fax: (01603) 713972
Mawson Triton Mouldings Ltd, 4-8 Waterside Industrial Estate, Doulton Road, Rowley Regis, West Midlands, B65 8JG Tel: (01384) 633321 Fax: (01384) 565782 E-mail: sales@mawsontriton.co.uk
Quantum Mouldings Ltd, Emville Street, Stourbridge, West Midlands, DY8 3TD Tel: (01384) 834422 Fax: (01384) 443743 E-mail: sales@quantummouldings.co.uk
Security Composites Ltd, The Farriers, Annscroft, Shrewsbury, SY5 8AN Tel: (01743) 860778 Fax: 01743 860015
Southdown Composites Ltd, Lasham Airfield, Lasham, Alton, Hampshire, GU34 5SR Tel: (01256) 381359 Fax: (01256) 381359 E-mail: sales@southdowncomposites.com
Westway Composites, Unit H The Factory, Dippenhall, Farnham, Surrey, GU10 5DW Tel: (01252) 820200 Fax: (01252) 820217 E-mail: enquiries@westway.co.uk

COMPOSITE COMPONENT SHORT CUT FIBRE FILLERS

Goonvean Fibres Ltd, Ottery Moor Lane, Honiton, Devon, EX14 1BW Tel: (01404) 44194 Fax: (01404) 45102 E-mail: office@goonveanfibres.co.uk
John Peel & Son Ltd, Baildon Mills, Northgate, Baildon, Shipley, West Yorkshire, BD17 6JY Tel: (01274) 583276 Fax: (01274) 598533 E-mail: mail@peelflock.com

COMPOSITE COMPONENT/ PRODUCT RESEARCH AND DEVELOPMENT SERVICES

▶ Aeroform Ltd, Dawkins Road Industrial Estate, Hamworthy, Poole, Dorset, BH15 4JW Tel: (01202) 683496 Fax: (01202) 622033 E-mail: sales@aeroform.co.uk

The Composites Centre, Imperial College, Prince Consort Road, London, SW7 2AZ Tel: (020) 7594 5084 Fax: (020) 7594 5083 E-mail: composites@imperial.ac.uk

COMPOSITE CONTAINERS

Cardboard Tubes Ltd, Unit D2 Zenith, Paycocke Road, Basildon, Essex, SS14 3DW Tel: (01268) 247380 Fax: (01268) 271979 E-mail: sales@cardboardtubes.co.uk

Cores & Tubes Ltd, 42 Vulcan Way, New Addington, Croydon, CR0 9UG Tel: (01689) 848586 Fax: (01689) 841468 E-mail: info@coresandtubes.co.uk

Curran Packaging Co. Ltd, Thames Industrial Park, Princess Margaret Road, East Tilbury, Tilbury, Essex, RM18 8RH Tel: (01375) 857131 Fax: (01375) 856884 E-mail: sales@curran.co.uk

▶ Fibrefusion Ltd, Unit 9e, Spencer Carter Works, Tregoniggie Industrial Estate, Falmouth, Cornwall, TR11 4SN Tel: (01326) 378787 Fax: (01326) 377065 E-mail: paul@fibrefusion.com

Smurfit Composites, Richmond Works, Moresby Road, Hensingham, Whitehaven, Cumbria, CA28 8TS Tel: (01946) 61671 Fax: (01946) 592281

▶ Stonehaven Engineering Ltd, 2 Spurryhillock Industrial Estate, Broomhill Road, Stonehaven, Kincardineshire, AB39 2NH Tel: (01569) 766700 Fax: (01569) 766147 E-mail: info@stonehaven-eng.com

COMPOSITE DOORS

GBW Panels Ltd, 2 Berkeley Business Park, Wainwright Road, Worcester, WR4 9FA Tel: (01905) 340095 Fax: (01905) 340188 E-mail: mark_cuthbert@gbwuk.com

▶ Hurst Plastics Ltd, 1 Kingston Int Business Park, Somerden Road, Hull, HU9 5PE Tel: (01482) 790790 Fax: (01482) 790690 E-mail: sales@hurst-plastics.co.uk

▶ IDM Doors Ltd, Rock Wharf, Mill Parade, Newport, Gwent, NP20 2UL Tel: (01633) 843098 Fax: (01633) 259079 E-mail: info@idmdoorsltd.co.uk

COMPOSITE FLOOR DECKING

L B Plastics Ltd, Firs Works, Heage Firs, Nether Heage, Belper, Derbyshire, DE56 2JJ Tel: (01773) 852311 Fax: (01773) 857080 E-mail: sheerframe@lbplastics.co.uk

COMPOSITE MATERIAL ENGINEERING

C2 Composites, 7 Venture Court, Bradley Lane, Newton Abbot, Devon, TQ12 1NB Tel: (01626) 356611 Fax: (01626) 356659 E-mail: silvan@c2-composites.co.uk

▶ Fibrefusion Ltd, Unit 9e, Spencer Carter Works, Tregoniggie Industrial Estate, Falmouth, Cornwall, TR11 4SN Tel: (01326) 378787 Fax: (01326) 377065 E-mail: paul@fibrefusion.com

White Young Green Ltd, The Mill Yard, Nursling Street, Nursling, Southampton, SO16 0AJ Tel: (0870) 6091084 E-mail: southampton@wyg.com

COMPOSITE MATERIAL FORMING

Aeroform H L M Ltd, Southway, Walworth Industrial Estate, Andover, Hants, SP10 5AF Tel: (01264) 337788 Fax: (01264) 337755 E-mail: hlm@andover.co.uk

COMPOSITE MATERIAL MOULDS

▶ Composite Integration, Unit 21f Saltash Industrial Estate, Saltash, Cornwall, PL12 6LF Tel: (01752) 849998 Fax: (01752) 849808 E-mail: info@composite-integration.co.uk

P P Composites Ltd, Unit 39c Vale Business Park, Llandow, Cowbridge, South Glamorgan, CF71 7PF Tel: (01446) 775885 Fax: (01446) 775822 E-mail: sales@ppcomposites.ltd.uk

COMPOSITE MATERIAL PIPES

Corus Ltd, 20 Inch Pipe Mill Tube Works, Hartlepool, Cleveland, TS25 2EG Tel: (01429) 266611 Fax: (01429) 527283

Pipeline Centre, Unit 3 Dominion Way Industrial Estate, Cardiff, CF24 1RF Tel: (029) 2048 0046 Fax: (029) 2049 6517

Primco Ltd, Grimshaw Lane, Middleton, Manchester, M24 2AE Tel: 0161-653 4876 Fax: 0161-655 3673 E-mail: sales@northwesternblanks.co.uk

COMPOSITE MATERIAL REPAIR SYSTEMS

J R Technology Ltd, 81 North End, Meldreth, Royston, Hertfordshire, SG8 6NU Tel: (01763) 260721 Fax: (01763) 260809 E-mail: enquiries@jrtech.co.uk

COMPOSITE MATERIAL TESTING SERVICES

Bodycote Materials Testing Ltd, Shields Road, Newcastle upon Tyne, NE6 2YD Tel: 0191-275 2800 Fax: 0191-276 0177 E-mail: sales-mt@bodycote-mt.com

The Composites Centre, Imperial College, Prince Consort Road, London, SW7 2AZ Tel: (020) 7594 5084 Fax: (020) 7594 5083 E-mail: composites@imperial.ac.uk

COMPOSITE MATERIAL TUBES

Aavf Co. Ltd, Clovelly Road, Bideford, Devon, EX39 3EX Tel: (01237) 475501 Fax: (01237) 479879 E-mail: sales@aavf.co.uk

COMPOSITE PARTITIONING

T P P Interiors Ltd, Rysted Lane, Westerham, Kent, TN16 1EP Tel: (01959) 563575 Fax: (01959) 561032 E-mail: des@tppinteriors.co.uk

Ultimate Office Interiors, 307 Mariners House Queens Dock Commercial Centre, Norfolk Street, Liverpool, L1 0BG Tel: 0151-708 7700 Fax: 0151-708 7701 E-mail: liverpool@unilock.co.uk

COMPOSITE TAPE LAYING SYSTEMS

Ingersoll International UK Ltd, 7 Sopwith Way, Drayton Fields, Daventry, Northamptonshire, NN11 5PB Tel: (01327) 313500 Fax: (01327) 313509 E-mail: inggmbh@ingersoll-uk.co.uk

COMPOSITE WALL CLADDING

Ruukki UK Ltd, The Old Granary, Riccall Grange King Rudding Lane, Riccall, York, YO19 6QL Tel: (01757) 249334 Fax: (01757) 249335 E-mail: claddingsalesuk@ruukki.com

▶ Vivalda Ltd, Unit 27, Bergan Way, Sutton Field Industrial Estate, Hull, HU7 0YQ Tel: (01482) 310865 Fax: (01482) 824946 E-mail: sales@vivalda_hull.co.uk

COMPRESSED AIR AMPLIFIERS

A C L Engineering Ltd, Anglia House, Sandown Road Industrial Estate, Watford, WD24 7UA Tel: (01923) 249444 Fax: (01923) 242368 E-mail: sales@aclengineering.co.uk

COMPRESSED AIR AND GAS BLOW GUNS

Meech Air Technology, 2 Network Point, Range Road, Witney, Oxfordshire, OX29 0YN Tel: (01993) 706700 Fax: (01993) 776977 E-mail: sales@meech.com

COMPRESSED AIR AND GAS COALESCING FILTERS

R A Driair Ltd, 9 Maguire Industrial Estate, Torrington Avenue, Coventry, CV4 9HN Tel: (024) 7646 6061 Fax: (024) 7669 4516 E-mail: sales@driair.co.uk

COMPRESSED AIR AND GAS CONDENSATE MANAGEMENT SYSTEMS

Airflow Compressors & Pneumatics Ltd, 100 Lord Street, Leigh, Lancashire, WN7 1BY Tel: (01942) 673529 Fax: (01942) 604672 E-mail: mail@airflow-compressors.co.uk

Beko Technologies Ltd, Unit 2-3 Buntsford Park Road, Bromsgrove, Worcestershire, B60 3DX Tel: (01527) 575778 Fax: (01527) 575779

COMPRESSED AIR AND GAS DRYERS

▶ Cambs Compressor Engineering, Grovemere House, Lancaster Way Business Park, Ely, Cambridgeshire, CB6 3NW Tel: (01353) 668925 Fax: (01353) 669595 E-mail: sales@cambscompressors.co.uk

Donaldson Filtration (GB) Ltd, Humberstone Lane, Thurmaston, Leicester, LE4 8HP Tel: 0116-269 6161 Fax: 0116-269 3028 E-mail: peter.cowing@emea.donaldson.com

GF Compressors, Unit 4 Wainwright Street, Birmingham, B6 5TG Tel: 0121-326 9122 Fax: 0121-327 4492 E-mail: sales@gfcompressors.co.uk

Hankison Ltd, Hazleton Interchange, Lakesmere Road, Horndean, Waterlooville, Hampshire, PO8 9JU Tel: (023) 9257 2828 Fax: (0870) 7367377 E-mail: hankisonuk@aol.com

Hiross, Thame Valley Industrial Estate, 1 Claymore, Wilnecote, Tamworth, Staffordshire, B77 5DQ Tel: (01827) 260056 Fax: (01827) 261196 E-mail: sales@zanderuk.com

L B Bentley Ltd, Fromehall Mill, Lodgemore Lane, Stroud, Gloucestershire, GL5 3EH Tel: (01453) 761500 Fax: (01453) 761505 E-mail: sales@lb-bentley.com

P C M Engineering Services Ltd, Castleblair Works, Castle Blair Lane, Dunfermline, Fife, KY12 9DP Tel: (01383) 733334 Fax: (01383) 739496

R A Driair Ltd, 9 Maguire Industrial Estate, Torrington Avenue, Coventry, CV4 9HN Tel: (024) 7646 6061 Fax: (024) 7669 4516 E-mail: sales@driair.co.uk

S P X Air Treatment Ltd, Hazleton Interchange, Lakesmere Road, Horndean, Waterlooville, Hampshire, PO8 9JU Tel: (023) 9257 2820 Fax: (023) 9257 2830 E-mail: enquiries@airtreatment.spx.com

COMPRESSED AIR AND GAS FILTERS

Advanced Vacuum Services Ltd, The Fluid Power Centre, Watling Street, Nuneaton, Warwickshire, CV11 6BQ Tel: (024) 7632 0768 Fax: (024) 7635 0842 E-mail: sales@avs-vacuum.co.uk

Filter Technology, Unit 11 Boundary Business Centre, Boundary Way, Woking, Surrey, GU21 5DH Tel: (01483) 776649 Fax: (01483) 740588 E-mail: dennis@filtertechnology.co.uk

Filterworld, 4a Middlebrook Way, Cromer, Norfolk, NR27 9JR Tel: (01263) 510118 Fax: (01263) 514335 E-mail: enquiry@filterworld.co.uk

Hankison Ltd, Hazleton Interchange, Lakesmere Road, Horndean, Waterlooville, Hampshire, PO8 9JU Tel: (023) 9257 2828 Fax: (0870) 7367377 E-mail: hankisonuk@aol.com

Hiross, Thame Valley Industrial Estate, 1 Claymore, Wilnecote, Tamworth, Staffordshire, B77 5DQ Tel: (01827) 260056 Fax: (01827) 261196 E-mail: sales@zanderuk.com

M I F Filter Systems Ltd, M I F Ho, Waterfall Lane Trading Estate, Cradley Heath, West Midlands, B64 6PU Tel: 0121-561 5380 Fax: 0121-561 3711 E-mail: sales@mif-filters.com

Midland Diving Equipment Ltd, 57 Sparkenhoe Street, Leicester, LE2 0TD Tel: 0116-212 4262 Fax: 0116-212 4263 E-mail: info@midlanddiving.com

Multi-Factor Europe Ltd, Harrison House, Rackery Lane, Llay, Wrexham, Clwyd, LL12 0PB Tel: (0845) 5314030 Fax: (01978) 855222 E-mail: mark.beeston@mfeuk.co.uk

Porvair Technology Ltd, Clywedog Road South, Wrexham Industrial Estate, Wrexham, Clwyd, LL13 9XS Tel: (01978) 661144 Fax: (01978) 664554E-mail: enquiries@porvairfiltration.com

S P X Air Treatment Ltd, Hazleton Interchange, Lakesmere Road, Horndean, Waterlooville, Hampshire, PO8 9JU Tel: (023) 9257 2820 Fax: (023) 9257 2830 E-mail: enquiries@airtreatment.spx.com

Walker Filtration Ltd, Spire Road, Glover East, Washington, Tyne & Wear, NE37 3ES Tel: 0191-417 7816 Fax: 0191-415 3748 E-mail: sales@walkerfiltration.co.uk

COMPRESSED AIR OPERATED PUMPS

Axflow Ltd, 3 Harlaw Centre Howe Moss Crescent, Kirkhill Industrial Estate, Dyce, Aberdeen, AB21 0GN Tel: (01224) 729367 Fax: (01224) 729368 E-mail: infoscot@axflow.co.uk

Hydraulic Pneumatic Services, Unit 3b King Street Trading Estate, Middlewich, Cheshire, CW10 9LF Tel: (01606) 835725 Fax: (01606) 737358 E-mail: kinfo@madan.uk.com

COMPRESSED AIR OR GAS EQUIPMENT

A E Industrial & Air Equipment Ltd, Burma Road, Blidworth, Mansfield, Nottinghamshire, NG21 0RT Tel: (01623) 797897 Fax: (01623) 796318

A J Metal Products Ltd, Cookley Wharf Industrial Estate, Bay 11, Leys Rd, Brierley Hill, West Midlands, DY5 3UP Tel: (01384) 74301 Fax: (01384) 485772 E-mail: sales@ajmetals.co.uk

Airco Pneumatics Ltd, Malmesbury Road, Kingsditch Trading Estate, Cheltenham, Gloucestershire, GL51 9PL Tel: (01242) 690480 Fax: (01242) 690490 E-mail: info@aircopneumatics.co.uk

▶ AR-EL Workshop Equipment Ltd, PO Box 200, Aberdeen, AB32 6GW Tel: (01224) 749051 Fax: (01244) 749051 E-mail: raymond@workshop-equipment.co.uk

Atlas Copco Compressors Ltd, 34 Telford Road, Lenzie Mill Industrial Estate, Cumbernauld, Glasgow, G67 2AX Tel: (01236) 733722 Fax: (01236) 735601 E-mail: admin@atlascopco.com

Atlas Copco Compressors Ltd, 11 Harvey Close, Crowther, Washington, Tyne & Wear, NE38 0AB Tel: 0191-417 5764 Fax: 0191-415 7452

▶ C H Power Tools, Bentley Road, Doncaster, South Yorkshire, DN5 9QP Tel: (01302) 821821

Caledonian Air Service, St. Andrews Works, Bonnyhill Road, Bonnybridge, Stirlingshire, FK4 2EJ Tel: (01324) 812122 Fax: (01324) 812128 E-mail: caledonian@airservice.fsnet.co.uk

Compressed Air Contracts, 5b Alleysbank Road, Rutherglen, Glasgow, G73 1LX Tel: 0141-647 0007 Fax: 0141-647 9090 E-mail: glasgow@economatics.co.uk

Compressed Air Services Ltd, Unit 22 Bordesley Trading Estate, Bordesley Green Road, Birmingham, B8 1BZ Tel: 0121-327 1700 Fax: 0121-322 0970 E-mail: pthomas@cas-ltd.uk.com

▶ Compressor Maintenance Repair Services Ltd, Unit 24 Maybrook Industrial Estate, Maybrook Road, Walsall, WS8 7DG Tel: (01543) 453881 Fax: (01543) 453882 E-mail: sales@cmrs.co.uk

D M F Ltd, 2 Dewsbury Road, Wakefield, West Yorkshire, WF2 9BS Tel: (01924) 370685 Fax: (01924) 364160 E-mail: sales@dmfwakefield.ltd.uk

Durr Technik (UK) Ltd, Unit 5, Ashmead Business Centre, Ashmead Road, Keynsham, Bristol, BS31 1SX Tel: 0117-986 0414 Fax: 0117-986 0416 E-mail: info@durrtechnik.co.uk

▶ Eaton, Tay House, 300 Bath Street, Glasgow, G2 4NA Tel: 0141-331 7000 Fax: 0141-331 7001

Flow Serve Flow Control Ltd, Victoria Way, Burgess Hill, West Sussex, RH15 9NF Tel: (01444) 245826

▶ Gardner Denver (Alton) Ltd, Unit 1, Waterbrook Estate, Waterbrook Road, Alton, Hampshire, GU34 2UD Tel: (01420) 544184 Fax: (01420) 544183 E-mail: ukinfo@eu.gardnerdenver.com

▶ I F P Systems Ltd, 10 Cameron Drive, Falkland, Cupar, Fife, KY15 7DL Tel: (01337) 857198 Fax: (01337) 857175

Interworld, Avenue Road, Lasham, Alton, Hampshire, GU34 5SU Tel: (01256) 381641 Fax: (01256) 381378

▶ London Hermetics P.L.C., Unit 42, Weir Road, Durnsford Industrial Estate, London, SW19 8UG Tel: (020) 8947 0886 Fax: (020) 8947 1007 E-mail: sales@lh-plc.co.uk

Norgren Ltd, Unit A3, Brookside Business Park, Greengate, Middleton, Manchester, M24 1GR Tel: 0161-655 7300 Fax: 0161-655 7373 E-mail: manchester@norgren.com

Norman Walker, Anchor House, Reservoir Road, Hull, HU6 7QD Tel: (01482) 493982 Fax: (01482) 493983 E-mail: info@walkerair.co.uk

Oscott Air Ltd, Sherlock Street, Birmingham, B5 6LT Tel: 0121-622 2789 Fax: 0121-666 6012 E-mail: sales@oscottair.com

▶ Pennine Pneumatic Services, 5-7 Pellon New Road, Halifax, West Yorkshire, HX1 4UB Tel: (01422) 321772 Fax: (01422) 342430

▶ R L Engineering Services Ltd, Polmadie Works, Jessie Street, Glasgow, G42 0PZ Tel: 0141-423 2367 Fax: 0141-422 2156

Rodwell H T B, Bentalls, Basildon, Essex, SS14 3SD Tel: (01268) 286646 Fax: (01268) 287799 E-mail: sales@rodwell-autoclave.com

▶ Sabroe Ltd, 86 Melchett Road, Kings Norton Business Centre, Birmingham, B30 3HX Tel: 0121-683 7800 E-mail: sales@sabroe.co.uk

South Coast Hydraulics Ltd, Unit 1, Kings Crescent, Shoreham-by-Sea, West Sussex, BN43 5LE Tel: (01273) 446444 Fax: (01273) 446555

Sparrows Offshore Services Ltd, Woodside Road, Bridge Of Don Industrial Estate, Aberdeen, AB23 8BW Tel: (01224) 826032

Sunbury Tubing & Pneumatics Ltd, Unit 11 Littleton House, Littleton Road, Ashford, Middlesex, TW15 1UU Tel: (01784) 256309 Fax: (01784) 246470

▶ Tayside Compressor Services, Lindegaard Building, 1 Kilspindie Street, Dunsinane Industrial Estate, Dundee, DD2 3EW Tel: (01382) 813263 Fax: (01382) 819075

Thomas Wright, 6 Barge Street, St. Thomas's Road, Huddersfield, HD1 3LG Tel: (01484) 534245 Fax: (01484) 435023 E-mail: bradford@thorite.co.uk

TransAirVac International Ltd, PO Box 491, Newcastle, Staffordshire, ST5 0TW Tel: (01782) 710282 Fax: (01782) 710126 E-mail: office@transairvac.com

▶ Trolley Jack Services, 11 Smith Street, Falkirk, FK2 7NB Tel: (01324) 634526 Fax: (01324) 622176

▶ indicates data change since last edition

COMPRESSED AIR OR GAS EQUIPMENT – *continued*

▶ Unicorn Ltd, 1 Park Works Canal Bridge Enterprise Centre, Meadow Lane, Ellesmere Port, CH65 4EH Tel: 0151-355 5151 Fax: 0151-357 1733 E-mail: pumps@unicornltd.fsnet.co.uk

COMPRESSED AIR OR GAS INSTALLATION OR SERVICING

A & B Air Systems Ltd, Unit 41 Abenbury Way, Wrexham Industrial Estate, Wrexham, Clwyd, LL13 9UZ Tel: (01978) 661999 Fax: (01978) 664330 E-mail: sales@ab-airsystems.co.uk

Air Systems Ltd, 20-22 Grafton Road, Sparkbrook, Birmingham, B11 1JP Tel: 0121-772 1561 Fax: 0121-766 8727

Airchannel, 115 Burrell Road, Ipswich, IP2 8AE Tel: (01473) 690000 Fax: (01473) 685058 E-mail: enquiries@anglair.co.uk

B C A S Ltd, Unit 8 Thames Park, Lester Way, Wallingford, Oxfordshire, OX10 9TA Tel: (01491) 821737 Fax: (01491) 821730 E-mail: sales@bcaslimited.co.uk

B R E Ltd, Fowler Road, West Pitkerro Industrial Estate, Broughty Ferry, Dundee, DD5 3RU Tel: (01382) 739848 Fax: (01382) 739849 E-mail: info@breuk.com

Boge Compressors, Units 1-4, Bowen Industrial Estate, Aberbargoed, Bargoed, Mid Glamorgan, CF81 9EP Tel: (01443) 875163 Fax: (01443) 820909

Burford Engineering, 11 Denesway, Meopham, Gravesend, Kent, DA13 0EA Tel: (01474) 815228 Fax: 07970 086211 E-mail: pete@burfordair.co.uk

Caledonian Air Service, St. Andrews Works, Bonnyhill Road, Bonnybridge, Stirlingshire, FK4 2EJ Tel: (01324) 812122 Fax: (01324) 812128 E-mail: caledonian@airservice.fsnet.co.uk

▶ Cambs Compressor Engineering, Grovemere House, Lancaster Way Business Park, Ely, Cambridgeshire, CB6 3NW Tel: (01353) 668925 Fax: (01353) 669595 E-mail: sales@cambscompressors.co.uk

▶ H & E Installations, Telford Way, Severalls Industrial Park, Colchester, CO4 9QP Tel: (01206) 844334 Fax: (01206) 844992

H P C Engineering Plc, Victoria Gardens, Victoria Gardens Industrial Estate, Burgess Hill, West Sussex, RH15 9RQ Tel: (01444) 241671 Fax: (01444) 247304 E-mail: info@hpcplc.co.uk

Kettering Compressed Air Services Ltd, 16 Cross Street, Kettering, Northamptonshire, NN16 9DQ Tel: (01536) 516482 Fax: (01536) 411842 E-mail: sales@kcas.co.uk

P C M Engineering Services Ltd, Castleblair Works, Castle Blair Lane, Dunfermline, Fife, KY12 9DP Tel: (01383) 733334 Fax: (01383) 739496

▶ S A Gas Engineers Ltd, Burma Road, Blidworth, Mansfield, Nottinghamshire, NG21 0RT Tel: (01623) 796545 Fax: (01623) 796546

COMPRESSED AIR SERVICES

Babcock PTI, Lorne Road, Larbert, Stirlingshire, FK5 4AT Tel: (01324) 552599 Fax: (01324) 562006

▶ Cambs Compressor Engineering, Grovemere House, Lancaster Way Business Park, Ely, Cambridgeshire, CB6 3NW Tel: (01353) 668925 Fax: (01353) 669595 E-mail: sales@cambscompressors.co.uk

CompAir UK Ltd, Claybrook Drive, Washford Industrial Estate, Redditch, Worcestershire, B98 0DS Tel: (01527) 525522 Fax: (01527) 521140 E-mail: sales@compair.com

Compressor & Air Equipment, Abbey Gate, Leicester, LE4 0AA Tel: 0116-251 4914

Marshall Brewson Ltd, 6 Westside Industrial Estate, South Humberside Industrial Estate, Grimsby, South Humberside, DN31 2TG Tel: (01472) 359001 Fax: (01472) 359954 E-mail: sales@marshallbrewson.co.uk

North West Compressed Air Co. Ltd, Unit 361 Leach Place, Walton Summit Centre, Bamber Bridge, Preston, PR5 8AS Tel: (01772) 311999 Fax: (01772) 312888 E-mail: sales@nwca.co.uk

COMPRESSED AIR SYSTEMS

Compressor & Air Equipment, Abbey Gate, Leicester, LE4 0AA Tel: 0116-251 4914

Marshall Brewson Ltd, 6 Westside Industrial Estate, South Humberside Industrial Estate, Grimsby, South Humberside, DN31 2TG Tel: (01472) 359001 Fax: (01472) 359954 E-mail: sales@marshallbrewson.co.uk

Nothern Gas Installation, 7 Alder Road, Failsworth, Manchester, M35 0GH Tel: 0161-682 8323 Fax: 0161-682 0043 E-mail: info@northerngasinstallations.com

COMPRESSED FIBRE PLUGS

Moorland Woodturning Co. Ltd, Woodlands Mill, Luke Lane, Thongsbridge, Holmfirth, HD9 7TB Tel: (01484) 683126

COMPRESSION COIL SPRINGS

Active Springs, Redditch Road, Studley, Warwickshire, B80 7AY Tel: (01527) 854932 Fax: (01527) 854969 E-mail: robert@active-springs.co.uk

COMPRESSION FITTINGS

Aston Fittings, Springcroft Road, Birmingham, B11 3EL Tel: 0121-778 6001 Fax: 0121-778 6002 E-mail: sales@astonfittings.com

Astore UK, Walsall Road, Norton Canes, Cannock, Staffordshire, WS11 9PU Tel: (01543) 272400 Fax: (01543) 272413 E-mail: sales@astore.uk.com

Cronation Ltd, Carlton Business Centre, 104 Nechells Place, Birmingham, B7 5AB Tel: 0121-359 7567 Fax: 0121-359 5339 E-mail: sales@cronation.co.uk

Delta Fluid Products Ltd, Delta Road, St. Helens, Merseyside, WA9 2ED Tel: (01744) 611811 Fax: (01744) 611818 E-mail: enquiries@deltafluidproducts.com

Flowflex Components Ltd, Samuel Blaser Works, Tongue Lane Industrial Estate, Buxton, Derbyshire, SK17 7LR Tel: (01298) 77211 Fax: (01298) 72362 E-mail: flowflex@compuserve.com

▶ Glynwed Pipe Systems Ltd, St. Peters Road, Huntingdon, Cambridgeshire, PE29 7DA Tel: (01480 52121 Fax: (01480) 450430 E-mail: enquiries@gpsuk.com

Hydraflow Hydraulics (UK) Ltd, Unit 1, Price Street, Bristol Road, Gloucester, GL1 5SZ Tel: (01452) 387061 Fax: (01452) 381332

Ionic Instruments Ltd, Henfield Road, Small Dole, Henfield, West Sussex, BN5 9XE Tel: (01273) 493522 Fax: (01273) 493630 E-mail:

Melnei Engineering, Unit F4 Heath Place, Bognor Regis, West Sussex, PO22 9SL Tel: (01243) 829103 Fax: (01243) 829103 E-mail: melnei@melneiengineering.co.uk

Serto UK Ltd, Unit 3 West Court, Buntsford Park Road, Bromsgrove, Worcestershire, B60 3DX Tel: (01527) 573960 Fax: (01527) 870291 E-mail: sales@serto.co.uk

Sherriff Sales Agency, 1 The Limes, Porton, Salisbury, SP4 0LT Tel: (01980) 610844 Fax: (01980) 611866 E-mail: sherriff.sales@ntlworld.com

▶ SpeedPlumb.co.uk, Casemill, Temeside, Ludlow, Shropshire, SY8 1JW Tel: 0845 3732738

Wade, Delta Road, Parr, St. Helens, Merseyside, WA9 2ED Tel: (01744) 451616 Fax: (01744) 26791 E-mail: enquiries@deltafluidproducts.com

Yorkshire Copper Tube, East Lancashire Road, Liverpool, L33 7TU Tel: 0151-546 2700 Fax: 0151-546 5881 E-mail: sales@yorkshirecoppertube.com

COMPRESSION RINGS

J P Olives Ltd, 31a Heming Road, Redditch, Worcestershire, B98 0DH Tel: (01527) 516600 Fax: (01527) 516611 E-mail: sales@jpolives.co.uk

COMPRESSION SPRINGS

A S K Springs, Edward Street, Clive Works, Redditch, Worcestershire, B97 6HA Tel: (01527) 63300 Fax: (01527) 63300

The Active Spring Company Ltd, Sibleys Green, Sibleys Lane, Thaxted, Dunmow, Essex, CM6 2NU Tel: (01371) 830557 Fax: (01371) 831151 E-mail: sales@tascuk.com

All Spring Ltd, C/O Multistroke Ltd, King Street, Old Hill, Cradley Heath, West Midlands, B64 6JJ Tel: (01384) 567773 Fax: (01304) 566589 E-mail: allspringltd@btconnect.com

Ashfield Springs Ltd, Nunn Brook Rise, Huthwaite, Sutton-in-Ashfield, Nottinghamshire, NG17 2PD Tel: 0845 4941745 Fax: (01623) 455502 E-mail: bryan.smith@ashfield-springs.com

Bywell Springs & Pressings Ltd, Unit 4, Millsborough House, Ipsley St, Redditch, Worcestershire, B98 7AL Tel: (01527) 66551 Fax: (01527) 66024 E-mail: sales@bywell.co.uk

Dan (UK) Ltd, Unit 1, Mucklow Hill 1 Trading Estate, Mucklow Hill, Halesowen, West Midlands, B62 8DF Tel: 0121-585 7171 Fax: 0121-585 7272 E-mail: sales@danlyuk.com

Flexo Springs Ltd, Hill Street, Kingswood, Bristol, BS15 4HB Tel: 0845 4941786 Fax: 0117-935 2597 E-mail: sales@flexosprings.com

Harris Springs Ltd, Ruscombe Works Tavistock Industrial Estate, Ruscombe Lane, Ruscombe, Reading, RG10 9LR Tel: 0118-934 0024 Fax: 0118-934 1365 E-mail: sales@harris-springs.com

Lee Spring Ltd, Latimer Road, Wokingham, Berkshire, RG41 2WA Tel: 0118-978 1800 Fax: 0118-977 4832 E-mail: abinding@leespring.co.uk

Lion Springs Ltd, Summer Street, Rochdale, Lancashire, OL16 1SY Tel: (01706) 861352 Fax: (01706) 657863 E-mail: sales@lionsprings.co.uk

Mortimer Springs Ltd, Coleman Works, Villiers Road, London, NW2 5PU Tel: (020) 8459 1420 Fax: (020) 8451 7614 E-mail: sales@mortimersprings.com

C. Norris (Spring Specialists) Ltd, Ladyhouse Spring Works, Newhey Road, Milnrow, Rochdale, Lancashire, OL16 4JD Tel: (01706) 642555 Fax: (01706) 648347 E-mail: andrewward@btconnect.com

Penning Springs, Bolton Road North, Ramsbottom, Bury, Lancashire, BL0 0LY Tel: (01706) 824614 Fax: (01706) 821636

Performance Springs Ltd, Queensway Industrial Estate, Scafell Road, St Annes, Lytham St. Annes, Lancashire, FY8 3HE Tel: (01253) 716900 Fax: (01253) 716911 E-mail: sales@performance-springs.com

Reliable Spring & Manufacturing Co. Ltd, Unit 4a Princes End Industrial Estate, Nicholls Road, Tipton, West Midlands, DY4 9LG Tel: 0121-557 4999 Fax: 0121-557 6959 E-mail: sales@reliablespring.co.uk

Frederick Spring Co., Princes End Industrial Park, Nicholls Road, Tipton, West Midlands, DY4 9LG Tel: 0121-557 4080 Fax: 0121-557 6959 E-mail: robjenkins@btclick.com

Springco (N I) Ltd, Tavanagh Factory, Armagh Road, Craigavon, County Armagh, BT62 3EG Tel: (028) 3833 3482 Fax: (028) 3833 8721 E-mail: sales@springco.co.uk

Springstop Ltd, Unit 11 Block 3, Nuneaton Street, Glasgow, G40 3JU Tel: 0141-554 4424 Fax: 0141-554 4423 E-mail: springstop1@aol.com

Valley Spring Co. Ltd, Pottery Lane East, Chesterfield, Derbyshire, S41 9BH Tel: (01246) 451981 Fax: (01246) 454327 E-mail: sales@valleyspring.com

COMPRESSION TEST EQUIPMENT

▶ Testometric Co. Ltd, Unit 1 Lincoln Business Park, Lincoln Close, Rochdale, Lancashire, OL11 1NR Tel: (01706) 654039 Fax: (01706) 646089 E-mail: info@testometric.co.uk

COMPRESSOR FILTERS

Multi-Factor Europe Ltd, Harrison House, Rackery Lane, Llay, Wrexham, Clwyd, LL12 0PB Tel: (0845) 5314030 Fax: (01978) 855222 E-mail: mark.beeston@mfeuk.co.uk

COMPRESSOR (GAS) DEVELOPMENT CONSULTANTS OR DESIGNERS

M S E Consultants Ltd, North House, 31 North Street, Carshalton, Surrey, SM5 2HW Tel: (020) 8773 4500 Fax: (020) 8773 4600 E-mail: enquiries@mse.co.uk

COMPRESSOR (GAS) MAINTENANCE/RECONDITION/ REMANUFACTURE/REPAIR SERVICES

Dresser Rand UK Ltd, Hareness Circle, Altens Industrial Estate, Aberdeen, AB12 3LY Tel: (01224) 879445 Fax: (01224) 894616 E-mail: geoff_king@dresser-rand.com

COMPRESSOR HIRE

Add Plant Ltd, Grovehill Road, Beverley, East Yorkshire, HU17 0JN Tel: (01482) 867227 Fax: (01482) 872868 E-mail: hire@addplant.karoo.co.uk

N.A. Robson Ltd, Robson Way, Highfurlong, Blackpool, FY3 7PP Tel: (01253) 393406 Fax: (01253) 300160 E-mail: sales@robson.uk.com

COMPRESSOR LUBRICANTS

Hydralube Ltd, 72A Parker Road, Hastings, East Sussex, TN34 3TT Tel: (01424) 465527 Fax: (01424) 201363 E-mail: sales@hydralube.co.uk

COMPRESSOR MAINTENANCE OR REPAIR

▶ Gardner Denver Alton Ltd, Larkfield Trading Estate, New Hythe Lane, Larkfield, Aylesford, Kent, ME20 6SW Tel: (01622) 716816 Fax: (01622) 715115 E-mail: ukinfo@eu.gardnerdenver.com

COMPRESSOR (RECIPROCATING) SPARE PARTS

Garlock GB Ltd, Premier Way, Lowfields Business Park, Elland, West Yorkshire, HX5 9HF Tel: (01422) 313600 Fax: (01422) 313601 E-mail: jasonsedgwick@compuserve.com

COMPRESSOR SPARE PARTS/ WEARING PARTS

Aces Ltd, Unit 10 Manor Farm, Peppard Common, Henley-on-Thames, Oxfordshire, RG9 5LA Tel: (01491) 629671 Fax: (01491) 629621 E-mail: sales@acescomp.co.uk

Air Systems Ltd, 20-22 Grafton Road, Sparkbrook, Birmingham, B11 1JP Tel: 0121-772 1561 Fax: 0121-766 8727

Compressor Valve Engineering Ltd, 4 Burnell Road, Ellesmere Port, CH65 5EX Tel: 0151-355 5937 Fax: 0151-357 1098 E-mail: sales@compvalve.co.uk

F J Engineering Ltd, 4 Keyhaven Road, Milford on Sea, Lymington, Hampshire, SO41 0QY Tel: (01590) 644644 Fax: (01590) 644644 E-mail: fjengineer@aol.com

G & M Venditti Compressors Ltd, Unit 1 Park Road, Bury, Lancashire, BL9 5BQ Tel: 0161-764 5667 Fax: 0161-764 1316

G P Compressed Air Services, Unit 2, Bodmin Road, Wyken, Coventry, CV2 5DB Tel: (024) 7662 2200 Fax: (024) 7662 2300 E-mail: info@gpair.co.uk

Hydro Pneumatic Services, Bastion House, Harlequin Avenue, Brentford, Middlesex, TW8 9EW Tel: (020) 8560 4968 Fax: (020) 8560 4958

Kompressors Ltd, Southgate Avenue, Mildenhall, Bury St. Edmunds, Suffolk, IP28 7AT Tel: (01638) 715361 Fax: (01638) 510762

Machine Mart Ltd, 211 Lower Parliament Street, Nottingham, NG1 1GN Tel: (0870) 7707830 Fax: (0870) 7707811 E-mail: sales@machinemart.co.uk

Motivair Compressors Ltd, 9 Mount Road Industrial Estate, Mount Road, Feltham, Middlesex, TW13 6AR Tel: (020) 8744 8833 Fax: (020) 8744 8822 E-mail: international@motivair.co.uk

Motivair Compressors Ltd, Chase Link, Lichfield Road, Brownhills, Walsall, WS8 6JZ Tel: (01543) 454454 Fax: (01543) 454334 E-mail: brownhills@motivair.co.uk

Sulzer Pumps UK Ltd, Manor Mill Lane, Leeds, LS11 8BR Tel: 0113-270 1244 Fax: 0113-272 4404 E-mail: sales@sulzerpumps.com

COMPRESSOR VALVES

Hoerbiger UK Ltd, 1649 Pershore Road, Stirchley, Birmingham, B30 3DR Tel: 0121-433 3636 Fax: 0121-433 3854 E-mail: info.huk@hoerbiger.com

Steadvale Air Systems Ltd, Boston Road, Glenrothes, Fife, KY6 2RE Tel: (01592) 771891 Fax: (01592) 772759 E-mail: sales@steadvale.co.uk

COMPRESSORS, *See also headings for particular types*

Atlas Copco Compressors Ltd, 34 Telford Road, Lenzie Mill Industrial Estate, Cumbernauld, Glasgow, G67 2AX Tel: (01236) 733722 Fax: (01236) 735601 E-mail: admin@atlascopco.com

Atlas Copco Compressors Ltd, 11 Harvey Close, Crowther, Washington, Tyne & Wear, NE38 0AB Tel: 0191-417 5764 Fax: 0191-415 7452

▶ C H Power Tools, Bentley Road, Doncaster, South Yorkshire, DN5 9QP Tel: (01302) 821821

Compass Oilfield Supply Co. Ltd, James Watt Close, Great Yarmouth, Norfolk, NR31 0NX Tel: (01493) 667037 Fax: (01493) 653603 E-mail: intray@compass-hq.com

Compressor & Air Equipment, Abbey Gate, Leicester, LE4 0AA Tel: 0116-251 4914

▶ Compressor Maintenance Repair Services Ltd, Unit 24 Maybrook Industrial Estate, Maybrook Road, Walsall, WS8 7DG Tel: (01543) 453881 Fax: (01543) 453882 E-mail: sales@cmrs.co.uk

▶ Eaton, Tay House, 300 Bath Street, Glasgow, G2 4NA Tel: 0141-331 7000 Fax: 0141-331 7001

H & M Compressors & Pumps Ltd, B Enterprise Centre, Paycocke Road, Basildon, Essex, SS14 3DY Tel: (01268) 531288 Fax: (01268) 532013 E-mail: hmcompressos@tiscali.co.uk

▶ I F P Systems Ltd, 10 Cameron Drive, Falkland, Cupar, Fife, KY15 7DL Tel: (01337) 857198 Fax: (01337) 857175

▶ Johnston Engineering (Falkirk) Ltd, Dunipace Mill, Denovan Road, Larbert, Stirlingshire, FK5 4RY Tel: (01324) 821122 Fax: (01324) 821122

▶ London Hermetics P.L.C., Unit 42, Weir Road, Durnsford Industrial Estate, London, SW19 8UG Tel: (020) 8947 0886 Fax: (020) 8947 1007 E-mail: sales@lh-plc.co.uk

▶ indicates data change since last edition

COMPRESSORS – *continued*

Machine Mart Ltd, 8-10 Holderness Road, Hull, HU9 1EG Tel: (01482) 223161 Fax: (01482) 225085

Norgren Ltd, Unit A3, Brookside Business Park, Greengate, Middleton, Manchester, M24 1GR Tel: 0161-655 7300 Fax: 0161-655 7373 E-mail: manchester@norgren.com

P G Reeves & Sons, 129-133 Dogsthorpe Road, Peterborough, PE1 3AH Tel: (01733) 563887 Fax: (01733) 555582

▶ Pennine Pneumatic Services, 5-7 Pellon New Road, Halifax, West Yorkshire, HX1 4UB Tel: (01422) 321772 Fax: (01422) 342430

▶ R L Engineering Services Ltd, Polmadie Works, Jessie Street, Glasgow, G42 0PZ Tel: 0141-423 2367 Fax: 0141-422 2156

▶ S W P Hydraulics Ltd, 4 Bell Close, Newnham Industrial Estate, Plympton, Plymouth, PL7 4JH Tel: (01752) 338772 Fax: (01752) 336588

South Coast Hydraulics Ltd, Unit 1, Kings Crescent, Shoreham-by-Sea, West Sussex, BN43 5LE Tel: (01273) 446444 Fax: (01273) 446555

Sparrows Offshore Services Ltd, Woodside Road, Bridge Of Don Industrial Estate, Aberdeen, AB23 8BW Tel: (01224) 826032

▶ Trolley Jack Services, 11 Smith Street, Falkirk, FK2 7NB Tel: (01324) 634526 Fax: (01324) 622176

▶ Unicorn Ltd, 1 Park Works Canal Bridge Enterprise Centre, Meadow Lane, Ellesmere Port, CH65 4EH Tel: 0151-355 5151 Fax: 0151-357 1733 E-mail: pumps@unicornltd.fsnet.co.uk

COMPRESSORS, AIR CONDITIONING (AC) UNIT

▶ Johnson Controls Ltd, Unit 17, Royal Portsbury, Bristol, BS20 7XE Tel: (01275) 375713 Fax: (01275) 375714

COMPUTATIONAL FLUID DYNAMIC (CFD) SIMULATION SOFTWARE

▶ Cambridge Flow Solutions, Compass House, Vision Park, Histon, Cambridge, CB4 9AD Tel: 01223 257978 Fax: 01223 257800 E-mail: ed.lewis@cambridgeflowsolutions.com

Computational Dynamics Ltd, Hythe House, 200 Shepherds Bush Road, London, W6 7NL Tel: (020) 7471 6200 Fax: (020) 7471 6201

▶ K8T Ltd, 8 Simmonds Buildings, Bristol Road, Bristol, BS16 1RY Tel: 0117-956 8477 E-mail: paulkingston@k8t.ltd.uk

COMPUTER ACCESSORIES AND CONSUMABLES

A D P Supplies Ltd, 65 Peach Street, Wokingham, Berkshire, RG40 1XP Tel: 0118-977 0554 Fax: 0118-978 5525

A G M Media Group, 212-214 Hylton Road, Sunderland, SR4 7UZ Tel: 0191-565 6776 Fax: 0191-565 5604

A T S S (East Anglia) Ltd, Station Road East, Stowmarket, Suffolk, IP14 1RQ Tel: (01449) 674944 Fax: (01449) 678678 E-mail: sales@atssea.co.uk

A W W Computers, South Road, Harlow, Essex, CM20 2AS Tel: (01279) 626354 Fax: (01279) 421500 E-mail: admin@wenham.co.uk

▶ A1 Cad, 19 Totnes Close, Poulton-le-Fylde, Lancashire, FY6 7TP Tel: (01253) 882812 Fax: (01253) 882812

Abbotts Office Solutions, Station Yard, Thame, Oxfordshire, OX9 3UH Tel: (01844) 268360 Fax: (01844) 268370 E-mail: abbott@officesolutions.co.uk

Absoft Ltd, Units B3-B4 Aberdeen Science & Technology Park, Balgownie Road, Bridge of Don, Aberdeen, AB22 8GT Tel: (01224) 707088 Fax: (01224) 707099 E-mail: info@absoft.co.uk

ACS (UK) Ltd, Park View House, 6 Woodside Place, Glasgow, G3 7QF Tel: 0141- 572 3020 Fax: 0141- 572 4020

Adept Scientific plc, Amor Way, Letchworth Garden City, Hertfordshire, SG6 1ZA Tel: (01462) 480055 Fax: (01462) 480213 E-mail: info@adeptscience.co.uk

Advanced 24, 40 Potton Road, St. Neots, Cambridgeshire, PE19 2NP Tel: (01480) 381632 Fax: 01480 381632

Allsoprint Designers, 3 Titan House, Calleva Park, Aldermaston, Reading, RG7 8AA Tel: 0118-982 0007 Fax: 0118-982 0004

Arena Computer Supplies Ltd, 18 Sandeman Way, Horsham, West Sussex, RH13 6EL Tel: (01403) 272156 Fax: (01403) 252620

Armari Ltd, 5 Woodshots Meadow, Croxley Business Park, Watford, WD18 8QD Tel: (01923) 225550 Fax: (01923) 221161 E-mail: sales@amari.co.uk

Ashby Computer Services, Sywell Airport Business Park, Wellingborough Road, Sywell, Northampton, NN6 0BN Tel: (01604) 790979 Fax: (01604) 491859 E-mail: enquiries@ashbycomputers.co.uk

Automated Services (London) Ltd, 42B Oakwood Hill Industrial Estate, Oakwood Hill, Loughton, Essex, IG10 3TZ Tel: (020) 8502 3111 Fax: (020) 8508 0322

Avenga Computer Services, 34 Morse Road, Whitnash, Leamington Spa, Warwickshire, CV31 2LH Tel: (01926) 882639 Fax: (01926) 882639 E-mail: nigel@avenga.co.uk

Beyond 2000 PC Systems Software, 97-103 Upper Parliament Street, Nottingham, NG1 6LA Tel: 0115-924 3000 Fax: (0870) 3304300

Big Fish Ltd, Ribbon Light House, Newtown Street, Prestwich, Manchester, M25 1HU Tel: 0161-798 0040 Fax: 0161-798 8884 E-mail: manvent@bigfishhook.com

Bingo Office Supplies Ltd, PO Box 845, Halifax, West Yorkshire, HX3 6YR Tel: (0800) 0424646 Fax: (0800) 0424329 E-mail: sales@bingo-office.co.uk

Black & White Consumables Ltd, 22 St.Johns North, Wakefield, West Yorkshire, WF1 3QA Tel: (01924) 210236 Fax: (01924) 782037 E-mail: info@bwconsumables.co.uk

▶ Blinkin Ink Cartridge Service, 15 Bucknall New Road, Stoke-on-Trent, ST1 2BA Tel: (01782) 859933 Fax: (01782) 861130

Blue Dolphin Supplies Ltd, 4 Portland Place, Hamilton, Lanarkshire, ML3 7JU Tel: (0870) 7479101 Fax: (01698) 297048 E-mail: info@bluedolphinsupplies.co.uk

Brightmedia Computer Consumables, 3 Chiltern Street, London, W1U 7PB Tel: (020) 7224 3363 Fax: (020) 7224 3373

Bristol Office Products, Woodview House, 47 Woodleaze, Bristol, BS9 2HX Tel: 0117-968 5016 Fax: 0117-968 5993 E-mail: sales@bop.uk.com

▶ Bubble Distribution Ltd, Edison Court, Pinchbeck, Spalding, Lincolnshire, PE11 3FX Tel: (0845) 4084671 Fax: (0845) 4084672

Business Computer Resources Ltd, 1b Dyke Road Drive, Brighton, BN1 6AJ Tel: (01273) 542759 Fax: (01273) 889898 E-mail: sales@bcrltd.co.uk

Byte Back, 4 Rex Corner, Broxholme Lane, Doncaster, South Yorkshire, DN1 2LP Tel: (01302) 812809

▶ C K Media (UK) Ltd, 300 Westfield Lane, Mansfield, Nottinghamshire, NG19 6NQ Tel: (01623) 652200

Calibre Computing, 19 Daish Way, Newport, Isle of Wight, PO30 5XJ Tel: (01983) 530548 Fax: (01983) 530548 E-mail: sales@calibrecomputing.co.uk

Cambridge Computer Systems, Rosemary House, Lanwades Business Park, Kennett, Newmarket, Suffolk, CB8 7PW Tel: (01638) 751485 Fax: (01638) 751058 E-mail: linda@ccsys.co.uk

▶ Cartridge Cellar, 10 Blenheim Parade, Allestree, Derby, DE22 2GP Tel: (01332) 551514 Fax: (01332) 606790 E-mail: sales@cartridgecellar.co.uk

▶ Cartridge City, 187 Queensway, Bletchley, Milton Keynes, MK2 2ED Tel: (01908) 366616

▶ Cartridge City, 49 Midland Road, Wellingborough, Northamptonshire, NN8 1HF Tel: (01933) 226555 Fax: (01933) 275372

▶ Cartridge World Ltd, Unit K-20 Westminster House, Town Centre, Basingstoke, Hampshire, RG21 7LS Tel: (01256) 323000 Fax: (01256) 323011 E-mail: cwbassingstoke@cartridgeworld.org

▶ Cartridge World Ltd, 3 Bassett Avenue, Bicester, Oxfordshire, OX26 4TZ Tel: (01869) 252627 Fax: (01869) 252625 E-mail: cwbicester@cartridgeworld.org

▶ Cartridge World Ltd, 24 Hockerill Street, Bishop's Stortford, Hertfordshire, CM23 2DW Tel: (01279) 466664 Fax: (01279) 467466

▶ Cartridge World Ltd, 22 Temple Street, Keynsham, Bristol, BS31 1EH Tel: 0117-986 8686 Fax: 0117-986 6222 E-mail: cwkeynsham@cartridgeworld.org

▶ Cartridge World Ltd, 40 Duke Street, Doncaster, South Yorkshire, DN1 3EA Tel: (01302) 325511 Fax: (01302) 360607

▶ Cartridge World Ltd, 7 Shellons Street, Folkestone, Kent, CT20 1BW Tel: (01303) 247474 Fax: (01303) 247427 E-mail: cwfolkstone@cartridgeworld.org

Cartridge World Ltd, 15 Woodford Avenue, Ilford, Essex, IG2 6UF Tel: (020) 8551 2277 Fax: (020) 8551 2442

▶ Cartridge World Ltd, 8 Clarendon Avenue, Leamington Spa, Warwickshire, CV32 5PZ Tel: (01926) 888131 Fax: (01926) 888767 E-mail: cartridgeworld@leamingtonspa.org

▶ Cartridge World Ltd, 1 Stainburn Parade, Leeds, LS17 6NA Tel: 0113-268 6868 Fax: 0113-268 1614

Cartridge World Ltd, 1575 London Road, Leigh-on-Sea, Essex, SS9 2SG Tel: (01702) 477449 Fax: (01702) 474449 E-mail: Franchise@cartridgeworld.org

▶ Cartridge World Ltd, 20 Surrey Street, Littlehampton, West Sussex, BN17 5BG Tel: (01903) 714444 Fax: (01903) 717102 E-mail: cwlittlehampton@cartridgeworld.org

▶ Cartridge World Ltd, 458 Romford Road, London, E7 8DF Tel: (020) 8470 2189 Fax: (020) 8475 0486

▶ Cartridge World, 192 King Street, London, W6 0RA Tel: (020) 8834 7070 Fax: (020) 8834 7171 E-mail: cwhammersmith@cartridgeworld.org

▶ Cartridge World Ltd, 2-2a Greenford Avenue, London, W7 3QP Tel: (020) 8566 3666 Fax: (020) 8566 0111 E-mail: cwgreenford@cartridgeworld.org

▶ Cartridge World Ltd, 370 Hornsey Road, London, N19 4HT Tel: (020) 7281 7600 Fax: (020) 7281 8789

▶ Cartridge World Ltd, 464 Hoe Street, London, E17 9AH Tel: (020) 8556 6030 Fax: (020) 8556 6050 E-mail: cwwalthamstow@cartridgeworld.org

▶ Cartridge World Ltd, 367 Green Lanes, Palmers Green, London, N13 4JG Tel: (020) 8886 8877

▶ Cartridge World Ltd, 49 St. Georges Terrace, Jesmond, Newcastle upon Tyne, NE2 2SX Tel: 0191-212 1610 Fax: 0191-212 1611 E-mail: cwjesmond@cartridgeworld.org

▶ Cartridge World Ltd, 96 High Street, Newport, Isle of Wight, PO30 1BQ Tel: (01983) 532323 Fax: (01983) 825477

▶ Cartridge World, 165 Queen Street, Newton Abbot, Devon, TQ12 2BS Tel: (01626) 337444 Fax: (01626) 334819

▶ Cartridge World Ltd, 46 High Street, Northallerton, North Yorkshire, DL7 8EG Tel: (01609) 771123 Fax: (01609) 771203

▶ Cartridge World Ltd, 78 Witton Street, Northwich, Cheshire, CW9 5AE Tel: (01606) 354554 Fax: (01606) 354553

▶ Cartridge World Ltd, 126 Front Street, Arnold, Nottingham, NG5 7EG Tel: 0115-967 1133 Fax: 0115-967 6644 E-mail: cwarnold@cartridgeworld.org

▶ Cartridge World Ltd, 19 Shoe Market, Pontefract, West Yorkshire, WF8 1AP Tel: (01977) 600111 Fax: (01977) 600222

▶ Cartridge World Ltd, High Street, Street, Somerset, BA16 0EX Tel: (01458) 841269 Fax: (01458) 841269 E-mail: cwstreet@cartridgeworld.co.uk

▶ Cartridge World Ltd, Faringdon Road, Swindon, SN1 5AR Tel: (01793) 714100 Fax: (01793) 714100

▶ Cartridge World Ltd, 25 Broad Street, Truro, Cornwall, TR1 1JD Tel: (01872) 222121 Fax: (01872) 222262

▶ Cartridge World Ltd, 8 Monson Road, Tunbridge Wells, Kent, TN1 1ND Tel: (01892) 614142 Fax: (01892) 614142 E-mail: cwturnbridgewells@cartridgeworld.co.uk

▶ Cartridge World Ltd, 152 Widnes Road, Widnes, Cheshire, WA8 6BA Tel: 0151-422 9876

▶ Cartridge World Ltd, 902 New Chester Road, Wirral, Merseyside, CH62 6AU Tel: 0151-343 0999 Fax: 0151-343 0008

▶ Cartridge World Ltd, 74 Clifton Green, York, YO30 6AW Tel: (01904) 733999 Fax: (01904) 700770

▶ Cartridge World Ltd, 16 Hull Road, York, YO10 3JG Tel: (01904) 870870

CBC Computer Systems Ltd, 64 Balby Road, Doncaster, South Yorkshire, DN4 0JL Tel: (01302) 768500 Fax: (01302) 761783 E-mail: sales-donc@cbccomputers.com

CCS Media Holdings Ltd, Old Birdholme House, Derby Road, Chesterfield, Derbyshire, S40 2EX Tel: (01246) 200200 Fax: (01246) 207048 E-mail: enquiries@ccsmedia.com

Charterhouse Muller plc, Little Johns Lane, Reading, RG30 1RA Tel: 0118-958 8700 Fax: 0118-958 4444 E-mail: sales@pcbroker.co.uk

Chevin Computer Systems Ltd, East Mill, Bridge Foot, Belper, Derbyshire, DE56 2UA Tel: (01773) 821992 Fax: (01773) 829910 E-mail: sales@chevincomputers.com

Christchurch Computer Centre, 2-4 Fairmile Parade, Fairmile Road, Christchurch, Dorset, BH23 2LP Tel: (01202) 486338 Fax: (0845) 8622661 E-mail: sales@c-c-c.co.uk

Clean Card Systems Ltd, Unit 3 Spring Gardens, Middleton, Manchester, M24 6DQ Tel: 0161-654 6611 Fax: 0161-643 1040 E-mail: info@cleancardsystems.co.uk

Cobra Systems, 5 Morven Park, Glenrothes, Fife, KY6 3PX Tel: (01592) 620067 Fax: (01592) 620067 E-mail: info@cobra-systems.com

Colebrook Bosson & Saunders Products Ltd, 18 Bowden Street, London, SE11 4DS Tel: (020) 7587 5283 Fax: (020) 7587 5275 E-mail: sales@cbsproducts.co.uk

College Computers, 169 Hollow Way, Cowley, Oxford, OX4 2NE Tel: (01865) 774410 Fax: (01865) 774410 E-mail: sales@college-computers.com

Colvin Ltd, 34 Silverwing Estate, Croydon, CR0 4RR Tel: (01737) 771311 Fax: (01737) 773268 E-mail: tarbot@tarbot.co.uk

Compfix Enterprises Ltd, 119 Manchester Road, Chorlton cum Hardy, Manchester, M21 9PG Tel: 0161-881 2395 Fax: 0161-881 2395 E-mail: sales@compfixpc.co.uk

▶ Complete Business Logistics, Hill Farm, Fillongley Road, Coleshill, Birmingham, B46 2QU Tel: (01675) 467890

Computaform, 4 Merivale Road, Harrow, Middlesex, HA1 4BH Tel: (020) 8423 5005 Fax: (020) 8422 7216 E-mail: mail@computaform.com

Computer Care Centre, 890 Romford Rd, London, E12 5JP Tel: (020) 8478 4789 Fax: (020) 8478 5699

Computer Plus, 14 Scarrots Lane, Newport, Isle of Wight, PO30 1JD Tel: (01983) 826555 Fax: (01983) 821222

Computer Press, 1 Rowles Way, Kidlington, Oxfordshire, OX5 1LA Tel: (01865) 849158 Fax: (01865) 374007 E-mail: sales@cpdirect.co.uk

Computer Systems Support, 74 Eglinton Avenue, Guisborough, Cleveland, TS14 7BX Tel: (01287) 610433 Fax: (01287) 610438 E-mail: info@computersystemssupport.co.uk

Computeraid Ltd, The Innovation Centre Swansea University, Singleton Park, Swansea, SA2 8PP Tel: (01792) 610550 Fax: (01792) 610560 E-mail: computeraid@computeraidwales.com

Computing Matters, C M House, Bowers, Wimborne, Dorset, BH21 7DL Tel: (01202) 888990 Fax: (01202) 888383 E-mail: ian@computing-matters.com

Comtel Communication Supplies Ltd, School Road, Great Yarmouth, Norfolk, NR30 1LA Tel: (01493) 851865 Fax: (01493) 851767

▶ Contrast Media Solutions, Unit 7A, St. Martins House, St. Martins Gate, Worcester, WR1 2DT Tel: (01905) 330566 Fax: (01905) 330566

▶ Copytek Duplication, Unit 8B, Cromwell Centre, Roebuck Road, Ilford, Essex, IG6 3UG Tel: (020) 8500 3773 Fax: (020) 8500 3773

▶ Coss Computer Consumables, Unit 10-10a Waterloo Industrial Park, Upper Brook Street, Stockport, Cheshire, SK1 3BP Tel: 0161-476 6633 Fax: 0161-476 6611

Creative Computers UK Ltd, 65 West Main Street, Whitburn, Bathgate, West Lothian, EH47 0QD Tel: (01501) 742600 Fax: (01501) 742600 E-mail: sales@creativegroup.co.uk

Croft Computer Supplies, 7 Croft Road, Kiltarlity, Beauly, Inverness-Shire, IV4 7HZ Tel: (01463) 741683 Fax: (01463) 741683

Croydon Computer Supplies Ltd, Unit 4, Broadfield Close, Progress Way, Croydon, CR0 4XR Tel: (020) 8686 0046 Fax: (020) 8667 1552 E-mail: sales@croydoncomputersupplies.co.uk

▶ Cygma Partnership, Kings Court, 5 Waterloo Road, Stalybridge, Cheshire, SK15 2AU Tel: 0161-338 5000 Fax: 0161-304 9961

D P I Systems Ltd, L C S House, Ainleys Industrial Estate, Huddersfield Road, Elland, West Yorkshire, HX5 9JP Tel: (01422) 375444 Fax: (01422) 370037 E-mail: elland@dpisystems.co.uk

Datamail Business Forms Ltd, 141 Kinghorn Road, Burntisland, Fife, KY3 9JW Tel: (01592) 872346 Fax: (01592) 874839

Dataproof, The Bond, 180-182 Fazeley Street, Birmingham, B5 5SE Tel: 0121-753 7930 Fax: 0121-753 7939 E-mail: office@dataproof.biz

Diskel Ltd, 212-214 Farnham Road, Slough, SL1 4XE Tel: (01753) 821091 Fax: (01753) 512438 E-mail: sales@diskel.co.uk

Dominion Business Supplies Ltd, Dominion House, Medway City Industrial Estate, Medway City Estate, Rochester, Kent, ME2 4DU Tel: (01634) 716666 Fax: (01634) 290620 E-mail: sales@dominion-group.com

Duplex Telecom Ltd, The Widford Hall, Widford Hall Lane, Chelmsford, CM2 8TD Tel: (0870) 7481408 Fax: (0870) 7481407 E-mail: sales@duplex.co.uk

Durable UK Ltd, East Dorset Trade Park, 10 Nimrod Way, Wimborne, Dorset, BH21 7SH Tel: (01202) 897071 Fax: (01202) 873381 E-mail: marketing@durable-uk.com

Eason & Son Ni Ltd, 21-25 Boucher Road, Belfast, BT12 6QU Tel: (028) 9038 1200 Fax: (028) 9068 2544 E-mail: accountsreceivable@eason.co.uk

Easy PC'S, 38 Abbotsbry Road, Weymouth, Dorset, DT4 0AE Tel: (01305) 760350 Fax: (0870) 0940321

Ego Computers Ltd, Salisbury Hall, London Colney, St. Albans, Hertfordshire, AL2 1BU Tel: (01727) 828400 Fax: (01727) 824141 E-mail: rdrinkwater@ego-computers.ltd.uk

Electronics Boutique Ltd, 39 Princess Square, Bracknell, Berkshire, RG12 1LS Tel: (01344) 305500

Electronics Boutique, 9 Havelock Square, Swindon, SN1 1LE Tel: (01793) 436946 Fax: (01793) 436946

Elmbrook Computer Services Ltd, Alpha Place, Garth Road, Morden, Surrey, SM4 4TS Tel: (020) 8410 4444 Fax: (020) 8410 4445

Ergo Computer Accessories Ltd, 5 Pipers Industrial Estate, Pipers Lane, Thatcham, Berkshire, RG19 4NA Tel: (01635) 877979 Fax: (01635) 877676 E-mail: sales@ergo-consumables.co.uk

▶ Ergotron UK Ltd, Suite 3 The Carlton Centre, Outer Circle Road, Lincoln, LN2 4WA Tel: (01522) 523034 Fax: (01522) 523280 E-mail: info.uk@ergotron.com

Eurotec Distribution Ltd, Church Croft House, Station Road, Rugeley, Staffordshire, WS15 2HE Tel: (01889) 503100 Fax: (01889) 503101 E-mail: sales@media-resources.co.uk

Eximedia UK Ltd, 4 Black Swan Yard, London, SE1 3XW Tel: (020) 7403 1555 Fax: (020) 7403 8524 E-mail: info@eximedia.co.uk

Explan Computer Ltd, PO Box 32, Tavistock, Devon, PL19 8YU Tel: (01822) 613868 Fax: (01822) 610868 E-mail: info@explan.co.uk

Falcon Computers, 11a Hay Street, Sunderland, SR5 1BG Tel: 0191-567 6669 Fax: 0191-567 6664 E-mail: sales@falconcomputers.co.uk

Faxlink Communications, 7-9 Bellegrove Parade, Welling, Kent, DA16 2RE Tel: (020) 8856 1166 Fax: (020) 8319 4074 E-mail: faxlink@dial.pipex.com

▶ Fillink Computer Consumables, 572 London Road, Isleworth, Middlesex, TW7 4EP Tel: (020) 8560 4444 Fax: (020) 8560 0694 E-mail: sales@fillink.co.uk

▶ Firscall Data Ltd, Unit 4, Carlton Court, Brown Lane West, Leeds, LS12 6LT Tel: 0113-242 7220 Fax: 0113-242 7217 E-mail: sales@firscall.co.uk

FOCUS Print & Marketing Ltd, Digital House, Stourport Road, Kidderminster, Worcestershire, DY11 7QH Tel: (01562) 862888 Fax: (01562) 820144

Fort House Systems Ltd, Fort House Factory, East Street, South Molton, Devon, EX36 3DF Tel: (01769) 574603 Fax: (01769) 573035 E-mail: sales@forthouse.com

COMPUTER ACCESSORIES AND CONSUMABLES – *continued*

Forward Group plc, 57 Buckland Road, London, E10 6QS Tel: (020) 8558 7110 Fax: (020) 8558 5974E-mail: sales@forward-group.co.uk

Freelance Software Ltd, East Street, Bingham, Nottingham, NG13 8DS Tel: (01949) 838988 Fax: (01949) 838112 E-mail: info@centralone.co.uk

Fujitsu Services, Trafalgar House, Temple Court, Risley, Warrington, WA3 6GD Tel: (01925) 432000 Fax: (01925) 432233

Future Labs Ltd, Regus House, 400 Thames Valley Park Drive, Reading, RG6 1PT Tel: (01344) 301155 Fax: (01344) 450380 E-mail: sales@computabits.com

▶ G E Computer Supplies, 3 Church View, Wyverstone, Stowmarket, Suffolk, IP14 4SQ Tel: (01449) 782059 E-mail: info@gecomputersupplies.co.uk

G M S Technologies, Unit 22, Brambles Enterprise Centre, Waterberry Drive, Waterlooville, Hampshire, PO7 7TH Tel: (023) 9223 1880 Fax: (023) 9223 1990

Golding Products Ltd, Unit 24 Hortonwood 33, Telford, Shropshire, TF1 7YQ Tel: (01952) 606667 Fax: (01952) 670267 E-mail: sales@goldingproducts.com

▶ Grade 1 Computers, Hamlin Lodge, Station Road, Ollerton, Newark, Nottinghamshire, NG22 9BN Tel: (01623) 825885 Fax: (01623) 824524E-mail: sales@grade1computers.co.uk

H W Dansies, 409 Chatsworth Road, Chesterfield, Derbyshire, S40 2DH Tel: (01246) 235455 Fax: (01246) 220862 E-mail: sales@dansies.co.uk

Harp Software, PO Box 1101, Stourbridge, West Midlands, DY9 8YL Tel: (0845) 2261671 Fax: (01384) 892169 E-mail: harp@harpsoftware.co.uk

Headliners European Ltd, Unit 10 Abbey Court, Wallingford Road, Leicester, LE4 5RD Tel: 0116-266 6629 Fax: 0116-266 6679 E-mail: info@pc-headliners.freeserve.co.uk

▶ Hinckley Computer Peripherals Ltd, Telford Way, Stephenson Industrial Estate, Coalville, Leicestershire, LE67 3HE Tel: (01530) 838555 Fax: (01530) 814250 E-mail: hcpuk@btclick.com

I B M (UK) Ltd, 1 New Square, Feltham, Middlesex, TW14 8HB Tel: (020) 8818 6060 Fax: (020) 8818 5499

Icon Technologies Ltd, Broadgate Court, 199 Bishopsgate, London, EC2M 3TY Tel: (020) 7814 6669 Fax: (020) 7814 7934 E-mail: sales@icontech.co.uk

Imagestore Ltd, Ecchinswell Road, Kingsclere, Newbury, Berkshire, RG20 4QG Tel: (01635) 297297 Fax: (01635) 298603 E-mail: sales@imagestore.co.uk

Indus (International) Ltd, Britannia Wharf, Monument Road, Woking, Surrey, GU21 5LW Tel: (01483) 722777 Fax: (01483) 721166 E-mail: sales@indusinternational.com

▶ Ink Xpress, 6 The Wharf Centre, Wharf Street, Warwick, CV34 5LB Tel: (01926) 411060 Fax: (01926) 498258

▶ Inkley Ink, 65 Stockwell Head, Hinckley, Leicestershire, LE10 1RD Tel: (01455) 619222

Inkost Ltd, Signal Buildings, Brunel Road, Newton Abbot, Devon, TQ12 4FD Tel: (01626) 333485 Fax: (01626) 335441

Inktec Midlands, PO Box 567, Wolverhampton, WV8 2JW Tel: (01902) 846060 Fax: (01902) 846360

▶ The Inkwell, 64 West Gate, Mansfield, Nottinghamshire, NG18 1RR Tel: (01623) 636222 Fax: (01623) 636222

▶ Inkxpress, 202 Nutgrove Road, St. Helens, Merseyside, WA9 5JP Tel: 0151-493 1005 Fax: 0151-493 1005

Inkxpress, 106 Rhosddu Road, Wrexham, Clwyd, LL11 2NG Tel: (01978) 261368 Fax: (01978) 262735 E-mail: sales@inkxperts.co.uk

Interchange, 2 The Western Centre, Western Road, Bracknell, Berkshire, RG12 1RW Tel: (01344) 861861 Fax: (01344) 487299 E-mail: sales@i-change.co.uk

Inter-Media, 196 Causeway Green Road, Oldbury, West Midlands, B68 8LS Tel: 0121-552 6622 Fax: 0121-544 5404 E-mail: sales@trackzone.demon.co.uk

Interpro Computers, 40 Blackburn Road, Darwen, Lancashire, BB3 1QJ Tel: (01254) 760917 Fax: (01254) 606797

Intona Imaging, Middlebrook Way, Holt Road, Cromer, Norfolk, NR27 9JR Tel: (01263) 517007 Fax: (01263) 517002 E-mail: info@intona.com

▶ It Print, 3 Cockridden Farm Indust Estate, Herongate, Brentwood, Essex, CM13 3LH Tel: (01277) 812501

Itec Associates, 735 Washwood Heath Road, Birmingham, B8 2JY Tel: 0121-322 2444 Fax: 0121-322 2700

J H Business Forms Ltd, Adams Street, Birmingham, B7 4LT Tel: 0121-359 6693 Fax: 0121-333 3118 E-mail: jhbf@cyberphile.co.uk

J & J Associates, 112 Ridgeway, Plymouth, PL7 2HN Tel: (01752) 336465 Fax: (01752) 336466 E-mail: sales@jj-associates.com

JBL Office, 168-170 Cumnor Road, Boars Hill, Oxford, OX1 5JS Tel: (01865) 739056 Fax: (01865) 326754 E-mail: sales@jbl.co.uk

▶ Jobero Ltd, 4 New Lane Galleries, New Street, Alfreton, Derbyshire, DE55 7BP Tel: (01773) 521500 E-mail: sales@jobero.com

Johnston Reid & Co., 224 Hardgate, Aberdeen, AB10 6AA Tel: (01224) 212255 Fax: (01224) 211146 E-mail: sales@johnstonreid.co.uk

Jubilee Printers, 430 Edgware Road, London, W2 1EG Tel: (020) 7724 1094 Fax: (020) 7706 0518 E-mail: info@jubileeprinters.co.uk

K B S Computer Supplies Ltd, Unit 3a West Bank Business Park, 5 West Bank Drive, Belfast, BT3 9LA Tel: (028) 9037 0088 Fax: (028) 9077 4767 E-mail: sales@kbs-computer-supplies.co.uk

K.C. Inks Ltd, Unit 13 Blackhall Yard, Kendal, Cumbria, LA9 4LU Tel: (01539) 738200 Fax: (01539) 738822 E-mail: sales@kc-inks.co.uk

K M P Crusader Manufacturing Co. Ltd, Oldmedow Road, King's Lynn, Norfolk, PE30 4LD Tel: (01553) 817200 Fax: (01553) 691909 E-mail: sales@kmp-uk.co.uk

S.J. Kennedy Group, 25 Main Street, Cambuslang, Glasgow, G72 7EX Tel: (0845) 6588899 Fax: (0845) 6588898

Kenroy Thompson Ltd, 25 Cobourg Street, Plymouth, PL1 1SR Tel: (01752) 227693 Fax: (0800) 7836322 E-mail: sales@kenroythompson.co.uk

Keystone Media, Units 4 & 5, The Old Creamery, Highbridge, Somerset, TA9 3DF Tel: (01278) 780438 Fax: (01278) 793858

Klassic Computers Services Ltd, 9 Church Meadow, Long Ditton, Surbiton, Surrey, KT6 5EP Tel: (020) 8398 3504 E-mail: sales@klassic.co.uk

Kudos Computer Supplies, 7 Orwell Court, Hurricane Way, Wickford, Essex, SS11 8YJ Tel: (01268) 571122 Fax: (01268) 570771 E-mail: sales@kudos-supplies.com

Lane Business Systems Ltd, 7 Denbigh Street, London, SW1V 2HF Tel: (020) 7828 6767 Fax: (020) 7828 2211 E-mail: enquiries@lanebus.com

Langford & Hill Ltd, Unit 17 Kings Exchange, Tileyard Road, London, N7 9AH Tel: (020) 7619 0527 Fax: (020) 7619 9856 E-mail: info@langfordhill.co.uk

Lark Computers Ltd, 65 James Carter Road, Mildenhall, Bury St Edmunds, Suffolk, IP28 7DE Tel: (01638) 716423 Fax: (01638) 716779

Laser Cartridge Recycling Co., Lower Kingsdown Road, Kingsdown, Corsham, Wiltshire, SN13 8BG Tel: (01225) 740022 Fax: (01225) 740092

Lasercharge UK Ltd, 70 Main Street, Garforth, Leeds, LS25 1AA Tel: 0113-286 4535 Fax: 0113-287 4232 E-mail: laserchargeuk@btinternet.com

Leco Computer Supplies Ltd, Unit 1, Ashwellthorpe Industrial Estate, Ashwellthorpe, Norwich, NR16 1ER Tel: (01508) 489535 Fax: (01508) 489331E-mail: sales@leco.co.uk

Linc It, North Street, Gainsborough, Lincolnshire, DN21 2HS Tel: (01427) 811770 Fax: (01427) 811780 E-mail: office@lincit.com

Lindy Electronics Ltd, Sadler Foster Way, Teesside Industrial Estate, Stockton-on-Tees, Cleveland, TS17 9JY Tel: (01642) 754000 Fax: (01642) 754027 E-mail: postmaster@lindy.co.uk

Lodestar Technologies Ltd, The Coach House, Gymnasium Street, Ipswich, IP1 3NX Tel: (01473) 408888 Fax: (01473) 400336 E-mail: sales@lodestar.co.uk

M & A Office Supplies Ltd, Unit 12 Westwood Court, Brunel Road, Totton, Southampton, SO40 3WX Tel: (023) 8066 7110 Fax: (023) 8066 7136 E-mail: simon@maoffice.demon.co.uk

M C W Group, Wrexham Technology Park, Wrexham, Clwyd, LL13 7YP Tel: (01978) 340340 Fax: (01978) 340345 E-mail: admin@mcwgroup.co.uk

▶ M M Marketing Ltd, Devonshire Road, Heathpark Industrial Estate, Honiton, Devon, EX14 1SD Tel: (01404) 44446 Fax: (01404) 42484 E-mail: info@mmmarketing.net

Magictype Computer Consumables, 22 Swallow Rise, Knaphill, Woking, Surrey, GU21 2LG Tel: (01483) 888813 Fax: (01483) 888814 E-mail: magictype@ntlworld.com

Mainstream Software Solutions, 43 Longway Avenue, Charlton Kings, Cheltenham, Gloucestershire, GL53 9JH Tel: (01242) 227377 Fax: (01242) 251319 E-mail: mainstream@bitstream.com

▶ Matrix Media World, 5-9 Vernon Street, Bolton, BL1 2QB Tel: (01204) 522066 Fax: (0870) 0113694

Micro Supply Company Ltd, Kamarhatty 40 Lynedoch Road, Scone, Perth, PH2 6RJ Tel: (01738) 551250 Fax: (01738) 551156 E-mail: sales@microsupplies.co.uk

Micro Warehouse Ltd, Stuarts Road, Manor Park, Runcorn, Cheshire, WA7 1TH Tel: (01928) 595252 Fax: (01928) 579810 E-mail: derek.lloyd@inmac.co.uk

Mills Computer Products International Ltd, 7 Amber Drive, Langley Mill, Nottingham, NG16 4BE Tel: (01773) 761246 Fax: (01773) 531246 E-mail: sales@millsimage.co.uk

Mitac Synnex UK Ltd, Synnex House, Nedge Hill, Telford, Shropshire, TF3 3AH Tel: (01952) 207200 Fax: (01952) 201216

Mobifax UK Ltd, Units 3-4 Ash Court, Crystal Drive, Sandwell Business Park, Smethwick, West Midlands, B66 1QG Tel: 0121-541 1604 Fax: 0121-541 1605

Mr Computer, 145 Victoria Street, St. Albans, Hertfordshire, AL1 3TA Tel: (01727) 834904 Fax: (01727) 834652 E-mail: ajones@mrcomputer-shop.co.uk

▶ MT Distribution, 4a Carron Place, Edinburgh, EH6 7RE Tel: 0131-555 4500 Fax: 0131-555 4789

▶ N B Computer Maintenance Ltd, 50 Leys Road, Pattishall, Towcester, Northamptonshire, NN12 8JZ Tel: (01327) 831404 Fax: (01327) 830982 E-mail: sales@nbmaintenance.co.uk

▶ N K Computer Supplies, Unit 5a Caxton Trading Estate, Printing House Lane, Hayes, Middlesex, UB3 1BE Tel: (020) 8813 6070 Fax: (020) 8574 3642 E-mail: sales@nkcomputersupplies.co.uk

N K Computer Supplies, Unit 5a Caxton Trading Estate, Printing House Lane, Hayes, Middlesex, UB3 1BE Tel: (020) 8813 6070 Fax: (020) 8574 3642 E-mail: sales@nkcomputers.co.uk

Nexcen Ltd, 16C Horse Street, Chipping Sodbury, Bristol, BS37 6DB Tel: (01454) 318686 Fax: 0171-433 4533

North West Continuers Ltd, 20 Fylde Road Industrial Estate, Fylde Road, Preston, PR1 2TY Tel: (01772) 561144 Fax: (01772) 253392 E-mail: sales@nwestco.com

▶ Nutronic Ltd, 36 Towerfield Road, Shoeburyness, Southend-On-Sea, SS3 9QT Tel: (0845) 1235626 Fax: (01702) 382812

▶ Oneprint International, 34 Flairs Avenue, Arbroath, Angus, DD11 5DY Tel: (01241) 872288 Fax: (01241) 872288

▶ P C Consumables, Headingley Lane, Leeds, LS6 1BL Tel: 0113-289 9555

P C Food, Blackbird Road, Leicester, LE1 5DR Tel: 0116-251 9933 Fax: 0116-251 5510 E-mail: sales@pc-food.co.uk

▶ Parts For Laptops.Com, 88 High Street, Colliers Wood, London, SW19 2BT Tel: (020) 8545 0222

PC Express, 185 Washway Road, Sale, Cheshire, M33 4AH Tel: 0161-291 1044 Fax: 0161-291 1077 E-mail: info@pc-xp.com

▶ PC Friend, Printing Office Street, Doncaster, South Yorkshire, DN1 1TR Tel: (01302) 322486 E-mail: doncaster@pcfriend-online.com

PC Partnership Ltd, 15 Brookfield Road, Bury, Lancashire, BL9 5LA Tel: 0161-763 5976 Fax: 0161-763 7082 E-mail: pcpartnership@btconnect.com

PC World, Tollgate West, Stanway, Colchester, CO3 8RG Tel: (0870) 2420444 Fax: (01206) 572969 E-mail: enquiries@pcworld.co.uk

Pelikan Hardcopy Scotland Ltd, Markethill Road, Turriff, Aberdeenshire, AB53 4AW Tel: (01888) 564200 Fax: (01888) 562042 E-mail: sales@phi-psl.co.uk

Perforag Ltd, Unit 4, Greaves Way, Leighton Buzzard, Bedfordshire, LU7 4UB Tel: (01525) 376743 Fax: (01525) 850297 E-mail: sales@perforag.com

Phoenix Grace Ltd, 8 Worset Lane, Hartlepool, Cleveland, TS26 0LJ Tel: (01429) 279814 Fax: (01429) 231255

▶ Pickup Pc's, 78 Crossley Road, St. Helens, Merseyside, WA10 3ND Tel: (01744) 26660 Fax: (01744) 26660

Pied Piper (UK) Ltd, Flat 22, Tempsford Ct, Sheepcote Rd, Harrow, Middlesex, HA1 2JJ Tel: 020 89061459 Fax: 0208 8646184

Plantech Ltd, 160 Queen Victoria Street, London, EC4V 4BF Tel: (020) 7202 8100 Fax: (020) 7928 8060 E-mail: sales@plantechltd.co.uk

▶ Plymouth Ink Jets, Unit 87 & 95, 68 Market Stalls, Plymouth, PL1 1PR Tel: (01752) 222527 Fax: (01752) 606868

Polytypos Ltd, Radstock, BA3 3WD Tel: (01761) 411018 Fax: (01761) 411551 E-mail: karenn@polytypos.com

Printer Connections Ltd, Unit 445 Oakshop Place, Walton Summit Industrial Estate, Bamber Bridge, Preston, PR5 8AT Tel: (01772) 314880 Fax: (01772) 314900 E-mail: sales@printerconnections.co.uk

Probrand Ltd, 37-55 Camden Street, Birmingham, B1 3BP Tel: (0800) 262629 E-mail: tony.sheen@proband.co.uk

Prosys Computing Ltd, Titan House Cardiff Bay Business Centre, Titan Road, Cardiff, CF24 5EJ Tel: (029) 2049 4757 Fax: (029) 2049 4737 E-mail: sales@prosyscom.co.uk

Q C Supplies Ltd, The Forum, Callendar Park, Falkirk, FK1 1XR Tel: (01324) 630022 Fax: (01324) 630055

Quay I T Computers, 7-9 Ticklemore Street, Totnes, Devon, TQ9 5EJ Tel: (01803) 868009 Fax: (01803) 863092 E-mail: sales@quayitcomputers.com

Quayshels Co. 677 Ltd, Top Floor, 5 Princes Road, Shepton Mallet, Somerset, BA4 5HL Tel: (01749) 330677 Fax: (01749) 330177

R B S Office Supplies, Tollgate Business Centre, Tollgate Drive, Tollgate Industrial Estate, Stafford, ST16 3HS Tel: (01785) 254859 Fax: (01785) 220400 E-mail: sales@rbsofficesupplies.co.uk

Raco Laser Supplies, 6 Elm Way, Hackleton, Northampton, NN7 2BT Tel: (0845) 3273431 Fax: (01604) 870970

▶ Re Cartridge, 59 Queens Road, Leicester, LE2 1TT Tel: 0116-270 5505 E-mail: recartridge@hotmail.co.uk

▶ Rectron Computer Consumables, 5-6 Northfield Drive, Northfield, Milton Keynes, MK15 0DQ Tel: (01908) 235600 Fax: (01908) 235620

▶ Refill Express, 6 New Union Street, Coventry, CV1 2HN Tel: (024) 7663 3333 Fax: (024) 7663 2331 E-mail: sales@refillexpress.co.uk

Rentmeister Distribution (N I), Unit 29 Cido Business Complex, Charles Street, Lurgan, Craigavon, County Armagh, BT66 6HG Tel: (028) 3834 6736 Fax: (028) 3834 6738 E-mail: sales@rentmeister.co.uk

▶ Revolution Ink, 1b Market Place, Holt, Norfolk, NR25 6BE Tel: (01263) 711102 Fax: (01263) 578314

Ryman The Stationer, 336 North End Road, London, SW6 1NB Tel: (020) 7381 8885 Fax: (020) 7381 8885

S B Computers, 88 Wilsthorpe Road, Long Eaton, Nottingham, NG10 3JZ Tel: 0115-946 3898 Fax: 0115-972 2225 E-mail: steve@sb-computers.co.uk

S & H Computers Ltd, Godfrey Drive, Ilkeston, Derbyshire, DE7 4HU Tel: 0115-875 8164 Fax: 0115-875 8164 E-mail: sales.shcomputers@ntlworld.com

S T S Computers, Tylney House, 23 High Street, Leatherhead, Surrey, KT22 8AB Tel: (01372) 378608 Fax: (01372) 374592 E-mail: info@stscomputers.co.uk

Shibro Computer Consumables, 26 Tottenham Court Road, London, W1T 1BR Tel: (020) 7323 6948 Fax: (020) 7724 5087 E-mail: mmm@mmmltd.com

▶ Showprice Accessories, J3-J4 Widnes Market Hall, Bradley Way, Widnes, Cheshire, WA8 6UE Tel: 0151-420 0544 Fax: 0151-420 0544

▶ Smart Cartridge, 119 Bruntsfield Place, Edinburgh, EH10 4EQ Tel: 0131-466 0067 Fax: 0131-466 0989

▶ Smart Cartridge, Unit 6, B S S House, Cheney Manor Industrial Estate, Swindon, SN2 2PJ Tel: (01793) 532251 Fax: (01793) 532258 E-mail: enquiries@smart-cartridge.co.uk

▶ Smart Cartridge, 15 Ardsheal Road, Worthing, West Sussex, BN14 7RN Tel: (01903) 202292 Fax: (01903) 202303 E-mail: info@smart-cartridge.com

▶ Smart Cartridge Hitchin, 43 Hermitage Road, Hitchin, Hertfordshire, SG5 1BY Tel: (01462) 434007 Fax: (01462) 451117

Southern Media Maintenance Ltd, Bridge House, R/O 1A Bensham Manor Road, Thornton Heath, Surrey, CR7 7AA Tel: (020) 8665 6760 Fax: (020) 8689 9541

Stat Plus, A1 New Pudsey Square, Bradford Road, Stanningley, Pudsey, West Yorkshire, LS28 6PX Tel: 0113-256 9494 Fax: 0113-204 7044

Supplies Team Scotland, Custom House, Union Street, Bo'Ness, West Lothian, EH51 9AQ Tel: (0870) 8715929 Fax: (0870) 8715928 E-mail: sales@supplies-team.co.uk

Systems Support Of Cambridge, Great Chesterford Court, Great Chesterford, Saffron Walden, Essex, CB10 1PF Tel: (01799) 531777 Fax: (01799) 531778

Techpoint Services, 133 Mains Lane, Poulton-le-Fylde, Lancashire, FY6 7LD Tel: (01253) 895999 Fax: (01253) 895999 E-mail: sales@diplidata.co.uk

Tekno Computer Systems Ltd, 41 Bartlett Street, Caerphilly, Mid Glamorgan, CF83 1JS Tel: (029) 2088 5421 Fax: (029) 2088 5235 E-mail: info@tekno.co.uk

Total Computer & Office Supplies Ltd, 100 Squirrels Heath Road, Harold Wood, Romford, RM3 0LU Tel: (01708) 780300

Trust Co. P.L.C., 2-3 Namrik Mews, Hove, East Sussex, BN3 2TF Tel: (01273) 735999 Fax: (01273) 736999 E-mail: info@trustco.co.uk

Tudor Business Forms Ltd, 2 Meridian Centre, Vulcan Way, New Addington, Croydon, CR0 9UG Tel: (01689) 844888 Fax: (01689) 844999 E-mail: sales@tudorofficesupplies.co.uk

▶ TV One, V Continental Approach, Westwood Industrial Estate, Margate, Kent, CT9 4JG Tel: (01843) 873311 Fax: (01843) 873301 E-mail: web@vinemicros.com

Vernon Computer Forms, 5 Spring Mill Business Centre, Avening Road, Nailsworth, Stroud, Gloucestershire, GL6 0BS Tel: (01453) 834466 Fax: (01453) 834554 E-mail: sales@vernoncf.co.uk

Visual Computer Technologies Ltd, Unit 207 Solent BSNS Centre 3, Millbrook Road West, Southampton, SO15 0HW Tel: (023) 8077 9162 Fax: (023) 8078 8222 E-mail: sales@focused.co.uk

Vital Office Products, Brokers House, 2A Ada Street, London, E8 4QU Tel: (020) 7923 2277 Fax: (020) 7923 4646

Watermark Business Forms Ltd, 353 Stratford Road, Shirley, Solihull, West Midlands, B90 3BW Tel: 0121-733 1633 Fax: 0121-733 1683 E-mail: sales@watermark.print.com

Watford Electronics, Finway, Dallow Road, Luton, LU1 1WE Tel: (0870) 0270900 Fax: (0870) 0270901 E-mail: info@watford.co.uk

Westway Business Services, 2 St. Marys Way, Baldock, Hertfordshire, SG7 6JF Tel: (01462) 490900 Fax: (01462) 490411

▶ What's in the Box?, 93 Derby Road, Bramcote, Nottingham, NG9 3GW Tel: (0845) 0524200 Fax: (0845) 0524300 E-mail: sales@printer-stuff.co.uk

Wiles Group Ltd, Walmgate Road, Greenford, Middlesex, UB6 7LN Tel: (020) 8758 7700 Fax: (020) 8758 7722 E-mail: sales@wilesgreenworld.co.uk

Wordflow, 32-38 Scrutton Street, London, EC2A 4RQ Tel: (020) 7377 1182 Fax: (020) 7377 2942 E-mail: help@wordflow.co.uk

X T & A T Computers Ltd, 77c St Pancras, Chichester, West Sussex, PO19 7LS Tel: (01243) 533367 Fax: (01243) 536018 E-mail: sales@xtat.co.uk

▶ Xma Ltd, 44 Nottingham South & Wilford Industrial Estate, Nottingham, NG11 7EP Tel: 0115-846 4000 Fax: 0115-981 0180 E-mail: sales@bsfitness.co.uk

York Distribution Ltd, 23-24 Auster Road, York, YO30 4XA Tel: (01904) 693969 Fax: (01904) 693255 E-mail: sales@ydl.co.uk

COMPUTER ACCESSORIES AND CONSUMABLES – *continued*

Zoo Computer Consumables, Edward House, 217 King Cross Road, Halifax, West Yorkshire, HX1 3JL Tel: (01422) 323232 Fax: (01422) 323233 E-mail: info@zoodirect.com

COMPUTER ACCESSORIES, SECURITY

▶ click4it.co.uk, Unit 2, Hope House Farm, Martley, Worcester, WR6 6QF Tel: 0845 2303084 E-mail: sales@click4it.co.uk

COMPUTER ACCESSORIES/ CONSUMABLES CARTRIDGE RECYCLING SERVICES

A M B Technical Expertise Ltd, 20 Falsgrave Road, Scarborough, North Yorkshire, YO12 5AT Tel: (01723) 363477 Fax: (01723) 363477 E-mail: sales@it-department.co.uk
Action P C's, 20 Canford Av, Bournemouth, BH11 8RX Tel: 01202 538141
Advisory Data, 20 Butt Haw Close, Hoo, Rochester, Kent, ME3 9BA Tel: (01634) 251906 Fax: (01634) 256823 E-mail: ifor@advisorydata.co.uk
Anderson Software, 23 Bernay Gardens, Bolbeck Park, Milton Keynes, MK15 8QD Tel: (01908) 668544
Associates Partnerships, 59 High Street, Maidstone, Kent, ME14 1SR Tel: (01622) 685588 Fax: (01622) 764660
Back To Black Ltd, 55 Barkby Road, Leicester, LE4 9HN Tel: 0116-261 1817 Fax: 0116-261 1841 E-mail: sales@back2black.co.uk
▶ Berkshire Clearance, 9 Church Road, Earley, Reading, RG6 1EY Tel: 0118-961 0112 Fax: (0870) 4321014 E-mail: help@berkshireclearance.com
Bruce R.I.D. Recycling Ltd, March Street, Sheffield, S9 5DQ Tel: 0114-243 3637 Fax: 0114-244 8521 E-mail: info@weee-recycler.co.uk
Business Systems Design Ltd, 185 Upper Selsdon Rd, South Croydon, Surrey, CR2 0DY Tel: 020 86514421
C C C & School Care Ltd, Unit 1, Armtech Row, Yeovil, Somerset, BA22 8RT Tel: (01935) 470300 Fax: (01935) 470302 E-mail: all@schoolcare.co.uk
C I M Systems Ltd, 1st Floor, Ross House, Kempson Way, Suffolk Business Park, Bury St. Edmunds, Suffolk, IP32 7AR Tel: (01284) 727200 Fax: (01284) 706602 E-mail: info@cimsystems.co.uk
C P L, Anglo House, Worcester Road, Stourport-On-Severn, Worcestershire, DY13 9AW Tel: (01299) 877004 Fax: (01299) 877226 E-mail: enquiries@computerproof.co.uk
▶ Cartridge Swop Shop, 201 Hoylake Road, Wirral, Merseyside, CH46 0SJ Tel: 0151-606 1435 Fax: 0151-606 0763 E-mail: Mark@cartridgeswopshop.com
Cartridge World Ltd, 506 Stafford Road, Wolverhampton, WV10 6AN Tel: (01902) 788240 Fax: (01902) 789283 E-mail: cwoxley@cartridgeworld.org
Commercial Software Management Ltd, Devereux House, Church Hill, Coleshill, Birmingham, B46 3AA Tel: (01675) 466731 Fax: (01675) 466734 E-mail: sales@csmltd.co.uk
Compaq Ltd, 50 The Highlands, Edgware, Middlesex, HA8 5HL Tel: (020) 8381 1180 Fax: (020) 8621 3050 E-mail: sales@netlineltd.co.uk
The Computer Shop, 8 South Mall, Frenchgate Centre, Doncaster, South Yorkshire, DN1 1TT Tel: (01302) 326111 Fax: (01302) 326222
Corsair Computer Systems Ltd, Fourth Floor 1, Old Hall Street, Liverpool, L3 9HF Tel: (0845) 3901001 Fax: 0151-255 1943 E-mail: info@Corsairsoftware.co.uk
Digital Systems, Solutions House Derby Road, Sandiacre, Nottingham, NG10 5HU Tel: 0115-849 9984 Fax: 0115-849 9993
Digital Workshop, 42-44 North Bar Street, Banbury, Oxfordshire, OX16 0TH Tel: (01295) 258335 Fax: (01295) 254590
Electronic Data Processing Group P.L.C., Sunrise Parkway, Linford Wood, Milton Keynes, MK14 6LJ Tel: (01908) 665522
Fort House Systems Ltd, Fort House Factory, East Street, South Molton, Devon, EX36 3DF Tel: (01769) 574603 Fax: (01769) 573035 E-mail: sales@forthouse.com
Giga Computer Systems, 30 Mill Road, Billericay, Essex, CM11 2SF Tel: (01277) 630493 Fax: (01277) 651666
Grafx Digital Technologies, 73 Market Street, Cheltenham, Gloucestershire, GL50 3NJ Tel: (01242) 704330 Fax: (01242) 704338 E-mail: sales@grafx.co.uk
H V S Cartridge Services, 9-13 Hart Lane, Hartlepool, Cleveland, TS26 8RJ Tel: (01429) 262568 Fax: (01429) 860257 E-mail: t-teef@hvs.uk.com
Hartley Bancks, 15 Britannia Road, Sale, Cheshire, M33 2XX Tel: 0161-905 1314 Fax: 0161-905 1381 E-mail: info@hbcc.co.uk
Hewlett Packard Ltd, Erskine Ferry Road, Bishopton, Renfrewshire, PA7 5PP Tel: 0141-814 8000 Fax: 0141-812 7745
The Ink Cycle, 24 Savile Rd, Huddersfield, HD3 3DQ Tel: (01484) 450987 Fax: (01484) 450987
Inkxpress, 106 Rhosddu Road, Wrexham, Clwyd, LL11 2NG Tel: (01978) 261368 Fax: (01978) 262735 E-mail: sales@inkxperts.co.uk
Item Systems, Albany House, 26 Nunholm Road, Dumfries, DG1 1JW Tel: (01387) 261969 Fax: (01387) 261969 E-mail: sales@itemsystems.co.uk
Kudlian Soft, 8a Nunhold Business Centre, Dark Lane, Hatton, Warwick, CV35 8XB Tel: (01926) 842544
Laserus Cartridges, 24 Whellock Road, London, W4 1DZ Tel: (020) 8723 3116 Fax: (020) 8995 8653
National Laser Toner Distribution, 30 Parsons Mead, Abingdon, Oxfordshire, OX14 1LS Tel: (01235) 525600 Fax: (01235) 520580 E-mail: julian@nationaltoners.com
Omnibus Solutions Ltd, Hollinwood Business Centre, Albert Street, Oldham, OL8 3QL Tel: 0161-683 3100 Fax: 0161-683 3102
Operandi, 62 St. Peters Road, Croydon, CR0 1HJ Tel: (020) 3251 0251 Fax: (020) 3251 0252
Orchard Networks, 1 Fieldways, The Drift, Chard, Somerset, TA20 4DN Tel: (01460) 68787 Fax: (01460) 63519 E-mail: admin@orchardnetworks.com
Parity Computers Ltd, Port Causeway, Bromborough, Wirral, Merseyside, CH62 3PS Tel: 0151-343 0200 Fax: 0151-343 0300
PC Tech International Ltd, 25 Loretto Gardens, Harrow, Middlesex, HA3 9LY Tel: (020) 8206 1505 Fax: (020) 8204 4579
Rabbitt Recycling, 27-29 New Street, Charfield, Wotton-under-Edge, Gloucestershire, GL12 8ES Tel: (01453) 844343 Fax: (01453) 521330 E-mail: info@rabbittrecycling.co.uk
Rebourn Ltd, 14 The Green, Chipping Norton, Oxfordshire, OX7 5NH Tel: (01608) 642020 Fax: (01608) 642031
Repeat Marketing, 2 Moor Knoll Drive, E Ardsley, Wakefield, West Yorkshire, WF3 2DR Tel: (01924) 871730 Fax: (01924) 823381
S D S Infotech Training Ltd, 5 Haig Court, Haig Road, Parkgate Industrial Estate, Knutsford, Cheshire, WA16 8XZ Tel: (01565) 654526
Sencam UK Ltd, Unit 107 Cariocca Business Park, Hellidon Close, Ardwick, Manchester, M12 4AH Tel: 0161-273 5747 Fax: 0161-273 6077 E-mail: sales@sencam.co.uk
Servicecare Support Services Ltd, Manchester Road, Hollinwood, Oldham, OL9 7AA Tel: 0161-688 1999 Fax: 0161-688 1998
Sigma Computer Engineering & Maintenance Ltd, 316-318 Salisbury Road, Totton, Southampton, SO40 3ND Tel: (023) 8066 3636 Fax: (023) 8086 1213
Softsell Computers Ltd, 199 High Street, Blackwood, Gwent, NP12 1AA Tel: (01495) 221166 Fax: (01495) 221177
South Notts Computers, 246-248 Southchurch Drive, Nottingham, NG11 8AA Tel: 0115-914 7066 Fax: 0115-914 7077 E-mail: info@southnottscomputers.co.uk
Sprint Systems, Unit 8 Bath Road Business Centre, Bath Road, Devizes, Wiltshire, SN10 1XA Tel: (01380) 729365 Fax: (01380) 729616
Thistle Ltd, Morebath, Tiverton, Devon, EX16 9BZ Tel: (0870) 9005449 Fax: (08709) 005449 E-mail: enquires@agridata.co.uk
Vortex Computers Ltd, 13-15 St. Michaels Square, Ashton-under-Lyne, Lancashire, OL6 6LF Tel: 0161-343 5555 Fax: 0161-343 7777 E-mail: sales@vortex.manc.co.uk
▶ What's in the Box?, 93 Derby Road, Bramcote, Nottingham, NG9 3GW Tel: (0845) 0524200 Fax: (0845) 0524300 E-mail: sales@printer-stuff.co.uk

COMPUTER AIDED DESIGN (CAD) COMPUTER HARDWARE

▶ Next Generation Computer Systems, 15 Tamworth Road, Amington, Tamworth, Staffordshire, B77 3BS Tel: (01827) 58100 Fax: (01827) 58100 E-mail: info@ngcstamworth.co.uk
Oracle Computers, 932 Shettleston Road, Glasgow, G32 7XW Tel: 0141-778 2906 E-mail: sales@oraclecomputers.co.uk

COMPUTER AIDED DESIGN (CAD) CONSULTANCY

Arrowflight, High Croft, Coldharbour Lane, Bletchingley, Redhill, RH1 4NA Tel: (01883) 744644 Fax: (01883) 744530 E-mail: sales@arrowflight.co.uk
Aryan Computer Associates Ltd, 5 Pepper Close, Caterham, Surrey, CR3 6BJ Tel: (01883) 344094 Fax: (01883) 341908
Causeway Technologies Ltd, Bucknalls Lane, Watford, WD25 9XX Tel: (01923) 892600 Fax: (01923) 679288 E-mail: partners@ecl.uk.com
▶ Complicad Ltd, 75a Phyllis Avenue, Peacehaven, East Sussex, BN10 7RA Tel: (01273) 582347 Fax: (01273) 582347 E-mail: complicad@btopenworld.com
Data Crown Ltd, Bearnshaw Tower Farm, Carr Road, Todmorden, Lancashire, OL14 7ES Tel: (01706) 817885 Fax: (01706) 817165
Digicad Designs, Martens Business Centre, Coney Lane, Keighley, West Yorkshire, BD21 5JE Tel: (01535) 691763 Fax: (01535) 691763 E-mail: digicad@hotmail.com
Digital Metal Ltd, The Church Gatehouse, Skinner Lane, Pontefract, West Yorkshire, WF8 1HG Tel: (01977) 706121 Fax: (01977) 705226
Electro Avionics, D Burnham Road, Dartford, DA1 5BN Tel: (01322) 288698 Fax: (01322) 277520 E-mail: colin@electroavionics.co.uk
Femsys Ltd, 158 Upper New Walk, Leicester, LE1 7QA Tel: 0116-254 1475 Fax: 0116-255 8982 E-mail: info@senses.co.uk
Fern Computer Consultancy Ltd, Fern Court, Derby Road, Denby, Ripley, Derbyshire, DE5 8LG Tel: (01332) 780790 Fax: (01332) 780788
▶ Fourquarters IS Ltd, Technology House, Lissadel Street, Salford, M6 6AP Tel: 0161-278 2444 Fax: (0870) 199 1225 E-mail: info@fourquarters.biz
▶ FourSquare Innovations LLP, 6 Hawksworth Grove, Leeds, LS5 3NB Tel: (0870) 3930044 Fax: (0870) 1326527 E-mail: info@foursquareinnovations.co.uk
Heron Conversions, 45 Herons Way, Pembury, Tunbridge Wells, Kent, TN2 4DW Tel: (01892) 823891 Fax: (01892) 825287 E-mail: bdwhero@aol.com
▶ Hi-Spec Engineering, Unit 9 Windmill Industrial Estate, Windmill, Fowey, Cornwall, PL23 1HB Tel: (01726) 833844 Fax: (01726) 833811 E-mail: sales@hi-spec-eng.com
Im Technical Services Ltd, Eagle House, Craigshaw Road, West Tullos Industrial Estate, Aberdeen, AB12 3AR Tel: (01224) 870004 Fax: (01224) 870004 E-mail: sales@imtechnical.com
It Innovation Centre Ltd, 2 Venture Road, Chilworth Science Park, Chilworth, Southampton, SO16 7NP Tel: (023) 8076 0834 Fax: (023) 8076 0833 E-mail: info@it-innovation.soton.ac.uk
J E G Design, PO Box 28, Stowmarket, Suffolk, IP14 3AZ Tel: (01449) 770459 Fax: (01449) 678444 E-mail: sales@babypoint.co.uk
Lan 2 Lan Ltd, 5 Genises Park, Woking, Surrey, GU21 5RW Tel: (01483) 594100 Fax: (01483) 594101
Martech Design Services, 109 London Road, Bagshot, Surrey, GU19 5DH Tel: (01276) 476922 Fax: (01276) 451622 E-mail: office@martechds.co.uk
Midpoint Ltd, 18 Leeds Road, Harrogate, North Yorkshire, HG2 8AA Tel: (01423) 528520 Fax: (01423) 529484 E-mail: enquiries@midpoint.co.uk
▶ Mode Associates Ltd, 8 Museum Place, Cardiff, CF10 3BG Tel: (029) 2035 9200 Fax: (0871) 6613854 E-mail: info@modestudio.co.uk
▶ Modis, Swan House, 33 Queen Street, London, EC4R 1BR Tel: (020) 7383 3888 Fax: (020) 7038 6401 E-mail: info@modisintl.com
Morson Projects Ltd, Unit 8, Furnace Lane, Moira, Swadlincote, Derbyshire, DE12 6AT Tel: (01283) 211711 Fax: (01283) 226868 E-mail: enquiries@mavitta.com
Quantum Manufacturing Ltd, 1 Heathcote Way, Heathcote Industrial Estate, Warwick, CV34 6TE Tel: (01926) 885564 Fax: (01926) 450387 E-mail: info@quantumprecisiontoolmakers.co.uk
Resources Computer Support Ltd, Norwich Road, Attleborough, Norfolk, NR17 2JX Tel: (01953) 457977 Fax: (01953) 457978
▶ RFA Design & Prototyping, 6 Willaim Lee Buildings, Science & Technology Park, University Boulevard, Nottingham, NG7 2RQ Tel: 0115-967 3107 Fax: 0115-925 6147 E-mail: richard.fletcher@rfadesign.co.uk
▶ Peter Thomas & Associates, 113 High Street, Codicote, Hitchin, Hertfordshire, SG4 8UA Tel: (01438) 821408 E-mail: sales@ptadesign.com
Transcendata Europe Ltd, 4 Carisbrooke Court, Buckingway Business Park, Anderson Road, Cambridge, CB24 4UQ Tel: (01954) 234300 Fax: (01954) 234349 E-mail: sales@transcendata.com
Tregartha Dinnie, Chancery House, 199 Silbury Boulevard, Milton Keynes, MK9 1JL Tel: (01908) 306500 Fax: (01908) 306505
▶ Trotman & Taylor, 40 Deer Park, Ivybridge, Devon, PL21 0HY Tel: (01752) 698410 Fax: (01752) 698410 E-mail: enquiries@trotmantaylor.com
Tunedata Ltd, 21 Bournes Row, Hoghton, Preston, PR5 0DR Tel: (01254) 853174 Fax: (01254) 853174 E-mail: john.abbott@btinternet.com

COMPUTER AIDED DESIGN (CAD) ENGINEERING PROJECTS

▶ Delta Motorsport, Litchlake Barns, Buckingham Road, Silverstone, Towcester, Northamptonshire, NN12 8TJ Tel: (01327) 858200 Fax: (01327) 858134 E-mail: enquiries@delta-motorsport.com
▶ Future Cad Services Ltd, 44 Chandlers, Orton Brimbles, Peterborough, PE2 5YW Tel: (01733) 230008 E-mail: chris@futurecadservices.co.uk
Gauge Service & Supply Co (Leamington) Ltd, 3 Park Street, Leamington Spa, Warwickshire, CV32 4QN Tel: (01926) 336137 Fax: (01926) 450636 E-mail: sales@gss.co.uk

COMPUTER AIDED DESIGN (CAD) EQUIPMENT

▶ Ace Design & Development Ltd, 10 Goldington Crescent, Billericay, Essex, CM12 0QJ Tel: (01277) 627240 Fax: 01277 659617 E-mail: ace.design@btconnect.com

COMPUTER AIDED DESIGN (CAD) SERVICES

A H Electrical Services Ltd, 21 Manshead Court, Galley Hill, Milton Keynes, MK11 1NR Tel: (01908) 569754 Fax: (01908) 569754 E-mail: alanholland2000@yahoo.com
B J Computers Ltd, 259 Eversholt Street, London, NW1 1BA Tel: (020) 7383 3444 E-mail: jass@bjcomputers.co.uk
C A Design Services Ltd, The Design Centre, Hewett Road, Gapton Hall, Great Yarmouth, Norfolk, NR31 0NN Tel: 01493 440444 Fax: 01493 442480 E-mail: sales@cadesignservices.co.uk
C A E Solutions Ltd, Unit D4 Hilton Trading Estate, Hilton Road, Lanesfield, Wolverhampton, WV4 6DW Tel: (01902) 403555 Fax: (01902) 401952 E-mail: sales@cae-solutions.co.uk
C T L Engineering Co. Ltd, Cromwell Road, Bredbury, Stockport, Cheshire, SK6 2RH Tel: 0161-430 3173 Fax: 0161-430 8643 E-mail: sales@ctl-eng.com
▶ CADVanced Ltd, 5 Thorne Rd, Doncaster, S. Yorkshire, DN1 2HJ Tel: (01909) 506655 Fax: (01909) 506655 E-mail: info@cadvancedltd.co.uk
Ceema Technology, 4 The Omega Centre, Stratton Business Park, Biggleswade, Bedfordshire, SG18 8QB Tel: (01767) 319800 Fax: (01767) 317621 E-mail: reception@ceema.co.uk
▶ Charttape Ltd, 14 Witt Road, Fair Oak, Eastleigh, Hampshire, SO50 7FR Tel: (07836) 671676 Fax: (023) 8069 6743 E-mail: charttape@btinternet.com
Crescent Draughting & Design, PO Box 914, Market Harborough, Leicestershire, LE16 9YJ Tel: (01858) 410320 Fax: (01858) 410320 E-mail: cresdesign@aol.com
▶ Flynn Product Design, 5 Crewkerne, Nailsea, Bristol, BS48 2SN Tel: (07730) 530636 E-mail: chris@flynn-product-design.com
▶ David Fox Design, Briars Lane, Stainforth, Doncaster, South Yorkshire, DN7 5AZ Tel: (01302) 849299 Fax: (01302) 849299 E-mail: info@davidfoxdesign.com
▶ Future Cad Services Ltd, 44 Chandlers, Orton Brimbles, Peterborough, PE2 5YW Tel: (01733) 230008 E-mail: chris@futurecadservices.co.uk
H D S Design Consultants Ltd, 22 South Street, Rochford, Essex, SS4 1BQ Tel: (01702) 530043 Fax: (01702) 530051 E-mail: projects@hdsdesign.com
Heron Conversions, 45 Herons Way, Pembury, Tunbridge Wells, Kent, TN2 4DW Tel: (01892) 823891 Fax: (01892) 825287 E-mail: bdwhero@aol.com
K R Graphics Ltd, 121 University Street, Belfast, BT7 1HP Tel: (028) 9033 3792 Fax: (028) 9033 0549 E-mail: studio@krgraphics.co.uk
Maidenbury Ltd, 360 Blackfen Road, Sidcup, Kent, DA15 9NY Tel: (020) 8303 4253 Fax: (020) 8303 4253 E-mail: kenhillard@maidenbury.co.uk
Memotrace Controls, 13 The Avenue, Spinney Hill, Northampton, NN3 6BA Tel: (01604) 642808 Fax: (01604) 642808 E-mail: memotrace@lineone.net
Merpro Leisure Ltd, Brent Avenue, Forties Road Industrial Estate, Montrose, Angus, DD10 9JA Tel: (01674) 662200 Fax: (01674) 662266 E-mail: sales@merpro.com
▶ Mode Associates Ltd, 8 Museum Place, Cardiff, CF10 3BG Tel: (029) 2035 9200 Fax: (0871) 6613854 E-mail: info@modestudio.co.uk
Modern Moulds & Tools, Commerce Way, Lancing, West Sussex, BN15 8TA Tel: (01903) 851905 Fax: (01903) 851907 E-mail: mail@modernmoulds.co.uk
Music & Design Ltd, 12 Linnell Road, Redhill, RH1 4DH Tel: (01737) 768272 E-mail: chris.bayley@virgin.net
P R Designs, 13 Davenport Park Road, Davenport Park, Stockport, Cheshire, SK2 6JU Tel: 0161-483 2655 Fax: 0161-483 2655 E-mail: info@prdesigns.co.uk
P-CAD, 3 Sycamore Road, Bournville, Birmingham, B30 2AA Tel: 0121-472 0235 E-mail: paul@bourniville51.freeserve.co.uk
Printed Circuit Design, 5 Holbrook Close, Great Waldingfield, Sudbury, Suffolk, CO10 0XX Tel: (01787) 310990 E-mail: d.holdaway@virgin.net
▶ Promac Process Design Ltd, 109 Norwood Grove, Beverley, North Humberside, HU17 9JP Tel: (01482) 860049 E-mail: promac_design@yahoo.co.uk
Radioscape Ltd, 2 Albany Terrace, London, NW1 4DS Tel: (020) 7224 1586 Fax: (020) 7224 1595 E-mail: info@radioscape.com
▶ RFA Design & Prototyping, 6 Willaim Lee Buildings, Science & Technology Park, University Boulevard, Nottingham, NG7 2RQ Tel: 0115-967 3107 Fax: 0115-925 6147 E-mail: richard.fletcher@rfadesign.co.uk

COMPUTER AIDED DESIGN (CAD) SERVICES – *continued*

Roevin Management Services Ltd, 40-44 Rothesay Road, Luton, LU1 1QZ Tel: (01582) 727216 Fax: (01582) 732188 E-mail: luton@roevin.co.uk
Solid Solutions Management Ltd, Innovation Centre Warwick Technology Park, Gallows Hill, Warwick, CV34 6UW Tel: (01926) 623160 Fax: (01926) 623161 E-mail: sales@solidsolutions.co.uk
Soluis Technologies Ltd, 31a King Street, Stenhousemuir, Larbert, Stirlingshire, FK5 4HD Tel: (01324) 878788 Fax: (01324) 878799 E-mail: martin@soluis.com
Toolbox (UK) Ltd, At Hurco, Hallifax Road, Cressex Business Park, High Wycombe, Buckinghamshire, HP12 3SN Tel: (01494) 558333 Fax: (01494) 558388
Toolroom Technology Ltd, Unit 1a & 1b, Haddenham Business Park, Thame Road, Haddenham, Buckinghamshire, HP17 8LJ Tel: (01844) 296650 Fax: (01844) 296651 E-mail: solutions@ttl-3d.co.uk
Trilobyte Design Ltd, Mersa House, Haroldslea Drive, Horley, Surrey, RH6 9DT Tel: (01293) 774747 E-mail: info@trilobytedesigns.co.uk
Woods Radio Frequency Services Ltd, Bullocks Farm, Bullocks Lane, Takeley, Bishop's Stortford, Hertfordshire, CM22 6TA Tel: (01279) 870432 Fax: (01279) 871689

COMPUTER AIDED DESIGN (CAD) SOFTWARE

4d Engineering Ltd, Phoenix House, Phoenix Way, Cirencester, Gloucestershire, GL7 1QG Tel: (01285) 650111 Fax: (01285) 650150 E-mail: sales@mastercam.co.uk
Advantage Automation Ltd, 21 Broadway, Maidenhead, Berkshire, SL6 1NJ Tel: (01628) 777759 Fax: (01628) 778681
Alta Systems Ltd, Ashleigh House, 81 Birmingham Road, West Bromwich, West Midlands, B70 6PX Tel: 0121-553 6665 Fax: 0121-553 6661 E-mail: sales@altasystems.co.uk
Amtech Power Software Ltd, Bank House, 171 Midsummer Boulevard, Milton Keynes, MK9 1EB Tel: (01908) 608833 Fax: (01908) 234355 E-mail: sales@amtech-power.co.uk
▶ ANSYS Europe Ltd, West Central 127, Milton Park, Abingdon, Oxfordshire, OX14 4SA Tel: (0870) 1420333 Fax: (0870) 1420301
Aveva Engineering It Ltd, High Cross, Madingley Road, Cambridge, CB3 0HB Tel: (01223) 556655 Fax: (01223) 556666 E-mail: info@aveva.com
CAD Academy Ltd, Sherwood House, Gregory Boulevard, Nottingham, NG7 6LB Tel: 0115-969 1114 Fax: 0115-969 1115 E-mail: info@cadacademy.co.uk
Cadalec Control Systems, Three Boundaries Business Park, Coventry Road, Croft, Leicester, LE9 3GP Tel: (01455) 286900 Fax: (01455) 286999 E-mail: sales@cadalec.com
Cadence Design Systems Ltd, Bagshot Road, Bracknell, Berkshire, RG12 0PH Tel: (01344) 360333 Fax: (01344) 869647
Cadserve Ltd, Beede House, St. Cuthberts Way, Newton Aycliffe, County Durham, DL5 6DX Tel: (01325) 318111 Fax: (01325) 318444 E-mail: info@cadserve.co.uk
Cadtek Systems Ltd, Cadek House, Station Road, Furness Vale, High Peak, Derbyshire, SK23 7QA Tel: (01663) 741405 Fax: (01663) 741605 E-mail: info@cadtek.co.uk
Catena Software Ltd, Terence House, 24 London Road, Thatcham, Berkshire, RG18 4LQ Tel: (01635) 866395 E-mail: sales@catenauk.com
Computer Aided Business Systems Ltd, 8 Forum Place, Fiddlebridge Lane, Hatfield, Hertfordshire, AL10 0RN Tel: (01707) 258338 Fax: (01707) 258339 E-mail: sales@cabs-cad.com
Crusader Ltd, Oxford House, Easthorpe Street, Ruddington, Nottingham, NG11 6LA Tel: 0115-940 5550 Fax: 0115-940 6660 E-mail: sales@crusaderltd.com
▶ Dragoncad, 9 St. Maughans Close, Monmouth, Gwent, NP25 5BU Tel: (07920) 054495 E-mail: info@dragoncad.co.uk
Eagland Machine Tools Ltd, The Studio, Hill Road, Lyme Regis, Dorset, DT7 3PG Tel: (01297) 446000 Fax: (01297) 446001 E-mail: info@eagland.co.uk
Euro Products Ltd, Yardley House, Yardley Street, Stourbridge, West Midlands, DY9 7AT Tel: (01384) 895000 Fax: (01384) 897000 E-mail: sales@europroducts.co.uk
Exitech Computers Ltd, Units 2-3, Sovereign Business Centre, Stockingswater Lane, Enfield, Middlesex, EN3 7JX Tel: (020) 8804 9942 Fax: (0845) 3701400
Femsys Ltd, 158 Upper New Walk, Leicester, LE1 7QA Tel: 0116-254 1475 Fax: 0116-255 8982 E-mail: info@senses.co.uk
Fern Computer Consultancy Ltd, Fern Court, Derby Road, Denby, Ripley, Derbyshire, DE5 8LG Tel: (01332) 780790 Fax: (01332) 780788
Harp Software, PO Box 1101, Stourbridge, West Midlands, DY9 8YL Tel: (0845) 2261671 Fax: (01384) 892169 E-mail: harp@harpsoftware.co.uk
Hebbard, 18 Park Lane, Little Downham, Ely, Cambridgeshire, CB6 2TF Tel: (01353) 698338 Fax: (01353) 698995 E-mail: workshop@hebbard3d.com
▶ ITMAX Ltd, Abbey Drive, Abbots Langley, Hertfordshire, WD5 0TL Tel: (01923) 464105 Fax: (01923) 464106 E-mail: bash@itmax.co.uk
Leonardo Computer Systems, Woodlands Business Village, Woodlands Business Village C Oronation Road, Basingstoke, Hampshire, RG22 4BH Tel: (01256) 322445 E-mail: sales@leonardo-cad.co.uk
Mentor Graphic UK Ltd, Rivergate Newbury Business Park, London Road, Newbury, Berkshire, RG14 2QB Tel: (01635) 811411 Fax: (01635) 810108
Merlin Software International Ltd, 6 Bancombe Road, Somerton, Somerset, TA11 6SB Tel: (01458) 271300 Fax: (01458) 224044 E-mail: info@caliburn-software.com
Midpoint Ltd, 18 Leeds Road, Harrogate, North Yorkshire, HG2 8AA Tel: (01423) 528520 Fax: (01423) 529484 E-mail: enquiries@midpoint.co.uk
Number 1 Systems, Oak Lane, Bredon, Tewkesbury, Gloucestershire, GL20 7LR Tel: (01684) 773662 Fax: (01684) 773664 E-mail: sales@numberone.com
Paradigm Geo-Physical UK Ltd, Mackenzie Buildings, 168 Skene Street, Aberdeen, AB10 1PE Tel: (01224) 649555 Fax: (01224) 649496
Rex Software Ltd, Chesil House, Arrow Close, Eastleigh, Hampshire, SO50 4SY Tel: (023) 8062 9429 Fax: (0870) 0548257
Rhinocad Ltd, 23 Avon Road, Kenilworth, Warwickshire, CV8 1DH Tel: (0845) 6037223 E-mail: info@rhinocad.co.uk
S T M Systems Ltd, 32 Bernard Street, Edinburgh, EH6 6PR Tel: 0131-467 7891 Fax: 0131-467 7448 E-mail: sales@systems.com
▶ Solutions Inc, 255 Old Shoreham Road, Hove, East Sussex, BN3 7ED Tel: (01273) 200800 Fax: (01273) 889030 E-mail: richard@solutionsinc.co.uk
Zuken, 1500 Aztec West, Almondsbury, Bristol, BS32 4RF Tel: (01454) 207800 Fax: (01454) 207803 E-mail: info@zuken.co.uk

COMPUTER AIDED DESIGN (CAD) SYSTEM HIRE

Computerhire South West Ltd, 5 Kingsway, Kingswood, Bristol, BS15 8BF Tel: 0117-907 7101 Fax: 0117-907 7105 E-mail: sales@computerhire-sw.co.uk
N T C Microcad, Morton Road, Darlington, County Durham, DL1 4PT Tel: (01325) 350220 Fax: (01325) 350767
Road Recruitment, Trioka House 2, East Union Street, Rugby, Warwickshire, CV22 6AJ Tel: (01788) 572841 Fax: (01788) 578609 E-mail: sales@rdrecruit.com

COMPUTER AIDED DESIGN (CAD) SYSTEMS

4d Engineering Ltd, Phoenix House, Phoenix Way, Cirencester, Gloucestershire, GL7 1QG Tel: (01285) 650111 Fax: (01285) 650150 E-mail: sales@mastercam.co.uk
A S P Electronic Design Ltd, 3a Warren House Road, Wokingham, Berkshire, RG40 5PN Tel: 0118-979 0825 Fax: 0118-977 1749 E-mail: enquiries@asp.uk.com
Cadence Design Systems Ltd, Bagshot Road, Bracknell, Berkshire, RG12 0PH Tel: (01344) 360333 Fax: (01344) 360324
Concept Northern, 14 St Bryde Street, East Kilbride, Glasgow, G74 4HQ Tel: (01355) 573173 Fax: (01355) 573073 E-mail: louiset@cc2000.co.uk
Leonardo Computer Systems, Woodlands Business Village, Woodlands Business Village C Oronation Road, Basingstoke, Hampshire, RG22 4BH Tel: (01256) 322445 E-mail: sales@leonardo-cad.co.uk
M E V Ltd, Baxall Business Centre Adswood Industrial Estate, Adswood Road, Stockport, Cheshire, SK3 8LF Tel: 0161-477 1898 Fax: 0161-718 3587 E-mail: sales@mev.co.uk
PCs R Us, Drumbrughas North, Lisnaskea, Enniskillen, County Fermanagh, BT92 0PE Tel: (028) 6772 3242 Fax: (028) 6772 3131 E-mail: zubbie75@hotmail.com
Planit International Ltd, 1 Trinity Road, Eureka Science Park, Ashford, Kent, TN25 4AB Tel: (01233) 635566 Fax: (01233) 627855 E-mail: sales@planit.com
Radan, Limpley Mill, Limpley Stoke, Bath, BA2 7FJ Tel: (0844) 8001248 Fax: (01225) 721333 E-mail: sales@uk.radan.com
▶ Solutions Inc, 255 Old Shoreham Road, Hove, East Sussex, BN3 7ED Tel: (01273) 200800 Fax: (01273) 889030 E-mail: richard@solutionsinc.co.uk
Toolbox (UK) Ltd, At Hurco, Hallifax Road, Cressex Business Park, High Wycombe, Buckinghamshire, HP12 3SN Tel: (01494) 558333 Fax: (01494) 558388
▶ Zed Computer Systems Ltd, 54 St.Johns Road, Slough, SL2 5EZ Tel: (01753) 823828 E-mail: enquiries@zedcomputers.com
Zuken, 1500 Aztec West, Almondsbury, Bristol, BS32 4RF Tel: (01454) 207800 Fax: (01454) 207803 E-mail: info@zuken.co.uk

COMPUTER AIDED DESIGN COMPUTER AIDED MANUFACTURING (CADCAM) DRAWING OR DRAFTING SERVICES

Adris Ltd, Riverise House Brunel Road, Totton, Southampton, SO40 3WX Tel: (023) 8086 8947 Fax: (023) 8086 1618 E-mail: sales@adris.co.uk
▶ Blue Aardvark Design, The Grange Business Centre, Belasis Avenue, Billingham, Cleveland, TS23 1LG Tel: (01642) 658783 Fax: (01642) 552820 E-mail: blueaardvarkdesign@tiscali.co.uk
Bluearc, Queensgate House, Cookham Road, Bracknell, Berkshire, RG12 1RB Tel: (01344) 408200 Fax: (01344) 408202
▶ CADVanced Ltd, 5 Thorne Rd, Doncaster, S. Yorkshire, DN1 2HJ Tel: (01909) 506655 Fax: (01909) 506655 E-mail: info@cadvancedltd.co.uk
▶ Computool, 5 Bilberry Close, Eaton Ford, St. Neots, Cambridgeshire, PE19 7GU Tel: (01480) 476670 Fax: (01480) 476670 E-mail: computool@ntlworld.com
▶ Concept To Reality, Unit 2, The Factory, Lightsfield, Oakley, Basingstoke, Hampshire, RG23 7BY Tel: 01256 782764 Fax: 01256 782764 E-mail: enquiries@ctr-design.co.uk
Digital Metal Ltd, The Church Gatehouse, Skinner Lane, Pontefract, West Yorkshire, WF8 1HG Tel: (01977) 706121 Fax: (01977) 705226
▶ Hi-Spec Engineering, Unit 9 Windmill Industrial Estate, Windmill, Fowey, Cornwall, PL23 1HB Tel: (01726) 833844 Fax: (01726) 833811 E-mail: sales@hi-spec-eng.com
Inspire2Design Limited, 17C Mill Road, Stourport-on-Severn, Worcestershire, DY13 9BG Tel: (01299) 827646 E-mail: info@inspire2design.co.uk
Mason Land Surveys Ltd, Dickson Street, Dunfermline, Fife, KY12 7SL Tel: (01383) 727261 Fax: (01383) 739480 E-mail: sales@mason.co.uk
Pathtrace P.L.C., 45 Boulton Road, Reading, RG2 0NH Tel: 0118-975 6084 Fax: 0118-975 6143 E-mail: enquiry@pathtrace.com
▶ Promac Process Design Ltd, 109 Norwood Grove, Beverley, North Humberside, HU17 9JP Tel: (01482) 860049 E-mail: promac_design@yahoo.co.uk
▶ Unique Fire Safety Solutions, Suite 39, 792 Wilmslow Road, Didsbury, Manchester, M20 6UG Tel: (07969) 664105 E-mail: sales@uniquefiresafety.com
▶ WebCad, The Barn, HodgeHill Farm, Blakedown, Kidderminster, Worcestershire, DY10 3NR Tel: 01562 515318 Fax: 0709 2394102 E-mail: sales@webcad2005.co.uk

COMPUTER AIDED DESIGN, COMPUTER AIDED MANUFACTURING (CADCAM) ENGINEERING

▶ C2m(Uk) Ltd, Suite 48 Gear House, Saltmeadows Road, Gateshead, Tyne & Wear, NE8 3AH Tel: 0191-490 1154 E-mail: c2muk@aol.com
Class 100 Ltd, Units 32-33 London Road Industrial Estate, Baldock, Hertfordshire, SG7 6NG Tel: (01462) 893336 Fax: (01462) 893377 E-mail: cadcam@class100.co.uk
Destech UK Ltd, 3 Millbrook Business Park, Hoe Lane, Nazeing, Waltham Abbey, Essex, EN9 2RJ Tel: (01992) 899002 Fax: (01992) 899003 E-mail: sales@destech-uk.co.uk
▶ Octo Product Development Ltd, Design Works, William Street, Felling, Gateshead, Tyne & Wear, NE10 0JP Tel: 0191-469 3888 Fax: 0191-469 1888 E-mail: danm@octodesign.co.uk
▶ Original Video UK, Central Way, Cheltenham Trade Park, Cheltenham, Gloucestershire, GL51 8LX Tel: (01242) 526565 Fax: (01242) 526565 E-mail: contact@original-video.com

COMPUTER AIDED DESIGN, COMPUTER AIDED MANUFACTURING (CADCAM) PROGRAMMING BUREAU SERVICES

Class 100 Ltd, Units 32-33 London Road Industrial Estate, Baldock, Hertfordshire, SG7 6NG Tel: (01462) 893336 Fax: (01462) 893377 E-mail: cadcam@class100.co.uk
▶ Computool, 5 Bilberry Close, Eaton Ford, St. Neots, Cambridgeshire, PE19 7GU Tel: (01480) 476670 Fax: (01480) 476670 E-mail: computool@ntlworld.com
Exitech Computers Ltd, Units 2-3, Sovereign Business Centre, Stockingswater Lane, Enfield, Middlesex, EN3 7JX Tel: (020) 8804 9942 Fax: (0845) 3701400
U G S Ltd, Milford House, Priory End, Hitchin, Hertfordshire, SG4 9AL Tel: (01462) 440222 Fax: (01462) 440522 E-mail: betty.waterhouse@ugs.com

COMPUTER AIDED DESIGN, COMPUTER AIDED MANUFACTURING (CADCAM) PROTOTYPING SERVICES

Aided Design & Draughting Supplies, Spreadeagle Court, Northgate Street, Gloucester, GL1 1SL Tel: (01452) 505040 Fax: (01452) 505040
Berry Place Models Ltd, 1 Berry Place, Sebastian Street, London, EC1V 0HE Tel: (020) 7490 8222 Fax: (020) 7336 8482 E-mail: enquiries@berryplace.co.uk
▶ Computool, 5 Bilberry Close, Eaton Ford, St. Neots, Cambridgeshire, PE19 7GU Tel: (01480) 476670 Fax: (01480) 476670 E-mail: computool@ntlworld.com
Retrac Productions Ltd, 3-5 Bramble Road, Techno Trading Estate, Swindon, SN2 8HB Tel: (01793) 524616 Fax: (01793) 511899 E-mail: andycarter@retrac-group.com
Rojac Patterns Ltd, Automotive Components Park, Hallens Drive, Wednesbury, West Midlands, WS10 7DD Tel: 0121-556 0909 Fax: 0121-556 4343 E-mail: sales@rojac.com
U G S Ltd, Milford House, Priory End, Hitchin, Hertfordshire, SG4 9AL Tel: (01462) 440222 Fax: (01462) 440522 E-mail: betty.waterhouse@ugs.com

COMPUTER AIDED DESIGN, COMPUTER AIDED MANUFACTURING (CADCAM)SYSTEMS, MECHANICAL APPLICATIONS

B J Computers Ltd, 259 Eversholt Street, London, NW1 1BA Tel: (020) 7383 3444 E-mail: jass@bjcomputers.co.uk
Toolbox (UK) Ltd, At Hurco, Hallifax Road, Cressex Business Park, High Wycombe, Buckinghamshire, HP12 3SN Tel: (01494) 558333 Fax: (01494) 558388

COMPUTER AIDED LIGHT MICROSCOPY SYSTEMS

Carl Zeiss Ltd, PO Box 78, Welwyn Garden City, Hertfordshire, AL7 1LU Tel: (01707) 331144 Fax: (01707) 330237 E-mail: info@zeiss.co.uk

COMPUTER AIDED MANUFACTURING (CAM) CONSULTANTS

Cambashi Ltd, 52 Mawson Road, Cambridge, CB1 2HY Tel: (01223) 460439 Fax: (01223) 461055 E-mail: info@cambashi.com
Pathtrace P.L.C., 45 Boulton Road, Reading, RG2 0NH Tel: 0118-975 6084 Fax: 0118-975 6143 E-mail: enquiry@pathtrace.com
Solution & Communications Services Ltd, 57 Crwys Road, Cardiff, CF24 4NE Tel: (029) 2066 6133 Fax: (029) 2066 6017 E-mail: sales@solutions-and-communications.com
Tarion Communication Services Ltd, 27 Almond Grove, Hempstead, Gillingham, Kent, ME7 3SE Tel: (01634) 378428 Fax: (01634) 262595

COMPUTER AIDED MANUFACTURING (CAM) SYSTEMS

4d Engineering Ltd, Phoenix House, Phoenix Way, Cirencester, Gloucestershire, GL7 1QG Tel: (01285) 650111 Fax: (01285) 650150 E-mail: sales@mastercam.co.uk
Althacam Ltd, Licom House, 8 Davenport Road, Coventry, CV5 6PY Tel: (024) 7671 3434 Fax: (024) 7671 3449 E-mail: sales@uk.althacam.com
Camtek Ltd, Camtek House, 117 Church Street, Malvern, Worcestershire, WR14 2AJ Tel: (01684) 892290 Fax: (01684) 892269 E-mail: sales@camtek.co.uk
Dia-Nielsen UK Ltd, Enfield Lock, South Ordnance Road, Enfield, Middlesex, EN3 6JG Tel: (01992) 787110
▶ Eclipse PC's, Suite 221, 26-32 Oxford Road, Bournemouth, BH8 8EZ Tel: (01202) 311052 Fax: (01202) 314513 E-mail: eclipsepcs@btinternet.com
Hex A Tec Systems Ltd, The Courtyard, Ochrelands, Fellside, Hexham, Northumberland, NE46 1SB Tel: (01434) 605575 Fax: (01434) 607800 E-mail: sales@hexatec.com
Hyde Group Ltd, Hadfield Street, Dukinfield, Cheshire, SK16 4QX Tel: 0161-308 2111 Fax: 0161-330 2680 E-mail: sales@hydetool.co.uk
Radan, Limpley Mill, Limpley Stoke, Bath, BA2 7FJ Tel: (0844) 8001248 Fax: (01225) 721333 E-mail: sales@uk.radan.com

COMPUTER AIDED MANUFACTURING (CAM) SYSTEMS

– continued

Retrac Productions Ltd, 3-5 Bramble Road, Techno Trading Estate, Swindon, SN2 8HB Tel: (01793) 524616 Fax: (01793) 511899 E-mail: andycarter@retrac-group.com
Trapese Group, Millbrook House, 141 Milton Road, Weston-super-Mare, Avon, BS22 8AA Tel: (01934) 413547 Fax: (01934) 413418 E-mail: sales@southerncomputersystems.co.uk
Zuken, 1500 Aztec West, Almondsbury, Bristol, BS32 4RF Tel: (01454) 207800 Fax: (01454) 207803 E-mail: info@zuken.co.uk

COMPUTER AIDED RETRIEVAL MICROFILM BUREAU SERVICES

Cosmo Imaging Ltd, Systems House, Ocean Street, Altrincham, Cheshire, WA14 5DP Tel: 0161-928 6042 Fax: 0161-929 7327 E-mail: info@cgil.co.uk
Drayton Data Ltd, 4 Willow Park, Upton Lane, Stoke Golding, Nuneaton, Warwickshire, CV13 6EU Tel: (01455) 213075 Fax: (01455) 213075 E-mail: draytondata@aol.com
M C2 Micrographic, 19 Heron Road, Belfast, BT3 9LE Tel: (028) 9046 6337 Fax: (028) 9046 6397
Micro Services (Eastern) Ltd, Unit 4 Craven Way Industrial Estate, Newmarket, Suffolk, CB8 0BW Tel: (01638) 661055 Fax: (01638) 664098

COMPUTER AIDED TEACHING SYSTEMS

▶ Alpha Tutors, No. 6, Russell Flint House, Royal Docks, London, E16 1UT Tel: 0207 4732360
Emco Education Ltd, Unit 4 Hayling Billy Business, Furniss Way, Hayling Island, Hampshire, PO11 0ED Tel: (023) 9263 7100 Fax: (023) 9263 7660
Northwood Computer Tutorial Centre Ltd, Paget, Flaunden Lane, Flaunden, Bovingdon, Hemel Hempstead, Hertfordshire, HP3 0PQ Tel: (01442) 831234

COMPUTER AIDED TESTING (CAT) SYSTEMS

Leysen Associates Ltd, Padmores Yard, St. Johns Mews, Woking, Surrey, GU21 7ZE Tel: (01483) 881188 Fax: (01483) 881189
Merit, Alloa Business Centre, The Whins, Alloa, Clackmannanshire, FK10 3SA Tel: (01259) 726640 Fax: (01259) 726620 E-mail: info@merit-at.com

COMPUTER AUDIT/ASSET MANAGEMENT SERVICES

Arc, Western House, 7 Knutsford Road, Wilmslow, Cheshire, SK9 6JA Tel: (01625) 543430 Fax: (01625) 543431 E-mail: sales@arcit.co.uk
Computer Research Consultant, Bell House, Kingsland, Leominster, Herefordshire, HR6 9RU Tel: (01568) 709180 Fax: (08456) 008250
Computer Research Consultants Ltd, 9 Duke Street, Alderley Edge, Cheshire, SK9 7HX Tel: (01625) 582228 Fax: (01993) 822701 E-mail: sales@crc-computeraudit.co.uk
Concorde Informatics Ltd, Stoneleigh, 39 Halifax Road, Brighouse, West Yorkshire, HD6 2AQ Tel: (01484) 405405 Fax: (01484) 405400 E-mail: info@concordeinf.com
End O Line Services, 1-3 Station Road, Maldon, Essex, CM9 4LQ Tel: (01621) 843535 Fax: (01621) 843534E-mail: sales@eols.co.uk
White Waghorn Ltd, 9 High Street, Stevenage, Hertfordshire, SG1 3BG Tel: (01438) 726393 E-mail: info@whitewaghorn.co.uk

COMPUTER BADGES

Key Factors, 11 Cannon Grove, Fetcham, Leatherhead, Surrey, KT22 9LG Tel: (01372) 376904 Fax: (01372) 376904 E-mail: sales@keyfactors.co.uk
Recognition Express, Venture Business Park, Grimsby, South Humberside, DN31 2UW Tel: (01472) 362900 Fax: (01472) 267647 E-mail: mailbox@recog-grimsby.co.uk

COMPUTER BASE UNITS

▶ click4it.co.uk, Unit 2, Hope House Farm, Martley, Worcester, WR6 6QF Tel: 0845 2303084 E-mail: sales@click4it.co.uk
▶ Compu-Tech, 11 Balmoral CR, Okehampton, Devon, EX20 1GN Tel: (01837) 659714
▶ Croft Networking, 20 Jardine Way, Dunstable, Bedfordshire, LU5 4AX Tel: (01582) 513234
▶ Equity PC, Heath Road, Woolpit, Bury St. Edmunds, Suffolk, IP30 9RL Tel: (07774) 768172 E-mail: services@equitypc.co.uk
▶ Interlogistics Ltd, Waldeck House, Waldeck Road, Maidenhead, Berkshire, SL6 8BR Tel: (01628) 621300 Fax: (01628) 621309 E-mail: info@justsurplus.co.uk
▶ Lyon Computer Solutions, 62, Lyon Road, Crowthorne, Berkshire, RG45 6RT Tel: (01344) 750147
▶ SJ Consultancy, 6 Flaxfields End, Fordingbridge, Hampshire, SP6 1RT Tel: 01425 652961 Fax: 01425 652961 E-mail: enquiries@sjcfb.co.uk

COMPUTER BASED COMMUNICATION SYSTEMS

Accutest Ltd, Wren Nest Road, Glossop, Derbyshire, SK13 8HB Tel: (01457) 866613 Fax: (01457) 856789 E-mail: sales@accutest.co.uk
Key Communication Systems Ltd, Key House, 21 Bourne Road, Bexley, Kent, DA5 1LW Tel: (01322) 555522 Fax: (01322) 555227 E-mail: info@keycoms.co.uk
Lan Com International Ltd, Birchwood, Main Road, Curbridge, Witney, Oxfordshire, OX29 7NT Tel: (01993) 776543 Fax: (01993) 776899 E-mail: jc.lancom@btinternet.com
Nec Europe Ltd, N E C House, 1 Victoria Road, London, W3 6BL Tel: (020) 8993 8111 Fax: (020) 8992 7161
▶ Panrix Computer, Unit 19, Sheepscar Street South, Leeds, LS7 1AD Tel: 0113-244 4958 Fax: 0113-244 4268 E-mail: gulberg@panrix.co.uk
Readycrest Ltd, PO Box 75, Chatham, Kent, ME5 9DL Tel: (01634) 304060 Fax: (01634) 304070 E-mail: info@readycrest.co.uk
Symicron Computer Communications Ltd, Technical Support Green Lane Business Park, 238 Green Lane, London, SE9 3TL Tel: (020) 8857 5577 Fax: (020) 8857 1945 E-mail: sales@symicron.com
Toltec Systems, Exchange Quay, Salford, M5 3EQ Tel: 0161-876 4447 Fax: 0161-876 4448 E-mail: sales-uk@etoltec.com
▶ Y O G Marine Computer Systems, Suite 19, 46 Warwick Way, Westminster, London, SW1V 1RY Tel: (0870) 8733750 Fax: (0870) 8733760 E-mail: info@yog-it.co.uk
Zoom Hayes, Lapwing, 430 Frimley Business Park, Frimley, Camberley, Surrey, GU16 7SG Tel: (01276) 704400 Fax: (01276) 704500 E-mail: eurosales@hayes.co.uk

COMPUTER BASED PROCESS CONTROLLER SYSTEMS

A Ii D Solutions Ltd, 2 Wyvern Avenue, Stockport, Cheshire, SK5 7DD Tel: 0161-480 3163 Fax: 0161-480 3043 E-mail: info@aiid.co.uk
Adaptive Control Solutions Ltd, 1 Ashfield Road, Greetland, Halifax, West Yorkshire, HX4 8HY Tel: (01422) 313456 Fax: (01422) 313567 E-mail: richardarmitage@adaptivecontrol.com
Advanced Control Systems Ltd, 140 Aberford Road, Woodlesford, Leeds, LS26 8LG Tel: 0113-282 7123 Fax: 0113-282 5252
Cougar Automation Ltd, Cougar House Parklands Business Park, Forest Road, Denmead, Waterlooville, Hampshire, PO7 6XP Tel: (023) 9226 9960 Fax: (023) 9226 9968 E-mail: info@cougar-automation.com
Geedev Ltd, 21 Barndale Drive, Arne, Wareham, Dorset, BH20 5BX Tel: (01929) 551122 Fax: (01929) 552936 E-mail: design@geedev.co.uk
Golconda, Links House, Southglade Business Park, Hucknall Road, Nottingham, NG5 9RA Tel: 0115-977 1101 Fax: 0115-977 0047 E-mail: golconda@golconda.co.uk
Hex A Tec Systems Ltd, The Courtyard, Ochrelands, Fellside, Hexham, Northumberland, NE46 1SB Tel: (01434) 605575 Fax: (01434) 607800 E-mail: sales@hexatec.com
Rospen Industries Ltd, Oldends Lane Industrial Estate, Oldends Lane, Stonehouse, Gloucestershire, GL10 3RQ Tel: (01453) 825212 Fax: (01453) 828279 E-mail: enquiries@rospen.com
Tascomp Ltd, Newburgh Court, Belasis Hall Technology Park, Billingham, Cleveland, TS23 4EE Tel: (01642) 370666 Fax: (01642) 370012 E-mail: sales@tascomp.com
Zella Instrumentation & Control Ltd, Brunel Drive, Newark, Nottinghamshire, NG24 2EG Tel: (01636) 704370 Fax: (01636) 640296 E-mail: sales@zella-instrumentation.co.uk

COMPUTER BATTERIES

Absolute Battery UK Ltd, Darrell House, Darrell Road, Felixstowe, Suffolk, IP11 3UU Tel: (01394) 674949 Fax: (01394) 279005
P S A Batteries Ltd, Faraday House, 39 Thornton Road, Wimbledon, London, SW19 4NQ Tel: (0870) 873 2002 Fax: (020) 8944 6694 E-mail: jem@psaparts.co.uk

COMPUTER BOARD LEVEL PRODUCTS

Pro Face UK Ltd, Orchard Court Binley Business Park, Harry Weston Road, Coventry, CV3 2TQ Tel: (024) 7644 0088 Fax: (024) 7644 0099 E-mail: sales@profaceuk.com
▶ Triangle Digital Support Ltd, 64a Market Place, Thirsk, North Yorkshire, YO7 1LW Tel: (01845) 527437 Fax: (0870) 7059860 E-mail: business@triangledigital.com

COMPUTER BOOKS

▶ All Top Books, 30 Marischal Road, London, SE13 5LG Tel: (0845) 0542730 E-mail: contact@alltopbooks.co.uk

COMPUTER BREAKDOWN EMERGENCY COMPUTER SUPPLY SERVICES

Aa Computer Maintenance Ltd, 4 Edge Business Centre, Humber Road, London, NW2 6EW Tel: (020) 8452 8033 Fax: (020) 8450 6360
L A Computers, 12 Magister Road, Bowerhill, Melksham, Wiltshire, SN12 6FE Tel: (01225) 793337 Fax: (01225) 793335
Network Disaster Recovery Ltd, 220 Chester Street, Aston, Birmingham, B6 4AH Tel: 0121-380 2000 Fax: 0121-359 0534 E-mail: sales@ndr.co.uk
Network Logic Ltd, 2 St Josephs Close, Droitwich, Worcestershire, WR9 0RY Tel: (01905) 795725 E-mail: network.logic@lineone.net
Unigold Computer Maintenance, 34 Stringers Avenue, Guildford, Surrey, GU4 7NW Tel: (01483) 459045 Fax: (01483) 459046 E-mail: enquiries@unigold2000.co.uk

COMPUTER BUS BASED SYSTEMS, COMPACT PERIPHERAL COMPONENT INTERCONNECT (PCI)

Hauppauge Computer Works Ltd, Bank Chambers, 6 Borough High Street, London, SE1 9QQ Tel: (020) 7378 1997 Fax: (020) 7357 9771 E-mail: support@hauppauge.co.uk
▶ Y O G Marine Computer Systems, Suite 19, 46 Warwick Way, Westminster, London, SW1V 1RY Tel: (0870) 8733750 Fax: (0870) 8733760 E-mail: info@yog-it.co.uk

COMPUTER CABLE INSTALLATION SERVICES

Ashby Computer Services, Sywell Airport Business Park, Wellingborough Road, Sywell, Northampton, NN6 0BN Tel: (01604) 790979 Fax: (01604) 491859 E-mail: enquiries@ashbycomputers.co.uk
Brandt Computer Systems Ltd, 20 Barclay Road, Croydon, CR0 1JN Tel: (020) 8760 9173 Fax: (020) 8760 9180 E-mail: croydon@brandt.co.uk
Brimalk Ltd, Unit 8, Apollo, Lichfield Road Industrial Estate, Tamworth, Staffordshire, B79 7TA Tel: (01827) 51550 Fax: (01827) 51188 E-mail: sales@brimalk.co.uk
Cable Team UK Limited, Unit 3, Daaker House, Two Rivers, Station Lane, Witney, Oxfordshire, OX28 4BH Tel: 01993 702300 Fax: 08709 509369 E-mail: enquiries@ct-uk.net
Cleanline Installations Ltd, Terminal House, Station Approach, Shepperton, Middlesex, TW17 8AS Tel: (01932) 260490 Fax: (01932) 227037 E-mail: cleanline@compuserve.com
Complete Connections, 75 Milford Road, Reading, RG1 8LG Tel: 0118-959 4286 Fax: 0118-950 5263 E-mail: sales@cableshop.co.uk
Conex Data Communications Ltd, Connex House, Follingsby Close, Gateshead, Tyne & Wear, NE10 8YG Tel: 0191-416 5444 Fax: 0191-416 0707 E-mail: sales@conexdata.com
D L S Services, Unit 2 Union Park Industrial Estate, Triumph Way, Kempston, Bedford, MK42 7QB Tel: (01234) 840104 E-mail: dls@kbnet.co.uk
D R S Rugged Systems (Europe) Ltd, Lynwood House, The Trading Estate, Farnham, Surrey, GU9 9NN Tel: (01252) 734488 Fax: (01252) 730530
Excel I T Ltd, Trafalgar House, 712 London Road, Grays, Essex, RM20 3JT Tel: (01708) 865855 Fax: (01708) 866856 E-mail: enquiries@excelit.com
Lancaster Communications Ltd, Tarn View, Denny Beck, Lancaster, LA2 9HG Tel: (01524) 846900 Fax: (01524) 846900 E-mail: enq@lancastercomms.co.uk
Le Computer, School Road, Rayne, Braintree, Essex, CM77 6SR Tel: (01376) 348886 Fax: (01376) 349996 E-mail: info@lecomputer.co.uk
Network Engineering Technology Ltd, 6 Church Road, Swallowfield, Reading, RG7 1TH Tel: 0118-988 7014 Fax: 0118-988 7114 E-mail: sale@netec.co.uk
Pulse Installations Ltd, 292 Worton Road, Isleworth, Middlesex, TW7 6EL Tel: (020) 8560 4040 Fax: (020) 8568 0133 E-mail: enquiries@pulse-inst.co.uk
R B Emerson, 8a Temple Farm Industrial Estate, Coopers Way, Temple Farm Industrial Estate, Southend-on-Sea, SS2 5TE Tel: (01702) 461999 Fax: (01702) 462001 E-mail: sales@emersons.uk.com
Structured Cabling Services Ltd, 13 Portland Road, Birmingham, B16 9HN Tel: (0845) 2300041 Fax: (0845) 2300042 E-mail: info@structured-cabling.co.uk
Ulysses Ltd, Unit A Troon Way Business Centre, Humberstone Lane, Leicester, LE4 9HA Tel: 0116-276 9152 Fax: (0845) 1300259 E-mail: info@ulysses.uk.com

COMPUTER CARRYING CASES

Fellowes Ltd, Yorkshire Way, Armthorpe, Doncaster, South Yorkshire, DN3 3FB Tel: (01302) 836800 Fax: (01302) 836899 E-mail: sales@fellowes.com
Lance Leathers, 14 Bedford Road, Stagsden, Bedford, MK43 8TP Tel: (01234) 823200 Fax: (01234) 826110 E-mail: david@lanceleathers.co.uk
Nomad plc, Rockingham Road, Market Harborough, Leicestershire, LE16 7QE Tel: (01858) 464878 Fax: (01858) 410175 E-mail: nomadsolutions@aol.com
Praybourne Ltd, Unit 11, Dunlop Road, Hunt End Industrial Estate, Redditch, Worcestershire, B97 5XP Tel: (0870) 2420004 Fax: (01527) 543752 E-mail: inquiries@praybourne.co.uk
Topper Cases Ltd, St. Peter's Hill, Huntingdon, Cambridgeshire, PE29 7DX Tel: (01480) 457251 Fax: (01480) 452107 E-mail: sales@toppercases.co.uk

COMPUTER (CD-ROM) SERVICES

CD Team Group Ltd, Unit 1 Fairview Trading Estate, Reading Road, Henley-on-Thames, Oxfordshire, RG9 1HE Tel: (01491) 636373 Fax: (01491) 636374 E-mail: info@cdteam.co.uk
Cir-Comm Systems Ltd, Bailey Brook House, Amber Drive, Langley Mill, Nottingham, NG16 4BE Tel: (01773) 761999
Compfix Enterprises Ltd, 119 Manchester Road, Chorlton cum Hardy, Manchester, M21 9PG Tel: 0161-881 2395 Fax: 0161-881 2395 E-mail: sales@compfixpc.co.uk
CTM Communications Ltd, Unit 15, Lamplight Way, Swinton, Manchester, M27 8UJ Tel: (0870) 0271122 Fax: 0161-925 0478
Innovative Systems Incorporated Ltd, 14 Westminster Court, Hipley St, Woking, Surrey, GU22 9LG Tel: (01483) 730118 Fax: (01483) 730536 E-mail: sales@innovativesystems.net
Marathon Microfilming Ltd, St. Marys Place, Southampton, SO14 3HY Tel: (023) 8022 0481 Fax: (023) 8023 0452 E-mail: sales@marathonmicro.com
Software Futures Ltd, 2 Waterloo Way, Cheltenham Road, Bredon, Tewkesbury, Gloucestershire, GL20 7NA Tel: (01684) 772691 Fax: (01684) 772639 E-mail: information@softwarefutures.ltd.uk

COMPUTER CLEANING CONTRACTORS/PREVENTIVE MAINTENANCE SERVICES

Astrocare Ltd, Bolton Enterprise Centre, Washington Street, Bolton, BL3 5EY Tel: (01204) 370861 Fax: (01204) 548742 E-mail: astrocare@aol.com
▶ Clean Impact, 103 Junction Road, Burgess Hill, West Sussex, RH15 0JL Tel: (07811) 107268 E-mail: sales@cleanimpact.ws
▶ Cleaner Systems Ltd, 108 Preston Road, Birmingham, B26 1TQ Tel: (0800) 7561331 Fax: (0800) 7569821 E-mail: info@cleaner-systems.co.uk
Cleanscreen Computer Services, 6 Woodmere Avenue, Croydon, CR0 7PA Tel: (020) 8656 7114 Fax: (020) 8406 4931 E-mail: enquiries@cleanscreen.co.uk
Computaclean Computer Cleaning, 3 Church Road, Cam, Dursley, Gloucestershire, GL11 5PJ Tel: (01453) 544442 Fax: (01453) 544442
Deja Vu Computer Cleaners, 149 Bramley Close, London, E17 6EG Tel: (020) 8523 4661 Fax: (020) 8523 4661
Envirotec Support Services, Cornwall House, London Road, Purfleet, Essex, RM19 1PS Tel: (01708) 685230 Fax: (01708) 861862
Hy Tec East London, 303 Higham Hill Road, London, E17 5RG Tel: (020) 8925 0400 Fax: (020) 8925 0411 E-mail: sales@hy-tec.co.uk
Inverness Computer Centre, 21-23 Greig Street, Inverness, IV3 5PX Tel: (01463) 239999 Fax: (01463) 710003 E-mail: info@invcomps.co.uk
L C M I T Cleaning Specialists, Main Road, Boreham, Chelmsford, CM3 3AJ Tel: (01245) 450320 Fax: (01245) 462020
M A S S Computers Ltd, 53 Dereham Road, Norwich, NR2 4HZ Tel: (01603) 630768 Fax: (01603) 610657 E-mail: sales@masscomputers.co.uk
My Problems Solved, 39-43 Church Street, Cannock, Staffordshire, WS11 1DS Tel: (01543) 469499 Fax: (07000) 432985

▶ indicates data change since last edition

COMPUTER CLEANING CONTRACTORS/PREVENTIVE MAINTENANCE SERVICES – *continued*

S & M Computer Cleaning Services Ltd, Midland House, New Road, Halesowen, West Midlands, B63 3HY Tel: 0121-550 4008 Fax: 0121-550 5272 E-mail: sales@computercleaners.co.uk

▶ Square Mile Marine Co., 1 Willett Close, Orpington, Kent, BR5 1QH Tel: (01689) 890888 Fax: (01689) 891100 E-mail: sales@smm.co.com

Techclean Services, 102 Queslett Road East, Sutton Coldfield, West Midlands, B74 2EZ Tel: 0121-353 0074 Fax: 0121-693 0074 E-mail: birmingham@techclean.co.uk

COMPUTER CLEANING EQUIPMENT

S & M Computer Cleaning Services Ltd, Midland House, New Road, Halesowen, West Midlands, B63 3HY Tel: 0121-550 4008 Fax: 0121-550 5272 E-mail: sales@computercleaners.co.uk

S & M Computer Cleaning Services Ltd, Midland House, New Road, Halesowen, West Midlands, B63 3HY Tel: 0121-550 4008 Fax: 0121-550 5272 E-mail: sales@computercleaners.co.uk

COMPUTER CLEANING MATERIALS/KITS

CCS Media Holdings Ltd, Old Birdholme House, Derby Road, Chesterfield, Derbyshire, S40 2EX Tel: (01246) 200200 Fax: (01246) 207048 E-mail: enquiries@ccsmedia.com

Jack Dusty's Stores, 400 Sandwell Road, Kingswood, Bristol, BS15 1JJ Tel: 0117-949 6686 Fax: 0117-949 6495 E-mail: enquiries@jackdusty.co.uk

S & M Computer Cleaning Services Ltd, Midland House, New Road, Halesowen, West Midlands, B63 3HY Tel: 0121-550 4008 Fax: 0121-550 5272 E-mail: sales@computercleaners.co.uk

COMPUTER COMMUNICATIONS CONSULTANTS

Barron Mccann Ltd, Meteor Centre, Mansfield Road, Derby, DE21 4SY Tel: (01332) 866500 Fax: (01332) 866501

C N S, Earley, Reading, RG10 8NF Tel: 0118-940 1313 Fax: 0118-940 3754 E-mail: enquire@cnscommunications.co.uk

Cir-Comm Systems Ltd, Bailey Brook House, Amber Drive, Langley Mill, Nottingham, NG16 4BE Tel: (01773) 761999

Harold Cloutt Associates Ltd, PO Box 87, Battle, East Sussex, TN33 9XR Tel: (01424) 838829 Fax: (0870) 1365618 E-mail: cloutt.hr@bcs.org.uk

Commontime Ltd, 568 Burton Road, Derby, DE23 6DG Tel: (01332) 368500 Fax: (01332) 366880 E-mail: sales@commontime.com

Computer Project Services Ltd, 16 Bank Street, Lutterworth, Leicestershire, LE17 4AG Tel: (01455) 558231 Fax: (01455) 554299 E-mail: cv@cps-euro.com

Computer Support Services, 8 Baker Street, Rochester, Kent, ME1 3DW Tel: (01634) 407462 Fax: (01634) 409568 E-mail: tony@pobgee.demon.co.uk

Computeraid Ltd, The Innovation Centre Swansea University, Singleton Park, Swansea, SA2 8PP Tel: (01792) 610550 Fax: (01792) 610560 E-mail: computeraid@computeraidwales.com

Create Form International Ltd, Instone House, Instone Road, Dartford, DA1 2AG Tel: (01322) 279797 Fax: (01322) 279779 E-mail: info@createform.com

Data Crown Ltd, Bearnshaw Tower Farm, Carr Road, Todmorden, Lancashire, OL14 7ES Tel: (01706) 817885 Fax: (01706) 817165

Data Strategy Ltd, 44 Kingswood Road, London, SW19 3NE Tel: (020) 8296 0643 E-mail: info@datadtrategy.com

Dataplex Systems Ltd, Orbit House, Albert Street, Eccles, Manchester, M30 0BL Tel: 0161-707 3355 Fax: 0161-707 3344 E-mail: sales@dataplex-systems.com

Davmark Ltd, 63 Keats Way, West Drayton, Middlesex, UB7 9DU Tel: (07824) 638853 Fax: (01895) 905902 E-mail: david.slade@davmark.co.uk

Discspeed Computer Consultants, Farley Common, Westerham, Kent, TN16 1UB Tel: (01959) 562117

E2 Systems Ltd, Broadway House, 21 Broadway, Maidenhead, Berkshire, SL6 1NJ Tel: (01628) 418128 E-mail: e2web@e2systems.co.uk

Electronic Vision International Ltd, 39-43 Newarke Street, Leicester, LE1 5SP Tel: 0116-222 0919 Fax: 0116-222 1964

Eris Technical Support Ltd, 21 Helen Road, Hornchurch, Essex, RM11 2EW Tel: (01708) 453997 E-mail: makkywebb@ec2uz.com

▶ Holbeach Computing Solutions, 17 Spalding Road, Holbeach, Spalding, Lincolnshire, PE12 7HG Tel: (01406) 426342 E-mail: don.scott@holbeachcomputing.co.uk

I Soft P.L.C., Lomond Court, The Castle Business Park, Stirling, FK9 4TU Tel: (01786) 450532 Fax: (01786) 449504

Intec Telecom Systems plc, 2 Wells Court, Albert Drive, Woking, Surrey, GU21 5UB Tel: (01483) 745800 Fax: (01483) 745860 E-mail: sales@intec-telecom-systems.com

▶ InterSys Solutions Limited, 22 Pump Hill, loughton, Essex, IG10 1RU Tel: 07970 610002 E-mail: mg@intsl.com

Libiros Research Ltd, 2 Chestnut Road, Towcester, Northamptonshire, NN12 7TW Tel: (01908) 543090 E-mail: info@librios.com

Linear Software Ltd, 17 Pulborough Road, London, SW18 5UN Tel: (020) 8877 0159 Fax: (020) 8877 0552

The Logic Group Enterprises Ltd, Logic House, Waterfront Business Park, Fleet Road, Fleet, Hampshire, GU51 3SB Tel: (01252) 776755 Fax: (01252) 776738 E-mail: marketing@the-logic-group.com

Mac Computers & Communications Centre, 20 Western Av, London, W3 7TZ Tel: 020 87491438

Neil S Bapty, Bayview, Low Askomil, Campbeltown, Argyll, PA28 6EP Tel: (01586) 552467 E-mail: nsbapty@btinternet.com

Oxygen 8, 10 Mount Ephraim, Tunbridge Wells, Kent, TN4 8AS Tel: (01825) 762444 Fax: (01892) 527652 E-mail: info@oxygenonline.co.uk

Smart Computers Ltd, Enterprise Way, Cheltenham Trade Park, Cheltenham, Gloucestershire, GL51 8LZ Tel: (01242) 580654 Fax: (01242) 580652

Systems Communications & Networks (Scn) Ltd, High Trees, 15A Salisbury Road, Blandford Forum, Dorset, DT11 7HN Tel: (01258) 480121 Fax: (01258) 455366 E-mail: infa@scnltd.com

Zest Computing Ltd, Summerhayes House, Croxeaston, Newbury, Berkshire, RG20 9QF Tel: (01635) 250559 Fax: (01635) 255337 E-mail: richard.holt@zestcomputing.com

COMPUTER COMMUNICATIONS, NETWORK ADAPTERS, WIRELESS

▶ Chrisalis Ltd, 19 Mount House Close, Formby, Liverpool, L37 3LH Tel: (01704) 870942 E-mail: kellysearch@chrisalis-uk.com

▶ Cleartron Computers, 636 First Floor, Southchurch Road, Southend-on-Sea, SS1 2PT Tel: (01702) 602436 Fax: (01702) 602429 E-mail: sales@cleartron.co.uk

▶ Digit Computers, PO Box 47761, London, NW10 5UN Tel: (08700) 420490 Fax: (070) 92844761 E-mail: info@digitcomputers.co.uk

▶ Fwa Solutions, Springboard Innovation Centre, Llantarnam Park, Cwmbran, Gwent, NP44 3AW Tel: (01633) 488080 Fax: (01633) 647806 E-mail: sales@fwasolutions.com

▶ Internormen Technology, Unit G14, Westthorpe Fields Road, Killamarsh, Sheffield, S21 1TZ Tel: 0114-218 0614 Fax: 0114-218 0615 E-mail: northsales@reacttechnologies.com

▶ Khipu Networks Ltd, Infineon House, Minley Road, Fleet, Hampshire, GU51 2RD Tel: (01252) 773184 Fax: (01252) 629008 E-mail: sales@khipu-networks.com

▶ LinWin Computer Services, 123 Tradewinds, Wards Wharf Appproach, London, London, E16 2ER Tel: 079 71695701 Fax: 0870 7064637 E-mail: info@linwin.co.uk

▶ Premier Management, 18 Balmoral CR, Oswestry, Shropshire, SY11 2XG Tel: (01691) 653505 E-mail: carl.palmer@premierconsultancy.com

▶ Tecnia, 63 Cromwell Road, Norwich, NR7 8XJ Tel: (01603) 488434 Fax: (0870) 1211941 E-mail: info@TECNiA.co.uk

▶ theLogic Limited IT Services, 65 Sycamore Gardens, Kirkmuirhill, Lanark, ML11 9SX Tel: (0789) 1997294 E-mail: info@thelogic.co.uk

COMPUTER COMPONENTS, REFURBISHED

Astra Distribution Ltd, 29 Roseberry Crescent, Great Ayton, Middlesbrough, Cleveland, TS9 6EP Tel: (01642) 724367 E-mail: info@astradistribution.com

▶ Interlogistics Ltd, Waldeck House, Waldeck Road, Maidenhead, Berkshire, SL6 8BR Tel: (01628) 621300 Fax: (01628) 621309 E-mail: info@justsurplus.co.uk

▶ www.letsspendless.org, John Clarke Centre, Middlesbrough, Cleveland, TS6 6UZ Tel: (07739) 509097

COMPUTER COMPONENTS/ SPARE PARTS

2 U Computers, Stambourne Road, Hawkes Farm, Little Sampford, Saffron Walden, Essex, CB10 2QS Tel: (01799) 586300 Fax: (01799) 586210 E-mail: admin@2ucomputers.co.uk

Active Electronics Plc, Albion House, Gordon Road, High Wycombe, Buckinghamshire, HP13 6ET Tel: (01494) 441414 Fax: (01494) 524674 E-mail: pool@active-electronics.co.uk

Alcom Computing, 84 The Broadway, High Street, Chesham, Buckinghamshire, HP5 1EG Tel: (01494) 784784 Fax: (01494) 778424 E-mail: sales@alcomcomputing.com

Arrow International Technologies Ltd, Arrow House, 4 Malabar Fields, Daventry, Northamptonshire, NN11 4DP Tel: (01327) 301160 Fax: (01327) 301180 E-mail: arrowteks@aol.com

Ashlyn Computer Services, The Garth, Doddington Road, Stubton, Newark, Nottinghamshire, NG23 5BX Tel: (01636) 627900 Fax: (01636) 627909 E-mail: sales@ashlyn.co.uk

Ashtel Systems Ltd, Unit 12, Central Business Centre, Great Central Way, London, NW10 0UR Tel: (0870) 9221140 Fax: (0870) 9221141

Camlab Computer Systems, 27 Faringdon Road, Swindon, SN1 5AR Tel: (01793) 534917 Fax: (01793) 513120 E-mail: sales@camlab.net

Cannon Computers Ltd, 2 Kingsmead Road, London, SW2 3JB Tel: (020) 8671 4140 E-mail: leonard@cannon-computers.co.uk

Computec Computers, 67 Frog Lane, Wigan, Lancashire, WN6 7DU Tel: (01942) 493400 Fax: (01942) 736967

Computer Centre Direct, 56 Battersea Rise, London, SW11 1EJ Tel: (020) 7228 1888 Fax: (020) 7228 8881 E-mail: ccconnect@btconnect.com

Coniston Computers Ltd, Hylton Park, Wessington Way, Sunderland, SR5 3NR Tel: 0191-516 0088 Fax: 0191-516 0476

Cybernaut Solutions, 30 Little Newport St, Walsall, WS1 1SA Tel: 01922 645554

D M C Products, P O Box 22, Derby, DE1 9ZU Tel: (01332) 205822 Fax: (01332) 205822 E-mail: info@dmc-systems.com

Davel Technology, Woodlands, Branksome Avenue, Wickford, Essex, SS12 0JD Tel: (01268) 763336 Fax: (01268) 763305 E-mail: davtech@onetel.com

Delphic Computer Services Ltd, White House, Preston Wynne, Hereford, HR1 3PB Tel: (01432) 820220 Fax: (01432) 820456 E-mail: sdent@delphic.uk.com

Digital Systems, Solutions House Derby Road, Sandiacre, Nottingham, NG10 5HU Tel: 0115-849 9984 Fax: 0115-849 9993

Dins Technologies Ltd, 45 Commerce Street, Glasgow, G5 8AD Tel: 0141-420 3735 Fax: 0141-429 1914

E C I Europe Ltd, The Coach House, 52a Priory Street, Colchester, CO1 2QB Tel: (01206) 864600

Europa Computers Ltd, 11-13 Edward Street, Salford, M7 1SN Tel: 0161-279 0000 Fax: 0161-832 9104 E-mail: sales@europacomputers.com

Fuselodge Ltd, 267 Acton Lane, Chiswick, London, W4 5DG Tel: (020) 8994 6275 Fax: (020) 8994 6275 E-mail: fuse.lodge@virgin.net

Hardware Associates Ltd, Colhook Indust Park, Petworth, West Sussex, GU28 9NB Tel: (01428) 707900 Fax: (01428) 707866 E-mail: sales@hardwarespairs.com

IntTechCo, 88 Maplewell Road, Woodhouse Eaves, Loughborough, Leicestershire, LE12 8RA Tel: (01509) 891172

Kew Computers, 78 Woolmer Way, Bordon, Hampshire, GU35 9QF Tel: (01420) 479666 Fax: (01420) 488348 E-mail: info@kewcomputers.com

Micro Direct Ltd, 275a Upper Brook Street, Manchester, M13 0HR Tel: 0161-248 4949 Fax: (0870) 4444432 E-mail: sales@microdirect.co.uk

Middlestown PCS Ltd, 52 High Street, Horbury, Wakefield, West Yorkshire, WF4 5LE Tel: (01924) 260615 Fax: (01924) 270245 E-mail: info@middlestownpcs.co.uk

Mighty Micro, 268 Wilmslow Road, Manchester, M14 6JR Tel: 0161-224 8117 Fax: 0161-257 2803 E-mail: info@mighty-micro.co.uk

Net Comp Ltd, 21 Shaftesbury Street South, Derby, DE23 8YH Tel: (01332) 290509 Fax: (01332) 384873 E-mail: sales@netcomp.ltd.uk

Paperchain Technology Ltd, Unit 9 Sandwell Business & Tec, Oldbury, W. Midlands, B68 8NA Tel: 0121-552 1144 Fax: 0121 552 1144

PC Planet, 4 Gateford Road, Worksop, Nottinghamshire, S80 1EB Tel: (01909) 470044 Fax: (0870) 7052609

Priceless Computing, 45 Commerce Street, Glasgow, G5 8AD Tel: 0141-420 3735 Fax: 0141-429 1914 E-mail: sales@pless.co.uk

Quadnet Ltd, Power House Cromwell Industrial Estate, Staffa Road, London, E10 7QZ Tel: (020) 8988 7710 Fax: (020) 8988 7719 E-mail: enquiries@quadnet.co.uk

Scan Computers International Ltd, 27-28 Enterprise Park, Horwich, Bolton, BL6 6PE Tel: (01204) 474747 Fax: (01204) 474748 E-mail: sales@scan.co.uk

Selkom Ltd, Unit D1 Riverside Industrial Estate, Bridge Road, Littlehampton, West Sussex, BN17 5DF Tel: (01903) 723645 Fax: (01903) 721362 E-mail: tonyselkom@aol.com

Spire Technology Ltd, 5 Black Moor Road, Verwood, Dorset, BH31 6AX Tel: (01202) 821300 Fax: (01202) 813966 E-mail: pcsales@spire.co.uk

Tekno Computer Systems Ltd, 41 Bartlett Street, Caerphilly, Mid Glamorgan, CF83 1JS Tel: (029) 2088 5421 Fax: (029) 2088 5235 E-mail: info@tekno.co.uk

Time Global Ltd, 21 Cornwall Rd, St. Albans, Herts, AL1 1SQ Tel: (01727) 847454 Fax: (01727) 847453 E-mail: sales@timeglobal.co.uk

Utopia Computers Ltd, 29-31 High Glencairn Street, Kilmarnock, Ayrshire, KA1 4AE Tel: (01563) 574280 Fax: (01563) 574280 E-mail: sales@utopiacomputers.co.uk

COMPUTER COMPONENTS/ SPARE PARTS IMPORT/EXPORT MERCHANTS OR AGENTS

▶ Goldstock Epos Systems, Unit 13, Rea Industrial Estate, Inkerman Street, Birmingham, B7 4SH Tel: 0121-359 0191 Fax: 0121-359 5387

COMPUTER COMPONENTS/ SPARE PARTS, USED

Ashlyn Computer Services, The Garth, Doddington Road, Stubton, Newark, Nottinghamshire, NG23 5BX Tel: (01636) 627900 Fax: (01636) 627909 E-mail: sales@ashlyn.co.uk

Computer Junk Shop, 10 Waterloo Road, Widnes, Cheshire, WA8 0PY Tel: 0151-420 6671 Fax: 0151-420 6671 E-mail: info@computer-junkshop.co.uk

Delphic Computer Services Ltd, White House, Preston Wynne, Hereford, HR1 3PB Tel: (01432) 820220 Fax: (01432) 820456 E-mail: sdent@delphic.uk.com

IT Disposal, 1 Brook Farm, Stapleford Road, Stapleford Abbotts, Romford, RM4 1EJ Tel: (0845) 6445303 Fax: (01708) 688019 E-mail: info@itdisposal.co.uk

New World Tech, 1776 Coventry Rd, Yardley, Birmingham, B26 1PB Tel: 0121-743 4570 Fax: 0121 7422171

Nexpress Ltd, Unit 16, Gelders Hall Road, Shepshed, Loughborough, Leicestershire, LE12 9NH Tel: (01509) 501100 Fax: (01509) 601186 E-mail: sales@nexpress.co.uk

COMPUTER CONFIGURATION MANAGEMENT (CM) CONSULTANCY

▶ Hot Tool, 7 The Frenches, Redhill, RH1 2HF Tel: (01737) 778589 Fax: (01737) 778549 E-mail: martin@hottool.co.uk

P C Supplies, 119 Cavendish Street, Barrow-in-Furness, Cumbria, LA14 1DJ Tel: (01229) 833595 Fax: (01229) 877677 E-mail: sales@pcsuppliesuk.co.uk

COMPUTER CONNECTORS

D L S Services, Unit 2 Union Park Industrial Estate, Triumph Way, Kempston, Bedford, MK42 7QB Tel: (01234) 840104 E-mail: dls@kbnet.co.uk

G T K (U K) Ltd, Unit 1 Maxdata Centre, Downmill Road, Bracknell, Berkshire, RG12 1QS Tel: (01344) 304123 Fax: (01344) 301414 E-mail: sales@gtk.co.uk

Interconnect Products Ltd, Marlborough Road, Wootton Bassett, Swindon, SN4 7SA Tel: (01793) 849811 Fax: (01793) 849809 E-mail: sales@interconnect.demon.co.uk

Swale Components Ltd, Unit 88 John Wilson Business Park, Chestfield, Whitstable, Kent, CT5 3QT Tel: (01227) 771100 Fax: (01227) 771117 E-mail: sales@swalecomponents.com

Wadsworth Electronics Ltd, Central Avenue, West Molesey, Surrey, KT8 2QB Tel: (020) 8268 7000 Fax: (020) 8268 6565 E-mail: info@wadsworth.co.uk

COMPUTER CONSULTANCY

A T E Technology Ltd, ATE House, 48 Green Meadows, Westhoughton, Bolton, BL5 2BN Tel: (01942) 815603 Fax: (01942) 815321 E-mail: info@ate-technology.com

▶ Columbia Precision Ltd, 125 Cheston Road, Birmingham, B7 5EA Tel: 0121-327 1500 Fax: 0121-327 1511 E-mail: enquires@columbia.uk.com

Ecoro Ltd, 3 Rowanside Close, Headley Down, Bordon, Hampshire, GU35 8HH Tel: (01428) 717070 E-mail: info@ecoro.co.uk

KTSX, 2 Eastgate, Llanboidy, Whitland, Carmarthenshire, SA34 0EJ Tel: (01994) 448771 Fax: (01994) 448771 E-mail: info@ktsx.co.uk

▶ R. Latham Computer Consultants, 2 Albion Road, Chesterfield, Derbyshire, S40 1NB Tel: (07904) 120638 E-mail: richardlatham@ntlworld.com

Sirius Corporation, Rivermead House, Hamm Moor Lane, Addlestone, Surrey, KT15 2SF Tel: (01932) 820467 E-mail: mail@siriusit.co.uk

▶ indicates data change since last edition

COMPUTER CONSULTANCY, SECURITY ASSESSMENT

Ecoro Ltd, 3 Rowanside Close, Headley Down, Bordon, Hampshire, GU35 8HH Tel: (01428) 717070 E-mail: info@ecoro.co.uk

COMPUTER CONTROLLED PRODUCTION CONTROL SYSTEMS

Advantec Systems Ltd, 39 Westfield Close, Dorridge, Solihull, West Midlands, B93 8DY Tel: (01564) 739134
Ceres System Ltd, Unit 15 The Old Malthouse, Springfield Road, Grantham, Lincolnshire, NG31 7BG Tel: (01476) 563188 E-mail: sales@vertexplus.co.uk
Industrial Electronics Consultants, 855 Holderness Road, Hull, HU8 9BA Tel: (01482) 374437 Fax: (01482) 796853 E-mail: ray@rayeldred.carouy.co.uk
Kalms Associates, 17 Lyon Road, London, SW19 2RL Tel: (020) 8286 6066 Fax: (020) 8547 7668 E-mail: sales@kalms-associates.com
Pentland Systems, 8 Alderstone Business Park, Macmillan Road, Livingston, West Lothian, EH54 7DF Tel: (01506) 464666 Fax: (01506) 463030 E-mail: sales@pentlandsys.com
Trio Motion Technology Ltd, Shannon Way, Tewkesbury, Gloucestershire, GL20 8ND Tel: (01684) 292333 Fax: (01684) 297929 E-mail: sales@triomotion.com

COMPUTER CONTROLLED TEST EQUIPMENT

Peak Production Equipment Ltd, Peak House, Works Road, Letchworth Garden City, Hertfordshire, SG6 1GB Tel: (01462) 475605 Fax: (01462) 480294 E-mail: sales@thepeakgroup.com
Special Purpose Equipment Ltd, 3 Loaland Business Centre, Maritime Close, Medway City Estate, Rochester, Kent, ME2 4AZ Tel: (01634) 295396 Fax: (01634) 718879 E-mail: johnlambell@special-purpose-equipment.co.uk

COMPUTER CONTROLLED TYPESETTING SERVICES

Robin Clay Ltd, 31 St. Leonards Road, Bexhill-on-Sea, East Sussex, TN40 1HP Tel: (01424) 730302 Fax: (01424) 730291 E-mail: sarah@ashbuscent.co.uk
Dalton Printers, Dalton House, Thesiger Street, Cardiff, CF24 4BN Tel: (029) 2023 6832 Fax: (029) 2066 6516 E-mail: daltonprinters@dial.pipex.com
Dolphin Design, 17 Invincible Road, Farnborough, Hampshire, GU14 7QU Tel: (01252) 518028 Fax: (01252) 518351 E-mail: thomas-frear@btconnect.com
Express Typesetters Ltd, 11 Riverside Park, Dogflud Way, Farnham, Surrey, GU9 7UG Tel: (01252) 724112 Fax: (01252) 721874 E-mail: sales@arrowpress.co.uk
Santype International Ltd, Harnham Trading Estate, Netherhampton Road, Salisbury, SP2 8PS Tel: (01722) 334261 Fax: (01722) 333171 E-mail: post@santype.com

COMPUTER COVER, *See Acoustic Covers/Hoods*

COMPUTER DATA AND MEDIA STORAGE EQUIPMENT

Acardia, Venture House 2 Arlington Square, Downshire Way, Bracknell, Berkshire, RG12 1WA Tel: (0845) 2301055 Fax: (01344) 868333 E-mail: admin@acardia.co.uk
Acco UK Ltd, Gatehouse Road, Aylesbury, Buckinghamshire, HP19 8DT Tel: (01296) 397444 Fax: (01296) 311000 E-mail: info@acco-uk.co.uk
Animal Systems, Threshing House, Berwick St. Leonard, Salisbury, SP3 5SN Tel: (01747) 827000 Fax: (01747) 820127 E-mail: sales@animalsystems.co.uk
Dot Hill Systems Europe Ltd, Network House, Basing View, Basingstoke, Hampshire, RG21 4HG Tel: (01256) 840600 Fax: (01256) 814462 E-mail: uk@dothill.com
Fellowes Ltd, Yorkshire Way, Armthorpe, Doncaster, South Yorkshire, DN3 3FB Tel: (01302) 836800 Fax: (01302) 836899 E-mail: sales@fellowes.com
H W Dansies, 409 Chatsworth Road, Chesterfield, Derbyshire, S40 2DH Tel: (01246) 235455 Fax: (01246) 220862 E-mail: sales@dansies.co.uk
K Russell, Brackenwood, Collinswood Road, Farnham Common, Slough, SL2 3LH Tel: (01753) 645569 Fax: (01753) 645230 E-mail: kr@keithrussell.com
Msa Focus International Ltd, Ground Floor Suite, St Hilary Court Copthorne Way, Cardiff, CF5 6ES Tel: (029) 2067 1760 Fax: (029) 2059 9733 E-mail: marketing@msafocus.com
P M D Magnetics, Avenue Farm Industrial Estate, Birmingham Road, Stratford-upon-Avon, Warwickshire, CV37 0HR Tel: (01789) 268579 Fax: (01789) 414450 E-mail: sales@pmdmagnetics.co.uk
PCS, Wakefield Road, Ossett, West Yorkshire, WF5 9AJ Tel: (01924) 281777 Fax: (01924) 266920
Redstor Ltd, 1 London Road, Reading, RG1 5BJ Tel: 0118 9011969 Fax: 0118-377 6501 E-mail: sales@redstor.com
Storagetek Ltd, 36 South Gyle Crescent, Edinburgh, EH12 9EB Tel: 0131-338 6515 Fax: 0131-339 3900
Transam Microsystems Ltd, 2 Bakers Yard, Bakers Row, London, EC1R 3HT Tel: (020) 7837 4050 Fax: (020) 7837 3804 E-mail: transam@transam.co.uk
Ultima Business Systems Ltd, 448 Basingstoke Road, Reading, RG2 0LP Tel: 0118-902 7500 Fax: 0118-902 7400 E-mail: sales@ultimabusiness.com

COMPUTER DATA PROCESSING, *See Data Processing etc*

COMPUTER DATA PROTECTION DEVICES

R S A Security Inc, R S A House, Western Road, Bracknell, Berkshire, RG12 1RT Tel: (01344) 781000 Fax: (01344) 781010

COMPUTER DATA SECURITY CONSULTANCY

▶ Computer Security Co., 79 London Road, Whitchurch, Hampshire, RG28 7LX Tel: (01256) 893662 E-mail: info@computersecuritycompany.co.uk
▶ Red Kestrel Consulting, 17 Constance Avenue, Trentham, Stoke-on-Trent, ST4 8TE Tel: (01782) 643438 E-mail: info@redkestrel.co.uk

COMPUTER DATA/MEDIA STORAGE CONSUMABLES

K Russell, Brackenwood, Collinswood Road, Farnham Common, Slough, SL2 3LH Tel: (01753) 645569 Fax: (01753) 645230 E-mail: kr@keithrussell.com

COMPUTER DATA/MEDIA STORAGE CONTRACTORS

Redstor Ltd, 1 London Road, Reading, RG1 5BJ Tel: 0118 9011969 Fax: 0118-377 6501 E-mail: sales@redstor.com

COMPUTER DEALERS/ BROKERS/DISTRIBUTORS/ AGENTS, COMPUTER HARDWARE

24Store Ltd, Siberia House, Church Street, Basingstoke, Hampshire, RG21 7QN Tel: (01256) 867700 Fax: (01256) 867701 E-mail: sales@24store.com
321 Systems Ltd, 6 Maryon Mews, London, NW3 2PU Tel: (020) 7794 3236 Fax: (020) 7431 3213 E-mail: info@321systems.com
4 Mat Systems Ltd, 69 High Street, Swadlincote, Derbyshire, DE11 8JA Tel: (01283) 512333 Fax: (01283) 229905
5 Fifteen Ltd, 180 Bedford Avenue, Slough, SL1 4RA Tel: (01753) 440515 Fax: (01753) 440567 E-mail: info@5fifteen.com
A B K Group Finance Ltd, Lower Meadow Road Brooke Park, Steadings House, Handforth, Wilmslow, Cheshire, SK9 3LP Tel: 0161-486 6721 Fax: 0161-482 6301 E-mail: sales@abkplc.com
A D C Technology Ltd, A D C Ho, Broomfield Place, Coventry, CV5 6GY Tel: (024) 7671 5858 Fax: (024) 7671 4462
A K-IT Solutions (UK) Ltd, 205-207 City Road, London, EC1V 1JN Tel: (020) 7684 6543 Fax: (020) 7684 8807
A & T Computer Rentals Ltd, Robert Cort Industrial Estate, Britten Road, Reading, RG2 0AU Tel: 0118-986 4666 Fax: 0118-986 4777 E-mail: admin@aandt.co.uk
A T Computers (Applemac), Unit E2 Green La Business Park, Green Lane, Tewkesbury, Gloucestershire, GL20 8SJ Tel: (01684) 291112 Fax: (01684) 274829
A T M Ltd, Knaves Beech Industrial Estate, Knaves Beech Way, Loudwater, High Wycombe, Buckinghamshire, HP10 9QY Tel: (01628) 642200 Fax: (01628) 642226
A U Computers, 20 Glebe Road, Bedlington, Northumberland, NE22 6JT Tel: (01670) 829763 Fax: (01670) 823454 E-mail: joe@aucomputers.com
A W C, 97 Commercial Road, Bournemouth, BH2 5RT Tel: (01202) 789269 Fax: (01202) 789277 E-mail: sales@awc.co.uk
Abs Technology plc, Technology House, Church Road, Shottermill, Haslemere, Surrey, GU27 1NU Tel: (01428) 664900 Fax: (01428) 664901
Acardia, Venture House 2 Arlington Square, Downshire Way, Bracknell, Berkshire, RG12 1WA Tel: (0845) 2301055 Fax: (01344) 868333 E-mail: admin@acardia.co.uk
Access Unlimited, 20 George Street, Alderley Edge, Cheshire, SK9 7EJ Tel: (01625) 584130 Fax: (01625) 584623 E-mail: info@accessunlimited.co.uk
Actual Reality, Stainton Moor View, Matlock, Derbyshire, DE4 3NE Tel: (01629) 760801 Fax: (08702) 201805 E-mail: admin@ar-computers.co.uk
Ada Computer Systems Ltd, Network House House, Albert Drive, Burgess Hill, West Sussex, RH15 9TN Tel: (01444) 232000 Fax: (01444) 247754E-mail: sales@ada.co.uk
Adris Ltd, Riverside House Brunel Road, Totton, Southampton, SO40 3WX Tel: (023) 8086 8947 Fax: (023) 8086 1618 E-mail: sales@adris.co.uk
Advanced Digital Technology UK Ltd, Unit 10 Lord Wilmot House, Bristol Road, Bumpers Farm, Chippenham, Wiltshire, SN14 6LH Tel: (01249) 653654 Fax: (01249) 659258
Advanced Modular Computers Ltd, Union House Deseronto Estate, St. Marys Road, Slough, SL3 7EW Tel: (01753) 580660 Fax: (01753) 580653 E-mail: moreinfo@amcuk.com
Albion Computers P.L.C., 112 Strand, London, WC2R 0AG Tel: (020) 7212 9090 Fax: (020) 7212 9091 E-mail: sales@albion.co.uk
Alpha Business Computers Ltd, Bentley House Newby Road Industrial Estate, Newby Road, Hazel Grove, Stockport, Cheshire, SK7 5DA Tel: 0161-483 5650 Fax: 0161-483 5576 E-mail: info@alphacom.co.uk
Alpha Telecommunications Ltd, 359a Hagley Rd, Edgbaston, Birmingham, B17 8DL Tel: 0121-434 4003 Fax: 0121-434 4043
Altus Adtek, Unit E The Coppetts Centre, Coneyhatch Lane, London, N12 0AJ Tel: (020) 8920 4800 Fax: (020) 8920 4827 E-mail: info@adtek.co.uk
Ama Business Systems Ltd, The Old Tabernacle, Palmyra Road, Bristol, BS3 3JQ Tel: 0117-923 1133 Fax: 0117-923 1144 E-mail: sales@ama-it.com
Angoss Software Ltd, Unit 23 Surrey Technology Centre, Occam Road, Surrey Research Park, Guildford, Surrey, GU2 7YG Tel: (01483) 452303 Fax: (01483) 453303 E-mail: ncb@angoss.com
Apex Computer International Ltd, Apex House, The Mallards, South Cerney, Cirencester, Gloucestershire, GL7 5TQ Tel: (01285) 862100 Fax: (01285) 862111
Applications Unlimited, 20 Glebe Road, Bedlington, Northumberland, NE22 6JT Tel: (01670) 824679 Fax: (01670) 823454 E-mail: sales@aucomputers.com
Applied Data Technologies, 92 Bedminster Parade, Bedminster, Bristol, BS3 4HL Tel: 0117-987 2170 Fax: 0117-941 0935 E-mail: sales@adtsystems.co.uk
Armagh Computer World, 43 Scotch Street, Armagh, BT61 7DF Tel: (028) 3751 0002 Fax: (028) 3751 0009 E-mail: sales@computerworlds.co.uk
Arun Computer Equipment Ltd, 72-74 Clifton Road, Worthing, West Sussex, BN11 4DP Tel: (01903) 529077 Fax: (01903) 529088 E-mail: sales@aruncomputers.co.uk
Ashtel Systems Ltd, Unit 12, Central Business Centre, Great Central Way, London, NW10 0UR Tel: (0870) 9221140 Fax: (0870) 9221141
Automaster UK Ltd, Centaur House, Ancells Road, Fleet, Hampshire, GU51 2UJ Tel: (0845) 4666070 Fax: (0845) 4666080 E-mail: info@automaster.ltd.uk
Avatea Ltd, Bulldog House, 267-269 Reading Road, Winnersh, Wokingham, Berkshire, RG41 5AB Tel: 0118-977 0270 Fax: 0118-977 0278 E-mail: peter@avatea.co.uk
Banbury Computers, 55 Middleton Road, Banbury, Oxon, OX16 3QR Tel: (01295) 272627E-mail: sales@banburycomputers.com
Belmonte Business Equipment Ltd, Carlton House, 230 Manchester Road, Stockport, Cheshire, SK4 1NN Tel: 0161-480 5556 Fax: 0161-480 6546 E-mail: sales@belmonte.co.uk
▶ Bioteknik Ltd, Unit 1, City Business Park Marshwood Close, Canterbury, Kent, CT1 1DX Tel: (01227) 470007 Fax: (01227) 470070 E-mail: enquiries@bioteknik.net
Bom Group Ltd, Clue House, Petherton Road, Bristol, BS14 9BZ Tel: (01275) 890100 Fax: (01275) 890111 E-mail: info@bom.co.uk
Box42 Ltd, PO Box 42, Prescot, Merseyside, L35 4PH Tel: 0151-426 9988 Fax: 0151-426 994 E-mail: jeffhughes@box42.com
Boxclever, The Mount, Selby Road, Garforth, Leeds, LS25 2AQ Tel: 0113-286 0795 Fax: 0113-286 4525 E-mail: sales@boxcleverbrokers.com
Brother (U K) Ltd, Shepley St, Guide Bridge, Manchester, M34 5JD Tel: 0161-330 6531 Fax: 0161-308 3281 E-mail: sales@brother-uk.com
Business Management Promotions Ltd, Lower Weaven, Little Dewchurch, Hereford, HR2 6QB Tel: (01432) 840456 Fax: (01432) 840450 E-mail: bmpltd@ticali.co.uk
C A Design Services Ltd, The Design Centre, Hewett Road, Gapton Hall, Great Yarmouth, Norfolk, NR31 0NN Tel: (01493) 440444 Fax: (01493) 442480 E-mail: sales@cadesignservices.co.uk
C C C & School Care Ltd, Unit 1, Armtech Row, Yeovil, Somerset, BA22 8RT Tel: (01935) 470300 Fax: (01935) 470302 E-mail: all@schoolcare.co.uk
C C M Flintex Ltd, Linden Lea House, High Pitfold, Hindhead, Surrey, GU26 6BN Tel: (01483) 426980 Fax: (01428) 608608 E-mail: tony@flintex.freeserve.co.uk
C C S Division Of Consumerdata Ltd, Meridian House, Artist St, Armley, Leeds, LS12 2EW Tel: 0113-242 0520 Fax: 0113-242 0050 E-mail: info@consumerdata.com
C K S Entertainment Systems, Logistics Centre, Willoughby Road, Bracknell, Berkshire, RG12 8FD Tel: (01344) 307788 Fax: (01344) 456710 E-mail: sales@cksgroup.co.uk
C P L, Anglo House, Worcester Road, Stourport-On-Severn, Worcestershire, DY13 9AW Tel: (01299) 877004 Fax: (01299) 877226 E-mail: enquiries@computerproof.co.uk
C S F Solutions Ltd, 920 Birchwood Boulevard, Birchwood, Warrington, WA3 7QS Tel: (01925) 852020 Fax: (01925) 811522
Cameo Computer Services Ltd, Unit 6, Maizefield, Hinckley, Leicestershire, LE10 1YF Tel: (01455) 618893 Fax: (01455) 254878 E-mail: info@cameouk.com
Cascade Water Gardens, Bury Road, Radcliffe, Manchester, M26 2WW Tel: 0161-725 8142 Fax: 0161-723 0004 E-mail: info@cascadekoi.com
Cconline Computer Systems, 33 Main Street, Turriff, Aberdeenshire, AB53 4AB Tel: (01888) 562180 E-mail: sales@cconlineuk.com
Centresoft Ltd, 6 Pavilion Drive, Holford, Birmingham, B6 7BB Tel: 0121-625 3399 Fax: 0121-625 3236 E-mail: sales@centresoft.co.uk
Century Business Systems, 19-21 Mid Stocket Road, Aberdeen, AB15 5JL Tel: (01224) 644064 Fax: (01224) 643407 E-mail: info@century.uk.net
Chaplin Computer Consultants, 331 Walsall Road, Great Wyrley, Walsall, WS6 6DR Tel: (01922) 411117 Fax: (01922) 411001 E-mail: chris@ccc1.demon.co.uk
Chevin Computer Systems Ltd, East Mill, Bridge Foot, Belper, Derbyshire, DE56 2UA Tel: (01773) 821992 Fax: (01773) 829910 E-mail: sales@chevincomputers.com
Chimera C M T Ltd, 9 Blenheim Court, Lustleigh Close, Marsh Barton Industrial Estate, Exeter, EX2 8PW Tel: (01392) 667444 Fax: (01392) 667440
Church Micros, Causeway Side, 1 High Street, Haslemere, Surrey, GU27 2JZ Tel: (01428) 644122 Fax: (01428) 656300 E-mail: churchmicros@haslemere.com
Cifer Data Systems Ltd, 1 Main Street, West Wilts Trading Estate, Westbury, Wiltshire, BA13 4JU Tel: (01373) 824129 Fax: (01373) 824127 E-mail: sales@cifer.co.uk
Civica UK Ltd, Castlegate House, Castlegate Drive, Dudley, West Midlands, DY1 4TD Tel: (01384) 453400 Fax: (01384) 453600
Clyde Computers Southern Ltd, Lovelace Works, High Street, Ripley, Woking, Surrey, GU23 6AF Tel: (01483) 225930 Fax: (01483) 225931 E-mail: sales@clydecomputers.co.uk
Compatibility Ltd, Park Road, Crowborough, East Sussex, TN6 2QX Tel: (01892) 665326 Fax: (01892) 665607 E-mail: info@compatibility.co.uk
Computaform, 4 Merivale Road, Harrow, Middlesex, HA1 4BH Tel: (020) 8423 5005 Fax: (020) 8422 7216 E-mail: mail@computaform.com
Computer Aided Business Systems Ltd, 8 Forum Place, Fiddlebridge Lane, Hatfield, Hertfordshire, AL10 0RN Tel: (01707) 258338 Fax: (01707) 258339 E-mail: sales@cabs-cad.com
Computer Doctor Services Ltd, 20a Portland Road, Kilmarnock, Ayrshire, KA1 2BS Tel: (01563) 537733 Fax: (01563) 537733 E-mail: kellyenquiry@computerdoctorservice.co.uk
Computer Precision Ltd, 185 Upper Street, London, N1 1RQ Tel: (020) 7359 9797 Fax: (020) 7359 9507 E-mail: 185@cipi.co.uk
Computer Repair Centre, 32 The Avenue, St. Pauls Cray, Orpington, Kent, BR5 3DJ Tel: (020) 8556 5331 Fax: (020) 8556 8890
Computer Resourcing, 1 Woodlea Grove, Northwood, Middlesex, HA6 2DW Tel: (01923) 828848
The Computer Shop, 2 New Rents, Ashford, Kent, TN23 1JH Tel: (01233) 613113
Computer Solutions, 83 Station Road, West Wickham, Kent, BR4 0PX Tel: (020) 8777 2228 Fax: (020) 8777 2276 E-mail: sales@thecomputersolution.co.uk
Computer Store, 16 Priory Street, Carmarthen, Dyfed, SA31 1NA Tel: (01267) 221661 Fax: (01267) 222214 E-mail: sales@perfectcomputers.com
Computer Systems Ltd, 33 Malmesbury Close, Pinner, Middlesex, HA5 2NG Tel: (01895) 623555 Fax: (01895) 631541 E-mail: enquiries@computer.dircon.co.uk
Computer Warehouse, 61 Low Street, Keighley, West Yorkshire, BD21 3QP Tel: (01535) 691157 Fax: (01535) 691157 E-mail: sales@computer-warehouse.net

▶ indicates data change since last edition

COMPUTER DEALERS/BROKERS/ DISTRIBUTORS/AGENTS, COMPUTER HARDWARE – *continued*

Connect Computers, 6 Durlston Parade, Durlston Drive, Bognor Regis, West Sussex, PO22 9DJ Tel: (01243) 830300 Fax: (01243) 830298 E-mail: trade@computers.uk.com
Continental Ltd, Unit C2 Herrick Way, Staverton Technology Park, Staverton, Cheltenham, Gloucestershire, GL51 6TQ Tel: (01452) 855222 Fax: (01452) 856794 E-mail: sales@continental.co.uk
Contrac Computer Supplies North East, Pinetree Centre, Durham Road, Birtley, Chester le Street, County Durham, DH3 2TD Tel: 0191-492 2999 Fax: 0191-492 3011 E-mail: enquiries@contrac.co.uk
Crayfield Computer Consultants, 64 Cuckfield Road, Hurstpierpoint, Hassocks, West Sussex, BN6 9SB Tel: (01273) 834999 Fax: (01273) 835550 E-mail: systems@crayfield.net
Crusader Ltd, Oxford House, Easthorpe Street, Ruddington, Nottingham, NG11 6LA Tel: 0115-940 5550 Fax: 0115-940 6660 E-mail: sales@crusaderltd.com
▶ Curve It Ltd, Riverside Place, Bridgewater Road, Leeds, LS9 0RQ Tel: 0113-248 8080 Fax: 0113-249 4006
Cynetix Group Ltd, Unit C1, Aven Industrial Park, Tickhill Road, Maltby, Rotherham, South Yorkshire, S66 7QR Tel: (01709) 819922 Fax: (01709) 798804 E-mail: sales@cynetix.co.uk
D & P Data Systems Ltd, 15 Carnarvon Street, Manchester, M3 1HJ Tel: 0161-832 6969 Fax: 0161-832 6970 E-mail: sales@dpdata.co.uk
Danter Automatics, 11a Copse Cross Street, Ross-on-Wye, Herefordshire, HR9 5PD Tel: (01989) 563604 Fax: (01989) 563604
Data Set Ready, 25 Leygreen Close, Luton, LU2 0SQ Tel: (01582) 618080 Fax: (01582) 618081E-mail: datatasteready@ntlworld.co.uk
▶ Datadesk Computer Services Ltd, 21 Anniesdale Avenue, Stepps, Glasgow, G33 6DW Tel: 0141-779 9162 Fax: 0141-779 9083 E-mail: info@datadesk.it
▶ Datamate Computers, 37 Darkes Lane, Potters Bar, Hertfordshire, EN6 1BJ Tel: (01707) 664499 Fax: (01707) 649964
Datapact Ltd, 188 St. John Street, London, EC1V 4JY Tel: (020) 7336 7511 E-mail: sales@datapact.co.uk
Delta Business Equipment, Unit G3 Meadow Mill, Water Street, Stockport, Cheshire, SK1 2BY Tel: 0161-480 1222 Fax: 0161-480 0022 E-mail: sales@deltaoffice.co.uk
Demand It, Units 19-21, Deacon Way, Tilehurst, Reading, RG30 6QG Tel: 0118-945 8600 Fax: 0118-945 3737 E-mail: sales@demand-it.co.uk
Deverill plc, Itec House, 34-40 West Street, Poole, Dorset, BH15 1LA Tel: (01202) 785000 Fax: (01202) 785001 E-mail: marketing@deverill.co.uk
Devon Computers Ltd, 39 Totnes Road, Paignton, Devon, TQ4 5LA Tel: (01803) 526303 Fax: (01803) 663289
Diamond Point International, Unit 9 North Point Business Estate, Enterprise Close, Medway City Estate, Rochester, Kent, ME2 4LX Tel: (01634) 722390 Fax: (01634) 722398 E-mail: sales@dpie.com
Digi International Ltd, Ashwood House, Almondsbury Business Park, Bradley Stoke, Bristol, BS32 4QH Tel: (01454) 643444 Fax: (01454) 619048
Direct It Distribution Ltd, 12 The Markham Centre, Station Road, Theale, Reading, RG7 4PE Tel: 0118-912 6400 Fax: 0118-912 6444 E-mail: sales@direct-it.co.uk
Diskel Ltd, 212-214 Farnham Road, Slough, SL1 4XE Tel: (01753) 821091 Fax: (01753) 512438 E-mail: sales@diskel.co.uk
Diskovery Systems, 123 Bournemouth Road, Poole, Dorset, BH14 9HR Tel: (01202) 746353 Fax: (01202) 737184 E-mail: sales@diskovery.co.uk
Dragon Systems, Gyllellog, Pennal, Machynlleth, Powys, SY20 9DU Tel: (01654) 791642 Fax: (01654) 791277 E-mail: dragoncom@aol.com
E Play Ltd, 62 The Elmsleigh Centre, Staines, Middlesex, TW18 4QF Tel: (01784) 451222 Fax: (01784) 451444
Eastar-solutions Ltd, 123 Bath Row, Birmingham, B15 1LS Tel: 0121-643 5500 Fax: 0121 6337537
▶ The Easy P C Store, 114 Moorfield Road, Widnes, Cheshire, WA8 3HX Tel: 0151-424 5671 Fax: 0151-424 5671 E-mail: info@easypcstore.co.uk
Ecieurope, Buckingway Business Park, Rowles Way, Swavesey, Cambridge, CB24 4UG Tel: (01954) 278000 Fax: (01954) 278001 E-mail: sales@ipuk.com
Eet UK, Unit 4 Service Road, Cornwall Road, Pinner, Middlesex, HA5 4UH Tel: (020) 8421 0101 Fax: (020) 8421 3364 E-mail: sales@romtronics.co.uk
Ego Computers Ltd, Salisbury Hall, London Colney, St. Albans, Hertfordshire, AL2 1BU Tel: (01727) 828400 Fax: (01727) 824141 E-mail: rdrinkwater@ego-computers.ltd.uk
Elcom ITG Ltd, Elcom House, 203 Bedford Avenue, Slough, SL1 4RY Tel: (01753) 442500 Fax: (01753) 442501 E-mail: info@elcom.co.uk
Elect Computer Systems, 257 Wick Rd, London, E9 5DG Tel: (020) 8986 8014 Fax: (020) 8986 8180
Electronic Data Processing Group P.L.C., Sunrise Parkway, Linford Wood, Milton Keynes, MK14 6LJ Tel: (01908) 665522
Sion Elliiott Ltd, 124A High Street, Nailsea, Bristol, BS48 1AH Tel: (01275) 851460 E-mail: info@sioncomputers.co.uk
Empire Computers, Northern Ho, Moss Street East, Ashton-under-Lyne, Lancs, OL6 7BX Tel: 0161-330 1544 Fax: 0161-330 1616
Equanet Ltd, Red Lion Road, Surbiton, Surrey, KT6 7RG Tel: (020) 8974 2321 Fax: (020) 8974 2982
Equinox Meridian, 18 Haycroft Road, Surbiton, Surrey, KT6 5AU Tel: (020) 8397 7347 Fax: (020) 8397 2652 E-mail: sales@equinoxmeridian.com
Eurosimm Ltd, Unit 9 Pilsworth Road, Heywood Distribution Park, Heywood, Lancashire, OL10 2TA Tel: (01706) 360000 Fax: (01706) 620000 E-mail: sales@eurosimm.com
Evesham Technology Ltd, Vale Park, Evesham, Worcestershire, WR11 1TD Tel: (01386) 769600 Fax: (01386) 769795
Extra Technology Services Ltd, 52-56 Shambles Street, Barnsley, South Yorkshire, S70 2SH Tel: (01226) 771117 Fax: (01226) 771118 E-mail: sales@extracomputers.co.uk
F M K Ltd, 3a Crown Buildings, The Green, London, E4 7EX Tel: (020) 8524 3595 Fax: (020) 8524 3566 E-mail: sales@fmk.co.uk
Fast Micros, 87 Canterbury Road, Margate, Kent, CT9 5AX Tel: (01843) 227522 Fax: (01843) 225109
Fast Software, East Street, Olney, Buckinghamshire, MK46 4BT Tel: (01234) 712184 Fax: (01234) 712184
FBH Associates Ltd, Hi Point House, Thomas Street, Taunton, Somerset, TA2 6HB Tel: (01823) 335292 Fax: (01823) 332104 E-mail: sales@fbh.co.uk
First Micronics Ltd, 602-604 Kingsbury Road, Erdington, Birmingham, B24 9PJ Tel: 0121-250 5000 Fax: 0121-250 5019 E-mail: sales@fml.net
Friendly Computers, 274 Harehills Lane, Leeds, LS9 7BD Tel: 0113-216 1999 Fax: 0113-216 1400
Fujitsu Services Ltd, Wenlock Way, West Gorton, Manchester, M12 5DR Tel: (08702) 345555
Fujitsu Services, Trafalgar House, Temple Court, Risley, Warrington, WA3 6GD Tel: (01925) 432000 Fax: (01925) 432233
G B Business Supplies, 17 Leek Road, Werrington, Stoke-on-Trent, ST9 0HX Tel: (01782) 550830 Fax: (01782) 550813 E-mail: info@gbbusiness.demon.co.uk
G M Computer Systems, Ferguson House, 5 Queen Street, Coleraine, County Londonderry, BT52 1BG Tel: (028) 7032 1888 Fax: (028) 7032 1999
Gamma Global, 157 Warwick Road, Solihull, West Midlands, B92 7AR Tel: 0121-706 8080 Fax: 0121-706 1188
Gold Chip Computer Systems Ltd, 45 Newcastle Road, Sunderland, SR5 1JB Tel: 0191-549 4477 Fax: 0191-549 5577 E-mail: sales@goldchip-uk.com
Goodsell & Co., PO Box 3, Teignmouth, Devon, TQ14 8XS Tel: (01626) 778820 Fax: (01626) 772556 E-mail: sales@goodco.demon.co.uk
H F Systems, 97 Hill Top, West Bromwich, West Midlands, B70 0RU Tel: 0121-556 5821 Fax: (0845) 8689918 E-mail: info@hfsystems.co.uk
Hawke Systems, Unit 1 14 Newlands Drive, Colnbrook, Slough, SL3 0DX Tel: (01753) 686686 Fax: (01753) 686747 E-mail: sales@hawke.co.uk
Helpdesk Institute, 21 High Street, Green Street Greens, Orpington, Kent, BR6 6BG Tel: (01689) 862999 Fax: (01689) 889227 E-mail: info@hdi-europe.com
Hi Tec Bradford Ltd, Cliffe House Prospect Road, Otley Road, Bradford, West Yorkshire, BD3 0HT Tel: (01274) 626379 Fax: (01274) 626381 E-mail: sales@hi-tecbradford.co.uk
Hi-Tech Distribution Ltd, Unit 5 Phoenix Trading Estate, Bilton Road, Perivale, Greenford, Middlesex, UB6 7DZ Tel: (020) 8991 8700 Fax: (020) 8991 8776
I S C Computers Plc, 2 Pioneer Way, Lincoln, LN6 3DH Tel: (01522) 686464
Innovations To Industry, Bowden Rooms The Firs, Bowdon, Altrincham, Cheshire, WA14 2TQ Tel: 0161-929 1062 Fax: 0161-928 7800 E-mail: debbie@i2iuk.com
Integrex Ltd, Portwood Industrial Estate, Church Gresley, Swadlincote, Derbyshire, DE11 9PT Tel: (01283) 550880 Fax: (01283) 552028 E-mail: sales@integrex.co.uk
Interchange, 2 The Western Centre, Western Road, Bracknell, Berkshire, RG12 1RW Tel: (01344) 861861 Fax: (01344) 487299 E-mail: sales@i-change.co.uk
Interface Solutions International Ltd, International Park, Starley Way, Birmingham, B37 7GN Tel: 0121-780 6000 Fax: 0121-780 6111 E-mail: sales@iface.co.uk
Interlan Computer Maintenance, The Mill, Glasshouses, Harrogate, North Yorkshire, HG3 5QH Tel: (01423) 712222 Fax: (01423) 712958
Interquad Distribution Ltd, Rath House, 55-65 Uxbridge Road, Slough, SL1 1SG Tel: (01753) 536464 Fax: (01753) 898306 E-mail: info@interquad.com
Isis Computer & Electronics (UK) Ltd, 8 Ranmore Road, Dorking, Surrey, RH4 1HA Tel: (01306) 740525 Fax: (01306) 740515 E-mail: peter@isiscomputer.co.uk
J P C (GB) Ltd, Capitol Ho, Sea St, Herne Bay, Kent, CT6 6PB Tel: 01227 371721 Fax: 01227 371 722
Jennings Computer Engineering Ltd, 24-28 Gain Lane, Bradford, West Yorkshire, BD3 7LS Tel: (01274) 637587 Fax: (01274) 633197 E-mail: info@jencomp.co.uk
Jentech Computers Ltd, Whitburn Street, Bridgnorth, Shropshire, WV16 4QP Tel: (01746) 761458 Fax: (01746) 768710 E-mail: alan@jentech.co.uk
John Bennison, 10a Clarence Road, Sutton Coldfield, West Midlands, B74 4AE Tel: 0121-323 2370
Keltec Ltd, Unit 2 Bracknell Enterprise Centre, Bracknell, Berkshire, RG12 1NF Tel: (01344) 306700 Fax: (01344) 306800 E-mail: sales@keltec.co.uk
Kira Supplies, Holt Lane, Lea, Matlock, Derbyshire, DE4 5GQ Tel: (01629) 534934 Fax: (01629) 534933 E-mail: admin@kira.co.uk
Lazer Printing, 65 Coniston Road, Peterborough, PE4 7UL Tel: (01733) 324404 Fax: (01733) 324404
Lynx Automotive Systems Ltd, Delta 500, Delta Business Park, Welton Road, Swindon, SN5 7XE Tel: (01793) 645300 Fax: (01793) 645301 E-mail: enquiries@mmi-automotive.co.uk
Lynx Technology Ltd, 3 Midland Way, Barlborough, Chesterfield, Derbyshire, S43 4XA Tel: (01246) 574000 Fax: (01246) 819401 E-mail: enquiries@lynxtec.com
M C W Group, Wrexham Technology Park, Wrexham, Clwyd, LL13 7YP Tel: (01978) 340340 Fax: (01978) 340345 E-mail: admin@mcwgroup.co.uk
M & M Computing Services Ltd, Dial Post Court, Horsham Road, Rusper, Horsham, West Sussex, RH12 4QX Tel: (01293) 871971 Fax: (01293) 871796 E-mail: sales@mm-computing.com
Ma Rich, 50 Sunnymead Road, London, NW9 8BU Tel: (020) 8205 3172 Fax: (020) 8205 2642
Mach One Design Equipment Ltd, Columbia House, Columbia Drive, Worthing, West Sussex, BN13 3HD Tel: (01903) 525100 Fax: (01903) 525155 E-mail: sales@machone.co.uk
MacXperts Ltd, London, W4 3UW Tel: (0871) 5504050 Fax: (020) 8181 7798 E-mail: info@macxperts.com
Maestro Solutions Ltd, 5 Woodland Road, Maple Cross, Rickmansworth, Hertfordshire, WD3 9ST Tel: (01923) 770856 Fax: (01923) 771143 E-mail: maestrosoloutions@aol.com
Manhattan Electronics, 4 Cooksey Lane, Birmingham, B44 9QN Tel: 0121-605 2957 Fax: 0121-605 3031 E-mail: manhattanelec@hotmail.com
Matrix Computer Services, Matrix Buildings, Darenth Road, Dartford, DA1 1LU Tel: (01322) 292391 Fax: (01322) 229908 E-mail: matrixcomputers@compuserve.com
Maxresponse Ltd, 55 Linkside Avenue, Oxford, OX2 8JE Tel: (01865) 316251 Fax: (0870) 0518845 E-mail: sales@maxresponse.co.uk
Mayfair Business Systems Ltd, 85 Market Street, Watford, WD18 0PT Tel: (01923) 800800 Fax: (01923) 800810 E-mail: info@mayfairbs.co.uk
MCP Microsystems, 369 Warrington Road, Rainhill, Prescot, Merseyside, L35 8LD Tel: 0151-431 0133 Fax: 0151-431 0072 E-mail: admin@mcpmicro.co.uk
Micro Check, 75 North Street, Wellington, Somerset, TA21 8NA Tel: (01823) 664943 Fax: (01823) 665747 E-mail: sales@microcheckcomputers.co.uk
Micro Engineering Ltd, 155 Kingston Road, New Malden, Surrey, KT3 3NS Tel: (020) 8949 2191 Fax: (020) 8336 1127 E-mail: sales@microeng.co.uk
Micro Peripherals Ltd, Shorten Brook Way, Altham Business Park, Altham, Accrington, Lancashire, BB5 5YJ Tel: (01282) 776776 Fax: (01282) 770001 E-mail: sales@micro-p.com
Microtec Ware Ltd, 146 Cherry Hinton Road, Cambridge, CB1 7AJ Tel: (01223) 416641 Fax: (01223) 413341 E-mail: purchasing@microtecware.com
Middlestown PCS Ltd, 52 High Street, Horbury, Wakefield, West Yorkshire, WF4 5LE Tel: (01924) 260615 Fax: (01924) 270245 E-mail: info@middlestownpcs.co.uk
Midland Business Equipment Ltd, Unit 4 Highlands House, Stirling Road, Shirley, Solihull, West Midlands, B90 4NE Tel: (01675) 470061 Fax: 01675 470889 E-mail: info@m-b-e.co.uk
Mighty Micro, 268 Wilmslow Road, Manchester, M14 6JR Tel: 0161-224 8117 Fax: 0161-257 2803 E-mail: info@mighty-micro.co.uk
Milequip Computer Maintenance Ltd, Hepworth House, 115 Southgate Street, Gloucester, GL1 1UT Tel: (01452) 305430 Fax: (01452) 411010 E-mail: mcmcomputers@freeuk.com
Misco, Darby Close, Park Farm South, Wellingborough, Northamptonshire, NN8 6GS Tel: (08707) 208720 Fax: (08707) 208686 E-mail: salesdesk@misco.co.uk
Mobifax UK Ltd, Units 3-4 Ash Court, Crystal Drive, Sandwell Business Park, Smethwick, West Midlands, B66 1QG Tel: 0121-541 1604 Fax: 0121-541 1605
Models & Computers Plus, 55-55a West Street, Boston, Lincolnshire, PE21 8QN Tel: (01205) 365102 Fax: (01205) 369949 E-mail: sales@modcomp.net
Monitor Shop, 574 Carlton Road, Nottingham, NG3 7AB Tel: 0115-911 0366 Fax: 0115-959 0932
Moorgate Ltd, 2 Cedar Court, Taylor Business Park, Risley, Warrington, WA3 6BT Tel: (01925) 765432 Fax: (01925) 765422 E-mail: sales@moorgate.co.uk
Morgan Computer Co., 11-12 Gateway House, Piccadilly South, Manchester, M1 2GH Tel: 0161-237 1111 Fax: 0161-237 3146 E-mail: man@morgancomputers.co.uk
N B Group It Consultancy, 34 Bedford Road, Gregans House, Hitchin, Hertfordshire, SG5 1HF Tel: (01462) 452452 E-mail: info@online-it.com
N C S Group P.L.C., Belville House, Ponteland, Newcastle Upon Tyne, NE20 9BF Tel: (01661) 803000 Fax: (01661) 860069 E-mail: marketing@ncs-plc.co.uk
Native Systems Ltd, 22 St. Annes Grove, Knowle, Solihull, West Midlands, B93 9JB Tel: 0121-743 0875 E-mail: info@nativesystems.co.uk
Nebula Computers, 73 Biggin Hall Cresent, Coventry, CV3 1HA Tel: (024) 7643 1211 Fax: (024) 7643 1711 E-mail: info@nebulacomputers.co.uk
Netbuyer, 1 International House, St. Katharines Way, London, E1W 1UN Tel: (020) 7903 6807 Fax: (020) 7903 6000 E-mail: geoff.inns@cnet.com
Next Day Computer Services, 32 Burnham Cl, Enfield, Middx, EN1 3RA Tel: 020 83665031 Fax: 020 83666323
Nike Consultants Ltd, Raynor House, 6 Raynor Road, Wolverhampton, WV10 9QY Tel: (01902) 566200 Fax: (01902) 566201 E-mail: sales@nike.co.uk
North East Communications, 76 High Street, Elgin, Morayshire, IV30 1BJ Tel: (01343) 551551 Fax: (01343) 540340
Omega Computers, 685 Cranbrook Road, Ilford, Essex, IG2 6SY Tel: (020) 8550 9295 Fax: (020) 8550 0830 E-mail: sale@omegacomputer.uk
Opal Services, 24 Aldershot Road, Fleet, Hampshire, GU51 3NN Tel: (01252) 812607 Fax: (01252) 812625
Orac Computer Services, 143 Tankerton Rd, Whitstable, Kent, CT5 2AW Tel: (01227) 280522 Fax: (01227) 280533 E-mail: dave@orac.co.uk
Organised Computer Systems Ltd, East House, Newpound, Wisborough Green, Billingshurst, West Sussex, RH14 0AZ Tel: (01403) 700959 Fax: (01403) 700969E-mail: sales@ocsl.co.uk
Oryx X L Ltd, XL House, Woodburn Road, Blackburn, Aberdeen, AB21 0PS Tel: (01224) 798400 Fax: (01224) 798401 E-mail: admin@xlg.co.uk
P A Business Systems Ltd, 5-7 The Pathway, Bowlalley Lane, Hull, HU1 1XJ Tel: (01482) 328607 Fax: (01482) 218236 E-mail: headoffice@pa-business.co.uk
P C Link Supplies Ltd, Ruxox House, Maulden Road, Flitwick, Bedford, MK45 5BN Tel: (01525) 717772 Fax: (01525) 717773 E-mail: sales@businesshomecomputers.com
P C Microfix Ltd, 149 Uxbridge Road, London, W7 3ST Tel: (020) 8579 7474 Fax: (020) 8579 1667 E-mail: microfix@aol.com
P & P Installation P.L.C., Unit 5 Empire Centre, Imperial Way, Watford, WD24 4YH Tel: (01923) 226357 Fax: (01923) 254434
Paisley Computer Exchange, 7 Wellmeadow St, Paisley, Renfrewshire, PA1 2WE Tel: 0141-889 9691 Fax: 01418896060
Panacea Ltd, Winton House, Winton Square, Basingstoke, Hampshire, RG21 8EN Tel: (01256) 305050 Fax: (01256) 305030
PC 2000, 7 Bridge Street, Dumbarton, G82 1NY Tel: (01389) 739290 Fax: (01389) 726885 E-mail: enquiries@pc2000.co.uk
Pershore Leisure Centre, PO Box 2000, Pershore, Worcestershire, WR10 1QU Tel: (01386) 552346 Fax: (01386) 556559 E-mail: post@c2000.com
Phoenix I T Group plc, Technology House, Hunsbury Hill Avenue, Northampton, NN4 8QS Tel: (01604) 769000 Fax: (01604) 706666 E-mail: sales@phoenixitservices.co.uk
Pisces Computers, Moor Street, Chepstow, Gwent, NP16 5DE Tel: (01291) 625100 Fax: (01291) 621068 E-mail: piscescomputers@aol.com
Planet Micro, Unit 1 Beresford Street, Failsworth, Manchester, M35 0HD Tel: (08707) 453555 Fax: (08707) 454555 E-mail: sales@planetmicro.co.uk
Portables Direct Ltd, Unit 5 Westmoreland House Cumberland Park, Scrubs Lane, London, NW10 6RE Tel: (020) 8968 1222 Fax: (020) 8968 1777 E-mail: sales@portables.co.uk
▶ Pro Source I T Ltd, Unit 1, Princess Mews Horace Road, Kingston upon Thames, Surrey, KT1 2SZ Tel: (020) 8541 0333 Fax: (020) 8549 1333
Proband Ltd, 37-55 Camden Street, Birmingham, B1 3BP Tel: (0800) 262629 E-mail: tony.sheen@proband.co.uk
Professional Computer Group Ltd, Merley House, Merley House Lane, Wimborne, Dorset, BH21 3AA Tel: (01202) 857000 Fax: (01202) 857007 E-mail: enquiries@pcgl.co.uk
Prosoft Systems Ltd, Marchwood House 934 St Albans, Road Watford, Watford, WD25 9NN Tel: (01923) 680223 Fax: (01923) 680683 E-mail: sales@prosoftonline.co.uk
Pyramid Valley Computers, Heapriding Mill, Ford Street, Stockport, Cheshire, SK3 0BT Tel: 0161-477 3880 Fax: 0161-480 8741 E-mail: sales@pyramidvalley.co.uk
R & A Software Systems Ltd, Bank Chambers, 244 Fulwood Road, Sheffield, S10 3BB Tel: 0114-267 9669 Fax: 0114-267 9670 E-mail: info@rasoft.co.uk

▶ indicates data change since last edition

COMPUTER DEALERS/BROKERS/ DISTRIBUTORS/AGENTS, COMPUTER HARDWARE – *continued*

R M P.L.C., New Mill House, 183 Milton Park, Abingdon, Oxfordshire, OX14 4SE Tel: (01235) 826000 Fax: (01235) 826999 E-mail: salesdesk@rm.com
Raven Systems, Gear House, Saltmeadows Road, Gateshead, Tyne & Wear, NE8 3AH Tel: 0191-478 6262 Fax: 0191-478 6363 E-mail: info@raven-systems.co.uk
Redview Computers, 17A North End, Longhoston, Alnwick, Northumberland, NE66 3AG Tel: (01665) 572027 E-mail: tom@redview.co.uk
Retellin Ltd, 78 Rainham Road, Rainham, Essex, RM13 7RL Tel: (01708) 553310
Root Computers Ltd, Templars Way Industrial Estate, Marlborough Road, Wootton Bassett, Swindon, SN4 7SR Tel: (01793) 850880 Fax: (01793) 850960 E-mail: sales@rootcomputers.co.uk
Rusholme Consoles Khan & Sons, 157 Dickenson Road, Manchester, M14 5HZ Tel: 0161-225 1475 Fax: 0161-225 1475
S C A Systems Ltd, 12 Littlehampton Road, Worthing, West Sussex, BN13 1QE Tel: (01903) 262688 Fax: (01903) 695311 E-mail: sales@scasystems.com
S I Systems Ltd, 64 Killigrew Street, Falmouth, Cornwall, TR11 3PP Tel: (01326) 315200 E-mail: sisystems@btinternet.com
S & S Systems Ltd, Bretton Court, Manor Road, Wales, Sheffield, S26 5PS Tel: (08456) 441670 E-mail: info@astraaccounts.co.uk
S T S Computers, Tylney House, 23 High Street, Leatherhead, Surrey, KT22 8AB Tel: (01372) 378608 Fax: (01372) 374592 E-mail: info@stscomputers.co.uk
Select Computers, Suite 2 Rawmec Industrial Park, Plumpton Road, Hoddesdon, Hertfordshire, EN11 0EE Tel: (01992) 448899 Fax: (01992) 471314 E-mail: mailorder@selectcomputers.co.uk
Silicon Group, 95 Whins Road, Alloa, Clackmannanshire, FK10 3RF Tel: (01259) 725200 Fax: (01259) 725270 E-mail: info@silicon-group.co.uk
Solsoft Computers, 2 Bosuen Road, Newquay, Cornwall, TR7 3BA Tel: (01637) 878933 Fax: (01637) 852666 E-mail: admin@solsoftsw.com
Solsoft S W Bespoke Software Systems, 2 Bosuen Road, Newquay, Cornwall, TR7 3BA Tel: (01637) 852666 Fax: (01637) 852666 E-mail: info@solsoftaw.com
Sphinx C S T, Woodside House, Osier Drive, Annesley, Nottingham, NG15 0DS Tel: (01623) 726282 Fax: (01623) 726292 E-mail: sales@sphinx.co.uk
Sujitsu Services Ltd, Viables Industrial Estate, Jays Close, Basingstoke, Hampshire, RG22 4BY Tel: (0870) 234 5555 Fax: (0870) 853 3262
Suntech Computer Services, 9 St. Colmans Park, Newry, County Down, BT34 2BX Tel: (028) 3026 6650 Fax: (028) 3083 4974 E-mail: messages@suntech.co.uk
Sussex Computers Ltd, Suite F10, Waterside Centre, North Street, Lewes, East Sussex, BN7 2PE Tel: (01273) 407360 Fax: (01273) 464880 E-mail: gm@sussexcomputers.co.uk
Syan Ltd, The Mill, King Coughton, Alcester, Warwickshire, B49 5QG Tel: (01789) 400464 Fax: (01789) 400470
T M S Ltd, 7 Central Park Avenue, Central Avenue, Larbert, Stirlingshire, FK5 4RX Tel: (01324) 550760 Fax: (0871) 2225035
Team Management PC Hire Ltd, 3 Hermitage Court, Wapping High Street, London, E1 9PL Tel: (020) 7702 9242 Fax: (020) 7702 9747 E-mail: tanya@pchire.com
Tecfacs Ltd, 6 Oaklands Business Centre, Oaklands Park, Wokingham, Berkshire, RG41 2FD Tel: 0118-977 6645 Fax: 0118-989 4461 E-mail: sales@tecfacs.com
Technical Data Systems Ltd, Unit A, Watchmoor Trade Centre, Watchmoor Road, Camberley, Surrey, GU15 3AJ Tel: (01276) 684835 Fax: (0870) 1607050 E-mail: sales@tdsltd.co.uk
Technol 2000 Ltd, 5-7 Chester Road, Northwich, Cheshire, CW8 1EZ Tel: (01606) 784044 Fax: (01606) 784055 E-mail: info@technol.co.uk
Technomatic, Horizon 1, Studio Way, Borehamwood, Hertfordshire, WD6 5WH Tel: (020) 8327 5000 Fax: (0870) 5133919
Tempus Computers Ltd, St Pauls House, St Pauls Square, Birmingham, B3 1RB Tel: 0121-233 3100 Fax: 0121-233 4560 E-mail: sales@tempa.co.uk
Tigra Solutions Ltd, 16 Queens Road, Farnborough, Hampshire, GU14 6DN Tel: (01252) 816699 Fax: (01252) 812375 E-mail: info@tigra-solutions.co.uk
Time Computers, Unit 2 Coypool Retail Park, Coypool Road, Plympton, Plymouth, PL7 4TB Tel: (01752) 338882 Fax: (01752) 339497 E-mail: info@thecomputershop.com
Tomorrows World, 29 Paragon Street, Hull, HU1 3NA Tel: (01482) 324887 Fax: (01482) 325854
Torex Retail, Manor Farm Courtyard, 57-61 Main Street, Frolesworth, Lutterworth, Leicestershire, LE17 5EE Tel: (01455) 202727 Fax: (01455) 202728 E-mail: info@torexretail.com
The Total Package Ltd, The Granary, Birling, West Malling, Kent, ME19 5JF Tel: (01732) 526910 Fax: (01732) 526939 E-mail: info@thetotalpackage.co.uk
Tower Digital Ltd, 312 Central Drive, Blackpool, FY1 6LE Tel: (01253) 400011 Fax: (01253) 400022 E-mail: info@towerdigital.co.uk
Trust Co. P.L.C., 2-3 Namrik Mews, Hove, East Sussex, BN3 2TF Tel: (01273) 735999 Fax: (01273) 736999 E-mail: info@trustco.co.uk
▶ U P S Direct, 6 Camross Drive, Shrewsbury, SY1 3XH Tel: (01743) 243833 Fax: (01743) 340555 E-mail: ghollis@upsdirect.com
Ultima Business Systems Ltd, 448 Basingstoke Road, Reading, RG2 0LP Tel: 0118-902 7500 Fax: 0118-902 7400 E-mail: sales@ultimabusiness.com
Unified Solutions Ltd, 883-884 Plymouth Road, Slough, SL1 4LP Tel: (01753) 775050 Fax: (01753) 775020 E-mail: info@unified.co.uk
Unitek Computers, Unitek House, Oxford Road, Tatling End, Gerrards Cross, Buckinghamshire, SL9 7BB Tel: (01753) 890500 Fax: (01753) 891916 E-mail: sales@chilternelectronics.co.uk
Vertical Systems, 14 Hemmells, Basildon, Essex, SS15 6ED Tel: (01268) 416155 Fax: (01268) 541287 E-mail: peter.healey@tarsc.net
Viglen Technology Ltd, 7 Handley Page Way Colney Street, Colney Street, St. Albans, Hertfordshire, AL2 2DQ Tel: (01923) 858700 Fax: (01727) 201888 E-mail: marketing@viglen.co.uk
Visual Computer Technologies Ltd, Unit 207 Solent BSNS Centre 3, Millbrook Road West, Southampton, SO15 0HW Tel: (023) 8077 9162 Fax: (023) 8078 8222 E-mail: sales@focused.co.uk
W D P Co., 37 Park Road, Bromley, BR1 3HJ Tel: (020) 8464 9011 Fax: (020) 8464 8977 E-mail: wdpco@aol.com
Wade Computing Services Ltd, 263 Buxton Road, Stockport, Cheshire, SK2 7NR Tel: 0161-456 0104 Fax: 0161-483 9119 E-mail: sales@wadecomputing.co.uk
West Country Business Systems Holdings Ltd, Somerset House, Magdalene Street, Glastonbury, Somerset, BA6 9EJ Tel: (01458) 833344 Fax: (01458) 835297 E-mail: sales@wcbs.co.uk
Westcom Computer Consultants, 6-8 Wilson Street, Workington, Cumbria, CA14 4AZ Tel: (01900) 870455 Fax: (01900) 606665 E-mail: sales@west-comm.co.uk
Westek Holdings Ltd, Unit 1 Lancaster Park Industrial Estate, Bowerhill, Melksham, Wiltshire, SN12 6TT Tel: (01225) 790600 Fax: (01225) 702968 E-mail: sales@westekuk.com
Western Computer Group Ltd, Victoria House, Temple Gate, Bristol, BS1 6PW Tel: 0117-922 5661 Fax: 0117-922 6504 E-mail: applecentre@western.co.uk
Wiztek, P C Upgrade Centre, 8 Bond St, Redruth, Cornwall, TR15 2QB Tel: (01209) 314296 E-mail: wiztek@hotmail.com
Worldwide PC UK Ltd, 88-90 Manningham Lane, Bradford, West Yorkshire, BD1 3ES Tel: (01274) 745515E-mail: gary@wwpc.co.uk
Wyvern Business Systems, Wyvern House, Netherwood Road, Rotherwas Industrial Estate, Hereford, HR2 6JJ Tel: (01432) 271233 Fax: (01432) 263550 E-mail: buyer@wbs.uk.com
Xenon Network Services Ltd, Anchorage Court Caspian Road, Atlantic Street, Broadheath, Altrincham, Cheshire, WA14 5HH Tel: 0161-929 5282 Fax: 0161-929 5264 E-mail: sales@xenon-uk.co.uk
Xperience Peg Associates Ltd, Belmont House, Lambdon Road, London, SW20 0LW Tel: (020) 8880 4440 Fax: (020) 8880 4442 E-mail: sales@xperience-group.co.uk
Yellowstone Electronic Solutions Ltd, 17 Lyneham Road, Luton, LU2 9JS Tel: (01582) 722011 Fax: (01582) 654440 E-mail: sales@yellowstone.co.uk

COMPUTER DESIGN CONSULTANTS/SERVICES

A R M Holdings, Moorbridge Road, Maidenhead, Berkshire, SL6 8LT Tel: (01628) 427700 Fax: (01628) 427701 E-mail: enquiries@arm.com
Actual Reality, Stainton Moor View, Matlock, Derbyshire, DE4 3NE Tel: (01629) 760801 Fax: (08702) 201805 E-mail: admin@ar-computers.co.uk
Britelec Network Services Ltd, 39 London Road, Braintree, Essex, CM7 2LD Tel: (01376) 552323 Fax: (01376) 340006
C N S, Earley, Reading, RG10 8NF Tel: 0118-940 1313 Fax: 0118-940 3754 E-mail: enquire@cnscommunications.co.uk
Client Management Systems, Holmes Chapel Rd, Sproston, Crewe, CW4 7LW Tel: 01606 738080 Fax: 01606 837540
D & M Systems Ltd, 28 Langdale Avenue, Chichester, West Sussex, PO19 8JQ Tel: (01243) 781950 Fax: (01243) 784478 E-mail: info@dandmsystems.co.uk
Davmark Ltd, 63 Keats Way, West Drayton, Middlesex, UB7 9DU Tel: (07824) 638853 Fax: (01895) 905902 E-mail: david.slade@davmark.co.uk
Ema Technology, 15 Stevens Lane, Breaston, Derby, DE72 3BU Tel: (01332) 875657 Fax: (01332) 875658 E-mail: info@ema-tech.co.uk
Excel Consultants Ltd, 10 Laburnham Road, Maidenhead, Berkshire, SL6 4DB Tel: (01628) 631991
Fellowes Industrial Technology Ltd, 133 Newhall Street, Cannock, Staffordshire, WS11 1AD Tel: (01543) 503842 Fax: (01543) 503842
Haas Associates, 20 Baldock Road, Buntingford, Hertfordshire, SG9 9DA Tel: (01763) 272865 Fax: (01763) 273869 E-mail: sales@haas-uk.com
▶ Harmony Internet Ltd, 3 The Granary Buildings, Millow, Biggleswade, Bedfordshire, SG18 8RH Tel: (01767) 317614 Fax: (01767) 317647 E-mail: info@harmony.co.uk
IRevoltion Ltd, Station House, 4-8 High Street, West Drayton, Middlesex, UB7 7DJ Tel: (01895) 444420 Fax: (01895) 444460
The It Partnership, 4 Upper Mulgrave Road, Sutton, Surrey, SM2 7AZ Tel: (0870) 7270089 Fax: (0870) 7270090
▶ J J Computing Ltd, 9 Stamford Close, Potters Bar, Hertfordshire, EN6 5NW Tel: (01707) 642767 E-mail: johnjohnson64@hotmail.com
Jemcare Training, Churchill House, Stirling Way, Borehamwood, Hertfordshire, WD6 2HP Tel: (020) 8736 0536 Fax: (020) 8736 0535 E-mail: mslyper@kinetictraining.com
Lloyd Savage Services Ltd, 25 The Green, Richmond, Surrey, TW9 1LY Tel: (020) 8332 7266
M5 Data Ltd, Mendip Court, Bath Road, Wells, Somerset, BA5 3DG Tel: (01749) 679222 Fax: (01749) 673928
Medway Computer Supplies, 2-11 Enterprise Close, Medway City Estate, Rochester, Kent, ME2 4LY Tel: (01634) 297575 Fax: (01634) 723227 E-mail: sales@medwaycomputers.fsnet.co.uk
Gregory Micallef Associates, 63 Croydon Road, London, SE20 7TB Tel: (020) 8778 7759 Fax: (020) 8778 3090 E-mail: sales@gmal.co.uk
Mos Computers Ltd, Queen Square, Saltford, Bristol, BS31 3EL Tel: (01225) 873117 Fax: (01225) 873776 E-mail: info@moscomputers.co.uk
Netwinner Ltd, 15 The Maltings, Longton, Preston, PR4 5ZS Tel: (01772) 616078 Fax: (01772) 616086 E-mail: sales@netwinner.co.uk
▶ PC Emergency, 2 Sycamore Rise, Berkhamsted, Hertfordshire, HP4 2JZ Tel: (07746) 555729 E-mail: office@pcmrg.com
Pericom SW Ltd, 46b Sea King Road, Lynx Trading Estate, Yeovil, Somerset, BA20 2NZ Tel: (01935) 410377 Fax: (01935) 410755 E-mail: mail@lbts.co.uk
Q P Share LLP, 8 Park Drive, Eldwick, Bingley, West Yorkshire, BD16 3DF Tel: (01274) 551007 Fax: (01274) 552932
Soft Sell Computers, 74 Darwen St, Blackburn, BB2 2BL Tel: (01254) 693593 Fax: (01254) 668975 E-mail: info@soft-sell.co.uk
Softgen Ltd, 92 Harrowdene Road, Wembley, Middlesex, HA0 2JF Tel: (020) 8900 0333 Fax: (020) 8900 9646 E-mail: admin@softegenltd.co.uk
Spruce Technology, 40 High Street, Langholm, Dumfriesshire, DG13 0JH Tel: (01387) 381529 Fax: (01387) 381779 E-mail: office@sprucetechnology.com
Superplate Graphics Ltd, 2 Apex Business Park, Apex Way, Leeds, LS11 5LN Tel: 0113-234 0800 Fax: 0113-234 0944

COMPUTER DISASTER RECOVERY SERVICES

▶ Advanced Media Engineering Ltd, Sannerville Chase, Main Road, Exminster, Exeter, EX6 8AT Tel: (01392) 824022 Fax: (01392) 824838 E-mail: sales@amesolutions.co.uk
Barnsley Yesco, 17 Fishdam La, Monk Bretton, Barnsley, S. Yorkshire, S71 2PX Tel: (01226) 200338 Fax: (01226) 200338 E-mail: yesco@computers97.freeserve.co.uk
Core Consultancy Ltd, 7 Kings Bench Street, London, SE1 0QX Tel: (020) 7928 3338 Fax: (0871) 6613393 E-mail: info@core-consultancy.com
Elan Support Services, Allerton Bywater Business Park, Newton Lane, Allerton Bywater, Castleford, West Yorkshire, WF10 2AL Tel: (01977) 604384 Fax: (01977) 604021 E-mail: evahorbury@elansupports.co.uk
Gapint Ltd, The Old Mill, Wellington Street, Ripley, Derbyshire, DE5 3EH Tel: (01773) 741174 Fax: (01773) 570247 E-mail: enquiries@gapint.co.uk
▶ Itflex, 1 Victory Close, Grays, Essex, RM16 6RT Tel: (01708) 209924 E-mail: info@itflex.co.uk
M & M Computing Services Ltd, Dial Post Court, Horsham Road, Rusper, Horsham, West Sussex, RH12 4QX Tel: (01293) 871971 Fax: (01293) 871796 E-mail: sales@mm-computing.com
MJM Data Recovery, Unit B2, Pixmore Industrial Estate, Letchworth Garden City, Hertfordshire, SG6 1JJ Tel: (01462) 680333 Fax: (01462) 483648 E-mail: sales@mjm.co.uk
Rescue IT Ltd, 6 Braham Street, London, E1 8EE Tel: (0870) 6090999 Fax: (07092) 102103 E-mail: info@rescueit.co.uk
Sacrosanct Technology Ltd, 3 Sambourn Close, Solihull, West Midlands, B91 2SA Tel: 0121-711 2100 E-mail: robthomas@sacrosanct.co.uk
Strand Technology Group, 10-12 Westgate, Skelmersdale, Lancashire, WN8 8AZ Tel: (0845) 6607968 E-mail: mail@standtech.co.uk
Tectonic Ltd, Meridian Business Park, 1A Jupitor Court, Dominus Way, Leicester, LE19 1RP Tel: 0116-282 0567 Fax: 0116-282 0599 E-mail: info@tectonic.com

COMPUTER DISC DRIVE (FLOPPY/HARD) MAINTENANCE/ REPAIR SERVICES

▶ All Solutions, 1 Merton Court, 54 Christchurch Road, Bournemouth, BH1 3PF Tel: (01202) 551862
▶ Apex Technology Ltd, PO Box 2364, Stafford, ST16 3DA Tel: (01785) 227989 E-mail: enquiry@apextechnology.co.uk
▶ Bluejays PC Services, 76 Davidson Road, Croydon, CR0 6DB Tel: 0208 6561056 E-mail: info@bluejayspc.co.uk
Brockham Computers, 7 Bishops Cottages Chalkpit Lane, Betchworth, Dorking, Surrey, RH3 7HA Tel: (01737) 842075 E-mail: keith@brockhamcomputers.co.uk
Computer Surgery, Apple Barn, Maidstone Road, Pembury, Tunbridge Wells, Kent, TN2 4AD Tel: (0845) 1303343 Fax: (0870) 0118128 E-mail: sales@computer-surgery.co.uk
▶ Computersave.Co.Uk, 45 Windmill Road, Hampton Hill, Hampton, Middlesex, TW12 1QZ Tel: (07950) 412207 Fax: (0795) 0412207 E-mail: info@computersave.co.uk
▶ Danoli Solutions Ltd, 116 Yew Tree Road, Ormskirk, Lancashire, L39 1NX Tel: (01695) 579442 E-mail: enquiries@danoli.co.uk
▶ DataInterpreters, 276 West Park Drive West, Leeds, LS8 2BD Tel: 07886 847024
Datastor Technology Ltd, Old Mushroom Farm, Heathend, Wotton-under-Edge, Gloucestershire, GL12 8AX Tel: (01454) 299399 Fax: (01454) 299400 E-mail: sales@datastor.co.uk
Davel Technology, Woodlands, Branksome Avenue, Wickford, Essex, SS12 0JD Tel: (01268) 763336 Fax: (01268) 763305 E-mail: davtech@onetel.com
▶ Get To It, 8 Coulson Way, Alconbury, Huntingdon, Cambridgeshire, PE28 4WU Tel: (01480) 896704 E-mail: sales@get-to-it.co.uk
▶ Hampshire Computer Clinics Ltd, 203E West Street, Fareham, Hampshire, PO16 0EN Tel: (023) 9243 5675 E-mail: mail@gosportpccentre.com
Harthill House Group Ltd, Harthill House, Woodhall Lane, Harthill, Sheffield, S26 7YQ Tel: (0870) 3501309 Fax: (01909) 772785 E-mail: sales@hhg.uk.com
▶ Hybrid Computers, 15 Rembrandt End, Aylesbury, Buckinghamshire, HP19 8SL Tel: (01296) 484888 E-mail: info@hybrid-computers.biz
Kew Computers, 78 Woolmer Way, Bordon, Hampshire, GU35 9QF Tel: (01420) 479666 Fax: (01420) 488348 E-mail: info@kewcomputers.com
Livenet Computing Ltd, 214 School Rd, Sheffield, S10 1GL Tel: 0114-268 7030
MH CompuTech, 6 Blackwell Close, Higham Ferrers, Northamptonshire, NN10 8PJ Tel: (01933) 315900 E-mail: info@mhcomputech.co.uk
▶ P C Sos 24 7, Europa House, Adlington Industrial Estate, Adlington, Macclesfield, Cheshire, SK10 4NL Tel: (0870) 2863767 E-mail: help@pcsos247.com
▶ PC Angells, 11 Tuxford Close, Borehamwood, Hertfordshire, WD6 4LE Tel: (07941) 153532 E-mail: paul@pcangells.co.uk

COMPUTER DISC PRODUCTION MACHINERY

Manufacturing Techniques Corporation UK Ltd, Units 5-6 North Avon Business Centre, Dean Road, Yate, Bristol, BS37 5NH Tel: (01454) 318491 Fax: (01454) 318575

COMPUTER DISK DRIVES, *See also headings for particular types*

Eurosimm Ltd, Unit 9 Pilsworth Road, Heywood Distribution Park, Heywood, Lancashire, OL10 2TA Tel: (01706) 360000 Fax: (01706) 620000 E-mail: sales@eurosimm.com
Phoenix I T Group plc, Technology House, Hunsbury Hill Avenue, Northampton, NN4 8QS Tel: (01604) 769000 Fax: (01604) 706666 E-mail: sales@phoenixitservices.co.uk
Probrand Ltd, 37-55 Camden Street, Birmingham, B1 3BP Tel: (0800) 262629 E-mail: tony.sheen@proband.co.uk
Quantum Peripheral Products Ltd, Quantum House 3 Bracknell Beeches, Old Bracknell La West, Bracknell, Berkshire, RG12 7BW Tel: (01344) 353500 Fax: (01344) 353510

COMPUTER DISK DRIVES, FLOPPY DISC

Continental Ltd, Unit C2 Herrick Way, Staverton Technology Park, Staverton, Cheltenham, Gloucestershire, GL51 6TQ Tel: (01452) 855222 Fax: (01452) 856794 E-mail: sales@continental.co.uk

COMPUTER DISK DRIVES, FLOPPY DISC – *continued*

Discount Computer Supplies, 58 Copley Road, Doncaster, South Yorkshire, DN1 2QW Tel: (01302) 364155 Fax: (01302) 366062 E-mail: sales@dcs.uk.com
Hexel Developments Ltd, Wash Lane, Warrington, WA4 1HS Tel: (01925) 444439 Fax: (01925) 655899E-mail: admin@hexel.net
Level 7 Computers Ltd, 39 Eastover, Bridgwater, Somerset, TA6 5AW Tel: (01278) 444770 E-mail: mail@level7.co.uk
PC World, Leeds Road Retail Park, Leeds Road, Huddersfield, HD1 6PF Tel: (0870) 2420444 Fax: (01484) 437302 E-mail: customer.services@pcworld.co.uk
Sunitek Marshan Ltd, 176 Newhampton Road East, Wolverhampton, WV1 4PQ Tel: (01902) 773329 Fax: (01902) 773328

COMPUTER DISK DRIVES, FLOPPY DISK, PORTABLE

▶ A J Computing, 12 Church Lane, Little Bytham, Grantham, Lincolnshire, NG33 4QP Tel: (01780) 410998 E-mail: alex@aj-computing.co.uk
▶ At Your Fingertips, 26 Greywell Precinct, Havant, Hampshire, PO9 5AL Tel: (023) 9247 1434 Fax: (023) 9247 1434
▶ Croft Networking, 20 Jardine Way, Dunstable, Bedfordshire, LU5 4AX Tel: (01582) 513234
P K N D Computer Services, 26 Parkfield Row, Leeds, LS11 7LT Tel: 0113-276 5758 Fax: 0871 5216882 E-mail: info@pknd.co.uk
▶ Penzance Computer Centre, 76 Market Jew Street, Penzance, Cornwall, TR18 2LG Tel: (01736) 366999 Fax: (01736) 366999 E-mail: sales@pzcomputers.com
▶ Retrolutions Ltd, 85 Lincoln Road, Stevenage, Herts, SG1 4PL Tel: 01438 743346 E-mail: richard.thatcher@retrolutions.com
▶ Twighlightzone, Green Pastures, Kentisbury, Barnstaple, Devon, EX31 4NN Tel: (0845) 2268145 Fax: (0845) 2268145 E-mail: frankie@twighlightzone.com

COMPUTER DISK DRIVES, HARD DISK (HDD), REFURBISHED

▶ www.letsspendless.org, John Clarke Centre, Middlesbrough, Cleveland, TS6 6UZ Tel: (07739) 509097

COMPUTER DISK DRIVES, HARD DISK (HDD), SMALL COMPUTER SYSTEM INTERFACE (SCSI)

▶ Absolutely PC Ltd, 11 Bradley Road, Patchway, Bristol, BS34 5LF Tel: 0117-975 9523 E-mail: Sales@AbsolutelyPC.co.uk

COMPUTER DISK DUPLICATING

Data Business, 1-4 Bankside, Kidlington, Oxfordshire, OX5 1JE Tel: (01865) 848574 Fax: (0870) 766 5210 E-mail: sales@databiz.com
Ram Peripherals, 14 Lombard Road, Merton, London, SW19 3TZ Tel: (020) 8543 9696 Fax: (020) 8543 3419 E-mail: sales@ram-peripherals.co.uk

COMPUTER DISMANTLING

End O Line Services, 1-3 Station Road, Maldon, Essex, CM9 4LQ Tel: (01621) 843535 Fax: (01621) 843534E-mail: sales@eols.co.uk
IT Disposal, 1 Brook Farm, Stapleford Road, Stapleford Abbotts, Romford, RM4 1EJ Tel: (0845) 6445303 Fax: (01708) 688019 E-mail: info@itdisposal.co.uk

COMPUTER DISPOSAL

Arc, Western House, 7 Knutsford Road, Wilmslow, Cheshire, SK9 6JA Tel: (01625) 543430 Fax: (01625) 543431 E-mail: sales@arcit.co.uk
Bruce R.I.D. Recycling Ltd, March Street, Sheffield, S9 5DQ Tel: 0114-243 3637 Fax: 0114-244 8521 E-mail: info@weee-recycler.co.uk
End O Line Services, 1-3 Station Road, Maldon, Essex, CM9 4LQ Tel: (01621) 843535 Fax: (01621) 843534E-mail: sales@eols.co.uk
▶ First Choice It Ltd, 13 Renshaw Close, Luton, LU2 8TD Tel: (0845) 0510136 Fax: (0871) 8729611 E-mail: info@firstchoiceit.co.uk
IT Disposal, 1 Brook Farm, Stapleford Road, Stapleford Abbotts, Romford, RM4 1EJ Tel: (0845) 6445303 Fax: (01708) 688019 E-mail: info@itdisposal.co.uk
Secure I.T. Disposals Ltd, Unit 12, 53 Kettles Wood Drive, Woodgate Business Park, Woodgate Valley, Birmingham, B32 3DB Tel: (0870) 7271578 Fax: (0870) 7271469 E-mail: @sitd.co.uk

COMPUTER DOCUMENT IMAGING

Cyptec UK Ltd, 134 Timbercroft Lane, London, SE18 2SG Tel: (020) 8855 6664 Fax: (020) 8855 1714 E-mail: sales@vellumfile.com
Document Control Services Ltd, 10 Stapledon Road, Orton Southgate, Peterborough, PE2 6TB Tel: (01733) 366800 Fax: (01733) 366801 E-mail: dcs@sapasolutions.co.uk
Gapint Ltd, The Old Mill, Wellington Street, Ripley, Derbyshire, DE5 3EH Tel: (01773) 741174 Fax: (01773) 570247 E-mail: enquiries@gapint.co.uk
In Form Consultants Ltd, Weathervane House, Old Shire Lane, Chorleywood, Rickmansworth, Hertfordshire, WD3 5PW Tel: (01923) 283694 E-mail: info@inform-consult.com

COMPUTER DOCUMENT MANAGEMENT SYSTEMS

▶ Docman Solutions Ltd, Charter House, Pittman Way, Preston, PR2 9ZD Tel: (01772) 907087 Fax: (01772) 707114 E-mail: enquiries@docmansolutions.co.uk
E D M Group Ltd, Woden Road, Wolverhampton, WV10 0AY Tel: (01902) 459907 Fax: (01902) 351243 E-mail: docman@edm.co.uk
Effective Case Management Ltd, The Depository, Lewes Road, Lindfield, Haywards Heath, West Sussex, RH16 2LE Tel: (01444) 483968 Fax: (01444) 484852 E-mail: sales@casedocs.co.uk
Euro-Scot Design Ltd, James Watt Avenue, East Kilbride, Glasgow, G75 0QD Tel: (01355) 272300 Fax: (01355) 272153
Im Technical Services Ltd, Eagle House, Craigshaw Road, West Tullos Industrial Estate, Aberdeen, AB12 3AR Tel: (01224) 870004 Fax: (01224) 870004 E-mail: sales@imtechnical.com
Imscan Systems Ltd, Yew Tree House Yew Tree Court, Warrington Road, Risley, Warrington, WA3 6WP Tel: (01925) 761000 Fax: (01925) 766334 E-mail: sales@imscan.co.uk
Interwoven Europe, Novell House, 1 Arlington Square Downshire Way, Bracknell, Berkshire, RG12 1WA Tel: (01344) 418600 Fax: (01344) 418602 E-mail: info@interwoven.com
Microgen P.L.C., Fleet House Fleetwood Park, 3 Barley Way, Fleet, Hampshire, GU51 2QJ Tel: (01252) 772300 Fax: (01252) 772301 E-mail: marketing@microgen.co.uk
S S I Solutions Ltd, Fordbrook Business Centre, Marlborough Road, Pewsey, Wiltshire, SN9 5NU Tel: (01672) 565300 Fax: (01672) 563001 E-mail: general.enquireis@ssi.co.uk
Storofile Ltd, Shirewood Store, Woodlands, Wimborne, Dorset, BH21 8LX Tel: (01202) 822115 Fax: (01202) 822866 E-mail: sales@storofile.com

COMPUTER EQUIPMENT ENCLOSURES

Armagard Ltd, Unit 9 Fortnum Close, Birmingham, B33 0LG Tel: 0121-608 7210 Fax: 0121-608 4477 E-mail: sales@armagard.co.uk
▶ Bosstech UK, Borodin Close, Basingstoke, Hampshire, RG22 4EW Tel: (01256) 470444 Fax: (0871) 6613031 E-mail: phil@bosstechuk.co.uk
Dalen Ltd, Garretts Green Trading Estate, Valepits Road, Birmingham, B33 0TD Tel: 0121-783 3838 Fax: 0121-784 6348 E-mail: sales@top-tec.co.uk

COMPUTER ESTIMATING SOFTWARE

Business Micros, Main Street, Penpont, Thornhill, Dumfriesshire, DG3 4BP Tel: (01848) 330588 Fax: (01848) 331531 E-mail: info@businessmicros.co.uk
CCM Ace Ltd, 223 Bury New Road, Whitefield, Manchester, M45 8GW Tel: 0161-766 4686 Fax: 0161-767 9217 E-mail: sales@ccmace.co.uk
E E S Data, 41 George Street, Wakefield, West Yorkshire, WF1 1LW Tel: (01924) 200103 Fax: (01924) 200104 E-mail: info@ees-data.co.uk
Gridmaster Ltd, Weekley, Kettering, Northamptonshire, NN16 9UP Tel: (01536) 484948 Fax: (01536) 484948 E-mail: sales@gridmaster.co.uk
▶ LibeRATE Estimating Software, 25B The Borough, Farnham, Surrey, GU9 7NJ Tel: (01252) 725513 Fax: (01252) 727828 E-mail: info@landpro.co.uk
Mentat Systems Ltd, 21 Porthleven Crescent, Astley, Tyldesley, Manchester, M29 7FZ Tel: (01942) 749444 E-mail: sales@mentat.co.uk
Price Systems Ltd, Meridian Office Park, Osborn Way, Hook, Hampshire, RG27 9HY Tel: (01256) 760012 Fax: (01256) 762122 E-mail: sales@pricesystems.com
Sysnet Ltd, Avon Court, Cowbridge Road, Bridgend, Mid Glamorgan, CF31 3SR Tel: (01656) 647111 Fax: (01656) 651038 E-mail: enquiries@sysnetltd.co.uk

COMPUTER FINANCING SERVICES

▶ 247 Finance Services, Regent Street, London, W1B 2QD Tel: 0560 0029542 E-mail: contact@247-services.co.uk
The Boss Corporation, 31 Wren Gardens, Alderholt, Fordingbridge, Hampshire, SP6 3PJ Tel: (0845) 2574685 Fax: (0871) 4332393 E-mail: sales@thebosscorporation.co.uk
Causeway Technologies Ltd, Comino House Furlong Road, Bourne End, Buckinghamshire, SL8 5AQ Tel: (01628) 552000 Fax: (01628) 552001 E-mail: sales@causeway.com
▶ Golf Finance Ltd, 4 Church Road, North Berwick, East Lothian, EH39 4AD Tel: (01620) 890200 Fax: (01620) 895895 E-mail: sales@golffinance.co.uk
HSBC Invoice Finance, 12 Calthorpe Road, Edgbaston, Birmingham, B15 1RA Tel: 0121-455 2611 Fax: 0121-455 2190 E-mail: sales@invoicefinance.hsbc.co.uk
Infosculpt Ltd, 36 Dorien Road, London, SW20 8EJ Tel: (020) 8544 0592 Fax: (020) 8544 1043 E-mail: cdrequest@infosculpt.org
Lynx Ltd, 269 Banbury Road, Oxford, OX2 7JF Tel: (01865) 310150 Fax: (01865) 310499
▶ Optima Partnership, 1 Howarth Court, Vicarage Lane, Water Orton, Birmingham, B46 1RF Tel: (0870) 9041188 Fax: (0871) 4337050E-mail: info@optimapartnership.co.uk

COMPUTER FIXED DISK DRIVES

Pro Logic Computers, 6-8 Doncaster Road, South Elmsall, Pontefract, West Yorkshire, WF9 2HZ Tel: (01977) 649100 Fax: (01977) 651411 E-mail: paul@pro-logic.co.uk

COMPUTER FORM, *See Computer Stationery etc*

COMPUTER FURNITURE

Acco UK Ltd, Gatehouse Road, Aylesbury, Buckinghamshire, HP19 8DT Tel: (01296) 397444 Fax: (01296) 311000 E-mail: info@acco-uk.co.uk
Acco UK Ltd, Bretton Way, Bretton, Peterborough, PE3 8YE Tel: (01733) 264711 Fax: (01733) 269910
Bennett, 1 Iremonger Road, Off London Road, Nottingham, NG2 3BL Tel: 0115-955 8000 Fax: 0115-955 8008 E-mail: sales@bennittsykes.co.uk
▶ Bicester Furniture Studio, 24 Church Street, Bicester, Oxfordshire, OX26 6AZ Tel: (01869) 325669 Fax: (01869) 323164 E-mail: sezzybfs@tesco.net
Business Improvement Techniques Ltd, 11 Capricorn Centre, Cranes Farm Road, Basildon, Essex, SS14 3JJ Tel: (01268) 663320 Fax: (0845) 1232931
Colebrook Bosson & Saunders Products Ltd, 18 Bowden Street, London, SE11 4DS Tel: (020) 7587 5283 Fax: (020) 7587 5275 E-mail: sales@cbsproducts.co.uk
Diamik Solutions Ltd, A W Nielsen Road, Goole, North Humberside, DN14 6UE Tel: (0845) 1300690 Fax: (0845) 1300691 E-mail: sales@diamikbymorris.co.uk
Mauve Furniture Ltd, Arnlie, 79 Edinburgh Road, Dumfries, DG1 1JX Tel: (01387) 248889 Fax: (01387) 248889 E-mail: info@mauvefurniture.co.uk
Offizone Office Stationery Supplies, 1-15 Middle Hillgate, Stockport, Cheshire, SK1 3AY Tel: 0161-480 2010 Fax: 0161-480 4133 E-mail: sales@offizone.co.uk
R B S Office Supplies, Tollgate Business Centre, Tollgate Drive, Tollgate Industrial Estate, Stafford, ST16 3HS Tel: (01785) 254859 Fax: (01785) 220400 E-mail: sales@rbsofficesupplies.co.uk
Royal Strathclyde Blindcraft Industries Beds Mattresses Office Re, 12 Edgefauld Avenue, Glasgow, G21 4BB Tel: 0141-287 0800 Fax: 0141-287 0880
S & B UK Ltd, Labtec Street, Swinton, Manchester, M27 8SE Tel: 0161-793 9333 Fax: 0161-728 9149E-mail: info@splusb.co.uk
▶ Total Install Ltd, Unit 3, Hanworth Trading Estate Hampton, Feltham, Middlesex, TW13 6DH Tel: (020) 8898 5644 Fax: (020) 8898 5642 E-mail: info@totalinstall.co.uk
▶ Waxall Wood Finishes, Unit 1 Kilroot Park, Carrickfergus, County Antrim, BT38 7PR Tel: (028) 9336 5690 Fax: (028) 9336 5690 E-mail: enquiries@waxall.co.uk

COMPUTER GENERATED SIGN MAKING EQUIPMENT

A C D C Signs, 1 Hill Street, Milford, Armagh, BT60 3NZ Tel: (028) 3752 4755 Fax: (028) 3752 4755 E-mail: enquiries@acdcsigns.co.uk
Advertising Signs, 11 Teal Court, Strathclyde Business Park, Bellshill, Lanarkshire, ML4 3NN Tel: (01698) 844114 Fax: (01698) 844377
Avon Displays, Unit 4, Redhill Business Park, Elberton, Bristol, BS35 4AL Tel: (01454) 411144 E-mail: info@avondisplays.com
Border Signs & Graphix Ltd, St. Marys Industrial Estate, Dumfries, DG1 1NA Tel: (01387) 269582 Fax: (01387) 259396
C D T Signs, 9 Woodlands Road, Cirencester, Gloucestershire, GL7 1SP Tel: (01285) 640680 Fax: (01285) 652346
Central c.n.c. Machinery Ltd, Unit 12B, Scar La, Milnsbridge, Huddersfield, HD3 4PE Tel: 0845 4941645 Fax: (01484) 460101 E-mail: enquiries@centralcnc.co.uk
Euroscreen UK Ltd, Unit 3 Butts Court, Leigh, Lancashire, WN7 3AW Tel: (01942) 673333 Fax: (01942) 673344
Eyecatchers Signs Ltd, Old Mill Victoria Road, Eccleshill, Bradford, West Yorkshire, BD2 2BH Tel: (01274) 630640 Fax: (01274) 630644
Fast Signs Scotland Ltd, Unit 1, Millstreet Industrial Estate, Airdrie, Lanarkshire, ML6 6JJ Tel: (01236) 766050 Fax: (01236) 751647 E-mail: fastsigns@btconnect.com
Fastsigns, 12 Boar Lane, Leeds, LS1 6EN Tel: 0113-246 9300 Fax: 0113-246 9393
▶ Fastsigns Signs & Graphics, 6 Victoria Court, New Street, Chelmsford, CM1 1GP Tel: (01245) 350450 Fax: (01245) 280022 E-mail: chelmsford.uk@863fastsigns.com
Grafityp (UK) Ltd, 103 Mariner, Tamworth, Staffordshire, B79 7UL Tel: (01827) 300500 Fax: (01827) 51333 E-mail: sales@grafityp.co.uk
High Street Signs, 5b Denham Road, Sheffield, S11 8NE Tel: 0114-268 4224 Fax: 0114-268 4224 E-mail: info@high-street-signs.co.uk
Impact Signs, 13-14 Hutton Street, Boldon Colliery, Tyne & Wear, NE35 9LW Tel: 0191-536 0536 Fax: 0191-536 5536 E-mail: info@inpact3dsigns.co.uk
K B S Group, 41 Marsh Green Road West, Marsh Barton Trading Estate, Exeter, EX2 8PN Tel: (01392) 208208 Fax: (01392) 208200 E-mail: sales@kbs-group.com
Lloyd Signs Of Birkenhead, Units 7-10, Cavendish Enterprise Centre, Birkenhead, Merseyside, CH41 8BY Tel: 0151-653 8053 Fax: 0151-653 8053
McKay Signs & Graphics, Unit 7 Chipping Edge Estate, Hatters Lane, Chipping Sodbury, Bristol, BS37 6AA Tel: (01454) 319483 Fax: (01454) 312912
N I S Sign Group, Oakland Road, Leicester, LE2 6AN Tel: 0116-270 6228 Fax: 0116-270 3347 E-mail: info@signs-nis.co.uk
Prestige Signs, 33 Daryl Road, Wirral, Merseyside, CH60 5RD Tel: 0151-342 6372 Fax: 0151-342 6372
▶ Scorpio Signs (Design & Display) Ltd, Hartford House Yard, School Lane, Hartford, Northwich, Cheshire, CW8 1NP Tel: (01606) 74912 Fax: (01606) 76036 E-mail: mail@scorpiosigns.co.uk
Select Signs, 68 Ballysallagh Road, Bangor, County Down, BT19 1UT Tel: (028) 9185 3301 Fax: (028) 9185 3301
Sign Shop, 93 West Main Street, Broxburn, West Lothian, EH52 5LE Tel: (01506) 853601 Fax: (01506) 853601
Sign Systems, Unit 4a Shipley Court, Manners Avenue Industrial Estate, Manners Industrial Estate, Ilkeston, Derbyshire, DE7 8EF Tel: 0115-944 1678 Fax: 0115-944 1495 E-mail: enquiries@signsystems.uk.com
Signdisplay, Unit 7 Long Island Park, Carlisle, CA2 5AS Tel: (01228) 819144 Fax: (01228) 514145 E-mail: maurice@albanysigndisplay.wannado.co.uk
Signet Signs Ltd, 45 West Town Road, Backwell, Bristol, BS48 3HG Tel: (01275) 463601 Fax: (01275) 462990 E-mail: mail@signetsigns.co.uk
Signs & Labels Of Shrewsbury, Unit 7a Hardwicke Stables Industrial Estate, Hadnall, Shrewsbury, SY4 4AS Tel: (01939) 210230 Fax: (01939) 210231
Signs & Lighting Services, Easterton Farm, Stirling Road, Denny, Stirlingshire, FK6 6RG Tel: (01324) 824218 Fax: (01324) 823794
Signtec Signs & Nameplates, The Lawns, Chargrove Lane, Shurdington, Cheltenham, Gloucestershire, GL51 4XB Tel: (01242) 862008 Fax: (01242) 862008
Southpark Signs, 258 Green Lane, Ilford, Essex, IG1 1YF Tel: (020) 8553 1123 Fax: (020) 8553 0789
Spectrum Menu Systems Ltd, Units 12 &13, Hixon Industrial Estate, Church Lane, Hixon, Stafford, ST18 0PY Tel: (01889) 271440 Fax: (01889) 271449
Swift Signs Ltd, Vere Court, Grantham, Lincolnshire, NG31 8FB Tel: (01476) 563981 Fax: (01476) 590655
T & E Signs, Unit 4b Nalken House Eley Estate, Nobel Road, London, N18 3BH Tel: (020) 8345 7007 Fax: (020) 8345 7117
Vital Signs, 1-15 Union Street, Cookstown, County Tyrone, BT80 8NN Tel: (028) 8676 5551 E-mail: sales@vitalsigns.org.uk

COMPUTER GENERATED SIGN MAKING EQUIPMENT – *continued*

Xpose Media Ltd, Unit 3 Mona Industrial Park, Gwalchmai, Holyhead, Gwynedd, LL65 4RJ Tel: (01407) 720222 Fax: (01407) 720066 E-mail: sales@angleseysigns.co.uk

COMPUTER GRAPHIC PRINTING OR PROCESSING SERVICES

▶ A & H Commercial Printers, 153-155 Ley Street, Ilford, Essex, IG1 4BL Tel: (020) 8478 2558 Fax: (020) 8514 5366 E-mail: info@ahprinters.com

Funasset Ltd, Orchards, 14 Townsend, Ilminster, Somerset, TA19 0AU Tel: (01460) 57065 Fax: (01460) 53538 E-mail: enquiries@funasset.com

▶ IDVE Design, 2 Hillside Road, HASTINGS, East Sussex, TN34 2QT Tel: 0845 2571965 E-mail: contact@idve.co.uk

COMPUTER GRAPHICS CONSULTANTS OR SERVICES

▶ Aboutalluneed, Fletcher House, 4 Betley Court, Main Road, Betley, Crewe, CW3 9BH Tel: (01270) 820344 Fax: (01270) 820344 E-mail: thisis@aboutalluneed.co.uk

Active Computer Graphics, Robin Lodge, Heynes West End, Haynes, Bedford, MK45 3RB Tel: 01234 740257

Aztec Presentations Ltd, Unit 7B, Browns Place, Leeds, LS11 0EF Tel: 0113-277 7799 E-mail: sales@aztecpresentations.co.uk

C G P Associates Ltd, 2 Maple Road, Enigma Business Park, Malvern, Worcestershire, WR14 1GQ Tel: (01684) 584700 Fax: (0870) 0522410 E-mail: derekc@cgp.co.uk

▶ Citrus Media Ltd, Trivarden House, Milton Road, Shipton-under-Wychwood, Chipping Norton, Oxfordshire, OX7 6BD Tel: (01993) 830955 Fax: (01993) 831906 E-mail: info@citrus-media.co.uk

Computer Junction, 276 Arundel Street, Portsmouth, PO1 1NT Tel: (023) 9282 5210 Fax: (023) 9282 5210 E-mail: cjsolent@btconnect.com

▶ Digital Progression, 123 Old Christchurch Road, Bournemouth, BH1 1EP Tel: (01202) 316660 Fax: (01202) 311185 E-mail: mail@digitalprogression.co.uk

I S G Direct Ltd, 31 Courthouse Road, London, N12 7PH Tel: (020) 8445 1631 Fax: (020) 8343 8326

Intercad Workstation Graphics Ltd, 43 Manse Road, Bearsden, Glasgow, G61 3PN Tel: 0141-942 2232 Fax: 0141-942 6555

Light Stop Ltd, 52 Furze Platt Road, Maidenhead, Berkshire, SL6 7NN Tel: (01628) 632632 Fax: (01628) 686900

London Graphic Centre, 16-18 Shelton Street, London, WC2H 9JL Tel: (020) 7759 4500 Fax: (020) 7759 4585 E-mail: mailorder@londongraphics.co.uk

▶ Pixel Perfect, The White House, Copse Road, Haslemere, Surrey, GU27 3QQ Tel: (01428) 643500 E-mail: sales@pixelperfect.co.uk

R H Colvill Associates, Pointers South, Pointers Road, Cobham, Surrey, KT11 1PQ Tel: (01932) 860950 Fax: (01932) 860950

Service Graphics, 3 Osiers Road, London, SW18 1NL Tel: (020) 8877 6600 Fax: (020) 8871 3521 E-mail: scott.king@servicegraphics.co.uk

Top Banana, The Studio, Broome, Stourbridge, West Midlands, DY9 0HA Tel: (01562) 700404 Fax: (01562) 700930 E-mail: info@top-b.com

Trilobyte Design Ltd, Mersa House, Haroldslea Drive, Horley, Surrey, RH6 9DT Tel: (01293) 774747 E-mail: info@trilobytedesigns.co.uk

COMPUTER GRAPHICS SYSTEM DESIGN

3-D Labs, Meadlake Place, Thorpe Lea Road, Egham, Surrey, TW20 8HE Tel: (01784) 470555 Fax: (01784) 470699 E-mail: info@3dlabs.co.uk

Design House, 52 Hollins Lane, Marple Bridge, Stockport, Cheshire, SK6 5BD Tel: 0161-427 1426 Fax: 0161-427 9316 E-mail: siddesigns@aol.com

Hauppauge Computer Works Ltd, Bank Chambers, 6 Borough High Street, London, SE1 9QQ Tel: (020) 7378 1997 Fax: (020) 7357 9771 E-mail: support@hauppauge.co.uk

Lawrence Creative Ltd, 1 Newton Place, Glasgow, G3 7PR Tel: 0141-333 9009 Fax: 0141-333 9495 E-mail: design@lawrencecreative.com

▶ Remote New Media, 17 Lower Down, Lydbury North, Shropshire, SY7 8BB Tel: (01588) 680480 E-mail: info@remote.uk.com

Stone Group, 58 Edison Road, Rabans Lane Industrial Area, Aylesbury, Buckinghamshire, HP19 8TE Tel: (01785) 812100 Fax: (01296) 424165 E-mail: info@compusys.co.uk

Tector Visual Systems, Woodhill Road, Collingham, Newark, Nottinghamshire, NG23 7NR Tel: (01636) 892246 Fax: (01636) 893317 E-mail: sales@graffelectronics.co.uk

Wordcrafts, Unit 9 The Beaver Centre, Putney Road West, Freemans Common, Leicester, LE2 7TD Tel: 0116-255 8422 Fax: 0116-255 0624 E-mail: info@wordcrafts.co.uk

Zucker & Staub Ltd, Flat 13 Nursery Walk Court, Sunningfields Road, Handon, London, NW4 4RJ Tel: (020) 8203 6499 Fax: (020) 8203 6499 E-mail: info@zucker-staub.com

COMPUTER HARD DISKS

Quantum Peripheral Products Ltd, Quantum House 3 Bracknell Beeches, Old Bracknell La West, Bracknell, Berkshire, RG12 7BW Tel: (01344) 353500 Fax: (01344) 353510

COMPUTER HARDWARE CLEANING PRODUCTS

HK Wentworth Ltd, Kingsbury Park, Midlington Road, Swadlincote, Derbyshire, DE11 0AN Tel: (01283) 222111 Fax: (01283) 550177 E-mail: afsales@hkw.co.uk

S & M Computer Cleaning Services Ltd, Midland House, New Road, Halesowen, West Midlands, B63 3HY Tel: 0121-550 4008 Fax: 0121-550 5272 E-mail: sales@computercleaners.co.uk

Techclean Services Ltd, V D U House, Old Kiln Lane, Farnham, Surrey, GU10 2JH Tel: (01428) 713713 Fax: (01428) 713798 E-mail: info@techclean.co.uk

COMPUTER HARDWARE DESIGN, EMBEDDED

▶ Spheroid (UK) Ltd, Unit 27, Balfour Road, Balfour Business Centre, Southall, Middlesex, UB2 5BD Tel: (0870) 4582222 Fax: (020) 8893 5588 E-mail: sales@compubits.com

COMPUTER HARDWARE EXPORT

Astra Distribution Ltd, 29 Roseberry Crescent, Great Ayton, Middlesbrough, Cleveland, TS9 6EP Tel: (01642) 724367 E-mail: info@astradistribution.com

▶ Cladswell House Systems Ltd, The Old Fishery, Holborrow Lodge, Holberrow Green, Redditch, Worcestershire, B96 6SF Tel: (01386) 793377 Fax: (01386) 793376 E-mail: sales@chs.eu.com

▶ Computer England, Quadro, Ivy Mill, Failsworth, Manchester, M35 9BD Tel: 0870 2201835 Fax: 0870 2201836

▶ Genstar Trading, Unit 2, Colne Way Court, Watford, WD24 7NE Tel: (01923) 806806 Fax: (01923) 805805 E-mail: sales@genstar.co.uk

▶ Global Tech Associates Limited, 2nd Floor, 145 - 157 St. John Street, London, EC1V 4PY Tel: 0207 7887717 Fax: 0870 7628453

▶ Logicus Technologies Ltd, 16 The Drive, Wembley, Middlesex, HA9 9EG Tel: (0870) 0637010 Fax: (0870) 0638010 E-mail: sme@logicus-technologies.com

P K N D Computer Services, 26 Parkfield Row, Leeds, LS11 7LT Tel: 0113-276 5758 Fax: 0871 5216882 E-mail: info@pknd.co.uk

COMPUTER HARDWARE INSTALLATION

▶ Adeptias Ltd, 37 Beauchamp Avenue, Leamington Spa, Warwickshire, CV32 5TD Tel: (01926) 831555 Fax: 01926 422600

Computer Doctor Services Ltd, 20a Portland Road, Kilmarnock, Ayrshire, KA1 2BS Tel: (01563) 537733 Fax: (01563) 537733 E-mail: kellyenquiry@computerdoctorservice.co.uk

▶ Computer Orbit Ltd, 36-44 West Road, Newcastle upon Tyne, NE4 9PY Tel: 0191-242 0120

▶ Computer Sos Gampian Ltd, Howford, Inverurie, Aberdeenshire, AB51 4DL Tel: (01467) 622766 E-mail: info@comp-sos.co.uk

▶ Labyrinth Computers Ltd, Unit 3 Lufton Heights Commerce Park, Boundary Way, Lufton, Yeovil, Somerset, BA22 8UY Tel: (01935) 421299 Fax: (01935) 421887 E-mail: sales@labyrinth-computers.com

▶ Spheroid (UK) Ltd, Unit 27, Balfour Road, Balfour Business Centre, Southall, Middlesex, UB2 5BD Tel: (0870) 4582222 Fax: (020) 8893 5588 E-mail: sales@compubits.com

Twisted Fish Ltd, 1 Stan Hill, Charlwood, Horley, Surrey, RH6 0EP Tel: (01293) 863763 Fax: (01293) 863201

Ulysses Ltd, Unit A Troon Way Business Centre, Humberstone Lane, Leicester, LE4 9HA Tel: 0116-276 9152 Fax: (0845) 1300259 E-mail: info@ulysses.uk.com

White Lightning Solutions, 97 Brighton Road, Godalming, Surrey, GU7 1PW Tel: (01483) 429040 Fax: (01483) 429030

Wizzbitz Ltd, 792 Wilmslow Road, Didsbury, Manchester, M20 6UG Tel: (08701) 657310 E-mail: customerservice@wizzbitz.com

COMPUTER HARDWARE MAINTENANCE SUPPORT

▶ Ade Sims, 23 Heathfield, Chippenham, Wiltshire, SN15 1BQ Tel: 01249 461295 E-mail: adesims@supanet.com

A1 Computer Services, 6 Wheatfield Road, Westerhope, Newcastle upon Tyne, NE5 5HQ Tel: (07757) 612978 E-mail: a1computers@mail.com

▶ Ask The Geek, Bruntsfield, Edinburgh, EH3 9LP Tel: (0797) 4224472 E-mail: sales@askthegeek.it

▶ Bat I T Solutions Ltd, 20 Briskman Way, Oakwood Park, Aylesbury, Buckinghamshire, HP21 8FP Tel: (01296) 483631 Fax: (01296) 331510 E-mail: tris@bat-it.com

Brockham Computers, 7 Bishops Cottages Chalkpit Lane, Betchworth, Dorking, Surrey, RH3 7HA Tel: (01737) 842075 E-mail: keith@brockhamcomputers.co.uk

▶ Computafixit.Com, 49 Oxford Road, Acocks Green, Birmingham, B27 6DS Tel: (0845) 8900689 E-mail: sales@computafixit.com

▶ Computer Solutions, 7 Sandringham Cresent, Harrow, Middlesex, HA2 9BW Tel: (020) 8422 7570 Fax: (020) 8248 0548 E-mail: info@1001solutions.co.uk

▶ Computers Doctor, 19 Bolton Walk, London, N7 7RW Tel: (0845) 3307881 E-mail: info@computersdoctor.com

▶ Computersurgeon, 3 High Copse, Farnham, Surrey, GU9 0BL Tel: (01252) 717096 Fax: (01252) 717096 E-mail: derek@computersurgeon.net

▶ Crownhill Consulting Ltd, 1 Lansbury Road, Halesworth, Suffolk, IP19 8SA Tel: (01986) 875814 Fax: (0870) 7058775 E-mail: kevin.holland@crownhill-consulting.com

Deepdale Technical Services Ltd, 33A Scalbie Road, Scarborough, North Yorkshire, YO12 5PZ Tel: (0870) 2201486 Fax: (01723) 377571 E-mail: info@deepdale.co.uk

Delta Pc Services Ltd, Bridge House, Bridge Street, Walton-On-Thames, Surrey, KT12 1AL Tel: (01932) 252514 Fax: (01932) 252818

▶ Elan Consulting, 52 St Marks Road, Henley-on-Thames, Oxfordshire, RG9 1LW Tel: 07920 112909 E-mail: nick@elanconsulting.co.uk

▶ Eserve It Ltd, Dealtree House, Blackmore Road Hook End, Brentwood, Essex, CM15 0DS Tel: (01277) 822005 Fax: (0870) 1166422 E-mail: info@eserve.it

▶ The Gosport PC Clinic, 69 Brockhurst Road, Gosport, Hampshire, PO12 3AR Tel: (023) 9252 2777 Fax: (023) 9252 2777 E-mail: support@coppcomm.com

▶ Hybrid Computers, 15 Rembrandt End, Aylesbury, Buckinghamshire, HP19 8SL Tel: (01296) 484888 E-mail: info@hybrid-computers.biz

▶ ITC Service Ltd, 45 Wedderlaw, Cramlington, Northumberland, NE23 6PA Tel: (07919) 154375 Fax: 0191-416 3003 E-mail: info@itcservive.co.uk

J W Cooper UK Limited, 25 Glenmore Road, Minehead, Somerset, TA24 6GA Tel: 0845 8380394 Fax: 0871 9942178 E-mail: info@jwcgroup.co.uk

Keen IT Solutions Limited, 79 Ansell Road, Frimley, Camberley, Surrey, GU16 8DH Tel: 0845 0940320 E-mail: info@keenit.co.uk

▶ Mac PC Solutions Ltd, 53 Shirley Gardens, Barking, Essex, IG11 9XB Tel: (07956) 168242 E-mail: info@macpcsolutions.co.uk

▶ N F M Solutions Ltd, 7 Standrigg Gardens, Brightons, Falkirk, FK2 0GJ Tel: (0870) 7776698 Fax: (0870) 7776398 E-mail: info@nfmsolutions.com

▶ Net Solutions London, 40 Sheen Lane, London, SW14 8LW Tel: 0208 2552483 Fax: 0208 2554022E-mail: info@netsols.co.uk

Ogl Computer Services Group, Worcester Road, Stourport-on-Severn, Worcestershire, DY13 9AT Tel: (01299) 873873 Fax: (01299) 873700 E-mail: enquiries@ogl.co.uk

▶ On-It Ltd, 32 Demesne Road, Wallington, Surrey, SM6 8PP Tel: (020) 8773 9900

▶ PC Cure, PO Box 332, Manchester, M16 0NB Tel: 0161-872 5297 Fax: 0870 2203165 E-mail: info@pccure.co.uk

▶ PC Help Centre, High St South, Dunstable, Bedfordshire, LU6 3HR Tel: (01582) 672606 Fax: (01582) 602508 E-mail: marketing@pchelpcentre.com

Persimmon Consultants Ltd, Pine View, Forest Dale Road, Marlborough, Wiltshire, SN8 2AS Tel: (01672) 514500 E-mail: info@persim.com

▶ Protec UK, The Underwater Studio, Archers Field, Burnt Mills Industrial Estate, Basildon, Essex, SS13 1DL Tel: 0845 8802253 Fax: 0845 8802254 E-mail: support@protecuk.com

▶ S R S Computer Systems Ltd, 1 Dewar House, 1 Enterprise Way, Dunfermline, Fife, KY11 8PY Tel: (01383) 624446 Fax: (01383) 840880 E-mail: kellyanne@srsnet.co.uk

SMG Computers, 34 Hallen Close, Emersons Green, Bristol, BS16 7JE Tel: (0788) 0731672 E-mail: smg@smg-computers.com

▶ T & S Technologies Ltd, 6 Tollgate Road, Stone, Dartford, DA2 6BS Tel: (01474) 824503

▶ Technology Zoo Ltd, 31 Kenway Collier Row, Romford, RM5 3EH Tel: (01708) 507716 E-mail: help@techzoo.co.uk

V M S Ltd, Blenheim Road, Pocklington Industrial Estate, York, YO42 1NR Tel: (01759) 305030 Fax: (01759) 305816 E-mail: admin@vmsl.co.uk

▶ Westlake Information Technology Ltd, 9 Windmill Field Denmead, Waterlooville, Hampshire, PO7 6PL Tel: (023) 9226 9594 E-mail: info@westlake-it.com

White Lightning Solutions, 97 Brighton Road, Godalming, Surrey, GU7 1PW Tel: (01483) 429040 Fax: (01483) 429030

COMPUTER HIRE

▶ Aria Desktops, Unit 12, Harmill Industrial Estate, Grovebury Road, Leighton Buzzard, Bedfordshire, LU7 4FF Tel: (01525) 853233

▶ Bear Assembly, 203 Longford Road, Longford, Coventry, CV6 6BG Tel: (024) 7636 7771 Fax: (024) 7664 5020

Blakelan Communications Ltd, Railway Cottage, Mill Road, Brighton, BN1 8ZF Tel: (01273) 564092 Fax: (01273) 564111 E-mail: mike.blakeman@blakelan.com

Causeway Technologies Ltd, Comino House Furlong Road, Bourne End, Buckinghamshire, SL8 5AQ Tel: (01628) 552000 Fax: (01628) 552001 E-mail: sales@causeway.com

Computerhire South West Ltd, 5 Kingsway, Kingswood, Bristol, BS15 8BF Tel: 0117-907 7101 Fax: 0117-907 7105 E-mail: sales@computerhire-sw.co.uk

▶ Conductive Inkjet Technology, The Power House, Lumen Road, Royston, Hertfordshire, SG8 7AG Tel: (01223) 437933 Fax: (01763) 245400 E-mail: sales@rentit.net

▶ Csi Leasing, 2 Newton Business Centre Thorncliffe Park Estate, Newton Cham, Chapeltown, Sheffield, S35 2PH Tel: 0114-232 9200 Fax: 0114-232 9216

E & M Office Equipment Ltd, 94 Gray's Inn Road, London, WC1X 8AD Tel: (020) 7713 1591 Fax: (020) 7242 0239 E-mail: sales@emofficeequipment.co.uk

G K M Technical Services, 14 Whessoe Road, Darlington, County Durham, DL3 0QP Tel: (01325) 361670 Fax: (01325) 361670 E-mail: sales@gkm.co.uk

Hamilton Rentals P.L.C., Hamilton House, North Circular Road, London, NW10 7UB Tel: (020) 8963 8080 Fax: (020) 8961 8385 E-mail: info@hamilton.co.uk

Hilton Charles Ltd, Airey House, 57 Shepherd Road, Lytham St. Annes, Lancashire, FY8 3ST Tel: (01253) 789444 Fax: (01253) 722989

▶ Hire Intelligence (Leicester) Ltd, 3 Hawthorn Grove, Oadby, Leicester, LE2 4ED Tel: 0116-271 0091 Fax: 0116-271 0095 E-mail: leicester@hire-intelligence.co.uk

▶ Hire Intelligence Southwest England - Exeter, 40 Southernhay East, Exeter, EX1 1PE Tel: (0800) 0857667 Fax: (0870) 2202752 E-mail: sales@hiresouthwest.co.uk

Hire It, Magnum House, Cookham Road, Bracknell, Berkshire, RG12 1RB Tel: (01344) 477744 Fax: (01344) 477789 E-mail: sales@hireit.co.uk

Livingston Services plc, Livingston House, 2-6 Queens Road, Teddington, Middlesex, TW11 0LR Tel: (020) 8943 1142 Fax: (020) 8977 6431 E-mail: info@livingston.co.uk

Micro Rent plc, 6 The Gateway Centre, Coronation Road, Cressex Business Park, High Wycombe, Buckinghamshire, HP12 3SU Tel: (01494) 768768 Fax: (01494) 768700 E-mail: sales@microrent.co.uk

Office Electronics Centre UK Ltd, Electronics House Enterprise Court, Gapton Hall Road, Great Yarmouth, Norfolk, NR31 0ND Tel: (01493) 600500 Fax: (01493) 650398 E-mail: sales@oecuk.co.uk

▶ PC 2 U, Design Works, William Street, Gateshead, Tyne & Wear, NE10 0JP Tel: 0191-420 5345 Fax: 0191-420 5345 E-mail: sales@pc2u.co.uk

▶ Summit Asset Management Ltd, Melita House, 124 Bridge Road, Chertsey, Surrey, KT16 8LA Tel: (01932) 575888 Fax: (01932) 575889

Tapestry Audio Visual, Nordic House, Baltic Quay, Grangemouth, Stirlingshire, FK3 8TX Tel: (0845) 2308999 Fax: (01324) 489349 E-mail: sales@tapestryav.net

▶ Tuskala, Clarendon Business Centre, 38 Clarendon Road, Eccles, Manchester, M30 9EF Tel: 0161-789 5153 Fax: 0161-788 9470 E-mail: sales@tuskala.com

COMPUTER INDUSTRIAL ROBOT CONTROLLERS

Cougar Automation Ltd, Cougar House Parklands Business Park, Forest Road, Denmead, Waterlooville, Hampshire, PO7 6XP Tel: (023) 9226 9960 Fax: (023) 9226 9968 E-mail: info@cougar-automation.com

Kuka Automation & Robotics Ltd, Hereward Rise, Halesowen, West Midlands, B62 8AN Tel: 0121-585 0800 Fax: 0121-585 0900 E-mail: sales@kuka.co.uk

COMPUTER INSTALLATION LOCAL AREA NETWORK (LAN) SYSTEM ENCLOSURES OR CABINETS

ADC Communications (UK) Ltd, Runnings Road, Kingsditch Trading Estate, Cheltenham, Gloucestershire, GL51 9NQ Tel: (01242) 264400 Fax: (01242) 264488 E-mail: christianname.surname@adckrone.com

▶ indicates data change since last edition

COMPUTER INSTALLATION LOCAL AREA NETWORK (LAN) SYSTEM ENCLOSURES OR CABINETS – *continued*

Cannon Technologies Europe Ltd, 13 Queensway, Stem Lane Industrial Estate, New Milton, Hampshire, BH25 5NU Tel: (01425) 638148 Fax: (01425) 619276 E-mail: sales@cannontech.co.uk

COMPUTER INSTALLATION SERVICES

A D C Technology Ltd, A D C Ho, Broomfield Place, Coventry, CV5 6GY Tel: (024) 7671 5858 Fax: (024) 7671 4462
A1 Netservices, 23 Tudor Road, Wheathampstead, St. Albans, Hertfordshire, AL4 8NW Tel: (01582) 834208 Fax: (0871) 7501428 E-mail: info@a1-netservices.co.uk
Aml Computers, Sir Francis Drake, Gayhurst, Newport Pagnell, Buckinghamshire, MK16 8LG Tel: (01908) 551550 Fax: (01908) 551545
Arena Computer Supplies Ltd, 18 Sandeman Way, Horsham, West Sussex, RH13 6EL Tel: (01403) 272156 Fax: (01403) 252620
▶ Astral Installations Ltd, 279 Marlborough Road, Gillingham, Kent, ME7 5HS Tel: (01634) 280763 Fax: (01634) 302110 E-mail: enquiries@astraluklimited.co.uk
Atlas Security, 226 Psalter Lane, Sheffield, S11 8UT Tel: 0114-266 9850
▶ Auxilior Ltd, 6 Steventon Road, Southampton, SO18 5HA Tel: (023) 8047 3441 E-mail: kevin.haynes@auxilior.co.uk
Aztech Microcentres Ltd, 322 Hemdean Road, Caversham, Reading, RG4 7QS Tel: 0118-946 6600 Fax: 0118-946 1076 E-mail: sales@aztechmicros.com
Barkers International Communication Ltd, Barkers Lane, Bedford, MK41 9TR Tel: (01234) 327772 Fax: (01234) 325526 E-mail: richard@barkers-int.co.uk
Brandt Computer Systems Ltd, 20 Barclay Road, Croydon, CR0 1JN Tel: (020) 8760 9173 Fax: (020) 8760 9180 E-mail: croydon@brandt.co.uk
Cameo Computer Services Ltd, Unit 6, Maizefield, Hinckley, Leicestershire, LE10 1YF Tel: (01455) 618893 Fax: (01455) 254878 E-mail: info@cameouk.com
▶ Columbia Precision Ltd, 125 Cheston Road, Birmingham, B7 5EA Tel: 0121-327 1500 Fax: 0121-327 1511 E-mail: enquires@columbia.uk.com
Comart ITM, Technology House, Ridge Road, Rotherham, South Yorkshire, S65 1NS Tel: (01709) 363418 Fax: (01709) 835369 E-mail: enquiries@comartplc.co.uk
Command Alkon Ltd, 21 St Annes Road, St Annes Park, St. Annes Park, Bristol, BS4 4AB Tel: 0117-972 4777 Fax: 0117-972 4888
Computer Precision Ltd, 185 Upper Street, London, N1 1RQ Tel: (020) 7359 9797 Fax: (020) 7359 9507 E-mail: 185@cipi.co.uk
▶ Computer Sos Gampian Ltd, Howford, Inverurie, Aberdeenshire, AB51 4DL Tel: (01467) 622766 E-mail: info@comp-sos.co.uk
Computers In Construction, 337 Brook Street, Broughty Ferry, Dundee, DD5 2DS Tel: (01382) 776733 Fax: (01382) 521438
Contrac Computer Supplies North East, Pinetree Centre, Durham Road, Birtley, Chester le Street, County Durham, DH3 2TD Tel: 0191-492 2999 Fax: 0191-492 3011 E-mail: enquiries@contrac.co.uk
Corporate Upgrade Centre Ltd, Ornhams Hall, Boroughbridge, York, YO51 9JH Tel: (01423) 324777 Fax: (01423) 324113
Creative Computing Solutions Ltd, Bishops Gate, Station Road, Taplow, Maidenhead, Berkshire, SL6 0PA Tel: (01628) 660600 Fax: (01628) 605434 E-mail: sales@creative-computing.co.uk
Cumbria Communications 2000 Ltd, Westgate, Milburn, Penrith, Cumbria, CA10 1TW Tel: (01768) 361416 Fax: (01768) 362000
Daystar, Daystar House, 102 Burnage Lane, Manchester, M19 2NG Tel: 0161-248 8088 Fax: 0161-224 2522
Dome Products Ltd, Burnside Business Centre, Burnside Road, Boddam, Peterhead, Aberdeenshire, AB42 3AW Tel: (01779) 481964 Fax: (01779) 481965
Durham Computer Centre Ltd, 6 New Elvet, Durham, DH1 3AQ Tel: 0191-386 8989 Fax: 0191-384 4556 E-mail: info@durhamcomputercentre.co.uk
Griffiths Associates Ltd, Penylan House, Penprysg Road, Pencoed, Bridgend, Mid Glamorgan, CF35 6LT Tel: (01656) 862653 Fax: (01656) 864243 E-mail: john.griffiths@galtd.co.uk
Groestar Ltd, 1 Morley Business Centre, Tonbridge, Kent, TN9 1RA Tel: (01732) 771121 Fax: (01732) 771124 E-mail: sales@groestar.co.uk
Hewlett Packard Ltd, 3 Dunlop Square, Deans, Livingston, West Lothian, EH54 8SB Tel: (01506) 419111 Fax: (01506) 460135
I S C Computers Plc, 2 Pioneer Way, Lincoln, LN6 3DH Tel: (01522) 686464
Ideal Software & Systems, 49 High St, Sandy, Beds, SG19 1AG Tel: 01767 682851 Fax: 01767 683884
J A V Controls, 26 Reson Way, Hemel Hempstead, Hertfordshire, HP1 1NU Tel: (01442) 256617 Fax: (01442) 233099 E-mail: jgurney@javgroup.co.uk
Jordan IT Services, 28 Carter Ave, Broughton, Kettering, Northants, NN14 1LZ Tel: (01536) 790425 Fax: (08701) 367829 E-mail: info@jordanitservices.com
Kezvale Ltd, 5 Johnsons Industrial Estate, Silverdale Road, Hayes, Middlesex, UB3 3BA Tel: (020) 8569 2731 Fax: (020) 8569 2790 E-mail: info@kezvale.co.uk
Kindways.Com, 4 Trinity Avenue, Llandudno, Gwynedd, LL30 2NQ Tel: (01492) 879312 Fax: (01492) 873811
Lawmax Electrical Contractors Ltd, Lawmax House, 30-32 Nottingham Road, Stapleford, Nottingham, NG9 8AA Tel: 0115-939 4248 Fax: 0115-939 9412 E-mail: sales@lawmaxelec.co.uk
M L R Networks Ltd, St. Michaels House, Hale Road, Widnes, Cheshire, WA8 8XL Tel: 0151-423 3633 Fax: 0151-495 1665 E-mail: pmorris@mlrnetworks.co.uk
Majenta Solutions, Coptfold Road, Brentwood, Essex, CM14 4BN Tel: (01277) 263244 Fax: (01277) 263245 E-mail: info@majentasolutions.co.uk
Middlestown PCS Ltd, 52 High Street, Horbury, Wakefield, West Yorkshire, WF4 5LE Tel: (01924) 260615 Fax: (01924) 270245 E-mail: info@middlestownpcs.co.uk
Milequip Computer Maintenance Ltd, Hepworth House, 115 Southgate Street, Gloucester, GL1 1UT Tel: (01452) 305430 Fax: (01452) 411010 E-mail: mcmcomputers@freeuk.com
Mintra Ltd, 963 Stockport Road, Manchester, M19 3NP Tel: 0161-256 4030 Fax: 0161-225 2848 E-mail: sales@mintra.com
Nexus Graphic Systems Ltd, Apartment 11, Generator Hall, Electric Wharf, Coventry, CV1 4JL Tel: (024) 7622 3865 Fax: (024) 7622 3872
On Line Support Computing Ltd, The Old Station Works, 119 Sandycomb Road, Richmond, Surrey, TW9 2EP Tel: (020) 8940 9484 Fax: (020) 8948 2114
P & P Installation P.L.C., Unit 5 Empire Centre, Imperial Way, Watford, WD24 4YH Tel: (01923) 226357 Fax: (01923) 254434
S & H Computers Ltd, Godfrey Drive, Ilkeston, Derbyshire, DE7 4HU Tel: 0115-875 8164 Fax: 0115-875 8164 E-mail: sales.shcomputers@ntlworld.com
Harry Shaw Business Computers Ltd, 29-31 Leicester Street, Bedworth, Warwickshire, CV12 8GG Tel: (024) 7631 6666 Fax: (024) 7631 6187 E-mail: info@harryshaw.net
Stack Computer Solutions Ltd, Bridle House, Bridle Way, Bootle, Merseyside, L30 4UA Tel: 0151-521 2202 Fax: 0151-525 2298 E-mail: sales@stack.co.uk
STS 2000 Ltd, Unit 11 Bowmans Trading Estate, Bessemer Drive, Stevenage, Hertfordshire, SG1 2DL Tel: (01438) 747474 Fax: (01438) 747476
Ufcc, 9 Withcote Avenue, Leicester, LE5 6SW Tel: 0116-241 6776

COMPUTER INTEGRATED MANUFACTURING (CIM) CONSULTANTS

J Wilson & Co., 96 David Street, Glasgow, G40 2UH Tel: 0141-551 0268 Fax: 0141-554 4620 E-mail: info@jwilsongroup.co.uk
M A Computing Ltd, 52A Church Street, Broughty Ferry, Dundee, DD5 1HB Tel: (01382) 770044 Fax: (0870) 0557796 E-mail: ian@macomputing.demon.co.uk
Vector Data Systems UK Ltd, Ho, Newark Road, Peterborough, PE1 5FL Tel: (01733) 296866 Fax: (01733) 296868 E-mail: plowdens@anteonuk.com

COMPUTER INTEGRATED MANUFACTURING (CIM) SYSTEMS

M A Computing Ltd, 52A Church Street, Broughty Ferry, Dundee, DD5 1HB Tel: (01382) 770044 Fax: (0870) 0557796 E-mail: ian@macomputing.demon.co.uk
North West Time Recording Co., 197 Bury Old Road, Prestwich, Manchester, M25 1JF Tel: 0161-798 8002 Fax: 0161-773 2441 E-mail: terry@nwtr.co.uk

COMPUTER INTERFACE CABLES

PC World, Leeds Road Retail Park, Leeds Road, Huddersfield, HD1 6PF Tel: (0870) 2420444 Fax: (01484) 437302 E-mail: customer.services@pcworld.co.uk

COMPUTER INTERFACE CARDS (CIC)

Hauppauge Computer Works Ltd, Bank Chambers, 6 Borough High Street, London, SE1 9QQ Tel: (020) 7378 1997 Fax: (020) 7357 9771 E-mail: support@hauppauge.co.uk
Intelligent Interfaces Ltd, PO Box 80, Eastleigh, Hampshire, SO53 2YX Tel: (023) 8026 1514 Fax: (0870) 0521281 E-mail: sales@intint.demon.co.uk

COMPUTER INTERFACE EQUIPMENT

Aculab plc, Lakeside Bramley Road, Mount Farm, Bletchley, Milton Keynes, MK1 1PT Tel: (01908) 273800 Fax: (01908) 273801
B A L Broadcast, Unit 23 Croft Road Industrial Estate, Newcastle, Staffordshire, ST5 0TW Tel: (024) 7631 6500 Fax: (024) 7649 1117 E-mail: sales@bal.co.uk
Computer Connection Retail, Unit 25, Holden Industrial Estate, Wombwell, Barnsley, South Yorkshire, S73 8HA Tel: (01226) 732975 Fax: (01226) 238139 E-mail: sales@ccretail.co.uk
▶ Cursor Controls Ltd, Conroi House, Brunel Drive, Newark, Nottinghamshire, NG24 2EG Tel: (01636) 615600 Fax: (01636) 615601 E-mail: sales@cursorcontrols.com
Flite Electronics Ltd, Church House Farm, Clewer Hill, Waltham Chase, Southampton, SO32 2LN Tel: (01489) 892422 Fax: (01489) 897929 E-mail: sales@flite.co.uk
Greenwich Instruments, Meridian House, Park Road, Swanley, Kent, BR8 8AH Tel: (0870) 0505404 Fax: (0870) 0505405 E-mail: sales@greenwichinst.co.uk
Intelligent Interfaces Ltd, PO Box 80, Eastleigh, Hampshire, SO53 2YX Tel: (023) 8026 1514 Fax: (0870) 0521281 E-mail: sales@intint.demon.co.uk
Thorcom Network Services Ltd, Unit 4 96b Blackpole Trading Estate We, St, Worcester, WR3 8TJ Tel: (01905) 756700 Fax: (01905) 755777 E-mail: sales@thorcom.co.uk
▶ Traxsys, Embankment Way, Ringwood, Hampshire, BH24 1EU Tel: (01425) 463100 Fax: (01425) 463111 E-mail: sales@penny-gilescp.co.uk

COMPUTER INTERFACE EQUIPMENT TO SPECIFICATION

▶ Traxsys, Embankment Way, Ringwood, Hampshire, BH24 1EU Tel: (01425) 463100 Fax: (01425) 463111 E-mail: sales@penny-gilescp.co.uk

COMPUTER INTERFACE SYSTEMS

Electric Software, Stream House, Castle Hill, Rotherfield, Crowborough, East Sussex, TN6 3RU Tel: (01825) 830388
Solstone Plus, 48a Old Steine, Brighton, BN1 1NH Tel: (01273) 206555 Fax: (01273) 387769 E-mail: solestoneplus@solestonegroup.com

COMPUTER LISTINGS SUPPLIERS/SERVICES

A D P Supplies Ltd, 65 Peach Street, Wokingham, Berkshire, RG40 1XP Tel: 0118-977 0554 Fax: 0118-978 5525
Central Computers Supplies, Washwood Heath Road, Birmingham, B8 2HQ Tel: (0870) 0434049 Fax: 0121-684 8885
Commercial Facilities & Logistics, 89 Park Road, Didcot, Oxfordshire, OX11 8QT Tel: (01235) 511054 Fax: (01235) 511056 E-mail: mhall@cfl-ltd.co.uk
Kirkland Ltd, 95 Main Street, Golspie, Sutherland, KW10 6TG Tel: (01408) 633109 Fax: (01408) 634468 E-mail: webad@kirkland.ltd.uk
Limetree Marketing, Unit 1, Warboys Road, Old Hurst, Huntingdon, Cambridgeshire, PE28 3AL Tel: (01487) 823823 Fax: (01487) 823898 E-mail: earl@limetreemarketing.co.uk
▶ Nettfar Technology Ltd, Panda, Tweentown, Cheddar, Somerset, BS27 3JF Tel: 01934 743716 E-mail: mail@netttfar.co.uk

COMPUTER LOGISTICS SERVICES

Arc, Western House, 7 Knutsford Road, Wilmslow, Cheshire, SK9 6JA Tel: (01625) 543430 Fax: (01625) 543431 E-mail: sales@arcit.co.uk

COMPUTER MAINTENANCE/ REPAIR SERVICES

@Pcproblem Co UK Ltd, Hillside House 215 Ashby Road, Burton On Trent, Burton-on-Trent, Staffordshire, DE15 0LA Tel: (0870) 1994812 E-mail: sales@pcproblem.co.uk
▶ 533 Software, Arable Centre, Winterbourne Monkton, Swindon, SN4 9NW Tel: (01672) 539000 Fax: (01672) 539111
A.1. Electronics, Warren Avenue, Koloma, Fakenham, Norfolk, NR21 8NP Tel: (01328) 856226 Fax: (0845) 1665227 E-mail: enquiries@a1electronics.co.uk
▶ A 1 Monitor Repairs Ltd, D Spring Hill Industrial Park, 110 Steward Street, Birmingham, B18 7AF Tel: 0121-454 6396
▶ A B Computer Repairs, 1 Miramar Way, Hornchurch, Essex, RM12 6LP Tel: (01708) 455192 E-mail: sales@abcomputerrepairs.co.uk
▶ A B M I T Solutions Ltd, 79 Lee High Road, London, SE13 5NS Tel: (020) 8297 4450 Fax: (020) 8297 0052 E-mail: b.chakarto@abm-itsolutions.co.uk
A C & C Service Centre, 15 Herbert Road, London, NW9 6AJ Tel: (020) 8203 4555 Fax: (020) 8203 6444
A D 2000 Strathallan Electronics, 7 Bay Terrace, Girvan, Ayrshire, KA26 0AS Tel: (01465) 715200 Fax: (01465) 712575
A G M Media Group, 212-214 Hylton Road, Sunderland, SR4 7UZ Tel: 0191-565 6776 Fax: 0191-565 5604
▶ A G S Computers Ltd, 29 Queen Elizabeth Avenue, East Tilbury, Tilbury, Essex, RM18 8SP Tel: (01375) 844478
A I T London Technologies, 2 25 Downham Road, London, N1 5AA Tel: (020) 7923 1011 Fax: (020) 7275 8344
▶ A J Computer Services, 1 Grasmere, Sunderland, SR6 7QF Tel: 0191-537 2094 Fax: 0191-537 2094
▶ A & L Computers, 8 High Street, Rhyl, Clwyd, LL18 1ES Tel: (01745) 338200 Fax: (01745) 356682 E-mail: sales@al-computers.co.uk
A P C Solutions (UK) Ltd, Unit 18 The Old Cinema, Allshots Industrial Estate, Kelvedon, Colchester, CO5 9DF Tel: (01376) 585554 Fax: (01376) 585727 E-mail: info@apcsolutionuk.com
▶ A S G I Systems 2000, 14a Cambridge Street, Wellingborough, Northamptonshire, NN8 1DJ Tel: (01933) 223005 Fax: (01933) 223005
A T Computers (Applemac), Unit E2 Green La Business Park, Green Lane, Tewkesbury, Gloucestershire, GL20 8SJ Tel: (01684) 291112 Fax: (01684) 274829
▶ A T X Computers, 114 Bancroft Road, Widnes, Cheshire, WA8 3LL Tel: 0151-422 0088
A U Computers, 20 Glebe Road, Bedlington, Northumberland, NE22 6JT Tel: (01670) 829763 Fax: (01670) 823454 E-mail: joe@aucomputers.com
▶ A1 PC Support, 39 Stirling Road, Bournemouth, BH3 7JQ Tel: (01202) 386292
A1 Vision, Vision House, 25 Bradford Road, Riddlesden, Keighley, West Yorkshire, BD21 4ET Tel: (01535) 607080 Fax: (01535) 603010 E-mail: sales@a1vision.com
Aa Computer Maintenance Ltd, 4 Edge Business Centre, Humber Road, London, NW2 6EW Tel: (020) 8452 8033 Fax: (020) 8450 6360
▶ AA Computer Solutions, 173 Northview, Swanley, Kent, BR8 7TB Tel: (01322) 664774
Abacus Computer Systems, 97 Bryant Road, Rochester, Kent, ME2 3ES Tel: (01634) 291310 Fax: (01634) 717569 E-mail: sales@abacusjb.co.uk
Abitech Systems, 13 Main Street, Keyworth, Nottingham, NG12 5AA Tel: 0115-937 4549 Fax: 0115-937 3662 E-mail: sales@abitech.co.uk
Abra Systems, 37 Crossall Street, Macclesfield, Cheshire, SK11 6QF Tel: (01625) 503448 Fax: (01625) 503448
▶ Absolute It Solutions Ltd, Fodol Cottage, Y Felinheli, Gwynedd, LL56 4QD Tel: (01248) 671007 Fax: (01248) 671099
Accent Business Solutions Ltd, 6 Upper Stone Street, Maidstone, Kent, ME15 6EX Tel: (01732) 841794 Fax: (01622) 671477 E-mail: accentsolu@aol.com
Access Computers, 411 Bearwood Road, Smethwick, West Midlands, B66 4DF Tel: 0121-429 5558 Fax: 0121-429 5558
▶ Ace Software Engineering, High Street, Berkhamsted, Herts, HP4 2DJ Tel: (01442) 875910
▶ Acs Computers Ltd, 2f South Hams Business Park, Churchstow, Kingsbridge, Devon, TQ7 3QH Tel: (01548) 853358 Fax: (01548) 856540
Active Computing & Telecoms Ltd, 3 Larks Way, Tree Beech Enterprise Park Gunn, Goodleigh, Barnstaple, Devon, EX32 7NZ Tel: (01271) 831325 Fax: (01271) 830987 E-mail: sales@activecomputing.co.uk
▶ Acuma Solutions Ltd, Waterside Court, 1 Crewe Road, Manchester, M23 9BE Tel: (0870) 7894321 Fax: (0870) 7894002 E-mail: enquiries@acuma.co.uk
Advanced Computer Centre Ltd, 59 George Lane, London, E18 1JJ Tel: (020) 8518 8353 Fax: (020) 8518 8056 E-mail: info@accldn.co.uk
Advanced Security Systems, 932 Ashton Road, Oldham, OL8 3JS Tel: 0161-785 8000 Fax: 0161-785 8888
▶ Adventi, 10 James Street, Righead Industrial Estate, Bellshill, Lanarkshire, ML4 3LU Tel: (0845) 6582080 Fax: 0131-623 7279 E-mail: info@scotsys.co.uk
▶ Ahead4, 11 Trinity Square, South Woodham Ferrers, Chelmsford, CM3 5JX Tel: (0845) 4584192 E-mail: info@ahead4.com
Ajt Computing, The Westbrook Centre, Grassmere Way, Waterlooville, Hampshire, PO7 8SE Tel: (023) 9224 0080 Fax: (023) 9224 0080 E-mail: ajt@ajtcomputing.co.uk
Alcom Computing, 84 The Broadway, High Street, Chesham, Buckinghamshire, HP5 1EG Tel: (01494) 784784 Fax: (01494) 778424 E-mail: sales@alcomcomputing.com

COMPUTER MAINTENANCE/REPAIR SERVICES – *continued*

Alg Enterprise, 312 Wandsworth Bridge Road, London, SW6 2UA Tel: (020) 7736 7714 Fax: (020) 7384 1329 E-mail: enquiries@algcomputers.co.uk

▶ All Solutions, 1 Merton Court, 54 Christchurch Road, Bournemouth, BH1 3PF Tel: (01202) 551862

Alnwick Computerware, Market Place, Alnwick, Northumberland, NE66 1HS Tel: (01665) 604816 Fax: (01665) 604160 E-mail: sales@alnwickcomputerware.co.uk

▶ Alpha Computer Maintenance, 22 Lyndon Avenue, Wallington, Surrey, SM6 7JT Tel: (020) 8254 9920 Fax: (020) 8254 9921

Alpha Computer Services UK Ltd, 69 Bransgrove Road, Edgware, Middlesex, HA8 6HZ Tel: (020) 8905 7245 Fax: (020) 8905 7245

▶ Alphaone Computing Services, 126 Ladies Mile Road, Brighton, BN1 8TE Tel: (01273) 552955

Altek, Bath Road, Beckington, Bath, BA11 6SQ Tel: (01373) 831231 Fax: (01373) 831813 E-mail: sales@altek-computers.co.uk

▶ Alternatum, 22-24, Homecroft Road, London, N22 5EL Tel: (020) 8888 7956 Fax: (020) 8888 2521

▶ Altus Computers Ltd, Abbeyfields, Lodge Road, Sandbach, Cheshire, CW11 3HD Tel: (01270) 750800

Ama Business Systems Ltd, The Old Tabernacle, Palmyra Road, Bristol, BS3 3JQ Tel: 0117-923 1133 Fax: 0117-923 1144 E-mail: sales@ama-it.com

Amco FM Ltd, 3 Sun Street, Baldock, Hertfordshire, SG7 6QA Tel: (01462) 896959 Fax: (01462) 896597 E-mail: support@amcofm.co.uk

Amsys plc, Byron House, Lower Road, Kenley, Surrey, CR8 5NB Tel: (020) 8660 9999 Fax: (020) 8763 9332 E-mail: info@amsys.co.uk

Andrews Computer Services Ltd, Nash House, London Road, Hemel Hempstead, Hertfordshire, HP3 9SR Tel: (01442) 241200 Fax: (01442) 241201 E-mail: admin@andrews-computers.com

Anita Business Systems, 29 Bentley Road, London, N1 4BY Tel: (020) 7249 6666 Fax: (020) 7923 1852E-mail: info@anita.co.uk

Apex Computer Services Wales Ltd, Unit 2 St. Michaels Court, Church Street, Newport, Gwent, NP20 2BY Tel: (01633) 215123 Fax: (01633) 215124 E-mail: sales@apexcs.co.uk

Apollo Computers Ltd, Unit 34, Eurolink Business Centre, 49 Effra Road, London, SW2 1BZ Tel: (020) 7924 0753 Fax: (020) 7274 8376

Applied Computer Services, Hunts End, Waterworks Lane, Martin, Dover, Kent, CT15 5JW Tel: (01304) 852772 Fax: (01304) 852772 E-mail: acsjohndyer@aol.com

Applied Data Technologies, 92 Bedminster Parade, Bedminster, Bristol, BS3 4HL Tel: 0117-987 2170 Fax: 0117-941 0935 E-mail: sales@adtsystems.co.uk

Aquila Systems, Aquila House, 283 Laygate, South Shields, Tyne & Wear, NE33 4QN Tel: 0191-455 9440 Fax: 0191-456 1259 E-mail: sales@aquilasystems.co.uk

Archway Systems Ltd, 31 Parolles Road, London, N19 3RE Tel: (020) 7272 3530 Fax: (020) 7263 1951 E-mail: admin@arsy.co.uk

▶ Argyll Computer Services, Unit 3, 46 Argyll Street, Lochgilphead, Argyll, PA31 8NE Tel: (01546) 603674 Fax: (01546) 603674 E-mail: info@argyllcomputers.com

▶ Artisan Solutions Ltd, Venture House 2 Arlington Square, Downshire Way, Bracknell, Berkshire, RG12 1WA Tel: (01344) 742808 Fax: (01344) 742908

Ashgoal Ltd, Cqueens Road, Barnet, Hertfordshire, EN5 4DJ Tel: (020) 8275 5100 Fax: (020) 8441 7240 E-mail: info@ashgoal.co.uk

▶ Associated Network Engineers, Mardale Road, Penrith, Cumbria, CA11 9EH Tel: (01768) 868555 Fax: (01768) 868777 E-mail: sales@ane.co.uk

▶ Astraware, Unit IC2, Keele Science Park, Newcastle, Staffordshire, ST5 5NH Tel: (01782) 638140 Fax: (01782) 667828

Astrun Computers, 78 High Street, Lee-on-the-Solent, Hampshire, PO13 9DA Tel: (023) 9255 6007 Fax: (023) 9255 3514 E-mail: sales@smsit.co.uk

▶ Autotron Computer Systems, 35 Hazelwood Avenue, New Milton, Hampshire, BH25 5LX Tel: (01425) 612470 Fax: (07092) 308410

Avenga Computer Services, 34 Morse Road, Whitnash, Leamington Spa, Warwickshire, CV31 2LH Tel: (01926) 882639 Fax: (01926) 882639 E-mail: nigel@avenga.co.uk

▶ Axem Computers, 30-31 Caroline Street, Hull, HU2 8DY Tel: (01482) 226899 E-mail: sales@axemcomputers.co.uk

B R M Computers, 101 Winchester Road, Chandler's Ford, Eastleigh, Hampshire, SO53 2GG Tel: (023) 8034 1094 Fax: (023) 8064 7207 E-mail: info@brmcomputers.demon.co.uk

▶ Back Up & Running, Tong Hall, Tong Lane, Bradford, W. Yorkshire, BD4 0RR Tel: 0113-285 2004

▶ Badger Computer Services Ltd, The Business Innovation Centre 1 Innova Business Park, Electric, Enfield, Middlesex, EN3 7XU Tel: (020) 8344 8344 Fax: (020) 8344 8345 E-mail: sales@badgercomputerservices.co.uk

▶ BCS, 364 Two Mile Hill Road, Bristol, BS15 1AH Tel: 0117-967 5707 Fax: 0117-940 7555 E-mail: b.c.s@virgin.net

▶ Bedford Home Computers, Poplar Avenue, Bedford, MK41 8BL Tel: (07754) 093885

▶ Beech Systems, Riversmead 1 Longridge Road, Hurst Green, Clitheroe, Lancashire, BB7 9QW Tel: (01254) 826570 Fax: (01254) 826763

Beetee, 139 Taplow, Thurlow Street, London, SE17 2UJ Tel: (07956) 868418 E-mail: lewis@btcomputers.com

▶ Berry Computers, Grove House, Lutyens Close, Lychpit, Basingstoke, Hampshire, RG24 8AG Tel: (01256) 316525 E-mail: info@berrycomputers.com

▶ BHCS, 64a Market Place, Chippenham, Wiltshire, SN15 3HG Tel: (01249) 652682 Fax: (0871) 2771259 E-mail: nstuart@businessandhome.co.uk

▶ Bhi Solutions, Coombe Lodge, Bourne Lane, Bristol, BS40 7RG Tel: (01761) 462244 Fax: (01761) 462775

Bigfish, Unit 8 Adam Smith Street, Grimsby, South Humberside, DN31 1SJ Tel: (01472) 268180 Fax: (01472) 268170 E-mail: humberside@bigfishhooked.com

▶ Biosilico, 34, Maple Street, London, W1T 6HD Tel: (020) 7436 8554 Fax: (020) 7436 8476

▶ Bits & PC's, Unit 10 Cwmtillery Industrial Estate, Cwmtillery, Abertillery, Gwent, NP13 1LZ Tel: (01495) 321300 E-mail: bitznpcz@aol.com

▶ Blackboard Associates, 5 Barton Villas, Dawlish, Devon, EX7 9QJ Tel: (01626) 863888 Fax: (0709) 219048 E-mail: info@blackboard-associates.com

▶ Blackrock Computers, 85 Church Road, Caldicot, Gwent, NP26 4HT Tel: (07906) 329794

Blue Baron, 1089 Pollokshaws Road, Glasgow, G41 3YG Tel: 0141-649 3101 Fax: 0141-649 3101 E-mail: bluebar@btconnect.com

Blue Chip Customer Engineering Ltd, Franklin Court, Priory Business Park, Bedford, MK44 3JZ Tel: (01234) 327700 Fax: (01234) 831580 E-mail: sales@bluechip.co.uk

Blue Fish Co., The Barm, Holt Lane, Ashby Magna, Lutterworth, Leicestershire, LE17 5NJ Tel: (01455) 201010 Fax: (01455) 201001 E-mail: bluefish@thebluefishcompany.com

▶ Blue Line Trading Ltd, Grapes House, 79A High Street, Esher, Surrey, KT10 9QA Tel: (01372) 468141 Fax: (01372) 467891

▶ Bluespier International Ltd, Priory Barn, The Priory, Alcester Road, Feckenham, Redditch, Worcestershire, B96 6JD Tel: (01527) 894216 Fax: (01527) 893089

Bradleys Electronic & Computer Services, Andross, Forest Road, Ruardean Woodside, Ruardean, Gloucestershire, GL17 9XW Tel: (01594) 544093 Fax: (01594) 544093 E-mail: becs@aic.co.uk

Bugbusters, Mcb Business Centre, Argoed Rd, Buckley, Clwyd, CH7 3HZ Tel: (01244) 546299 Fax: (01244) 543926

Bulli Computer Maintenance, Gatehouse Lane, Goddards Green, Hassocks, West Sussex, BN6 9LD Tel: (01444) 871609 Fax: (01444) 871216E-mail: bullicomputers@btconnect.com

Bullock Bros Electronics, 132 Cheltenham Road, Gloucester, GL2 0LY Tel: (01452) 529806 Fax: (01452) 529806 E-mail: sales@bullock-bros.com

Burway Computer Services, 24 Central Avenue, Church Stretton, Shropshire, SY6 6EF Tel: (01694) 722520 Fax: (01694) 724070 E-mail: kevan@burwaycomputers.co.uk

Business Computer Resources Ltd, 1b Dyke Road Drive, Brighton, BN1 6AJ Tel: (01273) 542759 Fax: (01273) 889898 E-mail: sales@bcrltd.co.uk

Bytes & PC's, 4 Stockwell Head, Hinckley, Leicestershire, LE10 1RE Tel: (01455) 613232 Fax: (01455) 615164 E-mail: derrick@themousepad.co.uk

Bytes & PC's UK Ltd, Gosford House, 26/27 Far Gosford Street, Coventry, CV1 5DW Tel: (024) 7655 5265 Fax: (024) 7655 1100 E-mail: sales@bytespcs.co.uk

C E B Computer Services, 12 Elm Lane, Capel St. Mary, Ipswich, IP9 2HS Tel: (01473) 312072 E-mail: info@cebcom.fsnet.co.uk

▶ Cando It, 42 Wolfe Road, Norwich, NR1 4HT Tel: (01603) 498999 E-mail: sales@cando-it.co.uk

Cannon Computers Ltd, 2 Kingsmead Road, London, SW2 3JB Tel: (020) 8671 4140 E-mail: leonard@cannon-computers.co.uk

Canon UK Ltd, Cockshot Hill, Reigate, Surrey, RH2 8BF Tel: (01737) 220000 Fax: (01737) 220022

▶ Care Micro Systems, Columbus House, 77-79 Columbus Ravine, Scarborough, North Yorkshire, YO12 7QU Tel: (01723) 351111 Fax: (01723) 351199 E-mail: sales@caremicro.co.uk

▶ Cartwright Computers, 35 The Arches, Maryport, Cumbria, CA15 8JE Tel: (0845) 2578630 Fax: (0870) 7060333 E-mail: lee@cartwrightcomputers.co.uk

Castlepoint Associates Ltd, Castle Point House 180 Kiln Road, Benfleet, Essex, SS7 1SU Tel: (01702) 558165 Fax: (01702) 552550 E-mail: sales@castle-point-computers.co.uk

▶ Cats-Whiskers.com Ltd, 14 Camelot Court, Somerton, Somerset, TA11 6SB Tel: (01458) 274383 Fax: (01458) 274388

▶ CD Writer Com Ltd, Greenwich High Road, London, SE10 8JL Tel: (020) 8694 7820 Fax: (020) 8694 3754

Central Computer Technology, 11 Greskine Clo, Bedford, MK41 0NW Tel: (01234) 357932

▶ Central Computers UK Ltd, Shop 284, Brentwood Road, Romford, RM2 5TA Tel: (01708) 453311 Fax: (01708) 458930 E-mail: sales@centralcomputersuk.co.uk

The Change Organisation, Units 70-71, John Wilson Business Park, Harvey Drive, Chestfield, Whitstable, Kent, CT5 3QT Tel: (01227) 779000 Fax: (01227) 779222

▶ Charteris, 85 Southdown Road, Harpenden, Hertfordshire, AL5 1PR Tel: (01582) 716100 Fax: (01582) 469051

▶ Chetwynd Computers, 38 Chetwynd Road, Edgmond, Newport, Shropshire, TF10 8HL Tel: (01952) 811402 Fax: (01952) 811402 E-mail: info@chetwyndcomputers.co.uk

▶ Choice Computers, 32 Buckingham Drive, Dukinfield, Cheshire, SK16 5BZ Tel: (0870) 7776755

Cifer Data Systems Ltd, 1 Main Street, West Wilts Trading Estate, Westbury, Wiltshire, BA13 4JU Tel: (01373) 824129 Fax: (01373) 824127 E-mail: sales@cifer.co.uk

Cir-Comm Systems Ltd, Bailey Brook House, Amber Drive, Langley Mill, Nottingham, NG16 4BE Tel: (01773) 761999

▶ Colleague Ltd, Catherine House, Coventry Road, Hinckley, Leics, LE10 0JT Tel: (01455) 633233 Fax: (01455) 639404

College Computers, 169 Hollow Way, Cowley, Oxford, OX4 2NE Tel: (01865) 774410 Fax: (01865) 774410 E-mail: sales@college-computers.com

Comart ITM, Technology House, Ridge Road, Rotherham, South Yorkshire, S65 1NS Tel: (01709) 363418 Fax: (01709) 835369 E-mail: enquiries@comartplc.co.uk

▶ Comfit Computer Services, 37, Wackerfield Road, Rendlesham, Woodbridge, Suffolk, IP12 2UT Tel: (01394) 420166 Fax: (01394) 420166

▶ Command Software Services Ltd, Bassett Court, Newport Pagnell, Buckinghamshire, MK16 0JN Tel: (01908) 283580 Fax: (07002) 227374 E-mail: info@commandsoftware.plus.com

Compfix Enterprises Ltd, 119 Manchester Road, Chorlton cum Hardy, Manchester, M21 9PG Tel: 0161-881 2395 Fax: 0161-881 2395 E-mail: sales@compfixpc.co.uk

Compu Hut, 54 Union Street, Melksham, Wiltshire, SN12 7PR Tel: (01225) 708181 Fax: (01225) 708181

Compuchange, 14 Parson Street, London, NW4 1QB Tel: (020) 8203 3363 Fax: (020) 8202 0860

▶ Compusence, 6, Market Street, Soham, Ely, Cambs, CB7 5JG Tel: (01353) 722759 Fax: (01353) 725185

▶ Computafixit.Com, 49 Oxford Road, Acocks Green, Birmingham, B27 6DS Tel: (0845) 8900689 E-mail: sales@computafixit.com

Computec Computers, 67 Frog Lane, Wigan, Lancashire, WN6 7DU Tel: (01942) 493400 Fax: (01942) 736967

Computec Solutions Ltd, 566 Streatham High Road, London, SW16 3QQ Tel: (020) 8679 1717 Fax: (020) 8679 5245 E-mail: mail@computecltd.com

Computer Care 2000, 14 St. Bryde Street, East Kilbride, Glasgow, G74 4HQ Tel: (01355) 241628 Fax: (01355) 573073 E-mail: sales@cc2000.co.uk

▶ The Computer Centre, Belmont Road, Exeter, EX1 2HF Tel: (01392) 204690 Fax: (01392) 204128 E-mail: sales@cobrexcomputers.com

Computer Centre Direct, 56 Battersea Rise, London, SW11 1EJ Tel: (020) 7228 1888 Fax: (020) 7228 8881 E-mail: ccconnect@btconnect.com

Computer Clinic Ltd, 204 Rayleigh Road, Hutton, Brentwood, Essex, CM13 1PN Tel: (01277) 261597 Fax: (01277) 261599 E-mail: guy@clinic2.freeserve.co.uk

Computer Connection Retail, Unit 25, Holden Industrial Estate, Wombwell, Barnsley, South Yorkshire, S73 8HA Tel: (01226) 732975 Fax: (01226) 238139 E-mail: sales@ccretail.co.uk

▶ Computer Doctors Ltd, Unit 12 Blackthorn Industrial Estate, 40 Blackthorn Road, Northampton, NN3 8PT Tel: (01604) 411444 Fax: (0871) 2519099 E-mail: sales@computerdoctors.uk.net

▶ Computer Home Help, 14 West Park Cr, Inverbervie, Montrose, Angus, DD10 0TX Tel: (01561) 362902 E-mail: lincoln.callander@btinternet.com

▶ Computer Home Help, The Vineyard, Welwyn Garden City, Hertfordshire, AL8 7PU Tel: (01707) 690468

▶ Computer Hospital, 100 Camlough Road, Bessbrook, Newry, County Down, BT35 7EE Tel: (028) 3083 9888 E-mail: newrycomputerhospital@yahoo.co.uk

Computer Junction, 276 Arundel Street, Portsmouth, PO1 1NT Tel: (023) 9282 5210 Fax: (023) 9282 5210 E-mail: cjsolent@btconnect.com

▶ Computer M8, 159 Hale Lane, Edgware, Middlesex, HA8 9QW Tel: (020) 8959 0088

Computer Maintenance Services, 11 Carvoza Road, Truro, Cornwall, TR1 1BA Tel: (01872) 241062 Fax: (01872) 241062

▶ The Computer Point, 19C East Princes Street, Helensburgh, Dunbartonshire, G84 7DE Tel: (01436) 676017 Fax: (01436) 670136 E-mail: sales@thecomputerpoint.co.uk

Computer Precision Ltd, 185 Upper Street, London, N1 1RQ Tel: (020) 7359 9797 Fax: (020) 7359 9507 E-mail: 185@cipi.co.uk

Computer Repair Centre, 32 The Avenue, St. Pauls Cray, Orpington, Kent, BR5 3DJ Tel: (020) 8556 5331 Fax: (020) 8556 8890

▶ Computer Repair Shop, 141c High Road, Loughton, Essex, IG10 4LT Tel: (0845) 1342003 Fax: (020) 8502 5900 E-mail: sales@crs2004.com

▶ Computer Repair Shop, Weedon Road, Northampton, NN5 5DA Tel: (0800) 0933072 Fax: (01604) 590160

▶ Computer Resale Brokers, High Pavement, Nottingham, NG1 1HF Tel: 0115-959 6464 Fax: 0115-959 6467

Computer Response, Response House, Foundry Street, Chesterfield, Derbyshire, S41 9AU Tel: (01246) 450540 Fax: (01246) 450483 E-mail: sales@computer-response.com

Computer Risk Management, 2 Davyhulme Circle, Urmston, Manchester, M41 0SS Tel: 0161-749 7250 Fax: 0161-747 2476

Computer Scene, 5 Kings Street, Mildenhall, Bury St. Edmunds, Suffolk, IP28 7EZ Tel: (01638) 717726 Fax: (01638) 510079 E-mail: sales@computerscene.co.uk

▶ Computer Services & Engineers, Unit 4a Stag Industrial Estate, Atlantic Street, Broadheath, Altrincham, Cheshire, WA14 5DW Tel: 0161-941 4555 Fax: 0161-941 6182 E-mail: sales@cselimited.co.uk

Computer Shop, 15 Hencotes, Hexham, Northumberland, NE46 2EQ Tel: (01434) 600022 Fax: (01434) 609262 E-mail: info@600022.com

▶ Computer Shop, Unit 8 Bargate Shopping Centre, Southampton, SO14 2YB Tel: (023) 8023 2261 Fax: (023) 8023 6560

Computer Solutions Grimsby Ltd, Wellowgate, Grimsby, South Humberside, DN32 0RA Tel: (01472) 311777 Fax: (01472) 311778

Computer Station Ltd, Station House, Station Road, Rayleigh, Essex, SS6 7HL Tel: (01268) 746746 Fax: (01268) 746747 E-mail: sales@computerstation.co.uk

▶ Computer Store, 82 Boothferry Road, Goole, North Humberside, DN14 6AA Tel: (01405) 720099

Computer Systems Support, 74 Eglinton Avenue, Guisborough, Cleveland, TS14 7BX Tel: (01287) 610433 Fax: (01287) 610438 E-mail: info@computersystemssupport.co.uk

▶ Computer Trouble Shooters (South Warwickshire), The Laurels, Birmingham Road, Pathlow, Stratford-upon-Avon, Warwickshire, CV37 0ES Tel: (01789) 296642 E-mail: douglas@comptroub.com

▶ Computer Troubleshooters, 44 Alberta Avenue, Sutton, Surrey, SM1 2LL Tel: (020) 8395 0182 E-mail: sales@cts-sutton.co.uk

Computer Wizard, 405 Hatfield Road, St. Albans, Hertfordshire, AL4 0XP Tel: (01727) 861010 E-mail: sales@computerwizard.co.uk

▶ Computer World Cookstown, 11 James Street, Cookstown, County Tyrone, BT80 8AA Tel: (028) 8675 8177 Fax: (028) 8675 8188 E-mail: info@computerworlds.co.uk

Computers In Construction, 337 Brook Street, Broughty Ferry, Dundee, DD5 2DS Tel: (01382) 776733 Fax: (01382) 521438

▶ Computersave.Co.Uk, 45 Windmill Road, Hampton Hill, Hampton, Middlesex, TW12 1QZ Tel: (07950) 412207

▶ Computing Solutions, Unit 3b North Castle Street, Banff, AB45 1JJ Tel: (01261) 815511 Fax: (01261) 815511 E-mail: sales@cseltham.co.uk

Computing Solutions, 14 Well Hall Parade, London, SE9 6SP Tel: (020) 8294 0090 Fax: (020) 8859 4562 E-mail: sales@cymc.com

▶ Computopia, 7 Riverside, Port Talbot, West Glamorgan, SA13 1PH Tel: (01792) 410516 Fax: (01639) 899943

Comtek Computers Manchester, 12 Silver Street, Bury, Lancashire, BL9 0EX Tel: 0161-761 2200 Fax: 0161-761 2211 E-mail: kazpenash@comtekcomputersmanchester.co.uk

Configuration Computer Services, 40 Surrey Technology Centre, Occam Road, Surrey Research Park, Guildford, Surrey, GU2 7YG Tel: (01483) 295796 Fax: (01483) 295797 E-mail: tony@configuration.co.uk

▶ Control & Display Systems Ltd, 1570 Parkway, Whiteley, Fareham, Hampshire, PO15 7AG Tel: (01489) 571771 Fax: (01489) 571555 E-mail: sales@cdsrail.com

▶ Cornwells, 65A High Street, Sawston, Cambridge, CB2 4BG Tel: (01223) 834533 Fax: (01223) 834533 E-mail: kevin.i.cornwell@btconnect.com

Courage & Co., Rye Hill Farm, Slaley, Hexham, Northumberland, NE47 0AH Tel: (01434) 673426 Fax: (01434) 673608 E-mail: info@consult-courage.co.uk

▶ CP Computers, 21 The Inlands, Daventry, Northants, NN11 4DD Tel: 01327 702182 Fax: 0871 2398138 E-mail: c.palmer@lycos.co.uk

▶ Crash It, Kettles Wood Drive, Birmingham, B32 3DB Tel: 0121-421 7601 Fax: 0121-421 7601 E-mail: enquire@crash-it.org

Creative Computers Ltd, 258 Old Christchurch Road, Bournemouth, BH1 1PS Tel: (01202) 775600 Fax: (01202) 775559 E-mail: sales@creativegroup.co.uk

Custard It Ltd, Lake View Drive Unit 1, Innovate Mews, Annesley, Nottingham, NG15 0EA Tel: (01623) 687650 Fax: (0870) 4019960 E-mail: info@custardgroup.co.uk

Cyptec UK Ltd, 134 Timbercroft Lane, London, SE18 2SG Tel: (020) 8855 6664 Fax: (020) 8855 1714 E-mail: sales@vellumfile.com

D C Trading, Copdock House, London Road, Copdock, Ipswich, IP8 3JW Tel: (01473) 730286 Fax: (01473) 730257 E-mail: info@dctrading.co.uk

COMPUTER MAINTENANCE/REPAIR SERVICES – *continued*

▶ D & D Computer Services, 2 Northfield Road, Narberth, Dyfed, SA67 7AA Tel: (01834) 869319 Fax: (01834) 860450 E-mail: enquiries@ddcs.co.uk

D M C Products, P O Box 22, Derby, DE1 9ZU Tel: (01332) 205822 Fax: (01332) 205822 E-mail: info@dmc-systems.com

D R L Systems Ltd, Woodside House, Woodside, Chilworth, Southampton, SO16 7LB Tel: (023) 8076 0808 Fax: (023) 8076 7900 E-mail: sales@drlsystems.co.uk

D S H Electronics Ltd, 206 Idle Road, Bradford, West Yorkshire, BD2 4JT Tel: (01274) 626261 Fax: (01274) 626299 E-mail: sales@dsh-electronics.co.uk

▶ Danoli Solutions Ltd, 116 Yew Tree Road, Ormskirk, Lancashire, L39 1NX Tel: (01695) 579442 E-mail: enquiries@danoli.co.uk

Dart Computers (Wales) Ltd, 26B Wellington Road, Rhyl, Clwyd, LL18 1BN Tel: (01745) 330128 Fax: (01745) 330128 E-mail: emquiries@dart-computers.com

Data Set Ready, 25 Leygreen Close, Luton, LU2 0SQ Tel: (01582) 618080 Fax: (01582) 618081E-mail: datatasteready@ntlworld.co.uk

▶ DataInterpreters, 276 West Park Drive West, Leeds, LS8 2BD Tel: 07886 847024

Datapact Ltd, 188 St. John Street, London, EC1V 4JY Tel: (020) 7336 7511 E-mail: sales@datapact.co.uk

Datastor Technology Ltd, Old Mushroom Farm, Heathend, Wotton-under-Edge, Gloucestershire, GL12 8AX Tel: (01454) 299399 Fax: (01454) 299400 E-mail: sales@datastor.co.uk

Davel Technology, Woodlands, Branksome Avenue, Wickford, Essex, SS12 0JD Tel: (01268) 763336 Fax: (01268) 763305 E-mail: davtech@onetel.com

DDF Computer Systems, Horsham Road, Walliswood, Dorking, Surrey, RH5 5QD Tel: (01306) 627155 Fax: (01306) 627166 E-mail: info@ddf.co.uk

Des Computers, Cardiff University, Senghennydd Road, Cardiff, CF24 4AG Tel: (029) 2025 0000 Fax: (029) 2025 9600 E-mail: sales@descom.co.uk

▶ Digital Error, 6a High Street, Wincanton, Somerset, BA9 9JP Tel: (0845) 2266432 Fax: (0845) 2266432 E-mail: sales@digitalerror.co.uk

▶ Digital Office Systems, Unit 424 Parkers House, 48 Regent Street, Cambridge, CB2 1FD Tel: (0870) 7655565 Fax: (08707) 654565

Direct Sales Agency Ltd, 4 Bankside, Hanborough Business Park, Long Hanborough, Witney, Oxfordshire, OX29 8SP Tel: (01993) 883606 Fax: (01993) 882733 E-mail: sales@direct.co.uk

▶ Discount Computer Warehouse Ltd, Unit 5 Bordesley Trading Estate, Bordesley Green Road, Birmingham, B8 1BZ Tel: (0800) 1804599 Fax: 0121-327 9521

▶ Discount Computers, 7 Canvey Road, Canvey Island, Essex, SS8 0LL Tel: (01268) 511716 Fax: (01268) 511716

Dna Computer Services Ltd, 64d Sutton Court Road, London, W4 3EG Tel: (020) 8742 3524 Fax: (020) 8995 8312 E-mail: info@dnacomputers.co.uk

▶ Dolphin Computer Upgrades Ltd, 30 Arlington Gardens, Brighton, BN2 8QE Tel: (01273) 248871 Fax: (01273) 245717 E-mail: sales@dolphinupgrades.com

▶ Domain Technologies Ltd, 284 Upper Richmond Road West, London, SW14 7JE Tel: (020) 8878 4994 Fax: (020) 8878 1554 E-mail: info@domtech.co.uk

E C Computers Ltd, Mead Court, Cooper Road, Thornbury, Bristol, BS35 3UW Tel: (01454) 281500 Fax: (0870) 7776444 E-mail: info@eccomputers.co.uk

E & M Office Equipment Ltd, 94 Gray's Inn Road, London, WC1X 8AD Tel: (020) 7713 1591 Fax: (020) 7242 0239 E-mail: sales@emofficeequipment.co.uk

E S L Ltd, 301-303 Kennington Lane, London, SE11 5QU Tel: (020) 7820 7718 Fax: (020) 7820 7754 E-mail: ind-esl@msn.com

Elan Support Services, Allerton Bywater Business Park, Newton Lane, Allerton Bywater, Castleford, West Yorkshire, WF10 2AL Tel: (01977) 604384 Fax: (01977) 604021 E-mail: evahorbury@elansupports.co.uk

Elect Computer Systems, 257 Wick Rd, London, E9 5DG Tel: (020) 8986 8014 Fax: (020) 8986 8180

Electronic & General Services Ltd, 3 Hitchs Yard, Church Street, Ware, Hertfordshire, SG12 9ES Tel: (01920) 468991 Fax: (01920) 469938 E-mail: klick@egs.co.uk

▶ Element A V, 59 St. Michaels Close, Aveley, South Ockendon, Essex, RM15 4SY Tel: (01708) 402977 Fax: (01708) 402977 E-mail: andy@elementav.com

Elite Contract Services Ltd, 6 Petsworth Lane, Great Notley, Braintree, Essex, CM77 7XS Tel: (0845) 2262796 E-mail: enquiries@ecsit.co.uk

Enlight Ltd, Suite 308 Third Floor, Whiteleys Centre, Queensway, London, W2 4YN Tel: (020) 7792 9065 Fax: (020) 7792 9089 E-mail: info@enlight.net

Enterprise Data Systems, Enterprise House, 130-134 Bristnall Hall Road, Oldbury, West Midlands, B68 9TX Tel: (0845) 6444774 Fax: (0871) 2205363 E-mail: andy@edsuk.co.uk

▶ Escape Systems, 9 Salamanca Crescent, Penicuik, Midlothian, EH26 0LT Tel: (07764) 304166

▶ Eserve It Ltd, Dealtree House, Blackmore Road Hook End, Brentwood, Essex, CM15 0DS Tel: (01277) 822005 Fax: (0870) 1166422 E-mail: info@eserve.it

▶ Essex Computer Services, 42 Brooklyn Road, Harwich, Essex, CO12 3QF Tel: (01255) 243235

▶ Eurocom Components Ltd, 22 Amhurst Parade, Amhurst Park, London, N16 5AA Tel: (020) 8802 7300 Fax: (020) 8802 7349

Eurotech Computer Services Ltd, Cambridge House, Cambridge Road, Walton-on-Thames, Surrey, KT12 2DP Tel: (01932) 260470 Fax: (01932) 260471 E-mail: sales@eurotech-computers.com

▶ Exlen Technology, 172 Chatsworth Road, Chesterfield, Derbyshire, S40 2AR Tel: (01246) 236363 Fax: (01246) 557391 E-mail: mo@exlen.net

Extra Technology Services Ltd, 52-56 Shambles Street, Barnsley, South Yorkshire, S70 2SH Tel: (01226) 771117 Fax: (01226) 771118 E-mail: sales@extracomputers.co.uk

F 1 Services, 19 Bridge Street, Newark, Nottinghamshire, NG24 1EE Tel: (01636) 701832 Fax: (01636) 707114 E-mail: a.forman@f1services.co.uk

Fast & Easy Computers, Unit 5b Marcliffe Industrial Estate, Macclesfield Road, Hazel Grove, Stockport, Cheshire, SK7 5EG Tel: 0161-483 6656 Fax: 0161-483 6667 E-mail: sales@fasteasy.com

Fast Micros, 87 Canterbury Road, Margate, Kent, CT9 5AX Tel: (01843) 227522 Fax: (01843) 225109

▶ Fastfix, 3 The Maltings, George Street, Newark, Nottinghamshire, NG24 1LU Tel: (0845) 8882001 Fax: (01636) 640029 E-mail: sales@fastfixcomputers.co.uk

▶ Featherstone Computer Centre, 10 Station Lane, Featherstone, Pontefract, West Yorkshire, WF7 5BE Tel: (01977) 700230

▶ Firewire Computer Solutions, 86 Coniston Road, Kings Langley, Hertfordshire, WD4 8DE Tel: (07909) 518101

▶ First Line, Unit B7 Evans Easyspace, Deeside Industrial Park, Deeside, Clwyd, CH5 2JZ Tel: (01244) 289714 Fax: (01244) 289713 E-mail: sales@firstlinemaintenance.co.uk

First Link Computing Ltd, York House, High Street, Amblecote, Stourbridge, West Midlands, DY8 4BT Tel: (01384) 377007 Fax: (01384) 377178 E-mail: sales@pcwarranty.co.uk

▶ Fix It Devon, 24 Jasmine Grove, Paignton, Devon, TQ3 3TH Tel: (01803) 404326 Fax: (01803) 404326 E-mail: sales@fix-it-devon.com

▶ Fixmeathome Computer Maintenance, 8 Lower Sand Hills, Surbiton, Surrey, KT6 6RP Tel: (020) 8399 5949

Flex Computer Services, 62 Clifton Road, Shefford, Bedfordshire, SG17 5AN Tel: (01462) 638777

▶ Freedom Computing, 23 Caldervale, Orton Longueville, Peterborough, PE2 7HX Tel: (01733) 361117

▶ Frost Computer Services, 2 Church Mount, Guilsborough, Northampton, NN6 8QA Tel: (01604) 743017 Fax: (01604) 743017 E-mail: sales@frostcomputerservices.co.uk

Fujitsu Services Ltd, Swan House, The Causeway, Staines, Middlesex, TW18 3BF Tel: (0870) 2345555 Fax: (0870) 2424445

▶ Fullpoints Ltd, 40, Nursery Road, London, SW9 8BP Tel: (020) 7924 9971

▶ Futureware Ltd, 115 London Road, Braintree, Essex, CM77 8PT Tel: (01376) 320276 Fax: (01376) 320288 E-mail: sales@futureware.co.uk

G C H Test & Computer Services Ltd, I S C House 5 Progress Business Centre, Whittle Parkway, Slough, SL1 6DQ Tel: (01628) 559980 Fax: (01628) 559990 E-mail: sales@gch-services.com

G & J Computing, 81 Etherley Lane, Bishop Auckland, County Durham, DL14 7QZ Tel: (01388) 603009 Fax: (01388) 662332 E-mail: sales@gandjcomputing.co.uk

G K M Technical Services, 14 Whessoe Road, Darlington, County Durham, DL3 0QP Tel: (01325) 361670 Fax: (01325) 361670 E-mail: sales@gkm.co.uk

▶ G S L, Ledcom Industrial Estate, Bank Road, Larne, County Antrim, BT40 3SF Tel: (028) 2827 2827 Fax: (028) 2827 9084

G T I Computers Portsmouth Ltd, Unit 219, Victory Business Centre, Somers Road North, Portsmouth, PO1 1PJ Tel: (023) 9275 0212 Fax: (0870) 0601868 E-mail: sales@gticomputers.co.uk

▶ Gazelle Solutions Ltd, York Place Buildings, 6-8 York Place, Leeds, LS1 2DS Tel: 0113-245 3777 Fax: 0113-244 1968

▶ Gen Tek, 20 Thornton Gate, Thornton-Cleveleys, Lancashire, FY5 1JN Tel: (01253) 855589

▶ Gendata Ltd, 3, Church Street, Cirencester, Glos, GL7 1LE Tel: (01285) 659810 Fax: (01285) 644388

▶ Generalsoft Computer Systems, Gibbs House, Kennel Ride, Ascot, Berkshire, SL5 7NT Tel: (01344) 890979 Fax: (01344) 884735 E-mail: info@generalsoft.co.uk

Genie Computing, Unit 1, Gelligron Industrial Estate, Tonyrefail, Porth, Mid Glamorgan, CF39 8ES Tel: (0800) 0198069 E-mail: sales@geniecomputing.co.uk

▶ Get To It, 8 Coulson Way, Alconbury, Huntingdon, Cambridgeshire, PE28 4WU Tel: (01480) 896704 E-mail: sales@get-to-it.co.uk

Gibbz Dot Biz, 42 Hilley Field Lane, Fetcham, Leatherhead, Surrey, KT22 9UX Tel: (01372) 373825

▶ Global Distribution, Unit 4 Penketh Business Park, Cleveleys Road, Great Sankey, Warrington, WA5 2TJ Tel: (01925) 411441 Fax: 0151-210 2606

Global System Computers North East, 24 John Street, Cullercoats, North Shields, Tyne & Wear, NE30 4PL Tel: 0191-252 4440 Fax: 0191-257 9057 E-mail: bkenyon@fsl.co.uk

▶ Gold Octopus Software, Liberty Barn, Illand, Launceston, Cornwall, PL15 7LS Tel: (01566) 782221 Fax: (01566) 782090

▶ Grapevine Computers Ltd, 20 Greenwood Street, Altrincham, Cheshire, WA14 1RZ Tel: 0161-941 6978 Fax: 0161-941 6979 E-mail: sales@grapevinecomputers.co.uk

Gray's Electronic Services, 10a Union Street, Troon, Ayrshire, KA10 6BS Tel: (01292) 313430 Fax: (01292) 318888

Griffiths Associates Ltd, Penylan House, Penprysg Road, Pencoed, Bridgend, Mid Glamorgan, CF35 6LT Tel: (01656) 862653 Fax: (01656) 864243 E-mail: john.griffiths@galtd.co.uk

Gerald Grundy Computer Services Ltd, 78 Vicarage Lane, Coventry, CV7 9AE Tel: (024) 7664 5990 Fax: (024) 7636 5445 E-mail: gerald.grundy@btinternet.com

▶ Guildford Computers, 5 High Street, Guildford, Surrey, GU2 4AB Tel: (01483) 458468 Fax: (01483) 458468

H & B Computer Services, 46 Coombe Drive, Sittingbourne, Kent, ME10 3DA Tel: (01795) 422560 Fax: (08701) 375225 E-mail: enquiries@handbcomputers.co.uk

▶ H E Computing Ltd, Grosvenor Road, Bircotes, Doncaster, South Yorkshire, DN11 8EY Tel: (01302) 746053 Fax: (01302) 752643 E-mail: hec@harworth.biz

H & S Computer Solutions Ltd, 9-10 Gilchrist Close, Norwich, NR4 3AT Tel: (01603) 617677 Fax: (01603) 617144

▶ H S M Computers, 1 Afan Valley Close, Neath, West Glamorgan, SA11 3AJ Tel: (01639) 761503 Fax: (0871) 2771665 E-mail: sales@hsmcomputers.co.uk

Halifax Computers, 55 Pellon Lane, Halifax, West Yorkshire, HX1 5SP Tel: (01422) 347868 Fax: (01422) 256666

▶ Halo Data Recovery, 9 June Crescent, Amington, Tamworth, Staffordshire, B77 3BH Tel: (0870) 3501012 Fax: (08703) 501013

Harthill House Group Ltd, Harthill House, Woodhall Lane, Harthill, Sheffield, S26 7YQ Tel: (0870) 3501309 Fax: (01909) 772785 E-mail: sales@hhg.uk.com

▶ Haverill PC Bureau, Homefield Road, Haverhill, Suffolk, CB9 8QP Tel: (0871) 8712100 Fax: (0871) 8712101 E-mail: sales@hpcb.co.uk

▶ Home & Business Computer Service, 12 David Close, Braunton, Devon, EX33 2AT Tel: (01271) 815262 E-mail: info@handbcs.co.uk

▶ Home Computer Services, 6 Lower Road, Breachwood Green, Hitchin, Hertfordshire, SG4 8NS Tel: (0845) 3105645 E-mail: peter@home-computer-services.co.uk

▶ Hylton Nomis Computer Services, Unit D, Greenforde Farm, Stoner Hill Road, Froxfield, Petersfield, Hants, GU32 1DY Tel: (01730) 266123 Fax: (01730) 263645

I B M (UK) Ltd, Palace Street, Plymouth, PL1 2DE Tel: (01752) 660042 Fax: (01752) 224230

I C M Team Computer Group, 27 Wells Street, Inverness, IV3 5JU Tel: (01463) 711302 Fax: (01463) 713825 E-mail: icm@computergroup.co.uk

▶ I C T Solutions & Services Ltd, 78 Cavalry Drive, March, Cambridgeshire, PE15 9DP Tel: (01354) 659587 Fax: (01354) 659601 E-mail: enquiries@ictss.com

▶ I F S UK Ltd, Oakdale House, Penny Pot Lane, Killinghall, Harrogate, North Yorkshire, HG3 2SD Tel: (01423) 509189 Fax: (01423) 562842

▶ I T C Group, 1 Wearington Business Centre, Piparates Road, Peterborough, PE4 5BH Tel: (01733) 292810 Fax: (01733) 327112 E-mail: sales@itcgroup.co.uk

▶ I T Solutions, 2 Lea Court, Orchard End Avenue, Amersham, Buckinghamshire, HP7 9LS Tel: 01494 765494 E-mail: jeremy@it-solutions.me.uk

I T Solutions UK Ltd, Alpine House, Honeypot Lane, London, NW9 9RX Tel: (020) 8206 2874 Fax: (020) 8204 8487 E-mail: enquiries@swiftpro.com

▶ I View Multimedia, 30-40, Elcho Street, London, SW11 4AU Tel: (020) 7223 8691 Fax: (020) 7504 3619 E-mail: info@iview-multimedia.com

▶ Ideal PC's, The Maltings, Roydon Road, Stanstead Abbotts, Ware, Hertfordshire, SG12 8UU Tel: (01920) 871687 E-mail: sales@ideal-pcs.co.uk

Impetus Technologies Ltd, Castle Farm, Cholmondeley, Malpas, Cheshire, SY14 8AQ Tel: (01829) 773200 Fax: (01829) 773208 E-mail: sales@impetusuk.net

▶ Indigo Computing, First Floor St. Marys House, St. Marys Road, Market Harborough, Leicestershire, LE16 7DS Tel: (0800) 5428814

▶ Induna IT Ltd, Unit 9, Station Yard Workshops, Alston, Cumbria, CA9 3HN Tel: (01434) 382825 Fax: (01434) 382825 E-mail: enquires@indunait.com

▶ Infosoft Solutions, Kenton Park Parade, Kenton Road, Harrow, Middlesex, HA3 8DQ Tel: (020) 8909 1313 Fax: (020) 8909 1414 E-mail: info@infosoftsolutions.co.uk

▶ Infotech Enterprises Europe Ltd, Holborn Hall, 100 Gray's Inn Road, London, WC1X 8AL Tel: (020) 7404 0640 Fax: (020) 7404 0664 E-mail: info@insotech-europe.com

▶ In-I-T.Co.Uk, 5, The Courtyard, 51 St. Marys Road, Weybridge, Surrey, KT13 9PX Tel: (01932) 821127 Fax: (01932) 821137

▶ Inta Computer Trading Ltd, 22 Alfreton Road, Derby, DE21 4AS Tel: (01332) 616091 Fax: (01332) 200997

Intelligent Corporate Machines Ltd, North Block, Westminster BSNS Square Durham Street, London, SE11 5JH Tel: (020) 7820 9777 Fax: (020) 7820 9860 E-mail: icmachines@aol.com

▶ Interfire Ltd, The Gatehouse, Naworth, Brampton, Cumbria, CA8 2HF Tel: (01697) 742336 Fax: (0870) 1634677

Interlan Computer Maintenance, The Mill, Glasshouses, Harrogate, North Yorkshire, HG3 5QH Tel: (01423) 712222 Fax: (01423) 712958

▶ Intranetmanagers, Swan House, White Hart Street, High Wycombe, Buckinghamshire, HP11 2HL Tel: (01494) 463311 E-mail: sales@intranetmanagers.co.uk

▶ Isg UK Ltd, 830 Romford Road, London, E12 5JG Tel: (020) 8514 8886 Fax: (020) 8553 4440

▶ ITC Solutions, 2 Riverside Industrial Park, Rapier Street, Ipswich, IP2 8JX Tel: (01473) 604391

J C S Computing Solutions Ltd, 31 Church Street, Oldbury, West Midlands, B69 3AG Tel: 0121-543 6996 Fax: 0121-543 6997 E-mail: sales@jcs.co.uk

▶ J D Personal Computers, 126, High Street, Canvey Island, Essex, SS8 7SH Tel: (01268) 510101

▶ J K Communications, 4 The Courtyard, 188 Galgorm Road, Ballymena, County Antrim, BT42 1HL Tel: (028) 2563 1767 Fax: (0870) 7623785 E-mail: info@jkcomm.co.uk

J S Computer Services Ltd, 61 Pinnocks Lane, Baldock, Hertfordshire, SG7 6DD Tel: (01462) 641556 Fax: (01462) 641557 E-mail: jscomputerservices@yahoo.co.uk

Japhlin Computer Repairs, 77 Weeping Cross, Stafford, ST17 0DQ Tel: (01785) 663400 Fax: (01785) 665807 E-mail: phil@japhlin.co.uk

Jennings Computer Engineering Ltd, 24-28 Gain Lane, Bradford, West Yorkshire, BD3 7LS Tel: (01274) 637867 Fax: (01274) 633197 E-mail: info@jencomp.co.uk

▶ Johnston's PC Clinic, 98 Black Bull Road, Folkestone, Kent, CT19 5QX Tel: (01303) 244500 Fax: (01303) 244500

▶ Jupiter It Soultions, 205-207 West End Road, Haydock, St. Helens, Merseyside, WA11 0AW Tel: (01744) 20085 Fax: (01744) 20085

▶ K 4 Komputers, 21 London Street, Larkhall, Lanarkshire, ML9 1AQ Tel: (01698) 889123

Kalms Associates, 17 Lyon Road, London, SW19 2RL Tel: (020) 8286 6066 Fax: (020) 8547 7668 E-mail: sales@kalms-associates.com

Keltec Ltd, Unit 2 Bracknell Enterprise Centre, Bracknell, Berkshire, RG12 1NF Tel: (01344) 306700 Fax: (01344) 306800 E-mail: sales@keltec.co.uk

▶ Kerio Technologies Ltd, Sheraton House, Castle Park, Cambridge, CB3 0AX Tel: (01223) 370136 Fax: (01223) 370040

Kew Computers, 78 Woolmer Way, Bordon, Hampshire, GU35 9QF Tel: (01420) 479666 Fax: (01420) 488348 E-mail: info@kewcomputers.com

▶ Kim Software Solutions Ltd, 1 The Square, Sawbridgeworth, Hertfordshire, CM21 9AE Tel: (01279) 600171 Fax: (01279) 600557 E-mail: mikepj@kimsp.com

▶ Kronons, 25-27 Wateny Market, Watney Street, London, E1 9PP Tel: (020) 7790 7144 Fax: (0870) 7062842 E-mail: info@kronons.com

L E T S S, The Lodge, Crown Woods School, Riefield Road, London, SE9 2QL Tel: (020) 8850 0100 Fax: (020) 8850 0400 E-mail: letss@compuserve.com

▶ Laptop Specialists, Lane End House, Green Lane, Tansley, Matlock, Derbyshire, DE4 5FJ Tel: (01629) 584456

▶ Laptop Support, No. 1 Factory Road, Poole, Dorset, BH16 5SJ Tel: (0800) 1977665 E-mail: repairs@testlink.co.uk

▶ LB Computer Solutions, 6 Whitelees Road, Cleghorn, Lanark, ML11 7SP Tel: (01555) 870394

Level 7 Computers Ltd, 39 Eastover, Bridgwater, Somerset, TA6 5AW Tel: (01278) 444770 E-mail: mail@level7.co.uk

▶ Liant Software Ltd, 5-8 The Sanctuary, London, SW1P 3JS Tel: (020) 7799 2434 Fax: (020) 7799 2552

▶ Lightening Computers, 107 Duke Street, St. Helens, Merseyside, WA10 2JG Tel: (01744) 751110 Fax: (01744) 882746

Linden Computer Services, Laverham House, 77 St Georges Place, Cheltenham, Gloucestershire, GL50 3PP Tel: (01242) 269369 Fax: (01242) 231341

Link Level Services Ltd, Business & Technology Centre, Radway Green, Crewe, CW2 5PR Tel: (01270) 886113 Fax: (01270) 886237 E-mail: sales@linklevel.co.uk

COMPUTER MAINTENANCE/REPAIR SERVICES – *continued*

▶ Linklan Solutions Ltd, The Lodge, 66 St. Leonards Road, Windsor, Berks, SL4 3BY Tel: (01753) 621660 Fax: (01753) 621690

▶ Lithium Systems, Unit 4 Block 1 Crookaridge Way, Alloa, Clackmannanshire, FK10 3LP Tel: (01259) 727847 Fax: (01259) 729963

▶ Loafdom Computers, Units 10-11, Stratford Antiques Centre, 60 Ely Street, Stratford-upon-Avon, Warwickshire, CV37 6LN Tel: (01789) 296515

Logo Systems, 8 Greenwich Quay, Clarence Road, London, SE8 3EY Tel: (020) 8469 2222 Fax: (020) 8469 2211 E-mail: service@logosystems.co.uk

▶ The Lost Connection, 13 Gordon Crescent, Brierley Hill, West Midlands, DY5 1HS Tel: (01384) 347597

Lyndon Co., Unit 14 Saxon Business Centre, Windsor Avenue, London, SW19 2RR Tel: (020) 8543 9969 Fax: (020) 8543 9765 E-mail: sales@lydongroup.co.uk

M I J Technology, PO Box 158, Deal, Kent, CT14 9GZ Tel: (01304) 360223 Fax: (0870) 7061577

M2 Technical Services Ltd, 18 Glebe Street, Glasgow, G4 0ET Tel: 0141-552 3877 Fax: 0141-552 3896 E-mail: admin@m2ltd.co.uk

▶ Mac PC Solutions Ltd, 53 Shirley Gardens, Barking, Essex, IG11 9XB Tel: (07956) 168242 E-mail: info@macpcsolutions.co.uk

Magnacom Ltd, Crossford Mill, Beith Road, Kilbarchan, Johnstone, Renfrewshire, PA10 2NS Tel: (01505) 706000 Fax: (01505) 706067 E-mail: office@magnacom.co.uk

▶ Mail Order Systems Ltd, Unit 3, Mercia Business Village, Torwood Close, Westwood Business Park, Coventry, CV4 8HX Tel: (024) 7688 3434 Fax: (024) 7688 3773

Maindec Computer Engineering Ltd, Maindec House, Holtspur Lane, Wooburn Green, High Wycombe, Buckinghamshire, HP10 0AB Tel: (01628) 810977 Fax: (01628) 810733 E-mail: roger.timms@maindec.co.uk

Maintenance Direct Ltd, 50c Coldharbour Lane, Hayes, Middlesex, UB3 3EP Tel: (0870) 7494044 Fax: (020) 8569 0399 E-mail: sales@maintenance-direct.com

Majenta Solutions, Coptfold Road, Brentwood, Essex, CM14 4BN Tel: (01277) 263244 Fax: (01277) 263245 E-mail: info@majentasolutions.co.uk

Manhattan Electronics, 4 Cooksey Lane, Birmingham, B44 9QN Tel: 0121-605 2957 Fax: 0121-605 3031 E-mail: manhattanelec@hotmail.com

▶ Maple Computer Components, 37 Measham Way, Lower Earley, Reading, RG6 4ES Tel: 0118-987 5522

Marlborough Data Systems Ltd, 2 The Parade Mews, The Parade, Marlborough, Wiltshire, SN8 1NE Tel: (01672) 511198 Fax: (01672) 511836 E-mail: sales@mdsltd.org

▶ MAS Computers, 310 Ruislip Road East, Greenford, Middlesex, UB6 9BH Tel: (020) 8575 0777 Fax: (020) 8575 0777 E-mail: arifsiddiqi@hotmail.com

Matrix Computer Services, Matrix Buildings, Darenth Road, Dartford, DA1 1LU Tel: (01322) 292391 Fax: (01322) 229908 E-mail: matrixcomputers@compuserve.com

▶ Matrix Memory Technology, Burlyns Coach House, Ball Hill, Newbury, Berkshire, RG20 0NU Tel: (01635) 255039

▶ M-audio, Floor 6, Gresham House, 53 Clarendon Road, Watford, WD17 1LA Tel: (01923) 204010 Fax: (0871) 7177101

Maxi Million Ltd, 21a Whitmore Street, Whittlesey, Peterborough, PE7 1HE Tel: (01733) 208283 Fax: (01733) 208366 E-mail: peterborough@maxi-million.co.uk

▶ Maximillion, Halesfield 20, Telford, Shropshire, TF7 4QU Tel: (01952) 585100 Fax: (01952) 585332

▶ MCL Cadcam Ltd, Block 2 Office 5 Nortonthorpe Industrial Estate, Wakefield Road, Scissett, Huddersfield, HD8 9LA Tel: (01484) 866311 Fax: (01484) 866575 E-mail: sales@mclsolutions.com

Media Magic Computers, Media House, 196a Abbey Road, Leeds, LS5 3NG Tel: 0113-228 9911 Fax: 0113-228 9933

Megatronics Group Ltd, 240 Wellesley Road, Methil, Leven, Fife, KY8 3BW Tel: (01333) 421116 Fax: (01333) 307004 E-mail: info@megatronicsgroup.com

▶ Merac Computer Systems, 10 King Street, Exeter, EX1 1BQ Tel: (01392) 679653 Fax: (01392) 491008 E-mail: sales@merac.co.uk

▶ Merryfields, Merryfields, Church Road, Partridge Green, Horsham, West Sussex, RH13 8JS Tel: (07732) 437628 Fax: (07876) 892851

▶ Meson Solutions, B9 Bicester Innovation Centre, Telford Road, Bicester, Oxfordshire, OX26 4LD Tel: (01869) 255777 Fax: (01869) 255801 E-mail: sales@mesonsolutions.com

▶ Micks Computer Clinic, 31 Milner Road, Long Eaton, Nottingham, NG10 1LB Tel: 0115-849 1797

Micro Rent plc, 6 The Gateway Centre, Coronation Road, Cressex Business Park, High Wycombe, Buckinghamshire, HP12 3SU Tel: (01494) 768768 Fax: (01494) 768700 E-mail: sales@microrent.co.uk

Micro Services, 293a Newark Road, Lincoln, LN5 8PE Tel: (01522) 522128 Fax: (01522) 522128

Micro System Support, The Common East, Premier House, Bradley Stoke, Bristol, BS34 6BH Tel: (01454) 626463 Fax: (01454) 626462

Microcare Corporation, 34 Chantry Close, Harrow, Middlesex, HA3 9QZ Tel: (020) 8204 3630 Fax: (020) 8204 3638 E-mail: microcare@breathemail.net

Microcraft Ltd, PO Box 3252, Tamworth, Staffs, B79 0BF Tel: (01827) 373551 Fax: (01827) 284667 E-mail: harryke@microcraft.ltd.uk

Micro-Fix, Hemlock Place, Hyssop Close, Cannock, Staffordshire, WS11 7GA Tel: (01543) 467579 Fax: (01543) 469624 E-mail: info@on2net.co.uk

▶ Microgaming Software Systems Ltd, M G S House, Circular Road, Douglas, Isle Of Man, IM1 1BL Tel: (01624) 647777 Fax: (01624) 647778

Microlog Computer Software, 7 Stainland Road, Greetland, Halifax, West Yorkshire, HX4 8AD Tel: (01422) 310031 Fax: (01422) 371694 E-mail: sales@micrlog.co.uk

Microtec Ware Ltd, 146 Cherry Hinton Road, Cambridge, CB1 7AJ Tel: (01223) 416641 Fax: (01223) 413341 E-mail: purchasing@microtecware.com

▶ Mikom Systems Ltd, 110 Parkgate, Darlington, County Durham, DL1 1RX Tel: (01325) 465683 Fax: (01325) 463930 E-mail: sales@mikom.co.uk

Milequip Computer Maintenance Ltd, Hepworth House, 115 Southgate Street, Gloucester, GL1 1UT Tel: (01452) 305430 Fax: (01452) 411010 E-mail: mcmcomputers@freeuk.com

▶ Mobile PC Fix, 23 Norton Road, London, E10 7LQ Tel: (020) 8556 3044

Modern Computers Ltd, 181 Old Kent Road, London, SE1 5NA Tel: (020) 7231 1313 Fax: (020) 7231 3225 E-mail: sales@moderncomputers.com

The Mousepad, Stockwell Head, Hinckley, Leicestershire, LE10 1RE Tel: (01455) 233893 Fax: (0870) 0567193 E-mail: derick@themouse.co.uk

▶ M-Tek Computer Services, Units 25-26, Holman Road, Caradon Business Centre, Liskeard, Cornwall, PL14 3UT Tel: (07918) 664540 Fax: (01579) 348094 E-mail: sales@mtek.co.uk

▶ Multimodal Applied Systems Europe Ltd, 5 Hunters Walk, Canal Street, Chester, CH1 4EB Tel: (01244) 403294 Fax: (01244) 348471

▶ My Computes, Unit 1, Central Buildings, Kingsway, Manchester, M19 1SP Tel: 0161-975 0220 Fax: 0161-975 0330

▶ N B Computer Maintenance Ltd, 50 Leys Road, Pattishall, Towcester, Northamptonshire, NN12 8JZ Tel: (01327) 831404 Fax: (01327) 830982 E-mail: sales@nbmaintenance.co.uk

N C S Group P.L.C., Belville House, Ponteland, Newcastle Upon Tyne, NE20 9BF Tel: (01661) 803000 Fax: (01661) 860069 E-mail: marketing@ncs-plc.co.uk

N E C Europe Ltd, Unit G Stafford Park 12, Telford, Shropshire, TF3 3BJ Tel: (01952) 237000 Fax: (01952) 237006 E-mail: kevin.emlyn@uk.neceur.com

▶ Naked Knowledge, 138, Watling Street East, Towcester, Northants, NN12 6BT Tel: 0870-112 3000

▶ Netcomm Data Solutions Ltd, 93-95, Carshalton Grove, Sutton, Surrey, SM1 4NB Tel: (020) 8643 4908 Fax: (020) 8770 0831

Nettech Solutions, 20 Branch Road, Batley, West Yorkshire, WF17 5RY Tel: (01924) 524873 Fax: (01924) 501183 E-mail: nettech.solutions@ntlworld.com

▶ New Health Network Ltd, The Leather Market, Weston Street, London, SE1 3ER Tel: (020) 7407 1618

Newcom Computer Systems, 1a Sugarhouse Quay, Newry, County Down, BT35 6HZ Tel: (028) 3026 3149 Fax: (028) 3026 3149

Nexus Graphic Systems Ltd, Apartment 11, Generator Hall, Electric Wharf, Coventry, CV1 4JL Tel: (024) 7622 3865 Fax: (024) 7622 3872

NKC Computers Ltd, Unit 22 Ogmore Crescent, Bridgend, Mid Glamorgan, CF31 3TE Tel: (01656) 655009 Fax: (01656) 669025

▶ No Limits, 28, Grenville Road, London, N19 4EH Tel: (020) 7263 0328

Norsk Data Ltd, The Coach House, Turners Drive, Thatcham, Berkshire, RG19 4QB Tel: (01635) 35544 Fax: (01635) 865634

▶ Nortech Computers Ltd, 10 High Street, Portishead, Bristol, BS20 6EW Tel: (01275) 818699 Fax: (01275) 849316

▶ Nurul Mobile PC Repairs, 3 Mount Pleasant Road, Sheffield, S7 1BA Tel: 0114-255 1188 Fax: (0870) 7052705

O B S Computer Maintenance & Sales, 113 Beech Hill Ave, Wigan, Lancs, WN6 7RP Tel: (01257) 421278 E-mail: sales@obscomputers.com

O N C, Unit 220 Tedco Business Centre, Jarrow, Tyne & Wear, NE32 3DT Tel: 0191-422 0229 Fax: 0191-428 3365 E-mail: s.owens@onc-computers.co.uk

▶ Oden Services Ltd, Unit 17 Highcroft Industrial Estate, Enterprise Road, Waterlooville, Hampshire, PO8 0BT Tel: (023) 9259 9898 Fax: (023) 9259 9696

Odyssey Technologies Ltd, Hurlands Close, Farnham, Surrey, GU9 9JE Tel: (01252) 721821 Fax: (01252) 721211 E-mail: sales@odessey.co.uk

▶ Olat Ltd, James House, 22-24 Corsham Street, London, N1 6DR Tel: (020) 72518556 Fax: (020) 72533806

▶ Omagh Computer Repair Centre, E Mountjoy Road, Omagh, County Tyrone, BT79 7AD Tel: (028) 8225 9564 Fax: (028) 8225 1687 E-mail: ocrc@btconnect.com

▶ Omicron Parts & Services, 5 Grand Union Enterprise Park, Grand Union Way, Southall, Middlesex, UB2 4EX Tel: (020) 8574 0647 Fax: (020) 8890 3418

▶ The Open Server Project, 370 Welcombe Avenue, Swindon, SN3 2PB Tel: (01793) 619595 Fax: (01793) 619595

▶ Oriel Computers, Enkalon Indust Estate, Randalstown Road, Antrim, BT41 4LJ Tel: (028) 9446 0021 Fax: (028) 9446 4545 E-mail: orielcomputers@tiscali.co.uk

Owen Coyle Anodising, 144 Blyth Road, Hayes, Middlesex, UB3 1BY Tel: (020) 8573 0184 Fax: (020) 8848 1170 E-mail: sales@owencoyle-anodising.co.uk

Oxford Computers, 30 Bulan Road, Headington, Oxford, OX3 7HT Tel: (01865) 747968 Fax: (01865) 747968 E-mail: oxford.computers@virgin.net

P A Computers, Highcross Road, Southfleet, Gravesend, Kent, DA13 9PH Tel: (01474) 833933 Fax: (01474) 834446 E-mail: mail@pacomputers.co.uk

▶ P C C Maintenance Ltd, 162 Oundle Road, Thrapston, Kettering, Northamptonshire, NN14 4PQ Tel: (0845) 1662916

▶ P C Clinic Plus, 28 Lenton Boulevard, Nottingham, NG7 2ES Tel: (0800) 5191010 Fax: E-mail: help@pcclinicplus.co.uk

P C Computer Clinic, Clyde Street, Londonderry, BT48 7EJ Tel: (028) 7128 3355 Fax: (028) 7128 3356 E-mail: jerry@pccomputerclinic.com

P C Ideals, 89 Albert Road, Southsea, Hampshire, PO5 2SG Tel: (023) 9282 9239 Fax: (023) 9286 2111 E-mail: sales@pcideals.com

▶ P C Image, Unit 4-5, The Square, Vicarage Farm Road, Peterborough, PE1 5TS Tel: (01733) 349032 Fax: (01733) 352472 E-mail: sales@pcimage.co.uk

P C Microfix Ltd, 149 Uxbridge Road, London, W7 3ST Tel: (020) 8579 7474 Fax: (020) 8579 1667 E-mail: microfix@aol.com

P C S Technical Services, 70 Church Road, Aston, Birmingham, B6 5TY Tel: 0121-326 0011 Fax: 0121-366 0022 E-mail: sales@pcs-technical.com

▶ P C Sos 24 7, Europa House, Adlington Industrial Estate, Adlington, Macclesfield, Cheshire, SK10 4NL Tel: (0870) 2863767 E-mail: help@pcsos247.com

▶ P C Stuff, 22 Albion Road, Bradford, West Yorkshire, BD10 9PY Tel: (01274) 616201

P C Supplies, 119 Cavendish Street, Barrow-in-Furness, Cumbria, LA14 1DJ Tel: (01229) 833595 Fax: (01229) 877677 E-mail: sales@pcsuppliesuk.co.uk

▶ P C Support & Networking, Unit 14, Prospect Way, Selby, North Yorkshire, YO8 8BD Tel: (0800) 1613395 Fax: (0871) 6617934

▶ P C Worxs, 89 Foxberry Road, London, SE4 2SS Tel: (020) 8691 9215

▶ P Ferguson Computers, PO BOX 29437, Glasgow, G67 9AX Tel: (07709) 264553 E-mail: pferguson22@hotmail.com

P M Associates, Lyjon House, Merseyton Road, Ellesmere Port, CH65 2AP Tel: 0151-357 2196 Fax: 0151-357 1120

P M P Micros, Rock Cottage, Hawber Lane, Silsden, Keighley, West Yorkshire, BD20 0LE Tel: (07967) 173739 Fax: (01535) 653006 E-mail: peter@pmp-micros.co.uk

Pace Computers, Greenways, Hudswell, Richmond, North Yorkshire, DL11 6BQ Tel: (01748) 850310 Fax: (01748) 850413 E-mail: pacecomputers@talk21.com

▶ Pagazzi Lighting Ltd, Unit 4, Almondvale South Retail Park, Livingston, West Lothian, EH54 6XG Tel: (01506) 407610 Fax: (01506) 464907 E-mail: lighting@pagazzi.com

Park Computers, 100 Darwen Street, Blackburn, BB2 2AJ Tel: (01254) 696111 Fax: (01254) 696111 E-mail: sales@parkcomputers.co.uk

PC 2000, 7 Bridge Street, Dumbarton, G82 1NY Tel: (01389) 739290 Fax: (01389) 726885 E-mail: enquiries@pc2000.co.uk

▶ PC Angells, 11 Tuxford Close, Borehamwood, Hertfordshire, WD6 4LE Tel: (07941) 153532 E-mail: paul@pcangells.co.uk

▶ PC Doctor, 26c London Road, Hertford Heath, Hertford, SG13 7PN Tel: (0870) 7771251 E-mail: enquiries@ukpcdoctor.co.uk

PC Express, 185 Washway Road, Sale, Cheshire, M33 4AH Tel: 0161-291 1044 Fax: 0161-291 1077 E-mail: info@pc-xp.com

PC Guru, 68 North Drive, Troon, Ayrshire, KA10 7DF Tel: (01292) 311688 E-mail: mark@pcguru-scotland.com

PC Healthcare Ltd, 767 Wimborne Road, Bournemouth, BH9 2BA Tel: (01202) 525952 Fax: (01202) 526843 E-mail: sales@pchealthcare.co.uk

▶ PC Home Help, Hillfield, Ringland Circle, Newport, Gwent, NP19 9PL Tel: (01633) 673272

▶ PC Medik, 66 Valley Gardens, Wallsend, Tyne & Wear, NE28 7HB Tel: (07960) 961593 E-mail: info@pcmedik.co.uk

▶ PC North, 79 Allhallowgate, Ripon, North Yorkshire, HG4 1LE Tel: (01765) 608400 Fax: (01765) 608400

▶ PC Paramedics, 36 Sefton Close, Stoke Poges, Slough, SL2 4LJ Tel: (01753) 645983

▶ PC Parts, 28 Sandy Lane, Stockport, Cheshire, SK5 7NZ Tel: 0161-476 1199 Fax: 0161-477 0703

PC Repair Centre Ltd, 22 Haydon Place, Guildford, Surrey, GU1 4LL Tel: (01483) 567817 Fax: (01483) 567817 E-mail: pcrepaircentre@yahoo.co.uk

PC Tech Ltd, 33 Cleveland Street, Normanby, Middlesbrough, Cleveland, TS6 0LT Tel: (01642) 460704 Fax: (01642) 461002 E-mail: sales@pctechcomputers.com

▶ PC Tekit, 25 Churchill Terrace, Barry, South Glamorgan, CF63 2QX Tel: (01446) 405104

PC World, Leeds Road Retail Park, Leeds Road, Huddersfield, HD1 6PF Tel: (0870) 2420444 Fax: (01484) 437302 E-mail: customer.services@pcworld.co.uk

▶ Pcbee Computer Maintenance, 156 High Street, Broadstairs, Kent, CT10 1JB Tel: (01843) 604207 Fax: (01843) 604207

▶ PCC Support Ltd, 162 Oundle Road, Thrapston, Kettering, Northamptonshire, NN14 4PQ Tel: (0845) 1662916 Fax: (0870) 7664154 E-mail: sales@pccsystems.co.uk

Pericom SW Ltd, 46b Sea King Road, Lynx Trading Estate, Yeovil, Somerset, BA20 2NZ Tel: (01935) 410377 Fax: (01935) 410755 E-mail: mail@lbts.co.uk

Persimmon Consultants Ltd, Pine View, Forest Dale Road, Marlborough, Wiltshire, SN8 2AS Tel: (01672) 514500 E-mail: info@persim.com

▶ Phase 4, 29 Regent Parade, Harrogate, North Yorkshire, HG1 5AZ Tel: (01423) 525277 Fax: (01423) 709922

Phase C R S Ltd, Beacon Lodge, Texas Street, Morley, Leeds, LS27 0HG Tel: 0113-238 0558 Fax: 0113-238 0484 E-mail: sales@phase.crs.co.uk

▶ Pinkroccade Group, Old Greenock Road, Inchinnan, Renfrew, PA4 9LH Tel: 0141-814 1000 Fax: 0141-814 1151

Pisces Computers, Moor Street, Chepstow, Gwent, NP16 5DE Tel: (01291) 625100 Fax: (01291) 621068 E-mail: piscescomputers@aol.com

Plum Technology, 21-23 Wordsworth Avenue, Sinfin, Derby, DE24 9HQ Tel: (01332) 272210 Fax: (01332) 272203 E-mail: sales@plum.co.uk

PNJ Monitors, 41 Brookfield, Bayston Hill, Shrewsbury, SY3 0LR Tel: (01743) 872935 Fax: (01743) 872935

▶ Poindexters Ltd, 103 Newgate Street, Bishop Auckland, County Durham, DL14 7EW Tel: (01388) 604004 Fax: (01388) 604004 E-mail: poindexters@dsl.pipex.com

Port PCS Ltd, Port Elphinstone Post Office, Elphinstone Road, Port Elphinstone, Inverurie, Aberdeenshire, AB51 3UR Tel: (01467) 629935

▶ Portlock Software, Vickers House Vickers Business Centre, Priestley Road, Basingstoke, Hampshire, RG24 9NP Tel: (01256) 392990 Fax: (01256) 473010 E-mail: sales@portlock.com

Premier Source Ltd, Cott Abbey, Winstone, Cirencester, Gloucestershire, GL7 7JT Tel: (01285) 821599 Fax: (01285) 821444 E-mail: ralph@premiresourceorg.org

▶ Prestige Network Solutions, Baynard House, 135 Queen Victoria Street, London, EC4V 4AA Tel: (020) 7601 0000 Fax: (020) 7495 5177 E-mail: sales@prestige.networks.com

▶ Pro-Com Computer Services London Ltd, 53 St. Helier Avenue, Morden, Surrey, SM4 6HY Tel: (020) 8287 2772 Fax: (020) 8395 3565 E-mail: sales@procomcomputers.co.uk

▶ Professional IT Logistics Ltd, Unit 5, Station Approach, Wendover, Buckinghamshire, HP22 6BN Tel: (0870) 3802999 Fax: (0870) 3802998 E-mail: support@professionalit.com

▶ Prophecy, 85-103, Queens Road, Reading, RG1 4DA Tel: 0118-958 9955 Fax: 0118-958 9977

Pyramid Valley Computers, Heapriding Mill, Ford Street, Stockport, Cheshire, SK3 0BT Tel: 0161-477 3880 Fax: 0161-480 8741 E-mail: sales@pyramidvalley.co.uk

R A M Computers, 260d Gospel Lane, Birmingham, B27 7AH Tel: 0121-707 3353 Fax: 0121-706 1413 E-mail: sales@ramcomputers.co.uk

R & J Computer Services, Unit 17, Bingham Park Farm, Potten End Hill, Water End, Hemel Hempstead, Hertfordshire, HP1 3BN Tel: (01442) 231943 Fax: (01442) 255207 E-mail: sales@max-technology.co.uk

R S Systems, 79 Blaney Road, Altnamachin, Newry, County Down, BT35 0EA Tel: (028) 3087 8602 Fax: (028) 3087 8141

▶ Rapid Group, Unit 18 Avon Trading Park, Reid Street, Christchurch, Dorset, BH23 2BT Tel: (01202) 703040 Fax: (01202) 470212 E-mail: sales@rapidgroup.net

▶ Real Time World Ltd, 152 West Market Gate, Dundee, DD1 1NJ Tel: (01382) 202821 Fax: (01382) 228188

▶ Reboot Computer Services, 106 Walcot Street, Bath, BA1 5BG Tel: (01225) 447227 Fax: (01225) 471166

▶ Recyber Direct, The Old Town Hall, St. Andrews Street, Droitwich, Worcs, WR9 8DY Tel: (01905) 779993 Fax: (01905) 773080

Redkyte Computers, 142 Flixton Road, Urmston, Manchester, M41 5BG Tel: 0161-749 7861 E-mail: sales@redkyte.com

Redstone Computers UK Ltd, Suit 3 Stone House Business Centre, Market Street, Chipping Norton, Oxfordshire, OX7 5NA Tel: (0870) 0119433 Fax: (01608) 811359 E-mail: emac@sagesolutions.co.uk

Regenersis Ltd, 1 James Wort Avenue, Westwood Park, Glenrothes, Fife, KY7 4UA Tel: (01592) 774704 Fax: (01592) 774150 E-mail: margaret.lessels@crc-group.com

COMPUTER MAINTENANCE/REPAIR SERVICES – *continued*

▶ Rekar Ltd, Sandy Cross, Heathfield, East Sussex, TN21 8QR Tel: (01435) 860100 Fax: (01435) 869718

Rental Options Ltd, Hillfoot House, Beenham Hill, Beenham, Reading, RG7 5LS Tel: 0118-971 2864 Fax: 0118-971 2820 E-mail: sales@rentaloptions.co.uk

▶ Rock Computer Corp, 1 Collins Road, Heathcote Industrial Estate, Warwick, CV34 6TF Tel: (0870) 2203600 Fax: (0870) 9909091 E-mail: sales@rockdirect.com

Roswell It Services Ltd, James Watt Centre Scottish Enterprise Technology Park, James, East Kilbride, Glasgow, G75 0QD Tel: (01355) 265588 Fax: (01355) 265975 E-mail: sales@roswell-it.co.uk

▶ S P C International, Unit 1-3, Station Road, Templecombe, Somerset, BA8 0JR Tel: (01963) 370504 Fax: (01963) 370101 E-mail: sales@spcint.com

S S I Solutions Ltd, Fordbrook Business Centre, Marlborough Road, Pewsey, Wiltshire, SN9 5NU Tel: (01672) 565300 Fax: (01672) 563001 E-mail: general.enquireis@ssi.co.uk

Sahara Presentation Systems P.L.C., Williams House, Hailey Road, Erith, Kent, DA18 4AA Tel: (020) 8319 7777 Fax: (020) 8319 7775 E-mail: jsa@sahara-products.com

▶ Samtec Computer Maintenance, 11 King Street, Luton, LU1 2DW Tel: (01582) 402705 E-mail: samtec@aol.com

▶ Scenic Compact, 3, Amarylis Close, Fareham, Hants, PO15 5LQ Tel: (01329) 849849

Scorpio Computers, 6 Fore Street, Devonport, Plymouth, PL1 4DW Tel: (01752) 606011 Fax: (01752) 606011 E-mail: scorpio@myisp.co.uk

SCS Technology Solutions Ltd, Unit 1 Exchange Close, North Hykeham, Lincoln, LN6 3TR Tel: (01522) 883636 Fax: (01522) 884467 E-mail: sales@scstechsolutions.co.uk

▶ Second Byte It, Unit D2 Mercia Way, Foxhills Industrial Estate, Scunthorpe, South Humberside, DN15 8RE Tel: (01724) 280055 Fax: (01724) 852925 E-mail: secondbyteit@mail.com

▶ Sector Systems Ltd, 18 Milton Road, Caterham, Surrey, CR3 5JD Tel: (01883) 334641 Fax: (01883) 334641 E-mail: rdavies@sectorsystems.co.uk

▶ Seldos Computers, 211 Kingland Road, London, E2 8AN Tel: (07984) 340359 E-mail: sales@seldos.co.uk

Seohun Co Ltd, Excel Ho, 6 Pepys Rd, London, SW20 8NH Tel: 020 89479313 Fax: 020 88793958

ServiceTec Ltd, ServiceTec House, 3 Rutherford Close, Medway Technology Park, Stevenage, Hertfordshire, SG1 2EF Tel: (01438) 341900 Fax: (01438) 341901 E-mail: info@servicetec.com

Servo, Oakwell Way, Birstall, Batley, West Yorkshire, WF17 9LU Tel: (01924) 422111 Fax: (0870) 1218302 E-mail: info@icm-computer.co.uk

Sherlock Computer Services Ltd, 28 Cornfield Road, Woodley, Reading, RG5 4QA Tel: 0118-954 0097 Fax: 0118-954 0097

Shore Electronic Services, 32 Heacham Drive, Leicester, LE4 0LF Tel: 0116-235 1858 Fax: 0116-235 1858 E-mail: shoreelectronicservices@shoreb.freeserve.co.uk

▶ Sinclair Computers, 16 Nisbet Drive, Denny, Stirlingshire, FK6 6AQ Tel: (01324) 829829

▶ Sipher Computer Maintenance, 39 English Street, Dumfries, DG1 2BU Tel: (01387) 253353 Fax: (01387) 270999 E-mail: enquiries@siphercomputing.co.uk

Sirton Computer Services Ltd, Unit 19 Windsor Park Indutrail Estate, 50 Windsor Avenue, London, SW19 2TJ Tel: (020) 8542 2255 Fax: (020) 8542 2266 E-mail: office@sirton.co.uk

SMG Computers, 34 Hallen Close, Emersons Green, Bristol, BS16 7JE Tel: (0788) 0731672 E-mail: smg@smg-computers.com

Soft Priced Hardware, 209-215 Padiham Road, Burnley, Lancashire, BB12 0HB Tel: (01282) 431113 Fax: (01282) 425550 E-mail: sphard@tiscali.co.uk

▶ Soho Computer Services, 164 Dulverton Avenue, Coventry, CV5 8HB Tel: (024) 7626 9533 E-mail: sales@soho-computer-services.co.uk

Solution & Communications Services Ltd, 57 Crwys Road, Cardiff, CF24 4NE Tel: (029) 2066 6133 Fax: (029) 2066 6017 E-mail: sales@solutions-and-communications.com

▶ Solutions, The Trent Business Centre, Canal Street, Long Eaton, Nottingham, NG10 4HN Tel: 0115-946 3215 Fax: 0115-946 3332

▶ Sorsis Ltd, 20 Normandy Close, Northwold, Thetford, Norfolk, IP26 5NN Tel: (01366) 727661 Fax: (01366) 727661

▶ Sort IT, 120 Holmes Avenue, Hove, East Sussex, BN3 7LE Tel: 01273 227709 E-mail: info@sortitquick.co.uk

South Wales Computer Repairs, 1-2 Usk Street, Newport, Gwent, NP19 7BE Tel: (01633) 252306 Fax: (01633) 252304 E-mail: jeoff@swcr.net

Spa Advanced Systems Ltd, 40 Holden Park Road, South Borough, Tunbridge Wells, Kent, TN4 0ER Tel: (01892) 548998 Fax: (01892) 548175 E-mail: spa@spadata.co.uk

SPC International Ltd, 106 Oxford Road, Uxbridge, Middlesex, UB8 1NA Tel: (01895) 454850 Fax: (01895) 454851 E-mail: sales@spcint.com

▶ Spear Technologies Ltd, Station Rise, York, YO1 6HT Tel: (01904) 624009 Fax: (01904) 655411E-mail: admin@speartechnologies.com

Specialist Computer Centre, 16 Dargan Crescent, Belfast, BT3 9JP Tel: (028) 9037 0160 Fax: (028) 9037 0195 E-mail: belfast.sales@scc.com

▶ Star Accountancy, Park Royal Metro Centre, Britannia Way, London, NW10 7PA Tel: (020) 8961 5151 Fax: (020) 8961 4546 E-mail: info@sacs-uk.com

▶ Steve Cornish Solutions, Imex Business Centre, Brookfield Road, Arnold, Nottingham, NG5 7ER Tel: 0115-920 5740 Fax: 0115-966 7427

▶ Stoctech Solutions, 21 Naples Road, Stockport, Cheshire, SK3 0TN Tel: (0800) 4583548 Fax: (07792) 528875

▶ Stripes, 1a Old Church Buildings, Cramlington, Northumberland, NE23 1DN Tel: (01670) 737014 Fax: (01670) 734026

▶ Stroud PC (Cinderford), 20 Victoria Street, Cinderford, Gloucestershire, GL14 2HQ Tel: (0870) 8034246 Fax: (07092) 812233 E-mail: bryan@stroud-pcs.com

▶ Stroud-PC's (RuralDean), 27 Victoria Street, Cinderford, Gloucestershire, GL14 2ET Tel: (0845) 2260173 E-mail: info@stroud-pcs.com

Swansea Itec Ltd, 250 Carmarthen Road, Swansea, SA1 1HG Tel: (01792) 464561 Fax: (01792) 648375 E-mail: info@swansea-itec.co.uk

▶ Swift Software Solutions Ltd, 2 Warner House, Harrovian Business Village, Bessborough Road, Harrow, Middlesex, HA1 3EX Tel: (020) 8423 8333 Fax: (020) 8423 9627

▶ Swinton Technology Ltd, Unit 3 Park Farm Courtyard, Easthorpe, Malton, North Yorkshire, YO17 6QX Tel: (01653) 698844 Fax: (01653) 605679 E-mail: allison_knaggs@swintontechnology.co.uk

Syan Ltd, Holton Wood 37, Telford, Shropshire, TF1 7GT Tel: (01952) 607000 Fax: (01952) 677278 E-mail: administration.team@syansmb.co.uk

▶ Syscom Business Computing Ltd, Blackpool Technology Centre, Faraday Way, Blackpool, FY2 0JW Tel: (01253) 316333 Fax: (01253) 316338 E-mail: sales@syscom.co.uk

T G M Resource, Technology House, Chasewater Court, Corbett Road, Chasewater Heaths Business Park, Burntwood, Staffordshire, WS7 3GL Tel: (01543) 458714 Fax: (01543) 458542

▶ T T Enterprises, Knighton, Canada Hill, Newton Abbot, Devon, TQ12 6AF Tel: (01626) 208928

▶ Taylor Systems, Lane End Court, 2a Lane End Road, Bembridge, Isle of Wight, PO35 5UE Tel: (01983) 875222 Fax: (01983) 875222

▶ Techies Ltd, Triumph Way, Woburn Road Industrial Estate, Kempston, Bedford, MK42 7QB Tel: (01234) 299000 Fax: (01234) 299009 E-mail: sales@techies.co.uk

Technical Progress Ltd, 96 Telford Road, Cumbernauld, Glasgow, G67 2NJ Tel: (01236) 453266 Fax: (01236) 458274 E-mail: sales@technicalprogressltd.co.uk

▶ Technically Yours Ltd, 20 Thompson Road, Newhaven, East Sussex, BN9 0RT Tel: (01273) 611178

▶ Technology Zoo Ltd, 31 Kenway Collier Row, Romford, RM5 3EH Tel: (01708) 507716 E-mail: help@techzoo.co.uk

▶ Techobox Ltd, 20 Nicholas Street, Manchester, M1 4EJ Tel: 0161-228 1010 Fax: 0161-228 0707 E-mail: sales@techobox.com

▶ Techsure Computer Maintenance, Bolton Enterprise Centre, Washington Street, Bolton, BL3 5EY Tel: (01204) 363399 Fax: (01204) 363369

▶ Tek Computers, 16 Lancer Close, Christchurch, Dorset, BH23 2TU Tel: (0870) 1994344 Fax: (0870) 1991324 E-mail: admin@tek-computers.com

▶ Teknocom Ltd, 49 Perth Road, Ilford, Essex, IG2 6BX Tel: (020) 8518 9090 Fax: (020) 8518 9091

Teleplan, Roman House 12 Cowdray Centre, Mason Road, Colchester, CO1 1BX Tel: (01206) 785000 Fax: (01206) 785008 E-mail: enquiries@teleplan-int.com

Tempus Computers Ltd, St Pauls House, St Pauls Square, Birmingham, B3 1RB Tel: 0121-233 3100 Fax: 0121-233 4560 E-mail: sales@tempa.co.uk

▶ Ten Ten Systems, Abbey Square, Chester, CH1 2HU Tel: (01244) 408990 Fax: (01244) 408991 E-mail: enquiries@1010systems.co.uk

Colin Thomas Electronics, 138 Port Tennant Road, Swansea, SA1 8JQ Tel: (01792) 469885 Fax: (01792) 522221

▶ Top End Computers, Wearde, Saltash, Cornwall, PL12 4AT Tel: (01752) 844881 E-mail: alan@topendcomputers.co.uk

Torex Services Ltd, 7 Brixham Enterprise Estate, Rea Barn Road, Brixham, Devon, TQ5 9DF Tel: (01803) 854616 Fax: (01803) 855936

▶ Total IT Ltd, Unit 6, Chase Park, Daleside Road, Nottingham, NG2 4GT Tel: 0115-924 0020 Fax: 0115-947 6176

▶ Total PC Solutions Ltd, 44 Lynton Road, Benfleet, Essex, SS7 2QQ Tel: (01702) 554077 E-mail: support@total-pc-solutions.com

Trase UK Ltd, 311 Gloucester Road, Cheltenham, Gloucestershire, GL51 7AR Tel: (01242) 690600 Fax: (01242) 528681 E-mail: sales@trase.co.uk

TVM Systems, 2 Newgate Court, Paradise Street, Coventry, CV1 2RU Tel: (024) 7625 7875 Fax: (024) 7625 6433 E-mail: sales@tvm-systems.co.uk

▶ UK Maintenance Contractors, 497A Bolton Road, Ashton-in-Makerfield, Wigan, Lancashire, WN4 8TJ Tel: (01942) 716800 Fax: (01942) 712588

▶ Uni PC, 168, Woodhouse Lane, Leeds, LS2 9HB Tel: 0113-242 9778 Fax: 0113-242 9842

▶ Uniplex Computer Systems Ltd, Unit 32 Harmill Industrial Estate, Grovebury Road, Leighton Buzzard, Bedfordshire, LU7 4FF Tel: (01525) 217321 Fax: (01525) 217328 E-mail: info@uniplex.co.uk

▶ Unipro Computer Systems, Top Cart Shed, Chilgrove Farm, Chilgrove, Chichester, West Sussex, PO18 9HU Tel: (01243) 535399 E-mail: sales@up.com

▶ Universal IT (UK) Ltd, Unit 11, TewinRoad Business Centre, Garden Court, Welwyn Garden City, Hertfordshire, AL7 1BH Tel: (01707) 322320 Fax: (01707) 322032

Unlimited Service, Rickett Street, London, SW6 1RU Tel: (020) 7386 6150

▶ V A G Systems Computer Engineers, 112 Wincolmlee, Hull, HU2 0PZ Tel: (01482) 609069 E-mail: info@vagsystems.co.uk

▶ Vardells Ltd, Staden Lane Business Park, Ashbourne Road, Buxton, Derbyshire, SK17 9RN Tel: (01298) 767600 Fax: (01298) 767619 E-mail: vardells@vardells.com

▶ Verbo Computers Ltd, 11 Station Road, Northfleet, Gravesend, Kent, DA11 9DY Tel: (01474) 353277

▶ Vertical Solutions, Juniper Gardens, Shenley, Radlett, Hertfordshire, WD7 9LA Tel: (01923) 839393 Fax: (01923) 839394 E-mail: admin@vsolutions.uk.com

Viking Computer Services, 10 Slingsby Grove, York, YO24 1LS Tel: (01904) 708022 E-mail: vikingcs@hotmail.com

Vision Computers, 84 King Street, Alfreton, Derbyshire, DE55 7DD Tel: (01773) 834666 E-mail: sales@visioncomputers.fsnet.co.uk

▶ Vivatech, Shambria, Woodvill Road, Leatherhead, Surrey, KT22 7BP Tel: (01372) 377362 Fax: (01372) 373927 E-mail: viva.tech@virgin.net

Wadebridge Computers Ltd, Laura House, Fair Park Road, Wadebridge, Cornwall, PL27 7NT Tel: (01208) 815956 Fax: (01208) 815968 E-mail: wadcom@btconnect.com

Webcom Puters, 22 Station Road, Teignmouth, Devon, TQ14 8PE Tel: (01626) 779636 Fax: (01626) 779636

▶ Webnet Systems, 141 Church Street, Malvern, Worcestershire, WR14 2AN Tel: (01684) 574990 Fax: (01684) 574412

West Wiltshire Micros, White Hart Yard, Trowbridge, Wiltshire, BA14 8BY Tel: (01225) 762759 Fax: (01225) 764120 E-mail: sales@wwmicros.co.uk

▶ Western I T Services, 1, Tindal Street, Chelmsford, CM1 1ER Tel: (01245) 284886

▶ Wishbone Technology Ltd, 6 Bolebridge Mews, Bolebridge Street, Tamworth, Staffordshire, B79 7PA Tel: (01827) 319988

▶ Woolleys World Of Computers, 80 Salters Road, Walsall, WS9 9JB Tel: (01543) 453411 Fax: (01543) 453411

▶ Xamtec Ltd, 2 Swinstead Road, Corby Glen, Grantham, Lincolnshire, NG33 4NU Tel: (01476) 550874 Fax: (01476) 550284 E-mail: info@xamtec.com

Xenopus Systems Ltd, The Anchorage, Central Lydbrook, Lydbrook, Gloucestershire, GL17 9SB Tel: (01594) 862000 Fax: (01594) 862001 E-mail: sales@xenopus.co.uk

COMPUTER MANAGEMENT SYSTEMS

Artemis Corporation, Kingsclere Park, Kingsclere, Newbury, Berkshire, RG20 4SW Tel: (01635) 291800 Fax: (01635) 291801 E-mail: sales@artemiscorp.com

C I Systems Ltd, Brunel Road, Churchfields, Salisbury, SP2 7PX Tel: (01722) 336938 Fax: (01722) 323222 E-mail: sales@cielec.com

Custom IT Security UK Ltd, Custom Ho, Kenn Rd, Clevedon, Avon, BS21 6EX Tel: (01275) 874233 Fax: (01275) 874235

D C S Automotive Ltd, Clarendon House, Clarendon Square, Leamington Spa, Warwickshire, CV32 5QJ Tel: (01926) 831401 Fax: (01926) 450183 E-mail: info@dcs-automotive.co.uk

Qube Global Software, Pyrford Road, West Byfleet, Surrey, KT14 6LD Tel: (01932) 334700 Fax: (01932) 355654 E-mail: sales@fdsltd.co.uk

Serco Solutions, P O Box 57 Laburnum House, Birmingham, B30 2BD Tel: 0121-459 1155 Fax: 0121-459 2199 E-mail: mediaanddesign@serco.com

Warwick I C Systems Ltd, Warwick House, Woodhouse Road, Horsley Woodhouse, Ilkeston, Derbyshire, DE7 6AY Tel: (01332) 781882 Fax: (01332) 781410 E-mail: sales@warwickicsystems.com

COMPUTER MEMORY

Sion Elliott Ltd, 124A High Street, Nailsea, Bristol, BS48 1AH Tel: (01275) 851460 E-mail: info@sioncomputers.co.uk

Greenwich Instruments, Meridian House, Park Road, Swanley, Kent, BR8 8AH Tel: (0870) 0505404 Fax: (0870) 0505405 E-mail: sales@greenwichinst.co.uk

Hypertec Ltd, Unit 2 Swangate, Hungerford, Berkshire, RG17 0YX Tel: (01488) 686844 Fax: (01488) 686845 E-mail: info@hypertec.co.uk

Megabytes, 90 Central Road, Worcester Park, Surrey, KT4 8HU Tel: (020) 8335 4224 Fax: (020) 8715 0914 E-mail: sales@megabytes.co.uk

Mid-Blue International Ltd, Great Queen Street, Dartford, DA1 1TJ Tel: (01322) 407000 Fax: (07092) 364351 E-mail: nigel.scott@mid-blue.com

P C Ideals, 89 Albert Road, Southsea, Hampshire, PO5 2SG Tel: (023) 9282 9239 Fax: (023) 9286 2111 E-mail: sales@pcideals.com

PC Tech Ltd, 33 Cleveland Street, Normanby, Middlesbrough, Cleveland, TS6 0LT Tel: (01642) 460704 Fax: (01642) 461002 E-mail: sales@pctechcomputers.com

Phoenix I T Group plc, Technology House, Hunsbury Hill Avenue, Northampton, NN4 8QS Tel: (01604) 769000 Fax: (01604) 706666 E-mail: sales@phoenixitservices.co.uk

R A M Computers, 260d Gospel Lane, Birmingham, B27 7AH Tel: 0121-707 3353 Fax: 0121-706 1413 E-mail: sales@ramcomputers.co.uk

Rombyte Ltd, Unit 6-7 Kingfisher Court, Newbury, Berkshire, RG14 5SJ Tel: (01635) 528006 Fax: (01635) 528115 E-mail: sales@rombyte.co.uk

Simple Tech, The Brunel Building, The Scottish Enterprise Technology Park, East Kilbride, Glasgow, G75 0QD Tel: (01355) 572850 Fax: (01355) 572868 E-mail: salesuk@simpletech.com

Sweet Valley Solutions Ltd, East Lodge House, 116 High Street, Cranleigh, Surrey, GU6 8AJ Tel: (01483) 273838 Fax: (01483) 275983 E-mail: sales@sweetvalley.co.uk

Tandon Europe, 4th Floor Long Wing, Grosvenor House Prospect Hill, Redditch, Worcestershire, B97 4DQ Tel: (01527) 599900 Fax: (01527) 599911 E-mail: aneile@tandon.com

VTEC Industry Europe, Eagleside House, Chantry Street, Andover, Hampshire, SP10 1DE Tel: (01264) 336901 Fax: (01264) 355768 E-mail: sales@vtec.co.uk

COMPUTER MONITOR ARMS

▶ G T Emergo Ltd, 30 Paxton Road, Northampton, NN3 3RL Tel: (01604) 248042 Fax: (01604) 513365 E-mail: sales@gtemergo.co.uk

COMPUTER MONITOR REPAIR

▶ Click4PC Ltd, Station House, 150 New Road, Bromsgrove, Worcestershire, B60 2LG Tel: (0800) 0852143 Fax: (01527) 576611 E-mail: enquiries@click4pc.co.uk

▶ K J H, Woodpeckers, Wildcroft Drive, Wokingham, Berkshire, RG40 3HY Tel: (07932) 671564 Fax: 0118-977 5957 E-mail: aardy@btinternet.com

▶ Kabam Computer Services, 248 Broadlands Drive, Lawrence Weston, Bristol, BS11 0PN Tel: (07876) 250434 E-mail: sales@kabam.co.uk

▶ S E O Computers, Waterside House, Falmouth Road, Penryn, Cornwall, TR10 8BE Tel: (01326) 378424 Fax: (01326) 376667 E-mail: info@seo-computers.com

COMPUTER MOUSE MATS, GEL

▶ One Stop Promotions, 38 Hayhill, Barrow upon Soar, Loughborough, Leicestershire, LE12 8LD Tel: (01509) 814380 Fax: (01509) 814929 E-mail: info@onestoppromotions.co.uk

▶ Promotional Business Ltd, 95 Welham Road, London, SW16 6QH Tel: (020) 8677 3738

COMPUTER MOUSE MATS, PHOTO

▶ The Mug Man, Unit 2 Horsbeck Way, Horsford, Norwich, NR10 3SS Tel: (01603) 898538 Fax: (01603) 893486 E-mail: sales@themugman.co.uk

▶ One Stop Promotions, 38 Hayhill, Barrow upon Soar, Loughborough, Leicestershire, LE12 8LD Tel: (01509) 814380 Fax: (01509) 814929 E-mail: info@onestoppromotions.co.uk

▶ Promotional Business Ltd, 95 Welham Road, London, SW16 6QH Tel: (020) 8677 3738

COMPUTER MOUSE MATS/PADS

Biblio Products Ltd, The Broadway, High Street, Chesham, Buckinghamshire, HP5 1EG Tel: (01494) 776655 Fax: (01494) 776677 E-mail: sales@biblioproducts.com

Fellowes Ltd, Yorkshire Way, Armthorpe, Doncaster, South Yorkshire, DN3 3FB Tel: (01302) 836800 Fax: (01302) 836899 E-mail: sales@fellowes.com

Mikkis Mouse Mats, Flat 3, 34 Croft Road, Clacton-on-Sea, Essex, CO15 3EF Tel: (01255) 225301 Fax: (01255) 225311 E-mail: sales@mikkis.com

COMPUTER MOUSE MATS/ PADS, PROMOTIONAL

Goldpress, 1 Lower Green Avenue, Scholes, Cleckheaton, West Yorkshire, BD19 6PB Tel: (01274) 878488 Fax: (01274) 878488 E-mail: davidkelly@goldpress.co.uk

Kirkfield Ltd, Unit 1/2 Schofield Business Park, Sugarbrook Road, Bromsgrove, Worcestershire, B60 3DN Tel: (01527) 559345 Fax: (01527) 835690 E-mail: sales@kirkfield.co.uk

Mikkis Mouse Mats, Flat 3, 34 Croft Road, Clacton-on-Sea, Essex, CO15 3EF Tel: (01255) 225301 Fax: (01255) 225311 E-mail: sales@mikkis.com

▶ The Promotional Gift Superstore, 79 Villa Road, Stanway, Colchester, CO3 0RN Tel: (0845) 3701022 Fax: (0845) 3701033 E-mail: sales@promogift-superstore.com

COMPUTER MULTIMEDIA SYSTEMS

Apcom Computer Services Ltd, 104 Newbury Gardens, Epsom, Surrey, KT19 0PD Tel: (020) 8224 9015 Fax: (020) 8224 9015 E-mail: atul@apcom.co.uk

B Y G Systems Ltd, 1-2 William Lee Building, Nottingham Science & Technical Park, University Boulevard, Nottingham, NG7 2RQ Tel: 0115-925 2221 Fax: 0115-922 3496 E-mail: info@bygsystems.com

Blue Baron, 1089 Pollokshaws Road, Glasgow, G41 3YG Tel: 0141-649 3101 Fax: 0141-649 3101 E-mail: bluebar@btconnect.com

Computer Clinic Ltd, 204 Rayleigh Road, Hutton, Brentwood, Essex, CM13 1PN Tel: (01277) 261597 Fax: (01277) 261599 E-mail: guy@clinic2.freeserve.co.uk

Connect It, Aizlewoods Mill, Nursery Street, Sheffield, S3 8GG Tel: 0114-282 3307 Fax: 0114-282 3302

Extra Technology Services Ltd, 52-56 Shambles Street, Barnsley, South Yorkshire, S70 2SH Tel: (01226) 771117 Fax: (01226) 771118 E-mail: sales@extracomputers.co.uk

F 1 Services, 19 Bridge Street, Newark, Nottinghamshire, NG24 1EE Tel: (01636) 701832 Fax: (01636) 707114 E-mail: a.forman@f1services.co.uk

▶ Keane Computer Services, 50 Kenmore Crescent, Coalville, Leicestershire, LE67 4RQ Tel: (01530) 451663 E-mail: mark@keaneservices.com

Mediamax, 25A Chertsey Road, Chobham, Woking, Surrey, GU24 8PD Tel: (01276) 856144 Fax: (01276) 855958 E-mail: sales@mediamax.co.uk

▶ Techdivision, 118 St. Margarets Road, Twickenham, TW1 2AA Tel: (020) 8891 3010 Fax: (020) 8288 2591 E-mail: info@techdivison.co.uk

▶ Zed Computer Systems Ltd, 54 St.Johns Road, Slough, SL2 5EZ Tel: (01753) 823828 E-mail: enquiries@zedcomputers.com

COMPUTER NETWORK ACCESSORIES

Arrowflight, High Croft, Coldharbour Lane, Bletchingley, Redhill, RH1 4NA Tel: (01883) 744644 Fax: (01883) 744530 E-mail: sales@arrowflight.co.uk

▶ Communications Express Ltd, 7 Grafton Place, Dukes Park Industrial Estate, Chelmsford, CM2 6TG Tel: (01245) 459490 Fax: (0845) 2000257 E-mail: sales@comms-express.com

Computer Clinic Ltd, 204 Rayleigh Road, Hutton, Brentwood, Essex, CM13 1PN Tel: (01277) 261597 Fax: (01277) 261599 E-mail: guy@clinic2.freeserve.co.uk

Computer Connection Retail, Unit 25, Holden Industrial Estate, Wombwell, Barnsley, South Yorkshire, S73 8HA Tel: (01226) 732975 Fax: (01226) 238139 E-mail: sales@ccretail.co.uk

Computer Junk Shop, 10 Waterloo Road, Widnes, Cheshire, WA8 0PY Tel: 0151-420 6671 Fax: 0151-420 6671 E-mail: info@computer-junkshop.co.uk

Computer Support Services, 8 Baker Street, Rochester, Kent, ME1 3DW Tel: (01634) 407462 Fax: (01634) 409568 E-mail: tony@pobgee.demon.co.uk

Discovery Computer Services Ltd, Burnham Business Park, Springfield Road, Burnham-on-Crouch, Essex, CM0 8TE Tel: (01621) 786860 Fax: (01621) 786861 E-mail: info@buy-it-back.com

Emulex Corporation, 7-8 Forest Court, Oaklands Park, Wokingham, Berkshire, RG41 2FD Tel: 0118-977 2929 Fax: 0118-977 3237 E-mail: enquire.europe@emulex.com

Hermes Datacommunications International Ltd, Hermes House, Oxon Business Park, Bicton Heath, Shrewsbury, SY3 5DD Tel: (01743) 235555 Fax: (01743) 271717 E-mail: info@hermes.com

M S G Computer Services, 4 Uplands Court, London Road, Luton, LU1 3RQ Tel: (01582) 731848 Fax: (01582) 484430 E-mail: sales@msgcomp.co.uk

Merlin Solutions, 5 Gaskells End, Tokers Green, Reading, RG4 9EW Tel: 0118-972 4666 Fax: 0118-972 4535 E-mail: terriw@mersol.co.uk

Micro Plus Computers, 33 Bailey Street, Oswestry, Shropshire, SY11 1PX Tel: (01691) 656875 Fax: (01691) 671285 E-mail: chris@micro-plus.co.uk

Perle Systems Europe Ltd, Abbey House, Wellington Way, Brooklands Business Park, Weybridge, Surrey, KT13 0TT Tel: (01932) 268591 Fax: (01932) 268592 E-mail: mwebster@perle.com

Sitecom UK Ltd, Falcon House, 16 Fernhill Road, Farnborough, Hampshire, GU14 9RX Tel: (01252) 551050 Fax: (01252) 511333 E-mail: sales@sitecom.com

COMPUTER NETWORK COMPONENTS, BUILDING AUTOMATION AND CONTROL NETWORKS (BACNET)

▶ RED Control Systems Otley Ltd, Wharfebank House, Wharfebank Business Centre, Ilkley Road, Otley, West Yorkshire, LS21 3JP Tel: (01943) 851000 Fax: (08714) 259742 E-mail: enquiries@redcontrolsystems.com

COMPUTER NETWORK DATA LINK SYSTEMS

Cablenet Cable & Wire Suppliers, Cablenet House, Lightwater Road, Lightwater, Surrey, GU18 5XQ Tel: (01276) 851900 Fax: (01276) 851909 E-mail: sales@cablenet.uk.com

Mindshare, 140 Walcot Street, Bath, BA1 5BL Tel: (01225) 329577 Fax: (01225) 329675 E-mail: sales@mindsharesecurity.co.uk

Ukerna, Atlas Centre, Fermi Avenue, Chilton, Didcot, Oxfordshire, OX11 0QS Tel: (01235) 822200 Fax: (01235) 822399

Xpert Systems Ltd, 910 Birchwood Boulevard, Birchwood, Warrington, WA3 7QN Tel: (01925) 851111 Fax: (01925) 811182

COMPUTER NETWORK DESIGN CONSULTANCY

A T E Technology Ltd, ATE House, 48 Green Meadows, Westhoughton, Bolton, BL5 2BN Tel: (01942) 815603 Fax: (01942) 815321 E-mail: info@ate-technology.com

Affiniti, Unit 2630, Kings Court, Birmingham, B37 7YE Tel: 0121-770 4141 Fax: 0121-779 7222 E-mail: info@affiniti.com

▶ AGIS Business Communications, Blairs Business Centre, South Deeside Road, Aberdeen, AB12 5LF Tel: (01224) 860335 Fax: (0870) 1645149 E-mail: johnw@agis.uk.com

Channel Partners Ltd, Albury Park, Albury, Guildford, Surrey, GU5 9BH Tel: (01483) 205011 Fax: (01483) 205022 E-mail: astbury@channelp.co.uk

CNS Computer Networks Ltd, Transport Hall, Gloucester Road, Avonmouth, Bristol, BS11 9AQ Tel: (0870) 7771650 Fax: (0870) 7771655 E-mail: sales@c-n-s.co.uk

Comcare Technology Ltd, Anglo House, Chapel Road, Manchester, M22 4JN Tel: 0161-902 0330 Fax: 0161-946 0126 E-mail: info@comcare.co.uk

Compunet Technology Ltd, 14 Carolina Place, Finchampstead, Wokingham, Berkshire, RG40 4PQ Tel: 0118-973 0584 E-mail: sales@compunet-technology.co.uk

Computer Links Ltd, 7 Grange Road, Houston Industrial Estate, Houstoun Industrial Estate, Livingston, West Lothian, EH54 5DE Tel: (01506) 434811 Fax: (01506) 441997 E-mail: service@computer-links.co.uk

Computer Solutions Grimsby Ltd, Wellowgate, Grimsby, South Humberside, DN32 0RA Tel: (01472) 311777 Fax: (01472) 311778

Computer Technocentre Ltd, 182 High Road Leytonstone, London, E11 3HU Tel: (020) 8519 9052 Fax: (020) 8519 9052 E-mail: isrealctc@aol.co

Delta Comtech Ltd, Artillery House, Gunco Lane, Macclesfield, Cheshire, SK11 7JL Tel: (01625) 430055 Fax: (0870) 2200568 E-mail: sales@delta-comtech.co.uk

Doncaster Computer Exchange, 250 Great North Road, Woodlands, Doncaster, South Yorkshire, DN6 7HP Tel: (01302) 728737 Fax: (01302) 725129 E-mail: dceexchange@aol.com

E H L Networks Ltd, 13 Stevenson Court, Priory Park, Frazer Road, Bedford, MK44 4WH Tel: (01234) 831888 Fax: (01234) 832501 E-mail: sales@ehl.co.uk

▶ Elan Consulting, 52 St Marks Road, Henley-on-Thames, Oxfordshire, RG9 1LW Tel: (07920) 112909 E-mail: nick@elanconsulting.co.uk

Fands Systems Integrator Ltd, 12 Saxonville, Benfleet, Essex, SS7 5TD Tel: (01268) 795757 Fax: (01268) 795858 E-mail: sales@fands.uk.com

HCL Technologies Europe Ltd, Network House, Norreys Drive, Maidenhead, Berkshire, SL6 4FJ Tel: (01628) 778555 Fax: (01628) 777566 E-mail: semipractice@hcltech.com

▶ Holbeach Computing Solutions, 17 Spalding Road, Holbeach, Spalding, Lincolnshire, PE12 7HG Tel: (01406) 426342 E-mail: don.scott@holbeachcomputing.co.uk

Icode Systems Ltd, Icode System Ltd Grange Business Park, Sandy Lane, Shedfield, Southampton, SO32 2HQ Tel: (01329) 835335 Fax: (01329) 835338 E-mail: sales@icode.co.uk

Infosystems, Bridge Farm, Holt Lane, Ashby Magna, Lutterworth, Leicestershire, LE17 5NJ Tel: (01455) 201000 Fax: (01455) 201001 E-mail: sales@infosystems.co.uk

▶ J K Computer Solutions, The Dairy, Lynn Road, Hillington, King's Lynn, Norfolk, PE31 6BJ Tel: (07775) 941121 E-mail: john@jkcomputersolutions.com

▶ Know I.T. Consulting Ltd, 1st Floor, 17 Station Road, Kettering, Northamptonshire, NN15 7HH Tel: (0845) 8382645 E-mail: info@knowitconsulting.co.uk

L E T S S, The Lodge, Crown Woods School, Riefield Road, London, SE9 2QL Tel: (020) 8850 0100 Fax: (020) 8850 0400 E-mail: letss@compuserve.com

Lima Networks, 5-6 Carolina Way, Quays Reach, Salford, M50 2ZY Tel: 0161-743 3000 Fax: (0845) 3451220 E-mail: sales@lima.com

Lineartron Maintenance Ltd, Lineartron House, 7 Black Moor Road, Ebblake Industrial Estate, Verwood, Dorset, BH31 6AX Tel: (01202) 828001 Fax: (01202) 828089 E-mail: sales@lineartron.co.uk

Marsden's Computer Systems, Unit 168 Glenfield Park Lomeshaye Business Village, Turner Road, Nelson, Lancashire, BB9 7DR Tel: (01282) 616176 Fax: (01282) 616152 E-mail: info@marsdens.net

Marsworth Computing, 34 Byron Hill Road, Harrow, Middlesex, HA2 0HY Tel: (020) 8864 4842 Fax: (020) 8864 4842 E-mail: sales@marsworth.net

MCP Microsystems, 369 Warrington Road, Rainhill, Prescot, Merseyside, L35 8LD Tel: 0151-431 0133 Fax: 0151-431 0072 E-mail: admin@mcpmicro.co.uk

Merlin Solutions, 5 Gaskells End, Tokers Green, Reading, RG4 9EW Tel: 0118-972 4666 Fax: 0118-972 4535 E-mail: terriw@mersol.co.uk

Gregory Micallef Associates, 63 Croydon Road, London, SE20 7TB Tel: (020) 8778 7759 Fax: (020) 8778 3090 E-mail: sales@gmal.co.uk

P C Innovations, 3 Cardine Close, Sittingbourne, Kent, ME10 2HY Tel: (01795) 410264 Fax: (01795) 410283 E-mail: enquiries@pc-i.co.uk

Procyon Ltd, 44 Oxford Street, Wellingborough, Northamptonshire, NN8 4JH Tel: (01933) 278787 Fax: (01933) 278789 E-mail: julia@procyon.ltd.uk

R Q Consultancy, The Gables, Pankridge Drive, Prestwood, Great Missenden, Buckinghamshire, HP16 9BZ Tel: (01494) 862406 Fax: (01494) 862382 E-mail: info@trqc.co.uk

Sala Consultancy, Forum House, Stirling Road, Chichester, West Sussex, PO19 7DN Tel: (01243) 775757 Fax: (01243) 787110 E-mail: info@ismc.co.uk

TSG Ltd, 1 Gosforth Park Way, Salters Lane, Newcastle upon Tyne, NE12 8ET Tel: 0191-256 1166 Fax: 0191-256 1167 E-mail: sales@tsg.com

Windmill Business Systems Ltd, Cattells Mill Road, Willingham, Cambridge, CB4 5LA Tel: (01954) 261661 Fax: (01954) 261661 E-mail: info@windmillweb.net

COMPUTER NETWORK EQUIPMENT

Apcom Computer Services Ltd, 104 Newbury Gardens, Epsom, Surrey, KT19 0PD Tel: (020) 8224 9015 Fax: (020) 8224 9015 E-mail: atul@apcom.co.uk

▶ com,mas, 18 Sussex Mansions, 39-40 Sussex Square, Brighton, BN2 5AD Tel: (0845) 0095083 Fax: (0700) 3401419 E-mail: sales@com-mas.co.uk

▶ Communications Express Ltd, 7 Grafton Place, Dukes Park Industrial Estate, Chelmsford, CM2 6TG Tel: (01245) 459490 Fax: (0845) 2000257 E-mail: sales@comms-express.com

▶ Computer Services & Engineers, Unit 4a Stag Industrial Estate, Atlantic Street, Broadheath, Altrincham, Cheshire, WA14 5DW Tel: 0161-941 4555 Fax: 0161-941 6182 E-mail: sales@cselimited.co.uk

Computer Systems Ltd, 33 Malmesbury Close, Pinner, Middlesex, HA5 2NG Tel: (01895) 623555 Fax: (01895) 631541 E-mail: enquiries@computer.dircon.co.uk

D S H Electronics Ltd, 206 Idle Road, Bradford, West Yorkshire, BD2 4JT Tel: (01274) 626261 Fax: (01274) 626299 E-mail: sales@dsh-electronics.co.uk

Dash Consulting, 4 Friars Cottage, off Copyground Lane, High Wycombe, Bucks, HP12 3XB Tel: (01923) 256655 Fax: (01923) 222494 E-mail: duncan@dashconsulting.com

E2 Systems Ltd, Broadway House, 21 Broadway, Maidenhead, Berkshire, SL6 1NJ Tel: (01628) 418128 E-mail: e2web@e2systems.co.uk

Electronic Vision International Ltd, 39-43 Newarke Street, Leicester, LE1 5SP Tel: 0116-222 0919 Fax: 0116-222 1964

Enterprise Data Systems, Enterprise House, 130-134 Bristnall Hall Road, Oldbury, West Midlands, B68 9TX Tel: (0845) 6444774 Fax: (0871) 2205363 E-mail: andy@edsuk.co.uk

Eurorealm Consultants Ltd, 29 Ivanhoe Road, Finchampstead, Wokingham, Berkshire, RG40 4QQ Tel: 0118-973 2977 Fax: 0118-973 4470 E-mail: sales@eurorealm.co.uk

Fast Software, East Street, Olney, Buckinghamshire, MK46 4BT Tel: (01234) 712184 Fax: (01234) 712184

Hytec Information Security Ltd, Units 9-10, Oasis Park, Stanton Harcourt Road, Eynsham, Witney, Oxfordshire, OX29 4TP Tel: (01865) 887423 Fax: (01865) 887444 E-mail: info@hytec.co.uk

▶ It's Here, 3 Holgate Court, Western Road, Romford, RM1 3JS Tel: (01708) 737500 Fax: (01708) 737500 E-mail: info@itshere.uk.com

Lan Com International Ltd, Birchwood, Main Road, Curbridge, Witney, Oxfordshire, OX29 7NT Tel: (01993) 776543 Fax: (01993) 776899 E-mail: jc.lancom@btinternet.com

▶ N-able Technologies Inc UK, 20 Garrick Street, London, WC2E 9BT Tel: (020) 7664 7821 Fax: (020) 7664 7878 E-mail: sales@n-able.com

▶ Network & Cabling Solutions Ltd, Endeavour House, 259 Forstal Road, Aylesford, Kent, ME20 7AP Tel: (01622) 791001 Fax: (01622) 791101 E-mail: info@networkandcabling.co.uk

▶ Online-Edge Ltd, The Old Smithy, 59 Lanark Road, Crossford, Carluke, Lanarkshire, ML8 5RE Tel: (01555) 860113 E-mail: sales@online-edge.co.uk

Perle Systems Europe Ltd, Abbey House, Wellington Way, Brooklands Business Park, Weybridge, Surrey, KT13 0TT Tel: (01932) 268591 Fax: (01932) 268592 E-mail: mwebster@perle.com

▶ Protocol Data Services Ltd, Wyndburgh, Lincoln Crescent, Wrockwardine Wood, Telford, Shropshire, TF2 6LU Tel: (01952) 412312 Fax: (0871) 2640312 E-mail: support@pdsnet.co.uk

▶ Sharpe Systems, Westthorpe Innovation Centre, Killamarsh, Sheffield, S21 1TZ Tel: 0114-251 4775 Fax: (0870) 1221505 E-mail: tim.sharpe@sharpe-systems.co.uk

Solution, Claydon Court, Old Ipswich Road, Claydon, Ipswich, IP6 0AE Tel: (01473) 833070 Fax: (01473) 833053 E-mail: sales@sw4it.com

▶ Wharf Systems, 37 Ullin Street, London, E14 6PN Tel: 020 75179943 E-mail: admin@wharfsystems.com

COMPUTER NETWORK MANAGEMENT SERVICES

▶ AGIS Business Communications, Blairs Business Centre, South Deeside Road, Aberdeen, AB12 5LF Tel: (01224) 860335 Fax: (0870) 1645149 E-mail: johnw@agis.uk.com

Arrowflight, High Croft, Coldharbour Lane, Bletchingley, Redhill, RH1 4NA Tel: (01883) 744644 Fax: (01883) 744530 E-mail: sales@arrowflight.co.uk

B D S Solutions, Heywood House, 12 High Street, Cullompton, Devon, EX15 1AA Tel: (01884) 33221 Fax: (01884) 34555 E-mail: info@bds-solutions.co.uk

Clearwater Consultancy Ltd, 18 St Georges Street, Chorley, Lancashire, PR7 2AA Tel: (01257) 272730 Fax: (01257) 272731 E-mail: info@clearwater-consultancy.co.uk

Combined Office System Services, PO Box 31, Hemel Hempstead, Hertfordshire, HP3 0JA Tel: (01442) 834216 Fax: (01442) 831352 E-mail: info@combinedoffice.co.uk

Coveford Data Systems Ltd, Old Bank House, 59 High Street, Odiham, Hampshire, RG29 1LF Tel: (01256) 704333 Fax: (07031) 159754 E-mail: cds@coveford.com

Digica Ltd, Phoenix House, Colliers Way, Nottingham, NG8 6AT Tel: 0115-977 1177 Fax: 0115-977 7000 E-mail: niki_torrance@digica.com

Direct Sales Agency Ltd, 4 Bankside, Hanborough Business Park, Long Hanborough, Witney, Oxfordshire, OX29 8SP Tel: (01993) 883606 Fax: (01993) 882733 E-mail: sales@direct.co.uk

▶ Elegant IT Ltd, PO Box 381, Northampton, NN4 6WL Tel: (01604) 420001 Fax: (01604) 420002 E-mail: ian.jenkins@elegant-it.co.uk

▶ Fresh Technical Solutions, Artillery Lane, London, E1 7LP Tel: (0845) 4587500 E-mail: info@fresh-uk.com

Hermes Datacommunications International Ltd, Hermes House, Oxon Business Park, Bicton Heath, Shrewsbury, SY3 5DD Tel: (01743) 235555 Fax: (01743) 271717 E-mail: info@hermes.com

Icm Computer Group plc, 3 Phoenix Place, Nottingham, NG8 6BA Tel: 0115-870 1000 Fax: (0870) 1218354 E-mail: sales@icm-computer.co.uk

COMPUTER NETWORK MANAGEMENT SERVICES – *continued*

Logma Systems Design Ltd, 27 Victoria Street, Chorley, Lancashire, PR7 2TX Tel: (01257) 233123 Fax: (01257) 237215 E-mail: sales@logma.net

Micro Business Maintenance Ltd, 8a Windmill Bank, Wombourne, Wolverhampton, WV5 9JD Tel: (01902) 324494 Fax: (01902) 324748 E-mail: nigel@twfinternet.com

Softgen Ltd, 92 Harrowdene Road, Wembley, Middlesex, HA0 2JF Tel: (020) 8900 0333 Fax: (020) 8900 9646 E-mail: admin@softegenltd.co.uk

Solution, Claydon Court, Old Ipswich Road, Claydon, Ipswich, IP6 0AE Tel: (01473) 833070 Fax: (01473) 833053 E-mail: sales@sw4it.com

Specialist Computer Centre, Kingsway House, Kingsway North, Team Valley Trading Estate, Gateshead, Tyne & Wear, NE11 0JS Tel: 0191-497 0000 Fax: 0191-497 0001

Trend U K, Unit 75 Questor, Powder Mill Lane, Dartford, DA1 1JA Tel: (0870) 1218326 Fax: (0870) 1218328

Typex Group, Newcastle House, Albany Court, Newcastle Business Park, Newcastle Upon Tyne, NE4 7YB Tel: 0191-256 4400 Fax: 0191-226 0252 E-mail: info@typex.com

Ukerna, Atlas Centre, Fermi Avenue, Chilton, Didcot, Oxfordshire, OX11 0QS Tel: (01235) 822200 Fax: (01235) 822399

Use-It Computers, 7 High Street, Rishton, Blackburn, BB1 4JZ Tel: (01254) 877009 Fax: (01254) 885281

White Waghorn Ltd, 9 High Street, Stevenage, Hertfordshire, SG1 3BG Tel: (01438) 726393 E-mail: info@whitewaghorn.co.uk

COMPUTER NETWORK SERVICES

Active Information Systems, Unit 3 Brooks Green Road, Coolham, Horsham, West Sussex, RH13 8GR Tel: (01403) 740400 Fax: (01403) 741125 E-mail: active@activegrp.co.uk

▶ AGIS Business Communications, Blairs Business Centre, South Deeside Road, Aberdeen, AB12 5LF Tel: (01224) 860335 Fax: (0870) 1645149 E-mail: johnw@agis.uk.com

▶ Alliband Business Services Ltd, 14a-14b Enville Road, Kingswinford, West Midlands, DY6 0JT Tel: (01384) 287483 Fax: (01384) 280186 E-mail: phil@alliband.co.uk

Alpha Business Computers Ltd, Bentley House Newby Road Industrial Estate, Newby Road, Hazel Grove, Stockport, Cheshire, SK7 5DA Tel: 0161-483 5650 Fax: 0161-483 5576 E-mail: info@alphacom.co.uk

Alpha Business Support Ltd, Cavendish House, Cavendish Avenue, New Malden, Surrey, KT3 6QQ Tel: (0845) 1110060 Fax: (020) 8942 1100 E-mail: info@alphabusiness.net

Alpha Computer Services, Laurel Bank, Chester Road, Kelsall, Tarporley, Cheshire, CW6 0RT Tel: (01829) 759440 Fax: (01829) 741106 E-mail: admin@alphacomputer.uk.com

▶ AMS-IT, Merlin House, Langstone Business Village, Priory Drive, Langstone, Newport, Gwent, NP18 2HJ Tel: (01633) 415310 Fax: (01633) 415366 E-mail: peter.oddy@amsolve.co.uk

Andrew Charles Associates, 119 Mulberry Road, Northfleet, Gravesend, Kent, DA11 8QA Tel: (01474) 532865 Fax: (01474) 320442 E-mail: enquires@andrewcharles.co.uk

Ashgoal Ltd, Cqueens Road, Barnet, Hertfordshire, EN5 4DJ Tel: (020) 8275 5100 Fax: (020) 8441 7240 E-mail: info@ashgoal.co.uk

Astley Computer Services, 37 The Farthings, Chorley, Lancashire, PR7 1TP Tel: (01257) 277057 Fax: (01257) 277057 E-mail: ast_com_serve@btinternet.com

▶ Badger Computer Services Ltd, The Business Innovation Centre 1 Innova Business Park, Electric, Enfield, Middlesex, EN3 7XU Tel: (020) 8344 8344 Fax: (020) 8344 8345 E-mail: sales@badgercomputerservices.co.uk

Ball & Co., 5 Harpton Parade, Villiage Way, Yateley, Hampshire, GU46 7SB Tel: (01252) 879884 Fax: (01252) 878067

Bits N Bytes Computer Solutions Ltd, 22-24 Ravendale St North, Scunthorpe, South Humberside, DN15 6NJ Tel: (01724) 282627 Fax: (01724) 280605 E-mail: sales@bitsnbytes.co.uk

▶ Blenkins Computer Services Ltd, 34 Rochester Road, Bournemouth, BH11 8AQ Tel: (01202) 568794 E-mail: info@blenkins.co.uk

Bryan Powercom, 19 University Street, Belfast, BT7 1FY Tel: (028) 9032 6315 Fax: (028) 9032 3144 E-mail: bryanprcom@aol.com

C C T Infotech Ltd, Unit 7C Priory Tech Park, Saxon Way, Hull, HU13 9PB Tel: (01482) 647044 Fax: (01482) 647046 E-mail: sales@cct-infotech.co.uk

C D R Computing Ltd, 12-14 Thames Street, Sunbury-on-Thames, Middlesex, TW16 5QP Tel: (01252) 838400 Fax: (01845) 3452396 E-mail: support@crdcomputing.com

▶ Can It Ltd, 53 Awsworth Lane Cossall, Cossall, Nottingham, NG16 2SA Tel: (0870) 4329919 E-mail: Sale@Can-IT.co.uk

Central Business Services, C B S House, 153 Enderby Road, Whetstone, Leicester, LE8 6JJ Tel: 0116-277 8111 Fax: 0116-278 8332 E-mail: info@cbs-osn.co.uk

▶ Cilix Ltd, Dell Cottage Menin Way, Farnham, Surrey, GU9 8DY Tel: (01252) 711532 Fax: (01252) 719612 E-mail: sean.connolly@cilix.co.uk

▶ Columbia Precision Ltd, 125 Cheston Road, Birmingham, B7 5EA Tel: 0121-327 1500 Fax: 0121-327 1511 E-mail: enquires@columbia.uk.com

Comcare Technology Ltd, Anglo House, Chapel Road, Manchester, M22 4JN Tel: 0161-902 0330 Fax: 0161-946 0126 E-mail: info@comcare.co.uk

▶ com,mas, 18 Sussex Mansions, 39-40 Sussex Square, Brighton, BN2 5AD Tel: (0845) 0095083 Fax: (0700) 3401419 E-mail: sales@com-mas.co.uk

Computec Solutions Ltd, 566 Streatham High Road, London, SW16 3QQ Tel: (020) 8679 1717 Fax: (020) 8679 5245 E-mail: mail@computecltd.com

Computer Technocentre Ltd, 182 High Road Leytonstone, London, E11 3HU Tel: (020) 8519 9052 Fax: (020) 8519 9052 E-mail: isrealctc@aol.co

Computers In Action, 30 The Spinney, Beaconsfield, Buckinghamshire, HP9 1SB Tel: (01494) 675202 E-mail: powers@systemsworld.net

Conex Data Communications Ltd, Connex House, Follingsby Close, Gateshead, Tyne & Wear, NE10 8YG Tel: 0191-416 5444 Fax: 0191-416 0707 E-mail: sales@conexdata.com

Configuration Computer Services, 40 Surrey Technology Centre, Occam Road, Surrey Research Park, Guildford, Surrey, GU2 7YG Tel: (01483) 295796 Fax: (01483) 295797 E-mail: tony@configuration.co.uk

Crayford Ltd, The Old Fire Station, Christchurch St West, Frome, Somerset, BA11 1EH Tel: (01373) 474466 Fax: (01373) 474499 E-mail: roger@crayford.ltd.uk

D C S Associates, 50 High Street, Kingswood, Bristol, BS15 4AJ Tel: 0117-960 3242 Fax: 0117-960 3282 E-mail: sales@dcs-imago.com

Dash Consulting, 4 Friars Cottage, off Copyground Lane, High Wycombe, Bucks, HP12 3XB Tel: (01923) 256655 Fax: (01923) 222494 E-mail: duncan@dashconsulting.com

Dataplex Systems Ltd, Orbit House, Albert Street, Eccles, Manchester, M30 0BL Tel: 0161-707 3355 Fax: 0161-707 3344 E-mail: sales@dataplex-systems.com

Datashare Solutions Ltd, 10 Chandler Court, Tolworth Rise South, Surbiton, Surrey, KT5 9NN Tel: (020) 8337 2700 Fax: (020) 8337 2701 E-mail: info@datasharesolutions.com

DDF Computer Systems, Horsham Road, Walliswood, Dorking, Surrey, RH5 5QD Tel: (01306) 627155 Fax: (01306) 627166 E-mail: info@ddf.co.uk

Delta Comtech Ltd, Artillery House, Gunco Lane, Macclesfield, Cheshire, SK11 7JL Tel: (01625) 430055 Fax: (0870) 2200568 E-mail: sales@delta-comtech.co.uk

Discspeed Computer Consultants, Farley Common, Westerham, Kent, TN16 1UB Tel: (01959) 562117

▶ EESSIS, 1 Wellgreen, Killearn, Glasgow, G63 9RT Tel: (01360) 449468 Fax: (0871) 9940715 E-mail: info@eessis.co.uk

Electronic Vision International Ltd, 39-43 Newarke Street, Leicester, LE1 5SP Tel: 0116-222 0919 Fax: 0116-222 1964

▶ Elegant IT Ltd, PO Box 381, Northampton, NN4 6WL Tel: (01604) 420001 Fax: (01604) 420002 E-mail: ian.jenkins@elegant-it.co.uk

Enterprise Data Systems, Enterprise House, 130-134 Bristnall Hall Road, Oldbury, West Midlands, B68 9TX Tel: (0845) 6444774 Fax: (0871) 2205363 E-mail: andy@edsuk.co.uk

Fast & Easy Computers, Unit 5b Marcliffe Industrial Estate, Macclesfield Road, Hazel Grove, Stockport, Cheshire, SK7 5EG Tel: 0161-483 6656 Fax: 0161-483 6667 E-mail: sales@fasteasy.com

First Choice Computers West Midlands Ltd, 40 Waterloo Road, Wolverhampton, WV1 4BL Tel: (01902) 712166 Fax: (01902) 427900 E-mail: enquiries@fcc-online.co.uk

▶ First Choice It Ltd, 13 Renshaw Close, Luton, LU2 8TD Tel: (0845) 0510136 Fax: (0871) 8729611 E-mail: info@firstchoiceit.co.uk

▶ Fresh Technical Solutions, Artillery Lane, London, E1 7LP Tel: (0845) 4587500 E-mail: info@fresh-uk.com

Future Labs Ltd, Regus House, 400 Thames Valley Park Drive, Reading, RG6 1PT Tel: (01344) 301155 Fax: (01344) 450380 E-mail: sales@computabits.com

G N T Ltd, Waterside Estate, Cradley Road, Dudley, West Midlands, DY2 9RG Tel: (01384) 236007 Fax: (01384) 236929 E-mail: info@gnt.co.uk

Hydra P.L.C., 145 Cannon Street, London, EC4N 5BQ Tel: (020) 7337 2777 Fax: (020) 7337 2772 E-mail: sales@hydranet.co.uk

Hytec Information Security Ltd, Units 9-10, Oasis Park, Stanton Harcourt Road, Eynsham, Witney, Oxfordshire, OX29 4TP Tel: (01865) 887423 Fax: (01865) 887444 E-mail: info@hytec.co.uk

Ict Networks Ltd, Unit 8 Palmerston Street, Joiners Square Industrial Estate, Stoke-on-Trent, ST1 3EU Tel: (01782) 406406 Fax: (01782) 406444 E-mail: sales@ict-networks.co.uk

Iken Business Ltd, Froomsgate House, Rupert Street, Bristol, BS1 2QJ Tel: (0845) 4509201 Fax: (0845) 4509209 E-mail: info@iken.com

Insurance Technology Solutions Ltd, International House, 1 St. Katharines Way, London, E1W 1UN Tel: (020) 7553 2500 Fax: (020) 7702 3074 E-mail: sales@intechsolutions.co.uk

Interfuture Systems Ltd, Kemps Farm, London Road, Balcombe, Haywards Heath, West Sussex, RH17 6JH Tel: (0845) 4522411 Fax: (0845) 4522412 E-mail: david.williams@interfuture.co.uk

Kingdom Computers, 129 High Street, Staines, Middlesex, TW18 4PD Tel: (01784) 466800 Fax: (01784) 466899

L M Computers Ltd, Arcade Chambers, Little Wellington Street, Aldershot, Hampshire, GU11 1EE Tel: (01252) 406323 Fax: (01252) 406324 E-mail: sales@lmcomputers.co.uk

Lakes Consultants Ltd, Flecket House, Helton, Penrith, Cumbria, CA10 2QA Tel: (01931) 712232 Fax: (01931) 712336

Lan Com International Ltd, Birchwood, Main Road, Curbridge, Witney, Oxfordshire, OX29 7NT Tel: (01993) 776543 Fax: (01993) 776899 E-mail: jc.lancom@btinternet.com

Lancaster Communications Ltd, Tarn View, Denny Beck, Lancaster, LA2 9HG Tel: (01524) 846900 Fax: (01524) 846900 E-mail: enq@lancastercomms.co.uk

▶ Lanteeh Network Solutions, 24 Ribble Avenue, Southport, Merseyside, PR9 8LZ Tel: (0870) 3505268 Fax: (0870) 7066048 E-mail: info@lantechnetworks.co.uk

▶ Linctec, 81 Saxon Way, Bourne, Lincolnshire, PE10 9QY Tel: (01778) 393757 E-mail: info@linctec.co.uk

M S G Computer Services, 4 Uplands Court, London Road, Luton, LU1 3RQ Tel: (01582) 731848 Fax: (01582) 484430 E-mail: sales@msgcomp.co.uk

Maindec Computer Engineering Ltd, Maindec House, Holtspur Lane, Wooburn Green, High Wycombe, Buckinghamshire, HP10 0AB Tel: (01628) 810977 Fax: (01628) 810733 E-mail: roger.timms@maindec.co.uk

▶ Matrix PCs, 5 Willow Drive, Wimborne, Dorset, BH21 2RA Tel: (01202) 840902 E-mail: info@matrix-pcs.co.uk

Micro Design Consultancy, Kenilworth Ho, 60 Kenilworth Rd, Leamington Spa, Warwickshire, CV32 6JY Tel: 01926 778899 Fax: 01926 778888

Micro Peripherals Ltd, Shorten Brook Way, Altham Business Park, Altham, Accrington, Lancashire, BB5 5YJ Tel: (01282) 776776 Fax: (01282) 770001 E-mail: sales@micro-p.com

▶ N-able Technologies Inc UK, 20 Garrick Street, London, WC2E 9BT Tel: (020) 7664 7821 Fax: (020) 7664 7878 E-mail: sales@n-able.com

Network Logic Ltd, 2 St Josephs Close, Droitwich, Worcestershire, WR9 0RY Tel: (01905) 795725 E-mail: network.logic@lineone.net

Noble Computer Services, 9 Newton Road, Ipswich, IP3 8HE Tel: (01473) 424342 Fax: (01473) 424466 E-mail: info@noble-online.co.uk

Orange Business Services, 217 Bath Road, Slough, SL1 4AA Tel: (020) 8321 4300 Fax: (020) 8321 4040

P C S Technical Services, 70 Church Road, Aston, Birmingham, B6 5TY Tel: 0121-326 0011 Fax: 0121-366 0022 E-mail: sales@pcs-technical.com

P & L Networks Ltd, Solway Court, Crewe, CW1 6LD Tel: (01270) 259740 Fax: (01270) 259759

Paradise Computing Ltd, Albion House, Albion Place, Northampton, NN1 1UD Tel: (01604) 604575 Fax: (01604) 670375 E-mail: sales@paradisecomputing.co.uk

Perle Systems Europe Ltd, Abbey House, Wellington Way, Brooklands Business Park, Weybridge, Surrey, KT13 0TT Tel: (01932) 268591 Fax: (01932) 268592 E-mail: mwebster@perle.com

▶ Quaytech Ltd, 1 Wesley Yard, Newquay, Cornwall, TR7 1LB Tel: (01637) 876737 E-mail: sales@quaytech.co.uk

R P T Computer Installations Ltd, 41 Anson Grove, Fareham, Hampshire, PO16 8JQ Tel: (023) 9234 8819

R Q Consultancy, The Gables, Pankridge Drive, Prestwood, Great Missenden, Buckinghamshire, HP16 9BZ Tel: (01494) 862406 Fax: (01494) 862382 E-mail: info@trqc.co.uk

Sala Consultancy, Forum House, Stirling Road, Chichester, West Sussex, PO19 7DN Tel: (01243) 775757 Fax: (01243) 787110 E-mail: info@ismc.co.uk

Sealpoint Computing, 130 Highland Road, Southsea, Hampshire, PO4 9NH Tel: (023) 9287 7688 Fax: (023) 9287 7688 E-mail: enquiries@sealpoint-computing.co.uk

▶ Steady Networking, PO Box 7025, London, WC2R 0DZ Tel: (0845) 2265983 Fax: 0871 2778988E-mail: sales@steadynetworking.com

Stone Group, 58 Edison Road, Rabans Lane Industrial Area, Aylesbury, Buckinghamshire, HP19 8TE Tel: (01785) 812100 Fax: (01296) 424165 E-mail: info@compusys.co.uk

Synetrix Ltd, Innovation Centre, University of Keele, Keele, Newcastle, Staffordshire, ST5 5NB Tel: (01782) 338200 Fax: (01782) 629600 E-mail: enq@synetrix.co.uk

▶ Tended Net Computer Services, 79 Kyrkeby, Letchworth Garden City, Hertfordshire, SG6 2PG Tel: (01462) 670225 Fax: (01462) 670225 E-mail: roy.stapleton@tendednet.com

Tigra Solutions Ltd, 16 Queens Road, Farnborough, Hampshire, GU14 6DN Tel: (01252) 816699 Fax: (01252) 812375 E-mail: info@tigra-solutions.co.uk

▶ TopHat IT Services, 80B St. James's Street, Brighton, BN2 1PA Tel: (01273) 311224 E-mail: enquiries@tophatit.com

Total Computer & Network Support Ltd, Business & Innovation Centre, 9 Aston Science Park, Love Lane, Birmingham, B7 4BJ Tel: 0121-693 6224 Fax: 0121-693 6225

Triumph Technologies, Unit A, Station Yard, Thame, Oxfordshire, OX9 3UH Tel: (01844) 261666 Fax: (01844) 261666 E-mail: technical@triumphtech.co.uk

Typex Group, Newcastle House, Albany Court, Newcastle Business Park, Newcastle Upon Tyne, NE4 7YB Tel: 0191-256 4400 Fax: 0191-226 0252 E-mail: info@typex.com

Unified Solutions Ltd, 883-884 Plymouth Road, Slough, SL1 4LP Tel: (01753) 775050 Fax: (01753) 775020 E-mail: info@unified.co.uk

Upgraders Computer Systems, 23 Ivatt Way, Peterborough, PE3 7PG Tel: (01733) 703269 Fax: (01733) 750767 E-mail: sales@upgraders.co.uk

▶ Wharf Systems, 37 Ullin Street, London, E14 6PN Tel: 020 75179943 E-mail: admin@wharfsystems.com

Windmill Business Systems Ltd, Cattells Mill Road, Willingham, Cambridge, CB4 5LA Tel: (01954) 261661 Fax: (01954) 261661 E-mail: info@windmillweb.net

Yellowstone Electronic Solutions Ltd, 17 Lyneham Road, Luton, LU2 9JS Tel: (01582) 722011 Fax: (01582) 654440 E-mail: sales@yellowstone.co.uk

COMPUTER NETWORK SWITCHBOX CABLES

▶ Camnet, 11 Mill View, London Road, Great Chesterford, Saffron Walden, Essex, CB10 1PD Tel: (01799) 530831 E-mail: james@camnet-communications.co.uk

COMPUTER NETWORKING PRODUCTS, NETWORK MANAGEMENT, VOICE OVER INTERNET PROTOCOL (VOIP)

▶ Bunny Connect Ltd, 11 Parade House, 135 The Parade High Street, Watford, WD17 1ND Tel: (0800) 0970238

▶ Centric, 2nd Floor, Europe House, Bancroft Road, Reigate, Surrey, RH2 7RP Tel: (0870) 7703769 Fax: (0870) 7703769 E-mail: sales@centriccc.co.uk

Commbinary Ltd, Citrus House, Dale Street, Liverpool, L2 5SF Tel: 0151-255 2121 Fax: 0151-255 2122 E-mail: sales@telecom2l.co.uk

▶ Felltech Ltd, St Johns House, Garrigill, Alston, Cumbria, CA9 3DS Tel: (01434) 380000 E-mail: info@felltech.com

▶ Highspeed Office Ltd, Epworth House, 25 City Road, London, EC1Y 1AA Tel: (020) 7847 4500 Fax: (020) 7847 4599 E-mail: sales@highspeedoffice.net

▶ Infinity Technologies Ltd, Hamlet House, 366-368 London, Westcliff-on-Sea, Essex, SS0 7HZ Tel: (01268) 777039 Fax: (08700) 548697 E-mail: bpb@inftech.co.uk

▶ Internet For Business Ltd, 387 Union Street, Aberdeen, AB11 6BX Tel: (01224) 333300 Fax: (01224) 333321 E-mail: sales@ifb.net

▶ Internormen Technology, Unit G14, Westthorpe Fields Road, Killamarsh, Sheffield, S21 1TZ Tel: 0114-218 0614 Fax: 0114-218 0615 E-mail: northsales@reacttechnologies.com

▶ IP Centrex Ltd, Unit 5, South Lodge Court, Ironsbottom, Sidlow, Reigate, Surrey, RH2 8QG Tel: (0870) 0487777 E-mail: admin@ipcentrex.ltd.uk

▶ M X Digital, Dunley Hill Court, Ranmore Common, Dorking, Surrey, RH5 6SX Tel: (01483) 286650 Fax: (01483) 286658 E-mail: sales@mxdigital.co.uk

▶ NAPSYS Ltd, 6 Laurel Grove, Sidemoor, Bromsgrove, Worcestershire, B61 8LU Tel: (0870) 0638606 Fax: (0870) 0638607 E-mail: sales@napsys.co.uk

▶ PC Systems, 19 Borthwick Close, Bransholme, Hull, HU7 5BE Tel: (01482) 827461 Fax: (01482) 827461 E-mail: info@pcsystems-ss.co.uk

▶ Red Galleon Ltd, Beech House Docking Road, Sedgeford, Hunstanton, Norfolk, PE36 5LR Tel: (01485) 579363 Fax: (01485) 579396 E-mail: info@redgalleon.com

▶ Smarttalk Communications, 23 Burlington Lane, London, W4 2RN Tel: (020) 8742 0321 Fax: 0870 2854888 E-mail: solutions@smarttalkuk.com

▶ Vaioni Group Ltd, 39 Salford University Business Park, Leslie Hough Way, Salford, M6 6AJ Tel: (0870) 1600650 Fax: (0870) 1600651E-mail: richard.chapman@vaioni.com

COMPUTER NUMERICAL CONTROL (CNC) SYSTEMS

Control Applications Ltd, Unit 12, Steeton Grove, Steeton, West Yorkshire, BD20 6TT Tel: (01535) 650890 Fax: (01535) 658824 E-mail: info@controlapplications.co.uk

▶ enviro-pc.com, Unit2 Duncote Mill, Walcot, Telford, Shropshire, TF6 5ER Tel: (01952) 740200

G E Fanuc Automation (UK) Ltd, 15 Basset Court, Loake Close, Grange Park, Northampton, NN4 5EZ Tel: (01604) 744130 Fax: (01604) 744140 E-mail: gef.uk@gefanuceur.ge.com

J T R Controls Ltd, Bank Street, Walshaw, Bury, Lancashire, BL8 3AZ Tel: 0161-764 3829 Fax: 0161-764 3829

Osai UK Ltd, Mount House, Bond Avenue, Bletchley, Milton Keynes, MK1 1SF Tel: (01908) 642687 Fax: (01908) 642688 E-mail: sales@osai.co.uk

▶ Red Rock Controls, 36 Sunnyside Lane, Balsall Common, Coventry, CV7 7FY Tel: (07968) 217494 E-mail: roger@redrockcontrols.co.uk

▶ Teknek Manufacturing Ltd, Inchinnan Business Park, Newmains Avenue, Inchinnan, Renfrew, PA4 9RR Tel: 0141-568 8100 Fax: 0141-568 8101 E-mail: sales@teknek.com

COMPUTER OUTSOURCING

Alternet, 5 Cardiff Road, Luton, LU1 1PP Tel: (0870) 6009968 Fax: (0870) 6009969 E-mail: jimrudd@alternetuk.com

Atos Origin (UK) Ltd, Walsall Road, Cannock, Staffordshire, WS11 0JA Tel: (01543) 465800 Fax: (01543) 464895

Bristlecone UK Ltd, Fulton House, Fulton Road, Wembley, Middlesex, HA9 0TF Tel: (0870) 7368880 Fax: (0870) 7368889 E-mail: sunilk@bcone.co.uk

Digica Ltd, Phoenix House, Colliers Way, Nottingham, NG8 6AT Tel: 0115-977 1177 Fax: 0115-977 7000 E-mail: niki_torrance@digica.com

▶ Elegant IT Ltd, PO Box 381, Northampton, NN4 6WL Tel: (01604) 420001 Fax: (01604) 420002 E-mail: ian.jenkins@elegant-it.co.uk

▶ First Choice It Ltd, 13 Renshaw Close, Luton, LU2 8TD Tel: (0845) 0510136 Fax: (0871) 8729611 E-mail: info@firstchoiceit.co.uk

Gates B 2 B Ltd, Electric Wharf, Coventry, CV1 4JF Tel: (024) 7652 5558 Fax: (0870) 6001092 E-mail: steve.williams@gatesb2b.com

▶ Goldnet Ltd, 3 Shire Close, Whiteley, Fareham, Hampshire, PO15 7BQ Tel: (01489) 886843 Fax: (01489) 886828 E-mail: info@goldnetltd.co.uk

iDeveloperNetwork, Suite 7, Grove House, Kensal Road, London, W10 5BZ Tel: (020) 7900 2071 Fax: (020) 7900 2071 E-mail: uk_contact@ideveloper network.com

J Wilson & Co., 96 David Street, Glasgow, G40 2UH Tel: 0141-551 0268 Fax: 0141-554 4620 E-mail: info@jwilsongroup.co.uk

Saic Ltd, Berkshire House, Queen Street, Maidenhead, Berkshire, SL6 1NF Tel: (01628) 686100 Fax: (01628) 686200

Stone Group, 58 Edison Road, Rabans Lane Industrial Area, Aylesbury, Buckinghamshire, HP19 8TE Tel: (01785) 812100 Fax: (01296) 424165 E-mail: info@compusys.co.uk

Syan Ltd, The Mill, King Coughton, Alcester, Warwickshire, B49 5QG Tel: (01789) 400464 Fax: (01789) 400470

Unisys Group Services Ltd, Bakers Court, Bakers Road, Uxbridge, Middlesex, UB8 1RG Tel: (01895) 237137 Fax: (01895) 862092 E-mail: sales@unisys.com

COMPUTER PERIPHERAL EQUIPMENT, *See also headings for particular types*

321 Systems Ltd, 6 Maryon Mews, London, NW3 2PU Tel: (020) 7794 3236 Fax: (020) 7431 3213 E-mail: info@321systems.com

A W W Computers, South Road, Harlow, Essex, CM20 2AS Tel: (01279) 626354 Fax: (01279) 444800 E-mail: admin@wenham.co.uk

Actual Reality, Stainton Moor View, Matlock, Derbyshire, DE4 3NE Tel: (01629) 760801 Fax: (08702) 201805 E-mail: admin@ar-computers.co.uk

Adept Scientific plc, Amor Way, Letchworth Garden City, Hertfordshire, SG6 1ZA Tel: (01462) 480055 Fax: (01462) 480213 E-mail: info@adeptscience.co.uk

Akhter Group Holdings P.L.C., Akhter House, Perry Road, Harlow, Essex, CM18 7PN Tel: (01279) 443521 Fax: (01279) 821300

Asdon Business Centre, Systems House, Enterprise Crescent, Ballinderry Road, Lisburn, County Antrim, BT28 2BH Tel: (028) 9267 5114 Fax: (028) 9266 0256 E-mail: sales@asdon.co.uk

▶ Avanti Elektronik Ltd, 37 Forest Avenue, Aberdeen, AB15 4TU Tel: (01224) 319849

Avenga Computer Services, 34 Morse Road, Whitnash, Leamington Spa, Warwickshire, CV31 2LH Tel: (01926) 882639 Fax: (01926) 882639 E-mail: nigel@avenga.co.uk

Banbury Computers, 55 Middleton Road, Banbury, Oxon, OX16 3QR Tel: (01295) 272627E-mail: sales@banburycomputers.com

Basic Business Systems Ltd, Brookside Road, Ruddington, Nottingham, NG11 6AT Tel: 0115-940 5000 Fax: 0115-940 5450

BDS Computer, 1 Rookery Court, Weller Drive, Finchampstead, Wokingham, Berkshire, RG40 4QZ Tel: 0118-973 7000 Fax: 0118-973 7070 E-mail: gen@bds.co.uk

Bridgeworks Ltd, 135 Summerford Road, Christchurch, Dorset, BH23 3PY Tel: (01425) 478811 Fax: (0870) 1210709 E-mail: sales@4bridgeworks.com

Ceratech Holdings plc, Ceratech House, Omega Park, Alton, Hampshire, GU34 2QE Tel: (01420) 85470 Fax: (01420) 83545 E-mail: sales@ceratech.co.uk

Cognitronics Ltd, Claylands Avenue, Worksop, Nottinghamshire, S81 7DJ Tel: (01909) 477272 Fax: (01909) 486260 E-mail: sales@cognitronics.co.uk

Computerworld Western, Unit 1 Fernhill Court, Fernhill, Almondsbury, Bristol, BS32 4LX Tel: (01454) 275400 Fax: (01454) 619931 E-mail: enquiries@computerworld.co.uk

Comtek Computers Manchester, 12 Silver Street, Bury, Lancashire, BL9 0EX Tel: 0161-761 2200 Fax: 0161-761 2211 E-mail: kazpenash@ comtekcomputersmanchester.co.uk

Configuration Computer Services, 40 Surrey Technology Centre, Occam Road, Surrey Research Park, Guildford, Surrey, GU2 7YG Tel: (01483) 295796 Fax: (01483) 295797 E-mail: tony@configuration.co.uk

Contech Electronics Ltd, Unit C Mindenhall Court, High Street, Stevenage, Hertfordshire, SG1 3BG Tel: (01438) 315757 Fax: (01438) 313679 E-mail: sales@contech.co.uk

Cristie Ltd, Cristie Mill, Chestnut Lane, Stroud, Gloucestershire, GL5 3EH Tel: (01453) 847000 Fax: (01453) 847001 E-mail: sales@cristie.com

▶ Cursor Controls Ltd, Conroi House, Brunel Drive, Newark, Nottinghamshire, NG24 2EG Tel: (01636) 615600 Fax: (01636) 615601 E-mail: sales@cursorcontrols.com

▶ Cyberia Systems, 6 Broom Wynd, Shotts, Lanarkshire, ML7 4HP Tel: (0845) 4565329 Fax: (01501) 826868 E-mail: sales@cyberiasystems.co.uk

Cynetix Group Ltd, Unit C1, Aven Industrial Park, Tickhill Road, Maltby, Rotherham, South Yorkshire, S66 7QR Tel: (01709) 819922 Fax: (01709) 798804 E-mail: sales@cynetix.co.uk

Deandray, 5 Monmouth Street, Lyme Regis, Dorset, DT7 3PX Tel: (01297) 445632 Fax: (01297) 445464 E-mail: deandray@btinternet.com

Dell Inc, Technology House Dell Campus, Cain Road, Bracknell, Berkshire, RG12 1BF Tel: (01344) 860456 Fax: (01344) 372767

Duplex Telecom Ltd, The Widford Hall, Widford Hall Lane, Chelmsford, CM2 8TD Tel: (0870) 7481408 Fax: (0870) 7481407 E-mail: sales@duplex.co.uk

Hawke Systems, Unit 1 14 Newlands Drive, Colnbrook, Slough, SL3 0DX Tel: (01753) 686686 Fax: (01753) 686747 E-mail: sales@hawke.co.uk

Hills Components Ltd, Valley Park, Olds Approach, Watford, WD18 9TL Tel: (01923) 772773 Fax: (01923) 421421 E-mail: sales@hillscomponents.co.uk

Ibm UK Ltd, Weybridge Business Park, Addlestone Road, Addlestone, Surrey, KT15 2UF Tel: (01932) 814000 Fax: (01932) 850011 E-mail: enquiries@uk.ibm.com

Integrex Ltd, Portwood Industrial Estate, Church Gresley, Swadlincote, Derbyshire, DE11 9PT Tel: (01283) 550880 Fax: (01283) 552028 E-mail: sales@integrex.co.uk

Interface Solutions International Ltd, International Park, Starley Way, Birmingham, B37 7GN Tel: 0121-780 6000 Fax: 0121-780 6111 E-mail: sales@iface.co.uk

Interquad Distribution Ltd, Rath House, 55-65 Uxbridge Road, Slough, SL1 1SG Tel: (01753) 536464 Fax: (01753) 898306 E-mail: info@interquad.com

Isis Computer & Electronics (UK) Ltd, 8 Ranmore Road, Dorking, Surrey, RH4 1HA Tel: (01306) 740525 Fax: (01306) 740515 E-mail: peter@isiscomputer.co.uk

Kendata Services Ltd, Nutsey Lane, Totton, Southampton, SO40 3NB Tel: (023) 8086 9922 Fax: (023) 8086 0800 E-mail: kpsales@kenda.co.uk

Keyzone Computer Products Ltd, 497 Sunleigh Road, Wembley, Middlesex, HA0 4LY Tel: (020) 8900 1525 Fax: (020) 8903 1486 E-mail: enquiries@keyzone.com

Matrox Vite Ltd, C Sefton Park, Bells Hill, Stoke Poges, Slough, SL2 4JS Tel: (01753) 665500 Fax: (01753) 665599

Micro Warehouse Ltd, Horizon One, Studio Way, Borehamwood, Hertfordshire, WD6 5WH Tel: (020) 8327 5000 Fax: (020) 8953 7617 E-mail: sales@microwarehouse.co.uk

Microtest Ltd, Technology House, 18 Normandy Way, Bodmin, Cornwall, PL31 1EX Tel: (01208) 73812 Fax: (01208) 77677 E-mail: sales@microtest.co.uk

Nec Europe Ltd, N E C House, 1 Victoria Road, London, W3 6BL Tel: (020) 8993 8111 Fax: (020) 8992 7161

Net Comp Ltd, 21 Shaftesbury Street South, Derby, DE23 8YH Tel: (01332) 290509 Fax: (01332) 384873 E-mail: sales@netcomp.ltd.uk

Nikad Electronics Ltd, Buchanan House, Malthouse Square, Princes Risborough, Buckinghamshire, HP27 9AQ Tel: (01844) 347350 Fax: (01844) 273888 E-mail: a.ward@nikad.com

North Time & Data Ltd, Enterprise Crescent, Lisburn, County Antrim, BT28 2BP Tel: (028) 9260 4000 Fax: (028) 9260 5595 E-mail: sales@ntd.ltd.uk

Northamber P.L.C., 23 Davis Road, Chessington, Surrey, KT9 1HS Tel: (020) 8296 7000 Fax: (020) 8296 7330

O K I (Europe) Ltd, Central House, Balfour Road, Hounslow, TW3 1HY Tel: (020) 8219 2190 Fax: (020) 8219 2199

Primary Storage Ltd, Units D7-D9, Hortonwood 7, Telford, Shropshire, TF1 7YY Tel: (01952) 602600 Fax: (01952) 670063 E-mail: sales@primaryuk.com

Pro-Byte Computers Ltd, 163 Cleethorpe Road, Grimsby, South Humberside, DN31 3AX Tel: (01472) 235500 Fax: (01472) 235501 E-mail: sales@pro-byte.co.uk

Ringdale UK Ltd, 26 Victoria Way, Burgess Hill, West Sussex, RH15 9NF Tel: (01444) 871349 Fax: (01444) 870228 E-mail: sales@ringdale.com

Roland UK Ltd, Atlantic House, Atlantic Close, Swansea Enterprise Park, Swansea, SA7 9FJ Tel: (01792) 702701 Fax: (01792) 600520 E-mail: sales@roland.co.uk

Rotronic Distribution Services, Unit 1a Crompton Fields, Crompton Way, Crawley, West Sussex, RH10 9EE Tel: (01293) 565556 Fax: (01293) 843710 E-mail: sales@rotronic.co.uk

Soft Brands ' Evolution, Glenfield Park 2, Blakewater Road, Blackburn, BB1 5QH Tel: (01254) 724400 Fax: (01254) 724404 E-mail: joanne.slater@softbrands.com

Steadlands International Marketing Ltd, PO Box 41, Blyth, Northumberland, NE24 3YE Tel: (01670) 361261 Fax: (0870) 9006097 E-mail: info@steadlands.com

Sun Micro Systems, Units 27-30, Number One Industrial Estate, Consett, County Durham, DH8 6TJ Tel: (01207) 580000 Fax: (01207) 591002 E-mail: postmaster@uk.sun.com

Tekdata Distribution Ltd, Technology House, Crown Road, Stoke-on-Trent, ST1 5NJ Tel: (01782) 274255 Fax: (01782) 665511 E-mail: sales@tekdata.co.uk

Tigra Solutions Ltd, 16 Queens Road, Farnborough, Hampshire, GU14 6DN Tel: (01252) 816699 Fax: (01252) 812375 E-mail: info@tigra-solutions.co.uk

▶ Traxsys, Embankment Way, Ringwood, Hampshire, BH24 1EU Tel: (01425) 463100 Fax: (01425) 463111 E-mail: sales@penny-gilescp.co.uk

Wordflow, 32-38 Scrutton Street, London, EC2A 4RQ Tel: (020) 7377 1182 Fax: (020) 7377 2942 E-mail: help@wordflow.co.uk

Wyse Technology (U K) Ltd, 1 The Pavilions, Ruscombe Park, Twyford, Reading, RG10 9NN Tel: 0118-934 5345 Fax: (01734) 340749 E-mail: sales@wyse.com

▶ Xma Ltd, 44 Nottingham South & Wilford Industrial Estate, Nottingham, NG11 7EP Tel: 0115-846 4000 Fax: 0115-981 0180 E-mail: sales@bsfitness.co.uk

York Distribution Ltd, 23-24 Auster Road, York, YO30 4XA Tel: (01904) 693969 Fax: (01904) 693255 E-mail: sales@ydl.co.uk

COMPUTER PERIPHERAL EQUIPMENT DESIGN

Adder Technology Ltd, Technology House, Trafalgar Way, Bar Hill, Cambridge, CB3 8SQ Tel: (01954) 780044 Fax: (01954) 780081 E-mail: sales@addertec.com

Fands Systems Integrator Ltd, 12 Saxonville, Benfleet, Essex, SS7 5TD Tel: (01268) 795757 Fax: (01268) 795858 E-mail: sales@fands.uk.com

Fontware Ltd, 25 Barnes Wallis Road, Fareham, Hampshire, PO15 5TT Tel: (01489) 505075 Fax: (0870) 0515816 E-mail: sales@fontware.com

COMPUTER PERIPHERAL EQUIPMENT HIRE

A & T Computer Rentals Ltd, Robert Cort Industrial Estate, Britten Road, Reading, RG2 0AU Tel: 0118-986 4666 Fax: 0118-986 4777 E-mail: admin@aandt.co.uk

Computerhire South West Ltd, 5 Kingsway, Kingswood, Bristol, BS15 8BF Tel: 0117-907 7101 Fax: 0117-907 7105 E-mail: sales@computerhire-sw.co.uk

Hamilton Rentals P.L.C., Hamilton House, North Circular Road, London, NW10 7UB Tel: (020) 8963 8080 Fax: (020) 8961 8385 E-mail: info@hamilton.co.uk

Hire It, Magnum House, Cookham Road, Bracknell, Berkshire, RG12 1RB Tel: (01344) 477744 Fax: (01344) 477789 E-mail: sales@hireit.co.uk

Microlease plc, Unit 6 Whitefriars Trading Estate, Tudor Road, Harrow, Middlesex, HA3 5SS Tel: (020) 8420 0200 Fax: (020) 8420 0299 E-mail: info@microlease.com

COMPUTER PERIPHERAL EQUIPMENT SERVICING/ MAINTENANCE SERVICES

Aa Computer Maintenance Ltd, 4 Edge Business Centre, Humber Road, London, NW2 6EW Tel: (020) 8452 8033 Fax: (020) 8450 6360

Bulli Computer Maintenance, Gatehouse Lane, Goddards Green, Hassocks, West Sussex, BN6 9LD Tel: (01444) 871609 Fax: (01444) 871216E-mail: bullicomputers@btconnect.com

Burway Computer Services, 24 Central Avenue, Church Stretton, Shropshire, SY6 6EF Tel: (01694) 722520 Fax: (01694) 724070 E-mail: kevan@burwaycomputers.co.uk

Cameo Computer Services Ltd, Unit 6, Maizefield, Hinckley, Leicestershire, LE10 1YF Tel: (01455) 618893 Fax: (01455) 254878 E-mail: info@cameouk.com

Cennin Ltd, Pen-Y-Maes Lodge, Clocaenog, Llanfwrog, Ruthin, Clwyd, LL15 2AP Tel: (01824) 750369 Fax: (01824) 750544

D S H Electronics Ltd, 206 Idle Road, Bradford, West Yorkshire, BD2 4JT Tel: (01274) 626261 Fax: (01274) 626299 E-mail: sales@dsh-electronics.co.uk

Electronic & General Services Ltd, 3 Hitchs Yard, Church Street, Ware, Hertfordshire, SG12 9ES Tel: (01920) 468991 Fax: (01920) 469938 E-mail: klick@egs.co.uk

Laser Services Cartridge Master, 2 Woodview Business Centre, Lockwood Close, Nottingham, NG5 9JN Tel: 0115-967 3445 Fax: 0115-967 3899 E-mail: sales@laserservices.co.uk

Regenersis Ltd, 1 James Wort Avenue, Westwood Park, Glenrothes, Fife, KY7 4UA Tel: (01592) 774704 Fax: (01592) 774150 E-mail: margaret.lessels@crc-group.com

UK Computer Maintenance Ltd, Unit 13 The Glennmore Center, Waterwell Business Park, Quedgley, Gloucester, GL2 2 AP Tel: 0870 0261234 Fax: 0870 0262345 E-mail: Sales@ukcm.co.uk

COMPUTER PERIPHERAL EQUIPMENT TO SPECIFICATION

First Micronics Ltd, 602-604 Kingsbury Road, Erdington, Birmingham, B24 9PJ Tel: 0121-250 5000 Fax: 0121-250 5019 E-mail: sales@fml.net

COMPUTER PERIPHERALS AND ACCESSORIES

A W W Computers, South Road, Harlow, Essex, CM20 2AS Tel: (01279) 626354 Fax: (01279) 444800 E-mail: admin@wenham.co.uk

C D R Computing Ltd, 12-14 Thames Street, Sunbury-on-Thames, Middlesex, TW16 5QP Tel: (01252) 838400 Fax: (0845) 3452396 E-mail: support@crdcomputing.com

▶ C M C Mobile Computing Ltd, The Heath Business & Technical Park, Runcorn, Cheshire, WA7 4QX Tel: (0870) 1651465 Fax: (0870) 7623701 E-mail: sales@cmc.org.uk

▶ Check Computer Services Ltd, Unit 7, Globe Park, Moss Bridge Road, Rochdale, Lancashire, OL16 5EB Tel: (01706) 651555 Fax: (01706) 651666 E-mail: Gareth@check.co.uk

Church Micros, Causeway Side, 1 High Street, Haslemere, Surrey, GU27 2JZ Tel: (01428) 644122 Fax: (01428) 656300 E-mail: churchmicros@haslemere.com

Comcen Computer Supplies Ltd, 1 York Place, Leeds, LS1 2DS Tel: 0113-234 5000 Fax: 0113-234 2757 E-mail: leeds@comcen.co.uk

Computing Matters, C M House, Bowers, Wimborne, Dorset, BH21 7DL Tel: (01202) 888990 Fax: (01202) 888383 E-mail: ian@computing-matters.com

Cybis Computer Systems, 34 Sudley Road, Bognor Regis, West Sussex, PO21 1ER Tel: (01243) 840000 Fax: (01243) 840084 E-mail: sales@cybis.co.uk

Electronic Data Processing Group P.L.C., Sunrise Parkway, Linford Wood, Milton Keynes, MK14 6LJ Tel: (01908) 665522

▶ E-Trade Enterprises Ltd, 21 Betchworth Road, Ilford, Essex, IG3 9JF Tel: (020) 8599 5259 E-mail: fismail@gadgetscene.co.uk

Intec, 35 Trelowarren Street, Camborne, Cornwall, TR14 8AD Tel: (01209) 716717 Fax: (01209) 610580

Livingston Services plc, Livingston House, 2-6 Queens Road, Teddington, Middlesex, TW11 0LR Tel: (020) 8943 1142 Fax: (020) 8977 6431 E-mail: info@livingston.co.uk

Lyndon Co., Unit 14 Saxon Business Centre, Windsor Avenue, London, SW19 2RR Tel: (020) 8543 9969 Fax: (020) 8543 9765 E-mail: sales@lydongroup.co.uk

MacXperts Ltd, London, W4 3UW Tel: (0871) 5504050 Fax: (020) 8181 7798 E-mail: info@macxperts.com

Mayflower Arosoft Systems Ltd, Mayflower House, Herbert Road, Stafford, ST17 9BH Tel: (01785) 240073 Fax: (01785) 245266 E-mail: b.bartlett@mfc-group.co.uk

COMPUTER PERIPHERALS AND ACCESSORIES – *continued*

Micro Check, 75 North Street, Wellington, Somerset, TA21 8NA Tel: (01823) 664943 Fax: (01823) 665747 E-mail: sales@microcheckcomputers.co.uk
Sitecom UK Ltd, Falcon House, 16 Fernhill Road, Farnborough, Hampshire, GU14 9RX Tel: (01252) 551050 Fax: (01252) 511333 E-mail: sales@sitecom.com
USB-FlashDrive.com, Nash House, Datchet Road, Slough, SL3 7LR Tel: (01753) 491470 Fax: (01753) 539801 E-mail: sales@usb-flashdrive.co.uk

COMPUTER PERIPHERALS, CARDS, PERIPHERAL COMPONENT INTERCONNECT (PCI) BUS, UNIVERSAL SERIAL BUS (USB)

▶ J Tech Suffolk Computer Systems Ltd, 27-29 Orwell Road, Felixstowe, Suffolk, IP11 7DD Tel: (01394) 271555 Fax: 05600 766700 E-mail: sales@jtechsuffolk.com

COMPUTER PERIPHERALS, PERIPHERAL COMPONENT INTERCONNECT MEZZANINE CARDS (PMC), QUAD SERIAL CONTROLLER

Images Storage & Partitioning Ltd, 68 Iron Mill Lane, Dartford, DA1 4RR Tel: (01322) 525975 Fax: (01322) 558032 E-mail: mrimages@globalnet.co.uk

COMPUTER PERSONNEL/IT TECHNOLOGY RECRUITMENT AGENCIES/CONSULTANTS/ SERVICES

Abraxas plc, 47 Eastcastle Street, London, W1W 8DY Tel: (020) 7255 5555 Fax: (020) 7636 0333 E-mail: corporate@abraxas.com
Accountancy Divisions, 37 George Street, Croydon, CR0 1LB Tel: (020) 8686 5353 Fax: (020) 8686 2666 E-mail: croydon@hays.com
Adecco UK Ltd, 44 Shenley Road, Borehamwood, Hertfordshire, WD6 1DR Tel: (020) 8953 6700 Fax: (020) 8207 4686 E-mail: info@adecco.co.uk
▶ Altmore General Recruitment, Office 15 Townsend Enterprise Park, 28 Townsend Street, Belfast, BT13 2ES Tel: (028) 9032 8411 Fax: (028) 9032 8400 E-mail: cr@altmore.co.uk
Altus Recruitment Services Ltd, Moseley, Birmingham, B13 9ZQ Tel: 0121-442 4030 Fax: 0121-442 4030
Andaire Computer Services, Plainlands, Drake Lane, Dursley, Gloucestershire, GL11 5HF Tel: (01453) 541800 Fax: (01453) 541808 E-mail: mail@andaire.co.uk
The Aristotle Corporation, Blenheim House, 56 Old Steine, Brighton, BN1 1NH Tel: (01273) 222400 Fax: (01273) 778464 E-mail: candidates@aristotlecorp.com
Aspectus Global Resource Solutions Ltd, Suite 353, 405 Kings Road, London, SW10 0BB Tel: (07002) 773288 Fax: (020) 8549 8592 E-mail: bmadmin@aspectusltd.co.uk
Atlan Ltd, Six Acre House, 17 Town Square, Sale, Cheshire, M33 7WZ Tel: 0161-282 1770 Fax: 0161-962 0316 E-mail: cbsnorth@atlanrecruitment.com
Badenoch & Clark, 16-18 New Bridge Street, London, EC4V 6HU Tel: (020) 7583 0073 Fax: (020) 7353 3908 E-mail: corp.comms@badenochandclark.com
The Business Connection, 4 Heritage Court, Lower Bridge Street, Chester, CH1 1RD Tel: (01244) 350303 Fax: (01244) 313004 E-mail: info@tbc-recruit.com
▶ Buzz House Keeping, Trocoll House, Wakering Road, Barking, Essex, IG11 8PD Tel: (020) 8507 9906 Fax: (020) 8507 9066 E-mail: peter@buzzservices.co.uk
C & D Recruitment, College Court, Regent Circus, Swindon, SN1 1PZ Tel: (01793) 488057 Fax: (01793) 488056 E-mail: enquiries@cdrecruitment.co.uk
C G Resources Ltd, 62 Wellington Street West, Broughton, Manchester, M7 2FD Tel: 0161-792 8234 Fax: 0161-792 7080 E-mail: enq@cgresources.com
C V Screen, 12 Octagon Court, High Wycombe, Buckinghamshire, HP11 2HS Tel: (01494) 769191 Fax: (01494) 447621 E-mail: matt@cvscreen.co.uk
Calibre Recruitment, 71 Patrick Way, Aylesbury, Buckinghamshire, HP21 9XJ Tel: (01296) 420456 Fax: (01296) 393723 E-mail: calibre_uk@compuserve.com
Castle International, 9 Woodcocks Cresent, Bournemouth, BH7 7JW Tel: (01202) 422447
▶ Cathedral Appointments, 33 Southernhay East, Exeter, EX1 1NX Tel: (01392) 413577 Fax: (01392) 425690 E-mail: sales@cathedralappointments.co.uk
Cliveden House, Taplow, Maidenhead, Berkshire, SL6 0JF Tel: (01628) 668561 Fax: (01628) 661837 E-mail: reservations@clivedenhouse.co.uk
Comms Resources, 1 Sherman Road, Bromley, BR1 3JH Tel: (020) 8663 1999 Fax: (020) 8313 6601 E-mail: mail@commsresources.com
Computeach International Ltd, University House, Jews Lane, Dudley, West Midlands, DY3 2AH Tel: (01384) 458515 Fax: (01384) 455650 E-mail: info@computeach.co.uk
Computer People Ltd, Anglo City House, 2-6 Shirley Road, Southampton, SO15 3EU Tel: (023) 8021 0400 Fax: (023) 8021 0410 E-mail: southampton@computerpeople.co.uk
Computer People Midlands Ltd, Alpha Tower, Suffolk St Queensway, Birmingham, B1 1TT Tel: 0121-643 8501 Fax: 0121-632 5996 E-mail: cpbirmingham@computerpeople.co.uk
Computer Two Thousand Ltd, Eclipse Court, 14B Chequer Street, St. Albans, Hertfordshire, AL1 3YD Tel: (01727) 868176 Fax: (01727) 831202 E-mail: mail@2000group.co.uk
Convert Recruitment Solutions Ltd, 127 Hillcroft Crescent, Oxhey, Watford, WD19 4PA Tel: (08700) 333370 Fax: (08700) 333371 E-mail: enquiry@convertrecruitment.co.uk
D P Connect, Garrard House, 2-6 Homesdale Road, Bromley, BR2 9LZ Tel: (020) 8466 5666 Fax: (020) 8313 1716 E-mail: info@dpconnect.co.uk
▶ Dart Resourcing, Mda House, The Grove, Slough, SL1 1RH Tel: (01753) 828900 Fax: 0870 8700299 E-mail: slo@mdarg.com
Elan I T Computing, St Johns House, Barrington Road, Altrincham, Cheshire, WA14 1JY Tel: 0161-924 3900 Fax: 0161-924 3901 E-mail: info.alt@elanit.co.uk
Excel I T Ltd, Trafalgar House, 712 London Road, Grays, Essex, RM20 3JT Tel: (01708) 865855 Fax: (01708) 866856 E-mail: enquiries@excelit.com
▶ Exectec Solutions, National Deposit House, 11-13 Goldsmith Street, Nottingham, NG1 5JS Tel: 0115-988 1810 Fax: 0115-950 8900 E-mail: awalker@exectecsolutions.co.uk
Executive Facilities Ltd, 43 High Street, Marlow, Buckinghamshire, SL7 1BA Tel: (01628) 898556 Fax: (01628) 898139 E-mail: eft@efrecruitment.co.uk
▶ Exodus Recruitment, Tower Bridge Business Centre, 46-48 East Smiths Field, London, E1W 1AW Tel: (020) 770 92070 Fax: (020) 770 92069 E-mail: nic@exodus-recruitment.com
Forest Personnel Ltd, Cross Keys House, 11 Bridge Street, Reading, RG1 2LR Tel: 0118-958 7272 Fax: 0118-939 1404 E-mail: mail@forestpersonnel.co.uk
G S A Tech Source Ltd, Cathedral House, 5 Beacon Street, Lichfield, Staffordshire, WS13 7AA Tel: (0845) 2267200 Fax: (0845) 2267210 E-mail: gsa@gsatechsource.com
G T Systems, Alba House, 218 Union Street, Aberdeen, AB10 1TL Tel: (01224) 620200 Fax: (01224) 620020
▶ Goldeneye Executive Resourcing Ltd, Flat 6 Kings Court, 40 Hersham Road, Walton-on-Thames, Surrey, KT12 1JE Tel: (07779) 134007
Gresham Computer Services Ltd, Mitchell House, Brook Avenue, Southampton, SO31 9ZA Tel: (01489) 555500 Fax: (01489) 555560 E-mail: info@gresham-computing.com
▶ The Harris Lord Group Ltd, 45a Carfax, Horsham, West Sussex, RH12 1EQ Tel: (01403) 273370 Fax: (01403) 273364
▶ Harvey Hays Ltd, PO BOX 4544, Walsall, WS9 1AJ Tel: 01922 44 21 58 E-mail: admin@harveyhays.com
▶ I T R M Ltd, Thames House, St. Johns Road, Sidcup, Kent, DA14 4HD Tel: (07000) 284876 Fax: (020) 8308 3301 E-mail: info@itrm.co.uk
Informatiq Consulting Ltd, Gresham House, 53 Clarendon Road, Watford, WD17 1FT Tel: (01923) 224481 Fax: (01923) 224493 E-mail: permanant@informatiq.co.uk
▶ Interquest UK Ltd, 20-23 Grevibbe Street, London, EC1N 8SS Tel: (020) 7025 0100 Fax: (020) 7025 0101 E-mail: info@interquest.co.uk
J H P Training, Sutherland House, Matlock Road, Coventry, CV1 4JQ Tel: (024) 7666 2096 Fax: (024) 7663 8214 E-mail: coventry.sales@jhp-group.com
J M, Chandos House, 12-14 Berry Street, London, EC1V 0AQ Tel: (020) 7253 7172 Fax: (020) 7253 0420
J P M Associates, 322 Upper Shoreham Rd, Shoreham-by-Sea, West Sussex, BN43 6BA Tel: (01273) 452305 Fax: (01273) 464228 E-mail: jpm_associates@compuserve.com
▶ Jeevan Technologies Pvt Ltd, 79 St. Marys Wharf, Blackburn, BB2 3AF Tel: (01225) 335477 Fax: E-mail: v.sathish@jeevantechnologies.com,d.kannan@jeevantechnologies.com
Kotschy Pauline Associates, 83 Mansel Street, Swansea, SA1 5TY Tel: (01792) 472725 Fax: (01792) 479828 E-mail: info@paulinek.com
Kramer Westfield, Old Pound House, London Road, Sunningdale, Ascot, Berkshire, SL5 0DJ Tel: (01344) 875087 Fax: (01344) 874877 E-mail: enquiries@kramwest.com
L A International, International House, Festival Way, Stoke-on-Trent, ST1 5UB Tel: (01782) 203000 Fax: (01782) 203050 E-mail: mail@lainternational.co.uk
M C W Group, Wrexham Technology Park, Wrexham, Clwyd, LL13 7YP Tel: (01978) 340340 Fax: (01978) 340345
Manpower UK Ltd, Capital Court, 30 Windsor Street, Uxbridge, Middlesex, UB8 1AB Tel: (01895) 205200 Fax: (01895) 205201
Merrivale IT Resourcing, Coborn House Suite 210, 3 Coborn Road, London, E3 2DA Tel: (0800) 1077850 Fax: (0871) 6619084 E-mail: mvit@mvit.co.uk
Metropolitano Ltd, Communications House, 26 York Street, Westminster, London, W1U 6PZ Tel: (020) 7060 2501 Fax: (020) 7060 6031 E-mail: info@metropolitano.co.uk
▶ Modis, Swan House, 33 Queen Street, London, EC4R 1BR Tel: (020) 7383 3888 Fax: (020) 7038 6401 E-mail: info@modisintl.com
Monroe Systems, Tubs Hill House South, London Road, Sevenoaks, Kent, TN13 1BL Tel: (0845) 6003233 Fax: (0845) 6445733 E-mail: monroe@monroe.co.uk
Montreal Associates Systems, Newbury House, 890 Eastern Avenue, Ilford, Essex, IG2 7HY Tel: (020) 8548 3500 Fax: (020) 8548 3501 E-mail: cvs@montreal.co.uk
Parity Solutions Ltd, Wimbledon Bridge House, 1 Hartfield Road, London, SW19 3RU Tel: (020) 8543 5353 Fax: (020) 8545 6456 E-mail: marketing@parity.co.uk
▶ Payne Associates Ltd, R B R House, Hawksworth Road, Central Park, Telford, Shropshire, TF2 9TU Tel: (01952) 210300 Fax: (01952) 210301 E-mail: ian.payne@payne-associates.co.uk
Project People Ltd, Whitefriars, Lewins Mead, Bristol, BS1 2NT Tel: 0117-908 7000 Fax: 0117-925 4676 E-mail: sales@handsets.com
▶ Proveya Ltd, Abbey Mill, Station Road, Bishops Waltham, Southampton, SO32 1DH Tel: (01489) 899103 Fax: (01489) 895542 E-mail: sandy@proveya.co.uk
▶ PurpleWeb, Bedford Heights, Brickhill Drive, Bedford, MK41 7PH Tel: 01234 272570 Fax: 01234 272545 E-mail: chris@purplewebit.com
▶ R D F Consulting, Fairways Business Park, 5 Deer Park Road, Livingston, West Lothian, EH54 8AF Tel: (01506) 836200 Fax: (01506) 444222 E-mail: sales@rdf-consulting.co.uk
Reflex Computer Recruitment Ltd, Regent House 1-3 Queensway, Redhill, RH1 1QT Tel: (01737) 778282 Fax: (01737) 778950 E-mail: reflexgroup@reflexgroup.co.uk
▶ ReformIS, 18 Christchurch Hill, London, NW3 1LG Tel: (020) 7152 9638 Fax: (020) 7152 9639
▶ Sales Network (UK) Ltd, Globe Centre, Penistone Road, Sheffield, S6 3AE Tel: (0870) 4441074 Fax: E-mail: glenn@salesnetworkuk.co.uk
Sanderson Recruitment P.L.C., Somerset House, 18 Canynge Road, Clifton, Bristol, BS8 3JX Tel: 0117-970 6666 Fax: 0117-970 6665 E-mail: mail@sandersonplc.com
Scottish IT Jobs, 10 Paladin Av, Glasgow, G13 3HP Tel: 0141-954 6511 E-mail: mlow200@netscapeonline.co.uk
Sector Contracts Ltd, 12 Well Court, London, EC4M 9DW Tel: (020) 7489 0165 Fax: (020) 7236 2824 E-mail: mail@sector.co.uk
▶ Skillquest Ltd, Bordesley Hall, The Holloway, Alvechurch, Birmingham, B48 7QA Tel: (01527) 585855 Fax: (01527) 60140 E-mail: skillquest@btconnect.com
Source Logistics Ltd, 75 Bothwell Street, Glasgow, G2 6TS Tel: 0141-572 2100 Fax: 0141-572 2101 E-mail: mail@sourceuk.com
▶ The Spencer Group Ltd, 308-314 Kings Road, Reading, RG1 4NR Tel: 0118-935 9444 Fax: 0118 935 9445 E-mail: sales@spencergroup.co.uk
Spring Group Ltd, Hazlitt House, 4 Bouverie Street, London, EC4Y 8AX Tel: (020) 7300 9000 Fax: (020) 7300 9090 E-mail: info@spring.com
Spring It Solutions Ltd, 1-3 Museum Place, Cardiff, CF10 3BD Tel: (029) 2064 9400 Fax: (029) 2038 3750 E-mail: pete-heaven@spring.com
▶ Technology Resourcing, Unit 29, Surrey Technology Centre, Occam Road, Guildford, Surrey, GU2 7YG Tel: (01483) 302211 Fax: (01483) 301222 E-mail: recruit@tech-res.co.uk
Towers Recruitment Services, Chiltern Chambers, St Peters Avenue, Caversham, Reading, RG4 7DH Tel: 0118-946 1200 Fax: 0118-946 3318 E-mail: jobs@towers.co.uk
▶ Unix Recruitment Ltd, Brightside Business Centre, 60 Lonnen Road, Wimborne, Dorset, BH21 7AX Tel: (01202) 888021 E-mail: richard@unixrecruitment.co.uk
W M S Development Services P.L.C., 45 Beech St, London, EC2Y 8AD Tel: (020) 7614 4828 Fax: (020) 7614 4801

COMPUTER PRINTER ACCESSORIES AND CONSUMABLES

▶ Cartridge World Ltd, 203 Whalley Road, Accrington, Lancashire, BB5 5AD Tel: (01254) 399991 Fax: (01254) 399199 E-mail: cwaccrington@cartridgeworld.org
▶ G E Computer Supplies, 3 Church View, Wyverstone, Stowmarket, Suffolk, IP14 4SQ Tel: (01449) 782059 E-mail: info@gecomputersupplies.co.uk
▶ SJP Business Supplies Ltd, 6 Acorn Drive, Leeds, LS14 2HH Tel: (0800) 0431044 Fax: (0870) 0429348 E-mail: sjpbusinesssupplies@ntlworld.com

COMPUTER PRINTER MAINTENANCE/REPAIR SERVICES

@Pcproblem Co UK Ltd, Hillside House 215 Ashby Road, Burton On Trent, Burton-on-Trent, Staffordshire, DE15 0LA Tel: (0870) 1994812 E-mail: sales@pcproblem.co.uk
▶ A D Young, Greenacre Court Ruffet Road, Kendleshire, Winterbourne, Bristol, BS36 1AN Tel: (01454) 252910 Fax: (01454) 252911 E-mail: admin@adyoung.com
Alcom Computing, 84 The Broadway, High Street, Chesham, Buckinghamshire, HP5 1EG Tel: (01494) 784784 Fax: (01494) 778424 E-mail: sales@alcomcomputing.com
Best Office Services Sussex, Five Ash Down, Uckfield, East Sussex, TN22 3AP Tel: (01825) 732020 Fax: (01825) 733506 E-mail: bos.s@virgin.net
Big Fish Ltd, Ribbon Light House, Newtown Street, Prestwich, Manchester, M25 1HU Tel: 0161-798 0040 Fax: 0161-798 8884 E-mail: manvent@bigfishhook.com
Bigfish, Unit 8 Adam Smith Street, Grimsby, South Humberside, DN31 1SJ Tel: (01472) 268180 Fax: (01472) 268170 E-mail: humberside@bigfishhooked.com
Blazepoint Ltd, Unit 2 Tower Estate, Warpsgrove Lane, Oxford, OX44 7XZ Tel: (01865) 891666 Fax: (01865) 891118 E-mail: sales@blazepoint.co.uk
Brockham Computers, 7 Bishops Cottages Chalkpit Lane, Betchworth, Dorking, Surrey, RH3 7HA Tel: (01737) 842075 E-mail: keith@brockhamcomputers.co.uk
Burway Computer Services, 24 Central Avenue, Church Stretton, Shropshire, SY6 6EF Tel: (01694) 722520 Fax: (01694) 724070 E-mail: kevan@burwaycomputers.co.uk
Business Computer Resources Ltd, 1b Dyke Road Drive, Brighton, BN1 6AJ Tel: (01273) 542759 Fax: (01273) 889898 E-mail: sales@bcrltd.co.uk
▶ Castle Business Services Ltd, 28 Grange Road, South Croydon, Surrey, CR2 0NA Tel: (020) 8407 0632 Fax: (020) 8407 0587 E-mail: service@faxandprinterrepairs.co.uk
Computer Risk Management, 2 Davyhulme Circle, Urmston, Manchester, M41 0SS Tel: 0161-749 7250 Fax: 0161-747 2476
Datasharp Independent Solutions, The Old Stockyard, Farleigh Road, Cliddesden, Basingstoke, Hampshire, RG25 2JS Tel: (01256) 811519 Fax: (01256) 818211 E-mail: sales@datasharp.uk.com
Des Computers, Cardiff University, Senghennydd Road, Cardiff, CF24 4AG Tel: (029) 2025 0000 Fax: (029) 2025 9600 E-mail: sales@descom.co.uk
Electronic & General Services Ltd, 3 Hitchs Yard, Church Street, Ware, Hertfordshire, SG12 9ES Tel: (01920) 468991 Fax: (01920) 469938 E-mail: klick@egs.co.uk
▶ Fuser Tech, Plaistow Road, Loxwood, Billingshurst, West Sussex, RH14 0TS Tel: (01403) 752520 Fax: (01403) 752520
▶ Home & Business Computer Service, 12 David Close, Braunton, Devon, EX33 2AT Tel: (01271) 815262 E-mail: info@handbcs.co.uk
Japhlin Computer Repairs, 77 Weeping Cross, Stafford, ST17 0DQ Tel: (01785) 663400 Fax: (01785) 665807 E-mail: phil@japhlin.co.uk
Link Level Services Ltd, Business & Technology Centre, Radway Green, Crewe, CW2 5PR Tel: (01270) 886113 Fax: (01270) 886237 E-mail: sales@linklevel.co.uk
▶ Maine Business Systems Plc, 81 Gloucester Road, Croydon, CR0 2DN Tel: 08709 088099 Fax: 08709 088098 E-mail: service@printerrepair.co.uk
Maine Business Systems P.L.C., Hanover Park House, Merebank Lane, Croydon, CR0 4NP Tel: (020) 8688 8855 Fax: (020) 8688 8897 E-mail: post@maine-plc.com
▶ Mind Machine, 69 Hutton Close, Crowther, Washington, Tyne & Wear, NE38 0AH Tel: 0191-417 9295 Fax: 0191-417 0643 E-mail: admin@mindmachine.co.uk
▶ MJ Servicing, 60 Haytor Road, Wrexham, LL11 2PU Tel: 01978 310384 Fax: 0870 7062999 E-mail: support@mjservicing.co.uk
Odyssey Technologies Ltd, Hurlands Close, Farnham, Surrey, GU9 9JE Tel: (01252) 721821 Fax: (01252) 721211 E-mail: sales@odessey.co.uk
Printer Rescue, PO Box 198, Manchester, M32 0ZQ Tel: (0845) 3451498 E-mail: john.regan@printerrescue.co.uk
▶ S V P Services, 106 Nevile Road, Salford, M7 3PL Tel: 0161-792 7501 E-mail: enquires@svpservices.co.uk
Sebserv Business Machine Repairs, Ramsay House, 18 Vera Avenue, London, N21 1RA Tel: (020) 8360 8845 Fax: (020) 8360 6688 E-mail: info@sebserv.com
Service Copier Supplies, 1 Swan Lane, Harleston, Norfolk, IP20 9AN Tel: (01379) 853713 Fax: (01379) 852158 E-mail: enq@servicesupplies.com

COMPUTER PRINTER MAINTENANCE/REPAIR SERVICES

– continued

▶ Solent Printer Services, 12b Walworth Enterprise Centre, West Way, Andover, Hampshire, SP10 5AP Tel: (0870) 7667511 E-mail: sales@solent-printer-services.co.uk
▶ Yorkshire Office Machines, 9 Harley View, Leeds, LS13 4RA Tel: 0113-229 6770 Fax: 0113-229 6770 E-mail: y.o.m@ntlworld.com

COMPUTER PRINTER MECHANISMS

Cartridge Express, 1 Phoenix Business Centre, Low Mill Road, Ripon, North Yorkshire, HG4 1NS Tel: (0870) 2435610 Fax: (0870) 2435611 E-mail: sales@cartex.co.uk

COMPUTER PRINTER PRINT HEAD MAINTENANCE/REPAIR SERVICES

▶ Castle Business Services Ltd, 28 Grange Road, South Croydon, Surrey, CR2 0NA Tel: (020) 8407 0632 Fax: (020) 8407 0587 E-mail: service@faxandprinterrepairs.co.uk
▶ MJ Servicing, 60 Haytor Road, Wrexham, LL11 2PU Tel: 01978 310384 Fax: 0870 7062999 E-mail: support@mjservicing.co.uk
▶ S V P Services, 106 Nevile Road, Salford, M7 3PL Tel: 0161-792 7501 E-mail: enquires@svpservices.co.uk
▶ Solent Printer Services, 12b Walworth Enterprise Centre, West Way, Andover, Hampshire, SP10 5AP Tel: (0870) 7667511 E-mail: sales@solent-printer-services.co.uk

COMPUTER PRINTERS

3d Computer Systems Ltd, Albany House, 11 New Road, Chippenham, Wiltshire, SN15 1HJ Tel: (01249) 460766 Fax: (01249) 460583 E-mail: sales@3d-computers.co.uk
Adris Ltd, Riverise House Brunel Road, Totton, Southampton, SO40 3WX Tel: (023) 8086 8947 Fax: (023) 8086 1618 E-mail: sales@adris.co.uk
Bom Group Ltd, Clue House, Petherton Road, Bristol, BS14 9BZ Tel: (01275) 890100 Fax: (01275) 890111 E-mail: info@bom.co.uk
Burrups Ltd, St. Ives House, Lavington Street, London, SE1 0NX Tel: (020) 7928 8844 Fax: (020) 7902 6572 E-mail: london@burrups.com
CBC Ltd, 91C-91D Mora Road, London, NW2 6TB Tel: (020) 8450 9185 Fax: (020) 8450 6090
Church Micros, Causeway Side, 1 High Street, Haslemere, Surrey, GU27 2JZ Tel: (01428) 644122 Fax: (01428) 656300 E-mail: churchmicros@haslemere.com
Compuchange, 14 Parson Street, London, NW4 1QB Tel: (020) 8203 3363 Fax: (020) 8202 0860
Computaform, 4 Merivale Road, Harrow, Middlesex, HA1 4BH Tel: (020) 8423 5005 Fax: (020) 8422 7216 E-mail: mail@computaform.com
Computer Junction, 276 Arundel Street, Portsmouth, PO1 1NT Tel: (023) 9282 5210 Fax: (023) 9282 5210 E-mail: cjsolent@btconnect.com
Computing Solutions, 14 Well Hall Parade, London, SE9 6SP Tel: (020) 8294 0090 Fax: (020) 8859 4562 E-mail: sales@cymc.com
Concept Labelling Solutions, The Old Sunday School, Bakes Street, Bradford, West Yorkshire, BD7 3EX Tel: (01274) 404400 Fax: (01274) 405599 E-mail: sales@concept-labelling.co.uk
Contrac Computer Supplies North East, Pinetree Centre, Durham Road, Birtley, Chester le Street, County Durham, DH3 2TD Tel: 0191-492 2999 Fax: 0191-492 3011 E-mail: enquiries@contrac.co.uk
Copywise, Unit 6, Block A6, Coombswood Way, Halesowen, West Midlands, B62 8BH Tel: 0121-559 9998
Core Estates Ltd, 3 Pendeford Place, Pendeford Industrial Estate, Wolverhampton, WV9 5HD Tel: (0870) 7014343 Fax: (01902) 557701 E-mail: sales@coresystems.co.uk
Elite Contract Services Ltd, 6 Petsworth Lane, Great Notley, Braintree, Essex, CM77 7XS Tel: (0845) 2262796 E-mail: enquiries@ecsit.co.uk
Equinox Meridian, 18 Haycroft Road, Surbiton, Surrey, KT6 5AU Tel: (020) 8397 7347 Fax: (020) 8397 2652 E-mail: sales@equinoxmeridian.com
Exel Management Ltd, 83-89 Phoenix Street, Sutton-in-Ashfield, Nottinghamshire, NG17 4HL Tel: (01623) 442211 Fax: (01623) 442844 E-mail: enquiries@exelmanagement.com
G M S Technologies, Unit 22, Brambles Enterprise Centre, Waterberry Drive, Waterlooville, Hampshire, PO7 7TH Tel: (023) 9223 1880 Fax: (023) 9223 1990
Hexel Developments Ltd, Wash Lane, Warrington, WA4 1HS Tel: (01925) 444439 Fax: (01925) 655899E-mail: admin@hexel.net
Jigsaw Systems Ltd, The Old Mill, High Church Street, Nottingham, NG7 7JA Tel: (0870) 7306868 Fax: (0870) 7306850 E-mail: sales@jigsaw24.com
K S Computers, 3 Dyneley Road, Blackburn, BB1 3AB Tel: (01254) 505500 Fax: (01254) 691466 E-mail: purchasing@javelincomputers.co.uk
Laser Traders, 83 Horton Road, Datchet, Slough, SL3 9LY Tel: (01753) 580082 Fax: (01753) 580082
Lasercare Bristol Ltd, 8 Bromley Heath Avenue, Bristol, BS16 6JS Tel: 0117-908 3463 Fax: 0117-907 7538 E-mail: sales@lasercarebristol.co.uk
Limetree Marketing, Unit 1, Warboys Road, Old Hurst, Huntingdon, Cambridgeshire, PE28 3AL Tel: (01487) 823823 Fax: (01487) 823898 E-mail: earl@limetreemarketing.co.uk
Mayflower Arosoft Systems Ltd, Mayflower House, Herbert Road, Stafford, ST17 9BH Tel: (01785) 240073 Fax: (01785) 245266 E-mail: b.bartlett@mfc-group.co.uk
MCP Microsystems, 369 Warrington Road, Rainhill, Prescot, Merseyside, L35 8LD Tel: 0151-431 0133 Fax: 0151-431 0072 E-mail: admin@mcpmicro.co.uk
Models & Computers Plus, 55-55a West Street, Boston, Lincolnshire, PE21 8QN Tel: (01205) 365102 Fax: (01205) 369949 E-mail: sales@modcomp.net
Modern Computers Ltd, 181 Old Kent Road, London, SE1 5NA Tel: (020) 7231 1313 Fax: (020) 7231 3225 E-mail: sales@moderncomputers.com
On Line It Ltd, 34 Bedford Road, Hitchin, Hertfordshire, SG5 1HF Tel: (01462) 624624 Fax: (01462) 452452
P C Innovations, 3 Cardine Close, Sittingbourne, Kent, ME10 2HY Tel: (01795) 410264 Fax: (01795) 410283 E-mail: enquiries@pc-i.co.uk
P M P Micros, Rock Cottage, Hawber Lane, Silsden, Keighley, West Yorkshire, BD20 0LE Tel: (07967) 173739 Fax: (01535) 653006 E-mail: peter@pmp-micros.co.uk
PCs R Us, Drumbrughas North, Lisnaskea, Enniskillen, County Fermanagh, BT92 0PE Tel: (028) 6772 3242 Fax: (028) 6772 3131 E-mail: zubbie75@hotmail.com
Performance Computers North East Ltd, 10-11 Post House Wynd, Darlington, County Durham, DL3 7LU Tel: (01325) 267333 Fax: (01325) 489093 E-mail: sales@performancecomputers.co.uk
▶ Printerbase, Victoria House, Victoria Street, Millbrook, Stalybridge, Cheshire, SK15 3HY Tel: 0161-304 7594 Fax: 0161-304 7598 E-mail: info@printerbase.co.uk
Pro Logic Computers, 6-8 Doncaster Road, South Elmsall, Pontefract, West Yorkshire, WF9 2HZ Tel: (01977) 649100 Fax: (01977) 651411 E-mail: paul@pro-logic.co.uk
R A M Computers, 260d Gospel Lane, Birmingham, B27 7AH Tel: 0121-707 3353 Fax: 0121-706 1413 E-mail: sales@ramcomputers.co.uk
S T S Computers, Tylney House, 23 High Street, Leatherhead, Surrey, KT22 8AB Tel: (01372) 378608 Fax: (01372) 374592 E-mail: info@stscomputers.co.uk
Silicon Group, 95 Whins Road, Alloa, Clackmannanshire, FK10 3RF Tel: (01259) 725200 Fax: (01259) 725270 E-mail: info@silicon-group.co.uk
▶ SJ Consultancy, 6 Flaxfields End, Fordingbridge, Hampshire, SP6 1RT Tel: 01425 652961 Fax: 01425 652961 E-mail: enquiries@sjcfb.co.uk
Spot On Computers Ltd, 122 Waterloo Road, Manchester, M8 8AF Tel: (0845) 3453111 Fax: (0870) 1121953 E-mail: sales@spotonuk.com
▶ Three Counties Computers, 14 Woodsage Drive, Gillingham, Dorset, SP8 4UF Tel: (01747) 823994 E-mail: sales@threecountiescomputers.co.uk
West Country Business Systems Holdings Ltd, Somerset House, Magdalene Street, Glastonbury, Somerset, BA6 9EJ Tel: (01458) 833344 Fax: (01458) 835297 E-mail: sales@wcbs.co.uk
Worldwide PC UK Ltd, 88-90 Manningham Lane, Bradford, West Yorkshire, BD1 3ES Tel: (01274) 745515E-mail: gary@wwpc.co.uk

COMPUTER PRINTERS TO SPECIFICATION

Bulli Computer Maintenance, Gatehouse Lane, Goddards Green, Hassocks, West Sussex, BN6 9LD Tel: (01444) 871609 Fax: (01444) 871216E-mail: bullicomputers@btconnect.com
C C M Sussex Ltd, PO Box 2004, Peacehaven, East Sussex, BN10 7HZ Tel: (01273) 586963 Fax: (01273) 584000 E-mail: sales@ccm.gb.com
▶ Toosey Print, 87 Spring Road, St. Osyth, Clacton-on-Sea, Essex, CO16 8RU Tel: (01255) 820264 E-mail: sales@tooseyprint.com

COMPUTER PRINTERS, LABEL/ PLASTIC CARDS

PMC Systems, Whitehill Industrial Estate, Whitehill Lane, Wootton Bassett, Swindon, SN4 7DB Tel: (01793) 848817 Fax: (01793) 848846 E-mail: pmccards@aol.com

COMPUTER PROTECTION UNINTERRUPTIBLE POWER SUPPLIES (UPS)

B T I Computer Systems UK Ltd, Burnt Meadow Road, Moons Moat North Industrial Estate, Redditch, Worcestershire, B98 9PA Tel: (01527) 598500 Fax: (01527) 598555 E-mail: sales@bticomputer.com
Chloride Power Protection, Unit C George Curl Way, Southampton, SO18 2RY Tel: (023) 8061 0311 Fax: (023) 8061 0852 E-mail: uk.sales@chloridepower.com
Computing Solutions, 14 Well Hall Parade, London, SE9 6SP Tel: (020) 8294 0090 Fax: (020) 8859 4562 E-mail: sales@cymc.com
E P I Service Ltd, Witan Park, Avenue Two, Station Lane, Witney, Oxfordshire, OX28 4FH Tel: (01993) 708855 Fax: (01993) 708850 E-mail: admin@epi-uk.com
N D S L Ltd, Unit 2 Oakfield Industrial Estate, Eynsham, Witney, Oxfordshire, OX29 4TS Tel: (01865) 884288 Fax: (01865) 884289 E-mail: sales@ndsl.co.uk
QPQ, Exchange House, Elsthorpe Road, Stainfield, Bourne, Lincolnshire, PE10 0RS Tel: (01778) 570879 E-mail: sales@qpq.co.uk
▶ Technology Ventures Maritime Ltd, Suite B 29 Harley Street, London, W1G 9QR Tel: (020) 7016 2664 Fax: (07092) 013175 E-mail: info@kinetec.uk.com

COMPUTER RECYCLING, REMARKETING AND RESELLING

A M I Systems Ltd, 1159-1163 New Chester Road, Wirral, Merseyside, CH62 0BY Tel: 0151-200 2121 Fax: 0151-200 2122
Clyde Computers Southern Ltd, Lovelace Works, High Street, Ripley, Woking, Surrey, GU23 6AF Tel: (01483) 225930 Fax: (01483) 225931 E-mail: sales@clydecomputers.co.uk
Else Refining & Recycling Ltd, Unit 7-8 Pole Hanger Farm, Shefford Road, Meppershall, Shefford, Bedfordshire, SG17 5LH Tel: (01462) 812000 Fax: (01462) 817117 E-mail: enquiries@elserefining.co.uk
▶ G R P (Electronic) Ltd, 2 Wham Cottages, Slackgate Lane, Denshaw, Oldham, OL3 5TZ Tel: (01457) 820864 Fax: (01457) 820864 E-mail: pollardgraham@talk21.com
Kingsfield Computer Product Ltd, Kingsfield Centre, Moulton Park, Northampton, NN3 6RB Tel: (0870) 8888410 Fax: (0870) 8888460 E-mail: purchase@kingsfieldcomputers.co.uk
Moorhouse Software Services, Capital House, 45 The Broadway, West Ealing, London, W13 9BP Tel: (020) 8567 7817 Fax: (020) 8840 4153
P S A Professionals Solutions, 67 Park Street, Thame, Oxfordshire, OX9 3HT Tel: (01844) 261750 Fax: (01840) 261751 E-mail: info@psaconnect.com
Secure I.T. Disposals Ltd, Unit 12, 53 Kettles Wood Drive, Woodgate Business Park, Woodgate Valley, Birmingham, B32 3DB Tel: (0870) 7271578 Fax: (0870) 7271469 E-mail: @sitd.co.uk
Technical Asset Management Ltd, Falcon House City Park, Watchmead, Welwyn Garden City, Hertfordshire, AL7 1AT Tel: (01707) 333555 Fax: (01707) 390893 E-mail: sales@tam-uk.com
Twisted Fish Ltd, 1 Stan Hill, Charlwood, Horley, Surrey, RH6 0EP Tel: (01293) 863763 Fax: (01293) 863201
Westwood Associates Ltd, Hampden House, Hampden Road, Chalfont St. Peter, Gerrards Cross, Buckinghamshire, SL9 9DP Tel: (01753) 887161 Fax: (01753) 891214

COMPUTER REFURBISHMENT

Twisted Fish Ltd, 1 Stan Hill, Charlwood, Horley, Surrey, RH6 0EP Tel: (01293) 863763 Fax: (01293) 863201
▶ www.letsspendless.org, John Clarke Centre, Middlesbrough, Cleveland, TS6 6UZ Tel: (07739) 509097

COMPUTER RELOCATION

Ar Computing, 8 Friday Street, Minehead, Somerset, TA24 5UA Tel: (01643) 707381 Fax: (01643) 707431 E-mail: enquiries@arcomputing.co.uk
Beacon Computer Technology Ltd, 43 Clifton Road, Cambridge, CB1 7ED Tel: (01223) 506616 Fax: (01223) 506620 E-mail: sales@beacon-ct.co.uk
Blakelan Communications Ltd, Railway Cottage, Mill Road, Brighton, BN1 8ZF Tel: (01273) 564092 Fax: (01273) 564111 E-mail: mike.blakeman@blakelan.com
Breakthrough Ltd, 145 Willington Street, Maidstone, Kent, ME15 8QX Tel: (01622) 670609 Fax: (01622) 670212
▶ CML Group, Bluebell Farm, Hewitts Road, Orpington, Kent, BR6 7QR Tel: (01959) 533833 Fax: (01689) 821893 E-mail: alyson@ah-design.co.uk
CMS Broadband Ltd, Conchieton, Twynholm, Kirkcudbright, DG6 4TA Tel: (01557) 870256 Fax: (01557) 870400 E-mail: info@thinkcms.co.uk
J J Network Services Ltd, Meridian House, 62 Station Road, London, E4 7BA Tel: (020) 8559 3211 Fax: (020) 8559 3223 E-mail: info@jjnet.co.uk
Malbrook, C.S. Ltd, 8 Millbank Court, Millbank Way, Bracknell, Berkshire, RG12 1RP Tel: (01344) 424458 Fax: (01344) 424459 E-mail: support@csmb.co.uk

COMPUTER REMOVAL/ TRANSPORTATION CONTRACTORS

Beacon Computer Technology Ltd, 43 Clifton Road, Cambridge, CB1 7ED Tel: (01223) 506616 Fax: (01223) 506620 E-mail: sales@beacon-ct.co.uk
Commercial Trading Co. Ltd, Unit D6 Sandown Industrial Park, Mill Road, Esher, Surrey, KT10 8BL Tel: (01372) 468383 Fax: (01372) 468576 E-mail: admin@ctc.co.uk
Computer Move Ltd, Unit 1, Lakeside Industrial Estate, Colnbrook By Pass, Colnbrook, Slough, SL3 0ED Tel: (01753) 283260 Fax: (01753) 689004
Else Refining & Recycling Ltd, Unit 7-8 Pole Hanger Farm, Shefford Road, Meppershall, Shefford, Bedfordshire, SG17 5LH Tel: (01462) 812000 Fax: (01462) 817117 E-mail: enquiries@elserefining.co.uk
Exclusive Move Solutions, 1 Cooks Road, London, E15 2PW Tel: (020) 8555 5179 Fax: (020) 8555 5172 E-mail: info@move-ems.com
▶ Express Moves, 116 Greyhound Lane, London, SW16 5RN Tel: (020) 8677 3436 Fax: (020) 8769 1098 E-mail: sales@expressmoves.co.uk
▶ H Mcclelland & Sons, Unit 7, Cadzow Industrial Estate, Hamilton, Lanarkshire, ML3 7QU Tel: (01698) 283314 Fax: (01698) 286677 E-mail: info@mcclellandremovals.co.uk
Tibbett & Britten Group P.L.C., Centennial Park, Centennial Avenue, Elstree, Borehamwood, Hertfordshire, WD6 3TL Tel: (020) 8327 2000 Fax: (020) 8327 2199 E-mail: info@tandb.co.uk

COMPUTER REPAIR, LAPTOP

Beetee, 139 Taplow, Thurlow Street, London, SE17 2UJ Tel: (07956) 868418 E-mail: lewis@btcomputers.com
▶ Cando It, 42 Wolfe Road, Norwich, NR1 4HT Tel: (01603) 498999 E-mail: sales@cando-it.co.uk
Datastor Technology Ltd, Old Mushroom Farm, Heathend, Wotton-under-Edge, Gloucestershire, GL12 8AX Tel: (01454) 299399 Fax: (01454) 299400 E-mail: sales@datastor.co.uk
▶ Escape Systems, 9 Salamanca Crescent, Penicuik, Midlothian, EH26 0LT Tel: (07764) 304166
Giga Computer Systems, 30 Mill Road, Billericay, Essex, CM11 2SF Tel: (01277) 630493 Fax: (01277) 651666
▶ Hampshire Computer Clinics Ltd, 203E West Street, Fareham, Hampshire, PO16 0EN Tel: (023) 9243 5675 E-mail: mail@gosportpccentre.com
▶ Laptop Specialists, Lane End House, Green Lane, Tansley, Matlock, Derbyshire, DE4 5FJ Tel: (01629) 584456
▶ Laptop Support, No. 1 Factory Road, Poole, Dorset, BH16 5SJ Tel: (0800) 1977665 E-mail: repairs@testlink.co.uk
Link Level Services Ltd, Business & Technology Centre, Radway Green, Crewe, CW2 5PR Tel: (01270) 886113 Fax: (01270) 886237 E-mail: sales@linklevel.co.uk
MBM Group, 11 Railway Street, Newcastle, County Down, BT33 0AL Tel: (028) 4372 2257 Fax: (028) 4372 2257 E-mail: sales@thembmgroup.com
▶ Pro-Com Computer Services London Ltd, 53 St. Helier Avenue, Morden, Surrey, SM4 6HY Tel: (020) 8287 2772 Fax: (020) 8395 3565 E-mail: sales@procomcomputers.co.uk
S & D Electronics, Unit 34, Winpenny Road, Parkhouse Industrial Estate East, Newcastle, Staffordshire, ST5 7RB Tel: (01782) 565797 Fax: (01782) 565181 E-mail: sales@sdelectronics.co.uk
▶ Stroud PC (Cinderford), 20 Victoria Street, Cinderford, Gloucestershire, GL14 2HQ Tel: (0870) 8034246 Fax: (07092) 812233 E-mail: bryan@stroud-pcs.com
▶ Stroud-PC's (RuralDean), 27 Victoria Street, Cinderford, Gloucestershire, GL14 2ET Tel: (0845) 2260173 E-mail: info@stroud-pcs.com

COMPUTER RESELLERS, ONLINE

▶ C-Ram Ltd, 126 Malvern Road, Leytonstone, London, E11 3DL Tel: (0845) 0589813 Fax: (0709) 2087787 E-mail: sales@c-ram.co.uk

COMPUTER RESELLERS, ONLINE – *continued*

Diamond Group, 145 Willington Street, Maidstone, Kent, ME15 8QX Tel: (01622) 688817 Fax: (01622) 670212 E-mail: sales@diamondgroup.org.uk

European Electronique Ltd, Forward House, Oakfield Industrial Estate, Eynsham, Witney, Oxfordshire, OX29 4TT Tel: (01865) 883300 Fax: (01865) 883371 E-mail: sales@euroele.com

COMPUTER ROOM AIR CONDITIONING (AC) EQUIPMENT

A C Engineers Ltd, Unit 7, Mill Industrial Estate, Kings Coughton, Alcester, Warwickshire, B49 5QG Tel: (01789) 763956 Fax: (01789) 400565 E-mail: ace@acegroup.co.uk

Acrol Air Conditioning Co. Ltd, Salt Meadows Road, East Gateshead Industrial Estate, Gateshead, Tyne & Wear, NE8 3AH Tel: 0191-477 7999 Fax: 0191-477 7222 E-mail: sales@acrolairconditioningco.co.uk

Advanced, PO Box 6433, Birmingham, B30 3HG Tel: 0121-459 3838 Fax: 0121-459 1415

Cleanair Group Ltd, Technology House, 5 Newton Close, Drayton Fields, Daventry, Northamptonshire, NN11 5RR Tel: (01327) 301383 Fax: (01327) 301384 E-mail: info@cleanair.com

M S N Network Power Ltd, Fourth Avenue, Globe Park, Marlow, Buckinghamshire, SL7 1YG Tel: (01628) 403200 Fax: (01628) 403203 E-mail: sales@emersonnetworkpower.com

▶ Qualitas Ltd, Suite 9, Coach House Cloisters, Hitchin Street, Baldock, Hertfordshire, SG7 6AE Tel: (01462) 491155 Fax: (01462) 896611 E-mail: enquiries@qualitaslimited.com

Simer Environmental Services Ltd, 15 Arnside Road, Waterlooville, Hampshire, PO7 7UP Tel: (023) 9225 8059 Fax: (023) 9226 7059 E-mail: sales@simer-environmental.co.uk

Warwick Fraser, Unit 9 Alfold Business Centre, Loxwood Road, Alfold, Cranleigh, Surrey, GU6 8HP Tel: (01403) 753069 Fax: (01403) 752469 E-mail: sales@warwickfraser.co.uk

COMPUTER ROOM AIR CONDITIONING (AC) INSTALLATION OR SERVICING

A C 2000, North Bridge Place, Frog Island, Leicester, LE3 5BG Tel: 0116-262 0411 Fax: 0116-251 8967 E-mail: aircon@ac2000.co.uk

Acm Air Conditioning, Unit 10 Armley Workshops, Pickering Street, Leeds, LS12 2QG Tel: 0113-203 8240 Fax: 0113-279 7088

Comserve Ltd, Comserve House, 54 Watling Street, Radlett, Hertfordshire, WD7 7NN Tel: (01923) 853269 Fax: (01923) 857370 E-mail: service@comserve.co.uk

Elyo UK Industrial Ltd, Unit 3-4 Sheffield Airport Business Park, Europa Link, Sheffield, S9 1XU Tel: 0114-280 0000 Fax: 0114-280 0099 E-mail: sheffield@elyo.co.uk

Ensys Ltd, Unit 10 Rivermead, Thatcham, Berkshire, RG19 4EP Tel: (01635) 872227 Fax: (01635) 872206 E-mail: sales@ensys.co.uk

Refrigeration Service (Ruislip) Ltd, 288 West End Road, Ruislip, Middlesex, HA4 6LS Tel: (01895) 622286 Fax: (01895) 622259

Sirocco Air Co. Ltd, Unit 4, Carew Street Industrial Estate, London, SE5 9DF Tel: (020) 7326 1272 Fax: (020) 7326 1272

Team National Ltd, Triumph House, Birmingham Road, Millisons Wood, Coventry, CV5 9AZ Tel: (01676) 526000 Fax: (01676) 522966 E-mail: sales@teamnational.co.uk

COMPUTER ROOM AIR CONDITIONING (AC) SYSTEMS

Denco Air Conditioning, Dolphin House, Morton On Legg, Hereford, HR4 8DS Tel: (01432) 277277 Fax: (01432) 268005

Edenaire Ltd, Station Road, Edenbridge, Kent, TN8 6EG Tel: (01732) 866066 Fax: (01732) 866653

COMPUTER ROOM CLEANING CONTRACTORS OR SERVICES

▶ Aquacair Ltd, 40 Parklands Road, Chichester, West Sussex, PO19 3DT Tel: (01243) 790808 Fax: (01243) 790809 E-mail: sales@aquacair.co.uk

▶ Atlas Clean Air Ltd, 5 Carrside, Lomeshaye Industrial Estate, Nelson, Lancashire, BB9 6RX Tel: (01282) 447666 Fax: (01282) 447789 E-mail: info@atlascleanair.com

▶ Clean Impact, 103 Junction Road, Burgess Hill, West Sussex, RH15 0JL Tel: (07811) 107268 E-mail: sales@cleanimpact.ws

(ECSO) Express Computer Services, 636 Cathcart Road, Crosshill, Govanhill, Glasgow, G42 8AA Tel: (0871) 7890247 Fax: (0871) 7890248 E-mail: info@ecso.co.uk

▶ Kizza Business Consultants Ltd, Seaton Close, Plaistow, London, E13 8JJ Tel: (020) 7511 8187 E-mail: pollykidza@yahoo.com

▶ Qualitas Ltd, Suite 9, Coach House Cloisters, Hitchin Street, Baldock, Hertfordshire, SG7 6AE Tel: (01462) 491155 Fax: (01462) 896611 E-mail: enquiries@qualitaslimited.com

COMPUTER ROOM FIRE ALARM OR PROTECTION SYSTEM INSTALLATION OR SERVICING

▶ Ace Systems Installations Ltd, 103 Elsenham Street, London, SW18 5NY Tel: (020) 8874 8966 Fax: (020) 8265 6050 E-mail: sales@fire-alarms.uk.com

Building Research Establishment Ltd, Bucknalls Lane, Garston, Watford, WD25 9XX Tel: (01923) 664237 Fax: (01923) 664994 E-mail: enquiries@brecertification.com

Erif UK Ltd, Prospect House, 6 Archipelago, Lyon Way, Frimley, Camberley, Surrey, GU16 7ER Tel: (0845) 8877999 Fax: (01276) 601337 E-mail: tim@erif.co.uk

Nobel Fire Systems Ltd, Unit 6, Southgate Industrial Estate, Green Lane, Heywood, Lancashire, OL10 1ND Tel: (01706) 625777 Fax: (01706) 625325 E-mail: info@nobel-fire-systems.com

COMPUTER ROOM FIRE ALARM OR PROTECTION SYSTEMS

Nobel Fire Systems Ltd, Unit 6, Southgate Industrial Estate, Green Lane, Heywood, Lancashire, OL10 1ND Tel: (01706) 625777 Fax: (01706) 625325 E-mail: info@nobel-fire-systems.com

COMPUTER ROOM FIRE PROTECTION EQUIPMENT OR SYSTEMS

Eagle Fire Systems, 100 Liverpool Street, Salford, M5 4LP Tel: 0161-745 9578 Fax: 0161-745 9578 E-mail: eaglfirsys@aol.com

COMPUTER ROOM FLOORING SYSTEMS

Bathgate Flooring Ltd, 1 Fir Tree Lane, Rotherwas, Hereford, HR2 6LA Tel: (01432) 353003 Fax: (01432) 353004

Raised Floor Systems, Peak House, Works Road, Letchworth Garden City, Hertfordshire, SG6 1GB Tel: (01582) 734161 Fax: (01582) 400946 E-mail: sales@raisedfloorsystems.co.uk

COMPUTER ROOM FURNITURE

▶ Aiveen Daly Upholstery & Design, 2 Letchford Gardens, London, NW10 6AS Tel: 0208 962 0044 E-mail: info@aiveendaly.com

Praxis Farm Ltd, Hoe Lane, Flansham, Bognor Regis, West Sussex, PO22 8NN Tel: (01243) 587354 Fax: (01243) 587353

▶ Total Install Ltd, Unit 3, Hanworth Trading Estate Hampton, Feltham, Middlesex, TW13 6DH Tel: (020) 8898 5644 Fax: (020) 8898 5642 E-mail: info@totalinstall.co.uk

COMPUTER SCREEN SAVER GRAPHIC DESIGN AND DEVELOPMENT SERVICES

Active Media Technology Ltd, Golden Gate Lodge, Weston Road, Crewe, CW2 5XN Tel: (01270) 580400 Fax: (01270) 589800 E-mail: info@active-media-online.com

▶ Blinding Web Site Design, 8 Dalkeith Street, Barrow-in-Furness, Cumbria, LA14 1SP Tel: (01229) 828028 E-mail: info@blindingwebdesign.co.uk

Dax Printing Co. Ltd, Free Street, Bishops Waltham, Southampton, SO32 1EE Tel: (01489) 891006 Fax: (01489) 891699 E-mail: general@daxprinting.co.uk

Effective Multimedia, 1107 Evesham Road, Astwood Bank, Redditch, Worcestershire, B96 6EB Tel: (01527) 892394 E-mail: sales@effectivemultimedia.co.uk

▶ Harmony Internet Ltd, 3 The Granary Buildings, Millow, Biggleswade, Bedfordshire, SG18 8RH Tel: (01767) 317614 Fax: (01767) 317647 E-mail: info@harmony.co.uk

COMPUTER SECURITY ALARM SYSTEMS

▶ Ace Security Systems Ltd, 12 Triumph Way, Kempston, Bedford, MK42 7QB Tel: (01234) 854455 Fax: (01234) 855345 E-mail: sales@acesecurity.co.uk

Blanchards Home Hardware, 51 Mill Street, Bideford, Devon, EX39 2JS Tel: (01237) 472084 E-mail: kellysearch@blanchardsecurity.co.uk

▶ Covert Surveillance & Investigations, 107 Brookdale Road, Liverpool, L15 3JF Tel: 0151-222 1188 Fax: 0151-222 1188 E-mail: enquiries@csilimited.co.uk

Dent Ltd, 191-195 Sturton St., Cambridge, CB1 2QH Tel: (01223) 350038 Fax: (01223) 300996 E-mail: dentsecur@aol.com

Destec Systems, 21 Grovelands Avenue, Swindon, SN1 4ET Tel: (01793) 496217 Fax: (01793) 610739 E-mail: info@destecsystems.co.uk

▶ Sparc Systems Ltd, 430 Allesley Old Road, Coventry, CV5 8GF Tel: (07930) 854033 E-mail: wilson@sparcsys.co.uk

COMPUTER SECURITY CONTAINERS/CAGE SYSTEMS

Aegis Security, Dane Road, Bletchley, Milton Keynes, MK1 1JQ Tel: (01908) 375451 Fax: (01908) 375044 E-mail: info@kemco-aegis.com

Alliance Sales (Europe) Ltd, Units 22-24, Brunel Way, Thetford, Norfolk, IP24 1HP Tel: (01842) 822150 Fax: (01842) 820300 E-mail: info@alliance-sales.com

Dalen Ltd, Garretts Green Trading Estate, Valepits Road, Birmingham, B33 0TD Tel: 0121-783 3838 Fax: 0121-784 6348 E-mail: sales@top-tec.co.uk

Data Encryption Systems Ltd, Silver Street House, Silver Street, Taunton, Somerset, TA1 3DL Tel: (01823) 352357 Fax: (01823) 352358 E-mail: enquiries@des.co.uk

Intercede Ltd, Lutterworth Hall, St. Marys Road, Lutterworth, Leicestershire, LE17 4PS Tel: (01455) 558111 Fax: (01455) 558222

J P J Business Services, 49 Whitefield Avenue, Liverpool, L4 1XJ Tel: 0151-284 1914 Fax: 0151-284 1914

Remtech Computer Security Ltd, PO Box 60, Epsom, Surrey, KT17 2YT Tel: (020) 8786 8788 Fax: (020) 8786 8788 E-mail: sales@remtech.uk.com

Safemark Computer Security, 92 Tadcaster Road, Dringhouses, York, YO24 1LT Tel: (01904) 778899 Fax: (01904) 778623 E-mail: sales@safemark.co.uk

COMPUTER SERVER CABINETS WITH AIR CONDITIONING (AC)

▶ KVM, 1 Southern Court, South Street, Reading, RG1 4QS Tel: (0870) 2202370 Fax: (0870) 2202371 E-mail: sales@kvmpartnership.co.uk

COMPUTER SERVER PROTECTION PRODUCTS

Adecs Ltd, 1 Mercia Business Village, Torwood Close, Westwood Business Park, Coventry, CV4 8HX Tel: (024) 7646 4753 Fax: (08453) 109600 E-mail: services@adecs.co.uk

COMPUTER SERVER RACKING SYSTEMS

▶ KVM, 1 Southern Court, South Street, Reading, RG1 4QS Tel: (0870) 2202370 Fax: (0870) 2202371 E-mail: sales@kvmpartnership.co.uk

COMPUTER SERVICES CONSULTANTS/BUREAUX

1 Can Help P C Problem Solving & Training Services, 60 Springwood Road, Heathfield, East Sussex, TN21 8JX Tel: (01435) 866575 E-mail: gordon@1canhelp.com

A A T Computer Services, 57 High Street, Donaghadee, County Down, BT21 0AQ Tel: (028) 9188 8114 Fax: (028) 9188 8370 E-mail: andrew@aatcs.co.uk

A W Computer Solutions Ltd, 8e Port Road, Carlisle, CA2 7AF Tel: (01228) 594682 Fax: (01228) 594683 E-mail: info@armstrongwatson.co.uk

Aa Computer Repair Centre, 1 Bridle Road, Bootle, Merseyside, L30 4XR Tel: 0151-524 2524 Fax: 0151-524 1010

▶ Abc Computer Services, Highview, 5a King Edward Road, Stanford-le-Hope, Essex, SS17 0EF Tel: (01375) 404495 E-mail: sales@mitefixit.com

Acxiom, Counting House, 53 Tooley Street, London, SE1 2QN Tel: (020) 7526 5100 Fax: (020) 7526 5200

Adare Ltd, Vantage House, 1 Weir Road, London, SW19 8UX Tel: (020) 8946 7537 Fax: (020) 8947 2740

Advanced Computer Installations Ltd, Unit W8 141 Charles Street, Glasgow, G21 2QA Tel: 0141-552 6366 Fax: 0141-552 6388

Advantage Technologies Ltd, Nether Hall, Nether Row, Thetford, Norfolk, IP24 2EG Tel: (01842) 763131 Fax: (01842) 766778

Advisory Data, 20 Butt Haw Close, Hoo, Rochester, Kent, ME3 9BA Tel: (01634) 251906 Fax: (01634) 256823 E-mail: ifor@advisorydata.co.uk

Alpine Computer Systems, 5 Church Road, Bishops Cleeve, Cheltenham, Gloucestershire, GL52 8LR Tel: (01242) 673322 Fax: (01242) 674845 E-mail: sales@alpinesystems.co.uk

Aquila Systems, Aquila House, 283 Laygate, South Shields, Tyne & Wear, NE33 4QN Tel: 0191-455 9440 Fax: 0191-456 1259 E-mail: sales@aquilasystems.co.uk

Audit & Computer Security Services Ltd, 46 Queens Road, Hertford, SG13 8AZ Tel: (01992) 582439 Fax: 01992 582439

B N E Electronics Ltd, 44 Main Street, Toomebridge, Antrim, BT41 3TF Tel: (028) 7965 0502 Fax: (028) 7965 4830 E-mail: edward.duffin@bne.onyxnet.co.uk

Basic Business Systems Ltd, Brookside Road, Ruddington, Nottingham, NG11 6AT Tel: 0115-940 5000 Fax: 0115-940 5450

Bluebell Associates Ltd, Cresta House, 42 Water Lane, Wilmslow, Cheshire, SK9 5AL Tel: (01625) 539288 Fax: (01625) 539211

Boothville Computer Services, 4 Boothville Green, Northampton, NN3 6JR Tel: (01604) 452967 E-mail: info@boothville.co.uk

Bruce Data Networks, 22 Duthie Road, Tarves, Ellon, Aberdeenshire, AB41 7JX Tel: (01651) 851568 Fax: (01651) 851416 E-mail: jim.bruce@btinternet.com

Bryan Powercom, 19 University Street, Belfast, BT7 1FY Tel: (028) 9032 6315 Fax: (028) 9032 3144 E-mail: bryanprcom@aol.com

Business Computers Hillsborough Ltd, Unit 225, City Business Park, Belfast, BT17 9HY Tel: (028) 9030 1526 Fax: (028) 9061 7766 E-mail: info@bch.eu.com

Business Computing Services, Linden, East Side, North Littleton, Evesham, Worcestershire, WR11 8QW Tel: (01386) 830444 Fax: (01386) 830444

C C S Division Of Consumerdata Ltd, Meridian House, Artist St, Armley, Leeds, LS12 2EW Tel: 0113-242 0520 Fax: 0113-242 0050 E-mail: info@consumerdata.com

C R M Associates, 72 Mytchett Rd, Mytchett, Camberley, Surrey, GU16 6EZ Tel: (01252) 513232 Fax: (01252) 517298

Career Soft Ltd, Mulcture House, 3 Mulcture Hall Road, Halifax, West Yorkshire, HX1 1SP Tel: (01422) 330450 Fax: (01422) 348024 E-mail: info@careersoft.co.uk

Civica UK Ltd, Castlegate House, Castlegate Drive, Dudley, West Midlands, DY1 4TD Tel: (01384) 453400 Fax: (01384) 453600

Class Business Systems Ltd, 77 Yew Tree Road, Ormskirk, Lancashire, L39 1RY Tel: (01695) 579988 E-mail: enquiries@classbusiness.uk.com

Combined Office System Services, PO Box 31, Hemel Hempstead, Hertfordshire, HP3 0JA Tel: (01442) 834216 Fax: (01442) 831352 E-mail: info@combinedoffice.co.uk

Comice Ltd, 12A Lower Church Street, Chepstow, Gwent, NP16 5HJ Tel: (01291) 628886 Fax: (01291) 628334 E-mail: comice@comice.co.uk

Computa Services & Consultants Ltd, 310 Broughty Ferry Road, Dundee, DD4 7NJ Tel: (01382) 450011 Fax: (01382) 450601 E-mail: admin@computa.co.uk

Computacenter Ltd, The Glover Pavillion, Aberdeen Science And Tecnology Park, Balgownie Road, Bridge Of Don, Aberdeen, AB22 8GH Tel: (01224) 825000

Computaphile Software Soltuions Ltd, 13 Surrey Close, Rugeley, Staffordshire, WS15 1JZ Tel: (01889) 579572 Fax: (01889) 579572 E-mail: brian@computaphile.com

Context Information Security Ltd, Blake House, Admirals Way, London, E14 9UJ Tel: (020) 7537 7515 Fax: (020) 7537 1071 E-mail: michael.leviseur@contextis.co.uk

Creative Computers UK Ltd, 65 West Main Street, Whitburn, Bathgate, West Lothian, EH47 0QD Tel: (01501) 742600 Fax: (01501) 742600 E-mail: sales@creativegroup.co.uk

Crombie Computer Consultants, 28 Bolney Avenue, Peacehaven, East Sussex, BN10 8NA Tel: (01273) 583304 Fax: (01273) 575312E-mail: ccc@crombies.freeserve.co.uk

CSC, Alliance House Clayton Green Business Park, Library Road, Clayton-le-Woods, Chorley, Lancashire, PR6 7EN Tel: (01772) 323555 Fax: (01772) 318000

Csm Computer Ltd, Lighthouse Farm, Main Road, Ashton, Helston, Cornwall, TR13 9SX Tel: (0845) 4561016 Fax: (0845) 4561621 E-mail: sales@csmcomputers.co.uk

CTS, 7-9 Moorland Road, Stoke-on-Trent, ST6 1DP Tel: (01782) 836194 Fax: (01782) 814818 E-mail: sales@names.co.uk

D C S Associates, 50 High Street, Kingswood, Bristol, BS15 4AJ Tel: 0117-960 3242 Fax: 0117-960 3282 E-mail: sales@dcs-imago.com

D & C TV's, 152 Holdenhurst Road, Bournemouth, BH8 8AS Tel: (01202) 318708 Fax: (01202) 380280

The Database Group Ltd, Colston Tower, Colston Street, Bristol, BS1 4UH Tel: 0117-918 3500 Fax: 0117-918 3501 E-mail: sales@databasegroup.co.uk

DDF Computer Systems, Horsham Road, Walliswood, Dorking, Surrey, RH5 5QD Tel: (01306) 627155 Fax: (01306) 627166 E-mail: info@ddf.co.uk

Digica Ltd, Phoenix House, Colliers Way, Nottingham, NG8 6AT Tel: 0115-977 1177 Fax: 0115-977 7000 E-mail: niki_torrance@digica.com

COMPUTER SERVICES CONSULTANTS/BUREAUX – *continued*

Donovan Data Systems Ltd, 7 Farm Street, London, W1J 5RX Tel: (020) 7255 7222 Fax: (020) 7255 7171 E-mail: ukinfo@dds.co.uk

D-trak Ltd, 8 Becket Way, Laverstock, Salisbury, SP1 1PZ Tel: (01722) 415144 Fax: (01722) 415143 E-mail: info@d-trak.com

Edinburgh Solutions, 6 York Place, Basement Flat 2, Edinburgh, EH1 3EP Tel: 0131-557 1001E-mail: graeme.thomas-green@virgin.net

Electronic Data Processing P.L.C., Beauchief Hall, Beauchief, Sheffield, S8 7BA Tel: 0114-262 1621 Fax: 0114-262 1126

Equinox Business Solutions Ltd, Technology House, Commerce Business Centre, West Wilts Trading Estate, Westbury, Wiltshire, BA13 4JB Tel: (01373) 825664 Fax: (01373) 859318 E-mail: enquiries@equinox-solutions.co.uk

Exportmaster Systems Ltd, 33 St Peters Street, South Croydon, Surrey, CR2 7DG Tel: (020) 8681 2321 Fax: (020) 8667 1816 E-mail: info@exportmaster.co.uk

F T Mail Solutions Ltd, Unit 36, Stephenson Road, South Hampshire Industrial Park, Totton, Southampton, SO40 3YD Tel: (023) 8066 5050 Fax: (023) 8066 5066 E-mail: sales@ftmailsolutions.co.uk

Fern Computer Services Ltd, Kennedy Enterprise Centre, Kennedy Way Industrial Estate, Belfast, BT11 9DT Tel: (028) 9080 8000 Fax: (028) 9080 8001 E-mail: sales@fern.co.uk

Foursys Ltd, 14 Science Park, Milton Road, Cambridge, CB4 0FQ Tel: (01223) 423311 Fax: (01223) 423855 E-mail: info@fourcys.co.uk

GEDYS-DISKUS, Spencer House, 91 Dewhurst Road, Birchwood, Warrington, WA3 7PG Tel: (01925) 848484 Fax: (01925) 848485 E-mail: info@gedys.co.uk

Gigabyte Computers, St. Johns Business Park, Penzance Road, Helston, Cornwall, TR13 8HN Tel: (01326) 565676 Fax: (01326) 565676

Global Exchange Services, 1-3 Station Road, Sunbury-On-Thames, Middlesex, TW16 6SU Tel: (01932) 776000 Fax: (01932) 776020

Grampian Business Bureau, 23 Carden Place, Aberdeen, AB10 1UQ Tel: (01224) 625836 Fax: (0845) 4508346 E-mail: info@gbb.co.uk

Grove Systems Ltd, 3 Ashlyn Grove, Manchester, M14 6YG Tel: 0161-224 4465 E-mail: donald@grove.demon.co.uk

Harris Systems Ltd, Ferry Works, Summer Road, Thames Ditton, Surrey, KT7 0QJ Tel: (020) 8339 1800 Fax: (020) 8390 5087

Hebbard, 18 Park Lane, Little Downham, Ely, Cambridgeshire, CB6 2TF Tel: (01353) 698338 Fax: (01353) 698995 E-mail: workshop@hebbard3d.com

Hymans Robertson, Finsbury Tower, 103-105 Bunhill Row, London, EC1Y 8LZ Tel: (020) 7847 6000 Fax: (020) 7847 6060

I C L Sorbus (UK) Ltd, Unit 9 Amelia St, London, SE17 3PY Tel: 020 77082481

Iconology Computer Consultants, Park Farm, Brabourne Lees, Ashford, Kent, TN25 6RG Tel: (01303) 813700 Fax: (01303) 813900 E-mail: info@iconology.co.uk

Insight Training, 67 Main Road, Cumbernauld, Glasgow, G67 4ED Tel: (01236) 733898 Fax: (01236) 733898

Instalec Networking Ltd, Arnhall Business Park, Westhill, Aberdeenshire, AB32 6UF Tel: (01224) 746400 Fax: (01224) 746401 E-mail: instalec@instalec.co.uk

Interlink Computer Communications, 154 Fore Street, London, N18 2XA Tel: (020) 8482 5211 Fax: (020) 8482 5224 E-mail: enquiries@interlink-computers.com

Intex Software Ltd, Diamond Court, Douglas Close, Preston Farm Industrial Estate, Stockton-on-Tees, Cleveland, TS18 3TP Tel: (01642) 672200 Fax: (01642) 671199 E-mail: sales@intex.co.uk

J R K & Co, Flat 61, Jepson Ho, Pearscroft Rd, London, SW6 2BG Tel: 020 77369012

Kam Computers Ltd, 509 Finchley Road, London, NW3 7BB Tel: (020) 7431 1223 Fax: (020) 7431 3804 E-mail: sales@kamcomputers.co.uk

Keplens Ltd, 94 Chester Road, Buckley, Clwyd, CH7 3AH Tel: (0870) 7418860 Fax: (0870) 7418861 E-mail: info@keplens.co.uk

Lailey Ltd, 25 Harewood Avenue, Bournemouth, BH7 6NJ Tel: (01202) 388840 Fax: (01202) 417748 E-mail: martinking@layley.co.uk

▶ Logic Business Systems Ltd, Logic House, Allenbrook Road, Rosehill Industrial Estate, Carlisle, CA1 2UT Tel: (01228) 527676 Fax: (01228) 515900

Logical Computers Ltd, 25 Henley Street, Stratford-upon-Avon, Warwickshire, CV37 6QW Tel: (01789) 296200 Fax: (01789) 261250 E-mail: pancho@logical-computers.co.uk

Logix Computer Service, 2 Mill Road, Harpley, King's Lynn, Norfolk, PE31 6TT Tel: (01485) 520338 Fax: (01485) 520889

Loveden Computer Services Ltd, Lovedon Beck, Casthorpe Road, Denton, Grantham, Lincolnshire, NG32 1JT Tel: (01476) 870000 E-mail: info@loveden.co.uk

Mailord Mail Order Services Ltd, 115 Park Avenue, Potters Bar, Hertfordshire, EN6 5EW Tel: (01707) 662442 Fax: (01707) 664180 E-mail: mike@mailord.co.uk

Marsworth Computing, 34 Byron Hill Road, Harrow, Middlesex, HA2 0HY Tel: (020) 8864 4842 Fax: (020) 8864 4842 E-mail: sales@marsworth.net

Metascybe Systems Ltd, 89 Hartfield Road, London, SW19 3TJ Tel: (01937) 543500 Fax: (020) 8544 0700 E-mail: info@metascybe.co.uk

Meteor, 239 Drum Road, Cookstown, County Tyrone, BT80 9HP Tel: (028) 8675 1515 Fax: (028) 8672 8961 E-mail: sales@meteorelectrical.com

Micas Solutions Ltd, Baldwin Road, Stourport-On-Severn, Worcestershire, DY13 9AX Tel: (01299) 825588 Fax: (01299) 828840 E-mail: info@micas.co.uk

Micro Focus Ltd, The Lawn, 22-30 Old Bath Road, Newbury, Berkshire, RG14 1QN Tel: (01635) 32646 Fax: (01635) 33966 E-mail: ukmarketing@microfocus.com

Micro-HELP (Scotland), 47 Parkhill Circle, Dyce, Aberdeen, AB21 7FN Tel: (01224) 773438 Fax: (01224) 773438E-mail: dwh@mh-s.co.uk

Microtech Services Ltd, 160 Westgate, Wakefield, West Yorkshire, WF2 9SR Tel: (01924) 332373 Fax: (01924) 216300 E-mail: sales@microtechservices.co.uk

N C S Group P.L.C., Belville House, Ponteland, Newcastle Upon Tyne, NE20 9BF Tel: (01661) 803000 Fax: (01661) 860069 E-mail: marketing@ncs-plc.co.uk

N Sys, Balgownie Road, Bridge of Don, Aberdeen, AB22 8GT Tel: (0845) 0559944 Fax: (0845) 0559945

Noble Computer Services, 9 Newton Road, Ipswich, IP3 8HE Tel: (01473) 424342 Fax: (01473) 424466 E-mail: info@noble-online.co.uk

Norbeck Data Ltd, Lenten House, The Gravel, Trowbridge, Wiltshire, BA14 6QL Tel: (01225) 782865 Fax: (01225) 783284

North West Office Services, Grove House, 27 Hawkin Street, Londonderry, BT48 6RE Tel: (028) 7126 1271 Fax: (028) 7126 5284

Northern Computer Markets, Tara House, Grains Road, Shaw, Oldham, OL2 8JB Tel: (01706) 299902 Fax: (01706) 840444 E-mail: sales@computermarkets.co.uk

Offtek Ltd, Claremont House Broad Lane, Tanworth-in-Arden, Solihull, West Midlands, B94 5DY Tel: (01564) 742064 Fax: (01564) 743087 E-mail: sales@offtek.co.uk

Opal Services, 24 Aldershot Road, Fleet, Hampshire, GU51 3NN Tel: (01252) 812607 Fax: (01252) 812625

Open International Ltd, Buckholt Drive, Warndon, Worcester, WR4 9SR Tel: (01905) 754455 Fax: (01905) 754441

Oryx X L Ltd, XL House, Woodburn Road, Blackburn, Aberdeen, AB21 0PS Tel: (01224) 798400 Fax: (01224) 798401 E-mail: admin@xlg.co.uk

P C Services, 4-5 Cottesbrooke Park, Heartlands Business Park, Daventry, Northamptonshire, NN11 8YL Tel: (01327) 312222 Fax: (01327) 301633 E-mail: email@pcservices.co.uk

P T Services Co Ltd, Unit 2, Priory Ct, 71 St. Leonards Rd, Norwich, NR1 4JW Tel: (01603) 762233 Fax: (01603) 664098

Penny Lane Computers Ltd, 243 Dales Road, Ipswich, IP1 4JY Tel: (01473) 255955 Fax: (01473) 255900 E-mail: tech@pennylane.co.uk

Phil Partners Micro Help, 8 Bleak Hill Way, Mansfield, Nottinghamshire, NG18 5EZ Tel: (01623) 651444 Fax: (01623) 633661 E-mail: philj@microhelpuk.net

Press Start Ltd, 9 Wragg Drive, Newmarket, Suffolk, CB8 7SD Tel: (01638) 608046 Fax: (01638) 603203 E-mail: sales@pressstart.co.uk

Prism Data Management Ltd, Colombia House, 1 Apollo Rise, Farnborough, Hampshire, GU14 0GT Tel: (01252) 556900 Fax: (01252) 556911

Prolog Systems Ltd, Century House, Station Way, Sutton, Surrey, SM3 8SW Tel: (020) 8715 1555 Fax: (020) 8715 1556 E-mail: sales@prologsystems.com

Prologic Computer Consultants Ltd, Redwood House, Rectory Lane, Berkhamsted, Hertfordshire, HP4 2DH Tel: (01442) 876277 Fax: (01442) 877245E-mail: info@prologic.net

Pugh Computers Ltd, Denver House, Llanon, Dyfed, SY23 5LP Tel: (01974) 200200 Fax: (01974) 202628 E-mail: sales@pugh.co.uk

Pythagoras Communications Ltd, Clivemont Road, Maidenhead, Berkshire, SL6 7BZ Tel: (01628) 590700 Fax: (01628) 590717

▶ Quality Financial Software Ltd, 3ND Floor, George Street House, George Street, Macclesfield, Cheshire, SK11 6HU Tel: (01625) 443210 Fax: (01625) 443219 E-mail: info@qfsl.co.uk

Quarrymead Ltd, 6 Foxes Pde, Sewardstone Rd, Waltham Abbey, Essex, EN9 1PH Tel: (01992) 712233 Fax: (01992) 650933

R O C C Computers Ltd, Stanford Gate, South Road, Brighton, BN1 6SB Tel: (01273) 274700 Fax: (01273) 274707 E-mail: marketing@rocc.co.uk

Reed Microsonix, 7a Station Road, Hednesford, Cannock, Staffordshire, WS12 4DH Tel: (01543) 426174 Fax: 01543 277211

Regency Computers, 67 Whitchurch Road, Shrewsbury, SY1 4EE Tel: (01743) 461829 Fax: (01743) 460880 E-mail: sales@regencycomputers.com

Rhw Computers, 22 Cow Wynd, Falkirk, FK1 1PU Tel: 01324 635761

Rockport Software Ltd, 551 Fairlie Road, Slough, SL1 4PY Tel: (01753) 577201 Fax: (01753) 577202 E-mail: info@rockportsoft.com

Rolfe & Nolan Systems Ltd, Lowndes House, 1-9 City Road, London, EC1Y 1AE Tel: (020) 7374 4841 Fax: (020) 7374 0732

Rosswood Studios Ltd, 114 Wendover Road, Stoke Mandeville, Aylesbury, Buckinghamshire, HP22 5TE Tel: (01296) 612009 E-mail: marianne@rosswood.co.uk

S B I Computers, 201-203 Park Lane, Kidderminster, Worcestershire, DY11 6TQ Tel: (01562) 829677 Fax: (01562) 862841 E-mail: sales@sbi-uk.net

S P S S Ltd, 65 Maygrove Road, London, NW6 2SP Tel: (020) 7625 7222 Fax: (020) 7624 5297

Sacrosanct Technology Ltd, 3 Sambourn Close, Solihull, West Midlands, B91 2SA Tel: 0121-711 2100 E-mail: robthomas@sacrosanct.co.uk

Servicecare UK, 551 Warwick Road, Tyseley, Birmingham, B11 2EX Tel: 0121-707 6011 Fax: 0121-707 6011

Snai International Ltd, 5 Berners Rd, London, N1 0PW Tel: 020 73541991 Fax: 020 73542474

Softlink Solutions Ltd, 417 Baddow Road, Chelmsford, CM2 7QL Tel: (01245) 475669 Fax: (01245) 473993 E-mail: info@softlinksolutions.co.uk

Solar Soft PMS Ltd, Hampshire Int Business Park, Crockford Lane, Chineham, Basingstoke, Hampshire, RG24 8WH Tel: (01256) 685200 Fax: (01256) 685201 E-mail: sales@ssi-world.com

Speech Centre, Croft Road, Crowborough, East Sussex, TN6 1DL Tel: (01892) 661116 Fax: (01892) 668177 E-mail: info@speechcentre.co.uk

Sphinx C S T, Woodside House, Osier Drive, Annesley, Nottingham, NG15 0DS Tel: (01623) 726282 Fax: (01623) 726292 E-mail: sales@sphinx.co.uk

Springwater Software Ltd, 101 Park St, Luton, LU1 3HG Tel: 01582 483399

Sprint Systems, Unit 8 Bath Road Business Centre, Bath Road, Devizes, Wiltshire, SN10 1XA Tel: (01380) 729365 Fax: (01380) 729616

Strand Technology Group, 10-12 Westgate, Skelmersdale, Lancashire, WN8 8AZ Tel: (0845) 6607968 E-mail: mail@standtech.co.uk

Sweet Valley Solutions Ltd, East Lodge House, 116 High Street, Cranleigh, Surrey, GU6 8AJ Tel: (01483) 273838 Fax: (01483) 275983 E-mail: sales@sweetvalley.co.uk

Syscom Group Ltd, Hampshire House, High Street, Kingswinford, West Midlands, DY6 8AW Tel: (01384) 400600 Fax: (01384) 400601 E-mail: info@syscom.plc.uk

System Solutions, P O Box 3768, Bracknell, Berks, RG42 7YL Tel: 01344890008 Fax: 01344 890009 E-mail: sales@system-solutions.co.uk

T A L Computer Services Ltd, 1 Egham Business Village, Crabtree Road, Egham, Surrey, TW20 8RB Tel: (01784) 434350 Fax: (01784) 470599 E-mail: talcs@talcs.co.uk

▶ Taskforce Software Ltd, 158 Sturminster Road, Bristol, BS14 8AT Tel: (01458) 835097 E-mail: info@taskforce-software.co.uk

TCS Computer Services Ltd, The Brewhouse 19 Old Bexley Business Park, Bourne Road, Bexley, Kent, DA5 1LR Tel: (01322) 559840 Fax: (01322) 550010 E-mail: rodney.gent@tcscs.co.uk

Technology Helpdesk, Unit 3, Turnbull Way, Livingston, West Lothian, EH54 8RB Tel: (01506) 436700 Fax: (01506) 436703 E-mail: sales@technologyhelpdesk.co.uk

Tectrade Computers Ltd, Unit A1, Godalming Business Centre, Godalming, Surrey, GU7 1XW Tel: (01483) 521910 Fax: (01483) 861449 E-mail: sales@tectrade.co.uk

Torex Retail, Manor Farm Courtyard, 57-61 Main Street, Frolesworth, Lutterworth, Leicestershire, LE17 5EE Tel: (01455) 202727 Fax: (01455) 202728 E-mail: info@torexretail.com

Total Computers & Accessories Ltd, Westfield House, Bratton Road, Westbury, Wiltshire, BA13 3EP Tel: (01373) 864627 Fax: (01373) 824952 E-mail: sales@tcaonline.co.uk

Total Computing, 1a Sterling Industrial Estate, Kings Road, Newbury, Berkshire, RG14 5RQ Tel: (01635) 523860 Fax: (01635) 524860

Typex Group, Newcastle House, Albany Court, Newcastle Business Park, Newcastle Upon Tyne, NE4 7YB Tel: 0191-256 4400 Fax: 0191-226 0252 E-mail: info@typex.com

U C M S, Brook Road, Wimborne, Dorset, BH21 2BJ Tel: (01202) 840111 Fax: (01202) 840204

Wallingford Computing Services Ltd, 142 Wantage Road, Wallingford, Oxfordshire, OX10 0LU Tel: (01491) 835959 Fax: (01491) 838071 E-mail: barry.harris@btconnect.com

Warnes Mail Marketing Ltd, 577 Kingston Road, London, SW20 8YA Tel: (020) 8687 3800 Fax: (020) 8545 2701 E-mail: sales@warnes.co.uk

Waterstar, Chester House, Westgate, Bishop Auckland, County Durham, DL13 1PG Tel: (01388) 517513 E-mail: john.mccutheon@waterstar.co.uk

COMPUTER SOFTWARE, *See also headings for particular types*

1spatial Group Ltd, Unit 6 Cambridge Business Park, Cowley Road, Cambridge, CB4 0WZ Tel: (01223) 420414 Fax: (01223) 420044 E-mail: info@1spatial.com

▶ 1st Computer Systems, 539 Moseley Road, Birmingham, B12 9BU Tel: 0121-446 4646

4th Hospitality Ltd, Unit 3 Des Roches Square, Witney, Oxfordshire, OX28 4LQ Tel: (01993) 899200 Fax: (01993) 775081 E-mail: info@abs-ltd.com

▶ A L K Technologies Ltd, 4 Bloomsbury Square, London, WC1A 2RP Tel: (020) 7404 4222 Fax: (020) 7404 7778

A & O Consultancy Ltd, 92A The Maltings, Roydon Road, Stanstead Abbotts, Ware, Hertfordshire, SG12 8UU Tel: (01920) 872321 E-mail:

▶ A P Computing, Unit 2, Bentinck Street, Birkenhead, Merseyside, CH41 4DY Tel: 0151-647 6789

Abacus Software Ltd, 6-14 Underwood Street, London, N1 7JQ Tel: (020) 7549 2500 Fax: (020) 7549 2501 E-mail: info@abacusemedia.com

Above Average Computers, 21 William Avenue, Blythe Bridge, Stoke-on-Trent, ST3 6HN Tel: (07909) 547211 E-mail: info@aacomps.co.uk

Access Unlimited, 20 George Street, Alderley Edge, Cheshire, SK9 7EJ Tel: (01625) 584130 Fax: (01625) 584623 E-mail: info@accessunlimited.co.uk

Accord Computer Systems Ltd, 7-9 Union Street, Stratford-upon-Avon, Warwickshire, CV37 6QT Tel: (01789) 415541 Fax: (01789) 414410 E-mail: info@accordltd.co.uk

▶ Accounting Technology Ltd, Europe House, 10 Bancroft Road, Reigate, Surrey, RH2 7RP Tel: (01737) 222261 Fax: (01737) 225585

Active Software Solutions Ltd, Jaywick Enterprise Centre, Lotus Way, Clacton-on-Sea, Essex, CO15 2LU Tel: (01255) 688286 Fax: (01255) 436205

Adapt Technology Ltd, 11a Green Lane, London, NW4 2NL Tel: (020) 8203 2222 Fax: (020) 8203 2259E-mail: info@adapt-technology.com

Added Value Software, 2-4 York Road, Felixstowe, Suffolk, IP11 7HX Tel: (01394) 286828 Fax: (0870) 0941003 E-mail: angus@a-v-s.co.uk

Adept Scientific plc, Amor Way, Letchworth Garden City, Hertfordshire, SG6 1ZA Tel: (01462) 480055 Fax: (01462) 480213 E-mail: info@adeptscience.co.uk

▶ Adroit Technologies Ltd, PO Box 19, Nantwich, Cheshire, CW5 6FF Tel: (01270) 627072 Fax: (01270) 629399 E-mail: sales@adroit-europe.com

Advance, 3 Wootton Road, King's Lynn, Norfolk, PE30 4EZ Tel: (01553) 691587

Advanced Manufacturing Management, Wentworth House, 3 Lichfield Road, Burntwood, Staffordshire, WS7 0HQ Tel: (01543) 677635 Fax: (0870) 0547750

▶ Advanced Ticket Systems Ltd, 10 Barley Mow Passage, London, W4 4PH Tel: (0870) 3506071

▶ AEYE, 1 Glencairn House, 70 Ridgway, London, London, SW19 4RA Tel: (020) 8879 9832 Fax: (020) 9212 9079 E-mail: info@aeye.biz

Aim, 20 Coales Gardens, Market Harborough, Leicestershire, LE16 7NY Tel: (01858) 434177 Fax: (01858) 466699

Airops Ltd, Fairoaks Airport, Chobham, Woking, Surrey, GU24 8HU Tel: (0870) 7655100 Fax: (01276) 858485

Akwil Projects Ltd, 493-495 Chester Road, Manchester, M16 9HF Tel: 0161-872 7337 Fax: (08712) 205338E-mail: sales@akwil.com

Alaric Systems Ltd, 22-24 Devonshire Street, Keighley, West Yorkshire, BD21 2AU Tel: (01535) 680000 Fax: (01535) 610223 E-mail: sales@alaric.co.uk

▶ Aldex Software Ltd, 6 High Street, Sutton, Ely, Cambridgeshire, CB6 2RB Tel: (01353) 778012 Fax: (01353) 776055 E-mail: devlabs@aldex.co.uk

▶ All Digital, Rear of, 198 Howard Road, Sheffield, S6 3RX Tel: 0114-231 5050

▶ Alligator Business Solutions, 17 Whinhill Road, Glasgow, G53 5RQ Tel: 0141-882 5678 Fax: 0141-882 1443 E-mail: enquiries@alligatorsolutions.com

Allpower 2 Computers, West Bergholt, Colchester, CO6 3WB Tel: (01206) 247094 Fax: (01206) 247094 E-mail: softwaresales@allpower2computers.co.uk

▶ Alpha Business Systems Ltd, Chorley Business & Technology Centre, Euxton Lane, Euxton, Chorley, Lancashire, PR7 6TE Tel: (01257) 249017 Fax: (08700) 517171 E-mail: info@alphasys.co.uk

American Software (UK) Ltd, St Georges Business Park, Brooklands Road, Weybridge, Surrey, KT13 0TS Tel: (01932) 855554 Fax: (01932) 854563 E-mail: sales@amsoftware.com

Amonite Ltd, 7b King St, Belper, Derbyshire, DE56 1PW Tel: (01773) 822211 E-mail: sales@amonite.com

▶ Angove Associates, 5 Marsh Grove Road, Huddersfield, HD3 3AQ Tel: 01484 539229 Fax: 01484 539229 E-mail: info@angoveassociates.co.uk

Apex Software, 11 Broadway, Knaphill, Woking, Surrey, GU21 2DR Tel: (01483) 797700 Fax: (01483) 797960

▶ Applestorm Ltd, Unit 3, Homefarm, Luton Hoo Estate, Luton, LU1 3TD Tel: (0800) 5655565 Fax: (0870) 4670447 E-mail: sales@applestorm.com

Application Specific Computers Ltd, Chapel Lane, Emley, Huddersfield, HD8 9ST Tel: (01924) 844600 Fax: (01924) 844606

COMPUTER SOFTWARE – *continued*

▶ Arxcis Europe Ltd, Palmerston House, Palmerston Road, Barry, South Glamorgan, CF63 2YZ Tel: (01446) 744381 Fax: (01446) 744381

Aspentech Ltd, Birkdale House, Kelvin Close, Warrington, WA3 7RB Tel: (01925) 844400 Fax: (01925) 844455

Associated Consultants Ltd, The Old Mill, Ewenny, Bridgend, Mid Glamorgan, CF35 5BN Tel: (01656) 768916 Fax: (01656) 662007

Atex Ltd, Wilsthorpe Road, Long Eaton, Nottingham, NG10 3LL Tel: 0115-973 5900 Fax: 0115-973 6605

Autodesk Ltd, 1 Meadow Gate Avenue, Farnborough Business Park, Farnborough, Hampshire, GU14 6FG Tel: (01252) 456600 Fax: (01252) 456601

Automaster UK Ltd, Centaur House, Ancells Road, Fleet, Hampshire, GU51 2UJ Tel: (0845) 4666070 Fax: (0845) 4666080 E-mail: info@automaster.ltd.uk

▶ Avansys UK Ltd, Business & Technology Centre, Radway Green, Crewe, CW2 5PR Tel: (01270) 878555 Fax: (0870) 2010600

Avis Software Consultants, 22 Balmoral Way, Sutton, Surrey, SM2 6PD Tel: (020) 8643 6899 Fax: (020) 8642 6005 E-mail: info@avissoft.co.uk

Avisoft Ltd, 11 Church Street, Kirkby In Ashfield, Nottingham, NG17 8LA Tel: (01623) 755555 E-mail: sales@avisoft.co.uk

▶ Axzona Ltd, 36 Dean Park Mews, Edinburgh, EH4 1ED Tel: 0131-315 0181 Fax: 0131-315 0185

Aztec Computing, Monument House, Marsh Road, Pinner, Middlesex, HA5 5NE Tel: (020) 8866 5577 E-mail: info@azteccomputing.com

B S A Prophet Systems Ltd, 3 Church Street, Leamington Spa, Warwickshire, CV31 1EG Tel: (01926) 430023 Fax: (01926) 431010 E-mail: sales@hccm.co.uk

B W C L, B W C L House, Brook Farm Estate, Kimbolton, Leominster, Herefordshire, HR6 0ES Tel: (01568) 750365 Fax: (01568) 750369 E-mail: admin@bwcl.co.uk

Banks Software Ltd, 74 Forest Road, Oldbury, West Midlands, B68 0EF Tel: 0121-421 8295 E-mail: sales@banks-software.co.uk

▶ Bde Group, Blackpole Trading Estate West, Worcester, WR3 8ZP Tel: (0870) 1287800 Fax: (01905) 756574 E-mail: sales@bdegroup.co.uk

Belair Software, Unit 16 Orchard Road Industrial Estate, Strabane, County Tyrone, BT82 9FR Tel: (07710) 344940 Fax: (028) 7138 3792

Big Red Computers P.L.C., 84 Aldermans Hill, London, N13 4PP Tel: (0870) 0711117 Fax: (0870) 0733337

▶ Bits & P C's Bognor Regis, 92 Highfield Road, Bognor Regis, West Sussex, PO22 8PH Tel: (01243) 849001 Fax: (01243) 849001 E-mail: sales@computerandy.co.uk

▶ Bits & PC's, High Cross Street, St. Austell, Cornwall, PL25 4AB Tel: (01726) 76999

▶ Blue Bell Computers, 14 Chalfont Walk, Norwich, NR4 7NH Tel: (01603) 507777 Fax: (01603) 507701 E-mail: sales@bluebellcomputers.co.uk

Bluespier International Ltd, Wood End House, Grafton Flyford, Worcester, WR7 4PH Tel: (01905) 391120 Fax: (01905) 391121 E-mail: susan.williams@bluespier.com

Bond International, Unit 10 Coped Hall Business Park, Wootton Bassett, Swindon, SN4 8DP Tel: (01793) 856300 Fax: (01793) 856301 E-mail: helpdesk@infosupport.co.uk

Boulevard Business Partnership Ltd, Island Farm, Black Lane, Nateby, Preston, PR3 0LH Tel: (0845) 4560050 Fax: (01995) 606045

▶ Breeze Media Ltd, Gleann Cottage, 1 The Terrace, Glenlomond, Kinross, KY13 9HF Tel: (01592) 840640 E-mail: info@breezemedia.co.uk

▶ Bridgehead Software Ltd, 215 Barnett Wood Lane, Ashtead, Surrey, KT21 2DD Tel: (01372) 221950 Fax: (01372) 221977 E-mail: bridgehead@bridgeheadsoftware.com

▶ Bristol Mac Centre, 233 Gloucester Road, Bishopston, Bristol, BS7 8NR Tel: (0800) 0714417

▶ Broseley Computers, 6 Instones Building, The Square, Broseley, Shropshire, TF12 5EW Tel: (01952) 884682

Bruhn Newtech Ltd, The Portway Centre, 1 Old Sarum Park, Old Sarum, Salisbury, SP4 6EB Tel: (01722) 417000 Fax: (01722) 417014 E-mail: info@bruhn-newtech.co.uk

Business Management Software Ltd, Old Music School, West Street, Oundle, Peterborough, PE8 4EJ Tel: (01832) 275004 Fax: (01832) 275006 E-mail: enquiries@bms.uk.com

▶ Business Systems UK Ltd, 462 London Road, Isleworth, Middlesex, TW7 4ED Tel: (020) 8326 8200 Fax: (020) 8326 8400 E-mail: sales@businesssystemsuk.com

▶ Byteback Computers Ltd, 69 Princess Avenue, Stainforth, Doncaster, South Yorkshire, DN7 5RA Tel: (01302) 846555 E-mail: enquiries@bytebackcomputers.net

C C L Software Ltd, Battenhall Lodge, 60 Battenhall Road, Worcester, WR5 2BX Tel: (0800) 0199853 Fax: (0845) 4900201 E-mail: nick@ccl-uk.com

▶ C C M A Services, Chappell, High Peak, Derbyshire, SK23 9HF Tel: (0870) 7559700 Fax: (0870) 7559707

C M A Solutions Ltd, Fleet Mill, Minley Road, Fleet, Hampshire, GU51 2RD Tel: (01252) 861500 Fax: (01252) 861550 E-mail: cma@cma-sol.co.uk

C P L Ltd, Liverpool House, Penlan Street, Pwllheli, Gwynedd, LL53 5DE Tel: (01758) 613035 Fax: (01758) 612485 E-mail: cplltd@compuserve.com

C P S, Drury Lane, St. Leonards-on-Sea, East Sussex, TN38 9BA Tel: (01424) 442663 Fax: (01424) 433835

C S S P, 29 London Road, Bromley, BR1 1DG Tel: (020) 8460 0022 Fax: (020) 8460 1196

▶ C Software, Tayside Software Centre, Dundee Technology Park, Dundee, DD2 1TY Tel: (01382) 598450 Fax: (01382) 598449

Cabsoft Ltd, Orwell House, Cowley Road, Cambridge, CB4 0PP Tel: (01223) 470022 Fax: (01223) 470023

Cambrian Software UK Ltd, 26 Lombard Street, Porthmadog, Gwynedd, LL49 9AP Tel: (01766) 514969

▶ Cambridge Computers, The Boiler House, Botley Mills Botley, Southampton, SO30 2GB Tel: (01489) 799955 E-mail: info@cambridgeci.com

Cambridge IT Solutions Ltd, May Ho, 4 Sheepcoat Clo, Shenley Church End, Milton Keynes, MK5 6JL Tel: (01908) 506888 Fax: (01908) 507088

Care Data Systems Ltd, Patrick House Lakeside, Lifford Lane, Birmingham, B30 3NU Tel: 0121-458 7887 Fax: 0121-451 2166

Carval Computing Ltd, Innovation & Technology Transfer Centre, Tamar Science Park, Plymouth, PL6 8BX Tel: (01752) 764290 Fax: (01752) 764291 E-mail: mail@carval.co.uk

▶ Catalan IS Services Ltd, Glenbervie Business Centre, Larbert, Stirlingshire, FK5 4RB Tel: (01324) 682150 Fax: 01324 682149

Cavalier Software, 1 Bryn Tirion, Nebo Road, Llanrwst, Gwynedd, LL26 0HL Tel: (01492) 641548

Centresoft Ltd, 6 Pavilion Drive, Holford, Birmingham, B6 7BB Tel: 0121-625 3399 Fax: 0121-625 3236 E-mail: sales@centresoft.co.uk

CEX Ltd, 143 Whitfield Street, London, W1T 5EP Tel: (020) 7916 8422 Fax: (020) 7916 8434

Chess Logistics Technology, Commerce Way, Trafford Park, Manchester, M17 1HW Tel: 0161-888 2580 Fax: 0161-888 2590 E-mail: info@chess.uk.com

Chorus Application Software Ltd, Devonshire House, Riverside Road, Pottington Business Park, Barnstaple, Devon, EX31 1SW Tel: (01271) 346738 Fax: (01271) 379250

Civica Financial Systems Ltd, Plain Tree Crescent, Feltham, Middlesex, TW13 7DT Tel: (020) 8844 2141 Fax: (020) 8751 4386 E-mail: enquiries@civica.co.uk

▶ Cladswell House Systems Ltd, The Old Fishery, Holborrow Lodge, Holberrow Green, Redditch, Worcestershire, B96 6SF Tel: (01386) 793377 Fax: (01386) 793376 E-mail: sales@chs.eu.com

▶ Cleaford Services Ltd, 46 Hazell Road, Farnham, Surrey, GU9 7BP Tel: (01252) 717166 Fax: (01252) 717137 E-mail: sales@cleaford.co.uk

Harold Cloutt Associates Ltd, PO Box 87, Battle, East Sussex, TN33 9XR Tel: (01424) 838829 Fax: (0870) 1365618 E-mail: cloutt.hr@bcs.org.uk

Code Computing, Global House, Berry Hill, Berry Hill Industrial Estate, Droitwich, Worcestershire, WR9 9AB Tel: (01905) 775566 Fax: (01905) 621676

▶ Coffeenetonline, 118 High Street, Bloxwich, Walsall, WS3 2DG Tel: (01922) 409007

▶ Complex Online, Rear of, 130 Handsworth Road, Sheffield, S9 4AE Tel: 0114-256 1010 Fax: 0114-256 1010 E-mail: sales@complexonline.co.uk

▶ Component Solution, 3 Lyme Drive, Parklands, Stoke-on-Trent, ST4 6NW Tel: (01782) 610211 Fax: (01782) 715316

Compurange Ltd, 337 Derby Street, Bolton, BL3 6LR Tel: (01204) 651212 Fax: (01204) 658060 E-mail: info@compurange.co.uk

▶ Computec UK Ltd, 28A Bath Road, Swindon, SN1 4BA Tel: (01793) 420333 Fax: (01793) 541911

Computer Associates Ltd, First Floor, Lynnfield House, Church St, Altrincham, Cheshire, WA14 4DZ Tel: 0161-928 9334 Fax: 0161-929 0292 E-mail: sales@cai.com

Computer Chaos, 1 Brookfield Dirve, Cannock, Staffordshire, WS11 0JN Tel: (01543) 578579 Fax: (01543) 571218

▶ Computer Future, Training at 2nd Floor , St Clare House, St Clare House, 30-33 The Minories, London, EC3N 1DD Tel: (020) 7798 5648 E-mail: sarah@computerfuture.net

Computer Hotline, 7 Blossom Waye, Hounslow, TW5 9HB Tel: (020) 8570 8275 Fax: (020) 8570 1152

The Computer Shop, 8 South Mall, Frenchgate Centre, Doncaster, South Yorkshire, DN1 1TT Tel: (01302) 326111 Fax: (01302) 326222

Computer Software Group, Pepper House, Market Street, Nantwich, Cheshire, CW5 5DQ Tel: (01270) 613800 Fax: (01270) 613801 E-mail: info@computersoftware.com

▶ Computer Surplus, 106 Walcot Street, Bath, BA1 5BG Tel: (01225) 470077 Fax: (01225) 471166

Computer Time Ltd, 363 Lugtrout Lane, Catherine-de-Barnes, Solihull, West Midlands, B91 2TN Tel: 0121-711 4006 Fax: 0121-711 2373

Computerlinks, Suffolk House, Newmarket, Suffolk, CB8 7AN Tel: (01638) 569600 Fax: (01638) 569601 E-mail: info@computerlinks.co.uk

Computers In Personnel Ltd, Abbey House, 28-30 Chapel Street, Marlow, Buckinghamshire, SL7 1DD Tel: (01628) 814000 Fax: (0870) 3662346 E-mail: sales@ciphr.com

Computing Needs Ltd, 9-11 Manor Road, Felixstowe, Suffolk, IP11 2EJ Tel: (01394) 278067 Fax: (01394) 458140 E-mail: sales@computingneeds.co.uk

▶ Com-Tek, 46 Welsh Row, Nantwich, Cheshire, CW5 5EJ Tel: (01270) 624300 Fax: (01270) 624300

Concept Computers, 390 High Street, Winsford, Cheshire, CW7 2DP

Construction Computer Software Ltd, Wester Kerse, Lochwinnoch, Renfrewshire, PA12 4DU Tel: (01505) 506118 Fax: (01505) 506117 E-mail: info@ccsuk.com

▶ ControlLoop, 14 St. Davids, Newtongrange, Midlothian, EH22 4LG Tel: (0131) 4540499

Convergent Development Ltd, Wortham, Lewdown, Okehampton, Devon, EX20 4QJ Tel: (01837) 871544 Fax: (01837) 871558

Cordingley Barnes Ltd, 5 The Courtyard, Hall Lane, Haughton, Tarporley, Cheshire, CW6 9RJ Tel: (01829) 260029 Fax: (01829) 261209 E-mail: karen@cordingleybarnes.com

Core UK Ltd, Cellphone House, North Circular Road, London, NW10 7SH Tel: (020) 8961 9990 Fax: (020) 8961 4371 E-mail: info@core-business.com

▶ Cornerstone Computer Centre, 15 The Arcade, Bognor Regis, West Sussex, PO21 1LH Tel: (01243) 820082

Corrin Software Products Ltd, SATRA Innovation Park, Rockingham Road, Kettering, Northamptonshire, NN16 9JH Tel: (01536) 414633 Fax: (01536) 414655

▶ CRE8 Computer Systems, Unit K Chadwell Heath Industrial Park, Kemp Road, Dagenham, Essex, RM8 1SL Tel: (020) 8597 4400 Fax: (020) 8597 4400

Creative Computing Solutions Ltd, Bishops Gate, Station Road, Taplow, Maidenhead, Berkshire, SL6 0PA Tel: (01628) 660600 Fax: (01628) 605434 E-mail: sales@creative-computing.co.uk

▶ Crest Technology, 5 East Glebe, Stonehaven, Kincardineshire, AB39 2HW Tel: (01569) 766662 Fax: (07876) 881265 E-mail: info@crest2000.com

Csc Computer Sciences Ltd, Sovereign House, Vision Park Chivers Way, Histon, Cambridge, CB4 9BY Tel: (01223) 547000 Fax: (01223) 547158

Cyberscience Corporation Ltd, Rawdon House, High Street, Hoddesdon, Hertfordshire, EN11 8BD Tel: (01992) 441111 Fax: (01992) 442740 E-mail: info@cyberscience.com

D R C Computer Services, 66 Snipe Street, Ellon, Aberdeenshire, AB41 9FW Tel: (01358) 722007 Fax: (01358) 721628 E-mail: info@drc-ellon.co.uk

D S Callards Ltd, 2 Station Yard, Ashburton, Newton Abbot, Devon, TQ13 7EF Tel: (01364) 654222 Fax: (01364) 652288 E-mail: ray.kemp@developersolutions.co.uk

Dart Computers (Wales) Ltd, 26B Wellington Road, Rhyl, Clwyd, LL18 1BN Tel: (01745) 330128 Fax: (01745) 330128 E-mail: emquiries@dart-computers.com

Dash Associates, 50 Binswood Avenue, Leamington Spa, Warwickshire, CV32 5RX Tel: (01926) 315862 Fax: (01926) 315854 E-mail: sales@dashoptimization.com

Data Development Services Ltd, Blythe Valley Innovation Centr, Central Boulevard, Blythe Valley Park, Solihull, West Midlands, B90 8AJ Tel: 0121-506 9310

Data Discovery Solutions LRD, 2 Venture Road, Chilworth, Southampton, SO16 7NP Tel: (023) 8076 7678 Fax: (023) 8076 7665 E-mail: sales@activenavigation.com

Dataflair Systems Ltd, PO Box 271, Fleet, Hampshire, GU51 3FD Tel: (01252) 812221 Fax: (01252) 819337

Datag Ltd, Holly Farm, Somerford Booths, Congleton, Cheshire, CW12 2JX Tel: (01260) 224794 Fax: (01260) 224794 E-mail: enquiries@datag.co.uk

Datamaster Training Services Ltd, Unit 4 Crescent Court, 51 High Street, Billericay, Essex, CM12 9AQ Tel: (01277) 624007 Fax: (01277) 630044 E-mail: enquiries@datamaster.uk.com

Datastart (Wales) Ltd, Unit 1 Dolphin Court, Brunel Quay, Neyland, Milford Haven, Dyfed, SA73 1PY Tel: (01646) 602770 Fax: (01646) 602721

Dealer Systems, 11 Market Hill, Southam, Warwickshire, CV47 0HF Tel: (01926) 815792 Fax: (01926) 813395

Deepdale Technical Services Ltd, 33A Scalbie Road, Scarborough, North Yorkshire, YO12 5PZ Tel: (0870) 2201486 Fax: (01723) 377571 E-mail: info@deepdale.co.uk

Dental Channel Ltd, 128 Woodward Road, London, SE22 8UT Tel: (020) 8299 9742 Fax: (020) 8399 4554

▶ Dev-Soft Ltd, 125 Thomas Street, Abertridwr, Caerphilly, Mid Glamorgan, CF83 4AY Tel: (029) 20 830339 E-mail: enquiries@dev-soft.co.uk

▶ Diamond Computers Ltd, 36 New England Road, Brighton, BN1 4GG Tel: (01273) 625032 Fax: (01273) 711504

Diamond People Ltd, The Chestnuts, Munderfield, Bromyard, Herefordshire, HR7 4JT Tel: (01885) 490480 Fax: (01885) 490484 E-mail: enquiries@diamondpeople.co.uk

Diamond Point International, Unit 9 North Point Business Estate, Enterprise Close, Medway City Estate, Rochester, Kent, ME2 4LX Tel: (01634) 722390 Fax: (01634) 722398 E-mail: sales@dpie.com

Diamond Software Ltd, Ryecroft Hall, Manchester Road, Audenshaw, Manchester, M34 5ZJ Tel: 0161-301 3888 Fax: 0161-371 7337 E-mail: info@diamondsoftware.co.uk

Digita International Ltd, Liverton Business Park, Exmouth, Devon, EX8 2NR Tel: (01395) 270273 Fax: (01395) 268893 E-mail: info@digita.com

▶ Digitalzone UK Ltd, 28 William Street, Ystrad, Pentre, Mid Glamorgan, CF41 7QR Tel: (01443) 422322 Fax: (01443) 422327 E-mail: sales@digitalzone.co.uk

Diversified Software Systems Europe Ltd, Unit 110, Wharfedale Road, Winnersh, Wokingham, Berkshire, RG41 5RB Tel: 0118-944 4000 Fax: 0118-944 4030 E-mail: elisabeth.hager@diversifiedsoftware.com

DPR Services, 171 Ranworth Avenue, Hoddesdon, Hertfordshire, EN11 9NU Tel: (01992) 470654 Fax: (0871) 6613985 E-mail: info@dprservices.co.uk

▶ Drivebuddy Ltd, Unit 3, Waterhouse Mill, Albert Street, Huddersfield, HD1 3PR Tel: (0870) 1657218 Fax: (0870) 0117748

▶ E Net Europe, Heathrow Boulevard, Bath Road, Sipson, West Drayton, Middlesex, UB7 0DQ Tel: (020) 8754 7894 Fax: (020) 8754 0862

▶ East Neuk Technology, 21 Rodger Street, Anstruther, Fife, KY10 3DU Tel: (01333) 313300 Fax: (01333) 313067

▶ Easy PC, 2 Margaret Road, Whitley Bay, Tyne & Wear, NE26 2PQ Tel: 0191-252 4534 Fax: 0191-252 4534

▶ Ecatenate, 37 Otago Street, Top Floor, Glasgow, G12 8JJ Tel: 0141-334 6043 Fax: 0141-334 6044

▶ Elcosystems Computer Systems, Unit 54 Imex Business Centre, Shobnall Road, Burton-on-Trent, Staffordshire, DE14 2AU Tel: (01283) 544582 Fax: (01283) 544582 E-mail: dh@elcocad.com

▶ Electronic Business Services Ltd, Cavalry Park, Peebles, EH45 9BU Tel: (01721) 724881 Fax: (01721) 724882 E-mail: info@ebs-europe.com

Electronics Boutique, 6 Castle La, Belfast, BT1 5DA Tel: (028) 9024 8386 Fax: (028) 9024 7545

▶ Enableit Technologies Ltd, Foxwood House, Dobbs Lane, Kesgrave, Ipswich, IP5 2QQ Tel: (01473) 618980 Fax: (01473) 618989 E-mail: david@e-nableit.com

▶ Entec Computer Systems, Ic2 Building Keele University, Science Park, Keele, Newcastle, Staffordshire, ST5 5NH Tel: (01782) 740900 Fax: (01782) 740600

Enterprise Software Systems, Enterprise House, Atlantic Street, Broadheath, Altrincham, Cheshire, WA14 5EN Tel: 0161-925 2400 Fax: 0161-925 2401 E-mail: sales@essl.co.uk

▶ Entire Computers, Riverside Avenue East, Lawford, Manningtree, Essex, CO11 1US Tel: (01206) 396413 Fax: (01206) 396413

Environmental Services Design, Inglewood House, Unit 8a, Inglewood, Alloa, Clackmannanshire, FK10 2HU Tel: (01259) 729545 Fax: (01259) 729545

▶ Epic Software Ltd, 105 Hanover Street, Edinburgh, EH2 1DJ Tel: 0131-477 2545 Fax: 0131-624 0071 E-mail: sales@epicsoftware.co.uk

Essential Computing Ltd, PO Box 49, Clevedon, Avon, BS21 7NB Tel: (01275) 343199 Fax: (01275) 340974 E-mail: sales@essential.co.uk

Essential Information Systems Ltd, 166 Station Road, Addlestone, Surrey, KT15 2BD Tel: (01932) 700370 Fax: (01932) 700380

Experience Payment, Eiger Point Swift Park, Old Leicester Road, Rugby, Warwickshire, CV21 1DZ Tel: (01788) 554800 Fax: (01788) 554900 E-mail: enquiries@eiger.co.uk

▶ Extech 2000 Ltd, Albion House, 25 Bridge Street, Macclesfield, Cheshire, SK11 6EG Tel: (01625) 422992 Fax: (01625) 427150 E-mail: sales@extech.co.uk

Farsight Technologies Ltd, 18 Guildford Road, Brighton, BN1 3LU Tel: (01273) 747487 Fax: (01273) 747333 E-mail: info@farsighttechnologies.com

Fasttrak Software Publishing Ltd, 20 Greenhill Crescent, Watford Business Park, Watford, WD18 8JA Tel: (01923) 495496 Fax: (01923) 800190 E-mail: fasttrak.info@polaron.co.uk

Fathom Technologies Ltd, 8 Windsor Square, Silver Street, Reading, RG1 2TH Tel: 0118-975 0044 Fax: 0118-975 0742 E-mail: info@fathom.co.uk

Financial Objects International Ltd, Seven Dials Village, 45 Monmouth Street, London, WC2H 9DG Tel: (020) 7836 3010 Fax: (020) 7240 5790 E-mail: enquiries@finobj.com

Financial Planning Software Ltd, Mill House, High Street, Kinver, Stourbridge, West Midlands, DY7 6ER Tel: (01384) 873430

Flare Software Systems UK Ltd, Kings Court, Parsonage Lane, Bath, BA1 1ER Tel: (01225) 485000 Fax: (01225) 485020

Flowmaster International, The Maltings, Alderton Road, Towcester, Northamptonshire, NN12 7TB Tel: (01327) 306000 Fax: (01327) 306020

Fontworks UK Ltd, New North House, 202-208 New North Road, London, N1 7BJ Tel: (020) 7226 4411 Fax: (020) 7226 4422 E-mail: sales@type.co.uk

▶ indicates data change since last edition

COMPUTER SOFTWARE – *continued*

Fordman Systems Ltd, The Broadway, Woodhall Spa, Lincolnshire, LN10 6ST Tel: (01526) 354000 Fax: (01526) 354511 E-mail: lorraine@fordman.co.uk

Formwise Export Ltd, 15 The Promenade, Swansea, SA1 6EN Tel: (01792) 462113 Fax: (01792) 650850 E-mail: sales@formwise.co.uk

Freight Data 2000 Ltd, Foremost House, Radford Way, Billericay, Essex, CM12 0BT Tel: (01622) 861323 E-mail: uksales@freightdata.com

Friedman Corporation Ltd, 1 Chapel Court, Holly Walk, Leamington Spa, Warwickshire, CV32 4YS Tel: (01926) 741600 Fax: (01926) 741601 E-mail: uksales@friedmancorp.co.uk

▶ Game, Unit 19 Gallions Reach Shopping Park, Armada Way, London, E6 7ER Tel: (020) 7511 3600 Fax: (020) 7511 3600

▶ Game Box, 85 High Street, Lochee, Dundee, DD2 3AT Tel: (01382) 612159

▶ Game Stores Ltd, 17 Chapel Street, Exmouth, Devon, EX8 1HS Tel: (01395) 260240

▶ Game Stores Ltd, 38 High Street, Rhyl, Clwyd, LL18 1ET Tel: (01745) 355060

Game Stores Ltd, 45-46 Fore Street, Taunton, Somerset, TA1 1HR Tel: (01823) 321558 Fax: (01823) 354106

▶ Gamma Dataware, Hillington Park Innovation Centre, 1 Ainslie Road, Glasgow, G52 4RU Tel: 0141-585 6338

Geo Designs Ltd, 17A Sea Grove Avenue, Hayling Island, Hampshire, PO11 9EU Tel: (023) 9246 6750 Fax: (023) 9263 7390 E-mail: info@gdesigns.co.uk

▶ Geowise Ltd, Edinburgh Business Centre, 11 Maritime Street, Edinburgh, EH6 6SB Tel: 0131-624 8935 Fax: 0131-624 8936 E-mail: krystal.badenoch@geowise.co.uk

Gerber Technology Ltd, 302 Metroplex Business Park, Broadway, Salford, M50 2UE Tel: 0161-772 2000 Fax: 0161-772 2020

Gerrard Associates, Mansard, Neston Rd, Burton, Neston, CH64 5SZ Tel: 0151-353 1056 Fax: 0151 3531082

Giant Technologies, 91 Western Road, Brighton, BN1 2NW Tel: (01273) 243030 Fax: (01273) 270271 E-mail: sales@giant-technologies.com

▶ Glasscalc Ltd, 5 Valmont Road, Nottingham, NG5 1GA Tel: (0845) 1662624 E-mail: sales@glasscalc.co.uk

Grange Technology Ltd, Rosebank, Stream Road, Upton, Didcot, Oxfordshire, OX11 9JG Tel: (01235) 851818 Fax: (01235) 851818 E-mail: gkt@gtech.demon.co.uk

Gresham Computer Services Ltd, Mitchell House, Brook Avenue, Southampton, SO31 9ZA Tel: (01489) 555500 Fax: (01489) 555560 E-mail: info@gresham-computing.com

Grove Systems Ltd, 3 Ashlyn Grove, Manchester, M14 6YG Tel: 0161-224 4465 E-mail: donald@grove.demon.co.uk

GSD Associates Ltd, 48 High Street, Stourport-on-Severn, Worcestershire, DY13 8BX Tel: (01299) 827592 Fax: (01299) 827593 E-mail: support@gsdassociates.co.uk

Gultronics, 45 New Oxford Street, London, WC1A 1BH Tel: (020) 7240 6030 Fax: (020) 7240 6030

H S C Ltd, Welsh Harp, Trelystan, Leighton, Welshpool, Powys, SY21 8JB Tel: (01938) 570428 Fax: (01938) 570653 E-mail: enquiries@hyteq.com

Halcyon Software Ltd, 5 The Forum, Minerva BSNS Park, Orton Wistow, Peterborough, PE2 6FT Tel: (01733) 234995 Fax: (01733) 234994 E-mail: sales@halcyonsoftware.com

▶ Hardwareability Computer Systems, Endeavour House, 8a Cambridge Road, Kingston upon Thames, Surrey, KT1 3JU Tel: (020) 8547 3600 Fax: (020) 8547 3698

Harp Software, PO Box 1101, Stourbridge, West Midlands, DY9 8YL Tel: (0845) 2261671 Fax: (01384) 892169 E-mail: harp@harpsoftware.co.uk

▶ HB Computers, 264 Hesketh Lane, Tarleton, Preston, PR4 6RJ Tel: (01772) 811409 Fax: (01772) 811409

▶ Helpit Systems Ltd, 9 North Street, Leatherhead, Surrey, KT22 7AX Tel: (01372) 360070 Fax: (01372) 360081 E-mail: sales@helpit.com

▶ Henton & Co., St. Andrews House, St. Andrews Street, Leeds, LS3 1LF Tel: 0113-246 7900 Fax: 0113-246 9200

Hewlett Packard Ltd, Cain Road, Bracknell, Berkshire, RG12 1HN Tel: (01344) 360000 Fax: (01344) 363344E-mail: info@jobshp.com

Hexagon Software Ltd, Unit 8 Highnam Business Centre, Highnam, Gloucester, GL2 8DN Tel: (01608) 811801 Fax: (01608) 811852 E-mail: sales@hexagon.co.uk

Hoge 100 Business Systems Ltd, I M S House, Prescott Drive, Worcester, WR4 9NE Tel: (01905) 455227 Fax: (01905) 455035 E-mail: sales@hoge100.co.uk

Housing Software Services Ltd, 89 Gleneagle Road, London, SW16 6AZ Tel: (020) 8677 2253 Fax: (020) 8677 2101

I Mediation Ltd, Sussex Ho, 6 The Forbury, Reading, RG1 3EJ Tel: 0118-925 3338 Fax: 0118 9253200

▶ I T @ Spectrum Ltd, 1 Trinity Street, Hull, HU3 1JR Tel: (01482) 586732 Fax: (01482) 211428E-mail: smonkman@itatspectrum.co.uk

▶ I T C (Epos) Ltd, Barnsley Business & Innovation Centre, Innovation Way, Barnsley, South Yorkshire, S75 1JL Tel: (01226) 731785 Fax: (01226) 731867 E-mail: sales@itcepos.co.uk

▶ I T Solutions, 31a The Broadway, St. Ives, Cambridgeshire, PE27 5BX Tel: (01480) 494908 Fax: (01480) 494913

I T Source International, Sheldon House, 29 Morley Street, Bradford, West Yorkshire, BD7 1AG Tel: (01274) 725572 Fax: (01274) 725572

▶ I T Supplies, 7 Grange Road, Houstoun Industrial Estate, Livingston, West Lothian, EH54 5DE Tel: (01506) 430400 Fax: (01506) 430500 E-mail: sales@itsuppliesuk.com

▶ I T West, 5 Dowren House, Foundry Lane, Hayle, Cornwall, TR27 4HD Tel: (01736) 758370 Fax: (01736) 758348 E-mail: info@itwest.co.uk

Identalink Ltd, Bedrup Moor, Forthbridge, Cheltenham, Gloucestershire, GL54 3JR Tel: (01285) 721030

▶ Indigo Software Ltd, Indigo House, Belmont Business Park, Durham, DH1 1TW Tel: 0191-375 6700 Fax: 0191-375 6702

▶ Info Logic It, Unit 2 Hertfordshire Business Centre, Alexander Road, London Colney, St. Albans, Hertfordshire, AL2 1JG Tel: (01727) 823000 Fax: (01727) 822332

Inforalgo Information Technology Ltd, 131 Lincoln Road North, Birmingham, B27 6RT Tel: 0121-708 1155 Fax: 0121-707 7331

Informatica Computer Solutions Ltd, 40 St. Peters Street, Bedford, MK40 2NN Tel: (01234) 273700 Fax: (01234) 365163 E-mail: sales@informatica200.co.uk

Insurance Technology Solutions Ltd, International House, 1 St. Katharines Way, London, E1W 1UN Tel: (020) 7553 2500 Fax: (020) 7702 3074 E-mail: sales@intechsolutions.co.uk

▶ Intec Microsystems Ltd, Unit 32, The Business Centre, 20 James Road,, Tyseley, Birmingham, B11 2BA Tel: 0121-707 2121 Fax: 0121-707 4242 E-mail: sales@intecmicros.co.uk

Intec Systems Ltd, Intec House, St. Nicholas Close, Fleet, Hampshire, GU51 4JA Tel: (01252) 775400 Fax: (01252) 775444 E-mail: info@intec.co.uk

▶ Integrate Software, 18 Knightsbridge, Northwich, Cheshire, CW9 8GE Tel: (0845) 1249800

Integrated Geochemical Interpretation, Hallsannery, Bideford, Devon, EX39 5HE Tel: (01237) 471749 Fax: (01237) 421700 E-mail: info@hallsannery.co.uk

Inter Active Software Services Ltd, Westwood House, Littleton Drive, Huntington, Cannock, Staffordshire, WS12 4TS Tel: (01543) 503611 Fax: (01543) 574566 E-mail: ifs@winteracter.com

Interactive Ideas Ltd, Centenary Estate, Jeffreys Road, Enfield, Middlesex, EN3 7HB Tel: (020) 8805 1000 Fax: (020) 8805 8962 E-mail: sales@interactiveideas.com

Interconnect Direct Ltd, 22 Edward Road, Arnos Vale, Bristol, BS4 3ES Tel: 0117-907 1880 E-mail: enquiries@interconnect-direct.com

Interlan Computer Maintenance, The Mill, Glasshouses, Harrogate, North Yorkshire, HG3 5QH Tel: (01423) 712222 Fax: (01423) 712958

Interlogic Ltd, Bestway House, Handen Road, Gerrards Cross, Buckinghamshire, SL9 9RY Tel: (01753) 889749 Fax: (01753) 540990 E-mail: sales@wrkgrp.com

Intersoft Entertainment, Unit 1 Matherian Ho, 24 Newlands, Daventry, Northants, NN11 4DU Tel: 01327 703030 Fax: (01327) 703397

Intertex Data Systems Ltd, 29 Abington Road, Kensington, London, W8 6AH Tel: (020) 8870 6924 Fax: 020 88706924

▶ Invention Machine Ltd, 26 Granta Park, Great Abington, Cambridge, CB21 6AL Tel: (01223) 890873 E-mail: sales@invention-machine.com

▶ Island Technology, Highbury, La Route Du Marais, St. Ouen, Jersey, JE3 2GG Tel: (01534) 484151 Fax: (01534) 481202

▶ It Centre Plus, 2 Stafford Street, Eccleshall, Stafford, ST21 6BH Tel: (01785) 850710 Fax: (01785) 859386

IT Partnership, 123 Radford Road, Leamington Spa, Warwickshire, CV31 1LG Tel: (01926) 314011 E-mail: help@itpartnership.com

▶ It Software Solutions, Dunstable Road, Toddington, Dunstable, Bedfordshire, LU5 6DT Tel: (07811) 741568 E-mail: zoltan@it-software-solutions.com

▶ i-teamworks, PO Box 556, Peterborough, PE4 6WL Tel: (0845) 4900126 Fax: (0845) 4900127 E-mail: info@iteamworks.com

J F Stevens & Co, The Retreat, South Road, South Somercotes, Louth, Lincolnshire, LN11 7QD Tel: (01507) 358714 Fax: (01507) 358758

▶ J & M Computers, 46c Green Arbour Road, Thurcroft, Rotherham, South Yorkshire, S66 9DB Tel: (01709) 547900

▶ J & S Computing, 114 Abbey Street, Nuneaton, Warwickshire, CV11 5BX Tel: (024) 7675 7672 Fax: (024) 7638 5178

Jentech Computers Ltd, Whitburn Street, Bridgnorth, Shropshire, WV16 4QP Tel: (01746) 761458 Fax: (01746) 768710 E-mail: alan@jentech.co.uk

John Bennison, 10a Clarence Road, Sutton Coldfield, West Midlands, B74 4AE Tel: 0121-323 2370

▶ Jungle I T Ltd, 2 Drury Lane, Horsforth, Leeds, LS18 4BQ Tel: 0113-258 4433 Fax: 0113-258 4499

▶ Justice Laboratory Services, JLS House, 25 - 27 Low Road, Auchtermuchty, Auchtermuchty, Fife, KY14 7BB Tel: (01337) 828404

K V Computer Services Ltd, North Sands Business Centre, Dame Dorothy Street, Sunderland, SR6 0QA Tel: 0191-510 9566 Fax: 0191-510 0686 E-mail: kvinfo@kvcomputerservices.co.uk

Kaspersky Lab UK Ltd, Orwell Ho, Cowley Rd, Cambridge, CB4 0PP Tel: 01223 500450 Fax: 01223 470072

▶ Kims Computers, 223 Maiden Lane, Dartford, DA1 4PL Tel: (01322) 310492

Kiosk World, 21 Fownhope Road, Sale, Cheshire, M33 4RF Tel: 0161-969 3005 Fax: 0161-969 3966

KK Systems Ltd, PO Box 2770, Brighton, BN45 7ED Tel: (01273) 857185 Fax: (01273) 857186 E-mail: sales@kksystems.com

Knowhow Consulting, Elmbridge House, Elmbridge Lane, Woking, Surrey, GU22 9AF Tel: (01483) 776000 Fax: (01483) 433317 E-mail: info@knowhowconsultinglco.uk

▶ L D D, Wira House, Ring Road, Leeds, LS16 6EB Tel: 0113-224 2222 Fax: 0113-224 2234 E-mail: sales@ldd.co.uk

L M Software Ltd, Apak House Badminton Court, Station Road, Yate, Bristol, BS37 5HZ Tel: (01454) 871060 Fax: (01454) 871199 E-mail: enquiries@lmsoft.co.uk

Lalpac, 8 The Causeway, Chippenham, Wiltshire, SN15 3BT Tel: (01249) 660088 Fax: (01249) 660099

▶ Landesk Software UK Ltd, Theale House, Brunel Road, Theale, Reading, RG7 4AQ Tel: (0845) 2305580 Fax: 0118-902 6201

▶ Landour Ltd, 27 Old Gloucester Street, London, WC1N 3XX Tel: (0870) 3213858 Fax: (0870) 1354533 E-mail: info@landourcom.net

▶ Lapwing Computers, Cowshill, Bishop Auckland, County Durham, DL13 1DA Tel: (01388) 537337 E-mail: info@lapwing.net

Le Software Man Ltd, Aberdeen House, 22 Highbury Grove, London, N5 2EA Tel: (020) 7354 8414 Fax: (020) 7226 2015 E-mail: sales@answersthatwork.com

Learning & Teaching Scotland, 58 Robertson Street, Glasgow, G2 8DU Tel: 0141-282 5000 Fax: 0141-282 5050 E-mail: equiries@ltscotland.org.uk

Leckhampton Computers Ltd, Leckhampton House, Lund House Green, Harrogate, North Yorkshire, HG3 1QG Tel: (01423) 879202 Fax: (01423) 870741 E-mail: pkl@leckhampton.com

Linear Software Ltd, 17 Pulborough Road, London, SW18 5UN Tel: (020) 8877 0159 Fax: (020) 8877 0552

▶ Logical Resources Ltd, 22 Regent Street, Leeds, LS2 7QA Tel: 0113-212 0000 Fax: (0870) 9906959 E-mail: info@logicalresources.co.uk

London Graphic Centre, 16-18 Shelton Street, London, WC2H 9JL Tel: (020) 7759 4500 Fax: (020) 7759 4585 E-mail: mailorder@londongraphics.co.uk

▶ Lowcost IT, Suites 1-2, Caxton House, 243 South Coast Road, Peacehaven, East Sussex, BN10 8NN Tel: (01273) 589222 E-mail: info@lowcost-it.com

Lucas Software Solutions, 95 Tilehouse St, Hitchin, Hertfordshire, SG5 2DW Tel: (01462) 440885 Fax: (01462) 440954 E-mail: sales@lucas-software.co.uk

Lusas Computer Systems, 66 High Street, Kingston upon Thames, Surrey, KT1 1HN Tel: (020) 8541 1999 Fax: (020) 8549 9399 E-mail: info@lusas.com

Lynx Automotive Systems Ltd, Delta 500, Delta Business Park, Welton Road, Swindon, SN5 7XE Tel: (01793) 645300 Fax: (01793) 645301 E-mail: enquiries@mmi-automotive.co.uk

Lyquidity Solutions, Ground Floor Office Suite, 16 Lynton Road, New Malden, Surrey, KT3 5EE Tel: (020) 7043 2777 Fax: (0870) 1373744 E-mail: sarah.seddon@lyquidity.com

M A S Business Systems Ltd, 8 Crown Court, Clough Road, Severalls Industrial Park, Colchester, CO4 9TZ Tel: (01206) 852827 Fax: (01206) 855009 E-mail: sagesales@masbs.co.uk

M C G Systems Ltd, The Hayloft, Condover Mews, Condover, Shrewsbury, SY5 7BG Tel: (01743) 875150 Fax: (01743) 875155 E-mail: info@mcgsystems.co.uk

M C W Group, Wrexham Technology Park, Wrexham, Clwyd, LL13 7YP Tel: (01978) 340340 Fax: (01978) 340345 E-mail: admin@mcwgroup.co.uk

M H Systems Ltd, 12 Tunbridge Chambers, Dembery Road, Tonbridge, Kent, TN9 2HZ Tel: (01732) 367227 Fax: (01732) 367447 E-mail: tech@gcgold.co.uk

Maars Software International Ltd, 7 High Street, Maidenhead, Berkshire, SL6 1JN Tel: (01628) 633115 Fax: (01628) 633114

▶ Mackey Software Design Ltd, Parnella House, 23 Market Place, Devizes, Wiltshire, SN10 1JQ Tel: (01380) 724688 E-mail: info@mackeysoftware.co.uk

Macrovision Europe Ltd, 14-18 Bell Street, Maidenhead, Berkshire, SL6 1BR Tel: (01628) 786100 Fax: (0870) 8711161 E-mail: info@macrovison.com

▶ Management Services 2000 Ltd, Middleton House, 38 Monkgate, York, YO31 7PF Tel: (01904) 659009 E-mail: enquiries@ms2m.com

Marilake Instruments Ltd, Building 97, Bournemouth International Airport, Christchurch, Dorset, BH23 6SE Tel: (01202) 570055 Fax: (01202) 581369 E-mail: phil@mailake.com

▶ Markell Computer, 47 Greygoose Park, Harlow, Essex, CM19 4JW Tel: (01279) 441000 Fax: (01279) 441110 E-mail: sales@marcelcomputers.com

Mascolo Support Systems, 6 Dean Park Crescent, Bournemouth, BH1 1HL Tel: (01202) 311826 Fax: (01202) 311830 E-mail: support@salongenius.com

Mastek UK Ltd, Crown House, 1a High Street Theale, Theale, Reading, RG7 5AH Tel: 0118-930 5190 Fax: 0118 -932-3354

▶ Masterlink Management Ltd, Hearts Court, Wearish Lane, West Houghton, Bolton, BL5 2DG Tel: (0845) 2701212 Fax: (0845) 2701210

Match-It Ltd, 95 Stansted Road, Bishop's Stortford, Hertfordshire, CM23 2DU Tel: (0845) 1300510 Fax: (01279) 757447 E-mail: enquiries@match-it.com

Matrikon, 81 Dale Road, Matlock, Derbyshire, DE4 3LU Tel: (01629) 580886 Fax: (01629) 582104 E-mail: info@ics-ltd.co.uk

▶ Matrix Technologies, Sheldon House, 29 Morley Street, Bradford, West Yorkshire, BD7 1AG Tel: (01274) 394111

▶ Matrix World, 14 New Street, Dudley, West Midlands, DY1 1LP Tel: (01384) 242867 Fax: (01384) 239585 E-mail: sale@matrixworld.co.uk

Maxima, 84 Coombe Road, New Malden, Surrey, KT3 4QS Tel: (020) 8336 8800 Fax: (020) 8336 8899

Mayfair Business Systems Ltd, 85 Market Street, Watford, WD18 0PT Tel: (01923) 800800 Fax: (01923) 800810 E-mail: info@mayfairbs.co.uk

Mentor Communications Ltd, PO Box 21, Wellingborough, Northamptonshire, NN8 1PB Tel: (08454) 581552 Fax: (08708) 401553 E-mail: mentor.comms@fsbdial.co.uk

Menzies Engineering Design Ltd, Dornoch, Sutherland, IV25 3RW Tel: (01862) 810788 Fax: (01862) 810771

▶ Micro At Home, 4A South Street, Wincanton, Somerset, BA9 9DL Tel: (01963) 824808 E-mail: sales@microathome.biz

MicroMedia UK Ltd, 74 Gloucester Road, London, E17 6AE Tel: (07762) 660697 Fax: (020) 8527 3302

Micron Software Ltd, 22 Lonsdale Road, Rackheath, Norwich, NR13 6QW Tel: (01603) 721600 Fax: (01603) 721607 E-mail: sales@micronds.com

▶ Micro-Pension Systems, 12 Burlington Place, Reigate, Surrey, RH2 9HT Tel: (01737) 237859

Miles Better Software, 221 Cannock Road, Cannock, Staffordshire, WS11 5DD Tel: (01543) 466577 Fax: (01543) 466579

Millennium Computer Systems Ltd, B11 The Seedbed Centre, Wyncolls Road, Colchester, CO4 9HT Tel: (01206) 855288 Fax: (01206) 855285 E-mail: info@millennium-computer.co.uk

▶ Mind Mapping Software Shop, 100 Vale Road, Windsor, Berkshire, SL4 5JL Tel: (01753) 621426 Fax: (01753) 621427

Misco, Darby Close, Park Farm South, Wellingborough, Northamptonshire, NN8 6GS Tel: (08707) 208720 Fax: (08707) 208686 E-mail: salesdesk@misco.co.uk

Misys P.L.C., Burleigh House, Chapel Oak, Salford Priors, Evesham, Worcestershire, WR11 8SP Tel: (01386) 871373 Fax: (01386) 871045

▶ Mode Designer PC's, 112 Deansgate, Bolton, BL1 1BD Tel: (01204) 366849 Fax: (01204) 366900

Moneysoft Ltd, Enterprise House, Cherry Orchard Lane, Salisbury, SP2 7LD Tel: (01722) 327707 Fax: (020) 8743 8073 E-mail: info@moneysoft.co.uk

Mountain Software, Withambrook Park Industrial Estate, Grantham, Lincolnshire, NG31 9ST Tel: (01476) 573718 Fax: (01476) 590563 E-mail: info@mountainsoftware.co.uk

Multi Resource Marketing Ltd, Barberton House, Farndon Road, Market Harborough, Leicestershire, LE16 9NR Tel: (01858) 410510 Fax: (01858) 434190

Mundane Software Co., 78a Chapel Street, Thatcham, Berkshire, RG18 4QN Tel: (01635) 876387 Fax: (01635) 876388 E-mail: sales@mundanesoftware.co.uk

Nasa Computers Ltd, 23 Stonefield Way, Ruislip, Middlesex, HA4 0YF Tel: (020) 8842 0931 Fax: (020) 8845 8577

▶ Company Net Ltd, Research Park North, Riccarton, Edinburgh, EH14 4AP Tel: 0131-559 7500 Fax: 0131-559 7501 E-mail: info@company-net.com

Netbuyer, 1 International House, St. Katharines Way, London, E1W 1UN Tel: (020) 7903 6807 Fax: (020) 7903 6000 E-mail: geoff.inns@cnet.com

Neutral Ltd, 167 Ardleigh Green Road, Hornchurch, Essex, RM11 2LF Tel: (01708) 701522 Fax: (01708) 701994 E-mail: info@neutral.co.uk

New Wave Concepts, 59 St Andrews Street, St Andrews House, Cambridge, CB2 3BQ Tel: (0870) 6090911 E-mail: sales@new-wave-concepts.com

Newcom Computer Systems, 1a Sugarhouse Quay, Newry, County Down, BT35 6HZ Tel: (028) 3026 3149 Fax: (028) 3026 3149

Newton Information Technology Ltd, 1 Central Business Centre, Great Central Way, London, NW10 0UR Tel: (020) 8451 0027 Fax: (020) 8451 0029 E-mail: sales@newtonit.co.uk

Newton Software Ltd, Hawthorn Dene, Gloucester Road, Tutshill, Chepstow, Gwent, NP16 7DB Tel: (01291) 627278 Fax: (01291) 627278

COMPUTER SOFTWARE – *continued*

Nexsoft, Lyth Business Centre, Crosthwaite, Kendal, Cumbria, LA8 8BP Tel: (01539) 568860 E-mail: sales@nexsoft.co.uk

▶ Next Generation Computer Systems, 15 Tamworth Road, Amington, Tamworth, Staffordshire, B77 3BS Tel: (01827) 58100 Fax: (01827) 58100 E-mail: info@ngcstamworth.co.uk

Nexus Open Systems Ltd, Vale House, Pynes Hill, Exeter, EX2 5AZ Tel: (01392) 205095 Fax: (01392) 205096

Northgate Information Solutions Ltd, Channel House, South Road, Midsomer Norton, Radstock, BA3 2EZ Tel: (01761) 411664 Fax: (01761) 411159

Norton Waugh Managment Software, The Old School, School Lane, Weston-Under-Lizard, Shifnal, Shropshire, TF11 8SZ Tel: (01952) 850333 Fax: (01952) 850649 E-mail: sales@nortonwaugh.co.uk

The Notebook Centre, 17 Oxford Street, London, W1D 2DJ Tel: (020) 7287 4247

Novolla Systems, 18 Lavender Road, London, SW11 2UG Tel: (020) 7228 5830 Fax: (020) 7228 5830

Nt2 Ltd, Unit A Warwick House, Market Pl, Braintree, Essex, CM7 3HQ Tel: (0870) 2410997 Fax: (0870) 2411717

▶ Nusoft Distribution, High Road, Chigwell, Essex, IG7 5BJ Tel: (020) 8500 5885 Fax: (020) 8500 6065

Nycom Ltd, Julia Avenue, Huntington, York, YO32 9JR Tel: (01904) 653383 Fax: (01904) 653005 E-mail: info@nycom.co.uk

▶ O E R Franchising, 5 High Street, Seaford, East Sussex, BN25 1PE Tel: (01323) 873555

Ocean Road, Unit 43, Kersey Road, Flushing, Falmouth, Cornwall, TR11 5TR Tel: (0845) 0034220 Fax: (0870) 9159418 E-mail: enquiries@oceanroad.co.uk

▶ Oilcats, Clydesdale Bank Buildings, Little Square, Oldmeldrum, Aberdeen, AB51 0AY Tel: (01651) 873171 Fax: (01651) 873214 E-mail: sales@oilcats.co.uk

One Step Beyond Ltd, 9-11 Bedford Street, Norwich, NR2 1AR Tel: (08703) 500252 Fax: (01603) 617378

▶ Onecallpc.Com, 25-29 High Street, Leatherhead, Surrey, KT22 8AB Tel: (0870) 7770999 Fax: (01372) 377092

▶ OnTrack Systems Ltd, 27 Sandyford Place, Glasgow, G3 7NG Tel: 0141-248 7999 Fax: 0141-248 7998 E-mail: info@ontracksystems.co.uk

Open Text, Mulberry Business Park, Fishponds Road, Wokingham, Berkshire, RG41 2GY Tel: 0118-978 2800 Fax: 0118-936 0606 E-mail: enquiries@hummingbird.com

Open Text UK Ltd, Webster House, 22 Wycombe End, Beaconsfield, Buckinghamshire, HP9 1NB Tel: (01494) 679700 Fax: (01494) 679707 E-mail: info.uk@opentext.com

Optimal Geomatics Ltd, 44-46 King Street, Knutsford, Cheshire, WA16 6DT Tel: (0870) 7876728 Fax: 0161-367 9328

Options Mail Order Software Ltd, Samuel House, Chinnor Road, Thame, Oxfordshire, OX9 3NU Tel: (01844) 211820 Fax: (01844) 212999

▶ Opulent Computers, 23 Larkhill Walk, Leeds, LS8 1RA Tel: (0845) 0705145 Fax: (08450) 705154 E-mail: jay@opulentcomputers.co.uk

Oracle Computers, 932 Shettleston Road, Glasgow, G32 7XW Tel: 0141-778 2906 E-mail: sales@oraclecomputers.co.uk

Oracle Corporation UK Ltd, Oracle Parkway, Reading, RG6 1RA Tel: 0118-924 0000 Fax: 0118-924 3000 E-mail: sales@uk.oracle.com

▶ Orbital Solutions, Hall Road, Heybridge, Maldon, Essex, CM9 4LA Tel: (01621) 878480 Fax: (01621) 851213

Co Ordination Technologies Ltd, 5 Green Court, Eaton Bishop, Hereford, HR2 9QD Tel: (01981) 251529 E-mail: sales@coordtec.globalnet.co.uk

Original Business Systems Ltd, The Stables, The Vatch, Stroud, Gloucestershire, GL6 7LE Tel: (01453) 751515 Fax: (01453) 753525 E-mail: info@obs.co.uk

▶ Ovedas, 53 Wray Lane, Reigate, Surrey, RH2 0HX Tel: (01737) 222980 Fax: (01737) 245478

Oxford Software Engineering Ltd, 9 Spinners Court, West End, Witney, Oxfordshire, OX28 1NH Tel: (01993) 700878 Fax: (01993) 774132 E-mail: enquiries@ocl.co.uk

P A Business Systems Ltd, 5-7 The Pathway, Bowlalley Lane, Hull, HU1 1XJ Tel: (01482) 328607 Fax: (01482) 218236 E-mail: headoffice@pa-business.co.uk

P A C Software Ltd, Worcester Road, Hanley Swan, Worcester, WR8 0EA Tel: (01684) 311226 Fax: (01684) 311227 E-mail: sales@pacsoftware.co.uk

▶ P C, Langley Parade, Crawley, West Sussex, RH11 7RS Tel: (01293) 530823 Fax: (01293) 530823

▶ P C Friend, Unit 2, Windsor Court, Morley, Leeds, LS27 9BG Tel: 0113-259 7595 Fax: 0113-275 1552

P C M Technologies, 45 Borthwick Road, London, E15 1UE Tel: (020) 8519 4497 Fax: (020) 8519 1429 E-mail: sales@pcmtec.co.uk

▶ P C Speed, Wessex House, 2B8 Upper Market Street, Eastleigh, Hampshire, SO50 9FD Tel: (023) 8064 4912

P C T I Solutions Ltd, The Old Coach House, Button Park, Pontefract, West Yorkshire, WF8 4HT Tel: (01977) 690977 Fax: (01977) 690966

P C Tech Service & Support, 216 Kingston Road, New Malden, Surrey, KT3 3RJ Tel: (020) 8605 1641

▶ P & P Computer Centre, Contract House, Stafford Street, Stone, Staffordshire, ST15 8QW Tel: (01785) 812299 Fax: (01785) 812277

P P Systems, Templandshaw, Sorn, Mauchline, Ayrshire, KA5 6NG Tel: (01290) 551543 Fax: (01290) 552165

Parallel Computer Systems, 14 Trent Road, Bulkington, Bedworth, Warwickshire, CV12 9QD Tel: (024) 7631 4447 E-mail: support@parasys.co.uk

Parguild Ltd, 41 Lordsmead, Cranfield, Bedford, MK43 0HP Tel: 01234 752299 Fax: 01234 752266

Paybacs Ltd, 2 Ashleigh Meadow, Tregondale, Liskeard, Cornwall, PL14 3RG Tel: (0845) 0670333 Fax: (01579) 349440 E-mail: info@paybacs.co.uk

▶ PC Bits & Bytes, 7 Bath Street, Leek, Staffordshire, ST13 6JQ Tel: (01538) 385351

▶ PC Place, 198 High Street, Barnet, Hertfordshire, EN5 5SZ Tel: (020) 8447 5700 Fax: (020) 8447 5711

▶ PC Specialist Ltd, Abbey Road, Huddersfield, HD8 8EL Tel: (0845) 2264036 Fax: (0845) 2264046

▶ PC Tech Discount Computers, 55 Station Road, Redcar, Cleveland, TS10 1DT Tel: (01642) 481888 Fax: (01642) 461002

Pelican Software Ltd, 35D Newland Street, Eynsham, Witney, Oxfordshire, OX29 4LB Tel: (01865) 883644 Fax: (01865) 883365 E-mail: jobs@pelicansoftware.co.uk

Peregrine Systems Ltd, Peregrine House, 26-28 Paradise Road, Richmond, Surrey, TW9 1SE Tel: (020) 8332 9666 Fax: (020) 8939 1170

Performance Monitoring Systems Ltd, 52 Coventry Street, Southam, Warwickshire, CV47 0EP Tel: (01926) 814846 Fax: (01926) 815516

Phoebus Solutions Ltd, 2a Market Street, Heanor, Derbyshire, DE75 7NR Tel: (0870) 7270300 Fax: (08707) 270400 E-mail: sales@pheobus-solutions.com

Pinnacle Software, Heather Court, 6 Maidstone Road, Sidcup, Kent, DA14 5HH Tel: (01322) 665652 E-mail: info@pinnacle-software.co.uk

Pipex Internet Ltd, Unit 1 Pipex House, Medway Technology Park, Rutherford Close, Stevenage, Hertfordshire, SG1 2EF Tel: (08706) 004454 Fax: (01438) 311100 E-mail: sales@dial.pipex.com

Pixel Management, 125 Dove House Lane, Solihull, West Midlands, B91 2EL Tel: 0121-688 8990 E-mail: sales@pml.co.uk

Plus Components, Harlequin Business Park, Kenny Hill, Bury St. Edmunds, Suffolk, IP28 8DS Tel: (01353) 675555 Fax: (01353) 675555 E-mail: info@pco.co.uk

▶ Point Digital, 18 Union Street, Hereford, HR1 2BT Tel: (01432) 276335 Fax: (01432) 276335

Portcullis Computer Security Ltd, Grange Barn, Pikes End, Pinner, Middlesex, HA5 2EX Tel: (020) 8868 0098 Fax: (020) 8868 0017

▶ Positive Focus Ltd, Unit 12 C Shepperton Business Park, Govett Avenue, Shepperton, Middlesex, TW17 8BA Tel: (01458) 250603 Fax: (01458) 250604 E-mail: sales@positivefocus.co.uk

▶ Powersoft Systems Ltd, 3 Finchley Close, Troedyrhiw, Merthyr Tydfil, Mid Glamorgan, CF48 4HR Tel: (01443) 693326 Fax: (01443) 693326

Primo Computers, 20 Fern Road, Godalming, Surrey, GU7 3EW Tel: (01483) 860777 E-mail: info@primocomputers.co.uk

▶ Principle Management Ltd, Britannia House, 29 Station Road, Kettering, Northamptonshire, NN15 7HJ Tel: (01536) 515855 Fax: (01536) 414000 E-mail: principle@principletechnology.com

Procon Systems, 7 St. Johns Close, Aberford, Leeds, LS25 3BP Tel: 0113-393 5085 Fax: 0113-393 5087

Prolog Systems Ltd, Century House, Station Way, Sutton, Surrey, SM3 8SW Tel: (020) 8715 1555 Fax: (020) 8715 1556 E-mail: sales@prologsystems.com

Prologic Computer Consultants Ltd, Redwood House, Rectory Lane, Berkhamsted, Hertfordshire, HP4 2DH Tel: (01442) 876277 Fax: (01442) 877245E-mail: info@prologic.net

Protean Software Ltd, 101 Lockhurst Lane, Coventry, CV6 5SF Tel: (024) 7666 6612 Fax: (024) 7670 3566 E-mail: enquiries@proteansoftware.co.uk

The Publishing Software Co., 6 Trevithick Close, Stourport-on-Severn, Worcestershire, DY13 8AN Tel: (0870) 0101780 Fax: (0870) 0101783 E-mail: laurence@p-s-c.co.uk

Pugh Computers Ltd, Denver House, Llanon, Dyfed, SY23 5LP Tel: (01974) 200200 Fax: (01974) 202628 E-mail: sales@pugh.co.uk

▶ Qikker Solutions Ltd, 17 Marble Street, Lowry House, Manchester, M2 3AW Tel: (0870) 7876611 Fax: (0870) 7876612 E-mail: sales@qikker.com

Q-Tron Ltd, The Ross Wing, Redhill Court, Doncaster, South Yorkshire, DN11 9ED Tel: (01302) 311066 Fax: (01302) 311774 E-mail: q-tron@btconnect.com

▶ Quality PC's, 26 Henderson Road, Norwich, NR4 7JW Tel: (01603) 506050 Fax: (01603) 453100 E-mail: sales@qualitypc.co.uk

Quantum System Management Ltd, 67 Tweedy Road, Bromley, BR1 3NH Tel: (020) 8460 2747 Fax: (020) 8313 3468

▶ Quartile Management Consulting Ltd, 10 Melville Crescent, Edinburgh, EH3 7LU Tel: 0131-666 1237 Fax: (07092) 313096

Qube Global Software, Pyrford Road, West Byfleet, Surrey, KT14 6LD Tel: (01932) 334700 Fax: (01932) 355654 E-mail: sales@fdsltd.co.uk

Qudos Computer Software Ltd, Ashmead House, 3 The Common, Siddington, Cirencester, Gloucestershire, GL7 6EY Tel: (01285) 656812

Quest Software, Ascot House, Westacott Way, Littlewick Green, Maidenhead, Berkshire, SL6 3QQ Tel: (01628) 518000 Fax: (01628) 822815

Quovadx, Ambassador House, Maxted Road, Hemel Hempstead Industrial Estate, Hemel Hempstead, Hertfordshire, HP2 7DX Tel: (01442) 231081 Fax: (01442) 235775

R C P Consultants Ltd, Richards House, 81 Broadway, Didcot, Oxfordshire, OX11 8AJ Tel: (01235) 510116 Fax: (01235) 515302 E-mail: sales@acp.co.uk

R.E.D. Computing Ltd, 179 Malden Road, New Malden, Surrey, KT3 6AA Tel: (020) 8336 1513 Fax: (020) 8942 9385 E-mail: sales@redcomputing.com

▶ R I E Consultancy, Eastway Road, Wigston, Leicestershire, LE18 1NJ Tel: 0116-281 2274

R & R Systems Ltd, 390 Bolton Road, Aspull, Wigan, Lancashire, WN2 1PR Tel: (01942) 833402 Fax: (01942) 833107 E-mail: info@rarsys.co.uk

R T S Computers, 13 New Street, Louth, Lincolnshire, LN11 9PT Tel: (01507) 606600 Fax: (01507) 606600 E-mail: rtscomputers@freebie.net

Rai Computing Services Ltd, 20 Cawnpore Rd, Coventry, CV6 4EN Tel: 024 76666610

Rand Worldwide, Unit 3 Interchange 25 Business Park, Bostock Lane, Sandiacre, Nottingham, NG10 5QG Tel: 0115-921 0000 Fax: 0115-921 0001

Rare It Ltd, Unit 35 Meridian House, Road One, Winsford Industrial Estate, Winsford, Cheshire, CW7 3QG Tel: (01606) 860607 Fax: (01606) 860608 E-mail: info@rareit.com

Red Ledge Ltd, Red Ledge Business Centre, 289-291 Huddersfield Road, Thongsbridge, Holmfirth, HD9 3UA Tel: (01484) 686769 Fax: (01484) 687879 E-mail: sales@redledge.co.uk

▶ Red Paw Solutions Ltd, 5a/1 Starbank Road, Edinburgh, EH5 3BW Tel: (07745) 428130

▶ Redprairie, Beacon House, Ibstone Road, Stokenchurch, High Wycombe, Buckinghamshire, HP14 3AQ Tel: (01494) 486500 Fax: (01494) 485465 E-mail: sales@online-internet.co.uk

▶ Redvers Consulting Ltd, Channelsea House, Canning Road, Stratford, London, E15 3ND Tel: (020) 8503 1211 E-mail: info@redversconsulting.co.uk

▶ Reform Technologies, Unit 5, Building 2, 2 Sandwich Industrial Estate, Sandwich, Kent, CT13 9LY Tel: (01304) 611875 Fax: (0870) 2203346

Resource Engineering Projects, Waterlinks House, Richard Street, Birmingham, B7 4AA Tel: 0121-678 7880 Fax: 0121-678 7899 E-mail: technical@topmode.co.uk

Ressoft Soft Ltd, Wesley Chmbers, Queens Road, Aldershot, Hampshire, GU11 3JD Tel: (01252) 337377 Fax: (01252) 338111

Retriever Software, 47 St. Georges Terrace, Jesmond, Newcastle upon Tyne, NE2 2SX Tel: 0191-212 1029 Fax: (07092) 281285

Retriever Technology Ltd, PO Box 3, Tenbury Wells, Worcestershire, WR15 8YX Tel: (01584) 781444 Fax: (01584) 781403 E-mail: support@reetec.co.uk

Rex Software Ltd, Chesil House, Arrow Close, Eastleigh, Hampshire, SO50 4SY Tel: (023) 8062 9429 Fax: (0870) 0548257

Reynolds Software Services, 37 Ratby Close, Lower Earley, Reading, RG6 4ER Tel: 0118-986 4579 Fax: 0118-986 2838 E-mail: rss@reynoldssoftwareservices.co.uk

Rivendale Systems Ltd, The Old Bakery, North End, Newbury, Berkshire, RG20 0AY Tel: (01635) 254464 Fax: (01635) 255359 E-mail: enquiries@rivendale.co.uk

Roevin Management Services Ltd, 40-44 Rothesay Road, Luton, LU1 1QZ Tel: (01582) 727216 Fax: (01582) 732188 E-mail: luton@roevin.co.uk

S C A Systems Ltd, 12 Littlehampton Road, Worthing, West Sussex, BN13 1QE Tel: (01903) 262688 Fax: (01903) 695311 E-mail: sales@scasystems.com

S Calvert, 30 Elmwood Avenue, Barwick in Elmet, Leeds, LS15 4JT Tel: 0113-281 2281 Fax: (07971) 114375 E-mail: scalvert@tiscali.co.uk

S M M Software Ltd, 42a High Street, Egham, Surrey, TW20 9DP Tel: (01784) 436234 Fax: (01784) 433315 E-mail: sales@smm.co.uk

▶ S M S Support, Support Centre, Tayside Software Centre, Technology Park, Dundee, DD2 1TY Tel: (01382) 598483 Fax: (01382) 598465

S & S Systems Ltd, Bretton Court, Manor Road, Wales, Sheffield, S26 5PS Tel: (08456) 441670 E-mail: info@astraaccounts.co.uk

▶ Saffron Computers Ltd, 4 Ash Drive, Haughton, Stafford, ST18 9EU Tel: (0871) 7233766 Fax: (01785) 780390 E-mail: sales@saffroncomputers.org

▶ SalesCentric, Worting House, Church Lane, Worting, Basingstoke, Hampshire, RG23 8PX Tel: (01256) 345575 Fax: (01256) 345553

▶ Mark Salter Ltd, PO Box 61, Swanley, Kent, BR8 8YZ Tel: (0870) 2406694 E-mail: sales@marksalter.com

Sapphire Ltd, Lambourne House, 7 Western Road, Romford, RM1 3LD Tel: (01708) 333700 Fax: (01708) 333800 E-mail: sales@dataease.com

Sas, Wittington House, Henley Road, Medmenham, Marlow, Buckinghamshire, SL7 2EB Tel: (01628) 486933 Fax: (01628) 483203

SBL, Eastmoor House Greenpark Business Centre, Goose Lane, Sutton-on-the-Forest, York, YO61 1ET Tel: (01347) 812100 Fax: (01347) 811220 E-mail: sales@softbox.co.uk

▶ SCC, 4 Redheughs Rigg, Edinburgh, EH12 9DQ Tel: 0131-339 0001 Fax: 0131-317 1683

Scientific Computers Ltd, Jubliee House, Jubilee Walk, Crawley, West Sussex, RH10 1LQ Tel: (01293) 403636 Fax: (01293) 403641 E-mail: info@scl.com

▶ Scorpio Computers, 2 Corporation Road, Plymouth, PL2 3NT Tel: (01752) 770027

Second Byte Computers, Market Square, Ellesmere Port, CH65 0HW Tel: 0151-356 8339 Fax: 0151-355 2851

Select Business Products Ltd, 65 Castle Street, Hull, HU1 1SE Tel: (01482) 586550 Fax: (01482) 211109 E-mail: info@selectgroup.co.uk

▶ Selsey PC, 79 High Street, Selsey, Chichester, West Sussex, PO20 0QL Tel: (01243) 607605 Fax: (01243) 606597 E-mail: sales@selseypc.net

Seltek Solutions, Unit 25, Stockwood Business Park, Stockwood, Redditch, Worcestershire, B96 6SX Tel: (01386) 793274 Fax: (01386) 792154 E-mail: info@selteksolutions.co.uk

Sense Computer Systems, Corner House, Robey Close, Linby, Nottingham, NG15 8AA Tel: 0115-964 6646 Fax: 0115-964 6647

Serion Systems, St Francis Centre, Pembroke Road, Woking, Surrey, GU22 7DY Tel: (01483) 747151 Fax: (01483) 721722

Service Works Ltd, 2 Burston Road, London, SW15 6AR Tel: (0870) 7360000 Fax: (0870) 7360001 E-mail: info@serviceworks.co.uk

Sherston Software Ltd, Angel House, High Street, Sherston, Malmesbury, Wiltshire, SN16 0LH Tel: (01666) 843200 Fax: (01666) 843216 E-mail: info@sherston.com

Siemens Products Life Cycle Management Software Iii (GB) Ltd, Park House, Castle Park, Cambridge, CB3 0DU Tel: (01223) 722600 Fax: (01223) 722601 E-mail: sales@d-cubed.co.uk

▶ Sigtec Computer Systems, 121 Giles Street, Edinburgh, EH6 6BZ Tel: 0131-553 5599 Fax: 0131-553 5599

▶ Simply Computers, 1 Ferry Lane Industrial Estate, Wickford Way, London, E17 6HG Tel: (0870) 7274020 Fax: (0870) 7274002

SIR Learning Systems Ltd, Blackbrook House, Ashbourne Road, Blackbrook, Belper, Derbyshire, DE56 2DB Tel: (01773) 820011 Fax: (01773) 820206 E-mail: sales@sirplc.co.uk

Smartstream Technologies, 1690 Park Avenue, Aztec West, Bristol, BS32 4RA Tel: (01454) 855100 Fax: (01454) 888503

Soft Option Technology, 2 The Old School, High Street, Wilburton, Ely, Cambridgeshire, CB6 3RB Tel: (01353) 741641 Fax: (01353) 741341 E-mail: info@softoption.com

▶ Soft Point Multi Media, Green Dragon House, 64-70 High Street, Croydon, CR0 9XN Tel: (020) 8681 7100 Fax: (020) 8681 8080

Soft Sell Computers, 74 Darwen St, Blackburn, BB2 2BL Tel: (01254) 693593 Fax: (01254) 668975 E-mail: info@soft-sell.co.uk

SoftBrands Ltd, SoftBrands House, 11 Worton Drive, Reading, RG2 0LX Tel: 0118-975 4000 Fax: 0118-975 4011 E-mail: info.emea@softbrands.com

▶ Software Central Ltd, 28 Vista Drive, Ilford, Essex, IG4 5JF Tel: (020) 8551 6262

Software Index Ltd, Matrix House, Gelders Hall Road, Shepshed, Loughborough, Leicestershire, LE12 9NH Tel: (01509) 505333 Fax: (01509) 505444

Software & Training Ltd, 71 Crombey Street, Swindon, SN1 5QW Tel: (01793) 485761 Fax: (01793) 421725 E-mail: arun.bedi9@ntlworld.com

▶ Softwide, Unit 134 The Harlequin, Watford, WD17 2UB Tel: (01923) 630259 Fax: (01923) 630261

Solcom Ltd, 79 George Street, Ryde, Isle Of Wight, PO33 2JF Tel: (01983) 817000 Fax: (01983) 817001 E-mail: info@solcom.com

Solidbase (UK) Ltd, Egerton Court, Haig Road, Knutsford, Cheshire, WA16 8FB Tel: (01565) 621150 Fax: (01565) 653950 E-mail: info@solidbase.co.uk

Soliton Associates Ltd, Coventry Point, Market Way, Coventry, CV1 1EA Tel: (024) 7622 0018

▶ Solutions 2 Enterprise Ltd, Church Road, Rainford, St. Helens, Merseyside, WA11 8HE Tel: (01744) 885860 Fax: (01744) 885872

Solutions With Software, 4 Yonder Way, Wanborough, Swindon, SN4 0BX Tel: (01793) 790379 Fax: (01793) 790379

South Bank Systems P.L.C., Compass Centre North, Chatham Maritime, Chatham, Kent, ME4 4YG Tel: (01634) 880141 Fax: (01634) 880383 E-mail: corporate@southbanksystems.com

Springdata, 116a Groby Road, Glenfield, Leicester, LE3 8GL Tel: 0116-232 0116

Stable Software, Stable Cottage, 3 Blind Lane, Hurworth, Darlington, County Durham, DL2 2JB Tel: (01325) 720039 E-mail: office@stablesoft.co.uk

▶ indicates data change since last edition

COMPUTER SOFTWARE – *continued*

Steanne Solutions, Hyde Park House, Cartwright Street, Hyde, Cheshire, SK14 4EH Tel: 0161-367 8137 Fax: 0161-367 8717 E-mail: info@steanne.co.uk

▶ Steller Performance Ltd, Unit 13 Silwood Park, Buckhurst Road, Ascot, Berkshire, SL5 7PW Tel: (01344) 870350 Fax: (01344) 870359

Summit Directions, The Innovation Centre, 217 Portobello, Sheffield, S1 4DP Tel: 0114-224 2624 Fax: 0114-224 2222 E-mail: innovations@the-summit.co.uk

Sunguard Systems Ltd, 33 St. Mary Axe, London, EC3A 8AA Tel: (020) 7337 6000 Fax: (020) 7337 6010

Sunrise Software Ltd, 50 Barwell Business Park, Leatherhead Road, Chessington, Surrey, KT9 2NY Tel: (020) 8391 9000 Fax: (020) 8391 4445 E-mail: enquiries@sunrisesw.com

Sunshine Solutions Ltd, 1 Hatchfield Cottages, Knighton Road, Broad Chalke, Salisbury, SP5 5DU Tel: (01722) 780885 Fax: (01722) 780886 E-mail: enquiries@sunshine-solutions.co.uk

Suntech Computer Services, 9 St. Colmans Park, Newry, County Down, BT34 2BX Tel: (028) 3026 6650 Fax: (028) 3083 4974 E-mail: messages@suntech.co.uk

▶ Support Force, Nionisle House, Station Road, Betchworth, Surrey, RH3 7BZ Tel: (0870) 7594357 E-mail: sales@thesupportforce.com

Sychron Ltd, Southern House, 1 Cambridge Terrace, Oxford, OX1 1RR Tel: (01865) 200211 Fax: (01865) 249666

Symantec Ltd, Green Park, 350 Brook Drive, Reading, RG2 6UH Tel: (0870) 2431080 Fax: (0870) 2431081

▶ Sysmax Ltd, Innovation Centre, Exploration Drive, Bridge of Don, Aberdeen, AB23 8GX Tel: (01224) 827217 Fax: (01224) 827218

System Access Europe Ltd, Tower 42 International Financial Centre, 25 Old Broad Street, London, EC2N 1HQ Tel: (020) 7588 8887 Fax: (020) 7588 8989

System Link (U K) Ltd, First Floor Holgate House, Holgate Court, 4-10 Western Road, Romford, RM1 3JF Tel: (01708) 733422 Fax: (01708) 730446

▶ Systemlogic Ltd, 2 Pell Street, Swansea, SA1 3ES Tel: (01792) 461577 Fax: (01792) 464411

Systems In Micro, 47 Gainsborough Street, Sudbury, Suffolk, CO10 2ET Tel: (01787) 313317 Fax: (01787) 372226 E-mail: admin@sysim.co.uk

Systems & Information Resources Ltd, 4 Hostle Park, Ilfracombe, Devon, EX34 9HW Tel: (01271) 867555 Fax: (01271) 867999 E-mail: info@softekltd.com

Systems & Software Ltd, 85 Alvechurch Road, Birmingham, B31 3PG Tel: 0121-604 7001 Fax: 0121-604 7002

Systemware Services Ltd, Unit 220, Fort Dunlop, Fort Parkway, Birmingham, B24 9FD Tel: 0121-749 8050 Fax: 0121-749 8075 E-mail: swhitehouse@ssl-uk.com

T I S Software Ltd, Regatta Place, Marlow Road, Bourne End, Buckinghamshire, SL8 5TD Tel: (01628) 532565 Fax: (01628) 532514 E-mail: info@tissoft.co.uk

Tadpole Cartesia plc, Waterloo House, Waterloo Street, Clifton, Bristol, BS8 4BT Tel: 0117-923 8853 Fax: 0117-923 8834

Technology Helpdesk, Unit 3, Turnbull Way, Livingston, West Lothian, EH54 8RB Tel: (01506) 436700 Fax: (01506) 436703 E-mail: sales@technologyhelpdesk.co.uk

Technology Services Group Edinburgh, Pentland Estate, Straiton, Edinburgh, EH20 9QW Tel: 0131-448 2400 Fax: 0131-448 0064 E-mail: enquiries@tsg.com

Teeside Education Support Services, Horsehouse, Leyburn, North Yorkshire, DL8 4TS Tel: (01969) 640364 Fax: (01969) 640383 E-mail: info@readindsoftware.com

Thamesdown SDC, Frankland Road, Blagrove, Swindon, SN5 8YU Tel: (01793) 428700 Fax: (01793) 511125 E-mail: sales@tsfltd.co.uk

▶ That Pc, 4 Wolseley Close, Plymouth, PL2 3BY Tel: (01752) 558000 Fax: (01752) 558008

Thesaurus Computer Services Ltd, Bank House, 171 Midsummer Boulevard, Milton Keynes, MK9 1EB Tel: (01908) 246500 Fax: (01908) 246555 E-mail: marketing@i-tcs.com

▶ Thought Technologies Ltd, Suite 28, 2 Upper York Street, Bristol, BS2 8QN Tel: 0117-924 8277

Time Technology Ltd, Brook House, Mint Street, Godalming, Surrey, GU7 1HE Tel: (01483) 863000 Fax: (01483) 425075 E-mail: sales@time-technology.co.uk

TMS Associates Ltd, 168 Clare Road, Cardiff, CF11 6RX Tel: (029) 2025 8900 Fax: (029) 2025 8255 E-mail: h.g.patel@ntlworld.com

Torex Ltd, Innovation House, Alcester, Warwickshire, B49 6HA Tel: (01789) 766755 Fax: 01789 766788 E-mail: sales@swl.co.uk

Total Home Entertainment International, Unit 1 Rosevale Business Park, Newcastle, Staffordshire, ST5 7QT Tel: (01782) 561000 Fax: (01782) 565400

Touch Systems Ltd, 261 Lyndon Road, Solihull, West Midlands, B92 7QP Tel: 0121-248 2448 Fax: 0121-248 2450 E-mail: sales@touchsystems.co.uk

Transware Computer Services Ltd, 218 Eagle Tower, Montpellier Drive, Cheltenham, Gloucestershire, GL50 1TA Tel: (01242) 583583 Fax: (01242) 523258 E-mail: transware@btinternet.com

▶ Tribeka, 134 The Harlequin, Watford, WD17 2UB Tel: (01923) 630259

Trilogy Publishing, Aries House, 43 Selkirk Street, Cheltenham, Gloucestershire, GL52 2HJ Tel: (01242) 222132 Fax: (01242) 235103 E-mail: sales@trilogypublishing.com

Tripoint Ltd, 1090 Guillat Avenue, Kent Science Park, Sittingbourne, Kent, ME9 8GU Tel: (01795) 434000 Fax: (01795) 434001 E-mail: admin@tripoint.co.uk

Tritech Computer Services Ltd, Forge House, Mill Road, Liss, Hampshire, GU33 7DX Tel: (01730) 893789 Fax: (01730) 894589 E-mail: sales@tritech.org.uk

Trog Associates Ltd, PO Box 243, South Croydon, Surrey, CR2 6WF Tel: (020) 8786 3614 Fax: (020) 8405 8049 E-mail: gostwrighter@dslpipex.com

Trustmark Solutions, Trustmark House, Alpha Court, Monks Cross Drive, Huntington, York, YO32 9WN Tel: (0870) 1210321 Fax: (0870) 1210320

▶ Turnkey Computer Technology Ltd, Thornton Lodge, East Kilbride Road, Clarkston, Glasgow, G76 9HW Tel: 0141-644 5444 Fax: 0141-644 5446

Ubiquity Software Corporation, Suite B Building 3 The Eastern Business Park, Wern Fawr Lane, St. Mellons, Cardiff, CF3 5EA Tel: (029) 2081 7500 Fax: (029) 2081 7501

Ultrasoft Technologies Ltd, 29 Knoll Park Road, Chertsey, Surrey, KT16 9LR Tel: (01932) 570057 Fax: (01932) 570103 E-mail: enquiry@ultrasoft-tech.co.uk

V T Software Solutions, Unit 4Thornbury Office Park, Midland Way, Thornbury, Bristol, BS35 2BS Tel: (01454) 874002 Fax: (01454) 874001 E-mail: enquire@vtsoftwaresolutions.com

V4Technical Ltd, 1 Quay Point, Station Road, Woodbridge, Suffolk, IP12 4AL Tel: (01394) 382400

▶ Vannypeco Consulting, Corsham Street, London, N1 6DR Tel: (020) 7490 4009 Fax: (020) 7490 8070

VBS Support Ltd, Gala House, 3, Raglan Road, Birmingham, B5 7RA Tel: (0870) 7534020 Fax: (0870) 7534022 E-mail: info@vbs.co.uk

▶ Venus Computers & Communications Ltd, 66 Ridgeways, Harlow, Essex, CM17 9HG Tel: (01279) 422211

▶ VeriSIM Ltd, Forsyth House, Rosyth Europarc, Rosyth, Dunfermline, Fife, KY11 2UU Tel: (01383) 428059 Fax: (01383) 428060

Vertical Systems, 14 Hemmells, Basildon, Essex, SS15 6ED Tel: (01268) 416155 Fax: (01268) 541287 E-mail: peter.healey@tarsc.net

Vigo Computer Systems Ltd, Hewell Lane, Malt Shovel Barn, Tardebigge, Bromsgrove, Worcestershire, B60 1LL Tel: 0121-447 7222 Fax: 0121-447 7333 E-mail: support@vigosoftware.co.uk

Virtual Image, 184 Reddish Road, Stockport, Cheshire, SK5 7HS Tel: 0161-480 1915 Fax: 0161-612 2965E-mail: virimage@cs.com

Virtual Reality Marketing Ltd, PO Box 26, Moreton-in-Marsh, Gloucestershire, GL56 0ZD Tel: (01608) 652676 Fax: (01608) 652533

▶ Vision Computing, Treleigh Industrial Estate, Jon Davey Drive, Redruth, Cornwall, TR16 4AX Tel: (01209) 315566

▶ Visual Data Concepts, Home Farm, Minety, Malmesbury, Wiltshire, SN16 9PL Tel: (01666) 861015 Fax: (01666) 861181

▶ Visual Technology Solutions Ltd, Church Hatch, Market Place, Ringwood, Hampshire, BH24 1AW Tel: (0870) 7542269 Fax: (0870) 7542279

▶ Visualfiles Computer Systems, Rownhams, Southampton, SO16 8LS Tel: (023) 8073 8539 Fax: (023) 8079 9768

Wade Computing Services Ltd, 263 Buxton Road, Stockport, Cheshire, SK2 7NR Tel: 0161-456 0104 Fax: 0161-483 9119 E-mail: sales@wadecomputing.co.uk

Wildings Professional Systems Ltd, 14 Dunlop Road, Hadleigh Road Industrial Estat, Ipswich, IP2 0UG Tel: (01473) 219819 Fax: (01473) 219955 E-mail: wildings@wildings.com

Glyn Williams & Associates, Ladywood, Droitwich, Worcestershire, WR9 0AJ Tel: (01905) 757700 Fax: (01905) 757800

Williams Ian Computer Software Consultancy, 12 High Green, Norwich, NR1 4AP Tel: (01603) 300301

▶ Wincan Computer Systems, 13 Cherry Street, Woking, Surrey, GU21 6EE Tel: (01483) 762226 Fax: (01483) 762226 E-mail: info@wincaneurope.com

Windowlink Ltd, Station Road, Minety, Malmesbury, Wilts, SN16 9QY Tel: (0870) 7701640 Fax: (01666) 860889

Windows & SQL Programmers Ltd, 31 Leconfield Road, London, N5 2RZ Tel: (020) 7359 0099 Fax: (020) 7359 0110 E-mail: services@winsql.com

Worldwide Solutions Ltd, Unit 5, Alfred Court, Saxon Business Park, Hanbury Road, Stoke Prior, Bromsgrove, Worcestershire, B60 4AD Tel: (01527) 870849 Fax: (01527) 874499 E-mail: enquiries@wwsolutions.co.uk

▶ www.allpower2computers.co.uk, PO Box 7327, Colchester, CO6 3WB Tel: 0845 4308732 Fax: 01206 247094 E-mail: softwaresales@allpower2computers.co.uk

Wych Tree Technology, 22 Afan Valley Road, Neath, West Glamorgan, SA11 3SN Tel: (01639) 645016 E-mail: sw@wychtree.com

X K O Group P.L.C., Clyde House, 16 Milburn Avenue, Oldbrook, Milton Keynes, MK6 2WA Tel: (01908) 295400 Fax: (01908) 393633

▶ Xchange International, 17-18 Britton Street, London, EC1M 5NQ Tel: (020) 7490 4455 Fax: (020) 7490 4466 E-mail: sales@xchangeuk.com

Xerox Ltd Technical Centre, PO Box 17, Welwyn Garden City, Hertfordshire, AL7 1BU Tel: (01707) 353535 Fax: (01707) 353424

▶ Xinit Systems Ltd, 7 Skylines Village, Limeharbour, London, E14 9TS Tel: (020) 7538 8230 Fax: (020) 7538 8246

Xperience Support Ltd, 11 Ferguson Drive, Knockmore Hill Industrial Park, Lisburn, County Antrim, BT28 2EX Tel: (028) 9267 7533 Fax: (028) 9267 2887 E-mail: info@xperience-group.com

▶ XPT Solutions, One St. Colme Street, Edinburgh, EH3 6AA Tel: 0131-220 8253 Fax: 0131-220 8201

▶ Xtreme Technology, 87 Hawthorn Road, Bognor Regis, West Sussex, PO21 2BE Tel: (01243) 825255 Fax: (01243) 825255

Y D P Ltd, 151 Knox Road, Wellingborough, Northamptonshire, NN8 1HX Tel: (01933) 229335 Fax: (01933) 223975 E-mail: info@ydpltd.co.uk

Yardi Apb, 201-249 Avebury Boulevard, Milton Keynes, MK9 1AX Tel: (01908) 308400 Fax: (01908) 550022 E-mail: personnel@apb.co.uk

Yo6 Computing, White Lodge, Tollerton Road, Huby, York, YO61 1HX Tel: (0845) 6441440 Fax: (0871) 2205371 E-mail: enquiries@yo6.co.uk

COMPUTER SOFTWARE DESIGN

A & O Consultancy Ltd, 92A The Maltings, Roydon Road, Stanstead Abbotts, Ware, Hertfordshire, SG12 8UU Tel: (01920) 872321 E-mail:

▶ AEYE, 1 Glencairn House, 70 Ridgway, London, London, SW19 4RA Tel: (020) 8879 9832 Fax: (020) 9212 9079 E-mail: info@aeye.biz

Affirm Ltd, The Barn, Upton-upon-Severn, Worcester, WR8 0ST Tel: (01684) 291710 Fax: (01684) 291712 E-mail: sales@screenjet.com

▶ Applications Management Ltd, 11g Kingwood Road, Fulham, London, SW6 6SW Tel: (020) 7386 9916 Fax: (020) 7386 9916 E-mail: info@applicationsmanagement.com

▶ ATMT Group P.L.C., 3 Central Business Centre, Great Central Way, London, NW10 0UR Tel: (0870) 4102868 Fax: (0870) 4102869 E-mail: info@atmtgroup.com

▶ Baker Automation, 3 Butternab Road, Huddersfield, HD4 7AH Tel: (07802) 495848 Fax: 0161-881 9376E-mail: john@ukelo.co.uk

Breeze It Ltd, 5 Colwick Quays Business Park, Colwick, Nottingham, NG4 2JY Tel: (0845) 0092788 Fax: (0845) 0092789 E-mail: steve.watkins@breezeassist.com

Geoff Bullen Electronics, Unit 1-2 Woods Way, Goring-by-Sea, Worthing, West Sussex, BN12 4QY Tel: (01903) 244500 Fax: (01903) 700715 E-mail: sales@gbelectronics.com

Celoxica Ltd, 66 Milton Park, Abingdon, Oxfordshire, OX14 4RX Tel: (01235) 863656 Fax: (01235) 863648 E-mail: sales.emea@celoxica.com

Chameleon Services, Senior House, 59-61 High Street, Rickmansworth, Hertfordshire, WD3 1RH Tel: (01923) 896939 Fax: (01923) 896526 E-mail: sims@infoflex-sims.co.uk

Cognos Ltd, Adlington Court Greencourts Business Park, Styal Road, Manchester, M22 5LG Tel: 0161-436 8888 Fax: 0161-436 6918

▶ D C A Data Solutions, 17 Gayfield Square, Edinburgh, EH1 3NX Tel: 0131-556 7787 Fax: 0131-556 2856

Data Development Services Ltd, Blythe Valley Innovation Centr, Central Boulevard, Blythe Valley Park, Solihull, West Midlands, B90 8AJ Tel: 0121-506 9310

▶ Epic Software Ltd, 105 Hanover Street, Edinburgh, EH2 1DJ Tel: 0131-477 2545 Fax: 0131-624 0071 E-mail: sales@epicsoftware.co.uk

Gissing Software Ltd, 21-23 Elmfield Road, Bromley, BR1 1LT Tel: (020) 8315 6550 Fax: (020) 8315 6530 E-mail: sales@mighter-gissing.com

Halcyon Software Ltd, 5 The Forum, Minerva BSNS Park, Orton Wistow, Peterborough, PE2 6FT Tel: (01733) 234995 Fax: (01733) 234994 E-mail: sales@halcyonsoftware.com

IT Networks Ltd, 19-21 High Street, Coleshill, Birmingham, B46 1AY Tel: 0870 1616611 Fax: 0870 1616622 E-mail: info@acutec.co.uk

▶ It Software Solutions, Dunstable Road, Toddington, Dunstable, Bedfordshire, LU5 6DT Tel: (07811) 741568 E-mail: zoltan@it-software-solutions.com

▶ J V F Consultants Ltd, 4 Loughborough Road, Mountsorrel, Loughborough, Leicestershire, LE12 7AT Tel: 0116-230 2880 Fax: 0116-237 6115 E-mail: sales@jvf.co.uk

▶ Karlan Digital Ltd, 76 Howdale Road, Hull, HU8 9JZ Tel: (07841) 870659 E-mail: enquiries@karlandigital.co.uk

Linear Blue Ltd, 400 Thames Valley Park Drive, Thames Valley Park, Reading, RG6 1PT Tel: (0870) 351 6594 E-mail: info@linearblue.com

Richard Moon Consulting, PO Box 425, Bedford, MK44 2ZW Tel: (01234) 772509 E-mail: richard@richardmoon.com

Mos Computers Ltd, Queen Square, Saltford, Bristol, BS31 3EL Tel: (01225) 873117 Fax: (01225) 873776 E-mail: info@moscomputers.co.uk

Myco Systems Ltd, 17 Criss Grove, Chalfont St. Peter, Gerrards Cross, Buckinghamshire, SL9 9HG Tel: (01753) 893390 E-mail: enquiries@mycosystems.co.uk

Network Associates (Midlands) Ltd, Vincent House, Buntsford Park Road, Bromsgrove, Worcestershire, B60 3DX Tel: (01527) 576933 Fax: (0870) 706 2522 E-mail: enquiries@network-associates.co.uk

P T C (UK) Ltd, Inavation House, Harvest Crescent, Fleet, Hampshire, GU51 2QR Tel: (01252) 817000 Fax: (01252) 817000

Radioscape Ltd, 2 Albany Terrace, London, NW1 4DS Tel: (020) 7224 1586 Fax: (020) 7224 1595 E-mail: info@radioscape.com

Selectactive Ltd, 67a Frimley Green Road, Frimley, Camberley, Surrey, GU16 8AL Tel: (01276) 683891 Fax: (01276) 683891 E-mail: alan@selectactive.co.uk

Sigmer, The Sussex Innovation Centre, Science Park Square, Falmer, Brighton, BN1 9SB Tel: (01273) 234663 Fax: (01273) 669 701 E-mail: info@sigmer.com

▶ Streamline Computer Solutions Ltd, Orchard House, Barncroft Road, Berkhamsted, Hertfordshire, HP4 3NL Tel: (01442) 405768 E-mail: alan@streamline-solutions.co.uk

TCS Computer Services Ltd, The Brewhouse 19 Old Bexley Business Park, Bourne Road, Bexley, Kent, DA5 1LR Tel: (01322) 559840 Fax: (01322) 550010 E-mail: rodney.gent@tcscs.co.uk

Tricostar, 11 Limes Court, Conduit Lane, Hoddesdon, Hertfordshire, EN11 8EP Tel: (01992) 442800 Fax: (01992) 442810 E-mail: info@tricostar.com

▶ Waveplus Systems Ltd, Broadhaven Cottage, Honeysuckle Lane, Headley Down, Bordon, Hampshire, GU35 8JA Tel: (01428) 713 430 E-mail: enquiries@waveplus.co.uk

COMPUTER SOFTWARE DEVELOPMENT

A C K Ltd, 35 Grosvenor Road, Caversham, Reading, RG4 5EN Tel: 0118-948 2588 Fax: 0118-946 5984 E-mail: sales@ackltd.co.uk

A D Developments Ltd, 5a London Road, Loughton, Milton Keynes, MK5 8AB Tel: (01908) 222606 E-mail: enquiries@addevelopments.com

A & L Services Ltd, Millcraig Farm Cottages, Alness, Ross-Shire, IV17 0YA Tel: (01349) 882344 Fax: (01349) 884800 E-mail: sales@software-scotland.co.uk

A & O Consultancy Ltd, 92A The Maltings, Roydon Road, Stanstead Abbotts, Ware, Hertfordshire, SG12 8UU Tel: (01920) 872321 E-mail:

A R M Ltd, 110 Fulbourn Road, Cherry Hinton, Cambridge, CB1 9NJ Tel: (01223) 400400 Fax: (01223) 400410 E-mail: info@arm.com

▶ Aardvark Wisdom, 126 Station Road, Tempsford, Sandy, Bedfordshire, SG19 2AY Tel: (0870) 3500880 Fax: (0870) 3500881

Abba Consultants, Calamare, Holly Close, Woking, Surrey, GU21 7QZ Tel: (01483) 833021 Fax: (01483) 833022

▶ Abc Computer, Whitfield Buildings, 192-200 Pensby Road, Heswall, Wirral, Merseyside, CH60 7RJ Tel: 0151-342 2791

▶ Abraqsys Business Systems, 13 Duncan Close, Moulton Park Industrial Estate, Northampton, NN3 6WL Tel: (01604) 797950 Fax: (01604) 797951 E-mail: sales@abraqsys.co.uk

▶ Absolute It Solutions Ltd, 1 Lon Pobty, Bangor, Gwynedd, LL57 1HR Tel: (01248) 360047

Acardia, Venture House 2 Arlington Square, Downshire Way, Bracknell, Berkshire, RG12 1WA Tel: (0845) 2301055 Fax: (01344) 868333 E-mail: admin@acardia.co.uk

▶ Accelrys Ltd, 334 Science Park, Milton Road, Cambridge, CB4 0WN Tel: (01223) 228500 Fax: (01223) 228501 E-mail: admin@accelrys.com

Ace Webmasters, 34-40 Wormgate, Boston, Lincolnshire, PE21 6NR Tel: (07050) 224352 E-mail: firstatboston@yahoo.co.uk

Achiever Software, Ashted Lock Way, Birmingham, B7 4AZ Tel: 0121-380 1010 Fax: 0121-380 1011 E-mail: sales@achiever.co.uk

ACI Worldwide Ltd, 27-33 Cookridge Street, Leeds, LS2 3AG Tel: 0113-394 0100 Fax: 0113-394 0129

▶ Actinic Holdings Ltd, Globe House, Lavender Park Road, West Byfleet, Surrey, KT14 6ND Tel: (01932) 358340 Fax: (01932) 358341 E-mail: enquiries@actinic.co.uk

Action Information Technologies Ltd, 1 Butler Road, Shrewsbury, SY3 7AJ Tel: (01743) 244377 Fax: (01743) 244367 E-mail: sales@actionit.demon.co.uk

Active Media Technology Ltd, Golden Gate Lodge, Weston Road, Crewe, CW2 5XN Tel: (01270) 580400 Fax: (01270) 589800 E-mail: info@active-media-online.com

Adelard Computer Consultants, 10 Northampton Square, London, EC1V 0HB Tel: (020) 7490 9450 Fax: (020) 7490 9451 E-mail: sales@adelard.co.uk

▶ Adjusting Solutions, 1 Alie Street, London, E1 8DE Tel: (020) 7488 3066 E-mail: support@iss-web.co.uk

COMPUTER SOFTWARE DEVELOPMENT - *continued*

Adobe Systems (U K) Ltd, 3 Roundwood Avenue, Stockley Park, Uxbridge, Middlesex, UB11 1AY Tel: (020) 8606 4000 Fax: (020) 8606 4004 E-mail: jobs@adobe.co.uk

Advanced Analysis & Integration Ltd, Riverpark Road, Manchester, M40 2XP Tel: 0161-231 1800 Fax: 0161-231 0509 E-mail: sales@aail.co.uk

Advensys Computer Systems, 63a Borough Street, Castle Donington, Derby, DE74 2LB Tel: (01332) 853113 Fax: (01332) 853949 E-mail: info@advensys.co.uk

Affinite Europe, 32 Station Road, Burley in Wharfedale, Ilkley, West Yorkshire, LS29 7JL Tel: (01943) 864124 Fax: (01943) 864917 E-mail: office@affinite.co.uk

Agency Sector Management UK Ltd, Ashford House, 41-45 Church Road, Ashford, Middlesex, TW15 2TQ Tel: (01784) 242200 Fax: (01784) 242012 E-mail: info@asm.org.uk

Aldebaran Systems Ltd, Unit 47 Cressex Enterprise Centre, Lincoln Road, High Wycombe, Buckinghamshire, HP12 3RL Tel: (01494) 614630 E-mail: info@aldebaran.co.uk

Alias Ltd, Stuart Road, Manor Park, Runcorn, Cheshire, WA7 1TS Tel: (01928) 579311 Fax: (01928) 579389 E-mail: info@alias.ltd.uk

▶ Allcomm Communications Ltd, 44 Mount Road, Tettenhall Wood, Wolverhampton, WV6 8HW Tel: (01902) 743000 Fax: (01902) 744665 E-mail: cburgwinn@allcomm.co.uk

▶ Alligator Business Solutions, 17 Whinhill Road, Glasgow, G53 5RQ Tel: 0141-882 5678 Fax: 0141-882 1443 E-mail: enquiries@alligatorsolutions.com

Alpha Business Support Ltd, Cavendish House, Cavendish Avenue, New Malden, Surrey, KT3 6QQ Tel: (0845) 1110060 Fax: (020) 8942 1100 E-mail: info@alphabusiness.net

Alpha Co Consulting Engineers Ltd, 30 Stowell Cresent, Wareham, Dorset, BH20 4PZ Tel: (01929) 551207 Fax: (07802) 431378 E-mail: info@alpha-comp.co.uk

Alterian Holdings Ltd, Century Place, Bond Street, Bristol, BS2 9AG Tel: 0117-970 3200 Fax: 0117-970 3201E-mail: info@alterian.com

Amadeus Software Ltd, Orchard Farm, Witney Lane, Leafield, Witney, Oxfordshire, OX29 9PG Tel: (01993) 878287 Fax: (01993) 878042 E-mail: info@amadeus.co.uk

▶ Amas Europe, 76 Lancefield Quay, Glasgow, G3 8HP Tel: (0870) 7471350 Fax: (0870) 1277477

And Technology Research Ltd, 4 Forest Drive, Theydon Bois, Epping, Essex, CM16 7EY Tel: (01992) 814655 Fax: (01992) 813362

Anglia Business Computers Training Ltd, Harston Mill, Royston Road, Harston, Cambridge, CB22 7GG Tel: (01223) 873400 Fax: (01223) 873401 E-mail: mktg@angliabs.com

Anite Mobile Working Solutions, 353 Buckingham Avenue, Slough, Slough, SL1 4PF Tel: (01753) 804000 Fax: (01753) 735735

Annite Public Sector Ltd, Sheridan House, Pitfield, Kiln Farm, Milton Keynes, MK11 3LW Tel: (01908) 264500 Fax: (01908) 264501 E-mail: enquiries@aniteps.com

Another Dimension Ltd, 167 Ardleigh Green Road, Hornchurch, Essex, RM11 2LF Tel: (01708) 701511 Fax: (01708) 701994 E-mail: info@anotherdimension.co.uk

Ant Software Ltd, Cambridge Business Park, Cowley Road, Cambridge, CB4 0WZ Tel: (01223) 716400 Fax: (01223) 716401 E-mail: info@antlimited.com

Aonix Europe, Newtown House, Newtown Road, Henley-on-Thames, Oxfordshire, RG9 1HG Tel: (01491) 415000 Fax: (01491) 575033 E-mail: info@aonix.co.uk

Aquarius Software, The Purlins, Black Robin Lane, Kingston, Canterbury, Kent, CT4 6HR Tel: (01227) 830131 E-mail: aquariussoft@freeuk.com

Aquatec Electronics Ltd, High Street, Hartley Wintney, Hook, Hampshire, RG27 8NY Tel: (01252) 843072 Fax: (01252) 843074 E-mail: sales@aquatec.org.uk

▶ Arbico Computers, 120 Franciscan Road, London, SW17 8HL Tel: (020) 8772 4090 Fax: (020) 8772 4090 E-mail: info@arbico.co.uk

Arcontech Ltd, 31-35 Kirby Street, London, EC1N 8TE Tel: (020) 7405 2111 Fax: (020) 7831 6667 E-mail: mail@arcontech.com

Arena Q S Ltd, Arena House, 23 Plough Way, London, SE16 2LS Tel: (020) 7237 1415 Fax: (020) 7237 1452

Aries Commercial Machinery Ltd, The Hollies School Lane, Auckley, Doncaster, South Yorkshire, DN9 3JR Tel: (01302) 770777 Fax: (01302) 770787 E-mail: info@aries.co.uk

Aries Software Service, 23 Surbiton Road, Southend-on-Sea, SS2 4NR Tel: (01702) 463833 Fax: (01702) 466122 E-mail: ariessoftware@btconnect.com

Armada Software, Glendower, Llangynog, Oswestry, Shropshire, SY10 0EX Tel: (01691) 860304 E-mail: armada@onetel.net.uk

▶ Ash Associates, PO Box 5374, Ferndown, Dorset, BH22 0ZX Tel: (0845) 1232701 E-mail: recruit@ash-associates.com

▶ Ash Transport Solutions, Priory Coach House, Ash Priors, Taunton, Somerset, TA4 3ND Tel: (01823) 431600

Asset Business Systems Ltd, 8a Milburn Road, Bournemouth, BH4 9HJ Tel: (01202) 757599 Fax: (01202) 757588 E-mail: davemac@assetsystems.co.uk

Astech Consultants, Albion Street, Chipping Norton, Oxfordshire, OX7 5BL Tel: (01608) 645251 Fax: (01608) 646510 E-mail: info@astech.uk.com

Atrium Ltd, Yateley Lodge, Reading Road, Yateley, Hampshire, GU46 7AA Tel: (01252) 862423 Fax: (01252) 890596 E-mail: info@atriumcom.com

▶ Autoconnect Contact Centre, Hewell Road, Redditch, Worcestershire, B97 6AY Tel: (01527) 61661

Avisoft Ltd, 11 Church Street, Kirkby In Ashfield, Nottingham, NG17 8LA Tel: (01623) 755555 E-mail: sales@avisoft.co.uk

Avon Control Engineering & Software, The Old Vicarage, Somerset Square, Nailsea, Bristol, BS48 1RN Tel: (01275) 853721 Fax: (01275) 857746 E-mail: sales@graynailsea.freeserve.co.uk

Aw Computer Systems Ltd, 16 Dundry Lane, Winford, Bristol, BS40 8AN Tel: (01275) 474591 Fax: (0870) 9004911 E-mail: awcs@dial.pipex.com

Axiom Connection Ltd, 2A Station Yard, Hungerford, Berkshire, RG17 0DY Tel: (01488) 683033 Fax: (01488) 683133 E-mail: axiom@axiomconnection.com

▶ Aztec Software & Technology Services Ltd., 1, Berkeey Street, London, W1J 8DJ Tel: (020) 7016 9852 E-mail: rphanee@aztecsoft.com

▶ B B N Communicatios, 18 Strand Street, Poole, Dorset, BH15 1SB Tel: (01202) 669922 Fax: (01202) 669922 E-mail: sales@bbncomms.co.uk

Babbage Software Ltd, Victoria House, Victoria Street, Totnes, Devon, TQ9 5EF Tel: (01803) 864328

▶ Back Scatter Ltd, 7 Grantley Gardens, Glasgow, G41 3PY Tel: 0141-636 1222

Baillie Associates Ltd, 50 Main Street, Lowdham, Nottingham, NG14 7BE Tel: 0115-966 3929 Fax: 0115-966 4745 E-mail: binfo@baillies.com

Banks Software Ltd, 74 Forest Road, Oldbury, West Midlands, B68 0EF Tel: 0121-421 8295 E-mail: sales@banks-software.co.uk

▶ Bargain Outlet Ltd, Unit 18 Mildmay House, Foundry Lane, Burnham-on-Crouch, Essex, CM0 8BL Tel: (0871) 2211422 Fax: (01621) 781199 E-mail: sales@bargainoutlet.co.uk

Belton Technological Services Ltd, 2 Church Street, Henfield, West Sussex, BN5 9NR Tel: (01273) 492320 Fax: (01273) 494849 E-mail: bts.ltd@btopenworld.com

Birla Technologies Ltd, 5Th Floor Congress House, 14 Lyon Road, Harrow, Middlesex, HA1 2FD Tel: (020) 8424 7320 Fax: (020) 8861 5062 E-mail: ketanm@birlatechnologies.com

▶ Blackstaff It, 1 Mill Court, 500-502 Falls Road, Belfast, BT12 6EP Tel: (028) 9062 9991

Blade Interactive Studios, Suite A, Great Northern Warehouse, Deansgete Mews, Manchester, M3 4EN Tel: 0161-839 6622 Fax: 0161-839 6688 E-mail: info@bladeinteractive.com

Blueberry Consultants Ltd, 22 Clarendon Street, Leamington Spa, Warwickshire, CV32 4PG Tel: (01926) 430168 Fax: (01926) 430133 E-mail: penny.oddy@bbconsult.co.uk

BMTGroup Ltd, Goodrich House, 1 Waldegrave Road, Teddington, Middlesex, TW11 8LZ Tel: (020) 8943 5544 Fax: (020) 8943 5347 E-mail: enquiries@bmtmail.com

Bond International Software Ltd, Courtlands, Parklands Avenue, Goring-by-Sea, Worthing, West Sussex, BN12 4NG Tel: (01903) 707070 Fax: (01903) 707080 E-mail: sales@bond.co.uk

▶ Borsdane Wood Ltd, 76a Market Street, Farnworth, Bolton, BL4 7NY Tel: (01204) 577776 Fax: (01204) 575600 E-mail: info@borsdane.com

▶ Brit Software Ltd, Unit 6, Quayside Business Centre, Lowestoft Enterprise Park, School Road, Lowestoft, Suffolk, NR33 9NW Tel: (0870) 7664965 Fax: (0870) 0117596 E-mail: info@britsoftware.com

Brown's Operating System Services Ltd, Brigade Street, London, SE3 0TW Tel: (020) 8297 9797 Fax: (020) 8318 3939 E-mail: mail@browns.co.uk

▶ Business Dispatch, Unit 3-4 Kingspark Business Centre, Kingston Road, New Malden, Surrey, KT3 3ST Tel: (020) 8605 1771 Fax: (020) 8605 1886 E-mail: sales@businessdispatch.com

Business Electronic & Computer Services, 74-75 Victoria Road, Great Yarmouth, Norfolk, NR30 3BA Tel: (01493) 330498 Fax: (01493) 332436

▶ Buzitech Computer Systems & It Support, 23 Furzy Park, Haverfordwest, Dyfed, SA61 1HG Tel: (01437) 779201 Fax: (01437) 767892 E-mail: info@buzinetsolutions.com

C C T Infotech Ltd, Unit 7C Priory Tech Park, Saxon Way, Hull, HU13 9PB Tel: (01482) 647044 Fax: (01482) 647046 E-mail: sales@cct-infotech.co.uk

C G P Associates Ltd, 2 Maple Road, Enigma Business Park, Malvern, Worcestershire, WR14 1GQ Tel: (01684) 584700 Fax: (0870) 0522410 E-mail: derekc@cgp.co.uk

C J Microsystems, Walnut Tree Cottage, Sutton Road, Cookham, Maidenhead, Berkshire, SL6 9SY Tel: (01628) 520113 E-mail: colin@cjmicro.co.uk

C P C Computers Ltd, Hay House, 21 Stroud Road, Gloucester, GL1 5AA Tel: (01452) 553344 Fax: (01452) 553345 E-mail: sales@cpccomputers.co.uk

C P L Ltd, Liverpool House, Penlan Street, Pwllheli, Gwynedd, LL53 5DE Tel: (01758) 613035 Fax: (01758) 612485 E-mail: cplltd@compuserve.com

Caliach Ltd, 7 The Green, West Drayton, Middlesex, UB7 7PL Tel: (01895) 430313 Fax: (01895) 448226 E-mail: sales@caliach.com

Cambridge Algorithmica Ltd, 9 Oakdene, Beaconsfield, Buckinghamshire, HP9 2BZ Tel: (01494) 678989 Fax: (01494) 678990 E-mail: info@camalg.co.uk

Cameleon Systems, Cuckoo Lane, Pinchbeck, Spalding, Lincolnshire, PE11 3XT Tel: (01775) 680481 E-mail: martin@chameleon-systems.net

▶ Cams Software, Whitehall, 75 School Lane, Hartford, Northwich, Cheshire, CW8 1PF Tel: (01606) 781261 Fax: (01606) 784566 E-mail: info@camssoftware.com

Capita Business Services Ltd, Manvers House, Manvers Street, Trowbridge, Wiltshire, BA14 8YX Tel: (01225) 773000 Fax: (01225) 777625

Capita Education Services, 5 Mercian Close, Cirencester, Gloucestershire, GL7 1LT Tel: (01285) 647500 Fax: (01285) 647599 E-mail: sales@dolphin-cs.co.uk

▶ Carallon Ltd, Studio G9 Shepherds Studios, Rockley Road, London, W14 0DA Tel: (020) 7371 2032

▶ Cardinale, Regus House, 400 Thames Valley Park Drive, Reading, RG6 1PT Tel: 0118-965 3444 Fax: 0118-965 3544

Cauldron Business Systems, 2 Walley Grove, High Road Well, Halifax, West Yorkshire, HX2 0AE Tel: (01422) 329500 Fax: (01422) 329500 E-mail: cauldronuk@aol.com

CCM Ace Ltd, 223 Bury New Road, Whitefield, Manchester, M45 8GW Tel: 0161-766 4686 Fax: 0161-767 9217 E-mail: sales@ccmace.co.uk

CCSS Europe Ltd, 6 The Courtyard, Campus Way, Gillingham Business Park, Gillingham, Kent, ME8 0NZ Tel: (01634) 370444 Fax: (01634) 370555E-mail: info@ccssltd.com

▶ Cede Tech, 78 London Road, Worcester, WR5 2DY Tel: (01905) 831599

Cellar Systems Ltd, 7 Grange Mills, Weir Road, London, SW12 0NE Tel: (020) 8673 5104 Fax: (020) 8673 2649

Centrereed Ltd, Thames House, Thames Street, Rotherham, South Yorkshire, S60 1LU Tel: (01709) 827700 Fax: (01709) 827715 E-mail: sales@centrereed.co.uk

Cham Ltd, 40 High St Wimbledon, London, SW19 5AU Tel: (020) 8947 7651 Fax: (020) 8879 3497 E-mail: phoenics@cham.co.uk

▶ Chameleon Services, Senior House, 59-61 High Street, Rickmansworth, Hertfordshire, WD3 1RH Tel: (01923) 896939 Fax: (01923) 896526 E-mail: cims@infoflex-cims.co.uk

Chelton Desant Comunications Ltd, Emblem House, Pynes Hill, Exeter, EX2 5BA Tel: (01392) 667777 Fax: (01392) 667778 E-mail: info@whiskyalpha.com

Cincom Systems UK Ltd, 1 Grenfell Road, Maidenhead, Berkshire, SL6 1HN Tel: (01628) 542300 Fax: (01628) 542310

Claremont Controls Ltd, Suite 4 Wansbeck Business Centre, Rotary Parkway, Ashington, Northumberland, NE63 8QZ Tel: (01670) 819000 Fax: (01670) 857886 E-mail: honet@claremont-controls.co.uk

▶ Clarity Computing, 33 Fryent Grove, London, NW9 7HE Tel: (020) 8205 4242 Fax: (020) 8205 4242 E-mail: jon@clarity-computing.com

▶ Cleaford Services Ltd, 46 Hazell Road, Farnham, Surrey, GU9 7BP Tel: (01252) 717166 Fax: (01252) 717137 E-mail: sales@cleaford.co.uk

▶ Coalition Computer Systems, 1 Newhams Row, London, SE1 3UZ Tel: (020) 7234 0312 Fax: (020) 7504 8233

Cobweb Computers, 471 Buxton Road, Stockport, Cheshire, SK2 7HE Tel: 0161-484 0100

Codel Computer Systems, 71 St. Helens Road, Swansea, SA1 4BG Tel: (01792) 654154 Fax: (01792) 644392 E-mail: info@codelsoftware.com

Commontime Ltd, 568 Burton Road, Derby, DE23 6DG Tel: (01332) 368500 Fax: (01332) 366880 E-mail: sales@commontime.com

▶ Community Network Services Ltd, 204-207 Berth, Western Docks, Southampton, SO15 1DA Tel: (023) 8079 9601 Fax: (023) 8079 9602

▶ Component One Europe Ltd, Knapp House, Howley, Chard, Somerset, TA20 3DU Tel: (01460) 234636 Fax: (01460) 234616 E-mail: info@componentone.co.uk

Component Source, 30 Greyfriars Road, Reading, RG1 1PE Tel: 0118-958 1111 Fax: 0118-958 9999 E-mail: sales@componentsource.com

Computential Computer Systems, 70 Norris Road, Sale, Cheshire, M33 3QR Tel: 0161-969 2663

Computer Associates UK plc, Ditton Park, Riding Court Road, Datchet, Slough, SL3 9LL Tel: (01753) 577733 Fax: (01753) 825464

▶ Computer Craft, Unit 26 Shaftesbury Centre, 83 Barlby Road, London, W10 6BN Tel: (020) 8964 0734

Concorde Informatics Ltd, Stoneleigh, 39 Halifax Road, Brighouse, West Yorkshire, HD6 2AQ Tel: (01484) 405405 Fax: (01484) 405400 E-mail: info@concordeinf.com

▶ Connective Logic Projects, Paceycombe House, Paceycombe Way, Poundbury, Dorchester, Dorset, DT1 3WB Tel: (01305) 251123 Fax: (01305) 251123

▶ Contron Computer Systems, Station House North, Mercer Road, Warnham, Horsham, West Sussex, RH12 3SR Tel: (01403) 261029 Fax: (01403) 261120

Convergys Emea Ltd, Building 1020, Cambourne Business Park, Cambourne, Cambridge, CB3 6DN Tel: (01223) 705000 Fax: (01223) 705001

Coral Ltd, The Forge, Grange Court, Tongham, Farnham, Surrey, GU10 1DW Tel: (01252) 781000 Fax: (01252) 781001 E-mail: sales@coral.ltd.uk

▶ Corelogic Computer Systems, Studley Road, Redditch, Worcestershire, B98 7HR Tel: (01527) 503691 E-mail: sales@corelogic.co.uk

▶ Cormorant Information Systems, Leveret House, Manor Park Estate, Nailsea, Bristol, BS48 4DD Tel: (01275) 854455 Fax: (0871) 4338600 E-mail: sales@cormorant.co.uk

Corporate Upgrade Centre Ltd, Ornhams Hall, Boroughbridge, York, YO51 9JH Tel: (01423) 324777 Fax: (01423) 324113

Counter Solutions Ltd, Lakeside Business Centre, Shipley, Heanor, Derbyshire, DE75 7JQ Tel: (01773) 530303 Fax: (01773) 530404 E-mail: sales@countersolutions.com

Crayford Ltd, The Old Fire Station, Christchurch St West, Frome, Somerset, BA11 1EH Tel: (01373) 474466 Fax: (01373) 474499 E-mail: roger@crayford.ltd.uk

CRC Associates, 41 The Park, Stow on the Wold, Cheltenham, Gloucestershire, GL54 1DX Tel: (01451) 831048 Fax: (01451) 832297

Croft Computer Systems, 124 Heath Lane, Croft, Warrington, WA3 7DS Tel: (01925) 764999 Fax: (01925) 765655 E-mail: croft.computers@virgin.net

Crombie Computer Consultants, 28 Bolney Avenue, Peacehaven, East Sussex, BN10 8NA Tel: (01273) 583304 Fax: (01273) 575312E-mail: ccc@crombies.freeserve.co.uk

Crown Max Investments Ltd, Halesfield 19, Telford, Shropshire, TF7 4QT Tel: (01952) 581121 Fax: (01952) 588284 E-mail: info@crownmax.co.uk

Cruse Control Ltd, 6 Wolsey Mansions, Main Avenue, Moor Park, Northwood, Middlesex, HA6 2HL Tel: (01923) 842295 Fax: (01923) 842698 E-mail: mail@crusecontrol.com

Custom Software Systems, 2 Undercliff Rd, Wemyss Bay, Renfrewshire, PA18 6AQ Tel: 01475 522541 Fax: 01475 522572

Cygnet Solutions Ltd, Swan House, The Straith, Priestland, Darvel, Ayrshire, KA17 0LP Tel: (01560) 323444 Fax: (01560) 323432

D K Computing Services, Kebbell House, Delta Gain, Watford, WD19 5EF Tel: (020) 8428 1000 Fax: (020) 8428 1111 E-mail: dennis@dkcomputing.co.uk

D & L Computer Services, The Crescent, Spalding, Lincolnshire, PE11 1AE Tel: (01775) 768287 Fax: (01775) 713591 E-mail: services@d-l.co.uk

D L K Ltd, 8 Stather Road, Burton-upon-Stather, Scunthorpe, South Humberside, DN15 9DH Tel: (01724) 720982 Fax: (01724) 720313 E-mail: sales@dlk.co.uk

D P S Integro, Unit 1 Langley House Business Park, Wykeham, Scarborough, North Yorkshire, YO13 9QP Tel: (01723) 866700 Fax: (01723) 865705 E-mail: info@dps-integro.co.uk

D R L Systems Ltd, Woodside House, Woodside, Chilworth, Southampton, SO16 7LB Tel: (023) 8076 0808 Fax: (023) 8076 7900 E-mail: sales@drlsystems.co.uk

D S T, Afinity House, Beaufort Court, Rochester, Kent, ME2 4FD Tel: (01634) 292292 Fax: (01293) 554600

▶ Da Media Ltd, 8 Fallowfield, Sittingbourne, Kent, ME10 4UT Tel: (01795) 559456 E-mail: info@da-media.co.uk

Dancerace plc, 2 Brock Street, Bath, BA1 2LN Tel: (0870) 7773033 Fax: (0870) 7772022 E-mail: info@dancerace.com

Data Connection Ltd, 100 Church Street, Enfield, Middlesex, EN2 6BQ Tel: (020) 8366 1177 Fax: (020) 8363 1468 E-mail: recruit@dataconnection.com

Data Discovery Solutions LRD, 2 Venture Road, Chilworth, Southampton, SO16 7NP Tel: (023) 8076 7678 Fax: (023) 8076 7665 E-mail: sales@activenavigation.com

Data One Ltd, Unit 12 Loughborough Technology Centre, Epinal Way, Loughborough, Leicestershire, LE11 3GE Tel: (01509) 215662 Fax: (01509) 212571 E-mail: danny@dataone.ltd.uk

Data Works Ltd, Priory House, 25 St. Johns Lane, London, EC1M 4HD Tel: (020) 7553 7800 Fax: (020) 7553 7801 E-mail: info@strategicdataworks.co.uk

Database Developments Ltd, 2 South Street, Uley, Dursley, Gloucestershire, GL11 5SS Tel: (01453) 861155 Fax: (01453) 861166 E-mail: sales@databasedevelopments.com

▶ Datapa Ltd, Midlothian Innovation Centre, Roslin, Midlothian, EH25 9RE Tel: 0131-440 9075 Fax: 0131-445 3941 E-mail: info@datapa.com

Datel Direct Ltd, Stafford Road, Stone, Staffordshire, ST15 0DG Tel: (01785) 810800 Fax: (01785) 810820 E-mail: sales@datel.co.uk

Gary Day Associates, 7 Unity Court, Broadmead Lane, Keynsham, Bristol, BS31 1ST Tel: 0117-986 9911 Fax: 0117-986 9944

Dean Microcomputers Ltd, 1 Abenhall Technolgy Centre, Abenhall Road, Mitcheldean, Gloucestershire, GL17 0DT Tel: (01594) 542116 Fax: (01594) 542643 E-mail: mary@deanmicros.co.uk

Delian Systems, 21 Lakin Close, Springfield, Chelmsford, CM2 6RU Tel: (01245) 450012 Fax: (01245) 602533

COMPUTER SOFTWARE DEVELOPMENT – *continued*

Delta Software Ltd, Whitwood Lodge, Whitwood Lane, Whitwood, Wakefield, West Yorkshire, WF10 5QD Tel: (01204) 529171 Fax: (01977) 668378 E-mail: info@deltasoftware.co.uk

Deltace Systems Ltd, Pierremont Hall, Pierremont Avenue, Broadstairs, Kent, CT10 1JX Tel: (01843) 861888 Fax: (01843) 865006

▶ Derwent Systems Technology, 8 Hugh Parke Close, Loughton, Milton Keynes, MK5 8FG Tel: (01908) 678686E-mail: rsapk@espuk.com

▶ Design Interface Ltd, Thurston Grange, Thurston End, Hawkedon, Bury St. Edmunds, Suffolk, IP29 4LQ Tel: (01284) 789608 Fax: (01284) 789617 E-mail: enquiries@design-interface.com

Desktop Design & Draughting Ltd, 27 Hall Drive, Lincoln, LN6 7SW Tel: (01522) 531861 Fax: (01522) 546795

▶ Digimode IT Ltd, 5 Boxworth Close, London, N12 9HJ Tel: (020) 8446 2642

Digital Development, The Old School, East Baldwin, Isle Of Man, IM4 5EP Tel: (01624) 851482 Fax: (01624) 851482

▶ Digitalarkitec Ltd, 121 Eastern Avenue, Lichfield, Staffordshire, WS13 6RL Tel: (01543) 251123 E-mail: enquiries@digitalarkitec.co.uk

Diptec Computer Systems Ltd, 80 Cleveland Avenue, Long Eaton, Nottingham, NG10 2BT Tel: 0115-946 4773 Fax: 0115-946 4719

Diskel Ltd, 212-214 Farnham Road, Slough, SL1 4XE Tel: (01753) 821091 Fax: (01753) 512438 E-mail: sales@diskel.co.uk

▶ Diversity Solutions Ltd, 18 Westminster Palace Gardens, Artillery Row, London, SW1P 1RR Tel: (0870) 7606227 Fax: (07092) 228007

Documation Software Ltd, Wessex House, Market Street, Eastleigh, Hampshire, SO50 9FD Tel: (023) 8064 7776 Fax: (023) 8064 7775 E-mail: info@documatation.co.uk

▶ Documation Software Ltd, Wessex House, Market Street, Eastleigh, Hampshire, SO50 9FD Tel: (023) 8064 7776 Fax: (023) 8064 7775 E-mail: info@documation.co.uk

▶ Dore IT Consultants Ltd, 24 Bonners Field, Bentley, Farnham, Surrey, GU10 5LH Tel: (01420) 520542

Drive Technology Ltd, Bibsworth Lane, Broadway, Worcestershire, WR12 7LW Tel: (01386) 852089

▶ Dutton Ltd, 2 Ocean Mews, 10 Fore Street, Budleigh Salterton, Devon, EX9 6NG Tel: (01395) 445092E-mail: info@paritor.co.uk

Dynis Ltd, The Chequers, St. Marys Way, Chesham, Buckinghamshire, HP5 1LL Tel: (01494) 777666 Fax: (01494) 777555 E-mail: sales@dynix.com

E B C Computers, The Orchard, The Highway, Croesyceiliog, Cwmbran, Gwent, NP44 2NH Tel: (01633) 869670 Fax: (01633) 485547

▶ E C A, The Brackens, London Road, Ascot, Berkshire, SL5 8BE Tel: (01344) 882240 Fax: (01344) 882219

E D S, Matrix House, Northern Boulevard, Matrix Park, Swansea Enterprise Park, Swansea, SA6 8RE Tel: (01792) 785500 Fax: (01792) 785555

E E S Data, 41 George Street, Wakefield, West Yorkshire, WF1 1LW Tel: (01924) 200103 Fax: (01924) 200104 E-mail: info@ees-data.co.uk

E Media Ltd, Ember House, Pleasant Place, Walton-on-Thames, Surrey, KT12 4HR Tel: (01932) 254787 Fax: (01932) 254786 E-mail: info@e-media.co.uk

E T C Global Solutions Ltd, 75 Woodside Road, Amersham, Buckinghamshire, HP6 6AA Tel: (01494) 720600 Fax: (01494) 720601 E-mail: mail@etcgs.com

Eaglecrest Computer Systems Ltd, Brytirion, Chapel Street, Llanarmon-yn-Ial, Mold, Clwyd, CH7 4QE Tel: (01824) 780565 Fax: (01824) 780375 E-mail: mike.wheeler@eaglecrest-cs.com

Easy Peasy, 1 Winder Gate, Frizington, Cumbria, CA26 3QS Tel: (01946) 813065

Ecieurope, Buckingway Business Park, Rowles Way, Swavesey, Cambridge, CB24 4UG Tel: (01954) 278000 Fax: (01954) 278001 E-mail: sales@ipuk.com

Eclipse Energy Controls Ltd, Unit 4, Wombourne Enterprise Park, Bridgnorth Road, Wombourne, Wolverhampton, WV5 0AL Tel: (01902) 897760 Fax: (01902) 897613 E-mail: sales@eclipse-energy.co.uk

Econintel Treasury Systems Ltd, The Octagon, 27 Middleborough, Colchester, CO1 1TG Tel: (01206) 760033 Fax: (01206) 760133 E-mail: colchester@econintel.com

▶ E-ld.Co.Uk, 52A Denton Road, Twickenham, TW1 2HQ Tel: (020) 8538 9898 Fax: (020) 8538 9898

▶ Elf Software, Whitchurch Road, Wellington, Telford, Shropshire, TF1 3DS Tel: (01952) 249900 Fax: (01952) 249907 E-mail: info@elf-soft.co.uk

▶ Empetus, Cleveland House, 39 Old Station Road, Newmarket, Suffolk, CB8 8QE Tel: (01638) 669440 Fax: (0870) 1299246

▶ Energy Solutions International Ltd, Hastings House, Falcon Court, Preston Farm Industrial Estate, Stockton-on-Tees, Cleveland, TS18 3TS Tel: (01642) 677755 Fax: (01642) 606655 E-mail: sales@energy-solutions.com

Engineering Designs With It Solutions, 17 Parkfield Drive, Sowerby Bridge, West Yorkshire, HX6 3PJ Tel: (01422) 834893 Fax: (01422) 835723 E-mail: sales@editsltd.co.uk

Ensign Advanced Systems Ltd, 56 Regent Road, Leicester, LE1 6YD Tel: 0116-254 9444 E-mail: ensignsys@aol.com

Entrust Technologies Ltd, Apex Plaza, Forbury Road, Reading, RG1 1AX Tel: 0118-953 3000 Fax: 0118-953 3001

Era Technology Ltd, Cleeve Road, Leatherhead, Surrey, KT22 7SA Tel: (01372) 367000 Fax: (01372) 367099 E-mail: info@era.co.uk

Esker, Durham House, Wyvern Business Park, Chaddesden, Derby, DE21 6BF Tel: (01332) 548181 Fax: (01332) 548160 E-mail: sam.townsend@esker.co.uk

▶ Esolutions Media Ltd, Unit 26, 140 Battersea Park Road, London, SW11 4NB Tel: (0870) 7477548 Fax: (0870) 7477549

Esp Music Ltd, Ladywood Lodge, Spondon Road, Dale Abbey, Ilkeston, Derbyshire, DE7 4PS Tel: 0115-944 4140 Fax: 0115-944 4150 E-mail: sales@espmusic.co.uk

Esri UK Ltd, Prebendal House, Parsons Fee, Aylesbury, Buckinghamshire, HP20 2QZ Tel: (01296) 745500 Fax: (01296) 745544 E-mail: info@esriuk.com

Estimation Ltd, Highland House, Stirling Road, Shirley, Solihull, West Midlands, B90 4NE Tel: 0121-704 3221 Fax: 0121-711 2664 E-mail: info@estimation.co.uk

▶ Eureka Solutions (Scotland) Ltd, James Watt Building, Scottish Enterprise Technology Park, East Kilbride, Glasgow, G75 0QD Tel: (01355) 813500 Fax: (0870) 224730 E-mail: enquiries@eurekasolutions.co.uk

Eurorealm Consultants Ltd, 29 Ivanhoe Road, Finchampstead, Wokingham, Berkshire, RG40 4QQ Tel: 0118-973 2977 Fax: 0118-973 4470 E-mail: sales@eurorealm.co.uk

Eurosoft (U K) Ltd, 3 St Stephens Road, Bournemouth, BH2 6JL Tel: (01202) 297315 Fax: (01202) 558280 E-mail: info@eurosoft-uk.com

Peter Evans & Associates Ltd, 52 The Parade, Roath, Cardiff, CF24 3AB Tel: (029) 2040 2200 Fax: (029) 2040 2213 E-mail: info@peterevans.com

▶ Exant Software, West Midland House, Gipsy Lane, Willenhall, West Midlands, WV13 2HA Tel: 0121-609 7102

Excel Computer Systems, Bothe Hall, Tamworth Road, Long Eaton, Nottingham, NG10 3XL Tel: 0115-946 0101 Fax: 0115-946 0606 E-mail: sales@exel.co.uk

▶ Exde Software, 2-4 Hoxton Square, London, N1 6NU Tel: (020) 7739 7641 Fax: (020) 7739 7641

Exel Management Ltd, 83-89 Phoenix Street, Sutton-in-Ashfield, Nottinghamshire, NG17 4HL Tel: (01623) 442211 Fax: (01623) 442844 E-mail: enquiries@exelmanagement.com

▶ Eximbills Ltd, 31 Bury Street, London, EC3A 5AG Tel: (020) 7648 6060 Fax: (020) 7648 6061

Exportmaster Systems Ltd, 33 St Peters Street, South Croydon, Surrey, CR2 7DG Tel: (020) 8681 2321 Fax: (020) 8667 1816 E-mail: info@exportmaster.co.uk

▶ Fairfax Communications, 58 Chester Road, Hartlepool, Cleveland, TS24 8QL Tel: (01429) 894089 Fax: (01429) 894089

Farmade Management Systems Ltd, Clearwater House, Bell Lane, Uckfield, East Sussex, TN22 1QL Tel: (01825) 729000 Fax: (01825) 760932 E-mail: sales@farmade.com

Fathom Technologies Ltd, 8 Windsor Square, Silver Street, Reading, RG1 2TH Tel: 0118-975 0044 Fax: 0118-975 0742 E-mail: info@fathom.co.uk

▶ Fernhall Associates Ltd, 15 Sturdon Road, Bristol, BS3 2BA Tel: 0117-378 9137 Fax: (07092) 229193 E-mail: info@fernhall.co.uk

▶ Field Solutions, 1 Windsor Court, Clarence Drive, Harrogate, North Yorkshire, HG1 2PE Tel: (01423) 532990

Fifth Dimension Computer Solutions Ltd, Park House, Maidenhead Road, Cookham, Maidenhead, Berkshire, SL6 9DS Tel: (01628) 851970

Financial Management Systems (UK) P.L.C., 4 Hillbrow House, Linden Drive, Liss, Hampshire, GU33 7RJ Tel: (01730) 894789 Fax: (01730) 892387 E-mail: info@fmsuk.com

Fingerpost Co. Ltd, 11 Northington Street, London, WC1N 2JF Tel: (020) 7404 0107 Fax: (020) 7404 0558 E-mail: sales@fingerpost.co.uk

Finmatica Ltd, Finmatica House, Ashted Lock, Aston Science Park, Birmingham, B7 4AZ Tel: 0121-359 5096 Fax: 0121-359 0375 E-mail: enquiries@finmatica.com

First Class Buisness Solutions Ltd, 8 Hanover Street, London, W1S 1YE Tel: (020) 7290 2650 Fax: (020) 7290 2655

Fisher Technology Ltd, Acre House, 11-15 William Road, London, NW1 3ER Tel: (020) 7874 7888 Fax: (020) 7380 4900 E-mail: enquiries@fishtech.net

Forcefield Software Ltd, 9 Hall Lane, Wiveton, Holt, Norfolk, NR25 7TG Tel: (01263) 741368

James Fortune Associates, 32 Plough Lane, Purley, Surrey, CR8 3QA Tel: (020) 8763 1995 Fax: (020) 8763 1539 E-mail: sales@jfaworld.com

▶ Fortyefi Ltd, Lumber House, Ashwell Bus Pk, Ashwell, Ilminster, Somerset, TA19 9DX Tel: (01935) 706077 Fax: (01935) 706077

▶ Franek Computer Systems, Holly Tree Cottage, Sprigs Holly Lane, Chinnor, Oxfordshire, OX39 4BY Tel: (01494) 482345 Fax: (01494) 482244

Functionpoint Ltd, Newlands Cottage, Weedon Hill, Hyde Heath, Amersham, Buckinghamshire, HP6 5RN Tel: (01494) 791995 Fax: (01494) 792014 E-mail: alan@functionpoint.co.uk

▶ Futronics Ltd, Nepicar House, London Road, Wrotham Heath, Sevenoaks, Kent, TN15 7RS Tel: (01732) 783130 Fax: (01732) 887227

Future Data International Ltd, 14 High Street, Lyndhurst, Hampshire, SO43 7BD Tel: (023) 8028 4369 Fax: (023) 8028 4369 E-mail: gary@futuredata.com

▶ Future Route Ltd, 2 Hatfields, London, SE1 9PG Tel: (020) 7960 9650 Fax: (020) 7960 9651 E-mail: info@validis.com

G T S Cadbuild Ltd, Woodbrook House, 30 Bridge Street, Loughborough, Leicestershire, LE11 1NH Tel: (08700) 509101 Fax: (08700) 509102 E-mail: sales@gtscad.com

Gamma Projects Ltd, Willcrick Magor, Undy, Caldicot, Gwent, NP26 3DA Tel: (01633) 883000 Fax: (01633) 882990 E-mail: enquiries@gammaprojects.com

▶ Gemsoft Computers, 13 Naworth Drive, Carlisle, CA3 0DD Tel: (01228) 547444 Fax: (01228) 547444

▶ Genus Systems, Prospect House, Halesfield 22, Telford, Shropshire, TF7 4QX Tel: (01952) 587196 Fax: (0845) 1110275

▶ Geoplex Computer Systems, 66 Cumbrian Way, Shepshed, Loughborough, Leicestershire, LE12 9BP Tel: (01509) 507995 Fax: (01509) 507996 E-mail: sales@geoplex.co.uk

▶ Global Address Ltd, Venturers House, Prince St Roundabout, Bristol, BS1 4PB Tel: 0117-915 4018 Fax: 0117-915 4348 E-mail: sales@globaladdress.net

Go Data, Unity Ct, 431 Meanwood Rd, Leeds, LS7 2LL Tel: 0113-217 9990 Fax: 0113 2179991

▶ Goodbitz Ltd, 52-54 Pillard House Lane, Gainsborough, Lincolnshire, DN21 1HX Tel: (01427) 677399 Fax: (01427) 677433

Gower Business Systems Ltd, 2 Newmill Court, Enterprise Park, Swansea, SA7 9FG Tel: (01792) 762646 Fax: (01792) 796292 E-mail: gbs@gowerbiz.co.uk

The Graphics Network Ltd, 27 Moor Lane, Fairford, Gloucestershire, GL7 4AL Tel: (01285) 713297 E-mail: enquiries@tgn.co.uk

Greycon Ltd, 7 Calico House, Clove Hitch Quay, London, SW11 3TN Tel: (020) 7978 0700 Fax: (020) 7978 6222 E-mail: jm@greycon.com

▶ GW Severn Software, The White House, Hockliffe Street, Leighton Buzzard, Bedfordshire, LU7 1HD Tel: (01525) 243570 Fax: (01525) 243571

H C C M Systems Ltd, 3 Church Street, Leamington Spa, Warwickshire, CV31 1EG Tel: (01926) 451551 Fax: (01926) 451556 E-mail: sales@hccm.co.uk

▶ H R Dashboards, 22A Clarence Road, Southend-On-Sea, SS1 1AN Tel: (01702) 342266 Fax: (01702) 342266

Halcyon Software Ltd, 5 The Forum, Minerva BSNS Park, Orton Wistow, Peterborough, PE2 6FT Tel: (01733) 234995 Fax: (01733) 234994 E-mail: sales@halcyonsoftware.com

Hamilton Grant Software Ltd, Seymour House, Lower South Street, Godalming, Surrey, GU7 1BZ Tel: (01483) 422404 Fax: (01483) 422401 E-mail: sales@hamilton-grant.com

Hamlet Computer Group Ltd, 5 Oriel Court, Omega Park, Alton, Hampshire, GU34 2YT Tel: (01420) 83550 Fax: (01420) 541364 E-mail: sales@hamletcg.co.uk

▶ Handysoft, 288 Bishopsgate, London, EC2M 4QP Tel: (020) 7959 3042 Fax: (020) 7959 3041

Hanlon Computer Systems, Unit 4 Victoria Court, Kent Street, Nottingham, NG1 3LZ Tel: 0115-959 0077 Fax: 0115-941 7432 E-mail: info@hcs-ltd.co.uk

▶ Hawkriver Software Designs, 8 St. Pauls Terrace, Easton, Wells, Somerset, BA5 1DX Tel: (0870) 1993812 Fax: (07092) 807649

Helmstone Communications Ltd, 18 Guildford Road, Brighton, BN1 3LU Tel: (01273) 747447 Fax: (01273) 747333 E-mail: nisbett@helmstone.com

▶ Hexaware Technology UK Ltd, Cornwall House, High Street, Slough, SL1 1BZ Tel: (01753) 217160 Fax: (01753) 217161 E-mail: sales@euhexaware.com

Hi Tech Solutions, 6 Fairwater Drive, Woodley, Reading, RG5 3HH Tel: 0118-926 7252

▶ Highway Electronics Ltd, Unit 2, Metherell Avenue, Brixham, Devon, TQ5 9QB Tel: (01803) 850460 Fax: (01803) 850470 E-mail: enquiries@highwaysoftware.co.uk

Hoge 100 Business Systems Ltd, I M S House, Prescott Drive, Worcester, WR4 9NE Tel: (01905) 455227 Fax: (01905) 455035 E-mail: sales@hoge100.co.uk

Honeypass Ltd, 16 Ardsheal Close, Worthing, West Sussex, BN14 7RP Tel: (01903) 212774 Fax: (01903) 238226 E-mail: info@honeypass.com

House Builder XL Ltd, Citypoint, Temple Gate, Bristol, BS1 6PL Tel: (0870) 8502444 Fax: (0870) 8502555E-mail: sales@hbxl.co.uk

Howells Associates Ltd, 32 Freemans Way, Harrogate, North Yorkshire, HG3 1DH Tel: (01423) 812800

▶ Hunted Cow Studios Ltd, 100 High Street, Elgin, Morayshire, IV30 1BW Tel: (01343) 550855 Fax: (01343) 550855

I B M (UK) Ltd, Palace Street, Plymouth, PL1 2DE Tel: (01752) 660042 Fax: (01752) 224230

I C S London Ltd, 26 Thackeray Mall, Fareham, Hampshire, PO16 0PQ Tel: (01329) 228200 Fax: (01329) 233191

I D Business Solutions Ltd, 2 Occam Court, Occam Road, Surrey Research Park, Guildford, Surrey, GU2 7QB Tel: (01483) 595000 Fax: (01483) 595001 E-mail: info@idbs.com

I I C O N Ltd, Regent House, Hubert Road, Brentwood, Essex, CM14 4JE Tel: (01277) 264404 Fax: (01277) 264405

I O Systech Ltd, 8 Willow Walk, Englefield Green, Egham, Surrey, TW20 0DQ Tel: (01784) 432058 E-mail: enquiries@iosystech.co.uk

I P A Systems Ltd, 3 Aberford Road, Garforth, Leeds, LS25 1PZ Tel: 0113-287 5337 Fax: 0113-287 5338 E-mail: sales@ipasystems.co.uk

I P L Information Processing Ltd, Eveleigh House, Grove Street, Bath, BA1 5LR Tel: (01225) 475000 Fax: (01225) 444400 E-mail: sales@iplbath.com

I S C Computers Plc, 2 Pioneer Way, Lincoln, LN6 3DH Tel: (01522) 686464

▶ Iconium Computer Systems, Exchange House, Worthing Road, Horsham, West Sussex, RH12 1UU Tel: (01403) 754300

Icore Ltd, 10-12 King Henry Terrace, Sovereign Close, London, E1W 3HE Tel: (020) 7464 8414 Fax: (020) 7481 9230

Illuminaries Ltd, Sheffield Science Park Cooper Buildings, Arundel Street, Sheffield, S1 2NS Tel: 0114-270 0800 Fax: 0114-221 1801 E-mail: enquiries@illuminaries.co.uk

Imass Ltd, Northumbria House, Regent Centre, Gosforth, Newcastle upon Tyne, NE3 3PX Tel: 0191-213 0526 Fax: 0191-213 0526 E-mail: servicedesk@imass.co.uk

Impact Computer Consultants Ltd, 210 Church Road, Hove, East Sussex, BN3 2DJ Tel: (01273) 821820 Fax: (01273) 821010 E-mail: sales@impactcc.co.uk

In4tek Ltd, Unisys House, 20 Barrington Road, Altrincham, Cheshire, WA14 1HB Tel: 0161-941 5833 Fax: 0161-927 7629 E-mail: in4mation@in4tek.com

▶ Incisus Ltd, Geddes House, Kirkton North, Livingston, West Lothian, EH54 6GU Tel: (01506) 407680 Fax: (01506) 407689

Indus (International) Ltd, Britannia Wharf, Monument Road, Woking, Surrey, GU21 5LW Tel: (01483) 722777 Fax: (01483) 721166 E-mail: sales@indusinternational.com

▶ Infatrans Ltd, 4 New Road, Great Kingshill, High Wycombe, Buckinghamshire, HP15 6DR Tel: (01494) 712212 Fax: (01494) 712212 E-mail: sales@infatrans.co.uk

▶ Info Basis, 9 Napier Court, Barton Lane, Abingdon, Oxfordshire, OX14 3YT Tel: (0870) 2000350 Fax: (0870) 2000351

Infogain Ltd, 18 Forlease Road, Maidenhead, Berkshire, SL6 1RU Tel: (01628) 580600 Fax: (01628) 580610 E-mail: info@infogain.com

Infogrames UK Ltd, 21 Castle Street, Manchester, M3 4SW Tel: 0161-827 8000 Fax: 0161-827 8001

▶ Infographics UK Ltd, Leslie House, Allen Road, Livingston, West Lothian, EH54 6TQ Tel: (01592) 750677 Fax: (01592) 610534

Infomatrix Ltd, The Old School, High Street, Fen Drayton, Cambridge, CB24 4SJ Tel: (01954) 232010 Fax: (01954) 230031 E-mail: chris.jones@infomatrix.com

Inform Atika, 25 Parkholme Rd, London, E8 3AG Tel: (020) 7241 2269 Fax: (020) 7241 2269 E-mail: cameron.martin@btinternet.com

▶ Information Data Systems Ltd, Exchange House, Exchange Street, Attleborough, Norfolk, NR17 2AB Tel: (01953) 452249

Inphase Software Ltd, Salamander Quay, Harefield, Uxbridge, Middlesex, UB9 6NY Tel: (01895) 829111 Fax: (01895) 829112 E-mail: info@inphase.com

▶ Intamission, Thames Court, 1 Victoria Street, Windsor, Berkshire, SL4 1YB Tel: (01753) 626860 Fax: (01753) 626861 E-mail: info@intamission.com

Intec Systems Blackburn Ltd, 12 Strawberry Bank, Blackburn, BB2 6AA Tel: (01254) 667106 Fax: (01254) 675925 E-mail: sales@intec-systems.co.uk

▶ Integral Mobile Data, Pembroke House, Ty Coch Lane, Llantarnam Park Way, Cwmbran, Gwent, NP44 3AU Tel: (0870) 0801808 Fax: (0870) 0801809

Integrated Manufacturing Systems, Nelson Street, Rotherham, South Yorkshire, S65 1ET Tel: (01709) 839933 Fax: (01709) 838848 E-mail: info@ims-uniplan.co.uk

Inter Active Software Services Ltd, Westwood House, Littleton Drive, Huntington, Cannock, Staffordshire, WS12 4TS Tel: (01543) 503611 Fax: (01543) 574566 E-mail: ifs@winteracter.com

▶ International Decision Systems, 1 Stewart Road, Basingstoke, Hampshire, RG24 8NF Tel: (01256) 302000 Fax: (01256) 302005

Intrinsyc Europe, Fountain House, Great Cornbow, Halesowen, West Midlands, B63 3BL Tel: 0121-501 6000 Fax: 0121-501 6035

▶ It Software Solutions, Dunstable Road, Toddington, Dunstable, Bedfordshire, LU5 6DT Tel: (07811) 741568 E-mail: zoltan@it-software-solutions.com

▶ Italik, 2B Rudgate Court, Walton, Wetherby, West Yorkshire, LS23 7BF Tel: (01937) 848380 Fax: (01937) 848381 E-mail: info@italik.co.uk

▶ indicates data change since last edition

COMPUTER SOFTWARE DEVELOPMENT - *continued*

Itech Quality Business Solutions Ltd, Lion Court Storten Harolrd, Whitick Business Park, Stenson Road, Coalville, Leicestershire, LE65 1RT Tel: (0870) 2249295 Fax: (0870) 8519295 E-mail: info@itechqbs.co.uk

Itheon Ltd, 1 The Boulevard, Welwyn Garden City, Hertfordshire, AL7 1EL Tel: (01707) 336600 Fax: (01707) 336622 E-mail: sales@itheon.com

J Computer Logic Ltd, Golden Valley Software Factory, New Mills, Clehonger, Hereford, HR2 9QS Tel: (01981) 251359 E-mail: sales@jclsoftware.com

▶ J & D Software, 161 Ashley Road, Hale, Cheshire, WA15 9SD Tel: (0845) 4504588

▶ J V F Consultants Ltd, 4 Loughborough Road, Mountsorrel, Loughborough, Leicestershire, LE12 7AT Tel: 0116-230 2880 Fax: 0116-237 6115 E-mail: sales@jvf.co.uk

▶ Jem Business Systems, Abbey Lakes Hall, Orrell Road, Orrell, Wigan, Lancashire, WN5 8QZ Tel: (01695) 627217

▶ Johnson Technical Systems, Unit 6 Essex Technology Centre, The Gables, Ongar, Essex, CM5 0GA Tel: (01277) 364530 E-mail: mail@jtechnical.com

K C C Ltd, TLM Ho, Percy St, Eastwood, Nottingham, NG16 3EP Tel: (01773) 760900 Fax: (01773) 760985 E-mail: emsales@flomerics.co.uk

K T S L Ltd, PO Box 2637, Corsham, Wiltshire, SN13 0RP Tel: (0870) 0275587 Fax: (01249) 700650 E-mail: sales@ktsl.com

K3 Business Technology Group, 1 Tavern Lane, Dereham, Norfolk, NR19 1PX Tel: (01362) 691999 Fax: (01362) 691710

Kappa Lambda Squared Ltd, Erskine House, 53 London Road, Maidstone, Kent, ME16 8JH Tel: (01622) 670095 Fax: (01622) 200119 E-mail: sales@kl2.com

Key It Systems Ltd, Brake Lane, Boughton, Newark, Nottinghamshire, NG22 9HQ Tel: (01623) 863556 Fax: (01623) 863203 E-mail: brian@keyits.co.uk

Khan Consultants Ltd, 7 Beech Drive, Woodville, Swadlincote, Derbyshire, DE11 7DA Tel: (01283) 552994 Fax: (01283) 558209 E-mail: info@khanconbsultants.co.uk

▶ Khaydor Ltd, Yr Hen Swyddfa Bost, Waunfawr, Aberystwyth, Dyfed, SY23 3QD Tel: (01970) 611320

▶ Kingsword Ltd, Unit 5, The Boundary Business Park, Wheatley Road, Garsington, Oxford, OX44 9EJ Tel: (01865) 361840 Fax: (01865) 361850 E-mail: sales@cssg.co.uk

Kudos Software Ltd, Cliff House, Cliff Road, Salcombe, Devon, TQ8 8JQ Tel: (01548) 843586 Fax: (01548) 843503 E-mail: kudos@kudos-software.co.uk

L M Computers Ltd, Arcade Chambers, Little Wellington Street, Aldershot, Hampshire, GU11 1EE Tel: (01252) 406323 Fax: (01252) 406324 E-mail: sales@lmcomputers.co.uk

Laganside Computer Consultants Ltd, Studio A, Hollywood Road, Belfast, BT4 3D Tel: (028) 9065 3006 Fax: (028) 9065 3005

Lalpac, 8 The Causeway, Chippenham, Wiltshire, SN15 3BT Tel: (01249) 660088 Fax: (01249) 660099

Laserform International Ltd, Higher Lane, Lymm, Cheshire, WA13 0RZ Tel: (01925) 750000 Fax: (01925) 750021 E-mail: admin@laserform.co.uk

Last Party, 7 Carlingnose Park, North Queensferry, Inverkeithing, Fife, KY11 1EX Tel: (01383) 415022 E-mail: sales@lastparty.co.uk

▶ Latens Systems, 1-3 Upper CR, Belfast, BT7 1NT Tel: (028) 9057 1500

▶ LeSoftCo Ltd, Carlson Suite, Vantage Point Business Village, Mitcheldean, Gloucestershire, GL17 0DD Tel: (01594) 544120 E-mail: info@lesoftco.co.uk

Lexicon Distribution, 11 Ackroyd St, Morley, Leeds, LS27 8QX Tel: 0113-252 2727 Fax: 0113-252 3177 E-mail: rob@xic.co.uk

Librios Research Ltd, 2 Chestnut Road, Towcester, Northamptonshire, NN12 7TW Tel: (01908) 543090 E-mail: info@librios.com

Linear Blue Ltd, 400 Thames Valley Park Drive, Thames Valley Park, Reading, RG6 1PT Tel: (0870) 351 6594 E-mail: info@linearblue.com

Liquid Software Solutions Ltd, 2 Wilsons Road, Knowle, Solihull, West Midlands, B93 0HZ Tel: (01564) 779090 Fax: (01564) 776161 E-mail: info@liquid-soft.com

▶ Logical Minds Ltd, Leigh House, Varley Street, Stanningley, Pudsey, West Yorkshire, LS28 6AN Tel: 0113-236 1199 Fax: 0113-236 1188 E-mail: mail@logicalminds.co.uk

Logistics Business, 17 The Crescent, Bromsgrove, Worcestershire, B60 2DF Tel: (01527) 889060 Fax: (01527) 559192 E-mail: info@logistics.co.uk

M C L Software Ltd, Hesketh Mount, Lord Street, Southport, Merseyside, PR8 1JR Tel: (01704) 501001 Fax: (01704) 533003 E-mail: info@mclsoftware.co.uk

▶ M D B Software, 26 Adbolton Grove, West Bridgford, Nottingham, NG2 5AR Tel: 0115-981 9986

M J H Engineering Services, Maycot, Quay Lane, Kirby-le-Soken, Frinton-on-Sea, Essex, CO13 0DP Tel: (01255) 675515 E-mail: info@mjh-engineering.co.uk

M S G Computers, Summit Chambers, Castle Hill Terrace, Maidenhead, Berkshire, SL6 4JP Tel: (01628) 671621 Fax: (01628) 623953

M & S Systems Ltd, 21 Excelsior Grove, Pelsall, Walsall, WS3 4PX Tel: (01922) 685615 E-mail: simon@mandssys.demon.co.uk

Mcneill Associates Ltd, 14 Well Hall Parade, London, SE9 6SP Tel: (020) 8294 1565 Fax: (020) 8859 4562 E-mail: post@mcneill.co.uk

Maestro Solutions Ltd, 5 Woodland Road, Maple Cross, Rickmansworth, Hertfordshire, WD3 9ST Tel: (01923) 770856 Fax: (01923) 771143 E-mail: maestrosoloutions@aol.com

Magic Systems Ltd, Unit 3 Sandridge Park, Porters Wood, St. Albans, Hertfordshire, AL3 6PH Tel: (01727) 855511 Fax: (01727) 864351 E-mail: sales@magicgroup.com

▶ Maginus Software Solutions, Dallimore Road, Roundthorn Industrial Estate, Manchester, M23 9NX Tel: 0161-953 0000 Fax: 0161-945 3806 E-mail: mail@maginus.com

▶ Majic Solutions, 15 Swanwick Walk, Broughton, Milton Keynes, MK10 9LJ Tel: (01908) 236678 E-mail: sales@majic.co.uk

Major Gold, Harbour House, Coldharbour Lane, Rainham, Essex, RM13 9YB Tel: (01708) 523233 Fax: (01708) 559818 E-mail: j.majorgold@btclick.com

MAM Software Ltd, 1 Station Road, Deepcar, Sheffield, S36 2SQ Tel: (0870) 7667012 Fax: (0870) 7667023

Marcmoor Computer Systems, 5a Church Sq, Market Harborough, Leics, LE16 7HB Tel: (01858) 465746 Fax: (01858) 434628 E-mail: paul@marcmoor.co.uk

▶ Marlin Design (MD) Ltd, 24 North Street, Chichester, West Sussex, PO19 1LB Tel: (01243) 773552 Fax: (01243) 787227 E-mail: marlindesign@btconnect.com

Matech Computers, North Quay, Great Yarmouth, Norfolk, NR30 1RE Tel: (01493) 331591 Fax: (01493) 851852

Matts Business Centre, Station Crescent, Llandrindod Wells, Powys, LD1 5BD Tel: (01597) 827940 E-mail: info@matts.co.uk

Maxima, 84 Coombe Road, New Malden, Surrey, KT3 4QS Tel: (020) 8336 8800 Fax: (020) 8336 8899

▶ Mayne Computer Technology Ltd, 13b Dalewood Road, Lymedale Business Park, Newcastle, Staffordshire, ST5 9QH Tel: (01782) 562522 Fax: (01782) 562299 E-mail: cathy-lou@maynetechnology.co.uk

▶ Mayrise Ltd, The Wheelhouse Bonds Mill, Stonehouse, Gloucestershire, GL10 3RF Tel: (01453) 827400 Fax: (01453) 853753 E-mail: office@mayrise.co.uk

MCC Ltd, 2 Milford Road, Sherburn in Elmet, Leeds, LS25 6AF Tel: (01977) 682880 Fax: (0870) 0518693 E-mail: tim@mccltd.org.uk

Mejdaf Europe Ltd, 196 Preston Road, Wembley, Middlesex, HA9 8PA Tel: (020) 8933 0727 Fax: (020) 8930 0944

Mentat Systems Ltd, 3 Rutland Road, Southport, Merseyside, PR8 6PB Tel: (01704) 514506 E-mail: sale@mentat.co.uk

Merula Ltd, 25-31 Huntingdon Street, St. Neots, Cambridgeshire, PE19 1BG Tel: (01480) 222940 Fax: (01480) 222941 E-mail: info@merula.net

Micad Systems & F M Data Services, Lansdown House, 85 Buxton Road, Stockport, Cheshire, SK2 6LR Tel: 0161-474 7174 Fax: 0161-474 7163 E-mail: support@micad.co.uk

Micas Solutions Ltd, Baldwin Road, Stourport-On-Severn, Worcestershire, DY13 9AX Tel: (01299) 825588 Fax: (01299) 828840 E-mail: info@micas.co.uk

Micro Nav Ltd, Gild House, 64-68 Norwich Avenue West, Bournemouth, BH2 6AW Tel: (01202) 764444 Fax: (01202) 545079 E-mail: sales@micronav.co.uk

Microfinance Systems Ltd, Milestone House, North Malvern Road, Malvern, Worcestershire, WR14 4LX Tel: (01684) 560141 Fax: (01684) 569186

Midsoft Computer Systems, Aston Lane, Aston, Stone, Staffordshire, ST15 0BW Tel: (01785) 818054 Fax: (01785) 817513 E-mail: sales@midsoft.co.uk

▶ Mill Systems, Unit 4, Heritage Business Centre, Derby road, Belper, Derbyshire, DE56 1SW Tel: (01773) 824400 Fax: (0870) 0515380 E-mail: sales@millsystems.com

Millennium Computer Systems Ltd, B11 The Seedbed Centre, Wyncolls Road, Colchester, CO4 9HT Tel: (01206) 855288 Fax: (01206) 855285 E-mail: info@millennium-computer.co.uk

▶ Monitor Computer Systems Ltd, Marlborough House, Westminster Place, Nether Poppleton, York, YO26 6RW Tel: (0870) 7551153 E-mail: sales@monitorsoft.com

Richard Moon Consulting, PO Box 425, Bedford, MK44 2ZW Tel: (01234) 772509 E-mail: richard@richardmoon.com

Mos Computers Ltd, Queen Square, Saltford, Bristol, BS31 3EL Tel: (01225) 873117 Fax: (01225) 873776 E-mail: info@moscomputers.co.uk

Mountain Software, Withambrook Park Industrial Estate, Grantham, Lincolnshire, NG31 9ST Tel: (01476) 573718 Fax: (01476) 590563 E-mail: info@mountainsoftware.co.uk

▶ N 4 Solutions Ltd, 1-4 Priory Court, Poulton, Cirencester, Gloucestershire, GL7 5JB Tel: (01285) 852200 Fax: (0870) 6085120

N B Information Ltd, 570 Lanark Road West, Balerno, Midlothian, EH14 7BN Tel: 0131-449 7922 E-mail: support@-info.co.uk

N Sys, Balgownie Road, Bridge of Don, Aberdeen, AB22 8GT Tel: (0845) 0559944 Fax: (0845) 0559945

Nathan Software Ltd, 352 New Trows Road, Lesmahagow, Lanark, ML11 0JS Tel: (01555) 893548 Fax: (01555) 893589

▶ Naturalmotion Ltd, Innovation House, Mill Street, Oxford, OX2 0JX Tel: (01865) 250575 Fax: (01865) 250577 E-mail: sales@naturalmotion.com

▶ Navayuga Europe Ltd, Progress Park, Ribocon Way, Chalton, Luton, LU4 9UU Tel: (01582) 585820 E-mail: info@navayuga.co.uk

▶ Neoworks Ltd, 2-3 North Mews, London, WC1N 2JP Tel: (020) 7025 0950 Fax: (020) 7637 9631 E-mail: sales@neoworks.com

Neptune Radar Ltd, Gardiners Farmhouse, Sandhurst Lane, Sandhurst, Gloucester, GL2 9NW Tel: (01452) 730479 Fax: (01452) 731315 E-mail: seawaves@enterprise.net

Net Formation Ltd, Godstone Green, Godstone, Surrey, RH9 8DZ Tel: (01883) 740000 Fax: (01883) 744465 E-mail: info@forfront.net

The Netpoint Project Ltd, Hove, East Sussex, BN3 3RZ Tel: (01273) 778122 Fax: (07092) 385043

Netserv Ltd, 51a Station Road, Marston Green, Birmingham, B37 7AB Tel: 0121-770 3730 Fax: 0121-779 4131 E-mail: info@netservuk.com

Netshift Software Ltd, Kennet Side, Newbury, Berkshire, RG14 5PX Tel: (01635) 568800 Fax: (01635) 568850 E-mail: admin@netshift.com

Netwinner Ltd, 15 The Maltings, Longton, Preston, PR4 5ZS Tel: (01772) 616078 Fax: (01772) 616086 E-mail: sales@netwinner.co.uk

Network Associates (Midlands) Ltd, Vincent House, Buntsford Park Road, Bromsgrove, Worcestershire, B60 3DX Tel: (01527) 576933 Fax: (0870) 706 2522 E-mail: enquiries@network-associates.co.uk

Neutral Ltd, 167 Ardleigh Green Road, Hornchurch, Essex, RM11 2LF Tel: (01708) 701522 Fax: (01708) 701994 E-mail: info@neutral.co.uk

New Wave Concepts, 59 St Andrews Street, St Andrews House, Cambridge, CB2 3BQ Tel: (0870) 6090911 E-mail: sales@new-wave-concepts.com

Nexus Alpha Ltd, Unit 8 Beaufort Ho, Beaufort Court, Sir Thomas Longley Rd, Rochester, Kent, ME2 4FB Tel: (01634) 304226 Fax: (01634) 301315

▶ Njini, 1 Dome Buildings, The Square, Richmond, Surrey, TW9 1DT Tel: (020) 8334 8760 Fax: (020) 8334 8761

▶ Novotronix, Creative Industry Centre, Mammoth Drive, Wolverhampton Science Park, Wolverhampton, WV10 9TG Tel: (01902) 424277

▶ Nu Vision Associates, 5A Prospect Street, Caversham, Reading, RG4 8JB Tel: 0118-947 5500 Fax: 0118-947 5588

▶ Open Destinations Ltd, Unit 11 Estilo, 7 Wenlock Road, London, N1 7SL Tel: (020) 7553 9220 Fax: (0870) 1343397 E-mail: surrport@opendestinations.com

▶ Openfield Systems Ltd, South Knoll, Southstoke Lane, Southstoke, Bath, BA2 7DN Tel: (01225) 833622

Optisoft Ltd, Whinchat Hall, Skipwith Road, Escrick, York, YO19 6EJ Tel: (01904) 727300 Fax: (01904) 727332 E-mail: info@optisoft.co.uk

Orchid Software Ltd, 63 Westgate Road, Newcastle Upon Tyne, NE1 1SG Tel: 0191-232 5750 E-mail: adrian@orchidsoft.com

Original Business Systems Ltd, The Stables, The Vatch, Stroud, Gloucestershire, GL6 7LE Tel: (01453) 751515 Fax: (01453) 753525 E-mail: info@obs.co.uk

Outsourced H R Solutions, 54 Clarendon Road, Watford, WD17 1DU Tel: (01923) 431675 Fax: (01923) 431875 E-mail: info@invosoftsolutions.com

Oxford Software Engineering Ltd, 9 Spinners Court, West End, Witney, Oxfordshire, OX28 1NH Tel: (01993) 700878 Fax: (01993) 774132 E-mail: enquiries@ocl.co.uk

▶ Oyster Software, Alexander House, Fleming Way, Swindon, SN1 2NG Tel: (01793) 530111 Fax: (01793) 530333

▶ P E P Technologys Ltd, Acorn House, 2 Greenhill Crescent, Watford, WD18 8AH Tel: (01923) 212611 Fax: (01923) 238344 E-mail: pep@peptech.co.uk

P & Q International plc, Wickham House, Station Road, Braughing, Ware, Hertfordshire, SG11 2PB Tel: (0845) 1300707 Fax: (0845) 1300727 E-mail: sales@pandq.com

Paloma Systems Ltd, 2 Frederick Terrace, Frederick Place, Brighton, BN1 1AX Tel: (01273) 778688 Fax: (01273) 323927 E-mail: sales@paloma.co.uk

Pansoft Ltd, 28 Landport Terrace, Portsmouth, PO1 2RG Tel: (023) 9285 1513 Fax: (023) 9285 1529 E-mail: sales@pansoft.co.uk

▶ Paramet Computer Systems, Northgate House, Plough Road, Great Bentley, Colchester, CO7 8LG Tel: (01206) 255300 E-mail: sales@paramet.cpm

Paravizion Ltd, 16 Lyndhurst Road, Heswall, Wirral, Merseyside, CH61 0HB Tel: 0151-648 7223 E-mail: ajc@discframe.co.uk

Passfield Data Systems Ltd, Passfield Business Centre, Lynchborough Road, Passfield, Liphook, Hampshire, GU30 7SB Tel: (01428) 751155 Fax: (01428) 751137

Pathtrace P.L.C., 45 Boulton Road, Reading, RG2 0NH Tel: 0118-975 6084 Fax: 0118-975 6143 E-mail: enquiry@pathtrace.com

Pear Computing Systems Ltd, The Pentagon Centre, 44 Washington Street, Glasgow, G3 8AZ Tel: 0141-221 3115 Fax: (0870) 2411589 E-mail: enquiries@pearsystems.com

▶ Philantech Computer Systems, 207 Waterloo Road, London, SE1 8XD Tel: (020) 7401 9901 Fax: (020) 7401 9901

Pipistrel Retail Software Ltd, 23 Woodbridge Road, Guildford, Surrey, GU1 1DY Tel: (01483) 440099 Fax: (0870) 1164400 E-mail: support@pipistrel.com

Pisys Ltd, Campus 1, Balgownie Road, Bridge of Don, Aberdeen, AB22 8GT Tel: (01224) 332014 Fax: (01224) 332055 E-mail: info@pisysltd.co.uk

Planmaster Systems Ltd, York House, Wycombe End, Beaconsfield, Buckinghamshire, HP9 1XA Tel: (01494) 672184 Fax: (01494) 670218 E-mail: sales@planmaster.co.uk

Poole Computers Ltd, 865 Ringwood Road, Bournemouth, BH11 8LL Tel: (01202) 591548 Fax: (01202) 590944 E-mail: pcl@lds.co.uk

Portech Systems, The Green House, Gibb Street, Birmingham, B9 4AA Tel: 0121-224 7890 Fax: 0121-624 0550 E-mail: info@portech.co.uk

Powervac Ltd, 111 Lightburn Road, Cambuslang, Glasgow, G72 8XN Tel: 0141-641 6611 Fax: 0141-641 9988

Practiceworks Ltd, Elopak House, Rutherford Close, Stevenage, Hertfordshire, SG1 2PR Tel: (01438) 245000 Fax: (01438) 245001

▶ Premier Barcode Systems, 27 Bromhurst Way, Warwick, CV34 6NS Tel: (01926) 499139

Premier Systems Technology Ltd, Newton Silk Mill, Holyoak Street, Manchester, M40 1HA Tel: 0161-682 2100 Fax: 0161-682 2090 E-mail: sales@premier-tech.com

Preview, Unit 4 Babbage Ho, Dukes Meadow, Millboard Rd, Bourne End, Bucks, SL8 5XF Tel: (01628) 819200 Fax: (01628) 810314

▶ The Princes Trust, Ashfield Avenue, Mansfield, Nottinghamshire, NG18 2AE Tel: (01623) 404520 Fax: (01623) 404502 E-mail: sales@solar-digital.co.uk

Proactis Group Ltd, Holtby Manor, Stamford Bridge Road, Dunnington, York, YO19 5LL Tel: (01904) 481999 Fax: (01904) 481666

Process Intelligence Ltd, Ebrington, Chipping Campden, Gloucestershire, GL55 6NL Tel: (01386) 593084 Fax: (01386) 593132

▶ Proscene Software, 198 Northfield Road, Sheffield, S10 1QU Tel: 0114-267 9679 Fax: 0114-268 7331 E-mail: proscene.software@proscenesoftware.com

▶ Proton Storm, 22 Market Place, Wetherby, West Yorkshire, LS22 6NE Tel: (01937) 586888 Fax: (01937) 588709

The Publishing Software Co., 6 Trevithick Close, Stourport-on-Severn, Worcestershire, DY13 8AN Tel: (0870) 0101780 Fax: (0870) 0101783 E-mail: laurence@p-s-c.co.uk

▶ Purple Business Solutions, Sidney Avenue, Hesketh Bank, Preston, PR4 6PD Tel: (01772) 816060

Q M Systems Ltd, 4 Manor Park Estate, Wyndham Street, Aldershot, Hampshire, GU12 4NZ Tel: (01252) 336612 Fax: (01252) 343018 E-mail: sales@qm-systems.com

▶ Q Software Global Ltd, Ranmore Manor, Ranmore Common, Dorking, Surrey, RH5 6SX Tel: (01483) 280400 Fax: (01483) 280401 E-mail: info@qsoftware.com

Q2 Systems Ltd, Mill Studio Business Centre, Crane Mead, Ware, Hertfordshire, SG12 9PY Tel: (01920) 444285 Fax: (01920) 468686 E-mail: q2@q2systems.co.uk

▶ Quality Financial Software Ltd, 3ND Floor, George Street House, George Street, Macclesfield, Cheshire, SK11 6HU Tel: (01625) 443210 Fax: (01625) 443219 E-mail: info@qfsl.co.uk

Qube Global Software, Pyrford Road, West Byfleet, Surrey, KT14 6LD Tel: (01932) 334700 Fax: (01932) 355654 E-mail: sales@fdsltd.co.uk

Qubix International Ltd, Highclere House, 5 High Street, Knaphill, Woking, Surrey, GU21 2PG Tel: (01483) 480222 Fax: (01483) 473050 E-mail: sales@qubixinternational.com

R B I Recovery Services, Geddings Road, Hoddesdon, Hertfordshire, EN11 0NW Tel: (01992) 445566 Fax: (01992) 441785

R G Software, Stocktons Courtyard, Overbury, Tewkesbury, Gloucestershire, GL20 7NT Tel: (01242) 233255 Fax: (01386) 725109 E-mail: sales@rgsoftware.co.uk

R S C Partnership Ltd, 1A Belmont Road, Wallington, Surrey, SM6 8TE Tel: (020) 8773 2299 E-mail: mail@rscpartnership.com

React Computer Partnership, Unit 5, Old Maltings Approach, Woodbridge, Suffolk, IP12 1EF Tel: (01394) 387337 Fax: (01394) 610554 E-mail: enquiries@reactcp.co.uk

▶ Read Riggs, St. Clare House, 30-33 Minories, London, EC3N 1DD Tel: (020) 7265 2060 Fax: (020) 7265 2066

▶ Red Kestrel Consulting, 17 Constance Avenue, Trentham, Stoke-on-Trent, ST4 8TE Tel: (01782) 643438 E-mail: info@redkestrel.co.uk

▶ Redblack Software Ltd, Kings House, 12 King Street, York, YO1 9WP Tel: (01904) 622888 Fax: (01904) 654888 E-mail: enquiries@redblacksoftware.co.uk

▶ Redcliffe Computers Ltd, 1st Floor Unity Court, 431 Meanwood Road, Leeds, LS7 2LD Tel: 0113-246 0777 Fax: 0113-245 0944 E-mail: info@redcliffe-computers.co.uk

▶ Redtrap Ltd, 6 Heron Way, Chippenham, Wiltshire, SN14 0XE Tel: (01793) 480133 E-mail: info@redtrap.com

COMPUTER SOFTWARE DEVELOPMENT – *continued*

▶ Regie (UK) Ltd, Bearley, Stratford-Upon-Avon, Warwickshire, CV37 0TY Tel: (0870) 8810167 Fax: (0870) 8810168

Renaissance Corporate (Barnet) Ltd, Unit 1 Stroud Wood Business Centre, Frogmore, St. Albans, Herts, AL2 2NN Tel: (01727) 875500 Fax: (01727) 874808 E-mail: sales@rencorp.co.uk

Risk Factor Solutions Ltd, Units B-C Kemps Farm, London Road, Balcombe, Haywards Heath, West Sussex, RH17 6JH Tel: (01444) 819460 Fax: (01444) 819461 E-mail: info@riskfactor-solutions.com

Riva Consulting Ltd, Chedeham House, Cot Lane, Chichester, West Sussex, PO18 8ST Tel: (01243) 575955 Fax: (01243) 575966 E-mail: sales@riva-consulting.com

▶ Riva Financial Systems, Old Chapple, Main Road, Union Mills, Isle of Man, IM4 4AD Tel: (01624) 853712 Fax: (01624) 853712 E-mail: sales@revafs.com

▶ Riverhall Systems, Warnford Court, 29 Throgmorton Street, London, EC2N 2AT Tel: (0870) 3210034 E-mail: andrew@riverhall.co.uk

Riverscape Ltd, Business & Innovation Centre, Wearfield, Sunderland Enterprise Park, Sunderland, SR5 2TA Tel: 0191-516 6456 Fax: 0191-516 6457 E-mail: info@riverscape.co.uk

Robelle Consulting Ltd, 91 Cumberland Road, London, E13 8LH Tel: (020) 7473 2558 Fax: (020) 7473 2558 E-mail: robelle_oldfield@msn.com

Rolfe & Nolan Systems Ltd, Lowndes House, 1-9 City Road, London, EC1Y 1AE Tel: (020) 7374 4841 Fax: (020) 7374 0732

Rombus Computers Ltd, Fairney House Wesley Drive, Benton Square Industrial Estate, Newcastle upon Tyne, NE12 9UP Tel: 0191-259 9756 Fax: (0870) 7021112 E-mail: action@rombus.com

Roundhill Computer Systems Ltd, Orchard Ho, Ogbourne St George, Marlborough, Wilts, SN8 1SU Tel: (01672) 841535 Fax: (01672) 841525

▶ Roundtrip Solutions Ltd, 15 Freuchie Mill, Freuchie, Cupar, Fife, KY15 7JL Tel: (01337) 858826 E-mail: sales@roundtripsolutions.com

▶ RS (UK) Computer Services Ltd, 71 Leonard Street, London, EC2A 4QS Tel: 020 70339003 Fax: 020 70339004

R-Utility Software Consultants Ltd, 10 Charles Street, Rossendale, Lancashire, BB4 9JG Tel: (01706) 830565 Fax: (01706) 225306 E-mail: sales@r-utility.co.uk

S F K Information, Langdale House, Lothersdale, Keighley, West Yorkshire, BD20 8HB Tel: (01535) 637390E-mail: info@sfkinfo.co.uk

S S I Solutions Ltd, Fordbrook Business Centre, Marlborough Road, Pewsey, Wiltshire, SN9 5NU Tel: (01672) 565300 Fax: (01672) 563001 E-mail: general.enquireis@ssi.co.uk

S S S Consultants, Alfriston, Traps Lane, New Malden, Surrey, KT3 4RT Tel: (020) 8949 3753 Fax: (020) 8949 0809 E-mail: info@sss-it.co.uk

Saa Consultants Ltd, The Computer Complex, Somerset Place, Plymouth, PL3 4BB Tel: (01752) 606000 Fax: (01752) 606838 E-mail: sales@saaconsultants.com

Safe Computing Ltd, 20 Freeschool Lane, Leicester, LE1 4FY Tel: 0116-262 9321 Fax: 0116-251 5535 E-mail: sales@safecomputing.co.uk

▶ Salespage Technologies Ltd, Chord Business Park, London Road, Godmanchester, Huntingdon, Cambridgeshire, PE29 2NX Tel: (01480) 424400 Fax: (01480) 424401

Sanderson Retail Sytems Ltd, Lakeside House, Waltham Business Park Brickyard Road, Swanmore, Southampton, SO32 2SA Tel: (01489) 896266 Fax: (01489) 892045 E-mail: enquiries@megabyte.co.uk

▶ Sapphire Accounting Systems, New Manor Farm, West Harptree, Bristol, BS40 6HW Tel: (01761) 222010 Fax: (01761) 222011

Saqqara Technology Ltd, 47 Sandfield Road, Headington, Oxford, OX3 7RW Tel: (01865) 744505 Fax: (01865) 744505

▶ Scalable Communications, Wycombe Lane, Wooburn Green, High Wycombe, Buckinghamshire, HP10 0HH Tel: (01628) 852500 E-mail: info@scalablenetworks.co.uk

▶ Schlumberger, Lambourn Court, Wyndyke Furlong, Abingdon, Oxfordshire, OX14 1UJ Tel: (01235) 559595 Fax: (01235) 535565 E-mail: info@geoquest.com

Scientia Ltd, St. Johns Innovation Centre, Cowley Road, Cambridge, CB4 0WS Tel: (01223) 421221 Fax: (01223) 421218 E-mail: info@scientia.com

Seeburger UK Ltd, Heathrow Boulevard 4, 280 Bath Road, West Drayton, Middlesex, UB7 0DQ Tel: (020) 8564 3914 E-mail: c.blomstedt@seeburger.co.uk

Select Software Ltd, Home Farm Road, Ellingham, Bungay, Suffolk, NR35 2EL Tel: (01508) 518112 Fax: (01508) 518113 E-mail: sales@selectsoftware.net

Serif Software Ltd, 141 St. James Road, Glasgow, G4 0LT Tel: 0141-552 3513 Fax: 0141-552 3506

Servo, Oakwell Way, Birstall, Batley, West Yorkshire, WF17 9LU Tel: (01924) 422111 Fax: (0870) 1218302 E-mail: info@icm-computer.co.uk

▶ Sharpowl International, Wood Cottage Ketteringham Hall, Church Road, Ketteringham, Wymondham, Norfolk, NR18 9RS Tel: (01603) 813620 Fax: (01603) 813629

▶ Sharpowl (International), Ketteringham Hall, Church Road, Ketteringham, Wymondham, Norfolk, NR18 9RS Tel: (01603) 813620 Fax: (01603) 813629

▶ SharpOWL (Software International), Ketteringham Hall, Church Road, Ketteringham, Wymondham, Norfolk, NR18 9RS Tel: (0870) 2242574 Fax: (0870) 2242577 E-mail: info@sharpowl.com

▶ Shaunsoft Computer Systems, Unit 18 Blencathra Business Centre, Threlkeld, Keswick, Cumbria, CA12 4TR Tel: (01768) 779988

Sidneyplus International Library System, Rodney House, Castle Gate, Nottingham, NG1 7AW Tel: 0115-955 5936 Fax: 0115-955 5937 E-mail: sales@sydneyplus.com

▶ Sigmapi Systems Ltd, Poplar Grove, Newcastle, Staffordshire, ST5 1JW Tel: (01782) 740134 Fax: (01782) 619908 E-mail: ch@sigmapisystems.com

▶ Silverlink Software, Atmel Way, Wallsend, Tyne & Wear, NE28 9NZ Tel: 0191-280 4322

Sinara Consultants Ltd, 63 Tanner Street, London, SE1 3PL Tel: (020) 7940 7950 Fax: (020) 7378 1074 E-mail: sales@sinara.co.uk

Sirsi, Unicorn House, Station Close, Potters Bar, Hertfordshire, EN6 3JW Tel: (01707) 646848 Fax: (01707) 858111 E-mail: sirsi@sirsi.co.uk

Skyewright, 24 Elgol, Isle of Skye, IV49 9BL Tel: (01599) 534046

Smartstream Technologies Ltd, 3 St Helens Place, London, EC3A 6AB Tel: (020) 7847 8000 Fax: (020) 7847 8003

Smartt Software Ltd, 3 Queens Road, Exeter, EX2 9ER Tel: (01392) 424299 Fax: (01392) 425254 E-mail: sales@exetermicro.co.uk

▶ Smews, 108 Nalders Road, Chesham, Buckinghamshire, HP5 3DA Tel: (01494) 776732 E-mail: sales@smews.com

Soft Brands ' Evolution, Glenfield Park 2, Blakewater Road, Blackburn, BB1 5QH Tel: (01254) 724400 Fax: (01254) 724404 E-mail: joanne.slater@softbrands.com

SoftBrands Ltd, SoftBrands House, 11 Worton Drive, Reading, RG2 0LX Tel: 0118-975 4000 Fax: 0118-975 4011 E-mail: info.emea@softbrands.com

▶ Softcaw Computer Systems, 7 Wetherby Close, Chippenham, Wiltshire, SN14 0SU Tel: (01249) 444496 Fax: (07043) 326267 E-mail: enquiries@softcaw.co.uk

Softlogic Solutions Ltd, 1 Bath Road, Stonehouse, Gloucestershire, GL10 2JD Tel: (01453) 827366

Softrilogy Ltd, 16 Albert Road, London, NW4 2SG Tel: (020) 8202 8431 Fax: (020) 8202 8431 E-mail: info@softrilogy.com

Solution, Claydon Court, Old Ipswich Road, Claydon, Ipswich, IP6 0AE Tel: (01473) 833070 Fax: (01473) 833053 E-mail: sales@sw4it.com

Solutions PT, Unit 1, Oakfield Road, Cheadle Royal Business Park, Cheadle, Cheshire, SK8 3GX Tel: 0161-495 4600 Fax: 0161-495 4690 E-mail: sales@solutionspt.co.uk

Sol-Vox, 13 Station Rd, Horsforth, Leeds, LS18 5PA Tel: 0113-225 2266

Sopra Group Ltd, Northbrook House, Robert Robinson Avenue, Oxford, OX4 4GA Tel: (01865) 781781 Fax: (01865) 781777

▶ Southern IT Ltd, Estate Office, Eridge Park, Eridge Green, Tunbridge Wells, Kent, TN3 9JT Tel: (01892) 750880 Fax: (0845) 2600644 E-mail: info@southernit.co.uk

▶ Special Source Ltd, 58A Chaplin Road, London, NW2 5PN Tel: (0845) 0573136 E-mail: info@special-source.co.uk

Spectrum Computer Services plc, PO Box 199, Bradford, West Yorkshire, BD1 5RJ Tel: (01274) 308188 Fax: (01274) 307264 E-mail: admin@spectrumplc.co.uk

Sphere IT Ltd, Fernhill House, St. Catherines Hill Lane, Christchurch, Dorset, BH23 2NL Tel: (08707) 373001 Fax: (08707) 373002 E-mail: admin@sphereit.com

Spiral Computers Ltd, 22 London Street, Southport, Merseyside, PR9 0UE Tel: (01704) 500977 Fax: (01704) 540977 E-mail: steve@spiral.co.uk

▶ Spook Ltd, Ayleswade Lane, Biddenden, Ashford, Kent, TN27 8LE Tel: (01580) 292202 Fax: (01580) 292202 E-mail: sales@spook.eu.com

▶ Spur Information Solutions Ltd, Hayward House 2a-2b Hayward Business Centre, New Lane, Havant, Hampshire, PO9 2NL Tel: (023) 9245 5564 Fax: (023) 9247 0874 E-mail: info@spursolutions.com

▶ Stablemate Systems, 63-65 Chilton Business Centre, Woodside Road, Amersham, Buckinghamshire, HP6 6AA Tel: (01494) 434323 Fax: (01494) 434643 E-mail: stablemateltd@aol.com

Stilo Technology, North Quay, Temple Back, Bristol, BS1 6FL Tel: 0117-311 6500 Fax: 0117-311 6599 E-mail: info@stilo.com

Strategic Thought Group plc, Old Town Hall, Centre Court Shopping Centre, Queens Road, London, SW19 8YB Tel: (020) 8410 4000 Fax: (020) 8410 4030 E-mail: sales@strategicthought.com

Strategix, Regatta Place, Marlow Road, Bourne End, Buckinghamshire, SL8 5TD Tel: (01628) 532565 Fax: (01628) 551490 E-mail: strategix@tissoft.co.uk

▶ Studio Box, Far End, Priest Hill, Caversham, Reading, RG4 7RY Tel: 0118-946 3336 Fax: 0118-948 2556 E-mail: studio@studiobox.com

Suilven Associates Computer Systems, PO Box 1, Leominster, Herefordshire, HR6 9YP Tel: (01568) 720194 Fax: (01568) 720195 E-mail: sales@suilven.com

Sunrise Systems Ltd, Flint Bridge Bus Centre, Flint Lane, Ely Road, Cambridge, CB5 9QZ Tel: (01223) 441311 Fax: (01223) 441297 E-mail: info@sunrise-sys.com

Sword Business Technology Solutions Ltd, Johnston House, 52-54 Rose Street, Aberdeen, AB10 1UD Tel: (01224) 704704 Fax: (01224) 704604 E-mail: enquiries@realtimeengineering.co.uk

▶ Symbiant Technologies, 10 Upper Bridge Street, Canterbury, Kent, CT1 2NA Tel: (01227) 455002 Fax: (01227) 454367

Synchro Arts, 13 Links Road, Epsom, Surrey, KT17 3PP Tel: (01372) 811934 Fax: (01372) 817976 E-mail: info@synchroarts.com

Syncron UK Ltd, Baskerville House, Centenary Square, Birmingham, B1 2ND Tel: 0121-503 2650 Fax: 0121-503 2651

Synergy Systems Manchester Ltd, 219 Stockport Road, Stockport, Cheshire, SK3 0RH Tel: 0161-428 1517 Fax: 0161-428 8528

▶ Syntagm, 10 Oxford Road, Abingdon, Oxfordshire, OX14 2DS Tel: (01235) 522859 Fax: (01235) 554449 E-mail: william.hudson@syntagm.co.uk

Syscom Group Ltd, Hampshire House, High Street, Kingswinford, West Midlands, DY6 8AW Tel: (01384) 400600 Fax: (01384) 400601 E-mail: info@syscom.plc.uk

Sysnet Ltd, Avon Court, Cowbridge Road, Bridgend, Mid Glamorgan, CF31 3SR Tel: (01656) 647111 Fax: (01656) 651038 E-mail: enquiries@sysnetltd.co.uk

▶ System Lynx Ltd, Holland House, Bath Street, Walsall, WS1 3BZ Tel: (01922) 622044 Fax: (01922) 709235

System One Ltd, Lavant House, 39 Lavant Street, Petersfield, Hampshire, GU32 3EL Tel: (01730) 267000 Fax: (01730) 266676 E-mail: sales@systemone.co.uk

System Red Ltd, Prospidnick, Helston, Cornwall, TR13 0RY Tel: (01326) 563300 Fax: (01326) 565680 E-mail: sales@systemred.co.uk

▶ Sytel Ltd, 1-2 Cromwell Court, New Street, Aylesbury, Buckinghamshire, HP20 2PB Tel: (01296) 381200

T M A Data Management Ltd, Surrey House, 34 Eden Street, Kingston upon Thames, Surrey, KT1 1ER Tel: (020) 8481 3988 Fax: (020) 8546 9794 E-mail: info@tma.co.uk

Tailormade Software, Poolside, 43 Pool Lane, Brocton, Stafford, ST17 0TY Tel: (01785) 660005 Fax: (01785) 660005 E-mail: sales@tailormadesw.co.uk

Tarantella Ltd, Richmond House, Lawnswood Business Park, Redbers Close, Leeds, LS16 6RD Tel: 0113-251 2000 Fax: 0113-368 6001

Target Group plc, Target House, 5-19 Cowbridge Road East, Cardiff, CF11 9AB Tel: (029) 2030 1401 Fax: (029) 2030 1400 E-mail: marketing@targetgroup.net

Task Computer Logic Ltd, 70 Skene Street, Aberdeen, AB10 1QE Tel: (0870) 7410292 Fax: (0871) 7333523 E-mail: seals@etcl.co.uk

Taylor Investments UK Ltd, 72 Commercial Road, Hereford, HR1 2BP Tel: (01432) 354439 Fax: (01432) 352799

TCS Computer Services Ltd, The Brewhouse 19 Old Bexley Business Park, Bourne Road, Bexley, Kent, DA5 1LR Tel: (01322) 559840 Fax: (01322) 550010 E-mail: rodney.gent@tcscs.co.uk

Tech Op Ltd, 268 London Road, Cheltenham, Gloucestershire, GL52 6HS Tel: (01242) 570999 Fax: (01242) 588955 E-mail: sales@techop.co.uk

Teleca Ltd, 137 Barlow Moor Road, Manchester, M20 2PW Tel: 0161-447 6900 Fax: 0161-447 6901

▶ Telefax Holdings Ltd, St. Augustines Business Park, Estuary Close, Whitstable, Kent, CT5 2QJ Tel: (01227) 791901 Fax: (01227) 266280E-mail: info@telefaxdatasystems.co.uk

Telesis Systems Ltd, 20 Stryd Y Castell, Ruthin, Clwyd, LL15 1DR Tel: (01824) 704040 Fax: (01824) 704020

▶ Temposoft UK, 59-60 Thames Street, Windsor, Berkshire, SL4 1TX Tel: (01753) 272040 Fax: (01753) 272049 E-mail: info@temposoft.com

Tera (UK) Ltd, Park Farm Business Centre, Fornham St. Genevieve, Bury St. Edmunds, Suffolk, IP28 6TS Tel: (01284) 753263 Fax: (01284) 753257 E-mail: sales@tera-uk.com

Tigerridge Consultancy Services Ltd, 4 Bonneys, The Street, Eversley, Hook, Hampshire, RG27 0PJ Tel: 0118-973 6875 Fax: (0845) 2303635 E-mail: sales@tigerridge.co.uk

▶ TMSC Ltd, 13 Helions Road, Steeple Bumpstead, Steeple Bumpstead, Haverhill, Suffolk, CB9 7DU Tel: (01440) 730211 E-mail: sales@tmsc.co.uk

TPOS Ltd, Mitre House, Lodge Road, Long Hanborough Business Park, Witney, Oxfordshire, OX29 8LP Tel: (01993) 883688 Fax: (01993) 883611

▶ TQS Ltd, The Stables, Station Road West, Oxted, Surrey, RH8 9EE Tel: (01883) 732002 Fax: (01883) 724638 E-mail: davidforester@tqsltd.co.uk

Trade Point Systems Ltd, Phoenix House, 2A Amity Grove, London, SW20 0LJ Tel: (020) 8944 1003 Fax: (020) 8971 6767 E-mail: info@tradepointsys.co.uk

Transtel Communications Ltd, Baileys House, Stoke Poges Lane, Slough, SL1 3PB Tel: (01753) 691869 Fax: (01753) 505639 E-mail: admin@transtel.com

Trax UK Ltd, Suite 4B Christchurch House, Beaufort Court, Medway City Estate, Rochester, Kent, ME2 4FX Tel: (01634) 724724 Fax: (01634) 290524 E-mail: sales@trax-uk.co.uk

Treasures, 6 Brendon Road, Watchet, Somerset, TA23 0AU Tel: (01984) 634903 Fax: (01984) 634903 E-mail: laurence.welbourne@btopenworld.com

Triad Group P.L.C., Weyside Park, Catteshall Lane, Godalming, Surrey, GU7 1XE Tel: (01483) 860222 Fax: (01483) 860198 E-mail: mail@triad.plc.uk

▶ Trifusion Ltd, 105 The Broadway, London, NW7 3TG Tel: (020) 8959 6677 Fax: (020) 8959 9206

▶ Trinem Consulting, 10 Montrose Terrace, Edinburgh, EH7 5DL Tel: 0131-652 8190 Fax: 0131-652 3512 E-mail: info@trinem.com

Tritec Systems Ltd, Riverview House, London Road, Old Basing, Basingstoke, Hampshire, RG24 7JL Tel: (01256) 477778 Fax: (01256) 477776 E-mail: sales@tritec.co.uk

True Systems Ltd, Systems House, 127 High Street, Teddington, Middlesex, TW11 8HH Tel: (020) 8977 5151 E-mail: sales@truesystems.co.uk

The Turtle Partnership, Hofer House, 185 Uxbridge Road, Hampton, Middlesex, TW12 1BN Tel: (020) 8941 6994 Fax: (020) 8941 4730 E-mail: mike@turtleweb.com

Ukerna, Atlas Centre, Fermi Avenue, Chilton, Didcot, Oxfordshire, OX11 0QS Tel: (01235) 822200 Fax: (01235) 822399

Unified Solutions Ltd, 883-884 Plymouth Road, Slough, SL1 4LP Tel: (01753) 775050 Fax: (01753) 775020 E-mail: info@unified.co.uk

Unitas Software, 1 Kingsgate Street, Coleraine, County Londonderry, BT52 1LB Tel: (02870) 320732 Fax: (02870) 321333 E-mail: info@unitassoftware.com

V T Software Solutions, Unit 4Thornbury Office Park, Midland Way, Thornbury, Bristol, BS35 2BS Tel: (01454) 874002 Fax: (01454) 874001 E-mail: enquire@vtsoftwaresolutions.com

Vbug, 4 Park Parade, Park Road, Farnham Royal, Slough, SL2 3AU Tel: (01753) 649680 Fax: (01753) 647222 E-mail: sales@vbug.co.uk

Vertex Financial Services Holdings Ltd, Allen Jones House, Jessop Avenue, Cheltenham, Gloucestershire, GL50 3SH Tel: (01242) 547000 Fax: (01242) 547016

Vertex Systems Ltd, 47 Holmlea Road, Goring, Reading, RG8 9EX Tel: (01491) 872812

Viewlocity Software Ltd, 165 Burwood Road, Walton-on-Thames, Surrey, KT12 4AT Tel: (01932) 260340 Fax: (01932) 260341

▶ Virtio, Alba Centre, Alba Campus, Livingston, West Lothian, EH54 7EG Tel: (01506) 402410

Vixon Computer Systems, 29-33 Grimsby Road, Cleethorpes, South Humberside, DN35 7AQ Tel: (01472) 362672 Fax: (01472) 350806 E-mail: vixsoft@vixsoft.co.uk

W P C Software Ltd, 9 Wellsway, Keynsham, Bristol, BS31 1HS Tel: 0117-908 1484 Fax: 0117-940 2060 E-mail: wpc@wpcsoft.com

Waterstar, Chester House, Westgate, Bishop Auckland, County Durham, DL13 1PG Tel: (01388) 517513 E-mail: john.mccutheon@waterstar.co.uk

Wilco International Ltd, 1 America Square, London, EC3N 2LS Tel: (020) 7418 4500 Fax: (020) 7418 4504 E-mail: reception@adpwilco.co.uk

Wild Strawberry Interactive Multimedia Ltd, 1 Cartland Avenue, Shrewsbury, SY2 5UW Tel: (01743) 354386 Fax: (01743) 354386

▶ WinIT Consultancy Ltd, West Mills, Newbury, Berkshire, RG14 5HG Tel: (0870) 2000635 Fax: (0870) 2000755 E-mail: robin@winitconsultancy.co.uk

Woodstock Computer Solutions Ltd, Malvern, Oakhanger, Bordon, Hampshire, GU35 9JJ Tel: (01420) 474722 E-mail: roly@wcsweb.co.uk

▶ Worksmart Solutions, 41 Tickford Street, Newport Pagnl, Newport Pagnell, Buckinghamshire, MK16 9AW Tel: (01908) 613613 E-mail: sales@worksmart.co.uk

▶ Worth Solutions Ltd, 66 Leonard Street, London, EC2A 4LW Tel: (020) 7739 3861

X K S Ltd, Unit 19 St. Asaph Business Park, Glascoed Road, St. Asaph, Clwyd, LL17 0LJ Tel: (01745) 584953 Fax: (01745) 583047

▶ Xecore Ltd, 59 Highbury Gardens, Seven Kings Ilford, Ilford, Essex, IG3 8AF Tel: (07800) 590908 E-mail: sales@xecore.co.uk

▶ Xperience, Xperience House, 25 Paterson Road, Finedon Road Industrial Estate, Wellingborough, Northamptonshire, NN8 4BZ Tel: (01933) 231100 Fax: (01933) 231111

▶ Y3k Systems Ltd, The Bearings, Bowbridge Road, Newark, Nottinghamshire, NG24 4BZ Tel: (01636) 708342 Fax: (01636) 708343 E-mail: info@y3k.info

COMPUTER SOFTWARE DEVELOPMENT SERVICES

▶ Faber Systems Ltd, 2Nd Floor Unit 2, Century Place, Lamberts Road, Tunbridge Wells, Kent, TN2 3EH Tel: (01892) 517388 Fax: (01892) 774801 E-mail: chris.smith@fabsys.com

▶ indicates data change since last edition

COMPUTER SOFTWARE DEVELOPMENT SERVICES – *continued*

Sigmer, The Sussex Innovation Centre, Science Park Square, Falmer, Brighton, BN1 9SB Tel: (01273) 234663 Fax: (01273) 669 701 E-mail: info@sigmer.com

COMPUTER SOFTWARE DEVELOPMENT SERVICES, INTERNET

▶ Mosketo, 1 Webster Street, Preston, PR2 1BY Tel: (07723) 042246 E-mail: enquiries@mosketo.net

COMPUTER SOFTWARE DUPLICATING

Ram Peripherals, 14 Lombard Road, Merton, London, SW19 3TZ Tel: (020) 8543 9696 Fax: (020) 8543 3419 E-mail: sales@ram-peripherals.co.uk

West Street Studios, West Street Studios, 3 West Street, Buckingham, MK18 1HL Tel: (01280) 822814 Fax: E-mail: jamie@weststreetstudios.co.uk

COMPUTER SOFTWARE ENGINEERING CONSULTANCY

▶ BitBolt Software Limited, 22b Petticoat Tower, Petticoat Square, London, E1 7EF Tel: 08704 860 498 Fax: 08704 860 497 E-mail: info@bitbolt.com

▶ Business Intelligence Solutions Ltd, 9 Southlands Close, Badsworth, West Bridgford, Pontefract, West Yorkshire, WF9 1AU Tel: (01977) 650944 E-mail: info@bi-solutions.co.uk

C H Media, 20 Marigold Walk, Bristol, BS3 2PD Tel: 0117-939 4061 Fax: (08701) 328330 E-mail: enquiries@chmedia.co.uk

▶ Demopad Software Ltd, Midwest House, Canal Road, Timperley, Cheshire, WA14 1TF Tel: 08700 551100 Fax: 08707 062171 E-mail: sales@sentrypad.com

▶ Enterprise Systems UK Ltd, 303-305 King Street, Aberdeen, AB24 5AP Tel: (01224) 339815 Fax: 01224 339801 E-mail: jm@enterprisesystems.co.uk

▶ John Gocher Computing, St Clair, Rouge Huis Avenue, St. Peter Port, Guernsey, GY1 1RX Tel: (01481) 724778 E-mail: john@gocher.co.uk

▶ HeronSoft Ltd, 29 Chatteris Park, Sandymoor, Runcorn, Cheshire, WA7 1XE Tel: (01928) 571620 Fax: (01928) 571620 E-mail: heronsoft@aol.com

▶ InterSys Solutions Limited, 22 Pump Hill, loughton, Essex, IG10 1RU Tel: 07970 610002 E-mail: mg@intsl.com

▶ MPBA Ltd, PO Box 190, Burgess Hill, West Sussex, RH15 8WN Tel: (0870) 0800667 Fax: (0870) 4325211E-mail: info@mpba.co.uk

Network Associates (Midlands) Ltd, Vincent House, Buntsford Park Road, Bromsgrove, Worcestershire, B60 3DX Tel: (01527) 576933 Fax: (0870) 706 2522 E-mail: enquiries@network-associates.co.uk

▶ PC Wizards, 97 Gordon Road, Gillingham, Kent, ME7 2NG Tel: (01634) 324188 E-mail: service@thepcwizards.net

▶ Stortford Computer Services Ltd, 9 Boundary Road, Bishop's Stortford, Hertfordshire, CM23 5LE Tel: (01279) 657855 E-mail: contact@stortfordcomputerservices.co.uk

TMS Associates Ltd, 168 Clare Road, Cardiff, CF11 6RX Tel: (029) 2025 8900 Fax: (029) 2025 8255 E-mail: h.g.patel@ntlworld.com

COMPUTER SOFTWARE ENGINEERS

A A T Computer Services, 57 High Street, Donaghadee, County Down, BT21 0AQ Tel: (028) 9188 8114 Fax: (028) 9188 8370 E-mail: andrew@aatcs.co.uk

▶ Ash Associates, PO Box 5374, Ferndown, Dorset, BH22 0ZX Tel: (0845) 1232701 E-mail: recruit@ash-associates.com

▶ Computa Centre, Carrick Business Centre, 4-5 Bonville Road, Bristol, BS4 5NZ Tel: 0117-316 0344 Fax: 0117-316 0399 E-mail: computacentre@blitz-it.com

▶ LinuSoft, 10 Silfield Road, Wymondham, Norfolk, NR18 9AU Tel: (01953) 601294 E-mail: enquiries@linusoft.co.uk

Pca Engineers Ltd, Homer House, Sibthorp Street, Lincoln, LN5 7SL Tel: (01522) 530106 Fax: (01522) 511703 E-mail: sales@pcaeng.co.uk

COMPUTER SOFTWARE HOUSE

Abington Business Systems, 121 The Drive, Northampton, NN1 4SW Tel: (01604) 714241 Fax: (01604) 714847

Achiever Software, Ashted Lock Way, Birmingham, B7 4AZ Tel: 0121-380 1010 Fax: 0121-380 1011 E-mail: sales@achiever.co.uk

Russell Adams Ltd, Beechwood House, Tanners Lane, Berkswell, Coventry, CV7 7DA Tel: (024) 7685 6400 Fax: (024) 7685 6401 E-mail: sales@russelladams.com

American Software (UK) Ltd, St Georges Business Park, Brooklands Road, Weybridge, Surrey, KT13 0TS Tel: (01932) 855554 Fax: (01932) 854563 E-mail: sales@amsoftware.com

Ariel Communications Ltd, 2 Harvingwell Place, 129-32 Mark Road, Hemel Hempstead, Hertfordshire, HP2 7BW Tel: (01442) 418460 E-mail: sales@arielcommunications.co.uk

Asl Financial Solutions, Fountain House Suite 9, Great Cornbow, Halesowen, West Midlands, B63 3BL Tel: (0870) 6002131 Fax: 0121-585 7294 E-mail: info@finobj.com

Avis Software Consultants, 22 Balmoral Way, Sutton, Surrey, SM2 6PD Tel: (020) 8643 6899 Fax: (020) 8642 6005 E-mail: info@avissoft.co.uk

B M S Ltd, Sproughton House, Sproughton, Ipswich, IP8 3AW Tel: (01473) 240024 Fax: (01473) 240043E-mail: info@b-m-s.co.uk

Barwick Systems Ltd, Merchants Wharf, Teesdale Park, Thornaby, Stockton-on-Tees, Cleveland, TS17 6BA Tel: (01642) 632900 Fax: (01642) 632915 E-mail: admin@barwicksystems.co.uk

Basic Business Systems Ltd, Brookside Road, Ruddington, Nottingham, NG11 6AT Tel: 0115-940 5000 Fax: 0115-940 5450

Bond International Software Ltd, Courtlands, Parklands Avenue, Goring-by-Sea, Worthing, West Sussex, BN12 4NG Tel: (01903) 707070 Fax: (01903) 707080 E-mail: sales@bond.co.uk

CCM Ace Ltd, 223 Bury New Road, Whitefield, Manchester, M45 8GW Tel: 0161-766 4686 Fax: 0161-767 9217 E-mail: sales@ccmace.co.uk

Coda P.L.C., Cardale Park, Beckwith Head Road, Harrogate, North Yorkshire, HG3 1RY Tel: (01423) 509999 Fax: (01423) 530525 E-mail: info@coda.com

Compsoft plc, Equinox House, Oriel Court, Alton, Hampshire, GU34 2YT Tel: (01420) 89545 Fax: (01420) 81444 E-mail: sales@compsoft.co.uk

Corby & Fellas, First Floor, 284-5 Southtown Rd, Great Yarmouth, Norfolk, NR31 0JB Tel: (01493) 658800 Fax: (01493) 442308 E-mail: sales@corby-fellas.co.uk

Data Collection Systems Ltd, 6 Station Court, Station Approach, Borough Green, Sevenoaks, Kent, TN15 8AD Tel: (01732) 780456 Fax: (01732) 780445 E-mail: sales@dcs-sol.com

Data Connection Ltd, 100 Church Street, Enfield, Middlesex, EN2 6BQ Tel: (020) 8366 1177 Fax: (020) 8363 1468 E-mail: recruit@dataconnection.com

Data Discovery Solutions LRD, 2 Venture Road, Chilworth, Southampton, SO16 7NP Tel: (023) 8076 7678 Fax: (023) 8076 7665 E-mail: sales@activenavigation.com

Datag Ltd, Holly Farm, Somerford Booths, Congleton, Cheshire, CW12 2JX Tel: (01260) 224794 Fax: (01260) 224794 E-mail: enquiries@datag.co.uk

Datapro Software Ltd, North Street, Portslade, Brighton, BN41 1DH Tel: (01273) 886000 Fax: (01273) 886066 E-mail: sales@datapro.co.uk

Dendrite Europe Ltd, 2 Windsor Dials, Arthur Road, Windsor, Berkshire, SL4 1RS Tel: (01753) 834200 Fax: (01753) 834399 E-mail: denuk@dendrite.co.uk

Di-Soft Research, Little Frankley, Hook Heath Road, Woking, Surrey, GU22 0QL Tel: (01483) 727906 Fax: (01483) 727906 E-mail: colin.howard@comdaq.net

Document Plus Ltd, The Station House, Hever, Edenbridge, Kent, TN8 7ER Tel: (01732) 867792 Fax: (01732) 865585 E-mail: sales@chamnet.com

▶ DPM Systems Ltd, Suite 4, Cornerstone House, Stafford Park 13, Telford, Shropshire, TF3 3AZ Tel: (01952) 504400 Fax: (01952) 504500 E-mail: info@dpmsys.com

Eastar-solutions Ltd, 123 Bath Row, Birmingham, B15 1LS Tel: 0121-643 5500 Fax: 0121 6337537

Elite Training & Consultancy Services Ltd, Thomas House, 14-16 James Street South, Belfast, BT2 7GA Tel: (028) 9031 6840 Fax: (028) 9031 6841 E-mail: sales@elitetraining.com

Estate Computer Systems, 4-6 Dukes Road, London, WC1H 9AD Tel: (020) 7388 3400 Fax: (020) 7388 6006 E-mail: info@qubeglobal.com

Exegesis S D M, 4 New Street, Talgarth, Brecon, Powys, LD3 0AH Tel: (01874) 711145 Fax: (01874) 711156 E-mail: sales@esdm.co.uk

Farmdata Ltd, Westertown, Rothienorman, Inverurie, Aberdeenshire, AB51 8US Tel: (01467) 671457 Fax: (01467) 671448 E-mail: sales@farmdata.co.uk

Fathom Technologies Ltd, 8 Windsor Square, Silver Street, Reading, RG1 2TH Tel: 0118-975 0044 Fax: 0118-975 0742 E-mail: info@fathom.co.uk

Formwise Export Ltd, 15 The Promenade, Swansea, SA1 6EN Tel: (01792) 462113 Fax: (01792) 650850 E-mail: sales@formwise.co.uk

Friedman Corporation Ltd, 1 Chapel Court, Holly Walk, Leamington Spa, Warwickshire, CV32 4YS Tel: (01926) 741600 Fax: (01926) 741601 E-mail: uksales@friedmancorp.co.uk

Future Data International Ltd, 14 High Street, Lyndhurst, Hampshire, SO43 7BD Tel: (023) 8028 4369 Fax: (023) 8028 4369 E-mail: gary@futuredata.com

Game Stores Ltd, 43-44 Western Road, Brighton, BN1 2EB Tel: (01273) 734737

GL Trade Ltd, 47-53 Cannon Street, London, EC4M 5SH Tel: (020) 7665 6200 Fax: (020) 7665 6299 E-mail: enquiries@gltrade.co.uk

Gordon Associates, Suite G1 Monpellier House, Monpellier Drive, Cheltenham, Gloucestershire, GL50 1TY Tel: (01242) 529820 Fax: (01242) 226021 E-mail: sales@gordonassociates.co.uk

I C C S Ltd, 4 Market Street, Edenfield, Ramsbottom, Bury, Lancashire, BL0 0JN Tel: (01706) 822233 Fax: (01706) 822277 E-mail: info@iccs-ltd.co.uk

I K Portable Solutions Ltd, I K House, Plough Road, Wellington, Telford, Shropshire, TF1 1ET Tel: (01952) 242000 Fax: (01952) 223789 E-mail: iki@netcomuk.co.uk

I P C Systems Computer & Telecommunications Systems, Fairview House, Rigg Road, Cumnock, Ayrshire, KA18 3JB Tel: (01290) 421613 Fax: (01290) 425586

▶ I T C (Epos) Ltd, Barnsley Business & Innovation Centre, Innovation Way, Barnsley, South Yorkshire, S75 1JL Tel: (01226) 731785 Fax: (01226) 731867 E-mail: sales@itcepos.co.uk

I T S L Net Ltd, 2 Marsh Lane, Birmingham, B23 6NX Tel: (0870) 7437780 Fax: (0870) 7437781 E-mail: sales@itslnet.com

Index Software Ltd, 4 Highfield Road, Weston-super-Mare, Avon, BS24 9LZ Tel: (01934) 811190 Fax: (01934) 811191 E-mail: indexsoftwarelimited@btinternet.com

Infor, Needles House, Birmingham Road, Studley, Warwickshire, B80 7AS Tel: (01527) 496200 Fax: (01527) 496300

▶ i-teamworks, PO Box 556, Peterborough, PE4 6WL Tel: (0845) 4900126 Fax: (0845) 4900127 E-mail: info@iteamworks.com

Kingfisher Associates UK Ltd, Nine Yews, Cranborne, Wimborne, Dorset, BH21 5PW Tel: (01725) 517744 Fax: (01725) 517766 E-mail: sales@kfa.co.uk

Kiwiplan, Unit 5, Crompton Court, Burntwood Business Park, Burntwood, Staffordshire, WS7 3GG Tel: (01543) 273073 Fax: (01543) 273074 E-mail: info@kiwiplan-europe.com

Lablogic Systems Ltd, Paradigm House, 3 Melbourne Avenue, Sheffield, S10 2QJ Tel: 0114-266 7267 Fax: 0114-266 3944 E-mail: solutions@lablogic.com

Langton Software Ltd, Holly Road, Twickenham, TW1 4EG Tel: (0845) 1235714 Fax: (020) 8831 7522 E-mail: admin@langton.com

Laser Byte Ltd, Burstow Park, Antlands Lane, Shipley Bridge, Horley, Surrey, RH6 9TF Tel: (01293) 772201 Fax: (01293) 774694 E-mail: support@lazerbyte.com

Laserform International Ltd, Higher Lane, Lymm, Cheshire, WA13 0RZ Tel: (01925) 750000 Fax: (01925) 750021 E-mail: admin@laserform.co.uk

Liber8 Ltd, Asher House, Barsbank Lane, Lymm, Cheshire, WA13 0ED Tel: (01925) 758283 Fax: (01925) 758470E-mail: info@liber8.co.uk

▶ Liverpool Data Research Associates Ltd, Monks Ferry, Portside, Birkenhead, Merseyside, CH41 5LH Tel: 0151-649 9300 Fax: 0151-649 9666 E-mail: info@ldra.co.uk

Logicscope Realisations Ltd, 64 Great Eastern Street, London, EC2A 3QR Tel: (020) 7880 5950 Fax: (020) 7880 5999 E-mail: info@logicscope.com

Lucas Software Solutions, 95 Tilehouse St, Hitchin, Hertfordshire, SG5 2DW Tel: (01462) 440885 Fax: (01462) 440954 E-mail: sales@lucas-software.co.uk

Macdonald Associates Ltd, 6 Cecil Aldin Drive, Tilehurst, Reading, RG31 6YP Tel: 0118-945 2862 Fax: 0118-962 4854 E-mail: info@macd.com

Macrovision Europe Ltd, 14-18 Bell Street, Maidenhead, Berkshire, SL6 1BR Tel: (01628) 786100 Fax: (0870) 8711161 E-mail: info@macrovison.com

Mailord Mail Order Services Ltd, 115 Park Avenue, Potters Bar, Hertfordshire, EN6 5EW Tel: (01707) 662442 Fax: (01707) 664180 E-mail: mike@mailord.co.uk

Mapsoft Computer Services Ltd, Idstone, Loddiswell, Kingsbridge, Devon, TQ7 4EJ Tel: (01548) 550047 E-mail: impdeved@mapsoft.com

Marcmoor Computer Systems, 5a Church Sq, Market Harborough, Leics, LE16 7HB Tel: (01858) 465746 Fax: (01858) 434628 E-mail: paul@marcmoor.co.uk

Maxima, 2 Bell Business Park, Smeaton Close, Aylesbury, Buckinghamshire, HP19 8JR Tel: (01296) 318060 Fax: (01296) 318089

Media Services Group Ltd, 64 Charlotte Street, London, W1T 4QD Tel: (020) 7436 0070 Fax: (020) 7580 5706 E-mail: hbrantley@msgl.com

Mentat Systems Ltd, 3 Rutland Road, Southport, Merseyside, PR8 6PB Tel: (01704) 514506 E-mail: sale@mentat.co.uk

Micro Focus Ltd, The Lawn, 22-30 Old Bath Road, Newbury, Berkshire, RG14 1QN Tel: (01635) 32646 Fax: (01635) 33966 E-mail: ukmarketing@microfocus.com

Microsec Computer Systems, 3b The Old Flour Mill, Queen Street, Emsworth, Hampshire, PO10 7BT Tel: (01243) 370073 Fax: (01243) 379997 E-mail: info@microsec.co.uk

Netmanage UK Ltd, Lyon Court, Walsworth Road, Hitchin, Hertfordshire, SG4 9SX Tel: (01462) 755050 Fax: (01462) 755055

Neutral Ltd, 167 Ardleigh Green Road, Hornchurch, Essex, RM11 2LF Tel: (01708) 701522 Fax: (01708) 701994 E-mail: info@neutral.co.uk

Norton Waugh Managment Software, The Old School, School Lane, Weston-Under-Lizard, Shifnal, Shropshire, TF11 8SZ Tel: (01952) 850333 Fax: (01952) 850649 E-mail: sales@nortonwaugh.co.uk

Orchid Software Ltd, 63 Westgate Road, Newcastle Upon Tyne, NE1 1SG Tel: 0191-232 5750 E-mail: adrian@orchidsoft.com

▶ P C S Personal Computer Systems Ltd, 531 Millbrook Road West, Regents Park, Southampton, SO15 0LN Tel: (023) 8078 0548 E-mail: info@pcs-on-line.co.uk

P N L Tools, 5 The Hawthorns, Hawthorns Lane, Staunton, Gloucester, GL19 3NY Tel: (01452) 840966 Fax: (01452) 840965

P & Q International plc, Wickham House, Station Road, Braughing, Ware, Hertfordshire, SG11 2PB Tel: (0845) 1300707 Fax: (0845) 1300727 E-mail: sales@pandq.com

Pansoft Ltd, 28 Landport Terrace, Portsmouth, PO1 2RG Tel: (023) 9285 1513 Fax: (023) 9285 1529 E-mail: sales@pansoft.co.uk

Paxton Computers Ltd, 15 Kingsway, Bedford, MK42 9EZ Tel: (01234) 216666 Fax: (01234) 212705 E-mail: info@paxsoft.co.uk

Pipistrel Retail Software Ltd, 23 Woodbridge Road, Guildford, Surrey, GU1 1DY Tel: (01483) 440099 Fax: (0870) 1164400 E-mail: support@pipistrel.com

Pisys Ltd, Campus 1, Balgownie Road, Bridge of Don, Aberdeen, AB22 8GT Tel: (01224) 332014 Fax: (01224) 332055 E-mail: info@pisysltd.co.uk

Pregem Computing Ltd, 9 Oriel Business Park, Omega Park, Alton, Hampshire, GU34 2YT Tel: (01420) 544514 Fax: (01420) 544599 E-mail: sales@pregem.com

Proact International Ltd, 9a Vale Street, Denbigh, Clwyd, LL16 3AD Tel: (01745) 813586 Fax: (01745) 815096

The Publishing Software Co., 6 Trevithick Close, Stourport-on-Severn, Worcestershire, DY13 8AN Tel: (0870) 0101780 Fax: (0870) 0101783 E-mail: laurence@p-s-c.co.uk

R O C C Computers Ltd, Stanford Gate, South Road, Brighton, BN1 6SB Tel: (01273) 274700 Fax: (01273) 274707 E-mail: marketing@rocc.co.uk

Rapid Prototyping Systems Ltd, Bowden Hall, Bowden Lane, Marple, Stockport, Cheshire, SK6 6ND Tel: 0161-426 0465 Fax: 0161-426 0467 E-mail: sales@rpsys.co.uk

Re-engineering Maintenance Conversion Ltd, 30 Christchurch Rd, Bournemouth, BH1 3PD Tel: 01202 438344 Fax: 01202 438388

Rhyme Systems Ltd, Stapeley House, London Road, Stapeley, Nantwich, Cheshire, CW5 7JW Tel: (01270) 626023 Fax: (01270) 625948

Safam 786 Ltd, 392a High Street, Cheltenham, Gloucestershire, GL50 3JD Tel: (01242) 693786 Fax: (01242) 252786 E-mail: safam786@dial.pipex.com

Safe Computing Ltd, 20 Freeschool Lane, Leicester, LE1 4FY Tel: 0116-262 9321 Fax: 0116-251 5535 E-mail: sales@safecomputing.co.uk

Scientia Ltd, St. Johns Innovation Centre, Cowley Road, Cambridge, CB4 0WS Tel: (01223) 421221 Fax: (01223) 421218 E-mail: info@scientia.com

Sci-sys Ltd, Clothier Road, Bristol, BS4 5SS Tel: 0117-971 7251 Fax: 0117-972 1846 E-mail: marketing@scisys.co.uk

Scomagg Ltd, Scomagg House, Crosshill Street, Motherwell, Lanarkshire, ML1 1RU Tel: (01698) 266199 Fax: (01698) 253672 E-mail: sales@scomagg.com

Selwell Computers (Software) Ltd, Selwood House, Hough Road, Frieston, Grantham, Lincolnshire, NG32 3DA Tel: (01400) 273311 Fax: (01400) 273312

Shire Management Services, Centre Court, 1301 Stratford Road, Hall Green, Birmingham, B28 9HH Tel: 0121-702 2431 Fax: 0121-778 6668 E-mail: admin@shireman.com

Sidneyplus International Library System, Rodney House, Castle Gate, Nottingham, NG1 7AW Tel: 0115-955 5936 Fax: 0115-955 5937 E-mail: sales@sydneyplus.com

Silvon Software Ltd, Pinewood Studios, Pinewood Road, IVER, Buckinghamshire, SL0 0NH Tel: 01753 631133 Fax: (01753) 653192

Sinara Consultants Ltd, 63 Tanner Street, London, SE1 3PL Tel: (020) 7940 7950 Fax: (020) 7378 1074 E-mail: sales@sinara.co.uk

Snap Survey Software Mercator Research Group Ltd, 5 Mead Court, Cooper Road, Thornbury, Bristol, BS35 3UW Tel: (01454) 280800 Fax: (01454) 281216 E-mail: info@snapsurveys.com

Soft Machine Ltd, Tilshead Ho, High St, Tilshead, Salisbury, SP3 4RX Tel: (01980) 621300 Fax: (01980) 621340 E-mail: hrh@softmachine.co.uk

Streets Heaver Computer Systems Ltd, 4 Low Moor Road, Lincoln, LN6 3JY Tel: (01522) 872000 Fax: (01522) 872255 E-mail: control@streetsheaver.com

Sum-It Computer Systems Ltd, Samuel House, Chinnor Road, Thame, Oxfordshire, OX9 3NU Tel: (01844) 213003 Fax: (01844) 214722 E-mail: sales@sum-it.co.uk

COMPUTER SOFTWARE HOUSE - *continued*

Symology Ltd, Cotswold Farm Business Park, Millfield Lane, Caddington, Luton, LU1 4AJ Tel: (01582) 842626 Fax: (01582) 842600 E-mail: webmaster@symology.co.uk

The Systems Practice plc, 134-135 High Street, Southampton, SO14 2BR Tel: (023) 8048 0001 Fax: (023) 8048 0002 E-mail: sales@tspplc.com

▶ Taskforce Software Ltd, 158 Sturminster Road, Bristol, BS14 8AT Tel: (01458) 835097 E-mail: info@taskforce-software.co.uk

Tecfacs Ltd, 6 Oaklands Business Centre, Oaklands Park, Wokingham, Berkshire, RG41 2FD Tel: 0118-977 6645 Fax: 0118-989 4461 E-mail: sales@tecfacs.com

Total Systems plc, 394 City Road, London, EC1V 2QA Tel: (020) 7294 4888 Fax: (020) 7294 4999 E-mail: sales@totalsystems.co.uk

Trackit Systems Ltd, Trival House, Unit 3 Hawthorne Park, Coal Road, Leeds, LS14 1PQ Tel: 0113-306 0306 Fax: 0113-276 0685

Tribal Asset Management Ltd, Unit E Gillette Close, Staffordshire Technology Park, Stafford, ST18 0LQ Tel: (0870) 0601040 Fax: (0870) 0607040 E-mail: info@tribalassetmanagement.co.uk

Trisoft Ltd, Accent Park, Bakewell Road, Orton Southgate, Peterborough, PE2 6XS Tel: (01733) 372700 Fax: (01733) 372729

True Systems Ltd, Systems House, 127 High Street, Teddington, Middlesex, TW11 8HH Tel: (020) 8977 5151 E-mail: sales@truesystems.co.uk

Unify Corp (UK) Ltd, Malt House, Hummer Road, Egham, Surrey, TW20 9BD Tel: (01784) 487940 Fax: (01784) 487941 E-mail: info@unify.com

V I Software, St. Michaels Square, Ashton-under-Lyne, Lancashire, OL6 6XN Tel: 0161-343 1322 Fax: 0161-343 1355 E-mail: robert@visoftware.co.uk

Version One Ltd, London House, London Road South, Poynton, Stockport, Cheshire, SK12 1YP Tel: (01625) 856500 Fax: (01625) 856501 E-mail: info@versionone.co.uk

Visibility Europe Ltd, 3Rd Floor, 1 Ashley Road, Altrincham, Cheshire, WA14 2DT Tel: 0161-927 2500 Fax: 0161-928 9700

W D M Software Ltd, Greensfield Business Centre, Mulgrave Terrace, Gateshead, Tyne & Wear, NE8 1PQ Tel: 0191-478 6666 Fax: 0191-478 1283 E-mail: info@wdmsoft.co.uk

Warwick I C Systems Ltd, Warwick House, Woodhouse Road, Horsley Woodhouse, Ilkeston, Derbyshire, DE7 6AY Tel: (01332) 781882 Fax: (01332) 781410 E-mail: sales@warwickicsystems.com

West Country Business Systems Holdings Ltd, Somerset House, Magdalene Street, Glastonbury, Somerset, BA6 9EJ Tel: (01458) 833344 Fax: (01458) 835297 E-mail: sales@wcbs.co.uk

Wiztek, P C Upgrade Centre, 8 Bond St, Redruth, Cornwall, TR15 2QB Tel: (01209) 314296 E-mail: wiztek@hotmail.com

Zone Cross Software Ltd, Talbot House, 2 Talbot Road, Northampton, NN1 4JB Tel: (01604) 231656 Fax: (01604) 602799

COMPUTER SOFTWARE LICENCE SUPPORT SERVICES

▶ A New Solution Ltd, 59 Elmfield Way, South Croydon, Surrey, CR2 0EJ Tel: (020) 8657 7441 Fax: (0870) 7060376 E-mail: sales@anewsolution.co.uk

COMPUTER SOFTWARE MANUAL PRINTING

Renault Printing Co. Ltd, 54 Factory Estate, College Road, Perry Barr, Birmingham, B44 8BS Tel: 0121-356 0331 Fax: 0121-356 0153 E-mail: sales@renaultprint.co.uk

Synergie Ltd, Digital House, The Loddon Centre, Wade Road, Basingstoke, Hampshire, RG24 8QW Tel: (01256) 467771 Fax: (01256) 840383 E-mail: alison@synergie.uk.com

COMPUTER SOFTWARE PUBLISHERS/WRITERS

C C L Software Ltd, Battenhall Lodge, 60 Battenhall Road, Worcester, WR5 2BX Tel: (0800) 0199853 Fax: (0845) 4900201 E-mail: nick@ccl-uk.com

Cincom Systems UK Ltd, 1 Grenfell Road, Maidenhead, Berkshire, SL6 1HN Tel: (01628) 542300 Fax: (01628) 542310

Computer Systems For Distribution plc, Croughton Lodge, High Street, Croughton, Brackley, Northamptonshire, NN13 5LT Tel: (01869) 810913 Fax: (01869) 810993 E-mail: sales@csfd.co.uk

Computerisation Ltd, Washington Chambers, Stanwell Road, Penarth, South Glamorgan, CF64 2AF Tel: (029) 2071 2664 Fax: (029) 2071 2997 E-mail: admin@computerisation.co.uk

Corbett Engineering Ltd, Unit 1 2 Mercia Villas, Torwood Close Westwood Business Park, Coventry, CV4 8HX Tel: (024) 7646 9930 Fax: (024) 7642 0994E-mail: info@celcat.com

D T A Computer Systems Ltd, 58 Norbiton Avenue, Kingston upon Thames, Surrey, KT1 3QR Tel: (020) 8974 5114 Fax: (07092) 314906 E-mail: info@dta.co.uk

Datamore, 7 Lake View, Alsager, Kidsgrove, Stoke-on-Trent, ST7 2FY Tel: (01270) 878552

Diamond Management Services Ltd, Diamond House, 149 Frimley Road, Camberley, Surrey, GU15 2PS Tel: (01276) 691415 Fax: (01276) 692903 E-mail: info@dms-management.com

Digital Development, The Old School, East Baldwin, Isle Of Man, IM4 5EP Tel: (01624) 851482 Fax: (01624) 851482

Farmplan Computer Systems, Farmplan House, Rank Xerox Business Park, Mitcheldean, Gloucestershire, GL17 0SN Tel: (01594) 545011 Fax: (01594) 545012 E-mail: sales@farmplan.co.uk

Fasttrak Software Publishing Ltd, 20 Greenhill Crescent, Watford Business Park, Watford, WD18 8JA Tel: (01923) 495496 Fax: (01923) 800190 E-mail: fasttrak.info@polaron.co.uk

FOCUS Microsystems, Belmont House, Bayswater Farm Road, Headington, Oxford, OX3 8BX Tel: (0871) 2500021 Fax: (01865) 750937 E-mail: enquiries@focus-property.co.uk

Freelance Software Ltd, East Street, Bingham, Nottingham, NG13 8DS Tel: (01949) 838988 Fax: (01949) 838112 E-mail: info@centralone.co.uk

▶ Global Address Ltd, Venturers House, Prince St Roundabout, Bristol, BS1 4PB Tel: 0117-915 4018 Fax: 0117-915 4348 E-mail: sales@globaladdress.net

Global Software Publishing, Meadow Lane, St. Ives, Cambridgeshire, PE27 4LG Tel: (01480) 496666 Fax: (01480) 460206 E-mail: sales@gsp.cc

Goldcrest Computer Services Ltd, 12 Vermont Place, Tongwell, Milton Keynes, MK15 8JQ Tel: (01908) 211330 Fax: (01908) 211326 E-mail: sales@goldcrest-uk.com

Hex A Tec Systems Ltd, The Courtyard, Ochrelands, Fellside, Hexham, Northumberland, NE46 1SB Tel: (01434) 605575 Fax: (01434) 607800 E-mail: sales@hexatec.com

▶ i-teamworks, PO Box 556, Peterborough, PE4 6WL Tel: (0845) 4900126 Fax: (0845) 4900127 E-mail: info@iteamworks.com

L M Software Ltd, Apak House Badminton Court, Station Road, Yate, Bristol, BS37 5HZ Tel: (01454) 871060 Fax: (01454) 871199 E-mail: enquiries@lmsoft.co.uk

John Lamb Media Ltd, 2 Dairy Cottages, Wolterton, Norwich, NR11 7LX Tel: (01263) 768572

Laserprint Software International, 23 Townmead Business Centre, William Morris Way, London, SW6 2SZ Tel: (020) 7610 9697 Fax: (07000) 486226 E-mail: info@laserprintsoftware.com

Media Services Group Ltd, 64 Charlotte Street, London, W1T 4QD Tel: (020) 7436 0070 Fax: (020) 7580 5706 E-mail: hbrantley@msgl.com

Micro Focus Ltd, The Lawn, 22-30 Old Bath Road, Newbury, Berkshire, RG14 1QN Tel: (01635) 32646 Fax: (01635) 33966 E-mail: ukmarketing@microfocus.com

Minnie Business Systems Ltd, 65 London Wall, London, EC2M 5TU Tel: (020) 7638 3815 Fax: (020) 7638 1481 E-mail: ad@minniebusiness.co.uk

Moneywise Software, 1 Joanna House, 34 Central Road, Worcester Park, Surrey, KT4 8JB Tel: (020) 8337 0663 Fax: (020) 8715 9909 E-mail: itmltd@aol.com

Neonstream Ltd, 23 Woodcote, Maidenhead, Berkshire, SL6 4DU Tel: (01628) 622022 Fax: (01628) 785458 E-mail: rws@neonstream.net

O N C, Unit 220 Tedco Business Centre, Jarrow, Tyne & Wear, NE32 3DT Tel: 0191-422 0229 Fax: 0191-428 3365 E-mail: s.owens@onc-computers.co.uk

P T C (UK) Ltd, Inavation House, Harvest Crescent, Fleet, Hampshire, GU51 2QR Tel: (01252) 817000 Fax: (01252) 817000

The PCMS Group plc, PCMS House, Torwood Close, Westwood Business Park, Coventry, CV4 8HX Tel: (024) 7669 4455 Fax: (024) 7642 1390 E-mail: mail@pcms-group.co.uk

Soft Options Custom Software, Wood Lodge, Calmore, Southampton, SO40 2UP Tel: (023) 8087 1580 Fax: (023) 8087 1582

Solar Soft PMS Ltd, Hampshire Int Business Park, Crockford Lane, Chineham, Basingstoke, Hampshire, RG24 8WH Tel: (01256) 685200 Fax: (01256) 685201 E-mail: sales@ssi-world.com

Solarsoft Ltd, Unit 3, Maridian Office Park, Osbourne Way, Hook, Hampshire, RG27 9HY Tel: (01256) 769769 Fax: (0870) 8728210

Solcom Ltd, 79 George Street, Ryde, Isle Of Wight, PO33 2JF Tel: (01983) 817000 Fax: (01983) 817001 E-mail: info@solcom.com

Systems In Micro, 47 Gainsborough Street, Sudbury, Suffolk, CO10 2ET Tel: (01787) 313317 Fax: (01787) 372226 E-mail: admin@sysim.co.uk

Target Achievement Ltd, Mercury Park, Amber Close, Amington, Tamworth, Staffordshire, B77 4RP Tel: (01827) 309709 Fax: (01827) 309719 E-mail: sales@maydown.co.uk

Timeslice Ltd, William Gaitskill House, 23 Paradise St, London, SE16 4QD Tel: (020) 7231 0073 Fax: (020) 7237 9806 E-mail: sales@timeslice.co.uk

Trace Group plc, 224-232 St John Street, London, EC1V 4QR Tel: (020) 7825 1000 Fax: (020) 7825 1001 E-mail: sales@tracegroup.com

Transcendata Europe Ltd, 4 Carisbrooke Court, Buckingway Business Park, Anderson Road, Cambridge, CB24 4UQ Tel: (01954) 234300 Fax: (01954) 234349 E-mail: sales@transcendata.com

Travellers Tales UK Ltd, Canute Court, Toft Road, Knutsford, Cheshire, WA16 0NL Tel: (01565) 757300 Fax: (01565) 757308 E-mail: emma@t-tales.com

Trax UK Ltd, Suite 4B Christchurch House, Beaufort Court, Medway City Estate, Rochester, Kent, ME2 4FX Tel: (01634) 724724 Fax: (01634) 290524 E-mail: sales@trax-uk.co.uk

COMPUTER SOFTWARE PULSATION ANALYSIS

Pulsation Dampers At Pulseguard Ltd, Unit 1, Greg Street Industrial Centre, Greg Street, Reddish, Stockport, Cheshire, SK5 7BS Tel: 0161-480 9625 Fax: 0161-480 9627 E-mail: sales@pulsation-dampers.co.uk

COMPUTER SOFTWARE SALES STAFF RECRUITMENT

▶ Brighter Recruiting, Elmsland House, Kirk Hammerton, York, YO26 8BX Tel: (01423) 331535 Fax: (01423) 331536 E-mail: recruiting@brighter-recruiting.co.uk

▶ Dart Resourcing, Mda House, The Grove, Slough, SL1 1RH Tel: (01753) 828900 Fax: 0870 8700299 E-mail: slo@mdarg.com

▶ Excelsior Professional Search Ltd, 34 South Molton Street, London, W1K 5RG Tel: 020 7495 3088 Fax: 020 7495 3089 E-mail: general@excelsiorsearch.com

Flexiskills Recruitment, Washington House, 14-16 High Street, Belfast, BT1 2BD Tel: (028) 9032 4436 Fax: (028) 9032 4436 E-mail: info@flexiskills.co.uk

Metropolitano Ltd, Communications House, 26 York Street, Westminster, London, W1U 6PZ Tel: (020) 7060 2501 Fax: (020) 7060 6031 E-mail: info@metropolitano.co.uk

▶ S R S Pensions, Broad Quay House, Broad Quay, Bristol, BS1 4DJ Tel: 0117-905 8734 Fax: 0117-963 7949 E-mail: sales@srs-pensions.co.uk

▶ Sales Network (UK) Ltd, Globe Centre, Penistone Road, Sheffield, S6 3AE Tel: (0870) 4441074 Fax: E-mail: glenn@salesnetworkuk.co.uk

COMPUTER SOFTWARE SECURITY MODULES

▶ Biject Ltd, 4 Kingston Close, Knott End-on-Sea, Poulton-le-Fylde, Lancashire, FY6 0DJ Tel: (01253) 812363

Causeway Technologies Ltd, Comino House Furlong Road, Bourne End, Buckinghamshire, SL8 5AQ Tel: (01628) 552000 Fax: (01628) 552001 E-mail: sales@causeway.com

DBL Software Ltd, Tytherley Road, Winterslow, Salisbury, SP5 1PY Tel: (01980) 863505 Fax: (0845) 2269028 E-mail: sales@dbl.co.uk

Ec Advantage Ltd, 30 Marsh Lane, Hemingford Grey, Huntingdon, Cambridgeshire, PE28 9EN Tel: (01480) 355034 Fax: (01480) 355036 E-mail: enquiries@call.uk.com

▶ PCS Ltd, 9-11 Wellington Street, Gateshead, Tyne & Wear, NE8 2AJ Tel: 0191-477 4779 Fax: 0191-477 7929 E-mail: sales@profcom.co.uk

▶ Pulse Computer Services Ltd, 10 Orchard Road, Basingstoke, Hampshire, RG22 6NU Tel: (01256) 422395 E-mail: pcsl@ntlworld.com

Secon Solutions Ltd, River House, 85 Esher Road, Walton-on-Thames, Surrey, KT12 4LN Tel: (020) 8255 0777 Fax: (020) 8255 7511 E-mail: sales@secon.co.uk

Sophos plc, Pentagon West, The Pentagon, Abingdon, Oxfordshire, OX14 3YP Tel: (01235) 559933 Fax: (01235) 559935 E-mail: sales@sophos.com

COMPUTER SOFTWARE TEST MANAGEMENT

E B D Computing Solutions Ltd, 57 Woodside, Ponteland, Newcastle upon Tyne, NE20 9JB Tel: (01661) 820389 Fax: (01661) 820389 E-mail: akeogh@excellencebydesign.co.uk

COMPUTER SOFTWARE TESTING SERVICES

Atos Origin (UK) Ltd, Walsall Road, Cannock, Staffordshire, WS11 0JA Tel: (01543) 465800 Fax: (01543) 464895

Beetee, 139 Taplow, Thurlow Street, London, SE17 2UJ Tel: (07956) 868418 E-mail: lewis@btcomputers.com

Island Systems Ltd, 83 Knightwood Crescent, New Malden, Surrey, KT3 5JP Tel: (020) 8949 4422 E-mail: enquirey@islandsys.com

Leysen Associates Ltd, Padmores Yard, St. Johns Mews, Woking, Surrey, GU21 7ZE Tel: (01483) 881188 Fax: (01483) 881189

Magic Systems Ltd, Unit 3 Sandridge Park, Porters Wood, St. Albans, Hertfordshire, AL3 6PH Tel: (01727) 855511 Fax: (01727) 864351 E-mail: sales@magicgroup.com

Resource Engineering Projects, Waterlinks House, Richard Street, Birmingham, B7 4AA Tel: 0121-678 7880 Fax: 0121-678 7899 E-mail: technical@topmode.co.uk

S I M Ltd, Albion House, Chertsey Road, Woking, Surrey, GU21 6BF Tel: (01483) 733100 Fax: (01483) 733101 E-mail: sales@simgroup.co.uk

Sweet Valley Solutions Ltd, East Lodge House, 116 High Street, Cranleigh, Surrey, GU6 8AJ Tel: (01483) 273838 Fax: (01483) 275983 E-mail: sales@sweetvalley.co.uk

Tescom UK Ltd, 21-22 Great Sutton Street, London, EC1V 0DY Tel: (020) 7022 6700 Fax: (020) 7022 6701 E-mail: info@tescom-intl.com

COMPUTER SOFTWARE TO SPECIFICATION

▶ Custom Software Systems, 16 Auchengreoch Avenue, Johnstone, Renfrewshire, PA5 0RJ Tel: (01505) 358223

▶ OnTrack Systems Ltd, 27 Sandyford Place, Glasgow, G3 7NG Tel: 0141-248 7999 Fax: 0141-248 7998 E-mail: info@ontracksystems.co.uk

▶ Red Paw Solutions Ltd, 5a/1 Starbank Road, Edinburgh, EH5 3BW Tel: (07745) 428130

▶ Turnkey Computer Technology Ltd, Thornton Lodge, East Kilbride Road, Clarkston, Glasgow, G76 9HW Tel: 0141-644 5444 Fax: 0141-644 5446

COMPUTER SOFTWARE TRAINING SERVICES

▶ Any Key Training Ltd, 15 Ongar Close, Addlestone, Surrey, KT15 1BX Tel: (01932) 820064 Fax: (0870) 7626550 E-mail: akt@anykeytraining.co.uk

Applied Electronics, Onslow House, Magham Down, Hailsham, East Sussex, BN27 1PL Tel: (01323) 844709 Fax: (01323) 844725

Beechbrook Consulting Ltd, 24 Clermont Terrace, Brighton, BN1 6SH Tel: (01273) 561714 Fax: (01273) 561772 E-mail: info@fastrak-consulting.co.uk

▶ Bristol Computer Training, 92 Egerton Road, Bishopston, Bristol, BS7 8HP Tel: 0117 9247567 E-mail: mail@bristolcomputertraining.co.uk

Business Training Partnership, 96 High Street, Burnham, Slough, SL1 7JT Tel: (01628) 664040 Fax: (01628) 660042 E-mail: dawn.oxley@btp.uk.com

C F C Sollutions, 1310 Solihull Parkway, Birmingham Business Park, Birmingham, B37 7YB Tel: 0121-717 7040 Fax: 0121-717 7011 E-mail: enquiries@cfcsolutions.co.uk

▶ C S D Training Partnership, 33 Grange Drive, Castle Donington, Derby, DE74 2QU Tel: (01332) 810117 E-mail: admin@csd-training.co.uk

Chimera C M T Ltd, 9 Blenheim Court, Lustleigh Close, Marsh Barton Industrial Estate, Exeter, EX2 8PW Tel: (01392) 667444 Fax: (01392) 667440

Computers In Personnel Ltd, Abbey House, 28-30 Chapel Street, Marlow, Buckinghamshire, SL7 1DD Tel: (01628) 814000 Fax: (0870) 3662346 E-mail: sales@ciphr.com

▶ Computersolutions-online, PO Box 24, Cardiff, CF23 0AA Tel: (08701) 999 630 Fax: (07092) 860228 E-mail: enquiries@cs-o.co.uk

▶ Dac Systems, 4 Balloo Drive, Bangor, County Down, BT19 7QY Tel: (028) 9185 7711 Fax: (028) 9185 7722 E-mail: sales@dacsystems.co.uk

Davian Systems, c/o The Punch Hotel, 25, Chapels, Darwen, Lancashire, BB3 OEE Tel: 07792 287416 E-mail: info@daviansystems.co.uk

Domian Electronics Ltd, The Bungalow, Portland Road, Burgess Hill, West Sussex, RH15 9RL Tel: (01444) 254583 Fax: (01444) 254584 E-mail: domianelec@aol.com

F1 Computing Systems Ltd, 3 Kelso Place, Upper Bristol Road, Bath, BA1 3AU Tel: (01225) 427285 Fax: (01225) 444728 E-mail: sales@f1comp.co.uk

Farmdata Ltd, Westertown, Rothienorman, Inverurie, Aberdeenshire, AB51 8US Tel: (01467) 671457 Fax: (01467) 671448 E-mail: sales@farmdata.co.uk

Generation Software, 59 Victoria Road, Tilehurst, Reading, RG31 5AB Tel: 0118-948 2468 Fax: 0118-948 2470 E-mail: office@generationsoftware.com

▶ Hardy Technical Services Ltd, 69 Lake Drive, Hainworthy, Poole, Poole, Dorset, BH15 4LR Tel: (01202) 674916 Fax: (0871) 2420922 E-mail: info@hardytechnicalservices.co.uk

Hexagon Software Ltd, Unit 8 Highnam Business Centre, Highnam, Gloucester, GL2 8DN Tel: (01608) 811801 Fax: (01608) 811852 E-mail: sales@hexagon.co.uk

COMPUTER SOFTWARE TRAINING SERVICES – *continued*

Ibex Systems Maidstone Ltd, Mill House Quarry Wood Industrial Estate, Mills Road, Aylesford, Kent, ME20 7NA Tel: (01622) 791991 Fax: (01622) 882900 E-mail: sales@ibexsystems.co.uk
Imtex Computer Consultants, Stratford Arcade, 75 High Street, Stony Stratford, Milton Keynes, MK11 1AY Tel: (01908) 261216 Fax: (01908) 261216
In4tek Ltd, Unisys House, 20 Barrington Road, Altrincham, Cheshire, WA14 1HB Tel: 0161-941 5833 Fax: 0161-927 7629 E-mail: in4mation@in4tek.com
Indus (International) Ltd, Britannia Wharf, Monument Road, Woking, Surrey, GU21 5LW Tel: (01483) 722777 Fax: (01483) 721166 E-mail: sales@indusinternational.com
▶ Inform I T, 55 Beauchamp Place, London, SW3 1NY Tel: (020) 7350 0191 Fax: (07050) 616471 E-mail: info@inform-it.com
▶ JayrConsulting Ltd Freelance Training Consultants, 33 Ixworth Close, Watermeadow Estate, Northampton, NN3 8TW Tel: 01604 642041 Fax: 01604 642041 E-mail: john.roberts@jayrconsulting.co.uk
Lexicon Lifeline Ltd, Unit 3, 78 Blandford Road, Corfe Mullen, Wimborne, Dorset, BH21 3HQ Tel: (01202) 657252 Fax: (01202) 657252 E-mail: office@lexiconlifeline.co.uk
Marcmoor Computer Systems, 5a Church Sq, Market Harborough, Leics, LE16 7HB Tel: (01858) 465746 Fax: (01858) 434628 E-mail: paul@marcmoor.co.uk
▶ Maxtar Ltd, 14 Chanctonbury View, Henfield, West Sussex, BN5 9TW Tel: (07714) 850950 Fax: (01273) 491848 E-mail: juergen.brinner@maxtar.co.uk
Midas Computer Systems, Gilnockie Station Ho, Canonbie, Dumfriesshire, DG14 0SG Tel: (01387) 371526 Fax: (01387) 371526
▶ MidWinter Computer Services Ltd, 385 Cricklade Road, Swindon, SN2 1AQ Tel: (01793) 522175 Fax: (0871) 6616186 E-mail: enquiries@midwintercomputers.com
▶ MK Training, Sunningdale Avenue, Feltham, Middlesex, TW13 5JU Tel: (07976) 515095 E-mail: mk.training@virgin.net
▶ Mobal Solutions, 20 Hop Garden, Church Crookham, Fleet, Hampshire, GU52 0YL Tel: (01252) 623499 E-mail: info@mobalsolutions.co.uk
▶ Motivating Moves, 3 Cotswold Gardens, Downswood, Maidstone, Kent, ME15 8TB Tel: (07968) 947999 Fax: (01622) 863199 E-mail: enquires@motivatingmoves.co.uk
Pennant International Group Ltd, Pennant Court, Staverton Technology Park, Old Gloucester Road, Staverton, Cheltenham, Gloucestershire, GL51 6TL Tel: (01452) 714914 Fax: (01452) 714920 E-mail: ptsl@pennantplc.co.uk
Renaissance Corporate (Barnet) Ltd, Unit 1 Stroud Wood Business Centre, Frogmore, St. Albans, Herts, AL2 2NN Tel: (01727) 875500 Fax: (01727) 874808 E-mail: sales@rencorp.co.uk
▶ Rutland Itc Computer Services Ltd, 4 Queen Street, Uppingham, Oakham, Leicestershire, LE15 9QR Tel: (01572) 821468 E-mail: support@rict.co.uk
▶ The Software Practice, Bullbeck Mill, Mill Lane, Barrington, Cambridge, CB2 5QY Tel: (01223) 872874 Fax: (01223) 872876 E-mail: enquiries@softwarepractice.co.uk
▶ South Devon Solutions, 6a Prings Court, Market Street, Brixham, Devon, TQ5 8ET Tel: (01803) 850875 E-mail: enquiries@southdevonsolutions.com
Tabs Training Ltd, Brunel House, Mitchell Road, Salisbury, SP2 7PY Tel: (01722) 338668 Fax: (01722) 332052 E-mail: sales@tabsltd.co.uk
The Technology Forge, Top Floor Pegholme, Wharfebank Business Centre, Otley, Leeds, LS21 3JP Tel: (01943) 464844 Fax: (01943) 464833 E-mail: sales@technologyforge.com
▶ Wellhouse Consultants, 404 The Spa, Melksham, Wiltshire, SN12 6QL Tel: (01225) 708225 Fax: (01225) 707126 E-mail: graham@wellho.net
▶ WPM Group, Mindenhall Court, High Street, Stevenage, Hertfordshire, SG1 3BG Tel: (01438) 311486 Fax: (01438) 311487 E-mail: enquiries@wpm-group.com

COMPUTER SOFTWARE, ACCOUNTING, CONSTRUCTION INDUSTRY CONTRACTS

▶ Cambot Technologies Ltd, 135 Edgar Street, Hereford, HR4 9JR Tel: (01432) 370950 E-mail: adrian@camcot.co.uk

COMPUTER SOFTWARE, ASSET INVENTORY MANAGEMENT

▶ Accelerate Consultancy Ltd, Bryn Tirion Brynford Road, Pentre Halkyn, Holywell, Clwyd, CH8 8AW Tel: (0845) 1259573 E-mail: information@accelerate-consultancy.co.uk
▶ Sure Count Stocktakers, Unit 8, 88 Clyde Road, Didsbury, Manchester, M20 2JN Tel: 0161-448 9491 E-mail: info@surecount.co.uk

COMPUTER SOFTWARE, AUTOMOTIVE ENGINEERING

▶ International Exports, 2 Southleigh Road, Taunton, Somerset, TA1 2XZ Tel: (07976) 084155 Fax: (01823) 254487 E-mail: postmaster@internationalexports.co.uk

COMPUTER SOFTWARE, BACKGROUND MUSIC

▶ 18records Ltd, 16 Folly Terrace, Pity Me, Durham, DH1 5DS Tel: 0191-384 3415
▶ Backtracks Record Mart, 17 Brougham Street, Edinburgh, EH3 9JS Tel: 0131-228 4898 E-mail: kelly@backtracksmusic.co.uk
▶ Bonners Music Superstore, 56 Langney Road, Eastbourne, East Sussex, BN21 3JN Tel: (01323) 649100 Fax: (01323) 649100 E-mail: info@bonnersmusic.co.uk
▶ ComputerDJ, Unit 5 The Shine, St. Marks Street, Hull, HU8 7FB Tel: (01482) 319700 Fax: (01482) 319701 E-mail: info@comptuerdj.net
▶ Contemporary Music Design, 50 Washington Street, Brighton, BN2 9SR Tel: 07789 435036 E-mail: info@comd.co.uk

COMPUTER SOFTWARE, BUSINESS CONTINUITY

Flexsys (UK) Ltd, The Courtyard, Green Lane, Heywood, Lancashire, OL10 2EX Tel: (01706) 362130 Fax: (01706) 362133 E-mail: sales@flexsys-group.com

COMPUTER SOFTWARE, BUSINESS PERFORMANCE MANAGEMENT

Affinite Europe, 32 Station Road, Burley in Wharfedale, Ilkley, West Yorkshire, LS29 7JL Tel: (01943) 864124 Fax: (01943) 864917 E-mail: office@affinite.co.uk
▶ Manusoft UK Ltd, The Groveange, Welford Road, Long Marston, Stratford-upon-Avon, Warwickshire, CV37 8RH Tel: (01789) 721930 Fax: (01789) 721901 E-mail: sales@menusoft.co.uk

COMPUTER SOFTWARE, BUSINESS PLAN

London Net Solutions UK Ltd, 4 Mead Way, Bromley, BR2 9EU Tel: 0208 4622655 Fax: 0208 4626389 E-mail: info@wsiworldclassnetsolutions.com
▶ Palo Alto Software Ltd, Crown House, 72 Hammersmith Road, London, W14 8TH Tel: (020) 7559 3500 Fax: (020) 7559 3401

COMPUTER SOFTWARE, CALL CENTRE

▶ Ansaback, Melford Court 2 The Havens, Ransomes Europark, Ipswich, IP3 9SJ Tel: (01473) 322900 Fax: (01473) 321801 E-mail: mtaylor@ansaback.co.uk
▶ AnServe, Redbourne Mere, Kirton Lindsey, Gainsborough, Lincolnshire, DN21 4NN Tel: (01652) 641100 Fax: (01652) 640720 E-mail: anserve_uk@yahoo.co.uk
▶ Call One Ltd, 5 The Foxwood, Charnock Richard, Chorley, Lancashire, PR7 5JQ Tel: (01257) 791599 Fax: (01257) 791599 E-mail: info@callone.uk.com
▶ Centric, 2nd Floor, Europe House, Bancroft Road, Reigate, Surrey, RH2 7RP Tel: (0870) 7703769 Fax: (0870) 7703769 E-mail: sales@centricc.co.uk
▶ Kerr Multilingual, 41-42 Haven Green, Ealing, London, W5 2NX Tel: (020) 8810 7839 Fax: (020) 8998 0388 E-mail: info@kerr-recruitment.co.uk
▶ M X Digital, Dunley Hill Court, Ranmore Common, Dorking, Surrey, RH5 6SX Tel: (01483) 286650 Fax: (01483) 286658 E-mail: sales@mxdigital.co.uk
▶ Priam Software Ltd, The Old Telephone Exchange, 32-42 Albert Street, Rugby, Warwickshire, CV21 2SA Tel: (01788) 558000 Fax: (01788) 558001 E-mail: andrewk@priamsoftware.com

COMPUTER SOFTWARE, CALL CENTRE MANAGEMENT

▶ International Marketing & Logistics, 11c Stephenson Road, Clacton-on-Sea, Essex, CO15 4XA Tel: (01255) 479864 Fax: (01255) 474705 E-mail: paul.quenet@iml.uk.com

COMPUTER SOFTWARE, CAR DEALER

▶ Delaceys Of Huddersfield, Royd Business Park, Dye House Lane, Brighouse, West Yorkshire, HD6 1LL Tel: (01484) 401011 Fax: (01484) 401447 E-mail: enquires@delaceys.co.uk

COMPUTER SOFTWARE, CHAT APPLICATIONS, INTERNET

▶ Mosketo, 1 Webster Street, Preston, PR2 1BY Tel: (07723) 042246 E-mail: enquires@mosketo.net

COMPUTER SOFTWARE, CHROMATOGRAPHY

▶ Justice Laboratory Services, JLS House, 25 - 27 Low Road, Auchtermuchty, Auchtermuchty, Fife, KY14 7BB Tel: (01337) 828404

COMPUTER SOFTWARE, COMPUTER AIDED DESIGN (CAD), ELECTRICAL

▶ eCad Solutions - AutoCAD Electrical Design, 37 Ridgeway East, Sidcup, Kent, DA15 8RY Tel: (020) 8850 4217 Fax: (020) 8331 6893 E-mail: design@ecad-solutions.co.uk
▶ Ecado Ltd, 29 Lindley Street, Holgate, York, YO24 4JG Tel: (01904) 332214 E-mail: neil.ferguson@ecado.co.uk

COMPUTER SOFTWARE, COMPUTER AIDED DESIGN, COMPUTER AIDED MANUFACTURING (CADCAM), THREE DIMENSIONAL (3D), INDUSTRIAL CONTROL AUTOMATION

▶ J. Randalls of Dunstable, 38 Downs Road, Dunstable, Bedfordshire, LU5 4DD Tel: (07967) 247788 E-mail: jim.randall@btinternet.com

COMPUTER SOFTWARE, COMPUTER BASED TRAINING

B Y G Systems Ltd, 1-2 William Lee Building, Nottingham Science & Technical Park, University Boulevard, Nottingham, NG7 2RQ Tel: 0115-925 2221 Fax: 0115-922 3496 E-mail: info@bygsystems.com
▶ Bourne Training, Bourne House, Sandy Lane, Romsey, Hampshire, SO51 0PD Tel: 01794 523301 Fax: 01794 516720 E-mail: info@bournetraining.co.uk
Business Training Partnership, 96 High Street, Burnham, Slough, SL1 7JT Tel: (01628) 664040 Fax: (01628) 660042 E-mail: dawn.oxley@btp.uk.com
Camsoft, 10 Wheatfield Close, Maidenhead, Berkshire, SL6 3PS Tel: (01628) 825206 Fax: (01628) 820431
Cognitive Network Solutions Ltd, High Street, Lye, Stourbridge, West Midlands, DY9 8LX Tel: (01384) 340666 Fax: (01384) 350666
Pageforward Learning, PO Box 230, Diss, Norfolk, IP22 1TA Tel: (01379) 650927 Fax: (01379) 642555 E-mail: info@pageforward.co.uk
▶ Pitman Training, Bishops Stortford, Suite 3, 15 Market Square, Bishop's Stortford, Hertfordshire, CM23 3UT Tel: (01279) 466200 Fax: (01279) 466220 E-mail: bishopsstortford@pitman-training.net
▶ Rescue From Technology, 17 Linley Court, Thicket Road, Sutton, Surrey, SM1 4QA Tel: 0870 3831519 Fax: 07092 309964 E-mail: enquiries@rescuefrom.com
Tabs Training Ltd, Brunel House, Mitchell Road, Salisbury, SP2 7PY Tel: (01722) 338668 Fax: (01722) 332052 E-mail: sales@tabsltd.co.uk
Tutorpro Ltd, 10 High Street, Wellington, Somerset, TA21 8RA Tel: (01823) 661669 Fax: (01823) 661668 E-mail: general@tutorpro.com

COMPUTER SOFTWARE, COMPUTER GAMES

▶ Aqua Pacific Ltd, 87A Warwick Street, Leamington Spa, Warwickshire, CV32 4RJ Tel: (01926) 339100 Fax: (01926) 889134
Blade Interactive Studios, Suite A, Great Northern Warehouse, Deansgate Mews, Manchester, M3 4EN Tel: 0161-839 6622 Fax: 0161-839 6688 E-mail: info@bladeinteractive.com
Code Masters Software Co. Ltd, Lower Farm, Stoneythorpe, Southam, Warwickshire, CV47 2DL Tel: (01926) 814132 Fax: (01926) 817595 E-mail: enquiries@codemasters.com
Game Stores Ltd, 13 Harvey Centre, Harlow, Essex, CM20 1XN Tel: (01279) 435486
Game Stores Ltd, 19 Tavern Street, Ipswich, IP1 3AA Tel: (01473) 230162 Fax: (01473) 230162
Game Stores Ltd, 56-72 Market Place, Romford, RM1 3ET Tel: (01708) 768206
Game Stores Ltd, F Churchway Potteries Shopping Centre, Market Square, Stoke-on-Trent, ST1 1PS Tel: (01782) 280596 Fax: (01782) 280596
Global Software Publishing, Meadow Lane, St. Ives, Cambridgeshire, PE27 4LG Tel: (01480) 496666 Fax: (01480) 460206 E-mail: sales@gsp.cc
Slough Computers, The Observatory, High Street, Slough, SL1 1LE Tel: (01753) 521594 Fax: (01753) 694633
▶ Spiky, 116A Fillongley Road, Meriden, Meriden, Coventry, CV7 7LT Tel: 01676 523759 Fax: 01676 523759 E-mail: spiky@myspiky.co.uk
That'Z Entertainment, Market Place, Romford, RM1 3AB Tel: (01708) 744338 Fax: (01708) 744338
Warthog plc, 10 Eden Place, Cheadle, Cheshire, SK8 1AT Tel: 0161-608 1200 Fax: 0161-610 3033 E-mail: info@warthog.co.uk

COMPUTER SOFTWARE, COURIER SERVICE

▶ A S A P Same Day Delivery Service, 30 Clarendon Court, Winwick Quay, Warrington, WA2 8QP Tel: (01925) 637453 E-mail: pete@asapsameday.com
▶ Corby Courier Services, 4 Lovap Way, Great Oakley, Corby, Northamptonshire, NN18 8JL Tel: (01536) 742412 Fax: (01536) 742412 E-mail: sales@corbycouriers.co.uk
▶ Silverbirch Sameday Couriers, Silverbirch Estate, Middleton, Manchester, M24 5JU Tel: 0161-654 7439 E-mail: contact@sscouriers.co.uk

COMPUTER SOFTWARE, CREDIT REPORTING

▶ www.debttrack.com, 40 Garswood Street, Ashton-in-Makerfield, Wigan, Lancashire, WN4 9AF Tel: (01942) 292432 E-mail: enquires@debttrack.com

COMPUTER SOFTWARE, CUSTOMER EXPERIENCE MANAGEMENT (CEM)

▶ Niche Technologies Ltd, Ternion Court, 264-268 Upper Fourth Street, Milton Keynes, MK10 1DP Tel: 0870 7504471 Fax: 0870 1335371 E-mail: sales@niche-technologies.co.uk

COMPUTER SOFTWARE, DATA CENTRE MANAGEMENT

▶ Accelerate Consultancy Ltd, Bryn Tirion Brynford Road, Pentre Halkyn, Holywell, Clwyd, CH8 8AW Tel: (0845) 1259573 E-mail: information@accelerate-consultancy.co.uk

COMPUTER SOFTWARE, DATA LOGGER

▶ C D L Products, Kennoway House, 34 Kennoway Place, Broughty Ferry, Dundee, DD5 3HT Tel: (01382) 732580 E-mail: sales@cdl-products.com

COMPUTER SOFTWARE, DATA RECOVERY

▶ Bat I T Solutions Ltd, 20 Briskman Way, Oakwood Park, Aylesbury, Buckinghamshire, HP21 8FP Tel: (01296) 483631 Fax: (01296) 331510 E-mail: tris@bat-it.com
Bisley Computency, 1 The Cottages, Stroud Road, Bisley, Stroud, Gloucestershire, GL6 7BQ Tel: (01452) 770832 Fax: 08717 333315 E-mail: enquiries@bisleydesign.co.uk
▶ Click4PC Ltd, Station House, 150 New Road, Bromsgrove, Worcestershire, B60 2LG Tel: (0800) 0852143 Fax: (01527) 576611 E-mail: enquiries@click4pc.co.uk
▶ IT Support Partners, St Johns Innovation Centre, Cowley Road, Cambridge, CB4 0WS Tel: (0870) 2403564 E-mail: info@itsp.co.uk
▶ PC Restore Ltd, 56 Glenarm Road, London, E5 0LZ Tel: (020) 8525 9795
▶ Pilgrim Technical Security Services, 65 Duke Street, Mayfair, London, W1M 6PP Tel: 0870 041 6457 Fax: 0871 236 1944 E-mail: ops@pilgrimtechnical.com

COMPUTER SOFTWARE, DEBT COLLECTION

Debt Collect, Baltic Chambers, 50 Wellington Street, Glasgow, G2 6HJ Tel: (0845) 1202935 Fax: (0845) 1302936 E-mail: enquiries@debtcollectuk.com

▶ Debt Collection Services UK Ltd, 1 Queen Street, Mirfield, West Yorkshire, WF14 8AH Tel: (01924) 499824 Fax: (0870) 7581125 E-mail: colette.rhodes@btconnect.com

COMPUTER SOFTWARE, EBUSINESS

Abba Consultants, Calamare, Holly Close, Woking, Surrey, GU21 7QZ Tel: (01483) 833021 Fax: (01483) 833022

Ace Webmasters, 34-40 Wormgate, Boston, Lincolnshire, PE21 6NR Tel: (07050) 224352 E-mail: firstatboston@yahoo.co.uk

Affinite Europe, 32 Station Road, Burley in Wharfedale, Ilkley, West Yorkshire, LS29 7JL Tel: (01943) 864124 Fax: (01943) 864917 E-mail: office@affinite.co.uk

Aldebaran Systems Ltd, Unit 47 Cressex Enterprise Centre, Lincoln Road, High Wycombe, Buckinghamshire, HP12 3RL Tel: (01494) 614630 E-mail: info@aldebaran.co.uk

B & M Europe Ltd, Heath End House, West Street, Tadley, Hampshire, RG26 3ST Tel: 0118-981 1880 Fax: 0118-981 1881 E-mail: info@bmeurope.com

Bottom Line Technologies Ltd, Ground Floor, Cromwell House, Bartley Wood Business Park, Bartley Way, Hook, Hampshire, RG27 9XA Tel: (01252) 618600 Fax: 0118-956 9988 E-mail: info@bottomline.com

C A L Software Ltd, Rivington House, Drumhead Road, Chorley North Industrial Estate, Chorley, Lancashire, PR6 7BX Tel: (01257) 231011 Fax: (01257) 230927 E-mail: sales@calsoftware.co.uk

Ciber UK Ltd, Sketchley Meadows Business Park, 2 Watling Drive, Hinckley, Leicestershire, LE10 3EY Tel: (01455) 898800 Fax: (0870) 0000205 E-mail: enquiries@c.co.uk

Di-Soft Research, Little Frankley, Hook Heath Road, Woking, Surrey, GU22 0QL Tel: (01483) 727906 Fax: (01483) 727906 E-mail: colin.howard@comdaq.net

Eaglecrest Computer Systems Ltd, Brytirion, Chapel Street, Llanarmon-yn-Ial, Mold, Clwyd, CH7 4QE Tel: (01824) 780565 Fax: (01824) 780375 E-mail: mike.wheeler@eaglecrest-cs.com

Edm, Daisyfield Business Centre, Appleby Street, Blackburn, BB1 3BL Tel: (01254) 722033 Fax: (01254) 583003

Equinox Business Solutions Ltd, Technology House, Commerce Business Centre, West Wilts Trading Estate, Westbury, Wiltshire, BA13 4JB Tel: (01373) 825664 Fax: (01373) 859318 E-mail: enquiries@equinox-solutions.co.uk

James Fortune Associates, 32 Plough Lane, Purley, Surrey, CR8 3QA Tel: (020) 8763 1995 Fax: (020) 8763 1539 E-mail: sales@jfaworld.com

Friedman Corporation Ltd, 1 Chapel Court, Holly Walk, Leamington Spa, Warwickshire, CV32 4YS Tel: (01926) 741600 Fax: (01926) 741601 E-mail: uksales@friedmancorp.co.uk

G N T Ltd, Waterside Estate, Cradley Road, Dudley, West Midlands, DY2 9RG Tel: (01384) 236007 Fax: (01384) 236929 E-mail: info@gnt.co.uk

Gresham Computer Services Ltd, Mitchell House, Brook Avenue, Southampton, SO31 9ZA Tel: (01489) 555500 Fax: (01489) 555560 E-mail: info@gresham-computing.com

Interchange Group, Garden Court, Lockington, Derby, DE74 2SJ Tel: (08700) 716716 Fax: (08700) 716789 E-mail: info@interchangegroup.com

Invensys Systems (UK) Ltd, Highbank House, Exchange Street, Stockport, Cheshire, SK3 0ET Tel: 0161-429 6744 Fax: 0161-480 9063

Itheon Ltd, 1 The Boulevard, Welwyn Garden City, Hertfordshire, AL7 1EL Tel: (01707) 336600 Fax: (01707) 336622 E-mail: sales@itheon.com

J Computer Logic Ltd, Golden Valley Software Factory, New Mills, Clehonger, Hereford, HR2 9QS Tel: (01981) 251359 E-mail: sales@jclsoftware.com

Jordan IT Services, 28 Carter Ave, Broughton, Kettering, Northants, NN14 1LZ Tel: (01536) 790425 Fax: (08701) 367829 E-mail: info@jordanitservices.com

Jotika Midlands Software Ltd, Carmichael House, Village Green, Inkberrow, Worcester, WR7 4DZ Tel: (01386) 793415 Fax: (01386) 793407 E-mail: sales@jotika.com

Lailey Ltd, 25 Harewood Avenue, Bournemouth, BH7 6NJ Tel: (01202) 388840 Fax: (01202) 417748 E-mail: martinking@layley.co.uk

Level Seven Communications Ltd, 10-16 Tiller Road, London, E14 8PX Tel: (020) 7345 5125 Fax: (020) 7345 9476 E-mail: sales@l7c.com

Lucas Software Solutions, 95 Tilehouse St, Hitchin, Hertfordshire, SG5 2DW Tel: (01462) 440885 Fax: (01462) 440954 E-mail: sales@lucas-software.co.uk

Magic Systems Ltd, Unit 3 Sandridge Park, Porters Wood, St. Albans, Hertfordshire, AL3 6PH Tel: (01727) 855511 Fax: (01727) 864351 E-mail: sales@magicgroup.com

Our-Info, 279 Garstang Road, Fulwood, Preston, PR2 9XH Tel: (01772) 719648 E-mail: david@joyner.co.uk

PCS, Wakefield Road, Ossett, West Yorkshire, WF5 9AJ Tel: (01924) 281777 Fax: (01924) 266920

Proquis Ltd, Building 1050 Cornforth Drive, Sittingbourne Research Centre, Sittingbourne, Kent, ME9 8PX Tel: (01795) 479001 Fax: (01795) 479009 E-mail: mark.fowler@proquis.com

R B I Recovery Services, Geddings Road, Hoddesdon, Hertfordshire, EN11 0NW Tel: (01992) 445566 Fax: (01992) 441785

Storwave Ltd, 1 Flowers Hill Close, Flowers Hill Trading Estate, Bristol, BS4 5LF Tel: 0117-972 8855 Fax: 0117-916 9234 E-mail: sales@theedmgroup.co.uk

The Systems Practice plc, 134-135 High Street, Southampton, SO14 2BR Tel: (023) 8048 0001 Fax: (023) 8048 0002 E-mail: sales@tspplc.com

Tib Co., Castlebridge Office Village, Kirtley Drive, Nottingham, NG7 1LD Tel: 0115-948 6500 Fax: 0115-948 6595 E-mail: sales@tibco.com

Unify Corp (UK) Ltd, Malt House, Hummer Road, Egham, Surrey, TW20 9BD Tel: (01784) 487940 Fax: (01784) 487941 E-mail: info@unify.com

Westbay Technology Ltd, Main Street, Baycliff, Ulverston, Cumbria, LA12 9RN Tel: (01229) 869108 Fax: (01229) 869108 E-mail: sales@westbay.ndirect.co.uk

Wise Systems Ltd, 7a High Street, Corsham, Wiltshire, SN13 0ES Tel: (01249) 717000 Fax: (01249) 717002 E-mail: info@wisesystems.co.uk

Workstation Technologies Ltd, 21 Sovereign Road, Kings Norton Business Centre, Birmingham, B30 3HN Tel: 0121-486 1234 Fax: (0870) 9901918 E-mail: info@wtluk.com

COMPUTER SOFTWARE, ELECTRONIC COMMERCE (ECOMMERCE), FINANCIAL

Davin Fowler, 15 Queens Square, Leeds, LS2 8AJ Tel: 0113 2255517 E-mail: info@giant-systems.co.uk

COMPUTER SOFTWARE, ELECTRONIC LEARNING (ELEARNING) MANAGEMENT

▶ Learning Expanse Ltd, Technology House, Lissadel Street, Salford, M6 6AP Tel: 0161 2782595 E-mail: info@learning-expanse.co.uk

COMPUTER SOFTWARE, EMPLOYMENT SERVICES

▶ Harvey Hays Ltd, PO BOX 4544, Walsall, WS9 1AJ Tel: 01922 44 21 58 E-mail: admin@harveyhays.com

COMPUTER SOFTWARE, ENTERPRISE SYSTEMS MANAGEMENT (ESM)

▶ Accelerate Consultancy Ltd, Bryn Tirion Brynford Road, Pentre Halkyn, Holywell, Clwyd, CH8 8AW Tel: (0845) 1259573 E-mail: information@accelerate-consultancy.co.uk

COMPUTER SOFTWARE, EXPENSE MANAGEMENT

▶ GlobalExpense Ltd, South Wing, 157 Edgware Road, London, W2 2HR Tel: 0207 2985757 E-mail: andy.bottrill@globalexpense.com

COMPUTER SOFTWARE, GRAPHIC DESIGN

▶ Icon Republic, 14 Orchard Street, Bristol, BS1 5EH Tel: 0117-905 5338

COMPUTER SOFTWARE, HAND HELD COMPUTERS TO DATA LOGGERS

▶ PC Systems, 19 Borthwick Close, Bransholme, Hull, HU7 5BE Tel: (01482) 827461 Fax: (01482) 827461 E-mail: info@pcsystems-ss.co.uk

COMPUTER SOFTWARE, HAND HELD TERMINALS

Action Information Technologies Ltd, 1 Butler Road, Shrewsbury, SY3 7AJ Tel: (01743) 244377 Fax: (01743) 244367 E-mail: sales@actionit.demon.co.uk

Blueleaf Ltd, 73 Steventon Road, Drayton, Abingdon, Oxfordshire, OX14 4LA Tel: (01235) 554677 Fax: (01235) 554977

Fifth Dimension Computer Solutions Ltd, Park House, Maidenhead Road, Cookham, Maidenhead, Berkshire, SL6 9DS Tel: (01628) 851970

▶ IGroup Ltd, 16-17 Yorke Street, Wrexham, Clwyd, LL13 8LW Tel: (0845) 8382184 E-mail: info@igroupltd.co.uk

Productivity Solutions Ltd, PO Box 2133, Stoke-on-Trent, ST3 4WP Tel: (01782) 855739 Fax: (01782) 855739 E-mail: headoffice@psleurope.com

Productivity Solutions Ltd, PO Box 3272, Stourbridge, West Midlands, DY8 2ZA Tel: (01562) 720630 Fax: (01562) 720630 E-mail: info@psleurope.com

COMPUTER SOFTWARE, HEALTHCARE INDUSTRY

Integrity Software Systems Ltd, Crockham Park, Main Road, Edenbridge, Kent, TN8 6SR Tel: (01732) 867555 Fax: (01732) 867115

COMPUTER SOFTWARE, INFORMATION DISPLAY

▶ Viewtouch Ltd., COf Hilton Studios, Park Lane, Lichfield, Staffordshire, WS14 OEU Tel: (0870) 7605756 Fax: (0870) 1309350 E-mail: info@viewtouch.co.uk

COMPUTER SOFTWARE, INFORMATION TECHNOLOGY (IT) INFRASTRUCTURE MANAGEMENT

Fujitsu Services Ltd, Swan House, The Causeway, Staines, Middlesex, TW18 3BF Tel: (0870) 2345555 Fax: (0870) 2424445

COMPUTER SOFTWARE, INFORMATION TECHNOLOGY (IT) SERVICE MANAGEMENT

▶ bcrodda, bcrodda, Tavistock, Devon, PL19 8BN Tel: 07989 893658

▶ SNS It, 18 Mount Close, Mount Avenue, London, W5 2RQ Tel: (020) 8991 4200 E-mail: info@snsitltd.com

COMPUTER SOFTWARE, INFORMATION TECHNOLOGY (IT) TRAINING

▶ Agile Training Limited, 8 Grafton Court, Canning Circus, Nottingham, NG7 3GH Tel: 07932 696228 E-mail: enquiries@agile-training.co.uk

▶ Business It Central, Sussex College, College Road, Crawley, West Sussex, RH10 1NR Tel: (01293) 442326 Fax: (01293) 453421 E-mail: business1@centralsussex.ac.uk

COMPUTER SOFTWARE, INFORMATION TECHNOLOGY MANAGEMENT

▶ bcrodda, bcrodda, Tavistock, Devon, PL19 8BN Tel: 07989 893658

▶ SNS It, 18 Mount Close, Mount Avenue, London, W5 2RQ Tel: (020) 8991 4200 E-mail: info@snsitltd.com

COMPUTER SOFTWARE, INTEGRATED ELECTRONIC COMMERCE (ECOMMERCE)

Davin Fowler, 15 Queens Square, Leeds, LS2 8AJ Tel: 0113 2255517 E-mail: info@giant-systems.co.uk

COMPUTER SOFTWARE, INTERNET BASED PAYMENT

▶ Anything It, 14 Mary Seacole Road, Plymouth, PL1 3JY Tel: (01752) 667771 Fax: (01752) 667771 E-mail: sales@anything-it.biz

▶ Castle I T Consulting Ltd, 128/7 Brunton Gardens, Edinburgh, EH7 5ET Tel: 0131-477 9536 E-mail: gillian@castleitconsulting.co.uk

▶ D B C M Web Design, 14 Walkerbrae Drive, Danestone, Aberdeen, AB22 8YB Tel: (01224) 825401 E-mail: info@dbcmtest.co.uk

▶ DJ Services, 44 Melbourne Street, Worcester, WR3 8AX Tel: (01905) 745339 E-mail: sales@djservicesuk.net

▶ Energo Limited, 3 The Square, Ellon, Aberdeenshire, AB41 9JB Tel: 01358 725139 E-mail: info@implement.it

▶ J T Projects Ltd, 32 Bellevue Terrace, Edinburgh, EH7 4DS Tel: (07980) 750040 Fax: E-mail: info@jtprojects.com

MDTS UK Ltd, 65 Redwood Drive, Laindon, Basildon, Essex, SS15 4AF Tel: (0870) 2427319 Fax: 07092 043571 E-mail: enquiries@mdts.uk.com

▶ NAPSYS Ltd, 6 Laurel Grove, Sidemoor, Bromsgrove, Worcestershire, B61 8LU Tel: (0870) 0638606 Fax: (0870) 0638607 E-mail: sales@napsys.co.uk

▶ - Swayo - Internet Solutions, PO Box 37491, London, United Kingdom, N3 2XR Tel: 0845 257 0392 Fax: 0871 242 5970 E-mail: sales@swayo.co.uk

COMPUTER SOFTWARE, INTERNET TRACKING

▶ Creative Cellular Solutions Ltd, Fox Covert Farm, South Cave Road, Riplingham, Brough, East Yorkshire, HU15 1QT Tel: (0845) 1298297 Fax: (01482) 652727 E-mail: info@creativecellular.co.uk

▶ DIY Tracking Ltd, Brooklands House, 3 Kingdom Close, Fareham, Hampshire, PO15 5TJ Tel: (01489) 571600 Fax: (01489) 571010 E-mail: sales@diytracking.com

▶ DJ Services, 44 Melbourne Street, Worcester, WR3 8AX Tel: (01905) 745339 E-mail: sales@djservicesuk.net

▶ Energo Limited, 3 The Square, Ellon, Aberdeenshire, AB41 9JB Tel: 01358 725139 E-mail: info@implement.it

▶ Illy Computer Systems Ltd, 11 Hoxton Square, London, N1 6NU Tel: (020) 7749 2222 Fax: (020) 7749 2233 E-mail: info@illycorp.com

▶ J T Projects Ltd, 32 Bellevue Terrace, Edinburgh, EH7 4DS Tel: (07980) 750040 Fax: E-mail: info@jtprojects.com

▶ VSI-Thinking, Royal Stuart Workshops Unit 8, Adelaide Place, Cardiff, CF10 5BR Tel: (029) 2033 1188 Fax: (029) 2025 1400 E-mail: jon@vsi-thinking.com

COMPUTER SOFTWARE, LEARNING AND DEVELOPMENT

▶ Franklin College, Chelmsford Avenue, Grimsby, North East Lincolnshire, DN34 5BY Tel: (01472) 875000 Fax: (01472) 875019

▶ Learning Expanse Ltd, Technology House, Lissadel Street, Salford, M6 6AP Tel: 0161 2782595 E-mail: info@learning-expanse.co.uk

COMPUTER SOFTWARE, MACHINERY DESIGN

▶ Camlinks Ltd, Dallas, Newtown, Little Neston, Neston, CH64 4BP Tel: 0151-353 1441 Fax: 0151-353 1441 E-mail: kjs@camlinks.com

COMPUTER SOFTWARE, MARKETING AND CAMPAIGN MANAGEMENT

▶ Tigersmart Marketing, Unit 2b Everoak Industrial Estate, Bromyard Road, Tattenhoe, Milton Keynes, MK4 3BN Tel: (01908) 330770 E-mail: info@tigersmartmarketing.co.uk

COMPUTER SOFTWARE, MARKETING COMMUNICATION

▶ Tigersmart Marketing, Unit 2b Everoak Industrial Estate, Bromyard Road, Tattenhoe, Milton Keynes, MK4 3BN Tel: (01908) 330770 E-mail: info@tigersmartmarketing.co.uk

COMPUTER SOFTWARE, MATHEMATICAL MODELLING

Oscar Kilo Ltd, Broad Parkham, Parkham, Bideford, Devon, EX39 5PJ Tel: (01237) 451517

COMPUTER SOFTWARE, MATHEMATICAL/STATISTICAL

Acropolis Computers Ltd, 2D Dolphin Way, Stapleford, Cambridge, CB2 5DW Tel: (01223) 841700 Fax: (01223) 841802 E-mail: info@biosoft.com

COMPUTER SOFTWARE, MATHEMATICAL/STATISTICAL – *continued*

D L K Ltd, 8 Stather Road, Burton-upon-Stather, Scunthorpe, South Humberside, DN15 9DH Tel: (01724) 720982 Fax: (01724) 720313 E-mail: sales@dlk.co.uk

Easy Peasy, 1 Winder Gate, Frizington, Cumbria, CA26 3QS Tel: (01946) 813065

Target Achievement Ltd, Mercury Park, Amber Close, Amington, Tamworth, Staffordshire, B77 4RP Tel: (01827) 309709 Fax: (01827) 309719 E-mail: sales@maydown.co.uk

COMPUTER SOFTWARE, MECHANICAL ENGINEERING

▶ HeronSoft Ltd, 29 Chatteris Park, Sandymoor, Runcorn, Cheshire, WA7 1XE Tel: (01928) 571620 Fax: (01928) 571620 E-mail: heronsoft@aol.com

COMPUTER SOFTWARE, MULTIMEDIA DESIGN

▶ Creative Rage Ltd, Wassell Wood House, Habberley Road, Bewdley, Worcestershire, DY12 1LD Tel: (01299) 409062 E-mail: contact@creativerage.co.uk

COMPUTER SOFTWARE, OFFICE MANAGEMENT

▶ Herts & Essex Business Supplies, Unit 1 Lea Road, Waltham Abbey, Essex, EN9 1AE Tel: (01920) 413685 Fax: (01992) 651651 E-mail: sales@heb-supplies.co.uk

COMPUTER SOFTWARE, PACKAGING MATERIALS

▶ Bowater Engineering (EU), PO Box 63, Stamford, Lincs, PE9 4SW Tel: 01780 480877 Fax: 01780 480878 E-mail: info@bowater.eu.com

COMPUTER SOFTWARE, PROCESS SIMULATION

Advanced Process Engineering & Simulation Services, 6 Milford Street, Cambridge, CB1 2LP Tel: (01223) 521149 E-mail: martin.sneesby@apess.co.uk

COMPUTER SOFTWARE, RETAIL

▶ BDE Group, 5 Tun Yard, Peardon Street, London, SW8 3HT Tel: 0870 128 7800 Fax: 020 7801 8866 E-mail: sales@bdegroup.co.uk

Brandt Computer Systems Ltd, 20 Barclay Road, Croydon, CR0 1JN Tel: (020) 8760 9173 Fax: (020) 8760 9180 E-mail: croydon@brandt.co.uk

COMPUTER SOFTWARE, SECURE WEBSITE SERVERS

▶ Chapter Eight Ltd, Medius House, 2 Sheraton Street, Soho, London, W1F 8BH Tel: (020) 7788 9861 Fax: (020) 7788 9862

COMPUTER SOFTWARE, STATISTICAL PROCESS CONTROL

Cadar Measurement Solutions Ltd, 100 Fitzwalter Road, Sheffield, S2 2SP Tel: 0114-275 0722 Fax: 0114-275 2912 E-mail: info@cadar.co.uk

I C C S Ltd, 4 Market Street, Edenfield, Ramsbottom, Bury, Lancashire, BL0 0JN Tel: (01706) 822233 Fax: (01706) 822277 E-mail: info@iccs-ltd.co.uk

COMPUTER SOFTWARE, SUPPLY CHAIN COLLABORATION (SCC)

▶ Openda Ltd, PO Box 2774, Swindon, SN5 3NY Tel: (0870) 0411890 Fax: (0870) 0411899 E-mail: enquiries@openda.com

COMPUTER SOFTWARE, SUPPLY CHAIN EXECUTION (SCE)

▶ Openda Ltd, PO Box 2774, Swindon, SN5 3NY Tel: (0870) 0411890 Fax: (0870) 0411899 E-mail: enquiries@openda.com

COMPUTER SOFTWARE, SUPPLY CHAIN INTEGRATION (SCI)

▶ Synchro Ltd, Design Centre 2.3, Coventry Universtiy, Technology Park, Puma Way, Coventry, CV1 2TT Tel: (024) 7679 2200 E-mail: info@synchroltd.com

COMPUTER SOFTWARE, TELEPHONE MARKETING

▶ VHO, Suite 24 Basepoint Business Centre, Rivermead Drive, Swindon, SN5 7EX Tel: 01793 608701 Fax: 01793 608704 E-mail: vivienne@vhorg.co.uk

COMPUTER SOFTWARE, THREE DIMENSIONAL (3D) CHARACTER ANIMATION

▶ Sketch 3D Design & Drafting, 130 Cambridge Street, Wolverton, Milton Keynes, MK12 5AQ Tel: (07789) 002945 E-mail: info@sketch3d.co.uk

T R S U, 1 Cranside Avenue, Bristol, BS6 7RA Tel: (07748) 740874 E-mail: ben@trsu.com

▶ Type In Motion Ltd, 169 High Street, Boston Spa, Wetherby, West Yorkshire, LS23 6BH Tel: (01937) 844815 Fax: (01937) 845327 E-mail: enquiries@typeinmotion.co.uk

COMPUTER SOFTWARE, TIME RECORDING

Data Time Systems Time Recorders Systems, 5 Lowlands Drive, Keyworth, Nottingham, NG12 5HG Tel: 0115-937 3368 Fax: 0115-937 6611 E-mail: info@datatime.co.uk

COMPUTER SOFTWARE, WEBSITE ANALYSIS

▶ Club Together Ltd, 31 Strathmore Road, Teddington, Middlesex, TW11 8UJ Tel: (020) 8943 2682 E-mail: dave.weston@teddingtontennis.org

COMPUTER SOFTWARE, WEBSITE DESIGN

▶ Alderdesigns, 79 Forrestal Street, Edzell, Brechin, Angus, DD9 7XG Tel: (01356) 648069 E-mail: phil.alder@alderdesigns.co.uk

Ask Web Design, Dam Hill Farm, Malton Road, York, YO32 9TL Tel: (01904) 400047 E-mail: tom@askwebdesign.com

▶ Golden Solutions Ltd, 245 Markfield, Courtwood Llane, Forestdale, Croydon, CR0 9HW Tel: 020 84059337

COMPUTER SOFTWARE, WEBSITE DEVELOPMENT

▶ Golden Solutions Ltd, 245 Markfield, Courtwood Llane, Forestdale, Croydon, CR0 9HW Tel: 020 84059337

COMPUTER SOLUTIONS HOUSE

▶ Abraqsys Business Systems, 13 Duncan Close, Moulton Park Industrial Estate, Northampton, NN3 6WL Tel: (01604) 797950 Fax: (01604) 797951 E-mail: sales@abraqsys.co.uk

Beaumont Colson Ltd, 133 New Bridge Street, Newcastle upon Tyne, NE1 2SW Tel: 0191-261 7117 Fax: 0191-230 4090

Burns E-commerce Solutions, Mansion House, Manchester Road, Altrincham, Cheshire, WA14 4RW Tel: 0161-929 8673 Fax: 0161-929 8674 E-mail: info@burnsecs.com

Chimera C M T Ltd, 9 Blenheim Court, Lustleigh Close, Marsh Barton Industrial Estate, Exeter, EX2 8PW Tel: (01392) 667444 Fax: (01392) 667440

Computer Solutions, 38 Chingford Mount Rd, London, E4 9AB Tel: 020 85318880 Fax: 020 85392338

Enline P.L.C., Newchase Court, Hopper Hill Road, Scarborough, North Yorkshire, YO11 3YS Tel: (0870) 5502015 Fax: (0870) 5673018 E-mail: marketing@enline.com

Epic Computers Ltd, 4 Sybron Way, Crowborough, East Sussex, TN6 3DZ Tel: (01892) 667770 Fax: (01892) 665777 E-mail: sales@epicpc.co.uk

Equinox Business Solutions Ltd, Technology House, Commerce Business Centre, West Wilts Trading Estate, Westbury, Wiltshire, BA13 4JB Tel: (01373) 825664 Fax: (01373) 859318 E-mail: enquiries@equinox-solutions.co.uk

Exordia Software Ltd, PO Box 7973, Ayr, KA7 4UQ Tel: (01292) 445599 Fax: (01292) 443343 E-mail: sales@exordia.co.uk

Fmi, Queens House, 1 Leicester Place, London, WC2H 7BP Tel: (020) 7758 0700 Fax: (020) 7758 0701

I T Solution Ltd, Concord House, Providence Drive, Stourbridge, West Midlands, DY9 8HQ Tel: (0871) 7000081 Fax: (01384) 892777

Interconnect Direct Ltd, 22 Edward Road, Arnos Vale, Bristol, BS4 3ES Tel: 0117-907 1880 E-mail: enquiries@interconnect-direct.com

Livesey Business Systems, 95 Princes Avenue, Hull, HU5 3QR Tel: (01482) 343453 E-mail: sales@livbiz.com

Maindec Computer Engineering Ltd, Maindec House, Holtspur Lane, Wooburn Green, High Wycombe, Buckinghamshire, HP10 0AB Tel: (01628) 810977 Fax: (01628) 810733 E-mail: roger.timms@maindec.co.uk

Merlin Software International Ltd, PO Box 27, Somerton, Somerset, TA11 6SB Tel: (01458) 271300 Fax: (01458) 224044 E-mail: info@caliburn-software.com

Morpheus, 6-7 The Courtyard, Eastern Road, Bracknell, Berkshire, RG12 2XB Tel: (01344) 458188 Fax: (01344) 458189 E-mail: info@morpheus.co.uk

N B S Solutions, Kelvin Way, Crawley, West Sussex, RH10 9WE Tel: (01293) 442797 Fax: (01293) 442798 E-mail: sales@nbs-solutions.co.uk

Nexillis Ltd, 1 Canada Square, Canary Wharf, London, E14 5DY Tel: (020) 7538 2533 Fax: (020) 7538 2534 E-mail: info@nexillis.com

Nybble Information Systems, 86 Darwen Street, Blackburn, BB2 2AJ Tel: (01254) 296590 Fax: (0870) 3301200 E-mail: enquiries@nybble.co.uk

Oakland Associates, Westmead House, 123 Westmead Road, Sutton, Surrey, SM1 4JH Tel: (020) 8395 7799 Fax: (020) 8395 7676 E-mail: info@oaklandassociates.co.uk

Office Software Solutions Ltd, 52 Chart La, Reigate, Surrey, RH2 7DZ Tel: 01737 241000 Fax: 01737 241000

Option Systems Ltd, Osl House, East Link, Leicester, LE19 1XU Tel: 0116-291 6666 Fax: 0116-291 6667 E-mail: sales@styleman.com

Parity Solutions Ltd, Wimbledon Bridge House, 1 Hartfield Road, London, SW19 3RU Tel: (020) 8543 5353 Fax: (020) 8545 6456 E-mail: marketing@parity.co.uk

Phase 2 Computers Services, The Mansley Centre, 19 Timothys Bridge Road, Stratford-upon-Avon, Warwickshire, CV37 9NQ Tel: (01789) 295444 Fax: (01789) 298444 E-mail: sales@phase2.co.uk

Portix, Belvedere, Basing View, Basingstoke, Hampshire, RG21 4HG Tel: (0870) 4607710 Fax: (01256) 396501

Quorum Business Systems Ltd, Unit 36 Watford Metro Centre, Dwight Road, Watford, WD18 9YA Tel: (01923) 231536 Fax: (01923) 221971 E-mail: mail@quorum-business.co.uk

Servo, Oakwell Way, Birstall, Batley, West Yorkshire, WF17 9LU Tel: (01924) 422111 Fax: (0870) 1218302 E-mail: info@icm-computer.co.uk

Starcol Ltd, 7 Cork Place, Bath, BA1 3BB Tel: (01225) 311276 Fax: (01225) 446828 E-mail: info@starcol.com

Systems Advisers Group UK Ltd, Enterprise House, Donaldson Crescent, Kirkintilloch, Glasgow, G66 1XF Tel: 0141-578 2237 Fax: 0141-578 2306 E-mail: sales@systemsadvisers.com

T M E Ltd, 11 Church Street, Walton-On-Thames, Surrey, KT12 2QP Tel: (01932) 232123 Fax: (01932) 232110E-mail: info@tme-ltd.com

Taylor Made Training Ltd, 132 Station Road, Glenfield, Leicester, LE3 8BR Tel: 0116-232 4800 Fax: 0116-232 4811 E-mail: mailbox@taylormadetraining.co.uk

Tenet Technology Ltd, North Heath Lane, Horsham, West Sussex, RH12 5UX Tel: (01403) 273173 Fax: (01403) 273123 E-mail: tenet@tenetsystems.com

Vantage Micro Systems Ltd, 2 Airfield Park, Cheddington Lane, Long Marston, Tring, Hertfordshire, HP23 4QR Tel: (01296) 668966 Fax: (01296) 662798 E-mail: sales@vantageit.co.uk

COMPUTER SPEECH RECOGNITION EQUIPMENT

▶ Cameo It, 5 Elizabeth Drive, Wantage, Oxfordshire, OX12 9YA Tel: (01235) 768660 Fax: (01235) 768660

Fluency Voice Technology Ltd, Block 6, 1St Floor Westbrook Centre, Cambridge, CB4 1YG Tel: (01223) 300101 Fax: (01223) 326701 E-mail: enquires@vocalis.com

Philips Speech Processing, 8 The Courtyards, Wyncolls Road, Severalls Industrial Park, Colchester, CO4 9PE Tel: (01206) 755755 Fax: (01206) 755888 E-mail: info@speech.philips.com

COMPUTER STATIONERY

A D P Supplies Ltd, 65 Peach Street, Wokingham, Berkshire, RG40 1XP Tel: 0118-977 0554 Fax: 0118-978 5525

Associated Print & Training Ltd, PO Box 107, Bury St. Edmunds, Suffolk, IP31 2UF Tel: (01284) 788333 Fax: (01284) 788336 E-mail: sales@apt.gb.com

Black & White Consumables Ltd, 22 St.Johns North, Wakefield, West Yorkshire, WF1 3QA Tel: (01924) 210236 Fax: (01924) 782037 E-mail: info@bwconsumables.co.uk

▶ Cartridge Swop Shop, 201 Hoylake Road, Wirral, Merseyside, CH46 0SJ Tel: 0151-606 1435 Fax: 0151-606 0763 E-mail: Mark@cartridgeswopshop.com

Chart Right Ltd, Units 34, Aston Fields Trading Estate, Bromsgrove, Worcestershire, B60 3DW Tel: (01527) 571500 Fax: (01527) 571516 E-mail: sales@chartright.com

Cubix Ltd, 34 Candlemas Lane, Beaconsfield, Buckinghamshire, HP9 1AF Tel: (01494) 678661 Fax: (01494) 678663 E-mail: sales@cubix.co.uk

D W Direct, 4 Merivale Road, Harrow, Middlesex, HA1 4BH Tel: (020) 8423 2030 Fax: (020) 8422 7216 E-mail: sales@computaform.force9.co.uk

Datagraphic UK Ltd, Cottage Leap, Butler's Leap, Rugby, Warwickshire, CV21 3XP Tel: (01788) 535383 Fax: (01788) 535351 E-mail: sales@datagraphic.co.uk

The Draughtsmans Centre Ltd, 819 Hagley Road West, Birmingham, B32 1AD Tel: 0121-423 1412 Fax: 0121-423 1812

DTS Computer Print Ltd, Adams Street, Birmingham, B7 4LT Tel: 0121-359 5551 Fax: 0121-359 7300E-mail: sales@dts-ltd.com

E C S Business Forms Ltd, Harbour House, Coldharbour Lane, Rainham, Essex, RM13 9YA Tel: (01708) 555241 Fax: (01708) 525244

Etrinsic, 473 Stratford Road, Shirley, Solihull, West Midlands, B90 4AD Tel: (0870) 4646131 Fax: (0870) 4646040

Formula Business Form, 5 Block 5 Shenstone Trading Estate, Bromsgrove Road, Halesowen, West Midlands, B63 3XB Tel: 0121-585 6333 Fax: 0121-585 5620 E-mail: sales@formulabusinessforms.co.uk

J H Business Forms Ltd, Adams Street, Birmingham, B7 4LT Tel: 0121-359 6693 Fax: 0121-333 3118 E-mail: jhbf@cyberphile.co.uk

Fred Johnson, Unit D2, Impirial Business Centre, West Mill, Gravesend, Kent, DA11 0DL Tel: (01474) 569919 Fax: (01474) 533261 E-mail: info@fjpaper.co.uk

Lonsdale Print Solutions Ltd, Denington Road, Denington Industrial Estate, Wellingborough, Northamptonshire, NN8 2RA Tel: (01933) 228855 Fax: (01933) 442405 E-mail: info@lonsdaleps.co.uk

Meridian Computer Stationery, 9-17 Crompton Way, Crawley, West Sussex, RH10 9QG Tel: (01293) 400210 Fax: (01293) 551703

Merlin Forms Ltd, Unit 3, 222 London Road Business Park, St. Albans, Hertfordshire, AL1 1PN Tel: (01727) 845077 Fax: (01727) 845013 E-mail: sales@merlinformsltd.co.uk

Multisets Ltd, Suite 2B, Second Floor, Eastheath House, Eastheath Avenue, Wokingham, Berkshire, RG41 2PR Tel: 0118-936 7600 Fax: 0118-936 7601 E-mail: info@multisets.co.uk

Office Depot UK, Guilbert House, Greenwich Way, Andover, Hampshire, SP10 4JZ Tel: (0870) 7556611 Fax: (0870) 4114735 E-mail: name@officedepot.com

Osborne Stationers Ltd, 27 Market Street, Wolverhampton, WV1 3AG Tel: (01902) 427071 Fax: (01902) 771070

P F C Group Ltd, Roman Way Business Centre, Berry Hill Industrial Estate, Droitwich, Worcestershire, WR9 9AJ Tel: (01905) 797000 Fax: (01905) 797274 E-mail: marketsales@pfcgroup.co.uk

Paragon Group UK Ltd, Pallion Trading Estate, Sunderland, SR4 6ST Tel: 0191-514 0716 Fax: 0191-567 1842 E-mail: enquiries@paragonuk.com

R W Pierce & Co. Ltd, 17 Dargan CR, Belfast, BT3 9HJ Tel: (028) 9037 1010 Fax: (028) 9037 2501

Rediset Business Forms Ltd, Factory Road, Upton Industrial Estate, Poole, Dorset, BH16 5SJ Tel: (01202) 622679 Fax: (01202) 623375

Reelprint Register Sets Ltd, Spring Road Industrial Estate, 13 Lanesfield Drive, Wolverhampton, WV4 6UA Tel: (01902) 405177 Fax: (01902) 405178 E-mail: reelprint@lineone.net

Scotforms Computer Stationery Ltd, 3 Hatton Square, Livingston, West Lothian, EH54 9BJ Tel: (01506) 410871 Fax: (01506) 416805 E-mail: info@scotforms.co.uk

Statco, Evett Close, Stocklake, Aylesbury, Buckinghamshire, HP20 1DN Tel: (01296) 392379 Fax: (01296) 435940 E-mail: statco@uk.uumail.com

Taws Printers Ltd, 1 Hortonwood, Telford, Shropshire, TF1 7GN Tel: (01952) 281281 Fax: (01952) 281282 E-mail: info@taws.co.uk

Trilogybrookes Printing, Ashbourne Way, Shirley, Solihull, West Midlands, B90 4QU Tel: 0121-745 9600 Fax: 0121-745 6200 E-mail: tkeatet@trilogymediagroup.com

COMPUTER STATIONERY – *continued*

Tudor Business Forms Ltd, 2 Meridian Centre, Vulcan Way, New Addington, Croydon, CR0 9UG Tel: (01689) 844888 Fax: (01689) 844999
E-mail: sales@tudorofficesupplies.co.uk

▶ UK Business Print Ltd, 15 Hendersyde Park, Kelso, Roxburghshire, TD5 7TU Tel: (01573) 224889 Fax: (01573) 223854
E-mail: sales@ukbrand.com

COMPUTER STATIONERY PRINTING

Computer Press, 1 Rowles Way, Kidlington, Oxfordshire, OX5 1LA Tel: (01865) 849158 Fax: (01865) 374007
E-mail: sales@cpdirect.co.uk

DTS Computer Print Ltd, Adams Street, Birmingham, B7 4LT Tel: 0121-359 5551 Fax: 0121-359 7300E-mail: sales@dts-ltd.com

Formula Business Form, 5 Block 5 Shenstone Trading Estate, Bromsgrove Road, Halesowen, West Midlands, B63 3XB Tel: 0121-585 6333 Fax: 0121-585 5620
E-mail: sales@formulabusinessforms.co.uk

▶ Micro Computer Forms Ltd, 9 Blackbrook Valley Industrial Estate, Narrowboat Way, Dudley, West Midlands, DY2 0XQ Tel: (01384) 455221 Fax: (01384) 455223
E-mail: lsm@mcforms.co.uk

Partners in Print, Venture Place, 45 Lord Street, Birmingham, B7 4DQ Tel: 0121-359 0202 Fax: 0121-359 5550
E-mail: mail@partnersinprint.co.uk

Print Systems (Midlands) Ltd, Steel House, 37 Church Street, Oldbury, West Midlands, B69 3AG Tel: 0121-541 1376 Fax: 0121-541 2292
E-mail: sales@printsystemsmidlands.co.uk

Rediset Business Forms Ltd, Factory Road, Upton Industrial Estate, Poole, Dorset, BH16 5SJ Tel: (01202) 622679 Fax: (01202) 623375

S Barber & Co. Ltd, 66-68 Kitchen Street, Liverpool, L1 0AN Tel: 0151-709 7323 Fax: 0151-709 6608
E-mail: sales@barbersprn.co.uk

Wordcrafts, Unit 9 The Beaver Centre, Putney Road West, Freemans Common, Leicester, LE2 7TD Tel: 0116-255 8422 Fax: 0116-255 0624 E-mail: info@wordcrafts.co.uk

COMPUTER STATIONERY TO SPECIFICATION

Business Wise, Bank House, Bank Cresent, Ledbury, Herefordshire, HR8 1AA Tel: (01531) 634636 Fax: (01531) 634637

COMPUTER STORAGE SERVICES

Network Appliance, Riley Court, Millburn Hill Road, Coventry, CV4 7HS Tel: (024) 7683 8838 Fax: (024) 7683 8801
E-mail: info@netapp.com

COMPUTER SUPPORT SERVICES

Abitech Systems, 13 Main Street, Keyworth, Nottingham, NG12 5AA Tel: 0115-937 4549 Fax: 0115-937 3662
E-mail: sales@abitech.co.uk

Ace Computer Services Ltd, 19 Westerby Lane, Smeeton Westerby, Leicester, LE8 0RA Tel: 0116-279 3673

Anglia Business Computers Training Ltd, Harston Mill, Royston Road, Harston, Cambridge, CB22 7GG Tel: (01223) 873400 Fax: (01223) 873401 E-mail: mktg@angliabs.com

▶ Applestorm Ltd, Unit 3, Homefarm, Luton Hoo Estate, Luton, LU1 3TD Tel: (0800) 5655565 Fax: (0870) 4670447
E-mail: sales@applestorm.com

Arun Computer Equipment Ltd, 72-74 Clifton Road, Worthing, West Sussex, BN11 4DP Tel: (01903) 529077 Fax: (01903) 529088
E-mail: sales@aruncomputers.co.uk

B C Computing Ltd, 57 Ferrybridge Road, Castleford, West Yorkshire, WF10 4JW Tel: (01977) 667777 Fax: (01977) 667701

▶ C F Systems Ltd, 17 Trewirgie Hill, Redruth, Cornwall, TR15 2TB Tel: (01209) 210195 Fax: (01209) 313841
E-mail: info@cfsystems.biz

Compliant Business Systems Ltd, PO Box 25, King's Lynn, Norfolk, PE30 4AR Tel: (01553) 660500 Fax: (01553) 660500
E-mail: mail@compliant.co.uk

Computer Surgery, Apple Barn, Maidstone Road, Pembury, Tunbridge Wells, Kent, TN2 4AD Tel: (0845) 1303343 Fax: (0870) 0118128
E-mail: sales@computer-surgery.co.uk

Comtech Telecommunications Ltd, 30 Bradford Road, Stanningley, Pudsey, West Yorkshire, LS28 6DD Tel: 0113-255 3927 Fax: 0113-205 7567 E-mail: info@comtech-telecom.co.uk

Connect Support Services Ltd, South Quay Plaza 2, 183 Marsh Wall, London, E14 9SH Tel: (020) 7517 2000 Fax: (020) 7517 2099
E-mail: connect@connect.co.uk

Core Consultancy Ltd, 7 Kings Bench Street, London, SE1 0QX Tel: (020) 7928 3338 Fax: (0871) 6613393
E-mail: info@core-consultancy.com

Creative Computers Ltd, 258 Old Christchurch Road, Bournemouth, BH1 1PS Tel: (01202) 775600 Fax: (01202) 775559
E-mail: sales@creativegroup.co.uk

Crusader Technologies, 34 Northill Road, Cople, Bedford, MK44 3UD Tel: (01234) 838040 Fax: (01234) 838152

Dash Consulting, 4 Friars Cottage, off Copyground Lane, High Wycombe, Bucks, HP12 3XB Tel: (01923) 256655 Fax: (01923) 222494 E-mail: duncan@dashconsulting.com

▶ Digit Info Tec, Unit 1a Victoria Business Park, Roche, St. Austell, Cornwall, PL26 8LX Tel: (01726) 890546 Fax: (01726) 890597
E-mail: sales@digit-info-tec.co.uk

▶ Doctor Software, Suite 3, Stanta Business Centre, 3 Soothouse Spring, St. Albans, Hertfordshire, AL3 6PF Tel: (01727) 869806 Fax: (0871) 4742864
E-mail: chris.beere@doctorsoftware.co.uk

Dsys Plus Ltd, Swan Business Centre, Fishers Lane, London, W4 1RX Tel: (020) 8994 5050 Fax: (020) 8994 0510

E C S Computers Ltd, 98-99 London Road, King's Lynn, Norfolk, PE30 5HA Tel: (01553) 692727 Fax: (01553) 764564
E-mail: support@ecscomputers.co.uk

G T I Computers Portsmouth Ltd, Unit 219, Victory Business Centre, Somers Road North, Portsmouth, PO1 1PJ Tel: (023) 9275 0212 Fax: (0870) 0601868
E-mail: sales@gticomputers.co.uk

Grove Systems Ltd, 3 Ashlyn Grove, Manchester, M14 6YG Tel: 0161-224 4465
E-mail: donald@grove.demon.co.uk

Gryphon Computer Support Ltd, 7 Nightingale Gardens, Nailsea, Bristol, BS48 2BH Tel: (01275) 857990 Fax: (01275) 851558
E-mail: sales@gryphon-group.co.uk

Helpdesk Institute, 21 High Street, Green Street Greens, Orpington, Kent, BR6 6BG Tel: (01689) 862999 Fax: (01689) 889227
E-mail: info@hdi-europe.com

Ilkley It Services Ltd, Nat West Bank Chambers The, Grove Ilkley, Ilkley, West Yorkshire, LS29 9LS Tel: (01943) 601601
E-mail: info@ilkleyitservices.co.uk

▶ Imitza Systems, 26 High Street, Spennymoor, County Durham, DL16 6DB Tel: (01388) 818844 E-mail: info@imitza.co.uk

Intalect Ltd, Office 7, Grange Farm Business Park, Newtown Unthank, Leicester, LE9 9FL Tel: (0845) 6448860 Fax: (0845) 6448861
E-mail: info@intalect.co.uk

Sam Kane Ltd, 40 Howard Business Park, Howard Close, Waltham Abbey, Essex, EN9 1XE Tel: (01992) 712746 Fax: (01992) 700211 E-mail: helen@samkane.ltd.uk

Kaye Instruments, Unit 1 Apollo House, Calleva Park, Aldermaston, Reading, RG7 8TN Tel: 0118-981 7100 Fax: 0118-981 7102

Keen IT Solutions Limited, 79 Ansell Road, Frimley, Camberley, Surrey, GU16 8DH Tel: 0845 0940320 E-mail: info@keenit.co.uk

Key Computer Applications, Cavern House, Ellesmere Street, Leigh, Lancashire, WN7 4LQ Tel: (01942) 261671 Fax: (01942) 260262

Linden Computer Services, Laverham House, 77 St Georges Place, Cheltenham, Gloucestershire, GL50 3PP Tel: (01242) 269369 Fax: (01242) 231341

Liquid Software Solutions Ltd, 2 Wilsons Road, Knowle, Solihull, West Midlands, B93 0HZ Tel: (01564) 779090 Fax: (01564) 776161
E-mail: info@liquid-soft.com

M & M Computing Services Ltd, Dial Post Court, Horsham Road, Rusper, Horsham, West Sussex, RH12 4QX Tel: (01293) 871971 Fax: (01293) 871796
E-mail: sales@mm-computing.com

Mcneill Associates Ltd, 14 Well Hall Parade, London, SE9 6SP Tel: (020) 8294 1565 Fax: (020) 8859 4562
E-mail: post@mcneill.co.uk

Maxresponse Ltd, 55 Linkside Avenue, Oxford, OX2 8JE Tel: (01865) 316251 Fax: (0870) 0518845 E-mail: sales@maxresponse.co.uk

▶ Microgator Ltd, 15A Bramford Road, Ipswich, IP1 2LZ Tel: (0800) 2986258
E-mail: sales@microgator.biz

Nexcen Ltd, 16C Horse Street, Chipping Sodbury, Bristol, BS37 6DB Tel: (01454) 318686 Fax: 0171-433 4533

Nitec Solutions, Unit 9 Technology Park, Belfast Road, Muckamore, Antrim, BT41 1QS Tel: (028) 9442 7000 Fax: (028) 9442 7030
E-mail: support@nitec.com

Office Support Ltd, Old Farn House, Moreton-on-Lugg, Hereford, HR4 8DE Tel: (01432) 761884 Fax: (01432) 760866
E-mail: enquiries@office-support.co.uk

Our-Info, 279 Garstang Road, Fulwood, Preston, PR2 9XH Tel: (01772) 719648
E-mail: david@joyner.co.uk

Q-Tron Ltd, The Ross Wing, Redhill Court, Doncaster, South Yorkshire, DN11 9ED Tel: (01302) 311066 Fax: (01302) 311774
E-mail: q-tron@btconnect.com

Quantum Data Solutions Ltd, 3-5 Marischal Street, Peterhead, Aberdeenshire, AB42 1BS Tel: (01779) 490426 Fax: (01779) 480074
E-mail: purchasing@qds.uk.net

Quintech Computer Systems Ltd, Ashton Road, Beckford, Tewkesbury, Gloucestershire, GL20 7AU Tel: (01386) 883800 Fax: (01386) 883801 E-mail: info@quintech.co.uk

▶ Spear Technologies Ltd, Station Rise, York, YO1 6HT Tel: (01904) 624009 Fax: (01904) 655411E-mail: admin@speartechnologies.com

Syscomm Ltd, Syscomm House, 2 Park Road, Kenilworth, Warwickshire, CV8 2GF Tel: (01926) 856000 Fax: (01926) 851158
E-mail: sales@syscomm.co.uk

Wisdom Information Technolgolist Ltd, 6 Flemring Road, Livingston, West Lothian, EH54 7BN Tel: (01506) 497490 Fax: (01506) 497494
E-mail: admin@wisdomit.co.uk

COMPUTER SWITCHES, KEYBOARD-VIDEO-MOUSE (KVM)

End Design Ltd, Unit 37, Bookham Industrial Park, Church Road, Leatherhead, Surrey, KT23 3EU Tel: (01372) 458080 Fax: (01372) 450592 E-mail: sales@end-design.co.uk

COMPUTER SYSTEMS

▶ A & J Computers, 50 Tamworth Road, Long Eaton, Nottingham, NG10 3LW Tel: 0115-946 2020 Fax: 0115 9462020
E-mail: enquiries@aj-computers.co.uk

▶ Amber Computing & It Services Ltd, Coilacriech, Ballater, Aberdeenshire, AB35 5UH Tel: (01339) 742019 Fax: (01339) 742292

▶ Crest Technology, 5 East Glebe, Stonehaven, Kincardineshire, AB39 2HW Tel: (01569) 766662 Fax: (07876) 881265
E-mail: info@crest2000.com

Deegee Systems Ltd, 15 Hawksley Rise, Oughtibridge, Sheffield, S35 0JB Tel: 0114-286 4400 Fax: 0114-286 4400
E-mail: sales@deegee.co.uk

Electrical Electronic Services, Sotherby Road, Middlesbrough, Cleveland, TS3 8BS Tel: (01642) 241600

▶ PCEazy Computer Systems, 172 Park Road, Bedworth, Warwickshire, CV12 8LA Tel: (0870) 3834821 E-mail: sales@pceazy.com

Silicon City Distribution, 50 Temple Avenue, London, N20 9EH Tel: (020) 8445 5251 Fax: (0870) 7052314E-mail: sales@silcity.com

Spa Advanced Systems Ltd, 40 Holden Park Road, South Borough, Tunbridge Wells, Kent, TN4 0ER Tel: (01892) 548998 Fax: (01892) 548175 E-mail: spa@spadata.co.uk

▶ Tribal Education Ltd, St. Leonards House, St. Leonards Gate, Lancaster, LA1 1NN Tel: (01524) 384050
E-mail: info.education@tribalgroup.co.uk

▶ Vivatech, Shambria, Woodvill Road, Leatherhead, Surrey, KT22 7BP Tel: (01372) 377362 Fax: (01372) 373927
E-mail: viva.tech@virgin.net

Welcome Computer Systems Ltd, The Pytchley Unit, Victors Barns, Brixworth, Northampton, NN6 9DQ Tel: (0845) 4582121 Fax: (0845) 4582020
E-mail: sales@welcome-computers.co.uk

COMPUTER SYSTEMS CONSULTANTS OR SERVICES, SOFTWARE ETC

1 Can Help P C Problem Solving & Training Services, 60 Springwood Road, Heathfield, East Sussex, TN21 8JX Tel: (01435) 866575
E-mail: gordon@1canhelp.com

1 Entity Software Ltd, Thames Acre, Hamm Court, Weybridge, Surrey, KT13 8YD Tel: (01932) 847784 Fax: (0870) 2203896

1st Computer Consultancy, 55 Argarmeols Road, Liverpool, L37 7BY Tel: (01704) 833588 Fax: (01704) 833588

▶ 1st Port, Allen House, The Maltings, Station Road, Sawbridgeworth, Hertfordshire, CM21 9JX Tel: (01279) 602150 Fax: (01279) 723957

1t Solutions, 3 The Crescent, Doncaster Road, Rotherham, South Yorkshire, S65 1NL Tel: (01709) 371441 Fax: (01709) 371440
E-mail: sales@1t-s.com

321 Systems Ltd, 6 Maryon Mews, London, NW3 2PU Tel: (020) 7794 3236 Fax: (020) 7431 3213 E-mail: info@321systems.com

360 Solutions, Unit 1, Nobles Gate Yard, Bell Yews Green, Tunbridge Wells, Kent, TN3 9AT Tel: (0870) 7606404 Fax: (0870) 7606404
E-mail: info@360ss.com

▶ 3c Technology Ltd, 29-33 Lower Kings Road, Berkhamsted, Hertfordshire, HP4 2AB Tel: (01442) 863388 Fax: (01442) 863444
E-mail: sales@3ctech.co.uk

3l1t3 Ltd, 43 Beckfield Road, Bingley, West Yorkshire, BD16 1QR Tel: (01274) 820102 Fax: (01274) 825558
E-mail: admin@3l1t3.com

3tech Systems Ltd, Whitwick Business Park, Stenson Road, Coalville, Leicestershire, LE67 4JP Tel: (01530) 276500 Fax: (01530) 813526 E-mail: info@3techsystems.co.uk

4 S Informations Systems Ltd, 4 The Square, Milnthorpe, Cumbria, LA7 7QJ Tel: (01539) 563091 Fax: (01539) 562475
E-mail: sales@4s-dawn.com

5 Fifteen Ltd, 180 Bedford Avenue, Slough, SL1 4RA Tel: (01753) 440515 Fax: (01753) 440567 E-mail: info@5fifteen.com

▶ A A C C Ltd, 32 Beaumaris Grove, Shenley Church End, Milton Keynes, MK5 6EN Tel: (01908) 330800

A A Computer Services, The Old Smithy, Henllan Amgoed, Whitland, Dyfed, SA34 0SN Tel: (01994) 240832 Fax: (01994) 240786

A A T Computer Services, 57 High Street, Donaghadee, County Down, BT21 0AQ Tel: (028) 9188 8114 Fax: (028) 9188 8370
E-mail: andrew@aatcs.co.uk

A I M Ltd, Victoria House, Derringham Street, Hull, HU3 1EL Tel: (01482) 326971 Fax: (01482) 228465 E-mail: aim@aim.co.uk

A K Consultancies Ltd, 141a Prestbury Road, Cheltenham, Gloucestershire, GL52 2DU Tel: (01242) 234123 E-mail: sales@akc.co.uk

A K I T Solutions (UK) Ltd, 110-114 Grafton Road, London, NW5 4BA Tel: (020) 7482 0304 Fax: (020) 7482 3852

▶ A & M IT Solutions, 93 Lever Street, London, EC1V 3RQ Tel: (020) 7253 6123

A R Business Systems & Software Ltd, Wrang Beck House, Leyburn Road, Middleham, Leyburn, North Yorkshire, DL8 4PN Tel: (01325) 481647 Fax: (01325) 369744
E-mail: office@arbs.net

A R M Holdings, Moorbridge Road, Maidenhead, Berkshire, SL6 8LT Tel: (01628) 427700 Fax: (01628) 427701
E-mail: enquiries@arm.com

A T Computers (Applemac), Unit E2 Green La Business Park, Green Lane, Tewkesbury, Gloucestershire, GL20 8SJ Tel: (01684) 291112 Fax: (01684) 274829

A T E Technology Ltd, ATE House, 48 Green Meadows, Westhoughton, Bolton, BL5 2BN Tel: (01942) 815603 Fax: (01942) 815321
E-mail: info@ate-technology.com

A T T & C, Tudor House, Catherine Road, Benfleet, Essex, SS7 1HY Tel: (01268) 759398 Fax: (01268) 565102

A W Computer Solutions Ltd, 8e Port Road, Carlisle, CA2 7AF Tel: (01228) 594682 Fax: (01228) 594683
E-mail: info@armstrongwatson.co.uk

A1 Netservices, 23 Tudor Road, Wheathampstead, St. Albans, Hertfordshire, AL4 8NW Tel: (01582) 834208 Fax: (0871) 7501428 E-mail: info@a1-netservices.co.uk

A4 Computers, 2nd Floor, 32 B Church Road, Ashford, Middlesex, TW15 2UY Tel: (0870) 0634283 Fax: (0870) 0632106
E-mail: info@a4it.co.uk

Aba Key Ltd, 5 Spring Garden Lane, Gosport, Hampshire, PO12 1HY Tel: (023) 9251 1617 Fax: (023) 9251 1416
E-mail: abakey@dhbaccountants.co.uk

Abacus Data Management Ltd, PO Box 67, Teddington, Middlesex, TW11 8QR Tel: (020) 8977 6367 Fax: (020) 8943 9473

Abacus Services, 1 Strand, Torquay, TQ1 2AA Tel: (01803) 211187 Fax: (01803) 290648

Abacus Software Ltd, 6-14 Underwood Street, London, N1 7JQ Tel: (020) 7549 2500 Fax: (020) 7549 2501
E-mail: info@abacusemedia.com

Abba Consultants, Calamare, Holly Close, Woking, Surrey, GU21 7QZ Tel: (01483) 833021 Fax: (01483) 833022

▶ Abbey IT Consultants, Lafone House, 11-13 Leathermarket Street, London, SE1 3HN Tel: (020) 7378 6616

Ability Plus Software (UK) Ltd, 4 King Charles Terr, Sovereign Court, London, E1W 3HL Tel: (020) 7231 1004 Fax: (020) 7231 6310
E-mail: info@ability.com

Abs Ltd, 1 Ridge Close, Hatch Warren, Basingstoke, Hampshire, RG22 4RN Tel: (01256) 357270 Fax: (01256) 301521
E-mail: admin@ABSuk.com

Absolute Computers Ltd, 19 Old High Street, Headington, Oxford, OX3 9HS Tel: (01865) 744115 Fax: (01865) 744155
E-mail: admin@absolute.co.uk

▶ Absolute It Solutions, 22 St. Michaels Road, Woking, Surrey, GU21 5PY Tel: (01483) 834887

Aca Systems Ltd, Sovereign House, Ellen Terrace, Washington, Tyne & Wear, NE37 3AS Tel: 0191-417 3166 Fax: 0191-417 3288

Academy Solutions Ltd, 46 Brasenose Drive, Kidlington, Oxfordshire, OX5 2EQ Tel: (01865) 371012 Fax: (01865) 847276
E-mail: paul.guest@acadsol.co.uk

▶ Acamology, 74 Retallick Meadows, St. Austell, Cornwall, PL25 3BY Tel: (01726) 69001 Fax: (0870) 0519348

Accel, 5 Chickney Rd, Henham, Bishop's Stortford, Herts, CM22 6BE Tel: (01279) 850547

Access Accounting (Scotland) Ltd, The Business Centre, Denside School, Glenogil, Forfar, Angus, DD8 3SQ Tel: (01356) 650222 Fax: (01356) 650322
E-mail: info@access-scotland.co.uk

Access To Data Solutions Ltd, 3 Beech Lees, Farsley, Pudsey, W. Yorkshire, LS28 5JY Tel: 0113-236 1134

Accessible I T Ltd, 9 Rees Drive, Coventry, CV3 6QF Tel: (024) 7669 3901
E-mail: rbs@accessibleit.co.uk

Accord Computer Systems Ltd, 7-9 Union Street, Stratford-upon-Avon, Warwickshire, CV37 6QT Tel: (01789) 415541 Fax: (01789) 414410
E-mail: info@accordltd.co.uk

Accurate Business Solutions Ltd, 80 Peach Street, Wokingham, Berkshire, RG40 1XH Tel: 0118-977 3880 Fax: 0118-977 1260
E-mail: info@accurate.co.uk

Ace Computer Services Ltd, 19 Westerby Lane, Smeeton Westerby, Leicester, LE8 0RA Tel: 0116-279 3673

Ace Systems, 72 Albert Road, Carrickfergus, County Antrim, BT38 8AE Tel: (028) 9336 2266 Fax: (028) 9336 2422
E-mail: info@ace-systems.co.uk

COMPUTER SYSTEMS CONSULTANTS OR SERVICES, SOFTWARE ETC – *continued*

Ace Works, 216 Chorley New Rd, Horwich, Bolton, BL6 5NP Tel: (01204) 668667 Fax: (0870) 845 9049 E-mail: info@aceworks.com

ACI Worldwide Ltd, 27-33 Cookridge Street, Leeds, LS2 3AG Tel: 0113-394 0100 Fax: 0113-394 0129

Actia UK Ltd, Unit 81, Mochdre Industrial Estate, Newtown, Powys, SY16 4LE Tel: (01686) 611150 Fax: (01686) 621068 E-mail: mail@actia.co.uk

Actionwest, 5 Orchard Industrial Estate South, Union Road, Kingsbridge, Devon, TQ7 1EG Tel: (01548) 856696 Fax: (01548) 856616 E-mail: sales@actionwest.co.uk

Activ Computer Services, PO Box 15, York, YO26 9YE Tel: (01423) 331646 Fax: (01423) 331647 E-mail: links@activ.co.uk

Active Data Management, West Malvern Road, Mathon, Malvern, Worcestershire, WR13 5NZ Tel: (01684) 576022 Fax: (01684) 576026 E-mail: info@activedatamanagement.co.uk

Active Logic Ltd, 46 Victoria Road, Penarth, South Glamorgan, CF64 3HY Tel: (029) 2070 2100 E-mail: enquiries@active-logic.co.uk

▶ Active Networks Ltd, Copperfield, Coppice Drive, Wraysbury, Staines, Middlesex, TW19 5JG Tel: (01784) 488420

Actual Systems UK, 9 Bankhead Drive, Edinburgh, EH11 4EJ Tel: 0131-538 8538 Fax: 0131-538 8539

Acumen Agencies, 161 Cregagh Road, Belfast, BT6 0LB Tel: (028) 9080 8150 Fax: (028) 9080 8155 E-mail: sales@acumenagencies.com

Adecs Ltd, 1 Mercia Business Village, Torwood Close, Westwood Business Park, Coventry, CV4 8HX Tel: (024) 7646 4753 Fax: (08453) 109600 E-mail: services@adecs.co.uk

Adelard Computer Consultants, 10 Northampton Square, London, EC1V 0HB Tel: (020) 7490 9450 Fax: (020) 7490 9451 E-mail: sales@adelard.co.uk

Adit Ltd, Tyn Rardd, Dwyran, Llanfairpwllgwyngyll, Gwynedd, LL61 6AJ Tel: (01248) 430075 Fax: (01248) 430771 E-mail: sales@adit.co.uk

Admicra Computer Systems, Unit 5b Factory Lane, Beeston, Nottingham, NG9 4AA Tel: 0115-925 2627 Fax: 0115-925 2626 E-mail: info@admicra.co.uk

▶ Adnett, Butcher Close, Staplehurst, Kent, TN12 0TJ Tel: (01580) 892682 E-mail: sales@adnett.co.uk

▶ Advance U K, 73 Chapel Street, Leigh, Lancashire, WN7 2DA Tel: (01942) 609996 Fax: (01942) 269508 E-mail: sales@advanceuk.com

Advanced Computer Group, The Pentagon Centre, 36 Washington Street, Glasgow, G3 8AZ Tel: 0141-248 4000 Fax: 0141-248 4001

Advanced Computer Installations Ltd, Unit 7 Salford Enterprise Centre, 5 Guide St, Salford, M50 1EW Tel: 0161-737 5654 Fax: 0161-737 5227 E-mail: veronica@acimanchester.co.uk

Advanced Data Management, 1 Candelan Way, High Legh, Knutsford, Cheshire, WA16 6TP Tel: (01925) 758543 Fax: (01925) 757950 E-mail: enquiries@adm-partnership.co.uk

Advanced Digital Technology UK Ltd, Unit 10 Lord Wilmot House, Bristol Road, Bumpers Farm, Chippenham, Wiltshire, SN14 6LH Tel: (01249) 653654 Fax: (01249) 659258

Advanced Expert Systems Ltd, Woburn House, Vernon Gate, Derby, DE1 1UL Tel: (01332) 383521 Fax: (01332) 383532

Advantage Business Group Ltd, East St, Farnham, Surrey, GU9 7TB Tel: (01252) 738500 Fax: (01252) 717065 E-mail: enquiries@advantage-business.co.uk

Advantec Systems Ltd, 39 Westfield Close, Dorridge, Solihull, West Midlands, B93 8DY Tel: (01564) 739134

Advice By Telephone Ltd, 306 St. Marys Lane, Upminster, Essex, RM14 3HL Tel: (01708) 640110 Fax: (01708) 224802 E-mail: admin@advice.uk.com

Aerosystems International Ltd, Turing House, Grovewood Road, Malvern, Worcestershire, WR14 1GD Tel: (01684) 585700 Fax: (01684) 585711

Agarwal Associates, Clockhouse, Partridge Lane, Newdigate, Dorking, Surrey, RH5 5EE Tel: (01306) 631888 Fax: (01306) 631011 E-mail: alokagarwal@nch.it

Ainsdale Computer Consultants Ltd, Goodyear Business Park, New Street, Mawdesley, Ormskirk, Lancashire, L40 2QP Tel: (01704) 823430 Fax: (01704) 823232 E-mail: post@ainsdale-computers.co.uk

Airedale Computer Centre, 33 Station Road, Baildon, Shipley, West Yorkshire, BD17 6HS Tel: (01274) 581777 Fax: (01274) 581777 E-mail: royston.moore@btinternet.com

Albion Computers P.L.C., 112 Strand, London, WC2R 0AG Tel: (020) 7212 9090 Fax: (020) 7212 9091 E-mail: sales@albion.co.uk

Alchemy Plus, Halliday House, Dingwall Business Park, Dingwall, Ross-Shire, IV15 9XL Tel: (01349) 865000 Fax: (01349) 865111 E-mail: info@alchemyplus.com

Alexsys Communications, Manor Farm, High Street, Chewton Mendip, Radstock, BA3 4LL Tel: (01761) 241695 Fax: (01761) 241696 E-mail: enquiries@alexsys.co.uk

Alistair Clark Associates, Rait, Perth, PH2 7RT Tel: (01821) 670570 Fax: (01821) 670570

Alpha Computer Services, Laurel Bank, Chester Road, Kelsall, Tarporley, Cheshire, CW6 0RT Tel: (01829) 759440 Fax: (01829) 741106 E-mail: admin@alphacomputer.uk.com

Alpha Co Consulting Engineers Ltd, 30 Stowell Cresent, Wareham, Dorset, BH20 4PZ Tel: (01929) 551207 Fax: (07802) 431378 E-mail: info@alpha-comp.co.uk

▶ Alpha One Consultants Ltd, 24 Elm Way, Messingham, Scunthorpe, South Humberside, DN17 3UR Tel: (01724) 764892

Alphameric Broadcast Solutions Ltd, Pear Mill Industrial Estate, Stockport Road West, Bredbury, Stockport, Cheshire, SK6 2BP Tel: 0161-476 7770 Fax: 0161-476 7771 E-mail: lynsey.rothwell@alphameric.com

Alpheus Solutions Ltd, 60 Lombard Street, London, EC3V 9EA Tel: (020) 7464 8444 Fax: (020) 7464 8745

Altera Europe Ltd, Holmers Farm Way, High Wycombe, Buckinghamshire, HP12 4XF Tel: (01494) 602000 Fax: (01494) 602001 E-mail: newsroom@altera.com

Altis Consulting Ltd, 11 Thatcham Business Village, Colthrop Way, Thatcham, Berkshire, RG19 4LW Tel: (01635) 867575 Fax: (01635) 867576 E-mail: sales@altisltd.com

▶ Alton It Support Ltd, 51 Greenfields Avenue, Alton, Hampshire, GU34 2EE Tel: (01420) 86315

Altrix Healthcare plc, Garret House, Warrington, WA3 7BP Tel: (01925) 828916 Fax: (01925) 848949

▶ Alver Services Ltd, 1 The Anchorage, Gosport, Hampshire, PO12 1LY Tel: (023) 9252 9191 Fax: (023) 9252 9191

Amac Services Ltd, 82 Ashenground Road, Haywards Heath, West Sussex, RH16 4QB Tel: (01444) 416305

Amdocs, Clarify Court, London Road, Earley, Reading, RG6 1BW Tel: 0118-955 5200 Fax: 0118-955 5201

Amethyst Associates Ltd, The Old Barn, Oak House, Main Road, Farthinghoe, Brackley, Northamptonshire, NN13 5PB Tel: (01295) 714056 Fax: (0870) 1219961 E-mail: geoff.wenmouth@amethystassociates.co.uk

Amfax Ltd, 3 Clump Farm Industrial Estate, Blandford Heights, Blandford Forum, Dorset, DT11 7TE Tel: (01258) 480777 Fax: (01258) 480728 E-mail: sales@amfax.co.uk

AMJ (UK), Epps Buildings, Bridge Road, Ashford, Kent, TN23 1BB Tel: (01233) 663205 Fax: (01233) 664181E-mail: info@amj-uk.com

▶ Ammar Professionals Ltd, Flat 12, Jellicoe House, Osnaburgh Street, London, NW1 3AY Tel: (020) 7387 7600 Fax: (0870) 1323077 E-mail: ammar@btconnect.com

Ammnet Ltd, Wentworth House, 3 Lichfield Road, Burntwood, Staffordshire, WS7 0HQ Tel: (01543) 305133 Fax: (0870) 0547750 E-mail: sales@ammnet.com

Amtec Consulting plc, Millennium Centre, 2 Crosby Way, Farnham, Surrey, GU9 7XX Tel: (01252) 737866 Fax: (01252) 737855 E-mail: post@amtec.co.uk

Amtech Power Software Ltd, Bank House, 171 Midsummer Boulevard, Milton Keynes, MK9 1EB Tel: (01908) 608833 Fax: (01908) 234355 E-mail: sales@amtech-power.co.uk

And Technology Research Ltd, 4 Forest Drive, Theydon Bois, Epping, Essex, CM16 7EY Tel: (01992) 814655 Fax: (01992) 813362

Anderson Ross Associates, Wellhall Road, Hamilton, Lanarkshire, ML3 9BY Tel: (01698) 493420 Fax: (01698) 493423 E-mail: info@andersonross.com

Andrew Charles Associates, 119 Mulberry Road, Northfleet, Gravesend, Kent, DA11 8QA Tel: (01474) 532865 Fax: (01474) 320442 E-mail: enquires@andrewcharles.co.uk

Andrews Computer Services Ltd, Nash House, London Road, Hemel Hempstead, Hertfordshire, HP3 9SR Tel: (01442) 241200 Fax: (01442) 241201 E-mail: admin@andrews-computers.com

Anix Computers Ltd, The Alpha Centre, Armstrong Way, Yate, Bristol, BS37 5NG Tel: (01454) 329555 Fax: (01454) 329666

Anjec Computer Services, The Mansard Suite The Robbins Building, Albert Street, Rugby, Warwickshire, CV21 2AA Tel: (01788) 540484 Fax: (01788) 540493 E-mail: anjec@via-anjec.co.uk

Anodyne Technology, 140 Castellain Mansions, Castellain Road, London, W9 1HB Tel: (020) 7266 5315 Fax: (020) 7266 5315

Ansty Computer Systems, 1 North Cottages, Cuckfield Road, Ansty, Haywards Heath, West Sussex, RH17 5AG Tel: (01444) 455760 Fax: (01444) 458067 E-mail: peterhutchinson@lineone.net

Anton Wylam Personal Computers, 10 Union Place, Tewkesbury, Gloucestershire, GL20 5RE Tel: (01684) 273800

Aonix Europe, Newtown House, Newtown Road, Henley-on-Thames, Oxfordshire, RG9 1HG Tel: (01491) 415000 Fax: (01491) 575033 E-mail: info@aonix.co.uk

Apak Group plc, Apak House Badminton Court, Station Road, Yate, Bristol, BS37 5HZ Tel: (01454) 871000 Fax: (01454) 871199 E-mail: enquiries@apakgroup.com

Applabs Ltd, Preston Technology Centre, Marsh Lane, Preston, PR1 8UQ Tel: (01772) 885850 Fax: (01772) 558881 E-mail: info@isintegration.com

Applications Design Ltd, 91 Melciss Road, Wickersley, Rotherham, South Yorkshire, S66 2BU Tel: (01709) 543025 Fax: (01709) 543025 E-mail: appsdesign@btinternet.com

Applied Computer Solutions Ltd, 2 Thatched Cottages, Longford, Ashbourne, Derbyshire, DE6 3DR Tel: (01335) 330097 E-mail: enquires@acslimited.org

Applied Electronics, Onslow House, Magham Down, Hailsham, East Sussex, BN27 1PL Tel: (01323) 844709 Fax: (01323) 844725

Applied Interactive Ltd, Cranfield Innovation Centre, University Way, Cranfield, Bedford, MK43 0BT Tel: (01234) 756050 Fax: (01234) 756138 E-mail: sales@applied-interactive.co.uk

Applinet, Unit 14 Thatcham Business Village, Colthrop Way, Thatcham, Berkshire, RG19 4LW Tel: (01635) 848900 Fax: (01635) 848920 E-mail: sales@applinet.co.uk

Aquarius Software, The Purlins, Black Robin Lane, Kingston, Canterbury, Kent, CT4 6HR Tel: (01227) 830131 E-mail: aquariussoft@freeuk.com

Aqute Ltd, 500 Chiswick High Road, London, W4 5RG Tel: (020) 8956 2505 Fax: (020) 8956 2504 E-mail: info@aqute.co.uk

Arcas Computing Ltd, 5 Grange Road, Edinburgh, EH9 1UH Tel: 0131-620 8110 Fax: 0131-620 8112 E-mail: sales@arcas.co.uk

Arch Consulting Ltd, The Mews, 1b Elliott Road, London, W4 1PF Tel: (020) 8987 0440 Fax: (020) 8747 8330 E-mail: info@arch.co.uk

Archway Systems Ltd, 31 Parolles Road, London, N19 3RE Tel: (020) 7272 3530 Fax: (020) 7263 1951 E-mail: admin@arsy.co.uk

Arcontech Ltd, 31-35 Kirby Street, London, EC1N 8TE Tel: (020) 7405 2111 Fax: (020) 7831 6667 E-mail: mail@arcontech.com

▶ Argon Computing, 125 Southend Road, Rochford, Essex, SS4 1HX Tel: (01702) 547625 E-mail: sales@argoncomputing.com

▶ Ariser Computer Services, 188 Blythe Road, London, W14 0HD Tel: (020) 7371 2227

Aristotle Corporation Ltd, 6 Hope Street, Edinburgh, EH2 4DB Tel: 0131-220 0420 Fax: 0131-220 1973

Armstrong Laing plc, 25 King Street, Knutsford, Cheshire, WA16 6DW Tel: (01565) 687000 Fax: (01565) 750030

Artemis Corporation, Kingsclere Park, Kingsclere, Newbury, Berkshire, RG20 4SW Tel: (01635) 291800 Fax: (01635) 291801 E-mail: sales@artemiscorp.com

Arun Computer Equipment Ltd, 72-74 Clifton Road, Worthing, West Sussex, BN11 4DP Tel: (01903) 529077 Fax: (01903) 529088 E-mail: sales@aruncomputers.co.uk

Arunday Computer Services, 41 Fairford Cl, Redditch, Worcs, B98 9LU Tel: 01527 63742

Aryan Computer Associates Ltd, 5 Pepper Close, Caterham, Surrey, CR3 6BJ Tel: (01883) 344094 Fax: (01883) 341908

▶ Ash Hill Data, 20 CWRT Pen-Y-Twyn, Dukestown, Tredegar, Gwent, NP22 4DL Tel: (01495) 711422 Fax: (01495) 711439 E-mail: richard@ashhilldata.co.uk

Ash Information Systems Ltd, Mile End Barn, Hemel Hempstead Road, Dagnall, Berkhamsted, Hertfordshire, HP4 1QR Tel: (01442) 842624 Fax: (01442) 842683 E-mail: ash@ashsys.co.uk

Ashlyn Computer Services, The Garth, Doddington Road, Stubton, Newark, Nottinghamshire, NG23 5BX Tel: (01636) 627900 Fax: (01636) 627909 E-mail: sales@ashlyn.co.uk

▶ Aspect It Ltd, County End Business Centre, Jackson Street, Springhead, Oldham, OL4 4TZ Tel: (01457) 872636 Fax: (01457) 872637

Aspentech UK Ltd, Sheraton House, Castle Park, Cambridge, CB3 0AX Tel: (01223) 312220 Fax: (01223) 350653 E-mail: info@aspentech.com

▶ Assign It, 4 Brick Knoll Park, Ashley Road, St. Albans, Hertfordshire, AL1 5UG Tel: (01727) 843888 Fax: (01727) 839999 E-mail: sales@assign-it.co.uk

Associates Partnerships, 59 High Street, Maidstone, Kent, ME14 1SR Tel: (01622) 685588 Fax: (01622) 764660

▶ Assured I T Services Ltd, Head Office 8 Apsley Mill Cottage, London Road, Hemel Hempstead, Hertfordshire, HP3 9QU Tel: (0870) 4608802 Fax: (0870) 7065656 E-mail: sales@assuredit.com

▶ Assured Systems, 154 London Road, Sevenoaks, Kent, TN13 1DJ Tel: (01732) 455911 Fax: (01732) 465018

Astec Computing UK Ltd, Astec House, 10-12 Sedlescombe Road South, St. Leonards-on-Sea, East Sussex, TN38 0TA Tel: (01424) 460721 Fax: (01424) 430888 E-mail: enquiries@asteccomputing.com

Astech Consultants, Albion Street, Chipping Norton, Oxfordshire, OX7 5BL Tel: (01608) 645251 Fax: (01608) 646510 E-mail: info@astech.uk.com

Astley Computer Services, 37 The Farthings, Chorley, Lancashire, PR7 1TP Tel: (01257) 277057 Fax: (01257) 277057 E-mail: ast_com_serve@btinternet.com

Atex Media Command Ltd, Woodside House, Latimer, Chesham, Buckinghamshire, HP5 1UQ Tel: (01494) 546500 Fax: (01494) 766761 E-mail: info@atex.com

W.S. Atkins Ltd, Unit 3 Langstone Business Village, Langstone Park, Langstone, Newport, Gwent, NP18 2LG Tel: (01633) 415500 Fax: (01633) 411211

Aufait Systems, 54 High Street, Hail Weston, St. Neots, Cambridgeshire, PE19 5JW Tel: (01480) 474779 Fax: (01480) 217288 E-mail: aufaitsystems@btinternet.com

Aurion Computer Consultants, Laganside Studios, Ravenhill Business Park, Belfast, BT6 8AW Tel: (028) 9045 5244 Fax: (028) 9045 5244 E-mail: maureen@aurion.co.uk

Automaster UK Ltd, Centaur House, Ancells Road, Fleet, Hampshire, GU51 2UJ Tel: (0845) 4666070 Fax: (0845) 4666080 E-mail: info@automaster.ltd.uk

Avante Digital Ltd, Kirkton Business Centre, 1 Kirk Lane, Livingston Village, Livingston, West Lothian, EH54 7AY Tel: (01506) 419777 Fax: (01506) 415777 E-mail: post@av-digital.com

Avatar Systems, Davis House, 36 Market Place, Brackley, Northamptonshire, NN13 7DP Tel: (01280) 700711 Fax: (01280) 700711 E-mail: avatar.systems@virgin.net

Avington Systems Ltd, PO Box 82, Winchester, Hampshire, SO21 1WA Tel: (01962) 779894 E-mail: info@avington.com

Avon Business Computers, New Road, High Littleton, Bristol, BS39 6JH Tel: (01761) 470543

Avonquest (UK) Ltd, 151 Freston Road, London, W10 6TH Tel: (020) 7221 4600 Fax: (020) 7792 1611 E-mail: jobs@mediagold.com

▶ Awelfor Ltd, 2 Marine Drive, Rhyl, Clwyd, LL18 3AT Tel: (01745) 361801

Axia Distribution Ltd, Axia House, 111 St Albans Road, Watford, WD17 1UH Tel: (01923) 227007 E-mail: sales@axia.co.uk

B C Computing Ltd, 57 Ferrybridge Road, Castleford, West Yorkshire, WF10 4JW Tel: (01977) 667777 Fax: (01977) 667701

B D P Computers & Data Processing Centre, 88-90 Tredworth Road, Gloucester, GL1 4QS Tel: (01452) 381425 Fax: (01452) 414718

B D S Solutions, Heywood House, 12 High Street, Cullompton, Devon, EX15 1AA Tel: (01884) 33221 Fax: (01884) 34555 E-mail: info@bds-solutions.co.uk

B E C Systems Ltd, 11 Glen Grove, East Kilbride, Glasgow, G75 0BG Tel: (01355) 242302 E-mail: sales@becsystems.co.uk

B & G Software Consultancy Ltd, The Barn, Watery Lane, Monmouth, Gwent, NP25 5AT Tel: (01600) 715105 Fax: (01600) 772802 E-mail: info@bandgsoftware.com

B H Associates 2000 Ltd, Cromwell House, Elland Road, Brighouse, West Yorkshire, HD6 2RG Tel: (01756) 700138 Fax: (01422) 371337 E-mail: sales@bhassociates.sagehost.co.uk

B J Computers Ltd, 259 Eversholt Street, London, NW1 1BA Tel: (020) 7383 3444 E-mail: jass@bjcomputers.co.uk

B L Computer Services, McPhail Ho, 1 Alexandra Rd, Clevedon, Avon, BS21 7QE Tel: (01275) 340500 Fax: (01275) 340470 E-mail: admin@blcomp.co.uk

▶ B & M Consultancy, 118 Colinton Mains Drive, Edinburgh, EH13 9BL Tel: 0131-441 9576

B & M Europe Ltd, Heath End House, West Street, Tadley, Hampshire, RG26 3ST Tel: 0118-981 1880 Fax: 0118-981 1881 E-mail: info@bmeurope.com

B R L Consulting Ltd, 1 Amersham Road, Penn Street, Amersham, Buckinghamshire, HP7 0QW Tel: (01494) 716541 Fax: (01494) 716541

B S Group Consultancies, 36 Woodpond Avenue, Hockley, Essex, SS5 4PX Tel: (01702) 204073 Fax: (01702) 200759 E-mail: bob41@onetel.com

B T I Computer Systems UK Ltd, Burnt Meadow Road, Moons Moat North Industrial Estate, Redditch, Worcestershire, B98 9PA Tel: (01527) 598500 Fax: (01527) 598555 E-mail: sales@bticomputer.com

Baldane Ltd, Auchterhouse, Dundee, DD3 0QS Tel: (01382) 320404 Fax: (01382) 320461 E-mail: info@baldane.co.uk

Ballard Chalmers Ltd, 1 Christopher Road, East Grinstead, West Sussex, RH19 3BT Tel: (01342) 410223 Fax: (01342) 410225 E-mail: info@ballardchalmers.com

Baniftec Ltd, Farley Edge, Farley Common, Westerham, Kent, TN16 1UB Tel: (01959) 564526 E-mail: enquiries@baniftec.com

Barking Electronics, 432 Barking Rd, London, E6 2SA Tel: 020 84707722 Fax: 020 84707788

Barnard Mircosystems Ltd, 134 Crouch Hill, London, N8 9DX Tel: (020) 8341 0566 E-mail: enquiries@barnardmicrosystems.com

Barnham Telecottage, 49 Barnham Rd, Barnham, Bognor Regis, W. Sussex, PO22 0ER Tel: (01243) 553725 Fax: (01243) 554898 E-mail: barnham.telecottage@saqnet.co.uk

Barnsley Yesco, 17 Fishdam La, Monk Bretton, Barnsley, S. Yorkshire, S71 2PX Tel: (01226) 200338 Fax: (01226) 200338 E-mail: yesco@computers97.freeserve.co.uk

Barratt Computing Ltd, Larbreck House, Quernmore, Lancaster, LA2 9EF Tel: (01524) 388000 Fax: (01524) 388333 E-mail: enquiries@barcom.co.uk

Barron Mccann Ltd, Meteor Centre, Mansfield Road, Derby, DE21 4SY Tel: (01332) 866500 Fax: (01332) 866501

Base Computer Services Ltd, 154 Eltham Hill, London, SE9 5EA Tel: (020) 8488 4448 Fax: (020) 8488 4449 E-mail: sales@base.uk.com

Basic Strategies Ltd, Network Ho, 222 Ewell Rd, Surbiton, Surrey, KT6 7AF Tel: 020 83954240 Fax: 020 83399550

Batch Control Systems Ltd, Govanhill Workspace, 69 Dixon Road, Glasgow, G42 8AT Tel: 0141-423 0413 Fax: 0141-424 3149 E-mail: sales@bcs2000.co.uk

Adrian Bates Ltd, 10 Curlew Close, Porthcawl, Mid Glamorgan, CF36 3QB Tel: (01656) 785658 Fax: (01656) 785658

COMPUTER SYSTEMS CONSULTANTS OR SERVICES, SOFTWARE ETC – *continued*

▶ Baton Consulting Ltd, 41 Maple Crescent, Penketh, Warrington, WA5 2LE Tel: (01925) 790111 Fax: (01925) 790101

▶ Bde Group, Blackpole Trading Estate West, Worcester, WR3 8ZP Tel: (0870) 1287800 Fax: (01905) 756574 E-mail: sales@bdegroup.co.uk

▶ Beckingham Solutions, Walsall Road, Sutton Coldfield, West Midlands, B74 4NP Tel: 0121-580 8669

▶ Benefit 2 Business, 2A Red Lions Business Centre, Burnham Road, Latchingdon, Chelmsford, CM3 6JH Tel: 01621 743699 E-mail: info@benefit2business.com

Bentley Computer Consultants, Lower Bush, Stoke St. Milborough, Ludlow, Shropshire, SY8 2ES Tel: (01584) 823667 Fax: (01584) 823667 E-mail: tonybentley@hotmail.com

▶ Betta Solutions Limited, 86, Enfield Road, Redditch, Worcs, B97 5NH Tel: (01527) 541171

Bicel Industries Ltd, 64 Sandown Avenue, Swindon, SN3 1QQ Tel: (01793) 491988 Fax: (01793) 692462

Bidmuthin Technologies, Dudley House, 31 Lower Road, Harrow, Middlesex, HA2 0DE Tel: (020) 8866 9988 Fax: (020) 8422 9555 E-mail: info@bidmuthin.co.uk

Birlasoft UK Ltd, Cromwell House, 142 High Street, Stevenage, Hertfordshire, SG1 3HN Tel: (01438) 350270 Fax: (01438) 749309 E-mail: corp@birlasoft.co.uk

Bishop Consultancy, 639 Galleywood Road, Chelmsford, CM2 8BT Tel: (01245) 346985 Fax: (01245) 490736 E-mail: enquiries@bishop-consultancy.com

Bitco Systems Ltd, 46 Bankfield Avenue, Stockport, Cheshire, SK4 2JH Tel: 0161-442 8178 Fax: 0161-442 8178 E-mail: mark@bitco.co.uk

Bits N Bytes Computer Solutions Ltd, 22-24 Ravendale St North, Scunthorpe, South Humberside, DN15 6NJ Tel: (01724) 282627 Fax: (01724) 280605 E-mail: sales@bitsnbytes.co.uk

▶ Bits & PC's, High Cross Street, St. Austell, Cornwall, PL25 4AB Tel: (01726) 76999

Bitwise Ltd, Crescent House, Carnegie Campus, Dunfermline, Fife, KY11 8GR Tel: (01383) 625151 Fax: (01383) 625152 E-mail: admin@bitwise.co.uk

BJL Business Consultants, The Old Rectory, St Marys Lane, Claxby, Market Rasen, Lincolnshire, LN8 3YX Tel: (01673) 828345 Fax: (01673) 828345

Black Box Computers, 2 Norfolk Street, Lancaster, LA1 2BW Tel: (01524) 389400 Fax: (01524) 62925

Blackburn Starling & Co. Ltd, Queens Drive, Nottingham, NG2 3AY Tel: 0115-986 6331 Fax: 0115-986 0301 E-mail: sales@blackburn-starling.co.uk

Blackwood S Consultants Ltd, 15 Glengarry Crescent, Falkirk, FK1 5UD Tel: (01324) 630043

Blade Interactive Studios, Suite A, Great Northern Warehouse, Deansgete Mews, Manchester, M3 4EN Tel: 0161-839 6622 Fax: 0161-839 6688 E-mail: info@bladeinteractive.com

Blakelan Communications Ltd, Railway Cottage, Mill Road, Brighton, BN1 8ZF Tel: (01273) 564092 Fax: (01273) 564111 E-mail: mike.blakeman@blakelan.com

Bleep Computing Ltd, 7 St. Saviours Wharf, 23 Mill Street, London, SE1 2BE Tel: (020) 7717 0200 Fax: (020) 7717 0201 E-mail: jay@bleep2000-demon.co.uk

Blenheim Systems, 31 Blenheim Gardens, Wembley, Middlesex, HA9 7NP Tel: (020) 8904 9317 Fax: (07092) 215433 E-mail: enq@blenheim-systems.com

Blue Curve, 17-29 Sun Street, London, EC2M 2PT Tel: (020) 7392 1390

Bom Group Ltd, Clue House, Petherton Road, Bristol, BS14 9BZ Tel: (01275) 890100 Fax: (01275) 890111 E-mail: info@bom.co.uk

Bond International Software Ltd, Courtlands, Parklands Avenue, Goring-by-Sea, Worthing, West Sussex, BN12 4NG Tel: (01903) 707070 Fax: (01903) 707080 E-mail: sales@bond.co.uk

Boxclever, The Mount, Selby Road, Garforth, Leeds, LS25 2AQ Tel: 0113-286 0795 Fax: 0113-286 4525 E-mail: sales@boxcleverbrokers.com

Brainsmead Ltd, Tangley Brainsmead Close, Cuckfield, Haywards Heath, West Sussex, RH17 5EZ Tel: (01444) 441951 E-mail: richard@brainsmead.co.uk

Brainstorm Computing Ltd, 3 White Hart Close, Sevenoaks, Kent, TN13 1RH Tel: (01732) 465786 E-mail: mark@brainstorm-uk.co.uk

Bransom Retail Systems Ltd, The Old Church, 48 Verulam Road, St. Albans, Hertfordshire, AL3 4DH Tel: (01727) 810509 Fax: (01727) 854607 E-mail: rob@bransom.co.uk

Bridge House Services Ltd, Rectory House, Maltings Lane, Ingham, Bury St. Edmunds, Suffolk, IP31 1NS Tel: (01284) 728100 Fax: (0870) 1671963

▶ Bright New World, 3 Woodbrook Crescent, Billericay, Essex, CM12 0EQ Tel: (01277) 656200 Fax: (01277) 653342

Britelec Network Services Ltd, 39 London Road, Braintree, Essex, CM7 2LD Tel: (01376) 552323 Fax: (01376) 340006

Brittanic Software Services Ltd, 2 Mount Pleasant Rd, Aldershot, Hants, GU12 4NL Tel: 01252 334469 Fax: 01252 334434

Broadband Connections Ltd, 6-8 Oakway, London, SW20 9JE Tel: (020) 8543 5228 Fax: (020) 8241 2061

Broadskill Ltd, Hinderton Grange, Quarry Road, Neston, CH64 7UD Tel: 0151-336 8899 Fax: 0151-336 7799 E-mail: admin@broadskill.com

▶ Broch Computer Services, 21 Commerce Street, Fraserburgh, Aberdeenshire, AB43 9AQ Tel: (01346) 512754

Bronzefern Ltd, 9 Orchard Close, Gravenhurst, Bedford, MK45 4JF Tel: (01462) 711400 Fax: (01462) 713162 E-mail: john@bronzefern.demon.co.uk

Brooks Associates, Honeyhill, Bismore, Eastcombe, Stroud, Gloucestershire, GL6 7DG Tel: (01452) 770060 Fax: (01452) 770078 E-mail: admin@brooksassociates.com

Brunel Computer Services Ltd, 87 - 89 Prince Avenue, Southend-on-Sea, SS2 6RL Tel: (01702) 302000 Fax: (01702) 305000 E-mail: brunel@email.com

Bta Ltd, 100 The High Street, Wandsworth, London, SW18 4LA Tel: (020) 8871 4240 Fax: (020) 8871 4584 E-mail: info@bta.com

Burns E-commerce Solutions, Mansion House, Manchester Road, Altrincham, Cheshire, WA14 4RW Tel: 0161-929 8673 Fax: 0161-929 8674 E-mail: info@burnsecs.com

Business Information Technology Services Ltd, 75 Longford Road, Coventry, CV6 6DY Tel: (024) 7683 5600 Fax: (024) 7683 5601 E-mail: bits@b-i-t-s.co.uk

Business Insights Group Ltd, Brandiston House, 98 High Street, Ingatestone, Essex, CM4 0BA Tel: (01277) 355755 Fax: (01277) 355753 E-mail: info@digroup.co.uk

Business Interface Ltd, 7 Garden Court, Wheathampstead, St. Albans, Hertfordshire, AL4 8RE Tel: (01582) 834477 Fax: (01582) 833200 E-mail: info@business-interface.co.uk

Business Management Promotions Ltd, Lower Weaven, Little Dewchurch, Hereford, HR2 6QB Tel: (01432) 840456 Fax: (01432) 840450 E-mail: bmpltd@ticali.co.uk

Business Micros, Main Street, Penpont, Thornhill, Dumfriesshire, DG3 4BP Tel: (01848) 330588 Fax: (01848) 331531 E-mail: info@businessmicros.co.uk

Business Numbers Ltd, 2 Magnolia Wharf, Strand On The Green, London, W4 3NY Tel: (020) 8995 8316 Fax: (020) 8995 8316

Business Resource, 30 High Street, Winterbourne, Bristol, BS36 1JN Tel: (01454) 250758 Fax: (01454) 858125

Byte Technology, 12-13 The Street, Yatesbury, Calne, Wiltshire, SN11 8YG Tel: (01672) 539559

Bytes Technology, Matrix House, North Fourth Street, Milton Keynes, MK9 1NJ Tel: (08707) 774646 Fax: (08707) 771021

C B R P Ltd, 20 Fernwood Drive, Radcliffe-on-Trent, Nottingham, NG12 1AA Tel: 0115-933 6123 Fax: 0115-841 3328 E-mail: enquiries@cbrp.co.uk

C B W Associates Ltd, 15 Station Rise, Marlow, Buckinghamshire, SL7 1EJ Tel: (01628) 482282 E-mail: bm.watson@btclick.com

C C S IT Ltd, The Octagon, Middleborough, Colchester, CO1 1RA Tel: (01206) 216200 Fax: (01206) 767770 E-mail: info@ccsit.co.uk

▶ C C S (Leeds) Ltd, 31 Birchfields Avenue, Leeds, LS14 2HT Tel: 0113-294 6699 Fax: 0113-273 0058

C D R Computing Ltd, 12-14 Thames Street, Sunbury-on-Thames, Middlesex, TW16 5QP Tel: (01252) 838400 Fax: (0845) 3452396 E-mail: support@crdcomputing.com

C F P Software, Propser House, Cardrew Industrial Estate, Redruth, Cornwall, TR15 1SS Tel: (01209) 314371 Fax: (01209) 314368 E-mail: general@cfp-software.co.uk

C G T Ltd, 314 Midsummer Boulevard, Milton Keynes, MK9 2UB Tel: (01908) 690361 Fax: (01908) 669922 E-mail: sales@cgt.co.uk

C J Consulting Ltd, 1 Hyde Drive, Worsley, Manchester, M28 3SG Tel: 0161-703 9972 E-mail: sales@cjconsulting.co.uk

C J E Micros Ltd, 78 Brighton Road, Worthing, West Sussex, BN11 2EN Tel: (01903) 523222 Fax: (01903) 523679 E-mail: sales@cjemicros.co.uk

C J G Consultants Ltd, 21e Heathmans Road, Parsons Green, London, SW6 4TJ Tel: (020) 7371 8889 Fax: (020) 7371 9998

▶ C K S Consulting Ltd, Regent House, Beam Heath Way, Nantwich, Cheshire, CW5 6PQ Tel: (01270) 619571 Fax: (0871) 2360387 E-mail: sales@cksconsulting.com

▶ C M R Intech, 124 Churchill Road, Bicester, Oxfordshire, OX26 4XD Tel: (01869) 248400

C P S, Drury Lane, St. Leonards-on-Sea, East Sussex, TN38 9BA Tel: (01424) 442663 Fax: (01424) 433835

C Pac, 33a Morland Way, Nelson Park, Cramlington, Northumberland, NE23 1WE Tel: 0191-491 0405 Fax: 0191-491 0465 E-mail: sales@c-pac.co.uk

▶ C S D, 10 New Road, Rayne, Braintree, Essex, CM77 6TG Tel: (01376) 340240 Fax: (01376) 550853E-mail: info@csd-it.co.uk

C S T Group Ltd, 94 Lewes Road, Brighton, BN2 3QA Tel: (01273) 621393 Fax: (01273) 621390 E-mail: info@cst-group.com

C T A Services, 1 Drake Road, Newport, Isle of Wight, PO30 1EQ Tel: (01983) 524129 Fax: (01983) 528001 E-mail: sales@ctaservices.co.uk

C Ways, Lora House, Wykeham, Scarborough, North Yorkshire, YO13 9QP Tel: (0870) 3502920 Fax: (0870) 3502919 E-mail: info@c-ways.co.uk

C&D, 2a Hoghatch Lane, Farnham, Surrey, GU9 0BY Tel: (01252) 714956

Cabrio Management Services, 6 Ash Meadow, Willesborough, Ashford, Kent, TN24 0LW Tel: (01233) 623230 E-mail: enquiries@cabrio.co.uk

Caci Consulting, Manor Court Yard, Grateley, Andover, Hampshire, SP11 8LE Tel: (01264) 889845 Fax: (01264) 889846 E-mail: sales@imaj.co.uk

CAD Academy Ltd, Sherwood House, Gregory Boulevard, Nottingham, NG7 6LB Tel: 0115-969 1114 Fax: 0115-969 1115 E-mail: info@cadacademy.co.uk

▶ Callidus Computer Centre, 91 Pall Mall, Leigh-on-Sea, Essex, SS9 1RF Tel: (01702) 478600 Fax: (01702) 479122 E-mail: enquirer@caladercomputercentre.com

Caltec Publications Ltd, Petticoat Court, Strait Bargate, Boston, Lincolnshire, PE21 6EE Tel: (01205) 358877 Fax: (01205) 359977 E-mail: sales@caltec.co.uk

▶ Cambridge Online Systems Ltd, 163 Milton Road, Cambridge, CB4 0GP Tel: (01223) 422600 Fax: (01223) 422601 E-mail: enquiries@cosl.co.uk

Cameleon Systems, Cuckoo Lane, Pinchbeck, Spalding, Lincolnshire, PE11 3XT Tel: (01775) 680481 E-mail: martin@chameleon-systems.net

▶ Camwood, 5-25, Scrutton Street, London, EC2A 4HJ Tel: (020) 7426 9700 Fax: (020) 7749 1201

Cantab Millennium Ltd, 95 Mill Road, Cambridge, CB1 2AW Tel: (01223) 322306 Fax: (01223) 322816 E-mail: cantab.millennium@virgin.net

Cap Gemini, 1 Forge End, Woking, Surrey, GU21 6DB Tel: (01483) 764764 Fax: (01483) 786161 E-mail: sales@uk.ggey.com

Cap Gemini Ernst & Young, 36 South Gyle Cresent, Edinburgh, EH12 9EB Tel: 0131-339 9339 Fax: 0131-200 3700 E-mail: sales@uk.cgey.com

Capita Business Services Ltd, Kemp House, Cumnor Hill, Cumnor, Oxford, OX2 9PH Tel: (01865) 861300 Fax: (01865) 861301

R.S. Capp Ltd, Masters House, Guildford Road, Westcott, Dorking, Surrey, RH4 3NG Tel: (01306) 887785 Fax: (01306) 887800 E-mail: info@rscapp.ltd.uk

Capstone Systems, Oak Mead, Honington, Bury St. Edmunds, Suffolk, IP31 1RE Tel: (01359) 268711 Fax: (01359) 268870 E-mail: dcg@capstonesystems.co.uk

Cardium Solutions, Unit 4 Dominion Court, Billington Road, Burnley, Lancashire, BB11 5UB Tel: (01282) 425111 Fax: (01282) 425444 E-mail: info@cardium.co.uk

Career Vision Ltd, Unit 3-4 Brickfield Business Centre, 60 Manchester Road, Northwich, Cheshire, CW9 7LS Tel: (0870) 0116713 Fax: (01606) 836977 E-mail: hq@careervision.co.uk

Carl Communications Ltd, 84 Beal Lane, Shaw, Oldham, OL2 8PH Tel: (01706) 292700 Fax: (01706) 880800 E-mail: sales@carlcomms.co.uk

▶ Kennedy Carter Ltd, Hatchlands, East Clandon, Guildford, Surrey, GU4 7SJ Tel: (01483) 226180 Fax: (01483) 226199 E-mail: sales@kc.com

Castlepoint Associates Ltd, Castle Point House 180 Kiln Road, Benfleet, Essex, SS7 1SU Tel: (01702) 558165 Fax: (01702) 552550 E-mail: sales@castle-point-computers.co.uk

CDC Software, 7 Rushmills, Northampton, NN4 7YB Tel: (01604) 630050 Fax: (01604) 630495

CDM Software Services Ltd, The Business Centre, Edward Street, Redditch, Worcestershire, B97 6HA Tel: (01527) 68688 Fax: (01527) 68816 E-mail: support@cdmsoftware.co.uk

Cedalion Ltd, Great Michael House, 14 Links Place, Edinburgh, EH6 7EZ Tel: 0131-477 7741 Fax: 0131-477 7742 E-mail: info@cedalion.co.uk

Cedar Systems Ltd, 2440 The Quadrant, Aztec West, Almondsbury, Bristol, BS32 4AQ Tel: (01454) 878708 Fax: (01454) 878608 E-mail: cedar@cedar.co.uk

Cellar Systems Ltd, 7 Grange Mills, Weir Road, London, SW12 0NE Tel: (020) 8673 5104 Fax: (020) 8673 2649

Central Computer Corporation (UK) Ltd, 32 St. Peters Street, London, N1 8JT Tel: (020) 7454 1222 Fax: (0870) 2408871 E-mail: info@ccc-uk.net

Centralis Ltd, Centralis House Upper Wawensmoor, Wawensmere Road Wootton Wawen, Wootton Wawen, Henley-in-Arden, West Midlands, B95 6BS Tel: (01564) 795911 Fax: (01564) 795912 E-mail: recruitment@centralis.co.uk

Centrix Networking Ltd, Centrix House, Oxford Road, Newbury, Berkshire, RG14 1PD Tel: (01635) 239800 Fax: (01635) 239801 E-mail: sales@centrix.co.uk

Century Business Systems, 19-21 Mid Stocket Road, Aberdeen, AB15 5JL Tel: (01224) 644064 Fax: (01224) 643407 E-mail: info@century.uk.net

Century Computers UK Ltd, 48 Barry Road, Barry, South Glamorgan, CF63 1BA Tel: (01446) 410070 Fax: 01446 410070

Century IT Group, 88 Watling Street, Radlett, Hertfordshire, WD7 7AB Tel: (01923) 856590 Fax: (01923) 853025 E-mail: info@century-networks.co.uk

Channel Partners Ltd, Albury Park, Albury, Guildford, Surrey, GU5 9BH Tel: (01483) 205011 Fax: (01483) 205022 E-mail: astbury@channelp.co.uk

Chaplin Computer Consultants, 331 Walsall Road, Great Wyrley, Walsall, WS6 6DR Tel: (01922) 411117 Fax: (01922) 411001 E-mail: chris@ccc1.demon.co.uk

Chapman Marsden Partnership, 1 West Street, Welford, Northampton, NN6 6HU Tel: (01858) 575123

Chartwell Systems, Malens, Beacon Gardens, Crowborough, East Sussex, TN6 1BG Tel: (01892) 669597 Fax: (01892) 669597 E-mail: chartwell.sys@btconnect.com

Charybdis Ltd, The Cowshed Strelley Hall, Main St, Strelley, Nottingham, NG8 6PE Tel: 0115-942 6962

Check Tek Ltd, 38-42 Newport Street, Swindon, SN1 3DR Tel: (01793) 480022 Fax: (01793) 480066 E-mail: sales@check-tek.co.uk

Checkpoint Computing Ltd, 2 Millfield, Lambourn, Hungerford, Berkshire, RG17 8YQ Tel: (01488) 71467 Fax: (01488) 71467

Chelton Desant Communications Ltd, Emblem House, Pynes Hill, Exeter, EX2 5BA Tel: (01392) 667777 Fax: (01392) 667778 E-mail: info@whiskyalpha.com

▶ Cheshire IT Services, 7 Holmes Chapple Road, Sproston, Crewe, CW4 7LW Tel: (01606) 841577 Fax: (01606) 841577

Chips Computers, Stall 29, Duke Street, Barrow-in-Furness, Cumbria, LA14 1HU Tel: (01229) 822115 Fax: (01229) 822115

Christchurch Computer Centre, 2-4 Fairmile Parade, Fairmile Road, Christchurch, Dorset, BH23 2LP Tel: (01202) 486338 Fax: (0845) 8622661 E-mail: sales@c-c-c.co.uk

Ciber UK Ltd, Sketchley Meadows Business Park, 2 Watling Drive, Hinckley, Leicestershire, LE10 3EY Tel: (01455) 898800 Fax: (0870) 0000205 E-mail: enquiries@c.co.uk

Cifer Data Systems Ltd, 1 Main Street, West Wilts Trading Estate, Westbury, Wiltshire, BA13 4JU Tel: (01373) 824129 Fax: (01373) 824127 E-mail: sales@cifer.co.uk

Cing Technologies Ltd, 3 Malt House Cottages, 31 Byfield Road, Chipping Warden, Banbury, Oxfordshire, OX17 1LE Tel: (01295) 660682 E-mail: nigel.galletly@cingtech.com

Citrix Systems Research and Development Ltd, Venture House, Cambourne Business Park, Cambourne, Cambridge, CB23 6DW Tel: (01954) 283600 Fax: (01954) 283601

Citrus Lime Ltd, County Square, Ulverston, Cumbria, LA12 7AL Tel: (01229) 588628 Fax: (0870) 7065088 E-mail: sales@citrus-lime.com

Civica Financial Systems Ltd, Plain Tree Crescent, Feltham, Middlesex, TW13 7DT Tel: (020) 8844 2141 Fax: (020) 8751 4386 E-mail: enquiries@civica.co.uk

Civica UK Ltd, Castlegate House, Castlegate Drive, Dudley, West Midlands, DY1 4TD Tel: (01384) 453400 Fax: (01384) 453600

Clark Computer & Management Services Ltd, 6-8 High Street, Shoreham-by-Sea, West Sussex, BN43 5DA Tel: (01273) 454064 Fax: (01273) 440515

Martin Clark Consultants, Trendle Cottage, Trendal Street, Sherborne, Dorset, DT9 3NT Tel: (01935) 815777 Fax: (0870) 1360933 E-mail: victor@cahor.plus.com

Clarke Computer Systems, 43 Cannock Road, Burntwood, Staffordshire, WS7 0BL Tel: (01543) 670756 Fax: (01543) 670756 E-mail: info@clarkecomputers.co.uk

Class Business Systems Ltd, 77 Yew Tree Road, Ormskirk, Lancashire, L39 1RY Tel: (01695) 579988 E-mail: enquiries@classbusiness.uk.com

▶ Clear I T, 328 Meanwood Road, Leeds, LS7 2JE Tel: 0113-200 7500 Fax: 0113-200 7508

Clearview Computers, 1A Parklands Avenue, Billingham, Cleveland, TS23 1DZ Tel: (01642) 868690 Fax: (01642) 868691 E-mail: clearviewcomputers@hotmail.co.uk

Clearwater Consultancy Ltd, 18 St Georges Street, Chorley, Lancashire, PR7 2AA Tel: (01257) 272730 Fax: (01257) 272731 E-mail: info@clearwater-consultancy.co.uk

Clerkdrive Ltd, 3 Tolliday Close, Wivenhoe, Colchester, CO7 9SL Tel: (01206) 827676

Clicksoftware Europe Ltd, 65 New Cavendish Street, London, W1G 7LS Tel: (01753) 701066 Fax: (01753) 553127

Client Management Solutions, Avonmore, Wilmslow Road, Alderley Edge, Cheshire, SK9 7QW Tel: (01625) 585050

Cliff Technologies, Pentlandfield Business Park, Roslin, Midlothian, EH25 9RE Tel: 0131-448 2006 Fax: 0131-448 2006

Clik Ltd, The Tobacco Factory, Raleigh Road, Bristol, BS3 1TF Tel: 0117-902 2012 Fax: 0117-902 2010

Harold Cloutt Associates Ltd, PO Box 87, Battle, East Sussex, TN33 9XR Tel: (01424) 838829 Fax: (0870) 1365618 E-mail: cloutt.hr@bcs.org.uk

Clover Consultancy, 21 The Crescent, Taunton, Somerset, TA1 4EB Tel: (01823) 336220 Fax: (01823) 270105 E-mail: info@cloveruk.net

Club Systems (International) Ltd, Club House, 34-36 Fairacres Road, High Lane, Stockport, Cheshire, SK6 8JQ Tel: (01663) 766999 Fax: (01663) 762499 E-mail: sales@club2000.co.uk

Coalesence, 9-10 St. Andrews Square, Edinburgh, EH2 2AF Tel: (0870) 0439901 Fax: 0131-718 6100E-mail: info@edincc.co.uk

Coates Consulting, Lower Flat, 126 Main Street, Lower Largo, Leven, Fife, KY8 6BP Tel: (01333) 329118 Fax: (01333) 329118

COMPUTER SYSTEMS CONSULTANTS OR SERVICES, SOFTWARE ETC – *continued*

Cobham Computer Systems Ltd, 56-58 Smithbrook Kiln, Cranleigh, Surrey, GU6 8JJ Tel: (01483) 275515 Fax: (01483) 277067 E-mail: sales@cobhamsystems.co.uk

Cobweb Computers, 471 Buxton Road, Stockport, Cheshire, SK2 7HE Tel: 0161-484 0100

Code Masters Software Co. Ltd, Lower Farm, Stoneythorpe, Southam, Warwickshire, CV47 2DL Tel: (01926) 814132 Fax: (01926) 817595 E-mail: enquiries@codemasters.com

Codebyte Ltd, 9 Belleisle, Purley on Thames, Reading, RG8 8AP Tel: 0118-941 6244

Codel Computer Systems, 71 St. Helens Road, Swansea, SA1 4BG Tel: (01792) 654154 Fax: (01792) 644392 E-mail: info@codelsoftware.com

Codis Ltd, 38-44 St Anns Road, Harrow, Middlesex, HA1 1LA Tel: (020) 8861 0610 Fax: (020) 8515 7049 E-mail: codis@codis.co.uk

Cognitive Network Solutions Ltd, High Street, Lye, Stourbridge, West Midlands, DY9 8LX Tel: (01384) 340666 Fax: (01384) 350666

Coherent Technology Ltd, 33 Belgrade Road, London, N16 8DH Tel: (020) 7690 7075 Fax: (020) 7923 0110

Colmi Ltd, The Brackens, London Road, Ascot, Berkshire, SL5 8BE Tel: (01344) 885050 Fax: (01344) 884141

Colophon Corporate Ltd, 59 Churchfield Road, Acton, London, W3 6AU Tel: (020) 8992 2555 Fax: (020) 8993 4598

Comapex, The Glebe, Culsalmond, Insch, Aberdeenshire, AB52 6UJ Tel: 01464 841209 Fax: 01464 841241

Combase Information Systems, 5 Buckingham Road, Cheadle Hulme, Cheadle, Cheshire, SK8 5EG Tel: 0161-283 1813 Fax: 0161-486 0779 E-mail: info@combase.co.uk

Combined Office System Services, PO Box 31, Hemel Hempstead, Hertfordshire, HP3 0JA Tel: (01442) 834216 Fax: (01442) 831352 E-mail: info@combinedoffice.co.uk

Comcare Technology Ltd, Anglo House, Chapel Road, Manchester, M22 4JN Tel: 0161-902 0330 Fax: 0161-946 0126 E-mail: info@comcare.co.uk

Comcen Computer Supplies Ltd, 1 York Place, Leeds, LS1 2DS Tel: 0113-234 5000 Fax: 0113-234 2757 E-mail: leeds@comcen.co.uk

Comino Services P.L.C, 11th Floor Amp House, Dingwall Road, Croydon, CR0 2LX Tel: (08708) 466111 Fax: (08708) 466888

Commonsense Computing Ltd, East Furlong Farmhouse, Littleham, Bideford, Devon, EX39 5HW Tel: (01237) 474795 Fax: (01237) 421216

Communicating Ltd, Incom House, 370 Old Street, London, EC1V 9LT Tel: (020) 7613 4747 Fax: (020) 7353 4949

Communication Technology 2000, Hardy Street, Eccles, Manchester, M30 7NB Tel: 0161-789 0222 Fax: 0161-788 0111 E-mail: sales@commtech2000.co.uk

Communications Software Airline Systems Ltd, 8 The Centre, Church Road, Colchester, CO5 0HF Tel: (01621) 817425 Fax: (01621) 817262 E-mail: info@commsoft.co.uk

Compaq Ltd, 50 The Highlands, Edgware, Middlesex, HA8 5HL Tel: (020) 8381 1180 Fax: (020) 8621 3050 E-mail: sales@netlineltd.co.uk

Compelsolve Ltd, Bishops Court, Solihull Parkway, Birmingham Business Park, Birmingham, B37 7YD Tel: 0121-329 0200 Fax: 0121-329 0201 E-mail: birmingham.reception@compelsolve.com

Compex Development & Marketing Ltd, Century House, The Lake, Northampton, NN4 7HD Tel: (01604) 233333 Fax: (01604) 233334 E-mail: sales@compexdm.co.uk

Compliant Business Systems Ltd, PO Box 25, King's Lynn, Norfolk, PE30 4AR Tel: (01553) 660500 Fax: (01553) 660500 E-mail: mail@compliant.co.uk

Component Source, 30 Greyfriars Road, Reading, RG1 1PE Tel: 0118-958 1111 Fax: 0118-958 9999 E-mail: sales@componentsource.com

Compserve Ltd, 130 Cowley Road, Cambridge, CB4 0DL Tel: (01223) 425777 Fax: (01223) 424387 E-mail: info@compserve.co.uk

Compsoft plc, Equinox House, Oriel Court, Alton, Hampshire, GU34 2YT Tel: (01420) 89545 Fax: (01420) 81444 E-mail: sales@compsoft.co.uk

Compucorp Ltd, Unit 37 Watford Metro Centre, Dwight Road, Watford, WD18 9SB Tel: (01923) 220121 E-mail: info@compucorp.co.uk

Compunet Technology Ltd, 14 Carolina Place, Finchampstead, Wokingham, Berkshire, RG40 4PQ Tel: 0118-973 0584 E-mail: sales@compunet-technology.co.uk

Computer Associates UK plc, Ditton Park, Riding Court Road, Datchet, Slough, SL3 9LL Tel: (01753) 577733 Fax: (01753) 825464

Computer Base Ltd, 21 Market Avenue, Plymouth, PL1 1PG Tel: (01752) 672128 Fax: (01752) 668490 E-mail: sales@computerbase.co.uk

Computer Communications Systems Consulting Ltd, 35 Thurloe Street, London, SW7 2LQ Tel: (020) 7581 5400 Fax: (020) 7584 4319 E-mail: enq@compcom.co.uk

Computer Consultancy Group Ltd, Cathedral House, Beacon Street, Lichfield, Staffordshire, WS13 7AA Tel: (01543) 410498 Fax: (01543) 254307

Computer Consultants, 22a Bellside Road, Cleland, Motherwell, Lanarkshire, ML1 5NP Tel: (01698) 861849 Fax: (01698) 861326

Computer Consultants Ltd, Guild Street, Stratford-upon-Avon, Warwickshire, CV37 6RP Tel: (01789) 261200 Fax: (01789) 262525 E-mail: sales@cclnet.co.uk

Computer Help, 4 Roslyn Gardens, Llandudno, Gwynedd, LL30 1BS Tel: (01492) 871290 Fax: (01492) 871997 E-mail: y2000pc@aol.com

Computer Hospital, 7 Kings Parade, King St, Stanford-le-Hope, Essex, SS17 0HR Tel: (01375) 643690

Computer Maintenance Cost Control, Windsor Bridge Works, Windsor Bridge Road, Bath, BA2 3DT Tel: (01225) 426066 E-mail: mail@cmcc.co.uk

The Computer Partnership Ltd, Berwick House, 8-10 Knoll Rise, Orpington, Kent, BR6 0EJ Tel: (01689) 898000 Fax: (01689) 898089 E-mail: marketing@tcplifesystems.com

Computer Performance International Ltd, Outwoods, Oxford Road, Gerrards Cross, Buckinghamshire, SL9 7PU Tel: (01753) 890808 Fax: (01753) 890918 E-mail: mail@cpiuk.co.uk

Computer Repair Centre, 32 The Avenue, St. Pauls Cray, Orpington, Kent, BR5 3DJ Tel: (020) 8556 5331 Fax: (020) 8556 8890

Computer Research Consultants Ltd, 9 Duke Street, Alderley Edge, Cheshire, SK9 7HX Tel: (01625) 582228 Fax: (01993) 822701 E-mail: sales@crc-computeraudit.co.uk

Computer Sciences Corporation, Bristol Data Centre, Station Road, Kingswood, Bristol, BS15 4NR Tel: 0117-991 2600 Fax: 0117-991 2650

Computer Sciences Corporation, Euxton House, Euxton Lane, Chorley, Lancashire, PR7 6FE Tel: (01257) 265507 Fax: (01257) 242609

Computer Software Group Plc, Merchants House, Wapping Wharf, Bristol, BS1 4RW Tel: 0117-926 6281 Fax: 0117-925 1330

Computer Support Services, 8 Baker Street, Rochester, Kent, ME1 3DW Tel: (01634) 407462 Fax: (01634) 409568 E-mail: tony@pobgee.demon.co.uk

Computer Systems (Ireland) Ltd, Old Crow Building, Glen Road, Comber, Newtownards, County Down, BT23 5EL Tel: (028) 9187 3700 Fax: (028) 9087 4421 E-mail: cfiltd@btconnect.com

Computer Systems Support, 74 Eglinton Avenue, Guisborough, Cleveland, TS14 7BX Tel: (01287) 610433 Fax: (01287) 610438 E-mail: info@computersystemssupport.co.uk

Computer Technocentre Ltd, 182 High Road Leytonstone, London, E11 3HU Tel: (020) 8519 9052 Fax: (020) 8519 9052 E-mail: isrealctc@aol.co

Computer Village, 76 Lorne Road, Bath, BA2 3BZ Tel: (01225) 405111 Fax: (01225) 466665 E-mail: sales@computervillage.biz

Computeraid Ltd, Neptune Point, Nettlefold Road, Cardiff, CF24 5JQ Tel: (029) 2066 4285 Fax: (029) 2045 5515 E-mail: training@computeraidwales.com

Computeraid Ltd, The Innovation Centre Swansea University, Singleton Park, Swansea, SA2 8PP Tel: (01792) 610550 Fax: (01792) 610560 E-mail: computeraid@computeraidwales.com

Computerisation Ltd, Washington Chambers, Stanwell Road, Penarth, South Glamorgan, CF64 2AF Tel: (029) 2071 2664 Fax: (029) 2071 2997 E-mail: admin@computerisation.co.uk

Computerlinks, Suffolk House, Newmarket, Suffolk, CB8 7AN Tel: (01638) 569600 Fax: (01638) 569601 E-mail: info@computerlinks.co.uk

Computers In Action, 30 The Spinney, Beaconsfield, Buckinghamshire, HP9 1SB Tel: (01494) 675202 E-mail: powers@systemsworld.net

Computing Advisory Services, Unit 1b Kennedy Way Industrial Estate, Belfast, BT11 9DT Tel: (028) 9061 6287 Fax: (028) 9061 6287

Computing Matters, C M House, Bowers, Wimborne, Dorset, BH21 7DL Tel: (01202) 888990 Fax: (01202) 888383 E-mail: ian@computing-matters.com

Computing (UK) Ltd, 7 London Stile, London, W4 3AU Tel: (020) 8742 3336 Fax: (020) 8995 3991 E-mail: info@computinguk.co.uk

Compuvision Computer Consultants, 25 Mucklets Court, Musselburgh, Midlothian, EH21 6SP Tel: 0131-665 6728 Fax: 0131-665 6728

Comset Ltd, Ilex Court, 94 Holly Road, Twickenham, TW1 4HF Tel: (020) 8831 7700 Fax: (020) 8831 7711 E-mail: sales@comset.co.uk

▶ Comsoft Computer Consultants, Edon Business Park, Thame Road, Wheatley, Oxford, OX33 1JN Tel: (01865) 297842 Fax: (01865) 297848

Comtec Computers Ltd, 96-98 Merritt Road, Greatstone, New Romney, Kent, TN28 8SZ Tel: (01797) 366333 Fax: (01797) 366333 E-mail: stuart.sayer@comteccomputers.co.uk

Comtech Telecommunications Ltd, 30 Bradford Road, Stanningley, Pudsey, West Yorkshire, LS28 6DD Tel: 0113-255 3927 Fax: 0113-205 7567 E-mail: info@comtech-telecom.co.uk

Comtek Accounts Ltd, Venture House Venture Court, Boleness Road, Wisbech, Cambridgeshire, PE13 2XQ Tel: (01945) 464854 Fax: (01945) 465575 E-mail: accounts@comtekaccounts.com

Comverse Kenan UK, 1a Stoke Road, Slough, SL2 5AA Tel: (01753) 745300 Fax: (01753) 745304

Conchango (UK) P.L.C., Heritage House, Church Road, Egham, Surrey, TW20 9QD Tel: (01784) 470448 Fax: (01784) 222200 E-mail: talktous@conchango.com

Concord Computer Services, Meridian Centre, King St, Oldham, OL8 1EZ Tel: 0161-627 2370 Fax: 0161-628 9429 E-mail: enq@concordservices.co.uk

Concorde Informatics Ltd, Stoneleigh, 39 Halifax Road, Brighouse, West Yorkshire, HD6 2AQ Tel: (01484) 405405 Fax: (01484) 405400 E-mail: info@concordeinf.com

Configuration Management Services Ltd, 20 The Avenue, Crowthorne, Berkshire, RG45 6PG Tel: (01344) 761155

▶ Connect Computer Consultants Ltd, 6 Crumplins Business Court, Dunleys Hill, Odiham, Hook, Hampshire, RG29 1DU Tel: (01256) 704693 Fax: (01256) 702659

Consilium UK Ltd, 141 St. James Road, Glasgow, G4 0LT Tel: 0141-847 1545 Fax: (07020) 935560 E-mail: info@consilium-uk.com

Constellation I X Ltd, Post Office House, Main Street, Leicester, LE9 2AL Tel: 0116-239 2300 E-mail: sales@conix.co.uk

Contek Software Ltd, Camkins House, Risborough Road, Little Kimble, Aylesbury, Buckinghamshire, HP17 0UE Tel: (01296) 612121 E-mail: sales@anaclara.net

Context Information Security Ltd, Blake House, Admirals Way, London, E14 9UJ Tel: (020) 7537 7515 Fax: (020) 7537 1071 E-mail: michael.leviseur@contextis.co.uk

▶ Convergis Ltd, The Old School House, Castle Ashby, Northampton, NN7 1LF Tel: (01604) 696704 Fax: (01604) 696852 E-mail: sales@convergis.co.uk

Conversion Co Ltd, Unit F9 St. Hildas Business Centre, The Ropery, Whitby, North Yorkshire, YO22 4ET Tel: (01947) 605859 Fax: (01947) 600023

Cool Tools Ltd, 144 St James Road, Croydon, CR0 2UY Tel: (020) 8684 5663 E-mail: enquiries@cooltoolsuk.com

Coral Ltd, The Forge, Grange Court, Tongham, Farnham, Surrey, GU10 1DW Tel: (01252) 781000 Fax: (01252) 781001 E-mail: sales@coral.ltd.uk

Corbett Engineering Ltd, Unit 1 2 Mercia Villas, Torwood Close Westwood Business Park, Coventry, CV4 8HX Tel: (024) 7646 9930 Fax: (024) 7642 0994E-mail: info@celcat.com

Core Consultancy Ltd, 7 Kings Bench Street, London, SE1 0QX Tel: (020) 7928 3338 Fax: (0871) 6613393 E-mail: info@core-consultancy.com

Core Estates Ltd, 3 Pendeford Place, Pendeford Industrial Estate, Wolverhampton, WV9 5HD Tel: (0870) 7014343 Fax: (01902) 557701 E-mail: sales@coresystems.co.uk

Core Facts, 68 Queensway, Mildenhall, Bury St Edmunds, Suffolk, IP28 7JY Tel: 01638 711931 Fax: 01638 711865

▶ Corporate Computing UK Ltd, Unit 14 Miller 3, Southmill Road, Bishop's Stortford, Hertfordshire, CM23 3DH Tel: (01279) 755339

Cotech Software Consultants Ltd, 9 Drakefield Road, London, SW17 8RT Tel: (020) 8682 0123 Fax: (020) 8682 4550 E-mail: faisal@cotech.co.uk

County Computers, Aranway House, Dyserth Road, Rhyl, Clwyd, LL18 4DS Tel: (01745) 330663 Fax: (01745) 337515 E-mail: admin@countycomputers.co.uk

Courage & Co., Rye Hill Farm, Slaley, Hexham, Northumberland, NE47 0AH Tel: (01434) 673426 Fax: (01434) 673608 E-mail: info@consult-courage.co.uk

Court Consultancy Ltd, 5 Fairholme Avenue, Romford, RM2 5UP Tel: (01708) 704650 Fax: (01708) 438952 E-mail: ngs_tcc@yahoo.com

Court Management & Accounting Services, Court Ho, Hooe, Battle, East Sussex, TN33 9HJ Tel: (01424) 842600 Fax: (01424) 846161

Courtyard Consultants Ltd, 27 Lichfield St, Bilston, W. Midlands, WV14 0AQ Tel: 0121-609 7279 Fax: 0121-609 7001 E-mail: srudd@court.co.uk

Coveford Data Systems Ltd, Old Bank House, 59 High Street, Odiham, Hampshire, RG29 1LF Tel: (01256) 704333 Fax: (07031) 159754 E-mail: cds@coveford.com

Cpio Ltd, Arden House The Courtyard, Gorsey Lane, Coleshill, Birmingham, B46 1JA Tel: (01675) 467046 Fax: (01675) 467682 E-mail: rcf@cpio.co.uk

Cravenplan Computers Ltd, Wilbury Barn, Swallowcliffe, Salisbury, SP3 5QH Tel: (01747) 858000 Fax: (01747) 858010 E-mail: info@cravenplan.co.uk

Crayfield Computer Consultants, 64 Cuckfield Road, Hurstpierpoint, Hassocks, West Sussex, BN6 9SB Tel: (01273) 834999 Fax: (01273) 835550 E-mail: systems@crayfield.net

Create Form International Ltd, Instone House, Instone Road, Dartford, DA1 2AG Tel: (01322) 279797 Fax: (01322) 279779 E-mail: info@createform.com

Creative Computers UK Ltd, 65 West Main Street, Whitburn, Bathgate, West Lothian, EH47 0QD Tel: (01501) 742600 Fax: (01501) 742600 E-mail: sales@creativegroup.co.uk

Creative Database Projects Ltd, Queens Wharf, Queen Caroline Street, London, W6 9RJ Tel: (020) 8600 2605 Fax: (020) 8600 2603 E-mail: enquiry@cdproj.com

Creative Technology Management Solutions Ltd, Westall Centre, Holberrow Green, Redditch, Worcestershire, B96 6JY Tel: (01386) 791900 Fax: (0870) 0518715 E-mail: info@ctms-uk.com

Crombie Computer Consultants, 28 Bolney Avenue, Peacehaven, East Sussex, BN10 8NA Tel: (01273) 583304 Fax: (01273) 575312E-mail: ccc@crombies.freeserve.co.uk

Crusader Ltd, Oxford House, Easthorpe Street, Ruddington, Nottingham, NG11 6LA Tel: 0115-940 5550 Fax: 0115-940 6660 E-mail: sales@crusaderltd.com

Cti Data Solutions Ltd, Nordic House, 120 High Street, Purley, Surrey, CR8 2AD Tel: (020) 8763 3888 Fax: (020) 8763 3863 E-mail: info@ctidata.co.uk

▶ Culex Ltd, 7 Telford Court, Chestergates Business Park, Chester, CH1 6LT Tel: (01244) 853838 Fax: (01244) 853800 E-mail: info@culex.co.uk

Custom Computers UK Ltd, Custom House, Kenn Road, Clevedon, Avon, BS21 6EX Tel: (01275) 874233 Fax: (01275) 874235

Cutec Ltd, 19 Branson Court, Plymouth, PL7 2WU Tel: (0870) 3211801 Fax: (0870) 3211802 E-mail: sales@cutec.co.uk

▶ Cyber Networks, Stratford Road, Hall Green, Birmingham, B28 8AE Tel: 0121-778 6008

Cybernex Computers Ltd, Unit 17, Bingham Park Farm, Potten End Hill, Hemel Hempstead, Hertfordshire, HP1 3BN Tel: (01442) 288469 Fax: (01442) 255207

Cybis Computer Systems, 34 Sudley Road, Bognor Regis, West Sussex, PO21 1ER Tel: (01243) 840000 Fax: (01243) 840084 E-mail: sales@cybis.co.uk

Cym Consulting Ltd, 14 Well Hall Parade, London, SE9 6SP Tel: (020) 8294 1622 Fax: (020) 8859 4562E-mail: cym@cymc.com

▶ Cymbal Corporation, 22 Upper Grosvenor Street, London, W1K 7PE Tel: (020) 7629 4243 E-mail: sales@cymbal.com

D C Trading, Copdock House, London Road, Copdock, Ipswich, IP8 3JW Tel: (01473) 730286 Fax: (01473) 730257 E-mail: info@dctrading.co.uk

D H Systems Consultancy Ltd, Studio 107, Abbey Mill Business Centre, Paisley, Renfrewshire, PA1 1TJ Tel: 0141-561 0320 Fax: 0141-561 2136

D J Consultants, The Leas, Elsworth Road, Conington, Cambridge, CB3 8LW Tel: (01954) 267441 Fax: (01954) 267441 E-mail: enquiries@djinter.net

D K Computing Services, Kebbell House, Delta Gain, Watford, WD19 5EF Tel: (020) 8428 1000 Fax: (020) 8428 1111 E-mail: dennis@dkcomputing.co.uk

D M Resources Ltd, 10 Slimbridge Rd, Burgess Hill, W. Sussex, RH15 8QE Tel: (01444) 246391

D & M Systems Ltd, 28 Langdale Avenue, Chichester, West Sussex, PO19 8JQ Tel: (01243) 781950 Fax: (01243) 784478 E-mail: info@dandmsystems.co.uk

D N A Computers, Lamorna Haven, 17 Rosebery Avenue, Eastbourne, East Sussex, BN22 9QB Tel: (01323) 508810 Fax: (01323) 521228

D N Consultancy Services, 60 Southover, London, N12 7ES Tel: (020) 8446 6001 Fax: (020) 8445 3711 E-mail: chains@dnconsultancy.com

D P Systems Ltd, 85 Longbridge Road, Barking, Essex, IG11 8TB Tel: (020) 8594 2244 Fax: (020) 8594 2777 E-mail: sales@d-p-systems.com

D R L Systems Ltd, Woodside House, Woodside, Chilworth, Southampton, SO16 7LB Tel: (023) 8076 0808 Fax: (023) 8076 7900 E-mail: sales@drlsystems.co.uk

D S Callards Ltd, 2 Station Yard, Ashburton, Newton Abbot, Devon, TQ13 7EF Tel: (01364) 654222 Fax: (01364) 652288 E-mail: ray.kemp@developersolutions.co.uk

D S T International Ltd, DST House, St. Marks Hill, Surbiton, Surrey, KT6 4QD Tel: (020) 8390 5000 Fax: (020) 8390 7000 E-mail: webmaster@dstintl.com

D T A Computer Systems Ltd, 58 Norbiton Avenue, Kingston upon Thames, Surrey, KT1 3QR Tel: (020) 8974 5114 Fax: (07092) 314906 E-mail: info@dta.co.uk

D T P Services, 39 Bridle Road, Croydon, CR0 8HN Tel: (020) 8777 2735 Fax: (020) 8777 0299 E-mail: sales@dtp-services.co.uk

D2 Information Solutions, Law Street, Cleckheaton, West Yorkshire, BD19 3QR Tel: (01274) 866006 Fax: (01274) 875549 E-mail: info@d2.com

▶ Dac Systems, 4 Balloo Drive, Bangor, County Down, BT19 7QY Tel: (028) 9185 7711 Fax: (028) 9185 7722 E-mail: sales@dacsystems.co.uk

Dancerace plc, 2 Brock Street, Bath, BA1 2LN Tel: (0870) 7773033 Fax: (0870) 7772022 E-mail: info@dancerace.com

Danecroft Consultants Ltd, The Old Station House, Off Wilson Close, Compton, Newbury, Berkshire, RG20 6QT Tel: (01635) 579596 E-mail: danecroft@consultant57.fsnet.co.uk

▶ Dark Blue, Unit K, Trecenydd Industrial Estate, Caerphilly, Mid Glamorgan, CF83 2RZ Tel: (0870) 8736800 Fax: (0870) 8736802

Dart Computers (Wales) Ltd, 26B Wellington Road, Rhyl, Clwyd, LL18 1BN Tel: (01745) 330128 Fax: (01745) 330128 E-mail: emquiries@dart-computers.com

Dartsoft Ltd, Noland Park, South Brent, Devon, TQ10 9DE Tel: (01364) 646000 Fax: (01364) 646002 E-mail: kevin@dartsoft.co.uk

▶ indicates data change since last edition

COMPUTER SYSTEMS CONSULTANTS OR SERVICES, SOFTWARE ETC – *continued*

Data Base Unlimited, The Old School, Bagwell Lane, Winchfield, Hook, Hampshire, RG27 8DB Tel: (01256) 393050 Fax: (01256) 393051 E-mail: techsupport@dbu.co.uk

Data Crown Ltd, Bearnshaw Tower Farm, Carr Road, Todmorden, Lancashire, OL14 7ES Tel: (01706) 817885 Fax: (01706) 817165

Data Day It Ltd, The Old Stack Yard, Shrawardine, Shrewsbury, SY4 1AH Tel: (01743) 851188 Fax: (01743) 850088

Data Graphic Application Ltd, 26 Felpham Road, Bognor Regis, West Sussex, PO22 7AZ Tel: (01243) 861621 Fax: (01243) 869326 E-mail: info@dga-ltd.co.uk

Data One Ltd, Unit 12 Loughborough Technology Centre, Epinal Way, Loughborough, Leicestershire, LE11 3GE Tel: (01509) 215662 Fax: (01509) 212571 E-mail: danny@dataone.ltd.uk

Data Strategy Ltd, 44 Kingswood Road, London, SW19 3NE Tel: (020) 8296 0643 E-mail: info@datadtrategy.com

Data Technology Group Ltd, Unit 3-4 The Long Room, Coppermill Lock, Uxbridge, Middlesex, UB9 6JA Tel: (01895) 829300 Fax: (01895) 820555 E-mail: general.information@datatechnology.co.uk

Database Developments Ltd, 2 South Street, Uley, Dursley, Gloucestershire, GL11 5SS Tel: (01453) 861155 Fax: (01453) 861166 E-mail: sales@databasedevelopments.com

Datacore Consultants, 319 Broomfield Road, Chelmsford, CM1 4DU Tel: (01245) 261578 Fax: (01245) 356146 E-mail: pstevdata@aol.com

Dataflow I T Ltd, 26 George Street, Richmond, Surrey, TW9 1HY Tel: (020) 8332 7733 Fax: (020) 8332 7456 E-mail: info@dataflowit.com

Datamirror UK Ltd, Elizabeth House, 39 York Road, London, SE1 7NQ Tel: (020) 7633 5200 Fax: (020) 7633 5210

Dataplex Computers Ltd, 129 Bath Road, Slough, SL1 3UW Tel: (01753) 678405 Fax: (01753) 811127 E-mail: info@dataplex.co.uk

Dataplex Systems Ltd, Orbit House, Albert Street, Eccles, Manchester, M30 0BL Tel: 0161-707 3355 Fax: 0161-707 3344 E-mail: sales@dataplex-systems.com

Datareason Ltd, College View, Hollington, Stoke-on-Trent, ST10 4HH Tel: (01889) 507348 E-mail: jslim@datareason.co.uk

Datarota Ltd, High Street, Denford, Kettering, Northamptonshire, NN14 4EQ Tel: (01832) 733671 Fax: (01832) 734188 E-mail: peter@datarota.com

Datasmith Ltd, 30 Helen Street, Golborne, Warrington, WA3 3QR Tel: (01942) 700828 Fax: (01942) 516572 E-mail: tony@datasmith.co.uk

▶ Datatech DTP, First Floor Offices, 16 Mere Street, Diss, Norfolk, IP22 4AD Tel: (01379) 742772

Datavalley Sales Ltd, 32 London Road, Southborough, Tunbridge Wells, Kent, TN4 0QA Tel: (01892) 514545 Fax: (01892) 518282 E-mail: sales@datavalley.co.uk

▶ Daubeneys, Daubeneys High Street, Colerne, Chippenham, Wiltshire, SN14 8DB Tel: (01225) 745732 Fax: (01225) 744384

DB Graphics, 162 Blackstock Road, London, N5 1HA Tel: (01438) 261305 Fax: (020) 7226 6217 E-mail: sales@dbgraphics.co.uk

DBL Software Ltd, Tytherley Road, Winterslow, Salisbury, SP5 1PY Tel: (01980) 863505 Fax: (0845) 2269028 E-mail: sales@dbl.co.uk

De Facto Software Ltd, The Rutherford Centre, 8 Dunlop Road, Ipswich, IP2 0UG Tel: (01473) 230202 Fax: (01473) 230247 E-mail: sales@defactosoftware.com

Dealer Consultancy, 12 Crofton Close, Christchurch, Dorset, BH23 2JN Tel: (01202) 478600 E-mail: dealer-consultancy@hotmail.com

Dealer Systems, 11 Market Hill, Southam, Warwickshire, CV47 0HF Tel: (01926) 815792 Fax: (01926) 813395

Dealogic, 231-232 The Strand, London, WC2R 1DA Tel: (020) 7379 5650 Fax: (020) 7379 7505

Decisions Express Ltd, 15 17 Hatherley House, Wood Street, Barnet, Hertfordshire, EN5 4AT Tel: (020) 8441 9800 Fax: (020) 8449 9597 E-mail: info@decisions.co.uk

Deep Blue Systems Ltd, Unit 1, Lawrence Parade, Lower Square, Isleworth, Middlesex, TW7 6RG Tel: (020) 8541 4131 Fax: (020) 8569 9691 E-mail: sales@deepbluesystems.com

Definite Software P.L.C., 3 Waterloo Road, Stockport, Cheshire, SK1 3BD Tel: (0870) 7406575 Fax: (0870) 7406576

Delian Systems, 21 Lakin Close, Springfield, Chelmsford, CM2 6RU Tel: (01245) 450012 Fax: (01245) 602533

Demack Company Chartered Accountants, 120 Towngate, Leyland, PR25 2LQ Tel: (01772) 491769 Fax: (01772) 622935 E-mail: info@demacks.com

Demand Solutions (Europe) Ltd, Mid-Day Court, 30 Brighton Road, Sutton, Surrey, SM2 5BN Tel: (020) 8770 9320 Fax: (020) 8770 9303 E-mail: info@demandmanagement.com

Desktop Associates Ltd, Unit 1, 6 Putney Common, London, SW15 1HL Tel: (020) 8789 2250 Fax: (020) 8789 2249 E-mail: info@desktop-associates.co.uk

▶ Desktop Network Systems Ltd, 8 Croydon Road, Nottingham, NG7 3DS Tel: (07710) 394296 Fax: 0115-841 3761 E-mail: sales@dns-direct.com

Deverill plc, Itec House, 34-40 West Street, Poole, Dorset, BH15 1LA Tel: (01202) 785000 Fax: (01202) 785001 E-mail: marketing@deverill.co.uk

Deycom Ltd, I T Solution Centre, 35-37 Esther Road, London, E11 1JB Tel: (020) 8988 7700 Fax: (020) 8988 7701 E-mail: sales@deycom.co.uk

Dial Solutions Ltd, PO Box 84, Leeds, LS15 8UZ Tel: 0113-294 5111 Fax: (0870) 0517288

Diam Software Ltd, 4 Lincoln Avenue, Canterbury, Kent, CT1 3YD Tel: (01227) 479333 E-mail: enquiries@diam.co.uk

Diamond Management Services Ltd, Diamond House, 149 Frimley Road, Camberley, Surrey, GU15 2PS Tel: (01276) 691415 Fax: (01276) 692903 E-mail: info@dms-management.com

Digital Applications International Ltd, Axtell House, 24 Warwick Street, London, W1B 5NQ Tel: (020) 7292 7500 Fax: (020) 7439 2077 E-mail: enquiries@dai.co.uk

Digital Peninsula Network, 1 Brewery Yard, Penzance, Cornwall, TR18 2SL Tel: (01736) 333700 Fax: (01736) 366700 E-mail: office@digitalpeninsula.com

Digital Sales, Chip House, Byron CR, Coppull, Chorley, Lancashire, PR7 5BE Tel: (01257) 471204 Fax: (01257) 793525 E-mail: sales@digitalsales.co.uk

Dimension Graphics, 43 Hergest Road, Kington, Herefordshire, HR5 3EL Tel: (01544) 231887 E-mail: dimensions@btinternet.com

Direct Sales Agency Ltd, 4 Bankside, Hanborough Business Park, Long Hanborough, Witney, Oxfordshire, OX29 8SP Tel: (01993) 883606 Fax: (01993) 882733 E-mail: sales@direct.co.uk

Discount Computer Supplies, 58 Copley Road, Doncaster, South Yorkshire, DN1 2QW Tel: (01302) 364155 Fax: (01302) 366062 E-mail: sales@dcs.uk.com

Discreet, Ingeni, 15-17 Broadwick Street, London, W1F 0DE Tel: (020) 7851 8000 Fax: (020) 7851 8001

Discspeed Computer Consultants, Farley Common, Westerham, Kent, TN16 1UB Tel: (01959) 562117

Di-Soft Research, Little Frankley, Hook Heath Road, Woking, Surrey, GU22 0QL Tel: (01483) 727906 Fax: (01483) 727906 E-mail: colin.howard@comdaq.net

Distinctive Systems Ltd, Amy Johnson Way, York, YO30 4XT Tel: (01904) 692269 Fax: (01904) 690810E-mail: sales@distinctive-systems.com

DLW Computing, 1 Crowley Crescent, Croydon, CR0 4EE Tel: (020) 8686 8484 Fax: (020) 8239 0024

Doherty It Solutions Ltd, Doherty House, 2 Heathfield Terrace, London, W4 4JE Tel: (020) 8742 3338 Fax: 0845 6010597 E-mail: info@doherty.co.uk

Domain 2000 Ltd, Old Rectory, Church Lane, Whaddon, Gloucester, GL4 0UE Tel: (01452) 306410 Fax: (01452) 306530

Dotted Eyes Ltd, Hanbury Court Harris Business Park, Hanbury Road, Stoke Prior, Bromsgrove, Worcestershire, B60 4JJ Tel: (01527) 556920 Fax: (01527) 556939 E-mail: info@dottedeyes.com

▶ Double V Design & Support Services, Langarth, Stoke Road, Westbury sub Mendip, Wells, Somerset, BA5 1HD Tel: (01749) 871104 Fax: (01749) 871105

Doulos, Church Hatch Centre, 22 Market Place, Ringwood, Hampshire, BH24 1AW Tel: (01425) 471223 Fax: (01425) 471573 E-mail: info@doulos.com

Dragon Systems, Gyllellog, Pennal, Machynlleth, Powys, SY20 9DU Tel: (01654) 791642 Fax: (01654) 791277 E-mail: dragoncom@aol.com

Drayton Data Ltd, 28 Old Forge Road, Fenny Drayton, Nuneaton, Warwickshire, CV13 6BD Tel: (01827) 715214 Fax: (01827) 713858

Drive Technology Ltd, Bibsworth Lane, Broadway, Worcestershire, WR12 7LW Tel: (01386) 852089

▶ Drummond Associates, 37 Duffryn Avenue, Cardiff, CF23 6LE Tel: (029) 2076 4555 Fax: (029) 2076 4555 E-mail: info@drummondassociates.co.uk

Dsi, Empire Centre, Imperial Way, Watford, WD24 4YH Tel: (01923) 800430 Fax: (01923) 800556

D-trak Ltd, 8 Becket Way, Laverstock, Salisbury, SP1 1PZ Tel: (01722) 415144 Fax: (01722) 415143 E-mail: info@d-trak.com

Durham Computer Centre Ltd, 6 New Elvet, Durham, DH1 3AQ Tel: 0191-386 8989 Fax: 0191-384 4556 E-mail: info@durhamcomputercentre.co.uk

Durham Systems Management Ltd, PO Box 38, Washington, Tyne & Wear, NE38 9YX Tel: 0191-492 0429 E-mail: sales@dunelmsystems.co.uk

Duskpoint Ltd, 27 Hockley Road, Poynton, Stockport, Cheshire, SK12 1RW Tel: (01625) 871101 Fax: (01625) 871102

E C Computers Ltd, Mead Court, Cooper Road, Thornbury, Bristol, BS35 3UW Tel: (01454) 281500 Fax: (0870) 7776444 E-mail: info@eccomputers.co.uk

▶ E Cocoon, Gaddesden Place, Great Gaddesden, Hemel Hempstead, Hertfordshire, HP2 6EX Tel: (01442) 231000 Fax: (01442) 231600

E M Computers Ltd, 13 Victoria Street, Wigston, Leicestershire, LE18 1AJ Tel: 0116-288 1088

E O S International Ltd, On Site Lodge, 9 Mansfield Road, Eastwood, Nottingham, NG16 3AR Tel: (01773) 766936 Fax: (01773) 767555 E-mail: general@eosintl.co.uk

E Q Consultants, Allt-An-Fhionn, St. Fillans, Crieff, Perthshire, PH6 2NG Tel: (01764) 685220 Fax: (01764) 685241 E-mail: biz@eqc.co.uk

E S I T Computer Consultancy, Suite A, Loughborough Technology Centre, Epinal Way, Loughborough, Leicestershire, LE11 3GE Tel: (01509) 235544 Fax: (01509) 260661 E-mail: info@esit.co.uk

E2 Systems Ltd, Broadway House, 21 Broadway, Maidenhead, Berkshire, SL6 1NJ Tel: (01628) 418128 E-mail: e2web@e2systems.co.uk

Eaglecrest Computer Systems Ltd, Brytirion, Chapel Street, Llanarmon-yn-Ial, Mold, Clwyd, CH7 4QE Tel: (01824) 780565 Fax: (01824) 780375 E-mail: mike.wheeler@eaglecrest-cs.com

Easy Web, 10 St Andrews Cresent, Cardiff, CF10 3DD Tel: (029) 2034 4006 Fax: (029) 2034 4008 E-mail: enquiries@eazyweb.co.uk

Ec Advantage Ltd, 30 Marsh Lane, Hemingford Grey, Huntingdon, Cambridgeshire, PE28 9EN Tel: (01480) 355034 Fax: (01480) 355036 E-mail: enquiries@call.uk.com

Eclipse Computer Supplies Ltd, 106 St. Nicholas Street, Coventry, CV1 4BT Tel: (024) 7650 0100 Fax: (0870) 7436000 E-mail: sales@eclipse-computers.com

▶ Ecommnet Ltd, Aidan House Tynegate Precinct, Sunderland Road, Gateshead, Tyne & Wear, NE8 3HU Tel: 0191-478 8315 Fax: 0191-478 9466 E-mail: robert.campbell@ecommnet.co.uk

Edeva Solutions Ltd, 73 Queensway, Taunton, Somerset, TA1 4NJ Tel: (01823) 279702 Fax: (01823) 352292

Edge Designs Ltd, Enterprise House, Courtaulds Way, Coventry, CV6 5NX Tel: (024) 7666 7337 Fax: (024) 7666 7657 E-mail: sales@edgedesigns.co.uk

Edimatrix Ltd, 411-413 High Road, Woodford Green, Essex, IG8 0XG Tel: (020) 8559 2454 Fax: (020) 8559 2497 E-mail: sales@edimatrix.co.uk

Editt Group, 2 White Hart Fold, Todmorden, Lancashire, OL14 7BD Tel: (01706) 818271 Fax: (01706) 818271

Edm, Daisyfield Business Centre, Appleby Street, Blackburn, BB1 3BL Tel: (01254) 722033 Fax: (01254) 583003

E-Exchange Ltd, 32 Ludgate Hill, London, EC4M 7DR Tel: 020 72486060 Fax: 020 72486060

Effective Solutions For Business, Acquest Ho, 183 Kingston Rd, London, SW19 1LH Tel: (020) 8395 6472 Fax: (020) 8241 2502 E-mail: sales@effects.co.uk

Effisoft Ltd, 69 King William Street, London, EC4N 7HR Tel: (020) 7626 5166 Fax: (020) 7626 5177

▶ Egolight Computer Consultants, 2.2 Queens Bridge Road, Nottingham, NG2 1NB Tel: 0115-986 4555E-mail: egolight@mac.com

▶ Eight Technology, 6 Park Fire Business Centre, Harrier Way, Exeter, EX2 7HU Tel: (0870) 3501888

Elcome Ltd, The Engine Shed, Overtown Farm, Wroughton, Swindon, SN4 0SH Tel: (01793) 845144 Fax: (01793) 845177 E-mail: sales@elcome.ltd.co.uk

Electric Software, Stream House, Castle Hill, Rotherfield, Crowborough, East Sussex, TN6 3RU Tel: (01825) 830388

Electronic Archive Solutions Ltd, 14 The Briars, Waterberry Drive, Waterlooville, Hampshire, PO7 7YH Tel: (023) 9223 3833 Fax: (023) 9223 8577 E-mail: info@e-asl.com

Electronic Data Processing P.L.C., Beauchief Hall, Beauchief, Sheffield, S8 7BA Tel: 0114-262 1621 Fax: 0114-262 1126

Electronic Media Services, Lynchborough Road, Passfield, Liphook, Hampshire, GU30 7SB Tel: (01428) 751655 Fax: (01428) 751654 E-mail: info@ems-uk.com

Electronic Payments & Commerce Ltd, 139 Tankerton Road, Whitstable, Kent, CT5 2AW Tel: (01227) 273000 E-mail: epaycom@compuserve.com

Elf Ltd, Unit 1, Forest Close, Ebblake Industrial Estate, Verwood, Dorset, BH31 6DE Tel: (01202) 822206 Fax: (01202) 823382 E-mail: sales@elf.co.uk

Elite Training & Consultancy Services Ltd, Thomas House, 14-16 James Street South, Belfast, BT2 7GA Tel: (028) 9031 6840 Fax: (028) 9031 6841 E-mail: sales@elitetraining.com

▶ Elliptica Computers, Maylite Business Centre, Berrow Green Road, Martley, Worcester, WR6 6PQ Tel: (01886) 887712 Fax: (01886) 887731

Eltham Park Information Technology Services, 16 Glenlyon Rd, London, SE9 1AJ Tel: 020 88596958

Ema Technology, 15 Stevens Lane, Breaston, Derby, DE72 3BU Tel: (01332) 875657 Fax: (01332) 875658 E-mail: info@ema-tech.co.uk

Emergent Systems Solutions Ltd, 9 Briarwood, Finchampstead, Wokingham, Berks, RG40 4XA Tel: 0118-973 6077 Fax: 0118-973 6088 E-mail: consult@emergent.co.uk

Emerthames Ltd, City Cloisters, 196 Old Street, London, EC1V 9FR Tel: (020) 7253 7900 Fax: (020) 7017 3901

Empower Dynamics Ltd, Moor Park House, Moor Park Lane, Farnham, Surrey, GU10 1QP Tel: (0870) 2435701 Fax: (0870) 2435702 E-mail: general@empdyna.com

▶ Enigma Software Solutions Ltd, 9 Carden Place, Aberdeen, AB10 1UR Tel: (01224) 631101 Fax: (01224) 586678

Entee Global Services Ltd, 2morrow Court, Appleford Road, Sutton Courtenay, Abingdon, Oxfordshire, OX14 4FH Tel: (01235) 845100 Fax: (01235) 845108 E-mail: mail@entee.co.uk

Enterprise Management Consulting Ltd, Crystal Palace Park Road, London, SE26 6EF Tel: (020) 8659 2000 Fax: (020) 8778 0101 E-mail: info@emcuk.com

Entrust Technologies Ltd, Apex Plaza, Forbury Road, Reading, RG1 1AX Tel: 0118-953 3000 Fax: 0118-953 3001

Epcot Systems Ltd, PO Box 114, Pinner, Middlesex, HA5 1TQ Tel: (020) 8537 0395 Fax: (020) 8931 5218

Epos Computing Services Ltd, Demby West Business Park, Third Avenue, Milton Keynes, MK1 1DH Tel: (01908) 802345 Fax: (0845) 0450546

Equanet Ltd, Red Lion Road, Surbiton, Surrey, KT6 7RG Tel: (020) 8974 2321 Fax: (020) 8974 2982

Eris Technical Support Ltd, 21 Helen Road, Hornchurch, Essex, RM11 2EW Tel: (01708) 453997 E-mail: makkywebb@ec2uz.com

▶ Es Tech Network Solutions Ltd, 4 Avon Crescent, Bicester, Oxfordshire, OX26 2LZ Tel: (01869) 356018 Fax: (01869) 253005 E-mail: support@es-tech.co.uk

▶ Escape Business Technologies, 5 Carden Place, Aberdeen, AB10 1UT Tel: (01224) 630600 Fax: (01224) 652969 E-mail: sales@escape-tech.co.uk

Esdu International Ltd, 27 Corsham Street, London, N1 6UA Tel: (020) 7490 5151 Fax: (020) 7490 2701E-mail: esdu@esdu.com

Esker, Durham House, Wyvern Business Park, Chaddesden, Derby, DE21 6BF Tel: (01332) 548181 Fax: (01332) 548160 E-mail: sam.townsend@esker.co.uk

Espi Ltd, Network House, St. Neots Road, Dry Drayton, Cambridge, CB3 8AY Tel: (01954) 213999 Fax: (01954) 213998 E-mail: sales@espi.net

Esri UK Ltd, Prebendal House, Parsons Fee, Aylesbury, Buckinghamshire, HP20 2QZ Tel: (01296) 745500 Fax: (01296) 745544 E-mail: info@esriuk.com

Estuary Personal Computers, 318 Chartwell North, Victoria Plaza, Southend-on-Sea, SS2 5SR Tel: (01702) 543300

Euro Fire Guard Ltd, PO Box 95, Cirencester, Gloucestershire, GL7 5YX Tel: (01285) 850720 Fax: (01285) 850605 E-mail: carol@euro-fire-guard.co.uk

EuroLAN Research, Peter Thompsom House, Market Close, Poole, Dorset, BH15 1NE Tel: (01202) 670170 Fax: (01202) 670456 E-mail: info@erolanresearch.com

Euro-News Computer Consultants, 13 Trinity Road, Ilford, Essex, IG6 2BQ Tel: (020) 8550 6458 E-mail: euronews@ingamells.biz

Eurorealm Consultants Ltd, 29 Ivanhoe Road, Finchampstead, Wokingham, Berkshire, RG40 4QQ Tel: 0118-973 2977 Fax: 0118-973 4470 E-mail: sales@eurorealm.co.uk

Evesham Technology, 1 Gloucester Court, Gloucester Terrace, Leeds, LS12 2ER Tel: 0113-203 2000 Fax: 0113-203 2001 E-mail: leeds.showroom@evesham.com

Evolution Computers, 135 Bradford Road, Shipley, West Yorkshire, BD18 3TB Tel: (01274) 773394 Fax: (01274) 778788 E-mail: info@evolutiondirect.com

Exe Ltd, Mayfield, Pound Lane, Mannings Heath, Horsham, West Sussex, RH13 6JL Tel: (01403) 243444 E-mail: enquiries@exe.sk

▶ Exedos Computer Services Ltd, 3 Lancaster Mews, South Marston Industrial Estate, Swindon, SN3 4YF Tel: (01793) 822833 Fax: (01793) 822433

Exegesis S D M, 4 New Street, Talgarth, Brecon, Powys, LD3 0AH Tel: (01874) 711145 Fax: (01874) 711156 E-mail: sales@esdm.co.uk

F C F Ltd, Suite 210 Spitfire Studios, 63-71 Collier Street, London, N1 9BE Tel: (020) 7713 6888 Fax: (020) 7713 5749

F M K Ltd, 3a Crown Buildings, The Green, London, E4 7EX Tel: (020) 8524 3595 Fax: (020) 8524 3566 E-mail: sales@fmk.co.uk

F1 Computing Systems Ltd, 3 Kelso Place, Upper Bristol Road, Bath, BA1 3AU Tel: (01225) 427285 Fax: (01225) 444728 E-mail: sales@f1comp.co.uk

▶ Fait UK, 8 Moons Park, Burnt Meadow Road, Moons Moat North Industrial Es, Redditch, Worcestershire, B98 9PA Tel: (01527) 591804 Fax: (0870) 2405957E-mail: sales@faituk.com

Fands Systems Integrator Ltd, 12 Saxonville, Benfleet, Essex, SS7 5TD Tel: (01268) 795757 Fax: (01268) 795858 E-mail: sales@fands.uk.com

▶ Fanfield Ltd, Oxley House Cottage, Oxley Hill, Tolleshunt D'Arcy, Maldon, Essex, CM9 8EN Tel: (01621) 810095 Fax: (01621) 810095

Fast & Easy Computers, Unit 5b Marcliffe Industrial Estate, Macclesfield Road, Hazel Grove, Stockport, Cheshire, SK7 5EG Tel: 0161-483 6656 Fax: 0161-483 6667 E-mail: sales@fasteasy.com

▶ Fast Lane Consulting & Education Services Ltd, Park House, Park Street, Maidenhead, Berkshire, SL6 1SL Tel: (01628) 673900 Fax: (01628) 673910

Fast Software, East Street, Olney, Buckinghamshire, MK46 4BT Tel: (01234) 712184 Fax: (01234) 712184

COMPUTER SYSTEMS CONSULTANTS OR SERVICES, SOFTWARE ETC – *continued*

Fayers Bespoke Software, 1A Barton Buisness Park, Barton Road, Bury St. Edmunds, Suffolk, IP32 7BE Tel: (01284) 760276 Fax: (08707) 515984 E-mail: chrisandian@fayresbespoke.com

FBH Associates Ltd, Hi Point House, Thomas Street, Taunton, Somerset, TA2 6HB Tel: (01823) 335292 Fax: (01823) 332104 E-mail: sales@fbh.co.uk

Feltham Associates Ltd, Carlton House, Carlton Road, Kibworth Harcourt, Leicester, LE8 0PE Tel: 0116-279 3232 Fax: 0116-279 2473 E-mail: fal@btinternet.com

Fern Computer Consultancy Ltd, Fern Court, Derby Road, Denby, Ripley, Derbyshire, DE5 8LG Tel: (01332) 780790 Fax: (01332) 780788

Filenet Ltd, Waterside House 4 Cowley Business Park, High Street, Cowley, Uxbridge, Middlesex, UB8 2FN Tel: (01895) 207300 Fax: (01895) 207365

Firefly Ltd, 6 Odun Road, Appledore, Bideford, Devon, EX39 1PT Tel: (01237) 478014 Fax: (01237) 425741 E-mail: david@firefly.ltd.uk

Firesoft Computer Consultants, 13 Roe Green Lane, Hatfield, Hertfordshire, AL10 0SH Tel: (01707) 271073

Firmware Computer Systems, 68 Hendre Road, Pencoed, Bridgend, Mid Glamorgan, CF35 6TN Tel: (01656) 863639 Fax: (01656) 863639 E-mail: plynham@technologist.com

First Choice Computers West Midlands Ltd, 40 Waterloo Road, Wolverhampton, WV1 4BL Tel: (01902) 712166 Fax: (01902) 427900 E-mail: enquiries@fcc-online.co.uk

First EBusiness Solutions Ltd, Burghmuir Way, Inverurie, Aberdeenshire, AB51 4FT Tel: (01467) 622720 Fax: (01467) 624120 E-mail: info@firstebusiness.co.uk

First Micronics Ltd, 602-604 Kingsbury Road, Erdington, Birmingham, B24 9PJ Tel: 0121-250 5000 Fax: 0121-250 5019 E-mail: sales@fml.net

First Training, Woodford Road, Wilmslow, Cheshire, SK9 2LT Tel: (01625) 549287 Fax: (01625) 537284 E-mail: sales@firsttraining.net

Firstworld Systems Ltd, 20 Bytham Heights, Castle Bytham, Grantham, Lincolnshire, NG33 4ST Tel: (01780) 410847

Fleet Computer Services Ltd, Station Road, Ruabon, Wrexham, Clwyd, LL14 6DL Tel: (01978) 810746 Fax: (01978) 810603 E-mail: mail@fleet-computers.co.uk

Flexible Management Systems Ltd, Fielden Ho, 28 London Bridge St, London, SE1 9SG Tel: (020) 7378 6788 Fax: (020) 7357 0577

Flowsolve Ltd, 130 Arthur Road, London, SW19 8AA Tel: (020) 8944 0940 Fax: (020) 8944 1218 E-mail: cfd@flowsolve.com

Ford & Wright Ltd, 73 Spencer Bridge Road, Northampton, NN5 7DP Tel: (01604) 587021

Forest Software Ltd, 9 Pembroke Grove, Glinton, Peterborough, PE6 7LG Tel: (01733) 253332 Fax: (0870) 7474942 E-mail: sales@forestsoftware.co.uk

Formwise Export Ltd, 15 The Promenade, Swansea, SA1 6EN Tel: (01792) 462113 Fax: (01792) 650850 E-mail: sales@formwise.co.uk

Fortent, 56th Floor 18 Manesll, 80-110 New Oxford Street, London, E1 8AA Tel: (020) 7255 1065 Fax: (020) 7436 9443

Forvus Computer Services, Forvus House, 53 Clapham Common South Side, London, SW4 9BX Tel: (020) 7819 1000 Fax: (020) 7498 1939 E-mail: sales@forvus.co.uk

Fossoft, Newstead House, Lake View Drive, Annesley, NG15 0DT Tel: (01623) 720012 Fax: (01623) 720006

The Foundry Visionmongers Ltd, 1 Wardour Street, London, W1D 6PA Tel: (020) 7434 0449 Fax: (020) 7434 1550 E-mail: info@thefoundry.co.uk

Francis & Thomson Ltd, Postgate House, Castleton, Whitby, North Yorkshire, YO21 2ET Tel: (01287) 660757 E-mail: moira@franthom.co.uk

Freeway Commerce Ltd, Unit 12, Sceptre Court, Sceptre Way, Bamber Bridge, Preston, PR5 6AW Tel: (01772) 646000 Fax: (01772) 646001 E-mail: info@freewaycommece.co.uk

▶ Freshwebdesign Com Ltd, 28 Imperial Park, Rawreth Lane, Rayleigh, Essex, SS6 9RS Tel: (0870) 8302999

The Fridge Group, Suite 6 Broomburn Court, 8 Broomburn Drive, Newton Mearns, Glasgow, G77 5JL Tel: 0141-577 7644 Fax: 0141-577 7645

Frog Networking Solutions Ltd, 1 Lion Works, Cambridge, CB2 4NL Tel: (01223) 493500 Fax: (0870) 4446772 E-mail: system@frog.co.uk

Frontline Consultancy Business Services Ltd, Frontline House, Epsom Avenue, Handforth, Wilmslow, Cheshire, SK9 3PW Tel: (0870) 2410715 Fax: (0870) 6067300 E-mail: sales@frontline-consultancy.co.uk

Fruition Systems Ltd, Unit 3, Claylands Road, Bishops Waltham, Southampton, SO32 1BH Tel: (01489) 890820 Fax: (01489) 897690 E-mail: info@fruitionsystems.co.uk

FTC Fastrak Ltd, 39 Beaufort Crescent, Stoke Gifford, Bristol, BS34 8QY Tel: 0117-987 7737

Functionpoint Ltd, Newlands Cottage, Weedon Hill, Hyde Heath, Amersham, Buckinghamshire, HP6 5RN Tel: (01494) 791995 Fax: (01494) 792014 E-mail: alan@functionpoint.co.uk

▶ Fusion Business Solutions, 1 Wallbrook Business Centre, Green Lane, Hounslow, TW4 6NW Tel: (020) 8814 4888 Fax: (020) 8570 8240 E-mail: info@fusion.co.uk

Futura Consulting UK Ltd, 51 Downside Close, Blandford Forum, Dorset, DT11 7SD Tel: (01258) 451007 Fax: (01258) 451007 E-mail: mick.gordon@futuraconsulting.com

Future Perfect, 14 Harebell Close, Minster on Sea, Sheerness, Kent, ME12 3ER Tel: (01795) 877577 Fax: (0870) 0558977 E-mail: info@contactmanager.co.uk

G B Business Supplies, 17 Leek Road, Werrington, Stoke-on-Trent, ST9 0HX Tel: (01782) 550830 Fax: (01782) 550813 E-mail: info@gbbusiness.demon.co.uk

G B Direct, The Design Exchange, 34 Peckover Street, Bradford, West Yorkshire, BD1 5BD Tel: (0870) 2007273 E-mail: info@gbdirect.co.uk

▶ G C Tech, Unit G70, Chapel Place, Northampton, NN1 4AQ Tel: (01604) 601873 Fax: (01604) 601893

G K S Computers Ltd, One Oclock Lane, Burgess Hill, West Sussex, RH15 0EX Tel: (01444) 250404 Fax: (01444) 250405 E-mail: sales@gkscomputers.co.uk

G P W Consultancy, 3 Redcourt, Woking, Surrey, GU22 8RA Tel: (01932) 355770 Fax: (01932) 336454 E-mail: information@gpw.co.uk

G R C Electronics Systems Ltd, 157-159 West Street, Bedminster, Bristol, BS3 3PN Tel: 0117-963 9830 Fax: 0117-963 9567 E-mail: sales@grcelex.demon.co.uk

G R Wallace Computer Systems, 11 Queen Street, Carnoustie, Angus, DD7 7AX Tel: (01241) 856249 Fax: (01241) 856250 E-mail: sales@grwallace.co.uk

▶ G7 Business Solutions, 104 High Street, London Colney, St. Albans, Hertfordshire, AL2 1QL Tel: (01727) 829190 Fax: (01727) 829199

Gallery Partnership Ltd, 53-55 The Hop Exchange, 24 Southwark Street, London, SE1 1TY Tel: (020) 7096 2800 Fax: (020) 7096 2810 E-mail: mkemp@gallerypartnership.co.uk

Game Stores Ltd, 120 High Street, Ayr, KA7 1PR Tel: (01292) 266066

Game Stores Ltd, 13 Harvey Centre, Harlow, Essex, CM20 1XN Tel: (01279) 435486

Game Stores Ltd, 142-144 The Luton Arndale Centre, Luton, LU1 2TJ Tel: (01582) 457823

Gardner Systems plc, 1 Faraday Road, Wavertree, Liverpool, L13 1EH Tel: 0151-220 5552 Fax: 0151-220 5715 E-mail: sales@gardsys.co.uk

C. Gaunt Technical Services, 14 Hurst Road, Hebden Bridge, West Yorkshire, HX7 8HR Tel: (01422) 842321 E-mail: c.gaunt@c-gaunt.com

GB It Services, PO Box 429, Sheffield, S13 8YZ Tel: 0114-248 6200 Fax: (0870) 0517730 E-mail: admin@gbits.com

General Facilities Management Ltd, Enterprise House, Terrace Road, Walton-on-T, Walton-on-Thames, Surrey, KT12 2SD Tel: (01932) 221191 Fax: (0870) 0527012 E-mail: sales@doctec.co.uk

Gensys Technology Ltd, 15 Percy Street, London, W1T 1DS Tel: (020) 7255 2022 Fax: (020) 7255 3033

Geotech Systems Ltd, 3000 Cathedral Hill Industrial Estate, Guildford, Surrey, GU2 7YB Tel: (01483) 243530 Fax: (01483) 245330

Geotechnix Computer Services Ltd, 39 West Hill Road, London, SW18 1LL Tel: (020) 8871 1497 Fax: (020) 8333 6714

Gibson Information Systems, Tamarisk, The Lizard, Helston, Cornwall, TR12 7PF Tel: (01326) 290304 E-mail: enquiries@gibsoninformationsystems.co.uk

Glass House Technologies UK, Ocean House, Bourne Business Park, Addlestone, Surrey, KT15 2QW Tel: (0870) 7770017 Fax: (0870) 7770018

Glenfield Associates, 2b Mossop Drive, Langtoft, Peterborough, PE6 9LY Tel: (01778) 343567 Fax: (01778) 347382 E-mail: sales@glenfieldbs.co.uk

Globebyte Computer Consultants, Kingsgate Business Centre, 12-50 Kingsgate Road, Kingston upon Thames, Surrey, KT2 5AA Tel: (020) 8541 3426 Fax: (020) 8546 7248 E-mail: info@globebyte.com

▶ Glue Ltd, Windsor House, Spittal Street, Marlow, Buckinghamshire, SL7 3HJ Tel: (01628) 481553 Fax: (01628) 481579 E-mail: sales@glueltd.com

Glycar Computing, 3 Rushton Road, Cheadle Hulme, Cheadle, Cheshire, SK8 6NS Tel: 0161-355 3052 Fax: 0161-355 3052 E-mail: glycar@aol.com

Goldtec Astell Ltd, 16 London Road, Peterborough, PE2 8AR Tel: (01733) 558267 Fax: (01733) 558287 E-mail: info@goldtec.co.uk

Goodwood Communications Ltd, 5 The Square, Petersfield, Hampshire, GU32 3HL Tel: (01730) 235500 Fax: (01730) 235501

Graham Systems, Lagan Mills, Dromore, County Down, BT25 1AS Tel: (028) 9269 0291 Fax: (028) 9269 3854 E-mail: info@grahamsystems.co.uk

D. Grant Crawley Ltd, Henrys Farm Cottage, Carr Lane, Lathom, Ormskirk, Lancashire, L40 4BT Tel: (0845) 1473626 Fax: (0870) 4602061 E-mail: grant@dgc.co.uk

Grant Systems Ltd, Crown House, 72 Hammersmith Road, London, W14 8TH Tel: (020) 7559 9778 Fax: (020) 7559 3401

Granthams, Corporation Street, Preston, PR1 2UQ Tel: (01772) 250207 Fax: (01772) 555108 E-mail: sales@granthams.co.uk

▶ Greenduck, Confectionery Works, Western Way, Bury St. Edmunds, Suffolk, IP33 3SP Tel: (01284) 700015 Fax: (01284) 700016 E-mail: info@greenduck.co.uk

Grey Matter Ltd, 2 Prigg Meadow, Ashburton, Newton Abbot, Devon, TQ13 7DF Tel: (01364) 654100 Fax: (0870) 3665577 E-mail: info@greymatter.com

▶ Grey Tone Services, Yew Tree Cottage, Deepdean, Ross-on-Wye, Herefordshire, HR9 5SQ Tel: (01989) 768403 Fax: (01989) 768115

Griffiths Associates Ltd, Penylan House, Penprysg Road, Pencoed, Bridgend, Mid Glamorgan, CF35 6LT Tel: (01656) 862653 Fax: (01656) 864243 E-mail: john.griffiths@galtd.co.uk

Grok Developments Ltd, 103 Acre Road, Kingston upon Thames, Surrey, KT2 6ES Tel: (020) 8547 2304 Fax: (020) 8547 2305 E-mail: support@grok.co.uk

Grove Consultants Software Engineering, 40 Ryles Park Road, Macclesfield, Cheshire, SK11 8AH Tel: (01625) 616279

GSD Associates Ltd, 48 High Street, Stourport-on-Severn, Worcestershire, DY13 8BX Tel: (01299) 827592 Fax: (01299) 827593 E-mail: support@gsdassociates.co.uk

H B S Consultants Ltd, 6 Brooks Road, Raunds, Wellingborough, Northamptonshire, NN9 6NS Tel: (0800) 0199850 Fax: (01933) 461663

H M B, 24 Springfield Cresent, Harpenden, Hertfordshire, AL5 4LF Tel: (01582) 712889 Fax: (01582) 760680 E-mail: hb@hmbolg.demon.co.uk

H P D Software Ltd, Aspley House, 176 Upper Richmond Road, London, SW15 2SH Tel: (020) 8780 6800 Fax: (020) 8780 6801 E-mail: sales@hpdsoftware.com

Haas Associates, 20 Baldock Road, Buntingford, Hertfordshire, SG9 9DA Tel: (01763) 272865 Fax: (01763) 273869 E-mail: sales@haas-uk.com

Hadley Healthcare Solutions Ltd, 96 Worcester Road, Malvern, Worcestershire, WR14 1NY Tel: (01684) 578678 Fax: (01684) 578510 E-mail: enquiries@hadleyhealthcare.co.uk

▶ Alexander Haines Ltd, Hatherley Lane, Cheltenham, Gloucestershire, GL51 6PN Tel: (01242) 225500

▶ Harbeam Systems, Merlin House, 122-126 Kilburn High Road, London, NW6 4HY Tel: (020) 7692 0879 Fax: (020) 8529 1793

Harlequin Software Consultants Ltd, The Old Vicarage Coach House, Finches Lane, Baydon, Marlborough, Wiltshire, SN8 2JJ Tel: (01672) 541541 Fax: (01672) 542111 E-mail: enquiries@hquin.co.uk

Harmoni Its Ltd, Parklands Business Park, Forest Road, Denmead, Waterlooville, Hampshire, PO7 6XP Tel: (023) 9226 8133 Fax: (023) 9226 8160 E-mail: wci@wcigroup.com

Harri Roberts Computer Training, 99 Mansel Street, Mansel House, Swansea, SA1 5UE Tel: (01792) 411991 Fax: 01792 411991

J. Harris, 31 Trinity Avenue, Llandudno, Gwynedd, LL30 2SJ Tel: (01492) 873157 Fax: (01492) 871997 E-mail: y2000pc@aol.com

Harris Systems Ltd, Ferry Works, Summer Road, Thames Ditton, Surrey, KT7 0QJ Tel: (020) 8339 1800 Fax: (020) 8390 5087

Harthill House Group Ltd, Harthill House, Woodhall Lane, Harthill, Sheffield, S26 7YQ Tel: (0870) 3501309 Fax: (01909) 772785 E-mail: sales@hhg.uk.com

Havering College, 81-85 High Street, Brentwood, Essex, CM14 4RR Tel: (01708) 769235 Fax: (01277) 202752 E-mail: bw.iltlc@topenworld.com

Hayford Systems Ltd, 147 Commercial St, London, E1 6BJ Tel: (020) 7247 3005

HCL Technologies Europe Ltd, Network House, Norreys Drive, Maidenhead, Berkshire, SL6 4FJ Tel: (01628) 778555 Fax: (01628) 777566 E-mail: semipractice@hcltech.com

Heartfield Technologies Ltd, Bromley, BR2 0WL Tel: (020) 8313 3088 Fax: (020) 8313 3002 E-mail: info@heartfield.co.uk

Helmdart Ltd, 10a Robin Hood Road, Woking, Surrey, GU21 8SP Tel: (01483) 760338 Fax: (01483) 729158 E-mail: helmdart@btconnect.com

Helmstone Communications Ltd, 18 Guildford Road, Brighton, BN1 3LU Tel: (01273) 747447 Fax: (01273) 747333 E-mail: nisbett@helmstone.com

Herschel Systems, PO Box 598, Beaconsfield, Buckinghamshire, HP9 1HB Tel: (01494) 675104 Fax: (01494) 677831 E-mail: sales@herschel.co.uk

Hewlett Packard Office Centre, 57 Holborn Viaduct, London, EC1A 2FD Tel: (020) 7651 6651 Fax: (020) 7236 4385 E-mail: service@ebm.co.uk

Hex Solutions Ltd, 6 Queen Street, Burntwood, Staffordshire, WS7 4QH Tel: (01543) 677792

Heywood Ltd, 2 Victoria Street, Altrincham, Cheshire, WA14 1ET Tel: 0161-613 4200 Fax: 0161-927 7132 E-mail: sales@heywood.co.uk

Hi Tech Solutions, 6 Fairwater Drive, Woodley, Reading, RG5 3HH Tel: 0118-926 7252

Hibrow Computing Consultancy, 40 North Street, Hornchurch, Essex, RM11 1EW Tel: (01708) 449999 Fax: (01708) 447555 E-mail: admin@hibrow.co.uk

Highgrove Computer Services, Melbourne Road, Staunton Harold, Ashby-de-la-Zouch, Leicestershire, LE65 1RT Tel: (01332) 695050 Fax: (01332) 695001 E-mail: postmaster@highgrove.co.uk

Highlander Ltd, Islington Business Design Centre, 52 Upper Street, London, N1 0QH Tel: (0800) 1560777 Fax: (0870) 3309911 E-mail: info@highlander.co.uk

▶ Highlander Computing Solutions Ltd, Systems House, Unit 7 Shepcote Office Village, Shepcote Lane, Sheffield, S9 1TG Tel: 0114-292 3800 Fax: 0114-292 3838 E-mail: sales@highlanderuk.com

Highridge Computers Ltd, 275 Tutbury Road, Burton-on-Trent, Staffordshire, DE13 0NZ Tel: (01283) 500530 Fax: (01283) 500540 E-mail: karl@highridge.net

Hiserve Computing Ltd, 11 Chiltern Close, Warminster, Wiltshire, BA12 8QU Tel: (01985) 846266

▶ Hobs (UK) Ltd, 29 Lilley Drive, Kingswood, Tadworth, Surrey, KT20 6JA Tel: (01737) 831426

Hoburne Business Systems Ltd, 9a Saulfland Place, Christchurch, Dorset, BH23 4QP Tel: (01425) 280009 Fax: (01425) 280905 E-mail: sales@hoburnesystems.co.uk

Holborn Enterprises Ltd, 8 & 9 Scott Skinner Square, Banchory, Kincardineshire, AB31 5SE Tel: (01330) 824545 Fax: (01330) 824545

▶ Home Computing, 12 Camps Close, Waterbeach, Cambridge, CB25 9NT Tel: (01223) 860242 E-mail: l.l@virgin.net

Honeypass Ltd, 16 Ardsheal Close, Worthing, West Sussex, BN14 7RP Tel: (01903) 212774 Fax: (01903) 238226 E-mail: info@honeypass.com

Hook Data Services, The Old Village Stores, Slinfold, Horsham, West Sussex, RH13 0RP Tel: (01403) 790739 Fax: (01403) 790160 E-mail: malcolmb@hookdata.co.uk

Human Computer Interaction York Ltd, 3 Innovation Close, Heslington, York, YO10 5ZF Tel: (01904) 428600 Fax: (01904) 428628

Hunter Systems Ltd, 46-48 Alfreton Road, Nottingham, NG7 3NN Tel: 0115-847 5210 Fax: 0115-847 5212 E-mail: info@hunter-systems.co.uk

Hytec Electronics Ltd, 5 Craddock Road, Reading, RG2 0JT Tel: 0118-975 7770 Fax: 0118-975 7566 E-mail: sales@hytec-electronics.co.uk

Company I Ltd, 42 New Broad Street, London, EC2M 1SB Tel: (020) 7382 0750 Fax: (08701) 667001

I B N, 138-140 Wapping High Street, London, E1 9NQ Tel: (020) 7369 1200 Fax: (020) 7369 1217

I D Business Solutions Ltd, 2 Occam Court, Occam Road, Surrey Research Park, Guildford, Surrey, GU2 7QB Tel: (01483) 595000 Fax: (01483) 595001 E-mail: info@idbs.com

I D O M Consulting Ltd, Royal London House, 22-25 Finsbury Square, London, EC2A 1DX Tel: (020) 7588 1118 Fax: (020) 7588 1117 E-mail: info@idom.co.uk

I E P, 21 Mapleton Rd, Risley, Derby, DE72 3QQ Tel: 01332 874290 Fax: 01332 874040

I I C O N Ltd, Regent House, Hubert Road, Brentwood, Essex, CM14 4JE Tel: (01277) 264404 Fax: (01277) 264405

I K Portable Solutions Ltd, I K House, Plough Road, Wellington, Telford, Shropshire, TF1 1ET Tel: (01952) 242000 Fax: (01952) 223789 E-mail: iki@netcomuk.co.uk

I Net Synergy Ltd, Martini House, 55 Newbury Street, Wantage, Oxfordshire, OX12 8DJ Tel: (01235) 766788 Fax: (01235) 766788 E-mail: phil-smith@inet-synergy.co.uk

I O Systech Ltd, 8 Willow Walk, Englefield Green, Egham, Surrey, TW20 0DQ Tel: (01784) 432058 E-mail: enquiries@iosystech.co.uk

I Q Software Systems, Old Brewery House, Redbrook, Monmouth, Gwent, NP25 4LU Tel: (01600) 719229 Fax: (01600) 719049 E-mail: enquiries@iqss.co.uk

I S Integration Ltd, Westpoint, 4 Redheughs Rigg, Edinburgh, EH12 9DQ Tel: (0131) 338 6106 Fax: (0131) 338 6700

▶ I Support Ltd, 8-9 Rodney Road, Southsea, Hampshire, PO4 8SY Tel: (023) 9286 3504 Fax: (023) 9273 4510 E-mail: martin@isupport-uk.com

I T Business Solutions Ltd, 17 Park Mans, London, W6 0YD Tel: 0208 563 2188 Fax: 0208 5638634

▶ I T Logic, Unit G10 Malthouse Business Centre, 48 Southport Road, Ormskirk, Lancashire, L39 1QR Tel: (01695) 580102 Fax: (01695) 580100 E-mail: info@it-logic.biz

I T S L Net Ltd, 2 Marsh Lane, Birmingham, B23 6NX Tel: (0870) 7437780 Fax: (0870) 7437781 E-mail: sales@itslnet.com

▶ Ian Ryall, 157a, Wood Street, London, E17 3LX Tel: (07775) 933371

Ibex Business Systems Ltd, 63a Brighton Road, Shoreham-By-Sea, West Sussex, BN43 6RE Tel: (01273) 565699 Fax: (01273) 728275

Ibex Systems Maidstone Ltd, Mill House Quarry Wood Industrial Estate, Mills Road, Aylesford, Kent, ME20 7NA Tel: (01622) 791991 Fax: (01622) 882900 E-mail: sales@ibexsystems.co.uk

Ibs Open Systems, Carrs Road, Cheadle, Cheshire, SK8 2EE Tel: 0161-491 5111 Fax: 0161-491 5892 E-mail: sales@ibs-public-services.co.uk

ICB COMPUTERS, 4 Downlands Road, Purley, Surrey, CR8 4JE Tel: (020) 8668 8828 Fax: (020) 8668 8828

COMPUTER SYSTEMS CONSULTANTS OR SERVICES, SOFTWARE ETC – *continued*

Icm Computer Group plc, 3 Phoenix Place, Nottingham, NG8 6BA Tel: 0115-870 1000 Fax: (0870) 1218354 E-mail: sales@icm-computer.co.uk

Icode Systems Ltd, Icode System Ltd Grange Business Park, Sandy Lane, Shedfield, Southampton, SO32 2HQ Tel: (01329) 835335 Fax: (01329) 835338 E-mail: sales@icode.co.uk

Icon, Allbright House, 156 St. Albans Road, Sandridge, St. Albans, Hertfordshire, AL4 9LP Tel: (08707) 587600 Fax: (08707) 587636 E-mail: ray.pitchforth@icon-plc.co.uk

Icore Ltd, 10-12 King Henry Terrace, Sovereign Close, London, E1W 3HE Tel: (020) 7464 8414 Fax: (020) 7481 9230

Iken Business Ltd, Froomsgate House, Rupert Street, Bristol, BS1 2QJ Tel: (0845) 4509201 Fax: (0845) 4509209 E-mail: info@iken.com

▶ I-Konic Ltd, 60 Grayshill Road, Cumbernauld, Glasgow, G68 9HQ Tel: (01236) 729435 Fax: (01236) 729515

▶ Ikonik Ltd, Unit 19, Victoria Way, Pride Park, Derby, DE24 8AN Tel: (01332) 224176

Ilfield Computer Consultancy Ltd, 7 Halsford Park Road, East Grinstead, West Sussex, RH19 1PW Tel: (01342) 321873 Fax: (01342) 316182 E-mail: enquiries@icc-ltd.co.uk

Image HQ Ltd, 15a Balgownie Road, Bridge of Don, Aberdeen, AB23 8JN Tel: (01224) 825900 Fax: (01224) 709440

Impact Computer Consultants Ltd, 210 Church Road, Hove, East Sussex, BN3 2DJ Tel: (01273) 821820 Fax: (01273) 821010 E-mail: sales@impactcc.co.uk

Impaq UK Ltd, Lantern House, Walnut Tree Close, Guildford, Surrey, GU1 4TX Tel: (01483) 466900 Fax: (01483) 466901 E-mail: enquiries@impaq.co.uk

Impreza Computer Services Ltd, Lingley House, Commissioners Road, Rochester, Kent, ME2 4EE Tel: (01634) 299801 Fax: (01634) 297161

In Form Consultants Ltd, Weathervane House, Old Shire Lane, Chorleywood, Rickmansworth, Hertfordshire, WD3 5PW Tel: (01923) 283694 E-mail: info@inform-consult.com

In Synergy Ltd, 2 Carver Hill Rd, High Wycombe, Bucks, HP11 2TY Tel: (01494) 444104 Fax: (01494) 637163

▶ Inca Infotech Ltd, Unit 6 Radford Crescent, Billericay, Essex, CM12 0DU Tel: (01277) 631773 Fax: (01277) 623800

▶ Indus Object Technologies, Jolyon House, Amberley Way, Hounslow, TW4 6BH Tel: (0870) 8700140 Fax: (020) 85729461

Infocomp Ltd, 48 Front Street, Framwellgate Moor, Durham, DH1 5BL Tel: 0191-384 7734 Fax: 0191-384 7734 E-mail: sales@infocomp.co.uk

Infologistix Ltd, 4 Wesleyan Chapel Walk, Stapleford, Nottingham, NG9 8BQ Tel: 0115-939 9907 Fax: 0115-939 9117 E-mail: info@infologistix.co.uk

▶ Infolonx5 Computer Consultants, 5 Lenton Boulevard, Nottingham, NG7 2BY Tel: 0115-970 8111 Fax: 0115-970 5111 E-mail: sales@infolonxf.com

Infor Global Solutions Frimley Ltd, 1 Lakeside Road, Farnborough, Hampshire, GU14 6XP Tel: (01276) 417200 Fax: (01276) 417201

Inform Atika, 25 Parkholme Rd, London, E8 3AG Tel: (020) 7241 2269 Fax: (020) 7241 2269 E-mail: cameron.martin@btinternet.com

Information Flow Ltd, 280 Yorktown Road, Sandhurst, Berkshire, GU47 0PZ Tel: (01276) 35323E-mail: ray.ursell@informationflow.co.uk

Information Technology Services, 4 Ashley Road, Epsom, Surrey, KT18 5AX Tel: (01372) 800466 Fax: (01372) 740544 E-mail: sales@it-services.co.uk

Information Technology Systems, 16 Gremista Industrial Estate, Gremista/Lerwick, Lerwick, Shetland, ZE1 0PX Tel: (01595) 741400 Fax: (01595) 741401 E-mail: mail@its-online.co.uk

Informed Solutions Ltd, The Old Bank, Old Market Place, Altrincham, Cheshire, WA14 4PA Tel: 0161-942 2000 Fax: 0161-942 2015

Infotrends Ltd, Sceptre House, 7-9 Castle Street, Luton, LU1 3AJ Tel: (01582) 400120 Fax: (01582) 411001 E-mail: info@capv.com

Initiative.Net, 7 Gewans Meadow, South Orne Road, St. Austell, Cornwall, PL25 4RS Tel: (01872) 223100 Fax: (01872) 223134

Ink 4 U Ltd, Unit 11, Sharp St, Dewsbury, West Yorkshire, WF13 1QZ Tel: (01924) 455556 Fax: (01924) 458060 E-mail: nancybell@ink4u.co.uk

▶ Innovative Computer Engineering Ltd, 20 Butley Street, Hazel Grove, Stockport, Cheshire, SK7 4BL Tel: 0161-456 6337 E-mail: info@icesolutions.co.uk

Innovative Software Solutions Ltd, 5 The Willows, Strensall, York, YO32 5YG Tel: (01904) 492425 Fax: (01904) 492772

Innovise Software Ltd, Hellier House, Wychbury Court, Brierley Hill, West Midlands, DY5 1TA Tel: (01384) 484032 Fax: (01277) 822566 E-mail: info@innovise.com

Inphase Software Ltd, Salamander Quay, Harefield, Uxbridge, Middlesex, UB9 6NY Tel: (01895) 829111 Fax: (01895) 829112 E-mail: info@inphase.com

Insite Ltd, PO Box 77, Tunbridge Wells, Kent, TN2 5ZL Tel: (01892) 686000 Fax: (01892) 676002 E-mail: sales@insite-europe.co.uk

Institute of Public Care, 8 Palace Yard Mews, Bath, BA1 2NH Tel: (01225) 484088 Fax: (01225) 330313 E-mail: ipc@brookes.ac.uk

Inta-Act Ltd, Littleleys, Gosden Common, Bramley, Guildford, Surrey, GU5 0AQ Tel: (01483) 891040 E-mail: cpeatroy@inta-act.co.uk

▶ Intaconnet, Unit 40, New Greenham Park, Greenham, Thatcham, Berkshire, RG19 6HW Tel: (01635) 529803 Fax: (01635) 523678 E-mail: info@intaconnet.co.uk

Intec Systems Ltd, Intec House, St. Nicholas Close, Fleet, Hampshire, GU51 4JA Tel: (01252) 775400 Fax: (01252) 775444 E-mail: info@intec.co.uk

Intec Systems Blackburn Ltd, 12 Strawberry Bank, Blackburn, BB2 6AA Tel: (01254) 667106 Fax: (01254) 675925 E-mail: sales@intec-systems.co.uk

▶ Integer Consulting, Sussex House, 6 The Forbury, Reading, RG1 3EJ Tel: 0118-925 3336 Fax: 0118-925 3326

Integranet Networking Services Ltd, 71 High Street, Harrold, Bedford, MK43 7BJ Tel: (01234) 721755 E-mail: info@integranet.co.uk

Integratech Ltd, 1 Wainwright Road, Worcester, WR4 9FA Tel: (0870) 3661366 Fax: (0870) 3661333 E-mail: info@integratech.co.uk

Integrated Broadcast Information Systems Ltd, The Maltings, Charlton Road, Shepton Mallet, Somerset, BA4 5QE Tel: (07002) 255424 Fax: (07002) 329424 E-mail: sales@ibistv.co.uk

Integrated Solutions, New Enterprise House, 149-151 High Road, Chadwell Heath, Romford, RM6 6PL Tel: (020) 8599 8866 Fax: (020) 8597 5971

Integration Services Ltd, 119 Kingston Road, Leatherhead, Surrey, KT22 7SU Tel: (01372) 227400 Fax: (01372) 225120 E-mail: sales@isluk.com

Integrity Software Systems Ltd, Centenary House, Whisby Way, Lincoln, LN6 3LQ Tel: (01522) 887200 E-mail: lincolncall@integrity-software.net

Intelligent Business Strategies Ltd, Springfield House, Water Lane, Wilmslow, Cheshire, SK9 5BG Tel: (01625) 520700 Fax: (01625) 520700

Intelligroup Europe Ltd, 1 2 Challenge House, Sherwood Drive, Bletchley, Milton Keynes, MK3 6DP Tel: (01908) 443100 Fax: (01908) 443166

Interactive Sound & Vision, 11 Ladywood Ave, Cove, Farnborough, Hants, GU14 9SS Tel: 01252 668976

Interchange Group, Garden Court, Lockington, Derby, DE74 2SJ Tel: (08700) 716716 Fax: (08700) 716789 E-mail: info@interchangegroup.com

Interchange Technical Consultancy Ltd, 53 Northop Road, Flint, Clwyd, CH6 5LG Tel: (01352) 733319 E-mail: sales@compumedic.co.uk

Interconnect Direct Ltd, 22 Edward Road, Arnos Vale, Bristol, BS4 3ES Tel: 0117-907 1880 E-mail: enquiries@interconnect-direct.com

Interfaces UK Ltd, 128 Radcliffe New Road, Whitefield, Manchester, M45 7RW Tel: 0161-796 2783 Fax: 0161-796 2783

Interfuture Systems Ltd, Kemps Farm, London Road, Balcombe, Haywards Heath, West Sussex, RH17 6JH Tel: (0845) 4522411 Fax: (0845) 4522412 E-mail: david.williams@interfuture.co.uk

Interglossa Computer Consultants, 31a Chain Street, Reading, RG1 2HX Tel: 0118-956 1919 E-mail: info@glossa.co.uk

International Technical Support Ltd, 42 Hackwood Road, Basingstoke, Hampshire, RG21 3AF Tel: (01256) 333226 Fax: (01256) 333860 E-mail: info@itsupports.co.uk

Intersystem Ltd, 10 Edenham Close, Lower Earley, Reading, RG6 3TH Tel: 0118-926 1187 Fax: 0118-926 2224 E-mail: sales@intersystem.co.uk

Interwoven Europe, Novell House, 1 Arlington Square Downshire Way, Bracknell, Berkshire, RG12 1WA Tel: (01344) 418600 Fax: (01344) 418602 E-mail: info@interwoven.com

Intex Software Ltd, Diamond Court, Douglas Close, Preston Farm Industrial Estate, Stockton-on-Tees, Cleveland, TS18 3TP Tel: (01642) 672200 Fax: (01642) 671199 E-mail: sales@intex.co.uk

Intra Systems Ltd, 202 Northwood Lane, Newcastle, Staffordshire, ST5 4DD Tel: (01270) 753509

Intuitive Business Solutions Ltd, 8 The Spinney, Haywards Heath, W. Sussex, RH16 1PL Tel: 01444 443175

▶ Intutive IT, Ladypool Road, Birmingham, B12 8LF Tel: 0121-446 6951

Invensys Systems (UK) Ltd, Highbank House, Exchange Street, Stockport, Cheshire, SK3 0ET Tel: 0161-429 6744 Fax: 0161-480 9063

Ioko 365 UK Ltd, Innovation Close, York Centre Science Park, Heslington, York, YO1 5ZD Tel: (01904) 438000

Iqual Ltd, Crown House, Home Gardens, Dartford, DA1 1DZ Tel: (0870) 1633320 Fax: (0870) 1633316

IRevoltion Ltd, Station House, 4-8 High Street, West Drayton, Middlesex, UB7 7DJ Tel: (01895) 444420 Fax: (01895) 444460

Island Computer Systems Ltd, 41 Horsebridge Hill, Newport, Isle of Wight, PO30 5TJ Tel: (01983) 821717 Fax: (01983) 521608 E-mail: sales@islanddcomputers.co.uk

Isys Computers Ltd, 8 Upper Glenburn Road, Bearsden, Glasgow, G61 4BW Tel: 0141-943 1533 E-mail: enquiries@isysdirect.com

It Architechture Ltd, Chancery House, Tolworth Close, Surbiton, Surrey, KT6 7EW Tel: (020) 8399 6070 Fax: (020) 8399 6696 E-mail: info@it-arc.co.uk

▶ IT.com Solutions (UK), 1-2 North End, Boston, Lincolnshire, PE20 3LR Tel: (01205) 820199 Fax: (01205) 821662 E-mail: enq@itcom-online.co.uk

The It Partnership, 4 Upper Mulgrave Road, Sutton, Surrey, SM2 7AZ Tel: (0870) 7270089 Fax: (0870) 7270090

Itas Computers, 27a Quay Street, Ammanford, Dyfed, SA18 3DB Tel: (01269) 591810 Fax: (01269) 591810 E-mail: andrew@aingerfield.freeserve.co.uk

Itech Quality Business Solutions Ltd, Lion Court Storten Harolrd, Whitick Business Park, Stenson Road, Coalville, Leicestershire, LE65 1RT Tel: (0870) 2249295 Fax: (0870) 8519295 E-mail: info@itechqbs.co.uk

▶ It-Freedom Ltd, Minster Court, Tuscam Way, Camberley, Surrey, GU15 3YY Tel: (01276) 686686 Fax: (01276) 671648 E-mail: sales@it-freedom.com

Its Computers Ltd, 377 Ladbroke Grove, London, W10 5AA Tel: (020) 8960 1494 Fax: (020) 8960 1484 E-mail: itscomputers@atlas.co.uk

▶ Ittalent Computer Consultants, 5 Aykley Vale, Aykley Heads, Durham, DH1 5WA Tel: 0191-383 0440

Ivy Learning Software, Ivy House, 235 Roehampton Lane, London, SW15 4LB Tel: (020) 8780 1494 Fax: (020) 8780 1420 E-mail: sales@ivysoft.co.uk

J B Computer Management, 39 Luckley Road, Wokingham, Berkshire, RG41 2ES Tel: 0118-978 5161 Fax: 0118-977 4108 E-mail: sales@cdc-jbcm.com

J C Microsystems, 66 Hampstead Way, London, NW11 7XX Tel: (020) 8455 4271 E-mail: jclynes@aol.com

J J Network Services Ltd, Meridian House, 62 Station Road, London, E4 7BA Tel: (020) 8559 3211 Fax: (020) 8559 3223 E-mail: info@jjnet.co.uk

J & J Systems UK Ltd, Systems House, Downs Park, Herne Bay, Kent, CT6 6BY Tel: (01227) 371375 Fax: (01227) 371377 E-mail: mail@jjsystems.co.uk

J P M Associates, 322 Upper Shoreham Rd, Shoreham-by-Sea, West Sussex, BN43 6BA Tel: (01273) 452305 Fax: (01273) 464228 E-mail: jpm_associates@compuserve.com

J P Programming Ltd, 6 Lark Cl, Leicester Forest East, Leicester, LE3 3NX Tel: 0116-238 6758

J R Computer Services, 58 Elmroyd Avenue, Potters Bar, Hertfordshire, EN6 2EF Tel: (01707) 655185 Fax: (01707) 655185

J R Stones, 4 Rose Hill, Dorking, Surrey, RH4 2EG Tel: (01306) 886754 Fax: (01306) 886754

Jackson Kent Associates, 112 Harpenden Road, St. Albans, Hertfordshire, AL3 6DA Tel: (01727) 834690 Fax: (01727) 834678 E-mail: robk@jka.co.uk

▶ Jaire Consultants, 398 Long Lane, Bexleyheath, Kent, DA7 5JN Tel: (020) 8303 2196 Fax: (020) 8298 9782

▶ Jansoft Computer Consultants, 5 Penrwyn Court, Eynesbury, St. Neots, Cambridgeshire, PE19 2SU Tel: (01480) 218536

Japanese Computer Services, Suffolk House, George Street, Croydon, CR0 1PE Tel: (020) 8662 4450 Fax: (020) 8662 4455 E-mail: info@japancs.com

Jardine & Associates Ltd, Scottish Technology Park, James Watt Avenue, East Kilbride, Glasgow, G75 0QD Tel: (01355) 581150 Fax: (01355) 581151

Jatech Ltd, 2 Springfield Business Centre, Brunel Way, Stroudwater Business Park, Stonehouse, Gloucestershire, GL10 3SX Tel: (01453) 791909 Fax: (01453) 828893 E-mail: info@jatech.co.uk

Javelin Computers, Unit C, Varis Business Park, Challenge Way, Blackburn, BB1 5QB Tel: (01254) 505505 Fax: (01254) 691466 E-mail: purchasing@javelincomputers.com

▶ Jays Information Systems, 384 Baring Road, London, SE12 0EF Tel: (020) 8857 8200 Fax: (020) 8857 8200

JD & MFS Wood Ltd, 3 Townfield, Rickmansworth, Hertfordshire, WD3 7DD Tel: (01923) 441644 Fax: (01923) 441644 E-mail: jon@wood-ltd.fsnet.co.uk

▶ Jdisoftware Computer Consultants, 2 Hillside Cottage, Soot Hill, Anderton, Northwich, Cheshire, CW9 6AA Tel: (01606) 871110 E-mail: sales@jdisoftware.co.uk

Jen Advisory Services, 14 Briar Road, Harrow, Middlesex, HA3 0DR Tel: (020) 8907 1300 Fax: (020) 8907 5088

Jigsaw Systems Ltd, The Old Mill, High Church Street, Nottingham, NG7 7JA Tel: (0870) 7306868 Fax: (0870) 7306850 E-mail: sales@jigsaw24.com

▶ JK Consultants, 110 The Brook, Chatham, Kent, ME4 4LB Tel: (01634) 818163 Fax: (01634) 818164

Jobmatch Ltd, 159 High St, London, SE20 7EN Tel: (020) 8778 8322 Fax: (020) 8659 1324

John Burke Associates, 117 Belgrave Avenue, Romford, RM2 6PS Tel: (01708) 770770 Fax: (01708) 770759 E-mail: office@jba.uk.com

Jotika Midlands Software Ltd, Carmichael House, Village Green, Inkberrow, Worcester, WR7 4DZ Tel: (01386) 793415 Fax: (01386) 793407 E-mail: sales@jotika.com

Jumpstart Ltd, 3 Medway Road, Birkenhead, Merseyside, CH42 2BD Tel: 0151-645 9398 Fax: 0151-645 9999 E-mail: nigel.birchenough@jumpstart.co.uk

Jungle Junction Ltd, 35 Aveley La, Farnham, Surrey, GU9 8PR Tel: (01252) 747940 Fax: (01252) 747941

K C S Management Systems Ltd, Royal Oak Centre, Brighton Road, Purley, Surrey, CR8 2PG Tel: (020) 8660 2444 Fax: (020) 8668 8196 E-mail: sales@kcsconnect.com

K D Computers, 38 Borough Road, Middlesbrough, Cleveland, TS1 5DW Tel: (01642) 244477 Fax: (01642) 242415 E-mail: kdc@themail.co.uk

K P Service Group, 12 Hammond Drive, Northleach, Cheltenham, Gloucestershire, GL54 3JF Tel: (01451) 860087 Fax: (01451) 860087 E-mail: ken@kpsg.net

K S Computers, 3 Dyneley Road, Blackburn, BB1 3AB Tel: (01254) 505500 Fax: (01254) 691466 E-mail: purchasing@javelincomputers.co.uk

K T S L Ltd, PO Box 2637, Corsham, Wiltshire, SN13 0RP Tel: (0870) 0275587 Fax: (01249) 700650 E-mail: sales@ktsl.com

KAI Consulting, 7C Bayham Street, London, NW1 0EY Tel: (020) 7383 3700 E-mail: sales@kaiuk.co.uk

Kanbay Europe Ltd, Regus House, 1010 Cambourne Business Park, Cambourne, Cambridge, CB3 6DP Tel: (01223) 597836 Fax: (01223) 598062

Sam Kane Ltd, 40 Howard Business Park, Howard Close, Waltham Abbey, Essex, EN9 1XE Tel: (01992) 712746 Fax: (01992) 700211 E-mail: helen@samkane.ltd.uk

Kanection Computer Systems, 275 Uttoxeter Road, Stoke-on-Trent, ST3 5LQ Tel: (01782) 595989 Fax: (01782) 595939 E-mail: male@kanection.co.uk

▶ Kavanagh, Bollin House, Bollin Walk, Wilmslow, Cheshire, SK9 1DP Tel: (01625) 543630 Fax: (01625) 538890 E-mail: info@kavanagh.co.uk

▶ Kayani Systems Consultancy Ltd, 6 Ladbrooke Road, Slough, SL1 2SR Tel: (01753) 550888 Fax: (01753) 550333

KBC Process Technology Ltd, 42-50 Hersham Road, Walton-on-Thames, Surrey, KT12 1RZ Tel: (01932) 242424 Fax: (01932) 224214 E-mail: info@kbcat.com

▶ Kelicomp Computing Ltd, 2a Croham Road, South Croydon, Surrey, CR2 7BA Tel: (020) 8760 9220 Fax: (0845) 1669072

Kencom Computer Services, Aberfoyle Road, Dumgoyne, Glasgow, G63 9LA Tel: (01360) 550085 E-mail: sales@kencom.co.uk

Key Information Systems Ltd, P O Box 7283, Tamworth, Staffs, B77 1QQ Tel: 01827 250807

Key It Systems Ltd, Brake Lane, Boughton, Newark, Nottinghamshire, NG22 9HQ Tel: (01623) 863556 Fax: (01623) 863203 E-mail: brian@keyits.co.uk

Keynote Business Services Ltd, Unit 46 Alpha Business Centre, 60 South Grove, London, E17 7NX Tel: (020) 8926 9216 Fax: (020) 8926 9216 E-mail: info@keynotes.co.uk

Keys Electrical Wholesalers, 4 Elder Road, Leeds, LS13 4DL Tel: 0113-236 1486 Fax: 0113-236 1487 E-mail: keysdata@nildram.co.uk

M.B. King, 109 Gladstone St, Darlington, County Durham, DL3 6LA Tel: 01325 252088

Kingsfield Computer Product Ltd, Kingsfield Centre, Moulton Park, Northampton, NN3 6RB Tel: (0870) 8888410 Fax: (0870) 8888460 E-mail: purchase@kingsfieldcomputers.co.uk

▶ Kingsword Ltd, Unit 5, The Boundary Business Park, Wheatley Road, Garsington, Oxford, OX44 9EJ Tel: (01865) 361840 Fax: (01865) 361850 E-mail: sales@cssg.co.uk

Ray Kirkham & Partners, 13 High Street, Prestwood, Great Missenden, Buckinghamshire, HP16 9EE Tel: (01494) 863423 E-mail: raykirkham@clara.co.uk

▶ KMS, 63 Tanner Street, London, SE1 3PL Tel: (020) 7939 0740 Fax: (020) 7407 2810 E-mail: rachelb@kms-software.com

Knowledge Solutions UK Ltd, 4b The Lanterns, Melbourn Street, Royston, Hertfordshire, SG8 7BX Tel: (01763) 257100 Fax: (01763) 257112 E-mail: sales@knowledgeuk.com

▶ Kodela Computer Consultants, 433 Porters Avenue, Dagenham, Essex, RM9 4ND Tel: (020) 8984 0606 Fax: (020) 89840606

Kontron UK Ltd, 9 Ben Turner Industrial Estate, Oving Road, Chichester, West Sussex, PO19 7ET Tel: (01243) 523500 Fax: (01243) 532949 E-mail: uksales@kontron.com

▶ Kopo Greenwood, Unit 3, Trident Industrial Estate, Blackthorne Road, Colnbrook, Slough, SL3 0AX Tel: (01753) 682828 Fax: (01753) 687338

Kramer Lee & Associates Ltd, Vermont House, Chrisy Close, Southfields Business Park, Basildon, Essex, SS15 6EA Tel: (01268) 494500 Fax: (01268) 494555 E-mail: info@kramerlee.com

Kudos Software Ltd, Cliff House, Cliff Road, Salcombe, Devon, TQ8 8JQ Tel: (01548) 843586 Fax: (01548) 843503 E-mail: kudos@kudos-software.co.uk

▶ Kudos Systems UK Ltd, Unit 17 Louis Pearlman Centre, Goulton Street, Hull, HU3 4DL Tel: (01482) 321210 Fax: (01482) 322019 E-mail: info@kudos-systems.com

Kue Software Ltd, 28 Ashpole Spinney, Northampton, NN4 9QB Tel: (01604) 592121 Fax: (01604) 592120 E-mail: simonk@kueservices.co.uk

COMPUTER SYSTEMS CONSULTANTS OR SERVICES, SOFTWARE ETC – *continued*

L C S Group Ltd, 7-9 Alexandra Road, Grimsby, South Humberside, DN31 1RD Tel: (01472) 501234 Fax: (01472) 501501 E-mail: info@lcsgroup.com

▶ L L G Solutions, 21 Kings Avenue, Prestatyn, Clwyd, LL19 9AA Tel: (01745) 886954

L P C Computer Solutions, Unit 2 Buslingthorpe Green, Leeds, LS7 2HG Tel: 0113-262 2626 Fax: 0113-262 6622 E-mail: len@lpconline.co.uk

L P L Ltd, 19 Thorndale Croft, Wetwang, Driffield, North Humberside, YO25 9XZ Tel: (01377) 236282 Fax: (01377) 236303 E-mail: info@lpl.co.uk

L R D Systems Ltd, 37 Robert Moffat, High Legh, Knutsford, Cheshire, WA16 6PS Tel: (01925) 758700 Fax: (01925) 758700 E-mail: enquiries@lrd.co.uk

Ladybridge Systems, 17b Coldstream Lane, Hardingstone, Northampton, NN4 6DB Tel: (01604) 709200 Fax: (01604) 709200 E-mail: sales@ladybridge.com

Laganside Computer Consultants Ltd, Studio A, Hollywood Road, Belfast, BT4 3D Tel: (028) 9065 3006 Fax: (028) 9065 3005

Lailey Ltd, 25 Harewood Avenue, Bournemouth, BH7 6NJ Tel: (01202) 388840 Fax: (01202) 417748 E-mail: martinking@layley.co.uk

Lake Financial Systems, Stable Mews Beechwoods Estate, Elmete Lane, Leeds, LS8 2LQ Tel: 0113-273 7788 Fax: 0113-273 9300 E-mail: info@lake.co.uk

Lalcrest Ltd, Woods Lane, Flintham, Newark, Nottinghamshire, NG23 5LR Tel: (01636) 525584 E-mail: enquiries@lalcrest.co.uk

Lalpac, 8 The Causeway, Chippenham, Wiltshire, SN15 3BT Tel: (01249) 660088 Fax: (01249) 660099

Lambie Gilchrist Consultancy, Wamphray Mill, Wamphray, Moffat, Dumfriesshire, DG10 9NP Tel: (01576) 470880 Fax: (01576) 470881

▶ Lamri, The Aske Stables, Aske, Richmond, North Yorkshire, DL10 5HG Tel: (01748) 821824 E-mail: marketing@lamri.com

Landmark Systems Ltd, Unit 6, Swan Court, Station Road, Pulborough, West Sussex, RH20 1RL Tel: (01798) 877100 Fax: (01798) 875392 E-mail: info@landmarksystems.co.uk

Langdon Systems Ltd, Westward House, King Street West, Wigan, Lancashire, WN1 1LP Tel: (01942) 202202 Fax: (01942) 206000

Language Technology Centre, 5&7 Kingston Hill, Kingston Upon Thames, Surrey, KT2 7PW Tel: (020) 8549 2359 Fax: (020) 8974 6994 E-mail: admin@langtec.co.uk

Lanmark Technical Services Ltd, 30-32 Thames Street, Hampton, Middlesex, TW12 2DX Tel: (020) 8783 3260 Fax: (020) 8783 3270 E-mail: sales@lanmark.co.uk

The Lapworth Consultancy Ltd, The Barn, Hambridge Farm, Hambridge Road, Newbury, Berkshire, RG14 2QG Tel: (01635) 567777 Fax: (01635) 550067 E-mail: tlc@tlc-ltd.com

Laser Byte Ltd, Burstow Park, Antlands Lane, Shipley Bridge, Horley, Surrey, RH6 9TF Tel: (01293) 772201 Fax: (01293) 774694 E-mail: support@lazerbyte.com

Laseread Software Ltd, 10 Medway Close, Newport Pagnell, Buckinghamshire, MK16 9DT Tel: (01908) 211116 Fax: (01908) 211120 E-mail: sales@laseread.com

▶ Lasso Computer Consultants, 2 Kingsfield Road, Biggleswade, Bedfordshire, SG18 8AT Tel: (01767) 600288 Fax: (01767) 600289

Le Software Man Ltd, Aberdeen House, 22 Highbury Grove, London, N5 2EA Tel: (020) 7354 8414 Fax: (020) 7226 2015 E-mail: sales@answersthatwork.com

Level Seven Communications Ltd, 10-16 Tiller Road, London, E14 8PX Tel: (020) 7345 5125 Fax: (020) 7345 9476 E-mail: sales@l7c.com

Leysen Associates Ltd, Padmores Yard, St. Johns Mews, Woking, Surrey, GU21 7ZE Tel: (01483) 881188 Fax: (01483) 881189

Liber8 Ltd, Asher House, Barsbank Lane, Lymm, Cheshire, WA13 0ED Tel: (01925) 758283 Fax: (01925) 758470E-mail: info@liber8.co.uk

Library Information Technology Centre, South Bank University, 103 Borough Road, London, SE1 0AA Tel: (020) 7815 7872 Fax: (020) 7815 7050

Librios Research Ltd, 2 Chestnut Road, Towcester, Northamptonshire, NN12 7TW Tel: (01908) 543090 E-mail: info@librios.com

▶ Lilley Information Systems Ltd, 16 Kingsway, Hayes, Middlesex, UB3 2TY Tel: (020) 8573 3911 E-mail: vlilley@lilleyinfosys.co.uk

Lilliput UK, 20-21 Worcester Street, Wolverhampton, WV2 4LD Tel: (01902) 688886 Fax: (01902) 399915 E-mail: sales@ucs.co.uk

Lima Networks, 5-6 Carolina Way, Quays Reach, Salford, M50 2ZY Tel: 0161-743 3000 Fax: (0845) 3451220 E-mail: sales@lima.com

Linc It, North Street, Gainsborough, Lincolnshire, DN21 2HS Tel: (01427) 811770 Fax: (01427) 811780 E-mail: office@lincit.com

Lingley Control Systems Ltd, Lingley House, Lingley Road, Great Sankey, Warrington, WA5 3ND Tel: (01925) 729933 Fax: (01925) 791331 E-mail: caloffice@cal.uk

Linhill Associates Ltd, Dunston House, Portland Street, Lincoln, LN5 7NN Tel: (01522) 535022 Fax: (01522) 518185

Linnhoff March Ltd, Targeting House, Gadbrook Park, Northwich, Cheshire, CW9 7UZ Tel: (01606) 815100 Fax: (01606) 815151

Lloyd Savage Services Ltd, 25 The Green, Richmond, Surrey, TW9 1LY Tel: (020) 8332 7266

Local Computing Ltd, The Old Bakery, Rosemary Lane, Bampton, Oxfordshire, OX18 2NF Tel: (01993) 851006 Fax: (01993) 851007

Logica UK Ltd, Stephenson House, 75 Hampstead Road, London, NW1 2PL Tel: (020) 7637 9111 Fax: (020) 7468 7006 E-mail: webmaster@logicacmg.com

▶ Logistics International plc, 5 Lion Park Avenue, Chessington, Surrey, KT9 1ST Tel: (020) 8974 1144 Fax: (020) 8974 2999

Logsys, Logsys House, Ashville Way, Wokingham, Berkshire, RG41 2PL Tel: 0118-979 4121 Fax: 0118-977 2506 E-mail: info@logsys.org

London College Of Business & Computing, 206 Cambridge Heath Road, London, E2 9NQ Tel: (020) 8983 4193 Fax: (020) 8983 4286 E-mail: lcbc@compuserve.com

Look Systems, 1 The Grouse, 52 High Street, Gargrave, Skipton, North Yorkshire, BD23 3RB Tel: (01756) 749922 Fax: (01756) 749933 E-mail: sales@1ooksystems.co.uk

Lothbury Software Ltd, Suite 1 Warnford Court, 29 Throgmorton Street, London, EC2N 2AT Tel: (020) 7256 8734 Fax: (020) 7256 9026

Lynx Ltd, 269 Banbury Road, Oxford, OX2 7JF Tel: (01865) 310150 Fax: (01865) 310499

Lynx Computing, 171 Junction Road, London, N19 5PZ Tel: (020) 7263 6232

Lynx Systems (West), Beaconfield, Pitts Lane, West Melbury, Shaftesbury, Dorset, SP7 0BU Tel: (01747) 855999 Fax: (01747) 852871 E-mail: sales@lynxssytems.co.uk

Lyons Associates, 98 Wick Lane, Bournemouth, BH6 4LB Tel: (01202) 433379 Fax: (01202) 419676 E-mail: info@l-a.co.uk

Lyrical Computing Ltd, 21 Chriswick High Road, London, W4 2ND Tel: (0844) 4822250 Fax: (0844) 4822251

M B A Michael Bailey Associates plc, 12 Brook House, Chapel Place, London, EC2A 3SJ Tel: (020) 7739 2022 Fax: (020) 7739 4280

M B A Systems Ltd, Staple House, Staple Gardens, Winchester, Hampshire, SO23 8SR Tel: (01962) 841494 Fax: (01962) 864770

M C G Applications Ltd, 150 Hastings Road, Battle, East Sussex, TN33 0TW Tel: (01424) 774748 Fax: (01424) 777190 E-mail: gill@mcg-applications.co.uk

▶ M C Research, 28 Hornsby Square, Southfields Business Park, Basildon, Essex, SS15 6SD Tel: (01268) 490242 Fax: (01268) 410595 E-mail: info@mcresearch.co.uk

M C S, 134 Stanney Lane, Ellesmere Port, CH65 9AQ Tel: 0151-355 1935 Fax: 0151-355 6253 E-mail: mcs@mcsbowling.com

▶ M C T Ltd, Liss Business Centre, Station Road, Liss, Hampshire, GU33 7AW Tel: (01730) 894834 Fax: (01730) 892641 E-mail: info@mctl.co.uk

M C T Ltd, 129 London Rd, Ongar, Essex, CM5 9PP Tel: (01277) 362112 Fax: (01277) 362112

M E V Ltd, Baxall Business Centre Adswood Industrial Estate, Adswood Road, Stockport, Cheshire, SK3 8LF Tel: 0161-477 1898 Fax: 0161-718 3587 E-mail: sales@mev.co.uk

M F C Partnership, 21 Bedford Square, Brighton, BN1 2PL Tel: (01273) 821084 Fax: (01273) 202350 E-mail: info@mfcpartnership.co.uk

M I S Cooperate Defence Solutions, Hermitage Lane, Maidstone, Kent, ME16 9NT Tel: (0800) 243649 Fax: (01622) 728690 E-mail: webmaster@mis-cds.com

M I S UK Ltd, Lime House, The Quadrant, 135 Salusbury Road, London, NW6 6RJ Tel: (020) 7625 9900 Fax: (020) 7625 9901 E-mail: info@misag.com

▶ M L System Services Ltd, Glenfield Park, 1 Philips Road, Blackburn, BB1 5PF Tel: (01254) 691444 E-mail: sales@mlsystemservices.com

M R Consultants, Greshop Industrial Estate, Forres, Morayshire, IV36 2GW Tel: (01309) 675605 Fax: (01309) 678909

M Rocker Associates Ltd, 54 Home Close, Greens Norton, Towcester, Northamptonshire, NN12 8AY Tel: (01327) 358044 Fax: (01327) 358044

M S G Computer Services, 4 Uplands Court, London Road, Luton, LU1 3RQ Tel: (01582) 731848 Fax: (01582) 484430 E-mail: sales@msgcomp.co.uk

M S Tech Ltd, 9 St. Marys Avenue, Northwood, Middlesex, HA6 3AY Tel: (07956) 317392 E-mail: sales@mstech.org.uk

M V M Holdings Ltd, M V M House, 2 Oakfield Road, Bristol, BS8 2AL Tel: 0117-974 4477 Fax: 0117-970 6897E-mail: mvm@mvm.co.uk

M5 Data Ltd, Mendip Court, Bath Road, Wells, Somerset, BA5 3DG Tel: (01749) 679222 Fax: (01749) 673928

Mc2 Data Innovation Ltd, 9 Barn Road, Broadstone, Dorset, BH18 8NH Tel: (01202) 657434 E-mail: enquiries@mc2data.co.uk

J.P. McCool, Artasooley, Maydown Road, Dungannon, County Tyrone, BT71 7LN Tel: (028) 3754 8074

Macdonald Associates Ltd, 6 Cecil Aldin Drive, Tilehurst, Reading, RG31 6YP Tel: 0118-945 2862 Fax: 0118-962 4854 E-mail: info@macd.com

Macfaction, Tew Lane, Wootton, Woodstock, Oxfordshire, OX20 1HA Tel: (01993) 811197 Fax: (01993) 812686 E-mail: info@macfaction.co.uk

MacKenzie Tribbeck Associates & (Computer Consultants) Ltd, Suite 2 92 Gloucester Place, London, W1H 3DA Tel: (020) 7224 3146

Macola UK, 4 The Potteries, Wickham Road, Fareham, Hampshire, PO16 7ET Tel: (01329) 235846 Fax: (01329) 221425 E-mail: sales@macola.co.uk

Macro 4 plc, The Orangery, Turners Hill Road, Worth, Crawley, West Sussex, RH10 4SS Tel: (01293) 872000 Fax: (01293) 872001 E-mail: market@macro4.com

Mactherapy Consulting Ltd, Unit 41 Kings Exchange, Tileyard Road, London, N7 9AH Tel: (020) 7700 0044 Fax: (020) 7700 7071

MacXperts Ltd, London, W4 3UW Tel: (0871) 5504050 Fax: (020) 8181 7798 E-mail: info@macxperts.com

Maddox Ford Ltd, Rosedale House, Rosedale Road, Richmond, Surrey, TW9 2SZ Tel: (020) 8939 9048 Fax: (020) 8939 9090

Maestro Computer Services Ltd, 5 Smitham Bottom Lane, Purley, Surrey, CR8 3DE Tel: (020) 8763 9513 Fax: (020) 8763 0027 E-mail: mail@maestrocompserv.co.uk

Maestro Solutions Ltd, 5 Woodland Road, Maple Cross, Rickmansworth, Hertfordshire, WD3 9ST Tel: (01923) 770856 Fax: (01923) 771143 E-mail: maestrosoloutions@aol.com

Magals Solutions Ltd, 258, Kingsland Road, London, E8 4DG Tel: (020) 7254 6481 Fax: (020) 7503 7959

Major Gold, Harbour House, Coldharbour Lane, Rainham, Essex, RM13 9YB Tel: (01708) 523233 Fax: (01708) 559818 E-mail: j.majorgold@btclick.com

Malbrook, C.S. Ltd, 8 Millbank Court, Millbank Way, Bracknell, Berkshire, RG12 1RP Tel: (01344) 424458 Fax: (01344) 424459 E-mail: support@csmb.co.uk

MAM Software Ltd, 1 Station Road, Deepcar, Sheffield, S36 2SQ Tel: (0870) 7667012 Fax: (0870) 7667023

Management Technology Services Ltd, 29 Bleasdale Avenue, Greenford, Middlesex, UB6 8LB Tel: (020) 8991 8066 Fax: (020) 8904 8055 E-mail: sramos@mtsl-net.co.uk

Manas Ltd, PO Box 26273, London, W3 6FN Tel: (0870) 7335000 Fax: (0870) 7336000 E-mail: mail@manas.co.uk

Manhattan Electronics, 4 Cooksey Lane, Birmingham, B44 9QN Tel: 0121-605 2957 Fax: 0121-605 3031 E-mail: manhattanelec@hotmail.com

Mantarun Systems Ltd, 310 Green La, Ilford, Essex, IG1 1XT Tel: (020) 8599 9980 Fax: (020) 8599 2498 E-mail: mantarun@btconnect.com

Mantra Information Services Ltd, 12 Ash Close, Abbots Langley, Hertfordshire, WD5 0DN Tel: (01923) 266572 Fax: (01923) 351394 E-mail: nkg@mantra95.freeserve.co.uk

Manumit Computers Ltd, Scope House, Weston Road, Crewe, CW1 6DD Tel: (01270) 250022 Fax: (01270) 250033 E-mail: contact@manumit-computers.com

Marandy Computers Ltd, 21 Lowswater Drive, Loughborough, Leicestershire, LE11 3RR Tel: 0115-911 8808 Fax: 0115-958 2400 E-mail: info@marandy.com

Marsden's Computer Systems, Unit 168 Glenfield Park Lomeshaye Business Village, Turner Road, Nelson, Lancashire, BB9 7DR Tel: (01282) 616176 Fax: (01282) 616152 E-mail: info@marsdens.net

Marsworth Computing, 34 Byron Hill Road, Harrow, Middlesex, HA2 0HY Tel: (020) 8864 4842 Fax: (020) 8864 4842 E-mail: sales@marsworth.net

▶ Martello Bay Tele Consultants Ltd, 5 Stephenson Road, Clacton-on-Sea, Essex, CO15 4XA Tel: (01255) 221110

Martingale Associates Ltd, 64 Cliffords Inn, Fetter Lane, London, EC4A 1BX Tel: (020) 7242 0064 Fax: (020) 7404 1862 E-mail: sales@martingale.com

Masterkey Systems Ltd, 27a Queens Road, Southend-on-Sea, SS1 1LT Tel: (01702) 437146

Matrice, Hawthorn Cottage, Hadham Road, Bishop's Stortford, Hertfordshire, CM23 2QT Tel: (01279) 501955 E-mail: info@matrice.co.uk

Matrix Computer Services, Matrix Buildings, Darenth Road, Dartford, DA1 1LU Tel: (01322) 292391 Fax: (01322) 229908 E-mail: matrixcomputers@compuserve.com

▶ Matter Solutions, 51 Back Church Lane, London, E1 1DQ Tel: (020) 7702 2200

Maxima, 2 Bell Business Park, Smeaton Close, Aylesbury, Buckinghamshire, HP19 8JR Tel: (01296) 318060 Fax: (01296) 318089

Mayfield Systems Ltd, 89 Mayfield Gardens, Brentwood, Essex, CM14 4UN Tel: (01277) 200292 Fax: (01277) 200292 E-mail: malcolmcree@msn.com

Mayflower Arosoft Systems Ltd, Mayflower House, Herbert Road, Stafford, ST17 9BH Tel: (01785) 240073 Fax: (01785) 245266 E-mail: b.bartlett@mfc-group.co.uk

Mayflower Computing Consultants, Spindrift, West Looe Hill, West Looe, Looe, Cornwall, PL13 2HE Tel: (01503) 263688 Fax: (0870) 7407649 E-mail: sales@mayflower-cc.com

MCC Ltd, 2 Milford Road, Sherburn in Elmet, Leeds, LS25 6AF Tel: (01977) 682880 Fax: (0870) 0518693 E-mail: tim@mccltd.org.uk

Meap Ltd, 1 Bath Road, Stonehouse, Gloucestershire, GL10 2JD Tel: (01453) 828088 Fax: (01453) 828980 E-mail: roger.hughes@softlogic.co.uk

Media Information Solutions Ltd, 32 Ballmoor, Buckingham Industrial Estate, Buckingham, MK18 1RQ Tel: (01280) 824488 Fax: (01280) 824489 E-mail: info@m-i-s.co.uk

Media Logic Ltd, PO Box 3214, Sheffield, S10 5WT Tel: 0114-230 3758 Fax: 0114-263 0868 E-mail: info@medialogic.net

Mediatech Ltd, 3 Ferndale Close, Thornton-Cleveleys, Lancashire, FY5 4PD Tel: (01253) 825251 Fax: (01253) 863839

Medical Marine Computing Ltd, 9b Bowthorpe Road, Wisbech, Cambridgeshire, PE13 2DX Tel: (01945) 580021 Fax: (01945) 580044 E-mail: support@medicalmarine.co.uk

Megabytes, 90 Central Road, Worcester Park, Surrey, KT4 8HU Tel: (020) 8335 4224 Fax: (020) 8715 0914 E-mail: sales@megabytes.co.uk

Megatype, Unit 6, Genesis Business Centre, Redkiln Way, Horsham, West Sussex, RH13 5QH Tel: (01403) 217613 Fax: (01403) 217612E-mail: sales@megatype.demon.co.uk

Mehdi & Ward Information Systems, 23 Aldermans Hill, London, N13 4YD Tel: (020) 8245 4545 Fax: (020) 8245 0151 E-mail: sales@mehdiward.com

▶ Mental Solutions Ltd, 1 The Arcade, Northgate, Bridgnorth, Shropshire, WV16 4ER Tel: (01746) 761133 Fax: (07092) 262950 E-mail: info@mentalsolutions.com

Mentat Systems Ltd, 21 Porthleven Crescent, Astley, Tyldesley, Manchester, M29 7FZ Tel: (01942) 749444 E-mail: sales@mentat.co.uk

Mentor Communications Ltd, PO Box 21, Wellingborough, Northamptonshire, NN8 1PB Tel: (08454) 581552 Fax: (08708) 401553 E-mail: mentor.comms@fsbdial.co.uk

Mentor Computer Consultants, 18 Old Stack Yard, Village Road, Great Barrow, Chester, CH3 7JE Tel: (01829) 740794

Andreas Menzies Associates, 14 Kestrel Road, Oakham, Leicestershire, LE15 6BU Tel: (01572) 770653 Fax: (01572) 722575 E-mail: andreas@amanet.co.uk

Mere Developments, Tangley Mere, New Road, Chilworth, Guildford, Surrey, GU4 8LZ Tel: (01483) 562631 Fax: (01483) 532022

Merit Technology Europe Ltd, 935bsittingbourne Research Centre, Cornforth Drive, Sittingbourne, Kent, ME9 8PX Tel: (01795) 418900 Fax: (01795) 418929 E-mail: sales@mtel.co.uk

▶ Merlin International Projects Ltd, 115a High Street, Selsey, Chichester, West Sussex, PO20 0QB Tel: (01243) 606876

Merlin It Ltd, 4 Main Road, Long Hanborough, Witney, Oxfordshire, OX29 8BE Tel: (01993) 880002 Fax: 01993 880002

Merlin Software International Ltd, 6 Bancombe Road, Somerton, Somerset, TA11 6SB Tel: (01458) 271300 Fax: (01458) 224044 E-mail: info@caliburn-software.com

Merlin Solutions, 5 Gaskells End, Tokers Green, Reading, RG4 9EW Tel: 0118-972 4666 Fax: 0118-972 4535 E-mail: terriw@mersol.co.uk

Merula Ltd, 25-31 Huntingdon Street, St. Neots, Cambridgeshire, PE19 1BG Tel: (01480) 222940 Fax: (01480) 222941 E-mail: info@merula.net

Metadata Ltd, 39 Pemberton Terrace, London, N19 5RX Tel: (020) 7272 3726

Metascybe Systems Ltd, 89 Hartfield Road, London, SW19 3TJ Tel: (01937) 543500 Fax: (020) 8544 0700 E-mail: info@metascybe.co.uk

Methods Application Ltd, 39 King Street, London, WC2E 8JS Tel: (020) 7240 1121 Fax: (020) 7379 8561 E-mail: central@methods.co.uk

Mha Computer Services, 42 Wheatsheaf Road, Alconbury Weston, Huntingdon, Cambridgeshire, PE28 4LF Tel: (01480) 891338 Fax: (01480) 891343

Gregory Micallef Associates, 63 Croydon Road, London, SE20 7TB Tel: (020) 8778 7759 Fax: (020) 8778 3090 E-mail: sales@gmal.co.uk

Mican Ltd, Oakmere, Horsemans Green, Whitchurch, Shropshire, SY13 3DY Tel: (01948) 830069

Michael Kinder Ltd, 1 Rectory Meadow, Bradwell, Braintree, Essex, CM77 8EX Tel: (01376) 561522 Fax: (01376) 561522

Michael Smith & Associates, Chemix Building, Dudley Road, Halesowen, West Midlands, B63 3NT Tel: 0121-585 0662 Fax: 0121-585 0649 E-mail: info@msasystems.co.uk

▶ Mico Trends, 4 Pendle Street, Nelson, Lancashire, BB9 7NH Tel: (01282) 447197 E-mail: info@micotrends.co.uk

Micro Check, 75 North Street, Wellington, Somerset, TA21 8NA Tel: (01823) 664943 Fax: (01823) 665747 E-mail: sales@microcheckcomputers.co.uk

Micro Data Systems Ltd, 65 Lower Olland Street, Bungay, Suffolk, NR35 1BY Tel: (01986) 895004 Fax: (01986) 896563 E-mail: sales@microdata.co.uk

Micro Plus Computers, 33 Bailey Street, Oswestry, Shropshire, SY11 1PX Tel: (01691) 656875 Fax: (01691) 671285 E-mail: chris@micro-plus.co.uk

Microcare Corporation, 34 Chantry Close, Harrow, Middlesex, HA3 9QZ Tel: (020) 8204 3630 Fax: (020) 8204 3638 E-mail: microcare@breathemail.net

Microforce Computer Systems, 327 Moseley Road, Birmingham, B12 0DX Tel: 0121-440 0440 Fax: 0121-440 1440 E-mail: info@microforce.co.uk

Microgen Solutions P.L.C., 320 City Road, London, EC1V 2PT Tel: (020) 7239 8400 Fax: (020) 7239 8401 E-mail: enquiry@imagoqa.com

▶ indicates data change since last edition

COMPUTER SYSTEMS CONSULTANTS OR SERVICES, SOFTWARE ETC – *continued*

Microguide Corporate Computer Consultants Ltd, Wyndham House, 82 Shortlands Road, Kingston upon Thames, Surrey, KT2 6HE Tel: (020) 8549 7152 Fax: (020) 8549 8112 E-mail: enquiry@microguide.co.uk

Microlise Business Computing, Farrington Way, Eastwood, Nottingham, NG16 3AG Tel: (01773) 535111 Fax: (01773) 537373 E-mail: enquiries@microlise.co.uk

Micrsolog Computer Software, 7 Stainland Road, Greetland, Halifax, West Yorkshire, HX4 8AD Tel: (01422) 310031 Fax: (01422) 371694 E-mail: sales@microlog.co.uk

MicroMedia UK Ltd, 74 Gloucester Road, London, E17 6AE Tel: (07762) 660697 Fax: (020) 8527 3302

Micropack Engineering Ltd, Fir Training Centre, Portlethen, Aberdeen, AB12 4RR Tel: (01224) 784055 Fax: (01224) 784056 E-mail: info@micropack.co.uk

Micros For Managers Ltd, 149 Gloucester Road, London, SW7 4TH Tel: (020) 7565 2111 Fax: (020) 7565 2114

Microsoft Ltd, 10 Great Pulteney Street, London, W1F 9NB Tel: (0870) 6010100

Microsystems Consultants, 26 Dunstall Way, West Molesey, Surrey, KT8 1PD Tel: (020) 8979 4099 Fax: (020) 8979 5898 E-mail: ivorhughes15@hotmail.com

▶ Microtek Computer Consultants, 49 Cheylesmore Drive, Frimley, Camberley, Surrey, GU16 9BN Tel: (01276) 61940 Fax: (01276) 61940

Microtest Ltd, Technology House, 18 Normandy Way, Bodmin, Cornwall, PL31 1EX Tel: (01208) 73812 Fax: (01208) 77677 E-mail: sales@microtest.co.uk

Midas Computer Systems, Gilnockie Station Ho, Canonbie, Dumfriesshire, DG14 0SG Tel: (01387) 371526 Fax: (01387) 371526

Mid-Blue International Ltd, Great Queen Street, Dartford, DA1 1TJ Tel: (01322) 407000 Fax: (07092) 364351 E-mail: nigel.scott@mid-blue.com

▶ Midwest Computer Consultants, The Old Coach House, Felton, Hereford, HR1 3PH Tel: (01432) 820033 Fax: (01432) 820044

Scott Mihajlovic Associates Ltd, 25 Aden Gro, London, N16 9NP Tel: (020) 7690 9700 Fax: (020) 7690 9711

Mikado Computer Support, 38 Gravel Hill, Wimborne, Dorset, BH21 1RR Tel: (01202) 883808 Fax: (01202) 883808 E-mail: sales@mikado.co.uk

Mill Tech Computers, 39c James Street, Whitehaven, Cumbria, CA28 7HZ Tel: (01946) 696200 Fax: (01946) 656208

Millennium Computer Systems Ltd, B11 The Seedbed Centre, Wyncolls Road, Colchester, CO4 9HT Tel: (01206) 855288 Fax: (01206) 855285 E-mail: info@millennium-computer.co.uk

Mills, 13 Fairway Drive, Fairway Industrial Estate, Greenford, Middlesex, UB6 8PW Tel: (020) 8833 2626 E-mail: sales@millsltd.com

Minca Computing Ltd, 42 Main Street, Milngavie, Glasgow, G62 6BU Tel: 0141-956 2260 Fax: 0141-956 2234 E-mail: info@CUIS.co.uk

Minitech Systems Ltd, Bridle Way, St. Vincents Close, Girton, Cambridge, CB3 0PB Tel: (01223) 277049 Fax: (01223) 277632 E-mail: sales@minitech-systems.com

Minnie Business Systems Ltd, 65 London Wall, London, EC2M 5TU Tel: (020) 7638 3815 Fax: (020) 7638 1481 E-mail: ad@minniebusiness.co.uk

▶ MJS It Services Ltd, Florida House, 13 Comberton Hill, Kidderminster, Worcestershire, DY10 1QG Tel: (01562) 748573 Fax: (01562) 753621 E-mail: enquiry@mjsits.co.uk

Modular, 103 Chatsworth Drive, Mansfield, Nottinghamshire, NG18 4QU Tel: (01623) 622144 Fax: (01623) 438308 E-mail: admin@modcompsys.demon.co.uk

Moffat Communications Ltd, 1 Bow Lane, London, EC4M 9EE Tel: (020) 7489 4567 Fax: (020) 7489 4568

Moneywise Software, 1 Joanna House, 34 Central Road, Worcester Park, Surrey, KT4 8JB Tel: (020) 8337 0663 Fax: (020) 8715 9909 E-mail: itmltd@aol.com

Monostar Ltd, Peggs Barn, Drinkstone, Bury St. Edmunds, Suffolk, IP30 9TW Tel: (01449) 736081 Fax: (01449) 736083 E-mail: info@monostar.co.uk

Montague Tate Ltd, PO Box 179, Cirencester, Gloucestershire, GL7 7YT Tel: (0870) 4030007 Fax: (0870) 4030008 E-mail: admin@montague-tate.co.uk

Monterpoint Ltd, 22 Belvedie Road, London, SE19 2HN Tel: (020) 8771 1666 Fax: (020) 8771 2249 E-mail: info@monterpoint.co.uk

Adrian Moss Associates, PO Box 473, Chichester, West Sussex, PO18 8BT Tel: (01243) 574500 Fax: (01243) 528923 E-mail: adrian@business-initiatives.com

Mountain Software, Withambrook Park Industrial Estate, Grantham, Lincolnshire, NG31 9ST Tel: (01476) 573718 Fax: (01476) 590563 E-mail: info@mountainsoftware.co.uk

▶ Multi Network Solutions Ltd, Priory Gate House, 7 Priory Road, High Wycombe, Bucks, HP13 6SE Tel: 0870-746 1343 Fax: (01494) 793439

Multilink Edi Ltd, 118-120 Dominion Road, Multilink House, Worthing, West Sussex, BN14 8JP Tel: (01903) 821554 Fax: (01903) 235216 E-mail: sales@blueflag.co.uk

Multipix Imaging Ltd, 1 Tilmore Road, Petersfield, Hampshire, GU32 2HG Tel: (01730) 233332 Fax: (01730) 231062 E-mail: sales@multipix.com

Myco Systems Ltd, 17 Criss Grove, Chalfont St. Peter, Gerrards Cross, Buckinghamshire, SL9 9HG Tel: (01753) 893390 E-mail: enquiries@mycosystems.co.uk

Myriad, 10 Lawn Avenue, Peterborough, PE1 3RB Tel: (01733) 766617 Fax: (01733) 759727 E-mail: enquiries@myriadit.net

▶ N 2 N Ltd, Unit 26, Rosehill Business Centre, Normanton Road, Derby, DE23 6RH Tel: (01332) 200009 Fax: (01332) 292625

N A G Ltd, Wilkinson House Jordan Hill, Banbury Road, Oxford, OX2 8DR Tel: (01865) 311744 Fax: (01865) 310139 E-mail: info@nag.co.uk

N C Soft, 12 Nicholas Lane, London, EC4N 7BN Tel: (01252) 556000 Fax: (020) 7623 0442 E-mail: info@ncsoft.co.uk

N Code International Ltd, Innovation Technology Center, Advanced Manufacturing Park, Brunel Way, Catcliffe, Rotherham, South Yorkshire, S60 5WG Tel: 0114-254 1246 Fax: 0114-254 1245 E-mail: info@ncode.com

N D C Ltd, 72 Crooksbury Road, Farnham, Surrey, GU10 1QD Tel: (01252) 782666 Fax: (01252) 782666

N M D Computer Consultants, 27 Friar Rd, Brighton, BN1 6NH Tel: (01273) 551060 Fax: (01273) 551060 E-mail: nick@mndconsulting.com

N N R Ltd, 94 Gervase Road, Edgware, Middlesex, HA8 0EP Tel: (020) 8906 1497

N T T Contracts Ltd, 307 Park Ho, 21 Park St, Croydon, CR0 1YE Tel: (020) 8405 8196 Fax: (020) 8681 5963

NCC Group, Oxford Road, Manchester, M1 7EF Tel: 0161-209 5200 Fax: 0161-209 5400 E-mail: response@nccgroup.co.uk

Neill King Partnership, 25 Garrard Close, Salford Priors, Evesham, Worcestershire, WR11 8XG Tel: (01789) 778462 Fax: (01789) 490486 E-mail: neil@neil-king.co.uk

Nemothon Computer Systems, Farleigh, East Grafton, Marlborough, Wiltshire, SN8 3DB Tel: (01672) 810901 Fax: (01672) 810883

Neonstream Ltd, 23 Woodcote, Maidenhead, Berkshire, SL6 4DU Tel: (01628) 622022 Fax: (01628) 785458 E-mail: rws@neonstream.net

Neosys Ltd, 14 Lomond Place, Erskine, Renfrewshire, PA8 6AP Tel: 0141-812 5937 Fax: 0141-812 5937

▶ Net Lynk, The Courtyard, Roman Way, Coleshill, Birmingham, B46 1HQ Tel: (01675) 466555 Fax: (01675) 466050

Net Resources Ltd, 26a Palmerston Place, Edinburgh, EH12 5AL Tel: 0131-477 7127 Fax: 0131-477 7126 E-mail: info@netresources.co.uk

Netcraft Ltd, Rockfield House, Charlcombe, Bath, BA1 9BQ Tel: (01225) 447500 Fax: (01225) 448600 E-mail: sales@netcraft.com

▶ Netfix Solutions Ltd, Heath House, West Drayton Road, Uxbridge, Middlesex, UB8 3LA Tel: (020) 8589 9966 Fax: (020) 8589 9955

Netik Consulting Ltd, Sir John Lyon Ho, 5 High Timber St, London, EC4V 3LS Tel: (020) 7489 5899 Fax: (020) 7329 0829

▶ Netron Wireless, 6 Wilmer Industrial Estate, Wilmer Place, London, N16 0LW Tel: (0870) 3509474 Fax: (020) 7249 3111

Network Perspectives Ltd, Elmbank Mill, The Charrier, Menstrie, Clackmannanshire, FK11 7BU Tel: (01259) 726636 Fax: (01259) 763388 E-mail: enquiries@net-spex.co.uk

▶ New Century Technology International Ltd, NCT House, Worley Road, Rotherham, South Yorkshire, S61 1LZ Tel: (0870) 7874833 Fax: (0870) 7874839

Newburgh Technologies Ltd, 2 Sandy Lane, Newburgh, Wigan, Lancashire, WN8 7TT Tel: (01257) 464200 Fax: (01257) 464200

Newmind Ltd, Yarburgh House, King Street, Yarburgh, Louth, Lincolnshire, LN11 0PN Tel: (01507) 363636 Fax: (01507) 363764 E-mail: sales@newmind.ltd.uk

▶ Newtyne Computer Consultants, 6 Howe Street, Edinburgh, EH3 6TD Tel: 0131-225 6952 Fax: 0131-225 9324 E-mail: enquiry@newtyne.com

Nexpress Ltd, Unit 16, Gelders Hall Road, Shepshed, Loughborough, Leicestershire, LE12 9NH Tel: (01509) 501100 Fax: (01509) 601186 E-mail: sales@nexpress.co.uk

Nexsan Technologies, 33-35 Parker Industrial Estate, Mansfield Road, Derby, DE21 4SZ Tel: (01332) 291600 Fax: (01332) 291616 E-mail: info@nexsan.com

▶ Nexsys Consultants, 22 Frys Lane, Yateley, Hampshire, GU46 7TJ Tel: (01252) 890633

▶ Nexus Data Solutions Ltd, Douglas House, 140 Hanham Road, Bristol, BS15 8NP Tel: (0845) 2263160

Noblestar Systems Ltd, Liberty House, 222 Regent Street, London, W1B 5TR Tel: (020) 7297 2038 Fax: (020) 7297 2142 E-mail: info@noblestar.co.uk

Norbeck Data Ltd, Lenten House, The Gravel, Trowbridge, Wiltshire, BA14 6QL Tel: (01225) 782865 Fax: (01225) 783284

Norman Data Defense Systems UK Ltd, Exchange House, 494 Midsummer Boulevard, Milton Keynes, MK9 2EA Tel: (01908) 847410 Fax: (0871) 7176999 E-mail: info@normanuk.com

Norsys Ltd, Citadel House, Solvay Road, Northwich, Cheshire, CW8 4DP Tel: (01606) 784884 Fax: (01606) 784082

North Gate Public Services, Sx3 House, Market Street, Bracknell, Berkshire, RG12 1QD Tel: (01344) 401111 Fax: (01344) 401100

Northern Connection Ltd, 23 Kelso Gardens, Newcastle upon Tyne, NE15 7DB Tel: 0191-274 5600 Fax: 0191-274 5625

N-Tire Systems Ltd, P O Box 215, Brentford, Middlesex, TW8 8RT Tel: (0845) 658 1505 Fax: (0845) 658 1505 E-mail: office@n-tiresystems.co.uk

▶ O S Solutions, 5 High West Street, Dorchester, Dorset, DT1 1UJ Tel: (01305) 751713

Oakhurst Business Systems Ltd, 11 Randiddles Close, Hurstpierpoint, Hassocks, West Sussex, BN6 9BG Tel: (01273) 835617 Fax: (01273) 832485

Oaklea Direct, Oaklea Pk, Tunbridge La, Bramshott, Liphook, Hants, GU30 7RF Tel: (01428) 727790 Fax: (01428) 787427

Oakleaf Consultancy Ltd, 2A Talbot Road, Northampton, NN1 4JB Tel: (01604) 633566 Fax: (01604) 601102 E-mail: sales@oakleafconsultancy.com

Oasys, Unit 1, Briar Close, Bramble Lane, Wye, Ashford, Kent, TN25 5HB Tel: (01233) 812050 Fax: (01233) 812082 E-mail: enquiries@o-a-sys.co.uk

Ocean Wave Digital Ltd, 138 Shepherds Bush Rd, London, W6 7PB Tel: 020 76104321 Fax: 020 76104453

Ohm Electronics Ltd, 515 Pinner Road, Harrow, Middlesex, HA2 6EH Tel: (020) 8427 0545 Fax: (020) 8863 7930 E-mail: sales@ohmelectronics.co.uk

OK Solutions Ltd, Albion Ho, 113 Station Rd, Hampton, Middlesex, TW12 2AL Tel: 020 84011301 Fax: 020 84011302

Omega Computers, 685 Cranbrook Road, Ilford, Essex, IG2 6SY Tel: (020) 8550 9295 Fax: (020) 8550 0830 E-mail: sale@omegacomputer.uk

O'Neil Software, Unit 6 Joplin Court, Crownhill, Milton Keynes, MK8 0JP Tel: (01908) 635320 Fax: (01908) 635328 E-mail: sales@oneilsoft.com

Opecsystem Ltd, 1 Beech Leys, Steeple Claydon, Buckingham, MK18 2RP Tel: (01296) 730110 Fax: (07070) 653124 E-mail: trevor@opecsystem.com

Open Answers Ltd, Masons House, 1-3 Valley Drive, London, NW9 9NG Tel: (020) 8204 8600 Fax: (020) 8905 0156

Open Business Solutions, 1 Highlands Court, Cranmore Avenue, Shirley, Solihull, West Midlands, B90 4LE Tel: 0121-711 2015 Fax: 0121-711 2873 E-mail: sales@novar-solutions.co.uk

Open File, 17 Springett Avenue, Ringmer, Lewes, East Sussex, BN8 5HD Tel: (01273) 814409 Fax: (01273) 814409

Open International Ltd, Buckholt Drive, Warndon, Worcester, WR4 9SR Tel: (01905) 754455 Fax: (01905) 754441

Open Link Software Ltd, Carolyn Ho, 22-26 Dingwall Rd, Croydon, CR0 9XS Tel: (020) 8681 7701 Fax: (020) 861 7702

Open Logistics Ltd, PO Box 147, Harrogate, North Yorkshire, HG2 8AH Tel: (01423) 569642

Open Seas, 7 Nuffield Way, Abingdon, Oxfordshire, OX14 1RJ Tel: (01235) 537391 Fax: (01235) 535168 E-mail: info@openseas.co.uk

Open Systems Professional Services Ltd, Oak View Lodge, Friezland Lane, Greenfield, Oldham, OL3 7EU Tel: (01457) 820667 Fax: (01457) 877388

Optima Systems Ltd, Optima Court Mill Court, Spindle Way, Crawley, West Sussex, RH10 1TT Tel: (01293) 562700 Fax: (01293) 562699 E-mail: sales@optima-systems.co.uk

Optimage Ltd, 26 St Fillans Terrace, Edinburgh, EH10 5PJ Tel: 0131-447 8800

Optimus UK Ltd, 131 Warwick Road, Kenilworth, Warwickshire, CV8 1HY Tel: (01926) 852352 E-mail: info@optimus.co.uk

Optinet Ltd, 115-117 Barnards Green Road, Malvern, Worcestershire, WR14 3LT Tel: (01684) 893857 Fax: (01684) 893859

Oracle Corporation UK Ltd, Oracle Parkway, Reading, RG6 1RA Tel: 0118-924 0000 Fax: 0118-924 3000 E-mail: sales@uk.oracle.com

Orb 2000 Ltd, 30 Cannon St, London, EC4M 6YN Tel: (020) 7653 5700 Fax: (020) 7653 5701

Orbit Information Systems Ltd, 6 Jasmine Close, Manchester, M23 9EY Tel: 0161-945 3886 Fax: 0161 945 3886

Oriel Systems Ltd, Unit 1, Industry Park, Cricketts Lane, Chippenham, Wiltshire, SN15 3EQ Tel: (01249) 705070 Fax: (01249) 705071 E-mail: sales@orielsystems.com

Original Business Systems Ltd, The Stables, The Vatch, Stroud, Gloucestershire, GL6 7LE Tel: (01453) 751515 Fax: (01453) 753525 E-mail: info@obs.co.uk

Oris GB Systems, 108 Henderson Street, Bridge of Allan, Stirling, FK9 4HF Tel: (01786) 833162 Fax: (01786) 834230 E-mail: sales@gbsystems.co.uk

Ottma Ltd, 30 Leicester Villas, Hove, East Sussex, BN3 5SQ Tel: (01273) 414586 Fax: 01273 414586

Our-Info, 279 Garstang Road, Fulwood, Preston, PR2 9XH Tel: (01772) 719648 E-mail: david@joyner.co.uk

Owta Ltd, Stratton House, Over Stratton, South Petherton, Somerset, TA13 5LQ Tel: (01460) 249170 Fax: (01460) 242235

Oxford Computer Consultants Ltd, 23-38 Hythe Bridge Street, Oxford, OX1 2ET Tel: (01865) 305200 Fax: (01865) 793124 E-mail: oxford@cc.co.uk

Oxford Software Engineering Ltd, 9 Spinners Court, West End, Witney, Oxfordshire, OX28 1NH Tel: (01993) 700878 Fax: (01993) 774132 E-mail: enquiries@ocl.co.uk

P A G Computers, 5 Bell Close, Knebworth, Hertfordshire, SG3 6AJ Tel: (01438) 814650 Fax: (01438) 814111 E-mail: admin@pagcomputers.com

P B S Computers, 72-74 Ashley Road, Poole, Dorset, BH14 9BN Tel: (01202) 668822 Fax: (01202) 772627 E-mail: info@pbscomputers.co

P C Computer Services, 16 South Avenue, Bognor Regis, West Sussex, PO21 3QS Tel: (01243) 820840 Fax: (01243) 842961 E-mail: sales@pc-computers.co.uk

P C Consultants, Enterprise Court, Ryde Business Park, Ryde, Isle of Wight, PO33 1BD Tel: (01983) 811711 Fax: (01934) 811801 E-mail: sales@pcconsultants.co.uk

P C Innovations, 3 Cardine Close, Sittingbourne, Kent, ME10 2HY Tel: (01795) 410264 Fax: (01795) 410283 E-mail: enquiries@pc-i.co.uk

P C Part X Computers, 77 Bawtry Road, Bramley, Rotherham, South Yorkshire, S66 2TN Tel: (01709) 701200 Fax: (01709) 701200 E-mail: sales@pcpartx.com

▶ P C Solutions & Support, 25 Marriotts Way, Hemel Hempstead, Hertfordshire, HP3 9EN Tel: (01442) 219149

P D P Associates Ltd, 23 Darlington Rd, Stockton-on-Tees, Cleveland, TS18 5BL Tel: (01642) 657010

P D S Consultants, 82 London Road, Leicester, LE2 0QR Tel: 0116-254 4645 Fax: 0116-247 0092 E-mail: info@pds-consultants.co.uk

P I A Software Ltd, 10 Brunel Close, Hedge End, Southampton, SO30 2TA Tel: (01489) 799364 Fax: (01489) 795191 E-mail: sales@pia.co.uk

P L W Associates Ltd, 37 Elmers Green, Skelmersdale, Lancashire, WN8 6RZ Tel: (01695) 559990 Fax: (01695) 559990 E-mail: plwunderscoreass@msn.com

P & Q International plc, Wickham House, Station Road, Braughing, Ware, Hertfordshire, SG11 2PB Tel: (0845) 1300707 Fax: (0845) 1300727 E-mail: sales@pandq.com

Paget Computer Services, 32 Paget Lane, Enniskillen, County Fermanagh, BT74 7HT Tel: (028) 6632 8868 Fax: (028) 6632 8854

Paloma Systems Ltd, 2 Frederick Terrace, Frederick Place, Brighton, BN1 1AX Tel: (01273) 778688 Fax: (01273) 323927 E-mail: sales@paloma.co.uk

Panacea Services Ltd, 20 St Mary at Hill, London, EC3R 8EE Tel: (020) 7375 3757 Fax: (020) 7375 1525 E-mail: info@panacea-services.co.uk

▶ Panther Computing, 2 Lions Way, Sleaford, Lincolnshire, NG34 8GN Tel: (01529) 415566 Fax: (01529) 415588

Paradigm Geo-Physical UK Ltd, Mackenzie Buildings, 168 Skene Street, Aberdeen, AB10 1PE Tel: (01224) 649555 Fax: (01224) 649496

Paragon Business Solutions Ltd, 3 Greenock Road, London, W3 8DU Tel: (020) 8993 8995 Fax: (020) 8993 8999 E-mail: info@credit-scoring.co.uk

Paravizion Ltd, 16 Lyndhurst Road, Heswall, Wirral, Merseyside, CH61 0HB Tel: 0151-648 7223 E-mail: ajc@discframe.co.uk

Partpulse Ltd, Aelred, Ballfield Road, Godalming, Surrey, GU7 2HE Tel: (01483) 419190 Fax: 01483418039

Patech Solutions Ltd, Tame House, Wellington Crescent, Fradley Park, Lichfield, Staffordshire, WS13 8RZ Tel: (01543) 444707 Fax: (01543) 444709

▶ Pathfinder Technologies UK Ltd, Lancaster Street, Birmingham, B4 7AR Tel: 0121-333 7000 E-mail: sales@pftec.co.uk

Patsystems UK Ltd, 22 Shand Street, London, SE1 2ES Tel: (020) 7940 0490 Fax: (020) 7940 0499 E-mail: info@patsystems.com

Paymaster Systems Ltd, Moorlands, Oldfield Road, Bromley, BR1 2LE Tel: (020) 8467 6107 Fax: (020) 8467 6121 E-mail: paymaster@btclick.com

PC World, 1 Priory Retail Park, 131 High St Colliers Wood, London, SW19 2PP Tel: (0870) 2420444 Fax: 020 82541201

PCS, Wakefield Road, Ossett, West Yorkshire, WF5 9AJ Tel: (01924) 281777 Fax: (01924) 266920

Pearl Technology Ltd, 34 Cecil Avenue, Barking, Essex, IG11 9TF Tel: (020) 8507 0507 E-mail: pearl@ukenet.com

Pearsons Professional Services Ltd, Rushton House, Nantwich Road, Audley, Stoke-on-Trent, ST7 8DL Tel: (01782) 720753 Fax: (01782) 720798E-mail: ppsltd@a-b.co.uk

Pegasus Group Public Ltd Company, Orion House, Orion Way, Kettering, Northamptonshire, NN15 6PE Tel: (01536) 495000 Fax: (01536) 495001 E-mail: sales@pegasus.co.uk

Pelstar Computing Ltd, Merlin House, 122-126 Kilburn High Road, London, NW6 4HY Tel: (020) 7624 6880 Fax: (020) 7328 9626 E-mail: info@pelstar.co.uk

Pendle Business Micro, Riverside, Bridge Street, Colne, Lancashire, BB8 0DR Tel: (01282) 861511 Fax: (01282) 871560 E-mail: peter@pendlebusinessmicro.fsbusiness.co.uk

Pendrigh Computer Services, 31-37 Church Street, Reigate, Surrey, RH2 0AD Tel: (01737) 221510 E-mail: info@pendrighcomputerservices.co.uk

COMPUTER SYSTEMS CONSULTANTS OR SERVICES, SOFTWARE ETC – *continued*

Pennycress Computers, 5 St. James Street, Weston-super-Mare, Avon, BS23 1SS Tel: (01934) 644893 Fax: (01934) 644863 E-mail: pennycress@hotmail.com

Penta Consulting, Chervil House, 28 Stafford Road, Wallington, Surrey, SM6 9BH Tel: (020) 8647 3999 Fax: (020) 8647 2777

Performance Computers North East Ltd, 10-11 Post House Wynd, Darlington, County Durham, DL3 7LU Tel: (01325) 267333 Fax: (01325) 489093 E-mail: sales@performancecomputers.co.uk

Pericom SW Ltd, 46b Sea King Road, Lynx Trading Estate, Yeovil, Somerset, BA20 2NZ Tel: (01935) 410377 Fax: (01935) 410755 E-mail: mail@lbts.co.uk

Peripheral Store, 2 Manorial Road, Sutton Coldfield, West Midlands, B75 5UD Tel: 0121-323 3633 Fax: 0121-323 3535

Pervasic Ltd, 2 Queen Caroline Street, London, W6 9DX Tel: (020) 8741 8777 Fax: (020) 8323 8013 E-mail: sales@pervasic.com

Phantasia Ltd, 5 Fenlock Court, Blenheim Office Park, Long Hanborough, Witney, Oxfordshire, OX29 8RX Tel: (01993) 883700 Fax: (01993) 883750 E-mail: sales@phantasia.net

Phoebus Solutions Ltd, 2a Market Street, Heanor, Derbyshire, DE75 7NR Tel: (0870) 7270300 Fax: (08707) 270400 E-mail: sales@pheobus-solutions.com

Piercy Adams Computer & Electronic Systems Ltd, Cochrane House, Church Road, Bookham, Leatherhead, Surrey, KT23 3JP Tel: (01372) 459577 Fax: (01372) 459343

▶ Pinnacle Business Solutions Ltd, Unit 10a, Balmakeith Industrial Estate, Nairn, IV12 5QW Tel: (01667) 458450 Fax: (0870) 0746644 E-mail: pinnacle@pinsol.com

Pipistrel Retail Software Ltd, 23 Woodbridge Road, Guildford, Surrey, GU1 1DY Tel: (01483) 440099 Fax: (0870) 1164400 E-mail: support@pipistrel.com

Plastics Software Ltd, Unit 1, Farmcroft, Farnham Lane, Haslemere, Surrey, GU27 1HD Tel: (01428) 656595 Fax: (01428) 656595 E-mail: sales@plasware.co.uk

Platinum Computer Consultants Ltd, Woodfield Way, Redhill, RH1 2DP Tel: (01737) 789555 E-mail: sales@platinumcc.co.uk

Plus Online Stores Ltd, Natson Mill, Bow, Crediton, Devon, EX17 6JE Tel: (01363) 82923 Fax: (01363) 82931 E-mail: ch@base10.ws

Pluscrab Ltd, 30 St Phillips Avenue, Wolverhampton, WV3 7DU Tel: (01902) 340529

Pneutrol Ireland Ltd, 5 Caulside Drive, Antrim, BT41 2DU Tel: (028) 9448 1800 Fax: (028) 9448 1801 E-mail: info@pneutrol.com

Positive Computer Systems, New Forest Enterprise Centre, Chapel Lane, Totton, Southampton, SO40 9LA Tel: (023) 8057 7733 Fax: (023) 8057 7755 E-mail: sales@positive-computers.co.uk

Powell & Associates, Bilbrook Cottage, 36 Dukes Wood Avenue, Gerrards Cross, Buckinghamshire, SL9 7JT Tel: (01753) 893162 Fax: (01753) 893162 E-mail: david.powell@powell-assoc.com

Powersoft Computer Services, 4 Pelham Court, Pelham Place, Crawley, West Sussex, RH11 9SH Tel: (01293) 562730 Fax: (01293) 522006 E-mail: support@powersoft-services.co.uk

Powertech Systems & Consultancy Ltd, 35 Maiden La Centre, Lower Earley, Reading, RG6 3HD Tel: 0118-935 0000 Fax: 0118-935 0001 E-mail: sales@powertech.co.uk

Pracctice Ltd, 216 Straight Mile Road, Rotherwas, Hereford, HR2 6JP Tel: (01432) 372100 Fax: (01432) 372111

Precision Plus, 6 Fiery Hillock, Fortrose, Ross-Shire, IV10 8SE Tel: (01381) 620480 Fax: (01381) 621534

Premier Software Solutions, Premier House, Hollys Court, Hollys Park Road, Cannock, Staffordshire, WS11 1DB Tel: (01543) 466580 Fax: (01543) 466579 E-mail: sales@chasebs.com

▶ Premium Source Ltd, 30 Whiteladies Road, Bristol, BS8 2LG Tel: 0117-949 0088 Fax: 0117-949 0088

Price Systems Ltd, Meridian Office Park, Osborn Way, Hook, Hampshire, RG27 9HY Tel: (01256) 760012 Fax: (01256) 762122 E-mail: sales@pricesystems.com

Princeton Consulting Ltd, 43-51 Windsor Road, Slough, SL1 2EE Tel: (01753) 217700 Fax: (01753) 217701

Pristine Computers & Computing Ltd, 45 High Street, Charing, Ashford, Kent, TN27 0HU Tel: (01233) 713660 Fax: (01233) 713727 E-mail: peter@pristineuk.com

▶ Pro Drive IT Ltd, Headley House, Parklands-Queens Elizabeth Park, Railton Road, Guildford, Surrey, GU2 9JX Tel: (01483) 236000 Fax: (01483) 236111 E-mail: sales@prodriveit.co.uk

Pro It Ltd, 24 Saffron Close, Chineham, Basingstoke, Hampshire, RG24 8XQ Tel: (01256) 358303 Fax: (01256) 358015

Pro Logic Computers, 6-8 Doncaster Road, South Elmsall, Pontefract, West Yorkshire, WF9 2HZ Tel: (01977) 649100 Fax: (01977) 651411 E-mail: paul@pro-logic.co.uk

Proactive Computing Ltd, 28 Telford Close, High Shincliffe, Durham, DH1 2YJ Tel: 0191-386 7605 Fax: 0191-386 7605 E-mail: proactivecomputing@ic24.net

Pro-Byte Computers Ltd, 163 Cleethorpe Road, Grimsby, South Humberside, DN31 3AX Tel: (01472) 235500 Fax: (01472) 235501 E-mail: sales@pro-byte.co.uk

Process Intelligence Ltd, Ebrington, Chipping Campden, Gloucestershire, GL55 6NL Tel: (01386) 593084 Fax: (01386) 593132

Profile, Tingewick Mill, Church Lane, Tingewick, Buckingham, MK18 4RB Tel: (01280) 847494 Fax: (01280) 847495 E-mail: info@profile.co.uk

Program Products (Services) Ltd, Enterprise House, Station Approach, West Byfleet, Surrey, KT14 6NJ Tel: (01932) 345566 Fax: (01932) 336333 E-mail: info@program-products.co.uk

Progress Partnership, 4 Garden Street, Hebden Bridge, West Yorkshire, HX7 8AQ Tel: (01422) 845245 Fax: (01422) 843964

Project Central Ltd, 163 Turnpike Link, Croydon, CR0 5NW Tel: (020) 8688 8002 Fax: (07079) 013173 E-mail: sales@projectcentral.co.uk

▶ Project Management Software Centre, 6 Whinmoor Way, Silkstone, Barnsley, South Yorkshire, S75 4JE Tel: (01226) 792222 Fax: (01226) 792945 E-mail: kelly@pmscsolutions.co.uk

Prolinx Ltd, View Farm Barn, Windmill Hill, Great Milton, Oxford, OX44 7NW Tel: (01844) 279199 Fax: (01844) 279144 E-mail: contact@prolinx.co.uk

Prologic Systems Ltd, 65 Fortess Rd, London, NW5 1AG Tel: (020) 7485 3225 Fax: (020) 7209 0399

Promark Systems Ltd, 9 Clydach Road, Enfield, Middlesex, EN1 3SL Tel: (020) 8363 0467 Fax: (020) 8364 4300

Promentum Technologies Ltd, 3 Cobden Road, London, SE25 5NZ Tel: (020) 8656 8666 Fax: (020) 8656 8606 E-mail: technologies@promentum.co.uk

Prosig Ltd, 44a High Street, Fareham, Hampshire, PO16 7BQ Tel: (01329) 239925 Fax: (01329) 239159 E-mail: info@prosig.com

Psytech Ltd, Suite 11, 216-218 Main Road, Biggin Hill, Westerham, Kent, TN16 3BD Tel: (01959) 541415 Fax: (01959) 541096 E-mail: admin@psytech.demon.co.uk

Puissance Computer Associates, 1 Bushey Coopers Cottage, Pond Hall Road, Hadleigh, Ipswich, IP7 5PS Tel: (01473) 822002 Fax: (01473) 829665 E-mail: sales@puissance.co.uk

Puma Computer Systems Ltd, 29 Waterloo Road, Wolverhampton, WV1 4DJ Tel: (01902) 714500 Fax: (01902) 710630 E-mail: info@pumacomputersystems.co.uk

▶ Purple Lattice Solutions Ltd, Ealing House, 33 Hanger Lane, London, W5 3HJ Tel: (020) 8566 7772 Fax: (020) 8566 7772 E-mail: sales@purplelattice.com

▶ Purple Triangle Ltd, 3 Hawk Close, Nuneaton, Warwickshire, CV11 6TG Tel: (024) 7632 0788

Pyramid Ltd, Turner House, 9-10 Mill Lane, Alton, Hampshire, GU34 2QG Tel: (01420) 593300 Fax: (01420) 593311 E-mail: sales@pyramid-ltd.co.uk

Pyramid Consultancy, Murlain House, Union Street, Chester, CH1 1QP Tel: (01244) 357277 Fax: (01244) 357278 E-mail: sales@pyramidconsultancy.co.uk

Pythagoras Communications Ltd, Clivemont Road, Maidenhead, Berkshire, SL6 7BZ Tel: (01628) 590700 Fax: (01628) 590717

QA, QA House, Delta Office Business Park, Welton Road, Swindon, SN5 7WZ Tel: (08709) 060090 Fax: (01793) 696007 E-mail: responsecentre@qa.com

▶ QDS, 2 Glebelands Road, Sale, Cheshire, M33 6LB Tel: 0161-962 6600 Fax: 0161-962 8800

Quadnet Ltd, Power House Cromwell Industrial Estate, Staffa Road, London, E10 7QZ Tel: (020) 8988 7710 Fax: (020) 8988 7719 E-mail: enquiries@quadnet.co.uk

Qualsoft Computer Consultants, 53 The Springs, Middleham, Leyburn, North Yorkshire, DL8 4RB Tel: (01969) 624575 Fax: (01969) 624637 E-mail: sales@qualsoft.com

Quantum Data Solutions Ltd, 3-5 Marischal Street, Peterhead, Aberdeenshire, AB42 1BS Tel: (01779) 490426 Fax: (01779) 480074 E-mail: purchasing@qds.uk.net

Quantum System Management Ltd, 67 Tweedy Road, Bromley, BR1 3NH Tel: (020) 8460 2747 Fax: (020) 8313 3468

Qubix International Ltd, Highclere House, 5 High Street, Knaphill, Woking, Surrey, GU21 2PG Tel: (01483) 480222 Fax: (01483) 473050 E-mail: sales@qubixinternational.com

Quest Computing, Queen St Chambers, 68 Queen Street, Sheffield, S1 1WR Tel: 0114-275 0006 Fax: 0114-276 1312 E-mail: general@questcomputing.co.uk

Quickdrive Data Systems Ltd, 292-308 Southbury Road, Enfield, Middlesex, EN1 1TS Tel: (020) 8443 4260 Fax: (020) 8350 4029

Quiss Technology P.L.C., Unit 2 Tudor Estate, Abbey Road, London, NW10 7UW Tel: (020) 8961 9535 Fax: (020) 8961 9536 E-mail: contracts@quiss.co.uk

Qurius UK Ltd, Waterfall Business Park, Bury, Lancashire, BL9 7BR Tel: 0161-705 6000 Fax: 0161-705 6001 E-mail: mike.dickson@cedilla.co.uk

R & A Software Systems Ltd, Bank Chambers, 244 Fulwood Road, Sheffield, S10 3BB Tel: 0114-267 9669 Fax: 0114-267 9670 E-mail: info@rasoft.co.uk

R B I Recovery Services, Geddings Road, Hoddesdon, Hertfordshire, EN11 0NW Tel: (01992) 445566 Fax: (01992) 441785

▶ R B Networks, Copthorne Common, Copthorne, Crawley, West Sussex, RH10 3LG Tel: (01342) 715396E-mail: sales@e-delta.net

R D Computer Systems, 39 Ballyroney Rd, Rathfriland, Newry, Co. Down, BT34 5NQ Tel: (028) 4063 1626 Fax: (028) 4063 1636

R D F Consulting Ltd, 15 Queen Square, Brighton, BN1 3FD Tel: (01273) 200100 Fax: (01273) 205005 E-mail: sales@rdfgroup.com

R H Associates, 79 Cherry Grove, Sketty, Swansea, SA2 8AX Tel: (01792) 410500 Fax: (01792) 410506 E-mail: tracey@jackland.demon.co.uk

R K D Computers Liverpool, 6 Glenluce Road, Liverpool, L19 9BX Tel: 0151-281 0860 Fax: 0151-427 3022

R S M J Computers Ltd, 11 Lammas Way, Ampthill, Bedford, MK45 2TR Tel: (01525) 841800 Fax: (01525) 841800

▶ R W A Ltd, R W A House 66 Cardiff Road, Glan-Y-Llyn, Taffs Well, Cardiff, CF15 7QE Tel: (029) 2081 5050 Fax: (029) 2081 5051 E-mail: enquiries@rwa-net.co.uk

R2 B2, Wyse Hill House, Finchampstead, Wokingham, Berkshire, RG40 4JR Tel: 0118-973 7171 Fax: 0118-973 7172 E-mail: r2b2@r2b2.co.uk

Radius Solutions Ltd, Manor House, High Street, Dronfield, Derbyshire, S18 1PY Tel: (01246) 290331 Fax: (01246) 412401 E-mail: infouk@radiussolutions.co.uk

Raining Data, Mitford House, Benhall, Saxmundham, Suffolk, IP17 1JS Tel: (01728) 603011 Fax: (01728) 604154

Ram Computer Systems Ltd, 2 Chandos Place, Bletchley, Milton Keynes, MK2 2SQ Tel: (01908) 371086 Fax: (01908) 643961 E-mail: enquiries@ramcom.co.uk

Ramesys E Business Services Ltd, Glaisdale Dr East, Nottingham, NG8 4GU Tel: 0115-971 2000 Fax: 0115-971 4600 E-mail: enq@ramesys.com

Ramsay Systems, Bratton House, Dogpole, Shrewsbury, SY1 1ES Tel: (01743) 232278 E-mail: charlie@ramseysystems.co.uk

Rapport Software Ltd, 33 Clerkenwell Cl, London, EC1R 0AU Tel: (020) 7713 9233 Fax: (020) 7490 5785

React Computer Partnership, Unit 5, Old Maltings Approach, Woodbridge, Suffolk, IP12 1EF Tel: (01394) 387337 Fax: (01394) 610554 E-mail: enquiries@reactcp.co.uk

Readycrest Ltd, PO Box 75, Chatham, Kent, ME5 9DL Tel: (01634) 304060 Fax: (01634) 304070 E-mail: info@readycrest.co.uk

Real Solutions Ltd, Alexander House, Atlantic Street, Altrincham, Cheshire, WA14 5EW Tel: 0161-926 2600 Fax: 0161-996 1778 E-mail: enquiries@realsolutionsuk.com

Real Time Associates Ltd, Canning Ho, 59 Canning Rd, Croydon, CR0 6QF Tel: (020) 8656 7333

Real Time Micro Systems Ltd, 2 Grange Park, London, W5 3PL Tel: 020 88409038 Fax: 020 88409038

Real World, Unit 10 Broughton Manor Business Park, Broughton, Newport Pagnell, Buckinghamshire, MK16 0HF Tel: (01908) 676812 Fax: (01908) 698463 E-mail: sales@realworldsolutions.co.uk

Realtime Business Services, The Birches, 82 Church Street, Pinchbeck, Spalding, Lincolnshire, PE11 3YA Tel: (01775) 769731 Fax: (01775) 711582 E-mail: allan@realtime-bs.com

Red Ant Innovations Ltd, 3-4 Southernhay West, Exeter, EX1 1JG Tel: (01392) 274707 Fax: (01392) 421475 E-mail: sales@redant.uk.com

Redstor Ltd, 1 London Road, Reading, RG1 5BJ Tel: 0118 9011969 Fax: 0118-377 6501 E-mail: sales@redstor.com

Redtitan Ltd, 5 Regius Court, Penn, High Wycombe, Buckinghamshire, HP10 8RL Tel: (0870) 8705432 Fax: (0870) 8704560 E-mail: sales@redtitan.com

Redwood Systems Ltd, Headway Business Park, Denby Dale Road, Wakefield, West Yorkshire, WF2 7AZ Tel: (01924) 880760 Fax: (01924) 880759

Relational Consultants Ltd, 38 Northgate Street, Bury St. Edmunds, Suffolk, IP33 1HY Tel: (01284) 765723E-mail: info@relcon.co.uk

Result Technology Ltd, President Drive, Rooksley, Milton Keynes, MK13 8PP Tel: (01296) 641944 Fax: (01908) 201148

Retail Business Solutions Ltd, 24-26 Vincent Avenue, Crownhill, Milton Keynes, MK8 0AB Tel: (01908) 226226 Fax: (01908) 225533

Ricardo Tarragon Ltd, Ground Floor Block 5, The Westbrook Centre, Milton Road, Cambridge, CB4 1YG Tel: (01223) 323336 Fax: (01223) 323337 E-mail: sales@tarragon-et.co.uk

Rimington Solutions Ltd, The Vine, St David Street, Presteigne, Powys, LD8 2BP Tel: (01544) 260098 Fax: (0870) 7053329 E-mail: enquiries@rimington.co.uk

Risk Factor Solutions Ltd, Units B-C Kemps Farm, London Road, Balcombe, Haywards Heath, West Sussex, RH17 6JH Tel: (01444) 819460 Fax: (01444) 819461 E-mail: info@riskfactor-solutions.com

Riva Consulting Ltd, Chedeham House, Cot Lane, Chichester, West Sussex, PO18 8ST Tel: (01243) 575955 Fax: (01243) 575966 E-mail: sales@riva-consulting.com

Riverscape Ltd, Business & Innovation Centre, Wearfield, Sunderland Enterprise Park, Sunderland, SR5 2TA Tel: 0191-516 6456 Fax: 0191-516 6457 E-mail: info@riverscape.co.uk

▶ Roade IT Training, 23 Abbotts Way, Roade, Northampton, NN7 2LY Tel: (07709) 336819

Rockport Software Ltd, 551 Fairlie Road, Slough, SL1 4PY Tel: (01753) 577201 Fax: (01753) 577202 E-mail: info@rockportsoft.com

Ronin Group, 637 Forest Road, London, E17 4NE Tel: (020) 8531 4001 Fax: (020) 8531 2223

Rothbury Computers, Townfoot, Rothbury, Morpeth, Northumberland, NE65 7SL Tel: (01669) 620070 E-mail: johnrayner@rothburycomputers.com

Roundhouse Software Ltd, The Cavendish Centre, Winnall Close, Winchester, Hampshire, SO23 0LB Tel: (01962) 877649 Fax: (01962) 834085 E-mail: sales@roundhouse-sw.com

Rowan Associates, 77 Albert Road, Gourock, Renfrewshire, PA19 1NJ Tel: (01475) 631200 Fax: (01475) 638971 E-mail: enquiries@rowanassociates.co.uk

Roxar Ltd, Heritage Gate, Sandy Lane West, Littlemore, Oxford, OX4 6LB Tel: (01865) 712828 Fax: (01865) 712829

Royce Development, Stowick, Evesham Road, Broadway, Worcestershire, WR12 7HU Tel: (01386) 830858 Fax: (01386) 830858

▶ Rubicon Workflow Solutions, Pump Lathurley Farm Business Unitsgrazeley, Grazeley, Reading, RG7 1LL Tel: 0118-988 8780 Fax: 0118-988 8782 E-mail: sales@rubicon-solutions.co.uk

Rup Ltd, Unit 16 Netherton Business Centre, Kemnay, Inverurie, Aberdeenshire, AB51 5LX Tel: (01467) 642950 E-mail: rupltd@rup.co.uk

R-Utility Software Consultants Ltd, 10 Charles Street, Rossendale, Lancashire, BB4 9JG Tel: (01706) 830565 Fax: (01706) 225306 E-mail: sales@r-utility.co.uk

Ryecomp Ltd, Woodside, Easthorpe Hall, Malton, North Yorkshire, YO17 6QX Tel: (01653) 697212

S B S Computer Services, 23 Thistlecroft Gardens, Stanmore, Middlesex, HA7 1PJ Tel: (020) 8951 0564 Fax: (020) 8951 3962 E-mail: sales@sbsnet.com

S C A Systems Ltd, 12 Littlehampton Road, Worthing, West Sussex, BN13 1QE Tel: (01903) 262688 Fax: (01903) 695311 E-mail: sales@scasystems.com

S C Consultancy, Grey Tiles, Broad Oak, Heathfield, East Sussex, TN21 8SN Tel: (01435) 865527

S D Partners Ltd, The White House, 9a Belvedere Road, Southbank, London, SE1 8AB Tel: (020) 7401 9399 Fax: (020) 7401 9499 E-mail: sales@sd-partners.com

S E S Computing, 5 Market Street, Weymouth, Dorset, DT4 8DD Tel: (01305) 774402 Fax: (01305) 784502 E-mail: sales@sescomputors.com

S H E Management, Barham Court, Teston, Maidstone, Kent, ME18 5BZ Tel: (01622) 618613 Fax: (01622) 205950 E-mail: info@formsmaster.com

S I M Ltd, Albion House, Chertsey Road, Woking, Surrey, GU21 6BF Tel: (01483) 733100 Fax: (01483) 733101 E-mail: sales@simgroup.co.uk

S P C Systems, 69 Merton Hall Road, London, SW19 3PX Tel: (020) 8540 8409 E-mail: sales@spc-systems.com

S S S Consultants, Alfriston, Traps Lane, New Malden, Surrey, KT3 4RT Tel: (020) 8949 3753 Fax: (020) 8949 0809 E-mail: info@sss-it.co.uk

S V I Ltd, 7 Chapel Street, Peterhead, Aberdeenshire, AB42 1TH Tel: (01779) 474000 Fax: (01779) 474800 E-mail: sales@svi.co.uk

S X 3, Queens Court, Wilmslow Road, Alderley Edge, Cheshire, SK9 7RR Tel: (01625) 587111 Fax: (01625) 587100 E-mail: sales@sx3.com

Sabrefame Ltd, Brook House, Duck Street, Wendens Ambo, Saffron Walden, Essex, CB11 4JU Tel: (01799) 542287 Fax: (01799) 541954 E-mail: sabrefame@aol.com

Sala Consultancy, Forum House, Stirling Road, Chichester, West Sussex, PO19 7DN Tel: (01243) 775757 Fax: (01243) 787110 E-mail: info@ismc.co.uk

The Salamander Organisation Ltd, 5 Innovation Close, York Science Park, York, YO10 5ZF Tel: (0870) 1611700 Fax: (0870) 1611701 E-mail: matthew.bosson@tsorg.com

Sanderson Ltd, 720 Waterside Drive, Aztec West, Almondsbury, Bristol, BS32 4UD Tel: (01454) 892500 Fax: (01454) 892610 E-mail: enquiries@sanderson.com

Sanderson P C S L Ltd, Batley Bus & Technology Centre, Technology Drive, Batley, West Yorkshire, WF17 6ER Tel: (01924) 520300 Fax: (01924) 520301 E-mail: info@sanderson.com

Sandford Partnership Ltd, 77-83 Walnut Tree Cl, Guildford, Surrey, GU1 4UH Tel: 01483 881600 Fax: 01483 881601 E-mail: ldon@sandford.co.uk

Sandhill Consultants Ltd, St Johns Court, Brewery Hill, Grantham, Lincolnshire, NG31 6DW Tel: (01476) 568708 Fax: (01476) 568620 E-mail: info@sandhill.co.uk

Sapphire Ltd, Lambourne House, 7 Western Road, Romford, RM1 3LD Tel: (01708) 333700 Fax: (01708) 333800 E-mail: sales@dataease.com

▶ Sapphire Computing & Consulting Ltd, Shapphire House, 50 Leyes Lane, Kenilworth, Warwickshire, CV8 2QT Tel: (01926) 779700

Sapphire Instrument Co., 25 Friar Road, Brighton, BN1 6NG Tel: (01273) 556008 Fax: (01273) 556008

Savant Systems Ltd, 45a Chigwell Rd, London, E18 1NG Tel: (020) 8530 7809 E-mail: guy@savantsystems.co.uk

COMPUTER SYSTEMS CONSULTANTS OR SERVICES, SOFTWARE ETC – *continued*

Savcom Ltd, Little Acre, Coopers Hill Road, Nutfield, Redhill, RH1 4HS Tel: (01737) 822343 E-mail: martin@savcom.co.uk

Savcor Ltd, 8a Bridgend Road, Dingwall, Ross-Shire, IV15 9SL Tel: (01349) 867970 Fax: (01349) 867978 E-mail: info@savador.co.uk

Save9 Ltd, Cayley Court, Hopper Hill Road, Eastfield, Scarborough, North Yorkshire, YO11 3YJ Tel: (01723) 588099 E-mail: sales@save9.com

Savoy Data Systems Ltd, 10 Leicester Road, Barnet, Hertfordshire, EN5 5DA Tel: (020) 8441 4426 Fax: (020) 8441 4428 E-mail: info@savoydata.co.uk

SBC Group Ltd, City Gates, 2-4 Southgate, Chichester, West Sussex, PO19 8DJ Tel: (01243) 779526 Fax: (01243) 785503 E-mail: info@sbcgroup.co.uk

Sciclone Ltd, 24a Angel Hill, Bury St. Edmunds, Suffolk, IP33 1UZ Tel: (01284) 777432 Fax: (01284) 701080 E-mail: info@miuk.com

Scientia Ltd, St. Johns Innovation Centre, Cowley Road, Cambridge, CB4 0WS Tel: (01223) 421221 Fax: (01223) 421218 E-mail: info@scientia.com

Scientific Computers Ltd, Jubilee House, Jubilee Walk, Crawley, West Sussex, RH10 1LQ Tel: (01293) 403636 Fax: (01293) 403641 E-mail: info@scl.com

Sci-sys Ltd, Clothier Road, Bristol, BS4 5SS Tel: 0117-971 7251 Fax: 0117-972 1846 E-mail: marketing@scisys.co.uk

Scott Adam Systems Ltd, Ramsay House, 18 Vera Avenue, London, N21 1RA Tel: (020) 8360 6600 Fax: (020) 8360 6688 E-mail: sales@scottadam.co.uk

Scottish Data Systems, Bawer Drive, Old Minniguff, Newton Stewart, Wigtownshire, DG8 6AH Tel: (01671) 402483 Fax: (01671) 402283 E-mail: sales@scottishdatasystems.com

Scytala Ltd, 181 St. Johns Road, Congleton, Cheshire, CW12 2EJ Tel: (01260) 276919

Sea Bass Software Ltd, Abbotts Tower, Goring Heath, Reading, RG8 7RZ Tel: (01491) 682585 Fax: (01491) 682586 E-mail: sarah.bell@seabass.co.uk

Secon Solutions Ltd, River House, 85 Esher Road, Walton-on-Thames, Surrey, KT12 4LN Tel: (020) 8255 0777 Fax: (020) 8255 7511 E-mail: sales@secon.co.uk

Selcom Systems, 65-71 York Road, Acomb, York, YO24 4LN Tel: (01904) 788181 Fax: (01904) 788194 E-mail: info@selcom.co.uk

Senior Consultants, 113 Station Road, Ellon, Aberdeenshire, AB41 9AZ Tel: (01358) 725161 Fax: (01358) 725171 E-mail: sales@ellon.co.uk

Sennock Computer Services Ltd, 3 Nightingale Road, Kemsing, Sevenoaks, Kent, TN15 6RU Tel: (01959) 525153 Fax: (01959) 525153 E-mail: info@sennock.co.uk

Sensible People, Romary House, 26 Church Road, Tunbridge Wells, Kent, TN1 1JP Tel: (01892) 612320 Fax: (01892) 612328 E-mail: sales@sensible-people.co.uk

Sequel Technology Ltd, 2 Hart House, The Hart, Farnham, Surrey, GU9 7HJ Tel: (01252) 734321 Fax: (01252) 734355 E-mail: sales@seqtec.co.uk

Serco Geografix Ltd, Hurricane Way, Norwich, NR6 6EW Tel: (01603) 788940 Fax: (01603) 788964 E-mail: sales@premiergeografix.com

Serenity Computer Services, 86 Leyburne Road, Dover, Kent, CT16 1SH Tel: (01304) 242188 Fax: (01304) 242088

Servicepower Business Solutions Ltd, Petersgate House, St. Petersgate, Stockport, Cheshire, SK1 1HE Tel: 0161-476 2277 Fax: 0161-480 8088 E-mail: info@servicepower.com

Services Online, 42 Kirby Drive, Luton, LU3 4AW Tel: (01582) 583823 Fax: (01582) 491384 E-mail: webmaster@services-online.co.uk

Sevagram Ltd, 26 Hodder Drive, Greenford, Middlesex, UB6 8LH Tel: (020) 8998 5191 Fax: (020) 8998 5191 E-mail: info@sevagram.co.uk

▶ S. A. Shaw, Hoylake Business Centre, 38-42 Birkenhead Road, Hoylake, Wirral, Merseyside, CH47 3BW Tel: (0870) 0780202 Fax: 0151-632 4624 E-mail: enquiries@shawbusiness.co.uk

Shopper Trak Ltd, 42 Ivanhoe Road, Hogwood Industrial Estate, Finchampstead, Wokingham, Berkshire, RG40 4QQ Tel: (0870) 8908725 Fax: (0870) 4102604 E-mail: information@shoppertrak.co.uk

Shyamtronics Computer Systems, 246 Tottenham Court Road, London, W1T 7QU Tel: (020) 7637 1990 Fax: (020) 7637 0085 E-mail: sales@shyamtronicds.com

Sigma Computer Services, 8 Adbolton Avenue, Gedling, Nottingham, NG4 3NB Tel: 0115-940 3041 E-mail: sigma@innotts.co.uk

Silicon 2000 (UK) Ltd, 82 Church Rd, Hove, E. Sussex, BN3 2EB Tel: 01273 388883

Silicon Heart Ltd, 6-8 Sedley Pl, London, W1C 2HE Tel: (020) 7355 3344 Fax: (020) 7355 2266

Silicon Valley Group plc, Lakeview House, Lightwater Road, Lightwater, Surrey, GU18 5XQ Tel: (01276) 455900 Fax: (01276) 455910 E-mail: svg@silicon-valley.co.uk

Silkmoth Ltd, Cara House, Crossall Street, Macclesfield, Cheshire, SK11 6QF Tel: (01625) 433388 Fax: (01625) 616760 E-mail: keith.jones@silkmoth.com

Silverstream UK Ltd, Stretton Road, Greetham, Oakham, Leicestershire, LE15 7NP Tel: (01572) 812251 E-mail: sales@silverstream.uk.com

Silvertech Ltd, Holmwood Broadlands Business Campus, Langhurstwood Road, Horsham, West Sussex, RH12 4PN Tel: (01403) 211611 Fax: (01403) 211058 E-mail: sales@silvertech.co.uk

Simex Systems, Unit 44 Canal Bridge Enterprise Centre, Meadow Lane, Ellesmere Port, CH65 4EH Tel: 0151-356 3040 Fax: 0151-356 3049 E-mail: sales@pcmouse.co.uk

Simply Agile, 25 Lindberg Way, Woodley, Reading, RG5 4XE Tel: 0118-969 7100 Fax: (0870) 1388551 E-mail: rod@train400.com

Sinara Consultants Ltd, 63 Tanner Street, London, SE1 3PL Tel: (020) 7940 7950 Fax: (020) 7378 1074 E-mail: sales@sinara.co.uk

SIR Learning Systems Ltd, Blackbrook House, Ashbourne Road, Blackbrook, Belper, Derbyshire, DE56 2DB Tel: (01773) 820011 Fax: (01773) 820206 E-mail: sales@sirplc.co.uk

Sirius Corporation, Rivermead House, Hamm Moor Lane, Addlestone, Surrey, KT15 2SF Tel: (01932) 820467 E-mail: mail@siriusit.co.uk

Sita Advanced Travel Solutions, Thornbrook House Weyside Park, Catteshall Lane, Godalming, Surrey, GU7 1XE Tel: (020) 8756 8000 Fax: (01483) 414122

Sixty Six Software, 128 Melton Road, West Bridgford, Nottingham, NG2 6EP Tel: 0115-945 5150 Fax: 0115-945 5152

SKTS, 451 Bushey Mill Lane, Bushey, WD23 2AT Tel: (01923) 223657 Fax: (01923) 333731 E-mail: enquiries@shkata.com

▶ Sli Developments, 94 Dawpool Road, London, NW2 7JY Tel: (020) 8830 6943

Sly Development Ltd, 15 The Avenue, Acocks Green, Birmingham, B27 6NG Tel: 0121-707 0060 Fax: 0121-707 0032 E-mail: info@slynet.co.uk

▶ Small Biz It Ltd, 13 Avenue Road, Trowbridge, Wiltshire, BA14 0AQ Tel: (01225) 765182 Fax: (01225) 765340

Small World Connections Ltd, PO Box 132, Manchester, M20 3BB Tel: 0161-445 0630 E-mail: info@swcltd.co.uk

Smart Systems (Essex) Ltd, 33 President Road, Colchester, CO3 9ED Tel: (01206) 549291 Fax: (01206) 769749

Smartdrive Ltd, 8 Colne Road, Earith, Huntingdon, Cambridgeshire, PE28 3PX Tel: (01487) 843663 Fax: (01487) 843661 E-mail: info@smartdrive.co.uk

▶ Smith Ivanson, 28 New Road, Penn, High Wycombe, Buckinghamshire, HP10 8DJ Tel: (01494) 817103

▶ Smr2 Computer Consultants, 44 High Street, Aylesbury, Buckinghamshire, HP20 1SE Tel: (01296) 428525

Soda Creative Ltd, 17-25 Cremer Street, London, E2 8HD Tel: (020) 7739 6217 Fax: (020) 7739 8650 E-mail: info@soda.co.uk

Softcase Consulting, 32 Canford Cliffs Road, Poole, Dorset, BH13 7AA Tel: (01202) 749643 Fax: (01202) 749643 E-mail: howard@softcase.co.uk

Softech Global, Softech House, London Road, Albourne, Hassocks, West Sussex, BN6 9BN Tel: (01273) 833844 Fax: (01273) 833044 E-mail: info@softechglobal.com

▶ Softedge Technology, Unit 6, Mavros House, 95 Vale Road, London, N4 1TG Tel: (020) 8809 1666 Fax: (020) 8809 5984

Softgen Ltd, 92 Harrowdene Road, Wembley, Middlesex, HA0 2JF Tel: (020) 8900 0333 Fax: (020) 8900 9646 E-mail: admin@softegenltd.co.uk

Software Futures Ltd, 2 Waterloo Way, Cheltenham Road, Bredon, Tewkesbury, Gloucestershire, GL20 7NA Tel: (01684) 772691 Fax: (01684) 772639 E-mail: information@softwarefutures.ltd.uk

Software Integrators Ltd, New London Bridge House, 25 London Bridge Street, London, SE1 9SG Tel: (020) 7378 9309 Fax: (020) 7378 9310 E-mail: admin@software-integrators.co.uk

Software Spectrum Ltd, Mallard House, Peregrine Business Park, Gomm Road, High Wycombe, Buckinghamshire, HP13 7DL Tel: (0870) 5771100 Fax: (0870) 5771104

Software & Training Ltd, 71 Crombey Street, Swindon, SN1 5QW Tel: (01793) 485761 Fax: (01793) 421725 E-mail: arun.bedi9@ntlworld.com

▶ Solak Technology Solutions, 25 Merryfields, Strood, Rochester, Kent, ME2 3ND Tel: (01634) 290983 Fax: (01634) 290983

Solar Soft PMS Ltd, Hampshire Int Business Park, Crockford Lane, Chineham, Basingstoke, Hampshire, RG24 8WH Tel: (01256) 685200 Fax: (01256) 685201 E-mail: sales@ssi-world.com

▶ Solidtech Solutions, Southgate House, Plough Road, Great Bentley, Colchester, CO7 8LG Tel: (01206) 252062 Fax: (0870) 1314474

Solstone Plus, 48a Old Steine, Brighton, BN1 1NH Tel: (01273) 206555 Fax: (01273) 387769 E-mail: solestoneplus@solestonegroup.com

Sopra Group Ltd, Northbrook House, Robert Robinson Avenue, Oxford, OX4 4GA Tel: (01865) 781781 Fax: (01865) 781777

▶ Sottek Ltd, 16 Warren Avenue, Sutton, Surrey, SM2 7QL Tel: (020) 8643 3487 Fax: (020) 8770 3997

Sourcing Partnership, 24 Alva Street, Edinburgh, EH2 4PY Tel: 0131-226 4747 Fax: 0131-226 4708 E-mail: admin@sourcingpartners.co.uk

South Bank Systems P.L.C., Compass Centre North, Chatham Maritime, Chatham, Kent, ME4 4YG Tel: (01634) 880141 Fax: (01634) 880383 E-mail: corporate@southbanksystems.com

Southdown House Software Ltd, Southdown House, Guildford Road, Westcott, Dorking, Surrey, RH4 3NR Tel: (01306) 877998 Fax: (01306) 887755 E-mail: info@southdown.co.uk

Southern Computer Service Ltd, 15 Blandford Gardens, Sittingbourne, Kent, ME10 4HW Tel: (01795) 429398

Southgate Accounting & Computer Consultants Ltd, The Grange, 100 High Street, London, N14 6TG Tel: (0870) 8506007 Fax: (0870) 8506008 E-mail: info@southgate.sagehost.co.uk

Spectrum O A Ltd, 7 121 Lansdowne Road, London, W11 2LF Tel: (020) 7221 3877 Fax: (020) 7221 6568

Speech Centre, Croft Road, Crowborough, East Sussex, TN6 1DL Tel: (01892) 661116 Fax: (01892) 668177 E-mail: info@speechcentre.co.uk

Sportcal Global Communications Ltd, 56 High St Wimbledon, London, SW19 5EE Tel: (020) 8944 8786 Fax: (020) 8944 8740 E-mail: sales@sportcal.com

Spot On Computers Ltd, 122 Waterloo Road, Manchester, M8 8AF Tel: (0845) 3453111 Fax: (0870) 1121953 E-mail: sales@spotonuk.com

▶ Spots Consulting, Knaves Beech Business Centre, Loudwater, High Wycombe, Buckinghamshire, HP10 9ZN Tel: (01628) 530404 Fax: (01628) 530404 E-mail: info@spots.co.uk

Sprezzatura Ltd, 45 St Mary's Road, Ealing, London, W5 5RG Tel: (020) 8912 1010 Fax: (020) 8912 1011 E-mail: info@sprezzatura.com

▶ Spring Associates, Roland Road, St. Sampson, Guernsey, GY2 4PF Tel: (07781) 149134

Spring It Solutions Ltd, 1-3 Museum Place, Cardiff, CF10 3BD Tel: (029) 2064 9400 Fax: (029) 2038 3750 E-mail: pete-heaven@spring.com

SRS, 3 Heol Mostyn, Village Farm Industrial Estate, Pyle, Bridgend, Mid Glamorgan, CF33 6BJ Tel: (01656) 745514 Fax: (01656) 749741

Stanford Technologies Ltd, Rayner House, Higher Hillgate, Stockport, Cheshire, SK1 3ER Tel: 0161-480 4051 Fax: 0161-429 0966 E-mail: sales@stanfordtec.co.uk

Star Computer Group plc, King Edward Court, 23 High Street, Sutton Coldfield, West Midlands, B72 1XS Tel: 0121-355 6171 Fax: 0121-354 4656 E-mail: info@starplc.co.uk

Star Computer Services (U K) Ltd, Unit 21 Woodside Park, Rugby, Warwickshire, CV21 2NP Tel: (01788) 551522 Fax: (01788) 551523

Star Seaford, 10 Broad Street, Seaford, East Sussex, BN25 1ND Tel: (01323) 490565 Fax: (01323) 491599

Strand Business Systems Ltd, 542 Chigwell Road, Woodford Green, Essex, IG8 8PA Tel: (020) 8559 2555 Fax: (020) 8506 0561

Strand Technology Group, 10-12 Westgate, Skelmersdale, Lancashire, WN8 8AZ Tel: (0845) 6607968 E-mail: mail@standtech.co.uk

Strategic Systems Technology Ltd, 14 Landons Close, London, E14 9QQ Tel: (020) 7538 8228 Fax: (0870) 2351411 E-mail: info@sst.co.uk

Strategic Thought Group plc, Old Town Hall, Centre Court Shopping Centre, Queens Road, London, SW19 8YB Tel: (020) 8410 4000 Fax: (020) 8410 4030 E-mail: sales@strategicthought.com

Strategy In Computing Ltd, Mooring Business Centre Willows End House, 9 Carolus Creek, Penn Island, Milton Keynes, MK15 8AZ Tel: (01908) 201202 Fax: (01908) 201170 E-mail: reply@strategy-in-computing.co.uk

Strategy Partners International Ltd, Chappell House, The Green, Datchet, Slough, SL3 9EH Tel: (01753) 592787 Fax: (01753) 592789

▶ Strawberry Global Technology, 1-2 219 High Street, Hampton Hill, Hampton, Middlesex, TW12 1NP Tel: (020) 8973 1414 Fax: (020) 8973 1515 E-mail: sales@strawberrygt.com

▶ Stroz Friedberg, Baird House, 15-17 St. Cross Street, London, EC1N 8UW Tel: (020) 7841 5870 Fax: (020) 7242 7860 E-mail: mail@strozfriedberg.co.uk

Stuart Wright, Warp Farm, Newsholme, Goole, North Humberside, DN14 7JS Tel: (01757) 638205 Fax: (01757) 630412 E-mail: stuart@dn14.co.uk

Styleware Ltd, 28 Wittering Road, Hayling Island, Hampshire, PO11 9SP Tel: (023) 9246 1561 Fax: (023) 9246 1501 E-mail: sales@styleware.co.uk

Styx Information Systems Ltd, 12 St Giles Grove, Haughton, Stafford, ST18 9HP Tel: (01785) 780583 Fax: (01785) 780641 E-mail: styx@styx.co.uk

Suilven Associates Computer Systems, PO Box 1, Leominster, Herefordshire, HR6 9YP Tel: (01568) 720194 Fax: (01568) 720195 E-mail: sales@suilven.com

▶ Sumari Business Systems Ltd, Branston Court, Branston Street, Birmingham, B18 6BA Tel: 0121-244 8111 Fax: 0121-244 8811 E-mail: sumari@sumari.co.uk

Sun Microsystems Ltd, Solaris House, Minley Road, Blackwater, Camberley, Surrey, GU17 9QG Tel: (01252) 420000 Fax: (01252) 420001

Sunflower Consulting Ltd, 2 Days Folley, Haytor, Newton Abbot, Devon, TQ13 9XR Tel: (01364) 661422 Fax: (01364) 661461

Sunitek Marshan Ltd, 176 Newhampton Road East, Wolverhampton, WV1 4PQ Tel: (01902) 773329 Fax: (01902) 773328

Support & Development Ltd, 43 Cottesford Clo, Hadleigh, Ipswich, IP7 5JA Tel: 01473 824642

Supportive Ltd, Old Studios, Hyde Park Road, Leeds, LS6 1RU Tel: 0113-245 7302 Fax: 0113-245 7304 E-mail: post@supportive.co.uk

▶ Supportkey Ltd, Ladywell Business Centre, 94 Duke Street, Glasgow, G4 0UW Tel: 0141-552 8505 Fax: 0141-552 0246 E-mail: sales@supportkey.com

Syan Ltd, The Mill, King Coughton, Alcester, Warwickshire, B49 5QG Tel: (01789) 400464 Fax: (01789) 400470

Syan Technology Ltd, Unit 2, Stafford Park 17, Telford, Shropshire, TF3 3DG Tel: (01952) 291670 Fax: (01952) 291845

The Synapse Partnership Ltd, 1A Cecil Road, Hale, Altrincham, Cheshire, WA15 9NY Tel: 0161-929 5777 Fax: 0161-929 0805

Syne Qua Non Ltd, Navire House, Mere Street, Diss, Norfolk, IP22 4AG Tel: (01379) 644449 Fax: (01379) 644445 E-mail: sales@synequanon.com

Synectics Solutions Ltd, Synectics House The Hollies, The Brampton, Newcastle, Staffordshire, ST5 0QY Tel: (01782) 664000 Fax: (01782) 664050 E-mail: enq@synectics-solutions.com

Synergy Financial Systems Ltd, 8-9 Edison Village, Nottingham Science Technology Park, Nottingham, NG7 2RF Tel: 0115-967 7933 Fax: 0115-967 7933 E-mail: info@synergy-sf.com

Synergy Systems Ltd, 43 Ashbarn Cresent, Winchester, Hampshire, SO22 4QH Tel: (01962) 840174 Fax: (01962) 877266 E-mail: admin@synsys.com

▶ Synetix Group, Unit C1, Aven Industrial Park, Tickhill Road, Maltby, Rotherham, South Yorkshire, S66 7QR Tel: (01709) 819933 Fax: (01709) 798804

Synetrix Ltd, Innovation Centre, University of Keele, Keele, Newcastle, Staffordshire, ST5 5NB Tel: (01782) 338200 Fax: (01782) 629600 E-mail: enq@synetrix.co.uk

Syport Systems, 5 Moorlands Avenue, Kenilworth, Warwickshire, CV8 1HR Tel: (01926) 864910E-mail: info@syport.co.uk

Syscom Group Ltd, Hampshire House, High Street, Kingswinford, West Midlands, DY6 8AW Tel: (01384) 400600 Fax: (01384) 400601 E-mail: info@syscom.plc.uk

Syscon Ltd, PO Box 119, North Shields, Tyne & Wear, NE30 2YD Tel: 0191-296 5542 Fax: 0191-296 5595E-mail: info@shotel.co.uk

Sysnet Computer Consultants, Newton House, 457 Sauchiehall Street, Glasgow, G2 3LG Tel: 0141-333 1020 Fax: 0141-572 1732

System Integration (UK) Ltd, Unit 1, Reddicap Trading Estate, Sutton Coldfield, West Midlands, B75 7BU Tel: (01283) 224222 Fax: (01283) 819615 E-mail: sales@simail.co.uk

System Red Ltd, Prospidnick, Helston, Cornwall, TR13 0RY Tel: (01326) 563300 Fax: (01326) 565680 E-mail: sales@systemred.co.uk

System Solutions Norwich, 19 Mahoney Green, Rackheath, Norwich, NR13 6JY Tel: (01603) 722590 Fax: (01603) 721308 E-mail: c.turner@systemsolutions.co.uk

▶ System Wise, 107 Saughtonhall Drive, Edinburgh, EH12 5TS Tel: 0131-313 0707 Fax: 0131-313 0808 E-mail: info@systemwise.co.uk

Systeme Evolutif Ltd, Third Floor, 9 Cavendish Place, London, W1G 0QD Tel: (020) 7636 6060 E-mail: info@evolutif.co.uk

Systems Advisers Group UK Ltd, Enterprise House, Donaldson Crescent, Kirkintilloch, Glasgow, G66 1XF Tel: 0141-578 2237 Fax: 0141-578 2306 E-mail: sales@systemsadvisers.com

Systems & Communications Ltd, 10 Moreland Close, Alton, Hampshire, GU34 2SA Tel: (01420) 88482 Fax: (01420) 544754

Systems For Dentists Ltd, 90 High Street, Gosforth, Newcastle upon Tyne, NE3 1HB Tel: 0191-285 9192 Fax: 0191-285 9192

Systems Plus, 14 Kintyre, Antrim, BT41 2AN Tel: (028) 9448 7497 Fax: (028) 9448 7497

The Systems Practice P.L.C., Parkside Business Park, Curstead Way, Golborne, Warrington, WA3 3PY Tel: (01942) 270222 Fax: (01942) 275220 E-mail: janet.houghton@tspplc.com

Systems Technology Consultants Ltd, Bedford Street, Stoke-on-Trent, ST1 4PZ Tel: (01782) 286300 Fax: (01782) 280036 E-mail: sytech@ebstar.co.uk

▶ Systemsoft Communications Ltd, Lilford Lodge, Lilford, Peterborough, PE8 5SA Tel: (01832) 272049 Fax: (01832) 270028 E-mail: stan.bell@systemssoft.co.uk

T A Computer Consultants, 41 Oakmead Road, St. Osyth, Clacton-on-Sea, Essex, CO16 8NW Tel: (01255) 821979 E-mail: help@tacomputers.co.uk

T A M Computer Equipment, 40 Hunter Drive, Bletchley, Milton Keynes, MK2 3LR Tel: (01908) 366929 Fax: (01908) 649009

T L P Consultancy Ltd, Robert Denholm House, Bletchingley Road, Nutfield, Redhill, RH1 4HW Tel: (01737) 824000 Fax: (01737) 824001

COMPUTER SYSTEMS CONSULTANTS OR SERVICES, SOFTWARE ETC – *continued*

T M A Data Management Ltd, Surrey House, 34 Eden Street, Kingston upon Thames, Surrey, KT1 1ER Tel: (020) 8481 3988 Fax: (020) 8546 9794 E-mail: info@tma.co.uk

T M E Ltd, 11 Church Street, Walton-On-Thames, Surrey, KT12 2QP Tel: (01932) 232123 Fax: (01932) 232110E-mail: info@tme-ltd.com

T S L Technology Ltd, The Station Mill, Station Road, Alresford, Hampshire, SO24 9DE Tel: (01962) 735707 Fax: (01962) 735502 E-mail: enquiries@tsltechnology.com

T T W Services Ltd, Suite 3, The Octagon, Brighton Marina Village, Brighton, BN2 5WB Tel: (01273) 699003 E-mail: ttw@winman.co.uk

Tadpole Contracts Ltd, The Old Bakery, High Street, Great Bardfield, Braintree, Essex, CM7 4RF Tel: (01371) 810817 Fax: (01371) 810024

Tadware Ltd, 31 Hill Field, Oadby, Leicester, LE2 4RW Tel: 0116-271 6137 Fax: 0116-271 6137 E-mail: tadnet@globalnet.co.uk

Tanist Computer Systems Ltd, Penbury, Pendrift, Blisland, Bodmin, Cornwall, PL30 4JT Tel: (01208) 851166 Fax: (01208) 850044

Tapcast Ltd, Russet House, Appletree Lane, Inkberrow, Worcester, WR7 4JA Tel: (01386) 792196 Fax: (01386) 793087 E-mail: steve.neal@tapcast.co.uk

Target Achievement Ltd, Mercury Park, Amber Close, Amington, Tamworth, Staffordshire, B77 4RP Tel: (01827) 309709 Fax: (01827) 309719 E-mail: sales@maydown.co.uk

Target Group plc, Target House, 5-19 Cowbridge Road East, Cardiff, CF11 9AB Tel: (029) 2030 1401 Fax: (029) 2030 1400 E-mail: marketing@targetgroup.net

Task Computer Systems, Breakspeare, College Road, London, SE21 7NB Tel: (020) 8693 5103 Fax: (020) 8299 2540

Tata Consultancy Services, 12 Rutland Square, Edinburgh, EH1 2BB Tel: 0131-229 9725 Fax: 0131-228 3637

Team Management PC Hire Ltd, 3 Hermitage Court, Wapping High Street, London, E1 9PL Tel: (020) 7702 9242 Fax: (020) 7702 9747 E-mail: tanya@pchire.com

Tecfacs Ltd, 6 Oaklands Business Centre, Oaklands Park, Wokingham, Berkshire, RG41 2FD Tel: 0118-977 6645 Fax: 0118-989 4461 E-mail: sales@tecfacs.com

Tech Cadcam, Minster House, Western Way, Bury St. Edmunds, Suffolk, IP33 3SP Tel: (01284) 754781 Fax: (01284) 750344 E-mail: sales@techcadcam.net

Tech Op Ltd, 268 London Road, Cheltenham, Gloucestershire, GL52 6HS Tel: (01242) 570999 Fax: (01242) 588955 E-mail: sales@techop.co.uk

▶ Techfield Software, 4 Banksfield Grove, Yeadon, Leeds, LS19 7LN Tel: (01943) 884478 Fax: (01943) 884478

Technical Software Consultants Ltd, 6 Mill Square, Featherstone Road, Wolverton Mill, Milton Keynes, MK12 5RB Tel: (01908) 317444 Fax: (01908) 220959 E-mail: info@tscinspectionsystems.com

The Technical Support Service, Forrest Rd, Stirling, FK8 1UJ Tel: 01786 478694 Fax: 01786 447672

▶ Techno-Craft (UK) Ltd, 16 The Mount, Guildford, Surrey, GU2 4HS Tel: (020) 7430 0777 Fax: (020) 7430 1777

Technology Blueprint Ltd, 45b High Street, St. Neots, Cambridgeshire, PE19 1BN Tel: (01480) 356226 Fax: (01480) 356227 E-mail: support@propco.co.uk

Technology For Business plc, 1-2 Kingdom Close, Fareham, Hampshire, PO15 5TJ Tel: (01489) 609000 Fax: (01489) 609999 E-mail: sales@tfbplc.co.uk

The Technology Forge, Top Floor Pegholme, Wharfebank Business Centre, Otley, Leeds, LS21 3JP Tel: (01943) 464844 Fax: (01943) 464833 E-mail: sales@technologyforge.com

Technology Helpdesk, Unit 3, Turnbull Way, Livingston, West Lothian, EH54 8RB Tel: (01506) 436700 Fax: (01506) 436703 E-mail: sales@technologyhelpdesk.co.uk

Technology Management Ltd, 1 Sunray Avenue, Whitstable, Kent, CT5 4ED Tel: (01227) 276590

Technology Management (Midlands) Ltd, The Old Rectory, 57 Waterloo Road, Wolverhampton, WV1 4QH Tel: (01902) 578300 Fax: (01902) 578301 E-mail: admin@tecman.co.uk

Technology Tamed Ltd, Hadleigh Business & Learning Centre, Crockatt Lane, Hadleigh, Ipswich, IP7 6RH Tel: (01473) 826180

Tectonic Ltd, Meridian Business Park, 1A Jupitor Court, Dominus Way, Leicester, LE19 1RP Tel: 0116-282 0567 Fax: 0116-282 0599 E-mail: info@tectonic.com

Tekno Computer Systems Ltd, 41 Bartlett Street, Caerphilly, Mid Glamorgan, CF83 1JS Tel: (029) 2088 5421 Fax: (029) 2088 5235 E-mail: info@tekno.co.uk

Telecetera Computer Consultants, Carden Close, Worcester, WR1 2AR Tel: (01905) 612220 Fax: (01905) 612226 E-mail: info@telecetera.co.uk

Telemere Group Ltd, 128 Greenstead Road, Colchester, CO1 2SN Tel: (01206) 867188 Fax: (01206) 503444 E-mail: david.johnson@telemere.co.uk

Teleport Ltd, The Pound, Cookham, Maidenhead, Berkshire, SL6 9QE Tel: (01628) 810100 Fax: (01628) 810300 E-mail: sales@teleport.co.uk

Telescan Computer Services, PO Box 1, Thornton-Cleveleys, Lancashire, FY5 1SH Tel: (01253) 829292

Tempus Computers Ltd, St Pauls House, St Pauls Square, Birmingham, B3 1RB Tel: 0121-233 3100 Fax: 0121-233 4560 E-mail: sales@tempa.co.uk

Tertio Ltd, 1 Angel Square, Torrens Street, London, EC1V 1PL Tel: (01225) 478000 Fax: (01225) 478001

Tescom UK Ltd, 21-22 Great Sutton Street, London, EC1V 0DY Tel: (020) 7022 6700 Fax: (020) 7022 6701 E-mail: info@tescom-intl.com

Tessella Support Service plc, Chadwick House Warrington Road, Birchwood Park, Birchwood, Warrington, WA3 6AE Tel: (01925) 286800 Fax: (01925) 286808 E-mail: sales@tesella.com

Texellent Solutions, Unit 13b Stephenson Court Fraser Road, Priory Business Park, Bedford, MK44 3WJ Tel: (01234) 832540 Fax: (01234) 832541 E-mail: admin@texellent.co.uk

Thames Information Systems Ltd, 11b Greenwich South Street, London, SE10 8NJ Tel: (020) 8858 6651 Fax: (020) 8305 1090 E-mail: info@tisl.co.uk

Thermo Fisher Scientific, 1 St Georges Court, Hanover Business Park, Broadheath, Altrincham, Cheshire, WA14 5TP Tel: 0161-942 3000 Fax: 0161-942 3001 E-mail: info@thermoinformatics.com

Thompson Consultants Ltd, The Mow Barton, Northend, Clutton, Bristol, BS39 5QS Tel: (01761) 453673 Fax: (01761) 452707 E-mail: sales@thompson-consultants.co.uk

Thorogood Associates Ltd, Dralda House, 24-28 Crendon Street, High Wycombe, Buckinghamshire, HP13 6LS Tel: (01494) 684200 Fax: (01494) 684223

Tib Co., Castlebridge Office Village, Kirtley Drive, Nottingham, NG7 1LD Tel: 0115-948 6500 Fax: 0115-948 6595 E-mail: sales@tibco.com

Tiertex Ltd, 67 Palatine Rd, Didsbury, Manchester, M20 3LJ Tel: 0161-446 2251 Fax: 0161-446 2589 E-mail: contact@tiertex.co.uk

Tietoenator UK Ltd, Berwick House, 8-10 Knoll Rise, Orpington, Kent, BR6 0EL Tel: (01689) 836909 Fax: (01689) 833780 E-mail: info@tietoenator.com

Tigerridge Consultancy Services Ltd, 4 Bonneys, The Street, Eversley, Hook, Hampshire, RG27 0PJ Tel: 0118-973 6875 Fax: (0845) 2303635 E-mail: sales@tigerridge.co.uk

Time Global Ltd, 21 Cornwall Rd, St. Albans, Herts, AL1 1SQ Tel: (01727) 847454 Fax: (01727) 847453 E-mail: sales@timeglobal.co.uk

Timeframe Software Ltd, The Pump House, Queens Avenue, Christchurch, Dorset, BH23 1BZ Tel: (01202) 499414 Fax: (01202) 482535 E-mail: info@timeframe.co.uk

TL Computer Systems Ltd, 40 Holton Road, Barry, South Glamorgan, CF63 4HD Tel: (01446) 747702 Fax: (01446) 744699 E-mail: mail@tlsystems.co.uk

TMC, 113 Sandringham Road, Birmingham, B42 1PX Tel: 0121-356 3327

TMS Associates Ltd, 168 Clare Road, Cardiff, CF11 6RX Tel: (029) 2025 8900 Fax: (029) 2025 8255 E-mail: h.g.patel@ntlworld.com

Topspeed Consultants Ltd, 90 Reeds Avenue, Earley, Reading, RG6 5SR Tel: 0118-961 0848 Fax: 07971618391 E-mail: info@topspeed.co.uk

Torex, Telfer House, Range Road, Witney, Oxfordshire, OX29 0YN Tel: (0870) 0509900 Fax: (0870) 0509901 E-mail: retail-info@torex.co.uk

▶ Torex Retail Ltd, Imperial House, Imperial Way, Coedkernew, Newport, Gwent, NP10 8UH Tel: (01633) 811822 Fax: (01633) 811820 E-mail: dthomas@torex.co.uk

The Total Package Ltd, The Granary, Birling, West Malling, Kent, ME19 5JF Tel: (01732) 526910 Fax: (01732) 526939 E-mail: info@thetotalpackage.co.uk

Touch Finder, 10 Burnell Road, Sutton, Surrey, SM1 4EE Tel: (020) 8770 3700 Fax: (020) 8661 9295 E-mail: info@touchfinder.co.uk

Touch I.T Mobile, 27 Goldsmith Avenue, Romford, RM7 0EX Tel: (07071) 222856 E-mail: admin@touchit.co.uk

▶ Touchpoint Media Ltd, Frodsham Business Centre, Bridge Lane, Frodsham, WA6 7FZ Tel: (01928) 736610 Fax: (01928) 736611

Touchstone, 1 Triton Square, London, NW1 3DX Tel: (020) 7121 4700 Fax: (020) 7121 4740 E-mail: charlie.davies@touchstone.co.uk

Touchstone C T A, 89 Barnham Road, Barnham, Bognor Regis, West Sussex, PO22 0EQ Tel: (01243) 553479 E-mail: malcolm@tcta.co.uk

Trade Wind Technology Ltd, The Old Stores, 11 North Street, Tillingham, Southminster, Essex, CM0 7TR Tel: (01621) 779037 Fax: (01621) 779034 E-mail: sales@t-w-t.co.uk

Trading Technologies UK Ltd, 1st Floor, 36 Poultry Street, London, EC2R 8AJ Tel: (020) 7600 2121 Fax: (020) 7600 3344 E-mail: support@tradingtechnologies.com

Trans European Technology, 132 Goswell Road, London, EC1V 7DY Tel: (020) 7553 9950 Fax: (020) 7608 3588 E-mail: sales@tet.co.uk

Transam Microsystems Ltd, 2 Bakers Yard, Bakers Row, London, EC1R 3HT Tel: (020) 7837 4050 Fax: (020) 7837 3804 E-mail: transam@transam.co.uk

Transenigma Ltd, 33 Soundwell Road, Bristol, BS16 4QQ Tel: 0117-956 4429 Fax: 0117-956 4430 E-mail: info@transenigma.co.uk

Transition Computing Ltd, 12 Challenge House, Sherwood Drive, Bletchley, Milton Keynes, MK3 6DP Tel: (0870) 0110999 Fax: (08700) 514550 E-mail: enquiries@transitioncomputing.com

Trantor Ltd, Green Hedges Bungalow, Pontadawe Road, Neath, West Glamorgan, SA10 7YL Tel: (01639) 633072

Trapese Group, Millbrook House, 141 Milton Road, Weston-super-Mare, Avon, BS22 8AA Tel: (01934) 413547 Fax: (01934) 413418 E-mail: sales@souterncomputersystems.co.uk

Travel Management Systems Ltd, 33 Dee View Rd, Connah's Quay, Deeside, Clwyd, CH5 4AY Tel: (01244) 811777 E-mail: davidweigh@lineone.net

Travel Port, Galileo House Unit 10, Hurricane Way, Slough, SL3 8US Tel: (01753) 288000 Fax: (01753) 288001 E-mail: info@galileo.uk.com

Travelocity Business Ltd, Edward House, Stockport, Cheshire, SK1 3DQ Tel: (0845) 7110011 Fax: 0161-968 9300 E-mail: hotels@first-option.co.uk

Trend Consulting Ltd, Swan Business Centre, Fishers Lane, London, W4 1RX Tel: (020) 8747 2400 Fax: (020) 8747 2401 E-mail: barrett@trend.co.uk

Trend U K, Unit 75 Questor, Powder Mill Lane, Dartford, DA1 1JA Tel: (0870) 1218326 Fax: (0870) 1218328

Triad Group P.L.C., Weyside Park, Catteshall Lane, Godalming, Surrey, GU7 1XE Tel: (01483) 860222 Fax: (01483) 860198 E-mail: mail@triad.plc.uk

Triangle Development Services Ltd, 8 Cross & Pillory Lane, Alton, Hampshire, GU34 1HL Tel: (01420) 547500 Fax: (01420) 547501

Triangular Business Systems, 1 Marlston Court, Rough Hill, Marlston-cum-Lache, Chester, CH4 9JT Tel: (01244) 683450 Fax: (01244) 674949 E-mail: enquiries@triangularsystems.co.uk

Tribune Business Systems Ltd, 30 City Road, London, EC1Y 2AY Tel: (020) 7870 0000 Fax: (020) 7870 0011 E-mail: info@tribune.co.uk

▶ Trident Systems Consulting Ltd, 6-7, Hockley Hill, Birmingham, B18 5AA Tel: 0121-523 5333 Fax: 0121-523 2111

TripleTrack Business Systems Ltd, 25 Market Place, Warminster, Wiltshire, BA12 9BB Tel: (01985) 214260 Fax: (01985) 215806 E-mail: enquiries@tbs-net.com

Trireme Object Technology International Ltd, Regents House, Heaton Lane, Stockport, Cheshire, SK4 1BS Tel: 0161-225 3240 E-mail: clive@trireme.com

Tritech Computer Services Ltd, Forge House, Mill Road, Liss, Hampshire, GU33 7DX Tel: (01730) 893789 Fax: (01730) 894589 E-mail: sales@tritech.org.uk

Triumph Technologies, Unit A, Station Yard, Thame, Oxfordshire, OX9 3UH Tel: (01844) 261666 Fax: (01844) 261666 E-mail: technical@triumphtech.co.uk

▶ Tron Systems Ltd, Tron House, Quarrywood Court, Livingston, West Lothian, EH54 6AX Tel: (01506) 400450 E-mail: sales@tronsystems.co.uk

▶ Trovum Computer Consultants, 49 Calderfield Close, Stockton Heath, Warrington, WA4 6PJ Tel: (01925) 600435 Fax: (01925) 600435

Trust Co. P.L.C., 2-3 Namrik Mews, Hove, East Sussex, BN3 2TF Tel: (01273) 735999 Fax: (01273) 736999 E-mail: info@trustco.co.uk

TSG Ltd, High Street, Broom, Alcester, Warwickshire, B50 4HN Tel: (01789) 778900 Fax: (01789) 772272

TSG Ltd, 1 Gosforth Park Way, Salters Lane, Newcastle upon Tyne, NE12 8ET Tel: 0191-256 1166 Fax: 0191-256 1167 E-mail: sales@tsg.com

The Turtle Partnership, Hofer House, 185 Uxbridge Road, Hampton, Middlesex, TW12 1BN Tel: (020) 8941 6994 Fax: (020) 8941 4730 E-mail: mike@turtleweb.com

Tutorpro Ltd, 10 High Street, Wellington, Somerset, TA21 8RA Tel: (01823) 661669 Fax: (01823) 661668 E-mail: general@tutorpro.com

Type Help, Unit 2 Triangle Ho, 2 Broomhill Rd, London, SW18 4HX Tel: 020 88752450 Fax: 020 88752422

Co U Help Ltd, 32 Beech Hill, Haywards Heath, West Sussex, RH16 3RX Tel: (01444) 440551 Fax: (01444) 441698 E-mail: info@compuhelp.co.uk

U K C Distribution Ltd, Unit 3, Tan La, Exeter, EX2 8EG Tel: (01392) 491919 Fax: (01392) 494567

U P S Installations NI Ltd, 25B Somerville Road, Clady, Strabane, County Tyrone, BT82 9QZ Tel: (028) 7188 2257

▶ U R U Computer, 2 Nobel Square, Burnt Mills Industrial Estate, Basildon, Essex, SS13 1LS Tel: (01268) 728111E-mail: sales@uru.uk.com

Ubiquity Software Corporation, Suite B Building 3 The Eastern Business Park, Wern Fawr Lane, St. Mellons, Cardiff, CF3 5EA Tel: (029) 2081 7500 Fax: (029) 2081 7501

Uct Ltd, Abbot Street, London, E8 3DP Tel: (020) 7254 1650 Fax: (020) 7518 0302 E-mail: info@uctltd.com

UK C M G, Suite A1, Kebbell House, Delta Gain, Watford, WD19 5BE Tel: (020) 8421 5330 Fax: (020) 8421 5457 E-mail: ukcmg@ukcmg.org.uk

UK Software Ltd, Innovation Centre, Millenium Way, Thanet, Broadstairs, Kent, CT10 2WA Tel: (01843) 609345 Fax: (01843) 609351 E-mail: sales@uksoftware.ltd.uk

▶ Ultimate It Ltd, 42a High Street, Egham, Surrey, TW20 9DP Tel: (01784) 477474

▶ Umtali Ltd, 51 Arundel Road, Woodley, Reading, RG5 4JR Tel: 0118-944 1111 Fax: (0871) 2360368 E-mail: info@umtali.co.uk

▶ Uniserve Consulting Ltd, Berger House, 38 Berkeley Square, London, W1J 5AE Tel: (020) 7493 9323 Fax: (020) 7493 9324

Unitron Systems & Developments Ltd, 76A Jameson House, High Street, Broseley, Shropshire, TF12 5EX Tel: (01952) 883817 Fax: (01952) 883672

Universal Rentals (UK) Ltd, Unit 31, Spaces Business Centre, Ingate Place, London, SW8 3NS Tel: (020) 7720 8787 Fax: (020) 7627 4586E-mail: info@universalrentals.co.uk

V X L Instruments Ltd, Rayner House, 23 Higher Hillgate, Stockport, Cheshire, SK1 3ER Tel: 0161-429 7767 Fax: 0161-429 7477 E-mail: warranty@vxl.net

Vbug, 4 Park Parade, Park Road, Farnham Royal, Slough, SL2 3AU Tel: (01753) 649680 Fax: (01753) 647222 E-mail: sales@vbug.co.uk

VcsTimeless, 249 Upper Third Street, Witan Gate West, Milton Keynes, MK9 1DS Tel: 01908 350550 Fax: 01908 350551 E-mail: contact@vcstimeless.com

Veryan Ltd, Wellhouse Road, Beech, Alton, Hampshire, GU34 4AH Tel: (01420) 543131 Fax: (01420) 543232 E-mail: solutions@veryan.com

Videcom Travel Systems Ltd, Newtown Road, Henley-on-Thames, Oxfordshire, RG9 1HG Tel: (01491) 578951 Fax: (01491) 579368 E-mail: sales@videcom.com

Viglen Technology Ltd, 7 Handley Page Way Colney Street, Colney Street, St. Albans, Hertfordshire, AL2 2DQ Tel: (01923) 858700 Fax: (01727) 201888 E-mail: marketing@viglen.co.uk

Virkonnen Ltd, 17a High Street, Reigate, Surrey, RH2 9AA Tel: (01737) 223233 Fax: (01737) 243061 E-mail: sales@virkonnen.co.uk

Virtalis, Chester House, 79 Dane Road, Sale, Cheshire, M33 7BP Tel: 0161-969 1155 Fax: 0161-969 1166 E-mail: info@vrweb.com

Virtual Image, 184 Reddish Road, Stockport, Cheshire, SK5 7HS Tel: 0161-480 1915 Fax: 0161-612 2965E-mail: virimage@cs.com

Visi Group Ltd, Ram House, Chalky Lane, Chessington, Surrey, KT9 2NF Tel: (01372) 748749 Fax: (01372) 748148

Visual Computer Technologies Ltd, Unit 207 Solent BSNS Centre 3, Millbrook Road West, Southampton, SO15 0HW Tel: (023) 8077 9162 Fax: (023) 8078 8222 E-mail: sales@focused.co.uk

VMS UK, 120-126 Holme Lane, Sheffield, S6 4JW Tel: 0114-285 2595 Fax: 0114-231 4145 E-mail: vms@vms.fsbusiness.co.uk

Vox Solutions Ltd, 8 Adlington Court, Birchwood, Warrington, WA3 6PL Tel: (0870) 7770660 Fax: (0870) 0113552 E-mail: sales@voxsolutions.co.uk

W H B Stevenson, 19 Alder Hill Avenue, Leeds, LS6 4JQ Tel: 0113-278 4751 Fax: 0113-295 7864 E-mail: design@whbs.net

W I T Systems, Unit1 7 Business Development Centre, Main Avenue, Treforest Industrial Estate, Pontypridd, Mid Glamorgan, CF37 5UR Tel: (01443) 844565 Fax: (01443) 842925 E-mail: info@wit-systems.net

W W Computer Systems, Mowbray House, 58-70 Edgware Way, Edgware, Middlesex, HA8 8DJ Tel: (020) 8958 1347 Fax: (020) 8958 1348 E-mail: simone@wwcomputers.co.uk

Warren Point Ltd, Pixmore House, Pixmore Centre, Pixmore Avenue, Letchworth Garden City, Hertfordshire, SG6 1JG Tel: (01462) 483733 Fax: (01462) 786103

▶ WASP Managed Services, 88 Gracechurch Street, London, EC3V 0DN Tel: (020) 7283 0088 Fax: (020) 7337 6370

Waterstar, Chester House, Westgate, Bishop Auckland, County Durham, DL13 1PG Tel: (01388) 517513 E-mail: john.mccutheon@waterstar.co.uk

▶ Wdit Solutions Ltd, Unit 20 Bumpers Enterprise Centre, Vincients Road, Bumpers Farm, Chippenham, Wiltshire, SN14 6QA Tel: (01249) 709000 Fax: (01249) 467050 E-mail: sales@wdit.biz

Wealth Management Software P.L.C., 45 Beech Street, London, EC2Y 8AD Tel: (020) 7614 4800 Fax: (020) 7614 4801

Web-Services.Com, Forge Farm, Cropedy, Banbury, Oxfordshire, OX17 1QF Tel: (01295) 758474 Fax: (01295) 758474

Welcom Software Ltd, The Exchange, Station Parade, Harrogate, North Yorkshire, HG1 1TS Tel: (0845) 4565859 Fax: E-mail: info@welcom.co.uk

Wengo Information Services, 82 London Road, Biggleswade, Bedfordshire, SG18 8EB Tel: (01767) 313972 Fax: (01767) 222273 E-mail: geoffreybuzzard@compuserve.com

Westwood Associates Ltd, Hampden House, Hampden Road, Chalfont St. Peter, Gerrards Cross, Buckinghamshire, SL9 9DP Tel: (01753) 887161 Fax: (01753) 891214

Wheatley Associates, 9 Main Street, Witchford, Ely, Cambridgeshire, CB6 2HG Tel: (01353) 664605 E-mail: enquiries@wheatley-associates.net

White Waghorn Ltd, 9 High Street, Stevenage, Hertfordshire, SG1 3BG Tel: (01438) 726393 E-mail: info@whitewaghorn.co.uk

Whitehouse Consultants Ltd, 29 Harcourt Road, Dorney Reach, Maidenhead, Berkshire, SL6 0DT Tel: (01628) 630459 Fax: (01524) 411037 E-mail: sales@whitehouse-consult.co.uk

COMPUTER SYSTEMS CONSULTANTS OR SERVICES, SOFTWARE ETC – *continued*

Whitewedge Systems Ltd, 42 Jacklyns Lane, Alresford, Hampshire, SO24 9LG Tel: (01962) 734165 Fax: (01962) 734214 E-mail: nick.stone@www.sys.co.uk

Wilan Technologies Ltd, Wilan, Thimbleby, Horncastle, Lincolnshire, LN9 5RB Tel: (01507) 525008 Fax: (01507) 525008 E-mail: info@wilan-technologies.ltd.uk

▶ Wilcom Services, 6 Amersham Road, Chalfont St. Peter, Gerrards Cross, Buckinghamshire, SL9 0NY Tel: (01494) 876600 Fax: (01494) 876600

Windmill Business Systems Ltd, Cattells Mill Road, Willingham, Cambridge, CB4 5LA Tel: (01954) 261661 Fax: (01954) 261661 E-mail: info@windmillweb.net

▶ Winfoware Technologies, 786 London Road, Thornton Heath, Surrey, CR7 6JB Tel: (020) 8683 3193 Fax: (020) 8683 3193

Wise Systems Ltd, 7a High Street, Corsham, Wiltshire, SN13 0ES Tel: (01249) 717000 Fax: (01249) 717002 E-mail: info@wisesystems.co.uk

Wizard UK, 8 Tanners Yard, 239 Long La, London, SE1 4PT Tel: (020) 7940 4654 Fax: (020) 7407 7969

Wizards Ltd, Alpha House, Ashridge Road, Chesham, Buckinghamshire, HP5 2RE Tel: (01494) 837515 Fax: (01494) 837013 E-mail: info@wizards.co.uk

Woodchip Computers, 15 Walker Close, Glusburn, Keighley, West Yorkshire, BD20 8PW Tel: (01535) 636981 Fax: (0870) 7061967 E-mail: sales@woodchipcomputers.co.uk

Woodford Computer Consultants, Little Fairwood, Fairwood Road, Dilton Marsh, Westbury, Wiltshire, BA13 4EL Tel: (01373) 824966 Fax: (01373) 825966 E-mail: woodford@fairwood.co.uk

Work Group Support Systems, The Studio, Craigleth Road, Edinburgh, EH4 2EB Tel: 0131-477 7775 Fax: 0131-332 7467 E-mail: n.hill@wgss.co.uk

▶ Workforce Systems, Unit 13 Nortex Business Centre, 105 Chorley Old Road, Bolton, BL1 3AS Tel: (01204) 842225 Fax: (01204) 497197 E-mail: sales@workforce.co.uk

X K S Ltd, Unit 19 St. Asaph Business Park, Glascoed Road, St. Asaph, Clwyd, LL17 0LJ Tel: (01745) 584953 Fax: (01745) 583047

Xansa Employee Trustee Company Ltd, 420 Thames Valley Park Drive, Thames Valley Park, Reading, RG6 1PU Tel: (0870) 2416181 Fax: (0870) 2426282 E-mail: info@xansa.com

▶ Xantium Consulting, 34 Buckingham Palace Road, London, SW1W 0RH Tel: (020) 7354 4664

Xenopus Systems Ltd, The Anchorage, Central Lydbrook, Lydbrook, Gloucestershire, GL17 9SB Tel: (01594) 862000 Fax: (01594) 862001 E-mail: sales@xenopus.co.uk

X-GL Systems Ltd, 24 Hunters Reach, Waltham Cross, Hertfordshire, EN7 6HQ Tel: (01992) 638763 Fax: (0870) 0521734 E-mail: sales@xgl.com

Xicon Education Ltd, Bank House, 1 Bank Street, Warrington, WA1 2AP Tel: (01925) 240342 Fax: (01925) 244894 E-mail: info@xicon.com

Xperience Peg Associates Ltd, Belmont House, Lambdon Road, London, SW20 0LW Tel: (020) 8880 4440 Fax: (020) 8880 4442 E-mail: sales@xperience-group.co.uk

Xperience Support Ltd, 11 Ferguson Drive, Knockmore Hill Industrial Park, Lisburn, County Antrim, BT28 2EX Tel: (028) 9267 7533 Fax: (028) 9267 2887 E-mail: info@xperience-group.com

Yacc, Old Vicarage, Old Vicarage Lane, Monk Fryston, Leeds, LS25 5EA Tel: (01977) 687980 Fax: (01977) 687998 E-mail: sales@yacc.co.uk

▶ Yampy Solutions Ltd, The Courtyard, 3 Abbey Street, Dudley, West Midlands, DY3 2ND Tel: (01384) 255000

Yo6 Computing, White Lodge, Tollerton Road, Huby, York, YO61 1HX Tel: (0845) 6441440 Fax: (0871) 2205371 E-mail: enquiries@yo6.co.uk

Youel Murray Ltd, 2 Gladstone Grove, Stockport, Cheshire, SK4 4DA Tel: 0161-442 8544 Fax: 0161-442 3594E-mail: ymltd@ymltd.com

Zigzak Computers, 29 Millgate, Arbroath, Angus, DD11 1NN Tel: (01241) 435900 Fax: (0870) 7053180 E-mail: sales@zigzak.co.uk

Zipzap Ltd, Unit 18 Exchange Road, Lincoln, LN6 3JZ Tel: (01522) 684705 Fax: (01522) 684627 E-mail: sales@zipzap.co.uk

Zone Cross Software Ltd, Talbot House, 2 Talbot Road, Northampton, NN1 4JB Tel: (01604) 231656 Fax: (01604) 602799

Zoomwatch Ltd, Down The Line, Station Road, Draycott, Cheddar, Somerset, BS27 3TQ Tel: (01934) 740040

COMPUTER SYSTEMS INTEGRATORS, COMPUTER AIDED DESIGN, COMPUTER AIDED MANUFACTURING (CADCAM) SOLUTIONS

3 T H Ltd, 9 Hinksey Business Centre, North Hinksey Lane, Oxford, OX2 0NR Tel: (01865) 791452 Fax: (01865) 794267 E-mail: sales@3th.co.uk

COMPUTER SYSTEMS INTEGRATORS, SPECIAL PURPOSE

3 T H Ltd, 9 Hinksey Business Centre, North Hinksey Lane, Oxford, OX2 0NR Tel: (01865) 791452 Fax: (01865) 794267 E-mail: sales@3th.co.uk

Mayfair Business Systems Ltd, 85 Market Street, Watford, WD18 0PT Tel: (01923) 800800 Fax: (01923) 800810 E-mail: info@mayfairbs.co.uk

Media Information Solutions Ltd, 32 Ballmoor, Buckingham Industrial Estate, Buckingham, MK18 1RQ Tel: (01280) 824488 Fax: (01280) 824489 E-mail: info@m-i-s.co.uk

Microlise Business Computing, Farrington Way, Eastwood, Nottingham, NG16 3AG Tel: (01773) 535111 Fax: (01773) 537373 E-mail: enquiries@microlise.co.uk

COMPUTER SYSTEMS TO SPECIFICATION

Abitech Systems, 13 Main Street, Keyworth, Nottingham, NG12 5AA Tel: 0115-937 4549 Fax: 0115-937 3662 E-mail: sales@abitech.co.uk

▶ Badger Computer Services Ltd, The Business Innovation Centre 1 Innova Business Park, Electric, Enfield, Middlesex, EN3 7XU Tel: (020) 8344 8344 Fax: (020) 8344 8345 E-mail: sales@badgercomputerservices.co.uk

Cablink UK Ltd, 74 Tenter Road, Moulton Park Industrial Estate, Northampton, NN3 6AX Tel: (01604) 670005 Fax: (01604) 670011

Codis Ltd, 38-44 St Anns Road, Harrow, Middlesex, HA1 1LA Tel: (020) 8861 0610 Fax: (020) 8515 7049 E-mail: codis@codis.co.uk

College Computers, 169 Hollow Way, Cowley, Oxford, OX4 2NE Tel: (01865) 774410 Fax: (01865) 774410 E-mail: sales@college-computers.com

Computec Computers, 67 Frog Lane, Wigan, Lancashire, WN6 7DU Tel: (01942) 493400 Fax: (01942) 736967

Durodata, 5 Castle Street, Canterbury, Kent, CT1 2FG Tel: (01227) 781037 Fax: (01227) 762416 E-mail: info@durodata.co.uk

Enabling Computer Supplies Ltd, Castlefields, Stafford, ST16 1BU Tel: (01785) 243111 Fax: (01785) 243222 E-mail: sales@enablingtechnology.net

The Environ & Process Engineering Ltd, Monza House, Unit 4, Milbrook Trading Estate, Southampton, SO15 0LD Tel: (023) 8070 3344 Fax: (023) 8070 2679 E-mail: wel@workingenvironments.co.uk

Highworth Computer Centre, 27 Newburgh Place, Highworth, Swindon, SN6 7DN Tel: (01793) 766866 Fax: (01793) 766162

Iken Business Ltd, Froomsgate House, Rupert Street, Bristol, BS1 2QJ Tel: (0845) 4509201 Fax: (0845) 4509209 E-mail: info@iken.com

J L A Computer Services Ltd, 1 Enterprise Court, Lakes Road, Braintree, Essex, CM7 3QS Tel: (01376) 343456 Fax: (01376) 321277 E-mail: sales@jla-computers.co.uk

Japhlin Computer Repairs, 77 Weeping Cross, Stafford, ST17 0DQ Tel: (01785) 663400 Fax: (01785) 665807 E-mail: phil@japhlin.co.uk

Letts Compute, Unit 1, 71 Kings Street, Derby, DE1 3GZ Tel: (01332) 386500 Fax: (01332) 386500

Media Magic Computers, Media House, 196a Abbey Road, Leeds, LS5 3NG Tel: 0113-228 9911 Fax: 0113-228 9933

Nexus Alpha Ltd, 5a Old Town, London, SW4 0JT Tel: (020) 7622 6816 Fax: (020) 7622 6817

O N C, Unit 220 Tedco Business Centre, Jarrow, Tyne & Wear, NE32 3DT Tel: 0191-422 0229 Fax: 0191-428 3365 E-mail: s.owens@onc-computers.co.uk

Ohm Electronics Ltd, 515 Pinner Road, Harrow, Middlesex, HA2 6EH Tel: (020) 8427 0545 Fax: (020) 8863 7930 E-mail: sales@ohmelectronics.co.uk

▶ Outlook It Ltd, Unit 14 Enterprise House, Dalziel Street, Motherwell, Lanarkshire, ML1 1PJ Tel: (01698) 264266

P C Link Supplies Ltd, Ruxox House, Maulden Road, Flitwick, Bedford, MK45 5BN Tel: (01525) 717772 Fax: (01525) 717773 E-mail: sales@businesshomecomputers.com

P C Supplies, 119 Cavendish Street, Barrow-in-Furness, Cumbria, LA14 1DJ Tel: (01229) 833595 Fax: (01229) 877677 E-mail: sales@pcsuppliesuk.co.uk

Prima Solutions Ltd, Loughborough Technology Park, Ashby Road, Loughborough, Leicestershire, LE11 3NG Tel: (01509) 232200 Fax: (01509) 262323

Pristine Computers & Computing Ltd, 45 High Street, Charing, Ashford, Kent, TN27 0HU Tel: (01233) 713660 Fax: (01233) 713727 E-mail: peter@pristineuk.com

Systems Created Ltd, Old Chapel, White Horse Road, East Bergholt, Colchester, CO7 6TU Tel: (01206) 299228 Fax: (01206) 299232

▶ Voyager Computers, 90a Frankwell, Shrewsbury, SY3 8JR Tel: 01743 341755 E-mail: voyagercomputers@hotmail.com

W C S Computer Services, Sovereign House, 53 Broadwater Street West, Worthing, West Sussex, BN14 9BY Tel: (01903) 209320 Fax: (01903) 232767 E-mail: admin@wcscomputers.com

Wind River UK Ltd, Unit 10 Viscount Way, South Marston Industrial Estate, Swindon, SN3 4TN Tel: (01793) 831831 Fax: (01793) 831808

X T & A T Computers Ltd, 77c St Pancras, Chichester, West Sussex, PO19 7LS Tel: (01243) 533367 Fax: (01243) 536018 E-mail: sales@xtat.co.uk

Xenopus Systems Ltd, The Anchorage, Central Lydbrook, Lydbrook, Gloucestershire, GL17 9SB Tel: (01594) 862000 Fax: (01594) 862001 E-mail: sales@xenopus.co.uk

COMPUTER SYSTEMS, ELECTRONIC POINT OF SALE (EPOS), HOSPITALITY

Peter Berry Associates, Unit 1B, Station Road, Tewkesbury, Gloucestershire, GL20 5DR Tel: (01684) 290629 Fax: (01684) 275231 E-mail: info@pbaservice.co.uk

▶ The Hammond Recruitment Group, 217 West Street, Fareham, Hampshire, PO16 0ET Tel: (01329) 825925 Fax: (01329) 826926 E-mail: enquiries@hrguk.com

Microtek Services Ltd, Gateway House, Gate Way Drive, Yeadon, Leeds, LS19 7XY Tel: 0113-238 7300 Fax: 0113-238 7320 E-mail: enquiries@microtek-services.co.uk

▶ Retail Technology, Armstrong House 3rd Floor, 38 Market Square, Uxbridge, Middlesex, UB8 1TG Tel: (01895) 421111 Fax: (01895) 431252 E-mail: info@retailtechnology.co.uk

Shelfguard Systems, 91 St Leonards Road, Windsor, Berkshire, SL4 3BZ Tel: (01753) 867257 Fax: (01753) 830024 E-mail: sales@shelfguard-systems.co.uk

COMPUTER SYSTEMS, HOTEL

▶ Black Boy Inn, Northgate Street, Caernarfon, Gwynedd, LL55 1RW Tel: (01286) 673604 Fax: (01286) 674130 E-mail: black@welsh-historic-inns.com

▶ Room Rates, 85 Cavendish Drive, Northampton, NN3 3HL Tel: 0870 1439055

COMPUTER SYSTEMS, POINT OF SALE (POS)/PURCHASE

Business Information Technology Services Ltd, 75 Longford Road, Coventry, CV6 6DY Tel: (024) 7683 5600 Fax: (024) 7683 5601 E-mail: bits@b-i-t-s.co.uk

▶ Coventry Computer Repairs, 26 Canon Drive, Shilton, Coventry, CV7 9HJ Tel: (0870) 3834068 E-mail: info@coventrycomputerrepairs.co.uk

▶ PCEazy Computer Systems, 172 Park Road, Bedworth, Warwickshire, CV12 8LA Tel: (0870) 3834821 E-mail: sales@pceazy.com

COMPUTER SYSTEMS, STOCK CONTROL, ELECTRONIC POINT OF SALE (EPOS)

Peter Berry Associates, Unit 1B, Station Road, Tewkesbury, Gloucestershire, GL20 5DR Tel: (01684) 290629 Fax: (01684) 275231 E-mail: info@pbaservice.co.uk

▶ The Hammond Recruitment Group, 217 West Street, Fareham, Hampshire, PO16 0ET Tel: (01329) 825925 Fax: (01329) 826926 E-mail: enquiries@hrguk.com

▶ InSync Retail Business Solutions, The Dairy,, Old Brookend Farm, Hurley, Atherstone, Warwickshire, CV9 2JP Tel: 01827 873899 Fax: 01827 872647 E-mail: sales@insync-rbs.com

▶ Retail Technology, Armstrong House 3rd Floor, 38 Market Square, Uxbridge, Middlesex, UB8 1TG Tel: (01895) 421111 Fax: (01895) 431252 E-mail: info@retailtechnology.co.uk

COMPUTER SYSTEMS, TO SPECIFICATION/TURNKEY

4th Hospitality Ltd, Unit 3 Des Roches Square, Witney, Oxfordshire, OX28 4LQ Tel: (01993) 899200 Fax: (01993) 775081 E-mail: info@abs-ltd.com

Access Computers, 411 Bearwood Road, Smethwick, West Midlands, B66 4DF Tel: 0121-429 5558 Fax: 0121-429 5558

Accord Computer Systems Ltd, 7-9 Union Street, Stratford-upon-Avon, Warwickshire, CV37 6QT Tel: (01789) 415541 Fax: (01789) 414410 E-mail: info@accordltd.co.uk

Alphameric Solutions Ltd, Bishopsgate House, Broadford Park, Guildford, Surrey, GU4 8ED Tel: (01483) 293900 Fax: (01483) 533333 E-mail: enquiries@alphameric.com

Anglia Business Computers Training Ltd, Harston Mill, Royston Road, Harston, Cambridge, CB22 7GG Tel: (01223) 873400 Fax: (01223) 873401 E-mail: mktg@angliabs.com

Apex Computer Services Wales Ltd, Unit 2 St. Michaels Court, Church Street, Newport, Gwent, NP20 2BY Tel: (01633) 215123 Fax: (01633) 215124 E-mail: sales@apexcs.co.uk

Ar Computing, 8 Friday Street, Minehead, Somerset, TA24 5UA Tel: (01643) 707381 Fax: (01643) 707431 E-mail: enquiries@arcomputing.co.uk

Astley Computer Services, 37 The Farthings, Chorley, Lancashire, PR7 1TP Tel: (01257) 277057 Fax: (01257) 277057 E-mail: ast_com_serve@btinternet.com

Brookes Data Products Ltd, Brookes House, Cradock Street, Loughborough, Leicestershire, LE11 1AJ Tel: (01509) 237410 Fax: (01509) 610506 E-mail: sales@brookesdata.co.uk

Bytes & PC's UK Ltd, Gosford House, 26/27 Far Gosford Street, Coventry, CV1 5DW Tel: (024) 7655 5265 Fax: (024) 7655 1100 E-mail: sales@bytespcs.co.uk

C Pac, 33a Morland Way, Nelson Park, Cramlington, Northumberland, NE23 1WE Tel: 0191-491 0405 Fax: 0191-491 0465 E-mail: sales@c-pac.co.uk

Cannon Computers Ltd, 2 Kingsmead Road, London, SW2 3JB Tel: (020) 8671 4140 E-mail: leonard@cannon-computers.co.uk

Compurange Ltd, 337 Derby Street, Bolton, BL3 6LR Tel: (01204) 651212 Fax: (01204) 658060 E-mail: info@compurange.co.uk

Computer Chaos, 1 Brookfield Dirve, Cannock, Staffordshire, WS11 0JN Tel: (01543) 578579 Fax: (01543) 571218

Comtech Solutions, 2 Moor Allerton Gardens, Leeds, LS17 6QU Tel: 0113-269 1034

D T A Computer Systems Ltd, 58 Norbiton Avenue, Kingston upon Thames, Surrey, KT1 3QR Tel: (020) 8974 5114 Fax: (07092) 314906 E-mail: info@dta.co.uk

Dalbrook Ltd, Box Cottage, West Kington Wick, Chippenham, Wiltshire, SN14 7JD Tel: (01249) 782146 Fax: (01249) 782948

Datawright Computer Services Ltd, Parsons House, Parsons Road, Washington, Tyne & Wear, NE37 1EZ Tel: 0191-419 4190 Fax: 0191-419 5800 E-mail: sales@datawright.co.uk

E M Computers Ltd, 13 Victoria Street, Wigston, Leicestershire, LE18 1AJ Tel: 0116-288 1088

E S L Ltd, 301-303 Kennington Lane, London, SE11 5QU Tel: (020) 7820 7718 Fax: (020) 7820 7754 E-mail: ind-esl@msn.com

Enabling Computer Supplies Ltd, Castlefields, Stafford, ST16 1BU Tel: (01785) 243111 Fax: (01785) 243222 E-mail: sales@enablingtechnology.net

Fretwell-Downing Hospitality, Brincliffe House, 861 Ecclesall Road, Sheffield, S11 7AE Tel: 0114-281 6060 Fax: 0114-281 6061 E-mail: info@fdhospitality.com

G K S Computers Ltd, One Oclock Lane, Burgess Hill, West Sussex, RH15 0EX Tel: (01444) 250404 Fax: (01444) 250405 E-mail: sales@gkscomputers.co.uk

Gamma Global, 157 Warwick Road, Solihull, West Midlands, B92 7AR Tel: 0121-706 8080 Fax: 0121-706 1188

Grampian Electronic Components Ltd, 19-25 Don Street, Woodside, Aberdeen, AB24 2RR Tel: (01224) 481000 Fax: (01224) 480111 E-mail: info@grampian-electronics.com

H F Systems, 97 Hill Top, West Bromwich, West Midlands, B70 0RU Tel: 0121-556 5821 Fax: (0845) 8689918 E-mail: info@hfsystems.co.uk

Hoburne Business Systems Ltd, 9a Saulfland Place, Christchurch, Dorset, BH23 4QP Tel: (01425) 280009 Fax: (01425) 280905 E-mail: sales@hoburnesystems.co.uk

Honeycomb Information Services Ltd, 23 Cedarland Crescent, Nuthall, Nottingham, NG16 1AG Tel: 0115-927 4521

Honeypass Ltd, 16 Ardsheal Close, Worthing, West Sussex, BN14 7RP Tel: (01903) 212774 Fax: (01903) 238226 E-mail: info@honeypass.com

Hussey & Greaves Ltd, 52 Moulsham Street, Chelmsford, CM2 0JA Tel: (01245) 268601 Fax: (01245) 491230 E-mail: chel@husseyandgreaves.co.uk

Imaj Computer Systems Group, Mill Street, Newton Moor Industrial Estate, Hyde, Cheshire, SK14 4LG Tel: 0161-368 1476 Fax: 0161-367 8145 E-mail: sales@imajsystems.co.uk

Infoquest Systems Ltd, Lawday Place Lane, Farnham, Surrey, GU9 0BT Tel: (01252) 723721 Fax: (01252) 723721 E-mail: sales@infoquest-systems.co.uk

Leading Edge Systems Ltd, 203 High La West, West Hallam, Ilkeston, Derbyshire, DE7 6HP Tel: 0115-944 7994

M & S Systems Ltd, 21 Excelsior Grove, Pelsall, Walsall, WS3 4PX Tel: (01922) 685615 E-mail: simon@mandssys.demon.co.uk

Magnacom Ltd, Crossford Mill, Beith Road, Kilbarchan, Johnstone, Renfrewshire, PA10 2NS Tel: (01505) 706000 Fax: (01505) 706067 E-mail: office@magnacom.co.uk

COMPUTER SYSTEMS, TO SPECIFICATION/TURNKEY – *continued*

Microtest Ltd, Technology House, 18 Normandy Way, Bodmin, Cornwall, PL31 1EX Tel: (01208) 73812 Fax: (01208) 77677 E-mail: sales@microtest.co.uk

Minnie Business Systems Ltd, 65 London Wall, London, EC2M 5TU Tel: (020) 7638 3815 Fax: (020) 7638 1481 E-mail: ad@minniebusiness.co.uk

Netlogic Consulting Ltd, Harlow, Essex, CM18 7NT Tel: (01279) 413355 Fax: (020) 8830 4173 E-mail: info@netlogicconsulting.com

Newton Information Technology Ltd, 1 Central Business Centre, Great Central Way, London, NW10 0UR Tel: (020) 8451 0027 Fax: (020) 8451 0029 E-mail: sales@newtonit.co.uk

Norsk Data Ltd, The Coach House, Turners Drive, Thatcham, Berkshire, RG19 4QB Tel: (01635) 35544 Fax: (01635) 865634

▶ Outlook It Ltd, Unit 14 Enterprise House, Dalziel Street, Motherwell, Lanarkshire, ML1 1PJ Tel: (01698) 264266

Paragon Electronics, 10 Market Place, Flat 1, Bideford, Devon, EX39 2DR Tel: (01237) 421324 Fax: (01237) 421016 E-mail: computers@paragon2.fsnet.co.uk

Performance Computers North East Ltd, 4 Zetland Street, Northallerton, North Yorkshire, DL6 1NA Tel: (01609) 772442 Fax: (0871) 2771281 E-mail: northallerton@performancecomputers.co.uk

Playsafe Monitoring, 14 The Maltings Industrial Estate, Brassmill Lane, Bath, BA1 3JL Tel: (01225) 311323 Fax: (01225) 445217 E-mail: sales@playsafemonitoring.com

Press Computer Systems Ltd, Castle Street, Wolverhampton, WV1 3AD Tel: (01902) 374757 Fax: (01902) 373622 E-mail: postmaster@presscomputers.com

Programming Research Ltd, 9-11 Queens Road, Walton-on-Thames, Surrey, KT12 5LU Tel: (01932) 888080 Fax: (01932) 888081 E-mail: web@prqa.co.uk

Prom UK, 23 Ash Close, Walters Ash, High Wycombe, Buckinghamshire, HP14 4TR Tel: (01494) 562253

R T S Computers, 13 New Street, Louth, Lincolnshire, LN11 9PT Tel: (01507) 606600 Fax: (01507) 606600 E-mail: rtscomputers@freebie.net

Redkyte Computers, 142 Flixton Road, Urmston, Manchester, M41 5BG Tel: 0161-749 7861 E-mail: sales@redkyte.com

Reon Computing, 3 Aghanloo Industrial Estate, Aghanloo Road, Limavady, County Londonderry, BT49 0HE Tel: (028) 7776 7273 E-mail: reon@btinternet.com

Sanderson Ltd, 720 Waterside Drive, Aztec West, Almondsbury, Bristol, BS32 4UD Tel: (01454) 892500 Fax: (01454) 892610 E-mail: enquiries@sanderson.com

Sapphire Instrument Co., 25 Friar Road, Brighton, BN1 6NG Tel: (01273) 556008 Fax: (01273) 556008

Scotland Electronics (International) Ltd, 28 West Road, Greshop Industrial Estate, Forres, Morayshire, IV36 2GW Tel: (01309) 678900 Fax: (01309) 678909 E-mail: sales@scotlandelectronics.co.uk

SCS Ltd, Multifreight House Cromwell Court, 16 St. Peters Street, Ipswich, IP1 1XG Tel: (01473) 212421 Fax: (01473) 212110 E-mail: sales@multifreight.com

Selectweb Computers, 51 Scotforth Road, Lancaster, LA1 4SA Tel: (01524) 383268 Fax: (01524) 382675E-mail: sales@select.net

Solutions PT, Unit 1, Oakfield Road, Cheadle Royal Business Park, Cheadle, Cheshire, SK8 3GX Tel: 0161-495 4600 Fax: 0161-495 4690 E-mail: sales@solutionspt.co.uk

Sopra Group Ltd, Northbrook House, Robert Robinson Avenue, Oxford, OX4 4GA Tel: (01865) 781781 Fax: (01865) 781777

Sound Technology, 23 Townhead Street, Hamilton, Lanarkshire, ML3 7BQ Tel: (01698) 458754 Fax: (01698) 421116

Sussex Computers Ltd, Suite F10, Waterside Centre, North Street, Lewes, East Sussex, BN7 2PE Tel: (01273) 407360 Fax: (01273) 464880 E-mail: gm@sussexcomputers.co.uk

Technology Shop, 10 Railway Street, Malton, North Yorkshire, YO17 7NR Tel: (01653) 600002 Fax: (01653) 690721 E-mail: shop@the-technology-shop.com

Total Media Communications, Unit 6, Berkshire Business Centre Berkshire Drive, Thatcham, Berkshire, RG19 4EW Tel: (01635) 869297 Fax: (01635) 869342

Trace Group plc, 224-232 St John Street, London, EC1V 4QR Tel: (020) 7825 1000 Fax: (020) 7825 1001 E-mail: sales@tracegroup.com

Trackit Systems Ltd, Trival House, Unit 3 Hawthorne Park, Coal Road, Leeds, LS14 1PQ Tel: 0113-306 0306 Fax: 0113-276 0685

Viglen Technology Ltd, 7 Handley Page Way Colney Street, Colney Street, St. Albans, Hertfordshire, AL2 2DQ Tel: (01923) 858700 Fax: (01727) 201888 E-mail: marketing@viglen.co.uk

W C S Computer Services, Sovereign House, 53 Broadwater Street West, Worthing, West Sussex, BN14 9BY Tel: (01903) 209320 Fax: (01903) 232767 E-mail: admin@wcscomputers.com

Workstation Technologies Ltd, 21 Sovereign Road, Kings Norton Business Centre, Birmingham, B30 3HN Tel: 0121-486 1234 Fax: (0870) 9901918 E-mail: info@wtluk.com

Your PC, 23-25 Station Road, Holmfirth, HD9 1AB Tel: (01484) 687814 Fax: (01484) 687685

COMPUTER TAPE DRIVES

Bull Information Systems Ltd, Maxted Road, Hemel Hempstead, Hertfordshire, HP2 7DZ Tel: (01442) 232222 Fax: (01442) 884361 E-mail: information@bull.co.uk

D & P Data Systems Ltd, 15 Carnarvon Street, Manchester, M3 1HJ Tel: 0161-832 6969 Fax: 0161-832 6970 E-mail: sales@dpdata.co.uk

M5 Data Ltd, Mendip Court, Bath Road, Wells, Somerset, BA5 3DG Tel: (01749) 679222 Fax: (01749) 673928

Storagetek Ltd, 36 South Gyle Crescent, Edinburgh, EH12 9EB Tel: 0131-338 6515 Fax: 0131-339 3900

COMPUTER TELEPHONE INTEGRATION (CTI) APPLICATION CONSULTANTS OR DESIGNERS

▶ A C T Comms Ltd, Hexagon House, 71 Lower Road, Kenley, Caterham, Surrey, CR8 5NH Tel: (0870) 7747576 Fax: (0870) 1600094 E-mail: sales@actcomms.co.uk

Aculab plc, Lakeside Bramley Road, Mount Farm, Bletchley, Milton Keynes, MK1 1PT Tel: (01908) 273800 Fax: (01908) 273801

Ascobra Ltd, 12 Abbots Rise, Kings Langley, Hertfordshire, WD4 8AP Tel: (01923) 264067

C I M Systems Ltd, 1st Floor, Ross House, Kempson Way, Suffolk Business Park, Bury St. Edmunds, Suffolk, IP32 7AR Tel: (01284) 727200 Fax: (01284) 706602 E-mail: info@cimsystems.co.uk

Commercial Software Management Ltd, Devereux House, Church Hill, Coleshill, Birmingham, B46 3AA Tel: (01675) 466731 Fax: (01675) 466734 E-mail: sales@csmltd.co.uk

Mitel Networks, Mitel Business Park, Portskewett, Caldicot, Gwent, NP26 5YR Tel: (0870) 9092020 Fax: (0870) 9094040 E-mail: sales@mitel.com

R G T Ltd, Chapel Road, Smallfield, Horley, Surrey, RH6 9NW Tel: (01342) 844411 Fax: (0870) 7771333 E-mail: sales@rgt.co.uk

Westcon Convergents, 1 Clayton Manor, Victoria Gardens, Burgess Hill, West Sussex, RH15 9NB Tel: (01444) 230004 Fax: (01444) 243889 E-mail: info@cranetel.co.uk

COMPUTER TELEPHONY INTEGRATION (CTI) SYSTEMS

Ecentric Media Ltd, PO Box 473, Horsham, West Sussex, RH12 5YL Tel: (01403) 253022 Fax: 01403 253022 E-mail: enquiries@ecentricmedia.co.uk

COMPUTER TELEPHONY SYSTEMS TO SPECIFICATION

▶ A C T Comms Ltd, Hexagon House, 71 Lower Road, Kenley, Caterham, Surrey, CR8 5NH Tel: (0870) 7747576 Fax: (0870) 1600094 E-mail: sales@actcomms.co.uk

Aculab plc, Lakeside Bramley Road, Mount Farm, Bletchley, Milton Keynes, MK1 1PT Tel: (01908) 273800 Fax: (01908) 273801

Iqual Ltd, Crown House, Home Gardens, Dartford, DA1 1DZ Tel: (0870) 1633320 Fax: (0870) 1633316

Sheldon Reed Ltd, Seymore House, 4 Tudor Avenue, Watford, WD24 7NX Tel: (0870) 7454580 E-mail: admin@sheldonreed.com

COMPUTER TERMINAL VISUAL DISPLAY UNITS (VDU)

Calibre UK Ltd, Cornwall House, Cornwall Terrace, Bradford, West Yorkshire, BD8 7JS Tel: (01274) 394125 Fax: (01274) 730960 E-mail: lisas@calibreuk.com

Microvitec Display Ltd, Drumhill Works, Clayton Lane, Bradford, West Yorkshire, BD14 6RF Tel: (01274) 816700 Fax: (01274) 817733 E-mail: sales@microvitec.co.uk

COMPUTER TIME-SHARING SERVICES, *See Computer Services/Bureaus*

COMPUTER TRAINING SERVICES OR CENTRES

1 Can Help P C Problem Solving & Training Services, 60 Springwood Road, Heathfield, East Sussex, TN21 8JX Tel: (01435) 866575 E-mail: gordon@1canhelp.com

▶ 1st Byte, Cade Road, Ashford, Kent, TN23 6JE Tel: (01233) 637056

▶ 2 Evolve UK, 2a Cunningham Road, Stirling, FK7 7SW Tel: (0870) 3501795 Fax: (0870) 3507096 E-mail: sales@2e-volve.com

A T T & C, Tudor House, Catherine Road, Benfleet, Essex, SS7 1HY Tel: (01268) 759398 Fax: (01268) 565102

A W Computer Solutions Ltd, 8e Port Road, Carlisle, CA2 7AF Tel: (01228) 594682 Fax: (01228) 594683 E-mail: info@armstrongwatson.co.uk

Aba Key Ltd, 5 Spring Garden Lane, Gosport, Hampshire, PO12 1HY Tel: (023) 9251 1617 Fax: (023) 9251 1416 E-mail: abakey@dhbaccountants.co.uk

Abs Ltd, 1 Ridge Close, Hatch Warren, Basingstoke, Hampshire, RG22 4RN Tel: (01256) 357270 Fax: (01256) 301521 E-mail: admin@ABSuk.com

Accountancy Systems & Training Ltd, 35 Church Walk, Denny, Stirlingshire, FK6 6DF Tel: (01324) 822222 E-mail: info@astl.co.uk

▶ Acordia, 46-48 Alfreton Road, Nottingham, NG7 3NN Tel: 0115-978 4513 Fax: 0115-847 5212

▶ Admiral Business Centre, Suite F1-2 Venture Tower, Fratton Road, Portsmouth, PO1 5DL Tel: (023) 9275 4002 Fax: (023) 9275 4002

Advance Training & Consultancy Ltd, Unit 10, 225 Putney Bridge Road, London, SW15 2PX Tel: (020) 8871 9886 Fax: (020) 8871 9781

▶ Advantage Computer Training Ltd, 83-85 Bridge Road, East Molesey, Surrey, KT8 9HH Tel: (020) 8979 8977

Amadeus Software Ltd, Orchard Farm, Witney Lane, Leafield, Witney, Oxfordshire, OX29 9PG Tel: (01993) 878287 Fax: (01993) 878042 E-mail: info@amadeus.co.uk

▶ Amazon Consultants, 29 St. Peters Street, Stamford, Lincolnshire, PE9 2PF Tel: (01780) 764430 Fax: (01780) 764430 E-mail: info@amazonconsultants.co.uk

Ashbee Computer Services, Wood Lea, Priorswood, Guildford, Surrey, GU3 1DR Tel: (01483) 810500 Fax: (01483) 811577

Astec Computing UK Ltd, Astec House, 10-12 Sedlescombe Road South, St. Leonards-on-Sea, East Sussex, TN38 0TA Tel: (01424) 460721 Fax: (01424) 430888 E-mail: enquiries@asteccomputing.com

Aylesbury Training Group, Gatehouse Close, Gatehouse Industrial Area, Aylesbury, Buckinghamshire, HP19 8DN Tel: (01296) 481818 Fax: (01296) 437391 E-mail: training@atg-training.co.uk

▶ Best Computer Training Ltd, 189 London Road, Staines, Middlesex, TW18 4HR Tel: (01784) 451288 Fax: (01784) 451287 E-mail: staines@best-training.co.uk

Best Training, 18 Fisher Street, Carlisle, CA3 8RH Tel: (01228) 590750 Fax: (01228) 596740 E-mail: carlisle@best-training.co.uk

Bores Signal Processing, Pond Road, Woking, Surrey, GU22 0JZ Tel: (01483) 740138 Fax: (01483) 740136

▶ Burridge Coursewear, Unit 23 The Steadings, Maisemore Court, Maisemore, Gloucester, GL2 8EY Tel: (01452) 872080 Fax: (01452) 872081 E-mail: sales@burridge-courseware.com

Business Computing Services, Linden, East Side, North Littleton, Evesham, Worcestershire, WR11 8QW Tel: (01386) 830444 Fax: (01386) 830444

Business & Employment Skills Training Ltd, 20 Eglinton Street, Irvine, Ayrshire, KA12 8AS Tel: (01294) 313144 Fax: (01294) 313177

Cameo Network Services Ltd, 91 Gainsborough Road, Felixstowe, Suffolk, IP11 7HR Tel: (01394) 672004E-mail: info@cameo.co.uk

Cheshire Training Centre, 41 Hightown, Crewe, CW1 3BZ Tel: 01270 500886 Fax: 01270 582 036

▶ Clays Lane Advise & Training Centre, High Meads, Temple Mill Lane, London, E15 2EW Tel: (020) 8522 0088 Fax: (020) 8522 0088

Click Here Ltd, Globe Ii Business Centre, 128 Maltravers Road, Sheffield, S2 5AZ Tel: 0114-281 4477 Fax: 0114-281 4478 E-mail: info@clickhere.co.uk

▶ College Of Technology London, Bow House, 153-159 Bow Road, London, E3 2SE Tel: (020) 8980 7888 Fax: (020) 8983 4911

Complete Integrated Services, 4 Seville House, Wapping High Street, London, E1W 1NX Tel: (020) 7481 0943

Computeach International Ltd, University House, Jews Lane, Dudley, West Midlands, DY3 2AH Tel: (01384) 458515 Fax: (01384) 455650 E-mail: info@computeach.co.uk

Computer Scene, 5 Kings Street, Mildenhall, Bury St. Edmunds, Suffolk, IP28 7EZ Tel: (01638) 717726 Fax: (01638) 510079 E-mail: sales@computerscene.co.uk

▶ Corbitt Greenwood Associates, 2 Phoenix Terrace, Hartley Wintney, Hook, Hampshire, RG27 8RU Tel: (01252) 844567 Fax: (01252) 844567

Cordingley Barnes Ltd, 5 The Courtyard, Hall Lane, Haughton, Tarporley, Cheshire, CW6 9RJ Tel: (01829) 260029 Fax: (01829) 261209 E-mail: karen@cordingleybarnes.com

▶ Crash It, Kettles Wood Drive, Birmingham, B32 3DB Tel: 0121-421 7601 Fax: 0121-421 7601 E-mail: enquire@crash-it.org

Cyberscience Corporation Ltd, Rawdon House, High Street, Hoddesdon, Hertfordshire, EN11 8BD Tel: (01992) 441111 Fax: (01992) 442740 E-mail: info@cyberscience.com

▶ Dac Systems, 4 Balloo Drive, Bangor, County Down, BT19 7QY Tel: (028) 9185 7711 Fax: (028) 9185 7722 E-mail: sales@dacsystems.co.uk

▶ Data Results, Suite 10, Sackville Place, 44-48 Magdalen Street, Norwich, NR3 1JU Tel: (01603) 768465 Fax: (07092) 155445

Datamaster Training Services Ltd, Unit 4 Crescent Court, 51 High Street, Billericay, Essex, CM12 9AQ Tel: (01277) 624007 Fax: (01277) 630044 E-mail: enquiries@datamaster.uk.com

▶ Develop IT Ltd, Springfield House, Springfield Business Park, Springfield Road, Grantham, Lincolnshire, NG31 7BG Tel: 01476 514670 Fax: 01476 514679 E-mail: info@develop-it.com

Deverill plc, Itec House, 34-40 West Street, Poole, Dorset, BH15 1LA Tel: (01202) 785000 Fax: (01202) 785001 E-mail: marketing@deverill.co.uk

Direct Computer Training Ltd, Argyle Ho, 29-31 Euston Rd, London, NW1 2SD Tel: (020) 7837 4800 Fax: (020) 7837 1090

Distinction Computer Training, 273 Liverpool Road, Eccles, Manchester, M30 0QN Tel: 0161-788 7560 Fax: 0161-788 7560 E-mail: enquires@go2dct.co.uk

Dorset Merc, 851 Wimborne Road, Bournemouth, BH9 2BG Tel: (01202) 775566 E-mail: david.bridgewater@dorset-merc.net

▶ Ealing Hammersmith & West London College, Southall Library, Osterley Park Road, Southall, Middlesex, UB2 4BL Tel: (020) 8574 1472

Elite Training & Consultancy Services Ltd, Thomas House, 14-16 James Street South, Belfast, BT2 7GA Tel: (028) 9031 6840 Fax: (028) 9031 6841 E-mail: sales@elitetraining.com

Elyzium, 12 Queensbrook, Bolton, BL1 4AY Tel: (01204) 528628 Fax: (01204) 534678 E-mail: sales@elyzium.co.uk

Enabling Computer Supplies Ltd, Castlefields, Stafford, ST16 1BU Tel: (01785) 243111 Fax: (01785) 243222 E-mail: sales@enablingtechnology.net

Evolution Training & Development, 3 Whitebeam Road, Oadby, Leicester, LE2 4EA Tel: 0116-271 4616

Fortec T A Ltd, 5 Upminster Trading Park, Warley Street, Upminster, Essex, RM14 3PJ Tel: (01708) 224713 Fax: (01708) 641029 E-mail: kp@fortectraining.co.uk

Gateway Centre, Clarence House, Clarence Place, Newport, Gwent, NP19 7AA Tel: (01633) 235110 Fax: (01633) 235111

Geotechnix Computer Services Ltd, 39 West Hill Road, London, SW18 1LL Tel: (020) 8871 1497 Fax: (020) 8333 6714

The Graphics Network Ltd, 27 Moor Lane, Fairford, Gloucestershire, GL7 4AL Tel: (01285) 713297 E-mail: enquiries@tgn.co.uk

Grove Consultants Software Engineering, 40 Ryles Park Road, Macclesfield, Cheshire, SK11 8AH Tel: (01625) 616279

▶ Grove Training, 16 The Precinct, Romiley, Stockport, Cheshire, SK6 4EA Tel: 0161-406 0201 Fax: 0161-291 9176

Harquejas Publications Ltd, 2 Shenley Close, Leighton Buzzard, Bedfordshire, LU7 3DG Tel: (01525) 852370 E-mail: sales@harquejas.co.uk

▶ Peter Harrison, Bonds Mill, Bristol Road, Stonehouse, Gloucestershire, GL10 3RG Tel: (01453) 826406 Fax: (01453) 826406

Highfield Computing Services Ltd, Highfields, Haselor, Alcester, Warwickshire, B49 6LX Tel: (01789) 488088 Fax: (01789) 488770 E-mail: hcsl@compuserve.com

Hoxton Bibliotech, 239 Old Street, London, EC1V 9EY Tel: (020) 7553 4470 Fax: (020) 7251 3130

▶ Icon College Of Technology & Management Ltd, Unit 21 St. Boniface Church, 1-13 Adler Street, London, E1 1EE Tel: (020) 7377 2800 Fax: (020) 7377 0822

▶ Impact, Balcony, 60 Merrion Centre, Leeds, LS2 8NG Tel: 0113-234 9186

In Tuition, 210 Borough High Street, London, SE1 1JX Tel: (020) 7403 7259 Fax: (020) 7403 2861 E-mail: mktmgn@intuition.co.uk

▶ Infinity I O Ltd, The Old Waterhouse, The Elvetham, Hook, Hampshire, RG27 8AS Tel: (01252) 847400 Fax: (01252) 848608 E-mail: info@infinityio.co.uk

▶ Infotec Computer Training, 29 College Road, Moseley, Birmingham, B13 9LS Tel: 0121-248 1416

▶ Insight Associates, Meadowview House, 191 Queens Road, Norwich, NR1 3PP Tel: (01603) 767669 Fax: (01603) 776585

Interactive, 84 Marsh Road, Rhyl, Clwyd, LL18 2AF Tel: (01745) 339331 Fax: (01745) 354494 E-mail: admin@womensevillage.co.uk

Intertrain Executrain, Witan Court, 294 Witan Gate West, Milton Keynes, MK9 1EJ Tel: (01908) 206700 Fax: (01908) 206701

▶ indicates data change since last edition

COMPUTER TRAINING SERVICES OR CENTRES – *continued*

▶ Isca Vision Ltd, Isca House 3 Bay Tree Close, Caerleon, Newport, NP18 3RT Tel: (01633) 431551 E-mail: sales@iscavision.com

IT First Ltd, St. Nicholas Way, Sutton, Surrey, SM1 1AT Tel: (020) 8643 3344 Fax: (020) 8643 3356

J T Computer Training Solutions, 16 Longpark Hill, Maidencombe, Torquay, TQ1 4TL Tel: (01803) 313386 Fax: (01803) 313376 E-mail: jt_training@msn.com

J & T Systems Ltd, 6 Northlands Road, Southampton, SO15 2LF Tel: (023) 8023 5280 Fax: (023) 8023 3358

JHP Training Sheffield, 40 Castle Square, Sheffield, S1 2GF Tel: 0114-275 7286 Fax: 0114-279 7503 E-mail: sheffield.business.centre@jhp-group.com

Jigsaw Consultancy, 272 Bath Street, Glasgow, G2 4JR Tel: 0141-353 9460 Fax: 0141-353 9386 E-mail: dorothy@westfieldtraining.co.uk

Jupitar Ltd, 68 Great Eastern Street, London, EC2A 3JT Tel: (020) 7729 8626 Fax: (020) 7729 8628 E-mail: info@jupitar.com

▶ Kaz Training, 575, Charminster Road, Bournemouth, BH8 9RG Tel: (01202) 515553

Kirkland Ltd, 95 Main Street, Golspie, Sutherland, KW10 6TG Tel: (01408) 633109 Fax: (01408) 634468 E-mail: webad@kirkland.ltd.uk

▶ L A G A T, Ariazne House, 25 Tentercroft Street, Lincoln, LN5 7DB Tel: (01522) 513227 Fax: (01522) 545533 E-mail: enquiries@lagat.co.uk

Law Leisure & Learning, Community Hall, 2-10 Queens Head Road, Birmingham, B21 0QG Tel: 0121-551 5115 Fax: 0121-554 6417

Learning & Teaching Scotland, 58 Robertson Street, Glasgow, G2 8DU Tel: 0141-282 5000 Fax: 0141-282 5050 E-mail: equiries@ltscotland.org.uk

Linden Computer Services, Laverham House, 77 St Georges Place, Cheltenham, Gloucestershire, GL50 3PP Tel: (01242) 269369 Fax: (01242) 231341

▶ LM Matters, Unit 26 Daniels Industrial Estate, 104 Bath Road, Stroud, Gloucestershire, GL5 3TJ Tel: (0845) 1707700 Fax: (01453) 759950

Longridge Teaching Centre, Berry Lane, Longridge, Preston, PR3 3JA Tel: (01772) 786668 Fax: (01772) 784578

▶ Looe Enterprise Centre, Enterprise House, Higher Market Street, Looe, Cornwall, PL13 1BN Tel: (01503) 265947 Fax: (01503) 265947 E-mail: looe.centre@btconnect.com

▶ McAuley, 14B Stone Row, Coleraine, County Londonderry, BT52 1EP Tel: (028) 7032 9104 Fax: (028) 7034 4246

▶ Manchester College Of Draughting & Technology, 2 Hellidon Close, Ardwick, Manchester, M12 4AH Tel: 0161-272 8900 Fax: 0161-230 6613

Matrice, Hawthorn Cottage, Hadham Road, Bishop's Stortford, Hertfordshire, CM23 2QT Tel: (01279) 501955 E-mail: info@matrice.co.uk

▶ Matrix Information Technology Ltd, Imperial Chambers, 41-43 Longsmith Street, Gloucester, GL1 2HT Tel: (01452) 387002 Fax: (01452) 309693 E-mail: sales@matrixinfotech.co.uk

Matrix Information Technology Ltd, Imperial Chambers, 41-43 Longsmith Street, Gloucester, GL1 2HT Tel: (01452) 387002 Fax: (01452) 309693 E-mail: sales@matrixinfotech.co.uk

Maxim Training Knowledgepool, 42 Bond Street, Brighton, BN1 1RD Tel: (01273) 827751 Fax: (01273) 738829 E-mail: tracy.capaldi-drewett@knowledgepool.com

▶ Meggs Costoya Attfield, 3 Warberry Road, London, N22 7TQ Tel: (020) 8826 0044 Fax: (020) 8829 0441

Mikado Computer Support, 38 Gravel Hill, Wimborne, Dorset, BH21 1RR Tel: (01202) 883808 Fax: (01202) 883808 E-mail: sales@mikado.co.uk

Millennium Software Solutions Centre Scotland Ltd, Burnfield Avenue, Thornliebank, Glasgow, G46 7TP Tel: 0141-633 5885 Fax: 0141-633 5733 E-mail: amanda@milleniumsoftware2000.com

▶ Minerva Centre, Bradtrad House, Ripley Street, Bradford, West Yorkshire, BD5 7JW Tel: (01274) 726754 Fax: (01274) 722368

Mosaic Missions, 217a Forest Rd, Walthamstow, London, E17 6HE Tel: 020 85232444 Fax: 020 85232475

New College, New College Drive, Swindon, SN3 1AH Tel: (01793) 436437 Fax: (01793) 436437E-mail: admissions@newcollege.ac.uk

▶ Newark Learn Direct Business Centre, 31 Albert Street, Newark, Nottinghamshire, NG24 4BJ Tel: (01636) 611900 Fax: (01636) 611988

Newham London Borough Of Inspection Development Service Education, Kirton Road, Credon Centre, London, E13 9BT Tel: (020) 8548 5034 Fax: (020) 8548 5068

Oakwood Computing Ltd, 1 Dornton Road, South Croydon, Surrey, CR2 7DR Tel: (020) 8686 7213 E-mail: enquiries@oakwoodcomputing.co.uk

▶ On Line Learning, 510 Wilbraham Road, Manchester, M21 9AW Tel: 0161-860 6814

Oxford House College, 30 Market Place, London, W1W 8AW Tel: (020) 7436 4872 Fax: (020) 7323 4582E-mail: english@oxfordhouse.co.uk

P T R Associates Ltd, 21A Peach Street, Wokingham, Berkshire, RG40 1XJ Tel: 0118-979 4000 Fax: 0118-979 4035 E-mail: sales@ptr.co.uk

Paradise Computing Ltd, Albion House, Albion Place, Northampton, NN1 1UD Tel: (01604) 604575 Fax: (01604) 670375 E-mail: sales@paradisecomputing.co.uk

▶ Paramount Training Group, 24 High Street, Cheadle, Cheshire, SK8 1AL Tel: 0161-428 8002

Parity Solutions Ltd, Wimbledon Bridge House, 1 Hartfield Road, London, SW19 3RU Tel: (020) 8543 5353 Fax: (020) 8545 6456 E-mail: sales@paritytraining.com

Path Way, 6 Netherwood Road, London, W14 0BJ Tel: (020) 7603 3393 Fax: (020) 7603 4222

Pathfinder Trust, Unit 1, The Candar, Ilfracombe, Devon, EX34 9DS Tel: (01271) 866761 Fax: (01271) 866761 E-mail: info@path-finder.org.uk

PC Coaching, Innova Park, Kinetic CR, Enfield, Middlesex, EN3 7XH Tel: (020) 8350 4848 Fax: (0845) 6650744 E-mail: sales@pccoaching.com

▶ Peritus Training, Kingsland House, 512 Wimborne Road East, Ferndown, Dorset, BH22 9NG Tel: (01202) 871971 Fax: (01202) 871971

Pershore Leisure Centre, PO Box 2000, Pershore, Worcestershire, WR10 1QU Tel: (01386) 552346 Fax: (01386) 556559 E-mail: post@c2000.com

Phase C R S Ltd, Beacon Lodge, Texas Street, Morley, Leeds, LS27 0HG Tel: 0113-238 0558 Fax: 0113-238 0484 E-mail: sales@phase.crs.co.uk

Pitman Training Centre Ltd, Ferrari House, 258 Field End Road, Ruislip, Middlesex, HA4 9UU Tel: (020) 8868 0111 Fax: (020) 8868 1001 E-mail: harrowanduxbridge@pitman-training.net

▶ Premier Computer Training Services, Unit 144, Enkalon Industrial Estate, Randalstown Road, Antrim, BT41 4LD Tel: (028) 9446 9442 Fax: (028) 4468 9256

Professional Computer Group Ltd, Merley House, Merley House Lane, Wimborne, Dorset, BH21 3AA Tel: (01202) 857000 Fax: (01202) 857007 E-mail: enquiries@pcgl.co.uk

Pygmalion Ltd, Latham House, 16 Minories, London, EC3N 1AX Tel: (020) 7680 9499 Fax: (020) 7480 7606 E-mail: training@pygmalion.com

▶ Q A P.L.C., Ashurst Manor, Church Lane, Ascot, Berkshire, SL5 7DD Tel: (01344) 876471 Fax: (0870) 4001841

Qa Scotland Ltd, 32 South Gyle Cresent, Edinburgh, EH12 9EB Tel: 0131-317 7600 Fax: 0131-317 7606

QAIQ Ltd, 55-65 Uxbridge Road, Slough, SL1 1SG Tel: (01753) 534421 Fax: (01753) 898305 E-mail: info@qa-iq.com

Mark Rastin IT Help, Support & Training, Croft House, Cymdda, Bridgend, Mid Glamorgan, CF32 9SL Tel: (01656) 729971 E-mail: mark@rastin.net

▶ Recruitment Training (Edinburgh) Ltd, 32 & 34 Heriot Hill Terrace, Edinburgh, EH7 4DY Tel: 0131-558 9209 Fax: 0131-558 9187 E-mail: info@rtl-training.com

Ronin Group, 637 Forest Road, London, E17 4NE Tel: (020) 8531 4001 Fax: (020) 8531 2223

▶ Rugeley Training Centre, 16 Upper Brook Street, Rugeley, Staffordshire, WS15 2DN Tel: (01889) 579579 Fax: 01889 579579

▶ St Peters Community Partnership, Richmond Suite, Portland House, Katherine Street, Ashton-Under-Lyne, Lancashire, OL6 7BS Tel: 0161-343 7560 Fax: 0161-343 7560

ServiceTec Ltd, ServiceTec House, 3 Rutherford Close, Medway Technology Park, Stevenage, Hertfordshire, SG1 2EF Tel: (01438) 341900 Fax: (01438) 341901 E-mail: info@servicetec.com

▶ Set Solutions, 14 Bacon Street, London, E1 6LF Tel: (020) 7729 7906 E-mail: sales@s-e-t.co.uk

Sigta Ltd, 26 Abinger Road, Portslade, Brighton, BN41 1RZ Tel: (01273) 420029 Fax: (01273) 423982 E-mail: sales@sigta.co.uk

Simply Agile, 25 Lindberg Way, Woodley, Reading, RG5 4XE Tel: 0118-969 7100 Fax: (0870) 1388551 E-mail: rod@train400.com

▶ Skillmarque Ltd, 27, East Street, Chichester, W. Sussex, PO19 1HS Tel: 0845-129 7299 Fax: 0845-129 7298

The Skills Centre, 3 The Adelaide, Higham, Rochester, Kent, ME3 7LU Tel: (01474) 824555

Smallpiece Enterprises, 27 Newbold Terrace, Leamington Spa, Warwickshire, CV32 4ES Tel: (01926) 336423 Fax: (01926) 450679 E-mail: train@smallpeice.co.uk

Softech Global, Softech House, London Road, Albourne, Hassocks, West Sussex, BN6 9BN Tel: (01273) 833844 Fax: (01273) 833044 E-mail: info@softechglobal.com

Softsmart Ltd, Minster House, York Road, Eastbourne, East Sussex, BN21 4ST Tel: (01323) 419682 Fax: (01323) 419558 E-mail: sales@softsmart.co.uk

Software Generation Training, 339 Plungington Road, Fulwood, Preston, PR2 3PS Tel: (01772) 712499 Fax: (01772) 787943 E-mail: info@sgtoday.co.uk

▶ Software Skills Centre, Unit 5, Zurich House, 299 High Street, Sutton, Surrey, SM1 1LG Tel: (020) 8770 9817 Fax: (020) 8652 7374 E-mail: judy@softwareskills.info

▶ Soo Consultant Ltd, 54-57, Key Hill, Birmingham, B18 5NX Tel: 0121-507 1512 Fax: 0121-554 4982

Sound Sense Training, The Old Manor Ho, Bush Rd, London, SE8 5AP Tel: 020 73940131

Southern Gilcrest Services, 63 Silverberry Road, Weston-super-Mare, Avon, BS22 6RY Tel: (01934) 521682 Fax: (01934) 513268

Specialist Computer Centres Ltd, Applied House, Killingbeck Drive, York Road, Leeds, LS14 6UF Tel: 0113-240 5250 Fax: 0113-240 1093

Square One Computer Training, Egerton House, Tower Road, Birkenhead, Merseyside, CH41 1FN Tel: 0151-650 6907 Fax: 0151-649 8567 E-mail: sales@squareonetraining.com

▶ Sunrise Systems, 52 Albany Street, Edinburgh, EH1 3QR Tel: 0131-478 7781 Fax: 0131-478 0239

▶ Sunrise Systems (Scotland), Arbikie Farm, Inverkeilor, Arbroath, Angus, DD11 4UZ Tel: (01241) 830770 Fax: (01241) 830755 E-mail: sales@sunsys.com

Swansea Itec Ltd, 250 Carmarthen Road, Swansea, SA1 1HG Tel: (01792) 464561 Fax: (01792) 648375 E-mail: info@swansea-itec.co.uk

Sys Dynamics Ltd, Unit 3, Burley Road, Angel Court, Leeds, LS3 1BS Tel: 0113-244 2176 Fax: 0113-244 2168

Tabs Training Ltd, Brunel House, Mitchell Road, Salisbury, SP2 7PY Tel: (01722) 338668 Fax: (01722) 332052 E-mail: sales@tabsltd.co.uk

Tadpole Contracts Ltd, The Old Bakery, High Street, Great Bardfield, Braintree, Essex, CM7 4RF Tel: (01371) 810817 Fax: (01371) 810024

Technocurve, Unit 52 Enterprise Centre, Bryn Road, Aberkenfig, Bridgend, Mid Glamorgan, CF32 9BS Tel: (0845) 0515014 Fax: (0870) 0940776

Technology Tamed Ltd, Hadleigh Business & Learning Centre, Crockatt Lane, Hadleigh, Ipswich, IP7 6RH Tel: (01473) 826180

Tigerridge Consultancy Services Ltd, 4 Bonneys, The Street, Eversley, Hook, Hampshire, RG27 0PJ Tel: 0118-973 6875 Fax: (0845) 2303635 E-mail: sales@tigerridge.co.uk

Touch I.T Mobile, 27 Goldsmith Avenue, Romford, RM7 0EX Tel: (07071) 222856 E-mail: admin@touchit.co.uk

Touchstone C T A, 89 Barnham Road, Barnham, Bognor Regis, West Sussex, PO22 0EQ Tel: (01243) 553479 E-mail: malcolm@tcta.co.uk

▶ Train 4 It Ltd, 275-285 High Street, London, E15 2TF Tel: (020) 8519 9243 Fax: (020) 8519 9243

Train & Grow Ltd, 73 Green Lane, Cookridge, Leeds, LS16 7ET Tel: 0113-226 4303 Fax: 0113 2264303 E-mail: enquiries@trainandgrow.com

The Training Foundry, City Campus, Pond Street, Sheffield, S1 1WB Tel: 0114-225 5888 Fax: 0114-225 5889 E-mail: itfoundry@shu.ac.uk

Training For The Millennuim, Rocheway, Rochford, Essex, SS4 1DQ Tel: (01702) 543680 Fax: (01268) 690133 E-mail: tftmrochford@yahoo.cp.uk

TSG Ltd, High Street, Broom, Alcester, Warwickshire, B50 4HN Tel: (01789) 778900 Fax: (01789) 772272

▶ Tutors 4 Computers, 25 Lower Bartons, Fordingbridge, Hampshire, SP6 1JB Tel: (07919) 094523 E-mail: Tutors4Computers@hotmail.co.uk

▶ Upgrade, 13 Fore Lane Avenue, Sowerby Bridge, West Yorkshire, HX6 1BQ

Veryan Ltd, Wellhouse Road, Beech, Alton, Hampshire, GU34 4AH Tel: (01420) 543131 Fax: (01420) 543232 E-mail: solutions@veryan.com

▶ Westward Training & Personnel, 34 Rolle Street, Exmouth, Devon, EX8 2SH Tel: (01392) 490167 Fax: (01395) 279297 E-mail: wtp.training@btconnect.com

Wheatley Associates, 9 Main Street, Witchford, Ely, Cambridgeshire, CB6 2HG Tel: (01353) 664605 E-mail: enquiries@wheatley-associates.net

COMPUTER TRAINING/ TEACHING SYSTEMS

▶ Alpha Tutors, No. 6, Russell Flint House, Royal Docks, London, E16 1UT Tel: 0207 4732360

Amadeus Software Ltd, Orchard Farm, Witney Lane, Leafield, Witney, Oxfordshire, OX29 9PG Tel: (01993) 878287 Fax: (01993) 878042 E-mail: info@amadeus.co.uk

Ascot Systems (UK) Ltd, Woods Way, Goring-By-Sea, Worthing, West Sussex, BN12 4QY Tel: (01903) 503041 Fax: (01903) 507250 E-mail: sales@ascot-systems.co.uk

Capita Business Services Ltd, Kemp House, Cumnor Hill, Cumnor, Oxford, OX2 9PH Tel: (01865) 861300 Fax: (01865) 861301

▶ Develop IT Ltd, Springfield House, Springfield Business Park, Springfield Road, Grantham, Lincolnshire, NG31 7BG Tel: 01476 514670 Fax: 01476 514679 E-mail: info@develop-it.com

Elyzium, 12 Queensbrook, Bolton, BL1 4AY Tel: (01204) 528628 Fax: (01204) 534678 E-mail: sales@elyzium.co.uk

I T At Bicester, 15 Manorsfield Road, Bicester, Oxfordshire, OX26 6EH Tel: (01869) 353939 E-mail: apine@occ.ac.uk

L J Technical Systems Ltd, 5-6 Francis Way, Bowthorpe Employment Area, Norwich, NR5 9JA Tel: (01603) 740421 Fax: (01603) 746340 E-mail: uksales@ljgroup.com

Lexicon Lifeline Ltd, Unit 3, 78 Blandford Road, Corfe Mullen, Wimborne, Dorset, BH21 3HQ Tel: (01202) 657252 Fax: (01202) 657252 E-mail: office@lexiconlifeline.co.uk

Matrix Information Technology Ltd, Imperial Chambers, 41-43 Longsmith Street, Gloucester, GL1 2HT Tel: (01452) 387002 Fax: (01452) 309693 E-mail: sales@matrixinfotech.co.uk

Meap Ltd, 1 Bath Road, Stonehouse, Gloucestershire, GL10 2JD Tel: (01453) 828088 Fax: (01453) 828980 E-mail: roger.hughes@softlogic.co.uk

COMPUTER VISION SYSTEMS

Azure Ltd, Unit 10 Herringston Barn, Herringston, Dorchester, Dorset, DT2 9PU Tel: (01305) 251771 Fax: (01305) 251779 E-mail: info@azure.com

COMPUTER/ TELECOMMUNICATION EQUIPMENT SCRAP MERCHANTS/RECOVERY CONTRACTORS/SPECIALIST SERVICES

Absolute Computers Ltd, 19 Old High Street, Headington, Oxford, OX3 9HS Tel: (01865) 744115 Fax: (01865) 744155 E-mail: admin@absolute.co.uk

Bruce R.I.D. Recycling Ltd, March Street, Sheffield, S9 5DQ Tel: 0114-243 3637 Fax: 0114-244 8521 E-mail: info@weee-recycler.co.uk

▶ G R P (Electronic) Ltd, 2 Wham Cottages, Slackgate Lane, Denshaw, Oldham, OL3 5TZ Tel: (01457) 820864 Fax: (01457) 820864 E-mail: pollardgraham@talk21.com

Micro Peripherals Ltd, Shorten Brook Way, Altham Business Park, Altham, Accrington, Lancashire, BB5 5YJ Tel: (01282) 776776 Fax: (01282) 770001 E-mail: sales@micro-p.com

COMPUTERISED PROCESS ENGRAVERS

Don Browning Trophies, 4 St. Georges Street, Cheltenham, Gloucestershire, GL50 4AF Tel: (01242) 690314 Fax: (01242) 690313 E-mail: richard@dbtrophies.co.uk

C A Grant, Orgreave Crescent, Sheffield, S13 9NQ Tel: 0114-269 5498 Fax: 0114-269 5412 E-mail: sales@cagrant.co.uk

Custom Components Ltd, Unit 3 Boxer Place, Leyland, PR26 7QL Tel: (01772) 455520 Fax: (01772) 436472 E-mail: sales@customcomponents.co.uk

Fortune UK Ltd, Wyvenhoe, Farnham Road, Farnham Royal, Slough, SL2 3AE Tel: (01753) 669471 Fax: (01753) 669472 E-mail: info@fortuneuk.com

G R S Sign Co. Ltd, Tateshall Way, Fairfield Industrial Estate, Louth, Lincolnshire, LN11 0YZ Tel: (01507) 609485 Fax: (01507) 609489 E-mail: sales@grssigns.co.uk

Gilmour Tools Ltd, Baird Avenue, Strutherhill Industrial Estate, Larkhall, Lanarkshire, ML9 2PJ Tel: (01698) 884856 Fax: (01698) 886634 E-mail: info@gilmourtools.co.uk

Industrial Signs Ltd, 8 Astor Park, Padholme Road, Peterborough, PE1 5XL Tel: (01733) 555153 Fax: (01733) 555157 E-mail: isignsltd@compuserve.com

J T S Engravers, 30-34 Aire Street, Leeds, LS1 4HT Tel: 0113-242 2158 Fax: 0113-242 8903 E-mail: jtsengravers@hotmail.co.uk

Lymm Engraving, 199 Liverpool Road, Cadishead, Manchester, M44 5XH Tel: 0161-775 7625 Fax: 0161-775 7247 E-mail: enquires@lymmengraving.co.uk

Nash & Co., 14 Bridge Street, Caversham, Reading, RG4 8AA Tel: 0118-947 2295 Fax: 0118-947 7010 E-mail: paulthejewel@aol.com

P M E Engraving & Screen Printing Ltd, 11 Robert Cort Industrial Estate, Britten Road, Reading, RG2 0AU Tel: 0118-986 4858 Fax: 0118-975 3415 E-mail: pms-sales@compuserve.com

Peter Devine, 94 Matilda Street, Sheffield, S1 4QF Tel: 0114-275 0479 Fax: 0114-275 0479

Michael Smith Engraving Services Ltd, Unit 3, Leicester, LE2 8AA Tel: 0116-283 0712 Fax: 0116-244 0198 E-mail: sales@michaelsmithswitchgear.co.uk

COMPUTERISED SIMULATION

Elonex P.L.C., 2 Apsley Way, London, NW2 7LF Tel: (020) 8452 4444 Fax: (020) 8452 6422 E-mail: sales@elonex.co.uk

FlowTech Design Ltd, 355 Green Lane, Bolton, BL3 2LU Tel: (01204) 362622 Fax: (01204) 362622 E-mail: clive.fenn@flowtechdesign.com

COMPUTERISED SIMULATION – *continued*

I3s, Higher Barn, Wildboarclough, Macclesfield, Cheshire, SK11 0BD Tel: (01260) 227377 Fax: (01260) 227399

Pennant International Group Ltd, Pennant Court, Staverton Technology Park, Old Gloucester Road, Staverton, Cheltenham, Gloucestershire, GL51 6TL Tel: (01452) 714914 Fax: (01452) 714920 E-mail: ptsl@pennantplc.co.uk

Thales Training & Simulation, Gatwick Road, Crawley, West Sussex, RH10 9RL Tel: (01293) 562822 Fax: (01293) 563366

COMPUTERISED SIMULATORS

Bull Information Systems Ltd, Maxted Road, Hemel Hempstead, Hertfordshire, HP2 7DZ Tel: (01442) 232222 Fax: (01442) 884361 E-mail: information@bull.co.uk

▶ Esd Simulation Training Ltd, Craigearn Business Park, Morrison Way, Kintore, Inverurie, Aberdeenshire, AB51 0TH Tel: (01467) 634934 Fax: (01467) 634949

Pennant International Group Ltd, Pennant Court, Staverton Technology Park, Old Gloucester Road, Staverton, Cheltenham, Gloucestershire, GL51 6TL Tel: (01452) 714914 Fax: (01452) 714920 E-mail: ptsl@pennantplc.co.uk

Rocs Computer Services Ltd, 3rd Floor, 35 William Road, London, NW1 3ER Tel: (020) 7383 4447 Fax: (020) 7383 5831 E-mail: sales@rocs.co.uk

Simutech Electronics Ltd, Unit 42 Louis Pearlman Centre, Goulton Street, Hull, HU3 4DL Tel: (01482) 212961 Fax: (01482) 585608 E-mail: simutechpt@compuserve.com

T & T Consultancy, Advantage House, Trentham Business Quarter, Stoke-on-Trent, ST4 8GQ Tel: (01782) 644141 Fax: (01782) 646142 E-mail: enqruies@tandt.com

Tector Visual Systems, Woodhill Road, Collingham, Newark, Nottinghamshire, NG23 7NR Tel: (01636) 892246 Fax: (01636) 893317 E-mail: sales@graffelectronics.co.uk

Thales Training & Simulation, Gatwick Road, Crawley, West Sussex, RH10 9RL Tel: (01293) 562822 Fax: (01293) 563366

COMPUTERS, CD-ROM

B W C L, B W C L House, Brook Farm Estate, Kimbolton, Leominster, Herefordshire, HR6 0ES Tel: (01568) 750365 Fax: (01568) 750369 E-mail: admin@bwcl.co.uk

Bridgewater Computers, 42 Green End, Whitchurch, Shropshire, SY13 1AA Tel: (01948) 666630 Fax: (01948) 666630 E-mail: bridgewatermcg@aol.com

Dominion Software Ltd, 63 Parkside, London, SW19 5NL Tel: (020) 8947 4059

Glowbird Computing Ltd, 157 Alma St, Abertillery, Gwent, NP13 1QD Tel: (01495) 212223

I T Protocol Ltd, 3 Weston Farm, The Street, Albury, Guildford, Surrey, GU5 9BZ Tel: (01483) 203000 Fax: (01483) 203030 E-mail: sales@itprotocol.com

P C Concepts, 9 Bolton Road, Worsley, Manchester, M28 3AX Tel: 0161-703 9025 Fax: 0161-703 9426 E-mail: sales@pc-concepts.co.uk

▶ PC Systems, 19 Borthwick Close, Bransholme, Hull, HU7 5BE Tel: (01482) 827461 Fax: (01482) 827461 E-mail: info@pcsystems-ss.co.uk

Sony DADC Ltd, Southwater Business Park, Worthing Road, Southwater, Horsham, West Sussex, RH13 9YT Tel: (01403) 732302 Fax: (01403) 732313

COMPUTERS, HANDHELD, TOUCH SCREEN

Crymatics Ltd, Oakwood House, Bishop Thornton, Harrogate, North Yorkshire, HG3 3JN Tel: (01423) 771133 Fax: (01423) 770093

Fujitsu Siemens Computers Ltd, The Boulevard, Cain Road, Bracknell, Berkshire, RG12 1HH Tel: (01344) 475000 Fax: (01344) 475666 E-mail: sales@fujitsu-siemens.com

Microscribe, PO Box 738, Cambridge, CB2 5WY Tel: 0845 064 5555 E-mail: info@microscribe.co.uk

Tectime Data Systems Ltd, Copthall House, Nelson Place, Newcastle, Staffordshire, ST5 1EZ Tel: (01782) 799567 Fax: (01782) 799447 E-mail: info@tectime.com

Touchstar Technologies Ltd, 7 Commerce Way, Trafford Park, Manchester, M17 1HW Tel: 0161-874 5050 Fax: 0161-874 5088 E-mail: enq@touchstar.com

COMPUTERS, NOTEBOOK

Blue Baron, 1089 Pollokshaws Road, Glasgow, G41 3YG Tel: 0141-649 3101 Fax: 0141-649 3101 E-mail: bluebar@btconnect.com

Cheap-IT, 338 City Road, Angel, London, EC1V 2PY Tel: (01582) 600883 E-mail: sales@cheap-it.com

Clarke Computer Systems, 43 Cannock Road, Burntwood, Staffordshire, WS7 0BL Tel: (01543) 670756 Fax: (01543) 670756 E-mail: info@clarkecomputers.co.uk

Crofton Micro Systems Ltd, Forest Hill Industrial Estate, Perry Vale, London, SE23 2LX Tel: (020) 8699 7575 E-mail: sales@crofton.co.uk

Evesham Technology Ltd, Vale Park, Evesham, Worcestershire, WR11 1TD Tel: (01386) 769600 Fax: (01386) 769795

Gamma Global, 157 Warwick Road, Solihull, West Midlands, B92 7AR Tel: 0121-706 8080 Fax: 0121-706 1188

I B M (UK) Ltd, Po Box 41, Portsmouth, PO6 3AU Tel: (023) 9256 1000 Fax: (023) 9238 8914 E-mail: uk_crc@uk.ibm.com

N B Group It Consultancy, 34 Bedford Road, Gregans House, Hitchin, Hertfordshire, SG5 1HF Tel: (01462) 452452 E-mail: info@online-it.com

▶ PCS Computers, Unit 50 Elms Business Centre, Main Road, Great Haywood, Stafford, ST18 0ST Tel: (01889) 883091 E-mail: sales@staffordshirelaptopcentre.co.uk

Siemens Business Services Ltd, 62 Boucher CR, Belfast, BT12 6HU Tel: (028) 9066 4331 Fax: (028) 9068 2168 E-mail: owen.mckenna@siemens.ie

▶ Think4 Ltd, Block P1 Unit, Heywood Distribution Park, Pilsworth Road, Heywood, Lancashire, OL10 2TT Tel: (0870) 1644446 Fax: (01706) 620000

Triangular Business Systems, 1 Marlston Court, Rough Hill, Marlston-cum-Lache, Chester, CH4 9JT Tel: (01244) 683450 Fax: (01244) 674949 E-mail: enquiries@triangularsystems.co.uk

COMPUTING MAGAZINES

Computer Trade Shopper, Quadrant House, The Quadrant, Sutton, Surrey, SM2 5AS Tel: (020) 8652 3500 Fax: (020) 8652 3793

Computer Weekly, Quadrant House The Quadrant, Brighton Road, Sutton, Surrey, SM2 5AS Tel: (020) 8652 8642 Fax: (020) 8652 8979

MicroScope, Quadrant House, The Quadrant, Sutton, Surrey, SM2 5AS Tel: (020) 8652 3500 Fax: (020) 8652 8297 E-mail: microscope@rbi.co.uk

CONCAVE OR CONVEX MIRRORS

D C Carter Ltd, Meadow Farm, Packards Lane, Wormingford, Colchester, CO6 3AH Tel: (01206) 243309 Fax: (01206) 242161 E-mail: dccarter@onetel.com

Opals (Mirror-Flex) Co. Ltd, Unit 3 B Seaden Court, Steveson Road, Gorse Lane Industrial Estate, Clacton-On-Sea, Essex, CO15 4XN Tel: (01255) 423927 Fax: (01255) 221117 E-mail: sales@mirrorflex.co.uk

CONCEALED HINGES

Salice UK Ltd, Kingfisher Way, Hinchingbrooke Business Park, Huntingdon, Cambridgeshire, PE29 6FN Tel: (01480) 413831 Fax: (01480) 451489 E-mail: info.salice@saliceuk.co.uk

CONCENTRATED OR TERPENELESS ESSENTIAL OILS

Adrian Essential Oils Ltd, 1 Essence House, Crabtree Road, Thorpe Industrial Estate, Egham, Surrey, TW20 8RN Tel: (01784) 485600 Fax: (01784) 472255 E-mail: uksales@adrian.fr

Forrester Wood & Co. Ltd, Heron Street, Hawksley Industrial Estate, Oldham, OL8 4UJ Tel: 0161-620 4124 Fax: 0161-627 1050 E-mail: info@forresterwood.com

R D Campbell & Co. Ltd, Unit 14 Mill Farm Business Park, Millfield Road, Hounslow, TW4 5PY Tel: (020) 8898 6611 Fax: (020) 8898 6622

R.C. Treatt & Co. Ltd, Northern Way, Bury St. Edmunds, Suffolk, IP32 6NL Tel: (01284) 702500 Fax: (01284) 703809 E-mail: marketing@rctreatt.com

CONCERT STAGING

▶ Ra'Alloy Trading Company Ltd, Hortonwood 10, Telford, Shropshire, TF1 7ES Tel: (01952) 677877 Fax: (01952) 677883 E-mail: sales@raalloy.com

CONCRETE ADDITIVES

Cemex, Station Yard, Bletchley, Milton Keynes, MK2 2JU Tel: (01908) 370259

Edenhall Concrete Ltd, Evergreen, Hale Purlieu, Fordingbridge, Hampshire, SP6 2NN Tel: (01725) 510174 Fax: (01725) 512824

Gamallt Ready Mix Concrete Ltd, Gamallt, Pantygrwndy, Cardigan, Dyfed, SA43 3NP Tel: (01239) 613257 Fax: (01239) 613257 E-mail: sales@gamalt.co.uk

Hanson Aggregates Ltd, 23 Queen St, Wigan, Lancashire, WN3 4DZ Tel: (01942) 239617

Hillhouse Precast Concrete, Mains Road, Beith, Ayrshire, KA15 2HR Tel: (01505) 502711 Fax: (01505) 502569 E-mail: info@hillhousegroup.co.uk

J Linham & Sons Ltd, Westhay, Meare, Glastonbury, Somerset, BA6 9TL Tel: (01458) 860216

Landywood Concrete Products Ltd, Stafford Road, Wolverhampton, WV10 7EG Tel: (01902) 786696

Marshalls, Llay Road, Llay, Wrexham, Clwyd, LL12 0TL Tel: (01978) 858200 Fax: (01978) 858212

Mobile Concrete Supplies, Hethersett Road, East Carleton, Norwich, NR14 8HX Tel: (01603) 811492 Fax: (01603) 814328

Peakmix Concrete, Peak Forest, Buxton, Derbyshire, SK17 8EW Tel: (01298) 23013

R M C South West Ltd, Moorlands Trading Estate, Saltash, Cornwall, PL12 6LX Tel: (01752) 481011 Fax: (01752) 848862

R M C Western Ltd, Warmwell Quarry, Moreton Road, Warmwell, Dorchester, Dorset, DT2 8HU Tel: (01305) 852553

Ready Mixed Concrete South West Ltd, 10 Concrete Works, Trewoon, St. Austell, Cornwall, PL25 5SL Tel: (01726) 74201 Fax: (01726) 73027

Ready Mixed Concrete (West Midlands) Ltd, Brick Kiln Lane, Stoke-On-Trent, ST4 7BN Tel: (01782) 202227 Fax: (01782) 267008

Ready Mixed Concrete Western Ltd, RMC House, 82-87 Feeder Road, Bristol, BS2 0UE Tel: 0117-977 9534 Fax: 0117-971 7534

Ready Mixed Concrete (Western) Ltd, C/O Bromfield Sand & Gravel, Bromfield, Ludlow, Shropshire, SY8 2JR Tel: (01584) 856253 Fax: (01584) 856261

RMC Readymix Southwest Ltd, Haye Quarry, Stag Lane, Plymouth, PL9 8AX Tel: (01208) 74321

Sika Ltd, Watchmead, Welwyn Garden City, Hertfordshire, AL7 1BQ Tel: (01707) 394444 Fax: (01707) 329129 E-mail: info@sika.com

Tarmac Northern Ltd, Lingerfield, Scotton, Knaresborough, North Yorkshire, HG5 9JN Tel: (01423) 796800 Fax: (01423) 796808 E-mail: info@tarmac-northern.co.uk

CONCRETE ADMIXTURES

A.S. Charles, RMC Aggregates Eastern Counties, Mentmore Rd, Leighton Buzzard, Beds, LU7 7PA Tel: 01525 381042

Chelmix Concrete Ltd, 2 Kendrick Trading Estate, Galton Way, Swindon, SN2 2DU Tel: (01793) 610420 Fax: (01793) 610420

David Ball Group plc, Huntingdon Road, Cambridge, CB23 8HN Tel: (01954) 780687 Fax: (01954) 782912 E-mail: sales@davidballgroup.com

Don Construction Products, Station Road, Churnetside Business Park, Cheddleton, Leek, Staffordshire, ST13 7RS Tel: (01538) 361799 Fax: (01538) 361899 E-mail: info@donconstruction.co.uk

Dudley Mixed, Peartree Lane, Dudley, West Midlands, DY2 0UU Tel: (01384) 242474 Fax: (01384) 242499

Ernest Hinchliffe (Peak Mix Concrete) Ltd, Peak Works, Peak Forest, Buxton, Derbyshire, SK17 8EW Tel: (01298) 23671 Fax: (0870) 0638909

London Concrete Ltd, 77 Boston Manor Road, Brentford, Middlesex, TW8 9JQ Tel: (020) 8380 7300 Fax: (020) 8380 7301 E-mail: london.concrete@aggregate.com

M S West & Son, Swiss Cottage, Westminster Lane, Newport, Isle of Wight, PO30 5DP Tel: (01983) 522472 Fax: (01983) 825538

Minicrete, Able House Billingham Reach Industrial Estate, Haverton Hill Road, Billingham, Cleveland, TS23 1PX Tel: (01642) 730000 Fax: (01642) 312126

Ready Mixed Concrete Eastern Ltd, Woodhall Road, Tattershall Thorpe, Lincoln, LN4 4JT Tel: (01526) 342187

Ready Mixed Concrete North West Ltd, Barden Lane, Reedley, Burnley, Lancashire, BB12 0RZ Tel: (01282) 428545 Fax: (01772) 769826 E-mail: info@rmc.co.uk

Tarmac Topmix Ltd, Constarry Road, Kilsyth, Glasgow, G65 9HY Tel: (01236) 821500

CONCRETE AGGREGATES

Amman Concrete Products Ltd, Bryncethin Road, Garnant, Ammanford, Dyfed, SA18 1YP Tel: (01269) 823338 Fax: (01269) 823638

Builder Center, 1 Knowsley Street, Cheetham Hill Road, Manchester, M8 8QL Tel: 0161-834 9437 Fax: 0161-833 2706 E-mail: wolseley@center.co.uk

Cemex UK Materials, Equinox North, Great Park Road, Bradley Stoke, Bristol, BS32 4QL Tel: (01454) 451851 Fax: (01454) 451860

Humber Sand & Gravel Ltd, West Quay, Alexandra Dock, Hedon Road, Hull, HU9 1TA Tel: (01482) 328144 Fax: (01482) 585163

K R L Concrete Ltd, Manor Nurseries, Kenilworth Road, Hampton-in-Arden, Solihull, West Midlands, B92 0LR Tel: (01675) 443157 Fax: (01675) 443316

Kendall Bros Portsmouth Ltd, Kendalls Wharf, Eastern Road, Portsmouth, PO3 5LY Tel: (023) 9266 2801 Fax: (023) 9267 0889 E-mail: sales@kendalls.co.uk

Lafarge Aluminates Ltd, Dolphin Way, Purfleet, Essex, RM19 1NZ Tel: (01708) 863333 Fax: (01708) 861033

Lasarge Concrete Products, Newlands Road, Charing, Ashford, Kent, TN27 0AS Tel: (01233) 712267 Fax: (01233) 713720

Leswidden, Leswidden, St. Just, Penzance, Cornwall, TR19 7RU Tel: (01736) 788644 Fax: (01736) 788644

Ready Mixed Concrete (London) Ltd, Randells Roadlkings Cross, London, N1 0DJ Tel: (020) 7607 8881

Salop Sand & Gravel Supply Co. Ltd, Station Road, Admaston, Telford, Shropshire, TF5 0AN Tel: (01952) 254101 Fax: (01952) 223932 E-mail: info@gravel.co.uk

▶ Semex UK Materials Ltd, Kilmartin Place, Tannochside Park, Uddingston, Glasgow, G71 5PH Tel: (01698) 811100 Fax: (01698) 816068

Silver Fern Concrete, Milton Industrial Estate, Milton, Cambridge, CB4 4AZ Tel: (01223) 420669

Smiths Concrete Ltd, Waverley Wood Quarry, Weston Lane, Bubbenhall, Coventry, CV8 3BN Tel: (01926) 633186 Fax: (01926) 633478 E-mail: info@smithsconcrete.co.uk

CONCRETE AGRICULTURAL BUILDINGS

J. Airey, Scott Laithe Farm, Gisburn Road, Bolton By Bowland, Clitheroe, Lancashire, BB7 4LT Tel: (01200) 447616

Alexander Mills, 43 Main Street, Benburb, Dungannon, County Tyrone, BT71 7JY Tel: (028) 3754 8971 Fax: (028) 3754 8691 E-mail: sales@alexander-mills.co.uk

Banks Cargill Agriculture Ltd, Lineside, Weston, Newark, Nottinghamshire, NG23 6TL Tel: (01636) 821074 Fax: (01522) 822235 E-mail: enquiries@cargill.com

Chris Blackler Farm Buildings, Oaklands, Loddiswell, Kingsbridge, Devon, TQ7 4EA Tel: (01548) 821489 Fax: (01548) 821489

Caerleon Ready Mixed Concrete Ltd, Western Industrial Estate, Caerleon, Newport, NP18 3NN Tel: (01633) 423549 Fax: (01633) 430413

E M Hunt, Whitehirst Park Works, Kilwinning, Ayrshire, KA13 6PF Tel: (01294) 552682 Fax: (01294) 557949

Farm Chemicals Ltd, 82a Charles Street, Portadown, Craigavon, County Armagh, BT62 1DQ Tel: (028) 3833 3509 Fax: (028) 3835 0706

Highwood, Millers Close, Dorchester, Dorset, DT1 1HW Tel: (01305) 266058 Fax: (01305) 263155 E-mail: enquiry@highwood-farming.co.uk

Lakeland Agri Care, Agri House, Main Street, Lisnaskea, Enniskillen, County Fermanagh, BT92 0JG Tel: (028) 6772 2377 Fax: (028) 6772 3655

Philip Holden, Harmire Enterprise Park, Barnard Castle, County Durham, DL12 8XT Tel: (01833) 637224 Fax: (01833) 690312

R D Bennett Farming Contractors, Hollyhedge Farm, Hollyhedge Lane, Higher Walton, Warrington, WA4 5QP Tel: (01925) 262342 Fax: (01925) 268703

R G Bell & Sons, The Wath, Caldbeck, Wigton, Cumbria, CA7 8EY Tel: (01697) 478204

Suttons Buildings, 66 Blackgate Lane, Tarleton, Preston, PR4 6UT Tel: (01772) 814865 Fax: (01772) 815643

Turkington Engineering Ltd, 14 Tullylagan Road, Cookstown, County Tyrone, BT80 9AY Tel: (028) 8676 3372 Fax: (028) 8676 3484 E-mail: tls@lineone.net

W G Phillips, Rosemount, Princes Gate, Narberth, Dyfed, SA67 8TF Tel: (01834) 860244 Fax: 01834 860244

Whites Concrete Ltd, Ravensthorpe Road, Thornhill Lees, Dewsbury, West Yorkshire, WF12 9EF Tel: (01924) 464283 Fax: (01924) 459183 E-mail: whites@longley.uk.com

CONCRETE ANCHORING SYSTEMS

Alderdale Fixing Systems, New John Street, Halesowen, West Midlands, B62 8HT Tel: 0121-561 5500 Fax: 0121-561 3535 E-mail: sales@alderdale.com

Cintech International, 11 Gold Tops, Newport, Gwent, NP20 4PH Tel: (01633) 246614 Fax: (01633) 246110 E-mail: cintec@aol.com

▶ Excalibur Screwbolts Ltd, 10 Aldermans Hill, Hockley, Essex, SS5 4RW Tel: (01702) 206962 Fax: (01702) 207918 E-mail: charles.bickford@screwbolt.com

Halfen Ltd, 31 Humphrys Road, Woodside Estate, Dunstable, Bedfordshire, LU5 4TP Tel: (01582) 470300 Fax: (0870) 5316304 E-mail: sales@halfen.co.uk

Stainless UK Ltd, Newhall Works, Newhall Road, Sheffield, S9 2QL Tel: 0114-244 1333 Fax: 0114-244 1444

T M S Systems, Park Works, Main Road, Kingsley, Bordon, Hampshire, GU35 9LY Tel: (01420) 489313 Fax: (01420) 487218 E-mail: info@tms-systems.co.uk

CONCRETE BLOCK PRODUCTION PLANT

Brett Concrete Ltd, 7-9 Chapman Road, London, E9 5DW Tel: (020) 8986 6616 Fax: (020) 8985 8182

Readyblock, 20 Ballypalady Road, Doagh, Ballyclare, County Antrim, BT39 0QY Tel: (028) 9335 2259 Fax: (028) 9335 2223

Readymix Concrete, Hermitage Lane, Mansfield, Nottinghamshire, NG18 5HB Tel: (01623) 622174

S Morris Ltd, Tout Quarry, Tout Road, Charlton Adam, Somerton, Somerset, TA11 7AN Tel: (01458) 223991 Fax: (01458) 223181 E-mail: sales@smorris.co.uk

CONCRETE BLOCKS

Barnetts Buglawton, 24 Brook Street, Congleton, Cheshire, CW12 1RH Tel: (01260) 273170 Fax: (01260) 298150 E-mail: barnetsbuglawltd@thomasarmstrong.co.uk

Blackford Fencing Contractors, 92 Blackford Road, Shirley, Solihull, West Midlands, B90 4BX Tel: 0121-745 6691 Fax: 0121-745 6691

Bodmin Blocks Ltd, Penwithick, St. Austell, Cornwall, PL26 8YL Tel: (01726) 850461 Fax: (01726) 850866 E-mail: bodblocks@callnet.com

Brand & Rae Ltd, Russell Mill, Springfield, Cupar, Fife, KY15 5QX Tel: (01334) 652828 Fax: (01334) 655967

Brett Concrete Ltd, 7-9 Chapman Road, London, E9 5DW Tel: (020) 8986 6616 Fax: (020) 8985 8182

Brooke Concrete Products Ltd, Monksbridge Road, Dinnington, Sheffield, S25 3QS Tel: (01909) 550455 Fax: (01909) 568780 E-mail: claz.smyth@brooke.concrete.co.uk

Cary Concrete Ltd, Tor View Farm, Galhampton, Yeovil, Somerset, BA22 7AE Tel: (01963) 350409 Fax: (01963) 351712

Cemex UK Ltd, Coldharbour Lane, Thorpe/, Egham, Surrey, TW20 8TE Tel: (0845) 1559210 Fax: (01932) 568933 E-mail: enquiries@cemex-group.com

Centurion Concrete Products, Centurion Industrial Estate, Centurion Way, Farington, Leyland, PR25 4GU Tel: (01772) 622926 Fax: (01772) 622926

Cheshire Concrete Products Ltd, Road Beata, Middlewich, Cheshire, CW10 0QF Tel: (01606) 837364 Fax: (01606) 837365 E-mail: ccp@cheshireconcrete.co.uk

Coulthard's Concrete Products, Blackdyke Industrial Estate, Silloth, Wigton, Cumbria, CA7 4WY Tel: (01697) 331324 Fax: (01697) 331418

Dragon Blockworks Ltd, Concrete Works, Alltwalis, Carmarthen, Dyfed, SA32 7EE Tel: (01559) 384317 Fax: (01559) 384175 E-mail: dragonconcreteworksltd@hotmail.com

E.Wiltshire & Son (Torquay) Ltd, Walls Hill Quarry, Babbacombe Road, Torquay, TQ1 3TA Tel: (01803) 327706 Fax: (01803) 327793 E-mail: info@wiltshires-babbacombe.co.uk

Forticrete Ltd, Bridle Way, Bootle, Merseyside, L30 4UA Tel: 0151-521 3545 Fax: 0151-521 5696 E-mail: sswift@forticrete.com

Forticrete Ltd, Thornhill Works, Calder Road, Dewsbury, West Yorkshire, WF12 9HY Tel: (01924) 456416 Fax: (01924) 430697 E-mail: enquiries@forticrete.com

Hanson Aggregates Ltd, Ashby Road East, Shepshed, Loughborough, Leicestershire, LE12 9BU Tel: (01509) 507050 Fax: (01509) 504120

Hanson Aggregates Ltd, Station Road, South Molton, Devon, EX36 3LL Tel: (01769) 572817 Fax: (01769) 574733

Hanson Building Products, Stewartby, Bedford, MK43 9LZ Tel: (0870) 5258258 Fax: (01234) 762040 E-mail: info@hanson.biz

Hartigan Readymix Ltd, Chesney Wold, Bleak Hall, Milton Keynes, MK6 1NE Tel: (01908) 668766 Fax: (01908) 676323

Humberside Blocks Ltd, The Industrial Centre, Ellifoot Lane, Burstwick, Hull, HU12 9EF Tel: (01964) 670682 Fax: (01964) 671947 E-mail: enquiries@humberside-blocks.com

Lignacite Ltd, Meadgate Works, Meadgate Road, Nazeing, Waltham Abbey, Essex, EN9 2PD Tel: (01992) 464441 Fax: (01992) 445713 E-mail: info@lignacite.co.uk

Lignacite Brandon Ltd, Norfolk House, High Street, Brandon, Suffolk, IP27 0AX Tel: (01842) 810678 Fax: (01842) 814602 E-mail: info@lignacite.co.uk

Lincoln Concrete Products, Leckwith Bridge, Leckwith, Cardiff, CF11 8AS Tel: (029) 2022 5974 Fax: (029) 2031 8696

Llanharan Concrete Co. Ltd, Llanharry Road, Llanharan, Pontyclun, Mid Glamorgan, CF72 9RN Tel: (01443) 226212 Fax: (01443) 237685

Lovie Ltd, Cowbog, New Pitsligo, Fraserburgh, Aberdeenshire, AB43 6PR Tel: (01771) 653777 Fax: (01771) 653527 E-mail: sales@lovie.co.uk

Maxwell Concrete, 22 Folliard Road, Castlederg, County Tyrone, BT81 7JW Tel: (028) 8167 1326 Fax: (028) 8167 1157

Mona Precast Anglesey Ltd, Gaerwen Industrial Estate, Gaerwen, Gwynedd, LL60 6HR Tel: (01248) 421772 Fax: (01248) 421424 E-mail: monaprecast@aol.com

▶ Orkney Aggregates Ltd, Garrison Road, Hatston Industrial Estate, Kirkwall, Orkney, KW15 1RE Tel: (01856) 871187 Fax: (01856) 871188 E-mail: sales@orkagg.co.uk

Penygroes Concrete Products Ltd, Norton Road, Penygroes, Llanelli, Dyfed, SA14 7RU Tel: (01269) 842278 Fax: (01269) 845026

Plasmor Ltd, Womersley Road, Knottingley, West Yorkshire, WF11 0DN Tel: (01977) 673221 Fax: (01977) 607071 E-mail: sales@plasmor.co.uk

R M C Concrete Products Ltd, Dale Road, Dove Holes, Buxton, Derbyshire, SK17 8BG Tel: (01298) 22324 Fax: (01298) 815221

Readymix Concrete, Hermitage Lane, Mansfield, Nottinghamshire, NG18 5HB Tel: (01623) 622174

RMC, Twechar, Kilsyth, Glasgow, G65 9TW Tel: (01236) 822461 Fax: (01236) 825249 E-mail: admin@rmc.co.uk

Roadmix Ltd, Ballyvesey Road, Newtownabbey, County Antrim, BT36 4SY Tel: (028) 9034 2189 Fax: (028) 9084 8198

S Morris Ltd, Tout Quarry, Tout Road, Charlton Adam, Somerton, Somerset, TA11 7AN Tel: (01458) 223991 Fax: (01458) 223181 E-mail: sales@smorris.co.uk

Stocks Bros Ltd, Blocks, 5 Ninelands Lane, Garforth, Leeds, LS25 1NT Tel: 0113-232 0022 Fax: 0113-287 0839 E-mail: sales@stocks-blocks.co.uk

Alexandra Stone Co. Ltd, Kirby Muxloe, Leicester, LE9 2BR Tel: 0116-239 2513 Fax: 0116-239 3993

Stowell Concrete, Arnolds Way, Yatton, Bristol, BS49 4QN Tel: (01934) 833340 Fax: (01934) 835474 E-mail: sales@stowellconcrete.co.uk

Tarmac Topmix Ltd, John Street, Derby, DE1 2LU Tel: (01332) 384389

Tarmac Western Ltd, PO Box 1, Kington, Herefordshire, HR5 3LQ Tel: (01544) 388959 Fax: (01544) 231406 E-mail: info@tarmac-western.co.uk

Thomas Armstrong Ltd, Pickhill, Thirsk, North Yorkshire, YO7 4JQ Tel: (01845) 567282 Fax: (01845) 567606

Thomas Armstrong Concrete Blocks Ltd, Whinfield House, Whinfield Industrial Estate, Rowlands Gill, Tyne & Wear, NE39 1EH Tel: (01207) 544214 Fax: (01207) 541800

Trubloc Ltd, Concrete Works, Carew Airfield, Milton, Tenby, Dyfed, SA70 8SX Tel: (01646) 651531

Wheeler & Co. (Concrete Products) Ltd, Old Pit Yard, Clandown, Radstock, BA3 3DA Tel: (01761) 432296 Fax: (01761) 472220

CONCRETE BUILDING SYSTEMS

Cary Concrete Ltd, Tor View Farm, Galhampton, Yeovil, Somerset, BA22 7AE Tel: (01963) 350409 Fax: (01963) 351712

Coltman Precast Concrete Ltd, London Road, Canwell, Sutton Coldfield, West Midlands, B75 5SX Tel: (01543) 480482 Fax: (01543) 481587 E-mail: sales@coltman.co.uk

Eleco plc, 15 Gentlemens Field, Westmill Road, Ware, Hertfordshire, SG12 0EF Tel: (01920) 443830 Fax: (01920) 469681 E-mail: mail@eleco.com

Finlay B M E, Aghnagar Road, Ballygawley, Dungannon, County Tyrone, BT70 2HW Tel: (028) 8556 7799 Fax: (028) 8556 7007 E-mail: sales@finlaygroup.co.uk

R Page Concrete Buildings Ltd, 951-953 High Road, Romford, RM6 4HB Tel: (020) 8590 3701 Fax: (020) 8590 1791

Ready Mixed Home Counties, New Building, Hardwick Gravel Pits, Hardwick, Witney, Oxfordshire, OX29 7QF Tel: (01865) 300155 Fax: (01865) 300427

Tarmac Precast Concrete Ltd, Barholm Road, Tallington, Stamford, Lincolnshire, PE9 4RL Tel: (01778) 381000 Fax: (01778) 348041 E-mail: tall@tarmac.co.uk

Trent Concrete Ltd, Private Road 3, Colwick Industrial Estate, Nottingham, NG4 2BG Tel: 0115-987 9747 Fax: 0115-987 9948 E-mail: admin@trentconcrete.co.uk

CONCRETE CONSULTANCY

Chadburns Fence Suppliers, 22 Wortley View, Blacker Hill, Barnsley, South Yorkshire, S74 0RD Tel: (01226) 744028

Discon Concrete Products, Mearcloth Road, Sowerby Bridge, West Yorkshire, HX6 3LF Tel: (01422) 833776

Dudley Mixed, Peartree Lane, Dudley, West Midlands, DY2 0UU Tel: (01384) 242474 Fax: (01384) 242499

Lafarge Readymix Ltd, Harper Lane, Radlett, Hertfordshire, WD7 7HX Tel: (01923) 852302

Lafarge Readymix Ltd, Cheltenham Road, Stockton-on-Tees, Cleveland, TS18 2SA Tel: (01642) 673335 Fax: (01642) 679507

Lanes Engineering & Construction, 189 New Road, Rainham, Essex, RM13 8SH Tel: (01708) 553555 Fax: (01708) 630523

R M C Ready Mixed Concrete (Scotland) Ltd, Blackcastle Quarry, Nairn, IV12 5NX Tel: (01667) 452536 Fax: (01667) 452429

Ready Mixed Concrete Ulster Ltd, Quarry Road, Banbridge, County Down, BT32 3TW Tel: (028) 4066 2758 Fax: (028) 9061 9969

Tarmac Topmix Ltd, Rover Way, Cardiff, CF24 2RX Tel: (029) 2046 0308 Fax: (029) 2049 7232 E-mail: tonyford@tarmac.com

CONCRETE CONTRACTORS OR SPECIALIST SERVICES

Bowsprit Contracting Ltd, J The Henfield Business Park, Shoreham Road, Henfield, West Sussex, BN5 9SL Tel: (01273) 491499 Fax: (01273) 491982 E-mail: enquiries@bowspritltd.co.uk

Collier & Henry Concrete Floors Ltd, Unit 2 Mellors Road, Trafford Park, Manchester, M17 1PB Tel: 0161-872 8410 Fax: 0161-872 9875

Connop & Son Ltd, Folley Farm, Eardisland, Leominster, Herefordshire, HR6 9BS Tel: (01544) 388489 Fax: (01544) 388926

▶ John Cooper Construction Ltd, Cooper House, 25 Belmont Circle Kenton Lane, Harrow, Middlesex, HA3 8RF Tel: (020) 8907 8908 Fax: (020) 8907 8903 E-mail: info@johncooperconstruction.co.uk

F T Gearing Landscape Services Ltd, Crompton Road Depot, Stevenage, Hertfordshire, SG1 2EE Tel: (01438) 369321 Fax: (01438) 353039 E-mail: fred@ft-gearing.co.uk

▶ Fraser Bruce, Millhall, Stirling, FK7 7LT Tel: (01786) 448822 Fax: (01786) 451192 E-mail: info@fraser-bruce.com

Lanes Engineering & Construction, 189 New Road, Rainham, Essex, RM13 8SH Tel: (01708) 553555 Fax: (01708) 630523

Markham (Sheffield) Ltd, Marspal House, Lawn Road Industrial Estate, Carlton-In-Lindrick, Worksop, Nottinghamshire, S81 9LB Tel: (01909) 730861 Fax: (01909) 733584 E-mail: sales@markham-sheffield.co.uk

Tarmac Topmix Ltd, Belford Industrial Estate, Station Road, Belford, Northumberland, NE70 7DT Tel: (01668) 213839

Tilbury Douglas Projects Ltd, 395 George Road, Erdington, Birmingham, B23 7RZ Tel: 0121-344 3900 Fax: 0121-344 4801 E-mail: enquiries@tilbury.co.uk

CONCRETE CUTTING CONTRACTORS

Dependable Diamond Drilling, 4 Parkway House Ashley Industrial Estate, Wakefield Road, Ossett, West Yorkshire, WF5 9JD Tel: (01924) 265646 Fax: (01924) 267217 E-mail: d.d.drilling@btconnect.com

J C Jetting, 84 Bonnington Walk, Bristol, BS7 9XD Tel: 0117-904 1638 Fax: 0117-904 1638 E-mail: rachod@ukonline.co.uk

Rentajet Ltd, Paultons Park, Ower, Romsey, Hampshire, SO51 6AL Tel: (023) 8081 2921 Fax: (023) 8081 4016 E-mail: sales@rentajet.co.uk

CONCRETE CUTTING EQUIPMENT

Aggregate Industries Ltd, Old Station Yard, Beauly, Inverness-Shire, IV4 7BG Tel: (01463) 782868 Fax: (01463) 782873

Croft Engineering UK Ltd, 4 The Omni Business Centre, Omega Park, Alton, Hampshire, GU34 2QD Tel: (01420) 590009 Fax: (01420) 590009 E-mail: sales@croft-eng.co.uk

CONCRETE CUTTING EQUIPMENT HIRE

A1 Rentals Ltd, A1 House 22b Navigation Drive, Hurst Business Park, Brierley Hill, West Midlands, DY5 1UT Tel: (01384) 486200 Fax: (01384) 486204 E-mail: admin1@a1rentals.entadsl.com

Hewden Plant Hire Ltd, 21-23 Willis Way, Poole, Dorset, BH15 3SR Tel: (01202) 674371 Fax: (01202) 665560

CONCRETE DEMOLITION CONTRACTORS

▶ C A J Services Ltd, Unit K,, Higham Business Park, Bury Close, Higham Ferrers, Northamptonshire, NN10 8HQ Tel: (01933) 355001 Fax: (01933) 355009 E-mail: mail@cajservices.co.uk

▶ Drillcut Ltd, Unit 4b Cadleigh Close, Lee Mill Industrial Estate, Ivybridge, Devon, PL21 9GB Tel: (01752) 691992 Fax: (01752) 691993

▶ W F Button & Son Ltd, Button House, Pix Farm Lane, Hemel Hempstead, Hertfordshire, HP1 2RY Tel: (01442) 879440 Fax: (01442) 879442 E-mail: sales@wfbutton.co.uk

CONCRETE DRAINAGE PRODUCTS

Cooper Clarke Civils & Lintels, Bloomfield Road, Farnworth, Bolton, BL4 9LP Tel: (01204) 862222 Fax: (01204) 795296 E-mail: farnworth@civilsandlintels.co.uk

CONCRETE DRILLING CONTRACTORS OR ENGINEERS

Bardon Vectis Ltd, St Georges Down, Blackwater, Newport, Isle of Wight, PO30 3BX Tel: (01983) 524822 Fax: (01983) 825676

Barton Drilling Ltd, 1 Station Road Industrial Estate, Latchford, Warrington, WA4 1LB Tel: (01925) 653354 Fax: (01925) 230151 E-mail: sales@bartondrilling.co.uk

▶ Burridge Drilling Contractors, 84 Clun Street, Sheffield, S4 7JS Tel: 0114-278 7688 Fax: (0800) 3898508

Cocon Construction Ltd, North Shore Builders Yard, Holyhead, Gwynedd, LL65 3AG Tel: (01407) 742222 Fax: (01407) 769347 E-mail: cocon@btinternet.com

Concrete Cutters Sarum Ltd, 18 David Road, Colnbrook, Slough, SL3 0DG Tel: (01753) 689920 Fax: (01753) 689920 E-mail: info@concut.co.uk

▶ Crystal Cut Drilling Services, Cannock Chase Enterprise Centre, Walkers Rise, Hednesford, Cannock, Staffordshire, WS12 0QW Tel: (01543) 876511 Fax: (01543) 877821 E-mail: crystalcutpl@aol.com

D Drill, 12 Hazel Road, Four Marks, Alton, Hampshire, GU34 5EY Tel: (020) 7355 4444 Fax: (01420) 560187E-mail: info@d-drill.co.uk

D Drill Master Drillers Ltd, Unit 5 Coity Cresent, Bridgend Industrial Estate, Bridgend, Mid Glamorgan, CF31 3RS Tel: (01656) 662321 Fax: (01656) 667779

D Drill Master Drillers Ltd, 4 Westover Industrial Estate, Ermington Road, Ivybridge, Devon, PL21 9ES Tel: (01752) 698890 Fax: (01752) 698891 E-mail: plymouth@d-drill.co.uk

D Drill Master Drillers Ltd, Daleside Works, Craghead Colliery Industrial Estate, Stanley, County Durham, DH9 6HB Tel: (01207) 231671 Fax: (01207) 299541 E-mail: newcastle@d-drill.co.uk

D-Drill (Master Drillers) Ltd, Unit 1 Rosebridge Way, Ince, Wigan, Lancashire, WN1 3DP Tel: (01942) 824724 Fax: (01942) 829944 E-mail: wigan@d-drill.co.uk

Dependable Diamond Drilling, 4 Parkway House Ashley Industrial Estate, Wakefield Road, Ossett, West Yorkshire, WF5 9JD Tel: (01924) 265646 Fax: (01924) 267217 E-mail: d.d.drilling@btconnect.com

▶ Diamanttek Ltd, Unit 12 Raikes Clough Industrial Estate, Raikes Lane, Bolton, BL3 1RP Tel: (01204) 366435 Fax: (01204) 366437

Diamond Cutters Herts Ltd, 10 Silk Mill, Brook Street, Tring, Hertfordshire, HP23 5EF Tel: (01442) 891313 Fax: (01442) 890751 E-mail: diamond.cutters@virgin.net

▶ Drilltec Ltd, Diamond House, Dencora Way, Sundon Park, Luton, LU3 3HP Tel: (01582) 564455 Fax: (01582) 847016 E-mail: fiona@drilltec.co.uk

Holemasters Demtech, Unit 2-4 Dixon Street, Westhoughton, Bolton, BL5 3PX Tel: (01942) 840600 Fax: (01942) 840700 E-mail: enquiries@holemasters.co.uk

Holemasters (N I) Ltd, The Ferguson Centre, 57-59 Manse Road, Newtownabbey, County Antrim, BT36 6RW Tel: (028) 9034 2235 Fax: (028) 9034 2053 E-mail: holemastersni@btinternet.com

▶ Isis Diamond Drilling, 31 Bradley Road, Patchway, Bristol, BS34 5LF Tel: 0117-907 7265 Fax: 0117-907 7265 E-mail: info@isisdiamonddrilling.co.uk

▶ Pride North Sea (UK) Ltd, Torridon House, 73-75 Regent Quay, Aberdeen, AB11 5AR Tel: (01224) 587878

Speed Drill Ltd, Unit 17-18 Chingford Industrial Centre, Hall Lane, London, E4 8DJ Tel: (020) 8524 0004 Fax: (020) 8524 6778

Speedbore Diamond Drilling (Northern) Ltd, Unit 7, Wood St, Poulton-le-Fylde, Lancashire, FY6 8JY Tel: (01253) 891206 Fax: (01253) 893848 E-mail: peter@speedbore.com

CONCRETE DRILLING EQUIPMENT

Xcalibre Equipment Ltd, 3 Starley Court, Hotchkiss Way, Binley Industrial Estate, Coventry, CV3 2RL Tel: (024) 7644 4412 Fax: (024) 7663 5903 E-mail: xcalibre-equipt@btconnect.com

CONCRETE EXPANSION JOINTS, *See Expansion Joint etc*

CONCRETE FENCING

Anderton Concrete Products Ltd, Anderton Wharf, Soot Hill, Anderton, Northwich, Cheshire, CW9 6AA Tel: (01606) 79436 Fax: (01606) 871590 E-mail: sales@andertonconcrete.co.uk

D D Concrete Ltd, Blaenant Industrial Estate, Brynmawr, Ebbw Vale, Gwent, NP23 4AZ Tel: (01495) 311253 Fax: (01495) 311253

D & H Concrete Products, Fernbank Avenue, Barnoldswick, Lancashire, BB18 5UX Tel: (01282) 812299 Fax: (01282) 812659 E-mail: info@dhconcrete.co.uk

CONCRETE FENCING – *continued*

E F C Fencing, Estate Yard, Lawnhead, Stafford, ST20 0JQ Tel: (01785) 284477 Fax: (01785) 284825 E-mail: andy@efcfencing.com

Ebor Concretes Ltd, Ripon, North Yorkshire, HG4 1JE Tel: (01765) 604351 Fax: (01765) 690065 E-mail: sales@eborconcrete.co.uk

▶ First Fencing, 585, Southleigh Road, Emsworth, Hampshire, PO10 7TE Tel: 01243 430502 E-mail: info@firstfencing.co.uk

Gee-Co (Precast) Ltd, Upbrooksmill, Taylor Street, Clitheroe, Lancashire, BB7 1NL Tel: (01200) 427960 Fax: (01200) 426719 E-mail: geeco@supernet.com

▶ Id Fencing, 24 Hayle Avenue, Warwick, CV34 5TW Tel: (01926) 496753 Fax: (01926) 496753 E-mail: info@idfencing.co.uk

▶ Kirkaldy Fencing & Dyking, 64 Feus, Auchterarder, Perthshire, PH3 1DG Tel: (01764) 663115 E-mail: kirkaldyfencinganddyking@msn.com

Mcveigh Parker & Co Ltd, Southend Road, Southend, Reading, RG7 6HA Tel: (0845) 1207755 Fax: 0118-974 4123 E-mail: sales@mcveighparker.co.uk

Mcveigh-Parker & Co. Ltd, Six Acre Farm, Stane Street, Adversane, Billingshurst, West Sussex, RH14 9JR Tel: (01403) 784250 Fax: (01403) 786394 E-mail: sales@mcveighparker.co.uk

▶ Sticks & Stones, Colchester Main Road, Alresford, Colchester, CO7 8DD Tel: (01206) 826835 Fax: (01206) 827655 E-mail: info@stixandstones.co.uk

Supreme Concrete Ltd, Coppingford Hall, Coppingford Road, Sawtry, Huntingdon, Cambridgeshire, PE28 5GP Tel: (01487) 833300 Fax: (01487) 833305 E-mail: sales@supremeconcrete.co.uk

Trentham Fencing & Contractors Ltd, 17-19 Church Lane, Stoke-on-Trent, ST4 4QB Tel: (01782) 644165 Fax: (01782) 644490 E-mail: sales@trenthamfencing.co.uk

Welslot Fencing, Common Lane, Carrington, Manchester, M31 4QJ Tel: 0161-777 6705 Fax: 0161-777 6908

▶ Woodcraft Fencing, Mold Road, Cefn-y-Bedd, Wrexham, Clwyd, LL12 9YG Tel: (01978) 769330 Fax: (01978) 756490 E-mail: woodcraft_fencing@yahoo.co.uk

CONCRETE FLOOR SLABS

▶ I.C.F. (Industrial Concrete Flooring)., 51 Manor Road, Wakefield, West Yorkshire, WF2 8QN Tel: 01924 290292 Fax: 01924 377897 E-mail: industrialconcreteflooring@hotmail.co.uk

CONCRETE FLOOR TREATMENT SERVICES

Abs Brymar Floor's Ltd, Dane Road Industrial Estate, Sale, Cheshire, M33 7BH Tel: 0161-972 5000 Fax: 0161-972 5001 E-mail: sales@absbrymarfloors.co.uk

Aedean Chemical Industrial Ltd, 73A Old Woking Road, West Byfleet, Surrey, KT14 6LF Tel: (01932) 336171 Fax: (01932) 336758 E-mail: info@aedean.co.uk

Brand Precast, 2 Lockwood Court, Market Pl, Pocklington, York, YO42 2QW Tel: (01759) 304130 Fax: (01759) 306727

Diamond Cutters Herts Ltd, 10 Silk Mill, Brook Street, Tring, Hertfordshire, HP23 5EF Tel: (01442) 891313 Fax: (01442) 890751 E-mail: diamond.cutters@virgin.net

Floor Maintenance Services Ltd, 215 Melton Road, Edwalton, Nottingham, NG12 4AF Tel: 0115-945 2186 Fax: 0115-974 7656 E-mail: sonia.mabbott@ntlworld.com

Quickset Chemical Flooring Ltd, 30 Runcorn Road, Birmingham, B12 8RQ Tel: 0121-440 0737 Fax: 0121-440 2255 E-mail: sales@uk-quickset.com

CONCRETE FORMING FIBREGLASS MOULDS

▶ A J Glass Fibre Ltd, Carr Wood Industrial Estate, Carr Wood Road, Castleford, West Yorkshire, WF10 4SB Tel: (01977) 603651 Fax: (01977) 603650 E-mail: lynn.kenney@haglassfibre.co.uk

E & F Composites Ltd, Graythorp Industrial Estate, Hartlepool, Cleveland, TS25 2DF Tel: (01429) 272356 Fax: (01429) 861571 E-mail: sales@eandf-composites.co.uk

CONCRETE FORMING PLASTIC MOULDS

Thermovac Plastics Ltd, Unit 1 Low Mill Lane, Ravensthorpe Industrial Estate, Dewsbury, West Yorkshire, WF13 3LN Tel: (01924) 499268 Fax: (01924) 491440 E-mail: sales@thermovacplastics.co.uk

CONCRETE FORMING STEEL MOULDS

Chart Engineering Ltd, Pivington Works, Pluckley, Ashford, Kent, TN27 0PG Tel: (01233) 840555 Fax: (01233) 840687 E-mail: sales@chartengineering.com

W I G Engineering Ltd, Barnfield, Chesterton, Bicester, Oxfordshire, OX26 1TE Tel: (01869) 320515 Fax: (01869) 320513 E-mail: wig@oxford38.fsnet.co.uk

CONCRETE FORMING TIMBER MOULDS

E & M Composites Ltd, Unit Y1 Blaby Industrial Park, Winchester Avenue, Blaby, LE8 4GZ Tel: 0116-278 8954 Fax: 0116-278 9313

Grantham Woodmill Ltd, Ruston Road, Grantham, Lincolnshire, NG31 9SW Tel: (01476) 568175 Fax: (01476) 591427

Matrix Moulds & Models Ltd, Glover Street, St. Helens, Merseyside, WA10 3LF Tel: (01744) 24333 Fax: (01744) 27999 E-mail: mmm@rapid.co.uk

Patterns & Moulds Ltd, Unit D2 Wymeswold Industrial Park, Wymeswold Road, Burton-on-the-Wolds, Loughborough, Leicestershire, LE12 5TY Tel: (01509) 881581 Fax: (01509) 881681 E-mail: info@patternsandmoulds.com

Premier Pattern Leicester Co. Ltd, 79 Coleman Road, Leicester, LE5 4LE Tel: 0116-276 6094 Fax: 0116-276 5371

S P C Patterns Ltd, 191 Vincent Road, Sheffield, S7 1BZ Tel: 0114-255 0040 Fax: 0114-255 8023

Traffco Engineers Pattern Co, Midland Road, Scunthorpe, South Humberside, DN16 1DQ Tel: (01724) 842753 Fax: (01724) 865569

CONCRETE FORMWORK, *See also headings for particular types*

▶ A & T Group, 183 Manor Road North, Southampton, SO19 2DZ Tel: (023) 8044 3127 E-mail: andie@chessun.fsnet.co.uk

CONCRETE FORMWORK BACK PROPPING SYSTEMS

▶ Rapid Metal Developments Ltd, 4-7 Marsh Road, Wembley, Middlesex, HA0 1ES Tel: (020) 8998 1727

CONCRETE FORMWORK CONTRACTORS OR SUPPLIES

Chart Engineering Ltd, Pivington Works, Pluckley, Ashford, Kent, TN27 0PG Tel: (01233) 840555 Fax: (01233) 840687 E-mail: sales@chartengineering.com

Form Fab Worcester Ltd, 9-11 Bache Road, Sandy Lane Industrial Estate, Stourport-on-Severn, Worcestershire, DY13 9QB Tel: (01299) 879271 Fax: (01299) 877339 E-mail: sales@form-fab.com

Hanson Concrete Products plc, 21 Wilden Road, Pattinson Industrial Estate, Washington, Tyne & Wear, NE38 8QB Tel: 0191-417 0066 Fax: 0191-417 0131 E-mail: sales@omnideck.co.uk

CONCRETE FORMWORK TIE EQUIPMENT

▶ A & T Group, 183 Manor Road North, Southampton, SO19 2DZ Tel: (023) 8044 3127 E-mail: andie@chessun.fsnet.co.uk

CONCRETE FRAME BUILDING CONTRACTORS

▶ Axiom Contractors Ltd, The Cavendish Centre, Winnall Close, Winchester, Hampshire, SO23 0LB Tel: (01962) 890888 Fax: (01962) 890888 E-mail: gtabner@axiomcontractors.co.uk

B & S Builders Ltd, Churchill Farm, Dale Road, Haverfordwest, Dyfed, SA62 3AD Tel: (01437) 779303

▶ Kaybridge Construction Barnet Ltd, 24 Cecil Road, Enfield, Middlesex, EN2 6TG Tel: (020) 8366 3361 Fax: (020) 8363 1128 E-mail: enquiries@kaybridge.com

CONCRETE GLASS FIBRE REINFORCED (GFR) PRODUCTS

▶ Imperial Stone, New Barn Farm, Rake Road, Milland, Liphook, Hampshire, GU30 7JU Tel: (01428) 741175 Fax: (01428) 741175 E-mail: sales@imperialstone.co.uk

Wards Welding & Fabrications, Cranfield Road, Woburn Sands, Milton Keynes, MK17 8UR Tel: (01908) 586505 Fax: (01908) 587505 E-mail: steve@wardsweldingandfsnet.co.uk

CONCRETE KERBS

Dick Freecast Inverness, Dores Road, Inverness, IV2 4RP Tel: (01463) 237556 Fax: (01463) 222871

Ladds Concrete Products, Wilson Way, Pool, Redruth, Cornwall, TR15 3RY Tel: (01209) 213132 Fax: (01209) 314441 E-mail: sales@laddsconcrete.co.uk

Tom Langton & Son, Knowsthorpe Lane, Leeds, LS9 0AT Tel: 0113-249 9440 Fax: 0113-240 2287 E-mail: chris@tomlangtons.com

▶ Wilsons Drop Kerbs, Ger-Y-Mynydd, Seiriol Road, Penmaenmawr, Gwynedd, LL34 6HB Tel: (01492) 623170 E-mail: wilsonsdropkerbs@hotmail.co.uk

CONCRETE LINTELS

Naylor Concrete Products, Milner Way, Ossett, West Yorkshire, WF5 9JE Tel: (01924) 267286 Fax: (01924) 265674 E-mail: lintels@naylor.co.uk

Stressline Ltd, Station Road, Stoney Stanton, Leicester, LE9 4LX Tel: (01455) 272457 Fax: (01455) 274564 E-mail: info@stressline.ltd.uk

CONCRETE MACHINERY, *See also headings for particular types*

Champion Hire Ltd, 2 Roman Ridge Road, Sheffield, S9 1XG Tel: (0845) 3456900 Fax: 0114-249 4100 E-mail: sales@champion-hire.com

D & C Engineers Ltd, Unit 1, Mariner, Lichfield Road Industrial Estate, Tamworth, Staffs, B79 7UL Tel: (01827) 54824 Fax: (01827) 61203 E-mail: dandcengineers@compuseve.com

Ebc UK Ltd, PO Box 28, Ross-on-Wye, Herefordshire, HR9 6YD Tel: (01989) 762051 Fax: (01989) 762052

Morris Bros Ltd, Phoenix Works, 215 Scotia Road, Stoke-on-Trent, ST6 4HB Tel: (01782) 834242 Fax: (01782) 575686 E-mail: sales@morrisbrothers.com

Rapid International Ltd, 96 Mullavilly Road, Tandragee, Craigavon, County Armagh, BT62 2LX Tel: (028) 3884 0671 Fax: (028) 3884 0880E-mail: info@rapidinternational.com

Ian Sparrow Equipment Ltd, Grantham Road, Bottesford, Nottingham, NG13 0EE Tel: (01949) 842385 Fax: (01949) 843436

CONCRETE MANHOLES

Milton Pipes Ltd, Cooks Lane, Sittingbourne, Kent, ME10 2QF Tel: (01795) 425191 Fax: (01795) 420360 E-mail: sales@miltonpipes.com

CONCRETE MIXERS

A C Carey, 142 Wycombe Lane, Wooburn Green, High Wycombe, Buckinghamshire, HP10 0HH Tel: (01628) 524994 Fax: (01628) 524755

Ace Minimix Ltd, Bellhouse Pit, Warren Lane, Stanway, Colchester, CO3 0NN Tel: (01206) 330178 Fax: (020) 8555 2612 E-mail: easten.amix@tarmac.co.uk

Astwell Augers Ltd, A14 Huntingdon Road, Thrapston, Kettering, Northamptonshire, NN14 4PT Tel: (01832) 735300 Fax: (01832) 735533 E-mail: sales@astwell.co.uk

Brown & Potter Ltd, The Quarry, Boroughbridge Road, Ripon, North Yorkshire, HG4 1UG Tel: (01765) 603710 Fax: (01765) 698801

Builders Equipment (Norwich) Ltd, 24 City Road, Norwich, NR1 3AN Tel: (01603) 616211 Fax: (01603) 630408 E-mail: mail@builders-equipment.co.uk

Cemex UK, Aerodrome, Scorton, Catterick, Richmond, North Yorkshire, DL10 7NP Tel: (01748) 811362 Fax: (01748) 810808

Hanson Aggregates Ltd, Hall Lane, Bradford, West Yorkshire, BD4 7DN Tel: (0845) 1206293 Fax: (01274) 607855

Hanson Premix plc, Coldstores Road, Cardiff, CF10 4LR Tel: (029) 2046 5383

Ernest Hinchliffe (Peak Mix Concrete) Ltd, Peak Works, Peak Forest, Buxton, Derbyshire, SK17 8EW Tel: (01298) 23671 Fax: (0870) 0638909

Hymix Fabricators, C10-C11 Unit, Stafford Park 11, Telford, Shropshire, TF3 3AY Tel: (01952) 200900 Fax: (01952) 200901 E-mail: mail@hymix.com

J M Rennie, Depot, Hen Lon Parcwr, Ruthin, Clwyd, LL15 1NA Tel: (01824) 704842 Fax: (01824) 705400

Kilworth Agricultural Machinery, Annwell Lane, Smisby, Ashby-de-la-Zouch, Leicestershire, LE65 2TA Tel: (01530) 412690 Fax: (01530) 560002E-mail: sales@kilworthmachinery.co.uk

Lantonpark Ltd, Clipper Close, Medway City Estate, Rochester, Kent, ME2 4QP Tel: (01634) 724108 Fax: (0870) 7052305 E-mail: sales@lantonpark.co.uk

Leiths Precast Concrete, Durris, Banchory, Kincardineshire, AB31 6DD Tel: (01330) 844444 Fax: (01330) 844417

▶ McPhee Bros (Blantyre) Ltd, 58 John Street, Blantyre, Glasgow, G72 0JF Tel: (01698) 823422 Fax: (01698) 823853 E-mail: lorna@mcfeemixers.co.uk

Multi Marque Production Engineering Ltd, Unit 33 Monckton Road Industrial Estate, Wakefield, West Yorkshire, WF2 7AL Tel: (01924) 290231 Fax: (01924) 382241 E-mail: enquiry@multi-marque.co.uk

O'Brian Manufacturing Ltd, Robian Way, Swadlincote, Derbyshire, DE11 9DH Tel: (01283) 217588 Fax: (01283) 215613

Oswald Record Plant Sales (Midlands) Ltd, Whittington Way, Whittington Moor, Chesterfield, Derbyshire, S41 9AG Tel: (01246) 451057 Fax: (01246) 454078 E-mail: sales@oswaldrecord.co.uk

Rapid International Ltd, 96 Mullavilly Road, Tandragee, Craigavon, County Armagh, BT62 2LX Tel: (028) 3884 0671 Fax: (028) 3884 0880E-mail: info@rapidinternational.com

Ready Mixed Concrete Huddersfield Ltd, Sheffield Road, Penistone, Sheffield, S36 6HJ Tel: (01226) 762476 Fax: (01226) 760920

Ready Mixed Concrete South West Ltd, The Old Railway Sidings, Bridgerule, Holsworthy, Devon, EX22 7EB Tel: (01288) 381292 Fax: (01208) 74327

Tarmac Northern Ltd, Lingerfield, Scotton, Knaresborough, North Yorkshire, HG5 9JN Tel: (01423) 796800 Fax: (01423) 796808 E-mail: info@tarmac-northern.co.uk

Topmix Tarmac Ltd, Tunnel Industrial Estate, London Road, Grays, Essex, RM20 3HH Tel: (01708) 864732 Fax: (01708) 860220

CONCRETE MIXING OR BATCHING PLANT

Ace Minimix, Rover Way, Cardiff, CF24 2RX Tel: (029) 2045 3894 Fax: (029) 2045 3894

Base Minimix Concrete, A29 Red Scar Industrial Estate, Longridge Road, Ribbleton, Preston, PR2 5NA Tel: (01524) 720344 Fax: (01772) 655515

Brett Concrete Ltd, Foxhall Four Quarry, Foxhall Road, Brightwell, Ipswich, IP10 0HT Tel: (01473) 736441 Fax: (01473) 736721

C & H Quickmix Ltd, Woodlands, Dereham Road, New Costessey, Norwich, NR5 0TL Tel: (01603) 740333 Fax: (01603) 741336 E-mail: enquiries@tarmac-southern.co.uk

Cemex UK Ltd, Crown House, Evreux Way, Rugby, Warwickshire, CV21 2DT Tel: 0114-242 6050 Fax: (01788) 517221

D & C Engineers Ltd, Unit 1, Mariner, Lichfield Road Industrial Estate, Tamworth, Staffs, B79 7UL Tel: (01827) 54824 Fax: (01827) 61203 E-mail: dandcengineers@compuseve.com

Hanson Premix plc, Allerton Park Pit, Allerton Park, Knaresborough, North Yorkshire, HG5 0SD Tel: (0845) 1206297 Fax: (01423) 324967

Hanson Premix plc, Stacey Avenue, London, N18 3PL Tel: (020) 8807 4966 Fax: (020) 8803 8714

J R Plant Services Ltd, 6 Cedar Ave, Connah's Quay, Deeside, Clwyd, CH5 4BE Tel: (01244) 810306

Lantonpark Ltd, Clipper Close, Medway City Estate, Rochester, Kent, ME2 4QP Tel: (01634) 724108 Fax: (0870) 7052305 E-mail: sales@lantonpark.co.uk

Mixamate Concrete, 1 Cambridge Grove, Clevedon, Avon, BS21 7BW Tel: (01275) 340804 Fax: (01225) 792204

Mixamate Concrete, 11 West Down, Bookham, Leatherhead, Surrey, KT23 4LJ Tel: (01243) 860300 Fax: (0845) 7225555

▶ Quarry Fix, 6b Orritor Street, Cookstown, County Tyrone, BT80 8BE Tel: (028) 8676 6177 Fax: (028) 8676 6177 E-mail: info@quarryfix.co.uk

R M C Mortars Ltd, Weeford Quarry, London Rd, Canwell, Sutton Coldfield, W. Midlands, B75 5SZ Tel: 01543 481044 Fax: 01543 481380

Ready Mixed Concrete (Northern) Ltd, Wiltons Yard, Jarrow Road, South Shields, Tyne & Wear, NE34 9PL Tel: 0191-455 3381

Sandsfield Ready Mix Ltd, Elvington Industrial Estate, York Road, Elvington, York, YO41 4AR Tel: (01904) 608772 Fax: (01904) 608998

Skako A/S (UK), PO Box 563, Bury St. Edmunds, Suffolk, IP33 9AW Tel: (01284) 723846 Fax: (01284)) 723846 E-mail: rta@skako.com

Tarmac Northern Ltd, Drumshoreland Road, Pumpherston, Livingston, West Lothian, EH53 0LH Tel: (01506) 853606

Tarmac Topmix Ltd, Rover Way, Cardiff, CF24 2RX Tel: (029) 2046 0308 Fax: (029) 2049 7232 E-mail: tonyford@tarmac.com

Three Counties Concrete Ltd, Grove House Yard, Tewkesbury Road, Upton-upon-Severn, Worcester, WR8 0PW Tel: (01684) 594464 Fax: (01684) 594940

White Cross Plant Ltd, 135 Engineer Road, West Wilts Trading Estate, Westbury, Wiltshire, BA13 4JW Tel: (01373) 824422 Fax: (01373) 825234

CONCRETE MIXING OR BATCHING PLANT HIRE

Rhino Construction Services Ltd, Thanamar, Chester Road, Llong, Mold, Flintshire, CH7 4JP Tel: (01244) 543441 Fax: (01244) 543441 E-mail: rhinoconstruction@fsmail.net

CONCRETE MIXING OR BATCHING PLANT SPARE PARTS

Lantonpark Ltd, Clipper Close, Medway City Estate, Rochester, Kent, ME2 4QP Tel: (01634) 724108 Fax: (0870) 7052305 E-mail: sales@lantonpark.co.uk

London Concrete Ltd, Station Yard, Approach Road, Purley, Surrey, CR8 2AL Tel: (020) 8668 2111 Fax: (020) 8668 4532

Skako A/S (UK), PO Box 563, Bury St. Edmunds, Suffolk, IP33 9AW Tel: (01284) 723846 Fax: (01284)) 723846 E-mail: rta@skako.com

CONCRETE MOULD RELEASE AGENTS

Grace Construction Products Ltd, 851-852 Birchwood Boulevard, Birchwood, Warrington, WA3 7QZ Tel: (01925) 824824 Fax: (01925) 824033 E-mail: enquiries@gcp-grace.com

CONCRETE OVERLAY STENCILLED PATTERN BLOCK PAVING

Ashmead Building Supplies Ltd, Portview Road, Avonmouth, Bristol, BS11 9LD Tel: 0117-982 8281 Fax: 0117-982 0135 E-mail: avon@ashmead.co.uk

▶ J A Block Paving Ltd, Railstone Terminal, Marlborough Road, Wootton Bassett, Swindon, SN4 7EH Tel: (01793) 852129 Fax: (01793) 850162

▶ Premier Paving, Higher Polscoe Farm, Lostwithiel, Cornwall, PL22 0HR Tel: (01208) 871010 Fax: (01208) 871010 E-mail: sales@premierpaving.co.uk

Stencil Tech, 1 Upland Industrial Estate, Mere Way, Wyton, Huntingdon, Cambridgeshire, PE28 2JZ Tel: (01480) 435919 Fax: (01480) 435922 E-mail: sales@stencil-tech.co.uk

CONCRETE PAVING CONTRACTORS, *See Concrete Paving etc*

CONCRETE PIPE PRODUCTION PLANT

Johnston Pre-Cast Ltd, Doseley, Telford, Shropshire, TF4 3BX Tel: (01952) 630300 Fax: (01952) 501537

Puk Holdings Ltd, F Timothy'S Bridge, Stratford-upon-Avon, Warwickshire, CV37 9PR Tel: (01789) 206800 Fax: (01789) 206801 E-mail: puk@pukservices.co.uk

CONCRETE PIPES

F P McCann Ltd, Whitehill Road, Ellistown, Coalville, Leicestershire, LE67 1ET Tel: (01530) 240024 Fax: (01530) 240025 E-mail: info@fpmccann.co.uk

Johnston Pre-Cast Ltd, Doseley, Telford, Shropshire, TF4 3BX Tel: (01952) 630300 Fax: (01952) 501537

Milton Pipes Ltd, Cooks Lane, Sittingbourne, Kent, ME10 2QF Tel: (01795) 425191 Fax: (01795) 420360 E-mail: sales@miltonpipes.com

Stanton Bonna Concrete Ltd, Littlewell Lane, Stanton-by-Dale, Ilkeston, Derbyshire, DE7 4QW Tel: 0115-944 1448 Fax: 0115-944 1466 E-mail: sbc@stanton-bonna.co.uk

CONCRETE PLACING SKIPS

Railtec Engineering Ltd, Wakefield Road, Dearne Works, Scissett, Huddersfield, HD8 9HS Tel: (01484) 862001 Fax: (01484) 864793 E-mail: john@railtec.co.uk

CONCRETE PLANERS

Zoomlion Powermole Ltd, 35 Church Road Business Centre, Church Road, Sittingbourne, Kent, ME10 3RS Tel: (01795) 425425 Fax: (01795) 477177 E-mail: allen.kayes@zlpm.com

CONCRETE POSTS

Allen Concrete Ltd, 38 Willow Lane, Mitcham, Surrey, CR4 4NA Tel: (020) 8687 2222 Fax: (020) 8687 5400

Batchelor Concrete Products, Wood End Gardens, Northolt, Middlesex, UB5 4QH Tel: (020) 8422 6892 Fax: (020) 8863 1268

▶ Erith Concrete Co., Landau Way, Darent Industrial Park, Erith, Kent, DA8 2LF Tel: (01322) 333263

Fabcast Concrete Fencing Products, Unit 4 Speedwall Street, Stoke-on-Trent, ST3 5EB Tel: (01782) 324542

Hardman & Cain Fencing Ltd, Stotts Pit Yard, Church Street, Westhoughton, Bolton, BL5 3QW Tel: (01942) 815312 Fax: (01942) 815312 E-mail: enquiries@hardmancainfencing.co.uk

J R Concrete, Harcourt Street, Worsley, Manchester, M28 3GN Tel: (01204) 571004

Kelcamp Ltd, St. Albans Road Industrial Estate, Stafford, ST16 3DR Tel: (01785) 259415 Fax: (01785) 258022

CONCRETE PRECAST LINTELS

▶ Atspeed Distributors Ltd, Oakendene Industrial Estate, Bolney Road, Cowfold, Horsham, West Sussex, RH13 8AZ Tel: (01403) 864950 Fax: (01403) 864987 E-mail: andy.thompson@atspeed.co.uk

CONCRETE PRESTRESSING EQUIPMENT

E K C Systems Ltd, Walkley Works, Walkley Lane, Heckmondwike, West Yorkshire, WF16 0PH Tel: (01924) 411604 Fax: (01924) 403822 E-mail: info@ekcsystems.co.uk

Spiroll Precast Services Ltd, 2 Kingsway Industrial Park, Kingsway Park Close, Derby, DE22 3FP Tel: (01332) 365131 Fax: (01332) 291736 E-mail: enquiries@spiroll.co.uk

T M S Systems, Park Works, Main Road, Kingsley, Bordon, Hampshire, GU35 9LY Tel: (01420) 489313 Fax: (01420) 487218 E-mail: info@tms-systems.co.uk

CONCRETE PRODUCTS, *See also other nearby headings for particular types*

A W B S Ltd, Wyevale Garden Centre, South Hinksey, Oxford, OX1 5AR Tel: (01865) 327111 Fax: (01865) 327333

A1 Patios, The Old Bakehouse Yard, Maesteg Road, Sarn, Bridgend, Mid Glamorgan, CF32 9UH Tel: (01656) 720428

Abercarn Constitutional Club Ltd, Bridge Street, Abercarn, Newport, Gwent, NP11 4SE Tel: (01495) 243047 Fax: (01495) 244538

Achason & Glover Ltd, Lisdoonan, Belfast Road, Saintfield, Ballynahinch, County Down, BT24 7EP Tel: (028) 9081 3848 Fax: (028) 9081 4505

Acheson & Glover Ltd, Creenagho, Belcoo, Enniskillen, County Fermanagh, BT93 5HA Tel: (028) 6638 6555 Fax: (028) 6638 6554

Aggregate Industries Ltd, Sand Pit Road, Calne, Wiltshire, SN11 8TJ Tel: (01249) 811818 Fax: (01249) 821528

Aggregate Industries Plc, Uffculme Works, The Downs, Uffculme, Cullompton, Devon, EX15 3BL Tel: (01884) 841140 Fax: (01884) 841919

▶ Aggregate Industries Ltd, Auchengeich Road, Chryston, Glasgow, G69 0JL Tel: 0141-776 8410 Fax: 0141-776 2464

Albury Lodge Ltd, 5 Fieldings Road, Cheshunt, Waltham Cross, Hertfordshire, EN8 9TR Tel: (01992) 620107 Fax: (01992) 621879 E-mail: alburylodgeltd@btconnect.com

Allen Concrete Ltd, 38 Willow Lane, Mitcham, Surrey, CR4 4NA Tel: (020) 8687 2222 Fax: (020) 8687 5400

▶ Anglia Concrete Products, Skelmersdale Road, Clacton-on-Sea, Essex, CO15 6BZ Tel: (01255) 420018 Fax: (01255) 222880 E-mail: admin@angliagroup.co.uk

Ardmore Precast Concrete Ltd, 25 Ballybogie Road, Ardmore, Londonderry, BT47 3RE Tel: (028) 7134 9566 Fax: (028) 7131 1100 E-mail: info@ardmoreprecast.co.uk

Thomas Armstrong Ltd, Park Road, Consett, County Durham, DH8 5SP Tel: (01207) 505655 Fax: (01207) 592345 E-mail: sales@thomasarmstrong.co.uk

▶ Ashton Concrete Floors Ltd, B The Old Brickyard, North End, Ashton Keynes, Swindon, SN6 6QR Tel: (01285) 862344 Fax: (01285) 862655

▶ B & A Whelan, 52-54 High Street, Blue Town, Sheerness, Kent, ME12 1RW Tel: (01795) 663879 Fax: (01795) 661934

B & M Concrete Products, Grange Works, 22 Falkenham Road, Kirton, Ipswich, IP10 0NW Tel: (01394) 448556 Fax: (01394) 448586

B S Eaton Ltd, Coppice Lane, Cheslyn Hay, Walsall, WS6 7EY Tel: (01922) 413678 Fax: (01922) 416515 E-mail: enquiries@bseaton.co.uk

▶ Barcon Systems Ltd, Unit 12a Horwich Loco Industrial Estate, Chorley New Road, Horwich, Bolton, BL6 5UE Tel: (01204) 690088 Fax: (01204) 690779

Batchelor Concrete Products, Wood End Gardens, Northolt, Middlesex, UB5 4QH Tel: (020) 8422 6892 Fax: (020) 8863 1268

Berry & Vincent Ltd, 18 Union Road, Crediton, Devon, EX17 3AS Tel: (01363) 772078 Fax: (01363) 772814 E-mail: berryandvincent@btinternet.com

Bespoke Precast Ltd, 2 Concrete Works Wellthorne Lane, Ingbirchworth, Penistone, Sheffield, S36 7GJ Tel: (01226) 761000 Fax: (01226) 761216 E-mail: bespokeprecast@btconnect.com

Bowland Cumbria Ltd, Under Railway Bridge, Dockray Hall Mill, Kendal, Cumbria, LA9 4RU Tel: (01539) 723600 Fax: (01539) 740776 E-mail: sales@boland-stone.com

Bowland Paving Centre, Mogul Lane, Halesowen, West Midlands, B63 2QQ Tel: (01384) 636564 Fax: (01384) 411744

Bromsgrove Guild Ltd, 233 Worcester Road, Stoke Heath, Bromsgrove, Worcestershire, B61 7JA Tel: (01527) 833198

Busy Bees, Wath Road, Wath-upon-Dearne, Rotherham, South Yorkshire, S63 7EN Tel: (01709) 760195 Fax: (01709) 877829

Carew Patio Products, Unit 1 Carew Airfield, Sageston, Tenby, Dyfed, SA70 8SQ Tel: (01646) 651116 Fax: (01646) 650100

Carter Concrete Ltd, Britons Lane, Beeston Regis, Sheringham, Norfolk, NR26 8TP Tel: (01263) 823434 Fax: (01263) 825678 E-mail: mail@carter-concrete.co.uk

Cary Concrete Ltd, Tor View Farm, Galhampton, Yeovil, Somerset, BA22 7AE Tel: (01963) 350409 Fax: (01963) 351712

Castacrete Ltd, Plantation Works, Clevedon Road, Failand, Bristol, BS8 3UA Tel: (01275) 851131 Fax: (01275) 851133

▶ Castacrete Ltd, Commissioners Road, Rochester, Kent, ME2 4EQ Tel: (01634) 724667 Fax: (01634) 290284

Cementcraft Concrete Products Ltd, Beckhythe, Little Melton, Norwich, NR9 3NP Tel: (01603) 810394 Fax: (01603) 812821

Cemex Floors, London Road, Wick, Bristol, BS30 5SJ Tel: (01788) 542111 Fax: 0117-937 4695 E-mail: rmc@concreteproducts.co.uk

Chiltern Concrete & Stone Ltd, Faldo Road, Barton-le-Clay, Bedford, MK45 4RF Tel: (01582) 881414 Fax: (01582) 881855 E-mail: info@chilternprecast.co.uk

Coltman Precast Concrete Ltd, London Road, Canwell, Sutton Coldfield, West Midlands, B75 5SX Tel: (01543) 480482 Fax: (01543) 481587 E-mail: sales@coltman.co.uk

Concrete Developments Great Barr Ltd, Baltimore Road, Great Barr, Birmingham, B42 1DD Tel: 0121-356 5575 Fax: 0121-344 3285 E-mail: james@concrete-developers.freeserve.co.uk

▶ Concrete Fabrications Ltd, Crewshole Road Off, Blackswarth Road, St George, Bristol, BS5 8AU Tel: 0117-955 7530

▶ Con-Tech Services Ltd, Oaks Lane, Hoyle Mill, Barnsley, South Yorkshire, S71 1HT Tel: (01226) 244051

▶ Cornish Concrete Products Ltd, Point Mills, Bissoe, Truro, Cornwall, TR4 8QZ Tel: (01872) 864808 Fax: (01872) 863606

Crewkerne Concrete Products, Unit 12 Cropmead, Crewkerne, Somerset, TA18 7HQ Tel: (01460) 74415 Fax: (01460) 74415

▶ Crynant Concrete Products, Unit 6, Crynant Business Park, Crynant, Neath, West Glamorgan, SA10 8PX Tel: (01639) 750850

D D Concrete Ltd, Blaenant Industrial Estate, Brynmawr, Ebbw Vale, Gwent, NP23 4AZ Tel: (01495) 311253 Fax: (01495) 311253

D Littler, Chester Road, Backford, Chester, CH1 6PE Tel: (01244) 851635 Fax: (01244) 851363

Dabro Precast Concrete Ltd, The Old Colliery Yard, Pensford, Bristol, BS39 4BU Tel: (01761) 490664 Fax: (01761) 490758

Dick Freecast Inverness, Dores Road, Inverness, IV2 4RP Tel: (01463) 237556 Fax: (01463) 222871

Douglas Acheson, Navan Fort Road, Armagh, BT60 4PN Tel: (028) 3752 2667

E & I Williams, High View, The Doward, Whitchurch, Ross-on-Wye, Herefordshire, HR9 6DZ Tel: (01600) 890474 Fax: (01600) 890327

E.Wiltshire & Son (Torquay) Ltd, Walls Hill Quarry, Babbacombe Road, Torquay, TQ1 3TA Tel: (01803) 327706 Fax: (01803) 327793 E-mail: info@wiltshires-babbacombe.co.uk

Ely Concrete Products Ltd, Wisbech Road, Littleport, Ely, Cambridgeshire, CB6 1RA Tel: (01353) 861416 Fax: (01353) 862165 E-mail: sales@histonconcrete.co.uk

▶ Fairford Concrete, Wellford Lane, London Road, Fairford, Gloucestershire, GL7 4DS Tel: (01285) 711460 Fax: (01285) 711461

Farringdon Garden Stone, Sandshill, Faringdon, Oxfordshire, SN7 7PQ Tel: (01367) 240774 Fax: (01367) 242980 E-mail: rogers.gardenstone@btinternet.com

Forden Concrete Products, Station Yard, Forden, Welshpool, Powys, SY21 8NN Tel: (01938) 580309

Forticrete Roofing Products Ltd, Boss Avenue, Off Grovebury Road, Leighton Buzzard, Bedfordshire, LU7 4SD Tel: (01525) 244900 Fax: (01525) 850432 E-mail: forticretetechnical@compuserve.com

▶ Fyse Stone, Kemnay Quarry, Aquithie Road, Kemnay, Inverurie, Aberdeenshire, AB51 5PD Tel: (01467) 651000 Fax: (01467) 642342

G E M Concrete Products Ltd, Quarry Works, Moor Lane, Little Eaton, Derby, DE21 5AU Tel: (01332) 831449 Fax: (01332) 830198

Garden Supply Nursery, 1 Hill Cottage, Landermere Road, Thorpe-Le-Soken, Clacton-On-Sea, Essex, CO16 0NF Tel: (01255) 860073

▶ E. & J.W. Glendinning Ltd, Glentor, Ashburton, Newton Abbot, Devon, TQ13 7LF Tel: (01364) 652601 Fax: (01364) 651118 E-mail: sales@ejwglendinning.co.uk

▶ H Plus H Celcon Ltd, 3 Quartermaster Road, West Wilts Trading Estate, Westbury, Wiltshire, BA13 4JT Tel: (01732) 886333 Fax: (01373) 827631

Hanson Aggregates Ltd, Premix Concrete Plant, Horspath Road, Oxford, OX4 2RP Tel: (01865) 772956

Hanson Aggregates Ltd, Chywoon Quarry, Chywoon, St. Gluvias, Penryn, Cornwall, TR10 9AF Tel: (01209) 860555 Fax: (01209) 860555

Hanson Aggregates Ltd, Clifford House, York Road, Wetherby, West Yorkshire, LS22 7NS Tel: (01937) 581977 Fax: (01937) 545889 E-mail: sales.orderswest@hanson-aggregates.com

Hanson Building Products, Sutton Courtenay Lane, Milton, Sutton Courtenay, Abingdon, Oxfordshire, OX14 4DD Tel: (01235) 811811 Fax: (01235) 510342 E-mail: ron.leese@hansonplc.com

Hanson Building Products, Stewartby, Bedford, MK43 9LZ Tel: (0870) 5258258 Fax: (01234) 762040 E-mail: info@hanson.biz

▶ Hanson Concrete Products plc, Sproughton Road, Ipswich, IP1 5AN Tel: (01473) 461771 Fax: (01473) 464117 E-mail: alanharding@hanson.biz

Ernest Hinchliffe (Peak Mix Concrete) Ltd, Peak Works, Peak Forest, Buxton, Derbyshire, SK17 8EW Tel: (01298) 23671 Fax: (0870) 0638909

Hoddam Contracting Co. Ltd, Hoddom Road, Ecclefechan, Lockerbie, Dumfriesshire, DG11 3BY Tel: (01576) 300634 Fax: (01576) 300798

Houghton Concrete Ltd, 8 Firsdale Industrial Estate, Nangreaves Street, Leigh, Lancashire, WN7 4TN Tel: (01942) 676446 Fax: (01942) 608018

Inverurie Pre-Cast Ltd, 14 Keith Hall Road, Inverurie, Aberdeenshire, AB51 3UA Tel: (01467) 624367 Fax: (01467) 672145

▶ J P Naylor Co., Woodside Business Park Beach Hay, Bayton, Kidderminster, Worcestershire, DY14 9NE Tel: (01299) 832726 Fax: (01299) 832779

Kelcamp Ltd, St. Albans Road Industrial Estate, Stafford, ST16 3DR Tel: (01785) 259415 Fax: (01785) 258022

▶ Kingstone & Mortars, Monkredding Works, Kilwinning, Ayrshire, KA13 7QN Tel: (01294) 559888

Ladds Concrete Products, Wilson Way, Pool, Redruth, Cornwall, TR15 3RY Tel: (01209) 213132 Fax: (01209) 314441 E-mail: sales@laddsconcrete.co.uk

▶ Lancashire Cast Stone Ltd, Unit 35 Lune Industrial Estate, Lancaster, LA1 5QP Tel: (01524) 388501 Fax: (01524) 845007

Landworth Product Ltd, 555 London Road, Hadleigh, Benfleet, Essex, SS7 2EA Tel: (01702) 558373

Limavady Concrete Products, 68 Carlaragh Road, Limavady, County Londonderry, BT49 9LF Tel: (07886) 022597 Fax: (028) 7776 7816

▶ Longborough Concrete Ltd, The Sitch, Moreton Road, Longborough, Moreton-in-Marsh, Gloucestershire, GL56 0QJ Tel: (01451) 830140 Fax: (01451) 870065

M & M Paving Slabs, Old Manor Farm, Leigh Road, Wimborne, Dorset, BH21 2BT Tel: (01202) 840455 Fax: (01202) 840455

Mccann's Concrete Products, 256 Whitebridge Road, Sixmilecross, Omagh, County Tyrone, BT79 9HH Tel: (028) 8076 1257 Fax: (028) 8076 1239

Mackin's Concrete & Building Supplies, 27 Hilltown Road, Newry, County Down, BT34 2LJ Tel: (028) 3026 3384 Fax: (028) 3026 0514

Mcmillan Plant, Aird Quarry, Castle Kennedy, Stranraer, Wigtownshire, DG9 8RX Tel: (01776) 707241 Fax: (01776) 707264

Milbank Industries, Brandon Central Depot, Mundford Road, Weeting, Brandon, Suffolk, IP27 0PL Tel: (01842) 819818

Mona Precast Anglesey Ltd, Gaerwen Industrial Estate, Gaerwen, Gwynedd, LL60 6HR Tel: (01248) 421772 Fax: (01248) 421424 E-mail: monaprecast@aol.com

Multi-Mix, Unit 2 Praed Road, Trafford Park, Trafford Park, Manchester, M17 1PQ Tel: (07958) 922361 Fax: 0161-776 0092 E-mail: multimix2005@hotmail.com

Northern Minimix Ltd, New Building, Birch Road, Sheffield, S9 3XL Tel: 0114-244 6353 Fax: (01709) 790707

▶ Oakdale Contracts Ltd, Walkerville Industrial Park, Catterick Garrison, North Yorkshire, DL9 4SA Tel: (01748) 834184 Fax: (01748) 833033 E-mail: inquieres@oakdalecontracts.co.uk

▶ Orkney Aggregates Ltd, Garrison Road, Hatston Industrial Estate, Kirkwall, Orkney, KW15 1RE Tel: (01856) 871187 Fax: (01856) 871188 E-mail: sales@orkagg.co.uk

P Messenger, 6 Twin Lakes Industrial Park, Bretherton Road, Croston, Leyland, PR26 9RF Tel: (01772) 600889 Fax: (01772) 600255 E-mail: sales@stoneandconcrete.co.uk

Paver Systems Ltd, Road Meetings Industrial Estate, Carluke, Lanarkshire, ML8 4QG Tel: (01555) 770555 Fax: (01555) 772868

CONCRETE PRODUCTS – *continued*

PD Edenhall Ltd, Danygraig Works, Danygraig Road, Risca, Newport, Gwent, NP11 6DP Tel: (01633) 612671 Fax: (01633) 601280 E-mail: enquiries@pd-edenhall.co.uk

Peplow Concrete Products, 1 Swinton Road, Mexborough, South Yorkshire, S64 9JB Tel: (01709) 570812

Pinnegar & Barnes Patio Slabs, The Wharf, Bugbrooke, Northampton, NN7 3QB Tel: (01604) 830291 Fax: (01604) 830496

Pioneer Concrete (uk), Dunham Ho, Cross St, Sale, Cheshire, M33 7HH Tel: 0161-969 0702 Fax: 0161-969 6240

▶ Plasmor Halton Ltd, Tanhouse Lane, Widnes, Cheshire, WA8 0SQ Tel: 0151-423 1161 Fax: 0151-495 1015

Portex Concrete Products, Limekiln Farm Buildings, Easton Lane, Portland, Dorset, DT5 1BW Tel: (01305) 820064 Fax: (01305) 820064

▶ Premier Precast, Unit 11 Kelliebank, Alloa, Clackmannanshire, FK10 1NT Tel: (01259) 219966 Fax: (01259) 219988

▶ Neil Price Ltd, Bouthwood Road, Sowerby Woods Industrial Estate, Barrow-in-Furness, Cumbria, LA14 4RD Tel: (01229) 839966 Fax: (01229) 814310 E-mail: office.neilprice@tiscali.co.uk

R & J Paving, The Yard, Stone Lane, Lydiard Millicent, Swindon, SN5 3LD Tel: (01793) 770071

R M C Ltd, St. Omers Road, Dunston, Gateshead, Tyne & Wear, NE11 9EJ Tel: 0191-460 5085 Fax: 0191-460 0908

R S Concrete Products, 20 Balunasollus Road, Cookstown, County Tyrone, BT80 9TQ Tel: (028) 8675 1378 Fax: (028) 8675 1378

R Whitehead Concrete Ltd, Gin Close Way, near Afwsworth, Giltbrook, Nottingham, NG16 2HH Tel: 0115-930 3104 Fax: 0115-944 1935

▶ William Rainfords Concrete, Watery Lane, St. Helens, Merseyside, WA9 3SN Tel: (01744) 750206 Fax: (01744) 25895

Ramcke Concrete Products, Penyrheol Farm, Five Roads, Llanelli, Dyfed, SA15 5AJ Tel: (01269) 860505 Fax: (01269) 860505

Ready Mixed Concrete Ltd, Fairfield Way, Stainsacre Industrial Estate, Stainsacre, Whitby, North Yorkshire, YO22 4NT Tel: (01947) 604363 Fax: (01947) 821698

Ready Mixed Concrete South West Ltd, Priorswood Road, Taunton, Somerset, TA2 8DF Tel: (01823) 282331 Fax: (01823) 327928

Readymix Huddersfield Ltd, Red Doles Lane, Leeds Road, Huddersfield, HD2 1YD Tel: (01484) 535311 Fax: (01484) 558255 E-mail: sales@readymix-huddersfield.co.uk

Ian Rennie Precast, Alfred Street, Montrose, Angus, DD10 8HW Tel: (01674) 672792 Fax: (01674) 672792 E-mail: sales@rennierecast.co.uk

RMC Concrete Products UK Ltd, Shap, Penrith, Cumbria, CA10 3QQ Tel: (01931) 716444 Fax: (01931) 716617

Robinson Bros, 86 Cumber Road, Claudy, Londonderry, BT47 4JA Tel: (028) 7133 8300 Fax: (028) 7133 7007 E-mail: garthrobinson@btconnect.com

▶ I. Robinson, 75 Cumber Road, Claudy, Londonderry, BT47 4JA Tel: (028) 7133 8250 Fax: (028) 7133 7170

Ryburn Concrete Ltd, 9 Woodman Works, Woodman Avenue, Elland, West Yorkshire, HX5 0PE Tel: (01422) 374423 Fax: (01422) 370249

Salisbury & Wood Ltd, Old Coach Road, Tansley, Matlock, Derbyshire, DE4 5FY Tel: (01629) 582272 Fax: (01629) 583989

Scott Toomebridge Ltd, 7 Creagh Road, Toomebridge, Antrim, BT41 3SD Tel: (028) 7965 0461 Fax: (028) 7965 0238 E-mail: sales@scotttrooftiles.com

Southern Precast Concrete Ltd, Unit 6 Holm Farm, Stansted, Rowland's Castle, Hampshire, PO9 6DT Tel: (023) 9241 3544 Fax: (023) 9245 3779

Specialist Precast Products Ltd, Pantglas Industrial Estate, Bedwas, Caerphilly, Mid Glamorgan, CF83 8DR Tel: (029) 2088 0800 Fax: (029) 2088 0700 E-mail: consolidated.specialist@virgin.net

▶ Stocks Bros Ltd, Pontefract Road, Leeds, LS10 1SW Tel: 0113-271 7249 Fax: 0113-271 7249

Alexandra Stone Co. Ltd, Kirby Muxloe, Leicester, LE9 2BR Tel: 0116-239 2513 Fax: 0116-239 3993

Stoner Benton Concrete Ltd, Tilley Lane, Boreham Street, Hailsham, East Sussex, BN27 4UU Tel: (01323) 832334 Fax: (01323) 873791 E-mail: info@stonerbenton.co.uk

Stowell Concrete, Arnolds Way, Yatton, Bristol, BS49 4QN Tel: (01934) 833340 Fax: (01934) 835474 E-mail: sales@stowellconcrete.co.uk

Stowell Concrete Ltd, Edford Green, Holcombe, Radstock, BA3 5DA Tel: (01761) 232282 Fax: (01761) 232806 E-mail: enquiries@stowellconcrete.co.uk

▶ Stowell Concrete, Winterstoke Road, Weston-super-Mare, Avon, BS23 3YW Tel: (01934) 628185

Supermix Concrete, 76 Strabane Road, Newtownstewart, Omagh, County Tyrone, BT78 4JZ Tel: (028) 8166 1391 Fax: (028) 8166 1391

Supreme Concrete Ltd, Coppingford Hall, Coppingford Road, Sawtry, Huntingdon, Cambridgeshire, PE28 5GP Tel: (01487) 833300 Fax: (01487) 833305 E-mail: sales@supremeconcrete.co.uk

Supreme Concrete Ltd, Crown Quay Lane, Sittingbourne, Kent, ME10 3SL Tel: (01795) 475255 Fax: (01795) 433599 E-mail: enquiries@bourncrete.co.uk

▶ Supreme Concrete Ltd, Unit 2 Tweedale Industrial Estate, Madeley, Telford, Shropshire, TF7 4JR Tel: (01952) 684282 Fax: (01952) 580834

T N S Concrete Products, Normanby Road, Scunthorpe, South Humberside, DN15 6AD Tel: (01724) 720814

▶ T Sutcliffe & Co. Ltd, Weston Street, Bolton, BL3 2AL Tel: (01204) 535221 Fax: (01204) 380681 E-mail: sales@sutcliffegarages.co.uk

Tarmac Motors Ltd, Foundry Lane, Widnes, Cheshire, WA8 8YZ Tel: (0870) 6006969 Fax: (01744) 885673

▶ Tarmac Precast Concrete Ltd, Thornfalcon Works, Henlade, Taunton, Somerset, TA3 5DN Tel: (01823) 442000 Fax: (01823) 443786

▶ Tarmac Top Floor, Chainbridge Lane, Lound, Retford, Nottinghamshire, DN22 8RU Tel: (01777) 816616 Fax: (01777) 816617

▶ Tarmac Topblock Ltd, Hangar 1 Ford Airfield Industrial Estate, Ford, Arundel, West Sussex, BN18 0HY Tel: (01903) 723333 Fax: (01903) 711043

▶ Tayban Developments Ltd, Unit 9b Locomotion Industrial Estate, Chorley New Road, Horwich, Bolton, BL6 5UE Tel: (01204) 691313 Fax: (01204) 691777

Ternent Pre-Cast, Whitehall Estate, 123a Barras Garth Road, Leeds, LS12 4JB Tel: 0113-231 9099

Thurrock Flue Co, Sandy Lane, West Thurrock, Grays, Essex, RM20 4BH Tel: (01708) 864908 Fax: (01708) 869200

▶ Travis Perkins, Blackhouse Circle, Blackhouse Industrial Estate, Peterhead, Aberdeenshire, AB42 1BN Tel: (01779) 471500 Fax: (01779) 471237 E-mail: gavin.davidson@travisperkins.co.uk

Tudorstone Building Materials Ltd, Daneshill Road, Lound, Retford, Nottinghamshire, DN22 8RB Tel: (01777) 816589 Fax: (01777) 817115

W D L (Contracting) Ltd, Stuart Quarry, Penderyn, Aberdare, Mid Glamorgan, CF44 9JY Tel: (01685) 811525 Fax: (01685) 814326 E-mail: accounts@wdlewisaberdare.co.uk

Wain Bros Ltd, 774 Leek Road, Stoke-on-Trent, ST1 6AE Tel: (01782) 202180 Fax: (01782) 213127

Warr Bros, Nab Works, Long Lane, Pott Shrigley, Macclesfield, Cheshire, SK10 5SD Tel: (01625) 574634 Fax: (01625) 576372 E-mail: sales@bowlandmanchester.co.uk

Watts 4 X 4 Centre, 122 Scarborough Road, Bridlington, North Humberside, YO16 7NU Tel: (01262) 606782 Fax: (01262) 604629 E-mail: wattsmix@aol.com

▶ Waycon Precast Ltd, Western Wood Way, Plympton, Plymouth, PL7 5BQ Tel: (01752) 335777 Fax: (01752) 336777

Westcrete Pre-cast Concrete Ltd, Stoney Bridges, Membury Road, Axminster, Devon, EX13 5RL Tel: (01297) 32002 E-mail: sales@westcrete.fsnet.co.uk

Wheeler & Co. (Concrete Products) Ltd, Old Pit Yard, Clandown, Radstock, BA3 3DA Tel: (01761) 432296 Fax: (01761) 472220

Windmore Concrete Products, Windmore Green, Creca, Annan, Dumfriesshire, DG12 6RP Tel: (01461) 500350 Fax: (01461) 500350

Yates Concrete Products, 177 Agbrigg Road, Wakefield, West Yorkshire, WF1 5BU Tel: (01924) 200997

CONCRETE PUMPING SERVICES

Coonan Concrete Pumping, 147 Western Road, Mitcham, Surrey, CR4 3EF Tel: (020) 8648 2088 Fax: (020) 8648 2088

Pochin Contractors Ltd, Brooks Lane, Middlewich, Cheshire, CW10 0JQ Tel: (01606) 833333 Fax: (01606) 833331 E-mail: sales@pochins.plc.uk

CONCRETE PUMPS

Aintree Concrete Pumping, 21 Aintree Close, Gravesend, Kent, DA12 5AS Tel: (01474) 333616 Fax: (01474) 333616 E-mail: info@aintreeconcretepumping.co.uk

Gunform Equipment Supplies Ltd, 33 Carsthorne Road, Hoylake, Wirral, Merseyside, CH47 4FB Tel: 0151-632 6333 Fax: 0151-632 6444 E-mail: gunform@gunform.u-net.com

Putzmeister Ltd, Carrwood Road, Chesterfield Trading Estate, Chesterfield, Derbyshire, S41 9QB Tel: (01246) 264200 Fax: (01246) 260077 E-mail: info@putzmeister.co.uk

▶ UK Pumps Ltd, Knowsley Road, Haslingden, Rossendale, Lancashire, BB4 4RR Tel: (01706) 221979 Fax: (01706) 215620 E-mail: ukpumpsltd@hotmail.com

Venus Services, The Old Rectory, Church Street, Southwell, Nottinghamshire, NG25 0HG Tel: (01636) 814633 Fax: (01636) 815403 E-mail: audley@btopenworld.com

CONCRETE RAFT FOUNDATIONS

▶ Moorhouse Construction Ltd, 111-113 Melton Road, Barrow Upon Soar, Loughborough, Leicestershire, LE12 8NT Tel: (01509) 620200 Fax: 01509 412612 E-mail: sales@moorhouse-construction.co.uk

CONCRETE RAILWAY SLEEPERS

Railway Sleeper.com, Kilgraney, Owthorpe Road, Cotgrave, Nottingham, NG12 3PU Tel: 0115-989 0445 Fax: 0115-989 3366 E-mail: enquiries@kilgraney.com

CONCRETE RECYCLING

Construction & Commercial Recycling Ltd, Century Business Centre, Century Business Park, Manvers, Rotherham, South Yorkshire, S63 5DA Tel: 01709 300090 Fax: 01709 300102 E-mail: Candcrecycling@aol.com

CONCRETE RECYCLING OR RECLAIMING SYSTEMS

Concrete T S Ltd, Unit A8 Moss Industrial Estate, St. Helens Road, Leigh, Lancashire, WN7 3PT Tel: (01942) 261909 Fax: (01942) 261750

Construction & Commercial Recycling Ltd, Century Business Centre, Century Business Park, Manvers, Rotherham, South Yorkshire, S63 5DA Tel: 01709 300090 Fax: 01709 300102 E-mail: Candcrecycling@aol.com

CONCRETE REFUSE CHUTES

R.V. Weaver, Rectory Road, Grays, Essex, RM17 6BD Tel: (01375) 390820 Fax: (01375) 393333

CONCRETE REINFORCEMENT WIRE, *See Wire Strands etc*

CONCRETE REINFORCEMENTS

Philip Jones Construction Materials Ltd, 40 Wood Lane, Hawarden, Deeside, Clwyd, CH5 3JE Tel: (01691) 626262 Fax: (01244) 520944 E-mail: philip.jones@tggroup.co.uk

CONCRETE REINFORCING ACCESSORIES

Creteco Sales, 17 St. Martins Street, Wallingford, Oxfordshire, OX10 0EA Tel: (01491) 839488 Fax: (01491) 833879 E-mail: sales@creteco.co.uk

Erico Europa GB Ltd, 52 Milford Road, Reading, RG1 8LJ Tel: 0118-958 8386 Fax: 0118-959 4856

Grip Steel Reinforcements, Atlas Works, Robinson Street, Stalybridge, Cheshire, SK15 1TH Tel: 0161-338 2607 Fax: 0161-303 0871 E-mail: gripsteel@boltblue.com

A.K. Orme & Son, 114-122 Arundel Street, Sheffield, S1 4RE Tel: 0114-272 2409 Fax: 0114-272 2409 E-mail: ormerings@aol.com

Reinforcements Peterborough, 1 Fenlake Business Centre, Fengate, Peterborough, PE1 5BQ Tel: (01733) 558321 Fax: (01733) 555260

Stephenson Ltd, Oakwood House, Bucks Green, Rudgwick, Horsham, West Sussex, RH12 3JJ Tel: (01403) 824960 Fax: (01403) 824961 E-mail: m.s@stephenson-ssc.co.uk

Techmarkets Ltd, Fourth Avenue, Trafford Park, Manchester, M17 1DB Tel: 0161-876 4125 Fax: 0161-876 4146 E-mail: techmarkets@btconnect.com

CONCRETE REINFORCING BAR CUTTING OR BENDING

Collins Re Inforcements Ltd, 5 Dobson Park Industrial Estate, 234 Manchester Road, Ince, Wigan, Lancashire, WN2 2ED Tel: (01942) 322210 Fax: (01942) 820380 E-mail: info@collins-reinforcements.co.uk

Express Reinforcements Ltd, Eaglebush Works, Milland Road Industrial Estate, Neath, West Glamorgan, SA11 1NJ Tel: (01639) 645555 Fax: (01639) 645558 E-mail: sales@expressreinforcements.co.uk

Express Reinforcements Ltd, High Street, Newburn, Newcastle upon Tyne, NE15 8LN Tel: 0191-264 3311 Fax: 0191-264 7842

Valley Reinforcements Ltd, Endle Street, Southampton, SO14 5FZ Tel: (023) 8022 6126 Fax: (023) 8033 8832 E-mail: andy@vrconstruction.f2s.com

CONCRETE REINFORCING SPACERS

BRC Ltd, 79-81 Station Road, Sutton-in-Ashfield, Nottinghamshire, NG17 5FR Tel: (01623) 440932 Fax: (01623) 440932 E-mail: sales@eastmidlands.brc.ltd.uk

BRC, 11 Mulberry Business Park, Fishponds Road, Wokingham, Berkshire, RG41 2FH Tel: 0118-977 3822 Fax: 0118-977 3913 E-mail: sales@brc-uk.co.uk

Collins Re Inforcements Ltd, 5 Dobson Park Industrial Estate, 234 Manchester Road, Ince, Wigan, Lancashire, WN2 2ED Tel: (01942) 322210 Fax: (01942) 820380 E-mail: info@collins-reinforcements.co.uk

Creteco Sales, 17 St. Martins Street, Wallingford, Oxfordshire, OX10 0EA Tel: (01491) 839488 Fax: (01491) 833879 E-mail: sales@creteco.co.uk

Grip Steel Reinforcements, Atlas Works, Robinson Street, Stalybridge, Cheshire, SK15 1TH Tel: 0161-338 2607 Fax: 0161-303 0871 E-mail: gripsteel@boltblue.com

Reinforcements Peterborough, 1 Fenlake Business Centre, Fengate, Peterborough, PE1 5BQ Tel: (01733) 558321 Fax: (01733) 555260

Techmarkets Ltd, Fourth Avenue, Trafford Park, Manchester, M17 1DB Tel: 0161-876 4125 Fax: 0161-876 4146 E-mail: techmarkets@btconnect.com

CONCRETE REINFORCING STAINLESS STEEL REINFORCEMENT

Kierbeck Ltd, Kierbeck Business Complex, North Woolwich Road, London, E16 2BG Tel: (020) 7474 0055 Fax: (020) 7474 7778 E-mail: sales@kierbeck.com

▶ Propex Concrete Systems, No. 9, Royal Court, Basil Close, Chesterfield, Derbyshire, S41 7SL Tel: 0845 5314078 Fax: (01246) 564201 E-mail: trevor.atkinson@propexinc.co.uk

SSR Stainless Steel Reinforcement Ltd, Units B & C Burnt Common, London Road, Send, Woking, Surrey, GU23 7LN Tel: (01483) 226426 Fax: (01483) 226427 E-mail: ssr@btconnect.com

Stainless UK Ltd, Newhall Works, Newhall Road, Sheffield, S9 2QL Tel: 0114-244 1333 Fax: 0114-244 1444

CONCRETE REINFORCING STEEL PRODUCTS, *See Reinforcing, Concrete*

CONCRETE REINFORCING STEEL REINFORCEMENT

Henry T. Billson (Kettering) Ltd, Glendon Ironworks, Sackville St, Kettering, Northants, NN16 9EQ Tel: (01536) 512194 Fax: (01536) 484152 E-mail: sales@billsonssteel.co.uk

BRC Ltd, 79-81 Station Road, Sutton-in-Ashfield, Nottinghamshire, NG17 5FR Tel: (01623) 440932 Fax: (01623) 440932 E-mail: sales@eastmidlands.brc.ltd.uk

BRC, 11 Mulberry Business Park, Fishponds Road, Wokingham, Berkshire, RG41 2FH Tel: 0118-977 3822 Fax: 0118-977 3913 E-mail: sales@brc-uk.co.uk

Cannon Steels Ltd, 22 Walcot Road, Enfield, Middlesex, EN3 7NF Tel: (020) 8805 4070 Fax: (020) 8805 4525 E-mail: enquiries@cannonsteelsltd.co.uk

Clifda Steels Ltd, Northwick Corner, Canvey Island, Essex, SS8 0PS Tel: (01268) 510066 Fax: (01268) 683815 E-mail: clifdasteels@yahoo.com

Clwyd Re Inforcements Ltd, Rhosddu Industrial Estate, Main Road, Rhosrobin, Wrexham, Clwyd, LL11 4YL Tel: (01978) 354454 Fax: (01978) 291373 E-mail: sales@clwyd-reinforcements.co.uk

Collins Re Inforcements Ltd, 5 Dobson Park Industrial Estate, 234 Manchester Road, Ince, Wigan, Lancashire, WN2 2ED Tel: (01942) 322210 Fax: (01942) 820380 E-mail: info@collins-reinforcements.co.uk

Cotswold Steel Stockholders Ltd, Unit 1m2 Babdown Industrial Estate, Babdown, Tetbury, Gloucestershire, GL8 8YL Tel: (01666) 504889 Fax: (01666) 504891 E-mail: james@cotswoldsteels.com

Express Reinforcements Ltd, Fordwater Trading Estate, Ford Road, Chertsey, Surrey, KT16 8HG Tel: (01932) 579600 Fax: (01932) 579601 E-mail: chertseysales@expressreinforcements.co.uk

Express Reinforcements Ltd, Eaglebush Works, Milland Road Industrial Estate, Neath, West Glamorgan, SA11 1NJ Tel: (01639) 645555 Fax: (01639) 645558 E-mail: sales@expressreinforcements.co.uk

Fibre Technology Ltd, Brookhill Road, Pinxton, Nottingham, NG16 6NT Tel: (01773) 864205 Fax: (01773) 580287 E-mail: sales@fibretech.com

CONCRETE REINFORCING STEEL REINFORCEMENT – *continued*

General Steel Services, 45 Sydenham Road, Belfast, BT3 9DH Tel: (028) 9045 6327 Fax: (028) 9045 8096 E-mail: gss@metsteel.co.uk
K B Reinforcements (Northern) Ltd, Chaddock Lane, Boothstown, Worsley, Manchester, M28 4DR Tel: 0161-790 8635 Fax: 0161-799 7083 E-mail: sales@kb-northern.co.uk
Kierbeck Ltd, Kierbeck Business Complex, North Woolwich Road, London, E16 2BG Tel: (020) 7474 0055 Fax: (020) 7474 7778 E-mail: sales@kierbeck.com
Lemon Groundwork Supplies, Russell Gardens, Wickford, Essex, SS11 8BH Tel: (01268) 571571 Fax: (01268) 571555 E-mail: sales@lemon-gs.co.uk
R M Reinforcements Ltd, 3-5 Church Street, Brierley Hill, West Midlands, DY5 3PT Tel: (01384) 262601 Fax: (01384) 262605 E-mail: rmreinforcements@aol.com
R S J Steels Lincoln Ltd, 97 Sadler Road, Lincoln, LN6 3RS Tel: (01522) 500400 Fax: (01522) 500401 E-mail: sales@rsj-steels.co.uk
Radius Reinforcements Ltd, 1 Villa Place, Clackmannan, FK10 4HZ Tel: (01259) 215129 Fax: (01259) 215129 E-mail: radiusrebar1@freeuk.com
Rainham Steel Co. Ltd, Kathryn House, Manor Way, Rainham, Essex, RM13 8RE Tel: (01708) 522311 Fax: (01708) 559024 E-mail: info@rainhamsteel.co.uk
Reinforcements Peterborough, 1 Fenlake Business Centre, Fengate, Peterborough, PE1 5BQ Tel: (01733) 558321 Fax: (01733) 555260
Renforce Ltd, 26A Collegiate Crescent, Sheffield, S10 2BH Tel: 0114-266 7521 Fax: 0114-268 4331
Rom, Unit 3 4 Blaydon Industrial Park, Chainbridge Road, Blaydon-on-Tyne, Tyne & Wear, NE21 5AB Tel: 0191-414 9600 Fax: 0191-414 9650 E-mail: daniel_hall@rom.co.uk
Rom Ltd, Mill Street, Risca, Newport, Gwent, NP11 6LF Tel: (01633) 612751 Fax: (01633) 619841 E-mail: sales@rom.co.uk
Rom Group Ltd, Eastern Avenue, Trent Valley, Lichfield, Staffordshire, WS13 6RN Tel: (01543) 414111 Fax: (01543) 421605 E-mail: sales@rom.co.uk
Rowland Reinforcement Ltd, Goods Yard, Knollys Road, London, SW16 2JP Tel: (020) 8677 5228 Fax: (020) 8664 6473
Speedwell Reinforcement Ltd, White Lane, Chapeltown, Sheffield, S35 2YG Tel: 0114-246 7551 Fax: 0114-240 2519 E-mail: enquiries@speedwellreinforcement.co.uk

CONCRETE REINFORCING WIRE MESH

Grip Steel Reinforcements, Atlas Works, Robinson Street, Stalybridge, Cheshire, SK15 1TH Tel: 0161-338 2607 Fax: 0161-303 0871 E-mail: gripsteel@boltblue.com

CONCRETE REINFORCING WIRE STRANDS

Kent Wire Ltd, Chatham Docks, Chatham, Kent, ME4 4SW Tel: (01634) 830964 Fax: (01634) 830967
▶ Ormond Construction Ltd, 91b Mora Road, London, NW2 6TB Tel: (020) 8450 2244 Fax: (020) 8450 1148

CONCRETE REPAIR

▶ Multi Bore Structural Services Ltd, Unit 10 East Moors Business Park, East Moors Road, Cardiff, CF24 5JX Tel: (029) 2049 7373 Fax: (029) 2048 1370 E-mail: info@multibore.co.uk

CONCRETE REPAIR PRODUCTS

2K Polymer Systems Limited, PO Box 7, Alfreton, Derbyshire, DE55 7RA Tel: (01773) 540440 Fax: (01773) 607638 E-mail: info@2kps.net
Alfred Bagnall & Sons Restoration Ltd, St Thomas Road, Belvedere, Kent, DA17 6AG Tel: (020) 8311 3910 Fax: (020) 8311 3833
▶ Conspare Ltd, Bestwood Road, Brookhill Industrial Estate, Pinxton, Nottingham, NG16 6NT Tel: (01773) 860796 Fax: (01773) 860055 E-mail: sales@conspare.com
Factory Improvements Supplies Ltd, 24-26 Imperial Ave, Shirley, Southampton, SO15 8QH Tel: (023) 8078 6759 Fax: (023) 8070 2989
Kinder Marketing, Unit D Roe Cross Indust Park, Old Road, Mottram, Hyde, Cheshire, SK14 6LG Tel: (01457) 762758 Fax: (01457) 776547
Permarock Products Ltd, Jubilee Drive, Loughborough, Leicestershire, LE11 5TW Tel: (01509) 262924 Fax: (01509) 230063 E-mail: sales@permarock.com
Pick Quick Service, 380 Meanwood Road, Leeds, LS7 2JF Tel: 0113-216 8811 Fax: 0113-216 8833 E-mail: sales@pickquick.co.uk
Support Site P.L.C., Pedmore Road, Dudley, West Midlands, DY2 0RN Tel: (01384) 472250 Fax: (01384) 472251 E-mail: birmingham@supportsite.co.uk
Vandex (UK) Ltd, PO Box 200, Guildford, Surrey, GU2 4WD Tel: (0870) 2416264 Fax: (0870) 2416274 E-mail: info@vandex.co.uk

CONCRETE ROOF TILE MACHINES

Vortex Hydra UK Ltd, Kingmoor Industrial Estate, Kingmoor Road, Carlisle, CA3 9QJ Tel: (01228) 510800 Fax: (01228) 510808 E-mail: vh_sales_uk@vortexhydra.com

CONCRETE ROOF WALKWAY TILES

Spartan Tiles Ltd, Martells Pit, Slough Lane, Ardleigh, Colchester, CO7 7RU Tel: (01206) 230553 Fax: (01206) 230516 E-mail: david@spartantiles.com

CONCRETE ROOFING MATERIALS

Heys-Shawl Ltd, Waterloo House, Langham Street Industrial Estate, Ashton-Under-Lyne, Lancashire, OL7 9AX Tel: 0161-343 2060 Fax: 0161-343 1542
Marley Building Materials Ltd, Station Road, Coleshill, Birmingham, B46 1HP Tel: (01675) 468400 Fax: (01675) 468485

CONCRETE SAWING CONTRACTORS

Barcol Ltd, Oak Lodge, Studland Avenue, Wickford, Essex, SS12 0JF Tel: (01268) 764642 Fax: (01268) 764644
Barton Drilling Ltd, 1 Station Road Industrial Estate, Latchford, Warrington, WA4 1LB Tel: (01925) 653354 Fax: (01925) 230151 E-mail: sales@bartondrilling.co.uk
Concrete Cutters Sarum Ltd, 18 David Road, Colnbrook, Slough, SL3 0DG Tel: (01753) 689920 Fax: (01753) 689920 E-mail: info@concut.co.uk
D Drill, 12 Hazel Road, Four Marks, Alton, Hampshire, GU34 5EY Tel: (020) 7355 4444 Fax: (01420) 560187E-mail: info@d-drill.co.uk
D Drill Master Drillers Ltd, Unit 5 Coity Cresent, Bridgend Industrial Estate, Bridgend, Mid Glamorgan, CF31 3RS Tel: (01656) 662321 Fax: (01656) 667779
D Drill Master Drillers Ltd, 4 Westover Industrial Estate, Ermington Road, Ivybridge, Devon, PL21 9ES Tel: (01752) 698890 Fax: (01752) 698891 E-mail: plymouth@d-drill.co.uk
D Drill Master Drillers Ltd, Daleside Works, Craghead Colliery Industrial Estate, Stanley, County Durham, DH9 6HB Tel: (01207) 231671 Fax: (01207) 299541 E-mail: newcastle@d-drill.co.uk
D-Drill (Master Drillers) Ltd, Unit 1 Rosebridge Way, Ince, Wigan, Lancashire, WN1 3DP Tel: (01942) 824724 Fax: (01942) 829944 E-mail: wigan@d-drill.co.uk
▶ Drilltec Ltd, Diamond House, Dencora Way, Sundon Park, Luton, LU3 3HP Tel: (01582) 564455 Fax: (01582) 847016 E-mail: fiona@drilltec.co.uk
Holemasters Demtech, Unit 2-4 Dixon Street, Westhoughton, Bolton, BL5 3PX Tel: (01942) 840600 Fax: (01942) 840700 E-mail: enquiries@holemasters.co.uk
Speed Drill Ltd, Unit 17-18 Chingford Industrial Centre, Hall Lane, London, E4 8DJ Tel: (020) 8524 0004 Fax: (020) 8524 6778
Speedbore Diamond Drilling (Northern) Ltd, Unit 7, Wood St, Poulton-le-Fylde, Lancashire, FY6 8JY Tel: (01253) 891206 Fax: (01253) 893848 E-mail: peter@speedbore.com

CONCRETE SCULPTURES

Tryst, Kippen Station, Kippen, Stirling, FK8 3JA Tel: (01786) 870295

CONCRETE SPRAYING EQUIPMENT

Putzmeister Ltd, Carrwood Road, Chesterfield Trading Estate, Chesterfield, Derbyshire, S41 9QB Tel: (01246) 264200 Fax: (01246) 260077 E-mail: info@putzmeister.co.uk

CONCRETE SPREADING OR FINISHING EQUIPMENT

Amey plc, Sutton Courtenay, Abingdon, Oxfordshire, OX14 4PP Tel: (01235) 848811 Fax: (01235) 848822 E-mail: amey.fleet@amey.co.uk
Concrete T S Ltd, Unit A8 Moss Industrial Estate, St. Helens Road, Leigh, Lancashire, WN7 3PT Tel: (01942) 261909 Fax: (01942) 261750

CONCRETE STAIRCASES

Cornish Stairways Ltd, Kernick Industrial Estate, Penryn, Cornwall, TR10 9DQ Tel: (01326) 374662 Fax: (01326) 376596 E-mail: mikejordan@cornishstairways.co.uk

CONCRETE STRUCTURAL REPAIR CONTRACTORS

Castlework Contractors Ltd, 98 College Street, Kempston, Bedford, MK42 8LU Tel: (01234) 217941 Fax: (01234) 357232 E-mail: sales@castlework-contractors.co.uk
Cemplas Ltd, Holbrook House, 72 Lower Addiscombe Road, Croydon, CR9 6AD Tel: (020) 8654 3149 Fax: (020) 8656 6984 E-mail: info@cemplas.co.uk
Colebrand Ltd, Goodshawfeld Rd, Rossendale, Lancs, BB4 8QF Tel: (01706) 217226 Fax: (01706) 831712
Colt Construction, Witty Street, Hull, HU3 4TT Tel: (01482) 581880 Fax: (01482) 215037 E-mail: info@colt-industrial.co.uk
Concrete Repair & Grouting Ltd, 163 Sutton Road, Kidderminster, Worcestershire, DY11 6QN Tel: (01562) 748101 Fax: (01562) 829007 E-mail: enquiries@crg-ltd.co.uk
Concrete Repairs Ltd, Cathite House, 23a Willow Lane, Mitcham, Surrey, CR4 4TU Tel: (020) 8288 4848 Fax: (020) 8288 4847 E-mail: sales@concrete-repairs.co.uk
Concrete T S Ltd, Unit A8 Moss Industrial Estate, St. Helens Road, Leigh, Lancashire, WN7 3PT Tel: (01942) 261909 Fax: (01942) 261750
Currall Lewis & Martin Construction Ltd, 89-93 Broadwell Road, Oldbury, West Midlands, B69 4BL Tel: 0121-552 9292 Fax: 0121-544 9899 E-mail: office@clmconstruction.com
▶ Drilltec Ltd, Diamond House, Dencora Way, Sundon Park, Luton, LU3 3HP Tel: (01582) 564455 Fax: (01582) 847016 E-mail: fiona@drilltec.co.uk
Keller Ground Engineering, Thorp Arch Trading Estate, Thorp Arch, Wetherby, West Yorkshire, LS23 7BJ Tel: (01937) 541118 Fax: (01937) 541371 E-mail: info@keller-ge.co.uk
Kilrot, 928 Foleshill Road, Coventry, CV6 6GS Tel: (024) 7668 9998 Fax: (024) 7663 7562 E-mail: dickdixon@kilrot.fsbusiness.co.uk
George Law Ltd, 35 Mill Street, Kidderminster, Worcestershire, DY11 6XB Tel: (01562) 820421 Fax: (01562) 829205
Planned Maintenance (Pennine) Ltd, Vine Grove Works, Commerce St, Haslingden, Rossendale, Lancashire, BB4 5JT Tel: (01706) 227865 Fax: (01706) 836111 E-mail: info@pmp-ltd.co.uk
Ram Services, 240-244 Lowerhouse Lane, Burnley, Lancashire, BB12 6NG Tel: (01282) 452211 Fax: (01282) 452244 E-mail: sales@ramservices.co.uk
Stonbury Ltd, 4 Phoenix Enterprise Park, Grovehill Road, Beverley, North Humberside, HU17 0JG Tel: (01482) 881198 Fax: (01482) 868457 E-mail: admin@stonbury.co.uk
Tilbury Douglas Projects Ltd, 395 George Road, Erdington, Birmingham, B23 7RZ Tel: 0121-344 3900 Fax: 0121-344 4801 E-mail: enquiries@tilbury.co.uk
Universal Sealants UK Ltd, Kingston House, Pattinson North, Washington, Tyne & Wear, NE38 8QA Tel: 0191-416 1530 Fax: 0191-415 4377 E-mail: info@usluk.com

CONCRETE SURFACE PREPARATION

D Drill, 12 Hazel Road, Four Marks, Alton, Hampshire, GU34 5EY Tel: (020) 7355 4444 Fax: (01420) 560187E-mail: info@d-drill.co.uk
D Drill Master Drillers Ltd, Unit 5 Coity Cresent, Bridgend Industrial Estate, Bridgend, Mid Glamorgan, CF31 3RS Tel: (01656) 662321 Fax: (01656) 667779
D Drill Master Drillers Ltd, 4 Westover Industrial Estate, Ermington Road, Ivybridge, Devon, PL21 9ES Tel: (01752) 698890 Fax: (01752) 698891 E-mail: plymouth@d-drill.co.uk
D Drill Master Drillers Ltd, Daleside Works, Craghead Colliery Industrial Estate, Stanley, County Durham, DH9 6HB Tel: (01207) 231671 Fax: (01207) 299541 E-mail: newcastle@d-drill.co.uk
D-Drill (Master Drillers) Ltd, Unit 1 Rosebridge Way, Ince, Wigan, Lancashire, WN1 3DP Tel: (01942) 824724 Fax: (01942) 829944 E-mail: wigan@d-drill.co.uk
G C M Ltd, Ratcliffe Buildings, Tuttel Hill, Nuneaton, Warwickshire, CV10 0GA Tel: (024) 7635 2540 Fax: (024) 7635 3223 E-mail: sales@gcmsales.com
Hydro Pumps Ltd, 19 High Mead, Fareham, Hampshire, PO15 6BL Tel: (01329) 823420 Fax: (01329) 823425 E-mail: sales@hydro-pumps.co.uk

CONCRETE SURFACE PREPARATION EQUIPMENT

G C M Ltd, Ratcliffe Buildings, Tuttel Hill, Nuneaton, Warwickshire, CV10 0GA Tel: (024) 7635 2540 Fax: (024) 7635 3223 E-mail: sales@gcmsales.com

CONCRETE SURFACE PREPARATION, WATER JET

Hydro Pumps Ltd, 19 High Mead, Fareham, Hampshire, PO15 6BL Tel: (01329) 823420 Fax: (01329) 823425 E-mail: sales@hydro-pumps.co.uk

CONCRETE TANKS

Whites Concrete Ltd, Ravensthorpe Road, Thornhill Lees, Dewsbury, West Yorkshire, WF12 9EF Tel: (01924) 464283 Fax: (01924) 459183 E-mail: whites@longley.uk.com

CONCRETE TEST EQUIPMENT

Wykeham Farrance International Ltd, Chiltern House, Unit 4B, Knaves Beech Business Centre, Loadwater, High Wycombe, Buckinghamshire, HP10 9QY Tel: (01628) 521000 Fax: (01628) 530300 E-mail: sales@wfi.co.uk

CONCRETE TEST SERVICES

Scientifics, 4-6 Wharfside, Oldbury, West Midlands, B69 2BU Tel: 0121-552 1565 Fax: 0121-544 8581 E-mail: admin@scientifics.com
UK Analytical Ltd, Lower Ground Floor, Dison Building, Buslingthorpe Lane, Leeds, LS7 2DG Tel: (0113) 2392 572 Fax: (0113) 2392 575 E-mail: uka@kirkstall.fsbusiness.co.uk

CONCRETE TESTING CALORIMETERS

Martech, 21 Church Street, Sawtry, Huntingdon, Cambridgeshire, PE28 5SZ Tel: (01487) 832288 Fax: (01487) 832739 E-mail: techinical@martech.co.uk

CONCRETE TUNNEL FORMWORK

▶ A & T Group, 183 Manor Road North, Southampton, SO19 2DZ Tel: (023) 8044 3127 E-mail: andie@chessun.fsnet.co.uk

CONCRETE VIBRATING EQUIPMENT

Amey plc, Sutton Courtenay, Abingdon, Oxfordshire, OX14 4PP Tel: (01235) 848811 Fax: (01235) 848822 E-mail: amey.fleet@amey.co.uk
G C M Ltd, Ratcliffe Buildings, Tuttel Hill, Nuneaton, Warwickshire, CV10 0GA Tel: (024) 7635 2540 Fax: (024) 7635 3223 E-mail: sales@gcmsales.com
Standall Tools Ltd, Mickley Lane, Dronfield Woodhouse, Dronfield, Derbyshire, S18 8XB Tel: 0114-262 0626 Fax: 0114-262 0520 E-mail: sales@standall.com

CONCRETE WALL CLADDING

Trent Concrete Ltd, Private Road 3, Colwick Industrial Estate, Nottingham, NG4 2BG Tel: 0115-987 9747 Fax: 0115-987 9948 E-mail: admin@trentconcrete.co.uk

CONCRETE WATERPROOFING,

See Cement Waterproofing etc

CONCRETE WEIGH BATCHING EQUIPMENT

Practicon Ltd, Chapel Lane, Rode Heath, Stoke-on-Trent, ST7 3SD Tel: (01270) 876211 Fax: (01270) 878887 E-mail: sales.systems@practicon.co.uk

CONDENSATE RETURN PUMPS

Aspen Pumps Ltd, Aspen Building, Apex Way, Hailsham, East Sussex, BN27 3WA Tel: (01323) 848842 Fax: (01323) 848846
Automatic Pump Ltd, 36 Lanehead Road, Etruria, Stoke-On-Trent, ST1 5PT Tel: (01782) 279504 Fax: (01782) 279005 E-mail: enquiries@elipse.co.uk
Birch Sales & Marketing Ltd, 41 Green Lane, Burnham, Slough, SL1 8DZ Tel: (01628) 661475 Fax: (01628) 667999 E-mail: bob@birch-sales.co.uk
E.D.C. International Ltd, Brook House Station Road, Pangbourne, Reading, RG8 7AN Tel: 0118-984 2040 Fax: 0118-984 5300 E-mail: sales@edcinternational.com

CONDENSATE RETURN PUMPS – *continued*

Sandycott Pump Mnfrs, Manor House, Church Street, Eckington, Sheffield, S21 4BH Tel: (01246) 436632 Fax: (01246) 433372 E-mail: sales@hydron-pumps.com
Williamson Pumps, Aviation House, The Street, Poynings, Brighton, BN45 7AQ Tel: (01273) 857752 Fax: (0845) 2263639 E-mail: info@williamsonpumps.co.uk

CONDENSATION CONTROL PRODUCTS

Ferrob Ltd, Regency House, Kingsclere Park, Kingsclere, Newbury, Berkshire, RG20 4SW Tel: (01635) 299266 Fax: (01635) 299277 E-mail: sales@ferrob.co.uk
▶ Regency Preservation, Conbar House, Mead Lane, Hertford, SG13 7AP Tel: (01992) 509201 Fax: (01992) 552277 E-mail: enquiries@regencypreservation.co.uk
Safeguard Chemicals Ltd, Redkiln Close, Horsham, West Sussex, RH13 5QL Tel: (01403) 210204 Fax: (01403) 217529 E-mail: info@safeguardchem.com
Sprayseal Contracts Ltd, Bollin House, Blakeley Lane, Mobberley, Knutsford, Cheshire, WA16 7LX Tel: (01565) 872303 Fax: (01565) 872599 E-mail: sales@sprayseal.co.uk

CONDENSATION CONTROL SERVICES

▶ Dampcure Woodcure 30 Ltd, 41 Merton Road, Watford, WD18 0WJ Tel: (01923) 663322 Fax: (01923) 223842 E-mail: admin@dampcurewoodcure.com
Ferrob Ltd, Regency House, Kingsclere Park, Kingsclere, Newbury, Berkshire, RG20 4SW Tel: (01635) 299266 Fax: (01635) 299277 E-mail: sales@ferrob.co.uk
Haynes Manufacturing UK, Marlowe House, Stewkins, Stourbridge, West Midlands, DY8 4YW Tel: (01384) 371416 Fax: (01384) 371416 E-mail: info@haynes-uk.co.uk
Kiltox Contracts Ltd, 6 Chiltonian Industrial Estate, Manor Lane, London, SE12 0TX Tel: (020) 8463 9690 Fax: (0845) 1662050 E-mail: info@kiltox.co.uk
Sprayseal Contracts Ltd, Bollin House, Blakeley Lane, Mobberley, Knutsford, Cheshire, WA16 7LX Tel: (01565) 872303 Fax: (01565) 872599 E-mail: sales@sprayseal.co.uk

CONDENSER INSPECTION OR REPAIR OR RETUBING ENGINEERING

Malvern Boilers Ltd, Spring Lane North, Malvern, Worcestershire, WR14 1BW Tel: (01684) 893777 Fax: (01684) 893776 E-mail: sales@malvernboilers.co.uk

CONDENSER TUBE CLEANING EQUIPMENT

Multilink Resources Ltd, Suite 18, Vermont House, Bradley Lane, Standish, Wigan, Lancashire, WN6 0XF Tel: (01257) 427053 Fax: (01257) 427053 E-mail: enquire@multilink.co.uk
Taprogge U K Ltd, Unit 6, Hurlbutt Road, Heathcote Industrial Estate, Warwick, CV34 6TD Tel: (01926) 336614 Fax: (01926) 336617 E-mail: taprogge@taprogge.co.uk

CONDENSER TUBE PROTECTIVE INSERT

Ensign Plastics Ltd, PO Box 55, Leatherhead, Surrey, KT22 7TD Tel: (01372) 377827 Fax: (01372) 377828 E-mail: sales@ensign-uk.com

CONDENSER WATER TREATMENT SHELL AND TUBE HEAT EXCHANGERS

Forsyths, Station Road, Rothes, Aberlour, Banffshire, AB38 7AD Tel: (01340) 831787 Fax: (01340) 831558 E-mail: enquiries@forsyths.com

CONDIMENT SET BLANKS

Cole & Mason Ltd, Bridge House, Eelmoor Road, Farnborough, Hampshire, GU14 7UE Tel: (01252) 522322 Fax: (01252) 522542 E-mail: customer.service@coleandmason.co.uk
T & G Woodware Ltd, Old Mill Road, Portishead, Bristol, BS20 7BX Tel: (01275) 841841 Fax: (01275) 841800 E-mail: info@tg-woodware.com

CONDITION MONITORING, *See also specific types of service*

▶ Blueprint Engineering Services Ltd, Units 1-5, 28A Wellington Road, Prenton, Merseyside, CH43 2JE Tel: 0151-652 3516 Fax: (0870) 8362181 E-mail: sales@blueprint-eng.com
Bureau Veritas, Pavilion 1 Craig Shaw Business Park, Craig Shaw Road, Tullos, Aberdeen, AB12 3AR Tel: (01224) 892100 Fax: (01224) 898437
Diagnostic Solutions Ltd, Unit 1, Rossett Business Village, Rossett, Chester, LL12 0AY Tel: (01244) 571411 Fax: (01244) 571977 E-mail: office@diagnosticsolutions.co.uk
K C M Services Ltd, Mill View, Daisy Hill, Burstwick, Hull, HU12 9HE Tel: (01482) 227953 Fax: (08456) 445547 E-mail: info@kcmservices.com
Kuwait Petroleum International Lubricants UK Ltd, Knowsthorpe Gate, Cross Green Industrial Estate, Leeds, LS9 0NP Tel: 0113-235 0555 Fax: 0113-248 5026 E-mail: marketing@q8oils.com
Rotary Equipment Services Ltd, Unit 5-6 Castle Way, Severn Bridge Industrial Estate, Portskewett, Caldicot, Gwent, NP26 5YG Tel: (01291) 420670 Fax: (01291) 430165 E-mail: sales@reslimited.com
S F R East Anglia, 22 Clements Way, Beck Row, Bury St. Edmunds, Suffolk, IP28 8AB Tel: (01638) 713758 Fax: (01638) 715541 E-mail: gary@sfrea.co.uk
T C S (UK) Limited, Penmore House, Hasland Road, Chesterfield, Derbyshire, S41 0SY Tel: (01246) 279066 Fax: (01246) 274115 E-mail: dave@tcsukltd.com

CONDITION MONITORING EQUIPMENT

Diagnostic Solutions Ltd, Unit 1, Rossett Business Village, Rossett, Chester, LL12 0AY Tel: (01244) 571411 Fax: (01244) 571977 E-mail: office@diagnosticsolutions.co.uk
Monitran Ltd, 33 Hazlemere Road, Penn, High Wycombe, Buckinghamshire, HP10 8AD Tel: (01494) 816569 Fax: (01494) 812256 E-mail: sales@monitran.co.uk
Ramac Engineering, 142 Old Shoreham Road, Hove, East Sussex, BN3 7BD Tel: (01273) 622394 Fax: (01273) 202009 E-mail: nfo@whippendell-marine.co.uk
Rotary Equipment Services Ltd, Unit 2, Expressway Business Park, Station Road, Queensferry, Deeside, Clwyd, CH5 2TF Tel: (01244) 822402 Fax: (01244) 823960 E-mail: jeff.sheen@reslimited.com
Sensonics Ltd, North Bridge Road, Berkhamsted, Hertfordshire, HP4 1EF Tel: (01442) 876833 Fax: (01442) 876477 E-mail: sales@sensonics.co.uk
System Devices Ltd Automation Di, 17 Beeston Court, Stuart Road, Manor Park, Runcorn, Cheshire, WA7 1SS Tel: (01928) 571977 Fax: (01928) 571988 E-mail: sales@systemdevices.co.uk
T C S (UK) Limited, Penmore House, Hasland Road, Chesterfield, Derbyshire, S41 0SY Tel: 01246) 279066 Fax: (01246) 274115 E-mail: dave@tcsukltd.com

CONDITION MONITORING MACHINERY AND PROCESS PLANT

▶ Blueprint Engineering Services Ltd, Units 1-5, 28A Wellington Road, Prenton, Merseyside, CH43 2JE Tel: 0151-652 3516 Fax: (0870) 8362181 E-mail: sales@blueprint-eng.com
IGE Energy Services (UK) Ltd, 2 Kelvin Close, Science Park North, Birchwood, Warrington, WA3 7BL Tel: (01925) 818504 Fax: (01925) 817819
JC Fluid Power, 5 Readmans Industrial Estate, Station Road, East Tilbury, Tilbury, Essex, RM18 8QR Tel: (01375) 843995 Fax: (01375) 859010 E-mail: info@jcfluidpower.co.uk
▶ Macom Technologies Ltd, 17 Glasgow Road, Paisley, Renfrewshire, PA1 3QS Tel: 0141-849 6287 Fax: 0141-849 6497 E-mail: info@macomtech.net

CONDOMS

▶ MyLife, PO Box 743, Bromley, BR2 7XX Tel: 07961 943896 E-mail: enquiries@mylives.co.uk

CONDOMS, LATEX

▶ MyLife, PO Box 743, Bromley, BR2 7XX Tel: 07961 943896 E-mail: enquiries@mylives.co.uk

CONDOMS, LUBRICATED

▶ MyLife, PO Box 743, Bromley, BR2 7XX Tel: 07961 943896 E-mail: enquiries@mylives.co.uk

CONDUCTIVE MATERIALS/ COATINGS

Applied Coating Technologies Ltd, Tipton Road, Tividale, Oldbury, West Midlands, B69 3HY Tel: 0121-557 5324 Fax: 0121-557 7064 E-mail: sales@applicoat.com

CONDUCTIVE PACKAGING

Vacform Group Derbyshire Ltd, Unit B1 Stainsby Close, Holmwood Industrial Estate, Holmewood, Chesterfield, Derbyshire, S42 5UG Tel: (01246) 855811 Fax: (01246) 854963 E-mail: info@vac-form.com

CONDUCTIVITY MEASURING INSTRUMENTS

A W R Instruments Ltd, 1 Northpoint Business Estate, Enterprise Close, Rochester, Kent, ME2 4LX Tel: (01634) 290751 Fax: (01634) 290295 E-mail: info@awr-instruments.com
L T H Electronics Ltd, Eltelec Works, Chaul End Lane, Luton, LU4 8EZ Tel: (01582) 593693 Fax: (01582) 598036 E-mail: sales@lth.co.uk
R F Electronics Controls Ltd, 8 Nazeing New Road, Broxbourne, Hertfordshire, EN10 6SU Tel: (01992) 460046 Fax: (01992) 442299 E-mail: sales@rfeltd.com

CONDUCTOR COMPONENTS

Fuselodge Ltd, 267 Acton Lane, Chiswick, London, W4 5DG Tel: (020) 8994 6275 Fax: (020) 8994 6275 E-mail: fuse.lodge@virgin.net

CONDUCTOR PIPE DRIVING

Franks International Ltd, Unit 1 Bessemer Way, Great Yarmouth, Norfolk, NR31 0LX Tel: (01493) 443044 Fax: (01493) 443055 E-mail: email.barrywoodhouse@franks.co.uk

CONDUCTOR PIPES, *See Conductor Pipe etc*

CONDUIT CABLES

▶ Cable Management Products Ltd, Station Road, Coleshill, Birmingham, B46 1HT Tel: (01675) 468200 E-mail: info@cm-products.com

CONDUIT FITTINGS

Jegs Electrical Ltd, 20 Progress Road, Eastwood, Leigh-On-Sea, Essex, SS9 5LW Tel: (01702) 421555 Fax: (01702) 420363 E-mail: mail@jegs.co.uk

CONE ROLLING CONTRACTORS/FABRICATORS, STEEL

Steel Technic Ltd, Mells, Frome, Somerset, BA11 3RH Tel: (01373) 813323 Fax: (01373) 813325

CONFECTIONERY

Abbey Tablet, 1 High Street, Coupar Angus, Blairgowrie, Perthshire, PH13 9DB Tel: (01828) 627695 Fax: (01828) 627695
Aunt Sandra's Candy Factory, 60 Castlereagh Road, Belfast, BT5 5FP Tel: (028) 9073 2868 Fax: (028) 9073 2868
Barnett Confectioners Ltd, Stansfield Street, Nottingham, NG7 2AE Tel: 0115-978 4642 Fax: 0115-944 9236
Baxter Murray, Unit 2 69a Aigburth Park, Belfast, BT4 1PQ Tel: (028) 9065 0209 Fax: (028) 9065 0209
Bay Tree Candies, Unit 1f Barbican Rise Industrial Estate, Looe, Cornwall, PL13 1QQ Tel: (01503) 262413 Fax: (01503) 262413 E-mail: baytreecandies@btconnect.com
Big Bear Ltd, Fox'S Confectionery, Sunningdale Road, Braunstone, Leicester, LE3 1UE Tel: 0116-287 3561 Fax: 0116-232 0117 E-mail: info@foxs.co.uk
▶ Bon Bons Office, 17 Sandbeck Park, Sandbeck Lane, Wetherby, West Yorkshire, LS22 7TW Tel: (01937) 584600 Fax: (01937) 584600 E-mail: info@bonbon.co.uk
Booja Booja Company Ltd, Howe Pits, Norwich Road, Brooke, Norwich, NR15 1HJ Tel: (01508) 558888 Fax: (01508) 557844 E-mail: info@boojaboojj.com
Elizabeth Botham & Sons, 35-39 Skinner Street, Whitby, North Yorkshire, YO21 3AH Tel: (01947) 602823 Fax: (01947) 820269
British Bakeries Ltd, 783 Duke Street, Glasgow, G31 1LL Tel: 0141-556 5211 Fax: 0141-554 3508
Browne's Chocolates, Throwleigh, Okehampton, Devon, EX20 2HX Tel: (0845) 4560568 Fax: (01647) 231289 E-mail: sales@brownes.co.uk
Butties, 657 Ashton New Road, Manchester, M11 4QJ Tel: 0161-220 8000
Bysel Ltd, Selby House, 27a Batley Road, Heckmondwike, West Yorkshire, WF16 9ND Tel: (01924) 403857 Fax: (01924) 405368 E-mail: export@byselcandy.com
Cadbury Schweppes P.L.C., 25 Berkeley Square, London, W1J 6HB Tel: (020) 7409 1313 Fax: (020) 7830 5200 E-mail: info@cadburyschweppes.com
Cadbury Trebor Bassett Ltd, PO Box 12, Birmingham, B30 2LU Tel: 0121-458 2000 Fax: 0121-451 4139
Cadbury Trebor Bassett Ltd, PO Box 12, Birmingham, B30 2LU Tel: 0121-458 2000 Fax: 0121-451 4139
▶ Candagrove Ltd, Regent Road, Great Yarmouth, Norfolk, NR30 2AS Tel: (01493) 844676 Fax: (01493) 858381 E-mail: candagrove@btconnect.com
▶ Candy Designer, The Candy & Chocolate Factory, Hawthorn Road, Skegness, Lincolnshire, PE25 3TD Tel: 01754 896667 E-mail: info@candydesigner.co.uk
▶ Carousel, Unit 17-18 The Metropolitan Centre, Derby Road, Greenford, Middlesex, UB6 8UJ Tel: (020) 8575 9090 Fax: (020) 8575 3900
Casemir Chocolates UK Ltd, 5a Tetherdown, London, N10 1ND Tel: (020) 8365 2132 E-mail: info@casemirchocolates.co.uk
▶ Cheddar Chocolate Co., 3 Saxon Place, Station Road, Cheddar, Somerset, BS27 3AG Tel: (01934) 741777 Fax: (01934) 741666
▶ Chocolate Factory Hutton Le Hole, Chocolate Factory, Hutton-le-Hole, York, YO62 6UA Tel: (01751) 417084 E-mail: sales@the-chocolate-factory.co.uk
▶ Chocolate Graphics, Hawthorn Road, Skegness, Lincolnshire, PE25 3TD Tel: (01754) 896668 Fax: (01754) 896668 E-mail: info@chocolategraphics.co.uk
▶ Clarks Home Bakery Ltd, Algernon Industrial Estate, New York Road, Shiremoor, Newcastle upon Tyne, NE27 0NB Tel: 0191-251 3772 Fax: 0191-251 3772
▶ Coco Aura, Unit 5 Quayside Business Centre, Lowestoft Enterprise Park, Lowestoft, Suffolk, NR33 9NW Tel: (01502) 500520
Cocoa Tree, Chillington, Kingsbridge, Devon, TQ7 2LA Tel: (01548) 580009 Fax: (01548) 580009
▶ Cocoda, 61 London Road, Woolmer Green, Knebworth, Herts, SG3 6JE Tel: 01438 810999 Fax: 01438 817193 E-mail: mail@cocoda.biz
Cooplands (Doncaster) Ltd, Victoria Mill Business Park, Wharf Road Wheatley, Doncaster, South Yorkshire, DN1 2SX Tel: (01302) 361333 Fax: (01302) 329776 E-mail: info@cooplands.co.uk
Crilco Confections Ltd, 15 Flagstaff Road, Cloughoge, Newry, County Down, BT35 8NR Tel: (028) 3026 4877 Fax: (028) 3025 6311 E-mail: crilco@utinternet.com
Derwent Lynton Co. Ltd, Siddals Road, Derby, DE1 2QD Tel: (01332) 365121 Fax: (01332) 343173 E-mail: info@derwentlynton.co.uk
Devonshire Made, 6 Bitton Park Road, Teignmouth, Devon, TQ14 9BU Tel: (01626) 776893
Devonvale Ltd, 2 Duchy Road, Heathpark Industrial Estate, Honiton, Devon, EX14 1YD Tel: (01404) 549980 Fax: (01404) 549981 E-mail: enquiries@devonvale.com
Donaldsons Of St Andrews Ltd, 21 Crossgate, Cupar, Fife, KY15 5HA Tel: (01334) 656433 Fax: (01334) 653729
Dovedale Confectionery Ltd, Vernon St Industrial Estate, Shirebrook, Mansfield, Nottinghamshire, NG20 8SS Tel: (01623) 742277 Fax: (01623) 743020 E-mail: dovedale@o2.co.uk
Durga Sweets, 173-175 Ilford Lane, Ilford, Essex, IG1 2RT Tel: (020) 8478 3466 Fax: (020) 8514 7280
▶ Ekhaya Foods Ltd, 66 Potters Lane, Send, Woking, Surrey, GU23 7AL Tel: (01483) 773534 E-mail: info@ekhayafoods.co.uk
▶ Favouritesweetshop.co.uk, 10 Castle Drive, Kemsing, Sevenoaks, Kent, TN15 6RL Tel: 01732 760480 E-mail: info@favouritesweetshop.co.uk
Finishing Touches, 4 North Erskine Park, Bearsden, Glasgow, G61 4LZ Tel: 0141-942 2226 Fax: 0141-943 9103
Fletchers Bakeries Ltd, Claywheels Lane, Sheffield, S6 1LY Tel: 0114-234 8171 Fax: 0114-232 4987 E-mail: enquiries@fletchers.co.uk
▶ The Food & Packaging Company, 84 Tenter Road, Moulton Park, Northampton, NN3 6AX Tel: 01604 493020 Fax: 01604 492228 E-mail: info@thefandp.com
▶ Forever Foods, Unit 7-8 Leeway House, Leeway Industrial Estate, Newport, Gwent, NP19 4SL Tel: (01633) 281777 Fax: (01633) 280651
Lauries Galloway Tablet, 3 Station Road, Dalbeattie, Kirkcudbrightshire, DG5 4AN Tel: (01556) 610731
▶ Giles & Posner Ltd, Victor Works, Barnet Road, St. Albans, Hertfordshire, AL2 1BQ Tel: (01727) 826262 Fax: (01727) 828285 E-mail: sales@giles-posne.com
▶ Godiva Confectionery Mnfrs, 141 Regent Street, London, W1B 4JA Tel: (020) 7734 8113 Fax: (020) 7287 2518

CONFECTIONERY – *continued*

Gregton Confectionery Ltd, Wantz Road, Dagenham, Essex, RM10 8PR Tel: (020) 8984 8811 E-mail: sales@gregtons.freeserve.co.uk

Hadleigh Maid Ltd, 35-37 George Street, Hadleigh, Ipswich, IP7 5BD Tel: (01473) 822305 Fax: (01473) 824654 E-mail: sales@hadleighmaid.co.uk

Halo Foods Ltd, Pendre Industrial Estate, Tywyn, Gwynedd, LL36 9LW Tel: (01654) 711171 Fax: (01654) 711744 E-mail: sales@halofoods.co.uk

Heritage Chocolates Ltd, Unit 17, 1-21 Carew Street, London, SE5 9DF Tel: (020) 7733 7268 Fax: (020) 7274 0151

Holdsworth Chocolate Ltd, Station Road, Bakewell, Derbyshire, DE45 1GE Tel: (01629) 813573 Fax: (01629) 813850 E-mail: info@holdsworthchocolates.co.uk

Holdsworths, 91-93 St. James Mill Road, St. James Business Park, Northampton, NN5 5JP Tel: (01604) 581411 Fax: (01604) 581864

House Of Dorchester, Unit 10 Alton Business Centre, Omega Park, Alton, Hampshire, GU34 2YU Tel: (01420) 84181 Fax: (01420) 543047 E-mail: sales@hotchoc.com

House Of York, Norham Road, North Shields, Tyne & Wear, NE29 7UN Tel: 0191-257 0101 Fax: 0191-258 6649

▶ Household Essentials, 25 Amberley Close, Littlehampton, West Sussex, BN17 6HW Tel: 01903 714355 E-mail: enq@household-essentials.co.uk

J E Wilson & Sons Kendal Ltd, The Mint Cake Works, Cross Lane, Kendal, Cumbria, LA9 5LB Tel: (01539) 720279 Fax: (01539) 730109 E-mail: sales@creativeconfectionery.co.uk

Jackson Evans Ltd, 9 Market St, Rhyl, Clwyd, LL18 1RL Tel: (01745) 331257

John Farrah & Harrogate Toffee, Camwal Road, Harrogate, North Yorkshire, HG1 4PY Tel: (01423) 883000 Fax: (01423) 883029 E-mail: sales@farrahs.com

Kennedys Fine Chocolates Ltd, The Old School, Orton, Penrith, Cumbria, CA10 3RU Tel: (01539) 624781 Fax: (01539) 624781 E-mail: kennedys.chocolates@btinternet.com

La Baguette, 17 Picardy Street, Belvedere, Kent, DA17 5QQ Tel: (020) 8311 1113 Fax: (020) 8310 5179

Lansdowne Bakery, 16 Lansdown Road, Bude, Cornwall, EX23 8BH Tel: (01288) 352777 Fax: (01288) 352777

▶ Leaf (U K) Ltd, 66 Virginia St, Southport, Merseyside, PR8 6RX Tel: (01704) 502400

Lees Of Scotland Ltd, North Caldeen Road, Coatbridge, Lanarkshire, ML5 4EF Tel: (01236) 441600 Fax: (01236) 441601 E-mail: sales@leesofscotland.co.uk

Lofthouse Of Fleetwood Ltd, Maritime Street, Fleetwood, Lancashire, FY7 7LP Tel: (01253) 872435 Fax: (01253) 778725 E-mail: sales@fishermansfriend.com

Luckshmee Ltd, Woodside End, Wembley, Middlesex, HA0 1UR Tel: (020) 8900 1990 Fax: (020) 8900 9890

Mcadams Confectionery, Unit 15 Cocker Trading Estate, Cocker Street, Blackpool, FY1 2EP Tel: (01253) 296516 Fax: (01253) 296516

Mcallister's Confectionery Products, Unit 14 Thistle Business Pk, Ayr Rd, Cumnock, Ayrshire, KA18 1EQ Tel: 01290 426464

Mackays Ltd, James Chalmers Road Kirkton Indust Estate, Kirkton Industrial Estate, Arbroath, Angus, DD11 3LR Tel: (01241) 432500 Fax: (01241) 432444 E-mail: info@mackays.com

Manor Bakeries Ltd, 110 Reeds Lane, Wirral, Merseyside, CH46 1PR Tel: 0151-488 4800 Fax: 0151-488 4809 E-mail: cristianname.surname@manor-bakeries.co.uk

Marasu's Petits Fours Ltd, 8 Powergate Business Park, Volt Avenue, London, NW10 6PW Tel: (020) 8961 3399 Fax: (020) 8963 0088 E-mail: sales@marasu.co.uk

▶ Maxilin Ltd, Sharples Vale, Bolton, BL1 6NR Tel: (01204) 309111 Fax: (01204) 596596

▶ Mazza Confectionery, Unit 1a Cranleigh Gardens Industrial Estate, Southall, Middlesex, UB1 2BZ Tel: (020) 8571 6272 Fax: (020) 8571 6281 E-mail: mazzaconf@aol.com

▶ Michton, Kingsway, Fforestfach, Swansea, SA5 4HD Tel: (01792) 561617 Fax: (01792) 561619 E-mail: sales@michton.com

▶ Minerva Chocolates, 14 Cheap Street, Bath, BA1 1NA Tel: (01225) 464999 Fax: (01225) 464793

Mushtaq Sweet Centre, 143 Lozells Road, Birmingham, B19 2TP Tel: 0121-507 0732 Fax: 0121-258 2339

Mushtaq Sweet Centre, 102 Alum Rock Road, Birmingham, B8 1HU Tel: 0121-328 3837 Fax: 0121-258 2339

Nestle Rowntree UK Ltd, Rowan Drive, Newcastle upon Tyne, NE3 3TR Tel: 0191-202 4200 Fax: 0191-202 4300

Nestle UK Ltd, Nestle Rowntree Division, Albion Mills, Halifax, West Yorkshire, HX3 9XT Tel: (01422) 862286 Fax: (01422) 862233

Norba (UK) Ltd, 14-16 Thomas Road, Wooburn Industrial Park, Wooburn Green, High Wycombe, Buckinghamshire, HP10 0PE Tel: (01628) 535900 Fax: (01628) 530381 E-mail: sales@norbauk.com

▶ Park Cake, Bakewell Works, Duckworth Street, Bolton, BL3 4DY Tel: (01204) 61226 Fax: (01204) 660666

▶ Promotional Candy Co., 9 Burton Road, Blackpool, FY4 4NW Tel: (01253) 698298 Fax: (01253) 698600 E-mail: sales@promotionalcandy.com

R G Watts, Norville Steam Bakery, The Causeway, Mark, Highbridge, Somerset, TA9 4PX Tel: (01278) 788154

Rascal Confectionery Ltd, Samal House, Loxford Road, Barking, Essex, IG11 8PU Tel: (020) 8594 1122 Fax: (020) 8594 3645 E-mail: sales@rascal-chocolate.com

The Rock Factory, The Rock Factory, Back of Keswick Road, Blackpool, FY1 5PB Tel: (01253) 296554 Fax: (01253) 292745

George Romney Ltd, Mintsfeet Road North, Kendal, Cumbria, LA9 6NA Tel: (01539) 720155 Fax: (01539) 720155 E-mail: sales@kendal.mintcake.co.uk

▶ Rumseys Chocolaterie, 26 High Street, Wendover, Aylesbury, Buckinghamshire, HP22 6EA Tel: (01296) 625060 Fax: (01296) 625060 E-mail: sales@rumseys.co.uk

Sanitary San Francisco Fudge Factory, 6 Church Street, Bath, BA1 1NL Tel: (01225) 425714 Fax: (01225) 332031 E-mail: sales@sanfranciscofudge.co.uk

Scottish Confectionery Co., Unit 18 South Parks Industrial Estate, Peebles, EH45 9ED Tel: (01721) 723691 Fax: 01721 723691

▶ Shetland Fudge, 11 Harbour Street, Lerwick, Shetland, ZE1 0LR Tel: (01595) 694324 Fax: (01595) 694324

Southern Confectioners, 9 East Howe Lane, Bournemouth, BH10 5HX Tel: (01202) 581126 Fax: (01202) 582025

Stockley Sweets Ltd, Moscow Mill, Colliers St, Oswaldtwistle, Accrington, Lancashire, BB5 3DF Tel: (01254) 232807 Fax: (01254) 382220

Sunray Home Bakery, Carnbane Industrial Estate, Newry, County Down, BT35 6EF Tel: (028) 3026 2614

Sweet Thoughts, Hawthorn Road, Skegness, Lincolnshire, PE25 3TD Tel: (01754) 896667 E-mail: info@sweetthoughts.co.uk

Sweets For U, Unit 9, Bradley Hall Trading Estate, Bradley Lane, Standish, Wigan, Lancashire, WN6 0XQ Tel: (01257) 400780 E-mail: julierose_4@hotmail.com

Tangerine Confectionery Ltd, Clifton Road, Blackpool, FY4 4QB Tel: (01253) 761201 Fax: (01253) 792006

Thorntons plc, Head Office, Thornton Park, Somercotes, Alfreton, Derbyshire, DE55 4XJ Tel: (01773) 540550 Fax: (01773) 540757 E-mail: tplccustserve@thorntons.co.uk

▶ Tilleys Sweets Ltd, Springfield, Oundle Road, Thrapston, Kettering, Northamptonshire, NN14 4PQ Tel: (01832) 732151

▶ Tom Hannah Agencies Ltd, Walkinshaw Works, Walkinshaw Street, Johnstone, Renfrewshire, PA5 8AB Tel: (01505) 321131 Fax: (01505) 329281 E-mail: sales@hannahssweets.co.uk

Trebor Bassett Ltd, Monkhills Works, Ferrybridge Road, Pontefract, West Yorkshire, WF8 2JS Tel: (01977) 701431 Fax: (01977) 705491

Walkers Chocolate Emporium, 6 High Street, Ilfracombe, Devon, EX34 9DF Tel: (01271) 867193

Whitakers Chocolates Skipton Ltd, 85 Keighley Road, Skipton, North Yorkshire, BD23 2NA Tel: (01756) 792531 Fax: (01756) 700225 E-mail: sales@whitakerschocolates.com

Sid Wilson (Newcastle) Ltd, 3-5 Tundry Way, Chainbridge Road Industrial Estate, Blaydon-On-Tyne, Tyne & Wear, NE21 5SJ Tel: 0191-414 3344 Fax: 0191-414 5962 E-mail: sidwilsonsweets@aol.com

Winterbotham,Darby & Co.Limited, Granville House Gatton Park, Business Centre, Redhill, RH1 3AS Tel: (01737) 646646 Fax: (01737) 646600 E-mail: wdarby@windar.co.uk

CONFECTIONERY COATINGS

Sweets For U, Unit 9, Bradley Hall Trading Estate, Bradley Lane, Standish, Wigan, Lancashire, WN6 0XQ Tel: (01257) 400780 E-mail: julierose_4@hotmail.com

CONFECTIONERY DISPLAY CABINETS

Idea Systems UK Ltd, 2 Whiting Street, Sheffield, S8 9QR Tel: 0114-258 3155 Fax: 0114-255 4465 E-mail: info@idea-systems.co.uk

CONFECTIONERY MACHINERY/ EQUIPMENT MAINTENANCE/ REPAIR SERVICES

Cadbury Ltd, Somerdale, Keynsham, Bristol, BS31 2AU Tel: 0117-986 1789 Fax: 0117-937 6590

Guiseley Engineering Co. Ltd, Hallam Street, Guiseley, Leeds, LS20 8AG Tel: (01943) 874512 Fax: (01943) 879361 E-mail: sales@guiseley-eng.co.uk

CONFECTIONERY PRODUCTION PLANT/EQUIPMENT

A M P Rose, Heapham Road, Gainsborough, Lincolnshire, DN21 1QU Tel: (01427) 611969 Fax: (01427) 616854 E-mail: admin@amp-rose.com

Big Bear Ltd, Fox'S Confectionery, Sunningdale Road, Braunstone, Leicester, LE3 1UE Tel: 0116-287 3561 Fax: 0116-232 0117 E-mail: info@foxs.co.uk

Chemtech International Ltd, 448 Basingstoke Road, Reading, RG2 0LP Tel: 0118-986 1222 Fax: 0118-986 0028 E-mail: sales@chemtechinternational.com

Coates Engineering International Ltd, Millfold, Whitworth, Rochdale, Lancashire, OL12 8DN Tel: (01706) 852122 Fax: (01706) 853629 E-mail: info@bchltd.com

Clifford Coupe Ltd, 1 Royal Close, Worcester Park, Surrey, KT4 7JS Tel: (020) 8330 0660 Fax: (020) 8330 0660

Guiseley Engineering Co. Ltd, Hallam Street, Guiseley, Leeds, LS20 8AG Tel: (01943) 874512 Fax: (01943) 879361 E-mail: sales@guiseley-eng.co.uk

New Paradigm Consultants Ltd, Walthams, Chart Road, Sutton Valence, Maidstone, Kent, ME17 3AW Tel: (01622) 844333 Fax: (01622) 844999

Robinsons, Charlton House East Service Road, Raynesway, Spondon, Derby, DE21 7BF Tel: (01332) 679898 Fax: (01332) 671717 E-mail: tony@wsrobinson.com

Signs 2000, Unit 4 Kenworthy Road, Stafford, ST16 3DY Tel: (01785) 220561 Fax: (01785) 220969 E-mail: admin@signs2k.co.uk

CONFECTIONERY PRODUCTION PLANT/EQUIPMENT SPARE PARTS/WEARING PARTS

Clifford Coupe Ltd, 1 Royal Close, Worcester Park, Surrey, KT4 7JS Tel: (020) 8330 0660 Fax: (020) 8330 0660

Guiseley Engineering Co. Ltd, Hallam Street, Guiseley, Leeds, LS20 8AG Tel: (01943) 874512 Fax: (01943) 879361 E-mail: sales@guiseley-eng.co.uk

CONFECTIONERY WRAPPING MACHINES/EQUIPMENT

A M P Rose, Heapham Road, Gainsborough, Lincolnshire, DN21 1QU Tel: (01427) 611969 Fax: (01427) 616854 E-mail: admin@amp-rose.com

CONFECTIONERY WRAPPING MACHINES/EQUIPMENT, RECONDITIONED

Galley-Pak, Galley-Pak House, 38 Greenfields, Shillington, Hitchin, Hertfordshire, SG5 3NX Tel: (01462) 711545 Fax: (01462) 712970 E-mail: john@galley-pak.com

CONFECTIONERY WRAPPINGS

▶ Chocolate Graphics, Hawthorn Road, Skegness, Lincolnshire, PE25 3TD Tel: (01754) 896668 Fax: (01754) 896668 E-mail: info@chocolategraphics.co.uk

Frith's Flexible Packaging Ltd, 1 The Forum Coopers Way, Temple Farm Industrial Estate, Southend-on-Sea, SS2 5TE Tel: (01702) 462605 Fax: (01702) 616954 E-mail: sales@friths.co.uk

CONFERENCE AUDIO VISUAL PRODUCTION SERVICES

▶ 3DAV - video by numbers, Studio 2-11, Parkers House, 48 Regents Street, Cambridge, CB2 1FD Tel: 01223 505600 E-mail: jamie@3dav.com

▶ Avc Productions Ltd, 106 Kings Road, Brighton, BN1 2FU Tel: (01273) 746555 Fax: (01273) 746447 E-mail: sales@avcworld.com

Brahler Ics UK Ltd, Unit 2 The Business Centre, Church End, Cambridge, CB1 3LB Tel: (01223) 411601 Fax: (01223) 411602 E-mail: info@brahler-ics.co.uk

Cass Productions Ltd, The Point, Leigh Road, Eastleigh, Hampshire, SO50 9DE Tel: (023) 8065 2220 Fax: (023) 8065 2220 E-mail: sales@cassproductions.co.uk

▶ Conference Organisers & Event Management, Exhibition House, London Road, Macclesfield, Cheshire, SK11 7QX Tel: 0870 242 2305 Fax: (01625) 611699 E-mail: info@conference-event.co.uk

Forward Vision Solutions, 156 London Road, Ruscombe, Reading, RG10 9HJ Tel: 0118-932 0890 Fax: 0118-932 0891 E-mail: info@avspecialists.co.uk

Hammonds A V S Ltd, 34 -36 Oak End Way, Gerrards Cross, Buckinghamshire, SL9 8BR Tel: (01923) 239733 Fax: (01753) 887163

I T M A B Ltd, Unit 2 Rushtons Farm Estate, Warren House Road, Wokingham, Berkshire, RG40 5RE Tel: 0118-977 5977 Fax: 0118-977 5624

Lightsource Data Presentations, Fox Studio, King Street, Much Wenlock, Shropshire, TF13 6BL Tel: (01952) 727715 Fax: (0870) 4204316 E-mail: lights@lightsource.co.uk

▶ Mills Media Limited, 2 Morpeth Wharf, Twelve Quays, Wirral, Merseyside, CH41 1LF Tel: 0151 649 3600 Fax: 0151 649 3700 E-mail: norman@millsmediagroup.com

Moxhams Ltd, 56-56a Portswood Road, Southampton, SO17 2FW Tel: (023) 8055 6644 Fax: (023) 8067 1667 E-mail: john@moxhams.co.uk

▶ Paragon Europe Ltd, The Island, Wey Meadows, Weybridge, Surrey, KT13 8XY Tel: 0870 224 2644 E-mail: val@paragoneurope.com

Preview Productions Ltd, The Old Dairy Manor Farm, Hermitage, Thatcham, Berkshire, RG18 9SD Tel: (01635) 202972 Fax: (01635) 202973

▶ S L V, The Barn, Fifield Farm, Marslton Road, Marlston Hermitage, Thatcham, Berkshire, RG18 9UN Tel: (01635) 202500 Fax: (01635) 202088 E-mail: Info@s-l-v.co.uk

▶ Scorpion Event Production, Castle Lane, Ripponden, Sowerby Bridge, West Yorkshire, HX6 4JZ Tel: (01422) 823399 E-mail: chris.smith@scorpion-events.co.uk

▶ Spike Events Ltd, 419 London Road, Hemel Hempstead, Herts, HP3 9BD Tel: 01442 261851 Fax: 01442 397138 E-mail: info@spikeevents.co.uk

Stagecraft Ltd, Ashfield Trading Estate, Salisbury, SP2 7HL Tel: (01722) 326055 Fax: (01722) 414076 E-mail: myran@stagecraft.co.uk

CONFERENCE AUDIO/VISUAL EQUIPMENT HIRE

Auditel Ltd, 2 Devonport Vernon Trading Estate, Cock Lane, High Wycombe, Buckinghamshire, HP13 7DE Tel: (01494) 465335 Fax: (01494) 446013 E-mail: sales@auditel.ltd.uk

B B M Audio Visual Specialists Ltd, Studio 2, Northbrook, Mitcheldever, Winchester, Hampshire, SO21 3AJ Tel: (01962) 774857 Fax: (01962) 774144 E-mail: audiovisual.bbm@btinternet.com

Brahler Ics UK Ltd, Unit 2 The Business Centre, Church End, Cambridge, CB1 3LB Tel: (01223) 411601 Fax: (01223) 411602 E-mail: info@brahler-ics.co.uk

D & D Conference & Event Management Ltd, 66a High Street, Egham, Surrey, TW20 9EY Tel: (01784) 432233 Fax: (01784) 430088 E-mail: dd@ddconfrence.com

▶ Hire Intelligence Southwest England - Exeter, 40 Southernhay East, Exeter, EX1 1PE Tel: (0800) 0857667 Fax: (0870) 2202752 E-mail: sales@hiresouthwest.co.uk

Key Audio Visual Services, Black Tower Studios, 15 Bracondale, Norwich, NR1 2AL Tel: (01603) 616661 Fax: (01603) 616668 E-mail: sales@keyav.com

▶ MAN Audio Services, Catherine Court Farm, Coppershell, Gastard, Corsham, Wiltshire, SN13 9PZ Tel: (01249) 701363 Fax: (01249) 701236 E-mail: matt@manaudio.co.uk

▶ Newland Corperate Communications, 34 Blackstone Court, Blaydon-on-Tyne, Tyne & Wear, NE21 4HH Tel: 0191-256 6000 Fax: 0191-256 6056 E-mail: hire@newlandcc.co.uk

Pedler Robin, Empire Buildings, 47-49 Church Street, Stoke-on-Trent, ST4 1DQ Tel: (01782) 749749 Fax: (01782) 747840 E-mail: sales@sgbworldservice.com

Picture Perfect Audio Visuals Ltd, AV House, Wallingford Road, Uxbridge, Middlesex, UB8 2RW Tel: (01895) 454 650 Fax: (01895) 454 657 E-mail: enquiries@ppav.co.uk

Rapport Presentations, The Wheel House, Raypark Road, Maidenhead, Berkshire, SL6 8QU Tel: (01628) 770474

Spyx Audio Equipment, 36 Shaftesbury Road, Coventry, CV5 6FN Tel: (024) 7667 7896 Fax: (024) 7667 7896 E-mail: spyx@btinternet.com

Tapestry Audio Visual, Nordic House, Baltic Quay, Grangemouth, Stirlingshire, FK3 8TX Tel: (0845) 2308999 Fax: (01324) 489349 E-mail: sales@tapestryav.net

CONFERENCE CENTRES/HALLS/ ROOMS/SUITES

Abbey Lodge Hotel, 38 Belfast Road, Downpatrick, County Down, BT30 9AU Tel: (028) 4461 4511 Fax: (028) 4461 6415

Aberdeen Exhibition & Conference Centre, Exhibition Avenue, Bridge of Don, Aberdeen, AB23 8BL Tel: (01224) 824824 Fax: (01224) 825276 E-mail: aecc@aecc.co.uk

Abernant Lake Hotel, Station Road, Llanwrtyd Wells, Powys, LD5 4RR Tel: (01591) 610250 Fax: (01591) 610684

Alexandra Palace, Alexandra Palace Way, London, N22 7AY Tel: (020) 8365 2121 Fax: (020) 8883 3999 E-mail: sales@alexandrapalace.com

Angus Hotel, 46 Wellmeadow, Blairgowrie, Perthshire, PH10 6NH Tel: (01250) 872455 Fax: (01250) 875615 E-mail: reservations@theangushotel.com

Avant Hotel, Windsor Road, Oldham, OL8 4AS Tel: 0161-627 5500 Fax: 0161-627 5896 E-mail: avant@menzies-hotels.co.uk

Aviemore Highlands Resort, Aviemore Centre, Aviemore, Inverness-Shire, PH22 1PN Tel: (01479) 815100 Fax: (01479) 811478 E-mail: info@aviemorehighlandsresort.com

CONFERENCE CENTRES/HALLS/ ROOMS/SUITES – *continued*

Balmer Lawn Hotel, Lyndhurst Road, Brockenhurst, Hampshire, SO42 7ZB Tel: (01590) 623116 Fax: (01590) 623864 E-mail: blh@btinternet.com

Barbican Centre, Silk Street, Barbican, London, EC2Y 8DS Tel: (020) 7382 7043 Fax: (020) 7382 7237 E-mail: admin@barbican.org.uk

Bear Ramada Jarvis, 41 Charnham Street, Hungerford, Berkshire, RG17 0EL Tel: (01488) 682512 Fax: (01488) 684357 E-mail: enquiries@jarvishotels.co.uk

Berystede Hotel, Bagshot Road, Ascot, Berks, SL5 9JH Tel: (01344) 623311 Fax: (01344) 872301

Best Western Mount Sorrel, Porthkerry Road, Barry, South Glamorgan, CF62 7XY Tel: (01446) 740069 Fax: (01446) 746600 E-mail: reservations@mountsorrel.co.uk

Birch Hotel, Lewes Road, Haywards Heath, West Sussex, RH17 7SF Tel: (01444) 451565 Fax: (01444) 440109 E-mail: sales@birchhotel.co.uk

The Bolholt Hotel, Walshaw Road, Bury, Lancashire, BL8 1PU Tel: 0161-762 4000 Fax: 0161-762 4100 E-mail: sales@bolholt.co.uk

Bowburn Hall Hotel, Ramside Estates, Bowburn, Durham, DH6 5NH Tel: 0191-377 0311 Fax: 0191-377 3459 E-mail: info@bowburnhallhotel.co.uk

Brambletye Hotel, Lewes Road, Forest Row, East Sussex, RH18 5EZ Tel: (01342) 824144 Fax: (01342) 824833 E-mail: brambletye.hotel@fullers.co.uk

Brighton Centre, Kings Road, Brighton, BN1 2GR Tel: (01273) 290131 Fax: (01273) 779980 E-mail: info@brightoncentre.co.uk

Brighton Festival Society Ltd, 29 New Road, Brighton, BN1 1UG Tel: (01273) 700747 Fax: (01273) 707505 E-mail: info@brighton-festival.org.com

Britainia Hotels Wigan, Almond Brook Road, Standish, Wigan, Lancashire, WN6 0SR Tel: (01257) 499988 Fax: (01257) 427327

Brittania Leeds Bradford Airport, Leeds Road, Bramhope, Leeds, LS16 9JJ Tel: 0113-284 3966 Fax: (0845) 8385552

Brocket Hall Ltd, Brocket Hall, Brocket Park, Lemsford, Welwyn Garden City, Hertfordshire, AL8 7XG Tel: (01707) 335241 Fax: (01707) 375166 E-mail: mail@brocket-hall.co.uk

Burford Bridge Hotel, London Road, Mickleham, Dorking, Surrey, RH5 6BX Tel: (01306) 884561 Fax: (01306) 880386

Business Design Centre Ltd, 52 Upper Street, London, N1 0QH Tel: (020) 7359 3535 Fax: (020) 7226 0590

Cabarfeidh Hotel, Perceval Road South, Stornoway, Isle of Lewis, HS1 2EU Tel: (01851) 702604 Fax: (01851) 705572 E-mail: cabarfeidh@calahotels.com

Cannizaro House, West Side Common, London, SW19 4UE Tel: (0870) 3339124 Fax: (0870) 3339224 E-mail: sales@cannizarohouse.co.uk

Cardiff International Arena, Mary Ann Street, Cardiff, CF10 2EQ Tel: (029) 2022 4488 Fax: (029) 2023 4501 E-mail: cia.sales@clearchannel.co.uk

Castle Ashby House, Castle Ashby, Northampton, NN7 1LQ Tel: (01604) 696696 Fax: (01604) 696516 E-mail: admin@castleashby.co.uk

The Cavendish, 81 Jermyn Street, London, SW1Y 6JF Tel: (020) 7930 2111 Fax: (020) 7839 2125

Chaucer Hotel, Chantry House, 63 Ivy Lane, Canterbury, Kent, CT1 1TU Tel: (01227) 464427 Fax: (01227) 450397 E-mail: sales@heritage-hotel.com

Chilworth Manor Ltd, Chilworth Manor, Chilworth, Southampton, SO16 7PT Tel: (023) 8076 7333 Fax: (023) 8070 1743 E-mail: general@chilworth-manor.co.uk

City Conference Centre, 80 Coleman Street, London, EC2R 5BJ Tel: (020) 7382 2626 Fax: (020) 7382 2670 E-mail: info@cityconferencecentre.com

Cliff Hotel, Cliff Hill, Gorleston, Great Yarmouth, Norfolk, NR31 6DH Tel: (01493) 662179 Fax: (01493) 653617 E-mail: cliffhotel@aol.com

Cliveden House, Taplow, Maidenhead, Berkshire, SL6 0JF Tel: (01628) 668561 Fax: (01628) 661837 E-mail: reservations@clivedenhouse.co.uk

Complete Event Solutions, Lymington Bottom Road, Four Marks, Alton, Hampshire, GU34 5DL Tel: (01420) 561105 Fax: (01420) 561105 E-mail: info@completeeventsolutions.com

Conference Centre, Lancaster University, Boland Avenue, Lancaster, LA1 4YT Tel: (01524) 592444 Fax: (01524) 843695 E-mail: conferenceoffice@lancaster.ac.uk

Congress Centre, Congress House, 23-28 Great Russell Street, London, WC1B 3LS Tel: (020) 7467 1200 Fax: (020) 7467 1313 E-mail: congress.centre@tuc.org.uk

Copthorne Hotel Manchester, Clippers Quay, Salford, M50 3SN Tel: 0161-873 7321 Fax: 0161-873 7318 E-mail: manchester@mill-cop.com

Corner House Hotel, 78 High Street, Annan, Dumfriesshire, DG12 6DL Tel: (01461) 202754 Fax: (01461) 202193 E-mail: corner.house@btconnect.com

Corus Hotels Bristol, Beggar Bush Lane, Failand, Bristol, BS8 3TG Tel: (01275) 393901 Fax: (01275) 392104 E-mail: meetings.bristol@corushotels.com

County Conference & Banqueting Centre, Meadow Lane, Nottingham, NG2 3HJ Tel: 0115-955 7222 Fax: 0115-955 7238 E-mail: candb@nottscountysc.co.uk

The Court Hotel Bromley Ltd, Bromley Hill, Bromley, BR1 4JD Tel: (020) 8464 5011 Fax: (020) 8460 0899 E-mail: enquireys@bromleycourt.co.uk

Crieff Hydro Hotel, Sand Tower Road, Crieff, Perthshire, PH7 3LQ Tel: (01764) 655555 Fax: (01764) 653087

Crowne Plaza Manchester Airport, Ringway Road, Manchester Airport, Manchester, M90 3NS Tel: (0870) 4009055 Fax: 0161-436 2340 E-mail: manchesterairport@6c.com

The Cumberland Hotel, Great Cumberland Place, Marble Art, London, W1A 4RF Tel: (020) 7262 1234 Fax: (0870) 3339281 E-mail: enquiries@thecumberland.co.uk

D & D Conference & Event Management Ltd, 66a High Street, Egham, Surrey, TW20 9EY Tel: (01784) 432233 Fax: (01784) 430088 E-mail: dd@ddconfrence.com

Days Inn, Port Road, Rhoose, Barry, South Glamorgan, CF62 3BT Tel: (01446) 710787 Fax: (01446) 719318

De Vere Belton Woods, Belton, Grantham, Lincolnshire, NG32 2LN Tel: (01476) 593200 Fax: (01476) 574547 E-mail: belton.woods@belvere-hotels.com

De Vere Daresbury Park Hotel, Daresbury, Warrington, WA4 4BB Tel: (01925) 267331 Fax: (01925) 601496

De Vere Venues Ltd, Wokefield Park, Mortimer, Reading, RG7 3AE Tel: 0118-933 4000 Fax: 0118-9334001

Dunkenhalgh Hotel, Blackburn Road, Clayton Le Moors, Accrington, Lancashire, BB5 5JP Tel: (01254) 398021 Fax: (01254) 872230 E-mail: reception.dunkenhalgh@mcdonald-hotels.co.uk

Earls Court & Olympia Group Ltd, Exhibition Centre, Warwick Road, London, SW5 9TA Tel: (020) 7370 8078 Fax: (020) 7370 8390 E-mail: sales@eco.co.uk

Eastbourne Borough Council, Town Hall, Grove Road, Eastbourne, East Sussex, BN21 4UG Tel: (01323) 415000 Fax: (01323) 410322 E-mail: film@eastbourne.gov.uk

Elizabeth Hotel, Ferriby High Road, North Ferriby, North Humberside, HU14 3LG Tel: (01482) 645212 Fax: (01482) 643332 E-mail: elizabeth.hull@elizabethhotels.co.uk

Elmbank Hotel, The Mount, York, YO24 1GE Tel: (01904) 610653 Fax: (01904) 627139 E-mail: elmbank@hotmail.com

Executive Communications Centres, 252-256 Kings Road, Reading, RG1 4HP Tel: 0118-956 6660 Fax: 0118-956 6415

Executive Hotel Services, 165 Victoria Road, Swindon, SN1 3BU Tel: (01793) 615831 Fax: (01793) 513521 E-mail: ehs@btconnect.com

Forte Posthouse, 215 Haverstock Hill, Hampstead, London, NW3 4RB Tel: (0870) 4009037 Fax: (020) 7435 5586

Francis Hotel, Queen Square, Bath, BA1 2HH Tel: (0870) 4008223 Fax: (01225) 319715 E-mail: h6636-rm@accor.com

Grand Atlantic Hotel, The Grand Atlantic, Beach Road, Weston-super-Mare, Avon, BS23 1BA Tel: (01934) 626543 Fax: (01934) 415048

Harlow Moat House Hotel, Southern Way, Harlow, Essex, CM18 7BA Tel: (01279) 829988 Fax: (01279) 635094 E-mail: revhar@queensmoat.co.uk

Haycock Hotel, London Road, Wansford, Peterborough, PE8 6JA Tel: (01780) 782223 Fax: (01780) 783031 E-mail: sales@arcadianhotel.co.uk

Haydock Park Race Course Co. Ltd, Lodge Lane, Newton-le-Willows, Merseyside, WA12 0HQ Tel: (01942) 725963 Fax: (01942) 270879 E-mail: info@haydock-park.com

▶ Highpoint, 165 Glenfield Road, Leicester, LE3 6DJ Tel: 0116-258 0000 Fax: 0116-258 0033 E-mail: eventsales@highpoint.org.uk

Hilton Hotel, Maple Court, Reeds Cresent, Watford, WD24 4QQ Tel: (020) 7850 4000 Fax: (020) 7856 8001

Holiday Inn Ltd, Brook Street, Brentwood, Essex, CM14 5NF Tel: (0870) 4009012 Fax: (01277) 264264 E-mail: brentwoodm25@6c.com

The Holiday Inn, Pentwyn Road, Cardiff, CF23 7XA Tel: (08704) 008141 Fax: (029) 2054 9147

Holiday Inn Ltd, Leigh Road, Eastleigh, Hampshire, SO50 9PG Tel: (0870) 4009075 Fax: (023) 8064 3945 E-mail: reservations-eastleigh@6c.com

Holiday Inn Ltd, 132 Corstorphine Road, Edinburgh, EH12 6UA Tel: (0870) 4009026 Fax: 0131-334 9237

The Holiday Inn, Junction 18 M1, Crick, Northampton, NN6 7XR Tel: (0870) 4009059 Fax: (01788) 823955 E-mail: reservations-rugby@6c.com

Holiday Inn Ltd, Herbert Walker Avenue, Southampton, SO15 1HJ Tel: (0870) 4009073 Fax: (023) 8033 2510

Holiday Inn Ltd, Tadcaster Road, Dringhouses, York, YO24 1QF Tel: (0870) 4009085 Fax: (01904) 702804

Homestead Court Hotel, Homestead Lane, Welwyn Garden City, Hertfordshire, AL7 4LX Tel: (01707) 324336 Fax: (01707) 326447 E-mail: enquiries@homesteadcourt.co.uk

Hop Farm Country Park, Hop Farm, Maidstone Road, Paddock Wood, Tonbridge, Kent, TN12 6PY Tel: (01622) 872068 Fax: (01622) 872630 E-mail: info@thehopfarm.co.uk

Hotel Elizabeth Grimsby, Little Coates Road, Grimsby, South Humberside, DN34 4LX Tel: (01472) 240024 Fax: (01472) 241354 E-mail: elizabeth.grimsby@elizabethhotels.co.uk

Hunt Hotel, 19 Church Road, Leighton Buzzard, Bedfordshire, LU7 2LR Tel: (01525) 374692 Fax: (01525) 382782

Jarvis Piccadilly, Portland Street, Manchester, M1 4PH Tel: 0161-236 8414 Fax: 0161-228 1568 E-mail: jshaw@jarvis.co.uk

Jury's Cardiff Hotel, Mary Ann Street, Cardiff, CF10 2JH Tel: (029) 2034 1441 Fax: (029) 2022 3742

▶ Just Great Events, Deerings, Shaw Lane, Holywell Green, Halifax, West Yorkshire, HX4 9DW Tel: (01422) 312816 E-mail: enquiries@justgreatevents.co.uk

Kelvin Conference Centre, The West Of Scotland Science Park, 2317 Maryhill Road, Glasgow, G20 0TH Tel: 0141-330 3939 Fax: 0141-330 2828 E-mail: kcc@gla.ac.uk

Kilhey Court Hotel, Chorley Road, Standish, Wigan, Lancashire, WN1 2XN Tel: (01257) 472100 Fax: (01257) 422401

Kingston Theatre, Kingston Square, Hull, HU2 8DA Tel: (01482) 225828 Fax: (01482) 587969 E-mail: gary@kingstontheatrehotel.com

▶ Lancashire College, Southport Road, Chorley, Lancashire, PR7 1NB Tel: (01257) 276719 Fax: (01257) 241370 E-mail: dawn.shelton@ed.lancscc.gov.uk

Lancashire County Cricket Club, Talbot Road, Old Trafford, Manchester, M16 0PX Tel: 0161-282 4040 Fax: (0870) 0624614 E-mail: enquiries@lccc.co.uk

Larne Enterprise Development Co. Ltd, Ledcom Industrial Estate, Bank Road, Larne, County Antrim, BT40 3AW Tel: (028) 2827 0742 Fax: (028) 2827 5653 E-mail: davidgillespie@ledcom.org

Le Meridien, North Terminal, London Gatwick Airport, Gatwick, West Sussex, RH6 0PH Tel: (01293) 567070 Fax: (01293) 567739 E-mail: sales@1emeridien-gatwick.com

Le Strange Arms, Golf Course Road, Hunstanton, Norfolk, PE36 6JJ Tel: (01485) 534411 Fax: (01485) 534724

Leewood Hotel, 13 Manchester Road, Buxton, Derbyshire, SK17 6TQ Tel: (01298) 23002 Fax: (01298) 23228 E-mail: sales@leewoodhotel.co.uk

Lerwick Hotel, 15 South Road, Lerwick, Shetland, ZE1 0RB Tel: (01595) 692166 Fax: (01595) 694419 E-mail: reception@lerwickhotel.co.uk

Luton Travel Lodge, 641 Dunstable Road, Luton, LU4 8RQ Tel: (01582) 575955 Fax: (01582) 490065

Macdonald Bower Hotel, Hollinwood Avenue, Chadderton, Oldham, OL9 8DE Tel: 0161-682 7254 Fax: 0161-683 4605 E-mail: admin@macdonaldhotels.co.uk

Macdonald Hotel Group, Paternoster Row, Winchester, Hampshire, SO23 9LQ Tel: (01962) 861611 Fax: (01962) 849617

Mall Galleries, 17 Carlton House Terrace, London, SW1Y 5BD Tel: (020) 7930 6844 Fax: (020) 7839 7830 E-mail: info@mallgalleries.com

Maltings Hotel, The Street, Weybourne, Holt, Norfolk, NR25 7SY Tel: (01263) 588731 Fax: (01263) 588240

▶ Mandalay Venue Finding, East Wing, Stourton, Shipston-on-Stour, Warwickshire, CV36 5HJ Tel: (0870) 0201610 Fax: (0870) 0201611 E-mail: look@mandalaypartners.co.uk

Manor House, Portland House, Reading, RG7 4YJ Tel: 0118-981 9333 Fax: 0118-981 9025 E-mail: manor.reservations@compass-group.co.uk

Marriott Breadsall Priory, Moor Road, Morley, Ilkeston, Derbyshire, DE7 6DL Tel: (01332) 832235 Fax: (01332) 833509

Marriott Dalmahoy Hotel & Country Club, Kirknewton, Kirknewton, Midlothian, EH27 8EB Tel: 0131-333 1845 Fax: 0131-333 1433 E-mail: salesadmin.dalmahoy@marriotthotels.co.uk

Marriott St Pierre Hotel & Country Club, St. Pierre Park, Hayesgate, Chepstow, Gwent, NP16 6YA Tel: (01291) 635208 Fax: (01291) 629975 E-mail: mhrs.cwlgs.frontdesk@marriothotels.com

Marriott Sprowston Manor Golf Club, Wroxham Road, Norwich, NR7 8RP Tel: (01603) 254292 Fax: (01603) 788884 E-mail: sprowstonmanor@marriotthotels.co.uk

New Bath Hotel, New Bath Road, Matlock Bath, Matlock, Derbyshire, DE4 3PX Tel: (0870) 4008119 Fax: (01629) 580268

Newry Golf Inn Ltd, Forkhill Road, Newry, County Down, BT35 8QY Tel: (028) 3026 3871 Fax: (028) 3026 3871

North Stafford Hotel, Winton Square, Stoke-on-Trent, ST4 2AE Tel: (01782) 744477 Fax: (01782) 744580 E-mail: claire.portar@britanniahotels.co.uk

Ocean View Hotel, Park Road, Shanklin, Isle of Wight, PO37 6BB Tel: (01983) 863262 Fax: (01983) 867139

Old Jordans Guest House & Conference Centre, Jordans Lane, Jordans, Beaconsfield, Buckinghamshire, HP9 2SW Tel: (01494) 874586 Fax: (01494) 875657 E-mail: reception@oldjordans.org.uk

Olde House Trading Post, Loundsley Green Road, Chesterfield, Derbyshire, S40 4RN Tel: (01246) 274321 Fax: (01246) 221853

Olympia Conference Centre, Hammersmith Road, Kensington, London, W14 8UX Tel: (020) 7370 8532 Fax: (020) 7370 8144 E-mail: conferences@eco.co.uk

Paramount Marine Hotel, 8 Crosbie Road, Troon, Ayrshire, KA10 6HE Tel: (01292) 314444 Fax: (01292) 316922 E-mail: marine@paramount-hotels.co.uk

Park Crescent Conference Centre, 229 Great Portland Street, London, W1W 5PN Tel: (020) 7631 8306 Fax: (020) 7631 8307 E-mail: conference@ish.org.uk

Park Hotel, Dunnings Bridge Road, Bootle, Merseyside, L30 6YN Tel: 0151-525 7555 Fax: 0151-525 2481

Park In Heathrow, Bath Road, West Drayton, Middlesex, UB7 0DU Tel: (020) 8759 6611 Fax: (020) 8759 3421 E-mail: sales@lemeridian.com

Pennine Way Hotel, Manchester Street, Oldham, OL8 1UZ Tel: 0161-624 0555 Fax: 0161-627 2031 E-mail: sales@penninewayhotel.co.uk

Portland Thistle Hotel, 3-5 Portland Street, Manchester, M1 6DP Tel: 0161-228 3400 Fax: 0161-228 6347 E-mail: manchester@thistle.co.uk

Portsmouth Marriott Hotel, North Harbour, Portsmouth, PO6 4SH Tel: (023) 9238 3151 Fax: (023) 9238 8701

Posthouse Cardiff City, Castle Street, Cardiff, CF10 1XD Tel: (0870) 4008140 Fax: (029) 2037 1495

Praba UK Ltd, 300-310 High Road, Ilford, Essex, IG1 1QW Tel: (020) 8478 0606 Fax: (020) 8478 3766

Prince Rupert Hotel, Butcher Row, Shrewsbury, SY1 1UQ Tel: (01743) 499955 Fax: (01743) 357306E-mail: post@prince-rupert-hotel.co.uk

QMH Ltd, Queens Court, 9-17 Eastern Road, Romford, RM1 3NG Tel: (01708) 730522 Fax: (01708) 762691 E-mail: headoffice.reception@qmh-hotels.com

Quality Hotel, Bell Common, High Road, Epping, Essex, CM16 4DG Tel: (0870) 3509027 Fax: (01992) 560402

Radisson Edwardian Mayfair, Stratton Street, London, W1A 2AN Tel: (020) 7629 7777 Fax: (020) 7629 1459 E-mail: mayfair@radisson.com

Ramada Jarvis, Grange Park Lane, Willerby, Hull, HU10 6EA Tel: (01482) 656488 Fax: (01482) 655848

Ramada York, Shipton Road, Skelton, York, YO30 1XW Tel: (01904) 670222 Fax: (01904) 670311

Randolph Hotel, Beaumont Street, Oxford, OX1 2LN Tel: (0870) 4008200 Fax: (01865) 791678 E-mail: info@macdonald-hotels.co.uk

Redcliffe Catering Ltd, 100 Icknield Port Road, Edgbaston, Birmingham, B16 0AA Tel: 0121-456 4545 Fax: 0121-454 9118 E-mail: cc.conferences@redcliffe.com

Redhurst Hotel, 77 Eastwoodmains Road, Giffnock, Glasgow, G46 6QE Tel: 0141-638 6465 Fax: 0141-620 0419 E-mail: redhurst@line1.net

Regency Banqueting Suite, 113 Bruce Grove, London, N17 6UR Tel: (020) 8885 2490 Fax: (020) 8885 1739 E-mail: enquiries@regencybanqueting.com

Regus (Central London), 1 Northumberland Avenue, London, WC2N 5BW Tel: (020) 7872 5500 Fax: (020) 7872 5611 E-mail: karl.newman@regus.com

The Research House Ltd, 124 Wigmore St, London, W1U 3RY Tel: (020) 7935 4979 Fax: (020) 7224 2494 E-mail: researchhouse@btinternet.com

Riverdale Hall Hotel, Bellingham, Hexham, Northumberland, NE48 2JT Tel: (01434) 220254 Fax: (01434) 220457 E-mail: reservations@riverdalehallhotel.co.uk

Riverside At Branston, Riverside Drive, Branston, Burton-on-Trent, Staffordshire, DE14 3EP Tel: (01283) 511234 Fax: (01283) 511441 E-mail: riverside.branston@oldenglishinns.co.uk

Robinson College Enterprises Ltd, Grange Road, Cambridge, CB3 9AN Tel: (01223) 339100 Fax: (01223) 351794

Roker Hotel, Roker Terrace, Sunderland, SR6 9ND Tel: 0191-567 1786 Fax: 0191-510 0289 E-mail: info@rokerhotel.co.uk

Round House, 1 Meyrick Road, Bournemouth, BH1 2PR Tel: (01202) 553262 Fax: (01202) 557698

Rowton Hall Hotel, Rowton Lane, Rowton, Chester, CH3 6AD Tel: (01244) 336110 Fax: (01244) 335464 E-mail: sales@rowtonhallhotel.co.uk

Royal Horticultural Halls & Conference Centre, 80 Vincent Square, London, SW1P 2PE Tel: (020) 7828 4125 Fax: (020) 7834 2072 E-mail: horthalls@rhs.org.uk

Rushpool Hall Hotel, Saltburn Lane, Saltburn-by-the-Sea, Cleveland, TS12 1HD Tel: (01287) 624111 Fax: (01287) 625255 E-mail: sales@rushpoolhall.com

St Andrews & Blackfriars Halls, St. Andrews & Blackfriars Hall, St. Andrews Hall Plain, Norwich, NR3 1AU Tel: (01603) 628477 Fax: (01603) 762182 E-mail: kingorders@norwich.gov.uk

Saracens Head Hotel, High Street, Chelmsford, CM1 1BE Tel: (01245) 262368 Fax: (01245) 262418

▶ Saturn Facilities, Saturn Centre, Spring Road, Ettingshall, Wolverhampton, WV4 6JX Tel: (01902) 493192 Fax: (01902) 402553 E-mail: tjordan@saturnfacilities.com

▶ Saturn Facilities Birmingham, Ephraim Phillips House, Bissell Street, Birmingham, B5 7UP Tel: 0121 6221366 E-mail: tjordan@saturnfacilities.com

▶ indicates data change since last edition

CONFERENCE CENTRES/HALLS/ROOMS/SUITES – *continued*

▶ Saturn Facilities Mayfair, 5-6 Carlos Place, Mayfair, London, W1K 3AP Tel: (020) 7907 9700 E-mail: tjordan@saturnfacilities.com

▶ Saturn Facilities Worthing, Columbia House, Columbia Drive, Worthing, West Sussex, BN13 3hd Tel: (01903) 262663 E-mail: tjordan@saturnfacilities.com

Searcys Roof Garden Rooms, 30 Pavilion Road, London, SW1X 0HJ Tel: (020) 7584 4921 Fax: (020) 7823 8694 E-mail: rgr@searcys.co.uk

Shelleys Hotel, High Street, Lewes, East Sussex, BN7 1XS Tel: (01273) 472361 Fax: (01273) 483152 E-mail: info@the-shelleys.co.uk

▶ Shillingford Bridge Hotel, Shillingford Hill, Wallingford, Oxfordshire, OX10 8LZ Tel: (01865) 858567 Fax: (01865) 858636

Ship Inn, Thornbury Road, Alveston, Bristol, BS35 3LL Tel: (01454) 412521 Fax: (01454) 281664 E-mail: bristol.north@premierlodge.co.uk

▶ Silver Fern Venues, 81 Westbury Road, Brentwood, Essex, CM14 4JS Tel: (01277) 222546 E-mail: greg@silverfernvenues.com

Somerset Hotel, 6 Dorset Square, London, NW1 6QA Tel: (020) 7723 0741 Fax: (020) 7723 6081

Stirling Highland Hotel Ltd, Spittal Street, Stirling, FK8 1DU Tel: (01786) 272727 Fax: (01786) 272829 E-mail: stirling@paramount-hotels.co.uk

Stourbridge Navigation Trust, 2 Canal Street, Stourbridge, West Midlands, DY8 4LU Tel: (01384) 395216 Fax: (01384) 395216

Surrey Materials, Newmet House, Rue De St. Lawrence, Waltham Abbey, Essex, EN9 1PF Tel: (01992) 711111 Fax: (01992) 768393 E-mail: materials@newmet.co.uk

Swallow Churchgate Hotel, Churchgate Street, Old Harlow, Harlow, Essex, CM17 0JT Tel: (01279) 420246 Fax: (01279) 437720 E-mail: swallow.oldharlow@swallowhotels.com

Swans Nest, Bridgetown, Stratford-upon-Avon, Warwickshire, CV37 7LT Tel: (0870) 4008183 Fax: (01789) 414547

The Terraces Hotel, 4 Melville Terrace, Stirling, FK8 2ND Tel: (01786) 472268 Fax: (01786) 450314 E-mail: sales@terraceshotel.co.uk

Thistle East Midlands Airport, Castle Donington, Derby, DE74 2SH Tel: (01332) 850700 Fax: (01332) 850823 E-mail: east.midlandsairport@thistle.co.uk

Thistle Euston, 43-48 Cardington Street, London, NW1 2LP Tel: (0870) 3339107 Fax: (0871) 3769117 E-mail: euston@thistle.co.uk

Thistle Hotel, Brands Hatch, Fawkham, Longfield, Kent, DA3 8PE Tel: (01474) 854900 Fax: (01474) 854990 E-mail: brandshatch@thistle.co.uk

Thistle Hotel, The Luton Arndale Centre, Luton, LU1 2TR Tel: (01582) 734199 Fax: (01582) 402528 E-mail: luton@thistle.co.uk

Thistle Newcastle, Neville Street, Newcastle upon Tyne, NE1 5DF Tel: 0191-232 2471 Fax: 0191-232 1285 E-mail: newcastle@thistle.co.uk

Thistle Swindon Hotel, Fleming Way, Swindon, SN1 1TN Tel: (01793) 528282 Fax: (01793) 541283 E-mail: swindon@thistle.co.uk

U K C Hospitality, Tanglewood, Giles Lane, Canterbury, Kent, CT2 7LX Tel: (01227) 828000 Fax: (01227) 828019 E-mail: hospitality-enquiry@kent.ac.uk

Watershed Media Centre, 1 Canons Road, Bristol, BS1 5TX Tel: 0117-927 6444 Fax: 0117-921 3958 E-mail: admin@watershed.co.uk

Wellington Park Ltd, Wellington Park, Church Road, Leyland, PR25 3AB Tel: (01772) 432881 Fax: (01772) 453151

▶ Westminster Hotel, 16 Leinster Square, London, W2 4PR Tel: (020) 7221 9131 Fax: (020) 7221 4073 E-mail: reservations@thewestminsterhotel.com

Wish Tower Hotel, King Edwards Parade, Eastbourne, East Sussex, BN21 4EB Tel: (01323) 722676 Fax: (01323) 721474 E-mail: info@wishtower.co.uk

Wyck Hill House Hotel, Wyck Hill, Stow on the Wold, Cheltenham, Gloucestershire, GL54 1HY Tel: (01451) 831936 Fax: (01451) 832243 E-mail: sales@nichehotels.com

Wynnstay Hotel, 43 Church Street, Oswestry, Shropshire, SY11 2SZ Tel: (01691) 655261 Fax: (01691) 670606 E-mail: sales@wynnstayhotel.com

CONFERENCE MEETING TABLES

Bridge Ceilings Ltd, Interiors House, Samson Road, Coalville, Leicestershire, LE67 3FP Tel: (01530) 834777 Fax: (01530) 813388 E-mail: info@bridgeinteriors.co.uk

Hatherway Office Furniture Ltd, The Farmhouse On The Green, Upper Quinton, Stratford-Upon-Avon, Warwickshire, CV37 8SX Tel: (01789) 721113 Fax: (01789) 721220 E-mail: fbs@freeola.com

Premier Seating International Ltd, Parkside Mill, Walter Street, Blackburn, BB1 1TL Tel: (01254) 673400 Fax: (01254) 665571 E-mail: sales@premierseating.co.uk

Of Quest Ltd, Irton House, Tower Estate, Warpsgrove Lane, Chalgrove, Oxford, OX44 7TH Tel: (01865) 891444 Fax: (01865) 893722 E-mail: customerservice@ofquest.co.uk

Stenochair Ltd, 30 Stilebrook Road, Industrial Estate, Olney, Buckinghamshire, MK46 5EA Tel: (01234) 711354 Fax: (01234) 713652 E-mail: sales@stenochair.co.uk

CONFERENCE ORGANISING SERVICES/LOGISTICS

▶ 3DAV - video by numbers, Studio 2-11, Parkers House, 48 Regents Street, Cambridge, CB2 1FD Tel: 01223 505600 E-mail: jamie@3dav.com

Accommodations, Lion House, 6 Hawthorn Road, Newcastle upon Tyne, NE3 4DE Tel: 0191-213 2131 Fax: 0191-213 2211 E-mail: sales@accomodationsuk.co.uk

Agra Informa Ltd, 80 Calverley Road, Tunbridge Wells, Kent, TN1 2UN Tel: (020) 7017 7500 Fax: (01892) 544895 E-mail: marketing@agra-europe.com

▶ Amc Solutions UK Ltd, 16 St. James Avenue, Sutton, Surrey, SM1 2TH Tel: (020) 8642 7214 Fax: 0870 766 9675 E-mail: info@amc-solutions.com

Anage Productions, Quoin House, Adelaide Road, Ashford, Middlesex, TW15 3LJ Tel: (01784) 423993 Fax: (01784) 247203

Arena Events, Unit 1 Perimeter Road, The N.E.C., Birmingham, B40 1PJ Tel: (0870) 7203010 Fax: (0870) 7201101 E-mail: info@arenaevents.com

B W P Ltd, 24 Bloomsbury Way, London, WC1A 2SL Tel: (020) 7404 2525 Fax: (020) 7404 2084 E-mail: host@bwp.co.uk

Brintex Ltd, 32 Vauxhall Bridge Road, London, SW1V 2SS Tel: (020) 7973 6404 Fax: (020) 7233 5054 E-mail: sales@brintex.com

▶ Carousel Entertainments, 18 Westbury Lodge Close, Pinner, Middlesex, HA5 3FG Tel: (0870) 7518688 Fax: (0870) 7518668 E-mail: sales@carouselentertainments.co.uk

Complete Support Group Ltd, The Garden House, Castle Bromwich, Chester Road, Birmingham, B36 9DE Tel: 0121-776 7766 Fax: 0121-776 7666 E-mail: enquiries@completesupport.co.uk

Concorde Services Ltd, 42 Canham Road, London, W3 7SR Tel: (020) 8743 3106 Fax: (020) 8743 1010 E-mail: london@concorde-uk.com

Conference Business Ltd, The Priory, Syresham Gardens, Haywards Heath, West Sussex, RH16 3LB Tel: (01444) 416678 Fax: (01444) 441162 E-mail: enq@conferencebusiness.co.uk

Conference Contacts Ltd, 16a College Avenue, Maidenhead, Berkshire, SL6 6AX Tel: (01628) 773300 Fax: (01628) 621033 E-mail: enquiries@c-contacts.com

▶ Conference Organisers & Event Management, Exhibition House, London Road, Macclesfield, Cheshire, SK11 7QX Tel: 0870 242 2305 Fax: (01625) 611699 E-mail: info@conference-event.co.uk

Conference Search Ltd, 92 Church Lane, Marple, Stockport, Cheshire, SK6 7AR Tel: 0161-427 7057 Fax: 0161-427 2415 E-mail: sales@conferencesearch.co.uk

Consilium, The Old Stables, Onehouse Hall, Lower Road, Onehouse, Stowmarket, Suffolk, IP14 3BY Tel: (01449) 676435 Fax: (01449) 676436 E-mail: sb@exclusiveheritagevenues.co.uk

Creative Solutions, 32 Ford Lane, Wrecclesham, Farnham, Surrey, GU10 4SF Tel: (01252) 724680 Fax: (01252) 724900 E-mail: production@cresol.co.uk

D & D Conference & Event Management Ltd, 66a High Street, Egham, Surrey, TW20 9EY Tel: (01784) 432233 Fax: (01784) 430088 E-mail: dd@ddconfrence.com

Executive Hotel Services, 165 Victoria Road, Swindon, SN1 3BU Tel: (01793) 615831 Fax: (01793) 513521 E-mail: ehs@btconnect.com

Expotel Barton Ltd, Kingsgate House, Kingsgate Place, London, NW6 4TA Tel: (020) 7328 9841 Fax: (020) 7328 8021 E-mail: lores@expotel.com

Expotel Hotel Reservations Ltd, Albert Chambers, 13 Bath Street, Glasgow, G2 1HY Tel: 0141-331 1771 Fax: 0141-331 1117 E-mail: events@expotel.co.uk

Expotel Hotel Reservations Ltd, Leeds Bridge House, Hunslet Road, Leeds, LS10 1JN Tel: 0113-242 3434 Fax: 0113-234 2781 E-mail: info@expotel.co.uk

The First & Last, First & Last, Herne Common, Herne Bay, Kent, CT6 7JU Tel: (01227) 364465

Four Seasons, Hamilton Place, Park Lane, London, W1A 1AZ Tel: (020) 7499 0888 Fax: (020) 7493 1895

The Grass Roots Group UK Ltd, Pennyroyal, Station Road, Tring, Hertfordshire, HP23 5QY Tel: (01442) 829400 Fax: (01442) 829405 E-mail: contactus@grg.com

▶ Highpoint, 165 Glenfield Road, Leicester, LE3 6DJ Tel: 0116-258 0000 Fax: 0116-258 0033 E-mail: eventsales@highpoint.org.uk

Hopkinson White, 46 Brook Street, Aston Clinton, Aylesbury, Buckinghamshire, HP22 5ES Tel: (01296) 631898 Fax: (01296) 630321 E-mail: info@hopkinson-white.co.uk

Index Communications Meeting Services Ltd, Crown House, 28 Winchester Road, Romsey, Hampshire, SO51 8AA Tel: (01794) 511332 Fax: (01794) 511455 E-mail: icms@indexcommunications.com

Inside Communications Ltd, Bank House, 23 Warwick Road, Coventry, CV1 2EW Tel: (024) 7657 1000 Fax: (024) 7625 2241

J B Communications Group Ltd, 15 Brackenbury Road, London, W6 0BE Tel: (020) 8749 6036 Fax: (020) 8749 9676 E-mail: interest@jbcommunications.co.uk

Jack Morton Europe Ltd, 16-18 Acton Park Industrial Esta, The Vale, London, W3 7QE Tel: (020) 8735 2000 Fax: (020) 8735 2020

The John Mills Group, 11 Hope Street, Liverpool, L1 9BJ Tel: 0151-709 9822 Fax: 0151-709 6585 E-mail: sales@johnmillsgroup.com

▶ Just Great Events, Deerings, Shaw Lane, Holywell Green, Halifax, West Yorkshire, HX4 9DW Tel: (01422) 312816 E-mail: enquiries@justgreatevents.co.uk

Key Audio Visual Services, Black Tower Studios, 15 Bracondale, Norwich, NR1 2AL Tel: (01603) 616661 Fax: (01603) 616668 E-mail: sales@keyav.com

L G G, 67 Smithbrook Kilns, Cranleigh, Surrey, GU6 8JJ Tel: (01483) 275577 Fax: (01483) 277888 E-mail: info@lgg.org.uk

Malone Associates, Fordham House, 46 Newmarket Road, Fordham, Ely, Cambridgeshire, CB7 5LL Tel: (01638) 721770 Fax: (01638) 721771 E-mail: sean@malones.co.uk

▶ Mandalay Venue Finding, East Wing, Stourton, Shipston-on-Stour, Warwickshire, CV36 5HJ Tel: (0870) 0201610 Fax: (0870) 0201611 E-mail: look@mandalaypartners.co.uk

Maritz Europa Ltd, Alexander House, Globe Park, Marlow, Buckinghamshire, SL7 1YW Tel: (01628) 486011 Fax: (01628) 475737

Photosound Communications Ltd, Stansted Road, Birchanger, Bishop's Stortford, Hertfordshire, CM23 5PT Tel: (01279) 818400 Fax: (01279) 647746

Stakeholder Communications Ltd, 2 Donegall Square East, Belfast, BT1 5HB Tel: (028) 9033 9949 Fax: (028) 9033 9959 E-mail: gayle.armstrong@stakeholdergroup.com

▶ Talk Events UK Ltd, Unit 6, 229 Torrington Avenue, Coventry, CV4 9HN Tel: (024) 7646 2444 Fax: (0845) 6126013 E-mail: info@talkevents.com

Tarsus Group plc, Commonwealth House, Chalkhill Road, London, W6 8DW Tel: (020) 8846 2700 Fax: (020) 8846 2801 E-mail: sales@tarsus-exhibitions.com

▶ Telekinetix Ltd, 38 Park Road North, Bedford, MK41 7RH Tel: (01234) 307571 Fax: 01234 328330 E-mail: sally@kinetixevents.co.uk

Travel Lines Ltd, 3 Church Street, Shoreham-By-Sea, West Sussex, BN43 5DQ Tel: (01273) 464662 Fax: (01273) 464693 E-mail: info@travel-lines.co.uk

Trident Exhibitions Ltd, West Devon Business Park, Brook Lane, Tavistock, Devon, PL19 9DP Tel: (01822) 614671 Fax: (01822) 614818 E-mail: info@trident-exhibition.co.uk

Ventana UK Ltd, Gainsborough House, 33 Throgmorton Street, London, EC2N 2BR Tel: (020) 7861 9550 Fax: (01494) 677840 E-mail: enquiries@ventana.co.uk

CONFERENCE PRESENTATION PRODUCTS

▶ Arkadin UK Ltd, 26-28 Hammersmith Grove, London, W6 7JA Tel: (020) 8742 6380 Fax: (020) 8742 6355 E-mail: d.creigh@arkadin.co.uk

▶ Business Friend Ltd, 5 Mayland Quay, Maylandsea, Chelmsford, CM3 6GJ Tel: (07931) 759611 Fax: (01621) 744292 E-mail: telmemore@businessfriend.net

▶ Digital Cubed, The Hive, Nottingham, NG1 4BU Tel: (0870) 8148333 Fax: 0115-848 4612 E-mail: nicholas.timms@digitalcubed.co.uk

Horton & Newberry (Sales & Marketing) Ltd, 53a High Street Wanstead, London, E11 2AA Tel: (020) 8989 5903 Fax: (020) 8530 4118 E-mail: sales@hortonandnewberry.co.uk

TV One, V Continental Approach, Westwood Industrial Estate, Margate, Kent, CT9 4JG Tel: (01843) 873311 Fax: (01843) 873301 E-mail: web@vinemicros.com

CONFERENCE PRODUCTION SERVICES

Audio Visual Unit Ltd, 10 Leslie Road, Ipswich, IP3 9PL Tel: (01473) 705200 Fax: (01473) 705218 E-mail: info@avunit.co.uk

▶ Avc Productions Ltd, 106 Kings Road, Brighton, BN1 2FU Tel: (01273) 746555 Fax: (01273) 746447 E-mail: sales@avcworld.com

Conference Search Ltd, 92 Church Lane, Marple, Stockport, Cheshire, SK6 7AR Tel: 0161-427 7057 Fax: 0161-427 2415 E-mail: sales@conferencesearch.co.uk

The D H M Partnership, Forge House, Hunton, Bedale, N. Yorkshire, DL8 1PX Tel: 0845 1235129 Fax: 0845 1235130 E-mail: dhmp@dhm-partnership.co.uk

D R P Group, 252 Ikon Industrial Estate, Droitwich Road, Hartlebury, Kidderminster, Worcestershire, DY10 4EU Tel: (01299) 250531 Fax: (01299) 250173 E-mail: sales@drp.co.uk

Effective Presentations & Events Ltd, Viking Court, Shepshed Road, Hathern, Loughborough, Leicestershire, LE12 5LZ Tel: (01509) 844444 Fax: (01509) 844104 E-mail: enquiries@thepresentationgroup.co.uk

Expotel Barton Ltd, Kingsgate House, Kingsgate Place, London, NW6 4TA Tel: (020) 7328 9841 Fax: (020) 7328 8021 E-mail: lores@expotel.com

Heart Of England Promotions, Old Hall, Wallhill Road, Fillongley, Coventry, CV7 8DX Tel: (01676) 540333 Fax: (01676) 540365 E-mail: sales@heartofengland.co.uk

Istead Business Presentations, 14 Herald Business Park, Golden Acres Lane, Coventry, CV3 2SY Tel: (024) 7645 9702 Fax: (024) 7663 5624 E-mail: admin@istead.co.uk

Jack Morton Europe Ltd, 16-18 Acton Park Industrial Esta, The Vale, London, W3 7QE Tel: (020) 8735 2000 Fax: (020) 8735 2020

▶ Mandalay Venue Finding, East Wing, Stourton, Shipston-on-Stour, Warwickshire, CV36 5HJ Tel: (0870) 0201610 Fax: (0870) 0201611 E-mail: look@mandalaypartners.co.uk

▶ Mills Media Limited, 2 Morpeth Wharf, Twelve Quays, Wirral, Merseyside, CH41 1LF Tel: 0151 649 3600 Fax: 0151 649 3700 E-mail: norman@millsmediagroup.com

▶ Mindset Communications, Nelson Close, Farnham, Surrey, GU9 9AR Tel: (07771) 870868 Fax: (01252) 316881 E-mail: info@mindsetcomms.co.uk

One Whitehall Place, 1 Whitehall Place, London, SW1A 2HD Tel: (020) 7839 3344 Fax: (020) 7839 3366

▶ Pro-Stage Europe Ltd, The Stables, Watersplash Farm Ford Bridge Roa, Sunbury-on-Thames, Middlesex, TW16 6AU Tel: (01932) 779399 Fax: (01932) 779399 E-mail: info@prostageeurope.com

Reflex Communications, Arden Hall, 66 Brooklands Road, Sale, Cheshire, M33 3SJ Tel: 0161-973 4007 Fax: 0161-973 2150

▶ Scorpion Event Production, Castle Lane, Ripponden, Sowerby Bridge, West Yorkshire, HX6 4JZ Tel: (01422) 823399 E-mail: chris.smith@scorpion-events.co.uk

▶ Spike Events Ltd, 419 London Road, Hemel Hempstead, Herts, HP3 9BD Tel: 01442 261851 Fax: 01442 397138 E-mail: info@spikeevents.co.uk

Stage Plan Of London, 26-30 The Swan Centre, Rosemary Road, London, SW17 0AR Tel: (020) 8944 0899 Fax: (020) 8946 5454

Stagecraft Ltd, Ashfield Trading Estate, Salisbury, SP2 7HL Tel: (01722) 326055 Fax: (01722) 414076 E-mail: myran@stagecraft.co.uk

Think-CI International Ltd, 8 Progress Business Centre, Whittle Parkway, Slough, SL1 6DQ Tel: (01628) 666242 Fax: (01628) 559812 E-mail: jermary.britton@think-global-group.com

Trident Exhibitions Ltd, West Devon Business Park, Brook Lane, Tavistock, Devon, PL19 9DP Tel: (01822) 614671 Fax: (01822) 614818 E-mail: info@trident-exhibition.co.uk

TV One, V Continental Approach, Westwood Industrial Estate, Margate, Kent, CT9 4JG Tel: (01843) 873311 Fax: (01843) 873301 E-mail: web@vinemicros.com

United Business Media GP No 3 Ltd, Ludgate House, 245 Blackfriars Road, London, SE1 9UY Tel: (020) 7921 5000 Fax: (020) 7528 2772

William Martin Ltd, The Studio, Tubney Warren Barn, Tubney, Abingdon, Oxfordshire, OX13 5QJ Tel: (01865) 390258 Fax: (01865) 390234 E-mail: info@wmproductions.co.uk

Zibrant, 2 Prospect Place, Pride Park, Derby, DE24 8HG Tel: (01332) 285577 Fax: (01332) 294964 E-mail: enquiries@zibrant.co.uk

CONFERENCE SERVICES

▶ Absolute Audio Visual Solutions, Cheney Lodge, 81 Station Road, Odsey, Baldock, Hertfordshire, SG7 5RP Tel: (01462) 743003 E-mail: enquiry@absoluteavs.co.uk

▶ Conference Organisers & Event Management, Exhibition House, London Road, Macclesfield, Cheshire, SK11 7QX Tel: 0870 242 2305 Fax: (01625) 611699 E-mail: info@conference-event.co.uk

Embassy Suite, 2 Balkerne Hill, Colchester, CO3 3AA Tel: (01206) 575910 Fax: (01206) 763042

▶ Highpoint, 165 Glenfield Road, Leicester, LE3 6DJ Tel: 0116-258 0000 Fax: 0116-258 0033 E-mail: eventsales@highpoint.org.uk

▶ The Hill Education & Conference Centre, Pen Y Pound Road, Abergavenny, Gwent, NP7 7RP Tel: (01495) 333770 Fax: (01495) 333778 E-mail: hill@coleggwent.ac.uk

▶ James H, Redditch, Worcestershire, B97 Tel: 0845 6446570 Fax: 0845 6446570 E-mail: info@jameshuk.com

▶ Jigsaw Confex Ltd, Events Office - Raincliffe Manor, Lady Ediths Drive, Scarborough, North Yorkshire, YO12 5RJ Tel: (07951) 164820 Fax: (07092) 399780 E-mail: office@jigsaw-confex.co.uk

▶ Paragon Europe Ltd, The Island, Wey Meadows, Weybridge, Surrey, KT13 8XY Tel: 0870 224 2644 E-mail: val@paragoneurope.com

▶ Pro-Stage Europe Ltd, The Stables, Watersplash Farm Ford Bridge Roa, Sunbury-on-Thames, Middlesex, TW16 6AU Tel: (01932) 779399 Fax: (01932) 779399 E-mail: info@prostageeurope.com

Select Bio Sciences Ltd, 1 Bull La Industrial Estate, Bull Lane, Acton, Sudbury, Suffolk, CO10 0BD Tel: (01787) 319234 Fax: (01787) 319235E-mail: admin@selectbiosciences.com

CONFERENCE SERVICES – *continued*

Showtech Sound & Light Design, Unit 23 Hammond Business Centre, Hammond Close, Attleborough Fields Ind Estate, Nuneaton, Warwickshire, CV11 6RY Tel: (024) 7634 8890 Fax: (024) 7634 8890 E-mail: enquiries@ssld.co.uk

▶ Sorted Technical Services Ltd, Brafield on the Green, Northampton, NN7 1BT Tel: (01604) 890260 E-mail: enquiries@sortedtech.co.uk

Sound Services, Button Street, Swanley, Kent, BR8 8DX Tel: (01322) 667709 Fax: 0208-196 2387 E-mail: mail@sound-services.co.uk

▶ Spike Events Ltd, 419 London Road, Hemel Hempstead, Herts, HP3 9BD Tel: 01442 261851 Fax: 01442 397138 E-mail: info@spikeevents.co.uk

▶ Winchester Events Ltd, 272 Back Street, Winchester, Hampshire, SO23 7NN Tel: (01962) 889159 Fax: (01962) 884946 E-mail: sales@winchesterevents.co.uk

CONFERENCE SETS TO SPECIFICATION

Ardan Exhibition, Unit 7 North Medburn Farm, Watling Street, Elstree, Hertfordshire, WD6 3AA Tel: (020) 8207 4957 Fax: (020) 8207 3040 E-mail: info@ardan.co.uk

CONFINED SPACE CONSULTANCY AND CONTRACTORS

Ropetech International Ltd, The Old School, Brynrefail, Caernarfon, Gwynedd, LL55 3NB Tel: 01286 685471 Fax: 01286 685473 E-mail: info@ropetech.com

CONFINED SPACE SAFETY TRAINING

▶ W V Training, 27 King St Trading Estate, Middlewich, Cheshire, CW10 9LF Tel: (01606) 841954 Fax: (01606) 558200 E-mail: mickwvt@fsmail.net

CONFLICT MANAGEMENT CONSULTANCY

Arcadia Alive Ltd, Parkfield House, Park Street, Stafford, ST17 4AL Tel: 01785 214921 E-mail: enquiry@conflict-training.co.uk

▶ Coady Consultants Ltd, 87 The Straits Lower Gornal, Dudley, West Midlands, DY3 3AL Tel: (01902) 664837 Fax: (01902) 664837 E-mail: enquiries@coadyconsultants.co.uk

CONFORMAL COATING SPECIALIST SERVICES

Acota Ltd, Unit B1 Centrepoint Stafford Drive, Battlefield, Shrewsbury, SY1 3BF Tel: (01743) 466392 Fax: (01743) 466555 E-mail: admin@acota.co.uk

▶ Surface Treatment Specialists Ltd, 1B Nelson Street, Widnes, Cheshire, WA8 0QD Tel: 0151-424 1200

CONFORMAL COATINGS

Acota Ltd, Unit B1 Centrepoint Stafford Drive, Battlefield, Shrewsbury, SY1 3BF Tel: (01743) 466392 Fax: (01743) 466555 E-mail: admin@acota.co.uk

Specialty Coating Systems Ltd, Forsyth Road, Woking, Surrey, GU21 5RZ Tel: (01483) 541000 Fax: (01483) 541050

▶ V Tech SMT, Bandeath Industrial Estate, Throsk, Stirling, FK7 7NP Tel: (01786) 813999 Fax: (01786) 813998 E-mail: sales@vtech-smt.co.uk

CONNECTOR ACCESSORIES, *See also headings for particular types*

Lane Electronics, Slinfold Lodge, Stane Street, Slinfold, Horsham, West Sussex, RH13 0RN Tel: (01403) 790661 Fax: (01403) 790849 E-mail: sales@wealdelectronics.com

Selwyn Electronics Ltd, Unit B8 Chaucer Business Park, Watery Lane, Kemsing, Sevenoaks, Kent, TN15 6QY Tel: (01732) 765100 Fax: (01732) 765190 E-mail: connect@selwyn.co.uk

CONNECTOR PINS AND SOCKETS

Deutsch Ltd, 4 Stanier Road, St. Leonards-on-Sea, East Sussex, TN38 9RF Tel: (01424) 852721 Fax: (01424) 851532 E-mail: sales@deutsch.co.uk

Wearnes Cambion Ltd, Mill Bridge, Castleton, Hope Valley, Derbyshire, S33 8WR Tel: (01433) 621555 Fax: (01433) 621290 E-mail: sales@cambion.com

CONNECTOR SOCKETS, INTEGRATED CIRCUIT (IC)/ TRANSISTOR

B & T Printed Circuits Services Ltd, B&T House, 27 Eastways, Witham, Essex, CM8 3YG Tel: (01376) 519500 Fax: (01376) 500388 E-mail: btcircuits@clara.co.uk

Winslow Adaptics Ltd, Unit 5 Brecon Enterprise Park, Brecon, Powys, LD3 8BT Tel: (01874) 625555 Fax: (01874) 625500 E-mail: sales@winslowadaptics.com

CONNECTORS

C A Designs Ltd, The Coach House, 54 The Ridgeway, Rothley, Leicester, LE7 7LE Tel: 0116-237 5248 Fax: (08700) 521513 E-mail: sales@cadesigns.co.uk

Connector & Terminal Supplies Ltd, Unit A3 Mountbatten Business Park, Jackson Close, Portsmouth, PO6 1US Tel: (023) 9237 5966 Fax: (023) 9237 5904 E-mail: sales@connectors-uk.com

J S T U K Ltd, Blyth Road, Halesworth, Suffolk, IP19 8EW Tel: (01986) 874131 Fax: (01986) 874276 E-mail: sales@jst.co.uk

CONNECTORS, ELECTRICAL, MULTIPOLE

F Walther Electrics Ltd, Cromwell Road, Bredbury, Stockport, Cheshire, SK6 2RF Tel: 0161-494 1233 Fax: 0161-494 5055 E-mail: mail@walther.demon.co.uk

CONNECTORS, ELECTRICAL, SUBSEA/UNDERWATER

Custom Design Mouldings Ltd, Unit 212-215, Springvale Industrial Estate, Cwmbran, Gwent, NP44 5BJ Tel: (01633) 861441 Fax: (01633) 876412 E-mail: sales@cdg-uk.com

Groove Associates Ltd, Unit 2, Alton Business Centre, Omega Park, Alton, Hampshire, GU34 2YU Tel: (01420) 88776 Fax: (01420) 88777 E-mail: sales@groove-ltd.com

▶ Hydro Bond Engineering Ltd, 2b Woodside Road, Bridge of Don Industrial Estate, Aberdeen, AB23 8EF Tel: (01224) 822996 Fax: (01224) 825142 E-mail: sales@hydrohouse.co.uk

Remote Marine Systems, Derwent Road, York Road Business Park, Malton, North Yorkshire, YO17 6YB Tel: (01653) 690001 Fax: (01653) 690002 E-mail: sales@rmsltd.com

Simrad Ltd, Star Lane, Margate, Kent, CT9 4NP Tel: (01843) 290290 Fax: (01843) 290471

CONNECTORS, FIBRE OPTIC, PIG TAIL

Cooknell Optronics Ltd, 48 Lynch Lane, Weymouth, Dorset, DT4 9DN Tel: (01305) 781567 Fax: (01305) 759648 E-mail: sales@cooknelloptronics.co.uk

CONNECTORS, HOME CINEMA

▶ Purely Plasma, Bluewater, Greenhithe, Kent, DA9 9SJ Tel: (01322) 427409 E-mail: sales@purelyplasma.com

CONNECTORS, MIL-C SPECIFICATION

Hub Electronics Ltd, Unit 1 Foundry Court, Foundry Lane, Horsham, West Sussex, RH13 5PY Tel: (01403) 255225 Fax: (01403) 263154 E-mail: tina@hubelectronics.co.uk

Hypertac Ltd, 36-38 Waterloo Road, London, NW2 7UH Tel: (020) 8450 8033 Fax: (020) 8208 4114 E-mail: info@hypertac.co.uk

I Q C International Ltd, PO Box 1024, Arundel, West Sussex, BN18 0LT Tel: (0870) 0130999 Fax: (0870) 0130888 E-mail: sales@iqc.co.uk

Tony James Component Wiring Ltd, Unit E10 Speedwell Way, Harleston Industrial Estate, Harleston, Norfolk, IP20 9EH Tel: (01379) 854485 Fax: (01379) 852718 E-mail: enquires@tonyjames.co.uk

CONNECTORS, TO DIN STANDARDS

M & M International UK Ltd, 12 Railton Road, Kempston, Bedford, MK42 7PW Tel: (01234) 855888 Fax: (01234) 856999 E-mail: sales@mmint.co.uk

CONSERVATION CONSULTANCY

▶ Southwest Conservation, 15 Richmond Road, Taunton, Somerset, TA1 1EN Tel: (01823) 337447

CONSERVATION STANDARD ART MOUNTBOARD

▶ Britannia Mounts Co. Ltd, Unit E3-E4, Meltham Mills Industrial Estate, Meltham, Holmfirth, HD9 4DS Tel: (01484) 854444 Fax: (01484) 854433 E-mail: sales@britannia-mounts.co.uk

Nelder & Southam, Mulberry Street, Stratford-upon-Avon, Warwickshire, CV37 6RS Tel: (01789) 267974 Fax: (01789) 267974

CONSERVATORIES, *See also headings for particular types*

▶ 1st APS Conservatory Roof Repairs, Crawford Place, New Road, Staines, Middlesex, TW18 3DH Tel: (01784) 464613 Fax: (01784) 464663

Academy Windows & Conservatories Ltd, 21 Denmark Street, Wokingham, Berkshire, RG40 2AY Tel: 0118-977 1144 Fax: 0118-989 1268E-mail: academy.gordon@btconnect.com

▶ Adams Glass, St George St, Leicester, LE1 1QG Tel: 0116-251 1715

▶ Alpine Conservatory Roof Manufacturers, Unit 9 Barnes Road Industrail Estate, Barnes Road, Bradford, West Yorkshire, BD8 9TG Tel: (01274) 494940 Fax: (01274) 484850 E-mail: matt@alpineroofs.co.uk

Ambassador Windows Ltd, 8 Heol Gors, Dafen Industrial Estate, Dafen, Llanelli, Dyfed, SA14 8QR Tel: (01554) 752144 Fax: (01554) 753311 E-mail: ambassador@lineone.net

▶ Avon Bridge Conservatories, 8 Bidavon Industrial Estate, Waterloo Road, Bidford-on-Avon, Alcester, Warwickshire, B50 4JN Tel: (01789) 778592 Fax: (01789) 490939

▶ Breckenridge Conservatories Ltd, Unit 16, Sawston Trade Park, London Road, Sawston, Cambridge, CB2 4TR Tel: (01223) 839976 Fax: (01223) 839339 E-mail: sales@breckenridgeconservatories.co.uk

▶ Castle, Chelsham Place, Limpsfield Road, Warlingham, Surrey, CR6 9DZ Tel: (01883) 627300 Fax: (01883) 624571 E-mail: info@castlecon.com

▶ Classic Home Improvements Ltd, 4 362b Spring Road, Southampton, SO19 2PB Tel: (023) 8044 7744 Fax: (023) 8044 0033 E-mail: sales@classichome.co.uk

▶ Classique Conservatories, 1-3 Christleton Road, Chester, CH3 5UF Tel: (01244) 345355 Fax: (01244) 345255 E-mail: sales@classique.co.uk

▶ Clearview (Yorkshire) Limited, Unit 4, Sullivan Business Park, West Dock Street, Hull, HU3 4TG Tel: 01482 609310 Fax: 01482 218444 E-mail: sales@conservatoryroofskits.co.uk

▶ Conserva-Care Ltd, 40 Main Street, Egginton, Derby, DE65 6HL Tel: (0845) 0098854 Fax: (0845) 0098853 E-mail: info@conserva-care.co.uk

Conservatory Supplies Ltd, The Conservatory Centre, Leighsinton Road, Malvern, Worcestershire, WR14 1JP Tel: (01684) 575588 Fax: (01684) 576077 E-mail: sales@csltd.net

Conservatory World, Unit 1, Speedwell Unit, Nelson Road Industrial Estate, Dartmouth, Devon, TQ6 9SZ Tel: (01803) 839330 Fax: (01803) 835803

▶ Cottage Conservatories, 12 Clooney Road, Londonderry, BT47 6TB Tel: (028) 7134 5571 Fax: (028) 7134 9400

County Windows, 22 Stephenson Road, St. Ives, Cambridgeshire, PE27 3WJ Tel: (01480) 461505 Fax: (01480) 494407 E-mail: enquiries@countywindows.com

Crofton Conservatory Centre, 112 Stubbington Lane, Fareham, Hampshire, PO14 2PE Tel: (01329) 665025 Fax: (01329) 668526 E-mail: sales@croftonconservatorycentre.com

Colin Dawson Windows Ltd, Chapel Works, John Kennedy Road, King's Lynn, Norfolk, PE30 2AA Tel: (01553) 775191 Fax: (01553) 760639

Diamond Seal Ltd, Bowling Back Lane, Bradford, West Yorkshire, BD4 8SX Tel: (01274) 303400 Fax: (01274) 303401

Esograt Ltd, Caldervale Works, River Street, Brighouse, West Yorkshire, HD6 1JS Tel: (01484) 716228 Fax: (01484) 400107 E-mail: info@esograt.com

▶ Ezze UK Ltd, 619 Sewall Highway, Coventry, CV6 7JE Tel: (024) 7666 7755 Fax: (024) 7672 7819 E-mail: wah@ezzeconsevatories.com

Fairmitre Ltd, Village Way, Trafford Park, Manchester, M17 1AD Tel: 0161-872 1841 Fax: 0161-872 2501 E-mail: sales@fairmitre.uk

FOCUS Windows Fascias Cladding Soffits, 9-15 Christchurch Lane, Market Drayton, Shropshire, TF9 1DZ Tel: (01630) 655717 Fax: (0871) 2422482 E-mail: info@focuswindows.co.uk

▶ Force 8 Upvc Conservatories Ltd, Unit 1c School Street, Hazel Grove, Stockport, Cheshire, SK7 4RA Tel: 0161-483 1997 Fax: 0161-483 5374 E-mail: dennis@force8.co.uk

▶ Frost Conservatories, The Old Forge Tempsford, Great North Road, Sandy, Bedfordshire, SG19 2AG Tel: (01767) 640808 Fax: (01767) 640561 E-mail: sales@frostconservatories.co.uk

Garden Scenes Ltd, The Fourwinds, Bridge Hill Road, Newborough, Peterborough, PE6 7SA Tel: (01733) 810400 E-mail: sean@gardenscenes.fsnet.co.uk

▶ Gary Hall Windows, Dixon Street, Consett, County Durham, DH8 5UF Tel: (01207) 591867 Fax: (01207) 591096 E-mail: garyhall@garyhall.plus.com

Good Openings, Hockley Business Centre, Hooley Lane, Redhill, RH1 6ET Tel: (01737) 772277 Fax: (01737) 772288

▶ Hayley Roof Line, Unit 4, Old Forge Trading Estate, Dudley Road, Stourbridge, West Midlands, DY9 8EL Tel: (01384) 896989 Fax: (01384) 898303 E-mail: mike@hayleywindows.co.uk

▶ Heritage Hardwood, Star Crossroads, Star, Gaerwen, Gwynedd, LL60 6AL Tel: (01248) 715280 Fax: (01248) 713383 E-mail: sales@heritage-hardwood.co.uk

▶ Horizon Conservatories Ltd, Strikes Garden Centre, Red Hall Lane, Wellington Hill, Leeds, LS17 8NA Tel: 0845 2301560 Fax: 0845 2301570 E-mail: info@horizonconservatories.co.uk

▶ Hutton Leisure Buildings Ltd, Hutton Garden Centre, Banwell Road, Hutton, Weston-super-Mare, Avon, BS24 9UB Tel: (01934) 822392 Fax: (01934) 822021 E-mail: mike@huttonconservetories.co.uk

▶ Ivy House Conservatories, Taylors Farm, Stoneygate, Houghton le Spring, Tyne & Wear, DH4 4NL Tel: 0191-511 0262 Fax: 0191-528 1928

Lafford & Leavey, Arrowhead Road, Reading, RG7 4XB Tel: 0118-930 3333 Fax: 0118-932 3707 E-mail: sales@1afford.com

M B S Window Systems Ltd, Corringham Road Industrial Estate, Gainsborough, Lincolnshire, DN21 1QB Tel: (01427) 615050 Fax: (01427) 614436

▶ MHA-Turnkey, 1 Roundwood House, Roundwood Road, High Wycombe, Buckinghamshire, HP12 4HE Tel: (01494) 528006 Fax: (01494) 445154 E-mail: mha-turnkey@supanet.com

▶ Midland Plastic Windows (Hinckley) Ltd, Sapcote Road, Burbage, Hinckley, Leicestershire, LE10 2AZ Tel: (01455) 234635 Fax: (01455) 612880

Norfolk Greenhouses Ltd, Chiswick Avenue, Mildenhall, Bury St. Edmunds, Suffolk, IP28 7AZ Tel: (01638) 713418 Fax: (01638) 714715 E-mail: sales@norfolk-greenhouses.co.uk

▶ Omega Windows, Exchange Road, Lincoln, LN6 3JZ Tel: (01522) 685444 Fax: (01522) 521 898

▶ P B National Products Ltd, Unit 107 Marchington Industrial Estate, Stubby Lane, Marchington, Uttoxeter, Staffordshire, ST14 8LP Tel: (01283) 576860 Fax: (01283) 821180

Paxton Home Improvements, Goddards Yard, Thaxted Road, Saffron Walden, Essex, CB11 3AG Tel: (01799) 527542 Fax: (01799) 527541 E-mail: sales@paxtonsonline.com

▶ Redbrook Conservatories Ltd, Floor 3, 53 Hamilton Square, Birkenhead, Merseyside, CH41 5AS Tel: (0800) 1613034 E-mail: enquiries@redbrookconservatories.com

Regal Windows & Conservatories, 4 Callenders, Paddington Drive, Swindon, SN5 7YW Tel: (0800) 616200 Fax: (01793) 886778 E-mail: regalwindows@tinyworld.co.uk

Ringwood Glass, 14 Lions Wood, St. Leonards, Ringwood, Hampshire, BH24 2LU Tel: (01425) 478445 Fax: (01425) 478484

▶ David Salisbury Joinery Ltd, Bennett Road, Isleport Business Park, Highbridge, Somerset, TA9 4PW Tel: (01278) 764400 Fax: (01278) 764422 E-mail: sales@davidsalisbury.com

▶ Shapet Joinery Ltd, Booth Road, Bedminster, Bristol, BS3 1BP Tel: 0117-963 6953 Fax: 0117-963 6966 E-mail: shapetjoinery@btconnect.com

Sheerwater Glass Centre, 23-27 Dartmouth Avenue, Woking, Surrey, GU21 5PE Tel: (01932) 349247 Fax: (01932) 346580

▶ Shire Conservatories, Unit 7, Harlescott Barns, Battlefield Enterprise Park, Shrewsbury, SY1 3SY Tel: 01743 463333 Fax: 01743 462200E-mail: info@shireconservatories.co.uk

▶ South Coast Windows & Conservatories Ltd, 81 South Coast Road, Peacehaven, East Sussex, BN10 8UR Tel: (01273) 585077 Fax: (01273) 589555 E-mail: info@southcoastwindows.co.uk

▶ Spire Window Systems Ltd, Tattershall Way, Fairfield Industrial Estate, Louth, Lincolnshire, LN11 0YZ Tel: (01507) 607291 Fax: (01507) 600159

▶ Staybrite Conservatories, 16 Warwick Row, Coventry, CV1 1EJ Tel: (024) 7622 2956 Fax: (024) 7622 3290

▶ Style Improvements Ltd, Dunfords Yard, Main Road, Colden Common, Winchester, Hampshire, SO21 1TB Tel: (01962) 715435 Fax: (01962) 711021

▶ Toogood Plastics, Pritchetts Way, Rookley, Ventnor, Isle of Wight, PO38 3LT Tel: (01983) 721511 Fax: (01983) 721522

CONSERVATORIES – continued

▶ Trade Conservatories 2 U Ltd, 36 Temple Way, Heybridge, Maldon, Essex, CM9 4PX Tel: (01621) 852200 Fax: (0845) 1303872 E-mail: sales@tradeconservatories2u.co.uk

▶ Truplas Ltd, Vine Road, Johnston, Haverfordwest, Dyfed, SA62 3NZ Tel: (01437) 890999 Fax: (01437) 899388

▶ Vision (Yorkshire) Ltd, Unit 2a, Shaw Lane Industrial Estate, Ogden Road, Doncaster, South Yorkshire, DN2 4SE Tel: (01302) 328600 Fax: (01302) 760741

Wareham Window Centre Ltd, 4 Warren Way, Holton Heath Trading Park, Poole, Dorset, BH16 6NJ Tel: (01929) 553218 Fax: (01202) 622866E-mail: sales@warehamwindows.co.uk

▶ Westbury Conservatories Ltd, 2 Martels, High Easter Road, Barnston, Dunmow, Essex, CM6 1NA Tel: (01371) 876576 Fax: (01371) 872305

A.J. & B.J. Williams (Martley) Ltd, Hillend Sawmills, Martley, Worcester, WR6 6QL Tel: (01886) 888601 Fax: (01886) 888481

▶ Wilton Conservatories Ltd, Wilton House, Wilton, Salisbury, SP2 0BZ Tel: (01722) 742700

Wrights Property Services, Unit 317 Tedco Bus Centre, Viking Industrial Park, Jarrow, Tyne & Wear, NE32 3DT Tel: 0191-428 3362 Fax: 0191-428 3314 E-mail: homeshields@hotmail.co.uk

Zenith Staybrite Ltd, Suites 4-6, Joseph King House, Abbey Farm Commercial Park, Horsham St Faith, Norwich, NR10 3JU Tel: (0800) 123 555 Fax: (01603) 892116 E-mail: mike.holmes@zsltd.co.uk

CONSERVATORY BLINDS

Carolina Blind Co., 24 Leigh Drive, Elsenham, Bishop's Stortford, Hertfordshire, CM22 6BY Tel: (01279) 816580 Fax: (01279) 817132 E-mail: carolina@elsex.demon.co.uk

Charisma Blinds, 3 Manitoba Place, Chapel Allerton, Leeds, LS7 4LU Tel: 0113-228 7193 Fax: 0113-262 1626 E-mail: charismablindswetherby@yahoo.co.uk

▶ Reflexol Conservatory Blinds Northwest, 1 Cuba Industrial Estate, Bolton Road North, Ramsbottom, Bury, Lancashire, BL0 0NE Tel: (01706) 825511 Fax: (01706) 825522 E-mail: info@reflexol.com

CONSERVATORY COMPONENTS OR ACCESSORIES

All Trim Plastics, Unit 1-2, Spring Lane, Willenhall, West Midlands, WV12 4HL Tel: (0845) 6099922 Fax: (01422) 370953 E-mail: sales@dqs.co.uk

▶ Alpine Conservatory Roof Manufacturers, Unit 9 Barnes Road Industrail Estate, Barnes Road, Bradford, West Yorkshire, BD8 9TG Tel: (01274) 494940 Fax: (01274) 484850 E-mail: matt@alpineroofs.co.uk

Charisma Blinds, 3 Manitoba Place, Chapel Allerton, Leeds, LS7 4LU Tel: 0113-228 7193 Fax: 0113-262 1626 E-mail: charismablindswetherby@yahoo.co.uk

▶ Charles H Coward Ltd, 540 Ecclesfield Road, Sheffield, S5 0DJ Tel: 0114-257 7666 Fax: 0114-257 7565 E-mail: ccsltd@btconnect.com

▶ GR8-conservatories.co.uk, PO BOX 697, Telford, Shropshire, TF7 9AL Tel: 01952 282069 Fax: 0845 2802071 E-mail: info@gr8-services.co.uk

Heattend Ltd, 9 Concorde Road, Norwich, NR6 6BH Tel: (01603) 787505 Fax: (01603) 429500 E-mail: sales@heattend.co.uk

▶ Horizon Conservatories Ltd, Strikes Garden Centre, Red Hall Lane, Wellington Hill, Leeds, LS17 8NA Tel: 0845 2301560 Fax: 0845 2301570 E-mail: info@horizonconservatories.co.uk

Hyacinth, The Rickyard, Eashing Lane, Godalming, Surrey, GU7 2QA Tel: (01483) 417851 Fax: (01483) 417906 E-mail: sales@hyacinth.uk.com

J & J Engineering (Walsall) Ltd, Fryers Road, Leamore Enterprise Park, Bloxwich, Walsall, WS2 7LZ Tel: (01922) 710204 Fax: (01922) 710191 E-mail: jwoodall@btconnect.com

Newdawn & Sun Ltd, Springfield Business Park, Alcester, Warwickshire, B49 6EY Tel: (01789) 764444 Fax: (01789) 400164 E-mail: sales@newdawn-sun.co.uk

Oak Valley Fabrications, The Workshop, rear of 91 Chesterfield Road, North Wingfield, Chesterfield, Derbyshire, S42 5LF Tel: 0782 117 9985

▶ Redbrook Conservatories Ltd, Floor 3, 53 Hamilton Square, Birkenhead, Merseyside, CH41 5AS Tel: (0800) 1613034 E-mail: enquiries@redbrookconservatories.com

▶ Windowscreens UK, PO Box 181, Upminster, Essex, RM14 1GX Tel: (01708) 222273 Fax: (01708) 641898 E-mail: info@flyscreensuk.co.uk

CONSERVATORY DOORS

5 Star Windows & Conservatories Ltd, The Old Stores, Stanklyn Lane, Summerfield, Kidderminster, Worcestershire, DY11 7RY Tel: (01562) 66955 Fax: (01562) 66955 E-mail: sales@5star-online.co.uk

▶ Altro Window Frame Mnfrs, Unit 51 Barns Court, Turners Hill Road, Crawley Down, Crawley, West Sussex, RH10 4HQ Tel: (01342) 718702 Fax: (01342) 718942

Davian Designs, 81 Main Road, Waterside, Kilmarnock, Ayrshire, KA3 6JU Tel: (01563) 550091 Fax: (01563) 550091 E-mail: mark@davian79.fsnet.co.uk

▶ Double Plas, 1 Babington Park, Grange Park, Swindon, SN5 6EZ Tel: (01793) 875171 Fax: (01793) 878389

Europa Conservatories Ltd, Unit 35 Tolpits Lane Industrial Centre, Watford, WD1 8SP Tel: (01923) 212700 Fax: (01923) 212727 E-mail: sales@europaconservatories.co.uk

▶ Finesse PVC U Ltd, Arburn House Chapel Place, Dentonholme Trading Estate, Carlisle, CA2 5DF Tel: (01228) 522581 Fax: (01228) 810947 E-mail: info@finessegroup.co.uk

Glevum Conservatories, Riverside Lane, Broadoak, Newnham, Gloucestershire, GL14 1JF Tel: (01452) 760000 Fax: (01452) 760001 E-mail: mail@glevum.co.uk

▶ Horizon Conservatories Ltd, Strikes Garden Centre, Red Hall Lane, Wellington Hill, Leeds, LS17 8NA Tel: 0845 2301560 Fax: 0845 2301570 E-mail: info@horizonconservatories.co.uk

▶ Origin Frames, Unit 9 Lincolns Park Business Centre, Lincoln Road, Cressex Business Park, High Wycombe, Buckinghamshire, HP12 3RD Tel: (0845) 4506662 Fax: (0845) 4506663 E-mail: info@originframes.co.uk

▶ Peninsula Windows Ltd, Star Crossroads, Star, Gaerwen, Gwynedd, LL60 6AL Tel: (01248) 715555 Fax: (01248) 713383 E-mail: sales@peninsulawindows.co.uk

▶ Polycool Ltd, Church Lane, Kinwarton, Alcester, Warwickshire, B49 6HB Tel: (01789) 766880 Fax: (01789) 764162 E-mail: pol@polycool.co.uk

▶ Redbrook Conservatories Ltd, Floor 3, 53 Hamilton Square, Birkenhead, Merseyside, CH41 5AS Tel: (0800) 1613034 E-mail: enquiries@redbrookconservatories.com

▶ Spooner Bros, Hawksworth Trading Estate, Swindon, SN2 1EJ Tel: (01793) 336333 Fax: (01793) 336333 E-mail: Sales@spoonerbrothers.co.uk

▶ Trade Conservatories 2 U Ltd, 36 Temple Way, Heybridge, Maldon, Essex, CM9 4PX Tel: (01621) 852200 Fax: (0845) 1303872 E-mail: sales@tradeconservatories2u.co.uk

▶ Valley Windows Ltd, The Old Spray Shop, Woodside Trading Estate, Usk, Monmouthshire, NP15 1SS Tel: (01291) 675470 Fax: (01291) 675472 E-mail: ian@valleywindows.co.uk

CONSERVATORY FURNITURE

▶ Bracken Wood Furniture, Unit 8 Headway Business Park, Denby Dale Road, Wakefield, West Yorkshire, WF2 7AZ Tel: (01924) 381580 Fax: (01924) 290811 E-mail: sales@brackenwoodfurniture.co.uk

▶ In Focus Interiors, Oxenwood, Westhill Road South, South Wonston, Winchester, Hampshire, SO21 3HP Tel: (01962) 883092 Fax: (01962) 885144

CONSERVATORY ROOFING SYSTEMS

▶ A A A Conservatory Roof Repairs & Replacement, 8 Birchwood Drive, Lightwater, Surrey, GU18 5RX Tel: (01276) 453654 Fax: E-mail: timhayesaaa@msn.com

▶ Alpine Conservatory Roof Manufacturers, Unit 9 Barnes Road Industrail Estate, Barnes Road, Bradford, West Yorkshire, BD8 9TG Tel: (01274) 494940 Fax: (01274) 484850 E-mail: matt@alpineroofs.co.uk

▶ Aztec Conservatory Roof Systems Ltd, Haydock Lane, Haydock, St. Helens, Merseyside, WA11 0SN Tel: (01942) 720044 E-mail: sales@aztecsystems.co.uk

Balham Glass & Joinery, 260-262 Cavendish Road, London, SW12 0BT Tel: (020) 8675 1640 Fax: (020) 8657 6784 E-mail: balhamglass@btclick.com

▶ C B K Ltd, 90 Bristol Road, Gloucester, GL1 5SQ Tel: (01452) 422333 Fax: (01452) 312822

Coastal Ltd, D'Oriel House, Holton Heath Trading Park, Poole, Dorset, BH16 6LE Tel: (01202) 624011 Fax: (01202) 622465 E-mail: sales@coastalwindows.co.uk

Modern Fabrications (Barnsley) Ltd, Modern House, Summer Lane, Barnsley, South Yorkshire, S70 2NP Tel: (01226) 733337 Fax: (01226) 730004 E-mail: sales@modern-fabrications.co.uk

Newdawn & Sun Ltd, Springfield Business Park, Alcester, Warwickshire, B49 6EY Tel: (01789) 764444 Fax: (01789) 400164 E-mail: sales@newdawn-sun.co.uk

Novaseal Plastics Ltd, 4 Blackbrook Business Park, Blackbrook Road, Fareham, Hampshire, PO15 5DR Tel: (01329) 233500 Fax: (01329) 230012 E-mail: info@novaseal.co.uk

Plastics Stockholder Ltd, Unit 4 Cullwick Street, Wolverhampton, WV1 2UL Tel: (01902) 404145 Fax: (01902) 404858 E-mail: sales@plasticsstockholder.co.uk

Twinfix Ltd, 201 Cavendish Place, Birchwood, Warrington, WA3 6WU Tel: (01925) 811311 Fax: (01925) 852955 E-mail: gjk@twinfix.com

CONSTANT FORCE SPRINGS

Applied Spring Technology Ltd, Unit 8 Chapel Farm, Hartwell, Northampton, NN7 2EU Tel: 01908 511432 Fax: 01908 511432 E-mail: inbox@appliedspring.co.uk

Kern-Liebers Ltd, Corringham Road Industrial Estate, Gainsborough, Lincolnshire, DN21 1QB Tel: (01427) 612085 Fax: (01427) 610301 E-mail: kl-uk@kern-liebers.com

CONSTANT VELOCITY JOINT RE-MANUFACTURING SERVICES

Shaftec Automotive Components Ltd, 2 Cato Street, Birmingham, B7 4TS Tel: 0121-333 3555 Fax: 0121-359 3003 E-mail: shaftec@automotive8.freeserve.co.uk

CONSTANT VELOCITY JOINTS

G K N Hardy Spicer Ltd, Chester Road, Erdington, Birmingham, B24 0RB Tel: 0121-377 7000 Fax: 0121-377 7012

I M S International Marketing Services Ltd, Boulton Works, 54 College Road, Perry Barr, Birmingham, B44 8BS Tel: 0121-344 5500 Fax: 0121-344 5504 E-mail: sales@ims-ltd.co.uk

Reco-Prop UK Ltd, Unit 4 New Town Trading Estate, Chase Street, Luton, LU1 3QZ Tel: (01582) 412110 Fax: (01582) 480432 E-mail: info@reco-prop.com

CONSTANT VOLTAGE BATTERY CHARGERS

Envetron Standby Power Ltd, 28 Wash Road, Hutton, Brentwood, Essex, CM13 1TB Tel: (01277) 214455 Fax: (01277) 227341 E-mail: enquiry@nvtools.co.uk

CONSTRUCTION

▶ Acorn Building Services Ltd, Sefton St, Leigh, Lancashire, WN7 1LX Tel: (01942) 609966 Fax: (01942) 262444 E-mail: reception@acornbuilders.com

▶ Caplin Building Services, Valley Farm Cottages, London Road, Frostenden, Beccles, Suffolk, NR34 7HW Tel: (01502) 675291 Fax: (01502) 676027

▶ Clovemead Ltd, Telford House, 105 Parker Drive, Leicester, LE4 0JP Tel: 0116-234 2800

▶ Crest Plant Ltd, Portland House, 51 Colney Hatch Lane, London, N10 1LJ Tel: (020) 8444 4165 Fax: (020) 8444 1084

▶ D E Clegg Ltd, Bishops House, 42 High Pavement, Nottingham, NG1 1HN Tel: 0115-841 3121 Fax: 0115-841 3122 E-mail: info@declegg.co.uk

▶ DES Group Ltd, Unit 9, Shield Drive, West Cross Centre, Great West Road, Brentford, Middlesex, TW8 9EX Tel: (020) 8560 8787 Fax: (020) 8758 2184 E-mail: jo.chambers@d-e-s.co.uk

FOCUS Windows Fascias Cladding Soffits, 9-15 Christchurch Lane, Market Drayton, Shropshire, TF9 1DZ Tel: (01630) 655717 Fax: (0871) 2422482 E-mail: info@focuswindows.co.uk

Galliford Try Partnership Ltd, 50 Rainsford Road, Chelmsford, CM1 2XB Tel: (01245) 494849 Fax: (01245) 493494 E-mail: sales@gallifordtry.co.uk

▶ George & Harding Construction Ltd, Sunburst House, Elliott Road, Bournemouth, BH11 8LT Tel: (01202) 578585 Fax: (01202) 581139

Hawk Property Services Ltd, Unit 3A, Britland Estate, Northbourne Road, Eastbourne, East Sussex, BN22 8PW Tel: (01323) 641110 Fax: (01323) 641112 E-mail: mail@hawkps.co.uk

▶ Horbury Building Systems Ltd, South Grove House, South Grove, Rotherham, South Yorkshire, S60 2AF Tel: (01709) 515044 Fax: 01709 515066 E-mail: dpriestley@horburygroup.com

▶ J & E Regan Builders & Contractors Ltd, Unit 4 Barncoose Industrial Estate, Barncoose, Redruth, Cornwall, TR15 3RQ Tel: (01209) 211616 Fax: (01209) 210175

J N G Construction & Engineering Ltd, 23 Hornsby Square, Southfields Industrial Park, Basildon, Essex, SS15 6SD Tel: (01268) 240888

▶ Logan Construction, 121 Nuxley Road, Belvedere, Kent, DA17 5JX Tel: (01322) 443270 Fax: (01322) 437376

M B Engineering Solutions Ltd, Logans Road, Motherwell, Lanarkshire, ML1 3NP Tel: (01698) 266111 Fax: (01698) 269774 E-mail: info@mbgroup.com

▶ Mansell Construction General Works Division, 269d Queensway South, Team Valley Trading Estate, Gateshead, Tyne & Wear, NE11 0SD Tel: 0191-487 0004 Fax: 0191-482 5982

▶ Martin Group N W Ltd, Bouthwood Road, Sowerby Woods Industrial Estate, Barrow-in-Furness, Cumbria, LA14 4RD Tel: (01229) 813428 Fax: (01229) 430330

▶ Mowlem P.L.C., Askern Road, Carcroft, Doncaster, South Yorkshire, DN6 8DH Tel: (01302) 330491

▶ Nicholson Jones Partnership Ltd, 20 St. Andrews Crescent, Cardiff, CF10 3DD Tel: (029) 2072 9500 Fax: (029) 2072 9501

▶ Palmers Ltd, North Lane, Aldershot, Hampshire, GU12 4QN Tel: (0870) 0465188 Fax: (0870) 0465189 E-mail: aldershotenq@palmersgroup.co.uk

Products Plan Ltd, 67 Europa Business Park, Bird Hall Lane, Stockport, Cheshire, SK3 0XA Tel: 0161-428 9966 Fax: 0161-428 9977

▶ Promaintenance, 254 Walsall Road, Cannock, Staffordshire, WS11 0JL Tel: (01543) 469098

▶ Rok, Stanley Harrison House, Norton Road, Malton, North Yorkshire, YO17 7PD Tel: (01392) 354000 Fax: (01653) 691111

▶ S & J Graveson Ltd, The Orchard, 1 Lyddington Road, Caldecott, Market Harborough, Leicestershire, LE16 8TE Tel: (01536) 770334 Fax: (01536) 771894

▶ Spring Dale, 46 Theydon Road, London, E5 9NA Tel: (020) 8815 4411

▶ Stacey Construction Ltd, Station Road, Wiveliscombe, Taunton, Somerset, TA4 2LX Tel: (01984) 623802 Fax: (01984) 624497

▶ T R A K Residential Ltd, Seymour House, Whiteleaf Road, Hemel Hempstead, Hertfordshire, HP3 9DE Tel: (01442) 838450 Fax: (01442) 838501

▶ UK Forks, Central House, Beckwith Knowle, Otley Road, Beckwithshaw, Harrogate, North Yorkshire, HG3 1UD Tel: (0800) 123101 Fax: (01423) 565657 E-mail: info@ukforks.com

V B C Group, 16 Regent Park, Park Farm Industrial Estate, Wellingborough, Northamptonshire, NN8 6GR Tel: (01933) 679500 Fax: (01933) 679250 E-mail: sales@vbcgroup.com

CONSTRUCTION ALUMINIUM PROFILED SHEET

▶ Yorkshire Metal Roofing, Unit 2 The Old Station, Nidd, Harrogate, North Yorkshire, HG3 3BN Tel: (01423) 779555 Fax: (01423) 779666 E-mail: info@yorkshiremetalroofing.co.uk

CONSTRUCTION CHEMICALS

Advanced Admixtures Ltd, 147 Park Road, Timperley, Altrincham, Cheshire, WA15 6QQ Tel: 0161-962 6267 Fax: 0161-962 6267

Pepcon Ltd, PO Box 272, Sunbury-on-Thames, Middlesex, TW16 6WB Tel: (01932) 788545 Fax: (01932) 788496 E-mail: sales@pepcon.org

Specialist Building Products, 24 Beaufort Drive, London, NW11 6BU Tel: (020) 8458 8212 Fax: (020) 8458 4116 E-mail: sbpchemicals@yahoo.com

Stephenson Group Ltd, PO Box 305, Bradford, West Yorkshire, BD7 1HY Tel: (01274) 723811 Fax: (01274) 370108 E-mail: group@stephensongroup.co.uk

CONSTRUCTION COMPUTATIONAL FLUID DYNAMICS (CFD) CONSULTANCY

▶ Cambridge Flow Solutions, Compass House, Vision Park, Histon, Cambridge, CB4 9AD Tel: 01223 257978 Fax: 01223 257800 E-mail: ed.lewis@cambridgeflowsolutions.com

Computational Dynamics Ltd, Hythe House, 200 Shepherds Bush Road, London, W6 7NL Tel: (020) 7471 6200 Fax: (020) 7471 6201

▶ K8T Ltd, 8 Simmonds Buildings, Bristol Road, Bristol, BS16 1RY Tel: 0117-956 8477 E-mail: paulkingston@k8t.ltd.uk

CONSTRUCTION COMPUTER SYSTEMS

Alpine Computer Systems, 5 Church Road, Bishops Cleeve, Cheltenham, Gloucestershire, GL52 8LR Tel: (01242) 673322 Fax: (01242) 674845 E-mail: sales@alpinesystems.co.uk

Morgan Computer Co., 64-72 New Oxford Street, London, WC1A 1AX Tel: (020) 7255 2115 Fax: (020) 7436 6285 E-mail: info@morgancomputers.co.uk

New Media Distribution (UK) Ltd, Unit 7, Sunderland Estate, Church Lane, Kings Langley, Hertfordshire, WD4 8JX Tel: (01923) 267267 Fax: (01923) 267266 E-mail: mark@panthercomputers.co.uk

SCT Systems, Balcarres House, 134-136 Balcarres Road, Leyland, PR25 3ED Tel: (01772) 450200 Fax: (01772) 450201 E-mail: sales@sctsystems.co.uk

CONSTRUCTION COST CONSULTANCY

A J A Associates, 4 Portchester Court, Great Holm, Milton Keynes, MK8 9DU Tel: (01908) 569617 Fax: (01908) 569617 E-mail: aja.associates@virgin.net

Andrews & Boyd, 24 Old Burlington Street, Mayfair, London, W1S 3AW Tel: (020) 7494 0399 Fax: (020) 7494 0477 E-mail: info@andrewsboyd.co.uk

Babtie Group Murdoch Green, 1 Grand Parade, Brighton, BN2 9QB Tel: (01273) 676766 Fax: (01273) 696977 E-mail: mgk.brighton@babtie.com

Brack Meekins Partnership, Aberdeen House, 22 Highbury Grove, London, N5 2DQ Tel: (020) 7359 9245 Fax: (020) 7226 9522 E-mail: info@qs_1.com

Bristow Johnson & Partners, 146 Oxford St, London, W1D 1LZ Tel: (020) 7636 1036 Fax: (020) 7436 5347 E-mail: bristowjohnson@compuserve.com

Capita Symonds Services, Sunlight House, Quay Street, Manchester, M3 3JZ Tel: 0161-833 0711 Fax: 0161-835 2624 E-mail: man@mpmcapita.co.uk

Franklin & Andrews, Sea Containers House, 20 Upper Ground, London, SE1 9LZ Tel: (020) 7633 9966 Fax: (020) 7928 2471 E-mail: michelle.swales@franklinandrews.com

James R Knowles, 2 Amber Business Village, Amber Close, Tamworth, Staffordshire, B77 4RP Tel: (0870) 7530830 Fax: (0870) 7530835 E-mail: tamworth@jrknowles.com

Kneeshaw C C M Ltd, Manchester House, 48 High Street, Stokesley, Middlesbrough, Cleveland, TS9 5AX Tel: (01642) 711583 Fax: (01642) 711678E-mail: mail@kccm.co.uk

Northcroft, 1 Horse Guards Avenue, London, SW1A 2HU Tel: (020) 7839 7858 Fax: (020) 7930 2594 E-mail: surv@northcroft.co.uk

▶ Optimus Business Practice, The Manzar Centre, Whitlenge Lane, Hartlebury, Kidderminster, Worcestershire, DY10 4HD Tel: (01299) 250745 Fax: (01299) 250240 E-mail: info@optimusbp.co.uk

Quincey Mason Practices Ltd, 6a Highfield Road, Edgbaston, Birmingham, B15 3ED Tel: 0121-456 1110 Fax: 0121-452 1444 E-mail: mail@qmp.co.uk

Ivor Russell Partnership, Royal Building, 10 Princess Way, Swansea, SA1 3LW Tel: (01792) 655888 Fax: (01792) 648384 E-mail: irp@themail.co.uk

Turner & Townsend, 111 Charles Street, Sheffield, S1 2ND Tel: 0114-272 9025 Fax: 0114-275 3760 E-mail: she@turntown.co.uk

V B Johnson & Partners, 304-310 St. Albans Road, Watford, WD24 6PW Tel: (01923) 227236 Fax: (01923) 231134 E-mail: watford@vbjohnson.co.uk

CONSTRUCTION COST MANAGEMENT CONSULTANCY

Cameron Brook & Associates, 1 Royal Oak Passage, High Street, Huntingdon, Cambridgeshire, PE29 3EA Tel: (01480) 436236 Fax: (01480) 436336 E-mail: sales@cameronbrook.co.uk

James R Knowles, Suite 1a Cameron Court, Cameron Street, Hillington Industrial Estate, Glasgow, G52 4JH Tel: (0870) 7530820 Fax: 0141-883 9134 E-mail: glasgow@jrknowles.com

Kneeshaw C C M Ltd, Manchester House, 48 High Street, Stokesley, Middlesbrough, Cleveland, TS9 5AX Tel: (01642) 711583 Fax: (01642) 711678E-mail: mail@kccm.co.uk

Ivor Russell Partnership, Royal Building, 10 Princess Way, Swansea, SA1 3LW Tel: (01792) 655888 Fax: (01792) 648384 E-mail: irp@themail.co.uk

CONSTRUCTION ENGINEERING MANAGEMENT DOCUMENT CONTROL SYSTEMS

Tdoc Projects Ltd, Suite 308, The White Studios, Templeton on the Green, Glasgow, G40 1DA Tel: 0141-637 3124 Fax: 0141-556 1212 E-mail: sales@tdoc.net

CONSTRUCTION EQUIPMENT CABS

▶ Aberfeldy Construction Equipment, 9 Market Square, Aberfeldy, Perthshire, PH15 2RB Tel: (01887) 829536 E-mail: sinclairderek@hotmail.com

CONSTRUCTION EQUIPMENT CANOPIES

▶ Aberfeldy Construction Equipment, 9 Market Square, Aberfeldy, Perthshire, PH15 2RB Tel: (01887) 829536 E-mail: sinclairderek@hotmail.com

CONSTRUCTION EQUIPMENT OPERATION OR MAINTENANCE MANUALS

▶ C P Formstyle, 3 Weirside Court, Dockfield Road, Shipley, West Yorkshire, BD17 7AD Tel: (01274) 591400 Fax: (01274) 591811 E-mail: sales@formstyle.co.uk

▶ Harper Tether Associates, 3 Sansome Road, Shirley, Solihull, West Midlands, B90 2BJ Tel: 0121 745 2456 Fax: 0121 745 2456 E-mail: kdharper@h-t-a.co.uk

CONSTRUCTION EQUIPMENT PLANT, COMPONENTS AND SPARE PARTS

Lee Brothers Construction Supplies, Spring Road, Ettingshall, Wolverhampton, WV4 6JT Tel: (01902) 491911 Fax: (01902) 353228 E-mail: sales@leebrothers.co.uk

CONSTRUCTION EQUIPMENT SPARE PARTS

Apex Agencies International Ltd, Sportrite House, 155 Tame Road, Witton, Birmingham, B6 7DG Tel: 0121-328 9190 Fax: 0121-328 4175 E-mail: info@apex-world.com

Dominion (England) Ltd, 6 Strathmore Court, 143 Park Rd, London, NW8 7HY Tel: (020) 7483 2117 Fax: (020) 7586 6974 E-mail: dominionengland@cs.com

Essex Tractor Co. Ltd, Birchwood Road, Cock Clarks, Chelmsford, CM3 6RF Tel: (01621) 828880 Fax: (01621) 828944 E-mail: sales@tractor.net

Fairport Construction Equipment Ltd, Blagden Street, Sheffield, S2 5QS Tel: 0114-276 7921 Fax: 0114-272 0965 E-mail: sales@fairport.uk.com

Feldex Ltd, 93 Derwent Avenue, Garforth, Leeds, LS25 1HS Tel: 0113-232 0171 Fax: 0113-232 0171 E-mail: peterfeldex@supanet.com

Grain Plant Sales Ltd, Barton Road, Haslingfield, Cambridge, CB23 1LW Tel: (01223) 872595 Fax: (01223) 872600

Kellands Plant Sales Ltd, High Street, Delabole, Cornwall, PL33 9AE Tel: (01840) 212393 Fax: (01840) 212120 E-mail: sales@kellands.com

▶ KM Products Europe Ltd, The Forum, Unit B, Hanworth Lane Business Park, Hanworth Lane, Chertsey, Surrey, KT16 9JX Tel: (01932) 571991 Fax: (01932) 571994 E-mail: sales@kmpuk.com

M S W Machinery (International) Ltd, 84 St James Lane, London, N10 3RD Tel: (020) 8883 0734 Fax: E-mail: michael@mswmc.co.uk

Parts Export Ltd, Welham Street, Grantham, Lincolnshire, NG31 6QU Tel: (01476) 560161 Fax: (01476) 566723 E-mail: sales@partsexport.co.uk

Pressurefast Ltd, Forge Road, Machynlleth, Powys, SY20 8EG Tel: (01654) 702865 Fax: (01654) 703450 E-mail: info@pressurefast.com

Riverlea Construction Equipment, Millfield, Whitland, Dyfed, SA34 0QQ Tel: (01994) 240965 Fax: (01994) 240285 E-mail: paul.a@riverlea.co.uk

T.H. White Ltd, London Road, Marlborough, Wiltshire, SN8 2RN Tel: 01672 512328

Whites Material Handling Ltd, 10-12 Dixon Road, Bristol, BS4 5QW Tel: 0117-972 0006 Fax: 0117-972 3296 E-mail: enquiries@whitesmh.co.uk

CONSTRUCTION EQUIPMENT SPARE PARTS EXPORT

▶ Engine Spares, 82 Mitcham Road, London, SW17 9NG Tel: (020) 8767 5990 Fax: (020) 8767 5991 E-mail: smithaustin01@btconnect.com

Fairport Construction Equipment Ltd, Blagden Street, Sheffield, S2 5QS Tel: 0114-276 7921 Fax: 0114-272 0965 E-mail: sales@fairport.uk.com

Feldex Ltd, 93 Derwent Avenue, Garforth, Leeds, LS25 1HS Tel: 0113-232 0171 Fax: 0113-232 0171 E-mail: peterfeldex@supanet.com

Parmavex Services, 17 Perryhill Lane, Oldbury, West Midlands, B68 0AG Tel: 0121-422 9818 Fax: 0121-421 7114 E-mail: contact@parmavex.co.uk

Terrapart International Ltd, Blacksmith's Yard, Broad Hinton, Swindon, SN4 9PB Tel: (01793) 731990 Fax: (01793) 731791 E-mail: accounts@terrapart.com

Trowell Plant Sales Ltd, 111 Station Road, Selston, Nottingham, NG16 6FF Tel: (01773) 580878 Fax: (01773) 580881 E-mail: tpsl@btconnect.com

Universal 2000 Ltd, Bedford Rd, Houghton Conquest, Bedford, MK45 3LS Tel: (01234) 740922 Fax: (01234) 742505

CONSTRUCTION FEASIBILITY STUDIES OR SERVICES

W W P Consultants Ltd, 5-15 Cromer Street, London, WC1H 8LS Tel: (020) 7833 5767 Fax: (020) 7833 5766 E-mail: info@wwp-london.co.uk

CONSTRUCTION FINANCE LEASE PACKAGES

▶ Saracen Finance, The Old Barn, Hall Farm, Main Street, Kirklington, Newark, Nottinghamshire, NG22 8NN Tel: (01636) 815685 Fax: (01636) 817859 E-mail: vstrachan@saracenfinance.com

CONSTRUCTION FIRE SAFETY TRAINING

▶ A B Fire Safety Training Services, 16 Buttermere Drive, Millom, Cumbria, LA18 4PL Tel: (01229) 772653 Fax: (01229) 772653 E-mail: steve@abfire.co.uk

▶ Risk Assessment & Training, Fire House, 205 West Lake Avenue, Hampton Vale, Peterborough, PE7 8LN Tel: (01733) 247172 Fax: (01733) 247172 E-mail: angliafiresafety@btinternet.com

▶ Tme Training Ltd, 5 Lower Actis, Glastonbury, Somerset, BA6 8DP Tel: (01458) 832607

CONSTRUCTION INDUSTRY CONSULTANCY

James R Knowles, 2 Amber Business Village, Amber Close, Tamworth, Staffordshire, B77 4RP Tel: (0870) 7530830 Fax: (0870) 7530835 E-mail: tamworth@jrknowles.com

Modulex Systems Ltd, 9a North Portway Close, Round Spinney Industrial Estate, Northampton, NN3 8RQ Tel: (01604) 672100 Fax: (01604) 672161 E-mail: mxuk@modulex.co.uk

▶ Savant UK Ltd, 3-5 Rathbone Place, London, W1T 1HJ Tel: (020) 7291 0220 Fax: (020) 7291 0250 E-mail: sarah.briggs@savantinternational.co.uk

▶ Skerritt Ltd, 24 Union Road, Nottingham, NG3 1FH Tel: 0115-950 6722 Fax: 0115-958 8149 E-mail: info@skerritt.co.uk

▶ Trotman & Taylor, 40 Deer Park, Ivybridge, Devon, PL21 0HY Tel: (01752) 698410 Fax: (01752) 698410 E-mail: enquiries@trotmantaylor.com

CONSTRUCTION INDUSTRY CONTRACT CONSULTANCY

▶ All Services Management Ltd, 9 Tennyson Road, High Wycombe, Buckinghamshire, HP11 2XA Tel: (07968) 740788 Fax: (01494) 534279 E-mail: robert@services-management.co.uk

CONSTRUCTION INDUSTRY FABRICATORS

Evenwood Engineering Ltd, Evenwood, Bishop Auckland, County Durham, DL14 9NJ Tel: (01388) 832556 Fax: (01388) 832966

Gillman Group Ltd, Chipstead Road, Erdington, Birmingham, B23 5HD Tel: 0121-244 4141 Fax: 0121-244 4142 E-mail: info@gillman-group.com

Miller Homes, Miller House, 2 Lochside View, Edinburgh, EH12 9DH Tel: (0870) 3365000 Fax: 0131-315 6110

Mini Clipper Ltd, 7 Chartmoor Road, Leighton Buzzard, Bedfordshire, LU7 4WG Tel: (01525) 244700 Fax: (01525) 851445 E-mail: sales@miniclipper.co.uk

Warmglade Ltd, 2 College Farm, Church Street, Whaddon, Royston, Hertfordshire, SG8 5RU Tel: (01223) 208788

CONSTRUCTION INDUSTRY INSURANCE

▶ Blackmore Heath Ltd, Luffield House Eurolink Industrial Centre, Stadium Way, Sittingbourne, Kent, ME10 3SD Tel: (01795) 470471 Fax: (01795) 470475 E-mail: steve@bhl-insurance.co.uk

▶ LG Insurance Services Ltd, Unit C6, Seedbed Centre Davidson Way, Romford, RM7 0AZ Tel: (01708) 730830 Fax: (01708) 734505 E-mail: LGinsurance@aol.com

CONSTRUCTION INDUSTRY INTERMEDIARY SERVICES

Anglian Bridges, 3 Westbrook Close, Steeple Morden, Royston, Hertfordshire, SG8 0NY Tel: (01763) 852839 Fax: (01763) 852839

Cornelly Sales, 207 North Approach, Garston, Watford, WD25 0ES Tel: (01923) 670884 Fax: (01923) 670883 E-mail: fredstrous@cornelly.co.uk

J & P UK Ltd, 16 Hanover Street, London, W1S 1YL Tel: (020) 7493 6493 Fax: (020) 7493 0059 E-mail: sales@jandp.org

Royce Butterfield & Wilkey, Barbican Citygate, 1-3 Dufferin Street, London, EC1Y 8NA Tel: (020) 7374 0788 Fax: (020) 7638 1966 E-mail: michael.wilkey@virgin.net

CONSTRUCTION INDUSTRY LEGAL ADVISERS

Forde Edwards & Partners, Monton House, Monton Green, Eccles, Manchester, M30 9LE Tel: 0161-788 9099 Fax: 0161-788 9155 E-mail: forde@totalise.co.uk

Gibson Consulting Ltd, 3 The Quadrant, Coventry, CV1 2DY Tel: (024) 7624 3607 Fax: (024) 7624 3608 E-mail: mark.gibson@gibsonconsulting.co.uk

Hammond Suddards Edge Solicitors, 148 Edmund Street, Birmingham, B3 2JR Tel: 0121-222 3000 Fax: 0121-222 3001 E-mail: sales@hammondsuddardsedge.com

Martineau Johnson, St.Philips House, St. Phillips Place, Birmingham, B3 2PP Tel: 0121-200 3300 Fax: 0121-200 3300 E-mail: marketing@martjohn.com

Royce Butterfield & Wilkey, Barbican Citygate, 1-3 Dufferin Street, London, EC1Y 8NA Tel: (020) 7374 0788 Fax: (020) 7638 1966 E-mail: michael.wilkey@virgin.net

CONSTRUCTION INDUSTRY SOFTWARE

▶ Business Collaborator, North Reading Bridge House, George Street, Reading, RG1 8LS Tel: (0870) 1632555 Fax: (0870) 1632550 E-mail: sales@groupbc.com

CAD Academy Ltd, Sherwood House, Gregory Boulevard, Nottingham, NG7 6LB Tel: 0115-969 1114 Fax: 0115-969 1115 E-mail: info@cadacademy.co.uk

▶ Cambot Technologies Ltd, 135 Edgar Street, Hereford, HR4 9JR Tel: (01432) 370950 E-mail: adrian@camcot.co.uk

Causeway Technologies Ltd, Bucknalls Lane, Watford, WD25 9XX Tel: (01923) 892600 Fax: (01923) 679288 E-mail: partners@ecl.uk.com

Claremont Controls Ltd, Suite 4 Wansbeck Business Centre, Rotary Parkway, Ashington, Northumberland, NE63 8QZ Tel: (01670) 819000 Fax: (01670) 857886 E-mail: honet@claremont-controls.co.uk

Cobham Computer Systems Ltd, 56-58 Smithbrook Kiln, Cranleigh, Surrey, GU6 8JJ Tel: (01483) 275515 Fax: (01483) 277067 E-mail: sales@cobhamsystems.co.uk

Computer Aided Business Systems Ltd, 8 Forum Place, Fiddlebridge Lane, Hatfield, Hertfordshire, AL10 0RN Tel: (01707) 258338 Fax: (01707) 258339 E-mail: sales@cabs-cad.com

Hamilton Hall Consultants Ltd, 3-4 The Windmills, St Marys Close, Alton, Hampshire, GU34 1EF Tel: (01420) 548548 Fax: (01420) 548549 E-mail: admin@hamiltonhall.co.uk

▶ Jobmaster Ltd, Intake Lane, Cromford, Matlock, Derbyshire, DE4 3RH Tel: (01629) 56363 Fax: (01629) 580469 E-mail: general@jobmaster.co.uk

▶ KMS, 63 Tanner Street, London, SE1 3PL Tel: (020) 7939 0740 Fax: (020) 7407 2810 E-mail: rachelb@kms-software.com

Lusas Computer Systems, 66 High Street, Kingston upon Thames, Surrey, KT1 1HN Tel: (020) 8541 1999 Fax: (020) 8549 9399 E-mail: info@lusas.com

The Technology Forge, Top Floor Pegholme, Wharfebank Business Centre, Otley, Leeds, LS21 3JP Tel: (01943) 464844 Fax: (01943) 464833 E-mail: sales@technologyforge.com

CONSTRUCTION INDUSTRY SOLICITORS

▶ Campbell Fitzpatrick, 51 Adelaide Street, Belfast, BT2 8FE Tel: (028) 9032 7388 Fax: (028) 9032 7732 E-mail: sales@campbell-fitzpatrick.co.uk

Ferdinand Kelly Solicitors, Yew House, Tamworth, Staffordshire, B78 2EY Tel: (01827) 895039 Fax: (01827) 895039 E-mail: info@ferdinandkelly.co.uk

▶ Gill Akaster, 25 Lockyer Street, Plymouth, PL1 2QW Tel: (01752) 512000 Fax: (01752) 203503 E-mail: steve.turner@gillakaster.com

CONSTRUCTION INDUSTRY TRAINING

John Laing, Gate 14, Basin South, London, E16 2QY Tel: (020) 7055 2450 Fax: (020) 7055 2451 E-mail: info@jlaingtraining.co.uk

▶ National Construction College Midlands, 83 Lifford Lane, Birmingham, B30 3JH Tel: 0121-459 8000 Fax: 0121-459 8330 E-mail: nationalconstruction.college@citb.co.uk

CONSTRUCTION INSURANCE

▶ Giles Financial Services, 12 Beresford Terrace, Ayr, KA7 2EG Tel: (01292) 619900 Fax: (01292) 610037
▶ JCB Insurance Services Ltd, Rocester, Uttoxeter, Staffordshire, ST14 5BW Tel: (01889) 590219 Fax: (01889) 590742 E-mail: insurance@jcb.com

CONSTRUCTION MANAGEMENT

▶ Mukiwa Projects, 3 Augustus Road, London, SW19 6LL Tel: (020) 8788 6452 Fax: (020) 8788 6452 E-mail: info@mukiwaprojects.com

CONSTRUCTION MOVEMENT JOINTS

Genesis Aps International Ltd, Ellerbeck Way, Stokesley Industrial Park, Stokesley, Middlesbrough, Cleveland, TS9 5JZ Tel: (01642) 713000 Fax: (01642) 713777 E-mail: enquiries@genesis-aps.com

CONSTRUCTION NATIONAL VOCATIONAL QUALIFICATION (NVQ) TRAINING

John Laing, Gate 14, Basin South, London, E16 2QY Tel: (020) 7055 2450 Fax: (020) 7055 2451 E-mail: info@jlaingtraining.co.uk

CONSTRUCTION OCCUPATIONAL HEALTH SAFETY TRAINING

COPE Ergonomics, Unit 1, The Business Park, Technology Drive, Nottingham, NG9 2ND Tel: 0115-925 9222 Fax: 0115-925 2111 E-mail: nick.aubrey@copeohs.com
▶ Everwell Occupational Health Ltd, The Rowans, Holmes Chapel Road, Somerford, Congleton, Cheshire, CW12 4SP Tel: (01477) 544306 E-mail: enquiries@everwelloh.co.uk
▶ Lifestyle Assessment Ltd, 39 Watery Lane, Keresley, Coventry, CV6 2GF Tel: (0800) 2985521 Fax: 02476 722053

CONSTRUCTION PLANNING AND ESTIMATING SAFETY TRAINING

UK Estimating Support Ltd, First Floor, 125-129 Witton Street, Northwich, Cheshire, CW9 5DY Tel: 0845 644 5327 Fax: 0845 644 5328 E-mail: office@estimatingsupport.co.uk

CONSTRUCTION PLANT HYDRAULIC EQUIPMENT OR SYSTEMS

▶ Bosch Rexroth Ltd, 23 Queensbrook, Bolton, BL1 4AY Tel: (01204) 534083 Fax: (01204) 534084 E-mail: steve.smith@boschrexroth.co.uk

CONSTRUCTION PLANT OR EQUIPMENT, *See also headings under Contractors' Plant*

▶ A R Plant Hire Ltd, Tanglewood Derritt Lane, Bransgore, Christchurch, Dorset, BH23 8AR Tel: (01425) 673388 Fax: (01425) 674485 E-mail: mail@ar-planthire.co.uk
A U S A (UK) Ltd, Unit 6-7 Alma Industrial Estate, Regent Street, Rochdale, Lancashire, OL12 0HQ Tel: (01706) 649691 Fax: (01706) 649720 E-mail: ausa@comel.demon.co.uk
Bell Equipment UK, Unit 6c Graycar Business Park, Barton Turns Barton Under, Barton Under Needwood, Burton-on-Trent, Staffordshire, DE13 8EN Tel: (01283) 712862 Fax: (01283) 712687 E-mail: web@bell.co.za
Butler Reynolds Ltd, Loughborough Road, Costock, Loughborough, Leicestershire, LE12 6XB Tel: (01509) 854144 Fax: (01509) 854199 E-mail: sales@butlerreynolds.co.uk
Caterpillar UK Ltd, Peckleton Lane, Desford, Leicester, LE9 9JU Tel: (01455) 826826 Fax: (01455) 826900
Cocon Construction Ltd, North Shore Builders Yard, Holyhead, Gwynedd, LL65 3AG Tel: (01407) 742222 Fax: (01407) 769347 E-mail: cocon@btinternet.com
Construction Machinery Supplies (UK) Ltd, Dormers, Hawthorn Lane, Four Marks, Alton, Hampshire, GU34 5AU Tel: (01420) 587216 Fax: (01420) 588303 E-mail: douglas.bonham@virgin.net
▶ Corrie Construction Ltd, North Road, Fort William, Inverness-Shire, PH33 6PP Tel: (01397) 700680 Fax: (01397) 703933 E-mail: sales@corrieconstruction.com
▶ D.G. Simpson Plant, Unit 2, Mill Lane, Littleburn Industrial Estate, Langley Moor, Durham, DH7 8HE Tel: 0191-378 3666 Fax: 0191-378 2333 E-mail: dgequipt@aol.com
D L Pugh Plant, Pentreclwyda House, Pentreclwyda, Resolven, Neath, West Glamorgan, SA11 4DU Tel: (01639) 720017 Fax: (01639) 721122
Dean Konrad Plant Sales, 78 Moira Road, Crumlin, County Antrim, BT29 4JL Tel: (028) 9442 3787 Fax: (028) 9445 4144 E-mail: sales@kdplant.com
▶ Extec Screens & Crushers Ltd, Unit 9 Gortrush Industrial Estate, Omagh, County Tyrone, BT78 5EJ Tel: (028) 8224 3790 Fax: (028) 8224 1940
F T Construction Equipment, Norwich Road, Swainsthorpe, Norwich, NR14 8PU Tel: (01508) 471777 Fax: (01508) 471585 E-mail: sales@ft-construction.co.uk
▶ FarmEquip.co.uk, 16 Camperdown Road, Boathpark, Nairn, IV12 5AR Tel: (01667) 456842
Fields International C A Ltd, Cavendish Avenue, Sheffield, S17 3NJ Tel: 0114-235 0103 Fax: 0114-236 2815 E-mail: sales@fields-international.com
▶ Geddes Group Ltd, Swirlburn, Colliston, Arbroath, Angus, DD11 3SH Tel: (01241) 890266 Fax: (01241) 890445
Gomaco International Ltd, 769 Buckingham Avenue, Slough, SL1 4NL Tel: (01753) 821926 Fax: (01753) 693093 E-mail: pavinguk@gomaco.com
▶ Gordon Bow Plant Hire, 82-86 East Main St, Broxburn, West Lothian, EH52 5EG Tel: (01506) 855913 Fax: (01506) 856393 E-mail: info@gordonbow.co.uk
H M Plant Ltd, 964 Weston Road, Slough Trading Estate, Slough, SL1 4HR Tel: (01753) 213900 Fax: (01753) 213901 E-mail: info@hmplant.ltd.uk
H S S Lift & Shift, Eastern Avenue Industrial Estate, Eastern Avenue, Dunstable, Bedfordshire, LU5 4JY Tel: (01582) 673256 Fax: (01582) 411320
High Speed Hire, 47 High Street, Nailsea, Bristol, BS48 1AW Tel: (01275) 810364 Fax: (01275) 859464
HSS Hire, 166-178 Great Howard Street, Liverpool, L3 7DW Tel: 0151-207 4747 Fax: 0151-207 3386
Industrial & Construction Plant Ltd, Clarence Road, Stoke-on-Trent, ST3 1AZ Tel: (01782) 316791 Fax: (01782) 599411 E-mail: enquiries@longtoncranehire.co.uk
Interworld, Avenue Road, Lasham, Alton, Hampshire, GU34 5SU Tel: (01256) 381641 Fax: (01256) 381378
J C B Compact Products Ltd, Harewood Estate, Leek Road, Cheadle, Stoke-on-Trent, ST10 2JU Tel: (01538) 755641 Fax: (01538) 757590
Leach Lewis Ltd, Victoria House, Britannia Road, Waltham Cross, Hertfordshire, EN8 7NU Tel: (01992) 704100 Fax: (01992) 704170 E-mail: enquiries@leachlewis.co.uk
Leica Geosystems Ltd, Davy Avenue, Knowlhill, Milton Keynes, MK5 8LB Tel: (01908) 256500 Fax: (01908) 609992 E-mail: uk.construction@leica-geosystems.com
Lemac Engineering, Block 3 Barnpark Drive, Tillicoultry, Clackmannanshire, FK13 6BZ Tel: (01259) 751573 Fax: (01259) 751196
▶ McGarvey Construction, 86 Clark Street, Paisley, Renfrewshire, PA3 1RB Tel: 0141-848 7555
New Ventures Products, Queens Yard, Long Wittenham Road, North Moreton, Didcot, Oxfordshire, OX11 9AX Tel: (0845) 4304030 Fax: (0845) 130 5833 E-mail: sales@newventureproducts.co.uk
Oakes Brothers Ltd, Fareham Road, Wickham, Fareham, Hampshire, PO17 5DH Tel: (01329) 832345 Fax: (01329) 833944
On Site Supplies, Stephenson Way, Crawley, West Sussex, RH10 1TN Tel: (01293) 744444
P P S Construction Plant Sales Ltd, Tomlinson Road, Leyland, PR25 2DY Tel: (01772) 456392 Fax: (01772) 621368 E-mail: info@ppsplantsales.co.uk
Phoenix Fixings Ltd, 21 Park Road, Bingley, West Yorkshire, BD16 4BQ Tel: (01274) 779001 Fax: (01274) 771277 E-mail: info@phoenixfixings.co.uk
Powered Access, Drury Way, London, NW10 0JH Tel: (020) 8830 3333 Fax: (08702) 415949 E-mail: phillomax@poweredaccess.com
▶ Pure Hire & Sales, 167 Hampton Road, London, E4 8NS Tel: (020) 8524 5115 Fax: (020) 8523 8751 E-mail: sales@purehire.co.uk
Quartz Plant UK Ltd, 5 Thomas Avenue, Radcliffe-On-Trent, Nottingham, NG12 2HT Tel: 0115-933 4947 Fax: 0115-933 4947 E-mail: brassandpower@ntlworld.com
▶ Richmack Building Services, 14 Nettlehill Road, Uphall Station, Livingston, West Lothian, EH54 5PP Tel: (01506) 505010 Fax: (01506) 505007
S M Plants Services Ltd, Hoo Marina Industrial Estate, Hoo, Rochester, Kent, ME3 9LB Tel: (01634) 253333 Fax: (01634) 253112
▶ Southwest Roofing Services Ltd, 6 Green Street Lane, Ayr, KA8 8BL Tel: (01292) 287936 Fax: (01292) 619719
▶ Southwest Roofing Services Ltd, Commerce Road, Stranraer, Wigtownshire, DG9 7DZ Tel: (01387) 256176 Fax: (01776) 703523
▶ Southwest Roofing Services Ltd, Commerce Road, Stranraer, Wigtownshire, DG9 7DZ Tel: (01387) 256176 Fax: (01776) 703523
Taylor Construction Plant Ltd, Unit 2, Broadmeadows, Harburn, West Calder, West Lothian, EH55 8RT Tel: (01621) 850777 Fax: (01621) 843330 E-mail: mail@tcp.eu
Terex UK Ltd, Central Boulevard, Prologis Park, Coventry, CV6 4BX Tel: (024) 7633 9400 Fax: (024) 7633 9500 E-mail: enquiries@terexce.com
▶ Truckmixer UK Ltd, 1 Stainsby Close, Holmewood Industrial Estate, Chesterfield, Derbyshire, S42 5UG Tel: (01246) 854339 Fax: (01246) 854339
Yorkshire Handlers Ltd, Unit 3 Fryors Close, Murton, York, YO19 5UY Tel: (01904) 489988 Fax: (01904) 489061 E-mail: sales@yorkshirehandlers.co.uk
Young Plant & Equipment Sales Ltd, Lochhill Industrial Estate, Doune, Perthshire, FK16 6AD Tel: (01786) 841598 Fax: (01786) 841130 E-mail: sales@youngplant.co.uk

CONSTRUCTION PLANT OR EQUIPMENT ATTACHMENTS

HY-MAC Construction Equipment, No 1 Berkeley Street, Mayfair, London, WC1 1UH Tel: (0870) 7602671 Fax: (0870) 7602672 E-mail: info@hy-mac.com

CONSTRUCTION PLANT OR EQUIPMENT HIRE

▶ A G Thomson & Sons, Spott Road, Dunbar, East Lothian, EH42 1RR Tel: (01368) 862315 Fax: (01368) 863000
A L F Plant Hire, Lyndon Lodge, Kilby Road, Fleckney, Leicester, LE8 8BQ Tel: 0116-240 3749
▶ A Plant Ltd, Poole Lane, Bournemouth, BH11 9DU Tel: (01202) 582580 Fax: (01202) 582581
▶ A Plant Groundcare, Cootham Lea Workshop, Pulborough Road, Cootham, Pulborough, West Sussex, RH20 4JN Tel: (01903) 742348 Fax: (01903) 742351
ABBEY PLANT HIRE, Great Frenchstone, South Molton, DEVON, EX36 4JH Tel: (01769) 579460 E-mail: admin@graysplanthire.co.uk
Accom Ltd, 1 Cliffside Industrial Estate, Askew Farm Lane, Grays, Essex, RM17 5XR Tel: (01375) 396262 Fax: (01375) 396363
Ainscough Crane Hire Ltd, Stanlow Refinery, PO Box 3, Ellesmere Port, CH65 4HB Tel: 0151-355 8812
▶ Ainscough Crane Hire Ltd, Langmuir Way, Baillieston, Glasgow, G69 7RW Tel: 0141-773 0500 Fax: 0141-781 1010 E-mail: general@ainscough.co.uk
▶ Ainscough Crane Hire Ltd, Scott Lane, Morley, Leeds, LS27 0NQ Tel: 0113-253 4366 Fax: 0113-253 2321
▶ Alan Whiteford Contracts Ltd, Moulandale, Burnhervie, Fetternear, Inverurie, Aberdeenshire, AB51 5JU Tel: (01467) 642151 Fax: (01467) 643770
▶ Alexander Plant Hire, Office 3A, 7 York Street, Ayr, KA8 8AN Tel: (01292) 265335
▶ Amec Internal Asset Management Ltd, Meadowside Street, Renfrew, PA4 8SS Tel: 0141-886 2253 Fax: 0141-886 6510
▶ T.M. Andrew (Plant Hire) Ltd, Kirktonfield Road, Neilston, Glasgow, G78 3NY Tel: 0141-880 7119
▶ Andy Hire Sales & Services Ltd, Wykeham Street, Scarborough, North Yorkshire, YO12 7SB Tel: (01723) 500601 Fax: (01723) 500611
▶ Angus Jordan, Broomknowe House Struthers, Cupar, Fife, KY15 5PG Tel: (01334) 828433 Fax: (01334) 828177
▶ A-Plant Ltd, Ford Airfield Industrial Estate, Ford, Arundel, West Sussex, BN18 0HY Tel: (01903) 717431 Fax: (01903) 732246
▶ A-Plant Ltd, Humber Road, Barton-upon-Humber, South Humberside, DN18 5BN Tel: (01652) 637777 Fax: (01652) 637788
▶ A-Plant Ltd, B Swann Road, Cambridge, CB5 8JZ Tel: (01223) 464367 Fax: (01223) 350050
▶ A-Plant Ltd, Speedfields Park, Fareham, Hampshire, PO14 1TS Tel: (01329) 829998 Fax: (01329) 828088
A-Plant, Unit 1 Block E, 19 Nurseries Road, Baillieston, Glasgow, G69 6UL Tel: 0141-771 7388 Fax: 0141-771 4929
▶ A-Plant Ltd, Chaddock Lane Industrial Estate, Kennedy Road, Astley Tyldesley, Manchester, M29 7JY Tel: (01942) 884588
A-Plant Ltd, 5 Wood Street, Openshaw, Manchester, M11 2FB Tel: 0161-231 4035 Fax: 0161-223 3140
▶ A-Plant Ltd, King George Close, Romford, RM7 7PN Tel: (01708) 730206 Fax: (01708) 733839
▶ A-Plant Ltd, Lockheed Close, Preston Farm Industrial Estate, Stockton-on-Tees, Cleveland, TS18 3SE Tel: (01642) 615151 Fax: (01642) 614549
▶ Ash Build Ltd, 21a Ancaster Road, Beckenham, Kent, BR3 4DZ Tel: (020) 8663 6227 Fax: (020) 8663 6254
▶ Ashstead Plant Hire, 16 St Machar Road, Aberdeen, AB24 2UU Tel: (01224) 276760
Ashtead Plant Hire Co. Ltd, Greenwell Road, East Tullos Industrial Estate, Aberdeen, AB12 3AX Tel: (01224) 876538 Fax: (01224) 899032 E-mail: whitehaven@aplant.com
▶ Ashtead Plant Hire Co. Ltd, Rossfield Road, Ellesmere Port, CH65 3AW Tel: 0151-357 3075 Fax: 0151-356 8588
▶ Ashtead Plant Hire Company Ltd, James Corbett Road, Salford, M50 1DE Tel: 0161-736 3779
▶ B & M Davies Plant Hire Ltd, Lakeside, Lees Lane, Dalton, Wigan, Lancashire, WN8 7RE Tel: (01257) 254343
▶ Beaver 84 Ltd, Thingoe Hill, Bury St. Edmunds, Suffolk, IP32 6BE Tel: (01284) 724824 Fax: (01284) 765824 E-mail: sales@beaver84.co.uk
▶ Beaver 84 Ltd, Bunny Lane, Sherfield English, Romsey, Hampshire, SO51 6FT Tel: (01794) 884876 Fax: (01794) 884277
▶ Bicester Sweepers Ltd, Glebe Court, Fringford, Bicester, Oxfordshire, OX27 8RJ Tel: (01869) 277410 Fax: (01869) 277704
▶ Bob Francis, 31 Deeside Industrial Estate, Welsh Road, Deeside, Clwyd, CH5 2LR Tel: (01745) 591753 Fax: (01745) 591929
▶ Bobcat Midlands Limited, Ridgeway, Well Lane, Little Witley, Worcester, WR6 6LN Tel: 01886 888413 Fax: 01886 888561 E-mail: adam.bobcat@virgin.net
▶ Broadhempston Plant Hire Ltd, Fairfax Road, Heathfield Industrial Estate, Newton Abbot, Devon, TQ12 6UD Tel: (01626) 832290 Fax: (01626) 201131
▶ Buckingham Plant Hire Ltd, Blackpit Farm, Silverstone Road, Stowe, Buckingham, MK18 5LJ Tel: (01280) 823355 Fax: (01280) 812830 E-mail: mail@buckinghamplant.co.uk
▶ Bullimore Plant Hire, 3 Spalding Road Industrial Esta, Bourne, Lincolnshire, PE10 9LE Tel: (01778) 423309 Fax: (01778) 393139
▶ C B L Ltd, Banyard Road, Portbury, Bristol, BS20 7XH Tel: (01275) 372229
▶ C S J Plant Ltd, Harboro House Fairhills Industrial Estate, Woodrow Way, Irlam, Manchester, M44 6ZQ Tel: 0161-775 0805 Fax: 0161-775 0711
▶ Cadzow Plant Hire Ltd, 15 Forrest St, Blantyre, Glasgow, G72 0JP Tel: (01698) 713344 Fax: (01698) 713355
▶ Caledonian Industrial Ltd, Unit 23 Eldin Industrial Estate, Edgefield Road, Loanhead, Midlothian, EH20 9QX Tel: 0131-448 0889 Fax: 0131-448 0891
▶ Calico Plant & Transport Ltd, Dawber Industrial Area, Skull House Lane, Appley Bridge, Wigan, Lancashire, WN6 9DN Tel: (01257) 252962 Fax: (01257) 254199
▶ Cameron Plant Hire Holdings Ltd, Brownside Farm, Loganswell, Newton Mearns, Glasgow, G77 6RZ Tel: (01355) 500286
▶ Cappers Plant Hire, Station Road, Armadale, Bathgate, West Lothian, EH48 3LJ Tel: (01501) 733999 Fax: (01501) 735310 E-mail: sales@cphltd.com
▶ Carroll Plant, Brookfield Drive, Liverpool, L9 7HJ Tel: 0151-525 1947 Fax: 0151-523 8322
▶ Carter Cabin Hire, Garage Lane, Setch, King's Lynn, Norfolk, PE33 0BE Tel: (01553) 810778 Fax: (01553) 810793
▶ Catplant Ltd, The Bungalow, Holmsley Lane, Brierley, Barnsley, South Yorkshire, S72 9EX Tel: (01226) 716058 Fax: (01226) 781114
▶ Central Crane Hire Hull, Albert Dock, Hull, HU1 2DY Tel: (01482) 223859 Fax: (01482) 581098
▶ Centre Plant Ltd, 28 Muriel Street, Barrhead, Glasgow, G78 1QB Tel: 0141-880 4433 Fax: 0141-881 0828
▶ Charles Wilson Ltd, 317 Bromford Lane, Washwood Heath, Birmingham, B8 2SH Tel: 0121-325 8686 Fax: 0121-328 7475
▶ Clave & Barford Ltd, Plot 6, Village Farm Industrial Estate, Pyle, Bridgend, Mid Glamorgan, CF33 6BJ Tel: (01656) 743231
▶ Clearwater D C, Carnbroe Road, Bellshill, Lanarkshire, ML4 1RS Tel: (01698) 844771 Fax: (01698) 844723
▶ Collier Plant Hire York Ltd, Station Yard, Temple Lane, Copmanthorpe, York, YO23 3RS Tel: (01904) 707851 Fax: (01904) 700447
▶ Colmil Plant & Equipment Co. Ltd, High Street, Crigglestone, Wakefield, West Yorkshire, WF4 3HT Tel: (01924) 259411 Fax: (01924) 253427
▶ Contradig, Bethania, Capel Garmon, Llanrwst, Conwy, LL26 0RL Tel: (01690) 710309 Fax: (01690) 710154 E-mail: info@contradig.com
▶ Cosham Plant Hire & Construction, Gate 4, Southmoor Lane, Havant, Hampshire, PO9 1JW Tel: (023) 9247 6400 Fax: (023) 9245 1581 E-mail: info@coshamplant.co.uk
▶ Coul Plant Hire, Coul Road, Contin, Strathpeffer, Ross-Shire, IV14 9ES Tel: (01997) 421817
▶ D A Johnstone, Station Yard, Longhirst, Morpeth, Northumberland, NE61 3HZ Tel: (01670) 812244 Fax: (01670) 810088
▶ D A Mcdonald, Kilmory, Lochgilphead, Argyll, PA31 8RR Tel: (01546) 603583 Fax: (01546) 602576
▶ D Kerr & Sons, Helenslea, Castlecary Road, Cumbernauld, Glasgow, G68 0HQ Tel: (01324) 840337 Fax: (01324) 840885
▶ David Turner, 55 Easthouses Road, Easthouses, Dalkeith, Midlothian, EH22 4EB Tel: 0131-663 2900 Fax: 0131-663 2900
Dawson, Muirfield, Overthickside, Jedburgh, Roxburghshire, TD8 6QX Tel: (01835) 863003 Fax: (01835) 863003
▶ Demenex Plant Hire Ltd, Wick Lane, London, E3 2TB Tel: (020) 8981 7711 Fax: (020) 8983 1080

CONSTRUCTION PLANT OR EQUIPMENT HIRE – *continued*

▶ Didsbury Plant Hire Ltd, Limefield House, Limefield Brow, Bury, Lancashire, BL9 6QS Tel: 0161-764 2580 Fax: 0161-763 9511

▶ Duncan Plant Hire Ltd, Gatehead Farm, Mansefield Road, New Cumnock, Cumnock, Ayrshire, KA18 4NU Tel: (01290) 338206 Fax: (01290) 338206

▶ E Jones & Son, Bronallt, Clawddnewydd, Ruthin, Clwyd, LL15 2NA Tel: (01824) 750604 Fax: (01824) 750402

▶ Ellon Plant & Machinery Hire, Unit 1 Castle Street, Castlepark Industrial Estate, Ellon, Aberdeenshire, AB41 9RF Tel: (01358) 720991 Fax: (01358) 722417 E-mail: sales@ellon-plant-hire.co.uk

▶ Ellon Plant & Machinery Hire, Unit 1 Castle Street, Castlepark Industrial Estate, Ellon, Aberdeenshire, AB41 9RF Tel: (01358) 720991 Fax: (01358) 722417 E-mail: sales@ellon-plant-hire.co.uk

▶ Equipment Planthire Ltd, 6 Hydepark Road, Newtownabbey, County Antrim, BT36 4PY Tel: (028) 9034 2150 Fax: (028) 9083 6941 E-mail: info@eplhire.com

▶ Eric Carnaby & Son, Holton Farm, Town Street, South Killingholme, Immingham, South Humberside, DN40 3DA Tel: (01469) 540329 Fax: (01469) 541074

▶ Farm Power, Ivy House Farm, Course Lane, Newburgh, Wigan, Lancashire, WN8 7UG Tel: (01257) 463679

▶ First Refurbishment & Demolition Ltd, 16 Lyon Road, Walton-on-Thames, Surrey, KT12 3PU Tel: (01932) 269301 Fax: (01932) 269303

▶ Forth Paving Ltd, Jamieson Mcgregor Yard, Kelliebank, Alloa, Clackmannanshire, FK10 1NU Tel: (01259) 212945 Fax: (01259) 212945

▶ Foster Plant Hire, 74 Acredales, Haddington, East Lothian, EH41 4NU Tel: (01620) 824823 Fax: (01620) 829457

▶ G E Capital, Beacon Hill Garage, 19 Beacon Hill Lane, Corfe Mullen, Wimborne, Dorset, BH21 3RU Tel: (01202) 659909 Fax: (01202) 659077

▶ G E Capital Equipment Services, Cotes Park Lane, Cotes Park Industrial Estate, Somercotes, Alfreton, Derbyshire, DE55 4PU Tel: (01773) 520777 Fax: (01773) 521005 E-mail: daren.sharpe@ge.com

▶ G P Hire Ltd, The Pleasance, Lanark, ML11 9TG Tel: (01555) 663234 Fax: (01555) 666969 E-mail: info@gpplantscape.com

▶ Garriock Ltd, 11 Newbridge Industrial Estate, Newbridge, Midlothian, EH28 8PJ Tel: 0131-333 2009 Fax: 0131-333 1979

▶ Gavin Craig Plant Hire, Avonside Farm, Drumclog, Strathaven, Lanarkshire, ML10 6RQ Tel: (01357) 440388

▶ Glenn Davidson Plant Ltd, Glendal, Corstorphine Road, Thornhill, Dumfriesshire, DG3 5NB Tel: (01848) 330839

▶ Go Plant, Unit 14 Parham Drive, Eastleigh, Hampshire, SO50 4NU Tel: (023) 8061 2727 Fax: (023) 8061 1212 E-mail: sales@gpl-hire.co.uk

Graham Jones Crane Hire Ltd, Rhosddu Industrial Estate, Rhosrobin, Wrexham, Clwyd, LL11 4YL Tel: (01978) 366458 Fax: (01978) 310573 E-mail: jonescranehire@aol.com

▶ Gravelle Plant Hire, Riverside Works, Penybanc Road, Ammanford, Dyfed, SA18 3RB Tel: (01269) 591049 Fax: (01269) 591040

▶ Groundplant Ltd, Nuttaberry Works, Nuttaberry, Bideford, Devon, EX39 4DT Tel: (01237) 475048 Fax: (01237) 475049

▶ H E Services (Plant Hire) Ltd, Riverside Industrial Estate, Langley Park, Durham, DH7 9TT Tel: 0191-373 7114

H E Services (Plant Hire) Ltd, Membury Business Park, Lambourn Woodlands, Hungerford, Berkshire, RG17 7TJ Tel: (01488) 73444

▶ H M Price Ltd, Gelli Wern Ganol Farm, Felindre, Swansea, SA5 7PJ Tel: (01792) 885396 Fax: (01792) 885801

▶ H & S Contractors Ltd, Kingsnorth Industrial Estate, Hoo, Rochester, Kent, ME3 9ND Tel: (01634) 253545 Fax: (01634) 251145 E-mail: mail@hscontractors.co.uk

▶ Hall Plant Hire Ltd, The Birches, Hollins, Old Brampton, Chesterfield, Derbyshire, S42 7JH Tel: (01246) 567233 Fax: (01246) 567248

▶ Hatton Traffic Management Ltd, Brunswick Industrial Estate, Brunswick Village, Newcastle upon Tyne, NE13 7BA Tel: 0191-236 8060 Fax: 0191-236 2035

▶ Hawes Plant Hire, Navigation Way, Loughborough, Leicestershire, LE11 1QD Tel: (01509) 212024 Fax: (01509) 611655

▶ Hawkspare Ltd Commercial Vehicle Exptrs, Green St Groveeen Road, Dartford, DA2 8DP Tel: (01474) 706971 Fax: (01474) 703402 E-mail: info@hawkspare.co.uk

▶ Hember Plant Hire Ltd, Eagle House 8 Heol Mostyn, Village Farm Industrial Estate, Pyle, Bridgend, Mid Glamorgan, CF33 6NU Tel: (01656) 744240 Fax: (01656) 744460

▶ Hewden Crane Hire Ltd, Billingham Reach Industrial Estate, Haverton Hill Road, Billingham, Cleveland, TS23 1PX Tel: (01642) 853737 Fax: (01642) 853738

▶ Hewden Crane Hire Ltd, 8 Kings Road, Immingham, South Humberside, DN40 1AL Tel: (01469) 575158 Fax: (01469) 578303

▶ Hewden Hire Centres Ltd, Brunswick Road, Ashford, Kent, TN23 1EL Tel: (01233) 634885 Fax: (01233) 665636

▶ Hewden Hire Centres, Unit 5 Brett Drive, Bexhill-on-Sea, East Sussex, TN40 2JP Tel: (01424) 210601 Fax: (01424) 427722

▶ Hewden Hire Centres Ltd, 107 Slateford Road, Edinburgh, EH11 1QY Tel: 0131-337 9494 Fax: 0131-337 9595

▶ Hewden Hire Centres Ltd, 88-92 Kilbirnie Street, Glasgow, G5 8JD Tel: 0141-429 7431 Fax: 0141-429 5139

▶ Hewden Hire Centres, 1 Ringway Trading Estate, Shadow Moss Road, Manchester, M22 6LX Tel: 0161-499 9413 Fax: 0161-437 0114

▶ Hewden Hire Centres Ltd, Penn Street, Newcastle upon Tyne, NE4 7BG Tel: 0191-273 4491 Fax: 0191-226 1393

▶ Hewden Instant Access Ltd, 20 Carmaben Road, Glasgow, G33 4UN Tel: 0141-781 0555 Fax: 0141-781 0318

▶ Hewden Instant Access Ltd, 20 Carmaben Road, Glasgow, G33 4UN Tel: 0141-781 0555 Fax: 0141-781 0318

▶ Hewden Instant Access Ltd, Ashmore Lake Way, Willenhall, West Midlands, WV12 4LF Tel: (01902) 608666 Fax: (01902) 603322

▶ Hewden Plant Hire Ltd, 251 Bordesley Green Road, Birmingham, B8 1BY Tel: 0121-772 5900 Fax: 0121-772 4821

▶ Hewden Plant Hire Ltd, Sloper Road, Cardiff, CF11 8AB Tel: (029) 2023 3491 Fax: (029) 2038 3134

▶ Hewden Plant Hire Ltd, Pound Mead, Corsham, Wiltshire, SN13 9NZ Tel: (01249) 712362 Fax: (01249) 701080

▶ Hewden Plant Hire Ltd, 40 Old Glamis Road, Dundee, DD3 8JQ Tel: (01382) 889922 Fax: (01382) 884222

▶ Hewden Plant Hire Ltd, Unit 13 Parham Drive, Eastleigh, Hampshire, SO50 4NU Tel: (023) 8061 8733 Fax: (023) 8061 1758

▶ Hewden Plant Hire Ltd, New Elgin Road, Elgin, Morayshire, IV30 6BE Tel: (01343) 550400 Fax: (01343) 549965

▶ Hewden Plant Hire Ltd, 20 Carmaben Road, Glasgow, G33 4UN Tel: 0141-771 1777 Fax: 0141-771 2777

▶ Hewden Plant Hire Ltd, Cattle Market, St. Oswalds Road, Gloucester, GL1 2SR Tel: (01452) 500959 Fax: (01452) 307988

▶ Hewden Plant Hire Ltd, 158 Park Street, Motherwell, Lanarkshire, ML1 1PF Tel: (01698) 252424 Fax: (01698) 275188

▶ Hewden Plant Hire Ltd, Mount Carbis Road, Redruth, Cornwall, TR15 2QQ Tel: (01209) 218730 Fax: (01209) 315262

▶ Hewden Plant Hire Ltd, Kinmel Park, Abergele Road, Bodelwyddan, Rhyl, Clwyd, LL18 5TY Tel: (01745) 583121 Fax: (01745) 582528

▶ Hewden Plant Hire Ltd, 99 Station Road, Thatcham, Berkshire, RG19 4QH Tel: (01635) 864418 Fax: (01635) 866897

▶ Hewden Plant Hire Ltd, Meadow Road, Whitehaven, Cumbria, CA28 9HY Tel: (01946) 694311 Fax: (01946) 691431

▶ Hewden Plant Hire Ltd, Vauxhall Industrial Estate, Ruabon, Wrexham, Clwyd, LL14 6HA Tel: (01978) 821717

▶ Hewden Self-Drive, 119 Hamilton Road, Glasgow, G32 9QW Tel: 0141-764 0590

▶ Hewden Stewart Plc, 1 Ellis Muir Way, Tannochside Park, Uddingston, Glasgow, G71 5PX Tel: (01698) 805500

▶ Hewden Stuart Plc, 2300 London Road, Glasgow, G32 8YU Tel: 0141-778 8571

▶ Hodge Plant, Craighead Farm, Abington, Biggar, Lanarkshire, ML12 6SQ Tel: (01864) 502577 E-mail: hire@hodgeplant.com

▶ Hoist & Access Services Ltd, 2-2a Dalsholm Avenue, Glasgow, G20 0TS Tel: 0141-945 0101 Fax: 0141-946 5200 E-mail: sales@hoistandaccess.com

Hopkinson Construction & Plant Hire, Valley Farm, Middle Bridge Road, Gringley-on-the-Hill, Doncaster, South Yorkshire, DN10 4SD Tel: (01777) 816791 Fax: (01909) 731937

▶ House Builders Montrose Ltd, 20 Castle Place, Montrose, Angus, DD10 8AL Tel: (01674) 673429 Fax: (01674) 673002

▶ HSS Hire, Circle House, Lostock Road, Urmston, Manchester, M41 0HS Tel: 0161-749 4090 Fax: 0161-749 4094

HSS Hire, Unit 1 Bardell Terrace, Rochester, Kent, ME1 1NG Tel: (01634) 880227 Fax: (01634) 880259 E-mail: hire@hss.com

Hydrex Equipment UK Ltd, Duntilland Road, Salsburgh, Shotts, Lanarkshire, ML7 4NZ Tel: (0870) 3501350 Fax: (01698) 871350 E-mail: vincentscott-halton@hydrex.co.uk

▶ Hyndford Plant Ltd, Anstruther Place, Douglas Water, Lanark, ML11 9LR Tel: (01555) 880350 Fax: (01555) 880350

▶ I T Shaw Ltd, Low Mill Business Park, Ulverston, Cumbria, LA12 9EE Tel: (01229) 581928 Fax: (01229) 587624

▶ J M Dewar Plant Contractors, Broich Road, Crieff, Perthshire, PH7 3RT Tel: (01764) 653951 Fax: (01764) 655358

▶ J Rutherford Contractors Hutton Ltd, Hutton Crofts, Hutton, Berwick-upon-Tweed, TD15 1TS Tel: (01289) 386226 Fax: (01289) 386256

▶ J W Munnings Ltd, Harfreys Road, Great Yarmouth, Norfolk, NR31 0LS Tel: (01493) 603328 Fax: (01493) 442424

Jackson & Gocher Hire Centre, Harrow Lane, Farncombe Street, Godalming, Surrey, GU7 3LP Tel: (01483) 527000 Fax: (01483) 415523

James Jack Lifting Services Ltd, Old Coal Yard, South Shore Road, Grangemouth, Stirlingshire, FK3 8TQ Tel: (01324) 664777

▶ James King Plant Ltd, Northampton Road, Blisworth, Northampton, NN7 3DW Tel: (01604) 858558 Fax: (01604) 859204

▶ James Mchugh Contracts Ltd, West End, 127a Main Street, Cairneyhill, Dunfermline, Fife, KY12 8QX Tel: (01383) 881390 Fax: (01383) 881390

▶ Jarvie Plant Ltd, Craigentinny Avenue North, Edinburgh, EH6 7LJ Tel: 0131-553 6994 Fax: 0131-553 6982 E-mail: sales@jarvieplant.co.uk

▶ Jarvie Plant Ltd, 295 Edmiston Drive, Glasgow, G51 3RN Tel: 0141-445 2121 Fax: 0141-440 2847

▶ Jarvie Plant Ltd, Dalgrain Road, Grangemouth, Stirlingshire, FK3 8ET Tel: (01324) 496500 Fax: (01324) 665117 E-mail: info@jarvieplant.co.uk

▶ Jefberry Ltd, Bridgeman House, Pindar Road, Hoddesdon, Hertfordshire, EN11 0DA Tel: (01992) 442133

▶ Jewson Ltd, 265 Godstone Road, Kenley, Surrey, CR8 5BP Tel: (020) 8763 9440 Fax: (020) 8763 9445

▶ John Elliott Ltd, Great Clifton Farm, The Pow, Great Clifton, Workington, Cumbria, CA14 1TZ Tel: (01900) 603881 Fax: (01900) 603151

▶ John Gibbins (Contractors) Ltd, Crimond Airfield, Fraserburgh, Aberdeenshire, AB43 8QQ Tel: (01346) 532400 Fax: (01346) 532200

▶ John Nixon Ltd, Water Street, Newcastle upon Tyne, NE4 7AX Tel: 0191-226 0666 Fax: 0191-272 2176

▶ John Reeve Plant Hire Ltd, Old Chalk Pit, Heronden Road, Eastry, Sandwich, Kent, CT13 0ET Tel: (01304) 611288 Fax: (01304) 614462

▶ K E R Plant Co Ownership Ltd, Hannington Grange Farm, Redhouse Lane, Hannington, Northampton, NN6 9SZ Tel: (01604) 780180 Fax: (01604) 780129

▶ K J Hire Centre, Kemys Way, Swansea Enterprise Park, Swansea, SA6 8QF Tel: (01792) 790953 Fax: (01792) 781803

▶ K & J Plant Hire, West Park, Yarnscombe, Barnstaple, Devon, EX31 3LZ Tel: (01271) 858540 Fax: (01271) 858574 E-mail: training@ctacentre.co.uk

▶ Kent Sweepers Ltd, Station Yard, Nightingale Road, Horsham, West Sussex, RH12 2NW Tel: (01403) 249499 Fax: (01403) 254354

▶ Kent Sweepers Ltd, Tenter Street, Rotherham, South Yorkshire, S60 1LB Tel: (01709) 555153 Fax: (01709) 555013

▶ Keyway Gloucester, The Luther Challis Business Centre, Barnwood Road, Gloucester, GL4 3HX Tel: (01452) 300567 Fax: (01452) 381381 E-mail: sales@keyway.co.uk

▶ Les Searle Plant Hire & Sales Ltd, 16 Parsonage Road, Horsham, West Sussex, RH12 4AN Tel: (01403) 262033 Fax: (01403) 217060

▶ Lloyds Konecranes, Unit 1e Brighouse Business Village, Brighouse Road, Middlesbrough, Cleveland, TS2 1RT Tel: (01642) 223411 Fax: (01642) 225587

▶ Long Eaton Plant Hire Ltd, Crompton Road Industrial Estate, Crompton Road, Ilkeston, Derbyshire, DE7 4BG Tel: 0115-932 7121 Fax: 0115-930 5230

Lucebay Plant Hire Ltd, Drough Duil, Dunragit, Stranraer, Wigtownshire, DG9 8QA Tel: (01581) 400248

▶ M E Willis Sales & Hire Ltd, 38 Long Street, Easingwold, York, YO61 3HT Tel: (01347) 822368 Fax: (01347) 821655

▶ M K Leslie Ltd, Staneyhill Quarry, Staneyhill, Lerwick, Shetland, ZE1 0QW Tel: (01595) 695060 Fax: (01595) 697239

▶ M Webb, Oakdale Trading Estate, Ham Lane, Kingswinford, West Midlands, DY6 7JH Tel: (01384) 401067 Fax: (01384) 294880

▶ M&A, Blue House Point Road, Stockton-on-Tees, Cleveland, TS18 2PQ Tel: (01642) 670379 Fax: (01642) 654055

▶ Mabey Hire Ltd, Stag Industrial Estate, Oxford Street, Bilston, West Midlands, WV14 7HZ Tel: (01902) 404512 Fax: (01902) 494942

▶ Mabey Hire Ltd, Harris Road, Calne, Wiltshire, SN11 9PT Tel: (01249) 821193 Fax: (01249) 821535

▶ Mabey Hire Ltd, Travellers Lane, North Mymms, Hatfield, Hertfordshire, AL9 7HN Tel: (01707) 267171 Fax: (01707) 268971

▶ Mabey Hire Ltd, Commissioners Road, Rochester, Kent, ME2 4EQ Tel: (01634) 722465 Fax: (01634) 723976 E-mail: group@mabey.co.uk

▶ Mabey Hire Ltd, Cupernham Lane, Romsey, Hampshire, SO51 7LF Tel: (01794) 515666 Fax: (01794) 524196

▶ Mabey Hire Ltd, 198 Gibbons Road, Ashton-in-Makerfield, Wigan, Lancashire, WN4 0YA Tel: (01942) 725341 Fax: (01942) 721243

▶ Machinery Movements & Crane Hire Ltd, Queen Alexandra Dock, Cardiff, CF10 4LT Tel: (029) 2048 8360

▶ Mcintosh & Robertson, Broompark Terrace, Murthly, Perth, PH1 4HJ Tel: (01738) 710255 Fax: (01738) 710598

▶ Mackay Plant Hire Ltd, 39 High Meadow, Tollerton, Nottingham, NG12 4DZ Tel: 0115-937 2890 Fax: 0115-937 2889

▶ Maclarty, Galvelmore Street, Crieff, Perthshire, PH7 3QY Tel: (01764) 652892

▶ Mcleod, Glengarnock Technology Centre Caledonia Road, Lochshore Industrial Estate, Glengarnock, Beith, Ayrshire, KA14 3DD Tel: (01505) 684922 Fax: (01505) 684922

▶ Mcleod Plant Hire, Naurcris, Dyce, Aberdeen, AB21 0EY Tel: (01224) 723718 Fax: (01224) 772877

Main Road Ground Works, Unit 22 Coniston Road, Kitty Brewster Industrial Esta, Blyth, Northumberland, NE24 4RF Tel: (01670) 353049

▶ Mann Crane Hire Ltd, Unit 1 Balthane Industrial Estate, Ballasalla, Isle Of Man, IM9 2AJ Tel: (01624) 835758 Fax: (01624) 836040 E-mail: mancranehire@manx.net

▶ Map Plant, Brunswick House, Ripple Road, Barking, Essex, IG11 0SL Tel: (020) 8592 7070 Fax: (020) 8592 8080

▶ Marsh Plant Ltd, Leabrook Road, Wednesbury, West Midlands, WS10 7LZ Tel: 0121-556 2158

▶ Martin Group N W Ltd, Bouthwood Road, Sowerby Woods Industrial Estate, Barrow-in-Furness, Cumbria, LA14 4RD Tel: (01229) 813428 Fax: (01229) 430330

▶ Martin Plant Hire Ltd, B Etna Road, Falkirk, FK2 9EG Tel: (01324) 612842 Fax: (01324) 622116

▶ Martin Plant Hire Ltd, 17 Lancefield Street, Glasgow, G3 8HZ Tel: (0800) 9756851 Fax: 0141-248 8357

▶ Martin Plant Hire Ltd, Unit 7 Carberry Place, Mitchelston Industrial Estate, Kirkcaldy, Fife, KY1 3NQ Tel: (01592) 655535

▶ Mechplant Plant & Machinery Hire, Schofield Street, Littleborough, Lancashire, OL15 0JS Tel: (01706) 370111 Fax: (01706) 377634

▶ Metcalfe Plant Hire Ltd, 46 Gilwilly Road, Gilwilly Industrial Estate, Penrith, Cumbria, CA11 9BL Tel: (01768) 868686 Fax: (01768) 868688

Miller Plant, North Lurg, Midmar, Inverurie, Aberdeenshire, AB51 7NB Tel: (01330) 830033 Fax: (01330) 833478

▶ Morris Leslie, Moorlands Lane, Saltash, Cornwall, PL12 4HJ Tel: (01752) 843291 Fax: (01752) 840400

▶ Morris Leslie Plymouth Ltd, 53 Valley Road, Plymouth, PL7 1RF Tel: (01752) 341200 Fax: (01752) 330065

▶ Mulholland Plant Hire Ltd, Polbeth Indust Estate, West Calder, West Lothian, EH55 8TJ Tel: (01506) 870297

▶ N A L Plant Ltd, Farnsworth Farm, Welbeck Road, Bolsover, Chesterfield, Derbyshire, S44 6XF Tel: (01246) 241066 Fax: (01246) 241066

▶ Network Plant Ltd, 76 Pretoria Road North, London, N18 1SP Tel: (020) 8803 3555 Fax: (020) 8803 3553 E-mail: info@networkplant.co.uk

▶ Newel Plant Hire, 45 Colwyn Crescent, Rhos on Sea, Colwyn Bay, Clwyd, LL28 4RF Tel: (01492) 533612 Fax: (01492) 533612

▶ C. Nicol & Son, Westside, Skene, Westhill, Aberdeenshire, AB32 6UJ Tel: (01224) 744473

▶ Nicolson Plant, Brae, Shetland, ZE2 9QG Tel: (01806) 522259

▶ Nor E X Hire Rail Ltd, Draycott Cross Road, Brookhouse Industrial Estate, Cheadle, Stoke-On-Trent, ST10 1PN Tel: (01538) 751777

▶ O'Connor Constructions Plant Co. Ltd, 9 Colletts Drive, Tewksbury Road, Cheltenham, Gloucestershire, GL51 8JQ Tel: (01242) 241100 E-mail: info@oconnorplant.co.uk

▶ One Call Equipment Hire, Neptune Industrial Estate, Neptune Close, Medway City Estate, Rochester, Kent, ME2 4LT Tel: (01634) 723222 Fax: (01634) 723721

▶ P C S Sandbach, Craigneigh, Ashley Heath, Market Drayton, Shropshire, TF9 4PS Tel: (01630) 673867

▶ P G Common Ltd, Bredbury Park Way, Bredbury Park Industrial Estat, Bredbury, Stockport, Cheshire, SK6 2SN Tel: 0161-430 8060

▶ P J C Plant Services Ltd, 56 Sanvey Gate, Leicester, LE1 4BQ Tel: 0116-253 6177 Fax: 0116-251 6961

▶ Palmaris Services, 27 Waverley Street, Northburn Road, Coatbridge, Lanarkshire, ML5 2HY Tel: (01236) 438040

▶ Parker Plant Hire Ltd, East Moors Road, Cardiff, CF24 5EE Tel: (029) 2045 2255 Fax: (029) 2045 2205

▶ Pencroft Ltd, Old Road, Clifton-on-Teme, Worcester, WR6 6DR Tel: (01886) 812822 Fax: (01886) 812833

▶ Penman Plant Hire, Merchant Place, Mitchelston Industrial Estate, Kirkcaldy, Fife, KY1 3NJ Tel: (01592) 654555 Fax: (01592) 654554

▶ Philip Shovlin Plant Hire Ltd, Brook Business Complex, Bennett St, West Gorton, Manchester, M12 5AU Tel: 0161-273 8900

▶ Pochin P.L.C., Birniehill, Whitburn Road, Bathgate, West Lothian, EH48 2HR Tel: (01606) 833333

Powered Access Services Ltd, Middleton Depot Lochlibo Road, Beith, Ayrshire, KA15 1HZ Tel: (01505) 850150

▶ Powerflo Rentals P.L.C., Unit 1D, Blackness Road, Altens Industrial Estate, Aberdeen, AB12 3LH Tel: (01224) 891234

▶ Premier Oil Fuel Services Ltd, Kirkton Avenue, Dyce, Aberdeen, AB21 0BF Tel: (01224) 724900 Fax: (01224) 770191

Quartz Plant UK Ltd, 5 Thomas Avenue, Radcliffe-On-Trent, Nottingham, NG12 2HT Tel: 0115-933 4947 Fax: 0115-933 4947 E-mail: brassandpower@ntlworld.com

▶ R D Kearton & Sons Ltd, Museum View, Boldron, Barnard Castle, County Durham, DL12 9RQ Tel: (01833) 631229 Fax: (01833) 631866

CONSTRUCTION PLANT OR EQUIPMENT HIRE – *continued*

R Petrie & Sons Ltd, Lornshill Farm, Alloa, Clackmannanshire, FK10 2EP Tel: (01259) 725848

▶ Richard Murray Plant Hire, 26 Brierie Gardens, Crosslee, Johnstone, Renfrewshire, PA6 7BZ Tel: (01505) 615733 Fax: (01505) 610201

▶ Robert Mccarroll Ltd, 8 Crowhill Road, Bishopbriggs, Glasgow, G64 1QR Tel: 0141-772 1884 Fax: 0141-772 7172

▶ Robinson, Sandy Leas Lane, Elton, Stockton-on-Tees, Cleveland, TS21 1BT Tel: (01642) 588806 Fax: (01642) 588499

▶ S G B Rental & Sales, 8 The Drift, Nacton Road, Ipswich, IP3 9QR Tel: (01473) 271313 Fax: (01473) 710979

▶ S L D Pumps Ltd, Ailsa Road, Irvine Industrial Estate, Irvine, Ayrshire, KA12 8LL Tel: (01294) 278986 Fax: (01294) 271324

▶ S L D Specialist Hire Service Ltd, 98 Turnhouse Road, Edinburgh, EH12 8ND Tel: 0131-339 1060

▶ S R Hire Centre Ltd, 15-19 West Bowling Green St, Edinburgh, EH6 5PQ Tel: 0131-555 3500

▶ Scott Stores, Station Industrial Estate, Newton Stewart, Wigtownshire, DG8 6ND Tel: (01671) 402038

▶ Scotts Plant Hire Ltd, Radcliffe Bridge Yard, Radcliffe Road, Sutton, Macclesfield, Cheshire, SK11 0JE Tel: (01260) 252252 Fax: (01260) 252333

▶ Selwood Ltd, 32-36 Bournemouth Road, Chandler's Ford, Eastleigh, Hampshire, SO53 3ZL Tel: (023) 8026 6311 Fax: (023) 8026 0906

▶ Selwood Ltd, Derby Road, Langley Mill, Nottingham, NG16 4AA Tel: (01773) 714227 Fax: (01773) 716445 E-mail: nottingham@selwoodgroup.co.uk

▶ Simpson Oils Ltd, South Quay, Fishmart, Wick, Caithness, KW1 5HA Tel: (01955) 604444 Fax: (01955) 602316

▶ Simpson Plant Hire & Civil Engineering, 61 Trevithick Estate, St. Merryn, Padstow, Cornwall, PL28 8NN Tel: (01841) 520786 Fax: (01841) 521255

▶ Simpsons Excavating Contractors Woolacombe Ltd, Chilworth House, Woolacombe Station Road, Woolacombe, Devon, EX34 7HH Tel: (01271) 870386

▶ Andrew Sinclair, Hatston Industrial Estate, Kirkwall, Orkney, KW15 1RE Tel: (01856) 873178 Fax: (01856) 873351

Site Equipment Ltd, King Road Avenue, Avonmouth, Bristol, BS11 9HG Tel: 0117-982 8236

▶ Skelton Group, Aylesham Industrial Estate, Aylesham, Canterbury, Kent, CT3 3EP Tel: (01304) 840640 Fax: (01304) 840440

▶ Southern Hoist Services, A Culverlands Corner, Winchester Road, Shedfield, Southampton, SO32 2JF Tel: (01329) 833223 Fax: (01329) 833683

▶ Spey Valley Hire Centre, Myrtlefield, Aviemore, Inverness-Shire, PH22 1SB Tel: (01479) 810555 Fax: (01479) 810789

▶ Stephen Christian & Sons Ltd, Fuchsia Cottage, Kirk Michael, Isle of Man, IM6 1AX Tel: (01624) 878223 Fax: (01624) 878189

▶ Stephen Wormell, Langenhoe Hall, Hall Lane, Langenhoe, Colchester, CO5 7NA Tel: (01206) 735687 Fax: (01206) 735487

▶ Stoneledge (South Bank) Ltd, Estate Road 4, South Humberside Industrial Es, Grimsby, South Humberside, DN31 2TB Tel: (01472) 240265

▶ Stuart Plant Ltd, Stuart House, Crowshall Lane, Attleborough, Norfolk, NR17 1AD Tel: (01953) 458963 Fax: (01953) 456968

▶ Sweeney Plant Ltd, 1 A Petersburn Road, Airdrie, Lanarkshire, ML6 8RD Tel: (01236) 762290

▶ The Sweeper Centre Ltd, Broomlands Farm, West Kilbride, Ayrshire, KA23 9NX Tel: (01294) 829333

▶ Taberner Plant Hire Ltd, Bell House Lane, Anslow, Burton-on-Trent, Staffordshire, DE13 9PA Tel: (01283) 564017 Fax: (01283) 512243

▶ Tartan Plant Ltd, Stirling Road, Larbert, Stirlingshire, FK5 3NJ Tel: (01324) 622956

Tony Hudson, Moor Farm Buildings, Moor Lane, Murton, York, YO19 5XD Tel: (01904) 481891 Fax: (01904) 481930

Trax Portable Access, Dukeries Industrial Estate, Claylands Avenue, Worksop, Nottinghamshire, S81 7DJ Tel: (0870) 240 2381

▶ Tulloch Civil Engineering Ltd, Grigorhill Industrial Estate, Nairn, IV12 5HX Tel: (01667) 455014 Fax: (01667) 455128

▶ Turner Hire & Sales Ltd, Fitzwilliam House, Thames Street, Rotherham, South Yorkshire, S60 1LU Tel: 0114-258 1682 Fax: (01709) 830166

▶ Uplift Power Platforms, Unit 1 8 Flanshaw Way, Wakefield, West Yorkshire, WF2 9LP Tel: (01924) 383833 Fax: (01924) 383832

▶ Venco, Jenning Street, Hull, HU8 7AN Tel: (01482) 585101

▶ VHGC, Unit 2 Aston Street, Shifnal, Shropshire, TF11 8DT Tel: (01952) 461107 Fax: (01952) 463030

▶ Ward Plant Ltd, West Mains Farm, Newbigging, Carnwath, Lanark, ML11 8NB Tel: (01555) 840497

▶ Warnock Plant Hire Ltd, West Rogerton, East Kilbride, Glasgow, G74 4NU Tel: (01355) 242992 Fax: (01355) 249424

▶ Western Well Tool Ltd, Unit1 Airways Industrial Estate, Pitmedden Road, Dyce, Aberdeen, AB21 0DT Tel: (01224) 224646

▶ Whyte, Hindstones Farm, New Aberdour, Fraserburgh, Aberdeenshire, AB43 6LY Tel: (01346) 561219 Fax: (01346) 561484

▶ Wiggins Transport Ltd, Horton Road, Staines, Middlesex, TW19 6AQ Tel: (01753) 683324

▶ William Selwood Pumps & Plant Hire Ltd, 2236 London Road, Glasgow, G32 8YF Tel: 0141-778 5155 Fax: 0141-778 8652

▶ Williams Plant Hire Ltd, Aberbechan Wharf, Newtown, Powys, SY16 3AW Tel: (01686) 630244 Fax: (01686) 630557

▶ Witherley Services Ltd, Witherley House, Hazelway, Nuneaton, Warwickshire, CV10 7QG Tel: (024) 7635 1188

▶ Work Tool Hire Ltd, 43 Commercial Road, Port Talbot, West Glamorgan, SA13 1LN Tel: (01639) 898888 Fax: (01639) 884377

▶ Young Excavator Services Ltd, 3 Tornaroy Road, Hannahstown, Belfast, BT17 0ND Tel: (028) 9030 1392 Fax: (028) 9060 0222

CONSTRUCTION PLANT OR EQUIPMENT IMPORT OR EXPORT

▶ D.G. Simpson Plant, Unit 2, Mill Lane, Littleburn Industrial Estate, Langley Moor, Durham, DH7 8HE Tel: 0191-378 3666 Fax: 0191-378 2333 E-mail: dgequipt@aol.com

▶ DRY-OFF (UK) LTD, 23 Castalia Square, Docklands, London, UK, E14 3NG Tel: 0207 5441474 Fax: 0207 5441499 E-mail: EDWARD@DRY-OFF.COM

I N E C Engineering Co. Ltd, 73 Mornington Street, London, NW1 7QE Tel: (020) 7383 2385 Fax: (020) 7383 3471

Power Lift Plant, The Garage, Panfield Lane, Braintree, Essex, CM7 5RN Tel: (01376) 331812 Fax: (01376) 341742

CONSTRUCTION PLANT OR EQUIPMENT MAINTENANCE OR REPAIR

P P S Construction Plant Sales Ltd, Tomlinson Road, Leyland, PR25 2DY Tel: (01772) 456392 Fax: (01772) 621368 E-mail: info@ppsplantsales.co.uk

Thames Valley Pneumatic Ltd, Delta Way, Egham, Surrey, TW20 8RX Tel: (01784) 434999 Fax: (01784) 434499 E-mail: tvpltd@hotmail.com

Westside Welding and Engineering Ltd, 9 Broadfield Place, Welwyn Garden City, Hertfordshire, AL8 6LJ Tel: 01707 332872 Fax: 01707 332872 E-mail: westsideweld@hotmail.co.uk

CONSTRUCTION PLANT OR EQUIPMENT OPERATOR RECRUITMENT

Aalpha Solutions (North West) Ltd, 169 Cross Green Lane, Cross Green, Leeds, LS9 0BD Tel: 0113-249 6900 Fax: 0113-249 6906 E-mail: info@aalphasolutions.co.uk

▶ theCONSTRUCTIONjob.com, PO Box 2448, Slough, SL1 1ZB Tel: 0870 8701193 Fax: 0870 8701194 E-mail: coz.dauncey@theconstructionjob.com

CONSTRUCTION PLANT OR EQUIPMENT SPARE PARTS

▶ KM Products Europe Ltd, The Forum, Unit B, Hanworth Lane Business Park, Hanworth Lane, Chertsey, Surrey, KT16 9JX Tel: (01932) 571991 Fax: (01932) 571994 E-mail: sales@kmpuk.com

CONSTRUCTION PROJECT MANAGEMENT

▶ Emprima Limited, The Oracle Building, Blythe Valley Park, Solihull, West Midlands, B90 8AD Tel: 0121 506 9600 Fax: 0121 506 9601 E-mail: mail@emprima.co.uk

▶ Interspace Ltd, Gate House, 1-3 St. John's Square, London, EC1M 4DH Tel: (020) 7251 6868 Fax: (020) 7253 6868 E-mail: info@interspace.ltd.uk

▶ KMS, 63 Tanner Street, London, SE1 3PL Tel: (020) 7939 0740 Fax: (020) 7407 2810 E-mail: rachelb@kms-software.com

▶ Knowledge Train, 30 Mildenhall Road, London, E5 0RU Tel: 020 8986-5430 E-mail: info@knowledgetrain.co.uk

Kor, Pynes Hill, Exeter, EX2 5JL Tel: (01392) 266870 Fax: (01392) 445400 E-mail: admin@kor.uk.com

M H I Ltd, 10 Appleton Gate, Newark, Nottinghamshire, NG24 1JY Tel: (01636) 704814 Fax: (01636) 671113 E-mail: enquiries@mhidesign.co.uk

▶ Mckeating Ltd, 4 Wykeham Road, Glasgow, G13 3YT Tel: 0141-434 1117 Fax: 0141-954 2987

▶ Mercury Architectural Projects Ltd, 2 Shrike Close Clayton Heights, Bradford, West Yorkshire, BD6 3YG Tel: (01274) 816105 Fax: 01274 816105 E-mail: info@mercuryarchitectural.com

Osprey Mott Macdonald, Welken House, 10-11 Charterhouse Square, London, EC1M 6EH Tel: (020) 7566 7900 Fax: (020) 7566 7911 E-mail: brenda.wiggins@ospreymottmac.com

Pert Building Services Ltd, 31 Bunbury Road, Northfield, Birmingham, B31 2DR Tel: 0121-411 2333 Fax: 0121-411 2600 E-mail: barrieroberts@pert-aircon.co.uk

Woolf Ltd, 1 Procter Street, London, WC1V 6DW Tel: (020) 7492 0202 Fax: (020) 7492 0203 E-mail: enquiries@woolfltd.com

CONSTRUCTION SAFETY TRAINING

John Laing, Gate 14, Basin South, London, E16 2QY Tel: (020) 7055 2450 Fax: (020) 7055 2451 E-mail: info@jlaingtraining.co.uk

CONSTRUCTION SECURITY SERVICES

Siteguard UK Ltd, Unit 30 Canal Bridge Enterprise Centre, Meadow Lane, Ellesmere Port, CH65 4EH Tel: 0151-355 3456 Fax: 0151-355 7809 E-mail: info@siteguarduk.com

CONSTRUCTION SERVICES CONSULTANCY

▶ Heritage Hardwood, Star Crossroads, Star, Gaerwen, Gwynedd, LL60 6AL Tel: (01248) 715280 Fax: (01248) 713383 E-mail: sales@heritage-hardwood.co.uk

CONSTRUCTION STEEL PROFILED SHEET

Clonshall Ltd, Whiteacre House, 97 Whiteacre Road, Ashton-under-Lyne, Lancashire, OL6 9PJ Tel: 0161-339 9637 Fax: 0161-343 1036 E-mail: adrian.young@clonshall.co.uk

Main Welding Co. Ltd, Shawclough Road, Shawclough, Rochdale, Lancashire, OL12 6LN Tel: (01706) 655131 Fax: (01706) 655135 E-mail: enquiries@mainltd.co.uk

Northern Profiles, Elm Tree Street, Wakefield, West Yorkshire, WF1 5EQ Tel: (01924) 291655 Fax: (01924) 372010

▶ Yorkshire Metal Roofing, Unit 2 The Old Station, Nidd, Harrogate, North Yorkshire, HG3 3BN Tel: (01423) 779555 Fax: (01423) 779666 E-mail: info@yorkshiremetalroofing.co.uk

CONSTRUCTION VEHICLE SEATS

Milsco Manufacturing Ltd, Harrington Way, Bermuda Park, Nuneaton, Warwickshire, CV10 7SH Tel: (024) 7658 0400 Fax: (024) 7658 0401 E-mail: info@milsco.co.uk

CONSTRUCTIONAL ENGINEERING

A C L Structures Ltd, Holland Way, Blandford Forum, Dorset, DT11 7TA Tel: (01258) 456051 Fax: (01258) 450566 E-mail: enquiries@aclstructures.co.uk

A D T Joinery, Joinery Works, Llynfi St, Bridgend, Mid Glamorgan, CF31 1SY Tel: (01656) 653644 Fax: (01656) 653644 E-mail: arby.richard@virgin.net

A W G Utility Services, Hampden House, Hitchin Road, Arlesey, Bedfordshire, SG15 6RT Tel: (01462) 731133 Fax: (01462) 834829

Alf Wright Ltd, 31 Saffron Road, Wigston, Leicestershire, LE18 4UR Tel: 0116-278 1005 Fax: 0116-278 1006 E-mail: headoffice@alfwright.co.uk

Allen Engineering Ltd, Narlow Works, Thorpe, Ashbourne, Derbyshire, DE6 2AT Tel: (01335) 350419 Fax: (01335) 350533 E-mail: sales@allenandhunt.co.uk

Alto Plant Services Ltd, Railway Road, Brinscall, Chorley, Lancashire, PR6 8RJ Tel: (01254) 832132 Fax: (01254) 832121

B C Dyson & Co., Prescott Lodge, Prescott Street, Halifax, West Yorkshire, HX1 2QW Tel: (01422) 360934 Fax: (01422) 320379 E-mail: b.c.dyson@bt.openworld.com

T.M. Brooks Ltd, Unit 4, Dawley Estate, Stallings Lane, Kingswinford, West Midlands, DY6 7AP Tel: (01384) 400777 Fax: (01384) 400167 E-mail: office@tmbrooks.co.uk

Compressors Ltd, 145 Nottingham Road, Alfreton, Derbyshire, DE55 7FL Tel: (01773) 836816 Fax: (01773) 520556 E-mail: compressors@fsbdial.co.uk

Dean & Dyball Developments Ltd, Endeavour House, Crow Arch Lane, Ringwood, Hampshire, BH24 1PN Tel: (01425) 470000 Fax: (01425) 472724 E-mail: enquiries@deandyball.co.uk

Dew Construction Ltd, Featherstall Road South, Oldham, OL9 6HH Tel: 0161-624 5631 Fax: 0161-678 0289 E-mail: admin@dewconstruction.co.uk

▶ Hatrick-Bruce Properties Ltd, Market House, Milnathort, Kinross, KY13 9XB Tel: (01577) 863967 E-mail: sales@hatrickbruce.co.uk

Hyundai Heavy Industries Co. Ltd, Second Floor The Triangle, 5-17 Hammersmith Grove, London, W6 9LT Tel: (020) 8741 0501 Fax: (020) 8741 5620

Industrial Development & Farm Services, Newcastle, Monmouth, Gwent, NP25 5NF Tel: (01600) 772126 Fax: (01600) 750396

J Parkinson & Sons Ltd, 3 Hampson Lane, Hampson, Lancaster, LA2 0HY Tel: (01524) 753301 Fax: (01524) 753302 E-mail: bcampbell@askam.co.uk

Mccormick Macnaughton Ni Ltd, Blaris Industrial Estate, Altona Road, Lisburn, County Antrim, BT27 5QB Tel: (028) 9266 1221 Fax: (028) 9266 1355 E-mail: sales@mccormickmacnaughton.com

Mccroy Engineering, 49b Armaghlughey Road, Aughnacloy, County Tyrone, BT69 6DN Tel: (028) 8555 7790 Fax: (028) 8555 7790

N S P Building Services Ltd, 24 Nova Lane, Birstall, Batley, West Yorkshire, WF17 9LE Tel: (01924) 445648 Fax: (01924) 445648

Norwest Trading Co, 6 Buxton Old Road, Disley, Stockport, Cheshire, SK12 2BB Tel: (01663) 764668 Fax: (01663) 764668 E-mail: dr@norwest-trading.co.uk

Peter Sandham Associates, 2 Wesley Street, Castleford, West Yorkshire, WF10 1AE Tel: (01977) 519600 Fax: (01977) 555290 E-mail: paulsandham@totalise.co.uk

Scott Wilson, Central Boulevard, Blythe Valley Park, Shirley, Solihull, West Midlands, B90 8AH Tel: 0121-746 6200 Fax: 0121-746 6201 E-mail: birmingham@camerontaylor.co.uk

Selwyn Construction Engineering Ltd, Tarran Road, Tarran Industrial Estate, Wirral, Merseyside, CH46 4TU Tel: 0151-678 0236 Fax: 0151-678 8959 E-mail: enquiries@selwyngroup.co.uk

Shairwood Contracts Ltd, Colchester Road, Tendring, Clacton-on-Sea, Essex, CO16 9AA Tel: (01255) 830704 Fax: (01255) 831047 E-mail: Office@sherwood.Co.uk

Shaw Group, Witan Gate House, 500-600 Witan Gate West, Milton Keynes, MK9 1BA Tel: (01908) 668844 Fax: (01908) 602211 E-mail:

Smart Frame Tectonics, Burnmill Road, Leven, Fife, KY8 4RA Tel: (01333) 421525 Fax: (01333) 423886

Space Industries Ltd, 748 Wimborne Road, Bournemouth, BH9 2DZ Tel: (01202) 517616 Fax: (01202) 533955 E-mail: sales@spaceindustries.co.uk

Sussex Fencing & Construction Co., 1 Beaconsfield Road, Portslade, Brighton, BN41 1XA Tel: (01273) 418878 Fax: (01273) 881858

▶ T P Aspinall & Sons Ltd, Middleton Business Park, Middleton Road, Middleton, Morecambe, Lancashire, LA3 3PW Tel: (01524) 852883 Fax: (01524) 853303 E-mail: enquiries@aspinall.co.uk

Thircon Ltd, Hambleton Steel Works, York Road, Thirsk, North Yorkshire, YO7 3BT Tel: (01845) 522760 Fax: (01845) 524146

Thomfab Engineering Services, Unit 1 Blackhill Industrial Estate, Findon, Aberdeen, AB12 4RL Tel: (01224) 781615 Fax: (01224) 781615 E-mail: duncan@thomfab.com

Trimplex, Mulberry Way, Belvedere, Kent, DA17 6AN Tel: (020) 8312 0400 Fax: (020) 8312 1400 E-mail: saftytread@btconnect.com

Watson Steel Structures Ltd, PO Box 9, Bolton, BL6 4BL Tel: (01204) 699999 Fax: (01204) 694543

Wells Masonry Services Ltd, Ilsom Farm, Ilsom, Tetbury, Gloucestershire, GL8 8RX Tel: (01666) 504251 Fax: (01666) 502285 E-mail: sales@wells-group.co.uk

Whessoe Oil & Gas Ltd, Brinkburn Road, Darlington, County Durham, DL3 6DS Tel: (01325) 390000 Fax: (01325) 390001

CONSTRUCTIONAL MANAGEMENT CONTRACTORS

A W G Utility Services, Hampden House, Hitchin Road, Arlesey, Bedfordshire, SG15 6RT Tel: (01462) 731133 Fax: (01462) 834829

▶ ACO Contracting Services, 2 Newmin Way, Clavering Park Estate, Whickham, Newcastle upon Tyne, NE16 5RE Tel: 0191-488 4871 E-mail: andrewoliver1975@hotmail.com

Bovis Land Lease Ltd, Third Floor The Vinus, 1 Old Park Lane, Trafford, Manchester, M41 7HG Tel: 0161-254 1700 Fax: 0161-254 1701

Clarke Engineering & Construction Co. Ltd, 13 Sydenham Road, Belfast, BT3 9DH Tel: (028) 9045 8337 Fax: (028) 9073 2382 E-mail: mail@cecltd.co.uk

Construction Management & Design, Ty Capel, Yr Henffordd, Nercwys, Mold, Clwyd, CH7 4DL Tel: (01352) 755522 Fax: (01352) 754656 E-mail: constmanagdesign@aol.com

CONSTRUCTIONAL MANAGEMENT CONTRACTORS – *continued*

Dew Construction Ltd, Featherstall Road South, Oldham, OL9 6HH Tel: 0161-624 5631 Fax: 0161-678 0289 E-mail: admin@dewconstruction.co.uk

Forde Edwards & Partners, Monton House, Monton Green, Eccles, Manchester, M30 9LE Tel: 0161-788 9099 Fax: 0161-788 9155 E-mail: forde@totalise.co.uk

HBG Construction Scotland Ltd, Kelvin House, Buchanan Gate Business Park, Stepps, Glasgow, G33 6FB Tel: 0141-779 8888

Holrow Building Refurbishment, Jubilee Court, Copgrove, Harrogate, North Yorkshire, HG3 3TB Tel: (01423) 340888 Fax: (01423) 340999 E-mail: sales@holrow.co.uk

John Laing P.L.C., Allington House, 150 Victoria Street, London, SW1E 5LB Tel: (020) 7901 3200 Fax: (020) 7901 3520 E-mail: enquiries@equion.ltd.uk

Lindum BMS Grimsby, 1 Alexandra Road, Grimsby, South Humberside, DN31 1RD Tel: (01472) 355171 Fax: (01472) 236667 E-mail: ew@lindumgroup.co.uk

▶ Marpal Ltd, Room 34, College Business Centre, The College, Uttoxeter New Road, Derby, DE22 3WZ Tel: (01332) 869290 Fax: (01332) 869291 E-mail: info@marpal.co.uk

R & G Construction (Manchester) Ltd, Phoenix Buildings, Heywood Road, Prestwich, Manchester, M25 1FN Tel: 0161-773 7867 Fax: 0161-773 8617

Schal International Management Ltd, Elizabeth House, 39 York Road, London, SE1 7NQ Tel: (020) 7401 4800 Fax: (020) 7401 4900

Stace, 273 High Street, Epping, Essex, CM16 4DA Tel: (01992) 565565 Fax: (01992) 560597 E-mail: epping@stace.co.uk

CONSULAR DOCUMENTATION SERVICES, *See Export/Import etc*

CONSULTANTS, *See headings for particular types*

CONSULTANTS, BUSINESS EXPANSION PLANNING

London Net Solutions UK Ltd, 4 Mead Way, Bromley, BR2 9EU Tel: 0208 4622655 Fax: 0208 4626389 E-mail: info@wsiworldclassnetsolutions.com

CONSULTANTS, ELECTRON BEAM WELDING DESIGN

Technical Systems Ltd, Long View, Simms Lane, Reading, RG7 2JP Tel: 0118-933 3700

CONSULTANTS, ENGINEERS OR DESIGNERS, SPECIAL PURPOSE MACHINERY

▶ Cambridge Engineering Technology Ltd, 17 Fennec Close, Cambridge, CB1 9GG Tel: (01223) 413797 E-mail: enquiries@cambridge-engineering.com

▶ S. Eldridge Design & Draughting, 37 Hazelwood Close, Honiton, Devon, EX14 2XA Tel: (01404) 45054 E-mail: stephen.eldridge@btinternet.com

Pneumatic Systems Ltd, Unit 32 Poplar Industrial Estate, Witton, Birmingham, B6 7AD Tel: 0121-344 3800 Fax: 0121 344 3866 E-mail: pneumaticsys@aol.com

▶ Renewable Devices Energy Solutions, Bush Estate, Penicuik, Midlothian, EH26 0PH Tel: 0131-535 3403 Fax: 0131-535 3303 E-mail: info@renewabledevices.com

Tri Development Ltd, Loomer Road, Newcastle, Staffordshire, ST5 7LB Tel: (01782) 561526 Fax: (01782) 561584 E-mail: tridevltd@btconnect.com

CONSULTANTS, ENVIRONMENTAL NOISE

Acoustical Investigation & Research Organisation Ltd, Duxons Turn, Hemel Hempstead, Hertfordshire, HP2 4SB Tel: (01442) 247146 Fax: (01442) 256749 E-mail: airo@bcs.org.uk

▶ Advanced Noise Solutions Ltd, 13 Boissy Close, St Albans, St. Albans, Hertfordshire, AL4 0UE Tel: (01727) 864667

Bureau Veritas, Pavilion 1 Craig Shaw Business Park, Craig Shaw Road, Tullos, Aberdeen, AB12 3AR Tel: (01224) 892100 Fax: (01224) 898437

▶ dB Acoustics, The Old School, Ipswich Road, Gosbeck, Ipswich, IP6 9SN Tel: 01449 760689 E-mail: gordon@10db.co.uk

▶ Environmental Noise Solutions Ltd, Suite 15 Doncaster Business Innovation Centre, Ten Pound WK, Doncaster, South Yorkshire, DN4 5HX Tel: (01302) 644001 Fax: (01302) 644002 E-mail: sales@environmental-noise-solutions.co.uk

▶ Sandy Brown Associates, 16 West Terrace, South Queensferry, West Lothian, EH30 9LL Tel: 0131-331 2020 Fax: 0131-331 2187 E-mail: post@sandybrown.com

CONSULTANTS, INTERNET

▶ A Web Whisper, 103 Lower End, Leafield, Witney, Oxfordshire, OX29 9QG Tel: (01993) 878356 E-mail: info@webwhisper.co.uk

▶ Alternative Focus Media, 68 Castle Gate, Newark, Nottinghamshire, NG24 1BG Tel: (01636) 706106 Fax: (01636) 611149 E-mail: mike@alternativefocusmedia.com

▶ David Anderson Associates, Unit 3 Saffron Walden Business Centre, Elizabeth Cl, Saffron Walden, Essex, CB10 2BL Tel: (0797) 3227402 Fax: (0870) 0527516 E-mail: sales@anderson.ath.cx

▶ Byrne Consultancy Ltd, 34 Ashburnham Loan, South Queensferry, West Lothian, EH30 9LE Tel: 0131-331 3694 Fax: 0131-331 3694

▶ Chartus, 5 Gratton Road, Cheltenham, Gloucestershire, GL50 2BT Tel: (01242) 701014 Fax: (01242) 701014 E-mail: info@chartus.co.uk

Comverse Kenan UK, 1a Stoke Road, Slough, SL2 5AA Tel: (01753) 745300 Fax: (01753) 745304

Datasmith Ltd, 30 Helen Street, Golborne, Warrington, WA3 3QR Tel: (01942) 700828 Fax: (01942) 516572 E-mail: tony@datasmith.co.uk

Demand It, Units 19-21, Deacon Way, Tilehurst, Reading, RG30 6QG Tel: 0118-945 8600 Fax: 0118-945 3737 E-mail: sales@demand-it.co.uk

Des Computers, Cardiff University, Senghennydd Road, Cardiff, CF24 4AG Tel: (029) 2025 0000 Fax: (029) 2025 9600 E-mail: sales@descom.co.uk

▶ Digitalarkitec Ltd, 121 Eastern Avenue, Lichfield, Staffordshire, WS13 6RL Tel: (01543) 251123 E-mail: enquiries@digitalarkitec.co.uk

▶ Martin Dixon, 5B Julien Road, Ealing, London, W5 4XA Tel: (020) 8354 0510 E-mail: martin@m-dixon.com

D-trak Ltd, 8 Becket Way, Laverstock, Salisbury, SP1 1PZ Tel: (01722) 415144 Fax: (01722) 415143 E-mail: info@d-trak.com

Electronic Archive Solutions Ltd, 14 The Briars, Waterberry Drive, Waterlooville, Hampshire, PO7 7YH Tel: (023) 9223 3833 Fax: (023) 9223 8577 E-mail: info@e-asl.com

Feltham Associates Ltd, Carlton House, Carlton Road, Kibworth Harcourt, Leicester, LE8 0PE Tel: 0116-279 3232 Fax: 0116-279 2473 E-mail: fal@btinternet.com

▶ Gary Crook Ltd, Regus House, Southampton International Business Park, George Curl Way, Southampton, SO18 2RZ Tel: (023) 8030 2005 Fax: (023) 8030 2225 E-mail: gary@wsi-internet4business.com

Highlander Ltd, Islington Business Design Centre, 52 Upper Street, London, N1 0QH Tel: (0800) 1560777 Fax: (0870) 3309911 E-mail: info@highlander.co.uk

▶ ICOM International Ltd, Norwood House, 53 Brighton Grove, Manchester, M14 5JT Tel: 0161-259 0100 E-mail: info@internetcommunication.co.uk

Kingfisher Associates UK Ltd, Nine Yews, Cranborne, Wimborne, Dorset, BH21 5PW Tel: (01725) 517744 Fax: (01725) 517766 E-mail: sales@kfa.co.uk

M A Computing Ltd, 52A Church Street, Broughty Ferry, Dundee, DD5 1HB Tel: (01382) 770044 Fax: (0870) 0557796 E-mail: ian@macomputing.demon.co.uk

Macfaction, Tew Lane, Wootton, Woodstock, Oxfordshire, OX20 1HA Tel: (01993) 811197 Fax: (01993) 812686 E-mail: info@macfaction.co.uk

Marketing for Profits Ltd, Top Floor, 33 Southbourne Grove, Southbourne, Bournemouth, BH6 3QT Tel: 01202 257423 Fax: 01202 257423 E-mail: accounts@consultancymarketing.co.uk

Myriad, 10 Lawn Avenue, Peterborough, PE1 3RB Tel: (01733) 766617 Fax: (01733) 759727 E-mail: enquiries@myriadit.net

Net Resources Ltd, 26a Palmerston Place, Edinburgh, EH12 5AL Tel: 0131-477 7127 Fax: 0131-477 7126 E-mail: info@netresources.co.uk

Newdev UK, 52-54 Snow Hill, Melton Mowbray, Leicestershire, LE13 1PH Tel: (01664) 569805 Fax: (01664) 481581 E-mail: newdevuk@aol.com

Oxford Computer Consultants Ltd, 23-38 Hythe Bridge Street, Oxford, OX1 2ET Tel: (01865) 305200 Fax: (01865) 793124 E-mail: oxford@cc.co.uk

▶ Oxford Strategic Ltd, The Maggalen Centre, Oxford Science Park, Oxford, OX4 4GA Tel: (01865) 784110 Fax: (01865) 748111 E-mail: info@oxfordstrategic.com

P S Consultants, Hockham Hill House, Spring Elms Lane, Little Baddom, Chelmsford, CM3 4SD Tel: (01245) 224065 Fax: (01245) 287057 E-mail: info@ps-consultants.co.uk

Paloma Systems Ltd, 2 Frederick Terrace, Frederick Place, Brighton, BN1 1AX Tel: (01273) 778688 Fax: (01273) 323927 E-mail: sales@paloma.co.uk

Pipex Internet Ltd, Unit 1 Pipex House, Medway Technology Park, Rutherford Close, Stevenage, Hertfordshire, SG1 2EF Tel: (08706) 004454 Fax: (01438) 311100 E-mail: sales@dial.pipex.com

▶ S E Marketing, 6 Hallas Grove, Manchester, M23 0GZ Tel: 0161-946 1116 E-mail: semarketing@postmaster.co.uk

Sea Bass Software Ltd, Abbotts Tower, Goring Heath, Reading, RG8 7RZ Tel: (01491) 682585 Fax: (01491) 682586 E-mail: sarah.bell@seabass.co.uk

Soft Solutions International Ltd, 123 Mudford Road, Yeovil, Somerset, BA21 4AQ Tel: (01935) 474469 Fax: (01935) 426228 E-mail: enquiries@ssi-ltd.com

Strategic Thought Group plc, Old Town Hall, Centre Court Shopping Centre, Queens Road, London, SW19 8YB Tel: (020) 8410 4000 Fax: (020) 8410 4030 E-mail: sales@strategicthought.com

▶ Visualeze Design, Annandale Road, London, SE10 0DB Tel: (020) 8488 6856 E-mail: kelly@visualeze.net

▶ Web Warehouse Ltd, Unit 12, Strathclyde Business Centre, 416 Hamilton Road, Cambuslang, Glasgow, G72 7XR Tel: (0845) 1260325 E-mail: info@web-warehouse.net

▶ Webcredible Ltd, 99 Mansell Street, London, E1 8AX Tel: (020) 7423 6320 Fax: 0207 481 2569 E-mail: info@webcredible.co.uk

CONSULTANTS, LASER SAFETY

Lasermet Ltd, 67 Portchester Road, Bournemouth, BH8 8JX Tel: (01202) 770740 Fax: (01202) 770730 E-mail: sales@lasermet.com

CONSULTANTS, MANAGEMENT, INFORMATION TECHNOLOGY (IT)

3 Thinking, 34 Windermere, Swindon, SN3 6JZ Tel: (0870) 1283075 Fax: (01793) 474522 E-mail: sales@3thinking.com

▶ A E C P.L.C., 25 Southampton Row, Holborn, London, WC1B 5HJ Tel: (0845) 0506296 Fax: (0870) 4199001 E-mail: info@aec.com

▶ Assert I T Ltd, 10 Knowle Avenue, Blackpool, FY5 3PP Tel: (01253) 865467 Fax: (0871) 2216078 E-mail: info@assert-it.co.uk

▶ Au Consulting, 37 Palmer Rise, Livingston, West Lothian, EH54 6NP Tel: (07986) 494775 Fax: (0871) 6611605 E-mail: enquiries@au-consulting.co.uk

▶ Bawden Quinn Associates, Sanderum House, 38 Oakley Road, Chinnor, Oxfordshire, OX39 4TW Tel: (01844) 355622 Fax: (01844) 353553 E-mail: contact@bawden-quinn.co.uk

▶ Bawden Quinn Associates Ltd, Manchester Business Park, 3000 Aviator Way, Manchester, M22 5TG Tel: 0161-266 1017 Fax: 0161-266 1001 E-mail: sales@bawden-quinn.co.uk

▶ Beacon Associates, 18 Wrekin Drive, Wergs, Wolverhampton, WV6 8UJ Tel: (01902) 755347 Fax: (01902) 754446 E-mail: mpb@beacon-associates.co.uk

▶ Bites UK Ltd, PO Box 2294, Woodford Green, Essex, IG8 0YF Tel: (0845) 2211000 Fax: (0870) 1350684 E-mail: sales@bites-uk.com

▶ Blueline Business Solutions Ltd, The iD Centre, rtc Business Park, London Road, Derby, DE24 8UP Tel: 01332 258837 Fax: 01332 258833 E-mail: enquiry@bluelinesolutions.co.uk

▶ Bryteworks Ltd, 24 Hampden Road, Caversham, Reading, RG4 5ED Tel: (0870) 7770477 Fax: (0870) 7620794 E-mail: info@bryteworks.com

C M A Solutions Ltd, Fleet Mill, Minley Road, Fleet, Hampshire, GU51 2RD Tel: (01252) 861500 Fax: (01252) 861550 E-mail: cma@cma-sol.co.uk

▶ Chameleon - Global ITIL Experts, Bracken Lodge, Bay Horse Lane, Scarcroft, Leeds, LS14 3JQ Tel: 0113-289 3661 Fax: 0113-289 2335 E-mail: info@chameleon-itil.com

Computer Consultants Ltd, Guild Street, Stratford-upon-Avon, Warwickshire, CV37 6RP Tel: (01789) 261200 Fax: (01789) 262525 E-mail: sales@cclnet.co.uk

▶ Crox Tech, 48 Crompton Drive, Liverpool, L12 0JX Tel: 0151-222 4691 E-mail: sales@croxtech.com

D B I Associates Ltd, Stoneleigh Park Mews, Stonleigh Abbey, Kenilworth, Warwickshire, CV8 2DB Tel: (01926) 312481 Fax: (01926) 515616 E-mail: consultants@dbiconsulting.co.uk

▶ Dexter-IT, 11 Babylon Lane, Bishampton, Pershore, Worcestershire, WR10 2NN Tel: 0845 6442414 Fax: 0870 1328311 E-mail: enquiries@Dexter-IT.co.uk

Elcom ITG Ltd, Elcom House, 203 Bedford Avenue, Slough, SL1 4RY Tel: (01753) 442500 Fax: (01753) 442501 E-mail: info@elcom.co.uk

Exel Management Ltd, 83-89 Phoenix Street, Sutton-in-Ashfield, Nottinghamshire, NG17 4HL Tel: (01623) 442211 Fax: (01623) 442844 E-mail: enquiries@exelmanagement.com

▶ Fineline Networks Ltd, 37 Southwood Road, London, SE9 3QE Tel: (020) 8294 2499 E-mail: info@fineline-net.co.uk

G T P Group Ltd, White Cross Industrial Estate, South Road, Lancaster, LA1 4XE Tel: (01524) 380380 Fax: (01524) 844514

Infogrames UK Ltd, 21 Castle Street, Manchester, M3 4SW Tel: 0161-827 8000 Fax: 0161-827 8001

▶ Isys Computer Services Ltd, 4 Charlotte Street, Dumbarton, G82 4JB Tel: (0845) 1434040 Fax: (0845) 1434039 E-mail: info@isys-computers.co.uk

Itdynamics Ltd, Lion Court, Staunton Harold, Ashby-de-la-Zouch, Leicestershire, LE65 1RT Tel: (01332) 695090 Fax: (01332) 695009 E-mail: info@itdynamics.co.uk

▶ J J Computing Ltd, 9 Stamford Close, Potters Bar, Hertfordshire, EN6 5NW Tel: (01707) 642767 E-mail: johnjohnson64@hotmail.com

Knibbs Computer Services Ltd, Suite 1 Falmer Court, London Road, Uckfield, East Sussex, TN22 1HN Tel: (01825) 749416 Fax: (0870) 7051341 E-mail: info@knibbs.com

The Lapworth Consultancy Ltd, The Barn, Hambridge Farm, Hambridge Road, Newbury, Berkshire, RG14 2QG Tel: (01635) 567777 Fax: (01635) 550067 E-mail: tlc@tlc-ltd.com

Logicol Technical Services Ltd, Units 15-17 Abenbury Way, Wrexham Industrial Estate, Wrexham, LL13 9UZ Tel: (01978) 664482 E-mail: sales@logicol.co.uk

▶ Massie Consulting Ltd, 20 Upper Olland Street, Bungay, Suffolk, NR35 1BH Tel: 01986 895030 E-mail: harold@massieconsulting.co.uk

Newburn Consulting plc, 1 Wood Street, Swindon, SN1 4AN Tel: (01793) 435000 Fax: (01793) 435001 E-mail: sales@newburn.co.uk

Open Seas, 7 Nuffield Way, Abingdon, Oxfordshire, OX14 1RJ Tel: (01235) 537391 Fax: (01235) 535168 E-mail: info@openseas.co.uk

▶ Quartet Computer Services, Astridge Park, Gyfelia, Wrexham, Clwyd, LL13 0YH Tel: (01978) 820343 E-mail: info@quartetcs.co.uk

▶ ReformIS, 18 Christchurch Hill, London, NW3 1LG Tel: (020) 7152 9638 Fax: (020) 7152 9639

Tektonic Ltd, 118, Hastings Road, Battle, East Sussex, TN33 0TQ Tel: (07092) 046259 Fax: 07092 046259 E-mail: enquiries@tektonic.co.uk

▶ Templar Consulting Limited, 7 Lidgett Park Avenue, Roundhay, LEEDS, LS8 1EN Tel: 0113 2179261 E-mail: info@templar-consulting.co.uk

Co U Help Ltd, 32 Beech Hill, Haywards Heath, West Sussex, RH16 3RX Tel: (01444) 440551 Fax: (01444) 441698 E-mail: info@compuhelp.co.uk

▶ Virtual Systems Solutions Ltd, 2 Sable Court, Southfields Business Park, Basildon, Essex, SS15 6SR Tel: (01268) 582950 Fax: (01268) 582951 E-mail: jcampbell@vssolutions.co.uk

▶ W Accountancy Ltd, 369 Hertford Road, Enfield, Middlesex, EN3 5JW Tel: (020) 8804 0478 Fax: (020) 8804 0221 E-mail: c.wheatley@waccountancy.co.uk

W Accountancy Ltd, Victoria Rdknaphill, Knaphill, Woking, Surrey, GU21 2AA Tel: (01483) 797901 Fax: (01483) 797899 E-mail: m.wood@waccountancy.co.uk

▶ WellyIT, 8 Lower Westford, WELLINGTON, Somerset, TA21 0DN Tel: (07962) 174984 E-mail: ntdobson@hotmail.com

CONSULTANTS, MEDIA INDUSTRY

A N Q, The Manor House, 14 Market Street, Lutterworth, Leicestershire, LE17 4EH Tel: (01455) 559446 Fax: (01455) 558523 E-mail: lgibson@anq.com

A R M Direct, 1 Bentinck Mews, London, W1U 2AF Tel: (020) 7317 3230 Fax: (020) 7224 3041 E-mail: info@arm-direct.co.uk

A.K. Sawyer Consulting, 19 Capesthorne Rd, Hazel Grove, Stockport, Cheshire, SK7 6BP Tel: (01625) 263904 E-mail: alansawyer@ontel.net.uk

T N S Media Intelligence, PA Newcentre, 292 Vauxhall Bridge Road, London, SW1V 1AE Tel: (020) 7963 7600 E-mail: tnsmi_sales@tnsofres.com

CONSULTANTS, MYSTERY SHOPPING

▶ Blue Apple, 6 The Wroe, Higham Ferrers, Rushden, Northamptonshire, NN10 8NB Tel: (01933) 316149 Fax: (01933) 316149 E-mail: steve@theblueapple.co.uk

Ims, Ten Pound Walk, Doncaster, South Yorkshire, DN4 5HX Tel: (01302) 554996 Fax: (01302) 554996 E-mail: sales@ukims.co.uk

CONSULTANTS, PRODUCT DESIGN AND DEVELOPMENT, ORIGINAL EQUIPMENT MANUFACTURE (OEM)

Bda, The Studio, Pipits Croft, Bicester, Oxfordshire, OX26 6XW Tel: (01869) 322158 Fax: (01869) 322158E-mail: info@bda-uk.com

CONSULTANTS, PRODUCT DESIGN AND DEVELOPMENT, ORIGINAL EQUIPMENT MANUFACTURE (OEM)

– *continued*

▶ Carpentry & Structures, 19 Parkside, Northampton, NN3 5EW Tel: (01604) 415198 E-mail: cassinjohn@tiscali.co.uk
▶ Exdel Design, Redwood, Norfolk Road, Turvey, Bedford, MK43 8DU Tel: (01234) 881566 Fax: (01234) 881450 E-mail: exdelservices@aol.com
Gravatom Engineering Systems Ltd, William Kelvin Building, Claylands Road, Bishops Waltham, Southampton, SO32 1BH Tel: (01489) 896010 Fax: (01489) 894382 E-mail: sales@gravatom.com
P J C, 22 The Drive, Orpington, Kent, BR6 9AP Tel: (07718) 267453 E-mail: studio@pjcdesign.co.uk
Product Partners Ltd, Church Street, Biggleswade, Bedfordshire, SG18 0JS Tel: (01767) 600456 Fax: (01767) 600155 E-mail: sales@productpartners.co.uk
▶ Taeno Design Consultants, The Mill, Home Farm, Ardington, Wantage, Oxfordshire, OX12 8PD Tel: (01235) 833785 Fax: (01235) 833860
Western Tooling Ltd, 55-57 Sterte Avenue, Poole, Dorset, BH15 2AJ Tel: (01202) 677654 Fax: (01202) 677876 E-mail: sales@westerntooling.co.uk

CONSULTING CHEMISTS

Bodycote Health Sciences, 121 Shady Lane, Great Barr, Birmingham, B44 9ET Tel: 0121-206 4100 Fax: 0121-251 4040 E-mail: healthsciences@bodycote.com
Central Scientific Laboratories, 445 New Cross Road, London, SE14 6TA Tel: (020) 8694 9330 Fax: (020) 8694 9163
Chemical & Industrial Consultants Association, 6 Church Bank, Richmond Rd, Bowdon, Altrincham, Cheshire, WA14 3NW Tel: 0161-928 6681 Fax: 0161-929 8544
Chemical Solutions, 474 Reigate Road, Epsom, Surrey, KT18 5XA Tel: (01737) 351777 Fax: (01737) 371606
Euro Test, Lennox Mall, Shirley Avenue, Vale Road, Windsor, Berkshire, SL4 5LH Tel: (01753) 867267 Fax: (01753) 867847 E-mail: southern.analytical@bodycote-mt.com
G C Laboratories Ltd, 6 Fen End, Stotfold, Hitchin, Hertfordshire, SG5 4BA Tel: (01462) 733770 Fax: (01462) 733898 E-mail: g.c.labs@btinternet.com
▶ M G Associates Construction Consultancy Ltd, 11 The Quadrant, Manor Park CR, Edgware, Middlesex, HA8 7LU Tel: (020) 8381 1429 Fax: (020) 8381 1425 E-mail: info@mg-assoc.co.uk
Pattinson Scientific Services, Scott House, Penn Street, Newcastle upon Tyne, NE4 7BG Tel: 0191-226 1300 Fax: 0191-226 1266 E-mail: pattinsonscientic@btconnect.com
Phoenix Analytical, The Laboratory, 270 London Road, Wallington, Surrey, SM6 7DJ Tel: (020) 8647 0003 Fax: (020) 8647 0004
Vintec Laboratories, Bucknalls Lane, Watford, WD25 9XX Tel: (01923) 661144 Fax: (01923) 661115 E-mail: vinteclabs@aol.com

CONSULTING ENGINEERS OR DESIGNERS, *See also headings for particular types*

3t Productions, Hill House, 8 Warwick Road, Southam, Warwickshire, CV47 0HN Tel: (01926) 811822 Fax: (01926) 811823 E-mail: 3t@inovates.it
▶ A F Crudden Associates, 209 High Street, Elgin, Morayshire, IV30 1DJ Tel: (01343) 550500 Fax: (01343) 550886
A K S Ward Ltd, 1 West Midfield, London, EC1A 9JU Tel: (020) 7236 0161 Fax: (020) 7236 3239 E-mail: consult@aksward.com
A4 Plus Drawing Services Ltd, 11a Park Street, Chatteris, Cambridgeshire, PE16 6AB Tel: (01354) 691820 Fax: (01354) 691821 E-mail: enquiries@a4plus.co.uk
Abatec Staff Consultants plc, Abatec House, Old Mixon Cresent, Weston-super-Mare, Avon, BS24 9AX Tel: (01934) 635025 Fax: (01934) 419999 E-mail: mail@abatec.co.uk
Abbott Holliday Partnership, 9 Greens Court, Lansdowne Mews, London, W11 3AP Tel: (020) 7792 1147 Fax: (01233) 820755 E-mail: enquiries@peter-holliday.co.uk
Alan White, Woodside House, 20-23 Woodside Place, Glasgow, G3 7QF Tel: 0141-582 1419 Fax: 0141-582 1484 E-mail: alan@alanwhitedesign.com
Amar Engineering Consultants, Unit 70 Station Road Workshops, Station Road, Kingswood, Bristol, BS15 4PJ Tel: 0117-956 5522 Fax: 0117-956 5573 E-mail: webe-amar@demon.co.uk
Amec Process & Energy Ltd, 76-78 Old Street, London, EC1V 9RU Tel: (020) 7539 5800 Fax: (020) 7539 5900 E-mail: commercial@amec.com
Aquatic Engineering & Construction Ltd, Palmerston Centre, 29-31 Palmerston Road, Aberdeen, AB11 5QP Tel: (01224) 573359 Fax: (01224) 577361 E-mail: admin@aquatic.co.uk
Archibald Shaw LLP, One Little London, Chichester, West Sussex, PO19 1PP Tel: (01243) 786 471 E-mail: info@archibaldshaw.co.uk
Arup, 13 Fitzroy Steet, London, W1T 4BQ Tel: (020) 7636 1531 Fax: (020) 7755 3716 E-mail: corporate@arup.com
Austin (UK) Ltd, Cardinal Point, Park Road, Rickmansworth, Hertfordshire, WD3 1RE Tel: (01923) 432658 Fax: (01923) 432795 E-mail: sales@austin.co.uk
Auto Design Ltd, 12 Tallon Road, Hutton, Brentwood, Essex, CM13 1TF Tel: (01277) 225000 Fax: (01277) 225002 E-mail: harvey@autodesign.co.uk
Automotive Design Centre, Northern Ireland Technology Centre, Cloreen Park, Malone Road, Belfast, BT9 5HN Tel: (028) 9033 5424 Fax: (028) 9097 4332 E-mail: a.mcbride@qub.ac.uk
Avon Construction, 850 Wimborne Road, Bournemouth, BH9 2DS Tel: (01202) 523006
Avontech Computer Systems, Dark Lane, Backwell, Bristol, BS48 3NP Tel: (01275) 462260 Fax: (01275) 462203 E-mail: sales@avontech.co.uk
B.C. & T. Consultants Ltd, Arundel House, Byland Road, Whitby, North Yorkshire, YO21 1JH Tel: (01947) 604871 Fax: (01947) 600010 E-mail: general@bct-consultants.co.uk
▶ B D T (uk) Ltd, Beaconsfield Lodge, Fore Street, Ashton Keynes, Swindon, SN6 6NP Tel: (01285) 862399 Fax: (01285) 862399 E-mail: richard.long@bdukltd.com
B K Consultants Ltd, Paxton Lodge, London Road, Coventry, CV1 2JT Tel: (024) 7625 6423 Fax: (024) 7652 0783 E-mail: engineers@bkconsultants.co.uk
B M T Defence Services Ltd, 210 Lower Bristol Road, Bath, BA2 3DQ Tel: (01225) 448712 Fax: (01225) 448714 E-mail: info@bmtdsl.co.uk
Babtie Group Ltd, Sheldon Court, Wagon Lane, Birmingham, B26 3DU Tel: 0121-700 1250 Fax: 0121-700 1251 E-mail: birmingham@babtie.com
Babtie Group Ltd, 224-226 Tower Bridge Road, London, SE1 2UP Tel: (020) 7403 3330 Fax: (020) 7939 1418
Bailey Johnson Hayes, Dane House, 55 London Road, St. Albans, Hertfordshire, AL1 1LJ Tel: (01727) 841172 Fax: (01727) 841085 E-mail: wb@bjh.co.uk
David Barfield Associates, Tylston Cottage, Tunbridge Lane, Liphook, Hampshire, GU30 7QA Tel: (01428) 723325 Fax: (01428) 723325 E-mail: dab295@aol.com
P. Barraclough & Associates Ltd, 48 Top Lane, Copmanthorpe, York, YO23 3UJ Tel: (01904) 704065 Fax: (01904) 700496
Bayliss & Miles Construction, 20 Park Way, Newbury, Berkshire, RG14 1EE Tel: (01635) 32280 Fax: (01635) 32260 E-mail: baylissandmiles@lineone.net
▶ BDR Civil, 4c Belmont Buildings, High Street, Crowborough, East Sussex, TN6 2QB Tel: (01892) 660057 Fax: (01892) 660063
Beattie Watkinson, Network House, 1 Ariel Way, London, W12 7SL Tel: (020) 8743 2021 Fax: (020) 8740 5921 E-mail: london@beawat.co.uk
Beaumont Structural Consultants, Goose Green Marsh, La Rue Du Craslin, St. Peter, Jersey, JE3 7BU Tel: (01534) 822888 Fax: (01534) 822889 E-mail: mail@bsc.co.je
Benaim (UK) Ltd, Dilke House, 1 Malet Street, London, WC1E 7JN Tel: (020) 7580 6000 Fax: (020) 7580 6090 E-mail: london@benaimgroup.com
▶ Bespoke Cards, 9B Higham Road, Woodford Green, Essex, IG8 9JN Tel: (0845) 270 1410 Fax: (0845) 270 1411 E-mail: theteam@bespokecards.net
Black & Veatch, Grove House, 100 High Street, Hampton, Middlesex, TW12 2ST Tel: (020) 8783 1055 Fax: (020) 8979 5397
Bluefrog Design, 21 St Margarets Street, Leicester, LE1 3EB Tel: 0116-253 0612 Fax: 0116-226 5737 E-mail: mail@bluefrogdesign.co.uk
Boot Robin Design Associates, 295a Lichfield Road, Sutton Coldfield, West Midlands, B74 4BZ Tel: 0121-308 5913 Fax: 0121-308 5913
Norman Bromley Partnership, Bridge House, 99-101 High Street, Tonbridge, Kent, TN9 1DR Tel: (01732) 773737 Fax: (01732) 773353 E-mail: mail@normanbromley.co.uk
Broughton Civil Engineers, 7-9 Station Road, Newport Pagnell, Buckinghamshire, MK16 0AG Tel: (01908) 500888 Fax: (01908) 500889 E-mail: consult@bbltd.co.uk
Bullen Consultants Ltd, Copthall House, Station Square, Coventry, CV1 2GT Tel: (024) 7663 2299 Fax: (024) 7663 2221 E-mail: coventry@bullen.co.uk
Bureau Veritas, The Oast, Newnham Court, Bearsted Road, Maidstone, Kent, ME14 5LH Tel: (01622) 632100 Fax: (01622) 739620 E-mail: oasts@uk.bureauveritas.com
Butler & Young Associates, 54-62 Station Road East, Oxted, Surrey, RH8 0PG Tel: (01883) 717172 Fax: (01883) 717174 E-mail: enquiries@bya.co.uk
C E C P Ltd, 819a Chorley Old Road, Bolton, BL1 5SL Tel: (01204) 849484 Fax: (01204) 849192
C W Fletcher & Sons Ltd, Sterling Works, Mansfield Road, Wales Bar, Sheffield, S26 5PQ Tel: 0114-294 2200 Fax: 0114-294 2211
Cadogan Consultants, 4th Floor The Market Building, 72-82 Rosebury Avenue, Clerkenwell, London, EC1R 4RW Tel: (020) 7837 5918 Fax: (020) 7490 2160
Calvert Brain & Fraulo, 3 Portland Street, King's Lynn, Norfolk, PE30 1PB Tel: (01553) 761771 Fax: (01553) 766033 E-mail: info@c-b-f.co.uk
Cameron & Andrew, The A P L Centre, Stevenston Industrial Estate, Stevenston, Ayrshire, KA20 3LR Tel: (01294) 603778 Fax: (01294) 603778 E-mail: rcamaron@btconect.com
Campbell Reith Hill LLP, Artillery House, 11-19 Artillery Row, London, SW1P 1RT Tel: (020) 7340 1700 Fax: (020) 7340 1777 E-mail: engineers@campbellreith.com
Campbell Rigg Associates, 12 Apollo Studios, Charlton Kings Road, London, NW5 2SB Tel: (020) 7284 1515 Fax: (020) 7267 4112 E-mail: design@campbellrigg.com
Canard Design Ltd, Sidney House, 262 Aylestone Lane, Wigston, Leicestershire, LE18 1BD Tel: 0116-279 6532 Fax: 0116-291 0081 E-mail: info@canard-design.co.uk
Capita Building Services, Salter House, 263-265 High Street, Berkhamsted, Hertfordshire, HP4 1AB Tel: (01442) 872121 Fax: (01442) 866565
Carl Bro Group, Grove House, Mansion Gate Drive, Leeds, LS7 4DN Tel: 0113-262 0000 Fax: 0113-262 0737 E-mail: enquiries@carlbro.com
Caudles, 23 West One House, St. Georges Road, Cheltenham, Gloucestershire, GL50 3DT Tel: (01242) 222307 Fax: (01242) 222665
Ch2m Hill, Avon House, Avonmore Road, London, W14 8TS Tel: (020) 7471 6100 Fax: (020) 7471 6101
Charles Andrews, The Corner House, Fourth Avenue, Trafford Park, Manchester, M17 1DB Tel: 0161-848 9955 Fax: 0161-848 9966 E-mail: info@charlesandrews.co.uk
▶ Charles Scott & Partners, 9 Park Quadrant, Glasgow, G3 6BS Tel: 0141-332 2873 Fax: 0141-332 2873
Charter Building Services Ltd, Mayplace Road East, Bexleyheath, Kent, DA7 6EJ Tel: (01322) 558011 Fax: (01322) 520282 E-mail: mail@charter.uk.com
Chesim Engineering Ltd, 7 Brunel Way, Fareham, Hampshire, PO15 5TX Tel: (01489) 885994 Fax: (01489) 885931 E-mail: sales@chesim.co.uk
Civil Engineering Dynamics Ltd, 11 Oak Walk, Wallington, Surrey, SM6 7DE Tel: (020) 8647 1908 Fax: (020) 8395 1556 E-mail: sales@environmental.co.uk
Clarke Designs Ltd, Imberhorne Lane, East Grinstead, West Sussex, RH19 1RJ Tel: (01342) 321021 Fax: (01342) 321021
Clarke Nicholls & Marcel, Galena House, 8-30 Galena Road, London, W6 0LT Tel: (020) 8748 8611 Fax: (020) 8741 8171 E-mail: cnm@cnmlondon.com
Coastal Marine (Boatbuilders) Ltd, Browns Bank, Eyemouth, Berwickshire, TD14 5DQ Tel: (01890) 750328 Fax: (01890) 751325
▶ Complete CCTV, Ty Crwn, Llangoed, Beaumaris, Isle of Anglesey, LL58 8NR Tel: (01248) 490575 E-mail: info@completecctv.co.uk
Conseco International Security Ltd, 5 Manchester Square, London, W1U 3PD Tel: (020) 7486 3661 Fax: (020) 7487 4153 E-mail: marketing@pellfrischmann.com
J M P Consultants Ltd, 172 Tottenham Court Road, London, W1T 7NA Tel: (020) 7388 5331 Fax: (020) 7387 0078 E-mail: london@jmp.co.uk
Consulting Engineers' Co-Partnership London Ltd, 1528 London Road, London, SW16 4EU Tel: (020) 8679 5621 Fax: (020) 8679 7922 E-mail: mail@cecp.co.uk
Cooper Beal & Ross, 33 Shaw Road, Stockport, Cheshire, SK4 4AG Tel: 0161-442 9770 Fax: 0161-442 9775 E-mail: cooperbealross@aol.com
Cordell Group Ltd, 159-160 High Street, Stockton-on-Tees, Cleveland, TS18 1PL Tel: (01642) 662400 Fax: (01642) 662402 E-mail: enquiries@cordellgroup.com
Cotleigh Engineering Co. Ltd, 586 Green Lanes, London, N8 0RP Tel: (020) 8802 0111 Fax: (020) 8809 5516 E-mail: j.markham@cotleigh.com
Coupland Bell Ltd, Barclays Venture Centre University of Warwick, Science Park, Coventry, CV4 7EZ Tel: (01926) 777566 E-mail: info@couplandbell.com
Coventry Turned Parts Ltd, Wedgenock Industrial Estate, Warwick, CV34 5PZ Tel: (01926) 491583 Fax: (01926) 410583
Cudd Bentley Consulting Ltd, Suite 1 Shelly Cresent Centre, 20 Farm House Way, Monkspath, Solihull, West Midlands, B90 4EH Tel: 0121-711 4343 Fax: 0121-711 3535
Cundall Johnston & Partners, Horsley House, Regent Centre, Gosforth, Newcastle upon Tyne, NE3 3LU Tel: 0191-213 1515 Fax: 0191-213 1701
Cundell, Saffron House, 6-10 Kirby Street, London, EC1N 8TS Tel: (020) 7438 1600 Fax: (020) 7438 1601 E-mail: info@cundall.com
Curtins Consulting Engineers plc, 26-29 St. Cross Street, London, EC1N 8UH Tel: (020) 7213 9000 Fax: (020) 7213 9001 E-mail: london@curtins.com
Cuthbertson Maunsell Ltd, Dunedin House, 25 Ravelstone Terrace, Edinburgh, EH4 3TP Tel: 0131-311 4000 Fax: 0131-311 4090 E-mail: cml-edin@compuserve.com
Danum Tools & Equipment, Great North Road, Doncaster, South Yorkshire, DN5 7UN Tel: (01302) 390080 Fax: (01302) 390081
Dar Al-Handasah Consultants Shair & Partners UK Ltd, Darpen House, 3 Waterlane, Richmond, Surrey, TW9 1TJ Tel: (020) 8334 7676 Fax: (020) 8334 2701 E-mail: darlondon@darlondon.com
Dats (Holdings) Ltd, 1 Springfield Street, Palmyra Square, Warrington, WA1 1BB Tel: (01925) 428559 Fax: (01925) 403801 E-mail: dats@dats.co.uk
Davmark Ltd, 63 Keats Way, West Drayton, Middlesex, UB7 9DU Tel: (07824) 638853 Fax: (01895) 905902 E-mail: david.slade@davmark.co.uk
Dean & Dyball Developments Ltd, Endeavour House, Crow Arch Lane, Ringwood, Hampshire, BH24 1PN Tel: (01425) 470000 Fax: (01425) 472724 E-mail: enquiries@deandyball.co.uk
Derek Wilkinson, Winfield Road, Nuneaton, Warwickshire, CV11 5AZ Tel: (024) 7637 5198 Fax: (024) 7637 5198 E-mail: derekw@enta.net
Descon Ltd, Graphic House, Otley Road, Guiseley, Leeds, LS20 8BH Tel: (01943) 877721 Fax: (01943) 870247 E-mail: info@descon.co.uk
Destech UK Ltd, 3 Millbrook Business Park, Hoe Lane, Nazeing, Waltham Abbey, Essex, EN9 2RJ Tel: (01992) 899002 Fax: (01992) 899003 E-mail: sales@destech-uk.co.uk
Detail Design, 2d Metropolitan Wharf, Wapping Wall, London, E1W 3SS Tel: (020) 7488 1669 Fax: (020) 7488 2524 E-mail: gorden@detail.co.uk
Deva Electronic Controls Ltd, Unit 52 Woodside Business Park, Birkenhead, Merseyside, CH41 1EL Tel: 0151-647 3222 Fax: 0151-647 4511 E-mail: sales@deva.co.uk
Doxford Design Engineering Ltd, 3 Fellside, Ponteland, Newcastle upon Tyne, NE20 9JW Tel: 0191-519 1433
Doyle Partnership, 5 Waverley Road, Huddersfield, HD1 5NA Tel: (01484) 516977 Fax: (01484) 516958
DSSR, 9 Crown Terrace, Glasgow, G12 9EY Tel: 0141-334 6161 Fax: 0141-357 1993 E-mail: glasgow@dssr.co.uk
▶ Eclipse Petroleum Technology, Salvesen Tower, Blaikies Quay, Aberdeen, AB11 5PW Tel: (01224) 588355 Fax: (01224) 588356
▶ Edp Consulting Engineers, Munro House, Quarrywood Court, Livingston, West Lothian, EH54 6AX Tel: (01506) 497200 Fax: (01506) 497949
▶ Elder's Engineers, 9 Park CR, Edinburgh, EH16 6JD Tel: 0131-664 5176 Fax: 0131-664 5643
Eldred Geotechnics, Veitchii Barn, Newbarn Road, Swanley, Kent, BR8 7PW Tel: (01322) 663222
▶ S. Eldridge Design & Draughting, 37 Hazelwood Close, Honiton, Devon, EX14 2XA Tel: (01404) 45054 E-mail: stephen.eldridge@btinternet.com
Electroglass Ltd, 4 Brunel Road, Manor Trading Estate, Benfleet, Essex, SS7 4PS Tel: (01268) 565577 Fax: (01268) 565594 E-mail: info@electroglass.co.uk
▶ Electrospect Ltd, 240 Queensferry Road, Edinburgh, EH4 2BP Tel: 0131-443 1692
Elektro Magnetix Ltd, Sussex Innovation Centre, Science Park Square, Falmer, Brighton, BN1 9SB Tel: (01273) 704471 Fax: (01273) 704472 E-mail: elektro@elektro.co.uk
Engineering Design Partnership, 2 Barnet Road, Barnet, Hertfordshire, EN5 3LJ Tel: (020) 8449 9696 Fax: (020) 8449 6100 E-mail: edp@e-dp.co.uk
Engineering Designs With It Solutions, 17 Parkfield Drive, Sowerby Bridge, West Yorkshire, HX6 3PJ Tel: (01422) 834893 Fax: (01422) 835723 E-mail: sales@editsltd.co.uk
Engineering & Development Consultants Ltd, Keruing Cedar, Chess Hill, Loudwater, Rickmansworth, Hertfordshire, WD3 4HU Tel: (01923) 776567 Fax: (01923) 721438 E-mail: gmcrook@lineone.net
Engineering Co Partnership plc, Units 16-17 Metro Business Centre, Kangley Bridge Road, London, SE26 5BW Tel: (020) 8776 8070 Fax: (020) 8776 7372 E-mail: info@ecp.co.uk
Eoin Technology Ltd, 35 Warwick Terrace, East Street, Olney, Buckinghamshire, MK46 4BU Tel: (07775) 935422 Fax: (0871) 2564641 E-mail: postbox@eointech.co.uk
Esdu International Ltd, 27 Corsham Street, London, N1 6UA Tel: (020) 7490 5151 Fax: (020) 7490 2701E-mail: esdu@esdu.com
Expotec Ltd, 10 Harles Arces, Hickling, Melton Mowbray, Leicestershire, LE14 3AF Tel: (01664) 822725 Fax: (01664) 822725 E-mail: tony.fox2@ntlworld.com
Faber Maunsell Ltd, Marlborough House, 18 Upper Marlborough Road, St. Albans, Hertfordshire, AL1 3UT Tel: (020) 8784 5784 Fax: (020) 8784 5700 E-mail: enquiries@fabermaunsell.com
Fabermaunsell, Beaufort House, 94-96 Newhall Street, Birmingham, B3 1PB Tel: 0121-262 1900 Fax: 0121-262 1999 E-mail: libby.caughtry@fabermaunsell.com
Ferguson & Mcilveen, Beechill House, 40 Beechill Road, Belfast, BT8 7RP Tel: (028) 9070 5111 Fax: (028) 9070 5651 E-mail: belfast@fermac.com
Ferguson Mcilveen LLP, Victoria House, 159 Albert Road, Middlesbrough, Cleveland, TS1 2PX Tel: (01642) 218476 Fax: (01642) 223582 E-mail: postmaster@fermac.com

CONSULTING ENGINEERS OR DESIGNERS – *continued*

▶ fhp engineering services solutions, 178-202 Great Portland Street, London, W1W 5JD Tel: (020) 7291 7777 Fax: (020) 7580 4472 E-mail: london@fhpess.com

Fichtner Consulting Engineers Ltd, Frederick House, 8 Acorn Business Park, Heaton Lane, Stockport, Cheshire, SK4 1AS Tel: 0161-476 0032 Fax: 0161-474 0618 E-mail: sales@fichtner.co.uk

Flomar Ltd, Marlborough Drive, Fleckney, Leicester, LE8 8UR Tel: 0116-240 3430 Fax: 0116-240 4012 E-mail: admin@flomar.co.uk

Fluor Ltd, Portland House, Bressenden Place, London, SW1E 5BH Tel: (020) 7932 1700 Fax: (020) 7932 1722

Foster Wheeler Energy Ltd, Shinfield Park, Shinfield, Reading, RG2 9FW Tel: 0118-913 1234 Fax: 0118-913 2333 E-mail: fw-sales@fwuk.fwc.com

Frazer-Nash Consultancy Ltd, Quay Head House, Colston Ave., Bristol, BS1 1EB Tel: 0117-922 6242 Fax: 0117-922 6524 E-mail: sales@fnc.co.uk

Furness Engineering & Technology, Ellers Mill, The Ellers, Ulverston, Cumbria, LA12 0AQ Tel: (01229) 584043 Fax: (01229) 586440 E-mail: mail@fetl.co.uk

G K Salter & Associates, Azalea Drive, Swanley, Kent, BR8 8HX Tel: (01322) 668933 Fax: (01322) 666019E-mail: post@gksa.ltd.uk

G T Drawing Services Ltd, Cradock Road, Luton, LU4 0JF Tel: (01582) 502883 Fax: (01582) 572201 E-mail: mail@gtdrawings.com

G W Building Consulting Engineers Ltd, Treasure House, 19-21 Hatton Garden, London, EC1N 8NG Tel: (020) 7831 1717 Fax: (020) 7831 6429 E-mail: info@gwconsultants.co.uk

G X Design Engineers, The Mayfield, Usk, Gwent, NP15 1SY Tel: (01291) 673437 Fax: (01291) 673438 E-mail: info@gxl.co.uk

Gardline Information Solutions Ltd, The Design Centre, Hewet Road, Gapton Hall, Great Yarmouth, Norfolk, NR31 0NN Tel: (01493) 440400 Fax: (01493) 442480 E-mail: steve.brown@gardline.co.uk

Tony Gee & Partners, T.G.P. House, 45-47 High Street, Cobham, Surrey, KT11 3DP Tel: (01932) 868277 Fax: (01932) 866003 E-mail: gmd@tgp.co.uk

Glasspool & Thaiss, Coughtrey House, 112-116 Broad Street, Chesham, Buckinghamshire, HP5 3ED Tel: (01494) 771314 Fax: (01494) 791455 E-mail: mail@glasspoolandthaiss.com

Peter Goodhind Associates Ltd, Brunel House, George Street, Gloucester, GL1 1BZ Tel: (01452) 503501 Fax: (01452) 308794 E-mail: mail@goodhindassociates.co.uk

Goodrow Engineering Ltd, Unit 5, Ebbsfleet Industrial Estate, Northfleet, Gravesend, Kent, DA11 9DZ Tel: (01474) 359990 Fax: (01474) 359994

Greenway & Partners Ltd, 1 Bedford Street, Leamington Spa, Warwickshire, CV32 5DY Tel: (01926) 337430 Fax: (01926) 428964 E-mail: sales@gapl.co.uk

GSS Projects Ltd, 12 Ambassador Place, Stockport Road, Altrincham, Cheshire, WA15 8EQ Tel: 0161-926 9510 Fax: 0161-926 9536

H M Sitec Ltd, St. Georges Lodge, 33 Oldfield Road, Bath, BA2 3NE Tel: (01225) 428221 Fax: (01225) 444697 E-mail: info@hmbath.com

H S B Engineering, Marycutler Rd, Portlethen, Aberdeen, AB12 4RB Tel: (01224) 784785 Fax: (01224) 784785

Halcrow Asia Partnership Ltd, Vineyard House, 44 Brook Green, London, W6 7BY Tel: (020) 7602 7282 Fax: (020) 7603 0095 E-mail: info@halcrow.com

Halcrow Crouch Ltd, City Park, 368 Alexandra Parade, Glasgow, G31 3AU Tel: 0141-552 2000 Fax: 0141-552 2525 E-mail: hcglasgow@halcrow.com

Halcrow Group Ltd, Arndale House, Otley Road, Leeds, LS6 2UL Tel: 0113-220 8220 Fax: 0113-274 2924

Harding McDermott & Partners, 12 Exmouth Market, London, EC1R 4QE Tel: (020) 7833 9533 Fax: (020) 7833 3633

Harding-Crosweller, Unit G Imber Court Trading Estate, Orchard La, East Molesey, Surrey, KT8 0BY Tel: (020) 8398 9625 Fax: (020) 8398 7486

Harley Haddow Partnership, 8 Coates Crescent, Edinburgh, EH3 7BY Tel: 0131-226 3331 Fax: 0131-226 2563 E-mail: edin@harleyhaddow.com

Harnden Plastics, Manchester Road, Hyde, Cheshire, SK14 2BP Tel: 0161-368 1817 Fax: 0161-368 1140 E-mail: harnden@a-m.co.uk

Haskoning (UK) Ltd, 4 Deans Yard, London, SW1P 3NL Tel: (020) 7222 2115 Fax: (020) 7222 2659 E-mail: info@london.royalhaskoning.com

Charles Haswell & Partners Ltd, 3900 Parkside, Birmingham Business Park, Birmingham, B37 7YG Tel: 0121-717 7744 Fax: 0121-717 0902 E-mail: enquiries@severntrent.com

Haughton Design Ltd, Business Innovation Centre, Gates Court, Staffordshire Technology Park, Stafford, ST18 0AR Tel: (01785) 243767 Fax: (01785) 243768 E-mail: adm@haughtondesign.co.uk

Heap & Digby Ltd, 6a Park Road, Oxted, Surrey, RH8 0AL Tel: (01883) 717102 Fax: (01883) 381405 E-mail: sales@heapdigby.co.uk

High Point Rendel, Suite 3 Bowling Hill Business Park, Quarry Road, Chipping Sodbury, Bristol, BS37 6JL Tel: (01454) 312266 Fax: (01454) 312666 E-mail: bris-hpr@netcomuk.co.uk

High Point Rendel Ltd, 61 Southwark Street, London, SE1 1SA Tel: (020) 7654 0400 Fax: (020) 7654 0401 E-mail: london@highpointrendel.com

Hilbre Engineering Design Services, 71 Park Rd, Meols, Wirral, Merseyside, CH47 7BD Tel: 0151-632 2995 Fax: 0151-632 2850 E-mail: heds@tinyonline.co.uk

Hoare, Lea, Glen House, 200-208 Tottenham Court Road, London, W1T 7PL Tel: (020) 7890 2500 Fax: (020) 7436 8466 E-mail: joebrookes@londonhoarelea.com

Horizon Instruments Ltd, Unit 12 Ghyll Industrial Estate, Heathfield, East Sussex, TN21 8AW Tel: (01435) 864239 Fax: (01435) 865222 E-mail: mail@horizoninstruments.co.uk

Houlder Ltd, 59 Lafone Street, London, SE1 2LX Tel: (020) 7357 7317 Fax: (020) 7403 8201 E-mail: mail@houlder-offshore.co.uk

HTS Design Services Ltd, 379 Anlaby Road, Hull, HU3 6AB Tel: (01482) 351236 Fax: (01482) 566052 E-mail: office@ahgsltd.co.uk

George Hutchison Associates Ltd, 51 Brookfield Road, Cheadle, Cheshire, SK8 1ES Tel: 0161-491 4600 Fax: 0161-491 4700 E-mail: enquiries@stressstrain.com

Hyder Consulting Ltd, Wellington House, Market Street, Douglas, Isle of Man, IM1 2PQ Tel: (01624) 624694 Fax: (01624) 661760

Hyder Consulting UK Ltd, 10 Medawar Road, Surrey Research Park, Guildford, Surrey, GU2 7AR Tel: (01483) 535000 Fax: (01483) 535051

Hyder Consulting UK Ltd, 29 Pressenden Place, London, SW1E 5DZ Tel: (0870) 0003006 Fax: (0870) 0003906 E-mail: info@hyderconsulting.com

I H S Energy Group, 28 Church Street, Epsom, Surrey, KT17 4QP Tel: (01372) 745959 Fax: (01372) 727091

IMC Group Consulting Ltd, PO Box 18, Nottingham, NG15 0DT Tel: (01623) 726166 Fax: (01623) 729359 E-mail: mining@imcgcl.com

INBIS Ltd, Club Street, Bamber Bridge, Preston, PR5 6FN Tel: (01772) 645000 Fax: (01772) 645001 E-mail: mailbox@assystems.com

INBIS Group Ltd, St. Johns House, Church Street, Wolverhampton, WV2 4LS Tel: (01902) 427463 Fax: (01902) 714239

Inbis Technology Ltd, 1 The Brooms, Emersons Green, Bristol, BS16 7FD Tel: 0117-987 4000 Fax: 0117-987 4040 E-mail: careers@inbis.com

Interlink Systems Engineering Ltd, Po Box 3, Leighton Buzzard, Bedfordshire, LU7 3AG Tel: (01525) 372613 Fax: (01525) 372613 E-mail: interlink.consulting@dial.pipex.com

Iron By Design, Unit 31 Steeton Grove, Steeton, Keighley, West Yorkshire, BD20 6TT Tel: (01535) 654146 Fax: (01535) 654146 E-mail: enquiries@iron-by-design.co.uk

J D Woodward, 7 Higham Way, Burbage, Hinckley, Leicestershire, LE10 2PU Tel: (01455) 613432 Fax: (01455) 613432 E-mail: sales@jdwoodward.co.uk

J E B Engineering Design Ltd, Chiswick Avenue, Mildenhall, Bury St. Edmunds, Suffolk, IP28 7AY Tel: (01638) 718435 Fax: (01638) 717962 E-mail: info@jebeng.com

J M Feerick & Partners, 3-5 Church Street, Brierley Hill, West Midlands, DY5 3PT Tel: (01384) 77885 Fax: (01384) 76181 E-mail: johnfeerick@jmfeerickandpatns.co.uk

J & S Marine Ltd, Riverside Road, Pottington Business Park, Barnstaple, Devon, EX31 1LY Tel: (01271) 337500 Fax: (01271) 337501 E-mail: sales@jsmarine.co.uk

J T Electrons, 42 Torridge Road, Thornton Heath, Surrey, CR7 7EY Tel: (020) 8665 6595 Fax: (020) 8665 6595 E-mail: istc@istc.org.uk

Jacobs Engineering Ltd, 95 Bothwell Street, Glasgow, G2 7HX Tel: 0141-240 4700 Fax: 0141-226 3109

James Maxton & Co, Calor Gas Building, Airport Road West, Belfast, BT3 9EE Tel: (028) 9045 8238 Fax: (028) 9045 6428 E-mail: jmaxton@aol.com

Jampel Davison & Bell, 210a Tufnell Park Road, London, N7 0PZ Tel: (020) 7272 0562 Fax: (020) 7263 4005 E-mail: info@jamdavbell.co.uk

Jim Mccoll Associates, 6a Mill Lane, Edinburgh, EH6 6TJ Tel: 0131-555 0721 Fax: 0131-555 0723 E-mail: enquiries@mccollassoc.co.uk

John D Hotchkiss Ltd, Main Road, West Kingsdown, Sevenoaks, Kent, TN15 6ER Tel: (01474) 853131 Fax: (01474) 853288 E-mail: sales@hotchkiss-engineers.co.uk

Michael Jones & Associates, Crossway House, 8 London Road, Reigate, Surrey, RH2 9HY Tel: (01737) 245610 Fax: (01737) 241142 E-mail: info@mjassociates.co.uk

K Home International Ltd, Ingram House, Allensway, Stockton-on-Tees, Cleveland, TS17 9HA Tel: (01642) 765421 Fax: (01642) 760721 E-mail: enquiry@khomeint.co.uk

KBR, Hill Park Court, Springfield Drive, Leatherhead, Surrey, KT22 7NL Tel: (01372) 865000 Fax: (01372) 864400

Link Project Services Ltd, 12 The Parks, Haydock Park, Newton-Le-Willows, Merseyside, WA12 0JQ Tel: (01942) 408440 Fax: (01942) 408450 E-mail: uk@link-projects.com

▶ Lisle Design, 50 Lade Braes, St. Andrews, Fife, KY16 9DA Tel: (01334) 471435

List Design Group Ltd, Manby Road By Passage, Immingham, South Humberside, DN40 2DW Tel: (01469) 571888 Fax: (01469) 571450 E-mail: ldgltd@aol.com

List Design Group Ltd, Unit 2, Avon Terrace, Salisbury, SP2 7BX Tel: (01722) 335112 Fax: (01722) 412521 E-mail: engineering@listgroup.co.uk

London Offshore Consultants Ltd, 20 St Dunstans Hill, London, EC3R 8NP Tel: (020) 7283 5544 Fax: (020) 7600 0562 E-mail: loc@londonoffshore.co.uk

Long & Co Kent Ltd, Bybow Farm, Orchard Way, Dartford, DA2 7ER Tel: (01322) 273028 Fax: (01322) 228818

Lusas Computer Systems, 66 High Street, Kingston upon Thames, Surrey, KT1 1HN Tel: (020) 8541 1999 Fax: (020) 8549 9399 E-mail: info@lusas.com

M D Hughes & Partners, 52 High Street, Stonehouse, Gloucestershire, GL10 2NA Tel: (01453) 824551 Fax: (01453) 828624 E-mail: mdhp@btconnect.com

▶ M G Associates Construction Consultancy Ltd, 11 The Quadrant, Manor Park CR, Edgware, Middlesex, HA8 7LU Tel: (020) 8381 1429 Fax: (020) 8381 1425 E-mail: info@mg-assoc.co.uk

M S E Consultants Ltd, North House, 31 North Street, Carshalton, Surrey, SM5 2HW Tel: (020) 8773 4500 Fax: (020) 8773 4600 E-mail: enquiries@mse.co.uk

Mca Consulting Engineers Ltd, Newhouse Farm Business Centre, Horsham, West Sussex, RH12 4RU Tel: (01293) 851490 Fax: (01293) 852156 E-mail: sales@mcaltd.co.uk

MACAW Engineering Ltd, 1 Park Road, Gosforth Business Park, Newcastle upon Tyne, NE12 8DG Tel: 0191-216 4930 E-mail: info@macawengineering.com

McGown Snowden, 14-18 Emerald Street, London, WC1N 3QA Tel: (020) 7242 2412 Fax: (020) 7242 0460 E-mail: office@mcgowensnowden.co.uk

Mclellan & Partners Ltd, 7 Station Approach, West Byfleet, Surrey, KT14 6NL Tel: (01932) 343271 Fax: (01932) 348037 E-mail: mclellan_uk@compuserve.com

Macrodyne Electronics Ltd, The Birches, Birches Lane, Newent, Gloucestershire, GL18 1DN Tel: (01531) 828010 Fax: (01531) 821153 E-mail: mailbox@macrodyne.com

Manderstam International Group Ltd, Douglas House, 16-18 Douglas Street, London, SW1P 4PB Tel: (020) 7730 9224 Fax: (020) 7823 3056 E-mail: migl@manderstam.com

March Designs & Measurements, 11 Alfred Street, Dunstable, Bedfordshire, LU5 4HZ Tel: (01582) 600016 Fax: (01582) 600016 E-mail: info@marchdesigns.com

Maritime Progress Ltd, 3-5 Holmethorpe Avenue, Redhill, RH1 2LZ Tel: (01737) 763400 Fax: (01737) 782818 E-mail: info@maritimeprogress.com

Marks Heeley & Brothwell Ltd, The Stables, Cannons Mill Lane, Bishop's Stortford, Hertfordshire, CM23 2BN Tel: (01279) 465900 Fax: (01279) 465999 E-mail: general@mhb.co.uk

Peter Mason Associates, New Street, Mawdesley, Ormskirk, Lancashire, L40 2QP Tel: (01704) 823245 Fax: (01704) 823246 E-mail: steve.douglas@btinternet.com

Wilson Mason & Partners, 3 Chandos Street, London, W1G 9JU Tel: (020) 7637 1501 Fax: (020) 7631 0325 E-mail: enquiries@wilsonmason.co.uk

Max Fordham & Partners, 42-43 Gloucester Cresent, London, NW1 7PE Tel: (020) 7267 5161 Fax: (020) 7482 0329 E-mail: post@maxfordham.com

Medtec Design Services Ltd, Unit 34, JS White Eastate, Cowes, Isle Of Wight, PO31 7LP Tel: (01983) 294974 Fax: (01983) 290255 E-mail: design@medtec.co.uk

Melliss & Partners, Boundary House The Pines Business Park, Broad Street, Guildford, Surrey, GU3 3BH Tel: (01483) 567879 Fax: (01483) 574616 E-mail: mail@melliss.com

Michael Barclay Partnership, 105 Strand, London, WC2R 0AB Tel: (020) 7240 1191 Fax: (020) 7240 2241

Milsom Industrial Designs Ltd, 11 Kelso Place, Upper Bristol Road, Bath, BA1 3AU Tel: (01225) 444809 Fax: (01225) 444787 E-mail: enquiries@milsom.uk.com

Morris Engineering Design, Service, 36 Craighall Road, Edinburgh, EH6 4SA Tel: 0131-551 3333 Fax: 0131-551 3030 E-mail: mes@gamorris.co.uk

Morrish & Partners Ltd, 8 Parkway, Welwyn Garden City, Hertfordshire, AL8 6HG Tel: (01707) 336017 E-mail: eng@morrish.co.uk

Mott Macdonald Ltd, Prince House, 49-51 Prince Street, Bristol, BS1 4PS Tel: 0117-906 9500 Fax: 0117-922 1924

Mott MacDonald, 43 Lambourne Cres, Cardiff Business Pk, Llanishen, Cardiff, CF14 5GG Tel: (029) 2075 5755 Fax: (029) 2075 5756 E-mail: cardiff@mottmac.com

Mott Macdonald Ltd, St Anne House, 20-26 Wellesley Road, Croydon, CR9 2UL Tel: (020) 8774 2000 Fax: (020) 8681 5706 E-mail: marketing@mottmac.com

Mott Macdonald (Wales) Ltd, 11 Wynnstay Rd, Colwyn Bay, Clwyd, LL29 8NB Tel: (01492) 534601 Fax: (01492) 533063 E-mail: colwyn.bay@mottmac.com

Mouchel Parkman plc, West Hall, Parvis Road, West Byfleet, Surrey, KT14 6EZ Tel: (01932) 337000 Fax: (01932) 340673 E-mail: info@mouchelparkman.com

Mowlem Engineering Solutions, Bewley Court, Bylands Way, Belasis Hall Technology Park, Billingham, Cleveland, TS23 4EB Tel: (01642) 371313 Fax: (01642) 373101

Mowlem Water Engineering, Port Causeway, Bromborough, Wirral, Merseyside, CH62 4TP Tel: 0151-334 4990 Fax: 0151-334 9403

Moy Park Ltd, Screevagh, Lisnaskea, Enniskillen, County Fermanagh, BT92 0FA Tel: (028) 6772 1999 Fax: (028) 6772 2442 E-mail: fernefoods@btinternet.com

Multi Tech Contracts, Unit 6 Bowood Court, Calver Road, Winwick Quay, Warrington, WA2 8QZ Tel: (01925) 418333 Fax: (01925) 418800 E-mail: sales@mtcl.net

N Code International Ltd, Innovation Technology Center, Advanced Manufacturing Park, Brunel Way, Catcliffe, Rotherham, South Yorkshire, S60 5WG Tel: 0114-254 1246 Fax: 0114-254 1245 E-mail: info@ncode.com

N I S Holdings Ltd, Ackhurst Road, Chorley, Lancashire, PR7 1NH Tel: (01257) 265656 Fax: (01257) 275501 E-mail: info@nisltd.com

Nash Mynard Design Ltd, Dodford Mill, Dodford, Northampton, NN7 4SS Tel: (01327) 341643 Fax: (01327) 341801

National Industrial Fuel Efficiency Services Ltd, Nifes House, Sinderland Road, Altrincham, Cheshire, WA14 5HQ Tel: 0161-928 5791 Fax: 0161-926 8718 E-mail: hoffice@nifes.co.uk

Noble Denton Consultants Ltd, Noble House, 39 Tabernacle Street, London, EC2A 4AA Tel: (020) 7812 8700 Fax: (020) 7812 8701 E-mail: marketing@nobledenton.co.uk

▶ North West Technologies Ltd, 15 Acacia Drive, Great Sutton, Ellesmere Port, CH66 2UT Tel: 0151-355 8075 E-mail: enquiries@nw-tech.co.uk

Numerate Technology Ltd, 4 Ashley Gardens, Tunbridge Wells, Kent, TN4 8TY Tel: (01892) 545049

Offshore Design Engineering Ltd, 12 Princeton Mews, 167-169 London Road, Kingston upon Thames, Surrey, KT2 6PT Tel: (020) 8481 1190 Fax: (020) 8546 4346 E-mail: ode_london@ode-ltd.co.uk

P B Power, Unit 4-5, Ferrybridge Business Park, Knottingley, West Yorkshire, WF11 8NA Tel: (01977) 677664 Fax: (01977) 672009 E-mail: info@pbworld.com

P J B Systems Technology Ltd, Systems House, Blackbrook Business Park, Fareham, Hampshire, PO15 5DR Tel: (01329) 826156 Fax: (01329) 826111 E-mail: sales@pjbsystems.co.uk

P L S Associates Ltd, Brackendale, The Green, Palgrave, Diss, Norfolk, IP22 1AN Tel: (01379) 644500 Fax: (01379) 644038 E-mail: sales@webpressworld.co.uk

Paramode Ltd, Harbour Road, Lowestoft, Suffolk, NR32 3LZ Tel: (01502) 574213 Fax: (01502) 501503 E-mail: sales@paramode.co.uk

Parsons Brinckerhoff, Quadrant Court, 45 Calthorpe Road, Edgbaston, Birmingham, B15 1TH Tel: 0121-452 7400 Fax: 0121-452 1799

Parsons Brinckerhoff, Crown House, River Way, Harlow, Essex, CM20 2DL Tel: (01279) 450900 Fax: (01279) 450898

▶ Parsons Brinckerhoff, Calyx House, South Road, Taunton, Somerset, TA1 3DU Tel: (01823) 424400 Fax: (01823) 424401 E-mail: slocomben@pbworld.com

Peter Fraenkel Maritime Ltd, 21-37 South Street, Dorking, Surrey, RH4 2JZ Tel: (01306) 879797 Fax: (01306) 879798 E-mail: contact@fraenkel.co.uk

▶ Plastic Design Solutions Ltd, 80 Church Road, Stockton-on-Tees, Cleveland, TS18 1TW Tel: (01642) 671711 Fax: (01642) 671762 E-mail: admin@plastic-design-solutions.freeserve.co.uk

Posford Haskoning, Eastchester House, Harlands Road, Haywards Heath, West Sussex, RH16 1PG Tel: (01444) 458551 Fax: (01444) 440665 E-mail: info@royalhaskoing.com

Precision Supply Co., 5 Block 3, Thornliebank Industrial Estate, Thornliebank, Glasgow, G46 8TU Tel: 0141-638 9060 Fax: 0141-638 9848 E-mail: sales@scottishtools.co.uk

Professional Equipment, Mill Farm, 42 Main St, Repton, Derby, DE65 6EZ Tel: (01283) 704432 Fax: (01283) 704432 E-mail: bob@profequip.fsnet.co

Prototype Pressing Ltd, Unit 12C, Shefford Industrial Park, Shefford, Bedfordshire, SG17 5DZ Tel: (01462) 816978 Fax: (01462) 817242 E-mail: pashby@ashfen.demon.co.uk

Ramsay & Primrose Ltd, 18 Lynedoch Street, Glasgow, G3 6EY Tel: 0141-332 4015 Fax: 0141-333 9197 E-mail: rndpltd@btconnect.com

Rayleigh Engineering Ltd, 19 Nobel Square, Burnt Mills Industrial Estate, Basildon, Essex, SS13 1LP Tel: (01268) 728380 Fax: (01268) 728205 E-mail: rayleigh.engineer@btconnect.com

Raysun Machine Tools, 6 Prospect Park, Valley Drive, Rugby, Warwickshire, CV21 1TF Tel: (01788) 541777 Fax: (01788) 541577 E-mail: raysun@tinyonline.co.uk

Chris Reading Associates, 6 Charfield Close, Winchester, Hampshire, SO22 4PZ Tel: (07802) 618656 Fax: (01962) 861496 E-mail: consult@cvrassociates.freeserve.co.uk

▶ Redwood Partnership, Maritime House, Basin Road North, Portslade, Brighton, BN41 1WR Tel: (01273) 414515 Fax: 08716 618938 E-mail: consult@redwoodpartnership.co.uk

Andrew Reid & Partners, 36-37 Furnival Street, London, EC4A 1JQ Tel: (020) 7430 1611 Fax: (020) 7404 0553 E-mail: general@andrewreid.co.uk

Renfrew Group, 33 Rutland St, Leicester, LE1 1RE Tel: 0116-253 1961 Fax: 0116-253 9827 E-mail: info@renfrew.com

CONSULTING ENGINEERS OR DESIGNERS – *continued*

Rennie & Kirkwood Ltd, 95 Morrison Street, Glasgow, G5 8BE Tel: 0141-429 2810 Fax: 0141-420 3728 E-mail: mail@rkglasgow.fsnet.co.uk

Rhos Designs Ltd, 3 Heol Aur, Dafen Industrial Estate, Dafen, Llanelli, Dyfed, SA14 8QN Tel: (01554) 749366 Fax: (01554) 749377 E-mail: rhos@compuserve.com

Ricardo Consulting Engineers Ltd, Bridge Works, Old Shoreham Road, Shoreham-by-Sea, West Sussex, BN43 5FG Tel: (01273) 455611 Fax: (01273) 464124

Richard Watkins, 142 Lower Marsh, London, SE1 7AE Tel: (020) 7593 0088 Fax: (020) 7593 0080 E-mail: engineers@rwalondon.co.uk

Robinson Architects, Merchants Quay, Ashley Lane, Shipley, West Yorkshire, BD17 7DB Tel: (01274) 532500 Fax: (01274) 534000 E-mail: rce@robinsongroup.co.uk

Rooley Consultants, Greenways, Church Lane, Stoke Poges, Slough, SL2 4PB Tel: (01753) 648040 Fax: (01753) 648048 E-mail: richard@rooley.com

Roughton & Partners International Ltd, 321 Millbrook Road West, Southampton, SO15 0HW Tel: (023) 8070 5533 Fax: (023) 8070 1060 E-mail: hq@roughton.com

Royal Haskoning, Rightwell House, Bretton Centrel, Bretton, Peterborough, PE3 8DW Tel: (01733) 336157 Fax: (01733) 262243 E-mail: info@peterborough.royalhaskoning.com

RPS Consulting Engineers, Elmwood House, 74 Boucher Road, Belfast, BT12 6RZ Tel: (028) 9066 7914 Fax: (028) 9066 8286 E-mail: belfast@rpsgroup.com

RSD Technology Ltd, Kingsway Business Centre, Kingsway, Fforestfach, Swansea, SA5 4DL Tel: (01792) 585859 Fax: (01792) 580651 E-mail: admin@rsd.uk.com

Howard Ruse Associates Ltd, 2 Avery Hill Road, London, SE9 2BD Tel: (020) 8850 5678 E-mail: sales@hraconsulting.co.uk

Ken Rush Associates, Bowman House, 191 South Street, Braintree, Essex, CM7 3QB Tel: (01376) 326789 Fax: (01376) 342711 E-mail: engineer@ken-rush-assoc.demon.co.uk

Rybka Battle UK Ltd, 14-17 Wells Mews, London, W1T 3HF Tel: (020) 7637 1221 Fax: (020) 7637 2338

S G L Systems Ltd, Milton Industrial Estate, Lesmahagow, Lanark, ML11 0JN Tel: (01555) 894449 Fax: (01555) 894227

S.J Deegan Sons, Elstree Hill South, Edgwarebury House Farm, Elstree, Borehamwood, Hertfordshire, WD6 3DE Tel: (020) 8953 1042 Fax: (020) 8207 6550

S V M Consulting Engineers Ltd, 10 Kensworth Gate, Garden Road, Dunstable, Bedfordshire, LU6 3HS Tel: (01582) 660090 Fax: (01582) 660091 E-mail: solutions@svm.co.uk

St James Lovell Partnership, Southbank House, Black Prince Road, London, SE1 7SJ Tel: (020) 7793 2330 Fax: (020) 7793 2335 E-mail: mail@stjameslovell.com

Charles Scott & Partners (London) Ltd, 23 Skylines, Limeharbour, London, E14 9TS Tel: (020) 7538 1333 Fax: (020) 7538 3747 E-mail: cspll@aol.com

Scott Wilson, Central Boulevard, Blythe Valley Park, Shirley, Solihull, West Midlands, B90 8AH Tel: 0121-746 6200 Fax: 0121-746 6201 E-mail: birmingham@camerontaylor.co.uk

Scott Wilson Kirkpatrick & Co. Ltd, Bayheath House, Rose Hill West, Chesterfield, Derbyshire, S40 1JF Tel: (01246) 209221 Fax: (01246) 209229

Scott Wilson & kur Patrick Ltd, Scott House, Basing View, Basingstoke, Hants, RG21 4JG Tel: (01256) 461161 Fax: (01256) 460582

Scott Wilson Piesold Ltd, Kanthack House, 35-41 Station Road, Ashford, Kent, TN23 1PP Tel: (01233) 658200 Fax: (01233) 658299

▶ Services Management Ltd, Seymour House, 51 Praed Street, London, W2 1NR Tel: (020) 7565 5763 Fax: (020) 7565 5754 E-mail: c.bower@sml-ltd.com

Siemens V A I Metals Technologies Ltd, Loewy House 11 Enterprise Way, Aviation Park, Hurn, Christchurch, Dorset, BH23 6EW Tel: (01202) 331000 Fax: (01202) 581851 E-mail: sales@vai.co.at

Snamprogetti Ltd, Snamprogetti House, Basingview, Basingstoke, Hampshire, RG21 4YY Tel: (01256) 461211 Fax: (01256) 482211 E-mail: sales@snampro.co.uk

SNC Lavalin UK Ltd, Knollys House, Addiscombe Road, Croydon, CR0 6SR Tel: (020) 8681 4250 Fax: (020) 8681 4299 E-mail: sncl.uk@snclavalin.com

Softsol Ltd, 27 Buckingham Road, Shoreham-by-Sea, West Sussex, BN43 5UA Tel: (01273) 440100 Fax: (01273) 454709 E-mail: softsol@softsol.ltd.uk

▶ Staff Solution Limited, Lasyard House, Underhill Street, Bridgnorth, Shropshire, WV16 4BB Tel: 01746 767107 Fax: 01746 769217 E-mail: sales@staffsolution.co.uk

Stasys Ltd, The Granary, 1 Waverley Lane, Farnham, Surrey, GU9 8BB Tel: (01252) 732500 Fax: (01252) 732501 E-mail: stasys@stasys.co.uk

Stirling Maynard & Partners Ltd, Stirling House, Rightwell, Bretton, Peterborough, PE3 8DJ Tel: (01733) 262319 Fax: (01733) 331527 E-mail: enquires@stirlingmaynard.com

Tim Stower & Partners Ltd, Unit A, Waterfront House, New Brunswick Street, Wakefield, West Yorkshire, WF1 5QW Tel: (01924) 375947 Fax: (01924) 382707 E-mail: stower.tprs@btconnect.co.uk

Strange Jeens & Mathison, 84 Warwick Road, Carlisle, CA1 1DE Tel: (01228) 524406 Fax: (01228) 548057 E-mail: sj_m@btconnect.com

T Dunwoody & Partners, Dunwoody House, 396 Kenton Road, Harrow, Middlesex, HA3 9DH Tel: (020) 8621 2100 Fax: (020) 8621 2111 E-mail: admin@dunwoody.uk.com

T J Browne Ltd, 61 Ashford Road, Swindon, SN1 3NS Tel: (01793) 695752 Fax: (01793) 695752 E-mail: tim_browne@talk21.com

T S L Technology Ltd, The Station Mill, Station Road, Alresford, Hampshire, SO24 9DE Tel: (01962) 735707 Fax: (01962) 735502 E-mail: enquiries@tsltechnology.com

T W I Ltd, Granta Park, Great Abington, Cambridge, CB1 6AL Tel: (01223) 899000 Fax: (01223) 892794 E-mail: twi@twi.co.uk

▶ Tec Transnational, 48 Fentham Road, Hampton-in-Arden, Solihull, West Midlands, B92 0AY Tel: (01926) 851403 Fax: (01675) 442222 E-mail: mail@tectransnational.com

Technical Software Consultants Ltd, 6 Mill Square, Featherstone Road, Wolverton Mill, Milton Keynes, MK12 5RB Tel: (01908) 317444 Fax: (01908) 220959 E-mail: info@tscinspectionsystems.com

Technology Offshore Onshore Ltd, Woodcroft House, Crow Hill Drive, Mansfield, Nottinghamshire, NG19 7AE Tel: (01623) 654254 Fax: (01623) 420821 E-mail: kcutt@techoffonshore.com

Tees Components Ltd, North Skelton, Skelton-in-Cleveland, Saltburn-by-the-Sea, Cleveland, TS12 2AP Tel: (01287) 650621 Fax: (01287) 652642 E-mail: sales@teescomponents.co.uk

Tomlinson & Partners, 66 Eastgate, Cowbridge, South Glamorgan, CF71 7AB Tel: (01446) 773151 Fax: (01446) 775267 E-mail: adt@tomlinsonconsulting.co.uk

John Tooke & Partners, 1a Montford Place, London, SE11 5DE Tel: (020) 7582 0255 Fax: (020) 7820 0297 E-mail: lloyd@john-tooke.co.uk

Traditional Structures Contracts Ltd, Landywood Lane, Cheslyn Hay, Walsall, WS6 7AJ Tel: (01922) 414145 Fax: (01922) 416958

Tribologic Ltd, C/O Mechanical Engineering Dept, The University Of Leeds, Woodhouse Lane, Leeds, LS2 9JT Tel: 0113-233 2159 Fax: 0113-343 2160 E-mail: info@tribologic.co.uk

Trident Engineering Consultants, Gatehouse Offices Babcock Park, Porterfield Road, Renfrew, PA4 8DJ Tel: 0141-561 2202 Fax: 0141-561 2259 E-mail: trident@trident-engineering-consultants.co.uk

Troup Bywaters & Anders, 51 Praed Street, London, W2 1NR Tel: (020) 7565 5666 Fax: (020) 7565 5744

Derek Tunnah Design Ltd, 3 Witney Way, Boldon Business Park, Boldon Colliery, Tyne & Wear, NE35 9PE Tel: 0191-519 1437 Fax: 0191-519 1484 E-mail: mail@derek-tunnah.co.uk

Turner Contracting Services Ltd, 95 Rhyddwen Road, Craig Cefn Parc, Swansea, SA6 5RG Tel: (01792) 842732 Fax: (01792) 842732

U R S Corporation Ltd, St Georges House, 5 St Georges Road, London, SW19 4DR Tel: (020) 8944 3300 Fax: (020) 8944 3301 E-mail: europeaninformation@urscorp.com

▶ University Of Leeds Farms Ltd, Financial Services, 11-84 Ec Stoner Building, Leeds, LS2 9JT Tel: 0113-234 0206 Fax: 0113-343 4058 E-mail: consulting@leeds.ac.uk

Vectra Group Ltd, Europa House, 310 Europa Boulevard, Westbrook, Warrington, WA5 7YQ Tel: (01925) 444648 Fax: (01925) 444701 E-mail: info@vectragroup.co.uk

Veryards Ltd, 18a High St, Llandaff, Cardiff, CF5 2DZ Tel: (029) 2055 2444 Fax: (029) 2055 4447 E-mail: admin@veryards.com

W A Fairhurst & Partners, 88 Queens Road, Aberdeen, AB15 4YQ Tel: (01224) 321222 Fax: (01224) 323201 E-mail: sales@fairhurst.co.uk

W Kennedy, The Holmes, Holmes Lane, Bacup, Lancashire, OL13 8BS Tel: (01706) 876438 Fax: (01706) 852217

The W R Davidge Planning Practice, PO Box 463, Peterborough, PE8 6HU Tel: (01780) 763901 Fax: (01733) 235051 E-mail: davidge.planning@virgin.net

W S P Consulting Engineers, 4-5 Lochside View, Edinburgh, EH12 9DH Tel: (01382) 225308 Fax: (01382) 206029 E-mail: david.gray@wspgroup.com

W2O Environment, 58 Cecil Road, Northampton, NN2 6PQ Tel: (01604) 478415 Fax: (01604) 478415 E-mail: wolfram@w2oenvironment.net

Waterfield Odham & Associates Ltd, 22 London Road, Riverhead, Sevenoaks, Kent, TN13 2BT Tel: (01732) 465444 Fax: (01732) 452550 E-mail: engineer@woaltd.co.uk

Watson Hallam, Burlington House, 369 Wellingborough Road, Northampton, NN1 4EU Tel: (01604) 230823 Fax: (01604) 230923

Watts Engineering Services, 22d Orgreave Crescent, Sheffield, S13 9NQ Tel: 0114 2880667

WBR Design Ltd, 126 High Street West, Glossop, Derbyshire, SK13 8HJ Tel: (01457) 857664 Fax: (01457) 851580 E-mail: wbr@wbrdesign.com

Wheeler International, 33 Riverside Walk, Tamerton Foliot, Plymouth, PL5 4AQ Tel: (01752) 702077 Fax: (01752) 702077 E-mail: tonywheeler@btconnect.com

Wheeler & Jupp, 11b Holywell Hill, St. Albans, Hertfordshire, AL1 1EU Tel: (01727) 868127 Fax: (01727) 840931 E-mail: sales@wheelerandjupp.com

Whessoe Oil & Gas Ltd, Brinkburn Road, Darlington, County Durham, DL3 6DS Tel: (01325) 390000 Fax: (01325) 390001

White Young Green, 27-31 Cumberland Street, Bristol, BS2 8NL Tel: 0117-924 4144 Fax: 0117-924 4145 E-mail: bristol@wyg.com

White Young Green, 12 St. Andrews Crescent, Cardiff, CF10 3DD Tel: (029) 2023 1141 Fax: (029) 2072 7649 E-mail: cardiff@wyg.com

White Young Green, Wallington House, Starbeck Avenue, Newcastle upon Tyne, NE2 1RH Tel: 0191-232 3043 Fax: 0191-261 0986 E-mail: newcastle@wyg.com

White Young Green Ltd, The Mill Yard, Nursling Street, Nursling, Southampton, SO16 0AJ Tel: (0870) 6091084 E-mail: southampton@wyg.com

White Young Green Consulting, Family House, 4 Bedford Business Park, Croydon, CR0 2AP Tel: (020) 8649 6600 Fax: (020) 8649 6629

White Young Green Consulting, Family House, 4 Bedford Business Park, Croydon, CR0 2AP Tel: (020) 8649 6600 Fax: (020) 8649 6629 E-mail: londoncroydon@wyg.com

White Young Green Consulting Ltd, Arndale Court, Headingley, Leeds, LS6 2UJ Tel: 0113-278 7111 Fax: 0113-278 3487 E-mail: enquiries@wyg.com

Wilde UK Ltd, Brindley Lodge, Adcroft Street, Stockport, Cheshire, SK1 3HZ Tel: 0161-474 7479 Fax: 0161-474 7492 E-mail: info@wildeandpartners.co.uk

Willbros (Overseas) Ltd, The Old Rechtory, Barkston, Grantham, Lincolnshire, NG32 2NB Tel: (020) 8549 4471 Fax: (020) 8974 8536 E-mail: arthur.west@willbros.com

Owen Williams Railways Ltd, Meridian, 85 Smallbrook, Queensway, Birmingham, B5 4HY Tel: 0121-654 7059 Fax: 0121-654 7242 E-mail: meridianoffice@owenwilliams.co.uk

Scott Wilson Pavement Engineering Ltd, 12 Regan Way Faraday Building, Nottingham Science & Technology Park, Chilwell, Nottingham, NG9 6RZ Tel: 0115-907 7000 Fax: 0115 907 7001 E-mail: enquiry@swpe.co.uk

Woodhill Engineering, St Andrews House, West Street, Woking, Surrey, GU21 6EB Tel: (01483) 717600 Fax: (01483) 717630 E-mail: info@woodhill.co.uk

Wright Engineering Rainham Ltd, Imperial Trading Estate, Lambs La North, Rainham, Essex, RM13 9XL Tel: (01708) 554618 Fax: (01708) 553395 E-mail: wright0458@aol.com

WSP, Colston Avenue 33, Bristol, BS1 4UA Tel: 0117-930 2000 Fax: 0117-929 4624 E-mail: admin@wspgroup.com

WSP International Ltd, First Point, Buckingham Gate, London Gatwick Airport, Gatwick, West Sussex, RH6 0NT Tel: (01293) 602600 Fax: (01293) 602699 E-mail: info@wsp-int.com

CONSUMABLE PACKAGING EQUIPMENT

Global Enterprises, The Old Stores, Penny Royal Road, Danbury, Chelmsford, CM3 4ED Tel: (01245) 226004 Fax: (01245) 225995 E-mail: enquiries@globalheatseal.com

Pamarco Europe Ltd, New Cut Lane, Woolston, Warrington, WA1 4AQ Tel: (01925) 456789 Fax: (01925) 456778 E-mail: solutions@pamarco.co.uk

CONSUMER FINANCE SOFTWARE

D S T, Afinity House, Beaufort Court, Rochester, Kent, ME2 4FD Tel: (01634) 292292 Fax: (01293) 554600

CONSUMER GOODS, *See headings for particular types*

CONSUMER GOODS TEST SERVICES

E & C Engineering Services Ltd, Bargate House Woodside Park, Catteshall Lane, Godalming, Surrey, GU7 1LG Tel: (01483) 426766 Fax: (01483) 426708 E-mail: info@ecengineering.co.uk

CONSUMER LOAN SERVICES

▶ Maxcroft Securities Ltd, 632 Eastern Avenue, Ilford, Essex, IG2 6PG Tel: (020) 8518 1828 Fax: 020 85547296 E-mail: enquiries@maxcroft.co.uk

CONTACT CENTRE OUTSOURCING

▶ Direct Dialogue, 1 Call Flex Business Park, Golden Smithies Lane, Wath-upon-Dearne, Rotherham, South Yorkshire, S63 7ER Tel: 07917 811057 Fax: 01709 384372 E-mail: keir.woolhouse@directdialogue.co.uk

CONTACT LENS CARE PRODUCTS

▶ OneStopContactLenses, P O Box 5029, London, W1A 7ET Tel: 0207 323 9704 Fax: 0207 636 0281 E-mail: enquiries@onestopcontactlenses.co.uk

CONTACT LENS PRODUCTION MACHINERY

Optimec Ltd, Unit B 3The Haysfield, Malvern, Worcestershire, WR14 1GF Tel: (01684) 892859 Fax: (01684) 893037 E-mail: enquiries@optimec.com

CONTACT LENS PRODUCTION TOOLS

Apex Diamond Products Ltd, 10 Bartleet Road, Washford Industrial Estate, Redditch, Worcestershire, B98 0DQ Tel: (01527) 529011 Fax: (01527) 510740 E-mail: sales@apexdiamond.co.uk

Chase Diamond Tools International Ltd, 10 Shieling Court, Corby, Northamptonshire, NN18 9QD Tel: (01536) 461133 Fax: (01536) 461144 E-mail: sales@chasediamond.com

CONTACT LENS SOLUTION

Abatron Ltd, 24 Chapel Street, Potton, Sandy, Bedfordshire, SG19 2PT Tel: (01767) 261333 Fax: (01767) 262205

CIBA Vision (UK) Ltd, Flanders Road, Hedge End, Southampton, SO30 2LG Tel: (01489) 785580 Fax: (01489) 786802 E-mail: parkwest.reception@cibavision.com

CONTACT LENS/LENS BLANKS

Acuity Contact Lenses, Plumpton Road, Hoddesdon, Hertfordshire, EN11 0LB Tel: (01992) 445035 Fax: (01992) 451223 E-mail: enquiries@acuity-lenses.co.uk

Madden & Layman, Unit C2, 20 Theaklen Drive, Ponswood Industrial Estate, St. Leonards-On-Sea, East Sussex, TN38 9AZ Tel: (01424) 715977 Fax: (01424) 715320

Microsoft Research Ltd, 7 JJ Thomson Avenue, Madingley Road, Cambridge, CB3 0FB Tel: (01223) 479700 Fax: (01223) 479999

Shiels Ltd, 16 St. Andrews Road South, St. Annes On Sea, Lytham St. Annes, Lancashire, FY8 1SR Tel: (01253) 726064 Fax: (01253) 722684

Thompson Contact Lenses Ltd, Ring Road, West Park, Leeds, LS16 6QL Tel: 0113-230 4304 Fax: 0113-274 5645 E-mail: sales@thompsonlenses.co.uk

▶ Vista Optics Ltd, Cheshire Science Centre, Gorsey Lane, Widnes, Cheshire, WA8 0RP Tel: (0870) 0111620 Fax: (0870) 0111630 E-mail: sales@vista-optics.com

CONTACTOR INSTALLATION

Enbray Cooper (UK) Ltd, Derwent Drive, Derwent Howe Industrial Estate, Workington, Cumbria, CA14 3YW Tel: (01900) 68173 Fax: (01900) 68189 E-mail: sales@enbray.co.uk

CONTACTORS, *See also headings for particular types*

C M T S, 7 Churchfield Road, Sudbury, Suffolk, CO10 2YA Tel: (01787) 468685 Fax: (01787) 468687 E-mail: sales@cmts.co.uk

Chamjtes Ltd, Mason Fold, Lea Lane, Lea Town, Preston, PR4 0RN Tel: (01772) 726975 Fax: (01772) 721277 E-mail: john@chamjets.com

Enbray Cooper (UK) Ltd, Derwent Drive, Derwent Howe Industrial Estate, Workington, Cumbria, CA14 3YW Tel: (01900) 68173 Fax: (01900) 68189 E-mail: sales@enbray.co.uk

J M Geggus & Sons, 50 Ferniefields, High Wycombe, Buckinghamshire, HP12 4SL Tel: (01494) 439926 Fax: (01494) 439926

Machine Electrics Ltd, Whitefield Road, Bredbury, Stockport, Cheshire, SK6 2RW Tel: 0161-430 6825 Fax: 0161-494 8954 E-mail: sales@machineelectrics.com

CONTAINER DESIGN ENGINEERS

E P S Logistics Technology Ltd, Staplehurst Road, Sittingbourne, Kent, ME10 1XS Tel: (01795) 424433 Fax: (01795) 426970 E-mail: sales@epslt.co.uk

▶ Stonehaven Engineering Ltd, 2 Spurryhillock Industrial Estate, Broomhill Road, Stonehaven, Kincardineshire, AB39 2NH Tel: (01569) 766700 Fax: (01569) 766147 E-mail: info@stonehaven-eng.com

CONTAINER FITTINGS AND HARDWARE

Bloxwich Engineering Ltd, Fryers Road, Walsall, WS2 7LZ Tel: (01922) 710510 Fax: (01922) 713510 E-mail: bloxwich@bloxwich.u-net.com

Conserve Corporation plc, Hillview Road, East Tullos Industrial Estate, Aberdeen, AB12 3HB Tel: (01224) 873797 Fax: (01224) 871029 E-mail: enquiries@conserveplc.co.uk

Eldapoint Ltd, Charleywood Road, Knowsley Industrial Park, Liverpool, L33 7SG Tel: 0151-548 9838 Fax: 0151-548 7357 E-mail: control.liverpool@eldapoint.co.uk

GWR Engineering Ltd, 36 Derby Road, Liverpool, L20 1AB Tel: 0151-933 3150 Fax: 0151-944 2410 E-mail: gwrengineering@aol.com

Matano, Units 14-15 Whinfield Industrial Estate, Whinfield Way, Rowlands Gill, Tyne & Wear, NE39 1EH Tel: (01207) 549448 Fax: (01207) 549447 E-mail: james.harlend@metano.com

CONTAINER HANDLING CRANES

Roadways Container Logistics, Valley Farm Way, Leeds, LS10 1SE Tel: 0113-296 8400 Fax: 0113-296 8322

Walker Crane Services Ltd, Trading Estate, Motherwell Way, Grays, Essex, RM20 3XD Tel: (01708) 867251 Fax: (01708) 863636 E-mail: info@walkercranes.co.uk

CONTAINER HANDLING EQUIPMENT

NSL Engineering, 6 Selby Place, Skelmersdale, Lancashire, WN8 8EF Tel: (01695) 556355

Trio Skips & Hooks Ltd, Ashville Road, Gloucester, GL2 5DA Tel: (01452) 331022 Fax: (01452) 331566 E-mail: info@trio-waste.co.uk

CONTAINER HANDLING SERVICES

H D L Carson, Trafford Park Road, Trafford Park, Manchester, M17 1WH Tel: 0161-872 2694 Fax: 0161-877 9755 E-mail: fredrickcarson@aol.com

CONTAINER HIRE

Cabin Centre Ltd, Sandtoft Industrial Estate, Belton Road Road, Sandtoft, Doncaster, South Yorkshire, DN9 1PN Tel: (01427) 873285 Fax: (01427) 874248 E-mail: sales@cabincentreltd.co.uk

Chep, Unit 2,, Weybridge Business Park, Addlestone Road, Addlestone, Surrey, KT15 2UP Tel: (01932) 850085 Fax: (01932) 850144

Cronos Containers Ltd, The Ice House, Dean Street, Marlow, Buckinghamshire, SL7 3AB Tel: (01628) 405580 Fax: (01628) 405650 E-mail: bjp@cronos.com

D C V Container Conversions, Mardyke Works, St Marys Lane, North Ockendon, Upminster, Essex, RM14 3PA Tel: (01708) 641169 Fax: (01708) 641192 E-mail: derek@containerconversions.freeserve.co.uk

Glasfryn Hire, Glasfryn Uchaf, Pencaenewydd, Pwllheli, Gwynedd, LL53 6RD Tel: (01766) 810204 Fax: (01766) 810707 E-mail: ema@glasflyn.co.uk

Leavesley Container Services, Lichfield Rd, Branston, Burton-on-Trent, Staffordshire, DE14 3HD Tel: (01283) 537382 Fax: (01283) 511740 E-mail: sales@leavesley-containers.com

Mcleod Cabins Ltd, The Saw Mill, Ipsden, Wallingford, Oxfordshire, OX10 6AS Tel: (01491) 871502 Fax: (01491) 871504

Manchester Cabins Ltd, Tweedale Way, Oldham, OL9 7LD Tel: 0161-684 3333 Fax: 0161-684 1111 E-mail: info@manchestercabins.co.uk

Mobile Storage UK Ltd, Woodham Industrial Park, Creighton Road, Woodham, Aylesbury, Buckinghamshire, HP18 0QE Tel: (01296) 655411 Fax: (01296) 651894 E-mail: info@mobilestorage.com

Pennine Services, Bredbury Park Way, Bredbury Park Industrial Estate, Bredbury, Stockport, Cheshire, SK6 2SN Tel: 0161-406 7555 Fax: 0161-406 7555

Qualitank Services Ltd, Harrison Street, Widnes, Cheshire, WA8 8TN Tel: 0151-495 1116 Fax: 0151-424 6842 E-mail: sales@qualitank.co.uk

▶ Ravenstock MSG Ltd, Albion Parade, Gravesend, Kent, DA12 2RN Tel: (01474) 534665 Fax: (01474) 534668 E-mail: webenquiries@ravenstockmsg.com

▶ Ravenstock MSG Ltd, Herald Avenue, Truimph Trading Park, Speke Hall Road, Liverpool, L24 9GG Tel: 0151-448 1338 Fax: 0151-448 1929 E-mail: webenquiries@ravenstockmsg.com

Taylors Removals Ltd, The Potters, 13 Central Way, Cwmbran, Gwent, NP44 5HT Tel: (01633) 276555 Fax: (01633) 290888

Titan Containers (UK) Ltd, Suite 1, 1 Cecil Court, London Road, Enfield, Middlesex, EN2 6DE Tel: (020) 8362 1444 Fax: (01707) 664407 E-mail: uk@titancontainer.com

CONTAINER INSPECTION EQUIPMENT

Heuft, Unit 24 26 Innage Park, Abeles Way, Holly Lane Industrial Estate, Atherstone, Warwickshire, CV9 2QX Tel: (01827) 717002 Fax: (01827) 716146 E-mail: dominic.metcalfe@heuft.com

CONTAINER LIFTING OR TIPPING EQUIPMENT

Comcount Ltd, Unit 16 Cranham Estate, Shipston Close, Worcester, WR4 9XN Tel: (01905) 454710 Fax: (01905) 455849 E-mail: mail@comcount.co.uk

Empteezy Ltd, Alpha House, 4 Muir Road, Houstoun Industrial Estate, Livingston, West Lothian, EH54 5DR Tel: (01506) 430309 Fax: (01506) 441466 E-mail: sales@empteezy.co.uk

The Handling Conceps, Unit E, Swallow Court, Bromsgrove, Worcestershire, B60 4FE Tel: (01527) 570900 Fax: (01527) 570947 E-mail: sales@handlingconcepts.co.uk

CONTAINER LOADING EQUIPMENT

Rent A Ramp Ltd, Unit 37 Station Lane Industrial Estate, Station Lane, Old Whittington, Chesterfield, Derbyshire, S41 9QX Tel: (01246) 260602 Fax: (01246) 260493 E-mail: sales@rentaramp.com

Thorworld Industries Ltd, Unit 37, Station Lane Industrial Estate, Old Whittington, Chesterfield, Derbyshire, S41 9QX Tel: (01246) 260981 Fax: (01246) 260493 E-mail: info@thorworld.co.uk

CONTAINER STRADDLE CARRIER SPARE PARTS

Amba Dockside Technology Ltd, 1 The Parkwood Centre, Aston Road, Waterlooville, Hampshire, PO7 7HT Tel: (023) 9223 1200 Fax: (023) 9226 7047 E-mail: ambeng@aol.com

CONTAINER TRAILERS

Collease Ltd, Choats Road, Chequers Lane, Dagenham, Essex, RM9 6RJ Tel: (020) 8517 1171 Fax: (020) 8593 0300

CONTAINERISATION, *See Freight Container etc*

CONTAINERS, AIR FREIGHT

▶ Carousel, Gateway Centre Eurolink Industrial Centre, Castle Road, Sittingbourne, Kent, ME10 3RN Tel: (01795) 413600 Fax: (01795) 413610 E-mail: sales@carousellogistics.co.uk

▶ Sea Wing Cargo, Unit, 1 Beta Way, Thorpe Industrial Park, Egham, Surrey, TW20 8RE Tel: (01784) 435111 Fax: (01784) 439444

Smith's Solutions, 27 Kiln Lane, Hope, Wrexham, Clwyd, LL12 9PH Tel: (01978) 769090 Fax: 01978 769173 E-mail: sales@smiths-solutions.co.uk

CONTAINERS, CHEMICAL STORAGE

▶ Pentalver Container Sales, West Bay Road, Western Docks, Southampton, SO15 0GN Tel: (023) 8070 6070 Fax: (023) 8070 6074 E-mail: soupentsal@pentalver.com

CONTAINERS, PACKING ETC,

See particular types (sometimes called Box/Container/Case) such as Cardboard; Fibreboard etc

CONTAINERS, PLASTIC

▶ Alison Handling, Freckleton Road, Kirkham, Preston, PR4 3RB Tel: (01772) 687940 Fax: (01772) 685400 E-mail: enquiries@alison-handling.co.uk

Cambrian Containers, Unit 32 Mochdre Industrial Estate, Mochdre, Newtown, Powys, SY16 4LE Tel: (01686) 611360 Fax: (01686) 611361

Craemer UK Ltd, Craemer House, Hortonwood 1, Telford, Shropshire, TF1 7GN Tel: (01952) 641366 Fax: (01952) 607801 E-mail: sales@craemer.co.uk

F D L Packaging Group, Abbeyway South, Vista Road, Haydock, St. Helens, Merseyside, WA11 0RW Tel: (01942) 722299 Fax: (01942) 271325 E-mail: sales@fdlgroup.co.uk

Fibrestar Drums Ltd, Redhouse Lane, Disley, Stockport, Cheshire, SK12 2NW Tel: (01663) 764141 Fax: (01633) 762967 E-mail: sales@harcostar.co.uk

Kings Cross Truck, 41 Leighlands, Crawley, West Sussex, RH10 3DN Tel: (01293) 873767 Fax: (01293) 873767 E-mail: sales@kingscrosstruck.co.uk

L'hotellier Montrichard (UK) Ltd, Balena Close, Poole, Dorset, BH17 7DU Tel: (01202) 693409 Fax: (01202) 658657 E-mail: sparkesc@lcn.ltd.uk

Mailbox Mouldings International Ltd, Bayley Street, Stalybridge, Cheshire, SK15 1QQ Tel: 0161-330 5577 Fax: 0161-330 5576 E-mail: ch@mailboxmouldings.co.uk

▶ Nampak Plastics Europe Ltd, Jenna Way Interchange Park, Newport Pagnell, Buckinghamshire, MK16 9PQ Tel: (01908) 611554 Fax: (01908) 614994 E-mail: jon.sweet@eu.nampak.com

Plastohm UK Ltd, Unit 2 Pacemanor Centre, Bellbrook Industrial Estate, Uckfield, East Sussex, TN22 1YA Tel: (01825) 768812 Fax: (01825) 768780 E-mail: jsaleuk@plastohm.com

Ring Containers Ltd, 1 Southern Cross, London Road, Swanley, Kent, BR8 8DE Tel: (01322) 615302 Fax: (01322) 614931

Solent Plastics, Manor House Avenue, Southampton, SO15 0LF Tel: (023) 8057 2500 Fax: (023) 8057 7775 E-mail: sales@solentplastics.co.uk

Wheelie Bin Direct Ltd, 22 Hainge Road, Tividale, Oldbury, West Midlands, B69 2NH Tel: 0121-557 1302 Fax: (0870) 2420175 E-mail: info@wheeliebindirect.co.uk

CONTAINERS, STACKING AND NESTING

M R P Trucks & Trolleys, 40 Horringer Road, Bury St. Edmunds, Suffolk, IP33 2DR Tel: (01284) 766300 Fax: (01284) 766500 E-mail: sales@mrptruckstrolleys.co.uk

CONTAINERS, WATER COOLER

Coolwater (Essex) Ltd, Unit 9,Thurrock Business Centre, Breach Road, West Thurrock, Grays, Essex, RM20 3NR Tel: (01708) 252522 Fax: (01708) 862423 E-mail: info@coolwateressex.co.uk

▶ Crystal Clear Products 2000 Ltd, Grove Cottages, Wormingford Grove, Wormingford, Colchester, CO6 3AJ Tel: (01206) 243700 Fax: (01206) 241806 E-mail: sales@pure-watercoolers.co.uk

CONTAINMENT SUITES

M S S Clean Technology, Castle House, The Industrial Estate, York Road, York, YO60 6RZ Tel: (01347) 878877 Fax: (01347) 878878 E-mail: postbox@mss-ct.co.uk

▶ Saffron Scientific Equipment Ltd, GSPK Technology Park, Manse Lane, Knaresborough, North Yorkshire, HG5 8LF Tel: (01423) 796138 Fax: (01423) 798268 E-mail: sales@saffron-uk.com

CONTAMINATED LAND OR BUILDING CLEARANCE REMEDIATION CONSULTANCY OR CONTRACTORS OR SERVICES

Able (U K) Ltd, Able House, Billingham Reach Industrial Estate, Haverton Hill, Billingham, Cleveland, TS23 1PX Tel: (01642) 806080 Fax: (01642) 655655E-mail: info@ableuk.com

▶ Ashridge Construction Ltd, A A Workshop, Enterprise Way, Thatcham, Berkshire, RG19 4AE Tel: (01635) 879400 Fax: (01635) 879401 E-mail: enquiries@ashridge.co.uk

▶ The Civils, 500 Pavilion Drive, Northampton, NN4 7YJ Tel: (01604) 664200 Fax: (01604) 708373 E-mail: glyn.holt@birse.co.uk

Cobban Environmental Development & Remediation Ltd, 93 Clifton Street Roath, Cardiff, CF24 1LT Tel: (029) 2040 7330 Fax: (029) 2040 7330

▶ Stephen Elwis, The Oaklands, Barton Street, Laceby, Grimsby, South Humberside, DN37 7LF Tel: (01472) 750700 Fax: (01472) 885949 E-mail: sales@globalstockuk.com

▶ Geo Environmental Management, 4 Village Court, Village Farm Industrial Estate, Pyle, Bridgend, Mid Glamorgan, CF33 6BX Tel: (01656) 741932 Fax: (01656) 740814 E-mail: groundwater@naturalsols.demon.co.uk

▶ Leyden Kirby Associates Ltd, 49 Bury Business Centre, Kay Street, Bury, Lancashire, BL9 6BU Tel: 0161-763 7200 Fax: 0161-763 7318 E-mail: info@leydenkirby.co.uk

Nukem Nuclear Ltd, Kelburn Court, Daten Park, Warrington, WA3 6TW Tel: (01925) 858200 Fax: (01925) 811866 E-mail: info@nukem.co.uk

SA&R plc, Brickfield House, High Road, Thornwood, Epping, Essex, CM16 6TH Tel: 0845 331 2426 Fax: 0845 331 2427 E-mail: info@sarplc.com

CONTAMINATION CONTROL MATS

P H S Group Kleenair, Western Industrial Estate, Lon-Y-Llyn, Caerphilly, Mid Glamorgan, CF83 1XH Tel: (029) 2080 9111 Fax: (029) 2080 9091 E-mail: sales@phs.co.uk

CONTAMINATION CONTROL SPECIALIST SERVICES

Isotron, Thornhill Industrial Estate, South Marston, Swindon, SN3 4TA Tel: (01793) 823451 Fax: (01793) 827320 E-mail: smarston@isotron.co.uk

CONTEMPORARY DESIGN DINING FURNITURE

▶ The Cabinet Makers, Unit 12 Brighton Road Industrial Estate, Heaton Mersey, Stockport, Cheshire, SK4 2BQ Tel: 0161-432 4455 E-mail: duncan@thecabinetmakers.net

CONTEMPORARY FURNITURE

Greenapple Systems Ltd, 6 Curo Park, Park Street Frogmore, St. Albans, Hertfordshire, AL2 2DD Tel: (01727) 872525 Fax: (01727) 872525

Hillcrest Furnishings Ltd, Unit 18, Miners Road, Llay Industrial Estate, Llay, Wrexham, Clwyd, LL12 0PJ Tel: (01978) 854966 Fax: (01978) 854966

Luke Jones, Greinan Farm, Tower Hill, Chipperfield, Kings Langley, Hertfordshire, WD4 9LU Tel: (01442) 832891 Fax: (01442) 831115

Mccollin Furniture, 39 Urlwin Street, London, SE5 0NF Tel: (020) 7703 2262 Fax: (020) 7703 2262 E-mail: mccollinbryan@aol.com

Nangla Furniture, 1292-1296 Leeds Road, Bradford, West Yorkshire, BD3 8LF Tel: (01274) 664601 Fax: (01274) 664601

Pine Range, Pottery Hill, Ewenny, Bridgend, Mid Glamorgan, CF35 5AP Tel: (01656) 665468

Roger E Smith, Barflies, Broadford Bridge, Billingshurst, West Sussex, RH14 9EB Tel: (01798) 813695 Fax: (01798) 813695

T & R Pine, 90 Hamilton Road, Felixstowe, Suffolk, IP11 7AD Tel: (01394) 285550 Fax: (01394) 285550 E-mail: sales@tandrpine.co.uk

CONTEMPORARY PANELLING SYSTEM DESIGN

▶ United Excelsior, 2 Woodside Industrial Estate, Pedmore Road, Dudley, West Midlands, DY2 0RL Tel: (01384) 267770 Fax: (01384) 482127 E-mail: enquiries@exlcr.co.uk

CONTENT MANAGED WEBSITE DESIGN

▶ Atlantis Promotions UK Ltd, 2 Clements Green Lane, South Woodham Ferrers, Chelmsford, CM3 5JG Tel: (08701) 223247 E-mail: info@atlantispromotions.co.uk

▶ Techno Consultancy (UK) Ltd, 200 Norman Crescent, Hounslow, TW5 9JW Tel: (0870) 2850765 Fax: (0870) 2860766

CONTENT MANAGEMENT SOFTWARE

▶ Electronic Business Services Ltd, Cavalry Park, Peebles, EH45 9BU Tel: (01721) 724881 Fax: (01721) 724882 E-mail: info@ebs-europe.com

▶ Giles Smith, Corbin Business Park, Caring Lane, Bearsted, Kent, ME14 4NJ Tel: 0845 055 9040 Fax: 0845 055 9038 E-mail: giles.smith@gforces.co.uk

CONTENTS GAUGES

A J D Instruments, 9 Lindfield Enterprise Park, Lewes Road, Lindfield, Haywards Heath, West Sussex, RH16 2LX Tel: (01444) 484055 Fax: (01444) 484042 E-mail: sales@ajdinstruments.co.uk

CONTINENTAL STEEL SECTIONS

Hickman Steels International Ltd, PO Box 6, Bridgnorth, Shropshire, WV16 5JJ Tel: (01746) 761733 Fax: (01746) 767299 E-mail: mikemansfield@hickmansteels.com

Superior Sections Ltd, 32 Regal Drive, Walsall Enterprise Park, Walsall, WS2 9HQ Tel: (01922) 620333 Fax: (01922) 610555 E-mail: sales@superiorsections.co.uk

CONTINUOUS BAND DRYERS

C C Process Engineering Ltd, Unit 44 Carlisle Enterprise Centre, James Street, Carlisle, CA2 5BB Tel: (01228) 819550 Fax: (01228) 819551 E-mail: sales@ccprocessengineering.com

Caltherm UK Ltd, Rowhurst Industrial Estate, Newcastle, Staffordshire, ST5 6BD Tel: (01782) 563865 Fax: (01782) 561607 E-mail: info@caltherm.co.uk

Robank Engineering Ltd, Meridian Centre, King Street, Oldham, OL8 1EZ Tel: 0161-633 9126 Fax: 0161-633 9136 E-mail: robank@globalnet.co.uk

Telford Process Engineering Ltd, Business Development Centre, Stafford Park 4, Telford, Shropshire, TF3 3BA Tel: (01952) 293231 Fax: (01952) 201246 E-mail: dryers.ovens@tpe.co.uk

CONTINUOUS BUSINESS FORMS, *See also Stationery, Continuous etc*

Centrereed Ltd, Thames House, Thames Street, Rotherham, South Yorkshire, S60 1LU Tel: (01709) 827700 Fax: (01709) 827715 E-mail: sales@centrereed.co.uk

Jaguar Business Forms, 9-17 Crompton Way, Crawley, West Sussex, RH10 9QG Tel: (01293) 512688 Fax: (01293) 551703 E-mail: sales@jagforms.co.uk

Merchants Systems, 11 Paul Street, Liverpool, L3 6DX Tel: 0151-236 2253 Fax: 0151-236 0861 E-mail: sales@merchants-systems.co.uk

Paragon Group UK Ltd, Pallion Trading Estate, Sunderland, SR4 6ST Tel: 0191-514 0716 Fax: 0191-567 1842 E-mail: enquiries@paragonuk.com

CONTINUOUS CASTING MACHINES

Rautomead Ltd, Nobel Road, West Gourdie Industrial Estate, Dundee, DD2 4UH Tel: (01382) 622341 Fax: (01382) 622941 E-mail: sales@rautomead.com

CONTINUOUS CASTINGS

U C B Starkeys Technicast Ltd, 45 Kingston Way, Stockholm Road, Hull, HU7 0XW Tel: (01482) 825203 Fax: (01482) 878094 E-mail: enquiries@bi-group.com

CONTINUOUS EMISSION MONITORING SYSTEMS

Adc Gas Analysis Ltd, Hoddesdon Industrial Centre, Pindar Road, Hoddesdon, Hertfordshire, EN11 0FF Tel: (01992) 478600 Fax: (01992) 478938 E-mail: sales@adc-analysers.com

CONTINUOUS ENVELOPES

Maddison Commercial Printers, Knaves Beech Business Centre, Knaves Beech Indust Estate Knaves Beech Way, Loudwater, High Wycombe, Buckinghamshire, HP10 9QY Tel: (01628) 530717 Fax: (01628) 819459 E-mail: sales@worldofenvelopes.com

CONTINUOUS ZOOM BORE SIGHT STABILITY LENSES

IntroVision, Units 6-7, The Glover Centre, 23-25 Bury Mead Road, Hitchin, Hertfordshire, SG4 1RP Tel: (01462) 459400 Fax: (01462) 459500 E-mail: introvision@ukonline.co.uk

CONTRACEPTIVE VENDING MACHINES

Autonumis Ltd, Cirencester Road, Tetbury, Gloucestershire, GL8 8SA Tel: (01666) 502641 Fax: (01666) 505100 E-mail: info@autonumis.co.uk

CONTRACT AEROSOL FILLING SERVICES

Aerosol Products Ltd, West Carr Lane, Hull, HU7 0BU Tel: (01482) 836222 Fax: (01482) 839856

Hydrokem Aerosols Ltd, Hickmans Road, Birkenhead, Merseyside, CH41 1JH Tel: 0151-630 4414 Fax: 0151-638 2353 E-mail: sales@hydrokem.co.uk

Shirley Jones & Associates Ltd, C The Courtyard, Lonesome Lane, Reigate, Surrey, RH2 7QT Tel: (01737) 244844 Fax: (01737) 243266

P & O Aerosols, 2 Hale Industrial Estate, Lower Church Lane, Tipton, West Midlands, DY4 7PQ Tel: 0121-520 8883 Fax: 0121-520 8080 E-mail: sales@pxoaerosols.co.uk

Reabrook Ltd, Rawdon Road, Moira, Swadlincote, Derbyshire, DE12 6DA Tel: (01283) 221044 Fax: (01283) 225731 E-mail: sales@greenhill.co.uk

Specialised Chemicals Ltd, Spittlegate Level, Grantham, Lincolnshire, NG31 7UH Tel: (01476) 567615 Fax: (01476) 560837 E-mail: sales@specialisedchemicals.com

Swallowfield P.L.C., Station Road, Wellington, Somerset, TA21 8NL Tel: (01823) 662241 Fax: (01823) 663642 E-mail: scp@swallowfield.com

CONTRACT CLEANING

Anthony Jackson, Unit C2 Sheaf Bank Business Park, Prospect Road, Heeley, Sheffield, S2 3EN Tel: 0114-258 9889 Fax: 0114-258 5255 E-mail: info@jacksoncleaning.com

▶ Crawley Office Cleaning Services, 69 Gatwick Road, Crawley, West Sussex, RH10 9RD Tel: (01293) 619975 Fax: (01293) 619975 E-mail: crawleyoffice@cleaningservices.net

▶ Dustdees Domestic Cleaning, 4 Hartland Road, Reading, RG2 8BN Tel: 0118-986 0254 E-mail: djs180671@yahoo.co.uk

▶ Exceed Cleaning Ltd, PO Box 8781, Stansted, Essex, CM24 8AN Tel: 01279 814990 Fax: 01279 814551 E-mail: info@exceedcleaning.com

▶ Expert Home and Office Services Ltd, 19 Satanita Close, London, E16 3TJ Tel: 0800 0431143 Fax: 020 4762285 E-mail: info@experthomeandofficeservices.co.uk

▶ Gemini Cleaning, Trewilyn, Ruddlemoor, St. Austell, Cornwall, PL26 8XF Tel: (0845) 2260974 Fax: (0845) 2260974 E-mail: gemini_cleaners@hotmail.com

▶ Greenserve Cleaning Services, 63 Tenter Road, Moulton Park Industrial Estate, Moulton Park Industrial Estate, Northampton, NN3 6AX Tel: (01604) 494605 Fax: (01604) 645786 E-mail: enquiries@greenservecleaning.co.uk

▶ JJS Cleaning, 27 Lavers Oak, Martock, Somerset, TA12 6HG Tel: 01793 636359 Fax: 01935 825885 E-mail: info@jjscleaning.co.uk

▶ Parker Contract Cleaning, 141 Banbury Road, Kidlington, Oxfordshire, OX5 1AJ Tel: (01865) 376655 E-mail: benb40@hotmail.com

▶ WILSON CLEANING SERVICES, 20 RISHWORTH CLOSE, Stockport, Cheshire, SK2 5NG Tel: 0161 483 0571

CONTRACT CURTAIN CONTRACTORS OR SERVICES

A1 Fitting, 36 Oxgangs Crescent, Edinburgh, EH13 9HL Tel: 0131-441 4404 Fax: 0131-441 4404

All Tracks Ltd, 231 Brunswick Park Rd, London, N11 1EL Tel: 020 83610211

Cheshire Curtainsiders, Second Avenue, Crewe, CW1 6BZ Tel: (01270) 766131 Fax: (01270) 255798

Constables Curtain Services, Station House, Tarring Road, Worthing, West Sussex, BN11 4SR Tel: (01903) 533513 Fax: (01903) 505080 E-mail: info@ccscurtains.co.uk

Curtain & Blind Specialists, West Drive, Lancaster, LA1 5BY Tel: (01524) 383000

Just Fabrics, 29-30 Colemeadow Road, Moons Moat North Industrial Estate, Redditch, Worcestershire, B98 9PB Tel: (01527) 63246 Fax: (01527) 63247

L G M Ltd, Coppice Trading Estate, Kidderminster, Worcestershire, DY11 7QY Tel: (01562) 823700 Fax: (01562) 68237 E-mail: acook@lgm-ltd.co.uk

London Contracts Interiors Ltd, 88 Gillespie Road, London, N5 1LN Tel: (020) 7354 0077 Fax: (020) 7354 0077 E-mail: londoncontractsinteriors@hotmail.com

New Curtains Co. Ltd, 64 South Street, Epsom, Surrey, KT18 7PH Tel: (01372) 747970

▶ Shahina Textiles, Tivoli House, Derby Street, Bolton, BL3 6JY Tel: (01204) 361617 Fax: (01204) 261618 E-mail: sal92uk@yahoo.co.uk

CONTRACT DELIVERY SERVICES

A D V Transport, 42 Mill Hill, Shoreham-by-Sea, West Sussex, BN43 5TH Tel: (01273) 462696 Fax: (01273) 462697 E-mail: advtransport@btinternet.net

▶ Amazing Man & Van, Ford Place, Ford Road, Wrotham Heath, Sevenoaks, Kent, TN15 7SE Tel: (0800) 2986802 Fax: (0871) 4338214 E-mail: andrew@questforbest.org

▶ C & R Transport Ltd, 24-26 High Street, Snodland, Kent, ME6 5DF Tel: 08703 121247

▶ Dalepak Packing, The Business Centre, Ross Road, Weedon Road Industrial Estate, Northampton, NN5 5AX Tel: (01604) 580777 Fax: (01604) 756600

Federal Express Corporation, Federal Express House Bond Gate Chambers, Bond Gate, Nuneaton, Warwickshire, CV11 4AL Tel: (024) 7634 3333 Fax: (024) 7637 5257

H W Coates Ltd, Main Street, Cosby, Leicester, LE9 1UW Tel: 0116-284 8403 Fax: 0116-275 0417

Highwayman Couriers, 31 Firs St, Dudley, West Midlands, DY2 7DW Tel: (01384) 456976 Fax: (01384) 457146 E-mail: enquiries@hiwaymancouriers.co.uk

▶ Interlink Express, Unit 3 17 Deerpark Road, Bellaghy, Magherafelt, County Londonderry, BT45 8LB Tel: (028) 7938 6575 Fax: (028) 7938 6546

▶ Interlink Express Parcels Ltd, Unit 2a Meadowbrook Park, Halfway, Sheffield, S20 3PJ Tel: 0114-251 1110 Fax: 0114-251 0888 E-mail: depot444@interlinkexpress.com

▶ McDonald Transport Services, Unit 4a Wrexham Enterprise Park, Ash Road North, Wrexham, LL13 9JT Tel: (0845) 0547544

CONTRACT DRYING SERVICES

Drytec Contract Processing Ltd, Unit K3, 46 Morley Road, Tonbridge, Kent, TN9 1RA Tel: (01732) 362611 Fax: (01732) 770776 E-mail: dryteclttd@aol.com

CONTRACT EMPLOYMENT SERVICES

▶ InterProfile, Wellington Street, Long Eaton, Nottingham, NG10 4NF Tel: (07854) 435262 E-mail: info@interprofile.co.uk

▶ R D F Consulting, Fairways Business Park, 5 Deer Park Road, Livingston, West Lothian, EH54 8AF Tel: (01506) 836200 Fax: (01506) 444222 E-mail: sales@rdf-consulting.co.uk

CONTRACT ESTIMATING SOFTWARE

▶ LiberRATE Estimating Software, 25B The Borough, Farnham, Surrey, GU9 7NJ Tel: (01252) 725513 Fax: (01252) 727828 E-mail: info@landpro.co.uk

CONTRACT FILLING SERVICES, *See also headings for particular types*

Descalite Supply Co. Ltd, Unit 2 Loaland Business Centre, Maritime Close, Medway City Estate, Rochester, Kent, ME2 4AZ Tel: (01634) 294455 Fax: (01634) 294494 E-mail: descalite@aol.com

Laleham Healthcare Ltd, Sycamore Park, Mill Lane, Alton, Hampshire, GU34 2PR Tel: (01420) 566500 Fax: (01420) 566566

Newgate Simms Ltd, PO Box 32, Chester, CH4 0BY Tel: (01244) 660771 Fax: (01244) 661220 E-mail: info@newgatesimms.co.uk

Packaging Ltd, Dierden St Works, Dierden Street, Winsford, Cheshire, CW7 3DL Tel: (01606) 594149 Fax: (01606) 861390

Dr Reddy's Laboratories UK Ltd, Riverview Road, Beverley, North Humberside, HU17 0LD Tel: (01482) 860228 Fax: (01482) 872042

CONTRACT FURNISHERS

A & B Office Furnishers, 4 Charlton Mead Lane, Hoddesdon, Hertfordshire, EN11 0DJ Tel: (0870) 0502040

Abbey Furnishing Ltd, Unit 1a The Distribution Centre, Stoke Road, Stoke Orchard, Cheltenham, Gloucestershire, GL52 7RS Tel: (01242) 673555 Fax: (01242) 673666 E-mail: info@abbey-furnishings.co.uk

Blinds By Design Ltd, 34 Wagg Street, Congleton, Cheshire, CW12 4BA Tel: (01260) 299866 Fax: (01260) 290099 E-mail: blindsbydesign@compuserve.com

Boughtons Bedroom Design, 319 Grafton Street, Liverpool, L8 4YB Tel: 0151-709 5195 Fax: 0151-709 7390

Cazaly Hillstead Holdings Ltd, 9-10 Industrial Estate, Thomas Road, London, E14 7BN Tel: (020) 7515 4444 Fax: (020) 7537 2650 E-mail: nmp@cazaly.fsbusiness.co.uk

Clarke's Contracts, 71 Kings Road, Tyseley, Birmingham, B11 2AX Tel: 0121-707 6968 Fax: 0121-680 8108 E-mail: sales@clarkescontracts.co.uk

Coexistence Ltd, 288 Upper Street, London, N1 2TZ Tel: (020) 7354 8817 Fax: (020) 7354 9610

Comack Upholstery Co., Farington Sawmill, Stanifield Lane, Farington, Leyland, PR25 4QA Tel: (01772) 424491 Fax: (01772) 621347 E-mail: comackuph@btinternet.com

Demountable Partitions Ltd, 4 Twin Bridges Business Park, 232 Selsdon Road, South Croydon, Surrey, CR2 6PL Tel: (020) 8410 3800 Fax: (020) 8239 0083 E-mail: sales@demountables.co.uk

Domino Equipping Solutions, Ashmead Close, Newcastle Upon Tyne, NE12 6GB Tel: 0191-268 1171 Fax: 0191-268 1171

Downshire Interiors, The Cottage, 18 Townsend Street, Banbridge, County Down, BT32 3LF Tel: (028) 4066 2317 Fax: (028) 4062 6500

E & A Wates Ltd, 82-84 Mitcham Lane, London, SW16 6NR Tel: (020) 8769 2205 Fax: (020) 8677 4766 E-mail: sales@eandawates.co.uk

▶ Fisher Brian, 40 Fuller Road, Harleston, Norfolk, IP20 9EA Tel: (01379) 853052 Fax: (01379) 854713 E-mail: furnish@brianfisher.co.uk

FOCUS Interior Contracts Ltd, Unit 14 Victoria Way, Pride Park, Derby, DE24 8AN Tel: (01332) 200556 Fax: (01332) 299226 E-mail: sales@focusinteriors.co.uk

Huntleigh Renray, Huntleigh Renray Ltd, Road Five, Winsford Industrial Estate, Winsford, Cheshire, CW7 3RB Tel: (01606) 593456 Fax: (01606) 861354 E-mail: sales@renraydavidbaker.co.uk

▶ Kas Designs, 2 Langley Business Park, Station Road, Langley Mill, Nottingham, NG16 4DG Tel: (01773) 530444 Fax: (01773) 719600 E-mail: itskasdesign@aol.com

Keith Evans Contract Furnisher Ltd, Brackla Industrial Estate, Bridgend, Mid Glamorgan, CF31 2AE Tel: (01656) 655015 Fax: (01656) 658162 E-mail: sales@keithevans.com

Kinnarps UK Ltd, 8 Lindsay Square, Deans Industrial Estate, Deans, Livingston, West Lothian, EH54 8RL Tel: (01506) 415885 Fax: (01506) 411447 E-mail: sales@kinnarps.co.uk

▶ Laytrad, Fith Floor Northway House, 1379 High Road, London, N20 9LP Tel: (020) 8492 3604 Fax: (020) 8446 5944 E-mail: sales@1aytrad.co.uk

M D Hotel Interiors Ltd, 2 Station Road Industrial Estate, Latchford, Warrington, WA4 1LB Tel: (01925) 650412 Fax: (01925) 656538

Sabih Nashat Contracts, Mosterley Farm, Cound, Shrewsbury, SY5 6BH Tel: (01694) 731731 Fax: (01694) 731739 E-mail: info@sabihnashat.com

Office Principles, 472 Basingstoke Road, Reading, RG2 0QN Tel: 0118-986 9860 Fax: 0118-967 2283

Paddox Home Interiors, 282 Hillmorton Road, Rugby, Warwickshire, CV22 5BW Tel: (01788) 542461 Fax: (01788) 339239

Poplar Products (Leeds) Ltd, Ramshead Approach, Seacroft, Leeds, LS14 1LR Tel: 0113-273 2288 Fax: 0113-273 4744 E-mail: mail@poplarseating.co.uk

Protectavan Commercial Vehicle Bodybuilders, Orsett Fruit Farm, Orsett Road, Orsett, Grays, Essex, RM16 3BH Tel: (01375) 891646 Fax: (01375) 891646

Shire Business Interiors, Snowdown, PO Box 123 Dough Bank, Ombersley, Droitwich, Worcestershire, WR9 0HN Tel: (01905) 621691 Fax: (01905) 621345 E-mail: sales@shirebusinessinteriors.co.uk

Southern Crafts, Durweston, Blandford Forum, Dorset, DT11 0QE Tel: (01258) 453987

A.J. Tear & Co. Ltd, 76 Overstone Road, Northampton, NN1 3JS Tel: (01604) 639280 Fax: (01604) 633832 E-mail: sales@glanmar.co.uk

Turgelplan Ltd, 38-39 Somerset House, Somerset Road, London, SW19 5JA Tel: (020) 8947 8655 Fax: (020) 8947 8382

Warden Bros Newtownards Ltd, 43-45 High Street, Newtownards, County Down, BT23 7HS Tel: (028) 9181 2147 Fax: (028) 9182 0226 E-mail: wardenbros@aol.com

Windmill Sofas, 1 Picks Cottage Factory Unit, Sewardstone Road, London, E4 7RA Tel: (020) 8805 5084 Fax: (020) 8524 2444

CONTRACT FURNITURE

Bevan Funnell Ltd, Reprodux House, Norton Road, Newhaven, East Sussex, BN9 0BZ Tel: (01273) 513762 Fax: (01273) 516735 E-mail: enquiries@bevan-funnell.co.uk

Boss Design Ltd, Boss Drive, Dudley, West Midlands, DY2 8SZ Tel: (01384) 455570 Fax: (01384) 241628 E-mail: sales@boss-design.co.uk

Bramwell Furniture Ltd, Unit 50 Crayford Industrial Estate, Swaisland Drive, Crayford, Dartford, DA1 4HS Tel: (01322) 556223 Fax: (01322) 550900 E-mail: sales@bramwellfurniture.co.uk

CONTRACT FURNITURE – *continued*

Branson Leisure Ltd, Fosters Croft, Foster Street, Harlow, Essex, CM17 9HS Tel: (01279) 432151 Fax: (01279) 450542 E-mail: sales@bransonleisure.co.uk

Bryan Contract Seating Services, Bass Industrial Estate, Sleaford, Lincolnshire, NG34 7JT Tel: (01529) 306281 Fax: (01529) 414303 E-mail: sales@bryan-seating.co.uk

Cintique Ltd, 43 Andrews Road, London, E8 4RN Tel: (020) 7254 1262 Fax: (020) 7254 6774 E-mail: sales@cintique.co.uk

Colin Almack Furniture, Beaver Lodge, Sutton, Thirsk, North Yorkshire, YO7 2PR Tel: (01845) 597420 Fax: (01845) 597420 E-mail: enquiries@beaverfurniture.co.uk

Daniel Englender Furniture Projects Ltd, 37 Hopefield Avenue, London, NW6 6LJ Tel: (020) 7289 0000 Fax: (020) 7289 0303 E-mail: sales@englender.com

Ercol Furniture, Summerleys Road, Princes Risborough, Buckinghamshire, HP27 9PX Tel: (01844) 271800 Fax: (01844) 271888 E-mail: sales@ercol.com

▶ Geometric Furniture Ltd, Geometric House Lark Hill, Townley Street Middleton, Middleton, Manchester, M24 1AT Tel: 0161-653 2233 Fax: 0161-653 2299 E-mail: sales@geometric-furniture.co.uk

Hegartys (Fitted Furniture) Ltd, 79 Scraghy Road, Killen, Castlederg, County Tyrone, BT81 7SL Tel: (028) 8167 0979 Fax: (028) 8167 9979

Interform Contract Furniture, 8 West Hampstead Mews, London, NW6 3BB Tel: (020) 7328 2340 Fax: (020) 7624 1777 E-mail: enquiries@interform-furniture.co.uk

▶ K4 Contract Ltd, Tong Park, Baildon, Shipley, West Yorkshire, BD17 7QD Tel: (01274) 531617 Fax: (01274) 531718 E-mail: info@k4contracts.co.uk

Knightsbridge Ltd, 191 Thornton Road, Bradford, West Yorkshire, BD1 2JT Tel: (01274) 731442 Fax: (01274) 736641 E-mail: sales@knightsbridge-furniture.co.uk

Knoll International, 1 Lindsey Street, London Central Markets, London, EC1A 9PQ Tel: (020) 7236 6655 Fax: (020) 7248 1744

Lans Fine Furnishings, 1717 London Road, Leigh-on-Sea, Essex, SS9 2SW Tel: (01702) 480591 Fax: (01702) 480591

Martin & Frost, Kinnaird Park, Newcraighall Road, Edinburgh, EH15 3HP Tel: 0131-657 0820 Fax: 0131-657 0821

Wayne Maxwell Designs, Unit6, Resolution Way, Deptford, London, SE8 4NT Tel: (020) 8691 3000 E-mail: designs@waynemaxwell.com

H. Morris & Co. Ltd, 24 Rosyth Road, Glasgow, G5 0YD Tel: 0141-300 7200 Fax: 0141-300 7240

North Offshore Ltd, Saltire House, Blackness Avenue, Altens Industrial Estate, Aberdeen, AB12 3PG Tel: (01224) 871906 Fax: (01224) 878828 E-mail: northoffshore@northgroup.co.uk

▶ Oblong Furniture Ltd, 80a York Street, Leeds, LS9 8AA Tel: 0113-242 6111 Fax: 0113-243 1858 E-mail: info@oblongfurniture.co.uk

Osborne Cabinet Makers, 10 Mowbray Gardens, Dorking, Surrey, RH4 1LL Tel: (01306) 713007 Fax: (01306) 644999

Palace Furniture Ltd, Stour House, High Street, Wollaston, Stourbridge, West Midlands, DY8 4PF Tel: (01384) 377771 Fax: (01384) 377772 E-mail: info@palace-furniture.co.uk

Parker Knoll Cabinets Ltd, London Road, Chipping Norton, Oxfordshire, OX7 5AX Tel: (0870) 7429904 Fax: (0870) 7429906 E-mail: retailsales@parkerknoll.co.uk

Pedley Furniture International Ltd, Shire Hill, Saffron Walden, Essex, CB11 3AL Tel: (01799) 522461 Fax: (01799) 543403 E-mail: sales@pedley.com

Poplar Products (Leeds) Ltd, Ramshead Approach, Seacroft, Leeds, LS14 1LR Tel: 0113-273 2288 Fax: 0113-273 4744 E-mail: mail@poplarseating.co.uk

Richmond Reproduction (Manufacturing) Ltd, Balloo Industrial Estate, 40 Balloo Avenue, Bangor, County Down, BT19 7QT Tel: (028) 9127 0930 Fax: 028) 9127 0711 E-mail: enquiries@richmond.ltd.uk

Sauvagnat UK Ltd, Unit 12 Weights Farm Business Park, Weights Lane, Redditch, Worcestershire, B97 6RG Tel: (0845) 0536000 Fax: (0845) 0536001 E-mail: sales@edencontractfurniture.co.uk

Simpsons Of Norfolk, Unit G1-G4, Abbey Farm Commercial Park, Southwell Road, Horsham St. Faith, Norwich, NR10 3JU Tel: (01603) 270270 Fax: (01603) 893538 E-mail: sales@simpsonsofnorfolk.co.uk

Stokke Furniture, 3 Shredding Green Farm, Langley Park Road, Iver, Buckinghamshire, SL0 9QS Tel: (01753) 655873 Fax: (01753) 655878 E-mail: stokkeuk@stokke.com

Swanglen Furniture Ltd, Ashmead Business Park, Ashmead Road, Keynsham, Bristol, BS31 1SX Tel: 0117-986 0200 Fax: 0117-986 6100 E-mail: sales@swanglen.co.uk

Target Furniture Ltd, Studland Road, Northampton, NN2 6PZ Tel: (01604) 792929 Fax: (01604) 792500 E-mail: sales@targetfurniture.co.uk

CONTRACT LABOUR OR RECRUITMENT AGENCIES OR CONSULTANCY OR SERVICES,

See also specialist services

A S A, 12-18 Paul Street, London, EC2A 4JH Tel: (020) 7669 5200 Fax: (020) 7669 5208 E-mail: group@asagroup.co.uk

A S A International Ltd, 6 Coates Crescent, Edinburgh, EH3 7AL Tel: 0131-226 6222 Fax: 0131-226 5110 E-mail: edincoates@asainternational.co.uk

Aarron Personnel, Unit 12 Hollins Business Centre, Rowley Street, Stafford, ST16 2RH Tel: (0870) 7456587 Fax: (0870) 7456588 E-mail: lisa@kcen.co.uk

Aberdeen Appointments Agency Ltd, 461 Union Street, Aberdeen, AB11 6DB Tel: (01224) 211211 Fax: (01224) 211411 E-mail: info@aaa.uk.com

Abraxas plc, 47 Eastcastle Street, London, W1W 8DY Tel: (020) 7255 5555 Fax: (020) 7636 0333 E-mail: corporate@abraxas.com

▶ Action Drive Ltd, 15 Grove Market Place, Court Yard, London, SE9 5PU Tel: (020) 8850 3763 Fax: (020) 8850 4113 E-mail: actiondrive@hotmail.com

Action Staff Bureau Ltd, 47a High St, Tunbridge Wells, Kent, TN1 1XL Tel: (01892) 542822 Fax: (01892) 542827 E-mail: sales@asbrecruitment.com

Adams & Associates UK Ltd, 14 Barclay Road, Croydon, CR0 1JN Tel: (020) 8680 0766 Fax: (020) 8680 0066 E-mail: info@adamsandassocs.com

Adecco UK Ltd, 44 Shenley Road, Borehamwood, Hertfordshire, WD6 1DR Tel: (020) 8953 6700 Fax: (020) 8207 4686 E-mail: info@adecco.co.uk

Adecco UK Ltd, Mayflower House, 178 Armada Way, Plymouth, PL1 1LD Tel: (01752) 262526 Fax: (01752) 220481 E-mail: 638.plymouth@adecco.co.uk

Alan Mead, Severn House, 30 Ombersley St West, Droitwich, Worcestershire, WR9 8QZ Tel: (01905) 791050 Fax: (01905) 773226 E-mail: alan.mead@alanmeadrecruitment.co.uk

Alexander Chapel, Orchard Lea, Winkfield Lane, Windsor, Berkshire, SL4 4RU Tel: (0870) 1609610 Fax: 0117-985 9986 E-mail: windsor@alexanderchapel.co.uk

Allison International Ltd, 7 Birchin Lane, London, EC3V 9BW Tel: (020) 7626 2266

Angel Human Resources plc, 54 Uxbridge Rd, Shepherds Bush, London, W12 8LP Tel: (020) 8740 1999 Fax: (020) 8749 4950 E-mail: west@angelhr.org

Angel Human Resources plc, 2-4 Union Street, London, SE1 1SZ Tel: (020) 7940 2000 Fax: (020) 7940 2018 E-mail: admin@angelhr.org

Anglo European Workforce Ltd, 51 Waterloo Road, Wolverhampton, WV1 4QJ Tel: (01902) 426767 Fax: (01902) 421895 E-mail: contact@angloew.com

Arlington Consultants Group Ltd, 32 Brook Street, London, W1K 5DL Tel: (020) 7470 0057 Fax: (020) 7470 0074 E-mail: info@arlington-consultants.co.uk

Asap Personnel, 5a Sheep Market, Spalding, Lincolnshire, PE11 1BH Tel: (01775) 712212 Fax: (01775) 768090 E-mail: info@asap-personnel.co.uk

B C P Search & Selection Ltd, Unit 9b Intec 2, Wade Road, Basingstoke, Hampshire, RG24 8NE Tel: (01256) 470704 Fax: (01256) 844054 E-mail: mail@bcprecruitment.co.uk

Badenoch & Clark, 16-18 New Bridge Street, London, EC4V 6HU Tel: (020) 7583 0073 Fax: (020) 7353 3908 E-mail: corp.comms@badenochandclark.com

Beavers Ltd, Holden House, 57 Rathbone Place, London, W1T 1JU Tel: (020) 7636 0825 Fax: (020) 7255 1237 E-mail: dam@beaver.co.uk

Beechwood Recruitment Ltd, 221 High Street, London, W3 9BY Tel: (020) 8992 8647 Fax: (020) 8992 5658 E-mail: mail@beechwoodrecruit.com

Better Engineers, Abatec House, Oldmixon Crescent, Weston-Super-Mare, Avon, BS24 9AX Tel: (01934) 621262 Fax: (01934) 620619 E-mail: mail@betterengineers.co.uk

Blue Arrow, Portland House, Longbrook Street, Exeter, EX4 6AB Tel: (01392) 424733 Fax: (01392) 490486 E-mail: enquiries@bluearrow.co.uk

Blue Arrow, 32 Friar Lane, Nottingham, NG1 6DQ Tel: 0115-947 2252 Fax: 0115-950 3766 E-mail: nottingham@bluearrow.co.uk

BMS, Mead House, 49 High Street, Egham, Surrey, TW20 9EW Tel: (01784) 434334 Fax: (01784) 435584 E-mail: jobs@bms-uk.com

Brook Street Bureau, Hatfield Road, St. Albans, Hertfordshire, AL1 4JB Tel: (01727) 848292 Fax: (01727) 846654

Campbell Birch Executive Recruitment, Broadway, Bracknell, Berkshire, RG12 1AG Tel: (01344) 424117 Fax: (01344) 360534 E-mail: info@campbellbirch.com

Capital Engineering Personnel Ltd, Broadway House, 112-134 The Broadway, London, SW19 1RL Tel: (020) 8605 2800 Fax: (028) 8946 3899 E-mail: admin@cap-recruit.co.uk

Capital Group, 1a Bridge Street, Bishop's Stortford, Hertfordshire, CM23 2JU Tel: (01279) 508632 Fax: (01279) 758903 E-mail: admin@cap-recuirt.co.uk

Capital Group of Companies Ltd, Broadway House, 112-134 The Broadway, London, SW19 1RL Tel: (020) 8542 8131 Fax: (020) 8540 7385 E-mail: admin@cap-recruit.co.uk

Capital Technical Services Ltd, Broadway Ho, 112-134 The Broadway, London, SW19 1RL Tel: (020) 8542 8131 Fax: (020) 8540 7385 E-mail: admin@cap-recruit.co.uk

Cappo International Ltd, Global House, 38-40 High Street, West Wickham, Kent, BR4 0NJ Tel: (020) 8776 1850 Fax: (020) 8777 9952 E-mail: info@cappo.co.uk

▶ Cathedral Appointments, 33 Southernhay East, Exeter, EX1 1NX Tel: (01392) 413577 Fax: (01392) 425690 E-mail: sales@cathedralappointments.co.uk

CBS Butler, Kings Mill, Kings Mill Lane, South Nutfield, Redhill, RH1 5NB Tel: (01737) 822000 Fax: (01737) 823031 E-mail: admin@uk.butler.com

▶ Central European Staffing, Thanet Way, Whitstable, Kent, CT5 3JF Tel: (01227) 771888 Fax: (01227) 771666 E-mail: sales@centraleuropeanstaffing.co.uk

Alexander Chapel Associates, Fountain Court, 2 Victoria Square, Victoria Street, St. Albans, Hertfordshire, AL1 3TF Tel: (01727) 859977 Fax: (01727) 859594 E-mail: stalbans@alexanderchapel.co.uk

Choice Technical Recruitment Ltd, 8 West Alley, Hitchin, Hertfordshire, SG5 1EG Tel: (01462) 442929 Fax: (01462) 442828 E-mail: choicetec@ctr.uk.com

▶ Colega Limited, 5300 Lakeside, Cheadle Royal Business Park, Cheadle, Cheshire, SK8 3GP Tel: 0161 408 0505 E-mail: stephen@colega.co.uk

Comms Resources, 1 Sherman Road, Bromley, BR1 3JH Tel: (020) 8663 1999 Fax: (020) 8313 6601 E-mail: mail@commsresources.com

Computer People Ltd, Anglo City House, 2-6 Shirley Road, Southampton, SO15 3EU Tel: (023) 8021 0400 Fax: (023) 8021 0410 E-mail: southampton@computerpeople.co.uk

Computer Project Services Ltd, 16 Bank Street, Lutterworth, Leicestershire, LE17 4AG Tel: (01455) 558231 Fax: (01455) 554299 E-mail: cv@cps-euro.com

Connections Employment Agency Ltd, 182-186 Cross Street, Sale, Cheshire, M33 7AG Tel: 0161-962 9711 Fax: 0161-905 1413 E-mail: recruitment@connections.co.uk

CPCR, The Charcoal, Blagdon Estate, Seaton Burn, Newcastle upon Tyne, NE13 6DB Tel: (01670) 785100 Fax: (01670) 785108 E-mail: people@cpcr.co.uk

Crown Personnel Ltd, 2 St. Giles Square, Northampton, NN1 1DA Tel: (01604) 622244 Fax: (01604) 230825 E-mail: branch@crownjobs.com

Crownmain Ltd, 19 Buxton Avenue, Gorleston, Great Yarmouth, Norfolk, NR31 6HG Tel: (01493) 663639 Fax: (01493) 669622 E-mail: crownmain@aol.com

▶ Crystal Employment Services Ltd, Gilbert Wakefield House, 67 Bewsey Street, Warrington, WA2 7JQ Tel: 01925 631300 Fax: 01925 638440 E-mail: info@crystalemp.com

CV Honesty Box, 64 Burghley Street, Bourne, Lincolnshire, PE10 9NG Tel: (01778) 420407 E-mail: info@cvhonestybox.co.uk

▶ D T L Training & Recruitment, Unit 1, Dunstall Hill Industrial Estate, Gorsebrook Road, Wolverhampton, WV6 0PJ Tel: (01902) 422722 Fax: (01902) 422711 E-mail: info@d-t-l.co.uk

Davis Co. Ltd, 45-49 Mortimer Street, London, W1W 8HL Tel: (020) 7323 6696 Fax: (020) 7323 6697 E-mail: marketing@davisrecruitment.co.uk

Driver Hire, 4/Maple House, Wykeham Road Northminster Business Park, Upper Poppleton, York, YO26 6QW Tel: (0845) 6023652 Fax: (01904) 557647 E-mail: york@driver-hire.co.uk

Elite Service Personnel, Suite 6 St. Georges House, St. Georges Road Industrial Estate, Donnington, Telford, Shropshire, TF2 7AS Tel: (01952) 616002 Fax: (01952) 612006 E-mail: info@elite-services.co.uk

Ellis Fairbank P.L.C., Ellis Fairbank House, 2 Manor Road, Horsforth, Leeds, LS18 4DX Tel: 0113-259 3000 Fax: (0870) 0110883 E-mail: contactus@ellisfairbank.co.uk

Employment Service, Upper Holloway ESJ, North Star Ho, 554-556 Holloway Rd, London, N7 6JP Tel: (020) 7301 3700 Fax: (020) 7301 3752

▶ Encore Personnel Services, Market Chambers, Shelton Square, Coventry, CV1 1DG Tel: (024) 7623 8330 Fax: (024) 7625 6475 E-mail: coventry@encorepersonnel.co.uk

Fircroft Engineering Services Ltd, Trinity House, 114 Northenden Road, Sale, Cheshire, M33 3FZ Tel: 0161-905 2020 Fax: 0161-969 1743 E-mail: recruitment@fircroft.co.uk

Fleet Partnership, The Lower Court, Stationers' Hall, Ave Marie La, London, EC4M 7DS Tel: (020) 7246 6500 Fax: (020) 7246 6501

G T Systems, Alba House, 218 Union Street, Aberdeen, AB10 1TL Tel: (01224) 620200 Fax: (01224) 620020

Guildsrealm Recruitment Agency, 39 Ensign Way, Hamble, Southampton, SO31 4RF Tel: (023) 8074 4440 Fax: (023) 8045 8135 E-mail: office@guildsrealm.com

Hanson Green, 110 Park Street, London, W1K 6NX Tel: (020) 7493 0837 Fax: (020) 7355 1436 E-mail: info@hansongreen.co.uk

Hazell Engineering Ltd, 42 Union Terrace, Aberdeen, AB10 1NP Tel: (01224) 630123 Fax: (01224) 620622 E-mail: recruitment@hazelleng.com

Hi Tech Recruitment Services Ltd, 144 Evesham Street, Redditch, Worcestershire, B97 4HP Tel: (01527) 65999 Fax: (01527) 62500

Highfield Human Solutions Ltd, 1 London Road, Newbury, Berkshire, RG14 1JL Tel: (01635) 33923 Fax: (01635) 38837 E-mail: admin@highfielduk.co.uk

Horizon Recruitment Ltd, 6 Piccadilly, Bradford, West Yorkshire, BD1 3LW Tel: (01274) 744991 Fax: (01274) 744992

Hudson Global Resources Ltd, Grosvenor House, 14 Bennetts Hill, Birmingham, B2 5RS Tel: 0121-633 0010 Fax: 0121-633 0862

Hyde Group Ltd, Hadfield Street, Dukinfield, Cheshire, SK16 4QX Tel: 0161-308 2111 Fax: 0161-330 2680 E-mail: sales@hydetool.co.uk

I P S Group Ltd, Lloyds Avenue House, 6 Lloyds Avenue, London, EC3N 3ES Tel: (020) 7481 8111 Fax: (020) 7481 0994 E-mail: enquiries@ipsgroup.co.uk

INBIS Group Ltd, St. Johns House, Church Street, Wolverhampton, WV2 4LS Tel: (01902) 427463 Fax: (01902) 714239

Inbis Technology Ltd, 1 The Brooms, Emersons Green, Bristol, BS16 7FD Tel: 0117-987 4000 Fax: 0117-987 4040 E-mail: careers@inbis.com

Informatiq Consulting Ltd, Gresham House, 53 Clarendon Road, Watford, WD17 1FT Tel: (01923) 224481 Fax: (01923) 224493 E-mail: permanant@informatiq.co.uk

Infostaff Ltd, 16 North Silver Street, Aberdeen, AB10 1RL Tel: (01224) 336200 Fax: (01224) 428500 E-mail: info@infostaff.co.uk

Instore Merchandising & Demonstrating, 1 Wallace Avenue, Lisburn, County Antrim, BT27 4AA Tel: (028) 9267 4215 Fax: (028) 9267 2015

Instruments & Controls Hull, Faraday Works, Crowle Street, Hull, HU9 1RH Tel: (01482) 225607 Fax: (01482) 217122 E-mail: sales@instco.co.uk

▶ InterProfile, Wellington Street, Long Eaton, Nottingham, NG10 4NF Tel: (07854) 435262 E-mail: info@interprofile.co.uk

J H P Training, 9-13 Castle Street, Dumfries, DG1 1DJ Tel: (01387) 279828 Fax: (01387) 266050 E-mail: dumfries.business.centre@jhp-group.com

J H P Training, 25 Frederick Street, Edinburgh, EH2 2ND Tel: 0131-226 1647 Fax: 0131-226 1648 E-mail: edinburgh.business.centre@jhp-group.com

J H P Training, Crown Buildings, Raby Road, Hartlepool, Cleveland, TS24 8AS Tel: (01429) 860211 Fax: (01429) 866598 E-mail: hartlepool.business.centre@jhp-group.com

J L Communications Ltd, Ferry Lane, Pembroke, Dyfed, SA71 4RE Tel: (01646) 683123 Fax: (01646) 621111

Jobsearch Employment Agency, 25 Bridge Street, Burnley, Lancashire, BB11 1AD Tel: (01282) 412212 Fax: (01282) 412212 E-mail: sales@jobsearch-employment.co.uk

Justengineers.Net, York House, 76 Lancaster Road, Morecambe, Lancashire, LA4 5QN Tel: (0845) 0502000 Fax: (0845) 0502001 E-mail: info@justengineers.net

Kelly Services, 22 Hanover Buildings, Southampton, SO14 1JU Tel: (023) 8023 5835 Fax: (023) 8023 6519 E-mail: southampton@kellyservices.co.uk

▶ Kinetic plc, Duckworth House, Talbot Road, Stretford, Manchester, M32 0FP Tel: 0161-872 2333 Fax: 0161-872 2444 E-mail: info@kinetic-plc.co.uk

Kinetic plc, Duckworth House, Talbot Road, Stretford, Manchester, M32 0FP Tel: 0161-872 2333 Fax: 0161-872 2444 E-mail: info@kinetic-plc.co.uk

Kramer Westfield, Old Pound House, London Road, Sunningdale, Ascot, Berkshire, SL5 0DJ Tel: (01344) 875087 Fax: (01344) 874877 E-mail: enquiries@kramwest.com

L A Recruitment & Management Services Ltd, 173 Union St, Aberdeen, AB11 6BB Tel: (01224) 212929 Fax: (01224) 573845 E-mail: info@larecruitment.co.uk

Labour Ready Temporary Services UK Ltd, 2 Pilot Industrial Estate, Manchester Road, Bolton, BL3 2ND Tel: (01204) 525306 Fax: (01204) 525367 E-mail: sales@laboueady.com

▶ Leo Recruitment, 2 The Grand Union Office Park, Packet Boat Lane, Uxbridge, Middlesex, UB8 2GH Tel: (0870) 4214016 E-mail: jobs@leorecruitment.co.uk

Link Recruitment Services, 86a London Road, East Grinstead, West Sussex, RH19 1EP Tel: (01342) 313234 Fax: (01342) 313052 E-mail: linkrecruitment@talk21.com

Lloyd Management Ltd, Maidhurst, Arundel, West Sussex, BN18 0NL Tel: (020) 7405 3499 E-mail: lloydmanagement@maidhurst.fsnet.co.uk

▶ Local Personnel, 26 High Street, Wetherby, Leeds, Leeds, LS22 6LT Tel: 01937 588111 Fax: 01937 588444 E-mail: john@localpersonnel.co.uk

M P I Ltd, Suite 1 Syer House, Stafford Court, Telford, Shropshire, TF3 3BD Tel: (01952) 290862 Fax: (01952) 290864 E-mail: telford@mpi.ltd.uk

▶ indicates data change since last edition

CONTRACT LABOUR OR RECRUITMENT AGENCIES OR CONSULTANCY OR SERVICES – *continued*

Macmillan Davies Consultants Ltd, Salisbury House, Bluecoats Avenue, Hertford, SG14 1PU Tel: (01992) 552552 Fax: (01992) 514101 E-mail: contact@hodes.co.uk

Manpower UK Ltd, 12 Hall Quay, Great Yarmouth, Norfolk, NR30 1HP Tel: (01493) 853222 Fax: (01493) 330366 E-mail: great.yarmouth@manpower.co.uk

Matchtech Group plc, 1450 Parkway, Solent Business Park, Fareham, Hampshire, PO15 7AF Tel: (01489) 898150 E-mail: jdean@Matchtech.com

▶ Mavero Recruitment, 145-157 St John Street, London, EC1V 4PY Tel: 0207 8710727 Fax: 0207 7882992 E-mail: info@mavero.co.uk

Mayburn Design Ltd, 117 Piersfield Terrace, Edinburgh, EH8 7BS Tel: 0131-661 0590 Fax: 0131-652 1603

▶ Modis, Swan House, 33 Queen Street, London, EC4R 1BR Tel: (020) 7383 3888 Fax: (020) 7038 6401 E-mail: info@modisintl.com

▶ Morgan Blair Ltd, 12 Abbey Park Place, Dunfermline, Fife, KY12 7PD Tel: (01383) 738088 Fax: (01383) 620120 E-mail: info@morganblair.co.uk

▶ Nanny-Find Ltd Nanny Recruitment Agency, Bessemer Drive, Business & Technology Centre, Stevenage, Hertfordshire, SG1 2DX Tel: (0845) 6066162 E-mail: recruitment@nanny-find.co.uk

Network Design International Ltd, 34 Mortimer Street, London, W1W 7JS Tel: (020) 7580 5151 Fax: (020) 7580 6242 E-mail: get.work@networkdesign.cc

▶ Newburn Personnel Services, 5 Palmer Place, Kingseat, Dunfermline, Fife, KY12 0UQ Tel: (01383) 620239 Fax: (07968) 181610

Nigel Wright Consultancy, 78 Grey Street, Newcastle upon Tyne, NE1 6AF Tel: 0191-222 0770 Fax: 0191-222 1786 E-mail: enquiries@nwc.co.uk

Office Angels Ltd, 30-38 Hammersmith Broadway, London, W6 7AB Tel: (020) 8741 8080 Fax: (020) 8741 9212

Orin Engineering (UK) Ltd, PO Box 50, Wokingham, Berkshire, RG41 4HZ Tel: 0118-978 4646 Fax: 0118-977 0886 E-mail: orin@orin.co.uk

Orion Engineering Services Ltd, 21 Albert Street, Aberdeen, AB25 1XX Tel: (01224) 632121 Fax: (01224) 640046 E-mail: abz@orioneng.co.uk

Daniel Owen Associates, Unit 3 The Schoolhouse, Second Avenue, Trafford Park, Manchester, M17 1DZ Tel: 0161-888 2332 Fax: 0161-877 8088 E-mail: info@danielowen.co.uk

Daniel Owen Associates, Hadwyn House, Field Road, Reading, RG1 6AP Tel: 0118-957 1011 Fax: 0118-957 1011 E-mail: paul.wells@danielowen.co.uk

P S D Group plc, 7 Perrymount Road, Haywards Heath, West Sussex, RH16 3TN Tel: (01293) 802000 Fax: (01293) 802001 E-mail: finance@psdgroup.com

▶ Parc UK Ltd, Claremont House, 20 North Claremont Street, Glasgow, G3 7LE Tel: 0141-331 2383 Fax: 0141-331 2385

Park, 11 South Street, Havant, Hampshire, PO9 1BU Tel: (023) 9248 8500 Fax: (023) 9248 8501 E-mail: havent@parc-group.com

Park Recruitment Partnership, Webster House, Dudley Road, Tunbridge Wells, Kent, TN1 1LE Tel: (01892) 535351 Fax: (01892) 543020 E-mail: sales@partjobs.com

Part Time Careers Ltd, 10 Golden Square, London, W1F 9JA Tel: (020) 7437 3103 Fax: (020) 7494 1154 E-mail: parttimecareers@btinternet.com

Charles Paterson Search & Selection, 31 Ranelagh Grove, London, SW1W 8PA Tel: (020) 7730 6555 Fax: (020) 7730 6555 E-mail: charles@charlespaterson.com

People Marketing, 4 Bowden Drive, Boulevard Industrial Park, Beeston, Nottingham, NG9 2JY Tel: 0115-922 3335 Fax: 0115-922 6560 E-mail: sales@peoplemarketing.co.uk

Pertemps plc, 13 Bennetts Hill, Birmingham, B2 5RS Tel: 0121-643 5000 Fax: 0121-230 9116

Pertemps Group, Main Road, Meriden, Coventry, CV7 7LA Tel: (01676) 525598 Fax: (01676) 525259

Pertemps Recruitment Partnership Ltd, 16-18 Temple Street, Birmingham, B2 5BG Tel: 0121-233 2222 Fax: 0121-631 2278 E-mail: birmingham038@pertemps.co.uk

Pertemps Recruitment Partnership Ltd, 22 High Street, Cardiff, CF10 1PY Tel: (029) 2022 0776 Fax: (029) 2023 9345 E-mail: cardiff@pertemps.co.uk

Pertemps Recruitment Partnership Ltd, Butleigh Road, Glastonbury, Somerset, BA6 8AQ Tel: (01384) 455666 Fax: (01384) 239593

Pertemps Recruitment Partnership Ltd, 9-11 Bull Street, West Bromwich Ringway, West Bromwich, West Midlands, B70 6EU Tel: 0121-525 5151 Fax: 0121-553 3688

Petrogramme Management Services (UK) Ltd, 32 Alexandra Road, Lowestoft, Suffolk, NR32 1PJ Tel: (01502) 500050 Fax: (01502) 516574 E-mail: vacancies@petrogramme.co.uk

Phillips & Carpenter, 23 Bentinck Street, London, W1U 2EZ Tel: (020) 7486 5333 Fax: (020) 7491 7084

Premiere People, 55 Royal Avenue, Belfast, BT1 1FX Tel: (028) 9023 5777 Fax: (028) 9033 2792 E-mail: belfast@premiere-agency.com

Premmit Associates Ltd, 33 Eccleston Square, London, SW1V 1PB Tel: (020) 7834 7253 Fax: (020) 7834 3544 E-mail: info@premmit.com

Primat Recruitment, Haughton Road, Darlington, County Durham, DL1 2ED Tel: (01325) 376200 Fax: (01325) 358111

Probe Technical Recruitment, 6 Emmanuel Court, Sutton Coldfield, West Midlands, B72 1TJ Tel: 0121-321 4311 Fax: 0121-321 4312 E-mail: recruitment@probe-uk.com

Productivity Solutions Ltd, PO Box 2133, Stoke-on-Trent, ST3 4WP Tel: (01782) 855739 Fax: (01782) 855739 E-mail: headoffice@psleurope.com

Productivity Solutions Ltd, PO Box 3272, Stourbridge, West Midlands, DY8 2ZA Tel: (01562) 720630 Fax: (01562) 720630 E-mail: info@psleurope.com

Project Design Services Ltd, 19 Station Square, Lowestoft, Suffolk, NR32 1BA Tel: (01502) 564892 Fax: (01502) 531658 E-mail: sales@projectdesign.co.uk

▶ R & G Services Ltd, Hillhouse International Site, Fleetwood Road North, Thornton-Cleveleys, Lancashire, FY5 4QD Tel: (01253) 864033 Fax: (01253) 828603 E-mail: cleanup@ukonline.co.uk

Real Time Consultants International Ltd, 118-120 Warwick Street, Leamington Spa, Warwickshire, CV32 4QY Tel: (01926) 313133 Fax: (01926) 422165 E-mail: contract@rtc.co.uk

Reed Computing Personnel, 37 King Street, 2Nd Floor, Manchester, M2 7AT Tel: 0161-830 1691 Fax: 0161-830 1691 E-mail: northwest.computing@reed.co.uk

Reed Employment Ltd, 24 Victoria Road, Surbiton, Surrey, KT6 4LD Tel: (020) 8399 5367 Fax: (020) 8390 8051

Reed Employment Ltd, 68 High Street, Watford, WD17 2BS Tel: (01923) 471104 Fax: (01923) 471101 E-mail: watford.employment@reed.co.uk

Reed Technology Ltd, 33 Wine Street, Bristol, BS1 2BQ Tel: 0117-914 7340 Fax: 0117-914 7338

Reed Technology, East Wing Offices South Quay Plaza, 185 Marsh Wall, London, E14 9SH Tel: (020) 7001 2880 Fax: (020) 7001 2899 E-mail: london.computing@reed.co.uk

Reed Technology Group, Dominion House, Woodbridge Road, Guildford, Surrey, GU1 4PU Tel: (01483) 569061 Fax: (01483) 301151 E-mail: southeast.computing@reed.co.uk

Retail Human Resources, 12 Bristol Gardens, London, W9 2JG Tel: (020) 7432 8888 Fax: (020) 7289 1968 E-mail: enquiries@rhr.co.uk

Rigman Offshore (UK) Ltd, Wellheads Centre, 5A Wellheads Crescent, Wellheads Industrial Estate, Aberdeen, AB21 7GA Tel: (01224) 725532 Fax: (01224) 724047 E-mail: admin@rigman.ifb.co.uk

Robert Walters Ltd, 55 Strand, London, WC2N 5WR Tel: (020) 7379 3333 Fax: (020) 7509 8714 E-mail: contact@robertwalters.com

Rockall Recruitment, Unit 1 Cleeve House, Lambourne Crescent, Llanishen, Cardiff, CF14 5GP Tel: (029) 2074 7748 Fax: (029) 2074 7874

Rosta Engineering Ltd, Resource House, 144 Castle Street, Stockport, Cheshire, SK3 9JH Tel: 0161-429 5300 Fax: 0161-429 5322 E-mail: mail@rosta.com

Joslin Rowe Associates Ltd, Bell Court House, 11 Blomfield Street, London, EC2M 7AY Tel: (020) 7786 8055 Fax: (020) 7786 6451 E-mail: london@joslinrowe.com

Rullion Engineering Personnel Ltd, PO Box 124, Altrincham, Cheshire, WA14 4RJ Tel: 0161-926 1717 Fax: 0161-926 1727 E-mail: engineering@rullion.co.uk

▶ SAF- Recruitment, Marvell Rise, Harrogate, North Yorkshire, HG1 3LT Tel: (01423) 550756 E-mail: stuart@saf-recruitment.com

St James Consultancy, 35 Thurloe Street, London, SW7 2LQ Tel: (020) 7589 1866 Fax: (020) 7589 8142 E-mail: recruit@stjc.co.uk

Sanderson Recruitment P.L.C., Somerset House, 18 Canynge Road, Clifton, Bristol, BS8 3JX Tel: 0117-970 6666 Fax: 0117-970 6665 E-mail: mail@sandersonplc.com

▶ Scientific Staffing Solutions (Scotland) Ltd, Suite 26D, 8-10 Glasgow Road, Kirkintilloch, Glasgow, G66 1SH Tel: 0141-578 3600 Fax: 0141-578 0049

Select Appointments plc, Regent Court, Laporte Way, Luton, LU4 8SB Tel: (01582) 811600 Fax: (01582) 811611 E-mail: information@select.co.uk

Select Recruitment (Aberdeen) Ltd, 11 Diamond Street, Aberdeen, AB10 1QU Tel: (01224) 638383 Fax: (01224) 658383 E-mail: select1@connectthree.co.uk

Shannon Installations, 10 Hillmeads Drive, Dudley, West Midlands, DY2 7TS Tel: (01384) 257475 Fax: (01384) 243908 E-mail: shannoninst@cs.com

Shard Recruitment, 3 Cavendish Street, Keighley, West Yorkshire, BD21 3RB Tel: (01535) 690600 Fax: (01535) 610197 E-mail: info@shardrecruit.co.uk

Sue Sheppard, 2 Park Street, Bristol, BS1 5HS Tel: 0117-917 5900 Fax: 0117-917 5915 E-mail: post@sue-sheppard.co.uk

Silicon Valley Group plc, Lakeview House, Lightwater Road, Lightwater, Surrey, GU18 5XQ Tel: (01276) 455900 Fax: (01276) 455910 E-mail: svg@silicon-valley.co.uk

Source Logistics Ltd, 75 Bothwell Street, Glasgow, G2 6TS Tel: 0141-572 2100 Fax: 0141-572 2101 E-mail: mail@sourceuk.com

▶ The Spencer Group Ltd, 308-314 Kings Road, Reading, RG1 4NR Tel: 0118-935 9444 Fax: 0118 935 9445 E-mail: sales@spencergroup.co.uk

▶ SpiderWeb Recruitment Ltd, Kingfisher House, 2 Yarrow Road, Chatham, Kent, ME5 0SJ Tel: 01634 353131 E-mail: info@spiderweb-recruitment.co.uk

Spring Group Ltd, Hazlitt House, 4 Bouverie Street, London, EC4Y 8AX Tel: (020) 7300 9000 Fax: (020) 7300 9090 E-mail: info@spring.com

Spring Personnel, 15-17 South John Street, Liverpool, L1 8BN Tel: 0151-708 8800 Fax: 0151-708 7122 E-mail: personnel_liverpool@spring.com

Springfield Appointments, 11 Station Road, Ashford, Middlesex, TW15 2UW Tel: (01784) 256144 Fax: (01784) 240936

SSR Personnel Services Ltd, 5 Blackhorse Lane, London, E17 6DN Tel: (020) 8626 3100 Fax: (020) 8626 3101 E-mail: sales@ssrpersonnel.com

Staff Smart, Goodacre Son, Church Street, Donington, Spalding, Lincolnshire, PE11 4UA Tel: (01775) 820786 Fax: (01775) 820512 E-mail: info@staffsmartuk.com

Star Executives Ltd, 7 Fitz Roy Mews, London, W1T 6DQ Tel: (020) 7387 6999 Fax: (020) 7387 6999 E-mail: info@starexecutives.com

Sysco Services, PO Box 437, Harpenden, Hertfordshire, AL5 2BP Tel: (01582) 486000 Fax: (01582) 486086 E-mail: mail@desingteaminc.co.uk

T.E.D. (Recruitment) Ltd, 2nd Floor, 277-279 Bethnal Green Road, London, E2 6AH Tel: (020) 7613 5555 Fax: (020) 7613 1191 E-mail: info@tedrecruitment.com

Team 2000, The Heath, Runcorn, Cheshire, WA7 4SU Tel: (01928) 511333 Fax: (01928) 511334 E-mail: info@team-2000.co.uk

Technical Network Ltd, 81-82 Darlington Street, Wolverhampton, WV1 4JD Tel: (01902) 311313 Fax: (01902) 427235 E-mail: sales@netrec.co.uk

Tek Personnel Consultants Ltd, Bells Square, Sheffield, S1 2FY Tel: 0114-252 5730 Fax: 0114-252 5731 E-mail: enquiries@tekpersonel.co.uk

W A Durose & Son, Lordspiece, Stanton, Ashbourne, Derbyshire, DE6 2DD Tel: (01335) 324316

W M S Development Services P.L.C., 45 Beech St, London, EC2Y 8AD Tel: (020) 7614 4828 Fax: (020) 7614 4801

Westaff UK Ltd, Friary House, 46-50 Southgate Street, Gloucester, GL1 2DR Tel: (01452) 304090 Fax: (01452) 300332 E-mail: chichester@westaff.co.uk

Wheale Thomas Hodgins plc, Berkeley Square House, 13 Berkeley Square, Bristol, BS8 1HB Tel: 0117-927 2311 Fax: 0117-927 2315 E-mail: wth@wth.co.uk

Richard Wheeler Associates, 130 High Street, Hungerford, Berkshire, RG17 0DL Tel: (01488) 684944 Fax: (01488) 685233 E-mail: sales@rwaconsultants.com

Whitehall Recruitment Ltd, 37-41 High Street, Edenbridge, Kent, TN8 5AD Tel: (01732) 864777 Fax: (01732) 865777 E-mail: info@whitehall.uk.com

▶ Workforce, Forth Family Centre, Castle Road, Rosyth, Dunfermline, Fife, KY11 2AS Tel: (01383) 420000 Fax: (01383) 415500

Workforce (Employment) Ltd, Force Group House, 31-33 Albion Street, Stoke-on-Trent, ST1 1QF Tel: (01782) 221900 Fax: (01782) 281047 E-mail: enquiry@workforce-employment.co.uk

Year In Industry, Unit 27a Weltech Centre, Ridgeway, Welwyn Garden City, Hertfordshire, AL7 2AA Tel: (01707) 871504 Fax: (01707) 377453 E-mail: admin@yini.org.uk

CONTRACT LABOUR, BRICKLAYERS

John Morris Developments Ltd, Stanton House, 6 Eastham Village Road, Eastham, Wirral, Merseyside, CH62 0DE Tel: 0151-326 2275 Fax: 0151-326 2276E-mail: i.lee@tiscali.co.uk

▶ K & J Storton Contractors Ltd, 146 Cleveland Way, Stevenage, Hertfordshire, SG1 6BY Tel: (01438) 230671 Fax: (01438) 880449 E-mail: jimstorton@msn.com

▶ M Bliss Ltd, 1 Mallard Close, Earls Barton, Northampton, NN6 0JF Tel: (01604) 811122 Fax: (01604) 811198

▶ Mickiewicz S, 4 Rectory Lane, Byfleet, West Byfleet, Surrey, KT14 7LL Tel: (01932) 347179

CONTRACT LABOUR, CNC ELECTRICIANS'

▶ L Jenkins, 18 Beeches Drive, Bayston Hill, Shrewsbury, SY3 0PQ Tel: (01743) 871000 Fax: 01743 871000

CONTRACT LABOUR, CONSTRUCTION PLANT OR EQUIPMENT OPERATIVES

▶ 2NITY Machine Operatives, 37 Ripley Road, Canning Town, London, E16 3EA Tel: (020) 7366 4408 Fax: (020) 7366 4408 E-mail: info@2nitypersonnel.co.uk

▶ MDN Contractors Limited, 12 Burnham Road, Owston Ferry, Doncaster, South Yorkshire, DN9 1AY Tel: 01427 728744 Fax: 01427 728744 E-mail: mdn.contractors@btinternet.com

CONTRACT LABOUR, ELECTRICIANS'

▶ A2Z Electrical Ltd, Parkers Avenue, Wick, Bristol, BS30 5QX Tel: 0117-900 3450

▶ Accor Electrical Engineering Services Ltd, 63 Montonfields Rd, Monton, Eccles, Manchester, M30 8AW Tel: 0161-707 3692 E-mail: enquiries@accorgroup.co.uk

▶ Acquatech Plumbing, Heating & Electrical, 301 Amersham Road, Hazlemere, Bucks, HP15 7PX Tel: 01494 717777 E-mail: info@acquatech.co.uk

▶ Ford, 2 Alexandria Trading Estate, Alexandria Road, Sidmouth, Devon, EX10 9HA Tel: (01395) 571020 Fax: (01395) 571005

▶ Green Connections Ltd, 36 Shannon Drive, Walsall, WS8 7LA Tel: (01543) 361076 Fax: (01543) 361075 E-mail: greenconnections@btinternet.com

▶ Kilo Electrical, 1 Stackpool Road, Southville, Bristol, BS3 1NX Tel: 07903 243918 E-mail: nick-walsh@lycos.com

▶ L Jenkins, 18 Beeches Drive, Bayston Hill, Shrewsbury, SY3 0PQ Tel: (01743) 871000 Fax: 01743 871000

▶ Leylec Electrical Contractors, 26 Kennett Drive, Leyland, PR25 3QX Tel: (01772) 451172 Fax: (01772) 451172 E-mail: sales@leylec.co.uk

▶ M. Lovatt Electrical, 6 The Crescent, Mitcheldean, Gloucestershire, GL17 0SB Tel: (01594) 543907 E-mail: martin@mlovatt.co.uk

▶ Mitchell Maintenance Services, 33 Balkerach Street, Doune, Perthshire, FK16 6DE Tel: (01786) 842411 Fax: (01786) 842170 E-mail: bmscotland@yahoo.co.uk

▶ N Foster, 212 Cotswold Crescent, Billingham, Cleveland, TS23 2QJ Tel: (01642) 361932 Fax: (01642) 361932 E-mail: sales@nfosterelectrical.co.uk

CONTRACT LABOUR, GROUNDWORKER CONTRACTORS

James Boville, 35 Culnafay Road, Toomebridge, Antrim, BT41 3QG Tel: (028) 2587 8213 Fax: (028) 2587 8213

▶ Carey Construction Ltd, 20B Royal Chase, Tunbridge Wells, Kent, TN4 8AY Tel: (01892) 522069 E-mail: careybuild@aol.com

▶ Gladwish Excavation Contractors, F Mckay Way, Lynch Lane, Weymouth, Dorset, DT4 9DN Tel: (01305) 787200 Fax: (01305) 787200

▶ Golden Valley Tarmacadam Ltd, 62 Quarry Road, Tupsley, Hereford, HR1 1SL Tel: 01432 267670 E-mail: enquiries@goldenvalleytarmacadam.com

V Jackson, 103 Fairview Road, Stevenage, Hertfordshire, SG1 2NP Tel: (01438) 722016

CONTRACT LABOUR, PLASTERERS

▶ Able Plastering, 14 Wilson Avenue, Wigan, Lancashire, WN6 7HD Tel: 07838 251505 E-mail: enquiries@getplastered.biz

▶ Ash Plastering, 8 Benson Road, Kings Heath, Birmingham, B14 4PH Tel: 0121- 430 5058 E-mail: quote@ashplastering.co.uk

▶ HDias Construction, 83 Riffel Road, London, NW2 4PG Tel: (020) 8438 8806 Fax: (020) 8438 8806 E-mail: HDiasConstruction@yahoo.co.uk

CONTRACT LABOUR, SCAFFOLDING CONTRACTORS

▶ Ace Scaffolding Manchester Ltd, Weymouth Road, Eccles, Manchester, M30 8BT Tel: 0161-787 7872 Fax: 0161-787 7565

▶ Apex Scaffolding Anglia Ltd, Barnards Way, Lowestoft, Suffolk, NR32 2HF Tel: (01502) 537129 Fax: (01502) 537133

▶ Balloo Hire Centre Ltd, 31 Sydenham Road, Belfast, BT3 9DH Tel: (028) 9045 8080 Fax: (028) 9127 1239 E-mail: laura.corrigan@balloohire.com

▶ M Bliss Ltd, 1 Mallard Close, Earls Barton, Northampton, NN6 0JF Tel: (01604) 811122 Fax: (01604) 811198

CONTRACT LABOUR, SCAFFOLDING CONTRACTORS – *continued*

▶ Platinum Scaffolding, 28 Barnet Lane, Barnet, Hertfordshire, EN5 2DN Tel: (020) 8447 0957 E-mail: platinumscaffolding@yahoo.co.uk

CONTRACT LABOUR, SECURITY GUARDS

▶ Anglo Security, 33 Morecambe Road, Brighton, BN1 8TL Tel: (01273) 702500 Fax: (01273) 562479 E-mail: kenneth.mees@ntlworld.com

▶ Protek security, 89 Circular Road, Denton, Manchester, M34 6NQ Tel: 0161-292 0662 E-mail: steventurnbull@msn.com

CONTRACT MANAGEMENT RECRUITMENT CONSULTANCY

▶ Chase Consulting, 17 The Chase, Crowthorne, Berkshire, RG45 6HT Tel: (0845) 4501946 Fax: (08454) 501947 E-mail: mail@chaseconsulting.biz

CONTRACT OR INTERIOR DECORATING SERVICES

A B O S Wedding Services, 43 Grove Gdns, Enfield, Middx, EN3 5PG Tel: 020 88051706

▶ Acornley Decorating, 38 Chalk Hill, Watford, WD19 4BX Tel: (07956) 150093 E-mail: macornley@hotmail.com

▶ Agb Decorators, 6 Burdon Terrace, Newcastle upon Tyne, NE2 3AE Tel: 0191-281 9108 E-mail: sales@agb-decorators.co.uk

▶ A-LINE OCEANA LTD, P O BOX 322, RAMSGATE, KENT, CT12 6GL Tel: 01843 570791 Fax: 01843 570791 E-mail: LOISBRIAN8@AOL.COM

▶ Andrews Decorating, 79 Mortimer Street, Herne Bay, Kent, CT6 5PR Tel: (07762) 621300 E-mail: laurieandrews@gmail.com

Baines Herbert Ltd, No 2 Passage Chester Street, Stockport, Cheshire, SK3 0BR Tel: 0161-480 9796

▶ Brush Strokes, 801 London Road, Stoke-on-Trent, ST4 5NZ Tel: (01782) 874178 E-mail: foxy1@ntlworld.com

C L C Contractors Anglia, 7 Station Way, Brandon, Suffolk, IP27 0BH Tel: (01842) 813972 Fax: 01842 813113 E-mail: brandon@clcgroup.com

Cement Glaze Decorators Ltd, 5 Barry Parade, Barry Road, London, SE22 0JA Tel: (020) 8299 2553 Fax: (020) 8299 2346

▶ Chantilly, Reading Road, Cholsey, Wallingford, Oxon, OX10 9HL Tel: 01491 652848 Fax: 07889 644848 E-mail: susiegsmith@btinernet.com

▶ Chiltern Handiman Services, Forest Lodge, Christmas Common, Watlington, Oxfordshire, OX49 5HN Tel: (01491) 613074 E-mail: enquiries@chilternhandiman.co.uk

Collins Contractors Ltd, 31 Gillian Street, London, SE13 7AJ Tel: (020) 8690 0077 Fax: (020) 8690 4077 E-mail: info@collins-contractors.co.uk

Createability Ltd, 2 Woodlands Business Village, Coronation Road, Basingstoke, Hampshire, RG21 4JX Tel: (01256) 818915 Fax: (01256) 335704 E-mail: info@createability.co.uk

D M L Contracting, 29-31 North Cross Road, London, SE22 9HZ Tel: (020) 8693 0416 Fax: (020) 8693 6221 E-mail: info@dml.co.uk

Daly (Painting Contractors) Ltd, Decor House Terracotta Drive, Clay Lane, Coventry, CV2 4LG Tel: (024) 7665 0033 Fax: (024) 7665 0056 E-mail: sales@dalypaintings.co.uk

Donald Humberstone & Co. Ltd, Brackenborough Road, Louth, Lincolnshire, LN11 0AG Tel: (01507) 603003 Fax: (01507) 603003

▶ Drakesridge, 25 Dale Close, Hitchin, Hertfordshire, SG4 9AS Tel: (01462) 631900 E-mail: enquiries@drakesridge.co.uk

E G Lewis & Co. Ltd, Tank Farm Road, Llandarcy, Neath, West Glamorgan, SA10 6EN Tel: (01792) 323288 Fax: (01792) 323255 E-mail: timl@eglewis.com

▶ Eco-Dec, 27a Northgate, Cleckheaton, West Yorkshire, BD19 3HH Tel: (07974) 683111

▶ Express Maintenance Ltd, 122 Holderness Road, Hull, HU9 1JP Tel: (01482) 325000 Fax: (01482) 325000 E-mail: maintenancecrew@aol.com

G I Sykes Ltd, The Hayes, Lye, Stourbridge, West Midlands, DY9 8NX Tel: (01384) 891341 Fax: (01384) 894773

Grandisson, Unit 27, Finnimore Industrial Estate, Ottery St. Mary, Devon, EX11 1NR Tel: (01404) 814425 Fax: (01404) 813332

Helme & Hallett Ltd, 42b High Street, Cuckfield, Haywards Heath, West Sussex, RH17 5EL Tel: (01444) 454776 Fax: (01444) 417716 E-mail: office@helme.co.uk

▶ Ian Williams Ltd, Stratford St North, Birmingham, B11 1BP Tel: 0121-766 5700 Fax: 0121-766 8715

Jack Tighe Decorating Ltd, Redbourne Mere, Kirton Lindsey, Gainsborough, Lincolnshire, DN21 4NW Tel: (01652) 649215 Fax: (01652) 648159

▶ K D Decorating Ltd, 5 Constable Court, Andover, Hampshire, SP10 3PX Tel: (01264) 394194 E-mail: karl@k-d-decorating.co.uk

Kirby MacLean Ltd, Roman House, 159 Ravenscroft Road, Beckenham, Kent, BR3 4TN Tel: (020) 8778 9282 Fax: (020) 8676 8575 E-mail: kirby.maclean@messages.co.uk

▶ Les Tuileries, Pixholme Cottage, Pixham Lane, Dorking, Surrey, RH4 1PF Tel: 01306 881252 Fax: 01306 881252 E-mail: info@lestuileries.co.uk

▶ Mario Nova, 1 Southmead Road, London, SW19 6SS Tel: (07788) 505205 E-mail: mario_venetianplaster@yahoo.co.uk

John Miller & Sons (Painters) Ltd, 52 Main Street, Barrhead, Glasgow, G78 1RE Tel: 0141-881 1516 Fax: 0141-880 8113

Mitie Property Services Eastern Ltd, Davey Close, Colchester, CO1 2XL Tel: (01206) 871954 Fax: (01206) 863818 E-mail: property.colchester@mitie.co.uk

P J Rowley Paintors & Decorators, 18 Martin Drive, Willenhall, West Midlands, WV12 4QR Tel: (01902) 631510 Fax: (01902) 410948 E-mail: info@pjrowley.com

▶ Pete Haslam Painters and Decorators, 74 Riverside, Lowmoor, Clitheroe, Lancashire, BB7 2NS Tel: (01200) 425595 E-mail: peter@thedecorator55.fsnet.co.uk

Peveril Decorators Ltd, Peveril House, Alfreton Road, Derby, DE21 4AG Tel: (01332) 344739 Fax: (01332) 368622 E-mail: sales@peverildecorators.co.uk

Plant Care, The Nurseries Bath Road, Swineford, Bitton, Bristol, BS30 6LN Tel: 0117-932 5080 Fax: 0117-932 1339

▶ Ports Decor Limited, 46 Passingham Avenue, Billericay, Essex, CM11 2TD Tel: (01277) 657558 Fax: (01277) 657548 E-mail: enquiries@portsdecorltd.co.uk

Reilly & Warnock, 2 Pokelly Place, Stewarton, Kilmarnock, Ayrshire, KA3 5PF Tel: (01560) 484279

▶ Rickman Decorators Ltd, Charterhouse, 11 Marine Drive, Barton on Sea, New Milton, Hampshire, BH25 7EG Tel: (01425) 618883 Fax: (01425) 618883 E-mail: office@paint4you.co.uk

▶ S P Decorating, 78 Southbridge Road, Croydon, CR0 1AE Tel: (020) 8405 9676 E-mail: info@spdecorating.co.uk

▶ Smith Property Maintenance, 129 Albany Road, Hornchurch, Essex, RM12 4AQ Tel: (01708) 477764 Fax: (01708) 442100 E-mail: lg_smiths@hotmail.com

T.A. Smith & Co. Ltd, 53-55 Scrutton Street, London, EC2A 4PJ Tel: (020) 7739 1702 Fax: (020) 8500 4634

▶ South West Coatings Ltd, 8a The Lawn, Budleigh Salterton, Devon, EX9 6LR Tel: (0870) 0802978 E-mail: info@southwestcoatings.co.uk

Stapletons Systems Ltd, Queniborough Road Industrial Estate, 1489 Melton Road, Queniborough, Leicester, LE7 3FP Tel: 0116-260 6909 Fax: 0116-264 0165 E-mail: enquiries@stapletons-group.co.uk

Steve Church Carpentry & Interior Contractors, 15 Lampits Hill Avenue, Corringham, Stanford-le-Hope, Essex, SS17 7NY Tel: (07960) 140338 Fax: (01375) 678513 E-mail: enquiries@steve-church.com

T H Kenyon & Sons plc, Kenyon House, 14a Hockerill Street, Bishop's Stortford, Hertfordshire, CM23 2DW Tel: (01279) 858700 Fax: (01279) 653454

Ultimate Office Interiors, 307 Mariners House Queens Dock Commercial Centre, Norfolk Street, Liverpool, L1 0BG Tel: 0151-708 7700 Fax: 0151-708 7701 E-mail: liverpool@unilock.co.uk

Warley Painters Ltd, Winchester Works, Malt Mill Lane, Halesowen, West Midlands, B62 8JF Tel: 0121-561 5665 Fax: 0121-561 5556 E-mail: wp@warleypaint.co.uk

CONTRACT STAFF RECRUITMENT AGENCIES

▶ Agency Staff Ltd, PO Box 8315, Birmingham, B31 2AL Tel: 0121-476 8337 Fax: 0121-476 8337 E-mail: agency.staff@virgin.net

CONTRACT STERILISATION

Sterigenics (U K) Ltd, Cotes Park Industrial Estate, Somercotes, Alfreton, Derbyshire, DE55 4NJ Tel: (01773) 543200 Fax: (01773) 543210

CONTRACT TECHNICAL AUTHORS

▶ Codelog Logistic Support Solutions Ltd, Unit 22B, Progress Business Park, Orders Lane, Kirkham, PR4 2TZ Tel: (01772) 672080 E-mail: info@codelog.com

CONTRACTORS PLANT OR EQUIPMENT, *See also headings for particular types*

A.G.M. (Distributors) Ltd, 40b Ravenhill Road, Belfast, BT6 8EB Tel: (028) 9045 2613 Fax: (028) 9045 0023 E-mail: sales@agmbuckley.demon.co.uk

Airmech Engineering Services Ltd, Littleburn Lane, Langley Moor, Durham, DH7 8HA Tel: 0191-378 0045 Fax: 0191-378 0854 E-mail: airmechplant@hotmail.co.uk

Dennis Barnfield Ltd, Lodge Quarry, Carnforth, Lancashire, LA5 9DW Tel: (01524) 733422 Fax: (01524) 736450 E-mail: malcolm@dennisbarnfield.co.uk

Brandon Hire P.L.C., 184 New Road, Rainham, Essex, RM13 8RS Tel: (01708) 553541 Fax: (01708) 521010

Bridges of Minworth, Kingsbury Road, Minworth, Sutton Coldfield, West Midlands, B76 9DD Tel: 0121-351 1965 Fax: 0121-351 7793 E-mail: sales@bridges-bridmin.co.uk

C B L Ltd, Holmbush Potteries, Crawley Road, Faygate, Horsham, West Sussex, RH12 4SE Tel: (01293) 851352 Fax: (01293) 851205

▶ Chesterfield Equipment Sales, Lancaster House Common Bank Industrial Estate, Ackhurst Road, Chorley, Lancashire, PR7 1NH Tel: (01257) 266656

Contractors Equipment Sales Ltd, 1 Harrier Way, Airport Industrial Estate, Norwich, NR6 6HY Tel: (01603) 404620 Fax: (01603) 429717 E-mail: ces@ces.demon.co.uk

F G G Plant, Fyfield Hall, Fyfield, Ongar, Essex, CM5 0SA Tel: (01277) 899495 Fax: (01277) 899613

▶ H O S Plant Ltd, School Farm Buildings, School Road, Langham, Colchester, CO4 5PB Tel: (01206) 273131 Fax: (01206) 271919 E-mail: sales@hosplant.co.uk

Hewden Hire Plant Ltd, Howard Road, Park Farm, Redditch, Worcestershire, B98 7SE Tel: (01527) 524020 Fax: (01527) 527320

Hewden Plant Hire Ltd, Tank Farm Road, Llandarcy, Neath, West Glamorgan, SA10 6EN Tel: (01792) 321111 Fax: (01792) 321346

Hussey & Greenhow Ltd, Unit 4 Hercules Way, Bowerhill, Melksham, Wiltshire, SN12 6TS Tel: (01225) 707888 Fax: (01225) 790523 E-mail: judy@husseygreenhow.co.uk

▶ I T S Trac, Unit 6a Tractor Spares Industrial Estate, Strawberry Lane, Willenhall, West Midlands, WV13 3RN Tel: (01902) 633614 Fax: (01902) 633625 E-mail: pford@itstrac.co.uk

Kings Worldwide Ltd, 34 Junction Rd, London, N19 5RE Tel: (020) 7263 0963 Fax: (020) 7281 3966 E-mail: info@kingsww.com

Lewis & Co., Hinton Hall, Hinton, Whitchurch, Shropshire, SY13 4HB Tel: (01948) 662923 Fax: (01948) 667908 E-mail: lewisnco@btopenworld.com

▶ Link Tool & Plant Sales, 3 Old Station Yard, Station Road, Petworth, West Sussex, GU28 0JF Tel: (01798) 342342 Fax: (01798) 343555 E-mail: linktoolplantsales@btconnect.com

Manchester Safety Services Ltd, Fir Street, Heywood, Lancashire, OL10 1NW Tel: (01706) 364943 Fax: (01706) 360026 E-mail: sales@manchestersafety.co.uk

Miller Plant, Woodside House, Pedmore Road, Dudley, West Midlands, DY2 0RL Tel: (01384) 262400 Fax: (01384) 350269 E-mail: millplant@aol.com

A.C. Nurden Plant Hire Ltd, Park Road, Malmesbury, Wiltshire, SN16 0BX Tel: (01666) 823518 Fax: (01666) 824810

Provincial Planters Ltd, Chalcraft Nurseries, Shirehall Road, Dartford, DA2 7SE Tel: (01322) 292644

Rhoswell Plant, The Yard, Walton East, Clarbeston Road, Dyfed, SA63 4SU Tel: (01437) 731528

Ridgeway Plant Co. Ltd, Airport Road West, Belfast, BT3 9AD Tel: (028) 9045 4599 Fax: (028) 9045 4596 E-mail: info@ridgeway-online.com

Rosskerr Plant & Tools Ltd, Coombe Works, Coombe Road, London, NW10 0EB Tel: (020) 8450 6606 Fax: (020) 8450 7372

Seddon Ltd, PO Box 41, Bolton, BL4 0NN Tel: (01204) 570400 Fax: (01204) 570401 E-mail: p.winnington@seddonplant.co.uk

▶ Southam Hire Services Ltd, Manor Farm, Beachampton, Milton Keynes, MK19 6DT Tel: (01908) 262224 Fax: (01908) 240003 E-mail: info@southamhireservices.co.uk

Southeast Plant Ltd, Unit B1, Sweechbridge Road, Herne Bay, Kent, CT6 6TE Tel: (01227) 749009 Fax: (01227) 749009

T M Wood, Hollydale, Buildwas Road, Ironbridge, Telford, Shropshire, TF8 7BN Tel: (01952) 432292 Fax: (01952) 432736 E-mail: tmwood@enta.net

Viking Plant Hire Ltd, 2 Dewing Road, Rackheath Industrial Estate, Norwich, NR13 6LN Tel: (01603) 720771 Fax: (01603) 721779 E-mail: viking-plant@virgin.net

Walker Machinery, Lindsay Farm, High Cogges, Witney, Oxfordshire, OX29 6UN Tel: (01993) 772255 Fax: (01993) 771007 E-mail: sales@walkermachinery.fsnet.co.uk

Walker & Partners Ltd, Inkersall Road Industrial Estate, Speedwell Industrial Estate, Staveley, Chesterfield, Derbyshire, S43 3JN Tel: (01246) 472147 Fax: (01246) 473913 E-mail: sales@walkerandpartners.co.uk

CONTRACTORS PLANT OR EQUIPMENT SAFETY SYSTEMS

▶ Safe Access, 136 Derbyshire Lane, Sheffield, S8 8SE Tel: 0114-280 2020 Fax: 0114-280 2010 E-mail: info@the-access-group.com

CONTRACTORS' OR BUILDERS' TOOLS, *See also headings for individual types*

▶ 1st Call Changing Group, Monton House, Monton Green, Eccles, Manchester, M30 9LE Tel: 0161-281 7007 Fax: 0161-281 6006 E-mail: sales@1stcallbuildingservices.co.uk

▶ A & B Builders, 8 York Road South, Wigan, Lancashire, WN4 9DT Tel: (01942) 720968 Fax: (01942) 272388 E-mail: abconstruction@abtec.net

A J S Tools, 39 Mill Road, Waterlooville, Hampshire, PO7 7DH Tel: (023) 9223 1800 Fax: (023) 923 2221 E-mail: ajs-tools@virgin.net

Amada UK Ltd, 6 Atlas House, St. Georges Square, Bolton, BL1 2HB Tel: (01562) 749555 Fax: (01562) 749510 E-mail: info@amada.co.uk

Ashtead Plant Hire, 3 Dixon Way, Dixon Street, Lincoln, LN6 7DE Tel: (01522) 520688 Fax: (01522) 513577

Coxhire Ltd, Lower Walsall Street, Wolverhampton, WV1 2EX Tel: (01902) 351407 Fax: (01902) 453062

▶ Craighead Building Supplies, 1 Block 8, 9 Clydesmill Drive, Clydesmill Industrial Estate, Glasgow, G32 8RG Tel: 0141-641 0077 Fax: 0141-641 0073 E-mail: sales@craighead-supplies.co.uk

Exeter Construction Ltd, 1 Pinbrook Industrial Estate, Chancel Lane, Exeter, EX4 8JU Tel: (01392) 464433 Fax: (01392) 464436

Fleming & Co. (Machinery) Ltd, 60 Woodhead Road, Glasgow, G53 7NX Tel: 0141-881 8155 Fax: 0141-881 8268 E-mail: sales@flemingandcompany.co.uk

Freeway Tools & Fixings, 14 Victoria Way, Burgess Hill, West Sussex, RH15 9NF Tel: (01444) 873000 Fax: (01444) 873001 E-mail: admin@freewayfixings.com

▶ Geoffrey Osborne Ltd, 18-22 Disney Place, London, SE1 1HJ Tel: (020) 7234 0287 Fax: (020) 7234 0290

Greenham Ltd, Tinsley Lane North, Crawley, West Sussex, RH10 9TP Tel: (01293) 525955 Fax: (01293) 522971 E-mail: crawley.sales@greenham.co.uk

▶ H B H Fixings Ltd, Unit 4, Mardle Way Business Park, Mardle Way, Buckfastleigh, Devon, TQ11 0JL Tel: (01364) 644766 Fax: (01364) 644768

▶ The Hire Station, Unit 8, Warren Road, Trafford Park, Manchester, M17 1QR Tel: 0161-877 1234 Fax: 0161-888 5205 E-mail: sales@vp.com

Ken Taylor Ltd, Unit 1-2 Crown Business Centre, George Street, Failsworth, Manchester, M35 9BW Tel: 0161-682 9400 Fax: 0161-682 6833 E-mail: sales@kpsupplies.com

▶ Mtool Ltd, Unit1 & 2 Derker Street, Oldham, OL1 4BE Tel: 0161-626 5556 Fax: 0161-626 3061 E-mail: pr@mtooluk.com

Jack Pennington Ltd, 3 Hird Street, Shipley, West Yorkshire, BD17 7ED Tel: (01274) 534444 Fax: (01274) 534433 E-mail: sales@pennington.co.uk

▶ Reelfix Ltd, Unit 4, Norton Industrial Estate, Lower Norton Lane, Kewstoke, Weston-super-Mare, Avon, BS22 9YR Tel: (01934) 425222 Fax: (01934) 425028 E-mail: mk@reelfix.co.uk

Threadrive Components Ltd, The Gloucesters, Crompton Close, Basildon, Essex, SS14 3AY Tel: (01268) 288880 Fax: (01268) 288879 E-mail: sales@threadrive.co.uk

Whittington Tool Hire, 73 Mason Road, Birmingham, B24 9EH Tel: 0121-382 5770 Fax: 0121-373 4542

CONTRACTORS' PLANT ELECTRICAL ENGINEERING

▶ Dyas Electrical, 225 Cleethorpe Road, Grimsby, South Humberside, DN31 3BE Tel: (01472) 312999

▶ Glenace Electrical Ltd, 60a Station Road, Kiveton Park, Sheffield, S26 6QQ Tel: (01909) 773344 Fax: (01909) 773322

▶ Versotech Ltd, 81D Main Street, Calderbank, Airdrie, Lanarkshire, ML6 9SG Tel: (01236) 753875 Fax: (01236) 754497 E-mail: info@versotech.co.uk

CONTRACTORS' PLANT HIRE

2 Cousins Access Ltd, Shell House, Watlington Road, Cowley, Oxford, OX4 6NF Tel: (01865) 779778 Fax: (01865) 401041 E-mail: keith@2cousins.co.uk

A E Harrison Plant Hire London Ltd, 219 Horn Lane, London, W3 9ED Tel: (020) 8993 5981 Fax: (020) 8752 1211

CONTRACTORS' PLANT HIRE – *continued*

A M P L Ltd, Prospect House, Deva Industrial Park, Factory Road, Sandycroft, Deeside, Flintshire, CH5 2QJ Tel: (01244) 527600 Fax: (01244) 527601 E-mail: nicholas.learoyd@ampl.co.uk

A W Phillips Awp Ltd, 47-51 Plashet Grove, London, E6 1AD Tel: (020) 8472 6656 Fax: (020) 8471 8317

A1 Rentals Ltd, A1 House 22b Navigation Drive, Hurst Business Park, Brierley Hill, West Midlands, DY5 1UT Tel: (01384) 486200 Fax: (01384) 486204 E-mail: admin1@a1rentals.entadsl.com

A76 Plant & Tool Hire Ltd, 203-205 Etruria Road, Stoke-on-Trent, ST1 5NS Tel: (01782) 858998 Fax: (01782) 858999

Aaron White Ltd, 20 Bland Street, Sheffield, S4 8DG Tel: 0114-261 9519 Fax: 0114-261 9348

Abacus Plant Hire Ltd, 273 Willesden Lane, London, NW2 5JG Tel: (020) 8459 7744

Aberdare Demolition, Cwmbach New Road, Aberdare, Mid Glamorgan, CF44 0PN Tel: (01685) 882744 Fax: (01685) 882744

Adams Cundell Engineers Ltd, The Coach House, Wicken, Milton Keynes, MK19 6DH Tel: (01908) 562191 Fax: (01908) 260461 E-mail: info@aceplant.co.uk

Add Plant Ltd, Grovehill Road, Beverley, East Yorkshire, HU17 0JN Tel: (01482) 867227 Fax: (01482) 872868 E-mail: hire@addplant.karoo.co.uk

Cliff Addison Drainage, Far End Cottage, Worsall Road, Kirklevington, Yarm, Cleveland, TS15 9PE Tel: (01642) 782702 Fax: (01642) 790038 E-mail: sales@cliffaddisondrainage.co.uk

Addscan Hire Centre, 221 Edleston Road, Crewe, CW2 7HT Tel: (01270) 211061 Fax: (01270) 211353 E-mail: lynne_smith@btconnect.com

Albion Tower Properties Ltd, 177 Greets Green Road, West Bromwich, West Midlands, B70 9ET Tel: 0121-557 4000 Fax: 0121-522 2703

Sam Allon (Contracts) Ltd, Lincoln Street, Hull, HU2 0PE Tel: (01482) 320051 Fax: (01482) 216610 E-mail: user@samallon.co.uk

Ambrose & Cox, Heanor Gate Road, Heanor, Derbyshire, DE7 7RE Tel: (01773) 713094 Fax: (01773) 717709

Anderton Kitchen Ltd, Braconash Road, Leyland, PR25 3ZE Tel: (01772) 433577 Fax: (01772) 622402 E-mail: anderton-kitchen@btclick.com

A-Plant Ltd, Mansfield Road, Derby, DE1 3RF Tel: (01332) 382275 Fax: (01332) 295504 E-mail: derbynorth@aplant.com

A-Plant Ltd, Unit 8 Bridge End, Egremont, Cumbria, CA22 2RE Tel: (01946) 823073 Fax: (01946) 821792 E-mail: egremont@aplant.com

A-Plant Ltd, Unit B1 Swinton Bridge Industrial Estate, White Lee Road, Swinton, Mexborough, South Yorkshire, S64 8BH Tel: (01709) 588890 Fax: (01709) 584632

▶ A-Plant Ltd, 102 Dalton Avenue, Birchwood Park Birchwood, Warrington, WA3 6YE Tel: (01925) 281030 Fax: (01925) 281005 E-mail: enquiries@aplant.com

Ashtead Plant Hire Ltd, ST. Johns Road, Dock Approach, Boston, Lincolnshire, PE21 6BE Tel: (01205) 311672 Fax: (01205) 363300

Ashtead Plant Hire Co. Ltd, Wylds Road, Bridgwater, Somerset, TA6 4BH Tel: (01278) 423153 Fax: (01278) 444299 E-mail: sales@aplant.com

Ashtead Plant Hire Co. Ltd, 819 London Road, Alvaston, Derby, DE24 8UU Tel: (01332) 573566 Fax: (01332) 755660 E-mail: derbysouth@aplant.com

Ashtead Plant Hire Co. Ltd, Station Works, Westerfield, Ipswich, IP6 9AB Tel: (01473) 254822 Fax: (01473) 212060

Ashtead Plant Hire, Mintsfeet Road North, Kendal, Cumbria, LA9 6LZ Tel: (01539) 736444 Fax: (01539) 730870

Ashtead Plant Hire Co Ltd, 119 Bow Road, London, E3 2AN Tel: (020) 8981 2611 Fax: (020) 8980 5627 E-mail: bowtoolhire@aplant.com

Ashtead Plant Hire Co. Ltd, St Georges Road, Donnington, Telford, Shropshire, TF2 7RA Tel: (01952) 620320 Fax: (01952) 610708 E-mail: telford@aplant.com

Ashtead Plant Hire Co. Ltd, Vale Industrial Estate, Tolpits Lane, Watford, WD18 9QP Tel: (01923) 771577 Fax: (01923) 771090 E-mail: watford@aplant.com

B J Corridan Plant Hire Ltd, 42 Midland Road, Scunthorpe, South Humberside, DN16 1DQ Tel: (01724) 859228 Fax: (01724) 859228

B L Cranes Ltd, 60 Granary Street, Burghead, Elgin, Morayshire, IV30 5UA Tel: (01343) 835360 Fax: (01343) 830771

B P H Equipment Ltd, PO Box 12, Barton-upon-Humber, South Humberside, DN18 5XD Tel: (01652) 633340 Fax: (01652) 635920 E-mail: info@bphequipment.co.uk

B T G Plant Hire & Repairs Ltd, Hallsford Bridge Industrial Estate, Ongar, Essex, CM5 9RB Tel: (01277) 364444 Fax: (01277) 365239

Balloo Hire Centre Ltd, 21 Balloo Drive, Bangor, County Down, BT19 7QY Tel: (028) 9145 4457 Fax: (028) 9127 1239 E-mail: dan@balloohire.com

▶ Balloo Hire Centre Ltd, 31 Sydenham Road, Belfast, BT3 9DH Tel: (028) 9045 8080 Fax: (028) 9127 1239 E-mail: laura.corrigan@balloohire.com

Banner Plant Services, 36 London Road, Datchet, Slough, SL3 9JN Tel: (01753) 543029 Fax: (01753) 580511

Banner Total Maintenance Ltd, Callywhite Lane, Dronfield, Derbyshire, S18 2XS Tel: (01246) 299400 Fax: (01246) 290253 E-mail: dronfield@bannerplant.co.uk

Bedingfield Hirebase Ltd, Faraday Road, Harfreys Industrial Estate, Great Yarmouth, Norfolk, NR31 0NH Tel: (01493) 440522 Fax: (01493) 442555

Peter Bennie Ltd, Oxwich Close, Brackmills Industrial Estate, Northampton, NN4 7BH Tel: (01604) 766101 Fax: (01604) 760671 E-mail: admin@peter.bennie.co.uk

William Birch & Sons Ltd, 1 Link Road Court, Osbaldwick, York, YO10 3JQ Tel: (01904) 411411 Fax: (01904) 428428 E-mail: info@williambirch.co.uk

A.P. Blythe & Sons Ltd, Will-o-the-wisp, Main Rd, Wrangle, Boston, Lincs, PE22 9AE Tel: (01205) 870738

▶ Blythewood Plant Hire Ltd, Fenland District Industrial Estate, Station Road, Whittlesey, Peterborough, PE7 2EY Tel: (01733) 203201 Fax: (01733) 350308 E-mail: enquiries@blythewood-plant.co.uk

▶ Bobcat Midlands Limited, Ridgeway, Well Lane, Little Witley, Worcester, WR6 6LN Tel: 01886 888413 Fax: 01886 888561 E-mail: adam.bobcat@virgin.net

Boss Plant Hire Ltd, Shelford Farm Cottages, Shalloak Road, Broad Oak, Canterbury, Kent, CT2 0PR Tel: (01227) 454645 Fax: (01227) 769822

Brandon Hire plc, St Helen Way, St. Helen Auckland, Bishop Auckland, County Durham, DL14 9AX Tel: (01388) 663085 Fax: (01388) 607264

Brandon Hire plc, 151 Bute Street, Cardiff, CF10 5HQ Tel: (029) 2048 9898 Fax: (029) 2048 0772 E-mail: cardiff23@brandonhire.plc.uk

Brandon Hire plc, Llangunnor Road, Carmarthen, Dyfed, SA31 2PB Tel: (01267) 237405 Fax: (01267) 238299 E-mail: carmarthen@brandonhire.plc.uk

Brandon Hire plc, Unit 7-9, Holmstone Road, Dover, Kent, CT17 0UF Tel: (01304) 241622 Fax: (01304) 241981

Brandon Hire plc, 48 Ratcliffe Gate, Mansfield, Nottinghamshire, NG18 2JL Tel: (01623) 635136 Fax: (01623) 624006

Brandon Hire P.L.C., 184 New Road, Rainham, Essex, RM13 8RS Tel: (01708) 553541 Fax: (01708) 521010

Brandon Pipe Hire, Unit 1 Claremont Centre, Cornwall Street South, Kinning Park, Glasgow, G41 1AA Tel: 0141-427 9000 Fax: 0141-427 9009 E-mail: glagow.k65@wilsley.co.uk

Brennans Of Wiltshire Ltd, Harepath Farm, Burbage, Marlborough, Wiltshire, SN8 3BT Tel: (01672) 810380 Fax: (01672) 811157 E-mail: bofwilts@aol.com

Brett Aggregates, Waldringfield Road, Brightwell, Ipswich, IP10 0BL Tel: (01473) 621007 Fax: (01473) 736721

Briggs & Partner Ltd, The Storth, Huddersfield Road, Elland, West Yorkshire, HX5 9JR Tel: (01422) 372515 Fax: (01422) 311093 E-mail: briggs@zen.co.uk

British Contractors Plant Ltd, Feathers Lane, Wraysbury, Staines, Middlesex, TW19 5AN Tel: (01784) 482122 Fax: (01784) 483781

Brock plc, New Hey, Chester Road, Great Sutton, Ellesmere Port, CH66 2LS Tel: 0151-339 8113 Fax: 0151-347 1254

Brooks Haulage, Redcliffe Street, Sutton-in-Ashfield, Nottinghamshire, NG17 4ES Tel: (01623) 441255

Bryen & Langley Ltd, 48-60 Footscray Road, London, SE9 2SU Tel: (020) 8850 7775 Fax: (020) 8850 6772 E-mail: info@bryen-langley.com

Build Center, Cambrian Works, Station Approach, Wrexham, Clwyd, LL11 2NY Tel: (01978) 354444 Fax: (01978) 351688

▶ Builders Equipment Ltd, City Road, Norwich, NR1 3AN Tel: (01473) 236316 Fax: (01473) 281788E-mail: mail@builders.equipment.co.uk

A.G. Bunker & Sons, Old House Stud Farm, Station Road, Stanbridge, Leighton Buzzard, Bedfordshire, LU7 9JF Tel: (01525) 210984 Fax: (01525) 210984

Burlington Engineers Ltd, Unit 11 Perival Industrial Park, Horsenden Lane South, Perivale, Greenford, Middlesex, UB6 7RL Tel: (020) 8810 7266 Fax: (020) 8998 3517 E-mail: info@burlington-engineers.co.uk

▶ Dave Bushby Plant Hire Ltd, Clovelly Road Industrial Estate, Bideford, Devon, EX39 3HN Tel: (01237) 472878

C B L Ltd, Holmbush Potteries, Crawley Road, Faygate, Horsham, West Sussex, RH12 4SE Tel: (01293) 851352 Fax: (01293) 851205

C J Thorne & Co. Ltd, Union Point, Ridgewood, Uckfield, East Sussex, TN22 5SS Tel: (01825) 764123 Fax: (01825) 764126 E-mail: info@thornegroupuk.com

C N Greene & Sons Ltd, 22 Ashtree Bank, Rugeley, Staffordshire, WS15 1HN Tel: (01889) 582509 Fax: (01889) 582509 E-mail: cng.plants@aol.com

Cadman Cranes Ltd, Moss Road, Stanway, Colchester, CO3 0LF Tel: (01206) 543232 Fax: (01206) 763231 E-mail: info@cadmancontracts.com

Capel Plant Holdings Ltd, Stephenson Road, Severalls Industrial Park, Colchester, CO4 9QR Tel: (01206) 844004 Fax: (01206) 841409

Chamberlaine Plant Hire Ltd, Station Road, Odsey, Baldock, Hertfordshire, SG7 5RT Tel: (01462) 742501 Fax: (01462) 742866

Champion Hire Ltd, 2 Roman Ridge Road, Sheffield, S9 1XG Tel: (0845) 3456900 Fax: 0114-249 4100 E-mail: sales@champion-hire.com

Cheetham Hill Construction Ltd, Woodhill Road, Bury, Lancashire, BL8 1AR Tel: 0161-761 5109 Fax: 0161-761 1300 E-mail: enquiries@cheethamhillconstruction.co.uk

Chippindale Plant Hire & Sales Ltd, Gas Works Road, Keighley, West Yorkshire, BD21 4LY Tel: (01535) 606135 Fax: (01535) 690303 E-mail: general@chippindale-plant.co.uk

Clancy Docwra/Vws UK Jv Ltd, Clare House Coppermill Lane, Harefield, Uxbridge, Middlesex, UB9 6HZ Tel: (01895) 823711 Fax: (01895) 825263 E-mail: admin@theclancygroup.co.uk

▶ Claude Fenton (Plant Hire) Ltd, Unit 1 Kennet Weir Business Park, Arrowhead Road, Theale, Reading, RG7 4AE Tel: 0118-930 3066 Fax: 0118-930 3041 E-mail: reading@fentonplant.co.uk

Claude Fenton (Plant Hire) Ltd, Unit 1 Kennet Weir Business Park, Arrowhead Road, Theale, Reading, RG7 4AE Tel: 0118-930 3066 Fax: 0118-930 3411

▶ Clee Hill Plant Ltd, 41 Downiebrae Road, Rutherglen, Glasgow, G73 1PW Tel: 0141-647 0067 Fax: 0141-647 7600 E-mail: glasgow@cleehill.co.uk

Clee Hill Plants, Mansfield Road, Corbriggs, Chesterfield, Derbyshire, S41 0JW Tel: (01246) 551637 Fax: (01246) 551639 E-mail: sales@cleehill.co.uk

Coleman Tunnelling & Technology Services Ltd, Old Wolverton Road, Old Wolverton, Milton Keynes, MK12 5NL Tel: (01908) 312744 Fax: (01908) 220676 E-mail: ctil@btconnectaol.com

Colwill Plant & Contracting, Ashlea, Main Street, Hatfield Woodhouse, Doncaster, South Yorkshire, DN7 6NF Tel: (01302) 840680 Fax: (01302) 351704

Costain Ltd, Anchor Bay Wharf, Manor Road, Erith, Kent, DA8 2AW Tel: (01322) 397600 Fax: (01322) 397775

Cox Hire Centre, Cromwell Road, Bredbury, Stockport, Cheshire, SK6 2RP Tel: 0161-430 4324 Fax: 0161-494 5686

Coxhire Ltd, Lower Walsall Street, Wolverhampton, WV1 2EX Tel: (01902) 351407 Fax: (01902) 453062

▶ Crownlea Group Ltd, Crownlea House, 247-253 Wood Street, London, E17 3NT Tel: (020) 8521 8812 Fax: (020) 8509 1914 E-mail: cfisher@crownlea.com

Cullum Plant Hire & Sales Ltd, 11 Boleness Road, Wisbech, Cambridgeshire, PE13 2RB Tel: (01945) 463356 Fax: (01945) 463248 E-mail: cullumsales@btinternet.com

Curle M J Ltd, Sunnymead Farm, Naird Lane, Shifnal, Shropshire, TF11 9PJ Tel: (01952) 460382 Fax: (01952) 463238 E-mail: mjcurle@netscapeonline.co.uk

D H Willis & Sons Ltd, Carrbeck House, Gilling West, Richmond, North Yorkshire, DL10 5LN Tel: (01748) 822714 Fax: (01748) 822714

D Morgan Ltd, Chester Road, Great Sutton, New Hay, Ellesmere Port, CH66 2LS Tel: 0151-339 8113 Fax: 0151-347 1254 E-mail: ibyrne@dmorgan.co.uk

D Simmons, 4 Devonshire House, North Street, North Tawton, Devon, EX20 2EX Tel: (01837) 82564 Fax: (01837) 82564

Danbury Plant Hire, 2 Maldon Road, Danbury, Chelmsford, CM3 4QJ Tel: (01245) 223483 Fax: (01245) 226067 E-mail: danburyplanthire@aol.com

Dawson Plant Hire Ltd, 79 Middle Watch, Swavesey, Cambridge, CB24 4RW Tel: (01954) 200400 E-mail: info@dawsonplanthire.co.uk

Delaney Plant, Beckside Works, Old Corn Mill Lane, Bradford, West Yorkshire, BD7 2LB Tel: (01274) 579224 Fax: (01274) 503372

H.F.A. Dolman Ltd, Ajax Works, Potters Way, Temple Farm Industrial Estate, Southend-On-Sea, SS2 5SJ Tel: (01702) 461155 Fax: (01702) 464177

E Aston & Son Ltd, Dale Street, Bilston, West Midlands, WV14 7JY Tel: (01902) 402418 Fax: (01902) 493546

E C Y (Holdings) Ltd, Barley Castle Lane, Appleton, Warrington, WA4 4RB Tel: (01925) 860000 Fax: (01925) 861111 E-mail: sales@ecyltd.co.uk

E H Roberts & Co Southend Ltd, 251-255 Church Road, Benfleet, Essex, SS7 4QP Tel: (01268) 752811 Fax: (01268) 793416

E J Parkinson & Son Ltd, Kirk Lane, Yeadon, Leeds, LS19 7ET Tel: 0113-250 9111 Fax: 0113-250 0223

Equiphire Northern, Bradford Road, Cleckheaton, West Yorkshire, BD19 5YR Tel: (01274) 871817 Fax: (01274) 851224

Equiphire Northern Ltd, Morley Hire Centre, West Street, Morley, Leeds, LS27 9EU Tel: 0113-252 5320 Fax: (01274) 851224

Evans Gwyn Plant Ltd, Brackla Industrial Estate, Bridgend, Mid Glamorgan, CF31 2AN Tel: (01656) 655393 Fax: (01656) 655393

Eynesbury Warehousing, Eynesbury Hardwicke, St. Neots, Cambridgeshire, PE19 6XJ Tel: (01480) 215555 Fax: (01480) 470736 E-mail: eynesburyplant@btinternet.com

F G G Plant, Fyfield Hall, Fyfield, Ongar, Essex, CM5 0SA Tel: (01277) 899495 Fax: (01277) 899613

Fast Plant Swindon Ltd, Unit 2267, Dunbeath Road, Elgin Industrial Estate, Swindon, SN2 8EA Tel: (01793) 617854 Fax: (01793) 420809 E-mail: fastplantswindon@btconnect.com

Fawcett Agriculture, Ireby Hall, Cowan Bridge, Carnforth, Lancashire, LA6 2JH Tel: (01524) 242222 Fax: (01524) 42239 E-mail: richard@fawcetts.net

Folkes Plant & Aggregates Ltd, Welcome Pits, Butt Lane, Burgh Castle, Great Yarmouth, Norfolk, NR31 9PY Tel: (01493) 780274 Fax: (01493) 781118

Fosseway Homes, Coly House, Swan Hill Road, Colyford, Colyton, Devon, EX24 6HE Tel: (01297) 553562 Fax: (01297) 553563 E-mail: michael.gardener@totalise.co.uk

Franchi Hardware Merchants, 144-146 Kentish Town Road, London, NW1 9QB Tel: (020) 7267 3138 Fax: (020) 7485 4637 E-mail: sales@franchi.co.uk

Franchi Locks & Tools Ltd, 278 Holloway Road, London, N7 6NE Tel: (020) 7607 2200 Fax: (020) 7700 4050 E-mail: info@franchi.co.uk

G C N Plant Ltd, Foryd Bank, Green Avenue, Kinmel Bay, Rhyl, Clwyd, LL18 5ET Tel: (01745) 343089 Fax: (01745) 332115 E-mail: gari_hughes@hotmail.com

G E Capital Equipment Services Lnd, Geddington Road, Corby, Northamptonshire, NN18 8AA Tel: (01536) 265505 Fax: (01536) 201258

F.L. Gamble & Sons Ltd, Meadow Road Industrial Estate, Dale Road, Worthing, West Sussex, BN11 2RY Tel: (01903) 230906 Fax: (01903) 210569 E-mail: sales@gamble-jarvis.co.uk

Gardner Plant Hire, Belvoir Way, Fairfield Industrial Estate, Louth, Lincolnshire, LN11 0LQ Tel: (01507) 604849 Fax: (01507) 604849

Geoffrey Budd Partnership, 5 Rothermead, Petworth, West Sussex, GU28 0EW Tel: (01798) 342574 Fax: (01798) 342574

Gill Demolitions Ltd, Progress Works, Hall Lane, Bradford, West Yorkshire, BD4 7DT Tel: (01274) 733011 Fax: (01274) 392879 E-mail: info@gilldemolitions.co.uk

Goplant, 88 Hawkcliffe Road, Mount Sorrel, Mount Sorrel, Loughborough, Leicestershire, LE12 7AH Tel: (01509) 414677 Fax: (01509) 416853

Greenbooth Construction Co. Ltd, Hunt Lane, Chadderton, Oldham, OL9 0LR Tel: 0161-633 4815

H Dunstan & Sons, Carnsew Farm, Treliever Road, Penryn, Cornwall, TR10 9EY Tel: (01326) 372240 Fax: (01326) 372240 E-mail: dunstan@mabe25.go-plus.net

Harman Plant Hire Ltd, The Hyde, Brighton, BN2 4JE Tel: (01273) 603021 Fax: (01273) 690647 E-mail: info@harmanhire.co.uk

Hather Plant Hire, Aldwarke Road, Parkgate, Rotherham, South Yorkshire, S62 6BZ Tel: (01709) 528585 Fax: (01709) 710822 E-mail: gary@hatherplant.freeserve.co.uk

Hawk Plant Hire Ltd, Charleston House, The Grange, Loppington, Shrewsbury, SY4 5SY Tel: (01939) 233730 Fax: (01939) 235206 E-mail: hire@hawk-group.co.uk

Hewden, Trafford House, Chester Road, Stretford, Manchester, M32 0RL Tel: 0161-848 8621 Fax: 0161-848 2298 E-mail: brian.sherlock@hewden.co.uk

Hewden Crane Hire Ltd, Hawley Road, Dartford, DA1 1PD Tel: (01322) 351155 Fax: (01322) 351144

Hewden Hire Centres Ltd, Pinfold Road, Thurmaston, Leicester, LE4 8AZ Tel: 0116-269 4881 Fax: 0116-264 0039

Hewden Hire Centres Ltd, 2 Brandon Road, York Way, London, N7 9AA Tel: (020) 7607 8344 Fax: (020) 7607 9632

Hewden Hire Centres Ltd, Main Road, Long Hanborough, Witney, Oxfordshire, OX29 8SY Tel: (01993) 883939 Fax: (01993) 882877

Hewden Hire Plant Ltd, Howard Road, Park Farm, Redditch, Worcestershire, B98 7SE Tel: (01527) 524020 Fax: (01527) 527320

Hewden Instant Access Ltd, Hawley Road, Dartford, DA1 1PD Tel: (01322) 425800 Fax: (01322) 350920

Hewden Instant Access Ltd, Staceys Yard, Station Road, Langley, Slough, SL3 6DB Tel: (01753) 548849 Fax: (01753) 540655

Hewden Plant Hire Ltd, Bryn Works, Llandygai, Bangor, Gwynedd, LL57 4LE Tel: (01248) 364944 Fax: (01248) 370462

Hewden Plant Hire Ltd, Cambridge Road, Bedford, MK42 0LH Tel: (01234) 340801 Fax: (01234) 343423

Hewden Plant Hire Ltd, Shieldgate House, Shadon Way, Birtley, Chester le Street, County Durham, DH3 2SW Tel: 0191-492 9900 Fax: 0191-492 3086

Hewden Plant Hire Ltd, Ellis Road, Mitcham, Surrey, CR4 4HX Tel: (020) 8648 7070 Fax: (020) 8687 0482

Hewden Plant Hire Ltd, Tank Farm Road, Llandarcy, Neath, West Glamorgan, SA10 6EN Tel: (01792) 321111 Fax: (01792) 321346

Hewden Plant Hire Ltd, Vicarage Farm Road, Peterborough, PE1 5TN Tel: (01733) 564378 Fax: (01733) 566480

Hewden Plant Hire Ltd, 21-23 Willis Way, Poole, Dorset, BH15 3SR Tel: (01202) 674371 Fax: (01202) 665560

Hewden Tool Hire, Unit 1 Kingstanding Business Park, Tunbridge Wells, Kent, TN2 3UP Tel: (01892) 616318 Fax: (01892) 616353 E-mail: steve.davies@hewden.co.uk

High Speed Hire, 47 High Street, Nailsea, Bristol, BS48 1AW Tel: (01275) 810364 Fax: (01275) 859464

Hire Service Shops Ltd, 865 Fulham Road, London, SW6 5HP Tel: (020) 7736 1769 Fax: (020) 7736 3127

Holmwood Tractors, Norfolk Garage, Horsham Road, Holmwood, Dorking, Surrey, RH5 4ER Tel: (01306) 888627

CONTRACTORS' PLANT HIRE – *continued*

▶ HSS Hire, 2 Market Street, Bracknell, Berkshire, RG12 1JG Tel: (01344) 486060 Fax: (01344) 459418

▶ HSS Hire, 208-210 High Road, London, N2 9AY Tel: (020) 8883 3818 Fax: (020) 8444 1297

▶ HSS Hire, 25 Willow Lane, Mitcham, Surrey, CR4 4TS Tel: (020) 8260 3100 Fax: (020) 8687 5005 E-mail: hire@hss.co.uk

HSS Lift & Shift, 176-178 Shore Road, Belfast, BT15 3QA Tel: (028) 9078 1818 Fax: (028) 9078 1122

HSS Lift & Shift, 8 Oakwood Industrial Park, Gatwick Road, Crawley, West Sussex, RH10 9AZ Tel: (01293) 611010 Fax: (01293) 618041

HSS Lift & Shift, 4 Seafield Road, Edinburgh, EH6 7LD Tel: 0131-554 0298 Fax: 0131-554 9542

HSS Lift & Shift, 399 York Road, Leeds, LS9 6TA Tel: 0113-240 7707 Fax: 0113-240 9944

HSS Lift & Shift, Sotherby Road, Middlesbrough, Cleveland, TS3 8BS Tel: (01642) 246015 Fax: (01642) 251411

Hutchings & Carter Ltd, The Avenue, Lasham, Alton, Hampshire, GU34 5SU Tel: (01256) 381338 Fax: (01256) 381876 E-mail: robert.white@hncltd.com

Hydrex Equipment UK Ltd, Peartree Lane, Dudley, West Midlands, DY2 0UX Tel: (01384) 256600 Fax: (01384) 256200

I Macpherson, Conisby, Bruichladdich, Isle of Islay, PA49 7UN Tel: (01496) 850295 Fax: (01496) 850295

Ian Mitchell, Stones Top, Hebden Bridge Road, Oxenhope, Keighley, West Yorkshire, BD22 9QH Tel: (07973) 692225 Fax: (01535) 643893

J A B Hire Services Ltd, J A B House, Delamare Road, Cheshunt, Waltham Cross, Hertfordshire, EN8 9SS Tel: (01992) 634666 Fax: (01992) 634777

J A Chapman, The Forge, 45 Bonehurst Road, Horley, Surrey, RH6 8PJ Tel: (01293) 785060 Fax: (01293) 785060

J F L Harvey Ltd, The Bungalow, Polwhele, Truro, Cornwall, TR4 9AE Tel: (01872) 274757 Fax: (01872) 260226

John Innes Gilkes Ltd, Bugbrooke Road, Kislingbury, Northampton, NN7 4AY Tel: (01604) 830098 Fax: (01604) 832190

John Stacey & Son Ltd, Stacey Industrial Park, Silchester Road, Tadley, Hampshire, RG26 3PZ Tel: 0118-981 3531 Fax: 0118-981 3458 E-mail: info@john-stacey.co.uk

Jovic Plant Ltd, Mayes Lane, Sandon, Chelmsford, CM2 7RP Tel: (01245) 224211 Fax: (01245) 224258 E-mail: sales@jovicplant.co.uk

K M Construction North Wales Ltd, Lower Denbigh Road, St. Asaph, Clwyd, LL17 0EL Tel: (01745) 583752 Fax: (01745) 584705

Keller Ground Engineering, Thorp Arch Trading Estate, Thorp Arch, Wetherby, West Yorkshire, LS23 7BJ Tel: (01937) 541118 Fax: (01937) 541371 E-mail: info@keller-ge.co.uk

D.P. Kelly (Holdings) Ltd, Nether Handley, Sheffield, S21 5RP Tel: (01246) 451167 Fax: (01246) 451167

Kelly Plant Hire, Fowberry Road, Newcastle upon Tyne, NE15 6XP Tel: 0191-275 3339 Fax: 0191-275 3304 E-mail: tele.planthire@virgin.net

KSS Hire Services, Russell Gardens, Wickford, Essex, SS11 8BH Tel: (01268) 769531 Fax: (01268) 561034

L E Talbot Plant Hire Ltd, Holyhead Road, Oakengates, Telford, Shropshire, TF2 6DJ Tel: (01952) 610456 Fax: (01952) 619050

L & J Wilcock, 10 Walnut Avenue, Wigan, Lancashire, WN1 3XE Tel: (01942) 242705

L Rampling Plant Hire, 6 Victory Rd, West Mersea, Colchester, CO5 8LY Tel: (01206) 382989 Fax: (01206) 384782

Laverty Plant Hire, 24 Limavallaghan Rd, Clough, Ballymena, Co. Antrim, BT44 9RX Tel: (028) 2175 8613

Leggat Plant Ltd, Crossmill, Glasgow Road, Glasgow, G78 1TG Tel: 0141-881 8104 Fax: 0141-881 8334

Lewis Plant Hire Ltd, Peacock Road, Newcastle, Staffordshire, ST5 9HY Tel: (01782) 623776 Fax: (01782) 614738

▶ Loc, 100 Mildenhall Road, Fordham, Ely, Cambridgeshire, CB7 5NR Tel: (01638) 720653 Fax: (01638) 721376 E-mail: mmusridd@btconnect.com

M B Plant Hire, 14 Wilson Street, Peterhead, Aberdeenshire, AB42 1UD Tel: (01224) 575255 Fax: (01779) 479236

M J Beskeen, 1872 Melton Road, Rearsby, Leicester, LE7 4YS Tel: (01664) 424799 Fax: (01664) 424799

M T M Plant Hire & Sales Ltd, Milner Road, Chilton Industrial Estate, Sudbury, Suffolk, CO10 2XG Tel: (01787) 312007 Fax: (01787) 883395 E-mail: mtm.plantlesltd@virgin.net

John Macnamara & Co. Ltd, 19a Bush Road, London, SE8 5AR Tel: (020) 7237 1591 Fax: (020) 7231 5173

Maher, 131 Canwick Road, Lincoln, LN5 8EY Tel: (01522) 885727

Malcolm Plant, Murray Street, Paisley, Renfrewshire, PA3 1QQ Tel: 0141-889 8711 Fax: 0141-889 7510 E-mail: contact@whm.co.uk

Mansell Construction Services Ltd, Wollaston Road, Stourbridge, West Midlands, DY8 4HP Tel: (01384) 440330 Fax: (01384) 440169 E-mail: stourbridge@mansell.plc.uk

Marsh Plant Hire Ltd, 67 New Lane, Havant, Hampshire, PO9 2LZ Tel: (023) 9248 2323 Fax: (023) 9245 3813 E-mail: info@marshplant.com

Marsh Plant Hire Ltd, Wallingford Road, Uxbridge, Middlesex, UB8 2SS Tel: (01895) 231291 Fax: (01895) 811650

Marshall, 18 Johnson Street, Sheffield, S3 8GT Tel: 0114-276 7071 Fax: 0114-273 8084 E-mail: sales@geomarshall.co.uk

Martello Plant Hire Ltd, Potts Marsh Industrial Estate, Westham, Pevensey, East Sussex, BN24 5NA Tel: (01323) 761887 Fax: (01323) 461933

Martins Plant, 10a Hayes Road, Deanshanger, Milton Keynes, MK19 6HW Tel: (01908) 563437 Fax: (01908) 262429

Marwood Group Ltd, Fengate Eastern Industrial Area, Peterborough, PE1 5BN Tel: (01733) 311444 Fax: (01733) 349974 E-mail: enquire@marwoodgroup.co.uk

Megaplant Ltd, Wyke Street, Hull, HU9 1PA Tel: (01482) 323800 Fax: (01482) 223864

Merriman Mineral Processing, Charnwood Edge, Syston Road, Cossington, Leicester, LE7 4UZ Tel: 0116-269 5137 Fax: 0116-269 2261 E-mail: sales@merrimans.com

Midland Earthmoving Co. Ltd, Gibbs Road, Lye, Stourbridge, West Midlands, DY9 8SY Tel: (01384) 894488 Fax: (01384) 894489

Midland Plant & Scaffolding Ltd, 171 Gloucester Crescent, Wigston, Leicestershire, LE18 4YH Tel: 0116-278 6677

Miskin Plant & Tool Hire Co. Ltd, Alban House, Brownfields, Welwyn Garden City, Hertfordshire, AL7 1BE Tel: (01707) 371858 Fax: (01707) 373073

Mitchell Hire, 1 Lynch Road, Weymouth, Dorset, DT4 0SJ Tel: (01305) 770601 Fax: (01305) 761752

Moat Plant Hire Ltd, 105 Town Street, Stanningley, Pudsey, West Yorkshire, LS28 6ES Tel: 0113-256 4890

Modern Plant Hire, 6 Somers Road, Rugby, Warwickshire, CV22 7DE Tel: (01788) 565186 Fax: (01788) 579878

Moon's Plant Hire, 3 Laureate Industrial Estate, Newmarket, Suffolk, CB8 0AP Tel: (01638) 662622 Fax: (01638) 660961

Moons Of Selling 1982 Ltd, Grove Road, Sheldwich, Faversham, Kent, ME13 9RR Tel: (01227) 752217 Fax: (01227) 752217

Chris Moore Transport Co. Ltd, Mill Court Barns, Binsted, Alton, Hampshire, GU34 4JF Tel: (01420) 23555 E-mail: chris_moore2000@hotmail.com

N T Burton, Oaklands, Loughborough Road, Rempstone, Loughborough, Leicestershire, LE12 6RQ Tel: (01509) 856150 Fax: (01509) 856444

▶ Newel Plant Hire, 45 Colwyn Crescent, Rhos on Sea, Colwyn Bay, Clwyd, LL28 4RF Tel: (01492) 533612 Fax: (01492) 533612

North London Plant Hire, 4-16 Shacklewell Lane, London, E8 2EZ Tel: (020) 7254 3328 Fax: (020) 7923 4129 E-mail: sales@nlph.co.uk

▶ North Yorkshire Construction Plant Ltd, P O Box 157, Middlesbrough, Cleveland, TS9 7JB Tel: (01642) 778444

Northumbria Plant Hire, Great Lime Road, West Moor, Newcastle Upon Tyne, NE12 0RU Tel: 0191-268 7000 Fax: 0191-216 0838

▶ Ob Hire, Unit C-D Woodside, Brewery Road, Hoddesdon, Hertfordshire, EN11 8HF Tel: (01992) 468460 Fax: 01992 468463 E-mail: sales@obhire.com

On The Dot Ltd, Ripley Road, Bradford, West Yorkshire, BD4 7EX Tel: (01274) 723626 Fax: (01274) 723626

P T E Plant Co., Kelham St, Doncaster, South Yorkshire, DN1 3TA Tel: (01302) 321221

Panther Platform Rentals, Derby Dell, Lasham, Alton, Hampshire, GU34 5RX Tel: (01256) 381515 Fax: (01256) 381505 E-mail: basingstoke@panther.uk.com

Penfold Public Works (Sussex) Ltd, The Chalk Pit, Mile Oak Road, Portslade, Brighton, BN41 2RB Tel: (01273) 412224 Fax: (01273) 412563E-mail: info@penfoldpublicworks.co.uk

Penhow Plant Hire Ltd, Langstone, Newport, Gwent, NP18 2HJ Tel: (01633) 415333 Fax: (01633) 415334

James Penman Plant Hire, Glenleven Industrial Estate, Leslie, Glenrothes, Fife, KY6 3EU Tel: (01592) 654555 Fax: (01592) 620245 E-mail: penmanplant@yahoo.co.uk

Percliff Plant Hire Ltd, Percliff Way, Philips Road, Blackburn, BB1 5PF Tel: (01254) 676600 Fax: (01254) 676630 E-mail: info@percliff.co.uk

Peter Hare Ltd, The Cottage, Post Office Lane, Little Totham, Maldon, Essex, CM9 8JL Tel: (01621) 891591

PJP Plant Hire, Mill Street, Radcliffe, Manchester, M26 1AJ Tel: 0845 5314214 Fax: 0161-959 1111 E-mail: hire@pjpuk.com

Plant Hire Ltd, Unit 3, Aquarius Business Park, Priestley Way, London, NW2 7AN Tel: (020) 8208 3838 Fax: (020) 8450 3716

Plant Life, 9 Woodland Way, Morden, Surrey, SM4 4DS Tel: (020) 8286 9461 Fax: (020) 8542 4456 E-mail: sales@plantlife.me.uk

Pochin Contractors Ltd, Brooks Lane, Middlewich, Cheshire, CW10 0JQ Tel: (01606) 833333 Fax: (01606) 833331 E-mail: sales@pochins.plc.uk

Trevor Potts Plant Hire, Hellaby Lane, Hellaby, Rotherham, South Yorkshire, S66 8HN Tel: (01709) 700200 Fax: (01709) 701875 E-mail: trevor@pottsplanthire.fsnet.co.uk

Power Plant Hire Ltd, Power House, Whitehall Road, Halesowen, West Midlands, B63 3JS Tel: 0121-585 4200 Fax: 0121-585 4232 E-mail: birmingham@powerplanthire.co.uk

Power Plant Hire Glasgow Ltd, 25 Robert Street, Glasgow, G51 3HB Tel: 0141-445 4437 Fax: 0141-425 1764 E-mail: paul@powerplanthire.demon.co.uk

Power Plant UK Ltd, Shalowstones, Baldersby, Thirsk, North Yorkshire, YO7 4PP Tel: (01765) 640641 Fax: (01765) 640222

Price Bros, 1 Ross Road, Abergavenny, Gwent, NP7 5LT Tel: (01873) 853827 Fax: (01873) 853827

Priory Plant Ltd, Norman House, Wattons Lane, Southam, Warwickshire, CV47 0HX Tel: (01926) 812343 Fax: (01926) 813942 E-mail: vicky.t@prioryplant.co.uk

PSL Ltd, 135 Bridgeman Street, Bolton, BL3 6BS Tel: (01204) 366555 Fax: (01204) 368020

Pudsey Plant Hire Ltd, Carlisle Drive, Pudsey, West Yorkshire, LS28 8QS Tel: 0113-257 6116 Fax: 0113-236 1360 E-mail: mail@pudseyplanthire.co.uk

Q Plant Hire Ltd, Stampstone Street, Oldham, OL1 3PW Tel: 0161-620 2115 Fax: 0161-652 8342 E-mail: jamesquinnplanthire@jqph.co.uk

R B James, Ashdown Farm, Badsey Road, Evesham, Worcestershire, WR11 7PA Tel: (01386) 41585 Fax: (01386) 41541

R J Cannon Ltd, Maldon Road, Tiptree, Colchester, CO5 0PH Tel: (01621) 815396 Fax: (01621) 817939 E-mail: rjcannon@btclick.com

R J T Excavations Ltd, Oxnam Road Indust, Oxnam Road Industrial Estate, Jedburgh, Roxburghshire, TD8 6LS Tel: (01835) 862367 Fax: (01835) 863025

R Mansell (Developments) Ltd, Roman House, 13/27 Grant Road, Croydon, CR9 6BU Tel: (020) 8654 8191 Fax: (020) 8655 1286 E-mail: mailbox@mansell.plc.uk

R Savage Plant Hire Co. Ltd, 222 St Margarets Road, Ward End, Birmingham, B8 2BG Tel: 0121-328 1100 Fax: 0121-327 3548 E-mail: enquiries@savageplanthire.co.uk

R W Almond & Co. Ltd, Heysham Road, Bootle, Merseyside, L30 6UA Tel: 0151-521 5454 Fax: 0151-525 0115 E-mail: sales@rwalmond.co.uk

Regal Construction, La Grande Route De St. Laurent, St. Lawrence, Jersey, JE3 1NN Tel: (01534) 865333 Fax: (01534) 861431 E-mail: regal-con@jerseymail.co.uk

▶ RGS Plant Hire, 28 Whitley Spring Road, Ossett, West Yorkshire, WF5 0QA Tel: (07968) 722984 E-mail: rgsplanthire@fsmail.net

Ridgeway Plant Co. Ltd, Airport Road West, Belfast, BT3 9AD Tel: (028) 9045 4599 Fax: (028) 9045 4596 E-mail: info@ridgeway-online.com

Road Equipment Ltd, 32-34 Feltham Road, Ashford, Middlesex, TW15 1DL Tel: (01784) 256565 Fax: (01784) 240398 E-mail: roadequipment@aol.com

Rowlands Plant Services Ltd, Alchorne Place, Portsmouth, PO3 5QS Tel: (023) 9266 1143 Fax: (023) 9264 1656 E-mail: rowlandsplant@btconnect.com

▶ Roy Francis Plant Hire Ltd, The Old Saw Mills, Bath Road, Sells Green, Melksham, Wiltshire, SN12 6RW Tel: (01380) 828988

Royhire Plant & Machinery Hire, 231b Southend Road, Stanford-le-Hope, Essex, SS17 7AB Tel: (01375) 678225 Fax: (01375) 678225

▶ Ian Rylands Ltd, Pitts House Farm, Pitts House Lane, Southport, Merseyside, PR9 7QT Tel: (01704) 226590 Fax: (01704) 231747 E-mail: ian.rylands@care4free.net

S E L Clarke Plant Hire, New Road, Bideford, Devon, EX39 5AA Tel: (01237) 476375 Fax: (01237) 421532

S G B Ltd, 40 Bayton Road, Exhall, Coventry, CV7 9EJ Tel: (024) 7636 2255 Fax: (024) 7658 8042 E-mail: info@sgb.co.uk

S R B E Ltd, Stewkley Road, Soulbury, Leighton Buzzard, Bedfordshire, LU7 0DF Tel: (01525) 270591 Fax: (01525) 270727 E-mail: sales@srbe.co.uk

S Redhead, Helsay Farm, Old Helsay, Warkworth, Morpeth, Northumberland, NE65 0SN Tel: (01665) 712952 E-mail: stephenredhead@aol.com

Sangwin Concrete Products Ltd, Dansom Lane, Hull, HU8 7LN Tel: (01482) 329921 Fax: (01482) 215353 E-mail: info@sangwin.co.uk

Scott Plant Hire Ltd, Kent Road, Pudsey, West Yorkshire, LS28 9DR Tel: 0113-257 1421 Fax: 0113-255 2690

Search Liverpool Ltd, Hammond Road, Knowsley Industrial Park, Liverpool, L33 7UW Tel: 0151-546 3361 Fax: 0151-549 1914 E-mail: info@wgsearch.co.uk

▶ G. Segger Contracts Ltd, 6 Linden Drive, Hurworth Place, Darlington, County Durham, DL2 2DJ Tel: (01325) 720565 Fax: (01325) 720565 E-mail: seggercontracts@yahoo.co.uk

Selwood Group, Hixon Industrial Estate, Church Lane, Hixon, Stafford, ST18 0QB Tel: (01889) 270524 Fax: (01889) 270063

Shorts Group Ltd, Lyndhurst Road, Ascot, Berkshire, SL5 9ED Tel: (01344) 620316 Fax: (01344) 624572 E-mail: sales@shorts-services.co.uk

Six Mile Excavators, Little North Leigh Farm, Stelling Minnis, Canterbury, Kent, CT4 6BZ Tel: (01227) 709611 Fax: (01227) 709820

Ian Smith Plant Ltd, Scotter Common, Gainsborough, Lincolnshire, DN21 3JF Tel: (01724) 764185 Fax: (01724) 764649

South Lincs Plant Hire & Sales Ltd, Enterprise Way, Pinchbeck, Spalding, Lincolnshire, PE11 3YR Tel: (01775) 766131 Fax: (01775) 711305

Southdown Plant Hire Ltd, Daveys Lane, Lewes, East Sussex, BN7 2BQ Tel: (01273) 472177

▶ Southern Counties Engineering Services Ltd, Ailwood, Corfe Castle, Wareham, Dorset, BH20 5JA Tel: (01929) 481440 Fax: (01929) 425688 E-mail: keithshaw@shellbay.unioffice.co.uk

Gordon Sparrow Plant Sales Ltd, 3-4 Newlands House, Lansdown Hill, Lansdown, Bath, BA1 5RE Tel: (01225) 429522 Fax: (01225) 429496

Speedy Hire Centres Ltd, 572 Melton Road, Thurmaston, Leicester, LE4 8BB Tel: 0116-260 1019 Fax: 0116-260 0109

Speedy Hire Centres Northern Ltd, Lakeside Buildings, St. Helens, Merseyside, WA10 3TT Tel: (01744) 697000 Fax: (01744) 739975

Speedy Hire Centres Southern Ltd, 6 Bedford Road, Kempston, Bedford, MK42 8AD Tel: (01234) 353148 Fax: (01234) 363285

Speedy Lifting Ltd, Pentagon Island, Nottingham Road, Derby, DE21 6BW Tel: (01332) 380493 Fax: (01332) 372615

Stennett Self Drive Hire, Blakeney, Guildford Road, Cranleigh, Surrey, GU6 8QZ Tel: (01483) 273814 Fax: (01483) 275912 E-mail: sales@stennetts.com

Stott Concrete Pumping Ltd, PO Box 393, Wigan, Lancashire, WN6 7LA Tel: (01942) 497776 Fax: (01942) 515952 E-mail: enquiries@stottconcretepumping.co.uk

M.P. Sweeney, 123 Burnham La, Slough, SL1 6LA Tel: 01628 602390

T F Sammon Plant Hire Ltd, 138 Downhills Park Road, London, N17 6BP Tel: (020) 8881 3572 Fax: (020) 8881 3572 E-mail: csammon@tiscali.co.uk

T H Quirk (Plant Hire), Cess Road, Martham, Great Yarmouth, Norfolk, NR29 4RF Tel: (01493) 748178 Fax: (01493) 740201

T & T Ltd, Jarvis Brook Goods Yard, Crowborough, East Sussex, TN6 3DS Tel: (01892) 663392 Fax: (01892) 662094

Tallboat Plant Hire Ltd, Pedmore Road, Brierley Hill, West Midlands, DY5 1TQ Tel: (01384) 78002 Fax: (01384) 77846

Telford Crane Hire Ltd, Halesfield 22, Telford, Shropshire, TF7 4QX Tel: (01952) 586304 Fax: (01952) 587848 E-mail: sales@telfordcrane.co.uk

Tickhill Plant Hire, Apy Hill Lane, Tickhill, Doncaster, South Yorkshire, DN11 9PD Tel: (01302) 742383 Fax: (01302) 750924

Toga Plant Hire Ltd, 67-71 Kingsland Road, London, E2 8AG Tel: (020) 7729 1471 Fax: (020) 7729 1592

Toton Plant Hire Ltd, Private Road 4, Colwick Industrial Estate, Nottingham, NG4 2JT Tel: 0115-940 1302 Fax: 0115-940 1312 E-mail: sales@totonplant.co.uk

Trodham Plant Ltd, Liphook Road, Hollywater, Bordon, Hampshire, GU35 9AF Tel: (01428) 751588 Fax: (01428) 751550 E-mail: trodham@aol.com

U Mole Ltd, Unit 11 Hardwick Road Industrial Estatepark, Hardwick Road, Great Gransden, Sandy, Bedfordshire, SG19 3BJ Tel: (01767) 677503 Fax: (01767) 677827 E-mail: info@umole.co.uk

V P plc, Beckwith Knowle, Otley Road, Beckwithshaw, Harrogate, North Yorkshire, HG3 1UD Tel: (01423) 533400 Fax: (01423) 565657 E-mail: enquiries@vpplc.com

Vention Hire Centre, 74 Cannock Road, Willenhall, West Midlands, WV12 5RZ Tel: (0800) 7310589 Fax: (01922) 402085

Venus Services, The Old Rectory, Church Street, Southwell, Nottinghamshire, NG25 0HG Tel: (01636) 814633 Fax: (01636) 815403 E-mail: audley@btopenworld.com

Penfold Verrall Ltd, The Chalk Pit, Mile Oak Road, Portslade, Brighton, BN41 2RB Tel: (01273) 412224 Fax: (01273) 412563 E-mail: info@penfoldverrall.com

Vertical Transportation Ltd, Grovebury Road, Leighton Buzzard, Bedfordshire, LU7 4RU Tel: (01525) 850027 Fax: (01525) 851357

Viking Plant Hire Ltd, 2 Dewing Road, Rackheath Industrial Estate, Norwich, NR13 6LN Tel: (01603) 720771 Fax: (01603) 721779 E-mail: viking-plant@virgin.net

Volts Vehicle Auto Electrical Blandford Dorset, 9 Chettle, Chettle City, Blandford Forum, Dorset, DT11 8DB Tel: (01258) 830624 E-mail: volts@billynet.co.uk

Walker May Halifax Ltd, 7 The Market Business Centre, Hanson Lane, Halifax, West Yorkshire, HX1 5PF Tel: (01422) 347483 Fax: (01422) 342096 E-mail: walkermay@btclick.com

Watling JCB Ltd, Dog & Gun Lane, Whetstone, Leicester, LE8 6LJ Tel: 0116-286 3621 Fax: 0116-286 3171 E-mail: watjcb@atlas.co.uk

A.P. Webb Plant Hire, Tilcon Avenue, Stafford, ST18 0YJ Tel: (01785) 241335 Fax: (01785) 255178

William G Search Ltd, Whitehall Road, Leeds, LS12 6EP Tel: 0113-263 9081 Fax: 0113-231 0267 E-mail: info@wgsearch.co.uk

Williams Plant Hire Ltd, Henfaes Lane, Welshpool, Powys, SY21 7BE Tel: (01938) 552337 Fax: (01938) 555650

Wilmslow, Omega Works Stuart Road, Bredbury Park Industrial Estate, Bredbury, Stockport, Cheshire, SK6 2SR Tel: 0161-406 0666 Fax: 0161-406 0777 E-mail: enquiries@wimslowplant.com

CONTRACTORS' PLANT HIRE – *continued*

Charles Wilson Engineers Ltd, 63 High Street, Harpenden, Hertfordshire, AL5 2SL Tel: (01582) 763122 Fax: (01582) 462697 E-mail: hire@cwplant.co.uk
Wilsons Of Clifton Ltd, 97 Hitchin Road, Shefford, Bedfordshire, SG17 5JB Tel: (01462) 811000 Fax: (01462) 817475
Winnersh Plant Hire Ltd, 580 Reading Road, Winnersh, Wokingham, Berkshire, RG41 5HA Tel: 0118-979 2828 Fax: 0118-979 0333 E-mail: info@winnershplant.co.uk
Wright Brothers (Clayton) Ltd, Victoria Works, Barnard Road, Bradford, West Yorkshire, BD4 7DY Tel: (01274) 587777 Fax: (01274) 394629
Yorkshire Plant (Humber) Ltd, Clay Street, Chamberlain Road, Hull, HU8 8HF Tel: (01482) 329441 Fax: (01482) 225027 E-mail: jez@yorkshireplant.co.uk

CONTRACTORS' PLANT MAINTENANCE OR REPAIR

▶ Andy's Machine Start, Block J Ringstones Industrial Estate, Bridgemont, Whaley Bridge, High Peak, Derbyshire, SK23 7PD Tel: (01663) 719710
C B L Ltd, Holmbush Potteries, Crawley Road, Faygate, Horsham, West Sussex, RH12 4SE Tel: (01293) 851352 Fax: (01293) 851205
▶ C Morgan, 172 Crown Lane, Horwich, Bolton, BL6 7QX Tel: (01204) 697982
Costain Ltd, Anchor Bay Wharf, Manor Road, Erith, Kent, DA8 2AW Tel: (01322) 397600 Fax: (01322) 397775
D & S & P Humphrey, New House Farm, Newhouse Lane, East Dean, Chichester, West Sussex, PO18 0NJ Tel: (01243) 811685 Fax: (01243) 773676
▶ Ehl, Unit G2 Morton Park Way, Darlington, County Durham, DL1 4PJ Tel: (01325) 488533 Fax: (01325) 488533E-mail: info@ehluk.co.uk
Leach Lewis Ltd, Victoria House, Britannia Road, Waltham Cross, Hertfordshire, EN8 7NU Tel: (01992) 704100 Fax: (01992) 704170 E-mail: enquiries@leachlewis.co.uk
Lewis & Co., Hinton Hall, Hinton, Whitchurch, Shropshire, SY13 4HB Tel: (01948) 662923 Fax: (01948) 667908 E-mail: lewisnco@btopenworld.com
Reeds, Mount Pleasant Yard, White Street, Market Lavington, Devizes, Wiltshire, SN10 4DP Tel: (01380) 816516 Fax: (01380) 816457
Viking Plant Hire Ltd, 2 Dewing Road, Rackheath Industrial Estate, Norwich, NR13 6LN Tel: (01603) 720771 Fax: (01603) 721779 E-mail: viking-plant@virgin.net

CONTRACTORS' PLANT SPARE PARTS OR WEARING PARTS

Ace Plantline, 10 Aghaginduff Road, Dungannon, County Tyrone, BT70 3AX Tel: (028) 8776 1433 Fax: (028) 8776 7017 E-mail: ace.plantline@btclick.com
Barbrak Ltd, 5 Eden Court, Eden Way, Leighton Buzzard, Bedfordshire, LU7 4FY Tel: (01525) 376605 Fax: (01525) 370505 E-mail: chris@barbrak.co.uk
Chippindale Plant Hire & Sales Ltd, Gas Works Road, Keighley, West Yorkshire, BD21 4LY Tel: (01535) 606135 Fax: (01535) 690303 E-mail: general@chippindale-plant.co.uk
D Martindale Ltd, Crosse Hall Street, Chorley, Lancashire, PR6 0QQ Tel: (01257) 263504 Fax: (01257) 263504 E-mail: info@donaldmartindale.co.uk
Greenshields JCB Ltd, Clipper Close, Medway City Estate, Rochester, Kent, ME2 4QP Tel: (01634) 296660 Fax: (01634) 296670
Hoddesdon Plant Hire Ltd, Unit 21, Pindar Road, Hoddesdon, Hertfordshire, EN11 0DE Tel: (01992) 443161 Fax: (01992) 451679
Kellands Holdings Ltd, Salmon Parade, Bridgwater, Somerset, TA6 5JY Tel: (01278) 451601 Fax: (01278) 446381 E-mail: terry@kellandsplantsales.co.uk
Purser Plant Ltd, Nyes Wharf, Frensham Street, London, SE15 6TH Tel: (020) 7639 1344 Fax: (020) 7639 2155
Rickmar, Westminster Road Industrial Estate, Station Road, North Hykeham, Lincoln, LN6 3QY Tel: (01522) 691441 Fax: (01522) 694056E-mail: sales@rickmarplantsales.co.uk
Ripco Sales, Bulldozer House, New Road, Sheerness, Kent, ME12 1AU Tel: (01795) 660666 Fax: (01795) 661559 E-mail: info@atecoaccess.com
Service Engines (Newcastle) Ltd, Great Lime Road, Killingworth, Newcastle Upon Tyne, NE12 6RU Tel: 0191-268 1000 Fax: 0191-216 0838 E-mail: admin@serviceengines.co.uk
Gordon Sparrow Plant Sales Ltd, 3-4 Newlands House, Lansdown Hill, Lansdown, Bath, BA1 5RE Tel: (01225) 429522 Fax: (01225) 429496
Speedy Hire Centres Ltd, 572 Melton Road, Thurmaston, Leicester, LE4 8BB Tel: 0116-260 1019 Fax: 0116-260 0109
Speedy Hire Centres Southern Ltd, 6 Bedford Road, Kempston, Bedford, MK42 8AD Tel: (01234) 353148 Fax: (01234) 363285
Speedy Hire Centres Southern Ltd, Accademy House, Fengate, Peterborough, PE1 5SW Tel: (01733) 551092 Fax: (01733) 352089
Stewart Plant Sales Ltd, Townmill Road, Glasgow, G31 3AR Tel: 0141-554 6881 Fax: 0141-550 2358 E-mail: enquiries@stewart-plant-sales.co.uk
Summit Equipment Supplies Ltd, Clover Nook Road, Clover Nook Industrial Estate, Alfreton, Derbyshire, DE55 4RF Tel: (01773) 520488 Fax: (01773) 831004 E-mail: sumhyd@lineone.net
United Parts, Station Farm, Station Road, Kirton Lindsey, Gainsborough, Lincolnshire, DN21 4BD Tel: (01652) 648931 Fax: (01652) 640769 E-mail: jimg@unitedparts.co.uk
W A C Mccandless Engineering Ltd, 95-99 Limestone Road, Belfast, BT15 3AB Tel: (028) 9035 1811 Fax: (028) 9074 6015 E-mail: sales@wacmccandless.com

CONTROL CABLES, BRAKE/CLUTCH

Capro Europe, Building 54, Second Avenue, Pensnett Trading Estate, Kingswinford, West Midlands, DY6 7XJ Tel: (01384) 276300 Fax: (01384) 402010
Catton Control Cables Ltd, 33-35 Kings Road, Yardley, Birmingham, B25 8JB Tel: 0121-772 4297 Fax: 0121-766 6075 E-mail: nick@catton.co.uk
Century Cables & Controls Ltd, Century House, 8 South Street, Crowland, Peterborough, PE6 0AJ Tel: (01733) 211600 Fax: (01733) 211082 E-mail: kwhincup@yahoo.com
Crown Surveillance, 11 Huss's Lane, Long Eaton, Nottingham, NG10 1GS Tel: 0115-946 5422 Fax: 0115-946 5433 E-mail: info@crown-cctv.co.uk
Dura Shifter Systems Ltd, Yspitty Road, Llanelli, Carmarthenshire, SA14 9TF Tel: (01554) 772445 Fax: (01554) 756808 E-mail: sales@duraauto.com
Elmill Products Ltd, 139a Engineer Road, West Wilts Trading Estate, Westbury, Wiltshire, BA13 4JW Tel: (01373) 864267 Fax: (01373) 858266 E-mail: sales@elmill.co.uk
Gills Cables, 25 Apollo, Lichfield Road Industrial Estate, Tamworth, Staffordshire, B79 7TA Tel: (01827) 304777 Fax: (01827) 314568 E-mail: kevinhatton@gillscables.com
SWR Ltd, 3 Eastman Way, Hemel Hempstead Industrial Estate, Hemel Hempstead, Hertfordshire, HP2 7DU Tel: (01442) 219611 Fax: (01442) 259918 E-mail: sales@swrgaragedoors.com
Tuthill Controls Group, Diplocks Way, Hailsham, East Sussex, BN27 3JS Tel: (01323) 841510 Fax: (01323) 845848
Wicks & Martin Ltd, Bromyard Industrial Estate, Bromyard, Herefordshire, HR7 4HT Tel: (01885) 483636 Fax: (01885) 483692 E-mail: mike@wicksandmartin.co.uk

CONTROL CABLES, STEEL

Escadean, Baltimore Road, Birmingham, B42 1DP Tel: 0121-356 1001 Fax: 0121-356 7411

CONTROL ENGINEERING CONSULTANTS

▶ Automated Building Controls, Wellesley House, 7 Clarence Parade, Cheltenham, Gloucestershire, GL50 3NY Tel: (01242) 265781 Fax: (01242) 265781 E-mail: mail@abc.uk.net
Avon Control Engineering & Software, The Old Vicarage, Somerset Square, Nailsea, Bristol, BS48 1RN Tel: (01275) 853721 Fax: (01275) 857746 E-mail: sales@graynailsea.freeserve.co.uk
Conard Systems & Engineering Ltd, Unit 6d Lowick Close, Newby Road Industrial Estate, Hazel Grove, Stockport, Cheshire, SK7 5ED Tel: 0161-456 5285
D Wynn, 15 Kennington Road, Nuffield Industrial Estate, Poole, Dorset, BH17 0GF Tel: (01202) 677741 Fax: (01202) 667769 E-mail: david.wynn@lineone.net
▶ Global Instrumentation Ltd, Unit 1080 Galley Drive, Sittingbourne Research Centre, Sittingbourne, Kent, ME9 8GA Tel: (0870) 3820001 Fax: (0870) 3820002

CONTROL GEAR (ELECTRIC) MANUFRS

Acme Electrical Manufacturing Tottenham Ltd, Tariff Road, Tottenham, London, N17 0EP Tel: (020) 8808 2702 Fax: (020) 8801 9017
Agut Control Gear Ltd, Mosley Street Works, Mosley Street, Blackburn, BB2 3SU Tel: (01254) 683714 Fax: (01254) 663630 E-mail: sales@agut.co.uk
Alex Nangle Electrical Ltd, Unit 3 Oakbank Park Way, Mid Calder, Livingston, West Lothian, EH53 0TH Tel: (01506) 449400 Fax: (01506) 449404 E-mail: info@nangle.co.uk
Anglo American Electrical Co., 67 Bradley Lane, Bolton, BL2 6RA Tel: (01204) 527251 Fax: (01204) 527257 E-mail: angloamerican1@btconnect.com
B E White, Brantwood Road, London, N17 0ED Tel: (020) 8887 1690 Fax: (020) 8884 1865 E-mail: info@bewhite.co.uk
Baldwin & Francis, President Park, Sheffield, S4 7UQ Tel: 0114-286 6000 Fax: 0114-286 6059 E-mail: enquiries@baldwinandfrancis.com
M.C. Bignell Ltd, Horton Road, West Drayton, Middlesex, UB7 8EJ Tel: (01895) 448181 Fax: (01895) 431157
Britannia Enterprises Ltd, Unit 14 Canal Industrial Park, Canal Road, Gravesend, Kent, DA12 2PA Tel: (01474) 328051 Fax: (01474) 320564
Chappell & Tibbert Ltd, 50 Stamford Road, Easton on the Hill, Stamford, Lincolnshire, PE9 3PA Tel: (01780) 751014 Fax: (01780) 751014
Crompton Controls Ltd, Monckton Road, Wakefield, West Yorkshire, WF2 7AL Tel: (01924) 368251 Fax: (01924) 367274 E-mail: sales@cromptoncontrols.co.uk
Crosland Ltd, 502 Bradford Road, Batley, West Yorkshire, WF17 5JX Tel: (01924) 474625 Fax: (01924) 443554 E-mail: sales@crosland-electrical.com
Elecsis Ltd, Yeo Road, Bridgwater, Somerset, TA6 5NA Tel: (01278) 453198 Fax: (01278) 453198 E-mail: chris.pratt@elecsis.com
Giffen Distribution Systems Ltd., Lyon Way, St. Albans, Hertfordshire, AL4 0LQ Tel: (01727) 734600 Fax: (01727) 833680 E-mail: everyone@giffengroup.co.uk
Hte Controls, 4 Cala Trading Estate, Ashton Vale Road, Bristol, BS3 2HA Tel: 0117-966 5925 Fax: 0117-966 1940 E-mail: sales@htecontrols.co.uk
Kay Electrical Swansea Ltd, 345 Llangyfelach Road, Brynhyfryd, Swansea, SA5 9LQ Tel: (01792) 461753 Fax: (01792) 460470 E-mail: kay.electrical@virgin.net
Moeller Holding Ltd, PO Box 35 Gatehouse Close, Aylesbury, Buckinghamshire, HP19 8DH Tel: (01296) 393322 Fax: (01296) 421854 E-mail: marketingl@moeller.co.uk
Northern Electrical Engineering Co. Ltd, 40 Earsham Street, Sheffield, S4 7LS Tel: 0114-275 7020 Fax: 0114-273 0476 E-mail: nengcoltd@tiscali.co.uk
Park Electrical Services, Crown Trading Centre, Clayton Road, Hayes, Middlesex, UB3 1DU Tel: (020) 8813 5889 Fax: (020) 8813 5946 E-mail: info@pes-group.co.uk
Parmley Graham Ltd, Saltmeadows Road, Gateshead, Tyne & Wear, NE8 3BG Tel: 0191-477 4625 Fax: 0191-478 6801 E-mail: hq@parmley-graham.co.uk
Quinton Crane Electronics Ltd, Carnival Way, Castle Donington, Derby, DE74 2HP Tel: (01332) 810955 Fax: (01332) 810475 E-mail: info@systekcontrols.com
Ravenscroft Cameras, 61 Grimsby Road, Cleethorpes, South Humberside, DN35 7AF Tel: (01472) 342007 Fax: (01472) 250504 E-mail: ravenscroftcameras@btinternet.com
Sinelco Ltd, 16 Carlyle Avenue, Hillington Industrial Estate, Glasgow, G52 4XX Tel: 0141-810 1441 Fax: 0141-810 1711
Stroud Switchgear Developments Ltd, Unit 3, Lightpill Trading Estate, Stroud, Gloucestershire, GL5 3LL Tel: (01453) 762709 Fax: (01453) 751977 E-mail: sales@stroud-switchgear.com
Total Electrical Distributors, Crawford Street, Newport, Gwent, NP19 7AY Tel: (01633) 214348 Fax: (01633) 254328
Transtar, Glasgow, G52 4BL Tel: 0141-810 9644 Fax: 0141-810 8642 E-mail: sales@transtargear.co.uk
Vossloh-Schwabe (UK) Ltd, 42 Tanners Drive, Blakelands, Milton Keynes, MK14 5BW Tel: (01908) 517800 Fax: (01908) 517817 E-mail: sales@vsuk.vossloh.com
W F Electrical, Unit 6 Westerton Road, East Mains Industrial Estate, Broxburn, West Lothian, EH52 5AU Tel: (01506) 858833 Fax: (01506) 855257 E-mail: edinburgh.industrial@hagemeyerservicecentre.co.uk
Frank Warren Ltd, Terrace Street, Oldham, OL4 1HQ Tel: 0161-287 8118 Fax: 0161-287 5226 E-mail: sales@fwarren.co.uk
Whippendell Electrical Ltd, 477-479 Whippendell Road, Watford, WD18 7PU Tel: (01923) 228201 Fax: (01923) 228007 E-mail: sales@whippendell-electrical.co.uk
Whippendell Electrical Ltd, 477-479 Whippendell Road, Watford, WD18 7PU Tel: (01923) 228201 Fax: (01923) 228007 E-mail: kevin@wippendale-marine.co.uk

CONTROL HANDLES, AEROSPACE/DEFENCE INDUSTRY

Ultra Electronics Electrics, Kingsditch Lane, Cheltenham, Gloucestershire, GL51 9PG Tel: (01242) 221166 Fax: (01242) 221167 E-mail: admin@ultra-electronics.com

CONTROL INSTRUMENTATION DESIGN SERVICES

Fylde Electronic Laboratories Ltd, 49-51 Fylde Road, Preston, PR1 2XQ Tel: (01772) 257560 Fax: (01772) 821530E-mail: sales@fylde.com
Instrument & Control Services Ltd, Unit 2, Westlake Trading Estate, Canal Lane, Stoke-on-Trent, ST6 4NZ Tel: (01782) 819900 Fax: (01782) 575190 E-mail: admin@icsluk.com

CONTROL INSTRUMENTATION TO SPECIFICATION

Instrument & Control Services Ltd, Unit 2, Westlake Trading Estate, Canal Lane, Stoke-on-Trent, ST6 4NZ Tel: (01782) 819900 Fax: (01782) 575190 E-mail: admin@icsluk.com

CONTROL KNOBS

B U Industrial Components Ltd, Units B2-B5, Tweedale Industrial Estate, Madeley, Telford, Shropshire, TF7 4JR Tel: (01952) 586016 Fax: (01952) 586062
WDS, Richardshaw Road, Grangefield Industrial Estate, Pudsey, West Yorkshire, LS28 6LE Tel: 0113-290 9852 Fax: (0845) 6011173

CONTROL METERING SYSTEMS

DSL Systems Holdings Ltd, Adbolton Hall Adbolton Lane, West Bridgford, Nottingham, NG2 5AS Tel: 0115-981 3700 Fax: 0115-813702 E-mail: mail@dsl-systems.com

CONTROL OF SUBSTANCES HAZARDOUS TO HEALTH (COSHH) ASSESSMENT CONSULTANTS

Duscovent Engineering Ltd, 86 Wellington Road North, Stockport, Cheshire, SK4 1HT Tel: 0161-480 4811 Fax: 0161-480 6503 E-mail: sales@duscovent.co.uk
Fumex Coshh & Service Ltd, 23 Hoyland Road, Sheffield, S3 8AB Tel: 0114-234 1114 Fax: 0114-234 1441 E-mail: info@fumex-coshh.co.uk
▶ L R B Consulting Ltd, 2 Fairmeadows Way, Loughborough, Leicestershire, LE11 2QT Tel: (01509) 550023 Fax: (01509) 550023 E-mail: enquiries@lrbconsulting.co.uk
P & J Dust Extraction Ltd, Otterham Quay, Gillingham, Kent, ME8 8NA Tel: 01634 233933
▶ Safety Simply, 23 Cock Close Road, Yaxley, Peterborough, PE7 3HJ Tel: (0845) 2600710 Fax: (0845) 2600711 E-mail: info@safetysimplified.co.uk

CONTROL PANEL ASSEMBLY

▶ BCM Technologies Ltd, Battle Court, Mill Lane Boroughbridge, York, YO51 9LH Tel: (01423) 324842 Fax: (08701) 38757 E-mail: martin.henry@battlecourt.fsnet.co.uk
▶ J M G Systems Ltd, 68a Derry Road, Omagh, County Tyrone, BT78 5ED Tel: (028) 8224 4131 E-mail: info@jmgsystems.co.uk
▶ Randall & Hodgkinson, The Old Stables, Queens Square, Kirkby Lonsdale, Carnforth, Lancashire, LA6 2AZ Tel: (01524) 271136 Fax: (01524) 271136
▶ Sandford Electrical Services, Unit 2, Kelpatrick Road, Cippenham, Slough, SL1 6BW Tel: (01628) 668 808 E-mail: sales@sandfordelectrical.co.uk

CONTROL PANEL CABINETS,

See also headings for Enclosures etc

Archer Woodnutt Ltd, Pit Lane, Talke Pits, Stoke-on-Trent, ST7 1UH Tel: (01782) 785016 Fax: (01782) 776273 E-mail: info@archerwoodnutt.com
B & J Controls, Spa Fields Industrial Estate, New Street, Slaithwaite, Huddersfield, HD7 5BB Tel: (01484) 843449 Fax: (01484) 842058
Dacon Fabrications Ltd, Dukesway, Team Valley Trading Estate, Gateshead, Tyne & Wear, NE11 0PZ Tel: 0191-482 5464 Fax: 0191-482 5463 E-mail: info@daconfab.co.uk
Dero Fabrication Ltd, Unit 67, Blackpole Trading Estate West, Blackpole Road, Worcester, WR3 8TJ Tel: (01905) 455199 Fax: (01905) 754152 E-mail: sales@dero.co.uk
Electrical Cabinets (Bradford) Ltd, 2 Essex Street, Wakefield Road, Bradford, West Yorkshire, BD4 7PG Tel: (01274) 729076 Fax: (01274) 732297
H C Controls Ltd, Wetherby Close, Portrack Interchange Business Park, Stockton-on-Tees, Cleveland, TS18 2SL Tel: (01642) 671681 Fax: (01642) 676100 E-mail: admin@hccontrol.co.uk
I & M Controls Ltd, 75 Villa Street, Birmingham, B19 2XL Tel: 0121-551 7877 Fax: 0121-554 3846 E-mail: sales@iandmcontrols.co.uk
Lall Engineering Ltd, 343 Bedworth Road, Longford, Coventry, CV6 6BN Tel: (024) 7636 4904 Fax: (024) 7636 2083
M J Metalcraft Ltd, 32-34 Sampson Road North, Birmingham, B11 1BL Tel: 0121-771 3711 Fax: 0121-771 3766 E-mail: enquiries@mjmetalcraftltd.co.uk
Meade Bros Ltd, Eckersall Road, Birmingham, B38 8SS Tel: 0121-486 2291 Fax: 0121-486 2276 E-mail: meadebrothersltd@aol.com

CONTROL PANEL CABINETS –

continued

Metal Cabinets Sales Ltd, Moorfield Road Estate, Yeadon, Leeds, LS19 7BN Tel: 0113-250 8082 Fax: 0113-250 5138 E-mail: person@metalcabinets.co.uk

MK Air Controls Ltd, Vimy Road, Leighton Buzzard, Bedfordshire, LU7 1ED Tel: (01525) 374157 Fax: (01525) 374411 E-mail: sales@mkaircontrols.com

MSK Fabrication, Unit 4 Orchard Park Industrial Estate, Sandiacre, Nottingham, NG10 5BP Tel: 0115-949 1500 Fax: 0115-949 1600 E-mail: info@mskfab.co.uk

Polham Controls Ltd, Block E Bath Road Business Park, Bath Road, Bridgwater, Somerset, TA6 4SZ Tel: (01278) 433433 Fax: (01278) 436999 E-mail: polham.controls@btinternet.com

Prolec Automation Services, A5 Arkwright Suite Coppull Enterprise Centre, Mill Lane, Coppull, Chorley, Lancashire, PR7 5BW Tel: (01257) 470460 Fax: (01257) 470469 E-mail: smprolec@tiscali.co.uk

Shearfab Ltd, Oldgate, St. Michaels Industrial Estate, Widnes, Cheshire, WA8 8TL Tel: 0151-420 5200 Fax: 0151-420 5190 E-mail: info@shearfab.co.uk

Vangard Ltd, Schofield Street, Royton, Oldham, OL2 6PT Tel: 0161-652 1249 Fax: 0161-678 6790

CONTROL PANEL COMPONENT MANUFRS

A A Electric UK Ltd, Witty Street, Hull, HU3 4TT Tel: (01482) 229880 Fax: (01482) 589644 E-mail: sales@aaelectric.co.uk

Argosafe Ltd, Unit 11 Dawsons Lane, Barwell, Leicester, LE9 8BE Tel: (01455) 844801 Fax: (01455) 850280 E-mail: argosafe@btconnect.com

Central Southern Security Ltd, Station Street, Lymington, Hampshire, SO41 3BA Tel: (01590) 677366 Fax: (01590) 678024 E-mail: enquiries@central southern security.co.uk

Control Stockholders & Properties Ltd, Perry Road, Witham, Essex, CM8 3AS Tel: (01376) 513348 Fax: (01376) 513361 E-mail: mail@control-engineering.ltd.uk

Cranleigh Control Co., Unit 30 Hewitts Industrial Estate, Elmbridge Road, Cranleigh, Surrey, GU6 8LW Tel: (01483) 272663 Fax: (01483) 272663 E-mail: mail@cranleighcontrol.co.uk

Engineering Electrics (Wilmslow) Ltd, 67 Oldfield Road, Sale, Cheshire, M33 2AP Tel: 0161-973 8230 Fax: 0161-962 8648

Qed Industrial Controls plc, Premier House, Randalls Road, Leatherhead, Surrey, KT22 7LB Tel: (01372) 378666 Fax: (01372) 379667 E-mail: sales@qedindustrial.co.uk

Thomas & Whitley, 3 Wortley Moor La Trading Estate, Leeds, LS12 4HX Tel: 0113-279 8880 Fax: 0113-231 0479 E-mail: sales@thomasandwhitley.co.uk

Ucontrol Ltd, Units 24-25, Strawberry Lane Industrial Estate, Strawberry Lane, Willenhall, West Midlands, WV13 3RS Tel: (01902) 601441 Fax: (01902) 602503 E-mail: infr@ucontroll.com

Unitech Engineering Services Ltd, The Old Dairy, Ball Hill, Newbury, Berkshire, RG20 0NY Tel: (01635) 253997 Fax: (01635) 255180 E-mail: unitech@unitech-engineering.co.uk

Uttley & Thompson Electronics Ltd, 90 Abbey Street, Accrington, Lancashire, BB5 1EE Tel: (01254) 384850 Fax: (01254) 395474 E-mail: uttleyandthompson@farmore.net

CONTROL PANEL MANUFRS

A B B Ltd, Hanover Place, Sunderland, SR4 6BY Tel: 0191-514 4555 Fax: 0191-514 5505

A C D C Automated Systems Ltd, Unit 1 Horizon Park, Valley Way, Swansea Enterprise Park, Swansea, SA6 8RG Tel: (01792) 771440 Fax: (01792) 796916 E-mail: enquiries@automatedsystems.co.uk

A F Switchgear & Control Panels Ltd, Nunn Brook Road, Huthwaite, Sutton-in-Ashfield, Nottinghamshire, NG17 2HU Tel: (01623) 555600 Fax: (01623) 555800 E-mail: e-mail@afswitchgear.co.uk

A K Controls, Unit 17 Fleetsbridge Business Park, Upton Road, Poole, Dorset, BH17 7AF Tel: (01202) 660061 Fax: (01202) 660200 E-mail: office@akcontrols.com

A L P Electrical Ltd, 70 St. Marks Road, Maidenhead, Berkshire, SL6 6DW Tel: (01628) 633998 Fax: (01628) 760981 E-mail: alp@alpelectrical.com

A T S Panels Ltd, Unit B, Lammas Courtyard, Weldon Industrial Estate, Corby, Northamptonshire, NN17 5EZ Tel: (01536) 407474 Fax: (01536) 409443

Actemium, Meteor Business Park, Cheltenham Road East, Gloucester, GL2 9QL Tel: (01452) 713222 Fax: (01452) 713444 E-mail: actemium@actemium.co.uk

Active Controls, 6 Court Yard Workshops, Bath Street, Market Harborough, Leicestershire, LE16 9EW Tel: (01858) 466504 Fax: (01858) 463650 E-mail: activecontrols@ukonline.co.uk

Acton Delta Ltd, Wombrook Business Centre, Giggetty Lane, Wombourne, Wolverhampton, WV5 8LZ Tel: (01902) 326563 Fax: (01902) 326564 E-mail: mail@actondelta.co.uk

Agut Control Gear Ltd, Mosley Street Works, Mosley Street, Blackburn, BB2 3SU Tel: (01254) 683714 Fax: (01254) 663630 E-mail: sales@agut.co.uk

Aird, Walker & Ralston Ltd, 12F Lawson Street, Kilmarnock, Ayrshire, KA1 3JP Tel: (01563) 522236 Fax: (01563) 521304 E-mail: sales@airdwalker.co.uk

Alfa Electric Ltd, 14 Burgess Road, Ivyhouse Industrial Estate, Hastings, East Sussex, TN35 4NR Tel: (01424) 424040 Fax: (01424) 424040 E-mail: sales@alfaelectric.co.uk

Allam Marine Ltd, 10-12 Lime Street, Hull, HU8 7AB Tel: (01482) 224861 Fax: (01482) 226680

▶ Alpha Beta Controls Ltd, 14 Coles Lane, Sutton Coldfield, West Midlands, B72 1NE Tel: 0121-321 3844 Fax: 0121-321 3866 E-mail: sales@alphabetacontrols.co.uk

Amber Programmable Design Ltd, Newbie, Annan, Dumfriesshire, DG12 5QJ Tel: (01461) 206000 Fax: (01461) 206200 E-mail: info@apd-ltd.com

Amos Electronics, 4 Little Balmer, Buckingham Industrial Estate, Buckingham, MK18 1TF Tel: (01280) 817877 Fax: (01280) 814140 E-mail: purchasing@paramountelectronics.co.uk

Andross Electrics Ltd, Unit 12 Twyford Business Centre, London Road, Bishop's Stortford, Hertfordshire, CM23 3YT Tel: (01279) 657661 Fax: (01279) 506164 E-mail: sales@andross.net

Annicom Electronic Equipment Component, Highview, High Street, Bordon, Hampshire, GU35 0AX Tel: (01420) 487788 Fax: (01420) 487799 E-mail: sale@annicom.com

Apsley Controls Ltd, Unit 14 Kents Avenue, Hemel Hempstead, Hertfordshire, HP3 9XH Tel: (01442) 235464 Fax: (01442) 249479 E-mail: martinturnbull@virgin.net

Arden Control Systems Ltd, Arden Street, New Mills, High Peak, Derbyshire, SK22 4NS Tel: (01663) 746060 Fax: (01663) 746189 E-mail: sales@ardencontrolsystems.co.uk

Ashtronics Ltd, 119 Meldreth Road, Whaddon, Royston, Hertfordshire, SG8 5RS Tel: (01223) 208308 Fax: (01223) 208308 E-mail: ashtronics@aol.com

Autolux Control Panel Mnfrs, Sizers Court, Yeadon, Leeds, LS19 7DP Tel: 0113-250 1405 Fax: 0113-250 1449 E-mail: autolux@btconnect.com

Avw Controls Ltd, Finningham Road, Rickinghall, Diss, Norfolk, IP22 1LT Tel: (01379) 898340 Fax: (01379) 898386 E-mail: info@avw.co.uk

B E S Controls Ltd, Unit 7c Silver End Industrial Estate, Brettell Lane, Brierley Hill, West Midlands, DY5 3LA Tel: (01384) 75000 Fax: (01384) 74000 E-mail: bescontrol@aol.com

B & G Controls Ltd, Broadoak Enterprise Village, Broadoak Road, Sittingbourne, Kent, ME9 8AQ Tel: (01795) 423554 Fax: (01795) 428873 E-mail: sales@bt-controls.co.uk

B & J Controls, Spa Fields Industrial Estate, New Street, Slaithwaite, Huddersfield, HD7 5BB Tel: (01484) 843449 Fax: (01484) 842058

B K Automations, 4 Talisman Business Centre, Duncan Road, Park Gate, Southampton, SO31 7GA Tel: (01489) 582712 Fax: (01489) 583294 E-mail: bkautomamation@tinyworld.co.uk

B T J Drives & Controls Ltd, Heath Holdings, Stone Heath, Leigh, Stoke-on-Trent, ST10 4PG Tel: (01889) 505315 Fax: (01889) 505604 E-mail: enquiries@btjdrives.co.uk

M.C. Bignell Ltd, Horton Road, West Drayton, Middlesex, UB7 8EJ Tel: (01895) 448181 Fax: (01895) 431157

Bonus Plug In Systems, Citadel Trading Park, Citadel Way, Hull, HU9 1TQ Tel: (01482) 313700 Fax: (01482) 588753

Bryant Electrical Ltd, 3 Shamel Business Centre, Commissioners Road, Rochester, Kent, ME2 4HQ Tel: (01634) 297211 Fax: (01634) 226863 E-mail: bryant.electrical@bryantelectrical.com

C H S Switchgear Ltd, 3 Batford Mill Industrial Estate, Lower Luton Road, Harpenden, Hertfordshire, AL5 5BZ Tel: (01582) 766008 Fax: (01582) 461386 E-mail: mailbox@chsswitchgear.co.uk

C L Electrical Controls Ltd, Unit 1 Kendleshire Farm Down, Road Winterbourne, Bristol, BS36 1AU Tel: (01454) 250555 Fax: (01454) 250540 E-mail: enquiries@clelectricalcontrols.co.uk

C N Controls Ltd, Thorpe Way Indust Estate, Thorpe Way, Banbury, Oxfordshire, OX16 4SP Tel: (01295) 266704 Fax: (01295) 266704 E-mail: sales@cncontrols.co.uk

Caledon Controls Ltd, Unit 2, Block 4, Castlehill Industrial Estate, Carluke, Lanarkshire, ML8 5UF Tel: (01555) 773355 Fax: (01555) 772212 E-mail: info@caledoncontrols.co.uk

▶ Campbell Control Services, Dalhousie Business Park, Carrington Road, Bonnyrigg, Midlothian, EH19 3HY Tel: 0131-660 4791 Fax: 0131-660 6793 E-mail: admin@campbellcontrols.com

Campbell Control Services, Dalhousie Business Park, Carrington Road, Bonnyrigg, Midlothian, EH19 3HY Tel: 0131-660 4791 Fax: 0131-660 6793

Canham Controls Ltd, 14 Dodson Way, Peterborough, PE1 5XJ Tel: (01733) 894489 Fax: (01733) 894488 E-mail: canhamcontrols@compuserve.com

Cheltenham Controls, 183 Westgate Street, Gloucester, GL1 2RN Tel: (01452) 503390 Fax: (01452) 503630 E-mail: info.cheltcontrols@dis-ltd.co.uk

Circle Control & Design Systems Ltd, Unit 8 The Poplars Industrial Estate, Wetherby Road, Boroughbridge, York, YO51 9HS Tel: (01423) 323900 Fax: (01423) 323304

Ciretech Ltd, Unit 4 Huffwood Trading Estate, Billingshurst, West Sussex, RH14 9UR Tel: (01403) 784855 Fax: (01403) 783000

Coltan Electronics Ltd, Unit D16-17 Boston Industrial Centre, Norfolk Street, Boston, Lincolnshire, PE21 9HG Tel: (01205) 351027 Fax: (01205) 354296 E-mail: coltan@eletron.fsbusiness.co.uk

Compere Systems Ltd, Ivy Street, Birkenhead, Merseyside, CH41 5EE Tel: 0151-647 7457 Fax: 0151-666 2569 E-mail: davidj@comperesystems.com

Computer Aid, 4 Hothfield Road, Rainham, Gillingham, Kent, ME8 8BJ Tel: (01634) 262534 Fax: (01634) 267215 E-mail: denise@computer-aid.co.uk

Conard Systems & Engineering Ltd, Unit 6d Lowick Close, Newby Road Industrial Estate, Hazel Grove, Stockport, Cheshire, SK7 5ED Tel: 0161-456 5285

Control Applications Ltd, Unit 12, Steeton Grove, Steeton, West Yorkshire, BD20 6TT Tel: (01535) 650890 Fax: (01535) 658824 E-mail: info@controlapplications.co.uk

Control Design, Unit Z Paddock Wood Distribution Centre, Paddock Wood, Tonbridge, Kent, TN12 6UU Tel: (01892) 836350 Fax: (01892) 837292 E-mail: controldesign@btconnect.com

Control Stockholders & Properties Ltd, Perry Road, Witham, Essex, CM8 3AS Tel: (01376) 513348 Fax: (01376) 513361 E-mail: mail@control-engineering.ltd.uk

Controline Ltd, Crown Works, Dewsbury Road, Elland, West Yorkshire, HX5 9BG Tel: (01422) 311993 Fax: (01422) 311818 E-mail: info@controline.co.uk

Cord Controls Ltd, 29 Wigston Street, Countesthorpe, Leicester, LE8 5RP Tel: 0116-277 7396 Fax: 0116-277 7396 E-mail: cord.controls@btclick.com

Cranford Controls Systems Ltd, Unit 3 Pattenden La Buis Centre, Marden, Tonbridge, Kent, TN12 9QS Tel: (01622) 833300 Fax: (01622) 833311 E-mail: sales@cranfordcontrol.co.uk

▶ Crawford Controls Ltd, Unit D7 Templeborough Business Park, Bow Bridge Close, Rotherham, South Yorkshire, S60 1BY Tel: (01709) 837201 Fax: (01709) 839109 E-mail: info@crawfordcontrols.com

Crescent Sheet Metal Co., 6 Wood End No 2 Mill, Manchester Road, Mossley, Ashton-under-Lyne, Lancashire, OL5 9RR Tel: (01457) 836518 Fax: (01457) 833611

D B Brooks Electrical Engineers Ltd, Sinclair Close, Heanor, Derbyshire, DE75 7SP Tel: (01773) 763444 Fax: (01773) 530332 E-mail: admin@dbbrooks.co.uk

D Benson & Co. Ltd, Normanton Industrial Estate, Normanton, West Yorkshire, WF6 1QS Tel: (01924) 894162 Fax: (01924) 896518 E-mail: info@dbensoncontrols.co.uk

D D C Control Systems Ltd, Unit 1 Broadwyn Trading Estate, Waterfall Lane, Cradley Heath, West Midlands, B64 6PS Tel: 0121-561 3312 Fax: 0121-561 3541 E-mail: ian.biddle@ddccontrolsystems.co.uk

D P Fabrications Ltd, Chantry Road, Woburn Road Industrial Estate, Kempston, Bedford, MK42 7HU Tel: (01234) 840166 Fax: (01234) 840177 E-mail: sales@dpfabs.co.uk

D S C Controls Ltd, 8 Lea Green Business Park, Eurolink, St. Helens, Merseyside, WA9 4TR Tel: (01744) 820777 Fax: (01744) 820707 E-mail: derek@dsc-control.freeserve.co.uk

Dacon Fabrications Ltd, Dukesway, Team Valley Trading Estate, Gateshead, Tyne & Wear, NE11 0PZ Tel: 0191-482 5464 Fax: 0191-482 5463 E-mail: info@daconfab.co.uk

Dacs Electrical Ltd, Old Fire Station, Church Street, Connah's Quay, Deeside, Clwyd, CH5 4AS Tel: (01244) 834100 Fax: (01244) 831858 E-mail: sales@dacselectrical.co.uk

Daikin Airconditioning UK Ltd, The Heights, Brooklands, Weybridge, Surrey, KT13 0NY Tel: (0845) 6419000 Fax: (0845) 6419009 E-mail: marketing@daikin.co.uk

Davies Control Systems, Unit 20 South Pontypool Industrial Park, Panteg Way, New Inn, Pontypool, Gwent, NP4 0LS Tel: (01495) 764094 Fax: (01495) 756237 E-mail: info@daviescontrolsystems.co.uk

Delta Designs Systems Ltd, The Green, Tendring, Clacton-on-Sea, Essex, CO16 0BU Tel: (01255) 830355 Fax: (01255) 830356 E-mail: info@deltadesignsystems.co.uk

Delton Central Services Ltd, 62-70 Camden Street, Birmingham, B1 3DP Tel: 0121-233 1051 Fax: 0121-236 6178 E-mail: sales@deltongroup.co.uk

James Dring Power Plant Ltd, 8 Eagle Road, Quarry Hill Industrial Estate, Ilkeston, Derbyshire, DE7 4RB Tel: 0115-944 0072 Fax: 0115-944 0235 E-mail: enquiries@jamesdring.co.uk

E P Systems Ltd, Media House, 21 East Ways Industrial Estate, Witham, Essex, CM8 3YQ Tel: (01376) 531380 Fax: (01376) 531361 E-mail: neil-rowe@epsystems.co.uk

Easthill Ltd, 1 Martinfield Business Centre, Martinfield, Welwyn Garden City, Hertfordshire, AL7 1HG Tel: (01707) 377355 Fax: (01707) 377358 E-mail: sales@easthill.co.uk

Ebs Panels, 144b Leek Road, Endon, Stoke-on-Trent, ST9 9EW Tel: (01782) 503386 Fax: (01782) 502265 E-mail: ebspanels@btconnect.com

Eca Contracts Ltd, 3 Fortnum Close, Kitts Green, Birmingham, B33 0LG Tel: 0121-785 4100 Fax: 0121-783 3596 E-mail: info@e-c-a.co.uk

Electraspec Control Panel Mnfrs, 4 Shell Corner Industrial Estate, Long Lane, Halesowen, West Midlands, B62 9LD Tel: 0121-559 9335 Fax: 0121-559 9362

▶ Electrical Control Panels Ltd, Unit 17 Midway Centre Bridge St Industrial Estate, Bridge Street, Clay Cross, Chesterfield, Derbyshire, S45 9NU Tel: (01246) 865770 Fax: (01246) 865770

Electrical Control Systems, Cliff Nook Lane, Newark, Nottinghamshire, NG24 1LY Tel: (01636) 707309 Fax: (01636) 640003 E-mail: sales@ecscontroll.co.uk

Electrical Design & Automation Ltd, The Old Bakery, Main Road, Pontesbury, Shrewsbury, SY5 0RR Tel: (01743) 791986 Fax: (01743) 791555 E-mail: eda1987@aol.com

Electrical Design & Manufacturing Co. Ltd, Station Street, Whetstone, Leicester, LE8 6JS Tel: 0116-286 2165

Electrical & Mechanical Controls Ltd, 8 Europa Way, Martineau Lane, Norwich, NR1 2EN Tel: (01603) 625535 Fax: (01603) 625030 E-mail: emc@norwichlife.co.uk

Electron Systems Ltd, Unit 5b Drum Industrial Estate, Chester le Street, County Durham, DH2 1SS Tel: 0191-492 2007 Fax: 0191-492 2009 E-mail: sales@electronsystems.com

Eltek Systems Ltd, Eltek House, Nene Valley Business Park, Oundle, Peterborough, PE8 4HN Tel: (01832) 277590 Fax: (01832) 273941 E-mail: info@eltek-systems.com

Embedded Controls Ltd, Loyal Cottage, Alyth, Blairgowrie, Perthshire, PH11 8JG Tel: (01828) 633554 Fax: (01828) 633554

Environmental Control Systems (Anglia) Ltd, Pinelands Industrial Estate, Holt Road, Horsford, Norwich, NR10 3EB Tel: (01603) 890632 Fax: (01603) 891186 E-mail: enquiries@ecs-anglia.co.uk

F1 Manufacturing, 350 Melton Road, Leicester, LE4 7SL Tel: 0116-268 8484 Fax: 0116-268 8489 E-mail: sales@f1manufacturing.com

Fairburn Engineering Ltd, 73-79 Clarence Street, Hull, HU9 1DH Tel: (01482) 323352 Fax: (01482) 229873 E-mail: sales@fairburneng.co.uk

Fairfield Controlec Ltd, London House, King Edward Street, Grimsby, South Humberside, DN31 3LA Tel: (01472) 268141 Fax: (01472) 243049 E-mail: sales@fairfield-controlec.co.uk

Fenton Industrial Ltd, 291 Edge Lane, Droylsden, Manchester, M43 6BS Tel: 0161-370 1568 Fax: 0161-370 9116 E-mail: info@fentonindustrial.co.uk

Frostechnic, Power Park, Station Approach, Banbury, Oxfordshire, OX16 5AB Tel: (01295) 266500 Fax: (01295) 275434 E-mail: info@frostechnic.com

▶ Fulbourn Medical, 5 Station Yard, Wilbraham Road, Fulbourn, Cambridge, CB21 5ET Tel: (01223) 880909 Fax: (01223) 880078 E-mail: info@fulbournmedical.com

G K Switchgear Ltd, 4 Colts Holm Road, Old Wolverton, Milton Keynes, MK12 5QD Tel: (01908) 225777 Fax: (01908) 225818 E-mail: rjbgks@aol.com

G N Systems, Undershore Works, Brookside Road, Bolton, BL2 2SE Tel: (01204) 361533 Fax: (01204) 382879 E-mail: gnsystems@provider.co.uk

Gainsborough Electronic Controls Ltd, Unit 6 Warnford Industrial Estate, Clayton Road, Hayes, Middlesex, UB3 1BQ Tel: (020) 8573 9611 Fax: (020) 8569 2426 E-mail: info@gainsborough-controls.co.uk

Gainsborough Industrial Controls Ltd, Foxby House, Foxby Hill, Gainsborough, Lincolnshire, DN21 1PN Tel: (01427) 611885 Fax: (01427) 611883 E-mail: sales@gic.uk.net

General Panel Systems Ltd, 1-2 Leicester Street, Bedminster, Bristol, BS3 4DE Tel: 0117-953 1500 Fax: 0117-947 1700 E-mail: info@gpspanels.co.uk

Gilman Control Systems Ltd, 15 Bridge Gate Business Park, Gatehouse Way, Aylesbury, Buckinghamshire, HP19 8XN Tel: (01296) 434810 Fax: (01296) 434847 E-mail: sales@gilman-controls.co.uk

Global Power & Control Systems Ltd, Unit 3 Hill Farm Barns, School Road, Henley, Ipswich, IP6 0SA Tel: (01473) 785057 Fax: (01473) 785059 E-mail: sales@global-panels.co.uk

Golco Automation Systems, Unit 323-325, Hartlebury Trading Estate, Hartlebury, Kidderminster, Worcestershire, DY10 4JB Tel: (01299) 253009 Fax: (01299) 253013 E-mail: sales@golco.co.uk

Gordon Parkes, 1a Johnson Road, Birmingham, B23 6PU Tel: 0121-377 7524 Fax: 0121-377 7524 E-mail: gordon306@tiscali.co.uk

Graphic Controls, Southcombe House, Southcombe, Chipping Norton, Oxfordshire, OX7 5QH Tel: (01608) 646303 Fax: (01608) 646304 E-mail: rickfordham@btconnect.com

Gretton Ward Electrical Ltd, 112 Peckham Rye, London, SE15 4HA Tel: (020) 7639 3275 Fax: (020) 7358 1389 E-mail: grettonward@lineone.net

H C Controls Ltd, Wetherby Close, Portrack Interchange Business Park, Stockton-on-Tees, Cleveland, TS18 2SL Tel: (01642) 671681 Fax: (01642) 676100 E-mail: admin@hccontrol.co.uk

Halcyon Drives Ltd, 7 Butler Way, Stanningley, Pudsey, West Yorkshire, LS28 6EA Tel: 0113-236 1509 Fax: 0113-239 3776 E-mail: sales@halcyon-drives.co.uk

Hech Engineering Ltd, Barrington Industrial Estate, Bedlington, Northumberland, NE22 7DQ Tel: (01670) 823588 Fax: (01670) 826744 E-mail: hecheng@aol.com

CONTROL PANEL MANUFRS - *continued*

Howarth Switchgear Ltd, Finlas Street, Cowlairs Industrial Estate, Glasgow, G22 5DT Tel: 0141-557 3553 Fax: 0141-558 0614 E-mail: sales@howarthswitchgear.co.uk

Howdens Signs Ltd, 94 Burley Road, Leeds, LS3 1JP Tel: 0113-245 7752 Fax: 0113-242 6993 E-mail: sales@howdenssigns.com

Huggett Electrical Ltd, Twerton Mill, Lower Bristol Road, Bath, BA2 1EW Tel: (01225) 426271 Fax: (01225) 448154 E-mail: mail@huggettelectrical.co.uk

I & M Controls Ltd, 75 Villa Street, Birmingham, B19 2XL Tel: 0121-551 7877 Fax: 0121-554 3846 E-mail: sales@iandmcontrols.co.uk

I P A Controls, 30 Craftmans Way, East Goscote, Leicester, LE7 3SL Tel: 0116-269 7100 Fax: 0116-269 6880

Ica Solutions Ltd, 1 115 Loverock Road, Reading, RG30 1DZ Tel: 0118-939 3663 Fax: 0118-939 3653 E-mail: info@icasolutions.co.uk

Icel Group, Ashmill Bus Park, Ashford Road, Lenham, Maidstone, Kent, ME17 2GQ Tel: (01622) 858200 Fax: (01622) 850065 E-mail: sales@icel-group.co.uk

Ies Pca Ltd, The Millcourt Centre, Pleasley Vale, Mansfield, Nottinghamshire, NG19 8RL Tel: (01623) 819319 Fax: (01623) 819329 E-mail: info@iespca.com

Industrial Switchgear Ltd, 8 Howard Road, Park Farm Industrial Estate, Redditch, Worcestershire, B98 7SE Tel: (01527) 527346 Fax: (01527) 510186 E-mail: industrialswitch@btconnect.com

Intech Automation Ltd, Willow Hall Works Cote Hill, Halifax, West Yorkshire, HX2 7LZ Tel: (01422) 355885 Fax: (01422) 355885

Integrated Control Systems Ltd, Millars Business Centre, Fishponds Close, Wokingham, Berkshire, RG41 2TZ Tel: 0118-977 2226 Fax: 0118-977 4999 E-mail: sales@icsbms.co.uk

Inter Lec Ltd, Holland Hill, Low Road, North Wheatley, Retford, Nottinghamshire, DN22 9DS Tel: (01427) 880021 Fax: (01427) 880011

J B Systems Ltd, 8 Bridgegate Business Park, Gatehouse Way, Gatehouse Industrial Area, Aylesbury, Buckinghamshire, HP19 8XN Tel: (01296) 489967 Fax: (01296) 393515 E-mail: info@jbsystems.co.uk

J N Building Services Ltd, Cooper Yard, Old Cider Works, Abbotskerswell, Newton Abbot, Devon, TQ12 5NF Tel: (01626) 352056 Fax: (01626) 363599 E-mail: enquiries@jnbuildingservices.com

J W & E Morris & Son Ltd, South Road, Bridgend Industrial Estate, Bridgend, Mid Glamorgan, CF31 3RB Tel: (01656) 653705 Fax: (01656) 767187 E-mail: sales@jwmorris.co.uk

John Pipkin Control Panel Manufacturers, Uveco Business Centre, Dock Road, Birkenhead, Merseyside, CH41 1FD Tel: 0151-630 5577 Fax: 0151-630 5577 E-mail: johnpipkin@tiscali.co.uk

K A B Systems Ltd, Lansdowne Road, Chadderton, Oldham, OL9 9EG Tel: 0161-678 6367 Fax: 0161-678 6979 E-mail: sales@kabsystems.co.uk

K C Hickson Ltd, 89-91 Rolfe Street, Smethwick, West Midlands, B66 2AY Tel: 0121-558 1884 Fax: 0121-558 0017 E-mail: kchickson@george-jones-engineering.co.uk

K P Electromech, Unit 3 Cross Hill, Codnor, Ripley, Derbyshire, DE5 9SQ Tel: (01773) 748270 Fax: (01773) 743612

Kestral Controls Ltd, 3 Garrell Road, Kilsyth, Glasgow, G65 9JX Tel: (01236) 821564 Fax: (01236) 825676 E-mail: sales@kestralcontrols.co.uk

Kim Systems Ltd, 4 Brook Road, Bicton Industrial Park, Kimbolton, Huntingdon, Cambridgeshire, PE28 0LR Tel: (01480) 860730 Fax: (01480) 861251

▶ King Stag Ltd, 6 Hartfoot Close, Melcombe Bingham, Dorchester, Dorset, DT2 7TY Tel: (01963) 363611 Fax: (08700) 940778 E-mail: sales@kingstag.com

Kone plc, 137-145 South Liberty Lane, Bristol, BS3 2TL Tel: 0117-966 2741 Fax: 0117-963 6310

L C A Controls Ltd, 1 Boleyn Court, Manor Park, Runcorn, Cheshire, WA7 1SR Tel: (01928) 579677 Fax: (01928) 579086 E-mail: lcacontrols@btinternet.com

Lacegold Electrical & Mechanical Services, 1 Aerial House, School Aycliffe, Newton Aycliffe, County Durham, DL5 6QF Tel: (01325) 315316 Fax: (01325) 329940 E-mail: lacegoldems@upexgroup.co.uk

Leicester Switch & Control Co. Ltd, Ross Walk, Leicester, LE4 5HA Tel: 0116-299 9277 Fax: 0116-299 9278 E-mail: lsc@lsandc.co.uk

Lemsford Mill Controls Ltd, 5 Alders Court, Welwyn Garden City, Hertfordshire, AL7 1LT Tel: (01707) 334833 Fax: (01707) 328266

Lilleson Engineering Ltd, Unit 12 Brookside Court, Parkgate, Rotherham, South Yorkshire, S62 6NX Tel: (01709) 371188 Fax: (01709) 378232 E-mail: sales@lilleson.co.uk

Lintott Control System Ltd, Units 3, 5, 7, &9, Jarrold Way, Bowthorpe Industrial Estate, Norwich, NR5 9JD Tel: (01603) 201201 Fax: (01603) 749118

Lion Lift Controls Ltd, Littleton Mill, Chew Road, Winford, Bristol, BS40 8HJ Tel: (01275) 332515 Fax: (01275) 333085 E-mail: sales@lionliftcontrols.co.uk

▶ Lloret Controls Systems Ltd, 24 Ullswater Crescent, Coulsdon, Surrey, CR5 2HR Tel: (020) 8410 4600 Fax: (020) 8660 5469

Lloyd Morris Electrical Ltd, Unit 1 Pandy Industrial Estate, Plas Acton Road, Wrexham, Clwyd, LL11 2UD Tel: (01978) 291505 Fax: (01978) 365433 E-mail: enquiries@lloydmorris.co.uk

Loxton Installations Ltd, Unit 14 Mill Hall Business Estate, Mill Hall, Aylesford, Kent, ME20 7JZ Tel: (01622) 716131 Fax: (01622) 719217 E-mail: info@loxtons.com

Lymm Engraving, 199 Liverpool Road, Cadishead, Manchester, M44 5XH Tel: 0161-775 7625 Fax: 0161-775 7247 E-mail: enquires@lymmengraving.co.uk

M R P Control Ltd, 4 Crown Avenue, Dukestown, Tredegar, Gwent, NP22 4EE Tel: (01495) 726430 Fax: (01495) 718623

Magpie Computer Developments Ltd, The Old Telephone Exchange, Gnosall, Stafford, ST20 0EX Tel: (01785) 823315 E-mail: dtweed@magpiecd.co.uk

Main Systems Ltd, Beach Road, Newhaven, East Sussex, BN9 0BX Tel: (01273) 612000 Fax: (01273) 514324 E-mail: newhaven@main-systems.co.uk

Master Control UK Ltd, Loughborough Motorway Trading Estate, Gelders Hall Road, Shepshed, Loughborough, Leicestershire, LE12 9QX Tel: (01509) 650750 Fax: (01509) 600075 E-mail: info@mastercontrol.co.uk

Mercian Electric, 79-93 Ratcliffe Road, Sileby, Loughborough, Leicestershire, LE12 7PU Tel: (01509) 816181 Fax: (01509) 816060

Micaline Electrical Systems Ltd, Unit 9, Block B Wednesbury Trading Estate, Darlaston Road, Wednesbury, West Midlands, WS10 7JN Tel: 0121-556 5194 Fax: 0121-556 4953

Mictell Hillpress, Victoria House, 18 Dalston Gardens, Stanmore, Middlesex, HA7 1BU Tel: (020) 8905 0008 Fax: (020) 8732 2848

Midland Control & Automation, 13 Industrial Estate, Sanders Road, Bromsgrove, Worcestershire, B61 7DG Tel: (01527) 574224 Fax: (01527) 574225 E-mail: johnmca@fsbdial.co.uk

Midvale Electrical Engineering Co. Ltd, 20 Butlers Leap, Rugby, Warwickshire, CV21 3RQ Tel: (01788) 543216 Fax: (01788) 540899 E-mail: sales@midvale-electrical.com

Mitchell & Hewitt Ltd, Ascot Drive, Derby, DE24 8GZ Tel: (01332) 332177 Fax: (01332) 374769 E-mail: admin@mitchellandhewitt.co.uk

Mobile Electro Service Ltd, Units 1-2 Buntsford Park Road, Bromsgrove, Worcestershire, B60 3DX Tel: (01527) 579795 Fax: (01527) 579963 E-mail: sales@mesuk.co.uk

Modatec, Unit 14 Orchard Business Park, Cottismore Farm, Kingsclere, Newbury, Berkshire, RG20 4SY Tel: (01635) 291968 Fax: (01635) 291970 E-mail: david-lancaster@btconnect.com

Moorfield Control Systems Ltd, Unit 17/18 Ashbrooke Park, Parkside Lane, Leeds, LS11 5SF Tel: 0113-270 7177 Fax: 0113-270 0264

Neesham Controls Ltd, Twerton Mill, Lower Bristol Road, Bath, BA2 1EW Tel: (01225) 402140 Fax: (01225) 448154

Northern Electrical Engineering Co. Ltd, 40 Earsham Street, Sheffield, S4 7LS Tel: 0114-275 7020 Fax: 0114-273 0476 E-mail: nengcoltd@tiscali.co.uk

O S S Electrical Controls Ltd, 36 Bar Gap Road, Oldham, OL1 3RL Tel: 0161-633 9692 Fax: 0161-627 2352 E-mail: rss-elect@tiscali.co.uk

Ostcliffe Electronics Ltd, Barrowfield Road, Hoyland, Barnsley, South Yorkshire, S74 9TH Tel: (01226) 749233

P & B Power Engineering, Belle Vue Works, Boundary St, Manchester, M12 5NG Tel: 0161-223 5151 Fax: 0161-230 6464 E-mail: sales@pbeng.co.uk

Paktronic Engineering Co. Ltd, Alma Park Road, Grantham, Lincolnshire, NG31 9SE Tel: (01476) 567623 Fax: (01476) 566503 E-mail: info@paktronic.co.uk

Pandelco Ltd, Canal Street, Burton-on-Trent, Staffordshire, DE14 3TB Tel: (01283) 542738 Fax: (01283) 511774 E-mail: sales@pandelco.co.uk

Pentagon Control Systems, The Old Vicarage, Whitlingham Lane, Trowse, Norwich, NR14 8TN Tel: (01603) 629909 Fax: (01603) 666379 E-mail: enquiries@pentagon-controls.co.uk

Phoenix Control Systems, Unit 14 Dewar Court, Astmoor Industrial Estate, Runcorn, Cheshire, WA7 1PT Tel: (01928) 590500 Fax: (01928) 590811

Pix Electrical Co. Ltd, Unit 6, Muslin Street, Salford, M5 4NF Tel: (0161) 925 9829 Fax: (0161) 737 9438 E-mail: phillip.hall@pixelectrical.co.uk

Pneutrol Ireland Ltd, 5 Caulside Drive, Antrim, BT41 2DU Tel: (028) 9448 1800 Fax: (028) 9448 1801 E-mail: info@pneutrol.com

Power Panels Electrical Systems Ltd, Landywood Green, Cheslyn Hay, Walsall, WS6 7AL Tel: (01922) 419109 Fax: (01922) 418181 E-mail: sales@power-panels.co.uk

Process Control Systems Ltd, St. Chads Church, Fisher Street, Brindley Ford, Stoke-On-Trent, ST8 7QJ Tel: (01782) 517601 Fax: (01782) 516921

Purpose Electrical Controls Ltd, 7 Salisbury Place Industrial Estate, Rosebery Street, Wolverhampton, WV3 0BD Tel: (01902) 712909 Fax: (01902) 712909

Quantran Systems Ltd, Unit 6 Garnett Close, Watford, WD24 7GN Tel: (01923) 252512 E-mail: sales@quantran.com

Quest Ltd, Victoria House, Accrington Road, Burnley, Lancashire, BB11 5EF Tel: (01282) 838000 Fax: (01282) 452121 E-mail: sales@questelectrical.co.uk

Quinsee Swan Ltd, 6 Thames Industrial Estate, High Street South, Dunstable, Bedfordshire, LU6 3HL Tel: (01582) 471162 Fax: (01582) 609830 E-mail: sales@quinseeswan.co.uk

R M Electrical, 340a Thornton Road, Bradford, West Yorkshire, BD8 8LD Tel: (01274) 549252 Fax: (01274) 549253 E-mail: admin@rmelectrical.co.uk

Radway Control Systems, Business & Technology Centre, Radway Grn, Crewe, CW2 5PR Tel: (01270) 886176 Fax: (01270) 886275 E-mail: pjtomkinson@radway.co.uk

Rafi (GB) Ltd, Unit 1 Perrywood Business Park, Honeycrock Lane, Salfords, Redhill, RH1 5DZ Tel: (01737) 778660 Fax: (01737) 778722 E-mail: sales@rafi.co.uk

Rees Switchgear Ltd, 157 Clarence Avenue, Northampton, NN2 6NY Tel: (01604) 597860 Fax: (01604) 597861 E-mail: janwimpress@rf-plc.com

Riverside Automation Ltd, 103 Carlisle St East, Sheffield, S4 8DQ Tel: 0114-270 1997 Fax: 0114-270 1998 E-mail: kcowley@zoom.co.uk

Robell Control Systems Ltd, 56 Cato Street, Nechells, Birmingham, B7 4TS Tel: 0121-333 4306 Fax: 0121-333 4811

S.E.C. Electrical Ltd, 15 Stafford Place, Moulton Park Industrial Estate, Northampton, NN3 6NN Tel: (01604) 491101 Fax: (01604) 790542

S & H Systems Design & Installation Ltd, Unit 1 Beechwood Business Park, Burdock Close, Cannock, Staffordshire, WS11 7GB Tel: (01543) 462620 Fax: (01543) 432630 E-mail: mail@s-and-h-systems.com

S M Control Engineering Ltd, 1 Redhouse Industrial Estate, Middlemore Lane, Aldridge, Walsall, WS9 8DL Tel: (01922) 744020 Fax: (01922) 744001 E-mail: cbailey@smcontroleng.co.uk

S M G Control Systems, 9 Smestow Bridge, Bridgnorth Road, Wombourne, Wolverhampton, WV5 8AY Tel: (01902) 326886 Fax: (01902) 326883 E-mail: smg@smgcontrolsystems.co.uk

S R C Systems Ltd, 5 Leslie Road, Ipswich, IP3 9PL Tel: (01473) 726445 Fax: (01473) 727278 E-mail: info@srcsystems.co.uk

Sarum Electronics Ltd, Clump Farm Industrial Estate, Higher Shaftesbury Road, Blandford Forum, Dorset, DT11 7TD Tel: (01258) 480802 Fax: (01258) 480803 E-mail: sarumelec@btopenworld.com

Sherwood Control Panels, Lenton Business Centre, Lenton Boulevard, Nottingham, NG7 2BY Tel: 0115-978 1502

▶ Sigma Electrical, Woodbine Road, Bolton, BL3 3JH Tel: (01204) 64322 Fax: (01204) 64612 E-mail: admin@sigma-electrical.co.uk

Southern Industrial Controls, 118 Faulds Industrial Estate, Tutbury, Burton-on-Trent, Staffs, DE13 9HS Tel: (01283) 814488 Fax: (01283) 814480

Stonegrove Ltd, 3 Boyd Business Centre, Whitewall Road, Medway City Estate, Rochester, Kent, ME2 4DZ Tel: (01634) 291151 Fax: (01634) 719430 E-mail: chris@stonegrove.co.uk

Stroud Switchgear Developments Ltd, Unit 3, Lightpill Trading Estate, Stroud, Gloucestershire, GL5 3LL Tel: (01453) 762709 Fax: (01453) 751977 E-mail: sales@stroud-switchgear.com

Sulectric Control Panel Mnfrs, 52 Sherwell Road, Bristol, BS4 4JZ Tel: 0117-971 3917 Fax: 0117-983 4775

Switchgear & Instrumentation Ltd, Ripley Road, Bradford, West Yorkshire, BD4 7EH Tel: (01274) 734221 Fax: (01274) 731390 E-mail: sales@switchgear.co.uk

Switchgear International Ltd, Farthing Road Industrial Estate, Ipswich, IP1 5AP Tel: (01473) 240280 Fax: (01473) 242929 E-mail: sales@switchgearinternational.co.uk

System Panels Ltd, 104 Dudley Road East, Oldbury, West Midlands, B69 3EB Tel: 0121-552 4418 Fax: 0121-552 4018 E-mail: sales@marwel.com

Systems Integrators Ltd, 31 Wick Road, Teddington, Middlesex, TW11 9DN Tel: (020) 8614 8070 Fax: (020) 8614 8040 E-mail: enquiries@sys-int.co.uk

Taylor Durant Ltd, 2A London Avenue, North End, Portsmouth, PO2 9BU Tel: (023) 9266 8586

Technical Control Systems Ltd, Treefield Industrial Estate, Gildersome, Leeds, LS27 7JU Tel: 0113-252 5977 Fax: 0113-238 0095 E-mail: enquiries@tcspanels.co.uk

Tegrel Ltd, Tundry Way, Blaydon-on-Tyne, Tyne & Wear, NE21 5TT Tel: 0191-414 6111 Fax: 0191-414 0660 E-mail: sales@tegrel.co.uk

Tes Europe Ltd, Sandyland, North End, Wisbech, Cambridgeshire, PE13 1PE Tel: (01945) 474809 Fax: (01945) 589591 E-mail: tes_europe@freenet.co.uk

▶ Theocrest Ltd, Cavans Way, Binley Industrial Estate, Binley Industrial Estate, Coventry, CV3 2SF Tel: (024) 7644 5758 Fax: (024) 7645 6438 E-mail: brian@theocrest.co.uk

Thermosensing Ltd, 30-31 Devonshire Place, Brighton, BN2 1QB Tel: (01903) 214466 Fax: (01903) 214477

Towerglens Ltd, Dock Lane Industrial Estate, Turner St, Dudley, West Midlands, DY1 1SD Tel: (01384) 455025 Fax: (01384) 451300 E-mail: sales@towerglens.com

Trinity Controls Ltd, 41 Eton Wick Road, Eton Wick, Windsor, Berkshire, SL4 6LU Tel: (01753) 840022 Fax: (01753) 832808

Varcol Electrical Services Ltd, Cornwall Street, Manchester, M11 2WQ Tel: 0161-223 9696 Fax: 0161-223 0976 E-mail: sales@varcol.co.uk

A.J. Watson (Electrical Services) Ltd, Browning Street, Hoddlesden, Darwen, Lancashire, BB3 3NE Tel: (01254) 760048 Fax: (01254) 760034 E-mail: info@agele.co.uk

Weatherite Electrical Ltd, Weatherite House, Westgate Park, Tintagel Way, Aldridge, Walsall, WS9 8EX Tel: (01922) 741600 Fax: (01922) 741601 E-mail: sales@weatherite-electrical.com

Wellman Automation, 6 Appleby Glade Industrial Estate, Ryder Close, Swadlincote, Derbyshire, DE11 9EU Tel: (01283) 550052 Fax: (01283) 550064 E-mail: wellman-automation@btconnect.com

Westminster Controls Ltd, Unit 3 Pym Street, Leeds, LS10 1PG Tel: 0113-288 4500 Fax: 0113-246 0791 E-mail: info@westminstercontrols.com

X B R Electronics Ltd, Campbell Road, Eastleigh, Hampshire, SO50 5AE Tel: (023) 8061 3211 Fax: (023) 8061 3215 E-mail: sales@xbrelectronics.com

CONTROL PANEL SWITCHGEARS

▶ C & N Control Systems Ltd, Units 7-8 Sterling Industrial Park, Carr Wood Road, Castleford, West Yorkshire, WF10 4PS Tel: (01977) 603803 Fax: (01977) 603161 E-mail: info@cn-controls.co.uk

CONTROL PANEL TRANSFORMERS

Nottingham Transformers Co. Ltd, Unit 37 Little Tennis Street, Nottingham, NG2 4EL Tel: 0115-958 8340 Fax: 0115-958 8341 E-mail: tony_medri@hotmail.com

Transformer Manufacturing Co. Ltd, Riverside Industrial Estate, Mill Lane, Maldon, Essex, CM9 4LD Tel: (01621) 843322 Fax: (01621) 843355 E-mail: sales@tmc.co.uk

CONTROL PANELS TO SPECIFICATION

A K Controls, Unit 17 Fleetsbridge Business Park, Upton Road, Poole, Dorset, BH17 7AF Tel: (01202) 660061 Fax: (01202) 660200 E-mail: office@akcontrols.com

Acton Delta Ltd, Wombrook Business Centre, Giggetty Lane, Wombourne, Wolverhampton, WV5 8LZ Tel: (01902) 326563 Fax: (01902) 326564 E-mail: mail@actondelta.co.uk

Broadoak Controls Ltd, Broadoak Enterprise Centre, Broadoak Road, Sittingbourne, Kent, ME9 8AQ Tel: (01795) 421900 Fax: (01795) 421900

C & W Electronics Ltd, Pool Street, Wolverhampton, WV2 4HN Tel: (01902) 426714 Fax: (01902) 422544

A. Campbell, 7 Blane Avenue, Blanefield, Glasgow, G63 9HU Tel: (01360) 770437 Fax: (01360) 770495 E-mail: info@campbellcontrols.com

Charnvel Ltd, Charnvel House, Canterbury Road, Nottingham, NG8 1PQ Tel: 0115-985 4000 Fax: 0115-985 5558 E-mail: info@charnvel.co.uk

Cheltenham Controls, 183 Westgate Street, Gloucester, GL1 2RN Tel: (01452) 503390 Fax: (01452) 503630 E-mail: info.cheltcontrols@dis-ltd.co.uk

Control & Power Systems Ltd, 3D Burniston Industrial Estate, Willymath Close, Burniston, Scarborough, North Yorkshire, YO13 0HG Tel: (01723) 871112 Fax: (01723) 870625 E-mail: controlandpower@compuserve.com

Controline Ltd, Crown Works, Dewsbury Road, Elland, West Yorkshire, HX5 9BG Tel: (01422) 311993 Fax: (01422) 311818 E-mail: info@controline.co.uk

Cranford Controls Systems Ltd, Unit 3 Pattenden La Buis Centre, Marden, Tonbridge, Kent, TN12 9QS Tel: (01622) 833300 Fax: (01622) 833311 E-mail: sales@cranfordcontrol.co.uk

Curry & Bevans, Unit 1 Willow Row, Stoke-on-Trent, ST3 2PU Tel: (01782) 596109 Fax: (01782) 596356

D Benson & Co. Ltd, Normanton Industrial Estate, Normanton, West Yorkshire, WF6 1QS Tel: (01924) 894162 Fax: (01924) 896518 E-mail: info@dbensoncontrols.co.uk

Daybury Electrical Services Ltd, Coppice Trading Estate, Kidderminster, Worcestershire, DY11 7QY Tel: (01299) 822070 Fax: (01562) 829747 E-mail: sales@daybury.co.uk

Edwards Modular Controls Ltd, 25 Freehold Terrace, Brighton, BN2 4AB Tel: (01273) 688285 Fax: (01273) 570657 E-mail: sales@emc4controls.co.uk

Electraspec Control Panel Mnfrs, 4 Shell Corner Industrial Estate, Long Lane, Halesowen, West Midlands, B62 9LD Tel: 0121-559 9335 Fax: 0121-559 9362

Europa Electrical Ltd, Unit 22c Parker Industrial Estate, Mansfield Road, Derby, DE21 4SZ Tel: (01332) 295439 Fax: (01332) 383593 E-mail: sales@europalec.co.uk

CONTROL PANELS TO SPECIFICATION – *continued*

Genpart UK Ltd, 5 Threxton Road Industrial Estate, Watton, Thetford, Norfolk, IP25 6NG Tel: (01953) 882436 Fax: (01953) 885597 E-mail: sales@genpart.co.uk
Moorfield Control Systems Ltd, Unit 17/18 Ashbrooke Park, Parkside Lane, Leeds, LS11 5SF Tel: 0113-270 7177 Fax: 0113-270 0264
P A Electrical Ltd, Childerditch Industrial Park, Childerditch Hall Drive, Little Warley, Brentwood, Essex, CM13 3XU Tel: (01277) 812881 Fax: (01277) 812661 E-mail: cpettit55@aol.com
Panelec Ltd, 1 Hollies Trading Estate, Graiseley Row, Wolverhampton, WV2 4HE Tel: (01902) 712582 Fax: (01902) 712582
Phoenix Control Systems, Unit 14 Dewar Court, Astmoor Industrial Estate, Runcorn, Cheshire, WA7 1PT Tel: (01928) 590500 Fax: (01928) 590811
Process Control Panels Ltd, Unit 13 Dunstall Hill Industrial Estate, Gorsebrook Road, Wolverhampton, WV6 0PJ Tel: (01902) 329990 Fax: (01902) 310743
S M Control Engineering Ltd, 1 Redhouse Industrial Estate, Middlemore Lane, Aldridge, Walsall, WS9 8DL Tel: (01922) 744020 Fax: (01922) 744001 E-mail: cbailey@smcontroleng.co.uk
S2 Engineering, 4 Derwenthaugh Marina, Blaydon-on-Tyne, Tyne & Wear, NE21 5LL Tel: 0191-414 2300 Fax: 0191-414 2287 E-mail: info@s2eng.co.uk

CONTROL PANELS, WELLHEAD

▶ Alderley P.L.C., Alderley House, Arnolds Field Estate,, The Downs,, Wickwar,, Wotton-Under-Edge, Gloucestershire, GL12 8JD Tel: (01454) 294556 Fax: (01454) 299272 E-mail: marketing@alderley.com

CONTROL RELAYS

Broyce Control Ltd, Pool St, Wolverhampton, WV2 4HN Tel: (01902) 773746 Fax: (01902) 420639 E-mail: sales@broycecontrol.com
More Control (UK) Ltd, Control House, Mount Farm Industrial Estate, Clarke Road, Bletchley, Milton Keynes, MK1 1LG Tel: (01908) 364555 Fax: (01908) 364511 E-mail: more@more-control.com
Siemens Protection Devices Ltd, PO Box 7, Hebburn, Tyne & Wear, NE31 1TZ Tel: 0191-401 5555 Fax: 0191-401 5575

CONTROL ROOM CONSOLES

Enclosure Systems Ltd, Platt Industrial Estate, Maidstone Road, Borough Green, Sevenoaks, Kent, TN15 8JA Tel: (01732) 886552 Fax: (01732) 886443 E-mail: sales@enclosures.co.uk
Winsted Ltd, Units 7 & 8 Lovett Road, Hampton Lovett Industrial Estate, Droitwich, Worcestershire, WR9 0QG Tel: (01905) 770276 Fax: (01905) 779791 E-mail: harry@winsted.co.uk

CONTROL STATIONS

Aberdeen Control Ltd, Unit 1 Union Glen, Aberdeen, AB11 6ER Tel: (01224) 211133 Fax: (01224) 211177E-mail: gcraig@rsc.co.uk
Kestral Controls Ltd, 3 Garrell Road, Kilsyth, Glasgow, G65 9JX Tel: (01236) 821564 Fax: (01236) 825676 E-mail: sales@kestralcontrols.co.uk
Riverside Automation Ltd, 103 Carlisle St East, Sheffield, S4 8DQ Tel: 0114-270 1997 Fax: 0114-270 1998 E-mail: kcowley@zoom.co.uk
Roomfoss Ltd, Larch Road, Saddlebow, King's Lynn, Norfolk, PE34 3HP Tel: (01553) 771413 Fax: (01553) 691184 E-mail: sales@roomfoss.co.uk
Towerglens Ltd, Dock Lane Industrial Estate, Turner St, Dudley, West Midlands, DY1 1SD Tel: (01384) 455025 Fax: (01384) 451300 E-mail: sales@towerglens.com
Tufts & Whitton, 14 Old Norwich Road, Marsham, Norwich, NR10 5PS Tel: (01263) 732401 Fax: (01263) 734791 E-mail: mike@tuftswhitton.co.uk
Uttley & Thompson Electronics Ltd, 90 Abbey Street, Accrington, Lancashire, BB5 1EE Tel: (01254) 384850 Fax: (01254) 395474 E-mail: uttleyandthompson@farmore.net

CONTROL SWITCHES

N S F Controls Ltd, Ingrow Bridge Works, Keighley, West Yorkshire, BD21 5EF Tel: (01535) 661144 Fax: (01535) 661474 E-mail: sales@nsfcontrols.co.uk
Salzer UK Ltd, 44 Edison Road, Aylesbury, Buckinghamshire, HP19 8TE Tel: (01296) 399992 Fax: (01296) 392229 E-mail: info@salzeruk.co.uk
U K Solenoid Ltd, 115 London Road, Newbury, Berkshire, RG14 2AH Tel: (01635) 45991 Fax: (01635) 37807E-mail: sales@uksol.co.uk

CONTROL SYSTEM COMMISSIONING

▶ Clarke Chapman Services, Unit 15 Planetary Industrial Estate, Planetary Road, Willenhall, West Midlands, WV13 3XA Tel: (01902) 728844 Fax: (01902) 728822 E-mail: info@clerkchapman.co.uk

CONTROL SYSTEM INSTALLATIONS

DVS Computers, Unit 5 Gabalfa Workshops Clos Menter, Excelsior Industrial Estate, Cardiff, CF14 3AY Tel: (029) 2069 5020 E-mail: sales@dvscomputers.co.uk
Honeywell Control Systems Ltd, 150 Aztec West, Almondsbury, Bristol, BS32 4UB Tel: (01454) 848048 Fax: (01454) 848049

CONTROL SYSTEM SOFTWARE

Dexdyne Ltd, Oakley House, Tetbury Road, Cirencester, Gloucestershire, GL7 1US Tel: (01285) 658122 Fax: (01285) 655644 E-mail: sales@dexdyne.com

CONTROL SYSTEM SOFTWARE SERVICES

B K Automations, 4 Talisman Business Centre, Duncan Road, Park Gate, Southampton, SO31 7GA Tel: (01489) 582712 Fax: (01489) 583294 E-mail: bkautomamation@tinyworld.co.uk
Compere Systems Ltd, Ivy Street, Birkenhead, Merseyside, CH41 5EE Tel: 0151-647 7457 Fax: 0151-666 2569 E-mail: davidj@comperesystems.com
Orchid Software Ltd, 63 Westgate Road, Newcastle Upon Tyne, NE1 1SG Tel: 0191-232 5750 E-mail: adrian@orchidsoft.com
Tritec Systems Ltd, Riverview House, London Road, Old Basing, Basingstoke, Hampshire, RG24 7JL Tel: (01256) 477778 Fax: (01256) 477776 E-mail: sales@tritec.co.uk

CONTROL SYSTEMS DESIGN CONSULTANTS

4c Electronics Ltd, Diamond Court Douglas Close, Preston Farm Business Park, Preston Farm Industrial Estate, Stockton-on-Tees, Cleveland, TS18 3SB Tel: (01642) 616449 Fax: (01642) 605772 E-mail: sales@4celectronics.co.uk
Ace Visual & Sound Systems Ltd, Field House, Fieldside, Thorne, Doncaster, South Yorkshire, DN8 4BE Tel: (01405) 740393 Fax: (01405) 814807 E-mail: kevin@showmagic.com
B & G Controls Ltd, Broadoak Enterprise Village, Broadoak Road, Sittingbourne, Kent, ME9 8AQ Tel: (01795) 423554 Fax: (01795) 428873 E-mail: sales@bt-controls.co.uk
Calverley Control Installations, Blacup House, Royds Close, Leeds, LS12 6LL Tel: 0113-279 6611 Fax: 0113-231 0391 E-mail: info@calverley-control-systems.co.uk
Control Solutions Ltd, Avon House, 82 Wellington Street, Thame, Oxfordshire, OX9 3BN Tel: (01844) 216988 Fax: (01844) 261466 E-mail: mail@control-solutions.co.uk
E D G S B Ltd, The Mews, 70 London Road, Burgess Hill, West Sussex, RH15 8NB Tel: (01444) 248691 Fax: (01444) 248721 E-mail: sales@edg.co.uk
Electro Control Systems, Backlands, Church Way, Guilsborough, Northampton, NN6 8QF Tel: (01604) 740305 Fax: (01604) 740305
Engineering Electrics (Wilmslow) Ltd, 67 Oldfield Road, Sale, Cheshire, M33 2AP Tel: 0161-973 8230 Fax: 0161-962 8648
Fleetclean Ltd, Common Lane, Knottingley, West Yorkshire, WF11 8BN Tel: (01904) 674674 Fax: (01977) 607004 E-mail: enquiries@fleetclean.co.uk
J K Controls Ltd, 12a Rochester Airport Industrial Estate, Laker Road, Rochester, Kent, ME1 3QX Tel: (01634) 685858 Fax: (01634) 685850 E-mail: info@jkcontrols.co.uk
M C S Control Systems Ltd, Unit 4 Phoenix Park, Bayton Road Industrial Estate, Coventry, CV7 9QN Tel: (024) 7636 0211 Fax: (024) 7636 8219 E-mail: sales@mcscs.co.uk
Micro Robotics Ltd, 135 Ditton Walk, Cambridge, CB5 8QB Tel: (01223) 523100 Fax: (01223) 524242 E-mail: sales@microrobotics.co.uk
Press Control Systems, Unit 6 Tinsley Street, Tipton, West Midlands, DY4 7LH Tel: 0121-557 0001 Fax: 0121-557 0002

CONTROL SYSTEMS INSTALLATION

Microsys Controls Ltd, Fennels Way, Flackwell Heath, High Wycombe, Buckinghamshire, HP10 9BY Tel: (01628) 532195 Fax: (01628) 532196 E-mail: microsyscontrols@aol.com

CONTROL SYSTEMS MANUFRS, *See also headings for particular types*

A A W Control Systems Ltd, Unit 1, The Firs Farm, Leckhampstead, Newbury, Berkshire, RG20 8RD Tel: (01488) 638928 Fax: (01488) 638947 E-mail: aaw@aawcs.co.uk
Alpha Instrumentation Ltd, 6 Stoke Close, Seaford, East Sussex, BN25 3RN Tel: (01323) 897027 Fax: (01323) 897027
Arrow Technical Services Ltd, 58 Nursery Street, Sheffield, S3 8GG Tel: 0114-281 2018 Fax: 0114-281 5404 E-mail: info@arrowtechnical.com
Associated Control Systems Ltd, Unit 15 Spring Road, Industrial Estate, Wolverhampton, WV4 6UA Tel: (01902) 353811 Fax: (01902) 353818 E-mail: rob.acs@btconnect.com
Betta Tech Controls Ltd, 104 Tanners Drive, Blakelands, Milton Keynes, MK14 5BP Tel: (01908) 616784 Fax: (01908) 216264
▶ Brooklands Automation, 27a Brindley Road, Bayton Road Industrial Estate, Coventry, CV7 9EP Tel: (024) 7667 1030 Fax: (024) 7636 2244
▶ Calm Control Systems Ltd, 7 Mead Walk, Didcot, Oxfordshire, OX11 7PA Tel: (01235) 811117 Fax: (01235) 511551 E-mail: sale@calm-controls.co.uk
Calverley Control Installations, Blacup House, Royds Close, Leeds, LS12 6LL Tel: 0113-279 6611 Fax: 0113-231 0391 E-mail: info@calverley-control-systems.co.uk
Clift Controls Ltd, Unit 5 2 Perry Way, Witham, Essex, CM8 3SX Tel: (01376) 512604 Fax: (01376) 518187
Command Alkon Ltd, 21 St Annes Road, St Annes Park, St. Annes Park, Bristol, BS4 4AB Tel: 0117-972 4777 Fax: 0117-972 4888
Controline Ltd, Crown Works, Dewsbury Road, Elland, West Yorkshire, HX5 9BG Tel: (01422) 311993 Fax: (01422) 311818 E-mail: info@controline.co.uk
Cord Controls Ltd, 29 Wigston Street, Countesthorpe, Leicester, LE8 5RP Tel: 0116-277 7396 Fax: 0116-277 7396 E-mail: cord.controls@btclick.com
Damar Group Ltd, Unit 15-19, Mill Road, Radstock, BA3 5TX Tel: (01761) 439111 Fax: (01761) 439123 E-mail: info@damarnet.com
Deep Sea Electronics plc, Hunmanby Industrial Estate, Hunmanby, Filey, North Yorkshire, YO14 0PH Tel: (01723) 890099 Fax: (01723) 893303 E-mail: marketing@deepseaplc.com
▶ Eagle Lcs, Innovation House, Unit 3 Linton Business Park, Gourdon, Montrose, Angus, DD10 0NH Tel: (01561) 360068
▶ East Coast Controls Ltd, Acre House, Stirling Road, Kilsyth, Glasgow, G65 0PT Tel: (01236) 825490 Fax: (01236) 822307
▶ Eic Scotland Ltd, Dryden Road, Loanhead, Midlothian, EH20 9LZ Tel: 0131-440 0456 Fax: 0131-440 4546
Elite Control Systems Ltd, Elite House, Starlaw Business Park, Livingston, West Lothian, EH54 8SF Tel: (01506) 597900 Fax: (01506) 597919 E-mail: admin@elitecontrols.co.uk
Excel Industrial Systems Ltd, Unit 4, Beeston Court, Stuart Road, Manor Park, Runcorn, Cheshire, WA7 1SS Tel: 01928 597834 Fax: 01928 579308 E-mail: sales@xlg.co.uk
Fagor Automation UK Ltd, Unit 2a Brunel Close, Drayton Fields Industrial Estate, Daventry, Northamptonshire, NN11 8RB Tel: (01327) 300067 Fax: (01327) 300880 E-mail: sales@fagorautomation.co.uk
Fleetclean Ltd, Common Lane, Knottingley, West Yorkshire, WF11 8BN Tel: (01904) 674674 Fax: (01977) 607004 E-mail: enquiries@fleetclean.co.uk
Grapevine Instruments, PO Box 598, Canterbury, Kent, CT4 7GW Tel: (07010) 707940 Fax: (01227) 730892 E-mail: sfigures@netcomuk.co.uk
▶ Grosvenor Telecom, Unit 30 Whitegate Industrial Estate, Whitegate Road, Wrexham, Clwyd, LL13 8UG Tel: (01978) 291950 Fax: (01978) 312252 E-mail: mail@grosvenortelecom.co.uk
▶ Honeywell, 2 President Buildings, Savile St East, Sheffield, S4 7UQ Tel: 0114-286 0910 Fax: 0114-286 0911
Ica Solutions Ltd, 1 115 Loverock Road, Reading, RG30 1DZ Tel: 0118-939 3663 Fax: 0118-939 3653 E-mail: info@icasolutions.co.uk
Identify Ltd, Smugglers End, The Street, Hythe, Kent, CT21 4LQ Tel: (01303) 239939 Fax: (01303) 267671 E-mail: mjager@identify_ltd.co.uk
Ies Pca Ltd, The Millcourt Centre, Pleasley Vale, Mansfield, Nottinghamshire, NG19 8RL Tel: (01623) 819319 Fax: (01623) 819329 E-mail: info@iespca.com
Intelligent Motion Control Ltd, 4 Brunel Close, Drayton Fields Industrial Estate, Daventry, Northamptonshire, NN11 8RB Tel: (01327) 307600 Fax: (01327) 300319 E-mail: info@inmoco.co.uk
Jode Systems Technology Ltd, 37 High Street, Lutterworth, Leicestershire, LE17 4AY Tel: (01455) 559626 Fax: (01455) 559676 E-mail: sales@jodesystems.co.uk
K & S Engineering & Scientific Ltd, 18 Clifton Gardens, London, NW11 7EL Tel: (020) 8731 7461 Fax: (020) 8731 8604 E-mail: seedetails@www.kse-sci.com
Kistler Instruments Ltd, Murrell Green Business Park, London Road, Hook, Hampshire, RG27 9GR Tel: (01256) 741550 Fax: (01256) 741551 E-mail: sales.uk@kistler.com
L Tec Control Engineers Ltd, 125 Deerdykes View, Westfield, Cumbernauld, Glasgow, G68 9HN Tel: (01236) 727766 Fax: (01236) 733903
▶ Lester Control Systems, Unit 3 Wycliffe Industrial Estate, Lutterworth, Leicestershire, LE17 4HG Tel: (01455) 557780
▶ M J Wilson Ltd, Charlton Street, Grimsby, South Humberside, DN31 1SQ Tel: (01472) 345361 Fax: (01472) 340172 E-mail: sales@dcmarshinstruments.co.uk
▶ Matrix Control Solutions Ltd, Littlemoss Road, Droylsden, Manchester, M43 7EF Tel: 0161-371 0111 Fax: 0161-371 0880
Merlin Systems Ltd, Pandy Industrial Estate, Ty Gwyn Lane, Wrexham, Clwyd, LL11 2UA Tel: (01978) 313911 Fax: (01978) 313811 E-mail: sales@merlin-systems.ltd.uk
Newfield Automation, Newfield House, Brook Lane, Astbury, Congleton, Cheshire, CW12 4TJ Tel: (01260) 282200 Fax: (01260) 282201 E-mail: team@newfieldautomation.com
Next Control Systems Ltd, 6 Farnborough Business Centre, Eelmoor Road, Farnborough, Hampshire, GU14 7XA Tel: (01252) 406398 Fax: (01252) 406401 E-mail: jackie@nextcontrols.com
▶ Ocean Power Delivery, 104 Commercial Street, Edinburgh, EH6 6NF Tel: 0131-554 8444 Fax: 0131-554 8544 E-mail: enquiries@oceanpd.com
P A Electrical Ltd, Childerditch Industrial Park, Childerditch Hall Drive, Little Warley, Brentwood, Essex, CM13 3XU Tel: (01277) 812881 Fax: (01277) 812661 E-mail: cpettit55@aol.com
P L Control, 18 Holdsworth Road, Holmfield, Halifax, West Yorkshire, HX2 9TH Tel: (01422) 382052 Fax: (01422) 241956
Parmley Graham Ltd, Saltmeadows Road, Gateshead, Tyne & Wear, NE8 3BG Tel: 0191-477 4625 Fax: 0191-478 6801 E-mail: hq@parmley-graham.co.uk
Phoenix Control Systems, Unit 14 Dewar Court, Astmoor Industrial Estate, Runcorn, Cheshire, WA7 1PT Tel: (01928) 590500 Fax: (01928) 590811
Power System Components Ltd, Hawthorne House, Main Street, York, YO61 1RS Tel: (01347) 838154 Fax: (01347) 838154
Process Control Services UK Ltd, The Savoy, 4 Hall Bank, Buxton, Derbyshire, SK17 6EW Tel: (01298) 79969 Fax: (01298) 71151
Stratos Control System, Great Harrowden Lodge, The Slips, Great Harrowden, Wellingborough, Northamptonshire, NN9 5AE Tel: (01933) 677550 Fax: (01933) 677884
▶ Total Energy Controls, Unit 1 Crystal Business Centre, Sandwich, Kent, CT13 9QX Tel: (01304) 619816 Fax: (01304) 619819
Tricon Ltd, 60 High Craithall Road, Port Dundas, Glasgow, G4 9UD Tel: 0141-332 1551 Fax: 0141-332 8545
Watts Industries UK Ltd, Grosvenor Business Centre, Enterprise Way, Vale Park, Evesham, Worcestershire, WR11 1GA Tel: (01386) 446997 Fax: (01386) 41923 E-mail: sales@wattsindustries.com
Western Automation, Unit 1 Spitfire Road, Birmingham, B24 9PR Tel: 0121-328 2000 Fax: 0121-328 7156 E-mail: sales@etfbirmingham.co.uk
Woodhead Connectivity Ltd, Unit 9 Rassau Industrial Estate, Rassau, Ebbw Vale, Gwent, NP23 5SD Tel: (01495) 350436 Fax: (01495) 350877 E-mail: contact@whdhd.co.uk
Zeta Controls Ltd, Telford Road, Bisecter, Oxford, OX26 4LB Tel: (01869) 322500 Fax: (01869) 322614 E-mail: sales@zetacontrols.co.uk

CONTROL SYSTEMS TO SPECIFICATION

Don Controls Ltd, Low Lane, Horsforth, Leeds, LS18 5NY Tel: 0113-258 4286 Fax: 0113-239 0056 E-mail: mail@don.co.uk
Engineered Solutions, Unit 2, North Court, Armstrong Road, Maidstone, Kent, ME15 6JZ Tel: (01622) 750650 Fax: (01622) 355199 E-mail: sales@engsolutions.co.uk
Sercon Controls Ltd, Clay Lane, Spar Fields, Slarthwate, Huddersfield, HD7 5BG Tel: (01484) 845548 Fax: (01484) 847846 E-mail: gln@serconcontrols.com
Telesound Ltd, 31 Hall Green Close, Malvern, Worcestershire, WR14 3QY Tel: (01684) 572506 E-mail: sales@telesound.co.uk

CONTROL SYSTEMS, ACCESS

▶ Advanced Perimeter Systems, 16 Cunningham Road, Springkerse Industrial Estate, Stirling, FK7 7TP Tel: (01786) 479862 Fax: (01786) 470331 E-mail: sales@aps-perimeter-security.com
Andromica Video Systems Ltd, Victory House, 54 Wallingford Road, Uxbridge, Middlesex, UB8 2RW Tel: (01895) 257971 Fax: (01895) 273483 E-mail: admin@andromica.co.uk
▶ Band Systems, Unit 3, Twyford Business Park, Station Road, Twyford, Reading, RG10 9TU Tel: 0118-377 9000 Fax: 0118-970 6804
Barb Security Systems, Reeds, Colliers End, Ware, Hertfordshire, SG11 1EH Tel: (0845) 2304248
Bewator Ltd, Albany Street, Newport, Gwent, NP20 5XW Tel: (08713) 860800 Fax: (01633) 850893 E-mail: sales@bewator.co.uk

CONTROL SYSTEMS, ACCESS – *continued*

British Security Technologies, 19 Hackford Walk, 119-123 Hackford Road, London, SW9 0QT Tel: (01424) 883275 E-mail: britsectec@aol.com

Centurion Security System, Centurion House, Park Road West, Huddersfield, HD4 5RX Tel: (01484) 321321 Fax: (01484) 351888 E-mail: sales@centurion.net

Feedback Data Ltd, Park Road, Crowborough, East Sussex, TN6 2QR Tel: (01892) 601400 Fax: (01892) 601429 E-mail: info@feedback-data.com

G E Security Ltd, Unit 5, Ashton Gate, Ashton Road, Harold Hill, Romford, RM3 8UF Tel: (01708) 381496 Fax: (0870) 7773049

Group 4 Technology Ltd, Challenge House, International Drive, Tewkesbury, Gloucestershire, GL20 8UQ Tel: (01684) 277175 Fax: (01684) 294845 E-mail: sales@group4technology.com

H F X Ltd, The Clock House, Green Street, Elsenham, Bishop's Stortford, Hertfordshire, CM22 6DS Tel: (01279) 647474 Fax: (01279) 647700 E-mail: info@hfx.co.uk

▶ HomeLANs Ltd, 71 Windsor Road, Bray, Maidenhead, Berkshire, SL6 2DN Tel: 0845 1665106 Fax: 0777 9014223 E-mail: mail@homelans.co.uk

▶ Intelligent Access Systems Ltd, 16 Gladstone Terrace, Boldon Colliery, Tyne & Wear, NE35 9HL Tel: 0191-536 9255 Fax: 0191-536 9255E-mail: laurance.laidlaw@homecall.co.uk

▶ J M H Technology LLP, Unit 3, Highlands Farm, Berden, Bishop's Stortford, Hertfordshire, CM23 1AB Tel: (0845) 0537457 Fax: (07092) 002578 E-mail: sales@jmhtechnology.co.uk

▶ Multilink Access Control Systems Ltd, 71 Hampermill Lane, Watford, WD19 4NT Tel: (01923) 224900 Fax: (01923) 224970 E-mail: info@multilinksecurity.co.uk

▶ Raytel Security Systems Ltd, 3 Block 5 Oakbank Industrial Estate, Garscube Road, Glasgow, G20 7LU Tel: 0141-332 4232 Fax: 0141-332 6952 E-mail: sales@raytelsecurity.co.uk

▶ Safe N'Sound Security Systems Ltd, Head Office, 19 Hackford Walk, 119 - 123 Hackford Road, London, SW9 0QT Tel: (01424) 883275 Fax: (020) 7793 8188 E-mail: sales@safensoundsecurity.co.uk

▶ J. Wesley (Electrical Contractors) Ltd, Units 7-10 Station Approach, Hitchin, Hertfordshire, SG4 9UP Tel: (01462) 437677 Fax: (01462) 422738 E-mail: info@wesleyservices.co.uk

▶ Zeag UK Ltd, 17 Deer Park Road, London, SW19 3XJ Tel: 0208 543 3281 Fax: 0208 543 5344 E-mail: info@zeaguk.com

CONTROL SYSTEMS, AGRICULTURAL/ANIMAL HUSBANDRY/DAIRY FARMING

Davlec Ltd, Unit 16, Severn Farm Industrial Estate, Welshpool, Powys, SY21 7DF Tel: (01938) 555791 Fax: (01938) 555792 E-mail: sales@davlec.com

Robert J V Kelso, Oughterard Road, Dungannon, County Tyrone, BT70 3HT Tel: (028) 8775 8686 E-mail: moreeholsteans@hotmail.com

CONTROL SYSTEMS, FUME CUPBOARD/CABINET

▶ Air Science Technologies Ltd, Suite 8, Jubilee House, Altcar Road, Formby, Liverpool, L37 8DL Tel: (01704) 833338 Fax: (01704) 833500 E-mail: info@airscienceuk.com

▶ RQS Engineering Solutions Ltd, 110 Main Street, Lennoxtown, Glasgow, G66 7DA Tel: (01360) 310554 E-mail: alanjlawson@btinternet.com

CONTROL SYSTEMS, PRODUCTION

Ceres System Ltd, Unit 15 The Old Malthouse, Springfield Road, Grantham, Lincolnshire, NG31 7BG Tel: (01476) 563188 E-mail: sales@vertexplus.co.uk

CONTROL SYSTEMS, VARIABLE SPEED, ELECTRIC/ELECTRONIC

Data Systems & Solutions, Unit 14 Princes Park Princes Way, Team Valley Trading Estate, Gateshead, Tyne & Wear, NE11 0NF Tel: 0191-499 4000 Fax: 0191-499 4001 E-mail: tomsimpson@ds-s.com

Laurence, Scott & Electromotors Ltd, Po Box 25, Norwich, NR1 1JD Tel: (01603) 628333 Fax: (01603) 610604 E-mail: sales@laurence-scott.com

Uttley & Thompson Electronics Ltd, 90 Abbey Street, Accrington, Lancashire, BB5 1EE Tel: (01254) 384850 Fax: (01254) 395474 E-mail: uttleyandthompson@farmore.net

CONTROL TEST EQUIPMENT

Controls Testing Equipment Ltd, Icknield Way Industrial Estate, Icknield Way, Tring, Hertfordshire, HP23 4JX Tel: (01442) 828311 Fax: (01442) 828466 E-mail: sales@controlstesting.co.uk

CONTROL VALVES

Auld Valves Ltd, Finlas Street, Cowlairs Industrial Estate, Glasgow, G22 5DQ Tel: 0141-557 0515 Fax: 0141-558 1059 E-mail: bob@auldvalves.com

Copes-Vulcan, Road Two, Winsford Industrial Estate, Winsford, Cheshire, CW7 3QL Tel: (01606) 552041 Fax: (01606) 558275 E-mail: copes@processequipment.spx.com

D R B Power Transmission, First Avenue, Deeside Industrial Park, Deeside, Clwyd, CH5 2QR Tel: (01244) 280280 Fax: (01244) 288367 E-mail: sales@drbgroup.co.uk

Dresser Flow Control, Unit 4 Suite 1.1 Nobel House The Grand Union Office Park, Packe, Uxbridge, Middlesex, UB8 2GH Tel: (01895) 454900 Fax: (01895) 454919 E-mail: sales@dresser-valve.co.uk

Dynamic Pump Services Ltd, Unit 11 Loomer Road Industrial Estate, Loomer Road, Newcastle, Staffordshire, ST5 7LB Tel: (01782) 566116 Fax: (01782) 566556 E-mail: sales@dynamicpumps.co.uk

Emerson Process Management, Horsfield Way, Bredbury, Stockport, Cheshire, SK6 2SU Tel: 0161-430 7100 Fax: (0870) 2404389

Heap & Partners Ltd, Britannia House, Newton Road, Hoylake, Wirral, Merseyside, CH47 3DG Tel: 0151-632 3393 Fax: 0151-632 4453 E-mail: info@heaps.co.uk

K Controls Ltd, Stone Close, West Drayton, Middlesex, UB7 8JU Tel: (01895) 449601 Fax: (01895) 448586 E-mail: sales@k-controls.co.uk

Koso Kent Introl Ltd, Armytage Road, Brighouse, West Yorkshire, HD6 1QF Tel: (01484) 710311 Fax: (01484) 407407 E-mail: control.valve@kentintrol.com

Magisco Valves Ltd, 53 Limes Road, Wolverhampton, WV6 8RD Tel: (01902) 561111

Majorsell International Ltd, Unit G Springhill Business Park, 111 Steward Street, Birmingham, B18 7AF Tel: 0121-455 0200 Fax: 0121-455 0272 E-mail: sales@majorsell.co.uk

Metso Automation Ltd, 2 Lindenwood, Crockford Lane, Chineham, Basingstoke, Hampshire, RG24 8QY Tel: (0870) 6061478 Fax: (01256) 707661 E-mail: sales@metso.com

Northvale Korting Ltd, Uxbridge Road, Leicester, LE4 7ST Tel: 0116-266 5911 Fax: 0116-261 0050 E-mail: sales@northvalekorting.co.uk

Presreg Valve, 18 Bakewell Road, Loughborough, Leicestershire, LE11 5QY Tel: (01509) 264242 Fax: (01509) 263308

Severn Glocon Ltd, Olympus Park, Quedgeley, Gloucester, GL2 4NF Tel: (01452) 887900 Fax: (0845) 2232041 E-mail: sales@severnglocon.co.uk

▶ Smart Valves Ltd, Uxbridge Road, Leicester, LE4 7ST Tel: 0116-268 8120 Fax: 0116-261 0050 E-mail: sales@smartvalves.co.uk

Tomoe Valve Ltd, Estuary Road, Queensway Meadows Industrial Estate, Newport, Gwent, NP19 4SP Tel: (01633) 636800 Fax: (01633) 636801

Whittle Valve Repairs Ltd, Unit 3 Tower Enterprise Park, Great George Street, Wigan, Lancashire, WN3 4DP Tel: (01942) 493495 E-mail: sales@whittle-valves.co.uk

CONTROLLED ATMOSPHERE FURNACES

Can-Eng Furnaces UK Ltd, Unit 8, Ninian Park, Ninian Way, Wilnecote, Tamworth, Staffordshire, B77 5ES Tel: (01827) 262601 Fax: (01827) 262602 E-mail: can-enguk@mcmail.com

CONTROLLED EXPANSION ALLOYS

Imphy Ugine Precision UK Ltd, Wessex Road, Bourne End, Buckinghamshire, SL8 5DT Tel: (01628) 850234 Fax: (01628) 850119

CONTROLLER (PROGRAMMABLE) SOFTWARE DESIGNERS/SYSTEMS BUILDERS

Crown Max Investments Ltd, Halesfield 19, Telford, Shropshire, TF7 4QT Tel: (01952) 581121 Fax: (01952) 588284 E-mail: info@crownmax.co.uk

Dacs Electrical Ltd, Old Fire Station, Church Street, Connah's Quay, Deeside, Clwyd, CH5 4AS Tel: (01244) 834100 Fax: (01244) 831858 E-mail: sales@dacselectrical.co.uk

Deegee Systems Ltd, 15 Hawksley Rise, Oughtibridge, Sheffield, S35 0JB Tel: 0114-286 4400 Fax: 0114-286 4400 E-mail: sales@deegee.co.uk

Intech Automation Ltd, Willow Hall Works Cote Hill, Halifax, West Yorkshire, HX2 7LZ Tel: (01422) 355885 Fax: (01422) 355885

M C S Control Systems Ltd, Unit 4 Phoenix Park, Bayton Road Industrial Estate, Coventry, CV7 9QN Tel: (024) 7636 0211 Fax: (024) 7636 8219 E-mail: sales@mcscs.co.uk

Maximotive Design Ltd, 70 River Way, Christchurch, Dorset, BH23 2QR Tel: (01202) 565713 Fax: (01202) 565713 E-mail: mylne@maximotive.com

Micro Robotics Ltd, 135 Ditton Walk, Cambridge, CB5 8QB Tel: (01223) 523100 Fax: (01223) 524242 E-mail: sales@microrobotics.co.uk

Practicon Ltd, Chapel Lane, Rode Heath, Stoke-on-Trent, ST7 3SD Tel: (01270) 876211 Fax: (01270) 878887 E-mail: sales.systems@practicon.co.uk

Weirgrove Automation Ltd, Lords Mill, Oakridge Road, High Wycombe, Buckinghamshire, HP11 2PA Tel: (01494) 448387 Fax: (01494) 530734 E-mail: weirgrove@weirgrove.co.uk

CONTROLLERS

F G H Controls Ltd, Openshaw Way, Letchworth Garden City, Hertfordshire, SG6 3ER Tel: (01462) 686677 Fax: (01462) 480633 E-mail: sales@fgh.co.uk

CONTROLLERS, ELECTRICAL EQUIPMENT, ENERGY SAVING/ PEOPLE SENSING

Northern Design Electronics Ltd, 228 Bolton Road, Bradford, West Yorkshire, BD3 0QW Tel: (01274) 729533 Fax: (01274) 721074 E-mail: sales@ndmeter.co.uk

CONTROLLERS, LIGHTING, PROGRAMMABLE

Steinel (UK) Ltd, 25 Manasty Road, Axis Park, Orton Southgate, Peterborough, PE2 6UP Tel: (01733) 366700 Fax: (01733) 366701 E-mail: steinel@steineluk.co.uk

CONTROLLERS, PROGRAMMABLE

A A Electric UK Ltd, Witty Street, Hull, HU3 4TT Tel: (01482) 229880 Fax: (01482) 589644 E-mail: sales@aaelectric.co.uk

Abacus Automation, Seaview House, The Parade, Parkgate, Neston, CH64 6SB Tel: 0151-336 7754 Fax: 0151-336 7548 E-mail: mail@abacusautomation.co.uk

BPX Electro Mechanical Co, Unit 8 Decade Close, High Carr Business Park, Newcastle, Staffordshire, ST5 7UH Tel: (01782) 565500 Fax: (01782) 565500 E-mail: bpxstaffs@bpx.co.uk

C S E Seprol Ltd, Rotherside Road, Eckington, Sheffield, S21 4HL Tel: (01246) 436331 Fax: (01246) 432461 E-mail: products@cse-seprol.com

Colter Products Ltd, Unit 7 Zone C Chelmsford Road Industrial Estate, Chelmsford Road, Dunmow, Essex, CM6 1HD Tel: (01371) 876887 Fax: (01371) 875638 E-mail: sales@coltergroup.co.uk

G E Fanuc Automation (UK) Ltd, 15 Basset Court, Loake Close, Grange Park, Northampton, NN4 5EZ Tel: (01604) 744130 Fax: (01604) 744140 E-mail: gef.uk@gefanuceur.ge.com

Horstmann Group Ltd, Roman Farm Road, Bristol, BS4 1UP Tel: 0117-978 8700 Fax: 0117-987 8701 E-mail: reception@horstmann.co.uk

Lamonde Automation Ltd, Project House, Morris Road, South Nutfield, Redhill, RH1 5SA Tel: (01737) 824600 Fax: (01737) 821431 E-mail: sales@lamonde.com

Colin Mear Engineering Ltd, Combe Wood, Combe St Nicholas, Chard, Somerset, TA20 3NL Tel: (01460) 67351 Fax: (01460) 65661 E-mail: cme@cme-ltd.com

Moeller Holding Ltd, PO Box 35 Gatehouse Close, Aylesbury, Buckinghamshire, HP19 8DH Tel: (01296) 393322 Fax: (01296) 421854 E-mail: marketingl@moeller.co.uk

Motor Technology Ltd, Motec House, Chadkirk Business Park, Stockport, Cheshire, SK6 3NE Tel: 0161-217 7100 Fax: 0161-217 7101 E-mail: sales@motec.co.uk

Panasonic Electric Works UK Ltd, Sunrise Parkway, Linford Wood, Milton Keynes, MK14 6LF Tel: (01908) 231555 Fax: (01908) 231599 E-mail: info-uk@eu.pewg.panasonic.com

▶ Wilkie Electronics, 16 Muirhall Terrace, Perth, PH2 7ES Tel: (01738) 621492

CONTROLLING DAMPERS

G D L Air Systems Ltd, Air Diffusion Works, Woolley Bridge Road, Hadfield, Glossop, Derbyshire, SK13 1AB Tel: (01457) 861538 Fax: (01457) 866010 E-mail: sales@grille.co.uk

Lindab Ltd, Unit 9 - 10 Carousel Way, Riverside Business Park, Northampton, NN3 9HG Tel: (01604) 788350 Fax: (01604) 788351

CONVENTIONAL PRINTED CIRCUITS

Maxim Integrated Products Ltd, 612 Reading Road, Winnersh, Wokingham, Berkshire, RG41 5HE Tel: 0118-900 6300 Fax: 0118-900 6400

Printech Circuit Laboratories Ltd, 31-35 Haltwhistle Road, South Woodham Ferrers, Chelmsford, CM3 5ZA Tel: (01245) 323244 Fax: (01245) 329472 E-mail: sales@pcll.co.uk

Simclar International Ltd, Pitreavie Business Park, Queensferry Road, Dunfermline, Fife, KY11 8UN Tel: (01383) 735161 Fax: (01383) 739986 E-mail: sales@simclar.com

Southport Electronics Ltd, 22 Glebe Lane, Banks, Southport, Merseyside, PR9 8EU Tel: (01704) 228510 Fax: (01704) 211057

Systematics Printed Circuits Ltd, Unit 7 R.J. Mitchell Centre, Spitfire Quay, Hazel Road, Woolston, Southampton, SO19 7GB Tel: (023) 8068 5677 Fax: (023) 8068 5625 E-mail: pcbsales@systematicsprintedcircuits.com

CONVERGING EQUIPMENT, MULTI LANE CONVEYOR, AUTOMATIC

Converging Solutions Holdings Ltd, Unit 13, Waterloo Business Park, Bidford-on-Avon, Alcester, Warwickshire, B50 4JG Tel: (01789) 491144 Fax: (01789) 491155 E-mail: sale@convergingsolutions.co.uk

CONVERSION FOAM

Arms Technical Engineering, Arms House, 29 Glen Road, Oldham, OL4 1LP Tel: 0161-626 5293 Fax: 0161-626 5293 E-mail: sales@armstechnicalengineering.co.uk

Gordano Packaging Ltd, 2a Lansdown Industrial Estate, Gloucester Road, Cheltenham, Gloucestershire, GL51 8PL Tel: (01242) 263765 Fax: (01242) 263768 E-mail: jeb@gordano-packaging.co.uk

CONVERTING MACHINERY

C M Machinery, 50 Seagoe Industrial Area, Portadown, Craigavon, County Armagh, BT63 5QE Tel: (028) 3833 3341 Fax: (028) 3833 0915 E-mail: info@cmmachinery.co.uk

Charles Walker Ltd, 22-24 John Brannan Way, Bellshill, Lanarkshire, ML4 3HD Tel: (01698) 327600 Fax: (01698) 327602 E-mail: se.scotland@charleswalker.co.uk

Keely Machinery Ltd, Unit 11 Ronald Close, Woburn Road Industrial Estate, Kempston, Bedford, MK42 7SH Tel: (01234) 857744 Fax: (01234) 854219 E-mail: sales@keelymachinery.co.uk

M M Digital Ltd, Haig Road, Parkgate Industrial Estate, Knutsford, Cheshire, WA16 8DX Tel: (01565) 755356 Fax: (01565) 755357 E-mail: sales@mmdigital.co.uk

Parkland Machines Ltd, 6 Portland Street, Bury, Lancashire, BL9 6EY Tel: 0161-762 9737 Fax: 0161-762 9738 E-mail: sales@parkland-international.com

Polygraphica Equipment Ltd, 1 Benton Office Park, Horbury, Wakefield, West Yorkshire, WF4 5RA Tel: (01924) 200444 Fax: (01924) 363714 E-mail: sales@polygraphica.com

CONVEYOR ACCESSORY MANUFRS

Adept Engineering & Design, 7-2 Halas Industrial Estate, Forge Lane, Halesowen, West Midlands, B62 8EB Tel: 0121-602 5060 Fax: 0121-602 5080 E-mail: aedrollers@tiscali.co.uk

Brewpack Ltd, 2 Sky Business Park, Eversley Way, Thorpe Industrial Estate, Egham, Surrey, TW20 8RG Tel: (01784) 431331 Fax: (01784) 472313 E-mail: sales@brewpack.ltd.uk

Conveyor Accesories Direct, 16 James Watt Close, Drayton Fields Industrial Estate, Drayton Fields Industrial Esta, Daventry, Northamptonshire, NN11 8RJ Tel: (01327) 311122 Fax: (01327) 314188 E-mail: sales@conveyor-accessories-direct.co.uk

Euro Conveying Equipment, Shepley Street, Failsworth, Manchester, M35 9DY Tel: 0161-682 6966 Fax: 0161-688 4942 E-mail: trev@beltman.co.uk

Moving Methods Ltd, Brooks Lane, Middlewich, Cheshire, CW10 0JH Tel: (01606) 833262 Fax: (01606) 832304

CONVEYOR ACCESSORY MANUFRS

– continued

Nationwide Vulcanising Ltd, 100 Brownedge Road, Lostock Hall, Preston, PR5 5AD Tel: (01772) 698122 Fax: (01772) 335376

Olympic Mato Ltd, West Rose Works, St. Mewan, St. Austell, Cornwall, PL25 5SP Tel: (01726) 61141 Fax: (01726) 70211

Siegling (U K) Ltd, Unit 2, Pilton Industrial Estate, Pitlake, Croydon, CR0 3RY Tel: (020) 8681 8151

CONVEYOR BEARINGS

Bridge Bearings Ltd, Heath Field Road, Sandy Lane Industrial Estate, Stourport-On-Severn, Worcestershire, DY13 9AQ Tel: (01299) 878443 Fax: (01299) 878318 E-mail: bearingsales@bridge-bearings.co.uk

Commercial Bearings Ltd, Plume Street, Birmingham, B6 7RY Tel: 0121-322 2036 Fax: 0121-327 6926 E-mail: sales@commercialbearings.co.uk

R T Bearings Ltd., Units 19 & 20, Bevan Industrial Estate, Brockmoor, Brierley Hill, West Midlands, DY5 3TF Tel: (01384) 868458 Fax: (01384) 865458 E-mail: sales@rtbearings.com

System Plast Ltd, Unit 3-4, Churchlands Business Park, Ufton Road, Harbury, Leamington Spa, Warwickshire, CV33 9GX Tel: (01926) 614314 Fax: (01926) 614914 E-mail: info@systemplastuk.com

Taylor Precision Plastics Ltd, Mile Oak Industrial Estate, Maesbury Road, Oswestry, Shropshire, SY10 8GA Tel: (01691) 679516 Fax: (01691) 670538 E-mail: sales@plasticbearings.co.uk

CONVEYOR BELT CLEANER OR SCRAPER REFURBISHMENT

L V S I M A S Ltd, Swansey Mill, Swansey Lane, Whittle-le-Woods, Chorley, Lancashire, PR6 7NR Tel: (01257) 263666 Fax: (01257) 241821 E-mail: sales@rubberbelts.co.uk

M & J (Europe) Ltd, Tafarnaubach Industrial Estate, Tafarnaubach, Tredegar, Gwent, NP22 3AA Tel: (01495) 723444 Fax: (01495) 723555

P.P. Mackingdale Ltd, Claymore, Tame Valley Industrial Estate, Tamworth, Staffordshire, B77 5DQ Tel: (01827) 261100 Fax: (01827) 281223

CONVEYOR BELT CLEANERS/ SCRAPERS

H M E Technology, Priory House, Saxon Park, Hanbury Road, Stoke Prior, Bromsgrove, Worcestershire, B60 4AD Tel: (01527) 839000 Fax: (01527) 839001 E-mail: contactus@hme-tech.com

Hosch (GB) Ltd, 97 Sadler Forster Way, Teesside Industrial Estate, Stockton-On-Tees, Cleveland, TS17 9JY Tel: (01642) 751100 Fax: (01642) 751448 E-mail: mail@hosch.co.uk

JND Technologies Ltd, Thrumpton Lane, Retford, Nottinghamshire, DN22 7AN Tel: (01777) 706777 Fax: (01777) 713192 E-mail: info@jnd.co.uk

CONVEYOR BELT DRUMS

Adept Engineering & Design, 7-2 Halas Industrial Estate, Forge Lane, Halesowen, West Midlands, B62 8EB Tel: 0121-602 5060 Fax: 0121-602 5080 E-mail: aedrollers@tiscali.co.uk

Conveyor Lines Accessories Ltd, Unit 17 Millbrook Close, Northampton, NN5 5JF Tel: (01604) 592960 Fax: (01604) 592970 E-mail: sales@casrollers.com

Dynatork Air Motors Ltd, Merchant Drive, Hertford, SG13 7BL Tel: (01992) 501900 Fax: (01992) 509890 E-mail: dynatork@huco.com

William Hardill Sons & Co. Ltd, Westbury Works, Sticker Lane, Bradford, West Yorkshire, BD4 8RU Tel: (01274) 664422 Fax: (01274) 664433 E-mail: info@hardill.demon.co.uk

CONVEYOR BELT FASTENERS

MATO Ltd, Church Bank Works, Kirk Road, Church, Accrington, Lancashire, BB5 4JW Tel: (01254) 235411 Fax: (01254) 238023 E-mail: info@mato.co.uk

Red Box Supplies, Unit 19d, Bergen Way, Hull, HU7 0YQ Tel: (01482) 321713 Fax: (01482) 321714 E-mail: sales@redboxsupplies.co.uk

CONVEYOR BELT ROLLERS

Adept Engineering & Design, 7-2 Halas Industrial Estate, Forge Lane, Halesowen, West Midlands, B62 8EB Tel: 0121-602 5060 Fax: 0121-602 5080 E-mail: aedrollers@tiscali.co.uk

Drive Technics Ltd, 1 Langley Terrace Industrial Park, Latimer Road, Luton, LU1 3XQ Tel: (01582) 486679 Fax: (01582) 486676

CONVEYOR BELT WEIGHT TOTALISER/FEED RATE INDICATORS

Siemens Process Instruments, Century House, Bridgwater Road, Worcester, WR4 9ZQ Tel: (01905) 450500 Fax: (01905) 450501

Thermo Fisher Sceientific, Unit A2, Swift Park, Old Leicester Road, Rugby, Warwickshire, CV21 1DZ Tel: (01788) 820319 Fax: (01788) 820301 E-mail: saleswiuk@thermofisher.com

CONVEYOR BELTING MANUFRS, *See also headings under Belting*

A B C Conveyor Belting Ltd, Northfield Rd, Soham, Ely, Cambs, CB7 5UF Tel: (01353) 624322 Fax: (01353) 723859

▶ Ace Conveyor Equipment Ltd, Plumtree Farm Industrial Estate, Plumtree Road, Bircotes, Doncaster, South Yorkshire, DN11 8EW Tel: (01302) 718800 Fax: (01302) 711998 E-mail: info@ace247.com

Action Vulcanising Services, 37 Stretton Close, Doncaster, South Yorkshire, DN4 6UE Tel: (01302) 530510 Fax: (01302) 530510

Alldrives Ltd, Unit 6 Mead Park River Way, Harlow, Essex, CM20 2SE Tel: (01279) 445576 Fax: (01279) 425554 E-mail: alldrives@btconnect.co.uk

Ammeraal Beltech Ltd, Parkwood Street, Keighley, West Yorkshire, BD21 4PL Tel: (01535) 667015 Fax: (01535) 610250 E-mail: keighley@ammeraalbeltech.co.uk

Anaconda Belting Co., 2 Ashwood Place, Bean, Dartford, DA2 8BD Tel: (01474) 709784 Fax: (01474) 709896 E-mail: info@anacondabelting.co.uk

Apex Belting Co. Ltd, 9 Boldero Road, Bury St. Edmunds, Suffolk, IP32 7BS Tel: (01284) 752486 Fax: (01284) 750542 E-mail: sales@apex-belting.co.uk

Belting & Mechanical Leather Co. Ltd, 20 Cloberfield Road, Milngavie, Glasgow, G62 7LN Tel: 0141-956 6577 Fax: 0141-956 2126 E-mail: sales@beltingmechanical.co.uk

Belts Conveyors & Accessories Ltd, Unit 8 Terry Dicken Industrial Estate, Station Road, Stokesley, Middlesbrough, Cleveland, TS9 7AE Tel: (01642) 711270 Fax: (01642) 711919 E-mail: geoflett@btinternet.com

Benson Beltings Ltd, Spenvale Works, Balme Road, Cleckheaton, West Yorkshire, BD19 4EW Tel: (01274) 851600 Fax: (01274) 851620 E-mail: sales@benson-beltings.co.uk

Blackburn Conveyor, Delph Road, Great Harwood, Blackburn, BB6 7HT Tel: (01254) 888866 Fax: (01254) 829826

C P T Enterprises, 143 White Hart Lane, Portchester, Fareham, Hampshire, PO16 9BB Tel: (023) 9238 9521 Fax: (023) 9237 5181 E-mail: info@cptenterprises.co.uk

Chiorino UK, Phoenix Avenue, Featherstone, Pontefract, West Yorkshire, WF7 6EP Tel: (01977) 691880 Fax: (0870) 6065061 E-mail: sales@chiorino.co.uk

Conveyor Lines Accessories Ltd, Unit 17 Millbrook Close, Northampton, NN5 5JF Tel: (01604) 592960 Fax: (01604) 592970 E-mail: sales@casrollers.com

Cozens & Cole Ltd, Spring Road, Ettingshall, Wolverhampton, WV4 6JT Tel: (01902) 405971 Fax: (01902) 497021 E-mail: sales@cozensandcole.co.uk

Davies Woven Wire Ltd, Unit 38 Cradley Heath Factory Centre, Woods Lane, Cradley Heath, West Midlands, B64 7AQ Tel: (01384) 411991 Fax: (01384) 410999 E-mail: sales@davieswovenwire.co.uk

Drive Technics Ltd, 1 Langley Terrace Industrial Park, Latimer Road, Luton, LU1 3XQ Tel: (01582) 486679 Fax: (01582) 486676

Fenbelt Ltd, 107 Clay Street, Soham, Ely, Cambridgeshire, CB7 5HL Tel: (01353) 723955 Fax: (01353) 723953 E-mail: sales@fenbelt.co.uk

Fenner plc, Hesslewood Office Park, Ferriby Road, Hessle, North Humberside, HU13 0PW Tel: (01482) 626500 Fax: (01482) 626502 E-mail: info@fenner.com

Geppert Conveyors UK, Camberley, Surrey, GU17 0RP Tel: (01252) 875871 Fax: (01252) 878804 E-mail: gwilliams@geppert-band.de

H Ireland & Son, 201 Hillhead Rd, Ballyclare, County Antrim, BT39 9LP Tel: (028) 9335 2844 Fax: (028) 9334 2382 E-mail: sales@h-ireland.co.uk

Hulco UK Ltd, 21 Meadow Close, Ise Valley Industrial Estate, Wellingborough, Northamptonshire, NN8 4BH Tel: (01933) 223743 Fax: (01933) 441534

Interbelt Ltd, Unit 5, Glensyn Way, Burton-on-Trent, Staffordshire, DE14 1LX Tel: (01283) 562598 Fax: (01283) 515316

Intralox Ltd, Building 90, Third Avenue, Pensnett Trading Estate, Kingswinford, West Midlands, DY6 7FW Tel: (0800) 894392 Fax: (01384) 355655

J Vickers & Co., 6 Birchfield, Bolton, BL2 4AH Tel: (01204) 301092 Fax: (01204) 301092

Jason Industrial Ltd, Unit 29 Normanby Park Workshops, Normanby Road, Scunthorpe, North Lincolnshire, DN15 8QZ Tel: (01724) 861006 Fax: (01724) 869846

JD Vulcanising Services Ltd, Apple Orchard House, Skelton-in-Cleveland, Saltburn-by-the-Sea, Cleveland, TS12 2AZ Tel: (01287) 651194 Fax: (01287) 651194

George Lane & Sons Ltd, Bannerley Road, Birmingham, B33 0SL Tel: 0121-784 5525 Fax: 0121-783 6988 E-mail: info@georgelane.co.uk

M E S International Ltd, 11 Copdale Road, Leicester, LE5 4FG Tel: 0116-249 0333 Fax: 0116-249 0142 E-mail: sales@mesinternational.uk.com

Martens Conveyor Belting Ltd, 72 Wheathead Lane, Keighley, West Yorkshire, BD22 6NN Tel: (01535) 609028 Fax: (01535) 605425 E-mail: sales@martensbelt.co.uk

Multibelt Conveyor Belt Co., Unit 12 Kencot Way, Erith, Kent, DA18 4AB Tel: (020) 8310 9400 Fax: (020) 8310 2433

Olympic Mato Ltd, West Rose Works, St. Mewan, St. Austell, Cornwall, PL25 5SP Tel: (01726) 61141 Fax: (01726) 70211

Polymark (G B) Ltd, Unit 14, Sopwith Way, Drayton Field Industrial Estate, Daventry, Northamptonshire, NN11 8PB Tel: (01327) 308600 Fax: (01327) 308611 E-mail: polymark.sales@polymark.co.uk

Premier Power Products Ltd, 1 Dampier Mews Edward Close, Hounstone Business Park, Houndstone Business Park, Yeovil, Somerset, BA22 8RU Tel: (01935) 432412 Fax: (01935) 433557

RDB Belting Ltd, Perseverance Mill, Church Lane, Mow Cop, Stoke-on-Trent, ST7 4LS Tel: (01782) 511014 Fax: (01782) 523220

Red Box Supplies, Unit 19d, Bergen Way, Hull, HU7 0YQ Tel: (01482) 321713 Fax: (01482) 321714 E-mail: sales@redboxsupplies.co.uk

Response Conveyor Belting Services, 41 Holly Court, St. Modwen Road, Plymouth, PL6 8LG Tel: (01752) 267111 Fax: (01752) 662110 E-mail: response.conveyors@btinternet.com

Siegling (U K) Ltd, Unit 2, Pilton Industrial Estate, Pitlake, Croydon, CR0 3RY Tel: (020) 8681 8151

Specialised Belting Supplies Ltd, 26 Brunel Way, Thetford, Norfolk, IP24 1HP Tel: (01842) 754392 Fax: (01842) 765264 E-mail: sales@sbsbelting.com

Strathaven Belting Co. Ltd, 33 Colvilles Place, East Kilbride, Glasgow, G75 0PZ Tel: (01357) 529936 Fax: (01357) 521188

Strathcona Conveyors Ltd, UNIT 3A, 95 Westburn Drive, Camduslamg, Glasgow, G72 7NA Tel: 0141-876 4525 Fax: 0141-620 2165

Thorpe Contracts Ltd, Worksop Road, Thorpe Salvin, Worksop, Nottinghamshire, S80 3JX Tel: (01909) 501414 Fax: (01909) 770767

Toogood Industrial Ltd, Unit H7, Haysbridge Business Centre, Brickhouse Lane, South Godstone, Godstone, Surrey, RH9 8JW Tel: (01342) 844188 Fax: (01342) 844220 E-mail: office@toogood.co.uk

Transbelt Ltd, 36 Howe Street, Bootle, Merseyside, L20 8NG Tel: 0151-922 1314 Fax: 0151-922 3983 E-mail: transbelt@btconnect.com

Transbelt Ltd, 46 The Acorn Centre, Barry Street, Oldham, OL1 3NE Tel: 0161-620 0493 Fax: 0161-627 0084 E-mail: sales@transbelt.co.uk

Universal Vulcanising Services, Unit 4 Moss Lane, Little Hoole, Preston, PR4 4SX Tel: (01772) 614343 Fax: (01772) 614848

Stewart Vaughan & Co. Ltd, Unit 21 Riverside Business Park, Lyon Road, London, SW19 2RL Tel: (020) 8544 9199 Fax: (020) 8540 8884

Westcountry Conveyors, 23 Lowley Road, Pennygillam Industrial Estate, Launceston, Cornwall, PL15 7PY Tel: (01566) 777940 Fax: (01566) 777659 E-mail: westconveyors@aol.com

Westminster Plastic Fabrication Ltd, Wynstead, Parkgate Road, Saughall, Chester, CH1 6JS Tel: (01244) 881884 Fax: (01244) 880111 E-mail: westpack@tiscali.co.uk

Wildcat Taconic, School Close, Burgess Hill, West Sussex, RH15 9RD Tel: (01444) 247756 Fax: (01444) 248416 E-mail: sales@wildcat-taconic.com

Wire Belt Co. Ltd, Castle Road, Sittingbourne, Kent, ME10 3RF Tel: (01795) 421771 Fax: (01795) 428905 E-mail: sales@wirebelt.co.uk

CONVEYOR CHAINS

Elecon Ltd, Wharf Road, Hawkins Lane Industrial Estate, Burton-on-Trent, Staffordshire, DE14 1PZ Tel: (01283) 537575 Fax: (01283) 511227

Ewart Chain Ltd, Colombo Street, Derby, DE23 8LX Tel: (01332) 345451 Fax: (01332) 371753 E-mail: sales@ewartchain.co.uk

F B Chain Ltd, Jubilee Road, Letchworth Garden City, Hertfordshire, SG6 1NE Tel: (01462) 670844 Fax: (01462) 480745 E-mail: phil.taylor@fbchain.com

James Hesketh & Co. Ltd, New Works, Sion Street, Radcliffe, Manchester, M26 3SB Tel: 0161-723 2789 Fax: 0161-725 9072

Industrial Chains & Gears, 45 Copeland Avenue, Tittensor, Stoke-on-Trent, ST12 9JA Tel: (01782) 374300 Fax: (01782) 373804 E-mail: peter@i-c-g.fsnet.co.uk

John King Chains Ltd, Lancaster Close, New Climax Works, Sherburn In Elmet, Leeds, LS25 6NS Tel: (01977) 689442 Fax: (01977) 681899 E-mail: admin@johnking-chain.com

Mec A Tec Services Ltd, Boleness Road, Wisbech, Cambridgeshire, PE13 2RB Tel: (01945) 474685 Fax: (01945) 474687 E-mail: mecatec@aol.com

Precision Chains Ltd, Clee Road, Dudley, West Midlands, DY2 0YG Tel: (01384) 455455 Fax: (01384) 230751 E-mail: mark.kyte@precision-chains.co.uk

R J T Conveyors (International) Ltd, Unit 20 Beven Industrial Estate, Beven Road, Brierley Hill, West Midlands, DY5 3TF Tel: (01384) 864458 Fax: (01384) 827777 E-mail: sales@rjtconveyors.com

R U D Chains Ltd, Units 10-14, John Wilson Business Park, Thanet Way, Whitstable, Kent, CT5 3QT Tel: (01227) 276611 Fax: (01227) 276586 E-mail: sales@rud.co.uk

Sedis Co. Ltd, PO Box 6529, Wellingborough, Northamptonshire, NN8 4YS Tel: (0870) 1607840 Fax: (01604) 764162 E-mail: sedisco@sedis.com

Sigma Industries Ltd, 19 Dunlop Road, Redditch, Worcestershire, B97 5XP Tel: (01527) 547771 Fax: (01527) 547772 E-mail: sales.sigmaind@btopenworld.com

Silcoms Ltd, Victoria Mill, Piggott Street, Farnworth, Bolton, BL4 9QN Tel: (01204) 571305 Fax: (01204) 861723 E-mail: pep@silcoms.co.uk

Stalum Engineering Ltd, 3 Darnall Works, Leathley Road, Leeds, LS10 1BG Tel: 0113-242 2289 Fax: 0113-234 7951 E-mail: sales@stalum.co.uk

Transmission Development Co GB Ltd, 26 Dawkins Road, Poole, Dorset, BH15 4HF Tel: (01202) 675555 Fax: (01202) 677466 E-mail: sales@transdev.co.uk

Transtec International, 39, Westbrook Trading Estate, Westbrook Road, Trafford Park, Manchester, M17 1AY Tel: 0161-772 1844 Fax: 0161-772 1845 E-mail: info@transtecinternational.com

Tsubakimoto UK Ltd, Osier Drive, Annesley, Nottingham, NG15 0DX Tel: (01623) 688700 Fax: (01623) 688729 E-mail: sales@tsubaki.co.uk

CONVEYOR CONVERGING EQUIPMENT

Converging Solutions Holdings Ltd, Unit 13, Waterloo Business Park, Bidford-on-Avon, Alcester, Warwickshire, B50 4JG Tel: (01789) 491144 Fax: (01789) 491155 E-mail: sale@convergingsolutions.co.uk

CONVEYOR GUARDS/COVERS

Modular Robotic Systems Ltd, Cale Lane, Aspull, Wigan, Lancashire, WN2 1HQ Tel: (01942) 820088 Fax: (01942) 820431 E-mail: info@modular-ltd.co.uk

CONVEYOR IDLERS

Continental Conveyor Ltd, West Quay Road, Sunderland Enterprise Park, Sunderland, SR5 2TD Tel: 0191-516 5353 Fax: 0191-516 5399 E-mail: sales@continental-conveyor.co.uk

Hosch (GB) Ltd, 97 Sadler Forster Way, Teesside Industrial Estate, Stockton-On-Tees, Cleveland, TS17 9JY Tel: (01642) 751100 Fax: (01642) 751448 E-mail: mail@hosch.co.uk

CONVEYOR IDLERS/ROLLER END CAPS

Edwin Lowe Ltd, Perry Bridge Works, Aldridge Road, Perry Barr, Birmingham, B42 2HB Tel: 0121-356 5255 Fax: 0121-344 3172 E-mail: sales@edwinlowe.com

CONVEYOR INDEXING SYSTEMS

Durable UK Ltd, East Dorset Trade Park, 10 Nimrod Way, Wimborne, Dorset, BH21 7SH Tel: (01202) 897071 Fax: (01202) 873381 E-mail: marketing@durable-uk.com

Turbo Systems, 1 Gillett Street, Hull, HU3 4JA Tel: (01482) 325651 Fax: (01482) 211434 E-mail: mmoss@turbo-systems.com

CONVEYOR INSTALLATION OR SERVICING OR MAINTENANCE OR REPAIR

Brec Ltd, Moor Park Court, St. Georges Road, Preston, PR1 6AQ Tel: (01772) 555000 Fax: (01772) 555422 E-mail: info@brec-ltd.com

Jack Burrows & Sons, Unit 10 Field Gate Works, New Street, Walsall, WS1 3DN Tel: (01922) 644150 Fax: (01922) 724375

Continental Engineering (1986) Ltd, 24 Invincible Road, Farnborough, Hampshire, GU14 7QU Tel: (01252) 512122 Fax: (01252) 549291 E-mail: conteng86ltd@btinternet.com

▶ indicates data change since last edition

CONVEYOR INSTALLATION OR SERVICING OR MAINTENANCE OR REPAIR – *continued*

Fenner Dunlop Europe, Marfleet, Hull, HU9 5RA Tel: (01482) 781234 Fax: (01482) 785438 E-mail: paul.mackman@fennerdunlop.com
Fletcher Moorland Ltd, Elenora Street, Stoke-On-Trent, ST4 1QG Tel: (01782) 411021 Fax: (01782) 744470 E-mail: info@fletchermoorland.co.uk
M & J (Europe) Ltd, Tafarnaubach Industrial Estate, Tafarnaubach, Tredegar, Gwent, NP22 3AA Tel: (01495) 723444 Fax: (01495) 723555
Power System Services Ltd, Foxwood Close, Sheepbridge Industrial Estate, Chesterfield, Derbyshire, S41 9RB Tel: (01246) 268800 Fax: (01246) 268811 E-mail: info@powersystemsservices.co.uk
Rti Conveyors, Common Road, Eton Wick, Windsor, Berkshire, SL4 6QY Tel: (01753) 855888 Fax: (01753) 855800 E-mail: rtiservices@btinternet.com
Simpsons Engineering, Vowels Lane, Kingscote, East Grinstead, West Sussex, RH19 4LF Tel: (01342) 811040 Fax: (01342) 811040
V Installations Mechanical Handling Ltd, Saxon Business Park, Stoke Prior, Bromsgrove, Worcestershire, B60 4AD Tel: 01527 833248
Westcountry Conveyors, 23 Lowley Road, Pennygillam Industrial Estate, Launceston, Cornwall, PL15 7PY Tel: (01566) 777940 Fax: (01566) 777659 E-mail: westconveyors@aol.com

CONVEYOR LEVELLING FEET

Conveyor Accesories Direct, 16 James Watt Close, Drayton Fields Industrial Estate, Drayton Fields Industrial Esta, Daventry, Northamptonshire, NN11 8RJ Tel: (01327) 311122 Fax: (01327) 314188 E-mail: sales@conveyor-accessories-direct.co.uk
Conveyor Lines Accessories Ltd, Unit 17 Millbrook Close, Northampton, NN5 5JF Tel: (01604) 592960 Fax: (01604) 592970 E-mail: sales@casrollers.com
Nu Tech Engineering Services Ltd, Unit 7 & 14 Newtown Business Park, Albion Close, Poole, Dorset, BH12 3LL Tel: (01202) 724100 Fax: (01202) 724114 E-mail: sales@nutech-eng.com

CONVEYOR PULLEYS

Bankside Engineering Ltd, Woodhouse St, Hedon Road, Hull, HU9 1RJ Tel: (01482) 337700 Fax: (01482) 337742 E-mail: users@bie.co.uk
William Hardill Sons & Co. Ltd, Westbury Works, Sticker Lane, Bradford, West Yorkshire, BD4 8RU Tel: (01274) 664422 Fax: (01274) 664433 E-mail: info@hardill.demon.co.uk

CONVEYOR ROLLERS

Amber Industries Ltd, Brook House, Brook Street, Tipton, West Midlands, DY4 9DD Tel: 0121-530 8664 Fax: 0121-530 8665 E-mail: info@amber-industries.ltd.uk
Amberlan Ltd, Building No 2, Brick Kiln Street, Brierley Hill, West Midlands, DY5 1JG Tel: (01384) 74332 Fax: (01384) 74334 E-mail: amberlan@blueyonder.co.uk
Autotrack (Birmingham) Ltd, Ball Unit House Station Road Industrial Estate, Station Road, Woodchester, Stroud, Gloucestershire, GL5 5EQ Tel: (01453) 873155 Fax: (01453) 878500 E-mail: info@autotrack.co.uk
Bankside Engineering Ltd, Woodhouse St, Hedon Road, Hull, HU9 1RJ Tel: (01482) 337700 Fax: (01482) 337742 E-mail: users@bie.co.uk
Conveyor Accesories Direct, 16 James Watt Close, Drayton Fields Industrial Estate, Drayton Fields Industrial Esta, Daventry, Northamptonshire, NN11 8RJ Tel: (01327) 311122 Fax: (01327) 314188 E-mail: sales@conveyor-accessories-direct.co.uk
Fastrax Conveyors & Components, Shieling Court, Oakley Hay Industrial Estate, Great Oakley, Corby, Northamptonshire, NN18 9QD Tel: (01536) 747770 Fax: (01536) 747990 E-mail: fastraxcc@aol.com
Hallanshire Engineering Holdings Ltd, Unit 14, North Anston Trading Estate, Dinnington, Sheffield, S25 4JJ Tel: (01909) 562091 Fax: (01909) 550206E-mail: sales@heh.co.uk
Interroll Ltd, Brunel Road, Earlstrees Industrial Estate, Corby, Northamptonshire, NN17 4UX Tel: (01536) 200322 Fax: (01536) 748505 E-mail: gb-sales@interroll.com
M E S International Ltd, 11 Copdale Road, Leicester, LE5 4FG Tel: 0116-249 0333 Fax: 0116-249 0142 E-mail: sales@mesinternational.uk.com
Roll Ezy, Warrington Lane, Agden, Lymm, Cheshire, WA13 0SW Tel: (01925) 759554 Fax: (01925) 759588 E-mail: sales@rollezy.com
Wolverhampton Handling Ltd, Unit 10 Planetary Industrial Estate, Planetary Road, Willenhall, West Midlands, WV13 3XQ Tel: (01902) 726481 Fax: (01902) 864744 E-mail: sales@wolverhamptonhandling.co.uk

CONVEYOR SAFETY/ PERSONNEL DETECTION SYSTEMS

Calmtoken Ltd, 32C Ellesmere Court, Leechmere Industrial Estate, Sunderland, SR2 9UA Tel: 0191-521 4316 Fax: 0191-521 4317 E-mail: robert@safetechsystems.com

CONVEYOR SKIRTING/ SPILLAGE CONTROL SYSTEMS

M & J (Europe) Ltd, Tafarnaubach Industrial Estate, Tafarnaubach, Tredegar, Gwent, NP22 3AA Tel: (01495) 723444 Fax: (01495) 723555
Mistura Systems, 217 Kingsbury Road, London, NW9 9PQ Tel: (020) 8511 1854 Fax: (020) 8205 0055 E-mail: safety@mistura.co.uk

CONVEYOR SYSTEM COMPONENTS

Calmtoken Ltd, 32C Ellesmere Court, Leechmere Industrial Estate, Sunderland, SR2 9UA Tel: 0191-521 4316 Fax: 0191-521 4317 E-mail: robert@safetechsystems.com
Moving Methods Ltd, Brooks Lane, Middlewich, Cheshire, CW10 0JH Tel: (01606) 833262 Fax: (01606) 832304
System Plast Ltd, Unit 3-4, Churchlands Business Park, Ufton Road, Harbury, Leamington Spa, Warwickshire, CV33 9GX Tel: (01926) 614314 Fax: (01926) 614914 E-mail: info@systemplastuk.com
Transtec International, 39, Westbrook Trading Estate, Westbrook Road, Trafford Park, Manchester, M17 1AY Tel: 0161-772 1844 Fax: 0161-772 1845 E-mail: info@transtecinternational.com

CONVEYOR SYSTEM HIRE

Conveyor Hire, Unit 15d Nuralite Industrial Centre, Canal Road, Higham, Rochester, Kent, ME3 7JA Tel: (01474) 824747 Fax: (01474) 824747 E-mail: mokempen@blueyonder.co.uk
HSS Lift & Shift, 399 York Road, Leeds, LS9 6TA Tel: 0113-240 7707 Fax: 0113-240 9944
Portable Conveyors Ltd, Bowling Green Lane, Albrighton, Wolverhampton, WV7 3HB Tel: (01902) 373735 Fax: (01902) 374755 E-mail: enquiries@portable-conveyors.co.uk
Rako Products Ltd, Brunel Way, Stonehouse, Gloucestershire, GL10 3SX Tel: (01453) 829900 Fax: (01453) 829928 E-mail: sales@rako-products.co.uk
▶ Southern Conveyors, Unit 2 Denton Slipways Site, Wharf Road, Gravesend, Kent, DA12 2RU Tel: (01474) 564145

CONVEYOR SYSTEM PROTECTION EQUIPMENT

Mistura Systems, 217 Kingsbury Road, London, NW9 9PQ Tel: (020) 8511 1854 Fax: (020) 8205 0055 E-mail: safety@mistura.co.uk

CONVEYOR SYSTEMS MANUFRS

▶ 4 Conveyor Solutions Ltd, PO Box 87, Batley, West Yorkshire, WF17 9YB Tel: (01924) 422110 Fax: (01924) 422009 E-mail: enquiries@nuwavesystems.plus.com
A & M Engineering Hull Ltd, Unit 30 B, Foster Street, Hull, HU8 8BT Tel: (01482) 820806 Fax: (01482) 824614 E-mail: sales@am-engineering.co.uk
A S C Materials Handling Ltd, 67 Europa Business Park, Bird Hall Lane, Stockport, Cheshire, SK3 0XA Tel: 0161-428 8600 Fax: 0161-428 1112 E-mail: sales@as-c.co.uk
A U T (Wheels & Castors) Co. Ltd, The Wheel House, Egmont Street, Mossley, Ashton-under-Lyne, Lancashire, OL5 9NB Tel: (01457) 837772 Fax: (01457) 832472 E-mail: sales@aut.co.uk
Alma Engineering Co. Ltd, Montgomery Way, Biggleswade, Bedfordshire, SG18 8UB Tel: (01767) 317814 Fax: (01767) 317002 E-mail: almaen@globalnet.co.uk
Amber Industries, Amber House, Crompton Street, Chadderton, Oldham, OL9 9AA Tel: 0161-284 2222 Fax: 0161-627 0075 E-mail: sales@amber-industries.ltd.uk
Amber Industries Ltd, Brook House, Brook Street, Tipton, West Midlands, DY4 9DD Tel: 0121-530 8664 Fax: 0121-530 8665 E-mail: info@amber-industries.ltd.uk
Ambit Projects Ltd, North Lynn Industrial Estate, King's Lynn, Norfolk, PE30 2JL Tel: (01553) 692977 Fax: (01553) 692997 E-mail: ambit@btinternet.com
Anlyn Engineering, Taylor Street, Liverpool, L5 5AD Tel: 0151-207 5592 Fax: 0151-207 5594E-mail: anlynsales@agjengineering.co.uk
Ashworth Europe Ltd, Building 84, Bay 1 First Avenue, Pensnett Trading Estate, Kingswinford, West Midlands, DY6 7FN Tel: (01384) 355000 Fax: (01384) 355001 E-mail: info@ashworth.com
Asmech Systems Ltd, Units 108-111, Old Mill Lane Industrial Estate, Mansfield Woodhouse, Mansfield, Nottinghamshire, NG19 9BG Tel: (01623) 424442 Fax: (01623) 424433 E-mail: sales@asmechsystems.co.uk
Astwell Augers Ltd, A14 Huntingdon Road, Thrapston, Kettering, Northamptonshire, NN14 4PT Tel: (01832) 735300 Fax: (01832) 735533 E-mail: sales@astwell.co.uk
Ataroth Plastics Machinery Sales Ltd, 5 Maer Lane, Market Drayton, Shropshire, TF9 1QX Tel: (01630) 655148 Fax: (01630) 654055
Autarky Co. Ltd, Charlwoods Industrial Estate, Charlwoods Place, East Grinstead, West Sussex, RH19 2HY Tel: (01342) 311388 Fax: (01342) 323733 E-mail: sales@autarky.com
B B Conveyors Ltd, 5 Hallcroft Industrial Estate, Aurilac Way, Retford, Nottinghamshire, DN22 7PX Tel: (01777) 711111 Fax: (01777) 711501
▶ Beaufort Maintenance Ltd, Ashcombe House, Upper Swainswick, Bath, BA1 8AL Tel: (01225) 859286 Fax: (01225) 859286 E-mail: beaufortmaintenance@fsbdial.co.uk
Bevpak Ltd, 27-28 Arkwright Road, Astmore Industrial Estate, Runcorn, Cheshire, WA7 1NU Tel: (01928) 574815 Fax: (01928) 589487 E-mail: bevpak@hotmail.co.uk
▶ Blackburn Conveyor, Delph Road, Great Harwood, Blackburn, BB6 7HT Tel: (01254) 888866 Fax: (01254) 829826
Blackburn Conveyor, Delph Road, Great Harwood, Blackburn, BB6 7HT Tel: (01254) 888866 Fax: (01254) 829826
Braham & Dixon Ltd, 88 Hodgson Street, Hull, HU8 7JB Tel: (01482) 211853 Fax: (01482) 211865 E-mail: eric@bd-eng.co.uk
Brighouse Engineering Ltd, Martin House, 2 Martin Street, Brighouse, West Yorkshire, HD6 1DA Tel: (01484) 719999 Fax: (01484) 720422 E-mail: brigeng@compuserve.com
Jack Burrows & Sons, Unit 10 Field Gate Works, New Street, Walsall, WS1 3DN Tel: (01922) 644150 Fax: (01922) 724375
C I Logistics, 43 Wenlock Way, Troon Industrial Area, Leicester, LE4 9HU Tel: 0116-276 1691 Fax: 0116-276 9836 E-mail: sales@conveyors.co.uk
Calmtoken Ltd, 32C Ellesmere Court, Leechmere Industrial Estate, Sunderland, SR2 9UA Tel: 0191-521 4316 Fax: 0191-521 4317 E-mail: robert@safetechsystems.com
Canning Conveyor Co. Ltd, Sandy Lane Industrial Estate, Sandy Lane, Worksop, Nottinghamshire, S80 1TN Tel: (01909) 486166 Fax: (01909) 500638 E-mail: andrew.canning@canningconveyor.co.uk
▶ Castor Services Ltd, The Wheel House, Egmont Street, Mossley, Ashton-Under-Lyne, Lancashire, OL5 9NB Tel: (01457) 838001 Fax: (01457) 838998 E-mail: sales@castorserviceslimited.co.uk
Challenger Handling Ltd, 1 Warwick Street, Hull, HU9 1ET Tel: (01482) 224404 Fax: (01482) 210808 E-mail: sales@challenger-group.co.uk
CKF Systems Ltd, Unit 10 St Albans Road, Empire Way, Gloucester, GL2 5FW Tel: (01452) 424565 Fax: (01452) 423477 E-mail: sales@ckf.co.uk
Clyde Process Solutions plc, Carolina Court, Lakeside, Doncaster, South Yorkshire, DN4 5RA Tel: (01302) 321313 Fax: (01302) 554400 E-mail: solutions@clydematerials.co.uk
Cobra Engineering UK Ltd, Redmoor Lane, Wisbech, Cambridgeshire, PE14 0RN Tel: (01945) 860578 Fax: (01945) 860914
▶ Conveyor Hire, Unit 15d Nuralite Industrial Centre, Canal Road, Higham, Rochester, Kent, ME3 7JA Tel: (01474) 824747 Fax: (01474) 824747
Conveyor Units Ltd, Sandy Lane Industrial Estate, Titton, Stourport-On-Severn, Worcestershire, DY13 9PT Tel: 0845 5314049 Fax: (01299) 877921 E-mail: conveyorsales@conveyor-units.co.uk
Conveyors Direct, Unit 6, Fishburn Industrial Estate, Fishburn, Stockton-on-Tees, Cleveland, TS21 4AJ Tel: 01740 623338 Fax: 01740 622504 E-mail: sales@conveyorsdirect.co.uk
Cox & Plant Products Ltd, Monument Works, Balds Lane, Stourbridge, West Midlands, DY9 8SE Tel: (01384) 895121 Fax: (01384) 893611 E-mail: convey@cox-plant.com
Crossfield Engineering Co., Barrow Road, Sheffield, S9 1JZ Tel: 0114-243 8441 Fax: 0114-243 9266 E-mail: sales@crossfielduk.com
D J Installations & Fabrications, The Cottage, Backworth, Newcastle upon Tyne, NE27 0AP Tel: 0191-268 4215 Fax: 0191-268 4215
Dawson, Stephenson Way, Thetford, Norfolk, IP24 3RU Tel: (01842) 753505 Fax: (01842) 753508 E-mail: sales@bwi-dawson.com
Delta Systems Electrical, 65 Boleness Road, Wisbech, Cambridgeshire, PE13 2RB Tel: (01945) 466866 Fax: (01945) 466108 E-mail: sales@deltasystems-uk.co.uk
Dematic Ltd, Beaumont Rd, Banbury, Oxon, OX16 1QZ Tel: (01295) 274600 Fax: (01295) 274808 E-mail: sd.uk.ma-marketing@siemens.com
Domic Welding Services, Unit 8, Victor Business Centre, Arthur St, Redditch, Worcestershire, B98 8JY Tel: (01527) 510041 Fax: (01527) 510403 E-mail: paul@pjwelding.fsnet.co.uk
Don Valley Engineering Co. Ltd, Sandall Stones Road, Kirk Sandall Industrial Estate, Doncaster, South Yorkshire, DN3 1QR Tel: (01302) 881188 E-mail: info@donvalleyeng.com
East Yorkshire Engineering, Unit B 133 Marfleet Avenue, Hull, HU9 5SA Tel: (01482) 788008 Fax: (01482) 788008
Endoline Machinery Ltd, Stratton Business Park, London Road, Biggleswade, Bedfordshire, SG18 8QB Tel: (01767) 316422 Fax: (01767) 318033 E-mail: info@endoline.co.uk
Ewab Engineering Ltd, Stafford Park 16, Telford, Shropshire, TF3 3BS Tel: (01952) 239200 Fax: (01952) 239258 E-mail: pam.berry@ewab.net
Excel Automation Ltd, Gregorys Bank, Worcester, WR3 8AB Tel: (01905) 721500 Fax: (01905) 613024 E-mail: information@excel-automation.co.uk
Exito Conveyors Ltd, 1 Woodhill Industries, Nottingham Lane, Old Dalby, Melton Mowbray, Leicestershire, LE14 3LX Tel: (01664) 823351
F Askew Engineers Ltd, Thorpe Road, Howden, Goole, North Humberside, DN14 7AY Tel: (01430) 430035 Fax: (01430) 431869 E-mail: enquries@askewengineers.co.uk
Fastrax Conveyors & Components, Shieling Court, Oakley Hay Industrial Estate, Great Oakley, Corby, Northamptonshire, NN18 9QD Tel: (01536) 747770 Fax: (01536) 747990 E-mail: fastraxcc@aol.com
Ford Green Engineering Ltd, Clarence Road, Longton, Stoke-On-Trent, ST3 1AZ Tel: (01782) 342530 Fax: (01782) 599692 E-mail: mail@fge.co.uk
Forward Industrial Products Group Ltd, Unit 2 Tyseley Park, Wharfedale Road Tyseley, Birmingham, B11 2DF Tel: 0121-707 2555 Fax: 0121-708 3081 E-mail: info@forwardindustrial.com
Fredenhagen Ltd, Keynes House, Alfreton Road, Derby, DE21 4AS Tel: (01332) 340077 Fax: (01332) 340614 E-mail: sales@fredenhagen.co.uk
▶ Gatfield Systems, Surrey Saw Mills, 70 Wrecclesham Hill, Wrecclesham, Farnham, Surrey, GU10 4JX Tel: (01252) 737357 Fax: (01252) 737358 E-mail: info@gatfield-systems.co.uk
Geppert Conveyors UK, Camberley, Surrey, GU17 0RP Tel: (01252) 875871 Fax: (01252) 878804 E-mail: gwilliams@geppert-band.de
Hardie Secure Products Ltd, 17 Station Road, Flitwick, Bedford, MK45 1JT Tel: (01525) 716736 Fax: (01525) 716736 E-mail: hsfabrications@msn.com
Hargreaves Hamilton Gears Ltd, PO Box 33, Bolton, BL1 2QE Tel: (01204) 456190 Fax: (01204) 364002 E-mail: info@hargreaveshamilton.co.uk
Haven Equipment Co., Duncote Mill, Walcot, Telford, Shropshire, TF6 5ER Tel: (01952) 740484 Fax: (01952) 740464 E-mail: sales@havenequipment.co.uk
Ken Hope Material Handling Specialists, Unit 38 C WB House, Bingswood Industrial Estate, Whaley Bridge, High Peak, Derbyshire, SK23 7LY Tel: (01663) 734641 Fax: (01663) 734767 E-mail: kenhope@wbhouse.co.uk
Hulse Engineering, Duke Street, Stoke-on-Trent, ST4 3NR Tel: (01782) 316589 Fax: (01782) 598504 E-mail: hulsefabricationsltd@hotmail.com
Hunter Neil Packaging Ltd, Unit 5, Hilltop Meadows, Old London Road, Knockholt, Sevenoaks, Kent, TN14 7JW Tel: (01959) 532200 Fax: (01959) 534400 E-mail: info@hunterneil.co.uk
Intern Transport Systems (U K) Ltd, 421 Nottingham Road, Ilkeston, Derbyshire, DE7 5BP Tel: 0115-930 7724 Fax: 0115-930 1742 E-mail: sales@itsuk.org.uk
J L Engineering Rixton Ltd, Chapel Lane, Warrington, WA3 6HG Tel: 0161-775 0588 Fax: 0161-775 6613 E-mail: info@jleng.co.uk
J R Power Transmission Scotland Ltd, Faraday Street, Dryburgh Industrial Estate, Dundee, DD2 3QQ Tel: (01382) 813677 Fax: (01382) 833925 E-mail: info@jrpower.co.uk
J Stevens, Hull Road, Eastrington, Goole, North Humberside, DN14 7XL Tel: (01430) 410333 Fax: (01430) 410354 E-mail: gdae@uk2.net
James Mcgowan Engineering Ltd, Dechmont Works, Hamilton Road, Cambuslang, Glasgow, G72 7XS Tel: 0141-641 3648 Fax: 0141-641 5147 E-mail: info@mcgowaneng.co.uk
JD Vulcanising Services Ltd, Apple Orchard House, Skelton-in-Cleveland, Saltburn-by-the-Sea, Cleveland, TS12 2AZ Tel: (01287) 651194 Fax: (01287) 651194
Jervis B Webb Co. Ltd, Swan Valley Way, Northampton, NN4 8BD Tel: (0845) 1270222 Fax: (0845) 1270221 E-mail: sales@jervisbwebb.co.uk
▶ Jex Engineering Co. Ltd, Adam Smith Street, Grimsby, South Humberside, DN31 1SJ Tel: (01472) 361311 Fax: (01472) 240218 E-mail: phill.bodsworth@jexengineering.com
John Morgan Conveyors Ltd, 1 Purbrook Road, Wolverhampton, WV1 2EJ Tel: (01902) 455755 Fax: (01902) 452245 E-mail: jmconveyors@btinternet.com
Kaytu Systems Ltd, 6A & 6B Throckley Way, Middlefields Industrial Estate, South Shields, Tyne & Wear, NE34 0NU Tel: 0191-456 2046 Fax: 0191-456 1971 E-mail: kaytusystems@kaytu-systems.co.uk
Kimbermatics Ltd, Cheethams Mill, Park Street, Stalybridge, Cheshire, SK15 2BT Tel: 0161-368 4891 Fax: 0161-304 8152 E-mail: kimbermatics@aol.com

CONVEYOR SYSTEMS MANUFRS – *continued*

L A C Conveyors Ltd, Unit 3, Charles Park, Cinderhill Road, Bulwell, Nottingham, NG6 8RE Tel: 0115-975 3300 Fax: 0115-975 3384 E-mail: sales@lacconveyors.co.uk
Lancashire Transmissions & Conveyor Engineers Ltd, PO Box 33, Bolton, BL1 2QS Tel: (01204) 382241 Fax: (01204) 362275 E-mail: gary@ltce.co.uk
Locom Engineering Ltd, Units 34-35 Cranswick Industrial Estate, Beverley Road, Cranswick, Driffield, North Humberside, YO25 9PF Tel: (01377) 271474 Fax: (01377) 271535 E-mail: info@locom.co.uk
Logan Teleflex UK Ltd, Sutton Road, Kingston Upon Hull, Hull, HU7 0DR Tel: (01482) 785600 Fax: (01482) 785699 E-mail: marketing@loganteleflex.co.uk
Lynnmoore Engineering Co. Ltd, Horsleys Fields, King's Lynn, Norfolk, PE30 5DD Tel: (01553) 771122 Fax: (01553) 777105 E-mail: tech@lynnmooreeng.co.uk
M G Automation Ltd, 16 Stratfield Park, Elettra Avenue, Waterlooville, Hampshire, PO7 7XN Tel: (023) 9226 7727 Fax: (023) 9226 7747 E-mail: sales@mgautomation.co.uk
Harry Major Machine UK Ltd, 3 Gosforth Close, Middlefield Industrial Estate, Sandy, Bedfordshire, SG19 1RB Tel: (01767) 689500 Fax: (01767) 680893 E-mail: sales@hmm-uk.com
Marden Edwards Ltd, 2 East Dorset Trade Park, Nimrod Way, Wimborne, Dorset, BH21 7SH Tel: (01202) 861200 Fax: (01202) 861400 E-mail: sales@mardenedwards.com
Marwel Conveyors Ltd, 108 Dudley Road East, Oldbury, West Midlands, B69 3EB Tel: 0121-552 4418 Fax: 0121-552 4018 E-mail: sales@marwel.com
Mayfran (U K) Ltd, Orchard Court Binley Business Park, Harry Weston Road, Coventry, CV3 2TQ Tel: (024) 7645 9000 Fax: (024) 7645 9690 E-mail: sales@mayfran-europe.com
Mercia Mechanical Handling Ltd, Unit C4-C6, Guy Motors Industrial Park, Park Lane, Wolverhampton, WV10 9QF Tel: (01902) 739852 Fax: (01902) 739547 E-mail: merciamech@btconnect.com
▶ Middleton Engineering Ltd, Ashcott Road, Meare, Glastonbury, Somerset, BA6 9SU Tel: (01458) 860264 Fax: (01458) 860311 E-mail: middletonadmin@btconnect.com
Midland Handling Equipment Ltd, Stretton Road, Great Glen, Leicester, LE8 9GN Tel: 0116-259 3175 Fax: 0116-259 2820 E-mail: sales@mhel.co.uk
Miracon Conveyors Ltd, Drayton Road, Shirley, Solihull, West Midlands, B90 4NG Tel: 0121-705 8468 Fax: 0121-711 2074 E-mail: sales@miracon.com
MK Profile Systems, 9 Cowling Business Park, Canal Side, Chorley, Lancashire, PR6 0QL Tel: (01257) 263937 Fax: (01257) 271409 E-mail: info@mkprofiles.co.uk
Monk Conveyors, Unit 18 Woodside Park, Catteshall Lane, Godalming, Surrey, GU7 1LG Tel: (01483) 791700 Fax: (01483) 791701 E-mail: sales@monk-conveyors.co.uk
Newland Engineering Co. Ltd, Captain Clarke Road, Hyde, Cheshire, SK14 4RF Tel: 0161-368 0326 Fax: 0161-367 8004 E-mail: info@newland-conveyors.com
Newsmith Stainless Ltd, Fountain Works, Child Lane, Liversedge, West Yorkshire, WF15 7PH Tel: (01924) 405988 Fax: (01924) 403304 E-mail: sales@newsmiths.co.uk
NKC Conveyors UK Ltd, Sunrise Parkway, Linford Wood, Milton Keynes, MK14 6LS Tel: (01908) 695611 Fax: (01908) 694632
Northbourne Engineering Ltd, The Old Malt House, Easole Street, Nonington, Dover, Kent, CT15 4HF Tel: (01304) 842858 Fax: (01304) 842868 E-mail: northbourneeng@talk21.com
O Kay Engineering Services Ltd, Valley Way, Market Harborough, Leicestershire, LE16 7PS Tel: (01858) 435500 Fax: (01858) 435511 E-mail: sales@okay.co.uk
Opal Food Processing Systems Ltd, Unit 20-21 Earith Business Park, Meadow Drove, Earith, Huntingdon, Cambridgeshire, PE28 3QF Tel: (01487) 740131
Orbiter Food Machinery, Private Road 7, Colwick Industrial Estate, Nottingham, NG4 2JW Tel: 0115-940 0372 Fax: 0115-961 8741 E-mail: enquiries@orbiterfoodmachinery.co.uk
P L Plastics Machinery Ltd, Unit 6 Telmere Industrial Estate, Albert Road, Luton, LU1 3QF Tel: (01582) 429224 Fax: (01582) 459133 E-mail: info@pl-plasticsmachinery.co.uk
Patera Engineering Ltd, Unit 2a Galveston Grove, Oldfields Business Park, Stoke-on-Trent, ST4 3ES Tel: (01782) 318822 Fax: (01782) 318822 E-mail: pateraeng@cs.com
PJH Engineering Ltd, Unit 15e Bergen Way, Sutton Fields Industrial Estate, Hull, HU7 0YQ Tel: (01482) 370375 Fax: (01482) 370385
Powervac Ltd, 111 Lightburn Road, Cambuslang, Glasgow, G72 8XN Tel: 0141-641 6611 Fax: 0141-641 9988
Prelude Fabrications Ltd, 129 Mereside, Soham, Ely, Cambridgeshire, CB7 5EG Tel: (01353) 722402 Fax: (01353) 624608
▶ ProdAuto Ltd, Creative Industries, Science Park, Wolverhampton, WV10 9TG Tel: 01902 420877 Fax: (01902) 716312 E-mail: info@prodauto.co.uk
Quality Conveyors Ltd, 10 Elland Lane, Elland, West Yorkshire, HX5 9DU Tel: (01422) 377166 Fax: (01422) 377238 E-mail: qconveyor@aol.com
R & A F Engineers, Unit 5b Britannia Park Industrial Estate, North Road, Stoke-on-Trent, ST6 2PZ Tel: (01782) 201212 Fax: (01782) 201212
▶ Rabrook Design, 225 Orphanage Road, Birmingham, B24 0BD Tel: 0121-382 8111 Fax: 0121-382 8111
Rako Products Ltd, Brunel Way, Stonehouse, Gloucestershire, GL10 3SX Tel: (01453) 829900 Fax: (01453) 829928 E-mail: sales@rako-products.co.uk
Rayridge Conveyors Ltd, Willenhall Trading Estate, Midacre, Willenhall, West Midlands, WV13 2JW Tel: (01902) 603763 Fax: (01902) 605081 E-mail: mail@ercongroup.com
Redler Ltd, Dudbridge Works, Dudbridge, Stroud, Gloucestershire, GL5 3EY Tel: (01453) 763611 Fax: (01453) 763582 E-mail: sales@redler.com
Riley Product Handling Ltd, Unit 2b, Meteor Business Park Mansfield Ro, Derby, DE21 4ST Tel: (01332) 866000 Fax: (01332) 866127 E-mail: paolo.graziani@rileyproducthandling.com
Robert Flannigan Engineering, 1 Flemington Industrial Park, Craigneuk Street, Motherwell, Lanarkshire, ML1 2NT Tel: (01698) 309307 Fax: (01698) 309312 E-mail: rfeconveyors@aol.com
▶ Robot Units UK, Woodford Park Industrial Estate, Leslie Road, Woodford Park Industrial Estat, Winsford, Cheshire, CW7 2RB Tel: (01606) 869690 Fax: (01606) 869692 E-mail: info.uk1@robotunits.com
▶ Robson Handling Technology Ltd, Coleford Road, Darnall, Sheffield, S9 5PA Tel: 0114-244 4221 Fax: 0114-243 3066 E-mail: info@robson.co.uk
Rolamat Ltd, Unit 5 Bunas Park, Hollom Down Road, Lopcombe, Salisbury, SP5 1BP Tel: (01264) 782143 Fax: (01264) 782580 E-mail: info@rolamat.co.uk
Serpecon Ltd, 22 Fairmile Road, Halesowen, West Midlands, B63 3QJ Tel: 0121-550 5950 Fax: 0121-550 6222 E-mail: serpecon@btinternet.com
Shrinkwrap Machinery Co. Ltd, 145 Sterte Road, Poole, Dorset, BH15 2AF Tel: (01202) 674944 Fax: (01202) 671891 E-mail: sales@shrinkwrap.co.uk
Silcoms Ltd, Victoria Mill, Piggott Street, Farnworth, Bolton, BL4 9QN Tel: (01204) 571305 Fax: (01204) 861723 E-mail: pep@silcoms.co.uk
Soco System UK Ltd, Unit 18 Palmerston Street, Joiners Square Industrial Estate, Stoke-on-Trent, ST1 3EU Tel: (01782) 274100 Fax: (01782) 272696 E-mail: paul.bangs@socosystem.co.uk
▶ Southern Conveyors, Unit 2 Denton Slipways Site, Wharf Road, Gravesend, Kent, DA12 2RU Tel: (01474) 564145
Stewart Gill Conveyor Ltd, 2 Christy Estate, Ivy Road, Aldershot, Hampshire, GU12 4TX Tel: (01252) 332221 Fax: (01252) 334387 E-mail: info@stewart-gill.co.uk
▶ Stilcan Industrial Conveyors, 10 Westgarth Place, East Kilbride, Glasgow, G74 5NT Tel: (01355) 270788 Fax: (01355) 270789
Strathcona Conveyors Ltd, UNIT 3A, 95 Westburn Drive, Camduslang, Glasgow, G72 7NA Tel: 0141-876 4525 Fax: 0141-620 2165
▶ Tellure Rota, PO Box 29, Ashton-under-Lyne, Lancashire, OL5 9NB Tel: (01457) 832556 Fax: (01457) 838406 E-mail: sales@aut.co.uk
Thomas Shaw & Son (M/C) Ltd, Star Works, Holt Town, Manchester, M40 7FQ Tel: 0161-273 7686 Fax: 0161-274 3699 E-mail: tommy.shaw@virgin.net
Transbelt Ltd, 36 Howe Street, Bootle, Merseyside, L20 8NG Tel: 0151-922 1314 Fax: 0151-922 3983 E-mail: transbelt@btconnect.com
TSD Wakefield, Keys Road, Mixs Hill, Somercoates, Alfreton, Derbyshire, DE55 7FQ Tel: (0870) 6090111 Fax: (01773) 521015 E-mail: sales@wakefields.co.uk
Van Der Lande Industries, 59 Marsh Lane, Hampton-in-Arden, Solihull, West Midlands, B92 0AJ Tel: (01675) 443801 Fax: (01675) 443169 E-mail: roger.peart@vanderlande.co.uk
Vanriet UK Ltd, W Riverside Industrial Estate, Atherstone Street, Fazeley, Tamworth, Staffordshire, B78 3RW Tel: (01827) 288871 Fax: (01827) 250810 E-mail: sales@vanriet.co.uk
▶ W D Pulley's, 54 Cuckoo Road, Birmingham, B7 5SY Tel: 0121-327 5133 Fax: 0121-327 2756 E-mail: birminghamsales@afc-uk.com
Welco, 2 Parklands, Rednal, Birmingham, B45 9PZ Tel: (0800) 9549001 Fax: (0845) 6888900 E-mail: sales@welco.co.uk
D.P. White & Co., 58 Hackenden Cl, East Grinstead, West Sussex, RH19 3DS Fax: (01342) 335747
Wire Belt Co. Ltd, Castle Road, Sittingbourne, Kent, ME10 3RF Tel: (01795) 421771 Fax: (01795) 428905 E-mail: sales@wirebelt.co.uk

CONVEYOR SYSTEMS SPARE PARTS/WEARING PARTS

G P M Engineering Systems Ltd, 1585 Bristol Road South, Rednal, Birmingham, B45 9UA Tel: 0121-457 7132 Fax: 0121-457 9035 E-mail: scrow@gpmengineering.com

CONVEYOR SYSTEMS, FLAT BELT

Conveyor Lines Ltd, Unit 11 Scotia Close, Brackmills Industrial Estate, Northampton, NN4 7HR Tel: (01604) 762672 Fax: (01604) 708827 E-mail: sales@conveyorlines.com

CONVEYOR SYSTEMS, FROZEN/CHILLED FOODS

Glanbia Cheese Ltd, Glanhwfa Road, Llangefni, Gwynedd, LL77 7TT Tel: (01248) 750351 Fax: (01248) 750566

CONVEYOR SYSTEMS, ROUND/SPIRAL

C I Logistics, 43 Wenlock Way, Troon Industrial Area, Leicester, LE4 9HU Tel: 0116-276 1691 Fax: 0116-276 9836 E-mail: sales@conveyors.co.uk
Transnorm Systems Ltd, 4 Ashchurch Business Centre, Alexandra Way, Ashchurch, Tewkesbury, Gloucestershire, GL20 8TD Tel: (01684) 291100 Fax: (01684) 291550 E-mail: sales@transnorm.co.uk

CONVEYOR WEAR STRIPS/GUIDE RAILS, PLASTIC

J W Stead & Son Ltd, Preserve Works, Thackley Old Road, Shipley, West Yorkshire, BD18 1QB Tel: (01274) 597814 Fax: (01274) 532177 E-mail: info@jwstead.com

COOKER HOOD DUCTING

D R Cooker Hoods Ltd, 2 Alpha Road, Aldershot, Hampshire, GU12 4RG Tel: (01252) 351111 Fax: (01252) 311608 E-mail: sales@drcookerhoods.co.uk

COOKER HOODS

Bishop & Smith Stainless Fabrication, Unit 2 Thorn Business Park, Rotherwas, Hereford, HR2 6JT Tel: (01432) 342355 Fax: (01432) 352399E-mail: alan@bishop-smith.fsnet.co.uk
D R Cooker Hoods Ltd, 2 Alpha Road, Aldershot, Hampshire, GU12 4RG Tel: (01252) 351111 Fax: (01252) 311608 E-mail: sales@drcookerhoods.co.uk
W S Westin Group Ltd, Phoenix Mill, Leeds Road, Huddersfield, HD1 6NG Tel: (01484) 421585 Fax: (01484) 432420 E-mail: sales@westin.co.uk

COOKERS, *See also headings for particular types*

Aga Rayburn Reconditioned Ranges, Crowan, Praze, Camborne, Cornwall, TR14 9ND Tel: (01209) 718531 Fax: (01209) 718531 E-mail: sales@agarayburn.freeserve.co.uk
Aga Shop, 12 Widcombe Parade, Bath, BA2 4JT Tel: (01225) 335237 Fax: (01225) 443302
Aga Shop, 23 Queen Street, Derby, DE1 3DS Tel: (01332) 340057 Fax: (01332) 204256 E-mail: derby@aga-web.co.uk
Aga Shop, 66-68 Princes Street, Perth, PH2 8LJ Tel: (01738) 443642 Fax: (01738) 443641
Aga Shop, 10 Upper High Street, Thame, Oxfordshire, OX9 3ER Tel: (01844) 214214 Fax: (01844) 218445
▶ Big Cooker Repair Co., 41 Balcarres Road, Leyland, PR25 2EL Tel: (01772) 465676 Fax: (01772) 464757 E-mail: enquiry@bigcookerrepair.co.uk
▶ Cast Iron Range Cookers Ltd, 50 High Street, Princes Risborough, Buckinghamshire, HP27 0AX Tel: (01844) 344475 Fax: (01844) 342080
Chase Heating Ltd, Somerfield Stores, Racecourse Road, Pinvin, Pershore, Worcestershire, WR10 2EY Tel: (01386) 553542 Fax: (01386) 552269 E-mail: chasehtg@gxn.co.uk
John Cooper & Sons Ltd, 74 Baddow Road, Chelmsford, CM2 7PJ Tel: (01245) 261909 Fax: (01245) 493109 E-mail: info@johncooperandsons.co.uk
Hoad & Taylor Ltd, 5 Manfield Park, Cranleigh, Surrey, GU6 8PT Tel: (01483) 204800 Fax: (01483) 204801
Mega Bonus, 101 Ock Street, Abingdon, Oxfordshire, OX14 5DQ Tel: (01235) 550776 E-mail: sales@megabonus.co.uk
Stanley Cookers Ni, 5 Moygashel Mills Park, Moygashel, Dungannon, County Tyrone, BT71 7DH Tel: (028) 8772 2195 Fax: (028) 8775 2022E-mail: sales@stanley-cookers.com
Traditional Cookers, 28 London Road, Horndean, Waterlooville, Hampshire, PO8 0BY Tel: (023) 9259 9227 Fax: (023) 9259 8997 E-mail: sales@trad-cookers.co.uk
Twyford Cookers Ltd, Units 31-32 Three Elms Trading Estate, Bakers Lane, Hereford, HR4 9PU Tel: (01432) 355924 Fax: (01432) 272664 E-mail: sales@twyford-cookers.com
W Gilchrist & Co., 65a London Road, Sevenoaks, Kent, TN13 1AU Tel: (01732) 457666 Fax: (01732) 457246

COOKING OIL

▶ M & B Edible Oil, 2 Cannon Road, Heathfield, Newton Abbot, Devon, TQ12 6SH Tel: (01626) 836280 Fax: (01626) 836280 E-mail: mboils@btconnect.com

COOKING/BOILING VESSELS, FOOD PROCESSING

Chloroxy-Tech Ltd, Powke Lane Industrial Estate, Powke La, Blackheath, Birmingham, B65 0AH Tel: 0121-559 4141 Fax: 0121-559 2503 E-mail: chloroxoy.tech@virgin.net
Food Machinery Co. Ltd, Fenn Corner, Rochester, Kent, ME3 8RS Tel: (01634) 272345 Fax: 01634 272200 E-mail: sales@food-machineryco.com

COOKWARE, *See also headings for particular types*

Aga Shop, 12 Widcombe Parade, Bath, BA2 4JT Tel: (01225) 335237 Fax: (01225) 443302
Beagle Cookware, 72-78 Stour Street, Birmingham, B18 7AJ Tel: 0121-454 3323 Fax: 0121-454 3342
Colanders, Unit 15 Martinfield Business CNT, Martinfield, Welwyn Garden City, Hertfordshire, AL7 1HG Tel: (01707) 320757 Fax: (01707) 335131E-mail: sales@colanders.demon.co.uk
Lambert & Blaber Ltd, 25 Kings Road, Haslemere, Surrey, GU27 2QA Tel: (01428) 658534 Fax: (01428) 658341 E-mail: sales@lambertblaber.co.uk
Prima Catering Supplies, 2 Whitworth Industrial Estate, Tilton Road, Birmingham, B9 4PP Tel: 0121-771 3116 Fax: 0121-772 2616 E-mail: primacatering@hotmail.com

COOKWARE, CAST IRON

▶ UK On-Line Shop, Administration Centre, Unit 1, Bell Road, Walsall, WS5 3JW Tel: 0121-357 9865 Fax: E-mail: ukon@bgtcom.co.uk

COOLANT MANAGEMENT SYSTEMS

Airtech Air Conditioning Services Ltd, Devon House, Eastbourne Road, Lingfield, Surrey, RH7 6JJ Tel: (01342) 836000 Fax: (01342) 835930 E-mail: ac@airtech.uk.com

COOLER DESIGN OR INSTALLATION OR SERVICING

Constant Cooling Services, 2 London Road Industrial Estate, London Road, Pampisford, Cambridge, CB2 4EE Tel: (01223) 834711 Fax: (01223) 837818 E-mail: constantcooling@hotmail.com
Watford Refrigeration & Air Conditioning Ltd, Wiggenhall Industrial Estate, Watford, WD18 0FT Tel: (01923) 227726 Fax: (01923) 233525 E-mail: sales@watref.co.uk

COOLERS, *See also headings for particular types*

Central Cooling Services Ltd, Garrison House, Garrison Street, Bordesley, Birmingham, B9 4BN Tel: 0121-766 7227 Fax: 0121-766 6156 E-mail: centralcoolingservices@btinternet.com
Flowcool Systems, Wimsey Way, Somercotes, Alfreton, Derbyshire, DE55 4LS Tel: (01773) 608888 Fax: (01773) 609001 E-mail: sales@flowcool.com
F.J. Pirie & Co. Ltd, Unit 2 Palmermount Works, Bypass Road, Dundonald, Kilmarnock, Ayrshire, KA2 9BL Tel: (01563) 850325 Fax: (01563) 851081
Protocol Control Systems Ltd, 2 Knighton Enterprise Park, Ludlow Road, Knighton, Powys, LD7 1HJ Tel: (01547) 529238 Fax: (01547) 529090 E-mail: info@protocolcontrolsystems.co.uk
Stadco Ltd, Harlescott Lane, Shrewsbury, SY1 3AS Tel: (01743) 462227 Fax: (01743) 447709 E-mail: cooling@stadco.co.uk

COOLERS, DRAFT BEER

Dispense Technology Services Ltd, 19a Watts Road, Studley, Warwickshire, B80 7PT Tel: (01527) 853014 Fax: (01527) 853014 E-mail: j_pickering@btconnect.com

COOLING SYSTEMS, CONTROL PANEL

▶ Clever Air Conditioning Sales Ltd, 26 York Street, London, W1U 6PZ Tel: (0845) 0573097 Fax: (020) 7206 9432 E-mail: sales@cleverengineering.co.uk

COOLING TOWER CLEANING OR MAINTENANCE

Balticare Ltd, Princewood Road, Earlstrees Industrial Estate, Corby, Northamptonshire, NN17 4AP Tel: (01536) 200312 Fax: (01536) 408623 E-mail: info@baltaircoil.be

Intergrated Water Services Ltd, Vincients Road, Bumpers Farm Industrial Estate, Chippenham, Wiltshire, SN14 6NQ Tel: (01249) 461744 Fax: (01249) 461766

Northern Plastics, Perseverance Works, Dewsbury Road, Elland, West Yorkshire, HX5 9AZ Tel: (01422) 311569 Fax: (01422) 376841 E-mail: rharrison@northernplastics.co.uk

S P X Cooling Technologies UK Ltd, Gregory's Bank, Worcester, WR3 8AB Tel: (01905) 720200 Fax: (01905) 720201 E-mail: info@ct.spx.com

Sas Safe & Secure, Birchwoodmoor House, Roston, Ashbourne, Derbyshire, DE6 2EH Tel: (01889) 591595 Fax: (01889) 591595 E-mail: sales@legionnairesdisease.co.uk

COOLING TOWER CONTRACTORS

Northern Plastics, Perseverance Works, Dewsbury Road, Elland, West Yorkshire, HX5 9AZ Tel: (01422) 311569 Fax: (01422) 376841 E-mail: rharrison@northernplastics.co.uk

S P X Cooling Technologies UK Ltd, Gregory's Bank, Worcester, WR3 8AB Tel: (01905) 720200 Fax: (01905) 720201 E-mail: info@ct.spx.com

Thermal Energy Construction Ltd, Trent Lane, Castle Donington, Derby, DE74 2NP Tel: (01332) 810999 Fax: (01332) 855175 E-mail: info@thermalenergy.co.uk

COOLING TOWERS

Aquafan Cooling Towers Ltd, 47 Down St, West Molesey, Surrey, KT8 2SY Tel: (020) 8941 4378

Baltairco West Ltd, Ivy House Farm, Wolvershill, Banwell, Avon, BS29 6LB Tel: (01934) 824411 Fax: (01934) 824477

Balticare Ltd, Princewood Road, Earlstrees Industrial Estate, Corby, Northamptonshire, NN17 4AP Tel: (01536) 200312 Fax: (01536) 408623 E-mail: info@baltaircoil.be

Carter Environmental Engineers Ltd, 2 Lawley Middleway, Birmingham, B4 7XL Tel: 0121-250 1000 Fax: 0121-250 1400 E-mail: sales@cee.co.uk

▶ Droitwich Glass Fibre Mouldings Ltd, Hangar 5, Long Lane, Throckmorton, Pershore, Worcestershire, WR10 2JH Tel: (01386) 555787 Fax: (01386) 555748 E-mail: glassfibres@btconnect.com

Hamon UK Ltd, Units1-2 Ropery Park, Alferd Street, Hull, HU3 2DF Tel: (01482) 787767 Fax: (01482) 706151 E-mail: info.huk@hamon.com

Northern Plastics, Perseverance Works, Dewsbury Road, Elland, West Yorkshire, HX5 9AZ Tel: (01422) 311569 Fax: (01422) 376841 E-mail: rharrison@northernplastics.co.uk

S P X Cooling Technologies UK Ltd, Gregory's Bank, Worcester, WR3 8AB Tel: (01905) 720200 Fax: (01905) 720201 E-mail: info@ct.spx.com

Water Technology Ltd, Powke Lane Industrial Estate, Blackheath, Rowley Regis, West Midlands, B65 0AH Tel: 0121-561 3144 Fax: 0121-561 3329 E-mail: water.tech@virgin.net

Watermiser Ltd, Tower Works, 4-8 Stoneygate Road, Newmilns, Ayrshire, KA16 9AJ Tel: (01560) 320762 Fax: (01560) 323093 E-mail: info@watermiser.co.uk

COORDINATE MEASURING MACHINES (CMM)

Aberlink Ltd, Avening Mill, High Street, Avening, Tetbury, Gloucestershire, GL8 8LU Tel: (01453) 835737 Fax: (01453) 832574 E-mail: sales@aberlink.co.uk

Hexagon Metrology, Halesfield 13, Telford, Shropshire, TF7 4PL Tel: (01952) 681300 Fax: (01952) 681311 E-mail: enquiry@hexmet.co.uk

C.E. Johansson Ltd, Metrology House, Halesfield 13, Telford, Shropshire, TF7 4PL Tel: 0870 4462667 Fax: 0870 4462668 E-mail: enquiry@hexmet.co.uk

COPPER ALLOY OR COPPER SCRAP OR WASTE OR DROSS RECYCLING OR DISPOSAL OR RECOVERY

B & J Alloys Ltd, The Leys, Brierley Hill, West Midlands, DY5 3UJ Tel: (01384) 485533

COPPER ALLOY WELDING WIRES

Cerro (Manganese Bronze) Ltd, PO Box 22, Ipswich, IP2 0EG Tel: (01473) 252127 Fax: (01473) 218229 E-mail: sales@scerromb.com

Sifbronze Ltd, Prentice Road, Stowmarket, Suffolk, IP14 1RD Tel: (01449) 771443 Fax: (01449) 771945 E-mail: sif@sifbronze.co.uk

T J Smith & Son Grinding Services Ltd, 17 Clifton Street, Sheffield, S9 2DQ Tel: 0114-244 8335 Fax: 0114-244 8336 E-mail: sales@precision-grinding.co.uk

COPPER BARS OR SECTIONS

Metelec Ltd, Vulcan Industrial Estate, Walsall, WS2 7BZ Tel: (01922) 712665 Fax: (01922) 710919 E-mail: sales@metelec.co.uk

MKM Mansfelder Copper Ltd, 37-39 Compton, Ashbourne, Derbyshire, DE6 1BX Tel: (01335) 300585 Fax: (01335) 300577

COPPER BASED ALLOY COMPONENTS

James Brown & Sons Ltd, 92 The Grove, Marton-in-Cleveland, Middlesbrough, Cleveland, TS7 8AP Tel: (01642) 318370 Fax: (01642) 318370

Coppercraft Of Edinburgh Collection, Newbattle Road, Dalkeith, Midlothian, EH22 3LL Tel: 0131-660 1020 Fax: 0131-660 1020

COPPER BRAIDS

Amari Copper Alloys, Unit 47, Eagle Rd, Moons Moat North Industrial Estate, Redditch, Worcestershire, B98 9HF Tel: (01527) 405600 Fax: (01527) 405605 E-mail: sales@amaricopperalloys.co.uk

COPPER CABLE GRANULATING OR REPROCESSING

Caprina Ltd, Woodacre Outbarn, Hazelhead Lane, Barnacre, Preston, PR3 1BN Tel: (01995) 606519 Fax: (01995) 600242 E-mail: prefcable@aol.com

Mountstar Cable, Hobson Industrial Estate, Hobson, Newcastle upon Tyne, NE16 6EA Tel: (01207) 270731 Fax: (01207) 271004 E-mail: sales@mountstar.com

COPPER CLAD PRINTED CIRCUIT LAMINATES (PCL)

Cookson Electronics, 2 Dunlop Square, Deans South West, Livingston, West Lothian, EH54 8SB Tel: (01506) 412812 Fax: (01506) 410571

Crossley & Bradley Ltd, Ulnes Walton Lane, Leyland, PR26 8NB Tel: (01772) 622800 Fax: (01772) 456859 E-mail: info@crossley-bradley.co.uk

G T S Flexible Materials Ltd, G T S House, 3 Wellington Business Park, Dukes Ride, Crowthorne, Berkshire, RG45 6LS Tel: (01344) 762376 Fax: (01344) 761615 E-mail: mail@gts-flexible.co.uk

Option Technology Europe Ltd, Carrs Industrial Estate, Haslingden, Rossendale, Lancashire, BB4 5HR Tel: (01706) 605000 Fax: (01706) 605010 E-mail: sales@option.co.uk

COPPER CLAMP WASHERS

Hampton Works Ltd, Twyning Road, Stirchley, Birmingham, B30 2XZ Tel: 0121-458 2901 Fax: 0121-433 3819 E-mail: sales@hampton-works.co.uk

COPPER COMPOUNDS

Bardyke Chemicals Ltd, Hamilton Road, Cambuslang, Glasgow, G72 7XJ Tel: (01698) 823361 Fax: (01698) 820535 E-mail: sales@bardyke.com

COPPER CONDUCTOR CABLES

Brand Rex Ltd, Viewfield Industrial Estate, Glenrothes, Fife, KY6 2RS Tel: (01592) 772124 Fax: (01592) 775314 E-mail: loswald@brand-rex.com

COPPER DIES

Grabern Engraving, Oyster Place, 28 Montrose Rd, Chelmsford, CM2 6TX Tel: (01245) 468223 Fax: (01245) 469121 E-mail: sales@grabernengraving.com

COPPER DRAIN OR SANITARY PIPES

Konaflex Ltd, Unit 2 Northcote Road, Stechford, Birmingham, B33 9BE Tel: 0121-783 9778 Fax: 0121-784 8026E-mail: konaflex@aol.com

COPPER FABRICATORS

Forsyths, Station Road, Rothes, Aberlour, Banffshire, AB38 7AD Tel: (01340) 831787 Fax: (01340) 831558 E-mail: enquiries@forsyths.com

McCallum Water Heating, Glen Works, Barrhead, Glasgow, G78 1ND Tel: 0141-881 1051 Fax: 0141-881 8275 E-mail: info@mccallumwaterheating.co.uk

Manchester Calorifiers Ltd, Lund Street, Manchester, M16 9EJ Tel: 0161-872 3613 Fax: 0161-872 3027

Ormandy Rycroft, Duncombe Road, Bradford, West Yorkshire, BD8 9TB Tel: (01274) 490911 Fax: (01274) 498580 E-mail: sales@rycroft.com

R G Abercrombie, Caledonian Road, Alloa, Clackmannanshire, FK10 1NB Tel: (01259) 222500 Fax: (01259) 222528 E-mail: info@diageo.com

Risuda Fabrications Ltd, Hare Street, Hopwood Lane, Halifax, West Yorkshire, HX1 4DJ Tel: (01422) 369782 Fax: (01422) 348251

COPPER FACED HAMMERS

Thor Hammer Co. Ltd, Highlands Road, Shirley, Solihull, West Midlands, B90 4NJ Tel: 0121-705 4695 Fax: 0121-705 4727 E-mail: info@thorhammer.com

COPPER FOIL

▶ H P Foils Ltd, 6B Coopers Way, Temple Farm Industrial Estate, Southend-On-Sea, SS2 5TE Tel: (01702) 602444

COPPER MINING COMPANIES,

See Mining Company (Overseas) UK Offices

COPPER OXIDES

Bardyke Chemicals Ltd, Hamilton Road, Cambuslang, Glasgow, G72 7XJ Tel: (01698) 823361 Fax: (01698) 820535 E-mail: sales@bardyke.com

COPPER PLATERS/PLATING SERVICES

Argosy Control Engineering Ltd, Murcar Industrial Estate, Denmore Road, Bridge of Don, Aberdeen, AB23 8JW Tel: (01224) 704788 Fax: (01224) 704831

H D Simpson & Co Polishers Ltd, Downing Street Industrial Estate, Smethwick, West Midlands, B66 2JH Tel: 0121-558 3469 Fax: 0121-558 3469

COPPER POWDER MANUFRS

Makin Metal Powers Ltd, Buckley Road, Rochdale, Lancashire, OL12 9DT Tel: (01706) 717317 Fax: (01706) 717303 E-mail: mmp@makin-metals.com

COPPER PRODUCERS/ REFINERS/SMELTERS,

See Copper/Alloy etc

COPPER RODS

▶ Pirelli Cables Ltd, Carr Lane, Prescot, Merseyside, L34 1PD Tel: 0151-430 4300 Fax: 0151-430 4390 E-mail: neil.bootman@pirelli.com

COPPER ROOFING CONTRACTORS

Beckett Construction Solutions Ltd, 99 Kingsway, Dunmurry, Belfast, BT17 9NU Tel: (028) 9066 3631 Fax: (028) 9055 1309 E-mail: mail@whbeckett.com

J.H. Brill & Son Ltd, 1A Merivale Rd, Putney, London, United Kingdom, SW15 2NW Tel: (020) 8788 2217 Fax: (020) 8788 5800 E-mail: info@brillandson.co.uk

Peters Roofing Contractors, 564 Davidson Road, Croydon, CR0 6DG Tel: (020) 8655 3598 Fax: (020) 8655 3598 E-mail: pete@petersroofing.co.uk

COPPER ROOFING MATERIALS

Heys-Shawl Ltd, Waterloo House, Langham Street Industrial Estate, Ashton-Under-Lyne, Lancashire, OL7 9AX Tel: 0161-343 2060 Fax: 0161-343 1542

COPPER SHEET

MKM Mansfelder Copper Ltd, 37-39 Compton, Ashbourne, Derbyshire, DE6 1BX Tel: (01335) 300585 Fax: (01335) 300577

COPPER STOCKHOLDERS

Amari Copper Alloys, Unit 47, Eagle Rd, Moons Moat North Industrial Estate, Redditch, Worcestershire, B98 9HF Tel: (01527) 405600 Fax: (01527) 405605 E-mail: sales@amaricopperalloys.co.uk

J T P (Non-Ferrous Stockholders) Ltd, Rope Street, Shelton New Road, Hartshill, Stoke-on-Trent, ST4 6DJ Tel: (01782) 711755 Fax: (01782) 717301 E-mail: dgreer@jtpnonferrous.co.uk

KME UK Ltd, Severn House, Prescott Drive, Warndon Business Park, Worcester, WR4 9NE Tel: (01905) 751816 Fax: (01905) 751801 E-mail: info@kme.com

Maxim Industries Ltd, Bankfield Road, Tyldesley, Manchester, M29 8QH Tel: 0161-703 2244 Fax: 0161-702 6454 E-mail: info@themssgroup.co.uk

Southend Aluminium Co., 24 Milton Road, Westcliff-on-Sea, Essex, SS0 7JX Tel: (01702) 331601 Fax: (01702) 330525

COPPER STRIP MANUFRS

Eip Metals, Rabone Lane, Smethwick, West Midlands, B66 3JH Tel: 0121-555 1199 Fax: 0121-555 1188 E-mail:

Luvata Sales Oy (UK), Regency Chambers Regency Arcade, 154-156 Parade, Leamington Spa, Warwickshire, CV32 4BQ Tel: (01689) 825677 Fax: (01926) 459149 E-mail: enquiries@outokumpu.com

Von Roll UK Ltd, Unit 6, Lawrence Way, Dunstable, Bedfordshire, LU6 1BD Tel: (01582) 500500 Fax: (01582) 476456 E-mail: wire@vonroll.com

COPPER TANKS

Copper Cyl, E Bull Street Trading Estate, Bull Street, Brierley Hill, West Midlands, DY5 3RA Tel: (01384) 77357 Fax: (01384) 77357 E-mail: roger.child@btconnect.com

Elsy & Gibbons Ltd, Simonside, South Shields, Tyne & Wear, NE34 9PD Tel: 0191-427 0777 Fax: 0191-427 0888 E-mail: info@elsonhotwater.co.uk

Gledhill Water Storage Ltd, Sycamore Trading Estate, Squires Gate Lane, Blackpool, FY4 3RL Tel: (01253) 474401 Fax: (01253) 474445 E-mail: info@gledhill-cyls.co.uk

Gledhill Water Storage Ltd, Unit 22, Corngreves Trading Estate, Charlton Dive, Cradley Heath, West Midlands, B64 7BJ Tel: (01384) 636245 Fax: (01384) 413700

COPPER TUBE FITTINGS

BSS, Unit 6-7 Industrial Estate, Thomas Road, London, E14 7BN Tel: (020) 7531 3900 Fax: (020) 7537 4849 E-mail: 1920.sales@bssgroup.com

Danfast, English Street, Hull, HU3 2DZ Tel: (01482) 599333 Fax: (01482) 599321 E-mail: enquiries@danfast.co.uk

Delta Fluid Products Ltd, Delta Road, St. Helens, Merseyside, WA9 2ED Tel: (01744) 611811 Fax: (01744) 611818 E-mail: enquiries@deltafluidproducts.com

Flowflex Components Ltd, Samuel Blaser Works, Tongue Lane Industrial Estate, Buxton, Derbyshire, SK17 7LR Tel: (01298) 77211 Fax: (01298) 72362 E-mail: flowflex@compuserve.com

Furlong Services Ltd, 148 Sculcoates Lane, Hull, HU5 1EE Tel: (01482) 444666 Fax: (01482) 444664 E-mail: enquiries@furlong-services.co.uk

COPPER TUBE FITTINGS – *continued*

Marine Engineering Pipworks, Leechmere East Industrial Estate, Sunderland, SR2 9TE Tel: 0191-521 1941 Fax: 0191-523 6954 E-mail: info@mepsun.com

Outokumpu Copper Metal Supplies Ltd, Mill Road, Sharnbrook, Bedford, MK44 1NP Tel: (01234) 781234 Fax: (01234) 781915 E-mail: andrew.smith@outokumpu.com

Rabco Fittings Ltd, Unit 15 Palmers Road, East Moons Moat, Redditch, Worcestershire, B98 0RF Tel: (01527) 510733 Fax: (01527) 510735 E-mail: admin@rabco-fittings.com

COPPER TUBE MANIPULATION

▶ Bristol Bending Sanoh Ltd, Quedgeley Court, Shepherd Road, Gloucester, GL2 5EL Tel: (01452) 303062 Fax: (01452) 300575

Formbend Ltd, Unit 4-5 Charles St Industrial Estate, Charles Street, West Bromwich, West Midlands, B70 0AZ Tel: 0121-557 0555 Fax: 0121-557 0888 E-mail: sales@formbend.com

Tubetech Ltd, Arundel Road, Uxbridge, Middlesex, UB8 2RP Tel: (01895) 233268 Fax: (01895) 231933

COPPER TUBE MANUFRS

Blackheath Tube Co Ltd, Castle Mill Works, Birmingham New Road, Dudley, West Midlands, DY1 4DA Tel: (01384) 255300 Fax: (01384) 255400 E-mail: sales@blackheathtube.co.uk

BSS, Unit 6-7 Industrial Estate, Thomas Road, London, E14 7BN Tel: (020) 7531 3900 Fax: (020) 7537 4849 E-mail: 1920.sales@bssgroup.com

Dorset Tube, Thrush Road, Poole, Dorset, BH12 4NT Tel: (01202) 725000 Fax: (01202) 725025 E-mail: sales@dorsettubes.co.uk

Furlong Services Ltd, 148 Sculcoates Lane, Hull, HU5 1EE Tel: (01482) 444666 Fax: (01482) 444664 E-mail: enquiries@furlong-services.co.uk

Metal Agencies, Cobb House, 2 Oyster Lane, Byfleet, West Byfleet, Surrey, KT14 7DU Tel: (01932) 331111 Fax: (01932) 331190 E-mail: ngould@metalagencies.vionet.gr

Mueller Europe Ltd, Oxford Street, Bilston, West Midlands, WV14 7DS Tel: (01902) 499700 Fax: (01902) 405838 E-mail: sales@muellereurope.com

Reyton Metals Ltd, 1 Malvern View Business Park, Stella Way, Cheltenham, Gloucestershire, GL52 7DQ Tel: (01242) 631000 Fax: (01242) 631110

Yorkshire Copper Tube, East Lancashire Road, Liverpool, L33 7TU Tel: 0151-546 2700 Fax: 0151-546 5881 E-mail: sales@yorkshirecoppertube.com

COPPER TUNGSTEN ALLOYS

Thermal Spray Material Services Ltd, Brook Street Business Centre, Brook Street, Tipton, West Midlands, DY4 9DD Tel: 0121-520 0720 Fax: 0121-520 3002 E-mail: thermalsprayuk@aol.com

COPPER WASHERS

All Marque, Unit 5 Block F, St. Michaels Industrial Estate, Widnes, Cheshire, WA8 8TL Tel: 0151-424 1984 Fax: 0151-420 3144 E-mail: sales@allmarque.co.uk

Lock Engineering Co Ltd, Western Trading Estate, 22 Trading Estate Road, London, NW10 7LY Tel: (020) 8961 6649 Fax: (020) 8961 1036 E-mail: ss@lockeng.co.uk

COPPER WATER HEATING CYLINDERS OR BOILERS

Albion Water Heaters, Shelah Road, Halesowen, West Midlands, B63 3PG Tel: 0121-585 5151 Fax: 0121-501 3826 E-mail: sales@albionwaterheaters.com

Church Hill Systems Ltd, Unit 4h Hinckley Business Centre, Burbage Road, Burbage, Hinckley, Leicestershire, LE10 2TP Tel: (01455) 890685 Fax: (01455) 891341 E-mail: sales@churchhillsystems.co.uk

Gledhill Water Storage Ltd, Sycamore Trading Estate, Squires Gate Lane, Blackpool, FY4 3RL Tel: (01253) 474401 Fax: (01253) 474445 E-mail: info@gledhill-cyls.co.uk

Gledhill Water Storage Ltd, Unit 22, Corngreves Trading Estate, Charlton Dive, Cradley Heath, West Midlands, B64 7BJ Tel: (01384) 636245 Fax: (01384) 413700

Mcdonald Engineers Ltd, Flemington Road, Glenrothes, Fife, KY7 5QF Tel: (01592) 611123 Fax: (01592) 611166 E-mail: info@mcdonald-engineers.com

Stanley Cylinders Ltd, 82 Lime Pit Lane, Stanley, Wakefield, West Yorkshire, WF3 4DF Tel: (01924) 823320 Fax: (01924) 825283 E-mail: stanleycylinders@aol.com

Telford Copper Cylinders, Haybridge Road, Wellington, Telford, Shropshire, TF1 2NW Tel: (01952) 262300 Fax: (01952) 253452 E-mail: sales@telford-group.com

COPPER WIRE

Essex Nexans UK Ltd, Ellis Ashton Street, Liverpool, L36 6BW Tel: 0151-443 6000 Fax: 0151-443 6025 E-mail: sales@essexgroup.co.uk

Kay Electronics & Materials, 52 Albany Park Road, Kingston Upon Thames, Surrey, KT2 5SU Tel: (020) 8546 3235 Fax: (020) 8549 5712 E-mail: jaqueline_babinet@hotmail.com

Leoni Temco Ltd, Whimsey Industrial Estate, Cinderford, Gloucestershire, GL14 3HZ Tel: (01594) 820100 Fax: (01594) 823691 E-mail: general@leonitemco.com

▶ Pirelli Cables Ltd, Carr Lane, Prescot, Merseyside, L34 1PD Tel: 0151-430 4300 Fax: 0151-430 4390 E-mail: neil.bootman@pirelli.com

Tri Wire Ltd, Good Hope Close, Normanton, West Yorkshire, WF6 1TR Tel: (01924) 223744 Fax: (01924) 220098 E-mail: sales@nexanstriwire.com

Von Roll UK Ltd, Unit 6, Lawrence Way, Dunstable, Bedfordshire, LU6 1BD Tel: (01582) 500500 Fax: (01582) 476456 E-mail: wire@vonroll.com

W G H Wire Drawers Ltd, Imperial Works, 217 Oxford Street, Bilston, West Midlands, WV14 7HY Tel: (01902) 354142 Fax: (01902) 354250

COPPER/ALLOY INGOTS

Special Quality Alloys Ltd, Colwall St, Sheffield, S9 3WP Tel: 0114-243 4366 Fax: 0114-244 1199 E-mail: sales@specialqualityalloys.com

COPPER/ALLOY STOCKHOLDERS, *See also headings for particular types under Copper such as Copper Bars or Sections*

Advanced Alloys Ltd, Unit 17 Parham Drive, Eastleigh, Hampshire, SO50 4NU Tel: (023) 8061 8891 Fax: (023) 8061 1481 E-mail: sales@advancedalloysltd.co.uk

Advanced Metals International Ltd, Odhams Trading Estate, St.Albans Road, Watford, WD24 7RT Tel: (01923) 205599 Fax: (01923) 205588 E-mail: sales@advancedmetals.com

Ampco Metal Ltd, 17 Binns Close, Coventry, CV4 9TB Tel: (024) 7646 7011 Fax: (024) 7646 1455 E-mail: info@ampcometal.co.uk

Columbia Metals Ltd, Union Street South, Halifax, West Yorkshire, HX1 2LA Tel: (01422) 343026 Fax: (01422) 346587 E-mail: export@columbiametals.co.uk

Forged Products, Venture House, Cross Street, Macclesfield, Cheshire, SK11 7PG Tel: (01625) 428399 Fax: (01625) 508200 E-mail: forgedproducts@dial.pipex.com

Langley Alloys Ltd, Campbell Rd, Stoke-on-Trent, ST4 4ER Tel: (01782) 847474 Fax: (01782) 847476 E-mail: chris@meighs.co.uk

Luvaca Wolverhampton Ltd, Unit B, Smeston Bridge Industrial Estate, Bridgnorth Road, Wombourne, Wolverhampton, WV5 8AY Tel: (01902) 324747 Fax: (01902) 324501 E-mail: sales@thatcher-alloys.com

MKM Mansfelder Copper Ltd, 37-39 Compton, Ashbourne, Derbyshire, DE6 1BX Tel: (01335) 300585 Fax: (01335) 300577

Nemco Metals International Ltd, 5 Pennard Close, Brackmills Indus Estate, Brackmills Industrial Estate, Northampton, NN4 7BE Tel: (01604) 666100 Fax: (01604) 768414 E-mail: sales@nemcometals.co.uk

William Rowland Ltd, 7-23 Meadow Street, Sheffield, S3 7BL Tel: 0114-276 9421 Fax: 0114-275 9429 E-mail: e-mail@william-rowland.co.uk

Taybroh Alloys & Stainless Steels Ltd, Unit 2 Eastington Trading Estate, Stonehouse, Gloucestershire, GL10 3RY Tel: (01453) 828991 Fax: (01453) 828988 E-mail: sales@taybrohalloys.co.uk

COPPER/ALLOY TUBES

Yorkshire Copper Tube, East Lancashire Road, Liverpool, L33 7TU Tel: 0151-546 2700 Fax: 0151-546 5881 E-mail: sales@yorkshirecoppertube.com

COPPER/ALLOYS, PLASTIC MOULD PRODUCTION

Ampco Metal Ltd, 17 Binns Close, Coventry, CV4 9TB Tel: (024) 7646 7011 Fax: (024) 7646 1455 E-mail: info@ampcometal.co.uk

COPPERPLATE ENGRAVERS

Go Go Cobblers, 474 Bromley Road, Bromley, BR1 4PB Tel: (020) 8697 1509 Fax: (020) 8697 1509

James Stewart & Co. (Printers) Ltd, 151 Hertingfordbury Road, Hertford, SG14 1NL Tel: (01992) 582531 Fax: (01992) 500549 E-mail: sales@james-stewart.demon.co.uk

John White Trophies, 115 Lindon Road, Walsall, WS8 7DD Tel: (01543) 379070 Fax: (01543) 379070 E-mail: john.white@virgin.net

COPPERPLATE PRINTERS/ PRINTING SERVICES

Thomas Ross Ltd, St Marks Road, Binfield, Bracknell, Berkshire, RG42 4TR Tel: (01344) 862686 Fax: (01344) 862575 E-mail: sales@thomasross.co.uk

James Stewart & Co. (Printers) Ltd, 151 Hertingfordbury Road, Hertford, SG14 1NL Tel: (01992) 582531 Fax: (01992) 500549 E-mail: sales@james-stewart.demon.co.uk

COPPERSMITHS/WORKERS

Collier Castings, Raybar, Hooe, Battle, East Sussex, TN33 9EU Tel: (01424) 892248 Fax: (01424) 892248

Lenco Engineering (Hull) Ltd, Unit 1D Marfleet Lane Industrial Estate, Burma Drive, Hull, HU9 5SD Tel: (01482) 784988 Fax: (01482) 796661 E-mail: lenco98@hotmail.com

Manco, Garland Works, Bennett Street, Ardwick, Manchester, M12 5BW Tel: 0161-223 0303 Fax: 0161-231 6558

COPYING AND DUPLICATING CENTRES/SERVICES

Ashford Overload Services, Bottings Industrial Estate, Curdridge, Southampton, SO30 2DY Tel: (01489) 787071 Fax: (01489) 787621 E-mail: ashford.overload@dial.pipex.com

Barley Mow Reprographics Ltd, 10 Barley Mow Passage, London, W4 4PH Tel: (020) 8995 7042 Fax: (020) 8747 8530 E-mail: enjayrepro@btinternet.com

Blairgowrie Printers, 7 Reform Street, Blairgowrie, Perthshire, PH10 6BD Tel: (01250) 872102

Bradbury Graphics Ltd, 6-14 Donegall Pass, Belfast, BT7 1BS Tel: (028) 9023 3535 Fax: (028) 9057 2057 E-mail: info@bradbury-graphics.co.uk

Business By Technology Midlands Ltd, 5 Portway Close, Torrington Avenue, Coventry, CV4 9UY Tel: (024) 7647 1507 Fax: (024) 7646 3838 E-mail: sales@bbt-direct.com

▶ Busy Fingers, 2 Elliott Road, Love Lane Industrial Estate, Cirencester, Gloucestershire, GL7 1YS Tel: (01285) 656757 Fax: (01285) 657665 E-mail: bfcopying@aol.com

C S L Copy Shop, 84 St. Marys Road, Market Harborough, Leicestershire, LE16 7DX Tel: (01858) 465208 Fax: (01858) 465208

Charnwood Publishing Co. Ltd, Vaughan Street, Coalville, Leicestershire, LE67 3GG Tel: (01530) 832288 Fax: (01530) 510390 E-mail: chardwoodp@aol.com

Colourplus Print & Design, Unit 28 Monument Business Park, Warpsgrove Lane, Chalgrove, Oxford, OX44 7RW Tel: (01865) 400040 Fax: (01865) 400040 E-mail: design@colourplus.co.uk

Copy Centre, 70 Park Lane, London, N17 0JR Tel: (020) 8808 7275 Fax: (020) 8365 1430

Copybest (Essex) Ltd, 172-174 Coggeshall Road, Braintree, Essex, CM7 9ER Tel: (01376) 550164 Fax: (01376) 552857

Copymatt Drawing Office Supplies Solihull, 25 Henley Cresent, Solihull, West Midlands, B91 2JD Tel: 0121-711 1112 Fax: 0121-711 4844 E-mail: sales@copymatt.co.uk

Copyprint UK Ltd, Ground Floor West Block Westminster Business Square, Durham Street, London, SE11 5JH Tel: (020) 7735 0956 Fax: (020) 7793 0519 E-mail: sales@copyprint.co.uk

Copytext Business Machines, 29 Irish Street, Dungannon, County Tyrone, BT70 1DB Tel: (028) 8772 9277 Fax: (028) 8775 3929 E-mail: copytext@hotmail.com

Copyworld Duplicating Services, 6 Merville Garden Village, Newtownabbey, County Antrim, BT37 9TF Tel: (028) 9080 0500 Fax: (028) 9087 9087 E-mail: info@copyworld.co.uk

Cranmore Instant Print Ltd, Crompton Road Mill, Crompton Road, Macclesfield, Cheshire, SK11 8DS Tel: (01625) 615093 Fax: (01625) 613539 E-mail: copy@cranmoreprint.com

Edos Microfilm, Audit Drive, Abingdon, Oxfordshire, OX14 3NJ Tel: (01235) 550505 Fax: (01235) 536719 E-mail: enquiries@edos.co.uk

Heatherbank Drawing Office Supplies, 4 Milethorn Lane, Doncaster, South Yorkshire, DN1 2SU Tel: (01302) 325146

▶ Immedia Print, 215 North Street, Romford, RM1 4QA Tel: (01708) 733237 Fax: (01708) 733739 E-mail: Immediaprint@AOL.com

▶ Impress Bath Ltd, 6 Cork Place, Bath, BA1 3BB Tel: (01225) 315467 Fax: (01225) 470274 E-mail: info@impressbath.co.uk

John E Wright & Co Ltd, 9-11 Marble Street, Leicester, LE1 5XB Tel: 0116-255 6030 E-mail: leicester@johnewright.com

▶ Mercia Instant Print Ltd Trading As Prontaprint, 34 Chapel Ash, Wolverhampton, WV3 0TN Tel: (01902) 771177 Fax: (01902) 422255

Midgley Design & Print, Unit 2c, York Road Industrial Park, Malton, North Yorkshire, YO17 6YA Tel: (01653) 695115 Fax: (01653) 690680 E-mail: dmidgley@fsbdial.co.uk

Multi Media Duplication Ltd, Suite 3 The White House, 7 Station Road, Hagley, Stourbridge, West Midlands, DY9 0NU Tel: (01562) 886808 Fax: (01562) 886808

Office Equipment Servicing, 3 Trinstead Way, Nottingham, NG5 5RZ Tel: (07860) 787882 Fax: 0115-913 9901

Co Ordinated Surveys, The Old Stables, Garage Street, Llandudno, Gwynedd, LL30 1DW Tel: (01492) 870277 Fax: (01492) 877759 E-mail: sales@uksurveys.com

Phillips Duplicators Ltd, 149b Masons Hill, Bromley, BR2 9HW Tel: (020) 8460 2772 Fax: (020) 8460 2772

Print Express, 4 Sunnyside Terrace, London, NW9 5DL Tel: (020) 8200 0600 Fax: (020) 8200 6866 E-mail: printexpress@btclick.com

Qualitext Business Services Ltd, 1 Howard Road, Reigate, Surrey, RH2 7JE Tel: (01737) 242999 Fax: (01737) 248117 E-mail: hialje@qualitext.freeserve.co.uk

Quality Copies Ltd, 26 Durley Road, London, N16 5JS Tel: (020) 8809 3312

Rebourn Ltd, 14 The Green, Chipping Norton, Oxfordshire, OX7 5NH Tel: (01608) 642020 Fax: (01608) 642031

Sackville Oak Ltd, 30 Store Street, London, WC1E 7QD Tel: (020) 7636 8723 Fax: (020) 7636 8726 E-mail: pdfprint@btclick.com

▶ Service Point, Attenborough House, 15 Bennet Road, Reading, RG2 0QX Tel: 0118-975 3995 Fax: 0118-975 3997 E-mail: reading@servicepointuk.com

Solutions For Business, Royston Business & Design Centre, 8 Priory Lane, Royston, Hertfordshire, SG8 9DU Tel: (01763) 242939 Fax: (01763) 243332 E-mail: sales@solutions-for-business.co.uk

Stat Shop, 3-9 Station Street, Sittingbourne, Kent, ME10 3DU Tel: (01795) 425424 Fax: (0870) 7777827 E-mail: admin@statshop.co.uk

Thames Accounting Centre, Systems House, Desborough Business Park, High Wycombe, Buckinghamshire, HP12 3BG Tel: (01494) 451752 Fax: (01494) 464403 E-mail: alex@thames.uk.com

Thames Valley Copiers, 53 Besselsleigh Road, Wootton, Abingdon, Oxfordshire, OX13 6DX Tel: (01865) 736606 Fax: (01865) 736607

Torplan Ltd, 216 Heaton Moor Road, Stockport, Cheshire, SK4 4DU Tel: 0161-443 1881 Fax: 0161-431 0786 E-mail: sales@torplan.co.uk

U D O Mayfair, 28 North Audley Street, London, W1K 6JH Tel: (020) 7499 6216 Fax: (020) 7495 6136 E-mail: mayfair@servicepointuk.com

Wimbledon Copy Bureau, 257-261 Haydons Road, London, SW19 8TY Tel: (020) 8542 8342 Fax: (020) 8715 8959 E-mail: colour@wcb.co.uk

Word Processing Services, 107 Dashwood Avenue, High Wycombe, Buckinghamshire, HP12 3EB Tel: (01494) 538090 Fax: (01494) 538088 E-mail: info@wordproc.co.uk

CORD SETS

Sandal P.L.C., Number 5, Harold Close, The Pinnacles, Harlow, Essex, CM19 5TH Tel: (01279) 422022 Fax: (01279) 626304 E-mail: ctaylor@powerconnections.co.uk

CORD/CORDAGE, PLAITED/ BRAIDED

James Lever & Sons Ltd, Unit 26 Orient Works Morris Green, Business Park Prescott, Bolton, BL3 3PE Tel: (01204) 658154 Fax: (01204) 658154 E-mail: sales@jameslever.co.uk

Marlow Ropes Ltd, Rope Maker Park, Dipilocks Way, Hailsham, East Sussex, BN27 3GU Tel: (01323) 444444 Fax: (01323) 444455 E-mail: sales@marlowropes.com

Nu Ropes, Coker Ropery, West Coker, Yeovil, Somerset, BA22 9BN Tel: (01935) 862327 Fax: (01935) 862274 E-mail: evanstherope1@supanet.co.uk

Twistlink Ltd, Stadon Road, Anstey, Leicester, LE7 7AY Tel: 0116-236 1860 Fax: 0116-236 6423 E-mail: sales@fabmania.com

CORDLESS ALARM SYSTEMS

P A C International Ltd, 1 Park Gate Close, Bredbury Park Way, Bredbury, Stockport, Cheshire, SK6 2SZ Tel: 0161-494 1331 Fax: 0161-430 8658 E-mail: info@pac.co.uk

CORDLESS TELEPHONES

▶ Paul Conway, Suites A, Floor 8, St. James's House, Pendleton Way, Salford, M6 5FW Tel: 0161-737 9898 Fax: 0161-737 8989 E-mail: paul.conway@pmctelecom.co.uk

▶ Landline Phones, 27-29A New Broadway, Tarring Road, Worthing, West Sussex, BN11 4HP Tel: (0870) 7707191 Fax: (0870) 7707191 E-mail: info@landlinephones.co.uk

Look Now Optical, 5 Skinner Street, Gillingham, Kent, ME7 1HD Tel: (01634) 852600 Fax: (01634) 852600 E-mail: sales@easylenses.co.uk

CORDLESS TELEPHONES – *continued*

Westcon Convergents, 1 Clayton Manor, Victoria Gardens, Burgess Hill, West Sussex, RH15 9NB Tel: (01444) 230004 Fax: (01444) 243889 E-mail: info@cranetel.co.uk

CORDS, CURTAIN TIE BACK/ PULL

▶ Acorn Soft Furnishings, 12 Almond Drive, Burtonwood, Warrington, WA5 4QE Tel: 01925 291237 Fax: 01925 293255 E-mail: bev@acorn-soft-furnishings.co.uk

▶ Curtain Genius, Eallisaid, Corsock, Castle Douglas, Kirkcudbrightshire, DG7 3DW Tel: (01644) 440264 Fax: (01644) 440253 E-mail: info@curtaingenius.co.uk

Instant Home Ltd, Beaulieu House, 78 Ermine Street, Huntingdon, Cambridgeshire, PE29 3EZ Tel: 01480 432230 Fax: 01480 432868 E-mail: hollie@instanthome.co.uk

CORDUROY CLOTH

Brisbane Moss Corduroys Corduroy Manufacturers, Halifax Road, Bridgeroyd Works, Todmorden, Lancashire, OL14 6DF Tel: (01706) 815121 Fax: (01706) 818598 E-mail: brimoss@brisbanemoss.co.uk

Chapman, Bridgeroyd Works, Halifax Road, Todmorden, Lancashire, OL14 6DF Tel: (01706) 818587 Fax: (01706) 818598 E-mail: chapmans@chapmangroup.co.uk

Cudworth Of Norden, Baitings Mill, Rochdale, Lancashire, OL12 7TQ Tel: (01706) 641771 Fax: (01706) 641771

Image House Ltd, 67-73 Constitution Hill, Birmingham, B19 3JX Tel: 0121-233 3569 Fax: 0121-233 0139 E-mail: vchobera@compuserve.com

CORE ANALYSERS

Core Laboratories, 17 Howe Moss Drive, Kirkhill Industrial Estate, Dyce, Aberdeen, AB21 0GL Tel: (01224) 421000 Fax: (01224) 421003 E-mail: sales@corelab.co.uk

CORE DRILL BITS

Diamond Power Service, 1a Clarke Street, Farnworth, Bolton, BL4 9JH Tel: (01204) 793303 Fax: (01204) 403804 E-mail: diamondpsi@aol.com

CORE DRILLING EQUIPMENT

Croft Engineering UK Ltd, 4 The Omni Business Centre, Omega Park, Alton, Hampshire, GU34 2QD Tel: (01420) 590009 Fax: (01420) 590009 E-mail: sales@croft-eng.co.uk

Golz UK Ltd, Springhead Enterprise Park, Springhead Road, Gravesend, Kent, DA11 8HB Tel: (01474) 321679 Fax: (01474) 321477 E-mail: sales@goelz.com

Runrig International Ltd, Fairview House, 27 Sun Street, Biggleswade, Bedfordshire, SG18 0BP Tel: (01767) 601102 Fax: (01767) 312106 E-mail: runrigintlltd@btinternet.com

CORE FOUNDRY SAND MIXERS

Omega Foundry Machinery Ltd, 8 Stapledon Road, Orton Southgate, Peterborough, PE2 6TB Tel: (01733) 232231 Fax: (01733) 237012 E-mail: sales@omegafoundrymachinery.com

CORK

Amorim UK Ltd, Suite 1a Bishops Weald House, Albion Way, Horsham, West Sussex, RH12 1AH Tel: (01403) 710001 Fax: (01403) 710003 E-mail: sales@wicanders.co.uk

Bathgate & Co Cork Ltd, 75 Trafalgar Lane, Edinburgh, EH6 4DQ Tel: 0131-625 5485 Fax: 0131-625 5485 E-mail: bathgateco@aol.com

Cantrill Cork Products, 3 Alma Works, Darlaston Road, Wednesbury, West Midlands, WS10 7TG Tel: 0121-567 3140 Fax: 0121-567 3149E-mail: cancork@cantrill.fsbusiness.co.uk

Rankin Brothers & Sons, Unit 3c Drakes Farm, Drakes Drive, Long Crendon, Aylesbury, Buckinghamshire, HP18 9BA Tel: (01844) 203100 Fax: (01844) 203101 E-mail: sales@rankincork.co.uk

CORK PRODUCTS

Bathgate & Co Cork Ltd, 75 Trafalgar Lane, Edinburgh, EH6 4DQ Tel: 0131-625 5485 Fax: 0131-625 5485 E-mail: bathgateco@aol.com

Perkins Closure Ltd, Lion Gate Ct, Petworth Rd, Witley, Godalming, Surrey, GU8 5QW Tel: 01428 685577 Fax: 01428 684477

CORK STOPPERS

Bathgate & Co Cork Ltd, 75 Trafalgar Lane, Edinburgh, EH6 4DQ Tel: 0131-625 5485 Fax: 0131-625 5485 E-mail: bathgateco@aol.com

C Olley & Sons Ltd, Iberia House, 14 Finchley Avenue, Mildenhall, Bury St. Edmunds, Suffolk, IP28 7BJ Tel: (01638) 712076 Fax: (01638) 717304 E-mail: sales@olley-cork.com

Rankin Brothers & Sons, Unit 3c Drakes Farm, Drakes Drive, Long Crendon, Aylesbury, Buckinghamshire, HP18 9BA Tel: (01844) 203100 Fax: (01844) 203101 E-mail: sales@rankincork.co.uk

CORK TILES

C Olley & Sons Ltd, Iberia House, 14 Finchley Avenue, Mildenhall, Bury St. Edmunds, Suffolk, IP28 7BJ Tel: (01638) 712076 Fax: (01638) 717304 E-mail: sales@olley-cork.com

CORKSCREWS

Metaltex UK Ltd, Brunleys, Kiln Farm, Milton Keynes, MK11 3HR Tel: (01908) 262062 Fax: (01908) 262162 E-mail: info@metaltex.com

CORNER SOFAS

Nabru Ltd, Unit 12, Sarum Complex, Salisbury Road, Uxbridge, Middlesex, UB8 2RZ Tel: (01895) 256868 Fax: (01895) 239214 E-mail: service@nabru.co.uk

CORONA TREATMENT SERVICES

Boddingtons Ltd, Blackwater Trading Estate, The Causeway, Maldon, Essex, CM9 4GG Tel: (01621) 874200 Fax: (01621) 874299 E-mail: sales@boddingtons-ltd.com

Dyne Technology Ltd, PO Box 9593, Tamworth, Staffordshire, B78 3NU Tel: (01827) 284244 Fax: (01827) 286311 E-mail: info@dynetechnology.co.uk

CORONA TREATMENT SYSTEMS

BPM Engineering Services Ltd, Unit 18 Failsworth Indust Estate, Morton Street, Failsworth, Manchester, M35 0BN Tel: 0161-682 3377 Fax: 0161-682 7711 E-mail: brian.bpm@btconnect.com

Dyne Technology Ltd, PO Box 9593, Tamworth, Staffordshire, B78 3NU Tel: (01827) 284244 Fax: (01827) 286311 E-mail: info@dynetechnology.co.uk

Schleising Consultancy Ltd, 10 Victoria Mead, Thame, Oxfordshire, OX9 3HY Tel: (01844) 213492 Fax: (01844) 216751 E-mail: eddie.schleising@dsl.pipex.com

CORPORATE ADVENTURE TRAINING

Quad Bike Tours, Keepers Cottage, Inverlair, Fersit, Roy Bridge, Inverness-Shire, PH31 4AR Tel: (01397) 732371 E-mail: info@quadbiketours.co.uk

CORPORATE AWARD CEREMONY ORGANISING

▶ Amazing Days Ltd, 90-91 Luddesdown Road, Luddesdown, Gravesend, Kent, DA13 0XE Tel: (01474) 815589 Fax: (01474) 815589 E-mail: dawn.gibson@amazing-days.co.uk

▶ Aztec Innovations, Burnhouse Industrial Estate, Whitburn, Bathgate, West Lothian, EH47 0LQ Tel: (01506) 204188

▶ Excel Chauffeur Services, Warrington Business Park, Long Lane, Warrington, WA2 8TX Tel: (0871) 2881433 Fax: (0871) 2881433 E-mail: enquiries@xl-cars.co.uk

▶ Exclusively Skye Ltd, Tigh Shasaig Teangue, Sleat, Isle of Skye, IV44 8RD Tel: (01471) 820225 E-mail: ken@exclusively-skye.co.uk

▶ Hands On, 23 Seldon Road, Worthing, West Sussex, BN11 2LN Tel: 07731 522290 E-mail: info@five-minute-massage-company.com

▶ Hatters Catering Co., 6 Southgate Parade, Crawley, West Sussex, RH10 6ER Tel: (01293) 550333 Fax: (01293) 552254 E-mail: admin@hatterscatering.co.uk

▶ Millennium Awards, Smithy Market Hill, Glass, Huntly, Aberdeenshire, AB54 4XX Tel: (01466) 700311 Fax: (01466) 700344 E-mail: info@onlinetrophies.co.uk

▶ Mountain Leap LLP, 1st Floor, 25 Eccleston Square, London, SW1V 1NS Tel: (020) 7931 0621 Fax: (020) 7931 0613 E-mail: adam.honey@mountainleap.com

▶ Sterling Travel Management, H Medina Chamber, Town Quay, Southampton, SO14 2AQ Tel: (023) 8033 0111 Fax: (023) 8033 7397 E-mail: info@sterlingtravel.co.uk

▶ Uptown Events, PO Box 1492, London, North London, NW11 6WL Tel: 0870 1226971

CORPORATE BEACH ACTIVITY ORGANISING

▶ Unicorn Trails, 2, Acorn Centre, Chestnut Avenue, Biggleswade, Bedfordshire, SG18 ORA Tel: 01767 600606 E-mail: david@unicorntrails.com

CORPORATE CASINO EVENT ORGANISING

▶ Galaxy Casino, Highfield Road, Kettering, Northamptonshire, NN15 6HT Tel: (01536) 000000 E-mail: caleb158@hotmail.co.uk

▶ Poker Store Ltd, 10 Rutland Avenue, Southend On Sea, Southend-on-Sea, SS1 2XH Tel: (01702) 615413 E-mail: katy@poker-store.co.uk

CORPORATE CLAY PIGEON SHOOTING ORGANISING

▶ Smoking Barrels Leicestershire & Rutland, Glebe Farm, North End, Hallaton, Market Harborough, Leicestershire, LE16 8UZ Tel: 0116-247 8714 E-mail: max@jacquespad.fsnet.co.uk

CORPORATE COACHING

▶ Clairegodwincoaching.co.uk, 33 Yew Tree Gardens, Denmead, Waterlooville, Hampshire, PO7 6LH Tel: (023) 9225 5232

▶ Creative Mind Skills Therapeutic Training, Holden House, Holden Road, Leigh, Lancashire, WN7 1EX Tel: 08704 323423 E-mail: info@cmst.co.uk

▶ Den Caney, 182 Stonehouse Lane, Quinton, Birmingham, B32 3AH Tel: 0121-427 2693 Fax: 0121-427 8905 E-mail: dencaneycoaches@blueyonder.co.uk

CORPORATE COMMUNICATIONS SERVICES

Adodo, Howitt Buildings, Lenton Boulevard, Nottingham, NG7 2BG Tel: 0115-970 1471 Fax: 0115-970 1671 E-mail: solutions@adodo.co.uk

Atrium Ltd, Yateley Lodge, Reading Road, Yateley, Hampshire, GU46 7AA Tel: (01252) 862423 Fax: (01252) 890596 E-mail: info@atriumcom.com

Buchanan Communications Ltd, 107 Cheapside, London, EC2V 6DN Tel: (020) 7466 5000 Fax: (020) 7466 5001 E-mail: contact@buchanan.uk.com

▶ Houston Associates, 183-185 Kirkdale, London, SE26 4QH Tel: (020) 8778 1900 Fax: (020) 8659 9191 E-mail: richard@houston-associates.com

▶ Just Great Events, Deerings, Shaw Lane, Holywell Green, Halifax, West Yorkshire, HX4 9DW Tel: (01422) 312816 E-mail: enquiries@justgreatevents.co.uk

M R C Publications Ltd, 5 Worcester Street, Oxford, OX1 2BX Tel: (01865) 200202 Fax: (01865) 200509 E-mail: sales@mrc.info.com

▶ Mindset Communications, Nelson Close, Farnham, Surrey, GU9 9AR Tel: (07771) 870868 Fax: (01252) 316881 E-mail: info@mindsetcomms.co.uk

Redhouse Lane Communications, 14-15 Bedford Square, London, WC1B 3JA Tel: (020) 7462 2600 Fax: (020) 7462 2601 E-mail: sales@redhouselane.com

▶ Vidox Video Productions Ltd, Unit 1b Dane John Works, Gordon Road, Canterbury, Kent, CT1 3PP Tel: (01227) 781155 E-mail: info@vidox.co.uk

CORPORATE CREATIVE DESIGN

▶ GnD Creations, 6 Peterborough Rd, Whittlesey, Peterborough, PE7 1NJ Tel: 01733 206520 E-mail: design@gndcreations.com

▶ Hammond, Clive Villas, Cemetery Road, Shelton, Stoke-on-Trent, ST4 2DL Tel: (01782) 202255 Fax: (01782) 202266 E-mail: max@hammondcosschalk.co.uk

CORPORATE EVENT ORGANISATION

▶ 20five eight Lifestyle Management, 8 Rubislaw Terrace, Aberdeen, AB10 1XE Tel: 01224 611555 E-mail: sherida@20five8.co.uk

▶ Eventurous, The Water front, West Midlands Water Ski centre, Tamworth, Staffordshire, B78 2DL Tel: (0870) 6071258 E-mail: sales@eventurous.co.uk

▶ Finedining.co.uk, 9a Ty Draw, Little Mill, Pontypool, Gwent, NP4 0HR Tel: (01495) 785449 E-mail: tracey@finedining.co.uk

▶ Hurst Point Yacht Charters Ltd, Little Howdens, Rhinefield Close, Brockenhurst, Hampshire, SO42 7SU Tel: (01590) 623765 E-mail: info@hurstpointyachts.co.uk

▶ Nick Levi - Close Up Magic, 2 North Park Avenue, Norwich, NR4 7EG Tel: (07962) 252949 E-mail: nick@levimagic.com

▶ Mountain Leap LLP, 1st Floor, 25 Eccleston Square, London, SW1V 1NS Tel: (020) 7931 0621 Fax: (020) 7931 0613 E-mail: adam.honey@mountainleap.com

▶ Occasions Caterers Ltd, Unit 22 Bow Triangle Business, Centre Eleanor Street Bow, London, E3 4UR Tel: (020) 8980 2770

Orange Tree Events Ltd, 4 Furnival Close, Virginia Water, Surrey, GU25 4HR Tel: (01344) 430091E-mail: info@orange-tree-events.co.uk

▶ Orbis Events, 20 Elmfield Close, Woodfalls, Salisbury, SP5 2BF Tel: (01725) 511963 E-mail: info@orbisevents.com

▶ P C I London, Unit G4, Harbour Yard, Chelsea Harbour, London, SW10 0XD Tel: (020) 7544 7500 Fax: (020) 7352 7906 E-mail: reception@pci-live.com

▶ Rolling Productions Ltd, Winsford House, 189. Finchampstead Road, Wokingham, Berkshire, RG40 3HE Tel: 0118-9782463 E-mail: enquiries@rollingproductions.com

▶ Sas Paintball, Codsall Wood Road, Codsall Wood, Wolverhampton, WV8 1QR Tel: (01902) 844467 Fax: (01902) 713117 E-mail: info@saspaintball.co.uk

▶ Smoking Barrels Leicestershire & Rutland, Glebe Farm, North End, Hallaton, Market Harborough, Leicestershire, LE16 8UZ Tel: 0116-247 8714 E-mail: max@jacquespad.fsnet.co.uk

▶ Telekinetix Ltd, 38 Park Road North, Bedford, MK41 7RH Tel: (01234) 307571 Fax: 01234 328330 E-mail: sally@kinetixevents.co.uk

▶ Unicorn Trails, 2, Acorn Centre, Chestnut Avenue, Biggleswade, Bedfordshire, SG18 ORA Tel: 01767 600606 E-mail: david@unicorntrails.com

▶ Uptown Events, PO Box 1492, London, North London, NW11 6WL Tel: 0870 1226971

CORPORATE EVENT ORGANISATION, SAILING

▶ Parallel Blue Marine Corporate Sailing Events, Griffin Mill, London Road, Thrupp, Stroud, Gloucestershire, GL5 2AZ Tel: (01453) 887766

CORPORATE FINANCE ADVISERS/SERVICES

A Anthony, Rose Hill House, Pygons Hill Lane, Liverpool, L31 4JF Tel: 0151-526 4008 Fax: 0151-526 1673

▶ Axis International plc, 40 Park Street, London, W1K 2JG Tel: (020) 7290 9570 Fax: (020) 7629 1917 E-mail: admin@axisinternational.com

Barclays Mercantile Business Finance Ltd, Churchill Plaza, Churchill Way, Basingstoke, Hampshire, RG21 7GP Tel: (01256) 314108 Fax: (01256) 791850 E-mail: bassf@barclays.co.uk

▶ Bowers & Co, York House, 4 Sheepscar Way, Leeds, LS7 3JB Tel: 0113 2379500 Fax: 0113 2379550 E-mail: ajb@companydoctor.co.uk

Brown Shipley Asset Management Ltd, Founders Court, Lothbury, London, EC2R 7HE Tel: (020) 7606 9833 Fax: (020) 7606 6657

Charles Lucas & Marshall, Eastcott House, 4 High Street, Swindon, SN1 3EP Tel: (01793) 511055 Fax: (01635) 570275

E B C Corporate Consultants Ltd, East India Ho, 109-117 Middlesex St, London, E1 7JF Tel: (020) 7621 0101 Fax: (020) 7626 7915 E-mail: sales@ebcam.co.uk

▶ Eastwood Anglo European Investments Ltd, Burnell Arms, Winkburn, Newark, Nottinghamshire, NG22 8PQ Tel: (01636) 636132 Fax: (01636) 636643 E-mail: tom@eastwoodanglo.com

Electra Partners Europe Ltd, 65 Kingsway, London, WC2B 6QT Tel: (020) 7831 6464 Fax: (020) 7404 5388 E-mail: info@electraeurope.com

Harris Kafton, 54-58 High Street, Edgware, Middlesex, HA8 7EJ Tel: (020) 8381 3770 Fax: (020) 8381 3470

▶ HLB International, 21 Ebury Street, London, SW1W 0LD Tel: (020) 7881 1100 Fax: (020) 7881 1109 E-mail: mailbox@hlbi.com

HSBC Invoice Finance, 12 Calthorpe Road, Edgbaston, Birmingham, B15 1RA Tel: 0121-455 2611 Fax: 0121-455 2190 E-mail: sales@invoicefinance.hsbc.co.uk

I D J Ltd, 81 Piccadilly, London, W1J 8HY Tel: (020) 7355 1200 Fax: (020) 7495 1149 E-mail: sales@idj.co.uk

Intermediate Capital Group plc, 20 Old Broad Street, London, EC2N 1DP Tel: (020) 7628 9898 Fax: (020) 7628 2268

▶ International Foreign Exchange, 84 Brook Street, Mayfair, London, UK, W1K 5EH Tel: (020) 7495 8888 Fax: (020) 7495 8890 E-mail: info@internationalfx.com

CORPORATE FINANCE ADVISERS/ SERVICES – *continued*

KPMG UK Ltd, Peat House, 1 Waterloo Way, Leicester, LE1 6LP Tel: 0116-256 6000 Fax: 0116-256 6050

Manches & Co., Aldwych House, 81 Aldwych, London, WC2B 4RP Tel: (020) 7404 4433 Fax: (020) 7430 1133

Milsted Langdon Ltd, Winchester House, Deane Gate Avenue, Taunton, Somerset, TA1 2UH Tel: (01823) 445566 Fax: (01823) 445555 E-mail: simonlmilsted@milsted-langdon.co.uk

▶ Mortgage Advice Co., 111 Union Street, Glasgow, G1 3TA Tel: 0141-204 5770 Fax: 0141-221 4055 E-mail: sales@mortgageadvicecompany.co.uk

Newchurch Computer Systems, Causeway House, 13 The Causeway, Teddington, Middlesex, TW11 0JR Tel: (020) 8783 3300 Fax: (020) 8977 8198 E-mail: info@newchurch.co.uk

Optima Legal Services Ltd, Arndale House, Charles Street, Bradford, West Yorkshire, BD1 1UN Tel: (01274) 553150 Fax: (01274) 513718

Redleaf Vehicle Leasing, 28-29 Westhampnett Road, Chichester, West Sussex, PO19 7HH Tel: (08457) 669988 Fax: (01243) 780750

Rowan Dartington Ltd, Colston Tower, Colston Street, Bristol, BS1 4RD Tel: 0117-933 0000 Fax: 0117-933 0009

Uni Credito Italiano, 17 Moorgate, London, EC2R 6PH Tel: (020) 7606 9011 Fax: (020) 7606 3920 E-mail: info@unicredit.co.uk

W H Ireland Ltd, 11 St James's Square, Manchester, M2 6WH Tel: 0161-832 2174 Fax: 0161-833 0935 E-mail: laurie.beavers@wh-ireland.co.uk

▶ Western Standard Corporation, 49 Florence Road, Gedling, Nottingham, NG4 2QL Tel: 0115-940 3131 Fax: 0115-940 3134

CORPORATE FUNCTION BALLOON DECORATION SERVICES

▶ Poker Shop, Unit 2, Fletchers Square, Southend-on-Sea, SS2 5RN Tel: (0870) 8712007 Fax: (0870) 8736007 E-mail: srush@poker-shop.co.uk

CORPORATE GALA DINNER ORGANISING

▶ Amazing Days Ltd, 90-91 Luddesdown Road, Luddesdown, Gravesend, Kent, DA13 0XE Tel: (01474) 815589 Fax: (01474) 815589 E-mail: dawn.gibson@amazing-days.co.uk

▶ Exclusively Skye Ltd, Tigh Shasaig Teangue, Sleat, Isle of Skye, IV44 8RD Tel: (01471) 820225 E-mail: ken@exclusively-skye.co.uk

▶ Hatters Catering Co., 6 Southgate Parade, Crawley, West Sussex, RH10 6ER Tel: (01293) 550333 Fax: (01293) 552254 E-mail: admin@hatterscatering.co.uk

▶ Midsummer House, Midsummer Common, Cambridge, CB4 1HA Tel: (01223) 369299 Fax: (01223) 302672 E-mail: reservations@midsummerhouse.co.uk

▶ Sterling Travel Management, H Medina Chamber, Town Quay, Southampton, SO14 2AQ Tel: (023) 8033 0111 Fax: (023) 8033 7397 E-mail: info@sterlingtravel.co.uk

CORPORATE GOLF DAYS

▶ Golf & Leisure Breaks, 20 Greys Road, Henley-on-Thames, Oxfordshire, RG9 1RY Tel: (01491) 572580 Fax: (01491) 573763 E-mail: sales@golf-leisurebreaks.co.uk

▶ Golfsim, 30 Elvington, King'S Lynn, King's Lynn, Norfolk, PE30 4TA Tel: (07956) 090436 E-mail: info@golfsimulation.co.uk

Winning Golf, Winning Golf, 5 Carden Place, Aberdeen, AB10 1UT Tel: (0845) 4505090 Fax: (01224) 652969 E-mail: info@winninggolf.net

CORPORATE HOSPITALITY SERVICES

▶ 6 Nations, 12 South Bridge, Edinburgh, EH1 1DD Tel: (0870) 3500890 Fax: 0870 350 0891 E-mail: sales@6-nations-hospitality.com

Catering Equipment Engineers Ltd, Kildrum Indust Estate, Kildrum Road, Shankbridge, Ballymena, County Antrim, BT42 3EY Tel: (028) 2589 2122 Fax: (028) 2589 8208 E-mail: info@cee-group.com

▶ Chocolate Fountains from Hot Chocolate Lunch Ltd, St Hilda Close, Deepcar, Sheffield, S36 2TH Tel: 0784 0685595 E-mail: info@hotchocolatelunch.com

▶ Global Sporting Event, 29a Stamford New Road, Altrincham, Cheshire, WA14 1EB Tel: 0161-924 0069 Fax: 0161-929 5642 E-mail: anthony@seesportlive.co.uk

▶ Golfsim, 30 Elvington, King'S Lynn, King's Lynn, Norfolk, PE30 4TA Tel: (07956) 090436 E-mail: info@golfsimulation.co.uk

▶ Hurst Point Yacht Charters Ltd, Little Howdens, Rhinefield Close, Brockenhurst, Hampshire, SO42 7SU Tel: (01590) 623765 E-mail: info@hurstpointyachts.co.uk

▶ Kensingtons Ltd, 2 Dixon Place, Collage Milton, East Kilbride, Glasgow, G74 5JF Tel: (0845) 2722845 Fax: E-mail: enquiry@kensingtons-catering.co.uk

▶ Venue Reservations, 13 Bishopsgate, London, EC2N 3BA Tel: (020) 7334 3922 Fax: (020) 7334 3911 E-mail: enquiries@venuereservations.co.uk

CORPORATE IDENTITY (ID) CLOTHING

abacus Careerwear Ltd, Unit D6 Newton Business Park, Cartwright Street, Hyde, Cheshire, SK14 4EH Tel: 0161-351 1211 Fax: 0161-367 8819 E-mail: alan@abacus-careerwear.co.uk

Allen & Douglas Corporate Clothing Ltd, Compton Park, Wildmere Road, Banbury, Oxfordshire, OX16 3EZ Tel: (01295) 272700 Fax: (01295) 270486 E-mail: sales@aandd.co.uk

Bernard Uniforms Ltd, Harbour Crescent, Main Road, Harwich, Essex, CO12 3NT Tel: (01255) 502281 Fax: (01255) 241457

Blues Clothing Ltd, Brigade House, Parsons Green, London, SW6 4TN Tel: (020) 7371 9900 Fax: (020) 7371 9782 E-mail: marketing@blues-clothing.co.uk

Century Clothing, Swinburne Street, Nottingham, NG3 2GD Tel: 0115-950 4744 Fax: 0115-924 1896 E-mail: paul@centuryclothing.co.uk

Debaer Incorperating Rimac, 7 Langley Business Centre, Station Road, Langley, Slough, SL3 8DS Tel: (01753) 710071 Fax: (01753) 572772 E-mail: sales@rimac.co.uk

Dewhirst Corporate Clothing, 3 Burdon Drive, North West Industrial Estate, Peterlee, County Durham, SR8 2JH Tel: 0191-518 1888 Fax: 0191-586 3167

Dickies Workwear, Second Avenue, Westfield Trading Estate, Midsomer Norton, Radstock, BA3 4BH Tel: (01761) 410041 Fax: (01761) 414825 E-mail: uksales@dickies.com

Elms & Elms, 6-8 Brookfield Road, Cheadle, Cheshire, SK8 2PN Tel: 0161-428 8383 Fax: 0161-428 8855 E-mail: info@elmsandelms.co.uk

Fayers Bespoke Software, 1A Barton Buisness Park, Barton Road, Bury St. Edmunds, Suffolk, IP32 7BE Tel: (01284) 760276 Fax: (08707) 515984 E-mail: chrisandian@fayersbespoke.com

GDB Manufacturing, Leisurewear House, Barnes Road, Bradford, West Yorkshire, BD8 9TG Tel: (01274) 491110 Fax: (01274) 491112

Glynn Valley, Station Road, Liskeard, Cornwall, PL14 4DA Tel: (01579) 345677 Fax: (01579) 345677 E-mail: sales@glynnvalley.com

Hewats Of Edinburgh, 11-12 Teviot Place, Edinburgh, EH1 2RA Tel: 0131-225 5705 Fax: 0131-226 6885 E-mail: sales@hewats.com

Leonard Hudson, 2 Queen Anne Drive, Edinburgh, EH28 8LH Tel: 0800 0181412 Fax: 0808 1806030 E-mail: sales@leonardhudson.co.uk

International Insignia, Unit 3 Dunstall Hill Industrial Estate, Gorsebrook Road, Wolverhampton, WV6 0PJ Tel: (01902) 714265 Fax: (01902) 714853 E-mail: sales@internationalinsignia.net

J B Armstrong & Co. Ltd, Middleton Street, Ilkeston, Derbyshire, DE7 5TT Tel: 0115-932 4913 Fax: 0115-930 0083 E-mail: info@armstrongsmill.co.uk

Johnsons Apparelmaster UK Ltd, Unit 6, Curlew Park, Threemilestone, Truro, Cornwall, TR4 9LE Tel: (01872) 260506

Kisgap, Unit 7/8 Clifton House, 14 Wells Terrace, London, N4 3JU Tel: (020) 7272 8333 Fax: (020) 7272 8102

Kruger Tissue Industrial Division, Penygroes Industrial Estate, Penygroes, Caernarfon, Gwynedd, LL54 6DB Tel: (01286) 880969 Fax: (01286) 880026

Malro Ltd, Malro House, 245 Wood Street, London, E17 3NT Tel: (020) 8521 5137 Fax: (020) 8521 6862

Matrix Design Services, Unit 331e Vauxhall Industrial Estate, Greg Street, Stockport, Cheshire, SK5 7BR Tel: 0161-480 5610 Fax: 0161-474 1845 E-mail: office@matrixdesigns.co.uk

▶ Motif Magic Ltd, 1 Davis Road, Brooklands, Weybridge, Surrey, KT13 0XH Tel: (01932) 830800 Fax: (0870) 7052851 E-mail: linda@motifmagic.co.uk

Murray, Castle Court, Bodmin Road, Coventry, CV2 5DB Tel: (024) 7658 7980 Fax: (024) 7658 7981 E-mail: jheadley@jheadley.co.uk

New Angle Promotions, Temuka House, School Road, Foulden, Thetford, Norfolk, IP26 5AJ Tel: (01366) 328282 Fax: (01366) 328283 E-mail: mediagolf@aol.com

P & P Clothing, Old Mill La Industrial Estate, Mansfield Woodhouse, Mansfield, Nottinghamshire, NG19 9BG Tel: (01623) 422044 Fax: (01623) 424557 E-mail: sales@pandp.force9.co.uk

Pioner Fristads (UK) Ltd, 7 Wensum Mount Business Centre, Low Road, Hellesdon, Norwich, NR6 5AQ Tel: (01603) 786160 Fax: (01603) 414540 E-mail: enquiries@fristads-co.com

Portlantis Ltd, Queenscot House, Sandhurst Road, Wokingham, Berkshire, RG40 3LS Tel: 0118-977 4529 E-mail: info@portlantis.com

R K Styles Ltd, Unit 2 Alma Street, Smethwick, West Midlands, B66 2RL Tel: 0121-565 3630 Fax: 0121-565 1004 E-mail: sales@rkstyles.co.uk

Rael Brook (Group) Ltd, Grosvenor Street, Ashden Underline, Ashton-Under-Lyne, Lancashire, OL7 0JY Tel: 0161-344 5618 Fax: 0161-308 5060 E-mail: admin@raelbrookshirts.com

Relational Consultants Ltd, 38 Northgate Street, Bury St. Edmunds, Suffolk, IP33 1HY Tel: (01284) 765723E-mail: info@relcon.co.uk

Topaz Blue Ltd, Middlesex Building, Elstree Aerodrome, Elstree, Borehamwood, Hertfordshire, WD6 3AW Tel: (020) 8207 1007 Fax: (020) 8207 0307 E-mail: sales@topazblue.com

▶ Trustyle UK Ltd, Trustyle, Unit 50, Woodside, Thornwood, Epping, Essex, CM16 6LJ Tel: (01992) 578112 Fax: (01992) 572831 E-mail: enquiries@trustyle.co.uk

Wessex Textiles Ltd, Blake Industrial Park, Colley Lane, Bridgwater, Somerset, TA6 5LT Tel: (01278) 450450 Fax: (01278) 450550 E-mail: sales@wessextextiles.co.uk

Wise Worksafe, 3 Parr Road, Stanmore, Middlesex, HA7 1PZ Tel: (020) 8381 1811 Fax: (020) 8381 1827

Woollen Mill, 179 High Street, Edinburgh, EH1 1PD Tel: 0131-225 8023 Fax: 0131-220 3103 E-mail: info@woollenmill.co.uk

CORPORATE IDENTITY (ID) SIGNS

Colette Hill Associates, 18-20 Bromells Road, London, SW4 0BG Tel: (020) 7622 8252 Fax: (020) 7622 8253 E-mail: cha@chapr.co.uk

Dixon Signs, Stratford Rd, Drayton, Banbury, Oxon, OX15 6EE Tel: (01295) 730707 Fax: (01295) 730026 E-mail: mail@dixonsigns.co.uk

Futurama Ltd, Island Farm House, Island Farm Road, West Molesey, Surrey, KT8 2TR Tel: (020) 8941 1999 Fax: (020) 8783 1687 E-mail: postbox@futurama.ltd.uk

Hawes Group Ltd, Sandfield Close, Moulton Park, Northampton, NN3 6EU Tel: (01604) 790000 Fax: (01604) 790190 E-mail: info@hawes.co.uk

L & G Signs Ltd, Unit B9 Larkfield Trading Estate, New Hythe Lane, Larkfield, Aylesford, Kent, ME20 6SW Tel: (01732) 783640 Fax: (01622) 715758 E-mail: sales@landgsigns.co.uk

Lyons, 206 Lylehill Road, Belfast, BT14 8SN Tel: (028) 9082 5688 Fax: (028) 9082 5688

Martin Hopkins Partnership, 31 The Parade, Roath, Cardiff, CF24 3AD Tel: (029) 2046 1233 Fax: (029) 2049 7208 E-mail: info@martinhopkins.co.uk

Rivermeade Signs Ltd, Rowley Industrial Park, Roslin Road, London, W3 8BH Tel: (020) 8896 6900 Fax: (020) 8752 1691 E-mail: info@rivermeade.com

The Sign Factory, Burnbank Road, Bainsford, Falkirk, FK2 7PE Tel: (01324) 501950 Fax: (01324) 501951 E-mail: info@falkirk.gov.uk

Signpost Signs, 137 Upper Wickham Lane, Welling, Kent, DA16 3AL Tel: (020) 8854 8777 Fax: (020) 8855 0577 E-mail: enquiries@signpostsigns.co.uk

▶ Still Works Ltd, 76 Wells Street, Cardiff, CF11 6DY Tel: (029) 2035 3940 Fax: (029) 2035 3941 E-mail: info@stillsdesign.com

CORPORATE IMAGE/DESIGN CONSULTANTS

Addison Corporate Marketing Ltd, 2 Cathedral Street, London, SE1 9DE Tel: (020) 7403 7444 Fax: (020) 7403 1243 E-mail: peter.chodel@addison.co.uk

Cato Associates Ltd, 13 Chelsea Crescent Chelsea Harbour, Chelsea Harbour, London, SW10 0XB Tel: (020) 7352 1406 Fax: (020) 7326689 E-mail: mac@cato.co.uk

Davies Wise Design Co., 14 Spring Mill, Avening Road, Nailsworth, Stroud, Gloucestershire, GL6 0BS Tel: (01453) 839192 Fax: (01453) 839193 E-mail: sales@dwdc.co.uk

▶ Design Distillery Ltd, 12 Northgate, Chichester, West Sussex, PO19 1BA Tel: (01243) 537837 Fax: (01243) 839448 E-mail: leslie@design-distillery.co.uk

Design Group, 2nd Floor Quay House, 7 The Quay, Poole, Dorset, BH15 1HA Tel: (01202) 669090 Fax: (01202) 669930 E-mail: sales@designgroup.co.uk

▶ Eberhardt Signs Ltd, Victory Trading Estate, Kiln Road, Portsmouth, PO3 5LP Tel: (023) 9266 5466 Fax: (023) 9266 5681 E-mail: sales@eberhardtsigns.com

Fine-Focus, 55 Warren Terrace, Hertford, SG14 3JF Tel: (0845) 2261726 E-mail: info@fine-focus.co.uk

Fire Imc, Manley House, 10 Dargan Cresent, Belfast, BT3 9JP Tel: (028) 9077 4388 Fax: (028) 9077 6906 E-mail: sales@fireimc.co.uk

GIA Design Ltd, 46a Pevensey Road, Eastbourne, East Sussex, BN21 3HP Tel: (01323) 722131 Fax: (01323) 642940 E-mail: greg@duvacourt.co.uk

George Gidden Graphics Ltd, 14 Park Street, Guildford, Surrey, GU1 4XB Tel: (01483) 303040 Fax: (01483) 303222 E-mail: paul@giddenplace.com

Graphic Results, 99 Bridge Street, Belper, Derbyshire, DE56 1BA Tel: (01773) 599159 Fax: (01773) 599259 E-mail: sales@graphic-results.co.uk

Harkess Ord Ltd, Bellerive House, 3 Muirfield Crescent, Docklands, London, E14 9SZ Tel: (020) 7459 3300 Fax: (020) 7459 3333

Henrion, Ludlow & Schmidt Ltd, 12 Hobart Place, London, SW1W 0HH Tel: (020) 7245 4600 Fax: (020) 7245 4601 E-mail: info@henrion.com

M P S Group, 207 Desborough Road, High Wycombe, Buckinghamshire, HP11 2QL Tel: (01494) 452600 Fax: (01494) 449122 E-mail: bbi@bbi.co.uk

▶ Still Works Ltd, 76 Wells Street, Cardiff, CF11 6DY Tel: (029) 2035 3940 Fax: (029) 2035 3941 E-mail: info@stillsdesign.com

Watershed Design, 31 Freegrove Road, Islington, London, N7 9RG Tel: (020) 7700 1759 Fax: (020) 7700 1692 E-mail: peter@watershed-uk.com

Wolff Olins Brand Consultants, 10 Regents Wharf, All Saints Street, London, N1 9RL Tel: (020) 7713 7733 Fax: (020) 7713 0217 E-mail: enquiries@wolff-olins.com

Woodstock Computer Solutions Ltd, Malvern, Oakhanger, Bordon, Hampshire, GU35 9JJ Tel: (01420) 474722 E-mail: roly@wcsweb.co.uk

Zebra Studios, 52 Eldon St North, Barnsley, South Yorkshire, S71 1LG Tel: (01226) 299238 Fax: (01226) 299238 E-mail: sales@zebrastudios.co.uk

CORPORATE JEWELLERY

R J Smith Ltd, 41-42 Tenby St North, Birmingham, B1 3EG Tel: 0121-233 2160 Fax: 0121-233 9630E-mail: sales@rjs-ltd.com

Trio Jewellery, 197 Warstone Lane, Birmingham, B18 6JR Tel: 0121-200 1367 Fax: 0121-212 0982

CORPORATE MARKETING GIFTS

▶ Alan Hislop, 32 Holt Road, Horsford, Norwich, NR10 3DD Tel: (01603) 897428 E-mail: sales@ahengraving.co.uk

▶ Annie's Hampers, Bar Farm, Market Weighton Road, Holme-on-Spalding-Moor, York, YO43 4ED Tel: (01430) 860339 E-mail: enquires@annieshampers.com

▶ Archway Promotions, 7 Kempston Court, Kempston Hardwick, Bedford, MK43 9PQ Tel: (01234) 853500 Fax: (01234) 852826 E-mail: sales@archwaypromotions.co.uk

▶ Business Baubles, North Oast, Reed Court Farm, Hunton Road, Tonbridge, Kent, TN12 9SX Tel: (01622) 820005 Fax: (01622) 820006 E-mail: sales@businessbaubles.com

▶ Clipperlight Nautical Books, Albrighton, Wolverhampton, WV7 3WL Tel: (01902) 373217 E-mail: clipperuk@aol.com

▶ Creative Pod Ltd, Basepoint Business & Innovation Centre, Metcalf Way, Crawley, West Sussex, RH11 7XX Tel: (01293) 817228 Fax: (01293) 518201 E-mail: ideas@creative-pod.com

▶ Halcyon Card, Grimshaw Hill, Ullenhall, Henley-in-Arden, West Midlands, B95 5NJ Tel: (01564) 793337 Fax: (01564) 793274 E-mail: mailbox@thehalcyoncard.co.uk

▶ Longservice.com Ltd, The Granary, Ryehurst Lane, Binfield, Bracknell, Berkshire, RG42 5QZ Tel: (0870) 7705445 Fax: (0870) 7770536 E-mail: sales@longservice.com

Modern Images UK, P.O. Box 460, Rochdale, Lancashire, OL12 0WX Tel: (0870) 6091364 Fax: (01706) 354746 E-mail: enquiries@modern-imagesuk.com

▶ Nauticality Nautical Gifts, Albrighton, Wolverhampton, WV7 3WL Tel: (01902) 373217 Fax: (01902) 375317 E-mail: nauticalitygift@aol.com

▶ Swarovski Store Guilford, 10 White Lion Walk, Guildford, Surrey, GU1 3DN Tel: (01483) 568200 E-mail: swarovskiguildford@ntlworld.com

CORPORATE MOTORSPORT RACING DAY HOSPITALITY SERVICES

▶ Eyecandy Model & Promotions Agency, 11-13 Derby Street, Manchester, M8 8QE Tel: 0161-833 3888 E-mail: info@eyecandy-promo.co.uk

▶ Nottingham Girls Model Agency, 49 Penrhyn Cresent, Nottingham, NG9 5PA Tel: 0115 841 9685 E-mail: agency@nottinghamgirls.co.uk

▶ Ultimate Days Ltd, PO Box 54, Pickering, North Yorkshire, YO18 7WZ Tel: (0845) 0652201 E-mail: sales@ultimatedays.com

▶ Yorkshire 4x4, Portacabin, Felixkirk, Sutton, Thirsk, North Yorkshire, YO7 2ED Tel: (01845) 537766 Fax: (01845) 537440 E-mail: sales@yorkshire4x4.co.uk

CORPORATE PARTY ORGANISING

▶ The Bus Business, The Coach House, Spofforth Hall, Nickols Lane, Spofforth, Harrogate, North Yorkshire, HG3 1WE Tel: (0845) 2250320 Fax: (0845) 2802461 E-mail: info@thebusbusiness.com

▶ Chocolate Events, 71 High Street, Buckden, St. Neots, Cambridgeshire, PE19 5TA Tel: (01480) 819338 E-mail: chocolateevents@hotmail.co.uk

▶ Edinburgh Event Production Services, 5/6 Broughton Place Lane, Edinburgh, EH1 3RS Tel: 0131-558 3824 E-mail: eeps@warpro.co.uk

CORPORATE PRESENTATION AWARD DESIGNERS, PRODUCERS ETC

E Media Ltd, Ember House, Pleasant Place, Walton-on-Thames, Surrey, KT12 4HR Tel: (01932) 254787 Fax: (01932) 254786 E-mail: info@e-media.co.uk

Emfec, Robins Wood House, Robins Wood Road, Aspley, Nottingham, NG8 3NH Tel: 0115-854 1616 Fax: 0115-854 1617 E-mail: enquiries@emfec.co.uk

Louis Lejeune Ltd, The Rectory, 71 High Street, Wilburton, Ely, Cambridgeshire, CB6 3RA Tel: (01353) 740444 Fax: (01353) 741599

▶ Millennium Awards, Smithy Market Hill, Glass, Huntly, Aberdeenshire, AB54 4XX Tel: (01466) 700311 Fax: (01466) 700344 E-mail: info@onlinetrophies.co.uk

F.W. Needham Ltd, 84 Great Hampton Street, Birmingham, B18 6EP Tel: 0121-554 5453 Fax: 0121-554 9859 E-mail: fw-needham@btconnect.com

P C Engravers World Of Trophies, 29 Lower Addiscombe Road, Croydon, CR0 6PQ Tel: (020) 8680 1354 Fax: (020) 8686 8706 E-mail: pcengravers@btconnect.com

▶ Q R 8 Design, Arundel Street, Sheffield, S1 2NS Tel: 0114-221 1818 Fax: (0870) 1338957 E-mail: jerry@lampson.co.uk

CORPORATE PRODUCT LAUNCH ORGANISING

▶ Aztec Innovations, Burnhouse Industrial Estate, Whitburn, Bathgate, West Lothian, EH47 0LQ Tel: (01506) 204188

Bryce Curdy Productions, PO Box 400, Ayr, KA7 4NB Tel: (01292) 443398 Fax: (01292) 443398 E-mail: mail@bryce-curdy.com

▶ RS-Events Ltd, 72 Overcliff Road, Lewisham, London, SE13 7UA Tel: (020) 8473 5529 E-mail: info@rs-events.co.uk

▶ SpareRIBs RIB Hire Agency, PO Box 1352, Southampton, SO19 9WX Tel: (023) 8042 0303 E-mail: spareribs@spareribs.info

▶ Sterling Travel Management, H Medina Chamber, Town Quay, Southampton, SO14 2AQ Tel: (023) 8033 0111 Fax: (023) 8033 7397 E-mail: info@sterlingtravel.co.uk

▶ Yorkshire 4x4, Portacabin, Felixkirk, Sutton, Thirsk, North Yorkshire, YO7 2ED Tel: (01845) 537766 Fax: (01845) 537440 E-mail: sales@yorkshire4x4.co.uk

CORPORATE QUAD BIKING ORGANISING

▶ Amazon ATV Ltd (Quad Sales & Hire 6-6yrs), Green Street Industrial Estate, 1 Green Street, Eastbourne, East Sussex, BN21 1QN Tel: (01323) 645564 Fax: (01323) 645564 E-mail: elainechild@tiscali.co.uk

CORPORATE RESCUE SERVICES

R W Oliver, 38 Alma Street, Eccles, Manchester, M30 0EX Tel: 0161-789 8474

CORPORATE SECRETARIAL SERVICES

▶ AP Office Services, 44 Christchurch Road, Tring, Hertfordshire, HP23 4EH Tel: 01442 890597 Fax: 0871 661 3480 E-mail: alison@aptyping.f9.co.uk

▶ Virtual Office Bureau Limited, 4 Twyfords, Crowborough, East Sussex, TN6 1YE Tel: 01892 653325 Fax: 01892 665861 E-mail: virtualofficebureau@yahoo.co.uk

CORPORATE STRATEGY CONSULTANCY

Careybrook Ltd, PO Box 205, Southam, Warwickshire, CV47 0ZL Tel: (01926) 813619 Fax: (01926) 814898 E-mail: cb.ltd@btinternet.com

Charles Lucas & Marshall, Eastcott House, 4 High Street, Swindon, SN1 3EP Tel: (01793) 511055 Fax: (01635) 570275

Mckinsey & Co. (UK), 1 Jermyn Street, London, SW1Y 4UH Tel: (020) 7839 8040 Fax: (020) 7339 5000

Messrs G Owen & Co., Owen House, Barking, Essex, IG11 9HY Tel: (0845) 0958225 Fax: (0845) 0958235 E-mail: gowenandco@yahoo.com

▶ Quadrant Consultants Ltd, 35 Endell Street, Covert Garden, London, WC2H 9BA Tel: (020) 7240 7200 Fax: 0207 240 7201 E-mail: huw.watkins@qcl.co.uk

▶ Robb Fordyce, Greenburn Tornaveen, Torphins, Banchory, Kincardineshire, AB31 4LL Tel: (01339) 883832 E-mail: john@robb-fordyce.co.uk

CORPORATE TEAM BUILDING ORGANISING

▶ Amazing Days Ltd, 90-91 Luddesdown Road, Luddesdown, Gravesend, Kent, DA13 0XE Tel: (01474) 815589 Fax: (01474) 815589 E-mail: dawn.gibson@amazing-days.co.uk

▶ Campaign Paintball Park, Old Lane, Cobham, Surrey, KT11 1NH Tel: (01932) 865999 Fax: (01932) 865744 E-mail: sales@campaignpaintball.com

Complete Event Solutions, Lymington Bottom Road, Four Marks, Alton, Hampshire, GU34 5DL Tel: (01420) 561105 Fax: (01420) 561105 E-mail: info@completeeventsolutions.com

▶ Exclusively Skye Ltd, Tigh Shasaig Teangue, Sleat, Isle of Skye, IV44 8RD Tel: (01471) 820225 E-mail: ken@exclusively-skye.co.uk

▶ Exmoor Manor Hotel, Barbrook, Lynton, Devon, EX35 6LD Tel: (01598) 752404 Fax: (01598) 753636 E-mail: info@exmoormanorhotel.co.uk

▶ Hands On, 23 Seldon Road, Worthing, West Sussex, BN11 2LN Tel: 07731 522290 E-mail: info@five-minute-massage-company.com

▶ Knockout Show Ltd, Holly House Barn Bradkirk Lane, Bamber Bridge, Preston, PR5 6ZQ Tel: (01772) 335544 Fax: (01772) 746678 E-mail: Dave@itsaknockout.com

▶ London Canal Museum, 12-13 New Wharf Road, London, N1 9RT Tel: (020) 7713 0836 Fax: (020) 7689 6679 E-mail: hire@canalmuseum.org.uk

▶ Mountain Leap LLP, 1st Floor, 25 Eccleston Square, London, SW1V 1NS Tel: (020) 7931 0621 Fax: (020) 7931 0613 E-mail: adam.honey@mountainleap.com

▶ Orbis Events, 20 Elmfield Close, Woodfalls, Salisbury, SP5 2BF Tel: (01725) 511963 E-mail: info@orbisevents.com

▶ RS-Events Ltd, 72 Overcliff Road, Lewisham, London, SE13 7UA Tel: (020) 8473 5529 E-mail: info@rs-events.co.uk

▶ Sankofa Exchange Ltd, Africa House, 21 Shorwell Road, Nottingham, NG3 7HG Tel: 0115-911 0111 Fax: 0115-911 0110 E-mail: office@sankofa.co.uk

▶ SpareRIBs RIB Hire Agency, PO Box 1352, Southampton, SO19 9WX Tel: (023) 8042 0303 E-mail: spareribs@spareribs.info

▶ Thruxton Motor Sports Centre, Unit 29, Thruxton, Andover, Hampshire, SP11 8PW Tel: (01264) 882222 Fax: (01264) 882201 E-mail: sales@thruxtonracing.co.uk

▶ Ultimate Days Ltd, PO Box 54, Pickering, North Yorkshire, YO18 7WZ Tel: (0845) 0652201 E-mail: sales@ultimatedays.com

▶ Uptown Events, PO Box 1492, London, North London, NW11 6WL Tel: 0870 1226971

▶ Yorkshire 4x4, Portacabin, Felixkirk, Sutton, Thirsk, North Yorkshire, YO7 2ED Tel: (01845) 537766 Fax: (01845) 537440 E-mail: sales@yorkshire4x4.co.uk

CORPORATE TEAM BUILDING OUTDOOR EVENT ORGANISING

▶ Exmoor Manor Hotel, Barbrook, Lynton, Devon, EX35 6LD Tel: (01598) 752404 Fax: (01598) 753636 E-mail: info@exmoormanorhotel.co.uk

▶ Knockout Show Ltd, Holly House Barn Bradkirk Lane, Bamber Bridge, Preston, PR5 6ZQ Tel: (01772) 335544 Fax: (01772) 746678 E-mail: Dave@itsaknockout.com

Scotia Marine, Clyde Marina, The Harbour, Ardrossan, Ayrshire, KA22 8DB Tel: (01294) 469584 Fax: (01294) 469584 E-mail: enquiries@scotiamarine.com

▶ SpareRIBs RIB Hire Agency, PO Box 1352, Southampton, SO19 9WX Tel: (023) 8042 0303 E-mail: spareribs@spareribs.info

Teamwork & Teamplay, Unit 16-17, Ashley Heath Industrial Estate, Ringwood Road, Three Legged Cross, Wimborne, Dorset, BH21 6UZ Tel: (01202) 590009 Fax: (01202) 828593 E-mail: mail@splatltd.co.uk

▶ Ultimate Days Ltd, PO Box 54, Pickering, North Yorkshire, YO18 7WZ Tel: (0845) 0652201 E-mail: sales@ultimatedays.com

▶ Unicorn Trails, 2, Acorn Centre, Chestnut Avenue, Biggleswade, Bedfordshire, SG18 0RA Tel: 01767 600606 E-mail: david@unicorntrails.com

CORPORATE VIDEO FILM PRODUCTION

▶ Ambient Light Productions Ltd, 6 Shipquay Street, Londonderry, BT48 6DN Tel: (028) 7136 3525 E-mail: info@ambient-light.co.uk

▶ Casual Productions, Unit 52, Stafford Business Village, Staffordshire Technology Park, Stafford, ST18 0TW Tel: 01785 887979 Fax: 01785 887825 E-mail: info@casualproductions.com

▶ Clouds Hill Imaging Ltd., Rock House, Curland, Taunton, Somerset, TA3 5SB Tel: 01823 481894 E-mail: david@cloudshillimaging.co.uk

▶ Harliquin.co.uk, Dover Street, Totton, Southampton, SO14 6GL Tel: (07050) 196660 E-mail: ian@harliquin.co.uk

▶ Bob Sanderson Video Production, 82 Chapel Street, Wordsley, Stourbridge, West Midlands, DY8 5QP Tel: (01384) 271073 Fax: (01384) 271073 E-mail: bobsanderson@talk21.com

▶ WV Entertainment Limited, C/O The Suite, 3 Goldthorn Avenue, Wolverhampton, WV4 5AA Tel: 07939 930781

CORPORATE VISUAL IDENTITY SERVICES

Greenwich Design Associates, 11a Greenwich South Street, London, SE10 8NJ Tel: (020) 8853 3028 Fax: (020) 8858 2128 E-mail: simon@greenwich-design.co.uk

▶ S H O Design, 57 Farringdon Road, London, EC1M 3JB Tel: (020) 7993 5472 E-mail: adam@sho-mail.com

CORROSION CONTROL/ MONITORING SYSTEMS

Advanced NDT Ltd, Orchard House, Orchard Close, Severn Stoke, Worcester, WR8 9JJ Tel: (01905) 371460 Fax: (01905) 371477 E-mail: sales@advanced-ndt.co.uk

Caproco plc, 31 Davey House, St Neots Road, Eaton Ford, St. Neots, Cambridgeshire, PE19 7BA Tel: (01480) 407600 Fax: (01480) 407619 E-mail: caproco@btconnect.com

Cormon Ltd, Unit 3 Robell Building, Chartwell Road, Lancing, West Sussex, BN15 8TU Tel: (01903) 854800 Fax: (01903) 854854 E-mail: sales@cormon.com

Corrintec Ltd, Marine House, 18 Hipper Street South, Chesterfield, Derbyshire, S40 1SS Tel: (01246) 246700 Fax: (01246) 246701 E-mail: sales@corrintec.co.uk

European Corrosion Ltd, Meadow Mill Industrial Estate, Dixon Street, Kidderminster, Worcestershire, DY10 1HH Tel: (01562) 820288 Fax: (01562) 515594

▶ Iicorr Ltd, Greenbank Place, East Tullos, Aberdeen, AB12 3BT Tel: (01224) 898282 Fax: (01224) 898202 E-mail: dennis.parr@iicorr.co.uk

▶ M M E Engineering Ltd, Unit 3 Faversham Shipyard, Upper Brents, Faversham, Kent, ME13 7DZ Tel: (01795) 535559 Fax: (01795) 536374

Wilson UK Ltd, Unit 3 Bloxwich Lane Industrial Estate, Bloxwich Lane, Walsall, WS2 8TF Tel: (01922) 725800 Fax: (01922) 649888 E-mail: uksales@wilsononline.com

CORROSION INHIBITIVE PACKAGING

Protective Packaging Ltd, Dane Road Industrial Estate, Sale, Cheshire, M33 7BH Tel: 0161-976 2006 Fax: 0161-976 3330 E-mail: info@protpack.com

CORROSION INHIBITORS

Corrosion Solutions Ltd, 5 Kirkhill Place, Kirkhill Industrial Estate, Dyce, Aberdeen, AB21 0GU Tel: (01224) 772694 Fax: (01224) 775810 E-mail: info@corrsol.co.uk

Feedwater Ltd, Tarran Road, Tarran Industrial Estate, Wirral, Merseyside, CH46 4TU Tel: 0151-606 0808 Fax: 0151-678 5459 E-mail: enquiries@feedwater.co.uk

Fernox, Sheer Water, Forsyth Road, Woking, Surrey, GU21 5RZ Tel: (0870) 6015000 Fax: (0870) 6015005 E-mail: sales@fernox.com

Grace Construction Products Ltd, 851-852 Birchwood Boulevard, Birchwood, Warrington, WA3 7QZ Tel: (01925) 824824 Fax: (01925) 824033 E-mail: enquiries@gcp-grace.com

Hawks Chemical Co. Ltd, 2 Tower Street, Hyde, Cheshire, SK14 1JW Tel: 0161-367 9441 Fax: 0161-367 9443 E-mail: sales@hawks-chem.com

▶ Intercontinental Chemical Products Ltd, 56-62 Lincoln Road, Tuxford, Newark, Nottinghamshire, NG22 0HP Tel: (01777) 870756 Fax: (01777) 871766 E-mail: sales@intchems.com

Lawrence Industries Ltd, Lawrence House, Apollo, Tamworth, Staffordshire, B79 7TA Tel: (01827) 314151 Fax: (01827) 314152 E-mail: sales@l-i.co.uk

Lettergold Plastics Ltd, 4 Hammond Close, Newmarket, Suffolk, CB8 0AZ Tel: (01638) 666888 Fax: (01635) 666999 E-mail: info@lettergold.co.uk

Vapor Tek Ltd, Fairclough Street, Bolton, BL3 2AF Tel: (01204) 521795 Fax: (01204) 364576 E-mail: information@vapor-tek.co.uk

CORROSION MONITORING

Caproco plc, 31 Davey House, St Neots Road, Eaton Ford, St. Neots, Cambridgeshire, PE19 7BA Tel: (01480) 407600 Fax: (01480) 407619 E-mail: caproco@btconnect.com

Cormon Ltd, Unit 3 Robell Building, Chartwell Road, Lancing, West Sussex, BN15 8TU Tel: (01903) 854800 Fax: (01903) 854854 E-mail: sales@cormon.com

Corrpro Companies Europe Ltd, 2 Adam Street, Stockton-on-Tees, Cleveland, TS18 3HQ Tel: (01642) 614106 Fax: (01642) 614100 E-mail: ccel@corrpro.co.uk

D C Materials Supply Ltd, Selham, Petworth, West Sussex, GU28 0PJ Tel: (01798) 861625 Fax: (01798) 461702 E-mail: sales@deepwater.demon.co.uk

Frazer-Nash NDT Ltd, Bradshaw Street, Heywood, Lancashire, OL10 1PL Tel: (01706) 628794 Fax: (01706) 627289 E-mail: enquiries@frazer-nash-btconnect.com

▶ Iicorr Ltd, Greenbank Place, East Tullos, Aberdeen, AB12 3BT Tel: (01224) 898282 Fax: (01224) 898202 E-mail: dennis.parr@iicorr.co.uk

Inspection Ecosse Ltd, Unit 1d, Old Redding Road, Laurieston, Falkirk, FK2 9JU Tel: (01324) 627772 Fax: (01324) 627945

Read Well Services Ltd, Viking House, 1 Claymore Avenue, Bridge of Don, Aberdeen, AB23 8GW Tel: (01224) 336600 Fax: (01224) 336611 E-mail: sales@readgroupuk.com

CORROSION PREVENTION COATING MAINTENANCE

Corrpro Companies Europe, 4 Mill Court, The Sawmills, Durley, Southampton, SO32 2EJ Tel: (01489) 861980 Fax: (01489) 861981 E-mail: ccel@onyxnet.co.uk

Dickerman Overseas Contracting Co. Ltd, Unit 3 Adam Business Centre, Henson Way, Telford Way Industrial Estate, Kettering, Northamptonshire, NN16 8PX Tel: (01536) 525131 Fax: (01536) 412031 E-mail: info@dickermangroup.com

Joseph Ash Galvanising, Seven Stars Road, Oldbury, West Midlands, B69 4JS Tel: 0121-552 1682 Fax: 0121-511 1125 E-mail: albion@josephash.co.uk

North Kent Shot Blasting Co. Ltd, Grove Road, Northfleet, Gravesend, Kent, DA11 9AX Tel: (01474) 350030 Fax: (01474) 327329 E-mail: info@nksb.co.uk

CORROSION PREVENTION INSULATING PIPE JOINTS

Euro Trading Ltd, Shepperton Marina, Felix Lane, Shepperton, Middlesex, TW17 8NS Tel: (01932) 246153 Fax: (01932) 226711 E-mail: eurotrading.co@virgin.net

CORROSION PREVENTION OR PROTECTION COATINGS OR LININGS

Ancorite, Moston Road, Sandbach, Cheshire, CW11 3AB Tel: (01270) 761720 Fax: (01270) 761697

Andrews, Littles Lane, Wolverhampton, WV1 1JY Tel: (01902) 429190 Fax: (01902) 426574 E-mail: info@andrewscoatings.co.uk

Anglia Rustguard Ltd, 26 Crittall Road, Western Industrial Estate, Witham, Essex, CM8 3DR Tel: 01376 514152 Fax: 01376 512802 E-mail: angliarustguard@btconnect.com

Anochrome Technologies Ltd, Wood Lane, Wolverhampton, WV10 8HN Tel: (01902) 567567 Fax: (01902) 567777 E-mail: enquiries@anochrome-group.co.uk

Archco Rigidon, Denso House, 33-35 Chapel Road, London, SE27 0TR Tel: (020) 8761 6244 Fax: (020) 8761 2456 E-mail: mail@denso.net

Canusa Systems Ltd, 3 Sterling Park, Gatwick Road, Crawley, West Sussex, RH10 9QT Tel: (01293) 541254 Fax: (01293) 541777 E-mail: sales@canusa-cps.co.uk

▶ Alexander Cardew Ltd, Unit 27 Chelsea Wharf, 15 Lots Road, London, SW10 0QJ Tel: (020) 7235 3785 Fax: (020) 7352 4635 E-mail: sales@cardew.com

Corrocoat Services Ltd, Forster Street, Leeds, LS10 1PW Tel: 0113-276 0760 Fax: 0113-276 0700 E-mail: enquiries@corrocoat.com

Corroless Northern Ltd, Regent House, Regent Street, Oldham, OL1 3TZ Tel: 0161-624 4941 Fax: 0161-627 5072 E-mail: sales@kenyon-group.co.uk

Corrosion Solutions Ltd, 5 Kirkhill Place, Kirkhill Industrial Estate, Dyce, Aberdeen, AB21 0GU Tel: (01224) 772694 Fax: (01224) 775810 E-mail: info@corrsol.co.uk

CORROSION PREVENTION OR PROTECTION COATINGS OR LININGS – *continued*

Counter Corrosion, PO Box 18, Dewsbury, West Yorkshire, WF12 0JP Tel: (01924) 468559 Fax: (01924) 458019
E Wood Ltd, Standard Way Industrial Estate, Northallerton, North Yorkshire, DL6 2XA Tel: (01609) 778907 Fax: (01609) 783762 E-mail: thortex@ewood.co.uk
Fluoro Precision Coatings, Units 19-20 Hewitts Industrial Estate, Elmbridge Road, Cranleigh, Surrey, GU6 8LW Tel: (01483) 276887 Fax: (01483) 276130 E-mail: gs@fluoroprecision.co.uk
HCC Protective Coatings Ltd, Bates Business Centre, Church Road, Harold Wood, Romford, RM3 0JF Tel: (01708) 378666 Fax: (01708) 378868 E-mail: hcc.pc@btconnect.com
Hesco Bastion Ltd, Unit 41 Knowsthorpe Way, Leeds, LS9 0SW Tel: 0113-248 6633 Fax: 0113-248 3501 E-mail: info@hescobastion.com
Jay Rubber Linings Ltd, 132 Queen Street, Crewe, CW1 4AU Tel: (01270) 254655 Fax: (01270) 254526 E-mail: sales@jayrubberlinings.co.uk
John Lord Holdings Ltd, Wellington Cement Works, Ainsworth Road, Bury, Lancashire, BL8 2RS Tel: 0161-764 4617 Fax: 0161-763 1873 E-mail: enquiries@john-lord.co.uk
Liquid Plastics Ltd, PO Box 7, Preston, PR1 1EA Tel: (01772) 255017 Fax: (01772) 255671 E-mail: info@liquidplastics.co.uk
Neutra Rust International Ltd, 24-31 London Road, Newbury, Berkshire, RG14 1JX Tel: (01784) 455454 Fax: (01784) 450752
Pollyaim Ltd, 9 Churchill Court, 58 Station Road, North Harrow, Harrow, Middlesex, HA2 7SA Tel: (020) 8863 0457 Fax: (020) 8863 0459 E-mail: sales@pollyaim.com
▶ Sigma Coatings Ltd, Huddersfield Road, Birstall, Batley, West Yorkshire, WF17 9XA Tel: (01924) 354000 Fax: (01924) 354001
Teal & Mackrill Ltd, Lockwood Street, Hull, HU2 0HN Tel: (01482) 328053 Fax: (01482) 219266
Whitford Plastics Ltd, Christleton Court, Manor Park, Runcorn, Cheshire, WA7 1ST Tel: (01928) 571000 Fax: (01928) 571010 E-mail: sales@whitfordww.co.uk

CORROSION PREVENTION OR PROTECTION CONSULTANCY

▶ Bilt Hamber Ltd, Tye Barn, Tye Common Road, Little Burstead, Billericay, Essex, CM12 9SB Tel: (01277) 658899 Fax: (01277) 657533 E-mail: enquiries@bilthamber.com
▶ Commtech Associates Ltd, 149 Melrose Avenue, London, SW19 8AU Tel: (020) 8944 9036 Fax: (020) 8944 9036 E-mail: ctassociates@btconnect.com
Corrpro Companies Europe Ltd, 2 Adam Street, Stockton-on-Tees, Cleveland, TS18 3HQ Tel: (01642) 614106 Fax: (01642) 614100 E-mail: ccel@corrpro.co.uk
Dickerman Overseas Contracting Co. Ltd, Unit 3 Adam Business Centre, Henson Way, Telford Way Industrial Estate, Kettering, Northamptonshire, NN16 8PX Tel: (01536) 525131 Fax: (01536) 412031 E-mail: info@dickermangroup.com
Northeast Corrosion Engineers Ltd, Craigearn Business Park, Kintore, Inverurie, Aberdeenshire, AB51 0TH Tel: 01467 633593
Oil Plus Ltd, Unit E Dominion House, Kennet Side, Newbury, Berkshire, RG14 5PX Tel: (01635) 30226 Fax: (01635) 49618 E-mail: m.bowyer@oilplus.co.uk

CORROSION PREVENTION OR PROTECTION PAPER

A P I Coated Products Ltd, The Vineyards, Gloucester Road, Cheltenham, Gloucestershire, GL51 8NH Tel: (01242) 512345 Fax: (01242) 576633 E-mail: enquiries@adcoat.co.uk
▶ Antalis Ltd, Gateway House, Interlink Way West, Bardon Hill, Coalville, Leicestershire, LE67 1LE Tel: (0870) 6079014 Fax: (0870) 6073160 E-mail: contact@antalis.co.uk
Vapor Tek Ltd, Fairclough Street, Bolton, BL3 2AF Tel: (01204) 521795 Fax: (01204) 364576 E-mail: information@vapor-tek.co.uk

CORROSION PREVENTION OR PROTECTION PROCESSORS OR SERVICES

Aberdeen Blast Cleaning Services Ltd, Hillview Road, East Tullos Industrial Estate, Aberdeen, AB12 3HB Tel: (01224) 896565 Fax: (01224) 894989
Ltd Anti-Corrosion Services, Carrington Business Park, Carrington, Manchester, M31 4QW Tel: 0161-776 4019 Fax: 0161-775 8995
Argosy Control Engineering Ltd, Murcar Industrial Estate, Denmore Road, Bridge of Don, Aberdeen, AB23 8JW Tel: (01224) 704788 Fax: (01224) 704831
Bradleys (Stowmarket) Ltd, 49 Knightsdale Road, Ipswich, IP1 4JJ Tel: (01473) 461400 Fax: (01473) 461490
Corrocoat Services Ltd, Forster Street, Leeds, LS10 1PW Tel: 0113-276 0760 Fax: 0113-276 0700 E-mail: enquiries@corrocoat.com
Counter Corrosion, PO Box 18, Dewsbury, West Yorkshire, WF12 0JP Tel: (01924) 468559 Fax: (01924) 458019
Crewe Stove Enamelling Co. Ltd, Springvale Industrial Estate, Moston Road, Sandbach, Cheshire, CW11 3HL Tel: (01270) 769069 Fax: (01270) 768003
D C Materials Supply Ltd, Selham, Petworth, West Sussex, GU28 0PJ Tel: (01798) 861625 Fax: (01798) 461702 E-mail: sales@deepwater.demon.co.uk
Delta G B N Ltd, 115 Lodgefield Road, Halesowen, West Midlands, B62 8AX Tel: 0121-602 1221 Fax: 0121-602 3222 E-mail: rogerw@deltagbn.co.uk
Delta GBM, Unit 4 P D H Industrial Estate, Western Way, Moxley, Wednesbury, West Midlands, WS10 7DQ Tel: 0121-556 6262 Fax: 0121-556 6264
Dickerman Overseas Contracting Co. Ltd, Unit 3 Adam Business Centre, Henson Way, Telford Way Industrial Estate, Kettering, Northamptonshire, NN16 8PX Tel: (01536) 525131 Fax: (01536) 412031 E-mail: info@dickermangroup.com
Eftec Ltd, Rhigos, Aberdare, Mid Glamorgan, CF44 9UE Tel: (01685) 815400 Fax: (01685) 813997
Ferrous Protection Ltd, Hanson House, Grains Road, Delph, Oldham, OL3 5RN Tel: (01457) 873419 Fax: (01457) 871091 E-mail: ferrous_protection@yahoo.com
Hastie & Co, Morfa Road, Swansea, SA1 2EP Tel: (01792) 651541 Fax: (01792) 468119 E-mail: steven.miller@hastiegroup.co.uk
HCC Protective Coatings Ltd, Bates Business Centre, Church Road, Harold Wood, Romford, RM3 0JF Tel: (01708) 378666 Fax: (01708) 378868 E-mail: hcc.pc@btconnect.com
Joseph Ash Galvanising, Seven Stars Road, Oldbury, West Midlands, B69 4JS Tel: 0121-552 1682 Fax: 0121-511 1125 E-mail: albion@josephash.co.uk
Kelcoat Engineering Plastics Ltd, Barnfield Road Industrial Estate, Leek, Staffordshire, ST13 5QG Tel: (01538) 383547 Fax: (01538) 387918
Leyfos Plastics, Unit D1, Rosehill Industrial, Stoke Heath, Market Drayton, Shropshire, TF9 2JU Tel: (01630) 638557 Fax: (01630) 638651 E-mail: sales@leyfos.com
Mallatite Ltd, Hardwick View Road, Holmewood, Chesterfield, Derbyshire, S42 5SA Tel: (01246) 593280 Fax: (01246) 593281 E-mail: info@mallatite.co.uk
North Kent Shot Blasting Co. Ltd, Grove Road, Northfleet, Gravesend, Kent, DA11 9AX Tel: (01474) 350030 Fax: (01474) 327329 E-mail: info@nksb.co.uk
PLCS Ltd, Wartell Bank, Kingswinford, West Midlands, DY6 7QJ Tel: (01384) 298000 Fax: (01384) 400845 E-mail: sales@pressleakage.com
Salamis International Ltd, 3 Greenhole Place, Bridge of Don Industrial Estat, Aberdeen, AB23 8EU Tel: (01224) 246001 Fax: (01224) 246100
Scientific & Technical Services Ltd, 3 Summerhill, Blaydon-on-Tyne, Tyne & Wear, NE21 4JR Tel: 0191-414 7801 Fax: 0191-414 1245 E-mail: sts@stsltd.fsnet.co.uk
Spray Glass International, 3 Beckley Hill Works, Canal Road, Higham, Rochester, Kent, ME3 7HX Tel: (01474) 824499 Fax: (01474) 824482 E-mail: sales@sprayglass.co.uk
Surface Engineers Manchester Ltd, Globe Works Off Astley Street, Dukinfield, Cheshire, SK16 4QZ Tel: 0161-330 9224 Fax: 0161-343 2650
Techniques Surfaces (UK) Ltd, Wood Lane, Erdington, Birmingham, B24 9QL Tel: 0121-382 8060 Fax: 0121-377 8928 E-mail: info@ts-uk.com
Jack Tighe Coatings Ltd, Sandall Stones Road, Kirk Sandall Industrial Estate, Doncaster, South Yorkshire, DN3 1QR Tel: (01302) 880360 Fax: (01302) 880370
Universal Applied Coatings Ltd, Parish Lane, Pease Pottage, Crawley, West Sussex, RH10 5NY Tel: (01293) 514943 Fax: (01293) 552619

CORROSION PREVENTION OR PROTECTION PRODUCTS

Canusa Systems Ltd, 3 Sterling Park, Gatwick Road, Crawley, West Sussex, RH10 9QT Tel: (01293) 541254 Fax: (01293) 541777 E-mail: sales@canusa-cps.co.uk
CDS Consultants, Bwlch Tocyn Farm, Bwlchtocyn, Pwllheli, Gwynedd, LL53 7BN Tel: (01758) 712245 Fax: (01758) 712014 E-mail: cdsconsultants@btinternet.com
Classcoat, 21 High Street, Upper Heyford, Bicester, Oxfordshire, OX25 5LE Tel: (01869) 232793 Fax: (01869) 233625 E-mail: classcoat7921718@aol.com

CORROSION PREVENTION/ PROTECTION ADDITIVES

Ciba Additives, Charter Way, Macclesfield, Cheshire, SK10 2NX Tel: (01625) 421933 Fax: (01625) 619637

CORROSION PREVENTION/ PROTECTION PACKAGING

▶ Antalis Ltd, Gateway House, Interlink Way West, Bardon Hill, Coalville, Leicestershire, LE67 1LE Tel: (0870) 6079014 Fax: (0870) 6073160 E-mail: contact@antalis.co.uk

CORROSION RESEARCH/TEST SERVICES

▶ Accelerated Weathering Laboratory Ltd, Berkeley House, Hunts Rise, South Marston Industrial Estat, Swindon, SN3 4TG Tel: (01793) 834211 Fax: (01793) 721212 E-mail: info@awlltd.co.uk
European Corrosion Ltd, Meadow Mill Industrial Estate, Dixon Street, Kidderminster, Worcestershire, DY10 1HH Tel: (01562) 820288 Fax: (01562) 515594
MACAW Engineering Ltd, 1 Park Road, Gosforth Business Park, Newcastle upon Tyne, NE12 8DG Tel: 0191-216 4930 E-mail: info@macawengineering.com
Technology Offshore Onshore Ltd, Woodcroft House, Crow Hill Drive, Mansfield, Nottinghamshire, NG19 7AE Tel: (01623) 654254 Fax: (01623) 420821 E-mail: kcutt@techoffonshore.com

CORROSION RESISTANT ALLOYS (CRA)

Eden Material Services (UK) Ltd, Unit 42A No 1 Industrial Estate, Medomsley Road, Consett, County Durham, DH8 6TT Tel: (01207) 590055 Fax: (01207) 590059 E-mail: sales@edenmaterials.co.uk

CORROSION RESISTANT CHEMICAL PLANT

Resinfab & Associates, 6 Imex Business Park, Kings Road, Tyseley, Birmingham, B11 2AL Tel: 0121-706 1848 Fax: 0121-706 1848 E-mail: tech@resinfab.co.uk

CORROSION RESISTANT COATINGS OR LININGS

▶ 3 J Lining Systems Ltd, Unit 2g Lake Enterprise Park, Sandall Stones Road, Kirk Sandall Industrial Estate, Doncaster, South Yorkshire, DN3 1QR Tel: (01302) 880800 Fax: (01302) 880900 E-mail: jeff@3jlinings.co.uk
Kal-Gard UK Ltd, Canalwood Industrial Estate, Chirk, Wrexham, LL14 5RL Tel: (01691) 772070 Fax: (01691) 778303 E-mail: tony@kal-gard.co.uk
LWD Precision Engineering Co Ltd, 169 Elland Road, Leeds, LS11 8BY Tel: 0113-271 3097 Fax: 0113-271 8655 E-mail: sales@lwdeng.com
Protective Finishing Group, 33 Crossgate Road, Park Farm Industrial Estate, Redditch, Worcestershire, B98 7SN Tel: (01527) 524126 Fax: (01527) 510361 E-mail: sales@profingroup.co.uk

CORROSION RESISTANT FASTENERS

▶ Engineering Services Fasteners Ltd, Parson Street, Keighley, West Yorkshire, BD21 3HD Tel: (01535) 665414 Fax: (01535) 608377 E-mail: sales@engservfast.co.uk
Poly Fasteners Ltd, 11-12 Rabans Close, Rabans Lane Industrial Area, Aylesbury, Buckinghamshire, HP19 8TP Tel: (01296) 333500 Fax: (01296) 333509 E-mail: sales@polyfasteners.co.uk
Prosper Engineering Ltd, 3 Arkwright Way, North Newmoor Industrial Estate, Irvine, Ayrshire, KA11 4JU Tel: (01294) 224422 Fax: (01294) 215003 E-mail: sales@prosper-engineering.com

CORROSION RESISTANT PUMPS

Kecol Pumps Ltd, Faraday Drive, Bridgnorth, Shropshire, WV15 5BJ Tel: (01746) 764311 Fax: (01746) 764780 E-mail: sales@kecol.co.uk
Sterling Fluid Systems UK Ltd, Atlantic Street, Broadheath, Altrincham, Cheshire, WA14 5DH Tel: 0161-928 6371 Fax: 0161-925 2129 E-mail: sales@sterlingfluid.com

CORROSION RESISTANT TAPES

Cinque Products Ltd, Harbour Road, Rye, East Sussex, TN31 7TE Tel: (01797) 223561 Fax: (01797) 224530 E-mail: longproducts@aol.com

CORROSION RESISTANT VALVES

Prochem Services Ltd, Mill Street, Congleton, Cheshire, CW12 2AD Tel: (01260) 299770 Fax: (01260) 299880 E-mail: info@prochem-services.com

CORRUGATED BOARD

Abbey Board, Cromwell House, Altendiez Way, Burton Latimer, Kettering, Northamptonshire, NN15 5YZ Tel: (01536) 420055 Fax: (01536) 421726 E-mail: sales@abbeyboard.co.uk
Dairi Pak, Platt Bridge, Ruyton XI Towns, Shrewsbury, SY4 1LS Tel: (01939) 260342 Fax: (01939) 260275 E-mail: sales@dairi-pak.co.uk
William Gosling & Son Ltd, Northwood Works, 155 Tame Road, Birmingham, B6 7DG Tel: 0121-327 4081 Fax: 0121-326 6032
John Hargreaves (Collyhurst & Stalybridge) Ltd, Knowl Street, Stalybridge, Cheshire, SK15 3AJ Tel: 0161-338 6011 Fax: 0161-338 4194 E-mail: jack@john-hargreaves.co.uk
Kappa Corrugated UK Ltd, Knowl Street, Stalybridge, Cheshire, SK15 3AR Tel: 0161-338 3711 Fax: 0161-303 2647
▶ Majestic Corrugated Cases Ltd, Unit 30 Parkrose Industrial Estate, Middlemore Road, Smethwick, West Midlands, B66 2DZ Tel: (01902) 733330 Fax: 0121-558 7000 E-mail: kavi.jundu@majesticbox.com
Mondi Packaging UK Ltd, Mold Business Park, Mold, Clwyd, CH7 1XZ Tel: (01352) 750655 Fax: (01352) 750677 E-mail: mark.mccleery@mondipackaging.com
R H Fibreboard Containers Ltd, 18 Knights Road, Chelston Business Park, Wellington, Somerset, TA21 9JH Tel: (01823) 663918 Fax: (01823) 665560 E-mail: enquiries@r-h-f.co.uk
▶ Sigma Squared Solutions Ltd, Bedford Heights, Manton Lane, Bedford, MK41 7PH Tel: (0870) 4862682 Fax: (0870) 4862681 E-mail: enquiries@sigma2solutions.com
Smurfit Sheet Feeding, Fishergate, Norwich, NR3 1SJ Tel: (01603) 660041 Fax: (01603) 679876 E-mail: sales@smurfitgroup.com
TRM Packaging Ltd, Red Cat Lane, Burscough, Ormskirk, Lancashire, L40 0SY Tel: (01704) 892811 Fax: (01704) 895546 E-mail: sales@trmpack.co.uk
UK Packaging Supplies Ltd, 100 Brantwood Road, London, N17 0XY Tel: (020) 8801 8144 Fax: (020) 8365 0847 E-mail: sales@ukplc.co.uk
Western Corrugated Ltd, Unit 59 60 Springvale Industrial Estate, Cwmbran, Gwent, NP44 5BE Tel: (01633) 872525 Fax: (01633) 861524 E-mail: sales@western-corr.co.uk

CORRUGATED BOARD CONVERTING MACHINES

Autobox Ltd, Unit S1 Cherrycourt Way, Leighton Buzzard, Bedfordshire, LU7 4UH Tel: (01525) 852831 Fax: (01525) 382353 E-mail: enquiries@autobox.co.uk

CORRUGATED BOARD MACHINERY ENGINEERS, INSTALLATION OR SERVICE

▶ Sigma Squared Solutions Ltd, Bedford Heights, Manton Lane, Bedford, MK41 7PH Tel: (0870) 4862682 Fax: (0870) 4862681 E-mail: enquiries@sigma2solutions.com

CORRUGATED BOX/CASE/ CONTAINER (CARDBOARD) MANUFRS

A & J Brooks, 37-39 North Acton Road, London, NW10 6PF Tel: (020) 8965 1440 Fax: (020) 8965 1440
A S C Cartons Ltd, Hillside Works, Leeds Road, Shipley, West Yorkshire, BD18 1DZ Tel: (01274) 599842 Fax: (01274) 592225 E-mail: sales@asc-cartons.co.uk
Abbey Board, Cromwell House, Altendiez Way, Burton Latimer, Kettering, Northamptonshire, NN15 5YZ Tel: (01536) 420055 Fax: (01536) 421726 E-mail: sales@abbeyboard.co.uk
▶ Able Packaging Designs Ltd, 23 Buckland Road, Penmill Trading Estate, Pen Mill Trading Estate, Yeovil, Somerset, BA21 5HA Tel: (01935) 470070 Fax: (01935) 477706 E-mail: sales@ablebox.com
Alfred Harrold Containers Ltd, Sandyland, Wisbech, Cambridgeshire, PE13 1TF Tel: (01945) 583776 Fax: (01945) 585577 E-mail: elaine@harrolds.co.uk

CORRUGATED BOX/CASE/ CONTAINER (CARDBOARD) MANUFRS – *continued*

Allan Cartons, Unit 1d Langley House Middlegreen Trading Estate, Middlegreen Road, Slough, SL3 6DF Tel: (01753) 577900 Fax: (01753) 577900

Allens Removals, 161 Jackmans Place, Letchworth Garden City, Hertfordshire, SG6 1RG Tel: (07850) 872308 Fax: (01462) 621701

Allpoint Packaging Ltd, Witch Lane Industrial Estate, Charter Alley, Basingstoke, Hampshire, RG26 5PY Tel: (01256) 851081 Fax: (01256) 851305 E-mail: allpointp@aol.com

Answerpak Ltd, Unit M, Fircroft Way, Edenbridge, Kent, TN8 6EL Tel: (01732) 869930 Fax: (01732) 869939 E-mail: sales@answerpak.co.uk

Aylesbury Box, 19 Faraday Road, Rabans La Industrial Area, Rabans Lane Industrial Area, Aylesbury, Buckinghamshire, HP19 8RY Tel: (01296) 436888 Fax: (01296) 481955 E-mail: sales@abcbox.co.uk

B M Packaging Ltd, Unit 4 Crosland Road Industrial Estate, Netherton, Huddersfield, HD4 7DQ Tel: (01484) 667855 Fax: (01484) 663280 E-mail: sales@bmpackaging.co.uk

B S C Packaging, 127 Mereside, Soham, Ely, Cambridgeshire, CB7 5EG Tel: (01353) 723024 Fax: (01353) 723333 E-mail: mark@brimur.co.uk

BCP Fluted Packaging Ltd, Crompton House, Nuttall Way Shadsworth, Shadsworth Business Park, Blackburn, BB1 2JT Tel: (01254) 677790 Fax: (01254) 681736 E-mail: info@bcpflute.com

Beaucrest Ltd, Holdford Road, Birmingham, B6 7EP Tel: 0121-356 5668 Fax: 0121-356 6049 E-mail: sales@beaucrest.ltd.uk

Birmingham Packaging Co., 40 Rushey Lane, Tyseley, Birmingham, B11 2BL Tel: 0121-706 9171 Fax: 0121-708 2565 E-mail: sales@birminghampackaging.co.uk

Box Factory Ltd, 2 Caswell Road, Leamington Spa, Warwickshire, CV31 1QD Tel: (01926) 430510 Fax: (01926) 430505

Boxes & Packaging Ltd, Unit 2/A, Drakes Farm, Drakes Drive, Long Crendon, Aylesbury, Buckinghamshire, HP18 9BA Tel: (01844) 202188 Fax: (01844) 202198 E-mail: sales@mondipackaging.com

Boxes & Packaging, Unit 10 Southside, Bredbury Park Industrial Estate, Bredbury, Stockport, Cheshire, SK6 2SP Tel: 0161-406 4200 Fax: 0161-406 7217 E-mail: manchester@boxesandpackaging.co.uk

Boxes & Packaging (Manchester) Ltd, Gorse Lane, Tarleton, Preston, PR4 6LH Tel: (01772) 815689 Fax: (01772) 812234 E-mail: info@boxesandpackaging.co.uk

Boxline Ltd, Bradgate Street, Leicester, LE4 0AW Tel: 0116-262 7571 Fax: 0116-251 5090 E-mail: sales@boxline.co.uk

Boxshop Ltd, 1-3 Manson Place, Kelvin Industrial Estate, East Kilbride, Glasgow, G75 0QW Tel: (01355) 222960 Fax: (01355) 223147 E-mail: boxes@boxshop.com

Bruce Boxes Ltd, Timothys Bridge Road, Stratford-Upon-Avon, Warwickshire, CV37 9NQ Tel: (01789) 269811 Fax: (01789) 414489 E-mail: sales@brucebox.co.uk

Bunzl Cleaning & Hygiene Supplies, Unit 4c Swallowfield Way, Hayes, Middlesex, UB3 1DQ Tel: (020) 8581 2345 Fax: (020) 8581 3344 E-mail: admin@bunzlcleaningsupplies.co.uk

C L F Packaging, Orchard House, Heath Road, Warboys, Huntingdon, Cambridgeshire, PE28 2UW Tel: (01487) 823222 Fax: (01487) 824011 E-mail: sales@clfpack.co.uk

Caps Cases Ltd, Studlands Park Industrial Estate, Newmarket, Suffolk, CB8 7AU Tel: (01638) 667326 Fax: (01638) 667407 E-mail: info@capscases.co.uk

Cardboard Box Co. Ltd, Clayton Park Enterpsise Centre, Petre Road, Clayton Le Moors, Accrington, Lancashire, BB5 5JB Tel: (01254) 232223 Fax: (01254) 232636 E-mail: info@thecardboardbox.co.uk

Case & Container Supply Co Ltd, 11 Wilson Road, Wigston, Leicestershire, LE18 4TP Tel: 0116-277 0000 Fax: 0116-277 0072 E-mail: sales@casecontainer.co.uk

Castle Cartons Ltd, Kings Road, Kings Heath, Birmingham, B14 6TN Tel: 0121-444 6060 Fax: 0121-441 1446 E-mail: jgreen@castlecartons.co.uk

Charapak Ltd, Meadow Lane, Alfreton, Derbyshire, DE55 7EZ Tel: (01773) 835735 Fax: (01773) 520148 E-mail: sales@charapak.co.uk

Clifford Packaging Ltd, Network 65 Business Park, Bentley Wood Way, Hapton, Burnley, Lancashire, BB11 5ST Tel: (01282) 458550 Fax: (01282) 410650 E-mail: enquires@clifford.packaging.com

Clifford Packaging Ltd, Bradbourne Drive, Tilbrook, Milton Keynes, MK7 8AQ Tel: (0870) 1226333 Fax: (01908) 270429 E-mail: enquiries@cliffordpackaging.com

Connect Packaging, 6-8 Brunel Road, Manor Trading Estate, Benfleet, Essex, SS7 4PS Tel: (01268) 755206 Fax: (01268) 755206 E-mail: info@connectpackaging.com

Corrugated Case Co. Ltd, Unit 1, Pilsley Road, Danesmoor, Chesterfield, Derbyshire, S45 9BU Tel: (01246) 860990 Fax: (01246) 860991 E-mail: info@corrugatedcase.com

Coutts Retail Communications Ltd, Golden House, Great Pulteney Street, London, W1F 9NN Tel: (020) 7534 8800 Fax: (020) 7534 8805

Croftbench Ltd, Pindar Road, Hoddesdon, Hertfordshire, EN11 0DA Tel: (01992) 444133 Fax: (01992) 445296

CRP Print & Packaging Ltd, Cooks Road, Weldon North Industrial Estate, Corby, Northamptonshire, NN17 5JT Tel: (01536) 200333 Fax: (01536) 403329 E-mail: sales@crpprint.co.uk

Custom Cartons & Packaging Ltd, Custom House, Shire Hill, Saffron Walden, Essex, CB11 3AQ Tel: (01799) 525000 Fax: (01799) 525001

Cutts Box Co. Ltd, Lion Works, Mowbray Street, Sheffield, S3 8EZ Tel: 0114-272 8673 Fax: 0114-276 5757

D S Smith, First Avenue, Royal Portbury Dock, Portbury, Bristol, BS20 7XR Tel: (01275) 375311 Fax: (01275) 374939

D S Smith, Scarne Industrial Estate, Launceston, Cornwall, PL15 9HN Tel: (01566) 777700 Fax: (01566) 774489 E-mail: sales@launceston.dssp.com

D S Smith, Fordham Road, Newmarket, Suffolk, CB8 7TX Tel: (01638) 722100 Fax: (01638) 722101

D S Smith Celtic, 5 Rush Drive, Pen-Y-Fan Industrial Estate, Crumlin, Newport, Gwent, NP11 3EJ Tel: (01495) 248255 Fax: (01495) 247675

D S Smith Packaging, Common Side Lane, Featherstone, Pontefract, West Yorkshire, WF7 5DF Tel: (01977) 791121 Fax: (01977) 780356

D W Cases, Inveresk Mills Industrial Park, Musselburgh, Midlothian, EH21 7UQ Tel: 0131-665 4645 Fax: 0131-665 0792

David S Smith, Prickwillow Road, Queen Adelaide, Ely, Cambridgeshire, CB7 4TZ Tel: (01353) 660000 Fax: (01353) 660011 E-mail: steve.wills@ely.dssp.com

Dayworth Packaging, Unit Q1, Trecenydd Industrial Estate, Caerphilly, Mid Glamorgan, CF83 2RZ Tel: (029) 2085 4860 Fax: (029) 2085 4861 E-mail: enquiries@dayworthpackaging.co.uk

Dewar Bros Ltd, Cleuch Mills, Lower Mill Street, Tillicoultry, Clackmannanshire, FK13 6BP Tel: (01259) 750669 Fax: (01259) 750573 E-mail: email@dewarbrothers.com

▶ Dial a Box Ltd, 35 Riverside Close, Warrington, WA1 2JD Tel: (01925) 650964 Fax: (0800) 7316769 E-mail: sales@dial-a-box.co.uk

▶ Don Greenwood & Partners, Main Road, Nether Broughton, Melton Mowbray, Leicestershire, LE14 3HB Tel: (01664) 823000 Fax: (01664) 823408

Dunmar Packaging Ltd, Kus Industrial Estate, Manor Lane, Hawarden, Deeside, Clwyd, CH5 3PJ Tel: (01244) 526872 Fax: (01244) 537396

Encase Northern Ltd, 2 Yeadon Airport Industrial Estate, Harrogate Road, Yeadon, Leeds, LS19 7WP Tel: 0113-250 5616 Fax: 0113-239 1145 E-mail: operations.northern@encase.co.uk

English Corrugating Paper Co. Ltd, Wilson Place, Bristol, BS2 9HL Tel: 0117-955 2002 Fax: 0117-955 4004 E-mail: sales@english-corrugating.co.uk

F D L Packaging Group, Abbeyway South, Vista Road, Haydock, St. Helens, Merseyside, WA11 0RW Tel: (01942) 722299 Fax: (01942) 271325 E-mail: sales@fdlgroup.co.uk

S.H. Fiske Ltd, The Coachworks, Kingsfield Lane, Longwell Green, Bristol, BS30 6DL Tel: 0117-960 4136 Fax: 0117-960 0187 E-mail: info@sh-fiske.com

L.P. Foreman & Sons Ltd, Farrow Road, Wigford Industrial Estate, Chelmsford, CM1 3TH Tel: (01245) 264521 Fax: (01245) 495232 E-mail: sales@lpforeman.co.uk

Forton Packaging Ltd, 11 Brookgate, Bristol, BS3 2UN Tel: 0117-953 7222 Fax: 0117-953 7456 E-mail: sales@fortonpack.com

Geddes Packaging, Dumblederry Lane, Walsall, WS9 0DH Tel: (01922) 455988 Fax: (01922) 454988E-mail: sales@geddespackaging.co.uk

William Gosling & Son Ltd, Northwodd Works, 155 Tame Road, Birmingham, B6 7DG Tel: 0121-327 4081 Fax: 0121-326 6032

Grove Packaging, Unit 2c Old Park Industrial Estate, Old Park Road, Wednesbury, West Midlands, WS10 9LR Tel: 0121-556 4735 Fax: 0121-556 4579

H S G Packing Cases Ltd, Long Row, New Works Road, Low Moor, Bradford, West Yorkshire, BD12 0QN Tel: (01274) 601137 Fax: (01274) 678597 E-mail: sales@hsg-packing-cases.co.uk

Harleys Corrugated Cases Ltd, Lonsdale Road, Thurmaston, Leicester, LE4 8JF Tel: 0116-269 3303 Fax: 0116-269 2828

George Hill Ltd, Biddings Lane, Bilston, West Midlands, WV14 9NW Tel: (01902) 403631 Fax: (01902) 492308 E-mail: sales@g-hill2000.co.uk

Holmes Mann & Co. Ltd, 17 Harris Street, Bradford, West Yorkshire, BD1 5HZ Tel: (01274) 735881 Fax: (01274) 306324 E-mail: oscar@holman.co.uk

Interactive Packaging Solutions Ltd, Unit 3 Ash Road North, Wrexham Industrial Estate, Wrexham, Clwyd, LL13 9JT Tel: (01978) 661671 Fax: (01978) 661681 E-mail: sales@ips-uk.co.uk

J Looker & Sons Ltd, Bessell Lane, Stapleford, Nottingham, NG9 7BX Tel: 0115-939 5054 Fax: 0115-939 5978

J M L Packaging Services Ltd, Parnall Road Trading Estate, Parnall Road, Bristol, BS16 3JQ Tel: 0117-965 5259 Fax: 0117-958 5494 E-mail: user@jmlpackaging.co.uk

J Nicklin & Sons Ltd, 36 Erskine Street, Birmingham, B7 4LL Tel: 0121-359 8101 Fax: 0121-359 6673 E-mail: sales@nicklin.co.uk

Jardin Corrugated Cases Ltd, Elean Business Park, Sutton, Ely, Cambridgeshire, CB6 2QE Tel: (01353) 778522 Fax: (01353) 777708 E-mail: jcc.enquiries@jccltd.com

Jaxpal Ltd, Unit 37 Planetary Industrial Estate, Planetary Road, Willenhall, West Midlands, WV13 3XB Tel: (01902) 721066 Fax: (01902) 865839 E-mail: sales@jaxpal.co.uk

Jayfour Packaging, 93 Charles Henry Street, Birmingham, B12 0SJ Tel: 0121-622 4451 Fax: 0121-666 6502 E-mail: sales@jayfourpkg.com

Jelmead Ltd, Units 1 & 4 Francis Works, Geddings Road, Hoddesdon, Hertfordshire, EN11 0NT Tel: (01992) 442751 Fax: (01992) 463739

Johnson & Akam Ltd, Old Park Court, Harris Street, Bradford, West Yorkshire, BD1 5HW Tel: (01274) 726375 Fax: (01274) 307946 E-mail: general@johnsonandakam.co.uk

Johnson Packaging, Manor Farm, Main Street, Fenton, Newark, Nottinghamshire, NG23 5PX Tel: (01636) 626949 Fax: (01636) 626911 E-mail: sales@johnsonpackaging.biz

Frederick Jones (Belfast) Ltd, 17 Napier Street, Belfast, BT12 5FE Tel: (028) 9032 4467 Fax: (028) 9032 5252 E-mail: sales@fjones.com

July Packaging, Unit 8 Manford Industrial Estate, Manor Road, Erith, Kent, DA8 2AJ Tel: (01322) 342123 Fax: (01322) 334479 E-mail: charlesdavies@zyworld.com

K C M Packaging Ltd, Units 17-18 Etherow Industrial Estate, Woolley Bridge Road, Hadfield, Glossop, Derbyshire, SK13 2GA Tel: (01457) 862617 Fax: (01457) 861540 E-mail: sales@kcmpackaging.co.uk

Kappa Corrugated UK Ltd, Knowl Street, Stalybridge, Cheshire, SK15 3AR Tel: 0161-338 3711 Fax: 0161-303 2647

Kenross Containers Ltd, Kippax Mill, Goodshawfold Road, Rossendale, Lancashire, BB4 8QW Tel: (01706) 228381 Fax: (01706) 831523 E-mail: sales@kenross.co.uk

Lancashire Board & Paper Co. Ltd, Balderstone Lane, Heasandford Industrial Estate, Burnley, Lancashire, BB10 2AL Tel: (01282) 835033 Fax: (01282) 835044 E-mail: sales@lancsboard.co.uk

Lea Boxes Ltd, 38 Camford Way, Luton, LU3 3AN Tel: (01582) 505561 Fax: (01582) 490352 E-mail: maria@leaboxes.co.uk

Lee Packaging Ltd, Bull Lane Industrial Estate, Bull Lane, Acton, Sudbury, Suffolk, CO10 0BD Tel: (01787) 372874 Fax: (01787) 376707 E-mail: sales@leepackaging.co.uk

M P V Packaging Ltd, Swan Lane, Hindley Green, Wigan, Lancashire, WN2 4HA Tel: (01942) 522522 Fax: (01942) 522523 E-mail: mpvpackaging@aol.com

Macfarlane Group UK Ltd, Unit 2, Concorde Road, Patchway, Bristol, BS34 5TB Tel: (0870) 8500542 Fax: (0870) 8500543 E-mail: bristol@macfarlanegroup.net

▶ Majestic Corrugated Cases Ltd, Unit 30 Parkrose Industrial Estate, Middlemore Road, Smethwick, West Midlands, B66 2DZ Tel: (01902) 733330 Fax: 0121-558 7000 E-mail: kavi.jundu@majesticbox.com

Manchester Paper Box Ltd, 2 Bird Hall Lane, Stockport, Cheshire, SK3 0SZ Tel: 0161-428 4225 Fax: 0161-428 0797 E-mail: c@mpbox.co.uk

Peter Marsh & Sons Ltd, Dundee Works, 47 Canal Street, Bootle, Merseyside, L20 8AE Tel: 0151-922 1971 Fax: 0151-922 3804 E-mail: sales@petermarsh.co.uk

▶ Marshall Langston Ltd, Marlan House, Lower Tuffley Lane, Gloucester, GL2 5DT Tel: (01452) 529717 Fax: (01452) 309994 E-mail: sales@marshalllangston.co.uk

Metro Box Ltd, 25-30 Green Street, Birmingham, B12 0NB Tel: 0121-772 5411 Fax: 0121-771 4371 E-mail: ajf@metrobox.freeserve.co.uk

Midland Box Co. Ltd, Field Industrial Estate, Clover Street, Kirkby-in-Ashfield, Nottingham, NG17 7LH Tel: (01623) 758758 Fax: (01623) 757229 E-mail: sales@midlandbox.co.uk

Mondi Packaging, Unit 10 Southside, Bredbury Park Industrial Estate, Bredbury, Stockport, Cheshire, SK6 2SP Tel: 0161-406 4200 Fax: 0161-406 7217 E-mail: manchester@boxesandpackaging.co.uk

▶ Mondi Packaging Bux, Airfield Works, Pulham St. Mary, Diss, Norfolk, IP21 4QH Tel: (01379) 676531 Fax: (01379) 676275 E-mail: sales.bux@mondipackaging.com

Mondi Packaging Eastern Region Ltd, 11 Uxbridge Road, Leicester, LE4 7ST Tel: 0116-266 2666 Fax: 0116-266 2555 E-mail: sales@boxesandpackaging.co.uk

Mondi Packaging UK Ltd, Mold Business Park, Mold, Clwyd, CH7 1XZ Tel: (01352) 750655 Fax: (01352) 750677 E-mail: mark.mccleery@mondipackaging.com

N Smith & Co. Ltd, Leopold Works, 28 Hainge Road, Tividale, Oldbury, West Midlands, B69 2NZ Tel: 0121-557 1891 Fax: 0121-521 5700 E-mail: sales@nsmithbox.co.uk

Northdown Packaging, 13c Quarry Wood Industrial Estate, Mills Road, Aylesford, Kent, ME20 7NA Tel: (01622) 710695 Fax: (01622) 790889 E-mail: sales@northdownpackaging.co.uk

Northern Corrugated Cases Ltd, 16 Middlewich Road, Byley, Middlewich, Cheshire, CW10 9NX Tel: (01606) 836811 Fax: (01606) 836088 E-mail: sales@northcorr.co.uk

Northern Packaging Ltd, Selby Place, Stanley Industrial Estate, Skelmersdale, Lancashire, WN8 8EF Tel: (01695) 731445 Fax: (01695) 51865 E-mail: sales@northern-packaging.co.uk

Ozbox, Herald Way, Binley Industrial Estate, Binley Industrial Estate, Coventry, CV3 2RQ Tel: (024) 7656 1561 Fax: (024) 7656 1555 E-mail: tena.snell@ozbox.co.uk

P O S Packaging Ltd, Cressex Business Park, 30A Wellington Road, High Wycombe, Buckinghamshire, HP12 3PR Tel: (01494) 473701 Fax: (01494) 473801 E-mail: unique.pkg@online.rednet.co.uk

Packaging Products Ltd, Collyhurst Road, Manchester, M40 7RT Tel: 0161-205 4181 Fax: 0161-203 4678 E-mail: sales@packagingproducts.co.uk

Pak Wraps Ltd, Unit 16 Sefton Lane Industrial Estate, Liverpool, L31 8BX Tel: 0151-924 0767 Fax: 0151-924 6555

Playford Packaging, Ash Road, Wrexham, Clwyd, LL13 9JT Tel: (01978) 661043 Fax: (01978) 661273

Porter Packaging Co. Ltd, Hardwick Grange, Woolston, Warrington, WA1 4RT Tel: (01925) 822828 Fax: (01925) 837593

Potters Packaging, Govan Road, Fenton Industrial Estate, Stoke-On-Trent, ST4 2RS Tel: (01782) 848888 Fax: (01782) 848900

Quickcase Boxes, 2 Brimscombe Mills Estate, London Road, Brimscombe, Stroud, Gloucestershire, GL5 2SA Tel: (01453) 884572 Fax: (01453) 885552

Red Rose Packaging Ltd, Newby Road Industrial Estate, Newby Road, Hazel Grove, Stockport, Cheshire, SK7 5DA Tel: 0161-483 4433 Fax: 0161-487 2161 E-mail: redrose.packaging@virgin.net

Reedbut Ltd, Bond Avenue, Bletchley, Milton Keynes, MK1 1JJ Tel: (01908) 630200 Fax: (01908) 630210 E-mail: sales@reedbut.com

Ribble Packaging Ltd, Greengate Street, Oldham, OL4 1DF Tel: 0161-284 9000 Fax: 0161-627 5049 E-mail: ribble@ribble-pack.co.uk

Rigid Containers Ltd, Stoke Albany Road, Desborough, Kettering, Northamptonshire, NN14 2SR Tel: (01536) 760266 Fax: (01536) 762714

Rogar Products Ltd, 9-12 Tewin Court, Welwyn Garden City, Hertfordshire, AL7 1AU Tel: (01707) 371251 Fax: (01707) 334838 E-mail: sales@rogar.co.uk

Rowlinson Packaging Ltd, Unit 1 Green Lane, Wardle, Nantwich, Cheshire, CW5 6BN Tel: (01829) 260571 Fax: (01829) 260718 E-mail: packaging@rowlinson.co.uk

Rowpak Containers Ltd, Arrow Trading Estate, Corporation Road, Manchester, M34 5LR Tel: 0161-320 0026 Fax: 0161-335 0537 E-mail: john.lowe@rowpak.co.uk

Roydon Packaging Ltd, 16-19 Harolds Road, Harlow, Essex, CM19 5BJ Tel: (01279) 442772 Fax: (01279) 422727 E-mail: sales@roydonpkg.co.uk

S C A Heavy Duty Ltd, Heanor Gate Industrial Estate, Heanor Gate Road, Heanor, Derbyshire, DE75 7RJ Tel: (01773) 836456 Fax: (01773) 530427

S C A Packaging, Brook Road, Speedwell, Bristol, BS5 7TD Tel: 0117-951 7415 Fax: 0117-935 4260

S C A Packaging Ltd, North Road, Ellesmere Port, CH65 1AG Tel: 0151-355 2381 Fax: 0151-357 2676

S C A Packaging Oldbury, Rood End Road, Oldbury, West Midlands, B69 4HT Tel: 0121-552 0696 Fax: 0121-552 0623

S C A Packaging Oxford, Unit 9 Stanton Harcourt Industrial Estate, Stanton Harcourt, Witney, Oxfordshire, OX29 5UX Tel: (01865) 882972 Fax: (01865) 882917 E-mail: oxford.salesoffice@sca.com

Saica Packaging UK Ltd, Road Three, Winsford Industrial Estate, Winsford, Cheshire, CW7 3RJ Tel: (01606) 562700 Fax: (01606) 562762 E-mail: reception@saica-packaging.co.uk

Saxon Packaging Ltd, 28 Harvest Drive, Lowestoft, Suffolk, NR33 7NJ Tel: (01502) 513112 Fax: (01502) 583627 E-mail: sales@saxonpackaging.ltd.uk

Sca Packaging Ltd, UK Central Office, Papyrus Way, Larkfield, Aylesford, Kent, ME20 7TW Tel: (01622) 883000 Fax: (01622) 716308

Servispak Ltd, Beadle Trading Estate, Hithercroft Road, Wallingford, Oxfordshire, OX10 9EZ Tel: (01491) 834000 Fax: (01491) 834054 E-mail: sales@sevispak.com

Siddons Packaging, Kingsley Street, Leicester, LE2 6DL Tel: 0116-244 8555 Fax: 0116-244 8575 E-mail: sales@sipak.co.uk

Simpkin & Icke Holdings Ltd, Glaisdale Works, Glaisdale Drive, Nottingham, NG8 4JU Tel: 0115-929 2106 Fax: 0115-929 0446 E-mail: boxes@simpkin-and-icke.co.uk

D.S. Smith Packaging, Meadow Close, Ise Valley Industrial Estate, Wellingborough, Northamptonshire, NN8 4BH Tel: (01933) 440488 Fax: (01933) 441202

Smith Pack, Units 43-44, Brook House Road, Parkhouse Industrial Estate West, Newcastle, Staffordshire, ST5 7EF Tel: (01782) 565123 Fax: (01782) 565124 E-mail: northweston@wsmith.co.uk

Smurfit Kappa, 24-26 Robjohns Road, Chelmsford, CM1 3BB Tel: (01245) 493777 Fax: (01245) 353427

▶ indicates data change since last edition

CORRUGATED BOX/CASE/ CONTAINER (CARDBOARD) MANUFRS – *continued*

Smurfit South West, Riverside Road, Pottington Business Park, Barnstaple, Devon, EX31 1LX Tel: (01271) 345011 Fax: (01271) 346665
Star Pac Ltd, 23 Fernwood Close, Redditch, Worcestershire, B98 7TN Tel: (01527) 850022 Fax: (01527) 850033 E-mail: sales@starpac.co.uk
Henry Sutcliffe Ltd, Hulme Street, Salford, M5 4PX Tel: 0161-736 1337 Fax: 0161-745 7724 E-mail: sales@hsltd.co.uk
Tee-Kay Packaging, Fengate, Peterborough, PE1 5XG Tel: (01733) 311867 Fax: (01733) 311017 E-mail: robert@tee-kay.co.uk
Trafalgar Cases Ltd, Stanhope Works, Primrose Hill, Kings Langley, Hertfordshire, WD4 8HS Tel: (01923) 261155 Fax: (01923) 268064 E-mail: sales@trafalgarcases.com
TRM Packaging Ltd, Red Cat Lane, Burscough, Ormskirk, Lancashire, L40 0SY Tel: (01704) 892811 Fax: (01704) 895546 E-mail: sales@trmpack.co.uk
Tyne Tees Packaging Ltd, Grindon Way, Heighington Lane Business Park, Newton Aycliffe, County Durham, DL5 6DQ Tel: (01325) 311114 Fax: (01325) 311301 E-mail: sales@tyneteespackaging.co.uk
UK Packaging Supplies Ltd, 100 Brantwood Road, London, N17 0XY Tel: (020) 8801 8144 Fax: (020) 8365 0847 E-mail: sales@ukplc.co.uk
Universal Packaging Ltd, Units 3-4, Capitol Industrial Centre, Fulmar Way, Wickford, Essex, SS11 8YW Tel: (01268) 561400 Fax: (01268) 572900 E-mail: admin@uplgroupltd.com
West Packaging Ltd, Cornish Street, Sheffield, S6 3AA Tel: 0114-276 0555 Fax: 0114-275 7590 E-mail: info@westpack.co.uk
Wevax Ltd, Prospect Close, Lowmoor Business Park, Kirkby-in-Ashfield, Nottingham, NG17 7LF Tel: (01623) 754268 Fax: (01623) 723447
Wilmot Packaging Ltd, Rutherford Way, Swindon Village, Cheltenham, Gloucestershire, GL51 9TU Tel: (01242) 245151 Fax: (01242) 245155
Richard Wood Packaging Ltd, Guys Industrial Estate Tollgate Road, Burscough, Ormskirk, Lancashire, L40 8TG Tel: (01704) 893073 Fax: (01704) 895276 E-mail: woodpackaging@aol.co.uk

CORRUGATED BOX/CASE/ CONTAINER PRINTING SERVICES

Fast-Pak Packaging Ltd, Unit 1 Kayley Industrial Estate, Richmond Street, Ashton-under-Lyne, Lancashire, OL7 0AU Tel: 0161-339 0697 Fax: 0161-339 4700 E-mail: fastpak@talk21.com

CORRUGATED BOX/CASE/ CONTAINER, PLASTIC

Laserpack Cartons & Cases Ltd, Unit 4, Llandygai Industrial Estate, Bangor, Gwynedd, LL57 4YH Tel: (0845) 2575758 Fax: (0845) 2575759 E-mail: sales@laserpack.co.uk
Tri-Pack Plastics Ltd, Estate Road No. 1, South Humberside Industrial Estate, Grimsby, South Humberside, DN31 2TB Tel: (01472) 355038 Fax: (01472) 266930 E-mail: mail@tri-pack.co.uk

CORRUGATED CONVEYOR SYSTEMS

Avanti Conveyors, Calico Lane, Furness Vale, High Peak, Derbyshire, SK23 7SW Tel: (01663) 740011 Fax: (01663) 745097 E-mail: sales@avanti-conveyors.co.uk

CORRUGATED FASTENERS

R J Engineering, Derby Works, Liverpool Road South, Burscough, Ormskirk, Lancashire, L40 7SU Tel: (01704) 897771 Fax: (01704) 897772 E-mail: r.j.engineering@amserve.net
Spotnails Ltd, Unit 21, Pantglas Industrial Estate, Bedwas, Caerphilly, Mid Glamorgan, CF83 8DR Tel: (029) 2086 0222 Fax: (029) 2086 0999 E-mail: sales@spotnails.co.uk

CORRUGATED LITHO-LAMINATED CARTONS

Allied Packaging Ltd, Brabant House, Portsmouth Road, Thames Ditton, Surrey, KT7 0EY Tel: (020) 8398 8882 Fax: (020) 8398 4485 E-mail: sales@alliedpackaging.co.uk
David S Smith, Prickwillow Road, Queen Adelaide, Ely, Cambridgeshire, CB7 4TZ Tel: (01353) 660000 Fax: (01353) 660011

CORRUGATED PACKING FITMENTS OR DIVISIONS

Beaucrest Ltd, Holdford Road, Birmingham, B6 7EP Tel: 0121-356 5668 Fax: 0121-356 6049 E-mail: sales@beaucrest.ltd.uk
Boxes & Packaging (Manchester) Ltd, Gorse Lane, Tarleton, Preston, PR4 6LH Tel: (01772) 815689 Fax: (01772) 812234 E-mail: info@boxesandpackaging.co.uk
Castle Corrugated Cases Ltd, Hadnock Road, Monmouth, Gwent, NP25 3NQ Tel: (01600) 715727 Fax: (01600) 714942
M P V Packaging Ltd, Swan Lane, Hindley Green, Wigan, Lancashire, WN2 4HA Tel: (01942) 522522 Fax: (01942) 522523 E-mail: mpvpackaging@aol.com
Manchester Paper Box Ltd, 2 Bird Hall Lane, Stockport, Cheshire, SK3 0SZ Tel: 0161-428 4225 Fax: 0161-428 0797 E-mail: c@mpbox.co.uk
Quickcase Boxes, 2 Brimscombe Mills Estate, London Road, Brimscombe, Stroud, Gloucestershire, GL5 2SA Tel: (01453) 884572 Fax: (01453) 885552

CORRUGATED PAPER MACHINERY

Mansfield Board Machinery Ltd, 2 Horsley Road, Northampton, NN2 6LJ Tel: (01604) 713656 Fax: (01604) 791132 E-mail: sales@mansfieldboard.co.uk

CORRUGATED PAPER MANUFRS

BCP Fluted Packaging Ltd, Crompton House, Nuttall Way Shadsworth, Shadsworth Business Park, Blackburn, BB1 2JT Tel: (01254) 677790 Fax: (01254) 681736 E-mail: info@bcpflute.com
Graham's Cartons, Garston Quays, Blackburn Street, Liverpool, L19 8EL Tel: 0151-427 6565 Fax: 0151-427 5123 E-mail: colin.graham@grahams-cartons.co.uk
John Hargreaves (Collyhurst & Stalybridge) Ltd, Knowl Street, Stalybridge, Cheshire, SK15 3AJ Tel: 0161-338 6011 Fax: 0161-338 4194 E-mail: jack@john-hargreaves.co.uk
K & A Polystyrene, 30 Lavell Mews, Bradford, West Yorkshire, BD2 3HW Tel: (01274) 631341 Fax: (01274) 641781
Rigid Paper Ltd, Denison Road, Selby, North Yorkshire, YO8 8DB Tel: (01757) 705151 Fax: (01757) 210009 E-mail: paper@rigid.co.uk
Sca Packaging Ltd, UK Central Office, Papyrus Way, Larkfield, Aylesford, Kent, ME20 7TW Tel: (01622) 883000 Fax: (01622) 793333 E-mail: publicity.packaging.uk@sca.com
Smurfit Corrugated Sheet Sales Windrush Ltd, Windrush Park Road, Witney, Oxfordshire, OX29 7EX Tel: (01993) 771188 Fax: (01993) 701201

CORRUGATED PAPER ROLLS

Custom Cartons & Packaging Ltd, Custom House, Shire Hill, Saffron Walden, Essex, CB11 3AQ Tel: (01799) 525000 Fax: (01799) 525001
Rigid Paper Ltd, Denison Road, Selby, North Yorkshire, YO8 8DB Tel: (01757) 705151 Fax: (01757) 210009 E-mail: paper@rigid.co.uk

CORRUGATED PLASTIC PACKAGING PRODUCTS

Bloomfield Supplies, Naas Lane, Gloucester, GL2 5RG Tel: (01452) 883354 Fax: (01452) 725115 E-mail: info@bloomfieldsupplies.co.uk
Britton Decoflex Ltd, Skerne Road, Oakesway Industrial Estate, Hartlepool, Cleveland, TS24 0RH Tel: (01429) 272102 Fax: (01429) 860388 E-mail: smrsales@britton-group.com
Central Tin Canister Co. Ltd, Orrell Mount, Bootle, Merseyside, L20 6NS Tel: 0151-933 6704 Fax: 0151-933 5315 E-mail: centralplastic@freenetname.co.uk
Cheshire Packaging Ltd, Unit B2 Talbot Road, Newton Business Park, Hyde, Cheshire, SK14 4UQ Tel: 0161-367 8331 Fax: 0161-367 8417

CORRUGATED PLASTIC SHEET

Goran Plastics Ltd, 5 Caxton Way, Watford Business Park, Watford, WD18 8UA Tel: (01923) 255700 Fax: (01923) 255698 E-mail: sales@goran.co.uk
Mcarthur Group Ltd, Arctic House, Goulton Street, Hull, HU3 4DL Tel: (01482) 506907 Fax: (01482) 351558 E-mail: enquiries@mcarthur-group.com
Sol Systems, Unit 4 Mallorie House, Beaumont Road, Banbury, Oxfordshire, OX16 1RH Tel: (01295) 255536 Fax: (01295) 276492 E-mail: bworsley@btinternet.com

CORRUGATED SCREEN PRINTED CARTONS

David S Smith, Prickwillow Road, Queen Adelaide, Ely, Cambridgeshire, CB7 4TZ Tel: (01353) 660000 Fax: (01353) 660011

CORRUGATED STEEL

Brown & Glegg Edinburgh Ltd, Bankhead Crossway South, Sighthill Industrial Estate, Edinburgh, EH11 4EZ Tel: 0131-453 6611 Fax: 0131-453 1848 E-mail: info@brownglegg.co.uk
M E T Steel Ltd, 51 Mallusk Road, Newtownabbey, County Antrim, BT36 4RU Tel: (028) 9083 7311 Fax: (028) 9084 3548

CORRUGATED TRANSIT PACKAGING

Cheshire Packaging Ltd, Unit B2 Talbot Road, Newton Business Park, Hyde, Cheshire, SK14 4UQ Tel: 0161-367 8331 Fax: 0161-367 8417
Corstat Containers Ltd, Unit 7 Whitehill Industrial Estate, Whitehill Lane, Swindon, SN4 7DB Tel: (01793) 855168 Fax: (01793) 855209 E-mail: enquiries@corstat.co.uk
D S Smith, Muir Road, Houstoun Industrial Estate, Livingston, West Lothian, EH54 5DP Tel: (01506) 432841 Fax: (01506) 438347
S E A Packaging, Lavenham Road, Yate, Bristol, BS37 5QY Tel: (01454) 314509 Fax: (01454) 325711

CORRUGATING MACHINES

Avanti Conveyors, Calico Lane, Furness Vale, High Peak, Derbyshire, SK23 7SW Tel: (01663) 740011 Fax: (01663) 745097 E-mail: sales@avanti-conveyors.co.uk

COSMETIC APPLICATION ACCESSORIES

Barry M Cosmetics, Unit 1 Bittacy Business Centre, Bittacy Hill, London, NW7 1BA Tel: (020) 8349 2992 Fax: (020) 8346 7773 E-mail: info@barrym.co.uk
Foamline Ltd, Unit A-B Industrial Estate, Floors Street, Johnstone, Renfrewshire, PA5 8PE Tel: (01505) 327155 Fax: (01505) 503811 E-mail: sales@foamline.co.uk
The Hair Factory, 4 North Square, London, N9 0HW Tel: (020) 8660 5520
Harzer Cosmetik Pinsel UK Ltd, Taylor Lane, Loscoe, Heanor, Derbyshire, DE75 7TA Tel: (01773) 534314 Fax: (01773) 534314
Natural Active Materials Resources, 3A Magdalene Street, Glastonbury, Somerset, BA6 9EW Tel: (01458) 835970 Fax: (01458) 831361
Synlatex Ltd, Unit M2 Innsworth Technology Park, Innsworth Lane, Gloucester, GL3 1DL Tel: (01452) 730068 Fax: (01452) 730048 E-mail: enquiries@slguk.com

COSMETIC BAGS/PURSES

▶ Makeupworld, 5 Maes Street, St. Thomas, Swansea, SA1 8ES Tel: (07851) 734820 E-mail: customerservice@makeupworld.co.uk
▶ Scootles Bags, 19 High Street, Castle Donington, Derby, DE74 2PP Tel: 01332 811740 Fax: 01332 811740 E-mail: info@scootles.co.uk

COSMETIC BOTANICAL OILS

▶ Anita Grant Ltd, Wycombe Lane, Wooburn Green, Buckinghamshire, HP10 0HL Tel: 0845 4025240 E-mail: atyourservice@anitagrant.com

COSMETIC COLOURS

▶ Academy Hair & Beauty UK Ltd, 4 Kent Street Industrial Estate, 26 Kent Street, Leicester, LE5 3BD Tel: 0116-262 4946 Fax: 0116-251 6489 E-mail: mail@academy-beauty.com
Cosi Ltd, Watersmead Business Park, Littlehampton, West Sussex, BN17 6LS Tel: (01903) 734734 Fax: (01903) 844552 E-mail: sales@cosiworld.com
Creative Cosmetics Ltd, 6-7 Riverside Industrial Park, Rapier Street, Ipswich, IP2 8JX Tel: (01473) 685599 Fax: (01473) 680727 E-mail: alan@creativecosmetics.com
▶ The Forever Aloe Store, 1 Argyle Street, Gorse Hill, Swindon, SN2 8BP Tel: (01793) 641732 E-mail: sales@theforeveraloestore.co.uk
Holliday Pigments Ltd, Morley Street, Hull, HU8 8DN Tel: (01482) 329875 Fax: (01484) 329791 E-mail: sales@holliday-pigments.com
Sensient Colors Ltd, Old Meadow Road, King's Lynn, Norfolk, PE30 4LA Tel: (01553) 669444 Fax: (01553) 770707

COSMETIC CONTAINER/ CLOSURE/COMPONENT (PACKAGING) MANUFRS

De Maeyer International, Office, 77 Winchester Road, Four Marks, Alton, Hampshire, GU34 5HR Tel: (01420) 562776 Fax: (01420) 562874 E-mail: admin@demaeyer.co.uk
Medical & Cosmetic Mouldings Ltd, Gas Road, Sittingbourne, Kent, ME10 2QD Tel: (01795) 426452 Fax: (01795) 422790 E-mail: informationmcm@aol.com
Specialist Anodising Ltd, New Hall Works, Elm Street, Burnley, Lancashire, BB10 1NY Tel: (01282) 412500 Fax: (01282) 422804 E-mail: saco@sacoltd.com
Toly Products (UK) Ltd, Watkin Road, Wembley, Middlesex, HA9 0NL Tel: (020) 8902 3161 Fax: (020) 8900 2975 E-mail: info@toly.com

COSMETIC CREAMS

▶ Anita Grant Ltd, Wycombe Lane, Wooburn Green, Buckinghamshire, HP10 0HL Tel: 0845 4025240 E-mail: atyourservice@anitagrant.com
▶ Hygieia Healthcare Ltd, PO Box 117, Bideford, Devon, EX39 1AA Tel: (01237) 473128 Fax: (01237) 425742 E-mail: sales@hygieia.co.uk

COSMETIC MIRRORS

Fancy Metal Goods Ltd, 71 Lifford Lane, Birmingham, B30 3DY Tel: 0121-459 9777 Fax: 0121-459 9595 E-mail: fancymetalgoods@btconnect.com
Opals (Mirror-Flex) Co. Ltd, Unit 3 B Seaden Court, Steveson Road, Gorse Lane Industrial Estate, Clacton-On-Sea, Essex, CO15 4XN Tel: (01255) 423927 Fax: (01255) 221117 E-mail: sales@mirrorflex.co.uk

COSMETIC NAIL EXTENSIONS

▶ The Beauty Preference, 33 Lyon Close, Maidenbower, Crawley, West Sussex, RH10 7ND Tel: (01293) 883716 E-mail: rose@beautypref.com
▶ Noticeable Nails, 21 Boundary Street, Leyland, PR25 4ST Tel: 01772 455634 E-mail: info@nails-in-preston.co.uk
Sally Hair & Beauty Supplies, 17 Canal Road, Bradford, West Yorkshire, BD1 4AT Tel: (01274) 739261
▶ Soewitos Hair And Beauty Salon, Brunel Centre, Bletchley, Milton Keynes, MK2 2ES Tel: 01908 642985

COSMETIC POWDER COMPACTION PRESSES

Kemwall Engineering Co., 52 Bensham Grove, Thornton Heath, Surrey, CR7 8DA Tel: (020) 8653 7111 Fax: (020) 8653 9669 E-mail: sales@kemwall.co.uk

COSMETIC POWDER PUFFS

Caressa Kahn, Wellfield Road, Hatfield, Hertfordshire, AL10 0BS Tel: (01707) 262287 Fax: (01707) 263297 E-mail: mail@i-kahn.co.uk

COSMETIC PROCESSING MACHINERY

Provel Ltd, 46-48 Saville Street, Bolton, BL2 1BY Tel: (01204) 381911 Fax: (01204) 381891 E-mail: martyn@provel.fsbusiness.co.uk

COSMETIC RAW MATERIALS

Cosmetochem UK Ltd, Cunningham House, Westfield Lane, Harrow, Middlesex, HA3 9ED Tel: (020) 8907 7779 Fax: (020) 8927 0686 E-mail: cosmetochem@cheshamchemicals.co.uk
Croda Chemicals International Ltd, Cowick Hall, Snaith, Goole, North Humberside, DN14 9AA Tel: (01405) 860551 Fax: (01405) 861767
Dome Cosmetics, 30 West Hill, Epsom, Surrey, KT19 8JD Tel: (01372) 745577 Fax: (01372) 747274 E-mail: press@domeltd.freeserve.co.uk
H L C Engineering Ltd, 4 Harvey Road, Burnt Mills Industrial Estate, Basildon, Essex, SS13 1QJ Tel: (01268) 590080 Fax: (01268) 590141E-mail: steelwork@hlcengineering.com
Minelco, 3 Riverside Business Centre, Brighton Road, Shoreham-by-Sea, West Sussex, BN43 6RE Tel: (01273) 452331 Fax: (01273) 464741 E-mail: info@minelco.com

COSMETIC SPONGE MANUFRS

Caressa Kahn, Wellfield Road, Hatfield, Hertfordshire, AL10 0BS Tel: (01707) 262287 Fax: (01707) 263297 E-mail: mail@i-kahn.co.uk

Gilca Manufacturing Ltd, 853 Wolverhampton Road, Oldbury, West Midlands, B69 4RU Tel: 0121-544 1929 Fax: 0121-544 6301 E-mail: info@gilca.biz

Medisponge, 35 Water Drive, Standish, Wigan, Lancashire, WN6 0EH Tel: (01257) 473175 Fax: (01257) 473175

Recticel Corby, 83-84 Manton Road, Earlstrees Industrial Estate, Corby, Northamptonshire, NN17 4JL Tel: (01536) 402345 Fax: (01536) 400524 E-mail: enquiries@recticel.co.uk

Synlatex Ltd, Unit M2 Innsworth Technology Park, Innsworth Lane, Gloucester, GL3 1DL Tel: (01452) 730068 Fax: (01452) 730048 E-mail: enquiries@slguk.com

COSMETICS, *See also headings for particular types*

Advanced Care Products Ltd, Unit 6 Chalfont Square, Old Foundry Road, Ipswich, IP4 2AJ Tel: (01473) 219220 Fax: (01473) 219049 E-mail: sales@advancedcareproducts.co.uk

Advantis Laboratories Ltd, Unit 13, Lawson Hunt Industrial Park, Guildford Road, Broadbridge Heath, Horsham, West Sussex, RH12 3JR Tel: (01403) 263100 Fax: (01403) 254493

African Dream Ltd, 31-33 East Street, London, SE17 2DJ Tel: (020) 7701 3886 Fax: (020) 7701 3886

Alberto-Culver Co. (UK) Ltd, Lime Tree Way, Hampshire International Business Park, Chineham, Basingstoke, Hampshire, RG24 8ER Tel: (01256) 705000 Fax: (01256) 705001

▶ Alexandria Associates, 4a, Leyland Road, Penwortham, Preston, PR1 9XR Tel: (01772) 742224 Fax: (01772) 751124

▶ Thomas Ashton, Beaufort Court, Admirals Way, London, E14 9XL Tel: (020) 7863 1740 Fax: (020) 7863 7510

Avon Cosmetics Ltd, Nunn Mills Road, Northampton, NN1 5PA Tel: (01604) 232425 Fax: (01604) 232444 E-mail: info@avon.com

Barry M Cosmetics, Unit 1 Bittacy Business Centre, Bittacy Hill, London, NW7 1BA Tel: (020) 8349 2992 Fax: (020) 8346 7773 E-mail: info@barrym.co.uk

Beauty, 103-105 Cheetham Hill Road, Manchester, M8 8PY Tel: 0161-833 9163 Fax: 0161-833 1687 E-mail: beautyuk@btconnect.com

The Body Shop International P.L.C., Watersmead, Littlehampton, West Sussex, BN17 6LS Tel: (01903) 731500 Fax: (01903) 726250 E-mail: info@bodyshop.co.uk

Bodycare Health & Beauty Ltd, 100 Albany Way, Salford, M6 5HR Tel: 0161-736 6522

▶ Caring Industries Ltd, Unit 7, Kenfig Industrial Estate, Margam, Port Talbot, West Glamorgan, SA13 2PE Tel: (01656) 749085

Castle Care Cosmetics Ltd, Invincible Road, Farnborough, Hampshire, GU14 7QP Tel: (01252) 548887 Fax: (01252) 548880 E-mail: sales@castlecare.co.uk

Cosi Ltd, Watersmead Business Park, Littlehampton, West Sussex, BN17 6LS Tel: (01903) 734734 Fax: (01903) 844552 E-mail: sales@cosiworld.com

Creative Cosmetics Ltd, 6-7 Riverside Industrial Park, Rapier Street, Ipswich, IP2 8JX Tel: (01473) 685599 Fax: (01473) 680727 E-mail: alan@creativecosmetics.com

Culpeper Ltd, Pall Mall Deposit, Unit 47, 124-128 Barlby Road, London, W10 6BL Tel: (020) 8962 3010 Fax: (020) 8969 9247 E-mail: info@culpeper.co.uk

Dooa Wholesalers Ltd, Dooa House, 55-61 North Acton Road, London, NW10 6PH Tel: (020) 8961 7978 Fax: (020) 8961 8767 E-mail: info@dooa.co.uk

E A Ellison & Co. Ltd, Crondal Road, Bayton Industrial Estate, Exhall, Coventry, CV7 9NH Tel: (024) 7636 1619 Fax: (024) 7637 9183 E-mail: sales@ellisons.co.uk

▶ Face Talk, 61 Seamoor Road, Bournemouth, BH4 9AE Tel: (01202) 556000 Fax: (01202) 556000

Fairtrade International Co. Ltd, 12 Cockfosters Parade, Cockfosters Road, Barnet, Hertfordshire, EN4 0BX Tel: (020) 8447 0220 Fax: (020) 8447 0330 E-mail: info@fairtradeint.co.uk

G Creations plc, 2 Homefield Road, London, SW19 4QE Tel: (020) 8947 8652 Fax: (020) 8944 1650

Hanworth Laboratories Ltd, The Grip, Hadstock Road, Linton, Cambridge, CB21 4XN Tel: (01223) 892217 Fax: (01223) 893623 E-mail: sales@hanworthlabs.co.uk

Intercos UK Ltd, 26 The Strand, Bideford, Devon, EX39 2ND Tel: (01237) 476339 Fax: (01237) 471040

John Gosnell & Co. Ltd, North Street, Lewes, East Sussex, BN7 2QG Tel: (01273) 473772 Fax: (01273) 472217 E-mail: info@johngosnell.com

Kirker Europe Ltd, Davidson Drive, Castle Avenue Industrial Estate, Invergordon, Ross-Shire, IV18 0SA Tel: (01349) 856000 Fax: (01349) 852255

Laboratory Facilities Ltd, 24 Britwell Road, Burnham, Slough, SL1 8AG Tel: (01628) 604149 Fax: (01628) 667920 E-mail: officelabfacs@btconnect.com

Le-Belle International, 248 Lewisham High Street, London, SE13 6JU Tel: (020) 8852 3604 Fax: (020) 8852 3604

L'Oreal Luxury Products Ltd, 255 Hammersmith Road, London, W6 8AZ Tel: (020) 8762 4000 Fax: (020) 8762 4001 E-mail: sales@1oreal.com

▶ Love The Planet, 124 Crown Street, Aberdeen, AB11 6HQ Tel: (01224) 594411 Fax: (01224) 594411 E-mail: sales@1ovetheplanet.co.uk

▶ MakeUpMadness, 44 Barnard Avenue, Ludworth, Durham, DH6 1LS Tel: (01429) 821343 E-mail: chris@makeupmadness.co.uk

Matthews & Wilson Ltd, Forest Road, Charlbury, Chipping Norton, Oxfordshire, OX7 3HH Tel: (01608) 811539 Fax: (01608) 811834

▶ Northumbrian Soap Co., 89 Station Road, Ashington, Northumberland, NE63 8RS Tel: (01670) 858936

Nutrimetics International UK Ltd, 3 Garamonde Drive, Wymbush, Milton Keynes, MK8 8DF Tel: (01908) 262020 Fax: (01908) 262021 E-mail: info@nutrimetics.co.uk

▶ Odds & Suds, 30 The Market, Tavistock, Devon, PL19 0AL Tel: (01822) 618111

Phils (Wholesale) Ltd, 709 North Circular Road, London, NW2 7AX Tel: (020) 8830 8830 Fax: (020) 8830 8833 E-mail: mark@trimarkfsnet.co.uk

▶ Pot Of Gold, Akroyd Mill, 4 Akroyd Place, Halifax, West Yorkshire, HX1 1YH Tel: (01422) 380704 Fax: (01422) 380706

▶ Professional Beauty Systems, Unit 3 Newmains Avenue, Inchinnan, Renfrew, PA4 9RR Tel: 0141-812 5000 Fax: 0141-812 1919

Professional Solutions Ltd, 109 Friern Park, London, N12 9LH Tel: (020) 8492 0550

Regal Beauty Supplies, 22 Rigg Approach, London, E10 7QN Tel: (020) 8539 5112 Fax: (0870) 2000664 E-mail: sales@regalbeauty.co.uk

Renbow International Ltd, 60 Church Road, Leyton, London, E10 5JP Tel: (0870) 3665410 Fax: (0870) 3665411 E-mail: sales@renbow.co.uk

Revlon International Corporation, Highgate Studio, Highgate Road, London, NW5 1TL Tel: (020) 7284 8700 Fax: (020) 7428 5625

Sabel Cosmetics, Mount Pellon Works, Pellon Lane, Halifax, West Yorkshire, HX1 4TZ Tel: (01422) 366400 Fax: (01422) 366669 E-mail: sabel@sabel-cosmetics.co.uk

Sovereign Cosmetics Ltd, Unit 3 Gainsborough Close, Long Eaton, Nottingham, NG10 1PX Tel: 0115-973 0195 Fax: 0115-946 1935 E-mail: sales@dutyfreeperfume.co.uk

Surefil Beauty Products, The Bedford Centre, Bedford Street, Parr Industrial Estate, St. Helens, Merseyside, WA9 1PN Tel: (01744) 758820 Fax: (01744) 451859 E-mail: surefil@aol.com

Thomas Blake & Co., The Byre House, Fearby, Ripon, North Yorkshire, HG4 4NF Tel: (01765) 689042 Fax: (01765) 689042

Ultimate Hair Co., 104 Eastgate Centre, Basildon, Essex, SS14 1AG Tel: (01268) 282008

Whitman Laboratories Ltd, Bedford Road, Petersfield, Hampshire, GU32 3DD Tel: (01730) 266522 Fax: (01730) 261500

COST MANAGEMENT CONSULTANTS, ENGINEERING

▶ ASK Innovation Limited, Suite 104b, Discovery Court, 551-553 Wallisdown Road, Poole, Dorset, BH12 5AG Tel: (01202) 853221 Fax: 01202 853214 E-mail: enquiries@askinnovation.co.uk

Project Management & Procurement Services, Old Billingham Business Centre, 1 Chapel Road, Billingham, Cleveland, TS23 1EN Tel: (01642) 353400 Fax: (01642) 353401 E-mail: ericbphelps@pmps.co.uk

Nigel Rose & Partners, 6 Langley Street, London, WC2H 9JT Tel: (020) 7836 9527 Fax: (020) 7379 0892 E-mail: london@nigelrose.com

COST REDUCTION CONSULTANCY

Cost Index Ltd, 48 Meadow Rise, Barton under Needwood, Burton-on-Trent, Staffordshire, DE13 8DT Tel: 01283 716426 Fax: 01283 716426 E-mail: chris@costindex.co.uk

▶ Peninsula Business Services Ltd, Delphian House, New Bailey Street, Salford, M3 5PB Tel: 0161-834 2773 Fax: 0161-833 9517 E-mail: enquiries@peninsula-uk.com

▶ Select Sourcing, The Technocentre, Coventry Technology Park, Puma Way, Coventry, CV1 2TT Tel: (024) 7623 6818 Fax: (024) 7623 6024 E-mail: info@selectsourcing.com

▶ Silver Bullet Associates Ltd, 43 Temple Row, Birmingham, B2 5LS Tel: 0121 237 6073 E-mail: mark.bartrick@silverbulletassociates.com

Supply Chain & Logistics Consulting Ltd, The Chimes, 1 Park Road, Congleton, Cheshire, CW12 1DS Tel: (01260) 276469 E-mail: info@supplychainlogistics-consulting.co.uk

COSTING SOFTWARE

Armstrong Laing plc, 25 King Street, Knutsford, Cheshire, WA16 6DW Tel: (01565) 687000 Fax: (01565) 750030

Business Micros, Main Street, Penpont, Thornhill, Dumfriesshire, DG3 4BP Tel: (01848) 330588 Fax: (01848) 331531 E-mail: info@businessmicros.co.uk

Cincom Systems UK Ltd, 1 Grenfell Road, Maidenhead, Berkshire, SL6 1HN Tel: (01628) 542300 Fax: (01628) 542310

Gerber Technology Ltd, 302 Metroplex Business Park, Broadway, Salford, M50 2UE Tel: 0161-772 2000 Fax: 0161-772 2020

Interchain UK Ltd, 44 Shenley Pavilions, Chalkdell Drive, Shenley Wood, Milton Keynes, MK5 6LB Tel: (01908) 521000 Fax: (01908) 522000 E-mail: pbz@interchain.co.uk

Midsoft Computer Systems, Aston Lane, Aston, Stone, Staffordshire, ST15 0BW Tel: (01785) 818054 Fax: (01785) 817513 E-mail: sales@midsoft.co.uk

Tribal Asset Management Ltd, Unit E Gillette Close, Staffordshire Technology Park, Stafford, ST18 0LQ Tel: (0870) 0601040 Fax: (0870) 0607040 E-mail: info@tribalassetmanagement.co.uk

Windowlink Ltd, Station Road, Minety, Malmesbury, Wilts, SN16 9QY Tel: (0870) 7701640 Fax: (01666) 860889

COTS

Kiddy Care, 25 Hockley, Nottingham, NG1 1FH Tel: 0115-950 5169 Fax: 0115-950 6107 E-mail: sales@kiddycare.co.uk

▶ Rock'A'Bye Baby, Cotsford Lane, Peterlee, County Durham, SR8 4JJ Tel: 0191-569 1771

COTTAS

▶ Adoremus Contemporary Church Textiles, 14 Beamont Drive, Preston, PR1 8UN Tel: 01772 889111 E-mail: information@adoremus.co.uk

J & M Sewing Services, 1 Charlotte Square, Newcastle upon Tyne, NE1 4XF Tel: 0191-232 9589 Fax: 0191-230 1215 E-mail: jandmsewing@btconnect.com

COTTON BAGS/SACKS

Red Rose Products Ltd, Albion Works, Silver Street, Oldham, OL1 1HX Tel: 0161-624 5261 Fax: 0161-627 0946

S G Baker Ltd, Union St, Friockheim, Arbroath, Angus, DD11 4TD Tel: (01241) 828681 Fax: (01241) 828349 E-mail: sales@sgbaker.co.uk

COTTON BALERS

Planters Clayton Ltd, Unit 6, Rivington House, Horwich Business Park, Chorley New Road, Horwich, Bolton, BL6 5UE Tel: (01204) 690003 Fax: (01204) 690170 E-mail: office@plantersclayton.com

COTTON CANVAS

2canvas Limited, 155 Stockwell Street, Glasgow, G1 4LR Tel: 0141-552 0005 E-mail: design@2canvas.co.uk

COTTON FABRIC CONVERTERS

Wolfin Textiles Ltd, 359 Uxbridge Road, Hatch End, Pinner, Middlesex, HA5 4JN Tel: (020) 8428 9911 Fax: (020) 8428 9955 E-mail: cotton@wolfintextiles.co.uk

COTTON FABRIC FINISHERS TO THE TRADE

Harvey Quilting, 11 Robin Hood Industrial Estate, Alfred St South, Nottingham, NG3 1GE Tel: 0115-958 5777 Fax: 0115-950 3339 E-mail: tonyatharveys@hotmail.com

P W Greenhalgh & Co. Ltd, Newhey Bleach & Dye Works, Milnrow, Rochdale, Lancashire, OL16 3TH Tel: (01706) 847911 Fax: (01706) 881217 E-mail: sgreenhalgh@pwgreenhalgh.com

COTTON FABRICS

Bill Beaumont Textiles Ltd, Park Mills, Deighton Road, Chorley, Lancashire, PR7 2HP Tel: (01257) 263065 Fax: (01257) 241348 E-mail: sales@billbeaumont.co.uk

J.H. Birtwistle Ltd, Grane Road Mill, Grane Road, Haslingden, Rossendale, Lancashire, BB4 5ES Tel: (01706) 215351 Fax: (01706) 831054 E-mail: birtwhistle@johnlewis.co.uk

Brisbane Moss Corduroys Corduroy Manufacturers, Halifax Road, Bridgeroyd Works, Todmorden, Lancashire, OL14 6DF Tel: (01706) 815121 Fax: (01706) 818598 E-mail: brimoss@brisbanemoss.co.uk

Fabric Place, 12 High Road, Chilwell, Beeston, Nottingham, NG9 4AE Tel: 0115-943 6636 Fax: 0115-943 1336 E-mail: info@fabricsinternational.com

J.F. Hodgett & Co. Ltd, 66 Bedford Street South, Leicester, LE1 3JR Tel: 0116-251 0705 Fax: 0116-251 2877 E-mail: jfhodgett@hotmail.com

James Thornber Ltd, Holmes Mill, Greenacre Street, Clitheroe, Lancashire, BB7 1EB Tel: (01200) 423601 Fax: (01200) 429332 E-mail: sales@jamesthornber.com

John Spencer Textiles Ltd, Ashfield Mill, Active Way, Burnley, Lancashire, BB11 1BS Tel: (01282) 423111 Fax: (01282) 416283 E-mail: sales@johnspencer.com

L Littlewood & Son Exports Ltd, 3 Edwin Road, Beswick, Manchester, M11 3ER Tel: 0161-273 1344 Fax: 0161-273 3013 E-mail: l-littlewood@btconnect.com

M & N Textiles Ltd, Wrengate House, 221 Palatine Road, Didsbury, Manchester, M20 2EE Tel: 0161-438 1050 Fax: 0161-438 1021 E-mail: mandn@wrengate.co.uk

Maytex Fabrics Ltd, Curzon Works, Curzon Street, Leicester, LE1 2HH Tel: 0116-262 4422 Fax: 0116-262 4447 E-mail: maytexfab@aol.com

Norfolk Textured Yarns Cromer Ltd, Holt Road, Cromer, Norfolk, NR27 9JW Tel: (01263) 513188 Fax: (01263) 515347

Peter Greig & Co., Victoria Linen Works, 147-151 St Clair Street, Kirkcaldy, Fife, KY1 2BU Tel: (01592) 651901 Fax: (01592) 655596 E-mail: rosie@petergreig.co.uk

Platt Haworth & Co. Ltd, Fourways House, 18 Tariff Street, Manchester, M1 2FN Tel: 0161-236 0764 Fax: 0161-236 7543 E-mail: sales@platthaworth.com

Premier Textiles Ltd, Green Lane Industrial Estate, Green Lane, Stockport, Cheshire, SK4 2JR Tel: 0161-429 5770 Fax: 0161-429 5777 E-mail: sales@premier-textiles.com

R K Ross & Co. Ltd, Unit 1 George Leigh Street, Manchester, M4 6BD Tel: 0161-205 1822 Fax: 0161-203 4609

Peter Reed Textiles Ltd, 2 Gisburn Road, Bolton By Bowland, Clitheroe, Lancashire, BB7 4NP Tel: (01282) 692416 Fax: (01200) 447708 E-mail: mreed@peterreedtextiles.com

Sam Weller & Sons Ltd, Pickwick Mill, Thongsbridge, Holmfirth, HD9 3JL Tel: (01484) 683201 Fax: (01484) 689700 E-mail: info@samwellerltd.co.uk

COTTON GOODS, MADE-UP, *See also Textile Goods, Made-Up*

L Whitaker & Sons 1983 Ltd, Unit 4-5 Rochdale Industrial Centre, Albion Road, Rochdale, Lancashire, OL11 4HN Tel: (01706) 655611 Fax: (01706) 655611 E-mail: sales@lwhitaker.co.uk

S A N Ltd, 42 Bloom Street, Manchester, M1 3HR Tel: 0161-236 2246 Fax: 0161-236 5528 E-mail: sasltd@lineone.net

Sizma Ltd, Unit 2 Upper Wingbury Courtyard, Wingrave, Aylesbury, Buckinghamshire, HP22 4LW Tel: (01296) 688303 Fax: (01296) 682119 E-mail: sales@sizma.co.uk

COTTON GREY FABRICS

▶ Temptation Alley, 361 Portobello Road, London, W10 5SA Tel: (020) 8969 1295 Fax: (020) 7727 4432 E-mail: info@temptationalley.com

COTTON INSPECTION SERVICES

Wakefield Inspection Services Ltd, 14-20 Pall Mall, Liverpool, L3 6AL Tel: 0151-236 0752 Fax: 0151-236 0144 E-mail: wif@wakefieldinspection.com

COTTON SEWING THREADS

American & Efird GB Ltd, Chapelfield, Radcliffe, Manchester, M26 1JF Tel: 0161-766 1333 Fax: 0161-766 9965 E-mail: sales@amefird.co.uk

B S K Ltd, Murdock Rd, Bedford, MK41 7PD Tel: (01234) 217096 Fax: (01234) 271537 E-mail: info@bsk.co.uk

Cotton Mill Ltd, 2 Gourley Street, London, N15 5NG Tel: (020) 8802 2305 Fax: (020) 8802 2307

COTTON SPINNERS AND DOUBLERS, *See Cotton Yarn etc*

COTTON WASTE MERCHANTS/ PROCESSORS OR SERVICES

Walter Smith Nelson Ltd, Wenning Street, Nelson, Lancashire, BB9 0LE Tel: (01282) 698142 Fax: (01282) 619109 E-mail: wsmith@provider.co.uk

COTTON WASTE PROCESSING MACHINERY

Allertex Ltd, Paradise Street, Bradford, West Yorkshire, BD1 2HP Tel: (01274) 723783 Fax: (01274) 728267 E-mail: info@allertex.co.uk

COTTON WOOL

Cowens Ltd, Ellers Mill, Dalston, Carlisle, CA5 7QJ Tel: (01228) 710205 Fax: (01228) 710331 E-mail: info@cowens.co.uk
▶ Mariposa Alternative Bodycare, 15A Shelldale Road, Portslade, BN41 1LE Tel: (01273) 242925 Fax: (01273) 242925 E-mail: enquiries@mariposa-alternative-bodycare.co.uk
Sabre Supply Co., 35-37 Brent Street, London, NW4 2EF Tel: (020) 8457 1510 Fax: (020) 8201 7368 E-mail: sabre@sabresupply.co.uk

COTTON YARN

B S K Ltd, Murdock Rd, Bedford, MK41 7PD Tel: (01234) 217096 Fax: (01234) 271537 E-mail: info@bsk.co.uk
E Mesrie & Sons Ltd, 3 Brazil Street, Manchester, M1 3PJ Tel: 0161-236 6274 Fax: 0161-236 8086 E-mail: yarns@mdmresourcing.com
Fabrics & Yarns Macclesfield Ltd, Hulley Road, Macclesfield, Cheshire, SK10 2LP Tel: (01625) 427311 Fax: (01625) 424769
Highams Group Ltd, Grape Mill, New Coin Street, Royton, Oldham, OL2 5JB Tel: 0161-633 2241 Fax: 0161-627 3275 E-mail: mailbox@highamsgroup.co.uk
K.Azmeh (Textiles) Ltd, Richmond House, Richmond Grove, Manchester, M13 0LN Tel: 0161-274 4827 Fax: 0161-274 4815 E-mail: info@katuk.com
k1 Yarns Knitting Boutique, 6 Queen Margaret Drive, Glasgow, G20 8NY Tel: 0141 576 0113 E-mail: info@k1yarns.com
▶ Paint Box Textiles, 16 Valley Road, Liversedge, West Yorkshire, WF15 6JY Tel: (01924) 235123 Fax: (01924) 235223 E-mail: sales@paintboxtextiles.co.uk
Rex H Perkins Ltd, Hucknall Aerodrome, Watnall Rd, Hucknall, Nottingham, NG15 6EQ Tel: 0115-963 5712 Fax: 0115-963 0129 E-mail: sales@rhperkins.co.uk
Malcolm Ross & Sons Ltd, PO Box 4, Alderley Edge, Cheshire, SK9 7PR Tel: (01625) 583853 Fax: (01625) 586340 E-mail: sales@malcolmross.co.uk
Thornton Kelley & Co. Ltd, Spring Place Mills, Northorpe, Mirfield, West Yorkshire, WF14 0QT Tel: (01924) 493128 Fax: (01924) 495119 E-mail: david@thorntonkelley.co.uk

COUCHES, PHYSIOTHERAPY/ MANIPULATION/CHIROPODY ETC

Beaver Healthcare Equipment, Beaver House, 1 Vale Rise, Tonbridge, Kent, TN9 1TB Tel: (01732) 367777
C M E, 6 Ascot Park Estate, Lenton Street, Sandiacre, Nottingham, NG10 5DL Tel: 0115-949 9066 Fax: 0115-939 3102 E-mail: gcb@cme.globalnet.co.uk
Maheono Alternative Therapies, 99 Reading Road, Yateley, Hampshire, GU46 7LR Tel: (01252) 861351 Fax: E-mail: info@maheono.com
Marshcouch, 14 Robinsfield, Hemel Hempstead, Hertfordshire, HP1 1RW Tel: (01442) 862210 Fax: (01442) 866786 E-mail: nigel@marshcouch.com
Nomeq Ltd, Unit 25-26 North St Industrial Estate, Droitwich, Worcestershire, WR9 8JB Tel: (01905) 795005 Fax: (01905) 796655 E-mail: info@nomeq.co.uk
Rothband & Co. Ltd, 4-6 Knowsley Road, Haslingden, Rossendale, Lancashire, BB4 4RX Tel: (01706) 830086 Fax: (01706) 830324 E-mail: sales@rothband.co.uk

COUNTER JOINERY

A G Duck & Sons Ltd, Charlton Mead Lane, Hoddesdon, Hertfordshire, EN11 0DJ Tel: (01992) 462188 Fax: (01992) 450991
Acorn Joinery, Floodgates Farm, Castle Lane, West Grinstead, Horsham, West Sussex, RH13 8LH Tel: (01403) 711330 Fax: (01403) 711330 E-mail: acornjoinery@resource24.net
B W Dove & Son, The Old Dairy, Darrow Green Road, Denton, Harleston, Norfolk, IP20 0BA Tel: (01986) 788377
Brent Taunton Joinery, 3 Coopers Industrial Estate, Littlehampton Road, Ferring, Worthing, West Sussex, BN12 6PW Tel: (01903) 248169 Fax: (01903) 248169
Brian Fawcett Joinery, Ellifoot Lane, Burstwick, Hull, HU12 9EF Tel: (01964) 670818 Fax: (01964) 671138 E-mail: enquiries@brianfawcett-joinery.com
Chelford Joinery Co. Ltd, Boundary Cottage, Chelford Road, Ollerton, Knutsford, Cheshire, WA16 8TA Tel: (01565) 751012 Fax: (01565) 652087
County Joinery, The Workshop, 13 Felpham Road, Bognor Regis, West Sussex, PO22 7AS Tel: (01243) 842714 E-mail: info@countyjoinery.co.uk
Critchley & Curtis, 7 Clegg Street, Liverpool, L5 3SP Tel: 0151-207 2437 Fax: 0151-207 2437
D Davies & Sons, Cornerswell Road, Penarth, South Glamorgan, CF64 2UZ Tel: (029) 2070 8524 Fax: (029) 2051 3189
D & P Joinery Manufacturers, 32a George Road, Carlton, Nottingham, NG4 3AE Tel: 0115-987 0128 Fax: 0115-956 0095 E-mail: dpjoinery@ntlworld.com
Dale Joinery Lichfield Ltd, Europa Way, Britannia Enterprise Park, Lichfield, Staffordshire, WS14 9TY Tel: (01543) 414223 Fax: (01543) 255538
Datone Joiners, Cemetery Road, Pudsey, West Yorkshire, LS28 7LW Tel: 0113-255 5532 Fax: 0113-255 5532
Derek De'Ath Ltd, New Line, Bacup, Lancashire, OL13 9RY Tel: (01706) 879456 Fax: (01706) 878080 E-mail: office@derekd.co.uk
Design Woodworking, 7 Vernon Place, Northern Court, Nottingham, NG6 0DE Tel: 0115-977 0302
Dove Tail Joinery, 7 Field Barn Lane Industrial Estate, Field Barn Lane, Cropthorne, Pershore, Worcestershire, WR10 3LY Tel: (01386) 861123 Fax: (01386) 860975
East Joinery, Unit 2 Willow Lane, Rugby, Warwickshire, CV22 5LX Tel: (01788) 568427 Fax: (01788) 574252 E-mail: r.ingram@ntlworld.com
England Joinery, Holehouse Lane, Glue Hill, Sturminster Newton, Dorset, DT10 2AA Tel: (01258) 472846 Fax: (01258) 472846 E-mail: info@englandjoinery.co.uk
Essex Woodcraft, Commerce Way, Colchester, CO2 8HJ Tel: (01206) 795464 Fax: (01206) 796596 E-mail: sales@essexwoodcraft.co.uk
Field Developments Hull Ltd, Staithes Road, Hull, HU12 8TJ Tel: (01482) 896240 Fax: (01482) 896510 E-mail: info@shopfituk.co.uk
Fineline Joinery, Littlemoor Road, Mark, Highbridge, Somerset, TA9 4NQ Tel: (01278) 641352 Fax: (01278) 641352
Flacke Turner & James, Elm Street Lane, Cardiff, CF24 3QQ Tel: (029) 2049 2023 Fax: (029) 2049 2023
G Empson & Sons Ltd, Station Road, Gunness, Scunthorpe, South Humberside, DN15 8TR Tel: (01724) 782459 Fax: (01724) 783077
Hanson & Beards Ltd, Garden Field, Wyke, Bradford, West Yorkshire, BD12 9NH Tel: (01274) 601010 Fax: (01274) 601666 E-mail: sales@hansonandbeards.co.uk
Humber Joiners Ltd, Stepney Lane, Hull, HU5 1HX Tel: (01482) 341954 Fax: (01482) 449516
KSM Property Maintenance South East Ltd, PO Box 8002, Harlow, Essex, CM20 3XA Tel: (01279) 439777 Fax: (01279) 439750 E-mail: sales@ksm-maintenance.co.uk
Linden Bauer Ltd, Mid Kent Business Park, Sortmill Road, Snodland, Kent, ME6 5UA Tel: (01634) 243137 Fax: (01634) 249306 E-mail: christian@lindenbauer.freeserve.co.uk
Harry Spurr Ltd, Harvest Lane, Sheffield, S3 8EF Tel: 0114-272 4581 Fax: 0114-276 6246 E-mail: info@spurrs.co.uk
Wratten Joinery, Aylesford Cottage, Guildford Road, Normandy, Guildford, Surrey, GU3 2AS Tel: (01483) 235324 Fax: (01483) 232131

COUNTER SURVEILLANCE EQUIPMENT

Lorraine Electronics Surveillance, 716 Lea Bridge Road, London, E10 6AW Tel: (020) 8558 4226 Fax: (020) 8558 1338 E-mail: info@lorraine.co.uk
▶ Pda Electronics Ltd, 7 Bevan Hill, Chesham, Buckinghamshire, HP5 2QS Tel: (01494) 794949 Fax: (01494) 791820 E-mail: info@pdaelectronics.com
Research Associates, 282 Latimer Road, London, W10 6QW Tel: (020) 7854 9000 Fax: (020) 7854 9090 E-mail: paulhawkes@investigationservices.co.uk

COUNTER/COUNTING DEVICES

Kirby Devon Ltd, Elm Tree House, Yealmbury Hill, Yealmpton, Plymouth, PL8 2JH Tel: (01752) 881717 Fax: (01752) 881710 E-mail: sales@kirbydevon.freeserve.co.uk
▶ Lab Tek Instruments, Star House, The Drive, Hellingly, Hailsham, East Sussex, BN27 4EP Tel: (01323) 840584 Fax: (01323) 840583 E-mail: tom.howe@footfallcounters.com
LS Controls, 270 Abbey Road, Leeds, LS5 3ND Tel: (01943) 872025 Fax: 0113-259 0243 E-mail: ls.lee@amserve.com
Nortonics Ltd, Watts Street, Chadderton, Oldham, OL9 9LQ Tel: 0161-626 5316 Fax: 0161-627 0929
Paper Life Ltd, Unit 13 Ahed House, Sandbeds Trading Estate, Ossett, West Yorkshire, WF5 9ND Tel: (01924) 281666 Fax: (01924) 281444 E-mail: sales@paperlife.co.uk
Vacuumatic, Brunel Way 8, Severalls Industrial Park, Colchester, CO4 9QX Tel: (01206) 841100 Fax: (01206) 841166 E-mail: sales@vacuumatic.com

COUNTERBORES

Bradford Tool Group, Beta Works, 1 Tong Street, Bradford, West Yorkshire, BD4 9PW Tel: (01274) 683902 Fax: (01274) 651168 E-mail: sales@bradtool.co.uk
Robert Charles Engineering Ltd, Ashley CR, Southampton, SO19 9NA Tel: (023) 8044 0144 Fax: (023) 8068 5825 E-mail: uksales@robertcharlestools.com

COUNTERFEIT BANKNOTE DETECTION DEVICES

Innovative Technology Ltd, Derker, Oldham, OL1 4EQ Tel: 0161-620 1990 Fax: 0161 6202090 E-mail: sales@innovative-technology.co.uk

COUNTERSINKS, *See also headings for particular types*

Robert Charles Engineering Ltd, Ashley CR, Southampton, SO19 9NA Tel: (023) 8044 0144 Fax: (023) 8068 5825 E-mail: uksales@robertcharlestools.com

COUNTRY PURSUIT BOOTS

▶ Bushwear, Unit 5 Crest Business Centre, 2 Glen Tye Road, Stirling, FK7 7LH Tel: (0845) 2260469 Fax: (0845) 2269329 E-mail: sales@bushwear.co.uk

COUNTRY PURSUITS CLOTHING

Brian Holden Ltd, 14 Racca Green, Knottingley, West Yorkshire, WF11 8AT Tel: (01977) 672791 Fax: (01977) 672791
Stephen J Fawcett, 7 Great John Street, Lancaster, LA1 1NQ Tel: (01524) 32033 Fax: (01524) 843470 E-mail: sales@fawcettonline.com

COUPLINGS, *See also headings for particular types*

▶ A J Transmissions, 4 Stanhope Close, Wilmslow, Cheshire, SK9 2NN Tel: (01625) 533466 Fax: (01625) 533466 E-mail: tomatajt@aol.co.uk
ERIKS UK, 8 Brunel Gate, Brunel Industrial Estate, Harworth, Doncaster, South Yorkshire, DN11 8QB Tel: (01302) 752161 Fax: (01302) 752163 E-mail: couplings.drives@eriks.co.uk
Forster & Hales Ltd, 24 Wadsworth Road, Greenford, Middlesex, UB6 7JD Tel: (020) 8998 9057 Fax: (020) 8998 2922 E-mail: sales@forsterandhales.com
Francis and Francis Ltd (Schmidt, Poggi & KBK), The Stables Works, Station Road, Kenley, Surrey, CR8 5JA Tel: (020) 8668 9792 Fax: (020) 8668 9793 E-mail: sales@powertransmissions.co.uk
FSC (Halifax) Ltd, Grantham House, Grantham Road, Halifax, West Yorkshire, HX3 6PL Tel: (01422) 347872 Fax: (01422) 321758 E-mail: kw@fscooper.com
Gamma Hose Ltd, Gamma Works, New Street, Earl Shilton, Leicester, LE9 7FS Tel: (01455) 847081 Fax: (01455) 842940 E-mail: sales@gammahose.com
Longford Bearings Engineering Sales Ltd, Transmission House, 10a Lady Lane, Longford, Coventry, CV6 6AZ Tel: (024) 7636 0666 Fax: (024) 7636 0759
▶ Millennium Coupling Co. Ltd, 72b Roman Way Industrial Estate, Ribbleton, Preston, PR2 5BE Tel: (01772) 653530 Fax: (01772) 653531 E-mail: sales@mcc-ltd.com
Peak Transmissions Ltd, Unit 8 Hardwick Court, Hardwick View Road, Holmewood, Chesterfield, Derbyshire, S42 5SA Tel: (01246) 856758 Fax: (01246) 856850 E-mail: sales@peakgroupltd.com
▶ Pipeclear Ltd, Cliff Mount, Whins Lane, Simonstone, Burnley, Lancashire, BB12 7QU Tel: (01282) 776454 Fax: (01282) 779829 E-mail: stephenatpipeclear@btinternet.com
Taylor Kerr Couplings Ltd, Disraeli House, 12 Aylesbury End, Beaconsfield, Buckinghamshire, HP9 1LW Tel: (01494) 679500 Fax: (01494) 679505 E-mail: info@teekaycouplings.com

COUPLINGS, DISC PACK/ TORSIONALLY RIGID

Bibby Tranmissions Ltd, Cannon Way, Dewsbury, West Yorkshire, WF13 1EH Tel: (01924) 460801 Fax: (01924) 457668 E-mail: sales@bibbytransmissions.co.uk
NDE Power Transmissions Group, NDE Bldgs, Aldbourne Road, Coventry, CV1 4EQ Tel: (024) 7622 2272 Fax: (024) 7625 8499 E-mail: sales@ndeclarketransmissions.co.uk
▶ Piv Drive, Posiva Works 8 Skipping Dale Industrial Estate, Exmoor Avenue, Scunthorpe, South Humberside, DN15 8NJ Tel: (01724) 281868 Fax: (01724) 282808

COUPLINGS, VICTAULIC

Pipe Fabrication Equipment Services, Unit 4, Townley Business Park, Hanson Street, Middleton, Manchester, M24 2UF Tel: 0161-653 7459 Fax: 0161-654 7286

COURIER SERVICES

▶ 2nd 2 None Ltd, 235 Beehive Lane, Chelmsford, CM2 9SH Tel: (07815) 290214 Fax: (01245) 602046 E-mail: info@2nd2noneltd.com
▶ 3d Courier Services, 71 Furnace Lane, Sheffield, S13 9XD Tel: (07817) 708363 E-mail: info@3dcourier.com
3-Towns Courier Services, 1 New England Road, Saltcoats, Ayrshire, KA21 6JT Tel: (07890) 981 974 Fax: (01294) 471 294 E-mail: sean.docherty@3-townscourierservices.co.uk
A. B. A. Courier Services, Suite F, 2nd Floor, 10-14 West Street, Southend-on-Sea, SS2 6HJ Tel: (01702) 435855 Fax: (01702) 347837 E-mail: sales@abacouriers.co.uk
A Clarke & Co Smethwick Ltd, Union Road, Oldbury, West Midlands, B69 3ER Tel: 0121-552 2854 Fax: 0121-552 6385 E-mail: barry@clarketransport.co.uk
▶ A Spriggs Courier Services, 46 Garth Avenue, Normanton, West Yorkshire, WF6 1DJ Tel: (01924) 782005 E-mail: andy@aspriggs.com
Aardvark Couriers, 206 Thornbridge Avenue, Birmingham, B42 2AH Tel: 0121-360 5253
Access, Silkmoor, New Street, Shrewsbury, SY3 8LN Tel: (01743) 360607 Fax: (01743) 340706 E-mail: admin@access-taxis.co.uk
▶ Ace Courier Services, 13 Ullswater Road, Tyldesley, Manchester, M29 7AQ Tel: (01942) 873990 Fax: (01942) 709137 E-mail: al63@blueyonder.co.uk
Ace Garage Services, 34 Railway Approach, Worthing, West Sussex, BN11 1UR Tel: (01903) 233823 E-mail: cars@acecarhire.com
▶ Ads, Unit 6 7 Phoenix Industrial Estate, Loxdale Street, Bilston, West Midlands, WV14 0PR Tel: (01902) 409453 Fax: (01902) 409215 E-mail: www.geraldine@advanceddeliveryservices.co.uk
▶ Anc North Yorkshire Ltd, York Road, Flaxby, Knaresborough, North Yorkshire, HG5 0RP Tel: (01423) 869696 Fax: (01423) 862922
▶ Ans Logistics Ltd, 385 Brentwood Road, Gidea Park, Romford, RM2 5TH Tel: (01708) 500883 E-mail: info@anslogistics.co.uk
Apollo Distribution Solution, A5 Seedbed Centre, Avenue Road, Nechells, Birmingham, B7 4NT Tel: 0121-359 7707 Fax: 0121-359 7717
Arrow Express Couriers, 387 Railway Arches, Geffrye Street, London, E2 8HZ Tel: (020) 7294 2000 Fax: (020) 7294 2094 E-mail: sales@arrow-express.co.uk
Association Of International &Currier Express Services, Global House, Poyle Road, Colnbrook, Slough, SL3 0AY Tel: (01753) 680550 Fax: (01753) 681710 E-mail: sales@aices.org
Astral Max Couriers, 90a High Street, Rickmansworth, Hertfordshire, WD3 1AQ Tel: (01923) 711444 Fax: (01923) 711714 E-mail: sales@maxinternational.co.uk
Axa Couriers Ltd, Axa House, Blandford Road, Southall, Middlesex, UB2 4JY Tel: (020) 8571 4747 Fax: (020) 8574 5697
B X Tech Ltd, 19 Wainright Street, Aston, Birmingham, B6 5TH Tel: 0121-327 6411 Fax: 0121-327 6681
▶ Barry Ward, 10 Vowell Close, Bristol, BS13 9HS Tel: (07831) 447764 Fax: 0117-904 4859 E-mail: barry@barrywardcourierservices.co.uk
▶ Black Cat Cars Ltd, 312 Channelsea Business Centre, Canning Road, London, E15 3ND Tel: (020) 8555 4545 Fax: (020) 8519 2333 E-mail: office@BlackCatCouriers.co.uk
Blackheath Car Service Ltd, 2a Blackheath Village, London, SE3 9LA Tel: (020) 8318 5432 Fax: (020) 8297 0734 E-mail: sales@blackheath-car-services.co.uk
Bromley Sameday Couriers, 16 Amesbury Road, Bromley, BR1 2QJ Tel: 07783 238436 E-mail: jamesmaycock@bromleysamedaycouriers.co.uk
▶ The Bullit Courier Company Ltd, 12 Charlotte Street, Brighton, BN2 1AG Tel: (0845) 2268556 E-mail: info@bullitcouriers.com

▶ indicates data change since last edition

COURIER SERVICES – *continued*

▶ Business Post Ltd, Unit B-C Ronald Close, Woburn Road Industrial Estate, Kempston, Bedford, MK42 7SH Tel: (01234) 840088 Fax: (01234) 853918

▶ Business Post Ltd, 11 Crystal Way, Harrow, Middlesex, HA1 2BJ Tel: (020) 8861 1599 Fax: (020) 8424 0708

C C C Express Couriers Ltd, Office 1, The Roundhouse, Dormans Park Road, East Grinstead, West Sussex, RH19 2EN Tel: (01342) 322550 Fax: (01342) 316200 E-mail: courtesycarraige@btconnect.com

CCF Couriers, 5a Wild Ridings Square, Bracknell, Berkshire, RG12 7SJ Tel: (01344) 452113 Fax: (01344) 489509 E-mail: ccfcouriers@btconnect.com

▶ CDL Couriers, 32 Raymond Drive, Bradford, West Yorkshire, BD5 8HS Tel: (01274) 206329 E-mail: cdlcouriers@yahoo.co.uk

▶ CHILLFREEZE DIRECT LTD, UNIT 6C BASSET COURT, LOAKE CLOSE, GRANGE PARK, NORTHAMPTON, NN4 5EZ Tel: 0870 2407998 Fax: 0870 7202733 E-mail: enquires@chillfreezedirect.co.uk

City Air Express Ni Ltd, West Bank Drive, Belfast, BT3 9LA Tel: (028) 9078 1878 Fax: (028) 9078 1788 E-mail: sales@cityairexpress.com

▶ Confidential Couriers, The Willows, The Cadney, Bettisfield, Whitchurch, Shropshire, SY13 2LP Tel: (0800) 2983485 Fax: (01948) 710730 E-mail: confcouriers@aol.com

Connection Delivery Service Ltd, 6 Domingo Street, London, EC1Y 0TA Tel: (020) 7253 2211 Fax: (020) 7251 3381

Cooper Carriers Ltd, Tir Llwyd Industrial Estate, Kinmel Bay, Rhyl, Clwyd, LL18 5JA Tel: (01745) 362800 Fax: (01745) 362801

Courier Cars, 353 Norbury Avenue, London, SW16 3RW Tel: (020) 8764 4444 Fax: (020) 8679 5050

▶ Courier Please Ltd, Suite 44, 468 Walton Road, West Molesey, Surrey, KT8 8AE Tel: 07890 454428 Fax: 0208 3390859 E-mail: info@acourierplease.co.uk

▶ Crumlin Village Cabs Ltd, 28 Main Street, Crumlin, County Antrim, BT29 4UP Tel: (028) 9445 2829 E-mail: crumlinvillage@cabs.wannadoo.co.uk

▶ D L M Distribution, 54 Birch Avenue, Quarry Bank, Brierley Hill, West Midlands, DY5 1BG Tel: (01384) 820511 Fax: E-mail: davem65@hotmail.com

▶ D & R Couriers, Building 2, 47 Skelwith Road, Marton, Blackpool, FY3 9UL Tel: 01253 312713 Fax: 01253 312713 E-mail: richard@dandrcouriers.co.uk

▶ Dagmar Courier Services, 18 St. Rumbold Street, Lincoln, LN2 5AP Tel: (01522) 567588 Fax: (01522) 567588 E-mail: dagmarcouriers@fsmail.net

Dale Express Transport Ltd, Dale House, 232 Selsdon Road, Croydon, CR2 6PL Tel: (020) 8760 5000 Fax: (020) 8760 0202 E-mail: service@daleexpress.co.uk

▶ David Hathaway Ltd, Westerleigh Business Park, 30 Woodward Avenue, Yate, Bristol, BS37 5YS Tel: (01454) 334500 Fax: (01454) 334550 E-mail: contact@davidhathaway.co.uk

▶ Deca Freelance Couriers Ltd, 240 Burton Road, Lincoln, LN1 3UB Tel: (01522) 851612 Fax: (01522) 851613 E-mail: deca.couriers3@ntlworld.com

Delivered On Time, 4 Mercury Centre, Central Way, Feltham, Middlesex, TW14 0RN Tel: (020) 8890 5511 Fax: (020) 8890 5533 E-mail: sales@shand.co.uk

DHL Express (UK) Ltd, Orbital Pk, 178-188 Great South West Rd, Hounslow, TW4 6JS Tel: (08701) 100300

Diamond Logistics, 8 The Elms Centre, Glaziers Lane, Normandy, Guildford, Surrey, GU3 2DF Tel: (01483) 812020 Fax: (01483) 811500 E-mail: sales@thegcg.com

Direct Despatch International Ltd, D D I House, 1-21 Elkstone Road, London, W10 5NT Tel: (020) 7724 4000 Fax: (020) 8964 8244 E-mail: sales@ddi.co.uk

Direct Link South, 38 Millbrook Road East, Southampton, SO15 1HY Tel: (023) 8033 1541 E-mail: louis.roe@dirlinks.freeserve.co.uk

Double M Transport Ltd, The Courtyard, Warkworth, Banbury, Oxfordshire, OX17 2AG Tel: (01295) 712828 Fax: (01295) 711886 E-mail: stuartdoublem@aol.com

▶ Dove Despatch Ltd, 83 Essington Road, Willenhall, West Midlands, WV12 5DT Tel: (01922) 404857 Fax: (01922) 408803 E-mail: sales@dovedespatch.co.uk

▶ Dumfries Carriers, 12 Mosspark Road, Dumfries, DG1 4EE Tel: (01387) 266100 Fax: (01387) 266100 E-mail: samedaycourier@tiscali.co.uk

E M S Cargo Ltd, Unit 5, Ringway Trading Estate, Manchester, M22 5LH Tel: 0161-499 1344 Fax: 0161-499 0847 E-mail: man@ems-cargo.co.uk

Eagle Couriers Scotland, 1b Payne Street, Glasgow, G4 0LE Tel: 0141-332 1115 Fax: 0141-332 2567

▶ Ecourier.Co.Uk, Cityside House, 40 Adler Street, London, E1 1EE Fax: (020) 7877 6501 E-mail: mybigquestion@ecourier.co.uk

Euroexpress Delivery Services, 6e Arndale Road, Wick, Littlehampton, West Sussex, BN17 7HD Tel: (01903) 732733 Fax: (01903) 732734 E-mail: sales@euro-xpress.com

▶ Example Courier Services, 4 Hayfield Close, Baildon, Shipley, West Yorkshire, BD17 6TY Tel: (01274) 585321 Fax: (01274) 583609 E-mail: office@exsamplecourierservices.com

▶ Excel Couriers UK, 11 St. Johns Road, Peterborough, PE2 8BL Tel: (07786) 128197 Fax: (0870) 7625282 E-mail: pete@excel-couriers.co.uk

Exeter Express Dispatch, Unit 15 Exeter Business Centre, 39 Marsh Green Road, Marsh Barton Trading Estate, Exeter, EX2 8PN Tel: (01392) 213229 Fax: (01392) 423538

Express 2000 Ltd, Pembley Green, Copthorne Common, Copthorne, Crawley, West Sussex, RH10 3LF Tel: (01342) 713500 Fax: (01342) 713520 E-mail: sales@express2000.co.uk

▶ Express Courier Services, Unit 8d Northwood Business Park, Newport Road, Cowes, Isle of Wight, PO31 8PE Tel: (01983) 299944 Fax: (01983) 299944 E-mail: info@ecs-iow.co.uk

Falcon Couriers, 21a Brownlow Mews, London, WC1N 2LA Tel: (020) 7831 8734 Fax: (020) 7404 6045 E-mail: mach1ltd@aol.com

▶ Fastway Couriers, A1 Barton Industrial Estate, Faldo Road, Barton-le-Clay, Bedford, MK45 4RP Tel: (0845) 1088000 Fax: (01582) 881767 E-mail: sales@fastwaycouriers.com

Fastway Flyers Ltd, 78 Rivington Street, London, EC2A 3AY Tel: (020) 7729 3333 Fax: (020) 7729 3806 E-mail: fastwayflyers@1tel.net.uk

Fleet Street Flyers, 21a Brownlow Mews, London, WC1N 2LA Tel: (020) 7242 6666 Fax: (020) 7404 6045

Forest Freight Ltd, Fairview Indust Park, Barlow Way, Rainham, Essex, RM13 8BT Tel: (01708) 552222 Fax: (01708) 553330 E-mail: sales@forestfreight.co.uk

Furnell Transport, Enterprise House, Maxted Road, Hemel Hempstead, Hertfordshire, HP2 7BT Tel: (01442) 212744 Fax: (01442) 255244 E-mail: sales@furnell.com

▶ Gibson Taylor Tranzol Ltd, Bent Ley Farm, Bent Ley Road, Meltham, Holmfirth, HD9 4AP Tel: (01484) 859293 Fax: (01484) 859339 E-mail: zoltan.gibsontaylor@btconnect.com

▶ Glh Haulage, 220 Lynn Road, Broomhill, Downham Market, Norfolk, PE38 9QY Tel: 01366 383500 Fax: 01366 381267 E-mail: glhhaulage@hotmail.co.uk

The Go Betweens Couriers Ltd, Panther House, 38 Mount Pleasant, London, WC1X 0AN Tel: (020) 7278 1000 Fax: (020) 7278 1100

Goman Couriers Ltd, 58c Arthur Street, Redditch, Worcestershire, B98 8JY Tel: (01527) 515055 Fax: (01527) 510779

Grand Prix Express, Swan Road, Mochdre Business Park, Mochdre, Colwyn Bay, Clwyd, LL28 5HB Tel: (01492) 545293 Fax: (01492) 546241 E-mail: john@grandprixexpress.com

▶ Grease Lightning, 22 Windrush Road, Berinsfield, Wallingford, Oxfordshire, OX10 7PF Tel: (01865) 341166 Fax: (01865) 341176 E-mail: greaselightningcouriers@yahoo.co.uk

▶ The Great British Courier Co., 33 Harris Crescent, Needingworth, St. Ives, Cambridgeshire, PE27 4TE Tel: (01480) 465450 E-mail: gbcc@btinternet.com

Greater London Hire, GLH House, 12-18 High Road, London, N2 9PJ Tel: (020) 8883 5000 Fax: (020) 8444 2026

Guernsey Freight Services, Airport Complex, Forest, Guernsey, GY8 0DJ Tel: (01481) 238180 Fax: (01481) 235479

Handicars, 56 Lee High Road, London, SE13 5PT Tel: (020) 8852 1122 Fax: (020) 8244 2901 E-mail: handicars@freenet.uk.com

▶ Alan Harvey, 76 Curbar Road, Great Barr, Birmingham, B42 2AU Tel: (0786) 3555365 Fax: E-mail: aharvey76@hotmail.com

▶ Healthcare Logistics, Kilbuck Lane, Haydock, St. Helens, Merseyside, WA11 9UX Tel: (01942) 402690 Fax: (01942) 402697

Highwayman Couriers, 31 Firs St, Dudley, West Midlands, DY2 7DW Tel: (01384) 456976 Fax: (01384) 457146 E-mail: enquiries@hiwaymancouriers.co.uk

▶ IMEX Sameday Express Couriers, 54, Melton Road, Barrow on Soar, Loughborough, Leicestershire, LE12 8NX Tel: 01509 620178 Fax: 01509 620178 E-mail: ianmargetts@btinternet.com

Initial A To Z Couriers, 21a Brownlow Mews, London, WC1N 2LA Tel: (020) 7841 1741 Fax: (020) 7404 6045 E-mail: danbrown@initial-atoz.co.uk

▶ Initial City Link, Unit 15 Belton La Industrial Estate, Grantham, Lincolnshire, NG31 9HN Tel: (01476) 577428 Fax: (01476) 577173

Initial City Link Ltd, Wellington House, 61-73 Staines Road West, Sunbury-On-Thames, Middlesex, TW16 7AH Tel: (01932) 822622 Fax: (01932) 785560 E-mail: enquiries@city-link.co.uk

Interfreight Ltd, 8 The Felbridge Centre, The Birches Industrial Estate, Imberhorne Lane, East Grinstead, West Sussex, RH19 1XP Tel: (01342) 410454 Fax: (01342) 327237 E-mail: interfreight@lineone.net

Interlink Express Parcels Ltd, Earlesfield Lane, Grantham, Lincolnshire, NG31 7NT Tel: (01476) 570263 Fax: (01476) 570268 E-mail: depot634@interlinkexpress.com

▶ Interlink Express Parcels Ltd, Unit 2a Meadowbrook Park, Halfway, Sheffield, S20 3PJ Tel: 0114-251 1110 Fax: 0114-251 0888 E-mail: depot444@interlinkexpress.com

▶ J 4 Deliveries Ltd, Cromer House, Caxton Way, Stevenage, Hertfordshire, SG1 2DF Tel: (01438) 236022 Fax: (01438) 236023 E-mail: j4deliveries@aol.com

▶ J D Haulage, 1 Wayside Crescent, Eccleshill, Bradford, West Yorkshire, BD2 2JY Tel: (01274) 626999 Fax: (01274) 402381 E-mail: denise@jd-haulage.co.uk

▶ J G S Couriers, 13 Crown Meadow, Lower Broadheath, Worcester, WR2 6QJ Tel: (01905) 640518 Fax: (01905) 640518 E-mail: info@jgscouriers.co.uk

J W Services, 31 Woodview Avenue, Baildon, Shipley, West Yorkshire, BD17 7LG Tel: (01274) 530928 Fax: (01274) 530928 E-mail: jwservices999@hotmail.com

▶ JMC PARCELS T/A FASTWAY COURIERS, 37 SOUTHFIELD RD, CUMBERNAULD, G68 9DZ Tel: 01236 732016 E-mail: paul@paul474.wanadoo.co.uk

JMJ, 10 Abbey Court, Liverpool, L25 5HS Tel: 0151-428 7857 Fax: 0151-428 7857

▶ Kage Express Delivery, 24 Japonica Gardens, St. Helens, Merseyside, WA9 4WP Tel: (07841) 112210 E-mail: info@samedaynationwide.co.uk

▶ Kellylink Ltd, Unit 2, Arrow Road North, Lakeside, Redditch, Worcestershire, B98 8NT Tel: (01527) 62222 Fax: (01527) 62222 E-mail: info@kellylink.co.uk

Kent Link Transport & Storage, Unit 18 Henwood Business Centre, Henwood, Ashford, Kent, TN24 8DH Tel: (01233) 638889 Fax: (01233) 635869 E-mail: sales@kentlink.com

▶ Kimberley Couriers, 35 Cotswold Road, Stourbridge, West Midlands, DY8 4UW Tel: (0800) 7833681 Fax: (01384) 443396 E-mail: info@kimberleycouriers.com

▶ KP Couriers (Cambs) Ltd, Keepers Lodge, Gamlingay Road, Waresley, Sandy, Bedfordshire, SG19 3DD Tel: (01767) 651717 Fax: (01767) 652062 E-mail: kpcambs@hotmail.co.uk

Lewis Day Transport plc, 76 East Road, London, N1 6AB Tel: (020) 7014 1000 Fax: (020) 7014 1001

Lockson Services Ltd, Heath Park Industrial Estate, Freshwater Road, Dagenham, Essex, RM8 1RX Tel: (020) 8597 2889 Fax: (020) 8597 5265 E-mail: enquiries@lockson.co.uk

London & City Carriage Co., 18-20 Laystall Street, London, EC1R 4PG Tel: (020) 7880 4880 Fax: (020) 7250 0851

▶ Lucas Express Couriers, 11 Benbow Close, Hinckley, Leicestershire, LE10 1RQ Tel: (01455) 634705 E-mail: rich@lucasexpress.co.uk

Lynx Express Ltd, Coppetts Road, London, N10 1JR Tel: (020) 8365 2222 Fax: (020) 8883 7284

▶ M & A Couriers, 6 Stanley Close, Sherburn, Durham, DH6 1JS Tel: 0191-372 1210 Fax: 0191-372 1210 E-mail: info@maac.co.uk

M R Couriers, 45 Homefield, Shortwood, Nailsworth, Stroud, Gloucestershire, GL6 0SP Tel: (01453) 835868

Mailboxes Etc (UK) Ltd, 8 Camp Road, Farnborough, Hampshire, GU14 6EW Tel: (01252) 371711 Fax: (01252) 371811 E-mail: info@mbefarnborough.co.uk

Mailflight Ltd, Unit 2 Central Way, Feltham, Middlesex, TW14 0RX Tel: (020) 8893 1477 Fax: (020) 8893 1459 E-mail: ops@mfcourier.com

▶ MDBXPRESS, 9 Flax Gardens, Kings Norton, Birmingham, B38 9QY Tel: (07917) 784210 Fax: 0121-451 3272 E-mail: enquiries@mdbxpress.co.uk

Mercury Despatch Ltd, Unit 14 Central Business Centre, Great Central Way, London, NW10 0UR Tel: (020) 8459 8022 Fax: (020) 8451 6722 E-mail: sales@mercurydespatch.co.uk

▶ Mitchell Storage & Distribution Ltd, Unit 12 The Warren, East Goscote, Leicester, LE7 3XA Tel: 0116-260 4080 Fax: 0116-260 4081 E-mail: sales@ncexpress.com

▶ Monarkle Couriers, 154 Cannock Road, Wednesfield, Wolverhampton, WV10 8PX Tel: (01902) 563354 E-mail: courier@monarkle.com

▶ Mr D's Couriers Ltd, Gothic House, Barker Gate, Nottingham, NG1 1JU Tel: (0870) 7506396 Fax: (0870) 7506397 E-mail: mrdscouriers@hotmail.com

Multi Route Carriers, PO Box 287, Chertsey, Surrey, KT16 8LA Tel: (01932) 882882 Fax: (07005) 994213 E-mail: info@multiroutecargo.co.uk

The Music Corporation, 679 Christchurch Road, Bournemouth, BH7 6AE Tel: (01425) 470007 Fax: (01425) 480569 E-mail: sales@them.corporation.com

▶ N S T Direct Ltd, Premium House, Hambridge Road, Newbury, Berkshire, RG14 5SS Tel: (01635) 31177 Fax: (01635) 31184 E-mail: info@nstdirect.co.uk

Nationwide Express Parcels, Unit 4b Surrey Street, Glossop, Derbyshire, SK13 7AJ Tel: (01457) 860826 Fax: (01457) 855652

▶ Nightfreight GB Ltd, Josselin Road, Burnt Mills Industrial Estate, Basildon, Essex, SS13 1PU Tel: (01268) 728484

Olympic Express Ltd, Head Office, 90-91 Moseley Street, Birmingham, B12 0RT Tel: (08451) 255505 Fax: 0121-666 7541

▶ OneDay Couriers, Unit 629, Great Northern House, 275 Deansgate, Manchester, M3 4EL Tel: 0800 8818178

▶ The Online Courier, 17 Armada Drive, Teignmouth, Devon, TQ14 9NF Tel: (0845) 6447069 E-mail: info@theonlinecourier.co.uk

▶ P.D.Q.Logistics, 11 The Lizard, Wymondham, Norfolk, NR18 9BH Tel: (07944) 087289 E-mail: pdqlogistics@hotmail.co.uk

P D Q Storage, St Vincent Works, Silverthorne Lane, Bristol, BS2 0QD Tel: 0117-971 6009 Fax: 0117-908 9909

P F Couriers Ltd, Unit 2, Lowfield Heath Industrial Estate, Crawley, West Sussex, RH11 0PQ Tel: (01293) 515661 Fax: (01293) 547045 E-mail: reception@pfcouriers.co.uk

▶ P H D Couriers, 158 Coneygree Road, Stanground, Peterborough, PE2 8LQ Tel: (01733) 560270 E-mail: phday68@yahoo.co.uk

P Harcombe Couriers, Bretby Business Park, Ashby Road, Bretby, Burton-on-Trent, Staffordshire, DE15 0YZ Tel: (01283) 219903 Fax: (01283) 219903 E-mail: paulhark@madasafish.com

▶ Parcel Net, Unit 23 Mitcham Industrial Estate, Streatham Road, Mitcham, Surrey, CR4 2AP Tel: (020) 8646 6646 Fax: (020) 8648 5227

Parceline Ltd, Roebuck Lane, Smethwick, West Midlands, B66 1BY Tel: (0845) 9505505 Fax: 0121-500 2646 E-mail: info@parceline.com

▶ Pend Logistics, 62 St. Marys Road, Edmonton, London, N9 8NJ Tel: (07957) 728769 E-mail: sales@pendlog.com

Point To Point Couriers Ltd, Unit 11 Mitre Bridge Industrial Park, Mitre Way, London, W10 6AU Tel: (020) 8960 2222 Fax: (020) 8960 0956

Point To Point Couriers Ltd, Eve Road, Woking, Surrey, GU21 5JS Tel: (01483) 723511 Fax: (01483) 750427

Practical Services Southern, PO Box 112, Orpington, Kent, BR6 7HB Tel: (01689) 850233 Fax: (01689) 857876 E-mail: info@pss-couriers.com

Quickshift UK Ltd, Gatwick Buisness Centre, Unit 10 Kennel Lane, Hookwood, Horley, Surrey, RH6 0AH Tel: (01293) 541215 Fax: (01293) 539067 E-mail: info@quickshift-couriers.com

R S Express, Earlesfield Lane, Grantham, Lincolnshire, NG31 7NT Tel: (01476) 570601 Fax: (01476) 750268 E-mail: info@rsexpress.co.uk

▶ Reads light haulage & courier service 24/7, 92 Church Lane, Brinsley, Nottingham, NG16 5AB Tel: (07925) 17653 E-mail: david.read67@virgin.net

▶ Runcorn Express Deliveries, 17 Victoria Road, Runcorn, Cheshire, WA7 5BN Tel: 01928 830280 E-mail: enquiries@runcornexpresscourires.co.uk

S I S Stafford, 1 North Avenue, Stafford, ST16 1NP Tel: (01785) 600113 Fax: (01785) 600113E-mail: stafford.couriers@ntlworld.com

▶ St Austell Couriers, 69 Thornpark Road, St. Austell, Cornwall, PL25 4DP Tel: (07876) 507355

▶ Sameday Co., Unit 16, Focus 303 Business Centre, Focus Way, Andover, Hampshire, SP10 5NY Tel: (01264) 352352 Fax: (01264) 369001

Seabourne Mailpack Worldwide, 13 Saxon Way, West Drayton, Middlesex, UB7 0LW Tel: (020) 8897 3888 Fax: (020) 8897 3898 E-mail: info@seabourne-express.com

Secure Track, Vaughan Trading Estate, Sedgley Road East, Tipton, West Midlands, DY4 7UJ Tel: 0121-522 2266 Fax: 0121-522 3344

Skynet Worldwide Express, Unit 8-9 Maple Grove Business Centre, Lawrence Road, Hounslow, TW4 6DR Tel: (020) 8538 1988 Fax: (020) 8538 1921 E-mail: tustserv@deltec-international.com

▶ Southern Despatch, 87 Palmerston Road, Bournemouth, BH1 4HP Tel: (01202) 394357 Fax: (01202) 398954 E-mail: sales@southerndespatch.co.uk

Spatial Air Brokers & Forwarders Ltd, Unit 7c Willow Farm Business Park, Castle Donington, Derby, DE74 2TW Tel: (01332) 850925 Fax: (01332) 812427 E-mail: sales@the-spatial-group.com

Special Delivery Ltd, 531 Kings Road, London, SW10 0TZ Tel: (020) 7351 5133 Fax: (020) 7351 6076

▶ Steadfast Courier Services, 34 Caerhendy Street, Merthyr Tydfil, Mid Glamorgan, CF47 9NJ Tel: (07782) 162061 E-mail: steadfastcourier@aol.com

Streetwise Courier Services, 25 Johns Mews, London, WC1N 2NS Tel: (020) 7404 6161 Fax: (020) 7404 6045 E-mail: mach1ltd@aol.com

Sutton Cars, 302 High Street, Sutton, Surrey, SM1 1PQ Tel: (020) 8643 7004 Fax: (020) 8643 9000

SW Courier Services, 1 Willowbank, Favordale Road, Colne, Lancashire, BB8 7AG Tel: (01282) 861147 Fax: (01282) 861147

T N T Express, Abeles Way, Atherstone, Warwickshire, CV9 2RY Tel: (01827) 303030 Fax: (01827) 301301 E-mail: steve.doig@tnt.co.uk

▶ Tailored Transport Solutions Ltd, 12 Amos Crescent, Scunthorpe, South Humberside, DN16 1RA Tel: (01724) 339169 E-mail: bobby76_373@hotmail.com

▶ Andy Theaker Ltd, 49 Wordsworth Road, Stockport, Cheshire, SK5 6JH Tel: 0161-221 1296 Fax: 0161-221 1178

Thompson Transport, Unit 19 J B J Business Park, Northampton Road, Blisworth, Northampton, NN7 3DW Tel: (01604) 859066 Fax: (01604) 859006

Time Couriers, 36 East Avenue, Bournemouth, BH3 7DA Tel: (01202) 764765 E-mail: sales@timecouriers.co.uk

▶ TM Courier, 52 Chester Road, Stevenage, Hertfordshire, SG1 4LE Tel: (01438) 237667 E-mail: info@tmcourier.co.uk

Tornado Express, Suite 220, London, E15 2SP Tel: (020) 8519 7800 Fax: (020) 8519 0603

Trans World Couriers Ltd, 3 Bricklayers Arms Distribution Centre, Mandela Way, London, SE1 5SR Tel: (020) 7231 3131 Fax: (020) 7237 3048 E-mail: sales@twc.uk.com

▶ Transporter, Bexhill Road, Eastbourne, East Sussex, BN22 7JH Tel: (0781) 7332392 Fax:

COURIER SERVICES – *continued*

▶ U K Logistic Solutions, Unit 23 Parsonage Ind Est, Forest Hall Road, Stansted, Essex, CM24 8TY Tel: 01279 817001 Fax: 01279 817004 E-mail: uklogistics@btconnect.com
U P S Ltd, Newcastle House, Castle Boulevard, Nottingham, NG7 1FT Tel: (0845) 7877877 Fax: 0115-971 6049
▶ UK County Couriers Ltd, 21 Malvern Drive, Ilford, Essex, IG3 9DP Tel: (0870) 4460810 Fax: (0870) 4460740 E-mail: ukcountycouriers@btinternet.com
▶ Van & Deliver, 3 Warkton Close, Chilwell, Nottingham, NG9 5FR Tel: 0845 1214484 E-mail: enquiries@van-and-deliver.co.uk
Vanguard Couriers Ltd, 6 Bendall Mews, London, NW1 6SN Tel: (020) 7258 1818 Fax: (020) 7723 8274 E-mail: courierslondon@aol.com
▶ Wallace Couriers Ltd, 286 Muswell Hill Broadway, London, N10 2QR Tel: (020) 8352 3634 Fax: (07785) 789024 E-mail: paulwallace@blueyonder.co.uk
▶ Peter Watson, 57 Euston Grove, Crow, Ringwood, Hampshire, BH24 1FB Tel: (07866) 737655 E-mail: tasminservices@tiscali.co.uk
Weymouth Same Day Express Couriers, Unit 10 Links Estate, Surrey Close, Granby Industrial Estate, Weymouth, Dorset, DT4 9TY Tel: (01305) 782058 Fax: (01305) 766156
White Knight Express Couriers, 38 Whitebean Close, Paignton, Devon, TQ3 3GA Tel: (01803) 664822
▶ Wiltshire Couriers.co.uk, Abercarn, Newtown, Heytesbury, Warminster, Wiltshire, BA12 OHN Tel: 01985 840321 Fax: 01985 840321 E-mail: info@wiltshirecouriers.co.uk
▶ World Courier, Sea Containers House, 20 Upper Ground, London, SE1 9PD Tel: (020) 7717 1400 Fax: (020) 7928 7105 E-mail: contact@worldcourier.com
World's End Couriers, Unit 6b Farm Lane Trading Estate, Farm Lane, London, SW6 1QJ Tel: (020) 7381 8991 Fax: (020) 7385 4468
Zip Despatch, 63 Regent Street, Eccles, Manchester, M30 0BP Tel: 0161-787 7787 Fax: (07771) 889089 E-mail: sales@zipcouriers.co.uk

CRACK DETECTION SYSTEMS

Magnaflux, Faraday Road, Dorcan, Swindon, SN3 5HE Tel: (01793) 524566 Fax: (01793) 619498 E-mail: sales@magnaflux.co.uk

CRADLE SYSTEMS FOR EXTERNAL MAINTENANCE CONTRACTORS OR SUPPLIES

Ansoroy Ltd, 237 Railton Road, London, SE24 0LX Tel: (020) 7738 6030 Fax: (020) 7738 6030 E-mail: sales@ansoroy.co.uk
Apollo Cradles Ltd, 428 Carlton Road, Barnsley, South Yorkshire, S71 3HX Tel: (01226) 700079 Fax: (01226) 727108 E-mail: sales@apollocradles.co.uk
Cento Engineering Co. Ltd, Baddow Park, West Hanningfield Road, Great Baddow, Chelmsford, CM2 7SY Tel: (01245) 477708 Fax: (01245) 477748
Cradle Access Services Ltd, PO Box 70, Erith, Kent, DA8 3WY Tel: (01322) 345999 Fax: (01322) 345999 E-mail: cradle.access@btconnect.com
D & R Scaffold Eastern, Archers Fields, Burnt Mills Industrial Estate, Basildon, Essex, SS13 1DH Tel: (01268) 525678 Fax: (01268) 284478
Kobi, Unit 19 Seax Court, Southfields Industrial Estate, Basildon, Essex, SS15 6SL Tel: (01268) 416335 Fax: (01268) 542148 E-mail: cradles@kobi.co.uk
P J P Services Ltd, PO Box 173, Rochester, Kent, ME2 4SY Tel: (01634) 724393 Fax: (01634) 724699 E-mail: sales@pjpservices.co.uk

CRADLE SYSTEMS FOR EXTERNAL MAINTENANCE INSPECTION OR MAINTENANCE OR REPAIR OR TEST SERVICES

Electromec Access, Unit 11 Buslingthorpe Green, Leeds, LS7 2HG Tel: 0113-239 2818 Fax: 0113-237 4088 E-mail: sales@electromec-access.co.uk

CRANE BLOCKS

Calder Lifting Services Ltd, Warehouse 1, Cromwell House, Elland Road, Brighouse, West Yorkshire, HD6 2RG Tel: (01422) 376589 Fax: (01422) 374686 E-mail: sales@calderlifting.com

CRANE BOOM GUARDS

Baldwins Crane Hire Ltd, Crane House, Rover Way, Cardiff, CF24 2RX Tel: (01753) 648682 Fax: (01753) 648685

CRANE CANOPIES

Baldwins Crane Hire Ltd, Crane House, Rover Way, Cardiff, CF24 2RX Tel: (01753) 648682 Fax: (01753) 648685

CRANE CONDUCTOR SYSTEMS

Brookfields Garden Centre, 431 Mapperley Plains, Nottingham, NG3 5RW Tel: 0115-926 8200 Fax: 0115-967 3261
Colton Electrical Equipment Co. Ltd, 329 Front Lane, Upminster, Essex, RM14 1LW Tel: (01708) 224454 Fax: (01708) 221191 E-mail: sales@coltonelectricalequipment.co.uk
Conductix Ltd, 1 Michigan Avenue, Salford, M50 2GY Tel: 0161-848 0161 Fax: 0161-873 7017 E-mail: info@conductix.co.uk

CRANE CONSULTANCY OR DESIGN

Cymru Lifting Gear Ltd, Unit 31 Abenbury Way, Wrexham Industrial Estate, Wrexham, Clwyd, LL13 9UZ Tel: (01978) 661439 Fax: (01978) 661238 E-mail: rossgrp_cog@msm.com
I A M Engineering Services, Fornighty Schoolhouse, Nairn, IV12 5JB Tel: (01667) 453509 Fax: (01667) 453066 E-mail: iameng@btinternet.com

CRANE CONTROL SYSTEM INSTALLATION

Claxton International Services, Sarankot House Gell Farm, Kinnerton Road, Lower Kinnerton, Chester, CH4 9AE Tel: (01244) 661000 Fax: (01244) 660240 E-mail: claxtoninter@aol.com
Morris Material Handling, E1 Premier Business Centre, Speedfields Park, Fareham, Hampshire, PO14 1TY Tel: (01329) 825603 Fax: (01329) 825624
Servacrane Investments Ltd, Bagnall Street Industrial Estate, George Henry Road, Tipton, West Midlands, DY4 7BZ Tel: 0121-557 4401 Fax: 0121-557 3788

CRANE CONTROL SYSTEMS

Air Industrial Developments Ltd, Union Street, Kenrick Way, West Bromwich, West Midlands, B70 6DB Tel: 0121-553 4446 Fax: 0121-525 5983 E-mail: paint.sales@airind.co.uk
Cattron Theimeg UK Ltd, Riverdene Industrial Estate, Molesey Road, Hersham, Walton-On-Thames, Surrey, KT12 4RY Tel: (01932) 247511 Fax: (01932) 220937 E-mail: sales@cattronuk.com

CRANE DISTRIBUTORS OR AGENTS OR DEALERS

Concord Lifting Equipment Ltd, Unit 53/56, Wimbledon Stadium Business Centre, Riverside Road, London, SW17 0BE Tel: (020) 8946 7902 Fax: (020) 8946 7001
Foster Crane & Equipment Ltd, Unit 2A, Dunstal Court, Astwood Lane, Feckenham, Redditch, Worcestershire, B96 6QH Tel: (01527) 894400 Fax: (01527) 894940 E-mail: andrewfoster@fostercranes.co.uk
G Stewart, 7 Mitchell Court, Kilmarnock, Ayrshire, KA1 3DU Tel: (01563) 533845 Fax: (01563) 533845
I A M Engineering Services, Fornighty Schoolhouse, Nairn, IV12 5JB Tel: (01667) 453509 Fax: (01667) 453066 E-mail: iameng@btinternet.com
Krane Ltd, Unit 9 Broomers Hill Park, Broomers Hill Lane, Pulborough, West Sussex, RH20 2RY Tel: 0845 4941750 Fax: (01798) 872100 E-mail: kraneltd@aol.com
Manitowoc Europe Holdings Ltd, 1 Azure Court, Doxford International Business Park, Sunderland, SR3 3BE Tel: 0191-522 2000 Fax: 0191-522 2053 E-mail: info@manitowoc.com
NRC Plant Ltd, Neagron House, Stanford Road, Orsett, Grays, Essex, RM16 3BX Tel: (01375) 361616 Fax: (01375) 361818 E-mail: sales@nrcplant.co.uk
Outreach plc, Abbots Road, Middlefield Industrial Estate, Falkirk, FK2 9AR Tel: (01324) 889000 Fax: (01324) 888901 E-mail: cmarshall@outreachltd.co.uk
Terex Demag UK Ltd, Unit 324 Heyford Park, Camp Road, Upper Heyford, Bicester, Oxfordshire, OX25 5HA Tel: (01869) 232443 Fax: (01869) 232840 E-mail: phil.harvey@terex-demag.com
Valla Cranes, Unit 5 Sidings Court, Henry Boot Way, Hull, HU4 7DY Tel: (01482) 351546 Fax: (01482) 351091 E-mail: E.Finn@valla-cranes.co.uk

CRANE ERECTION

Cobal Cranes Ltd, Doctor Lane, Sheffield, S9 5AP Tel: 0114-261 8003 Fax: 0114-261 9003 E-mail: steven.hides@btconnect.com
Crane Care Ltd, 15 Avenue Road, Aston, Birmingham, B6 4DY Tel: 0121-333 3995 Fax: 0121-333 3996 E-mail: sales@cranecare.ltd.uk
▶ Cranetech (Bristol) Limited, 467 Bath Road, Brislington, Bristol, BS4 3JU Tel: 0778 995 3837 Fax: 0117 904 7142 E-mail: crane-tech@blueyonder.co.uk
K G A Ltd, 8 Attenburys Park Estate, Attenburys Lane, Timperley, Altrincham, Cheshire, WA14 5QE Tel: 0161-962 5076 Fax: 0161-962 5312
R B Engineering Services, Unit 43 College Street, Kempston, Bedford, MK42 8LU Tel: (01234) 211263 Fax: (01234) 328835
Seward Wyon Ltd, The Old Tannery, Kelston, Bath, BA1 9AN Tel: 0117-932 7565 Fax: 0117-932 7765 E-mail: sales@sewardwyon.co.uk

CRANE HIRE

A Bedingfield, Island Road, Hersden, Canterbury, Kent, CT3 4HD Tel: (0845) 2300970 Fax: (0845) 2300971 E-mail: bedcrane@btconnet.com
A Jardine & Sons, Northgate, White Lund Industrial Estate, Morecambe, Lancashire, LA3 3PA Tel: (01524) 33113 Fax: (01524) 843262
▶ A P, 3 Godfrey Avenue, Gosberton, Spalding, Lincolnshire, PE11 4HF Tel: (01775) 841819 Fax: (01775) 841819 E-mail: shazza@freeserve.co.uk
A W Plant Services Ltd, Eurocentre, North River Road, Great Yarmouth, Norfolk, NR30 1TE Tel: (01493) 330209 Fax: (01493) 843470
Ace Plantline, 10 Aghagindulff Road, Dungannon, County Tyrone, BT70 3AX Tel: (028) 8776 1433 Fax: (028) 8776 7017 E-mail: ace.plantline@btclick.com
Ainscough Ltd, Col Industrial Estate, Old Bath Road, Slough, SL3 0NJ Tel: (01753) 684811 Fax: (01753) 684005
Ainscough Crane Hire Ltd, Ipswich Road, Cardiff, CF23 9AQ Tel: (029) 2049 5455 Fax: (029) 2049 3967 E-mail: cardiff@inc.co.uk
Ainscough Crane Hire Ltd, Kings Road, Immingham, South Humberside, DN40 1AL Tel: (01469) 576266 Fax: (01469) 576351 E-mail: immingham@ainscough.co.uk
▶ Ainscough Crane Hire Ltd, Rugby Road, Princethorpe, Rugby, Warwickshire, CV23 9PN Tel: (01926) 634786 Fax: (01926) 634763 E-mail: coventry@ainscough.co.uk
Ainscough Crane Hire Ltd, Harewood Works, Middlesbrough Road, Thornaby, Stockton-on-Tees, Cleveland, TS17 7BN Tel: (01642) 661111 Fax: (01642) 612422 E-mail: general@ainscough.co.uk
Argo Crane Hire, Greenham Lock Cottage, London Road, Newbury, Berkshire, RG14 5SN Tel: (01635) 30306
Armstrong Crane Hire, 44 Pemberton Valley, Ayr, KA7 4UB Tel: (01292) 445645 Fax: (01292) 445645
▶ Ash Crane Services, 20 Royds Avenue, New Mill, Holmfirth, HD9 1LP Tel: (01484) 691890 Fax: (01484) 691896 E-mail: 1.ashmead@btopenworld.com
▶ B P Consultancy, Unit 3, Plot 14, Eagle Road, Quarry Hill Industrial Estate, Ilkeston, Derbyshire, DE7 4RB Tel: 0115-930 9275 Fax: 0115-930 4083
B P H Equipment Ltd, PO Box 12, Barton-upon-Humber, South Humberside, DN18 5XD Tel: (01652) 633340 Fax: (01652) 635920 E-mail: info@bphequipment.co.uk
▶ Baldwins Crane Hire Ltd, 52-54 River Road, Barking, Essex, IG11 0DW Tel: (020) 8591 9901 Fax: (020) 8591 9981 E-mail: info@baldwinscranehire.co.uk
Baldwins Crane Hire Ltd, Crane House, Rover Way, Cardiff, CF24 2RX Tel: (01753) 648682 Fax: (01753) 648685
Biwater Treatment Ltd, The Compound White Horse Business Park, Ware Road, Stanford in the Vale, Faringdon, Oxfordshire, SN7 8NY Tel: (01367) 710088 Fax: (01367) 710266
Brennan Site Services Ltd, Mill Way, Old Mill Lane Industrial Estate, Mansfield Woodhouse, Mansfield, Nottinghamshire, NG19 9BG Tel: (01623) 654221 Fax: (01623) 420390
Bronzeshield Lifting Ltd, Vitbe Bungalow, Thames Road, Crayford, Dartford, DA1 4QH Tel: (01322) 555050 Fax: (01322) 550099
Bronzeshield Lifting Ltd, Vitbe Bungalow, Thames Road, Crayford, Dartford, DA1 4QH Tel: (01322) 555050 Fax: (01322) 550099
▶ Buckley's Crane Hire, Bryn Garth, Garth Road, Glan Conwy, Colwyn Bay, Clwyd, LL28 5TD Tel: (01492) 580227 Fax: (01492) 580725 E-mail: enquiries@buckleyscranehire.co.uk
Burcombe Crane Hire, 23 Ridgeway, Coalpit Heath, Bristol, BS36 2PN Tel: (01454) 775471 Fax: (01454) 852845 E-mail: sales@burcombes.co.uk
Campbell Crane Hire, 112 Lisaclare Road, Stewartstown, Dungannon, County Tyrone, BT71 5QJ Tel: (028) 8773 8105 Fax: (028) 8774 0020 E-mail: kevincranehire@aol.com
City Lifting, Purfleet Industrial Park, Aveley, South Ockendon, Essex, RM15 4YA Tel: (01708) 805550 Fax: (01708) 805558 E-mail: hire@citylifting.co.uk
▶ Clarke Chapman Services, Unit 15 Planetary Industrial Estate, Planetary Road, Willenhall, West Midlands, WV13 3XA Tel: (01902) 728844 Fax: (01902) 728822 E-mail: info@clerkchapman.co.uk
Concord Lifting Equipment Ltd, Unit 53/56, Wimbledon Stadium Business Centre, Riverside Road, London, SW17 0BE Tel: (020) 8946 7902 Fax: (020) 8946 7001
Crane Enterprises, Brookhouse Road, Aston, Sheffield, S26 2AH Tel: 0114-287 5499 Fax: 0114-287 5388
▶ Crane Force, 67 Haigh Moor Way, Swallownest, Sheffield, S26 4SW Tel: 0114-288 0909
▶ Cranes (UK), Rockingham House, Wentworth Way, Tankersley, Barnsley, South Yorkshire, S75 3DH Tel: (0870) 0665466 Fax: (0870) 0665501
Davies Crane Hire Ltd, Pensarn Road, Carmarthen, Dyfed, SA31 2BS Tel: (01267) 234660 Fax: (01267) 232346 E-mail: enquiries@daviescranehire.co.uk
Dewsbury & Proud Ltd, Biddings Lane, Bilston, West Midlands, WV14 9NN Tel: (01902) 405553 Fax: (01902) 354420 E-mail: operations@cranehiremidlands.com
Dewsbury & Proud, Cedar House, Kingsbury Road, Marston, Sutton Coldfield, West Midlands, B76 0DS Tel: (01675) 443048
Dylan Thomas, Railway Yard, Boncath, Dyfed, SA37 0JW Tel: (01239) 841888 Fax: (01239) 841663
Emsley Crane Hire Of Harrogate, Unit 1-2 Claro Park, Harrogate, North Yorkshire, HG1 4BB Tel: (01423) 561929 Fax: (01423) 509772
Keith Faulkner Ltd, Park Garage, Macclesfield Street, Stoke-on-Trent, ST6 1EH Tel: (01782) 812990 Fax: (01782) 838991
Ford & Son Ltd, Station House, Station Road, Holton-le-Clay, Grimsby, South Humberside, DN36 5HR Tel: (01472) 840452 Fax: (01472) 840177
Freeland Freight Services Ltd, Blackness Road, Altens Industrial Estate, Aberdeen, AB12 3LH Tel: (01224) 873601 Fax: (01224) 879863 E-mail: enquiries@freelandfreight.co.uk
▶ G B K Rental Services Ltd, Green Elms Estate, Grays Road, Uddingston, Glasgow, G71 6ET Tel: (01698) 801000 Fax: (01698) 801144
G Cox Oldbury Ltd, 146 Dudley Road East, Oldbury, West Midlands, B69 3EB Tel: 0121-552 4413 Fax: 0121-552 1883
Gerald Hamill & Sons, 114 Obin Street, Portadown, Craigavon, County Armagh, BT62 1BP Tel: (028) 3833 2297 Fax: (028) 3839 3377
Hartland Crane Hire, Sneyd Hill, Stoke-on-Trent, ST6 2DY Tel: (01782) 575554 Fax: (01952) 587848
▶ HB Crane Hire UK, Carnaby Industrial Estate, Carnaby, Bridlington, East Riding of Yorkshire, YO15 3QY Tel: (01262) 673346 E-mail: hire@crane-hire-uk.com
Hewden Crane Hire Ltd, St Andrews Road, Holesmouth, Avonmouth, Bristol, BS11 9BN Tel: 0117-938 4777 Fax: 0117-938 4555
Hewden Crane Hire Ltd, Hawley Road, Dartford, DA1 1PD Tel: (01322) 351155 Fax: (01322) 351144
Hewden Crane Hire, Brigg Road, Scunthorpe, North Lincolnshire, DN16 1XA Tel: (01724) 277741 Fax: (01724) 843222
Hewden Hire Centres Ltd, Main Road, Long Hanborough, Witney, Oxfordshire, OX29 8SY Tel: (01993) 883939 Fax: (01993) 882877
Hewden Plant Hire Ltd, Cambridge Road, Bedford, MK42 0LH Tel: (01234) 340801 Fax: (01234) 343423
Hewden Plant Hire Ltd, Vicarage Farm Road, Peterborough, PE1 5TN Tel: (01733) 564378 Fax: (01733) 566480
Hewson Smith & Sons, Old Main Road, Scamblesby, Louth, Lincolnshire, LN11 9XG Tel: (01507) 343249 Fax: (01507) 343779
Highcliffe Engineering Ltd, Unit C Old Housecraft Yard, Church Street, Mexborough, South Yorkshire, S64 0HH Tel: (01709) 581656 Fax: (01709) 581656
Bernard Hunter Ltd, 600 Gilmerton Road, Edinburgh, EH17 8RY Tel: 0131-663 7268 Fax: 0131-654 2592 E-mail: info@bernardhunter.com
▶ Independent Crane Services Ltd, Worcester Road, Upton Warren, Bromsgrove, Worcs, B61 7ER Tel: (01527) 869028 Fax: (01527) 869147
J Exley Ltd, Park Works, 644 Bradford Road, Batley, West Yorkshire, WF17 8HG Tel: (01924) 472353 Fax: (01924) 440007 E-mail: greg@jexley.co.uk
▶ J G B Transport, Building 789, Murray Road, Europark, Dunfermline, Fife, KY11 2EB Tel: (01383) 416009 Fax: (01383) 414176
▶ J P Lifting Ltd, 95 Dover Avenue, Banbury, Oxfordshire, OX16 0JH Tel: (01295) 261126 Fax: (01295) 261126 E-mail: jclifting@btconnect.com
James Jack Lifting Services Ltd, 7-13 South Esplanade West, Aberdeen, AB11 9AA Tel: (01224) 897535 Fax: (01224) 897299 E-mail: sales@james-jack.co.uk
James Jack Listing Services Ltd, Oilfield Support Base, Shore Road, Invergordon, Ross-Shire, IV18 0EX Tel: (01349) 853000 Fax: (01349) 853416E-mail: invergordon@james-jack.co.uk
Jay & Davies (Crane Hire), 14 Sweetmans Yard, Harrow Road, Plough Lane, Hereford, HR4 0EE Tel: (01432) 267043 Fax: (01432) 270754

CRANE HIRE – *continued*

Graham Jones Crane Hire Ltd, 6-10 Haygate Road, Wellington, Telford, Shropshire, TF1 1QA Tel: (01952) 245455 Fax: (01978) 310573

L & D Mortimer, Birch Street, Bury, Lancashire, BL9 5AL Tel: 0161-764 1362 Fax: 0161-761 6836

Lewis J C Maidenhead Ltd, 117 Blackamoor Lane, Maidenhead, Berkshire, SL6 8RQ Tel: (01628) 621013 Fax: (01628) 781009

Lift-It Ltd, Sendalls Way, Glacis Park Crownhill, Plymouth, PL6 5JT Tel: (01752) 771311 Fax: (01752) 788093

▶ Linian North West Ltd, Unit 9 Shaw Street, St. Helens, Merseyside, WA10 1DQ Tel: (01744) 736330 Fax: (01744) 22013 E-mail: sales@linian.co.uk

Longton Crane Hire Ltd, Clarence Road, Longton, Stoke-On-Trent, ST3 1AZ Tel: (01782) 310911 Fax: (01782) 599411

Machinery Installations (Birmingham) Ltd, Unit 12A, Middlemore Lane West, Aldridge, Walsall, WS9 8BG Tel: (01922) 743187 Fax: (01922) 743206 E-mail: mibham@aol.com

Mcnally Crane Hire Ltd, Drumrainy, Newtownbutler, Enniskillen, County Fermanagh, BT92 6LY Tel: (028) 6773 8830

Mantid Ltd, Unit 16 Klondyke Trading Estate, Rushenden Road, Queenborough, Kent, ME11 5HB Tel: (01795) 580558

Marsden Crane Hire Ltd, 12 Ince Lane, Eccleston, Chorley, Lancashire, PR7 5TH Tel: (01257) 452689 Fax: (01257) 453776

Marsh Plant Hire Ltd, Wallingford Road, Uxbridge, Middlesex, UB8 2SS Tel: (01895) 231291 Fax: (01895) 811650

Mid Anglia Crane Hire Ltd, Shepherds Grove Industrial Estate, Stanton, Bury St. Edmunds, Suffolk, IP31 2AR Tel: (01359) 251451 Fax: (01359) 251313 E-mail: midangliacranehire@telco4u.net

Midland Electrical Services, 6 Moor Street Industrial Estate, Moor Street, Brierley Hill, West Midlands, DY5 3ST Tel: (01384) 262558 Fax: (01384) 480661

Millennium Crane Hire Ltd, Rear Of 400 Edgware Road, Cricklewood, London, NW2 6ND Tel: (020) 8208 1444 Fax: (020) 8452 1248

Mobile Freezer Rentals Ltd, Greensbury Farm, Thurleigh Road, Bolnhurst, Bedford, MK44 2ET Tel: (01234) 376999 Fax: (01234) 376060 E-mail: julie@mfrltd.co.uk

MSD, Unit 1 Red Barnes Way, Darlington, County Durham, DL1 2RR Tel: (01325) 340034 Fax: (01325) 382599 E-mail: hire@msdcranes.com

Thomas Muir Haulage Ltd, Randolph Industrial Estate, Kirkcaldy, Fife, KY1 2TX Tel: (01592) 651076 Fax: (01592) 651138

Nickell Crane Hire, 52 Church Road, Dover, Kent, CT17 9LR Tel: (01304) 211897 Fax: (01304) 211897

NRC Plant Ltd, Neagron House, Stanford Road, Orsett, Grays, Essex, RM16 3BX Tel: (01375) 361616 Fax: (01375) 361818 E-mail: sales@nrcplant.co.uk

▶ Onsite Crane & Commercial Ltd, Shrublands Avenue, Berkhamsted, Hertfordshire, HP4 3JG Tel: (01442) 878886 Fax: (01442) 878886

P Casey, 39 Carrycastle Road, Dungannon, County Tyrone, BT70 1PZ Tel: (028) 3754 8709 Fax: (028) 3754 8709

P Hird & Sons Ltd, English Street, Hull, HU3 2BT Tel: (01482) 227333 Fax: (01482) 587710 E-mail: sales@peter-hird.co.uk

P L Moors, Hillside Farm, Willington, Tarporley, Cheshire, CW6 0LX Tel: (01829) 732222 Fax: (01829) 730794

John Panes, Regal Garage, Hanley Road, Upton-upon-Severn, Worcester, WR8 0HU Tel: (01684) 592316

Power Lifting Services Limited, Linen Hall, 162-168 Regent Street, London, W1B 5TG Tel: 0207 0383881 Fax: 0207 0383845 E-mail: powerlifting@btinternet.com

Quinto Crane Hire, The Drift, Nacton Road, Ipswich, IP3 9QR Tel: (01473) 712041 Fax: (01473) 720386

Quinto Crane & Plant Ltd, Drakes Lane, Boreham, Chelmsford, CM3 3BE Tel: (01245) 360531 Fax: (01245) 362427

Quinto Crane & Plant Ltd, Admiralty Road, Great Yarmouth, Norfolk, NR30 3DY Tel: (01493) 331800 Fax: (01603) 407269

Quinto Crane & Plant Ltd, Wisbech Road, King's Lynn, Norfolk, PE30 5JL Tel: (01553) 764383 Fax: (01553) 768716

Quinto Crane & Plant Ltd, Markfield Road, Groby, Leicester, LE6 0FT Tel: (01530) 244181 Fax: (01530) 244808

Quinto Crane & Plant Ltd, Anson Road, Norwich Airport, Norwich, NR6 6EH Tel: (01603) 410881 Fax: (01603) 404565 E-mail: cranehire@quinto.co.uk

Quinto Crane & Plant Ltd, Royce Road, Peterborough, PE1 5YB Tel: (01733) 560338 Fax: (01733) 890829 E-mail: adrian@quinto.co.uk

▶ R S Cranes, Asrc Bussiness Centre, 2 Cassel Court, Haverton Hill Road, Billingham, Cleveland, TS23 1RB Tel: (01642) 674250 Fax: (01642) 673368

Rent-A-Crane Ltd, 25 Rock Road, Solihull, West Midlands, B92 7LB Tel: 0121-706 7340

Roadcraft (Crane & Plant Hire) Ltd, 8-18 Strand Road, Bootle, Merseyside, L20 1AN Tel: (0151) 922 4567 Fax: (0151) 922 2396

▶ S C H Site Services, Units G511 A, B & C, Whinbank Road, Aycliffe Industrial Estate, Newton Aycliffe, County Durham, DL5 6AY Tel: (01325) 327149 Fax: (01325) 327148 E-mail: b.smithies@schsiteservices.co.uk

▶ S J B Crane Co., Station Road, Halfway, Sheffield, S20 3GW Tel: 0114-247 9686 Fax: 0114-247 1527

Sarens UK Ltd, Dinsdale House, Riverside Park Road, Middlesbrough, Cleveland, TS2 1UT Tel: (01642) 621621 Fax: (01642) 621620 E-mail: sales@sarens.com

▶ Shires Crane Hire Ltd, Sheepbridge Lane, Chesterfield, Derbyshire, S41 9RX Tel: (01246) 452296 Fax: (01246) 451015 E-mail: louise@shirescrane.fsnet.co.uk

Somerset Lifting Supplies, Riverside, Bathpool, Taunton, Somerset, TA1 2DX Tel: (01823) 352029 Fax: (01823) 352029

South West Crane Hire Ltd, Tan Lane, Exeter, EX2 8EG Tel: (01392) 256148 Fax: (01392) 270603 E-mail: info@sw-crane-hire.co.uk

Steve Foster Crane Hire, Dovefields, Derby Road, Dovefields Industrial Estate, Uttoxeter, Staffordshire, ST14 8HU Tel: (01889) 568163 Fax: (01889) 568853 E-mail: sales@stevefostercranes.co.uk

Maurice Sutton Crane Hire, 1 Newstead Road, Urmston, Manchester, M41 0QQ Tel: 0161-748 1848 Fax: 0161-748 1848

T O Tomlins Ltd, Halfway House, Station Lane, Halfway House, Shrewsbury, SY5 9DB Tel: (01743) 884235 Fax: (01743) 884424

Taylor Crane Co. Ltd, 6 York St, Aberdeen, AB11 5DD Tel: (01224) 211188 Fax: (01224) 212803

Teesdale Crane Hire, 23 Leekworth Gardens, Middleton In Teesdale, Barnard Castle, County Durham, DL12 0TE Tel: (01833) 640395 Fax: (01833) 640395

Telford Crane Hire Ltd, Halesfield 22, Telford, Shropshire, TF7 4QX Tel: (01952) 586304 Fax: (01952) 587848 E-mail: sales@telfordcrane.co.uk

Telford Crane Hire Ltd, Halesfield 22, Telford, Shropshire, TF7 4QX Tel: (01952) 586304 Fax: (01952) 587848 E-mail: sales@telfordcrane.co.uk

Terranova, Bennet Road, Reading, RG2 0QX Tel: 0118-986 6577 Fax: 0118-931 4114 E-mail: sales@terranovagroup.co.uk

Thames Crane Services Ltd, 327 Heyford Park, Camp Road, Upper Heyford, Bicester, Oxfordshire, OX25 5HA Tel: (01869) 232001 Fax: (01869) 232004

Tilita Rosettes, 267 Hillbury Road, Warlingham, Surrey, CR6 9TL Tel: (01883) 622121 Fax: (01883) 622124 E-mail: tilita@bigfoot.com

Topcliffe Crane & Recovery, Station Road, Topcliffe, Thirsk, North Yorkshire, YO7 3SG Tel: (01845) 577330 Fax: (01845) 577007

Venture Lifting Services Ltd, 52 Grove Road, Newbury, Berkshire, RG14 1UL Tel: (01635) 40150 Fax: (01635) 40195

W M Arnold Boroughbridge Ltd, Station Yard, Boroughbridge, York, YO51 9BL Tel: (01423) 322871 Fax: (01423) 324380 E-mail: sales@wmarnold.demon.co.uk

West Country Crane Hire Ltd, 3 Slip North Internal P C 1310, Royal H M Dockyard, Plymouth, PL1 4SG Tel: (01752) 223344 Fax: (01752) 222229 E-mail: brian.metters@westcountrycranehire.com

▶ Winterlift Ltd, Fairhills Industrial Estate, Woodrow Way, Irlam, Manchester, M44 6ZQ Tel: 0161-775 4400 Fax: (0845) 1309003 E-mail: andrew.winter@btinternet.co.uk

Wright Brothers (Clayton) Ltd, Victoria Works, Barnard Road, Bradford, West Yorkshire, BD4 7DY Tel: (01274) 587777 Fax: (01274) 394629

CRANE MANUFACTURERS OR BUILDERS, *See also headings under Cranes*

A & B Crane & Electrical Services Ltd, Prince Consort Road, Hebburn, Tyne & Wear, NE31 1EH Tel: 0191-483 6767 Fax: 0191-428 0317

Advanced Lifting Equipment, Goosens Workshop, Broadclyst, Exeter, EX5 3JQ Tel: (01392) 461393 Fax: (01392) 462393

Allerton Engineering Ltd, Allerton House, Thurston Road, Northallerton, North Yorkshire, DL6 2NA Tel: (01609) 774471 Fax: (01609) 780364 E-mail: sales@allertonengineering.co.uk

Butterley Nuclear Engineering Ltd, Engineering Works, Ripley, Derbyshire, DE5 3BQ Tel: (01773) 573573 Fax: (01773) 749898 E-mail: admin@butterley.com

C Y Electrical & Cranes Co. Ltd, Hayes Lane, Stourbridge, West Midlands, DY9 8QT Tel: (01384) 895570 Fax: (01384) 892877 E-mail: sales@cyequip.co.uk

Chesterfield Crane Co., Whittington House, South St North, New Whittington, Chesterfield, Derbyshire, S43 2BP Tel: (01246) 454521 Fax: (01246) 260815

Coolmetal Steel Fabricators, 68-72 Bromley Street, Stourbridge, West Midlands, DY9 8JA Tel: (01384) 424424 Fax: (01384) 892810 E-mail: info@coolmetal.co.uk

D B Crane Ltd, Unit 10 Sovereign Works, Deepdale Lane, Dudley, West Midlands, DY3 2AF Tel: (01384) 458763 Fax: (01384) 459766

Demag Cranes & Components Ltd, Beaumont Rd, Banbury, Oxfordshire, OX16 1QZ Tel: (01295) 676100 Fax: (01295) 226106 E-mail: help@demagcranes.com

Dragon Crane Services, Unit 18 Lamby Workshops, Lamby Way, Rumney, Cardiff, CF3 2EQ Tel: (029) 2077 7444 Fax: (029) 2077 7404 E-mail: email@dragoncraneservices.co.uk

J Barnsley Cranes Ltd, Unit 16 Pedmore Road Industrial Estate, Pedmore Road, Brierley Hill, West Midlands, DY5 1TJ Tel: (01384) 484811 Fax: (01384) 484333 E-mail: jsatch@jbarnsleycranes.com

▶ Kobelco Cranes Europe Ltd, 9 The Felbridge Centre, Imberhorne Lane, East Grinstead, West Sussex, RH19 1XP Tel: (01342) 301122 Fax: (01342) 326987

Lebus International Engineers Ltd, Dane Works, Crown Quay Lane, Sittingbourne, Kent, ME10 3HU Tel: (01795) 475324 Fax: (01795) 428004 E-mail: enquiries@lebusintengineers.com

Lifting Gear Supplies Ltd, 23 Anstey Lane, Leicester, LE4 0FF Tel: 0116-262 8023 Fax: 0116-251 4862 E-mail: sales@liftinggearsuppliesltd.co.uk

Manitowoc Potain Ltd, Unit 2c Tomo Industrial Estate, Packet Boat Lane, Uxbridge, Middlesex, UB8 2JP Tel: (01895) 430053 Fax: (01895) 459500

Matterson King Cranes, PO Box 31, Glasgow, G15 8TE Tel: 0141-944 4000 Fax: 0141-944 0111 E-mail: pct@pctgroup.co.uk

Morris Material Handling Ltd, PO Box 7, Loughborough, Leicestershire, LE11 1RL Tel: (01509) 643200 Fax: (01509) 610666 E-mail: info@morriscranes.co.uk

Outreach plc, Abbots Road, Middlefield Industrial Estate, Falkirk, FK2 9AR Tel: (01324) 889000 Fax: (01324) 888901 E-mail: cmarshall@outreachltd.co.uk

▶ Pelloby Engineering Ltd, Halesfield 19, Telford, Shropshire, TF7 4QT Tel: (01952) 586626 Fax: (01952) 587871 E-mail: sales@pelloby.com

Servacrane Investments Ltd, Bagnall Street Industrial Estate, George Henry Road, Tipton, West Midlands, DY4 7BZ Tel: 0121-557 4401 Fax: 0121-557 3788

Stothert & Pitt, Lower Bristol Road, Bath, BA2 3DJ Tel: (01225) 314400 Fax: (01225) 332529

Terex Demag UK Ltd, Unit 324 Heyford Park, Camp Road, Upper Heyford, Bicester, Oxfordshire, OX25 5HA Tel: (01869) 232443 Fax: (01869) 232840 E-mail: phil.harvey@terex-demag.com

Tilita Rosettes, 267 Hillbury Road, Warlingham, Surrey, CR6 9TL Tel: (01883) 622121 Fax: (01883) 622124 E-mail: tilita@bigfoot.com

United Crane Services Ltd, Niagara Works, Beeley Wood Rd, Sheffield, S6 1NH Tel: 0114-285 2801 Fax: 0114-232 5626 E-mail: unitedcranes@aol.com

CRANE MOUNTED ATTACHMENTS

Cascade (UK) Ltd, Unit 5, Eden Close, Hellaby Industrial Estate, Hellaby, Rotherham, South Yorkshire, S66 8RW Tel: (01709) 704500 Fax: (01709) 704501 E-mail: uk-sales@cascorp.com

Kinshofer (UK) Ltd, 4 Milton Industrial Court, Horsfield Way, Bredbury, Stockport, Cheshire, SK6 2TA Tel: 0161-406 7046 Fax: 0161-406 7014 E-mail: info@kinshofer.com

▶ Speedy Lift, Unit B North Sea Supply Base, Riverside Park Road, Middlesbrough, Cleveland, TS2 1UT Tel: (01642) 246111 Fax: (01642) 249123 E-mail: teesside-lifting@speedydepots.co.uk

CRANE OPERATOR TRAINING

▶ Ainscough Training Services Ltd, Farington Business Park, Golden Hill Lane, Leyland, PR25 3GG Tel: (01772) 623591 Fax: (01772) 622654 E-mail: ianfisher@ainscoughtraining.co.uk

Bryn Thomas Training Services Ltd, 421 Chester Road, Oakenholt, Flint, CH6 5SE Tel: (01352) 733984 Fax: (01352) 761052 E-mail: nik@brynthomastrainingservices.co.uk

Sigma Studies Training, 121 Corringham Road, Stanford-le-Hope, Essex, SS17 0BA Tel: (01375) 671111 Fax: (07092) 380757 E-mail: info@sigmastudies.co.uk

CRANE RAILS

Crane Rail Installations UK Ltd, 9 Portersfield Road, Cradley Heath, West Midlands, B64 7BN Tel: (01384) 634466 Fax: (01384) 634277 E-mail: cri@btinternet.com

H.J. Skelton & Co. Ltd, 9 The Broadway, Thatcham, Berkshire, RG19 3JA Tel: (01635) 865256 Fax: (01635) 865710 E-mail: info@hjskelton.com

CRANE SAFETY OR OVERLOAD PROTECTION SYSTEMS

Ainscough Engineering Services Ltd, Farington Business Park, Leyland, PR25 3GG Tel: (01772) 622116 Fax: (01772) 622210 E-mail: a.keith@ainscoughengineering.co.uk

Claxton International Services, Sarankot House Gell Farm, Kinnerton Road, Lower Kinnerton, Chester, CH4 9AE Tel: (01244) 661000 Fax: (01244) 660240 E-mail: claxtoninter@aol.com

Wylie Systems, Drury Lane, St. Leonards-on-Sea, East Sussex, TN38 9XS Tel: (01424) 421235 Fax: (01424) 433760 E-mail: wylie@raycowylie.com

Weighload Systems Ltd, Watling Street Works, Watling St, Brownhills, Walsall, WS8 7JT Tel: (01543) 453494 Fax: (01543) 453167

CRANE SAFETY TRAINING

First Choice Training & Development Ltd, 37 Langdale Crescent Eston, Grange Middlesbrough, Middlesbrough, Cleveland, TS6 7RB Tel: (01642) 511877 E-mail: firstchoicetraining@ntlwolrd.com

▶ JH Training Services Ltd, 7 Baron Court, Peterborough, PE4 7ZE Tel: (07752) 847195

▶ Trans Plant Mastertrain, Schovella, Cliff Road, Gorran Haven, St. Austell, Cornwall, PL26 6JN Tel: (01392) 426242 Fax: (01392) 205006 E-mail: geoff_fox@hotmail.com

CRANE SPARE PARTS OR WEARING PARTS

Amba Dockside Technology Ltd, 1 The Parkwood Centre, Aston Road, Waterlooville, Hampshire, PO7 7HT Tel: (023) 9223 1200 Fax: (023) 9226 7047 E-mail: ambeng@aol.com

▶ Anbar Trading Co., 44 Belton Lane, Great Gonerby, Grantham, Lincolnshire, NG31 8NA Tel: (01476) 571966 Fax: (01476) 592093 E-mail: anbar@globalnet.co.uk

Doity Engineering Ltd, Isherwood Street, Rochdale, Lancashire, OL11 1JF Tel: (01706) 345515 Fax: (01706) 640454 E-mail: sales@doity.com

Krane Ltd, Unit 9 Broomers Hill Park, Broomers Hill Lane, Pulborough, West Sussex, RH20 2RY Tel: 0845 4941750 Fax: (01798) 872100 E-mail: kraneltd@aol.com

CRANE TESTING OR INSPECTION OR MAINTENANCE OR REPAIR OR MODIFICATION

A & B Crane & Electrical Services Ltd, Prince Consort Road, Hebburn, Tyne & Wear, NE31 1EH Tel: 0191-483 6767 Fax: 0191-428 0317

Advanced Lifting Equipment, Goosens Workshop, Broadclyst, Exeter, EX5 3JQ Tel: (01392) 461393 Fax: (01392) 462393

Ainscough Engineering Services Ltd, Farington Business Park, Leyland, PR25 3GG Tel: (01772) 622116 Fax: (01772) 622210 E-mail: a.keith@ainscoughengineering.co.uk

Amba Dockside Technology Ltd, 1 The Parkwood Centre, Aston Road, Waterlooville, Hampshire, PO7 7HT Tel: (023) 9223 1200 Fax: (023) 9226 7047 E-mail: ambeng@aol.com

Austin Engineering Shropshire Ltd, Cargotec Industrial Park, Ellesmere, Shropshire, SY12 9JW Tel: (01691) 622864 Fax: (01691) 622864E-mail: steve@austinengineering.co.uk

Barnes Lifting Services Ltd, Station Works, Main Road, Unstone, Dronfield, Derbyshire, S18 4AQ Tel: (01246) 417941 Fax: (01246) 410244

C Y Electrical & Cranes Co. Ltd, Hayes Lane, Stourbridge, West Midlands, DY9 8QT Tel: (01384) 895570 Fax: (01384) 892877 E-mail: sales@cyequip.co.uk

Central Steel Pickling Ltd, Nomex House, Powke Lane, Cradley Heath, West Midlands, B64 5PX Tel: (01384) 566373 Fax: (01384) 566376

Claxton International Services, Sarankot House Gell Farm, Kinnerton Road, Lower Kinnerton, Chester, CH4 9AE Tel: (01244) 661000 Fax: (01244) 660240 E-mail: claxtoninter@aol.com

Crane Care Ltd, 15 Avenue Road, Aston, Birmingham, B6 4DY Tel: 0121-333 3995 Fax: 0121-333 3996 E-mail: sales@cranecare.ltd.uk

Crane Enterprises, Brookhouse Road, Aston, Sheffield, S26 2AH Tel: 0114-287 5499 Fax: 0114-287 5388

Crane Inspection & Lifting Services Ltd, Unit 17 Neptune Industrial Estate, Neptune Close, Medway City Estate, Rochester, Kent, ME2 4LT Tel: (01634) 290030 Fax: (01634) 730584 E-mail: cils@btconnect.com

Crane & Lifting Services Ltd, Evtol Trading Estate, Frederick Street, Newport, Gwent, NP20 2DR Tel: (01633) 265445 Fax: (01633) 265446

Crane Services Ltd, Platts Road, Stourbridge, West Midlands, DY8 4YR Tel: (01384) 370318 Fax: (01384) 440203 E-mail: sales@craneservices.co.uk

CRANE TESTING OR INSPECTION OR MAINTENANCE OR REPAIR OR MODIFICATION – *continued*

D B Crane Ltd, Unit 10 Sovereign Works, Deepdale Lane, Dudley, West Midlands, DY3 2AF Tel: (01384) 458763 Fax: (01384) 459766
Delph Electrical Lifting Services Ltd, 3 The Wallows Industrial Estate, Fens Pool Avenue, Brierley Hill, West Midlands, DY5 1QA Tel: (01384) 76222 Fax: (01384) 75524
Elec-Tech Services, 132 Northfield Lane, Wickersley, Rotherham, South Yorkshire, S66 2HW Tel: (01709) 543211 Fax: (01709) 543211
Electromec Access, Unit 11 Buslingthorpe Green, Leeds, LS7 2HG Tel: 0113-239 2818 Fax: 0113-237 4088 E-mail: sales@electromec-access.co.uk
Fraser Crane & Lifting Services, 52 Block 3 Coltswood Road, Coatbridge, Lanarkshire, ML5 2AB Tel: (01236) 607063 Fax: (01236) 607063 E-mail: frasercranes@aol.com
I M E S Ltd, Tern Place, Denmore Road, Bridge of Don, Aberdeen, AB23 8JX Tel: (01224) 705777 Fax: (01224) 824808 E-mail: marketing@imes-group.com
K G A Ltd, 8 Attenburys Park Estate, Attenburys Lane, Timperley, Altrincham, Cheshire, WA14 5QE Tel: 0161-962 5076 Fax: 0161-962 5312
Konecranes Service Ltd, Albion Road, West Bromwich, West Midlands, B70 8AX Tel: 0121-569 1000 Fax: 0121-569 1099
Midland Safe Load Indicators Ltd, Watling Street Works, Watling Street, Brownhills, Walsall, WS8 7JT Tel: (01543) 453166 Fax: (01543) 453167
Morris Material Handling, 3 Lambhill Quadrant, Glasgow, G41 1SB Tel: 0141-429 4347 Fax: 0141-429 4347
Morris Material Handling Ltd, PO Box 7, Loughborough, Leicestershire, LE11 1RL Tel: (01509) 643200 Fax: (01509) 610666 E-mail: info@morriscranes.co.uk
Morris Material Handling, Lodge Way, Thetford, Norfolk, IP24 1HE Tel: (01842) 750252 Fax: (01842) 750909
Nuffield Radiographic Inspection, Unit B13-14, 46 Holton Road, Holton Heath Trading Park, Poole, Dorset, BH16 6LT Tel: (01202) 632200 Fax: (01202) 632042 E-mail: sales@nuffieldinspection.co.uk
Oilfield Maintenance Repairs Ltd, 4 Salmon Road, Great Yarmouth, Norfolk, NR30 3QS Tel: (01493) 859985 Fax: (01493) 853385
Olympia Testing Holdings Ltd, Oldbush Street, Off Level Street, Brierley Hill, West Midlands, DY5 1UB Tel: (01384) 573164 Fax: (01384) 265832
P P Engineering, Charles Street, Kilnhurst, Mexborough, South Yorkshire, S64 5TG Tel: (01709) 578877 Fax: (01709) 578555 E-mail: ppengineering@talk21.com
Servacrane Investments Ltd, Bagnall Street Industrial Estate, George Henry Road, Tipton, West Midlands, DY4 7BZ Tel: 0121-557 4401 Fax: 0121-557 3788
Severnside Machinery Ltd, Unit 57, Ditton Priors, Bridgnorth, Shropshire, WV16 6SS Tel: 01746 712433
▶ Sparrows Offshore Services Ltd, Denmore Road, Bridge of Don, Aberdeen, AB23 8JW Tel: (01224) 704868 Fax: (01224) 825191 E-mail: sales@sparrows.co.uk
Weighsafe, Meadow Croft, Denaby Lane, Old Denaby, Doncaster, S. Yorkshire, DN12 4JX Tel: (01709) 584752 Fax: (01709) 571197

CRANE TRACK CONTRACTORS OR SUPPLIES

Crane Rail Installations UK Ltd, 9 Portersfield Road, Cradley Heath, West Midlands, B64 7BN Tel: (01384) 634466 Fax: (01384) 634277 E-mail: cri@btinternet.com
▶ Cranequip Ltd, Cattell Road, Cape Industrial Estate, Warwick, CV34 4JN Tel: (01926) 406900 Fax: (01926) 406910 E-mail: robert.shearsby@uk.gantry.com
Gantry Railing Ltd, Sudmeadow Road, Gloucester, GL2 5HG Tel: (01452) 300688 Fax: (01452) 300198 E-mail: info@gantry.co.uk

CRANE TRACK FASTENINGS

▶ Cranequip Ltd, Cattell Road, Cape Industrial Estate, Warwick, CV34 4JN Tel: (01926) 406900 Fax: (01926) 406910 E-mail: robert.shearsby@uk.gantry.com
Gantry Railing Ltd, Sudmeadow Road, Gloucester, GL2 5HG Tel: (01452) 300688 Fax: (01452) 300198 E-mail: info@gantry.co.uk

CRANE TRACKS

Acorn Lifting Services Ltd, Northern Court, Off Vernon Road, Nottingham, NG6 0BJ Tel: 0115-976 2862 Fax: 0115-976 1406 E-mail: als@acorn-lifting.co.uk

CRANE WEIGHING ATTACHMENTS OR SCALES

Load Monitor (U K) Ltd, The Marchoness Building, Commercial Rd, Bristol, BS1 6TG Tel: 0117-925 2300 Fax: 0117-925 2300 E-mail: sales@loadmonitor.com

CRANES TO SPECIFICATION

Dragon Crane Services, Unit 18 Lamby Workshops, Lamby Way, Rumney, Cardiff, CF3 2EQ Tel: (029) 2077 7444 Fax: (029) 2077 7404 E-mail: email@dragoncraneservices.co.uk
Wellman Booth, 2 Kirkfields Industrial Centre, Kirk Lane, Yeadon, Leeds, LS19 7LX Tel: 0113-387 9730 Fax: 0113-250 6180 E-mail: sales@wellmanbooth.co.uk

CRANKSHAFT FORGINGS

Alfing Kessler Engineering Ltd, 56a Bramhall Lane South, Bramhall, Stockport, Cheshire, SK7 1AH Tel: 0161-440 0104 Fax: 0161-440 0115 E-mail: alfingkessler@btconnect.com

CRANKSHAFT GRINDING MACHINES

▶ S I M Machine Tools Ltd, 5-6a Unit, London Terrace, Darwen, Lancashire, BB3 3DF Tel: (01254) 777117 Fax: (01254) 774841 E-mail: sales@simmachinetools.com

CRANKSHAFT MAINTENANCE OR REPAIR

F J Payne & Son Ltd, Oakfield Industrial Estate, Eynsham, Witney, Oxfordshire, OX29 4AW Tel: (01865) 882299 Fax: (01865) 882309 E-mail: sales@fjpayne.com

CRANKSHAFTS

Albion Automotive Ltd, Lancashire Enterprises Business Park, Centurian Way, Leyland, PR26 6TZ Tel: (01772) 831400 Fax: (01772) 831401
Alfing Kessler Engineering Ltd, 56a Bramhall Lane South, Bramhall, Stockport, Cheshire, SK7 1AH Tel: 0161-440 0104 Fax: 0161-440 0115 E-mail: alfingkessler@btconnect.com
Bifrangi UK Ltd, PO Box 129, Sheffield, S9 1HR Tel: (01709) 562766 Fax: (01709) 857888
Britalco Engineering Ltd, 3 Villiers Trading Estate, Marston Road, Wolverhampton, WV2 4LA Tel: (01902) 771836 Fax: (01902) 717766
Chera Marine, 3 Overmoor Fold, Idle, Bradford, West Yorkshire, BD10 8UT Tel: (07976) 741327 Fax: (01274) 619663
Phoenix Crankshafts Ltd, 37 The Business Village, Wexham Road, Slough, SL2 5EJ Tel: (01753) 821303 Fax: (01753) 692485

CRASH OR TRAFFIC OR MOTORWAY BARRIER CONTRACTORS OR ERECTORS

▶ Border Barrier Systems Ltd, Head Office, Alstonby Grange, Westlinton, Carlisle, CA6 6AF Tel: (01228) 675764 Fax: (01228) 675215 E-mail: info@borderbarriers.com
Broughton Controls Ltd, Shaw Road, Oldham, OL1 4AW Tel: 0161-627 0060 Fax: 0161-627 1362 E-mail: info@broughton-controls.co.uk
Delta Scientific Corporation UK Ltd, Delta House, 70 South View Avenue, Caversham, Reading, RG4 5BB Tel: 0118-948 1133 Fax: 0118-948 1122 E-mail: deltascuk@aol.com
Protek Fencing Ltd, Coney Park, Harrogate Road, Yeadon, Leeds, LS19 7XS Tel: 0113-250 0995 Fax: 0113-250 1899 E-mail: contact@protek-fencing.co.uk
Joe Roocroft & Sons Ltd, Aston Way, Moss Side Development Park, Leyland, PR26 7UX Tel: (01772) 642810 Fax: (01772) 455714 E-mail: davidr@jroocroft.co.uk

CRASH REPAIR SERVICES, COMMERCIAL VEHICLE BODYWORK, *See Commercial Vehicle Body Builders*

CRATE HIRE

Badgers Removals, Unit 11 Nathan Way, London, SE28 0BQ Tel: (020) 8317 4500 Fax: (020) 8317 3539
Charter Crate, Berwick Barns, Terling Hall Road, Hatfield Peverel, Chelmsford, CM3 2EY Tel: (01245) 382001 Fax: (01245) 382999
G B Nationwide Crate Hire Ltd, Heritage House, 345 Southbury Road, Enfield, Middlesex, EN1 1UP Tel: (020) 8219 8180 Fax: (020) 8219 8181 E-mail: moreinfo@gbnationwide.com
Komfort Office Crate Hire, 7 Sipson Lane, Hayes, Middlesex, UB3 5EH Tel: (020) 8897 0414 Fax: (020) 8476 1370
▶ Company Moves, 39 Invinsible Road, Farnborough, Hampshire, GU14 7QU Tel: (01252) 549381 Fax: (01252) 376413 E-mail: comoves7@aol.com
PHS Teacrate, PO Box 43, London, NW10 6RH Tel: (020) 8202 0000 Fax: (020) 8282 0022 E-mail: info@teacrate.com
PHS Teacrate The Crate Rental Specialists, 151 Scrubs Lane, London, NW10 6RH Tel: (020) 8282 0000 Fax: (020) 8282 0022 E-mail: info@teacrate.com

CRATES, *See also headings for particular types*

Commercial Trading, Bridge Road, Kingswood, Bristol, BS15 4PT Tel: 0117-961 0710 Fax: 0117-960 2933 E-mail: commercial.trading@btinternet.com
Glenrothes Industrial Packing Ltd, 75-76 Whitecraigs Road, Glenrothes, Fife, KY6 2RX Tel: (01592) 771052 Fax: (01592) 620158
John Pipe Ltd, Mayflower Close, Chandler's Ford, Eastleigh, Hampshire, SO53 4AR Tel: (023) 8036 0100 Fax: (023) 8027 3080 E-mail: sales@johnpipe.co.uk

CRAWLER CRANE HIRE

▶ Anderson Crawler Crane Hire Ltd, Flaxton Grange, Flaxton, York, YO60 7RU Tel: (01904) 468689 Fax: (01904) 468775 E-mail: martyn@andersoncrawler.co.uk
▶ Baldwins Crane Hire Ltd, 52-54 River Road, Barking, Essex, IG11 0DW Tel: (020) 8591 9901 Fax: (020) 8591 9981 E-mail: info@baldwinscranehire.co.uk
Crane Enterprises, Brookhouse Road, Aston, Sheffield, S26 2AH Tel: 0114-287 5499 Fax: 0114-287 5388
Davies Crane Hire Ltd, Pensarn Road, Carmarthen, Dyfed, SA31 2BS Tel: (01267) 234660 Fax: (01267) 232346 E-mail: enquiries@daviescranehire.co.uk
P Burley & Son, Magna Mile, Ludford, Market Rasen, Lincolnshire, LN8 6AH Tel: (01507) 313620 Fax: (01507) 313620

CRAWLER MOUNTED CRANES

Davies Crane Hire Ltd, Phoenix Wharf, Harbour Road, The Docks, Port Talbot, West Glamorgan, SA13 1RA Tel: (01639) 883474 Fax: (01639) 897028 E-mail: enquiries@daviescrane.co.uk
R B Cranes Ltd, Thrumpton Lane, Retford, Nottinghamshire, DN22 7AN Tel: (01777) 700039 Fax: (01777) 713192 E-mail: info@jnd.co.uk

CRAYONS

Binney & Smith Europe Ltd, Ampthill Road, Bedford, MK42 9RS Tel: (01234) 266702 Fax: (01234) 342110
Creative Art Products Ltd, Manor Lane, Holmes Chapel, Crewe, CW4 8AG Tel: (01477) 535868 Fax: (01477) 535996 E-mail: sales@scolaquip.go-plus.net
Rowland Sandwith Ltd, 32 Canford Bottom, Wimborne, Dorset, BH21 2HD Tel: (01202) 882323 Fax: (01202) 842815 E-mail: hancocks@rowland-sandwith.co.uk
Stadium Chalk & Crayon Co. Ltd, Endle Street, Southampton, SO14 5AW Tel: (023) 8022 6765 Fax: (023) 8063 0304 E-mail: sales@stadium-chalk.fsnet.co.uk

CREASING MACHINE/SYSTEMS, *See Folding etc*

CREDIT CARD INDUSTRY RECRUITMENT

▶ Appoint Direct Ltd, PO Box 8828, Chelmsford, CM1 7WP Tel: (01245) 442777 Fax: (08456) 443005 E-mail: info@appointdirect.com
Sirona Consulting, 80 Bulkington Avenue, Worthing, West Sussex, BN14 7HZ Tel: (01903) 206249 Fax: (01903) 206249 E-mail: andy@sironaconsulting.com

CREDIT CARD SYSTEM TOOLMAKERS

Langdale Bros, Weatherhill Works, Hathersham Close, Smallfield, Horley, Surrey, RH6 9JE Tel: (01342) 843164 Fax: (01342) 843164 E-mail: langdalebros@aol.com

CREDIT CARD SYSTEMS

Credit Card Systems Ltd, 64 Walsworth Road, Hitchin, Hertfordshire, SG4 9SX Tel: (01462) 429400 Fax: (01462) 429401 E-mail: sales-ccs@fimak.com
Datum Automation Ltd, 18 Aston Road, Waterlooville, Hampshire, PO7 7XG Tel: (023) 9224 1154 Fax: (023) 9224 1156 E-mail: sales@datum-automation.com
Gemplus Ltd, 36 New Lane, Havant, Hampshire, PO9 2NR Tel: (023) 9248 6444 Fax: (023) 9247 0628 E-mail: felicity.best@gemplus.com
Magtek Europe, Unit 25-26, Shrivenham Hundred Business Park, Majors Road, Watchfield, Swindon, SN6 8TZ Tel: (01793) 786070 Fax: (01793) 786076 E-mail: sales@magtek.co.uk
Oasys Technologies Ltd, Unit 37 Jubilee Road, Letchworth Garden City, Hertfordshire, SG6 1NE Tel: (01462) 480933 Fax: (01462) 480292

CREDIT CARDS

▶ My Credit Zoo, 1 Park Lane, Leeds, LS3 1EP Tel: 0113-242 4747 E-mail: james.dobson@eurodirect.co.uk

CREDIT CONTROL CONSULTANCY

All Management Services Ltd, PO Box 8098, Birmingham, B38 9SP Tel: 0121-680 1981 Fax: 0121-243 8717 E-mail: amslimited@aol.com
Auto Exec Account Collections Ltd, Technology House, 492 London Road, Westcliff-on-Sea, Essex, SS0 9LD Tel: (01702) 431731 Fax: (01702) 431804 E-mail: info@accountcollection.com
Clanchatton Birmingham Ltd, Bell Way House, 7 Worcester Road, Bromsgrove, Worcestershire, B61 7DL Tel: (01527) 879000 Fax: (01527) 870071
Credit Protection Association plc, 350 King Street, London, W6 0RX Tel: (020) 8846 0000 Fax: (020) 8741 7459 E-mail: sales@cpa.co.uk
Credit Solutions Ltd, Barlow House, 3 Butter Hill, Carshalton, Surrey, SM5 2TW Tel: (020) 8773 7111 Fax: (020) 8773 9919 E-mail: credsol@globalnet.co.uk
▶ Crescent Credit Control, PO Box 459, Walton-on-Thames, Surrey, KT12 2WE Tel: (01932) 706590 Fax: (01932) 706590 E-mail: info@credit-specialists.co.uk
L P L Commercial Investigations, 890-900 Eastern Avenue, Ilford, Essex, IG2 7HH Tel: (020) 8597 2229 Fax: (020) 8597 1180 E-mail: info@lplgroup.com
Lewis Group Plc, Lawrence House, Riverside Drive, Cleckheaton, West Yorkshire, BD19 4DH Tel: (01274) 852000 Fax: (01274) 862602
M R C Publications Ltd, 5 Worcester Street, Oxford, OX1 2BX Tel: (01865) 200202 Fax: (01865) 200509 E-mail: sales@mrc.info.com
▶ Paperchase Business Services, Warrington, WA4 6QQ Tel: (07939) 145015 Fax: (01925) 638440
Prime Document Ltd, Unit 3, Park Seventeen, Moss Lane, Whitefield, Manchester, M45 8FJ Tel: 0161-766 5544 Fax: 0161-766 5599 E-mail: sthompson@primedoc.co.uk
Regal Credit Consultants Ltd, Regal House, 18 High Street, Bagshot, Surrey, GU19 5AA Tel: (01276) 470500 Fax: (01276) 470503 E-mail: sales@regalcredit.co.uk
▶ www.getpaidontime.co.uk, 1 Mill Lane, Westhoughton, BOLTON, BL5 2DN Tel: 01942 817905 E-mail: training@getpaidontime.co.uk

CREDIT INFORMATION SERVICES

Agricultural Credit Bureau, Suite 413, The Cotton Exchange Buildings, Old Hall Street, Liverpool, L3 9LQ Tel: 0151-236 6463 Fax: 0151-236 0922 E-mail: mail@lltps.co.uk
Aktiv Kapital (UK) Ltd, Merchants House, Crook Street, Chester, CH1 2BE Tel: (01244) 319912 Fax: (01244) 314635 E-mail: collect@aktivkapital.co.uk
Anthill Debt Collectors, 233a Golders Green Road, London, NW11 9ES Tel: (0800) 0742500 Fax: (020) 8905 5100
C A R E S GB Ltd, Suite, 8 Stoke Road, Stoke-on-Trent, ST4 2DP Tel: (01782) 212613 Fax: (01782) 212046
▶ China Company Research Services Ltd, Catherinefield House, Catherinefield Business Park, Dumfries, DG1 3PQ Tel: (01387) 247588 Fax: (01387) 257143 E-mail: info@ccrs.info
Credit Recovery Systems, 345 City Road, London, EC1V 1AS Tel: (020) 8295 7220 Fax: (020) 7833 4832
Equifax P.L.C., Capital House, 25 Chapel Street, London, NW1 5DS Tel: (020) 7298 3000 Fax: (020) 7723 7555 E-mail: info@equifax.co.uk
Graydon UK Ltd, 66 College Road, 2nd Floor Hygeia Building, Harrow, Middlesex, HA1 1BE Tel: (020) 8515 1400 Fax: (020) 8515 1499 E-mail: mail@graydon.co.uk

CREDIT INFORMATION SERVICES – *continued*

I C C Information Ltd, First Floor, Rooms 8-10, Scottish Mutual Building, 16 Donegall Square South, Belfast, BT1 5JG Tel: (028) 9055 9559 Fax: (028) 9055 0072 E-mail: reports@iccinformationni.com
International Co Profile, Paulton House, 8 Shepherdess Walk, London, N1 7LB Tel: (020) 7490 0049 Fax: (020) 7566 8319 E-mail: customerservice@icpcredit.com
Jack Russell Collections & Investigations, Bayleaf House, 10 York Road, Northampton, NN1 5QG Tel: (01604) 634170 Fax: (01604) 635507 E-mail: jrnorth@debtcollect.co.uk
Liverpool & London Trade Protection Society Ltd, 9 Hillview Close, Purley, Surrey, CR8 1AU Tel: (020) 8763 8807 Fax: (020) 8645 0601 E-mail: mail@lltps.co.uk
Mega Company Services P.L.C., Business Information House, Farmoor Court, Cumnor Road, Oxford, OX2 9LU Tel: (01865) 865666 Fax: (01865) 865465E-mail: info@mega.co.uk
S T A International, Watson House, St. Leonards Road, Maidstone, Kent, ME16 0SS Tel: (01622) 718222 Fax: (01622) 718444 E-mail: enqueries@staonline.com
Status Credit Reports Ltd, 21 Whitchurch Road, Cardiff, CF14 3JN Tel: (029) 2054 4333 Fax: (029) 2054 4300 E-mail: orders@statuscredit.com
Transaction Network Services UK Ltd, Unit 2 The Boulevard, Welwyn Garden City, Hertfordshire, AL7 1EL Tel: (01707) 362200 Fax: (01707) 371764
Transnational Corporation Ltd, Portland House, 4 Albion Street, Cheltenham, Gloucestershire, GL52 2LG Tel: (01242) 529424 Fax: (01242) 222834 E-mail: services@transnationalltd.com

CREDIT INSURANCE

Agricultural Credit Bureau, Suite 413, The Cotton Exchange Buildings, Old Hall Street, Liverpool, L3 9LQ Tel: 0151-236 6463 Fax: 0151-236 0922 E-mail: mail@lltps.co.uk
Atradius, 3 Harbour Drive, Cardiff, CF10 4WZ Tel: (029) 2082 4000 Fax: (029) 2082 4003 E-mail: reception@atradius.com
▶ Bruce Stevenson Risk Management, 38-40 New City Road, Glasgow, G4 9JT Tel: 0141 353 3539 Fax: 0141 353 3888 E-mail: mark.costello@brucestevenson.co.uk
▶ CIFF - Credit Insurance, Factoring & Finance., Cliff House, 75 Hill Top, Bolsover, Derbyshire, S44 6NJ Tel: 01246 241002 Fax: 0845 127 4385 E-mail: ciff1@holroydr.plus.com
Euler Hermes Guarantee plc, Surety House, Lyons Cresent, Tonbridge, Kent, TN9 1EN Tel: (01732) 770311 Fax: (01732) 770361
Euler Hermes UK plc, 1 Canada Square, London, E14 5DX Tel: (0800) 0565452 Fax: (0207) 8602455 E-mail: creditinfo@eulerhermes.com
Heath Lambert Overseas Ltd, 133 Houndsditch, London, EC3A 7AH Tel: (020) 7560 3000 Fax: (020) 7560 3000 E-mail: info@heathgroup.com
Liverpool & London Trade Protection Society Ltd, 9 Hillview Close, Purley, Surrey, CR8 1AU Tel: (020) 8763 8807 Fax: (020) 8645 0601 E-mail: mail@lltps.co.uk
Low Quote Limited, 2a Alton House Office Park, Gatehouse Way, Gatehouse Industrial Area, Aylesbury, Bucks, HP19 8YF Tel: (07834) 542976 E-mail: admin@low-quote.net
Provident Financial Management Services, Colonnade, Sunbridge Road, Bradford, West Yorkshire, BD1 2LQ Tel: (01274) 304044 Fax: (01274) 727300 E-mail: info@provident.co.uk
Rycroft Associates LLP, 16 Queens Avenue, Shirley, Solihull, West Midlands, B90 2NT Tel: 0121 7458978 Fax: 0121 7443562 E-mail: mikestott@rycroftassociates.com

CREDIT REPORTING SERVICES

▶ www.debttrack.com, 40 Garswood Street, Ashton-in-Makerfield, Wigan, Lancashire, WN4 9AF Tel: (01942) 292432 E-mail: enquires@debttrack.com

CREMATION FURNACES/ CREMATORS

Facultatieve Technologies Ltd, Moor Road, Leeds, LS10 2DD Tel: 0113-276 8888 Fax: 0113-271 8188 E-mail: sales@facultatieve.com
Furnace Construction Co. Ltd, Newton Moor Industrial Estate, Hyde, Cheshire, SK14 4LF Tel: 0161-368 8419 Fax: 0161-368 3813 E-mail: sales@furnace-construction.co.uk
Furnace Construction Co. Ltd, Newton Moor Industrial Estate, Hyde, Cheshire, SK14 4LF Tel: 0161-368 8419 Fax: 0161-368 3813 E-mail: sales@furnace-construction.co.uk
▶ Majic Systems Ltd, Hine Lodge, Ransom Road, Mapperley, Nottingham, NG3 5HN Tel: 0870 753 3641 Fax: 0870 753 3651 E-mail: enquiries@majicsystems.co.uk
J.G. Shelton & Co. Ltd, Unit 4, Gibbons Industrial Park, Kingswinford, West Midlands, DY6 8XF Tel: (01384) 293601 Fax: (01384) 293975 E-mail: terry.hawkins@btconnect.com

T & I Stockman Ltd, 19 Holwell Road, Brixham, Devon, TQ5 9NE Tel: (01803) 882385 E-mail: info@stockmanfuneralservice.co.uk
Techtrol Ltd, Gregson Road, Stockport, Cheshire, SK5 7SS Tel: 0161-476 6955 Fax: 0161-476 2674 E-mail: mailbox@techtrol.co.uk

CREPE PAPER

Felber Jucker & Co. Ltd, 48 Minerva Road, Park Royal, London, NW10 6HJ Tel: (020) 8965 9371 Fax: (020) 8961 3732

CRICKET REQUISITES

John Newbery Ltd, The Chalet, Eaton Road, Hove, East Sussex, BN3 3AF Tel: (01273) 775770 Fax: (01273) 775899 E-mail: enquiries@newbery.co.uk
Kookaburra Reader Ltd, Unit 25, The Alders, Seven Mile Lane, Mereworth, Maidstone, Kent, ME18 5JG Tel: (01622) 812230 Fax: (01622) 814224 E-mail: sales@alfredreader.co.uk
Three D Sports, The Runnings, Cheltenham, Gloucestershire, GL51 9NJ Tel: (01242) 241819 Fax: (01242) 222994 E-mail: sales@3dsports.co.uk

CRIMP CONNECTORS

J S T U K Ltd, Blyth Road, Halesworth, Suffolk, IP19 8EW Tel: (01986) 874131 Fax: (01986) 874276 E-mail: sales@jst.co.uk

CRIMP TERMINALS

Livewire Electronic Components Ltd, CWM Farm Barn, Llantrisant, Usk, Gwent, NP15 1LG Tel: (01291) 673003 Fax: (01291) 671001 E-mail: info@livewire.uk.com

CRIMPED PAPER GOODS

▶ Bartec Paper & Packaging, Wincham Avenue, Wincham, Northwich, Cheshire, CW9 6GB Tel: (01606) 354664 Fax: (01606) 354665 E-mail: ute.cooper@good.co.uk
Crimped Paper Works(M/C) Ltd, Bowden Park, Chapel-En-Le-Frith, High Peak, Derbyshire, SK23 0JX Tel: (01298) 812181 Fax: (01298) 815905 E-mail: sales@crimpedpaper.co.uk

CRIMPING (CABLE) END TERMINATIONS

Cable Services Liverpool, 43 St.Johns Road, Bootle, Merseyside, L20 8BH Tel: 0151-933 9022 Fax: 0151-933 9765 E-mail: lpool@cableservices.co.uk

CRITICAL SAFETY JOINTS

K J N Automation Ltd, 5 Peckleton Lane Business Park, Peckleton Common, Peckleton, Leicester, LE9 7RN Tel: (01455) 823304 Fax: (01455) 828186 E-mail: sales@kjnltd.co.uk

CROP SPRAYS, *See Agricultural Spray etc*

CROWD CONTROL BARRIER INSTALLATION

▶ Border Barrier Systems Ltd, Head Office, Alstonby Grange, Westlinton, Carlisle, CA6 6AF Tel: (01228) 675764 Fax: (01228) 675215 E-mail: info@borderbarriers.com

CRUCIBLE FURNACES

Morganite Crucible Ltd, Woodbury Lane, Norton, Worcester, WR5 2PU Tel: (01905) 728200 Fax: (01905) 767877 E-mail: marketing@morganitecrucible.com

CRUCIBLES

Dyson Precision Ceramics, Low Road, Earlsheaton, Dewsbury, West Yorkshire, WF12 8BU Tel: (01924) 468201 Fax: (01924) 459429
Morganite Crucible Ltd, Woodbury Lane, Norton, Worcester, WR5 2PU Tel: (01905) 728200 Fax: (01905) 767877 E-mail: marketing@morganitecrucible.com

CRUDE OIL VESSEL INSPECTION

Saybolt UK Ltd, Oliver Close, Grays, Essex, RM20 3EE Tel: (01708) 862611 Fax: (01708) 867401

CRUSHER HIRE

▶ A & S Crushing Services Ltd, Theedhams Farm, Steeple Road, Southminster, Essex, CM0 7BD Tel: 01621 772620
▶ Haulmark Equipment Ltd, Barleycastle Lane, Appleton, Warrington, WA4 4RB Tel: (01925) 269900 Fax: (01925) 269901 E-mail: sales@haulmarkltd.co.uk
▶ R K Bell Ltd, Dunwear Depot, Dunwear, Bridgwater, Somerset, TA7 0AA Tel: (01278) 424883 Fax: 01278 425944 E-mail: jerome@rkbell.com
Red Rhino Crushers, Unit 3 Triangle Business Park, Quilters Way, Stoke Mandeville, Aylesbury, Buckinghamshire, HP22 5BL Tel: (0870) 6064949 Fax: (0870) 6063939 E-mail: info@redrhinocrushers.net

CRUSHING AND SCREENING PLANT

▶ Kane Haulage Ltd, Construction House, Porters Wood, Valley Road Industrial Estate, St. Albans, Hertfordshire, AL3 6NW Tel: (01727) 733600 Fax: (01727) 733607 E-mail: info@kanehaulage.co.uk

CRUSHING (INDUSTRIAL) PLANT DISTRIBUTORS OR AGENTS

Parker Plant Ltd, PO Box 146, Leicester, LE4 6HD Tel: 0116-266 5999 Fax: 0116-261 0812 E-mail: sales@parkerplant.com

CRUSHING MACHINES

Lanway Ltd, PO Box 3568, Bewdley, Worcestershire, DY12 1ZU Tel: (01299) 861733 Fax: (0871) 7333899 E-mail: sales@lanway.ltd.uk
Xcalibre Equipment Ltd, 3 Starley Court, Hotchkiss Way, Binley Industrial Estate, Coventry, CV3 2RL Tel: (024) 7644 4412 Fax: (024) 7663 5903 E-mail: xcalibre-equipt@btconnect.com

CRYOGENIC ENGINEERING SERVICES

Anglitemp Ltd, Unit A3 Third Avenue, Tyne Tunnel Trading Estate, North Shields, Tyne & Wear, NE29 7SW Tel: 0191-258 6646 Fax: 0191-257 8445 E-mail: anglitemp@anglitemp.freeserve.co.uk

CRYOGENIC EQUIPMENT MANUFRS

Honeywell Hymatic Engineering Co. Ltd, Burnt Meadow Road, North Moons Moat, Redditch, Worcestershire, B98 9HJ Tel: (01527) 64931 Fax: (01527) 591117 E-mail: redwich.sales@honeywell.com
M1 Engineering Ltd, 5 Commondale Way, Bradford, West Yorkshire, BD4 6SQ Tel: (01274) 416000 Fax: (01274) 420307
Magnex Scientific Ltd, Oxford Industrial Park, 6 Mead Road, Yarnton, Oxford, OX5 1QU Tel: (01865) 853800 Fax: (01865) 842466 E-mail: sales@magnex.com
Oxford Instruments Superconductivity, Tubney Woods, Abingdon, Oxfordshire, OX13 5QX Tel: (01865) 393200 Fax: (01865) 393333 E-mail: nanoscience@oxinst.co.uk
Planer plc, 110 Windmill Road, Sunbury-on-Thames, Middlesex, TW16 7HD Tel: (01932) 755000 Fax: (01932) 755001 E-mail: sales@planer.co.uk
Quantum Production, Unit 25 Wornal Park, Menmarsh Road, Worminghall, Aylesbury, Buckinghamshire, HP18 9PH Tel: (01844) 339993 Fax: (01844) 339996 E-mail: info@quantumproduction.co.uk
Statebourne Cryogenics Ltd, 18 Parsons Road, Washington, Tyne & Wear, NE37 1EZ Tel: 0191-416 4104 Fax: 0191-415 0369 E-mail: sales@statebourne.com
Thames Cryogenics Ltd, Gooch Drive, Southmead Industrial Park, Didcot, Oxfordshire, OX11 7PR Tel: (01235) 815777 Fax: (01235) 815333 E-mail: sales@thamescryogenics.com
Wessington Cryogenics Ltd, Building 9, Philadelphia Complex, Houghton Le Spring, Tyne & Wear, DH4 4UG Tel: 0191-512 0677 Fax: 0191-512 0745 E-mail: info@wessingtoncryogenics.co.uk

CRYOGENIC PRESSURE VESSELS

Statebourne Cryogenics Ltd, 18 Parsons Road, Washington, Tyne & Wear, NE37 1EZ Tel: 0191-416 4104 Fax: 0191-415 0369 E-mail: sales@statebourne.com

CRYOGENIC PUMPS

Liquified Gas Pumping Services Ltd, 18 Abbotsinch Road, Grangemouth, Stirlingshire, FK3 9UX Tel: (01324) 485475 Fax: (01324) 485677 E-mail: sales@lgpservices.co.uk

CRYOGENIC SHRINK FITTING SERVICES

Bishop Pipefreezing Ltd, Pipefreezing House, 58A Shirley Road, Croydon, CR0 7EP Tel: (0800) 132750 Fax: (020) 8654 5459 E-mail: bishop@pipefreezingsales.co.uk
Cyril W Bishop, 58a Shirley Road, Croydon, CR0 7EP Tel: (020) 8656 8234 Fax: (020) 8654 5459 E-mail: pipefreezing@bishop.co.uk

CRYOGENIC TANK MAINTENANCE OR REPAIR

Wessington Cryogenics Ltd, Building 9, Philadelphia Complex, Houghton Le Spring, Tyne & Wear, DH4 4UG Tel: 0191-512 0677 Fax: 0191-512 0745 E-mail: info@wessingtoncryogenics.co.uk

CRYOGENIC VALVES

Ebtrade Ltd, Albion Dockside Works, Bristol, BS1 6UT Tel: 0117-927 9204 Fax: 0117-929 8193 E-mail: enquiries@seetru.com
Hindle Valves, Hindle Cockburns Ltd, Victoria Road, Leeds, LS11 5UG Tel: 0113-244 3741 Fax: 0113-244 1872 E-mail: sales_hindle@tyco-valves.com
Proteus Fittings Ltd, Unit 6 Stonegravels Lane, Chesterfield, Derbyshire, S41 7LF Tel: (01246) 211303 Fax: (01246) 209700 E-mail: info@proteusfittings.co.uk
Y P S Valves Ltd, Richardshaw Road, Grangefield Industrial Estate, Pudsey, West Yorkshire, LS28 6QW Tel: 0113-256 7725 Fax: 0113-236 1987 E-mail: info@yps-valves.co.uk

CRYOSTATS, LABORATORY/ INDUSTRIAL/RESEARCH ETC

Bright Instrument Co. Ltd, St. Margarets Way, Stukeley Meadows Industrial Estate, Huntingdon, Cambridgeshire, PE29 6EU Tel: (01480) 454528 Fax: (01480) 456031 E-mail: sales@brightinstruments.com
Magnex Scientific Ltd, Oxford Industrial Park, 6 Mead Road, Yarnton, Oxford, OX5 1QU Tel: (01865) 853800 Fax: (01865) 842466 E-mail: sales@magnex.com
Oxford Instruments Superconductivity, Tubney Woods, Abingdon, Oxfordshire, OX13 5QX Tel: (01865) 393200 Fax: (01865) 393333 E-mail: nanoscience@oxinst.co.uk

CRYSTAL BOUQUETS

▶ Caradan Designs, 13 Burrows Road, Kingswinford, West Midlands, DY6 8LS Tel: (01384) 273491

CRYSTAL CLOCK OSCILLATORS

Onspec Oscillators Ltd, Unit 10, Alliance Close, Attleborough Fields Industrial Estate, Nuneaton, Warwickshire, CV11 6SD Tel: (024) 7664 2024 Fax: (024) 7664 2073 E-mail: sales@onspec.co.uk

CRYSTAL FILTERS

Magna Frequency Management Ltd, Magna House Dales Manor Business Park, Grove Road, Sawston, Cambridge, CB2 4TJ Tel: (01223) 834800 Fax: (01223) 834600 E-mail: sales@magnafrequency.com

CRYSTAL GLASSWARE

Anthony Stern Glass Ltd, Unit 205 Avro House, Havelock Terrace, London, SW8 4AL Tel: (020) 7622 9463 Fax: (020) 7738 8100 E-mail: anthony@anthonysternglass.com
Brierley Hill Glass Co. Ltd, Mount Pleasant, Quarry Bank, Brierley Hill, West Midlands, DY5 2YS Tel: (01384) 77486 Fax: (01384) 77486 E-mail: sales@brierleycrystal.com

CRYSTAL GLASSWARE – *continued*

▶ Bristol Blue Glass Ltd, 7 Whitby Road, Bristol, BS4 3QF Tel: 0117-972 0888 Fax: 0117-972 1050 E-mail: bristolblueglass@bristol-glass.co.uk

Caithness Crystal, 9-12 Hardwick Industrial Estate, Paxman Road, King's Lynn, Norfolk, PE30 4NE Tel: (01553) 765111 Fax: (01553) 767628 E-mail: sales@caithnessglass.co.uk

Dartington Crystal Ltd, Town Park, Torrington, Devon, EX38 7AN Tel: (01805) 626262 Fax: (01805) 626263 E-mail: enquiries@dartington.co.uk

Georgian Crystal Tutbury Ltd, 1 Silk Mill Lane, Tutbury, Burton-on-Trent, Staffordshire, DE13 9LE Tel: (01283) 814534 Fax: (01283) 520186

Greatdale Ltd, The Lakes Glass Centre Oubas Hill, Ulverston, Cumbria, LA12 7LB Tel: (01229) 584400 Fax: (01229) 581132 E-mail: sales@cumbriacrystal.freeserve.co.uk

Nazeing Glassworks Ltd, Nazeing New Road, Broxbourne, Hertfordshire, EN10 6SU Tel: (01992) 464485 Fax: (01992) 450966 E-mail: admin@nazeing-glass.com

Royal Brierley Crystal Ltd, Tipton Road, Dudley, West Midlands, DY1 4SQ Tel: 0121-530 5607 Fax: (01384) 457302 E-mail: brierleyshop@dartington.co.uk

Royal Doulton, Sir Henry Doulton House, Forge Lane Etruria, Stoke-on-Trent, ST1 5NN Tel: (01782) 404040 Fax: (01782) 404000 E-mail: sales@royal-doulton.com

▶ Scribe Gifts, 1 Borehamgate King Street, Sudbury, Suffolk, CO10 2EG Tel: (01787) 373306 E-mail: sales@scribegifts.co.uk

Taylor & Whitlock, 170 Dukes Ride, Crowthorne, Berkshire, RG45 6DS Tel: (01344) 780212 Fax: (01344) 780212 E-mail: sales@twj.co.uk

Tutbury Crystal Glass Ltd, Burton Street, Tutbury, Burton-on-Trent, Staffordshire, DE13 9NR Tel: (01283) 813281 Fax: (01283) 813228 E-mail: info@tutburycrystal.co.uk

Waterford Wedgwood UK P.L.C., Barlaston, Stoke-On-Trent, ST12 9ES Tel: (01782) 204141 Fax: (01782) 204402 E-mail: customer.care@wedgwood.com

CRYSTAL GROWING EQUIPMENT

Crystalox Ltd, 1 Limborough Road, Wantage, Oxfordshire, OX12 9AJ Tel: (01235) 770044 Fax: (01235) 770111 E-mail: sales@crystalox.com

CRYSTAL GROWING SERVICES

Crystalox Ltd, 1 Limborough Road, Wantage, Oxfordshire, OX12 9AJ Tel: (01235) 770044 Fax: (01235) 770111 E-mail: sales@crystalox.com

Metal Crystals & Oxides Ltd, Unit B4 Button End Industrial Estate, Harston, Cambridge, CB22 7GX Tel: (01223) 872072 Fax: (01223) 872517 E-mail: sales@metal-crystals.com

CRYSTAL OSCILLATORS

▶ C-MAC MicroTechnology, Station Road, Crewkerne, Somerset, TA18 8AR Tel: 01460 270200 Fax: 01460 72578 E-mail: info@cmac.com

Euroquartz Ltd, Blacknell Lane, Crewkerne, Somerset, TA18 7HE Tel: (01460) 230000 Fax: (01460) 230001 E-mail: sales@euroquartz.co.uk

Eurosource Electronics Ltd, Parkway House, Sheen Lane, London, SW14 8LS Tel: (020) 8878 5355 Fax: (020) 8878 5733 E-mail: sales@eurosource.co.uk

Fordahl Sa), 225 Hampton Lane, Blackfield, Southampton, SO45 1XA Tel: (023) 8089 8899 Fax: (023) 8089 8899 E-mail: fordahluk@fordahl.com

Magna Frequency Management Ltd, Magna House Dales Manor Business Park, Grove Road, Sawston, Cambridge, CB2 4TJ Tel: (01223) 834800 Fax: (01223) 834600 E-mail: sales@magnafrequency.com

Onspec Oscillators Ltd, Unit 10, Alliance Close, Attleborough Fields Industrial Estate, Nuneaton, Warwickshire, CV11 6SD Tel: (024) 7664 2024 Fax: (024) 7664 2073 E-mail: sales@onspec.co.uk

CRYSTAL STONES

▶ Middleton On The Walds Natural Therapies, 2a Front Street, Middleton on the Wolds, Driffield, North Humberside, YO25 9UA Tel: (01377) 217623 E-mail: sales@middlemists.co

▶ Vivid Trading, Mere Farm Bell, Bell Lane, Saham Toney, Thetford, Norfolk, IP25 7HD Tel: (01953) 883264 E-mail: vividmail@hotmail.com

CUBICLES

Abacus Building Components, Manor House, Rise Road, Sigglesthorne, Hull, HU11 5QH Tel: (01964) 533720 Fax: (01964) 535958 E-mail: abacuscomp@aol.com

▶ Bushboard Ltd, Rixon Road, Wellingborough, Northamptonshire, NN8 4BA Tel: (01933) 232200 Fax: (01933) 232280 E-mail: washrooms@bushboard.co.uk

Deerite Partitions, 9 Eastway, Sale, Cheshire, M33 4DT Tel: 0161-969 5216 Fax: 0161-905 1774 E-mail: birddeerite@btinternet.com

Helmsman, Northern Way, Bury St. Edmunds, Suffolk, IP32 6NH Tel: (01284) 727600 Fax: (01284) 727601 E-mail: sales@helmsman.co.uk

▶ Liverpool Cubicles & Washroom Systems Ltd, Unit 5-7 Luton Street, Liverpool, L5 9XR Tel: 0151-298 1509 Fax: 0151-298 2276 E-mail: liverpoolcubicle@aol.com

Pow Sport & Leisure Co., PO Box 28, London, W4 4WT Tel: (0870) 3503650 Fax: (0870) 3503651 E-mail: info@pow-sport.co.uk

CUE REPAIR

B & W Billiards & Snooker Services Ltd, Unit 3 Sapcote Trading Centre, Powke Lane, Old Hill, Cradley Heath, West Midlands, B64 5QR Tel: (01384) 638191 Fax: (01384) 638195 E-mail: sales@bandwbilliards.co.uk

CUFF LINKS

Acorn Hip Flasks Ltd, Reliance Works, 62 Northwood Street, Birmingham, B3 1TT Tel: (0777) 9724408 Fax: 0121-233 4336 E-mail: peter@hipflasks.co.uk

Peter Dyson & Son Ltd, 3 Cuckoo Lane, Honley, Holmfirth, HD9 6AS Tel: (01484) 661062 Fax: (01484) 663709

Korporate Creations Ltd, 151 Utney Bridge Road Shire Place, Swaffield Road, London, SW15 2NZ Tel: (020) 8870 2070 Fax: (020) 8870 2012 E-mail: info@korporate-creations.com

Merit Badge & Regalia Co. Ltd, Merit House, Stanhope Street, Highgate, Birmingham, B12 0UX Tel: 0121-440 6861 Fax: 0121-440 1037 E-mail: sales@fcparry.com

Morton & Crowder Ltd, 14 Fortnum Close, Birmingham, B33 0JX Tel: 0121-783 7571 Fax: 0121-783 1327 E-mail: morcro@aol.com

Toye Kenning Spencer Stadden, 77 Warstone Lane, Birmingham, B18 6NL Tel: 0121-236 3253 Fax: 0121-236 7217 E-mail: sales@toyebirm.demon.co.uk

CULLETS, *See Glass Cullet etc*

CULTIVATORS

Bomford Turner Ltd, Station Road, Salford Priors, Evesham, Worcestershire, WR11 8SW Tel: (01789) 773383 Fax: (01789) 773238 E-mail: sales@bomford-turner.com

Kilworth Agricultural Machinery, Annwell Lane, Smisby, Ashby-de-la-Zouch, Leicestershire, LE65 2TA Tel: (01530) 412690 Fax: (01530) 560002E-mail: sales@kilworthmachinery.co.uk

P.J. Parmiter & Sons Ltd, Station Works, Tisbury, Salisbury, SP3 6QZ Tel: (01747) 870821 Fax: (01747) 871171 E-mail: mail@parmiter.co.uk

CULTURED PEARLS

Cultured Pearl Co. Ltd, 27 Hatton Garden, London, EC1N 8BR Tel: (020) 7405 3339 Fax: (020) 7405 5936 E-mail: info@theculturedpearl.co.uk

Imperial Pearl, 24 Hatton Garden, London, EC1N 8BQ Tel: (020) 7242 0575 Fax: (020) 7405 7373 E-mail: valdorltd@waitrose.com

La Jana Ltd, 34-35 Hatton Garden, London, EC1N 8DX Tel: (020) 7242 6668 Fax: (020) 7242 1991

Lotus Jewellery, Alexandra House, Chartwell Drive, Wigston, Leicestershire, LE18 2EZ Tel: (0870) 8508200 Fax: (0870) 8508201 E-mail: apollo.sales@timeproducts.co.uk

Matt Aminoff & Co., 26-27 Hatton Garden, London, EC1N 8BR Tel: (020) 7405 3587 Fax: (020) 7430 1073 E-mail: enquiries@mattaminoff.com

Val D'Or Ltd, 24 Hatton Gardens, London, EC1N 8BQ Tel: (020) 7405 5102 Fax: (020) 7405 7373

CUPOLA FURNACES

A1 Roper Ltd, Crown Works, Worth Way, Keighley, West Yorkshire, BD21 5LR Tel: (01535) 604215 Fax: (01535) 602689 E-mail: a1-roper@compuserve.com

CUPRO NICKEL

Aldruscilla, 8 Deer Park Road, London, SW19 3UU Tel: (020) 8543 8710 Fax: (020) 8543 0605 E-mail: metal@aldruscilla.co.uk

Dorset Tube, Thrush Road, Poole, Dorset, BH12 4NT Tel: (01202) 725000 Fax: (01202) 725025 E-mail: sales@dorsettubes.co.uk

CUPRO NICKEL FORGINGS

Newlo International Ltd, Market Place, Chapel-en-le-Frith, High Peak, Derbyshire, SK23 0EN Tel: (01298) 812973 Fax: (01298) 813282

CUPRO NICKEL TUBES

Dorset Tube, Thrush Road, Poole, Dorset, BH12 4NT Tel: (01202) 725000 Fax: (01202) 725025 E-mail: sales@dorsettubes.co.uk

CUPRO-NICKEL WIRE

Kanthal Ltd, Canal Arm, Festival Way, Stoke-on-Trent, ST1 5UR Tel: (01782) 224800 Fax: (01782) 224820 E-mail: info.uk@kanthal.se

Omega Resistance Wire Ltd, Hadley Works, Cranborne Road, Potters Bar, Hertfordshire, EN6 3JL Tel: (01707) 620111 Fax: (01707) 649225 E-mail: sales@omega-wire.com

CURING, *See headings for particular types*

CURRENCY EXCHANGE RATE BOARDS

▶ CorporateFX, 163 Eversholt Street, Euston, London, NW1 1BU Tel: 0207 3808400

▶ Moneycorp, 100 Brompton Road, London, SW3 1ER Tel: (020) 7823 7500 Fax: (020) 7235 4250 E-mail: smaguire@receptional.com

CURRENCY FUTURES BROKERS OR DEALERS

▶ Moneycorp, 100 Brompton Road, London, SW3 1ER Tel: (020) 7823 7500 Fax: (020) 7235 4250 E-mail: smaguire@receptional.com

CURRENT MEASUREMENT TRANSFORMERS

Instrument Transformers Ltd, 8 Lithgow Place, East Kilbride, Glasgow, G74 1PW Tel: (01355) 236057 Fax: (01355) 239259 E-mail: sales@itl-uk.com

Toroid Technology Ltd, 50 Mill Lane, Purley Way, Croydon, CR0 4AA Tel: (020) 8686 8646 Fax: (020) 8686 7177 E-mail: toroids@toroid-tech.com

CURRENT OPERATED EARTH LEAKAGE CIRCUIT BREAKERS (ELCB)

C M T S, 7 Churchfield Road, Sudbury, Suffolk, CO10 2YA Tel: (01787) 468685 Fax: (01787) 468687 E-mail: sales@cmts.co.uk

Doepke UK Ltd, Unit 19, Woodlands Business Park, Woodlands Park Avenue, Maidenhead, Berkshire, SL6 3UA Tel: (01628) 829133 Fax: (01628) 829149 E-mail: sales@doepke.co.uk

CURRENT TRANSFORMERS

Albar Associates, Meridian House, Road One, Winsford, Cheshire, CW7 3QG Tel: (01606) 861351 Fax: (01606) 861643 E-mail: albar@albar-energy.co.uk

Toroid Technology Ltd, 50 Mill Lane, Purley Way, Croydon, CR0 4AA Tel: (020) 8686 8646 Fax: (020) 8686 7177 E-mail: toroids@toroid-tech.com

CURRIERS, HIDE/LEATHER, *See Leather etc*

CURTAIN ACCESSORIES

▶ Curtain Calls, 6 Ambleside Close, Woodley, Reading, RG5 4JJ Tel: 0118-901 4632 Fax: 0118-901 4632 E-mail: studio@curtaincalls.co.uk

CURTAIN CLEANING SERVICES TO THE TRADE

Careclean Dry Cleaners, 117 Snakes Lane, Woodford Green, Essex, IG8 0DY Tel: (020) 8504 6955

Pilgrim Payne & Co. Ltd, Units 12-14 Wharfeside, Rosemont Road, Wembley, Middlesex, HA0 4PE Tel: (020) 8453 5350 Fax: (020) 8453 5604 E-mail: info@pilgrimpayne.co.uk

CURTAIN HOOKS AND RINGS

Kestrel, Heaton Road, Bradford, West Yorkshire, BD9 4SH Tel: (01274) 360404 Fax: (01274) 360401 E-mail: sales.kestrel@haddowholdingsplc.com

Charles Rowley & Co. Ltd, 22 Athole Street, Birmingham, B12 0DA Tel: 0121-440 7711 Fax: 0121-440 4837 E-mail: sales@charlesrowley.co.uk

Rufflette Ltd, Sharston Road, Sharston Industrial Area, Manchester, M22 4TH Tel: 0161-998 1811 Fax: 0161-945 1123 E-mail: sales@rufflette.com

CURTAIN INTERLININGS

Premier Textiles Ltd, Green Lane Industrial Estate, Green Lane, Stockport, Cheshire, SK4 2JR Tel: 0161-429 5770 Fax: 0161-429 5777 E-mail: sales@premier-textiles.com

R & J Partington, Failsworth Mill, Ashton Road West, Failsworth, Manchester, M35 0FR Tel: 0161-934 4040 Fax: 0161-683 4280 E-mail: partington@fabric.co.uk

CURTAIN LINING FABRICS, *See Lining Fabric etc*

CURTAIN LINING SERVICES

▶ Acorn Soft Furnishings, 12 Almond Drive, Burtonwood, Warrington, WA5 4QE Tel: 01925 291237 Fax: 01925 293255 E-mail: bev@acorn-soft-furnishings.co.uk

▶ Alandola Design, Midton House, By Alloway, Ayr, KA7 4EG Tel: (01292) 442226 Fax: (01292) 442226 E-mail: adrienne@alandola-design.fsworld.co.uk

Edmund Bell & Co. Ltd, Belfry House, Roydsdale Way, Euroway Industrial Estate, Bradford, West Yorkshire, BD4 6SU Tel: (01274) 680000 Fax: (01274) 680699 E-mail: sales@edmundbell.co.uk

Platt Haworth & Co. Ltd, Fourways House, 18 Tariff Street, Manchester, M1 2FN Tel: 0161-236 0764 Fax: 0161-236 7543 E-mail: sales@platthaworth.com

R & J Partington, Failsworth Mill, Ashton Road West, Failsworth, Manchester, M35 0FR Tel: 0161-934 4040 Fax: 0161-683 4280 E-mail: partington@fabric.co.uk

Samuel Simpson & Co. Ltd, 30 Broughton Street, Manchester, M8 8NN Tel: 0161-834 4920 Fax: 0161-834 3056 E-mail: sales@samuelsimpson.com

CURTAIN RAIL OR POLE OR FITTINGS

Bruva Renaissance, The Old Mill, Miry Lane, Yeadon, Leeds, LS19 7ER Tel: 0113-250 4499

Cope & Timmins Ltd, Innova House 4 Kinetic Crescent, Enfield, Middlesex, EN3 7XH Tel: (0845) 4588860 Fax: (0800) 0740078 E-mail: customerservice@copes.co.uk

CTS, 23 Belle Vue Road, London, E17 4DQ Tel: (020) 8527 2001 Fax: (020) 8527 1511

▶ Curtain & Blind, 39-41 Appleton Gate, Newark, Nottinghamshire, NG24 1JR Tel: (01636) 702102 Fax: (01609) 771669 E-mail: tony@hotmail.com

▶ Fit-Ex.Com, 30 Hans Apel Drive, Brackley, Northamptonshire, NN13 6HD Tel: (01280) 701090 Fax: (01280) 701090 E-mail: fitex@btinternet.com

Hallis Hudson Group Ltd, Unit B1, Redscar Business Park, Longridge Road, Preston, PR2 5NJ Tel: (01772) 909500 Fax: (01772) 909599 E-mail: info@hallishudson.com

Holbein, 142A Canbury Park Road, Kingston upon Thames, Surrey, KT2 6LE Tel: (020) 8974 5695 Fax: (020) 8974 5635

I D P (Europe) Ltd, Phoenix Works, Davis Road, Chessington, Surrey, KT9 1TH Tel: (020) 8391 3888 Fax: (020) 8974 2895 E-mail: info@holbine.co.uk

Jameson Curtains Ltd, 320 Cheapside, Birmingham, B5 6AX Tel: 0121-622 6620 Fax: 0121-622 6779 E-mail: furnishings@jamesons.demon.co.uk

John Downs Hull Ltd, 13 Unit Factory Estate, Boulevard, Hull, HU3 4AY Tel: (01482) 329099 Fax: (01482) 329099

Kestrel, Heaton Road, Bradford, West Yorkshire, BD9 4SH Tel: (01274) 360404 Fax: (01274) 360401 E-mail: sales.kestrel@haddowholdingsplc.com

▶ Poles4curtains, 4 Manywells Industrial Estate, Cullingworth, Bradford, West Yorkshire, BD13 5DX Tel: (01535) 273355 Fax: (01535) 273344 E-mail: info@poles4curtains.co.uk

R N Contract Blinds, 57 Dyott Avenue, Whittington, Lichfield, Staffordshire, WS14 9NF Tel: (01543) 433433 Fax: (01543) 304047

CURTAIN RAIL OR POLE OR FITTINGS – *continued*

Ritetrack, Harrowby Business Centre, Harrowby Place, Cardiff, CF10 5GB Tel: (029) 2049 9877 Fax: (029) 2046 2462
Neil Smith Ltd, 370 Gallowgate, Glasgow, G4 0TX Tel: 0141-552 1141 Fax: 0141-552 0623

CURTAIN SWAGS AND TAILS

▶ Contemporary Living, 25 Peaseland Road, Cleckheaton, West Yorkshire, BD19 3EZ Tel: (01274) 861855 Fax: (01274) 876529 E-mail: design@contemporaryliving.tv

CURTAIN TAPES

Mactapes Ltd, Heatherside, Stalybridge, Cheshire, SK15 2QN Tel: 0161-303 2244 Fax: 0161-303 2244
Rufflette Ltd, Sharston Road, Sharston Industrial Area, Manchester, M22 4TH Tel: 0161-998 1811 Fax: 0161-945 1123 E-mail: sales@rufflette.com

CURTAIN TIE BACKS

▶ Alandola Design, Midton House, By Alloway, Ayr, KA7 4EG Tel: (01292) 442226 Fax: (01292) 442226 E-mail: adrienne@alandola-design.fsworld.co.uk
Bruva Renaissance, The Old Mill, Miry Lane, Yeadon, Leeds, LS19 7ER Tel: 0113-250 4499

CURTAIN WALL SYSTEM ACOUSTIC PANELS

▶ House Couturier Ltd, 285 New Kings Road, London, SW6 4RD Tel: (020) 7371 9255 E-mail: info@housecouturier.eu

CURTAIN WALLING SYSTEMS

J P J Installations Ltd, 8 Swinbourne Drive, Springwood Industrial Estate, Braintree, Essex, CM7 2YP Tel: (01376) 528111 Fax: (01376) 528222 E-mail: jpj@btconnect.com
Modern Fabrications (Barnsley) Ltd, Modern House, Summer Lane, Barnsley, South Yorkshire, S70 2NP Tel: (01226) 733337 Fax: (01226) 730004 E-mail: sales@modern-fabrications.co.uk
▶ MTW Architectural, Trinity Business Park, Turner Way, Wakefield, West Yorkshire, WF2 8EF Tel: (01924) 239100 Fax: (01924) 239600 E-mail: neville.taylor@mtwarchitectural.co.uk
Parkside Group Ltd, 5 Willow Business Centre, 17 Willow Lane, Mitcham, Surrey, CR4 4NX Tel: (020) 8685 9685 Fax: (020) 8646 5096 E-mail: sales@parksidegrp.co.uk

CURTAIN WALLING SYSTEMS FABRICATORS OR SUBCONTRACTORS

A W S Turner-Fain Ltd, Roman Acre House, West Bank, Berry Hill Industrial Estate, Droitwich, Worcestershire, WR9 9AE Tel: (01905) 774267 Fax: (01905) 775565 E-mail: aws@turnerfainltd.co.uk
Albann Ltd, Unit 69 Third Avenue, Heatherhouse Industrial Estate, Irvine, Ayrshire, KA12 8HN Tel: (01294) 272311 Fax: (01294) 276677 E-mail: sales@albann.co.uk
Aluminium Sashes Ltd, Barnett Way, Barnwood, Gloucester, GL4 3RT Tel: (01452) 616581 Fax: (01452) 371923
Architectural Aluminium Systems Ltd, Sandleheath Industrial Estate, 6 Old Brickyard Road, Sandleheath, Fordingbridge, Hampshire, SP6 1PA Tel: (01425) 654080 Fax: (01425) 652038
Avdon Bristol Ltd, Ashton Vale Road, Bristol, BS3 2HT Tel: 0117-953 3300 Fax: 0117-966 4948 E-mail: sales@avdon.co.uk
Branston Engineering Ltd, Grange Farm Cottages, Grange Lane, Nocton Hth, Lincoln, LN4 2AQ Tel: (01522) 791101 Fax: (01522) 793242 E-mail: branston@globalnet.co.uk
C A P Aluminium Systems Ltd, Systems House, Spon Lane, West Bromwich, West Midlands, B70 6AA Tel: 0121-525 1000 Fax: 0121-525 5010
Duplus Architectural Systems Ltd, 370 Melton Road, Leicester, LE4 7SL Tel: 0116-261 0710 Fax: 0116-261 0539 E-mail: sales@duplus.co.uk
Euro Aluminium Systems Ltd, Bradley Junction Industrial Estate, Leeds Road, Huddersfield, HD2 1UR Tel: (01484) 429987 Fax: (01484) 429937 E-mail: info@euroalisys.freeserve.co.uk
HW Architectural Ltd, Birds Royd Lane, Birds Royd Lane, Brighouse, West Yorkshire, HD6 1NG Tel: (01484) 717677 Fax: (01484) 400148 E-mail: info@hwa.co.uk
▶ J S F Installations, 185 Garth Twentyfour, Killingworth, Newcastle Upon Tyne, NE12 6DJ Tel: 0191-268 5375 Fax: 0191-268 5375
Leay Ltd, Unit 3 Lake Road, Quarry Wood, Aylesford, Kent, ME20 7TQ Tel: (01622) 882345 Fax: (01622) 882208 E-mail: enquiries@leay.com
M D S Architectural Fabrications Ltd, Unit 3a Brandon Way, West Bromwich, West Midlands, B70 8JB Tel: 0121-525 3338 Fax: 0121-525 3348
Magnum Aluminium Products (1993) Ltd, Units 3-4 Blackwater Close, Marsh Way, Rainham, Essex, RM13 8RH Tel: (01708) 522417 Fax: (01708) 525840 E-mail: gary@magnumaluminium.co.uk
Melayway Glass Assemblies Ltd, Centennium House, Pyrford Road, West Byfleet, Surrey, KT14 6LD Tel: (01932) 349404 Fax: (01932) 349405 E-mail: info@melayway.co.uk
▶ MTW Architectural, Trinity Business Park, Turner Way, Wakefield, West Yorkshire, WF2 8EF Tel: (01924) 239100 Fax: (01924) 239600 E-mail: neville.taylor@mtwarchitectural.co.uk
Parry Bowen, Unit S Chasewater Industrial Estate, Burntwood Business Park, Burntwood, Staffordshire, WS7 3GQ Tel: (01543) 678000 Fax: (01543) 677237
▶ Pensher-Skytech, Felling Works, William Street, Gateshead, Tyne & Wear, NE10 0JP Tel: 0191-438 0455 Fax: 0191-438 2328 E-mail: sales@pensher.co.uk
Plus Facades Ltd, Unit 9, Woking Business Park, Woking, Surrey, GU21 5TY Tel: (01483) 757511 Fax: (01483) 757522 E-mail: pluswall@pluswall.com
S G Aluminium Ltd, Unit B Sett End Road West, Shadsworth Business Park, Blackburn, BB1 2QJ Tel: (01254) 691600 Fax: (01253) 340526 E-mail: info@sg-aluminium.co.uk
Stoakes Systems Ltd, 1 Banstead Road, Purley, Surrey, CR8 3EB Tel: (020) 8660 7667 Fax: (020) 8660 5707 E-mail: admin@stoakes.co.uk
Structura UK Ltd, Phoenix Works, Davis Road, Chessington, Surrey, KT9 1TH Tel: (020) 8397 4361 Fax: (020) 8391 5805 E-mail: sales@structura-uk.com
Thames Contract, Longreach Road, Barking, Essex, IG11 0JR Tel: (020) 8591 1555 Fax: (020) 8591 8889 E-mail: thames.c@virgin.net
Topside Group Ltd, Daimler Drive, Cowpen Lane Industrial Estate, Billingham, Cleveland, TS23 4JD Tel: (01642) 566611 Fax: (01642) 561196
The Window Glass Company Bristol Ltd, 11 Emery Road, Bristol, BS4 5PF Tel: 0117-977 9292 Fax: 0117-977 9299 E-mail: mail@windowglass.co.uk

CURTAINS TO SPECIFICATION

A & M Curtains, Ray Street, Huddersfield, HD1 6BL Tel: (01484) 307507 Fax: (01484) 307507
▶ Acorn Soft Furnishings, 12 Almond Drive, Burtonwood, Warrington, WA5 4QE Tel: 01925 291237 Fax: 01925 293255 E-mail: bev@acorn-soft-furnishings.co.uk
Albert E Chapman Ltd, 17 Crouch Hill, London, N4 4AP Tel: (020) 7272 2536 Fax: (020) 7263 1033
Apollo Blinds Ltd, 212 Argyle Street, Glasgow, G2 8HA Tel: 0141-226 3166 Fax: 0141-226 5444
▶ Ayshire Curtain Makers, 3 Montgomery Place, Irvine, Ayrshire, KA12 8PN Tel: (01294) 275603 Fax: (01294) 275603
Austin Berridge Ltd, 2 Buckminster Road, Blackbird Road, Leicester, LE3 9AR Tel: 0116-251 9922 Fax: 0116-251 9922
Briant Curtaining Ltd, 147-149 Albany Road, Coventry, CV5 6ND Tel: (024) 7671 3334 Fax: (024) 7671 2055 E-mail: bc@briantcurtaining.co.uk
Bury Soft Furnishings Ltd, 9 Brantwood Road, Salford, M7 4EN Tel: 0161-792 1492 Fax: 0161-792 1492
Cheshire Drapes Ltd, Chichister Road, Romley, Stockport, Cheshire, SK6 4BL Tel: 0161-430 4110 Fax: 0161-406 6327
Clarke S.J Company Ltd, Caxton Park, Caxton Road Elm Farm Indusrial Estate, Elm Farm Industrial Estate, Bedford, MK41 0TY Tel: (01234) 346513 Fax: (01234) 364047 E-mail: sales@sjclarke.co.uk
Courtney Contract Furnishers Ltd, J-K Unit Enterprise Centre, Paycocke Road, Basildon, Essex, SS14 3DY Tel: (01268) 531771 Fax: (01268) 271299 E-mail: sales@courtney-contracts.co.uk
Curtain & Blind Specialists, West Drive, Lancaster, LA1 5BY Tel: (01524) 383000
▶ Curtain Calls, 6 Ambleside Close, Woodley, Reading, RG5 4JJ Tel: 0118-901 4632 Fax: 0118-901 4632 E-mail: studio@curtaincalls.co.uk
Curtain Couture, 281 Stockport Road, Ashton-under-Lyne, Lancashire, OL7 0NT Tel: 0161-339 2227 Fax: 0161-339 2227 E-mail: curtaincouture@hotmail.com
Curtain Studio, Unit 10, Swallow Mill, Swallow Street, Higher Hillgate, Stockport, Cheshire, SK1 3HJ Tel: 0161-480 6480
Curtains Plus, 6 Bridge Close, Horsell, Woking, Surrey, GU21 4PD Tel: (01483) 472121 E-mail: rose.austin@ntlworld.com
Filigree Ltd, Carter Lane East, South Normanton, Alfreton, Derbyshire, DE55 2EG Tel: (01773) 811619 Fax: (01773) 862777 E-mail: enquiries@filigree.demon.co.uk
Thomas French Ltd, James Street, Bury, Lancashire, BL9 7EG Tel: 0161-764 5356 Fax: 0161-764 6416 E-mail: peter.owen@thomasfrench.com
Fuda International Trading Co. Ltd, Middle Engine Lane, North Shields, Tyne & Wear, NE29 8HG Tel: 0191-258 2233 Fax: 0191-258 2267
Fullwith Textiles Ltd, Sunnybank Mills, Town Street, Farsley, Pudsey, West Yorkshire, LS28 5UJ Tel: 0113-257 9811 Fax: 0113-257 7064
Gaf Interiors, 448 Queens Drive, West Derby, Liverpool, L13 0AR Tel: 0151-230 0033 Fax: 0151-230 0033 E-mail: jeanette@woolrich.fslife.co.uk
Gemini Blinds & Curtains, 732 Borough Road, Birkenhead, Merseyside, CH42 9JF Tel: 0151-608 7100 Fax: 0151-608 7100
Jameson Curtains Ltd, 320 Cheapside, Birmingham, B5 6AX Tel: 0121-622 6620 Fax: 0121-622 6779 E-mail: furnishings@jamesons.demon.co.uk
JP Soft Furnishings, Hitherford Workshop, Hitherford Lane, Over, Cambridge, CB24 5NY Tel: (01954) 230651 E-mail: mje@pjsoftfurnishings.co.uk
▶ K W Curtain Designs, 59 Holt Drive, Loughborough, Leicestershire, LE11 3HZ Tel: (01509) 210585 E-mail: kwalmsley@kwdesigns.fsnet.co.uk
▶ Loose Ends Fabrics & Workshop, Unit 8 Priory Place, Hankerton, Malmesbury, Wiltshire, SN16 9JZ Tel: (01666) 575300 Fax: (01666) 575300 E-mail: info@looseendsfabrics.co.uk
Mallards Interiors, Peter James Lane, Fairlight, Hastings, East Sussex, TN35 4AH Tel: (01424) 813853 Fax: (01424) 813853
New Curtains Co. Ltd, 64 South Street, Epsom, Surrey, KT18 7PH Tel: (01372) 747970
P E C Furniture Ltd, Amble Industrial Estate, Amble, Morpeth, Northumberland, NE65 0PE Tel: (01665) 710593 Fax: (01665) 712735 E-mail: pecfurn@aol.com
Perkins & Stockwell, 12 Abbey Gate, Leicester, LE4 0AB Tel: 0116-251 6501 Fax: 0116-251 0697
Pilgrim Payne & Co. Ltd, Units 12-14 Wharfeside, Rosemont Road, Wembley, Middlesex, HA0 4PE Tel: (020) 8453 5350 Fax: (020) 8453 5604 E-mail: info@pilgrimpayne.co.uk
Ann Poulter, 2a Worksop Road, Swallownest, Sheffield, S26 4WD Tel: 0114-287 6707 Fax: 0114-287 6707
Practical Upholsterers Ltd, 35a Pound Farm Road, Chichester, West Sussex, PO19 7PU Tel: (01243) 786090 Fax: (01243) 786090
Sinclair Fabrics, London Road, Bozeat, Wellingborough, Northamptonshire, NN29 7JR Tel: (01933) 663533 Fax: (01933) 663657
Suttons Furnishings Ltd, 56 Church Road, Hove, East Sussex, BN3 2FP Tel: (01273) 723728 Fax: (01273) 730837
Techniblinds Ltd, 16 Plumpton Way, Carshalton, Surrey, SM5 2DG Tel: (020) 8669 1122 Fax: (020) 8669 2244 E-mail: info@techniblinds.co.uk
Turners Of Felixstowe, 56 St Andrews Road, Felixstowe, Suffolk, IP11 7BT Tel: (01473) 610830 Fax: (01394) 273670
York Blind Co., Heworth House Studio, Melrosegate, York, YO31 0RP Tel: (01904) 416389 Fax: (01904) 416389

CURVED OR HOLE CUTTING SAWS

Garrison Dales Ltd, Unit 8, North St Industrial Estate, Droitwich, Worcestershire, WR9 8JB Tel: (01905) 794555 Fax: (01905) 794592 E-mail: sales@garrisondales.co.uk

CURVED STAIRCASES

▶ T B Staircases, Unit 1b Millenium Business Unit, Dawlish Business Park, Dawlish, Devon, EX7 0NH Tel: (01626) 866435 Fax: (01626) 866445 E-mail: tb.staircases@virgin.net

CURVED STAIRCASES TO SPECIFICATION

▶ MalcolmEWhite&Son, 28 Brick Hill, Bromham, Chippenham, Wiltshire, SN15 2JL Tel: (01380) 850562 Fax: (01380) 850562 E-mail: info@malcolmewhiteandson.co.uk

CUSHION COVERS

▶ Bay Ridge, Design House, 20-22 Beulah Road, London, SW19 3SB Tel: (020) 8543 8598 Fax: (020) 8542 6831 E-mail: office@bayridge-uk.com
Mystic East Cushions, PO BOX 51568, London, LONDON, SE1 2JT Tel: 0845 612 1551 E-mail: mysticeastcushions@miscobjects.com

CUSHIONS

▶ Bay Ridge, Design House, 20-22 Beulah Road, London, SW19 3SB Tel: (020) 8543 8598 Fax: (020) 8542 6831 E-mail: office@bayridge-uk.com

CUSTOM BUILT POWER SUPPLIES

P S U Designs Ltd, 7 Bloomfield Park, Bloomfield Road, Tipton, West Midlands, DY4 9AP Tel: 0121-557 6499 Fax: 0121-557 6498 E-mail: sales@psudesigns.co.uk
P S U Electronics Ltd, Unit 8 Tweedale Court, Tweedale North Industrial Estate, Telford, Shropshire, TF7 4JZ Tel: (01952) 583637 Fax: (01952) 583637
Power One, 24 Upper High Street, Worthing, West Sussex, BN11 1DL Tel: (01903) 823323 Fax: (01903) 823324 E-mail: sales@powerone.com
Qes Ltd, Niall House, 24-26 Boulton Road, Stevenage, Hertfordshire, SG1 4QX Tel: (01438) 749849 Fax: (01438) 318420 E-mail: sales@qesltd.co.uk
Wright Electric Company Ltd, 35 Clarendon Avenue, Trowbridge, Wiltshire, BA14 7BW Tel: (01225) 761188 Fax: (01225) 761188 E-mail: sales@wrightelec.demon.co.uk

CUSTOMER ANALYSIS SYSTEMS

▶ Niche Technologies Ltd, Ternion Court, 264-268 Upper Fourth Street, Milton Keynes, MK10 1DP Tel: 0870 7504471 Fax: 0870 1335371 E-mail: sales@niche-technologies.co.uk

CUSTOMER RELATION MANAGEMENT (CRM) SERVICES

▶ Autoview UK Ltd, Business & Innovation Centre, Wearfield, Sunderland Enterprise Park (East), Sunderland, SR5 2TA Tel: 0191 5166444 Fax: 0191 5166445 E-mail: info@autoviewsystems.co.uk
▶ Jane Phillips, The Quadrant, Parkway Avenue, Sheffield, S9 4WG Tel: 0114 227 0022

CUSTOMER RELATIONSHIP MANAGEMENT (CRM) ELECTRONIC MAIL (EMAIL) MARKETING

▶ Just C R M, Garden Cottage, Elsfield, Oxford, OX3 9UH Tel: (01865) 351771 E-mail: jonbowen@personal-computer-services.co.uk
▶ stream:20, Southbank house, Blackprince Road, London, SE1 7SJ Tel: 0207 7932450

CUSTOMER RELATIONSHIP MANAGEMENT (CRM) SUPPORT SOFTWARE

▶ Cobault Computer Systems, 29 Great George Street, Bristol, BS1 5QT Tel: 0117-920 0123 Fax: 0117-920 0124E-mail: info@cobault.com

CUSTOMER RELATIONSHIP MANAGEMENT (CRM) TRAINING

▶ Jane Phillips, The Quadrant, Parkway Avenue, Sheffield, S9 4WG Tel: 0114 227 0022

CUSTOMER RELATIONSHIP MANAGEMENT (CRM), PROPERTY

▶ Surf4apropety, Leeds, LS17 1BX Tel: 0113-266 9639 Fax: 0113-266 9639 E-mail: info@surf4aproperty.com

CUSTOMER SATISFACTION CONSULTANTS

Achieveglobal, Spencer House, 23 Sheen Road, Richmond, Surrey, TW9 1BN Tel: (020) 8322 4000 Fax: (020) 8322 4001 E-mail: service@achieveglobal.co.uk
Ashway Associates, Ashway House, Ickwell Green, Biggleswade, Bedfordshire, SG18 9EQ Tel: (01767) 627449 Fax: (01767) 627799 E-mail: ashcroftashway@aol.com
Linkbridge Ltd, 173 Quemerford, Calne, Wiltshire, SN11 8JX Tel: (01249) 811476 Fax: (01249) 811854 E-mail: lars@linkbridge.co.uk

CUSTOMER SATISFACTION CONSULTANTS – *continued*

Saratoga Systems Ltd, Ashlyn House, Terrace Road North, Binfield, Bracknell, Berkshire, RG42 5JA Tel: (01344) 868700 Fax: (01344) 421171 E-mail: sales@saratoga.co.uk

Work Group Support Systems, The Studio, Craigleth Road, Edinburgh, EH4 2EB Tel: 0131-477 7775 Fax: 0131-332 7467 E-mail: n.hill@wgss.co.uk

CUSTOMS CLEARANCE AGENTS

A Hartrodt UK Ltd, Unit 2 Pump Lane Industrial Estate, Hayes, Middlesex, UB3 3NB Tel: (020) 8848 3545 Fax: (020) 8561 0940 E-mail: london@hartrodt.co.uk

Archfield (Shipping) Ltd, Factory Road, London, E16 2HD Tel: (020) 7476 4386 Fax: (020) 7511 2238 E-mail: sales@archfield.co.uk

John Burke & Co. Ltd, 141 York Street, Belfast, BT15 1AB Tel: (028) 9032 2841 Fax: (028) 9032 3395 E-mail: smcready@burkebelfast.com

Chiltern Cargo Services Ltd, Willen Works, Willen Road, Newport Pagnell, Bucks, MK16 0DG Tel: (01908) 611222 Fax: (01908) 612221 E-mail: admin@chiltern.cargo.co.uk

Dolphin Movers, Unit 2 Haslemere Business Centre, Lincoln Way, Enfield, Middlesex, EN1 1DX Tel: (020) 8804 7700 Fax: (020) 8804 3232 E-mail: sales@dolphinmovers.com

▶ Stephen Elwis, The Oaklands, Barton Street, Laceby, Grimsby, South Humberside, DN37 7LF Tel: (01472) 750700 Fax: (01472) 885949 E-mail: sales@globalstockuk.com

G K N Freight Services Ltd, Equity House, 128-136 High St, Edgware, Middlesex, HA8 7EL Tel: (020) 8905 6688 Fax: (020) 8905 6951 E-mail: info.fsl@gkndriveline.com

Immediate Transportation Co. Ltd, First Floor, St Nicholas House, Chappel St, Liverpool, L2 8TX Tel: 0151-227 4521 Fax: 0151-236 8036 E-mail: itcolhr@itcolhr.co.uk

Kay Oneill Ltd, Unit 6, Horton Road, Colnbrook, Slough, SL3 0AT Tel: (01753) 684606 Fax: (01753) 682241 E-mail: lhr@kayoneill.com

Maersk Logistics, Unit 6 Orwell House, Ferry Lane, Felixstowe, Suffolk, IP11 3AQ Tel: (01394) 614600 Fax: (01394) 614636

Martintrux Dover, Lord Warden Square, Dover, Kent, CT17 9EQ Tel: (01304) 213122 Fax: (01304) 213247 E-mail: clearance@martintrux.co.uk

Mersey Forwarding Co Shipping Services Ltd, Mersey House, 1 Church Street, Bootle, Merseyside, L20 1AF Tel: 0151-933 2000 Fax: 0151-933 0883 E-mail: tlennonmfss@btconnect.com

New Alliance Services Ltd, 403A Trelawny House, The Dock, Felixstowe, Suffolk, IP11 3EQ Tel: (01394) 676212 Fax: (01394) 676423

Parkside Warehousing & Transport Co. Ltd, Parkside House, Tomo Industrial Estate, Creeting Road, Stowmarket, Suffolk, IP14 5AY Tel: (01449) 676551 Fax: (01449) 672954

Quality Freight (UK) Ltd, 1st Floor Port Office, Manisty Wharf, Ellesmere Port, CH65 1AF Tel: 0151-355 6006 Fax: 0151-355 3273 E-mail: info@quality-freight.co.uk

R H Group, Lenton Lane, Nottingham, NG7 2NR Tel: 0115-943 8000 Fax: 0115-943 8045

Roadways Container Logistics, Box Lane, Renwick Road, Barking, Essex, IG11 0SQ Tel: (020) 8700 4932 Fax: (020) 8700 2163 E-mail: rcl@roadways.co.uk

S T S Eurolink, Andes Road, Nursling, Southampton, SO16 0YZ Tel: (023) 8073 0816 Fax: (023) 8073 0819 E-mail: stseurolink@dial.pipex.com

TNT Freight Management, Unit 5 & 6 Park Way Trading Estate, Cranford Lane, Hounslow, TW5 9QA Tel: (020) 8814 7000 Fax: (020) 8814 7078 E-mail: info@uk.tntfreight.com

CUT AWAY SERVICES, *See Engine Sectionalising etc*

CUT WELDING EQUIPMENT

Arc Welding Services, 17 Sandy Lane, Aston, Birmingham, B6 5TP Tel: 0121-327 2249 Fax: 0121-327 4797 E-mail: service@arcweld.freeserve.co.uk

CUTLERY BLANKS

Jessop & Smith Ltd, Albert Works, Sidney Street, Sheffield, S1 4RG Tel: 0114-272 1515 Fax: 0114-276 1733

Nickel Blanks Co. Ltd, 6 Smithfield, Sheffield, S3 7AR Tel: 0114-272 5792 Fax: 0114-276 8519 E-mail: shefcutler@aol.com

CUTLERY HANDLES AND SCALE CUTTERS

Beatson Drake Ltd, Quarry Road, Handsworth, Sheffield, S13 9AZ Tel: 0114-244 6873 Fax: 0114-243 5915 E-mail: beatsondrakeltd@aol.com

Bierton & Staniforth Ltd, Crescent Works, 71-73 St. Mary's Road, Sheffield, S2 4AN Tel: (0114) 272 0514

CUTLERY IMPORT MERCHANTS OR AGENTS

Alpha Price, Station Road, Harrow, Middlesex, HA1 1NA Tel: (020) 8861 4710

CUTLERY WHOLESALE DISTRIBUTORS OR AGENTS

Amefa (UK) Ltd, Lion Works, 15 Orgreave Drive, Handsworth, Sheffield, S13 9NR Tel: (0844) 5553234 Fax: (0844) 5553435 E-mail: sales@amefa.co.uk

Bunzl Lockhart Catering Equipment, Lockhart House, Brunel Road, Theale, Reading, RG7 4XE Tel: (0870) 1678678 Fax: (0870) 1678679 E-mail: marketing@bunzl.co.uk

▶ David Baggaley, 79 West Bar, Sheffield, S3 8PS Tel: (07877) 162431 E-mail: david.baggaley1@btinternet.com

Samuel Eales Silverware Ltd, 26 Douglas Road, Sheffield, S3 9SA Tel: 0114 2720885

Europlus Mouldings, Unit 1a Bilston Key Industrial Estate, Oxford Street, Bilston, West Midlands, WV14 7DW Tel: (01902) 404852 Fax: (01902) 409354 E-mail: nick@euro-plas.com

Global Foodservice Equipment Ltd, Global House, 104-108 School Road, Tilehurst, Reading, RG31 5AX Tel: (0870) 6004333 Fax: (0870) 2434334 E-mail: sales@global-fse.co.uk

Heritage Group, 62 Green Lane, Small Heath, Birmingham, B9 5DB Tel: 0121-773 0724 Fax: 0121-766 6073 E-mail: sales@heritage-silverware.com

Lambert & Blaber Ltd, 25 Kings Road, Haslemere, Surrey, GU27 2QA Tel: (01428) 658534 Fax: (01428) 658341 E-mail: sales@lambertblaber.co.uk

C.J. Lang & Son Ltd, 78 Longtown Road, Dundee, DD4 8JU Tel: (01382) 512000 Fax: (01382) 508222E-mail: info@cjlang.co.uk

Lockhart Catering Equipment, 8 Fountain Court, New Leaze, Bradley Stoke, Bristol, BS32 4LA Tel: (01454) 202500 Fax: (01454) 202266

London Cutlery Co., 6 Plantagenet Road, Barnet, Hertfordshire, EN5 5JQ Tel: (020) 8441 9505

M & G Catering, 69/79 Hadfield Street, Old Trafford, Manchester, M16 9FE Tel: 0161-848 0959 Fax: 0161-848 0959 E-mail: mg-catering@ntlworld.com

PHD, Bromley Road, Congleton, Cheshire, CW12 1PP Tel: (01260) 271243

S & S Marketing, B8-B10 Unit Tenterfields Business Park, Burnley Road, Luddendenfoot, Halifax, West Yorkshire, HX2 6EQ Tel: (01422) 882754 Fax: (01422) 884978 E-mail: sales@sandsmarketing.co.uk

CUTLESS BEARINGS

Friedenthals Ltd, Marine Propeller Works, Croft Street, Preston, PR1 8XD Tel: (01772) 254255 Fax: (01772) 204829

CUTTER BLADE BOLTS

Edge Tool Co. Ltd, Unit 2a Dronfield, Callywhite Lane, Dronfield, Derbyshire, S18 2XR Tel: (01246) 415111 Fax: (01246) 415222 E-mail: sales@etmblades.co.uk

CUTTER GRINDING LUBRICANTS

Oel Held UK Ltd, 16 Colomendy Industrial Estate, Rhyl Road, Denbigh, Clwyd, LL16 5TA Tel: (01745) 814777 Fax: (01745) 813222 E-mail: info@oelheldgroup.co.uk

CUTTER SHARPENING

▶ Isherwood Engineering, 17 Hearts of Oak Cottages, Caerau, Maesteg, Mid Glamorgan, CF34 0TU Tel: (01656) 731459 E-mail: stephenisherwood@yahoo.co.uk

CUTTER SHARPENING MACHINES

Autool Grinders Ltd, Padiham Road, Sabden, Clitheroe, Lancashire, BB7 9EW Tel: (01282) 775000 Fax: (01282) 773486 E-mail: sales@autool.co.uk

▶ WEST SAW SERVICES LTD, UNIT 15, BALTIC WORKS, EFFINGAM ROAD, Sheffield, S9 3QA Tel: 0114 2426620 Fax: 0114 2426620 E-mail: josilk@btinternet.com

CUTTERS, FORME, PRINT/ PACKAGING

A1 Cutting Formes, 117 Whitehouse Lane, Bedminster, Bristol, BS3 4DN Tel: 0117-963 7897 Fax: 0117-953 8101 E-mail: info@a1cuttingformes.co.uk

Ace Cutters London Ltd, Unit 10 Lewisham Way Industrial Estate, 151-163 Lewisham Way, London, SE14 6QP Tel: (020) 8692 4671 Fax: (020) 8692 0433 E-mail: sales@acecutters.co.uk

Arden Dies Ltd, Shepley Lane Industrial Estate, Hawk Green, Marple, Stockport, Cheshire, SK6 7JW Tel: 0161-449 6000 Fax: 0161-449 0497 E-mail: orderdies@ardendies.com

Avon Dies Bristol Ltd, Unit 5-6 Carrick Business Centre, 4-5 Bonville Road, Bristol, BS4 5NZ Tel: 0117-977 1872 Fax: 0117-972 3703 E-mail: cad@avon-dies.co.uk

B I B Cutters & Formes, Hertford, SG14 3BT Tel: (07710) 255485 Fax: (01992) 419275

Channel Cutters, Unit 18 Lawrence Hill Industrial Park, Croydon Street, Bristol, BS5 0EB Tel: 0117-955 2443 Fax: 0117-955 2443 E-mail: channelcutters@btconnect.com

Clarke Cutters, 17 Offerton Industrial Estate, Hempshaw Lane, Stockport, Cheshire, SK2 5TH Tel: 0161-477 6440 Fax: 0161-477 8090 E-mail: sales@clarkecutters.co.uk

Crosland Cutters Ltd, Nimmings Road, Halesowen, West Midlands, B62 9JE Tel: 0121-559 7915 Fax: 0121-561 3064 E-mail: sales@croslandcuttersltd.co.uk

Cross Pak Ltd, 14 Calow Brook Drive, Hasland, Chesterfield, Derbyshire, S41 0DR Tel: (01246) 200183 Fax: (01246) 200183 E-mail: crosspak@wyldboy.demon.co.uk

Diamond Cutting Formes, 2 Monks Brook Industrial Park, School Close, Chandler's Ford, Eastleigh, Hampshire, SO53 4RA Tel: (023) 8026 7326 Fax: (023) 8027 5187 E-mail: dcformes@izrmail.com

East London Print Finishers, Unit 7 Lockwood Way, London, E17 5RB Tel: (020) 8527 5448 Fax: (020) 8527 0635

Elite Cutters Ltd, Oakfield Works, Branksome Hill Road, College Town, Sandhurst, Berkshire, GU47 0QE Tel: (01276) 32991 Fax: (01276) 600146 E-mail: kriswatling@elitecutters.fsnet.co.uk

Flexiforms Birmingham Ltd, 7 Lee Bank House, Blucher Street, Birmingham, B1 1HP Tel: 0121-643 7368 Fax: 0121-643 7366

Forme Display 1990 Ltd, 8 Millbrook Road, Birkenhead, Merseyside, CH41 1FL Tel: 0151-691 1592 Fax: 0151-639 0403

J & J Cutting Formes Ltd, Unit 20 Whitworth Drive, Aycliffe Industrial Park, Newton Aycliffe, County Durham, DL5 6SZ Tel: (01325) 319744 Fax: (01325) 304003 E-mail: mail@jandjcuttingformes.co.uk

Joseph Dixon Tool Company Ltd, Unit 2 Charles Street, Town Wharf Business Park, Walsall, WS2 9LZ Tel: (01922) 622051 Fax: (01922) 721168 E-mail: sales@josephdixon.co.uk

K E S Safetycutters, 147 Portland Road, London, SE25 4UX Tel: (020) 8656 6811 Fax: (020) 8656 6814 E-mail: sales@safetycutters.net

M P Vineis Ltd, 34 Henry Road, Barnet, Hertfordshire, EN4 8BD Tel: (020) 8449 4206 Fax: (020) 8449 4206 E-mail: vineis@btconnect.com

Maurice D Spencer & Co., Faircharm Trading Estate, Evelyn Drive, Leicester, LE3 2BU Tel: 0116-289 1313 Fax: 0116-289 3484 E-mail: mdspencer@ic24.net

Precision Formes Ltd, 13 Glegg Street, Liverpool, L3 7DX Tel: 0151-207 2446 Fax: 0151-298 1539 E-mail: info@pfl3.co.uk

Charles Robinson (Cutting Tools) Ltd, Unit C1, Castle Park Industrial Estate, Bower Street, Oldham, OL1 3LN Tel: 0161-628 5550 Fax: 0161-628 5599 E-mail: sales@c-robinson.co.uk

Rossendale Forme & Knife Co. Ltd, 245 Burnley Road East, Rossendale, Lancashire, BB4 9HU Tel: (01706) 213165 Fax: (01706) 831319 E-mail: info@rossforme.co.uk

Screen Technology, Maerdy Industrial Estate, Maerdy Road, Ferndale, Mid Glamorgan, CF43 4AB Tel: (01443) 730271 Fax: (01443) 730789 E-mail: info@screentec.co.uk

Wessex Formes Ltd, 2 Lindberg Road, Ferndown Industrial Estate, Wimborne, Dorset, BH21 7SP Tel: (01202) 870754 Fax: (01202) 870764

Wood Ash Formes Ltd, Kingsfield Ways, Kingsheath, Northampton, NN5 7QN Tel: (01604) 752242 Fax: (01604) 751727

CUTTERS, HEATED/KNIVES, INDUSTRIAL

Lyteze Products Ltd, 8 Colne Road, Brightlingsea, Colchester, CO7 0DL Tel: (01206) 302699 Fax: (01206) 302699 E-mail: annecook@lyteze.com

CUTTERS, ULTRASONIC

▶ Sonics & Materials (UK) Ltd, Unit 18 Tomo Business Park, Creeting Road, Stowmarket, Suffolk, IP14 5EP Tel: (01449) 770055 Fax: (01449) 770333 E-mail: sales@sonicsandmaterials.co.uk

CUTTERS, VINYL SIGN

▶ A & S Signs, 240 Holliday Street, Birmingham, B1 1SJ Tel: 0121-632 6222 Fax: 0121-632 6222 E-mail: designwithsigns@btinternet.com

Five Fish Ltd, 77 Richmond Road, Twickenham, TW1 3AW Tel: (020) 8538 9277 Fax: (020) 8538 9270 E-mail: info@fivefish.co.uk

▶ Graphics Store, Clough Mill, Bradford Road, Gomersal, West Yorkshire, BD19 4AZ Tel: (01274) 862051 Fax: (01274) 851173 E-mail: info@graphics-store.co.uk

MDLogistics, MDL House, 151 Mead Way, Old Coulsdon, Coulsdon, Surrey, CR5 1PR Tel: (0845) 4561914 E-mail: info@mdlogistics.co.uk

▶ The Sign King, 35 charles street, Swinton, Manchester, M27 9UG Tel: 0161-278 0199 Fax: 0161-278 0199 E-mail: thesignking@ntlworld.com

▶ Tayside Contracts Sign Shop, Signal Box Road, Blairgowrie, Perthshire, PH10 6ER Tel: (01250) 876091 Fax: (01250) 870293 E-mail: signshop@tayside-contracts.co.uk

CUTTING AND CREASING RULES

Channel Cutters, Unit 18 Lawrence Hill Industrial Park, Croydon Street, Bristol, BS5 0EB Tel: 0117-955 2443 Fax: 0117-955 2443 E-mail: channelcutters@btconnect.com

L. Hodge Engineering Ltd, Unit 12, Chiltern Business Village, Arundel Road, Uxbridge, Middlesex, UB8 2SN Tel: (01895) 813758 Fax: (01895) 812468 E-mail: john@lhodge-engineers.co.uk

Metal-Woods Ltd, 14 Church Street, Market Harborough, Leicestershire, LE16 7AB Tel: (01858) 462641 Fax: (01858) 431616 E-mail: sales@metal-woods.co.uk

▶ Pema Rules, Unit 15 Leyton Business Centre, Etloe Road, London, E10 7BT Tel: (020) 8988 4083 Fax: (020) 8556 8543 E-mail: sales@pemarules.com

CUTTING HYDRAULIC PRESSES

Robert Greig, The Mariners Hall, Irwell Lane, Runcorn, Cheshire, WA7 1RP Tel: (01928) 572638 Fax: (01928) 572638 E-mail: mike@robertgreig.co.uk

CUTTING MACHINES, FOR MATERIALS, *See also Cutter etc*

Cadcam Technology, 5 Crocus Street, Nottingham, NG2 3DE Tel: 0115-844 8050 Fax: 0115-844 8059 E-mail: info@cct-uk.com

Qualcot Profiling Machines Ltd, Oak Road, West Chirton North Industrial Estate, North Shields, Tyne & Wear, NE29 8SD Tel: 0191-257 5205 Fax: 0191-257 4961 E-mail: k.edmundson@qualcut.com

CUTTING OFF MACHINES, *See also headings for particular types*

Benetec Cutting Tools, Unit 5b Midland Trading Estate, Consul Road, Rugby, Warwickshire, CV21 1PB Tel: (01788) 561133 Fax: (01788) 560223 E-mail: sales@benetecmetlab.com

Kingsland Engineering Co. Ltd, Weybourne Road, Sheringham, Norfolk, NR26 8HE Tel: (01263) 822153 Fax: (01263) 825667 E-mail: info@kingsland.com

CUTTING OIL OR FLUID PRODUCTS

Fuchs Lubricants (UK) Plc, P O Box 20, Stoke-on-Trent, ST1 5HU Tel: (0870) 1200400 Fax: (01782) 202072 E-mail: contact-uk@fuchs-oil.com

Houghton plc, Beacon Road, Trafford Park, Manchester, M17 1AF Tel: 0161-874 5000 Fax: 0161-877 9764 E-mail: info@houghtonintl.com

Jemma Tools Kent Ltd, 16 Willesborough Industrial Park, Willesborough, Ashford, Kent, TN24 0TD Tel: (01233) 639600 Fax: (01233) 637300 E-mail: sales@jemma-kent.co.uk

John Clayden & Partners Lubysil Ltd, 9 Frensham Road, Sweet Briar Road Industrial Estate, Norwich, NR3 2BT Tel: (01603) 789924 Fax: (01603) 417335 E-mail: claydenlubysil@aol.com

Kuwait Petroleum International Lubricants UK Ltd, Knowsthorpe Gate, Cross Green Industrial Estate, Leeds, LS9 0NP Tel: 0113-235 0555 Fax: 0113-248 5026 E-mail: marketing@q8oils.com

Logtek C N C Cut, 12a Church Road, Formby, Liverpool, L37 8BQ Tel: (01704) 873222 Fax: (01704) 873222 E-mail: deslogan@supanet.com

Molyslip Atlantic, Unit 1 Danebrook Court, Langford Lane, Kidlington, Oxfordshire, OX5 1LQ Tel: (01865) 370032 Fax: (01865) 372030 E-mail: enquiries@molyslip.co.uk

CUTTING OIL OR FLUID PRODUCTS

– continued

Oil Inventions Ltd, Leamore Close, Walsall, WS2 7NJ Tel: (01922) 477904 Fax: (01922) 710108 E-mail: info@oilinventions.co.uk

Oiline Ltd, Whitehall Road, Tipton, West Midlands, DY4 7JZ Tel: 0121-557 1475 Fax: 0121-522 2311

Olenol Ltd, Olenol House, Plot 7 Greenfield Farm Industrial Estate, Congleton, Cheshire, CW12 4TR Tel: (01260) 298276 Fax: (01260) 298267

Petrofer UK plc, Harcourt Business Park, Halesfield 17, Telford, Shropshire, TF7 4PW Tel: (01952) 580100 Fax: (01952) 580101 E-mail: sales@petrofer.co.uk

CUTTING OIL/FLUID MIXING/ DISPERSING EQUIPMENT

Arrow Engineering Supply Co. Ltd, Hunters Lane Industrial Estate, Rugby, Warwickshire, CV21 1EA Tel: (01788) 574107 Fax: (01788) 542179 E-mail: frank@fasteng.co.uk

C N C Fluids Ltd, Whitehall Trading Estate, Gerrish Avenue, Whitehall, Bristol, BS5 9DF Tel: 0117-935 0033 Fax: 0117-935 0440 E-mail: sales@cncfluids.co.uk

CUTTING PRESSES, SHAPE/ PROFILE

Alpress Hydraulic Engineers, 65 Back Sneddon Street, Paisley, Renfrewshire, PA3 2DD Tel: 0141-848 7175 Fax: 0141-889 5280 E-mail: alpresshs@tiscali.co.uk

Hawkes Technical Ltd, Spencer Parade, Stanwick, Wellingborough, Northamptonshire, NN9 6QJ Tel: (01933) 622492 Fax: (01933) 624092 E-mail: info@hawkestechnical.com

Charles Robinson (Cutting Tools) Ltd, Unit C1, Castle Park Industrial Estate, Bower Street, Oldham, OL1 3LN Tel: 0161-628 5550 Fax: 0161-628 5599 E-mail: sales@c-robinson.co.uk

CUTTING ROOM CONSULTANTS AND DESIGN, TEXTILE INDUSTRY

S G Cuttings, Unit E4 Europa Trading Estate, Stoneclough Road, Radcliffe, Manchester, M26 1GG Tel: (01204) 574030 Fax: (01204) 574031 E-mail: simon.leigh@john-holden.com

CUTTING SERVICES, *See also headings for particular types*

▶ A M R (Burnley) Ltd, Unit 3, Gannow Business Park, Gannow Lane, Burnley, Lancashire, BB12 6JJ Tel: (01282) 448008 Fax: (01282) 448419 E-mail: sales@lasercutters.co.uk

Control Waterjet Cutting, Unit 18 Telford Crescent, Speedwell Industrial Estate, Staveley, Chesterfield, Derbyshire, S43 3PF Tel: (01246) 284000 Fax: (01246) 284003 E-mail: sales@controlwaterjet.co.uk

▶ Flexible Reinforcements Ltd, Bancroft Road, Burnley, Lancashire, BB10 2TP Tel: (01282) 478222 Fax: (01282) 478210 E-mail: sales@flexr.co.uk

J & J Cutting Formes Ltd, Unit 20 Whitworth Drive, Aycliffe Industrial Park, Newton Aycliffe, County Durham, DL5 6SZ Tel: (01325) 319744 Fax: (01325) 304003 E-mail: mail@jandjcuttingformes.co.uk

Kennametal UK Ltd, PO Box 29, Kingswinford, West Midlands, DY6 7NP Tel: (01384) 401000 Fax: (01384) 408015 E-mail: kingswinfold.service@kennametal.com

M P Vineis Ltd, 34 Henry Road, Barnet, Hertfordshire, EN4 8BD Tel: (020) 8449 4206 Fax: (020) 8449 4206 E-mail: vineis@btconnect.com

Medway Cutters, Joseph Wilson Industrial Estate, Millstrood Road, Whitstable, Kent, CT5 3PS Tel: (01227) 273138 Fax: (01227) 770344 E-mail: sales@medwaycutters.co.uk

Metal Goods Wales Ltd, North Road, Bridgend Industrial Estate, Bridgend, Mid Glamorgan, CF31 3TP Tel: (01656) 647755 Fax: (01656) 647744 E-mail: sales@metalgoods.co.uk

Mi-King Ltd, Bentall Business Park, Glover District 11, Washington, Tyne & Wear, NE37 3JD Tel: 0191-415 5919 Fax: 0191-415 1300 E-mail: sales@mi-king.co.uk

CUTTING TO LENGTH MACHINES

Bromley Car Audio, 50 Homesdale Road, Bromley, BR2 9LD Tel: (020) 8460 8704 Fax: (020) 8460 8704 E-mail: sales@caraudioonline.co.uk

CUTTING TOOL MANUFRS, *See also headings for particular types under Cutting Tools*

▶ A D P Diamond Cutting Solutions Ltd, Unit 29, Dunmere Road, Bodmin, Cornwall, PL31 2QN Tel: (01208) 269898 Fax: (01208) 264818 E-mail: sales@adpdiamex.co.uk

Arrow Engineering Supply Co. Ltd, Hunters Lane Industrial Estate, Rugby, Warwickshire, CV21 1EA Tel: (01788) 574107 Fax: (01788) 542179 E-mail: frank@fasteng.co.uk

Bass Stobart Ltd, 20 Obelisk Road, Southampton, SO19 9BN Tel: (023) 8068 5485 Fax: (023) 8068 5469 E-mail: sales@bass-stobart.co.uk

Ben Ford Paul Ltd, 41 West Princes Street, Glasgow, G4 9BU Tel: 0141-332 0585 Fax: 0141-333 1607 E-mail: benfordpaul@aol.com

Bencere Elliott Ltd, Broadstone Hill, Old Chalford, Chipping Norton, Oxfordshire, OX7 5QL Tel: (01608) 672800 Fax: (01789) 450785 E-mail: sales@bencere.co.uk

Benetec Ltd, PO Box 472, Edgware, Middlesex, HA8 7ZR Tel: (0845) 4563082 Fax: (0845) 4563085 E-mail: sales@benetecmetleb.com

Buck & Hickman Ltd, 4 Block A Hareness Park, Hareness Circle, Altens Industrial Estate, Aberdeen, AB12 3QY Tel: (01224) 895272 Fax: (01224) 895248 E-mail: aberdeen@buckhickmaninone.com

Buck & Hickman Ltd, 5 Mod Department, Spitfire Road, Birmingham, B24 9PR Tel: 0121-386 8000 Fax: 0121-386 8011 E-mail: manchester@buckhickman.co.uk

Buck & Hickman Ltd, 203 Longmead Road, Emersons Green, Bristol, BS16 7FG Tel: 0117-957 9797 Fax: 0117-957 9799 E-mail: bristol@buckhickmaninone.com

Buck & Hickman Ltd, R Kingsville Road, Kingsditch Trading Estate, Cheltenham, Gloucestershire, GL51 9NZ Tel: (01242) 519665 Fax: (01242) 224097 E-mail: cheltenham@buckhickmaninone.co.uk

Buck & Hickman Ltd, Unit 16 Gatwick Int Distribution Centre, Cobham Way, Crawley, West Sussex, RH10 9RX Tel: (01293) 561651 Fax: (01293) 561637 E-mail: crawley@buckhickmaninone.com

Buck & Hickman Ltd, Rosswood Road, Rossmore Industrial Estate, Ellesmere Port, CH65 3BU Tel: 0151-356 2160 Fax: 0151-357 2019 E-mail: ellesmere@buckhickmaninone.com

Buck & Hickman Ltd, Unit 19 Ringway Industrial Estate, Beck Road, Huddersfield, HD1 5DG Tel: (01484) 426611 Fax: (01484) 435368 E-mail: huddersfield@buckhickman.co.uk

▶ Buck & Hickman Ltd, C2 Waterside Road, Hamilton, Leicester, LE5 1TL Tel: 0116-299 2990 Fax: 0116-299 3301 E-mail: leicester@buckhickman.co.uk

Buck & Hickman Ltd, Unit 9a, Finway, Dallow Road, Luton, LU1 1TR Tel: (01582) 419887 Fax: (01582) 425824 E-mail: luton@buckhickmaninone.co.uk

Buck & Hickman Ltd, 7 Cannon Park Way, Cannon Park Industrial Estate, Middlesbrough, Cleveland, TS1 5JU Tel: (01642) 240116 Fax: (01642) 245299 E-mail: middlesbrough@buckhickmaninone.com

Buck & Hickman Ltd, A Hambridge Road, Newbury, Berkshire, RG14 5SS Tel: (01635) 521747 Fax: (01635) 32605 E-mail: newbury@buckhickmaninone.com

Buck & Hickman Ltd, Hamar Close, Tyne Tunnel Trading Estate, North Shields, Tyne & Wear, NE29 7UY Tel: 0191-296 0333 Fax: 0191-296 0335 E-mail: newcastle@buckhickman.co.uk

Buck & Hickman Ltd, Unit 2 Longwall Avenue, Queens Drive Industrial Estate, Nottingham, NG2 1NA Tel: 0115-986 8282 Fax: 0115-986 8486 E-mail: nottingham@buckhickmaninone.com

Buck & Hickman Ltd, Unit 2a Treelyn Park, Welbeck Way Woodston, Peterborough, PE2 7WH Tel: (01733) 371737 Fax: (01733) 232245 E-mail: peterborough@buckhickmaninone.co.uk

Buck & Hickman Ltd, 4 Phoenix Business Park, Estover Road, Plymouth, PL6 7PY Tel: (01752) 692700 Fax: (01752) 692701 E-mail: plymouth@buckhickmaninone.com

Buck & Hickman Ltd, Unit 12, Riverside Court, Don Road, Sheffield, S9 2TJ Tel: 0114-244 1012 Fax: 0114-244 5372 E-mail: sheffield@buckhickman.co.uk

Buck & Hickman Ltd, Building 110 Nursling Industrial Estate, Mauretania Road, Nursling, Southampton, SO16 0YS Tel: (023) 8074 2300 Fax: (023) 8074 2301 E-mail: southampton@buckhickmaninone.com

Buck & Hickman Ltd, Lyme Vale Court, Parklands Business Park, Parklands, Stoke-on-Trent, ST4 6NW Tel: (01782) 279927 Fax: (01782) 286355 E-mail: stoke@buckhickman.co.uk

Buck & Hickman Ltd, Unit 12 Ferryboat Close, Enterprise Park, Swansea Enterprise Park, Swansea, SA6 8QN Tel: (01792) 799998 Fax: (01792) 700678 E-mail: swansea@buckhickman.co.uk

Buck & Hickman Ltd, 103-109 Waldegrave Road, Teddington, Middlesex, TW11 8LL Tel: (020) 8977 8844 Fax: (020) 8943 2826 E-mail: teddington@buckhickman.co.uk

Buck Hickman In One Ltd, 70 Lancefield Street, Glasgow, G3 8JD Tel: 0141-221 7174 Fax: 0141-221 8877 E-mail: glasgow@buckhickman.co.uk

Buck In Hickman, Neptune Point, Vanguard Way, Ocean Park, Cardiff, CF24 5PG Tel: (029) 2030 6000 Fax: (029) 2030 6030 E-mail: cardiff@buckhickmaninone.co.uk

Buckhickman Ltd, Castleton Road, Armley, Leeds, LS12 2EN Tel: 0113-246 0911 Fax: 0113-244 6888 E-mail: sales@buckhickmaninone.com

BuckHickman InOne, Unit 2, Chartergate, Moulton Park, Northampton, NN3 6QF Tel: (01604) 797400 Fax: (01604) 797401 E-mail: northampton@buckhickmaninone.co.uk

Cambridge Tool Supplies Ltd, Unit 1 Brookfield Business Centre, Twentypence Road, Cottenham, Cambridge, CB4 8PS Tel: (01954) 251862 Fax: (01954) 251073 E-mail: camtool@btconnect.com

Carillon Industrial Services, 7 Marlborough Road, Colmworth Business Park, Eaton Socon, St. Neots, Cambridgeshire, PE19 8YP Tel: (01480) 225850 Fax: (01480) 225860 E-mail: sales@cis-tools.co.uk

Chase Diamond Tools International Ltd, 10 Shieling Court, Corby, Northamptonshire, NN18 9QD Tel: (01536) 461133 Fax: (01536) 461144 E-mail: sales@chasediamond.com

Cromwell Industrial Supplies Ltd, Unit 11 Manton Centre, Manton Lane, Manton Industrial Estate, Bedford, MK41 7PX Tel: (01234) 716470 Fax: (01234) 211214 E-mail: bedford@cromwell-tools.co.uk

Cromwell (Smethwick), Middlemore Road, Smethwick, West Midlands, B66 2DR Tel: 0121-558 1133 Fax: 0121-565 3530 E-mail: smethwick@cromwell.co.uk

Cromwell Tools Ltd, Gibraltar Island Road, Old Mill Business Park, Leeds, LS10 1RJ Tel: 0113-277 7730 Fax: 0113-277 7724 E-mail: leeds@cromwell.co.uk

Crosland Cutters Ltd, Nimmings Road, Halesowen, West Midlands, B62 9JE Tel: 0121-559 7915 Fax: 0121-561 3064 E-mail: sales@croslandcutterltd.co.uk

Cutting Edge Services Ltd, Unit 362A Walton Summit Centre, Bamber Bridge, Preston, PR5 8AS Tel: (0870) 062 1030 Fax: (0870) 062 1024 E-mail: accounts@cuttingedgeservices.co.uk

Derek Walmsley & Co Ltd, Lyons Street, Sheffield, S4 7QS Tel: 0114-243 0142 Fax: 0114-244 2870 E-mail: sales@derekwalmsley.com

Drill Service Horley Ltd, 23 Albert Road, Horley, Surrey, RH6 7HR Tel: (01293) 774911 Fax: (01293) 820463 E-mail: sales@drill-service.co.uk

Frio UK Ltd, Whitleys, Wolfscastle, Haverfordwest, Dyfed, SA62 5DY Tel: (01437) 741755 Fax: (01437) 741781 E-mail: frio@btinternet.com

FSG, Newtown Industrial Estate, Llantwit Fardre, Pontypridd, Mid Glamorgan, CF38 2EE Tel: (01443) 202281 Fax: (01443) 205747 E-mail: admin@fsgtoolanddie.co.uk

G & J Hall Ltd, Burgess Road, Sheffield, S9 3WD Tel: 0114-244 0562 Fax: 0114-244 9256 E-mail: sales@gjhall.co.uk

Hardmet Grinding Co., 18 The Meadows, Houston, Johnstone, Renfrewshire, PA6 7DJ Tel: (01505) 615066 Fax: (01505) 615066

Ingleson David Carbide Sales Services, Canada Crescent, Cleveleys, Rawdon, Leeds, LS19 6LT Tel: 0113-250 6013

▶ James Listers, 3 Riverside Industrial Estate, Meir Road, Redditch, Worcestershire, B98 7SY Tel: (01527) 500878 Fax: (01527) 510579 E-mail: redditch@lister.co.uk

Jemma Tools Kent Ltd, 16 Willesborough Industrial Park, Willesborough, Ashford, Kent, TN24 0TD Tel: (01233) 639600 Fax: (01233) 637300 E-mail: sales@jemma-kent.co.uk

John Young, 7 Cranbrook Court, Avenue Two, Witney, Oxfordshire, OX28 4YP Tel: (01993) 700337 Fax: (01993) 778123 E-mail: john-young1@btconnect.com

Logtek C N C Cut, 12a Church Road, Formby, Liverpool, L37 8BQ Tel: (01704) 873222 Fax: (01704) 873222 E-mail: deslogan@supanet.com

Marshall Drills Ltd, Metrology House, Dukinfield Road, Hyde, Cheshire, SK14 4SD Tel: 0161-882 9618 Fax: 0161-366 9800 E-mail: sales@marshalldrills.co.uk

Midway Tools Ltd, 9a Walsall Street, West Bromwich, West Midlands, B70 7NX Tel: 0121-553 3819 Fax: 0121-500 5453 E-mail: sales@midwaytools.co.uk

P J Tooling Ltd, Millers Road, Warwick, CV34 5AN Tel: (01926) 492693 Fax: (01926) 410057 E-mail: pj.tooling@virgin.net

Personna International UK Ltd, Unit 11 Ratcher Way, Forest Town, Mansfield, Nottinghamshire, NG19 0FS Tel: (01623) 638600 Fax: (01623) 638638 E-mail: sales@personna.co.uk

Portway Tool & Gauge Ltd, 27 Dudley Road, Lye, Stourbridge, West Midlands, DY9 8EX Tel: (01384) 892458 Fax: (01384) 424371 E-mail: info@portwaytoolgauge.co.uk

▶ Precision Tools, 40 Kingfisher Court, Hambridge Road, Newbury, Berkshire, RG14 5SJ Tel: (01635) 31977 Fax: (01635) 528865 E-mail: sales@precisiontoolsnewbury.co.uk

Quality Forms Ltd, 13-21 Church Street, Grimsby, South Humberside, DN32 7SR Tel: (01472) 241583 Fax: (01472) 358660

▶ S G S Carbide Tool UK Ltd, Unit 1 Metro Centre, Toutley Road, Wokingham, Berkshire, RG41 1QW Tel: 0118-979 5200 Fax: 0118-979 5295 E-mail: sales@sgstool.com

Scimitar Engineering Co. Ltd, Power House, 87 Mansel Street, Swansea, SA1 5TZ Tel: (01792) 651781 Fax: (01792) 646229

Stocdon Ltd, 2 Mackenzie Way, Swindon Village, Cheltenham, Gloucestershire, GL51 9TX Tel: (01242) 241123 Fax: (01242) 241133 E-mail: info@stocdon.co.uk

▶ T H S Tools Group, Salisbury House Unit 4, Centurion Business Park, Bessemer Way, Rotherham, South Yorkshire, S60 1FB Tel: (01709) 724000 Fax: (01709) 724014 E-mail: guy.farmer@thstools.co.uk

Tekron Hard Metals Ltd, 6 Marsh Green Close, Biddulph, Stoke-on-Trent, ST8 6TA Tel: (01782) 522563 Fax: (01782) 516452 E-mail: tekrontool@madasafish.com

Unimerco Ltd, Nanscawen Road, Fradley, Lichfield, Staffordshire, WS13 8LH Tel: (01543) 267777 Fax: (01543) 267778 E-mail: info@unimerco.com

Universal Engineering, Unit 10 Mid Wynd, Dundee, DD1 4JG Tel: (01382) 223592 Fax: (01382) 202506 E-mail: sales@universalengtool.co.uk

Vargus Tooling UK Ltd, Halesfield 4, Telford, Shropshire, TF7 4AP Tel: (01952) 583222 Fax: (01952) 583383 E-mail: sales@vargustooling.co.uk

Whitehill Woodworking Machinery, 6 Union Street, Luton, LU1 3AN Tel: (01582) 736881 Fax: (01582) 488987 E-mail: david@whitehill-tools.com

Wycombe Models & Engineering, Gomm Road, High Wycombe, Buckinghamshire, HP13 7DJ Tel: (01494) 447941 Fax: (01494) 461959

CUTTING TOOLS, PRECISION

R H C Consultancy, 202 Raedwald Drive, Bury St. Edmunds, Suffolk, IP32 7DW Tel: (01284) 717184 Fax: (01284) 717184 E-mail: rhcroft@btconnect.com

CUTTING TOOLS, SPECIAL/ ENGINEERS'

A S A P Tooling Ltd, Crondal Road, Exhall, Coventry, CV7 9NH Tel: (024) 7664 4555 Fax: (024) 7636 7019 E-mail: asaptooling@btconnect.com

Allied Maxcut Engineering Co. Ltd, 93 Vantage Point, Pensnett Estate, Kingswinford, West Midlands, DY6 7FR Tel: (01384) 400900 Fax: (01384) 400105 E-mail: rodcrawford@alliedmaxcut.com

Arden Dies Ltd, Shepley Lane Industrial Estate, Hawk Green, Marple, Stockport, Cheshire, SK6 7JW Tel: 0161-449 6000 Fax: 0161-449 0497 E-mail: orderdies@ardendies.com

Bardek Precision Tools, Britten Street, Redditch, Worcestershire, B97 6HD Tel: (01527) 67358 Fax: (01527) 65145

Bencere Elliott Ltd, Broadstone Hill, Old Chalford, Chipping Norton, Oxfordshire, OX7 5QL Tel: (01608) 672800 Fax: (01789) 450785 E-mail: sales@bencere.co.uk

Bradford Tool Group, Beta Works, 1 Tong Street, Bradford, West Yorkshire, BD4 9PW Tel: (01274) 683902 Fax: (01274) 651168 E-mail: sales@bradtool.co.uk

Bryar Group Ltd, 41 Catley Road, Darnall, Sheffield, S9 5JF Tel: 0114-291 7020 Fax: 0114-261 8186 E-mail: info@bryar.co.uk

Castle Tools Ltd, 33 Trent Street, Sheffield, S9 3XU Tel: 0114-261 7200 Fax: 0114-261 7370 E-mail: sales@castletools.co.uk

Cavat, 7 New Road, Burton Lazars, Melton Mowbray, Leicestershire, LE14 2UU Tel: (01664) 561761 Fax: (01664) 410280 E-mail: cavattools@cavattools.co.uk

Cutter Grinding Services, 22b Guildford Street, Luton, LU1 2NR Tel: (01582) 735626 Fax: (01582) 404164 E-mail: john.malia@tesco.net

F P Tools Ltd, Tyseley Lane, Birmingham, B11 3PX Tel: 0121-707 3838 Fax: 0121-707 3097 E-mail: sales@fptools.co.uk

James D. Gibson & Co. Ltd, 399 Petre Street, Sheffield, S4 8LL Tel: 0114-243 0385 Fax: 0114-242 5490 E-mail: admin@jamesgibson.co.uk

Glendower Cutting Tools Ltd, 21 Pinfold Road, Thurmaston, Leicester, LE4 8AS Tel: 0116-269 5999 Fax: 0116-269 3442 E-mail: sales@glendower.co.uk

Grindrite Grinding Equipment Es, 14 Hertburn Estate, Hertburn, Washington, Tyne & Wear, NE37 2SF Tel: 0191-416 3654 Fax: 0191-416 3729

Gun Drill & Reamers Ltd, 37 Southfields Industrial Park, Hornsby Square, Basildon, Essex, SS15 6SD Tel: (01268) 415197 Fax: (01268) 410692

H C S Tools Ltd, Unit T, Millmeade Industrial Estate, Staines, Middlesex, TW18 4UK Tel: (01895) 257265 Fax: (01895) 235630 E-mail: alan@hcstools.fsnet.co.uk

Halliburton Manufacturing & Services Ltd, Kirkhill Industrial Estate, Howemoss Cresent, Aberdeen, AB21 0GN Tel: (01224) 795000 Fax: (01224) 728495

Hempstead & Johnson Ltd, Oakridge Road, High Wycombe, Buckinghamshire, HP11 2PF Tel: (01494) 444971 Fax: (01494) 462636 E-mail: hemstead.johnson@btinternet.com

Impact Carbides Ltd, 36 East Bank Road, Sheffield, S2 3PS Tel: 0114-272 7216 Fax: 0114-272 4854 E-mail: sales@impactcarbides.co.uk

J B S Tooling Co. Ltd, Aizelewood Business Centre, Nursery Street, Sheffield, S3 8GG Tel: 0114-282 3160 Fax: 0114-282 3150

CUTTING TOOLS, SPECIAL/ ENGINEERS' – *continued*

J J Churchill Ltd, Station Road, Market Bosworth, Nuneaton, Warwickshire, CV13 0PF Tel: (01455) 299600 Fax: (01455) 292330 E-mail: sales@jjchurchill.com

J W Hill Precision Engineers Ltd, 22-26 Bath Road, Worcester, WR5 3EL Tel: (01905) 356712 Fax: (01905) 763155 E-mail: info@jwhill-engineering.co.uk

Kennametal UK Ltd, PO Box 29, Kingswinford, West Midlands, DY6 7NP Tel: (01384) 401000 Fax: (01384) 408015 E-mail: kingswinfold.service@kennametal.com

Kered Engineering Ltd, 32-34 Carron Place, Kelvin, East Kilbride, Glasgow, G75 0YL Tel: (01355) 237016 Fax: (01355) 264366 E-mail: sales@nesso.co.uk

M R Tool (Atherstone) Ltd, Unit 1, Netherwood Industrial Estate, Ratcliffe Road, Atherstone, Warwickshire, CV9 1HY Tel: (01827) 713097 Fax: (01827) 718518 E-mail: mrtoolsales@btconnect.com

Mapal Ltd, Swift Park, Old Leicester Road, Rugby, Warwickshire, CV21 1DZ Tel: (01788) 574700 Fax: (01788) 569551

Marshall Drills Ltd, Metrology House, Dukinfield Road, Hyde, Cheshire, SK14 4SD Tel: 0161-882 9618 Fax: 0161-366 9800 E-mail: sales@marshalldrills.co.uk

Menrica Engineering Ltd, 17 Paynes Lane, Rugby, Warwickshire, CV21 2UH Tel: (01788) 572434

Mitchell Fox & Co. Ltd, 9 Whitehouse Street, Leeds, LS10 1AD Tel: 0113-246 1000 Fax: 0113-246 5000 E-mail: sales@mitchellfox.co.uk

P & C Tools Ltd, 80 Cato Street North, Birmingham, B7 5AN Tel: 0121-333 7772 Fax: 0121-333 7776 E-mail: pctoolsltd@yahoo.co.uk

P J Tooling Ltd, Millers Road, Warwick, CV34 5AN Tel: (01926) 492693 Fax: (01926) 410057 E-mail: pj.tooling@virgin.net

P N Tools, Unit 33 34, Fourways, Carlyon Road Industrial Estate, Atherstone, Warwickshire, CV9 1LH Tel: (01827) 720013 Fax: (01827) 720039

Pen Cutting Tools Ltd, Bold Street, Sheffield, S9 2LR Tel: 0114-243 0055 Fax: 0114-243 0066 E-mail: sales@pencuttingtools.co.uk

Presto International Ltd, Penistone Road, Sheffield, S6 2FN Tel: 0114-234 9361 Fax: 0114-234 7446 E-mail: kevin.blackwell@presto-tools.com

W.J. Quinn Cutting Tools Ltd, 9 Wainwright Street, Aston, Birmingham, B6 5TH Tel: 0121-328 4640 E-mail: sales@quinntoolsgroup.co.uk

Ren Tools Ltd, 247 Great Lister Street, Birmingham, B7 4BS Tel: 0121-359 7231 Fax: 0121-359 7502 E-mail: sales@rentals.co.uk

David Richards Engineering Ltd, Unit 7B, Herald Industrial Estate, Hedge End, Southampton, SO30 2JW Tel: (01489) 790900 Fax: (01489) 790333 E-mail: drengineering@aol.com

▶ Rippon Cutting Tools, Hollingworth Road, Bredbury, Stockport, Cheshire, SK6 2AZ Tel: 0161-430 3660 Fax: 0161-430 3661 E-mail: info@rippontools.co.uk

Saint Gobain Abrasives Ltd, Millbrook Close, Chandler's Ford, Eastleigh, Hampshire, SO53 4BZ Tel: (023) 8025 4777 Fax: (023) 8025 5930 E-mail: terry.hughes@saint-gobain.com

Sorby (UK) Ltd, 7 Orgreave Close, Handsworth, Sheffield, S13 9NP Tel: 0114-269 3803 Fax: 0114-254 0523 E-mail: sales@sorbyuk.co.uk

Special Tooling Services, Exchange Road, Lincoln, LN6 3JZ Tel: (01522) 693993 Fax: (01522) 500993

Stellram, Bowerhill, Melksham, Wiltshire, SN12 6YH Tel: (01225) 897100 Fax: (01225) 897111

Steloc Tooling Co, 3 Brunswick Trading Estate, Hertford Street, Sparkbrook, Birmingham, B12 8NP Tel: 0121-440 3467 Fax: 0121-440 5194

▶ T H S Tools Group, Salisbury House Unit 4, Centurion Business Park, Bessemer Way, Rotherham, South Yorkshire, S60 1FB Tel: (01709) 724000 Fax: (01709) 724014 E-mail: guy.farmer@thstools.co.uk

Techni Grind Preston Machining Ltd, Unit 62 Red Scar Industrial Estate, Longridge Road, Ribbleton, Preston, PR2 5ND Tel: (01772) 797589 Fax: (01772) 797682 E-mail: sales@tgmeng.co.uk

Titex Tools Ltd, 1 The Courtyard, Buntsford Drive, Bromsgrove, Worcestershire, B60 3DJ Tel: (01527) 839450 Fax: (01527) 839482 E-mail: titex-prototyp@titex.com

Toolmatic Tool Design, 36 Hall Street, Birmingham, B18 6BS Tel: 0121-236 1417 Fax: 0121-233 9240

Tooloy (T S) Ltd, Sizers Court Trading Estate, Henshaw Lane, Yeadon, Leeds, LS19 7DP Tel: 0113-250 4717 Fax: 0113-239 1207 E-mail: paul@tooloytsltdco.co.uk

U T T Ltd, Ashton Close, Beaumont Leys, Leicester, LE4 2BN Tel: 0116-233 8884 Fax: 0116-233 8885 E-mail: sales@utt-ltd.co.uk

CUTTING TOOLS, ULTRA HARD

David Richards Engineering Ltd, Unit 7B, Herald Industrial Estate, Hedge End, Southampton, SO30 2JW Tel: (01489) 790900 Fax: (01489) 790333 E-mail: drengineering@aol.com

CYANOACRYLATE ADHESIVES

▶ 5 Star Adhesives, P O Box 96, Liverpool, L17 3BY Tel: 0151-733 7182 Fax: 0151-733 7182 E-mail: info@glue-shop.com

Bondloc UK Ltd, Alton Works, Long Bank, Bewdley, Worcestershire, DY12 2UJ Tel: (01299) 269269 Fax: (01299) 269210 E-mail: sales@bondloc.co.uk

Cedesa Ltd, Chater Lea Building, Icknield Way, Letchworth Garden City, Hertfordshire, SG6 1WT Tel: (01462) 480764 Fax: (01462) 480765 E-mail: neil.wildon@cedesa.co.uk

Chemence Ltd, 13 Princewood Road, Earlstrees Industrial Estate, Corby, Northamptonshire, NN17 4XD Tel: (01536) 402600 Fax: (01536) 400266 E-mail: sales@chemence.com

Delta Adhesives Ltd, 2 Lakeside Industrial Estate, Lakeside Road, Leeds, LS12 4QP Tel: 0113-279 6966 Fax: 0113-231 0828 E-mail: info@delta-adhesives.co.uk

Fast 10 Adhesives, Hollytree House, Leeds Road, Tadcaster, North Yorkshire, LS24 9NL Tel: (07949) 274474 Fax: (01937) 832337 E-mail: nrockcliff@fast10.co.uk

Polymer Systems Technology Ltd, 6 Vernon Building, Westbourne Street, High Wycombe, Buckinghamshire, HP11 2PX Tel: (01494) 446610 Fax: (01494) 528611 E-mail: sales@silicone-polymers.co.uk

CYCLE CARRIERS, MOTOR CAR

▶ Maxxraxx Trading, Unit 10 Hays Bridge Farm, Brickhouse Lane, South Godstone, Godstone, Surrey, RH9 8JW Tel: (01342) 841989 Fax: (01342) 844150 E-mail: info@maxxraxx.co.uk

Thule Ltd, Five C Business Centre, Concorde Drive, Clevedon, Avon, BS21 6UH Tel: (01275) 340404 Fax: (01275) 340686 E-mail: sales@thule.co.uk

Witter Towbars, 11 Drome Road, Deeside Industrial Park, Deeside, Clwyd, CH5 2NY Tel: (01244) 284500 Fax: (01244) 284577 E-mail: sales@witter-towbars.com

CYCLE COMPONENTS/ ACCESSORIES MANUFRS

Mealor-Clarke Cycle Spares, Unit 4 St. Johns Road, Saxmundham, Suffolk, IP17 1BE Tel: (01728) 605970 Fax: (0560) 0751879 E-mail: ray@mealorclarkecyclespares.com

Professional Cycle Manufacturing Ltd, Forge Lane, Cradley Heath, West Midlands, B64 5AL Tel: (01384) 568521 Fax: (01384) 634494 E-mail: enquires@pcmgroup.co.uk

S P P Extrusions, Timothys Bridge Road, Stratford-upon-Avon, Warwickshire, CV37 9NQ Tel: (01789) 298429 Fax: (01789) 414427 E-mail: sales@sp-plastics.co.uk

U C P Ltd, 117 Baltimore Road, Birmingham, B42 1AA Tel: 0121-358 0400 Fax: 0121-358 3683 E-mail: info@ucp.co.uk

Weldtite Products Ltd, Unit 9, Harrier Road, Humber Bridge Industrial Estate, Barton-Upon-Humber, South Humberside, DN18 5RP Tel: (01652) 660000 Fax: (01652) 660066 E-mail: sales@weldtite.co.uk

CYCLE DISPLAY EQUIPMENT, SHOP

Kestrel Engineering, 9 Dartmouth Buildings, Fort Fareham Industrial Site, Fareham, Hampshire, PO14 1AH Tel: (01329) 233443 Fax: (01329) 284148 E-mail: alan.s.walker@talk21.com

CYCLE FRAME TUBES/FORKS/ STAYS

Ceeway Bike Building Supplies, 80-82 West Street, Erith, Kent, DA8 1AQ Tel: (01322) 442990 Fax: (01322) 442886 E-mail: sales@framebuilding.com

Reynolds Cycle Technology (2000) Ltd, Redfern Road, Tyseley, Birmingham, B11 2BS Tel: 0121-706 5151 Fax: 0121-707 0081

Upgrade Bikes Ltd, PO Box 2518, Horsham, West Sussex, RH13 8RA Tel: (01403) 711611 Fax: (01403) 710753

CYCLE LIGHTING EQUIPMENT

Nimrod Reflectives, Rushton Spencer, Macclesfield, Cheshire, SK11 0RN Tel: (01260) 226600 Fax: (01260) 226699

CYCLE/COMPONENTS/ ACCESSORIES DEALERS OR DISTRIBUTORS, WHOLESALE

Arthur Neal & Co. Ltd, 6 Send Road, Caversham, Reading, RG4 8EH Tel: 0118-947 0519 Fax: 0118-946 1418E-mail: anealco@aol.com

Crabtree Sports & Leisure Ltd, Ebor Mills, Ebor Lane, Haworth, Keighley, West Yorkshire, BD22 8HS Tel: (01535) 640000 Fax: (01535) 640044 E-mail: info@acornsport.co.uk

Cyclesport North, 464 Ranglet Road, Walton Summit Centre, Bamber Bridge, Preston, PR5 8AR Tel: (01772) 339220 Fax: (01772) 339290 E-mail: sales@cyclesportnorth.co.uk

Fisher Outdoor Leisure, Unit 8 9 Brick Knoll Park, Ashley Road, St. Albans, Hertfordshire, AL1 5UG Tel: (01727) 798340 Fax: (0800) 9807129 E-mail: sales@fisheroutdoor.co.uk

D. Fudge & Sons Ltd, 564-566 Harrow Road, London, W9 3QH Tel: (020) 8969 5991 Fax: (020) 8964 1215

Halfords Ltd, Icknield St Drive, Redditch, Worcestershire, B98 0DE Tel: (01527) 517601 Fax: (01527) 513201

Hegan & Co., 56 Distillery Street, Belfast, BT12 5BJ Tel: (028) 9032 5143 Fax: (028) 9023 8349

▶ M & J Distributors, Unit A Hanix Building, Windmill Lane, Denton, Manchester, M34 3SP Tel: 0161-337 9600 Fax: 0161-337 0482

Mealor-Clarke Cycle Spares, Unit 4 St. Johns Road, Saxmundham, Suffolk, IP17 1BE Tel: (01728) 605970 Fax: (0560) 0751879 E-mail: ray@mealorclarkecyclespares.com

Moore Large & Co. Ltd, Grampian Buildings, Sinfin Lane, Derby, DE24 9GL Tel: (01332) 274200 Fax: (01332) 270635

On Your Bike, 52-54 Tooley Street, London, SE1 2SZ Tel: (020) 7378 6669 Fax: (020) 7357 7600 E-mail: enquiries@onyourbike.net

Rectro Ltd, 237 Bexley Road, Erith, Kent, DA8 3EX Tel: (01322) 340372 Fax: (01322) 335657

▶ Ride Low Ltd, 27-29 Church Street, Manchester, M4 1PE Tel: 0161-834 5788 E-mail: george@ridelow.co.uk

Tradewinds UK Ltd, 2 Lombard Way, Banbury, Oxfordshire, OX16 4TD Tel: (01295) 278866 Fax: (01295) 278855 E-mail: twuk@tradewindworldwide.co.uk

CYCLES

Bob Jackson Cycles 1993 Ltd, 320-322 Stanningley Road, Leeds, LS13 3EG Tel: 0113-255 9844 Fax: 0113-255 4444 E-mail: factory@bobjacksoncycles.demon.co.uk

▶ Cycleurope UK Ltd, 21-23 Mill Street, Bedford, MK40 3EU Tel: (01234) 245929 Fax: (01234) 270562 E-mail: sales@bianchi.com

Dawes Cycles, 35 Tameside Drive, Castle Vale, Birmingham, B35 7AG Tel: 0121-748 8050 Fax: 0121-748 8060

Falcon Cycles Ltd, PO Box 3, Brigg, South Humberside, DN20 8PB Tel: (01652) 656000 Fax: (01652) 650040 E-mail: sales@falconcycles.co.uk

I & M Steiner Ltd, 5 Reynard Business Park, Windmill Road, Brentford, Middlesex, TW8 9LY Tel: (020) 8847 4422 Fax: (020) 8847 3322

Moulton Developments Ltd, Holt Road, Bradford-on-Avon, Wiltshire, BA15 1AH Tel: (01225) 865895 Fax: (01225) 864742 E-mail: mail@alexmoulton.co.uk

Pace Cycles Ltd, Great Edstone, York, YO62 6PD Tel: (01751) 432929 Fax: (01751) 432691 E-mail: pace@pace-racing.co.uk

▶ Pacific Sports, Unit 4b, Exhibition House North View, Staple Hill, Bristol, BS16 4NY Tel: 0117-910 9876 Fax: 0117-910 9966

Pashley Holdings Ltd, Masons Road, Stratford-Upon-Avon, Warwickshire, CV37 9NL Tel: (01789) 292263 Fax: (01789) 414201 E-mail: enquiries@pashley.co.uk

Professional Cycle Manufacturing Ltd, Forge Lane, Cradley Heath, West Midlands, B64 5AL Tel: (01384) 568521 Fax: (01384) 634494 E-mail: enquires@pcmgroup.co.uk

Raleigh UK Ltd, Triumph Road, Nottingham, NG7 2DD Tel: 0115-942 0202 Fax: 0115-942 0214

▶ Ride Low Ltd, 27-29 Church Street, Manchester, M4 1PE Tel: 0161-834 5788 E-mail: george@ridelow.co.uk

Southern Trading (London) Co Ltd, 34 Eastdown Park, London, SE13 5HS Tel: 020 88528563

Thorn Cycles, 91-93 St. John Street, Bridgwater, Somerset, TA6 5HX Tel: (01278) 441526 E-mail: sales@sjcycles.com

Toucan Engineering Ltd, 40 Staindale, Cleverland Park, Guisborough, Cleveland, TS14 8JU Tel: (07944) 161643 E-mail: info@2cancycle.com

CYCLING GLOVES

▶ Awanstars Leather Fashion, 42 Foxton Road, Birmingham, B8 3HP Tel: (0781) 2817248 E-mail: awanstars@yahoo.co.uk

CYLINDER DESIGN, HYDRAULIC

▶ PDP Design Ltd, 74a Pine Avenue, Gravesend, Kent, DA12 1QZ Tel: (01474) 743334 Fax: 01474 746558 E-mail: mail@pdpdesign.co.uk

CYLINDER LINERS

G K N Ltd, Sheepbridge Works, Sheepbridge Lane, Chesterfield, Derbyshire, S41 9QD Tel: (01246) 260026 Fax: (01246) 260022

CYLINDER REBORING/ CRANKSHAFT GRINDING SPECIALIST SERVICES

Airport Engineering Co., 1 Harold Court Road, Romford, RM3 0YU Tel: (01708) 342358 Fax: (01708) 304598 E-mail: sales@propshafts.sagehost.co.uk

Ben Kent Precision Engineers, Riverside Industrial Estate, Marsh Lane, Boston, Lincolnshire, PE21 7PJ Tel: (01205) 362681 Fax: (01205) 362681

Ray Brown (Engineers) Ltd, Caroline Place, Plymouth, PL1 3QY Tel: 01752 662084

Coventry Boring & Metalling Co. Ltd, 3 Coniston Road, Coventry, CV5 6GU Tel: (024) 7667 2372 Fax: (024) 7667 9948

Dartford Rebore Ltd, 15 Overy Street, Dartford, DA1 1UP Tel: (01322) 220634 Fax: (01322) 220634

Foxwood Boring & Grinding Ltd, 17 Whitting Valley Road, Old Whittington, Chesterfield, Derbyshire, S41 9EY Tel: (01246) 260199 Fax: (01246) 455274 E-mail: ken@foxwooddiesel.com

Gosnay's Engineering Co. Ltd, Eastern Avenue West, Romford, RM7 7NS Tel: (01708) 740668 Fax: (01708) 733266 E-mail: sales@gosnays.co.uk

Green & Weatherly Ltd, 16 Bushey Hall Road, Bushey, WD23 2EA Tel: (01923) 228992 Fax: (01923) 241254

Bob Harman Performance Ltd, 101-107 Sutton Road, Watford, WD17 2QG Tel: (01923) 224303 Fax: (01923) 226596

Star Engineers, 157 Main Road, Broomfield, Chelmsford, CM1 7DJ Tel: (01245) 440501 Fax: (01206) 549167 E-mail: carhire@jdrobertson.freeserve.co.uk

West Midland Engines, Saltley Road, Saltley, Birmingham, B7 4TD Tel: 0121-359 4402 Fax: 0121-359 7340

CYLINDER SKIVING

A H Garner Ltd, Harrimans Lane, Lenton Lane Industrial Estate, Nottingham, NG7 2SD Tel: 0115-978 5161 Fax: 0115-924 4704 E-mail: sales@ahgarner.co.uk

CYLINDER TEST EQUIPMENT

Bancroft & Co., 5 Stairbridge Court, Stairbridge Lane, Bolney, Haywards Heath, West Sussex, RH17 5PA Tel: (01444) 248884 Fax: (01444) 242767 E-mail: sales@bancroft.co.uk

CYLINDER VALVES

Gas Control Equipment Ltd, Yew Tree Way, Golborne, Warrington, WA3 3JD Tel: (01942) 292950 Fax: (01942) 292951 E-mail: sales@gceuk.com

CYLINDERS, *See also headings for particular types*

Aircat Ltd, Unit A1, Milestone Business Park, Oslo Road, Sutton Fields Industrial Estate, Hull, HU7 0YN Tel: (01482) 878878 Fax: (01482) 878801 E-mail: sales@aircat.karoo.co.uk

G C E Fluid Power Ltd, Unit 17 Atlas Estate, Brookvale Road, Witton, Birmingham, B6 7EX Tel: 0121-356 5727 Fax: 0121-344 3629 E-mail: gcefluidpower@btinternet.com

▶ Hydraulic & Engineering Services Ltd, Unit 5-6 Victory Park, Trident Close, Medway City Estate, Rochester, Kent, ME2 4ER Tel: (01634) 295650 Fax: (01634) 295670 E-mail: info@hydraulicengineering.co.uk

McCallum Water Heating, Glen Works, Barrhead, Glasgow, G78 1ND Tel: 0141-881 1051 Fax: 0141-881 8275 E-mail: info@mccallumwaterheating.co.uk

▶ Universal Supplies Clydesdale Ltd, Hozier Street, Carluke, Lanarkshire, ML8 5DW Tel: (01555) 772474 Fax: (01555) 772426 E-mail: sales@uscltd.co.uk

CYLINDERS, AIR/PNEUMATIC

Airflow Compressors & Pneumatics Ltd, 100 Lord Street, Leigh, Lancashire, WN7 1BY Tel: (01942) 673529 Fax: (01942) 604672 E-mail: mail@airflow-compressors.co.uk

CYLINDERS, AIR/PNEUMATIC – *continued*

Cooper Freer Ltd, Kenilworth Drive, Oadby, Leicester, LE2 5LG Tel: 0116-271 0401 E-mail: sales@cooperfreer.co.uk

Era Hydraulics & Pneumatics Ltd, Unit 5 Loaland Business Centre, Maritime Close Medway City, Estate Rochester, Rochester, Kent, ME2 4AZ Tel: (01634) 717499 Fax: (0845) 2412446 E-mail: erahydraulice@btconnect.com

Hebble Hydraulic Services Ltd, Spring Grove Mills, Linthwaite, Huddersfield, HD7 5QG Tel: (01484) 846688 Fax: (01484) 847701 E-mail: hebble@btconnect.com

Hydramatics Ltd, Unit 2b The Quantum, Marshfield Bank Industrial Estate, Crewe, CW2 8UY Tel: (01270) 584348 Fax: (01270) 584348 E-mail: hydramatics@aol.com

Inovis Ltd, 1 Bracken Close, Lichfield, Staffordshire, WS14 9RU Tel: (0870) 3504707 Fax: (0870) 3504717 E-mail: info@inovis.uk.com

K V Ltd, Lunar House, Crownhill, Milton Keynes, MK8 0HB Tel: (01908) 561515 Fax: (01908) 561227 E-mail: marketing@kvautomation.co.uk

Miller Fluid Power, 3 Bailey Drive, Norwood Industrial Estate, Killamarsh, Sheffield, S21 2JF Tel: 0114-247 2936 Fax: 0114-247 8371

Parker Diving Ltd, A P Valves Building, Water Ma Trout Industrial Estate, Nancegollan, Helston, Cornwall, TR13 0BN Tel: (01326) 561040 Fax: (01326) 573605 E-mail: sales@apvalves.com

R G S Electro Pneumatics Ltd, West End Business Park, Oswaldtwistle, Accrington, Lancashire, BB5 4WZ Tel: (01254) 872277 Fax: (01254) 390133 E-mail: sales@rgs-e-p.co.uk

S M C Pneumatics, Vincent Avenue, Crownhill, Milton Keynes, MK8 0AN Tel: (01908) 563888 Fax: (01908) 561185 E-mail: sales@smcpneumatics.co.uk

Tox Pressotechnik Ltd, Unit 35, Stafford Business Village, Dyson Way, Staffordshire Technology Park, Stafford, ST18 0TW Tel: (01785) 887903 Fax: (01785) 887027 E-mail: sales@tox-uk.com

Univer Manufacturing Co. Ltd, Station Road, Bradford, West Yorkshire, BD1 4SF Tel: (01274) 725777 Fax: (01274) 725111 E-mail: enquiries@univer.co.uk

CYLINDERS, ALUMINIUM/ALLOY

Luxfer Gas Cylinders, Colwick Industrial Estate, Nottingham, NG4 2BH Tel: 0115-980 3800 Fax: 0115-980 3899 E-mail: info@luxfercylinders.com

CYLINDRICAL GRINDING MACHINES

Jones & Shipman Precision Ltd, Murrayfield Road, Braunstone Frith Industrial Estate, Leicester, LE3 1UW Tel: 0116-201 3000 Fax: 0116-201 3002 E-mail: sales@jonesshipman.com

CYLINDRICAL GRINDING SERVICES

Alpha Tool Grinding, Unit 6 Stafford Park 4, Telford, Shropshire, TF3 3BA Tel: (01952) 292988 Fax: (01952) 292988

Ambit Precision Grinding, 38a Kenilworth Drive, Oadby, Leicester, LE2 5LG Tel: 0116-271 1011 Fax: 0161-627 1101 E-mail: adam@ambit.fsnet.co.uk

BEP Surface Tecnologies, Eton Hill Road, Radcliffe, Manchester, M26 2XT Tel: 0161-724 9090 Fax: 0161-725 9539 E-mail: info@bepsurfacetecnologies.co.uk

Central Grinding Services, 3a Pomeroy Drive, Oadby, Leicester, LE2 5NE Tel: 0116-271 8188 Fax: 0116-271 8199 E-mail: central@grinding.fsnet.co.uk

Diesel Marine International Ltd, Gloucester Road, North Shields, Tyne & Wear, NE29 8RQ Tel: 0191-257 5577 Fax: 0191-258 6398 E-mail: david.murray@dmiuk.co.uk

J. Fairburn Ltd, Waterloo Works, Trafalgar Street, Burnley, Lancashire, BB11 1RF Tel: (01282) 422754 Fax: (01282) 422754 E-mail: pipeprofiling@compuserve.com

FCJ, 10a Bushey Hall Road, Bushey, WD23 2EA Tel: (01923) 220137 Fax: (01923) 233027 E-mail: sales@fcjprecisiongrinding.co.uk

G & W Grinding Services Ltd, Unit A Thomas Street, Walsall, WS2 8NE Tel: (01922) 723481 Fax: (01922) 724968

Leigh Precision Grinding, 132 Blyth Road, Hayes, Middlesex, UB3 1TD Tel: (020) 8573 0451 Fax: (020) 8561 6399 E-mail: leighgrinding@btinternet.co.uk

M & D Precision Grinding, Unit 8 North Weylands Industrial Estate, Molesey Road, Walton-on-Thames, Surrey, KT12 3PL Tel: (01932) 246270 Fax: (01932) 246270

Makewell & Skinner, 4 The Forest, Hatfield Broad Oak, Bishop's Stortford, Hertfordshire, CM22 7BT Tel: (01279) 718114 Fax: (01279) 718115

Multi-Grind Services Ltd, Unit 10, Harefield Road Industrial Estate, Rickmansworth, Hertfordshire, WD3 1PQ Tel: (01923) 725230 Fax: (01923) 777915 E-mail: steve@multigrind.co.uk

Poole Grinders Ltd, 81 Sterte Avenue West, Poole, Dorset, BH15 2AL Tel: (01202) 675650 Fax: (01202) 666388

Reddish Electroplating, Mersey Street, Stockport, Cheshire, SK1 2HX Tel: 0161-480 7890 Fax: 0161-480 4383 E-mail: rep-sales@btconnect.com

Scorpion Tooling Services, Unit 7 & 9, Libbys Drive, Stroud, Gloucestershire, GL5 1RN Tel: (01453) 751511 Fax: (01453) 766676

Charles Styles Ltd, New Bond Street, Birmingham, B9 4EJ Tel: 0121-772 2424 Fax: 0121-771 2597 E-mail: sales@hexasports.co.uk

Wolverhampton Grinding Company Ltd, Rosehill, Willenhall, West Midlands, WV13 2AR Tel: (01902) 606442 Fax: (01902) 636137 E-mail: sprint@btclick.com

CYLINDRICAL ROLLER BEARINGS

Timken Aerospace Uk Ltd, PO Box 667, Wolverhampton, WV2 4UH Tel: (01902) 719300 Fax: (01902) 719301 E-mail: talkbox@timken.com

DAIRY ENGINEERING SERVICES

E M & J R Evans, Priddbwll Mawr, Llangedwyn, Oswestry, Shropshire, SY10 9JZ Tel: (01691) 791203 Fax: (01691) 791203

Fullwood Ltd, 20 Merchants Quay, Pennygillam Industrial Estate, Launceston, Cornwall, PL15 7QA Tel: (01566) 777794 Fax: (01566) 777761 E-mail: launceston@fullwood.com

Goodrowes Of Chichester Ltd, 6 The Hornet, Chichester, West Sussex, PO19 7JQ Tel: (01243) 784411 Fax: (01243) 784339 E-mail: goodroweslt d@aol.com

H G Jones, Pantyrafallen Bach, Y Felinheli, Gwynedd, LL56 4QN Tel: (01248) 670194 Fax: (01248) 670194

M M T Services Ltd, 31 Vicarage Lane, Shrivenham, Swindon, SN6 8DT Tel: (01793) 784685 Fax: (01793) 784730 E-mail: andrew@mmtservicesltd.co.uk

Odescan Ltd, 37 Redhills Road, South Woodham Ferrers, Chelmsford, CM3 5UL Tel: (01245) 325135 Fax: (01245) 329035

Sepserv Ltd, 174 Liverpool Road, Southport, Merseyside, PR8 4NY Tel: (01704) 567401 Fax: (01704) 562644

Phil Squires Dairy & Electronic Engineers, Unit 1b, Dulford, Cullompton, Devon, EX15 2DY Tel: (01884) 266796 Fax: (01884) 266797

Thompson Food Co. Ltd, 9-11 Blount Street, London, E14 7RL Tel: (020) 7790 3408 Fax: (020) 7790 5162 E-mail: thompsondairy@aol.com

John Wallis Titt & Co. Ltd, Manor Road, Frome, Somerset, BA11 4BQ Tel: (01373) 463594 Fax: (01373) 451382

DAIRY LABORATORY TEST EQUIPMENT

Samuel James Outdoor Centre, 75-77 Gisburn Road, Barrowford, Barrowford, Nelson, Lancashire, BB9 6DX Tel: (07939) 502602 Fax: (01282) 613415 E-mail: broomsticktrav@aol.com

DAIRY PLANT AND EQUIPMENT MANUFRS

Ambic Equipment Ltd, Avenue 4, Station Lane, Witney, Oxfordshire, OX28 4XT Tel: (01993) 776555 Fax: (01993) 779039 E-mail: sales@ambix.co.uk

Bibbys Of Halifax Ltd, Jasper Street Works, Queens Road, Halifax, West Yorkshire, HX1 4NT Tel: (01422) 366331 Fax: (01422) 330086 E-mail: bibbysofhalifax@aol.com

Blyford Dairy Services, Oakley, Primes Lane, Blyford, Halesworth, Suffolk, IP19 9JS Tel: (01986) 872578 Fax: (01986) 875569

Cotswold Dairy Equipment Ltd, Avenue Three, Witney, Oxfordshire, OX28 4BP Tel: (01993) 774567 Fax: (01993) 774567 E-mail: sales@cotswold-dairy.co.uk

Dinting Metric, 8 Hadfield Industrial Estate, Waterside, Hadfield, Glossop, Derbyshire, SK13 1BS Tel: (01457) 855510 Fax: (01457) 838609 E-mail: sales@dintingmetric.com

Dunlop Design Engineering, 1 Sackville Street, Lisburn, County Antrim, BT27 4AB Tel: (028) 9267 2333 Fax: (028) 9267 2383 E-mail: info@dnet.co.uk

Fivemiletown & Brookeborough Co-Operative Agricultural & Dairy So, 14 Ballylurgan, Fivemiletown, County Tyrone, BT75 0RX Tel: (028) 8952 1209 Fax: (028) 8952 1863 E-mail: billcurry@fivemiletown.com

Fullwood Ltd, Grange Road, Ellesmere, Shropshire, SY12 9DF Tel: (01691) 627391 Fax: (01691) 627361 E-mail: sales@fullwood.com

Green Oak Equipment Ltd, 11 Boleyn Court, Manor Park, Runcorn, Cheshire, WA7 1SR Tel: (01928) 579971 Fax: (01928) 579269 E-mail: greenoak.runcorn@fsbdial.co.uk

J Wilson Agriculture, 75 Drumcroon Road, Garvagh, Coleraine, County Londonderry, BT51 4ED Tel: (028) 7086 8430 Fax: (028) 7086 8803 E-mail: cowcomfort@wilsonagri.co.uk

Jbi Technology Ltd, Unit 2-3 Bond Street, West Bromwich, West Midlands, B70 7DQ Tel: 0121-553 0500 Fax: 0121-553 5333 E-mail: info@jbitech.co.uk

Les Owen Ltd, Brook Street, Welshpool, Powys, SY21 7NA Tel: (01938) 552229 Fax: (01938) 552229

R.D. Mallory Milking Machine & Dairy Supplies Ltd, Unit 3, Strensham Business Park, Strensham, Worcester, WR8 9JZ Tel: (01684) 275040 Fax: (01684) 275020

Millar Mcdowell, 44 Lany Road, Moira, Craigavon, County Armagh, BT67 0NZ Tel: (028) 9262 1086 Fax: (028) 9262 1086

Moody plc, West Carr Road Industrial Estate, Retford, Nottinghamshire, DN22 7SN Tel: (01777) 701141 Fax: (01777) 709086 E-mail: info@moodyplc.com

Mueller Cooling Systems Ltd, Unit B Manor Farm, Main Street, Pinvin, Pershore, Worcestershire, WR10 2ES Tel: (01386) 561757 Fax: (01386) 561750 E-mail: phil.valentine@mueller-cooling.co.uk

Northern Dairy Supplies Ltd, Lea Road, Lea Town, Preston, PR4 0RA Tel: (01772) 720358 Fax: (01772) 726489 E-mail: admin@dairyhygiene.co.uk

▶ Novapak Equipment Ltd, 2 The Old Bakery, Stevington, Bedford, MK43 7QH Tel: (01234) 823018

S G E (Seal) Ltd, Church Street, Seal, Sevenoaks, Kent, TN15 0AT Tel: (01732) 761724 Fax: (01732) 761422 E-mail: sales@sgeseal.com

▶ South West Areas Services, Lower Upton Farm, Old Village, Cullompton, Devon, EX15 1RA Tel: (01884) 839393 Fax: (01884) 839399

V B Fabrications Ltd, Barnswood Farm, Rushton Spencer, Macclesfield, Cheshire, SK11 0RA Tel: (01260) 226261 Fax: (01260) 226544 E-mail: vic@milkingequipment.com

DAIRY PRODUCTS

A Gammie & Sons, Croftcrunie Farm, Tore, Muir of Ord, Ross-Shire, IV6 7SB Tel: (01463) 811240 Fax: (01463) 811240

Adams Food Ingredients Ltd, Prince St, Leek, Staffordshire, ST13 6DB Tel: (01538) 399686 Fax: 01538 399476 E-mail: sales@adams-food-ingredients.co.uk

Adams Food Ingredients Ltd, Prince St, Leek, Staffordshire, ST13 6DB Tel: (01538) 399686 Fax: (01538) 399766 E-mail: sales@adams-food-ingredients.co.uk

Aeron Valley Supplies, Perthi Yard, Llanrhystud, Dyfed, SY23 5ED Tel: (01974) 272585 Fax: (01974) 272585

Atkinson Sons Farmers, Main Street, Warton, Carnforth, Lancashire, LA5 9QF Tel: (01524) 732894 Fax: (01524) 720884

Bio Green Dairy Products, Home Farm, Hayes End Road, Hayes, Middlesex, UB4 8EN Tel: (020) 8848 1051 Fax: (020) 8813 5833

Bloomsbury Cheeses, 61b Judd Street, London, WC1H 9QT Tel: (020) 7387 7645 Fax: (020) 7387 7645

Castle Dairies Ltd, Pontygwindy Industrial Estate, Caerphilly, Mid Glamorgan, CF83 3HU Tel: (029) 2088 3981 Fax: (029) 2088 6506 E-mail: sales@castledairies.fsnet.co.uk

Caws Cenarth, Glyneithinog, Lancych, Boncath, Dyfed, SA37 0LH Tel: (01239) 710432

Caws Cymru, Wervil Grange, Pentregat, Llandysul, Dyfed, SA44 6HW Tel: (01239) 654800 Fax: (01239) 654800

▶ Central Supplies Brierley Hill Ltd, Unit 55 Enterprise Trading Estate, Pedmore Road, Brierley Hill, West Midlands, DY5 1TX Tel: (01384) 484629 Fax: (01384) 484829

▶ Cheese Shed, 8 Shepherds Business Park, Norwich Road, Lenwade, Norwich, NR9 5SG Tel: (01603) 879802 Fax: (01603) 879802

Cheese Wedge, Chester Market Hall, Princess Street, Chester, CH1 2HH Tel: (01244) 325458

Cheesework Cheese Makers, 1 Folly Hill Cottages, Folly Hill, Cranbrook, Kent, TN17 2LT Tel: (01580) 892021 Fax: (01580) 890774

Cheltenham Cheese, 147 Fairview Road, Cheltenham, Gloucestershire, GL52 2EX Tel: (01242) 584212 Fax: (01242) 577834

Chr. Hansen (UK) Ltd, 2 Tealgate, Charnham Park, Hungerford, Berkshire, RG17 0YT Tel: (01488) 689800 Fax: (01488) 685436 E-mail: contactus-gb@gb.chr-hansen.com

Classic Foods, Gratwicke Road, Worthing, West Sussex, BN11 4BH Tel: (01903) 231760 Fax: (01903) 231760

Giles Cooper Trading Ltd, Hetherson Green Farm, Hetherson Green, Malpas, Cheshire, SY14 8EL Tel: (01829) 720155 Fax: (01829) 720166

Cornish Country Larder Ltd, The Creamery, Trevarrian, Newquay, Cornwall, TR8 4AH Tel: (01637) 860331 Fax: (01637) 860133 E-mail: enquiries@ccl-ltd.co.uk

Country Fare Produce, Stall 7b-11b Fish Market, Market Place, Leicester, LE1 5HQ Tel: 0116-253 1432 Fax: 0116-288 0311

D J Sanders, Orchard Farm, Ockham Lane, Cobham, Surrey, KT11 1LP Tel: (01932) 866705 Fax: (01932) 860685

Dairy Crest Ltd, Pelton Road, Basingstoke, Hampshire, RG21 6XD Tel: (01256) 321329 Fax: (01256) 810833

▶ Dairy Crest Ltd, 4 Alexandra Road, Epsom, Surrey, KT17 4BJ Tel: (01372) 726551 Fax: (01372) 747231 E-mail: epson.depot@dairycrest.co.uk

Dairy Crest Ltd, Dudnance Lane, Pool, Redruth, Cornwall, TR15 3QT Tel: (01209) 713238 Fax: (01209) 612126

Dairyborn Foods Ltd, Eaton Green Road, Luton, LU2 9XF Tel: (01582) 457979 Fax: (01582) 400957

Dale Farm Ice Cream Ltd, 15 Dargan Road, Belfast, BT3 9LS Tel: (028) 9037 2200 E-mail: info@utdni.co.uk

Dale Farm Ingredients Ltd, Dargan Road, Belfast, BT3 9JU Tel: (028) 9037 0903 Fax: (028) 9077 1442 E-mail: k.lyons@halib.co.uk

▶ David South Ltd, Southdale House Holloway Drive, Wardley Industrial Estate, Worsley, Manchester, M28 2LA Tel: 0161-279 8020 Fax: 0161-279 8021

P. & C.A. Duncan, Stapleton Farm, Langtree, Torrington, Devon, EX38 8NP Tel: (01805) 601414 Fax: (01805) 601620 E-mail: sales@stapletonfarm.co.uk

E M Morgan, Nantybwla, Pentremeurig Road, Carmarthen, Dyfed, SA31 3QS Tel: (01267) 237905 Fax: (01267) 237905

Eurofayre Ltd, Hudds Mill Ho, Edington, Westbury, Wilts, BA13 4NH Tel: 01380 831323

Evan Rees Dyfed Ltd, Station Road, St. Clears, Carmarthen, SA33 4BP Tel: (01994) 230511 Fax: (01994) 231444

Everest Dairies Ltd, L Vulcan Business Centre, Vulcan Road, Leicester, LE5 3EB Tel: 0116-253 0909

Farmlea Foods Ltd, 199 Airport Road West, Belfast, BT3 9ED Tel: (028) 9045 4647 Fax: (028) 9073 4834

Farmview Dairies Ltd, 75a Lisnabreeny Road, Belfast, BT6 9SR Tel: (028) 9044 8553 Fax: (028) 9044 9120

Fayrefield Foods Ireland Ltd, 123 York Street, Belfast, BT15 1AB Tel: (028) 9024 7448 Fax: (028) 9032 6375 E-mail: info@fayrefieldireland.com

▶ Fior D I Latte, Unit 22, Jubilee Drive, Loughborough, Leicestershire, LE11 5XS Tel: (01509) 211310

First Milk, Cirrus House Glasgow Airport Business Park, Marchburn Drive, Abbotsinch, Paisley, Renfrewshire, PA3 2SJ Tel: 0141-887 6111 Fax: 0141-848 0015

▶ The First Milk Cheese Co. Ltd, Merlins Bridge, Haverfordwest, Dyfed, SA61 1JN Tel: (01437) 762852 Fax: (01437) 760624

Futura Foods UK Ltd, Wynchfield House, Calcot, Tetbury, Gloucestershire, GL8 8YJ Tel: (01666) 890500 Fax: (01666) 890522 E-mail: info@futura-foods.com

G Lloyd Evans & Sons, Bryn Hen, Groesffordd Marli, Abergele, Clwyd, LL22 9ED Tel: (01745) 583534

Golden Cow, 25-29 Artabrackagh Road, Portadown, Craigavon, County Armagh, BT62 4HB Tel: (028) 3833 8411 Fax: (028) 3835 0292

Hawkridge Dairy, Hawkridge Farm, Coldridge, Crediton, Devon, EX17 6AR Tel: (01363) 884222 Fax: (01363) 83939

Hunts Frozen Foods Bristol Ltd, Unit 3 Pucklechurch Trading Estate, Pucklechurch, Bristol, BS16 9QH Tel: 0117-937 2341 Fax: 0117-937 4160 E-mail: sales@hunts-food-service.co.uk

HXF Fine Foods Ltd, Pidney, Hazelbury Bryan, Sturminster Newton, Dorset, DT10 2EB Tel: (01258) 817529 Fax: (01258) 817561

International Cheese Centre, Unit 3 The Concourse Liverpool Street Station, Liverpool Street, London, EC2M 7PY Tel: (020) 7628 6637 Fax: (020) 7628 2343

Inverloch Cheese Co., 22 Kirk Street, Campbeltown, Argyll, PA28 6BL Tel: (01586) 552692 Fax: (01586) 554729

Isle Of Mull Cheese Ltd, Sgriob-Ruadh Farm, Tobermory, Isle of Mull, PA75 6QD Tel: (01688) 302235 Fax: (01688) 302546 E-mail: mull.cheese@btinternet.com

J J Herbert, High Normanby, Whitby, North Yorkshire, YO22 4PR Tel: (01947) 880459

Kerry Foodservice, Gatehouse Road, Gatehouse Industrial Area, Aylesbury, Buckinghamshire, HP19 8HH Tel: (01296) 318000 Fax: (01296) 338425 E-mail: info@kerry-foodservice.co.uk

L J Solomon, Little Laniley Farm, Bodrean, Truro, Cornwall, TR4 9AG Tel: (01872) 273909 Fax: (01872) 273909

▶ Langage Farm Dairy Produce, Langage Farm, Higher Chalonsleigh, Smithaleigh, Plymouth, PL7 5AY Tel: (01752) 337723 E-mail: sales@langagefarm.com

Little Town Farm Ltd, Burlington Cresent, Goole, North Humberside, DN14 5EQ Tel: (01405) 720198 Fax: (01405) 720365 E-mail: littletownfarm@btconnect.com

▶ Lloyds Animal Feeds Southern Ltd, Westover Trading Estate, Langport, Somerset, TA10 9RB Tel: (01458) 251170 Fax: (01458) 250073

▶ Long Clawson Dairy, 7 Langar Lane, Harby, Melton Mowbray, Leicestershire, LE14 4BL Tel: (01949) 860405 Fax: (01949) 860259

M Brigstock, Stallings Lane, Kingswinford, West Midlands, DY6 7HT Tel: (01384) 293817 Fax: (01384) 279357

DAIRY PRODUCTS – *continued*

M C Kelly Ltd, Elston Farm, Copplestone, Crediton, Devon, EX17 5PB Tel: (01363) 84545 Fax: (01363) 84060 E-mail: sales@mckelly.co.uk

▶ Mclelland Cheese Packaging, Commerce Road, Stranraer, Wigtownshire, DG9 7DA Tel: (01776) 706790 Fax: (01776) 707629

▶ Manor Lodge Dairy Products, 157a Sefton Street, Southport, Merseyside, PR8 5DA Tel: (01704) 538537 Fax: (01704) 501211

Mark Clegg & Co., Lower Road, Longridge, Preston, PR3 2YJ Tel: (01772) 785655 Fax: (01772) 784681 E-mail: mark@markclegg.co.uk

Mark Haigh Dairy Products, 19 Church Lane, Cayton, Scarborough, North Yorkshire, YO11 3SA Tel: (01723) 583192

Iain Mellis, 492 Great Western Road, Glasgow, G12 8EW Tel: 0141-339 8998 Fax: 0141-339 6006 E-mail: sales@ijmellischeesemonger.co.uk

Mentmore Foods Ltd, The Corner House, 9 The Green, Cheddington, Leighton Buzzard, Bedfordshire, LU7 0RJ Tel: (01296) 668117 Fax: (01296) 662737

Mervyn Cyril Clothier, Marston Mains Farm, Marston Bigot, Frome, Somerset, BA11 5BY Tel: (01373) 836276

Michael Lee Cheese Wholesalers, Wakefield Road, Ackworth, Pontefract, West Yorkshire, WF7 7AA Tel: (01977) 618828 Fax: (01977) 618828

Middledale Foods Ltd, 20 Abbey Road, Bourne End, Buckinghamshire, SL8 5NZ Tel: (01628) 521685 Fax: (01628) 521123 E-mail: sales@middledalefoods.co.uk

Mollington Farms Ltd, Grange Farm, Parkgate Road, Mollington, Chester, CH1 6NP Tel: (01244) 851982 Fax: (01244) 851226

▶ Morton's Ltd, Kenyons Lane, Lydiate, Liverpool, L31 0BP Tel: 0151-526 1046 Fax: 0151-520 1570

Muller Dairy (UK) Ltd, Shrewsbury Road, Market Drayton, Shropshire, TF9 3SQ Tel: (01630) 692000 Fax: (01630) 692001 E-mail: consumers@muller.co.uk

The Original Cheddar Cheese Co., The Cliffs, Cheddar, Somerset, BS27 3QE Tel: (01934) 743113 Fax: (01934) 744449

Park Tonks Ltd, 48 North Road, Great Abington, Cambridge, CB21 6AS Tel: (01223) 891721 Fax: (01223) 893571 E-mail: mail@parktonks.co.uk

Philpot Dairy Products Ltd, Philpot House, Station Road, Rayleigh, Essex, SS6 7HH Tel: (01268) 775522 Fax: (01268) 773848 E-mail: claud.bilbao@dairycrest.co.uk

Quickes Traditional Ltd, Home Farm, Newton St. Cyres, Exeter, EX5 5AY Tel: (01392) 851222 Fax: (01392) 851382 E-mail: sales@quickes.co.uk

R P Davidson Cheese Factors, 31 Market Hall, Chesterfield, Derbyshire, S40 1AR Tel: (01246) 201203 Fax: (01246) 201203

Rippon Cheese Stores, 26 Upper Tachbrook Street, London, SW1V 1SW Tel: (020) 7931 0668 Fax: (020) 7828 2368

Rowan Glen Dairy Products Ltd, Palnure, Palnure, Newton Stewart, Wigtownshire, DG8 7AX Tel: (01671) 403633 Fax: (01671) 402444 E-mail: enquiries@rowan-glen.co.uk

Saputo Cheese UK Ltd, The Creamery, Aberarad, Newcastle Emlyn, Carmarthenshire, SA38 9DQ Tel: (01239) 710424 Fax: (01239) 710175

▶ Scottish Milk Products Ltd, Townhead, Rothesay, Isle of Bute, PA20 9JH Tel: (01700) 503186

Scottish Milk Products Ltd, Castle Kennedy, Stranraer, Wigtownshire, DG9 8SH Tel: (01581) 400208 Fax: (01581) 400208

South Caernarfon Creameries Ltd, Chwilog, Pwllheli, Gwynedd, LL53 6SB Tel: (01766) 810251 Fax: (01766) 810578 E-mail: mail@sccwales.co.uk

Staple Dairy Products Ltd, Main Road, Orpington, Kent, BR5 3HS Tel: (01689) 888700 Fax: (01689) 888710 E-mail: sales@stapledairy.co.uk

T Pickles Farms Ltd, South Farm, Dowbridge, Kirkham, Preston, PR4 2YL Tel: (01772) 683032 Fax: (01772) 683157

Tanner Foods Ltd, Oxford Lane Dairy, Sible Hedingham, Halstead, Essex, CO9 3LE Tel: (01787) 460276 Fax: (01787) 465223

Harry Travis (Rishworth) Ltd, New Market, Otley, West Yorkshire, LS21 3AE Tel: (01943) 462530 Fax: (01943) 462530

▶ Turners Dairies, Myrtle Grove Farm, Myrtle Grove, Patching, Worthing, West Sussex, BN13 3XL Tel: (01903) 871520 Fax: (01903) 871524

Tuxford & Tebbutt, 46-56 Thorpe End, Melton Mowbray, Leicestershire, LE13 1RB Tel: (01664) 502900 Fax: (01664) 502901

Unilever Best Foods Ltd, London Road, Purfleet, Essex, RM19 1SD Tel: (01708) 863300 Fax: (01708) 684786

United Dairy Farmers, 15 Dargan Road, Belfast, BT3 9LS Tel: (028) 9037 2237 Fax: (028) 9037 2222 E-mail: info@utdni.co.uk

▶ Voyager Foods, B Sunrise Enterprise Park, Ferryboat Lane, Sunderland, SR5 3RX Tel: 0191-549 5700 Fax: 0191-549 3418

West Highland Dairy Sheep, Achmore, Strome Ferry, Ross-Shire, IV53 8UW Tel: (01599) 577203 Fax: (01599) 577331 E-mail: info@westhighlanddairy.co.uk

Robert Wiseman Dairies, Rolle Road, Torrington, Devon, EX38 8AU Tel: (01805) 622018 Fax: (01805) 624970 E-mail: claire.turner@robertwisemans.co.uk

Woodlands Park Dairy, Woodlands, Wimborne, Dorset, BH21 8LX Tel: (01202) 822687 Fax: (01202) 826051 E-mail: sales@woodlands-park.co.uk

Woolsery Cheese, The Old Dairy, Up Sydling, Dorchester, Dorset, DT2 9PQ Tel: (01984) 623359 Fax: (01300) 341991 E-mail: woolsery.cheese@virgin.net

▶ Y D C Ltd, Littleworth Road, Esher, Surrey, KT10 9PD Tel: (01372) 476000 Fax: (01372) 476111

DAIRY PUMPS

Farmview Dairies Ltd, 75a Lisnabreeny Road, Belfast, BT6 9SR Tel: (028) 9044 8553 Fax: (028) 9044 9120

Fullwood Ltd, Grange Road, Ellesmere, Shropshire, SY12 9DF Tel: (01691) 627391 Fax: (01691) 627361 E-mail: sales@fullwood.com

DAMP PROOF COURSES (DPC)

▶ Lifecote Damp Proofing, 5 Higher Beacon, Ilminster, Somerset, TA19 9AJ Tel: (01460) 52669 Fax: (01460) 52669 E-mail: info@lifecote.net

▶ Regency Preservation, Conbar House, Mead Lane, Hertford, SG13 7AP Tel: (01992) 509201 Fax: (01992) 552277 E-mail: enquiries@regencypreservation.co.uk

DAMP PROOFING CHEMICAL PRODUCTS

John Newton & Co. Ltd, 12 Verney Road, London, SE16 3DH Tel: (020) 7237 1217 Fax: (020) 7252 2769 E-mail: sales@newton-membranes.co.uk

Safeguard Chemicals Ltd, Redkiln Close, Horsham, West Sussex, RH13 5QL Tel: (01403) 210204 Fax: (01403) 217529 E-mail: info@safeguardchem.com

Sovereign Chemical Ltd, Park Road, Barrow-In-Furness, Cumbria, LA14 4EQ Tel: (01229) 870800 Fax: (01229) 870850 E-mail: sales@sovchem.co.uk

Triton Chemical Manufacturing Co. Ltd, Unit 5 Lyndean Industrial Estate, 129 Felixstowe Road, London, SE2 9SG Tel: (020) 8310 3929 Fax: (020) 8312 0349 E-mail: info@triton-chemicals.com

DAMP PROOFING SERVICES OR CONTRACTORS

▶ Biocraft Ltd, 25b Chapel Hill, Tilehurst, Reading, RG31 5BT Tel: 0118-945 1144 E-mail: sales@biocraft.co.uk

▶ Bosa Contracts Ltd, Unit 5A, Ahed Business Centre, Dewsbury Road, Ossett, West Yorkshire, WF5 9ND Tel: (01924) 274930 Fax: (01924) 271728 E-mail: stevebosa@btconnect.com

Brick Lock Ltd, 8 Brexdale Avenue, Kippax, Leeds, LS25 7EJ Tel: 0113-232 0800

C R S Specialised Building Services Ltd, 45a Stoke Road, Gosport, Hampshire, PO12 1LS Tel: (023) 9258 3084 Fax: (023) 9258 3084 E-mail: enq@crsbuilders.co.uk

Complete Preservation Service Ltd, 4-5 Wyvern House, Harriers Trading Estate, Stadium Close, Kidderminster, Worcestershire, DY10 1NJ Tel: (01562) 69945 Fax: (01562) 69945 E-mail: complete.preservation@ukonline.co.uk

Coulson, William James House, Cowley Road, Cambridge, CB4 0WX Tel: (01223) 423800 Fax: (01223) 420550 E-mail: group@coulson.co.uk

Dampco (U.K.) Ltd, 21 Lythalls Lane, Coventry, CV6 6FN Tel: (0800) 626925 Fax: (024) 7668 7683 E-mail: info@dampco.org

Dampcoursing Ltd, 10-12 Dorset Road, London, N15 5AJ Tel: (020) 8802 2233 Fax: (020) 8809 1839 E-mail: dampcoursingltd@london.com

Dampcure Luton Co., 1 Ashton Road, Luton, LU1 3QE Tel: (01582) 735650

▶ Dampcure Woodcure 30 Ltd, 41 Merton Road, Watford, WD18 0WJ Tel: (01923) 663322 Fax: (01923) 223842 E-mail: admin@dampcurewoodcure.com

Gulliver Timber Treatments Ltd, Bank Buildings, Station Road, Sevenoaks, Kent, TN14 5QX Tel: (01959) 524966 Fax: (01959) 525176 E-mail: enquiries@gullivertt.co.uk

Homeguard (South East) Ltd, 19 Broadmead Road, Folkestone, Kent, CT19 5AN Tel: (01702) 471666 Fax: (0845) 3703883 E-mail: linda@dwcuk.com

J Charles & Son Ltd, Whitbygate, Thornton Dale, Pickering, North Yorkshire, YO18 7RY Tel: (01751) 474303

J H Garlick Ltd, 180 Park View Road, Welling, Kent, DA16 1ST Tel: (020) 8303 2941 Fax: (020) 8303 0951 E-mail: surveyors@jhgarlickltd.fsnet.co.uk

Henry Jones & Sons Ltd, Wyvern, 1 Brynhedydd Road, Rhyl, Denbighshire, LL18 3UH Tel: (01745) 351314 Fax: (01745) 351314 E-mail: office@hjs1923.f9.co.uk

Kilrot, 928 Foleshill Road, Coventry, CV6 6GS Tel: (024) 7668 9998 Fax: (024) 7663 7562 E-mail: dickdixon@kilrot.fsbusiness.co.uk

Kiltox Contracts Ltd, 6 Chiltonian Industrial Estate, Manor Lane, London, SE12 0TX Tel: (020) 8463 9690 Fax: (0845) 1662050 E-mail: info@kiltox.co.uk

▶ Lifecote Damp Proofing, 5 Higher Beacon, Ilminster, Somerset, TA19 9AJ Tel: (01460) 52669 Fax: (01460) 52669 E-mail: info@lifecote.net

Mercian Preservation Ltd, 74 Cinder Bank, Dudley, West Midlands, DY2 9BH Tel: (01384) 250154 Fax: (01384) 456068

John Newton & Co. Ltd, 12 Verney Road, London, SE16 3DH Tel: (020) 7237 1217 Fax: (020) 7252 2769 E-mail: sales@newton-membranes.co.uk

Pass & Co. (St. Albans) Ltd, 37 Thornton Road, Little Heath, Potters Bar, Hertfordshire, EN6 1JJ Tel: (01727) 851172 Fax: (01707) 654327

Plad Timber & Damp Proofing Specialists Ltd, 168 Birmingham Road, Shenstone Wood End, Lichfield, Staffordshire, WS14 0NX Tel: 0121-308 4241 Fax: 0121-323 3683

Protim Services Ltd, Cockersdale Works, Whitehall Road, Drighlington, Bradford, West Yorkshire, BD11 1NQ Tel: 0113-285 2173 Fax: 0113-285 2243 E-mail: leeds@protim-services.co.uk

Pro-Treat (Timber & Damp Co) Ltd, Premier House, Holmes Road, Sowerby Bridge, West Yorkshire, HX6 3LD Tel: (01422) 834096 Fax: (01422) 839898

R H Smith Worthing Ltd, Southdownview Way, Worthing, West Sussex, BN14 8NL Tel: (01903) 238316 E-mail: rhsmith1956@tiscali.co.uk

Renlon Holdings Ltd, Richardson House, Boundary Business Court, Mitcham, Surrey, CR4 3TD Tel: (020) 8687 4000 Fax: (020) 8687 4040 E-mail: survey@renlon.com

RLH Developments, 3 Coombe Avenue, Croydon, CR0 5SD Tel: (020) 8681 8811 Fax: (020) 8666 0147 E-mail: info@rlhdevelopments.co.uk

Roofrite (East Anglia) Ltd, The Street, Sheering, Bishop's Stortford, Hertfordshire, CM22 7LY Tel: (01279) 734515 Fax: (01279) 734568

Tapco Homecare Services, Commercial Unit, Pool House Estate, Bancroft Road, Reigate, Surrey, RH2 7RP Tel: (020) 8398 6663 Fax: (01737) 247265 E-mail: info@tapco.uk

▶ Timberwise (UK) Ltd, PO Box 4198, Cardiff, CF14 8BG Tel: (0800) 991100 E-mail: cardiff@timberwise.co.uk

▶ Timberwise UK plc, Chester Enterprise Centre, Hoole Bridge, Chester, CH2 3NE Tel: (01244) 321366 Fax: (01565) 621000 E-mail: chester@timberwise.co.uk

▶ Timberwise (UK) Ltd, 19 Eagle Close, Birdwood Park, Fareham, Hants, PO16 8QX Tel: (0800) 991100 Fax: (01329) 510186 E-mail: hants@timberwise.co.uk

▶ Timberwise UK plc, Kirkfields Business Centre, Kirk Lane, Yeadon, Leeds, LS19 7ET Tel: 0113-250 4402 Fax: 0113-250 9931 E-mail: leeds@timberwise.co.uk

▶ Timberwise (UK) Ltd, 1 Norman Road, Thurmaston, Leicester, LE4 8EL Tel: (0800) 991100 Fax: 0116-269 3678 E-mail: leics@timberwise.co.uk

▶ Timberwise (UK) Ltd, Unit B16, Brunswick Business Centre, Brunswick Business Park, Sefton Street, Liverpool, L3 4BD Tel: (0800) 991100 Fax: 0151-284 6837 E-mail: liverpool@timberwise.co.uk

▶ Timberwise UK plc, 3 CWRT Roger Mostyn, Builder Street, Llandudno, Gwynedd, LL30 1DS Tel: (01492) 535065 Fax: (01492) 864004 E-mail: llandudno@timberwise.co.uk

Timberwise UK plc, 1 Drake Mews, Gadbrook Park, Northwich, Cheshire, CW9 7XF Tel: (01606) 333636 Fax: (01606) 334664 E-mail: hq@timberwise.co.uk

▶ Timberwise (UK) Ltd, Bank House, 4 Wharf Road, Sale, Cheshire, M33 2AF Tel: (0800) 991100 Fax: 0161-972 0077 E-mail: sale@timberwise.co.uk

▶ Timberwise UK plc, 4 Finchwell Close, Sheffield, S13 9DF Tel: 0114-256 1411 Fax: 0114-256 1422 E-mail: sheffield@timberwise.co.uk

Timberwise UK, Coombe Works, Coombe, Sherborne, Dorset, DT9 4AU Tel: (01935) 812600 Fax: (01935) 814436 E-mail: hq@timberwise.co.uk

▶ Timberwise UK plc, 47 The Green, Cheadle, Stoke-on-Trent, ST10 1XS Tel: (01782) 599921 Fax: 0161 962 7610 E-mail: stoke@timberwise.co.uk

▶ Timberwise (UK) Ltd, 6 Rose Hill, Sutton, Surrey, SM1 3EU Tel: (0800) 991100 Fax: (020) 8641 4343 E-mail: sutton@timberwise.co.uk

▶ Timberwise (UK) Ltd, Wilwood, Smith Hill, Bishopsteignton, Teignmouth, Devon, TQ14 9QT Tel: (0800) 991100 Fax: (01935) 814436 E-mail: devon@timberwise.co.uk

▶ Timberwise (UK) Ltd, 7 Gooch Way, Worle, Weston-super-Mare, Avon, BS22 7YH Tel: (0800) 991100 Fax: (01935) 814436 E-mail: weston@timberwise.co.uk

▶ W P M R Ltd, 69 Trinity Street, Leamington Spa, Warwickshire, CV32 5YN Tel: (01926) 338845 Fax: (01926) 336613

DAMP PROOFING SYSTEMS

▶ Anscombe Property Maintenance, 8 Leybourne Parade, Brighton, BN2 4LW Tel: (01273) 693844 Fax: 01273 693844 E-mail: info@anscombepropertymaintenance.co.uk

DAMPER REGULATORS

Flowrite Industrial Dampers Ltd, The Glasshouse Kings Lane, Norwich, NR1 3PS Tel: (01603) 633163 Fax: (01603) 633763 E-mail: sales@industrialdampers.com

DANCEWEAR

▶ Baillando Dancewear, 12a Market Buildings, Maidstone, Kent, ME14 1HP Tel: (01622) 691190 E-mail: manager@baillando.co.uk

E Gandolfi Ltd, Mill Road, Wellingborough, Northamptonshire, NN8 1PR Tel: (01933) 224007 Fax: (01933) 227009 E-mail: gandolfisports@btconnet.com

Eternal Clothing Ltd, 275a Ley Street, Ilford, Essex, IG1 4BN Tel: (020) 8514 3544 Fax: (020) 8514 1786 E-mail: ecuk@aol.com

▶ Freed Of London Ltd, 35 Rydal Street, Leicester, LE2 7DS Tel: 0116-254 8010

GrooveDancewear, High Street, Chatteris, Cambridgeshire, PE16 6BE Tel: (01354) 693595E-mail: sales@groovedancewear.co.uk

▶ Hullachan Pro, 6 Milrig Road, Rutherglen, Glasgow, G73 2NH Tel: 0141-647 0257 E-mail: craig.coussins@btinternet.com

▶ ReetPetite, The Cottage, Ragnall Lane, Walkley Wood, Nailsworth, Gloucestershire, GL6 0RX Tel: 01453 833996 E-mail: reet@reetpetite.biz

▶ The Tutu Shop, 2-4 Pendarves Street, Beacon, Camborne, Cornwall, TR14 7SQ Tel: (01209) 716833 E-mail: sales@thetutushop.co.uk

DANGEROUS GOODS SAFETY ADVISER (DGSA)

▶ Barracuda Safety & Training Services, 19 Kingsmead, Nailsea, North Somerset, BS48 2XH Tel: (01275) 859285 Fax: (01275) 859285 E-mail: info@barracudatraining.co.uk

DARK RYE BREAD

▶ All Natural, 61e-61f Gorse Industrial Estate, Barnham, Thetford, Norfolk, IP24 2PH Tel: (01842) 890891 Fax: (01842) 890891 E-mail: michael@allnaturalbakery.co.uk

DATA ACQUISITION BOARDS

Concurrent UK Ltd, Chiltern House, Broad Lane, Bracknell, Berkshire, RG12 9GU Tel: (01344) 403280 Fax: (01344) 403283

DATA ACQUISITION SOFTWARE

Accurate Business Solutions Ltd, 80 Peach Street, Wokingham, Berkshire, RG40 1XH Tel: 0118-977 3880 Fax: 0118-977 1260 E-mail: info@accurate.co.uk

Advanced Analysis & Integration Ltd, Riverpark Road, Manchester, M40 2XP Tel: 0161-231 1800 Fax: 0161-231 0509 E-mail: sales@aail.co.uk

Anville Instruments, Unit 19 Pegasus Court, North Lane, Aldershot, Hampshire, GU12 4QP Tel: (01252) 351030 Fax: (01252) 323492 E-mail: stephen@anvilleinstrumemts.com

Elcome Ltd, The Engine Shed, Overtown Farm, Wroughton, Swindon, SN4 0SH Tel: (01793) 845144 Fax: (01793) 845177 E-mail: sales@elcome.ltd.co.uk

Eurotherm, Faraday Close, Durrington, Worthing, West Sussex, BN13 3PL Tel: (01903) 268500 Fax: (01903) 265982 E-mail: info@eurotherm.com

▶ Global Address Ltd, Venturers House, Prince St Roundabout, Bristol, BS1 4PB Tel: 0117-915 4018 Fax: 0117-915 4348 E-mail: sales@globaladdress.net

Richard Moon Consulting, PO Box 425, Bedford, MK44 2ZW Tel: (01234) 772509 E-mail: richard@richardmoon.com

Omicron Development Ltd, Station Road, Stalbridge, Sturminster Newton, Dorset, DT10 2RQ Tel: (01963) 363632 Fax: (01963) 363632 E-mail: neil@omicrondev.co.uk

Planworld Computers Ltd, 1 Farnham Road, Guildford, Surrey, GU2 4RG Tel: (01483) 549888 Fax: (01483) 549100 E-mail: kellysearch@planworld.co.uk

Somat Systems (UK) Ltd, 230 Woodburn Road, Sheffield, S9 3LQ Tel: 0114-275 5292 Fax: 0114-275 8272 E-mail: ajb@somat.com

Symdex Ltd, 3 Mill Lane, Broxbourne, Hertfordshire, EN10 7AZ Tel: 01992 451515 E-mail: info@symdex.co.uk

DATA ACQUISITION SYSTEM DESIGN

Outram Research Ltd, Haining House, Taylors Lane, Bosham, Chichester, West Sussex, PO18 8QQ Tel: (01243) 573050 Fax: (01243) 574136

DATA ACQUISITION SYSTEMS INTEGRATORS

Serco, Unit A-B Wellington Gate, Silverthorne Way, Waterlooville, Hampshire, PO7 7XY Tel: (023) 9278 4950 Fax: (023) 9226 9859

DATA ACQUISITION SYSTEMS MANUFRS

A Ii D Solutions Ltd, 2 Wyvern Avenue, Stockport, Cheshire, SK5 7DD Tel: 0161-480 3163 Fax: 0161-480 3043 E-mail: info@aiid.co.uk

Adaptive Computing Co., Crabtree Farm, Wisborough Green, Billingshurst, West Sussex, RH14 0AD Tel: (01403) 753333 Fax: (01403) 753386 E-mail: info@adaptive-instruments.com

Agilent Technologies UK Ltd, Eskdale Road, Winnersh, Wokingham, Berkshire, RG41 5DZ Tel: (07004) 666666 Fax: (07004) 444555 E-mail: contactcenter_uk@agilent.com

Anville Instruments, Unit 19 Pegasus Court, North Lane, Aldershot, Hampshire, GU12 4QP Tel: (01252) 351030 Fax: (01252) 323492 E-mail: stephen@anvilleinstrumemts.com

Astech Electronics Ltd, Forge Industrial Estate, The Street, Binsted, Alton, Hampshire, GU34 4PF Tel: (01420) 22689 Fax: (01420) 22636 E-mail: astech@astech.demon.co.uk

Blue Chip Technology Ltd, Chowley Oak, Chowley Oak Lane, Tattenhall, Chester, CH3 9EX Tel: (01829) 772000 Fax: (01829) 772001 E-mail: sales@bluechiptechnology.co.uk

C S E Seprol Ltd, Rotherside Road, Eckington, Sheffield, S21 4HL Tel: (01246) 436331 Fax: (01246) 432461 E-mail: products@cse-seprol.com

Cambridge Electronic Design Ltd, Science Park, Milton Road, Cambridge, CB4 0FE Tel: (01223) 420186 Fax: (01223) 420488 E-mail: info@ced.co.uk

Data Track Technology P.L.C., 153 Somerford Road, Christchurch, Dorset, BH23 3TY Tel: (01425) 270333 Fax: (01425) 270433 E-mail: sales@dtrack.com

Datel UK Ltd, 15 Campbell Court, Bramley, Tadley, Hampshire, RG26 5EG Tel: (01256) 880444 Fax: (01256) 880706 E-mail: datel.ltd@datel.com

Field Electronics Ltd, 23 Star Road, Star Trading Estate, Partridge Green, Horsham, West Sussex, RH13 8RA Tel: (01403) 713772 Fax: (0870) 0271033 E-mail: sales@fieldelectronics.com

G K N Aerospace Services, Ferry Road, East Cowes, Isle of Wight, PO32 6RA Tel: (01983) 294101 Fax: (01983) 291006 E-mail: info@gknwae.com

H B M UK Ltd, 1 Churchill Court, 58 Station Road, North Harrow, Harrow, Middlesex, HA2 7SA Tel: (020) 8515 6100 Fax: (020) 8515 6149 E-mail: info@uk.hbm.com

Halda Ltd, Quay Business Centre, 12 Harvard Court, Winwick Quay, Warrington, WA2 8LT Tel: (01925) 629926 Fax: (01925) 629929 E-mail: haldauk@aol.com

K UK Ltd, Suite 1, Homestead Farm, North Houghton, Stockbridge, Hampshire, SO20 6LG Tel: (01264) 810044 Fax: (01264) 810044

Kendata Services Ltd, Nutsey Lane, Totton, Southampton, SO40 3NB Tel: (023) 8086 9922 Fax: (023) 8086 0800 E-mail: kpsales@kenda.co.uk

Micro Movements Ltd, Eversley Centre, Hook, Hampshire, RG27 0NB Tel: 0118-973 0200 Fax: 0118-9328872 E-mail: info@micromovements.co.uk

Pentagon Instruments Ltd, Unit 4 Wayside, Commerce Way, Lancing, West Sussex, BN15 8SW Tel: (01903) 765225 Fax: (01903) 765547 E-mail: sales@pentagoninstruments.com

Protronix Industrial Services, 3-15 Cross Street, Luton, LU2 0DP Tel: (01582) 418490 Fax: (01582) 486588 E-mail: sales@protronix.co.uk

Radio Data Logger Co. Ltd, 75 Silver Street, Newport Pagnell, Buckinghamshire, MK16 0EQ Tel: (01908) 618932 Fax: (01908) 618932 E-mail: enq@radiolog.co.uk

Scotland Electronics (International) Ltd, 28 West Road, Greshop Industrial Estate, Forres, Morayshire, IV36 2GW Tel: (01309) 678900 Fax: (01309) 678909 E-mail: sales@scotlandelectronics.co.uk

Serco, Unit A-B Wellington Gate, Silverthorne Way, Waterlooville, Hampshire, PO7 7XY Tel: (023) 9278 4950 Fax: (023) 9226 9859

Somat Systems (UK) Ltd, 230 Woodburn Road, Sheffield, S9 3LQ Tel: 0114-275 5292 Fax: 0114-275 8272 E-mail: ajb@somat.com

Symbol Technologies Ltd, Symbol Place, Wharfedale Road, Winnersh, Wokingham, Berkshire, RG41 5TP Tel: 0118-945 7000 Fax: 0118-945 7500

Xicon Education Ltd, Bank House, 1 Bank Street, Warrington, WA1 2AP Tel: (01925) 240342 Fax: (01925) 244894 E-mail: info@xicon.com

Yokogawa Marex Ltd, 34 Medina Road, Cowes, Isle Of Wight, PO31 7DA Tel: (01983) 296011 Fax: (01983) 291776 E-mail: sales@ymx.yokogawa.com

DATA ACQUISITION/CONTROL SYSTEMS

A C I C International Ltd, Blacknest Road, Blacknest, Alton, Hampshire, GU34 4PX Tel: (01420) 23930 Fax: (01420) 23921 E-mail: sales@acic.co.uk

▶ CTES Ltd, 1 Claremont Street, Aberdeen, AB10 6QP Tel: (01224) 588788 Fax: (01224) 588840 E-mail: uksales@ctes.com

Hytec Electronics Ltd, 5 Craddock Road, Reading, RG2 0JT Tel: 0118-975 7770 Fax: 0118-975 7566 E-mail: sales@hytec-electronics.co.uk

Integrated Computer Services (Scotland) Ltd, 105a Shore Rd, Innellan, Dunoon, Argyll, PA23 7SR Tel: (01369) 830647 Fax: (01369) 830783 E-mail: ics_ltd@netcomuk.co.uk

DATA ACQUISITION/CONTROL SYSTEMS SERVICES

A C I C International Ltd, Blacknest Road, Blacknest, Alton, Hampshire, GU34 4PX Tel: (01420) 23930 Fax: (01420) 23921 E-mail: sales@acic.co.uk

Captec Ltd, Fareham, Hampshire, PO15 5TX Tel: (01489) 866066 Fax: (01489) 866088 E-mail: info@captec.co.uk

Expro North Sea Ltd, Unit B2, Kirkhill Place, Kirkhill Industrial Estate, Dyce, Aberdeen, AB21 0GU Tel: (01224) 214600 Fax: (01224) 770295 E-mail: marketing.enquiries@exprogroup.com

Hytec Electronics Ltd, 5 Craddock Road, Reading, RG2 0JT Tel: 0118-975 7770 Fax: 0118-975 7566 E-mail: sales@hytec-electronics.co.uk

DATA ANALYSIS SOFTWARE

▶ Terrington Data Management, IT Centre, Innovation Way, York Science Park, Heslington, York, YO10 5DG Tel: 0870 8508023 Fax: 01904 567719 E-mail: sales@terringtondm.com

DATA ANALYSIS SYSTEMS

Alterian Holdings Ltd, Century Place, Bond Street, Bristol, BS2 9AG Tel: 0117-970 3200 Fax: 0117-970 3201E-mail: info@alterian.com

Lake Financial Systems, Stable Mews Beechwoods Estate, Elmete Lane, Leeds, LS8 2LQ Tel: 0113-273 7788 Fax: 0113-273 9300 E-mail: info@lake.co.uk

S F K Information, Langdale House, Lothersdale, Keighley, West Yorkshire, BD20 8HB Tel: (01535) 637390E-mail: info@sfkinfo.co.uk

DATA ARCHIVING SERVICES

▶ EDA Ltd, c/o Simms Croft, Middleton, Milton Keynes, MK10 9GF Tel: 01908 393294 E-mail: info@eda-ltd.co.uk

DATA BACKUP CONSULTANCY

▶ Project Desk2Web, 5 Ashburn Avenue, Waterside, Londonderry, BT47 5QE Tel: (020) 8123 6355 E-mail: allannospam@desk2web.co.uk

DATA BACKUP SERVICES

▶ Project Desk2Web, 5 Ashburn Avenue, Waterside, Londonderry, BT47 5QE Tel: (020) 8123 6355 E-mail: allannospam@desk2web.co.uk

DATA BACKUP SOFTWARE

▶ Datascape Online Ltd, 24 Waters Edge Business Park, Modwen Road, Salford, M5 3EZ Tel: (0870) 0621200 Fax: (0870) 0621203

Rescue IT Ltd, 6 Braham Street, London, E1 8EE Tel: (0870) 6090999 Fax: (07092) 102103 E-mail: info@rescueit.co.uk

DATA CABLE ASSEMBLIES

Deval Ltd, Unit 6 Hamilton Way, New Milton, Hampshire, BH25 6TQ Tel: (01425) 620772 Fax: (01425) 638431 E-mail: sales@deval-ltd.co.uk

Ringtel Electronics (UK) Ltd, Ringtel House, Lakeview, Llantarnam Industrial Park, Cwmbran, Gwent, NP44 3HP Tel: (01633) 489550 Fax: (01633) 489570 E-mail: sales@ringtel.com

DATA CABLE INSTALLATION

A C Electrical Wholesale Ltd, 2 Parkway Industrial Estate, Heneage Street, Birmingham, B7 4LY Tel: 0121-333 4959 Fax: 0121-333 4403 E-mail: birmingham@ac-electrical.co.uk

Advance Communications, Business Development Centre, Main Avenue, Treforest Indust Estate, Pontypridd, Mid Glamorgan, CF37 5UR Tel: (01443) 843555 Fax: (01443) 841449

Allnet Ltd, Unit B4, Intergration House, Woton Grange, Reading, RG2 0TG Tel: (01923) 410415 Fax: 0118-921 6006

Avc Europe Ltd, Bessemer Drive, Stevenage, Hertfordshire, SG1 2DT Tel: (01438) 341300 Fax: (01438) 341301 E-mail: info@avcgroup.co.uk

Data Cabling Ltd, 6 Farrier Road, Lincoln, LN6 3RU Tel: (01522) 500699 Fax: (01522) 500882 E-mail: sales@data-cabling.co.uk

E C Electricals Ltd, 16C Wincombe Business Park, Warminster Road, Shaftesbury, Dorset, SP7 9QJ Tel: (01747) 853861 Fax: (01747) 855274 E-mail: enquiries@ecelectricals.co.uk

Edmundson Rickards Electrical, 30 Garrett Road, Lynx Trading Estate, Yeovil, Somerset, BA20 2TJ Tel: (01935) 472727 Fax: (01935) 472010 E-mail: mail@spectrumelectrical.co.uk

Eric Johnson Of Northwich Ltd, Ash House, Ash House Lane, Little Leigh, Northwich, Cheshire, CW8 4RG Tel: (01606) 892444 Fax: (01606) 892442 E-mail: irj@johnson42.fsnet.co.uk

F K B Electrical Ltd, Unit 10-12, Quakers Coppice, Crewe, CW1 6EW Tel: (01270) 501244 Fax: (01270) 251399 E-mail: fkb@fkb.co.uk

First Projects Ltd, City Business Centre, Station Rise, York, YO1 6GA Tel: (01904) 613361 Fax: (01904) 612936

Grapevine, 83 Broadway, Southbourne, Bournemouth, BH6 4EJ Tel: (01202) 429232 Fax: (01202) 424559 E-mail: sales1@grapevine-comms.co.uk

Netx Voice & Data Installations, 76 Broad St, Ely, Cambs, CB7 4AH Tel: 01353 664242 Fax: 01353 776266

Oxford Electronics, 5 Kendall Cresent, Oxford, OX2 8NE Tel: (01865) 510131 Fax: (01865) 311911E-mail: sales@oxford-electronics.co.uk

Paul Earl Ltd, 1 Euro Business Park, New Road, Newhaven, East Sussex, BN9 0DQ Tel: (01273) 514356 Fax: (01273) 611036 E-mail: info@paulearl.co.uk

Renaissance Corporate (Barnet) Ltd, Unit 1 Stroud Wood Business Centre, Frogmore, St. Albans, Herts, AL2 2NN Tel: (01727) 875500 Fax: (01727) 874808 E-mail: sales@rencorp.co.uk

Systemax Communications Ltd, Unit 7 Westerham Trade Centre, The Flyers Way, Westerham, Kent, TN16 1DE Tel: (01959) 563133 Fax: (01959) 563008

U K Cabling Ltd, 7 South View Road, Walton, Peterborough, PE4 6AG Tel: (01733) 321555 Fax: (01733) 322995 E-mail: sales@ukcabling.com

DATA CABLES

Cablelines (Nottingham) Ltd, Unit 4 Orchard Park Industrial Estate, Sandiacre, Nottingham, NG10 5BP Tel: 0115-949 1010 Fax: 0115-949 1019 E-mail: sales@cablelines.com

Central Systems Installations Ltd, 100 Central Street, London, EC1V 8AJ Tel: (020) 7608 0070 Fax: (020) 7253 0891 E-mail: shop@csigroup.co.uk

Comtec Cables, Unit 3 Cardinal Way, Godmanchester, Huntingdon, Cambridgeshire, PE29 2XN Tel: (01480) 415400 Fax: (01480) 454724 E-mail: sales@comtec-comms.com

Hagemeyer Group, Unit 34 Minworth Industrial Park, Forge Lane, Sutton Coldfield, West Midlands, B76 1AH Tel: 0121-351 5222 Fax: 0121-351 4851 E-mail: sales@hageneyer.com

Heart Electronics Ltd, 2 King Edward Road, Nuneaton, Warwickshire, CV11 4BB Tel: (024) 7635 3615 Fax: (024) 7635 3616 E-mail: info@heartelectronics.com

Icomm Structured Wiring Systems, 5 Wychwood Close, New Duston, Northampton, NN5 6QL Tel: (01604) 584655 Fax: (01604) 584652

Microcomms Ltd, New Portreath Road, Redruth, Cornwall, TR16 4QL Tel: (01209) 843636 Fax: (01209) 843666 E-mail: sales@microcomms.co.uk

Norbeck Data Ltd, Lenten House, The Gravel, Trowbridge, Wiltshire, BA14 6QL Tel: (01225) 782865 Fax: (01225) 783284

U K Cabling Ltd, 7 South View Road, Walton, Peterborough, PE4 6AG Tel: (01733) 321555 Fax: (01733) 322995 E-mail: sales@ukcabling.com

UK Telcom, UK House, Springfield Road, Hayes, Middlesex, UB4 0LG Tel: (020) 8573 5052 Fax: (020) 8561 7758

DATA CAPTURE SYSTEMS

Britsoft Barcode Systems Ltd, 1 Kings Road, Hertford, SG13 7EY Tel: (01992) 554552 Fax: (01992) 552426 E-mail: sales@britsoft.com

Documation Software Ltd, Wessex House, Market Street, Eastleigh, Hampshire, SO50 9FD Tel: (023) 8064 7776 Fax: (023) 8064 7775 E-mail: info@documatation.co.uk

Feedback Data Ltd, Park Road, Crowborough, East Sussex, TN6 2QR Tel: (01892) 601400 Fax: (01892) 601429 E-mail: info@feedback-data.com

Gardline Information Solutions Ltd, The Design Centre, Hewet Road, Gapton Hall, Great Yarmouth, Norfolk, NR31 0NN Tel: (01493) 440400 Fax: (01493) 442480 E-mail: steve.brown@gardline.co.uk

I D Data Ltd, The New Mint House, Bedford Road, Petersfield, Hampshire, GU32 3AL Tel: (01730) 235700 Fax: (01730) 235711 E-mail: enquiry@iddata.com

Itesoft Ltd, Headway House, Crosby Way, Farnham, Surrey, GU9 7XG Tel: (01252) 741500 Fax: (01252) 741515 E-mail: marketing@itesoft-uk.co.uk

▶ Itesoft UK Ltd, 19-21 The Woolneed, Farnham, Surrey, GU9 7TT Tel: (01252) 741500 Fax: (01252) 741515 E-mail: marketing@itesoft.com

Trax UK Ltd, Suite 4B Christchurch House, Beaufort Court, Medway City Estate, Rochester, Kent, ME2 4FX Tel: (01634) 724724 Fax: (01634) 290524 E-mail: sales@trax-uk.co.uk

DATA CAPTURE SYSTEMS, HANDHELD

▶ Ryzex plc, Unit 1, Bumpers Way, Bumpers Farm, Chippenham, Wiltshire, SN14 6LH Tel: (01249) 465100 Fax: (01249) 659777 E-mail: infouk@ryzex.com

TMS Insight (Data Capture) Ltd, 1 Chads Close, Dudley, West Midlands, DY3 2LJ Tel: (01384) 214950 Fax: (01384) 212683 E-mail: andrew.haywood@tmsinsight.com

DATA COLLECTION SYSTEMS

Barcode Connections Ltd, 18 King Harry Lane, St. Albans, Hertfordshire, AL3 4AR Tel: (01727) 833391 Fax: (01727) 838819 E-mail: info@tele-ticket.co.uk

Red Ledge Ltd, Red Ledge Business Centre, 289-291 Huddersfield Road, Thongsbridge, Holmfirth, HD9 3UA Tel: (01484) 686769 Fax: (01484) 687879 E-mail: sales@redledge.co.uk

Tectime Data Systems Ltd, Copthall House, Nelson Place, Newcastle, Staffordshire, ST5 1EZ Tel: (01782) 799567 Fax: (01782) 799447 E-mail: info@tectime.com

Unique Id Ltd, 1 Barnes Wallis Court, Wellington Road, Cressex Business Park, High Wycombe, Buckinghamshire, HP12 3PS Tel: (01494) 511022 Fax: (01494) 511033 E-mail: sales@barcodecentral.co.uk

DATA COLLECTION SYSTEMS, PORTABLE, HAND HELD

Electronic Reading Systems Ltd, 14 Wolsdon Business Park, Woburn Road Industrial Estate, Kempston, Bedford, MK42 7PW Tel: (01234) 855300 Fax: (01234) 855446 E-mail: sales@ersltd.co.uk

Tectime Data Systems Ltd, Copthall House, Nelson Place, Newcastle, Staffordshire, ST5 1EZ Tel: (01782) 799567 Fax: (01782) 799447 E-mail: info@tectime.com

DATA COMMUNICATION CONNECTORS

Ringtel Electronics (UK) Ltd, Ringtel House, Lakeview, Llantarnam Industrial Park, Cwmbran, Gwent, NP44 3HP Tel: (01633) 489550 Fax: (01633) 489570 E-mail: sales@ringtel.com

DATA COMMUNICATION ENCLOSURES

Dataracks, Stagwood House, Beach Road, Cottenham, Cambridge, CB4 8FP Tel: (01954) 252229 Fax: (01954) 251461 E-mail: sales@dataracks.co.uk

DATA COMMUNICATION MANAGED NETWORK SERVICES

Communication Centre (International) Ltd, 60 Riverside I I I, Sir Thomas Longley Road, Strood, Rochester, Kent, ME2 4BH Tel: (01634) 295295 Fax: (01634) 723895 E-mail: enquiries@commscentre.com

Federal Communications, PO Box 96, Hengoed, Mid Glamorgan, CF82 7ZR Tel: (0870) 2203995 Fax: (0870) 2203996 E-mail: info@federalcommunications.com

Global Exchange Services, 1-3 Station Road, Sunbury-On-Thames, Middlesex, TW16 6SU Tel: (01932) 776000 Fax: (01932) 776020

DATA COMMUNICATION MANAGED NETWORK SERVICES – *continued*

Intermail plc, Canal View Road, Newbury, Berkshire, RG14 5XF Tel: (01635) 565000 Fax: (01635) 41678 E-mail: sales@intermail.co.uk
J T S Datacom Ltd, 2 Crossfields Close, Shinfield, Reading, RG2 9AY Tel: (0845) 6443193 Fax: (0845) 6448195 E-mail: info@jtsdata.com
The Logic Group Enterprises Ltd, Logic House, Waterfront Business Park, Fleet Road, Fleet, Hampshire, GU51 3SB Tel: (01252) 776755 Fax: (01252) 776738 E-mail: marketing@the-logic-group.com
Metrodata Ltd, Blenheim House Crabtree Office Village, Eversley Way, Egham, Surrey, TW20 8RY Tel: (01784) 744700 Fax: (01784) 477423 E-mail: sales@metrodata.co.uk
Premier Voice & Data, Motokov House, North Lynn Indust Estate, North Lynn Industrial Estate, King's Lynn, Norfolk, PE30 2JG Tel: (01553) 779950 Fax: (01553) 779950 E-mail: info@premiervoiceanddata.co.uk
Soft-Ex UK Ltd, Unit 3b Juno House, Calleva Park, Aldermaston, Reading, RG7 8RA Tel: 0118-981 5555 Fax: 0118-981 5577 E-mail: sales@soft-ex.net

DATA COMMUNICATION SYSTEMS CONSULTANTS OR DESIGNERS, PROTOCOL CONVERSION

J & S Marine Ltd, Riverside Road, Pottington Business Park, Barnstaple, Devon, EX31 1LY Tel: (01271) 337500 Fax: (01271) 337501 E-mail: sales@jsmarine.co.uk

DATA COMMUNICATION SYSTEMS DESIGN

A W Perry Electrical Co. Ltd, 35 Stroud Road, London, SE25 5DR Tel: (020) 8654 3122 Fax: (020) 8656 8806 E-mail: mail@perryelectrical.co.uk

DATA COMMUNICATION SYSTEMS MANUFRS

Amplicon Liveline Ltd, Unit 11 Centenary Industrial Estate, Hughes Road, Brighton, BN2 4AW Tel: (01273) 570220 Fax: (01273) 570215 E-mail: sales@amplicon.co.uk
Avc Europe Ltd, Bessemer Drive, Stevenage, Hertfordshire, SG1 2DT Tel: (01438) 341300 Fax: (01438) 341301 E-mail: info@avcgroup.co.uk
Belgravium, 6 Campus Road, Listerhills Science Park, Bradford, West Yorkshire, BD7 1HR Tel: (01274) 741860 Fax: (01274) 741862 E-mail: sales@belgravium.com
Black Box Network Services Ltd, 464 Basingstoke Road, Reading, RG2 0BG Tel: 0118-965 5000 Fax: 0118-965 5001 E-mail: info@blackbox.co.uk
D A T A Services, 1 Coates Place, Edinburgh, EH3 7AA Tel: 0131-225 7707 Fax: 0131-225 7708
Dimension Data Advanced Infrastructure, Thelwall Industrial Estate, Thelwall New Road, Warrington, WA4 2LY Tel: (01925) 602942 Fax: (01925) 267464 E-mail: sales@uk.didata.com
Enterasys Networks Ltd, Nexus House Newbury Business Park, London Road, Newbury, Berkshire, RG14 2PZ Tel: (01635) 580000 Fax: (01635) 810300
Fibernet Group plc, Rosalind House, Jays Close, Basingstoke, Hampshire, RG22 4BS Tel: (01256) 858685 Fax: (01256) 858601
Hagemeyer Group, Unit 34 Minworth Industrial Park, Forge Lane, Sutton Coldfield, West Midlands, B76 1AH Tel: 0121-351 5222 Fax: 0121-351 4851 E-mail: sales@hageneyer.com
Icomm Structured Wiring Systems, 5 Wychwood Close, New Duston, Northampton, NN5 6QL Tel: (01604) 584655 Fax: (01604) 584652
KK Systems Ltd, PO Box 2770, Brighton, BN45 7ED Tel: (01273) 857185 Fax: (01273) 857186 E-mail: sales@kksystems.com
Lancaster Communications Ltd, Tarn View, Denny Beck, Lancaster, LA2 9HG Tel: (01524) 846900 Fax: (01524) 846900 E-mail: enq@lancastercomms.co.uk
Microcomms Ltd, New Portreath Road, Redruth, Cornwall, TR16 4QL Tel: (01209) 843636 Fax: (01209) 843666 E-mail: sales@microcomms.co.uk
Mitier Communications, 2 Rudgard Avenue, Cherry Willingham, Lincoln, LN3 4JG Tel: (01522) 754279 Fax: (01522) 751942 E-mail: info@radiolinc.co.uk
Newlife Data Communications Ltd, Beacon House, 10 Forest Road, Loughborough, Leicestershire, LE11 3NP Tel: 01509 267231 Fax: 01509 211019
Phoenix Datacom Group Ltd, Phoenix House, Smeaton Close, Aylesbury, Buckinghamshire, HP19 8UW Tel: (01296) 397711 Fax: (01296) 394431 E-mail: info@phoenixdata.com
Spitfire Technology Group, Unit 6-7 Southbank Business Centre, Ponton Road, London, SW8 5BL Tel: (020) 7501 3000 Fax: (020) 7501 3001 E-mail: sales@spitfire.co.uk
W F Electrical plc, 50-51 Burnt Mill, Elizabeth Way, Harlow, Essex, CM20 2HU Tel: (01279) 417171 Fax: (01279) 450902
I.S.G. Webb Ltd, Unit 2 Progress Estate, Bircholt Road, Maidstone, Kent, ME15 9YH Tel: (01622) 670281 Fax: (01622) 683528 E-mail: project.office@isgwebb.com
Westermo Data Communications Ltd, Talisman Business Centre, Duncan Road, Park Gate, Southampton, SO31 7GA Tel: (01489) 580585 Fax: (01489) 580586 E-mail: sales@westermo.co.uk

DATA COMMUNICATION SYSTEMS SERVICING/ INSTALLATION/MAINTENANCE SERVICES

A B B Ltd, Deben House, 1 Selsdon Way, City Harbour, London, NW10 6DH Tel: (020) 7515 5551 Fax: (020) 7515 5551 E-mail: abb.buildingtechnology@gb.abb.com
Barkers International Communication Ltd, Barkers Lane, Bedford, MK41 9TR Tel: (01234) 327772 Fax: (01234) 325526 E-mail: richard@barkers-int.co.uk
Capon Computer Environmental Services Ltd, 149 Putnoe Street, Bedford, MK41 8JR Tel: (01234) 359791 Fax: (01234) 269995
Computer Links Ltd, 7 Grange Road, Houston Industrial Estate, Houstoun Industrial Estate, Livingston, West Lothian, EH54 5DE Tel: (01506) 434811 Fax: (01506) 441997 E-mail: service@computer-links.co.uk
Crown House Technologies, Peal House, 50 Waterloo Road, Wolverhampton, WV1 4RU Tel: (01902) 428666 Fax: (01902) 428774
Matrix Technology Services Ltd, North Street, Maldon, Essex, CM9 5HL Tel: (01621) 841000 Fax: (01621) 843849 E-mail: sales@matrix-ts.com
Mitier Communications, 2 Rudgard Avenue, Cherry Willingham, Lincoln, LN3 4JG Tel: (01522) 754279 Fax: (01522) 751942 E-mail: info@radiolinc.co.uk
Worth Installations Ltd, Bramwell House, Park Lane, Keighley, West Yorkshire, BD21 4QX Tel: (01535) 210510 Fax: (01535) 691508 E-mail: sales@worthcomms.co.uk

DATA COMPUTER SERVER CABINETS

Data Room Supplies, Conbar House, Mead Lane, Hertford, SG13 7AP Tel: (01992) 558737 Fax: (01992) 558714 E-mail: sales@dataroomsupplies.co.uk

DATA CONFERENCING

▶ Arkadin UK Ltd, 26-28 Hammersmith Grove, London, W6 7JA Tel: (020) 8742 6380 Fax: (020) 8742 6355 E-mail: d.creigh@arkadin.co.uk

DATA ENTRY SERVICES

▶ Arcevia Services, 80 Oakland Avenue, Leicester, LE4 7SF Tel: 0116-220 4655 Fax: (0870) 7625207 E-mail: info@arcevia.com
▶ CMP Support, 46 Freshwater Drive, Poole, Dorset, BH15 4JE Tel: (01202) 245318 Fax: 01202 245318 E-mail: enquiries@cmpsupport.co.uk
▶ Damco Solutions Ltd, 23 Clayton Road, Hayes, Middlesex, UB3 1AN Tel: +44 (0) 208 817 1047 Fax: (020) 8573 9072 E-mail: sales@damcosoft.co.uk

DATA LOGGER HIRE

Emmco Ltd, The Old Stables, Cork Lane, 19 West Bar Street, Banbury, Oxfordshire, OX16 9SA Tel: (01295) 262826 Fax: (01295) 709091 E-mail: info@emmcolimited.co.uk

DATA LOGGING EQUIPMENT MANUFRS

A T C Ltd, Greenway House, Greenway Business Centre, Harlow, Essex, CM19 5QD Tel: 0161-406 1000 Fax: (0870) 0558081 E-mail: sales@atc.co.uk
Campbell Scientific Ltd, Campbell Park, 80 Hathern Road, Shepshed, Loughborough, Leicestershire, LE12 9GX Tel: (01509) 601141 Fax: (01509) 601091 E-mail: sales@campbellsci.co.uk
Deltronics Electronic Engineers, Unit 15 Church Road Industrial Estate, Gorslas, Llanelli, Dyfed, SA14 7NN Tel: (01269) 843728 Fax: (01269) 845527 E-mail: sales@deltronics.co.uk
Digitrol Ltd, Coronet Way, Swansea Enterprise Park, Swansea, SA6 8RH Tel: (01792) 796000 Fax: (01792) 701600E-mail: info@digitrol.com
R D S Technology Ltd, Cirencester Road, Minchinhampton, Stroud, Gloucestershire, GL6 9BH Tel: (01453) 733300 Fax: (01453) 733311 E-mail: info@rdstec.com
Radio Data Logger Co. Ltd, 75 Silver Street, Newport Pagnell, Buckinghamshire, MK16 0EQ Tel: (01908) 618932 Fax: (01908) 618932 E-mail: enq@radiolog.co.uk
Wylie Systems, Drury Lane, St. Leonards-on-Sea, East Sussex, TN38 9XS Tel: (01424) 421235 Fax: (01424) 433760 E-mail: wylie@raycowylie.com
Sailes Marketing Ltd, 15 Aintree Road, Keytec 7 Business Park, Pershore, Worcestershire, WR10 2JN Tel: (01386) 554210 Fax: (01386) 552461 E-mail: sales@sailesmarketing.com
Storm Products, 28 Hawbank Road, East Kilbride, Glasgow, G74 5EX Tel: (01355) 249358 Fax: (01355) 249197 E-mail: sales@cvcs.co.uk
Testo Ltd, Newman Lane, Alton, Hampshire, GU34 2QJ Tel: (01420) 544433 Fax: (01420) 544434 E-mail: caterer@testo.co.uk
Wessex Power Technology Ltd, 189 Ashley Road, Poole, Dorset, BH14 9DL Tel: (01202) 723000 Fax: (01202) 723400 E-mail: wpt@wessexpower.co.uk

DATA LOGGING SERVICES

Expro North Sea Ltd, Unit B2, Kirkhill Place, Kirkhill Industrial Estate, Dyce, Aberdeen, AB21 0GU Tel: (01224) 214600 Fax: (01224) 770295 E-mail: marketing.enquiries@exprogroup.com
I H S Energy Group, 28 Church Street, Epsom, Surrey, KT17 4QP Tel: (01372) 745959 Fax: (01372) 727091
▶ M D Electronics, 9 Quarry Fields, Leek Wootton, Warwick, CV35 7RS Tel: (01926) 850315 Fax: (01926) 850315 E-mail: info@mdelectronics.co.uk
Sonifex Ltd, 61 Station Road, Irthlingborough, Wellingborough, Northamptonshire, NN9 5QE Tel: (01933) 650700 Fax: (01933) 650726 E-mail: sales@sonifex.co.uk
Validation Centre, Unit 9 Sinclair Court, Great Yarmouth, Norfolk, NR31 0NH Tel: (01493) 443800 Fax: (01493) 443900 E-mail: sales@tvcalx.co.uk

DATA MINING SOFTWARE

Angoss Software Ltd, Unit 23 Surrey Technology Centre, Occam Road, Surrey Research Park, Guildford, Surrey, GU2 7YG Tel: (01483) 452303 Fax: (01483) 453303 E-mail: ncb@angoss.com
▶ ASTRAC Ltd, Innovation Centre, Warwick Technology Park, Warwick, CV34 6UW Tel: (01926) 623060 Fax: (01926) 623061 E-mail: info@astrac.com

DATA PREPARATION/ PROCESSING/PUNCHING/IMAGE CAPTURE CONSULTANTS OR SERVICES, *See also Computer Services etc*

A T S S (East Anglia) Ltd, Station Road East, Stowmarket, Suffolk, IP14 1RQ Tel: (01449) 674944 Fax: (01449) 678678 E-mail: sales@atssea.co.uk
Abacus E-Solutions Ltd, Albany House, Concorde Street, Luton, LU2 0JD Tel: (01582) 702702 Fax: (01582) 452106 E-mail: sales@abacusuk.com
Am Computing Direct Ltd, International House, Cray Avenue, Orpington, Kent, BR5 3RY Tel: (01689) 896489 Fax: (01689) 896659 E-mail: amaddalo@aol.com
Arrow Imaging Ltd, 34 Pebble Close, Tamworth Business Park, Amington, Tamworth, Staffordshire, B77 4RP Tel: (01827) 310350 Fax: (01827) 313880 E-mail: sales@arrow-imaging.co.uk
B N E Electronics Ltd, 44 Main Street, Toomebridge, Antrim, BT41 3TF Tel: (028) 7965 0502 Fax: (028) 7965 4830 E-mail: edward.duffin@bne.onyxnet.co.uk
Breeze Ltd, Breeze House, Albert Close Trading Estate, Whitefield, Manchester, M45 8EH Tel: 0161-796 3600 Fax: 0161-796 3700 E-mail: info@breez.co.uk
Business Database Production Ltd, 19 Hatherley Road, Sidcup, Kent, DA14 4BH Tel: (020) 8300 3661 Fax: (020) 8300 7367 E-mail: marilynbdp@aol.com
Ciber (U.K.) Ltd, 101 Wigmore Street, London, W1U 1QU Tel: (020) 7355 1101 Fax: (020) 7355 9000 E-mail: info.uk@ciber.com
Robin Clay Ltd, 31 St. Leonards Road, Bexhill-on-Sea, East Sussex, TN40 1HP Tel: (01424) 730302 Fax: (01424) 730291 E-mail: sarah@ashbuscent.co.uk
William Clowes Ltd, Copland Way, Ellough, Beccles, Suffolk, NR34 7TL Tel: (01502) 712884 Fax: (01502) 717003 E-mail: william@clowes.co.uk
D B I Associates Ltd, Stoneleigh Park Mews, Stonleigh Abbey, Kenilworth, Warwickshire, CV8 2DB Tel: (01926) 312481 Fax: (01926) 515616 E-mail: consultants@dbiconsulting.co.uk
▶ Damco Solutions Ltd, 23 Clayton Road, Hayes, Middlesex, UB3 1AN Tel: +44 (0) 208 817 1047 Fax: (020) 8573 9072 E-mail: sales@damcosoft.co.uk
Data & Research Services plc, Sunrise Parkway, Linford Wood, Milton Keynes, MK14 6LR Tel: (01908) 666088 Fax: (01908) 607668 E-mail: enquiries@drs.co.uk
Eurodata Computer Services Ltd, 8 Westmead Corner, Carshalton, Surrey, SM5 2NZ Tel: (020) 8643 0933 Fax: (020) 8643 1886 E-mail: eurodatacs@aol.com
▶ Exescan Ltd, 37 Rolle Street, Exmouth, Devon, EX8 2SN Tel: (01395) 224141 Fax: (01395) 268829 E-mail: info@exescan.co.uk
F M A Systems, Unit 37 Monument Business Park, Warpsgrove Lane, Chalgrove, Oxford, OX44 7RW Tel: (01865) 891682 Fax: (01865) 891685 E-mail: sales@fma-systems.com
I B M (UK) Ltd, Po Box 41, Portsmouth, PO6 3AU Tel: (023) 9256 1000 Fax: (023) 9238 8914 E-mail: uk_crc@uk.ibm.com
I K Portable Solutions Ltd, I K House, Plough Road, Wellington, Telford, Shropshire, TF1 1ET Tel: (01952) 242000 Fax: (01952) 223789 E-mail: iki@netcomuk.co.uk
Inputideal Ltd, Tame House, Wellington CR, Fradley Park, Lichfield, Staffordshire, WS13 8RZ Tel: (01543) 444708 Fax: (01543) 444709 E-mail: webmaster@patech-solutions.com
Itesoft Ltd, Headway House, Crosby Way, Farnham, Surrey, GU9 7XG Tel: (01252) 741500 Fax: (01252) 741515 E-mail: marketing@itesoft-uk.co.uk
Key Data Group Ltd, Lincoln Street, Old Basford, Nottingham, NG6 0FT Tel: 0115-942 2266 Fax: 0115-942 0065 E-mail: info@keydatagroup.co.uk
Lewis Direct Mail Marketing Ltd, 433-435 Caledonian Road, London, N7 9BG Tel: (020) 7607 6505 Fax: (020) 7607 0932 E-mail: info@ldm.co.uk
Line Scan, Unit 2, Seeking Road, Bartlett Court, Lynx Trading Estate, Yeovil, Somerset, BA20 2NZ Tel: (01935) 471440 Fax: (01935) 475285 E-mail: enquiries@linescan.co.uk
Lsi Logic Europe Ltd, Greenwood House, London Road, Bracknell, Berkshire, RG12 2UB Tel: (01344) 413200 Fax: (01344) 413329
Mailord Mail Order Services Ltd, 115 Park Avenue, Potters Bar, Hertfordshire, EN6 5EW Tel: (01707) 662442 Fax: (01707) 664180 E-mail: mike@mailord.co.uk
Market Developer Ltd, Bourne House, 10 Windmill Road, Hampton Hill, Middlesex, TW12 1RH Tel: (020) 8979 1122 Fax: (020) 8941 7595 E-mail: simon.davis@marketdeveloper.com
Meldrum Mailing Ltd, Units 1-2 Hainault Works, Hainault Road, Little Heath, Romford, RM6 5NF Tel: (020) 8597 3218 Fax: (0845) 6445675
Micad Systems & F M Data Services, Lansdown House, 85 Buxton Road, Stockport, Cheshire, SK2 6LR Tel: 0161-474 7174 Fax: 0161-474 7163 E-mail: support@micad.co.uk
Price Direct Ltd, 505A Norwood Road, London, SE27 9DL Tel: (020) 8761 7612 Fax: (020) 8761 7514 E-mail: info@pricedirect.com
Research & Marketing Ltd, Trefor House, Galdames Place, Cardiff, CF24 5RE Tel: (029) 2043 5800 Fax: (029) 2048 3540 E-mail: info@rmltd.net
Spectrum Computer Services plc, PO Box 199, Bradford, West Yorkshire, BD1 5RJ Tel: (01274) 308188 Fax: (01274) 307264 E-mail: admin@spectrumplc.co.uk
Storwave Ltd, 1 Flowers Hill Close, Flowers Hill Trading Estate, Bristol, BS4 5LF Tel: 0117-972 8855 Fax: 0117-916 9234 E-mail: sales@theedmgroup.co.uk
Wyman Dillon Ltd, Silverhill, Rudgeway, Bristol, BS35 3NS Tel: (01454) 200000 Fax: (01454) 200002 E-mail: mail@wymandillon.co.uk

DATA PROCESSING KEYBOARDS

Lamina Keyboards Ltd, 32 Southridge Rise, Crowborough, East Sussex, TN6 1LG Tel: (01892) 664633 Fax: (01892) 603928 E-mail: sales@lamina-keyboards.com
RTC International, 13-15 Osyth Close, Brackmills Industrial Estate, Northampton, NN4 7DY Tel: (01604) 541000 Fax: (01604) 541020

DATA PROCESSING SYSTEMS MANUFRS

Ashmead Applications Ltd, 28 Pigeon Farm Road, Stokenchurch, High Wycombe, Buckinghamshire, HP14 3TE Tel: (01494) 483623 E-mail: patrick@ashmeadapplications.co.uk
Cyberscience Corporation Ltd, Rawdon House, High Street, Hoddesdon, Hertfordshire, EN11 8BD Tel: (01992) 441111 Fax: (01992) 442740 E-mail: info@cyberscience.com
Datacourt Computer Systems, 198 Knutsford Road, Warrington, WA4 1AU Tel: (01925) 243898 Fax: (01925) 243732
Emc Computer Systems, E M C Tower, Great West Road, Brentford, Middlesex, TW8 9AN Tel: (0870) 6087777 Fax: (0870) 6087788 E-mail: sales@uk.emc.com

DATA PROCESSING SYSTEMS MANUFRS – *continued*

Hytec Information Security Ltd, Units 9-10, Oasis Park, Stanton Harcourt Road, Eynsham, Witney, Oxfordshire, OX29 4TP Tel: (01865) 887423 Fax: (01865) 887444 E-mail: info@hytec.co.uk

Infographics UK Ltd, 12 Hanover Court, North Street, Glenrothes, Fife, KY7 5SB Tel: (01592) 750677 Fax: (01592) 610534 E-mail: sales@infographics.co.uk

N C R UK Group Ltd, 206 Marylebone Road, London, NW1 6LY Tel: (020) 7723 7070 Fax: (020) 7725 8224

Spark Response Ltd, Follingsby Avenue, Gateshead, Tyne & Wear, NE10 8HQ Tel: 0191-495 9999 Fax: 0191-495 9900 E-mail: enquiries@sparkresponse.co.uk

DATA PROCESSING/STORAGE SERVICES, TECHNOLOGICAL

▶ Damco Solutions Ltd, 23 Clayton Road, Hayes, Middlesex, UB3 1AN Tel: +44 (0) 208 817 1047 Fax: (020) 8573 9072 E-mail: sales@damcosoft.co.uk

Market Developer Ltd, Bourne House, 10 Windmill Road, Hampton Hill, Middlesex, TW12 1RH Tel: (020) 8979 1122 Fax: (020) 8941 7595 E-mail: simon.davis@marketdeveloper.com

DATA PROTECTION AGENCIES

▶ Rsa Direct, Boundary House, Boston Road, London, W7 2QE Tel: (020) 8434 3680 Fax: (020) 8434 3449 E-mail: richard.gibson@rsadirect.com

DATA RACKING COOLING FANS

Data & Power Solutions, Unit 1 The Monarch Centre, Venture Way, Priorswood Industrial Estate, Taunton, Somerset, TA2 8DE Tel: (01823) 275100 Fax: (01823) 275002 E-mail: sales@dataandpower.com

DATA RECOVERY

▶ Apex Technology Ltd, PO Box 2364, Stafford, ST16 3DA Tel: (01785) 227989 E-mail: enquiry@apextechnology.co.uk

Data Clinic, Unit 9 The Pavilions, Bridge Hall Lane, Bury, Lancashire, BL9 7NY Tel: 0161-764 3060 E-mail: customer.services@dataclinic.co.uk

▶ Data Global Services Ltd, 6 Old Bath Road, The Lawns, Colnbrook, Slough, SL3 0NH Tel: (0776) 5788244 Fax: E-mail: dataglobalservices@yahoo.com

▶ Data Services 24/7, 124 Harborough Road, Rushden, Northamptonshire, NN10 0LP Tel: 08701 660724 Fax: (08709) 162101 E-mail: support@dataservices247.com

▶ Datascape Online Ltd, 24 Waters Edge Business Park, Modwen Road, Salford, M5 3EZ Tel: (0870) 0621200 Fax: (0870) 0621203

MJM Data Recovery, Unit B2, Pixmore Industrial Estate, Letchworth Garden City, Hertfordshire, SG6 1JJ Tel: (01462) 680333 Fax: (01462) 483648 E-mail: sales@mjm.co.uk

▶ Rawdata IT, 101-103 Corbiehall, Bo'ness, West Lothian, EH51 0AU Tel: (01506) 517037 Fax: (01506) 517038

▶ Tierra Data Rescue, 1 Barondale Cottages, Newbattle, Dalkeith, Midlothian, EH22 3LX Tel: (0845) 0940027 Fax: (0845) 0940028 E-mail: gill@tierra.co.uk

Xytron, Unit 4 Twyford Court, Twyford Road, Hereford, HR2 6JR Tel: 0800 8818900 Fax: (01432) 342742 E-mail: info@xytron.co.uk

DATA RECOVERY CONSULTANCY

▶ Tierra Data Rescue, 1 Barondale Cottages, Newbattle, Dalkeith, Midlothian, EH22 3LX Tel: (0845) 0940027 Fax: (0845) 0940028 E-mail: gill@tierra.co.uk

DATA RECOVERY SERVICES

▶ Tierra Data Rescue, 1 Barondale Cottages, Newbattle, Dalkeith, Midlothian, EH22 3LX Tel: (0845) 0940027 Fax: (0845) 0940028 E-mail: gill@tierra.co.uk

DATA RETRIEVAL SYSTEMS

Contek Software Ltd, Camkins House, Risborough Road, Little Kimble, Aylesbury, Buckinghamshire, HP17 0UE Tel: (01296) 612121 E-mail: sales@anaclara.net

Thorogood Associates Ltd, Dralda House, 24-28 Crendon Street, High Wycombe, Buckinghamshire, HP13 6LS Tel: (01494) 684200 Fax: (01494) 684223

DATA SAFE/DOCUMENT SAFE

Cyptec UK Ltd, 134 Timbercroft Lane, London, SE18 2SG Tel: (020) 8855 6664 Fax: (020) 8855 1714 E-mail: sales@vellumfile.com

Safetyworks GB Limited, P.O. Box 753, Aylesbury, Buckinghamshire, HP22 9BJ Tel: (01296) 655506 Fax: (01296) 655503 E-mail: david@safety-works.co.uk

DATA SCANNING

Arrow Imaging Ltd, 34 Pebble Close, Tamworth Business Park, Amington, Tamworth, Staffordshire, B77 4RP Tel: (01827) 310350 Fax: (01827) 313880 E-mail: sales@arrow-imaging.co.uk

▶ File Express Ltd, Walton Lane, Bosham, Chichester, West Sussex, PO18 8ED Tel: (01243) 575858 Fax: (01243) 575123 E-mail: enquiries@file-express.co.uk

DATA SECURITY/ENCRYPTION SYSTEMS

B D S Solutions, Heywood House, 12 High Street, Cullompton, Devon, EX15 1AA Tel: (01884) 33221 Fax: (01884) 34555 E-mail: info@bds-solutions.co.uk

Brown's Operating System Services Ltd, Brigade Street, London, SE3 0TW Tel: (020) 8297 9797 Fax: (020) 8318 3939 E-mail: mail@browns.co.uk

Commercial Collection Services, 797 London Road, Thornton Heath, Surrey, CR7 6YY Tel: (020) 8665 4900 Fax: (020) 8683 2283 E-mail: stephen.durrant@ccscollect.co.uk

Electronics 2000 Ltd, Grafton House, Grafton Street, High Wycombe, Buckinghamshire, HP12 3AJ Tel: (01494) 444044 Fax: (01494) 470499 E-mail: sales@e2000.com

M I S Cooperate Defence Solutions, Hermitage Lane, Maidstone, Kent, ME16 9NT Tel: (0800) 243649 Fax: (01622) 728690 E-mail: webmaster@mis-cds.com

Softek Computer Security, La Rue Du Pont Marquet, St. Brelade, Jersey, JE3 8DS Tel: (01534) 811182 Fax: (01534) 811183 E-mail: sales@softek.co.uk

Sophos plc, Pentagon West, The Pentagon, Abingdon, Oxfordshire, OX14 3YP Tel: (01235) 559933 Fax: (01235) 559935 E-mail: sales@sophos.com

DATA STORAGE SERVICES, ARCHIVE/COMMERCIAL RECORD

▶ 3D Space Ltd, Warwick Way, Pimlico, London, SW1V 1QT Tel: (020) 7840 8130 E-mail: enquiries@3dspacestorage.co.uk

▶ Archival Record Management plc, 53-57 Southampton Way, London, SE5 7SW Tel: (020) 7701 7018 Fax: (020) 7701 7026 E-mail: sales@armplc.com

Ardington Archives, White Horse Business Park, Ware Road, Stanford in the Vale, Faringdon, Oxfordshire, SN7 8NY Tel: (01367) 718710 Fax: (01367) 718501 E-mail: sales@ardingtonarchives.co.uk

British Movietone Ltd, North Orbital Road, Denham, Uxbridge, Middlesex, UB9 5HQ Tel: (01895) 833071 Fax: (01895) 834893 E-mail: library@mtone.co.uk

East Midlands Micro Imaging, 46 Tenter Road, Moulton Park Industrial Estate, Northampton, NN3 6AX Tel: (01604) 644665 Fax: (01604) 643673 E-mail: sales@em-micro-imaging.co.uk

Garrards Removals & Storage, Unit 9b Mill Lane Trading Estate, Mill Lane, Croydon, CR0 4AA Tel: (020) 8688 4979 Fax: (020) 8686 4140

Horsehay Ltd, Horsehay Estate, Telford, Shropshire, TF4 3PY Tel: (01952) 503344 Fax: (01952) 503356 E-mail: richard@horsehay.uk.com

Iron Mountain Ltd, Cottons Centre, Tooley Street, London, SE1 2TT Tel: (0800) 270270 Fax: (020) 7939 1501

Iron Mountain Ltd, 3 The Borough Industrial Estate, Leagrave Road, Luton, LU3 1RJ Tel: (0800) 270270 Fax: (01582) 391602 E-mail: tpowell@ironmountain.co.uk

Iron Mountain Ltd, Mill Way, Sittingbourne, Kent, ME10 2PT Tel: (01795) 479241 Fax: (01795) 427224 E-mail: info@ronmountain.co.uk

Jardin Corrugated Cases Ltd, Elean Business Park, Sutton, Ely, Cambridgeshire, CB6 2QE Tel: (01353) 778522 Fax: (01353) 777708 E-mail: jcc.enquiries@jccltd.com

▶ M R Studio, Liverpool, L12 0WW Tel: (07876) 518390 E-mail: info@mrstudio.biz

Management Archives, Parkside House, Parkside Lane, Leeds, LS11 5TD Tel: 0113-277 2525 Fax: 0113-387 7690 E-mail: guymanarch@aol.com

Micad Systems & F M Data Services, Lansdown House, 85 Buxton Road, Stockport, Cheshire, SK2 6LR Tel: 0161-474 7174 Fax: 0161-474 7163 E-mail: support@micad.co.uk

Mill Road Properties Ltd, Pressing Room Dye Works, Hartley Street, Dewsbury, West Yorkshire, WF13 2HR Tel: (01924) 465323 Fax: (01924) 502662

▶ Norfolk Storage Equipment Ltd, 15 Maurice Gaymer Road, Attleborough, Norfolk, NR17 2QZ Tel: (01953) 458800 Fax: (01953) 458819 E-mail: sales@nsel.biz

Philpot Enterprises Ltd, West Town Farm, Farm Road, Taplow, Maidenhead, Berkshire, SL6 0PT Tel: (01628) 602003 Fax: (01628) 660905 E-mail: angus@philpot-group.co.uk

▶ Red Devil Storage Ltd, 14 - 16 Kempson Close, Gatehouse Industrial Estate, Aylesbury, Buckinghamshire, HP19 8UQ Tel: (01296) 381818 Fax: (01296) 381919 E-mail: kempsonclose@reddevilstorage.co.uk

▶ Red Devil Storage, Units 1 - 2, The Wynne Jones Centre, Tring Road, Aylesbury, Buckinghamshire, HP21 7RL Tel: (01296) 397215 Fax: (01296) 397216 E-mail: tringroad@reddevilstorage.co.uk

▶ Red Devil Storage Ltd, 381 Kennington Road, London, SE11 4PT Tel: (0800) 0561773 Fax: (020) 7480 8120 E-mail: enquiries@reddevilstorage.co.uk

Restore Ltd, Redhill Distribution Centre, Salbrook Road, Redhill, RH1 5DY Tel: (01293) 446270 Fax: (01293) 446276 E-mail: john.minton@restore.co.uk

Square Group Ltd, 78 New Oxford Street, London, WC1A 1HB Tel: (020) 7692 9990 Fax: (020) 7692 6636 E-mail: sales@squaregroup.co.uk

Wansdyke Security Ltd, PO Box 179, Corsham, Wiltshire, SN13 9TL Tel: (01225) 810225 Fax: (01225) 810625 E-mail: sales@wansdyke.co.uk

DATA STORAGE SYSTEM REPAIR

Data Track Services Ltd, Unit 38 Basepoint Enterprise Centre, Basingstoke, Hampshire, RG24 8UP Tel: (01256) 406616 Fax: (01256) 406617E-mail: sales@datatrackservices.co.uk

▶ Prestige Computer Services, 3-4 Park Road, Malmesbury, Wiltshire, SN16 0BX Tel: (01666) 825620 Fax: (01666) 826686 E-mail: service@pcs-uk.net

DATA STORAGE SYSTEMS MANUFRS

Contek Software Ltd, Camkins House, Risborough Road, Little Kimble, Aylesbury, Buckinghamshire, HP17 0UE Tel: (01296) 612121 E-mail: sales@anaclara.net

Cristie Ltd, Cristie Mill, Chestnut Lane, Stroud, Gloucestershire, GL5 3EH Tel: (01453) 847000 Fax: (01453) 847001 E-mail: sales@cristie.com

Plasmon Data Systems, Whiting Way, Melbourn, Royston, Hertfordshire, SG8 6EN Tel: (01763) 261516 Fax: (01763) 264444 E-mail: sales@plasmon.co.uk

Storagetek Ltd, 36 South Gyle Crescent, Edinburgh, EH12 9EB Tel: 0131-338 6515 Fax: 0131-339 3900

Tectonic Ltd, Meridian Business Park, 1A Jupitor Court, Dominus Way, Leicester, LE19 1RP Tel: 0116-282 0567 Fax: 0116-282 0599 E-mail: info@tectonic.com

Ultima Business Systems Ltd, 448 Basingstoke Road, Reading, RG2 0LP Tel: 0118-902 7500 Fax: 0118-902 7400 E-mail: sales@ultimabusiness.com

DATA TAGGING (ELECTRONIC) EQUIPMENT MANUFRS

Borer Data Systems Ltd, Gotelee House, Market Place, Wokingham, Berkshire, RG40 1AN Tel: 0118-979 1137 Fax: 0118-977 3526 E-mail: borer@borer.co.uk

DATA TRANSCRIPTION SERVICES

▶ Business Friend Ltd, 5 Mayland Quay, Maylandsea, Chelmsford, CM3 6GJ Tel: (07931) 759611 Fax: (01621) 744292 E-mail: telmemore@businessfriend.net

▶ Easy Typing, 16 Burn View, Bude, Cornwall, EX23 8BZ Tel: 01288 355587 E-mail: easytyping@hotmail.co.uk

K International plc, Carina Building, Sunrise Parkway, Milton Keynes, MK14 6PW Tel: (01908) 670399 Fax: (01908) 670170 E-mail: info@k-international.com

Santype International Ltd, Harnham Trading Estate, Netherhampton Road, Salisbury, SP2 8PS Tel: (01722) 334261 Fax: (01722) 333171 E-mail: post@santype.com

▶ Sandrine Vaillant, Old Vallis Cottage, Vallis Road, Frome, Somerset, BA11 3EN Tel: (0777) 9668707 Fax: (01373) 474945 E-mail: sandrine.vaillant@btinternet.co.uk

DATA TRANSMISSION CABLES

A-B Accessories, 93 Ilchester Rd, Yeovil, Somerset, BA21 3BJ Tel: (08707) 450976 Fax: (01935) 434100 E-mail: andy@abaccessories.co.uk

Anixter UK Ltd, Anixter House, 1 York Road, Uxbridge, Middlesex, UB8 1RN Tel: (0845) 6041301 Fax: (01895) 818182

Commtech Trading Co. (Lancashire) Ltd, 5 Petre Road, Clayton Park Industrial Estate, Accrington, Lancashire, BB5 5JB Tel: (01254) 232638 Fax: (01254) 301197 E-mail: sales@commtechcomm.com

Data Cabling Ltd, 6 Farrier Road, Lincoln, LN6 3RU Tel: (01522) 500699 Fax: (01522) 500882 E-mail: sales@data-cabling.co.uk

DATA TRANSMISSION SYSTEMS MANUFRS

Black Box Network Services Ltd, 464 Basingstoke Road, Reading, RG2 0BG Tel: 0118-965 5000 Fax: 0118-965 5001 E-mail: info@blackbox.co.uk

Datamirror UK Ltd, Elizabeth House, 39 York Road, London, SE1 7NQ Tel: (020) 7633 5200 Fax: (020) 7633 5210

DATABASE MANAGEMENT

Abacus E-Solutions Ltd, Albany House, Concorde Street, Luton, LU2 0JD Tel: (01582) 702702 Fax: (01582) 452106 E-mail: sales@abacusuk.com

Another Dimension Ltd, 167 Ardleigh Green Road, Hornchurch, Essex, RM11 2LF Tel: (01708) 701511 Fax: (01708) 701994 E-mail: info@anotherdimension.co.uk

▶ Arden Business Consultants, PO Box 9900, Henley-in-Arden, Warwickshire, B95 5QW Tel: (01564) 796600 Fax: (0870) 0516753 E-mail: data@abcon.net

Blenheim Systems, 31 Blenheim Gardens, Wembley, Middlesex, HA9 7NP Tel: (020) 8904 9317 Fax: (07092) 215433 E-mail: enq@blenheim-systems.com

Cegedim Ltd, Fourth Floor, Nicholsons House, Nicholsons Walk, Maidenhead, Berkshire, SL6 1LD Tel: (01628) 773533 Fax: (01628) 771488

Compsoft plc, Equinox House, Oriel Court, Alton, Hampshire, GU34 2YT Tel: (01420) 89545 Fax: (01420) 81444 E-mail: sales@compsoft.co.uk

Coveford Data Systems Ltd, Old Bank House, 59 High Street, Odiham, Hampshire, RG29 1LF Tel: (01256) 704333 Fax: (07031) 159754 E-mail: cds@coveford.com

CTS, Curriers Close, Charter Avenue Industrial Estate, Coventry, CV4 8AW Tel: (0870) 7511400 Fax: (024) 7642 6401 E-mail: enquiries@ctsnet.co.uk

Data Base Unlimited, The Old School, Bagwell Lane, Winchfield, Hook, Hampshire, RG27 8DB Tel: (01256) 393050 Fax: (01256) 393051 E-mail: techsupport@dbu.co.uk

▶ Data Creative Ltd, 9 Elm Grove, Toddington, Dunstable, Bedfordshire, LU5 6BJ Tel: (01525) 877911 Fax: (01525) 877921 E-mail: enquiries@data-creative.com

▶ Data Systems UK, Data House, Kirton Lane, Thorne, Doncaster, South Yorkshire, DN8 5RJ Tel: (01405) 815848 Fax: (01405) 815848 E-mail: glynn@datasystemsuk.com

The Database Group Ltd, Colston Tower, Colston Street, Bristol, BS1 4UH Tel: 0117-918 3500 Fax: 0117-918 3501 E-mail: sales@databasegroup.co.uk

Epcot Systems Ltd, PO Box 114, Pinner, Middlesex, HA5 1TQ Tel: (020) 8537 0395 Fax: (020) 8931 5218

F E Burman Ltd, 4 Rich Industrial Estate, Crimscott Street, London, SE1 5TF Tel: (020) 7206 1000 Fax: (020) 7206 1040 E-mail: info@feburman.co.uk

▶ Fluent Contact Marketing, Lok' N' Store Building Unit 2, Etheridge Avenue, Brinklow, Milton Keynes, MK10 0BB Tel: (0870) 1277310 Fax: (0870) 1277329 E-mail: sales@fluent-marketing.co.uk

GB Group plc, GB House, Kingsfield Court, Chester Business Park, Chester, CH4 9GB Tel: (01244) 657333 Fax: (01244) 680808

Holborn Direct Mail, Capacity House, 2-6 Rothsay Street, London, SE1 4UD Tel: (020) 7407 6444 Fax: (020) 7357 6065 E-mail: peter@holborndirectmail.co.uk

The Institution Of Engineering & Technology Benevolent Fund, Michael Faraday House, Stevenage, Hertfordshire, SG1 2AY Tel: (01438) 313311 Fax: (01438) 313465 E-mail: postmaster@theiat.org

John Blackburn Group Ltd, Old Run Road, Leeds, LS10 2AA Tel: 0113-277 7711 Fax: 0113-277 4009 E-mail: sales@jblackburn.co.uk

M & M Secure Services Ltd, Station Yard, Whitehaven, Moor Row, Cumbria, CA24 3JP Tel: (01946) 815957 Fax: (01946) 815957

▶ Mediascene Ltd, A-D Unit, Bowen Industrial Estate, Aberbargoed, Bargoed, Mid Glamorgan, CF81 9AB Tel: (01443) 821877 Fax: (01443) 822055 E-mail: hi@mediascene.co.uk

Oracle Corporation UK Ltd, Southgate Centre Two, 321 Wilmslow Road, Heald Green, Cheadle, Cheshire, SK8 3PW Tel: 0161-499 1717 Fax: 0161-493 4966

▶ Paperchase Business Services, Warrington, WA4 6QQ Tel: (07939) 145015 Fax: (01925) 638440

Polypostals, Unit 21, Sea Vixen Industrial Estate, Wilverley Road, Christchurch, Dorset, BH23 3RU Tel: (01202) 479932 Fax: (01202) 488118

DATABASE MANAGEMENT – *continued*

Prism Data Management Ltd, Colombia House, 1 Apollo Rise, Farnborough, Hampshire, GU14 0GT Tel: (01252) 556900 Fax: (01252) 556911

Raining Data, Mitford House, Benhall, Saxmundham, Suffolk, IP17 1JS Tel: (01728) 603011 Fax: (01728) 604154

Safescript Ltd, 2 Deanhill Road, London, SW14 7DF Tel: (020) 8876 1853 Fax: (020) 8876 3249 E-mail: info@safescript.co.uk

Specialist Computer Centre, Kingsway House, Kingsway North, Team Valley Trading Estate, Gateshead, Tyne & Wear, NE11 0JS Tel: 0191-497 0000 Fax: 0191-497 0001

Sphere IT Ltd, Fernhill House, St. Catherines Hill Lane, Christchurch, Dorset, BH23 2NL Tel: (08707) 373001 Fax: (08707) 373002 E-mail: admin@sphereit.com

Trade Wind Technology Ltd, The Old Stores, 11 North Street, Tillingham, Southminster, Essex, CM0 7TR Tel: (01621) 779037 Fax: (01621) 779034 E-mail: sales@t-w-t.co.uk

Washington Direct Mail Ltd, Fourth Avenue, Team Valley, Gateshead, Tyne & Wear, NE11 0JS Tel: 0191-482 4291 Fax: 0191-491 0109 E-mail: wdm@wdml.co.uk

Weeks Computing Services, 6 Langley Street, London, WC2H 9JA Tel: (020) 7379 3548 Fax: (020) 7240 8870 E-mail: office@weekscomputing.com

DATABASE MARKETING

Acxiom, Park House, Station Road, Teddington, Middlesex, TW11 9AD Tel: (020) 8213 5500 Fax: (020) 8213 5588 E-mail: info-uk@claritaseu.com

▶ Arden Business Consultants, PO Box 9900, Henley-in-Arden, Warwickshire, B95 5QW Tel: (01564) 796600 Fax: (0870) 0516753 E-mail: data@abcon.net

Ark H Handling Ltd, 1 Wilstead Industrial Park, Kenneth Way, Wilstead, Bedford, MK45 3PD Tel: (01234) 742777 Fax: (01234) 742999 E-mail: sales@ark-h.co.uk

▶ Data Creative Ltd, 9 Elm Grove, Toddington, Dunstable, Bedfordshire, LU5 6BJ Tel: (01525) 877911 Fax: (01525) 877921 E-mail: enquiries@data-creative.com

The Database Group Ltd, Colston Tower, Colston Street, Bristol, BS1 4UH Tel: 0117-918 3500 Fax: 0117-918 3501 E-mail: sales@databasegroup.co.uk

Direct Mail Advertising & Marketing Services Ltd, 3 Wallis Court, Fleming Way, Crawley, West Sussex, RH10 9DA Tel: (01293) 541511 Fax: (01293) 562996 E-mail: reception@dmams.co.uk

Jemcare Training, Churchill House, Stirling Way, Borehamwood, Hertfordshire, WD6 2HP Tel: (020) 8736 0536 Fax: (020) 8736 0535 E-mail: mslyper@kinetictraining.com

▶ Mango Media, 49 Carnaby Street, London, W1F 9PY Tel: (020) 7292 9000 Fax: (020) 7434 1077 E-mail: info@mangomedia.net

▶ Mediascene Ltd, A-D Unit, Bowen Industrial Estate, Aberbargoed, Bargoed, Mid Glamorgan, CF81 9AB Tel: (01443) 821877 Fax: (01443) 822055 E-mail: hi@mediascene.co.uk

▶ Stewart Miller Associates, Na Mara, Innellan, Dunoon, Argyll, PA23 7QN Tel: (01369) 830000

▶ Stilton Surveys Ltd, 2 Turpins Ride, Stilton, Peterborough, PE7 3RE Tel: (01733) 240072 Fax: (01733) 240072 E-mail: info@stiltonsurveys.co.uk

▶ Worthington Brown Designs, 24 Huddersfield Road, Holmfirth, HD9 2JS Tel: (01484) 688808 Fax: (01484) 688818 E-mail: bt@worthingtonbrown.co.uk

Wyman Dillon Ltd, Silverhill, Rudgeway, Bristol, BS35 3NS Tel: (01454) 200000 Fax: (01454) 200002 E-mail: mail@wymandillon.co.uk

DATABASES, *See headings for particular types*

See also headings for particular types

▶ Data Creative Ltd, 9 Elm Grove, Toddington, Dunstable, Bedfordshire, LU5 6BJ Tel: (01525) 877911 Fax: (01525) 877921 E-mail: enquiries@data-creative.com

DATABASES, MATERIALS PROPERTY

▶ Granta Design Ltd, Rustat House, 62 Clifton Road, Cambridge, CB1 7EG Tel: (01223) 518895 Fax: (01223) 506432 E-mail: info@grantadesign.com

DATE CODING MACHINES

Rotech Machines Ltd, Bridge Road East, Welwyn Garden City, Hertfordshire, AL7 1JU Tel: (01707) 393700 Fax: (01707) 392800

DATER/DATING MACHINES

E M Richford Ltd, Curzon Road, Sudbury, Suffolk, CO10 2XW Tel: (01787) 375241 Fax: (01787) 310179 E-mail: sales@richstamp.co.uk

DAVITS AND FITTINGS

MacGREGOR (GBR) Ltd, Grampian House, 59 Palmerston Road, Aberdeen, AB11 5QJ Tel: (01224) 583300 Fax: (01224) 583450 E-mail: sales@macgregor-group.com

DAY CARE OPERATING TABLES

Rastrick Engineering Ltd, 7 Martin Street, Brighouse, West Yorkshire, HD6 1DA Tel: (01484) 715748 Fax: (01484) 720639

DEAERATION PLANT/ EQUIPMENT

Netzsch-Mastermix, 23 Lombard Street, Lichfield, Staffordshire, WS13 6DP Tel: (01543) 418938 Fax: (01543) 418926 E-mail: info@nmx.netzsch.com

DEALING OR COMPUTER ROOM CONSULTANCY OR CONTRACTORS

Key Communication Systems Ltd, Key House, 21 Bourne Road, Bexley, Kent, DA5 1LW Tel: (01322) 555522 Fax: (01322) 555227 E-mail: info@keycoms.co.uk

DEBRIS SAFETY NETTING

▶ R W P Scaffolding & Safety Netting Services, 1 Pelton Walk, Monsall, Manchester, M40 8QY Tel: 0161-277 9704 Fax: 0161-205 5981 E-mail: rwpscaffolding@aol.com

DEBT MANAGEMENT

▶ CDI DEBT RECOVERY, 9A The Esplanade, Sunderland, SR2 7BQ Tel: 0191 6666666

David & Co. Financial Advisers, Old Croft, Bogmoor, Spey Bay, Fochabers, Morayshire, IV32 7PB Tel: (01343) 829290 Fax: (01343) 821257

▶ Debt Aid, Chatton Mill, Chatton, Alnwick, Northumberland, NE66 5RA Tel: (01668) 215505 Fax: (01668) 215000 E-mail: marketing@debtaid.ltd.uk

▶ Gregory Pennington Ltd, Pennington House, Carolina Way, Salford, M50 2ZY Tel: (0800) 0839630 Fax: 0161-972 7100

Relief 4 Debt, 72 London Road, St. Albans, Hertfordshire, AL1 1NS Tel: (01727) 869966 Fax: (01727) 869149 E-mail: enquiries@relief4debt.co.uk

▶ Sheraz Iqbal, 6th Floor, Kings Gate House, Wellington Road North, Stockport, Cheshire, SK4 1LW Tel: (0800) 1386500 E-mail: marketing@consolidate-your-credit.com

DEBT RECOVERY

Agricultural Credit Bureau, Suite 413, The Cotton Exchange Buildings, Old Hall Street, Liverpool, L3 9LQ Tel: 0151-236 6463 Fax: 0151-236 0922 E-mail: mail@lltps.co.uk

Aktiv Kapital (UK) Ltd, Merchants House, Crook Street, Chester, CH1 2BE Tel: (01244) 319912 Fax: (01244) 314635 E-mail: collect@aktivkapital.co.uk

All Management Services Ltd, PO Box 8098, Birmingham, B38 9SP Tel: 0121-680 1981 Fax: 0121-243 8717 E-mail: amslimited@aol.com

▶ Allied International Credit UK Ltd, The Clocktower, Chineham, Basingstoke, Hampshire, RG24 8BQ Tel: (01256) 416400 Fax: (01256) 355155 E-mail: marketing@aiccorp.com

Anthill Debt Collectors, 233a Golders Green Road, London, NW11 9ES Tel: (0800) 0742500 Fax: (020) 8905 5100

Atradius, 3 Harbour Drive, Cardiff, CF10 4WZ Tel: (029) 2082 4000 Fax: (029) 2082 4003 E-mail: reception@atradius.com

Auto Exec Account Collections Ltd, Technology House, 492 London Road, Westcliff-on-Sea, Essex, SS0 9LD Tel: (01702) 431731 Fax: (01702) 431804 E-mail: info@accountcollection.com

Bond Pearce, Ballard House, West Hoe Road, Plymouth, PL1 3AE Tel: (0870) 1200000 Fax: (023) 8020 8050 E-mail: elcroft@bondpearce.com

Brindley Twist Tafft & James, Lowick Gate Coventry Trading Estate, Siskin Drive, Middlemarch Business Park, Coventry, CV3 4FJ Tel: (024) 7653 1532 Fax: (024) 7630 1300 E-mail: admin@bttj.com

C A R E S GB Ltd, Suite, 8 Stoke Road, Stoke-on-Trent, ST4 2DP Tel: (01782) 212613 Fax: (01782) 212046

Cattles plc, Kingston House Centre 27 Business Park, Woodhead Road, Birstall, Batley, West Yorkshire, WF17 9TD Tel: (01924) 444466 Fax: (01924) 442255

▶ CCI Legal Services Ltd, Unit 5, Snowdonia Business Park, Minffordd, Penrhyndeudraeth, Gwynedd, LL48 6LD Tel: (01766) 771166 Fax: (01766) 771840 E-mail: sales@ccilegal.co.uk

Clanchatton Birmingham Ltd, Bell Way House, 7 Worcester Road, Bromsgrove, Worcestershire, B61 7DL Tel: (01527) 879000 Fax: (01527) 870071

Commercial Collection Services, 797 London Road, Thornton Heath, Surrey, CR7 6YY Tel: (020) 8665 4900 Fax: (020) 8683 2283 E-mail: stephen.durrant@ccscollect.co.uk

Commercial & Domestic Investigations Ltd, 7 The Esplanade, Sunderland, SR2 7BQ Tel: 0191-510 8474 Fax: 0191-514 4225

Connaught Collections UK Ltd, Airport House, Purley Way, Croydon, CR0 0XZ Tel: (020) 8253 0350 Fax: (020) 8680 7661 E-mail: sales@connaught.uk.com

The Courthouse Project (Otley) Ltd, Courthouse Street, Otley, West Yorkshire, LS21 3AN Tel: (01943) 467216 Fax: (01943) 851033 E-mail: admin@courthousecredit.co.uk

Credit Protection Association plc, 350 King Street, London, W6 0RX Tel: (020) 8846 0000 Fax: (020) 8741 7459 E-mail: sales@cpa.co.uk

Credit Recovery Systems, 345 City Road, London, EC1V 1AS Tel: (020) 8295 7220 Fax: (020) 7833 4832

Credit Solutions Ltd, Barlow House, 3 Butter Hill, Carshalton, Surrey, SM5 2TW Tel: (020) 8773 7111 Fax: (020) 8773 9919 E-mail: credsol@globalnet.co.uk

▶ Credit Tel International, Network House, 45 Warwick Road, Thames Ditton, Surrey, KT7 0PR Tel: (020) 8398 9555 Fax: (020) 8398 7831 E-mail: info@credittel.com

Crosse & Crosse Ltd, 14 Southernhay West, Exeter, EX1 1PL Tel: (01392) 258451 Fax: (01392) 278938 E-mail: mail@crosse.co.uk

▶ CRS Debt Recovery Solicitors, 12 Park Place, Leeds, LS1 2RU Tel: 0113 2467887 Fax: 0113 2439822 E-mail: info@carrickread.com

D R S Legal Services, Tradewinds House, Otterham, Camelford, Cornwall, PL32 9SL Tel: (01840) 261136 Fax: (0871) 4339159 E-mail: mail@debtrecovery.me.uk

Debt Busters (Universal), Communications House, 9 St Johns Street, Colchester, CO2 7NN Tel: (01206) 761777 Fax: (01206) 763444 E-mail: info@debtbustersuniversal.com

Debt Collect, Baltic Chambers, 50 Wellington Street, Glasgow, G2 6HJ Tel: (0845) 1202935 Fax: (0845) 1302936 E-mail: enquiries@debtcollectuk.com

▶ Debt Sentinel, Acorn House, Nailsworth Mills Estate, Avening Road, Nailsworth, Stroud, Gloucestershire, GL6 0BS Tel: (0870) 3501870 Fax: (0870) 3501871 E-mail: info@debtsentinel.co.uk

Debtsave, Palmerston House, 814 Brighton Road, Purley, Surrey, CR8 2BR Tel: (020) 8655 8484 Fax: (020) 8655 8501 E-mail: debtsave@palmerston.co.uk

Eular Hermes Collections UK Ltd, 36 Floor, 1 Canada Square, Canary Wharf, London, E14 5DX Tel: (020) 7512 9333

Euler Hermes UK plc, 1 Canada Square, London, E14 5DX Tel: (0800) 0565452 Fax: (0207) 8602455 E-mail: creditinfo@eulerhermes.com

Hawkins Russell Jones, 7-8 Portmill Lane, Hitchin, Hertfordshire, SG5 1AS Tel: (01462) 628888 Fax: (01462) 631233 E-mail: hitchin@hrjlaw.co.uk

Hutton Debt Recovery, 7 Atholl Crescent, Perth, PH1 5NG Tel: (01738) 639864 Fax: (01738) 630043 E-mail: dept@aahutton.co.uk

Inter-Credit International Ltd, 1ST Floor Newby House, 309 Chase Road, Southgate, London, N14 6JS Tel: (020) 8482 4444 Fax: (020) 8482 4455 E-mail: brendanglover@intercred.com

Intrum Justitia Group, Warwick House, Birmingham Road, Stratford-Upon-Avon, Warwickshire, CV37 0BP Tel: (01789) 415181 Fax: (01789) 412072

Jack Russell Collections & Investigations, Bayleaf House, 10 York Road, Northampton, NN1 5QG Tel: (01604) 634170 Fax: (01604) 635507 E-mail: jrnorth@debtcollect.co.uk

Judge & Priestley Ltd, Justin House, 6 West Street, Bromley, BR1 1JN Tel: (020) 8290 0333 Fax: (020) 8464 3332 E-mail: info@judge-priestley.co.uk

L P L Commercial Investigations, 890-900 Eastern Avenue, Ilford, Essex, IG2 7HH Tel: (020) 8597 2229 Fax: (020) 8597 1180 E-mail: info@lplgroup.com

Lewis Group Plc, Lawrence House, Riverside Drive, Cleckheaton, West Yorkshire, BD19 4DH Tel: (01274) 852000 Fax: (01274) 862602

Liverpool & London Trade Protection Society Ltd, 9 Hillview Close, Purley, Surrey, CR8 1AU Tel: (020) 8763 8807 Fax: (020) 8645 0601 E-mail: mail@lltps.co.uk

Mega Company Services P.L.C., Business Information House, Farmoor Court, Cumnor Road, Oxford, OX2 9LU Tel: (01865) 865666 Fax: (01865) 865465E-mail: info@mega.co.uk

N C O Europe, 3 The Green, Stratford Road, Shirley, Solihull, West Midlands, B90 4LA Tel: (020) 8565 4700 Fax: 0121-733 3154

Northants Debt Recovery Services, 31 Wellingborough Road, Earls Barton, Northampton, NN6 0JR Tel: (01604) 811254 Fax: (01604) 812566 E-mail: hunter.m@btconnect.com

Optima Legal Services Ltd, Arndale House, Charles Street, Bradford, West Yorkshire, BD1 1UN Tel: (01274) 553150 Fax: (01274) 513718

Relief 4 Debt, 72 London Road, St. Albans, Hertfordshire, AL1 1NS Tel: (01727) 869966 Fax: (01727) 869149 E-mail: enquiries@relief4debt.co.uk

▶ Renaissance, 1 Emperor Way, Exeter Business Park, Exeter Business Park, Exeter, EX1 3QS Tel: (01803) 404047 Fax: (01803) 404048 E-mail: enquiries@debt-recovery-services.com

S T A International, Watson House, St. Leonards Road, Maidstone, Kent, ME16 0SS Tel: (01622) 718222 Fax: (01622) 718444 E-mail: enqueries@staonline.com

Southern Credit Services Kent Ltd, 64 Highfield Road, Willesborough, Ashford, Kent, TN24 0JU Tel: (01233) 631998 E-mail: scs_ashford@hotmail.com

Star Credit Services Ltd, 10-12 Lombard Road, London, SW19 3TZ Tel: (020) 8540 9691 Fax: (020) 8540 6021 E-mail: info@star-serv.com

Swift Credit Services, Hazeldene, 2 High Street, Penydarren, Merthyr Tydfil, Mid Glamorgan, CF47 9AH Tel: (01685) 721900 Fax: (0870) 0006210 E-mail: sales@swift-credit.com

Transnational Corporation Ltd, Portland House, 4 Albion Street, Cheltenham, Gloucestershire, GL52 2LG Tel: (01242) 529424 Fax: (01242) 222834 E-mail: services@transnationalltd.com

Wannop & Fox Ltd, South Pallant House, 8 South Pallant, Chichester, West Sussex, PO19 1TH Tel: (01243) 778844 Fax: (01243) 788349 E-mail: wannopfox@compuserve.com

▶ www.getpaidontime.co.uk, 1 Mill Lane, Westhoughton, BOLTON, BL5 2DN Tel: 01942 817905 E-mail: training@getpaidontime.co.uk

▶ Zero Cost Debt Recovery, Europa House, Barcroft Street, Bury, Lancashire, BL9 5BT Tel: 0161-447 8816 Fax: (0870) 4582900 E-mail: info@zero-cost-debt-recovery.com

DEBURRING EQUIPMENT MANUFRS

Anotronic Ltd, Stewkley Road, Soulbury, Leighton Buzzard, Bedfordshire, LU7 0DF Tel: (01525) 270261 Fax: (01525) 270235 E-mail: sales@anotronic.co.uk

Buck & Hickman Ltd, Unit 5 Waterside, Trafford Park, Manchester, M17 1WD Tel: 0161-877 7888 Fax: 0161-877 7111 E-mail: manchester@buckhickmaninone.com

C L A Manufacturing Ltd, 10 Binns Close, Coventry, CV4 9TB Tel: (024) 7646 5535 Fax: (024) 7669 4543 E-mail: info@clatools.co.uk

Extrude Hone Ltd, 1 Sovereign Business Park, Joplin Court, Crownhill, Milton Keynes, MK8 0JP Tel: (01908) 263636 Fax: (01908) 262141 E-mail: miltonkeynes.sales@extrudehone.com

R M B Engineering Services Ltd, Union Street, West Bromwich, West Midlands, B70 6BP Tel: 0121-500 1940 Fax: 0121-500 1941 E-mail: sales@rmbgroup.co.uk

Sharmic Engineering Ltd, Baldwin Road, Stourport-on-Severn, Worcestershire, DY13 9AX Tel: (01299) 878123 Fax: (01299) 879409 E-mail: info@sharmic.co.uk

T S Technology, Langwood, 87 Langley Road, Watford, WD17 4PW Tel: (01923) 221155 Fax: (01923) 218625 E-mail: sales@tstechnology.co.uk

DEBURRING MACHINES

Electrochemical Machining Services Ltd, High Street, Oadby, Leicester, LE2 5DE Tel: 0116-271 8022 Fax: 0116-271 8023 E-mail: ivan@electrochemical.co.uk

Qtech Mta Ltd, 34 Alcester Road, Hollywood, Birmingham, B47 5NB Tel: 0121-430 8848 Fax: 0121-430 8848 E-mail: qtechmtaltd@aol.com

Rhodes Barrellings, Unit 4, Victoria Avenue, Borrowash, Derby, DE72 3HE Tel: (07718) 160144 Fax: (01332) 666090 E-mail: rhodesbarrelling@aol.com

DECAL OR TRANSFER PAPER

Target Transfers Ltd, Anglia Way, Braintree, Essex, CM7 3RG Tel: (01376) 326351 Fax: (01376) 345876 E-mail: info@targettransfers.com

Tullis Russell Coaters Ltd, Brittains Paper Mills, Commercial Road, Hanley, Stoke-on-Trent, ST1 3QS Tel: (01782) 202567 Fax: (01782) 202157 E-mail: enquiries@trcoaters.co.uk

DECALS, HEAT TRANSFER

Pressmech Sewing Machines, 3 Walton New Road, Bruntingthorpe, Lutterworth, Leicestershire, LE17 5RD Tel: 0116-247 8071 Fax: (01455) 251320 E-mail: pressmech@aol.com

DECATISING WRAPPERS

Sam Weller & Sons Ltd, Pickwick Mill, Thongsbridge, Holmfirth, HD9 3JL Tel: (01484) 683201 Fax: (01484) 689700 E-mail: info@samwellerltd.co.uk
Whaleys Bradford Ltd, Harris Court, Bradford, West Yorkshire, BD7 4EQ Tel: (01274) 576718 Fax: (01274) 521309 E-mail: whaleys@btinternet.com

DECK CHAIR CLOTHS

Mitchell Interflex Ltd, County Brook Mill, County Brook Lane, Foulridge, Colne, Lancashire, BB8 7LT Tel: (01282) 813221 Fax: (01282) 813633 E-mail: sales@mitchell-interflex.co.uk

DECK CHAIRS

Dorset Enterprises, Elliott Road, Bournemouth, BH11 8JP Tel: (01202) 577966 Fax: (01202) 570049 E-mail: dorsetenterprises@bournemouth.gov.uk
Escor Toys, Elliott Road, Bournemouth, BH11 8JP Tel: (01202) 591081 Fax: (01202) 570049 E-mail: escortoys@bournemouth.gov.uk

DECK ELECTROLUMINESCENT (EL) LIGHTING PANELS

Apex Electrical Distribution Ltd, New York Way, New York Industrial Park, Newcastle upon Tyne, NE27 0QF Tel: 0191-293 0900 Fax: 0191-257 7722

DECKING CONTRACTORS

▶ Acorn Timber Decking, 158 Werrington Road, Stoke-on-Trent, ST2 9AW Tel: (01782) 869805 Fax: (07786) 001962 E-mail: simon.kearns@ntlworld.com
▶ CB Solutions, Wise Field, Beverley Road, Beeford, Driffield, East Yorkshire, YO25 8AD Tel: (01262) 488919 Fax: (01262) 488986 E-mail: info@cbsol.co.uk
Durastic, 47 Cuthbert Court, Bede Trading Estate, Jarrow, Tyne & Wear, NE32 3EG Tel: 0191-483 2299 Fax: 0191-483 2295
Far Landscapes, 2 Cedar Avenue, Methil, Leven, Fife, KY8 2AY Tel: (01333) 421506 E-mail: a.a.ritchie@homecall.co.uk
▶ Landscapes Of Bath, York Buildings, Bath, BA1 2EB Tel: (07739) 462855 Fax: (01225) 462358E-mail: sales@landscapesofbath.co.uk
Structural Metal Decks Ltd, Mallard House, Duck Island Lane, Ringwood, Hampshire, BH24 3AA Tel: (01425) 471088 Fax: (01425) 471408 E-mail: contactus@smdltd.co.uk

DECKING JOISTS

▶ Custom Creations, 1 Plot 120 Village Farm Road, Village Farm Industrial Estate, Pyle, Bridgend, Mid Glamorgan, CF33 6BL Tel: (01656) 749855 Fax: (01656) 749855 E-mail: customc@tiscali.co.uk

DECOILING SERVICES, *See Steel Coil etc*

DECONTAMINATION CONTRACTORS OR SERVICES

Scotoil Services Ltd, Miller Street, Aberdeen, AB11 5AN Tel: (01224) 571491 Fax: (01224) 580861 E-mail: enquiries@scotoil.co.uk

DECONTAMINATION EQUIPMENT AND UNITS

Bioquell UK Ltd, 52 Royce Close, West Portway, Andover, Hampshire, SP10 3TS Tel: (01264) 835835 Fax: (01264) 835836 E-mail: enquiries@bioquell.com
Hughes Safety Showers Ltd, Whitefield Road, Bredbury, Stockport, Cheshire, SK6 2SS Tel: 0161-430 6618 Fax: 0161-430 7928 E-mail: sales@hughes-safety-showers.co.uk
Professional Protection Systems Ltd, Protection House, Sherbourne Drive, Tilbrook, Milton Keynes, MK7 8HX Tel: (01908) 272240 Fax: (01908) 371605

DECORATED METAL BOXES

Specialist Materials Processing, Unit 22 Podington Airfield, Hinwick, Wellingborough, Northamptonshire, NN29 7JQ Tel: (01234) 782026 Fax: (01234) 782028

DECORATING SERVICES, WALLPAPERING

▶ Brush Strokes, 801 London Road, Stoke-on-Trent, ST4 5NZ Tel: (01782) 874178 E-mail: foxy1@ntlworld.com
▶ Ports Decor Limited, 46 Passingham Avenue, Billericay, Essex, CM11 2TD Tel: (01277) 657558 Fax: (01277) 657548 E-mail: enquiries@portsdecorltd.co.uk
▶ RA Mitchell Painting & Decorating, The Mayflower, Harriets Corner, Pilgrims Lane, Whitstable, Kent, CT5 3BL Tel: 01227 274317 E-mail: info@ramitchell.co.uk
▶ Rickman Decorators Ltd, Charterhouse, 11 Marine Drive, Barton on Sea, New Milton, Hampshire, BH25 7EG Tel: (01425) 618883 Fax: (01425) 618883 E-mail: office@paint4you.co.uk

DECORATION HIRE

Abba Party Land, 1a Greenford Avenue, Southall, Middlesex, UB1 2AA Tel: (020) 8574 8275 Fax: (020) 8574 6036

DECORATION MATERIALS

Abba Party Land, 1a Greenford Avenue, Southall, Middlesex, UB1 2AA Tel: (020) 8574 8275 Fax: (020) 8574 6036

DECORATIVE BELLS

▶ Copper Fayre, 48 High Rd, Benfleet, Essex, SS7 5LH Tel: (01268) 566855 Fax: 01268 683311 E-mail: Copperfayre@hotmail.com

DECORATIVE CANDLES

Custom Candles Ltd, 12 Cross Lane, Coal Aston, Dronfield, Derbyshire, S18 3AL Tel: (01246) 414740 Fax: (01246) 290012 E-mail: sales@customcandles.co.uk
▶ easyonlineshop, 68 Monument Road, Talke Pits, Stoke-on-Trent, ST7 1SJ Tel: (01782) 771592 E-mail: lisahughesann@yahoo.co.uk
Ethos Candles Ltd, Quarry Fields, Mere, Warminster, Wiltshire, BA12 6LA Tel: (01747) 860960 Fax: (01747) 860934 E-mail: sales@charlesfarris.co.uk
▶ Mobarak, 1 Harrogate Road, Rawdon, Leeds, LS19 6HW Tel: 0113-250 0880 E-mail: info@mobarak.co.uk
Shearer Candles Ltd, 23 Robert Street, Glasgow, G51 3HB Tel: 0141-445 1066 Fax: 0141-445 1061 E-mail: sales@shearer-candles.com
Stonewood Trading Ltd, Dunmere Road, Bodmin, Cornwall, PL31 2QN Tel: (01208) 73258 Fax: (01208) 74223 E-mail: stonewoodtrading@btconnect.com

DECORATIVE CASTINGS

Bruce & Hyslop (Brucast) Ltd, 1 Well Lane, Bootle, Merseyside, L20 3BS Tel: 0151-922 2404 Fax: 0151-922 5994 E-mail: colin.appleton@bruceandhyslop.com

DECORATIVE CEILING CONSTRUCTORS OR MANUFACTURERS OR CONTRACTORS

Arrow Ceilings Ltd, A9 Hucknall Road, Nottingham, NG5 1FD Tel: 0115-985 7016 Fax: 0115-985 6883 E-mail: mail@arrowceilings.co.uk
ESE (Scotland) Ltd, 3 Dunlop Court, Deans Industrial Estate, Deans, Livingston, West Lothian, EH54 8SL Tel: (01506) 413313 Fax: (01506) 416550 E-mail: info@ese-scotland.co.uk

DECORATIVE CONCRETE FLOOR COATINGS

▶ Creative Impressions Ltd, 237 Oldfield Road, Walton Summit Centre, Bamber Bridge, Preston, PR5 8BG Tel: (01772) 335435 Fax: (01772) 335434 E-mail: sales@creative-impressions.com

DECORATIVE FLOCK

Hiva Products, Disraeli Street, Leicester, LE2 8LX Tel: 0116-283 6977 Fax: 0116-283 5265 E-mail: info@hiva.co.uk
John Peel & Son Ltd, Baildon Mills, Northgate, Baildon, Shipley, West Yorkshire, BD17 6JY Tel: (01274) 583276 Fax: (01274) 598533 E-mail: mail@peelflock.com

DECORATIVE FURNITURE MOULDINGS

Rustin Allen Ltd, Darlaston Road, Wednesbury, West Midlands, WS10 7TN Tel: 0121-526 4048 Fax: 0121-526 4658 E-mail: sales@palextrusions.co.uk
Tectonics Ltd, 10 Caker Stream Road, Alton, Hampshire, GU34 2QA Tel: (01420) 83910 Fax: (01420) 541196 E-mail: sales@tectonics.co.uk

DECORATIVE GAS FIRES

▶ Amgas Fires & Fireplaces Ltd, Unit 12 12 Whingate, Leeds, LS12 3BL Tel: 0113-263 0700 Fax: 0113-263 0700 E-mail: info@amgas.tk
▶ Gas Style, 374 Blackpool Road, Ashton-on-Ribble, Preston, PR2 2DS Tel: (01772) 761006 Fax: (01772) 761006

DECORATIVE GLASSWARE

Caithness Crystal, 9-12 Hardwick Industrial Estate, Paxman Road, King's Lynn, Norfolk, PE30 4NE Tel: (01553) 765111 Fax: (01553) 767628 E-mail: sales@caithnessglass.co.uk
Glassart, Cross Bank Farm, Burnt Fen, Freckenham, Bury St. Edmunds, Suffolk, IP28 8EA Tel: (01353) 675285 Fax: (01353) 675285 E-mail: sales@glassartuk.com
Lichfield Studio Glass Ltd, Boston Industrial Estate, Power Station Road, Rugeley, Staffordshire, WS15 2HS Tel: (01889) 575551 Fax: (01889) 575551 E-mail: lich@globalnet.co.uk
Merlin Glass, Barn Street, Liskeard, Cornwall, PL14 4BJ Tel: (01579) 342399 Fax: (01579) 345110 E-mail: info@glassdoorhandles.com

DECORATIVE INTERIOR LIGHTING

▶ Accommodation Services Management Ltd, Greenhole Park, Greenhole Place, Bridge of Don Industrial Estate, Aberdeen, AB23 8EU Tel: (01224) 826100 Fax: (01224) 826101 E-mail: info@asm.co.uk

DECORATIVE LIGHTING

David Hunt Lighting Ltd, Tilemans Lane, Shipston-on-Stour, Warwickshire, CV36 4HP Tel: (01608) 661590 Fax: (01608) 662951
Derwent Lighting, Derwent Road, York Road Business Park, Malton, North Yorkshire, YO17 6YB Tel: (01653) 696444 Fax: (01653) 696965 E-mail: enquiries@derwentlighting.co.uk
H Tyson & Co. Ltd, Gibson House, Walpole St, Blackburn, BB1 1DB Tel: (01254) 266000 Fax: (01254) 266001 E-mail: info@tyson-lighting.co.uk
Impex (Glassware) Ltd, Impex House, 8 Scrubs Lane, London, NW10 6QR Tel: (020) 8969 6496 Fax: (020) 8960 5337 E-mail: moreinfo@impex.glassware.co.uk
J & M Parker Ltd, 9 New Summer Street, Birmingham, B19 3QN Tel: 0121-359 8897 Fax: 0121-359 4497 E-mail: enquiries@parker.co.uk
Lamps & Lighting, Bridgewater Court, Network 65 Business Park, Hapton, Burnley, Lancashire, BB11 5ST Tel: (01282) 448666 Fax: (01282) 417705 E-mail: sales@lamps-lighting.co.uk
▶ Lumino Ltd, Lumino House, Lovet Road, Harlow, Essex, CM19 5TB Tel: (01279) 635411 Fax: (01279) 626101 E-mail: info@lumino.co.uk
Mathmos, Sterte Avenue West, Poole, Dorset, BH15 2BE Tel: (01202) 644600 Fax: (01202) 669440

DECORATIVE LITTER BINS

Cigarette Bin.Co.Uk, 118 Woodside Business Park, Birkenhead, Merseyside, CH41 5LB Tel: (0870) 1212388 E-mail: info@ciggybins.co.uk

DECORATIVE OR ARCHITECTURAL PRECAST CONCRETE PRODUCTS TO SPECIFICATION

Bespoke Concrete Products Ltd, Tynedale Works, Princess Way, Prudhoe, Northumberland, NE42 6PL Tel: (01661) 839340 Fax: (01661) 833923 E-mail: info@bespokeconcrete.co.uk
▶ Imperial Stone, New Barn Farm, Rake Road, Milland, Liphook, Hampshire, GU30 7JU Tel: (01428) 741175 Fax: (01428) 741175 E-mail: sales@imperialstone.co.uk

DECORATIVE OR ROOM OR WALL MOULDINGS

Copley Decor Ltd, 1 Leyburn Business Park, Harmby Road, Leyburn, North Yorkshire, DL8 5QA Tel: (01969) 623410 Fax: (01969) 624398 E-mail: mouldings@copleydecor.co.uk
Renaissance Period Mouldings, 262 Handsworth Road, Sheffield, S13 9BS Tel: 0114-244 6622 Fax: 0114-261 0472
Winther,Browne & Company Ltd, 75 Bilton Way, Enfield, Middlesex, EN3 7ER Tel: (020) 8344 9050 Fax: (020) 8344 9051 E-mail: sales@wintherbrowne.co.uk

DECORATIVE PLAQUES

Brambley Furniture, 108 Westmoor Street, Charlton, London, SE7 8NQ Tel: (020) 8293 6662 Fax: (020) 8305 0907
Broadhurst Bros Burslem Ltd, Waterloo Road, Burslem, Stoke-on-Trent, ST6 2EL Tel: (01782) 834561 Fax: (01782) 832102
Leander Architectural, Hallsteads Close, Dove Holes, Buxton, Derbyshire, SK17 8BP Tel: (01298) 814941 Fax: (01298) 814970 E-mail: sales@1eanderarch.demon.co.uk
Metalprint Signs & Nameplates, 37 The Pentlands, Kintbury, Hungerford, Berkshire, RG17 9XB Tel: (01488) 658670 Fax: (01488) 658670 E-mail: fp@metalplaques.co.uk

DECORATIVE PLASTERWORK

Stevensons Of Norwich Ltd, Roundtree Way, Norwich, NR7 8SQ Tel: (01603) 400824 Fax: (01603) 405113 E-mail: sales@stevensons-of-norwich.co.uk
▶ VEN Systems Ltd, 25 Wingmore Road, London, SE24 0AS Tel: (07718) 159555 Fax: (020) 7837 8443 E-mail: info@venplaster.co.uk

DECORATIVE PROTECTIVE COATINGS

Anochrome Technologies Ltd, Wood Lane, Wolverhampton, WV10 8HN Tel: (01902) 567567 Fax: (01902) 567777 E-mail: enquiries@anochrome-group.co.uk

DECORATIVE RADIATOR COVERS

Johnny Egg, 32 Clarendon Road, Borehamwood, Hertfordshire, WD6 1BJ Tel: (020) 8207 1333 Fax: (020) 8207 1333 E-mail: johnnyegg@ntlworld.com
▶ Jo Howard, 2 Linnet Close, Hightown, Ringwood, Hampshire, BH24 3RE Tel: (01425) 476364 E-mail: info@coverrad.co.uk
Neil Smith Quality Home Improvements, 24 Hawthorn Hill, Trefechan, Merthyr Tydfil, Mid Glamorgan, CF48 2ES Tel: (01685) 723895 Fax: (01685) 723895
Alan Parkes Designs Ltd, Unit 1, Birch Lane Business Park, Birch Lane, Walsall, WS9 0NF Tel: (01543) 682111
R S Curving Services, Unit 8 Abbey Ct, Wallingford Rd, Leicester, LE4 5RD Tel: 0116-266 6803 Fax: 0166 266 6803
The Radiator Cover Co., Lincoln Avenue, Sandiacre, Nottingham, NG10 5GZ Tel: 0115-939 9125 Fax: 0115-939 9125 E-mail: theradiatorcovercompany@gmail.com

DECORATIVE RIBBONS

Brooklyn Bow & Ribbon Co. Ltd, Herald Business Park, Golden Acres Lane, Coventry, CV3 2RT Tel: (024) 7663 5599 Fax: (024) 7663 5525 E-mail: sales@brooklynbow.co.uk
Cole Fabrics plc, 3 Ludlow Hill Road, West Bridgford, Nottingham, NG2 6HF Tel: 0115-923 5251 Fax: 0115-923 3274 E-mail: info@colefabrics.com
Fashion Ribbon Ltd, Manners Avenue, Manners Industrial Estate, Ilkeston, Derbyshire, DE7 8EF Tel: 0115-930 8699 Fax: 0115-930 4555 E-mail: chris@fashionribbon.co.uk

DECORATIVE STREET LIGHTING STANDARDS OR COLUMNS

Marshalls Mono Ltd, Landscape House, Premiere Way, Housefield Business Park, Elland, West Yorkshire, HX5 9HT Tel: (01422) 306400 Fax: (0870) 6002426

DECORATIVE TELEPHONES

Ian Tofte Voice & Data Communications, 32 Bronte Close, Aylesbury, Buckinghamshire, HP19 8LF Tel: (01296) 487982 Fax: (01296) 488050 E-mail: itofte@tiscalli.co.uk

DECORATIVE WALLCOVERINGS

Muraspec Ltd, 74-78 Wood Lane End, Hemel Hempstead, Hertfordshire, HP2 4RF Tel: (01442) 268890 Fax: (0870) 5329020 E-mail: customerservices@muraspec.com
▶ Property Network Services Ltd., 29 Woodlands Crescent, Johnstone, Renfrewshire, PA5 0AZ Tel: 01505 320281

DECORATORS' SPRAYING EQUIPMENT

Crown Brolac Decorator Centre, 5 London Road, Bedford, MK42 0PB Tel: (01234) 360541 Fax: (01234) 360551 E-mail: cdc406.bedford@dwn.akzonobel.com
The Crown Decorating Centre, Unit 2 Southsea Works, Rodney Road, Southsea, Hampshire, PO4 8SP Tel: (023) 9283 8201 Fax: (023) 9285 1736 E-mail: cdc706.portsmouth@dwn.akzonobel.com
Dulux Ltd, 60-72 New Town Row, Birmingham, B6 4HP Tel: 0121-359 5511 Fax: 0121-359 3537

DECORATORS' SUPPLIES

Aldridge & Trillwood Ltd, 12 Railway Approach, East Grinstead, West Sussex, RH19 1BP Tel: (01342) 322519 Fax: (01342) 322519
Ayrshire Paint & Paper Co, 15 Church Street, Troon, Ayrshire, KA10 6HU Tel: (01292) 312111
C. Brewer & Sons Ltd, 81 Alston Drive, Bradwell Abbey, Milton Keynes, MK13 9HF Tel: (01908) 316719 Fax: (01908) 311423
Brewers Ltd, Priory Bridge Road, Taunton, Somerset, TA1 1QD Tel: (01823) 284532 Fax: (01823) 353712
C Brewer & Sons Ltd, 49 New England Street, Brighton, BN1 4GQ Tel: (01273) 570243 Fax: (01273) 693592 E-mail: brighton@brewers.co.uk
C Brewer & Sons Ltd, Albany House, Ashford Road, Eastbourne, East Sussex, BN21 3TR Tel: (01323) 437801 Fax: (01323) 721435 E-mail: decorating@brewers.co.uk
C Brewer & Sons Ltd, 5 Sphere Industrial Estate, Campfield Road, St. Albans, Hertfordshire, AL1 5HT Tel: (01727) 844737 Fax: (01727) 846672
Clifton Paints Ltd, 92-100 North Street, Bedminster, Bristol, BS3 1HF Tel: 0117-966 0321 Fax: 0117-963 1301 E-mail: sales@dacrylate.co.uk
Crown Brolac Decorator Centre, 5 London Road, Bedford, MK42 0PB Tel: (01234) 360541 Fax: (01234) 360551 E-mail: cdc406.bedford@dwn.akzonobel.com
The Crown Decorating Centre, Unit 2 Southsea Works, Rodney Road, Southsea, Hampshire, PO4 8SP Tel: (023) 9283 8201 Fax: (023) 9285 1736 E-mail: cdc706.portsmouth@dwn.akzonobel.com
Decor Centre, North Quay, Pwllheli, Gwynedd, LL53 5YR Tel: (01758) 612562 Fax: (01758) 704999 E-mail: sales@decorcentrewales.com
Dulex Decorators Ltd, 117-119 Hillingdon Hill, Uxbridge Road, Uxbridge, Middlesex, UB10 0JE Tel: (01895) 234523 Fax: (01895) 814359 E-mail: debcosales@zoom.co.uk
Dulux Ltd, Manchester Road, West Timperley, Altrincham, Cheshire, WA14 5PG Tel: 0161-968 3000 Fax: 0161-973 4202
Dulux Ltd, 60-72 New Town Row, Birmingham, B6 4HP Tel: 0121-359 5511 Fax: 0121-359 3537
Dulux Ltd, Swansey Mill, Swansey Lane, Clayton-le-Woods, Chorley, Lancashire, PR6 7HY Tel: (01257) 269570 Fax: (01257) 269564
Dulux Ltd, 66 Burleys Way, Leicester, LE1 3BD Tel: 0116-262 9471 Fax: 0116-251 2985
Dulux Ltd, Anglian House, Claydons Lane, Rayleigh, Essex, SS6 7UP Tel: (01268) 773891 Fax: (01268) 770314
DZD Blyco Ltd, Lower Ground Floor, 145 Tottenham Court Road, London, W1T 7NE Tel: (020) 7388 7488 Fax: (020) 7388 7499 E-mail: enquiries@dzd.co.uk
E W Moore & Son Ltd, 39-43 Plashet Grove, London, E6 1AD Tel: (020) 8472 0521 Fax: (020) 8472 4702 E-mail: sales@wallposters.org.uk
▶ Eco-Dec, 27a Northgate, Cleckheaton, West Yorkshire, BD19 3HH Tel: (07974) 683111
Ernest Griffith & Sons Ltd, Praed Rd, Trafford Park, Manchester, M17 1PQ Tel: 0161-877 1655 Fax: 0161-877 6577 E-mail: pdbrearley@aol.com
Halls Beeline Ltd, Northgate, White Lund Trading Estate, Morecambe, Lancashire, LA3 3PA Tel: (01524) 63233 Fax: (01524) 65792 E-mail: sales@hallsbeeline.net
Home-Key Ltd, Units 1-3 Admiral Park Estate, Airport Service Road, Portsmouth, PO3 5RQ Tel: (023) 9267 3535 Fax: (023) 9269 5543 E-mail: home.key@virgin.net
Mayalls of Wigan, Woodhouse Lane, Wigan, Lancashire, WN6 7TH Tel: (01942) 241711 Fax: (01942) 241271 E-mail: maywigan@travisperkins.co.uk
P W Cannon & Son Ltd, 36 Hythe Avenue, Bexleyheath, Kent, DA7 5NY Tel: (01322) 432247 Fax: (01322) 432248
Park Paints, Head Office, 493 Battersea Park Road, London, SW11 4LW Tel: (020) 7228 0547 Fax: (020) 7924 3927
Ray Lowe Ltd, Rohais Road, St. Peter Port, Guernsey, GY1 1YP Tel: (01481) 722618 Fax: (01481) 711903
Robinson & Neal Ltd, 129 Sefton Street, Toxteth, Liverpool, L8 5SN Tel: 0151-709 9481 Fax: 0151-707 1377
Rodbers Of Richmond Ltd, The Old Cinema, 2 Queens Road, Richmond, North Yorkshire, DL10 4DN Tel: (01748) 822491 Fax: (01748) 826497
Roger Hickman Paint & Wallcovering Ltd, Unit 32 The Wallows Industrial Estate, Fens Pool Avenue, Brierley Hill, West Midlands, DY5 1QA Tel: (01384) 75629 Fax: (01384) 483347
S J Dixon & Son Ltd, Garden Street, Walsall, WS2 8EG Tel: (01922) 647244 Fax: (01922) 722965
Sanderson & Co, High Street, Leyburn, North Yorkshire, DL8 5AQ Tel: (01969) 623143 Fax: (01969) 623364
Scotts Decorators Merchants Ltd, 5 Wharf Road, Avon Industrial Estate, Stratford-upon-Avon, Warwickshire, CV37 0AD Tel: (01789) 292171 Fax: (01789) 294073
Simpson's Paints Ltd, 122-124 Broadley Street, London, NW8 8BB Tel: (020) 7723 6657 Fax: (020) 7706 4662
Thompson Builders Merchants Ltd, Bilton Road, Chelmsford, CM1 2UB Tel: (01245) 266754 Fax: (01245) 359070 E-mail: info@thompson-online.co.uk
Thompson & Parkes Ltd, Oldington Trading Estate, Kidderminster, Worcestershire, DY11 7QP Tel: (01562) 745881 Fax: (01562) 515578
Travis Perkins plc, Mayors Avenue, Dartmouth, Devon, TQ6 9NG Tel: (01803) 832216 Fax: (01803) 835694
Wright's Of Lymm Ltd, Warrington Lane, Lymm, Cheshire, WA13 0SA Tel: (01925) 752226 Fax: (01925) 757569 E-mail: info@wrightsoflymm.co.uk

DECORATORS' TOOLS

Brewers Ltd, Priory Bridge Road, Taunton, Somerset, TA1 1QD Tel: (01823) 284532 Fax: (01823) 353712
C Brewer & Sons Ltd, 49 New England Street, Brighton, BN1 4GQ Tel: (01273) 570243 Fax: (01273) 693592 E-mail: brighton@brewers.co.uk
The Crown Decorating Centre, Unit 2 Southsea Works, Rodney Road, Southsea, Hampshire, PO4 8SP Tel: (023) 9283 8201 Fax: (023) 9285 1736 E-mail: cdc706.portsmouth@dwn.akzonobel.com
Crown Hand Tools Ltd, Excelsior Works, Burnt Tree Lane, Hoyle Street, Sheffield, S3 7EX Tel: 0114-272 3366 Fax: 0114-272 5252 E-mail: info@crowntools.com
Delta Manufacturing Co., 28f Park View West Industrial Estate, Hartlepool, Cleveland, TS25 1PE Tel: (01429) 276895 Fax: (01429) 865766 E-mail: info@brushmaster.com
Dulux Ltd, 60-72 New Town Row, Birmingham, B6 4HP Tel: 0121-359 5511 Fax: 0121-359 3537
Hamilton Acorn Ltd, Halford Road, Attleborough, Norfolk, NR17 2HZ Tel: (01953) 453201 Fax: (01953) 454943 E-mail: sales@hamilton-acorn.co.uk
Hamilton Acorn Ltd, Callywhite Lane, Dronfield, Derbyshire, S18 2XP Tel: (01246) 418306 Fax: (01246) 410334 E-mail: info@hamilton-acorn.co.uk
L G Harris & Co. Ltd, Hanbury Road, Stoke Prior, Bromsgrove, Worcestershire, B60 4AE Tel: (01527) 575441 Fax: (01527) 575366 E-mail: enquiries@lgharris.co.uk
Robinson & Neal Ltd, 129 Sefton Street, Toxteth, Liverpool, L8 5SN Tel: 0151-709 9481 Fax: 0151-707 1377

DEEP CLEANING

▶ At Chore Service, 10 Oak Court, North Road, South Ockendon, Essex, RM15 6PN Tel: (01708) 850931
Dougland Holdings Ltd, Little Park Farm, Segensworth West Industrial Estate, Fareham, Hampshire, PO15 5SN Tel: (01489) 574234 Fax: (01489) 576104 E-mail: margaret@dougland.co.uk
EDSCO, 118 Featherbed Lane, Hillmorton, Rugby, Warwickshire, CV21 4LQ Tel: 01788 331530 Fax: 01788 336858 E-mail: e.scholey@ntlworld.com
▶ Enserve, Metro House, 57 Pepper Road, Leeds, LS10 2RU Tel: (0800) 0377817 E-mail: sales@enserve.co.uk
Service Systems UK Ltd, Chester Road, Sandycroft, Deeside, Clwyd, CH5 2QW Tel: (01244) 535095 Fax: (01244) 538987 E-mail: service@servicesystems.co.uk

DEEP DRAWING GRADE STEEL BLANKS

Abbey Steel & Shearing Co. Ltd, 5 Cartwright Road, Pin Green Industrial Area, Stevenage, Hertfordshire, SG1 4QJ Tel: (01438) 741888 Fax: (01438) 740980 E-mail: sales@abbeysteel.co.uk

DEEP DRAWING SPECIALIST SERVICES

Accellent, Unit E3 Brookside Business Park, Greengate, Middleton, Manchester, M24 1GS Tel: 0161-643 0018 Fax: 0161-643 0019 E-mail: susan.ward@accellent.com

DEEP DRAWN PRESSINGS

A P Smith & Son Metal Pressing Ltd, 8 Kings St, Birmingham, B19 3AR Tel: 0121-523 0011 Fax: 0121-554 7244 E-mail: sales@apsmith.co.uk
Danglo Components Ltd, Unit 9-10, Wedgewood Way, Stevenage, Hertfordshire, SG1 4QB Tel: (01438) 735616 Fax: (01438) 735625 E-mail: sales@danglo.co.uk
Doby Ltd, Doby Ltd, Hare Law Industrial Estate, Stanley, County Durham, DH9 8UJ Tel: (01207) 299861 Fax: (01207) 283563 E-mail: sales@dobyverrolec.com
F E M, Bradware Industrial Park, Leonard Street, Bingley, West Yorkshire, BD16 1DP Tel: (01274) 511911 Fax: (01274) 511913
G & D Engineering Vickers Ltd, Poplars Industrial Estate, Moor Lane, Birmingham, B6 7AD Tel: 0121-356 3378
H T Brigham & Co. Ltd, Station Road, Coleshill, Birmingham, B46 1JQ Tel: (01675) 463882 Fax: (01675) 467441 E-mail: admin@htbrigham.co.uk
Metal Spinners Group Ltd, Newburn Industrial Estate, Shelley Road, Newcastle upon Tyne, NE15 9RT Tel: 0191-267 1011 Fax: 0191-264 7137 E-mail: sales@metal-spinners.co.uk
Press Metal Products Ltd, 5 Abberley Industrial Centre, Abberley Street, Smethwick, West Midlands, B66 2QL Tel: 0121-555 6061 Fax: 0121-555 6058 E-mail: sales@pressed-metal.com
Presspart Manufacturing Ltd, Phillips Road, Blackburn, BB1 5RF Tel: (01254) 582233 Fax: (01254) 584100 E-mail: sales@presspart.com
R J Vickers & Son Ltd, 152 Soho Hill, Birmingham, B19 1AF Tel: 0121-523 6235 Fax: 0121-523 9397 E-mail: vickers.metform@virgin.net
R S M Industries Ltd, School Lane, Exhall, Coventry, CV7 9NN Tel: (024) 7636 2082 Fax: (024) 7655 3715 E-mail: admin@rsmindustries.co.uk
Specialist Anodising Ltd, New Hall Works, Elm Street, Burnley, Lancashire, BB10 1NY Tel: (01282) 412500 Fax: (01282) 422804 E-mail: saco@sacoltd.com
Zero Cases (U K) Ltd, Alpha Park, Bevan Way, Smethwick, West Midlands, B66 1BZ Tel: 0121-558 2011 Fax: 0121-565 2115 E-mail: zero.cases.europe.sales@dial.pipex.com

DEEP HOLE BORING

Accure Geneva Ltd, 1-5 Goodwood Road, Pershore, Worcestershire, WR10 2JL Tel: (01386) 555335 Fax: (01386) 556739 E-mail: enquiries@geneva.accura.co.uk
Bored Bar Engineering Ltd, New Street, Halfway, Sheffield, S20 3GH Tel: 0114-248 3631 Fax: 0114-247 7133 E-mail: sales@bored-bar.co.uk
Darren Sbo, Canklow Meadows Industrial Estate, Rotherham, South Yorkshire, S60 2XL Tel: (01709) 722600 Fax: (01709) 722657 E-mail: pspeechley@darron.co.uk
P R V Engineering Ltd, Pegasus House, Polo Grounds, New Inn, Pontypool, Gwent, NP4 0TW Tel: (01495) 769697 Fax: (01495) 769776 E-mail: enquiries@prv-engineering.co.uk

DEEP HOLE BORING TOOLS

▶ CS Press Tools Ltd, Unit 23 Nutwood Trading Estate, Limestone Cottage Lane, Sheffield, S6 1NJ Tel: 0114-234 8563 Fax: 0114-234 6290 E-mail: david@cspresstools.co.uk

DEEP HOLE DRILLING

Accura Holdings, Hickman Avenue, Wolverhampton, WV1 2DW Tel: (01902) 454460 Fax: (01902) 451840 E-mail: enquiries@accura.co.uk
Darren Sbo, Canklow Meadows Industrial Estate, Rotherham, South Yorkshire, S60 2XL Tel: (01709) 722600 Fax: (01709) 722657 E-mail: info@darron-sbo.com
P R V Engineering Ltd, Pegasus House, Polo Grounds, New Inn, Pontypool, Gwent, NP4 0TW Tel: (01495) 769697 Fax: (01495) 769776 E-mail: enquiries@prv-engineering.co.uk
Partridge Microdrilling Services, Priestley Way, Crawley, West Sussex, RH10 9NT Tel: (01293) 526525 Fax: (01293) 526525 E-mail: partridill@aol.com
Saxton Drilling Ltd, Cardrew Industrial Estate, Redruth, Cornwall, TR15 1SS Tel: (01209) 315100 Fax: (01209) 315000
W R Clark & Co Engineers Ltd, Bridge St Industrial Estate, Bridge Street, Clay Cross, Chesterfield, Derbyshire, S45 9NU Tel: (01246) 862325 Fax: (01246) 250033

DEEP HOLE DRILLING MACHINES

Halliburton, Howe Moss Place, Dyce, Aberdeen, AB21 0GS Tel: (01224) 776600 Fax: (01224) 793193
Mollart Engineering Ltd, Roebuck Road, Chessington, Surrey, KT9 1EU Tel: (020) 8391 2282 Fax: (020) 8391 6626 E-mail: info@mollart.co.uk
T B T UK Ltd, Gorsey Lane, Coleshill, Birmingham, B46 1JU Tel: (01675) 433250

DEEP HOLE DRILLING TOOLS

Halliburton, Howe Moss Place, Dyce, Aberdeen, AB21 0GS Tel: (01224) 776600 Fax: (01224) 793193
Linear Tools Ltd, 1 Clock Tower Road, Isleworth, Middlesex, TW7 6DT Tel: (020) 8400 2020 Fax: (020) 8400 2021 E-mail: sales@lineartools.co.uk
Mollart Engineering Ltd, Roebuck Road, Chessington, Surrey, KT9 1EU Tel: (020) 8391 2282 Fax: (020) 8391 6626 E-mail: info@mollart.co.uk
T B T UK Ltd, Gorsey Lane, Coleshill, Birmingham, B46 1JU Tel: (01675) 433250

DEEP SEA FISHING GEAR

Advanced Netting, 157 St Osyth Road, Clacton-on-Sea, Essex, CO15 3HD Tel: (01255) 428988 Fax: (01255) 220668 E-mail: sales@advancednetting.co.uk
Edwin Ashworth Marine Ltd, 10 Dove Way, Kirkby Mills Industrial Estate, Kirkbymoorside, York, YO62 6QR Tel: (01751) 433039 Fax: (01751) 433039
B & T Angling, 11 Briar Road, Romford, RM3 8AH Tel: (01708) 370033 Fax: (01708) 370004
Barzillai Hingley & Sons Ltd, Lion Chain Works, Providence Street, Cradley Heath, West Midlands, B64 5DT Tel: (01384) 569141 Fax: (01384) 639177 E-mail: sales@barzillai.com
Beejay Welding Engineers, 5 Newlyn Road, Cradley Heath, West Midlands, B64 6BE Tel: (01384) 566205 Fax: (01384) 565245
▶ The Fly Factory, Unit 325, Vale Enterprise Centre, Hayes Road, Sully, Penarth, South Glamorgan, CF64 5SY Tel: (01446) 700401 Fax: (01446) 404646 E-mail: sales@theflyfactory.co.uk
▶ Rugby Tackle, 155a Bilton Road, Rugby, Warwickshire, CV22 7DS Tel: (01788) 544913 Fax: (01788) 570645 E-mail: sales@rugbytackle.co.uk

DEFLASHING EQUIPMENT TO SPECIFICATION

T I A Robotic Tooling Solutions, Unit 4C Derby Business Park, Canal Street, Derby, DE1 2RJ Tel: (01332) 204850 Fax: (01332) 204851 E-mail: info@tatem.co.uk

DEGREASERS, PARTS WASHER

▶ D-Grease UK Ltd, Unit 3 North Gawber Industrial Park, Blacker Road, Mapplewell, Barnsley, South Yorkshire, S75 6BS Tel: (01226) 230890 Fax: (01226) 381100 E-mail: enquiries@dgrease.fsnet.co.uk

DEGREASING CHEMICAL PRODUCTS OR DEGREASANTS

Concorde Chemicals P.L.C., Concorde Works, Bilton Way, Brimsdown, Enfield, Middlesex, EN3 7NH Tel: (020) 8404 7411 Fax: (020) 8805 6553 E-mail: dgoldberg@concordechemicals.co.uk
E P Laboratories Ltd, Amersham Road, Chesham, Buckinghamshire, HP5 1NE Tel: (01494) 791585 Fax: (01494) 771853 E-mail: sales@eplabs.com
Ecokem Ltd, 4 Trafalgar Court, Widnes, Cheshire, WA8 0SZ Tel: 0151-420 0172 Fax: 0151-510 5455 E-mail: dclarkson@ecokem.co.uk
High Technology Solvents UK Ltd, Millfield, Ashwells Road, Brentwood, Essex, CM15 9SF Tel: (01277) 375222 Fax: (01277) 373115 E-mail: htsukltd@aol.com
Mirj Hygiene Products Ltd, Unit 3, Antelope Industrial Park, Rhydymwyn, Mold, Clwyd, CH7 5JH Tel: (01352) 741919 Fax: (01352) 741920 E-mail: sales@mirjhygiene.co.uk
Quadralene Ltd, Bateman Street, Derby, DE23 8JL Tel: (01332) 292500 Fax: (01332) 295941 E-mail: info@quadralene.co.uk
Stowlin Ltd, Radnor Road, Wigston, Leicestershire, LE18 4XY Tel: 0116-278 5373 Fax: 0116-277 2616E-mail: kate@stowlin.com

DEGREASING CHEMICAL PRODUCTS OR DEGREASANTS – *continued*

Turbex Ltd, Unit 1, Riverwey Industrial Park, Newman Lane, Alton, Hampshire, GU34 2QL Tel: (01420) 544909 Fax: (01420) 542264 E-mail: sales@turbex.co.uk

DEGREASING PLANT/ DEGREASER, *See also headings for particular types*

Gimson Ltd, 30 Boston Road, Leicester, LE4 1AU Tel: 0116-236 8688 Fax: 0116-236 3663 E-mail: a_sims@gimsoneng.co.uk

DEGREASING PLANT/ DEGREASERS, CONVEYORISED

Environmental Cleaning Technologies Ltd, Unit 65 North Mersey Bus Centre, Woodward Road, Knowsley Industrial Park, Liverpool, L33 7UY Tel: 0151-548 4015 Fax: 0151-548 4122 E-mail: sales@ect-ltd.co.uk
Turbex Ltd, Unit 1, Riverwey Industrial Park, Newman Lane, Alton, Hampshire, GU34 2QL Tel: (01420) 544909 Fax: (01420) 542264 E-mail: sales@turbex.co.uk

DEGREASING PLANT/ DEGREASERS, INDUSTRIAL

Checo 2000, Brailwood Road, Bilsthorpe, Newark, Nottinghamshire, NG22 8UA Tel: (01623) 871976 Fax: (01623) 871964 E-mail: info@checo200.co.uk
Environmental Cleaning Technologies Ltd, Unit 65 North Mersey Bus Centre, Woodward Road, Knowsley Industrial Park, Liverpool, L33 7UY Tel: 0151-548 4015 Fax: 0151-548 4122 E-mail: sales@ect-ltd.co.uk
Mecwash Systems Ltd, Unit A 64 Hundred, 7 Drive, Tewkesbury Business Park, Tewkesbury, Gloucestershire, GL20 8TB Tel: (01684) 271600 E-mail: paulyoung@mecwash.co.uk
Metalas UK Ltd, White Cottages, Fuller Street, Fairstead, Chelmsford, CM3 2AY Tel: (01245) 233715 Fax: (01245) 381866 E-mail: admin@metalas.co.uk
Odlings M C R Ltd, Rosscliffe Road, Junction 8 Business Centre, Ellesmere Port, CH65 3AS Tel: 0151-355 0261 Fax: 0151-356 4423 E-mail: sales@odlingsmcr.co.uk
Projectworld Ltd, Morvern Works, Church Street, Briton Ferry, Neath, West Glamorgan, SA11 2JP Tel: (01639) 812332 Fax: (01639) 812496 E-mail: info@projectworld.co.uk
S M S Degreasers (Sheet Metal Structures) Ltd, Woodlands, Cliff Road, Salcombe, Devon, TQ8 8LD Tel: (01548) 842454 Fax: (01548) 843380
▶ Standard Industrial Systems Ltd, Stanton House, Eastham Village Rd, Eastham, Wirral, Merseyside, CH62 0DE Tel: (0845) 2571985 Fax: (0845) 2571986 E-mail: sales@standardindustrial.co.uk
Turbex Ltd, Unit 1, Riverwey Industrial Park, Newman Lane, Alton, Hampshire, GU34 2QL Tel: (01420) 544909 Fax: (01420) 542264 E-mail: sales@turbex.co.uk
Vixen Surface Treatments Ltd, Jay Avenue, Teeside Industrial Estate, Stockton-on-Tees, Cleveland, TS17 9LZ Tel: (01642) 769333 Fax: (01642) 769441

DEGREASING PLANT/ DEGREASERS, SPECIAL PURPOSE

Bio-Clean Equipment Sales Ltd, Waterhouse, Greenfields Road, Horley, Surrey, RH6 8HW Tel: (01293) 424200 Fax: (01293) 424444 E-mail: sales@bioclean.co.uk
Environmental Cleaning Technologies Ltd, Unit 65 North Mersey Bus Centre, Woodward Road, Knowsley Industrial Park, Liverpool, L33 7UY Tel: 0151-548 4015 Fax: 0151-548 4122 E-mail: sales@ect-ltd.co.uk
Mecwash Systems Ltd, Unit A 64 Hundred, 7 Drive, Tewkesbury Business Park, Tewkesbury, Gloucestershire, GL20 8TB Tel: (01684) 271600 E-mail: paulyoung@mecwash.co.uk
Metalas UK Ltd, White Cottages, Fuller Street, Fairstead, Chelmsford, CM3 2AY Tel: (01245) 233715 Fax: (01245) 381866 E-mail: admin@metalas.co.uk

DEGREASING SERVICES

Acorn Services, Unit 3 Access Point, Willenhall Industrial Centre, Bloxwich, Walsall, WS3 2XN Tel: (01922) 491676 Fax: (01922) 710305 E-mail: jane@acornservices.wannado.co.uk
Chemsquad Ltd, 23 Izons Industrial Estate, Oldbury Road, West Bromwich, West Midlands, B70 9BS Tel: 0121-553 1340 Fax: 0121-525 2077

DEHUMIDIFIER HIRE

Dehumidifier Co., Langsford Farm, Peter Tavy, Tavistock, Devon, PL19 9LY Tel: (01822) 810638 Fax: (01822) 810638 E-mail: mike@pidsley.com

DEHUMIDIFIERS

Air And Water Centre.Com, Artex Avenue, Rustington, Littlehampton, West Sussex, BN16 3LN Tel: (01903) 858657 Fax: (01903) 850345 E-mail: sales@airandwatercentre.com
Air Improve Ltd, Unit 4 City Business Centre, Hyde Street, Winchester, Hampshire, SO23 7TA Tel: (01962) 841366 Fax: (01962) 840185 E-mail: enquiries@airimprove.ltd.uk
Broughton Electroair Products, Clive Works, Edward Street, Redditch, Worcestershire, B97 6HA Tel: (01527) 597567 Fax: (01527) 67603 E-mail: sales@broughtoneap.com
Calorex Heat Pumps Ltd, Unit 2, The Causeway, Heybridge, Maldon, Essex, CM9 4XL Tel: (01621) 856611 Fax: (01621) 850871 E-mail: sales@calorex.com
Cool Heat Services, 167 Hullbridge Road, South Woodham Ferrers, Chelmsford, CM3 5LN Tel: (01245) 321615 Fax: (01245) 328981
Heatstar Ltd, 22 Daish Way, Newport, Isle of Wight, PO30 5XB Tel: (01983) 521465 Fax: (01983) 822016 E-mail: info@heatstar.co.uk
Karalex Ltd, The Clock House 4 Russley Park Mews, Russley Park, Baydon, Marlborough, Wiltshire, SN8 2JY Tel: (01672) 540934 Fax: (01672) 540934 E-mail: tech@karalex.co.uk
Motan Ltd, Unit 10 Blacklands Way, Abingdon Business Park, Abingdon, Oxfordshire, OX14 1RD Tel: (01235) 550011 Fax: (01235) 550033 E-mail: sales.ltd@motan.com
Taprex, 2-6 Victor Road, Harrow, Middlesex, HA2 6PU Tel: (020) 8863 4698
Watford Refrigeration & Air Conditioning Ltd, Wiggenhall Industrial Estate, Watford, WD18 0FT Tel: (01923) 227726 Fax: (01923) 233525 E-mail: sales@watref.co.uk

DEHYDRATED POULTRY FOOD EXTENDERS

▶ PCS Food Group, 5 Bilston Key Industrial Estate, Oxford Street, Bilston, West Midlands, WV14 7DW Tel: (01902) 401230 Fax: (01902) 409906

DEHYDRATION PLANT

Cable Pressure Systems Ltd, Borrowmeadow Road, Springkerse Industrial Estate, Stirling, FK7 7UW Tel: (01786) 449292 Fax: (01786) 449393 E-mail: cps@fernan.com
Hanover Maloney (U K) Ltd, Westgate, Aldridge, Walsall, WS9 8EX Tel: (01922) 450200 Fax: (01922) 450210 E-mail: info@hanover-maloney.co.uk

DEIONISED WATER

Purite Ltd, Bandet Way, Thame Industrial Estate, Thame, Oxfordshire, OX9 3SJ Tel: (01844) 217141
Transfair Llanllyr Spring Water Co., Llanllyr, Talsarn, Lampeter, Dyfed, SA48 8QB Tel: (01570) 470788 Fax: (01570) 471074

DEIONISED WATER TREATMENT PLANT AND EQUIPMENT

Silkstream Water Treatment Equipment, 36 Spencer Close, Potton, Sandy, Bedfordshire, SG19 2QY Tel: (01767) 261942 E-mail: sales@silkstream.co.uk

DELICATESSEN CONSULTANCY

▶ Chaplais Ltd, 9 High Street, Fairford, Gloucestershire, GL7 4AD Tel: (01285) 713610 E-mail: mauricechaplais@aol.com

DEMINERALISED WATER

Chance & Hunt Ltd, Alexander House, Crown Gate, Runcorn, Cheshire, WA7 2UP Tel: (01928) 793000 Fax: (01928) 714351 E-mail: passport@chance-hunt.com

DEMISTERS, FILTRATION/ SEPARATION

Knitwire Products, Dalton Court, Chadwick Road, Runcorn, Cheshire, WA7 1PU Tel: (01928) 566996 Fax: (01928) 566996 E-mail: sales@knitwire.com
Wirecloth Sales & Development Ltd, 11a East View, Grappenhall, Warrington, WA4 2QH Tel: (01925) 268417 Fax: (01925) 604861 E-mail: wireclothsales@aol.com

DEMOLITION BREAKERS

▶ Frac Roc, Islwyn, Lon Gernant, Menai Bridge, Anglesey, LL59 5SU Tel: (01248) 717999 Fax: (01248) 717999 E-mail: rockbusters@btinternet.com

DEMOLITION CONSULTANCY

▶ W F Button & Son Ltd, Button House, Pix Farm Lane, Hemel Hempstead, Hertfordshire, HP1 2RY Tel: (01442) 879440 Fax: (01442) 879442 E-mail: sales@wfbutton.co.uk

DEMOLITION CONTRACTORS

Aaron White Ltd, 20 Bland Street, Sheffield, S4 8DG Tel: 0114-261 9519 Fax: 0114-261 9348
Aberdare Demolition, Cwmbach New Road, Aberdare, Mid Glamorgan, CF44 0PN Tel: (01685) 882744 Fax: (01685) 882744
Able (U K) Ltd, Able House, Billingham Reach Industrial Estate, Haverton Hill, Billingham, Cleveland, TS23 1PX Tel: (01642) 806080 Fax: (01642) 655655E-mail: info@ableuk.com
Abrasive Chasers Drilling & Sawing LLP, 96 Broom Road, Stanford, Biggleswade, Bedfordshire, SG18 9JE Tel: (01462) 813666 Fax: (01462) 813351 E-mail: abrasive.chasers@btconnect.com
▶ Alf Kitching & Sons Ltd, Double Rivers, Crowle, Scunthorpe, South Humberside, DN17 4DD Tel: (01724) 710286 Fax: (01724) 710477
▶ Allan W J Wilson Ltd, Office, 1 Balnagore, Fearn, Tain, Ross-Shire, IV20 1RP Tel: (01862) 832840 Fax: (01862) 832840
Sam Allon (Contracts) Ltd, Lincoln Street, Hull, HU2 0PE Tel: (01482) 320051 Fax: (01482) 216610 E-mail: user@samallon.co.uk
▶ Amber Contracts, 29 Lochinvar Road, Cumbernauld, Glasgow, G67 4AR Tel: (01236) 453776
Anglia Building Suppliers Ltd, Waltham Road, Boreham, Chelmsford, CM3 3AY Tel: (01245) 467505 Fax: (01245) 467506 E-mail: angliabs@btinternet.com
B S Security, 25 Barnes Wallis Road, Fareham, Hampshire, PO15 5TT Tel: (01489) 885870 Fax: (01489) 889801 E-mail: enquiries@bssecurity.co.uk
Bagnall Group Ltd, 940 Lakeside Drive, Centre Park, Warrington, WA1 1RY Tel: (01925) 651191 Fax: (01925) 651192 E-mail: admin@bagnallgroup.co.uk
G. Baskerville Demolition Contractors Ltd, Leek New Road Trading Estate, Cobridge, Stoke-On-Trent, ST6 2PL Tel: (01782) 219455 Fax: (01782) 263666
Syd Bishop & Sons (Demolitition) Ltd, Waldens Depot, Waldens Road, St. Mary Cray, Orpington, Kent, BR5 4EU Tel: (01689) 820315 Fax: (01689) 873784 E-mail: info@sydbishop.co.uk
▶ Braithwaite Excavations Ltd, Claycliffe Road, Barnsley, South Yorkshire, S75 1HS Tel: (01226) 779527 Fax: (01226) 203080
D.J. Broady Ltd, Foster Street, Kingston Upon Hull, East Yorkshire, Hull, HU8 8BT Tel: (01482) 585985 Fax: (01482) 585995
Bromley Demolition Co. Ltd, 75 Siward Road, Bromley, BR2 9JY Tel: (020) 8464 3610 Fax: (020) 8313 3623 E-mail: info@bromleydem.co.uk
Brooks Haulage, Redcliffe Street, Sutton-in-Ashfield, Nottinghamshire, NG17 4ES Tel: (01623) 441255
Edward & John Brown (Contractors) Ltd, 288 Bordesley Grange, Birmingham, B9 5NA Tel: 0121-772 1191 Fax: 0121-766 5130
▶ Brown & Mason Ltd, New Loom House, 101 Back Church Lane, London, E1 1LU Tel: (020) 7264 1120 Fax: (020) 7481 8244 E-mail: b&m@brownandmason.ltd.uk
▶ Buckler Haulage Ltd, Marsh Road, Middlesbrough, Cleveland, TS1 5LB Tel: (01642) 222489 Fax: (01642) 249144 E-mail: mrk@bucker.fsbusiness.co.uk
▶ C A J Services Ltd, Unit K,, Higham Business Park, Bury Close, Higham Ferrers, Northamptonshire, NN10 8HQ Tel: (01933) 355001 Fax: (01933) 355009 E-mail: mail@cajservices.co.uk
C Jackson & Sons, Keysoe Road, Thurleigh, Bedford, MK44 2EA Tel: (01234) 771311 Fax: (01234) 771128 E-mail: info@cjacksonandsons.co.uk
Castlemoor Demolition Ltd, Transfer House, 53 Marshgate Lane, Stratford, London, E15 2NQ Tel: (020) 8503 1505 Fax: (020) 8519 5035
Cheshire Demolition & Excavation Contractors Ltd, 72 Moss Lane, Macclesfield, Cheshire, SK11 7TT Tel: (01625) 424433 Fax: (01625) 611094 E-mail: sales@cheshiredemolition.co.uk
▶ Clyde Demolition, Trump House, 15 Edison Street, Hillington Industrial Estate, Glasgow, G52 4JW Tel: 0141-883 2233 Fax: 0141-882 3840
Cramlington & District Metals Ltd, Appleby Street, North Shields, Tyne & Wear, NE29 6TE Tel: 0191-257 2049 Fax: 0191-257 9907
▶ Cuddy Demolition & Dismantling Ltd, Tank Farm Road, Llandarcy, Neath, West Glamorgan, SA10 6EN Tel: (01792) 321110 Fax: (01792) 321411 E-mail: info@cuddy-group.com
Curle M J Ltd, Sunnymead Farm, Naird Lane, Shifnal, Shropshire, TF11 9PJ Tel: (01952) 460382 Fax: (01952) 463238 E-mail: mjcurle@netscapeonline.co.uk
▶ D Hughes Demolition, Coteman Heights Farm, Hill Top Lane, Delph, Oldham, OL3 5RW Tel: 0161-624 3460 Fax: 0161-620 6295
D & M Demolitions Ltd, Meek Street, Royton, Oldham, OL2 6HL Tel: 0161-652 2550 Fax: 0161-652 5203 E-mail: sales@dandmdemolitions.ltd.uk
▶ Dalkeith Demolition Ltd, Mayfield Industrial Estate, Newtongrange, Dalkeith, Midlothian, EH22 4AH Tel: 0131-660 1939
▶ Dalkeith Demolition Ltd, Unit 27 Mayfield Industrial Estate, Newtongrange, Dalkeith, Midlothian, EH22 4AD Tel: 0131-660 1939 Fax: 0131-663 8138 E-mail: iwmg@btconnect.com
Davis & Samson Contractors, Billet Lane, Berkhamsted, Hertfordshire, HP4 1DP Tel: (01442) 878800 Fax: (01442) 878801 E-mail: sales@davisandsamson.co.uk
Stan Dawson Ltd, Kirkley Sawmills, Kirkley, Newcastle upon Tyne, NE20 0BD Tel: (01661) 860413 Fax: (01661) 822352
Demolition & Salvage Ltd, Ackworth Road, Portsmouth, PO3 5NS Tel: (023) 9267 7890 Fax: (023) 9267 0644 E-mail: sales@demolitionandsalvage.co.uk
H.F.A. Dolman Ltd, Ajax Works, Potters Way, Temple Farm Industrial Estate, Southend-On-Sea, SS2 5SJ Tel: (01702) 461155 Fax: (01702) 464177
▶ Drain Cure Services, 6 Strathmore Street, Perth, PH2 7HP Tel: (01738) 449300 Fax: (01738) 634167
Dundee Plant Co. Ltd, Longtown Street, Dundee, DD4 8LF Tel: (01382) 507506 Fax: (01382) 507550
E Nicholson & Sons, 445 Balmore Road, Glasgow, G22 6NX Tel: 0141-336 6065 Fax: 0141-336 5229 E-mail: sales@enicholson.co.uk
Econ Construction Ltd, Old Maidstone Road, Sidcup, Kent, DA14 5AZ Tel: (020) 8302 4691 Fax: (020) 8308 0483 E-mail: econconstruction@aol.com
Erith Contractors Ltd, Riverside House, Maypole Crescent, Darent Industrial Park, Erith, Kent, DA8 2JZ Tel: (01322) 346811 Fax: (01322) 341978 E-mail: info@erith.net
Essex Demolition Contractors Ltd, 1 Navigation Road, Chelmsford, CM2 6ND Tel: (01245) 258333 Fax: (01245) 266911
F C Richardson & Son Ltd, 194 Yardley Road, Acocks Green, Birmingham, B27 6LR Tel: 0121-706 6701 Fax: 0121-706 6701
Fenton Hadley Contracts Ltd, Arrowhead Road, Theale, Reading, RG7 4AE Tel: 0118-988 3266 Fax: 0118-988 4538 E-mail: waste@hadley.co.uk
Franklin Hire Ltd, 1 Rawreth Industrial Estate, Rawreth Lane, Rayleigh, Essex, SS6 9RL Tel: (01268) 784888 Fax: (01268) 782329
George Beattie & Sons Ltd, Auchinvole Castle, Kilsyth, Glasgow, G65 0SA Tel: (01236) 823160 Fax: (01236) 823201 E-mail: info@beattie-demolition.com
Gill Demolitions Ltd, Progress Works, Hall Lane, Bradford, West Yorkshire, BD4 7DT Tel: (01274) 733011 Fax: (01274) 392879 E-mail: info@gilldemolitions.co.uk
▶ Glenside Recycling Ltd, Colliery, Coalpit Lane, Rugeley, Smethwick, West Midlands, B66 2JN Tel: (01889) 574045 Fax: 0121-565 0646 E-mail: mikekillett@glensiderecycling.com
▶ Gothard Landscape & Land Reclamation Ltd, Gate House, Sandhurst Road, West Tilbury, Tilbury, Essex, RM18 8DH Tel: (01375) 842904 Fax: (01375) 859203
Griffiths - McGee Demolition Co. Ltd, Alperton Lane, Wembley, Middlesex, HA0 1EB Tel: (020) 8998 1101 Fax: (020) 8997 7689 E-mail: mail@mcgee.co.uk
H E Humphries Ltd, Monway House, Portway Road, Wednesbury, West Midlands, WS10 7DZ Tel: 0121-556 0097 Fax: 0121-556 9427
Hanson Recycling & Demolition, Sheffield Bottom, Off Station Road, Theale, Reading, RG7 4AJ Tel: 0118-957 6243
▶ Hegarty Demolition, 188-194 Barford Street, Highgate, Birmingham, B5 7EP Tel: 0121-622 2722
▶ Herts Demolition Contractors, 14 Waltham Gardens, Enfield, Middlesex, EN3 6PG Tel: (01992) 763669 Fax: (01992) 763669
Hughes & Salvidge, 11 Flathouse Road, Portsmouth, PO1 4QS Tel: (023) 9275 3733 Fax: (023) 9275 5189 E-mail: info@hughes-salvidge.co.uk
Humberside Aggregates & Excavations Ltd, The Quarry, Newport Road, North Cave, Brough, North Humberside, HU15 2NU Tel: (01430) 421503 Fax: (01430) 421116 E-mail: enquiries@hag.com
▶ Hutchinson Demolition (Yorkshire) Ltd, Day St, Ravensthorpe, Dewsbury, West Yorkshire, WF13 3LJ Tel: (01924) 491616
▶ J Hanley Builders Ltd, Jute Lane, Enfield, Middlesex, EN3 7PJ Tel: (020) 8804 0908 Fax: (020) 8805 0570
▶ J P Tisdale Demolition Ltd, Dock Road, Liverpool, L19 2JN Tel: 0151-427 7906
▶ J R D Demolition Ltd, 7 Somervell Street, Cambuslang, Glasgow, G72 7EB Tel: 0141-641 7771 Fax: 0141-641 7771

DEMOLITION CONTRACTORS – *continued*

J Sharples, Banastres at Bank, Nook Lane, Bamber Bridge, Preston, PR5 6BD Tel: (01772) 628644 Fax: (01772) 628644

J White & Co Tde Ltd, Meadow Bank Road, Rotherham, South Yorkshire, S61 2NF Tel: (01709) 740099 Fax: (01709) 740438 E-mail: jwhite-tde@jwhite-tde.co.uk

▶ Jersey Demolition Contractors, La Route Des Genets, St. Brelade, Jersey, JE3 8DB Tel: (01534) 498994 Fax: (01534) 498995

John Stacey & Son Ltd, Stacey Industrial Park, Silchester Road, Tadley, Hampshire, RG26 3PZ Tel: 0118-981 3531 Fax: 0118-981 3458 E-mail: info@john-stacey.co.uk

John Tinnelly & Sons, Forkhill Road, Cloughoge, Newry, County Down, BT35 8LZ Tel: (028) 3026 5331 Fax: (028) 3026 8491 E-mail: info@tinnelly.com

C.D. Jordans & Sons Ltd, Dundas Spur, Dundas Lane, Copnor, Portsmouth, PO3 5NX Tel: (023) 9266 1391 Fax: (023) 9267 9503 E-mail: michelle@cdjordan.co.uk

▶ Kane Haulage Ltd, Construction House, Porters Wood, Valley Road Industrial Estate, St. Albans, Hertfordshire, AL3 6NW Tel: (01727) 733600 Fax: (01727) 733607 E-mail: info@kanehaulage.co.uk

Keanes Ltd, 4 Iverson Road, London, NW6 2HT Tel: (020) 7625 5555 Fax: (020) 7624 8444 E-mail: office@ballyholmeps.bangor.ni.sch.uk

Kennedy Demolition Ltd, 219 Wickham Road, Croydon, CR0 8TG Tel: (020) 8655 1111 Fax: (020) 8655 1123

▶ KPH Environmental Services Ltd, 4 Paddock Barn Farm, Godstone Road, Caterham, Surrey, CR3 6RE Tel: (01883) 346604

▶ L A Moore Ltd, Old Railway Yard, Haybridge, Wells, Somerset, BA5 1AH Tel: (01749) 672870 Fax: (01749) 672072 E-mail: sales@lamoore.co.uk

L Rifkin (Liverpool) Ltd, Marsh Street, Kirkdale, Liverpool, L20 2BL Tel: 0151-922 3004 Fax: 0151-922 0780 E-mail: dhale.rifkin@cybase.co.uk

▶ Lancebox Ltd, Block O Kent Kraft Industrial Estate, Lower Road, Northfleet, Gravesend, Kent, DA11 9SR Tel: (01322) 427482 Fax: (01322) 427397 E-mail: lancebox@fsmail.net

▶ Ledge Associates (North West) Ltd, Warwick House Green Lane, Featherstone, Pontefract, West Yorkshire, WF7 6EH Tel: (01977) 709698 E-mail: info@ledge-associates.co.uk

▶ Leiths (Scotland) Ltd, Rigifa, Cove, Aberdeen, AB12 3LR Tel: (01224) 876333

▶ London Demolition Co. Ltd, 65 Church Street, Chalvey, Slough, SL1 2NN Tel: (01753) 572262

M.G.L. Demolition Ltd, Davison House Rennys Lane, Dragonville Industrial Estate, Durham, DH1 2RS Tel: 0191-374 0789 Fax: 0191-383 9911 E-mail: enquiries.mgl@sheal.co.uk

▶ McCormick Site Services Ltd, Park House, 56 Trench Road, Mallusk, Newtownabbey, County Antrim, BT36 4TY Tel: (028) 9084 8381

▶ Mcfletch Waste Management, The Barn, The Street, Pebmarsh, Halstead, Essex, CO9 2NH Tel: (01787) 882200 Fax: (01787) 269909 E-mail: sales@mcfletch.co.uk

McGuinness (P.) Co. Ltd, Romdin House, Romdin Road, Ardwick, Manchester, M12 6BF Tel: 0161-273 5272 Fax: 0161-274 3884 E-mail: demolition@pmcguinness.com

▶ McKenna Demolition Ltd, Sheetings Farm, Salt Box Hill, Biggin Hill, Westerham, Kent, TN16 3EE Tel: (01959) 571512 Fax: (01959) 572439 E-mail: mckennademo@btconnect.com

▶ Mcmillan Contracting, Unit 27 New Albion Industrial Estate, Halley Drive, Glasgow, G13 4DJ Tel: 0141-952 0444 Fax: 0141-952 0777

▶ Macwilliam, Hollandhurst Road, Coatbridge, Lanarkshire, ML5 2EG Tel: (01236) 421222 Fax: (01236) 422025

Mark Metals Ltd, Seven Stars Road, Oldbury, West Midlands, B69 4JR Tel: 0121-552 7479 Fax: 0121-552 9088

▶ Masterton Dismantling Contractors, Boyd Street, Falkirk, FK2 7BL Tel: (01324) 637816 Fax: (01324) 612142

▶ Matrixgrade Ltd, Matrix House, Meadow Road, Netherfield, Nottingham, NG4 2FF Tel: 0115-987 0871

▶ Micor Ltd, Templewood, Stock Road, West Hanningfield, Chelmsford, CM2 8LL Tel: (01277) 841288 Fax: (01277) 841882

▶ Mitchell Demolition, 1a Gunton Lane, Norwich, NR5 0AE Tel: (01603) 748060 Fax: (01603) 747170

▶ Monksview Demolition, 71 Narrow Lane, Leicester, LE2 8NA Tel: 0116-244 0590 Fax: (01406) 330323

Mountelm Ltd, 8 Junction Street, Carlisle, CA2 5XH Tel: (01228) 523136 Fax: (01228) 530550 E-mail: m.liddle@btconnect.com

Mountelm Ltd, Cannon House, Rutland Road, Sheffield, S3 8DP Tel: 0114-275 3030 Fax: 0114-272 8864 E-mail: info@wellsrichardson.co.uk

Murco, 40b Deacons Road, Kilsyth, Glasgow, G65 0BN Tel: (01236) 825297 Fax: (01236) 827697

▶ N M C Drainage Ltd, 140 Old Gartloch Road, Gartcosh, Glasgow, G69 8EH Tel: (01236) 870087 Fax: (01236) 870700

Norman Cull, 10 Morville Road, Dudley, West Midlands, DY2 9HR Tel: (01384) 255339

Notts Contractors Ltd, Barton Yards, Abbotsham, Bideford, Devon, EX39 5AP Tel: (01237) 479440 Fax: (01237) 478800

▶ Oldham Bros Scrap Merchants Dismantlers Demolition, Kirkby Bank Road, Clarence House, Knowsley Industrial Park, Liverpool, L33 7SY Tel: 0151-546 5233 Fax: 0151-546 1258 E-mail: demolition@oldhambros.co.uk

Pectel Group, Pectel Court, Burnt Mills Road, Basildon, Essex, SS13 1DT Tel: (01268) 591222 Fax: (01268) 590998 E-mail: info@pectel-group.co.uk

Potteries Demolition Co. Ltd, Brocksford Street, Stoke-on-Trent, ST4 3EZ Tel: (01782) 313234 Fax: (01782) 598371

▶ Powell Demolition, 91 Eastham Village Road, Eastham, Wirral, Merseyside, CH62 0AW Tel: 0151-327 5700 Fax: 0151-327 7153

Chas B. Pugh (Walsall) Ltd, Heath Road, Darlaston, Wednesbury, West Midlands, WS10 8LU Tel: 0121-568 7568 Fax: 0121-568 8666 E-mail: pughmail@supanet.com

▶ R Collard Ltd, Fleet Road, Hartley Wintney, Hook, Hampshire, RG27 8ED Tel: (01252) 844688 Fax: (01252) 844668

▶ R G L Contract Services, Burnfoot Yard, Old Carlisle Road, Moffat, Dumfriesshire, DG10 9QN Tel: (01683) 220122 Fax: (01683) 220644

▶ Randall Plant Ltd, 6 110 River Road, Barking, Essex, IG11 0DS Tel: (020) 8709 1870 Fax: (020) 8507 7002

Rentajet Ltd, Paultons Park, Ower, Romsey, Hampshire, SO51 6AL Tel: (023) 8081 2921 Fax: (023) 8081 4016 E-mail: sales@rentajet.co.uk

▶ Ross A D T Ltd, 30 Byron St, Dundee, DD3 6QX Tel: (01382) 825050

S D Demolition Ltd, PO Box 65, Biggleswade, Bedfordshire, SG18 9BE Tel: (01767) 314166 Fax: (01767) 318511 E-mail: enquiries@sddemolition.net

SA&R plc, Brickfield House, High Road, Thornwood, Epping, Essex, CM16 6TH Tel: 0845 331 2426 Fax: 0845 331 2427 E-mail: info@sarplc.com

T.E. Scudder Ltd, Carey House, Great Central Way, Wembley, Middlesex, HA9 0HR Tel: (020) 8903 9722 Fax: (020) 8903 6311 E-mail: scudder@carey-plc.co.uk

▶ Smalldene Midlands Ltd, Houndsfield Lane, Hollywood, Birmingham, B47 5QR Tel: (01564) 823085

H. Smith Engineers Ltd, Fordcroft Road, Orpington, Kent, BR5 2DB Tel: (01689) 833581 Fax: (01689) 820218 E-mail: mail@hsmith.co.uk

Southern Group (UK) Ltd, 23 Caker Stream Rd, Alton, Hampshire, GU34 2QA Tel: (01420) 88344 Fax: (01420) 88348 E-mail: info@southerngroupuk.com

Stephen Dalton Scrap Metal Merchants, Station Road, Gogarbank, Edinburgh, EH12 9BU Tel: 0131-339 5355 Fax: 0131-317 7168 E-mail: dalton@daltondemo.co.uk

▶ Stoneglen Demolition & Co. Ltd, 10 Queens Road, London, SE15 2PT Tel: (020) 7639 2267 Fax: (020) 7639 4323

▶ Technical Demolition Services, 17 Hamilton Square, Birkenhead, Merseyside, CH41 6AX Tel: 0151-666 1272 Fax: 0151-666 1624 E-mail: techdem@btinternet.com

▶ Total Reclaims Demolition, Kissingstone House, Radford Road, Nottingham, NG7 7EB Tel: 0115-942 1975 Fax: 0115-942 2049 E-mail: info@totalreclaims.co.uk

Tower Demolition Ltd, 264 Hanworth Road, Hounslow, TW3 3TY Tel: (020) 8569 5152 Fax: (020) 8569 4337 E-mail: mail@tower-demolition.co.uk

▶ Tutor Hall Ltd, 52 Braunston Gate, Leicester, LE3 5LG Tel: 0116-254 6798

▶ Underground Surveys, Unit G14 Warrington Business Park, Long Lane, Warrington, WA2 8TX Tel: (01925) 444664 Fax: (01925) 444663 E-mail: info@undergroundsurveys.co.uk

▶ United Demolition Ltd, 13B Hopetoun Lane, Bathgate, West Lothian, EH48 1PP Tel: (01506) 815800

W A Banham & Sons Ltd, The Pipeworks, Eye Road, Hoxne, Eye, Suffolk, IP21 5BA Tel: (01379) 668268 Fax: (01379) 668268

W Hayden & Son Ltd, Webb Street, Bilston, West Midlands, WV14 8XL Tel: (01902) 402341 Fax: (01902) 491832

W J Hatt Ltd, Foxcovert Farm, Goring Heath, Reading, RG8 7SL Tel: (01491) 680424 Fax: (01491) 680425 E-mail: wjhatt@aol.com

Walker May Halifax Ltd, 7 The Market Business Centre, Hanson Lane, Halifax, West Yorkshire, HX1 5PF Tel: (01422) 347483 Fax: (01422) 342096 E-mail: walkermay@btclick.com

Walsh Demolition, 257 Moorland Road, Cardiff, CF24 2LJ Tel: (029) 2046 0645 Fax: (029) 2046 0645

▶ Watkinson Industrial, 78 River Road, Barking, Essex, IG11 0DS Tel: (020) 8507 9642

Weaver Demolition Ltd, Farrington Fields, Farrington Gurney, Bristol, BS39 6UU Tel: (01761) 452391 Fax: (01761) 453644 E-mail: mike@weaverdemolition.com

▶ West Riding Crushing Services Ltd, Holme Lane, Tong, Bradford, West Yorkshire, BD4 0RJ Tel: (01274) 687852 Fax: (01274) 688695

▶ Windmill Demolition Co. Ltd, Windmill Lane, Denton, Manchester, M34 2JF Tel: 0161-320 9119

Wrightways Ltd, Beveridge Lane, Ellistown, Coalville, Leicestershire, LE67 1FB Tel: (01530) 263183 Fax: (01530) 263186 E-mail: info@wrightwaysltd.co.uk

Wye Valley Demolition, Lloyd George House, Fordshill Road, Rotherwas, Hereford, HR2 6NS Tel: (01432) 361670 Fax: (01432) 361689 E-mail: info@wyevalleygroup.co.uk

Yorkshire Demolition Contractors Ltd, 8 Weetworth Ave, Glasshoughton, Castleford, West Yorkshire, WF10 4QA Tel: (01977) 553117 Fax: (01977) 553117

DEMOLITION EQUIPMENT PROTECTION CAGES

Jays Of Yorkshire, Green Lane, Featherstone, Pontefract, West Yorkshire, WF7 6EH Tel: (01977) 792431 Fax: (01977) 600334 E-mail: info@jaysofyorkshire.co.uk

DEMOLITION TOOLS

▶ Haulmark Equipment Ltd, Barleycastle Lane, Appleton, Warrington, WA4 4RB Tel: (01925) 269900 Fax: (01925) 269901 E-mail: sales@haulmarkltd.co.uk

DEMOUNTABLE INTERMEDIATE BULK CONTAINERS (IBC)

Hydrair Ltd, Berry Hill, Berry Hill Industrial Estate, Droitwich, Worcestershire, WR9 9AB Tel: (01905) 772302 Fax: (01905) 770309 E-mail: name@hydrair.demom.co.uk

Manchester Drums Ltd, Bower Street, Newton Heath, Manchester, M40 2AS Tel: 0161-203 4611 Fax: 0161-203 5404

DEMOUNTABLE OR DRY CONSTRUCTION PARTITIONING

Anglia Partitions Ltd, Unit 3 Freisian Way, King's Lynn, Norfolk, PE30 4JQ Tel: (01553) 691202 Fax: (01553) 769808 E-mail: info@angliapartitions.demon.co.uk

Aztec Interiors, Hillcrest, Long Lane, Bursledon, Southampton, SO31 8BZ Tel: 023 80457036 Fax: 023 80457036

Barnards Ceilings & Partitions Ltd, Mulberry House, Holders Green, Lindsell, Dunmow, Essex, CM6 3QQ Tel: (01371) 870104 Fax: (01371) 870105

Bolts Of Hereford, 5-7 Perseverance Road, Hereford, HR4 9SN Tel: (01432) 269508 Fax: (01432) 263835 E-mail: nick.bolt@btclick.com

Boygle & Co. Ltd, Chichester Road, Romiley, Stockport, Cheshire, SK6 4BL Tel: 0161-406 8280 Fax: 0161-406 8244

Brysdales Interiors Ltd, Brysdale House Drumhead Road, Chorley North Business Park, Chorley, Lancashire, PR6 7DE Tel: (01257) 240000 Fax: (01257) 240024 E-mail: enquiries@brysdales.co.uk

Building Tecnics, Regents Trade Park, Barwell Lane, Gosport, Hampshire, PO13 0EQ Tel: (01329) 282900 Fax: (0870) 200517 E-mail: info@buildingtecnics.com

C F C Group Ltd, Kilnbrook House, Rosekiln Lane, Reading, RG2 0BY Tel: (0845) 0540040 Fax: (0845) 0540041 E-mail: cfc@cfcgroup.co.uk

C P Supplies Ltd, 95 Chester Street, Aston, Birmingham, B6 4AE Tel: 0121-380 1600 Fax: 0121-380 1616 E-mail: admin@cpsupplies.co.uk

Caledonian Contracts (Aberdeen) Ltd, 8 Holland Place, Aberdeen, AB25 3UW Tel: (01224) 630355 Fax: (01224) 639504

Ceipart Ltd, 1 Bowker Street, Worsley, Manchester, M28 0SG Tel: 0161-790 5905 Fax: 0161-703 8673 E-mail: ceipt@aol.com

Contarps North West Ltd, Unit D4 Newton Business Park, Talbot Road, Hyde, Cheshire, SK14 4UQ Tel: 0161-367 9341 Fax: 0161-367 9352 E-mail: sales@contarps.co.uk

CPS Interiors Ltd, 1 Prince William Way, Loughborough, Leicestershire, LE11 5DD Tel: (01509) 230429 Fax: (01509) 610617 E-mail: cpsinteriors@btconnect.com

Ek Partitions & Ceilings Ltd, 15 Arden Business Centre, Arden Road, Alcester, Warwickshire, B49 6HW Tel: (01789) 400404 Fax: (01789) 400505 E-mail: sales@ekpartitions.com

Exel Ltd, Storage & Interiors Centre, Northbank Industrial Park, Cadishead, Manchester, M44 5AH Tel: 0161-775 1611 Fax: 0161-775 4753 E-mail: sales@brookstore.co.uk

Flexi-Plan Partitions Ltd, Unit J1, Halesfield 19, Telford, Shropshire, TF7 4QT Tel: (01952) 586126 Fax: (01952) 581174 E-mail: flexplanpartitions@btopenworld.com

Flexiwall Co. Ltd, 15 Iliad Street, Liverpool, L5 3LU Tel: 0151-207 1103 Fax: 0151-207 1588

G I A Office Interiors Ltd, Unit 104 Portmanmoor Road Industrial Estate, Cardiff, CF24 5HB Tel: (029) 2044 3850 Fax: (029) 2044 3860

Hatmet Ltd, Interiors House, Lynton Road, London, N8 8SL Tel: (020) 8341 0200 Fax: (020) 8341 9878 E-mail: info@hatmet.co.uk

Heaton Shopfitters Ltd, 88 Tatton Road South, Stockport, Cheshire, SK4 4LX Tel: 0161-442 5786 Fax: 0161-718 3519

Hill Top, Ridgacre Road, West Bromwich, West Midlands, B71 1BB Tel: 0121-555 1470 Fax: 0121-555 1471 E-mail: sales.hts@hadleygroup.co.uk

Peter Howell Office Interiors, 105 Dockfield Road, Shipley, West Yorkshire, BD17 7BE Tel: (01274) 592337 Fax: (01274) 531595 E-mail: info@peter-howell.com

I T S Projects Ltd, 42-44 Portman Road, Reading, RG30 1EA Tel: 0118-950 0225 Fax: 0118-950 3267 E-mail: info@itsprojects.co.uk

Intec Storage & Partitioning, 21 Green Lane, Stapleton, Leicester, LE9 8JP Tel: (01455) 841698 Fax: (01455) 841769

Interior Concepts Ltd, Unit 1, 1 Russett Place, Kirdford, Billingshurst, West Sussex, RH14 0QQ Tel: (01403) 820000 Fax: (05603) 132034 E-mail: enquiry@interiorconcepts.uk.com

Interior Property Specialists Ltd, Interplan House, Chelmsford Road Industrial Estate, Dunmow, Essex, CM6 1HE Tel: (01371) 874241 Fax: (01371) 873848 E-mail: contact@ips-interiors.co.uk

Jennor Electrical, 57-59 Brynn Street, St. Helens, Merseyside, WA10 1JB Tel: (01744) 730717 Fax: (01744) 759657 E-mail: general@jennor.co.uk

Kaba Hufcor Operable Partitions, Trent Lane, Castle Donington, Derby, DE74 2NP Tel: (0870) 0005250 Fax: (01332) 811059 E-mail: hufcoruk@dial.pipex.com

Kappa Corrugated UK, London Road, Purfleet, Essex, RM19 1QY Tel: (01708) 861776 Fax: (01708) 861910

Leemo (Partitions) Ltd, Essex House, Kelfall Street, Oldham, OL9 6HR Tel: 0161-665 4666 Fax: 0161-624 4376

Linco PC Ltd, Edge Lane Street, Royton, Oldham, OL2 6DS Tel: 0161-624 7098 Fax: 0161-678 6162 E-mail: info@lincopc.com

Mcfeggan Brown Ltd, Unit 1, 38 Midland Road, Staplehill, Bristol, BS16 4NW Tel: 0117-957 3355 Fax: 0117-956 7221

Margolis Business Systems, Unit 4.02 Crayfield Business Park, New Mill Road, Orpington, Kent, BR5 3QA Tel: (01689) 891000 Fax: (01689) 890555 E-mail: sales@margolis.co.uk

T.J, Mee Contracts, 11 Tyler Road, Ratby, Leicester, LE6 0NQ Tel: 0116-238 7628 Fax: 0116-238 7628

Neo Interiors, The Old Dairy, Upper Thrift Street, Northampton, NN1 5HR Tel: (01604) 601981 Fax: (01604) 601989 E-mail: neointeriors@talk21.com

Nottingham Suspended Ceilings Ltd, Wright Street, Netherfield, Nottingham, NG4 2PG Tel: 0115-987 9880 Fax: 0115-940 0086 E-mail: info@nsceilings.co.uk

P K K Storage Systems Ltd, Gibbons Lane, Brierley Hill, West Midlands, DY5 4RY Tel: (01384) 79555 Fax: (01384) 75588 E-mail: pkkcontracts@aol.com

Paramount Office Interiors, Paramount House, Pascal Close, St. Mellons, Cardiff, CF3 0LW Tel: (029) 2083 9800 Fax: (029) 2083 9801 E-mail: sales@paramountinteriors.com

Pinnacle Partition Systems Ltd, 6 Cawley Hatch, Harlow, Essex, CM19 5AN Tel: (01279) 641317 Fax: (01279) 641329 E-mail: sales@pinnacle-partitions.co.uk

Planet, 23 Albert Drive, Burgess Hill, West Sussex, RH15 9TN Tel: (01444) 247933 Fax: (01444) 248799 E-mail: enquiries@planetpartitoning.co.uk

Prime Partitioning Systems Ltd, 7 Windmill Business Park, Windmill Road, Kenn, Clevedon, Avon, BS21 6SR Tel: (01275) 343646 Fax: (01275) 343898 E-mail: info@prime-partitioning.co.uk

Roskel Contracts Ltd, Suite 1a Old Bank House, 50 St Johns Close, Knowle, Solihull, West Midlands, B93 0JU Tel: (01564) 732292 Fax: (01564) 732296 E-mail: sales@roskel.co.uk

Sapphire Contractors Ltd, 18 Gladstone Road, Croydon, CR0 2BQ Tel: (020) 8665 6226 Fax: (020) 8665 6282 E-mail: enquiries@sapphirecontractors.co.uk

Stroud Office Interiors Ltd, Alder Ho, Inchbrook Trading Estate, Woodchester, Stroud, Glos, GL5 5EY Tel: (01453) 834867 Fax: (01453) 835818 E-mail: derek@stroudofficeinteriors.co.uk

Tedwood Storage Systems Ltd, 1489 Melton Road, Queniborough, Leicester, LE7 3FP Tel: 0116-269 3838

Total Concept Partitions Ltd, Unit 12 Anthonys Way, Medway City Estate, Rochester, Kent, ME2 4NW Tel: (01634) 290077 Fax: (01634) 297977 E-mail: info@totalconceptpartitions.co.uk

Trademark Interiors, 8 March Monte Gate, Hemel Hempstead, Hertfordshire, HP2 7BF Tel: (01442) 260022 Fax: (01442) 232244 E-mail: info@tmark.co.uk

TSD Wakefield, Keys Road, Mixs Hill, Somercoates, Alfreton, Derbyshire, DE55 7FQ Tel: (0870) 6090111 Fax: (01773) 521015 E-mail: sales@wakefields.co.uk

W K D Storage Systems Ltd, 3-4 Bourne Industrial Estate, Wrotham Road, Borough Green, Sevenoaks, Kent, TN15 8DF Tel: (01732) 882042 Fax: (01732) 885763 E-mail: sales@wkdstorage.co.uk

Westgate Factory Dividers, PO Box 21, Stafford, ST16 3DD Tel: (01785) 242171

DENATURANTS

Macfarlan Smith Ltd, Wheatfield Road, Edinburgh, EH11 2QA Tel: 0131-337 2434 Fax: 0131-337 9813 E-mail: msl@macsmith.com

DENIM CLOTHING

Original Blues Clothing Co. Ltd, Enterprise House, 133 Blyth Road, Hayes, Middlesex, UB3 1DD Tel: (020) 8813 7766 Fax: (020) 8813 7811 E-mail: sales@original-blues.com

DENIM FABRICS

Image House Ltd, 67-73 Constitution Hill, Birmingham, B19 3JX Tel: 0121-233 3569 Fax: 0121-233 0139 E-mail: vchobera@compuserve.com

DENSITY GAUGING INSTRUMENTS

A.D. Burs, 9 Madleaze Trading Estate, Bristol Road, Gloucester, GL1 5SG Tel: (01452) 307171 Fax: (01452) 307187 E-mail: sales@sswhite.com

A W R Instruments Ltd, 1 Northpoint Business Estate, Enterprise Close, Rochester, Kent, ME2 4LX Tel: (01634) 290751 Fax: (01634) 290295 E-mail: info@awr-instruments.com

Anton Paar Ltd, 13 Harforde Court, John Tate Road, Hertford, SG13 7NW Tel: (01992) 514730 Fax: (01992) 514739 E-mail: info.gb@anton-paar.com

J S Engineering, 102 Commercial Road, Skelmanthorpe, Huddersfield, HD8 9DS Tel: (01484) 866254 Fax: (01484) 866255 E-mail: jsengineeringuk@aol.com

Krohne Ltd, Rutherford Drive, Park Farm Industrial Estate, Wellingborough, Northamptonshire, NN8 6AE Tel: (01933) 408500 Fax: (01933) 408501 E-mail: info@krohne.co.uk

DENTAL CABINETS

Blueprint Dental Equipment Ltd, 12 Lessness Road, Morden, Surrey, SM4 6HP Tel: (0870) 4329786 Fax: (0870) 4324665 E-mail: info@blueprintdental.co.uk

Dental Style, Neroche House, Factory Lane, Bason Bridge, Highbridge, Somerset, TA9 4RN Tel: (01278) 789119 Fax: (01278) 781825 E-mail: sales@castleneroche.com

Mckillop Dental Equipment Ltd, 45a Derby Road, Southport, Merseyside, PR9 0TZ Tel: (01704) 538221 Fax: (01704) 538353 E-mail: office@mckillopdental.co.uk

▶ Stewart S Redman Dental Engineering Services, 63A Steam Mill Lane, Ripley, Derbyshire, DE5 3JR Tel: 07904 048102 E-mail: enquiries@ssredman.co.uk

DENTAL CHAIR MAINTENANCE OR REPAIR

Blueprint Dental Equipment Ltd, 12 Lessness Road, Morden, Surrey, SM4 6HP Tel: (0870) 4329786 Fax: (0870) 4324665 E-mail: info@blueprintdental.co.uk

Medontic, Medontic LTD., Spencer House, Northampton, NN1 5AA Tel: (01604) 633457 Fax: (01604) 633457 E-mail: info@medontic.co.uk

DENTAL CHAIRS

Levingstone Manufacturing Ltd, Cranmere House, 196 Upper Chobham Road, Camberley, Surrey, GU15 1HD Tel: (01276) 25915 Fax: (01276) 21251 E-mail: conroy@hendries.freeserve.co.uk

Medontic, Medontic LTD., Spencer House, Northampton, NN1 5AA Tel: (01604) 633457 Fax: (01604) 633457 E-mail: info@medontic.co.uk

Nesor Equipment Co. Ltd, 166 Gilmore Road, London, SE13 5AE Tel: (020) 8852 8545 Fax: (020) 8852 1230 E-mail: nesor@supanet.com

▶ Stewart S Redman Dental Engineering Services, 63A Steam Mill Lane, Ripley, Derbyshire, DE5 3JR Tel: 07904 048102 E-mail: enquiries@ssredman.co.uk

DENTAL CONSUMABLES

3M Health Care Ltd, 3M House, Morley Street, Loughborough, Leicestershire, LE11 1EP Tel: (01509) 611611 Fax: (01509) 613061 E-mail: jsmith123@mmm.com

A.D. Burs, 9 Madleaze Trading Estate, Bristol Road, Gloucester, GL1 5SG Tel: (01452) 307171 Fax: (01452) 307187 E-mail: sales@sswhite.com

Associated Dental Products Ltd, Kemdent Works, Cricklade Road, Purton, Swindon, SN5 4HT Tel: (01793) 770256 Fax: (01793) 772256 E-mail: sales@kemdent.co.uk

Den-Tal-Ez Dental Products (GB) Ltd, Cleveland Way, Hemel Hempstead, Hertfordshire, HP2 7DY Tel: (01442) 269301 Fax: (01442) 217594 E-mail: contact@dentalez.co.uk

Gillette Group UK, The Gillette Building, Great West Road, Isleworth, Middlesex, TW7 5NP Tel: (020) 8847 7800 Fax: (020) 8847 6165

Glaxo Smith Klein Leisure Club, Oldfield Lane North, Greenford, Middlesex, UB6 8QD Tel: (020) 8966 2280 Fax: (020) 8966 4499

Kent Express Ltd, Medcare House, Centurion Close, Gillingham Business Park, Gillingham, Kent, ME8 0SB Tel: (01634) 878750 Fax: (01634) 878788 E-mail: sales@kentexpress.co.uk

Wright Health Group Ltd, Dunsinane Avenue, Dunsinane Industrial Estate, Dundee, DD2 3QD Tel: (01382) 833866 Fax: (01382) 811042 E-mail: administrator@wright-dental.co.uk

DENTAL DRILLS/ENGINES/ INSTRUMENTS

▶ Commic International, Unit 9,, Phoenix Works, Willows Lane, Accrington, Lancashire, BB5 0RT Tel: (07984) 768938 Fax: (01254) 388422 E-mail: sales@commic-int.com

Kavo Dental Ltd, Corinium Industrial Estate, Raans Road, Amersham, Buckinghamshire, HP6 6JL Tel: (01494) 733000 Fax: (01494) 431168 E-mail: sales@kavo.com

Kent Express Ltd, Medcare House, Centurion Close, Gillingham Business Park, Gillingham, Kent, ME8 0SB Tel: (01634) 878750 Fax: (01634) 878788 E-mail: sales@kentexpress.co.uk

Metrodent Ltd, Lowergate Works, Huddersfield, HD3 4EP Tel: (01484) 461616 Fax: (01484) 462700 E-mail: admin@metrodent.com

▶ Nexday Handpiece Repairs, PO Box 334, Northampton, NN3 7XL Tel: (01604) 493308 Fax: (01604) 491139 E-mail: nexday@nexdayrepairs.co.uk

DENTAL EDUCATIONAL AIDS

Time Medical & Scientific Network, Unit 6, North End Industrial Estate, Bury Mead Road, Hitchin, Hertfordshire, SG5 1RT Tel: (01462) 422112 Fax: (01462) 422042 E-mail: sales@timemedical.co.uk

DENTAL LABORATORIES/ TECHNICIANS TO THE DENTAL PROFESSION

A Foster, Unit 4 Dove Court, Aylesbury Road, Aston Clinton, Aylesbury, Buckinghamshire, HP22 5AQ Tel: (01296) 631616 Fax: (01296) 631616

B & S Dental Laboratory, 18 Chilham Way, Bromley, BR2 7PR Tel: (020) 8462 7007 Fax: (020) 8462 7007

Bristol Crown Company, Albert Road Unit 7, Ferry Steps Trading Estate, St. Philips, Bristol, BS2 0XW Tel: 0117-977 3593 Fax: 0117-977 3593 E-mail: bcrown@dircon.co.uk

Byron George, 2 Gellideg, Pencoed Isaf Road, Bynea, Llanelli, Dyfed, SA14 9TL Tel: (01554) 773010

▶ Central Ceramics, 44 Higher Bridge Street, Bolton, BL1 2HA Tel: (01204) 361887 Fax: (01204) 362577

Ceramics Studios Ltd, 59a Chesson Road, London, W14 9QT Tel: (020) 7385 2061 Fax: (020) 7385 2235

▶ Crown Ceramics, 8 Mill Lane, Codnor, Ripley, Derbyshire, DE5 9QF Tel: (01773) 749278 Fax: (01773) 749278 E-mail: info@crown-ceramics.co.uk

D P Dental, 85 Seaward Street, Glasgow, G41 1HJ Tel: 0141-420 1111 Fax: 0141-420 3338 E-mail: mary@dpdental.co.uk

Dentacast Of Exeter Ltd, PO Box 21, Exeter, EX2 9BE Tel: (01392) 273489 Fax: (01392) 423036 E-mail: info@dentacast.co.uk

East Essex Dental Laboratory Ltd, Ford Road Industrial Estate, Clacton-on-Sea, Essex, CO15 3DT Tel: (01255) 424071 Fax: (01255) 424071

▶ Elite Dental Studios, 30 West Street, Burgess Hill, West Sussex, RH15 8NX Tel: (01444) 245145 Fax: (01444) 245145

Gordon Dental Laboratories, Pendrill House, Beverley Road, Hull, HU3 1UP Tel: (01482) 224944

Griffen Dental Laboratory, 9 High Road, Byfleet, West Byfleet, Surrey, KT14 7QH Tel: (01932) 340580 Fax: (01932) 340941 E-mail: griffindental@lineone.net

▶ Guisborough Dental Laboratory, 4 Redcar Road, Guisborough, Cleveland, TS14 6DB Tel: (01287) 635555 Fax: (01287) 634902

J J Thompson Ltd, 95 Hill Street, Sheffield, S2 4SP Tel: 0114-275 3090 Fax: 0114-275 8385 E-mail: jjt@eurodontic.co.uk

Kavo Dental Ltd, Corinium Industrial Estate, Raans Road, Amersham, Buckinghamshire, HP6 6JL Tel: (01494) 733000 Fax: (01494) 431168 E-mail: sales@kavo.com

Klasp Prosthesis Laboratory, 110 Church Street, Westhoughton, Bolton, BL5 3SF Tel: (01942) 819979 Fax: (01942) 812080

Lodge Dental Laboratory, Unit 10 Station Industrial Estate, Oxford Road, Wokingham, Berkshire, RG41 2YQ Tel: 0118-989 0202 Fax: 0118-989 2009

▶ Maurice Hood Dental Laboratory Ltd, Houghton Street, Oldbury, West Midlands, B69 2BB Tel: 0121-544 8855 Fax: 0121-544 8835 E-mail: sales@mauricehood.co.uk

N Royston Ltd, Carham Road, Hoylake, Wirral, Merseyside, CH47 4FF Tel: 0151-632 4141 Fax: 0151-632 0569 E-mail: charleshumphreys@1stdental.co.uk

North London Ceramics Ltd, 585 High Road, Tottenham, London, N17 6SB Tel: (020) 8808 9216 Fax: (020) 8801 6159

▶ Nouveau Ceramics, 223 Longbridge Lane, Birmingham, B31 4RE Tel: 0121-477 2038 Fax: 0121-475 4004

Oral Ceramics, Crown House, Wassage Way, Hampton Lovett, Droitwich, Worcestershire, WR9 0NX Tel: (01905) 778686 Fax: (01905) 774545

Oral Prosthetics, 121 Headstone Road, Harrow, Middlesex, HA1 1PG Tel: (020) 8863 6977

Phoenix Dental Castings Ltd, Unit 1 The Alpha Centre, Osprey Road, Sowton Industrial Estate, Exeter, EX2 7LH Tel: (01392) 444456 Fax: (01392) 445725 E-mail: phoenix.dental@btinternet.com

Portway Dental Laboratory, 203-205 (rear of) Avonmouth Road, Avonmouth, Bristol, BS11 9EG Tel: (0117) 982 2813

Rayner & Eve Ltd, Unit 5 37-39 Western Road, Mitcham, Surrey, CR4 3ED Tel: (020) 8646 2770 Fax: (020) 8646 3151

Regent Dental Laboratories Ltd, 4 Bassett Road, Leighton Buzzard, Bedfordshire, LU7 1AR Tel: (01525) 374646 Fax: (01525) 374887 E-mail: enquiries@regentdental.com

Sherring-Lucas Dental Laboratory Ltd, 14 Mark Road, Hemel Hempstead, Hertfordshire, HP2 7BN Tel: (01442) 244706 Fax: (01442) 247014 E-mail: info@sherringlucas.co.uk

Stocking Beer & Oborn Dental Laboratories, 120a Marylebone Lane, London, W1U 2QG Tel: (020) 7486 2097 Fax: (020) 7224 6382 E-mail: lab@sbodentallaboatory.co.uk

Alex Strang Dental Laboratory, Cross Street, Venture House, Macclesfield, Cheshire, SK11 7PG Tel: (01625) 421368

DENTAL LABORATORY EQUIPMENT

Chanter Bio Med Ltd, 1 Hanworth Road, Low Moor, Bradford, West Yorkshire, BD12 0SG Tel: (01274) 414666 Fax: (01274) 414470 E-mail: info@chanterbiomed.co.uk

Dental Style, Neroche House, Factory Lane, Bason Bridge, Highbridge, Somerset, TA9 4RN Tel: (01278) 789119 Fax: (01278) 781825 E-mail: sales@castleneroche.com

Metrodent Ltd, Lowergate Works, Huddersfield, HD3 4EP Tel: (01484) 461616 Fax: (01484) 462700 E-mail: admin@metrodent.com

Milnes Bros, Unit 9 Enterprise Close, Croydon, CR0 3RZ Tel: (020) 8665 9907 Fax: (020) 8665 9956 E-mail: milnesbros@aol.com

Plandent, Summit House, Cranborne Road, Potters Bar, Hertfordshire, EN6 3EE Tel: (01707) 822400 Fax: (01707) 649901

DENTAL LATHE BRUSHES

E. Berry & Sons, Unit 19, 308A Melton Road, Leicester, LE4 7SL Tel: (0845) 1306862 Fax: (0845) 3892144 E-mail: eberryson@aol.com

Stoddard Manufacturing Co. Ltd, Denturax Works, Icknield Way, Letchworth Garden City, Hertfordshire, SG6 4AH Tel: (01462) 686221 Fax: (01462) 480711 E-mail: admin@stoddard.co.uk

DENTAL PORCELAIN

▶ Atkinson Bailey Ceramics, 3a Groveley Road, Christchurch, Dorset, BH23 3HB Tel: (01202) 473330 Fax: (01202) 480686

▶ G W Ceramics, 80 North Street, Leighton Buzzard, Bedfordshire, LU7 1ES Tel: (01525) 381736 Fax: (01525) 377702 E-mail: sales@gwceramics.com

DENTAL PREPARATIONS

Advanced Healthcare Ltd, Dukes Factory, Chiddingstone Causeway, Tonbridge, Kent, TN11 8JU Tel: (01892) 870500 Fax: (01892) 870482 E-mail: sales@ahl.uk.com

Attenborough Dental Ltd, Viscosa House, George Street, Nottingham, NG1 3BN Tel: 0115-947 3562 Fax: 0115-950 9086 E-mail: info@attenborough.com

Dentsply Ltd, Hamm Moor Lane, Addlestone, Surrey, KT15 2SE Tel: (01932) 853422 Fax: (01932) 840168 E-mail: sales.weybridge@dentsply-gb.com

Gillette Group UK, The Gillette Building, Great West Road, Isleworth, Middlesex, TW7 5NP Tel: (020) 8847 7800 Fax: (020) 8847 6165

Klasp Prosthesis Laboratory, 110 Church Street, Westhoughton, Bolton, BL5 3SF Tel: (01942) 819979 Fax: (01942) 812080

MR Dental Supplies Ltd, 4 Manor Way, Woking, Surrey, GU22 9JX Tel: (01483) 773282 Fax: (01483) 740548 E-mail: mrdental@virgin.net

P S P Dental Co. Ltd, 3-5 Dylan Road, Belvedere, Kent, DA17 5QS Tel: (020) 8311 7337 Fax: (020) 8310 0920 E-mail: sales@pspdental.com

Schottlander Dental Equipment Supplies, Fifth Avenue, Letchworth Garden City, Hertfordshire, SG6 2WD Tel: (01462) 480848 Fax: (01462) 482802 E-mail: service@schottlander.co.uk

Septodont Ltd, Units R-S Orchard Business Centre, St. Barnabas Close, Allington, Maidstone, Kent, ME16 0JZ Tel: (01622) 695520 Fax: (01622) 686165 E-mail: information@septodont.co.uk

Westone Products Ltd, 8 Hampstead Gate, 1a Frognal, London, NW3 6AL Tel: (020) 7431 9001 Fax: (020) 7431 9002 E-mail: sales@westoneproducts.com

Wright Cottrell & Co., 76 Gravelly Industrial Park, Birmingham, B24 8TL Tel: 0121-328 2200 Fax: 0121-328 2233

DENTAL SUPPLIES DISTRIBUTORS/AGENTS/ SERVICES

Apollo Dental Ltd, Tempest House, Lyon Road, Walton-on-Thames, Surrey, KT12 3PU Tel: (01932) 240950 Fax: (01932) 246606

Av Surgery Supplies, 29 Cross Road, Croydon, CR0 6TE Tel: (020) 8760 9992

C Bolter Ltd, Carlton Works, St Johns Hill, Sevenoaks, Kent, TN13 3NS Tel: (01732) 457010 Fax: (01732) 740904

▶ Commic International, Unit 9,, Phoenix Works, Willows Lane, Accrington, Lancashire, BB5 0RT Tel: (07984) 768938 Fax: (01254) 388422 E-mail: sales@commic-int.com

Den-Tal-Ez Dental Products (GB) Ltd, Cleveland Way, Hemel Hempstead, Hertfordshire, HP2 7DY Tel: (01442) 269301 Fax: (01442) 217594 E-mail: contact@dentalez.co.uk

Dentocare Ltd, 7 Cygnus Business Centre, Dalmeyer Road, London, NW10 2XA Tel: (020) 8459 7550 Fax: (020) 8451 0063 E-mail: sales@dentocare.co.uk

Dentsply Ltd, Hamm Moor Lane, Addlestone, Surrey, KT15 2SE Tel: (01932) 853422 Fax: (01932) 840168 E-mail: sales.weybridge@dentsply-gb.com

E M Natt Ltd, 45-47 Friern Barnet Road, London, N11 3EG Tel: (020) 8361 4649 Fax: (020) 8361 4145 E-mail: info@silencer.com

Henry Schein Equipment, Commondale Court, Unit 14 Commondale Way, Euroway Industrial Estate, Bradford, West Yorkshire, BD4 6SF Tel: (01274) 474400 Fax: (01274) 474405

Claude Hill Dental Supplies, Unit 2 Premier Industrial Estate, The Leys, Brierley Hill, West Midlands, DY5 3UT Tel: (01384) 262121 Fax: (01384) 77781

Kent Express Ltd, Medcare House, Centurion Close, Gillingham Business Park, Gillingham, Kent, ME8 0SB Tel: (01634) 878750 Fax: (01634) 878788 E-mail: sales@kentexpress.co.uk

Mckillop Dental Equipment Ltd, 45a Derby Road, Southport, Merseyside, PR9 0TZ Tel: (01704) 538221 Fax: (01704) 538353 E-mail: office@mckillopdental.co.uk

Medontic, Medontic LTD., Spencer House, Northampton, NN1 5AA Tel: (01604) 633457 Fax: (01604) 633457 E-mail: info@medontic.co.uk

Minerva Dental Ltd, Courtney House Pacific Business Park, Pacific Road, Cardiff, CF24 5HJ Tel: (029) 2049 0504 Fax: (029) 2048 2139 E-mail: info@minervadental.co.uk

MR Dental Supplies Ltd, 4 Manor Way, Woking, Surrey, GU22 9JX Tel: (01483) 773282 Fax: (01483) 740548 E-mail: mrdental@virgin.net

Nesor Equipment Co. Ltd, 166 Gilmore Road, London, SE13 5AE Tel: (020) 8852 8545 Fax: (020) 8852 1230 E-mail: nesor@supanet.com

NFH Metal Co., 2b Selborne Road, London, N14 7DH Tel: (020) 8886 9667

Norwood Instruments Ltd, New Mill Road, Honley, Holmfirth, HD9 6QD Tel: (01484) 661318 Fax: (01484) 661319 E-mail: gpc@norwood.cc

Phoenix Dental Castings Ltd, Unit 1 The Alpha Centre, Osprey Road, Sowton Industrial Estate, Exeter, EX2 7LH Tel: (01392) 444456 Fax: (01392) 445725 E-mail: phoenix.dental@btinternet.com

Plandent, Summit House, Cranborne Road, Potters Bar, Hertfordshire, EN6 3EE Tel: (01707) 822400 Fax: (01707) 649901

Plas-Dent Co. Ltd, Middlemore Road, Smethwick, West Midlands, B66 2DQ Tel: 0121-558 3601 Fax: 0121-555 5567 E-mail: richard@plas-dent.co.uk

Schottlander Dental Equipment Supplies, Fifth Avenue, Letchworth Garden City, Hertfordshire, SG6 2WD Tel: (01462) 480848 Fax: (01462) 482802 E-mail: service@schottlander.co.uk

Septodont Ltd, Units R-S Orchard Business Centre, St. Barnabas Close, Allington, Maidstone, Kent, ME16 0JZ Tel: (01622) 695520 Fax: (01622) 686165 E-mail: information@septodont.co.uk

▶ Southern Smiles Ltd, 9a Catherine Street, Salisbury, SP1 2DF Tel: (01722) 410430

DENTAL SUPPLIES DISTRIBUTORS/ AGENTS/SERVICES – *continued*

Tricodent Ltd, 8 Teknol House, Victoria Road, Burgess Hill, West Sussex, RH15 9LH Tel: (01444) 247752 Fax: (01444) 239800 E-mail: tricodent@tricodent.com

▶ Walton Dental Arts Ltd, Kinawley, 3 Station Road, Leatherhead, Surrey, KT22 7AA Tel: (01372) 377154 Fax: (01372) 362369 E-mail: sales@waltondentalarts.co.uk

John Winter & Co. Ltd, Washer Lane Works, Halifax, West Yorkshire, HX2 7DP Tel: (01422) 364213 Fax: (01422) 330493 E-mail: sales@johnwinter.co.uk

Wright Health Group Ltd, Dunsinane Avenue, Dunsinane Industrial Estate, Dundee, DD2 3QD Tel: (01382) 833866 Fax: (01382) 811042 E-mail: administrator@wright-dental.co.uk

DENTAL SURGERY EQUIPMENT

A.D. Burs, 9 Madleaze Trading Estate, Bristol Road, Gloucester, GL1 5SG Tel: (01452) 307171 Fax: (01452) 307187 E-mail: sales@sswhite.com

Av Surgery Supplies, 29 Cross Road, Croydon, CR0 6TE Tel: (020) 8760 9992

▶ B D S Dental Equipment Ltd, 2b Stanley Road, Barnsley, South Yorkshire, S70 3PG Tel: (01226) 208810 Fax: (01226) 208815 E-mail: info@bds-dental.co.uk

Daray Lighting Ltd, Unit 6A, Commerce Way, Stanbridge Road, Leighton Buzzard, Bedfordshire, LU7 4RW Tel: (01525) 376766 Fax: (01525) 216519 E-mail: info@daray.com

▶ Dentafix UK Ltd, Unit 11-13, Helix Business Park, Camberley, Surrey, GU15 2QT Tel: (01276) 691821 Fax: (01276) 23490 E-mail: info@dentafix.co.uk

Dental Style, Neroche House, Factory Lane, Bason Bridge, Highbridge, Somerset, TA9 4RN Tel: (01278) 789119 Fax: (01278) 781825 E-mail: sales@castleneroche.com

Den-Tal-Ez Dental Products (GB) Ltd, Cleveland Way, Hemel Hempstead, Hertfordshire, HP2 7DY Tel: (01442) 269301 Fax: (01442) 217594 E-mail: contact@dentalez.co.uk

Kavo Dental Ltd, Corinium Industrial Estate, Raans Road, Amersham, Buckinghamshire, HP6 6JL Tel: (01494) 733000 Fax: (01494) 431168 E-mail: sales@kavo.com

Mckillop Dental Equipment Ltd, 45a Derby Road, Southport, Merseyside, PR9 0TZ Tel: (01704) 538221 Fax: (01704) 538353 E-mail: office@mckillopdental.co.uk

Medivance Instrumnets Ltd, Barretts Green Road, London, NW10 7AP Tel: (020) 8965 2913 Fax: (020) 8963 1270 E-mail: enquiries@velopex.com

Metrodent Ltd, Lowergate Works, Huddersfield, HD3 4EP Tel: (01484) 461616 Fax: (01484) 462700 E-mail: admin@metrodent.com

▶ S J T Medical, Spartan Works, 20 Carlisle Street, Sheffield, S4 7LJ Tel: 0114-272 8273 Fax: 0114-220 1172 E-mail: info@sjtmedical.com

Tridac Ltd, Elton House, Bushey Hall Road, Bushey, WD23 2HJ Tel: (01923) 242398 Fax: (01923) 250864

Virilium Co. Ltd, 9 Colne Way Court, Colne Way, Watford, WD24 7NE Tel: (01923) 233133 Fax: (01923) 251037

▶ W & H (U K) Ltd, 6 Stroud Wood Bus Centre, Park St, St. Albans, Hertfordshire, AL2 2NJ Tel: (01727) 874990

DENTISTRY AIR COMPRESSORS

Bambi Air Compressors Ltd, 152 Thimble Mill Lane, Birmingham, B7 5HT Tel: 0121-322 2299 Fax: 0121-322 2297 E-mail: sales@bambi-air.co.uk

▶ Stewart S Redman Dental Engineering Services, 63A Steam Mill Lane, Ripley, Derbyshire, DE5 3JR Tel: 07904 048102 E-mail: enquiries@ssredman.co.uk

DEPARTMENTAL STORE BUYING OFFICES/ REPRESENTATIVES/AGENTS

Associated Independent Stores Ltd, Cranmore Avenue, Shirley, Solihull, West Midlands, B90 4LF Tel: 0121-711 2200 Fax: 0121-711 1334 E-mail: mail@aistores.co.uk

Audio Education Ltd, 13A Airport Road West, Belfast, BT3 9ED Tel: (028) 9088 3555 Fax: (028) 9088 3539

Jack Barclay Ltd, 18 Berkeley Square, London, W1J 6AE Tel: (020) 7629 7444 Fax: (020) 7629 8258 E-mail: administration@jackbarclay.co.uk

Bentalls, Wood Street, Kingston Upon Thames, Surrey, KT1 1TX Tel: (020) 8546 1001 Fax: (020) 8549 6163 E-mail: bentallsonline@bentalls.co.uk

Bhs Ltd, Marylebone House, 129-137 Marylebone Road, London, NW1 5QD Tel: (020) 7262 3288 Fax: (020) 7723 1115

Botterills, Block, 9 South Avenue, Blantyre, Glasgow, G72 0XB Tel: (01698) 824311 Fax: (01698) 824231 E-mail: info@botterillconveniencestores.co.uk

R.H. Collier & Co. Ltd, 1-41 Sutton Road, Erdington, Birmingham, B23 6QH Tel: 0121-377 8888 Fax: 0121-377 6907 E-mail: fleetsales@colliers.co.uk

Fortnum & Mason P.L.C., 181 Piccadilly, London, W1A 1ER Tel: (020) 7734 8040 Fax: (020) 7437 3278

Kurt Geiger Ltd, 75 Bermondsey Street, London, SE1 3XF Tel: (020) 7546 1888 Fax: (020) 7546 1880 E-mail: info@kurtgeiger.com

Homers Of Quarry Bank, 46-47 High Street, Quarry Bank, Brierley Hill, West Midlands, DY5 2AA Tel: (01384) 564180 Fax: (01384) 636719 E-mail: homers@homersquarrybank.co.uk

House of Fraser (Stores) Ltd, Head Office, 1 Howick Place, London, SW1P 1BH Tel: (0870) 1607270 Fax: (020) 7821 5348

Jenners Princes Street Edinburgh Ltd, 47 Princes Street, Edinburgh, EH2 2YJ Tel: 0131-225 2442 Fax: 0131-260 2218 E-mail: info@jenners.com

L R G Sound & Vision Ltd, 171-175 Albertbridge Road, Belfast, BT5 4PS Tel: (028) 9045 1381 Fax: (028) 9073 1478 E-mail: lrg@btconnect.com

Liberty Plc, 210-220 Regent St, London, W1B 5AH Tel: (020) 7734 1234 Fax: (020) 7573 9876 E-mail: info@liberty.co.uk

Martin Dawes Solutions Ltd, Martin Dawes House, Europa Boulevard, Westbrook, Warrington, WA5 7WH Tel: (01925) 555000 Fax: (01925) 494835

Mitsukoshi, Dorland House, 14-20 Regent Street, London, SW1Y 4PH Tel: (020) 7930 0317 Fax: (020) 7839 1167

Pashley Bicycles, Harrods, 87-135 Brompton Road, London, SW1X 7QN Tel: (020) 7730 1234 Fax: (020) 7581 0470

Peacocks Stores Ltd, Atlantic House, Tyndall Street, Cardiff, CF10 4PS Tel: (029) 2027 0000 Fax: (029) 2044 0400

River Island Clothing Co. Ltd, Chelsea House, Westgate, London, W5 1DR Tel: (020) 8991 4500

Selfridges Retail Ltd, 400 Oxford Street, London, W1A 1AB Tel: (0870) 8377377 Fax: (020) 7495 8321 E-mail: paul.kelly@selfridges.co.uk

Somerfield Merchant Services Ltd, Summerfield House, Whtchurch Lane, Bristol, BS14 0TJ Tel: 0117-935 9359 Fax: 0117-978 0629

Superdrug Stores plc, 118 Beddington Lane, Croydon, CR0 4TB Tel: (020) 8684 7000 Fax: (020) 8684 6102

Top Man Retail, 214 Oxford St, London, W1C 1DD Tel: (020) 7636 7700 Fax: (020) 7291 2907 E-mail: oxford.circus.reception@arcadiagroup.co.uk

DEPARTMENTAL STORE (OVERSEAS) BUYING OFFICES/ REPRESENTATIVES/AGENTS IN UK

Hetheringtons Shoe Services Ltd, 80 Front Street West, Bedlington, Northumberland, NE22 5UA Tel: (01670) 821505 Fax: (01670) 821505

Joplings, John Street, Sunderland, SR1 1DP Tel: 0191-510 2105 Fax: 0191-510 5510

Tesco Stores Ltd, Tesco House, Delamare Road, Cheshunt, Waltham Cross, Hertfordshire, EN8 9SL Tel: (01992) 632222 Fax: (01992) 630794

DESALINATION PLANT

Alfalaval Ltd, Salvesen Tower, Blaikies Quay, Aberdeen, AB11 5PW Tel: (01224) 424300 Fax: (01224) 424315

Desal Supplies, Unit 4 Fletcher Street, Rochdale, Lancashire, OL11 1AE Tel: (01706) 869777 Fax: (01706) 713095 E-mail: sales@desal.co.uk

Salt Separation Services, Grosvenor House, Gorrell Street, Rochdale, Lancashire, OL11 1AP Tel: (01706) 655522 Fax: (01706) 654475 E-mail: sss@saltsep.co.uk

Seafresh Desalinators Ltd, A 4 Premier Centre, Romsey, Hampshire, SO51 9DG Tel: 01794 830363

VWS Westgarth Ltd, Orbital House, 3 Redwood Crescent, East Kilbride, Glasgow, G74 5PR Tel: (01355) 588038 Fax: (01355) 588001

DESCALING CALORIFIERS

A G S Environmental Maintenance, The Oaks, Boxhill Road, Tadworth, Surrey, KT20 7JT Tel: (01737) 843656 Fax: (01737) 842883 E-mail: sales@agsmaintenance.co.uk

DESCALING CHEMICALS

Descalite Supply Co. Ltd, Unit 2 Loaland Business Centre, Maritime Close, Medway City Estate, Rochester, Kent, ME2 4AZ Tel: (01634) 294455 Fax: (01634) 294494 E-mail: descalite@aol.com

Waterchem Ltd, Unit 2c, Derwent Close, Worcester, WR4 9TY Tel: (01905) 23669 Fax: (01905) 729959 E-mail: info@waterchem.co.uk

DESCALING EQUIPMENT

Descalite Supply Co. Ltd, Unit 2 Loaland Business Centre, Maritime Close, Medway City Estate, Rochester, Kent, ME2 4AZ Tel: (01634) 294455 Fax: (01634) 294494 E-mail: descalite@aol.com

Scimitar Engineering Co. Ltd, Power House, 87 Mansel Street, Swansea, SA1 5TZ Tel: (01792) 651781 Fax: (01792) 646229

Trelawny SPT Ltd, 13 Highdown Road, Leamington Spa, Warwickshire, CV31 1XT Tel: (01926) 883781 Fax: (01926) 450352 E-mail: sales@trelawny.co.uk

DESCALING NEEDLE GUNS

Trelawny SPT Ltd, 13 Highdown Road, Leamington Spa, Warwickshire, CV31 1XT Tel: (01926) 883781 Fax: (01926) 450352 E-mail: sales@trelawny.co.uk

DESCALING SERVICES OR CONTRACTORS

C & H Precision Finishers Ltd, Derby Road Trade Centre, Derby Road, Sandiacre, Nottingham, NG10 5HU Tel: 0115-939 4707 Fax: 0115-949 0146 E-mail: admin@chprecision.co.uk

Chemsquad Ltd, 23 Izons Industrial Estate, Oldbury Road, West Bromwich, West Midlands, B70 9BS Tel: 0121-553 1340 Fax: 0121-525 2077

T C & D Technical Services Ltd, Kirkcroft Farm, Thorpe Hesley, Rotherham, South Yorkshire, S61 2RP Tel: 0114-246 9410 Fax: 0114-257 7935

DESICCANT DRYERS

Hankison Ltd, Hazleton Interchange, Lakesmere Road, Horndean, Waterlooville, Hampshire, PO8 9JU Tel: (023) 9257 2828 Fax: (0870) 7367377 E-mail: hankisonuk@aol.com

DESICCANT, BREATHER

Absorbopak Ltd, Wilson Road, South Wigston, Leicester, LE18 4TQ Tel: 0116-258 1160 E-mail: patc@absorbopak.com

DESICCANT/MOISTURE DRYING AGENTS

Brownell Ltd, Commercial Way, Abbey Road, London, NW10 7XF Tel: (020) 8965 9281 Fax: (020) 8965 3239 E-mail: sales@brownell.co.uk

Cordstrap Ltd, Paddock Road, Skelmersdale, Lancashire, WN8 9PL Tel: (01695) 554700 Fax: (01695) 556644 E-mail: sales@cordstrap.net

GeeJay Chemicals Ltd, 1 Beamish Close, Sandy, Bedfordshire, SG19 1SD Tel: (01767) 682774 Fax: (01767) 699697 E-mail: sales@geejaychemicals.co.uk

▶ Humidity Control Systems Ltd, 8 The Green, Nettleham, Lincoln, LN2 2NR Tel: (01522) 753722 Fax: (01522) 753822 E-mail: sales@humiditycontrol.co.uk

Thompson & Capper Ltd, Hardwick Road, Astmoor Industrial Estate, Runcorn, Cheshire, WA7 1PH Tel: (01928) 573734 Fax: (01928) 580694 E-mail: info@tablets2buy.com

DESICCANT/MOISTURE DRYING SYSTEMS INSTALLATION SERVICES

Whitecross Engineering Ltd, Columbia House, Columbia Drive, Worthing, West Sussex, BN13 3HD Tel: (01903) 690807 Fax: (01903) 690807

DESIGN ADVISORY CONSULTANTS/SERVICES

3form Design, Unit 63 Basepoint Business & Innovation Centre, Caxton Close, Andover, Hampshire, SP10 3FG Tel: (01264) 326306 Fax: (01264) 326308 E-mail: info@3formdesign.com

Absolute Museum & Gallery Products, 66 Leonard Street, London, EC2A 4LW Tel: (020) 7729 5817 Fax: (020) 7613 4224 E-mail: info@absoluteproduct.com

Alton Design Ltd, Burnham House Park Street, Ripon, North Yorkshire, HG4 2BY Tel: (01765) 643830 Fax: (01765) 643831 E-mail: annabel@altoninteriors.com

Bang Communications Ltd, The Black Barn, Farleigh Road, Cliddesden, Basingstoke, Hampshire, RG25 2JL Tel: (01256) 370900 Fax: (01256) 370901 E-mail: info@bang-on.net

Brittan Design Partnership, 7 The Old Fire Station Annexe, Fairfield Road, Market Harborough, Leicestershire, LE16 9QJ Tel: (01858) 466950 Fax: (01858) 434632 E-mail: enquiry@goto-bdp.co.uk

Burness Corlett & Partners, 12-20 Camomile Street, London, EC3A 7PT Tel: (020) 7621 2943 Fax: (020) 7929 4167 E-mail: enquiries@bctq.com

Canard Design Ltd, Sidney House, 262 Aylestone Lane, Wigston, Leicestershire, LE18 1BD Tel: 0116-279 6532 Fax: 0116-291 0081 E-mail: info@canard-design.co.uk

Colebrook Bosson & Saunders Products Ltd, 18 Bowden Street, London, SE11 4DS Tel: (020) 7587 5283 Fax: (020) 7587 5275 E-mail: sales@cbsproducts.co.uk

Coley Porter Bell Ltd, 18 Grosvenor Gardens, London, SW1W 0DH Tel: (020) 7824 7700 Fax: (020) 7824 7701 E-mail: brand-design@cpb.co.uk

Conclusive Marketing Ltd, 76 The Downs, Harlow, Essex, CM20 3RF Tel: (01279) 303373

Crystal Structures Ltd, Crystal Park, Tunbridge Lane, Bottisham, Cambridge, CB25 9EA Tel: (01223) 811451 Fax: (01223) 811452 E-mail: sales@crystalstructures.co.uk

Davies Wise Design Co., 14 Spring Mill, Avening Road, Nailsworth, Stroud, Gloucestershire, GL6 0BS Tel: (01453) 839192 Fax: (01453) 839193 E-mail: sales@dwdc.co.uk

Design House, 52 Hollins Lane, Marple Bridge, Stockport, Cheshire, SK6 5BD Tel: 0161-427 1426 Fax: 0161-427 9316 E-mail: siddesigns@aol.com

Elpeeko Ltd, Wrightsway, Outer Circle Road, Lincoln, LN2 4JY Tel: (01522) 512111 Fax: (01522) 541796 E-mail: sales@elpeeko.com

Exposed Design, PO Box 35575, London, NW4 4UH Tel: 020 8202 5964 Fax: 0870 125 9115 E-mail: kellys@exposed.co.uk

F.M. Design Ltd, 2 Huntsworth Muse, London, N1 6DD Tel: (020) 7723 4188 Fax: (020) 7723 8644 E-mail: design@fmgroup.co.uk

Fire Imc, Manley House, 10 Dargan Crescent, Belfast, BT3 9JP Tel: (028) 9077 4388 Fax: (028) 9077 6906 E-mail: sales@fireimc.co.uk

▶ First Source & Supply Ltd, Unit 1 High Hall Farm, Oxley Hill, Heybridge, Maldon, Essex, CM9 8ES Tel: (01621) 810893 Fax: (01621) 840054 E-mail: info@firstsourcesupply.co.uk

Freshwater UK, Freshwater House, Cardiff Gate Business Park, Pontprennau, Cardiff, CF23 8RS Tel: (029) 2054 5370 Fax: (029) 2054 5380 E-mail: sales@freshwater-uk.com

Greenwich Design Associates, 11a Greenwich South Street, London, SE10 8NJ Tel: (020) 8853 3028 Fax: (020) 8858 2128 E-mail: simon@greenwich-design.co.uk

Haslimann Taylor Ltd, 1 Wrens Court, 53 Lower Queen Street, Sutton Coldfield, West Midlands, B72 1RT Tel: 0121-355 3446 Fax: 0121-355 3393 E-mail: info@haslimanntaylor.com

Hilbre Engineering Design Services, 71 Park Rd, Meols, Wirral, Merseyside, CH47 7BD Tel: 0151-632 2995 Fax: 0151-632 2850 E-mail: heds@tinyonline.co.uk

Hyde Group Ltd, Hadfield Street, Dukinfield, Cheshire, SK16 4QX Tel: 0161-308 2111 Fax: 0161-330 2680 E-mail: sales@hydetool.co.uk

▶ Hype Studios, 72 Princes Street, Dunstable, Bedfordshire, LU6 3AX Tel: (01582) 663925 Fax: (01582) 663925 E-mail: info@hypestudios.co.uk

Kirk John Design, 18 Hayhill, Barrow upon Soar, Loughborough, Leicestershire, LE12 8LD Tel: (01509) 817100 Fax: (01509) 817101 E-mail: accounts@johnkirkdesign.co.uk

Lloydnorthove Ltd, Pulpit House, 1 The Sqaure, Abingdon, Oxfordshire, OX14 5SZ Tel: (01235) 554499 Fax: (01235) 532878

Nexus Design & Print Ltd, 99-102 Preston Road, Brighton, BN1 6AF Tel: (01273) 702525 Fax: (01273) 887211 E-mail: sales@nexusdp.co.uk

One For One Ltd, 121-141 Westbourne Terrace, London, W2 6JR Tel: (020) 7706 2306 Fax: (020) 7258 3757

▶ Platform44, Sparkhouse Studios, Rope Walk, Lincoln, LN6 7DQ Tel: (01522) 837241 Fax: (01522) 837201 E-mail: projects@platform44.com

Quantum Print Services Ltd, 1b Bardsley Road, Earlstrees Industrial Estate, Corby, Northamptonshire, NN17 4AR Tel: (01536) 408392 Fax: (01536) 408492 E-mail: sales@quantum-print.co.uk

R F Insight Ltd, 47 Percival Road, Rugby, Warwickshire, CV22 5JU Tel: (01788) 541790 Fax: (01788) 541790E-mail: sales@vvlp.co.uk

Reddie & Grose, 16 Theobalds Road, London, WC1X 8PL Tel: (020) 7242 0901 Fax: (020) 7242 3290 E-mail: enquiries@reddie.co.uk

Richardson Carpenter, Manor Farm, Cliddesden, Basingstoke, Hampshire, RG25 2JB Tel: (01256) 353700 Fax: (01256) 358100

Serota Furniture, 92 Hilliard Road, Northwood, Middlesex, HA6 1SW Tel: (01923) 840697 E-mail: michael@serota.co.uk

Springetts Brand Design Consultants, 13 Salisbury Place, London, W1H 1FJ Tel: (020) 7486 7527 Fax: (020) 7487 3033 E-mail: all@springetts.co.uk

White Young Green, Regatta House, Clippers Quay, Salford, M50 3XP Tel: 0161-872 3223 Fax: 0161-872 3193 E-mail: manchester@wyg.com

DESIGN ADVISORY CONSULTANTS/ SERVICES – *continued*

Whyte Group Ltd, Marlborough House, 298 Regents Park Road, London, N3 2UA Tel: (020) 8346 5946 Fax: (020) 8349 4589 E-mail: sales@whytechem.co.uk

Works Design Ltd, The Co-Op Centre, 11 Mowll Street, London, SW9 6BG Tel: (020) 7820 8501 Fax: (020) 7820 8502 E-mail: sales@worksdesign.co.uk

DESIGN BUREAU

▶ Hype Studios, 72 Princes Street, Dunstable, Bedfordshire, LU6 3AX Tel: (01582) 663925 Fax: (01582) 663925 E-mail: info@hypestudios.co.uk

DESIGN DRAFTING SOFTWARE

Navigator Systems Ltd, 3 Fullerton Road, Hartford, Northwich, Cheshire, CW8 1SR Tel: (01606) 782655

Peak Document Solutions, Tapton Park Innovation Centre, Brimington Road, Chesterfield, Derbyshire, S41 0TZ Tel: (01246) 245490 Fax: (01246) 245491

Vero Software, The Mill, Brimscombe Port, Brimscombe, Stroud, Gloucestershire, GL5 2QG Tel: (01453) 732900 Fax: (01453) 887444

DESIGN REGISTRATION AGENT ASSOCIATIONS

Eric Potter Clarkson LLP, Park View House, 58 The Ropewalk, Nottingham, NG1 5DD Tel: 0115-955 2211 Fax: 0115-955 2201

DESIGN REGISTRATION AGENTS

Boult Wade Tennant, Verulam Gardens, 70 Gray's Inn Road, London, WC1X 8BT Tel: (020) 7430 7500 Fax: (020) 7831 1768 E-mail: boult@boult.com

Boult Wade Tennant, 34 Bridge Street, Reading, RG1 2LU Tel: 0118-956 5900 Fax: 0118-950 0442 E-mail: boult@boult.com

Bromhead Johnson, Kingsbourne House, 19 Buckingham Street, London, WC2N 6EF Tel: (020) 7839 4935 Fax: (020) 7839 6898 E-mail: mail@bromhead-johnson.com

Brookes Batchellor, 102-108 Clerkenwell Road, London, EC1M 5SA Tel: (020) 7253 1563 Fax: (020) 7253 1214

▶ Crossguard Trade Mark Agents, 4 Berkeley Road, Kenilworth, Warwickshire, CV8 1AP Tel: (0845) 0536675 Fax: (0870) 0468361 E-mail: mail@crossguard.info

Gallafent & Co., 9 Staple Inn, London, WC1V 7QH Tel: (020) 7242 3094 Fax: (020) 7539 4999 E-mail: rg@rkallafent.compulink.co.uk

Marks & Clerk, 27 Imperial Square, Cheltenham, Gloucestershire, GL50 1RQ Tel: (01242) 524520 Fax: (01242) 579383 E-mail: cheltonham@marks-clerk.com

Marks N Clarke, Cliffords Inn, Fetter Lane, London, EC4A 1BX Tel: (020) 7405 4916 Fax: (020) 7831 0343

Oliver & Graimes Design Associates Ltd, 1-3 Ship Street, Shoreham-by-Sea, West Sussex, BN43 5DH Tel: (01273) 748884 Fax: (01273) 465398 E-mail: info@oandg.co.uk

Urquhart Dykes & Lord, 30 Welbeck Street, London, W1G 8ER Tel: (020) 7487 1550 Fax: (020) 7487 1599E-mail: email@udl.co.uk

▶ Wilson Gunn Mccaw, 5th Floor, Blackfriars House, Manchester, M3 2JA Tel: 0161-827 9400 Fax: 0161-832 4905 E-mail: wgm@wilsongunn.com

DESIGN SERVICES

▶ 4Designs, 1 Gables Close, Maidenhead, Berkshire, SL6 8QD Tel: (01628) 675269 E-mail: info@4Designs.co.uk

▶ A2e Ltd, Adaptive House, Quarrywood Court, Livingston, West Lothian, EH54 6AX Tel: (01506) 463393 Fax: (01506) 461257

▶ AG Visible Projects Ltd, Locks Heath, Southampton, SO31 6ZE Tel: (0870) 7661085 Fax: (0871) 9906323 E-mail: studio@agvp.co.uk

Audio Engine, 1 Lower Luton Road, Harpenden, Hertfordshire, AL5 5AF Tel: (01582) 768560 Fax: (01582) 469532 E-mail: phaudio@aol.com

▶ Bentheim Interior Design, 3 Rosetti Studios, 72 Flood Street, London, SW3 5TF Tel: (020) 7376 3427 Fax: (020) 7376 3428 E-mail: david@bentheim.co.uk

C P I, Concorde House, 56 Station Road, Finchley Central, London, N3 2SA Tel: (020) 8235 3535 Fax: (020) 8235 3555 E-mail: info@cpilondon.com

Day-Timers Europe Ltd, Chene Court, Poundwell Street, Modbury, Devon, PL21 0QJ Tel: (08705) 143583 Fax: (08705) 143580

▶ Design Forte, Harewood Cottage, Main Street, Weeton, Leeds, LS17 0AY Tel: (01423) 734856 E-mail: chris@designforte.co.uk

▶ Edp Consulting Engineers, Munro House, Quarrywood Court, Livingston, West Lothian, EH54 6AX Tel: (01506) 497200 Fax: (01506) 497949

▶ Exel Designs Ltd, Danish Buildings, 44-46 High Street, Hull, HU1 1PS Tel: (01604) 517572 E-mail: info@exeldesigns.co.uk

▶ Fabre, 54 Ryde Avenue, Hull, HU5 1QA Tel: (07958) 346249E-mail: hello@fabre.co.uk

Finger Prints, Unit 3 Andrews Court, Andrews Way, Barrow-in-Furness, Cumbria, LA14 2UE Tel: (01229) 432959 Fax: (01229) 431955 E-mail: info@fingerprints.co.uk

▶ First Source & Supply Ltd, Unit 1 High Hall Farm, Oxley Hill, Heybridge, Maldon, Essex, CM9 8ES Tel: (01621) 810893 Fax: (01621) 840054 E-mail: info@firstsourcesupply.co.uk

▶ HDA Marketing Services Ltd, 58 Summerhouse Drive, Bexley, Kent, DA5 2HP Tel: (01322) 525224 Fax: (01322) 523209 E-mail: richardjones30@btinternet.com

▶ Hype Studios, 72 Princes Street, Dunstable, Bedfordshire, LU6 3AX Tel: (01582) 663925 Fax: (01582) 663925 E-mail: info@hypestudios.co.uk

▶ Igl Oil & Gas Consultants Ltd, Exchange House, Union Street, Aberdeen, AB11 5BJ Tel: (01224) 212300 Fax: (01224) 212301

▶ Lisle Design, 50 Lade Braes, St. Andrews, Fife, KY16 9DA Tel: (01334) 471435

Meadow Industrial Electronics, Newcastle Enterprise Centre, High Street, Knutton, Newcastle, Staffordshire, ST5 6BX Tel: (01782) 714200 Fax: (01782) 714204 E-mail: info@meadowindustrial.co.uk

▶ Plastic Design Solutions Ltd, 80 Church Road, Stockton-on-Tees, Cleveland, TS18 1TW Tel: (01642) 671711 Fax: (01642) 671762 E-mail: admin@plastic-design-solutions.freeserve.co.uk

▶ Platinum Print Ltd, Park House, Hookstone Park, Harrogate, North Yorkshire, HG2 7DB Tel: (01423) 881158 Fax: (01423) 886072 E-mail: sales@platinumprint.com

▶ Printing.Com@RasLtd, Lakeland House, 10 Boughton, Chester, CH3 5AG Tel: (01244) 343333 Fax: (01244) 346120 E-mail: sales@rasgroup.co.uk

▶ PROPS, Calais Gate, Cormont Road, Camberwell, London, SE5 9RQ Tel: (020) 7735 6940E-mail: contact@designprops.co.uk

▶ PWS, Ethel Street Studios, 78 Ethel Street, Hove, East Sussex, BN3 3LL Tel: (0845) 6585818 E-mail: stewart.h@pws-uk.com

▶ Red Seal, Technium Business Park, Kings Road, Swansea, SA1 8PH Tel: (01792) 295004 Fax: (01792) 485577 E-mail: studio@red-seal.com

▶ Studio Limonard, The Residence 43 Royal Clarence Yard, Weevil Lane, Gosport, Hampshire, PO12 1AX Tel: (023) 9258 9910 Fax: (023) 9258 9910

Tryco Designs Ltd, 8 Orchard Street, Norwich, NR2 4PP Tel: (01603) 627157 Fax: (01603) 665412 E-mail: trycodesigns@ukgateway.net

▶ Vosper International Ltd, 7 Killermont View, Glasgow, G20 0TZ Tel: 0141-945 5529 E-mail: design@vosper.co.uk

▶ Wave Marketing & Design, Upper Hey House, Barkisland, Halifax, West Yorkshire, HX4 0EQ Tel: (01422) 820787 Fax: (01422) 820790 E-mail: sales@wavemad.co.uk

▶ Websters Ltd, 40 Crossdene Road, Crosshouse, Kilmarnock, Ayrshire, KA2 0JU Tel: (01563) 534540 Fax: (0845) 1232561

▶ Zuan Ltd, Lytton Road, LCB Depot, 31 R, Leicester, LE2 1WJ Tel: 0116-212 9847 E-mail: info@zuan.co.uk

DESIGN SERVICES, GRP

▶ Leeson Designs Ltd, Brook St, Nelson, Lancs, BB9 9PU Tel: (01282) 696009 Fax: (01282) 411728 E-mail: sales@leesondesigns.co.uk

Pow Ltd, Conitor House, Denbury Road, Newton Abbot, Devon, TQ12 6AD Tel: (01626) 361490 Fax: (01626) 333359 E-mail: sales@powplastics.co.uk

DESIGN SYSTEM SOFTWARE

Ace Webmasters, 34-40 Wormgate, Boston, Lincolnshire, PE21 6NR Tel: (07050) 224352 E-mail: firstatboston@yahoo.co.uk

Bubball Systems Ltd, 60-62 Jenkin Road, Horbury, Wakefield, West Yorkshire, WF4 6DT Tel: (01924) 261158 Fax: (01924) 261158

C A L Software Ltd, Rivington House, Drumhead Road, Chorley North Industrial Estate, Chorley, Lancashire, PR6 7BX Tel: (01257) 231011 Fax: (01257) 230927 E-mail: sales@calsoftware.co.uk

Cadence Design Systems Ltd, Bagshot Road, Bracknell, Berkshire, RG12 0PH Tel: (01344) 360333 Fax: (01344) 869647

Computerlinks, Suffolk House, Newmarket, Suffolk, CB8 7AN Tel: (01638) 569600 Fax: (01638) 569601 E-mail: info@computerlinks.co.uk

Dalman Technical Services, Unit 36 Walworth Enterprise Centre Duke Close, West Way, Andover, Hampshire, SP10 5AP Tel: (01264) 357580 Fax: (01264) 351325 E-mail: sales@dalmants.co.uk

Design Computer, 16A Littleway, Exeter, EX2 9PB Tel: (01392) 435340 E-mail: mousepad@eurobell.co.uk

Ellipse Design, 45 Marsh Lane, Crosspool, Sheffield, S10 5NN Tel: 0114-268 2961 Fax: 0114-268 2961 E-mail: enquiries@ellipsedesign.co.uk

Explan Computer Ltd, PO Box 32, Tavistock, Devon, PL19 8YU Tel: (01822) 613868 Fax: (01822) 610868 E-mail: info@explan.co.uk

Gerber Technology Ltd, 302 Metroplex Business Park, Broadway, Salford, M50 2UE Tel: 0161-772 2000 Fax: 0161-772 2020

Haas Associates, 20 Baldock Road, Buntingford, Hertfordshire, SG9 9DA Tel: (01763) 272865 Fax: (01763) 273869 E-mail: info@haas-uk.com

Hanlon Computer Systems, Unit 4 Victoria Court, Kent Street, Nottingham, NG1 3LZ Tel: 0115-959 0077 Fax: 0115-941 7432 E-mail: info@hcs-ltd.co.uk

Interchange Group Ltd, 2 Plover Close, Interchange Park, Newport Pagnell, Buckinghamshire, MK16 9PS Tel: (01908) 618161 Fax: (0870) 0716789 E-mail: info@interchangegroup.com

Microhelp Ltd, Unit 2a, Caldey Road, Roundthorn Industrial Estate, Manchester, M23 9GE Tel: 0161-946 0193 Fax: 0161- 945 4947 E-mail: sales@microhelp.co.uk

Mitech Communications Engineering, 4 Lower Mill Street, Cheltenham, Gloucestershire, GL51 8JN Tel: (01242) 224015 Fax: (01242) 223988

Pisys Ltd, Campus 1, Balgownie Road, Bridge of Don, Aberdeen, AB22 8GT Tel: (01224) 332014 Fax: (01224) 332055 E-mail: info@pisysltd.co.uk

Promentum Technologies Ltd, 3 Cobden Road, London, SE25 5NZ Tel: (020) 8656 8666 Fax: (020) 8656 8606 E-mail: technologies@promentum.co.uk

Quantum System Management Ltd, 67 Tweedy Road, Bromley, BR1 3NH Tel: (020) 8460 2747 Fax: (020) 8313 3468

S F J Systems Ltd, Andil House, Court Street, Trowbridge, Wiltshire, BA14 8BR Tel: (01225) 775103 Fax: (01225) 774877 E-mail: info@sfjsystems.co.uk

Smart People Time plc, Node Court, Drivers End, Codicote, Hitchin, Hertfordshire, SG4 8TR Tel: (01438) 822222 Fax: (01438) 822240 E-mail: info@smarthumanlogistics.com

Welcom Software Ltd, The Exchange, Station Parade, Harrogate, North Yorkshire, HG1 1TS Tel: (0845) 4565859 Fax: E-mail: info@welcom.co.uk

DESIGN, MANUFACTURE AND COMMISSIONING SERVICES, PLASTICS INDUSTRY TOOLING

▶ RM Alderton Designs Ltd, 5 Temple Bar Business Park, Strettington, Chichester, West Sussex, PO18 0TU Tel: (0870) 754 2665 Fax: (0870) 622 0445 E-mail: sales@rmalderton.com

DESIGNERS/DESIGN CONSULTANTS/ENGINEERS, *See Consulting Engineers/Designers*

DESK CONTROL PANELS

Anstee & Wear (Wales) Ltd, Foreshore Road, Cardiff, CF10 4DF Tel: (029) 2048 1831 Fax: (029) 2049 6592 E-mail: info@ansteewear.co.uk

Conard Systems & Engineering Ltd, Unit 6d Lowick Close, Newby Road Industrial Estate, Hazel Grove, Stockport, Cheshire, SK7 5ED Tel: 0161-456 5285

East Midlands Instrument Co. Ltd, Laughton Lane, Morton, Gainsborough, Lincolnshire, DN21 3ET Tel: (01427) 616721 Fax: (01427) 810804 E-mail: emi@eminst.co.uk

H C Controls Ltd, Wetherby Close, Portrack Interchange Business Park, Stockton-on-Tees, Cleveland, TS18 2SL Tel: (01642) 671681 Fax: (01642) 676100 E-mail: admin@hccontrol.co.uk

DESK TOP PUBLISHING SERVICES/BUREAU SERVICES

Advent Publishing Systems, 3b2 House, 12 Bath Road, Swindon, SN1 4BA Tel: (01793) 511432 Fax: (01793) 536616 E-mail: info@3b2.com

▶ Ali Alwan DTP, 228 Seaforth Avenue, New Malden, Surrey, KT3 6JW Tel: (020) 8949 6048

Aspect Design, 89 Newtown Road, Malvern, Worcestershire, WR14 1PD Tel: (01684) 561567 Fax: (01684) 560041 E-mail: help@aspect-design.net

Bond Street Business Base, 3 Bond Street, St. Helier, Jersey, JE2 3NP Tel: (01534) 724100 Fax: (01534) 759662 E-mail: info@bondbase.info

Charlesworth China Ltd, 254 Deighton Road, Huddersfield, HD2 1JJ Tel: (01484) 517077 Fax: (01484) 517068 E-mail: mail@charlesworth.com

Composing Operations Ltd, Sheffield Road, Tunbridge Wells, Kent, TN4 0PD Tel: (01892) 511725 Fax: (01892) 511726 E-mail: compops@btconnect.com

Copyworld Duplicating Services, 6 Merville Garden Village, Newtownabbey, County Antrim, BT37 9TF Tel: (028) 9080 0500 Fax: (028) 9087 9087 E-mail: info@copyworld.co.uk

▶ Essex Communications, Unit 11, Olympic Business Centre, Paycocke Road, Basildon, Essex, SS14 3EX Tel: (01268) 287575 Fax: (01268) 287585

▶ Fakenham Photosetting Ltd, 16 Garrood Drive, Fakenham, Norfolk, NR21 8NN Tel: (01328) 851570 Fax: (01328) 864088 E-mail: info@fakphoto.co.uk

First Edition Translations, 22 Newmarket Rd, Cambridge, CB5 8DT Tel: (01223) 356733 Fax: (01223) 321488 E-mail: info@firstedit.co.uk

K International plc, Carina Building, Sunrise Parkway, Milton Keynes, MK14 6PW Tel: (01908) 670399 Fax: (01908) 670170 E-mail: info@k-international.com

Kandaprint Printers, 9 Oakley Hay Lodge, Great Fold Road, Corby, Northamptonshire, NN18 9AS Tel: (01536) 460890 Fax: (01536) 460890 E-mail: kandaprint@aol.com

Kopykat Printing Ltd, 76c Rivington Street, London, EC2A 3AY Tel: (020) 7739 2451 Fax: (020) 7729 5925 E-mail: print@kopykat.co.uk

Lexisnexis, Halsbury House, 35 Chancery Lane, London, WC2A 1EL Tel: (020) 7400 2500 Fax: (020) 7400 2611 E-mail: marketingdepartment@lexisnexis.co.uk

Office Overload, Peelers End, May Lane, Pilley, Lymington, Hampshire, SO41 5QR Tel: (01590) 688476 Fax: (01590) 675133 E-mail: sue@officeoverload.com

Output Ltd, 1 Amptronic Industrial Estate, Heath Mill Road, Wombourne, Wolverhampton, WV5 8AP Tel: (01902) 895107 Fax: (01902) 895113 E-mail: sales@outputdigital.com

Pinder P.L.C., Unit 481 Walton Summit Centre, Bamber Bridge, Preston, PR5 8AR Tel: (01772) 620999 Fax: (01772) 620888 E-mail: k.ashley@pinder.com

▶ Purple Creature, 6 Rosemount Square, Aberdeen, AB25 2UB Tel: (01224) 643673 E-mail: info@purplecreature.co.uk

Solutions For Business, Royston Business & Design Centre, 8 Priory Lane, Royston, Hertfordshire, SG8 9DU Tel: (01763) 242939 Fax: (01763) 243332 E-mail: sales@solutions-for-business.co.uk

Trog Associates Ltd, PO Box 243, South Croydon, Surrey, CR2 6WF Tel: (020) 8786 3614 Fax: (020) 8405 8049 E-mail: gostwrighter@dslpipex.com

Vivitext Designers, The Old School, Old Hunstanton Road, Hunstanton, Norfolk, PE36 6HZ Tel: (01485) 534566 Fax: (01485) 534828 E-mail: viv@vivitext.co.uk

Winstanley & Watkins, 104 Duke Street, Liverpool, L1 5AG Tel: 0151-709 0808 Fax: 0151-709 3060 E-mail: info@wwprint.co.uk

Zone 1 Media, Meeting House Lane, Baldock, Hertfordshire, SG7 5BP Tel: (01462) 491134 Fax: (01462) 491137 E-mail: pauline.rees@zone1media.co.uk

DESKTOP COMPUTERS

▶ Bellville Computers Ltd, 53 Second Drove, Peterborough, PE1 5XA Tel: (01733) 891414 Fax: (01733) 891415 E-mail: sales@bellville-computers.co.uk

▶ Envision Online, 6 Cockpit Hill, Cullompton, Devon, EX15 1DF Tel: 07740 778082 E-mail: info@Envision-Online.co.uk

DESKTOP PUBLISHING EQUIPMENT

Flame Ltd, 12 Kings Park, Primrose Hill, Kings Langley, Hertfordshire, WD4 8ST Tel: (01923) 272900 Fax: (01923) 270141 E-mail: sales@flame1.com

I P A Systems Ltd, 4 Liberty Court, 101-103 Bell Street, Reigate, Surrey, RH2 7JB Tel: (01737) 225010 Fax: (01737) 771827 E-mail: sales@ipasystems.co.uk

DESOLDERING TOOLS

▶ Dancap Electronics, 24 Trent Crescent, Thatcham, Berkshire, RG18 3DN Tel: (01635) 866394 Fax: (01635) 869589 E-mail: dancap@btinternet.com

DESUPERHEATERS

Copes-Vulcan, Road Two, Winsford Industrial Estate, Winsford, Cheshire, CW7 3QL Tel: (01606) 552041 Fax: (01606) 558275 E-mail: copes@processequipment.spx.com

Johnson Systems International Ltd, Little Lane, Ilkley, West Yorkshire, LS29 8HY Tel: (01943) 607550 Fax: (01943) 609463

DETACHABLE SLIDEWAYS

Slideway Grinding Services, Unit 4, Fullwood Close, Aldermans Green Industrial Estate, Coventry, CV2 2SS Tel: (024) 7661 3541 Fax: (024) 7660 2649

DETECTIVE AGENCIES/ CORPORATE/PRIVATE INVESTIGATION SERVICES

▶ A&D Surveillance and Security Consultants, 15, Chester Close, Dorking, Surrey, RH4 1PP Tel: 01306 885717 Fax: 01306 885717 E-mail: info@adssc.co.uk
▶ Albany Investigations Ltd, Albany House, Gannel Road, Newquay, Cornwall, TR7 2AD Tel: 08700 114314 E-mail: albanymc@hotmail.com
▶ Alliance Investigation Services, P.O. Box 1869, Bristol, BS37 9TP Tel: (0845) 6101442 E-mail: jantaylor@ allianceinvestigationservices.co.uk
▶ Beetecs Investigations, 1 Cranwell Rise, Mile Oak, Tamworth, Staffordshire, B78 3PU Tel: (01827) 285401 E-mail: petespencer1@ntlworld.com
▶ Britannia Support Services Ltd, 17 Ensign House, Admirals Way, London, E14 9XQ Tel: 020 7474 6108 Fax: 020 7474 1668 E-mail: info@britannia-supportservices.co.uk
▶ Cambrian Securities, 3 John Street, Llanelli, Carmarthenshire, SA15 1 UH Tel: (01554) 780502 Fax: (01554) 777708 E-mail: cambrian@clara.net
▶ Giles Higgitt, 7 Hazelwood Road, Walthamstow, London, E17 7AJ Tel: (020) 8509 1487 Fax: (020) 8509 1487 E-mail: info@blood-ties.com
Global, PO Box 101, Northampton, NN1 4BS Tel: (01604) 636531 Fax: (01604) 760656 E-mail: info@globalintelligence.ltd.uk
▶ Intrinsic Surveillance & Investigations, P.O. Box 170, St. Austell, Cornwall, PL25 5DS Tel: 01726 66419 Fax: 0871 2421051 E-mail: intrinsic@tiscali.co.uk
▶ Investigator Direct (Operations) Limited, Floor Six, 456 - 458 Strand, London, WC2R 0DZ Tel: 0870 9903211 Fax: 0870 9903212 E-mail: admin@id-net.co.uk
▶ Mike Lenny & Co., 35 Gondar Gardens, West Hampstead, London, NW6 1EP Tel: (020) 7794 3700 Fax: (020) 7443 9300 E-mail: m.lenny@btconnect.com
Luckett Investigation, 14 Barnfield Way, Stafford, ST17 4NB Tel: 01785 602075 Fax: 01785 602075 E-mail: info@luckett-investigation.co.uk
▶ Marine Security Worldwide, 41 Burnley Road, Newton Abbot, Devon, TQ12 1YD Tel: (01626) 200515
▶ North Wales Process Solutions, PO Box 226, Rhyl, Denbighshire, LL18 9AZ Tel: (0870) 0425071 Fax: (0870) 7627365 E-mail: contact@nwprocess-solutions.com
Pinkerton Consulting & Investigations Ltd, 102 College Road, Harrow, Middlesex, HA1 1ES Tel: (020) 8424 8884 Fax: (020) 8424 9744 E-mail: sales@pinkerton-europe.com
Renaissance, 1 Emperor Way, Exeter Business Park, Exeter Business Park, Exeter, EX1 3QS Tel: (01803) 404047 Fax: 01392 434047 E-mail: enquiries@commercial-investigation. com
Research Associates, 282 Latimer Road, London, W10 6QW Tel: (020) 7854 9000 Fax: (020) 7854 9090 E-mail: paulhawkes@investigationservices.co. uk
▶ Rose UK, Unit 13 Vision Business Park, Firth Way, Nottingham, NG6 8GF Tel: 0115-927 9542 Fax: 0115-976 1986 E-mail: rose@roseuksecurityservices.co.uk
▶ Verify, c/o Knox & Eames, Greys Green, Rotherfield Greys, Henley-on-Thames, Oxfordshire, RG9 4QG Tel: 0118-957 4046 Fax: 0118-958 4100 E-mail: office@verify24plus.com

DETERGENT CHEMICALS

C K Chemicals, Unit 16 Lady La Industrial Estate, Hadleigh, Ipswich, IP7 6BQ Tel: (01473) 822836 Fax: (01473) 824044 E-mail: sales@ckchemicals.co.uk
Croda Chemicals International Ltd, Cowick Hall, Snaith, Goole, North Humberside, DN14 9AA Tel: (01405) 860551 Fax: (01405) 861767
Echem Ltd, 147 Kirkstall Road, Leeds, LS3 1JN Tel: 0113-245 7471 Fax: 0113-244 5082 E-mail: info@echem.co.uk
Zok International Group, Airworthy House, Elsted, Midhurst, West Sussex, GU29 0JT Tel: (01730) 811920 Fax: (01730) 811930 E-mail: zok@zok.com

DETERGENT MANUFRS

A M B Products Ltd, Marriott Road, Swinton, Mexborough, South Yorkshire, S64 8AG Tel: (01709) 583132 Fax: (01709) 587252 E-mail: amb@walterblack.co.uk
Allens (Disinfectants) Ltd, 462 Cleveland St, Birkenhead, Merseyside, CH41 8EQ Tel: 0151-652 4877 Fax: 0151-652 3800
Bio-Clean Equipment Sales Ltd, Waterhouse, Greenfields Road, Horley, Surrey, RH6 8HW Tel: (01293) 424200 Fax: (01293) 424444 E-mail: sales@bioclean.co.uk
C M R Chemical Services Ltd, Moorhey Street, Oldham, OL4 1JE Tel: 0161-626 4143 Fax: 0161-628 5081
Ceetek Chemicals Ltd, Firs Industrial Estate, Kidderminster, Worcestershire, DY11 7QN Tel: (01562) 755337 Fax: (01562) 865660 E-mail: ceetek@aol.com
Chemisphere, 3, Trafford Park, Manchester, M17 1RE Tel: 0161-874 7200 Fax: 0161-874 7201
Christeyns UK Ltd, Rutland Street, Bradford, West Yorkshire, BD4 7EA Tel: (01274) 393286 Fax: (01274) 309143 E-mail: headoffice@christeyns.co.uk
▶ Cleenol Group Ltd, Neville House, Beaumont Road, Banbury, Oxfordshire, OX16 1RB Tel: (01295) 251721 Fax: (01295) 269561 E-mail: sales@cleanol.co.uk
William Clements (Chemicals) Ltd, 38a Witham Street, Belfast, BT4 1HP Tel: (028) 9073 8395 Fax: (028) 9045 0532
Clenal Ware Systems, Farnham Trading Estate, Farnham, Surrey, GU9 9NN Tel: (01252) 712789 Fax: (01252) 723719 E-mail: info@clenalware.com
Concorde Chemicals P.L.C., Concorde Works, Bilton Way, Brimsdown, Enfield, Middlesex, EN3 7NH Tel: (020) 8404 7411 Fax: (020) 8805 6553 E-mail: dgoldberg@concordechemicals.co.uk
Deb Ltd, 108 Spencer Road, Belper, Derbyshire, DE56 1JX Tel: (01773) 596700 Fax: (01773) 822548 E-mail: enquiry@deb.co.uk
Devons Catering Equipment, 1589-1593 London Road, London, SW16 4AA Tel: (020) 8679 8585 Fax: (020) 86796633 E-mail: info@devonscatering.co.uk
East Lancashire Chemical Co. Ltd, Edge Lane, Droylsden, Manchester, M43 6AU Tel: 0161-371 5585 Fax: 0161-301 1990 E-mail: info@eastlancschemical.com
Ecolab Ltd, Stanley Green Trading Estate, Duke Avenue, Cheadle Hulme, Cheadle, Cheshire, SK8 6RB Tel: 0161-485 6166 Fax: 0161-488 4127 E-mail: inge.van.der.linden@ecolab.com
Ecolab Ltd, David Murray John Building, Swindon, SN1 1NH Tel: (01793) 511221 Fax: (01793) 618552 E-mail: sales.uk@ecolab.co.uk
Johnson Diversey Ltd, 1/117 Dargan Road, Bushmills, County Antrim, BT57 8XQ Tel: (028) 9078 1636 Fax: (028) 9037 0456
Kemtec Manufacturing, 1a Caddick Road, Knowsley Business Park, Prescot, Merseyside, L34 9HP Tel: 0151-549 1559 Fax: 0151-549 1729 E-mail: enquiries@kemtec.co.uk
▶ Kilco Chemicals Ltd, 1a Trench Road, Newtownabbey, County Antrim, BT36 4TY Tel: (028) 9084 4344 Fax: (028) 9034 2494 E-mail: info@kilcogroup.com
Klenzan Ltd, 2 Cameron Court, Winwick Quay, Warrington, WA2 8RE Tel: (01925) 234696 Fax: (01925) 234693 E-mail: info@klenzan.co.uk
James Law (Chemicals) Ltd, Crossley Street Works, Royal Street, Smallbridge, Rochdale, Lancashire, OL16 2QA Tel: (01706) 644940 Fax: (01706) 644037
Lever Faberge, PO Box 69, Wirral, Merseyside, CH62 4ZD Tel: 0151-641 4000 Fax: 0151-641 4029
Libra Speciality Chemicals Ltd, Brinell Drive, Northbank Industrial Park, Irlam, Manchester, M44 5LF Tel: 0161-775 1888 Fax: 0161-777 9109 E-mail: sales@librachem.co.uk
Link Contract Supplies Ltd, Unit 1, 172-174 Mile Cross Lane, Norwich, NR6 6RY Tel: (01603) 415355 Fax: (01603) 401921
Lower Swell Chemicals Ltd, Sunnydale, Naunton, Cheltenham, Gloucestershire, GL54 3AD Tel: (01451) 850456 Fax: (01451) 810707 E-mail: enquiries@lscltd.fsnet.co.uk
McBride P.L.C., McBride House, Penn Road, Beaconsfield, Buckinghamshire, HP9 2FY Tel: (01494) 607050 Fax: (01494) 607056
Multex Chemicals, Multex House, Cannon Street, Hull, HU2 0AB Tel: (01482) 320432 Fax: (01482) 321777 E-mail: sales@multexchemicals.co.uk
Powder & Liquid Products Ltd, Factory 37, No 1 Industrial Estate, Consett, County Durham, DH8 6TW Tel: (01207) 591217 Fax: (01207) 592119 E-mail: sales@plp.co.uk
Quill International, Quill International Group Ltd, Castle Lane, Melbourne, Derby, DE73 8JB Tel: (01332) 863292 Fax: (01332) 863292 E-mail: sales@quillinternational.com
Reckitt Benckiser, Delta 1200, Welton Road, Delta Business Park, Swindon, SN5 7XZ Tel: (01793) 427200 Fax: (01793) 511572
S B Chemicals Ltd, Altona Road, Lisburn, County Antrim, BT27 5QB Tel: (028) 9267 3331 Fax: (028) 9267 3939 E-mail: postmaster@sbchemicals.co.uk
Zamo Household Products Ltd, 27 White Post Lane, London, E9 5EN Tel: (020) 8525 1177 Fax: (020) 8525 1166 E-mail: zamoproducts@aol.com

DETERGENT RAW MATERIALS

Anikem Ltd, 18 North Gate, Harborne, Birmingham, B17 9EP Tel: 0121-428 1355 Fax: 0121-428 1366 E-mail: sales@anikem.co.uk

DEUTERIUM LAMPS

▶ Spectro Service Ltd, Top Station Road, Top Station Road Industrial Estate, Brackley, Northamptonshire, NN13 7UG Tel: (01280) 705577 Fax: (01280) 705510 E-mail: sales@spectroservice.co.uk

DEVELOPMENT ENGINEERING SERVICES/CONSULTANTS, TECHNOLOGICAL

Adrian March, 5 The Paddock, Kings Worthy, Winchester, Hampshire, SO23 7QR Tel: (01962) 882277 E-mail: adrian@adrianmarch.com
▶ ASK Innovation Limited, Suite 104b, Discovery Court, 551-553 Wallisdown Road, Poole, Dorset, BH12 5AG Tel: 01202 853221 Fax: 01202 853214 E-mail: enquiries@askinnovation.co.uk
▶ Cambridge Engineering Technology Ltd, 17 Fennec Close, Cambridge, CB1 9GG Tel: (01223) 413797 E-mail: enquiries@cambridge-engineering.com
Cooke & Arkwright, 7-8 Windsor Place, Cardiff, CF10 3SX Tel: (029) 2034 6346 Fax: (029) 2034 6300 E-mail: sales@coark.com
Coupland Bell Ltd, Barclays Venture Centre University of Warwick, Science Park, Coventry, CV4 7EZ Tel: (01926) 777566 E-mail: info@couplandbell.com
Derek Wilkinson, Winfield Road, Nuneaton, Warwickshire, CV11 5AZ Tel: (024) 7637 5198 Fax: (024) 7637 5198 E-mail: derekw@enta.net
Fathomtree Ltd, 5 The Midway, Nottingham, NG7 2TS Tel: 0115-986 0096 Fax: 0115-986 0210 E-mail: sales@fathomtreeltd.com
Ferranti Technologies Group Ltd, Cairo Mill, Greenacres Road, Oldham, OL4 3JA Tel: 0161-624 0281 Fax: 0161-624 5244 E-mail: sales@ferranti-technologies.co.uk
The G H M Consultancy Group Ltd, Wheathampstead, St. Albans, Hertfordshire, AL4 8BU Tel: (01582) 834233 Fax: (01582) 832176 E-mail: ghm@ghm-group.co.uk
Bernard Hooper Engineering Ltd, PO Box 4155, Bridgnorth, Shropshire, WV15 5WY Tel: (01746) 761425 Fax: (01746) 761425 E-mail: bhe1@breathemail.net
Ice Guard Group, Mold Road, Cefn-y-Bedd, Wrexham, Clwyd, LL12 9UL Tel: (01978) 761881 Fax: (01978) 761789
Jay Engineering Consultancy Ltd, 178 Aldridge Road, Streetly, Sutton Coldfield, West Midlands, B74 3TP Tel: 0121-353 6400 Fax: 0121-353 9600 E-mail: john.butler@iee.org
Lafarge Roofing Technical Centers Ltd, Sussex Manor Business Park, Gatwick Road, Crawley, West Sussex, RH10 9NZ Tel: (01293) 618418 Fax: (01293) 614548
The Mathworks Ltd, Matrix House 10 Cowley Park, Cowley Road, Cambridge, CB4 0HH Tel: (01223) 423200 Fax: (01223) 423289 E-mail: sales@mathworks.co.uk
▶ North West Technologies Ltd, 15 Acacia Drive, Great Sutton, Ellesmere Port, CH66 2UT Tel: 0151-355 8075 E-mail: enquiries@nw-tech.co.uk
Rolls-Royce Aircraft Management Ltd, PO Box 31, Derby, DE24 8BJ Tel: (01332) 242424 Fax: (01332) 249936
Scott Gibbin Ltd, Padholme Road, Peterborough, PE1 5XP Tel: (01733) 561569 Fax: (01733) 552065
T W I Ltd, Granta Park, Great Abington, Cambridge, CB1 6AL Tel: (01223) 899000 Fax: (01223) 892794 E-mail: twi@twi.co.uk
Universal Applications, 2 Clarkes Road, Wigston, Leicestershire, LE18 2BG Tel: 0116-288 8038 Fax: 0116-288 8036
Works Design Ltd, The Co-Op Centre, 11 Mowll Street, London, SW9 6BG Tel: (020) 7820 8501 Fax: (020) 7820 8502 E-mail: sales@worksdesign.co.uk

DEVELOPMENT SYSTEM SOFTWARE

A R M Ltd, 110 Fulbourn Road, Cherry Hinton, Cambridge, CB1 9NJ Tel: (01223) 400400 Fax: (01223) 400410 E-mail: info@arm.com
Adelard Computer Consultants, 10 Northampton Square, London, EC1V 0HB Tel: (020) 7490 9450 Fax: (020) 7490 9451 E-mail: sales@adelard.co.uk
Adobe Systems (U K) Ltd, 3 Roundwood Avenue, Stockley Park, Uxbridge, Middlesex, UB11 1AY Tel: (020) 8606 4000 Fax: (020) 8606 4004 E-mail: jobs@adobe.co.uk
Avisoft Ltd, 11 Church Street, Kirkby In Ashfield, Nottingham, NG17 8LA Tel: (01623) 755555 E-mail: sales@avisoft.co.uk
▶ Aztec Software & Technology Services Ltd., 1, Berkeey Street, London, W1J 8DJ Tel: (020) 7016 9852 E-mail: rphanee@aztecsoft.com
The Big Internet, 32 Lipson Road, Plymouth, PL4 8PW Tel: (01752) 256162 Fax: (01752) 250733
Database Developments Ltd, 2 South Street, Uley, Dursley, Gloucestershire, GL11 5SS Tel: (01453) 861155 Fax: (01453) 861166 E-mail: sales@databasedevelopments.com
E A S E, Mill Farm Business Park, Mill Field Road, Hounslow, TW4 5PY Tel: (020) 8893 9121 E-mail: wilma@ease.co.uk
Electronic Media Services, Lynchborough Road, Passfield, Liphook, Hampshire, GU30 7SB Tel: (01428) 751655 Fax: (01428) 751654 E-mail: info@ems-uk.com
Eservglobal UK Ltd, 7th Floor East Gate House, Carr Street, Ipswich, IP4 1HA Tel: (01473) 289900 Fax: (01473) 289944
Fulcrum Software Ltd, 3 Saxon Gate, Back of The Walls, Southampton, SO14 3HA Tel: (023) 8071 0903 Fax: 023 80360333
I O Systech Ltd, 8 Willow Walk, Englefield Green, Egham, Surrey, TW20 0DQ Tel: (01784) 432058 E-mail: enquiries@iosystech.co.uk
Infographics UK Ltd, 12 Hanover Court, North Street, Glenrothes, Fife, KY7 5SB Tel: (01592) 750677 Fax: (01592) 610534 E-mail: sales@infographics.co.uk
Interchange Group, Garden Court, Lockington, Derby, DE74 2SJ Tel: (08700) 716716 Fax: (08700) 716789 E-mail: info@interchangegroup.com
Liber8 Ltd, Asher House, Barsbank Lane, Lymm, Cheshire, WA13 0ED Tel: (01925) 758283 Fax: (01925) 758470E-mail: info@liber8.co.uk
M S G Business Systems Ltd, 18 Harrowby Street, Cardiff, CF10 5GA Tel: (029) 2091 1700 Fax: (029) 2029 1171
Northgate Information Solutions Ltd, 6 Woodlands Workshops, Coedcae Lane, Pontyclun, Mid Glamorgan, CF72 9DW Tel: (01443) 228740
Omron Electronics Ltd, 1200 Parkway, Whiteley, Fareham, Hampshire, PO15 7AD Tel: (01489) 886772 Fax: (01489) 886762
Promentum Technologies Ltd, 3 Cobden Road, London, SE25 5NZ Tel: (020) 8656 8666 Fax: (020) 8656 8606 E-mail: technologies@promentum.co.uk
Propath Software Ltd, Manor House, 23 Robin Lane, Pudsey, West Yorkshire, LS28 7BR Tel: 0113-255 4115 Fax: 0113-255 4690 E-mail: sales@propath.com
Smart Golf, 30 Hopefield Avenue, Belfast, BT15 5AP Tel: (028) 9087 8001 Fax: (028) 9087 8001 E-mail: info@smartgolf.co.uk
Starsmore Ltd, Main Road, Rookley, Ventnor, Isle of Wight, PO38 3NL Tel: (01983) 721445 Fax: (01983) 721912 E-mail: sales@starsmore.com
Unify Corp (UK) Ltd, Malt House, Hummer Road, Egham, Surrey, TW20 9BD Tel: (01784) 487940 Fax: (01784) 487941 E-mail: info@unify.com
Warthog plc, 10 Eden Place, Cheadle, Cheshire, SK8 1AT Tel: 0161-608 1200 Fax: 0161-610 3033 E-mail: info@warthog.co.uk
Xara Ltd, Gaddesden Place, Great Gaddesden, Hemel Hempstead, Hertfordshire, HP2 6EX Tel: (01442) 350000 Fax: (01442) 350010 E-mail: sales@xara.com

DEVICE PROGRAMMERS

Crown Hill Associates Ltd, Station House, Station Road, Wilburton, Ely, Cambridgeshire, CB6 3PZ Tel: (01353) 749990 Fax: (01353) 749991 E-mail: sales@crownhill.co.uk
Euroeda Ltd, Britannia House, 29 Station Road, Kettering, Northamptonshire, NN15 7HJ Tel: (01536) 517657 Fax: (01933) 676372 E-mail: info@euro-eda.com
Lloyd Research Ltd, 7-7A Brook Lane, Warsash, Southampton, SO31 9FH Tel: (01489) 885515 Fax: (01489) 885853 E-mail: progs@lloydres.co.uk

DEW POINT INDICATORS/ METERS

IMA Ltd, Parkwell House, Otley Rd, Guiseley, Leeds, LS20 8BH Tel: 0845 4941692 Fax: (01943) 879988E-mail: sales@ima.co.uk
▶ Moisture Control & Measurement Ltd, Thorp Arch Trading Estate, Thorp Arch, Wetherby, West Yorkshire, LS23 7BJ Tel: (01937) 843927 Fax: (01937) 842524 E-mail: sales@mcm-moisture.com
Shaw Moisture Meters (UK) Ltd, Rawson Road, Westgate, Bradford, West Yorkshire, BD1 3SQ Tel: (01274) 733582 Fax: (01274) 370151 E-mail: mail@shawmeters.com

DEWATERING EQUIPMENT

Andritz Ltd, R & B Technology Centre, Speedwell Road, Parkhouse East Industrial Estate, Newcastle, Staffordshire, ST5 7RG Tel: (01782) 565656 Fax: (01782) 566130 E-mail: welcome@andritzltd.com
▶ Kilkie Paper Mill Services, Lovesta, Gowanlea Road, Comrie, Crieff, Perthshire, PH6 2HD Tel: (01764) 670141 Fax: (0870) 1301570 E-mail: sales@kilkie.com
Proquip Direct Ltd, Unit 1b Park Road Works, 125 Park Road, Beckenham, Kent, BR3 1QJ Tel: (020) 8639 0377 Fax: (020) 8639 0379 E-mail: sales@proquipdirect.com

DEWATERING SERVICES

W J Groundwater Ltd, 9 Park Road, Bushey, WD23 3EE Tel: (020) 8950 7256 Fax: (020) 8950 5207 E-mail: info@wjgl.com

DIAGNOSTIC KIT/SYSTEMS

Bio Diagnostics Ltd, Upton Industrial Estate, Rectory Road, Upton Upon Severn, Worcester, WR8 0LX Tel: (01684) 592262 Fax: (01684) 592501 E-mail: info@bio-diagnostics.co.uk

DIAGNOSTIC KIT/SYSTEMS – *continued*

Bio-Rad Laboratories Ltd, Bio-Rad House, Maylands Avenue, Hemel Hempstead, Hertfordshire, HP2 7TD Tel: (020) 8328 2000 Fax: (020) 8328 2500 E-mail: uk.lsg.marketing@bio-rad.com

Biotest (U.K.) Ltd, Unit 28 Monkspath Business Park, Highlands Road Shirley, Shirley, Solihull, West Midlands, B90 4NZ Tel: 0121-733 3393 Fax: 0121-733 3066 E-mail: sales@biotestuk.com

Clin-Tech Ltd, Unit G Perram Works, Merrow Lane, Guildford, Surrey, GU4 7BN Tel: (01483) 301902 Fax: (01483) 301907 E-mail: info@clin-tech.co.uk

Dako Ltd, Denmark House, Angel Drove, Ely, Cambridgeshire, CB7 4ET Tel: (01353) 669911 Fax: (01353) 668989

Euro DPC Ltd, Glyn Rhonwy, Llanberis, Caernarfon, Gwynedd, LL55 4EL Tel: (01286) 871871 Fax: (01286) 871802 E-mail: euro@dpconline.com

Mast Group Ltd, Mast House, Derby Road, Bootle, Merseyside, L20 1EA Tel: 0151-933 7277 Fax: 0151-944 1332 E-mail: sales@mastgrp.com

Omega Diagnostics Ltd, Omega House, Carsebridge Court, Whins Road, Alloa, Clackmannanshire, FK10 3LQ Tel: (01259) 763030 Fax: (01259) 723251 E-mail: odl@omegadiagnostics.co.uk

R S R Ltd, The Avenue Industrial Park, Croescadarn Close, Cardiff, CF23 8HE Tel: (029) 2073 2076 Fax: (029) 2073 2704

Sykes Pickervant Ltd, Lancaster House, Bowerhill Industrial Estate, Bowerhill, Melksham, Wiltshire, SN12 6TT Tel: (01225) 700750 Fax: (01225) 791845

Trek Diagnostic Systems Ltd, Imberhorne Lane, East Grinstead, West Sussex, RH19 1QX Tel: (01342) 318777 Fax: (01342) 318666 E-mail: info@trekds.com

Unipath Ltd, Priory Business Park, Bedford, MK44 3UP Tel: (01234) 835000 Fax: (01234) 835001 E-mail: info@unipath.com

DIAGNOSTIC PRODUCTS

Bayer UK plc, Bayer House, Strawberry Hill, Newbury, Berkshire, RG14 1JA Tel: (01635) 563000 E-mail: corporate.communications@bayer.co.uk

Bio Diagnostics Ltd, Upton Industrial Estate, Rectory Road, Upton Upon Severn, Worcester, WR8 0LX Tel: (01684) 592262 Fax: (01684) 592501 E-mail: info@bio-diagnostics.co.uk

Omega Diagnostics Ltd, Omega House, Carsebridge Court, Whins Road, Alloa, Clackmannanshire, FK10 3LQ Tel: (01259) 763030 Fax: (01259) 723251 E-mail: odl@omegadiagnostics.co.uk

Trek Diagnostic Systems Ltd, Imberhorne Lane, East Grinstead, West Sussex, RH19 1QX Tel: (01342) 318777 Fax: (01342) 318666 E-mail: info@trekds.com

Unipath Ltd, Priory Business Park, Bedford, MK44 3UP Tel: (01234) 835000 Fax: (01234) 835001 E-mail: info@unipath.com

DIAL GAUGES

▶ Mapra Technik Co., Unit D13, The Seedbed Centre, Langston Road, Loughton, Essex, IG10 3TQ Tel: (020) 8508 4207 Fax: (020) 8502 5107 E-mail: info@mapra.co.uk

DIAL THERMOMETERS

Instrument & Gauges Electronics Ltd, Gravel Lane, Banks, Southport, Merseyside, PR9 8DE Tel: (01704) 505333 Fax: (01704) 505334 E-mail: sales@instruments-gauges.co.uk

LG International, Marsh Road, Lords Meadow Industrial Estate, Crediton, Devon, EX17 1EU Tel: (01363) 777500 Fax: (01363) 777501

J.W. Ray & Co. Liverpool Ltd, Unit 87 North Mersey Business Centre, Woodward Road, Knowsley Industrial Park, Liverpool, L33 7UY Tel: 0151-546 2534 Fax: 0151-549 1645

DIALYSIS DISPOSABLE PRODUCTS

Associated Hospital Supply Ltd, Sherwood Road, Aston Fields, Bromsgrove, Worcestershire, B60 3DR Tel: (01527) 876776 Fax: (01527) 872022 E-mail: info@associatedhospitalsupply.com

Fresenius Medical Care (UK) Ltd, Nunn Brook Road, Huthwaite, Sutton-In-Ashfield, Nottinghamshire, NG17 2HU Tel: (01623) 445100 Fax: (01623) 552409

DIALYSIS MACHINES

Fresenius Medical Care (UK) Ltd, Nunn Brook Road, Huthwaite, Sutton-In-Ashfield, Nottinghamshire, NG17 2HU Tel: (01623) 445100 Fax: (01623) 552409

DIAMOND ABRASIVE MATERIALS

▶ UK Diamond Tools, Tyrells Hall, Fowlmere Road, Shepreth, Royston, Hertfordshire, SG8 6QS Tel: (01763) 260430 Fax: (01763) 260430 E-mail: queries@schereltd.co.uk

DIAMOND AND CUBIC BORON NITRIDE (CBN) GRINDING

Charles Styles Ltd, New Bond Street, Birmingham, B9 4EJ Tel: 0121-772 2424 Fax: 0121-771 2597 E-mail: sales@hexasports.co.uk

DIAMOND BLADE MANUFRS

Cutting Import & Distribution, 2 Arthur Street, Stanningley, Pudsey, West Yorkshire, LS28 6JY Tel: 0113-256 7111 Fax: 0113-274 4759

Diamondjack Ltd, 16 Huntsmead, Alton, Hampshire, GU34 2SE Tel: (01420) 542932 Fax: (01420) 542608

Diaquip Sales & Service, 1 Whitefield Road, Bredbury, Stockport, Cheshire, SK6 2QR Tel: 0161-406 0609 Fax: 0161-406 0211

Golz UK Ltd, Springhead Enterprise Park, Springhead Road, Gravesend, Kent, DA11 8HB Tel: (01474) 321679 Fax: (01474) 321477 E-mail: sales@goelz.com

Malvern Lapidary, 39 Broadlands Drive, Malvern, Worcestershire, WR14 1PW Tel: (01684) 561537 Fax: (01684) 891611

Marcrist International Limited, Marcrist House, Kirk Sandall Industrial Estate, Doncaster, S. Yorkshire, DN3 1QR Tel: (01302) 890888 Fax: (01302) 883864 E-mail: info@marcrist.com

Sovereign Diamond Services Ltd, 13 Duddingston Square West, Edinburgh, EH15 1RS Tel: 0131-669 4365 Fax: 0131-669 4365

DIAMOND CORE DRILLING MACHINERY OR EQUIPMENT

Abrasive Chasers Drilling & Sawing LLP, 96 Broom Road, Stanford, Biggleswade, Bedfordshire, SG18 9JE Tel: (01462) 813666 Fax: (01462) 813351 E-mail: abrasive.chasers@btconnect.com

Diaquip Sales & Service, 1 Whitefield Road, Bredbury, Stockport, Cheshire, SK6 2QR Tel: 0161-406 0609 Fax: 0161-406 0211

Golz UK Ltd, Springhead Enterprise Park, Springhead Road, Gravesend, Kent, DA11 8HB Tel: (01474) 321679 Fax: (01474) 321477 E-mail: sales@goelz.com

Marita (Diamond Tooling) Ltd, 8 Longacre Way, Holbrook, Sheffield, S20 3FS Tel: 0114-248 8194 Fax: 0114-251 0667 E-mail: info@mdt.eu.com

Xcalibre Equipment Ltd, 3 Starley Court, Hotchkiss Way, Binley Industrial Estate, Coventry, CV3 2RL Tel: (024) 7644 4412 Fax: (024) 7663 5903 E-mail: xcalibre-equipt@btconnect.com

DIAMOND CORE DRILLING TOOLS

Abrasive Chasers Drilling & Sawing LLP, 96 Broom Road, Stanford, Biggleswade, Bedfordshire, SG18 9JE Tel: (01462) 813666 Fax: (01462) 813351 E-mail: abrasive.chasers@btconnect.com

Bridge Abrasives Ltd, Unit E, Ford Road, Totnes Industrial Estate, Totnes, Devon, TQ9 5LQ Tel: (01803) 866667 Fax: (01803) 866001 E-mail: info@bridge-abrasives.co.uk

D F T, The Flax Mill, 134 Townhill Road, Portglenone, Ballymena, County Antrim, BT44 8AW Tel: (028) 2582 2877 Fax: (028) 2582 2805 E-mail: info@dftfixings.com

J D M Diamond Masters Ltd, Unit 1-2a Holmes Chapel Business Park, Manor Lane, Holmes Chapel, Crewe, CW4 8AB Tel: (0845) 3301319 Fax: (0845) 3301369 E-mail: sales@diamondmasters.co.uk

Marcrist International Limited, Marcrist House, Kirk Sandall Industrial Estate, Doncaster, S. Yorkshire, DN3 1QR Tel: (01302) 890888 Fax: (01302) 883864 E-mail: info@marcrist.com

DIAMOND CUTTING OR CORE DRILLING EQUIPMENT

Accurite Industries, Cumbria, Haws Bank, Coniston, Cumbria, LA21 8AP Tel: (01539) 441313 Fax: (01539) 441225

Duradiamond Ltd, Kingfisher House, Auld Mart Road, Milnathort, Kinross, KY13 9FR Tel: (01577) 863028 Fax: (01577) 866704 E-mail: enquiries@duradiamond.com

Exactaform Cutting Tools Ltd, G2 Little Heath Industrial Estate, Old Church Road, Coventry, CV6 7ND Tel: (024) 7666 5823 Fax: (024) 7663 8251 E-mail: sales@exactaform.co.uk

Premier Diamond Products, Chislet Close, Lakesview International Business Park, Hersden, Canterbury, Kent, CT3 4LB Tel: (01227) 711555 Fax: (01227) 710540

DIAMOND CUTTING TOOLS

Abrasive Technology Ltd, Roxby Place, London, SW6 1RT Tel: (020) 7471 0200 Fax: (020) 7471 0202 E-mail: info@abrasive-tech.com

DIAMOND CUTTING/MILLING/ POLISHING ACCESSORIES

Abrasive Technology Ltd, Roxby Place, London, SW6 1RT Tel: (020) 7471 0200 Fax: (020) 7471 0202 E-mail: info@abrasive-tech.com

Flextol Ltd, 20 Swannington Road, Cottage Lane Industrial Estate, Broughton Astley, Leicester, LE9 6TU Tel: (01455) 285333 Fax: (01455) 285238 E-mail: sales@flextol.co.uk

DIAMOND CUTTING/MILLING/ POLISHING SERVICES

Contract Diamond Drilling Ltd, Harvest Court, Harvest Drive, Lowestoft, Suffolk, NR33 7NB Tel: (01502) 566500 Fax: (01502) 585815

Martract, Ardent Link, Humber Bridge Industrial Estate, Humber Bridge Industrial Estat, Barton-upon-Humber, South Humberside, DN18 5RN Tel: (01652) 632172 Fax: (01652) 660295 E-mail: info@martract.co.uk

Opticron Plastics, Unit 3 Sabre Court, Gillingham Business Park, Gillingham, Kent, ME8 0RW Tel: (01634) 366385 Fax: (01634) 366397 E-mail: info@opticron.co.uk

DIAMOND DRILLING BITS

Diaquip Sales & Service, 1 Whitefield Road, Bredbury, Stockport, Cheshire, SK6 2QR Tel: 0161-406 0609 Fax: 0161-406 0211

Duradiamond Ltd, Kingfisher House, Auld Mart Road, Milnathort, Kinross, KY13 9FR Tel: (01577) 863028 Fax: (01577) 866704 E-mail: enquiries@duradiamond.com

Geo Gem Ltd, Unit 15, Colomendy Business Park, Denbigh, Clwyd, LL16 5TA Tel: (01745) 815315 Fax: (01745) 815495 E-mail: sales@geogem.co.uk

DIAMOND DRILLING ON LAND CONTRACTORS OR ENGINEERS

Barcol Ltd, Oak Lodge, Studland Avenue, Wickford, Essex, SS12 0JF Tel: (01268) 764642 Fax: (01268) 764644

Boldon Drilling Ltd, Private Road 3, Colwick Industrial Estate, Nottingham, NG4 2BB Tel: 0115-961 1250 Fax: 0115-961 7338 E-mail: drill@bds.co.uk

British Drilling and Freezing Co. Ltd, Private Road No 3, Colwick Industrial Estate, Colwick, Nottingham, NG4 2BB Tel: 0115-961 1300 Fax: 0115-961 7338 E-mail: drill@bdf.co.uk

CMT (Testing) Ltd, Prime Park Way, Prime Enterprise Park, Derby, DE1 3QB Tel: (01332) 383333 Fax: (01332) 602607 E-mail: testing@cmt-ltd.co.uk

Core Cut Ltd, Bankhead, Winchburgh, Broxburn, West Lothian, EH52 6PP Tel: (01506) 854710 Fax: (01506) 853068 E-mail: info@corecut.co.uk

D Drill Master Drillers Ltd, 84 Clun Street, Sheffield, S4 7JS Tel: 0114-273 9199 Fax: 0114-276 5884 E-mail: sheffield@d-drill.co.uk

Dependable Diamond Drilling, 4 Parkway House Ashley Industrial Estate, Wakefield Road, Ossett, West Yorkshire, WF5 9JD Tel: (01924) 265646 Fax: (01924) 267217 E-mail: d.d.drilling@btconnect.com

Geotechnical Engineering Ltd, Centurion House, Olympus Park, Quedgeley, Gloucester, GL2 4NF Tel: (01452) 527743 Fax: (01452) 507435 E-mail: sales@geoeng.co.uk

Giles Engineering Services, 18 William Street, Dunoon, Argyll, PA23 7JH Tel: (01369) 705043 Fax: (01369) 703478

H & F Drilling Supplies Ltd, 16a Cunningham Road, Stirling, FK7 7SW Tel: (01786) 479575 Fax: (01786) 465803

▶ Isis Diamond Drilling, 31 Bradley Road, Patchway, Bristol, BS34 5LF Tel: 0117-907 7265 Fax: 0117-907 7265 E-mail: info@isisdiamonddrilling.co.uk

KSS Hire Services, Russell Gardens, Wickford, Essex, SS11 8BH Tel: (01268) 769531 Fax: (01268) 561034

Lloyd Drilling Ltd, 72 Hutton Close, Crowther, Washington, Tyne & Wear, NE38 0AH Tel: 0191-419 0321 Fax: 0191-416 8863 E-mail: lloyddrill@msn.com

Speedbore Diamond Drilling (Northern) Ltd, Unit 7, Wood St, Poulton-le-Fylde, Lancashire, FY6 8JY Tel: (01253) 891206 Fax: (01253) 893848 E-mail: peter@speedbore.com

DIAMOND GLASS CUTTERS

Shaw Cutters, Ashwellthorpe Industrial Estate, Ashwellthorpe, Norwich, NR16 1ER Tel: (01508) 488400 Fax: (01508) 488058 E-mail: sales@dcdevs.co.uk

DIAMOND IMPREGNATED GRINDING WHEEL MANUFRS

Abrasive Technology Ltd, Roxby Place, London, SW6 1RT Tel: (020) 7471 0200 Fax: (020) 7471 0202 E-mail: info@abrasive-tech.com

Astley Diamond Tools, Unit 10, Chancel Way, Witton Moor Lane Industrial Estate, Witton, Birmingham, B6 7AU Tel: 0121-356 8035 Fax: 0121-356 8035 E-mail: benorpeter@astley-diamontools.co.uk

Consort Diamond Products Ltd, A1-A2 Unit, Tir Llwyd Industrial Estate, Kinmel Bay, Rhyl, Clwyd, LL18 5JA Tel: (01745) 343951 Fax: (01745) 342015 E-mail: info@consortprecision.co.uk

Crusader Abrasives Ltd, Unit 24 Crossfield Industrial Estate, Crossfield Road, Lichfield, Staffordshire, WS13 6RJ Tel: (01543) 263632 Fax: (01543) 415787

Star Industrial Tools Ltd, 42 Westfield Road, Kings Heath, Birmingham, B14 7ST Tel: 0121-444 4354 Fax: 0121-441 1838 E-mail: sales@starindustrialtools.co.uk

Wendt Boart (UK) Ltd, Station Road, Staplehurst, Tonbridge, Kent, TN12 0QD Tel: (01580) 890800 Fax: (01580) 890888 E-mail: sales@wbuk.wendtgroup.com

DIAMOND IMPREGNATED TOOLS

Breton International Ltd, Havelock Buildings, Jubilee Street, Llandudno, Gwynedd, LL30 2NZ Tel: (01492) 875268 Fax: (01492) 860731 E-mail: info@breton-international.com

Consort Diamond Products Ltd, A1-A2 Unit, Tir Llwyd Industrial Estate, Kinmel Bay, Rhyl, Clwyd, LL18 5JA Tel: (01745) 343951 Fax: (01745) 342015 E-mail: info@consortprecision.co.uk

Klingspor Abrasives Ltd, Dukeries Close, Worksop, Nottinghamshire, S81 7DN Tel: (01909) 504400 Fax: (01909) 504405 E-mail: sales@klingspor.co.uk

Wendt Boart (UK) Ltd, Station Road, Staplehurst, Tonbridge, Kent, TN12 0QD Tel: (01580) 890800 Fax: (01580) 890888 E-mail: sales@wbuk.wendtgroup.com

DIAMOND INDENTERS

Star Industrial Tools Ltd, 42 Westfield Road, Kings Heath, Birmingham, B14 7ST Tel: 0121-444 4354 Fax: 0121-441 1838 E-mail: sales@starindustrialtools.co.uk

DIAMOND (INDUSTRIAL) MANUFRS OR CUTTERS

Apex Diamond Products Ltd, 10 Bartleet Road, Washford Industrial Estate, Redditch, Worcestershire, B98 0DQ Tel: (01527) 529011 Fax: (01527) 510740 E-mail: sales@apexdiamond.co.uk

Cape Diamond Products Ltd, Castle Vale Industrial Estate, Maybrook Road, Minworth, Sutton Coldfield, West Midlands, B76 1DJ Tel: 0121-351 4371 Fax: 0121-351 3094 E-mail: sales@cape-diamond.co.uk

E I D Ltd, 12 St Cross Street, London, EC1N 8UB Tel: (020) 7405 6594 Fax: (020) 7831 0372 E-mail: eidlondon@aol.com

I D C Holdings Ltd, 86 Hatton Garden, London, EC1N 8QQ Tel: (020) 7242 5303 Fax: (020) 7242 9406 E-mail: idc@idcholdings.com

Marcon Diamond Products Ltd, Marcon House, 131 High Street, Codicote, Hitchin, Hertfordshire, SG4 8UB Tel: (01438) 820581 Fax: (01438) 821352

Nixon Industrial Diamonds Ltd, Albion Industrial Estate, Endermere Road, Coventry, CV6 5RR Tel: (024) 7668 6069 Fax: (024) 7663 7213 E-mail: sales@nixondiamonds.co.uk

Ultra Hard Products, Heath Farm Cottage, Cockaynes Lane, Alresford, Colchester, CO7 8DA Tel: (01206) 827121

DIAMOND LAPPING COMPOUND MANUFRS

Engis UK Ltd, Unit 9 Centenary Business Park, Station Road, Henley-on-Thames, Oxfordshire, RG9 1DS Tel: (01491) 411117 Fax: (01491) 412252 E-mail: sales@engis.uk.com

Kemet International Ltd, Sutton Road, Maidstone, Kent, ME15 9NJ Tel: (01622) 755287 Fax: (01622) 670915 E-mail: sales@kemet.co.uk

▶ Lamplan Industries Ltd, Unit 5, Pettings Court Farm, Hodsoll Street, Sevenoaks, Kent, TN15 7LH Tel: (01732) 824829 Fax: (01732) 824828 E-mail: jbroad@lamsplan.com

DIAMOND MERCHANTS, *See also Diamond (Industrial) Merchants*

A Roberts, 67 Hatton Garden, London, EC1N 8JY Tel: (020) 7405 4987

▶ Daniel Prince Of London, 24 Hatton Garden, London, EC1N 8BQ Tel: (0845) 1083684 Fax: (020) 8944 8418 E-mail: sales@danielprince.co.uk

Delta Watch Co., 12-13 Greville Street, London, EC1N 8SB Tel: (020) 7405 0784 Fax: (020) 7404 8200

E & W Hopkins Ltd, 32-33 Hatton Garden, London, EC1N 8BR Tel: (020) 7405 6354 Fax: (020) 7405 1170 E-mail: ew_hopkins@hotmail.com

Ellison Bros, 24 Donegall Street, Belfast, BT1 2GP Tel: (028) 9032 5320 Fax: (028) 9032 8143E-mail: sales@ellisonbrothers.co.uk

H L Brown & Son Ltd, Leopold Street, Sheffield, S1 1LZ Tel: 0114-272 5440 Fax: 0114-272 4580 E-mail: info@hl-brown.co.uk

Invedia Ltd, 32 Hatton Garden, London, EC1N 8DL Tel: (020) 7242 8965 Fax: (020) 7242 5036 E-mail: koppelman@clara.net

▶ J Shalev Diamonds, 100 Hatton Garden, London, EC1N 8NX Tel: (020) 7404 4022 Fax: (07900) 563551 E-mail: jacob@shalev.co.uk

Levy Gems Co., Minerva House, 26-27 Hatton Garden, London, EC1N 8BR Tel: (020) 7242 4547 Fax: (020) 7831 0102 E-mail: levey.gems@virgin.net

Monnickendam Diamonds Ltd, 9 Ely Place, London, EC1N 6RY Tel: (020) 7242 2333 Fax: (020) 7404 0223

David L. Solomons Ltd, 5 Hatton Place, London, EC1N 8RU Tel: (020) 7242 7659 Fax: (020) 7831 6647 E-mail: dsolo34962@aol.com

▶ Paul Thorney, 17 Bridgeman Rd, Oswestry, Shropshire, SY11 2JP Tel: (01691) 654610 E-mail: PlThrn@aol.com

DIAMOND MOUNTERS/SETTERS TO THE TRADE

Delta Watch Co., 12-13 Greville Street, London, EC1N 8SB Tel: (020) 7405 0784 Fax: (020) 7404 8200

William Griffith & Sons (Birmingham) Ltd, 55-57 Vittoria St, Birmingham, B1 3NY Tel: 0121-236 1772

V. & F. Parker Ltd, 51 Vyse Street, Hockley, Birmingham, B18 6HS Tel: 0121-554 3587 Fax: 0121-523 2232

R H B, Unit 115B The Big Peg, 120 Vyse Street, Hockley, Birmingham, B18 6NB Tel: 0121-236 5310 Fax: 0121-236 5310

DIAMOND ON LAND DRILLING EQUIPMENT

Drill Cut Ltd, 3 Verulam Court, St. Albans Road, Stafford, ST16 3DT Tel: (01785) 240045 Fax: (01952) 820822 E-mail: info@drill-cut.freeserve.co.uk

J K S - Boyles UK Ltd, Unit 9 Salcombe Road, Meadow Lane Industrial Estate, Alfreton, Derbyshire, DE55 7RG Tel: (01773) 835323 Fax: (01773) 835075 E-mail: sales@jks-boyles-ltd.co.uk

DIAMOND PLATING

Astley Diamond Tools, Unit 10, Chancel Way, Witton Moor Lane Industrial Estate, Witton, Birmingham, B6 7AU Tel: 0121-356 8035 Fax: 0121-356 8035 E-mail: benorpeter@astley-diamontools.co.uk

Delta Watch Co., 12-13 Greville Street, London, EC1N 8SB Tel: (020) 7405 0784 Fax: (020) 7404 8200

DIAMOND POWDERS

E I D Ltd, 12 St Cross Street, London, EC1N 8UB Tel: (020) 7405 6594 Fax: (020) 7831 0372 E-mail: eidlondon@aol.com

I D C Holdings Ltd, 86 Hatton Garden, London, EC1N 8QQ Tel: (020) 7242 5303 Fax: (020) 7242 9406 E-mail: idc@idcholdings.com

DIAMOND TIPPED TOOL MAINTENANCE OR REPAIR

▶ AbTec Industries Ltd, Unit 4, Venture Court, Boleness Road, Wisbech, Cambridgeshire, PE13 2XQ Tel: (01945) 585500 Fax: (01945) 585052 E-mail: sales@abrasivetechnology.net

Diamond Power Service, 1a Clarke Street, Farnworth, Bolton, BL4 9JH Tel: (01204) 793303 Fax: (01204) 403804 E-mail: diamondpsi@aol.com

DIAMOND TIPPED TOOLS

Adamas GB Ltd, Unit W3 Littlemoor Business Centre, Littlemoor, Eckington, Sheffield, S21 4EF Tel: (01246) 433965 Fax: (01246) 436895

Adept Tooling Ltd, 25b Tir Llwyd Industrial Estate, Kinmel Bay, Rhyl, Clwyd, LL18 5JA Tel: (01745) 345050 Fax: (01745) 345060

Apex Diamond Products Ltd, 10 Bartleet Road, Washford Industrial Estate, Redditch, Worcestershire, B98 0DQ Tel: (01527) 529011 Fax: (01527) 510740 E-mail: sales@apexdiamond.co.uk

Argon Corporation Ltd, Ridgeway, Aycliffe Industrial Park, Newton Aycliffe, County Durham, DL5 6EE Tel: (01325) 304166 Fax: (01325) 304167

▶ Brit Bit Ltd, Technology & Manufacturing Centre, Souter Head Road, Altens Industrial Estate, Aberdeen, AB12 3LF Tel: (01224) 380050 Fax: (01224) 380291

Cape Diamond Products Ltd, Castle Vale Industrial Estate, Maybrook Road, Minworth, Sutton Coldfield, West Midlands, B76 1DJ Tel: 0121-351 4371 Fax: 0121-351 3094 E-mail: sales@cape-diamond.co.uk

Castle Diamond Technology Ltd, Unit 27 Tir Llwyd Industrial Estate, Kinmel Bay, Rhyl, Clwyd, LL18 5JA Tel: (01745) 360877 Fax: (01745) 360862 E-mail: sales@castle-tech.co.uk

Chase Diamond Tools International Ltd, 10 Shieling Court, Corby, Northamptonshire, NN18 9QD Tel: (01536) 461133 Fax: (01536) 461144 E-mail: sales@chasediamond.com

Consolidated Diamond Products Ltd, Unit 9a2, Carcroft Enterprise Park, Carcroft, Doncaster, South Yorkshire, DN6 8DD Tel: (01302) 725553 Fax: (01302) 725523 E-mail: enquiries@consolidateddiamond.co.uk

Consort Diamond Products Ltd, A1-A2 Unit, Tir Llwyd Industrial Estate, Kinmel Bay, Rhyl, Clwyd, LL18 5JA Tel: (01745) 343951 Fax: (01745) 342015 E-mail: info@consortprecision.co.uk

Cranden Diamond Products Ltd, Mounts Hill, Cranbrook Road, Benenden, Cranbrook, Kent, TN17 4ET Tel: (01580) 241013 Fax: (01580) 241838 E-mail: andrew.cranshaw@diamondtoolsuk.com

Croft Diamond Tools (UK '91) Ltd, Plumpton House, Plumpton Road, Hoddesdon, Hertfordshire, EN11 0LB Tel: (01992) 447700 Fax: (01992) 447519 E-mail: rosecroft@btconnect.com

Dtas Ltd, Low Common Road, Dinnington, Sheffield, S25 2RJ Tel: (01909) 552470 Fax: (01909) 552472 E-mail: info@dtas-diamonds.co.uk

Hertfordshire (Diamond) Products Ltd, Unit F, Gunnels Wood Park, Gunnels Wood Road, Stevenage, Hertfordshire, SG1 2BH Tel: (01438) 748758 Fax: (01438) 362060

▶ Hertfordshire Diamonds Products, Unit 3 Heathfield Caravan Park, Hurn, Christchurch, Dorset, BH23 6AS Tel: (01202) 481282 Fax: (01202) 481282

High Speed Hire, 47 High Street, Nailsea, Bristol, BS48 1AW Tel: (01275) 810364 Fax: (01275) 859464

I D C Holdings Ltd, 86 Hatton Garden, London, EC1N 8QQ Tel: (020) 7242 5303 Fax: (020) 7242 9406 E-mail: idc@idcholdings.com

J B Industrial Tooling, 2 Mount Caburn CR, Peacehaven, East Sussex, BN10 8DW Tel: (0870) 1660041 Fax: (0870) 1660042

J D M Diamond Masters Ltd, Unit 1-2a Holmes Chapel Business Park, Manor Lane, Holmes Chapel, Crewe, CW4 8AB Tel: (0845) 3301319 Fax: (0845) 3301369 E-mail: sales@diamondmasters.co.uk

J & J Tooling Services, Bridge House, Railway Street, Radcliffe, Manchester, M26 3AA Tel: 0161-724 7799 Fax: 0161-724 0722 E-mail: sales@jjtooling.co.uk

Midland Precision Diamond Tools, 44 Hockley Street, Birmingham, B18 6BH Tel: 0121-515 2108 Fax: 0121-554 9674

Nixon Industrial Diamonds Ltd, Albion Industrial Estate, Endermere Road, Coventry, CV6 5RR Tel: (024) 7668 6069 Fax: (024) 7663 7213 E-mail: sales@nixondiamonds.co.uk

R T H Sales, Queen St, Houghton Regis, Dunstable, Beds, LU5 5BT Tel: 01582 867222 Fax: 01582 585758

Star Industrial Tools Ltd, 42 Westfield Road, Kings Heath, Birmingham, B14 7ST Tel: 0121-444 4354 Fax: 0121-441 1838 E-mail: sales@starindustrialtools.co.uk

T A B Diamond Tools Ltd, 66 Alston Drive, Bradwell Abbey, Milton Keynes, MK13 9HB Tel: (01908) 320770 Fax: (01908) 320770

DIAMOND TOOLS AND PRODUCTS

J B Industrial Tooling, 2 Mount Caburn CR, Peacehaven, East Sussex, BN10 8DW Tel: (0870) 1660041 Fax: (0870) 1660042

▶ UK Diamond Tools, Tyrells Hall, Fowlmere Road, Shepreth, Royston, Hertfordshire, SG8 6QS Tel: (01763) 260430 Fax: (01763) 260430 E-mail: queries@schereltd.co.uk

DIAMOND WHEELS

Hytek Europe, 11 Elliott Road, Love Lane Industrial Estate, Cirencester, Gloucestershire, GL7 1YS Tel: (01285) 659349 Fax: (01285) 657915 E-mail: enquiries@hytekeurope.co.uk

Joro Abrasives Ltd, Holly Farm, Holly Lane, Styal, Wilmslow, Cheshire, SK9 4JL Tel: (01625) 524558 Fax: (01625) 539330

DIAPHRAGM PUMPS

Energy Chemical & Equipment Co, Southwell Business Park, Crew Lane, Southwell, Nottinghamshire, NG25 0TX Tel: (01636) 816600 Fax: (01636) 816602 E-mail: energypumps@aol.com

Fullbrook Systems Ltd, Unit 4 Bourne End Mills, Hemel Hempstead, Hertfordshire, HP1 2UJ Tel: (01442) 876777 Fax: (01442) 877144 E-mail: sales@fullbrook.com

Hilta TW, Flowplant House, Unit 8A-B Summit Crescent, Summit Estate, Smethwick, West Midlands, B66 1BT Tel: 0121-525 9955 Fax: 0121-525 0748 E-mail: hilta@hiltapumps.com

Tapflo UK Ltd, B The Apex Centre, Church Lane, Colden Common, Winchester, Hampshire, SO21 1TN Tel: (01962) 717131 Fax: (01962) 717130 E-mail: mick@tapflo-demon.co.uk

Tri Ark, Burnham Business Park, Springfield Road, Burnham-on-Crouch, Essex, CM0 8TE Tel: (01621) 781144 Fax: (01621) 781155 E-mail: sales@tri-ark.com

DIAPHRAGM VALVES

Heap & Partners Ltd, Britannia House, Newton Road, Hoylake, Wirral, Merseyside, CH47 3DG Tel: 0151-632 3393 Fax: 0151-632 4453 E-mail: info@heaps.co.uk

DIARY CORNER/EDGING, METAL

D Leonardt & Co., New Road, Highley, Bridgnorth, Shropshire, WV16 6NN Tel: (01746) 861203 Fax: (01746) 862296 E-mail: sales@leonardt.com

DIARY DESIGNERS/ PRODUCERS/PUBLISHERS

Charles Letts Group Ltd, Thornybank Industrial Estate, Dalkeith, Midlothian, EH22 2NE Tel: 0131-663 1971 Fax: 0131-660 3225 E-mail: diaries@letts.co.uk

Cougar Designs, 6A Bart Street, Sparkhill, Birmingham, B11 4SA Tel: 0121-773 9491 Fax: 0121-771 0464

Filofax Time Management, Unit 3 Victoria Gardens, Burgess Hill, West Sussex, RH15 9NB Tel: (01444) 238100 Fax: (01444) 238119 E-mail: enquiries@filofax.co.uk

G H Enterprises, 10 Coope Road, Bollington, Kerridge, Macclesfield, Cheshire, SK10 5AE Tel: (01625) 574336 Fax: (01625) 573727 E-mail: ghe@breathemail.net

J M Tatler & Son Ltd, Abbey Street Works, Derby, DE22 3SW Tel: (01332) 342120 Fax: (01332) 293699 E-mail: willtat@fsbdial.co.uk

Moments Calendars, Wayzgoose Drive, Derby, DE21 6ST Tel: (01332) 285911 Fax: (01332) 285912 E-mail: sales@moments.co.uk

Neale Dataday Ltd, Charfleet Bindery, Canvey Island, Essex, SS8 0PA Tel: (0800) 0284536 Fax: (01268) 510636 E-mail: sales@nealedataday.co.uk

Pirongs Ltd, 10 Silverhills Road, Decoy Industrial Estate, Newton Abbot, Devon, TQ12 5NA Tel: (01626) 352655 Fax: (01626) 336574 E-mail: mail@pirongs.co.uk

DIARY DISTRIBUTORS OR AGENTS

Charles Letts Group Ltd, Thornybank Industrial Estate, Dalkeith, Midlothian, EH22 2NE Tel: 0131-663 1971 Fax: 0131-660 3225 E-mail: diaries@letts.co.uk

Cheshire Dairy Products, Congleton Road, Arclid, Sandbach, Cheshire, CW11 2UJ Tel: (01477) 500480 Fax: (01477) 500480

Impact Calendars, 1 Redwood Park, Capel, Tonbridge, Kent, TN12 6WB Tel: (01892) 838811 Fax: (01892) 836699 E-mail: impactcal@dial.pipex.com

Ryman The Stationer, 175-177 High Street, Guildford, Surrey, GU1 3AW Tel: (01483) 454088 Fax: (01483) 454088

W F S Ltd, 30 Main Road, Weston, Crewe, CW2 5NA Tel: (01270) 252001 Fax: (01270) 213131 E-mail: contact@wfsltd.co.uk

DIATHERMY CABLES

▶ Grazedean Ltd, Unit 27, 865 Ringwood Road, Bournemouth, BH11 8LL Tel: (01202) 581645 Fax: (01202) 593824 E-mail: info@grazedean.com

DICING OR SLICING PRECISION SAWS

Disco Hi-Tec, Second Floor, 151 London Road, East Grinstead, West Sussex, RH19 1ET Tel: (01342) 313165 Fax: (01342) 313177 E-mail: sales.uk@discoeurope.com

DICTATING MACHINE MAINTENANCE SERVICES

▶ Business Equipment Service, 6 Titan Court, Laporte Way, Luton, LU4 8EF Tel: (01582) 417332 Fax: (01582) 417332 E-mail: mike@besluton.co.uk

Electronic Recording Systems, Dundridge Lane, Bishops Waltham, Southampton, SO32 1GD Tel: (01489) 896682 Fax: (01489) 896682

T R M Scotland Ltd, 29 Cardowan Drive, Stepps, Glasgow, G33 6HE Tel: 0141-779 9991 Fax: 0141-779 9991

T R M Southern Ltd, 132 London Road, Waterlooville, Hampshire, PO7 5SU Tel: (023) 9225 5686 Fax: (023) 9225 5700 E-mail: services@trm-southern.co.uk

TRM (Southern) Ltd, 19 Willow Gdns, North Baddesley, Southampton, SO52 9FY Tel: (023) 8073 3824 Fax: (023) 8041 0992

Voice Products Ltd, Innovation House, Alexander Bell Centre, Hopkinson Way, Andover, Hampshire, SP10 3UR Tel: (0870) 0503870 Fax: (0870) 0503872 E-mail: info@voiceproducts.co.uk

DICTATING MACHINES

Dictating Machine Co Ltd, 22 Broadway, London, SW1H 0BH Tel: (020) 7222 2626 Fax: (020) 7222 6680

Electronic Recording Systems, Dundridge Lane, Bishops Waltham, Southampton, SO32 1GD Tel: (01489) 896682 Fax: (01489) 896682

Integrity Services Ltd, 23 Sandy Lane, Aston, Birmingham, B6 5TP Tel: 0121-327 2872 Fax: 0121-327 0454 E-mail: sales@integrityservices.co.uk

Offstat Office Supplies Ltd, 2nd Floor, 41 Dace Road, London, E3 2NG Tel: (020) 8525 7707 Fax: (020) 8525 7708 E-mail: office-services@offstat.sagehost.co.uk

Philips Speech Processing, 8 The Courtyards, Wyncolls Road, Severalls Industrial Park, Colchester, CO4 9PE Tel: (01206) 755755 Fax: (01206) 755888 E-mail: info@speech.philips.com

Sanyo Speechtek Ltd, Sanyo House, Otterspool Way, Watford, WD25 8JX Tel: (01923) 205900 Fax: (01923) 205935 E-mail: dictationsupport@sanyo.co.uk

Townley Office Equipment, Unit 4 Malham Road, London, SE23 1AG Tel: (020) 8291 1999 Fax: (020) 8291 9177

DIE AND PUNCH GRINDING MACHINES

Hunton Ltd, Hilton Rd, Cobbs Wood Industrial Estate, Ashford, Kent, TN23 1EW Tel: (01233) 628976 Fax: (01233) 664909 E-mail: sales@mjallen.co.uk

▶ Hunton - R M T - Gabro Machines, Cobbs Wood Industrial Estate, Hilton Road, Ashford, Kent, TN23 1EW Tel: (01233) 628976 Fax: (01233) 664909 E-mail: sales@mjallen.co.uk

DIE CASTING DIESINKING, *See Diecasting Mould/Die etc*

DIE CASTING LUBRICANTS

Acheson Industries Europe Ltd, Cattewater Road, Plymouth, PL4 0SP Tel: (01752) 218788 Fax: (01752) 207133 E-mail: acheson.plymouth@nstarch.com

Chem-Trend (UK) Ltd, Hough Mills, Bradford Road, Halifax, West Yorkshire, HX3 7BN Tel: (0870) 3504708 Fax: (0870) 3509427 E-mail: uksales@chemtrend.com

Cotswold Chemicals & Lubricants, Unit 16-17, Ryeford Industrial Estate, Ryeford, Stonehouse, Gloucestershire, GL10 2LB Tel: (01453) 825292 Fax: (01453) 791451 E-mail: sales@cotswoldchemicals.co.uk

Fenco-Aldridge (Barton) Ltd, Lovat Court, Caldecote St, Newport Pagnell, Buckinghamshire, MK16 0YZ Tel: (01908) 614646 Fax: (01908) 214482 E-mail: fab@fenco.co.uk

Petrofer UK plc, Harcourt Business Park, Halesfield 17, Telford, Shropshire, TF7 4PW Tel: (01952) 580100 Fax: (01952) 580101 E-mail: sales@petrofer.co.uk

DIE CASTING SLEEVES OR PLUNGERS

Precision Tool & Engineering Co., Pountney Street, Wolverhampton, WV2 4HX Tel: (01902) 459752 Fax: (01902) 458928 E-mail: mail@precisiontool.co.uk

DIE CASTINGS, *See also headings for particular types*

A M E Pressure Die Casting Ltd, Unit 59c Siddons Factory Estate, Howard Street, West Bromwich, West Midlands, B70 0SU Tel: 0121-505 5222 Fax: 0121-505 5444 E-mail: amediecasting@aol.com

Aacorn Engineering, Earlswood Trading Estate, Poolhead Lane, Earlswood, Solihull, West Midlands, B94 5EW Tel: (01564) 703545 Fax: (01564) 703511 E-mail: mail@aacorn-engineering.freeserve.co.uk

Avon P D C, 40 Holford Way, Witton, Birmingham, B6 7AX Tel: 0121-681 1160 Fax: 0121-344 3902 E-mail: enquiries@avonpdc.co.uk

Etma Engineering Ltd, Victoria Road, Halesowen, West Midlands, B62 8HY Tel: 0121-559 5333 Fax: 0121-559 2236E-mail: sales@etma.co.uk

Glen Castings Ltd, Meadows Mill, Burnley Road, Bacup, Lancashire, OL13 8BZ Tel: (01706) 873967 Fax: (01706) 879234 E-mail: glencas@lancs.co.uk

H & J Speake Ltd, Strawberry Lane Industrial Estate, Strawberry Lane, Willenhall, West Midlands, WV13 3RS Tel: (01902) 607188 Fax: (01902) 635802 E-mail: hjspeake@freenetname.co.uk

Haworth Castings Ltd, Budds Lane, Romsey, Hampshire, SO51 0HA Tel: (01794) 512685 Fax: (01794) 830086 E-mail: sales@haworthcastings.com

Hemphill Castings Ltd, 273 Bromford Lane, Washwood Heath, Birmingham, B8 2SG Tel: 0121-327 5459 Fax: 0121-322 2040

JC Trophies, The Business Centre, 21 James Road, Tyseley, Birmingham, B11 2BA Tel: 0121-707 0606 Fax: 0121-707 0609 E-mail: jdcmanufacturing@blueyonder.co.uk

Kemlows Diecasting Products Ltd, Charlton Mead Lane, Hoddesdon, Hertfordshire, EN11 0HB Tel: (01992) 460671 Fax: (01992) 446889 E-mail: sales@kemlows.co.uk

Archibald Kenrick & Sons Ltd, Union Street, Kenrick Way, West Bromwich, West Midlands, B70 6DB Tel: 0121-553 2741 Fax: 0121-500 6332 E-mail: enquiries@kenricks.co.uk

Kenwell Precision Die Casting Ltd, 1 Smallbridge Industrial Park, Riverside Drive, Rochdale, Lancashire, OL16 2SH Tel: (01706) 640412 Fax: (01706) 711894 E-mail: sales@kenwellprecisiondiecastings.co.uk

Lesney Industries Ltd, Norwood House, Temple Bank, River way, Harlow, Essex, CM20 2DY Tel: (01279) 260130 Fax: (01279) 413100 E-mail:

Moldmet Ltd, Sandall Stones Road, Kirk Sandall Industrial Estate, Doncaster, South Yorkshire, DN3 1QR Tel: (01302) 888810 Fax: (01302) 880333 E-mail: ken@moldmet.com

Norfran Aluminium Ltd, West Chirton Trading Estate, North Shields, Tyne & Wear, NE29 7TY Tel: 0191-258 2611 Fax: 0191-257 1549 E-mail: jb@norfran.co.uk

P M S Diecasting, Unit 11 Braithwell Way, Hellaby, Rotherham, South Yorkshire, S66 8QY Tel: (01709) 701901 Fax: (01709) 700833 E-mail: gpanter@pmsdiecasting.co.uk

Perry Castings, Bank Street, Wolverhampton, WV10 9DU Tel: (01902) 732910 Fax: (01902) 721046

Pressure Cast Products Ltd, Fairacres Industrial Estate, Dedworth Road, Windsor, Berkshire, SL4 4LE Tel: (01753) 868969 Fax: (01753) 840475 E-mail: info@pressurecast.co.uk

R D Castings Ltd, Leyton Avenue, Mildenhall, Bury St. Edmunds, Suffolk, IP28 7BL Tel: (01638) 717944 Fax: (01638) 716590

Roston Castings, Mill Lane, Ellastone, Ashbourne, Derbyshire, DE6 2HF Tel: (01335) 324368 Fax: (01335) 324544 E-mail: sales@rostoncastings.co.uk

Sant Products Ltd, Unit 42 Coneygre Industrial Estate, Tipton, West Midlands, DY4 8XP Tel: 0121-557 7066 Fax: 0121-557 2007

West Midlands Foundry Co. Ltd, Blakemore Road, West Bromwich, West Midlands, B70 8JF Tel: 0121-553 1515 Fax: 0121-500 5839

DIE CASTINGS, ZINC ALLOY

▶ Petchcast, 25 Trent Street, Digbeth, Birmingham, B5 5NL Tel: 0121 643 3130 Fax: 0121 633 4283 E-mail: david@petchcast.co.uk

DIE CUSHIONS

Worson Die Cushions Ltd, Linel Works, 89-91 Rolfe St, Smethwick, West Midlands, B66 2AY Tel: 0121-558 0939 Fax: 0121-558 0017

DIE CUT ADHESIVE MATERIALS

▶ IM3D Ltd, Axis 3, High Carr Business Park, Newcastle, Staffordshire, ST5 7UF Tel: (01782) 564888 Fax: (01782) 564344 E-mail: info@im3duk.com

DIE CUTTING

A E Davidson & Son Ltd, 3 Alton Road Industrial Estate, Ross-on-Wye, Herefordshire, HR9 5NB Tel: (01989) 764850 Fax: (01989) 768291 E-mail: aedties@btinternet.com

Atlas Laser Dies, 3 Northgate Industrial Park, Collier Row Road, Romford, RM5 2BG Tel: (020) 8548 7230 Fax: (020) 8548 7231 E-mail: sales@atlasdies.com

Crown Manufactory Rotherham Ltd, Chapel Walk, Masborough Street, Rotherham, South Yorkshire, S60 1EP Tel: (01709) 562957 Fax: (01709) 554728

Dies To Die For, Unit 1, Low Bank Garage, Ashton-in-Makerfield, Wigan, Lancashire, WN4 9RN Tel: (01942) 711063 Fax: (01942) 711063 E-mail: kirstywiseman@hotmail.com

Dunmar Packaging Ltd, Kus Industrial Estate, Manor Lane, Hawarden, Deeside, Clwyd, CH5 3PJ Tel: (01244) 526872 Fax: (01244) 537396

Farr Formes, 1-4 Piper Rd, Hardwick Narrows Industrial Estate, King's Lynn, Norfolk, PE30 4NG Tel: (01553) 762705 Fax: (01553) 765245 E-mail: cadroom@farrformes.co.uk

G S M Industrial Graphics, Avenue One, Witney, Oxfordshire, OX28 4BZ Tel: (01993) 776511 Fax: (01993) 778238 E-mail: gsmindustrialgraphics@gsmgroup.co.uk

Hartington Litho Ltd, Marlborough Road, Lancing Business Park, Lancing, West Sussex, BN15 8UF Tel: (01903) 761401 Fax: (01903) 767301 E-mail: micheal@hartingtonlitho.co.uk

Make A Dye Laser, 2 Abbey Road, London, E15 3LG Tel: (020) 8519 8161 Fax: (020) 8534 3248

MK Technology, 45 Bradgate Street, Leicester, LE4 0AW Tel: 0116-251 3001 Fax: 0116-251 7834

Paper Shapers, 10 Premier Drum Works, Canal Street, Wigston, Leicestershire, LE18 4PL Tel: 0116-277 4433 Fax: 0116-277 4300 E-mail: cutters@papershapers.co.uk

Paragon Cutting Forms, Unit 23 Blaydon Business Centre, Cowen Road, Blaydon-on-Tyne, Tyne & Wear, NE21 5TW Tel: 0191-487 9555 Fax: 0191-487 9666 E-mail: sales@paragoncfl.com

DIE CUTTING EQUIPMENT, ROTARY

▶ Gerhardt Ltd, Trent La Industrial Estate, Willow Road, Castle Donington, Derby, DE74 2NP Tel: (01332) 853434 Fax: (01332) 810274 E-mail: info@gerhardt.co.uk

DIE CUTTING MACHINE/ EQUIPMENT MANUFRS

Crosland V K Ltd, Unit 4, Lyons Road, Trafford Park, Manchester, M17 1RN Tel: 0161-877 8668 Fax: 0161-876 5234 E-mail: sales@croslandvk.com

D K Engineering Services, 7 Enterprise Industrial Estate, Enterprise Road, Waterlooville, Hampshire, PO8 0BB Tel: (023) 9259 3947 Fax: (023) 9259 3948 E-mail: sales@dkeltd.co.uk

Newfoil Machines, Moorhey Street, Oldham, OL4 1JE Tel: 0161-620 5688 Fax: 0161-627 0551 E-mail: sales@newfoilmachines.co.uk

Paper Shapers, 10 Premier Drum Works, Canal Street, Wigston, Leicestershire, LE18 4PL Tel: 0116-277 4433 Fax: 0116-277 4300 E-mail: cutters@papershapers.co.uk

DIE CUTTING TOOLS

Cutting Edge Tooling Ltd, Unit 75, Trent Business Centre, Canal Street, Long Eaton, Nottingham, NG10 4HN Tel: (0870) 7667681 Fax: (0870) 4602353 E-mail: sales@cuttingedgetooling.co.uk

DIE FORMS

Medway Cutters, Joseph Wilson Industrial Estate, Millstrood Road, Whitstable, Kent, CT5 3PS Tel: (01227) 273138 Fax: (01227) 770344 E-mail: sales@medwaycutters.co.uk

MK Technology, 45 Bradgate Street, Leicester, LE4 0AW Tel: 0116-251 3001 Fax: 0116-251 7834

Paragon Cutting Forms, Unit 23 Blaydon Business Centre, Cowen Road, Blaydon-on-Tyne, Tyne & Wear, NE21 5TW Tel: 0191-487 9555 Fax: 0191-487 9666 E-mail: sales@paragoncfl.com

Trade Cutting Formes Ltd, Unit 14b, Tanfield Lea Industrial Estate North, Tanfield Lea, Stanley, County Durham, DH9 9UU Tel: (01207) 230598 Fax: (01207) 290945 E-mail: sales@tcf-ltd.co.uk

DIE MAKING INDUSTRY SUPPLIES/DISTRIBUTORS/ FACTORS/AGENTS

Metal-Woods Ltd, 14 Church Street, Market Harborough, Leicestershire, LE16 7AB Tel: (01858) 462641 Fax: (01858) 431616 E-mail: sales@metal-woods.co.uk

DIE RECLAMATION ENGINEERS/ SERVICES

Kespar Engineering Ltd, Johnson House Bilston Industrial Estate, Oxford Street, Bilston, West Midlands, WV14 7EG Tel: (01902) 353848 Fax: (01902) 494939 E-mail: andywalker@kespar.co.uk

DIE SET TOOLS

Hunton Ltd, Hilton Rd, Cobbs Wood Industrial Estate, Ashford, Kent, TN23 1EW Tel: (01233) 628976 Fax: (01233) 664909 E-mail: sales@mjallen.co.uk

DIE SETS

A W Precision Ltd, Cosford Lane, Rugby, Warwickshire, CV21 1QN Tel: (01788) 542271 Fax: (01788) 561256 E-mail: sales@awp-ltd.com

Dan (UK) Ltd, Unit 1, Mucklow Hill 1 Trading Estate, Mucklow Hill, Halesowen, West Midlands, B62 8DF Tel: 0121-585 7171 Fax: 0121-585 7272 E-mail: sales@danlyuk.com

Danly UK Ltd, 2 Aintree Road, Perivale, Greenford, Middlesex, UB6 7LA Tel: (020) 8998 5381 Fax: (020) 8991 2461 E-mail: sales@danleyuk.com

DIE SINKING SERVICES, DROP FORGING TRADE

Dynamic Die & Steel (Sheffield) Ltd, 136 Savile Street East, Sheffield, S4 7UQ Tel: 0114-276 1100 Fax: 0114-275 0752

Hewmor Products Ltd, Unit D4 Hilton Trading Estate, Hilton Road, Lanesfield, Wolverhampton, WV4 6DW Tel: (01902) 491144 Fax: (01902) 401952 E-mail: hewmor.products@btconnect.com

DIE SPRINGS

Baron Springs, Unit 3 70 Strathclyde Street, Glasgow, G40 4JR Tel: 0141-550 3477 Fax: 0141-554 7240

Lee Spring Ltd, Latimer Road, Wokingham, Berkshire, RG41 2WA Tel: 0118-978 1800 Fax: 0118-977 4832 E-mail: abinding@leespring.co.uk

DIE STAMPING/EMBOSSING/ ENGRAVING/SINKING

Baddeley Reynolds & Dix Ltd, 23-31 Dennett Road, Croydon, CR0 3JD Tel: (020) 8684 1277 Fax: (020) 8689 8791

Documedia, Northern Way, Bury St. Edmunds, Suffolk, IP32 6NR Tel: (01284) 762201 Fax: (01284) 764033 E-mail: sales@documedia.co.uk

Downey & Co. Ltd, Unit 1 Peterley Business Centre, 472 Hackney Road, London, E2 9EG Tel: (020) 7739 8696 Fax: (020) 7739 9877 E-mail: orders@downey.co.uk

Emblem Die Sinking, 32 Hylton Street, Birmingham, B18 6HN Tel: 0121-554 8028 Fax: 0121-554 8028

Foil Ribbon & Impact Printing Scotland Ltd, 4 Rutherford Court, 15 North Avenue, Clydebank Business Park, Clydebank, Dunbartonshire, G81 2QP Tel: 0141-952 5525 Fax: 0141-952 5524 E-mail: scotland@foilribbon.com

Frewer Brothers Ltd, 3 Wealdstone Road, Sutton, Surrey, SM3 9QN Tel: (020) 8641 7171 Fax: (020) 8644 4779 E-mail: mail@frewerbrothers.co.uk

Oak Die Stamping & Engraving Co. Ltd, Tyburn Industrial Estate, Ashold Farm Road, Birmingham, B24 9QG Tel: 0121-382 4585 Fax: 0121-377 6359 E-mail: ordes-oak@btconnect.com

Shaftesbury Engraving/Printing Unit 7, 7 Plaza Business Centre, Stockingswater Lane, Enfield, Middlesex, EN3 7XT Tel: (020) 8443 3970 Fax: (020) 8443 3972 E-mail: sales@shaftesburyengraving.co.uk

Thomas L Wilkins Ltd, 2-4 Johnson Street, Leicester, LE1 4DN Tel: 0116-251 8996 Fax: (0870) 1659258 E-mail: sales@tlwilkins.co.uk

W Downing, 79 Spencer Street, Birmingham, B18 6DE Tel: 0121-236 7353 Fax: 0121-200 2429

Walsall Die & Tool Co. Ltd, Unit 2 Woodall Street, Walsall, WS3 3HG Tel: (01922) 492989 Fax: (01922) 492989

DIECASTING DIE, *See Diecasting Mould/Die etc*

DIECASTING MACHINE MAINTENANCE OR REPAIR SERVICES

E M B Diecasting Machines Ltd, Unit 1 Oldbury Road Industrial Estate, 132 Oldbury Road, Smethwick, West Midlands, B66 1JE Tel: 0121-565 3199 Fax: 0121-555 5275 E-mail: emba@embdiecast.fsbusiness.co.uk

Frech (UK) Ltd, The Production Centre, Boundary Industrial Estate, Fordhouses, Wolverhampton, WV10 7EL Tel: (01902) 786616 Fax: (01902) 786626 E-mail: info@frech.co.uk

Linear Motion, Park St South, Wolverhampton, WV2 3JH Tel: (01902) 425588 Fax: (01902) 425504

DIECASTING MACHINE MANUFRS

Frech (UK) Ltd, The Production Centre, Boundary Industrial Estate, Fordhouses, Wolverhampton, WV10 7EL Tel: (01902) 786616 Fax: (01902) 786626 E-mail: info@frech.co.uk

S M T Network Solutions Ltd, 20 Park Street, Princes Risborough, Buckinghamshire, HP27 9AH Tel: (01844) 275100 Fax: (01844) 275111 E-mail: info@smtnet.co.uk

▶ Worswick Engineering Ltd, Philips Road, Blackburn, BB1 5SG Tel: (01254) 261351 Fax: (01254) 682208 E-mail: sales@worswick.com

DIECASTING MOULD/DIE TOOL DESIGN

C A E Solutions Ltd, Unit D4 Hilton Trading Estate, Hilton Road, Lanesfield, Wolverhampton, WV4 6DW Tel: (01902) 403555 Fax: (01902) 401952 E-mail: sales@cae-solutions.co.uk

DIECASTING MOULD/DIE TOOLMAKERS

Abbey Tool & Dye, Unit 11 Old Canal Wharf, Navigation Road, Stoke-on-Trent, ST6 3BL Tel: (01782) 838137 Fax: (01782) 577372 E-mail: abbeytool@aol.com

Advanced Cooling Systems U.K Ltd, Highfield Industrial Estate, Warren Road, Folkestone, Kent, CT19 6DD Tel: (01303) 255465 Fax: (01303) 246186 E-mail: info@atsuk.com

Al Tools Ltd, Sidings Road, Lowmoor Road Business Park, Kirkby-in-Ashfield, Nottingham, NG17 7JZ Tel: (01623) 751577 Fax: (01623) 755590 E-mail: alanlockyear@altoolsltd.co.uk

Alexican Ltd, 177 King Street, Dukinfield, Cheshire, SK16 4LG Tel: 0161-339 1999 Fax: 0161-330 1555 E-mail: info@alexican.co.uk

Arvon Die & Tool Co., Oaks Street, Quarry Bank, Brierley Hill, West Midlands, DY5 2JH Tel: (01384) 567970 Fax: (01384) 567970 E-mail: enquires@arvon.co.uk

Astral Pattern Co. Ltd, Roway La, Oldbury, W. Midlands, B69 3EJ Tel: 0121-552 3507 Fax: 0121-544 2471

B & T Quality Engineering, Unit B Pooley Lane, Polesworth, Tamworth, Staffordshire, B78 1JA Tel: (01827) 895377 Fax: (01827) 895377

Bournville Engineering, Lifford Trading Estate, Lifford Lane, Birmingham, B30 3DY Tel: 0121-459 9339 Fax: 0121-459 9242

Burnac Ltd, Ohio Grove, Hot Lane Industrial Estate, Stoke-on-Trent, ST6 2BL Tel: (01782) 837599 Fax: (01782) 837149 E-mail: burnac@burnac.co.uk

C A E Solutions Ltd, Unit D4 Hilton Trading Estate, Hilton Road, Lanesfield, Wolverhampton, WV4 6DW Tel: (01902) 403555 Fax: (01902) 401952 E-mail: sales@cae-solutions.co.uk

C & L Patterns, Unit 5 Field Gate, Walsall, WS1 3DJ Tel: (01922) 628377 Fax: (01922) 628377

Constell Engineers Ltd, Nile Street, Rochdale, Lancashire, OL16 2JQ Tel: (01706) 646936 Fax: (01706) 647817 E-mail: office@constell.co.uk

D Harvey & Co., 4 Mill Park, Cannock, Staffordshire, WS11 7XT Tel: (01543) 573408 Fax: (01543) 462100 E-mail: sales@dharveyandco.co.uk

▶ D M E U K, Carrwood Road, Chesterfield Trading Estate, Chesterfield, Derbyshire, S41 9QB Tel: (020) 7133 0037 Fax: (020) 7133 0036 E-mail: dme_uk@dmeeu.com

D R Precision, 8 Shell Corner Industrial Estate, Long Lane, Halesowen, West Midlands, B62 9LD Tel: 0121-561 1874 Fax: 0121-561 1874

Diemould Service Co. Ltd, 11 Blenheim Road, Cressex Business Park, High Wycombe, Buckinghamshire, HP12 3RS Tel: (01494) 523811 Fax: (01494) 452898 E-mail: sales@dms-diemould.co.uk

DIECASTING MOULD/DIE TOOLMAKERS – *continued*

Elliott Musgrave Ltd, Jackson Street, Bradford, West Yorkshire, BD3 9SJ Tel: (01274) 731115 Fax: (01274) 722691 E-mail: sales@elliott-musgrave.co.uk

Frech (UK) Ltd, The Production Centre, Boundary Industrial Estate, Fordhouses, Wolverhampton, WV10 7EL Tel: (01902) 786616 Fax: (01902) 786626 E-mail: info@frech.co.uk

H C M Engineering Ltd, Pedmore Road, Stourbridge, West Midlands, DY9 7DZ Tel: (01384) 422643 Fax: (01384) 899210 E-mail: simonh@hcmeng.co.uk

Hi Spec Precision Toolmakers Ltd, 36 Rumer Hill Bus Estate, Rumer Hill Road, Cannock, Staffordshire, WS11 0ET Tel: (01543) 505323 Fax: (01543) 505230 E-mail: neil@hispec.uk.com

Howard 2000 Ltd, Howard Centre, Paper Mill End, Great Barr, Unit 4, Birmingham, B44 8NH Tel: 0121-356 9833 Fax: 0121-356 0280

I H C Plating (Nelson) Ltd, Unit 2 Valley Trading Estate, Southfield Street, Nelson, Lancashire, BB9 0LD Tel: (01282) 693195 Fax: (01282) 696117

I M S Supplies Ltd, 3 Clifton Road, Huntingdon, Cambridgeshire, PE29 7EJ Tel: (01480) 411763 Fax: (01480) 417170 E-mail: imssupplies@cs.com

Ironsun Ltd, Lindon Road, Brownhills, Walsall, WS8 7BG Tel: (01543) 454453 Fax: (01543) 454450 E-mail: admin@ironsun-ltd.com

Jaymark Mould & Tool Co. Ltd, Unit 1, Capital Place, Lovet Road, The Pinnacles, Harlow, Essex, CM19 5AS Tel: (01279) 427945 Fax: (01279) 641330 E-mail: jaymark@btinternet.com

Joal Engineering, 13 Orchard Road, Melbourn, Royston, Hertfordshire, SG8 6HL Tel: (01763) 245490 Fax: (01763) 247582

Lawday Engineering Ltd, Grafton Road, West Bromwich, West Midlands, B71 4EH Tel: 0121-553 4892 Fax: 0121-500 5842 E-mail: sales@lawday.co.uk

Lodent Precision, Colliers Close, Coppice Side Industrial Estate, Brownhills, Walsall, WS8 7EU Tel: (01543) 453700 Fax: (01543) 453800 E-mail: info@lodent.flyer.co.uk

M K Tool & Die Ltd, 19 Spackmans Way, Slough, SL1 2SA Tel: 01753 539159

Micromech Precision Tools, Wellfield Street, Rochdale, Lancashire, OL11 1AW Tel: (01706) 646505 Fax: (01706) 646505

Minium Tool Co. Ltd, Unit 1 & 2, Malmesbury Road, Kingsditch Trading Estate, Cheltenham, Gloucestershire, GL51 9PL Tel: (01242) 529352 Fax: (01242) 521737 E-mail: miniumtool@btconnect.com

Newark Tools Ltd, Coppice Side Industrial Estate, Brownhills, Walsall, WS8 7EX Tel: (01543) 454600

Oak Tree Plastic & Engineering Ltd, Spon La South, West Bromwich, West Midlands, B70 6AZ Tel: 0121-500 5164 Fax: 0121-500 5164

Pantograph Precision Ltd, 15 Willow Road, Colnbrook, Slough, SL3 0BS Tel: (01753) 684343 Fax: (01753) 681363 E-mail: stuart@pantagraph.demon.co.uk

Patterns & Dies Ltd, Bute Street, Stoke-on-Trent, ST4 3PW Tel: (01782) 343700 Fax: (01782) 343800 E-mail: sales@patterns-dies.co.uk

Playden Tools Ltd, Factory 5-6 The Elms, Church Road, Harold Wood, Romford, RM3 0JR Tel: (01708) 343874 Fax: (01708) 376531

Pobs Precision Tools Mould Toolmkrs, 44 Bickford Road, Birmingham, B6 7EE Tel: 0121-327 5736 Fax: 0121-328 5261 E-mail: pobs.tools@btconnect.com

R J Clark, Unit 7 Enterprise Trading Est, Pedmore Road, Brierley Hill, West Midlands, DY5 1TX Tel: (01384) 480290 Fax: (01384) 481961

Rojak Tool & Die Co. Ltd, Falkland Close, Coventry, CV4 8AU Tel: (024) 7646 7969 Fax: (024) 7669 4458 E-mail: rojak@ukf.net

Sarginsons Industries Ltd, Torrington Avenue, Coventry, CV4 9AG Tel: (024) 7646 6291 Fax: (024) 7646 8135 E-mail: keithb@sarginsons.co.uk

Skiller Engineering Ltd, Unit 1, Pig Lane, Bishop'S Stortford, Hertfordshire, CM23 3HG Tel: 01279 501631

Superite Tools, Unit 3 Hayward Industrial Park, Vigo Place, Walsall, WS9 8UG Tel: (01922) 455769 Fax: (01922) 743176 E-mail: enquiries@superite.co.uk

T S D Precision Ltd, Unit 11 Lion Industrial Park, Northgate Way, Walsall, WS9 8RL Tel: (01922) 457620 Fax: 01922 455443

Thurlow Tools, 79a Westbury Avenue, London, N22 6SA Tel: (020) 8889 1217

Trintools Ltd, 6 Cranford Way, Smethwick, West Midlands, B66 2RU Tel: 0121-558 0886 Fax: 0121-558 2986 E-mail: sales@trintools.co.uk

Triune Precision Engineering Co. Ltd, Spring Lane, Malvern, Worcestershire, WR14 1AJ Tel: (01684) 573331 Fax: (01684) 893201

W R Tooling Ltd, Armytage Road Industrial Estate, Armytage Road, Brighouse, West Yorkshire, HD6 1QF Tel: (01484) 719642 Fax: (01484) 716854 E-mail: info@wrtooling.co.uk

Wentworth Tool & Die, Woodbine House, Wold Newton, Driffield, North Humberside, YO25 3YD Tel: (01262) 470270 Fax: (01262) 470270 E-mail: woodbinehouse@aol.com

XL Tools Ltd, Unit 3, Aylesham Industrial Estate, Brighouse Road, Bradford, West Yorkshire, BD12 0NQ Tel: 01274 693505 Fax: 01274 694023

DIECASTING MOULD/DIE TOOLMAKERS, INVESTMENT

Investment Tooling International Ltd, Sidings Road, Lowmoor Business Park, Kirkby-in-Ashfield, Nottingham, NG17 7JZ Tel: (01623) 754814 Fax: (01623) 754914 E-mail: sales@iti-kirkby.co.uk

K L Precision Engineering Ltd, Athelney Way, Cheltenham, Gloucestershire, GL52 6RT Tel: (01242) 244847 Fax: (01242) 244847

DIECASTING MOULD/DIE TOOLMAKERS, PRESSURE

Abbey Tool & Dye, Unit 11 Old Canal Wharf, Navigation Road, Stoke-on-Trent, ST6 3BL Tel: (01782) 838137 Fax: (01782) 577372 E-mail: abbeytool@aol.com

D R B Precision Ltd, Unit H, Bowen Industrial Estate, Aberbargoed, Bargoed, Mid Glamorgan, CF81 9EP Tel: (01443) 828940 Fax: (01443) 879133 E-mail: sales@drbprecision.com

G T Tools Ltd, Coxmoor Road, Sutton-in-Ashfield, Nottinghamshire, NG17 4NE Tel: (01623) 551000 Fax: (01623) 550784 E-mail: sales@gttools.co.uk

Pantograph Precision Ltd, 15 Willow Road, Colnbrook, Slough, SL3 0BS Tel: (01753) 684343 Fax: (01753) 681363 E-mail: stuart@pantagraph.demon.co.uk

T S D Precision Ltd, Unit 11 Lion Industrial Park, Northgate Way, Walsall, WS9 8RL Tel: (01922) 457620 Fax: 01922 455443

DIECASTINGS, ALUMINIUM/ ALLOY

Alpac Alloys Holdings Ltd, Dale Street, Burton-on-Trent, Staffordshire, DE14 3TE Tel: (01283) 567737 Fax: (01283) 512359 E-mail: peter@alpacgroup.com

Alucast Ltd, Western Way, Wednesbury, West Midlands, WS10 7BW Tel: 0121-556 6111 Fax: 0121-505 1302 E-mail: sales@alucast.co.uk

Barton Aluminium Foundries, Rayboulds Bridge Rd, Walsall, WS2 8PG Tel: (01922) 637551 Fax: (01922) 644481 E-mail: sales@barton-aluminium.co.uk

Bridgnorth Castings Ltd, Alveley Industrial Estate, Alveley, Bridgnorth, Shropshire, WV15 6HG Tel: (01746) 781177 Fax: (01746) 781188 E-mail: vp32@dial.pipex.com

Brooks Crownhill Patternmakers Ltd, North Way, Andover, Hampshire, SP10 5AZ Tel: (01264) 355136 Fax: (01264) 332145 E-mail: info@bcplimited.co.uk

Daften Ltd, Trevilling Quay, Wadebridge, Cornwall, PL27 6EB Tel: (01208) 812148 Fax: (01208) 814092 E-mail: diecasting@daften.co.uk

Darlaston Diecast Alloys Ltd, Ashmore Lake Way, Willenhall, West Midlands, WV12 4LF Tel: (01902) 606436 Fax: (01902) 609405 E-mail: darlastondiecast@btconnect.com

Eutectic Alloy Castings Wolverhampton Ltd, Units 25-26, Wood Street, Park Village, Wolverhampton, WV10 9DS Tel: (01902) 726699 Fax: (01902) 726692

▶ G T Group Ltd, 8 Faraday Road, Peterlee, County Durham, SR8 5AP Tel: 0191-586 2366 Fax: 0191-587 2111 E-mail: info@gtgroup.co.uk

Glen Castings Ltd, Meadows Mill, Burnley Road, Bacup, Lancashire, OL13 8BZ Tel: (01706) 873967 Fax: (01706) 879234 E-mail: glencas@lancs.co.uk

Gravitech Ltd, 136 Kentish Road, Middlemore Industrial Estate, Birmingham, B21 0AY Tel: 0121-558 0847 Fax: 0121-555 8171

Kaye Presteigne, Harper Lane, Presteigne, Powys, LD8 2AH Tel: (01544) 267551 Fax: (01544) 267032 E-mail: reception@kayepresteigne.co.uk

Kemlows Diecasting Products Ltd, Charlton Mead Lane, Hoddesdon, Hertfordshire, EN11 0HB Tel: (01992) 460671 Fax: (01992) 446889 E-mail: sales@kemlows.co.uk

J.H. Lavender & Co. Ltd, Hall Green Works, Crankhall Lane, West Bromwich, West Midlands, B71 3JZ Tel: 0121-588 2273 Fax: 0121-588 7936 E-mail: lavender-diecast@city2000.net

Melloy Ltd, Main Avenue, Unit C10, Treforest Industrial Estate, Pontypridd, Mid Glamorgan, CF37 5UD Tel: (01443) 824880 Fax: (01443) 844797 E-mail: enquiries@melloy.co.uk

Norfran Aluminium Ltd, West Chirton Trading Estate, North Shields, Tyne & Wear, NE29 7TY Tel: 0191-258 2611 Fax: 0191-257 1549 E-mail: jb@norfran.co.uk

Norfran Products Ltd, Alveley Industrial Estate, Alveley, Bridgnorth, Shropshire, WV15 6HG Tel: (01746) 780919 Fax: (01746) 780297 E-mail: mail@norfran.com

Patay Bucks Castings Ltd, The Ridgeway, Iver, Buckinghamshire, SL0 9HW Tel: (01753) 652126 Fax: (01753) 651330

Thomas Bros Leeds Ltd, Stanningley Field Close, Leeds, LS13 4QG Tel: 0113-256 7210 Fax: 0113-256 9199E-mail: info@tbleeds.com

Truscanian Ltd, St. Martins Industrial Estate, Engine Street, Oldbury, West Midlands, B69 4NL Tel: 0121-552 3011 Fax: 0121-552 4672

West Midlands Foundry Co. Ltd, Blakemore Road, West Bromwich, West Midlands, B70 8JF Tel: 0121-553 1515 Fax: 0121-500 5839

DIECASTINGS, ALUMINIUM/ ALLOY, MACHINED

E M B Diecasting Machines Ltd, Unit 1 Oldbury Road Industrial Estate, 132 Oldbury Road, Smethwick, West Midlands, B66 1JE Tel: 0121-565 3199 Fax: 0121-555 5275 E-mail: emba@embdiecast.fsbusiness.co.uk

Eutectic Alloy Castings Wolverhampton Ltd, Units 25-26, Wood Street, Park Village, Wolverhampton, WV10 9DS Tel: (01902) 726699 Fax: (01902) 726692

DIECASTINGS, GRAVITY, ALUMINIUM/ALLOY

D R Precision, 8 Shell Corner Industrial Estate, Long Lane, Halesowen, West Midlands, B62 9LD Tel: 0121-561 1874 Fax: 0121-561 1874

Ferndowne, Reform Industrial Estate, Maidenhead, Berkshire, SL6 8BY Tel: (01628) 630211 Fax: (01628) 623459

Lenton Brook, Unit D Hawthorns Industrial Estate, Middlemore Road, Middlemore Road, Birmingham, B21 0BH Tel: 0121-523 9390 Fax: 0121-523 9390 E-mail: graham@lentonbrook.freeserve.co.uk

Melloy Ltd, Main Avenue, Unit C10, Treforest Industrial Estate, Pontypridd, Mid Glamorgan, CF37 5UD Tel: (01443) 824880 Fax: (01443) 844797 E-mail: enquiries@melloy.co.uk

DIEHEADS

Boston Matthews Machinery Ltd, Navigation Road, Diglis, Worcester, WR5 3DE Tel: (01905) 763100 Fax: (01905) 763101 E-mail: info@bostonmatthews.co.uk

Namco Tooling Ltd, New Road, Studley, Warwickshire, B80 7LZ Tel: (01527) 853667 Fax: (01527) 852668 E-mail: sales@namco-tooling.com

DIELECTRIC SPECTROMETERS

Mass Sectrometry International Ltd, Unit C, Tudor Road, Broadheath, Altrincham, Cheshire, WA14 5RZ Tel: 0161-929 7583 Fax: 0161-941 5540

DIES TO SPECIFICATION

Rectory Tool Company Ltd, 7 Port Hope Road, Camp Hill, Birmingham, B11 1JS Tel: 0121-773 9135 Fax: 0121-773 9342 E-mail: dianne@ctr.uk.com

DIES, DIE CASTING, *See also Diecasting Mould/Die etc*

Aluminium Castings Ltd, 3b Celtic Road, Moss Side Industrial Estate, Callington, Cornwall, PL17 7SD Tel: (01579) 383513 Fax: (01579) 384762 E-mail: info@alcast.co.uk

Ideal Sand & Die Casting Co., Unit 5, New Field Industrial Estate, High St, Stoke-on-Trent, ST6 5PB Tel: (01782) 818866 Fax: (01782) 836750 E-mail: sales@idealcasting.co.uk

DIES, EXTRUSION

Eroga Die Co. Ltd, 6a Eastbrook Road Trading Estate, Eastbrook Road, Gloucester, GL4 3DB Tel: (01452) 524039 Fax: (01452) 500615 E-mail: mail@erogadie.com

Extrusion Form Tools Ltd, Malvern View Business Park, Stella Way, Bishops Cleeve, Cheltenham, Gloucestershire, GL52 7DQ Tel: (01242) 673377 Fax: (01242) 677711 E-mail: ash@extrusionformtools.com

Hillside Adr Ltd, 9 Quarry Park Close, Moulton Park Industrial Estate, Northampton, NN3 6QB Tel: (01604) 671251 Fax: (01604) 670868 E-mail: sales@hillsideadr.co.uk

Minium Tool Co. Ltd, Unit 1 & 2, Malmesbury Road, Kingsditch Trading Estate, Cheltenham, Gloucestershire, GL51 9PL Tel: (01242) 529352 Fax: (01242) 521737 E-mail: miniumtool@btconnect.com

DIESEL CRANES

R B Cranes Ltd, Thrumpton Lane, Retford, Nottinghamshire, DN22 7AN Tel: (01777) 700039 Fax: (01777) 713192 E-mail: info@jnd.co.uk

Valla Cranes, Unit 5 Sidings Court, Henry Boot Way, Hull, HU4 7DY Tel: (01482) 351546 Fax: (01482) 351091 E-mail: E.Finn@valla-cranes.co.uk

DIESEL DRIVE PUMPING SETS

Pioneer Pump Ltd, Corner Farm Industrial Estate, Woolpit Road, Rattlesden, Bury St. Edmunds, Suffolk, IP30 0RZ Tel: (01449) 736777

DIESEL DRIVEN GENERATOR SETS

Advanced Diesel Engineering, Unit 14, Langthwaite Road, Langthwaite Business Park, South Kirkby, Pontefract, West Yorkshire, WF9 3AP Tel: (01977) 658100 Fax: (01977) 608111 E-mail: r.brown@adeltd.co.uk

Aggreko UK Ltd, Birch Road, Dumbarton, G82 2RF Tel: (01389) 742214 Fax: (01389) 742554

Allam Marine Ltd, 10-12 Lime Street, Hull, HU8 7AB Tel: (01482) 224861 Fax: (01482) 226680

Arc-Gen Ltd, Station Road, Four Ashes Industrial Estate, Four Ashes, Wolverhampton, WV10 7DB Tel: (01902) 790824 Fax: (01902) 790355 E-mail: andymunford@arc-gen.co.uk

Arun International (Power) Ltd, Unit F1, Dominion Way, Littlehampton, West Sussex, BN16 3HQ Tel: (01903) 850285 Fax: (01903) 850636 E-mail: sales@arunpower.co.uk

B Sinclair, Kirkton Cottage, Auchterless, Turriff, Aberdeenshire, AB53 8BA Tel: (01888) 511406 Fax: (01888) 511406

Clarke International Ltd, Hemnall Street, Epping, Essex, CM16 4LG Tel: (01992) 565300 Fax: (01992) 561562 E-mail: sales@clarkeinternational.com

Combustion Energy & Steam Specialists Ltd, 77-79 John Street, Stromness, Orkney, KW16 3AD Tel: (01856) 851177 Fax: (01856) 851199 E-mail: enquiries@cess.co.uk

Cummins Power Generation Ltd, Manston Park, Columbus Avenue, Manston, Ramsgate, Kent, CT12 5BF Tel: (01843) 255000 Fax: (01843) 255902 E-mail: graham.n.baldock@cummins.com

Dale Power Solutions Ltd, Salter Road, Eastfield, Scarborough, North Yorkshire, YO11 3DU Tel: (01723) 583511 Fax: (01723) 581231 E-mail: sales@dalepowersolutions.com

Eagle Power, Johnson Bridge Road, Off Church Lane, West Bromwich, West Midlands, B71 1DG Tel: 0121-580 3222 Fax: 0121-525 4796 E-mail: eagle@kw1.com

Eastleigh Power Plant, PO Box 199, Southampton, SO30 0WZ Tel: (023) 8040 7507 Fax: (01489) 780478 E-mail: epower@fpcad.com

Electromech Engineering Services, 174 Manchester Road, Astley, Tyldesley, Manchester, M29 7FB Tel: (01942) 888181 Fax: (01942) 888802 E-mail: sales@electromech.org

Euro-Diesel (U K) Ltd, Stato House, Somerford Road, Cirencester, Gloucestershire, GL7 1TW Tel: (01285) 640879 Fax: (01285) 652509 E-mail: info@euro-diesel.co.uk

Finning UK Ltd, 688-689 Stirling Road, Slough, SL1 4ST Tel: (01753) 497300 Fax: (01753) 497333 E-mail: mbarnes@finning.co.uk

Generated Power Services Ltd, Argosons Hunsdon Stud, Eastwick Road, Hunsdon, Ware, Hertfordshire, SG12 8PP Tel: (01920) 877171 Fax: (01920) 877128

International Power Generation, Unit 7c Carcroft Enterprise Park, Carcroft, Doncaster, South Yorkshire, DN6 8DD Tel: (01302) 722888 Fax: (01302) 721202 E-mail: sales@generator.co.uk

J Robinson Engineering Ltd, 12 Clarence Road, Fleet, Hampshire, GU51 3RZ Tel: (01252) 621312 Fax: (01252) 819100 E-mail: jim@jrobinsoneng.fsnet.co.uk

▶ Kentec Power Systems Ltd, Unit 18 Cannel Road, Chasetown Industrial Estate, Burntwood Business Park, Burntwood, Staffordshire, WS7 3FU Tel: (01543) 677802 Fax: (01543) 677508 E-mail: sales@kentec.uk.com

Man Diesel Ltd, Bramhall Moor Lane, Hazel Grove, Stockport, Cheshire, SK7 5AQ Tel: 0161-483 1000 Fax: 0161-487 1465

Musgrave Generators Ltd, 1 Enderby Road Industrial Estate, Whetstone, Leicester, LE8 6HZ Tel: 0116-286 1534 Fax: 0116-286 1559 E-mail: info@musgrave-generators.com

▶ North Lincs Engineering Ltd, College View Works, Manby Road, Grimoldby, Louth, Lincolnshire, LN11 8HE Tel: (01507) 328787 Fax: (01507) 329306 E-mail: mark@nle.demon.co.uk

Phase Hire, 140a Kents Hill Road, Benfleet, Essex, SS7 5PH Tel: (01268) 792648 Fax: (01268) 792641

Powerco (International) Ltd, 1 Strawberry Vale, Twickenham, TW1 4RY Tel: (0208) 831 6634 Fax: (0208) 891 6435 E-mail: radin.powerco@virgin.net

Powerplant Stamford Ltd, Wackerley Works, Bourne Road, Essendine, Stamford, Lincolnshire, PE9 4LT Tel: (01780) 766017 Fax: (01780) 750910 E-mail: sales@powerplantstamford.co.uk

Re Trem & Co. Ltd, Old Bawtry Road, Finningley, Doncaster, South Yorkshire, DN9 3BX Tel: (01302) 770203 Fax: (01302) 770868 E-mail: sales@enginesandgenerators.com

DIESEL DRIVEN GENERATOR SETS

– *continued*

Regulators Europa Ltd, Port Lane, Colchester, CO1 2NX Tel: (01206) 799556 Fax: (01206) 792685

Rollo UK Ltd, 2 Balm Road Industrial Estate, Beza Street, Leeds, LS10 2BG Tel: 0113-272 0444 Fax: 0113-272 0499 E-mail: info@rollouk.com

Rollo UK Ltd, 2 Rochester Airport Industrial Estate, Laker Road, Rochester, Kent, ME1 3QX Tel: (01634) 669100 Fax: (01634) 669101

Sandhurst Manufacturing, Belchmire Lane, Gosberton, Spalding, Lincolnshire, PE11 4HG Tel: (01775) 840020 Fax: (01775) 843063 E-mail: info@sandhurst-mfg.com

T W Generators, 2 Long Marston Road, Marsworth, Tring, Hertfordshire, HP23 4NF Tel: (01296) 668420 Fax: (01296) 662064 E-mail: sales@twgenerators.co.uk

Wagenaar Generators Ltd, Gilfach-Y-Rhiw, Abergwili, Carmarthen, SA32 7ER Tel: (01267) 237078 Fax: (01267) 234113 E-mail: johndenver@amgenerators.com

Watpower International Ltd, PO Box 1389, London, W5 1JJ Tel: (020) 8810 9148 Fax: (020) 8810 5509 E-mail: info@watpower.co.uk

Welland Engineering Ltd, 31a Cranmore Lane, Holbeach, Spalding, Lincolnshire, PE12 7HT Tel: (01406) 490660 Fax: (01406) 490444 E-mail: sales@generating-sets.com

DIESEL ENGINE COMPONENTS OR SPARE PARTS

2 M Power Systems Ltd, Howe Moss Drive, Kirkhill Industrial Estate, Dyce, Aberdeen, AB21 0GL Tel: (01224) 725506 Fax: (01224) 723717 E-mail: 2mpowerltd@btconnect.com

Abex Ltd, Abex House, 93 Cato Street, Birmingham, B7 4TS Tel: 0121-359 2623 Fax: 0121-359 7277 E-mail: enquiries@abexltd.co.uk

Bartech Marine Engineers, 11-12 Rushmere Close, West Mersea, Colchester, CO5 8QQ Tel: (01206) 384677 Fax: (01206) 385329 E-mail: sales@bartechmarine.com

C J Diesel Injection, 6 Wood Lane, Isleworth, Middlesex, TW7 5ER Tel: (020) 8560 2297 Fax: (020) 8560 1282 E-mail: sales@cjdiesel.com

Central Diesel, Unit 15 Hawksley Industrial Estate, Hawksley Street, Oldham, OL8 4PQ Tel: 0161-620 7070 Fax: 0161-620 6007 E-mail: steve.kay@central-diesel.co.uk

D.F. Coulam & Sons, Northfields Industrial Estate, 3 Stirling Way, Market Deeping, Peterborough, PE6 8LG Tel: (01778) 346518 Fax: (01778) 380495 E-mail: sales@dfcspares.com

Cummins Diesel, Rutherford Drive, Park Farm South, Wellingborough, Northamptonshire, NN8 6AN Tel: (01933) 672200 Fax: (01933) 334198 E-mail: cduksales@cummins.com

D & L Diesel Ltd, 75 Scot Lane, Wigan, Lancashire, WN5 0TU Tel: (01942) 825545 Fax: (01942) 493890 E-mail: davidlong@dldiesels.co.uk

Dalton Power Products Ltd, Unit 19 Autumn Park Industrial Estate, Dysart Road, Grantham, Lincolnshire, NG31 7DD Tel: (01476) 576666 Fax: (01476) 577127 E-mail: dppask@daltonpowerproducts.co.uk

Diesel Industrial Electrical Spares & Equipment (London), Units 19-20 Thurrock Commercial Park, Purfleet Industrial Park, London Road, Aveley, South Ockendon, Essex, RM15 4YA Tel: (01708) 890011 Fax: (01708) 862111 E-mail: dieseluk@aol.com

Diesel Marine International Ltd, Gloucester Road, North Shields, Tyne & Wear, NE29 8RQ Tel: 0191-257 5577 Fax: 0191-258 6398 E-mail: sales@dmiuk.co.uk

Donovan Diesel Engine Equipment, St. Bartholomew Building, Nelson Street, Bolton, BL3 2AH Tel: (01204) 527520 Fax: (01204) 524348 E-mail: donovanandson@aol.com

Engineering Products & Services Ltd, Unit 10 Newporte Business Park, 9 Cardinal Close, Lincoln, LN2 4SY Tel: (01522) 544218 Fax: (01522) 510720 E-mail: phil@epsltd.karoo.co.uk

Industrial & Marine Power Services Ltd, Whisby Way, North Hykeham, Lincoln, LN6 3LQ Tel: (01522) 881000 Fax: (01522) 883555 E-mail: chris@ind-marpower.co.uk

Kingsdown, Brook Street, Snodland, Kent, ME6 5BB Tel: (01634) 249555 Fax: (01634) 249550 E-mail: sales@kingsdownuk.com

Lincoln Diesels plc, Great Northern Terrace, Lincoln, LN5 8HJ Tel: (01522) 511512 Fax: (01522) 512935 E-mail: ld@lincolndiesels.com

M I Diesel Products, Chorley North Industrial Park, Chorley, Lancashire, PR6 7BX Tel: (01257) 239200 Fax: (01257) 241726 E-mail: sales@midiesel.co.uk

C.S. Martin (Alford) Ltd, 33 West Street, Alford, Lincolnshire, LN13 9DQ Tel: (01507) 463427 Fax: (01507) 466942

▶ Geoff Matthews Engineers, Unit 17 Pavilion Workshops, Holmewood Industrial Park, Park Road, Holmewood, Chesterfield, Derbyshire, S42 5UY Tel: (01246) 851118 Fax: (01246) 855502 E-mail: enquiries@gmengineers.co.uk

Power Torque Engineering Ltd, 27 Herald Way, Binley Industrial Estate, Coventry, CV3 2RQ Tel: (024) 7663 5757 Fax: (024) 7663 5878 E-mail: sales@powertorque.co.uk

Skagerak Co., 13 Byemoor Avenue, Great Ayton, Middlesbrough, Cleveland, TS9 6JP Tel: (01642) 723819 Fax: (01642) 722324 E-mail: info@skagerak.co.uk

Skandiaverken Ltd S K V, Cartside Avenue, Inchinnan, Renfrew, PA4 9RW Tel: 0141-812 8121 Fax: 0141-812 8124 E-mail: spares@skvuk.com

▶ Soni Exports Ltd, PO Box 7923, Leicester, LE4 9LS Tel: 0116-276 4000 Fax: 0116-276 4002 E-mail: sales@soniexports.co.uk

SSAB Swedish Steel UK (Dobel), Unit 17 Narrowboat Way, Hurst Business Park, Brierley Hill, West Midlands, DY5 1UF Tel: (01384) 74660 Fax: (01384) 77575 E-mail: sales@dobel.co.uk

Tayside Diesel Engineering Ltd, Fowler Road, Broughty Ferry, Dundee, DD5 3RU Tel: (01382) 735960 Fax: (01382) 735969 E-mail: sales@tdedundee.co.uk

Turner Diesel Ltd, Unit 1a Dyce Industrial Park, Dyce, Aberdeen, AB21 7EZ Tel: (01224) 723925 Fax: (01224) 723927 E-mail: burtbutchart@turner-diesel.co.uk

W R Clark & Co Engineers Ltd, Bridge St Industrial Estate, Bridge Street, Clay Cross, Chesterfield, Derbyshire, S45 9NU Tel: (01246) 862325 Fax: (01246) 250033

Wartsila UK Ltd, Riverside Business Centre, River Lawn Road, Tonbridge, Kent, TN9 1EP Tel: (01732) 783571 E-mail: uk.marine@wartsila.com

DIESEL ENGINE COMPONENTS, MARINE

▶ United Diesel Ltd, Unit 6 Leaton Industrial Estate, Bomere Heath, Shrewsbury, SY4 3AP Tel: (01939) 291155 Fax: (01939) 290791 E-mail: Keith@uniteddiesel.co.uk

DIESEL ENGINE FLAME PROOFING

Pyroban Ltd, Endeavour Works, Dolphin Road, Shoreham-By-Sea, West Sussex, BN43 6QG Tel: (01273) 463311 Fax: (01273) 465313 E-mail: customerservice@pyroban.com

DIESEL ENGINE MAINTENANCE EQUIPMENT

Skagerak Co., 13 Byemoor Avenue, Great Ayton, Middlesbrough, Cleveland, TS9 6JP Tel: (01642) 723819 Fax: (01642) 722324 E-mail: info@skagerak.co.uk

DIESEL ENGINE PROTECTION SYSTEMS

A R S Anglian Diesels Ltd, Unit 9c Headway Business Park, Denby Dale Road, Wakefield, West Yorkshire, WF2 7AZ Tel: (01924) 332492 Fax: (01924) 332493 E-mail: enquiries@arsangliandiesels.co.uk

Agrie Mach Ltd, Wayfarers, Domewood, Copthorne, Crawley, West Sussex, RH10 3HD Tel: (01342) 713743 Fax: (01342) 719181 E-mail: info@agriemach.com

Chalwyn Estates Ltd, Chalwyn Industrial Estate, St Clement Road, Poole, Dorset, BH12 4PF Tel: (01202) 715400 Fax: (01202) 715600 E-mail: sales@chalwyn.co.uk

Teddington Controls Ltd, Daniels Lane, St. Austell, Cornwall, PL25 3HG Tel: (01726) 74400 Fax: (01726) 67953 E-mail: info@tedcon.com

DIESEL ENGINE RECONDITIONING

D & R James Engineering Services Ltd, 16 Benson Road, Nuffield Industrial Estate, Poole, Dorset, BH17 0GB Tel: (01202) 678679

Engine Power, 7 Bryant Road, Bayton Road Industrial Estate, Coventry, CV7 9EN Tel: (024) 7664 4660 Fax: (024) 7664 4634

F J Payne & Son Ltd, Oakfield Industrial Estate, Eynsham, Witney, Oxfordshire, OX29 4AW Tel: (01865) 882299 Fax: (01865) 882309 E-mail: sales@fjpayne.com

Regal Engines, Unit B, 16 Juliet Way, Aveley, South Ockendon, Essex, RM15 4YD Tel: (01708) 868805 Fax: (01708) 868885 E-mail: info@engine-reconditioners.co.uk

Smiths Engineering Works N I Ltd, Larne Road, Ballymena, County Antrim, BT42 3HA Tel: (028) 2564 1621 Fax: (028) 2564 3724

Tilsley & Lovatt Ltd, Newstead Industrial Trading Estate, Stoke-on-Trent, ST4 8HT Tel: (01782) 657331 Fax: (01782) 644600 E-mail: sales@tilsleyandlovatt.co.uk

W Drake Bradford Ltd, Bolling Road, Bradford, West Yorkshire, BD4 7BG Tel: (01274) 733541 Fax: (01274) 740892 E-mail: info@wdrake.co.uk

DIESEL ENGINE SAFETY EQUIPMENT

Chalwyn Estates Ltd, Chalwyn Industrial Estate, St Clement Road, Poole, Dorset, BH12 4PF Tel: (01202) 715400 Fax: (01202) 715600 E-mail: sales@chalwyn.co.uk

Pyroban Ltd, Endeavour Works, Dolphin Road, Shoreham-By-Sea, West Sussex, BN43 6QG Tel: (01273) 463311 Fax: (01273) 465313 E-mail: customerservice@pyroban.com

DIESEL ENGINE STARTER SYSTEMS

Industrial Power Units Ltd, Churchbridge, Oldbury, West Midlands, B69 2AS Tel: 0121-511 0400 Fax: 0121-511 0401 E-mail: ipu@ipu.co.uk

Prestolite Electric Ltd, Larden Road, Acton, London, W3 7SX Tel: (020) 8735 4500 Fax: (020) 8735 4777

DIESEL ENGINE TEST EQUIPMENT

A V L United Kingdom Ltd, Avon House, Hartlebury Trading Estate, Hartlebury, Kidderminster, Worcestershire, DY10 4JB Tel: (01299) 254600 Fax: (01299) 253734 E-mail: uk.sales@avl.com

C J Diesel Injection, 6 Wood Lane, Isleworth, Middlesex, TW7 5ER Tel: (020) 8560 2297 Fax: (020) 8560 1282 E-mail: sales@cjdiesel.com

Crypton Ltd, Bristol Road, Bridgwater, Somerset, TA6 4BX Tel: (01278) 436205 Fax: (01278) 450567 E-mail: sales@cryptontechnology.com

Custom Technology Ltd, Brooks Road, Lewes, East Sussex, BN7 2BY Tel: (01273) 479101 Fax: (01273) 486727 E-mail: sales@customtechnology.co.uk

Hartridge, Tingewick Road, Buckingham, MK18 1EF Tel: (01280) 825600 Fax: (01280) 825601 E-mail: sales@hartridge.co.uk

DIESEL ENGINE VALVE ROTATORS

F J R Engineering Ltd, 65b Blackpole Trading Estate West, Worcester, WR3 8TJ Tel: (01905) 454143 Fax: (01905) 454143

DIESEL ENGINEERS SERVICE OR INSTALLATION OR MAINTENANCE

A L D Engineering (UK) Ltd, Les Searle Plant Yard, Parsonage Way, Horsham, West Sussex, RH12 4AL Tel: (01403) 271964 Fax: (01403) 271965

Bartech Marine Engineers, 11-12 Rushmere Close, West Mersea, Colchester, CO5 8QQ Tel: (01206) 384677 Fax: (01206) 385329 E-mail: sales@bartechmarine.com

British Polar Engines Ltd, 133 Helen Street, Glasgow, G51 3HD Tel: 0141-445 2455 Fax: 0141-445 2185 E-mail: sales@polareng.sagehost.co.uk

Custom Diesels, Unit 10, Blackhill Road West, Holton Heath Trading Park, Poole, Dorset, BH16 6LW Tel: (01202) 621935

D C Woodhead & Partners Ltd, Carlisle Drive, Pudsey, West Yorkshire, LS28 8QS Tel: 0113-257 2275 Fax: 0113-255 3224 E-mail: woodhdpl@dialstart.net

Daihatsu Diesel (Europe) Ltd, 5th Floor, Devon House, 58 St. Katharines Way, London, E1W 1LB Tel: (020) 7977 0280 Fax: (020) 7626 6020 E-mail: daihatsu@ddeuk.com

Diamond Diesels Ltd, Unit 4 Blackburn Industrial Estate, Enterprise Way, Sherburn In Elmet, Leeds, LS25 6NA Tel: (0844) 4996373 Fax: (0844) 4996383 E-mail: sales@diamonddiesels.co.uk

Diesel Industrial Electrical Spares & Equipment (London), Units 19-20 Thurrock Commercial Park, Purfleet Industrial Park, London Road, Aveley, South Ockendon, Essex, RM15 4YA Tel: (01708) 890011 Fax: (01708) 862111 E-mail: dieseluk@aol.com

Diesel Injection (Aylesbury) Ltd, Unit 20, Edison Road, Rabans Lane, Aylesbury, Buckinghamshire, HP19 8TE Tel: (01296) 487400 Fax: (01296) 422343

E Rand & Sons Ltd, Chapel Lane, Great Blakenham, Ipswich, IP6 0JY Tel: (01473) 832833 Fax: (01473) 832834 E-mail: sales@rand.uk.com

Euro Diesel, Vulcan Road South, Norwich, NR6 6AF Tel: (01603) 406525 Fax: (01603) 484046 E-mail: rayradford@btconnect.com

Eurotex International Ltd, Unit 20 Shipyard Estate, Brightlingsea, Colchester, CO7 0AR Tel: (01206) 304063 Fax: (01206) 304026 E-mail: terry.kershaw@virgin.net

G W Dale Diesel Engineer Ltd, 139 Newcastle Street, Stoke-on-Trent, ST6 3QJ Tel: (01782) 837824 Fax: (01782) 839550

Hartman Marine Services, Unit C2 The Boatyard, Stonar Industrial Estate, Sandwich, Kent, CT13 9LY Tel: (01304) 614121 Fax: (01304) 615070 E-mail: hartman.marine@virgin.net

Kelvin Diesels Ltd, 133 Helen Street, Glasgow, G51 3HD Tel: (01698) 810666 Fax: (01698) 810999 E-mail: sales@britishpolarengines.co.uk

Kestlin Diesel Services Ltd, Bar Lane, Waddington, Lincoln, LN5 9SA Tel: (01522) 722900 Fax: (01522) 722922 E-mail: kestlin.diesel@virgin.net

Lincoln Diesels plc, Great Northern Terrace, Lincoln, LN5 8HJ Tel: (01522) 511512 Fax: (01522) 512935 E-mail: ld@lincolndiesels.com

▶ Lynxdiesels, 405 Finchampstead Road, Finchampstead, Wokingham, Berkshire, RG40 3RL Tel: 0118-973 4469 Fax: 0118-973 4026 E-mail: alandarby@lynxdiesels.com

▶ North Lincs Engineering Ltd, College View Works, Manby Road, Grimoldby, Louth, Lincolnshire, LN11 8HE Tel: (01507) 328787 Fax: (01507) 329306 E-mail: mark@nle.demon.co.uk

Prior Diesel Ltd, Gapton Hall Road, Great Yarmouth, Norfolk, NR31 0NL Tel: (01493) 441383 Fax: (01493) 441796 E-mail: info@priordiesel.com

Ranburn Ltd, Tunnel Avenue, London, SE10 0PT Tel: (020) 8858 2293 Fax: (020) 8293 4373

Tilsley & Lovatt Ltd, Newstead Industrial Trading Estate, Stoke-on-Trent, ST4 8HT Tel: (01782) 657331 Fax: (01782) 644600 E-mail: sales@tilsleyandlovatt.co.uk

▶ James Troop, 4 Davy Road, Astmoor Industrial Estate, Runcorn, Cheshire, WA7 1PZ Tel: (01928) 566170 Fax: (01928) 577314 E-mail: sales@jamestroop.co.uk

Wartsila UK Ltd, Riverside Business Centre, River Lawn Road, Tonbridge, Kent, TN9 1EP Tel: (01732) 783571 E-mail: uk.marine@wartsila.com

Watson Diesel Ltd, Elm Grove, London, SW19 4HE Tel: (020) 8879 3854 Fax: (0870) 4441386 E-mail: sales@watsondiesel.com

DIESEL ENGINES

Aktion Automotive Ltd, Unit N3 Cardiff Bay Business Centre, Titan Road, Cardiff, CF24 5EJ Tel: (029) 2046 4668 Fax: (029) 2046 4669 E-mail: sales@aktionautomotive.co.uk

British Polar Engines Ltd, 133 Helen Street, Glasgow, G51 3HD Tel: 0141-445 2455 Fax: 0141-445 2185 E-mail: sales@polareng.sagehost.co.uk

Cummins Engine Co. Ltd, Royal Oak Way South, Royal Oak Industrial Estate, Daventry, Northamptonshire, NN11 8NU Tel: (01327) 886000 Fax: (01327) 886100

Daihatsu Diesel (Europe) Ltd, 5th Floor, Devon House, 58 St. Katharines Way, London, E1W 1LB Tel: (020) 7977 0280 Fax: (020) 7626 6020 E-mail: daihatsu@ddeuk.com

Deutz AG - UK, Willow Park, Burdock Close, Cannock, Staffordshire, WS11 7FQ Tel: (01543) 438900 Fax: (01543) 438932

Engine Power, 7 Bryant Road, Bayton Road Industrial Estate, Coventry, CV7 9EN Tel: (024) 7664 4660 Fax: (024) 7664 4634

Finning UK Ltd, 688-689 Stirling Road, Slough, SL1 4ST Tel: (01753) 497300 Fax: (01753) 497333 E-mail: mbarnes@finning.co.uk

Iveco Ltd, Iveco House, Road One, Winsford Industrial Estate, Winsford, Cheshire, CW7 3QP Tel: (01606) 541000 Fax: (01606) 541126

Kubota (UK) Ltd, Dormer Road, Thame, Oxfordshire, OX9 3UN Tel: (01844) 214500 Fax: (01844) 216685 E-mail: sales@kubota.co.uk

Man Ltd, 4-5 Grosvenor Place, London, SW1X 7DG Tel: (020) 7201 3366 Fax: (020) 7235 9450 E-mail: manfred.stelz@man-ltd.co.uk

MAN B & W Diesel Ltd, Hythe Hill, Colchester, CO1 2HW Tel: (01206) 795151 Fax: (01206) 797869 E-mail: sales@manbwltd.com

Man Diesel Ltd, Bramhall Moor Lane, Hazel Grove, Stockport, Cheshire, SK7 5AQ Tel: 0161-483 1000 Fax: 0161-487 1465

Marshalls Industrial Ltd, Hithercroft Road, Wallingford, Oxfordshire, OX10 9DG Tel: (01491) 834666 Fax: (01491) 839777 E-mail: sales@marshalls-industrial.co.uk

Mermaid Marine Ltd, 70-72 Cobham Road, Ferndown Industrial Estate, Wimborne, Dorset, BH21 7RN Tel: (01202) 891824 Fax: (01202) 895882 E-mail: engines@mermaid-marine.co.uk

Perkins Engine Co (Stafford) Ltd, Tixall Road, Stafford, ST16 3UB Tel: (01785) 215700 Fax: (01785) 215110

Perkins Engines Co. Ltd, Frank Perkins Way, Eastfield, Peterborough, PE1 5NA Tel: (01733) 583000 Fax: (01733) 582240 E-mail: purdy_claire@perkins.com

Regulators Europa Ltd, Port Lane, Colchester, CO1 2NX Tel: (01206) 799556 Fax: (01206) 792685

Sabre Engines Ltd, 22 Cobham Road, Ferndown Industrial Estate, Wimborne, Dorset, BH21 7PW Tel: (01202) 893720 Fax: (01202) 851700 E-mail: post@sabre-engines.co.uk

Scania (Great Britain) Ltd, Delaware Drive, Tongwell, Milton Keynes, MK15 8HB Tel: (01908) 210210 Fax: (01908) 215040

DIESEL ENGINES – *continued*

Wartsila UK Ltd, Riverside Business Centre, River Lawn Road, Tonbridge, Kent, TN9 1EP Tel: (01732) 783571 E-mail: uk.marine@wartsila.com

DIESEL ENGINES UP TO 100 HORSEPOWER

▶ Stuart Group Ltd, Stuart House, Crowshall Lane, Attleborough, Norfolk, NR17 1AD Tel: (01953) 454540 Fax: (01953) 456968 E-mail: info@stuartpumps.co.uk

DIESEL FORKLIFT TRUCKS

Crown Lift Trucks Ltd, The Quay Centre, West Quay Road, Winwick, Warrington, WA2 8TS Tel: (01925) 445777 Fax: (01925) 425656 E-mail: info@crown.com

▶ Handy Lift, 121a Bitterne Road West, Southampton, SO18 1AR Tel: (023) 8034 7750 Fax: (023) 8034 7752 E-mail: info@handylift.co.uk

DIESEL FUEL FILTERS

Glencoe Ltd, Glenco House, Drake Avenue, Staines, Middlesex, TW18 2AW Tel: (01784) 493555 Fax: (01784) 493222 E-mail: sales@fuelsystem.co.uk

Separ Distribution, 428 Whippendell Road, Watford, WD18 7QU Tel: (01923) 819041 Fax: (01923) 255052 E-mail: filtration@separ.co.uk

DIESEL FUEL INJECTION EQUIPMENT

Merlin Diesel Systems Ltd, Unit 3-4 Lincoln Place, Walton Summit Centre, Bamber Bridge, Preston, PR5 8NA Tel: (01772) 627676 Fax: (01772) 626220 E-mail: sales@merlindiesel.com

DIESEL FUEL SYSTEM TEST EQUIPMENT

Hartridge, Tingewick Road, Buckingham, MK18 1EF Tel: (01280) 825600 Fax: (01280) 825601 E-mail: sales@hartridge.co.uk

DIESEL FUELS

▶ Croft Fuels Ltd, PO BOX 0, LIVERPOOL, L38 0WY Tel: 0151 929 2900 Fax: 0151 929 3050 E-mail: sales@croft-fuels.co.uk

DIESEL GENERATOR CONTROL PANELS

Control & Power Systems Ltd, 3D Burniston Industrial Estate, Willymath Close, Burniston, Scarborough, North Yorkshire, YO13 0HG Tel: (01723) 871112 Fax: (01723) 870625 E-mail: controlandpower@compuserve.com

Direct Generation, Newstead Industrial Trading Estate, Stoke-on-Trent, ST4 8HX Tel: (01782) 646767 Fax: (01782) 646868 E-mail: sales@directgeneration.co.uk

DIESEL GENERATOR CONTROL SYSTEMS

Control & Power Systems Ltd, 3D Burniston Industrial Estate, Willymath Close, Burniston, Scarborough, North Yorkshire, YO13 0HG Tel: (01723) 871112 Fax: (01723) 870625 E-mail: controlandpower@compuserve.com

Direct Generation, Newstead Industrial Trading Estate, Stoke-on-Trent, ST4 8HX Tel: (01782) 646767 Fax: (01782) 646868 E-mail: sales@directgeneration.co.uk

DIESEL GENERATORS

Croxton Power Ltd, Croxton Kerrial, Grantham, Lincolnshire, NG32 1QX Tel: (01476) 870386 Fax: (01476) 879377 E-mail: enquiries@croxtonpower.com

▶ Event Plant & Access., Events House, Braye Road, Vale, Guernsey, GY3 5PB Tel: (01481) 243334 Fax: (01481) 243899 E-mail: admin@eventsci.com

Quartz Plant UK Ltd, 5 Thomas Avenue, Radcliffe-On-Trent, Nottingham, NG12 2HT Tel: 0115-933 4947 Fax: 0115-933 4947 E-mail: brassandpower@ntlworld.com

John A. Sparks & Co. Ltd., Western Industrial Estate, Caerphilly, CF83 1BQ Tel: (0845) 8503434 Fax: (029) 2080 7081 E-mail: tonysparks@a-sparks.com

▶ Yorpower Generators, Blenheim Road, Pocklington Industrial Estate, Pocklington, York, YO42 1NR Tel: (01759) 305400 Fax: (01759) 305405 E-mail: sales@yorpower.com

DIESEL HEATED BELT DRIVE PUMP PRESSURE WASHERS

William Lennon & Co. Ltd, The Bank, Stoney Middleton, Hope Valley, Derbyshire, S32 4TD Tel: (01433) 630451 Fax: (01433) 630954 E-mail: sales@williamlennon.co.uk

DIESEL LOCOMOTIVES

Brush Traction, PO Box 17, Loughborough, Leicestershire, LE11 1HS Tel: (01509) 617000 Fax: (01509) 617001 E-mail: sales@brushtraction.com

Hunslet-Barclay Ltd, Caledonia Works, West Langlands Street, Kilmarnock, Ayrshire, KA1 2QD Tel: (01563) 523573 Fax: (01563) 541076 E-mail: mail@hunsletbarclay.co.uk

DIESEL PUMPS

J R D Engineers Ltd, 5 Willow Road, Poyle Trading Estate, Colnbrook, Slough, SL3 0BU Tel: (01753) 682665 Fax: (01753) 681475

Midland Pump Manufacturing Co. Ltd, Tyseley Industrial Estate, Seeleys Road, Birmingham, B11 2LF Tel: 0121-773 8862 Fax: 0121-771 4363 E-mail: sales@midlandpump.co.uk

Purolator Products Automotive, Glenco Ho, Drake Ave, Staines, Middx, TW18 2AW Tel: (01784) 493555

DIESEL TANKS

▶ Main Ltd, Shawclough Road, Shawclough, ROCHDALE, LANCASHIRE, OL12 6LN Tel: 01706 655131 Fax: 01706 655132 E-mail: wendy@mainltd.co.uk

DIESINKING CUTTERS

Crosland Cutters Ltd, Nimmings Road, Halesowen, West Midlands, B62 9JE Tel: 0121-559 7915 Fax: 0121-561 3064 E-mail: sales@croslandcuttersltd.co.uk

DIETARY FIBRE

General Dietary Ltd, PO Box 38, Kingston upon Thames, Surrey, KT2 7YP Tel: (020) 8336 2323 Fax: (020) 8942 8274 E-mail: greareal.dietary@vigin.net

DIFFERENTIAL EPICYCLIC GEARS

Compact Orbitial Gears Ltd, Unit A Brynberth Industrial Estate, Rhayader, Powys, LD6 5EW Tel: (01597) 811676 Fax: (01597) 811677 E-mail: info@compactorbitalgears.com

Precision Motion (Cofil) Ltd, Unit 63, Roman Way, Longridge Road, Ribbleton, Preston, PR2 5BE Tel: (01772) 653366 Fax: (01772) 653163 E-mail: pmcofil@btconnect.com

DIFFERENTIAL GAUGES

Dwyer Instruments Ltd, Unit 16 The Wye Estate, London Road, High Wycombe, Buckinghamshire, HP11 1LH Tel: (01494) 461707 Fax: (01494) 465102 E-mail: sales@dwyer-inst.co.uk

G S M International, Upper Neatham Mill Farm, Upper Neatham Mill Lane, Holybourne, Alton, Hampshire, GU34 4EP Tel: (01420) 80617 Fax: (01420) 80617 E-mail: gsminternational@ukonline.co.uk

DIFFICULT ACCESS ABSEILING ENGINEERING OR INSPECTION

Can Geotechnical Ltd, Smeckley Wood Close, Chesterfield Trading Estate, Chesterfield, Derbyshire, S41 9PZ Tel: (01246) 261111 Fax: (01246) 261626 E-mail: info@can.ltd.uk

Central High Rise Ltd, Central House, Thoresby Avenue, Nottingham, NG2 3GA Tel: 0115-958 7637 Fax: 0115-941 1279 E-mail: info@abseiling.uk.com

Highline Access Ltd, PO Box 2089, Bristol, BS99 7SZ Tel: (0870) 0435531 Fax: (0870) 0435532 E-mail: enquiries@highlineaccess.com

M B Inspection Ltd, Wellhead Way, Wellhead Road, Aberdeen, AB12 7DG Tel: (01224) 772161 Fax: (01224) 772156 E-mail: operations@mbinspection.co.uk

Oilfield Testing Services, Viking Road, Great Yarmouth, Norfolk, NR31 0NU Tel: (01493) 440555 Fax: (01493) 440737 E-mail: ots@oilfieldtesting.com

Richardson, Courville House, 1 Ellerbeck Court, Stokesley, Middlesbrough, Cleveland, TS9 5PT Tel: (01642) 714791 Fax: (01642) 714387 E-mail: enquiries@pcrichardson.co.uk

▶ Safe Access, 136 Derbyshire Lane, Sheffield, S8 8SE Tel: 0114-280 2020 Fax: 0114-280 2010 E-mail: info@the-access-group.com

Sealtite Sealants Ltd, 66 Wodbrooke Way, Corringham, Stanford-le-Hope, Essex, SS17 9DW Tel: (01375) 641607 Fax: (01375) 361283

▶ Silocare Ltd, Grayingham Road, Blyborough, Gainsborough, Lincolnshire, DN21 4EY Tel: (01427) 668061 Fax: (01427) 668062 E-mail: silocare@aol.com

Tarrant S C S Ltd, 1st Floor Victoria Court, St. Pancras, Chichester, West Sussex, PO19 7GD Tel: (01243) 839992 Fax: (01243) 839993 E-mail: rita.brown.tarrant@breathemail.net

Trac International Ltd, Unit 12 Kirkhill Industrial Estate, Howe Moss Drive, Dyce, Aberdeen, AB21 0GL Tel: (01224) 725800 Fax: (01224) 725801 E-mail: info@tracinternational.com

Vertical Technology Ind Rope Access Specialists, Unit 15 Wren Centre, Westbourne Road, Emsworth, Hampshire, PO10 7SU Tel: (01243) 377599 Fax: (01243) 377227 E-mail: admin@vertical-technology.com

DIFFRACTION GRATING

Paton Hawksley Education Ltd, 59 Wellsway, Keynsham, Bristol, BS31 1PG Tel: 0117-986 2364 Fax: 0117-986 8285

DIFFUSED BONDED WOVEN WIRE CLOTH FILTER MEDIA

▶ G Bopp & Co. Ltd, Grange Close, Clover Nook Industrial Park, Somercotes, Alfreton, Derbyshire, DE55 4QT Tel: (01773) 521266 Fax: (01773) 521163 E-mail: info@gbopp.com

DIGITAL AUDIO SYSTEMS

▶ Sonaptic Ltd, Chancery Court, Lincolns Inn, Lincoln Road, High Wycombe, Bucks, HP12 3RE Tel: 01494 429368 E-mail: mail@sonaptic.com

DIGITAL BINOCULAR CAMERAS

▶ Mr.Amin, 3 Galen Place, London, WC1A 2JR Tel: (020) 7240 6774 Fax: (020) 7419 4729 E-mail: sales@microglobe.co.uk

DIGITAL CAMERAS

A B K Group Finance Ltd, Lower Meadow Road Brooke Park, Steadings House, Handforth, Wilmslow, Cheshire, SK9 3LP Tel: 0161-486 6721 Fax: 0161-482 6301 E-mail: sales@abkplc.com

Canon UK Ltd, Cockshot Hill, Reigate, Surrey, RH2 8BF Tel: (01737) 220000 Fax: (01737) 220022

▶ FotoStation, 146 High Street, Ruislip, Middlesex, HA4 8LJ Tel: (01895) 674000 E-mail: info@fotostation.co.uk

Genisys Group Ltd, Crockford Lane, Chineham, Basingstoke, Hampshire, RG24 8NA Tel: (01256) 816611 Fax: (01256) 816552 E-mail: sales@genisys.co.uk

Imagic UK P.L.C., Potterne, Devizes, Wiltshire, SN10 5XG Tel: (01380) 729099 Fax: (01380) 729092 E-mail: info@imageaccess.co.uk

Intec, 35 Trelowarren Street, Camborne, Cornwall, TR14 8AD Tel: (01209) 716717 Fax: (01209) 610580

Jigsaw Systems Ltd, The Old Mill, High Church Street, Nottingham, NG7 7JA Tel: (0870) 7306868 Fax: (0870) 7306850 E-mail: sales@jigsaw24.com

Kalms Associates, 17 Lyon Road, London, SW19 2RL Tel: (020) 8286 6066 Fax: (020) 8547 7668 E-mail: sales@kalms-associates.com

Kodak Ltd, Hemel One, Boundary Way, Hemel Hempstead, Hertfordshire, HP2 7YU Tel: (01442) 261122 E-mail: gb-ei-orders@kodak.com

Leica Microsystems UK Ltd, Davy Avenue, Knowlhill, Milton Keynes, MK5 8LB Tel: (0800) 437 0492 Fax: (01908) 609992 E-mail: sales@leica-geosystems.com

Martin Dawes Solutions Ltd, Martin Dawes House, Europa Boulevard, Westbrook, Warrington, WA5 7WH Tel: (01925) 555000 Fax: (01925) 494835

Nikon UK Ltd, Nikon House, 380 Richmond Road, Kingston upon Thames, Surrey, KT2 5PR Tel: (020) 8247 1718 Fax: (020) 8541 4584

Norbain SD Ltd, Eskdale Road, Winnersh, Wokingham, Berkshire, RG41 5TS Tel: 0118-944 0123 Fax: 0118-9440999 E-mail: james.smith@norbain.co.uk

Olympus UK Ltd, 2-8 Honduras St, London, EC1Y 0TX Tel: (020) 7253 2772 Fax: (020) 7251 6330 E-mail: info@olympus.uk.com

Polaroid UK Ltd, Vale of Leven Industrial Estate, Dumbarton, G82 3PW Tel: (01389) 712000 Fax: (01389) 755101

Brian Reece Scientific Ltd, 12 West Mills, Newbury, Berkshire, RG14 5HG Tel: (01635) 32827 Fax: (01635) 34542 E-mail: brian@brsl.co.uk

Spot On Computers Ltd, 122 Waterloo Road, Manchester, M8 8AF Tel: (0845) 3453111 Fax: (0870) 1121953 E-mail: sales@spotonuk.com

Sunitek Marshan Ltd, 176 Newhampton Road East, Wolverhampton, WV1 4PQ Tel: (01902) 773329 Fax: (01902) 773328

DIGITAL CLOCKS

Wharton Electronics, Unit 15 Thame Park Business Centre, Wenman Road, Thame, Oxfordshire, OX9 3XA Tel: (01844) 260567 Fax: (01844) 218855 E-mail: info@wharton.co.uk

DIGITAL COLOUR PRINTERS

▶ Arvanti UK Ltd, Unit 6, Morley Business Centre, Morley Road, Tonbridge, Kent, TN9 1RA Tel: (01732) 366063 Fax: (01732) 770890 E-mail: info@arvanti.co.uk

Giraffe Print, PO Box 453, Epsom, Surrey, KT18 7WJ Tel: 0800 328 4712 E-mail: info@giraffeprint.com

Print Partnership, Unit 11 Pacific Business Park, Pacific Road, Cardiff, CF24 5HJ Tel: (029) 2047 4010 Fax: (029) 2047 4011 E-mail: repro@printpartnership.co.uk

▶ Salisbury Printing Co. Ltd, 71a Greencroft Street, Salisbury, SP1 1JF Tel: (01722) 413330 Fax: (01722) 413242 E-mail: mail@salisburyprinting.co.uk

DIGITAL COMBINATION ACCESS LOCKS

▶ Access Hardware Ltd, Jewsons Ltd, The Slough, Spernal, Studley, Warwickshire, B80 7EN Tel: (01527) 852948 Fax: (01527) 854192 E-mail: sales@accesshardware.co.uk

Thomas Fox & Co. Ltd, 3 Rhodes Way, Watford, WD24 4YA Tel: (01923) 811700 Fax: (01923) 811710 E-mail: enquiries@thomasfox.co.uk

J&T Group Ltd, PO Box 5 Victoria Works, Stoke-on-Trent, ST4 6HA Tel: (01782) 202545 Fax: (01782) 349449 E-mail: sales@storagebins.co.uk

DIGITAL COMMUNICATION ANALYSERS

A R G Electrodesign Ltd, Querns Business Centre, Whitworth Road, Cirencester, Gloucestershire, GL7 1RT Tel: (01285) 658501 Fax: (01285) 885376 E-mail: info@arg.co.uk

DIGITAL COMPUTERS

Baydel Ltd, Brook Way, Leatherhead, Surrey, KT22 7NA Tel: (01372) 378811 Fax: (01372) 386960 E-mail: enquiry@baydel.com

Enterasys Networks Ltd, Nexus House Newbury Business Park, London Road, Newbury, Berkshire, RG14 2PZ Tel: (01635) 580000 Fax: (01635) 810300

Harris Systems Ltd, Eskdale Road, Winnersh, Wokingham, Berkshire, RG41 5TS Tel: 0118-969 8787 Fax: 0118-964 8001

DIGITAL DISPLAYS, LIQUID CRYSTAL (LCD)

B F Group Ltd, Unit 6 Cobhan Centre, Westmead Industrial Estate, Westlea, Swindon, SN5 7UJ Tel: (01793) 498020 Fax: (01793) 542019 E-mail: sales@bfgroup.co.uk

Ferrograph Ltd, New York Way, New York Industrial Park, Newcastle upon Tyne, NE27 0QF Tel: 0191-280 8800 Fax: 0191-280 8810

The Herts Meter Co. Ltd, Unit 10 Bury Road, Hatfield, Hertfordshire, AL10 8BJ Tel: (01707) 270404 Fax: (01707) 270152 E-mail: info@hertsmeter.com

Infotec Ltd, The Maltings, Tamworth Road, Ashby-de-la-Zouch, Leicestershire, LE65 2PS Tel: (01530) 560600 Fax: (01530) 560111 E-mail: sales@infotech.co.uk

Manhattan Skyline Ltd, 5 Bracknell Business Centre, Downmill Road, Bracknell, Berkshire, RG12 1QS Tel: (01344) 307733 Fax: (01344) 307744 E-mail: sales@mansky.co.uk

The ST. Albans Meter Company Ltd, Lombardy House, The Ridgeway, St. Albans, Hertfordshire, AL4 9AL Tel: (01727) 899911 Fax: (01727) 899922 E-mail: stalbansmeters@ukgateway.net

Trident Microsystems Ltd, Perrywood Business Park, Honeycrock Lane, Redhill, RH1 5JQ Tel: (01737) 780790 Fax: (01737) 771908 E-mail: sales@trident-uk.co.uk

▶ indicates data change since last edition

DIGITAL DOOR LOCKS

▶ GB Locking Systems Ltd, Redburn House, Redburn Road, Newcastle upon Tyne, NE5 1NB Tel: 0191-271 6344 Fax: 0191-271 3644 E-mail: sales@gblockingsystems.co.uk
▶ Torbay Security Solutions, 46 Bitton Avenue, Teignmouth, Devon, TQ14 8HD Tel: (01626) 776161 Fax: (01626) 772583 E-mail: enquiries@torbaysecuritysolutions.co.uk

DIGITAL ELECTRONIC EQUIPMENT DESIGN

▶ Design Interface Ltd, Thurston Grange, Thurston End, Hawkedon, Bury St. Edmunds, Suffolk, IP29 4LQ Tel: (01284) 789608 Fax: (01284) 789617 E-mail: enquiries@design-interface.com
Newbury Electronic Services Ltd, 1 Berwick Courtyard, Berwick St. Leonard, Salisbury, SP3 5UA Tel: (01747) 820615 E-mail: sales@nes-ltd.com

DIGITAL ENCODERS

T R Controls Ltd, 12a Oak Industrial Park, Chelmsford Road, Dunmow, Essex, CM6 1XN Tel: (01371) 876187 Fax: (01371) 876287 E-mail: alan@trcontrols.co.uk

DIGITAL IMAGING SYSTEMS

▶ C3 Imaging, Back New Bridge Street, Newcastle upon Tyne, NE1 2TY Tel: 0191-232 1517 Fax: 0191-232 0572 E-mail: info@c3newcastle.co.uk
Cognitronics Ltd, Claylands Avenue, Worksop, Nottinghamshire, S81 7DJ Tel: (01909) 477272 Fax: (01909) 486260 E-mail: sales@cognitronics.co.uk
Crailcrest Ltd, Coach House, Birch Grove, Horsted Keynes, Haywards Heath, West Sussex, RH17 7DJ Tel: (01825) 740190 Fax: (01825) 740178 E-mail: sales@crailcrest.com
▶ Creative Imaging (UK) Ltd, Waterside House, 60 Wharf Road, London, N1 7SF Tel: (020) 7251 6006
Durst (UK) Ltd, 9 Blenheim Road, Longmead Industrial Estate, Epsom, Surrey, KT19 9AR Tel: (01372) 726262 Fax: (01372) 740761 E-mail: info@durstuk.co.uk
Godiva Imaging Ltd, Little Heath Industrial Estate, Old Church Road, Coventry, CV6 7ND Tel: (024) 7663 7192 Fax: (024) 7663 7192
Harmen Technology Ltd, Ilford Way, Mobberley, Knutsford, Cheshire, WA16 7JL Tel: (01565) 650000 Fax: (01565) 872734
Imaging Associates Ltd, 6 Avonbury Business Park, Howes Lane, Bicester, Oxfordshire, OX26 2UA Tel: (01869) 356240 Fax: (01869) 356241 E-mail: sales@imas.co.uk
Leica Microsystems UK Ltd, Davy Avenue, Knowlhill, Milton Keynes, MK5 8LB Tel: (0800) 437 0492 Fax: (01908) 609992 E-mail: sales@leica-geosystems.com
Olympus UK Ltd, 2-8 Honduras St, London, EC1Y 0TX Tel: (020) 7253 2772 Fax: (020) 7251 6330 E-mail: info@olympus.uk.com
Photo Optix Ltd, 14 Clivemont Road, Maidenhead, Berkshire, SL6 7BU Tel: (01628) 778787 Fax: (01628) 776145
T D C I, Sopwith Close, Drayton Fields Industrial Esta, Daventry, Northamptonshire, NN11 8EA Tel: (01327) 312570 Fax: (01327) 312721 E-mail: info@tdci.eu.com
Xograph Imaging Systems, Xograph House, Hampton Street, Tetbury, Gloucestershire, GL8 8LD Tel: (01666) 501501 Fax: (01666) 501502 E-mail: enquiry@xograph.com
Your PC, 23-25 Station Road, Holmfirth, HD9 1AB Tel: (01484) 687814 Fax: (01484) 687685

DIGITAL INDICATORS

BEKA Associates Ltd, Old Charlton Road, Hitchin, Hertfordshire, SG5 2DA Tel: (01462) 438301 Fax: (01462) 453971 E-mail: sales@beka.co.uk

DIGITAL INTEGRATED CIRCUITS (IC)

Dialog Semiconductor UK Ltd, Windmill Hill Business Park, Whitehill Way, Swindon, SN5 6PJ Tel: (01793) 875327 Fax: (01793) 875328 E-mail: mixed_signal@diasemi.com

DIGITAL MAP PRODUCTION SYSTEMS

1spatial Group Ltd, Unit 6 Cambridge Business Park, Cowley Road, Cambridge, CB4 0WZ Tel: (01223) 420414 Fax: (01223) 420044 E-mail: info@1spatial.com
Lovell Johns Ltd, 10 Hanborough Business Park, Lodge Road, Long Hanborough, Witney, Oxfordshire, OX29 8RU Tel: (01993) 883161 Fax: (01993) 883096 E-mail: enquiries@lovelljohns.com

DIGITAL MAPPING SOLUTIONS

▶ Map Marketing Limited, Suite 23,, Hardmans Business Centre, New Hall Hey Road, Rawtenstall, Lancashire, BB4 6HH Tel: 01706 220444 E-mail: glen@mapmarketing.com

DIGITAL MEDIA PRODUCTION

▶ 360red Productions, LCB Depot, 31 Rutland Street, Leicester, LE1 1RE Tel: 0116-253 3420 E-mail: info@360red.co.uk
▶ Two Heads Global Design Ltd, Kit Lane, Checkendon, Reading, RG8 0TY Tel: (01491) 681061 Fax: (01491) 682095 E-mail: victoria@2heads.tv

DIGITAL OHMMETERS

Arbra Instruments, Advance Park, Park Road, Rhosymedre, Wrexham, Clwyd, LL14 3YR Tel: (01978) 823900 Fax: (01978) 822913 E-mail: sales@aslgroup.uk

DIGITAL PANEL METERS

Dalroad Distribution Ltd, Bramingham Business Park, Enterprise Way, Luton, LU3 4BU Tel: (01582) 505252 Fax: (01582) 560060 E-mail: sales@dalroad.com
London Electronics Ltd, Warren Court, Chicksands, Shefford, Bedfordshire, SG17 5QB Tel: (01462) 850967 Fax: (01462) 850968 E-mail: support@london-electronics.com
Martel Instruments Holdings Ltd, Stanelaw Way, Tanfield Lea Industrial Estate, Tanfield Lea, Stanley, County Durham, DH9 9XG Tel: (01207) 290266 Fax: (01207) 290239 E-mail: info@martelinstruments.com
Multitek Ltd, Lancaster Way, Earls Colne, Colchester, CO6 2NS Tel: (01787) 223228 Fax: (01787) 223607 E-mail: chris@multitek-ltd.com
▶ Rayleigh Instruments Ltd, Raytel House, 19 Brook Road, Rayleigh, Essex, SS6 7XH Tel: (01268) 749300 Fax: (01268) 749309 E-mail: sales@rayleigh.co.uk
Swiss Mimic Co Ltd, 26 Highfield Road, Chertsey, Surrey, KT16 8BU Tel: (01932) 569100 Fax: (01932) 569100 E-mail: swiss.mimic@tiscarly.co.uk

DIGITAL PHOTOGRAPHIC PROCESSING

▶ Your BLank Canvas, 14 Green Lake Close, Bourton on the Water, Cheltenham, Gloucestershire, GL54 2PR Tel: (01451) 822880 Fax: (01451) 824060 E-mail: info@yourblankcanvas.co.uk

DIGITAL PHOTOGRAPHY TRAINING

▶ Digital Imaging Services & Photography, 8 Odense Court, East Kilbride, G75 0SA Tel: 07855 669213 E-mail: alex_disp@yahoo.co.uk

DIGITAL PREPRESS SERVICES

Digital Repro, Cambridge Road Industrial Estate, Milton, Cambridge, CB4 6AZ Tel: (01223) 420444 Fax: (01223) 420783
Dunns Imaging Group Ltd, Chester Road, Cradley Heath, West Midlands, B64 6AA Tel: (01384) 564770 Fax: (01384) 637165 E-mail: enquiries@dunns.co.uk
Graphic Output Technology Ltd, South Bank Technopark, 90 London Road, London, SE1 6LN Tel: (020) 7928 8889 Fax: (020) 7928 9929
Keene Printing Co. Ltd, 33-41 Dallington St, London, EC1V 0BB Tel: (020) 7251 2722 Fax: (020) 7490 8736 E-mail: info@keenes.co.uk
Prism Digital Colour Ltd, 4 Moreton Park Industrial Estate, Moreton Road South, Luton, LU2 0TL Tel: (01582) 456144 Fax: (01582) 453396 E-mail: sales@prismdigital.co.uk
Speedlith Ltd, Longford Trading Estate, Thomas Street, Stretford, Manchester, M32 0JT Tel: 0161-864 2233 Fax: 0161-864 5238 E-mail: speedlith@aol.com
T G I Great Britain, 16 Swinton La, St.Johns, Worcester, WR2 4JT Tel: (01905) 748222 Fax: (01905) 748220 E-mail: charlesbone@btinternet.com
Taylowe Ltd, Malvern Road, Furze Platt, Maidenhead, Berkshire, SL6 7RF Tel: (01628) 413333 Fax: (01628) 413397 E-mail: taylowereception@taylowe.com

DIGITAL PRINTERS

Abbotts Creative Print Ltd, Turnpike Close, Bilton Way, Lutterworth, Leicestershire, LE17 4YB Tel: (01455) 552636 Fax: (01455) 551699 E-mail: info@abbottsuk.net
▶ The Allesley Press Ltd, Leofric House, Waterman Road, Coventry, CV6 5TP Tel: (024) 7663 8844 Fax: (024) 7663 8890
Alpha Graphics, 40 Carrmere Road, Leechmere Industrial Estate, Sunderland, SR2 9TW Tel: 0191-523 9100 Fax: 0191-523 6045
▶ Antony Rowe Ltd, 2 Whittle Drive, Eastbourne, East Sussex, BN23 6QH Tel: (01323) 434700 Fax: (01323) 521117 E-mail: info@antonyrowe.co.uk
Ashford Press, Bottings Industrial Estate, Curdridge, Southampton, SO30 2DY Tel: (01489) 785311 Fax: (01489) 780716 E-mail: production@asfordpress.co.uk
Aztec Group, Unit 18 Chiltern Business Village, Arundel Road, Uxbridge, Middlesex, UB8 2SN Tel: (01895) 520600 Fax: (01895) 520650 E-mail: sales@aztecgroup.net
Bradbury Graphics Ltd, 6-14 Donegall Pass, Belfast, BT7 1BS Tel: (028) 9023 3535 Fax: (028) 9057 2057 E-mail: info@bradbury-graphics.co.uk
▶ Bridenprint Ltd, Briden House, Condor Road, Quarry Hill Industrial Park, Ilkeston, Derbyshire, DE7 4RE Tel: 0115-944 7111 Fax: 0115-944 7222 E-mail: sales@bridenprint.co.uk
C3 Imaging Ltd, Severalls Business Park, Telford Way, Colchester, CO4 9QP Tel: (01206) 845544 Fax: (01206) 845856 E-mail: jacqueline@hilocolour.co.uk
Chameleon Print Ltd, Unit 3, Palmerston Drive, Fareham, Hampshire, PO14 1DJ Tel: (01329) 280197 Fax: (01329) 822379
▶ Creative Place Ltd, 4 Millfield House, Woodshots Meadow, Watford, WD18 8SS Tel: (01923) 227272 Fax: (01923) 246556 E-mail: sales@thecreativeplace.co.uk
▶ Cyan Group Ltd, Regal House, 70 London Road, Twickenham, TW1 3QS Tel: (0870) 6088808 Fax: (0870) 6060270 E-mail: enquiries@cyan-group.com
D M A Signs, Unit 5-6 Bridge Works, Kingston Road, Leatherhead, Surrey, KT22 7SU Tel: (01372) 363808 Fax: (01372) 363801 E-mail: sale@dmasigns.co.uk
▶ D P I Ltd, Printing House, Church Lane, Norton, Worcester, WR5 2PS Tel: (0845) 0700750 Fax: (0845) 0700751 E-mail: dclover@dpi4xerox.co.uk
▶ Direct Imaging Ltd, Demmings House, Brookfield Road, Cheadle, Cheshire, SK8 2PE Tel: 0161-491 2121
E S P Technologies Group Ltd, 2 Euroway, Wood Close, Quarry Wood, Aylesford, Kent, ME20 7UB Tel: (01622) 715000 Fax: (01622) 797000 E-mail: sales@esptech.co.uk
F & M Displays Ltd, Tower Hamlets Road, Dover, Kent, CT17 0BJ Tel: (01304) 208889 Fax: (01304) 205807
Fosco Hayes-Hurdley Ltd, Carlton House, 41 Smith Street, Hockley, Birmingham, B19 3EN Tel: 0121-554 7421 Fax: 0121-523 4452 E-mail: enquiries@foscos.co.uk
▶ Foxprint Printers, 1 Factory Street, Shepshed, Loughborough, Leicestershire, LE12 9AQ Tel: (01509) 505413 Fax: (01509) 650413 E-mail: print@foxprint.co.uk
G P Print, G P Print Edgerley Business, Challenger Way, Peterborough, PE1 5EX Tel: (01733) 340622 Fax: (08719) 940780 E-mail: info@gpprint.co.uk
Giraffe Print, PO Box 453, Epsom, Surrey, KT18 7WJ Tel: 0800 328 4712 E-mail: info@giraffeprint.com
▶ I T @ Spectrum Ltd, 1 Trinity Street, Hull, HU3 1JR Tel: (01482) 586732 Fax: (01482) 211428E-mail: smonkman@itatspectrum.co.uk
Ikon Office Solutions plc, James House, 55 Welford Road, Leicester, LE2 7AP Tel: 0116-254 0999 Fax: 0116-285 4812 E-mail: sales@ikon.com
Ikon Office Solutions plc, 160 Edinburgh Avenue, Slough, SL1 4UE Tel: (01753) 771000 Fax: (01753) 696045
▶ Impress Repro By Design, 2 A1 Parkway, Southgate Way, Orton Southgate, Peterborough, PE2 6YN Tel: (01733) 397350 Fax: (01733) 397351
Kingsway Press Ltd, Seventh Avenue, Team Valley Trading Estate, Gateshead, Tyne & Wear, NE11 0SL Tel: 0191-491 0455 Fax: 0191-491 0454 E-mail: sales@kingswaypress.co.uk
▶ Kinko's Ltd, 1 Curzon Street, London, W1J 5HD Tel: (020) 7717 4900 Fax: (020) 7717 4901
Midshire Business Systems Northern Ltd, Jones Court, Jones Square, Stockport, Cheshire, SK1 4LJ Tel: 0161-477 3277 Fax: 0161-477 3340 E-mail: info@midshire.co.uk
▶ Oriel Studios, Orrell Mount, Bootle, Merseyside, L20 6NS Tel: 0151-922 2785 Fax: 0151-933 5410
P J Signs, 37 Priory Avenue, Taunton, Somerset, TA1 1XZ Tel: (01823) 283985 Fax: (01823) 321391 E-mail: sales@pjsigns.co.uk
Pandaprint, 104 Park Road, Rosyth, Dunfermline, Fife, KY11 2JL Tel: (01383) 417847 Fax: (01383) 411863
▶ Pier House Ltd, Unit 3, Bourne Mill, Guildford Road, Farnham, Surrey, GU9 9PS Tel: (01252) 735000 Fax: (01252) 738110 E-mail: pam.hudson@pierhouse.co.uk
▶ Print By Design, 7-9 Imperial Square, Cheltenham, Gloucestershire, GL50 1QB Tel: (01242) 216123
Print Express, 4 Sunnyside Terrace, London, NW9 5DL Tel: (020) 8200 0600 Fax: (020) 8200 6866 E-mail: printexpress@btclick.com
▶ Printhouse Corporation Ltd, St Leonards Road, London, NW10 6ST Tel: (020) 8963 0123 Fax: (0871) 7171103 E-mail: sales@printhouse.co.uk
Prism Digital Colour Ltd, 4 Moreton Park Industrial Estate, Moreton Road South, Luton, LU2 0TL Tel: (01582) 456144 Fax: (01582) 453396 E-mail: sales@prismdigital.co.uk
▶ Ps2 Digital Imaging, 1 Sarus Court, Manor Park, Runcorn, Cheshire, WA7 1UL Tel: (01928) 597888 Fax: (01928) 597886 E-mail: sales@ps2-digital.com
▶ St Barnabas Press, Coldhams Road, Cambridge, CB1 3EW Tel: (01223) 413792
▶ Salisbury Printing Co. Ltd, 71a Greencroft Street, Salisbury, SP1 1JF Tel: (01722) 413330 Fax: (01722) 413242 E-mail: mail@salisburyprinting.co.uk
Swaingrove Ltd, Unit 3-4 Fourwheel Drive, Rougham Industrial Estate, Rougham, Bury St. Edmunds, Suffolk, IP30 9ND Tel: (01359) 271385 Fax: (01359) 271327 E-mail: systems@swaingrove.co.uk
▶ Xpress Business Services, Unit 30-31 The Bell Centre, Newton Road, Crawley, West Sussex, RH10 9FZ Tel: (01293) 616848 Fax: (01293) 511666 E-mail: sales@xpress-services.co.uk
Zero Signs Ltd, Grosvenor Works, Derby Street, Crewe, CW1 3ER Tel: (01270) 256258 Fax: (01270) 501603 E-mail: sales@zerosigns.co.uk

DIGITAL PRINTERS, WIDE FORMAT, MAINTENANCE AND REPAIR

▶ A D Young, Greenacre Court Ruffet Road, Kendleshire, Winterbourne, Bristol, BS36 1AN Tel: (01454) 252910 Fax: (01454) 252911 E-mail: admin@adyoung.com
▶ Castle Business Services Ltd, 28 Grange Road, South Croydon, Surrey, CR2 0NA Tel: (020) 8407 0632 Fax: (020) 8407 0587 E-mail: service@faxandprinterrepairs.co.uk

DIGITAL PRINTING

A D M Imaging, 59-61 Summer Lane, Birmingham, B19 3TH Tel: 0121-359 5424 Fax: 0121-359 7038 E-mail: info@abmimaging.co.uk
A Mcclay & Co. Ltd, Longwood Drive, Cardiff, CF14 7ZB Tel: (029) 2054 4100 Fax: (029) 2054 4123 E-mail: 106740.3652@compuserve.com
Abbotts Creative Print Ltd, Turnpike Close, Bilton Way, Lutterworth, Leicestershire, LE17 4YB Tel: (01455) 552636 Fax: (01455) 551699 E-mail: info@abbottsuk.net
▶ Aeroprinting, Unit 54B, Aidan Court, Bede Industrial Estate, Jarrow, Tyne & Wear, NE32 3EF Tel: 0191 4282428 Fax: 0191 4837266 E-mail: info@aeroprinting.co.uk
Age Communications, 20 Upper Ground, London, SE1 9PF Tel: (020) 7805 5590 Fax: (020) 7805 5910 E-mail: iln@ilng.co.uk
Allen Signs Ltd, Waddington House, Whisby Way, Lincoln, LN6 3LQ Tel: (01522) 501500 Fax: (01522) 501600 E-mail: enquiries@allensigns.co.uk
B E P Signs Ltd, 8a South Street, Greenock, Renfrewshire, PA16 8TX Tel: (01475) 784423 Fax: (01475) 729213 E-mail: enquiries@bepsigns.co.uk
Beaver Graphic Services, Graphic House, Wiggenhall Road, Watford, WD18 0FG Tel: (01923) 229387 Fax: (01923) 223957 E-mail: sales@beaver.co.uk
Border Reprographics, Tuppenny Lane, Emsworth, Hampshire, PO10 8HG Tel: (01243) 377721 Fax: (01243) 379200 E-mail: info@border-repro.co.uk
Cestrian, Stanley Green TRDG Estate, Earl Road, Cheadle Hulme, Cheadle, Cheshire, SK8 6QD Tel: 0161-488 3300 Fax: 0161-488 3301 E-mail: reception@cestrian.co.uk
Clanpress (Kings Lynn) Ltd, 1 Dundee Court, Hamburg Way, King's Lynn, Norfolk, PE30 2ND Tel: (01553) 772737 Fax: (01553) 768403 E-mail: clanpress@aol.com
Creative Display Group, Millersdale Close, Euroway Industrial Estate, Bradford, West Yorkshire, BD4 6RX Tel: (01274) 700690 Fax: (01274) 700699 E-mail: sales@creativedisplaygroup.co.uk
D X Imaging, Units 19 & 20, Watford Enterprise Centre, Watford, WD18 8EA Tel: (01923) 227644 Fax: (01923) 816896 E-mail: dximaging@dximaging.co.uk
Datagraphic UK Ltd, Cottage Leap, Butler's Leap, Rugby, Warwickshire, CV21 3XP Tel: (01788) 535383 Fax: (01788) 535351 E-mail: sales@datagraphic.co.uk
E S P Technologies Group Ltd, 2 Euroway, Wood Close, Quarry Wood, Aylesford, Kent, ME20 7UB Tel: (01622) 715000 Fax: (01622) 797000 E-mail: sales@esptech.co.uk
▶ Four Point Printing & Copying, Unit 3 Fordwater Trading Estate, Ford Road, Chertsey, Surrey, KT16 8HG Tel: (01932) 561163 Fax: (01932) 568010 E-mail: info@fourpoint.co.uk

DIGITAL PRINTING – *continued*

G&T, 9 Orwell Court, Hurricane Way, Wickford, Essex, SS11 8YJ Tel: (01268) 766500 Fax: (01268) 766530 E-mail: info@gtoffice.co.uk

Gemini Digital Colour, North Road, Bridgend Industrial Estate, Bridgend, Mid Glamorgan, CF31 3TP Tel: (01656) 652447 Fax: (01656) 661266 E-mail: sales@geminidigitalcolour.co.uk

Grasmere (Digital) Imaging Ltd, Bramley Business Centre, Stanningley Road, Leeds, LS13 4EN Tel: 0113-224 8600 Fax: 0113-239 3166 E-mail: admin@grasmeredigital.co.uk

Hobs Reprographic, 244-256 Deansgate, Manchester, M3 4BQ Tel: 0161-832 6670 Fax: 0161-833 2228

Image X P S Ltd, 11 North Street, Portslade, Brighton, BN41 1DH Tel: (01273) 421242 Fax: (01273) 421210

▶ Ips, Executive House, Mill Lane, Blaby, Leicester, LE8 4FG Tel: 0116-277 2666 Fax: 0116-276 1199 E-mail: susan@direct-ips.co.uk

Harold Jackson Screenprint Ltd, 986 Pollokshaws Road, Glasgow, G41 2HE Tel: 0141-649 1783 Fax: 0141-649 6087 E-mail: enquiries@jacksonscreenprint.co.uk

▶ Kelleway Media, Unit 8 Thesiger Close, Worthing, West Sussex, BN11 2RN Tel: (01903) 218111 Fax: (01903) 288659 E-mail: sales@kellewaymedia.com

Labute Colour Printers Ltd, Cambridge Printing Park, Milton, Cambridge, CB4 6AZ Tel: (01223) 420000 Fax: (01223) 420860 E-mail: info@labute.co.uk

Northampton Signs Ltd, Unit 5,, Stour Road,, Weedon Road Industrial Estate,, Northampton, NN5 5AA Tel: (01604) 758198 E-mail: sales@northamptonsigns.co.uk

Oyez Straker, 4 City Park Industrial Estate, Gelderd Road, Leeds, LS12 6DR Tel: 0113-203 2100 Fax: 0113-263 9011 E-mail: sales.pudsey@oyezstraker.co.uk

▶ Palm Signs Systems, 35a Greenfield Business Park, Bagillt Road, Greenfield, Holywell, Clwyd, CH8 7HJ Tel: (01352) 712222 Fax: (01352) 712255 E-mail: info@palmsigns.co.uk

Phoenix Colour plc, 11 Knighton Fields Road West, Leicester, LE2 6LH Tel: 0116-283 5817 Fax: 0116-244 0061 E-mail: admin@phoenix-photo.co.uk

Redwood Photographic, 7 Brunel Court, Brunel Way, Severalls Industrial Park, Colchester, CO4 9XW Tel: (01206) 751241 Fax: (01206) 855134 E-mail: info@redwoodphoto.com

Robert Horne Co. Ltd, 3 Nicholson Drive, Newtownabbey, County Antrim, BT36 4FB Tel: (028) 9034 2742 Fax: (028) 9034 2413 E-mail: rh.northern.ireland@roberthorne.co.uk

Robert Horne Group plc, Orleans House, Edmund Street, Liverpool, L3 9NG Tel: 0151-236 4411 Fax: 0151-255 0359 E-mail: total.support@roberthorne.co.uk

Robert Horne Group plc, Horse Fair House, St Faiths Lane, Norwich, NR1 1NE Tel: (01603) 610386 Fax: (01603) 633381 E-mail: rh.norwich@roberthorne.co.uk

Service Point, 32 Invincible Drive, Armstrong Industrial Park, Newcastle upon Tyne, NE4 7HX Tel: 0191-273 2834 Fax: 0191-272 3174

Teknigrafiks, Unit 110 Bradley Fold Trading Estate, Radcliffe Moor Road, Bradley Fold, Bolton, BL2 6RT Tel: (01204) 389686 Fax: (01204) 531597 E-mail: sales@teknigrafiks.co.uk

Wood & Richardson Ltd, Royden House, 156 Haxby Road, York, YO31 8JN Tel: (01904) 622712 Fax: (01904) 620352 E-mail: sales@woodrichardson.co.uk

DIGITAL PRINTING SUBSTRATES

Brissco Signs & Graphics, 25 Cater Road, Bristol, BS13 7TX Tel: 0117-311 3777 Fax: 0117-311 6777 E-mail: sales@brissco.co.uk

C P Arts Ltd, Alphin Brook Road, Marsh Barton Trading Estate, Exeter, EX2 8QF Tel: (01392) 210574 Fax: (01392) 412107 E-mail: cparts@cparts.co.uk

Charnwood Publishing Co. Ltd, Vaughan Street, Coalville, Leicestershire, LE67 3GG Tel: (01530) 832288 Fax: (01530) 510390 E-mail: chardwoodp@aol.com

Leopold Professional Services, 57 Lancaster Road, Barnet, Hertfordshire, EN4 8AS Tel: (020) 8441 4310 Fax: (020) 8449 0317 E-mail: paul@leopold.co.uk

▶ St James Litho Ltd, 21 Wates Way, Mitcham, Surrey, CR4 4HR Tel: (020) 8640 9438 Fax: (020) 8685 1719

DIGITAL PUBLISHING

▶ House of Hamilton Publishing, 0 Hamilton Road, Felixstowe, Suffolk, IP11 7BA Tel: 01394 274440 E-mail: enquiries@houseofhamiltonpublishing.co.uk

DIGITAL RADIOGRAPHY EQUIPMENT

▶ IDR Services Ltd, 32 St Peters Close, Crabbs Cross, Redditch, Worcestershire, B97 5LE Tel: 01527 542501 Fax: 01527 542501 E-mail: idrservices@blueyonder.co.uk

DIGITAL READOUT SYSTEMS MAINTENANCE/REPAIR SERVICES

Engineering Equipment Centre Ltd, 27 St Margarets Road, Bournemouth, BH10 4BG Tel: (01202) 528249 Fax: (01202) 528979

New England Engineering Ltd, Sandy Lane Industrial Estate, Stourport-on-Severn, Worcestershire, DY13 9QB Tel: (01299) 827399 Fax: (01299) 827400 E-mail: machines@newengland.co.uk

DIGITAL READOUT SYSTEMS MANUFRS

Beckmass Scientific Apparatus, 25 The Brambles, Haslington, Crewe, CW1 5RA Tel: (01270) 586707 Fax: (01270) 586707

Warren Carson Ltd, Dean Court, Upper Dean, Huntingdon, Cambridgeshire, PE28 0NL Tel: (01234) 708881 Fax: (01234) 708677

Engineering Equipment Centre Ltd, 27 St Margarets Road, Bournemouth, BH10 4BG Tel: (01202) 528249 Fax: (01202) 528979

Expect Precision Services, 449 Scarborough Avenue, Stevenage, Hertfordshire, SG1 2QB Tel: (07802) 277353 Fax: (01438) 364874 E-mail: sinned72@hotmail.com

Heidenhain (GB) Ltd, 200 London Road, Burgess Hill, West Sussex, RH15 9RD Tel: (01444) 247711 Fax: (01444) 870024 E-mail: sales@heidenhain.co.uk

Lascar Electronics Ltd, Module House, Whiteparish, Salisbury, SP5 2SJ Tel: (01794) 884567 Fax: (01794) 884616 E-mail: sales@lascar.co.uk

London Electronics Ltd, Warren Court, Chicksands, Shefford, Bedfordshire, SG17 5QB Tel: (01462) 850967 Fax: (01462) 850968 E-mail: support@london-electronics.com

New England Engineering Ltd, Sandy Lane Industrial Estate, Stourport-on-Severn, Worcestershire, DY13 9QB Tel: (01299) 827399 Fax: (01299) 827400 E-mail: machines@newengland.co.uk

The Red Corner Document Solutions Ltd, 7200 The Quorum, Oxford Business Park North, Oxford, OX4 2JZ Tel: (01865) 481488 Fax: (01865) 882164

Warren Measurement Systems, 15 Berwick Way, Kettering, Northamptonshire, NN15 5XF Tel: (01536) 310722 Fax: (01536) 310722 E-mail: sales@warrenmeasurement.co.uk

DIGITAL SATELLITE RECEIVERS

▶ AMOS Marketing Ltd, 28 Jermyn Way, Tharston, NORWICH, NR15 2ZA Tel: 01508 531482 E-mail: amosmarketing@btinternet.com

▶ Skyscope, 196 Morris Green Lane, Bolton, BL3 3LB Tel: (01204) 654901 E-mail: paul@skyscope.co.uk

DIGITAL SATELLITE RECEIVERS, DIGITAL VIDEO BROADCASTING (DVB), FREE TO AIR

▶ AMOS Marketing Ltd, 28 Jermyn Way, Tharston, NORWICH, NR15 2ZA Tel: 01508 531482 E-mail: amosmarketing@btinternet.com

DIGITAL SECURITY SYSTEMS OR EQUIPMENT

M J Security UK Ltd, Tudor Walk, Berry Hill, Coleford, Gloucestershire, GL16 7AE Tel: (01594) 834585 E-mail: enquiries@mjsecuritysystems.com

Sisys, Patrick House, West Quay Road, Poole, Dorset, BH15 1JF Tel: (01202) 660666 Fax: (01202) 330290

DIGITAL SIGNAL PROCESSORS (DSP)

Hunt Engineering, Chestnut Court, Burton Row, Brent Knoll, Highbridge, Somerset, TA9 4BP Tel: (01278) 760188 Fax: (01278) 760199 E-mail: sales@hunteng.co.uk

Sarsen Technology Ltd, 23 High Street, Marlborough, Wiltshire, SN8 1LW Tel: (01672) 511166 Fax: (01672) 511177 E-mail: sales@sarsen.net

Sundance Multiprocessor Technology Ltd, Chiltern Ho, Waterside, Chesham, Buckinghamshire, HP5 1PS Tel: (01494) 793167 Fax: (01494) 793168 E-mail: sales@sundance.com

DIGITAL SOUND STORES

Golding Audio, 8 Peartree Business Centre, Peartree Road, Stanway, Colchester, CO3 0JN Tel: (01206) 762462 Fax: (01206) 762633 E-mail: enquiries@goldingaudio.co.uk

DIGITAL THERMOMETERS

Anton Test & Measurement, Park House, 15-23 Greenhill Crescent, Watford, WD18 8PH Tel: (08704) 280073 Fax: (08704) 280076 E-mail: sales@anton-group.com

Edale Instruments (Cambridge) Ltd, Gresley House, Station Road, Longstanton, Cambridge, CB4 5DS Tel: (01954) 260853 Fax: (01954) 260894

▶ Heatmiser UK Ltd, Primrose House, Primrose Street, Darwen, Lancashire, BB3 2DE Tel: (01254) 776343 Fax: (01254) 704143 E-mail: info@heatmiser.co.uk

R & J Engineering, Gate House Cam Centre, Wilbury Way, Hitchin, Hertfordshire, SG4 0TW Tel: (01462) 620444 Fax: (01462) 620777

DIGITAL TRANSCRIPTION SERVICES

▶ 1st Class Secretarial Services, 34 New Hunterfield, Gorebridge, Midlothian, EH23 4BD Tel: (01875) 823215 Fax: (01875) 823215 E-mail: dawn.lawson@1stclass.uk.com

▶ A Virtual Solution, 11 Langley Close, Louth, Lincolnshire, LN11 8YP Tel: (01507) 609043 Fax: (01507) 609043 E-mail: sales@avirtualsolution.co.uk

Audio Experts, Springboard Business Centre, Ellerbeck Way, Middlesbrough, Cleveland, TS9 5JZ Tel: (01642) 715345 Fax: (01642) 715344 E-mail: office@audio-experts.co.uk

Voicescript, 31 Rickford Road, Nailsea, Bristol, BS48 4QB Tel: 01275 791184 E-mail: enquiries@voicescript.co.uk

DIGITAL VERSATILE DISC (DVD) AUTHORING

▶ A19 Duplication, PO Box 428, Middlesbrough, Cleveland, TS1 9AF Tel: (01642) 225283 E-mail: sales@a19duplication.co.uk

▶ Cinecosse Presentation Services, Unit 4 North Meadows, Oldmeldrum, Inverurie, Aberdeenshire, AB51 0GQ Tel: (01651) 873311 Fax: (01651) 873300

Data Business, 1-4 Bankside, Kidlington, Oxfordshire, OX5 1JE Tel: (01865) 848574 Fax: (0870) 766 5210 E-mail: sales@databiz.com

▶ Dicsmart Disc Services, 25a Caxton Avenue, Blackpool, FY2 9AP Tel: (01253) 508670 Fax: (01253) 508670

▶ DS Digital Video, The Corner Cot, Guildford Road, Chertsey, Surrey, KT16 9RU Tel: 08709 220032 Fax: 08707 601171 E-mail: admin@dsdigitalvideo.co.uk

▶ Pink Pigeon Ltd, 34-35 Berwick Street, London, W1F 8RP Tel: (020) 7439 3266 Fax: (020) 7439 3277 E-mail: info@pinkpigeon.net

▶ Redshark, Zetland House, Paul Street, London, EC2A 4LF Tel: (020) 7729 0030 Fax: (020) 7739 4918E-mail: info@redshark.tv

▶ Squire International Ltd, Skillion Business Centre, Hawley Road, London, N18 3SB Tel: (020) 8345 7474 Fax: (020) 8345 7373 E-mail: sales@squire.co.uk

DIGITAL VIDEO POST PRODUCTION EQUIPMENT

Brimar Ltd, Greenside Way, Middleton, Manchester, M24 1SN Tel: 0161-681 7072 Fax: 0161-683 5978 E-mail: dave.eldridge@brimar.ltd.uk

▶ Dynamite Pictures, 8 Wilkinson Terrace, Stutton, Tadcaster, North Yorkshire, LS24 9BP Tel: (07816) 319195 E-mail: richard.ball@lycos.co.uk

▶ Element A V, 59 St. Michaels Close, Aveley, South Ockendon, Essex, RM15 4SY Tel: (01708) 402977 Fax: (01708) 402977 E-mail: andy@elementav.com

▶ Harliquin.co.uk, Dover Street, Totton, Southampton, SO14 6GL Tel: (07050) 196660 E-mail: ian@harliquin.co.uk

▶ i2i Television Ltd, The Studio, Bankhead Farm Road, Strathaven, Lanarkshire, ML10 6TR Tel: (01698) 794100 E-mail: crews@i2itv.com

▶ The Post Factory, 7Th Floor Newcombe House, 45 Nottinghill Gate, London, W11 3LQ Tel: (020) 7229 6015 Fax: (020) 7727 8509 E-mail: info@postfactory.co.uk

▶ Retina Productions Ltd, 6 Mount Pleasant Crescent, London, N4 4HP Tel: (020) 7272 4448 Fax: (020) 7272 5756 E-mail: nisrine@retina-productions.co.uk

DIGITISING SERVICES

▶ Mcpherson Document Solutions, 102-112 Main Road, Elderslie, Johnstone, Renfrewshire, PA5 9AX Tel: (01505) 331534 Fax: (01505) 328266 E-mail: sales@trmcpherson.co.uk

DIMENSIONAL CONTROL SURVEY SERVICES

▶ Accura Surveys Ltd, The Granary, Breadstone, Berkeley, Glos, GL13 9HG Tel: 01453 511998 E-mail: info@accura-surveys.com

▶ Geomap Ltd, 8 Fairview Close, Watledge, Nailsworth, Stroud, Gloucestershire, GL6 0AX Tel: (07968) 428655 E-mail: info@geomapltd.co.uk

N B Surveys Ltd, 182 Market Street, Aberdeen, AB11 5PQ Tel: (01224) 212324 Fax: (01224) 212306 E-mail: admin@nbsurveys.com

Ocean Fix International Ltd, Waterton Grange, Stoneywood, Bucksburn, Aberdeen, AB21 9HX Tel: (01224) 714100 Fax: (01224) 714170 E-mail: pps@oceanfix-international.co.uk

▶ Sentripod Survey Company Ltd, The Lodge, 13 The Hamlet, Chippenham, Wiltshire, SN15 1BY Tel: (01249) 462039 Fax: (01249) 462039 E-mail: info@sentripod.co.uk

▶ Warner Land Surveys, Beaumont House, 59 High Street, Theale, Reading, RG7 5AL Tel: 0118-930 3314 Fax: 0118-930 1859 E-mail: wlsl@warnerlandsurveys.com

DIMENSIONAL MEASURING INSTRUMENTS

Intern Transport Systems (U K) Ltd, 421 Nottingham Road, Ilkeston, Derbyshire, DE7 5BP Tel: 0115-930 7724 Fax: 0115-930 1742 E-mail: sales@itsuk.org.uk

DIMMER SWITCHES

Lorlin Electronics, Enterprise Unit A-C, Harwood Road, Littlehampton, West Sussex, BN17 7AT Tel: (01903) 725121 Fax: (01903) 723919 E-mail: lorlin@btconnect.com

DIN RAIL TERMINAL BLOCKS

Asco Components, Unit 19 Green Lane Industrial Estate, Bordesley Green, Birmingham, B9 5QP Tel: 0121-773 3090 Fax: 0121-773 3390 E-mail: info@ascocomponents.co.uk

DINING CHAIRS

Artedi (U K) Ltd, Unit D, Everitt Road, London, NW10 6PL Tel: (020) 8961 6555 Fax: (020) 8961 9996

▶ Italcomma UK Llp, 1 Bell Lane, Byfield, Daventry, Northamptonshire, NN11 6US Tel: (01327) 260070 Fax: (01327) 260065 E-mail: info@italcomma.co.uk

Woodstock, 127 Wandsworth Bridge Road, London, SW6 2TT Tel: (020) 7371 8484 Fax: (020) 7731 3676

DINING FURNITURE

▶ Pine Tree, 69 Bruntcliffe Road, Morley, Leeds, LS27 0LQ Tel: 0113-252 0808 Fax: 0113-252 0808 E-mail: sales@thepinetreemorley.co.uk

▶ Timberline Pine Ltd, 1-2 Kingswalk, Winchester, Hampshire, SO23 8AF Tel: (01962) 861133 Fax: (01962) 884231 E-mail: sales@timberlinepine.co.uk

DINING TABLES

Artedi (U K) Ltd, Unit D, Everitt Road, London, NW10 6PL Tel: (020) 8961 6555 Fax: (020) 8961 9996

▶ Charlies Pine, 2 Narborough Road, Leicester, LE3 0BQ Tel: 0116-247 1474

▶ Italcomma UK Llp, 1 Bell Lane, Byfield, Daventry, Northamptonshire, NN11 6US Tel: (01327) 260070 Fax: (01327) 260065 E-mail: info@italcomma.co.uk

Woodstock, 127 Wandsworth Bridge Road, London, SW6 2TT Tel: (020) 7371 8484 Fax: (020) 7731 3676

DIODES

▶ The CR Supply Co., 44 Chapelfield Way, Rotherham, South Yorkshire, S61 2TL Tel: (07967) 990598 E-mail: ralph@crsupply.co.uk

N I C Components Europe, 14 Top Angel, Buckingham Industrial Estate, Buckingham, MK18 1TH Tel: (01280) 813737 Fax: (01280) 814737 E-mail: niesales@niccomp.com

DIPPED PRODUCTS, *See headings for particular types*

DIPSLIDES, LIQUID TESTING

Dimanco Ltd, 24 Henlow Industrial Estate, Henlow, Bedfordshire, SG16 6DS Tel: (01462) 813933 Fax: (01462) 817407 E-mail: dimanco@ltdhenlow.fsbusiness.co.uk

DIPSTICKS, MOTOR VEHICLE

Brookvale Manufacturing Co. Ltd, 15 Reddicap Trading Estate, Sutton Coldfield, West Midlands, B75 7DQ Tel: 0121-378 0833 Fax: 0121-311 1794 E-mail: enquiries@brookvale-manufacturing.co.uk

DIPSTICKS/DIP RODS

C G F Automation Ltd, York House, Fernie Road, Market Harborough, Leics, LE16 7PH Tel: (01858) 414616 Fax: (01858) 410196 E-mail: cgfnormondsales@veeder.co.uk

Dipsticks Calibration Services, Westacre, Belton Road, Portishead, Bristol, BS20 8DR Tel: (01275) 843651 Fax: (01275) 844784

DIRECT CURRENT (DC) BRUSHLESS ELECTRIC MOTORS

Coercive Group Ltd, Beta House, Laser Quay, Rochester, Kent, ME2 4HU Tel: (01634) 713053 Fax: (01634) 712541 E-mail: csl@coercive.com

Elektro Magnetix Ltd, Sussex Innovation Centre, Science Park Square, Falmer, Brighton, BN1 9SB Tel: (01273) 704471 Fax: (01273) 704472 E-mail: elektro@elektro.co.uk

Moog Controls Ltd, Ashchurch, Tewkesbury, Gloucestershire, GL20 8NA Tel: (01684) 296600 Fax: (01684) 296760 E-mail: sales@moog.co.uk

Muirhead Norcroft, East Portway, Andover, Hampshire, SP10 3LU Tel: (01264) 349600 Fax: (01264) 336444 E-mail: sales@muirheadaerospace.com

DIRECT CURRENT (DC) ELECTRIC MOTOR DRIVES

MFA/Como Drills, Felderland Lane, Worth, Deal, Kent, CT14 0BT Tel: (01304) 612132 Fax: (01304) 614696 E-mail: info@mfacomo.com

DIRECT CURRENT (DC) ELECTRIC MOTORS

Astrosyn International Technology plc, The Old Courthouse, New Road Avenue, Chatham, Kent, ME4 6BE Tel: (01634) 815175 Fax: (01634) 826552 E-mail: astrosyn@btinternet.com

T.A. Boxall & Co. Ltd, 20 Balcombe Road, Horley, Surrey, RH6 9HR Tel: (01293) 820133 Fax: (01293) 776139 E-mail: ronransley@taboxall.co.uk

Camis Motors & Drives, Wallows Industrial Estate, Brierley Hill, West Midlands, DY5 1QA Tel: (01384) 480645 Fax: (01384) 480745 E-mail: sales@camis.com

Comlec Units Ltd, Northgate Way, Northgate, Aldridge, Walsall, WS9 8TH Tel: (01922) 456237 Fax: (01922) 455251 E-mail: sales@comlec.co.uk

Control Techniques Dynamics Ltd, South Way, Andover, Hampshire, SP10 5AB Tel: (01264) 387600 Fax: (01264) 356561 E-mail: sales@ctdynamics.com

Crouzet Ltd, Intec 3, Wade Road, Basingstoke, Hampshire, RG24 8NE Tel: (01256) 318900 Fax: (01256) 318901 E-mail: sales@crouzet.com

Danfoss Bauer, Unit 1, Natlane Business Park, Winsford, Cheshire, CW7 3BS Tel: (01606) 868600 Fax: (01606) 868603 E-mail: sales@danfoss.com

Ebm-Papst, The Barn, Sheepdown, East Ilsley, Newbury, Berkshire, RG20 7ND Tel: (0870) 7665170 Fax: (08707) 665180 E-mail: aanddsales@uk.ebmpapst.com

Electric Vehicle Systems Ltd, 11 Glover Network Centre, Spire Road, Washington, Tyne & Wear, NE37 3HB Tel: 0191-416 1286 Fax: 0191-419 3746 E-mail: info@evsystems.co.uk

Euromotor Ltd, 5 Bolney Grange Business Park, Stairbridge Lane, Bolney, Haywards Heath, West Sussex, RH17 5PB Tel: (07000) 226276 Fax: (07002) 668677 E-mail: sales@euromotor.net

LEMAC Ltd, Hospital Road, Haddington, East Lothian, EH41 3PD Tel: (01620) 828700 Fax: (01620) 828730 E-mail: info@lemac.com

maxon motor uk ltd, Maxon House, Hogwood Lane, Finchampstead, Wokingham, Berkshire, RG40 4QW Tel: 0118-973 3337 Fax: 0118-973 7472 E-mail: salesuk@maxonmotor.com

MFA/Como Drills, Felderland Lane, Worth, Deal, Kent, CT14 0BT Tel: (01304) 612132 Fax: (01304) 614696 E-mail: info@mfacomo.com

Prestolite Electric, 12-16 Bristol Road, Greenford, Middlesex, UB6 8UP Tel: (020) 8231 1000 Fax: (020) 8575 9575 E-mail: sales@prestolite.co.uk

Rotalink Ltd, Cropmead, Crewkerne, Somerset, TA18 7HQ Tel: (01460) 72000 Fax: (01460) 74278 E-mail: info@rotalink.com

Scott Electromech Ltd, 314 Ravenhill Road, Belfast, BT6 8GN Tel: (028) 9045 7225 Fax: (028) 9073 2031 E-mail: info@s-em.com

Sem, Faraday House, Faraday Way, Orpington, Kent, BR5 3QT Tel: (01689) 884700 Fax: (01689) 884884 E-mail: info@sem.co.uk

T-T-Electric, Unit 7A, Waterloo Park Industrial Estate, Upper Brook Street, Stockport, Cheshire, SK1 3BP Tel: 0161-480 0037 Fax: 0161-476 4390 E-mail: john.legg@t-t-electric.com

DIRECT CURRENT (DC) FANS

Eao Ltd, Albert Drive, Burgess Hill, West Sussex, RH15 9TN Tel: (01444) 236000 Fax: (01444) 236641 E-mail: sales.euk@eao.com

DIRECT CURRENT (DC) GENERATORS

Driftgate 2000 Ltd, Little End Road, Eaton Socon, St. Neots, Cambridgeshire, PE19 8JH Tel: (01480) 470400 Fax: (01480) 470401 E-mail: sales@dg2k.co.uk

DIRECT CURRENT (DC) LINEAR POWER SUPPLIES

Contrel Ltd, PO Box 4127, Sudbury, Suffolk, CO10 1AB Tel: (01787) 881292 Fax: (01787) 881926 E-mail: intray7@contrel.co.uk

DIRECT CURRENT (DC) POWER SUPPLIES

Contrel Ltd, PO Box 4127, Sudbury, Suffolk, CO10 1AB Tel: (01787) 881292 Fax: (01787) 881926 E-mail: intray7@contrel.co.uk

Harrison & Greenwood Transformers Ltd, Mill Lane, Halifax, West Yorkshire, HX3 6TR Tel: (01422) 329003 Fax: (01422) 329009

Romarsh Ltd, Clarke Avenue, Portemarsh Industrial Estate, Calne, Wiltshire, SN11 9BS Tel: (01249) 812624 Fax: (01249) 816134 E-mail: sales@romarsh.co.uk

DIRECT CURRENT (DC) STABILISED POWER SUPPLIES

Davtrend Ltd, 7a Fitzherbert Spur, Farlington, Portsmouth, PO6 1TT Tel: (023) 9237 2004 Fax: (023) 9232 6307 E-mail: sales@davtrend.co.uk

E R L Ltd, Iroko House, Bolney Avenue, Peacehaven, East Sussex, BN10 8HF Tel: (01273) 581007 Fax: (01273) 581555 E-mail: erl@fastnet.co.uk

General High Voltage, New Road, Highley, Bridgnorth, Shropshire, WV16 6NN Tel: (01746) 862555 Fax: (01746) 862666 E-mail: info@genvolt.co.uk

K R P Power Source UK Ltd, 2 The Galloway Centre, Express Way, Newbury, Berkshire, RG14 5TL Tel: (01635) 32510 Fax: (01635) 32510 E-mail: sales@krp.co.uk

Secure Power Systems Ltd, 2A Watermoor Road, Cirencester, Gloucestershire, GL7 1JW Tel: (01285) 651768 Fax: (01285) 657053 E-mail: wknight756@aol.com

DIRECT CURRENT (DC) TO ALTERNATING CURRENT (AC) INVERTERS

Driftgate 2000 Ltd, Little End Road, Eaton Socon, St. Neots, Cambridgeshire, PE19 8JH Tel: (01480) 470400 Fax: (01480) 470401 E-mail: sales@dg2k.co.uk

Eltek Energy (UK) Ltd, Eltek House, Maxted Road, Hemel Hempstead, Hertfordshire, HP2 7DX Tel: (01442) 219355 Fax: (01442) 245894 E-mail: uksales@eltekenergy.com

Gresham Power Electronics, Gresham House, Telford Road, Salisbury, SP2 7PH Tel: (01722) 413060 Fax: (01722) 413034 E-mail: info@greshampower.com

Socomec Sicon Ltd, 401-402 Love Lane, Cirencester, Gloucestershire, GL7 1YG Tel: (01285) 644444 Fax: (01285) 644414 E-mail: enquires@socomec.com

DIRECT CURRENT (DC) TO DIRECT CURRENT (DC) CONVERTERS

Alfatronix Ltd, 29 Newtown Business Park, Albion Close, Poole, Dorset, BH12 3LL Tel: (01202) 715517 Fax: (01202) 715122 E-mail: sales@alfatronix.co.uk

C C Power Electronics Ltd, Unit 19, Haigh Park, Whitehill Industrial Estate, Stockport, Cheshire, SK4 1QR Tel: 0161-429 7923 Fax: 0161-474 1174 E-mail: info@ccpowerltd.co.uk

Datel UK Ltd, 15 Campbell Court, Bramley, Tadley, Hampshire, RG26 5EG Tel: (01256) 880444 Fax: (01256) 880706 E-mail: datel.ltd@datel.com

Eastern Transformer Ltd, Overland Industrial Park, Sudbury Road, Little Whelnetham, Bury St. Edmunds, Suffolk, IP30 0UL Tel: (01284) 388033 Fax: (01284) 386969 E-mail: info@ete.co.uk

Eurosource Electronics Ltd, Parkway House, Sheen Lane, London, SW14 8LS Tel: (020) 8878 5355 Fax: (020) 8878 5733 E-mail: sales@eurosource.co.uk

▶ M D Electronics, 9 Quarry Fields, Leek Wootton, Warwick, CV35 7RS Tel: (01926) 850315 Fax: (01926) 850315 E-mail: info@mdelectronics.co.uk

Mascot UK, PO Box 2090, Salisbury, SP2 2BH Tel: (01722) 504853 Fax: (01264) 396402 E-mail: andrew.parrish@mascot.no

Power One, 24 Upper High Street, Worthing, West Sussex, BN11 1DL Tel: (01903) 823323 Fax: (01903) 823324 E-mail: sales@powerone.com

Powerfactor Ltd, 8 Pear Tree Farm, Townsend, Marsh Gibbon, Bicester, Oxfordshire, OX27 0EY Tel: (01869) 278585 Fax: (01869) 278989 E-mail: sales@powerfactor.co.uk

Powernetics International Ltd, Jason Works, Clarence Street, Loughborough, Leicestershire, LE11 1DX Tel: (01509) 214153 Fax: (01509) 262460 E-mail: sales@powernetics.co.uk

DIRECT CURRENT (DC) TO DIRECT CURRENT (DC) POWER SUPPLY CONVERTERS

Alcatel Submarine Networks Ltd, Christchurch Way, London, SE10 0AG Tel: (020) 8293 2000 Fax: (020) 8293 2433

Lambda UK, Kingsley Avenue, Ilfracombe, Devon, EX34 8ES Tel: (01271) 856600 Fax: (01271) 864894 E-mail: powersolutions@lambda-europe.com

V X I Power Ltd, Westminster Industrial Estate, Station Road, North Hykeham, Lincoln, LN6 3QY Tel: (01522) 500511 Fax: (01522) 500515 E-mail: sales@vxipower.com

Young Ecc Electronics, Crown House, Coronation Road, Cressex Business Park, High Wycombe, Buckinghamshire, HP12 3TA Tel: (01494) 753500 Fax: (01494) 753501 E-mail: sales@youngelectronics.com

DIRECT DIGITAL RADIOGRAPHY EQUIPMENT

▶ IDR Services Ltd, 32 St Peters Close, Crabbs Cross, Redditch, Worcestershire, B97 5LE Tel: 01527 542501 Fax: 01527 542501 E-mail: idrservices@blueyonder.co.uk

DIRECT FIRED HEATERS

Flaretec Alloys & Equipment Ltd, Hardwick View Road, Holmewood, Chesterfield, Derbyshire, S42 5SA Tel: (01246) 853522 Fax: (01246) 852415 E-mail: contact@flaretec.com

DIRECT MAIL

20-20 Direct Mail, Unit 49 The Washford Industrial Estate, Heming Road, Redditch, Worcestershire, B98 0EA Tel: (01527) 510444 Fax: (01527) 510006 E-mail: sales@2020dml.com

A D C Marketing Ltd, Unit 4, Richardson Way, Crosspoint Business Park, Coventry, CV2 2TY Tel: (0870) 7525252 Fax: (0870) 7525251 E-mail: enquiries@adc-uk.com

A R M Direct, 1 Bentinck Mews, London, W1U 2AF Tel: (020) 7317 3230 Fax: (020) 7224 3041 E-mail: info@arm-direct.co.uk

Abstrakt Services Ltd, 58 Chester Street, Aston, Birmingham, B6 4LW Tel: 0121-380 2600 Fax: 0121-333 6537 E-mail: mail@abstrakt.co.uk

Accelerated Mailing & Marketing, The Penny Black, Marchants Way, Burgess Hill, West Sussex, RH15 8QY Tel: (01444) 245917 Fax: (01444) 870960 E-mail: info@accelerated-mail.co.uk

Acorn Mailing Services, Chaucer Business Park, Watery Lane, Kemsing, Sevenoaks, Kent, TN15 6HU Tel: (01732) 760042 Fax: (01732) 760043 E-mail: info@acornmailingservices.co.uk

Acxiom, Counting House, 53 Tooley Street, London, SE1 2QN Tel: (020) 7526 5100 Fax: (020) 7526 5200

Acxiom, Park House, Station Road, Teddington, Middlesex, TW11 9AD Tel: (020) 8213 5500 Fax: (020) 8213 5588 E-mail: info-uk@claritaseu.com

▶ Adare Ltd, Bankside, Dockfield Road, Shipley, West Yorkshire, BD17 7BJ Tel: (01274) 771111 Fax: (01274) 208308 E-mail: info@adare.com

Adare Carwin, Unit B Wellington Gate, Silverthorne Way, Waterlooville, Hampshire, PO7 7XY Tel: (023) 9224 5000 Fax: (023) 9224 5060 E-mail: info@adare.com

▶ Advanced Mailing Solutions, 2 Howard Court, Nerston Industrial Estate, East Kilbride, Glasgow, G74 4QZ Tel: (01355) 522839 Fax: (01355) 524839 E-mail: enquiries@amsnet.co.uk

Alpha Mail Ltd, 18 Victoria Way, Burgess Hill, West Sussex, RH15 9NF Tel: (01444) 871555 Fax: (01444) 871355 E-mail: sales@alphamail.co.uk

Alpha Media Direct Marketing, 38 Second Drove, Peterborough, PE1 5XA Tel: (01733) 898023 Fax: (01733) 898324 E-mail: sales@alphamedia.co.uk

Am Computing Direct Ltd, International House, Cray Avenue, Orpington, Kent, BR5 3RY Tel: (01689) 896489 Fax: (01689) 896659 E-mail: amaddalo@aol.com

Ark H Handling Ltd, 1 Wilstead Industrial Park, Kenneth Way, Wilstead, Bedford, MK45 3PD Tel: (01234) 742777 Fax: (01234) 742999 E-mail: sales@ark-h.co.uk

Askew Mailing Services Ltd, 1 Broadmead Business Park, Broadmead Road, Stewartby, Bedford, MK43 9NX Tel: (01234) 766202 Fax: (01234) 766388 E-mail: info@mailinghouse.co.uk

Astron Marketing Technology, Crawford House, Crawford Way, Liverpool, L7 9NG Tel: 0151-228 8003 Fax: 0151-259 6129

B H & P Direct Mail Ltd, Darby House, Bletchingley Road, Redhill, RH1 3DN Tel: (01737) 645233 Fax: (01737) 644283 E-mail: bhpdirectmailltd@onyxnet.co.uk

▶ B I Worldwide Ltd, 1 Vantage Court, Tickford Street, Newport Pagnell, Buckinghamshire, MK16 9EZ Tel: (01908) 214700 Fax: (01908) 214777 E-mail: enquires@eu.biworldwide.com

B J Mailing Services, 25-27 Whittle Road, Ferndown Industrial Estate, Wimborne, Dorset, BH21 7RP Tel: (01202) 897717 Fax: (01202) 870277 E-mail: admin@bjmailing.co.uk

Breeze Ltd, Breeze House, Albert Close Trading Estate, Whitefield, Manchester, M45 8EH Tel: 0161-796 3600 Fax: 0161-796 3700 E-mail: info@breez.co.uk

Business Lists (U K), Cheadle Court, Turves Road, Cheadle Hulme, Cheadle, Cheshire, SK8 6AW Tel: 0161-482 0500 Fax: 0161-488 4160 E-mail: info@businesslistsuk.com

Capital Communications Group Ltd, Farm Castle Estate, Duchess Place, Rutherglen, Glasgow, G73 1DR Tel: 0141-613 1314 Fax: 0141-643 1032 E-mail: info@scotsmail-online.com

Chase Perrin Ltd, 7 Littleton House, Littleton Road, Ashford, Middlesex, TW15 1UU Tel: (01784) 250200 Fax: (01784) 257283 E-mail: printmail@lineone.net

Chilworth Communications, 106 Star Street, London, W2 1QF Tel: (020) 7706 1014 Fax: (020) 7258 3852 E-mail: enquiries@chilworthcommunications.com

Circularising Ltd, 6 Landor Road, London, SW9 9PP Tel: (020) 7733 3177 Fax: (020) 7978 9059 E-mail: ross@circularising.freeserve.co.uk

Clovertone Ltd, 9 Canal Walk, London, N1 5SA Tel: (020) 7923 0300 Fax: (020) 7923 0266 E-mail: sales@clovertone.co.uk

Commercial Facilities & Logistics, 89 Park Road, Didcot, Oxfordshire, OX11 8QT Tel: (01235) 511054 Fax: (01235) 511056 E-mail: mhall@cfl-ltd.co.uk

Communisis Security Products Ltd, Trafford Wharf Road, Trafford Park, Manchester, M17 1HE Tel: 0161-869 1000 Fax: 0161-869 1010

Communitis Chorleys Ltd, Manston Lane, Leeds, LS15 8AH Tel: 0113-225 5000 Fax: 0113-225 5400 E-mail: sales@chorleys-communisis.co.uk

Compact Group Ltd, 4 Deacon Industrial Estate, Forstal Road, Aylesford, Kent, ME20 7SP Tel: (01622) 719365 Fax: (01622) 718831 E-mail: directmail@compactgroup.co.uk

Concorde Agency, 28a High Street, Harpenden, Hertfordshire, AL5 2SX Tel: (01582) 715000 Fax: (01582) 461306 E-mail: sue.churchhouse@concord-agency.com

Connelly Manton Printing Ltd, Albert Buildings, 49 Queen Victoria Street, London, EC4N 4SA Tel: (020) 7248 0404 Fax: (020) 7236 0353

Dawson Marketing P.L.C., The Arena, Stafferton Way, Maidenhead, Berkshire, SL6 1AY Tel: (01628) 628777 Fax: (01628) 789634 E-mail: sales@dawsonmarketing.co.uk

Dawsons Marketing Services, 200 Milton Park, Abingdon, Oxfordshire, OX14 4TB Tel: (01235) 824200 Fax: (01235) 824304 E-mail: sales@dawson-marketing.co.uk

DHL Global Mail Ltd, Mills Road, Quarry Wood, Aylesford, Kent, ME20 7WZ Tel: (01622) 792111 Fax: (01622) 792333

Diesel Power Ltd, Unit 12 Mitcham Industrial Estate, 85 Streatham Road, Mitcham, Surrey, CR4 2AP Tel: (020) 8648 0041 Fax: (020) 8640 8471 E-mail: info@dpdirect.net

DIRECT MAIL – *continued*

Direct Mail Advertising & Marketing Services Ltd, 3 Wallis Court, Fleming Way, Crawley, West Sussex, RH10 9DA Tel: (01293) 541511 Fax: (01293) 562996 E-mail: reception@dmams.co.uk

Direct Mail Publicity Birmingham Ltd, PO Box 581, Birmingham, B6 7ER Tel: 0121-327 1172 Fax: 0121-326 6139 E-mail: sales@dmpb.co.uk

Dsi Business Support Ltd, 73 Whitby Road, Slough, SL1 3DR Tel: (01753) 714000 Fax: (01753) 714005

Eagle Direct Marketing, Unit 1 Axis, Hawkfield Business Park, Whitchurch, Bristol, BS14 0BY Tel: 0117-902 0073 Fax: 0117-902 8220 E-mail: sc@eaglemailing.co.uk

Edward Thompson International Ltd, Richmond Street, Sheepfolds Industrial Estate, Sunderland, SR5 1BQ Tel: 0191-514 4199 Fax: 0191-567 7510 E-mail: info@edward-thompson.com

Elsdon Mailing Ltd, Unit 16 Nonsuch Industrial Estate, Kiln Lane, Epsom, Surrey, KT17 1DH Tel: (01372) 720613 E-mail: elsdonmailing@lineone.net

Emap Glenigan, 41-47 Seabourne Road, Bournemouth, BH5 2HU Tel: (0800) 373771 Fax: (01202) 431204 E-mail: info@glenigan.emap.com

Equifax P.L.C., Capital House, 25 Chapel Street, London, NW1 5DS Tel: (020) 7298 3000 Fax: (020) 7723 7555 E-mail: info@equifax.co.uk

F E Burman Ltd, 4 Rich Industrial Estate, Crimscott Street, London, SE1 5TF Tel: (020) 7206 1000 Fax: (020) 7206 1040 E-mail: info@feburman.co.uk

F T Mail Solutions Ltd, Unit 36, Stephenson Road, South Hampshire Industrial Park, Totton, Southampton, SO40 3YD Tel: (023) 8066 5050 Fax: (023) 8066 5066 E-mail: sales@ftmailsolutions.co.uk

▶ Farmpro Mail Marketing Ltd, Stephenson Road, Groundwell Industrial Estate, Swindon, SN25 5AN Tel: (01793) 451000 Fax: (01793) 451010

Finishing Plus Ltd, 34 Lanchester Way, Royal Oak Industrial Estate, Daventry, Northamptonshire, NN11 8PH Tel: (01327) 301155 Fax: (01327) 301070 E-mail: finishingplus@btconnect.com

Gildersons Ltd, 31-35 Pitfield Street, London, N1 6HB Tel: (020) 7324 0180 Fax: (020) 7490 4333 E-mail: studio@gildersons.co.uk

Halligan Direct Mail Ltd, 66 Addison Road, Bromley, BR2 9HQ Tel: (020) 8290 9000 Fax: (020) 8290 9002 E-mail: info@halligans.co.uk

Hamilton House Mailings Ltd, Earls Trees Court, Earls Trees Road, Corby, Northamptonshire, NN17 4HH Tel: (01536) 399000 Fax: (01536) 399012 E-mail: sales@hamilton-house.com

Hay Nisbet Press Ltd, 11 Dilwara Avenue, Glasgow, G14 0SQ Tel: 0141-959 3325 Fax: 0141-958 1161 E-mail: Studio@haynisbet.com

Holborn Direct Mail, Capacity House, 2-6 Rothsay Street, London, SE1 4UD Tel: (020) 7407 6444 Fax: (020) 7357 6065 E-mail: peter@holborndirectmail.co.uk

Hudson & Pearson Ltd, Bradwood Works, Manchester Road, Dunnockshaw, Burnley, Lancashire, BB11 5PW Tel: (01706) 210582 Fax: (01706) 215692

I D Data Ltd, The New Mint House, Bedford Road, Petersfield, Hampshire, GU32 3AL Tel: (01730) 235700 Fax: (01730) 235711 E-mail: enquiry@iddata.com

I D Mailing Ltd, 1-4 Fleming Close, Parkfarm Industrial Estate, Wellingborough, Northamptonshire, NN8 6UF Tel: (01933) 678650 Fax: (01933) 678651 E-mail: enq@id-mailing.co.uk

Intermail plc, Canal View Road, Newbury, Berkshire, RG14 5XF Tel: (01635) 565000 Fax: (01635) 41678 E-mail: sales@intermail.co.uk

Lewis Direct Mail Marketing Ltd, 433-435 Caledonian Road, London, N7 9BG Tel: (020) 7607 6505 Fax: (020) 7607 0932 E-mail: info@ldm.co.uk

▶ Lime P M Ltd, Unit 1A, Gresham Industrial Estate, Eastern Road, Aldershot, Hampshire, GU12 4TE Tel: (01252) 322252 Fax: (01252) 322315

▶ Logicall Results, 5 Beacontree Plaza, Gillette Way, Reading, RG2 0BS Tel: 0118-922 4400 Fax: 0118 922 4401 E-mail: info@logicallresults.co.uk

Lynx D P M Ltd, Unit 35a Monument Industrial Park, Warpsgrove Lane, Chalgrove, Oxford, OX44 7RW Tel: (01865) 891989 Fax: (01865) 891164 E-mail: sales@lynxdpm.com

M C M Direct Mail, Unit 10 Solent Industrial Estate, Shamblehurst Lane, Hedge End, Southampton, SO30 2FX Tel: (01489) 796611 Fax: (01489) 795511 E-mail: sales@mcmdirect.com

M & S Mailing & Support Ltd, Unit 17 18, Royce Road, Crawley, West Sussex, RH10 9NX Tel: (01293) 527711 Fax: (01293) 527713

Macdonald Mailing, Staplehurst Road, Sittingbourne, Kent, ME10 2NH Tel: (01795) 439513 Fax: (01795) 439551

Mail Marketing International Ltd, Springfield House, West Street, Bedminster, Bristol, BS3 3NX Tel: 0117-966 6900 Fax: 0117-963 6737 E-mail: sales@formpromm.co.uk

Mail Marketing (Scotland) Ltd, 42 Methil Street, Glasgow, G14 0SZ Tel: 0141-950 2222 Fax: 0141-950 2726 E-mail: glasgow@mailmarkscot.com

▶ Mail Shot International Ltd, Unit 2 Park House, Greenhill Crescent, Watford Business Park, Watford, WD18 8PH Tel: (01923) 800422 Fax: (01923) 800433 E-mail: info@mailshotinternational.co.uk

Mailcom P.L.C., Snowdon Drive, Winterhill, Milton Keynes, MK6 1HQ Tel: (0870) 5888222 Fax: (0870) 1261335 E-mail: info@mailcom.co.uk

Mailflight Ltd, Unit 2 Central Way, Feltham, Middlesex, TW14 0RX Tel: (020) 8893 1477 Fax: (020) 8893 1459 E-mail: ops@mfcourier.com

Mailings International Ltd, Unit 10, The Demcora Centre, Campfield Road, St. Albans, Hertfordshire, AL1 5HN Tel: (01727) 836062 Fax: (01727) 848863

Mailshot Services, 21 Upper Priory Street, Grafton Street Industrial Estate, Northampton, NN1 2PT Tel: (01604) 622290 Fax: (01604) 622290

Mailtime Services Ltd, 490 Gorton Road, Reddish, Stockport, Cheshire, SK5 6PP Tel: 0161-223 0044 Fax: 0161-223 0055

Media Cards, 108 Davies Road, West Bridgford, Nottingham, NG2 5HY Tel: 0115-914 2369 E-mail: sales@media-cards.co.uk

Meldrum Mailing Ltd, Units 1-2 Hainault Works, Hainault Road, Little Heath, Romford, RM6 5NF Tel: (020) 8597 3218 Fax: (0845) 6445675

Midlands Direct Mail & Packaging Services Ltd, Bellamy Road, Mansfield, Nottinghamshire, NG18 4LN Tel: (01623) 636337 Fax: (01623) 420917 E-mail: sales@mdmuk.co.uk

Moore Response Marketing, Studio 4, The Calls, Leeds, LS2 7EY Tel: 0113-222 3330 Fax: 0113-222 3331

Motronic Services, Peachley Court, Peachley Lane, Lower Broadheath, Worcester, WR2 6QR Tel: (01905) 640025 Fax: (01905) 640415

MPC, 3-4 Lawrence Way, Camberley, Surrey, GU15 3DL Tel: (01276) 21320 Fax: (01276) 21328 E-mail: sales@mpc4u.com

▶ MPF, The Slough, Studley, Warwickshire, B80 7EN Tel: (01527) 853840 Fax: (01527) 853843 E-mail: lee@mpfltd.co.uk

Multi Resource Marketing Ltd, Barberton House, Farndon Road, Market Harborough, Leicestershire, LE16 9NR Tel: (01858) 410510 Fax: (01858) 434190

Nelson Direct Mail Services, Unit 2, Quadrum Park Old Portsmouth Road, Peasmarsh, Guildford, Surrey, GU3 1LU Tel: (01483) 532737 Fax: (01483) 532837 E-mail: sales@nelsondirectmail.com

Nicom Ltd, Unit 9 Tamebridge Industrial Estate, Aldridge Road, Birmingham, B42 2TX Tel: 0121-356 1667 Fax: 0121-344 3336

Oliver & Graimes Design Associates Ltd, 1-3 Ship Street, Shoreham-by-Sea, West Sussex, BN43 5DH Tel: (01273) 748884 Fax: (01273) 465398 E-mail: info@oandg.co.uk

Orchestra Bristol Ltd, 17-19 Emery Road, Bristol, BS4 5PF Tel: 0117-972 4400 Fax: 0117-972 4501 E-mail: sales@orchestra.co.uk

Outmere Direct Mail Ltd, 5-6 Wellington Road, London, SW19 8EX Tel: (020) 8947 7577 Fax: (020) 8944 9736 E-mail: info@outmere.co.uk

P W P Direct Mail Services Ltd, A 21 Broadwater Road, Welwyn Garden City, Hertfordshire, AL7 3BQ Tel: (01707) 882255 Fax: (01707) 883322 E-mail: pwp@dial.pipex.com

Packpost (International) Ltd, Griffin House, Griffin Lane, Aylesbury, Buckinghamshire, HP19 8BE Tel: (01296) 487493 Fax: (01296) 392369 E-mail: sales@packpost.co.uk

Paton Brown Ltd, Calico House, Printwork Lane, Manchester, M19 3JP Tel: (0870) 4445501 Fax: (0870) 4445502 E-mail: info@patonbrown.co.uk

Pebble Business Services Ltd, 20 Bonville Road, Bristol, BS4 5QH Tel: 0117-971 5435 Fax: 0117-977 8863 E-mail: data@pebble.co.uk

Pennine Packaging Co Ltd, Dell Road, Rochdale, Lancashire, OL12 6BZ Tel: (01706) 655787 Fax: (01706) 860418 E-mail: penninepackaging@hotmail.com

Pillar Publications Ltd, 45 Woodland Grove, Weybridge, Surrey, KT13 9EQ Tel: (01932) 820282 Fax: (01932) 858035 E-mail: sales@pillardirect.demon.co.uk

Pims, 42-44 Stapledon Road, Orton Southgate, Peterborough, PE2 6TH Tel: (01733) 235523 Fax: (01733) 235522

Polestar Digital Labels Ltd, 501 Dewsbury Road, Leeds, LS11 5LL Tel: 0113-201 6600 Fax: 0113-276 2552 E-mail: leeds.direct@polestar-group.com

Polypostals, Unit 21, Sea Vixen Industrial Estate, Wilverley Road, Christchurch, Dorset, BH23 3RU Tel: (01202) 479932 Fax: (01202) 488118

Premier Mailing, Park House, 15-19 Greenhill CR, Watford, WD18 8PH Tel: (01923) 676319 Fax: (01923) 674333 E-mail: sales@premiermailing.co.uk

Projects Advertising & Marketing Ltd, Unit B5 Southways Park, London Road, Lowfield Heath, Crawley, West Sussex, RH10 9TQ Tel: (01293) 446949 Fax: (01293) 455071 E-mail: sales@projectsadv.co.uk

Promotional Logistics Ltd, Prolog House, Sudbury, Suffolk, CO10 2XG Tel: (01787) 370272 Fax: (01787) 379935 E-mail: bdm@prolog.uk.com

Push The Envelope Ltd, Unit 21/21a Merrett's Mills, Industrial Estate, Woodchester, Stroud, Gloucestershire, GL5 5EX Tel: (01453) 836200 Fax: (01453) 836 201 E-mail: info@pushtheenvelope.co.uk

Queen Elizabeth's Foundation, Bradmere House, Kingston Road, Leatherhead, Surrey, KT22 7NA Tel: (01372) 389940 Fax: (01372) 361386 E-mail: bradhouse@bradhouse.demon.co.uk

Research & Marketing Ltd, Trefor House, Galdames Place, Cardiff, CF24 5RE Tel: (029) 2043 5800 Fax: (029) 2048 3540 E-mail: info@rmltd.net

Rocket Mailing Ltd, 13 Lea Road, Waltham Abbey, Essex, EN9 1AS Tel: (01992) 788881 Fax: (01992) 788882 E-mail: sales@rocketmailing.co.uk

Rockhill Mailing Services Ltd, Unit 3 Brooks Road, Shepherd Industrial Estate, Lewes, East Sussex, BN7 2BY Tel: (01273) 479065 Fax: (01273) 479057

St. Ives Direct (Edenbridge) Ltd, Enterprise Way, Edenbridge, Kent, TN8 6HF Tel: (01732) 862788 Fax: (01732) 868868 E-mail: kevin.johnson@stivesdirect.com

Seward Direct Mail Ltd, Unit 107 Cannon Workshops, 5 Cannon Drive, London, E14 4AS Tel: (020) 7538 5120 E-mail: sewardkj@aol.com

Singer & Partners Ltd, Harrison Trading Estate, Longworth Street, Preston, PR1 5DL Tel: (01772) 651188 Fax: (01772) 652577 E-mail: info@singerpartners.com

▶ Sitel UK Ltd, Sitel House, Timothys Bridge Road, Stratford-upon-Avon, Warwickshire, CV37 9HY Tel: (01789) 299622 Fax: (01789) 292341 E-mail: info@sitel.com

Spark Response Ltd, Follingsby Avenue, Gateshead, Tyne & Wear, NE10 8HQ Tel: 0191-495 9999 Fax: 0191-495 9900 E-mail: enquiries@sparkresponse.co.uk

T M B International Ltd, Platt Industrial Estate, Maidstone Road, Platt, Sevenoaks, Kent, TN15 8TB Tel: (01732) 887456 Fax: (01732) 886345 E-mail: emmac@tmbmailing.com

T V P Ltd, Unit 5, First Avenue, Globe Business Park, Marlow, Buckinghamshire, SL7 1YA Tel: (01628) 473121 Fax: (01628) 477563 E-mail: sales@tvp.ltd.uk

Teamwork Handling Ltd, Allerthorpe Business Park, Pocklington, York, YO42 1NS Tel: (01759) 322400 Fax: (01759) 303265 E-mail: magnus@teamwork-handling.co.uk

Total Spectrum Ltd, 11 Intec 2, Wade Road, Basingstoke, Hampshire, RG24 8NE Tel: (01256) 814114 Fax: (01256) 814115 E-mail: sales@totalspectrum.co.uk

Transterra Ltd, 2 Copperfields Orchard, Kemsing, Sevenoaks, Kent, TN15 6QH Tel: (01732) 761687 Fax: (01732) 761687

Valldata Services Ltd, Halifax Road, Bowerhill, Melksham, Wiltshire, SN12 6UB Tel: (01225) 354200 Fax: (01225) 709689 E-mail: sales@valldata.co.uk

Vitesse Mailing, 17 Wellington Road, London, E10 7QF Tel: (020) 8558 8006 Fax: (020) 8558 8084 E-mail: aziz@vitessemailing.com

Warnes Mail Marketing Ltd, 577 Kingston Road, London, SW20 8YA Tel: (020) 8687 3800 Fax: (020) 8545 2701 E-mail: sales@warnes.co.uk

Washington Direct Mail Ltd, Fourth Avenue, Team Valley, Gateshead, Tyne & Wear, NE11 0JS Tel: 0191-482 4291 Fax: 0191-491 0109 E-mail: wdm@wdml.co.uk

Webscribe Ltd, PO Box 464, Berkhamsted, Hertfordshire, HP4 2UR Tel: (01442) 876000 Fax: (01442) 872279 E-mail: jenny@webscribe.co.uk

Wegener Sefton, G 7 Unit Liver Industrial Estate, Long Lane, Walton, Liverpool, L9 7ES Tel: 0151-521 7070 Fax: 0151-525 2458 E-mail: howardpaul@btconnect.com

World Wide Direct Mail Ltd, Unit 4, Clipper Close, Medway City Estate, Strood, Rochester, Kent, ME2 4QR Tel: (01634) 723135 Fax: (01634) 713399 E-mail: paul.barford@btconnect.com

DIRECT MAIL PRINT FINISHING

Spectrum Printing & Mailing Services, 1 50 Station Road, Chertsey, Surrey, KT16 8BE Tel: (01932) 569123 Fax: (01932) 569123 E-mail: spectrumpms@btconnect.com

DIRECT MARKETING

20-20 Direct Mail, Unit 49 The Washford Industrial Estate, Heming Road, Redditch, Worcestershire, B98 0EA Tel: (01527) 510444 Fax: (01527) 510006 E-mail: sales@2020dml.com

▶ ARCH Marketing Solutions Ltd, Kildare House, 102-104 Sheen Road, Richmond, Surrey, TW9 1UF Tel: (020) 8334 1137 Fax: E-mail: info@archmarketing.co.uk

▶ BusinessGrowth UK, Bristol & West House, Post Office Road, Bournemouth, BH1 1BL Tel: (01202) 313611 Fax: (01202) 313601 E-mail: info@businessgrowthuk.com

Case Alarms Ltd, Unit 5 Taff Workshops, Tresillian Terrace, Cardiff, CF10 5DE Tel: (029) 2038 7006 Fax: (029) 2038 7006 E-mail: cardiff@casesecurity.co.uk

Celebration File Ltd, Oakwood House, Spa Road, Melksham, Wiltshire, SN12 7TA Tel: (01225) 705582 Fax: (01225) 700277 E-mail: direct@cflmarketing.co.uk

Colette Hill Associates, 18-20 Bromells Road, London, SW4 0BG Tel: (020) 7622 8252 Fax: (020) 7622 8253 E-mail: cha@chapr.co.uk

Communique Public Relations Ltd, Waterside, 2 Canal Street, Manchester, M1 3HE Tel: 0161-228 6677 Fax: 0161-228 7391 E-mail: info@communiquepr.co.uk

Dataforce Group Ltd, Moulton House, 10 Pond Wood Close, Moulton Park Industrial Estate, Northampton, NN3 6DF Tel: (01604) 673800 Fax: (01604) 673801 E-mail: dfreception@dataforce.co.uk

Direct Mail Advertising & Marketing Services Ltd, 3 Wallis Court, Fleming Way, Crawley, West Sussex, RH10 9DA Tel: (01293) 541511 Fax: (01293) 562996 E-mail: reception@dmams.co.uk

▶ Duo Marketing Services, Primmers Green Cottages, Primmers Green, Wadhurst, East Sussex, TN5 6DU Tel: (01892) 783017 Fax: (01892) 783017 E-mail: enquiries@duomarketing.co.uk

▶ E-Consultancy.Com Publishing, 85 Clerkenwell Road, London, EC1R 5AR Tel: (020) 7681 4052 Fax: (020) 7681 4031 E-mail: ashley@e-consultancy.com

F S W Group Ltd, Manor Farm Barns, Fox Road, Framingham Pigot, Norwich, NR14 7PZ Tel: (01508) 491400 Fax: (01508) 494088 E-mail: mail@fsw.co.uk

▶ Farmpro Mail Marketing Ltd, Stephenson Road, Groundwell Industrial Estate, Swindon, SN25 5AN Tel: (01793) 451000 Fax: (01793) 451010

▶ gsa Ltd, Unit 3, Devonshire Business Park, Borehamwood, Herts, WD6 1NA Tel: 0208 236 2531

▶ H G S Marketing, Elmgrove Lodge, 47A Elmgrove Road, Weybridge, Surrey, KT13 8PB Tel: (01932) 829419 E-mail: info@hgsmarketing.com

John Blackburn Group Ltd, Old Run Road, Leeds, LS10 2AA Tel: 0113-277 7711 Fax: 0113-277 4009 E-mail: sales@jblackburn.co.uk

Key Note Ltd, Field House, 72 Oldfield Road, Hampton, Middlesex, TW12 2HQ Tel: (020) 8481 8750 Fax: (020) 8783 0049 E-mail: sales@keynote.co.uk

▶ Logicall Results, 5 Beacontree Plaza, Gillette Way, Reading, RG2 0BS Tel: 0118-922 4400 Fax: 0118 922 4401 E-mail: info@logicallresults.co.uk

Lynx D P M Ltd, Unit 35a Monument Industrial Park, Warpsgrove Lane, Chalgrove, Oxford, OX44 7RW Tel: (01865) 891989 Fax: (01865) 891164 E-mail: sales@lynxdpm.com

Mail Marketing International Ltd, Springfield House, West Street, Bedminster, Bristol, BS3 3NX Tel: 0117-966 6900 Fax: 0117-963 6737 E-mail: sales@formpromm.co.uk

▶ Mail Shot International Ltd, Unit 2 Park House, Greenhill Crescent, Watford Business Park, Watford, WD18 8PH Tel: (01923) 800422 Fax: (01923) 800433 E-mail: info@mailshotinternational.co.uk

Mailshot Services, 21 Upper Priory Street, Grafton Street Industrial Estate, Northampton, NN1 2PT Tel: (01604) 622290 Fax: (01604) 622290

▶ Mango Media, 49 Carnaby Street, London, W1F 9PY Tel: (020) 7292 9000 Fax: (020) 7434 1077 E-mail: info@mangomedia.net

Mealbox Ltd, 235 Farnham Road, Slough, SL2 1DE Tel: (01753) 554391 E-mail: enq@mealbox.com

▶ National Mailshot, Northgate House, St. Peters Street, Colchester, CO1 1HT Tel: (01206) 574674 Fax: (01206) 764040 E-mail: sales@nationalmailshot.net

Prism Data Management Ltd, Colombia House, 1 Apollo Rise, Farnborough, Hampshire, GU14 0GT Tel: (01252) 556900 Fax: (01252) 556911

▶ Prodo Ltd, Littleton Old Hall, Little Heath Road, Littleton, Chester, CH3 &DW Tel: 0870 7562828 Fax: 0870 7562838 E-mail: sales@prodo.com

Prospect Swetenhams, Field House, 72 Oldfield Road, Hampton, Middlesex, TW12 2HQ Tel: (020) 8481 8730 Fax: (020) 8783 1940 E-mail: sales@prospectshop.co.uk

Singer & Partners Ltd, Harrison Trading Estate, Longworth Street, Preston, PR1 5DL Tel: (01772) 651188 Fax: (01772) 652577 E-mail: info@singerpartners.com

▶ Soapbox Creative Marketing Ltd, 6 Billing Road, Northampton, NN1 5AN Tel: (01604) 638989 Fax: (01604) 638553 E-mail: jo@soapbox-creative.com

▶ Stilton Surveys Ltd, 2 Turpins Ride, Stilton, Peterborough, PE7 3RE Tel: (01733) 240072 Fax: (01733) 240072 E-mail: info@stiltonsurveys.co.uk

▶ TENFOUR writing, 65 The Beckers, Rectory Road, London, N16 7QU Tel: 07971 669206 E-mail: chris@tenfourwriting.co.uk

Tequila International Holdings Ltd, 82 Charing Cross Road, London, WC2H 0QB Tel: (020) 7557 6101 Fax: (020) 7557 6111 E-mail: info@tequila-uk.com

Xmark Media Ltd, Old Village Hall, The Street, Effingham, Leatherhead, Surrey, KT24 5JS Tel: (01372) 750555 Fax: (01372) 750666 E-mail: mobilex@zetnet.co.uk

Yes Response Ltd, Unit 15 Brookside Business Park, Brookside Road, Uttoxeter, Staffordshire, ST14 8AU Tel: (01889) 561400 Fax: (01889) 568264 E-mail: dhanley@yesresponse.co.uk

DIRECT NUMERICAL CONTROL (DNC) SYSTEMS

▶ D Lo UK Ltd, Select House, Popes Lane, Oldbury, West Midlands, B69 4PA Tel: 0121-544 6256 Fax: 0121-541 4264 E-mail: info@dlog.co.uk

DIRECT SCREW TRANSFER PLASTIC MOULDINGS

D T Industries Ltd, Unit 10, Coulman Road Industrial Estate, Doncaster, South Yorkshire, DN8 5JU Tel: (01405) 740313 Fax: (01405) 817903 E-mail: sales@dtindustries.co.uk

DIRECTION FINDING EQUIPMENT, AVIONICS ETC

Selex Centre At Airbourne Systems, Ferry Road, Edinburgh, EH5 2XS Tel: 0131-332 2411 Fax: 0131-343 4011

DIRECTIONAL DRILLING CONTRACTORS

Mole Plumbers, 123 Arrowe Park Road, Wirral, Merseyside, CH49 5PB Tel: 0151-605 1469 Fax: 0151-605 1472 E-mail: sales@moleuk.com

▶ Quick Drill Ltd, 92 Castle Terrace, Winchburgh, Broxburn, West Lothian, EH52 6RH Tel: (01506) 891048 Fax: (01506) 891607

Visser & Smit Hanab UK, Unit 1a Orion Way, Kettering Business Park, Kettering, Northamptonshire, NN15 6NL Tel: (01536) 314700 Fax: (01536) 314709 E-mail: info@vsh-uk.com

DIRECTIONAL DRILLING EQUIPMENT

Terex Halco, PO Box 25, Halifax, West Yorkshire, HX3 9TW Tel: (01422) 399900 Fax: (01422) 330186 E-mail: halco@halcodrilling.com

DIRECTIONAL SIGNS

Doric Productions Ltd, 6-8 Kellner Road, London, SE28 0AX Tel: (020) 8316 0222 Fax: (020) 8316 0316 E-mail: sales@doricsigns.co.uk

Info Sign Systems Ltd, 17 East Cromwell Street, Edinburgh, EH6 6HD Tel: 0131-553 6433 Fax: 0131-554 5259 E-mail: admin@ellinfo.co.uk

Rivermeade Signs Ltd, Rowley Industrial Park, Roslin Road, London, W3 8BH Tel: (020) 8896 6900 Fax: (020) 8752 1691 E-mail: info@rivermeade.com

Saltwell Signs (North East) Ltd, Princesway North, Team Valley Trading Estate, Gateshead, Tyne & Wear, NE11 0TU Tel: 0191-482 5555 Fax: 0191-491 0246 E-mail: sales@saltwellsigns.co.uk

Sign Centre, 1 Farrier Road, Lincoln, LN6 3RU Tel: (01522) 500024 Fax: (01522) 500054 E-mail: enquires@signcentre-uk.com

Signs & Labels Ltd, Willow Business Park, 21 Willow Lane, Mitcham, Surrey, CR4 4NA Tel: (020) 8274 3700 Fax: (020) 8274 3702 E-mail: sales@signsandlabels.co.uk

W R Advertising Ltd, Black Lake, West Bromwich, West Midlands, B70 0PL Tel: 0121-525 2626 Fax: 0121-525 2955 E-mail: sales@wradvertising.co.uk

DIRECTORIES

B Plan Information Sytems, The Square, Basing View, Basingstoke, Hampshire, RG21 4EB Tel: (01256) 691111 Fax: (01256) 692450 E-mail: enquiries@fiinfo.com

▶ Eat Out Cornwall, Chiverton Lodge, The Saltings, Lelant, St. Ives, Cornwall, TR26 3DL Tel: (01736) 755113 Fax: (01736) 759413 E-mail: admin@eatoutcornwall.com

i-cD Publishing (UK) Ltd, 50 Sulivan Road, London, SW6 3DX Tel: (020) 7909 2200 Fax: (020) 7610 9024

▶ Sandy Bedfordshire, Nursery House, Sandy, Bedfordshire, SG19 1BP Tel: 0845 2005165 Fax: 0845 2012190 E-mail: info@sandy-bedfordshire.co.uk

UK Electrical Links, 9 Marion Road, Furnace Green, Crawley, West Sussex, RH10 6QQ Tel: (0870) 7437802 Fax: (01293) 537436 E-mail: ajm@elec.co.uk

▶ Uk250 Ltd, 2 Alpha House, Farmer Ward Road, Kenilworth, Warwickshire, CV8 2ED Tel: (01926) 863004 Fax: (01926) 863005 E-mail: info@uk250.co.uk

DIRECTORY PUBLISHERS

A P Information Services Ltd, Marlborough House, 298 Regents Park Road, London, N3 2UU Tel: (020) 8349 9988 Fax: (020) 8349 9797 E-mail: info@apinfo.co.uk

Art Sales Index Ltd, 194 Thorpe Lea Road, Egham, Surrey, TW20 8HA Tel: (01784) 451145 Fax: (01784) 451144 E-mail: info@art-sales-index.com

Barbour Index, Kingswood, Kings Ride, Ascot, Berkshire, SL5 8AD Tel: (01344) 884999 Fax: (01344) 899377 E-mail: reception@barbourindex.co.uk

Beechwood House Publishing Ltd, Beechwood House 2-3 Commercial Way, Christy Close, Southfields Business Park, Basildon, Essex, SS15 6EF Tel: (01268) 495600 Fax: (01268) 495601 E-mail: info@binleys.co.uk

C B D Research Ltd, 15 Wickham Road, Beckenham, Kent, BR3 5JS Tel: (0871) 2223440 Fax: (020) 8650 0768 E-mail: cbd@cbdresearch.co.uk

C M P Data & Information Services, Riverbank House, Angel Lane, Tonbridge, Kent, TN9 1SE Tel: (01732) 377591 Fax: (01732) 377479 E-mail: orders@ubminternational.com

William Clowes Ltd, Copland Way, Ellough, Beccles, Suffolk, NR34 7TL Tel: (01502) 712884 Fax: (01502) 717003 E-mail: william@clowes.co.uk

E L C International, 5 Five Mile Drive, Oxford, OX2 8HT Tel: (01865) 513186 E-mail: snyderbub@aol.com

Elanders UK Ltd, 32 Kings Road, Harrogate, North Yorkshire, HG1 5JW Tel: (01423) 530362 Fax: (01423) 530610 E-mail: sales@elanders.co.uk

ESI Ltd, Ochil House, Springkerse Business Park, Stirling, FK7 7XE Tel: (01786) 407000 Fax: (01786) 407003 E-mail: info@endat.com

Europa Publications Ltd, 11 New Felter La, London, EC4P 4EE Tel: (020) 7589 9855 Fax: (020) 7842 2249 E-mail: sales@europapublications.co.uk

Executive Grapevine International Ltd, New Barns Mill, Cottonmill Lane, St. Albans, Hertfordshire, AL1 2HA Tel: (01727) 844335 Fax: (01727) 844779 E-mail: sales@executive-grapevine.co.uk

Franchise Development Services Ltd, Franchise House, Surrey Street, Norwich, NR1 3FD Tel: (01603) 620301 Fax: (01603) 630174 E-mail: sales@franchise-group.com

Gabriel Communications Ltd, 1st Floor, St. James's Buildings, Oxford Street, Manchester, M1 6FP Tel: 0161-236 8856 Fax: 0161-236 8530 E-mail: advertising@the-universe.net

Hemming Group, 32 Vauxhall Bridge Road, London, SW1V 2SS Tel: (020) 7973 6404 Fax: (020) 7233 5052 E-mail: customer@hgluk.com

Hobsons Publishing plc, 42 Adler Street, London, E1 1EE Tel: (020) 7958 5000 Fax: (020) 7958 5001 E-mail: london.recception@hobsons.co.uk

Hollis Publishing Ltd, Harlequin House, 7 High Street, Teddington, Middlesex, TW11 8EL Tel: (020) 8973 3400 Fax: (020) 8977 1133 E-mail: hollis@hollis-pr.co.uk

I H S Technical Indexes Ltd, Viewpoint One, Willoughby Road, Bracknell, Berkshire, RG12 8FB Tel: (01344) 426311 Fax: (01344) 328004 E-mail: info@ihs.com

Incisive Media, 32 & 34 Broadwick Street, London, W1A 2HG Tel: (020) 7316 9000 Fax: (020) 7316 9003

Jane's Information Group, 163 Brighton Road, Coulsdon, Surrey, CR5 2YH Tel: (020) 8700 3700 Fax: (020) 8763 1005 E-mail: info@janes.com

Jordan Publishing Ltd, 21 St Thomas Street, Bristol, BS1 6JS Tel: 0117-923 0600 Fax: 0117-925 0486 E-mail: customersupport@jordans.co.uk

Kemps Publishing Ltd, 11 Swan Courtyard, Charles Edward Road, Birmingham, B26 1BU Tel: 0121-765 4144 Fax: 0121-706 6210 E-mail: enquiries@kempspublishing.co.uk

Key Note Ltd, Field House, 72 Oldfield Road, Hampton, Middlesex, TW12 2HQ Tel: (020) 8481 8750 Fax: (020) 8783 0049 E-mail: sales@keynote.co.uk

Kingston Communications Hull plc, 35-37 Carr Lane, Hull, HU1 3RE Tel: (01482) 602100 Fax: (01482) 320652 E-mail: publicrelations@kcom.com

▶ Kingston Publishing Services, Broadway House, 105 Ferensway, Hull, HU1 3UN Tel: (01482) 602600 Fax: (01482) 216816 E-mail: sue.brightman@kcom.com

Kompass Publishers, Windsor Court, East Grinstead House, East Grinstead, West Sussex, RH19 1XA Tel: (0800) 0185882 Fax: (01342) 335747 E-mail: sales@kompass.co.uk

M R C Publications Ltd, 5 Worcester Street, Oxford, OX1 2BX Tel: (01865) 200202 Fax: (01865) 200509 E-mail: sales@mrc.info.com

Market Research Society, 15 Northburgh Street, London, EC1V 0JR Tel: (020) 7490 4911 Fax: (020) 7490 0608 E-mail: sales@mrs.org.uk

Metal Bulletin Journals Ltd, Park House, 3 Park Terrace, Worcester Park, Surrey, KT4 7HY Tel: (020) 7827 9977 Fax: (020) 8337 8943 E-mail: books@metalbulletin.co.uk

▶ Millers Publications Ltd, The Cellars, High Street, Tenterden, Kent, TN30 6BN Tel: (01580) 766411 Fax: (01580) 766100

O A G Worldwide, Church Street, Dunstable, Bedfordshire, LU5 4HB Tel: (01582) 600111 Fax: (01582) 695140 E-mail: sales@oag.com

Page Bros Norwich Ltd, Mile Cross Lane, Norwich, NR6 6SA Tel: (01603) 778800 Fax: (01603) 778801 E-mail: info@pagebros.co.uk

Pearson Eduction Ltd, Edinburgh Gate, Edinburgh Way, Harlow, Essex, CM20 2JE Tel: (01279) 623623 Fax: (01279) 431059 E-mail: sales@pearson.com

Pindar Set Ltd, Newlands House, Caxton Way, Scarborough, North Yorkshire, YO11 3YT Tel: (01723) 502000 Fax: (01723) 502002 E-mail: enquiries@pindarset.com

Prospect Swetenhams, Field House, 72 Oldfield Road, Hampton, Middlesex, TW12 2HQ Tel: (020) 8481 8730 Fax: (020) 8783 1940 E-mail: sales@prospectshop.co.uk

Reed Business Information, Windsor Court, East Grinstead Ho, Wood St, East Grinstead, West Sussex, RH19 1XA Tel: (01342) 326972 Fax: (01342) 335612 E-mail: information@reedinfo.co.uk

Reed Business Information Ltd, Quadrant House, The Quadrant, Sutton, Surrey, SM2 5AS Tel: (020) 8652 3500 E-mail: webmaster@rbi.co.uk

Roles & Associates Ltd, 3 Pucks Corner, Lower Hampton Road, Sunbury-on-Thames, Middlesex, TW16 5PR Tel: (020) 8783 0777 Fax: (020) 8783 0088 E-mail: roles@easynet.co.uk

Snyder William Publishing Associates Information Services, 5 Five Mile Drive, Oxford, OX2 8HT Tel: (01865) 311015 Fax: (01865) 513186 E-mail: snyderpub@cs.com

Spotlight Casting Directories & Contacts, 7 Leicester Place, London, WC2H 7RJ Tel: (020) 7437 7631 Fax: (020) 7437 5881 E-mail: sales@spotlightcd.com

▶ T S I Luckins Ltd, Cherryholt Road, Stamford, Lincolnshire, PE9 2EP Tel: (01780) 750500 Fax: (01780) 750567 E-mail: info@luckins.co.uk

Thomas Telford Services Ltd, Thomas Telford House, 1 Heron Quay, London, E14 4JD Tel: (020) 7987 6999 Fax: (020) 7538 4101 E-mail: sales@t-telford.co.uk

United Business Media GP No 3 Ltd, Ludgate House, 245 Blackfriars Road, London, SE1 9UY Tel: (020) 7921 5000 Fax: (020) 7528 2772

Waterlow Publishing Information Services Ltd, Paulton House, 8 Shepherdess Walk, London, N1 7LB Tel: (020) 7490 0049 Fax: (020) 7253 1308 E-mail: marketing@waterlow.com

J. Whitaker & Sons Ltd, Endeavour House, 189 Shaftesbury Avenue, London, WC2H 8TJ Tel: (020) 7420 6000 Fax: (020) 7836 6781

DISABILITY AWARENESS TRAINING

▶ Kasway Ltd, 1 Conyers Avenue, Southport, Merseyside, PR8 4SZ Tel: 01704 551212 Fax: (01704) 551212 E-mail: mohammadi@kasway.co.uk

▶ Sense-Ability, Felin Brithdir, Rhydlewis, Llandysul, Dyfed, SA44 5SN Tel: 0151-652 1053 E-mail: post@sense-ability.co.uk

▶ Yogabuds Ltd, 47 Algers Road, Loughton, Essex, IG10 4NG Tel: 020 8508 3653

DISABILITY DISCRIMINATION ACT (DDA) ACCESS AUDITING

▶ Enable Enterprises Ltd, 24 Treforest Road, Coventry, CV3 1FN Tel: (024) 7644 3830 Fax: 0800 358 8484 E-mail: simon.stevens@enableenterprises.com

▶ Kasway Ltd, 1 Conyers Avenue, Southport, Merseyside, PR8 4SZ Tel: 01704 551212 Fax: (01704) 551212 E-mail: mohammadi@kasway.co.uk

DISABILITY DISCRIMINATION ACT (DDA) ACCESS TRAINING

▶ Enable Enterprises Ltd, 24 Treforest Road, Coventry, CV3 1FN Tel: (024) 7644 3830 Fax: 0800 358 8484 E-mail: simon.stevens@enableenterprises.com

DISABILITY DISCRIMINATION ACT (DDA) CONSULTANCY

▶ Enable Enterprises Ltd, 24 Treforest Road, Coventry, CV3 1FN Tel: (024) 7644 3830 Fax: 0800 358 8484 E-mail: simon.stevens@enableenterprises.com

DISABLED ACCESS CONSULTANCY

Sparks Fire Protection, 89 Llewellyn Street, Port Talbot, West Glamorgan, SA12 8SG Tel: (01639) 885837 E-mail: kevin@sparksfire.org.uk

DISABLED ACCESS SURVEYS

▶ Sense-Ability, Felin Brithdir, Rhydlewis, Llandysul, Dyfed, SA44 5SN Tel: 0151-652 1053 E-mail: post@sense-ability.co.uk

DISABLED AND ELDERLY PERSON ACCESS CONTROL SYSTEMS

▶ Intelligent Access Systems Ltd, 16 Gladstone Terrace, Boldon Colliery, Tyne & Wear, NE35 9HL Tel: 0191-536 9255 Fax: 0191-536 9255E-mail: laurance.laidlaw@homecall.co.uk

DISABLED AND ELDERLY PERSON AID DESIGNERS AND MAKERS

Arjo Ltd, St. Catherine Street, Gloucester, GL1 2SL Tel: (01452) 428200 Fax: (01452) 428344 E-mail: info@arjo.com

Autochair, Wood St North, Meddow Lane Industrial Estate, Alfreton, Derbyshire, DE55 7JR Tel: (0800) 214045 Fax: (01773) 830444 E-mail: info@autochair.co.uk

Mike Ayres Design Ltd, Unit 8, Shepherds Grove, Stanton, Bury St. Edmunds, Suffolk, IP31 2AR Tel: (01359) 251551 Fax: (01359) 251707 E-mail: enquiries@mikeayresdesign.co.uk

Bennetts Of Bromsgrove Ltd, 53 Sherwood Road, Aston Fields Industrial Estate, Bromsgrove, Worcestershire, B60 3DR Tel: (01527) 870440 Fax: (01527) 575595 E-mail: sales@bennettsbathrooms.co.uk

Bodys Surgical Care Centre, 631 London Road, Westcliff-on-Sea, Essex, SS0 9PE Tel: (01702) 346204 Fax: (01702) 338631

Cee Vee Engineering Ltd, Shepherds Close, Cooden Sea Road, Bexhill-on-Sea, East Sussex, TN39 4SL Tel: (01424) 845566 Fax: (01424) 842144 E-mail: sales@ceevee.co.uk

Cit Realisations Ltd, 6 Wedgwood Road, Bicester, Oxfordshire, OX26 4UL Tel: (01869) 327173 Fax: (01869) 247214 E-mail: sales@chilterninvadex.co.uk

Clinical Engineering Consultants Ltd, 2 Harlow House, Dukes Road, Newdigate, Dorking, Surrey, RH5 5BY Tel: (01306) 631681 Fax: (01306) 631688 E-mail: cec.co@lineone.net

Elap Engineering Ltd, Fort Street, Accrington, Lancashire, BB5 1QG Tel: (01254) 871599 Fax: (01254) 389992 E-mail: mail@elap.co.uk

Langham Products Ltd, Willow Road, Castle Donington, Derby, DE74 2NP Tel: (01332) 850277 Fax: (01332) 850366 E-mail: enquiries@langhamproducts.co.uk

Mangar International Ltd, Presteigne Industrial Estate, Presteigne, Powys, LD8 2UF Tel: (01544) 267674 Fax: (01544) 260287 E-mail: sales@mangar.co.uk

Medeci Rehab Ltd, Hallsford Bridge Industrial Estate, Stondon Road, Ongar, Essex, CM5 9RB Tel: (01277) 364449 Fax: (01277) 364962 E-mail: sales@ponting.co.uk

Neves Mobility Services, 25-35 Birkbeck Road, Sidcup, Kent, DA14 4DD Tel: (020) 8300 1000 Fax: (020) 8302 8941

Portaramp, Roudham Road, Harling Road, Norwich, NR16 2QN Tel: (01953) 714599 Fax: (01842) 714598 E-mail: sales@portaramps.co.uk

Possum Controls Ltd, 8 Stocklake Park Industrial Estate, Farmborough Close, Aylesbury, Buckinghamshire, HP20 1DQ Tel: (01296) 481591 Fax: (01296) 394349 E-mail: info@possum.co.uk

Ross Care Centres, Units 2-3 & 11, Westfield Road, Wallasey, Merseyside, CH44 7HX Tel: 0151-653 6000 Fax: 0151-653 8543

Simorg Ltd, Room 13 Enterprise House, 7 Gordon St, Luton, LU1 2QP Tel: (01582) 484785 Fax: (01582) 484157 E-mail: admin@simorglimited.co.uk

Southern Care Systems Ltd, Spectra House Unit 1a, Hightown Industrial Estate, Ringwood, Hampshire, BH24 1NZ Tel: (01425) 471522 Fax: (01425) 479130 E-mail: sales@southerncaresystems.co.uk

Stannah Lift Services, 45 Carlyle Avenue, Hillington Industrial Estate, Glasgow, G52 4XX Tel: 0141-882 9946 Fax: 0141-882 7503

Waterbury Bathroom Accessories Ltd, 60 Adams Street, Birmingham, B7 4LT Tel: 0121-333 6062 Fax: 0121-333 6459 E-mail: sales@waterbury.co.uk

DISABLED AND ELDERLY PERSON AIDS, LIFTING AIDS

Move Man SKG, 123 Abbey Lane, Leicester, LE4 5QX Tel: 0116-266 5353

▶ Stairglide, Unit 8, Barshaw Park, Leycroft Road, Leicester, LE4 1ET Tel: (0800) 7812020 E-mail: info@equilift.com

DISABLED AND ELDERLY PERSON AIDS, MONITORED ALARMS

Sparks Fire Protection, 89 Llewellyn Street, Port Talbot, West Glamorgan, SA12 8SG Tel: (01639) 885837 E-mail: kevin@sparksfire.org.uk

DISABLED AND ELDERLY PERSON AIDS, PLASTIC HEALTHCARE PRODUCTS

Langham Products Ltd, Willow Road, Castle Donington, Derby, DE74 2NP Tel: (01332) 850277 Fax: (01332) 850366 E-mail: enquiries@langhamproducts.co.uk

DISABLED AND ELDERLY PERSON AIDS, SHOWER ACCESSORIES

▶ Apres Shower Dryers (UK) Ltd, Apres House, Woodhill Street, Bury, Lancashire, BL8 1AT Tel: 0161-761 7014 Fax: 0161-764 7013 E-mail: mike@apresshower.com

DISABLED AND ELDERLY PERSON AIDS, TOILET AIDS

Kirton Healthcare Group Ltd, 23 Rookwood Way, Haverhill, Suffolk, CB9 8PB Tel: (01440) 705352 Fax: (01440) 706199 E-mail: info@kirtonhealthcare.demon.co.uk

DISABLED AND ELDERLY PERSON BATHS

Arjo Ltd, St. Catherine Street, Gloucester, GL1 2SL Tel: (01452) 428200 Fax: (01452) 428344 E-mail: info@arjo.com

Athena Solid Surfaces, 14 Sedling Road, Wear Industrial Estate, Washington, Tyne & Wear, NE38 9BZ Tel: 0191-416 7275 Fax: 0191-417 7510 E-mail: admin@athenasolidsurfaces.co.uk

DISABLED AND ELDERLY PERSON CARRIAGE REPAIR

Brook Miller Mobility Ltd, Ability House, Owler Ings Road, Brighouse, West Yorkshire, HD6 1EH Tel: (01484) 721772 Fax: (01484) 401242 E-mail: sales@brookmobility.co.uk

J R Wooddisse & Co. Ltd, Dale Street, Bilston, West Midlands, WV14 7LE Tel: (01902) 494336 Fax: (01902) 354953

Midland Mobility Ltd, Torrington Avenue, Coventry, CV4 9BL Tel: (024) 7647 1124 Fax: (024) 7646 5288 E-mail: sales@midlandmobility.co.uk

Neves Mobility Services, 25-35 Birkbeck Road, Sidcup, Kent, DA14 4DD Tel: (020) 8300 1000 Fax: (020) 8302 8941

DISABLED AND ELDERLY PERSON CARRIAGES

All Handling Ltd, Mobility House, 492 Kingston Road, London, SW20 8DX Tel: (020) 8542 1021 Fax: (020) 8395 4410

Care Centres Ltd, 75 Rowlands Road, Worthing, West Sussex, BN11 3JN Tel: (01903) 821515 Fax: (01903) 235132 E-mail: carecentresltd@supanet.com

Midland Mobility Ltd, Torrington Avenue, Coventry, CV4 9BL Tel: (024) 7647 1124 Fax: (024) 7646 5288 E-mail: sales@midlandmobility.co.uk

Neves Mobility Services, 25-35 Birkbeck Road, Sidcup, Kent, DA14 4DD Tel: (020) 8300 1000 Fax: (020) 8302 8941

DISABLED AND ELDERLY PERSON DOORS

▶ Folding Sliding Doors, FSD Works, Hopbine Avenue West Bowling, Bradford, West Yorkshire, BD5 8ER Tel: (01274) 715880 Fax: (0845) 6446631 E-mail: info@foldingslidingdoors.co.uk

DISABLED AND ELDERLY PERSON LIFTING PLATFORMS

Disability Access Co, 16-18 Chapel Street, Glossop, Derbyshire, SK13 8AT Tel: (01457) 868547 Fax: (08717) 335071 E-mail: sales@disabilityaccessco.com

DISABLED AND ELDERLY PERSON LIFTS

Crown Lifts Ltd, Regancy House, 33-49 Farwig Lane, Bromley, BR1 3RE Tel: (020) 8464 5000 Fax: (020) 8290 7646

▶ Dolphin Stairlifts, 37 Chertsey Road, Chobham, Woking, Surrey, GU24 8PD Tel: (01276) 856060 Fax: (01276) 858689 E-mail: christian@dolphinlifts.co.uk

Enable Access Disabled Access Equipement, 16 Plantagenet Road, Barnet, Hertfordshire, EN5 5JG Tel: (020) 8275 0375 Fax: (020) 8449 0326

Equilift Ltd, 8 Barrington Park, Leycroft Road, Leicester, LE4 1ET Tel: 0116-234 4310 Fax: 0116-234 4360 E-mail: info@equilift.com

Pickerings Europe Ltd, 9 Glasgow Road, Baillieston, Glasgow, G69 6JT Tel: 0141-771 7575 Fax: 0141-771 8585 E-mail: info@pickerings.co.uk

Saxon Lifts Ltd, Grand Union Works, Whilton Locks, Whilton, Daventry, Northamptonshire, NN11 2NH Tel: (01327) 843355 Fax: (01327) 843887 E-mail: sales@saxonlifts.com

Southern Care Systems Ltd, Spectra House Unit 1a, Hightown Industrial Estate, Ringwood, Hampshire, BH24 1NZ Tel: (01425) 471522 Fax: (01425) 479130 E-mail: sales@southerncaresystems.co.uk

Stannah Lift Services, 45 Carlyle Avenue, Hillington Industrial Estate, Glasgow, G52 4XX Tel: 0141-882 9946 Fax: 0141-882 7503

ThyssenKrupp Accessibility, 62 Boston Road, Leicester, LE4 1AW Tel: 0116-234 4310 Fax: 0116-236 4134 E-mail: info@TKAccessibility.com

Wessex Medical Equipment Co. Ltd, Budds Lane, Romsey, Hampshire, SO51 0HA Tel: (01794) 830303 Fax: (01794) 512621 E-mail: info@wessexmedical.co.uk

Yorkshire Care Equipment, 6 Over Lane, Rawdon, Leeds, LS19 6DY Tel: (01423) 880399 Fax: 0113-250 7433

DISABLED AND ELDERLY PERSON MINIBUSES

Advanced Vehicle Builders Ltd, Bridge Street Industrial Estate, Bridge Street, Clay Cross, Chesterfield, Derbyshire, S45 9NU Tel: (01246) 250022 Fax: (01246) 250016 E-mail: info@minibus.co.uk

DISABLED AND ELDERLY PERSON POWERED MOBILITY SCOOTERS

Days Health, North Road, Bridgend Industrial Estate, Bridgend, Mid Glamorgan, CF31 3TP Tel: (01656) 657495 Fax: (01656) 767178 E-mail: info@dayshealthcare.com

Electric Mobility Euro Ltd, Canal Way, Ilminster, Somerset, TA19 9DL Tel: (01460) 258100 Fax: (01460) 258125 E-mail: sales@electricmobility.co.uk

Sunrise Medical Ltd, Sunrise Business Park, High Street, Wollaston, Stourbridge, West Midlands, DY8 4PS Tel: (01384) 446688 Fax: (01384) 446699 E-mail: sunmail@sunmed.co.uk

DISABLED AND ELDERLY PERSON SAFETY EQUIPMENT

N M I Safety Systems Ltd, 17 Lake Business Centre, Tariff Road, London, N17 0YX Tel: (020) 8801 5339 Fax: (020) 8801 3491 E-mail: sales@nmisafty.com

DISABLED AND ELDERLY PERSON SHOWER CABINETS OR CUBICLES

Arjo Ltd, St. Catherine Street, Gloucester, GL1 2SL Tel: (01452) 428200 Fax: (01452) 428344 E-mail: info@arjo.com

Contour Showers Ltd, Siddorn Street, Winsford, Cheshire, CW7 2BA Tel: (01606) 592586 Fax: (01606) 861260 E-mail: sales@contour-showers.co.uk

▶ Neaco Ltd, Norton Grove Industrial Estate, Norton, Malton, North Yorkshire, YO17 9HQ Tel: (01653) 695721 Fax: (01653) 600418 E-mail: alan.green@neaco.co.uk

DISABLED AND ELDERLY PERSON VEHICLE CONVERSION SPECIALIST SERVICES

A J Mobility Ltd, Unit 17 Diplocks Way, Hailsham, East Sussex, BN27 3JF Tel: (01323) 847250 Fax: (01323) 849707 E-mail: sales@ajmobility.co.uk

Autochair, Wood St North, Meddow Lane Industrial Estate, Alfreton, Derbyshire, DE55 7JR Tel: (0800) 214045 Fax: (01773) 830444 E-mail: info@autochair.co.uk

Chassis Development Ltd, 16 Botley Road, Park Gate, Southampton, SO31 1AJ Tel: (01489) 885738 Fax: (01489) 570227

Cowal Mobility Aid Ltd, Cowal Court, Heath End Road, Great Kingshill, High Wycombe, Buckinghamshire, HP15 6HL Tel: (01494) 714400 Fax: (01494) 714818 E-mail: sales@cowalmobility.co.uk

East Anglian Motor & Sheet Metal Co. Ltd, 10 Garden Street, Norwich, NR1 1QX Tel: (01603) 625664 Fax: (01603) 760545 E-mail: sales@ea-arc.co.uk

Minibus Options Ltd, PO Box 1, High Peak, Derbyshire, SK23 7LY Tel: (01663) 735355 Fax: (01663) 735352 E-mail: sales@minibusoptions.co.uk

Brian Page Controls, 18 Pooley Green Road, Egham, Surrey, TW20 8AF Tel: (01784) 435850 Fax: (01784) 434278 E-mail: brianpagecontrols@hotmail.com

R & S Mobility, 120 Courtney Street, Hull, HU8 7QF Tel: (01482) 320289 Fax: (01482) 320289 E-mail: rsmobility@hotmail.com

Steering Developments Group Ltd, Unit 5 Eastman Way, Hemel Hempstead, Hertfordshire, HP2 7HF Tel: (01442) 212918 Fax: (01442) 240254 E-mail: enquiries@steeringdevelopments.co.uk

DISABLED PERSON EMPLOYMENT TRAINING

▶ Yogabuds Ltd, 47 Algers Road, Loughton, Essex, IG10 4NG Tel: 020 8508 3653

DISABLED PERSON SEATS

Clinical Engineering Consultants Ltd, 2 Harlow House, Dukes Road, Newdigate, Dorking, Surrey, RH5 5BY Tel: (01306) 631681 Fax: (01306) 631688 E-mail: cec.co@lineone.net

Richards & Shaw (Trim) Ltd, 57 Cradley Road, Cradley Heath, West Midlands, B64 7BP Tel: (01384) 633800 Fax: (01384) 410791 E-mail: slynch@richards-shaw.co.uk

DISABLED/HANDICAPPED PERSON CHAIRS

Clinical Engineering Consultants Ltd, 2 Harlow House, Dukes Road, Newdigate, Dorking, Surrey, RH5 5BY Tel: (01306) 631681 Fax: (01306) 631688 E-mail: cec.co@lineone.net

Kirton Healthcare Group Ltd, 23 Rookwood Way, Haverhill, Suffolk, CB9 8PB Tel: (01440) 705352 Fax: (01440) 706199 E-mail: info@kirtonhealthcare.demon.co.uk

R J Mobility Ltd, Boxtree Mills, Wheatley, Halifax, West Yorkshire, HX3 5AE Tel: (01422) 358888 Fax: (01422) 355924 E-mail: sales@rjmobility.com

DISASTER MANAGEMENT/ PLANNING/RECOVERY SERVICES

Datashare Solutions Ltd, 10 Chandler Court, Tolworth Rise South, Surbiton, Surrey, KT5 9NN Tel: (020) 8337 2700 Fax: (020) 8337 2701 E-mail: info@datasharesolutions.com

Eastleigh Power Plant, PO Box 199, Southampton, SO30 0WZ Tel: (023) 8040 7507 Fax: (01489) 780478 E-mail: epower@fpcad.com

Hewlett Packard, 29 Valepits Road, Garretts Green, Birmingham, B33 0TD Tel: 0121-784 7445 Fax: 0121-783 4015 E-mail: enquiries@synstar.com

Merryhill Envirotec Ltd, Merryhill House, Budds Lane, Romsey, Hampshire, SO51 0HA Tel: (01794) 515848 Fax: (01794) 524386 E-mail: enquiries@merryhill-idm.co.uk

▶ Poppleton & Appleby, 32 High Street, Manchester, M4 1QD Tel: 0161-834 7025 Fax: 0161-833 1548 E-mail: enquires@pandamanchester.co.uk

DISC BRAKE PADS

Fibrax Ltd, Queensway, Wrexham, Clwyd, LL13 8YR Tel: (01978) 356744 Fax: (01978) 356206 E-mail: info@fibrax.co.uk

Pretech Engineering, Barrett Court, Cardiff Road, Reading, RG1 8ED Tel: 0118-957 3123 Fax: 0118-957 3123 E-mail: info@pretech.co.uk

DISC BRAKES

Robert Cupitt Ltd, 4 Joplin Court, Sovereign Business Park, Crownhill, Milton Keynes, MK8 0JP Tel: (01908) 563063 Fax: (01908) 562910 E-mail: sales@robertcupitt.co.uk

Fibrax Ltd, Queensway, Wrexham, Clwyd, LL13 8YR Tel: (01978) 356744 Fax: (01978) 356206 E-mail: info@fibrax.co.uk

High Precision Machining Ltd, Unit 10 Washington Centre, Washington Street, Dudley, West Midlands, DY2 9RE Tel: (01384) 233133 Fax: (01384) 212755 E-mail: enquiries@eurac-group.com

Peak Transmissions Ltd, Unit 8 Hardwick Court, Hardwick View Road, Holmewood, Chesterfield, Derbyshire, S42 5SA Tel: (01246) 856758 Fax: (01246) 856850 E-mail: sales@peakgroupltd.com

Portland Engineering Co. Ltd, Wide Street, Portland, Dorset, DT5 2JP Tel: (01305) 821273 Fax: (01305) 821499 E-mail: office@portlandengineering.com

Precision Disc Castings Ltd, 16 Mannings Heath Road, Poole, Dorset, BH12 4NJ Tel: (01202) 715050 Fax: (01202) 715068 E-mail: shumps@pdcastings.co.uk

Red Dot Ltd, 98 White Hart Lane, London, N22 5SG Tel: (020) 8888 2354 Fax: (020) 8881 0497 E-mail: sales@reddotracing.co.uk

Stromag Ltd, 29 Wellingborough Road, Rushden, Northamptonshire, NN10 9YE Tel: (01933) 350407 Fax: (01933) 358692 E-mail: sales@stromag.com

Wichita Co. Ltd, Ampthill Road, Bedford, MK42 9RD Tel: (01234) 350311 Fax: (01234) 350317 E-mail: clutch@wichita.co.uk

DISC SPRINGS

Long Technology Ltd, 1 Richmond Lane, Huntly, Aberdeenshire, AB54 8FJ Tel: (01466) 794646 Fax: (01466) 794111 E-mail: sales@longtechnology.com

DISCOTHEQUE EQUIPMENT HIRE

Apollo Light & Sound Ltd, Avonside Enterprise Park, Melksham, Wiltshire, SN12 8BS Tel: (01225) 707429 Fax: (01225) 707429 E-mail: apollo@lightandsound.fsnet.co.uk

▶ Beach Entertainments, 89 The Ridgway, Brighton, BN2 6PB Tel: (01273) 388424

▶ Chilli Sound, 8 Albert Road, Finsbury Park, London, N4 3RW Tel: (07973) 500651 Fax: (01273) 679416 E-mail: info@chillisound.co.uk

▶ Electro Entertainments (Karaoke & Disco), 6 Flintsham Grove, Hanley, Stoke-on-Trent, ST1 5QS Tel: (01782) 204152 E-mail: ianmaddock@wolfieselectro.co.uk

Kays Electronics of Chesterfield, 195 Sheffield Road, Chesterfield, Derbyshire, S41 7JQ Tel: (01246) 205361 E-mail: jk@kayselectronics.co.uk

▶ Lightspeed Entertainments, 108 Quay Road, Bridlington, East Yorkshire, YO16 4JB Tel: (07831) 192740 Fax: (01262) 679735 E-mail: lightspeed@trancefixed.fsnet.co.uk

▶ Newdecade Productions, 16 Stevenage Road, Hitchin, Hertfordshire, SG4 9DL Tel: (01438) 369545 Fax: (01438) 369545 E-mail: paul@newdecade.co.uk

Rossco Ltd, Croft Court, Grammar School Walk, Hitchin, Hertfordshire, SG5 1JD Tel: (01462) 431413 Fax: (01462) 431423

DISCOTHEQUE EQUIPMENT, SPECIAL EFFECTS

52nd Street, Unit 11 Oakwell Business Centre, Oakwell View, Barnsley, South Yorkshire, S71 1HX Tel: (01226) 200900 Fax: (01226) 200222 E-mail: shaun@52ndstreet.co.uk

▶ A B C Sound & Lighting, 36 Stepfield, Witham, Essex, CM8 3TH Tel: (01376) 511335 Fax: (01376) 511335

▶ Abacab Sound, Cambridge Road, Whetstone, Leicester, LE8 6LH Tel: 0116-286 7123 Fax: 0116-286 7123 E-mail: rockflightcases@aol.com

▶ Beach Entertainments, 89 The Ridgway, Brighton, BN2 6PB Tel: (01273) 388424

Central Sounds, 66 Laurel Road, Loughborough, Leicestershire, LE11 2NL Tel: (01509) 215560 Fax: (01509) 215560

▶ Destiny Entertainments, Unit 9 Bankside Park, 28 Thames Road, Barking, Essex, IG11 0HZ Tel: (0870) 3501079

Disco Equipment Hire, 214 High Road, Romford, RM6 6LS Tel: (020) 8597 4575 Fax: (020) 8590 4125

Discotechnology Ltd, 479a Wakefield Road, Liversedge, West Yorkshire, WF15 6BL Tel: (01924) 400700 Fax: (01924) 400700 E-mail: discotechnololgy@btconnect.com

▶ Electronic Lighting, 77-78 Fore Street, Buckfastleigh, Devon, TQ11 0BS Tel: (01364) 642111 Fax: (01364) 642111

▶ Enterprise Tyre Service, Unit 36-37, Neath Abbey Business Park, Neath Abbey, Neath, West Glamorgan, SA10 7DR Tel: (01792) 816731 Fax: (01792) 816503 E-mail: sales@entsuk.com

Gig Shop, 322 Beverley Road, Hull, HU5 1BA Tel: (01482) 440982 Fax: (01482) 440982

Huws Light & Sound, 2 Pisgah Street, Kenfig Hill, Bridgend, Mid Glamorgan, CF33 6BY Tel: (01656) 741414 Fax: (01656) 741414

▶ Jade's Entertainment Disco Mobile, 201 Union Street, Torquay, TQ1 4BY Tel: (0871) 7110627

Kaleidoscope, 84 Parkwood Road, Bournemouth, BH5 2BL Tel: (01202) 431691 Fax: (01202) 429669 E-mail: sales@ksl-online.co.uk

DISCOTHEQUE EQUIPMENT, SPECIAL EFFECTS – *continued*

Kays Electronics of Chesterfield, 195 Sheffield Road, Chesterfield, Derbyshire, S41 7JQ Tel: (01246) 205361 E-mail: jk@kayselectronics.co.uk
Knight Sound & Light, 98 Uxbridge Road, London, W7 3SU Tel: (020) 8579 0144 Fax: (020) 8579 8222 E-mail: info@knightsoundandlight.com
L S Direct Ltd, 44 Holcombe Crescent, Kearsley, Bolton, BL4 8JY Tel: (01204) 862776 Fax: (01204) 707865 E-mail: pat@lsdirect.co.uk
▶ Lightspeed Entertainments, 108 Quay Road, Bridlington, East Yorkshire, YO16 4JB Tel: (07831) 192740 Fax: (01262) 679735 E-mail: lightspeed@trancefixed.fsnet.co.uk
M2, Unit 3, City Commerce Centre, Marsh Lane, Southampton, SO14 3EW Tel: (023) 8063 4437 Fax: (023) 8022 5011 E-mail: sale@movement.com
Martin Manufacturing UK plc, Belvoir Way, Fairfield Industrial Estate, Louth, Lincolnshire, LN11 0LQ Tel: (01507) 604399 Fax: (01507) 601956 E-mail: sales@martin.dk
Orange DJ Gear Ltd, 734 Oxford Road, Reading, RG30 1EH Tel: 0118-950 9969 Fax: 0118-950 7072 E-mail: sales@djgear.co.uk
Premier Solutions (Nottingham) Ltd, Ascot Industrial Estate, Sandiacre, Nottingham, NG10 5DL Tel: 0115-939 4122 Fax: 0115-949 0453 E-mail: info@premier-solutions.biz
Pulsar Light Of Cambridge, 3 Coldhams Business Park, Norman Way, Cambridge, CB1 3LH Tel: (01223) 403500 Fax: (01223) 403501 E-mail: sales@pulsarlight.com
R G M Music Ltd, 24 Nelson Street, Kilmarnock, Ayrshire, KA1 1BA Tel: (01563) 537711 Fax: (01563) 530209
▶ Rs100, 56 Park Road, Glasgow, G4 9JF Tel: (08707) 661650
▶ Solo Lighting & Sound Ltd, 7 Derby Road, Stapleford, Nottingham, NG9 7AS Tel: 0115-917 1718 Fax: 0115-913 3577 E-mail: sales@lifeismusic.co.uk
South East Disco Supplies, 85 Baden Road, Gillingham, Kent, ME7 1QZ Tel: (01634) 281877
TTL Sales & Distribution Ltd, Units 1-3 CMS Business Park, Station Lane, Featherstone, Pontefract, West Yorkshire, WF7 6EQ Tel: (01977) 600064 Fax: (0870) 7449959 E-mail: sales@ttlonline.co.uk
▶ West Coast Radio, 3 Spen Farm Studios, Clifton Road, Blackpool, FY4 4QA Tel: (01253) 838828 Fax: (01253) 838828 E-mail: sales@westcoastradio.co.uk

DISHED/FLANGED ENDS, TANK/BOILER

Cerec, 95 Ashby High Street, Scunthorpe, South Humberside, DN16 2JX Tel: (01724) 846866 Fax: (01724) 280358 E-mail: colin-wilson@ntlworld.com
J Bown & Co Dukinfield Ltd, Wharf Street, Dukinfield, Cheshire, SK16 4PQ Tel: 0161-339 9888 Fax: 0161-343 1052 E-mail: sale@jbown.com

DISHWASHER RACKS FOR GLASSES

▶ Easicook Microwave Ltd, Unit 23 Cardiff Business Park, Lambourne Cresent, Llanishen, Cardiff, CF14 5GF Tel: (029) 2074 7567 Fax: (029) 2021 4100 E-mail: info@easicook.co.uk

DISHWASHER RINSING AGENTS

▶ Easicook Microwave Ltd, Unit 23 Cardiff Business Park, Lambourne Cresent, Llanishen, Cardiff, CF14 5GF Tel: (029) 2074 7567 Fax: (029) 2021 4100 E-mail: info@easicook.co.uk

DISHWASHER TRAY RACKS

▶ Easicook Microwave Ltd, Unit 23 Cardiff Business Park, Lambourne Cresent, Llanishen, Cardiff, CF14 5GF Tel: (029) 2074 7567 Fax: (029) 2021 4100 E-mail: info@easicook.co.uk

DISHWASHERS, *See also headings for particular types*

Alton Electrical Services, 25-27 Southview Rise, Alton, Hampshire, GU34 2AB Tel: (01420) 86194 Fax: (01420) 86194
▶ Axon Enterprises Ltd, 8a & 8b St. Martins Street, Hereford, HR2 7RE Tel: (01432) 359906 Fax: (01432) 352436 E-mail: sales@axon-enterprises.co.uk
Gde Services Ltd, Mayfield House, Tockholes Road, Darwen, Lancashire, BB3 1LL Tel: (01254) 761246 Fax: (01254) 775202
Pro Wash, 47 Milton Hill, Weston-super-Mare, Avon, BS22 9RE Tel: (01934) 418177 Fax: (01934) 643580 E-mail: prowash@btconnect.com

DISINFECTANTS

Allens (Disinfectants) Ltd, 462 Cleveland St, Birkenhead, Merseyside, CH41 8EQ Tel: 0151-652 4877 Fax: 0151-652 3800
Bonnett Maintenance Chemicals, Unit 44 Corringham Industrial Estate, Corringham Road, Gainsborough, Lincolnshire, DN21 1QB Tel: (01427) 613240 Fax: (01427) 617308 E-mail: enquiries@bonnetts.f9.co.uk
▶ Cleenol Group Ltd, Neville House, Beaumont Road, Banbury, Oxfordshire, OX16 1RB Tel: (01295) 251721 Fax: (01295) 269561 E-mail: sales@cleenol.co.uk
William Clements (Chemicals) Ltd, 38a Witham Street, Belfast, BT4 1HP Tel: (028) 9073 8395 Fax: (028) 9045 0532
Concorde Chemicals P.L.C., Concorde Works, Bilton Way, Brimsdown, Enfield, Middlesex, EN3 7NH Tel: (020) 8804 7411 Fax: (020) 8805 6553 E-mail: dgoldberg@concordechemicals.co.uk
Deb Ltd, 108 Spencer Road, Belper, Derbyshire, DE56 1JX Tel: (01773) 596700 Fax: (01773) 822548 E-mail: enquiry@deb.co.uk
Haji Cash & Carry Wholesalers, Haji House, Lower Tweedale Street, Rochdale, Lancashire, OL11 1HG Tel: (01706) 715959 Fax: (01706) 715960
Jeyes Group Ltd, Brunel Way, Thetford, Norfolk, IP24 1HF Tel: (01842) 757575 Fax: (01842) 757812
M & A Pharmachem Ltd, Allenby Laboratories, Wigan Road, Westhoughton, Bolton, BL5 2AL Tel: (01942) 816184 Fax: (01942) 813937 E-mail: info@mapharmachem.co.uk
Northern Dairy Supplies Ltd, Lea Road, Lea Town, Preston, PR4 0RA Tel: (01772) 720358 Fax: (01772) 726489 E-mail: admin@dairyhygiene.co.uk
Quatchem Chemicals Ltd, 1 Victoria Trading Estate, Drury Lane, Chadderton, Oldham, OL9 7PJ Tel: 0161-947 0177 Fax: 0161-947 0180 E-mail: sales@quatchem.co.uk
Solmedia Laboratory Supplies, 6 The Parade, Colchester Road, Romford, RM3 0AQ Tel: (01708) 343334 Fax: (01708) 372785 E-mail: labsupplies@solmedialtd.com
Thornton & Ross Ltd, Linthwaite, Huddersfield, HD7 5QH Tel: (01484) 842217 Fax: (01484) 847301 E-mail: mail@thorntonross.com
Zamo Household Products Ltd, 27 White Post Lane, London, E9 5EN Tel: (020) 8525 1177 Fax: (020) 8525 1166 E-mail: zamoproducts@aol.com

DISK DUPLICATING

▶ Dicsmart Disc Services, 25a Caxton Avenue, Blackpool, FY2 9AP Tel: (01253) 508670 Fax: (01253) 508670

DISMANTLING CONTRACTORS

C Soar & Sons, Tank Row, Grange Lane, Barnsley, South Yorkshire, S71 5AD Tel: (01226) 287951 Fax: (01226) 293146 E-mail: info@csoarandsons.co.uk
Albert Draper & Son Ltd, Black 5 Works, Ravenstreet, Hull, HU9 1PP Tel: (01482) 320712 Fax: (01482) 585312 E-mail: info@adraper.co.uk
Hicks Metals & Alloys, 170-176 Fazeley Street, Birmingham, B5 5SE Tel: 0121-772 1896 Fax: 0121-771 2085
Hughes & Salvidge, 11 Flathouse Road, Portsmouth, PO1 4QS Tel: (023) 9275 3733 Fax: (023) 9275 5189 E-mail: info@hughes-salvidge.co.uk
Robinson & Birdsell, Audby House, Audby Lane, Wetherby, West Yorkshire, LS22 7FD Tel: (01937) 548800 Fax: (01937) 548801 E-mail: r-b@robinson-birdsell.co.uk
Yorkshire Demolition Contractors Ltd, 8 Weetworth Ave, Glasshoughton, Castleford, West Yorkshire, WF10 4QA Tel: (01977) 553117 Fax: (01977) 553117

DISPENSERS, FLUID/LIQUID

Hingerose Ltd, 5 Ryder Court, Corby, Northamptonshire, NN18 9NX Tel: (01536) 461441 Fax: (01536) 461600 E-mail: info@hingerose.co.uk
Hook & Tucker Zenyx Ltd, Vulcan Way, New Addington, Croydon, CR0 9UG Tel: (01689) 843345 Fax: (01689) 841792 E-mail: sales@htz.biz
Ophardt Product UK Ltd, 18 Shaftesbury St South, Derby, DE23 8YH Tel: (01332) 297666 Fax: (01332) 343354 E-mail: sales@ophardt.com
Reliant Design Development Co. Ltd, 60 Woolmer Way, Bordon, Hampshire, GU35 9QF Tel: (01420) 478341 Fax: (01420) 489322 E-mail: sales@rdd.co.uk

DISPENSING EQUIPMENT, PU/RESIN ETC

Metix (UK) Ltd, Saxon House, Henson Way, Telford Way Industrial Estate, Kettering, Northamptonshire, NN16 8PX Tel: (01536) 312990 Fax: (01536) 312985 E-mail: sales@metix.co.uk

DISPERSANT CHEMICALS

Lawrence Industries Ltd, Lawrence House, Apollo, Tamworth, Staffordshire, B79 7TA Tel: (01827) 314151 Fax: (01827) 314152 E-mail: sales@l-i.co.uk
Stepan UK Ltd, Bridge House, Bridge Street, Stalybridge, Cheshire, SK15 1PH Tel: 0161-338 5511 Fax: 0161-338 4245 E-mail: sales@stepanuk.com

DISPERSANTS, OIL/PETROLEUM POLLUTION

Dasic International Ltd, Winchester Hill, Romsey, Hampshire, SO51 7YD Tel: (01794) 512419 Fax: (01794) 522346 E-mail: sales@dasicinter.com

DISPLACEMENT TRANSDUCERS

Rota Engineering Ltd, Wellington Street, Bury, Lancashire, BL8 2BD Tel: 0161-764 0424 Fax: 0161-762 9729 E-mail: sales@rota-eng.com
▶ Solartron Metrology Ltd, 1 Steyning Way, Bognor Regis, West Sussex, PO22 9ST Tel: (01243) 833300 Fax: (01243) 861244

DISPLAY BOARDS

Avon Displays, Unit 4, Redhill Business Park, Elberton, Bristol, BS35 4AL Tel: (01454) 411144 E-mail: info@avondisplays.com
Fastlane Displays Ltd, 19 Arkwright Court, Astmoor Industrial Estate, Runcorn, Cheshire, WA7 1NX Tel: (01928) 569846 Fax: (01928) 569846
Info Sign Systems Ltd, 17 East Cromwell Street, Edinburgh, EH6 6HD Tel: 0131-553 6433 Fax: 0131-554 5259 E-mail: admin@ellinfo.co.uk
M J Visual Systems Ltd, Unit 1, New Bury Park, Easthampnett, Chichester, West Sussex, PO18 0JY Tel: (01243) 780816 Fax: (01243) 783562 E-mail: sales@mjvisual.co.uk
Magiboards Ltd, Unit F, Stafford Park 12, Telford, Shropshire, TF3 3BJ Tel: (01952) 292111 Fax: (01952) 292280 E-mail: sales@magiboards.co.uk
Magna Display Systems Ltd, Unit 13 Alliance Close, Attleborough Fields Industrial Estate, Nuneaton, Warwickshire, CV11 6SD Tel: (024) 7632 0032 Fax: (024) 7635 0213 E-mail: info@magnadisplaysystems.co.uk
Oakleaf Graphics, Portland House, Bolsover Business Park, Woodhouse Lane, Bolsover, Chesterfield, Derbyshire, S44 6BD Tel: (01246) 828228 E-mail: sales@oakleafgraphics.co.uk
▶ Pitts Presentation Products Ltd, Hill Top Lane, Whittle-le-Woods, Chorley, Lancashire, PR6 7QR Tel: (01257) 220247 Fax: (01257) 220246 E-mail: info@pittspresentation.co.uk
Silvercases, Daux Road, Billingshurst, West Sussex, RH14 9SR Tel: (01403) 784671 Fax: (01403) 785353 E-mail: info@woodcon.co.uk
Vista Visuals UK, Unit 4 Old Mill Industrial Estate, Bamber Bridge, Preston, PR5 6SY Tel: (01772) 696725 Fax: (01772) 696726 E-mail: danny@vistavisuals.co.uk
Vultron International Ltd, Unit 2 City Park Industrial Estate, Gelderd Road, Leeds, LS12 6DR Tel: 0113-263 0323 Fax: 0113-279 4127 E-mail: vultronuk@aol.com

DISPLAY BOXES, WOODEN

Cuthbertson Maunsell Ltd, Dunedin House, 25 Ravelstone Terrace, Edinburgh, EH4 3TP Tel: 0131-311 4000 Fax: 0131-311 4090 E-mail: cml-edin@compuserve.com

DISPLAY BUBBLE TUBES AND COLUMNS

Blaze Bright Trading As Exterior, 8B Langthwaite Road, Langthwaite Grange Industrial Estate, South Kirkby, Pontefract, West Yorkshire, WF9 3AP Tel: (0845) 6440977 Fax: (0845) 6440988 E-mail: gareth.jones@exterior.innovations.co.uk

DISPLAY CABINET LOCKS

Clares Of Croydon Ltd, 54 Tamworth Road, Croydon, CR0 1XW Tel: (020) 8688 7952 Fax: (020) 8688 1867

DISPLAY CABINETS

3d Displays Ltd, Upper Brents, Faversham, Kent, ME13 7DR Tel: (01795) 532947 Fax: (01795) 539934 E-mail: info@3ddisplays.co.uk
A F Electrics, Millbank Street, Stoke-on-Trent, ST3 1AE Tel: (01782) 332276 Fax: (01782) 341036 E-mail: arnot@audemex.co.uk
Astabridge Ltd, Earlstrees Road, Earlstrees Industrial Estate, Corby, Northamptonshire, NN17 4AZ Tel: (01536) 267796 Fax: (01536) 402079 E-mail: info@astabmnge.co.uk
Avon Armour Holdings Ltd, Unit 12, 1-2 Portview Road, Bristol, BS11 9LD Tel: 0117-982 6288 Fax: 0117-982 8322 E-mail: sales@avonarmour.co.uk
▶ Bourne & Son Ltd, Unit 23a Firsland Park Estate, Henfield Road, Albourne, Hassocks, West Sussex, BN6 9JJ Tel: (01273) 491554 Fax: (01273) 491554 E-mail: furniture@bourneandson.com
Bradley Furniture Kent Ltd, Bradley House, Park Farm Close, Park Farm Industrial Estate, Folkestone, Kent, CT19 5ED Tel: (01303) 850011 Fax: (01303) 244028 E-mail: info@bradleyfurniture.co.uk
Click Display Systems Ltd, Unit 1a Goodson Industrial Mews, Wellington Street, Thame, Oxfordshire, OX9 3BX Tel: (01844) 212574 Fax: (01844) 211899 E-mail: click@netherfield.com
▶ DSC Showcases, Merrill Ville, Enborne Row, Wash Water, Newbury, Berkshire, RG20 0LX Tel: (01635) 34656 Fax: (01635) 34656 E-mail: admin@dscshowcases.co.uk
Lazawood Ltd, 79 Farleigh Road, Warlingham, Surrey, CR6 9EJ Tel: (01883) 622151 Fax: (01883) 624533
Robinson & Gronnow Ltd, 3 Mackenzie Industrial Estate, Bird Hall Lane, Stockport, Cheshire, SK3 0SB Tel: 0161-428 1199 Fax: 0161-428 0635 E-mail: info@robinson-gronnow.co.uk
Timbercraft Cabinet Displays, Abercorn House York Farm Business Centre, Watling Street, Towcester, Northamptonshire, NN12 8EU Tel: (01327) 830663 Fax: (01327) 830963 E-mail: sales@displaycases.co.uk

DISPLAY CASES

Designex Cabinets Ltd, Unit 10, Button Mill Industrial Estate, Lower Mill, Bridgend, Stonehouse, Gloucestershire, GL10 2BB Tel: (01453) 826868 Fax: (01453) 826868 E-mail: sales@designex-cabinets.co.uk
▶ DSC Showcases, Merrill Ville, Enborne Row, Wash Water, Newbury, Berkshire, RG20 0LX Tel: (01635) 34656 Fax: (01635) 34656 E-mail: admin@dscshowcases.co.uk

DISPLAY CASES, MODEL

▶ Lazenby Design Associates, Coach Cottage, Riverside Lane, Summerbridge, Harrogate, North Yorkshire, HG3 4JP Tel: (01423) 781781 E-mail: info@lazenbydesign.com
Uncle Tom's Dolls Houses Factory, 49 Ansty Road, Wyken, Coventry, CV2 3FG Tel: 0247 6278104 Fax: 0247 6278104 E-mail: info@dollshouses.atspace.com

DISPLAY CASES, PLASTIC MODEL

▶ Lazenby Design Associates, Coach Cottage, Riverside Lane, Summerbridge, Harrogate, North Yorkshire, HG3 4JP Tel: (01423) 781781 E-mail: info@lazenbydesign.com

DISPLAY CASES/CONTAINERS/STANDS, FOOD

Dalebrook Supplies Ltd, Eastways Industrial Estate, Witham, Essex, CM8 3UA Tel: (01376) 510101 Fax: (01376) 510153 E-mail: sales@dalebrook.com

DISPLAY COMPONENTS, LED

A & E Marketing Electronics Ltd, 9 Nicol Street, Kirkcaldy, Fife, KY1 1NY Tel: (01592) 261222 Fax: (01592) 261333 E-mail: sales@aemarketing.info
Hero Electronics Ltd, 10 Doolittle Mill Business Park, Froghall Road, Ampthill, Bedford, MK45 2ND Tel: (01525) 405015 Fax: (01525) 402383 E-mail: kelly@heroelec.co.uk
Selectronic Ltd, Book End, Witney, Oxfordshire, OX29 0YE Tel: (01993) 778000 Fax: (01993) 772512 E-mail: sales@selectronic-ltd.co.uk

DISPLAY COMPONENTS, LIQUID CRYSTAL (LCD)

Craft Data, 92 Broad Street, Chesham, Buckinghamshire, HP5 3ED Tel: (01494) 778235 Fax: (01494) 773645 E-mail: sales@craftdata.co.uk
Ginsbury Electronics Ltd, 1 Exeter House, Boufort Court, Rochester, Kent, ME2 4FE Tel: (01634) 298900 Fax: (01634) 290904 E-mail: sales@ginsbury.co.uk
The Herts Meter Co. Ltd, Unit 10 Bury Road, Hatfield, Hertfordshire, AL10 8BJ Tel: (01707) 270404 Fax: (01707) 270152 E-mail: info@hertsmeter.com
Selectronic Ltd, Book End, Witney, Oxfordshire, OX29 0YE Tel: (01993) 778000 Fax: (01993) 772512 E-mail: sales@selectronic-ltd.co.uk

DISPLAY DESIGNERS OR PRODUCERS OR SUPPLIERS

3d Displays Ltd, Upper Brents, Faversham, Kent, ME13 7DR Tel: (01795) 532947 Fax: (01795) 539934 E-mail: info@3ddisplays.co.uk
Ace Signs Group, Oak Tree Road, Binley, Coventry, CV3 2RR Tel: (024) 7660 8200 Fax: (024) 7660 8201 E-mail: info@asg.co.uk
Admiral Display, 18 Seas End Road, Surfleet, Spalding, Lincolnshire, PE11 4DQ Tel: (01775) 680410 Fax: (01775) 680921 E-mail: admiraldisplay@aol.com
Antone Displays Ltd, Wanstead Road, Leicester, LE3 1TR Tel: 0116-232 4700 Fax: 0116-287 8012 E-mail: lucy.orr@antone.co.uk
Arno GB Ltd, Discovery House, 125 Redcliff Street, Bristol, BS1 6HU Tel: 0117-929 2541 Fax: 0117-929 4684 E-mail: display@arno-online.co.uk
Aspect Graphics & Displays, Units 35-36 Bury Business Centre, Kay Street, Bury, Lancashire, BL9 6BU Tel: 0161-763 9955 Fax: 0161-763 9355 E-mail: sales@aspectdisplays.co.uk
Atlas Products, Unit F1 Ash Grove Industrial Park, Heath Place, Bognor Regis, West Sussex, PO22 9SL Tel: (01243) 830324 Fax: (01243) 868404
Bluefrog Design, 21 St Margarets Street, Leicester, LE1 3EB Tel: 0116-253 0612 Fax: 0116-226 5737 E-mail: mail@bluefrogdesign.co.uk
Buzzard Screen Print Ltd, 17 Wing Road, Leighton Buzzard, Bedfordshire, LU7 2NG Tel: (01525) 373527 Fax: (01525) 851260 E-mail: sales@buzzardscreenprint.co.uk
Creative Displays (UK) Ltd, St Helens Way, Thetford, Norfolk, IP24 1HG Tel: (01842) 751503 Fax: (01842) 754060 E-mail: chris@creativedisplaysltd.co.uk
Design Built Exhibitions Ltd, 46 Enfield Industrial Estate, Redditch, Worcestershire, B97 6DE Tel: (01527) 69132 Fax: (01527) 65692
Display Array Ltd, Unit 4 Britannia Industrial Estate, Cherry Holt Road, Bourne, Lincolnshire, PE10 9LA Tel: (01778) 423400 Fax: (01778) 423444 E-mail: display2u@aol.com
Display Containers Ltd, 19b Moor Road, Broadstone, Dorset, BH18 8AZ Tel: (01202) 658838 Fax: (01202) 698284 E-mail: sales@displaycontainers.co.uk
Display Promotions London Ltd, 17 Station Parade, Whitchurch Lane, Edgware, Middlesex, HA8 6RW Tel: (020) 8951 0088 Fax: (020) 8381 3229 E-mail: snb@display.freeserve.co.uk
Eden, 1 Little Dockray, Penrith, Cumbria, CA11 7HL Tel: (01768) 869000 Fax: (01768) 865578 E-mail: david@edengraphics.co.uk
Exhibition Department Ltd, South March, Long March Industrial Estate, Daventry, Northamptonshire, NN11 4PH Tel: (024) 7636 8474 Fax: (01327) 704488 E-mail: sales@theexhibitiondepartment.co.uk
The Exhibition & Interiors Co. Ltd, Station Road, Irthlingborough, Wellingborough, Northamptonshire, NN9 5QE Tel: (01933) 650222 Fax: (01933) 655688 E-mail: sales@exhibitionandinteriors.co.uk
Gordon Signs & Interior Displays Ltd, St. Faiths Road, Norwich, NR6 7BW Tel: (01603) 486142 Fax: (01603) 486172 E-mail: simon@gordonsigns.co.uk
▶ Innov-8 Ltd, Clayfield Industrial Estate, Tickhill Road, Doncaster, South Yorkshire, DN4 8QG Tel: (01302) 310888 Fax: (01302) 855060
Kleerex Group UK Ltd, River Way, Temple Bank, Harlow, Essex, CM20 2DY Tel: (01279) 451103 Fax: (01279) 451104 E-mail: solutions@kleerex.co.uk
Lansa UK Ltd, 4-5 The Big Peg, Warstone Lane, Birmingham, B18 6NA Tel: 0121-233 4588 Fax: 0121-233 4655
Mcrobb Display, 70 Montgomery Street, Edinburgh, EH7 5JA Tel: 0131-556 9633 Fax: 0131-556 7657 E-mail: info@mcrobb.co.uk
Polypal Ltd, Polypal House, Monckton Road Industrial Estate, Wakefield, West Yorkshire, WF2 7AL Tel: (01924) 200015 Fax: (01924) 201160 E-mail: enquiry@polypal.co.uk
Striking Displays UK Ltd, Display House, North Street, Portslade, Brighton, BN41 1DH Tel: (01273) 423623 Fax: (01273) 420424 E-mail: sales@strikingdisplays.com
W Thompson & Son Ltd, 2 Nobel Road, London, N18 3BH Tel: (020) 8807 7576 Fax: (020) 8807 9517 E-mail: wthompsons@lineone.net

DISPLAY DRIVERS

Maxim Integrated Products (UK) Ltd, 612 Reading Road, Winnersh, Wokingham, Berkshire, RG41 5HE Tel: 0118-930 3388 Fax: 0118-900 6400 E-mail: maximdallasdirect_sales@maximhq.com

DISPLAY (ELECTRONIC) PANEL/ MODULE/SYSTEMS MANUFRS

C W Micro-Systems, 11 Mitchell Point, Ensign Way, Southampton, SO31 4RF Tel: (023) 8045 6888 Fax: (023) 8045 6542 E-mail: info@signblazer.com
Whiteley Electronics Ltd, Victoria Street, Mansfield, Nottinghamshire, NG18 5RW Tel: (01623) 415600 Fax: (01623) 420484 E-mail: e-mail@whiteleyelectronics.com

DISPLAY EQUIPMENT/STANDS,

See also headings for particular types

3d Displays Ltd, Upper Brents, Faversham, Kent, ME13 7DR Tel: (01795) 532947 Fax: (01795) 539934 E-mail: info@3ddisplays.co.uk
Bell Packaging Ltd, Barratt Industrial Park, Airport Way, Luton, LU2 9NH Tel: (01582) 459292 Fax: (01582) 450181 E-mail: info@bellpackaging.com
Branston Plastics Ltd, 60 Spencer Street, Birmingham, B18 6DS Tel: 0121-236 8253 Fax: 0121-236 8253
Castle Plastic, Unit 16b Raleigh Hall Industrial Estate, Eccleshall, Stafford, ST21 6JL Tel: (01785) 851842 Fax: (01785) 851370 E-mail: sales@castleplastics.co.uk
Display Promotions London Ltd, 17 Station Parade, Whitchurch Lane, Edgware, Middlesex, HA8 6RW Tel: (020) 8951 0088 Fax: (020) 8381 3229 E-mail: snb@display.freeserve.co.uk
Drakes Display & Shop Aids, 45 Wessex Trade Centre, Ringwood Road, Poole, Dorset, BH12 3PG Tel: (01202) 735858 Fax: (01202) 733979 E-mail: sales@drakesdisplay.co.uk
Exhibition Services Ltd, 6 271 Merton Road, London, SW18 5JS Tel: (020) 8874 1787 Fax: (020) 8874 1587 E-mail: info@exhibitionservices.com
Eyeline Visual Merchandising Ltd, Amsterdam Road, Hull, HU7 0XF Tel: (01482) 824191 Fax: (01482) 824193 E-mail: enquiries@eyeline.co.uk
Fibrous Ltd, Unit E2, Newton Business Park, Talbot Road, Newton, Hyde, Cheshire, SK14 4UQ Tel: (0845) 4508935 Fax: (0845) 4508936 E-mail: info@fibrous.com
Harber Display Ltd, 10 Park Road, Irthlingborough, Wellingborough, Northamptonshire, NN9 5PW Tel: (01933) 624079 Fax: (01933) 460253 E-mail: harbersales@btconnect.com
Harewood Products Ltd, Unit 1, Union Road, The Valley, Bolton, BL2 2DT Tel: (01204) 395730 Fax: (01204) 388018 E-mail: info@adboards.com
Henry Hall Displays Fittings Ltd, Cherrytree, Union Road, Sheffield, S11 9EF Tel: 0114-255 1351 Fax: 0114-250 0006 E-mail: sales@retaildisplay.com
Thomas Hopkinson & Son Ltd, Victor Works, Bolton Hall Road, Bradford, West Yorkshire, BD2 1BQ Tel: (01274) 582056 Fax: (01274) 531328 E-mail: ian@triple-king.co.uk
I D S Plastics, Unit 42 The Acorn Centre, Barry Street, Oldham, OL1 3NE Tel: 0161-627 1054 Fax: 0161-624 4500 E-mail: info@showcasesonline.com
Insignia, 20 Common Road, Bristol, BS15 3LL Tel: (01249) 460006 Fax: 0117-935 3916 E-mail: richard@insignia-signs.co.uk
Kleerex Group UK Ltd, River Way, Temple Bank, Harlow, Essex, CM20 2DY Tel: (01279) 451103 Fax: (01279) 451104 E-mail: solutions@kleerex.co.uk
Klemetric Displays Ltd, Old Airfield Industrial Estate, Warboys Airfield, Warboys, Huntingdon, Cambridgeshire, PE28 2SH Tel: (01487) 824015 Fax: (01487) 823746 E-mail: sales@klemetricdisplays.co.uk
Lemarc Display Systems, 55 Chiswick Avenue, Mildenhall, Bury St. Edmunds, Suffolk, IP28 7AY Tel: (01638) 714909 Fax: (01638) 712500 E-mail: mail@lemarc.co.uk
Merit Display, 8-10 Maudslay Road, Coventry, CV5 8EL Tel: (024) 7667 6700
Nimlok Ltd, Nimlok House, 45 Booth Drive, Park Farm Industrial Estate, Wellingborough, Northamptonshire, NN8 6NL Tel: (01933) 409409 Fax: (01933) 409451 E-mail: info@nimlok.co.uk
R M D (U K) Ltd, Thornham Works, Oozewood Road, Royton, Oldham, OL2 5SQ Tel: 0161-620 4418
Roy John Design, 117 Christchurch Road, Ringwood, Hampshire, BH24 3AQ Tel: (01425) 477644 Fax: (01425) 480254 E-mail: enquiries@royjohndesign.co.uk
Technisteel, 47 Kenilworth Drive, Oadby, Leicester, LE2 5LT Tel: 0116-271 1889 Fax: 0116-271 1889 E-mail: rjadams@technisteel.co.uk
Topfit Ltd, 1 Aston Road North, Birmingham, B6 4DS Tel: 0121-608 6711 Fax: 0121-608 2008 E-mail: sales@e-shopfittings.com
Versatile Fittings Ltd, Bicester Road, Aylesbury, Buckinghamshire, HP19 8AU Tel: (01296) 483481 Fax: (01296) 437596 E-mail: info@versatile-fittings.co.uk
The Visual Partnership, 35 Purdeys Way, Purdeys Industrial Estate, Rochford, Essex, SS4 1ND Tel: (01702) 546539 Fax: (01702) 542490

DISPLAY EQUIPMENT/STANDS, ACRYLIC

Argo Plastics Ltd, Unit 6B, Park Street Industrial Estate, Kidderminster, Worcestershire, DY11 6TN Tel: (01562) 823531 Fax: (01562) 825417
Kolorgraphic Ltd, Unit 3a Stag Industrial Estate, Atlantic Street, Broadheath, Altrincham, Cheshire, WA14 5DW Tel: 0161-928 6014 Fax: 0161-928 7299 E-mail: kolorgraphic01@hotmail.com
Menu Shop, 38 High Street, Warminster, Wiltshire, BA12 9AF Tel: (01985) 217000 Fax: (01985) 218000 E-mail: sales@menushop.co.uk
Systemec, Radford Court Industrial Estate, Nottingham, NG7 3DY Tel: (0870) 4289180 Fax: (0870) 4289186 E-mail: mail@systemec.co.uk

DISPLAY EQUIPMENT/STANDS, CARPET

Creative Displays (UK) Ltd, St Helens Way, Thetford, Norfolk, IP24 1HG Tel: (01842) 751503 Fax: (01842) 754060 E-mail: chris@creativedisplaysltd.co.uk
Thomas Hopkinson & Son Ltd, Victor Works, Bolton Hall Road, Bradford, West Yorkshire, BD2 1BQ Tel: (01274) 582056 Fax: (01274) 531328 E-mail: ian@triple-king.co.uk
T & E Fabrications Ltd, Mucklow Hill, Halesowen, West Midlands, B62 8DL Tel: 0121-585 7600 Fax: 0121-585 7601 E-mail: teltd@btconnect.com

DISPLAY EQUIPMENT/STANDS, FURNITURE

Fairfield Displays, Fairfield House Vernon Drive, Battlefield Enterprise Park, Shrewsbury, SY1 3TF Tel: (01743) 462472 Fax: (01743) 462452

DISPLAY EQUIPMENT/STANDS, JEWELLERY

Lansa UK Ltd, 4-5 The Big Peg, Warstone Lane, Birmingham, B18 6NA Tel: 0121-233 4588 Fax: 0121-233 4655
Lazawood Ltd, 79 Farleigh Road, Warlingham, Surrey, CR6 9EJ Tel: (01883) 622151 Fax: (01883) 624533

DISPLAY EQUIPMENT/STANDS, METAL

A Harvey & Co The Wireworkers Ltd, 2 Stockton End, Sandy, Bedfordshire, SG19 1SB Tel: (01767) 681830 Fax: (01767) 683111 E-mail: sales@harveywire.freeserve.co.uk
A P Engineering (Portsmouth) Ltd, 6a Fitzherbert Spur, Farlington, Portsmouth, PO6 1TT Tel: (023) 9238 4012 Fax: (023) 9237 9454 E-mail: sales@apeng.co.uk
Arrow Display Fittings Ltd, 21 Bartleet Road, Redditch, Worcestershire, B98 0DG Tel: (01527) 527941 Fax: (01527) 510205 E-mail: sales@arrowdisplay.co.uk
Bullet Engineering Ltd, Vale Road, Spilsby, Lincolnshire, PE23 5HE Tel: (01790) 753320 Fax: (01790) 754530
Clark Engineering, 6 Cranborne Industrial Estate, Cranborne Road, Potters Bar, Hertfordshire, EN6 3JN Tel: (01707) 651393 Fax: (01707) 644094
Cotswald Design & Manufacture Ltd, The Daniel Gooch Building, Whitehill Lane, Wootton Bassett, Swindon, SN4 7DB Tel: (01793) 848007 Fax: (01793) 848526 E-mail: heather@ergotec-cdm.co.uk
Creative Displays (UK) Ltd, St Helens Way, Thetford, Norfolk, IP24 1HG Tel: (01842) 751503 Fax: (01842) 754060 E-mail: chris@creativedisplaysltd.co.uk
Crusader Plastics Ltd, Crown Street, Failsworth, Manchester, M35 9BD Tel: 0161-688 6466 Fax: 0161-683 5732 E-mail: geoffkay@crusader-ltd.co.uk
Hobday Ltd, Aston Brook St East, Aston, Birmingham, B6 4RR Tel: 0121-359 4431 Fax: 0121-608 2008
Thomas Hopkinson & Son Ltd, Victor Works, Bolton Hall Road, Bradford, West Yorkshire, BD2 1BQ Tel: (01274) 582056 Fax: (01274) 531328 E-mail: ian@triple-king.co.uk
Kestrel Engineering, 9 Dartmouth Buildings, Fort Fareham Industrial Site, Fareham, Hampshire, PO14 1AH Tel: (01329) 233443 Fax: (01329) 284148 E-mail: alan.s.walker@talk21.com
Lemarc Display Systems, 55 Chiswick Avenue, Mildenhall, Bury St. Edmunds, Suffolk, IP28 7AY Tel: (01638) 714909 Fax: (01638) 712500 E-mail: mail@lemarc.co.uk
Metallon Ltd, Unit D Lea Road Trading Estate, Lea Road, Waltham Abbey, Essex, EN9 1AE Tel: (01992) 715737 Fax: (01992) 767607 E-mail: sales@metallon.co.uk
Middlehurst Ltd, 103 Boyn Valley Road, Maidenhead, Berkshire, SL6 4EA Tel: (01628) 628044 Fax: (01628) 773143 E-mail: office@middlehurstlimited.com
Nova Display, Unit 1, Peckfield Business Park, Phoenix Avenue, Micklefield, Leeds, LS25 4DY Tel: 0113-385 0200 Fax: 0113-385 0201 E-mail: howard@novadisplay.co.uk
▶ Opus Fabrication, Unit 3, Phoenix Works, Windsor Road, Enfield, Redditch, Worcestershire, B97 6DJ Tel: (01527) 68533 Fax: (01527) 68534 E-mail: opus-fab@btconnect.com
Sloane Group (Holdings) Ltd, 2-20 Booth Drive, Park Farm Estate, Wellingborough, Northamptonshire, NN8 6GR Tel: (01933) 401555 Fax: (01933) 400507 E-mail: info@sloanegroup.co.uk
Tameside Metal Components, Dove House, Thorncliffe Wood, Hollingworth, Hyde, Cheshire, SK14 8NJ Tel: (01457) 766300 Fax: (01457) 766300
Two Wests & Elliott Ltd, Carrwood Road, Chesterfield, Derbyshire, S41 9RH Tel: (01246) 451077 Fax: (01246) 260115 E-mail: sales@twowests.co.uk
Universal Display Fittings Co. Ltd, 51 Mortimer Street, London, W1W 8JH Tel: (020) 7580 9471 Fax: (020) 7436 9732 E-mail: info@universaldisplay.co.uk
Versatile Fittings Ltd, Bicester Road, Aylesbury, Buckinghamshire, HP19 8AU Tel: (01296) 483481 Fax: (01296) 437596 E-mail: info@versatile-fittings.co.uk
▶ Walkers Manchester, Crabtree Lane, Manchester, M11 4GU Tel: 0161-223 7814 Fax: 0161-231 7212 E-mail: info@walkersmcr.com

DISPLAY EQUIPMENT/STANDS, PLASTIC

Antone Displays Ltd, Wanstead Road, Leicester, LE3 1TR Tel: 0116-232 4700 Fax: 0116-287 8012 E-mail: lucy.orr@antone.co.uk
Brochure Holders International Ltd, Victor Unit, Earls Colne Business Park, Earls Colne, Colchester, CO6 2NS Tel: (01787) 220700 Fax: (01787) 220701 E-mail: sales@brochureholders.co.uk
Display Matrix, Unit 14, Dixon Business Centre Dixon Road, Bristol, BS4 5QW Tel: 0117-300 9925 Fax: 0117-977 2457 E-mail: info@displaymatrix.co.uk
Durleigh Display Systems, 6 Symons Way, Bridgwater, Somerset, TA6 4DR Tel: (01278) 447447 Fax: (01278) 456376
I D S Plastics, Unit 42 The Acorn Centre, Barry Street, Oldham, OL1 3NE Tel: 0161-627 1054 Fax: 0161-624 4500 E-mail: info@showcasesonline.com
Inca, 12-13 Oaklands Business Park, Ferndale, Mid Glamorgan, CF43 4UG Tel: (01443) 733355 Fax: (01443) 733366
K2 Associates Ltd, 6 Haselmere Industrial Estate, Pig Lane, Bishop's Stortford, Hertfordshire, CM23 3HG Tel: (01279) 508305 Fax: (01279) 755530 E-mail: ken.day@k2a.co.uk
Kleerex Group UK Ltd, River Way, Temple Bank, Harlow, Essex, CM20 2DY Tel: (01279) 451103 Fax: (01279) 451104 E-mail: solutions@kleerex.co.uk
North West Prototypes, The Little Mill, Palatine Street, Denton, Manchester, M34 3LY Tel: 0161-320 5529 Fax: 0161-335 0928
Nova Display, Unit 1, Peckfield Business Park, Phoenix Avenue, Micklefield, Leeds, LS25 4DY Tel: 0113-385 0200 Fax: 0113-385 0201 E-mail: howard@novadisplay.co.uk
P.P.E. Ltd, Horsecroft Rd, The Pinnacles, Harlow, Essex, CM19 5BH Tel: (01279) 412345 Fax: (01279) 419533E-mail: sales@ppe.co.uk
Plastengrave Ltd, Unit 29 77-87 Trafalgar Business Centre, River Road, Barking, Essex, IG11 0JU Tel: (020) 8591 2595 Fax: (020) 8594 0459 E-mail: sales@plastengrave.co.uk
Striking Displays UK Ltd, Display House, North Street, Portslade, Brighton, BN41 1DH Tel: (01273) 423623 Fax: (01273) 420424 E-mail: sales@strikingdisplays.com
Superframe Ltd, The Old Electricity Works, Campfield Road, St. Albans, Hertfordshire, AL1 5HJ Tel: (01727) 865555 Fax: (01727) 865566 E-mail: sales@sf2.co.uk

DISPLAY EQUIPMENT/STANDS, RETAIL TRADE

Axiom Displays Ltd, Mersey Road North, Failsworth, Manchester, M35 9LT Tel: 0161-681 1371 Fax: 0161-683 4641 E-mail: info@axiom-displays.co.uk
R M D (U K) Ltd, Thornham Works, Oozewood Road, Royton, Oldham, OL2 5SQ Tel: 0161-620 4418
Retail Display Solutions, St. Andrew House, St. Andrews Trading Estate, Bridport, Dorset, DT6 3EX Tel: (01308) 459950 Fax: (01308) 424410 E-mail: sales@retaildisplaysolutions.co.uk

DISPLAY EQUIPMENT/STANDS, TUBULAR

Crusader Plastics Ltd, Crown Street, Failsworth, Manchester, M35 9BD Tel: 0161-688 6466 Fax: 0161-683 5732 E-mail: geoffkay@crusader-ltd.co.uk
Displad Ltd, Eton Hill Works, Eton Hill Road, Radcliffe, Manchester, M26 2DL Tel: 0161-723 3125 Fax: 0161-723 3125 E-mail: carpetdisplay@ukonline.co.uk
Lemarc Display Systems, 55 Chiswick Avenue, Mildenhall, Bury St. Edmunds, Suffolk, IP28 7AY Tel: (01638) 714909 Fax: (01638) 712500 E-mail: mail@lemarc.co.uk
Millers Retail Design Ltd, Granby House, Greenwood Street, Salford, M6 6PD Tel: 0161-743 1026 Fax: 0161-743 1598

DISPLAY EQUIPMENT/STANDS, TUBULAR – *continued*

Opto International Ltd, Bayley Street, Stalybridge, Cheshire, SK15 1QQ Tel: 0161-330 9136 Fax: 0161-343 7332 E-mail: enquiry@optoint.co.uk

DISPLAY EQUIPMENT/STANDS, WIRE

Crusader Plastics Ltd, Crown Street, Failsworth, Manchester, M35 9BD Tel: 0161-688 6466 Fax: 0161-683 5732 E-mail: geoffkay@crusader-ltd.co.uk

Gold Bros Ltd, Arches Abc, 408 Ellingfort Road, London, E8 3PA Tel: (020) 8985 7926 Fax: (020) 9898 5729 E-mail: info@goldbros.co.uk

M M C Ltd, 2ND Floor, Guide Bridge Mill, South Street, Ashton-Under-Lyne, Lancashire, OL7 0HU Tel: 0161-343 1740 Fax: 0161-343 1741 E-mail: pats@mmc93.co.uk

Roycott Ltd, Royston Road, Byfleet, West Byfleet, Surrey, KT14 7NY Tel: (01932) 343515 Fax: (01932) 351285 E-mail: info@charlesausten.com

Stoke On Trent Workshops For The Blind, 211 City Road, Stoke-on-Trent, ST4 2PN Tel: (01782) 233900 Fax: (01782) 234900 E-mail: sales@stokeworkshops.co.uk

DISPLAY EQUIPMENT/STANDS, WOODEN

Admiral Display, 18 Seas End Road, Surfleet, Spalding, Lincolnshire, PE11 4DQ Tel: (01775) 680410 Fax: (01775) 680921 E-mail: admiraldisplay@aol.com

Displad Ltd, Eton Hill Works, Eton Hill Road, Radcliffe, Manchester, M26 2DL Tel: 0161-723 3125 Fax: 0161-723 3125 E-mail: carpetdisplay@ukonline.co.uk

Driscoll Bros Group Ltd, 59 Grasmere Road, Gatley, Cheadle, Cheshire, SK8 4RS Tel: 0161-428 2109 Fax: (01625) 548466 E-mail: glynn@driscollbros.co.uk

W Thompson & Son Ltd, 2 Nobel Road, London, N18 3BH Tel: (020) 8807 7576 Fax: (020) 8807 9517 E-mail: wthompsons@lineone.net

DISPLAY FELT

Hardy & Hanson Ltd, Summit Works, Longlands Road, Staincliffe, Dewsbury, West Yorkshire, WF13 4AB Tel: (01924) 462353 Fax: (01924) 457883E-mail: enquiries@hardy-hanson.co.uk

DISPLAY HOOKS/HANGERS

System Marketing Ltd, 249-251 Merton Road, London, SW18 5EB Tel: (020) 8874 8285 Fax: (020) 8874 9325 E-mail: sales@system-marketing.co.uk

UK Point Of Sale Group Ltd, Emery Court, The Embankment Business Park, Heaton Mersey, Stockport, Cheshire, SK4 3GL Tel: 0161-431 4400 Fax: 0161-431 4411 E-mail: info@ukpos.com

▶ Younger Enterprizes, Newton Bank, St. Andrews, Fife, KY16 9TY Tel: (07903) 841590 Fax: (01334) 478905 E-mail: jmdy@sol.co.uk

DISPLAY MODELS, FIGURES AND MANNEQUINS

Adel Rootstein, 9 Beaumont Avenue, London, W14 9LP Tel: (020) 7381 1447 Fax: (020) 7381 3263 E-mail: sales@adelrootstein.co.uk

Alan Graham, Unit 7 Ayr Street, Nottingham, NG7 4FX Tel: 0115-970 1677 Fax: 0115-970 1677 E-mail: alan@agmodelmakers.co.uk

▶ Effigy, 4 Station Road, Thames Ditton, Surrey, KT7 0NR Tel: (020) 8972 9779 Fax: (020) 8972 9779 E-mail: info@effigy.uk.com

I D U Science Museum, 23 Blythe Road, London, W14 0QX Tel: (020) 7610 4074 Fax: (020) 7371 4885

K & M Model Trees, 4 North Street, Beaminster, Dorset, DT8 3DZ Tel: (01297) 21542 Fax: (01308) 363420

Models London Manufacturing Ltd, 160 Dukes Road, London, W3 0SL Tel: (020) 8896 2440 Fax: (020) 8752 1391 E-mail: info@models-london.com

Universal Display Fittings Co. Ltd, 51 Mortimer Street, London, W1W 8JH Tel: (020) 7580 9471 Fax: (020) 7436 9732 E-mail: info@universaldisplay.co.uk

The Visual Partnership, 35 Purdeys Way, Purdeys Industrial Estate, Rochford, Essex, SS4 1ND Tel: (01702) 546539 Fax: (01702) 542490

DISPLAY MODULES, LIQUID CRYSTAL (LCD), THIN FILM TRANSISTOR (TFT)

Arrow Electronics, London Road Campus, London Road, Harlow, Essex, CM17 9NA Tel: (01279) 441144 Fax: (01189) 683801 E-mail: embedded@arrowuk.com

▶ Hire Intelligence Southwest England - Exeter, 40 Southernhay East, Exeter, EX1 1PE Tel: (0800) 0857667 Fax: (0870) 2202752 E-mail: sales@hiresouthwest.co.uk

DISPLAY OR EXHIBITION LIGHTING

B D B Marketing Ltd, D161-162 Fruit & Vegetable Market, New Covent Garden, Vauxall, London, SW8 5LL Tel: (020) 7720 4444 Fax: (020) 7720 4808 E-mail: bryan1brown@hotmail.com

Graylands Trading Co., 38 Sherwood Road, Winnersh, Wokingham, Berkshire, RG41 5NJ Tel: 0118-989 0002 Fax: 0118-989 0003 E-mail: graylands@supernet.com

Hilclare Ltd, Unit 1 Bond Street Industrial Estate, Mancunian Way, Manchester, M12 6HW Tel: 0161-274 3626 Fax: 0161-274 3731 E-mail: sales@hilclare.com

Icon Display, 130-136 Maidstone Road, Sidcup, Kent, DA14 5HS Tel: (020) 8302 4921 Fax: (020) 8302 3971 E-mail: icondisplay@cix.co.uk

Illumination, Unit 7, North Medburn Farm, Watling Street, Elstree, Borehamwood, Hertfordshire, WD6 3AA Tel: (020) 8953 1414 Fax: (020) 8207 3040 E-mail: info@illumelec.co.uk

Klemetric Displays Ltd, Old Airfield Industrial Estate, Warboys Airfield, Warboys, Huntingdon, Cambridgeshire, PE28 2SH Tel: (01487) 824015 Fax: (01487) 823746 E-mail: sales@klemetricdisplays.co.uk

Lightique Ltd, 7 Bayton Way, Exhall, Coventry, CV7 9ER Tel: (024) 7636 5665 Fax: (024) 7636 5520 E-mail: lightique@btinternet.com

Normalite Ltd, Kingsley Street, Leicester, LE2 6DY Tel: 0116-270 0893 Fax: 0116-270 1221 E-mail: sales@normalite.fsnet.co.uk

Remco Signs Ltd, Mundy Street, Ilkeston, Derbyshire, DE7 8DH Tel: 0115-930 7769 Fax: 0115-932 7714 E-mail: sales@remcosigns.com

Sound Tech Ltd, 137 Western Road, Hockley, Birmingham, B18 7QD Tel: 0121-523 6344 Fax: 0121-507 0151 E-mail: chris@soundtech-ltd.freeserve.co.uk

Christopher Wray (Lighting Emporium) Ltd, 600 Kings Road, London, SW6 2YW Tel: (020) 7736 8434 Fax: (020) 7751 8699 E-mail: sales@christopherwray.com

DISPLAY OR EXHIBITION LIGHTING SERVICES INCLUDING HIRE

Event Lighting, 10 Palmerston Close, Kibworth, Leicester, LE8 0JJ Tel: 0116-279 3851

Illumination, Unit 7, North Medburn Farm, Watling Street, Elstree, Borehamwood, Hertfordshire, WD6 3AA Tel: (020) 8953 1414 Fax: (020) 8207 3040 E-mail: info@illumelec.co.uk

J P L Services, 15 High Street, Rampton, Cambridge, CB24 8QE Tel: (01954) 250851 Fax: (01954) 250543

Remco Signs Ltd, Mundy Street, Ilkeston, Derbyshire, DE7 8DH Tel: 0115-930 7769 Fax: 0115-932 7714 E-mail: sales@remcosigns.com

Tega Office, 58 Stockholm Road, Hull, HU7 0XW Tel: (01482) 831032 Fax: (01482) 831331 E-mail: sales@tega.co.uk

DISPLAY PANELS, ADVERTISING ETC

Anderson Spratt Group Holdings, Anderson House, 409 Holywood Road, Belfast, BT4 2GU Tel: (028) 9080 2000 Fax: (028) 9080 2021 E-mail: info@andersonspratt.com

Corrugated Case Co. Ltd, Unit 1, Pilsley Road, Danesmoor, Chesterfield, Derbyshire, S45 9BU Tel: (01246) 860990 Fax: (01246) 860991 E-mail: info@corrugatedcase.com

The Media Shop (Scotland) Ltd, 5 Royal Exchange Square, Glasgow, G1 3AH Tel: 0141-221 0280 Fax: 0141-204 0722 E-mail: info@the-media-shop.co.uk

Morelli Birmingham, 1 Stratford St North, Birmingham, B11 1BY Tel: 0121-772 7100 Fax: 0121-772 7713 E-mail: headoffice@morelli.co.uk

Transigns Display Ltd, Warish Hall, Warish Hall Road, Takeley, Bishop's Stortford, Hertfordshire, CM22 6NZ Tel: (01279) 871566 Fax: (01279) 871967

DISPLAY PANELS/MODULES/ SYSTEMS, LIGHT EMITTING DIODE (LED)

A & E Marketing Electronics Ltd, 9 Nicol Street, Kirkcaldy, Fife, KY1 1NY Tel: (01592) 261222 Fax: (01592) 261333 E-mail: sales@aemarketing.info

Conversion Engineering, 5 Dunsfold Rise, Coulsdon, Surrey, CR5 2ED Tel: (020) 8668 2898 Fax: (020) 8660 8656

E D C Technology, Suite 24, Mountbatten House, Hillcrest, Highgate, London, N6 4HJ Tel: (020) 8341 2689

Jayex Technology Ltd, Unit 13 Sovereign Park, Coronation Road, London, NW10 7QP Tel: (020) 8838 6222 Fax: (020) 8838 3222 E-mail: sales@jayex.com

P R P Optoelectronics Ltd, Woodburcote Way, Towcester, Northamptonshire, NN12 6TF Tel: (01327) 359135 Fax: (01327) 359602 E-mail: sales@prpopto.co.uk

The ST. Albans Meter Company Ltd, Lombardy House, The Ridgeway, St. Albans, Hertfordshire, AL4 9AL Tel: (01727) 899911 Fax: (01727) 899922 E-mail: stalbansmeters@ukgateway.net

Swiss Mimic Co Ltd, 26 Highfield Road, Chertsey, Surrey, KT16 8BU Tel: (01932) 569100 Fax: (01932) 569100 E-mail: swiss.mimic@tiscarly.co.uk

DISPLAY PORTABLE SYSTEMS MANUFRS

Independent Design & Display, Independent, 275 Meanwood Road, Leeds, LS7 2JD Tel: 0113-242 9944 Fax: 0113-242 9669 E-mail: info@independentdesign.co.uk

Oakleaf Graphics, Portland House, Bolsover Business Park, Woodhouse Lane, Bolsover, Chesterfield, Derbyshire, S44 6BD Tel: (01246) 828228 E-mail: sales@oakleafgraphics.co.uk

DISPLAY SCREENS

ADI UK Ltd, Pittman Court, Pittman Way, Fulwood, Preston, PR2 9ZG Tel: (0800) 592346 Fax: (01772) 708201 E-mail: sales@theadigroup.com

Global Display Solutions Ltd, Fairfax House, Cottingley Business Park, Bingley, West Yorkshire, BD16 1PE Tel: (01274) 230150 Fax: (01274) 230144 E-mail: sales@gds.com

DISPLAY SIGNS

A T Free & Co. Ltd, Jackson Street, St. Helens, Merseyside, WA9 1AH Tel: (01744) 22252 Fax: (01744) 453036

Adco Signs, 15 Cleggs Buildings, Bolton, BL1 4AN Tel: (01204) 529167 Fax: (01204) 399214 E-mail: adcoinfo.signs@virgin.net

Angletheme Partnership, Signal House, Charter Way, Macclesfield, Cheshire, SK10 2NF Tel: (01625) 501204 Fax: (01625) 560911 E-mail: enquiries@angletheme.co.uk

Display Ideas Ltd, 30 White Ladies Road, Clifton, Bristol, BS8 2LG Tel: 0117-970 6400 Fax: 0117-970 6401 E-mail: design@displayideas.co.uk

G B Signs, 5b-5c Chesterbank Business Park, River Lane, Saltney, Chester, CH4 8SL Tel: (01244) 682868 Fax: (01244) 683030 E-mail: sales@gbsigns.co.uk

Hardy Signs, Unit 10 Falcon Close, Burton-on-Trent, Staffordshire, DE14 1SG Tel: (01283) 569102 Fax: (01283) 540001 E-mail: sales@hardysigns.co.uk

I S Group, Unit 1 Enterprise House Aber Park, Aber Road, Flint, Clwyd, CH6 5EX Tel: (01352) 792000 Fax: (01352) 792001 E-mail: sales@impactsigns.co.uk

Interplan Sign Systems Ltd, Abbey Road Industrial Estate, Durham, DH1 5HB Tel: 0191-384 0645 Fax: 0191-384 2423 E-mail: sales@interplan-signs.co.uk

Low Cost Signs, 250 Upminster Road North, Rainham, Essex, RM13 9JL Tel: (01708) 500123 Fax: (01708) 500900

Manor Signs, 62 Knighton Lane, Leicester, LE2 8BE Tel: (0116) 283 5007 Fax: (0116) 283 8946

Mida Sign Services UK Ltd, Gatefield House, Blandford Street, Ashton-under-Lyne, Lancashire, OL6 7DW Tel: 0161-830 0600 Fax: 0161-830 0601 E-mail: enquiries@midasignservices.co.uk

Mockridge Labels (Sales) Ltd, Viaduct Works, Cavendish Street, Ashton-under-Lyne, Lancashire, OL6 7QL Tel: 0161-308 2331 Fax: 0161-343 1958 E-mail: mike.graham@mockridge.com

PW Signs, 21 Southgate, Pontefract, West Yorkshire, WF8 1LN Tel: (01977) 701701 Fax: (01977) 701701 E-mail: pwsigns@btconnect.com

The Sign Studio, Coach Fold Works, Haley Hill, Halifax, West Yorkshire, HX3 6ED Tel: (01422) 345179 Fax: (01422) 365400 E-mail: phil.rushworth@msl-signstudio.co.uk

Solito Graphics, 1137 Yardley Wood Road, Birmingham, B14 4LS Tel: 0121-474 4640 Fax: 0121-474 4640

Torbay Signs, Ashfield Road, Torquay, TQ2 6HE Tel: (01803) 605981 Fax: (01803) 605913

Widd Signs, 194 Armley Road, Leeds, LS12 2NB Tel: 0113-279 4144 Fax: 0113-279 7935 E-mail: admin@widdsigns.co.uk

DISPLAY STANDS, *See also headings for particular types*

▶ Graphic Pavement Signs Ltd, Letchworth Garden City, Hertfordshire, SG6 3XH Tel: (01462) 673831 Fax: (01462) 481703 E-mail: mail@posterholders.fsnet.co.uk

▶ Marsel Display Marketing, Marsel House, Belton Road, Silsden, Keighley, West Yorkshire, BD20 0EE Tel: (01535) 650000 Fax: (01535) 650001 E-mail: marsel@marsel.co.uk

DISPLAY TRAYS, JEWELLERY

R M Pugh & Co. Ltd, 35 Hylton Street, Birmingham, B18 6HJ Tel: 0121-554 4283 Fax: 0121-523 8709

DISPLAY UNITS, PORTABLE

▶ Supersine Duramark Ltd, Freemantle Road, Lowestoft, Suffolk, NR33 0EA Tel: (01502) 501234 Fax: (01502) 560620 E-mail: info@ssdm.co.uk

DISPLAYS, 7 SEGMENT

Nicomatic UK Ltd, Unit 8 Campus 5 Third Avenue, Letchworth Garden City, Hertfordshire, SG6 2JF Tel: (01462) 677886 Fax: (01462) 480548 E-mail: sales@nicomatic.co.uk

DISPLAYS, LED, LIGHT PIPES

A & E Marketing Electronics Ltd, 9 Nicol Street, Kirkcaldy, Fife, KY1 1NY Tel: (01592) 261222 Fax: (01592) 261333 E-mail: sales@aemarketing.info

DISPLAYS, LIQUID CRYSTAL (LCD), MAINTENANCE/REPAIR SERVICES

▶ T.J Butler (Electronics) Ltd, Unit 2 Catherine Court, Airfield View, Hawarden Industrial Park, Hawarden, Deeside, Flintshire, CH5 3NU Tel: (0871) 2224230 Fax: (01244) 538438 E-mail: service@tjbutlers.co.uk

DISPLAYS, LIQUID CRYSTAL (LCD), PANEL/MODULE/ SYSTEMS MANUFRS

Hero Electronics Ltd, 10 Doolittle Mill Business Park, Froghall Road, Ampthill, Bedford, MK45 2ND Tel: (01525) 405015 Fax: (01525) 402383 E-mail: kelly@heroelec.co.uk

DISPLAYS, VACUUM FLUORESCENT

Manhattan Skyline Ltd, 5 Bracknell Business Centre, Downmill Road, Bracknell, Berkshire, RG12 1QS Tel: (01344) 307733 Fax: (01344) 307744 E-mail: sales@mansky.co.uk

DISPOSABLE APRONS

▶ Dorset Nursing Supplies Co., 3 Wickham Road, Bournemouth, BH7 6JX Tel: (01202) 425070 Fax: (01202) 418332 E-mail: sales@dorsetnursing.co.uk

DISPOSABLE CATERING PRODUCTS

A & M Associates, Unit 2, Stuart Street, Off Fishwick Street, Rochdale, Lancashire, OL16 5NB Tel: (01706) 710747 Fax: (01706) 710746 E-mail: amasso@zen.co.uk

Kenthorp Supplies Wholesale Ltd, 83 Palmerston Road, Bournemouth, BH1 4HW Tel: (01202) 302030 Fax: (01202) 396000 E-mail: enquiries@kenthorpsupplies.co.uk

▶ R P C Tedeco-Gizeh UK Ltd, Kenfig Industrial Estate, Margam, Port Talbot, West Glamorgan, SA13 2PG Tel: (01656) 746655 Fax: (01656) 743074 E-mail: sales@rpc-tedeco-gizeh.com

Thomas Radcliffe Ltd, Unit 21, White Hoe, Old Castletown Road, Douglas, Isle Of Man, IM2 1QD Tel: (01624) 626767 Fax: (01624) 677337 E-mail: thomasradcliffe@mcb.net

DISPOSABLE CATERING PRODUCTS – *continued*

▶ Reliance Converting Ltd, Salters Lane, Sedgefield, Stockton-on-Tees, Cleveland, TS21 3EE Tel: (01740) 621415 Fax: (01740) 621424
E-mail: sales@relianceconverting.co.uk

▶ Restaurant Supplies Ltd, 10 Kishorn Court, Glenrothes, Fife, KY7 6ES Tel: (01592) 749149 Fax: (01592) 749149
E-mail: sales@restaurantsuppliesltd.com

Unita Packaging Ltd, Unit 15 Bloomsgrove Industrial Estate, Ilkeston Rd, Nottingham, NG7 3JG Tel: 0115-978 6172 Fax: 0115-978 6776 E-mail: sales@unita.co.uk

Welsh Boxes of Swansea Ltd, Bruce Road, Swansea Industrial Estate, Fforestfach, Swansea, SA5 4HX Tel: (01792) 586527 Fax: (01792) 585410
E-mail: sales@welshboxes.co.uk

West Midlands Food Machines, 108 Worcester Road, Kidderminster, Worcestershire, DY10 1JS Tel: (01562) 742592 Fax: (01562) 742592

DISPOSABLE CLEANING WIPES

Bunzl Cleaning & Hygiene Supplies, Bone Lane, Newbury, Berkshire, RG14 5SH Tel: (01635) 528550 Fax: (01635) 528822
E-mail: newbury@bunzlchs.co.uk

Esk Hygeine Supplies Ltd, Saffron Way, Leicester, LE2 6UP Tel: 0116-283 9362
E-mail: sales@eskgroup.co.uk

Multy Abrasives Ltd, First Avenue, Deeside Industrial Park, Deeside, Clwyd, CH5 2NU Tel: (01244) 288261 Fax: (01244) 280305
E-mail: clare@multyabrasives.co.uk

DISPOSABLE CONTACT LENSES

▶ OneStopContactLenses, P O Box 5029, London, W1A 7ET Tel: 0207 323 9704 Fax: 0207 636 0281
E-mail: enquiries@onestopcontactlenses.co.uk

DISPOSABLE FAST FOOD PACKAGING

▶ Middlewich Food Trays Ltd, 4 Montgomery Close, Parkgate Industrial Estate, Knutsford, Cheshire, WA16 8XW Tel: (01565) 652668 Fax: (01565) 633136

Nu-Line Marketing Ltd, Access Business Centre, First Way, Wembley Stadium Industrial Estate, Wembley, Middlesex, HA9 0JD Tel: (020) 8900 8660 Fax: (020) 8900 0606
E-mail: sales@nu-line.com

DISPOSABLE KITCHEN GREASE AIR FILTERS

C P L Filters, Unit 1-2 Alma Industrial Estate, Regent Street, Rochdale, Lancashire, OL12 0HQ Tel: (01706) 642823 Fax: (01706) 642537
E-mail: dorothy.clarke@pure-filters.com

Vianen Ventilation Systems, Coten House, 59-63 Coten End, Warwick, CV34 4NU Tel: (01926) 496644 Fax: (01926) 493977
E-mail: info@vianen.co.uk

DISPOSABLE LABORATORY PRODUCTS

Cellpath plc, Unit 66 Mochdre Industrial Estate, Mochdre, Newtown, Powys, SY16 4LE Tel: (01686) 611333 Fax: (01686) 622946
E-mail: sales@cellpath.co.uk

Medicell International Ltd, 239 Liverpool Road, London, N1 1LX Tel: (020) 7607 2295 Fax: (020) 7700 4156
E-mail: all@medicell.co.uk

Porvair Sciences Ltd, 6 Shepperton Business Park, Govett Avenue, Shepperton, Middlesex, TW17 8BA Tel: (01932) 224539 Fax: (01932) 254393 E-mail: int.sales@porvair.com

Ross Lab plc, Ross Lab House, Fence Avenue Industrial Estate, Macclesfield, Cheshire, SK10 1LT Tel: (01625) 610077 Fax: (01625) 619877 E-mail: sales@rosslab.com

DISPOSABLE MEDICAL PRODUCTS, *See Hospital Disposable Products*

DISPOSABLE MEDICAL/DENTAL/ SURGICAL GOWNS/DRAPES

B D S Ltd, Grangestone Industrial Estate, Ladywell Avenue, Girvan, Ayrshire, KA26 9PL Tel: (01465) 714848 Fax: (01465) 713857
E-mail: contact@bdf.ltd.uk

Kappler Europe Ltd, Unit 1 Crown Farm Way, Forest Town, Mansfield, Nottinghamshire, NG19 0FT Tel: (01623) 416200 Fax: (01623) 416250 E-mail: sales@kappler.com

Medipost (UK) Ltd, 17 Surrey Close, Granby Industrial Estate, Weymouth, Dorset, DT4 9TY Tel: (01305) 760750 Fax: (01305) 776917
E-mail: info@medipost.co.uk

Smith Medical Ltd, 52 Grayshill Road, Westfield, Cumbernauld, Glasgow, G68 9HQ Tel: (01236) 737138 Fax: (01236) 738503
E-mail: info@smiths-medical.com

Sterimedix Ltd, Unit 6/7, Kingfisher Business Park, Arthur Street, Redditch, Worcestershire, B98 8LG Tel: (01527) 501480 Fax: (01527) 501491 E-mail: sales@sterimedix.com

DISPOSABLE MEDICAL/DENTAL/ SURGICAL SUPPLIES MANUFRS

3M Health Care Ltd, 3M House, Morley Street, Loughborough, Leicestershire, LE11 1EP Tel: (01509) 611611 Fax: (01509) 613061
E-mail: jsmith123@mmm.com

Bibby Sterlin Ltd, Pengam Road, Aberbargoed, Bargoed, Mid Glamorgan, CF81 9FW Tel: (01443) 830830 Fax: (01443) 821545

Bullen Health Care Group, 85-87 Kempston Street, Liverpool, L3 8HE Tel: 0151-207 1239 Fax: 0151-207 3804E-mail: info@bullens.com

Consolidated Supply Services, Unit 7, Hastingwood Business Centre, Hastingwood, Harlow, Essex, CM17 9GD Tel: (01279) 641131 Fax: (01279) 635438

G E Bridge & Co. Ltd, 123-125 Old Christchurch Road, Bournemouth, BH1 1HF Tel: (01202) 204802 Fax: (01202) 204800

Medipost (UK) Ltd, 17 Surrey Close, Granby Industrial Estate, Weymouth, Dorset, DT4 9TY Tel: (01305) 760750 Fax: (01305) 776917
E-mail: info@medipost.co.uk

Mident Trading Co., Remmets House, Lord Street, Bury, Lancashire, BL9 0RE Tel: 0161-761 6060 Fax: 0161-763 1005
E-mail: midentuk@aol.com

Navrish Ltd, Navrish Nivas, 17 Bishops Close, Mays Lane, Arkley, Barnet, Hertfordshire, EN5 2QH Tel: (020) 8440 0803 Fax: (020) 8441 6813 E-mail: sales@navrish.co.uk

New Splint Ltd, Unitech House, Units B1 B2, Bond Close, Kingsland Buisiness Park, Basingstoke, Hampshire, RG24 8PZ Tel: (01256) 365480 Fax: (01256) 365486
E-mail: sales.dept@newsplint.co.uk

Pelican Healthcare Ltd, Cardiff Business Park, Cardiff, CF14 5WF Tel: (029) 2074 7000 Fax: (029) 2074 7001
E-mail: mailroom@pelicanhealthcare.co.uk

Plandent, Summit House, Cranborne Road, Potters Bar, Hertfordshire, EN6 3EE Tel: (01707) 822400 Fax: (01707) 649901

R J Supplies, Wellington House, 65 Wellington Street, Stapleford, Nottingham, NG9 7BE Tel: 0115-939 3933

Rocialle Medical Ltd, Dales Manor Business Park, Grove Road, Sawston, Cambridge, CB22 3TJ Tel: (01223) 495700 Fax: (01223) 495701 E-mail: info@rocialle.com

Smith Medical Ltd, 52 Grayshill Road, Westfield, Cumbernauld, Glasgow, G68 9HQ Tel: (01236) 737138 Fax: (01236) 738503
E-mail: info@smiths-medical.com

Vygon UK Ltd, Bridge Road, Cirencester, Gloucestershire, GL7 1PT Tel: (01285) 657051 Fax: (01285) 650293
E-mail: vygon@vygon.co.uk

DISPOSABLE NON WOVEN MACHINERY

C M Machinery, 50 Seagoe Industrial Area, Portadown, Craigavon, County Armagh, BT63 5QE Tel: (028) 3833 3341 Fax: (028) 3833 0915 E-mail: info@cmmachinery.co.uk

DISPOSABLE PAPER CUPS

Cherry Hinton Catering Supplies, 8 Home End, Fulbourn, Cambridge, CB21 5BS Tel: (01223) 506005 Fax: (01223) 506386

Edsol Ltd, Edsol House, Meanwood Road, Buslingthorpe Green, Leeds, LS7 2HG Tel: 0113-262 1122 Fax: 0113-262 3957
E-mail: info@edwardsofleeds.com

Falkingham & Taylor (Vending) Ltd, 40-50 New Cleveland St, Hull, HU8 7EX Tel: (01482) 320600 Fax: (01482) 585766
E-mail: sales@st-vending.com

Gaffar Packaging Ltd, 65 Cobden Street, Leicester, LE1 2LB Tel: 0116-253 7766 Fax: 0116-229 0290
E-mail: gaffarpackaging@aol.com

DISPOSABLE PAPER PRODUCTS MANUFRS

A S D International, PO Box 54, Bridgend, Mid Glamorgan, CF31 4YP Tel: (01656) 880013 Fax: (01656) 880865

▶ Able Packaging Group Ltd, Firmin Coates Indust Estate, Middlewich Road, Byley, Middlewich, Cheshire, CW10 9NT Tel: (01606) 836161 Fax: (01606) 836970
E-mail: info@ablepackaging.co.uk

Allchem Midlands Ltd, Wingate Close, Nottingham, NG8 4LP Tel: 0115-929 5258 Fax: 0115-929 2379

Amico Packaging Supplies, 4 Robinson Road, Leicester, LE5 4NS Tel: 0116-276 2786 Fax: 0116-276 9786

Amscan International Ltd, Brudenell Drive, Brinklow, Milton Keynes, MK10 0DA Tel: (01908) 288500 Fax: (01908) 288501
E-mail: sales@amscan-uk.co.uk

B & C Supplies Ltd, Unit 1 Burnham Way, London, SE26 5AG Tel: (020) 8776 5757 Fax: (020) 8776 5750
E-mail: sales@bandcsupplies.co.uk

Bell Brush Co., 286 Alma Road, Enfield, Middlesex, EN3 7BB Tel: (020) 8804 4144 Fax: (020) 8804 4235
E-mail: sales@bellbrush.com

▶ F. Bender Ltd, Gresford Industrial Park, Chester Road, Wrexham, LL12 8LX Tel: (01978) 855661 Fax: (01978) 855101
E-mail: info@benders.co.uk

Blanchet & Co., G7-G9 Blackpole Trading Estate East, Blackpole Road, Worcester, WR3 8SG Tel: (01905) 757144 Fax: (01905) 755705

Blue Diamond Hygiene Supplies, 104 Havest Lane, Sheffield, S3 8EG Tel: 0114-278 7777

C P D Ltd, Copenhagen Road, Suttonfields Industrial Estate, Hull, HU7 0XQ Tel: (01482) 625625 Fax: (01482) 625626
E-mail: info@cpd-clean.co.uk

Clean Solutions, Unit 1 Kenwood Road, Stockport, Cheshire, SK5 6PH Tel: 0161-947 9947 Fax: 0161-947 9940
E-mail: enquiries@cleansolutions.co.uk

Cotswold Industrial Products, Westmead Drive, Westmead Industrial Estate, Swindon, SN5 7YT Tel: (01793) 610880 Fax: (01793) 616941 E-mail: sales@cpkgg.com

Disposable Supplies, Movement House Soho Mills, London Road, Wallington, Surrey, SM6 7HN Tel: (020) 8773 2692 Fax: (020) 8669 1907
E-mail: sales@disposablesupplies.co.uk

Duni Ltd, Chester Road, Preston Brook, Runcorn, Cheshire, WA7 3FR Tel: (01928) 712377 Fax: (01928) 754580

Durham Tissue Supplies, Unit 1l The Dairies, Durham Road, Annfield Plain, Stanley, County Durham, DH9 7SR Tel: (01207) 237476 Fax: (01207) 237476
E-mail: durhamtissuesupplies@btinternet.com

East Anglia Cleaning & Safety Supplies, Langton Green, Eye, Suffolk, IP23 7HL Tel: (01379) 871110 Fax: (01379) 871160
E-mail: workwearunderstoreeastanglia@hotmail.com

Edicos Ltd, Unit 8-9 Cromwell Industrial Estate, Staffa Road, London, E10 7QZ Tel: (020) 8539 6102 Fax: (020) 8539 8061

Elof Hansson Pulp & Paper Ltd, Unit 22 Carlson Court, 116 Putney Bridge Road, London, SW15 2NQ Tel: 0845 5314057 Fax: (020) 8871 4689 E-mail: info@uk.elofhansson.com

Gaffar Packaging Ltd, 65 Cobden Street, Leicester, LE1 2LB Tel: 0116-253 7766 Fax: 0116-229 0290
E-mail: gaffarpackaging@aol.com

Georgia Pacific GB Ltd, Mansell Way, Horwich, Bolton, BL6 6JL Tel: (01204) 673300 Fax: (01204) 673301 E-mail:

Green of Lincoln, Pyke Road, Lincoln, LN6 3QS Tel: (01522) 500006

Hygenitec Disposables, Unit G7/9, Blackpole Trading Estate East, Worcester, WR3 8SG Tel: (01905) 755535 Fax: (01905) 755705

Icp Hygiene, 14 Ronald Close, Woburn Road Industrial Estate, Kempston, Bedford, MK42 7SH Tel: (01234) 843666 Fax: (01234) 843636 E-mail: icpsales@jangro.net

Industrial Supplies Wrayson Ltd, 3-4 Brookfield Road, Cheadle, Cheshire, SK8 2PN Tel: 0161-428 0707 Fax: 0161-428 1304
E-mail: sales@wrayson.com

Kerr & Noble Ltd, Welford Barn, Binton Road, Welford On Avon, Stratford-Upon-Avon, Warwickshire, CV37 8PT Tel: (01789) 751075 Fax: (01789) 751089

Kimberly Clark Ltd, 1 Tower View, Kings Hill, West Malling, Kent, ME19 4HA Tel: (01732) 594000 Fax: (01732) 594001

King UK Ltd, Unis 1-3 Conquest Industrial Estate, Knight Road, Rochester, Kent, ME2 2AL Tel: (01634) 290913 Fax: (01634) 716739

Kingsley, Tregoniggie Industrial Estate, Falmouth, Cornwall, TR11 4SN Tel: (01326) 373531 Fax: (01326) 372965
E-mail: kingsley_falmouth@hotmail.com

L P C Properties Ltd, Waterside Road, Hamilton Industrial Park, Leicester, LE5 1TZ Tel: 0116-246 0888 Fax: 0116-246 0222
E-mail: info@lpcgroup.co.uk

Lindisposables Ltd, King Street, Kirton, Boston, Lincolnshire, PE20 1HZ Tel: (01205) 724444 Fax: (01205) 722818

Lo Cost Packaging Ltd, 32 Stephenson Street, London, E16 4SA Tel: (020) 7474 3786 Fax: (020) 7474 5786

Mcnulty Wray, 4-6 Bypass Park Estate, Sherburn in Elmet, Leeds, LS25 6EP Tel: (01977) 681133 Fax: (01977) 681177
E-mail: sales@mcnultywray.co.uk

Mid Warwickshire Cleaning Supplies Ltd, Budbrooke Road Industrial Estate, Budbrooke Road, Budbrooke Industrial Estate, Warwick, CV34 5WQ Tel: (01926) 497272 Fax: (01926) 408407
E-mail: sales@mwcleaningsupplies.co.uk

Millwood Marketing, Fivefield House, Bennetts Road, Keresley End, Coventry, CV7 8HX Tel: (024) 7633 1433 Fax: (024) 7633 5663

Neatawash Laundriy, Boothen Green, Stoke-on-Trent, ST4 4BJ Tel: (01782) 413502 Fax: (01782) 747130
E-mail: service@neatawash.co.uk

P C S Amlico Ltd, Wakefield Commercial Park, Bridge Road, Horbury, Wakefield, West Yorkshire, WF4 5NW Tel: (01924) 280130 Fax: (01924) 280018
E-mail: info@pcsamlico.co.uk

Paramount Catering Disposables Ltd, 29 Byron Road, Wealdstone, Harrow, Middlesex, HA3 7SY Tel: (020) 8427 5617

Pollards Woodworking Machines Of Switzerland Ltd, 49 Aylesbury Street, Bletchley, Milton Keynes, MK2 2BQ Tel: (01908) 644877 Fax: (01908) 271552
E-mail: sales@pollards.co.uk

R J Supplies, Wellington House, 65 Wellington Street, Stapleford, Nottingham, NG9 7BE Tel: 0115-939 3933

Stadium Disposables Ltd, 161-162 Dukes Road, Acton, London, W3 0SL Tel: (020) 8993 7686 Fax: (0845) 450 0694

Staples Disposables Ltd, East Road, Sleaford, Lincolnshire, NG34 7EQ Tel: (01529) 411600 Fax: (01529) 411607
E-mail: admin@staplesdisposables.com

Swan Mill Holdings Ltd, Swan Mill, Goldsel Road, Swanley, Kent, BR8 8EU Tel: (01322) 665566 Fax: (01322) 666460
E-mail: sales@swantex.com

Thamesmead Business Services Ltd, 29 Pomeroy Street, London, SE14 5BW Tel: (020) 7639 0348 Fax: (020) 7639 3646
E-mail: info@thamesmeadonline.co.uk

Viceroy Trading Co. Ltd, 67 St. Johns Road, Hemel Hempstead, Hertfordshire, HP1 1QG Tel: (01442) 239770 Fax: (01442) 239124
E-mail: vtcltd@tesco.net

W K Thomas & Co. Ltd, Mount House, Mount Road, Chessington, Surrey, KT9 1HY Tel: (020) 8391 2211 Fax: (020) 8391 2980
E-mail: info@wkthomas.com

DISPOSABLE PLASTIC CUPS

Autobar Packaging & Veriplast International, Dragonville Industrial Estate, Durham, DH1 2RL Tel: 0191-386 5171 Fax: 0191-386 4429

B B P Marketing Ltd, Lowland Works, Lowland Road, Mirfield, West Yorkshire, WF14 8LY Tel: (01924) 480393 Fax: (01924) 480632
E-mail: sales@bb-plastics.co.uk

Central Catering Supplies, 140 Wood Street, Rugby, Warwickshire, CV21 2SP Tel: (01788) 546547 Fax: (01788) 565180
E-mail: sales@centralcatering.co.uk

Coffeeman Disposables, Unit 5 Endeavour Park, 11 Witney Road, Poole, Dorset, BH17 0GJ Tel: (01202) 684111 Fax: (01202) 685111
E-mail: sales@coffeeman.co.uk

Key Catering plc, 33-34 Eastbury Road, London, E6 6GP Tel: (020) 7511 4100 Fax: (020) 7511 0417 E-mail: sales@keycatering.co.uk

Solo Europe, Tower Close, Huntingdon, Cambridgeshire, PE29 7BZ Tel: (01480) 459413 Fax: (01480) 459274
E-mail: sales@soloeurope.co.uk

DISPOSABLE PLASTIC PRODUCTS

Alpha Packaging, Gooch, Didcot, Oxfordshire, OX11 7PR Tel: (01235) 511500 Fax: (01235) 510543
E-mail: alpha.packaging@btconnect.com

Ashwood, Crown House, Home Gardens, Dartford, DA1 1DZ Tel: (0845) 3700222 Fax: (0845) 3700223
E-mail: sales@ashwood.biz

Swiss Pack Ltd, 312a London Road, Waterlooville, Hampshire, PO7 7DU Tel: (023) 9224 0200 Fax: (023) 9224 0288
E-mail: sales@swisspack.co.uk

www.throwitaway.com, 211 Winchester Road, Basingstoke, Hampshire, RG21 8YH Tel: (07887) 993202
E-mail: sales@throwitaway.com

DISPOSABLE PLASTIC TABLEWARE

Europlus Mouldings, Unit 1a Bilston Key Industrial Estate, Oxford Street, Bilston, West Midlands, WV14 7DW Tel: (01902) 404852 Fax: (01902) 409354
E-mail: nick@euro-plas.com

Herald Marketing Ltd, 174 Billet Road, London, E17 5DX Tel: (020) 8507 7900 Fax: (020) 8507 2914

Linpac Plastics, Wakefield Road, Featherstone, Pontefract, West Yorkshire, WF7 5DE Tel: (01977) 692111 Fax: (01977) 692450

Plastic Development Techniques Ltd, Lyon Way, St. Albans, Hertfordshire, AL4 0LB Tel: (01727) 866317 Fax: (01727) 847060

Plastico Ltd, 100 Morden Road, Mitcham, Surrey, CR4 4DA Tel: (020) 8646 0456 Fax: (020) 8646 0500 E-mail: sales@plastico.co.uk

DISPOSABLE RESPIRATORY PRODUCTS

Wise Worksafe, 3 Parr Road, Stanmore, Middlesex, HA7 1PZ Tel: (020) 8381 1811 Fax: (020) 8381 1827

DISPUTE RESOLUTION

▶ Compromitto, 151 West George St, Glasgow, G2 2JJ Tel: 0141 2284737
▶ Soma Contract Services Ltd, 6 The Green, Dunchurch, Rugby, Warwickshire, CV22 6NX Tel: (01788) 817811 Fax: (01788) 817282 E-mail: maggieholman@somacontracts.co.uk

DISTILLERS, *See also headings for particular types*

Allied Distillers Ltd, Miltonduff Distillery, Elgin, Morayshire, IV30 8TQ Tel: (01343) 547433 Fax: (01343) 548802
Ben Nevis Distillery Fort William Ltd, Lochy Bridge, Fort William, Inverness-Shire, PH33 6TJ Tel: (01397) 700200 Fax: (01397) 702768 E-mail: colin.ross@bennevis.co.uk
G & J Greenall, Loushers Lane, Causeway Distillery, Warrington, WA4 6RY Tel: (01925) 650111 Fax: (01925) 414445 E-mail: sales@gjgreenall.com
Glen Moray Distillery, 1 Glenmoray Distillery Cottages, Elgin, Morayshire, IV30 1YE Tel: (01343) 542577 Fax: (01343) 546195 E-mail: edodson@glenmorangieplc.co.uk
J. & G. Grant, Glenfarclas Distillery, Ballindalloch, Banffshire, AB37 9BD Tel: (01807) 500209 Fax: (01807) 500234 E-mail: enquiries@glenfarclas.co.uk
J & A Mitchell Co. Ltd, Springbank Distillery, Well Close, Campbeltown, Argyll, PA28 6ET Tel: (01586) 552085 Fax: (01586) 553215 E-mail: info@jandamitchell.com
D. Johnston & Co. (Laphroaig) Ltd, Laphroaig Distillery, Laphroaig, Port Ellen, Isle Of Islay, PA42 7DU Tel: (01496) 302418 Fax: (01496) 302496 E-mail: robin.shields@adsweu.com
Morrison Bowmore Distillers Ltd, Bowmore Distilleries, School Street, Bowmore, Isle of Islay, PA43 7JS Tel: (01496) 810441 Fax: (01496) 810757 E-mail: emailinfo@morrisonbowmore.com
V & S Plymouth Ltd, Black Friars Distillery, Southside Street, Plymouth, PL1 2LQ Tel: (01752) 665292 Fax: (01752) 220062 E-mail: shaun@plymouthgin.com
Whyte & Mackay, Dalmore House, 310 St. Vincent Street, Glasgow, G2 5RG Tel: 0141-248 5771 Fax: 0141-221 1993

DISTILLERS YEAST

Mauri Products Ltd, Stockholm Road, Sutton Fields Industrial Estate, Hull, HU7 0XW Tel: (01482) 833133 Fax: (01482) 838460 E-mail: sue.fox@mauri.co.uk

DISTILLERS, FRESH WATER

▶ Bushy Tail Ltd, Staveley Mill Yard, Back Lane, Staveley, Kendal, Cumbria, LA8 9LR Tel: (01539) 822244 Fax: 0870 8362158

DISTILLERY PLANT AND EQUIPMENT

Brewing-Solutions Co UK Ltd, Unit 31, Osborne Mill Osborne Street, Oldham, OL9 6QQ Tel: 0161-622 1603 Fax: 0161-622 1662 E-mail: info@brewing-solutions.co.uk
McMillan Ltd, Prestonpans Industrial Estate, Mid Road, Prestonpans, East Lothian, EH32 9JB Tel: (01875) 811110 Fax: (01875) 814022 E-mail: sales@mcmillanltd.co.uk

DISTRIBUTION AGENTS OR SERVICES

1st Engravers & Trophies, Wimbledon Station, London, SW19 7NL Tel: (020) 8946 9037 Fax: (020) 8949 3330
A Clarke & Co Smethwick Ltd, Union Road, Oldbury, West Midlands, B69 3ER Tel: 0121-552 2854 Fax: 0121-552 6385 E-mail: barry@clarketransport.co.uk
A E Parker Ltd, Terminus Road, Chichester, West Sussex, PO19 8TX Tel: (01243) 783319 Fax: (01243) 532617 E-mail: transport@parkerltd.co.uk
▶ A & T Distribution, 19 Wainman Road, Peterborough, PE2 7BU Tel: (01733) 231005
Air Conditioning Accessories, 105 Ash Road, Sutton, Surrey, SM3 9LA Tel: (020) 8288 1181 Fax: (020) 8288 1185
Alarm Doctor Ltd, 59 Hempstalls Lane, Newcastle, Staffordshire, ST5 0SN Tel: (01782) 633532
Alpine Storage Ltd, West Road, Old Hooton Airfield, Hooton, Ellesmere Port, CH65 1BR Tel: 0151-327 5651 Fax: 0151-327 7870 E-mail: alpine@mersinet.co.uk
Andrew Johnson Knudtzon, Boulevard, Hull, HU3 4DY Tel: (01482) 326873 Fax: (01482) 327934 E-mail: info@ajkltd.co.uk
Anixter Industrial - Nottingham, Fastener House, Queens Bridge Road, Sheriffs Way, Nottingham, NG2 1NB Tel: 0115-986 0127 Fax: 0115-986 2574
Bakers Farm Feeds, Bakers Farm, Coat, Martock, Somerset, TA12 6AR Tel: (01935) 823417
Bewley's Coffee Man, 5 Mill Paddock, Letcombe Regis, Wantage, Oxfordshire, OX12 9JE Tel: (01235) 764145 Fax: (01235) 764145
▶ Bibby Distribution Services Ltd, 7 Yeadon Airport Industrial Estate, Harrogate Road, Yeadon, Leeds, LS19 7WP Tel: 0113-250 6787 Fax: 0113-239 1293 E-mail: info@bibbydist.co.uk
Blinds Wholesale, 7 Pound Close, Great Oakley, Corby, Northamptonshire, NN18 8JA Tel: (01536) 745575 Fax: (01536) 460369
Brown Bros Wines Europe Ltd, Ray Mead Road, Maidenhead, Berkshire, SL6 8NJ Tel: (01628) 776446 Fax: (01628) 776136
Burton Distribution Ltd, 1 Brewster Place, Riverside Business Park, Irvine, Ayrshire, KA11 5DD Tel: (01294) 277766 Fax: (01294) 315381
▶ Calderdale Distribution Ltd, Unit 3A Royds Mill, Royd Business Park, Dye House Lane, Brighouse, West Yorkshire, HD6 1LL Tel: (01484) 722011
Cavalier Of Brighton, 9-11 Nevill Road, Rottingdean, Rottingdean, Brighton, BN2 7HH Tel: (01273) 309224 Fax: (01273) 306321 E-mail: cavalierofbrighton@tiscali.co.uk
Chandis Ltd, 5 Great Union Road, St. Helier, Jersey, JE2 3YA Tel: (01534) 736401 Fax: (01534) 768442 E-mail: admin@chandis.com
Christian Salvesen P.L.C., Salvesen House, Lodge Way, Lodge Farm Industrial Estate, Northampton, NN5 7SL Tel: (01604) 737100
Churchills, 55 Hazell Close, Clevedon, Avon, BS21 5DW Tel: (01275) 341325 Fax: (01275) 341325
Clugston Distribution Services, Brigg Road, Scunthorpe, South Humberside, DN16 1BB Tel: (01724) 855029 Fax: (01724) 270240 E-mail: andrew.hansed@clugston.co.uk
Collectors Cellar, 11 Hencotes, Hexham, Northumberland, NE46 2EQ Tel: (01434) 601392 Fax: (01434) 601392 E-mail: sales@collectorscellar.co.uk
Complete, Midland House, London Road, Chesterton, Newcastle, Staffordshire, ST5 7JB Tel: (01782) 562249 Fax: (01782) 566612
▶ D H L, Western Avenue, Western Docks, Southampton, SO15 0HH Tel: (023) 8077 2200 Fax: (023) 8078 1111
Danish Bacon Co. P.L.C., Manors Industrial Estate, Manors Avenue, Ilkeston, Derbyshire, DE7 8EF Tel: 0115-932 5041 Fax: 0115-930 7854
Exel, McKinney Industrial Estate, Mallusk, Newtownabbey, County Antrim, BT36 8YZ Tel: (028) 9084 3481 Fax: (028) 9083 3153 E-mail: pam.millar@dhl.co.uk
Exel Freight Management UK Ltd, Great South West Road, Feltham, Middlesex, TW14 8NE Tel: (020) 8750 7000 Fax: (020) 8890 8444
Furnell Transport, Enterprise House, Maxted Road, Hemel Hempstead, Hertfordshire, HP2 7BT Tel: (01442) 212744 Fax: (01442) 255244 E-mail: sales@furnell.com
Geodis Overseas (U K) Ltd, PO Box 92, High Wycombe, Buckinghamshire, HP12 3TW Tel: (01494) 446541 Fax: (01494) 446329 E-mail: hwcustomerservies@geodisuk.com
Geoffrey Sumpter, Barton End House, Barton End, Horsley, Stroud, Gloucestershire, GL6 0QQ Tel: (01453) 833883 Fax: (01453) 833883
George Hammond plc, Hammond House, Limekiln Street, Dover, Kent, CT17 9EE Tel: (01304) 201201 Fax: (01304) 240374 E-mail: georgehammond@p.plc.uk
Gluten Free Foods Ltd, Unit 270 Centennial Park, Centennial Avenue, Elstree, Borehamwood, Hertfordshire, WD6 3SS Tel: (020) 8953 4444 Fax: (020) 8953 8285 E-mail: info@glutenfree-foods.co.uk
Glyn Thomas, Hendy Uchaf Farm, The Werm, Gowerton, Swansea, SA4 3NA Tel: (01792) 873241 Fax: (01792) 873989
Goddard Warehousing Ltd, Compton House, Furnace Lane, Finedon, Wellingborough, Northamptonshire, NN9 5NY Tel: (01536) 726060 Fax: (01536) 726006 E-mail: admin@goddardwarehousing.com
H W Coates Ltd, Main Street, Cosby, Leicester, LE9 1UW Tel: 0116-284 8403 Fax: 0116-275 0417
Hales, Hammond Road, Knowsley Industrial Park, Liverpool, L33 7UL Tel: 0151-546 5249 Fax: 0151-545 1010 E-mail: deb@halestrans.u-net.com
Hitek Electronic Materials Ltd, 15 Wentworth Road, Scunthorpe, South Humberside, DN17 2AX Tel: (01724) 851678 Fax: (01724) 280586 E-mail: sales@hitek-ltd.co.uk
IMG Industrial Maintenance Group Ltd, Unit M Riverside Industrial Estate, Fazeley, Tamworth, Staffordshire, B78 3RW Tel: (01827) 283322 Fax: (01827) 250143
J E Haith Ltd, Park Street, Cleethorpes, South Humberside, DN35 7LX Tel: (01472) 357515 Fax: (01472) 242883E-mail: sales@haith.com
J H Ingle Ltd, 74 Barkston House, Croydon Street, Leeds, LS11 9RS Tel: 0113-243 0239 Fax: 0113-242 6901 E-mail: jhingle@aol.com
Jim Brackenridge Transport Ltd, Unit 1 Dalcross Industrial Estate, Inverness, IV2 7XB Tel: (01667) 462999 Fax: (01667) 462788 E-mail: robert@jbt.co.uk
Kuehne & Nagel UK Ltd, Old Bath Road, Colnbrook, Slough, SL3 0NW Tel: (01895) 552000 Fax: (01753) 762401
Lenham Storage Ltd, Ham Lane, Lenham, Maidstone, Kent, ME17 2LH Tel: (01622) 858441 Fax: (01622) 850469 E-mail: info@lenhamstorage.co.uk
Lenham Storage Southern Ltd, Fyfield Road, Weyhill, Andover, Hampshire, SP11 8DL Tel: (01264) 772166 Fax: (01264) 773431 E-mail: administration@lenhamstoragesouthern.co.uk
Lloyds Pharmacy Ltd, Sapphire Court, Walsgrave Triangle, Walsgrave, Coventry, CV2 2TX Tel: (024) 7643 2400 Fax: (024) 7643 2301 E-mail: enquiries@lloydspharmacy.com
▶ London News Distribution, 1 Dockley Road Industrial Estate, Dockley Road, London, SE16 3SF Tel: (020) 7231 2065 Fax: (020) 7231 1866
Master Cleaning Supplies, Middlemore La West, Aldridge, Walsall, WS9 8BG Tel: (01922) 453682 Fax: (01922) 458687
The Max Distribution Co., The Old Bakery, High Street, East Malling, West Malling, Kent, ME19 6AJ Tel: (01732) 840845 E-mail: sales@the-max.co.uk
Nelsons Transport Keighley Ltd, Bocking Farm, Keighley, West Yorkshire, BD22 9BG Tel: (01535) 642097 Fax: (01535) 647015 E-mail: nelsonstransport@btinternet.com
Newport Commercial Refrigeration Ltd, 60 Commercial Road, Newport, Gwent, NP20 2PF Tel: (01633) 221100 Fax: (01633) 220810 E-mail: ntrltd@ntlworld.com
Newsquest Direct, 6 St Peters Court, Middleborough, Colchester, CO1 1WD Tel: (01206) 508250 Fax: (01206) 508266 E-mail: nqd@nqd.co.uk
Oriflame (UK) Ltd, Kiln Farm, Tilers Road, Milton Keynes, MK11 3EH Tel: (01908) 261126 Fax: (01908) 267444 E-mail: salesuk/ireland@oriflame.co.uk
P H M Plant Services Ltd, 117 Bath Road, Stroud, Gloucestershire, GL5 3JW Tel: (01453) 763532 Fax: (01453) 755083
▶ Park Logistics, Private Road No 4, Colwick Industrial Estate, Nottingham, NG4 2JT Tel: 0115-940 3332 Fax: 0115-940 2728 E-mail: sales@parklogistics.co.uk
Pearce Seeds, Rosedown Farm, Sandford Orcas, Sherborne, Dorset, DT9 4SX Tel: (01935) 811400 Fax: (01935) 816800
Playscene, Watering Farm, Creeting St. Mary, Ipswich, IP6 8ND Tel: (01449) 721729 Fax: (01449) 722477
Procon Engineering Ltd, Vestry Estate, Vestry Road, Sevenoaks, Kent, TN14 5EL Tel: (01732) 781300 Fax: (01732) 781311 E-mail: sales@procon-eng.com
▶ Product Development Corporation, Westminster Place, York Business Park, Nether Poppleton, York, YO26 6RW Tel: (01904) 606300 Fax: (01904) 606311 E-mail: sales@teampdc.co.uk
R Collett & Sons Transport Ltd, Albert Road, Halifax, West Yorkshire, HX2 0DF Tel: (01422) 255233 Fax: (01422) 255244 E-mail: sales@collett.co.uk
Rand Equipment Europe Ltd, Unit 8 Commonwealth Close, Leigh, Lancashire, WN7 3BD Tel: (01942) 606062 Fax: (01942) 606087
Ripponden Carriers Ltd, Oldham Road, Ripponden, Sowerby Bridge, West Yorkshire, HX6 4ED Tel: (01422) 822266 Fax: (01422) 823882 E-mail: info@rippondencarriers.co.uk
Sainsburys Supermarkets Ltd, Faraday Avenue, Hams Hall Distribution Park, Coleshill, Birmingham, B46 1AL Tel: (01675) 435800
sale echo, Unit 30 Wolverton Mill East, Mill Park, High Park Drive Wolverton, Milton Keynes, MK12 5TT Tel: (0845) 124 1700 Fax: (01908) 441750 E-mail: enquires@echoltd.com
Screwbolt Fixing, Unit 1a Eastlands Industrial Estate, Leiston, Suffolk, IP16 4LL Tel: (01728) 832076 Fax: (01728) 833312
Station Kitchens Ltd, 47 Station Road, Erdington, Birmingham, B23 6UE Tel: 0121-373 9160 Fax: 0121-377 7530
TDG UK Ltd, High Street, Coleshill, Birmingham, B46 3BP Tel: (01675) 467447 Fax: (01675) 467585
Teknion Distribution Services, 22-24 Southgate Industrial Estate, Cross Street, Heywood, Lancashire, OL10 1PW Tel: (01706) 669988 Fax: (01706) 669989 E-mail: info@teknion.co.uk
Tibbett & Britten, 10 Mossbell Road, Motherwell Food Park, Bellshill, Lanarkshire, ML4 3NW Tel: (01698) 748766 Fax: (01698) 743849
Tibbett & Britten Group P.L.C., Laverstoke Road, Allington, Maidstone, Kent, ME16 0LE Tel: (01622) 671400 Fax: (01622) 692495
Tomalin Associates, 12 Bardfield Centre, Great Bardfield, Braintree, Essex, CM7 4SL Tel: (01371) 811299 Fax: (01371) 811283 E-mail: sales@tomalinassociates.com
Trade Counter Ltd, Unit D Trading Estate Road, London, NW10 7LU Tel: (020) 8385 2753 Fax: (020) 8965 9765 E-mail: ptc@netcomuk.co.uk
Transit Retail Services, Manor Farm, Wibtoft, Lutterworth, Leicestershire, LE17 5BB Tel: (01455) 220221 Fax: (01455) 220208 E-mail: enquiries@trs-uk.co.uk
Victoria Health Foods, Unit 23 Broadwalk Shopping Centre, Station Road, Edgware, Middlesex, HA8 7BD Tel: (020) 8905 6931 Fax: (020) 8905 6931
▶ W H Barley Transport & Storage Ltd, Old Wolverton Road, Old Wolverton, Milton Keynes, MK12 5NL Tel: (01908) 227222 Fax: (01908) 227370 E-mail: sales@whbarley.co.uk
W H Bowker Ltd, Holme Road, Bamber Bridge, Preston, PR5 6BP Tel: (01772) 628800 Fax: (01772) 628801 E-mail: enquiries@bowker.co.uk
West Cornwall Storage & Distribution Ltd, Calloose, Leedstown, Hayle, Cornwall, TR27 5ET Tel: (01736) 850146 Fax: (01736) 850148
Wincanton Logistics Ltd, Central Way, Feltham, Middlesex, TW14 0XQ Tel: (020) 8831 1500 Fax: (020) 8831 1518
Wolf Garden Ltd, Crown Business Park, Dukestown, Tredegar, Gwent, NP22 4EF Tel: (01495) 306600 Fax: (01495) 303344 E-mail: info@wolf-garden.co.uk

DISTRIBUTION AUTOMATION EQUIPMENT

▶ Process Automation, 17 South Lodge Court, Chesterfield, Derbyshire, S40 3QG Tel: (01246) 568868 E-mail: process.automation@fsmail.net

DISTRIBUTION CONTROL SWITCHBOARDS

▶ Salem Automation Ltd, Sycamore Road, Eastwood Trading Estate, Rotherham, South Yorkshire, S65 1EN Tel: (01709) 538200 Fax: (01709) 376903 E-mail: sales@salemautomation.net

DISTRIBUTION SYSTEM SOFTWARE

B L Computer Services, McPhail Ho, 1 Alexandra Rd, Clevedon, Avon, BS21 7QE Tel: (01275) 340500 Fax: (01275) 340470 E-mail: admin@blcomp.co.uk
Capital Systems Ltd, 17 Princess Victoria Street, Bristol, BS8 4BX Tel: 0117-973 0506 Fax: 0117-973 0811
Ciber UK Ltd, Sketchley Meadows Business Park, 2 Watling Drive, Hinckley, Leicestershire, LE10 3EY Tel: (01455) 898800 Fax: (0870) 0000205 E-mail: enquiries@c.co.uk
Excel Computer Systems, Bothe Hall, Tamworth Road, Long Eaton, Nottingham, NG10 3XL Tel: 0115-946 0101 Fax: 0115-946 0606 E-mail: sales@exel.co.uk
Ferranti Air Systems Ltd, The Oaks Business Park, Crewe Road, Manchester, M23 9SS Tel: 0161-946 3600 Fax: 0161-946 3601 E-mail: sales@ultra-as.com
First Degree Software Systems Ltd, 28 Oakwood Close, Warsash, Southampton, SO31 9PW Tel: (01489) 603383 Fax: (01489) 603384
Infor Global Solutions Frimley Ltd, 1 Lakeside Road, Farnborough, Hampshire, GU14 6XP Tel: (01276) 417200 Fax: (01276) 417201
Interchain UK Ltd, 44 Shenley Pavilions, Chalkdell Drive, Shenley Wood, Milton Keynes, MK5 6LB Tel: (01908) 521000 Fax: (01908) 522000 E-mail: pbz@interchain.co.uk
Teeside Education Support Services, Horsehouse, Leyburn, North Yorkshire, DL8 4TS Tel: (01969) 640364 Fax: (01969) 640383 E-mail: info@readindsoftware.com

DIVANS

Baynell, 85-86 Darlington Street, Wolverhampton, WV1 4NG Tel: (01902) 425616 Fax: (01902) 311242
Bed Warehouse, Wrea Lane, Scarborough, North Yorkshire, YO12 7PN Tel: (01723) 351313 Fax: (01723) 353971
Bedding Superstore Studley, 1 Marble Alley, Studley, Warwickshire, B80 7LD Tel: (01527) 854488 Fax: (01527) 854488
Best Buy Carpet & Divan Centre, 2 Arksey Lane, Bentley, Doncaster, South Yorkshire, DN5 0RR Tel: (01302) 873586 Fax: (01302) 873586
Cheam Bedding, 34 The Broadway, Cheam, Sutton, Surrey, SM3 8BD Tel: (020) 8642 2232 Fax: (020) 8288 0785 E-mail: sales@cheambedding.co.uk
Dreams plc, 5 The Forum, Stevenage, Hertfordshire, SG1 1EH Tel: (01438) 759999 Fax: (01438) 749999 E-mail: enquiries@dreamsplc.co.uk
Fonad Products, 99a Webster Road, Liverpool, L7 4LG Tel: 0151-733 0000 Fax: 0151-733 0000
Highland Blindcraft, 38 Ardconnel Street, Inverness, IV2 3EX Tel: (01463) 233662 Fax: (01463) 710809 E-mail: sales@highlandblindcraft.co.uk
Malcolm Johnston, 156 Woodville Park Industrial Estate, Woodville Street, Glasgow, G51 2RL Tel: 0141-445 2368 Fax: 0141-445 2368
Northsleep Ltd, 19-21 St Clair Street, Aberdeen, AB24 5TA Tel: (01224) 632334 Fax: (01224) 649282
Peacock & Chandler Ltd, 134 Villiers Road, London, NW2 5PU Tel: (020) 8459 0519 Fax: (020) 8451 1049 E-mail: sales@peacockandchandler.com
Sealy, Station Road, Aspatria, Wigton, Cumbria, CA7 2AS Tel: (0870) 7473259 Fax: (0870) 7429884 E-mail: salesorders@sealyuk.co.uk

DIVANS - *continued*

Silent Night Beds, Spring Lane, Barnoldswick, Lancashire, BB18 6BJ Tel: (01282) 813051 Fax: (01282) 813466 E-mail: enquiries@silentnightgroup.co.uk
Skipton Bed & Suite Centre, 17 Water Street, Skipton, North Yorkshire, BD23 1PQ Tel: (01756) 794719 Fax: (01756) 796284
Staples Uk Ltd, Windover Road, Huntingdon, Cambridgeshire, PE29 7EF Tel: (01480) 442222 Fax: (01480) 442266 E-mail: enquiries@staplesbeds.co.uk
Swansea Water Bed Centre, Gorseinon Road, Penllergaer, Swansea, SA4 9GE Tel: (01792) 899110 Fax: (01792) 899110 E-mail: sales@swanseawaterbeds.co.uk
Towersleep Ltd, King Edward Street, Grimsby, South Humberside, DN31 3JW Tel: (01472) 355371 Fax: (01472) 242915 E-mail: sales@towersleep.co.uk

DIVERTER VALVES

Bush & Wilton Ltd, 6 Millennium Place, Tiverton Business Park, Tiverton, Devon, EX16 6SB Tel: (01884) 242233 Fax: (01884) 252555 E-mail: sales@bushandwilton.com
Industrial Plastics Ltd, Unit 13 Canterbury Industrial Park, 297 Ilderton Road, London, SE15 1NP Tel: (020) 7252 9600 Fax: (020) 7252 9601 E-mail: sales@ipl-london.co.uk
Midland Industrial Designers Ltd, Common Lane, Watnall, Nottingham, NG16 1HD Tel: 0115-938 2154 Fax: 0115-938 6315 E-mail: sales@mid.uk.com

DIVING EQUIPMENT OR ACCESSORIES OR SYSTEMS

▶ Air Tek Analytical, Unit 1-5 Meadow Mill, Water Street, Stockport, Cheshire, SK1 2BY Tel: 0161-477 3777
▶ All Oceans Engineering Ltd, Tyrebagger Works, Kinellar, Aberdeen, AB21 0TT Tel: (01224) 791001 Fax: (01224) 791002 E-mail: admin@alloceans.co.uk
Andark Promotions Ltd, 256 Bridge Road, Swanwick, Southampton, SO31 7FL Tel: (01489) 581755 Fax: (01489) 575223 E-mail: sales@andark.co.uk
Aquatec, 7 Russell Avenue, Weymouth, Dorset, DT4 9RA Tel: (01305) 776037 Fax: (01305) 769977 E-mail: info@aquatec.co.uk
Bel Air Sub Aqua Supplies, 82 Fairfax Drive, Westcliff-on-Sea, Essex, SS0 9AF Tel: (01702) 353205 Fax: (01702) 353205
Birchley Products, 7 Bush Hay, Church Down, Gloucester, GL3 2QR Tel: (01452) 855312 Fax: (01452) 859245 E-mail: ab@birchleyproducts.co.uk
▶ Birns (Scotland) Ltd, Denmore Road, Bridge of Don, Aberdeen, AB23 8JW Tel: (01224) 706816 Fax: (01224) 707280
Blandford Sub Aqua, Unit C Holly Industrial Park, Ryan Way, Watford, WD24 4YP Tel: (01923) 801572 Fax: (01923) 801573
Collins & Chambers Ltd, 197-199 Mare Street, London, E8 3QF Tel: (020) 8985 9970 Fax: (020) 8985 3123 E-mail: nautilus@talk21.com
Divex Ltd, Enterprise Drive, Westhill Industrial Estate, Westhill, Aberdeenshire, AB32 6TQ Tel: (01224) 740145 Fax: (01224) 740172 E-mail: info@divex.co.uk
Diving Services Anglesey, Heather Cliffe, Ravenspoint Road, Trearddur Bay, Holyhead, Gwynedd, LL65 2AQ Tel: (01407) 860318 Fax: (01407) 860318
Dorset Diving Services, Unit 6 & 7 West Howe Industrial Estate, Elliott Road, Bournemouth, BH11 8JX Tel: (01202) 580065 Fax: (01202) 593529 E-mail: mail@dorsetdiving.co.uk
Enjay Marine, 10 Somerset Road, Christchurch, Dorset, BH23 2ED Tel: (01202) 481286 Fax: (01202) 481286
Hydroweld Divers, 46 Bedford Drive, Sutton Coldfield, West Midlands, B75 6AX Tel: 0121-378 1230 Fax: 0121-378 1281 E-mail: info@hydroweld.com
▶ K S A Underwater Ltd, Unit 10 Skellgillside Workshops, Nenthead Road, Alston, Cumbria, CA9 3TR Tel: (01434) 382122 Fax: (01434) 382574 E-mail: ksauw@aol.com
M & S Sub Aqua Supplies Ltd, 1 Hackenden Close, East Grinstead, West Sussex, RH19 3DR Tel: (01342) 300162 Fax: (01342) 322500
Marsden Dive Centre, Diving Centre, 6 Fallow Road, South Shields, Tyne & Wear, NE34 7AG Tel: 0191-427 7820 Fax: 0191-427 7820 E-mail: sales@marsdendivecentre.co.uk
Mike's Waterfront Warehouse, Unit 1 Wyatts View, St. Anne's Park, Bristol, BS4 4WW Tel: 0117-977 6227
Namron Aqua Products Ltd, Canklow Meadows Industrial Estate, West Bawtry Road, Rotherham, South Yorkshire, S60 2XL Tel: (01709) 371006 Fax: (01709) 367295 E-mail: namron@scubauk.com
Oceanic (SW) Ltd, Pelagic House, Dunkeswell, Honiton, Devon, EX14 4RB Tel: (01404) 891819 Fax: (01404) 891909
Old Harbour Dive Centre, 11 Nothe Parade, Weymouth, Dorset, DT4 8TX Tel: (01305) 760888 Fax: (01305) 766889
▶ Orca Divers, 125 Manchester Road, Chorlton Cum Hardy, Manchester, M21 9PG Tel: 0161 7183118 E-mail: enquiries@orcadivers.com
Parker Diving Ltd, A P Valves Building, Water Ma Trout Industrial Estate, Nancegollan, Helston, Cornwall, TR13 0BN Tel: (01326) 561040 Fax: (01326) 573605 E-mail: sales@apvalves.com
R Mcmahon Engineering Ltd, Unit 5 Oldends Industrial Estate, Oldends, Stonehouse, Gloucestershire, GL10 3RQ Tel: (01453) 828666 Fax: (01453) 828360 E-mail: howard@mcmahon-engineering.com
Sandford & Down, 24 Pier Street, Plymouth, PL1 3BT Tel: (01752) 266248 Fax: (01752) 226131 E-mail: dive@sandforddandown.co.uk
Scuba Dream Ltd, 18 Greasbrough Road, Parkgate, Rotherham, South Yorkshire, S62 6HN Tel: (01709) 525480 Fax: (01709) 529580
Scubaaction, 9 Guy Place East, Leamington Spa, Warwickshire, CV32 4RG Tel: 01926 450193 Fax: 01926 435211
Seastyle, Unit 21 Three Springs Trading Estate, Vincent Road, Worcester, WR5 1BW Tel: (01905) 351528 Fax: (01905) 763776 E-mail: diving@seastyle.co.uk
Sub Aqua Divers, Rescuestation House, Station Road, Wath-upon-Dearne, Rotherham, South Yorkshire, S63 7DG Tel: (01709) 877222 Fax: (01709) 877555
▶ Sub Aqua Products Ltd, Lycroft Farm, 8 Upper Swanmore, Swanmore, Southampton, SO32 2QQ Tel: (01489) 878055 Fax: (01489) 878002 E-mail: info@subaqua-products.com
▶ Timuna Sea Ltd, 121 Cannon Workshops, 3 Cannon Drive, London, E14 4AS Tel: (020) 7719 9444
Undersea Ltd, 1 Forelle Centre, 30 Black Moor Road, Ebblake Industrial Estate, Verwood, Dorset, BH31 6BB Tel: (01202) 822025 Fax: (01202) 826626 E-mail: enquiries@undersea-ltd.demon.co.uk
Wade Precision Engineering, Unit 39 Penley Industrial Estate, Penley, Wrexham, Clwyd, LL13 0LQ Tel: (01948) 830268 Fax: (01948) 830268

DIVING EQUIPMENT OR ACCESSORIES OR SYSTEMS HIRE

Cornish Diving, Bar Road, Falmouth, Cornwall, TR11 4BN Tel: (01326) 313178 Fax: (01326) 311265 E-mail: info@cornishdiving.co.uk
Dorset Diving Services, Unit 6 & 7 West Howe Industrial Estate, Elliott Road, Bournemouth, BH11 8JX Tel: (01202) 580065 Fax: (01202) 593529 E-mail: mail@dorsetdiving.co.uk
▶ In2Scuba Dive School, 27 Poyntell Road, Staplehurst, Tonbridge, Kent, TN12 0SA Tel: (01580) 891711 E-mail: steve@in2scuba.co.uk
Mikes Waterfront Warehouse, 42 Lichfield Terrace, Upminster, Essex, RM14 3JX Tel: (01708) 227122 E-mail: info@waterfrontscuba.com
Sandford & Down, 24 Pier Street, Plymouth, PL1 3BT Tel: (01752) 266248 Fax: (01752) 226131 E-mail: dive@sandforddandown.co.uk
Searchwise Ltd, 6 Broomiesburn Road, Ellon, Aberdeenshire, AB41 9RD Tel: (01358) 722990 Fax: (01358) 722933 E-mail: sales@searchwise.co.uk
Seaways Diving & Marine, Commercial Road, Penryn, Cornwall, TR10 8AQ Tel: (01326) 375544 Fax: (01326) 375401 E-mail: colin@seawaysdiving.com
Sub Aqua Divers, Rescuestation House, Station Road, Wath-upon-Dearne, Rotherham, South Yorkshire, S63 7DG Tel: (01709) 877222 Fax: (01709) 877555

DIVING EQUIPMENT OR SYSTEM MAINTENANCE OR REPAIR

Cormeton Fire Protection Ltd, Unit 12 Delaval Trading Estate, Seaton Delaval, Whitley Bay, Tyne & Wear, NE25 0QT Tel: 0191-237 0790 Fax: 0191-237 5143 E-mail: sales@cormeton.co.uk

DIVING GASES

Air Products plc, Enterprise Drive, Westhill Industrial Estate, Westhill, Aberdeenshire, AB32 6TQ Tel: (0845) 6015163 Fax: (01224) 749065
Cambridge Fluid Systems, 12 Trafalgar Way, Bar Hill, Cambridge, CB3 8SQ Tel: (01954) 786800 Fax: (01954) 786818 E-mail: uhp@cam.cambridge-fluid.com

DIVING SERVICES OR CONTRACTORS

Acergy Ltd, Bucksburn House, Howes Road, Aberdeen, AB16 7QU Tel: (01224) 718200 Fax: (01224) 715129 E-mail: uk-hr@acergy-group.com
B C D Marine Ltd, Vanguard House, Vanguard Road, Gapton Hall Industrial Estate, Great Yarmouth, Norfolk, NR31 0NT Tel: (01493) 444002 Fax: (01493) 652576
Cambridge Dive Centre, 252 Cherry Hinton Road, Cambridge, CB1 7AU Tel: (01223) 240818 Fax: (01223) 240818 E-mail: sales@cambridge-dive-centre.co.uk
Houlder Ltd, 59 Lafone Street, London, SE1 2LX Tel: (020) 7357 7317 Fax: (020) 7403 8201 E-mail: mail@houlder-offshore.co.uk
Interdive Services Ltd, Unit 3a Stoke Damerel Business Centre, 5 Church Street, Plymouth, PL3 4DT Tel: (01752) 558080 Fax: (01752) 569090 E-mail: admin@interdive.co.uk
Northern Divers (Engineering) Ltd, Tower Street, Hull, HU9 1TU Tel: (01482) 227276 Fax: (01482) 215712 E-mail: contact@northerndivers.co.uk
Oceaneering International Services Ltd, Pitmedden Road, Dyce, Aberdeen, AB21 0DP Tel: (01224) 770444 Fax: (01224) 771583
Port of London Authority, Barkers Hall, 7 Harp Lane, London, EC3R 6LB Tel: (020) 7743 7900 Fax: (020) 7743 7998 E-mail: marketing@portoflondon.co.uk
▶ Pro Dive Europe, 268-270 Hillmorton Road, The Paddox, Rugby, Warwickshire, CV22 3BW Tel: (024) 7674 6397 Fax: (07092) 808864 E-mail: info@prodive.co.uk
Quest Explosive Disposal Ltd, Hethfelton Hollow East Stoke, Wareham, Dorset, BH20 6HJ Tel: (01929) 405029 Fax: (01929) 405472
Seaweld Engineering Ltd, The Limes, The Street, Acle, Norwich, NR13 3QJ Tel: (01493) 751421 Fax: (01493) 750064 E-mail: admin@seaweld.co.uk
Technip Offshore Ltd, Enterprise Drive, Westhill Industrial Estate, Westhill, Aberdeenshire, AB32 6TQ Tel: (01224) 744044 Fax: (01224) 271271
Wraysbury Dive Centre, Station Road, Wraysbury, Staines, Middlesex, TW19 5ND Tel: (01784) 488007 Fax: (01784) 488007 E-mail: info@learntodive.co.uk

DIVING SUPPORT VESSEL OR SUBMERSIBLE OPERATORS

Acergy Ltd, Bucksburn House, Howes Road, Aberdeen, AB16 7QU Tel: (01224) 718200 Fax: (01224) 715129 E-mail: uk-hr@acergy-group.com
Briggs Marine Contractors Ltd, West Dock, Seaforth Place, Burntisland, Fife, KY3 9AU Tel: (01592) 872939 Fax: (01592) 873975
Technip Offshore Ltd, Enterprise Drive, Westhill Industrial Estate, Westhill, Aberdeenshire, AB32 6TQ Tel: (01224) 744044 Fax: (01224) 271271

DIY WORKBENCHES

Tudor, 3 Ellesmere Business Park, Oswestry Road, Ellesmere, Shropshire, SY12 0EW Tel: (01691) 623424 Fax: (01691) 624479 E-mail: nevilletudor@virgin.net

DO IT YOURSELF (DIY) PRODUCTS/SUPPLIES, *See also Headings for particular types*

Acutech, Unit 5 York House, Langston Road, Loughton, Essex, IG10 3TQ Tel: (020) 8502 2155 Fax: (020) 8508 8562 E-mail: sales@acuutech.com
Ainsworth, Frenches Works, Chew Valley Road, Greenfield, Oldham, OL3 7AE Tel: (01457) 879000 Fax: (01457) 873279 E-mail: diyshop@ainsworthdiy.co.uk
Andrew & Co Spalding Ltd, Welland Sawmills, Little London, Spalding, Lincolnshire, PE11 2UJ Tel: (01775) 723016 Fax: (01775) 722499 E-mail: derek@andrewdiy.co.uk
▶ Art Plus Function Ltd, Macknade, Selling Road, Faversham, Kent, ME13 8XF Tel: (01795) 530400 Fax: (0870) 7627707 E-mail: info@artplusfunction.co.uk
Bartoline, Barmston Close, Woodmansey, Beverley, North Humberside, HU17 0LW Tel: (01482) 678710 Fax: (01482) 872606 E-mail: info@bartoline.co.uk
▶ Bitrex, 10 Wheatfield Road, Edinburgh, EH11 2QA Tel: 0131-337 2434 Fax: 0131-337 9813
Burcart Clacton Ltd, 259-265 Old Road, Clacton-on-Sea, Essex, CO15 3LU Tel: (01255) 422213 Fax: (01255) 476751 E-mail: burcart@supanet.com
C Brewer & Sons Ltd, Albany House, Ashford Road, Eastbourne, East Sussex, BN21 3TR Tel: (01323) 437801 Fax: (01323) 721435 E-mail: decorating@brewers.co.uk
D & M Builders Merchants, 73-81 Heath Road, Twickenham, TW1 4AW Tel: (020) 8892 3813 Fax: (020) 8744 1044
Dobsons, 104-106 Stoke Road, Slough, SL2 5AP Tel: (01753) 520978 Fax: (01753) 823821 E-mail: dobsons@hotmail.com
Driffield Hardware Centre, Cranwell Road, Driffield, North Humberside, YO25 6UH Tel: (01377) 241399 Fax: (01377) 241252
Eathornes Mica Hardware, 2 Drygate St, Larkhall, Lanarkshire, ML9 2AJ Tel: (01698) 881523 Fax: (01698) 882337
F S B Wholesale Ltd, Mirror Works, Cuckoo Hall Lane, London, N9 8DH Tel: (020) 8804 4333 Fax: (020) 8804 8777
Firth Manufacturing Ltd, Hole House Lane, Stocksbridge, Sheffield, S36 1BS Tel: 0114-288 3298 Fax: 0114-288 4176 E-mail: info@firths.co.uk
G E Collis & Sons Ltd, Queen St Industrial Estate, Queens Drive, Burntwood, Staffordshire, WS7 4QF Tel: (01543) 686370 Fax: (01543) 675221 E-mail: sales@collissheds.co.uk
Glyn Webb Group Ltd, Old Darby House, Derker Street, Oldham, OL1 3XF Tel: 0161-6214500 Fax: 0161-621 4501 E-mail: contactus@glynwebb.co.uk
H E Humphries Ltd, Monway House, Portway Road, Wednesbury, West Midlands, WS10 7DZ Tel: 0121-556 0097 Fax: 0121-556 9427
H J Cooper Timber Ltd, Thornleigh Trading Estate, Dudley, West Midlands, DY2 8UB Tel: (01384) 254591 Fax: (01384) 237119 E-mail: info@cooperstimber.co.uk
Hardy's D.I.Y. Ltd, 652 Warwick Rd, Tyseley, Birmingham, B11 2HJ Tel: 0121-706 2646 Fax: 0121-624 2662
Herne Hill Timber Co, 301 Railton Road, London, SE24 0JN Tel: (020) 7274 2548
Lamboard Ltd, 228 Leads Road, Hull, HU7 0DQ Tel: (01482) 701143 Fax: (01482) 712332
M & J Products, 20 Gresley Close, Drayton Fields Industrial Estate, Daventry, Northamptonshire, NN11 8RZ Tel: (01327) 872885 Fax: (01327) 300706 E-mail: mjproducts@btconnect.com
M & J Timber Ltd, 32 Union Street, Greenock, Renfrewshire, PA16 8DJ Tel: (01475) 723737 Fax: (01475) 722537
Malletts Home Hardware, 6-7 Victoria Square, Truro, Cornwall, TR1 2RT Tel: (01872) 274441 Fax: (01872) 240664 E-mail: sales@mallettshomehardware.co.uk
Monway Builders Supplies Ltd, Portway Road, Wednesbury, West Midlands, WS10 7EQ Tel: 0121-502 0911 Fax: 0121-556 9427
Oracstar, Weddell Way, Brackmills, Northampton, NN4 7HS Tel: (01604) 702181 Fax: (01604) 701743 E-mail: orac@oracstar.co.uk
Proops Manufacturing Ltd, Shaftesbury House, 46-47 New Street, Burton-On-Trent, Staffordshire, DE14 3QW Tel: (01283) 533280 Fax: (01283) 533280 E-mail: cjroe@lonw.fsnet.co.uk
Quick Fit, Unit 5 The Sidings, Leeds Road, Shipley, West Yorkshire, BD18 1BN Tel: (01274) 595127 Fax: (01274) 531271 E-mail: quickfit@btinternet.com
Rodbers Of Richmond Ltd, The Old Cinema, 2 Queens Road, Richmond, North Yorkshire, DL10 4DN Tel: (01748) 822491 Fax: (01748) 826497
S E Apex Ltd, 847-849 London Road, Westcliff-on-Sea, Essex, SS0 9SZ Tel: (01702) 477425 Fax: (01702) 480564
Saunders & Co. Ltd, 35-39 Trinity Street, Sheffield, S3 7AJ Tel: 0114-276 6733 Fax: 0114-275 0307
Shakespeare & Sons, 291-295 Dudley Road, Birmingham, B18 4HA Tel: 0121-454 1341 Fax: 0121-454 1341
Stairway Projects, Unit 16 Taylors, Gravel Lane, Chigwell, Essex, IG7 6DQ Tel: (020) 8559 9226 Fax: (020) 8559 9226
Strowger Ltd, 395-397 London Road, Mitcham, Surrey, CR4 4BG Tel: (020) 8648 2401 Fax: (020) 8648 2401
Taggart & Co. Ltd, 38-44 Main Street, Ballymoney, County Antrim, BT53 6AP Tel: (028) 2766 2130 Fax: (028) 2766 6129
Thornton Heath Dry Cleaners, 92 Brigstock Road, Thornton Heath, Surrey, CR7 7JA Tel: (020) 8683 2589 Fax: (020) 8240 0081 E-mail: thdiy-ltd@ukgateway.net
Tool-auctions-online, 13 Waveney Road, Lowestoft, Suffolk, NR32 1BT Tel: (01502) 564120 Fax: (01502) 564120 E-mail: kevin@tool-auctions-online.co.uk
Travis Perkins plc, Havyat Road Trading Estate, Havyat Road, Wrington, Bristol, BS40 5PA Tel: (01934) 862439 Fax: (01934) 863617
Travis Perkins plc, Mayors Avenue, Dartmouth, Devon, TQ6 9NG Tel: (01803) 832216 Fax: (01803) 835694
W L D Textiles, Lansdowne Terrace, York, YO10 3EA Tel: (01904) 413453 Fax: (01904) 413453
Washington & Riley Ltd, 1 William Clowes Street, Stoke-on-Trent, ST6 3AR Tel: (01782) 834363 Fax: (01782) 834366 E-mail: info@washingtonandriley.ltd.uk
▶ Wilkinson, Unit 1 28 St. Johns Walk, Colchester, CO2 7AL Tel: (01206) 767662
Woodcraft Industries & DIY, 191 London Road, Glasgow, G40 1PA Tel: 0141-552 1437 Fax: 0141-552 1437

DOCK (DRY) FACILITIES/ SERVICES

Canal Cruising Co. Ltd, Crown Street, Stone, Staffordshire, ST15 8QN Tel: (01785) 813982 Fax: (01785) 819041 E-mail: kwyatt5745@aol.com
Dunston Ship Repairs Ltd, William Wright Dock, Hull, HU3 4PG Tel: (01482) 326774 Fax: (01482) 226815 E-mail: sales@dunstons.co.uk
Lincoln & Hull Marine Contractors Ltd, 100 Lime Street, Hull, HU8 7AR Tel: (01482) 320727 Fax: (01482) 320727 E-mail: noel@siggle.fsnet.co.uk

DOCK (DRY) FACILITIES/SERVICES

– continued

▶ Milford Haven Ship Repairers, The Docks, Milford Haven, Dyfed, SA73 3DJ Tel: (01646) 696320 Fax: (01646) 696321 E-mail: mhsr@milford-docks.co.uk

Penzance Dry Dock Ltd, Wharf Road, Penzance, Cornwall, TR18 4BW Tel: (01736) 363838 Fax: (01736) 351207 E-mail: admiral.1@btconnect.com

Port Of Workington, Prince of Wales Dock, Workington, Cumbria, CA14 2JH Tel: (01900) 602301 Fax: (01900) 604696 E-mail: workington.port@cumbriacc.gov.uk

Southampton Container Terminals Ltd, Berth 204-206 Prince Charles Container Port, Western Docks, Southampton, SO15 1DA Tel: (023) 8070 1701 Fax: (023) 8052 8285 E-mail: admin@sct.uk.com

DOCK LOADING SYSTEMS

▶ Dockright Ltd, Forest Vale Road, Forest Vale Industrial Estate, Cinderford, Gloucestershire, GL14 2PH Tel: (01594) 822591 Fax: (01594) 823544 E-mail: service@dockright.co.uk

DOCK OR LOADING BAY DOOR SEALS OR SHELTERS

Easilift Loading Systems Ltd, Spring Grove, Penistone Road, Kirkburton, Huddersfield, HD8 0PL Tel: (01484) 601400 Fax: (01484) 601401 E-mail: sales@easilift-loading-systems.co.uk

Warehouse Direct Industrial Ltd, PO Box 928, Woking, Surrey, GU23 7ZN Tel: 08707 700709 Fax: 08707 700659 E-mail: sales@wdil.co.uk

DOCK OR LOADING BAY EQUIPMENT, *See also headings for particular types*

▶ Dockright Ltd, Forest Vale Road, Forest Vale Industrial Estate, Cinderford, Gloucestershire, GL14 2PH Tel: (01594) 822591 Fax: (01594) 823544 E-mail: service@dockright.co.uk

Envirohold Ltd, Viking Close, Willerby, Hull, HU10 6BS Tel: (01482) 651090 Fax: (01482) 651002 E-mail: sales@envirodoor.com

Industrial Doors Systems Ltd, Unit 51, Waverley Road, Beeches Industrial Estate, Bristol, BS37 5QR Tel: (01454) 324410 Fax: (01454) 324412 E-mail: idsbristol1@aol.com

KONE PLC, Blisworth Hill Farm, Stoke Road, Blisworth, Northampton, NN7 3DB Tel: 08451 999 999 Fax: 0870 7701144 E-mail: sales.marketinguk@kone.com

Move Man SKG, 123 Abbey Lane, Leicester, LE4 5QX Tel: 0116-266 5353

Oakland International, 3 The Chancery, Bramcote, Nottingham, NG9 3AJ Tel: 0115-967 7141 Fax: 0115-967 7653 E-mail: info@loadingbay.co.uk

Safety By Design, Safety House Aire & Calder Industrial Park, Lock Lane, Castleford, West Yorkshire, WF10 2JA Tel: (0800) 0858782 Fax: (01977) 555351 E-mail: sales@safetybydesign.co.uk

Warehouse Direct Industrial Ltd, PO Box 928, Woking, Surrey, GU23 7ZN Tel: 08707 700709 Fax: 08707 700659 E-mail: sales@wdil.co.uk

DOCK OR LOADING BAY EQUIPMENT MAINTENANCE OR REPAIR

Oakland International, 3 The Chancery, Bramcote, Nottingham, NG9 3AJ Tel: 0115-967 7141 Fax: 0115-967 7653 E-mail: info@loadingbay.co.uk

Stanair Industrial Door Services Ltd, Unit 11, Blundells Road, Bradville, Milton Keynes, MK13 7HA Tel: (01908) 222070 Fax: (01908) 222621 E-mail: info@stanair.co.uk

DOCK OR LOADING BAY EQUIPMENT SPARE PARTS

Oakland International, 3 The Chancery, Bramcote, Nottingham, NG9 3AJ Tel: 0115-967 7141 Fax: 0115-967 7653 E-mail: info@loadingbay.co.uk

DOCK OR LOADING BAY INSTALLATION OR CONTRACTORS

County Installations, 15 Moore Road, Church Crookham, Fleet, Hampshire, GU52 6JB Tel: (01252) 616093 Fax: (01252) 627755 E-mail: patlowe@countyinstallations.co.uk

Industrial Doors Systems Ltd, Unit 51, Waverley Road, Beeches Industrial Estate, Bristol, BS37 5QR Tel: (01454) 324410 Fax: (01454) 324412 E-mail: idsbristol1@aol.com

Redmill Fabrication Ltd, 19 Inchmuir Road, Whitehill Industrial Estate, Bathgate, West Lothian, EH48 2EP Tel: (01506) 634333 Fax: (01506) 634999

DOCK OR LOADING BAY LEVELLERS

▶ Armo UK, Unit A5, Halesfield 9, Telford, Shropshire, TF7 4QW Tel: (07838) 117354 Fax: (01952) 582321 E-mail: david.bruneau@armoweb.com

Chase Equipment Ltd, 53A Wellington Industrial Estate, Coseley, Bilston, West Midlands, WV14 9EE Tel: (01902) 675835 Fax: (01902) 674998 E-mail: sales@chaseequipment.com

▶ Dockright Ltd, Forest Vale Road, Forest Vale Industrial Estate, Cinderford, Gloucestershire, GL14 2PH Tel: (01594) 822591 Fax: (01594) 823544 E-mail: service@dockright.co.uk

Easilift Loading Systems Ltd, Spring Grove, Penistone Road, Kirkburton, Huddersfield, HD8 0PL Tel: (01484) 601400 Fax: (01484) 601401 E-mail: sales@easilift-loading-systems.co.uk

Lambourn Valley Projects Ltd, 13 Prospect Road, Hungerford, Berkshire, RG17 0JL Tel: (01488) 680680 Fax: (01488) 681258 E-mail: sales@dock-levellers.co.uk

Loading Bay Specialists Ltd, 4 Garnet Close, Watford, WD24 7JX Tel: (01923) 208888 Fax: (01923) 208899 E-mail: info@saralbs.co.uk

Rent A Ramp Ltd, Unit 37 Station Lane Industrial Estate, Station Lane, Old Whittington, Chesterfield, Derbyshire, S41 9QX Tel: (01246) 260602 Fax: (01246) 260493 E-mail: sales@rentaramp.com

Tecmach Ltd, PO Box 29, St. Albans, Hertfordshire, AL1 5NU Tel: (01727) 860355 Fax: (01727) 844062 E-mail: sales@tecmach.co.uk

Thorworld Industries Ltd, Unit 37, Station Lane Industrial Estate, Old Whittington, Chesterfield, Derbyshire, S41 9QX Tel: (01246) 260981 Fax: (01246) 260493 E-mail: info@thorworld.co.uk

DOCK WORKER RECRUITMENT

▶ Redco Recruitment Group Limited, Redco House, 165 Lea Road, Pennfelds, Wolverhampton, WV3 0LQ Tel: 0845 111 0735 Fax: 0845 111 0736 E-mail: info@redcorecruitment.com

DOCTOR BLADES

William Pinder & Sons Ltd, 4 Harling Road, Sharston Industrial Estate, Manchester, M22 4UZ Tel: 0161-998 1729 Fax: 0161-946 0734 E-mail: info@pinderblades.com

DOCUMENT CASES/ PORTFOLIOS, POLYPROPYLENE (PP)

E X X Projects, 72 Rivington Street, London, EC2A 3AY Tel: (020) 7684 8200 Fax: 0845-630 1282 E-mail: exx@plax.co.uk

DOCUMENT CD ROM DIGITAL SCANNING

Edos Microfilm, Audit Drive, Abingdon, Oxfordshire, OX14 3NJ Tel: (01235) 550505 Fax: (01235) 536719 E-mail: enquiries@edos.co.uk

H M S L Group Ltd, Mayflower House, 11 Caxton Hill, Hertford, SG13 7NE Tel: (01992) 500555 Fax: (01992) 554241 E-mail: sales@hmsl.co.uk

▶ Pagefree Ltd, 11 Pennine Road, Glossop, Derbyshire, SK13 6NN Tel: (01457) 857006 Fax: (01457) 857006 E-mail: sales@pagefree.co.uk

Pregem Computing Ltd, 9 Oriel Business Park, Omega Park, Alton, Hampshire, GU34 2YT Tel: (01420) 544514 Fax: (01420) 544599 E-mail: sales@pregem.com

DOCUMENT CONVEYING SYSTEMS

Air Tube Carrier Systems, 79 Turnberry, Bracknell, Berkshire, RG12 8ZH Tel: (01344) 423659 Fax: (01344) 423659

Quirepace Ltd, Cleveland Place, Cleveland Road, Gosport, Hampshire, PO12 2JG Tel: (023) 9251 1008 Fax: (023) 9251 3244 E-mail: info@quirepace.co.uk

DOCUMENT DESTRUCTION SERVICES

▶ Premier Shredding Ltd, Unit 3J, North Road, Marchwood Industrial Park, Marchwood, Southampton, SO40 4BL Tel: (023) 8086 8888 Fax: (023) 8086 7475 E-mail: sales@premiershredding.co.uk

DOCUMENT IMAGE PROCESSING SERVICES

Call Print 16 Ltd, 201 Shenley Road, Borehamwood, Hertfordshire, WD6 1AT Tel: (020) 8207 1188 Fax: (020) 8207 0193 E-mail: bwood@callprint.co.uk

▶ Compact Data Management Ltd, 6 Leons Way, Tollgate Drive, Tollgate Industrial Estate, Stafford, ST16 3HS Tel: (01785) 220846 Fax: (01785) 220876 E-mail: sales@compact.uk.com

Cosmo Imaging Ltd, Systems House, Ocean Street, Altrincham, Cheshire, WA14 5DP Tel: 0161-928 6042 Fax: 0161-929 7327 E-mail: info@cgil.co.uk

Dectel Information Systems, Swinbourne Road, Burnt Mills Industrial Estate, Basildon, Essex, SS13 1EF Tel: (01268) 727586 Fax: (01268) 591422 E-mail: sales@dectel.co.uk

Documation Software Ltd, Wessex House, Market Street, Eastleigh, Hampshire, SO50 9FD Tel: (023) 8064 7776 Fax: (023) 8064 7775 E-mail: info@documatation.co.uk

Document Imaging Services Ltd, Image House, Radford Way, Billericay, Essex, CM12 0BT Tel: (01277) 625000 Fax: (01277) 624999 E-mail: sales@document-imaging.co.uk

East Midlands Micro Imaging, 46 Tenter Road, Moulton Park Industrial Estate, Northampton, NN3 6AX Tel: (01604) 644665 Fax: (01604) 643673 E-mail: sales@em-micro-imaging.co.uk

Gapint Ltd, The Old Mill, Wellington Street, Ripley, Derbyshire, DE5 3EH Tel: (01773) 741174 Fax: (01773) 570247 E-mail: enquiries@gapint.co.uk

I I C O N Ltd, Regent House, Hubert Road, Brentwood, Essex, CM14 4JE Tel: (01277) 264404 Fax: (01277) 264405

Imscan Systems Ltd, Yew Tree House Yew Tree Court, Warrington Road, Risley, Warrington, WA3 6WP Tel: (01925) 761000 Fax: (01925) 766334 E-mail: sales@imscan.co.uk

In Form Consultants Ltd, Weathervane House, Old Shire Lane, Chorleywood, Rickmansworth, Hertfordshire, WD3 5PW Tel: (01923) 283694 E-mail: info@inform-consult.com

Microformat UK Ltd, 344 High Street, Rochester, Kent, ME1 1JE Tel: (01634) 813751 Fax: (01634) 831557 E-mail: sales@microformat.co.uk

Premier Systems Ltd, Fritham, Lyndhurst, Hampshire, SO43 7HH Tel: (023) 8081 1100

▶ Rapide Reprographics, St. James House, Pendleton Way, Salford, M6 5FW Tel: 0161-743 0302 Fax: 0161-743 0305 E-mail: sales@rapide-repro.co.uk

Scan Optics Ltd, 5 Brookside, Colne Way, Watford, WD24 7QJ Tel: (01923) 819581 Fax: (01923) 212633

Square Group Ltd, 78 New Oxford Street, London, WC1A 1HB Tel: (020) 7692 9990 Fax: (020) 7692 6636 E-mail: sales@squaregroup.co.uk

Tudor Business Forms Ltd, 2 Meridian Centre, Vulcan Way, New Addington, Croydon, CR0 9UG Tel: (01689) 844888 Fax: (01689) 844999 E-mail: sales@tudorofficesupplies.co.uk

DOCUMENT MANAGEMENT SYSTEMS

DocIndexer, St. Martins House, 16 St. Martins le Grand, London, EC1A 4EN Tel: (0870) 7668440 Fax: (0871) 2884087 E-mail: kellysearch@tickboxdb.com

▶ RPJ Document Management Ltd, Unit F2 Harlow Seedbed Centre, Coldharbour Road, Pinnacles East, Harlow, Essex, CM19 5AF Tel: (01279) 450600 Fax: (01279) 411400 E-mail: rpj.dm@btconnect.com

▶ SnowPrince Document Management, 1-3 Lime Hill Road, Tunbridge Wells, Kent, TN1 1LJ Tel: 0870 760 7879 E-mail: info@SnowPrince.co.uk

▶ Virtual Archive, Riverbank House, 1 Putney Bridge Approach, London, SW6 3JD Tel: (020) 7736 9002 Fax: 0207 6106162 E-mail: alex@vasat.co.uk

DOCUMENT PRESENTATION BINDING SYSTEMS

Ape Image Consultants, 36-40 Bloomfield Avenue, Luton, LU2 0PT Tel: (01582) 483718 Fax: (01582) 454518 E-mail: sales@apeimage.co.uk

Babs UK Ltd, Plot 1 Oakwood Hill Industrial Estate, Oakwood Hill, Loughton, Essex, IG10 3TZ Tel: (020) 8965 9821 Fax: (020) 8502 4187 E-mail: info@babs.co.uk

C L C Presentation Systems, Mill Road Industrial Estate, Linlithgow Bridge, Linlithgow, West Lothian, EH49 7SF Tel: (01506) 848779 Fax: (01506) 202779 E-mail: sales@clc-online.co.uk

Comtext Services Ltd, 2 Chatsworth Technology Park, Dunston Road, Whittington Moor, Chesterfield, Derbyshire, S41 8XA Tel: (01246) 260650 Fax: (01246) 260613 E-mail: info@comtextservices.co.uk

Dayfold Ltd, Unit 4-6 27 Black Moor Road, Ebblake Industrial Estate, Verwood, Dorset, BH31 6BE Tel: 01202 827401 Fax: (01202) 825841 E-mail: enquiries@dayfold.com

Harrison Products, East Gate House, Moreton Road, Longborough, Moreton-in-Marsh, Gloucestershire, GL56 0QJ Tel: (01451) 830083 Fax: (01451) 830830

Presentation For Business, L1-L2 Unit Kent Kraft Industrial Estate, Lower Road, Northfleet, Gravesend, Kent, DA11 9SR Tel: (01322) 386717 Fax: (01322) 385506 E-mail: info@p4b.co.uk

Press Co., Kiln Lane, Swindon, SN2 2NP Tel: (01793) 716316 Fax: (01793) 511345 E-mail: sales@presco-uk.com

Printaply Printers' Services, Highfield Lane, Sheffield, S13 9NA Tel: 0114-269 3322 Fax: (0845) 0850077 E-mail: printaply@yahoo.co.uk

R G Scales, 92 Southwark Bridge Road, London, SE1 0EX Tel: (020) 7928 9738 Fax: (0845) 3459182 E-mail: info@document-centre.co.uk

Single Source Binding Ltd, 223 East India Dock Road, London, E14 0ED Tel: (020) 7515 0539 Fax: (020) 7537 9839 E-mail: sales@single-source.co.uk

Unibind Systems Ltd, 3 Oak Court, Betts Way, Crawley, West Sussex, RH10 9GG Tel: (01293) 530182 Fax: (01293) 529272 E-mail: sales@unibindsystems.co.uk

W.H. Ware & Sons Ltd, Barns Ground, Ken Road, Clevedon, Avon, BS21 6ST Tel: (01275) 874327 Fax: (01275) 335480 E-mail: christinewilliams@waresbinding.com

DOCUMENT PROCESSING

▶ C F Systems UK Ltd, 7 Metro Centre, Ronsons Way, Sandridge, St. Albans, Hertfordshire, AL4 9QT Tel: (01727) 841048 Fax: (01727) 840944 E-mail: sales@cfsystems.co.uk

DOCUMENT SCANNING EQUIPMENT

Document Control Services Ltd, 10 Stapledon Road, Orton Southgate, Peterborough, PE2 6TB Tel: (01733) 366800 Fax: (01733) 366801 E-mail: dcs@sapasolutions.co.uk

Micrographic Techniques, Pennington House Unit 10, Commonwealth Close, Leigh, Lancashire, WN7 3BD Tel: (01942) 682562 Fax: (01942) 262867 E-mail: enquiries@paperscanning.co.uk

▶ Pagefree Ltd, 11 Pennine Road, Glossop, Derbyshire, SK13 6NN Tel: (01457) 857006 Fax: (01457) 857006 E-mail: sales@pagefree.co.uk

R W M Data Management Ltd, R W M House, 1-2 Boundry Road, Harfreys Industrial Estate, Great Yarmouth, Norfolk, NR31 0LY Tel: (0870) 2406053 Fax: (01493) 667657 E-mail: info@rwm.co.uk

DOCUMENT TO BRAILLE TRANSLATION SERVICES

▶ Braille Translations, 9 Wadham Gardens, Greenford, Middlesex, UB6 0BP Tel: (07005) 860169 Fax: (020) 8422 2237 E-mail: ghow@brailletranslations.co.uk

DOG COATS

▶ Doggie Coats, 59 Headroomgate Road, Lytham St. Annes, Lancashire, FY8 3BD Tel: (01253) 714713 Fax: (01253) 714713 E-mail: anne@doggiecoats.co.uk

DOG COMBS

Ancol Pet Products Ltd, Ancol House, 113 Leamore Lane, Walsall, WS2 7DA Tel: (01922) 402428 Fax: (01922) 404983 E-mail: sales@ancol.co.uk

Diamond Edge Ltd, 126 Gloucester Road, Brighton, BN1 4BU Tel: (01273) 605922 Fax: (01273) 625074 E-mail: diamondedge@btclick.com

Harry Irving & Co. Ltd, Hi Craft House, Sandy Road, Seaforth, Liverpool, L21 1AG Tel: 0151-928 2487 Fax: 0151-920 0617 E-mail: sales@hi-pet.com

DOG GROOMING PRODUCTS

▶ Four Paws, 34 Sedbury Road, Sompting, Lancing, West Sussex, BN15 0LL Tel: (01903) 521499 E-mail: sarahj@fourpaws.wanadoo.co.uk

DOG HANDLING SECURITY SERVICES

▶ Midland Patrol Dogs Ltd, PO Box 12241, Birmingham, B31 5LZ Tel: 0121-475 2615 E-mail: midlandpatroldog@aol.com

DOG KENNELS

▶ Barking Mad, Wishing Well Cottage, 285 Headley Road East, Woodley, Reading, RG5 4SE Tel: 0118 9693115 E-mail: val.walls@barkingmad.uk.com

PAWS4THOUGHT, 6 PARK COURT, Kidderminster, WORCESTERSHIRE, DY11 6TR Tel: 01562 510290 E-mail: elizabeth.watson63@tesco.net

▶ Trans-K9 Kennel & Dog Transit Products, High Carminnows, Dalry, Castle Douglas, Kirkcudbrightshire, DG7 3TB Tel: 0845 3308849 E-mail: info@transk9.co.uk

DOG SHAMPOOS

▶ Muttley's, Promsfield, Craigbreck, North Kessock, Inverness, IV1 3XG Tel: (01463) 731743 E-mail: info@muttleys.com

DOG TRAINING EQUIPMENT

Ancol Pet Products Ltd, Ancol House, 113 Leamore Lane, Walsall, WS2 7DA Tel: (01922) 402428 Fax: (01922) 404983 E-mail: sales@ancol.co.uk

▶ Doggie Solutions, Hazel Edge, Scotts Grove Road, Chobham, Woking, Surrey, GU24 8DX Tel: (01276) 488119 E-mail: info@doggiesolutions.co.uk

DOG TRANSPORTATION TRAILERS

▶ Muttley's, Promsfield, Craigbreck, North Kessock, Inverness, IV1 3XG Tel: (01463) 731743 E-mail: info@muttleys.com

▶ Trans-K9 Kennel & Dog Transit Products, High Carminnows, Dalry, Castle Douglas, Kirkcudbrightshire, DG7 3TB Tel: 0845 3308849 E-mail: info@transk9.co.uk

DOGSPIKE, *See Rail Spikes etc*

DOLLS HOUSE FURNITURE

▶ Dolly Dolittle Ltd, 23 High Street, Market Harborough, Leicestershire, LE16 7NJ Tel: (01858) 466262 Fax: (01536) 770160 E-mail: ray@dollydolittles.co.uk

▶ Looby Lou's Miniatures, 3 Brookside, Calcot, Reading, RG31 7PJ Tel: 0118-941 9500 E-mail: karen@loobylousminiatures.co.uk

▶ LYLLOY Co.,LTD, Unit 60, 3-9 Hyde Road, Ardwick Green, Manchester, M12 6BQ Tel: 0773 0383126

Seaton Hobby Shop, Goulden Lion House, 23 Fore Street, Seaton, Devon, EX12 2LE Tel: (01297) 22025 Fax: (01297) 22025 E-mail: email@seatonhobbyshop.com

Willow Models, 4 Willow Grove, Golcar, Huddersfield, HD7 4RX Tel: (01484) 658832 Fax: (01484) 658832 E-mail: sales@willowmodels.com

DOLLS HOUSES

▶ Looby Lou's Miniatures, 3 Brookside, Calcot, Reading, RG31 7PJ Tel: 0118-941 9500 E-mail: karen@loobylousminiatures.co.uk

Willow Models, 4 Willow Grove, Golcar, Huddersfield, HD7 4RX Tel: (01484) 658832 Fax: (01484) 658832 E-mail: sales@willowmodels.com

DOLLS HOUSES, WOODEN

▶ Looby Lou's Miniatures, 3 Brookside, Calcot, Reading, RG31 7PJ Tel: 0118-941 9500 E-mail: karen@loobylousminiatures.co.uk

DOMED ACRYLIC BADGES

Dectek Ltd, Unit 29 Business Development Centre, Main Ave, Treforest Industrial Estate, Pontypridd, M. Glam, CF37 5UR Tel: (01443) 841840 Fax: (01443) 842815 E-mail: sales@dectek.co.uk

Key Factors, 11 Cannon Grove, Fetcham, Leatherhead, Surrey, KT22 9LG Tel: (01372) 376904 Fax: (01372) 376904 E-mail: sales@keyfactors.co.uk

DOMED NUTS

Peter Abbott, Unit 10 Keyford Court, Marston Trading Estate, Frome, Somerset, BA11 4BD Tel: (01373) 461261 Fax: (01373) 451513 E-mail: sales@peterabbott.co.uk

DOMED PLASTIC LABELS

A P L Industrial Ltd, 14 Carlisle Road, London, NW9 0HL Tel: (020) 8205 2444 Fax: (020) 8200 8037 E-mail: info@apl-industrial.co.uk

G S M Graphic Art, Castlegarth Works, Masonic Lane, Thirsk, North Yorkshire, YO7 1PS Tel: (01845) 522184 Fax: (01845) 522206 E-mail: gsmgrapicarts@gsmgroup.co.uk

DOMESTIC AIR CONDITIONING (AC) UNITS

Heattend Ltd, 9 Concorde Road, Norwich, NR6 6BH Tel: (01603) 787505 Fax: (01603) 429500 E-mail: sales@heattend.co.uk

▶ Knightsbridge Property Services Ltd, Knightsbridge House, 42 Willow Lane, Mitcham, Surrey, CR4 4NA Tel: (020) 8287 3838 Fax: (020) 8287 3737 E-mail: enquiries@knightsbridgeproperty.co.uk

DOMESTIC AIR PURIFIERS AND CLEANERS

Aircare Europe Ltd, Unit 27 Tatton Court, Kingsland Grange, Woolston, Warrington, WA1 4RR Tel: (08707) 445588 Fax: (01925) 850325 E-mail: info@aircareeurope.com

▶ Elbow Grease Cleaners, Kestrel House, Gurnell Grove, West Ealing, London, W13 0AD Tel: 020 82211300 Fax: 020 85030400 E-mail: info@elbowgreasecleaners.co.uk

Garrett Air Cleaning, 21 Garrett Close, Dunstable, Bedfordshire, LU6 3EG Tel: (01582) 475900 Fax: (01582) 475900

Group 100 Electronics, 145 Avon Road, Worcester, WR4 9AH Tel: (01905) 22875 Fax: (01905) 22875

Health-Air UK, Norwich House, Water Street, Liverpool, L2 9XW Tel: 0151-236 8388 Fax: 0151-236 2369

DOMESTIC AND INDUSTRIAL ELECTRICITY SUPPLY COMPANIES

British Gas Business, Spinneyside, Penman Way, Grove Park, Leicester, LE19 1SZ Tel: 0845 850 0056 E-mail: customerservice@britishgasbusiness.co.uk

Guernsey Electricity, PO Box 4, Guernsey, GY1 3AD Tel: (01481) 200700 Fax: (01481) 246942 E-mail: admin@electricity.gg

Jersey Electricity Co. Ltd, PO Box 45, Jersey, JE4 8NY Tel: (01534) 505000 Fax: (01534) 505011 E-mail: jec@jec.co.uk

▶ Phoenix Power, 323 Goring Road, Goring-by-Sea, Worthing, West Sussex, BN12 4NX Tel: (01903) 248999 Fax: (01903) 249555 E-mail: sales@phoenixpower.net

Powergen plc, Westwood Way, Westwood Business Park, Coventry, CV4 8LG Tel: (024) 7642 4000 Fax: (024) 7642 5432 E-mail: domestic@powergen.co.uk

Powergen plc, Colliers Way, Nottingham, NG8 6AL Tel: (0870) 4191539 Fax: 0115-995 6738 E-mail: sales@eme.co.uk

Powergen plc, Kingsnorth & Grain Power Stations, Hoo, Rochester, Kent, ME3 9NQ Tel: (01634) 250088 Fax: (01634) 872130

R W E npower, Birchfield House, Joseph Street, Oldbury, West Midlands, B69 2AQ Tel: 0121 544 2988 Fax: 0121 541 2404

Scottish Power P.L.C, Corporate Office, 1 Atlantic Quay, Glasgow, G2 8SP Tel: 0141-248 8200 Fax: 0141-248 8300 E-mail: contactus@scottishpower.co.uk

Scottish & Southern Energy P.L.C., Centenary House, 10 Winchester Road, Basingstoke, Hampshire, RG21 8UQ Tel: (0845) 7210220 Fax: (01256) 304269 E-mail: national.sales@scottish-southern.co.uk

Scottish & Southern Energy plc, Inveralmond House, 200 Dunkeld Road, Perth, PH1 3AQ Tel: (01738) 456000 Fax: (01738) 456520 E-mail: info@scottish-southern.co.uk

SWALEC, Ty Meridian, Malthouse Avenue, Cardiff Gate Business Park, Cardiff, CF23 8AU Tel: (0800) 7834121 Fax: (01920) 249760 E-mail: ian.mason@scottish-7.co.uk

▶ Switch Utilities Ltd, New Brook House, 385 Alfreton Road, Nottingham, NG7 5LR Tel: (0845) 6341005 Fax: (0845) 6341006 E-mail: james@switchutilities.com

Utility Options, 78 Northgate Street, Chester, CH1 2HR Tel: (0800) 1950123 Fax: (01352) 781813 E-mail: enquiries@utility-options.co.uk

DOMESTIC APPLIANCE MAINTENANCE OR REPAIR

Electricare, 21 Shepherds Lane, Bracknell, Berkshire, RG42 2BN Tel: (01344) 452648 Fax: (01344) 640098 E-mail: c.onions@ntlworld.com

▶ J S Electrics Bookham, 36 Strathcona Avenue, Bookham, Leatherhead, Surrey, KT23 4HP Tel: (01372) 452617

▶ Sun Electrical Ltd, 17 Heol Nant Bran, Birchgrove, Swansea, SA7 9LS Tel: (01792) 815962 Fax: (01792) 815962 E-mail: sunelectrical@ntlworld.com

▶ A.C. Talbot - Appliance Repairs, 3 Carisbrooke Crescent, Barrow-in-Furness, Cumbria, LA13 0HU Tel: (01229) 835263 Fax: (0871) 2110099 E-mail: andee.talbot@tiscali.co.uk

DOMESTIC BOILERS

Atlantic 2000, PO Box 11, Ashton-under-Lyne, Lancashire, OL6 7TR Tel: 0161-621 5960 Fax: 0161-621 5966 E-mail: info@atlanticboilers.com

B B T Thermo Technology UK Ltd, Danesmoor Works, Pilsley Road, Danesmoor, Chesterfield, Derbyshire, S45 9BY Tel: (01246) 250251 Fax: (01246) 250313

Boulter Boilers Ltd, Magnet House, Whitehouse Road, Ipswich, IP1 5JA Tel: (01473) 241555 Fax: (01473) 241321 E-mail: sales@boulter-buderus.com

Crossling, 2 Kingstown Broadway, Kingstown Industrial Estate, Carlisle, CA3 0HA Tel: (01228) 541101 Fax: (01228) 539288 E-mail: marketing@crossling.co.uk

Dunsley Heat Ltd, Bridge Mills, Holmfirth, HD9 3TW Tel: (01484) 682635 Fax: (01484) 688428 E-mail: sales@dunsleyheat.co.uk

GAH Heating Products Ltd, Building 846, Bentwaters Park, Rendlesham, Woodbridge, Suffolk, IP12 2TW Tel: (01394) 421160 Fax: (01394) 421170 E-mail: mail@gah.co.uk

Heatcall Group Services, Nottingham Road, Belper, Derbyshire, DE56 1JT Tel: (01773) 828100 Fax: (01773) 828123

Ideal Boilers Ltd, PO Box 103, Hull, HU5 4JN Tel: (01482) 492251 Fax: (01482) 448858 E-mail: enquires@idealboilers.com

Malvern Boilers Ltd, Spring Lane North, Malvern, Worcestershire, WR14 1BW Tel: (01684) 893777 Fax: (01684) 893776 E-mail: sales@malvernboilers.co.uk

▶ Mistral Boilers Ltd, Unit C3, Halesfield 23, Telford, Shropshire, TF7 4NY Tel: (01952) 270082 Fax: (01952) 270086 E-mail: mistralboilers@aol.com

Parts Centre, PO Box 48, Ripon, North Yorkshire, HG4 5NB Tel: (01765) 690690

Ravenheat Manufacturing Ltd, Chartists Way, Morley, Leeds, LS27 9ET Tel: 0113-252 7007 Fax: 0113-238 0229

Trianco Heating Products Ltd, Thorncliffe, Chapeltown, Sheffield, S35 2PH Tel: 0114-257 2349 Fax: 0114-257 1419 E-mail: info@trianco.co.uk

DOMESTIC BUILDING STRUCTURAL OR ENGINEERING DESIGN

Consulting Engineers' Co-Partnership London Ltd, 1528 London Road, London, SW16 4EU Tel: (020) 8679 5621 Fax: (020) 8679 7922 E-mail: mail@cecp.co.uk

Cooper Beal & Ross, 33 Shaw Road, Stockport, Cheshire, SK4 4AG Tel: 0161-442 9770 Fax: 0161-442 9775 E-mail: cooperbealross@aol.com

▶ Rupee Design Ltd, 12a Sutherland Avenue, Maida Vale, London, W9 2HQ Tel: (020) 7289 3201 E-mail: rupeedesign@yahoo.co.uk

Leslie Wilks Associates, 1 Sunnyside, Claygate Road, Laddingford, Maidstone, Kent, ME18 6BQ Tel: (01892) 730863 Fax: (01892) 730864 E-mail: info@leslie-wilks.co.uk

DOMESTIC CEILING FANS

▶ Cannoc Electrical, Unit 5 Martindale Industrial Estate, Hawks Green, Cannock, Staffordshire, WS11 7XN Tel: (01543) 505104 Fax: (01543) 466034 E-mail: sales@cannockelectrical.com

DOMESTIC CIRCULATING PUMPS

Halstead Boilers Ltd, 16-22 First Avenue, Halstead, Essex, CO9 2EX Tel: (01787) 475557 Fax: (01787) 474588 E-mail: sales@halsteadboilers.co.uk

DOMESTIC CLEANING PRODUCTS, *See also headings for particular types*

A Baillie Hygiene & Co., Water Street, Kettering, Northamptonshire, NN16 0JR Tel: (01536) 519048 Fax: (01536) 417892

Advance Cleaning & Supplies, 4 Station Road, Ystradgynlais, Swansea, SA9 1NT Tel: (01639) 841444

Anglowide Marketing Ltd, County Ground Works, Deanstones Lane, Bradford, West Yorkshire, BD13 2AT Tel: (01274) 883668 Fax: (01274) 818980

▶ Clean-A-Home Leeds, Suite A, 43 Cardinal Grove, Leeds, LS11 8HG Tel: 0113 2171248 E-mail: denise.cleanahome@ntlworld.com

Home Care Products UK Ltd, Consort House, Princes Road, Ferndown, Dorset, BH22 9JG Tel: (01202) 871717 Fax: (01202) 876161 E-mail: homecare@btconnect.com

Hope & Brown Ltd, Blackburn Road, West End, Oswaldtwistle, Lancashire, BB5 4LL Tel: (01254) 390050 Fax: (01254) 223609

▶ Household Essentials, 25 Amberley Close, Littlehampton, West Sussex, BN17 6HW Tel: 01903 714355 E-mail: enq@household-essentials.co.uk

Hull Vac, Unit 8 South Orbital Trading Park, Hedon Road, Hull, HU9 1NJ Tel: (01482) 320633 Fax: (01482) 213671 E-mail: hullvac@aoil.com

Lancashire Hygiene, 12 Forest Road, Southport, Merseyside, PR8 6ST Tel: (01704) 535363 Fax: (01704) 514800

Moston Janitorial Supplies Ltd, 270 Lightbowne Road, Manchester, M40 5HQ Tel: 0161-688 8282 Fax: 0161-684 8791 E-mail: sales@mostonjanitorial.co.uk

▶ Oven Master, 12 Fuchsia Close, Priorslee, Telford, Shropshire, TF2 9PG Tel: (01952) 210067 Fax: (01952) 210067 E-mail: ovenmaster@tiscali.co.uk

Reckitt Benckiser, Delta 1200, Welton Road, Delta Business Park, Swindon, SN5 7XZ Tel: (01793) 427200 Fax: (01793) 511572

RJN Chemicals Ltd, 6 The Ridgeway, Iver, Buckinghamshire, SL0 9HX Tel: (01753) 655076 Fax: (01753) 652983 E-mail: info@rjnchemicals.com

St Margarets Mill Retreats, St. Margarets Mill, Caister Road, Acle, Norwich, NR13 3AX Tel: (01493) 752288

Spick & Span Supplies, Oakhurst, Bourton Road, Frankton, Rugby, Warwickshire, CV23 9NX Tel: (01926) 633090 Fax: (01926) 633090

Squeegee Clean Direct, 76 Leyland Rd, Penwortham, Preston, PR1 9XS Tel: 01772 491431

Tecserv, Unit 7, Parsons Green Estate, Boulton Road, Stevenage, Hertfordshire, SG1 4QG Tel: (01438) 750905 Fax: (01438) 315270 E-mail: macserv-fcm@btconnect.com

Total Hygiene Supplies, 3 Bedlay Place, Annathill, Coatbridge, Lanarkshire, ML5 2QR Tel: (01236) 870088 Fax: (01236) 870088

DOMESTIC COFFEE MAKERS

▶ Discount Appliance Centre Ltd, Cook House, Brunel Drive, Newark, Nottinghamshire, NG24 3FB Tel: (0870) 0671420 Fax: (01636) 707737 E-mail: info@thedac.co.uk

Evencray Ltd, Unit 8, Welbeck Way, Woodston, Peterborough, PE2 7WH Tel: (01733) 371700 Fax: (01733) 361065 E-mail: ashley_young@btclick.com

Fracino Catering Equipment, Unit 17-19 Birch Road East Industrial Estate, Birch Road East, Birmingham, B6 7DA Tel: 0121-328 5757 Fax: 0121-327 3333 E-mail: sales@fracino.com

Teknomat UK Ltd, Unit 27, Wornal Park, Menmarsh Road, Worminghall, Aylesbury, Buckinghamshire, HP18 9PH Tel: (01844) 339828 Fax: (01844) 339829

DOMESTIC DISHWASHERS

▶ Glebe Radio & Television Ltd, 33 Glebe Farm Road, Birmingham, B33 9LY Tel: 0121-783 3352 Fax: 0121-783 1498 E-mail: glebetv@freedomnames.co.uk

DOMESTIC DOOR LOCKS

Access & Security 24Hr Locksmiths, Key House Coombe Rise, Oadby, Leicester, LE2 5TT Tel: 0116-271 9003 Fax: 0116-271 9229 E-mail: info@leicesterlocksmith.com

Door Centre, Eastfield Industrial Estate, Penicuik, Midlothian, EH26 8HA Tel: (01968) 671680 Fax: (01968) 671684 E-mail: sales@thedoorcentre.co.uk

▶ Torbay Security Solutions, 46 Bitton Avenue, Teignmouth, Devon, TQ14 8HD Tel: (01626) 776161 Fax: (01626) 772583 E-mail: enquiries@torbaysecuritysolutions.co.uk

DOMESTIC ELECTRIC APPLIANCE COMPONENTS/ SPARE PARTS/WEARING PARTS MANUFRS

Allprep Weighing Equipment, 26 Church Lane, Caythorpe, Grantham, Lincolnshire, NG32 3DU Tel: (01400) 273877 Fax: (01400) 273877

DOMESTIC ELECTRIC APPLIANCE COMPONENTS/SPARE PARTS/ WEARING PARTS MANUFRS – *continued*

Babytec International Ltd, 5B Sunrise Business, Blandford Forum, Dorset, DT11 8ST Tel: (01258) 459554 Fax: (01258) 480225 E-mail: stephenbenson@babytec.co.uk
Bridisco Ltd, Devonshire House, 550 White Hart Lane, London, N17 7RQ Tel: (020) 8881 2001 Fax: (020) 8829 9210
Ces Microcare Ltd, 1 Muirhall Road, Larbert, Stirlingshire, FK5 4RR Tel: (01324) 552121 Fax: (01324) 562299 E-mail: service@ces-microcare.co.uk
Denmans Electrical Wholesalers Ltd, Unit 10 Pages Industrial Park, Eden Way, Leighton Buzzard, Bedfordshire, LU7 4TZ Tel: (01525) 374666 Fax: (01525) 852662 E-mail: denmans@theleightonbuzzard.freeserve.co.uk
Denmans Electrical Wholesalers Ltd, Hickman Avenue, Wolverhampton, WV1 2XD Tel: (01902) 453551 Fax: (01902) 456666 E-mail: wolverhampton@denmans.co.uk
Devondale Electrical Distributors, Unit 3 24 Marsh Green Road West, Marsh Barton Trading Estate, Exeter, EX2 8PN Tel: (01392) 667474 Fax: (01392) 420037 E-mail: sales@devondale.net
E T B Services Ltd, 7 James St Workshops, James Street, Carlisle, CA2 5AH Tel: (01228) 594747 Fax: (01228) 594665 E-mail: etb@btclick.com
Eastleigh Domestic Appliance Services, 53 Twyford Road, Eastleigh, Hampshire, SO50 4HH Tel: (023) 8064 4984 Fax: (023) 8061 2799 E-mail: sales@eastleigh-services.co.uk
Edmundson Electrical Ltd, 31C Ganton Way, Techno Trading Estate, Swindon, SN2 8ES Tel: (01793) 522241 Fax: (01793) 524504 E-mail: swindon.274@eel.co.uk
Electrical & Contractors Supplies, 177 Meanwood Road, Leeds, LS7 1JP Tel: 0113-242 9295 Fax: 0113-242 5021 E-mail: sales@ecs-electrical.com
Electrical Services (Nelson) Ltd, 43 Belgrave St., Nelson, Lancashire, BB9 9HS Tel: (01282) 696317 Fax: (01282) 611632 E-mail: david@electricialsales.co.uk
Electrical Supplies Bolton Ltd, 68 Chorley Old Road, Bolton, BL1 3AE Tel: (01204) 362959 Fax: (01204) 362503
Ems, 18-22 Queen Street, Leicester, LE1 1QR Tel: 0116-262 2588 Fax: 0116-251 1429 E-mail: emsleister@rexelscnet.co.uk
Evencray Ltd, Unit 8, Welbeck Way, Woodston, Peterborough, PE2 7WH Tel: (01733) 371700 Fax: (01733) 361065 E-mail: ashley_young@btclick.com
Eyre & Elliston Ltd, H Bolton Central Industrial Estate, St Marks Street, Bolton, BL3 6NR Tel: (01204) 366601 Fax: (01204) 366602 E-mail: bolton@eyreandelliston.co.uk
Eyre & Elliston Ltd, 40 Brownfields, Welwyn Garden City, Hertfordshire, AL7 1AX Tel: (01707) 326344 Fax: (01707) 372334
North Bristol Appliances, 42 Lockleaze Road, Bristol, BS7 9RT Tel: 0117-971 4964
Orion Electric (UK) Ltd, Unit 3, Kenfig Industrial Estate, Margam, Port Talbot, West Glamorgan, SA13 2PE Tel: (01656) 742400 Fax: (01656) 744700 E-mail: oeu@relay.co.uk
Panther UK Ltd, Panther House, 1 Panther Drive, London, NW10 0JP Tel: (020) 7887 7777 Fax: (020) 7887 7711 E-mail: products@pantheronline.co.uk
R Barker Tarring Ltd, 32 South Street, Tarring, Worthing, West Sussex, BN14 7LN Tel: (01903) 233680 Fax: (01903) 824690 E-mail: rbarkerltd@mail.com
Sale Appliances Ltd, 343 Victoria Avenue, Southend-on-Sea, SS2 6NH Tel: (01702) 390845 Fax: (01702) 390845 E-mail: sales@saleappliances.co.uk
Sharley Domestics, 6 Green Lane, Radnage, High Wycombe, Buckinghamshire, HP14 4DN Tel: (01494) 485926 Fax: (01494) 484140 E-mail: sharleydomestics@btconnect.com
▶ Vacuumbags2u.co.uk, 115 Sedlescombe Road North, St. Leonards-on-Sea, East Sussex, TN37 7EJ Tel: (01424) 729800 E-mail: silverhillapp@btconnect.com

DOMESTIC ELECTRIC FAN HEATERS

BN Thermic Ltd, 34 Woodside Road, London, SE25 5DY Tel: (01293) 547361 Fax: (01293) 531432 E-mail: sales@bnthermic.co.uk
Consort 1996 Ltd, Thornton Industrial Estate, Milford Haven, Dyfed, SA73 2RT Tel: (01646) 692172 Fax: (01646) 695195 E-mail: enquiries@consortepl.com
Edwards & Hope, 5 New Road, Brighton, BN1 1UF Tel: (01273) 775166 Fax: (01273) 746610
Glen Dimplex UK Ltd, Millbrook House, Grange Drive, Hedge End, Southampton, SO30 2DF Tel: (0845) 6005111 Fax: (0870) 7270109 E-mail: enquiries@dimplex.co.uk
Grate Glow Fires, Mill Lane, Old Swan, Liverpool, L13 4AJ Tel: 0151-252 6600 Fax: 0151-220 5277 E-mail: info@robinson-willey.com
Mercian Electric, 79-93 Ratcliffe Road, Sileby, Loughborough, Leicestershire, LE12 7PU Tel: (01509) 816181 Fax: (01509) 816060
W H Flinn Ltd, 77 Albony Road, Manchester, M21 0BN Tel: 0161-881 9591 Fax: 0161-862 9180 E-mail: whflinn@btconnect.com

DOMESTIC ELECTRIC FIRES

Edmundson Electrical Ltd, 2 Portland Road Industrial Estate, Portland Road, Hove, East Sussex, BN3 5NT Tel: (01273) 430789 Fax: (01273) 430650 E-mail: brighton.122@eel.co.uk
Edmundson Electrical Ltd, 31C Ganton Way, Techno Trading Estate, Swindon, SN2 8ES Tel: (01793) 522241 Fax: (01793) 524504 E-mail: swindon.274@eel.co.uk
Fires4U, PO Box 6843, Swadlincote, Derbyshire, DE12 7XX Tel: (0845) 6120001 E-mail: sales@fires4u.co.uk
Glen Dimplex UK Ltd, Millbrook House, Grange Drive, Hedge End, Southampton, SO30 2DF Tel: (0845) 6005111 Fax: (0870) 7270109 E-mail: enquiries@dimplex.co.uk
▶ Internetfiresdirect, Bent Ley Industrial Estate, Meltham, Holmfirth, HD9 4EP Tel: (0870) 2242847 Fax: (01484) 854867 E-mail: richard.kaye@adamsurrounds.co.uk
Seagoe Technology Ltd, Church Road, Portadown, Craigavon, County Armagh, BT63 5HU Tel: (028) 3833 3131 Fax: (028) 3835 1390 E-mail: info@jltgroup.com
W H Flinn Ltd, 77 Albony Road, Manchester, M21 0BN Tel: 0161-881 9591 Fax: 0161-862 9180 E-mail: whflinn@btconnect.com

DOMESTIC ELECTRIC IRONS

Rowenta (UK) Ltd, 1A Langley Business Centre, Station Road, Slough, SL3 8PH Tel: (01753) 796400 Fax: (01753) 796499

DOMESTIC ELECTRICAL APPLIANCE TAPES

▶ J C Electrics, 1-3 Verlands Court, Verlands Way, Pencoed, Bridgend, Mid Glamorgan, CF35 6JA Tel: (01656) 863536 Fax: (01656) 863536 E-mail: sales@jcelectrics.com

DOMESTIC ELECTRICAL ENGINEERING

B P D Building Services, 7 Sunnyside Grove, Ashton-under-Lyne, Lancashire, OL6 6TN Tel: 0161-612 7514 E-mail: paul@bpd-ltd.com
▶ Electrical Concepts, 55 Aylands Road, Enfield, Middlesex, EN3 6PW Tel: (01992) 700825 Fax: (01992) 700825 E-mail: electrician74@tiscali.co.uk
▶ Erleback engineering ltd, Dixies Barns, High Street, Ashwell, Baldock, Hertfordshire, SG7 5NT Tel: (0870) 7407481 Fax: (0870) 7407482 E-mail: michael@erlebach.freeserve.co.uk
H J M Services, 12 Regent Squsre, Northampton, NN1 2NQ Tel: (01604) 639792 Fax: (01604) 630919 E-mail: hjm@dial.pipex.com
▶ Nodal Engineering Ltd, Riverside House, Riverside Drive, Aberdeen, AB11 7LH Tel: 01224 224360 Fax: 01224 224301 E-mail: info@nodalengineering.com

DOMESTIC ELECTRONIC EQUIPMENT TESTING

▶ Fluke (UK) Ltd, 52 Hurricane Way, Norwich, NR6 6JB Tel: (020) 7942 0700 Fax: (020) 7942 0701 E-mail: industrial@uk.fluke.nl
Mercom, 5 Cowley Road, Nuffield Industrial Estate, Poole, Dorset, BH17 0UJ Tel: (01202) 661210 Fax: (01202) 661216 E-mail: kevin.hockney@mercom.org

DOMESTIC GAS FIRES

Grate Glow Fires, Mill Lane, Old Swan, Liverpool, L13 4AJ Tel: 0151-252 6600 Fax: 0151-220 5277 E-mail: info@robinson-willey.com
Strax Gas Ltd, Longfield Road, Sydenham Industrial Estate, Leamington Spa, Warwickshire, CV31 1XB Tel: (01926) 477511 Fax: (01926) 477510 E-mail: sales@straxgas.co.uk
▶ Verrall & Parks, 225-227 Seaside, Eastbourne, East Sussex, BN22 7NR Tel: (01323) 737633 Fax: (01323) 745789 E-mail: sales@verrallandparks.co.uk

DOMESTIC GAS METERS

▶ Trade Meter Supplies Ltd, I-Centre House, Hamilton Way, Mansfield, Nottinghamshire, NG18 5BR Tel: (01623) 600677 Fax: (01623) 422003E-mail: info@trademetersupplies.co.uk

DOMESTIC GOODS, *See headings for particular types such as Hardware*

DOMESTIC HARDWARE

J. Banks & Co. Ltd, Excelsior Works, Wood Street, Willenhall, West Midlands, WV13 1JY Tel: (01902) 605084 Fax: (01902) 603248 E-mail: contact@jbanks.co.uk
Beldorm Ltd, Kearsley Mill, Crompton Road, Radcliffe, Manchester, M26 1RH Tel: (01204) 702300 Fax: (01204) 854854 E-mail: sales@ruia.co.uk
Bodel Distributors Ltd, 9 Hulls Lane, Lisburn, County Antrim, BT28 2SR Tel: (028) 9267 2412 Fax: (028) 9267 1873 E-mail: sales@badel.com
Croydex Ltd, Central Way, Andover, Hampshire, SP10 5AW Tel: (01264) 365881 Fax: (01264) 356437 E-mail: admin@croydex.co.uk
Home Care Products UK Ltd, Consort House, Princes Road, Ferndown, Dorset, BH22 9JG Tel: (01202) 871717 Fax: (01202) 876161 E-mail: homecare@btconnect.com
John Anslow Ltd, Stafford Street, Wednesbury, West Midlands, WS10 7JX Tel: 0121-556 1125 Fax: 0121-556 5414
Miele Co. Ltd, Fairacres, Marcham Road, Abingdon, Oxfordshire, OX14 1TW Tel: (0845) 3303618 Fax: (01235) 554477 E-mail: miele-professional@miele.co.uk
Radmore Agencies Ltd, Perry House, Torton, Kidderminster, Worcestershire, DY10 4HY Tel: (01299) 250621 Fax: (01299) 251444
Spinnaker Products Ltd, Unit 15, Rylands Farm Industrial Estate, Bagley Road, Rockwell Grove, Wellington, Somerset, TA21 9PZ Tel: (01823) 400969 Fax: (01823) 665268
Titon Hardware, 11 Piperell Way, Haverhill, Suffolk, CB9 8PH Tel: (01440) 762223 Fax: (01440) 706808
W H Povoas Ltd, Radnor Street, Stretford, Manchester, M32 8LP Tel: 0161-865 1086 Fax: 0161-864 3584 E-mail: sales@whpovoas.co.uk
▶ Wilkinson, 14 The Chilterns, High Wycombe, Buckinghamshire, HP13 5ES Tel: (01494) 471608
William O'Hanlon & Co Ltd, Mochdre Industrial Estate, Mochdre, Newtown, Powys, SY16 4LE Tel: (01686) 611800 Fax: (01686) 611802 E-mail: info@williamohanlon.co.uk

DOMESTIC HEATERS, *See also Electric, Gas etc*

Potterton Commercial, Brooks House, Coventry Road, Warwick, CV34 4LL Tel: (0870) 6001991 Fax: (01926) 405305
R H Adams Forest Hill Ltd, Hindsleys Place, London, SE23 2NQ Tel: (020) 8699 4803 Fax: (020) 8699 8493
V A Heating Ltd, 30-38 Yeaman Street, Stoke-on-Trent, ST4 4AP Tel: (01782) 845633 Fax: (01782) 745371

DOMESTIC HOT WATER BOILER HIRE

Ready Heat UK Ltd, Unit B5 Bulwell Business Centre, Sellers Wood Drive, Bulwell, Nottingham, NG6 8GN Tel: 0115-975 4500 Fax: 0115-975 4500

DOMESTIC INCINERATORS

H & E Knowles (Lye) Ltd, Britannia Works, Talbots Lane, Brierley Hill, West Midlands, DY5 2YX Tel: (01384) 78877 Fax: (01384) 79012 E-mail: sales@heknowles.freeserves.co.uk

DOMESTIC LIGHTING

C B Lighting Co., 56 Staplehill Road, Fishponds, Bristol, BS16 5BS Tel: 0117-907 4906 Fax: 0117-966 0311
▶ Clitheroe Lighting Centre, 14 Moor Lane, Clitheroe, Lancashire, BB7 1BE Tel: (01200) 423757 Fax: (01200) 423757 E-mail: lights@clitheroelightingcentre.co.uk
Concord Marlin Ltd, Avis Way, Newhaven, East Sussex, BN9 0ED Tel: (01273) 515811 Fax: (01273) 512688 E-mail: info@concordmarlin.com
Dar Lighting Ltd, Wildmere Road, Banbury, Oxfordshire, OX16 3JZ Tel: (01295) 672200 Fax: (01295) 271743 E-mail: sales@darlighting.co.uk
David Hunt Lighting Ltd, Tilemans Lane, Shipston-on-Stour, Warwickshire, CV36 4HP Tel: (01608) 661590 Fax: (01608) 662951
Dernier & Hamlyn Ltd, Unit 5 Jaycee House, 214 Purley Way, Croydon, CR0 4XG Tel: (020) 8760 0900 Fax: (020) 8760 0955 E-mail: info@dernier-hamlyn.com
Eterna Lighting Ltd, Eterna Lighting Huxley Close, Park Farm South, Wellingborough, Northamptonshire, NN8 6AB Tel: (01933) 404140 Fax: (01933) 678083 E-mail: sales@eterna-lighting.co.uk
Firstlight Products Ltd, 22 Erica Road, Stacey Bushes, Milton Keynes, MK12 6HS Tel: (01908) 310221 Fax: (01908) 310229 E-mail: flp@firstlight-products.co.uk
Franklite Factory Shop, Snowdon Drive, Winterhill, Milton Keynes, MK6 1AP Tel: (01908) 443090 Fax: (01908) 691939 E-mail: info@franklite.ltd.uk
G E Lighting Ltd, 129 - 135 Camp Road, St. Albans, Hertfordshire, AL1 5HL Tel: (01727) 795493 Fax: (01727) 795422
Illuma Lighting Ltd, 11a Sills Road, Castle Donington, Derby, DE74 2US Tel: (01332) 818200 Fax: (01332) 818222 E-mail: info@illuma.co.uk
J & M Parker Ltd, 9 New Summer Street, Birmingham, B19 3QN Tel: 0121-359 8897 Fax: 0121-359 4497 E-mail: enquiries@parker.co.uk
Lightbulb Co. (UK) Ltd, Thomas Edison House, 74-77 Magdalen Road, Oxford, OX4 1RE Tel: (01865) 794500 Fax: (01865) 203996 E-mail: sales@thelightbulb.co.uk
▶ Lumino Ltd, Lumino House, Lovet Road, Harlow, Essex, CM19 5TB Tel: (01279) 635411 Fax: (01279) 626101 E-mail: info@lumino.co.uk
Noral Ltd, Unit 1 The Oaks, Mill Farm Courtyard, Stratford Road, Beechampton, Milton Keynes, MK19 6DS Tel: (01908) 561818 Fax: (01908) 569785 E-mail: lighting@noral-gb.co.uk
Poole Lighting Ltd, Cabot Lane, Poole, Dorset, BH17 7BY Tel: (01202) 690945 Fax: (01202) 600166 E-mail: vanessa.saxby@poolelighting.com
R V L Ltd, Sion Street, Radcliffe, Manchester, M26 3SB Tel: 0161-723 5039 Fax: 0161-724 9078 E-mail: rvl.ltd@ukgateway.net
Reggiani Ltd, 7-8 Warwick Road, Borehamwood, Hertfordshire, WD6 1US Tel: (020) 8953 0855 Fax: (020) 8236 3099 E-mail: reggiani@reggiani.net
Rutland Lighting, Thistleton Road Industrial Estate, Market Overton, Oakham, Leicestershire, LE15 7PP Tel: (01572) 767587 Fax: (01572) 767420 E-mail: Ab@rutlandlighting.sagehost.co.uk
Simplex Marketing Ltd, Lowerclough Mill, Pendle Street, Nelson, Lancashire, BB9 8PH Tel: (01282) 697777 Fax: (01282) 699929
West Midlands Lighting Centre, 10-12 York Road, Erdington, Birmingham, B23 6TE Tel: 0121-350 1999 Fax: 0121-377 7490 E-mail: westlight@msn.com

DOMESTIC LIGHTING CONTRACTORS, *See Electrical Contractors*

DOMESTIC LIGHTING DESIGN

▶ Fenton Mcintosh, 3 Eastern Terrace Mews, Kemptown, Brighton, BN2 1EP Tel: (01273) 628700 E-mail: iain@fenton-mcintosh.co.uk
▶ Firefly Lighting Design, 4th Floor Threshold House, 65-69 Shepherds Bush Green, London, W12 8TX Tel: (020) 8746 2991 E-mail: info@fireflylightingdesign.com
▶ Future Designs Ltd, The Lighthouse, Fircroft Way, Edenbridge, Kent, TN8 6EJ Tel: (01732) 867420 Fax: (01732) 863459
Lightiq Ltd, 1 Rylett Studios 77 Rylett Crescent, London, W12 9RP Tel: (020) 8749 1900 Fax: (020) 8749 1999 E-mail: abby@lighting.com
▶ Michael Warren Design, 275 Goldhawk Road, London, W12 8EU Tel: (07957) 195895 E-mail: mail@michaelwarrendesign.com

DOMESTIC LIGHTING LAMPS

Cascade Electrolite Ltd, Gorse Mill, Gorse Street, Chadderton, Oldham, OL9 9RJ Tel: 0161-628 6622 Fax: 0161-628 2831
▶ Clitheroe Lighting Centre, 14 Moor Lane, Clitheroe, Lancashire, BB7 1BE Tel: (01200) 423757 Fax: (01200) 423757 E-mail: lights@clitheroelightingcentre.co.uk
▶ Heathfield & Co., 2 Priory Road, Tonbridge, Kent, TN9 2AF Tel: (01732) 350450 Fax: (01732) 353525 E-mail: sales@heathfield.co.uk
Welwyn Lighting Designs Ltd, Bessemer Road, Welwyn Garden City, Hertfordshire, AL7 1HH Tel: (01707) 255300 Fax: (01707) 255357 E-mail: sales@wewyn-lighting.co.uk

DOMESTIC MIRRORS

Caplin Glass, Unit 9a Queens Yard, White Post Lane, London, E9 5EN Tel: (020) 8986 0047 Fax: (020) 8986 0455
Classic Glass, 6 Hillview Industrial Estate, Castle Road, Randalstown, Antrim, BT41 2ED Tel: (028) 9447 2920 Fax: (028) 9447 2964 E-mail: sales@classicglass.com
Dutton Glass & Mirrors Ltd, 66 Holloway Head, Birmingham, B1 1NG Tel: 0121-622 1221 Fax: 0121-643 5520
Gray & Mcdonnell, Unit 3 4 City Cross Business Park, Salutation Road, London, SE10 0AT Tel: (020) 8858 8050 Fax: (020) 8269 1513 E-mail: mirrors@graymcdonnell.co.uk
Home Improvement Bureau, 21-23 Station Road, New Barnet, Barnet, Hertfordshire, EN5 1PH Tel: (020) 8441 0352 Fax: (020) 8441 0219

DOMESTIC MIRRORS - *continued*

J Preedy & Sons Ltd, Lamb Works, North Road, London, N7 9DP Tel: (020) 7700 0377 Fax: (020) 7700 7579 E-mail: sales@preedyglass.com
McCollins, Boynton Hall, Boynton St, Hull, HU3 3BZ Tel: (01482) 329634 Fax: (01482) 329634
Manuscript Holdings Ltd, Moorswater, Moorswater, Liskeard, Cornwall, PL14 4LG Tel: (01579) 340340 Fax: (01579) 340341 E-mail: sales@manuscript.co.uk
Midland Framing, 988 Tyburn Road, Birmingham, B24 0TL Tel: 0121-384 4831 Fax: 0121-384 4831
Mirrors & Glass Stockport Ltd, 84 Wellington Road North, Stockport, Cheshire, SK4 1HW Tel: 0161-480 1875 Fax: 0161-480 7008 E-mail: sales@mirrorsandglass.co.uk
P Binnington, Botany Farm, East Lulworth, Wareham, Dorset, BH20 5QH Tel: (01929) 400224 Fax: (01929) 400744 E-mail: p.binnington@aol.co.uk
Spectrum Photos, Belgrave Gate, Leicester, LE1 3GQ Tel: 0116-251 9478 Fax: 0116-251 9478 E-mail: spectrumphoto@virginnet.co.uk
Universal Glass Co, 8-16 Camelon Street, Glasgow, G32 6AF Tel: 0141-764 0444 Fax: 0141-764 0044 E-mail: universalglass@btinternet.com
Witham Glass Works, 1 Wilton Street, Hull, HU8 7LG Tel: (01482) 329183 Fax: (01482) 211959
Wyndham Plastics & Glass, Unit 8 Horsefair Road, Waterton Industrial Estate, Bridgend, Mid Glamorgan, CF31 3TN Tel: (01656) 667767 Fax: (01656) 669915 E-mail: steve@wyndham-plastics.co.uk
Yearn Glass & Co., 55 Wallis Road, London, E9 5LH Tel: (020) 8533 3307 Fax: (020) 8533 7189 E-mail: sales@yearnglass.co.uk

DOMESTIC OR OFFICE FANS

CCL Veloduct, 1-3 Dean Road, Lincoln, LN2 4DR Tel: (01522) 567087 Fax: (01522) 563525

DOMESTIC OR STRUCTURAL SOUND INSULATION SERVICES

Domestic & General Insulation Ltd, 9 Bridges Business Park, Bridge Road, Horsehay, Telford, Shropshire, TF4 3EE Tel: (01952) 507777 Fax: (01952) 501111 E-mail: office@dgitelford.co.uk
Sheffield Insulation Ltd, South Port, Forshore Way, Cardiff, CF10 5SP Tel: (029) 2049 3371 Fax: (029) 2066 2911 E-mail: cardiff@sheffins.co.uk

DOMESTIC OR WHEELCHAIR LIFTS

The Britannic Lift Company plc, Riverview Buildings, Bradford Road, Riddlesden, Keighley, West Yorkshire, BD20 5JH Tel: (01535) 600066 Fax: (01535) 600077 E-mail: sales@lifts.co.uk
Stannah Stairlifts LTS, Watt Close, Andover, Hampshire, SP10 3SD Tel: (0800) 715492 E-mail: nigel_dickinson@stannah.co.uk
Wessex Medical Equipment Co. Ltd, Budds Lane, Romsey, Hampshire, SO51 0HA Tel: (01794) 830303 Fax: (01794) 512621 E-mail: info@wessexmedical.co.uk

DOMESTIC PROPERTY CLEANING

▶ Arleys Angels Ltd, 2 Old Farm, Arley Road, Appleton, Warrington, WA4 4RP Tel: (01925) 266834 Fax: (01925) 266895 E-mail: info@arleysangels.co.uk
▶ Clean 4 You, 7 Rosina Way, Penwithick, St. Austell, Cornwall, PL26 8TS Tel: 01726 851418 Fax: 01726 851418 E-mail: cleanforyou@btinternet.com
▶ Clean-A-Home Leeds, Suite A, 43 Cardinal Grove, Leeds, LS11 8HG Tel: 0113 2171248 E-mail: denise.cleanahome@ntlworld.com
▶ Crystal Clean Southwest, Carrick Business Centre, Commercial Road, Penryn, Cornwall, TR10 8AR Tel: (01326) 377999 Fax: 01326 377999 E-mail: crystal_cleaning@btconnect.com
▶ Domestic Perfection, 4 Speldhurst Road, Tunbridge Wells, Kent, TN4 0DP Tel: (07743) 933171 E-mail: d.perfection@btinternet.com
▶ Dustdees Domestic Cleaning, 4 Hartland Road, Reading, RG2 8BN Tel: 0118-986 0254 E-mail: djs180671@yahoo.co.uk
▶ Happy Hands Domestic Cleaning Agency, PO Box 30418, London, NW6 7FX Tel: (020) 8451 7070 Fax: (020) 8830 0443 E-mail: paul@happy-hands.biz
▶ L Razec, 82 Oakdale Road, Poole, Dorset, BH15 3LQ Tel: (07716) 529694 E-mail: contact@razec.co.uk
▶ M AND M DOMESTIC SERVICES, 5 Prudden Close, Elstow, Bedford, MK42 9EB Tel: 01234 219924 E-mail: mandmservices@fsmail.net
▶ Maids for You, 120 Mow Lane, Gillow Heath, Stoke-on-Trent, ST8 6RJ Tel: (01782) 515541 E-mail: avrily@aol.com
▶ Merediths Maids, 15 Crescent Road, Kidderminster, Worcestershire, DY11 6RN Tel: (07891) 815232 E-mail: tracey@meredithsmaids.com
▶ Oven Master, 12 Fuchsia Close, Priorslee, Telford, Shropshire, TF2 9PG Tel: (01952) 210067 Fax: (01952) 210067 E-mail: ovenmaster@tiscali.co.uk
▶ Perfect Example, Kendall, Roack Road, St. Minver, Wadebridge, Cornwall, PL27 6PN Tel: (01208) 869555 E-mail: info@perfectexample.co.uk
▶ Spicnspan, 5 Christie Avenue, Morecambe, Lancashire, LA4 5UR Tel: (01524) 310749 E-mail: cleaningcleanse@yahoo.co.uk
▶ Spotless Cleaning Services, 317 Coalburn Road, Coalburn, Lanark, ML11 0NF Tel: (01555) 820032 Fax: (01555) 820032 E-mail: spotless@email.com

DOMESTIC RADIATORS

Aestus Ltd, Unit 5, Strawberry Lane, Willenhall, West Midlands, WV13 3RF Tel: (01902) 632256 Fax: (01902) 635800 E-mail: sales@aestus-radiators.com
Coverad Ltd, The Brows, Farnham Road, Liss, Hampshire, GU33 6JG Tel: (01730) 893393 Fax: (01730) 893696
Express Radiators & Bathrooms Ltd, Abbey Mills, Charfield Road, Kingswood, Wotton-under-Edge, Gloucestershire, GL12 8RL Tel: (01453) 521166 Fax: (01453) 521799
M H S Ltd, 35 Nobel Square, Burnt Mills Industrial Estate, Basildon, Essex, SS13 1LT Tel: (01268) 591010 Fax: (01268) 728202 E-mail: sales@modular-heating-group.co.uk
Vogue Management Services Ltd, Unit 8-10 Strawberry La Industrial Estate, Strawberry Lane, Willenhall, West Midlands, WV13 3RS Tel: (0870) 4030107 Fax: (0870) 4030108 E-mail: info@vogue-uk.co.uk

DOMESTIC SECURITY DOORS

▶ ISYS Integrated Systems, Isys House, 23 Innotec Drive, Bangor, County Down, BT19 7PD Tel: (0845) 0945925 E-mail: info@isysni.com

DOMESTIC SECURITY INTERCOM SYSTEMS

▶ London Intercom, 119-123 Sandycombe Road, Richmond, Surrey, TW9 2EP Tel: 07790 145376 E-mail: londonintercom@yahoo.co.uk

DOMESTIC SEWING MACHINES

Bogod Group P.L.C., Fortran Road, St. Melons, Cardiff, CF3 0WJ Tel: (029) 2079 2079 Fax: (029) 2077 4999
Sewing Machine Services Luton Ltd, Unit 6-52 High Town Enterprise Centre, York Street, Luton, LU2 0HA Tel: (01582) 455112
▶ Singer Sewing Centre, 126 Park View, Whitley Bay, Tyne & Wear, NE26 3QN Tel: 0191-252 5825 Fax: 0191-292 5826 E-mail: sales@singermachines.co.uk

DOMESTIC SHOWER UNITS

Express, Unit 1b Thorn Business Park, Rotherwas, Hereford, HR2 6JT Tel: (01432) 278138 Fax: (01432) 278138
▶ H20 Products Ltd, Brestwers Corner, Pendicke Street, Southam, Warwickshire, CV47 1PN Tel: (01926) 810111 Fax: (01926) 811040 E-mail: mail@h-2-o.co.uk
Majestic Shower Co. Ltd, 1 North Place, Edinburgh Way, Harlow, Essex, CM20 2SL Tel: (01279) 443644 Fax: (01279) 635074 E-mail: info@majesticshowers.com
Matki Public Ltd Company, Churchward Road, Yate, Bristol, BS37 5PL Tel: (01454) 322888 Fax: (01454) 315284 E-mail: sales@matki.co.uk
Triton plc, Shepperton Business Park, Caldwell Road, Nuneaton, Warwickshire, CV11 4NR Tel: (024) 7634 4441 Fax: (024) 7634 9828 E-mail: reception@triton.plc.uk

DOMESTIC SWITCHGEARS

Eaton MEM, Grimshaw Lane, Middleton, Manchester, M24 1GQ Tel: 0161-655 8900 Fax: 0161-626 1709 E-mail: ukcommorders@eaton.com

DOMESTIC TAPS

Avilion, Gateway X111 Industrial Estate, Ferry Lane, Rainham, Essex, RM13 9YH Tel: (01708) 526361 Fax: (01708) 550220 E-mail: sales@avilion.co.uk
Barber Wilson & Co. Ltd, Crawley Road, London, N22 6AH Tel: (020) 8888 3461 Fax: (020) 8888 2041 E-mail: sales@barwil.co.uk
Bristan Group Ltd, 30 Lagrange, Lichfield Road Industrial Estate, Tamworth, Staffordshire, B79 7XD Tel: (01827) 68525 Fax: (01827) 68553 E-mail: enquire@bristan.com
KWC UK Ltd, 149 Balham Hill, London, SW12 9DJ Tel: (020) 8675 9335 Fax: (020) 8675 8568 E-mail: kwcuk@globalnet.co.uk
Marflow Engineering Ltd, Austin Way, Hampstead Industrial Estate, Birmingham, B42 1DU Tel: 0121-358 1555 Fax: 0121-358 1444 E-mail: sales@marflow.co.uk
Shavrin Levatap Co. Ltd, 32 Watersides, Kings Langley, Hertfordshire, WD4 8HH Tel: (01923) 267678 Fax: (01923) 265050 E-mail: sales@shavinlevatap.co.uk

DOMESTIC VACUUM CLEANERS

Bissell Homecare, The Boatyard, 105 Straight Road, Old Windsor, Windsor, Berkshire, SL4 2SE Tel: (0870) 2250109 Fax: (01753) 867684
Dyson Ltd, Tetbury Hill, Malmesbury, Wiltshire, SN16 0RP Tel: (01666) 827200 Fax: (01666) 827299 E-mail: james.ross-smith@dyson.com

DOMESTIC VENTILATORS

Greenwood Air Management Ltd, Brookside Industrial Estate, Rustington, Littlehampton, West Sussex, BN16 3LF Tel: (01903) 771021 Fax: (01903) 782398 E-mail: info@greenwood.co.uk
Timloc Building Products, Rawcliffe Road, Goole, North Humberside, DN14 6UQ Tel: (01405) 765567 Fax: (01405) 720479 E-mail: sales@timloc.co.uk

DOMESTIC WASHING MACHINES

▶ Dave Quirk Washing Machine, Unit 4 St. Michaels Industrial Estate, Widnes, Cheshire, WA8 8TL Tel: 0151-424 0539 E-mail: info@davequirkwashingmachines.com
Electrolux Ltd, Cornwall House, 55-57 High Street, Slough, SL1 1DZ Tel: (01753) 872500 Fax: (01753) 872501
▶ Masterpart, 4 Grainger Road, Southend-on-Sea, SS2 5BZ Tel: (01702) 310031 Fax: (01702) 312000 E-mail: sales@masterpart.com
Merloni Domestic Appliances Ltd, Merloni Ho, 3 Cowley Business Pk, High St, Cowley, Uxbridge, Middx, UB8 2AD Tel: (01895) 858200 Fax: (01895) 858270
Rayvac Electrics, East Thurrock Road, Grays, Essex, RM17 6SP Tel: (01375) 371253 Fax: (01375) 381381 E-mail: rayvac@btopenworld.com

DOMESTIC WASTE DISPOSAL SERVICES

2nd To None Rubbish Removals, Penarth Road, Deane, Bolton, BL3 5RJ Tel: (01204) 665569 E-mail: darren@2ndtonone.co.uk
▶ 3b Waste Solutions, Unit C Scotch Park Trading Estate, Forge Lane, Leeds, LS12 2PY Tel: 0113-279 2348 Fax: (0870) 7520745 E-mail: info@3bwaste.co.uk
▶ A1 Grafters, 83 Ermine Road, Lewisham, London, SE13 7JJ Tel: (020) 8690 6635 E-mail: advice@a1grafters.com
▶ C B Skip Hire Ltd, Southbourne, St. Thomas Farm, London Road, Salisbury, SP1 3YU Tel: (01722) 320544 Fax: (01722) 410329 E-mail: info@cbskiphire.co.uk

DOMESTIC WATER PURIFICATION EQUIPMENT

European WaterCare Systems, Regal House, South Road, Harlow, Essex, CM20 2BL Tel: (01279) 780250 Fax: (01279) 780268 E-mail: info@watercare.co.uk
Pre Mac International Ltd, Unit 5 Morewood Close, Sevenoaks, Kent, TN13 2HU Tel: (01732) 460333 Fax: (01732) 460222 E-mail: office@pre-mac.com

DOMESTIC WATER SOFTENING EQUIPMENT

E P Laboratories Ltd, Amersham Road, Chesham, Buckinghamshire, HP5 1NE Tel: (01494) 791585 Fax: (01494) 771853 E-mail: sales@eplabs.com
▶ Eastern Counties Pumps, 3 Burrell Road, Ipswich, IP2 8AD Tel: (01473) 400101 Fax: (01473) 400103 E-mail: sales@ecpgroup.com
Ecowater Systems Ltd, 1 Independent Business Park, Mill Road, Stokenchurch, High Wycombe, Buckinghamshire, HP14 3TP Tel: (01494) 484000 Fax: (01494) 484396 E-mail: sales@ecowater.co.uk
Ensign UK Ltd, A5 Faraday Road, Newbury, Berkshire, RG14 2AD Tel: (0870) 0113436 Fax: (0845) 6431882 E-mail: info@ensign-water.co.uk
European WaterCare Systems, Regal House, South Road, Harlow, Essex, CM20 2BL Tel: (01279) 780250 Fax: (01279) 780268 E-mail: info@watercare.co.uk
Silverline UK Ltd, Whitemoor, Iddesleigh, Winkleigh, Devon, EX19 8BN Tel: (01805) 804202 Fax: (01805) 804680 E-mail: enquiries@silverlineuk.co.uk

DOMESTIC WOODWARE

Dalescraft Art & Craft Materials, 26a Bondgate Green, Ripon, North Yorkshire, HG4 1QW Tel: (01765) 692053 Fax: (01765) 692053 E-mail: colin@dalescraft.com
F W Mason & Sons Ltd, Private Road, Number 8, Colwick Industrial Estate, Nottingham, NG4 2EQ Tel: 0115-911 3500 Fax: 0115-911 3555 E-mail: mail@masons-timber.co.uk
Jewson Ltd, Merchant House Binley Business Park, Harry Weston Road, Coventry, CV3 2TT Tel: (024) 7643 8400 Fax: (024) 7643 8401
N K Antcliffe, Brittania Works, Melton Road, Thurmaston, Leicester, LE4 8BD Tel: 0116-269 4743

DOOR AUTOMATION SYSTEMS

▶ A1 Access, Unit 8c Hybris Business Park, Warmwell Road, Crossways, Dorchester, Dorset, DT2 8BF Tel: (01305) 854990 Fax: (01305) 851983 E-mail: terry@a1access.org.uk
Advance Door Services, 227 Bolton Road, Turton, Bolton, BL7 0HY Tel: (01204) 853199 Fax: (01204) 853994
Electra Controls Ltd, 20 Acorn Close, Enfield, Middlesex, EN2 8LX Tel: (020) 8366 1433
Hillaldam Coburn Ltd, 6 Wyvern Estate, Beverley Way, New Malden, Surrey, KT3 4PH Tel: (020) 8336 1515 Fax: (020) 8336 1414 E-mail: sales@hillaldam.co.uk
M D F Designs, 153 Barton Lane, Eccles, Manchester, M30 0HN Tel: 0161-789 6602 Fax: 0161-789 6715 E-mail: sales@mdfdesign.com
▶ Openings Disability Access, 327 Holdenhurst Road, Bournemouth, BH8 8BT Tel: (01202) 309946 Fax: (01202) 727071 E-mail: doors@openings.co.uk
R T S Gate Automation, 224 Spen Lane, Gomersal, Cleckheaton, West Yorkshire, BD19 4PJ Tel: (01274) 852006 Fax: (01274) 871074 E-mail: info@rtsautomaticgates.co.uk
The Scandinavian Door Co., 10 Willowhayne Crescent, East Preston, Littlehampton, West Sussex, BN16 1PJ Tel: (01903) 776894 Fax: (01903) 776894
John Wainwright Systems Ltd, Third Avenue, Midsomer Norton, Radstock, BA3 4XD Tel: (01761) 414700 Fax: (01761) 414722 E-mail: post@jwsltd.co.uk

DOOR BOLTS

Fred Dennis Ltd, Eastern Avenue, Lichfield, Staffordshire, WS13 6UY Tel: (01543) 419700 Fax: (01543) 419755 E-mail: sales@freddennis.co.uk
Frank Allart & Co. Ltd, 15-35 Great Tindal Street, Birmingham, B16 8DR Tel: 0121-454 2977 Fax: 0121-456 2234E-mail: sales@allart.co.uk
Kirkpatrick Ltd, PO Box 17, Walsall, WS2 9NF Tel: (01922) 620026 Fax: (01922) 722525 E-mail: sales@kirkpatrick.co.uk
World of Brass, 9 Hebble Close, Bolton, BL2 3FS Tel: (0845) 260 9009 Fax: (0845) 260 9008 E-mail: info@worldofbrass.co.uk

DOOR CANOPIES

Bainbridge GRP Ltd, Unit 3D, Peel Mill, Chamberhall Street, Bury, Lancashire, BL9 0JU Tel: 0161-764 5034 Fax: 0161-764 5020
Multitex G R P, Unit 5 Dolphin Industrial Estate, Salisbury, SP1 2NB Tel: (01722) 332139 Fax: (01722) 338458 E-mail: sales@multitex.co.uk

DOOR CLOSER HOLDERS

▶ Door-Tech Solutions Ltd, 4 Kean Close, Lichfield, Staffordshire, WS13 7EL Tel: (01543) 252374 Fax: (01543) 256845 E-mail: sales@doortechsolutions.co.uk

DOOR CLOSER OR CLOSING EQUIPMENT MAINTENANCE OR REPAIR

Able Doorspring & Metal Window Co., Unit 29 Oakwood Hill Industrial Estate, Oakwood Hill, Loughton, Essex, IG10 3TZ Tel: (020) 8508 9703 Fax: (01277) 375141

DOOR CLOSERS OR CLOSING EQUIPMENT

Able Doorspring & Metal Window Co., Unit 29 Oakwood Hill Industrial Estate, Oakwood Hill, Loughton, Essex, IG10 3TZ Tel: (020) 8508 9703 Fax: (01277) 375141

Cartwright Hardware, Cartwright House, Springwell Road, Leeds, LS12 1AX Tel: 0113-243 6931 Fax: 0113-242 1716 E-mail: sales@cartwrighthardware.co.uk

Door Spring Supplies Co, 25 Knox Road, Wellingborough, Northamptonshire, NN8 1HW Tel: (01933) 222431 Fax: (01933) 222531 E-mail: tony@autodoorsprings.co.uk

Dorma UK, Wilbury Way, Hitchin, Hertfordshire, SG4 0AB Tel: (01462) 477602 Fax: (01462) 477603 E-mail: info@dorma-uk.co.uk

J B Architectural Ironmongery Ltd, Avis Way, Newhaven, East Sussex, BN9 0DU Tel: (01273) 514961 Fax: (01273) 516764 E-mail: info@jbai.co.uk

Jebron Ltd, Bright Street, Wednesbury, West Midlands, WS10 9HX Tel: 0121-526 2212 Fax: 0121-568 2131 E-mail: sales@jebron.co.uk

Laidlaw Solutions Ltd, 4-5 Bonville Road, Bristol, BS4 5NF Tel: 0117-316 0460 Fax: 0117-316 0491 E-mail: gateshead@laidlaw.net

Reilor Ltd, Astra Business Centre, Roman Way, Preston, PR2 5AP Tel: (01772) 793793 Fax: (01772) 797877E-mail: sales@reilor.com

Security Closures, Barnack Trading Centre, Bedminster, Bristol, BS3 5QE Tel: 0117-963 5382 Fax: 0117-963 5395

Security Closures, 11 Heybridge Way, Leabridge Road, London, E10 7NQ Tel: (020) 8558 9350 Fax: (020) 8558 4815

DOOR FINGERGUARD SAFETY SHIELDS

Boewood Prevention Ltd, PO Box 44, Newtown, Powys, SY16 1WD Tel: (01686) 622228 Fax: (01686) 622451 E-mail: sales@doorsafety.co.uk

DOOR FIRE RESISTANT (FR) HINGES

Modern Door Closures, Lloyds Bank Chambers, High Street, Littlehampton, West Sussex, BN17 5AG Tel: (01903) 724003 Fax: (01903) 739806 E-mail: tradersnetwork@btconnect.com

DOOR FITTINGS OR FURNITURE

Allendor Products Ltd, Bentinck Street, Ashton-under-Lyne, Lancashire, OL7 0PT Tel: 0161-330 6839 Fax: 0161-344 0741

Annstar Group Ltd, 57 Sutherland Road, London, E17 6BH Tel: (020) 8503 2323 Fax: (020) 8503 3947 E-mail: info@annstar.co.uk

Brassart Ltd, 76 Attwood Street, Lye, Stourbridge, West Midlands, DY9 8RY Tel: (01922) 740512 Fax: (01384) 898705 E-mail: davidgregory@brassards.co.uk

C B S (Midlands) Ltd, Kenilworth House, 118 Stourbridge Road, Dudley, West Midlands, DY1 2DP Tel: (01384) 254015 Fax: (01384) 456856

Carlton Industries Ltd, Units 1-4, Progress Business Park, Progress Way, Croydon, CR0 4XD Tel: (020) 8686 9898 Fax: (020) 8686 9848

Constant Aluminium Supplies Ltd, Unit B2 Junction 22 Business, Park Tweedale Way, Oldham, OL9 7LD Tel: 0161-681 9917 Fax: 0161-683 4182 E-mail: sales@constant-engineering.co.uk

Croft Architectural Hardware Ltd, 23 Lower Lichfield Street, Willenhall, West Midlands, WV13 1QQ Tel: (01902) 606493 Fax: (01902) 606933 E-mail: sales@croft-arch.co.uk

▶ Davemont Reproduction Ltd, 118-122 Cheshire Street, London, E2 6EJ Tel: (020) 7613 3505 Fax: (020) 7256 0366

Dortrend International Ltd, Riverside Business Centre, Worcester Road, Stourport-on-Severn, Worcestershire, DY13 9BZ Tel: (01299) 827837 Fax: (01299) 827094 E-mail: sales@dortrend.co.uk

Fred Duncombe Ltd, Progress Drive, Cannock, Staffordshire, WS11 0JE Tel: (01543) 578661 Fax: (01543) 570050 E-mail: sales@fredduncombe.co.uk

Home & Leisure Products, 13 Derby Road, Hinckley, Leicestershire, LE10 1QD Tel: (01455) 234448 Fax: (01455) 250277

Irm Bristol Ltd, Unit 1 2 Armstrong Court, Armstrong Way, Yate, Bristol, BS37 5NG Tel: (01454) 321311 Fax: (01454) 273411 E-mail: sales@irm-bristol.co.uk

J & J Engineering (Walsall) Ltd, Fryers Road, Leamore Enterprise Park, Bloxwich, Walsall, WS2 7LZ Tel: (01922) 710204 Fax: (01922) 710191 E-mail: jwoodall@btconnect.com

J & M Hardware, 75 Scotland Road, Nelson, Lancashire, BB9 7UY Tel: (01282) 613460 Fax: (01282) 617928

James Gibbons Format Ltd, Vulcan Road, Bilston, West Midlands, WV14 7JG Tel: (01902) 405500 Fax: (01902) 385915 E-mail: sales@jgf.co.uk

JC Trophies, The Business Centre, 21 James Road, Tyseley, Birmingham, B11 2BA Tel: 0121-707 0606 Fax: 0121-707 0609 E-mail: jdcmanufacturing@blueyonder.co.uk

▶ John Plank Ltd, 17-18 Haywards Place, Clerkenwell Green, London, EC1R 0EQ Tel: (020) 7608 0074 Fax: (020) 7608 0075 E-mail: sales@johnplanck.co.uk

Lloyd Worrall London, Unit F21, Riverside Business Centre, Haldane Place, London, SW18 4UQ Tel: (020) 8874 4755 Fax: (020) 8874 4624 E-mail: sales@london.lloydworrall.co.uk

Lloyd Worrall Sheffield Ltd, 10 Fell Road, Sheffield, S9 2AL Tel: 0114-244 3350 Fax: 0114-244 4219 E-mail: sales@sheffield.lloydworrall.co.uk

London Door Co., 153 St Johns Hill, London, SW11 1TQ Tel: (020) 7801 0877 Fax: (020) 7223 7296 E-mail: sales@londordoor.co.uk

M Marcus, 7 Blackbrook Industrial Estate, Peartree Lane, Dudley, West Midlands, DY2 0XW Tel: (01384) 457900 Fax: (01384) 457903 E-mail: info@m-marcus.com

P H Chandler Leyland Ltd, 5 The Forward Industrial Estate, Talbot Road, Leyland, PR25 2ZJ Tel: (01772) 421651 Fax: (01772) 621493 E-mail: carolw@phchandler.co.uk

Paddock Fabrications Ltd, Fryers Road, Walsall, WS2 7LZ Tel: (01922) 470940 Fax: (01922) 476021 E-mail: sales@paddockfabrications.co.uk

▶ Phoenix Fitted Furniture, Industrial Estate, Old Church Road, East Hanningfield, Chelmsford, CM3 8AB Tel: (01245) 400920 Fax: (01245) 401057

Reilor Ltd, Astra Business Centre, Roman Way, Preston, PR2 5AP Tel: (01772) 793793 Fax: (01772) 797877E-mail: sales@reilor.com

▶ Response Furniture Systems Ltd, 52 Tanners Drive, Blakelands, Milton Keynes, MK14 5BW Tel: (01908) 216466 Fax: (01908) 216467 E-mail: sales@responsefurnituresystems.co.uk

Roto Frank Ltd, Swift Point, Rugby, Warwickshire, CV21 1QH Tel: (01788) 558600 Fax: (01788) 558605 E-mail: uk_sales@roto-frank.com

Turnstyle Designs, Baron Way, Roundswell Business Park, Barnstaple, Devon, EX31 3TB Tel: (01271) 325325 Fax: (01271) 328248 E-mail: sales@turnstyledesigns.com

Valli & Valli Ltd, Unit 8 Hedging Lane Industrial Estate, Hedging Lane, Wilnecote, Tamworth, Staffordshire, B77 5HH Tel: (01827) 283655 Fax: (01827) 280553 E-mail: sales@valiandvali.co.uk

World of Brass, 9 Hebble Close, Bolton, BL2 3FS Tel: (0845) 260 9009 Fax: (0845) 260 9008 E-mail: info@worldofbrass.co.uk

DOOR HANDLE LOCKS

▶ Laird Security, 18 Burnbank Road, Falkirk, FK2 7PE Tel: (01324) 633889 Fax: (01324) 633767 E-mail: sales@lairdsecurity.co.uk

DOOR INFILL PANELS

Advanced Panels & Products, Grosvenor Road, Gillingham Business Park, Gillingham, Kent, ME8 0SA Tel: (01634) 378880 Fax: (01634) 378381

C R F Sections Ltd, Hale Trading Estate, Lower Church Lane, Tipton, West Midlands, DY4 7PQ Tel: 0121-557 1234 Fax: 0121-522 3003

GBW Panels Ltd, 2 Berkeley Business Park, Wainwright Road, Worcester, WR4 9FA Tel: (01905) 340095 Fax: (01905) 340188 E-mail: mark_cuthbert@gbwuk.com

▶ Hurst Plastics Ltd, 1 Kingston Int Business Park, Somerden Road, Hull, HU9 5PE Tel: (01482) 790790 Fax: (01482) 790690 E-mail: sales@hurst-plastics.co.uk

Rocal Insulating Panels, Atherton Way, Brigg, South Humberside, DN20 8AR Tel: (01652) 659259 Fax: (01652) 650983 E-mail: sales@rocal.co.uk

DOOR LOCKING SYSTEMS

▶ Laird Security, 18 Burnbank Road, Falkirk, FK2 7PE Tel: (01324) 633889 Fax: (01324) 633767 E-mail: sales@lairdsecurity.co.uk

▶ Safeways Wirral Locksmiths Ltd, 10 Grange Mount, Prenton, Merseyside, CH43 4XW Tel: 0151-653 3414 Fax: 0151-653 3414 E-mail: inneng@aol.com

DOOR LOCKS

Clares Of Croydon Ltd, 54 Tamworth Road, Croydon, CR0 1XW Tel: (020) 8688 7952 Fax: (020) 8688 1867

D P Security, Ryecroft House, Green St Green Road, Dartford, DA2 8DX Tel: (01474) 707030 Fax: (01474) 707313 E-mail: info@dpsecurity.co.uk

Era Products Ltd, Straight Road, Willenhall, West Midlands, WV12 5RA Tel: (01922) 490049 Fax: (01922) 494420 E-mail: bevans@era-security.com

Lloyd Worrall London, Unit F21, Riverside Business Centre, Haldane Place, London, SW18 4UQ Tel: (020) 8874 4755 Fax: (020) 8874 4624 E-mail: sales@london.lloydworrall.co.uk

Lloyd Worrall Sheffield Ltd, 10 Fell Road, Sheffield, S9 2AL Tel: 0114-244 3350 Fax: 0114-244 4219 E-mail: sales@sheffield.lloydworrall.co.uk

LSH Ltd, Western Road, Silver End, Witham, Essex, CM8 3QB Tel: (01376) 507507 Fax: (01376) 584687 E-mail: sales@lairdsecurity.co.uk

▶ multipointlocks.co.uk, 29 Westgate End, Wakefield, West Yorkshire, WF2 9RG Tel: (01924) 360444 E-mail: sales@multipointlocks.co.uk

N & C Building Products Ltd, 41-51 Freshwater Road, Dagenham, Essex, RM8 1SP Tel: (020) 8586 4600 Fax: (020) 8586 4646 E-mail: head.office@nichollsandclarke.com

Ronis-Dom Ltd, Moor Street South, Blakenhall, Wolverhampton, WV2 3JJ Tel: (01902) 715440 Fax: (01902) 715145

Securefast plc, Meadow Dale Works, Dimminsdale, Willenhall, West Midlands, WV13 2BE Tel: (01902) 607503 Fax: (01902) 609327 E-mail: sales@securefast.co.uk

DOOR MAINTENANCE OR REPAIR OR INSTALLATION, *See also particular types of Door*

Abbey Roller Shutters & Doors, Unit A-B Caxton St North, London, E16 1JL Tel: (020) 7476 4422 Fax: (020) 7476 4433

Access Industrial Door Co Midlands Ltd, 148a Crankhall Lane, Wednesbury, West Midlands, WS10 0ED Tel: 0121-505 1435 Fax: 0121-505 3318 E-mail: neelsangha@aol.com

All Style Door & Gate Services, 25 Woolacombe Lodge Road, Birmingham, B29 6PZ Tel: 0121-472 0675

Arkas Ltd, Nubal House, Headcorn Road, Sutton Valence, Maidstone, Kent, ME17 3EH Tel: 0845 5314195 Fax: (01622) 843488 E-mail: danny@arkas.co.uk

Central Shutters & Doors, Unit 39 Phoenix International Industrial Estate, Charles Street, West Bromwich, West Midlands, B70 0AY Tel: 0121-557 3434 Fax: 0121-557 3403

Door Repair Service, 5a Hilton Drive, Prestwich, Manchester, M25 9NN Tel: 0161-773 6370 Fax: 0161-773 2145

Door Services, Severnside Trading Estate, St. Andrews Road, Avonmouth, Bristol, BS11 9YQ Tel: 0117-949 4919 Fax: 0117-938 1711 E-mail: doorservices@free-online.co.uk

Dorma UK, Wilbury Way, Hitchin, Hertfordshire, SG4 0AB Tel: (01462) 477602 Fax: (01462) 477603 E-mail: info@dorma-uk.co.uk

Dorwingear, 107 Hospital Street, Birmingham, B19 3XA Tel: 0121-359 1744 Fax: 0121-333 3475 E-mail: dorwingearltd@btconnect.com

Brian Fuller & Co., 106 Brockhurst Rd, Gosport, Hants, PO12 3DG Tel: (023) 9258 3107 Fax: (023) 9258 3107 E-mail: brian.fuller3@btinternet.com

Guardian Industrial Doors Ltd, 45 Progress Road, Leigh-On-Sea, Essex, SS9 5PR Tel: (0800) 7836602 Fax: (01702) 510015 E-mail: ross@guardiandoors.com

H & C Fabrications Ltd, Corporation Road, Birkenhead, Merseyside, CH41 8FA Tel: 0151-653 7677 Fax: 0151-652 0626

Harling Security Products, 237 Church Road, Hayes, Middlesex, UB3 2LG Tel: (020) 8561 3787 Fax: (020) 8848 0999 E-mail: harlingsec@aol.com

▶ Harper Window Systems Ltd, The Gables, Ash Lane, Alvechurch, Birmingham, B48 7TT Tel: 0121-445 0104 Fax: 0121-445 3138 E-mail: enquiries@harperwindows.co.uk

I R Security & Safety, 1 Berrington Road, Leamington Spa, Warwickshire, CV31 1NB Tel: (01926) 437000 Fax: (01926) 437005 E-mail: ir_customerservice@eu.irco.com

Industrial Door Repair, Unit 4 Windmill La Industrial Estate, Denton, Manchester, M34 3RB Tel: 0161-336 2228 Fax: 0161-336 8742

Industrial Doors Scotland Ltd, 199 Broughton Road, Edinburgh, EH7 4LN Tel: 0131-553 6685 Fax: 0131-555 0482 E-mail: industrialdoors@talk21.com

Industrial Doors Systems Ltd, Unit 51, Waverley Road, Beeches Industrial Estate, Bristol, BS37 5QR Tel: (01454) 310005 Fax: (01454) 324412 E-mail: idsbristol1@aol.com

Lafford & Leavey, Arrowhead Road, Reading, RG7 4XB Tel: 0118-930 3333 Fax: 0118-932 3707 E-mail: sales@1afford.com

Lambourn Valley Projects Ltd, 13 Prospect Road, Hungerford, Berkshire, RG17 0JL Tel: (01488) 680680 Fax: (01488) 681258 E-mail: sales@dock-levellers.co.uk

Middleton Maintenance Services Ltd, The London Centre, 99 Queensland, London, N7 7AJ Tel: (020) 7700 7070 Fax: (020) 7609 3223 E-mail: sales@middleton-maintenance.co.uk

Mila Maintenance Services, Oaks Business Park, Oaks Lane, Barnsley, South Yorkshire, S71 1HT Tel: (01226) 203315 Fax: (01226) 249493 E-mail: sales@milamaintenance.co.uk

R N B Industrial Door Service Ltd, 6 Davenport Centre, Renwick Road, Barking, Essex, IG11 0SH Tel: (020) 8595 1242 Fax: (020) 8595 3849

Rallock Door Systems Ltd, 30 Hardhill Road, Bathgate, West Lothian, EH48 2BW Tel: (01506) 634134 Fax: (01506) 650333

Redmill Fabrication Ltd, 19 Inchmuir Road, Whitehill Industrial Estate, Bathgate, West Lothian, EH48 2EP Tel: (01506) 634333 Fax: (01506) 634999

Sabrina Traditional Oak Doors, Alma Yard, Alma Street, Shrewsbury, SY3 8QL Tel: (01743) 357977 Fax: (01743) 352233 E-mail: sales@oakdoors.co.uk

Sharp Maintenance Services, 57 Ballens Road, Chatham, Kent, ME5 8NX Tel: (01634) 683232 Fax: (01634) 200025

Specialized Door & Window Services, Unit 5-6 Merlin Way, Hillend Industrial Park, Hillend, Dunfermline, Fife, KY11 9JY Tel: (01383) 829912 Fax: (01383) 825372

System 2000 Group Ltd, 39-41 Wood End Lane, Erdington, Birmingham, B24 8AN Tel: 0121-350 2000 Fax: 0121-377 6300

Tambour Doors Ltd, 21 Marston Lane, Marston, Northwich, Cheshire, CW9 6DL Tel: (01606) 42423 Fax: (01606) 48118

Welding Engineers (Hertford) Ltd, Unit 1, Lower Road, Great Amwell, Ware, Hertfordshire, SG12 9TA Tel: (01920) 468634 Fax: (01920) 487463 E-mail: hertford@weldingengineers.co.uk

DOOR OR WINDOW SECURITY HARDWARE

Astraline Security Door Systems, Unit 6a Waterloo Works, Gorsey Way, Stockport, Cheshire, SK1 3BU Tel: 0161-477 9991 Fax: 0161-477 5742 E-mail: astraline4doors@aol.com

Avocet Hardware Taiwan Ltd, Brookfoot Mills, Elland Road, Brighouse, West Yorkshire, HD6 2RW Tel: (01484) 711700 Fax: (01484) 720124 E-mail: post@avocet-hardware.co.uk

Cotswold Architectural Products Ltd, Manor Park Industrial Estate, Manor Road, Cheltenham, Gloucestershire, GL51 9SQ Tel: (01242) 246624 Fax: (01242) 221146 E-mail: info@cotswold-windows.co.uk

Gosport Engineering Co. Ltd, Lordship Lane, London, N17 8NS Tel: (020) 8808 2326 Fax: (020) 8885 2867 E-mail: gosporteng@btconnect.com

Grange Welding Services, Earl Street, Sheffield, S1 4PY Tel: 0114-272 7606 Fax: 0114-272 7606

Leicester Wrought Iron Co., 25-27 Thurcaston Road, Leicester, LE4 5PG Tel: 0116-266 3566 Fax: 0116-266 3566

LSH Ltd, Western Road, Silver End, Witham, Essex, CM8 3QB Tel: (01376) 507507 Fax: (01376) 584687 E-mail: sales@lairdsecurity.co.uk

DOOR SEALS, REFRIGERATOR/ REFRIGERATION UNIT

Collins Extrusions Ltd, Bidavon Industrial Estate, Waterloo Road, Bidford-on-Avon, Alcester, Warwickshire, B50 4JW Tel: (01789) 773536 Fax: (01789) 490225 E-mail: coltec1@yahoo.com

DOOR SETS

Acorn Doors, 2 Abbas Business Centre, Main Road, Itchen Abbas, Winchester, Hampshire, SO21 1BQ Tel: (01962) 791111 Fax: (01962) 791111

Adcas 1997 Ltd, Unit 12a Parkview East Industrial Estate, Parkview Road East, Hartlepool, Cleveland, TS25 1PG Tel: (01429) 283212 Fax: (01429) 420900 E-mail: sales@adcas1997.co.uk

Blackpool DIY & Door Centre Ltd, 43b Caunce Street, Blackpool, FY1 3ND Tel: (01253) 622176

Bonlea Ltd, Q Net House, Malleable Way, Stockton-on-Tees, Cleveland, TS18 2SZ Tel: (01642) 617611 Fax: (01642) 674490 E-mail: enquiries@bonlea.co.uk

Bulldog Door Services Ltd, Unit D1 Adamson Industrial Estate, Hyde, Cheshire, SK14 1EF Tel: 0161-368 6011 Fax: 0161-368 5566

▶ Folding Sliding Doors, FSD Works, Hopbine Avenue West Bowling, Bradford, West Yorkshire, BD5 8ER Tel: (01274) 715880 Fax: (0845) 6446631 E-mail: info@foldingslidingdoors.co.uk

In Doors Manufacturing Ltd, 49 Creagh Road, Toomebridge, Antrim, BT41 3SE Tel: (028) 7965 9555 Fax: (028) 7965 9559

Ir Martin Roberts, Millen Road, Sittingbourne, Kent, ME10 2AA Tel: (01795) 476161 Fax: (01795) 422463

▶ J K Doors Ltd, Unit 4/6, Hanworth Road, Off Common Road, Low Moor, Bradford, West Yorkshire, BD12 0SG Tel: (0845) 0589420 Fax: (0845) 0589421 E-mail: kevin@jkdoors.co.uk

Mctavish Ramsay & Co. Ltd, Fowler Road, West Pitkerro Industrial Estate, Broughty Ferry, Dundee, DD5 3RN Tel: (01382) 737722 Fax: (01382) 480054 E-mail: sales@mctavish-ramsay.com

Spazio Folding Door Co., 3 Barnfield, St. Michaels, Tenterden, Kent, TN30 6NH Tel: (01580) 763593 Fax: (01580) 765883 E-mail: susie@spazio.co.uk

DOOR SPRING BARRELS OR ROLLERS

M & S Products Ltd, Unit 16 Riverside Industrial Estate, Thames Road, Barking, Essex, IG11 0ND Tel: (020) 8507 3940 Fax: (020) 8594 7033

DOOR STRIKE PLATES

Furnells Signs, Unit 5 Crusader Industrial Estate, 167 Hermitage Road, London, N4 1LZ Tel: (020) 8880 2771 Fax: (020) 8880 2333 E-mail: sales@furnells.com

DOORS, *See also headings for particular types*

Alternative Door Style, 9 St. Johns Street, Bridlington, North Humberside, YO16 7NL Tel: (01262) 400626 Fax: (01262) 400626

▶ Altro Window Frame Mnfrs, Unit 51 Barns Court, Turners Hill Road, Crawley Down, Crawley, West Sussex, RH10 4HQ Tel: (01342) 718702 Fax: (01342) 718942

C J Smith, 1 New Mill Street, Dudley, West Midlands, DY2 8PB Tel: (01384) 255172 Fax: (01384) 255172

Cardiff Door Centre Ltd, 185 Broadway, Cardiff, CF24 1QH Tel: (029) 2025 5674 Fax: (029) 2045 5534

Cashmores Joinery Ltd, 86-88 Essex Road, Leicester, LE4 9EG Tel: 0116-276 9948 Fax: 0116-276 9948

▶ Cheshire Industrial Doors, 8 Dalton Court, Astmoor Industrial Estate, Runcorn, Cheshire, WA7 1PU Tel: (01928) 500530 Fax: (01928) 500531 E-mail: sales@cheshireindustrialdoors.com

Classic Doors, 10-12 Cheapside, Morley, Leeds, LS27 9DQ Tel: 0113-238 0220 E-mail: sales@classic-doors.co.uk

▶ Classic Home Improvements Ltd, 4 362b Spring Road, Southampton, SO19 2PB Tel: (023) 8044 7744 Fax: (023) 8044 0033 E-mail: sales@classichome.co.uk

Devoran Metals, Devoran Joinery Works, Greenbank Road, Devoran, Truro, Cornwall, TR3 6PQ Tel: (01872) 863376 Fax: (01872) 862123 E-mail: richard@devoran-joinery.demon.co.uk

▶ Direct Doorpanels, Busk Road, Oldham, OL9 6QZ Tel: 0161-626 5539 Fax: 0161-626 4355

▶ Door System UK Ltd, 450a Bradford Road, Batley, West Yorkshire, WF17 5LW Tel: (01924) 471801 Fax: (01924) 471828

▶ Enfield Speciality Doors, Alexandra Road, Enfield, Middlesex, EN3 7EH Tel: (020) 8805 6662 Fax: (020) 8443 1290 E-mail: sales@infodoors.co.uk

▶ Everglade Windows Ltd, 22 Wadsworth Road, Greenford, Middlesex, UB6 7JD Tel: (020) 8998 8775 Fax: (020) 8997 0300 E-mail: sales@everglade.co.uk

▶ Folding Sliding Doors, FSD Works, Hopbine Avenue West Bowling, Bradford, West Yorkshire, BD5 8ER Tel: (01274) 715880 Fax: (0845) 6446631 E-mail: info@foldingslidingdoors.co.uk

▶ Jeld-Wen UK Ltd, 169 Watch House Lane, Doncaster, South Yorkshire, DN5 9LR Tel: (01302) 394000 Fax: (01302) 787383 E-mail: customer-services@jeld-wen.co.uk

Kaybee Door Sales Ltd, 52-60 St. Anne Street, Liverpool, L3 3DX Tel: 0151-207 2131 Fax: 0151-298 1004 E-mail: sales@kaybeedoors.co.uk

Laporte Doors, 31 Winchester Avenue, Winchester Trading Estate, Denny, Stirlingshire, FK6 6QE Tel: (01324) 820082 Fax: (01324) 820141 E-mail: info@la-porte.co.uk

▶ M B W Doors, Unit 8, Dale Street Industrial Estate, Radcliffe, Manchester, M26 1AD Tel: 0161-723 5577 Fax: 0161-723 5577 E-mail: mbwdoors1@btconnect.com

M & S Products Ltd, Unit 16 Riverside Industrial Estate, Thames Road, Barking, Essex, IG11 0ND Tel: (020) 8507 3940 Fax: (020) 8594 7033

▶ Midland Plastic Windows (Hinckley) Ltd, Sapcote Road, Burbage, Hinckley, Leicestershire, LE10 2AZ Tel: (01455) 234635 Fax: (01455) 612880

Moffett Thallon & Co. Ltd, 143 Northumberland Street, Belfast, BT13 2JF Tel: (028) 9032 2802 Fax: (028) 9024 1428 E-mail: info@moffett.demon.co.uk

▶ New Generation Doors, Tattersall Way, Chelmsford, CM1 3UB Tel: (01245) 255519 Fax: (01245) 255525

Nortech Ltd, Unit 14 Terrace Factory, Bassington Industrial Estate, Cramlington, Northumberland, NE23 8AD Tel: (01670) 736811 Fax: (01670) 731252 E-mail: sales@nortechgaragedoors.co.uk

Parry Bowen, Unit S Chasewater Industrial Estate, Burntwood Business Park, Burntwood, Staffordshire, WS7 3GQ Tel: (01543) 678000 Fax: (01543) 677237

Pellfold Parthos Ltd, 1 The Quadrant, Howarth Road, Maidenhead, Berkshire, SL6 1AP Tel: (01628) 773353 Fax: (01628) 773363 E-mail: sales@pellfoldparthos.co.uk

Roman Windows & Doors Ltd, Unit 3 Fir Ralph Trade Centre, Hopton Industrial Estate, London Road, Devizes, Wiltshire, SN10 2FD Tel: (01380) 729000 Fax: (01380) 729038 E-mail: romanwindows@romanglass.co.uk

S T P Group Ltd, Watford Bridge Road, New Mills, High Peak, Derbyshire, SK22 4HJ Tel: (01663) 744030 Fax: (01663) 745295 E-mail: stpgroupltd@btinternet.com

▶ Steelwood (UK) Ltd, Units 7-8, Venture Court, Metcalf Drive, Altham Industrial Estate, Accrington, Lancashire, BB5 5WH Tel: (01282) 777781 Fax: (01282) 777889 E-mail: sales@steelwood.com

Sunfold Systems, Unit 12 Chestnut Drive, Wymondham, Norfolk, NR18 9SB Tel: (01953) 423423 Fax: (01953) 423430 E-mail: info@sunfold.com

▶ Thetford Door Services, 21 Edith Cavell Close, Thetford, Norfolk, IP24 1TJ Tel: (01842) 764730 Fax: (01842) 764643

Totton Timber Co. Ltd, Maynard Road, Totton, Southampton, SO40 3DB Tel: (023) 8086 0077 Fax: (023) 8087 3168 E-mail: sales@tottontimber.com

▶ Wooden Door Co., Unit 10 Oystons Mill, Strand Road, Preston, PR1 8UR Tel: (01772) 430055 Fax: (01772) 430066

DOORS TO SPECIFICATION

▶ Advance Door Engineering Ltd, Malthouse Road, Tipton, West Midlands, DY4 9AE Tel: 0121-557 0611 Fax: 0121-520 1233 E-mail: sales@advancedooreng.com

B M C Security Systems N I Ltd, 2 Orchard Road, Strabane, County Tyrone, BT82 9QR Tel: (028) 7138 2936 Fax: (028) 7138 2937 E-mail: bmcsecsys@hotmail.com

▶ Caudle Contracts & Design Ltd, Everglades, Maiden St, Weston, Hitchin, Hertfordshire, SG4 7AA Tel: (01462) 790580 Fax: (01462) 790398 E-mail: sales@caudle.co.uk

Dovetail Enterprises Ltd, Dunsinane Avenue, Dunsinane Industrial Estate, Dundee, DD2 3QN Tel: (01382) 810099 Fax: (01382) 814816 E-mail: enquiries@dovetailenterprises.co.uk

Meridian Technology Ltd, Unit 24 Park Gate Business Centre Chandlers Way, Park Gate, Southampton, SO31 1FQ Tel: (01489) 577599 Fax: (01489) 579472 E-mail: sales@19inchracks.com

▶ Keith Preston Joinery Co. Ltd, 20 Brest Road, Plymouth, PL6 5XP Tel: (01752) 781700 Fax: (01752) 777423 E-mail: sales@keithprestonjoinery.co.uk

Protect Doors Ltd, Suite 13 Vickers Business Centre, Priestley Road, Basingstoke, Hampshire, RG24 9RA Tel: (01256) 814000 Fax: (01256) 814443

Pullman Doors, Chelsea House, Heysham Road, Liverpool, Bootle, L30 6UZ Tel: 0151-525 6022 Fax: 0151- 525 6022

DOORS, FOLDING

Access Door Services, Unit 6-7 Trent South Industrial Park, Nottingham, NG2 4EQ Tel: 0115-958 0768 Fax: 0115-985 9240

▶ Apex Enterprises, Kern House, Corporation Road, Birkenhead, Merseyside, CH41 1HB Tel: 0151-647 9323 Fax: 0151-647 9324

Deceuninck Ltd, Stanier Road, Porte Marsh Industrial Estate, Calne, Wiltshire, SN11 9PX Tel: (01249) 816969 Fax: (01249) 815234 E-mail: deceuninck.ltd@deceuninck.com

Good Openings, Hockley Business Centre, Hooley Lane, Redhill, RH1 6ET Tel: (01737) 772277 Fax: (01737) 772288

Guardian Industrial Doors Ltd, 45 Progress Road, Leigh-On-Sea, Essex, SS9 5PR Tel: (0800) 7836602 Fax: (01702) 510015 E-mail: ross@guardiandoors.com

L H Safety Ltd, Greenbridge Works, Fallbarn Road, Rossendale, Lancashire, BB4 7NX Tel: (01706) 235100 Fax: (01706) 235150 E-mail: enquiries@lhsafety.co.uk

Marquees Ltd, Keens Lane, Guildford, Surrey, GU3 3JS Tel: (01483) 232394 Fax: (01483) 236420 E-mail: sales@guildfordshades.co.uk

Stanair Industrial Door Services Ltd, Unit A-D Great Central Indust Estate, Great Central Way, Rugby, Warwickshire, CV21 3XH Tel: (01788) 568888 Fax: (01788) 568999 E-mail: sales@stanair.co.uk

Sunfold Systems, Unit 12 Chestnut Drive, Wymondham, Norfolk, NR18 9SB Tel: (01953) 423423 Fax: (01953) 423430 E-mail: info@sunfold.com

DOSIMETERS

Data Loop Ltd, Beare Green Court, Dorking, Surrey, RH5 4SL Tel: +44 (0) 1306 711088 Fax: +44 (0) 1306 713108 E-mail: sales@data-loop.co.uk

Thermo Electron, Grange Lane, Beenham, Reading, RG7 5PR Tel: 0118-971 2121 Fax: 0118-971 2835 E-mail: admin@thermormp.co.uk

DOT MATRIX COMPUTER PRINTERS

Abacus Leewell, 30b High Street, Langford, Biggleswade, Bedfordshire, SG18 9RR Tel: (01462) 700229 Fax: (01462) 701291 E-mail: sales@abacus-leewell.co.uk

Blazepoint Ltd, Unit 2 Tower Estate, Warpsgrove Lane, Oxford, OX44 7XZ Tel: (01865) 891666 Fax: (01865) 891118 E-mail: sales@blazepoint.co.uk

D C Trading, Copdock House, London Road, Copdock, Ipswich, IP8 3JW Tel: (01473) 730286 Fax: (01473) 730257 E-mail: info@dctrading.co.uk

Fujitsu U K Ltd, Hayes Park Central Building, Hayes End Road, Hayes, Middlesex, UB4 8FE Tel: (020) 8573 4444 Fax: (020) 8573 2643 E-mail: sales@uk.fujitsu.com

Limetree Marketing, Unit 1, Warboys Road, Old Hurst, Huntingdon, Cambridgeshire, PE28 3AL Tel: (01487) 823823 Fax: (01487) 823898 E-mail: earl@limetreemarketing.co.uk

O K I (Europe) Ltd, Central House, Balfour Road, Hounslow, TW3 1HY Tel: (020) 8219 2190 Fax: (020) 8219 2199

DOUBLE ACTING PNEUMATIC PISTON ACTUATORS

Inovis Ltd, 1 Bracken Close, Lichfield, Staffordshire, WS14 9RU Tel: (0870) 3504707 Fax: (0870) 3504717 E-mail: info@inovis.uk.com

DOUBLE DIAPHRAGM PUMPS

Flotronic Pumps Ltd, Ricebridge Works, Brighton Road, Bolney, Haywards Heath, West Sussex, RH17 5NA Tel: (01444) 881871 Fax: (01444) 881860 E-mail: salesdept@flotronicpumps.co.uk

DOUBLE GLAZED CONSERVATORIES

▶ 1st APS Conservatory Roof Repairs, Crawford Place, New Road, Staines, Middlesex, TW18 3DH Tel: (01784) 464613 Fax: (01784) 464663

Alframes Holdings Ltd, 1A Arnold Road, London, SW17 9HU Tel: (020) 8648 9394 Fax: (020) 8648 4985

Alucare Glaziers, 9 Flitwick Industrial Estate, Maulden Road, Flitwick, Bedford, MK45 1UX Tel: (01525) 713085 Fax: (01525) 715661 E-mail: info@alucare.co.uk

Ambassador Windows Ltd, 8 Heol Gors, Dafen Industrial Estate, Dafen, Llanelli, Dyfed, SA14 8QR Tel: (01554) 752144 Fax: (01554) 753311 E-mail: ambassador@lineone.net

Armour Custom Services Ltd, K Holder Road, Aldershot, Hampshire, GU12 4RH Tel: (01252) 350280 Fax: (01252) 350682 E-mail: info@totalinstallations.co.uk

B D G Group Ltd, 5 Wenlock Road, Lurgan, Craigavon, County Armagh, BT66 8QR Tel: (028) 3832 7741 Fax: (028) 3832 4358 E-mail: bdg@bdg.co.uk

Budget Windows, 2 Chain Lane, Newport, Isle of Wight, PO30 5QA Tel: (01983) 520327 Fax: (01983) 521600 E-mail: sales@bwconline.net

C R Building Plastics, 40 Main Road, Christian Malford, Chippenham, Wiltshire, SN15 4AZ Tel: (01249) 721700 E-mail: sales@crbuildingplastics.co.uk

▶ Clearview (Yorkshire) Limited, Unit 4, Sullivan Business Park, West Dock Street, Hull, HU3 4TG Tel: 01482 609310 Fax: 01482 218444 E-mail: sales@conservatoryroofskits.co.uk

Conservatory World, Unit 1, Speedwell Unit, Nelson Road Industrial Estate, Dartmouth, Devon, TQ6 9SZ Tel: (01803) 839330 Fax: (01803) 835803

▶ D-LUX UPVC Wigan, 20 Cloughwood Crescent, Shevington, Wigan, Lancashire, WN6 8EP Tel: (01257) 251631 E-mail: jm001j3373@blueyonder.co.uk

Elliott Group Fineline, Commissioners Road, Strood, Rochester, Kent, ME2 4ET Tel: (01634) 719701 Fax: (01634) 716394 E-mail: fineline.windows@virgin.net

▶ Ezze UK Ltd, 619 Sewall Highway, Coventry, CV6 7JE Tel: (024) 7666 7755 Fax: (024) 7672 7819 E-mail: wah@ezzeconsevatories.com

▶ Glass Doctor, 56 Little Glen Road, Glen Parva, Leicester, LE2 9TS Tel: (0800) 6346494 Fax: 0116-299 1898 E-mail: info@glassandlock.co.uk

▶ Glass Scratch Repair, 19 Harwood Lane, Great Harwood, Blackburn, BB6 7SN Tel: (01254) 808557 E-mail: peter_cornwell@lineone.net

C. Hughes, 89 Station Rd, Flitwick, Bedford, MK45 1LA Tel: (01525) 717270 Fax: (01525) 717270 E-mail: clive.hughes1@ntlworld.com

J & K Glass & Glazing Ltd, Units 4-5, Station Road, Terrington St. Clement, King's Lynn, Norfolk, PE34 4PL Tel: (01553) 828555 Fax: (01553) 827035 E-mail: info@jkwindowsanddoors.com

▶ M & D Wright Devlopment Ltd, 46 Park Lane, Bedhampton, Havant, Hampshire, PO9 3HL Tel: (023) 9247 5595 Fax: (023) 9247 6697 E-mail: dgolf@tiscali.co.uk

▶ New Age Systems P V C U Ltd, Units 38-40, Gelli Industrial Estate, Gelli, Pentre, Mid Glamorgan, CF41 7UW Tel: (01443) 431026 Fax: (01443) 422463 E-mail: sales@newagesystems.co.uk

▶ Peak Performance Upvc Installations, 1d Payne Street, Glasgow, G4 0LE Tel: 0141-353 1771 Fax: 0141-353 1996

Shaws Glass Ltd, 66 North Street, Horsham, West Sussex, RH12 1RD Tel: (01403) 211133 Fax: (01293) 852340

▶ Shire Conservatories, Unit 7, Harlescott Barns, Battlefield Enterprise Park, Shrewsbury, SY1 3SY Tel: 01743 463333 Fax: 01743 462200E-mail: info@shireconservatories.co.uk

▶ Space Solutions Ltd, 23 Ampthill Road, Shefford, Bedfordshire, SG17 5BD Tel: 01462 815206 Fax: 01462 641176 E-mail: space@space-solutions.co.uk

Staybrite Windows, Weston Road, Norwich, NR3 3TP Tel: (0800) 0832656 Fax: (01603) 406185 E-mail: mike.holmes@zsltd.co.uk

▶ Trade Conservatories 2 U Ltd, 36 Temple Way, Heybridge, Maldon, Essex, CM9 4PX Tel: (01621) 852200 Fax: (0845) 1303872 E-mail: sales@tradeconservatories2u.co.uk

▶ Zenith Conservatories, Weston Road, Norwich, NR3 3TP Tel: (0800) 0830125 Fax: (01603) 406185 E-mail: mike.holmes@zsltd.co.uk

Zenith Staybrite Ltd, Suites 4-6, Joseph King House, Abbey Farm Commercial Park, Horsham St Faith, Norwich, NR10 3JU Tel: (0800) 123 555 Fax: (01603) 892116 E-mail: mike.holmes@zsltd.co.uk

DOUBLE GLAZED EXTERNAL DOORS

▶ F V Conservatories & Windows, Colchester Road, Elmstead, Colchester, CO7 7EA Tel: (01206) 825374 Fax: (01206) 825405 E-mail: sales@fvconservatories.co.uk

DOUBLE GLAZED UNIT FABRICATING MACHINERY

▶ mh design, 6 Willand Court, Retford, Retford, Nottinghamshire, DN22 7GD Tel: 01777 704967 Fax: 01777 719517 E-mail: sales@mhdesign.co.uk

West Leigh Ltd, 11-13 Spa Road, London, SE16 3RB Tel: (020) 7232 0030 Fax: (020) 7232 1763 E-mail: info@west-leigh.co.uk

DOUBLE GLAZED WINDOWS

A Woodcock & Son, 8a Asfordby Street, Leicester, LE5 3QG Tel: 0116-262 2176

▶ Advanced Tempered & Insulating Glass Ltd, Ynyshir Industrial Estate, Llanwonno Road, Porth, Mid Glamorgan, CF39 0HU Tel: (01443) 681681 Fax: (01443) 681814

Albann Mckinney Window Co Ltd, Hyde Park, Mallusk, Newtownabbey, County Antrim, BT36 4PX Tel: (028) 9084 2611 Fax: (028) 9034 2317 E-mail: mailbox@mcneill-mcmanus.com

Alframes Holdings Ltd, 1A Arnold Road, London, SW17 9HU Tel: (020) 8648 9394 Fax: (020) 8648 4985

Allard Windows & Doors, Unit 3b Conners Yard, Crowborough Hill, Crowborough, East Sussex, TN6 2DA Tel: (01892) 665224 Fax: (01892) 669545 E-mail: john.allard@btclick.com

Armour Custom Services Ltd, K Holder Road, Aldershot, Hampshire, GU12 4RH Tel: (01252) 350280 Fax: (01252) 350682 E-mail: info@totalinstallations.co.uk

▶ Asf, 1 Old Station Road, Station Road, Uppingham, Oakham, Leicestershire, LE15 9TX Tel: (01572) 822486 Fax: (01572) 822475 E-mail: sales@asf-upvc.com

Budget Windows, 2 Chain Lane, Newport, Isle of Wight, PO30 5QA Tel: (01983) 520327 Fax: (01983) 521600 E-mail: sales@bwconline.net

Burley UPVC Windows, Unit 6-9, Bridle Way, Netherton, Liverpool, L30 4UW Tel: 0151-922 4888 Fax: 0151-944 2300

C Jenkins Ltd, Scotia Place, Falkirk, FK2 7AJ Tel: (01324) 631326 Fax: (01324) 629339

Conservatory & Window World Ltd, 149-151 Watling Road, Bishop Auckland, County Durham, DL14 9AU Tel: (01388) 458088 Fax: (01388) 810292

County Windows (Winchester) Ltd, Units 3-4, Winchester, Hampshire, SO23 7RU Tel: (01962) 840780 Fax: (01962) 841532 E-mail: ian@county-glass.co.uk

Crittall Windows Ltd, Springwood Drive, Braintree, Essex, CM7 2YN Tel: (01376) 324106 Fax: (01376) 349662 E-mail: hq@crittall-windows.co.uk

Crown Windows Hull Ltd, New Cleveland Street, Hull, HU8 7HA Tel: (01482) 329043 Fax: (01482) 39043

▶ D-LUX UPVC Wigan, 20 Cloughwood Crescent, Shevington, Wigan, Lancashire, WN6 8EP Tel: (01257) 251631 E-mail: jm001j3373@blueyonder.co.uk

Elliott Group Fineline, Commissioners Road, Strood, Rochester, Kent, ME2 4ET Tel: (01634) 719701 Fax: (01634) 716394 E-mail: fineline.windows@virgin.net

DOUBLE GLAZED WINDOWS – *continued*

▶ G T I Glazing Systems Ltd, The Pavillion Somerton Park, Newport Road, Cowes, Isle of Wight, PO31 8PB Tel: (01983) 280880 Fax: (01983) 290222
▶ Gardenia West Wales Ltd, Spring Gardens, Narberth, Dyfed, SA67 7BT Tel: (01834) 860849 Fax: (01834) 861527 E-mail: sales@gardenia.co.uk
▶ H & P Double Glazing Ltd, Kelsall Street, Oldham, OL9 6HR Tel: 0161-678 9144 E-mail: enquires@hpdoubleglazing.co.uk
Halls Mica Hardware, 116 Market Street, Chapel-en-le-Frith, High Peak, Derbyshire, SK23 0HZ Tel: (01298) 812260 Fax: (01298) 816143
Hi Seal Ltd, Bellbanks Corner, Mill Road, Hailsham, East Sussex, BN27 2AH Tel: (01323) 841392 Fax: (01323) 442719
J W Cooper Joinery, 6 Sea Lane, Rustington, Littlehampton, West Sussex, BN16 2RB Tel: (01903) 776941 Fax: (01903) 776941 E-mail: sales@cooperjoinery.co.uk
Juno Installations, 8 Carlton Park Avenue, London, SW20 8BL Tel: (020) 8543 1697 Fax: (020) 8543 1697 E-mail: harlea0@aol.com
Paignton Glassworks Ltd, 16 Marldon Road, Paignton, Devon, TQ3 3QZ Tel: (01803) 558096 Fax: (01803) 522044 E-mail: enquiries@paigntonglass.co.uk
Pandora Glaze, 41-45 Lind Road, Sutton, Surrey, SM1 4PP Tel: (020) 8643 2132 Fax: (020) 8642 1133
▶ Pilkington UK Ltd, 78 North Ormesby Road, Middlesbrough, Cleveland, TS4 2AG Tel: (01642) 242258 Fax: (01642) 232135
▶ Scott James Glass Ltd, 12A-14 Armstrong Close, St. Leonards-On-Sea, East Sussex, TN38 9ST Tel: (01424) 854161 Fax: (01424) 853418
Season Master, 1 Redan Hill Estate, Redan Road, Aldershot, Hampshire, GU12 4SJ Tel: (01252) 319670 Fax: (01252) 341983 E-mail: sales@seasonmaster.com
Solent Glass & Glazing Ltd, 1 Hackett Way, Fareham, Hampshire, PO14 1TH Tel: (01329) 828210 Fax: (01329) 828838
Supreme-O-Glaze Home Products Ltd, 4 Lyon Road, Romford, RM1 2BA Tel: (0208) 518 2221 Fax: (01708) 739 363
Taylor & Son (Joinery) Ltd, 42 A Vicarage Road, Halesowen, West Midlands, B62 8HU Tel: 0121-559 3955 Fax: 0121-559 5412
Trade Glass Supplies Ltd, Unit 2, Lythgoes Lane, Warrington, WA2 7XE Tel: (01925) 411488 Fax: (01925) 231420 E-mail: tradeglass@aol.com
Welcome Windows Ltd, Wembley Works, Hemingfield Road, Wombwell, Barnsley, South Yorkshire, S73 0LY Tel: (01226) 340240 Fax: (01226) 340327
Wolverhampton Glass & Windows, Pelham Street, Wolverhampton, WV3 0BJ Tel: (01902) 773831 Fax: (01902) 423294
Wrekin Windows Ltd, Units D1-D4, Stafford Park 4, Telford, Shropshire, TF3 3BA Tel: (01952) 290733 Fax: (01952) 290956 E-mail: les.burks@wrekin-windows.co.uk

DOUBLE GLAZING BEADS

▶ Greenwich Windows & Conservatories, Unit 5 Woodhouse Business Centre, Wakefield Road, Normanton, West Yorkshire, WF6 1BB Tel: (01924) 220770 E-mail: sales@greenwitchwindows.com

DOUBLE GLAZING CONTRACTORS

▶ Broadland Windows Ltd, 148 Hellesdon Park Road, Drayton High Road, Norwich, NR6 5DR Tel: (01603) 483002 Fax: (01603) 485946 E-mail: sales@broadlandwindows.co.uk
▶ Country Style, 220 Moulsham Street, Chelmsford, CM2 0LS Tel: (01245) 252277
▶ Country Window Systems Ltd, Unit 1 Hardys Monument Indus, 1 Blagdon Road, Dorchester, Dorset, DT1 2JN Tel: (01305) 889500
▶ DMC Glass & Glazing, 36 Marbles Way, Tadworth, Surrey, KT20 5LG Tel: (01737) 212687 Fax: (01737) 212687 E-mail: dmcglazingservices@hotmail.co.uk
▶ Express Windows, 1 Bishopgate Business Park, Widdrington Road, Coventry, CV1 4NA Tel: (024) 7663 0430 Fax: (024) 7623 1811
▶ F V Conservatories & Windows, Colchester Road, Elmstead, Colchester, CO7 7EA Tel: (01206) 825374 Fax: (01206) 825405 E-mail: sales@fvconservatories.co.uk
▶ First Choice Windows Ltd, 58 Castle Lane, Benfleet, Essex, SS7 2AL Tel: (01702) 555570 Fax: (01702) 555988
▶ Frameline PVC U Products, 16-17 Faraday Road, Knowsley Industrial Park, Liverpool, L33 7UT Tel: 0151-546 5577 Fax: 0151-546 5588
▶ G & T Trade Windows, Oswin Avenue, Balby, Doncaster, South Yorkshire, DN4 0NR Tel: (01302) 857555
▶ High Quality Joinery & Aluminium Services, Lynchford Lane, Farnborough, Hampshire, GU14 6JD Tel: (01252) 548702 Fax: (01252) 548898E-mail: sales@highqualityjoinery.co.uk
▶ Hour Glass, Abernant Enterprise Workshop, Pontardawe Road, Rhydyfro, Pontardawe, Swansea, SA8 4SX Tel: (01269) 825999 Fax: (01269) 825999
▶ Jersey Double Glazing, 1 St. Peters Technical Park, St. Peter, Jersey, JE3 7ZN Tel: (01534) 484459 Fax: (01534) 483309 E-mail: windows@jerseymail.co.uk
Kingston U P V C Ltd, Todmorden Road, Littleborough, Lancashire, OL15 9EQ Tel: (01706) 378824 Fax: (01706) 372138
▶ Orion Windows Ltd, Clifton Industrial Estate, Audax Road, York, YO30 4US Tel: (01904) 690881 Fax: (01904) 691504
▶ S & A Double Glazing Ltd, 111 Hopewell Drive, Chatham, Kent, ME5 7NP Tel: (01634) 843148 Fax: (01634) 818942
▶ Saran Window Ltd, Unit 12, Dale Street Industrial Estate, Radcliffe, Manchester, M26 1AD Tel: 0161-724 6400
▶ Supaglazing Ltd, Units 29 & 10, Deacon Trading Centre, Knight Road Strood, Rochester, Kent, ME2 2AU Tel: (01634) 727406
▶ Sureframe Windows Ltd, Oxford Works, Oxford Street, Accrington, Lancashire, BB5 1QX Tel: (01254) 235390 Fax: (01354) 388084
▶ W E Cox & Sons Ltd, 95 Stewart Road, Bournemouth, BH8 8PA Tel: (01202) 395863 Fax: (01202) 395863
▶ West Kent Windows Ltd, 6 Church Trading Estate, Slade Green Road, Erith, Kent, DA8 2JA Tel: (01322) 338158 Fax: (01322) 338159

DOUBLE GLAZING REPAIR

▶ Double Plas, 1 Babington Park, Grange Park, Swindon, SN5 6EZ Tel: (01793) 875171 Fax: (01793) 878389
▶ Greenwich Windows & Conservatories, Unit 5 Woodhouse Business Centre, Wakefield Road, Normanton, West Yorkshire, WF6 1BB Tel: (01924) 220770 E-mail: sales@greenwitchwindows.com
▶ Higman Windows, Unit 8, Treloggan Industrial Estate, Newquay, Cornwall, TR7 2SX Tel: (01637) 879343 E-mail: sales@higman-windows.co.uk
▶ Normandy Windows Ltd, 3 Crown Close, Crown Industrial Estate, Taunton, Somerset, TA2 8RX Tel: (01823) 256075 E-mail: info@normandy-windows.co.uk

DOUBLE GLAZING SEALANTS

▶ M & D Wright Devlopment Ltd, 46 Park Lane, Bedhampton, Havant, Hampshire, PO9 3HL Tel: (023) 9247 5595 Fax: (023) 9247 6697 E-mail: dgolf@tiscali.co.uk
Plas Tech Windows Ltd, Unit 1-2 Silverwood, Snow Hill, Crawley Down, Crawley, West Sussex, RH10 3EN Tel: (01342) 717714 Fax: (01342) 717715

DOUBLE GLAZING UNITS

A C Yule & Son Ltd, 1 Pinefield Parade, Elgin, Morayshire, IV30 6AG Tel: (01343) 545222 Fax: (01343) 542246 E-mail: elgin@acyule.com
Abbseal (U K) Ltd, Broadway, Broadway, Hyde, Cheshire, SK14 4QW Tel: 0161-368 5711 Fax: 0161-366 8155
Alframes Holdings Ltd, 1A Arnold Road, London, SW17 9HU Tel: (020) 8648 9394 Fax: (020) 8648 4985
Alucare Glaziers, 9 Flitwick Industrial Estate, Maulden Road, Flitwick, Bedford, MK45 1UX Tel: (01525) 713085 Fax: (01525) 715661 E-mail: info@alucare.co.uk
Aluclad Ltd, 140 Woodside Street, Coatbridge, Lanarkshire, ML5 5NS Tel: (01236) 422822
Andrew Wright, 4 Boundary Road, Heathfield Industrial Estate, Ayr, KA8 9DJ Tel: (01292) 611999 Fax: (01292) 610298
Anglian Home Improvements Ltd, PO Box 65, Norwich, NR6 6EJ Tel: (01603) 787000 Fax: (01603) 422298 E-mail: matt.carey@angliangroup.com
Arkay Windows Ltd, 573-575 Lordship Lane, London, N22 5LE Tel: (020) 8889 6821 Fax: (020) 8888 0398 E-mail: sales@arkaywindows.co.uk
B A C Ltd, Faringdon Avenue, Romford, RM3 8SP Tel: (01708) 382200 Fax: (01708) 382308 E-mail: sales@bac.ltd.uk
B B Glass Ltd, 7a Buddle Road, Clay Flatts Industrial Estate, Workington, Cumbria, CA14 3YD Tel: (01900) 65445 Fax: (01900) 64789
Bridgwater Glass, Unit 2-3 Park View, Gallamore Lane, Market Rasen, Lincolnshire, LN8 3HZ Tel: (01673) 842388 Fax: (01673) 842388
Britannia Windows (UK) Ltd, Britannia Houd, Stroud Road, Clevedon, Avon, BS21 6QH Tel: (01275) 878153 Fax: (01275) 343134 E-mail: info@britanniawindows.co.uk
Budget Windows, 2 Chain Lane, Newport, Isle of Wight, PO30 5QA Tel: (01983) 520327 Fax: (01983) 521600 E-mail: sales@bwconline.net
Cornpool Ltd, 174 Station Road, March, Cambs, PE15 8NG Tel: (01354) 655200 Fax: (01354) 656421
Country Window Systems Ltd, Flightway, Dunkeswell Industrial Estate, Dunkeswell, Honiton, Devon, EX14 4LN Tel: (01404) 891144 Fax: (01404) 891044 E-mail: info@countrywindows.com
CR Smith, Gardeners Street, Dunfermline, Fife, KY12 0RN Tel: (01383) 732181 Fax: (01383) 739095 E-mail: admin@crsmith.co.uk
Crescent Glass Ltd, Derby Road, Burton-On-Trent, Staffordshire, DE14 1RX Tel: (01283) 563070 Fax: (01283) 566898 E-mail: info@longlifewindows.co.uk
Crocodilla Ltd, East Cottage, Hill View Road, Michelmersh, Romsey, Hampshire, SO51 0NN Tel: (01794) 367286 Fax: (01794) 367286 E-mail: info@crocodilla.co.uk
Double Glazing Supplies Group plc, Sycamore Road, Castle Donington, Derby, DE74 2NW Tel: (01332) 811611 Fax: (01332) 812650 E-mail: reception@dgsgroup.co.uk
Excel Glass Ltd, Musgrave Park Industrial Estate, Stockmans Way, Belfast, BT9 7ET Tel: (028) 9038 2121 Fax: (028) 9038 1951 E-mail: bg@excel.dnet.co.uk
Express Windows, 1 Trovers Way, Holmethorpe Industrial Estate, Redhill, RH1 2LH Tel: (01737) 768833 Fax: (01737) 768832 E-mail: mail@expresswindows.co.uk
Don Farmer & Sons, Rendel Street, Birkenhead, Merseyside, CH41 3NJ Tel: 0151-666 1450 Fax: 0151-666 2540 E-mail: sales@doubleglaze.co.uk
Flat Glass Ltd, 186 Wigan Road, Westhoughton, Bolton, BL5 2AG Tel: (01942) 813037 Fax: (01942) 812203 E-mail: info@flatglass.co.uk
FOCUS Windows Ltd, Unit A Technology Centre, White Oak Square, London Road, Swanley, Kent, BR8 7AG Tel: (01322) 614551 Fax: (01322) 613366
Glas Seal Ni Ltd, 80 Belfast Road, Ballynahinch, County Down, BT24 8EB Tel: (028) 9756 2932 Fax: (028) 9756 1096 E-mail: post@glas-seal.co.uk
▶ Glass Doctor, 56 Little Glen Road, Glen Parva, Leicester, LE2 9TS Tel: (0800) 6346494 Fax: 0116-299 1898 E-mail: info@glassandlock.co.uk
▶ Glass Scratch Repair, 19 Harwood Lane, Great Harwood, Blackburn, BB6 7SN Tel: (01254) 888557 E-mail: peter_cornwell@lineone.net
Griffin Windows Ltd, Unit 37 Abergorki Industrial Estate, Treorchy, Mid Glamorgan, CF42 6DL Tel: (01443) 777333 Fax: (01443) 776773 E-mail: suzm@griffinwindows.co.uk
Hanwell Glass Co. Ltd, 183 Uxbridge Road, London, W7 3TH Tel: (020) 8567 2186 Fax: (020) 8840 0042
Holdens Supaseal Ltd, 505 Garretts Green Lane, Birmingham, B33 0SG Tel: 0121-789 7766 Fax: 0121-789 7237 E-mail: info@holdens-supaseal.co.uk
Isolated Systems Ltd, Adams Close, Heanor, Derbyshire, DE75 7SW Tel: (01773) 761226 Fax: (01773) 760408 E-mail: fshopkins@vitraseal.co.uk
K2 Glass Ltd, Sett End Road, Shadsworth Business Park, Blackburn, BB1 2PT Tel: (01254) 260040 Fax: (01254) 692389 E-mail: enquiry@k2glassltd.com
The London & Local Manufacturing Co. Ltd, 312B Kingston Road, London, SW20 8LX Tel: (020) 8644 5951 Fax: (020) 8641 4119 E-mail: londonandlocal1@aol.co.uk
Lyten Ltd, 1-3 Inchview Road, Wallyford, Musselburgh, Midlothian, EH21 8JZ Tel: 0131-653 2400 Fax: 0131-665 0040 E-mail: sales@lyten.co.uk
Nova, 3 Partnership House, Withambrook Park Industrial Estate, Grantham, Lincolnshire, NG31 9ST Tel: (01476) 577635 Fax: (01476) 577635 E-mail: novawindows@hotmail.com
P & M Dabner Ltd, Unit C2 Springhead Enterprise Park, Springhead Road, Northfleet, Gravesend, Kent, DA11 8HD Tel: (01474) 335678 Fax: (01474) 334678 E-mail: enquiries@etchedglass.co.uk
Pandora Glaze, 41-45 Lind Road, Sutton, Surrey, SM1 4PP Tel: (020) 8643 2132 Fax: (020) 8642 1133
Paxton Home Improvements, Goddards Yard, Thaxted Road, Saffron Walden, Essex, CB11 3AG Tel: (01799) 527542 Fax: (01799) 527541 E-mail: sales@paxtonsonline.com
Pilkington Plyglass, Cotes Park, Somercotes, Alfreton, Derbyshire, DE55 4PL Tel: (01773) 520000 Fax: (01773) 520052
Pilkington Sealed Units, Churchbridge Indust Estate, Oldbury, West Midlands, B69 4FH Tel: 0121-541 1601 Fax: 0121-552 3748 E-mail: sealed.units@pilkington.com
Pilkington UK Ltd, 1 Dunnswood Road, Wardpark South, Cumbernauld, Glasgow, G67 3EN Tel: (01236) 728298 Fax: (01236) 729876 E-mail: cumbernauld@pilkington.com
Pilkington UK Ltd, Orgreave Drive, Sheffield, S13 9NR Tel: 0114-254 0444 Fax: 0114-254 0861 E-mail: joanne.marlow@pilkington.com
Plas Tech Windows Ltd, Unit 1-2 Silverwood, Snow Hill, Crawley Down, Crawley, West Sussex, RH10 3EN Tel: (01342) 717714 Fax: (01342) 717715
Q Glazing Ltd, 83-89 Western Road, Wood Green, London, N22 6US Tel: (020) 8888 7733 Fax: (020) 8888 7744 E-mail: mail@qglazing.com
Ramsey Glass & Window Co (Chipwel), A Highlode Industrial Estate, Stocking Fen Road, Ramsey, Huntingdon, Cambridgeshire, PE26 2RB Tel: (01487) 813007 Fax: (01487) 710364 E-mail: salesramseyglass@hotmail.com
Ravensby Glass Co. Ltd, Fowler Road, West Pitkerro Industrial Estate, Broughtyferry, Dundee, DD5 3RU Tel: (01382) 480842 Fax: (01382) 480323
Regency Glass, Hope Carr Industrial Estate, Butt St, Leigh, Lancashire, WN7 3XA Tel: (01942) 262162 Fax: (01942) 261555 E-mail: dean@regencyglass.co.uk
River Street Glassworks, Bridgeman Street, Bolton, BL3 6BS Tel: (01204) 454444 Fax: (01204) 454445
Rugby Glass Centre, 17 Somers Road, Rugby, Warwickshire, CV22 7DG Tel: (01788) 543756 Fax: (01788) 540078
St George Glass Co., 108 Halliwell Road, Bolton, BL1 3QN Tel: (01204) 383811 Fax: (01204) 394758
Sash Products UK Ltd, Ferrymoor Way, Grimethorpe, Barnsley, South Yorkshire, S72 7BN Tel: (01226) 715619 Fax: (01226) 780701 E-mail: sales@sashuk.com
Sheerwater Glass Centre, 23-27 Dartmouth Avenue, Woking, Surrey, GU21 5PE Tel: (01932) 349247 Fax: (01932) 346580
Southern Counties Glass, Unit I Foundry Close, Horsham, West Sussex, RH13 5TX Tel: (01403) 264723 Fax: (01403) 268153 E-mail: derek@southerncountiesglass.co.uk
Southport Glass, 19 St James Street, Southport, Merseyside, PR8 5AE Tel: (01704) 537474 Fax: (01704) 534418
Southwest Glass, The Old Saw Mill Industrial Estate, The Street, Broughton Gifford, Melksham, Wiltshire, SN12 8PY Tel: (01225) 783207 Fax: (01225) 783273 E-mail: sales@swglass.co.uk
Sunit Glass, Napier Close, Hawkesworth Trading Estate, Swindon, SN2 1TY Tel: (01793) 615445 Fax: (01793) 491414
Supaseal Glass Ltd, 1-3 Lovat Place, Hillington Industrial Estate, Glasgow, G52 4DS Tel: 0141-810 5010 Fax: 0141-810 5020 E-mail: sales@supasealglass.co.uk
System 3 Ltd, Denton Hall Farm Road, Denton, Manchester, M34 2SY Tel: 0161-337 3000 Fax: 0161-337 0222
Technical Glass Ltd, Kelvin Way, West Bromwich, West Midlands, B70 7LB Tel: 0121-553 3334 Fax: 0121-553 3336 E-mail: sales@technicalglass.net
Tolland Glass & Windows, 11 Tudor Parade, Well Hall Road, London, SE9 6SX Tel: (020) 8850 9236 Fax: (020) 8294 0036
Tradelink Direct Ltd, Marwick Road, March, Cambridgeshire, PE15 8PH Tel: (01354) 657650 Fax: (01354) 657400
Triwarm Ltd, Unit E, Hamstead Industrial Estate, Austin Way, Great Barr, Birmingham, B42 1DU Tel: 0121-525 0500 Fax: 0121-525 6800 E-mail: sales@tri-warm.co.uk
Uni Seal (South Coast) Co. Ltd, 28 Balena Close, Poole, Dorset, BH17 7EB Tel: (01202) 602800 Fax: (01202) 658651
Weathershield Ltd, 82 Curries Close, Canley, Coventry, CV4 8AW Tel: (024) 7647 4447 Fax: (024) 7646 1977
Wessex Frames, Permaframe House, Georges Ground, Frome, Somerset, BA11 4RP Tel: (01373) 455955 Fax: (01373) 467650

DOUBLE PIPE HAIRPIN HEAT EXCHANGERS

Koch Heat Transfer Company, PO Box 790, Wimborne, Dorset, BH21 5BQ Tel: (01258) 840776 Fax: (01258) 840961 E-mail: bftuk@kochind.com

DOUBLE RIDGED MICROWAVE COMPONENTS

Q Par Angus Ltd, Barons Cross Laboratories, Barons Cross Road, Barons Cross, Leominster, Herefordshire, HR6 8RS Tel: (01568) 612138 Fax: (01568) 616373 E-mail: sales@q-par.com

DOUBLE SIDED ADHESIVE TAPES

3M Tapes & Adhesives Group, 3M Centre, Cain Road, Bracknell, Berkshire, RG12 8HT Tel: (01344) 858000 Fax: (01344) 858278
Action Tapes Ltd, Red Scar Industrial Estate, Longridge Road, Ribbleton, Preston, PR2 5NE Tel: (01280) 700591 Fax: (01280) 700590 E-mail: sales@prestec.co.uk
Adhesive Tape Manufacturing Co Ltd, 2 Bilston Industrial Estate, Oxford Street, Bilston, West Midlands, WV14 7EG Tel: (01902) 409598 Fax: (01902) 409599 E-mail: sales@atmuk.co.uk
Apollo Chemicals Holdings Ltd, Sandy Way, Amington Industrial Estate, Tamworth, Staffordshire, B77 4DS Tel: (01827) 54281 Fax: (01827) 53030 E-mail: sales@apolloadhesives.com
BDK Industrial Products, Levington Park, Bridge Road, Levington, Ipswich, IP10 0JE Tel: (01473) 659059 Fax: (01473) 659104 E-mail: sales@bdk.uk.com
Bruce Douglas Ultratape Ltd, Kilspindie Road, Dunsinane Industrial Estate, Dundee, DD2 3JP Tel: (01382) 832999 Fax: (01382) 833422 E-mail: sales@ultratape.com

DOUBLE SIDED ADHESIVE TAPES - *continued*

Cheshire Adhesives Tapes & Packaging, New Road, Winsford, Cheshire, CW7 2NU Tel: (01606) 863228 Fax: (01606) 863139 E-mail: bullfinchgroup@freeuk.com
▶ Creative Detail, 32 Thorncliffe Drive, Darwen, Lancashire, BB3 3QA Tel: 01254 773391 E-mail: val@creative-detail.co.uk
Delta Adhesives Ltd, 2 Lakeside Industrial Estate, Lakeside Road, Leeds, LS12 4QP Tel: 0113-279 6966 Fax: 0113-231 0828 E-mail: info@delta-adhesives.co.uk
Hi Bond Tapes Ltd, 1 Crucible Road, Corby, Northamptonshire, NN17 5TS Tel: (01536) 260022 Fax: (01536) 260044 E-mail: sales@hi-bondtapes.co.uk
Lewis Industrial Products, 25 Lichfield Close, New Arley, Coventry, Warwickshire, CV7 8PU Tel: (01676) 541792 Fax: (01676) 541184 E-mail: lewislip@aol.com
Litho Supplies Scotland Ltd, 8 Elphinstone Square, Deans Industrial Estate, Deans, Livingston, West Lothian, EH54 8RG Tel: (01506) 462555 Fax: (01506) 465678 E-mail: scotland@litho.co.uk
▶ Lohmann Adhesive Tape Systems, Cane End Lane, Bierton, Aylesbury, Buckinghamshire, HP22 5BH Tel: (01296) 337888 Fax: (01296) 337772 E-mail: info@lohmann-tapes.co.uk
P A L Adhesive Products Ltd, Old Park Industrial Estate, Old Park Road, Wednesbury, West Midlands, WS10 9LR Tel: 0121-556 6686 Fax: 0121-505 1487 E-mail: sales@paladhesives.co.uk
Pakex UK plc, 1 Prime Point, Bessemer Road, Welwyn Garden City, Hertfordshire, AL7 1FE Tel: (01707) 384858 Fax: (01707) 332838 E-mail: sales@pakexuk.com
Pamarco Europe Ltd, New Cut Lane, Woolston, Warrington, WA1 4AQ Tel: (01925) 456789 Fax: (01925) 456778 E-mail: sales-roll@pamarco.co.uk
Parafix, Spencer Road, Church Hill Industrial Estate, Lancing, West Sussex, BN15 8UA Tel: (01903) 750000 Fax: (01903) 767728 E-mail: sales@parafix.co.uk
Polar Seal Tapes & Conversions, Guildford Road Industrial Estate, Guildford Road, Farnham, Surrey, GU9 9PZ Tel: (01252) 726000 Fax: (01252) 728125
Premier Coatings & Converters, West Portway, Andover, Hampshire, SP10 3LF Tel: (01264) 358633 Fax: (01264) 334701 E-mail: sales@pcc-ltd.com
▶ Proton Supplies, Unit 18 Allshots Enterprises, Woodhouse Lane, Kelvedon, Colchester, CO5 9DF Tel: (01376) 584000 Fax: (01376) 583444 E-mail: sales@apcsolutionsuk.com
R G H Rubber & Plastics Ltd, Acorn House, Oak Industrial Park, Chelmsford Road, Great Dunmow, Dunmow, Essex, CM6 1XN Tel: (01371) 875941 Fax: (01371) 873804 E-mail: sales@rghrubber.co.uk
Saint Gobain Performance Plastics, 13 Earlstrees Road, Earlstrees Industrial Estate, Corby, Northamptonshire, NN17 4AZ Tel: (01536) 276000 Fax: (01536) 203427 E-mail: pplcorbyuk@aol.com
Scappa (U K) Ltd, The Woodside Estate, Dunstable, Bedfordshire, LU5 4TP Tel: (01582) 478111 Fax: (01582) 471085 E-mail: carole.price@scapatapes.com
▶ Sealking UK Ltd, Centrum House, Engine Lane, Brownhills, Walsall, WS8 7TE Tel: (01543) 453453 Fax: (01543) 452542 E-mail: uksales@seal-king-europe.com
▶ Steratape Ltd, Carnaby Industrial Estate, Lancaster Road, Carnaby, Bridlington, East Yorkshire, YO15 3QY Tel: (01262) 603721 Fax: (01262) 400028 E-mail: carl@steratape.com
tesa UK Ltd, Yeomans Drive, Blakelands, Milton Keynes, MK14 5LS Tel: 0845 4941752 Fax: (01908) 211555 E-mail: ukenquiry@tesa.com
V S A Products Ltd, Hardwick Trading Estate, Rollesby Road, King's Lynn, Norfolk, PE30 4JS Tel: (01553) 761521 Fax: (01553) 691464 E-mail: vsa-enquiries@btconnect.com

DOUBLED YARN

F. Harding (Macclesfield) Ltd, Kershaw Mill, Newton Street, Macclesfield, Cheshire, SK11 6QJ Tel: (01625) 429625 Fax: (01625) 612836 E-mail: sales@f-harding.com

DOWEL PINS

Emkay Screw Supplies, 74 Pepys Way, Strood, Rochester, Kent, ME2 3LL Tel: (01634) 717256 Fax: (01634) 717256 E-mail: emkaysupplies@talktalk.net
Industrial Trading Co. Ltd, PO Box 51, Worcester, WR1 1QE Tel: (01905) 20373 Fax: (01905) 27158

DOWN QUILTS

Amoire Linen, 82 Beech Farm Drive, Macclesfield, Cheshire, SK10 2ER Tel: (01625) 431166 Fax: (01625) 610955 E-mail: sales@armoirelinen.co.uk

DOWNHOLE TOOL HIRE

Andergauge Ltd, Hareness Road, Altens Industrial Estate, Aberdeen, AB12 3LE Tel: (01224) 336500 Fax: (01224) 336505 E-mail: sales@andergauge.com
Hall Green Hire Ltd, 282-284 Fox Hollies Road, Acocks Green, Birmingham, B27 7PT Tel: 0121-706 8940 Fax: 0121-604 6633
Valden Hire Services Ltd, 5 St Clements Road, Nechells, Birmingham, B7 5AF Tel: 0121-327 8920 Fax: 0121-327 7606

DOWNHOLE TOOLS

Baker Oil Tools UK Ltd, Kirkhill Road, Kirkhill Industrial Estate, Dyce, Aberdeen, AB21 0GQ Tel: (01224) 223500 Fax: (01224) 771400 E-mail: jim.moir@bakeroiltools.com
Halliburton Manufacturing & Services Ltd, Kirkhill Industrial Estate, Howemoss Cresent, Aberdeen, AB21 0GN Tel: (01224) 795000 Fax: (01224) 728495
Lion Engineering Services Ltd, Gapton Hall Road, Great Yarmouth, Norfolk, NR31 0NL Tel: (01493) 653642 Fax: (01493) 653353 E-mail: sales@lion-oil-tools.demon.co.uk
Mussett Group Ltd, Beccles Industrial Estate, Loddon, Norwich, NR14 6JD Tel: (01508) 522500 Fax: (01508) 528769 E-mail: enquire@mussett.co.uk
National Oilwell (U K) Ltd, Unit 10, Kirkton Avenue, Dyce, Aberdeen, AB21 0BF Tel: (01224) 875071 Fax: (01224) 723034
Wood Group Production Technology Ltd, Maersk House, Greenbank Road, East Tullos Industrial Estate, Aberdeen, AB21 3BR Tel: (01224) 840000 Fax: (01224) 216775

DOWNPROOF FABRICS

Platt Haworth & Co. Ltd, Fourways House, 18 Tariff Street, Manchester, M1 2FN Tel: 0161-236 0764 Fax: 0161-236 7543 E-mail: sales@platthaworth.com

DRAFTING SERVICES

▶ Blue Aardvark Design, The Grange Business Centre, Belasis Avenue, Billingham, Cleveland, TS23 1LG Tel: (01642) 658783 Fax: (01642) 552820 E-mail: blueaardvarkdesign@tiscali.co.uk
▶ D S Traditional Drawings, Birmingham, B44 8ET Tel: 0121-382 5544
▶ JBES, The Cottage, Sackville Street, Winterborne Kingston, Blandford Forum, Dorset, DT11 9BJ Tel: (01929) 471114 Fax: (01929) 472521 E-mail: jbes@supanet.com
▶ WebCad, The Barn, HodgeHill Farm, Blakedown, Kidderminster, Worcestershire, DY10 3NR Tel: 01562 515318 Fax: 0709 2394102 E-mail: sales@webcad2005.co.uk

DRAIN CLEANING OR CLEARANCE CONTRACTORS

24hourdrains.Com, 26 Colwyn Avenue, Morecambe, Lancashire, LA4 6EH Tel: (01524) 410410 Fax: (01524) 411880
▶ associated drain cleaning services, 80 hawthorn way, shepperton, middlesex, TW17 8QD Tel: 01932 765892 Fax: 01932 765892 E-mail: info@associated-services.co.uk
▶ Drainserve.com Ltd, 8 Scott Grove, Solihull, West Midlands, B92 7LJ Tel: 0121-707 7489
Drainways Ltd, 108 Summer Road, Erdington, Birmingham, B23 6DY Tel: 0121-377 6583 Fax: 0121-377 7769 E-mail: sales@drainways.com
Earl Road Sweepers Ltd, Shardlowes Farm, Hedingham Road, Gosfield, Halstead, Essex, CO9 1PL Tel: (01787) 273777 Fax: (01787) 273777 E-mail: office@ersweepers.wanadoo.co.uk
▶ Econorod, 6 Brownfields, Welwyn Garden City, Hertfordshire, AL7 1AN Tel: (01707) 333573 Fax: (01707) 333574
Envirotec Support Services, Cornwall House, London Road, Purfleet, Essex, RM19 1PS Tel: (01708) 685230 Fax: (01708) 861862
▶ Gracelands Landscapes Ltd, The Yard, Bramshill Close, Arborfield Cross, Reading, RG2 9PT Tel: 0118-976 0660 Fax: 0118-976 0990 E-mail: info@gracelands-landscapes.co.uk
Greens Water Systems, Longacre Business Park, Westminster Road, North Hykeham, Lincoln, LN6 3QH Tel: (01522) 697785 Fax: (01522) 823899 E-mail: info@water-systems.co.uk
J C Jetting, 84 Bonnington Walk, Bristol, BS7 9XD Tel: 0117-904 1638 Fax: 0117-904 1638 E-mail: rachod@ukonline.co.uk
Keep Clean Drain Services, E2-E3 Unit, Jaggard Way, London, SW12 8SG Tel: (020) 8772 9388 Fax: (020) 8772 9389 E-mail: sales@kcdrains.co.uk

DRAIN CLEANING OR CLEARANCE EQUIPMENT

24hourdrains.Com, 26 Colwyn Avenue, Morecambe, Lancashire, LA4 6EH Tel: (01524) 410410 Fax: (01524) 411880
▶ Accelerated Drain Services Ltd, 47 Suffolk Road, Barking, Essex, IG11 7QP Tel: (020) 8594 7171 E-mail: info@accelerated-drains.co.uk
Aqua Clenz Ltd, Unit 8-10 Chanters Industrial Estate, Tyldesley Old Road, Atherton, Manchester, M46 9BE Tel: (01942) 882664 Fax: (01942) 883733
Chadwicks Liverpool Ltd, 62-64 Kitchen Street, Liverpool, L1 0AN Tel: 0151-709 3081 Fax: 0151-709 9115
Horobin Ltd, Willenhall Trading Estate, Midacre, Willenhall, West Midlands, WV13 2JW Tel: (01902) 604060 Fax: (01902) 603366 E-mail: sales@horobin.co.uk
Kenmac (U K) Ltd, Unit D Wigan Hall Road, Good Yard, Wigan Hall Road, Watford, WD18 0EZ Tel: (01923) 218998 Fax: (01923) 818454 E-mail: enquiries@kenmacuk.com
Monument Tools, Restmor Way, Hackbridge Road, Hackbridge, Wallington, Surrey, SM6 7AH Tel: (020) 8288 1100 Fax: (020) 8288 1108 E-mail: info@monument-tools.com
Ridge Tools, Arden Press Way, Pixmore Avenue, Letchworth Garden City, Hertfordshire, SG6 1LH Tel: (01462) 485335 Fax: (01462) 485315 E-mail: sales.uk@ridgid.com
Rothenberger UK Ltd, 2 Kingsthorne Park, Henson Way, Telford Way Industrial Estate, Kettering, Northamptonshire, NN16 8PX Tel: (01536) 310300 Fax: (01536) 310600 E-mail: info@rothenberger.co.uk
Sexton Sales Ltd, D Wiggenhall Road Goods Yard, Wiggenhall Road, Watford, WD18 0EZ Tel: (01923) 240434 Fax: (01923) 818454 E-mail: enquiries@sextonsales.com
Tolbest Ltd, 10 Aston Court, Kingsland Grange, Woolston, Warrington, WA1 4SG Tel: (01925) 825335 Fax: (01925) 825336 E-mail: info@tolbest.co.uk
Ward's Flexible Rod Co. Ltd, 22 James Carter Road, Mildenhall, Bury St. Edmunds, Suffolk, IP28 7DE Tel: (01638) 713800 Fax: (01638) 716863 E-mail: sales@wardsflex.co.uk
▶ Wessex Plumbing & Heating Services Ltd, Unit 3 5b Surrey Close, Granby Industrial Estate, Weymouth, Dorset, DT4 9GD Tel: (01305) 766549 Fax: (01305) 766549 E-mail: colin-wessexplumbing@btconnect.com

DRAIN COUPLINGS

Fernco International Ltd, Newlands Way, Valley Park, Wombwell, Barnsley, South Yorkshire, S73 0UW Tel: (01226) 340209 Fax: (01226) 340400 E-mail: enquiries@fernco.co.uk

DRAIN OR SANITARY PIPES, *See also headings for particular materials*

Brett Martin Roofing Products Ltd, Langley Road, Burscough Industrial Estate, Ormskirk, Lancashire, L40 8JR Tel: (01704) 895345 Fax: (01704) 894229 E-mail: contact@daylightsystems.co.uk
Drainage Spares & Pipework Supplies Ltd, Fairy Farm Wethersfield, Wethersfield, Braintree, Essex, CM7 4EP Tel: (01371) 850808 Fax: (01371) 850120 E-mail: adam.dsps@btinternet.com
Euro Industrial Plastics Ltd, Chamberlain Road, Aylesbury, Buckinghamshire, HP19 8DY Tel: (01296) 482252 Fax: (01296) 425482 E-mail: enquiries@euroindustrialplastics.co.uk
J D P Ltd, Collett Way, Yate, Bristol, BS37 5NL Tel: (01454) 323000 Fax: (01454) 310037 E-mail: yate@jdpipes.co.uk
Pipeline Center Plastics Ltd, Braidhurst Industrial Estate, Motherwell, Lanarkshire, ML1 3SN Tel: (01698) 261414 Fax: (01698) 275424

DRAIN RODS

Bailey Bros (Engineers) Ltd, 105 Hospital St, Newtown, Birmingham, B19 3XB Tel: 0121-359 8361 Fax: 0121-359 0909 E-mail: sales@cerro-ems.co.uk
Ward's Flexible Rod Co. Ltd, 22 James Carter Road, Mildenhall, Bury St. Edmunds, Suffolk, IP28 7DE Tel: (01638) 713800 Fax: (01638) 716863 E-mail: sales@wardsflex.co.uk

DRAIN TEST OR INSPECTION OR SURVEY EQUIPMENT

Consoil Geotechnical Instruments UK, Clark House, 3 Brassey Drive, Aylesford, Kent, ME20 7QL Tel: (01622) 882093 Fax: (0870) 0543915 E-mail: info@consoil.co.uk
▶ Sunnyfield International. Ltd, Sunnyfield Farm, Ince Lane, Liverpool, L23 4UJ Tel: 0151-924 3692 Fax: 0151-924 8305 E-mail: enquiries@setting-out.com
Survequip.com, Centrix House, Ash 05, 26 Crow Lane East, Newton-le-Willows, Merseyside, WA12 9UY Tel: (0800) 13 13 435 Fax: (01925) 273001 E-mail: sales@survequip.com
▶ Survey Technology, Westmere Drive, Crewe, CW1 6ZG Tel: (01270) 250525 Fax: (01270) 580700 E-mail: info@surveytechnology.co.uk

DRAIN TESTING OR INSPECTION OR SURVEYING

Consoil Geotechnical Instruments UK, Clark House, 3 Brassey Drive, Aylesford, Kent, ME20 7QL Tel: (01622) 882093 Fax: (0870) 0543915 E-mail: info@consoil.co.uk
Drainways Ltd, 108 Summer Road, Erdington, Birmingham, B23 6DY Tel: 0121-377 6583 Fax: 0121-377 7769 E-mail: sales@drainways.com
▶ Geomap Ltd, 8 Fairview Close, Watledge, Nailsworth, Stroud, Gloucestershire, GL6 0AX Tel: (07968) 428655 E-mail: info@geomapltd.co.uk
Insewer Surveys, Unit 22 Lordswood Industrial Estate, Revenge Road, Chatham, Kent, ME5 8UD Tel: (01634) 861768 Fax: (01634) 201376 E-mail: enquiries@hydrogroup.demon.co.uk

DRAINAGE CHANNELS

ACO Buildings Drainage, Hitchin Road, Shefford, Bedfordshire, SG17 5TE Tel: (01462) 816666 Fax: (01462) 851490 E-mail: buildingdrainage@aco.co.uk
▶ Ashridge Construction Ltd, A A Workshop, Enterprise Way, Thatcham, Berkshire, RG19 4AE Tel: (01635) 879400 Fax: (01635) 879401 E-mail: enquiries@ashridge.co.uk
Isle of Wight Land Drainage, Newnham Farm, Newnham Lane, Ryde, Isle Of Wight, PO33 4ED Tel: (01983) 882423 Fax: (01983) 882423 E-mail: newnhamfarm@talk21.com
Webster-Wilkinson Ltd, Unit A, Halesfield 10, Telford, Shropshire, TF7 4QP Tel: (01952) 585701 Fax: (01952) 581901 E-mail: sales@webster-wilkinson.com

DRAINAGE INSTALLATION

▶ Berry Bank Bank Farm, Windmill Lane, Hundall, Apperknowle, Dronfield, Derbyshire, S18 4BQ Tel: (01246) 415986 E-mail: mark@berrybankfarm.co.uk
▶ Carey Construction Ltd, 20B Royal Chase, Tunbridge Wells, Kent, TN4 8AY Tel: (01892) 522069 E-mail: careybuild@aol.com
▶ Draincare Services Ltd, Unit 2, Batford Mill, Lower Luton Road, Harpenden, Hertfordshire, AL5 5BZ Tel: (01582) 467111

DRAINAGE SEWERAGE AND TRADE EFFLUENT CONSULTANCY

▶ A - Tanks, The Cottage Back Lane, Northwick Road, Mark Moor, Highbridge, Somerset, TA9 4PQ Tel: 01278 641410 Fax: 01278 641410 E-mail: natasha@a-tanks.co.uk
Marley Plumbing & Drainage Ltd, Rannoch Road, Uddingston, Glasgow, G71 5PA Tel: (01698) 815231 Fax: (01698) 810307
Peter Mason Associates, New Street, Mawdesley, Ormskirk, Lancashire, L40 2QP Tel: (01704) 823245 Fax: (01704) 823246 E-mail: steve.douglas@btinternet.com
TDK Groundworks, 140 Grantham Road, Waddington, Lincoln, LN5 9NU Tel: (01522) 722332 Fax: (01522) 722280
▶ Underground Surveys, Unit G14 Warrington Business Park, Long Lane, Warrington, WA2 8TX Tel: (01925) 444664 Fax: (01925) 444663 E-mail: info@undergroundsurveys.co.uk

DRAINAGE SYSTEM DESIGN

Hepworth Building Products Ltd, 47 Coppice Side, Swadlincote, Derbyshire, DE11 9AA Tel: (01283) 552467 Fax: (01283) 221034

DRAINAGE SYSTEMS, *See also headings for particular types*

▶ Clark-Drain, Station Works, Station Road, Yaxley, Peterborough, PE7 3EQ Tel: (01733) 765315 Fax: (01733) 246923
▶ Lanes For Drains Ltd, Sandleheath Industrial Estate, Old Brickyard Road, Sandleheath, Fordingbridge, Hampshire, SP6 1PA Tel: (01425) 656116 Fax: (01425) 657563
Brian Thompson, Barrock End, Hethersgill, Carlisle, CA6 6HT Tel: (01228) 675614 Fax: (01228) 675614

DRAUGHT EXCLUDERS

Slottseal Extrusions Ltd, Tyne Road, Weadon Road Industrial Estate, Northampton, NN5 5AF Tel: (01604) 759535 Fax: (01604) 752780 E-mail: tecplastics@btinternet

DRAUGHT EXCLUDERS – *continued*

TSL Extrusions, Elton Park Business Centre, Hadleigh Rd, Ipswich, IP2 0HN Tel: 0845 4940747 Fax: (01473) 236044 E-mail: sales@tubeway.co.uk

V S A Products Ltd, Hardwick Trading Estate, Rollesby Road, King's Lynn, Norfolk, PE30 4JS Tel: (01553) 761521 Fax: (01553) 691464 E-mail: vsa-enquiries@btconnect.com

DRAUGHT PROOF WINDOWS

Frostree Ltd, 31 Station Street, Middlesbrough, Cleveland, TS1 1SR Tel: (01642) 224151 Fax: (01642) 247973 E-mail: sales@frostree.co.uk

DRAUGHT STABILISERS

H Docherty Ltd, Red Shute Hill Industrial Estate, Red Shute Hill, Hermitage, Thatcham, Berkshire, RG18 9QL Tel: (01635) 200145 Fax: (01635) 201737 E-mail: info@docherty.co.uk

DRAWER (PLASTIC) MANUFRS

Hardex Fittings, Shilton Industrial Estate, Bulkington Road, Coventry, CV7 9JY Tel: (024) 7658 7600 Fax: (024) 7658 7606 E-mail: enquiries@hardex.co.uk

DRAWER SLIDES

Agostino Ferrari UK Ltd, Units H & L Strawberry Street Industrial Estate, Strawberry Street, Hull, HU9 1EN Tel: (01482) 594450 Fax: (01482) 594455 E-mail: info@aferrariuk.com

G S F Ltd, Unit 9 Gledrid Industrial Estate, Chirk, Wrexham, LL14 5DG Tel: (01691) 770303 Fax: (01691) 776900 E-mail: enquiries@gsfslides.com

Indaux UK Ltd, Mga House, Ray Mill Road East, Maidenhead, Berkshire, SL6 8ST Tel: (01628) 780250 Fax: (01628) 780251 E-mail: sales@indaux.com

DRAWER SUSPENSION SLIDES

G S F Ltd, Unit 9 Gledrid Industrial Estate, Chirk, Wrexham, LL14 5DG Tel: (01691) 770303 Fax: (01691) 776900 E-mail: enquiries@gsfslides.com

DRAWING BOARD CLIPS

▶ Walton Designs Ltd, 41 St Helens Way, Thetford, Norfolk, IP24 1HG Tel: (01842) 752522 Fax: (01842) 754060 E-mail: sales@waltondesignsltd.co.uk

DRAWING BOARDS/ ACCESSORIES/FITTINGS

Blundell Harling Ltd, 9 Albany Road, Granby Industrial Estate, Weymouth, Dorset, DT4 9TH Tel: (01305) 206000 Fax: (01305) 760598 E-mail: sales@blundellharling.co.uk

Orchard Drawing Boards, Union Square, Wakefield, West Yorkshire, WF1 1TT Tel: (01924) 291333 Fax: (01924) 290909

DRAWING INSTRUMENTS

Geometrix Ltd, Chase Road, Brownhills, Walsall, WS8 6JU Tel: (01543) 452424 Fax: (01543) 453012 E-mail: enquiries@geometrix.co.uk

DRAWING OFFICE EQUIPMENT AND MATERIALS, *See also headings for particular types*

A & B Office Furnishers, 4 Charlton Mead Lane, Hoddesdon, Hertfordshire, EN11 0DJ Tel: (0870) 0502040

A M I Supplies Ltd, 2 Centre 2000, St. Michaels Road, Sittingbourne, Kent, ME10 3DZ Tel: (01795) 420430 Fax: (01795) 426817 E-mail: sales@amigroup.co.uk

Aided Design & Draughting Supplies, 14-16 West Street, Exeter, EX1 1BA Tel: (01392) 445580 Fax: (01392) 444126

Aided Design & Draughting Supplies, Spreadeagle Court, Northgate Street, Gloucester, GL1 1SL Tel: (01452) 505040 Fax: (01452) 505040

Bayliss Wright Gados Ltd, 50 Park Street, Luton, LU1 3ET Tel: (01582) 722186 Fax: (01582) 727780 E-mail: baylisswright@eurotelbroadband.com

Bradbury Graphics Ltd, 6-14 Donegall Pass, Belfast, BT7 1BS Tel: (028) 9023 3535 Fax: (028) 9057 2057 E-mail: info@bradbury-graphics.co.uk

C.D.S Yorks Ltd, Ledgard Way, Reprographic House, Armley, Leeds, LS12 2ND Tel: 0113-263 0601 Fax: 0113-231 0305 E-mail: sales@cds-yorks.com

Copylogic Ltd, The Palmerston Centre, Oxford Road, Wealdstone, Harrow, Middlesex, HA3 7RG Tel: (020) 8863 4483 Fax: (020) 8861 1620 E-mail: mail@copylogic.co.uk

Cotech Ltd, Unit 13-16, Tafarnaubach Industrial Estate, Tafarnaubach, Tredegar, Gwent, NP22 3AA Tel: (01495) 711970 Fax: (01495) 725765 E-mail: sales@cotech-uk.com

Cross's, 20 Lower Bridge Street, Canterbury, Kent, CT1 2LG Tel: (01227) 458776 Fax: (01227) 760827

Dartex Office Furniture, Unit 6 Crayside Industiral Estate, Thames Road, Crayford, Dartford, DA1 4RF Tel: (01322) 521545 Fax: (01322) 558685 E-mail: sales@dartexofficefurniture.co.uk

Design & Reprographic Supplies, Repro House, Liverpool Road, Newcastle, Staffordshire, ST5 9HD Tel: (01782) 712024 Fax: (01782) 713083 E-mail: sales@drs-paper.com

Document Co. Xerox Ltd, Bridge House, Oxford Road, Uxbridge, Middlesex, UB8 1HS Tel: (01895) 251133 Fax: (01895) 254095

Donaldson & Weir Graphics Ltd, Unit 6a Maryland Industrial Estate, Moneyrea, Newtownards, County Down, BT23 6BL Tel: (028) 9044 8048 Fax: (028) 9044 8014

Draw Write, 72-74 Sandgate, Ayr, KA7 1BX Tel: (01292) 610735 Fax: (01292) 263877 E-mail: dwrite7274@aol.com

The Drawing Group Ltd, 3-9 West St, Hull, HU1 3UR Tel: (01482) 324263 Fax: (01482) 325176 E-mail: sales@drawgroup.co.uk

Drawing Office Systems, 160 Congleton Road, Talke, Stoke-on-Trent, ST7 1LT Tel: (01782) 774817 Fax: (01782) 782143 E-mail: drawingofficesys@aol.com

Eborcraft Ltd, 11-12 Chessingham Park Common Road, Dunnington, York, YO19 5SE Tel: (01904) 481020 Fax: (01904) 481022 E-mail: sales@eborcraft.co.uk

Heatherbank Drawing Office Supplies, 4 Milethorn Lane, Doncaster, South Yorkshire, DN1 2SU Tel: (01302) 325146

Helix Group plc, Lye, Engine Lane, Stourbridge, West Midlands, DY9 7AJ Tel: (01384) 424441 Fax: (01384) 892617 E-mail: info@helixhq.com

Hobs Reprographics, 56d Milton Park, Milton, Abingdon, Oxfordshire, OX14 4RX Tel: (01235) 833044 Fax: (01235) 831666 E-mail: abingdon@hobsrepro.com

Hobs Reprographics, 52-60 Woodlands Road, Glasgow, G3 6HA Tel: 0141-333 9535 Fax: 0141-332 6395 E-mail: glasgow@hobsrepro.com

Hussey & Greaves Ltd, 94 Hutton Road, Shenfield, Brentwood, Essex, CM15 8ND Tel: (01277) 226262 Fax: (01277) 261287 E-mail: sales@husseyandgreaves.co.uk

Hussey & Knights Ltd, 60 Bethel Street, Norwich, NR2 1NR Tel: (01603) 428110 Fax: (01603) 761032 E-mail: sales@hussey-knights.co.uk

Midland Business Supplies Ltd, Midland House, Cross Street, Oadby, Leicester, LE2 4DD Tel: 0116-272 0044 Fax: 0116-272 0050 E-mail: info@mbs-sales.co.uk

Millington York Ltd, Leighswood Road, Walsall, WS9 8AL Tel: (01922) 454121 Fax: (01922) 743045 E-mail: richard@millington-york.co.uk

P P Scene Ltd, 68 High Street, Chislehurst, Kent, BR7 5BL Tel: (020) 8467 0935 Fax: (020) 8467 7490

Pennine Drawing Office Supplies North East, 63g Lord Avenue, Thornaby, Stockton-on-Tees, Cleveland, TS17 9JX Tel: (01642) 763762 Fax: (01642) 763768 E-mail: sales@penninedrawing.co.uk

Polydraft Ltd, The Tracings, 3-5 Dunston Road, London, E8 4EH Tel: (020) 7923 1130 Fax: (020) 7249 6818 E-mail: info@polydraft.co.uk

Prizma Graphics, Broadfields Court Broadfields Retail Park, Bicester Road, Aylesbury, Buckinghamshire, HP19 8BU Tel: (01296) 393700 Fax: (01296) 393794 E-mail: sales@prizmagraphics.co.uk

Service Point, 68 Whiteladies Road, Bristol, BS8 2NH Tel: 0117-970 6500 Fax: 0117-970 6182 E-mail: Bristol@servicepointuk.com

Sir Ltd, 4 Carron Place, Kelvin Industrial Estate, East Kilbride, Glasgow, G75 0YL Tel: (01355) 264422 Fax: (01355) 244744 E-mail: sales@sir.ltd.uk

Standing Stone, Uni G10 Morton Park Way, Darlington, County Durham, DL1 4PJ Tel: (01325) 288877 Fax: (01325) 288855 E-mail: sales@standing-stone.co.uk

Standing Stone Drawing Office Supplies, Unit 1-2 Standing Stone, Matfen, Newcastle upon Tyne, NE20 0RQ Tel: (01661) 886653 Fax: (01661) 886988 E-mail: sales@standing-stone.co.uk

Talbot Plan Printing Co., 47 Wyle Cop, Shrewsbury, SY1 1XJ Tel: (01743) 343740 Fax: (01743) 343740 E-mail: d.chidlow@btconnect.com

West Design Products Ltd, West House, Shearway Business Park, Pent Road, Folkestone, Kent, CT19 4RJ Tel: (01303) 297888 Fax: (01303) 297877 E-mail: sales@westdesignproducts.co.uk

West Yorkshire Drawing Office Services Ltd, Swallow Hill Mills, Tong Road, Leeds, LS12 4QG Tel: 0113-220 5400 Fax: 0113-231 0615 E-mail: enquiries@wydos.co.uk

DRAWING OFFICE TECHNICAL SERVICES OR CARTOGRAPHY OR DRAFTING OR REPROGRAPHIC SERVICES

A4 Plus Drawing Services Ltd, 11a Park Street, Chatteris, Cambridgeshire, PE16 6AB Tel: (01354) 691820 Fax: (01354) 691821 E-mail: enquiries@a4plus.co.uk

Abatec Staff Consultants plc, Abatec House, Old Mixon Cresent, Weston-super-Mare, Avon, BS24 9AX Tel: (01934) 635025 Fax: (01934) 419999 E-mail: mail@abatec.co.uk

Claygate Digital Services Ltd, Airport House, Purley Way, Croydon, CR0 0XZ Tel: (020) 8288 3588 Fax: (020) 8288 3599 E-mail: sales@claygate.com

Comau Estil Systems, Midland Road, Luton, LU2 0HR Tel: (01582) 817600 Fax: (01582) 817700

Cosmographics, 1 Mowat Industrial Estate, Sandown Road, Watford, WD24 7UY Tel: (01923) 210909 Fax: (01923) 211657 E-mail: enquiries@cosmographics.co.uk

Crescent Draughting & Design, PO Box 914, Market Harborough, Leicestershire, LE16 9YJ Tel: (01858) 410320 Fax: (01858) 410320 E-mail: cresdesign@aol.com

Design Drafting Services, 4 Carr Street, Ramsbottom, Bury, Lancashire, BL0 9AE Tel: (01706) 823331 Fax: (01706) 827910

Edos Microfilm, Audit Drive, Abingdon, Oxfordshire, OX14 3NJ Tel: (01235) 550505 Fax: (01235) 536719 E-mail: enquiries@edos.co.uk

G T Drawing Services Ltd, Cradock Road, Luton, LU4 0JF Tel: (01582) 502883 Fax: (01582) 572201 E-mail: mail@gtdrawings.com

H M Sitec Ltd, St. Georges Lodge, 33 Oldfield Road, Bath, BA2 3NE Tel: (01225) 428221 Fax: (01225) 444697 E-mail: info@hmbath.com

HTS Design Services Ltd, 379 Anlaby Road, Hull, HU3 6AB Tel: (01482) 351236 Fax: (01482) 566052 E-mail: office@ahgsltd.co.uk

Kent Technical, 10 High Street, Snodland, Kent, ME6 5DF Tel: (01634) 248900 Fax: (01634) 248901

Leythorne Ltd, Hawthorns Business Centre, Halfords Lane, Smethwick, West Midlands, B66 1BB Tel: 0121-558 1181 Fax: 0121-555 4913 E-mail: sales@leythorne.co.uk

Long & Co Kent Ltd, Bybow Farm, Orchard Way, Dartford, DA2 7ER Tel: (01322) 273028 Fax: (01322) 228818

M F S Reprographics, 15 Blackmoor Gate, Furzton, Milton Keynes, MK4 1DS Tel: (01908) 504550 Fax: (01908) 504550 E-mail: mfsrepro@btinternet.com

P D M Office Supplies, 3 Parklands Parade, Bath Road, Hounslow, TW5 9AX Tel: (020) 8570 4488 Fax: (020) 8569 6050

Pinder P.L.C., Unit 481 Walton Summit Centre, Bamber Bridge, Preston, PR5 8AR Tel: (01772) 620999 Fax: (01772) 620888 E-mail: k.ashley@pinder.com

Service Point, 16 Rivers St, Bath, BA1 2QA Tel: (01225) 311972 Fax: (01225) 310124

Servicepoint, 81 Endell Street, London, WC2H 9AJ Tel: (020) 7836 9422 Fax: (020) 7836 4248 E-mail: coventgarden@servicepointuk.com

Shiptech (U K) Ltd, St. Andrews House, 33 Beverley Road, Hull, HU3 1XH Tel: (01482) 324964 Fax: (01482) 226679 E-mail: info@shiptech.co.uk

Timco Designs Ltd, Normans Cross, Forton, Chard, Somerset, TA20 4HD Tel: (01460) 239569 Fax: (01344) 628581

V C Digital Ltd, 44 Bridge Road, Crosby, Liverpool, L23 6SG Tel: 0151-931 2226 Fax: 0151-931 3136

DRAWING PINS

Prym Whitecroft (UK) Ltd, Whitecroft, Lydney, Gloucestershire, GL15 4QG Tel: (01594) 562631 Fax: (01594) 563662 E-mail: sales@whitecroft.co.uk

DRAWING STORAGE SYSTEMS

▶ The Drawing Co. Ltd, 8 Morton Close, Ely, Cambridgeshire, CB7 4FE Tel: (01353) 669952 Fax: (01353) 669952 E-mail: wc@thedrawingcompany.co.uk

Planline International Ltd, 3 Boddington Road, Byfield, Daventry, Northamptonshire, NN11 6UP Tel: (01327) 264406 Fax: (01327) 264406 E-mail: sales@planlineinternational.com

DREDGER BUILDERS

Humber Workboats Ltd, North Killingholme, Immingham, South Humberside, DN40 3LX Tel: (01469) 540156 Fax: (01469) 540303 E-mail: elliotmorton@humberworkboats.co.uk

Liverpool Water Witch Marine Engineering Co. Ltd, 4 Lightbody Street, Liverpool, L5 9UZ Tel: 0151-207 4874 Fax: 0151-298 1366 E-mail: sales@waterwitch.demon.co.uk

Seadrec Ltd, Blackhall House, Blackhall Lane, Paisley, Renfrewshire, PA1 1TA Tel: 0141-887 4131 Fax: 0141-887 6437 E-mail: info@lobnitz.com

DREDGING CONTRACTORS

Blueboar Farm Contracts Ltd, London Road, Dunchurch, Rugby, Warwickshire, CV23 9LH Tel: (01788) 810854 Fax: (01788) 817100 E-mail: enquiries@blueboarcontracts.co.uk

Circle Technical Services Ltd, Turulus Way, Midmill Business Park, Kintore, Aberdeenshire, AB51 0TG Tel: (01467) 632020 Fax: (01467) 632022 E-mail: info@circletechnical.co.uk

Dredging International UK Ltd, Greenstede House Wood Street, Station Road, East Grinstead, West Sussex, RH19 1UZ Tel: (01342) 323000 Fax: (01342) 326000 E-mail: diuk@dredging.com

French Equipment, Runnymede Boat House, Windsor Road, Old Windsor, Windsor, Berkshire, SL4 2JL Tel: (01784) 439626 Fax: (01784) 433309

Hanson Aggregates Ltd, Marine Parade, Southampton, SO14 5JF Tel: (023) 8023 7210 Fax: (023) 8082 8248

Lincoln & Hull Marine Contractors Ltd, 100 Lime Street, Hull, HU8 7AR Tel: (01482) 320727 Fax: (01482) 320727 E-mail: noel@siggle.fsnet.co.uk

M L (UK) Ltd, Kettering Terrace, Mile End, Portsmouth, PO2 7AE Tel: (023) 9281 9114 Fax: (023) 9282 3386 E-mail: martin@mluk.co.uk

J.T. Mackley & Co. Ltd, Bankside House, Henfield Road, Small Dole, Henfield, West Sussex, BN5 9XQ Tel: (01273) 492212 Fax: (01273) 494328 E-mail: construct@mackley.co.uk

▶ Teignmouth Maritime Services Ltd, 8 Ivy Lane, Teignmouth, Devon, TQ14 8BT Tel: (01626) 772197 Fax: (01626) 772197 E-mail: info@tmsmaritime.co.uk

Van Oord UK Ltd, Lockside Place, Newbury, Berkshire, RG14 5QS Tel: 01635 529101

W J Hatt Ltd, Foxcovert Farm, Goring Heath, Reading, RG8 7SL Tel: (01491) 680424 Fax: (01491) 680425 E-mail: wjhatt@aol.com

DREDGING PLANT AND EQUIPMENT

Seadrec Ltd, Blackhall House, Blackhall Lane, Paisley, Renfrewshire, PA1 1TA Tel: 0141-887 4131 Fax: 0141-887 6437 E-mail: info@lobnitz.com

▶ Teignmouth Maritime Services Ltd, 8 Ivy Lane, Teignmouth, Devon, TQ14 8BT Tel: (01626) 772197 Fax: (01626) 772197 E-mail: info@tmsmaritime.co.uk

DRESSING GOWNS

Direct Alarms, 11 Croft House Drive, Morley, Leeds, LS27 8NU Tel: 0113-289 7897 Fax: 0113-255 6919

DRESSINGS, THIN FILM

▶ Smith & Nephew Extruded Films Ltd, Gateway To Humberside Trading Estate, Gilberdyke, Brough, North Humberside, HU15 2TD Tel: (01430) 440757 Fax: (01430) 440211 E-mail: phil.redshaw@smith-nephew.com

DRIED PEANUTS

Trigon Snacks Ltd, Atherton Road, Liverpool, L9 7AQ Tel: 0151-523 8700 Fax: 0151-521 5370 E-mail: sales@trigon-snacks.com

DRILL BITS, *See also headings for particular types*

▶ Akromultihire, Unit 6 Naysmyth Place, Houston Industrial Estate, Livingston, West Lothian, EH54 5EG Tel: (01506) 441991 Fax: (01506) 441856

Alpen UK Ltd, 1 Laburnum Park, 72 Knutsford Road, Alderley Edge, Cheshire, SK9 7SF Tel: (01625) 586516 Fax: (01625) 586556

Bradford Tool Group, Beta Works, 1 Tong Street, Bradford, West Yorkshire, BD4 9PW Tel: (01274) 683902 Fax: (01274) 651168 E-mail: sales@bradtool.co.uk

Drillserve Ltd, Roscroggan Mill, Roscroggan, Camborne, Cornwall, TR14 0BA Tel: (01209) 710079 Fax: (01209) 717139

Fenn Tool Ltd, 44 Spring Wood Drive, Springwood Industrial Estate, Braintree, Essex, CM7 2YN Tel: (01376) 347566 Fax: (01376) 550827 E-mail: enquiries@fenntool.co.uk

Irwin Industrial Tool Co. Ltd, Parkway Works, Kettlebridge Road, Sheffield, S9 3BL Tel: 0114-244 9066 Fax: 0114-256 1788 E-mail: sales@record.co.uk

Presto International Ltd, Penistone Road, Sheffield, S6 2FN Tel: 0114-234 9361 Fax: 0114-234 7446 E-mail: kevin.blackwell@presto-tools.com

DRILL BITS TO SPECIFICATION

P J Tooling Ltd, Millers Road, Warwick, CV34 5AN Tel: (01926) 492693 Fax: (01926) 410057 E-mail: pj.tooling@virgin.net

DRILL BITS, CORE, DIAMOND, WET DRILLING

▶ Access Diamond Drilling Ltd, Elm View, 2 Longley Road, Croydon, CR0 3LH Tel: (020) 8239 1486 Fax: (020) 8239 1486 E-mail: davidhann@blueyonder.co.uk

▶ Sealant & Construction Services Ltd, Framsden, Stowmarket, Suffolk, IP14 6LH Tel: (01728) 860198 Fax: (01728) 860203

DRILL CHUCKS

Armeg Ltd, Callywhite Lane, Dronfield, Derbyshire, S18 2XJ Tel: (01246) 411081 Fax: (01246) 411882 E-mail: j.mowthorpe@armeg.co.uk

DRILL COLLARS

Bored Bar Engineering Ltd, New Street, Halfway, Sheffield, S20 3GH Tel: 0114-248 3631 Fax: 0114-247 7133 E-mail: sales@bored-bar.co.uk

Carrack Ltd, Badentoy Crescent, Badentoy Industrial Estate, Portlethen, Aberdeen, AB12 4YD Tel: (01224) 783100 Fax: (01224) 783400 E-mail: sandym@carrackltd.com

Carroll Tools Ltd, 16-18 Factory Lane, Croydon, CR0 3RL Tel: (020) 8781 1268 Fax: (020) 8781 1278 E-mail: info@carrolltools.com

Keeton,Sons & Co.,Limited, Keetona House, Acres Hill Lane, Sheffield, S9 4LR Tel: 0114-242 0328 Fax: 0114-261 8860 E-mail: keetons@keetons.com

DRILL HEADS

Colcrete Eurodrill, Tower Business Park, Derby Road, Clay Cross, Chesterfield, Derbyshire, S45 9AG Tel: (01246) 868700 Fax: (01246) 868701 E-mail: info@colcrete-eurodrill.co.uk

▶ J. S. Bruce Engineering, 5 French Street, Ashton-under-Lyne, Lancashire, OL6 9PP Tel: 0161 3399476 Fax: 0161 3399476 E-mail: john@jsbruceengineering.co.uk

Jectabore Ltd, East Side Road, Chesterfield, Derbyshire, S41 9AT Tel: (01246) 456124 Fax: (01246) 455289 E-mail: sales@jectabore.co.uk

Slack & Parr Hydraulics Ltd, Long Lane, Kegworth, Derby, DE74 2FL Tel: (01509) 672306 Fax: (01509) 674557 E-mail: info@slack-parr.com

Systematic Multi Head Co.Ltd, Trend Grey House, Tomlow Road, Southam, Warwickshire, CV47 8HX Tel: (01926) 810678 Fax: (01926) 810618 E-mail: sales@systematic-drill-head.co.uk

DRILL JIG BUSHES

Talbot Tool Co. Ltd, Grip Works, Crowhurst Road, Brighton, BN1 8AT Tel: (01273) 508881 Fax: (01273) 540544 E-mail: sales@talbot-tool.co.uk

DRILL POINT GRINDING MACHINES

Boremasters, High Street, Cleobury Mortimer, Kidderminster, Worcestershire, DY14 8DS Tel: (01299) 270942 Fax: (01299) 270212 E-mail: sales@boremasters.co.uk

Brierley Machine Tools Ltd, Ferry Farm Road, Llandudno Junction, Gwynedd, LL31 9SF Tel: (01492) 581777 Fax: (01492) 592558

DRILL STAND (MAGNETIC) MANUFRS

Rotabroach, Imperial Works, Sheffield Road, Tinsley, Sheffield, S9 2YL Tel: 0114-221 2510 Fax: 0114-221 2563 E-mail: info@rotabroach.co.uk

DRILLING FLANGES

Probe Oil Tools Ltd, Edison Way, Great Yarmouth, Norfolk, NR31 0NG Tel: (01493) 655471 Fax: (01493) 652746 E-mail: sales@probe-oil-tools.co.uk

DRILLING MACHINE MAINTENANCE OR REPAIR

Diamond Power Service, 1a Clarke Street, Farnworth, Bolton, BL4 9JH Tel: (01204) 793303 Fax: (01204) 403804 E-mail: diamondpsi@aol.com

DRILLING MACHINES, *See also headings for particular types*

Bowen Tools Div I R I International, Kirkton Avenue, Pitmedden Road Industrial Estate, Dyce, Aberdeen, AB21 0BF Tel: (01224) 771339 Fax: (01224) 723034

Herbert Tooling Ltd, Roseme, Sandy Lane, Fillongley, Coventry, CV7 8DD Tel: (01676) 540040 Fax: (01676) 540040 E-mail: info@herbert-tooling.com

▶ W B & A D Morgan Ltd, Presteigne Industrial Estate, Presteigne, Powys, LD8 2UF Tel: (0800) 5427613 Fax: (01544) 267981 E-mail: info@findingwater.co.uk

Pigott Shaft Drilling Ltd, PO Box 63, Preston, PR4 0BD Tel: (01772) 690076 Fax: (01772) 690840 E-mail: sales@psdmud.co.uk

Premier Plant Engineering, Hud Hey Road, Haslingden, Rossendale, Lancashire, BB4 5JH Tel: (01706) 222181 Fax: (01706) 222133 E-mail: info@premierplantengineering.co.uk

Rocbore Ltd, 6 Salcombe Road, Alfreton, Derbyshire, DE55 7RG Tel: (01773) 521391 Fax: (01773) 521377

▶ Universal Augers Ltd, Brook Road, Bicton Industrial Park, Kimbolton, Huntingdon, Cambridgeshire, PE28 0EY Tel: (01480) 861440 Fax: (01480) 861446 E-mail: info@universal-augers.com

DRILLING MONITORING INSTRUMENTATION

Electro-Flow Controls Ltd, Unit 3 Souter Head Industrial Centre, Souter Head Road, Altens, Aberdeen, AB12 3LF Tel: (01224) 249355 Fax: (01224) 249339 E-mail: efcltd@attglobal.net

Rigserv Ltd, Unit 9 Wellheads Crescent, Wellheads Industrial Estate, Aberdeen, AB21 7GA Tel: (01224) 724212 Fax: (01224) 724282 E-mail: information@rigserv.com

DRILLING SERVICES, *See also headings for particular types*

▶ Apex Drilling Services Ltd, 28 Sturmi Way, Village Farm Industrial Estate, Pyle, Bridgend, Mid Glamorgan, CF33 6BZ Tel: (01656) 749149 Fax: (01656) 749096

Automatic Forming, 7 Kinwarton Farm Road, Kinwarton, Alcester, Warwickshire, B49 6EH Tel: (01789) 400567 Fax: (01789) 765213

Drurys Engineering Ltd, 21 Knowl Piece, Wilbury Way, Hitchin, Hertfordshire, SG4 0TY Tel: (01462) 420123 Fax: (01462) 420124 E-mail: info@drurys.co.uk

Ground Restoration Ltd, Unit 15 Ingoldmells Court, Edinburgh Way, Corsham, Wiltshire, SN13 9XN Tel: (01225) 810818 Fax: (01225) 811030 E-mail: grla1cad@aol.com

Harbex Profiling & Grinding Ltd, Blackberry Farm, High Oak Hill, Bobbing, Sittingbourne, Kent, ME9 8QD Tel: (01795) 842925 Fax: (01795) 843868 E-mail: sales@harbex.co.uk

▶ Land-Drill Geotechnics Ltd, Drilling & Exploration Centre, Pardovan Estate, Philipstoun, Linlithgow, West Lothian, EH49 7RX Tel: (01506) 830044 Fax: (01506) 830055 E-mail: info@land-drill.com

Metalock Engineering, Hamilton, Glasgow, Tel: 0141-641 3368 E-mail: sales@metalock.co.uk

Metalock Engineering UK Ltd, Paragon Way, Bayton Road Industrial Estate, Coventry, CV7 9QS Tel: (01322) 290090 Fax: (01322) 290088 E-mail: sales@metalock.co.uk

PJP Precision Engineering Ltd, 5 Berkshire Business Centre, Berkshire Drive, Thatcham, Berkshire, RG19 4EW Tel: (01635) 872792 Fax: (01635) 864390 E-mail: pjpm@msn.com

Wheal Jane Enterprises Ltd, Old Mine Offices, Wheal Jane, Baldhu, Truro, Cornwall, TR3 6EE Tel: (01872) 560200 Fax: (01872) 562020 E-mail: carnon@wheal-jane.co.uk

DRILLING SERVICES, LASER

▶ Lairdside Laser Engineering Centre, Campbeltown Road, Birkenhead, Merseyside, CH41 9HP Tel: 0151-650 2305 Fax: 0151-650 2304 E-mail: info@llec.co.uk

Microkerf Ltd, 43 Boston Road, Leicester, LE4 1AW Tel: 0116-234 1500 Fax: 0116-234 1600 E-mail: sales@microkerf.com

DRIP MATS

Absorbent Dripmats Ltd, Aero Mill, Kershaw Street, Church, Accrington, Lancashire, BB5 4JS Tel: (01254) 234247 Fax: (01254) 383996 E-mail: info@naylergroup.co.uk

Burton Beer Mats Ltd, Moor St Works, Burton-on-Trent, Staffordshire, DE14 3TA Tel: (01283) 564769 Fax: (01283) 535492 E-mail: sales@burtonbeermatsltd.co.uk

Quarmby Promotions, Britannia Road, Milnsbridge, Huddersfield, HD3 4QE Tel: (01484) 653011 Fax: (01884) 460008

DRIP PROOF ELECTRIC MOTORS

Franklin Electric (Henley), Treetops House, Gillotts Lane, Henley-On-Thames, Oxfordshire, RG9 1PT Tel: (01491) 579118 Fax: (01491) 412211 E-mail: fesales@acdcsystems.com

Weg Electric Motors UK Ltd, Unit 28 29, Walkers Road, Moons Moat North Industrial Estate, Redditch, Worcestershire, B98 9HE Tel: (01527) 596748 Fax: (01527) 591133 E-mail: wegsales@wegelectricmotors.co.uk

DRIVE SYSTEMS, *See also headings for paricular types*

Cooper Control Ltd, 20 Greenhill Crescent, Watford Business Park, Watford, WD18 8XG Tel: (01923) 495495 Fax: (01923) 800190 E-mail: nelco@polaron-group.co.uk

▶ Newton Tesla (Electric Drives) Ltd, Unit G18 Warrington Business Park, Long Lane, Warrington, WA2 8TX Tel: (01925) 444773 Fax: (01925) 241477 E-mail: info@newton-tesla.com

S E W Eurodrive Ltd, 5 Sugarbrook Court, Aston Road, Bromsgrove, Worcestershire, B60 3EX Tel: (01527) 877319 Fax: (01527) 575245 E-mail: sales@sew-eurodrive.co.uk

S E W Eurodrive Ltd, 764 Finchley Road, London, NW11 7TH Tel: (020) 8458 8949 Fax: (020) 8458 7417

DRIVERS

▶ A Plus Driving School Ltd, 441 Dudley Road, Wolverhampton, WV2 3AQ Tel: (0845) 1308880 E-mail: info@thedrivingschool.co.uk

DRIVES

▶ EURO Driveshafts & Hydraulics, Tannahill, Kilmaurs, Kilmarnock, Ayrshire, KA3 2LN Tel: (01563) 538011 Fax: (01563) 572389

DRIVESHAFT REMANUFACTURING

Commercial Propshaft Services Ltd, 190 Kingsway South, Team Valley Trading Estate, Gateshead, Tyne & Wear, NE11 0SH Tel: 0191-482 1690 Fax: 0191-482 0582

Shaftec Automotive Components Ltd, 2 Cato Street, Birmingham, B7 4TS Tel: 0121-333 3555 Fax: 0121-359 3003 E-mail: shaftec@automotive8.freeserve.co.uk

DRIVESHAFTS

Drivelink UK Ltd, 190 Kingsway South, Team Valley Trading Estate, Gateshead, Tyne & Wear, NE11 0SH Tel: 0191-491 3666 Fax: 0191-487 1255 E-mail: enquiries@drivelink.com

▶ EURO Driveshafts & Hydraulics, Tannahill, Kilmaurs, Kilmarnock, Ayrshire, KA3 2LN Tel: (01563) 538011 Fax: (01563) 572389

G K N Driveline Ltd, Higher Woodcroft, Leek, Staffordshire, ST13 5QF Tel: (01538) 372444 Fax: (01538) 371265 E-mail: sales@gkndriveline.co.uk

NDE Power Transmissions Group, NDE Bldgs, Aldbourne Road, Coventry, CV1 4EQ Tel: (024) 7622 2272 Fax: (024) 7625 8499 E-mail: sales@ndeclarketransmissions.co.uk

Premier Propshaft Co Ltd, 24-26 Atherstone Road, Hartshill, Nuneaton, Warwickshire, CV10 0SP Tel: (024) 7639 3806 Fax: (024) 7639 3452

Reco-Prop UK Ltd, Unit 4 New Town Trading Estate, Chase Street, Luton, LU1 3QZ Tel: (01582) 412110 Fax: (01582) 480432 E-mail: info@reco-prop.com

Spicer Driveshaft UK Ltd, Rutherford Drive, Park Farm Industrial Estate, Wellingborough, Northamptonshire, NN8 6AQ Tel: (01933) 402000 Fax: (01933) 401322

DRIVING EXPERIENCE DAYS, CLASSIC CARS

▶ Fantastic Days Out Ltd, The Coach House, 4 Main Street, Humberstone, Leicester, LE5 1AE Tel: 0116-276 6061 Fax: 0116-276 5960 E-mail: enquiries@fantasticdaysout.com

▶ Well Wicked Limited, Southover, Hurst Lane, Egham, Surrey, TW20 8QJ Tel: 01344 844439 E-mail: Martinpcraven@BTinternet.com

DRIVING EXPERIENCE DAYS, HIGH PERFORMANCE CARS

▶ Well Wicked Limited, Southover, Hurst Lane, Egham, Surrey, TW20 8QJ Tel: 01344 844439 E-mail: Martinpcraven@BTinternet.com

DRIVING EXPERIENCE DAYS, MILITARY TANK

▶ Fantastic Days Out Ltd, The Coach House, 4 Main Street, Humberstone, Leicester, LE5 1AE Tel: 0116-276 6061 Fax: 0116-276 5960 E-mail: enquiries@fantasticdaysout.com

▶ Well Wicked Limited, Southover, Hurst Lane, Egham, Surrey, TW20 8QJ Tel: 01344 844439 E-mail: Martinpcraven@BTinternet.com

DRIVING INSTRUCTOR TRAINING

▶ A Plus Driving School Ltd, 441 Dudley Road, Wolverhampton, WV2 3AQ Tel: (0845) 1308880 E-mail: info@thedrivingschool.co.uk

▶ Ashby's Driving School, 29 Acres Gardens, Tadworth, Surrey, KT20 5LP Tel: (01737) 358430 Fax: (01737) 358430 E-mail: info@ashbysdrivingschool.gbr.cc

▶ Davids Driving School, 46 London Road, Ramsgate, Kent, CT11 0DN Tel: (01843) 851148

▶ Julie Martin, 10 Oakwood, Flackwell Heath, High Wycombe, Buckinghamshire, HP10 9DW Tel: (01628) 523235 Fax: (01628) 523235 E-mail: jglenister56@hotmail.com

▶ Kruze Driving Academy Ltd, 79 Blandford Waye, Hayes, Middlesex, UB4 0PB Tel: (020) 8561 6617 E-mail: info@kruzedrivingacademy.co.uk

▶ MinscuLe of Motoring, 11 Cherry Orchard, Wotton-under-Edge, Gloucestershire, GL12 7HT Tel: (01453) 521543 E-mail: andrew.shell@btinternet.com

▶ Nationwide Instructor Training College, 441 Dudley Road, Wolverhampton, WV2 3AQ Tel: (0845) 1304035 Fax: (0845) 1304507 E-mail: info@drivinginstructorcollege.co.uk

▶ Pass-n-Bye, 16 Reid Street, Burnbank, Hamilton, Lanarkshire, ML3 0RQ Tel: (01698) 300951 E-mail: info@pass-n-bye.co.uk

DROP FORGING DIES

Eyres Forgings Ltd, Lord North Street, Miles Platting, Manchester, M40 8HT Tel: 0161-205 1090 Fax: 0161-203 4513

Forge Tech Services Ltd, Gatefield Works, Whitelands Road, Ashton-under-Lyne, Lancashire, OL6 6UG Tel: 0161-339 1120 Fax: 0161-343 2257 E-mail: info@forgetechservices.com

DROP FORGINGS

Bifrangi (UK) Ltd, PO Box 22, Lincoln, LN2 5DT Tel: (01522) 585800 Fax: (01522) 529116

Dixons Forge, Unit 47 Salthouse Mills Industrial Estate, Barrow-in-Furness, Cumbria, LA13 0DH Tel: (01229) 431618 Fax: (01229) 431618

Eyres Forgings Ltd, Lord North Street, Miles Platting, Manchester, M40 8HT Tel: 0161-205 1090 Fax: 0161-203 4513

Firth Rixson Forgings Ltd, Meadowhall Road, Wincobank, Sheffield, S9 1HD Tel: 0114-219 3001 Fax: 0114-219 1131 E-mail: fsales@firthrixson.com

Mettis Aerospace Ltd, Windsor Road, Redditch, Worcestershire, B97 6EF Tel: (01527) 406400 Fax: (01527) 406401 E-mail: info@mettis-aerospace.com

Mills Forgings Ltd, Charterhouse Road, Coventry, CV1 2BJ Tel: (024) 7622 4985 Fax: (024) 7652 5453 E-mail: sales@millsforgings.co.uk

Premier Stampings Ltd, Station Street, Cradley Heath, West Midlands, B64 6AJ Tel: (01384) 353100 Fax: (01384) 353101

R A D Precision Die & Tool, Johnson House, Bilston Industrial Estate, Oxford Street, Bilston, West Midlands, WV14 7EG Tel: (01902) 494647 Fax: (01902) 604366 E-mail: andywalker@kespar.co.uk

Redfern Stevens Ltd, 40 Brickfield Road, Birmingham, B25 8HE Tel: 0121-766 6464 Fax: 0121-766 6651 E-mail: info@redfernstevens.co.uk

S J Humphries Ltd, Portersfield Road, Cradley Heath, West Midlands, B64 7BN Tel: (01384) 569326 Fax: (01384) 74070

Scottish Stampings Ltd, East Park Road, Ayr, KA8 9HR Tel: (01292) 267971 Fax: (01292) 613408

Stokes Forgings Ltd, Northcote St, Walsall, WS2 8BH Tel: (01922) 704800

W & P Forgings Ltd, 11 Hedon Road, Hull, HU9 1LL Tel: (01482) 323089 Fax: (01482) 324735 E-mail: info@wp-forging.co.uk

DRUG DELIVERY DEVICES

3M Neotechnic Ltd, UpBrooks, Clitheroe, Lancashire, BB7 1NX Tel: (01200) 422251 Fax: (01200) 428993 E-mail: neotechnic@mmm.com
Unichem Ltd, 24 Marsh Green Road, Marsh Barton Trading Estate, Exeter, EX2 8LZ Tel: (01392) 434941 Fax: (01392) 425781

DRUG DISCOVERY PARTICLES

▶ Polymer Laboratories Ltd, Essex Road, Church Stretton, Shropshire, SY6 6AX Tel: (01694) 723581 Fax: (01694) 722171 E-mail: sales@polymerlabs.com

DRUG SCREENING

Doctor's Laboratory plc, 60 Whitfield Street, London, W1T 4EU Tel: (020) 7460 4800 Fax: (020) 7460 4848
Evotec UK Ltd, 151 Milton Park, Milton, Abingdon, Oxfordshire, OX14 4SD Tel: (01235) 441200 Fax: (01235) 863139 E-mail: sales@evotecoai.com
▶ Nationwide Healthcare Connections Ltd, Connections House, 105 Bellingdon Road, Chesham, Buckinghamshire, HP5 2HQ Tel: (01494) 773007 Fax: (01494) 773008 E-mail: sales@healthcare-connections.com
Protherics P.L.C., The Heath Business & Technical Park, Runcorn, Cheshire, WA7 4QX Tel: (01928) 518000 Fax: (01928) 518002 E-mail: information@protherics.com

DRUGS, CRUDE/BOTANICAL/ MEDICINAL

▶ A D Allen Pharma Ltd, Bower Hill Industrial Estate, Epping, Essex, CM16 7BN Tel: (01992) 566366 Fax: (01992) 577582 E-mail: amanda@adallenpharma.com
Astrin Bros Ltd, 32 Prescot Street, London, E1 8BB Tel: (020) 7481 2110 Fax: (020) 7480 5030 E-mail: trading@johnkellysltd.demon.co.uk
▶ Avecia, Earls Road, Grangemouth, Stirlingshire, FK3 8XG Tel: (01324) 498300 Fax: (01324) 498350 E-mail: admin@avecia.com
▶ Ethigen Pharmaceutical Distributors, 15 Springburn Place, East Kilbride, Glasgow, G74 5NU Tel: (01355) 598150 Fax: (01355) 598159
▶ G & M Proctor Ltd, 8 Arran Place, North Muirton Industrial Estate, Perth, PH1 3RN Tel: (01738) 636145 Fax: (01738) 643466 E-mail: enquiries@gandmproctor.com
▶ Glaxosmithkline, Cobden Street, Montrose, Angus, DD10 8EA Tel: (01674) 672606 Fax: (01674) 666688
J R B Enterprises Ltd, Dixies Development, High Street, Ashwell, Baldock, Hertfordshire, SG7 5NT Tel: (01462) 742157 Fax: (01462) 742088 E-mail: johnrbonnett@aol.com
▶ Laser Fume Extraction Guidance, Unit 11 Solent Industrial Estate, Hedge End, Southampton, SO30 2FX Tel: 01489 782262 Fax: 01661 833010 E-mail: info@laser-fume-extraction.com
▶ Life Healthcare, Freepost JE723, St. Helier, Jersey, JE1 1AF Tel: (0845) 1667070 E-mail: help@elixireurope.com
Meconic P.L.C., 10 Wheatfield Road, Edinburgh, EH11 2QA Tel: 0131-313 1416
▶ Millipore (UK) Ltd, Gemini Crescent, Dundee Technology Park, Dundee, DD2 1SW Tel: (01382) 561600 Fax: (01382) 561601
▶ Quintiles, Almondvale Business Park, Almondvale Way, Livingston, West Lothian, EH54 6GA Tel: (01506) 818000 Fax: (01506) 818200 E-mail: sales@quintiles.co.uk
▶ Raven Supplies Ltd, A Great Bank Road, Westhoughton, Bolton, BL5 3XU Tel: (01942) 850500 Fax: (01942) 850511
▶ Vericroe Ltd, Kinnoull Road, Dunsinane Industrial Estate, Dundee, DD2 3XR Tel: (01382) 813838 Fax: (01382) 832721
White Rose Computer Supplies, Unit 10, Elvington Industrial Estate, York, YO41 4AR Tel: (01904) 608775 Fax: (01904) 608163

DRUM CLOSURES

Drum Closures Ltd, Borwick Rails, Millom, Cumbria, LA18 4JT Tel: (01229) 772101 Fax: (01229) 774972 E-mail: sales@drum-closures.co.uk

DRUM DEALERS/ RECONDITIONERS/SUPPLIERS

John Arthur & Son Ltd, Throckley Industrial Estate, Ponteland Road, Throckley, Newcastle upon Tyne, NE15 9EW Tel: 0191-267 1341 Fax: 0191-264 0329
G R & J Atkinson, 7 Baird Close, Drayton Fields Industrial Estate, Daventry, Northamptonshire, NN11 8RY Tel: (01327) 310464 Fax: (01327) 310451
Humber Cooperage Co. Ltd, Stone Ferry Industrial Estate, Rix Road, Hull, HU7 0BT Tel: (01482) 838965 Fax: (01482) 838965
J E Jones S & D Ltd, Moor Lane, Birmingham, B6 7HH Tel: 0121-356 9169 Fax: 0121-356 0595 E-mail: jejdrums@aol.com
J Milner & Sons Ltd, Ingram Road, Leeds, LS11 9RD Tel: 0113-245 3845 Fax: 0113-245 3845
J & S Simcox Ltd, Pikehelve Street, West Bromwich, West Midlands, B70 0TU Tel: 0121-557 3076 Fax: 0121-520 9674
Jacques Products, Greengate Industrial Estate, Greenside Way, Middleton, Manchester, M24 1SW Tel: 0161-688 7744 Fax: 0161-688 6060
Ken Rooms Ltd, Cumberland Street, Hull, HU2 0PU Tel: (01482) 320129 Fax: (01482) 586040 E-mail: name@ken-rooms.co.uk
M A K Drums & Containers, Unit 16 Garston Industrial Estate, Blackburne Street, Liverpool, L19 8JB Tel: 0151-494 3331 Fax: 0151-494 9580 E-mail: sales@makdrums.co.uk
Manchester Drums Ltd, Bower Street, Newton Heath, Manchester, M40 2AS Tel: 0161-203 4611 Fax: 0161-203 5404
Pack 2 Pack UK Ltd, Avonmouth Way, Avonmouth, Bristol, BS11 9HD Tel: 0117-982 3584 Fax: 0117-923 5396 E-mail: sales.avo@uk.pack2pack.com
pack2pack UK Ltd, Clifton Bridge Works, Wood Street, Brighouse, West Yorkshire, HD6 1PW Tel: (01484) 714484 Fax: (01484) 711172 E-mail: alan.mcgougan@uk.pack2pack.com
R Spivey & Son Ltd, 54 Upper Station Road, Batley, West Yorkshire, WF17 5TA Tel: (01924) 473372 Fax: (01924) 442921 E-mail: david@spiveydrums.co.uk
Ramsden & Whale Ltd, Harrold Street, Tipton, West Midlands, DY4 0JF Tel: 0121-557 3656 Fax: 0121-522 3144
Soptralentz UK Ltd, Ravell Drum Works, Gelderd Road, Leeds, LS12 6DL Tel: 0113-263 8573 Fax: 0113-263 7842 E-mail: ken@peaserecycling.co.uk
R. Spivey & Sons Ltd, 30 Pheasant Drive, Birstall, Batley, West Yorkshire, WF17 9LT Tel: (01924) 423200 Fax: (01924) 420006 E-mail: david@spiveydrums.co.uk
Suma Containers, Plot Z Robian Way, Swadlincote, Derbyshire, DE11 9DH Tel: (01283) 224114 Fax: (01283) 218280 E-mail: sales@sumacontainers.co.uk
Taylor Davis Ltd, Moat Road, West Wilts Trading Estate, Westbury, Wiltshire, BA13 4JF Tel: (01373) 864324 Fax: (01373) 858021 E-mail: sales@taylor-davis.co.uk

DRUM DISPOSAL, *See Waste Drum/Tank Disposal etc*

DRUM FILLING MACHINES

Drum Technology, 2 Green Lane, Hull, HU2 0HG Tel: (01482) 223824 Fax: (01482) 223824 E-mail: user@drumtech.karoo.co.uk
R C S Filling Machines Ltd, Unit 1 Brand Street, Nottingham, NG2 3GW Tel: 0115-985 1717 Fax: 0115-985 1948 E-mail: sales@rcsfilling.com

DRUM HANDLING EQUIPMENT

BX Plant Ltd, 20 Eastmead Industrial Estate, Lavant, Chichester, West Sussex, PO18 0DE Tel: (01243) 781970 Fax: (01243) 533547 E-mail: rhodge@bxplant.com
Drum Technology, 2 Green Lane, Hull, HU2 0HG Tel: (01482) 223824 Fax: (01482) 223824 E-mail: user@drumtech.karoo.co.uk
Marwel Conveyors Ltd, 108 Dudley Road East, Oldbury, West Midlands, B69 3EB Tel: 0121-552 4418 Fax: 0121-552 4018 E-mail: sales@marwel.com
Spencer Davis Handling Ltd, Glanmor Terrace, Burry Port, Dyfed, SA16 0LS Tel: (01554) 833358 Fax: (01554) 835338 E-mail: sales@sde.co.uk
Wilmat Handling Company Ltd, 43 Steward Street, Birmingham, B18 7AE Tel: 0121-454 7514 Fax: 0121-456 1792 E-mail: info@wilmat-handling.co.uk

DRUM HEATERS

British & Continental Traders Ltd, Oxford House, North Bridge Road, Berkhamsted, Hertfordshire, HP4 1EH Tel: (01442) 877415 Fax: (01442) 872782E-mail: sales@b-ct.co.uk
Stabilag (E.S.H.) Ltd, 34 Mark Road, Hemel Hempstead, Hertfordshire, HP2 7DD Tel: (0870) 9906763 Fax: (0870) 9906762 E-mail: sales@stabilag.com

DRUM MANUFRS, *See also headings under drums*

A & B Containers Ltd, Windsor Street, Salford, M5 4DG Tel: 0161-736 0716 Fax: 0161-743 8445 E-mail: info@aandbcontainers.co.uk
▶ Drumland UK, Langney Road, Eastbourne, East Sussex, BN21 3JP Tel: (01323) 636142 Fax: (01323) 649100
A.W. Stokes & Son (Drums) Ltd, Hall Street, West Bromwich, West Midlands, B70 7DN Tel: 0121-553 1713 Fax: 0121-553 0825 E-mail: sales@awsdrums.co.uk

DRUM OPENERS

Drum Technology, 2 Green Lane, Hull, HU2 0HG Tel: (01482) 223824 Fax: (01482) 223824 E-mail: user@drumtech.karoo.co.uk

DRUM OVENS

Hedinair Ovens Ltd, 3 Pilot Close, Fulmar Way, Wickford, Essex, SS11 8YW Tel: (01268) 761777 Fax: (01268) 760210 E-mail: sales@hedinair.co.uk

DRUM PUMPS

Kecol Pumps Ltd, Faraday Drive, Bridgnorth, Shropshire, WV15 5BJ Tel: (01746) 764311 Fax: (01746) 764780 E-mail: sales@kecol.co.uk
ScopeNEXT Ltd, UWSP Barclay Centre, Sir William Lyons Road, Coventry, CV4 7EZ Tel: (0845) 4505406 Fax: (0845) 4505407 E-mail: info@scopenext.com

DRUM TAPS

Brassey Export Co., Starbell House, Carr Lane, Hoylake, Wirral, Merseyside, CH47 4FB Tel: 0151-632 6464 Fax: 0151-632 6392 E-mail: bec@starbell.com

DRY AIR COOLERS

Trans Tronic, Whitting Valley Road, Old Whittington, Chesterfield, Derbyshire, S41 9EY Tel: (01246) 264260 Fax: (01246) 455281 E-mail: sales@trans-tronic.co.uk
Transtherm Ltd, 12 Banner Park, Wickmans Drive, Coventry, CV4 9XA Tel: (024) 7647 1120 Fax: (024) 7647 1125 E-mail: sales@transtherm.ltd.uk

DRY BREAK COUPLINGS

First Hose Ltd, 21 Denmore Industrial Estate, Denmore Road, Bridge of Don, Aberdeen, AB23 8JW Tel: (01224) 823413 Fax: (01224) 823113 E-mail: sales@1st-hose.co.uk
▶ Millennium Coupling Co. Ltd, 72b Roman Way Industrial Estate, Ribbleton, Preston, PR2 5BE Tel: (01772) 653530 Fax: (01772) 653531 E-mail: sales@mcc-ltd.com
Staubli Unimation Ltd, Lodge Park, Telford, Shropshire, TF1 7ET Tel: (01952) 604827 Fax: (01952) 608579 E-mail: connectors.uk@staubli.com
Walther Couplings, 29 Akeman Street, Tring, Hertfordshire, HP23 6AN Tel: (01442) 891929 Fax: (01442) 890812 E-mail: sales@walther-couplings.com

DRY CARPET CLEANING

▶ Advanced Carpet Care Services, 4 Elmanoak Grove, Llay, Wrexham, Clwyd, LL12 0LZ Tel: (01978) 855846 E-mail: brian@advancecarpetcare.co.uk
▶ Advanced Cleaning Services, 81 Parkfield Drive, Castle Bromwich, Birmingham, B36 9TJ Tel: 0121-749 3013 E-mail: leewitten@advanced-cleaning.co.uk
▶ Gunns Upholstery Cleaners, 65 Mitchell Gardens, South Shields, Tyne & Wear, NE34 6EF Tel: 0191-454 2819 E-mail: stevegunn@gunnscleaning.co.uk
▶ London Domestic Cleaners, 41 Grovebury Court, London, N14 4JR Tel: (020) 8374 3020 E-mail: info@london-domestic-cleaners.co.uk
▶ SDC Carpet & Upholstery Cleaning Systems, Park House, 26 Park Lane, Eastbourne, East Sussex, BN21 2UU Tel: (01323) 520044 Fax: (01323) 641775 E-mail: sdccleaning@hotmail.com
▶ Yashar Bish, 96 Gloucester Road, Brighton, BN1 4AP Tel: (01273) 671900 Fax: (01273) 671900 E-mail: kim@yashar-bish.com

DRY CLEANING MACHINES

Joseph H Wood & Son Ltd, 15 Hemmons Road, Manchester, M12 5ST Tel: 0161-248 9814 Fax: 0161-225 2044 E-mail: wood@steamforindustry.freeserve.co.uk
▶ Parrisianne Ltd, Brighton Road, Lower Kingswood, Kingswood, Tadworth, Surrey, KT20 6SY Tel: (01737) 830007 Fax: (01737) 830199 E-mail: info@parrisianne.com
R L Services, 1 Bryn Road, Loughor, Swansea, SA4 6PG Tel: (01792) 897594 Fax: (01792) 416505 E-mail: ritchieslaundry@hotmail.com

DRY CLEANING SUPPLY SERVICES

Ashburne, 16-20 Penallta Road, Ystrad Mynach, Hengoed, Mid Glamorgan, CF82 7AP Tel: (01443) 816618 Fax: (01443) 816880
Cole & Wilson Ltd, Nabbs Lane Chemical Works, Slaithwaite, Huddersfield, HD7 5AT Tel: (01484) 842353 Fax: (01484) 843598 E-mail: sales@colewilson.co.uk
Johnson Cleaners UK Ltd, Ruthvenfield Road, Perth, PH1 3SW Tel: (01738) 623456 Fax: (01738) 635160
Laundry Supplies Ltd, Vulcan Road, Lode Lane Industrial Estate, Solihull, West Midlands, B91 2JY Tel: 0121-705 4645 Fax: 0121-711 2051 E-mail: sales@slmarketing.co.uk
Perkins Dyers & Cleaners Ltd, 6 Holly Bush Vale, Hampstead, London, NW3 6TX Tel: (020) 7794 4849 Fax: (020) 7433 1088 E-mail: perkinscleaners@aol.com
Alex Reid Ltd, 128-130 Beddington Lane, Croydon, CR0 4YZ Tel: (020) 8684 7667 Fax: (020) 8683 4335 E-mail: sales@alexreid.co.uk
Spick 'N' Span, 121 Kentish Town Road, London, NW1 8PB Tel: (020) 7485 5203
Standard Laundry (N I) Ltd, 213 Donegall Avenue, Belfast, BT12 6LU Tel: (028) 9032 7295 Fax: (028) 9031 4026
The Sunlight Service Group Ltd, Princes Street, Penrith, Cumbria, CA11 7BQ Tel: (01768) 862744 Fax: (01768) 891881 E-mail: penrith@sunlight.co.uk
Super Hanger Manufacturing Co. Ltd, 100 Vale Road, Windsor, Berkshire, SL4 5JL Tel: (01753) 622500 Fax: (01753) 622770 E-mail: sales@super-hanger.co.uk
Tibard Laundry Services Ltd, Holden Street, Ashton-under-Lyne, Lancashire, OL6 9JB Tel: 0161-330 5106 Fax: 0161-339 9995
Waveney Laundry Ltd, Clonavon Road South, Ballymena, County Antrim, BT43 5BJ Tel: (028) 2564 2131 Fax: (028) 2564 3123 E-mail: mail@waveneylaundry.com

DRY COLOUR BLENDING PIGMENTS

Hampton Colours Ltd, Toadsmoor Mills, Brimscombe, Stroud, Gloucestershire, GL5 2UH Tel: (01453) 731555 Fax: (01453) 731234 E-mail: sales@hamptoncolours.co.uk

DRY ICE BLAST CLEANING SERVICES

Cryosonic UK Ltd, 11 Boundary Court Rathmore Road, Cambridge, CB1 7BB Tel: (01223) 720695 Fax: (0870) 1314500 E-mail: sales@cryosonic.co.uk

DRY ROT PREVENTATIVE SOLUTION

Kiltox Contracts Ltd, 6 Chiltonian Industrial Estate, Manor Lane, London, SE12 0TX Tel: (020) 8463 9690 Fax: (0845) 1662050 E-mail: info@kiltox.co.uk
▶ Timberwise (UK) Ltd, PO Box 4198, Cardiff, CF14 8BG Tel: (0800) 991100 E-mail: cardiff@timberwise.co.uk
▶ Timberwise UK plc, Chester Enterprise Centre, Hoole Bridge, Chester, CH2 3NE Tel: (01244) 321366 Fax: (01565) 621000 E-mail: chester@timberwise.co.uk
▶ Timberwise (UK) Ltd, 19 Eagle Close, Birdwood Park, Fareham, Hants, PO16 8QX Tel: (0800) 991100 Fax: (01329) 510186 E-mail: hants@timberwise.co.uk
▶ Timberwise UK plc, Kirkfields Business Centre, Kirk Lane, Yeadon, Leeds, LS19 7ET Tel: 0113-250 4402 Fax: 0113-250 9931 E-mail: leeds@timberwise.co.uk
▶ Timberwise (UK) Ltd, 1 Norman Road, Thurmaston, Leicester, LE4 8EL Tel: (0800) 991100 Fax: 0116-269 3678 E-mail: leics@timberwise.co.uk
▶ Timberwise (UK) Ltd, Unit B16, Brunswick Business Centre, Brunswick Business Park, Sefton Street, Liverpool, L3 4BD Tel: (0800) 991100 Fax: 0151-284 6837 E-mail: liverpool@timberwise.co.uk
▶ Timberwise UK plc, 3 CWRT Roger Mostyn, Builder Street, Llandudno, Gwynedd, LL30 1DS Tel: (01492) 535065 Fax: (01492) 864004 E-mail: llandudno@timberwise.co.uk
▶ Timberwise (UK) Ltd, Bank House, 4 Wharf Road, Sale, Cheshire, M33 2AF Tel: (0800) 991100 Fax: 0161-972 0077 E-mail: sale@timberwise.co.uk
▶ Timberwise UK plc, 4 Finchwell Close, Sheffield, S13 9DF Tel: 0114-256 1411 Fax: 0114-256 1422 E-mail: sheffield@timberwise.co.uk
▶ Timberwise UK plc, 47 The Green, Cheadle, Stoke-on-Trent, ST10 1XS Tel: (01782) 599921 Fax: 0161 962 7610 E-mail: stoke@timberwise.co.uk
▶ Timberwise (UK) Ltd, 6 Rose Hill, Sutton, Surrey, SM1 3EU Tel: (0800) 991100 Fax: (020) 8641 4343 E-mail: sutton@timberwise.co.uk

DRY ROT PREVENTATIVE SOLUTION – *continued*

▶ Timberwise (UK) Ltd, Wilwood, Smith Hill, Bishopsteignton, Teignmouth, Devon, TQ14 9QT Tel: (0800) 991100 Fax: (01935) 814436 E-mail: devon@timberwise.co.uk

▶ Timberwise (UK) Ltd, 7 Gooch Way, Worle, Weston-super-Mare, Avon, BS22 7YH Tel: (0800) 991100 Fax: (01935) 814436 E-mail: weston@timberwise.co.uk

DRY RUNNING VACUUM PUMPS

Northey Technologies Ltd, Nortech House, Allens Lane, Poole, Dorset, BH16 5DG Tel: (01202) 668600 Fax: (01202) 668500 E-mail: info@northey.net

DRY STONE WALLING

S B Cole, 24 Drury Lane, Biggin, Buxton, Derbyshire, SK17 0DL Tel: (01298) 84445 Fax: 01298 84445

DRY TRANSFORMERS

International Transformers, Longley Lane, Sharston Industrial Area, Manchester, M22 4RU Tel: 0161-428 9507 Fax: 0161-428 0052 E-mail: info@int-transformers.co.uk

A.C. Simpson (Transformers) 1981 Ltd, Unit 20, Olds Close, Watford, WD18 9RU Tel: (01923) 777495 Fax: (01923) 771257 E-mail: info@acstx.co.uk

T & R Group Ltd, 15-16 Woodbridge Meadows, Guildford, Surrey, GU1 1BJ Tel: (01483) 568281 Fax: (01483) 504961 E-mail: sales@transformers.co.uk

DRY WALL

Avonside Insulation Supplies Ltd, Unit 6a Pucklechurch Trading Estate, Pucklechurch, Bristol, BS16 9QH Tel: 0117-937 2232 Fax: 0117-937 2387

British Gypsum Ltd, Gotham Road, East Leake, Loughborough, Leicestershire, LE12 6JQ Tel: 0115-945 1050 Fax: 0115-945 1154 E-mail: bgtechnical.enquiries@bpb.com

J.F. Goodwillie Ltd, Saw Mills, 154 London Road, Waterlooville, Hampshire, PO7 5SR Tel: (08707) 705433 Fax: (08707) 705435

Hall & Rogers Ltd, Hillkirk Street, Manchester, M11 3EZ Tel: 0161-273 8800 Fax: 0161-273 7279 E-mail: prigby@hallandrogers.co.uk

Lafarge Aggregates Ltd, Marsh Lane, Easton-in-Gordano, Bristol, BS20 0NF Tel: (0800) 373636 Fax: (01275) 377700

DRY WALL ACCESSORIES

Cornercare Ltd, Unit 3-4 Walter Nash Road West, Birchen Coppice Trading Estate, Kidderminster, Worcestershire, DY11 7QY Tel: (01562) 515200 Fax: (01562) 864063 E-mail: cornercare@compuserve.com

Lafarge Aggregates Ltd, Marsh Lane, Easton-in-Gordano, Bristol, BS20 0NF Tel: (0800) 373636 Fax: (01275) 377700

Walls & Ceilings International Ltd, 31 Tything Road, Kinwarton, Alcester, Warwickshire, B49 6ES Tel: (01789) 763727 Fax: (01789) 400312E-mail: sales@walls-and-ceilings.co.uk

DRY WALL CONTRACTORS

▶ Cawdell Contracts, Malting Lane, Dagnall, Berkhamsted, Hertfordshire, HP4 1QY Tel: (01442) 843100 Fax: (01442) 842170

DRY WALL INSTALLATION

Avon Manufacturing Ltd, Viande House, Kineton Road, Southam, Warwickshire, CV47 0DR Tel: (01926) 817292 Fax: (01926) 814156 E-mail: sale@avonova.co.uk

DRY WALL LINING SYSTEMS

▶ JP taping & jointing, 57 Huntington terrace road, Cannock, Staffordshire, WS11 5HB Tel: 07976 284152 Fax: 01543 428578 E-mail: phasey@tiscli.co.uk

DRY WAREHOUSING

Potter Group Ltd, Cutnall Green, Rushock, Droitwich, Worcestershire, WR9 0NS Tel: (01299) 851441 Fax: (01299) 851390 E-mail: droitwich@pottergroup.co.uk

DRYERS, *See also headings for particular types*

Ceramic Drying Systems Ltd, Weston Coyney Road, Stoke-on-Trent, ST3 5JU Tel: (01782) 336666

Tek Machinery Ltd, 9 Stadium Court, Barbot Hall Industrial Estate, Parkgate, Rotherham, South Yorkshire, S62 6EW Tel: (01709) 820820 Fax: (01709) 382504 E-mail: info@tekmachinery.co.uk

Woodside Pneumatics Ltd, Stirling Road Industrial Estate, Dykehead Road, Airdrie, Lanarkshire, ML6 7UJ Tel: (01236) 756171 Fax: (01236) 751210 E-mail: sales@woodside-compressors.co.uk

DRYERS, CAN/BOTTLE

Secomak Holdings Ltd, Unit 330, Centennial Park, Elstree, Borehamwood, Hertfordshire, WD6 3TJ Tel: (020) 8732 1300 Fax: (020) 8732 1301 E-mail: sales@secomak.com

DRYERS, FLUID BED, VIBRATING

▶ Liquid Alternative Ltd, 2/4 Arran Mall, Ayr, KA7 1SQ Tel: 01292 886779 Fax: 01292 886602 E-mail: info@labeds.com

DRYERS, GAS, *See Gas Drying etc*

DRYING OVENS

Alphatech Ltd, Green House, Homefield Road, Haverhill, Suffolk, CB9 8QP Tel: (01440) 714709 Fax: (01440) 714706 E-mail: info@alphatech.eu.com

Cem Microwave Technology Ltd, 2 Middle Slade, Buckingham Industrial Estate, Buckingham, MK18 1WA Tel: (01280) 822873 Fax: (01280) 822342 E-mail: info.uk@cem.com

Greenbank Technology Ltd, Unit 420 Glenfield Park Two, Blakewater Road, Blackburn, BB1 5QH Tel: (01254) 690555 Fax: (01254) 690666 E-mail: info@greenbanktechnology.co.uk

J L S Redditch, Holberrow Green, Holberrow Green, Redditch, Worcestershire, B96 6JY Tel: (01386) 791513 Fax: 01386 791518 E-mail: sales@jlsovens.com

Robank Engineering Ltd, Meridian Centre, King Street, Oldham, OL8 1EZ Tel: 0161-633 9126 Fax: 0161-633 9136 E-mail: robank@globalnet.co.uk

DRYSUITS

C & L Products, Tall Trees, Lazenbys Estate, Walliswood, Dorking, Surrey, RH5 5RE Tel: (01306) 627721 Fax: (01306) 627721 E-mail: sales@c-lproducts.co.uk

Namron Aqua Products Ltd, Canklow Meadows Industrial Estate, West Bawtry Road, Rotherham, South Yorkshire, S60 2XL Tel: (01709) 371006 Fax: (01709) 367295 E-mail: namron@scubauk.com

Seastyle, Unit 21 Three Springs Trading Estate, Vincent Road, Worcester, WR5 1BW Tel: (01905) 351528 Fax: (01905) 763776 E-mail: diving@seastyle.co.uk

DUAL IN LINE (DIL) SWITCHES

Felco Electronics Ltd, 2 Rivermead, Pipers Way, Thatcham, Berkshire, RG19 4EP Tel: (01635) 866940 Fax: (01635) 866951 E-mail: sales@felco.co.uk

Knitter Switch UK Ltd, Grove House, Lutyens Close, Lychpit, Basingstoke, Hampshire, RG24 8AG Tel: (01256) 338670 Fax: (01256) 338671 E-mail: ksuk@knitter-switch.com

DUCKS

▶ Warrawee Duck Farm, Pollards Moor Road, Copythorne, Southampton, SO40 2NZ Tel: 023 80811457 E-mail: nicky.janaway@warraweeduckfarm.co.uk

DUCT HEATERS

Mitrechoice Ltd, Haynes Garage, The Knoll, Sherington, Newport Pagnell, Buckinghamshire, MK16 9NZ Tel: (01908) 611054 Fax: (01908) 611054

DUCTED PROPELLERS

Kart Propulsion Co. Ltd, Bank Chambers, 70 Pier Road, Erith, Kent, DA8 1BA Tel: (01322) 346346 Fax: (01322) 347346 E-mail: info@kortpropulsion.com

DUCTILE IRON CASTINGS

Durham Foundry (Sheffield) Ltd, Durham Foundry, Harleston Street, Sheffield, S4 7QB Tel: 0114-249 4977 Fax: 0114-249 4910 E-mail: castings@durhamfoundry.com

J T & E Castings Ltd, Leyland Mill Lane, Wigan, Lancashire, WN1 2SA Tel: (01942) 241966 Fax: (01942) 492136 E-mail: enquiries@jte-castings.co.uk

William Lee Ltd, Callywhite Lane, Dronfield, Derbyshire, S18 2XU Tel: (01246) 416155 Fax: (01246) 292194 E-mail: sales@wmlee.co.uk

Newby & Son Ironfounders Ltd, Smiths Road, Wednesbury, West Midlands, WS10 0PB Tel: 0121-556 4451 Fax: 0121-505 3626 E-mail: sales@newbyfoundries.co.uk

DUCTILE IRON MANHOLE COVERS OR FRAMES

Eccles UK Foundries Ltd, Portland Street, Walsall, WS2 8AA Tel: (01922) 613222 Fax: (01922) 613444

DUCTING, *See also headings for particular types*

Adams Sheet Metal Ltd, Mill Street, Wibsey, Bradford, West Yorkshire, BD6 3BQ Tel: (01274) 693630 Fax: (01274) 693631 E-mail: sales@a-s-m.co.uk

▶ Airware, Unit 5c Arrow Trading Estate, Corporation Road, Audenshaw, Manchester, M34 5LR Tel: 0161-320 4777 Fax: 0161-320 7829

Alpha Tube Co., Tameside Works, Park Road, Dukinfield, Cheshire, SK16 5PT Tel: 0161-339 8901 Fax: 0161-343 1750 E-mail: alpha@alphatube.freeserve.co.uk

C D M Ductwork, 19 Prince William Road, Loughborough, Leicestershire, LE11 5GU Tel: (01509) 611118 Fax: (01509) 232345 E-mail: cdmductwork@aol.com

Direct Air Supplies Ltd, 4 Brocklebank Industrial Estate, Brocklebank Road, London, SE7 7SX Tel: (020) 8853 2186 Fax: (020) 8293 5539 E-mail: direct.air@virgin.net

▶ K C G Installations Ltd, 20 Burrish Street, Droitwich, Worcestershire, WR9 8HX Tel: (01905) 770531 E-mail: enquiries@kcg-installations.com

Plasticon (U K) Ltd, Grovehill Industrial Estate, Beverley, North Humberside, HU17 0JT Tel: (01482) 862194 Fax: (01482) 871398 E-mail: sales@plasticon.co.uk

Ultimate Ducting Sales, Unit 14 Riverside Court, Don Road, Sheffield, S9 2TJ Tel: 0114-242 5377 Fax: 0114-261 0495

DUCTING OR DUCT CLEANING MACHINES OR EQUIPMENT

Envirocare Services Ltd, 5 Stratfield Park, Elettra Avenue, Waterlooville, Hampshire, PO7 7XN Tel: (023) 9264 4700 Fax: (023) 9264 4677 E-mail: info@envirocare-services.com

DUCTING OR DUCT COMPONENTS

A & K Partners, Hill House, 20 Hill House Road, Norwich, NR1 4AA Tel: (01603) 667142 Fax: (01603) 667159

Aces Dust Control Ltd, Unit 3 Fossil Bank, Upper Colwall, Malvern, Worcestershire, WR13 6PL Tel: (01684) 576573 Fax: (01684) 576583

Adams Sheet Metal Ltd, Mill Street, Wibsey, Bradford, West Yorkshire, BD6 3BQ Tel: (01274) 693630 Fax: (01274) 693631 E-mail: sales@a-s-m.co.uk

Airtight Ductwork Ltd, New Town, Kington Magna, Gillingham, Dorset, SP8 5EU Tel: (01747) 838777 Fax: (01747) 838999 E-mail: info@airtightductwork.co.uk

BH & Sons Ltd, 6 Hazel End, Swanley, Kent, BR8 8NU Tel: (01322) 667610 Fax: (01322) 614569

C C L Veloduct Ltd, 10 Redburn Industrial Estate, Woodall Road, Enfield, Middlesex, EN3 4LE Tel: (020) 8805 3656 Fax: (020) 8805 0558 E-mail: sales@cclveloduct.co.uk

Ductwork Wolverhampton Ltd, Unit 10-11, Spring Road, Ettingshall, Wolverhampton, WV4 6JT Tel: (01902) 353984 Fax: (01902) 353985

J D P Ltd, Collett Way, Yate, Bristol, BS37 5NL Tel: (01454) 323000 Fax: (01454) 310037 E-mail: yate@jdpipes.co.uk

Mechanical Air Supplies Ltd, Crouch Indust Estate, Barnett Wood Lane, Leatherhead, Surrey, KT22 7DG Tel: (01372) 370084 Fax: (01372) 370085

Millwrights Liverpool Ltd, 31-33 Naylor Street, Liverpool, L3 6DR Tel: 0151-236 0479 Fax: 0151-255 0198

DUCTWORK AIR FLOW MONITORS

Air Flow Measurements Ltd, 72 Manchester Road, Kearsley, Bolton, BL4 8NZ Tel: (01204) 571499 Fax: (01204) 571734 E-mail: info@airflowmeasurements.com

Temperature Electronics Ltd, 388-400 Manchester Road, Rochdale, Lancashire, OL11 4NW Tel: (01706) 633438 Fax: (01706) 524609 E-mail: sales@tel-uk.com

DUCTWORK CONTRACTORS

A I S Sheet Metal Ltd, Hoo Farm Industrial Estate, Worcester Road, Kidderminster, Worcestershire, DY11 7RA Tel: (01562) 820700 Fax: (01562) 829401 E-mail: sales@aissheetmetal.co.uk

D R Ventilation Ltd, 14 Bishop Close, Leighton Buzzard, Bedfordshire, LU7 4ST Tel: (01525) 630730 Fax: (01525) 630730 E-mail: dr.ventilation@ntlworld.com

▶ Prelite Plenums Ltd, Chainbridge Road, Blaydon-on-Tyne, Tyne & Wear, NE21 5ST Tel: 0191-414 3331 Fax: 0191-414 3331

S W & National Ventilation, 20 Brean Down Road, Peverell, Plymouth, PL3 5PX Tel: (01752) 201140 Fax: (01752) 201140 E-mail: swanvent@eurobell.co.uk

DUCTWORK INSTALLATION

Fabfold Ltd, Amington Industrial Estate, 30 Sandy Way, Tamworth, Staffordshire, B77 4DS Tel: (01827) 313396 Fax: (01827) 313289 E-mail: fabfold@fabfold.fsnet.co.uk

Tatetone Ventilation Systems, 4 Bridgewater Close, Reading, RG30 1JT Tel: 0118-950 8914 Fax: 0118-950 8913 E-mail: enquiries@tateoneltd.co.uk

DUCTWORK OR DUCTING OR DUCT CLEANING CONTRACTORS OR SERVICES

▶ Aquacair Ltd, 40 Parklands Road, Chichester, West Sussex, PO19 3DT Tel: (01243) 790808 Fax: (01243) 790809 E-mail: sales@aquacair.co.uk

Ductwork Wolverhampton Ltd, Unit 10-11, Spring Road, Ettingshall, Wolverhampton, WV4 6JT Tel: (01902) 353984 Fax: (01902) 353985

Filta Group Ltd, The Locks, Hillmorton, Rugby, Warwickshire, CV21 4PP Tel: (01788) 550100 Fax: (01788) 551839 E-mail: sales@filtagroup.com

Harbec Services, 1A Leaphill Road, Pokesdown, Bournemouth, BH7 6LS Tel: (01202) 417725 Fax: (01202) 417732 E-mail: sales@harbec.co.uk

Heasman & Sadler Ltd, 29 Park Road, Faringdon, Oxfordshire, SN7 7BP Tel: (01367) 240286 Fax: (01367) 242056

Intergrated Water Services Ltd, Vincients Road, Bumpers Farm Industrial Estate, Chippenham, Wiltshire, SN14 6NQ Tel: (01249) 461744 Fax: (01249) 461766

M F D Ductwork Installations Ltd, 16a York Road, Earls Colne, Colchester, CO6 2RN Tel: (01787) 222745 Fax: (01787) 222182

The Pure Group, 10 Mead Court, Cooper Road, Thornbury, Bristol, BS35 3UW Tel: (01454) 411888 Fax: (01454) 411117 E-mail: puregroup@puregroup.co.uk

Swiftclean (UK) Ltd, Aviation Way, Southend-On-Sea, SS2 6UN Tel: (01702) 531221 Fax: (01702) 531220 E-mail: info@swiftclean.co.uk

DUCTWORK WELDING

Domglade Ltd, 1a Desborough Avenue, High Wycombe, Buckinghamshire, HP11 2RS Tel: (01494) 437771 Fax: (01494) 462357

DUMPER TRUCKS

A U S A (UK) Ltd, Unit 6-7 Alma Industrial Estate, Regent Street, Rochdale, Lancashire, OL12 0HQ Tel: (01706) 649691 Fax: (01706) 649720 E-mail: ausa@comel.demon.co.uk

Arnold Plant Hire Ltd, Bredbury Park Way, Bredbury Park Industrial Estate, Bredbury, Stockport, Cheshire, SK6 2SN Tel: 0161-406 8734 Fax: 0161-406 8804 E-mail: hire@arnold-plant.co.uk

Beddoes Bros, Pentre Hyling, Church Stoke, Montgomery, Powys, SY15 6HU Tel: (01588) 620199 Fax: (01588) 620499 E-mail: paul@beddoesplant.co.uk

Bell Equipment UK, Unit 6c Graycar Business Park, Barton Turns Barton Under, Barton Under Needwood, Burton-on-Trent, Staffordshire, DE13 8EN Tel: (01283) 712862 Fax: (01283) 712687 E-mail: web@bell.co.za

Butler Reynolds Ltd, Loughborough Road, Costock, Loughborough, Leicestershire, LE12 6XB Tel: (01509) 854144 Fax: (01509) 854199 E-mail: sales@butlerreynolds.co.uk

DUMPER TRUCKS – *continued*

▶ Geddes Group Ltd, Swirlburn, Colliston, Arbroath, Angus, DD11 3SH Tel: (01241) 890266 Fax: (01241) 890445

Multi Marque Production Engineering Ltd, Unit 33 Monckton Road Industrial Estate, Wakefield, West Yorkshire, WF2 7AL Tel: (01924) 290231 Fax: (01924) 382241 E-mail: enquiry@multi-marque.co.uk

Thwaites Ltd, Welsh Road Works, Leamington Spa, Warwickshire, CV32 7NQ Tel: (01926) 422471 Fax: (01926) 337155 E-mail: name@thwaitesdumpers.co.uk

DUNNAGE BAGS

Gemini Industries UK Ltd., 18-20 Canterbury Road,, Whitstable, Kent, CT5 4EY Tel: 01406 350572 E-mail: info@geminiindustries.co.uk

Javah Ltd, Warwick Mills, Howard Street, Batley, West Yorkshire, WF17 6JH Tel: (01924) 452156 Fax: (01924) 455015 E-mail: sales@javah.com

DUPLEX METAL FABRICATORS

C P E (Pressure Vessels) Ltd, Apollo, Lichfield Road Industrial Estate, Tamworth, Staffordshire, B79 7TA Tel: 01827 68710 Fax: (01827) 54396 E-mail: sales@cpe-ltd.com

DUPLEX METAL FLANGES AND FITTINGS

Chemipetro Ltd, Plant A Peartree Indust Park, Pear Tree Lane, Dudley, West Midlands, DY2 0UW Tel: (01384) 239441 Fax: (01384) 238430 E-mail: sales@chemipetro.com

Full Supply Ltd, Unit 29a Dawley Trading Estate, Stallings Lane, Kingswinford, West Midlands, DY6 7AP Tel: (01384) 402101 Fax: (01384) 402501 E-mail: sales@fullsupply.co.uk

Mardale Pipes Plus Ltd, PO Box 86, Runcorn, Cheshire, WA7 1PX Tel: (01928) 580555 Fax: (01928) 591033 E-mail: sales@mardale-pipes.com

Special Piping Materials Ltd, Broadway, Dukinfield, Cheshire, SK16 4UU Tel: 0161-343 7005 Fax: 0161-343 7011 E-mail: sales@spm.co.uk

DUPLEX METALS

Langley Alloys Ltd, Campbell Rd, Stoke-on-Trent, ST4 4ER Tel: (01782) 847474 Fax: (01782) 847476 E-mail: chris@meighs.co.uk

Metals Group Ltd, Units 10-11 Walker Industrial Park, Guide, Blackburn, BB1 2QE Tel: (01254) 586700 Fax: (01254) 692063 E-mail: sales@metalsuk.com

Orchard Materials Ltd, 7 Brunel Way, Thornbury, Bristol, BS35 3UR Tel: (01454) 415222 Fax: (01454) 415333 E-mail: sales@orchardmaterials.com

DUPLEX STEEL CASTINGS

Goodwin International Ltd, Ivy House Foundry, Hanley, Stoke-on-Trent, ST1 3NR Tel: (01782) 220000 Fax: (01782) 208060 E-mail: goodwinplc@goodwin.co.uk

Norton Cast Products Ltd, Capital Steel Works, Tinsley Park Road, Sheffield, S9 5DL Tel: 0114-244 8722 Fax: 0114-242 5523 E-mail: info@nortoncast.com

DUPLICATE BOOKS

▶ Officepoint Fivestar, 326 Kensal Road, London, W10 5BZ Tel: (020) 8969 8348 Fax: (020) 8969 8349 E-mail: sales@officepointfivestar.com

DUPLICATING MACHINES

N R G Group Ltd, 4 Rushmills, Northampton, NN4 7YB Tel: (01604) 732700

DUPLICATOR STENCILS

▶ J F K Signs & Stamp Maker, 67 Tylecroft Road, Norbury, London, SW16 4BL Tel: (020) 8679 5428 Fax: (020) 8679 1928

Team Group Technologies, Stammerham Business Centre, Capel Road, Rusper, Horsham, West Sussex, RH12 4PZ Tel: (01306) 713410 Fax: (01306) 713408 E-mail: sales@teamgt.co.uk

DUST BARRIER MATS

Blue Diamond Industrial Supplies, Hatton, Peterhead, Aberdeenshire, AB42 0RX Tel: (01779) 841899

Bonar Floors Ltd, High Holborne Road, Ripley, Derbyshire, DE5 3XD Tel: (01773) 744121 Fax: (01773) 744142 E-mail: enquires@bonarfloors.com

Threshold Floorings Ltd, Marston Gate, South Marston Park, Swindon, SN3 4TQ Tel: (01793) 764301 Fax: (01793) 765319 E-mail: sales@thresholdflr.co.uk

W O M International, Cherrycourt Way, Leighton Buzzard, Bedfordshire, LU7 4AA Tel: (01525) 375033 Fax: (01525) 383552 E-mail: services@wom-int.com

DUST BINS, METAL

Brettell & Shaw, Allfor House, Hayes Lane, Stourbridge, West Midlands, DY9 8QT Tel: (01384) 898911 Fax: (01384) 899100 E-mail: jpc@bretshaweltex.com

Garrods of Barking Ltd, Abbey Wharf, Kings Bridge Road, Barking, Essex, IG11 0BD Tel: (020) 8594 0224 Fax: (020) 8594 0225 E-mail: info@garrods.com

H & E Knowles (Lye) Ltd, Britannia Works, Talbots Lane, Brierley Hill, West Midlands, DY5 2YX Tel: (01384) 78877 Fax: (01384) 79012 E-mail: sales@heknowles.freeserves.co.uk

DUST COLLECTING BAGS OR SLEEVES

Filter & Press Cloth Co. Ltd, 26 Town Road, Hillchurch Street, Stoke-on-Trent, ST1 2EX Tel: (01782) 281819 Fax: (01782) 281819

Filtrex Environmental, Unit 18 Burnt Mill Industrial Estate, Elizabeth Way, Harlow, Essex, CM20 2HS Tel: (01279) 457590 Fax: (01279) 457591

H R Filtration & Co., The Green Barn Complex, The Scarr, Newent, Gloucestershire, GL18 1DQ Tel: (01531) 820320 Fax: (01531) 822253 E-mail: sales@hrfiltration.com

Heath Filtration Ltd, PO Box 1, Stoke-on-Trent, ST6 4SH Tel: (01782) 838591 Fax: (01782) 835508 E-mail: info@heathfiltration.com

G. Hunt Filtration Ltd, Portland Mill, Portland Street South, Ashton-Under-Lyne, Lancashire, OL6 7SX Tel: 0161-330 7337 Fax: 0161-343 2365 E-mail: sales@hunt-filtration.co.uk

HVDS, Site B Hixon Industrial Estate, Church Lane, Hixon, Stafford, ST18 0PY Tel: (01889) 270079 Fax: (01889) 271616

Simpson Thomson Filtration, Virginia Mills, 187 Higher Hillgate, Stockport, Cheshire, SK1 3JG Tel: 0161-480 8991 Fax: 0161-429 8413

Tyne-Tees Filtration Ltd, Blue House Point Road, Portrack Industrial Estate, Stockton-On-Tees, Cleveland, TS18 2QL Tel: (01642) 617401 Fax: (01642) 617404 E-mail: enquiries@ttf-uk.com

DUST COLLECTING EQUIPMENT

A B Dust Control Ltd, 79-81 High Street, Albrighton, Wolverhampton, WV7 3JA Tel: (01902) 373155 Fax: (01902) 373133 E-mail: abdustconltd@aol.com

Cleen Flo Manchester Ltd, 5 Lower Chatham Street, Manchester, M1 5QL Tel: 0161-237 3880 Fax: 0161-236 9388

Climavent Systems Ltd, Units 1-3 Cairngorm Business Park, Liverpool Road, Ashton-in-Makerfield, Wigan, Lancashire, WN4 0YU Tel: (01942) 726164 Fax: (01942) 722300 E-mail: info@climavent.co.uk

Donaldson Filtration (GB) Ltd, Humberstone Lane, Thurmaston, Leicester, LE4 8HP Tel: 0116-269 6161 Fax: 0116-269 3028 E-mail: peter.cowing@emea.donaldson.com

Dulevo UK Ltd, Royds House Royds Mill, Leeds Road, Ossett, West Yorkshire, WF5 9YA Tel: (01924) 277026 Fax: (01924) 262074 E-mail: dulevo@dial.pipex.com

Dustcheck Ltd, Environmental House, Galveston Grove, Stoke-on-Trent, ST4 3PE Tel: (01782) 599454 Fax: (01782) 599478 E-mail: sales@dustcheck.co.uk

Dustraction Ltd, Mandervell Road, Oadby, Leicester, LE2 5ND Tel: 0116-271 3212 Fax: 0116-271 3215 E-mail: steve.matuska@dustraction.co.uk

Environmental Elements (UK) Ltd, Unit 2 Moor Street, Burton-on-Trent, Staffordshire, DE14 3SU Tel: (01283) 740536 Fax: (01283) 563969 E-mail: dcormack@eec1.com

Filtex Filters, 4 7 Union Park, Navigation Way, West Bromwich, West Midlands, B70 9DF Tel: 0121-553 1283 Fax: 0121-500 5289 E-mail: sales@ioi.co.uk

Freddy Products Ltd, Units 6-7, Goodwood Rd, Pershore, Worcestershire, WR10 2JL Tel: (01386) 561113 Fax: (01386) 556401 E-mail: sales@freddy-products.co.uk

Hamon UK Ltd, Units1-2 Ropery Park, Alferd Street, Hull, HU3 2DF Tel: (01482) 787767 Fax: (01482) 706151 E-mail: info.huk@hamon.com

Intensiv Filter (UK) Ltd, Bath House, Bath Street, Walsall, WS1 3DB Tel: (01922) 628893 Fax: (01922) 613875 E-mail: intensiv@intensiv-filter.co.uk

J E M (Environmental) Ltd, Furlong Lane, Burslem, Stoke-On-Trent, ST6 3LE Tel: (01782) 834823 Fax: (01782) 575656 E-mail: sales@jemenvironmental.co.uk

Luhrfilter Ltd, 58a Thornhill Road, Sutton Coldfield, West Midlands, B74 3EN Tel: 0121-353 8703 Fax: 0121-353 4066 E-mail: sales@luhrgb.demon.co.uk

Molyneux Dust Control Ltd, 7 Leicester Avenue, Alsager, Stoke-on-Trent, ST7 2BS Tel: (01270) 879359 Fax: (01270) 879355 E-mail: johnmolydust@aol.com

Porter Environmental Supplies Ltd, 18 Montpelier Avenue, Bexley, Kent, DA5 3AL Tel: (020) 8298 1919 Fax: (020) 8298 7737

Rock Drill Services, 11A Main Street, Hothan, York, YO43 4UF Tel: (01430) 424814 Fax: (01430) 424991 E-mail: rockdrill@btclick.com

Soho Sheet Metal Ltd, Furlong Lane, Stoke-on-Trent, ST6 3LE Tel: (01782) 817930 Fax: (01782) 575656

Steelform Ventilation Ltd, Unit 13 Attenburys Park Estate, Attenbury Lane, Timperley, Altrincham, Cheshire, WA14 5QE Tel: 0161-962 8639 Fax: 0161-973 6742 E-mail: sales@steelformvetilation.com

DUST COLLECTING MAT SUPPLY SERVICES

O C S Group Uk, 78 Gatwick Road, Crawley, West Sussex, RH10 9YB Tel: (01293) 553121 Fax: (01293) 663385 E-mail: info@catering.ocs.co.uk

W O M International, Cherrycourt Way, Leighton Buzzard, Bedfordshire, LU7 4AA Tel: (01525) 375033 Fax: (01525) 383552 E-mail: services@wom-int.com

DUST COLLECTING MATS

O C S Group Uk, 78 Gatwick Road, Crawley, West Sussex, RH10 9YB Tel: (01293) 553121 Fax: (01293) 663385 E-mail: info@catering.ocs.co.uk

W O M International, Cherrycourt Way, Leighton Buzzard, Bedfordshire, LU7 4AA Tel: (01525) 375033 Fax: (01525) 383552 E-mail: services@wom-int.com

DUST COLLECTOR VALVES

Goyen Controls Co. UK Ltd, Unit 3B, Beechwood, Chineham Business Park, Basingstoke, Hampshire, RG24 8WA Tel: (01256) 817800 Fax: (01256) 843164 E-mail:

DUST CONTROL FILTERS

Dustcheck Ltd, Environmental House, Galveston Grove, Stoke-on-Trent, ST4 3PE Tel: (01782) 599454 Fax: (01782) 599478 E-mail: sales@dustcheck.co.uk

Euro Filter, Hare Park Mills, 46 Hare Park Lane, Liversedge, West Yorkshire, WF15 8EP Tel: (01623) 412412 Fax: (01623) 412455 E-mail: sales@eurofilter.co.uk

Holdsworth Ventilations Ltd, Greenside Works, Stoke-on-Trent, ST6 4HU Tel: (01782) 811900 Fax: (01782) 811902 E-mail: mark@holdsworthventilations.co.uk

Leyland Filtration Ltd, Yarrow Road, Chorley, Lancashire, PR6 0LP Tel: (01257) 269292 Fax: (01257) 261056 E-mail: layland.filtration@talk21.com

Multi-Factor Europe Ltd, Harrison House, Rackery Lane, Llay, Wrexham, Clwyd, LL12 0PB Tel: (0845) 5314030 Fax: (01978) 855222 E-mail: mark.beeston@mfeuk.co.uk

DUST CONTROL OR MONITORING SYSTEMS

BPC Circuits Ltd, Sheene Road, Leicester, LE4 1BF Tel: 0116-233 4444 Fax: 0116-233 4466 E-mail: info@circuitcontroltechnology.com

▶ Dynoptic Systems Ltd, Furlong House, Crowfield, Brackley, Northamptonshire, NN13 5TW Tel: (01280) 850521 Fax: (01280) 850568 E-mail: contact@dynoptic.com

Goyen Controls Co. UK Ltd, Unit 3B, Beechwood, Chineham Business Park, Basingstoke, Hampshire, RG24 8WA Tel: (01256) 817800 Fax: (01256) 843164 E-mail:

Heaton Green (Dust Control) Ltd, Atlas Quarry Works, Upper Howard Street, Batley, West Yorkshire, WF17 6AA Tel: (01924) 430430 Fax: (01924) 430898 E-mail: user@heatongreen.co.uk

Holdsworth Ventilations Ltd, Greenside Works, Stoke-on-Trent, ST6 4HU Tel: (01782) 811900 Fax: (01782) 811902 E-mail: mark@holdsworthventilations.co.uk

Meridian Controls Ltd, 38 Galloway Close, South Ham, Basingstoke, Hampshire, RG22 6SX Tel: 0845 5314080 Fax: (01256) 324209 E-mail: sales@meridian-controls.co.uk

Pcme, Clearview Building, Edison Road, St. Ives, Cambridgeshire, PE27 3GH Tel: (01480) 468200 Fax: (01480) 463400 E-mail: sales@pcme.co.uk

Turnkey Instruments Ltd, Units 1-2 Dalby Court, Gadbrook Business Centre, Rudheath, Northwich, Cheshire, CW9 7TN Tel: (01606) 44520 Fax: (01606) 331526 E-mail: shop@turnkey-instruments.com

W T Products Ltd, Unit 3 Cedar Terrace, Leeds, LS12 1TQ Tel: 0113-279 7345 Fax: 0113-231 0725 E-mail: wtproducts1@btconnect.com

Worcester Ventilation Systems Ltd, PO Box 190, Droitwich, Worcestershire, WR9 7DE Tel: (01905) 794422 Fax: (01905) 794488 E-mail: mail@worcester-vent.co.uk

DUST COVERS

Tamar Specialist Brushes, Exeter, EX2 8WW Tel: (01392) 491818 Fax: (01392) 491818 E-mail: enquiries@tamarbrushes.co.uk

DUST EXTRACTION CONSULTANCY OR DESIGN

R & B Industrial Ltd, 41 Charlton Road, Andover, Hampshire, SP10 3JH Tel: (01264) 351844 Fax: (01264) 354191 E-mail: info@rbindustrial.co.uk

DUST EXTRACTION CONTROL SYSTEMS

Ansteygate Dust Extraction, 19 Marlow Road, Leicester, LE3 2BQ Tel: 0116-282 6333 Fax: 0116-282 6336 E-mail: carl@ansteygate.co.uk

Bofa UK Ltd, Unit 13 Fleetsbridge Business Park, Upton Road, Poole, Dorset, BH17 7AF Tel: (01202) 699444 Fax: (01202) 699446 E-mail: sales@bofa.co.uk

BPC Circuits Ltd, Sheene Road, Leicester, LE4 1BF Tel: 0116-233 4444 Fax: 0116-233 4466 E-mail: info@circuitcontroltechnology.com

Dust Pollution Systems Ltd, 2 Premacto Works, Queensmead Road, Loudwater, High Wycombe, Buckinghamshire, HP10 9XA Tel: (01494) 462333 Fax: (01494) 463777 E-mail: info@dustpollution.co.uk

Erskine Environmental Engineering Ltd., 16 Lady Lane, Paisley, Renfrewshire, PA1 2LJ Tel: 0141-887 7784 Fax: 0141-889 4338

Hird Fan Systems, Town Hall, Westfield Road, Horbury, Wakefield, West Yorkshire, WF4 6HR Tel: (01924) 273731 Fax: (01924) 263096

Ken Mills Engineering Ltd, New Street Works, Shawclough, Rochdale, Lancashire, OL12 6NS Tel: (01706) 644698 Fax: (01706) 649285 E-mail: ken.mills@zen.co.uk

R W Vesey Ltd, 734 Melton Road, Thurmaston, Leicester, LE4 8BD Tel: 0116-269 6241 Fax: 0116-269 6243 E-mail: info@vesey-airflow.com

Steelform Ventilation Ltd, Unit 13 Attenburys Park Estate, Attenbury Lane, Timperley, Altrincham, Cheshire, WA14 5QE Tel: 0161-962 8639 Fax: 0161-973 6742 E-mail: sales@steelformvetilation.com

DUST EXTRACTION FANS

Inman & Co Electrical Ltd, 2-4 Orgreave Place, Sheffield, S13 9LU Tel: 0114-254 2400 Fax: 0114-254 2410 E-mail: sales@inmanselectrical.co.uk

System Air GMPH, 20b Westside Centre, London Road, Stanway, Colchester, CO3 8PH Tel: (01206) 543311 Fax: (01206) 760497 E-mail: sales@matthews-yates.co.uk

DUST EXTRACTION INSTALLATION OR SERVICING

A B Dust Control Ltd, 79-81 High Street, Albrighton, Wolverhampton, WV7 3JA Tel: (01902) 373155 Fax: (01902) 373133 E-mail: abdustconltd@aol.com

A S Contracts Ltd, Warstock Road, Birmingham, B14 4RS Tel: 0121-436 7969 Fax: 0121-436 7970

A1 Extraction Ltd, Wentworth Road, Heathfield Industrial Estate, Newton Abbot, Devon, TQ12 6TL Tel: (01626) 832007 Fax: (01626) 834590

Advent Engineering Ltd, 9 Sherwood Road, Bromsgrove, Worcestershire, B60 3DR Tel: (01527) 874414 Fax: (01527) 831603 E-mail: info@adventmanchester.co.uk

Air Pollution Services, Suite 6 Chiltern House, Leys Road, Brierley Hill, West Midlands, DY5 3UP Tel: (01384) 78094 Fax: (01384) 480940 E-mail: martinwil@msn.com

Auto Extract Systems, Brearley House, Burnley Road, Halifax, West Yorkshire, HX2 6NB Tel: (01422) 888144 Fax: (01422) 888145

Carter Environmental Engineers Ltd, 2 Lawley Middleway, Birmingham, B4 7XL Tel: 0121-250 1000 Fax: 0121-250 1400 E-mail: sales@cee.co.uk

Cleen Flo Manchester Ltd, 5 Lower Chatham Street, Manchester, M1 5QL Tel: 0161-237 3880 Fax: 0161-236 9388

Cliftonair Ltd, 48 High Street, Newport Pagnell, Buckinghamshire, MK16 8AQ Tel: (01908) 216416 Fax: (01908) 616732 E-mail: brian@cliftonair.co.uk

DUST EXTRACTION INSTALLATION OR SERVICING - *continued*

Climavent Systems Ltd, Units 1-3 Cairngorm Business Park, Liverpool Road, Ashton-in-Makerfield, Wigan, Lancashire, WN4 0YU Tel: (01942) 726164 Fax: (01942) 722300 E-mail: info@climavent.co.uk

Constant Air Systems Ltd, Hillbottom Road, Sands Industrial Estate, High Wycombe, Buckinghamshire, HP12 4HJ Tel: (01494) 469529 Fax: (01494) 469549 E-mail: admin@constantair.co.uk

Crosskill Ventilation Ltd, Spar Road, Norwich, NR6 6BX Tel: (01603) 423028 Fax: (01603) 401136 E-mail: crosskill@btconnect.com

DST Engineering Ltd, 17 Chapmans Brae, Bathgate, West Lothian, EH48 4LH Tel: (01506) 631196 Fax: (01506) 634873

Duscovent Engineering Ltd, 86 Wellington Road North, Stockport, Cheshire, SK4 1HT Tel: 0161-480 4811 Fax: 0161-480 6503 E-mail: sales@duscovent.co.uk

Dust Control Systems Ltd, Churwell Vale, Shaw Cross Business Park, Dewsbury, West Yorkshire, WF12 7RD Tel: (01924) 482500 Fax: (01924) 482530 E-mail: sales@dcslimited.co.uk

Dustolex Ltd, Ebor Street, Littleborough, Lancashire, OL15 9AS Tel: (01706) 377344 Fax: (01706) 377332 E-mail: sales@dustolex.co.uk

Dy-rect Services Ltd, Unit 8 Hikers Way, Crendon Industrial Park, Long Crendon, Aylesbury, Buckinghamshire, HP18 9RW Tel: (01844) 202233 Fax: (01844) 208748 E-mail: info@dy-rect.co.uk

Filtex Filters, 4 7 Union Park, Navigation Way, West Bromwich, West Midlands, B70 9DF Tel: 0121-553 1283 Fax: 0121-500 5289 E-mail: sales@ioi.co.uk

Glenair Ltd, 171-177 Hessle Road, Hull, HU3 4AA Tel: (01482) 223313 Fax: (01482) 229962 E-mail: info@glenair.ltd.uk

Halifax Sheet Metal & Ventilation, Pellon Industrial Estate, Queens Road, Halifax, West Yorkshire, HX1 4PR Tel: (01422) 362361 Fax: (01422) 340591E-mail: info@hsmv.co.uk

Heaton Green (Dust Control) Ltd, Atlas Quarry Works, Upper Howard Street, Batley, West Yorkshire, WF17 6AA Tel: (01924) 430430 Fax: (01924) 430898 E-mail: user@heatongreen.co.uk

Holdsworth Ventilations Ltd, Greenside Works, Stoke-on-Trent, ST6 4HU Tel: (01782) 811900 Fax: (01782) 811902 E-mail: mark@holdsworthventilations.co.uk

Industrial Air Control Ltd, Bath Lodge, Park Street, Royton, Oldham, OL2 6QN Tel: 0161-626 0242 Fax: 0161-627 0231 E-mail: sales@iacontrol.co.uk

Intensiv Filter (UK) Ltd, Bath House, Bath Street, Walsall, WS1 3DB Tel: (01922) 628893 Fax: (01922) 613875 E-mail: intensiv@intensiv-filter.co.uk

Inventair Fabrications, Carnaby Industrial Estate, Lancaster Road, Carnaby, Bridlington, North Humberside, YO15 3QY Tel: (01262) 400919 Fax: (01262) 401358 E-mail: david@inventair.co.uk

J E M (Environmental) Ltd, Furlong Lane, Burslem, Stoke-On-Trent, ST6 3LE Tel: (01782) 834823 Fax: (01782) 575656 E-mail: sales@jemenvironmental.co.uk

▶ Jamieson (Environmental Services) Ltd, 142 Busby RF, Clarkston, Glasgow, G76 8BG Tel: 0141-644 5191 Fax: 0141-644 1696 E-mail: sales@jamiesonenvironmental.co.uk

L & J Mechanical Services Swindon Ltd, Unit 7, Lyndon Road, Cheney Manor, Swindon, SN2 2QJ Tel: (01793) 541419 Fax: (01793) 495759 E-mail: owen.bignenn-ljms@btinternet.com

Linscert UK Ltd, 25 Osborne Avenue, Aston, Sheffield, S26 2BY Tel: 0114-269 2513 Fax: 0114-287 7816

Maine Engineering Services Ltd, West Line Industrial Estate, Birtley, Chester le Street, County Durham, DH2 1AU Tel: 0191-410 0004 Fax: 0191-410 2053 E-mail: mick.main@dsl.pipex.com

Nederman Ltd, PO Box 503, Preston, PR5 8AF Tel: (01772) 334721 Fax: (01772) 315273

Nobles Engineering Solutions Ltd, 11 Mallard Close, Earls Barton, Northampton, NN6 0JF Tel: (01604) 810695 Fax: (01604) 812586

Ownglen Environmental Consultants, 169 Horbury Road, Wakefield, West Yorkshire, WF2 8BG Tel: (01924) 368822 Fax: (01924) 368833

P & J Dust Extraction Ltd, Otterham Quay, Gillingham, Kent, ME8 8NA Tel: 01634 233933

Quality Extraction Designs Ltd, 52 Sandiway Bank, Thornhill, Dewsbury, West Yorkshire, WF12 0SD Tel: (01924) 430802 Fax: (01924) 430892 E-mail: daviddenise@qedltd.fsnet.co.uk

R J Barrington Ltd, 3 Barrington Buildings, Clinton Road, Leominster, Herefordshire, HR6 0RJ Tel: (01568) 612101 Fax: (01568) 612501 E-mail: mary@rjbarringtonltd.co.uk

R P L (1983) Ltd, Unit 39, Nortonthorpe Industrial Park, Wakefield Road, Scissett, Huddersfield, HD8 9FB Tel: (01484) 868283 Fax: (01484) 868258 E-mail: info@rplltd.co.uk

Ray Rushin Ltd, Whiteley Road, Ripley, Derbyshire, DE5 3QL Tel: (01773) 512155 Fax: (01773) 512156 E-mail: sales@rayrushin.co.uk

S P E Ltd, 27 Dinghouse Wood, Buckley, Clwyd, CH7 3DH Tel: (01244) 549790 Fax: (01244) 549790 E-mail: s.mogridge@btinternet.com

Severn Ventilation Ltd, Rock Cottages, Hill Street, Kidderminster, Worcestershire, DY11 6TD Tel: (01562) 743869 Fax: (01562) 862018

Soho Sheet Metal Ltd, Furlong Lane, Stoke-on-Trent, ST6 3LE Tel: (01782) 817930 Fax: (01782) 575656

Steelform Ventilation Ltd, Unit 13 Attenburys Park Estate, Attenbury Lane, Timperley, Altrincham, Cheshire, WA14 5QE Tel: 0161-962 8639 Fax: 0161-973 6742 E-mail: sales@steelformvetilation.com

Techshare Ventilation Systems, 39 Leaplish, Washington, Tyne & Wear, NE38 0RB Tel: 0191-417 2424 Fax: 0191-415 1686 E-mail: sales@techshare.co.uk

TVM Workplace Improvements Ltd, PO Box 6, Wigan, Lancashire, WN6 8EF Tel: (01257) 254488 E-mail: sales@nofumes.co.uk

Versaduct Sheet Metal Ltd, Edwin Avenue, Hoo Farm Industrial Estate, Kidderminster, Worcestershire, DY11 7RA Tel: (01562) 824913 Fax: (01562) 823809

Work Place Safety Management Ltd, Unit 11A, Whitwick Business Centre, Whitwick Business Park, Stenson Road, Coalville, Leicestershire, LE67 4JP Tel: (01530) 276535 Fax: (01530) 276536

DUST EXTRACTION PLANT AND EQUIPMENT MANUFRS

A I S Sheet Metal Ltd, Hoo Farm Industrial Estate, Worcester Road, Kidderminster, Worcestershire, DY11 7RA Tel: (01562) 820700 Fax: (01562) 829401 E-mail: sales@aissheetmetal.co.uk

BPC Circuits Ltd, Sheene Road, Leicester, LE4 1BF Tel: 0116-233 4444 Fax: 0116-233 4466 E-mail: info@circuitcontroltechnology.com

Climavent Systems Ltd, Units 1-3 Cairngorm Business Park, Liverpool Road, Ashton-in-Makerfield, Wigan, Lancashire, WN4 0YU Tel: (01942) 726164 Fax: (01942) 722300 E-mail: info@climavent.co.uk

Dantherm Filtration Ltd, Limewood Approach, Seacroft, Leeds, LS14 1NG Tel: 0113-273 9400 Fax: 0113-265 0735 E-mail: info.uk@danthermfiltration.com

Dolphin Enterprises, 4 Eddington Drive, Newton Mearns, Glasgow, G77 5AX Tel: 0141-639 4551 Fax: 0141-639 4551 E-mail: dolphinenterprizes@btconnect.com

Donaldson Filtration (GB) Ltd, Humberstone Lane, Thurmaston, Leicester, LE4 8HP Tel: 0116-269 6161 Fax: 0116-269 3028 E-mail: peter.cowing@emea.donaldson.com

Duscovent Engineering Ltd, 86 Wellington Road North, Stockport, Cheshire, SK4 1HT Tel: 0161-480 4811 Fax: 0161-480 6503 E-mail: sales@duscovent.co.uk

Dust Control, 1b Pury Business Park, Alderton Road, Paulerspury, Towcester, Northamptonshire, NN12 7LS Tel: (01327) 811510 Fax: (01327) 811413 E-mail: sales@dustcontrol.co.uk

Dust Control Systems Ltd, Churwell Vale, Shaw Cross Business Park, Dewsbury, West Yorkshire, WF12 7RD Tel: (01924) 482500 Fax: (01924) 482530 E-mail: sales@dcslimited.co.uk

Dustcheck Ltd, Environmental House, Galveston Grove, Stoke-on-Trent, ST4 3PE Tel: (01782) 599454 Fax: (01782) 599478 E-mail: sales@dustcheck.co.uk

Dustolex Ltd, Ebor Street, Littleborough, Lancashire, OL15 9AS Tel: (01706) 377344 Fax: (01706) 377332 E-mail: sales@dustolex.co.uk

Dustraction Ltd, Mandervell Road, Oadby, Leicester, LE2 5ND Tel: 0116-271 3212 Fax: 0116-271 3215 E-mail: steve.matuska@dustraction.co.uk

E & F Services Ltd, 10 Westleigh Business Park, Winchester Avenue, Blaby, Leicester, LE8 4EZ Tel: 0116-247 7450 Fax: 0116-247 7487 E-mail: info@eandfservices.com

Envirocare Services Ltd, 5 Stratfield Park, Elettra Avenue, Waterlooville, Hampshire, PO7 7XN Tel: (023) 9264 4700 Fax: (023) 9264 4677 E-mail: info@envirocare-services.com

Ernest Morrison & Co., Unit 13 Loughside Industrial Estate, Dargan CR, Belfast, BT3 9JP Tel: (028) 9077 7093 Fax: (028) 9077 6299

Fercell Engineering Ltd, Unit 1, Old Mill Lane, Aylesford, Kent, ME20 7DT Tel: (01622) 791414 Fax: (01622) 791515 E-mail: info@fercell.com

Flextraction Ltd, 10 Digby Drive, Leicester Road Industrial Estate, Melton Mowbray, Leicestershire, LE13 0RQ Tel: (01664) 410641 Fax: (01664) 480244 E-mail: sales@flextraction.co.uk

Form Fabrications, 21-25 The Crescent, Hockley, Birmingham, B18 5LU Tel: 0121-551 3561 Fax: 0121-551 6258 E-mail: enquiries@formfabs.com

▶ Harold & Wylie Enviroflo Engineering, 10A Newton Court, Westrand, Pendeford Business Park, Wolverhampton, WV9 5HB Tel: (01902) 784848 Fax: (01902) 784242 E-mail: wylie@enviroflo.co.uk

Heaton Green (Dust Control) Ltd, Atlas Quarry Works, Upper Howard Street, Batley, West Yorkshire, WF17 6AA Tel: (01924) 430430 Fax: (01924) 430898 E-mail: user@heatongreen.co.uk

Intensiv Filter (UK) Ltd, Bath House, Bath Street, Walsall, WS1 3DB Tel: (01922) 628893 Fax: (01922) 613875 E-mail: intensiv@intensiv-filter.co.uk

J E M (Environmental) Ltd, Furlong Lane, Burslem, Stoke-On-Trent, ST6 3LE Tel: (01782) 834823 Fax: (01782) 575656 E-mail: sales@jemenvironmental.co.uk

Luhrfilter Ltd, 58a Thornhill Road, Sutton Coldfield, West Midlands, B74 3EN Tel: 0121-353 8703 Fax: 0121-353 4066 E-mail: sales@luhrgb.demon.co.uk

Mcluckie Engineering Ltd, 54 Barterholm Road, Paisley, Renfrewshire, PA2 6PF Tel: 0141-887 2201 Fax: 0141-889 5970 E-mail: sales@mcluckie.co.uk

Mardon Engineering Co. Ltd, Ditton Priors Trading Estate, Station Road, Ditton Priors, Bridgnorth, Shropshire, WV16 6SS Tel: (01746) 712616 Fax: (01746) 712349

Mastervent Ventilation Systems, 2 Engine Street, Smethwick, West Midlands, B66 3DT Tel: 0121-558 1559 Fax: 0121-565 4047 E-mail: home@masterventltd.go-plus.net

▶ Michael Williams Ltd, Wilbraham Road, Fulbourn, Cambridge, CB21 5ET Tel: (01223) 882222 Fax: (01223) 882598 E-mail: sales@mikewills.co.uk

Minden Industrial Ltd, Saxham Business Park, Little Saxham, Bury St. Edmunds, Suffolk, IP28 6RX Tel: (01284) 760791 Fax: (01284) 702156 E-mail: sales@minden-ind.co.uk

Modus Air Ltd, 75 Lifford Lane, Birmingham, B30 3JH Tel: 0121-459 3060 Fax: 0121-459 6417 E-mail: modusair@btinternet.com

Moldow Ltd, Unit 31 Britannia Way, Britannia Enterprise Park, Lichfield, Staffordshire, WS14 9UY Tel: (01543) 258844 Fax: (01543) 416311

Nederman Ltd, PO Box 503, Preston, PR5 8AF Tel: (01772) 334721 Fax: (01772) 315273

North & South Industries, Sidings Court, Doncaster, South Yorkshire, DN4 5NU Tel: (01302) 730037 Fax: (01302) 730073

Pentagon-Europe Ltd, No11 Earlsfield, Holyport, Maidenhead, Berkshire, SL6 2LZ Tel: (01628) 627247 Fax: (01628) 624553

Prompt Profiles Ltd, Liberator House, Bidwell Road, Norwich, NR13 6PT Tel: (01603) 720090 Fax: (01603) 720202

Quality Extraction Designs Ltd, 52 Sandiway Bank, Thornhill, Dewsbury, West Yorkshire, WF12 0SD Tel: (01924) 430802 Fax: (01924) 430892 E-mail: daviddenise@qedltd.fsnet.co.uk

Rowley & Hall Ventilation Ltd, 4 Canal Lane, Tunstall, Stoke-on-Trent, ST6 4NZ Tel: (01782) 837592 Fax: (01782) 833810

Sangre Engineering Ltd, Unit 32c The Washford Industrial Estate, Heming Road, Redditch, Worcestershire, B98 0DH Tel: (01527) 524782 Fax: (01527) 510323 E-mail: sales@sangre.co.uk

Severn Environmental Engineering Ltd, Scan Buildings, Oldbury Road, Cwmbran, Gwent, NP44 3JU Tel: (01633) 866241 Fax: (01633) 874664

Super Stork I P T Ltd, Carlisle Road, London, NW9 0HD Tel: (020) 8200 1144 Fax: (020) 8200 4385 E-mail: sales1@superstork.co.uk

Vented Services Telford Ltd, Unit A6 Hortonwood 10, Telford, Shropshire, TF1 7ES Tel: (01952) 677788 Fax: (01952) 677789 E-mail: addessee@vented-services.co.uk

Walker & Holmes Ltd, Linton Street, Bradford, West Yorkshire, BD4 7EZ Tel: (01274) 728655 Fax: (01274) 723678 E-mail: walkerholmesltd@aol.com

West Bromwich Sheet Metal Ltd, Unit 43n Siddons Factory Estate, Howard Street, West Bromwich, West Midlands, B70 0SU Tel: 0121-556 9120 Fax: 0121-556 9120

Wilson Bros Sheffield Ltd, 35 Kirk Street, Sheffield, S4 7JX Tel: 0114-272 6179 Fax: 0114-276 5889

The Woodwork Dust Control Company Ltd, Wotton Road, Brill, Aylesbury, Buckinghamshire, HP18 9UB Tel: (01844) 238833 Fax: (01844) 238899 E-mail: woodworkdust@ukonline.co.uk

DUST EXTRACTION SERVICES

Air Plants Environmental Control Systems, 295 Aylestone Road, Leicester, LE2 7PB Tel: 0116-283 7800 Fax: 0116-283 7311 E-mail: sales@airplants.co.uk

Cades Ltd, Commerce Close, Challenge Way, Bradford, West Yorkshire, BD4 8NW Tel: (01274) 661156 Fax: (01274) 661756

Dust Control Services Ltd, Brocus House, Parkgate Road, Dorking, Surrey, RH5 5AH Tel: (01306) 631505 Fax: 01306 631751 E-mail: sales@dustextraction.co.uk

Dust Plant Services, 87 Lothair Road, Leicester, LE2 7QE Tel: 0116-244 0150

Dustolex Ltd, Ebor Street, Littleborough, Lancashire, OL15 9AS Tel: (01706) 377344 Fax: (01706) 377332 E-mail: sales@dustolex.co.uk

Extech (Environmental Systems & Services) Ltd, Unit 2 Building 6, Stanmore Industrial Estate, Bridgnorth, Shropshire, WV15 5HR Tel: (01746) 767414 Fax: (01746) 767345

Fumex Ltd, 411 Effingham Rd, Sheffield, S9 3QD Tel: 0114-243 0538 Fax: 0114-243 2394 E-mail: enquiries@fumex.co.uk

L & J Mechanical Services Swindon Ltd, Unit 7, Lyndon Road, Cheney Manor, Swindon, SN2 2QJ Tel: (01793) 541419 Fax: (01793) 495759 E-mail: owen.bignenn-ljms@btinternet.com

Mcluckie Engineering Ltd, 54 Barterholm Road, Paisley, Renfrewshire, PA2 6PF Tel: 0141-887 2201 Fax: 0141-889 5970 E-mail: sales@mcluckie.co.uk

Merlin Industrial Services, 55 Merlin Way, East Grinstead, West Sussex, RH19 3XG Tel: (01342) 300818 Fax: (01342) 324562

▶ Michael Williams Ltd, Wilbraham Road, Fulbourn, Cambridge, CB21 5ET Tel: (01223) 882222 Fax: (01223) 882598 E-mail: sales@mikewills.co.uk

Modern Air Systems Ltd, 219 Humberstone Lane, Leicester, LE4 9JT Tel: 0116-269 3485 Fax: 0116-269 3543 E-mail: sales@parkerplant.com

P N Ventilation, 65 Southend Road, Bungay, Suffolk, NR35 1DN Tel: (01986) 893706 Fax: (01986) 895050

Quality Extraction Designs Ltd, 52 Sandiway Bank, Thornhill, Dewsbury, West Yorkshire, WF12 0SD Tel: (01924) 430802 Fax: (01924) 430892 E-mail: daviddenise@qedltd.fsnet.co.uk

R P L (1983) Ltd, Unit 39, Nortonthorpe Industrial Park, Wakefield Road, Scissett, Huddersfield, HD8 9FB Tel: (01484) 868283 Fax: (01484) 868258 E-mail: info@rplltd.co.uk

Unicorn Mucksuckers, 41 High Street, Clophill, Bedford, MK45 4AA Tel: (01525) 860255 Fax: (01525) 861635 E-mail: info@uti.co.uk

DUST EXTRACTION TEST CONSULTANCY

L & J Mechanical Services Swindon Ltd, Unit 7, Lyndon Road, Cheney Manor, Swindon, SN2 2QJ Tel: (01793) 541419 Fax: (01793) 495759 E-mail: owen.bignenn-ljms@btinternet.com

R & B Industrial Ltd, 41 Charlton Road, Andover, Hampshire, SP10 3JH Tel: (01264) 351844 Fax: (01264) 354191 E-mail: info@rbindustrial.co.uk

DUST SUPPRESSION SYSTEMS

Long Reach Irrigation Ltd, Unit 6, Furnham Close, Furnham Road, Chard, Somerset, TA20 1AX Tel: (01460) 261255 Fax: (01460) 261266 E-mail: sales@xlreach.com

DUTCH TO ENGLISH TRANSLATION

▶ Kerry Services Ltd, 6 The Walks East, Huntingdon, Cambridgeshire, PE29 3AP Tel: (01480) 391504 Fax: (01480) 386467 E-mail: info@kerrytrans.com

▶ Translation Agency TGV24, Crimond Croft, Whitehouse, Alford, Aberdeenshire, AB33 8DL Tel: (01577) 862702 E-mail: tgv24@e3internet.com

DVD ACCESSORIES

▶ Disccity Ltd, Unit 12, Westbrook Road, Westbrook Trading Estate, Trafford Park, Manchester, M17 1AY Tel: 0870 166 0757 Fax: 0870 166 0759 E-mail: enqs@disccity.co.uk

DVD COPYING SOFTWARE

▶ A19 Duplication, PO Box 428, Middlesbrough, Cleveland, TS1 9AF Tel: (01642) 225283 E-mail: sales@a19duplication.co.uk

DVD DUPLICATING

Davis Rubin Associates Ltd, PO Box 15, Towcester, Northamptonshire, NN12 8DJ Tel: (01327) 830999 Fax: (01327) 831000 E-mail: btrubin@davisrubin.com

DVD REPLICATING

Thamesdown SDC, Frankland Road, Blagrove, Swindon, SN5 8YU Tel: (01793) 428700 Fax: (01793) 511125 E-mail: sales@tsfltd.co.uk

DVDS

▶ Discount DVDs & Videos, 16 Craighead Drive, Huntly, Aberdeenshire, AB54 8LG Tel: (01466) 799142 E-mail: cheapstock@tiscali.co.uk

▶ Discovery Media Direct, 1 Brookhampton Lane, Kineton, CV35 0JA Tel: 0871 474 2724

▶ W R D Worldwide Music Ltd, 282 Camden Road, London, NW1 9AB Tel: (020) 7267 6762 Fax: (020) 7482 4029 E-mail: info@wrdmusic.com

DYE PENETRANTS

Johnson & Allen Ltd, Neocol Works, Smithfield, Sheffield, S3 7AR Tel: 0114-273 8066 Fax: 0114-272 9842 E-mail: info@johnsonandallen.co.uk

DYE PRODUCTS, HOME-USE

Mayborn Group P.L.C., Dylon House, Worsley Bridge Road, London, SE26 5HD Tel: (020) 8663 4801 E-mail: dylonimp@dylon.co.uk
Town End Leeds plc, Silver Court, Intercity Way, Leeds, LS13 4LY Tel: 0113-256 4251 Fax: 0113-239 3315E-mail: sales@dyes.co.uk

DYELINE PRINTING MACHINES, *See Plan Printing Machine etc*

DYERS/FINISHERS TO TEXTILE TRADES

A T C Dyers, Royds Hall Lane, Buttershaw, Bradford, West Yorkshire, BD6 2NE Tel: (01274) 691169 Fax: (01274) 690016 E-mail: atcdyers@legend.co.uk
Adam Dyeing Ltd, Greenhill Industrial Estate, Birmingham Road, Kidderminster, Worcestershire, DY10 2SH Tel: (01562) 821525 Fax: (01562) 827916 E-mail: aac@adamcarpets.com
Alltex Ltd, Sladen Mill, Halifax Road, Littleborough, Lancashire, OL15 0LB Tel: (01706) 377374 Fax: (01706) 377256 E-mail: alltex@alltechsdying.co.uk
Atkinson Dyeing Co. Ltd, Deal Street, Keighley, West Yorkshire, BD21 4LA Tel: (01535) 604288 Fax: (01535) 690710
Barford Bros Ltd, 111 North Street, Luton, LU2 7QG Tel: (01582) 720371 Fax: (01582) 611098
Belmont Bleaching & Dyeing Co. Ltd, Belmont Works, Egerton Road, Belmont, Bolton, BL7 8BN Tel: (01204) 811247 Fax: (01204) 811408 E-mail: info@belmont-bleaching.co.uk
Blackburn Yarn Dyers Ltd, Grimshaw Park Dye Works, Haslingden Road, Blackburn, BB2 3HN Tel: (01254) 53051 Fax: (01254) 672233 E-mail: info@bydltd.co.uk
The British Millerain Company Ltd, Melloroid Works, Belfield Road, Rochdale, Lancashire, OL16 2XA Tel: (01706) 649242 Fax: (01706) 527611 E-mail: sales@britishmillerain.com
Brook Dyeing Co. Ltd, Slaithwaite Dyeworks, Britannia Mills, Slaithwaite, Huddersfield, HD7 5HE Tel: (01484) 842345 Fax: (01484) 843640
Bulmer & Lumb, Royds Hall Lane, Buttershaw, Bradford, West Yorkshire, BD6 2NE Tel: (01274) 676321 Fax: (01274) 691239 E-mail: sales@bulmerandlumb.com
Century Dyeing Co., Century Road, Elland, West Yorkshire, HX5 9HQ Tel: (01422) 379411 Fax: (01422) 376592 E-mail: info@centurydyeing.co.uk
A.E. Charlesworth & Co.Ltd, Rugby St, Leicester, LE3 5FG Tel: 0116-251 0552 Fax: 0116-251 8629
D P Dyers Ltd, Thirstin Dye Works, Thirstin Road, Honley, Holmfirth, HD9 6JL Tel: (01484) 661215 Fax: (01484) 665591
Dewsbury Dyeing Co. Ltd, Oaklands Mill, Netherfield Road, Dewsbury, West Yorkshire, WF13 3JY Tel: (01924) 463321 Fax: (01924) 460899 E-mail: dews.dyeing@btclick.com
Francis Dinsmore Ltd, 25 Greenfield Road, Kells, Ballymena, County Antrim, BT42 3JL Tel: (028) 2589 1203 Fax: (028) 2589 2295 E-mail: info@dinsmore.co.uk
James Dyson Ltd, Hoyle Ing Dyeworks, Linthwaite, Huddersfield, HD7 5RU Tel: (01484) 842456 Fax: (01484) 847253 E-mail: enquiries@jamesdyson.co.uk
Glemsford Silk Mills Ltd, Chequers Lane, Glemsford, Sudbury, Suffolk, CO10 7PW Tel: (01787) 280244 Fax: (01787) 281730
Guilford (Europe) Ltd, Cotes Park Lane, Somercotes, Alfreton, Derbyshire, DE55 4NJ Tel: (01773) 841200 Fax: (01773) 547315
H & C Whitehead Ltd, Prospect Works, Bailiffe Bridge, Brighouse, West Yorkshire, HD6 4DJ Tel: (01484) 712151 Fax: (01484) 716187 E-mail: info@hcwhitehead.co.uk
Hebden Dyeing & Finishing Co. Ltd, Crimsworth Dye Works, Midgehole, Hebden Bridge, West Yorkshire, HX7 7AN Tel: (01422) 842888 Fax: (01422) 845689 E-mail: hebdyefin@dial.pipex.com
Hicking Pentecost & Co. (N.I) Ltd, 64-66 Leighinmohr Avenue, Ballymena, County Antrim, BT42 2AN Tel: (028) 2565 6551 Fax: (028) 2565 9868
Holmfirth Dyers Ltd, Ribbleden Dye Works, Dunford Road, Holmfirth, HD9 2DP Tel: (01484) 682271 Fax: (01484) 681084 E-mail: holmefirthdyers@aol.com
J Clegg & Bros Rakewood Ltd, Rakewood Mill, Rakewood Road, Littleborough, Lancashire, OL15 0AP Tel: (01706) 378342 E-mail: peter@jclegg.co.uk
Langholm Dyeing Co Ltd, Waterside Mill, Langholm, Dumfriesshire, DG13 0DG Tel: (01387) 381188 Fax: (01387) 381177
Linton Tweeds Ltd, Shaddon Mills, Shaddongate, Carlisle, CA2 5TZ Tel: (01228) 527569 Fax: (01228) 512062 E-mail: info@lintontweeds.co.uk
Maxilusta Ltd, 24A Main Road, Radcliffe-On-Trent, Nottingham, NG12 2FH Tel: 0115-933 4966 Fax: 0115-933 5974
Naylor Jennings Ltd, Green Lane Dye Works, Yeadon, Leeds, LS19 7XP Tel: 0113-250 2331 Fax: 0113-250 6698 E-mail: sales@naylorjennings.co.uk
P W Greenhalgh & Co. Ltd, Newhey Bleach & Dye Works, Milnrow, Rochdale, Lancashire, OL16 3TH Tel: (01706) 847911 Fax: (01706) 881217 E-mail: sgreenhalgh@pwgreenhalgh.com
Pile Fabric Dyers Ltd, Woodhouse Mill, Greenbooth Road, Norden, Rochdale, Lancashire, OL12 7TD Tel: (01706) 523535 Fax: (01706) 659490 E-mail: admin@storyvelvets.co.uk
Pin Croft Dyeing & Printing Co. Ltd, Adlington Works, Market Street, Adlington, Chorley, Lancashire, PR7 4HJ Tel: (01257) 480202 Fax: (01257) 480898
Pollock & Cochrane Ltd, Thrushcraig Works, Rowan Street, Paisley, Renfrewshire, PA2 6RT Tel: 0141-889 2009 Fax: 0141-840 2114
Regal Dyeing & Finishing Co. Nottingham, The Poplars, Wollaton Road, Beeston, Nottingham, NG9 2PD Tel: 0115-925 4416 Fax: 0115-925 4416 E-mail: johncharles@tiscali.co.uk
Herbert Roberts Ltd, Royd Works, Royd Lane, Keighley, West Yorkshire, BD20 6BN Tel: (01535) 602266 Fax: (01535) 611252
S Lyles & Sons Co, Calder Bank Mills, Calder Bank Road, Dewsbury, West Yorkshire, WF12 9QW Tel: (01924) 436500 Fax: (01924) 436511
Schofield Dyers & Finishers, Gala Mill, Huddersfield Street, Galashiels, Selkirkshire, TD1 3AY Tel: (01896) 754848 Fax: (01896) 754417 E-mail: galamill@aol.com
Small & Tidmas Ltd, Vicarage Street, Barnstaple, Devon, EX32 7HA Tel: (01271) 375972 Fax: (01271) 379753 E-mail: info@smallandtidmas.co.uk
Standfast Barracks, Caton Road, Lancaster, LA1 3PA Tel: (01524) 64334 Fax: (01524) 380157
Stevensons, Amber Dye Works, Bullbridge, Ambergate, Belper, Derbyshire, DE56 2EX Tel: (01773) 852222 Fax: (01773) 857078 E-mail: gordon.cawood@quantumclothing.com
Thomas Birkhead & Son, Yew Tree Mills, Holmbridge, Holmfirth, HD9 2NN Tel: (01484) 691510 Fax: (01484) 691515
W T Johnson & Sons Huddersfield Ltd, Bankfield Mills, Moldgreen, Huddersfield, HD5 9BB Tel: (01484) 549965 Fax: (01484) 448106 E-mail: office@wtjohnson.co.uk
WRTL Exterior Lighting, 2 Waterside Park, Golds Hill Way, Tipton, West Midlands, DY4 0PU Tel: 0121-521 1234 Fax: 0121-521 1250 E-mail: sales@wrtl.co.uk

DYESTUFFS, *See also headings for particular types*

Albion Dyestuffs Ltd, Rook Lane Mills, Law Street, Bradford, West Yorkshire, BD4 9NF Tel: (01274) 652907 Fax: (01274) 689359 E-mail: albiondyestuffs@aol.com
Amatar Ltd, Amatar House, Manor Road, Woodley, Stockport, Cheshire, SK6 1RT Tel: 0161-494 6692 Fax: 0161-406 6752 E-mail: djo171135@aol.com
Chekemcolour Ltd, Smithfield Works, South Lane, Elland, West Yorkshire, HX5 0HQ Tel: (01422) 378221 Fax: (01422) 310074 E-mail: enquiries@chekem.co.uk
Copras Specialities Ltd, Copperas House Terrace, Todmorden, Lancashire, OL14 7PU Tel: (01706) 817899 Fax: (01706) 813671 E-mail: copras@packing.fsbusiness.co.uk
John Hogg, Mellors Road, Trafford Park, Manchester, M17 1PB Tel: 0161-872 5611 Fax: 0161-848 8206 E-mail: info@johnhogg.co.uk
Magna Colours Ltd, 3 Dodworth Business Park, Upper Cliffe Road, Dodworth, Barnsley, South Yorkshire, S75 3SP Tel: (01226) 731751 Fax: (01226) 731752 E-mail: sales@magnacolours.com
Rapid Colour Services Ltd, D 2 Moss Industrial Estate, Leigh, Lancashire, WN7 3PT Tel: (01942) 675932 Fax: (01942) 602229 E-mail: sales@rapidcolour.co.uk
Tolbest Ltd, 10 Aston Court, Kingsland Grange, Woolston, Warrington, WA1 4SG Tel: (01925) 825335 Fax: (01925) 825336 E-mail: info@tolbest.co.uk
Town End Leeds plc, Silver Court, Intercity Way, Leeds, LS13 4LY Tel: 0113-256 4251 Fax: 0113-239 3315E-mail: sales@dyes.co.uk
Unicolour Ltd, Tandem Works, Wakefield Road, Waterloo, Huddersfield, HD5 0AN Tel: (01484) 516974 Fax: (01484) 510667 E-mail: dyes@unicolour.co.uk
Wilkinson & Scott Ltd, 58 Nelson Street, Bradford, West Yorkshire, BD5 0DZ Tel: (01274) 724059 Fax: (01274) 305389 E-mail: anne@mac56.com
Yorkshire Chemicals plc, 27 Kirkstall Road, Leeds, LS3 1LL Tel: 0113-244 3111 Fax: 0113-244 1670 E-mail: yorkshire.chemicals@yorkchem.com

DYNAMIC BALANCING MACHINES

C F R Giesler Ltd, Empson Street, London, E3 3LT Tel: (020) 7987 2161 Fax: (020) 7515 0483 E-mail: sales@giesler.co.uk
Coborn Engineering Co. Ltd, Chesham Close, Romford, RM7 7PJ Tel: (01708) 744666 Fax: (01708) 725187 E-mail: coborneng@aol.com
▶ I R D Ltd, Block 3 Brymau One Trading Estate, River Lane, Saltney, Chester, CH4 8RQ Tel: (01244) 682222 Fax: (01244) 675439 E-mail: sales@irdbalancing.com
Schmitt Europe Ltd, Sir William Lyons Road, University of Warwick Science Park, Coventry, CV4 7EZ Tel: (024) 7669 7192 Fax: (024) 7641 2697 E-mail: enquiries@schmitt.co.uk
Universal Balancing Ltd, Unit 12 Douglas Road Industrial Estate, Douglas Road, Kingswood, Bristol, BS15 8PD Tel: 0117-907 7403 Fax: 0117-907 7402 E-mail: sales@unibal.co.uk

DYNAMIC BALANCING SERVICES

A 1 Dynamic Balancing Ltd, 7-9 Hagley Road, Hayley Green, Halesowen, West Midlands, B63 1DG Tel: 0121-501 3705 Fax: 0121-501 3615 E-mail: sales@wdbltd.co.uk
Anstee & Ware Group Ltd, Unit 1 St Georges Industrial Estate, St Andrews Road, Bristol, BS11 9HS Tel: 0117-982 0081 Fax: 0117-982 3511 E-mail: admin@ansteeware.co.uk
Anstee & Wear (Wales) Ltd, Foreshore Road, Cardiff, CF10 4DF Tel: (029) 2048 1831 Fax: (029) 2049 6592 E-mail: info@ansteewear.co.uk
▶ Balancing, Unit 12, Logan Road, Birkenhead, Merseyside, CH41 1JJ Tel: 0151-639 9898 Fax: 0151-639 9898 E-mail: enquiries@dp-engineering.co.uk
C F R Giesler Ltd, Empson Street, London, E3 3LT Tel: (020) 7987 2161 Fax: (020) 7515 0483 E-mail: sales@giesler.co.uk
Clydesdale Engineering Services Ltd, Belvoir Way, Fairfield Industrial Estate, Louth, Lincolnshire, LN11 0LQ Tel: (01507) 605991 Fax: (01507) 605991 E-mail: info@clydesdale.fsbusiness.co.uk
Dynamic Balancing Services, Hughenden Avenue, High Wycombe, Buckinghamshire, HP13 5SQ Tel: (01494) 462977 Fax: (01494) 462916 E-mail: sales@dynamicbalancing.co.uk
The Ford Group (Nottingham) Ltd, Park Lane Works, Old Basford, Nottingham, NG6 0EU Tel: 0115-977 0724 Fax: 0115-976 1041 E-mail: ford@fordgroup.co.uk
Rewinds & J. Windsor & Sons (Engineers) Ltd, 81 Regent Road, Liverpool, L5 9SY Tel: 0151-207 2074 Fax: 0151-298 1442 E-mail: accounts@rjweng.com
Royston Fan Co. Ltd, Lumen Road, Royston, Hertfordshire, SG8 7AF Tel: (01763) 241400 Fax: (01763) 245654 E-mail: alan@roystonfan.co.uk
RWE npower, TS Ferrybridge, Old Great North Road, Knottingley, West Yorkshire, WF11 8PR Tel: (01977) 632201 Fax: (01977) 632311 E-mail: tsg@rwe.com
Scholar Engines, Blue House, Norwich Road, Mendlesham, Stowmarket, Suffolk, IP14 5NH Tel: (01449) 767711 Fax: (01449) 767772 E-mail: adwsre@aol.com
Turbine Support Ltd, 7 Dodnor Park, Newport, Isle of Wight, PO30 5XE Tel: (01983) 826252 Fax: (01983) 826253 E-mail: sales@turbine-support.com
Universal Balancing Ltd, Unit 12 Douglas Road Industrial Estate, Douglas Road, Kingswood, Bristol, BS15 8PD Tel: 0117-907 7403 Fax: 0117-907 7402 E-mail: sales@unibal.co.uk
Universal Balancing, Station Street, Cradley Heath, West Midlands, B64 6AJ Tel: (01384) 567550 Fax: (01384) 413997 E-mail: jblomer@unifabrcations.co.uk

DYNAMIC POSITIONING SYSTEMS

Dynamic Positioning Services Ltd, Unit 2, Denmore Place, Bridge Of Don, Aberdeen, AB23 8JS Tel: (01224) 226850 Fax: (01224) 226851 E-mail: egrant@dynamic-positioning.co.uk
Marinetronix Ltd, Unit 1, Airside Business Park, Dyce Drive, Kirkhill Industrial Estate, Dyce, Aberdeen, AB21 0GT Tel: (01224) 774423 Fax: (01224) 724396 E-mail: info@marinetronix.co.uk

DYNAMIC WEIGHBRIDGES

▶ Avery Weigh Tronix Ltd, 13-14 Monckton Road Industrial Estate, Wakefield, West Yorkshire, WF2 7BP Tel: (0870) 9050041 Fax: (0870) 9050042 E-mail: hiredivisionuk@awtxglobal.com

DYNAMOMETER CONTROLLERS

Custom Technology Ltd, Brooks Road, Lewes, East Sussex, BN7 2BY Tel: (01273) 479101 Fax: (01273) 486727 E-mail: sales@customtechnology.co.uk

DYNAMOMETERS, *See also headings for particular types*

Amber Instruments Ltd, Dunston House Sheepbridge Works, Dunston Road, Chesterfield, Derbyshire, S41 9QD Tel: (01246) 260250 Fax: (01246) 260955 E-mail: sales@amberinstruments.com
Bowmonk Ltd, Diamond Road, St. Faiths Industrial Estate, Norwich, NR6 6AW Tel: (01603) 485153 Fax: (01603) 418150 E-mail: info@bowmonk.co.uk
Custom Technology Ltd, Brooks Road, Lewes, East Sussex, BN7 2BY Tel: (01273) 479101 Fax: (01273) 486727 E-mail: sales@customtechnology.co.uk
David Mcclure Ltd, Mersey Dynamo Works, Range Road, Stockport, Cheshire, SK3 8EF Tel: 0161-474 7362 Fax: 0161-429 0251 E-mail: mail@david-mcclure.co.uk
Froude Hofmann, Blackpole Road, Worcester, WR3 8YB Tel: (01905) 856800 Fax: (01905) 856811 E-mail: sales@froude.fki-eng.com
N J Froment & Co. Ltd, Cliffe Road, Easton on the Hill, Stamford, Lincolnshire, PE9 3NP Tel: (01780) 480033 Fax: (01780) 480044 E-mail: sales@froment.co.uk

EAR DEFENDERS

Chapman & Smith Ltd, Safir Works, South Street, East Hoathly, Lewes, East Sussex, BN8 6EW Tel: (01825) 840323 Fax: 01825 840827 E-mail: sales@chapman-smith.co.uk
Jays Racewear, Throstle Nest Mill, Leeds Road, Nelson, Lancashire, BB9 7QZ Tel: (01282) 677907 Fax: (01282) 697319 E-mail: sales@jaysracewear.co.uk
R Glover Ascroft Ltd, Ace Works, 157 Ordnance Road, Enfield, Middlesex, EN3 6AW Tel: (01992) 717272 Fax: (01992) 714040 E-mail: enquiries@r-glover-ascroft.com
S M Alexander Plastics Ltd, Little End Road, Eaton Socon, St. Neots, Cambridgeshire, PE19 8JH Tel: (01480) 473140 Fax: (01480) 406968 E-mail: smalexanderplastics@btinternet.com

EAR PLUGS

Anti Noise Ltd, 67 Great Underbank, Stockport, Cheshire, SK1 1PE Tel: 0161-480 8454 Fax: 0161-429 9049 E-mail: sales@freehearingtest.co.uk
Jays Racewear, Throstle Nest Mill, Leeds Road, Nelson, Lancashire, BB9 7QZ Tel: (01282) 677907 Fax: (01282) 697319 E-mail: sales@jaysracewear.co.uk

EARLY STREAMER EMISSION LIGHTNING CONDUCTORS

Britannia Lightning Prevectron Ltd, Longue Drive, Calverton, Nottingham, NG14 6QF Tel: 0115-847 7113 Fax: 0115-847 5185 E-mail: sales@lightninguk.fsnet.co.uk

EARRINGS

▶ Beads & Sparkly Things, 24 Larchwood Avenue, Romford, RM5 2QJ Tel: (07976) 035539 E-mail: carol.norman@ntlworld.com
▶ The Pearls Company, 1 Thomson Green, Deer Park, Livingston, West Lothian, EH54 8TA Tel: 01506 201327 Fax: 01506 210327 E-mail: info@thepearlscompany.co.uk
▶ Style Overload, The Lodge, Links Rd, Worthing, West Sussex, BN14 9QY Tel: 0207 6694181 E-mail: info@styleoverload.com
▶ Wave Contemporary Jewellery, 18a Finkle Sti, Kendal, Cumbria, LA9 4AB Tel: (01539) 729805 Fax: (01539) 48067 E-mail: info@wavejewellery.co.uk

EARTH BORING EQUIPMENT

Archway Engineering (UK) Ltd, Ainleys Industrial Estate, Elland, West Yorkshire, HX5 9JP Tel: (01422) 373101 Fax: (01422) 374847 E-mail: sales@archway-engineering.com
Brewis Engineering, Handlemaker Road, Frome, Somerset, BA11 4RW Tel: (01373) 451387 Fax: (01373) 452714 E-mail: sales@brewisdirect.com
J K S - Boyles UK Ltd, Unit 9 Salcombe Road, Meadow Lane Industrial Estate, Alfreton, Derbyshire, DE55 7RG Tel: (01773) 835323 Fax: (01773) 835075 E-mail: sales@jks-boyles-ltd.co.uk
Nub Engineering Ltd, Newhouse Industrial Estate, Newhouse, Motherwell, Lanarkshire, ML1 5RX Tel: (01698) 833873 Fax: (01698) 734322 E-mail: sales@nubeng.com
Runrig International Ltd, Fairview House, 27 Sun Street, Biggleswade, Bedfordshire, SG18 0BP Tel: (01767) 601102 Fax: (01767) 312106 E-mail: runrigintlltd@btinternet.com
Zoomlion Powermole Ltd, 35 Church Road Business Centre, Church Road, Sittingbourne, Kent, ME10 3RS Tel: (01795) 425425 Fax: (01795) 477177 E-mail: allen.kayes@zlpm.com

EARTH BORING SERVICES, *See Earth Boring etc*

EARTH MOVING CONTRACTORS

▶ Alf Kitching & Sons Ltd, Double Rivers, Crowle, Scunthorpe, South Humberside, DN17 4DD Tel: (01724) 710286 Fax: (01724) 710477
Barton Plant Ltd, Cranford Road, Burton Latimer, Kettering, Northamptonshire, NN15 5TB Tel: (01536) 722100 Fax: (01536) 722714 E-mail: enquiries@barton-plant.co.uk
C.A. Blackwell (Contracts) Ltd, Coggeshall Road, Earls Colne, Colchester, CO6 2JX Tel: (01787) 223131 Fax: (01787) 224391 E-mail: enquires@cablackwell.co.uk
John Doyle Construction Ltd, John Doyle House, 2-3 Little Burrow, Welwyn Garden City, Hertfordshire, AL7 4SP Tel: (01707) 329481 Fax: (01707) 328213 E-mail: admin@john-doyle.co.uk
Fenton Hadley Contracts Ltd, Arrowhead Road, Theale, Reading, RG7 4AE Tel: 0118-988 3266 Fax: 0118-988 4538 E-mail: waste@hadley.co.uk
Hewden Plant Hire Ltd, Bryn Works, Llandygai, Bangor, Gwynedd, LL57 4LE Tel: (01248) 364944 Fax: (01248) 370462
▶ M D Clarke (Contractors) Ltd, Midland House, Brent, Ninian Way, Tame Valley Industrial Estate, Tamworth, Staffordshire, B77 5DF Tel: (01827) 282323
Midland Earthmoving Co. Ltd, Gibbs Road, Lye, Stourbridge, West Midlands, DY9 8SY Tel: (01384) 894488 Fax: (01384) 894489
Chris Moore Transport Co. Ltd, Mill Court Barns, Binsted, Alton, Hampshire, GU34 4JF Tel: (01420) 23555 E-mail: chris_moore2000@hotmail.com
R W Almond & Co. Ltd, Heysham Road, Bootle, Merseyside, L30 6UA Tel: 0151-521 5454 Fax: 0151-525 0115 E-mail: sales@rwalmond.co.uk
▶ Rosedene Construction Ltd, Tripes Farm Yard Chelsfield Lane, Orpington, Kent, BR6 7RS Tel: (01689) 835807 Fax: (01689) 835807 E-mail: joan.rosedene@btopenworld.com
Volvo Construction Equipment Ltd, Portobello Road, Birtley, Chester le Street, County Durham, DH3 2RR Tel: 0191-410 9863 Fax: 0191-410 7617
W Hayden & Son Ltd, Webb Street, Bilston, West Midlands, WV14 8XL Tel: (01902) 402341 Fax: (01902) 491832
▶ Weldon Plant Ltd, Lammas Road, Weldon North, Corby, Northamptonshire, NN17 5JF Tel: (01536) 260833 Fax: (01536) 261880 E-mail: sales@weldonplant.co.uk
Wheel Masters, Tufthorn Industrial Estate, Stepbridge Road, Coleford, Gloucestershire, GL16 8PJ Tel: (01594) 835678 Fax: (01594) 835789 E-mail: sales@wheelsuk.co.uk

EARTH MOVING EQUIPMENT

Con Mech Group Ltd, Cleary Court, Church Street East, Woking, Surrey, GU21 6HJ Tel: (01483) 714024 Fax: (01483) 714343
▶ D Kerr & Sons, Helenslea, Castlecary Road, Cumbernauld, Glasgow, G68 0HQ Tel: (01324) 840337 Fax: (01324) 840885
E C Hallam Engineering Leicester Ltd, Beaufield Smeeton Road, Kibworth, Leicester, LE8 0LG Tel: 0116-279 2330 E-mail: carey@hallam-eng.freeserve.co.uk
Falling Leaf, 1 Lodge Bank, Crown Lane, Horwich, Bolton, BL6 5HY Tel: (01204) 696621 Fax: (01204) 667559 E-mail: sales@bigbuckets.com
▶ G & W Plant Hire, Mill Lane, Coxley, Wells, Somerset, BA5 1QU Tel: (01749) 671393 Fax: (01749) 671394
J C B Landpower Ltd, Lakeside Works, Denstone Road, Rocester, Uttoxeter, Staffordshire, ST14 5JP Tel: (01889) 590312 Fax: (01889) 590588 E-mail: enq@jcbinfo.co.uk
Komatsu UK Ltd, Durham Road, Birtley, Chester le Street, County Durham, DH3 2QX Tel: 0191-410 3155 Fax: 0191-410 8156 E-mail: enquiries@komatsuuk.com
Liebherr Crane Hire, Stratton Business Park, Biggleswade, Bedfordshire, SG18 8QB Tel: (01767) 602100 Fax: (01767) 602110 E-mail: info.lgb@liebherr.com
▶ McGarvey Construction, 86 Clark Street, Paisley, Renfrewshire, PA3 1RB Tel: 0141-848 7555
Marubeni Komatsu Ltd, Church Farm, Gransden Road, Papworth Everard, Cambridge, CB23 3PL Tel: (01954) 719755 Fax: (01954) 719639 E-mail: sales@marubeni-komatsu.co.uk
New Ventures Products, Queens Yard, Long Wittenham Road, North Moreton, Didcot, Oxfordshire, OX11 9AX Tel: (0845) 4304030 Fax: (0845) 130 5833 E-mail: sales@newventureproducts.co.uk
Northern Track Ltd, Gerrard Road, Leeds, LS11 5JD Tel: 0113-276 2300
Strickland Direct Ltd, 5 Main Road, Cropthorne, Pershore, Worcestershire, WR10 3NE Tel: (01386) 860349 Fax: (01386) 860057
Terex Equipment Ltd, Newhouse Industrial Estate, Motherwell, Lanarkshire, ML1 5RY Tel: (01698) 732121 Fax: (01698) 734046
Thwaites Ltd, Welsh Road Works, Leamington Spa, Warwickshire, CV32 7NQ Tel: (01926) 422471 Fax: (01926) 337155 E-mail: name@thwaitesdumpers.co.uk

EARTH MOVING EQUIPMENT SPARE PARTS OR WEARING PARTS

Barbrak Ltd, 5 Eden Court, Eden Way, Leighton Buzzard, Bedfordshire, LU7 4FY Tel: (01525) 376605 Fax: (01525) 370505 E-mail: chris@barbrak.co.uk
Claron Hydraulic Seals Ltd, Station Road, Cradley Heath, West Midlands, B64 6PN Tel: 0121-559 9711 Fax: 0121-559 1036 E-mail: sales@claron-seals.co.uk
Con Mech Group Ltd, Cleary Court, Church Street East, Woking, Surrey, GU21 6HJ Tel: (01483) 714024 Fax: (01483) 714343
Falling Leaf, 1 Lodge Bank, Crown Lane, Horwich, Bolton, BL6 5HY Tel: (01204) 696621 Fax: (01204) 667559 E-mail: sales@bigbuckets.com
Hydrema Plant & Machinery Dealer, Barker Business Park, Melmerby Green Lane, Melmerby, Ripon, North Yorkshire, HG4 5NB Tel: (01765) 641940 Fax: (01765) 641942 E-mail: twa@hydrema.com
Interpart (U K) Ltd, 2 Warsall Road, Wythenshawe, Manchester, M22 4RH Tel: 0161-998 9911 Fax: 0161-946 0131 E-mail: info@interpart.co.uk
S R Equipment, 33-35 Dawf Lane, London, NW7 4SD Tel: (020) 8906 6600 Fax: (020) 8906 6611 E-mail: admin@sreq.com
Strickland Direct Ltd, 5 Main Road, Cropthorne, Pershore, Worcestershire, WR10 3NE Tel: (01386) 860349 Fax: (01386) 860057 E-mail: sales@stricklanduk.com
W M Arnold Boroughbridge Ltd, Station Yard, Boroughbridge, York, YO51 9BL Tel: (01423) 322871 Fax: (01423) 324380 E-mail: sales@wmarnold.demon.co.uk

EARTH OR LAND SITE ANCHORS

Dywidag Systems International Ltd, Northfield Road, Kineton Road Industrial Estate, Southam, Warwickshire, CV47 0FG Tel: (01926) 813980 Fax: (01926) 813817 E-mail: sales@dywidag.co.uk
▶ UK Land Solutions, Field House, 7 Victoria Avenue,, Westgate-on-Sea, Kent, CT8 8BG Tel: (01843) 834938

EARTH TEST EQUIPMENT

W.J. Furse Ltd, Wilford Road, Nottingham, NG2 1EB Tel: 0115-964 3800 Fax: 0115-986 0538 E-mail: sales@furse.com

EARTH TUNNELLING MOLES

Essig Products Ltd, 4 Courtyard 3, Wentworth Road, Mapplewell, Barnsley, South Yorkshire, S75 6DT Tel: (01226) 383384 Fax: (01226) 390880 E-mail: sales@essig.co.uk
T T UK Ltd, Windsor Road, Bedford, MK42 9SU Tel: (01234) 342566 Fax: (01234) 352184 E-mail: info@tt-uk.com

EARTHENWARE OR POTTERY LAMP BASES

▶ Emma Bridgewater Ltd, Eastwood Pottery, Lichfield Street, Stoke-on-Trent, ST1 3EJ Tel: (01782) 201200 Fax: (01782) 271508

EARTHENWARE TABLEWARE, *See Chinaware etc*

EARTHING BARS

S M G Control Systems, 9 Smestow Bridge, Bridgnorth Road, Wombourne, Wolverhampton, WV5 8AY Tel: (01902) 326886 Fax: (01902) 326883 E-mail: smg@smgcontrolsystems.co.uk

EARTHING CLIPS

W.J. Furse Ltd, Wilford Road, Nottingham, NG2 1EB Tel: 0115-964 3800 Fax: 0115-986 0538 E-mail: sales@furse.com

EARTHING RODS

Britannia Lightning Prevectron Ltd, Longue Drive, Calverton, Nottingham, NG14 6QF Tel: 0115-847 7113 Fax: 0115-847 5185 E-mail: sales@lightninguk.fsnet.co.uk
HVR International Ltd, Bede Trading Estate, Jarrow, Tyne & Wear, NE32 3EN Tel: 0191-489 7771 Fax: 0191-483 9501 E-mail: info@hvrint.com
T N Robinson Ltd, 5 Priestley Business Centre, Priestley Street, Warrington, WA5 1TF Tel: (01925) 650501 Fax: (01925) 418614 E-mail: sales@tnr.com

ECOLOGICAL SURVEYS

▶ A D K Environmental Management, 2 Foldside, Freckleton, Preston, PR4 1JX Tel: (01772) 493215 Fax: (01772) 467094 E-mail: adk@adk-environmental.co.uk
▶ Mab Environment & Ecology Ltd, The Old Chapel, Knayton, Thirsk, North Yorkshire, YO7 4AZ Tel: (01845) 537845 E-mail: Giles@mab.uk.com

ECONOMIC CONSULTANCY

A C Nielsen Ltd, Nielsen House, London Road, Headington, Oxford, OX3 9RX Tel: (01865) 742742 Fax: (01865) 742222 E-mail: graham.northfield@acnielsen.co.uk
Dr Barry Bracewell-Milnes, 26 Lancaster Court, Banstead, Surrey, SM7 1RR Tel: (01737) 350736 Fax: (01737) 371415
The Building Centre Bookshop, 26 Store Street, London, WC1E 7BT Tel: (020) 7692 4040 Fax: (020) 7636 3628 E-mail: agagliano@buildingcentre.co.uk
Business Strategies Ltd, Nightingale House, 65 Curzon Street, London, W1J 8PE Tel: (0870) 1968201 Fax: (0870) 1968200 E-mail: business-strategies@uk.experian.com
Cambridgeshire Chamber Of Commerce, 5 The Forum, Minerva Business Park, Lynch Wood, Peterborough, PE2 6FT Tel: (01733) 393330 Fax: (01733) 393335 E-mail: emquiries@cambscci.co.uk
Campbell Lee Computer Services Ltd, Unit G1 Exploration House, Exploration Drive, Bridge Of Don, Aberdeen, AB23 8GX Tel: (01224) 355435 Fax: (01224) 677201 E-mail: info@campbell-lee.co.uk
Castings Technology International, Waverley Advance Manufacturing Park, Brunel Way, Rotherham, South Yorkshire, S60 5WG Tel: 0114-272 8647 Fax: 0114-273 0852 E-mail: info@castingstechnology.com
Centre for Economics & Business Research Ltd, Unit 1, 4 Bath Street, London, EC1V 9DX Tel: (020) 7324 2850 Fax: (020) 7324 2855 E-mail: enquiries@cebr.com
Chown Dewhurst L L P, 51 Lafone Street, London, SE1 2LX Tel: (020) 7403 0787 Fax: (020) 7403 6693 E-mail: info@chowndewhurst.com
D T Z Pieda Consulting, 1 Edinburgh Quay, 133 Fountainbridge, Edinburgh, EH3 9QG Tel: 0131-222 4500 Fax: 0131-222 4501
▶ First Economics Ltd, 48 Westway Gardens, Redhill, RH1 2JB Tel: (020) 7537 3605 E-mail: info@first-economics.com
The Henley Centre, 9 Bridewell Place, Bridewell Gate, London, EC4V 6AW Tel: (020) 7955 1800 Fax: (020) 7353 2899 E-mail: future@henleycentre.com
I H S Global Insight, Wimbledon Bridge House, 1 Hartfield Road, London, SW19 3RU Tel: (020) 8544 7800 Fax: (020) 8544 7801 E-mail: receptionist.london@globalinsight.com
I-DocumentSystems Ltd, Tontine House, 8 Gordon Street, Glasgow, G1 3PL Tel: 0141-574 1900 Fax: 0141-574 1901 E-mail: ruth.rintoul@idoxplc.com
Logistech Ltd, Exchange House, 494 Midsummer Boulevard, Milton Keynes, MK9 2EA Tel: (01908) 255985 E-mail: info@logistech.co.uk
Maxwell Stamp Group plc, Abbots Court, 34 Farringdon Lane, London, EC1R 3AX Tel: (020) 7251 0147 Fax: (020) 7251 0140 E-mail: london@maxwellstamp.com
One North East, Stella House, Goldcrest Way, Newcastle upon Tyne, NE15 8NY Tel: (0870) 1601781 Fax: 0191-229 6201 E-mail: enquiries@onenortheast.co.uk
▶ Reckon LLP, 20 Theobalds Road, London, WC1X 8PF Tel: (020) 7841 5850 Fax: (020) 7841 5850 E-mail: feedback@reckon.co.uk
S Q W Ltd, Enterprise House, Vision Park, Histon, Cambridge, CB4 9ZR Tel: (01223) 209400 Fax: (01223) 209401 E-mail: mailbox@sqw.co.uk
Scottish Enterprise, 3 Greenmarket, Dundee, DD1 4QB Tel: (01382) 223100 Fax: (01382) 305576 E-mail: set.reception@scotent.co.uk
Scottish Enterprise Renfrewshire, 25 Causeyside Street, Paisley, Renfrewshire, PA1 1UL Tel: 0141-848 0101 Fax: 0141-848 6930 E-mail: network.helpline@scotent.co.uk

ECONOMIC DEVELOPMENT AGENCIES

Highlands & Islands Enterprise, Cowan House, Highlander Way, Inverness Business & Retail Pa, Inverness, IV2 7GF Tel: (01463) 234171 Fax: (01463) 244469 E-mail: hie.general@hient.co.uk
Preston City Council, Premier House, Church Street, Preston, PR1 3BQ Tel: (01772) 563957 Fax: (01772) 558524
Scottish Enterprise Network, 150 Broomielew, Atlantic Quay, Glasgow, G2 8LU Tel: 0141-248 2700 Fax: 0141-221 3217 E-mail: network.helpline@scotent.co.uk

EDDY CURRENT EQUIPMENT/ SYSTEMS MANUFRS

Fischer Instrumentation (GB) Ltd, Department K, Gordleton Industrial Park, Hannah Way, Pennington, Lymington, Hampshire, SO41 8JD Tel: (01590) 684100 Fax: (01590) 684110 E-mail: mail@fischergb.co.uk
Foerster UK Ltd, 2 Bonehill Mews, Fazeley, Tamworth, Staffordshire, B78 3QU Tel: (01827) 831290 Fax: (01827) 284982 E-mail: sales@foersteruk.com
G E Inspection Technologies, Inspec Ho, 129-135 Camp Rd, St. Albans, Herts, AL1 5HL Tel: (01727) 795500 Fax: (01727) 795400

EDGE BANDING

Hallmark Fraulo Ltd, Units 55-56, Hillgrove Business Park, Nazeing Road, Nazeing, Waltham Abbey, Essex, EN9 2HB Tel: (01992) 899025 Fax: (01992) 899026 E-mail: info@hallmarkfraulo.co.uk

EDGE DRESSING SERVICES

Stafford Stainless Steels, Meaford Power Station, Meaford, Stone, Staffordshire, ST15 0UU Tel: (01782) 796868 Fax: (01782) 374410 E-mail: sales@stainless.st

EDGE DRESSING, STAINLESS STEEL STRIP

▶ Colter Steels Ltd, Unit 10 Owen Road Industrial Estate, Willenhall, West Midlands, WV13 2PY Tel: 0121-526 6066 Fax: 0121-526 3044 E-mail: sales@coltersteels.co.uk
▶ Firebird Metals Ltd, 1 Canal Street, Sheffield, S4 7ZE Tel: (0870) 7622333 Fax: (0870) 7622334 E-mail: neil@firebirdmetals.com

EDGE GLUED TIMBER BOARD

▶ Panel Supplies, Harvey Road, Basildon, Essex, SS13 1ES Tel: (01268) 729100 Fax: (01268) 729700 E-mail: jonhaak@panelsupplies.co.uk

EDGE PROTECTORS

Celltex Fabrications Ltd, Unit 9a Barnfield Trading Estate, Ramsey Road, Tipton, West Midlands, DY4 9DU Tel: 0121-520 3443 Fax: 0121-520 1772 E-mail: sales@celltex.co.uk

EDGE TOOLS

Bullock Bros Edge Tools Ltd, Landywood Lane, Cheslyn Hay, Walsall, WS6 7AL Tel: (01922) 414360 Fax: (01922) 410359 E-mail: sales@bullocktools.co.uk

EDGE TRIMS, METAL

Universal Flooring Accessories Ltd, Interserve House, Ruscombe Park, Twyford, Reading, RG10 9JU Tel: 0870 770 4330 Fax: 0118 934 3667 E-mail: info@uniflooring.co.uk

EDGEBANDING MACHINES

Avontech Machines, Park Yard, Old Down, Tockington, Bristol, BS32 4PB Tel: (0845) 070 4343 Fax: (0845) 070 4346 E-mail: avontech@blueyonder.co.uk

EDIBLE CAKE DECORATIONS

▶ Alice's Cake Store, C/o Latteridge House, Latteridge Green, Iron Acton, Bristol, BS37 9TS Tel: (0870) 1995481
Confectionery Supplies, 31 Lower Cathedral Road, Cardiff, CF11 6LU Tel: (029) 2037 2161 Fax: (029) 2039 6632
Culpitt Ltd, Jubilee Industrial Estate, Ashington, Northumberland, NE63 8UQ Tel: (01670) 814545 Fax: (01670) 815248 E-mail: reception@culpitt.com
Sugar Shack, 87 Burnt Oak Broadway, Edgware, Middlesex, HA8 5EP Tel: (0800) 5975097 Fax: (020) 8951 4888 E-mail: sales@sugarshack.co.uk
▶ Wendy's Cakes, 285 Sheldon Heath Road, Birmingham, B26 2TY Tel: 0121-243 7341 E-mail: wendyscakes@yahoo.co.uk

EDIBLE GUM

C P Kelco UK Ltd, Cleeve Court, Cleeve Road, Leatherhead, Surrey, KT22 7UD Tel: (01372) 369400 Fax: (01372) 369401

EDIBLE OIL/FAT PRODUCTION MACHINERY

Chemtech International Ltd, 448 Basingstoke Road, Reading, RG2 0LP Tel: 0118-986 1222 Fax: 0118-986 0028 E-mail: sales@chemtechinternational.com

De Smet Rosedowns Ltd, Cannon Street, Hull, HU2 0AD Tel: (01482) 329864 Fax: (01482) 325887 E-mail: info@rosedowns.co.uk

Signs 2000, Unit 4 Kenworth Road, Stafford, ST16 3DY Tel: (01785) 220561 Fax: (01785) 220969 E-mail: admin@signs2k.co.uk

EDIBLE OIL/FAT WASTE RECYCLING/MERCHANTS OR PROCESSORS

▶ M & B Edible Oil, 2 Cannon Road, Heathfield, Newton Abbot, Devon, TQ12 6SH Tel: (01626) 836280 Fax: (01626) 836280 E-mail: mboils@btconnect.com

EDIBLE OILS/FATS

ADM Pura Foods Ltd, Erith Oil Works, Church Manorway, Erith, Kent, DA8 1DL Tel: (01322) 443000 Fax: (01322) 443027

Broadland Foods Ltd, Great Barr Street, Birmingham, B9 4BB Tel: 0121-773 5955 Fax: 0121-771 1207 E-mail: broadland@chobby.fsnet.co.uk

Cardowan Creameries Ltd, 49 Holywell Street, Glasgow, G31 4BT Tel: 0141-554 1137 Fax: 0141-551 0619

Henry Colbeck Ltd, Seventh Avenue, Team Valley Trading Estate, Gateshead, Tyne & Wear, NE11 0HG Tel: 0191-482 4242 Fax: 0191-491 0357 E-mail: sales@colbeck.co.uk

Edible Oils Ltd, Crabtree Manorway South, Belvedere, Kent, DA17 6BB Tel: (020) 8311 7171 Fax: (020) 8310 7505 E-mail: name@edible-oils.co.uk

Edicos Ltd, Unit 8-9 Cromwell Industrial Estate, Staffa Road, London, E10 7QZ Tel: (020) 8539 6102 Fax: (020) 8539 8061

G T Products Ltd, 3-4 Loomer Road, Newcastle, Staffordshire, ST5 7LB Tel: (01782) 562056 Fax: (01782) 564757 E-mail: sales@gtproducts.co.uk

William Hodgson & Co., 73A London Road, Alderley Edge, Cheshire, SK9 7DY Tel: (01625) 599111 Fax: (01625) 599222

Holland UK Ltd, 12 Conway Units, Stephenson Road, Clacton-on-Sea, Essex, CO15 4XA Tel: (01255) 431773 Fax: (01255) 221393 E-mail: sales@hollanduk.co.uk

J L Owen Ltd, 13 Blossom Street, Manchester, M4 5AF Tel: 0161-236 0507 Fax: 0161-236 7831

Kassero Edible Oils Ltd, 6-8 Albert Road, St. Philips, Bristol, BS2 0XA Tel: 0117-971 4331 Fax: 0117-972 4183 E-mail: sales@kassero.co.uk

▶ M & B Edible Oil, 2 Cannon Road, Heathfield, Newton Abbot, Devon, TQ12 6SH Tel: (01626) 836280 Fax: (01626) 836280 E-mail: mboils@btconnect.com

Microcide Ltd, Shepherd's Grove, Stanton, Bury St. Edmunds, Suffolk, IP31 2AR Tel: (01359) 251077 Fax: (01359) 251545 E-mail: microcide@microcide.co.uk

Mid Ulster Proteins Ltd, 47 Seagoe Industrial Estate, Craigavon, County Armagh, BT63 5QD Tel: (028) 3833 7217 Fax: (028) 3833 6114 E-mail: atrfood@btinternet.com

S O P Edibles Ltd, 7 Aston Fields Road, Whitehouse Industrial Estate, Runcorn, Cheshire, WA7 3DL Tel: (01928) 712822 Fax: (01928) 719593 E-mail: sopinternational@btconnect.com

Smilde Food Group Ltd, PO Box 27, Crowborough, East Sussex, TN6 3DZ Tel: (01892) 669616 Fax: (01892) 669617 E-mail: bobwilliams@smildefood.uk.com

United Fish Products Ltd, Greenwell Place, East Tullos Industrial Estate, Aberdeen, AB12 3AY Tel: (01224) 854444 Fax: (01224) 854333

V A Whitley & Co. Ltd, Milward House, Fir Street, Heywood, Lancashire, OL10 1NW Tel: (01706) 364211 Fax: (01706) 366828 E-mail: mine@vawhitley.co.uk

EDIBLE WHITE OIL, *See Edible Oils etc*

EDITORIAL SERVICES, *See Publishers etc; also Technical etc*

EDUCATIONAL AIDS/ EQUIPMENT

BBC Childrens Learning, P O Box 234, Wetherby, West Yorkshire, LS23 7EU Tel: (0870) 8308000 Fax: (0870) 8308002

C Y Education, 33 Foy Lane, Portadown, Craigavon, County Armagh, BT62 1PY Tel: (028) 3833 4916 Fax: (028) 3833 4916

Classroom Video, Northavon Business Centre, Dean Road, Yate, Bristol, BS37 5NH Tel: (01454) 324222 Fax: (01454) 325222 E-mail: sales@classroomvideo.co.uk

Cochranes of Oxford Ltd, Grove Farm Barns, High Street, Shipton-under-Wychwood, Chipping Norton, Oxfordshire, OX7 6DG Tel: (01993) 832868 Fax: (01993) 832578 E-mail: cochranes@mailbox.co.uk

Coningsby International, 22 School Lane, Coningsby, Lincoln, LN4 4WX Tel: (01526) 342231 Fax: (01526) 344367 E-mail: info@coningsby.com

The Countryside Centre, Chapel Lane, Ullenhall, Henley-In-Arden, West Midlands, B95 5RT Tel: (01564) 793244

Cuisenaire Co., Unit 5, Feidr Castell, Fishguard, Dyfed, SA65 9BB Tel: (0845) 6122912 Fax: (0845) 6123912 E-mail: cuisenaire@cuisenaire.co.uk

Cybernetic Applications Ltd, West Portway Industrial Estate, Andover, Hampshire, SP10 3LF Tel: (01264) 350093 Fax: (01264) 333771

Denford Ltd, Birds Royd, Brighouse, Brighouse, West Yorkshire, HD6 1NB Tel: (01484) 712264 Fax: (01484) 722160 E-mail: sales@denford.co.uk

Drake Educational Associates Ltd, 89 St. Fagans Road, Fairwater, Cardiff, CF5 3AE Tel: (029) 2056 0333 Fax: (029) 2055 4909 E-mail: info@drakeav.com

Eagle Scientific Ltd, Regent House, Lenton Street, Sandiacre, Nottingham, NG10 5DJ Tel: 0115-949 1111 Fax: 0115-939 1144 E-mail: equip@eagle-scientific.co.uk

Easylearn, Trent House, Rolleston Road, Fiskerton, Southwell, Nottinghamshire, NG25 0UH Tel: (01636) 830240 Fax: (01636) 830162 E-mail: enquiry@easylearn.co.uk

Educational Aids (London) Ltd, 25 Bradfield Close, Finedon Road Industrial Estate, Wellingborough, Northamptonshire, NN8 4RQ Tel: (01933) 274434 Fax: (01933) 274313 E-mail: edaids@aol.com

Educational & Scientific Products Ltd, Unit A2 Dominion Way, Rustington, Littlehampton, West Sussex, BN16 3HQ Tel: (01903) 773340 Fax: (01903) 771108 E-mail: sales@espmodels.co.uk

Educational Technology Ltd, Locomotion Way, Camperdown Industrial Estate, Newcastle upon Tyne, NE12 5US Tel: 0191-268 2222 Fax: 0191-268 1137 E-mail: sales@edtech.co.uk

Escor Toys, Elliott Road, Bournemouth, BH11 8JP Tel: (01202) 591081 Fax: (01202) 570049 E-mail: escortoys@bournemouth.gov.uk

Feedback Instruments Ltd, Park Road, Crowborough, East Sussex, TN6 2QR Tel: (01892) 653322 Fax: (01892) 663719 E-mail: feedback@fdbk.co.uk

Findel Education Ltd, Gazelle Road, Weston-super-Mare, Avon, BS24 9BJ Tel: (01934) 413606 Fax: (01934) 626421

Formative Fun, 5 Charles Street, Worcester, WR1 2AQ Tel: (01905) 22353 Fax: (01905) 22353 E-mail: worcester@formativefun.com

Fun Junction, 29 County Place, Perth, PH2 8EE Tel: (01738) 444222 Fax: (01738) 450481 E-mail: perth@funjunctiononline.com

G W Chadwick Ltd, Unit 40 Chorley North Industrial Park, Chorley, Lancashire, PR6 7BX Tel: (01257) 234242 Fax: (01257) 234213 E-mail: email@gwchadwick.co.uk

Esmond Hellerman Ltd, Hellerman House, Harris Way, Sunbury-on-Thames, Middlesex, TW16 7EW Tel: (01932) 781888 Fax: (01932) 789573 E-mail: sales@hellermans.com

▶ Institute For Outdoor Learning, Plumpton, Penrith, Cumbria, CA11 9NP Tel: (01768) 885800 Fax: (01768) 885801 E-mail: institute@outdoor-learning.org

Invicta Toys & Games Ltd, PO Box 9, Leicester, LE2 4LB Tel: 0116-272 0555 Fax: 0116-272 0626 E-mail: sales@invictagroup.co.uk

▶ Johnsons Innovations Ltd, 14 Vale Walk, Woodhill, Bishopbriggs, Glasgow, G64 1LG Tel: 0141 5636475 E-mail: support@disc2drive.com

L D A, Abbeygate House, East Road, Cambridge, CB1 1DB Tel: (01223) 357744 Fax: (01223) 460557

Learning & Teaching Scotland, 58 Robertson Street, Glasgow, G2 8DU Tel: 0141-282 5000 Fax: 0141-282 5050 E-mail: equiries@ltscotland.org.uk

Limrose Group Ltd, Aerial Road, Llay Industrial Estate, Llay, Wrexham, Clwyd, LL12 0TU Tel: (01978) 855555 Fax: (01978) 855556 E-mail: limrose@aol.com

Mill House Manufacturing Design Ltd, Roughton Road, Kirkby-on-Bain, Woodhall Spa, Lincolnshire, LN10 6YL Tel: (01526) 354404 Fax: (01526) 354424 E-mail: sales@millhouse-md.co.uk

Paton Hawksley Education Ltd, 59 Wellsway, Keynsham, Bristol, BS31 1PG Tel: 0117-986 2364 Fax: 0117-986 8285

Philip & Tacey Ltd, North Way, Andover, Hampshire, SP10 5BA Tel: (01264) 332171 Fax: (01264) 384808 E-mail: export@philipandtacey.co.uk

Rainbow Crafts Fife, Crosshill Centre, Main Street, Crosshill, Lochgelly, Fife, KY5 8BJ Tel: (01592) 860444 Fax: (01592) 861527

S T E UK Ltd, Staple Hurst Road, Sittingbourne, Kent, ME10 2NH Tel: (01795) 474700 Fax: (01795) 438901E-mail: info@steuk.co.uk

St Josephs Workshop Ltd, 190-194 Bag Lane, Atherton, Manchester, M46 0JZ Tel: (01942) 883210 Fax: (01942) 878087

Seamstress Playchutes Ltd, 23 Banbury Road, Byfield, Daventry, Northamptonshire, NN11 6XJ Tel: (01327) 263933 Fax: (01327) 263933 E-mail: sales@playchutes.com

Sound Vision (UK) Ltd, 86 Kingsley Road, Hounslow, TW3 1QA Tel: (020) 8570 1999 Fax: (020) 8577 3033

Storysacks Support Project, Pinehurst Infant School, Beech Av, Swindon, SN2 1JT Tel: 01793 421168 Fax: 01793 421168

Super Stickers, PO Box 55, Bangor, County Down, BT19 7PJ Tel: (028) 9145 4344 Fax: (028) 9146 6474 E-mail: info@motivationinlearning.co.uk

T Q Education & Training Ltd, Bonsall Street, Long Eaton, Nottingham, NG10 2AN Tel: 0115-972 2611 Fax: 0115-973 1520 E-mail: info@tq.com

Taskmaster Ltd, Morris Road, Leicester, LE2 6BR Tel: 0116-270 4286 Fax: 0116-270 6992 E-mail: info@taskmasteronline.co.uk

Technician Service Centre, Main Street, Chapelhall, Airdrie, Lanarkshire, ML6 8SF Tel: (01236) 756552 Fax: (01236) 756542 E-mail: techcentre@ea.n-lanark.sch.uk

Three Bears Playthings, Steward House, Rothbury, Morpeth, Northumberland, NE65 7TL Tel: (01669) 620315 Fax: (01669) 621900 E-mail: wwwthreebearsplay@aol.com

Time Medical & Scientific Network, Unit 6, North End Industrial Estate, Bury Mead Road, Hitchin, Hertfordshire, SG5 1RT Tel: (01462) 422112 Fax: (01462) 422042 E-mail: sales@timemedical.co.uk

▶ Tracline UK Ltd, Bennett House, 1 High Street, Edgware, Middlesex, HA8 7TA Tel: (020) 8952 7770 Fax: (020) 8951 5149 E-mail: sales@tracline.co.uk

Wesco, 114 Highfields Road, Witham, Essex, CM8 2HH Tel: (01376) 503590 Fax: (01376) 514236 E-mail: sales@wesco-uk.com

Wilson & Garden Ltd, 2 Carrington Road, Spalding, Lincolnshire, PE11 1LY Tel: (01775) 712332 Fax: (01775) 712332

Witzig's Ltd, Unit 5, George Edwards Road Industrial Estate, Fakenham, Norfolk, NR21 8NL Tel: (01328) 864941 Fax: (01328) 864943 E-mail: info@witzigs.co.uk

EDUCATIONAL BOOKS

▶ Terry Allen Education, Lower Bramblewood, Mill Hill Lane, Brockham, Betchworth, Surrey, RH3 7LR Tel: (01737) 843212 Fax: (01737) 843212 E-mail: contacts@terryalleneducation.co.uk

▶ Artworkshops, 43 Broomleaf Road, Farnham, Surrey, GU9 8DQ Tel: 01252 714221

▶ In2Scuba Dive School, 27 Poyntell Road, Staplehurst, Tonbridge, Kent, TN12 0SA Tel: (01580) 891711 E-mail: steve@in2scuba.co.uk

▶ Passionet Ltd, 537 Norwood Road, Entrance 1 Chestnut Road, West Norwood, London, SE27 9DL Tel: 0845 330 9498 Fax: 020 8761 1469 E-mail: info@passionet.net

EDUCATIONAL CONTRACTORS, *See Educational Supplies etc*

EDUCATIONAL ELECTRONIC EQUIPMENT

Abitec Products, Oak House, 50 Barton Drive, New Milton, Hampshire, BH25 7JJ Tel: (01425) 617852 Fax: (01425) 617852 E-mail: sales@abitec.co.uk

Cambridge Microprocessor Systems Ltd, 17-18 Zone D, Chelmsford Road Industrial Estate, Great Dunmow, Dunmow, Essex, CM6 1XG Tel: (01371) 875644 Fax: (01371) 876077 E-mail: info@cms.uk.com

Deltronics Electronic Engineers, Unit 15 Church Road Industrial Estate, Gorslas, Llanelli, Dyfed, SA14 7NN Tel: (01269) 843728 Fax: (01269) 845527 E-mail: sales@deltronics.co.uk

EDUCATIONAL EQUIPMENT TURNKEY/PROJECTS

Pendax UK Ltd, 57 Sutton Park Avenue, Earley, Reading, RG6 1AZ Tel: 0118-966 8383 Fax: 0118-966 8895 E-mail: sales@pendax.co.uk

EDUCATIONAL FURNITURE

▶ Active Learning Ltd, Hartley Business Centre, 28 Hucknall Road, Nottingham, NG5 1FD Tel: 0115-960 6111 Fax: 0115-960 6111 E-mail: sales@activelearning-uk.com

Ambic Ltd, 41-44 Stella Gill Industrial, Estate Pelton Fell, Pelton Fell, Chester le Street, County Durham, DH2 2RH Tel: 0191-389 1888 Fax: 0191-389 1999 E-mail: enquiries@ambic.ltd.uk

Armare School Furniture & Equipment, 3 Peartree Industrial Estate, Bath Road, Langford, Bristol, BS40 5DJ Tel: (01934) 853808 Fax: (01934) 853141

Associated Joinery Techniques Ltd, Marks Hall, Marks Hall Lane, Margaret Roding, Dunmow, Essex, CM6 1QT Tel: (01245) 231881 Fax: (01245) 231818 E-mail: ajt.ltd@btinternet.com

Atkinson Vari-Tech Ltd, Unit 4, Sett End Road, Shadsworth, Blackburn, BB1 2PT Tel: (01254) 678777 Fax: (01254) 678782 E-mail: sales@vari-tech.co.uk

Budget Paper Supplies Ltd, Arborfield Mill, Helpston, Peterborough, PE6 7DH Tel: (01733) 252868 Fax: (01733) 253555 E-mail: enquiries@budget-paper.co.uk

Crossbrook Furniture Ltd, 8 Marshgate Industrial Estate, 20 Marshgate Drive, Hertford, SG13 7AJ Tel: (01992) 557000 Fax: (01992) 501666 E-mail: sales@crossbrook.co.uk

Diamik Solutions Ltd, A W Nielsen Road, Goole, North Humberside, DN14 6UE Tel: (0845) 1300690 Fax: (0845) 1300691 E-mail: sales@diamikbymorris.co.uk

E J Herok Ltd, Charlton Mead Lane, Hoddesdon, Hertfordshire, EN11 0DJ Tel: (01992) 462943 Fax: (01992) 464792 E-mail: info@herok.com

▶ The Education Furniture Co. Ltd, Education House, 22A Cobbet Road, Burntwood, Staffordshire, WS7 3GL Tel: (01543) 495086 Fax: (01543) 495089

Educational Aids (London) Ltd, 25 Bradfield Close, Finedon Road Industrial Estate, Wellingborough, Northamptonshire, NN8 4RQ Tel: (01933) 274434 Fax: (01933) 274313 E-mail: edaids@aol.com

Educational Furniture Manufacturers, Pottery Lane West, Chesterfield, Derbyshire, S41 9BN Tel: (01246) 455191 Fax: (01246) 456506 E-mail: sales@efmchesterfield.co.uk

Educational & Municipal Equipment Scotland, Blackaddie Road, Sanquhar, Dumfriesshire, DG4 6DE Tel: (01659) 50404 Fax: (01659) 50107 E-mail: sales@emescotland.co.uk

Emmerich (Berlon) Ltd, Kingsnorth Industrial Estate, Wotton Road, Ashford, Kent, TN23 6JY Tel: (01233) 622684 Fax: (01233) 645801 E-mail: emmerick@emir.co.uk

Esa Mcintosh Ltd, Mitchelston Drive, Mitchelston Industrial Estate, Kirkcaldy, Fife, KY1 3LX Tel: (01592) 656200 Fax: (01592) 656299 E-mail: sales@esamcintosh.co.uk

▶ Exclusive, Unit 20, Butts Pond Industrial Estate, Sturminster Newton, Dorset, DT10 1AZ Tel: (01258) 472001 Fax: (01258) 473884 E-mail: sales@exclusive-furniture.co.uk

Hope Education, Hyde Building, Ashton Road, Hyde, Cheshire, SK14 4SH Tel: (0870) 2433400 Fax: 0161-367 2009 E-mail: enquiries@hope-educational.co.uk

J R Bourne Powder Coatings Ltd, Beckingham Road, Great Totham, Maldon, Essex, CM9 8EA Tel: (01621) 892972 Fax: (01621) 893299 E-mail: sales@jrbourne.co.uk

John F White Cabinet Makers, Unit 6 Veasey Close, Attleborough Fields Industrial Estate, Nuneaton, Warwickshire, CV11 6RT Tel: (024) 7634 7347 Fax: (024) 7638 2077 E-mail: enquiries@jfw-cabinet.com

Jubilee Joinery Hull Ltd, Eagle House, Cleveland Street, Hull, HU8 7AU Tel: (01482) 224275 Fax: (01482) 217672 E-mail: jubilee@sagehost.co.uk

▶ K M Furniture Ltd, Newton House, Pottery La West, Chesterfield, Derbyshire, S41 9BN Tel: (01246) 260123 Fax: (01246) 260221

Klick Technology Ltd, Claverton Road, Roundthorn Industrial Estate, Manchester, M23 9FT Tel: 0161-998 9726 Fax: 0161-946 0419 E-mail: sales@klicktechnology.co.uk

L F C DespatchLine, Grange House, 2 Geddings Road, Hoddesdon, Hertfordshire, EN11 0NT Tel: (01992) 454500 Fax: (01992) 448989 E-mail: enquiries@lfcdespatch.co.uk

Liddell's Cabinet Works Ltd, Marsh Lane, Lords Meadow Industrial Estate, Crediton, Devon, EX17 1ES Tel: (01363) 772032 Fax: (01363) 774838 E-mail: liddells@eclipse.co.uk

Little Dreams Ltd, Campbell Road, Stoke-on-Trent, ST4 4ES Tel: (01782) 413600 Fax: (01782) 413601 E-mail: info@littledreams.co.uk

Matrix Educational Furniture Ltd, Unit 10 Shawbridge Industrial Estate, 237-239 Shawbridge Street, Glasgow, G43 1QN Tel: 0141-636 5700 Fax: 0141-649 0909 E-mail: matrixed@ukonline.co.uk

EDUCATIONAL FURNITURE – *continued*

▶ Metalliform Holdings, Chambers Road, Hoyland, Barnsley, South Yorkshire, S74 0EZ Tel: (01226) 350555 Fax: (01226) 350112 E-mail: sales@metalliform.co.uk

Mill House Manufacturing Design Ltd, Roughton Road, Kirkby-on-Bain, Woodhall Spa, Lincolnshire, LN10 6YL Tel: (01526) 354404 Fax: (01526) 354424 E-mail: sales@millhouse-md.co.uk

Milton Laboratory Furniture Ltd, Unit 17 Birksland Industrial Estate, Bradford, West Yorkshire, BD4 8TY Tel: (01274) 395110 Fax: (01274) 395111 E-mail: paul@miltonfurniture.com

Oblique, Stamford Works, Gillett Street, London, N16 8JH Tel: (020) 7249 7363 Fax: (020) 7275 7495

Point Eight Ltd, Unit 14 Blackbrook Valley Industrial Estate, Narrowboat Way, Dudley, West Midlands, DY2 0EZ Tel: (01384) 238282 Fax: (01384) 455746 E-mail: sales@point8.co.uk

▶ Print Services UK Ltd, Print House, 66 Hartlebury Trading Estate, Hartlebury, Kidderminster, Worcestershire, DY10 4JB Tel: (01299) 250001 E-mail: visiboard@hotmail.com

Remploy Furniture Group, Baglan Energy Park, Central Avenue, Baglan, Port Talbot, West Glamorgan, SA12 7AX Tel: (01639) 824637 Fax: (01639) 424685 E-mail: furniture@remploy.co.uk

S & B UK Ltd, Labtec Street, Swinton, Manchester, M27 8SE Tel: 0161-793 9333 Fax: 0161-728 9149E-mail: info@splusb.co.uk

S O S Group, Westways Business Park, 2 Apollo Road, Belfast, BT12 6HP Tel: (028) 9066 1133 Fax: (028) 9068 2616 E-mail: sales@sosgroup.co.uk

Satoris Products Ltd, 25 Bradfield Close, Finedon Road Industrial Estate, Wellingborough, Northamptonshire, NN8 4RQ Tel: (01933) 274323 Fax: (01933) 274313 E-mail: edaids@aol.com

▶ Simply Direct, Adelphi Mill, Grimshaw Lane, Bollington, Macclesfield, Cheshire, SK10 5JB Tel: (01625) 576527 Fax: (01625) 576545 E-mail: sales@simplydirect.net

Washbourn & Garrett Ltd, Ashcroft Road, Knowsley Industrial Park North, Liverpool, L33 7TW Tel: 0151-546 2901 Fax: 0151-548 5562 E-mail: enquiries@washbourngarrett.co.uk

Whitehouse Furniture Ltd, Whytehouse Farm, Greenway, Rock, Kidderminster, Worcestershire, DY14 9SJ Tel: (01299) 832466 Fax: (01299) 832576 E-mail: sales@whitehousefurniture.co.uk

EDUCATIONAL INFORMATION SERVICES

Institute Of Measurement & Control, 87 Gower Street, London, WC1E 6AF Tel: (020) 7387 4949 Fax: (020) 7388 8431 E-mail: instmc@instmc.org.uk

▶ Kip Mcgrath Education Centre (Southall), The Arches, Merrick Road, Southall, Middlesex, UB2 4AU Tel: (020) 8574 7338 E-mail: enquiries@kmgsouthall.com

EDUCATIONAL MAGNETS

▶ Guys Magnets, 12 Barbel Close, Calne, Wiltshire, SN11 9QP Tel: (01249) 811372 Fax: (01249) 812778 E-mail: guy@guysmagnets.com

EDUCATIONAL MATERIAL PUBLISHERS

A & C Black Publishers Ltd, 38 Soho Square, London, W1D 3HB Tel: (020) 7758 0200 Fax: (020) 7758 0222 E-mail: enquiries@acblack.com

A M S Educational, 38 Parkside Road, Leeds, LS6 4QG Tel: 0113-275 9900 Fax: 0113-275 7799 E-mail: admin@amseducational.co.uk

A1 Copying Systems & Supplies Ltd, 36 Church Street, Leighton Buzzard, Bedfordshire, LU7 1BT Tel: (01525) 371333 Fax: (01525) 371339 E-mail: a1copyingsys@btclick.com

Burrows Communications Ltd, 106 Stafford Road, Wallington, Surrey, SM6 9AY Tel: (020) 8773 3000 Fax: (020) 8773 8888 E-mail: generalservices@burrows.co.uk

Egon Publishers Ltd, Royston Road, Baldock, Hertfordshire, SG7 6NW Tel: (01462) 894498 Fax: (01462) 894660 E-mail: information@egon.co.uk

W. Foulsham & Co. Ltd, The Publishing House, Bennetts Close, Slough, SL1 5AP Tel: (01753) 526769 Fax: (01753) 535003 E-mail: belasco@foulsham.com

Harcourt Education, Linacre House, Jordan Hill, Oxford, OX2 8DP Tel: (01865) 888000 Fax: (01865) 314222

Institute Of Measurement & Control, 87 Gower Street, London, WC1E 6AF Tel: (020) 7387 4949 Fax: (020) 7388 8431 E-mail: instmc@instmc.org.uk

Learning Materials Ltd, Dixon Street, Wolverhampton, WV2 2BX Tel: (01902) 454026 Fax: (01902) 457596 E-mail: learning.materials@btinternet.com

Marshall Cavendish International Ltd, 119 Wardour Street, London, W1F 0UW Tel: (020) 7734 6710 Fax: (020) 7734 6221

Microform Imaging Ltd, Main Street, East Ardsley, Wakefield, West Yorkshire, WF3 2AP Tel: (01924) 825700 Fax: (01924) 871005 E-mail: info@microform.co.uk

Nelson Thornes Ltd, Delta Place, 27 Bath Road, Cheltenham, Gloucestershire, GL53 7TH Tel: (01242) 267100 Fax: (01242) 221914 E-mail: sales@nelsonthornes.com

Pearson Eduction Ltd, Edinburgh Gate, Edinburgh Way, Harlow, Essex, CM20 2JE Tel: (01279) 623623 Fax: (01279) 431059 E-mail: sales@pearson.com

Royal Society For The Prevention Of Accidents Ltd, 353 Bristol Road, Edgbaston, Birmingham, B5 7ST Tel: 0121-248 2000 Fax: 0121-248 2001 E-mail: help@rospa.com

Trotman Publishing & Empower Group Ltd, 2 The Green, Richmond, Surrey, TW9 1PL Tel: (020) 8486 1150 Fax: (020) 8486 1151 E-mail: management@trotman.co.uk

Western Mail, Newsdesk, Havelock Street, Cardiff, CF1 1WR Tel: (029) 2058 3668 Fax: (029) 2058 3443

EDUCATIONAL MICROSCOPES

Griffin Education, Bishop Meadow Road, Loughborough, Leicestershire, LE11 5RG Tel: (01509) 233344 Fax: (01509) 231893 E-mail: info@fisher.co.uk

EDUCATIONAL PREPARED MATERIALS

Askews Library Services Ltd, 218-222 North Road, Preston, PR1 1SY Tel: (01772) 555947 Fax: (01772) 492768 E-mail: info@askews.co.uk

Creative Art Products Ltd, Manor Lane, Holmes Chapel, Crewe, CW4 8AG Tel: (01477) 535868 Fax: (01477) 535996 E-mail: sales@scolaquip.go-plus.net

Insect Lore, PO Box 1420, Milton Keynes, MK19 6ZH Tel: (01908) 563338 Fax: (01908) 262654

▶ Kip Mcgrath Education Centre (Southall), The Arches, Merrick Road, Southall, Middlesex, UB2 4AU Tel: (020) 8574 7338 E-mail: enquiries@kmgsouthall.com

EDUCATIONAL SCIENCE EQUIPMENT

Time Medical & Scientific Network, Unit 6, North End Industrial Estate, Bury Mead Road, Hitchin, Hertfordshire, SG5 1RT Tel: (01462) 422112 Fax: (01462) 422042 E-mail: sales@timemedical.co.uk

EDUCATIONAL SOFTWARE

Angel Multimedia, 32 Blue Street, Carmarthen, Dyfed, SA31 3LE Tel: (01267) 221175 Fax: (01267) 223196 E-mail: sales@angelmm.co.uk

Avp, School Hill Centre, Chepstow, Gwent, NP16 5PH Tel: (01291) 625439 Fax: (01291) 629671 E-mail: sales@info.avp.co.uk

Box42 Ltd, PO Box 42, Prescot, Merseyside, L35 4PH Tel: 0151-426 9988 Fax: 0151-426 994 E-mail: jeffhughes@box42.com

Capita Education Services, 5 Mercian Close, Cirencester, Gloucestershire, GL7 1LT Tel: (01285) 647500 Fax: (01285) 647599 E-mail: sales@dolphin-cs.co.uk

Carron Practicals, 8 Harley Drive, Condover, Shrewsbury, SY5 7AY Tel: (01743) 872120 Fax: (01743) 872792

Cascaid Ltd, Holywell Buildings, Holywell Way, Loughborough, Leicestershire, LE11 3UZ Tel: (01509) 283390 Fax: (01509) 283401 E-mail: enquire@cascaid.co.uk

Computer Associates UK plc, Ditton Park, Riding Court Road, Datchet, Slough, SL3 9LL Tel: (01753) 577733 Fax: (01753) 825464

D L K Ltd, 8 Stather Road, Burton-upon-Stather, Scunthorpe, South Humberside, DN15 9DH Tel: (01724) 720982 Fax: (01724) 720313 E-mail: sales@dlk.co.uk

Easy Peasy, 1 Winder Gate, Frizington, Cumbria, CA26 3QS Tel: (01946) 813065

Esp Music Ltd, Ladywood Lodge, Spondon Road, Dale Abbey, Ilkeston, Derbyshire, DE7 4PS Tel: 0115-944 4140 Fax: 0115-944 4150 E-mail: sales@espmusic.co.uk

Global Software Publishing, Meadow Lane, St. Ives, Cambridgeshire, PE27 4LG Tel: (01480) 496666 Fax: (01480) 460206 E-mail: sales@gsp.cc

Hamlet Computer Group Ltd, 5 Oriel Court, Omega Park, Alton, Hampshire, GU34 2YT Tel: (01420) 83550 Fax: (01420) 541364 E-mail: sales@hamletcg.co.uk

Philip Harris International, Hyde Building, Ashton Road, Hyde, Cheshire, SK14 4SH Tel: (01530) 418550 E-mail: exportsales@philipharris.co.uk

Institute Of Measurement & Control, 87 Gower Street, London, WC1E 6AF Tel: (020) 7387 4949 Fax: (020) 7388 8431 E-mail: instmc@instmc.org.uk

Kaniko Computing, 23 Edward Road, Harrow, Middlesex, HA2 6QB Tel: (020) 8861 6543 Fax: (020) 8861 6543 E-mail: kanikoc@aol.com

L E T S S, The Lodge, Crown Woods School, Riefield Road, London, SE9 2QL Tel: (020) 8850 0100 Fax: (020) 8850 0400 E-mail: letss@compuserve.com

Learning Materials Ltd, Dixon Street, Wolverhampton, WV2 2BX Tel: (01902) 454026 Fax: (01902) 457596 E-mail: learning.materials@btinternet.com

Multilingual Solutions Ltd, 27A Stonor Road, London, W14 8RZ Tel: (020) 7602 7555 Fax: (020) 7602 4190

N A G Ltd, Wilkinson House Jordan Hill, Banbury Road, Oxford, OX2 8DR Tel: (01865) 311744 Fax: (01865) 310139 E-mail: info@nag.co.uk

React Computer Partnership, Unit 5, Old Maltings Approach, Woodbridge, Suffolk, IP12 1EF Tel: (01394) 387337 Fax: (01394) 610554 E-mail: enquiries@reactcp.co.uk

Rem, Great Western House, Westover Trading Estate, Langport, Somerset, TA10 9YU Tel: (01458) 254700 Fax: (01458) 254701

Software Production Associates Ltd, PO Box 59, Tewkesbury, Gloucestershire, GL20 6AB Tel: (01684) 833700 Fax: (0845) 2301306 E-mail: sales@spasoft.co.uk

Tag Learning Ltd, 25 Pelham Road, Gravesend, Kent, DA11 0HU Tel: (01474) 357350 Fax: (01474) 537887

Virtual Image, 184 Reddish Road, Stockport, Cheshire, SK5 7HS Tel: 0161-480 1915 Fax: 0161-612 2965E-mail: virimage@cs.com

EDUCATIONAL SUPPLIES, *See also headings for particular types*

A B K Group Finance Ltd, Lower Meadow Road Brooke Park, Steadings House, Handforth, Wilmslow, Cheshire, SK9 3LP Tel: 0161-486 6721 Fax: 0161-482 6301 E-mail: sales@abkplc.com

B Garrad Ltd, Water Lane, Kings Langley, Hertfordshire, WD4 8HW Tel: (01923) 264088 Fax: (01923) 264089 E-mail: artcraft@bgarrad.co.uk

B P C Courseware, 4 Apple Barn Court, Old Church Lane, Bury St. Edmunds, Suffolk, IP33 3TJ Tel: (01284) 703300

Beecroft & Partners Ltd, Northfield Road, Rotherham, South Yorkshire, S60 1RR Tel: (01709) 377881 Fax: (01709) 369264 E-mail: sales@beecroft-science.co.uk

Budget Paper Supplies Ltd, Arborfield Mill, Helpston, Peterborough, PE6 7DH Tel: (01733) 252868 Fax: (01733) 253555 E-mail: enquiries@budget-paper.co.uk

Cheltenham College Enterprises Ltd, Cheltenham College, Bath Road, Cheltenham, Gloucestershire, GL53 7LD Tel: (01242) 513540 Fax: (01242) 513540 E-mail: higley.helen@cheltcoll.gloucs.sch.uk

Christian Education Europe Ltd, Marantha House, Northford Close, Shrivenham, Swindon, SN6 8HL Tel: (01793) 783783 Fax: (01793) 783775 E-mail: info@christian-education.org

College Engineering Supply, 2 Sandy Lane, Codsall, Wolverhampton, WV8 1EJ Tel: (01902) 842284 Fax: (01902) 842284 E-mail: enquiries@collegeengineering.co.uk

Craft Packs, Unit 3 Axis Park, Fort Fareham Industrial Site, Fareham, Hampshire, PO14 1FD Tel: (01329) 238282 Fax: (01329) 234550 E-mail: sales@craftpacks.co.uk

Crossbow Eductional, 1 Sawpit Lane, Brocton, Stafford, ST17 0TE Tel: (01785) 660902 Fax: (01785) 661431 E-mail: sales@crossboweducation.com

D & V Engineering, 17 Browning Avenue, Sutton, Surrey, SM1 3QU Tel: (020) 8642 5127 Fax: (020) 8770 1992

Eagle Scientific Ltd, Regent House, Lenton Street, Sandiacre, Nottingham, NG10 5DJ Tel: 0115-949 1111 Fax: 0115-939 1144 E-mail: equip@eagle-scientific.co.uk

Educational Co. Ltd, High Park House, 54 Mallusk Road, Newtownabbey, County Antrim, BT36 4WU Tel: (028) 9084 4023 Fax: (028) 9084 0705

Educational Aids (London) Ltd, 25 Bradfield Close, Finedon Road Industrial Estate, Wellingborough, Northamptonshire, NN8 4RQ Tel: (01933) 274434 Fax: (01933) 274313 E-mail: edaids@aol.com

Educational & Scientific Products Ltd, Unit A2 Dominion Way, Rustington, Littlehampton, West Sussex, BN16 3HQ Tel: (01903) 773340 Fax: (01903) 771108 E-mail: sales@espmodels.co.uk

Fieldyork International Ltd, The Manor, 306 -308 Leicester Road, Wigston, Leicestershire, LE18 1JX Tel: 0116-257 1572 Fax: 0116-257 8969

Fun to Learn, 5 Ardfreelin, Newry, County Down, BT34 1JG Tel: (028) 3025 0960 Fax: (028) 3025 0960

H M E Technology, Priory House, Saxon Park, Hanbury Road, Stoke Prior, Bromsgrove, Worcestershire, B60 4AD Tel: (01527) 839000 Fax: (01527) 839001 E-mail: contactus@hme-tech.com

Hamelin Stationery Ltd, River Street, Brighouse, West Yorkshire, HD6 1LU Tel: (01484) 385600 Fax: (01484) 385602 E-mail: sales@oxfordstationery.com

Harcourt Education, Linacre House, Jordan Hill, Oxford, OX2 8DP Tel: (01865) 888000 Fax: (01865) 314222

Hope Education, Hyde Building, Ashton Road, Hyde, Cheshire, SK14 4SH Tel: (0870) 2433400 Fax: 0161-367 2009 E-mail: enquiries@hope-educational.co.uk

Imex Systems Ltd, 34 Old Kilmore Road, Moira, Craigavon, County Armagh, BT67 0LZ Tel: (028) 9261 9233 Fax: (028) 9261 9234 E-mail: sales@ulster.imex.co.uk

K & J Moxham, Laburnum Road, Stonehouse, Gloucestershire, GL10 2NS Tel: (01453) 822368 Fax: (01453) 827432

K & M Wholesale Suppliers Ltd, Unit 24 Lion Park New Street, Holbrook Industrial Estate, Holbrook, Sheffield, S20 3GH Tel: 0114-247 4733 Fax: 0114-247 5335

L F C DespatchLine, Grange House, 2 Geddings Road, Hoddesdon, Hertfordshire, EN11 0NT Tel: (01992) 454500 Fax: (01992) 448989 E-mail: enquiries@lfcdespatch.co.uk

Laburnum House Educational, Carlisle Street, Gainsborough, Lincolnshire, DN21 2HZ Tel: (01427) 811109 Fax: (01427) 811109 E-mail: sales@laburnumhouse.co.uk

Learning Materials Ltd, Dixon Street, Wolverhampton, WV2 2BX Tel: (01902) 454026 Fax: (01902) 457596 E-mail: learning.materials@btinternet.com

▶ Learning Partnership, Unit 8 The Old Power Station, 121 Mortlake High Street, London, SW14 8SN Tel: (020) 8876 9322 Fax: (020) 8876 9322 E-mail: info@tlp.org

London College Of Business & Computing, 206 Cambridge Heath Road, London, E2 9NQ Tel: (020) 8983 4193 Fax: (020) 8983 4286 E-mail: lcbc@compuserve.com

Lonsdale Revision Guides, Elmsfield Park, Holme, Carnforth, Lancashire, LA6 1RJ Tel: (01539) 565920 Fax: (01539) 564167 E-mail: enquiries@lonsdalesrg.co.uk

Mill House Manufacturing Design Ltd, Roughton Road, Kirkby-on-Bain, Woodhall Spa, Lincolnshire, LN10 6YL Tel: (01526) 354404 Fax: (01526) 354424 E-mail: sales@millhouse-md.co.uk

Montessori Trading Co. Ltd, 13 Hewer Street, London, W10 6DU Tel: (020) 8960 7585 Fax: (020) 7328 5341

Music Education Supplies Ltd, Unit 1 Bentinck Workshops, Park Lane, Kirkby-in-Ashfield, NG17 9LE Tel: (0845) 0264703 Fax: (01623) 726871 E-mail: sales@mesdirect.com

Philip & Tacey Ltd, North Way, Andover, Hampshire, SP10 5BA Tel: (01264) 332171 Fax: (01264) 384808 E-mail: export@philipandtacey.co.uk

Philip & Tacey Ltd, Riverside Road, Pottington Business Park, Barnstaple, Devon, EX31 1LR Tel: (01271) 340300 Fax: (01271) 345086

▶ Pink Cow, Unit 5 Bracknell Beeches, Bracknell Old La West, Bracknell, Berkshire, RG12 7BW Tel: (01344) 867007 Fax: (01344) 860217 E-mail: enquiries@pinkcowselect.com

Pirongs Ltd, 10 Silverhills Road, Decoy Industrial Estate, Newton Abbot, Devon, TQ12 5NA Tel: (01626) 352655 Fax: (01626) 336574 E-mail: mail@pirongs.co.uk

Pisces, Westwood Studios, Marshfield Bank, Crewe, CW2 8UY Tel: (01270) 216211 Fax: (01270) 586150 E-mail: info@pisces-art.co.uk

Playpoint Playground Equipment, 5 Woodside Walk, Strathaven, Lanarkshire, ML10 6HL Tel: (01357) 520929 Fax: (01357) 529239

Rotherham EAL Service, Eastwood Youth Centre, Cranworth Road, Rotherham, South Yorkshire, S65 1LN Tel: (01709) 828608 Fax: (01709) 828608

S E N Marketing, 618 Leeds Road, Wakefield, West Yorkshire, WF1 2LT Tel: (01924) 871697 Fax: (01924) 871697 E-mail: info@sem.com

S T E UK Ltd, Staple Hurst Road, Sittingbourne, Kent, ME10 2NH Tel: (01795) 474700 Fax: (01795) 438901E-mail: info@steuk.co.uk

Sheiling School, Beggars Roost, Horton Road, Ashley Heath, Ringwood, Hampshire, BH24 2EB Tel: (01425) 477488 Fax: (01425) 479536

Specialist Crafts, PO Box 247, Leicester, LE7 1PD Tel: 0116-269 7711 Fax: 0116-269 7722 E-mail: sales@speccrafts.co.uk

Studiocraft Ltd, 17 Arden Business Centre, Arden Forest Industrial Estate, Alcester, Warwickshire, B49 6HW Tel: (01283) 840380 Fax: (01283) 840980 E-mail: sales@studiocraft.co.uk

Tayside Education Link, Barns of Claverhouse, Dundee, DD4 9RA Tel: (01382) 505683

Technology Supplies Ltd, Phoenix House, Tern Hill, Market Drayton, Shropshire, TF9 3PX Tel: (01630) 637301 Fax: (01630) 637302 E-mail: info@technologysupplies.co.uk

West Yorkshire Fabrics Ltd, 20 High Ash Drive, Leeds, LS17 8RA Tel: (0870) 4439842 Fax: 0113-225 6550 E-mail: info@stroud-brothers.demon.co.uk

EDUCATIONAL SUPPLIES, COMPUTER/DESIGN/ TECHNOLOGY

▶ Artastik Ltd, Unit 6 Shorade Industrial Estate, New Street, Bridgtown, Cannock, Staffordshire, WS11 0DH Tel: (01543) 468434 E-mail: info@artastik.co.uk

Box 42 Ltd, PO Box 42, St. Helens, Merseyside, WA10 3BF Tel: (0845) 3700442 Fax: (0845) 3700542 E-mail: welcome@box42.com

C E S Holdings Ltd, Unit 11 Shepley Industrial Estate South, Audenshaw, Manchester, M34 5EX Tel: 0161-337 9337 Fax: 0161-337 9099 E-mail: sales@cesholdings.co.uk

EDUCATIONAL SUPPLIES, COMPUTER/DESIGN/TECHNOLOGY
– *continued*

Educational Co. Ltd, 47-49 Queen Street, Belfast, BT1 6HP Tel: (028) 9032 4687 Fax: (028) 9043 8115 E-mail: theshop@edco.co.uk
Findel Education Ltd, Hyde Building, Ashton Road, Hyde, Cheshire, SK14 4SH Tel: 0161-882 5300 Fax: 0161-882 5300
Philip Harris International, Hyde Building, Ashton Road, Hyde, Cheshire, SK14 4SH Tel: (01530) 418550 E-mail: exportsales@philipharris.co.uk
Klick Technology Ltd, Claverton Road, Roundthorn Industrial Estate, Manchester, M23 9FT Tel: 0161-998 9726 Fax: 0161-946 0419 E-mail: sales@klicktechnology.co.uk
Limrose Group Ltd, Aerial Road, Llay Industrial Estate, Llay, Wrexham, Clwyd, LL12 0TU Tel: (01978) 855555 Fax: (01978) 855556 E-mail: limrose@aol.com
Progressive Educational Tools Ltd, 139 Warwick Road, Kenilworth, Warwickshire, CV8 1HY Tel: (01926) 863360 Fax: (01926) 863360 E-mail: ssexton@petlanguages.co.uk
▶ Quasar Electronics Ltd, PO Box 6935, Bishop's Stortford, Hertfordshire, CM23 4WP Tel: (0870) 2461826 Fax: (0870) 4601045 E-mail: sales@quasarelectronics.com

EDUCATIONAL SUPPLIES, TEST/ MEASUREMENT

Griffin Education, Bishop Meadow Road, Loughborough, Leicestershire, LE11 5RG Tel: (01509) 233344 Fax: (01509) 231893 E-mail: info@fisher.co.uk
▶ S J Electronics, Unit 3 Vernon Court, Henson Way, Telford Way Industrial Estate, Kettering, Northamptonshire, NN16 8PX Tel: (01536) 416200 Fax: (01536) 416300 E-mail: sales@sjelectronics.co.uk
Sanako Educational Equipment, Woodland Park, Bradford Road, Chain Bar, Cleckheaton, West Yorkshire, BD19 6BW Tel: (01274) 863380 Fax: (01274) 863381 E-mail: ukenquiries@sanako.com

EDUCATIONAL TOYS

▶ Doodlebugz, Marton, Marton cum Grafton, York, YO51 9QE Tel: (01347) 830100 Fax: (01347) 830100 E-mail: info@doodlebugz.co.uk

EFFLUENT ANALYSIS EQUIPMENT

A E Jones, 11 Mortimer Street, Cleckheaton, West Yorkshire, BD19 5AR Tel: (01274) 851126 Fax: (01274) 870155 E-mail: sales@aejones.co.uk
Palintest Ltd, Kingsway, Team Valley Trading Estate, Gateshead, Tyne & Wear, NE11 0NS Tel: 0191-491 0808 Fax: 0191-482 5372 E-mail: sales@palintest.com

EFFLUENT RECYCLING OR DISPOSAL OR RECOVERY OR MERCHANTS OR PROCESSORS OR SERVICES

Central Waste Oil Collections Ltd, 143 Queen Street, Walsall, WS2 9NT Tel: (01922) 725966 Fax: (01922) 721966
Cleansing Service Group Ltd, Botley Road, Hedge End, Southampton, SO30 2HE Tel: (01489) 785856 Fax: (01489) 789821 E-mail: enquiries@csgwasteman.co.uk
Crewdson & Co. Ltd, Beck Mills, Shap Road, Kendal, Cumbria, LA9 6NY Tel: (01539) 730990 Fax: (01539) 725316 E-mail: crewco@btconnect.com
Dirk European Holdings Ltd, Dirk House, 29-31 Woodchurch Lane, Prenton, Birkenhead, Merseyside, CH42 9PJ Tel: 0151-608 8552 Fax: 0151-608 7579 E-mail: gdirk@dirkgroup.com
Viridor Waste Managment, Thames House, Wood Lane, Slough, SL1 9EB Tel: (01753) 512832 Fax: (01753) 536230

EFFLUENT TREATMENT CHEMICAL PRODUCTS

Colloid Treatment Technologies, Rovert House, Water Tower Road, Clayhill Light Industrial Park, Neston, CH64 3US Tel: 0151-336 7775 Fax: 0151-336 7733E-mail: colltreat@aol.com
E A West, Pyewipe, Grimsby, South Humberside, DN31 2SW Tel: (01472) 232000 Fax: (01472) 232200 E-mail: hmats_uk@huntsman.com
Feedwater Ltd, Tarran Road, Tarran Industrial Estate, Wirral, Merseyside, CH46 4TU Tel: 0151-606 0808 Fax: 0151-678 5459 E-mail: enquiries@feedwater.co.uk
Feralco (UK) Ltd, Ditton Road, Widnes, Cheshire, WA8 0PH Tel: 0151-802 2940 Fax: 0151-802 2999 E-mail: info@feralco.com
Watermarc Chemical Services, Unit 38 Nine Mile Point Industrial Estate, Cwmfelinfach, Ynysddu, Newport, Gwent, NP11 7HZ Tel: (01495) 200005 Fax: (01495) 200844

EFFLUENT TREATMENT PLANT CONSULTANCY

First Effluent Ltd, 42a High Street, Sutton Coldfield, West Midlands, B72 1UJ Tel: 0121-355 2907 Fax: 0121-355 6134
Hytec Industrie, PO Box 642, Guildford, Surrey, GU2 7WE Tel: (01483) 827065 Fax: (01483) 827075 E-mail: uk@hytec-industrie.com

EFFLUENT TREATMENT PLANT CONTRACTORS

Black & Veatch Ltd, Stirling House, Danebury Court Old Sarum Park, Old Sarum, Salisbury, SP4 6EB Tel: (01722) 413339 Fax: (01722) 413306

EFFLUENT TREATMENT PLANT MANUFRS

Adams Hydraulics Ltd, PO Box 15, York, YO30 4XE Tel: (01904) 695695 Fax: (01904) 695600 E-mail: sales@adamshydraulics.co.uk
Amafiltergroup Ltd, Navigation Road, Stoke-on-Trent, ST6 3RU Tel: (01782) 575611 Fax: (01782) 577001 E-mail: salesuk@amafilter.com
Aquatec Consultancy Services Ltd, Pocket Nook Lane, Lowton, Warrington, WA3 1AB Tel: (01942) 603268 Fax: (01942) 261521 E-mail: info@aquatecchemicalservices.com
B E W T Environmental Services Ltd, Warwick, CV35 8PY Tel: (01926) 843233 Fax: (01926) 843233
Bioclear Environmental Ltd, Unit 10, Carver Road, Astonfields Industrial Estate, Stafford, ST16 3HR Tel: (01785) 254410 Fax: (01785) 254553 E-mail: sales@bioclear.fsnet.co.uk
Black & Veatch Ltd, Stirling House, Danebury Court Old Sarum Park, Old Sarum, Salisbury, SP4 6EB Tel: (01722) 413339 Fax: (01722) 413306
Brightwater Engineering, Unit 2 The Business Centre, Avenue One, Letchworth, Letchworth Garden City, Hertfordshire, SG6 2HB Tel: (01462) 485005 Fax: (01462) 485003 E-mail: enquiries@brightwater.uk.com
Colloid Treatment Technologies, Rovert House, Water Tower Road, Clayhill Light Industrial Park, Neston, CH64 3US Tel: 0151-336 7775 Fax: 0151-336 7733E-mail: colltreat@aol.com
Copa Waste Water Controls Ltd, Lisduff Industrial Estate, Newry, County Down, BT35 6QH Tel: (028) 3026 7996 Fax: (028) 3026 6777 E-mail: kieran@glv.com
De Smet Rosedowns Ltd, Cannon Street, Hull, HU2 0AD Tel: (01482) 329864 Fax: (01482) 325887 E-mail: info@rosedowns.co.uk
Esmil Process Systems Ltd, 30 Abbey Barn Road, High Wycombe, Buckinghamshire, HP11 1RW Tel: (01494) 474515 Fax: (01494) 474515 E-mail: info@esmil.co.uk
First Effluent Ltd, 42a High Street, Sutton Coldfield, West Midlands, B72 1UJ Tel: 0121-355 2907 Fax: 0121-355 6134
G F Price & Co., Littlecroft, Chetton, Bridgnorth, Shropshire, WV16 6UE Tel: (01746) 789330 Fax: (01746) 789330
Gee & Co Effluent Control & Recovery Ltd, Gee House, Holborn Hill, Birmingham, B7 5JR Tel: 0121-326 1700 Fax: 0121-326 1779 E-mail: info@geeco.co.uk
Hodge Separators Ltd, 1 Jennings Road, Kernick Road Industrial Estate, Penryn, Cornwall, TR10 9LY Tel: (01326) 375388 Fax: (01326) 377235 E-mail: sales@hodge-separators.com
Hydro-X Water Treatment Ltd, Unit 3a Eden Place, Outgang Lane Dinnington, Dinnington, Sheffield, S25 3QT Tel: (01909) 565133 Fax: (01909) 564301 E-mail: office@hydro-x.co.uk
Hytec Industrie, PO Box 642, Guildford, Surrey, GU2 7WE Tel: (01483) 827065 Fax: (01483) 827075 E-mail: uk@hytec-industrie.com
J R G Engineering Services Ltd, 7 Weaver St, Kirkstall Rd, Leeds, LS4 2AU Tel: 0113-263 8731 Fax: 0113-231 0294
▶ Kilkie Paper Mill Services, Lovesta, Gowanlea Road, Comrie, Crieff, Perthshire, PH6 2HD Tel: (01764) 670141 Fax: (0870) 1301570 E-mail: sales@kilkie.com
Koch Membrane Systems, The Granary, Telegraph Street, Stafford, ST17 4AT Tel: (01785) 272500 Fax: (01785) 223149
Mbe Fabrications Ltd, 1 Town Drove, Quadring, Spalding, Lincolnshire, PE11 4PU Tel: (01775) 821222 Fax: (01775) 820914 E-mail: sales@mbefabs.com
Pollution Control UK Ltd, Mounsey Road, Bamber Bridge, Preston, PR5 6LS Tel: (01772) 620066 Fax: (01772) 628996 E-mail: sales@pollution-control.co.uk
Puriflo Ltd, 44 Holton Road, Holton Heath Trading Park, Poole, Dorset, BH16 6LT Tel: (01202) 625656 Fax: (01202) 621002 E-mail: sales@rhe-puriflo.co.uk
Rodway & Taylor Birmingham Ltd, 85 Buckingham Street, Birmingham, B19 3HU Tel: 0121-236 4027 Fax: 0121-233 2972 E-mail: paul.rodway@virgin.net
Trojan Mixers, 1191 Stratford Road, Hall Green, Birmingham, B28 8BX Tel: 0121-777 5555 Fax: 0121-777 5555 E-mail: trojanmixers@hotmail.com
Wyatt Ltd, Unit 3, Whittington Buissness Park, Oswestry, Shropshire, SY11 4ND Tel: (01691) 662592 Fax: (01691) 658346 E-mail: wyattltd@aol.com

EFFLUENT TREATMENT SERVICES

Civil & Environmental Project Services Ltd, 1 Port Street, Evesham, Worcestershire, WR11 3LA Tel: (01386) 424007 Fax: (01386) 424007 E-mail: info@civenv.co.uk

EFFLUENT TREATMENT SYSTEM INSTALLATION OR MAINTENANCE OR REFURBISHMENT

C D Bissell Engineering Services Ltd, Unit 28, Moorfields Industrial Estate, Cotes Heath, Stafford, ST21 6QY Tel: (01782) 791711 Fax: (01782) 791511 E-mail: mick@cdbissell.com
C W T Ltd, Hempstalls Lane, Newcastle, Staffordshire, ST5 0SW Tel: (01782) 625222 Fax: (01782) 625333 E-mail: cwtlimited@aol.com
Cleveland Biotech Ltd, 3 Vanguard Court, Preston Farm Business Pk, Stockton-on-Tees, Cleveland, TS18 3TR Tel: (01642) 606606 Fax: (01642) 606040 E-mail: bugs@clevebio.com
Copa Waste Water Controls Ltd, Lisduff Industrial Estate, Newry, County Down, BT35 6QH Tel: (028) 3026 7996 Fax: (028) 3026 6777 E-mail: kieran@glv.com
First Effluent Ltd, 42a High Street, Sutton Coldfield, West Midlands, B72 1UJ Tel: 0121-355 2907 Fax: 0121-355 6134
Goodwater Ltd, 23-24 Ivanhoe Road, Hogwood Industrial Estate, Finchampstead, Wokingham, Berkshire, RG40 4QQ Tel: 0118-973 5003 Fax: 0118-973 5004 E-mail: info@goodwater.co.uk
Hydroklear Services Ltd, 50 Linister Crescent, Howwood, Johnstone, Renfrewshire, PA9 1DS Tel: (01505) 704111 Fax: (01505) 706500 E-mail: sales@hydroklear.co.uk
RPS Consulting Engineers, Elmwood House, 74 Boucher Road, Belfast, BT12 6RZ Tel: (028) 9066 7914 Fax: (028) 9066 8286 E-mail: belfast@rpsgroup.com

EFFLUENT TREATMENT SYSTEMS

Ashbrook Simon-Hartley Ltd, 10/11 Brindley Court, Dalewood Road, Lymedale Business Park, Newcastle-under-Lyme, Staffordshire, ST5 9QH Tel: (01782) 578650 Fax: (01782) 260534 E-mail: enquiries@as-h.com
B L T Circuit Services Ltd, Airfield Industrial Estate, Eye, Suffolk, IP23 7HN Tel: (01379) 870870 Fax: (01379) 870970 E-mail: sales@blt.keme.co.uk
J R G Engineering Services Ltd, 7 Weaver St, Kirkstall Rd, Leeds, LS4 2AU Tel: 0113-263 8731 Fax: 0113-231 0294
Kurion Technologies Ltd, 43 Brunel Close, Drayton Fields Industrial Estate, Daventry, Northamptonshire, NN11 8RB Tel: (01327) 876600 Fax: (01327) 705131 E-mail: sales@kurion.co.uk
Locker Wire Weavers, Farrell Street, Warrington, WA1 2WW Tel: (01925) 406600 Fax: (01925) 444386 E-mail: sales@lockerwire.co.uk
PIE International Ltd, The Exchange, Express Park, Bridgwater, Somerset, TA6 4RR Tel: (0870) 7877872 Fax: (0870) 7877873 E-mail: info@pieinternational.com

EGG WHITES

▶ D Wise Ltd, Parkfields, Nomansheath, Malpas, Cheshire, SY14 8DY Tel: (01948) 820418 Fax: (01948) 820452

EGGS

▶ D Wise Ltd, Parkfields, Nomansheath, Malpas, Cheshire, SY14 8DY Tel: (01948) 820418 Fax: (01948) 820452

EIDERDOWN, *See Down etc*

EJECTOR PINS

Berger Tools Ltd, Units B 1-2 Chaucer Business Park, Watery Lane, Kemsing, Sevenoaks, Kent, TN15 6QY Tel: (01732) 763377 Fax: (01732) 763335 E-mail: sales@berger-tools.co.uk
K M A Grinding, Unit 62 Western Business Park, Great Western Close, Birmingham, B18 4QF Tel: 0121-554 5537 Fax: 0121-554 1933

EJECTORS, STEAM/AIR OPERATED

Nash Elmo UK Ltd, Road One, Winsford Industrial Estate, Winsford, Cheshire, CW7 3PL Tel: (01606) 542400 Fax: (01606) 542434 E-mail: sales@nasheng.com
Northvale Korting Ltd, Uxbridge Road, Leicester, LE4 7ST Tel: 0116-266 5911 Fax: 0116-261 0050 E-mail: sales@northvalekorting.co.uk

ELASTIC BRAID MANUFRS

Artistic Trims Ltd, Aston House, 77 Upper Trinity Street, Birmingham, B9 4EG Tel: 0121-766 6167 Fax: 0121-766 6360 E-mail: elastic@artistictrims.co.uk
Malmic Lace Ltd, Malmic House, Brookside Road, Ruddington, Nottingham, NG11 6AT Tel: 0115-940 5151 Fax: 0115-984 5706 E-mail: info@malmiclace.co.uk
S & T Trimmings Ltd, 56-66 Cambridge Street, Coventry, CV1 5HW Tel: (024) 7622 3366 Fax: (024) 7666 4401 E-mail: info@sttrimmings.com
Twistlink Ltd, Stadon Road, Anstey, Leicester, LE7 7AY Tel: 0116-236 1860 Fax: 0116-236 6423 E-mail: sales@fabmania.com

ELASTIC CORDS

Artistic Trims Ltd, Aston House, 77 Upper Trinity Street, Birmingham, B9 4EG Tel: 0121-766 6167 Fax: 0121-766 6360 E-mail: elastic@artistictrims.co.uk
Ibex, 92-94 Manchester Road, Mossley, Ashton-under-Lyne, Lancashire, OL5 9AY Tel: (01457) 831600 Fax: (01457) 831669 E-mail: sales@ibexropes.com
Marlow Ropes Ltd, Rope Maker Park, Dipilocks Way, Hailsham, East Sussex, BN27 3GU Tel: (01323) 444444 Fax: (01323) 444455 E-mail: sales@marlowropes.com

ELASTIC FABRICS

Pennine Trims, 5 Rosewood Business Park, St James's Road, Blackburn, BB1 8ET Tel: (01254) 582715 Fax: (01254) 663309

ELASTIC TAPES

Artistic Trims Ltd, Aston House, 77 Upper Trinity Street, Birmingham, B9 4EG Tel: 0121-766 6167 Fax: 0121-766 6360 E-mail: elastic@artistictrims.co.uk
G.C. Moore (U.K.) Ltd, PO Box 6541, Burton-On-Trent, Staffordshire, DE13 8WY Tel: (01283) 712901 Fax: (01283) 716690 E-mail: grahamhughes@btconnect.com

ELASTIC WEBBING MANUFRS

H Seal & Co. Ltd, Church Lane, Whitwick, Coalville, Leicestershire, LE67 5DJ Tel: (01530) 832351 Fax: (01530) 813382 E-mail: sales@hseal.co.uk
Nottingham Narrow Fabrics, Block A Harrington Mills, Leopold Street, Long Eaton, Nottingham, NG10 4QG Tel: 0115-946 8883 Fax: 0115-946 8652
Walter Melville Ltd, Fanshaws Lane, Brickendon, Hertford, SG13 8PG Tel: (01992) 511285 Fax: (01992) 511286 E-mail: melville_trimmings@yahoo.co.uk

ELASTIC YARN

Wykes International Ltd, 434 Thurmaston Boulevard, Leicester, LE4 9LD Tel: 0116-276 8282 Fax: 0116-274 2506 E-mail: sales@wykes.co.uk

ELASTOMER CASTINGS

Hippo Marine Ltd, 1 Gilston Road, Saltash, Cornwall, PL12 6TW Tel: (01752) 843333 Fax: (01752) 843333

ELASTOMER COATED ROLLERS

Bowers & Jones Ltd, Patrick Gregory Road, Wolverhampton, WV11 3DU Tel: (01902) 732110 Fax: (01902) 864654 E-mail: jim.willmott@bowers.jones.freeserve.co.uk

ELECTRIC ACCESSORIES, *See also headings for particular types*

Contactum Ltd, Victoria Works, Edgware Road, London, NW2 6LF Tel: (020) 8452 6366 Fax: (020) 8208 3340 E-mail: general@contactum.co.uk
Eric Thacker Industrial Control Ltd, 110 Lichfield Road, Bloxwich, Walsall, WS3 3LY Tel: (01922) 475865 Fax: (01922) 711770

ELECTRIC ACCESSORIES – *continued*

Harding Electricals Distributors, 475-499 Lichfield Road, Birmingham, B6 7SP Tel: 0121-326 9229 Fax: 0121-328 0589 E-mail: aston.268@eel.co.uk
K B Electrical, 7 Wentworth Drive, Lancaster, LA1 3RJ Tel: (01524) 37822 E-mail: kbelectrical@yahoo.com
R Hamilton & Co. Ltd, Quarryfield Industrial Estate, Mere, Warminster, Wiltshire, BA12 6LA Tel: (01747) 860088 Fax: (01747) 861032 E-mail: info@hamilton-litestat.com
Strickland & Co. (Electrical) Ltd, 113-117 Springfield Road, Windsor, Berkshire, SL4 3PZ Tel: (01753) 830040 Fax: (01753) 867894 E-mail: ccelectrical@btconnect.com
Tele Control Ltd, Unit 21 Three Point Business Park, Charles Lane, Haslingden, Rossendale, Lancashire, BB4 5EH Tel: (01706) 226333 Fax: (01706) 226444 E-mail: sales@tele-control.co.uk
Timms Electrics, 40 Malmains Way, Beckenham, Kent, BR3 6SB Tel: 020 86505772
Turnock Ltd, Reaymer Close, Walsall, WS2 7QZ Tel: (01922) 710422 Fax: (01922) 710428

ELECTRIC ACTUATORS

Auma Actuators Ltd, Britannia Way, Clevedon, Avon, BS21 6QH Tel: (01275) 871141 Fax: (01275) 875492E-mail: sales@alma.com
C R D Devices Ltd, 3 All Saints Industrial Estate, Darlington Road, Shildon, County Durham, DL4 2RD Tel: (01388) 778400 Fax: (01388) 778800 E-mail: sales@crd-devices.co.uk
D J Automation Engineering Ltd, 11d Old Bridge Way, Shefford, Bedfordshire, SG17 5HQ Tel: (01462) 813703 Fax: (01462) 816810 E-mail: enquiries@djautomation.co.uk
Flowserve, Abex Road, Newbury, Berkshire, RG14 5EY Tel: (01635) 42297 Fax: (01635) 36034 E-mail: jrobinson@flowserve.com
▶ Industrial Devices (GB) Ltd, Glebe House, Ratlinghope, Shrewsbury, SY5 0SN Tel: (01588) 650551 Fax: (01588) 650130 E-mail: sales@actuators-electric.co.uk
Kinetrol Ltd, Farnham Trading Estate, Farnham, Surrey, GU9 9NU Tel: (01252) 733838 Fax: (01252) 713042 E-mail: sales@kinetrol.com
Muirhead Norcroft, East Portway, Andover, Hampshire, SP10 3LU Tel: (01264) 349600 Fax: (01264) 336444 E-mail: sales@muirheadaerospace.com
Paladon Systems Ltd, Ferro Fields, Brixworth Industrial Estate, Brixworth, Northampton, NN6 9UA Tel: (01604) 880700 Fax: (01604) 882424 E-mail: enquiries@paladon.co.uk
Valve Center, 2 Bold Business Centre, Bold Lane, St. Helens, Merseyside, WA9 4TX Tel: (01925) 290660 Fax: (01925) 227463 E-mail: sales@valvecenter.co.uk

ELECTRIC AIR HEATERS

F A T I International Ltd, 9 Wight Way, Selsey, Chichester, West Sussex, PO20 0UD Tel: (01243) 606007 Fax: (01243) 606007 E-mail: fatiint@btconnect.com
Process Heating Services, 12 Noddington Avenue, Lichfield, Staffordshire, WS14 9NQ Tel: (01543) 432661 Fax: (01543) 432782 E-mail: sales@processheatingservices.com

ELECTRIC BELL PUSHES

Knight & Gibbins Ltd, Windham Road, Chilton Industrial Estate, Sudbury, Suffolk, CO10 2XD Tel: (01787) 377264 Fax: (01787) 378258 E-mail: sales@knightandgibbins.co.uk

ELECTRIC BELLS

Fulleon, Llantarnam Industrial Park, Cwmbran, Gwent, NP44 3AW Tel: (01633) 628500 Fax: (01633) 866346 E-mail: sales@fulleon.co.uk

ELECTRIC BEVELLING TOOLS

S K S Plant & Equipment Ltd, 11 Redehall Road, Smallfield, Horley, Surrey, RH6 9PY Tel: (01342) 843688 Fax: (01342) 842140 E-mail: sks@sks-group.co.uk

ELECTRIC BLANKET HEATING ELEMENTS

De Icers M H G Ltd, 11 Hamilton Street, Charlton Kings, Cheltenham, Gloucestershire, GL53 8HN Tel: (01242) 573321 Fax: (01242) 573543
Thermocable (Flexible Elements) Ltd, Pasture Lane, Clayton, Bradford, West Yorkshire, BD14 6LU Tel: (01274) 882359 Fax: (01274) 882229 E-mail: info@thermocable.com

ELECTRIC BLINDS

Anglia Window Blinds, 27a Forge Road, Port Talbot, West Glamorgan, SA13 1US Tel: (01639) 891045 Fax: (01639) 884995
Artek Contracts, 173 Red Lion Road, Surbiton, Surrey, KT6 7RG Tel: (020) 8397 2121
Betta Blinds, Unit Ps5, Market Precinct, Carmarthen, Dyfed, SA31 1QY Tel: (01267) 232263 Fax: (01267) 232263
BSB Signs.Co.Uk, Orchard Works, Grove Road, London, E4 9SU Tel: (020) 8529 3330 Fax: (020) 8529 3331 E-mail: info@bsbsigns.co.uk
Castle Blinds, 2 Ayton House, North Road, Berwick-upon-Tweed, TD15 1PR Tel: (01289) 306090 Fax: (01289) 332020 E-mail: micheal@mullan4245.fsnet.co.uk
Charisma, Sligo Road, Enniskillen, County Fermanagh, BT74 7JY Tel: (028) 6632 7111 Fax: (028) 6632 7999
Crusader Cleaning Services, 17 Bulmer Way, Cannon Park Industrial Estate, Middlesbrough, Cleveland, TS1 5JT Tel: (01642) 226403 Fax: (01642) 226403
Direct Blinds, 21 Kaimes View, Danderhall, Dalkeith, Midlothian, EH22 1QZ Tel: 0131-660 2622 Fax: 0131-660 6622
Evendale Blinds, Indoor Market, 62-72 Titchfield Street, Kilmarnock, Ayrshire, KA1 1PH Tel: (01563) 573767 Fax: (01563) 573767
Fiesta Blinds & Fabrics Ltd, 36 Waterloo Street, Londonderry, BT48 6HF Tel: (028) 7126 1961 Fax: (028) 7137 4387
Fiesta Blinds & Fabrics Ltd, 1 Springgrowth Business Park, Springtown Road, Londonderry, BT48 0LY Tel: (028) 7126 2605 Fax: (028) 7137 4387
G A Blinds & Curtains, 8 Norland House Business Centre, Hackworth Industrial Park, Shildon, County Durham, DL4 1HE Tel: (01388) 777171
Galea Sunblinds, 2 Station Shops, Westborough, Scarborough, North Yorkshire, YO11 1TR Tel: (01723) 353513 Fax: (01723) 341010
Kingfisher Blinds Bath Ltd, Unit C The Hawthorns, Old Pit Road, Midsomer Norton, Radstock, BA3 4BQ Tel: (01761) 417807 Fax: (01761) 417807
Reynolds Blinds, 254 High Street, Erdington, Birmingham, B23 6SN Tel: 0121-373 7017 Fax: 0121-373 7059 E-mail: sales@reynoldsblinds.co.uk
See More Blinds, 24 Church Square, Midsomer Norton, Radstock, BA3 2HX Tel: (01761) 411063 Fax: (01761) 411063 E-mail: seemoreblinds@yahoo.com
Shades Window Blind Specialists, 2B Chingford Road, London, E17 4PJ Tel: (020) 8527 3991 Fax: (020) 8523 4476 E-mail: info@shades-london.co.uk
Shadow Blinds Ltd, Unit E Newark Road South, Glenrothes, Fife, KY7 4NS Tel: (01592) 630660 Fax: (01592) 630188
Smart Shading Systems, Crown Business Centre, 195 Horton Road, West Drayton, Middlesex, UB7 8HP Tel: (01895) 448217 Fax: (01895) 448503 E-mail: sales@smartshading.co.uk
Suncolor Blinds, Almond Business Centre, Craigshill Road, Livingston, West Lothian, EH54 5DT Tel: (0800) 3898825 Fax: (01506) 497265 E-mail: sales@suncolor.co.uk
Trade Blinds, 104 Oak Road, Sittingbourne, Kent, ME10 3PR Tel: (01795) 428793

ELECTRIC BOILERS

Atlantic 2000, PO Box 11, Ashton-under-Lyne, Lancashire, OL6 7TR Tel: 0161-621 5960 Fax: 0161-621 5966 E-mail: info@atlanticboilers.com
Church Hill Systems Ltd, Unit 4h Hinckley Business Centre, Burbage Road, Burbage, Hinckley, Leicestershire, LE10 2TP Tel: (01455) 890685 Fax: (01455) 891341 E-mail: sales@churchhillsystems.co.uk
▶ Heat & Cool, Sands Business Centre, Sands Road, Farnham, Surrey, GU10 1PX Tel: (0870) 0427484 E-mail: sales@heatandcool.co.uk
Heatrae Sadia, 1 Hurricane Way, Norwich, NR6 6EA Tel: (01603) 420100 Fax: (01603) 420218 E-mail: sales@heatraesadia.com
Howden Electro Heating (Howden Electroheating), 10-12 Belgowan Street, Bellshill Industrial Estate, Bellshill, Lanarkshire, ML4 3NS Tel: (01698) 573111 Fax: (01698) 573121 E-mail: sales@howden-electroheating.com

ELECTRIC BUZZERS

▶ Fleet Electrical & Safety Direct Ltd, Unit 10, Commerce Business Centre, Commerce Close, West Wilts Trading Estate, Westbury, Wiltshire, BA13 4LS Tel: (01373) 823242 Fax: (01373) 823206 E-mail: sales@fleetelectrical.co.uk

ELECTRIC CABLE ACCESSORIES/EQUIPMENT/ MACHINERY, *See Cable etc*

ELECTRIC CABLES

Globe Electrical Co., 25 Crown Street, Ayr, KA8 8AG Tel: (01292) 269529 Fax: (01292) 611918

ELECTRIC CALL SYSTEMS

Lismore Instruments Ltd, 2 Tristar Business Centre, Star Road, Partridge Green, Horsham, West Sussex, RH13 8RA Tel: (01403) 713121 Fax: (01403) 713141 E-mail: sales@intercall.com

ELECTRIC COMMUTATORS

CTL/EDM Ltd, Green Street, Green Road, Mile End Green, Dartford, DA2 8EB Tel: (01474) 708621 Fax: (01474) 708948 E-mail: ctl.edm@lineone.net
Lye Commutators, The White House, Pearson Street, Stourbridge, West Midlands, DY9 8BB Tel: (01384) 893025 Fax: (01384) 422398
Southern Commutators Ltd, 16B Mill Lane, Carshalton, Surrey, SM5 2JY Tel: (020) 8669 3876 Fax: (020) 8773 4082 E-mail: southerncommutators@tiscali.co.uk
Sudatek Ltd, 59 Barn Meadow Lane, Bookham, Leatherhead, Surrey, KT23 3EZ Tel: (01372) 450008 Fax: (01372) 450006 E-mail: sales@sudatek.com

ELECTRIC COMPONENTS, *See also headings for particular types*

Norlec Ltd, 2 Newton Court, Norwich Road, Dereham, Norfolk, NR20 3ES Tel: (01362) 696072 Fax: (01362) 696842
Pallas Connections Ltd, Unit 1 Field Farm Business Centre, Launton, Bicester, Oxfordshire, OX26 5EL Tel: (01869) 277053 Fax: (01869) 277058 E-mail: hornby@pallasconnections.co.uk
Pristine Computers & Computing Ltd, 45 High Street, Charing, Ashford, Kent, TN27 0HU Tel: (01233) 713660 Fax: (01233) 713727 E-mail: peter@pristineuk.com
Sumitomo Electrical Wiring Systems Europe Ltd, Unit1 Woodlands Business Park, Ystradgynlais, Swansea, SA9 1GW Tel: (01639) 842281 Fax: (01639) 849853

ELECTRIC CONDUIT FITTINGS OR ACCESSORIES

Adaptaflex Ltd, Station Road Industrial Estate, Station Road, Coleshill, Birmingham, B46 1HT Tel: (01675) 468200 Fax: (01675) 462090 E-mail: sales@adaptaflex.co.uk
Mark Davis Engineering Co. Ltd, Hayes Lane, Lye, Stourbridge, West Midlands, DY9 8RA Tel: (01384) 424404 Fax: (01384) 424707 E-mail: enquiries@markdavis.co.uk
Dyson Products, Moor St Industrial Estate, Moor Street, Brierley Hill, West Midlands, DY5 3ST Tel: (01384) 77833 Fax: (01384) 263724
Flexicon Ltd, Roman Way, Coleshill, Birmingham, B46 1HG Tel: (01675) 466900 Fax: (01675) 466901 E-mail: sales@flexicon.uk.com
Harnessflex Ltd, PO Box 7690, Birmingham, B46 1HT Tel: (01675) 468200 Fax: (01675) 464930 E-mail: sales@harnessflex.co.uk
Kopex International Ltd, 3rd Floor Crossbow House, 40 Liverpool Road, Slough, SL1 4QZ Tel: (01753) 502502 Fax: (01753) 693521 E-mail: jaustin@kopex.co.uk
Niglon Ltd, Highlands Road, Shirley, Solihull, West Midlands, B90 4NP Tel: 0121-711 1990 Fax: 0121-711 1344
P F P Electrical Products Ltd, 22 Fortnum Close, Mackadown Lane, Kitts Green, Birmingham, B33 0LB Tel: 0121-783 7161 Fax: 0121-783 5717 E-mail: sales@pfp-elec.co.uk
Plastube Ltd, The Old Foundry, Leech Street, Stalybridge, Cheshire, SK15 1SD Tel: 0161-338 5505 Fax: 0161-338 5502 E-mail: admin@plastube.co.uk
Stephen Glover & Co. Ltd, Long Street, Walsall, WS2 9DU Tel: (01922) 611311 Fax: (01922) 721824 E-mail: verglo@btconnect.com
Zed Duct Systems Ltd, 5-5a Unit, Hill Street, Kidderminster, Worcestershire, DY11 6TD Tel: (01562) 824261 Fax: (01562) 746435

ELECTRIC CONDUITS, *See also other nearby headings for particular types*

Adaptaflex Ltd, Station Road Industrial Estate, Station Road, Coleshill, Birmingham, B46 1HT Tel: (01675) 468200 Fax: (01675) 462090 E-mail: sales@adaptaflex.co.uk
▶ Bowbros Ltd, Newby Road Industrial Estate, Newby Road, Hazel Grove, Stockport, Cheshire, SK7 5DD Tel: (01656) 661224 Fax: (01656) 660009
Flexicon Ltd, Roman Way, Coleshill, Birmingham, B46 1HG Tel: (01675) 466900 Fax: (01675) 466901 E-mail: sales@flexicon.uk.com
Kopex International Ltd, 3rd Floor Crossbow House, 40 Liverpool Road, Slough, SL1 4QZ Tel: (01753) 502502 Fax: (01753) 693521 E-mail: jaustin@kopex.co.uk
T S Industrial Products Ltd, 75 Somers Road, Rugby, Warwickshire, CV22 7DG Tel: (01788) 543387 Fax: (01788) 541311 E-mail: sales@tsindustrial.co.uk
Trident Sections Ltd, Unit 33 Dawley Trading Estate, Dawlings Lane, Kingswinford, West Midlands, DY6 7AP Tel: (01384) 401700 Fax: (01384) 292785

ELECTRIC CONTROL SYSTEMS

Autolux Control Panel Mnfrs, Sizers Court, Yeadon, Leeds, LS19 7DP Tel: 0113-250 1405 Fax: 0113-250 1449 E-mail: autolux@btconnect.com
B & F Group Ltd, Sovereign Way, Chester West Employment Park, Chester, CH1 4QJ Tel: (01244) 390215 Fax: (01244) 382747
Brush Electrical Machines Ltd, PO Box 18, Loughborough, Leicestershire, LE11 1HJ Tel: (01509) 611511 Fax: (01509) 610440 E-mail: sales@bem.fki-et.com
C & W Electronics Ltd, Pool Street, Wolverhampton, WV2 4HN Tel: (01902) 426714 Fax: (01902) 422544
Carlton Controls Ltd, 3c Lea Road, Waltham Abbey, Essex, EN9 1AE Tel: (01992) 767609 Fax: (01992) 788446 E-mail: mail@carlton-controls.co.uk
Control Electrics Leicester Ltd, 30 Fowke Street, Rothley, Leicester, LE7 7PJ Tel: 0116-237 4233 E-mail: enquire@controlelectrics.co.uk
Control Solutions Ltd, Avon House, 82 Wellington Street, Thame, Oxfordshire, OX9 3BN Tel: (01844) 216988 Fax: (01844) 261466 E-mail: mail@control-solutions.co.uk
Dobbie McInnes, 42 Methil Street, Glasgow, G14 0AN Tel: 0141-959 2247 Fax: 0141-954 1172 E-mail: dobbie@yandc.co.uk
Electric Vehicle Systems Ltd, 11 Glover Network Centre, Spire Road, Washington, Tyne & Wear, NE37 3HB Tel: 0191-416 1286 Fax: 0191-419 3746 E-mail: info@evsystems.co.uk
Electrical Control Systems, 89 Queslett Road East, Sutton Coldfield, West Midlands, B74 2AH Tel: 0121-353 1231 E-mail: info@ecscontrol.co.uk
Endress & Hauser Ltd, Floats Road, Roundthorn Industrial Estate, Manchester, M23 9NF Tel: 0161-286 5000 Fax: 0161-998 1841 E-mail: info@uk.endress.com
Fridge Controls Ltd, 4-5 Plantagaenet Estate, Kineton, Warwick, CV35 0HU Tel: (01926) 640171 Fax: (01926) 641707 E-mail: sales@fridgecontrols.co.uk
Gainsborough Industrial Controls Ltd, Foxby House, Foxby Hill, Gainsborough, Lincolnshire, DN21 1PN Tel: (01427) 611885 Fax: (01427) 611883 E-mail: sales@gic.uk.net
Jetter Distributors Ltd, Leighswood House, 43 Leighswood Road, Walsall, WS9 8AH Tel: (01922) 745200 Fax: (01922) 745045 E-mail: jetteruk@btinternet.com
Kensal Handling Systems Ltd, Kensal House, President Way, Luton, LU2 9NR Tel: (01582) 425777 Fax: (01582) 425776 E-mail: sales@kensal.com
Lawtronic Ltd, Hamlin Way, King's Lynn, Norfolk, PE30 4NG Tel: (01553) 765247 Fax: (01553) 692147
M B Controls & Installation, 3 White Swan Industrial Estate, Derker Street, Oldham, OL1 3LY Tel: 0161-628 5026 Fax: 0161-628 5027 E-mail: mikeholt@mbcontrols.fsnet.co.uk
Macdonald Humfrey Automation Ltd, 29-35 Bolton Road, Luton, LU1 3HY Tel: (01582) 405741 Fax: (01582) 453237 E-mail: sales@mhaltd.co.uk
Measurement Aids Ltd, 90-92 Tontine Street, Folkestone, Kent, CT20 1JW Tel: (01303) 850722 Fax: (01303) 220380
Micaline Electrical Systems Ltd, Unit 9, Block B Wednesbury Trading Estate, Darlaston Road, Wednesbury, West Midlands, WS10 7JN Tel: 0121-556 5194 Fax: 0121-556 4953
Midvale Electrical Engineering Co. Ltd, 20 Butlers Leap, Rugby, Warwickshire, CV21 3RQ Tel: (01788) 543216 Fax: (01788) 540899 E-mail: sales@midvale-electrical.com
Moeller Holding Ltd, PO Box 35 Gatehouse Close, Aylesbury, Buckinghamshire, HP19 8DH Tel: (01296) 393322 Fax: (01296) 421854 E-mail: marketingl@moeller.co.uk
PD Electronics Ltd, The Old Barn, Woods Lane, Potterspury, Towcester, Northamptonshire, NN12 7PT Tel: (01908) 543150 Fax: (01908) 543139
Press Control Systems, Unit 6 Tinsley Street, Tipton, West Midlands, DY4 7LH Tel: 0121-557 0001 Fax: 0121-557 0002
Systech UK Ltd, Willow House, Kingswood Business Park, Albrighton, Wolverhampton, WV7 3AU Tel: (01902) 373276 Fax: (01902) 373081 E-mail: john@systechuk.com
Tes Europe Ltd, Sandyland, North End, Wisbech, Cambridgeshire, PE13 1PE Tel: (01945) 474809 Fax: (01945) 589591 E-mail: tes_europe@freenet.co.uk

ELECTRIC CONTROL SYSTEMS – *continued*

Testbank Ship Repair & Boiler Co. Ltd, Western Avenue, Western Docks, Southampton, SO15 0HH Tel: (023) 8078 7878 Fax: (023) 8078 7826 E-mail: admin@testbank.co.uk
▶ Theocrest Ltd, Cavans Way, Binley Industrial Estate, Binley Industrial Estate, Coventry, CV3 2SF Tel: (024) 7644 5758 Fax: (024) 7645 6438 E-mail: brian@theocrest.co.uk
Towerglens Ltd, Dock Lane Industrial Estate, Turner St, Dudley, West Midlands, DY1 1SD Tel: (01384) 455025 Fax: (01384) 451300 E-mail: sales@towerglens.com
Ultra Electronics Ltd, Armitage Road, Rugeley, Staffordshire, WS15 1DR Tel: (01889) 503300 Fax: (01889) 572929 E-mail: enquiries@pmes.com
Varcol Electrical Services Ltd, Cornwall Street, Manchester, M11 2WQ Tel: 0161-223 9696 Fax: 0161-223 0976 E-mail: sales@varcol.co.uk
Volex, Butts Mill, Butts Street, Leigh, Lancashire, WN7 3AD Tel: (01942) 672393 Fax: (01942) 677395 E-mail: sales@volexwiring.com
Westminster Controls Ltd, Unit 3 Pym Street, Leeds, LS10 1PG Tel: 0113-288 4500 Fax: 0113-246 0791 E-mail: info@westminstercontrols.com
Wyke Electrical Control Ltd, Unit 1, St Marks Square, Hull, HU3 2DQ Tel: (01482) 328630 Fax: (01482) 320674

ELECTRIC COOKERS

Aga Factory Shop, Station Road, Ketley, Telford, Shropshire, TF1 5AQ Tel: (01952) 642024 Fax: (01952) 243138 E-mail: info@aga-web.co.uk
Electrolux, Merrington Lane Trading Estate, Spennymoor, County Durham, DL16 7UU Tel: (01388) 814141 Fax: (01388) 812753 E-mail: graham.metcalfe@electrolux.co.uk
Glen Dimplex Cooking Ltd, Stoney Lane, Whiston, Prescot, Merseyside, L35 2XW Tel: 0151-426 6551 Fax: 0151-426 3261
Inman & Co Electrical Ltd, 2-4 Orgreave Place, Sheffield, S13 9LU Tel: 0114-254 2400 Fax: 0114-254 2410 E-mail: sales@inmanselectrical.co.uk
Johnson & Johnson Furniture plc, Unit 12-19 Guinness Road Trading Estate, Guinness Road, Trafford Park, Manchester, M17 1SB Tel: 0161-872 7041 Fax: 0161-872 7351 E-mail: mail@jjff.co.uk

ELECTRIC CURRENT CONDUCTORS

Wampfler Co Ltd, Unit B4, Altrincham Business Park, Stuart Road, Broadheath, Altrincham, Cheshire, WA14 5GJ Tel: 0161-929 6032 Fax: 0161-928 9126 E-mail: wampfler.uk@wampfler.com

ELECTRIC DRILL HEADS

▶ J. S. Bruce Engineering, 5 French Street, Ashton-under-Lyne, Lancashire, OL6 9PP Tel: 0161 3399476 Fax: 0161 3399476 E-mail: john@jsbruceengineering.co.uk

ELECTRIC FENCING

Electranets Ltd, 31 Westfield Avenue, Brockworth, Gloucester, GL3 4AU Tel: (01452) 617841 Fax: (01452) 617841 E-mail: roy@electranets.fsnet.co.uk
Horizont UK Ltd, Gloucester, GL2 8YS Tel: (01452) 300450 Fax: (01452) 308776 E-mail: bramley@horizont.com
Hotline Electric Fencing Ltd, Wharf Road, NEWTON ABBOT, Devon, TQ12 2DA Tel: (01626) 331188 Fax: (01626) 331810 E-mail: sales@hotline-fencing.co.uk
Knox Industries Ltd, Clearview, Scholague Road, Abbeylands, Isle of Man, IM4 5BU Tel: (01624) 674434 Fax: (01624) 674434
Rappa Fencing Ltd, Steepleton Hill, Stockbridge, Hampshire, SO20 6JE Tel: (01264) 810665 Fax: (01264) 810079 E-mail: sales@rappa.co.uk
Renco, Bath Road Trading Estate, Lightpill, Stroud, Gloucestershire, GL5 3QF Tel: (01453) 752154 Fax: (01453) 752155 E-mail: sales@renco-netting.co.uk
Rutland Electric Fencing Co Ltd, Fencing House, 8 Landsend Way, Oakham, Rutland, LE15 6RF Tel: (01572) 722455 Fax: (01572) 757614 E-mail: enquiries@rutland-electric-fencing.co.uk

ELECTRIC FIRES

▶ Creative Fires UK Ltd, Unit 14, Arnside Road, Waterlooville, Hampshire, PO7 7UP Tel: (023) 9223 3030
Fires4U, PO Box 6843, Swadlincote, Derbyshire, DE12 7XX Tel: (0845) 6120001 E-mail: sales@fires4u.co.uk
▶ Gibson and Goold, 1-3 Scotland Street, Glasgow, G5 8LS Tel: (01292) 268478

ELECTRIC FLASH BUTT WELDING EQUIPMENT

Donald Engineering Services Ltd, 131 Walmley Road, Sutton Coldfield, West Midlands, B76 1QL Tel: 0121-351 4057 E-mail: donaldengser@aol.com

ELECTRIC FURNACES

Efco Group Ltd, 29 Avro Way, Brooklands Business Park, Weybridge, Surrey, KT13 0YZ Tel: (01932) 350534 Fax: (01932) 350543
Eurofusion Ltd, Ituri, Darcy Rise, Little Baddow, Chelmsford, CM3 4SN Tel: (01245) 221235 Fax: (0870) 4296791 E-mail: glass@eurofusion.co.uk
Furnace Construction Co. Ltd, Newton Moor Industrial Estate, Hyde, Cheshire, SK14 4LF Tel: 0161-368 8419 Fax: 0161-368 3813 E-mail: sales@furnace-construction.co.uk
Hendrick Industrial Equipment Ltd, Unit 32d The Washford Industrial Estate, Heming Road, Redditch, Worcestershire, B98 0DH Tel: (01527) 523712 Fax: (01527) 514545 E-mail: heat@hendrick.co.uk
Inductotherm Europe Ltd, The Furlong, Berry Hill Industrial Estate, Droitwich, Worcestershire, WR9 9AH Tel: (01905) 795100 Fax: (01905) 795138 E-mail: sales@inductotherm.co.uk
Isoheat, Unit 5, Aurillac Court, Hallcroft Industrial Estate, Aurilac Way, Retford, Nottinghamshire, DN22 7PX Tel: (01777) 708811 Fax: (01777) 708866 E-mail: isoheat@fsbdial.co.uk
Monometer Holdings Ltd, Monometer House, Rectory Grove, Leigh-on-Sea, Essex, SS9 2HN Tel: (01702) 472201 Fax: (01702) 715112 E-mail: sales@monometer.co.uk
Vecstar Furnaces, Unit 11-12 Dunston Trading Estate, Foxwood Road, Chesterfield, Derbyshire, S41 9RF Tel: (01246) 260094 Fax: (01246) 450213 E-mail: enquiries@vecstar.co.uk
W P A Furnaces & Engineering Projects Ltd, 24 Monmer Close Industrial Estate, Willenhall, West Midlands, WV13 1JR Tel: (01902) 631155 Fax: (01902) 602615

ELECTRIC FUSES

Eaton MEM, Grimshaw Lane, Middleton, Manchester, M24 1GQ Tel: 0161-655 8900 Fax: 0161-626 1709 E-mail: ukcommorders@eaton.com
Lawson Fuses Ltd, Meadowfield, Ponteland, Newcastle upon Tyne, NE20 9SW Tel: (01661) 823232 Fax: (01661) 824213 E-mail: sales@lawson-fuses.co.uk
Le Carbone Great Britain Ltd, South Street, Portslade, Brighton, BN41 2LX Tel: (01273) 415701 Fax: (01273) 415673
Vernon's Fuse Co, 22 Trinity Trading Estate, Tribune Drive, Sittingbourne, Kent, ME10 2PG Tel: (01795) 471234 Fax: (01795) 476996

ELECTRIC GATE KITS

▶ Instant Access Garage Doors, Caenant House, Mill Road, Caerphilly, Mid Glamorgan, CF83 3FE Tel: (029) 2088 4622 E-mail: info@autogateswales.co.uk

ELECTRIC GEARED MOTORS

Amir Power Transmission Ltd, Amir House, Maxted Road, Hemel Hempstead Industrial Estate, Hemel Hempstead, Hertfordshire, HP2 7DX Tel: (01442) 212671 Fax: (01442) 246640 E-mail: amirpower@amirpower.co.uk
Bennett Electrical Co, 6-8 Reginald St, Burslem, Stoke-on-Trent, ST6 1DU Tel: (01782) 825281 Fax: (01782) 575120 E-mail: motors@bennettelectrical.com
Danfoss Bauer, Unit 1, Natlane Business Park, Winsford, Cheshire, CW7 3BS Tel: (01606) 868600 Fax: (01606) 868603 E-mail: sales@danfoss.com
H B Industrial Services Ltd, 15 Kingdom Close, Fareham, Hampshire, PO15 5TJ Tel: (01489) 575222 Fax: (01489) 575666 E-mail: sales@hbindustrialservices.co.uk
Mellor Electrics Ltd, Sett End Road, Shadsworth Business Park, Blackburn, BB1 2NW Tel: (01254) 53854 Fax: (01254) 678625 E-mail: info@mellorelectrics.co.uk
Nord Gear Ltd, 11 Barton Lane, Abingdon, Oxfordshire, OX14 3NB Tel: (01235) 534404 Fax: (01235) 534414 E-mail: info@nord.uk.com
Opperman Mastergear Ltd, Hambridge Lane, Newbury, Berkshire, RG14 5TS Tel: (01635) 811500 Fax: (01635) 811501 E-mail: sales@opperman-mastergear.co.uk
Specialty Electric Motor Sales, 23 Winston Business Centre, Chartwell Road, Lancing, West Sussex, BN15 8TU Tel: (01903) 765652 Fax: (01903) 765654 E-mail: info@sp-t.co.uk
Zella Instrumentation & Control Ltd, Brunel Drive, Newark, Nottinghamshire, NG24 2EG Tel: (01636) 704370 Fax: (01636) 640296 E-mail: sales@zella-instrumentation.co.uk

ELECTRIC GRADE STEEL

Cogent Orb Electrical Steels, PO Box 30, Newport, Gwent, NP19 0XT Tel: (01633) 290033 Fax: (01633) 294592 E-mail: sales@cogent-power.com
Union Steel Products Ltd, Row End, Berrow Green Road, Martley, Worcester, WR6 6PQ Tel: (01886) 888828 Fax: (01886) 888853

ELECTRIC GREENHOUSE HEATERS

▶ Cambridge Glass House Co. Ltd, 236 Main Road, Newport, Brough, North Humberside, HU15 2RH Tel: (01430) 449440 Fax: (01430) 449331 E-mail: info@cambridgeglasshouse.co.uk
▶ Parwin Heaters UK Ltd, 21 High Haden Road, Glatton, Huntingdon, Cambridgeshire, PE28 5RU Tel: (01487) 834630 Fax: (01487) 830407 E-mail: paul@metalspec.freeserve.co.uk

ELECTRIC HAMMER COMPONENT TOOLS

Black & Decker Ltd, 210 Bath Road, Slough, SL1 3YD Tel: (01753) 511234 Fax: (01753) 551155 E-mail: info@blackdecker.co.uk

ELECTRIC HAND DRYERS

Dudley Industries, Preston Road, Lytham St. Annes, Lancashire, FY8 5AT Tel: (01253) 738311 Fax: (01253) 794393 E-mail: dudley@cyberscape.net
Heatrae Sadia, 1 Hurricane Way, Norwich, NR6 6EA Tel: (01603) 420100 Fax: (01603) 420218 E-mail: sales@heatraesadia.com
The Wandsworth Group Ltd, Albert Drive, Sheerwater, Woking, Surrey, GU21 5SE Tel: (01483) 713400 Fax: (01483) 740384 E-mail: info@wandsworthgroup.com
Warner Howard Group Ltd, Woodgrange Avenue, Harrow, Middlesex, HA3 0XD Tel: (020) 8927 0100 Fax: (020) 8927 0101 E-mail: sales@warnerhoward.co.uk

ELECTRIC HAND TOOLS

▶ I T W Contstructions Products, Unit R8, Blair Coart, 110 Borain Street, Portdundas Business Park, Glasgow, G4 9XG Tel: 0141-342 1660 Fax: 0141-332 7489 E-mail: sales@itwcp.co.uk
▶ Pen Tools Ltd, Jubilee Building, Westfields Trading Estate, Hereford, HR4 9NS Tel: (01432) 273018

ELECTRIC HARNESSES, *See Cable Assembly etc*

ELECTRIC HEATERS

Astra Distribution Manchester Ltd, Unit 6, Lowercroft Business Park, Lowercroft Road, Bury, Lancashire, BL8 3PA Tel: 0161-797 3222 Fax: 0161-797 3444 E-mail: support@astra247.com
Brooks Partners Ltd, The Paddocks, Honey Hill, Wokingham, Berkshire, RG40 3BD Tel: (01344) 772456 Fax: (01344) 776733 E-mail: sales@brookspartners.co.uk
Delonghi Ltd, 15-16 Bridle Close, Finedon Road Industrial Estate, Wellingborough, Northamptonshire, NN8 4RN Tel: (01933) 442040 Fax: (01933) 441891 E-mail: marketing@delonghi.co.uk
H E Randall & Son, Longworth Street, Chorley, Lancashire, PR7 2HT Tel: (01257) 263854 Fax: (01257) 263854
▶ Heat & Cool, Sands Business Centre, Sands Road, Farnham, Surrey, GU10 1PX Tel: (0870) 0427484 E-mail: sales@heatandcool.co.uk
Howden Electro Heating (Howden Electroheating), 10-12 Belgowan Street, Bellshill Industrial Estate, Bellshill, Lanarkshire, ML4 3NS Tel: (01698) 573111 Fax: (01698) 573121 E-mail: sales@howden-electroheating.com
Lectroheat Industrial Heating Ltd, Unit 16 Pantglas Industrial Estate, Bedwas, Caerphilly, Mid Glamorgan, CF83 8DR Tel: (029) 2088 9300 Fax: (029) 2086 1872 E-mail: info@lectroheat.com
Noble Heating (U K) Ltd, Unit 19-21, Small Heath Trading Estate, Armoury Road, Birmingham, B11 2RJ Tel: 0121-773 0114 Fax: 0121-766 6589 E-mail: info@noboheatinguk.com
Scanlock Overseas Property Agents, 208 Pensby Road, Heswall, Wirral, Merseyside, CH60 7RJ Tel: 0151-342 6530 Fax: 0151-342 6530 E-mail: sales@scanlock.com
Thama Holdings Ltd, Sharrocks Street, Wolverhampton, WV1 3RP Tel: (01902) 457575 Fax: (01902) 457797

ELECTRIC HEATERS FOR GAS OR AIR

Heatrae Industrial, Duncombe Road, Bradford, West Yorkshire, BD8 9TB Tel: (01274) 362798 Fax: (01274) 493580 E-mail: sales@heatrae-industrial.com

ELECTRIC HEATING MANTLES OR PADS

Electrothermal Engineering Ltd, 419 Sutton Road, Southend-on-Sea, SS2 5PH Tel: (01702) 612211 Fax: (01702) 619888 E-mail: sales@electrothermal.co.uk

ELECTRIC HIGH VOLTAGE TEST EQUIPMENT

Megar Ltd, Archcliffe Road, Dover, Kent, CT17 9EN Tel: (01304) 502100 Fax: (01304) 241491 E-mail: uksales@megger.com
Oxford Applied Research Ltd, Unit 31 Crawley Mill Industrial Estate, Dry Lane, Crawley, Witney, Oxfordshire, OX29 9SP Tel: (01993) 773575 Fax: (01993) 702326 E-mail: sales@oaresearch.co.uk
T. & R. Test Equipment Ltd, 15-16 Woodbridge Meadows, Guilford, Guildford, Surrey, GU1 1BJ Tel: (01483) 207428 Fax: (01483) 235759 E-mail: sales@trtest.com

ELECTRIC HOISTS

Abc Lifting Equipment Ltd, 4 Alliance Business Park, Corporation Street, Accrington, Lancashire, BB5 0RR Tel: (01254) 233349 Fax: (01254) 233533 E-mail: sales@abclifting.co.uk
Crane Services Ltd, Platts Road, Stourbridge, West Midlands, DY8 4YR Tel: (01384) 370318 Fax: (01384) 440203 E-mail: sales@craneservices.co.uk
Lifting Gear Hire plc, 120 Bolton Road, Atherton, Manchester, M46 9YZ Tel: (01942) 878081 Fax: (01942) 895018 E-mail: info@lgh.co.uk
London Hoist Ltd, Rifle Street, London, E14 6PB Tel: (020) 7538 4833 Fax: (020) 7515 3593 E-mail: info@londonhoist.co.uk
Matterson King Cranes, PO Box 31, Glasgow, G15 8TE Tel: 0141-944 4000 Fax: 0141-944 0111 E-mail: pct@pctgroup.co.uk
Pfaff-Silberblau Ltd, Prenton Way, North Cheshire Trading Estate, Prenton, Merseyside, CH43 3DU Tel: 0151-609 0099 Fax: 0151-609 0852 E-mail: anyone@pfaff-silberblau.co.uk
R Stahl Ltd, Unit 43 Stahl House Elmdon Trading Estate, Bickenhill Lane, Birmingham, B37 7HE Tel: 0121-767 6400 Fax: 0121-767 6480 E-mail: info@rstahl.co.uk

ELECTRIC LAMP/LIGHT BULB CAPPING ADHESIVES

Glass Bond N W Ltd, Westside Industrial Estate, Jackson Street, St. Helens, Merseyside, WA9 3AT Tel: (01744) 730334 Fax: (01744) 451661 E-mail: sales@glassbond.co.uk

ELECTRIC LAMPS OR LIGHT BULBS, *See also headings under Lamps*

▶ Abbeylite Ltd, 3 Longmead, Shaftesbury, Dorset, SP7 8PL Tel: (01747) 852583 Fax: (01747) 851169
Albion Electric Stores Ltd, South Accommodation Road, Leeds, LS10 1PR Tel: 0113-245 0196 Fax: 0113-234 1408 E-mail: sales@albionelectric.co.uk
▶ Astro Lighting Ltd, Unit 21 Mead Industrial Park, Riverway, Harlow, Essex, CM20 2SE Tel: (01279) 427001 Fax: (01279) 427002 E-mail: sales@astrolighting.co.uk
Ceravision Lighting Mnfrs, Innovation Centre, Bletchley Park, Bletchley, Milton Keynes, MK3 6EB Tel: (01908) 371463 Fax: (01908) 370792
Designed Architectural Lighting Ltd, 6 Conqueror Court, Spilsby Road, Harold Hill, Romford, RM3 8SB Tel: (01708) 381999 Fax: (01708) 381585
▶ Direct Lighting Distributors Ltd, Gibbs Marsh Trading Estate, Stalbridge, Sturminster Newton, Dorset, DT10 2RY Tel: (01963) 362697 Fax: (01963) 363445
Eldis Electrical Distributors, 239-242 Great Lister Street, Birmingham, B7 4BS Tel: 0121-359 4521 Fax: 0121-333 1432 E-mail: eldis@eldis.co.uk
▶ Heathfield & Co., 2 Priory Road, Tonbridge, Kent, TN9 2AF Tel: (01732) 350450 Fax: (01732) 353525 E-mail: sales@heathfield.co.uk
▶ The Lighting & Interiors Group Ltd, Cobden Mill, Bentinck Street, Farnworth, Bolton, BL4 7EP Tel: (01204) 707277 Fax: (01204) 861890

ELECTRIC LAMPS OR LIGHT BULBS

– continued

▶ Mallatite Ltd, Units 5-6 Creswell Industrial Estate, Colliery Road, Creswell, Worksop, Nottinghamshire, S80 4BX Tel: (01909) 724465 Fax: (01909) 724198

Martech UK Ltd, Conway House, Thornhill Road, Dewsbury, West Yorkshire, WF12 9QQ Tel: (01924) 482700 Fax: (01924) 438388 E-mail: sales@martech-uk.com

▶ Peter Martin Lighting Design Ltd, Unit 1 Lincoln Business Park, Lincoln Road, High Wycombe, Buckinghamshire, HP12 3RD Tel: (01494) 464363 Fax: (01494) 462413

Primarc Marketing, Unit 8 Wycombe Road, Wembley, Middlesex, HA0 1RH Tel: (020) 8900 8535 Fax: (020) 8900 2232 E-mail: sales@primarc.co.uk

▶ Seven Day Signs Ltd, Millhall, Stirling, FK7 7LT Tel: (01786) 470111 Fax: (01786) 470111

Specialist Lighting Co. Ltd, 49 The Broadway, Cheam, Sutton, Surrey, SM3 8BL Tel: (020) 8643 3110 Fax: (020) 8770 1911 E-mail: sic-@hotmail.com

Specialist Lighting Co. Ltd, 49 The Broadway, Cheam, Sutton, Surrey, SM3 8BL Tel: (020) 8643 3110 Fax: (020) 8770 1911 E-mail: elc-ltd@hotmail.com

Strickland & Co. (Electrical) Ltd, 113-117 Springfield Road, Windsor, Berkshire, SL4 3PZ Tel: (01753) 830040 Fax: (01753) 867894 E-mail: ccelectrical@btconnect.com

▶ Tamlite Lighting, Warwick House, Station Road, Kenilworth, Warwickshire, CV8 1JJ Tel: (01926) 858126

▶ Victory Lighting, Quay West, Salamander Quay, Harefield, Uxbridge, Middlesex, UB9 6NZ Tel: (01895) 821821 Fax: (01895) 821822

W F O L C Ltd, Unit 6 Woking Business Park, Albert Drive, Woking, Surrey, GU21 5JY Tel: (01483) 727571 Fax: (01483) 725066

Wilson Electrical Distributors, Unit 6 Waterside, Hamm Moor Lane, Addlestone, Surrey, KT15 2SN Tel: (01932) 848020 Fax: (01932) 820600 E-mail: sales@wilsonelectrical.com

ELECTRIC LIFT CABLES

Cortland Fibron B X Ltd, Unitc R D Park, Stephenson Close, Hoddesdon, Hertfordshire, EN11 0BW Tel: (01992) 471444 Fax: (01992) 471555

ELECTRIC LIFTS

Accord Lift Services Ltd, Unit 5A Beechcroft Farm Industries, Chapel Wood Road, Ash, Sevenoaks, Kent, TN15 7HX Tel: (01474) 879858 Fax: (01474) 874143 E-mail: info@accordlifts.co.uk

Ace Elevators Ltd, Galven House, Bakewell Road, Loughborough, Leicestershire, LE11 5QY Tel: (01509) 265383 Fax: (01509) 269275E-mail: midlands@ace-elevators.co.uk

Ace Elevators Southern Ltd, Millennium House, 74 South Street, Keighley, West Yorkshire, BD21 1DQ Tel: (01535) 602239 Fax: (01535) 661268 E-mail: sales@ace-elevators.co.uk

H. Breakell & Co. (Blackburn) Ltd, P1/15 Parklands, Heywood Distribution Park, Heywood, Lancashire, OL10 2TT Tel: (01706) 369272 Fax: (01706) 629448 E-mail: enquiries@breakell-lifts.co.uk

HSS Lift & Shift, 3 Barnfield Road, Swindon, SN2 2DJ Tel: (01793) 480044 Fax: (01793) 480257

Kone Ltd, 31 Clarendon Road, Belfast, BT1 3DD Tel: (028) 9031 2180 Fax: (028) 9024 6604 E-mail: info@kone.com

Kone plc, Global House Station Place, Fox La North, Chertsey, Surrey, KT16 9HW Tel: (0870) 7701122 Fax: (0870) 7701122 E-mail: salesandmarketing.uk@kone.com

Kone plc, 86 Broad Street, Glasgow, G40 2PX Tel: 0141-554 7604 Fax: 0141-554 6762

Lift & Engineering Services Ltd, 16 Portersfield Road, Cradley Heath, West Midlands, B64 7BN Tel: (01384) 633115 Fax: (01384) 633119 E-mail: mailbox@lift-engineering.co.uk

Oakland Elevators Ltd, 6 Mandervell Road, Oadby, Leicester, LE2 5LL Tel: 0116-272 0800 Fax: 0116-272 0904 E-mail: sales@oakland-elevators.co.uk

Pickerings Europe Ltd, PO Box 19, Stockton-on-Tees, Cleveland, TS20 2AD Tel: (01642) 607161 Fax: (01642) 677638 E-mail: sales@pickerings.com

Propbrook Ltd, 389 Lichfield Road, Birmingham, B6 7SS Tel: 0121-327 7909 Fax: 0121-327 7423

Schindler, Benwell House, Green Street, Sunbury-on-Thames, Middlesex, TW16 6QT Tel: (01932) 785281 Fax: (020) 8818 7999 E-mail: marketing@schindler.com

Stannah Stairlifts LTS, Watt Close, Andover, Hampshire, SP10 3SD Tel: (0800) 715492 E-mail: nigel_dickinson@stannah.co.uk

ELECTRIC LOCOMOTIVES

Clayton Equipment Ltd, Unit 2a, Second Avenue, Centrum One Hundred, Burton-on-Trent, Staffordshire, DE14 2WF Tel: (01283) 524470 Fax: (0870) 1129192 E-mail: info@claytonequipment.com

ELECTRIC MEASURING INSTRUMENT ENGINEERING

A J Mare Instruments, 110 Church Road, Perry Barr, Birmingham, B42 2LF Tel: 0121-356 8511 Fax: 0121-344 3644 E-mail: pimmy-21@hotmail.com

Algo Schetronics Ltd, Crinacott Farm, Pyworthy, Holsworthy, Devon, EX22 6LJ Tel: (01409) 254595 E-mail: info@algo-sales.co.uk

Bells Instrument Engineers, 153 Sunbridge Road, Bradford, West Yorkshire, BD1 2NU Tel: (01274) 720677 Fax: (01274) 720677 E-mail: bells@legend.co.uk

ELECTRIC MEASURING INSTRUMENT MANUFRS

Accent Optical Technologies (U K) Ltd, Haxby Road, York, YO31 8SD Tel: (01904) 715500 Fax: (01904) 645624 E-mail: admin@accentopto.com

C I E Group, Blenheim Industrial Estate, Widdowson Close, Bulwell, Nottingham, NG6 8WB Tel: 0115-977 0075 Fax: 0115-977 0081 E-mail: marketing@cie-ltd.co.uk

Chauvin Arnoux UK Ltd, Waldeck House, Waldeck Road, Maidenhead, Berkshire, SL6 8BR Tel: (01628) 788888 Fax: (01628) 628099 E-mail: sales@chauvin-arnoux.co.uk

Eltime Ltd, 10-14 Hall Road, Heybridge, Maldon, Essex, CM9 4NF Tel: (01621) 859500 Fax: (01621) 855335 E-mail: sales@eltime.co.uk

P & B Weir, Unit 10 Leafield Industrial Estate, Leafield Way, Corsham, Wiltshire, SN13 9SW Tel: (01225) 811449 Fax: (01225) 810909 E-mail: sales@pbweir.com

▶ Rayleigh Instruments Ltd, Raytel House, 19 Brook Road, Rayleigh, Essex, SS6 7XH Tel: (01268) 749300 Fax: (01268) 749309 E-mail: sales@rayleigh.co.uk

ELECTRIC MOTOR BRAKES

Koncar, Unit 43, Brittania Way, Enterprise Industrial Pk, Lichfield, Staffs, WS14 9UY Tel: (01543) 255995 Fax: (01543) 250316

ELECTRIC MOTOR BRUSH HOLDERS

Morgan Rekofa Tinsley Division, 37 John Swains Way, Long Sutton, Spalding, Lincolnshire, PE12 9DQ Tel: (01406) 366400 Fax: (01406) 366626 E-mail: sales@morgan-rekofa.co.uk

ELECTRIC MOTOR COMPONENTS

Child Rewinds, Fairfield Road, Downham Market, Norfolk, PE38 9ET Tel: (01366) 382946 Fax: (01366) 383299

Classic Rewinds Ltd, 50a Park Road, Nottingham, NG7 1JG Tel: 0115-947 3758 Fax: 0115-947 3758

ELECTRIC MOTOR CONTROL EQUIPMENT TO SPECIFICATION

E L F Electric (London) Ltd, 511 Garratt Lane, London, SW18 4SW Tel: (020) 8874 2952 Fax: (020) 8874 2952 E-mail: elfelectric@tiscali.co.uk

ELECTRIC MOTOR CONTROL MAINTENANCE AND REPAIR

Anstee & Ware Group Ltd, Unit 1 St Georges Industrial Estate, St Andrews Road, Bristol, BS11 9HS Tel: 0117-982 0081 Fax: 0117-982 3501 E-mail: admin@ansteeware.co.uk

Mick Davis Rewinds Ltd, Unit 27 Marlow Road Industrial Estate, Marlow Road, Leicester, LE3 2BQ Tel: 0116-282 6956

E L F Electric (London) Ltd, 511 Garratt Lane, London, SW18 4SW Tel: (020) 8874 2952 Fax: (020) 8874 2952 E-mail: elfelectric@tiscali.co.uk

Electric Motor Rewinds, 114 Islingword Road, Brighton, BN2 9SG Tel: (01273) 685925 Fax: (01273) 685925 E-mail: sales@electricmotorrewinds.co.uk

S K Engineering, 16a Tamlaghduff Road, Bellaghy, Magherafelt, County Londonderry, BT45 8JQ Tel: (028) 7938 6561 Fax: (028) 7938 6561

ELECTRIC MOTOR CONTROL MODULES

Central Electrical Co., West Midland House, Gipsy Lane, Willenhall, West Midlands, WV13 2HA Tel: (01902) 482477 Fax: (01902) 482478 E-mail: sales@centralelec.co.uk

ELECTRIC MOTOR CONTROL PANELS

Process Control Panels Ltd, Unit 13 Dunstall Hill Industrial Estate, Gorsebrook Road, Wolverhampton, WV6 0PJ Tel: (01902) 329990 Fax: (01902) 310743

ELECTRIC MOTOR CONTROL SYSTEMS

Child Rewinds, Fairfield Road, Downham Market, Norfolk, PE38 9ET Tel: (01366) 382946 Fax: (01366) 383299

Classic Rewinds Ltd, 50a Park Road, Nottingham, NG7 1JG Tel: 0115-947 3758 Fax: 0115-947 3758

Cortex Controllers Ltd, 50 St. Stephens Place, Cambridge, CB3 0JE Tel: (01223) 368000 Fax: (01223) 462800 E-mail: info@cortexcontrollers.com

Merlyn Electronics, Bridge Mills, Holland Street, Salford, M6 6EL Tel: 0161-745 7697 Fax: 0161-737 5615 E-mail: sales@merlyn-electronics.co.uk

MFA/Como Drills, Felderland Lane, Worth, Deal, Kent, CT14 0BT Tel: (01304) 612132 Fax: (01304) 614696 E-mail: info@mfacomo.com

Modern Drives & Controls Ltd, 5 Barrington Park, Leycroft Road, Leicester, LE4 1ET Tel: 0116-234 0234 Fax: 0116-236 6310 E-mail: modern.drives@connectfree.co.uk

ELECTRIC MOTOR CONTROLLERS

Child Rewinds, Fairfield Road, Downham Market, Norfolk, PE38 9ET Tel: (01366) 382946 Fax: (01366) 383299

ELECTRIC MOTOR DRIVE CONTROL SYSTEMS ENGINEERS

Betech 100pt Ltd, Four Square Building, Thomas Street, Heckmondwike, West Yorkshire, WF16 0LS Tel: (0870) 7573344 Fax: (0870) 7573388 E-mail: sales@betech100pt.co.uk

C J Controls Ltd, Crofty Industrial Estate, Penclawdd, Swansea, SA4 3RS Tel: (01792) 851083 Fax: (01792) 850442 E-mail: sales@cjcontrols.co.uk

Control Gear Distributors Ltd, 3 Farthing Road, Ipswich, IP1 5AP Tel: (01473) 741404 Fax: (01473) 240904 E-mail: sales@controlgear.co.uk

Hadfield CNC & Electronics Co. Ltd, 15 Retford Road, Worksop, Nottinghamshire, S80 2PT Tel: (01909) 500760 Fax: (01909) 542800 E-mail: service@hcnc.co.uk

Masterpower Electronics Ltd, Badentoy Cresent, Badentoy Industrial Estate, Portlethen, Aberdeen, AB12 4YD Tel: (01224) 783700 Fax: (01224) 783701 E-mail: sales@masterpower.co.uk

Motech Control Ltd, Unit 14, Lloyds Court, Manor Royal, Crawley, West Sussex, RH10 9QX Tel: (01293) 440710 Fax: (01293) 440711 E-mail: sales@motech.co.uk

S W Electrical Repairs Ltd, Ashley Street Works, Ashley Street, Princess Way, Burnley, Lancashire, BB12 0BE Tel: (01282) 452411 Fax: (01282) 830167 E-mail: swrewinds@aol.com

Southern Industrial Controls, 118 Faulds Industrial Estate, Tutbury, Burton-on-Trent, Staffs, DE13 9HS Tel: (01283) 814488 Fax: (01283) 814480

Wilson Electric Motor Sales Ltd, 12-18 Radstock Street, Battersea, London, SW11 4AT Tel: (01622) 687128 Fax: (020) 7924 1887

ELECTRIC MOTOR DRIVEN PUMPS

Calpeda Ltd, Wedgwood Road Industrial Estate, Bicester, Oxfordshire, OX26 4UL Tel: (01869) 241441 Fax: (01869) 240681 E-mail: pumps@calpeda.co.uk

Elmbridge Pump Co., 6a Shepherd Road, Gloucester, GL2 5EQ Tel: (01452) 501102 Fax: (01452) 303691 E-mail: sales@elmbridgepump.com

Midland Pump Manufacturing Co. Ltd, Tyseley Industrial Estate, Seeleys Road, Birmingham, B11 2LF Tel: 0121-773 8862 Fax: 0121-771 4363 E-mail: sales@midlandpump.co.uk

ELECTRIC MOTOR MAINTENANCE/REPAIR EQUIPMENT

Mick Davis Rewinds Ltd, Unit 27 Marlow Road Industrial Estate, Marlow Road, Leicester, LE3 2BQ Tel: 0116-282 6956

▶ Ellahi Servo Specialists, 34 Collingwood Court, Riverside Park Industrial Estate, Middlesbrough, Cleveland, TS2 1RP Tel: (01642) 249678 Fax: (01642) 249678

G E M Rewinds Ltd, 4 Welton Road, Wedgnock Industrial Estate, Warwick, CV34 5PZ Tel: (01926) 497778 Fax: (01926) 410128 E-mail: mike@gem-group.co.uk

Whitelegg Machines Ltd, Horsham Road, Beare Green, Dorking, Surrey, RH5 4LQ Tel: (01306) 713200 Fax: (01306) 711865 E-mail: sales@whitelegg.com

ELECTRIC MOTOR MANUFRS,

See also headings under Electric Motors

A E R Ltd, Wotton Road, Kingsnorth Industrial Estate, Ashford, Kent, TN23 6LN Tel: (01233) 632777 Fax: (01233) 661673 E-mail: sales@aer.co.uk

Ace Rewinds Ltd, 25 Ivatt Way, Westwood Industrial Estate, Peterborough, PE3 7PG Tel: (01733) 331464 Fax: (01733) 334075 E-mail: meeksruss@aol.com

Adc Electrical Co. Ltd, Burtree Works, Hertburn Estate, Hertburn, Washington, Tyne & Wear, NE37 2SF Tel: 0191-416 5222 Fax: 0191-416 3996 E-mail: info@adc-electrical.co.uk

Amco Marelli Ltd, Meadow Lane, Loughborough, Leicestershire, LE11 1NB Tel: (01509) 615518 Fax: (01509) 615514 E-mail: sales@amco.fki-et.com

Amir Power Transmission Ltd, Amir House, Maxted Road, Hemel Hempstead Industrial Estate, Hemel Hempstead, Hertfordshire, HP2 7DX Tel: (01442) 212671 Fax: (01442) 246640 E-mail: amirpower@amirpower.co.uk

Anstee & Ware Gloucester Ltd, Bonds Mill, Bristol Road, Stonehouse, Gloucestershire, GL10 3RF Tel: (01453) 826433 Fax: (01453) 827653 E-mail: awglass@aol.com

▶ AS Bearings and Drives Services, 5 Oadby Drive, Hasland, Chesterfield, Derbyshire, S41 0YF Tel: 07813 717741 Fax: 01246 224995 E-mail: alastair.stewart@astewart.fsnet.co.uk

Aston Edwards Electrical Co. Ltd, C Salford Trading Estate, Salford Street, Birmingham, B6 7SH Tel: 0121-327 4064 Fax: 0121-327 7759

Astrosyn International Technology plc, The Old Courthouse, New Road Avenue, Chatham, Kent, ME4 6BE Tel: (01634) 815175 Fax: (01634) 826552 E-mail: astrosyn@btinternet.com

Automotive Industrial Partnerships Ltd, 52 Heming Road, Redditch, Worcestershire, B98 0EA Tel: (01527) 504200 Fax: (01527) 516195 E-mail: sales@aip.demon.co.uk

B E White, Brantwood Road, London, N17 0ED Tel: (020) 8887 1690 Fax: (020) 8884 1865 E-mail: info@bewhite.co.uk

Ball Bearing Centre Ltd, Unit 1-55, 57 Park Royal Road, London, NW10 7JJ Tel: (020) 8965 8833 Fax: (020) 8965 7080 E-mail: ballbrgctr@btconnect.com

Barr R & T Electrical Ltd, 142-158 Pittencrieff Street, Dunfermline, Fife, KY12 8AN Tel: (01383) 722096 Fax: (01383) 739226 E-mail: rtbarr@hotmail.co.uk

Beta Power Engineering Ltd, Beta House Discovery Park, Crossley Road, Stockport, Cheshire, SK4 5BN Tel: 0161-432 9995 Fax: 0161-431 7800 E-mail: beta_power@btconnect.com

Bosch Rexroth Ltd, Cromwell Road, St. Neots, Cambridgeshire, PE19 2ES Tel: (01480) 223200 Fax: (01480) 219052 E-mail: info@boschrexroth.co.uk

Brook Crompton, St. Thomas Road, Huddersfield, HD1 3LJ Tel: (01484) 557200 Fax: (01484) 557201 E-mail: csc@brookcrompton.com

Brush Electrical Machines Ltd, PO Box 18, Loughborough, Leicestershire, LE11 1HJ Tel: (01509) 611511 Fax: (01509) 610440 E-mail: sales@bem.fki-et.com

Burscough Rewinds, Units 1-10, Red Cat Lane, Burscough, Ormskirk, Lancashire, L40 0RA Tel: (01704) 894501 Fax: (01704) 897787 E-mail: sales@burscough-rewinds.co.uk

C H Rewinds Ltd, Smithfold Lane, Worsley, Manchester, M28 0GP Tel: 0161-702 8737 Fax: 0161-702 8730 E-mail: sales@chrewinds.com

Camis Motors & Drives, Wallows Industrial Estate, Brierley Hill, West Midlands, DY5 1QA Tel: (01384) 480645 Fax: (01384) 480745 E-mail: sales@camis.com

Charion Spares Ltd, Unit 7 Paper Mill End Industrial Estate, Birmingham, B44 8NH Tel: 0121-344 4540 Fax: 0121-344 3017 E-mail: charionspares@yahoo.co.uk

▶ Cookstown Rewinds, Derryloran Industrial Estate, Sandholes Road, Cookstown, County Tyrone, BT80 9LU Tel: (028) 8676 1070

Cooper Control Ltd, 20 Greenhill Crescent, Watford Business Park, Watford, WD18 8XG Tel: (01923) 495495 Fax: (01923) 800190 E-mail: nelco@polaron-group.co.uk

▶ Covelec Electric Motor Sales, 1 171 Church Hill Road, Thurmaston, Leicester, LE4 8DH Tel: 0116-269 8111 Fax: 0116-269 8222 E-mail: enquires@covelec.co.uk

D N R Services (Dudley) Ltd, Bay 4, 84 Pensnett Trading Estate, First Avenue, Kingswinford, West Midlands, DY6 7FN Tel: (01384) 400800 Fax: (01384) 298042 E-mail: dnrservices@tiscali.co.uk

David Mcclure Ltd, Mersey Dynamo Works, Range Road, Stockport, Cheshire, SK3 8EF Tel: 0161-474 7362 Fax: 0161-429 0251 E-mail: mail@david-mcclure.co.uk

ELECTRIC MOTOR MANUFRS - *continued*

Mick Davis Rewinds Ltd, Unit 27 Marlow Road Industrial Estate, Marlow Road, Leicester, LE3 2BQ Tel: 0116-282 6956

Deebridge Electrical Engineers, Craigshaw Road, West Tullos Industrial Estate, Aberdeen, AB12 3AR Tel: (01224) 871548 Fax: (01224) 899910 E-mail: info@deebridge.co.uk

Delta Designs Systems Ltd, The Green, Tendring, Clacton-on-Sea, Essex, CO16 0BU Tel: (01255) 830355 Fax: (01255) 830356 E-mail: info@deltadesignsystems.co.uk

Demag Cranes & Components Ltd, Beaumont Rd, Banbury, Oxfordshire, OX16 1QZ Tel: (01295) 676100 Fax: (01295) 226106 E-mail: help@demagcranes.com

E M R Sliverthorn Ltd, 4 Abercorn Commercial Centre, Manor Farm Road, Wembley, Middlesex, HA0 1AN Tel: (020) 8903 1390 Fax: (020) 8903 9092 E-mail: emrsilverthorn@ndirect.co.uk

E O Culverwell Ltd, Station Road, Robertsbridge, East Sussex, TN32 5DG Tel: (01580) 880567 Fax: (01580) 881022 E-mail: cars@eo-culverwell.ltd.uk

Electric Motor Sales Birmingham Ltd, Unit 39 Rovex Business Park, Hay Hall Road, Birmingham, B11 2AG Tel: 0121-765 4899 Fax: 0121-706 5080

Electrical Repairs & Rewind Service Ltd, 2 Charlotte Street, Wakefield, West Yorkshire, WF1 1UL Tel: (01924) 365117 Fax: (01924) 200268

Electro Power Engineering, Brian Royd Lane, Greetland, Halifax, West Yorkshire, HX4 8PE Tel: (01422) 379570 Fax: (01422) 370612 E-mail: enquiries@electropowerengineering.co.uk

▶ Ellahi Servo Specialists, 34 Collingwood Court, Riverside Park Industrial Estate, Middlesbrough, Cleveland, TS2 1RP Tel: (01642) 249678 Fax: (01642) 249678

Feig Electrical, 98 Clarence Road, London, E5 8HB Tel: (020) 8985 7004 Fax: (020) 8985 0107 E-mail: feigelec@aol.com

Francis Chambers & Co., Taylors Lane, Parkgate, Rotherham, South Yorkshire, S62 6EE Tel: (01709) 522175 Fax: (01709) 522944 E-mail: fcco@freenetname.co.uk

G B Electrical Engineering Co, Springvale Street, Willenhall, West Midlands, WV13 1EJ Tel: (01902) 605934 Fax: (01902) 632198 E-mail: sales@gbelectrical.co.uk

Grants Electrical Services (NI) Ltd, Queens Road, Queens Island, Belfast, BT3 9DU Tel: (028) 9045 7061 Fax: (028) 9045 0708 E-mail: sales@grantselectrical.co.uk

Grundfos Pumps Ltd, Orford Court, Green Fold Way, Leigh, Lancashire, WN7 3XJ Tel: (0870) 7503888 Fax: (01942) 605970

Halolux Electric Motors, 606 Romford Road, London, E12 5AF Tel: (020) 8478 8262 Fax: (020) 8478 1686

The Invincible Electrical Engineering Company Ltd, Bay 2 Building 1, Dandy Bank Road, Pensnett Trading Estate, Kingswinford, West Midlands, DY6 7PP Tel: (01384) 270114 Fax: (01384) 400155

John H Rundle Ltd, Main Road, New Bolingbroke, Boston, Lincolnshire, PE22 7LN Tel: (01205) 480431 Fax: (01205) 480132 E-mail: jhrundle@globalnet.co.uk

Johnson Engineering Co., 319 Kennington Road, London, SE11 4QE Tel: (020) 7735 1412 Fax: (020) 7582 1161

Kirkby Lindsey Electrical Engineering Ltd, Crowle Street, Hull, HU9 1RH Tel: (01482) 223937 Fax: (01482) 218261 E-mail: sales@kirkby-lindsey.co.uk

Lincolnshire Rewinds, Long Leys Road, Lincoln, LN1 1DX Tel: (01522) 524283 Fax: (01522) 521122

Lojer Products Ltd, 56 The Broadway, Thatcham, Berkshire, RG19 3HP Tel: (01635) 865882 Fax: (01635) 871087 E-mail: sales@lojerproducts.co.uk

M B K Motor Rewinds Ltd, 10a Lythalls Lane, Coventry, CV6 6FG Tel: (024) 7668 9510 Fax: (024) 7666 2944 E-mail: sales@mbk-rewinds.co.uk

Micro Clutch Developments Ltd, Unit 8-9 Kiln Park Industrial Estate, Searle CR, Weston-super-Mare, Avon, BS23 3XP Tel: (01934) 415606 Fax: (01934) 636658 E-mail: sales@microclutch.com

Microclutch, Units 8-9, Kiln Park, Searle Crescent, Weston-super-Mare, Avon, BS23 3XP Tel: (01934) 415606 Fax: (01934) 636658 E-mail: info@microclutch.com

MPTC Elektrotechnik Ltd, Unit 9, Nether Friarton Ind Units, Friarton Rd, Perth, PH2 8DF Tel: 01738 643433 Fax: 01738 643678

N M B-Minebea (UK) Ltd, Suite 2.2, Doncastle House, Doncastle Road, Bracknell, Berkshire, RG12 8PE Tel: (01344) 426611 Fax: (01344) 485522

Oriental Motor (UK) Ltd, Unit 5, Faraday Office Park, Rankine Road, Basingstoke, Hampshire, RG24 8AH Tel: (01256) 347090 Fax: (01256) 347099 E-mail: info@oriental-motor.co.uk

Re Nu Electrical Service, Murdock Road, Manton Industrial Estate, Bedford, MK41 7PE Tel: (01234) 261933 Fax: (01234) 269120 E-mail: sales@renu-electrical.com

Repairs & Rewinds, 7 Walsall Street, Wednesbury, West Midlands, WS10 9BZ Tel: 0121-556 0806 Fax: 0121-556 0806

Rewinds & J. Windsor & Sons (Engineers) Ltd, 81 Regent Road, Liverpool, L5 9SY Tel: 0151-207 2074 Fax: 0151-298 1442 E-mail: accounts@rjweng.com

Rossi Gearmotors Ltd, Unit 8-9 Phoenix Park, Bayton Road Industrial Estate, Coventry, CV7 9QN Tel: (024) 7664 4646 Fax: (024) 7664 4535 E-mail: sales@rossigears.com

S E W Eurodrive Ltd, Beckbridge Road, Normanton Industrial Estate, Normanton, West Yorkshire, WF6 1QR Tel: (01924) 893855 Fax: (01924) 893702 E-mail: sales@sew-eurodrive.co.uk

▶ Sabar UK Ltd, 17 Duckworth Street, Darwen, Lancashire, BB3 1AR Tel: (01254) 702456 Fax: (01254) 702456 E-mail: sabaruk@ntlworld.com

Leroy Somer Ltd, Heathrow Interchange, Bullsbrook Road, Hayes, Middlesex, UB4 0JR Tel: (020) 8756 7000 Fax: (020) 8756 7028 E-mail: leroy-somer@leroy.somer.co.uk

Specialty Electric Motor Sales, 23 Winston Business Centre, Chartwell Road, Lancing, West Sussex, BN15 8TU Tel: (01903) 765652 Fax: (01903) 765654 E-mail: info@sp-t.co.uk

▶ SPEED Laboratory, University Of Glasgow, Oakfield Avenue, Glasgow, G12 8LT Tel: 0141-330 3157 Fax: 0141-330 3158

Star Electrical Repairs, 5 Englehard Industrial Estate Valley Road, Bilson, Cinderford, Gloucestershire, GL14 2PB Tel: (01594) 826433 Fax: (01594) 826433

Stebon Ltd, Unit 2C Chase Park Industrial Estate, Ring Road, Burntwood, Staffordshire, WS7 8JQ Tel: (01543) 677211 Fax: (01543) 675005 E-mail: sales@stebon.net

Teco Electric Europe Ltd, Teco Building Centrepoint, Marshall Stevens Way, Trafford Park, Manchester, M17 1PP Tel: 0161-877 8025 Fax: 0161-877 8030 E-mail: enquiries@teco.co.uk

Transpower Drives Ltd, 4 Bridle Close, Finedon Road Industrial Estate, Wellingborough, Northamptonshire, NN8 4RN Tel: (01933) 441101 Fax: (01933) 443326 E-mail: sales@transpower.co.uk

Trasfor Electric Ltd, Belwell House, 1A Belwell Lane, 4 Oaks, Sutton Coldfield, West Midlands, B74 4AA Tel: 0121-323 3339 Fax: 0121-323 3301 E-mail: andrew.jackson@trasfor.co.uk

Tyco Networks (UK) Ltd, Wheatley Hall Road, Doncaster, South Yorkshire, DN2 4NB Tel: (01302) 812712 Fax: (01302) 364738

URENCO (Capenhurst) Ltd, Capenhurst, Chester, CH1 6ER Tel: 0151-473 4000 Fax: 0151-473 4384 E-mail: cad@cap.urenco.co.uk

W S Henderson & Son Ltd, Bute Street, Salford, M50 1DU Tel: 0161-736 1511 Fax: 0161-745 8159 E-mail: motorrepairs@wshendersons.freeserve.co.uk

Weg Electric Motors UK Ltd, Unit 28 29, Walkers Road, Moons Moat North Industrial Estate, Redditch, Worcestershire, B98 9HE Tel: (01527) 596748 Fax: (01527) 591133 E-mail: wegsales@wegelectricmotors.co.uk

Wilson Electric Motor Sales Ltd, 12-18 Radstock Street, Battersea, London, SW11 4AT Tel: (01622) 687128 Fax: (020) 7924 1887

Wynnstruments Ltd, Wynn House, Lansdown Estate, Cheltenham, Gloucestershire, GL51 8PL Tel: (01242) 232266 Fax: (01242) 231131 E-mail: sales@wynn.co.uk

ELECTRIC MOTOR POWER CONTROL UNITS

Accurate Controls, 25 Cowley Road, Nuffield Industrial Estate, Poole, Dorset, BH17 0UJ Tel: (01202) 678108 Fax: (01202) 670161 E-mail: info@accurate-controls.ltd.uk

Switchgear & Instrumentation Ltd, Ripley Road, Bradford, West Yorkshire, BD4 7EH Tel: (01274) 734221 Fax: (01274) 731390 E-mail: sales@switchgear.co.uk

ELECTRIC MOTOR REPAIR/ REWIND SPECIALIST SERVICES

A E R Ltd, Wotton Road, Kingsnorth Industrial Estate, Ashford, Kent, TN23 6LN Tel: (01233) 632777 Fax: (01233) 661673 E-mail: sales@aer.co.uk

A E S (Birmingham) Ltd, Unit 39 Rovex Business Park, Hayhall Road, Tyseley, Birmingham, B11 2AG Tel: 0121-706 8251 Fax: 0121-706 5080E-mail: bernard@aesltd63freeserve.co.uk

A J S Electrical Ltd, 14A Brewery Street, Aston, Birmingham, B6 4JB Tel: 0121-685 9991 Fax: 0121-685 9992

A K Controls, Unit 17 Fleetsbridge Business Park, Upton Road, Poole, Dorset, BH17 7AF Tel: (01202) 660061 Fax: (01202) 660200 E-mail: office@akcontrols.com

A S K Rewinds Ltd, Unit 5 Laneside, Metcalf Drive, Altham Industrial Estate, Accrington, Lancashire, BB5 5TU Tel: (01282) 776475 Fax: (01282) 779438 E-mail: sales@ask-rewinds-ltd.co.uk

Adc Electrical Co. Ltd, Burtree Works, Hertburn Estate, Hertburn, Washington, Tyne & Wear, NE37 2SF Tel: 0191-416 5222 Fax: 0191-416 3996 E-mail: info@adc-electrical.co.uk

Aish Electro, Unit 2b Cowley Road, Nuffield Industrial Estate, Poole, Dorset, BH17 0UJ Tel: (01202) 677100 Fax: (01202) 677233 E-mail: serbite@aishem.co.uk

Alpha Electrics Ltd, Unit 11, 158 Tithe St, Leicester, LE5 4BN Tel: 0116-276 8686 Fax: 0116-276 6776 E-mail: info@alphaelectrics.com

Anstee & Ware Gloucester Ltd, Bonds Mill, Bristol Road, Stonehouse, Gloucestershire, GL10 3RF Tel: (01453) 826433 Fax: (01453) 827653 E-mail: awglass@aol.com

Aston Edwards Electrical Co. Ltd, C Salford Trading Estate, Salford Street, Birmingham, B6 7SH Tel: 0121-327 4064 Fax: 0121-327 7759

B & T Rewinds Ltd, 134 Brearley Street, Hockley, Birmingham, B19 3XJ Tel: 0121-359 8398 Fax: 0121-359 7072 E-mail: bandt.rewind@btconnect.com

R. Baker (Electrical) Ltd, Evans Road, Speke, Liverpool, L24 9PB Tel: 0151-486 6760 Fax: 0151-448 1225 E-mail: mail@rbaker.co.uk

Boardley & Roberts Ltd, Plummers Dell, Gipping Road, Great Blakenham, Ipswich, IP6 0JG Tel: (01473) 830272 Fax: (01473) 830274 E-mail: carl@boardley-roberts.co.uk

Bowers Electricals Ltd, Slack Lane, Heanor, Derbyshire, DE75 7GX Tel: (01773) 531531 Fax: (01773) 716171 E-mail: enquiries@bowerselec.co.uk

T.A. Boxall & Co. Ltd, 20 Balcombe Road, Horley, Surrey, RH6 9HR Tel: (01293) 820133 Fax: (01293) 776139 E-mail: ronransley@taboxall.co.uk

Bradford Armature Winding Co. Ltd, 429 Bowling Old Lane, Bradford, West Yorkshire, BD5 8HN Tel: (01274) 728379 Fax: (01274) 731518 E-mail: info@bawco.com

Brook Crompton, St. Thomas Road, Huddersfield, HD1 3LJ Tel: (01484) 557200 Fax: (01484) 557201 E-mail: csc@brookcrompton.com

Brownings Electric Co. Ltd, 11 Thames Road, Barking, Essex, IG11 0HG Tel: (020) 8591 3030 Fax: (020) 8594 7708 E-mail: enquiries@browningselectric.co.uk

Burscough Rewinds, Units 1-10, Red Cat Lane, Burscough, Ormskirk, Lancashire, L40 0RA Tel: (01704) 894501 Fax: (01704) 897787 E-mail: sales@burscough-rewinds.co.uk

C B S Rotary Power Motion Ltd, Lupin Works, Worcester Road, Kidderminster, Worcestershire, DY10 1JR Tel: (01562) 741808 Fax: (01562) 744312 E-mail: kidderminster@cbs-rpm.co.uk

C H Rewinds Ltd, Smithfold Lane, Worsley, Manchester, M28 0GP Tel: 0161-702 8737 Fax: 0161-702 8730 E-mail: sales@chrewinds.com

C & R Munro Ltd, Unit 7e, Bandeath Industrial Estate, Throsk, Stirling, FK7 7NP Tel: (01786) 813618 Fax: (01786) 815113

Cambridge Rewinds Ltd, Cambridge Road Ind Estate, Milton, Cambridge, CB4 6AZ Tel: (01223) 420555 Fax: (01223) 424113

Cegelec Repair & Maintenance Services, Pyewipe, Gilbey Road, Grimsby, South Humberside, DN31 2SJ Tel: (01472) 355869 Fax: (01472) 250363 E-mail: info.uk@cegelec.com

Chappell & Tibbert Ltd, 50 Stamford Road, Easton on the Hill, Stamford, Lincolnshire, PE9 3PA Tel: (01780) 751014 Fax: (01780) 751014

Clark Electrical Industries Ltd, 1e North Crescent, London, E16 4TG Tel: (020) 7474 7404 Fax: (020) 7473 1961 E-mail: enquries@ceiltd.co.uk

Classic Rewinds Ltd, 50a Park Road, Nottingham, NG7 1JG Tel: 0115-947 3758 Fax: 0115-947 3758

Cleveland Electrical Co. Ltd, 50 Park Lane, Liverpool, L1 8HE Tel: 0151-709 6883 Fax: 0151-709 8861 E-mail: enquiries@cleveland-electrical.co.uk

Colchester Rewind & Repairs Ltd, Moss Road, Stanway, Colchester, CO3 0LE Tel: (01206) 768886 Fax: (01206) 768915 E-mail: sales@colchesterrewinds.co.uk

Comlec Units Ltd, Northgate Way, Northgate, Aldridge, Walsall, WS9 8TH Tel: (01922) 456237 Fax: (01922) 455251 E-mail: sales@comlec.co.uk

▶ Coventry Rewinds Ltd, Unit 3b Maguire Industrial Estate, 219 Torrington Avenue, Coventry, CV4 9HN Tel: (024) 7646 7960 Fax: (024) 7647 1460 E-mail: coventryrewinds@btopenworld.com

D L D Rewinds Ltd, Unit 52 Westbrook Trading Estate, Westbrook Road, Trafford Park, Manchester, M17 1AY Tel: 0161-848 7601 Fax: 0161-876 0680

D N R Services (Dudley) Ltd, Bay 4, 84 Pensnett Trading Estate, First Avenue, Kingswinford, West Midlands, DY6 7FN Tel: (01384) 400800 Fax: (01384) 298042 E-mail: dnrservices@tiscali.co.uk

J.W. Davis (Plymouth) Ltd, 14 Stonehouse Street, Plymouth, PL1 3PE Tel: (01752) 664756 Fax: (01752) 660720 E-mail: jwdavisltd@aol.com

Deebridge Electrical Engineers, Craigshaw Road, West Tullos Industrial Estate, Aberdeen, AB12 3AR Tel: (01224) 871548 Fax: (01224) 899910 E-mail: info@deebridge.co.uk

Delta Designs Systems Ltd, The Green, Tendring, Clacton-on-Sea, Essex, CO16 0BU Tel: (01255) 830355 Fax: (01255) 830356 E-mail: info@deltadesignsystems.co.uk

Delton Central Services Ltd, 62-70 Camden Street, Birmingham, B1 3DP Tel: 0121-233 1051 Fax: 0121-236 6178 E-mail: sales@deltongroup.co.uk

Deritend, Shoolbred Works, Cumberland Street, Luton, LU1 3BP Tel: (01582) 729301 Fax: (01582) 729977 E-mail: luton@deritend.co.uk

Deritend, Rollingmill Street, Walsall, WS2 9EN Tel: (01922) 621664 Fax: (01922) 723128 E-mail: walsall@deritend.co.uk

Dowding & Mills Calibration, The Service Centre Watchmoor Point, Watchmoor Road, Camberley, Surrey, GU15 3AD Tel: (01276) 701717 Fax: (01276) 700245 E-mail: calibration.camberley@dowdingandmills.com

Dowding & Mills Engineering Services Ltd, Third Way, Avonmouth, Bristol, BS11 9HL Tel: 0117-938 1188 Fax: 0117-938 0066

Dowding & Mills Engineering Services Ltd, Colwall Street, Sheffield, S9 3WP Tel: 0114-244 6661 Fax: 0114-243 6782 E-mail: engineering.sheffield@dowdingandmills.com

Dowding & Mills Southern Ltd, 24-26 White Post Lane, London, E9 5EP Tel: (020) 8985 8351 Fax: (020) 8985 9615 E-mail: engineering.london@dowdingandmills.com

Dynamic Balancing Services, Hughenden Avenue, High Wycombe, Buckinghamshire, HP13 5SQ Tel: (01494) 462977 Fax: (01494) 462916 E-mail: sales@dynamicbalancing.co.uk

E L F Electric (London) Ltd, 511 Garratt Lane, London, SW18 4SW Tel: (020) 8874 2952 Fax: (020) 8874 2952 E-mail: elfelectric@tiscali.co.uk

E M R Sliverthorn Ltd, 4 Abercorn Commercial Centre, Manor Farm Road, Wembley, Middlesex, HA0 1AN Tel: (020) 8903 1390 Fax: (020) 8903 9092 E-mail: emrsilverthorn@ndirect.co.uk

E M R Windings Ltd, Units 5 & 6, Kiln Park Industrial Park, Searle Crescent, Weston-super-Mare, Somerset, BS23 3XP Tel: (01934) 631374 Fax: (01934) 622698 E-mail: lee.graham@emrelectronics.co.uk

Electric Motor Rewinds, 114 Islingword Road, Brighton, BN2 9SG Tel: (01273) 685925 Fax: (01273) 685925 E-mail: sales@electricmotorrewinds.co.uk

Electric Motor Rewinds, 6 Upper Wharf, Fareham, Hampshire, PO16 0LZ Tel: (01329) 233154 Fax: (01329) 280679

Electric Motor Sales Birmingham Ltd, Unit 39 Rovex Business Park, Hay Hall Road, Birmingham, B11 2AG Tel: 0121-765 4899 Fax: 0121-706 5080

Electric Motor Services, Unit C, Lyttleton Road, Northampton, NN5 7ET Tel: (01604) 587700 Fax: (01604) 580073 E-mail: sales@elemoto.com

Electrical Repairs & Rewind Service Ltd, 2 Charlotte Street, Wakefield, West Yorkshire, WF1 1UL Tel: (01924) 365117 Fax: (01924) 200268

Electro Power Engineering, Brian Royd Lane, Greetland, Halifax, West Yorkshire, HX4 8PE Tel: (01422) 379570 Fax: (01422) 370612 E-mail: enquiries@electropowerengineering.co.uk

European Drives & Motor Repairs Ltd, 9 Mansion Close, Moulton Park Industrial Estate, Northampton, NN3 6RU Tel: (01604) 499777 Fax: (01604) 492777 E-mail: sales@edmr.co.uk

Eurotronix, 19, Telford, Shropshire, TF6 6HD Tel: (01952) 541873 Fax: (01952) 541874 E-mail: sales@eurotronixgb.co.uk

Express Rewinds, 28 Meteor Close, Norwich, NR6 6HR Tel: (01603) 411971 Fax: (01603) 426704

Feig Electrical, 98 Clarence Road, London, E5 8HB Tel: (020) 8985 7004 Fax: (020) 8985 0107 E-mail: feigelec@aol.com

Fletcher Moorland Ltd, Elenora Street, Stoke-On-Trent, ST4 1QG Tel: (01782) 411021 Fax: (01782) 744470 E-mail: info@fletchermoorland.co.uk

Forco Electrical Services Ltd, Alphinbrook Road, Marsh Barton Trading Estate, Exeter, EX2 8RG Tel: (01392) 272639 Fax: (01392) 270498 E-mail: post@forco.co.uk

Francis Chambers & Co., Taylors Lane, Parkgate, Rotherham, South Yorkshire, S62 6EE Tel: (01709) 522175 Fax: (01709) 522944 E-mail: fcco@freenetname.co.uk

Fulmak Rewinding Co., 236a Bennett Street, Long Eaton, Nottingham, NG10 4HH Tel: 0115-973 3216 Fax: 0115-946 9493 E-mail: fulmak@supernet.com

Fyfe Wilson & Co. Ltd, Raynham Road, Bishop's Stortford, Hertfordshire, CM23 5PF Tel: (01279) 653333 Fax: (01279) 504941 E-mail: sales@fyfewilson.co.uk

G B Electrical Engineering Co, Springvale Street, Willenhall, West Midlands, WV13 1EJ Tel: (01902) 605934 Fax: (01902) 632198 E-mail: sales@gbelectrical.co.uk

G E M Rewinds Ltd, 4 Welton Road, Wedgnock Industrial Estate, Warwick, CV34 5PZ Tel: (01926) 497778 Fax: (01926) 410128 E-mail: mike@gem-group.co.uk

Gardner Electrical Group, Unit D Albion Road, Sileby, Loughborough, Leicestershire, LE12 7RA Tel: (01509) 813111 Fax: (01509) 814254

Glasswell & Last Ltd, 28 Eastern Way, Bury St. Edmunds, Suffolk, IP32 7AB Tel: (01284) 761528 Fax: (01284) 723528 E-mail: sales@glasswell-last.com

Goodmarriott & Hursthouse Ltd, Hooton Street, Nottingham, NG3 5GL Tel: 0115-950 5100 Fax: 0115-958 1200E-mail: mail@gandh.co.uk

H M Electric Motor Repair & Sales, 65 Nile Street, London, N1 7RD Tel: (020) 7253 9496 Fax: (020) 7490 2743

Hereford Rewinds Ltd, Unit 12a Thorn Business Park, Rotherwas, Hereford, HR2 6JT Tel: (01432) 275002 Fax: (01432) 353484 E-mail: admin@herefordrewinds.co.uk

ELECTRIC MOTOR REPAIR/REWIND SPECIALIST SERVICES – *continued*

Holt & Martin Electrical Ltd, 100 & 102 Gigg Lane, Bury, Lancashire, BL9 9EW Tel: 0161-797 7782 Fax: 0161-761 5127 E-mail: holt.martin@btinternet.com

Hulme & Gibson Ltd, Mount Pleasant, Stoke-on-Trent, ST1 4AY Tel: (01782) 262525 Fax: (01782) 274057 E-mail: hgrewinds@btinternet.com

Industrial Electrical Repairs, Mount Ambrose, Redruth, Cornwall, TR15 1NR Tel: (01209) 214764 Fax: (01209) 213631

The Invincible Electrical Engineering Company Ltd, Bay 2 Building 1, Dandy Bank Road, Pensnett Trading Estate, Kingswinford, West Midlands, DY6 7PP Tel: (01384) 270114 Fax: (01384) 400155

J Hirst, New Bank Street, Morley, Leeds, LS27 8NT Tel: 0113-253 4679 Fax: 0113-201 2977 E-mail: sales@jhirst.co.uk

J K Electric, East Mews, Station Fields, Church Lane, Garforth, Leeds, LS25 1PL Tel: 0113-286 5857 Fax: 0113-286 0659

J N Building Services Ltd, Cooper Yard, Old Cider Works, Abbotskerswell, Newton Abbot, Devon, TQ12 5NF Tel: (01626) 352056 Fax: (01626) 363599 E-mail: enquiries@jnbuildingservices.com

J R S Rewinds, 71 Halifax Road, Maidenhead, Berkshire, SL6 5ES Tel: (01628) 628964 Fax: (01628) 672333

Jarvis & Evered Ltd, Priorswood Industrial Estate, Taunton, Somerset, TA2 8DG Tel: (01823) 337141 Fax: (01823) 323475 E-mail: jon@jarvisevered.com

John Mcnicol & Co Electrical Engineers Ltd, 123 Elliot Street, Glasgow, G3 8EY Tel: 0141-221 0725 Fax: 0141-248 4569 E-mail: info@johnmcnicol.co.uk

Johnson Engineering Co., 319 Kennington Road, London, SE11 4QE Tel: (020) 7735 1412 Fax: (020) 7582 1161

Kirkby Lindsey Electrical Engineering Ltd, Crowle Street, Hull, HU9 1RH Tel: (01482) 223937 Fax: (01482) 218261 E-mail: sales@kirkby-lindsey.co.uk

Knowlton & Newman, Belvidere Terrace, Southampton, SO14 5QR Tel: (023) 8022 5869 Fax: (023) 8063 1969 E-mail: sales@knsoton.co.uk

Knowlton & Newman (Portsmouth) Ltd, Unit 4, Admiral Park, Portsmouth, PO3 5RQ Tel: (023) 9265 0100 Fax: (023) 9265 1097 E-mail: sales@knports.co.uk

L C Kittow Ltd, 34 Spear Road, Southampton, SO14 6UH Tel: (023) 8032 2650 Fax: (023) 8032 2651 E-mail: info@lckittow.com

L E G Electrical Ltd, 83 High St South, London, E6 6EJ Tel: (020) 8471 8229 Fax: (020) 8472 1817

L S UK Rewind, 12 Bucklands Road, Penmill Trading Estate, Yeovil, Somerset, BA21 5EA Tel: (01935) 476255 Fax: (01935) 433627 E-mail: rewind@rgillard.wannado.co.uk

Laurence, Scott & Electromotors Ltd, Po Box 25, Norwich, NR1 1JD Tel: (01603) 628333 Fax: (01603) 610604 E-mail: sales@laurence-scott.com

Lincolnshire Rewinds, Long Leys Road, Lincoln, LN1 1DX Tel: (01522) 524283 Fax: (01522) 521122

Lutterworth Electrical Services, 1a Market Street, Lutterworth, Leicestershire, LE17 4EJ Tel: (01455) 552511 Fax: (01455) 557812 E-mail: enquiries@lutterworthelectrical.co.uk

M B K Motor Rewinds Ltd, 10a Lythalls Lane, Coventry, CV6 6FG Tel: (024) 7668 9510 Fax: (024) 7666 2944 E-mail: sales@mbk-rewinds.co.uk

M E R Electrical & Mechanical, The Broadway, Mansfield, Nottinghamshire, NG18 2RL Tel: (01623) 621522 Fax: (01623) 627719 E-mail: sales@mer-electrical.co.uk

M J Gilbert & Co., Mill Road, Barnstaple, Devon, EX31 1JQ Tel: (01271) 343442 Fax: (01271) 343442

M & M Rewinds, 15 Dinsdale Road, Croft Business Park, Bromborough, Wirral, Merseyside, CH62 3PY Tel: 0151-334 6808 Fax: 0151-334 6808 E-mail: mandmrew@amserve.com

▶ Massey Coldbeck, Lyntown Trading Estate, Eccles, Manchester, M30 9QG Tel: 0161-789 8867 Fax: 0161-787 7790

Mawdsley's Bristol Electrical Repairs, Barton Manor, Midland Road, Bristol, BS2 0RL Tel: 0117-955 2481 Fax: 0117-955 2483 E-mail: info@mawdsleys.com

Midland Electrical Holdings Ltd, 14 Abbotsinch Road, Grangemouth, Stirlingshire, FK3 9UX Tel: (01324) 486817 Fax: (01324) 474834 E-mail: info@midlandgroup.co.uk

Motor & Armature Rewinds Ltd, 242 London Road, Westcliff-on-Sea, Essex, SS0 7JG Tel: (01702) 330756 E-mail: dnagy69@hotmail.com

P & B Electrical Company, 1a St Dunstans Road, London, SE25 6EU Tel: (020) 8771 6555 Fax: (020) 8771 9867

P G A Rewinds, 58 Temperance Street, Manchester, M12 6DP Tel: 0161-273 4484 Fax: 0161-273 4484

Pennine Electrical Rewinding Ltd, Clamark House, 63 Stalker Lees Road, Sheffield, S11 8NP Tel: 0114-266 3131 Fax: 0114-266 4944 E-mail: info@crystal-abrasives.com

Premium Power Units Ltd, Block 10, Unit 4, Beardmore Way, Clydebank, Dunbartonshire, G81 4HT Tel: 0141-952 4344 Fax: 0141-952 6350 E-mail: sales@premiumpowerunits.co.uk

R W Wilson Ltd, 166 Findon Road, Worthing, West Sussex, BN14 0EL Tel: (01903) 264979 Fax: (01903) 264979 E-mail: mikejupp@btconnect.com

Re Nu Electrical Service, Murdock Road, Manton Industrial Estate, Bedford, MK41 7PE Tel: (01234) 261933 Fax: (01234) 269120 E-mail: sales@renu-electrical.com

Repairs & Rewinds, 7 Walsall Street, Wednesbury, West Midlands, WS10 9BZ Tel: 0121-556 0806 Fax: 0121-556 0806

Rewinds & J. Windsor & Sons (Engineers) Ltd, 81 Regent Road, Liverpool, L5 9SY Tel: 0151-207 2074 Fax: 0151-298 1442 E-mail: accounts@rjweng.com

Romford Electrical Services Ltd, 608 Romford Road, London, E12 5AF Tel: (020) 8478 6065 Fax: (020) 8478 1686

Rotamec Ltd, 4 Winchester Farm, Draycott Road, Cheddar, Somerset, BS27 3RP Tel: (01934) 743165 Fax: (01934) 743168 E-mail: sales@rotamec.co.uk

S W Electrical Repairs Ltd, Ashley Street Works, Ashley Street, Princess Way, Burnley, Lancashire, BB12 0BE Tel: (01282) 452411 Fax: (01282) 830167 E-mail: swrewinds@aol.com

Samco Industrial Rewinds, Irthlingborough Road, Wellingborough, Northamptonshire, NN8 1RA Tel: (01933) 442597 Fax: (01933) 225965 E-mail: samcorewinds@aol.com

Samuel Vickers, 15 Leyland Way, Boston, Lincolnshire, PE21 7SW Tel: (01205) 363289 Fax: (01205) 363289

Scott Electromech Ltd, 314 Ravenhill Road, Belfast, BT6 8GN Tel: (028) 9045 7225 Fax: (028) 9073 2031 E-mail: info@s-em.com

Semec Electrical, Northfleet Industrial Estate, Lower Road, Northfleet, Gravesend, Kent, DA11 9SN Tel: (01322) 382070 Fax: (01322) 382143

Star Electrical Repairs, 5 Englehard Industrial Estate Valley Road, Bilson, Cinderford, Gloucestershire, GL14 2PB Tel: (01594) 826433 Fax: (01594) 826433

Stewart Rewinds Ltd, 1 Mafeking Street, Glasgow, G51 2UZ Tel: 0141-445 3055 Fax: 0141-445 3008

Swift Electrical, Unit 1 Craven Way, Newmarket, Suffolk, CB8 0BW Tel: (01638) 661001 Fax: (01638) 560195 E-mail: swiftsescrubes@hotmail.com

T K Rewinds, 21 Airfield Road, Christchurch, Dorset, BH23 3TG Tel: (01202) 476641 Fax: (01202) 480450

T M J Power Rewinds Ltd, Unit G3 Newington Industrial Estate, London Road, Newington, Sittingbourne, Kent, ME9 7NU Tel: (01795) 843476 Fax: (01795) 843476

Taylor & Goodman Ltd, 7 Cradock Road, Reading, RG2 0LB Tel: 0118-987 1773 Fax: 0118-931 4945 E-mail: sales@taylorgoodman.co.uk

Team Services Ltd, Riverside Road, Pottington, Barnstaple, Devon, EX31 1TE Tel: (01271) 374019 Fax: (01271) 375977 E-mail: sales@teamservices.co.uk

Telford Rewinds Ltd, Unit 5, Halesfield 18, Telford, Shropshire, TF7 4PP Tel: (01952) 580703 Fax: (01952) 580703

Transformotor Ltd, Unit 43 Coneygre Industrial Estate, Tipton, West Midlands, DY4 8XU Tel: 0121-557 4491 Fax: 0121-557 3175

T-T-Electric, Unit 7A, Waterloo Park Industrial Estate, Upper Brook Street, Stockport, Cheshire, SK1 3BP Tel: 0161-480 0037 Fax: 0161-476 4390 E-mail: john.legg@t-t-electric.com

Universal Rewinds Ltd, 273 Wincolmlee, Hull, HU2 0PZ Tel: (01482) 226238 Fax: (01482) 586654 E-mail: rewinds@lineone.net

W S Henderson & Son Ltd, Bute Street, Salford, M50 1DU Tel: 0161-736 1511 Fax: 0161-745 8159 E-mail: motorrepairs@wshendersons.freeserve.co.uk

Walker Rewinds, Unit 4 Station Road Industrial Estate, Madeley, Telford, Shropshire, TF7 5EF Tel: (01952) 582594 Fax: (01952) 582594

Westcliff Armature Winding Co., 369 Westborough Road, Westcliff-On-Sea, Essex, SS0 9TS Tel: (01702) 341854

Wilson Electric Motor Sales Ltd, 12-18 Radstock Street, Battersea, London, SW11 4AT Tel: (01622) 687128 Fax: (020) 7924 1887

Wyre Repairs Ltd, J Boyn Valley Industrial Estate, Boyn Valley Road, Maidenhead, Berkshire, SL6 4EJ Tel: (01628) 674691 Fax: (01628) 674691 E-mail: info@wyrerepairs.co.uk

ELECTRIC MOTOR REWIND SEALS

Industrial (Motor) Rewinds Ltd, Haut De L'Orme, Rue De Haut De L'Orme, Trinity, Jersey, JE3 5FP Tel: (01534) 865782 Fax: (01534) 865786 E-mail: rayimp@hotmail.com

ELECTRIC MOTOR SLIDE RAILS

Cooper Slide Rails Ltd, Unit 12 Pedmore Road Industrial Estate, Pedmore Road, Brierley Hill, West Midlands, DY5 1TJ Tel: (01384) 75500 Fax: (01384) 79712 E-mail: coopersliderails@aol.com

ELECTRIC MOTOR SPEED CONTROL EQUIPMENT

Toshiba International (Europe) Ltd, Albany House, 71-79 Station Road, West Drayton, Middlesex, UB7 7LT Tel: (01895) 427400 Fax: (01895) 449493 E-mail: info@til.toshiba-global.com

ELECTRIC MOTOR SPEED CONTROLLERS

A & M Drive Systems, 16 Bayfield Avenue, Frimley, Camberley, Surrey, GU16 8TU Tel: (01276) 26651 Fax: (01276) 685193

Alpha Electrics Ltd, Unit 11, 158 Tithe St, Leicester, LE5 4BN Tel: 0116-276 8686 Fax: 0116-276 6776 E-mail: info@alphaelectrics.com

▶ Cadamp Ltd, Wharfedale House, Great Pasture Lane, Burley in Wharfedale, Ilkley, West Yorkshire, LS29 7DB Tel: (01943) 863884 Fax: (01943) 862630 E-mail: info@cadamp.co.uk

Mobile Electro Service Ltd, Units 1-2 Buntsford Park Road, Bromsgrove, Worcestershire, B60 3DX Tel: (01527) 579795 Fax: (01527) 579963 E-mail: sales@mesuk.co.uk

Ralspeed Ltd, Hurstwood Court, Mercer Way Shadsworth BSNS Park, Shadsworth Business Park, Blackburn, BB1 2QU Tel: (01254) 582345 Fax: (01254) 668414 E-mail: sales@ralspeed.com

▶ Standel Dawman Ltd, Pasture Lane Works, Factory La, Barrowford, Nelson, Lancs, BB9 6ES Tel: (01282) 613175 Fax: (01282) 615429E-mail: sales@standeldawman.uk.com

Stock Electronics Ltd, 10 Edison Road, Salisbury, SP2 7NU Tel: (01722) 321758 Fax: (01722) 413079 E-mail: enquiries@stockelectronics.co.uk

ELECTRIC MOTOR STARTER SYSTEMS

Interstart Ltd, Unit 8a Shirebrook Business Park, Acreage Lane, Shirebrook, Mansfield, Nottinghamshire, NG20 8RN Tel: (01623) 748987 Fax: (01623) 748987

▶ P S V Transport Systems Ltd, Unit 21 Impresa Park, Pindar Road, Hoddesdon, Hertfordshire, EN11 0DL Tel: (01992) 479950 Fax: (01992) 471676 E-mail: sales@psv-transport-systems.co.uk

Prestolite Electric, 12-16 Bristol Road, Greenford, Middlesex, UB6 8UP Tel: (020) 8231 1000 Fax: (020) 8575 9575 E-mail: sales@prestolite.co.uk

ELECTRIC MOTOR WINDING/ REWINDING EQUIPMENT

Pennine Electrical Rewinding Ltd, Clamark House, 63 Stalker Lees Road, Sheffield, S11 8NP Tel: 0114-266 3131 Fax: 0114-266 4944 E-mail: info@crystal-abrasives.com

Stralfors P.L.C., Cardew Way, Redruth, Cornwall, TR15 1SH Tel: (01209) 312800 Fax: (01209) 312900 E-mail: enquiries@stralfors.co.uk

ELECTRIC MOTORS, AIRCRAFT/ AEROSPACE

Airscrew Ltd, 111 Windmill Road, Sunbury-on-Thames, Middlesex, TW16 7EF Tel: (01932) 765822 Fax: (01932) 761098 E-mail: airscrew@ametek.co.uk

ELECTRIC MOTORS, MIL SPECIFICATIONS

Haydon Switch (HSI) (Henley), Treetops House, Gillotts Lane, Henley-on-Thames, Oxfordshire, RG9 1PT Tel: (01491) 579118 Fax: (01491) 412211 E-mail: sales@acdcsystems.com

ELECTRIC MOTORS, TO CUSTOMER SPECIFICATION

Airscrew Ltd, 111 Windmill Road, Sunbury-on-Thames, Middlesex, TW16 7EF Tel: (01932) 765822 Fax: (01932) 761098 E-mail: airscrew@ametek.co.uk

Electric Motor Sales Birmingham Ltd, Unit 39 Rovex Business Park, Hay Hall Road, Birmingham, B11 2AG Tel: 0121-765 4899 Fax: 0121-706 5080

The Morley Electrical Engineering Co. Ltd, Bradford Road, Stanningley, Pudsey, West Yorkshire, LS28 6QB Tel: 0113-257 1734 Fax: 0113-257 0751 E-mail: sales@morleymotors.com

ELECTRIC PANEL HEATERS

▶ Heat & Cool, Sands Business Centre, Sands Road, Farnham, Surrey, GU10 1PX Tel: (0870) 0427484 E-mail: sales@heatandcool.co.uk

ELECTRIC POWER MANAGEMENT

▶ Energy Integration Ltd, The Lodge, Nettlestead Place, Maidstone Road, Nettlestead, Maidstone, Kent, ME18 5HA Tel: (07752) 539887 E-mail: info@energy-integration.com

ELECTRIC PROJECTION SCREENS

Sahara Presentation Systems P.L.C., Williams House, Hailey Road, Erith, Kent, DA18 4AA Tel: (020) 8319 7777 Fax: (020) 8319 7775 E-mail: jsa@sahara-products.com

ELECTRIC RADIATOR HEATERS

Heattend Ltd, 9 Concorde Road, Norwich, NR6 6BH Tel: (01603) 787505 Fax: (01603) 429500 E-mail: sales@heattend.co.uk

ELECTRIC RESISTANCE WELDING (ERW) EQUIPMENT

C G & W Young Ltd, 15a Colne Road, Twickenham, TW2 6QQ Tel: (020) 8894 5168 Fax: (020) 8898 1316 E-mail: ryoung@youngswelding.co.uk

M H Spencer Ltd, Charter Avenue, Coventry, CV4 8AF Tel: (024) 7646 4044 Fax: (024) 7669 4011 E-mail: james.evans@mhspencer.co.uk

R W Cushway & Co. Ltd, 180 Brooker Road, Waltham Abbey, Essex, EN9 1HT Tel: (01992) 713749 Fax: (01992) 788367 E-mail: info@cushways.co.uk

R W M Wolverhampton Ltd, 34 Commercial Road, Wolverhampton, WV1 3RD Tel: (01902) 871272

Sciaky Electric Welding Machines Ltd, 212 Bedford Avenue, Slough, SL1 4RH Tel: (01753) 525551 Fax: (01753) 821416 E-mail: sales@sciaky.co.uk

Sureweld UK Ltd, Sanders Lodge Industrial Estate, Rushden, Northamptonshire, NN10 6BQ Tel: (01933) 357005 Fax: (01933) 357606 E-mail: info@surerweld.co.uk

ELECTRIC RESISTANT WELD (ERW) STEEL TUBES

Bull Tubes Ltd, Unit 4, Park Road, Willenhall, West Midlands, WV13 1AH Tel: (01902) 608881 Fax: (01902) 602221 E-mail: enquiries@bulltube.com

Hayes Tubes Ltd, Balds Lane, Lye, Stourbridge, West Midlands, DY9 8NN Tel: (01384) 422373 Fax: (01384) 422877 E-mail: hayestubes@enterprise.net

ELECTRIC SAFETY LAMPS

S A Equipment Sales, Edison Point, Millmarsh Lane, Enfield, Middlesex, EN3 7QG Tel: (020) 8443 7420 Fax: (020) 8804 2655

ELECTRIC SHOWER UNITS

Damixa Ltd, Edison Courtyard, Brunel Road, Earlstrees Industrial Estate, Corby, Northamptonshire, NN17 4LS Tel: (01536) 409222 Fax: (01536) 400144 E-mail: uksales@damixa.com

Gainsborough bathrooms Ltd, Seafield House, Claylands Avenue, Worksop, Nottinghamshire, S81 7BQ Tel: (01909) 471520 Fax: (01909) 471593 E-mail: keithtaylor@heatraesadia.com

Heatrae Sadia, 1 Hurricane Way, Norwich, NR6 6EA Tel: (01603) 420100 Fax: (01603) 420218 E-mail: sales@heatraesadia.com

Marleton Cross Ltd, Alpha Close, Tewkesbury, Gloucestershire, GL20 8JF Tel: (01684) 293311 Fax: (01684) 293900 E-mail: rhj@mxgroup.demon.co.uk

Salamander, 2-10 St. Johns Street, Bedford, MK42 0DH Tel: (0845) 3779160 Fax: (0845) 3779180 E-mail: info@salamanderpumps.co.uk

ELECTRIC SOLDERING IRONS

Cooper Tools, Pennine House, Washington, Tyne & Wear, NE37 1LY Tel: 0191-419 7700 Fax: 0191-417 9421 E-mail: sales@coopertools.com

ELECTRIC SOLUTION TURNKEY PROJECTS OR CONTRACTORS OR SERVICES

A B B Power Ltd, Stonefield Works, Oulton Road, Stone, Staffordshire, ST15 0RS Tel: (01785) 825050 Fax: (01785) 819019
Viridian Group Ltd, 120 Malone Road, Belfast, BT9 5HT Tel: (028) 9066 8416 Fax: (028) 9068 9117 E-mail: sales@viridiangroup.co.uk

ELECTRIC STEAM BOILERS

▶ Aktron Ltd, 8 Greenlea Park, Prince Georges Road, London, SW19 2JD Tel: (020) 8685 9461 Fax: (020) 8640 8688

ELECTRIC STEPPER MOTORS

Astrosyn International Technology plc, The Old Courthouse, New Road Avenue, Chatham, Kent, ME4 6BE Tel: (01634) 815175 Fax: (01634) 826552 E-mail: astrosyn@btinternet.com
H G Brunner, Bradbourne House, East Malling, West Malling, Kent, ME19 6DZ Tel: (01732) 873715 Fax: (01732) 875610 E-mail: sales@hgbrunner.com
Rotalink Ltd, Cropmead, Crewkerne, Somerset, TA18 7HQ Tel: (01460) 72000 Fax: (01460) 74278 E-mail: info@rotalink.com
Stebon Ltd, Unit 2C Chase Park Industrial Estate, Ring Road, Burntwood, Staffordshire, WS7 8JQ Tel: (01543) 677211 Fax: (01543) 675005 E-mail: sales@stebon.net
Unimatic Engineers Ltd, 130 Granville Road, London, NW2 2LN Tel: (020) 8922 1000 Fax: (020) 8922 1066 E-mail: sales@unimatic.com

ELECTRIC STORAGE HEATERS

Stiebel Eltron UK Ltd, Unit 12, Stadium Court Stadium Road, Wirral, Merseyside, CH62 3RP Tel: 0151-346 2300 Fax: 0151-334 2913 E-mail: aeinfo@appied-engery.com

ELECTRIC SUPPLIES/ APPLIANCE/EQUIPMENT IMPORT/EXPORT MERCHANTS OR AGENTS

Bennett & Fountain Ltd, 2-4 Argyle Road, London, W13 8AD Tel: (020) 8998 0061 Fax: (020) 8998 0085 E-mail: bandf@ealing514.fsbusiness.co.uk
Delonghi Ltd, 15-16 Bridle Close, Finedon Road Industrial Estate, Wellingborough, Northamptonshire, NN8 4RN Tel: (01933) 442040 Fax: (01933) 441891 E-mail: marketing@delonghi.co.uk
Edmundson Electrical Ltd, 15 Lister Lane, Halifax, West Yorkshire, HX1 5AS Tel: (01422) 359428 Fax: (01422) 330291 E-mail: halifax.139@eel.co.uk
Europa Import Export, 3-8 Porchester Gate, Bayswater Road, London, W2 3HP Tel: (020) 7221 3449 Fax: (020) 7221 7461 E-mail: eie@compuserve.com
Industrial Apparatus Consultants Ltd, 116 Baker Street, London, W1U 6TS Tel: (020) 7486 6474 Fax: (020) 7487 2757
Jendee Trading Ltd, Kebbell House, Delta Gain, Watford, WD19 5EF Tel: (020) 8421 4235 Fax: (020) 8421 4236 E-mail: info@jendee.co.uk
KPC Engineering Company Ltd, KPC House, Coventry Road, Yardley, Birmingham, B26 1DD Tel: 0121-707 0004 Fax: 0121-706 0065 E-mail: kpcengineering@btclick.com
M H Electrical Distributors Ltd, 2 Station House, Lowlands Road, Runcorn, Cheshire, WA7 5TQ Tel: (01928) 591888 Fax: (01928) 591555 E-mail: mhelec001@aol.com
Ormrod Electric Ltd, 173 Chiswick High Road, London, W4 2DR Tel: (020) 8994 0118 Fax: (020) 8994 6008
P U Electrical Wholesalers Ltd, 104 Soho Hill, Birmingham, B19 1AD Tel: 0121-554 1371 Fax: 0121-554 8190 E-mail: info@puelectrical.co.uk
Power Equipment Design & Supplies Ltd, Lyndhurst Cottage, Seymour Road, Bath, BA1 6DZ Tel: (01225) 463721 Fax: (0845) 2804920 E-mail: info@pedsltd.co.uk
Rabo Merchants Ltd, 267 Bearwood Road, Smethwick, West Midlands, B66 4NA Tel: (01386) 700193 Fax: 0121-429 4993 E-mail: reception@rabo.co.uk
Rexel Electrical Wholesalers, 2 Sidney Robinson Business Park, Ascot Drive, Derby, DE24 8EH Tel: (01332) 755918 Fax: (01332) 757673
Sefex International Ltd, 50 Frank Street, Preston, PR1 1PB Tel: (01772) 884020 Fax: (01772) 884020E-mail: sales@sefexinternational.co.uk
T T I Electrical Ltd, Tti House Millers Yard, Long Lane, London, N3 2QG Tel: (020) 8343 1661 Fax: (020) 8343 1771 E-mail: sales@tti-group.co.uk
Techna International, Unit 1 Metro Centre, Dwight Road, Watford, WD18 9HG Tel: (01923) 222227 Fax: (01923) 219700 E-mail: sales@techna.co.uk
TVI Home Appliance Centre, Unit 6 Peartree Lane, Dudley, West Midlands, DY2 0QU Tel: (01384) 571879 Fax: (01384) 482575 E-mail: tvi1@btconnect.com
W F Electrical plc, 1 Trinity Centre, Park Farm Industrial Estate, Wellingborough, Northamptonshire, NN8 6ZB Tel: (01933) 679009 Fax: (01933) 400264

ELECTRIC SUPPLIES/ APPLIANCE/EQUIPMENT MANUFACTURE, *See headings for particular types*

ELECTRIC TORCHES

▶ Uni-Lite International Ltd, Unit 7 Colemeadow Road, North Moors Moat, Redditch, Worcestershire, B98 9PB Tel: (01527) 584344 Fax: (01527) 584345 E-mail: sales@uni-lite.com

ELECTRIC TOWEL RAILS

▶ Pyramide UK Trading Ltd, Suite 306, Parkway House, Sheen Lane, East Sheen, London, SW14 8LS Tel: (020) 8392 1123 Fax: (0870) 7628545 E-mail: sales@towelradiator.co.uk

ELECTRIC TRACTION MOTORS

Charion Spares Ltd, Unit 7 Paper Mill End Industrial Estate, Birmingham, B44 8NH Tel: 0121-344 4540 Fax: 0121-344 3017 E-mail: charionspares@yahoo.co.uk
Prestolite Electric, 12-16 Bristol Road, Greenford, Middlesex, UB6 8UP Tel: (020) 8231 1000 Fax: (020) 8575 9575 E-mail: sales@prestolite.co.uk

ELECTRIC VEHICLE BATTERY CHARGERS

Electra Caddie, 99 Main Road, Bolton le Sands, Carnforth, Lancashire, LA5 8EQ Tel: (01902) 823300 Fax: (01524) 822382 E-mail: enquiries@kaddy.co.uk
Merlin Equipment, Unit 4, Cabot Business Village, Holyrood Close, Cabot Lane, Poole, Dorset, BH17 7BA Tel: (01202) 697979 Fax: (01202) 691919 E-mail: sales@merlinequipment.com

ELECTRIC VEHICLE MAINTENANCE AND REPAIR

Autolec Services, 101 Albert Street, Rugby, Warwickshire, CV21 2SW Tel: (01788) 573475 Fax: (01788) 550530 E-mail: autorug@yahoo.co.uk
Ful Ton Fork Lifts, Argyle Crescent, Hillhouse Industrial Estate, Hamilton, Lanarkshire, ML3 9BH Tel: (01698) 286490 Fax: (01698) 429531 E-mail: sales@ful-ton-forklifts.com

ELECTRIC VEHICLE SPARE PARTS

John Bradshaw Ltd, New Lane, Stibbington, Peterborough, PE8 6LW Tel: (01780) 782621 Fax: (01780) 783694 E-mail: sales@john-bradshaw.co.uk
Component Distributors Ltd, Blackwater Road, Newtownabbey, County Antrim, BT36 4UA Tel: (028) 9034 1900 Fax: (028) 9034 1977 E-mail: mail@cd-group.com
Machine Electrics Ltd, Unit 6 The Timberyard, East Moors Road, Cardiff, CF24 5ES Tel: (029) 2049 8840 Fax: (029) 2048 0469
S E V Group Ltd, Houghton Road, North Anston Trading Estate, Dinnington, Sheffield, S25 4JJ Tel: (01909) 568006 Fax: (01909) 564781 E-mail: enquiry@sev.co.uk

ELECTRIC VEHICLES

John Bradshaw Ltd, New Lane, Stibbington, Peterborough, PE8 6LW Tel: (01780) 782621 Fax: (01780) 783694 E-mail: sales@john-bradshaw.co.uk
Dac Handling Solutions, 7 Eldon Way, Bristol, BS4 3PZ Tel: (01264) 772012 Fax: (01264) 771083 E-mail: drock@dac-handling.co.uk
Electra Caddie, 99 Main Road, Bolton le Sands, Carnforth, Lancashire, LA5 8EQ Tel: (01902) 823300 Fax: (01524) 822382 E-mail: enquiries@kaddy.co.uk
Electric Mobility Euro Ltd, Canal Way, Ilminster, Somerset, TA19 9DL Tel: (01460) 258100 Fax: (01460) 258125 E-mail: sales@electricmobility.co.uk
Electricars Ltd, 15 Carlyon Road, Atherstone, Warwickshire, CV9 1LQ Tel: (01827) 716888 Fax: (01827) 717841 E-mail: electricars@lineone.net
▶ John Grose Group Ltd, Beveridge Way, Hardwick Narrows, King's Lynn, Norfolk, PE30 4NB Tel: (01553) 770060 Fax: (01553) 778226
Mobile Electrics, 2a Pwllmawr Avenue, Rumney, Cardiff, CF3 3HH Tel: (029) 2079 5689 Fax: (029) 2079 5689
P A Loading Systems Ltd, 9 Kineton Road, Kenilworth, Warwickshire, CV8 2AW Tel: (01926) 851619 Fax: (01926) 850478 E-mail: davidparry@mash-b.co.uk
S E V Group Ltd, Houghton Road, North Anston Trading Estate, Dinnington, Sheffield, S25 4JJ Tel: (01909) 568006 Fax: (01909) 564781 E-mail: enquiry@sev.co.uk
Sev, 356d Dukesway Court, Gateshead, Tyne & Wear, NE11 0BH Tel: 0191-487 1311 Fax: 0191-482 0243 E-mail: sales@sev.co.uk
Towrite Electric Vehicles (Harborough) Ltd, Albert Road, Market Harborough, Leicestershire, LE16 7LU Tel: (01858) 433548 Fax: (01858) 434209 E-mail: sales@towrite.co.uk
Towrite Fabrications Ltd, Albert Road, Market Harborough, Leicestershire, LE16 7LU Tel: (01858) 467805 Fax: (01858) 434209 E-mail: sales@towrite.co.uk
W S Barrett & Son Ltd, Riverside Industrial Estate, Marsh Lane, Boston, Lincolnshire, PE21 7PJ Tel: (01205) 362585 Fax: (01205) 310831 E-mail: info@wsbarrett.co.uk

ELECTRIC WASTE DISPOSAL UNITS

Tweeny, Kingfisher House, Wheel Park, Westfield, Hastings, East Sussex, TN35 4SE Tel: (07004) 893369 Fax: (01424) 751444 E-mail: sales@tweeny.co.uk

ELECTRIC WATER HEATERS

Crown Water Heaters Ltd, Sunbeam Studios, Sunbeam Street, Wolverhampton, WV2 4PF Tel: (01902) 310678 Fax: (01902) 425707 E-mail: sales@crownheat.force9.co.uk
Electric Water Heating Co., 2 Horsecroft Place, Harlow, Essex, CM19 5BT Tel: (0845) 0553811 Fax: (0845) 0553822E-mail: sales@ewh.co.uk
Gainsborough bathrooms Ltd, Seafield House, Claylands Avenue, Worksop, Nottinghamshire, S81 7BQ Tel: (01909) 471520 Fax: (01909) 471593 E-mail: keithtaylor@heatraesadia.com
Stiebel Eltron UK Ltd, Unit 12, Stadium Court Stadium Road, Wirral, Merseyside, CH62 3RP Tel: 0151-346 2300 Fax: 0151-334 2913 E-mail: aeinfo@appied-engery.com

ELECTRIC WELDING

A F Hussey London Ltd, Unit B10 Down Bounds Green Industrial Estate, Ringway, London, N11 2UD Tel: (020) 8368 3680 Fax: (020) 8361 2992
Astral Fabrications Ltd, 5 Phoenix House, Castle Street, Tipton, West Midlands, DY4 8HP Tel: 0121-522 4761 Fax: 0121-522 4761
B & R Welding Fabrications, Unit 1a Ribble Business Park, Challenge Way, Blackburn, BB1 5QB Tel: (01254) 670503 Fax: (01254) 670503
E R Burgess Macclesfield Ltd, Brunswick Works, Lowe Street, Macclesfield, Cheshire, SK11 7NJ Tel: (01625) 423735 Fax: (01625) 502025
Forg Welding & Engineering Co. Ltd, 4 Block 2 Mariner Way, Felnex Industrial Estate, Newport, Gwent, NP19 4PQ Tel: (01633) 274690 Fax: (01633) 270975 E-mail: sales@forg.co.uk
Frank Langfield Ltd, Hollins Mill Lane, Sowerby Bridge, West Yorkshire, HX6 2RF Tel: (01422) 835388 Fax: (01422) 834452 E-mail: sales@langfieldwelding.com
Lattis Ltd, New Loom Ho, 101 Back Church La, London, E1 1LU Tel: (020) 7366 6666 Fax: (020) 7366 1122
S & P Blair & Son, Bayswell Park, Dunbar, East Lothian, EH42 1AE Tel: (01368) 862371 Fax: (01368) 862051 E-mail: sales@spblair.com

ELECTRIC WELDING EQUIPMENT

C G & W Young Ltd, 15a Colne Road, Twickenham, TW2 6QQ Tel: (020) 8894 5168 Fax: (020) 8898 1316 E-mail: ryoung@youngswelding.co.uk
S I P Industrial Products Ltd, Gelders Hall Road, Shepshed, Loughborough, Leicestershire, LE12 9NH Tel: (01509) 500300 Fax: (01509) 503154 E-mail: sales@sip-group.com
Saf Welding Products Ltd, 2 Low March Industrial Estate, Low March, Daventry, Northamptonshire, NN11 4SD Tel: (01327) 705511 Fax: (01327) 701310 E-mail: sales@saf-wp.co.uk
Sureweld UK Ltd, Sanders Lodge Industrial Estate, Rushden, Northamptonshire, NN10 6BQ Tel: (01933) 357005 Fax: (01933) 357606 E-mail: info@surerweld.co.uk
Total Welding Supplies Ltd, Unit 12-13, St. Johns Road, Kirkdale, Liverpool, L20 8PR Tel: 0151-933 7213 Fax: 0151-944 1177 E-mail: totalwelding@btconnect.com
TPS Fronius Ltd, 5 Simonsburn Road, Kilmarnock, Ayrshire, KA1 5LE Tel: (01563) 529435 Fax: (01563) 523510 E-mail: sales@tps-fronius.co.uk

ELECTRIC WINCHES

Lebus International Engineers Ltd, Dane Works, Crown Quay Lane, Sittingbourne, Kent, ME10 3HU Tel: (01795) 475324 Fax: (01795) 428004 E-mail: enquiries@lebusintengineers.com
North Sea Winches Ltd, Dunslow Road, Eastfield, Scarborough, North Yorkshire, YO11 3UT Tel: (01723) 584080 Fax: (01723) 581605 E-mail: sales@nswinches.co.uk
Seatronics Ltd, 4 Denmore Industrial Estate, Denmore Road, Denmore Industrial Estate, Aberdeen, AB23 8JW Tel: (01224) 853100 Fax: (01224) 853101 E-mail: david.currie@seatronics-group.com

ELECTRIC WIRE

Belden C D T Ltd, Littleborough, Lancashire, OL15 8YJ Tel: (01706) 374015 Fax: (01706) 370576
E C Cables Ltd, Unit 4B, Waymills Industrial Estate, Waymills, Whitchurch, Shropshire, SY13 1TT Tel: (01948) 660950 Fax: (01948) 660959 E-mail: ec.cables@virgin.net
Leoni Temco Ltd, Whimsey Industrial Estate, Cinderford, Gloucestershire, GL14 3HZ Tel: (01594) 820100 Fax: (01594) 823691 E-mail: general@leonitemco.com
Leoni Wiring Systems Ltd, Lower Milehouse Lane, Newcastle, Staffordshire, ST5 9BT Tel: (01782) 563366 Fax: (01782) 604895 E-mail: sales@leoniwiring.com
Scientific Wire Co. Ltd, 18 Raven Road, London, E18 1HW Tel: (020) 8505 0002 Fax: (020) 8559 1114 E-mail: wire@enterprise.net
Vernon's Fuse Co, 22 Trinity Trading Estate, Tribune Drive, Sittingbourne, Kent, ME10 2PG Tel: (01795) 471234 Fax: (01795) 476996

ELECTRIC WIRE, PREPARED OR CUT OR TERMINATED FOR ASSEMBLY

D. Evans Electrical Ltd, Stretton Way, Wilson Road, Huyton Industrial Estate, Liverpool, L36 6JF Tel: 0151-489 1232 Fax: 0151-480 1496 E-mail: drowley@d-evans.co.uk
▶ Parkfield Electronics, 4 Parkfield Avenue, Rose Green, Bognor Regis, West Sussex, PO21 3BW Tel: 01243 261990 Fax: 01243 261990E-mail: info@parkfieldelectronics.co.uk

ELECTRIC WIRING ACCESSORIES

Alpha, Goudhurst Road, Marden, Tonbridge, Kent, TN12 9NW Tel: (01622) 832488 Fax: (01622) 832488
Contactum Ltd, Victoria Works, Edgware Road, London, NW2 6LF Tel: (020) 8452 6366 Fax: (020) 8208 3340 E-mail: general@contactum.co.uk
Deta Electrical Co. Ltd, Kingsway House, Laporte Way, Luton, LU4 8RJ Tel: (01582) 544544 Fax: (01582) 544501 E-mail: sales@detaelectrical.co.uk
Electrical & Contractors Supplies, 177 Meanwood Road, Leeds, LS7 1JP Tel: 0113-242 9295 Fax: 0113-242 5021 E-mail: sales@ecs-electrical.com
Electrium Ltd, Lichfield Road, Brownhills, Walsall, WS8 6JZ Tel: (01543) 455000
Electrium Sales Ltd, Walkmill Business Park, Walkmill Way, Cannock, Staffordshire, WS11 0XE Tel: (01543) 455000 Fax: (01543) 455001 E-mail: darren.garbett@electrium.co.uk
Ems, 18-22 Queen Street, Leicester, LE1 1QR Tel: 0116-262 2588 Fax: 0116-251 1429 E-mail: emsleister@rexelscnete.co.uk
Eyre & Elliston Ltd, 68 Arthur Street, Redditch, Worcestershire, B98 8JY Tel: (01527) 510101 Fax: (01527) 510131
Loblite International Ltd, 3rd Avenue, Team Valley Trading Estate, Gateshead, Tyne & Wear, NE11 0QQ Tel: 0191-487 8103 Fax: 0191-482 0270 E-mail: info@loblite.co.uk
Novar ED&S, The Arnold Centre, Paycocke Road, Basildon, Essex, SS14 3EA Tel: (01268) 563000 Fax: (01268) 563538 E-mail: mk_reception@nova.com
Stephen Glover & Co. Ltd, Long Street, Walsall, WS2 9DU Tel: (01922) 611311 Fax: (01922) 721824 E-mail: verglo@btconnect.com
Trident Sections Ltd, Unit 33 Dawley Trading Estate, Dawlings Lane, Kingswinford, West Midlands, DY6 7AP Tel: (01384) 401700 Fax: (01384) 292785
Turnock Ltd, Reaymer Close, Walsall, WS2 7QZ Tel: (01922) 710422 Fax: (01922) 710428

ELECTRIC WIRING ACCESSORIES – *continued*

Whitehouse Plastics Ltd, Unit 4 Tiber Way, Glebe Farm Industrial Estate, Rugby, Warwickshire, CV21 1ED Tel: (01788) 541042 Fax: (01788) 552314
E-mail: sales@whitehouseplastics.co.uk

ELECTRICAL AND ELECTRONIC CATERING EQUIPMENT SPARE PARTS

Grampian Catering Equipment Ltd, Unit 2, New Inn Buildings, Market Street, Ellon, Aberdeenshire, AB41 9JD Tel: (01358) 729500 Fax: (01358) 729501
E-mail: sales@grampiancateringequipment.co.uk

ELECTRICAL APPLIANCE REPAIR

▶ General Domestic Appliances, 120 Prime Street, Northwood, Stoke-on-Trent, ST1 6PS Tel: (01782) 204167
E-mail: generaldomestics@aol.com

▶ A.C. Talbot - Appliance Repairs, 3 Carisbrooke Crescent, Barrow-in-Furness, Cumbria, LA13 0HU Tel: (01229) 835263 Fax: (0871) 2110099 E-mail: andee.talbot@tiscali.co.uk

▶ Yates Electrical, 30 Clearmount Avenue, Newmilns, Ayrshire, KA16 9ER Tel: (01563) 573783 Fax: (01560) 323482
E-mail: sales@a-r-removals.vze.com

ELECTRICAL BACKPANELS

John Beaumont Ltd, Riverside Mills, Firth Street, Huddersfield, HD1 3BD Tel: 0845 8510215 Fax: (01484) 435302
E-mail: peter@beaumont-ltd.co.uk

ELECTRICAL CABLE CONNECTIONS

Cable First Ltd, 32-40 Harwell Road, Poole, Dorset, BH17 0GE Tel: (01202) 687337 Fax: (01202) 672501
E-mail: sales@cablefirst.co.uk

▶ Cable Solutions Worldwide Ltd, Unit A1, Wellheads Crescent, Wellheads Industrial Estate, Aberdeen, AB21 7GA Tel: (01224) 727910 Fax: (01224) 725360
E-mail: ricky.gill@1st4cables.com

City Electrical Factors Ltd, 19 Bedford Business Centre, Mile Road, Bedford, MK42 9TW Tel: (01234) 212444 Fax: (01234) 268081
E-mail: sales.bedford@cef.co.uk

City Electrical Factors Ltd, Units 4-6, St Nicholas Road, Beverley, North Humberside, HU17 0QT Tel: (01482) 869861 Fax: (01482) 866297

City Electrical Factors Ltd, 2 Blackstone Road, Stukeley Meadows Industrial Estate, Huntingdon, Cambridgeshire, PE29 6EF Tel: (01480) 456456 Fax: (01480) 457457
E-mail: sales.huntingdon@cef.co.uk

City Electrical Factors Ltd, Unit N6 Riverside Industrial Estate, Bridge Road, Littlehampton, West Sussex, BN17 5DF Tel: (01903) 723801 Fax: (01903) 730361

▶ Kew Electrical Distributor Ltd, 2 Chapel Road, Portslade, Brighton, BN41 1PF Tel: (01273) 420452 Fax: (01273) 418060
E-mail: darren@kewelectrical.co.uk

PDM Neptec Ltd, 4-6 Alton Business Centre, Omega Park, Alton, Hampshire, GU34 2YU Tel: (01420) 85848 Fax: (01420) 84288
E-mail: sales@pdmneptec.com

ELECTRICAL CATERING EQUIPMENT

A B C Catering Equipment, 196 Edgeware Bury Lane, Edgware, Middlesex, HA8 8QW Tel: (020) 8958 1958 Fax: (020) 8958 1958
E-mail: sales@abccatering.co.uk

A & M Supplies (Catering) Ltd, 8-10 Hallsteads, Dove Holes, Buxton, Derbyshire, SK17 8BJ Tel: (01298) 816023 Fax: (01298) 816153
E-mail: sales@a-mcateringsupplies.co.uk

Ace Business Machines, 21 Clarendon Road, Kenilworth, Warwickshire, CV8 1HZ Tel: (024) 7667 0715 Fax: (024) 7667 0715

Bond Catering Manufacturers, Bond Street, Denton, Manchester, M34 3AJ Tel: 0161-320 4065

Border Food Machinery, 39 Kingstown Broadway, Kingstown Industrial Estate, Carlisle, CA3 0HA Tel: (01228) 534996 Fax: (01228) 514260

Cabbola Food Service Equipment, 47 New Street, Hinckley, Leicestershire, LE10 1QY Tel: (01455) 612020 Fax: (01455) 636364
E-mail: sales@cabbola.com

City Electrical Factors Ltd, Tritton Road, Lincoln, LN6 7QY Tel: (01522) 682548 Fax: (01582) 694512 E-mail: info.lincoln@cef.co.uk

Denton's Catering Equipment Ltd, 2-4 Clapham High Street, London, SW4 7UT Tel: (020) 7622 7157 Fax: (020) 7622 5546
E-mail: sales@dentons.co.uk

Elro UK Ltd, 3 Furzton Lake, Shellwell Crescent, Furzton, Milton Keynes, MK4 1GA Tel: (01908) 526444 Fax: (01908) 526449
E-mail: info@elro-uk.ltd.uk

F R Stainless Ltd, Unit 7, Darrows Industrial Esate, John Branning Way, Bellshill, Lanarkshire, ML4 3HD Tel: (01698) 842779 Fax: (01698) 842770

G B Catering Engineers, 6 Alma Industrial Estate, Stafford Road, Wednesbury, West Midlands, WS10 8SX Tel: 0121-568 7669 Fax: 0121-568 7669

Highland Catering Resources, Suite 4 Upper Mall, Grampian Road, Aviemore, Inverness-Shire, PH22 1RH Tel: (01479) 810270 Fax: (01479) 810270

E & R Moffat Ltd, Bonnymuir Works, Seabegs Road, Bonnybridge, Stirlingshire, FK4 2BS Tel: (01324) 812272 Fax: (01324) 814107
E-mail: sales@ermoffat.co.uk

Scobie & Mcintosh Catering Equipment Ltd, 15 Brewster Square, Brucefield Industrial Estate, Livingston, West Lothian, EH54 9BJ Tel: (01506) 426200 Fax: (01506) 426279

Watco Refrigeration Ltd, Unit 1 Hardengreen Industrial Estate, Dalkeith, Midlothian, EH22 3NX Tel: 0131-561 9502 Fax: 0131-561 9503 E-mail: info@watco-refridgeration.co.uk

ELECTRICAL CERAMIC COMPONENTS

B.H.W Ceramics Ltd, Adelaide Street, Stoke-on-Trent, ST6 2BD Tel: (01782) 813855 Fax: (01782) 575647
E-mail: info@bhwceramics.sagehost.co.uk

ELECTRICAL CLEANING SOLVENTS

Fleming Technical Ltd, Brunel Road, Croft Business Park, Wirral, Merseyside, CH62 3NY Tel: 0151-343 1800 Fax: 0151-343 1801
E-mail: gil@fleming-tech.co.uk

ELECTRICAL COMPONENT CONTACTS

Ekaton Ltd, Jubilee House, Altcar Road, Formby, Liverpool, L37 8DL Tel: (01704) 870107 Fax: (01704) 831269
E-mail: colinmackay@ekaton.ltd.uk

Llandaff Engineering Co. Ltd, Paper Mill Road, Canton, Cardiff, CF11 8PH Tel: (029) 2083 8300 Fax: (029) 2056 5125
E-mail: majenkins@llandaffeng.com

Loxwood Contacts Ltd, Unit 11 Cardiff Road Industrial Estate, Cardiff Road, Watford, WD18 0DG Tel: (01923) 254521 Fax: (01923) 818027 E-mail: sales@loxwoodcontacts.co.uk

Metalor Technologies (UK) Ltd, 74 Warstone Lane, Birmingham, B18 6NG Tel: 0121-236 3241 Fax: 0121-236 3568
E-mail: electrotechnics@metalor.com

Noconn Electrical Contacts Ltd, Unit 71, Storforth Lane Trading Estate, Chesterfield, Derbyshire, S41 0QZ Tel: (01246) 209556 Fax: (01246) 201440 E-mail: info@electricalcontacts.com

Samuel Taylor Ltd, Arthur Street, Lakeside, Redditch, Worcestershire, B98 8JY Tel: (01527) 522687 Fax: (01527) 500869
E-mail: sales@samueltaylor.co.uk

Vacuum Impregnated Products Ltd, Hew Cut Lane, Woolston, Warrington, WA1 4AG Tel: (01925) 817213 Fax: (01925) 823862
E-mail: sales@viproducts.co.uk

ELECTRICAL COMPONENT IMPORT/EXPORT MERCHANTS OR AGENTS

▶ DRY-OFF (UK) LTD, 23 Castalia Square, Docklands, London, UK, E14 3NG Tel: 0207 5441474 Fax: 0207 5441499
E-mail: EDWARD@DRY-OFF.COM

Team Overseas Ltd, Meridian House, Nazeing Glass Works Estate, Nazeing New Road, Broxbourne, Hertfordshire, EN10 6SX Tel: +44 (01992) 788233 Fax: +44 (01992) 788695
E-mail: sales@teamoverseas.com

ELECTRICAL CONNECTOR DISTRIBUTORS OR AGENTS

Ambitron Components Ltd, 4 Station Road, Hungerford, Berkshire, RG17 0DY Tel: (01488) 685404 Fax: (01488) 685406
E-mail: sales@ambitron.co.uk

Ashlea Components Ltd, 4 Shrivenham Hundred Business Park, Majors Road, Watchfield, Swindon, SN6 8TZ Tel: (01793) 783784 Fax: (01793) 783646
E-mail: sales@ashlea.co.uk

Colton Electrical Equipment Co. Ltd, 329 Front Lane, Upminster, Essex, RM14 1LW Tel: (01708) 224454 Fax: (01708) 221191
E-mail: sales@coltonelectricalequipment.co.uk

Conec Electronic Equipment Component, Ringway House, Kelvin Road, Newbury, Berkshire, RG14 2DB Tel: (01635) 36929 Fax: (01635) 36925
E-mail: conec@conec.co.uk

Deutsch Ltd, 4 Stanier Road, St. Leonards-on-Sea, East Sussex, TN38 9RF Tel: (01424) 852721 Fax: (01424) 851532
E-mail: sales@deutsch.co.uk

Distributed Technology Ltd, Howard House, Amy Road, Oxted, Surrey, RH8 0PW Tel: (01883) 716161 Fax: (01883) 716865
E-mail: mail@dtl-connectors.co.uk

Dubilier Electronic Component Distributors, Station House Station Yard Industrial Park, Station Road, Dunmow, Essex, CM6 1XD Tel: (01371) 875758 Fax: (01371) 875075
E-mail: sales@dubilier.co.uk

Felco Electronics Ltd, 2 Rivermead, Pipers Way, Thatcham, Berkshire, RG19 4EP Tel: (01635) 866940 Fax: (01635) 866951
E-mail: sales@felco.co.uk

Flair Electronic Systems Ltd, Britannia House, Boulton Road, Stevenage, Hertfordshire, SG1 4QX Tel: (01438) 727391 Fax: (01438) 740232 E-mail: sales@flairelectronics.co.uk

Fujikura Europe Ltd, Unit C51 Barwell Business Park, Leatherhead Road, Chessington, Surrey, KT9 2NY Tel: (020) 8240 2000 Fax: (020) 8240 2010
E-mail: ddk_connectors@fujikura.co.uk

Future Electronics Ltd, Future House, Poyle Road, Colnbrook, Slough, SL3 0AA Tel: (01753) 763000 Fax: (01753) 689100
E-mail: lcdwizard@futureelectronics.com

Glenair UK Ltd, 40 Lower Oakham Way, Mansfield, Nottinghamshire, NG18 5BY Tel: (01623) 638100 Fax: (01623) 638111
E-mail: enquiries@glenair.co.uk

Hub Electronics Ltd, Unit 1 Foundry Court, Foundry Lane, Horsham, West Sussex, RH13 5PY Tel: (01403) 255225 Fax: (01403) 263154 E-mail: tina@hubelectronics.co.uk

Maplin Electronics P.L.C., National Distribution Centre, Valley Road, Wombwell, Barnsley, South Yorkshire, S73 0BS Tel: (0870) 4296000 Fax: (0870) 4296001
E-mail: sales@maplin.co.uk

Multi-Contact (UK) Ltd, 3 Presley Way, Crownhill, Milton Keynes, MK8 0ES Tel: (01908) 265544 Fax: (01908) 262080
E-mail: uk@multi-contact.com

Niglon Ltd, Highlands Road, Shirley, Solihull, West Midlands, B90 4NP Tel: 0121-711 1990 Fax: 0121-711 1344

RS Components (Watford), Unit 2A, Colonial Way, Watford, WD24 4WP Tel: (01923) 219696 Fax: (01923) 211777
E-mail: watford.tradecounter@rs-components.com

Selwyn Electronics Ltd, Unit B8 Chaucer Business Park, Watery Lane, Kemsing, Sevenoaks, Kent, TN15 6QY Tel: (01732) 765100 Fax: (01732) 765190
E-mail: connect@selwyn.co.uk

Takbro Ltd, 59 Church Street, Walshaw, Bury, Lancashire, BL8 3BN Tel: (01204) 887001 Fax: (01204) 545400
E-mail: sales@takbro.co.uk

ELECTRICAL CONNECTORS, *See also headings under Connectors*

Asbury Associates, 40 Croft Holm, Moreton-in-Marsh, Glos, GL56 0JH Tel: (01608) 652214 Fax: (01608) 652214

Ceep Ltd, Unit 7 Weydown Industrial Estate, Haslemere, Surrey, GU27 1DW Tel: (01428) 661515 Fax: (01428) 644147
E-mail: sales@ceep.co.uk

Cembre Ltd, Fair View Industrial Estate, Kingsbury Road, Curdworth, Sutton Coldfield, West Midlands, B76 9EE Tel: (01675) 470440 Fax: (01675) 470220
E-mail: sales@cembre.co.uk

Channel Ltd, Fairway, Orpington, Kent, BR5 1EG Tel: (01689) 871522 Fax: (01689) 833428

Cinch Connectors Ltd, Shireoaks Road, Worksop, Nottinghamshire, S80 3HA Tel: (01909) 474131 Fax: (01909) 478321
E-mail: sales@cinchuk.com

Deutsch Ltd, 4 Stanier Road, St. Leonards-on-Sea, East Sussex, TN38 9RF Tel: (01424) 852721 Fax: (01424) 851532
E-mail: sales@deutsch.co.uk

Elco Europe, Exning Road, Newmarket, Suffolk, CB8 0AT Tel: (01638) 675000 Fax: (01638) 675001

Electroustic Ltd, 1 Eaglesfield Industrial Estate, Main Street, Leire, Lutterworth, Leicestershire, LE17 5HF Tel: (01455) 202364 Fax: (01455) 209043 E-mail: sales@electroustic.co.uk

Alex Everett Ltd, 34 Victoria Road, Writtle, Chelmsford, CM1 3PA Tel: (01245) 421198 Fax: (01245) 422433
E-mail: aelconnectors@btclick.com

Fujikura Europe Ltd, Unit C51 Barwell Business Park, Leatherhead Road, Chessington, Surrey, KT9 2NY Tel: (020) 8240 2000 Fax: (020) 8240 2010
E-mail: ddk_connectors@fujikura.co.uk

Head Braiding Ltd, Armstrong Works, Raynham Rd, Bishop's Stortford, Herts, CM23 5PB Tel: (01279) 658271 Fax: (01279) 503566

Hypertac Ltd, 36-38 Waterloo Road, London, NW2 7UH Tel: (020) 8450 8033 Fax: (020) 8208 4114 E-mail: info@hypertac.co.uk

I T W McMurdo Connectors, Norway Road, Hilsea, Portsmouth, PO3 5HT Tel: (023) 9269 4971 Fax: (023) 9265 3356
E-mail: itwswitch1@aol.com

Itt Industries Ltd, Viables Industrial Estate, Jays Close, Basingstoke, Hampshire, RG22 4BA Tel: (01256) 311800 Fax: (01256) 811814

Kompress Holdings Ltd, Unit 5 Little Tennis Street, Nottingham, NG2 4EL Tel: 0115-958 1029 Fax: 0115-958 4180
E-mail: info@kompress.com

Lane Electronics, Slinfold Lodge, Stane Street, Slinfold, Horsham, West Sussex, RH13 0RN Tel: (01403) 790661 Fax: (01403) 790849
E-mail: sales@fclane.com

Lane Electronics, Slinfold Lodge, Stane Street, Slinfold, Horsham, West Sussex, RH13 0RN Tel: (01403) 790661 Fax: (01403) 790849
E-mail: sales@wealdelectronics.com

Lemo U K Ltd, 12 North Street, Worthing, West Sussex, BN11 1DU Tel: (01903) 234543 Fax: (01903) 206231
E-mail: uk.office.services@lemo.com

Lorlin Electronics, Enterprise Unit A-C, Harwood Road, Littlehampton, West Sussex, BN17 7AT Tel: (01903) 725121 Fax: (01903) 723919
E-mail: lorlin@btconnect.com

Machine Electrics Ltd, Whitefield Road, Bredbury, Stockport, Cheshire, SK6 2RW Tel: 0161-430 6825 Fax: 0161-494 8954
E-mail: sales@machineelectrics.com

Molex UK Ltd, The Millennium Centre, Crosby Way, Farnham, Surrey, GU9 7XX Tel: (01252) 720720 Fax: (01252) 720721
E-mail: mxuk@molex.com

Northern Electrical Connectors, Unit 8 Glover Centre, Egmont Street, Mossley, Ashton-Under-Lyne, Lancashire, OL5 9PY Tel: (01457) 837511 Fax: (01457) 835216
E-mail: martin@nec-ltd.net

PDM Neptec Ltd, 4-6 Alton Business Centre, Omega Park, Alton, Hampshire, GU34 2YU Tel: (01420) 85848 Fax: (01420) 84288
E-mail: sales@pdmneptec.com

Raffenday Ltd, 11 Fleming Close, Park Farm Industrial Estate, Wellingborough, Northamptonshire, NN8 6UF Tel: (01933) 673333 Fax: (01933) 675555
E-mail: sales@raffenday.com

Switchtec Electronics Ltd, Brooms Road, Stone Business Park, Stone, Staffordshire, ST15 0SH Tel: (01785) 818600 Fax: (01785) 811900 E-mail: sales@switchtec.co.uk

Takbro Ltd, Unit 5 Albert Drive, Burgess Hill, West Sussex, RH15 9TN Tel: (01444) 245601 Fax: (01444) 872316
E-mail: mail@takbro.co.uk

TTAB Connectors Ltd, Ynysboeth Industrial Estate, Abercynon, Mountain Ash, Mid Glamorgan, CF45 4SF Tel: (01443) 740331 Fax: (01443) 741676

Vitelec Electronics Ltd, Station Road, Bordon, Hampshire, GU35 0LG Tel: (01420) 488661 Fax: (01420) 488014
E-mail: sales@vitelec.co.uk

Wieland Electric Ltd, 1 The Riverside Business Centre, Walnut Tree Close, Guildford, Surrey, GU1 4UG Tel: (01483) 531213 Fax: (01483) 505029 E-mail: info@wieland.co.uk

ELECTRICAL CONSULTANCY OR CONSULTING ENGINEERS

A1 Electrical Installations Ltd, 120-122 Becontree Avenue, Dagenham, Essex, RM8 2TS Tel: (020) 8597 0953 Fax: (020) 8597 2556
E-mail: info@a1electrical.co.uk

Asa Consulting Engineers Ltd, Surrey Chambers, Surrey Street, Lowestoft, Suffolk, NR32 1LJ Tel: (01502) 518223 Fax: (01502) 567663
E-mail: sue@asaconsultants.co.uk

Babtie Group Ltd, Sheldon Court, Wagon Lane, Birmingham, B26 3DU Tel: 0121-700 1250 Fax: 0121-700 1251
E-mail: birmingham@babtie.com

▶ Broadhay Consulting Services, PO Box 6448, Poole, Dorset, BH12 9BZ Tel: 01202 650069 Fax: 0870 762 6135
E-mail: csh@broadhay.co.uk

Norman Bromley Partnership, Bridge House, 99-101 High Street, Tonbridge, Kent, TN9 1DR Tel: (01732) 773737 Fax: (01732) 773353
E-mail: mail@normanbromley.co.uk

Burgins News, 167 Wolverhampton Street, Dudley, West Midlands, DY1 3AH Tel: (01384) 255807

Butler & Young Associates, 54-62 Station Road East, Oxted, Surrey, RH8 0PG Tel: (01883) 717172 Fax: (01883) 717174
E-mail: enquiries@bya.co.uk

C G M Partners Ltd, Carradine House, 237 Regents Park Road, London, N3 3LF Tel: (020) 8349 2011 Fax: (020) 8349 2014
E-mail: cgmpartners@c.co.uk

Carl Bro Group, Grove House, Mansion Gate Drive, Leeds, LS7 4DN Tel: 0113-262 0000 Fax: 0113-262 0737
E-mail: enquiries@carlbro.com

Centra Controls Ltd, 14 Landywood Lane, Cheslyn Hay, Walsall, WS6 7AH Tel: (01922) 415510 Fax: (01922) 415510
E-mail: centra@tiscala.co.uk

Central Southern Security Ltd, Station Street, Lymington, Hampshire, SO41 3BA Tel: (01590) 677366 Fax: (01590) 678024
E-mail: enquiries@central southern security.co.uk

Dron & Dickson Group, Craigshaw Road, West Tullos Industrial Estate, Aberdeen, AB12 3AR Tel: (01224) 874554 Fax: (01224) 895220
E-mail: info@drondickson.co.uk

E P Systems Ltd, Media House, 21 East Ways Industrial Estate, Witham, Essex, CM8 3YQ Tel: (01376) 531380 Fax: (01376) 531361
E-mail: neil-rowe@epsystems.co.uk

Edmundson Rickards Electrical, 30 Garrett Road, Lynx Trading Estate, Yeovil, Somerset, BA20 2TJ Tel: (01935) 472727 Fax: (01935) 472010 E-mail: mail@spectrumelectrical.co.uk

ELECTRICAL CONSULTANCY OR CONSULTING ENGINEERS – *continued*

Electrical Services (Nelson) Ltd, 43 Belgrave St., Nelson, Lancashire, BB9 9HS Tel: (01282) 696317 Fax: (01282) 611632 E-mail: david@electricialsales.co.uk

▶ The Engineering Practice, Gunnery House, Gunnery Terrace, Leamington Spa, Warwickshire, CV32 5PE Tel: (01926) 436010 Fax: (01926) 470326

▶ Erleback engineering ltd, Dixies Barns, High Street, Ashwell, Baldock, Hertfordshire, SG7 5NT Tel: (0870) 7407481 Fax: (0870) 7407482 E-mail: michael@erlebach.freeserve.co.uk

Faber Maunsell Ltd, Marlborough House, 18 Upper Marlborough Road, St. Albans, Hertfordshire, AL1 3UT Tel: (020) 8784 5784 Fax: (020) 8784 5700 E-mail: enquiries@fabermaunsell.com

G J L Electrical, 43 New North Road, Reigate, Surrey, RH2 8LZ Tel: (01737) 246281

Harley Haddow Partnership, 8 Coates Crescent, Edinburgh, EH3 7BY Tel: 0131-226 3331 Fax: 0131-226 2563 E-mail: edin@harleyhaddow.com

Helix Services Consultancy, 5 Saturn House, Calleva Park, Aldermaston, RG7 3PW Tel: 0118-981 9000 Fax: 0118-981 9001 E-mail: mail@helixconsultancy.com

Integrated Building Services Design Partnership plc, Newton House Cambridge Business Park, Cowley Road, Cambridge, CB4 0WZ Tel: (01223) 436600 Fax: (01223) 436601 E-mail: mail@ibs-plc.co.uk

Leivers Associates, 6 Clinton Avenue, Nottingham, NG5 1AW Tel: 0115-960 3548 Fax: 0115-969 1147 E-mail: sales@1eiversassociates.co.uk

List Design Group Ltd, Manby Road By Passage, Immingham, South Humberside, DN40 2DW Tel: (01469) 571888 Fax: (01469) 571450 E-mail: ldgltd@aol.com

Ostcliffe Electronics Ltd, Barrowfield Road, Hoyland, Barnsley, South Yorkshire, S74 9TH Tel: (01226) 749233

P J G Electrical Ltd, 14 Silver Street, Stony Stratford, Milton Keynes, MK11 1JR Tel: (01908) 561100 Fax: (01908) 561181

Paul Earl Ltd, 1 Euro Business Park, New Road, Newhaven, East Sussex, BN9 0DQ Tel: (01273) 514356 Fax: (01273) 611036 E-mail: info@paulearl.co.uk

Regam Electric Ltd, Macaulay Street, Leeds, LS9 7SW Tel: 0113-245 0946 Fax: 0113-244 9397

Robert Collins Electrical Ltd, 30 Wood End Gardens, Northolt, Middlesex, UB5 4QJ Tel: (020) 8864 6939 Fax: (020) 8423 3177 E-mail: johnwhittle7@aol.com

S V M Consulting Engineers Ltd, 10 Kensworth Gate, Garden Road, Dunstable, Bedfordshire, LU6 3HS Tel: (01582) 660090 Fax: (01582) 660091 E-mail: solutions@svm.co.uk

▶ Services Management Ltd, Seymour House, 51 Praed Street, London, W2 1NR Tel: (020) 7565 5763 Fax: (020) 7565 5754 E-mail: c.bower@sml-ltd.com

Stemet Earthing Co. Ltd, 6 Downs View, Bow Brickhill, Milton Keynes, MK17 9JS Tel: (01908) 373907 Fax: (01908) 378658

▶ TTS, Celect House, 12a Fairbairn Road, Livingston, West Lothian, EH54 6TS Tel: (01506) 464448 Fax: (01506) 464430 E-mail: web@ttsce.co.uk

W W P Consultants Ltd, 5-15 Cromer Street, London, WC1H 8LS Tel: (020) 7833 5767 Fax: (020) 7833 5766 E-mail: info@wwp-london.co.uk

Williams & Shaw Ltd, Agar House, 31 Ballynahinch Road, Carryduff, Belfast, BT8 8BB Tel: (028) 9081 3075 Fax: (028) 9081 4135 E-mail: info@williams-shaw.co.uk

WSP, Colston Avenue 33, Bristol, BS1 4UA Tel: 0117-930 2000 Fax: 0117-929 4624 E-mail: admin@wspgroup.com

ELECTRICAL CONSULTANT/ CONSULTING ENGINEER ASSOCIATIONS

Erg Energy, Church House, Misterton, Lutterworth, Leicestershire, LE17 4JP Tel: (01455) 558236 Fax: (01455) 558237 E-mail: RGriff7944@aol.com

Institution of Incorporated Engineers, Savoy Hill House, Savoy Hill, London, WC2R 0BS Tel: (020) 7836 3357 E-mail: postmaster@theiet.org.uk

R W Gregory & Partners, Cathedral Buildings, Dean Street, Newcastle upon Tyne, NE1 1PJ Tel: 0191-232 6306 Fax: 0191-232 5359 E-mail: newcastle@rwgregory.co.uk

Stapak Services, Bankside, Youlgrave, Bakewell, Derbyshire, DE45 1WD Tel: (01629) 636855 Fax: (01629) 636187 E-mail: stapakservices@aol.com

ELECTRICAL CONTACT MATERIALS

Thessco Ltd, Royds Mill, Windsor Street, Sheffield, S4 7WB Tel: 0114-272 0966 Fax: 0114-275 2655 E-mail: metals@thessco.co.uk

ELECTRICAL CONTRACTORS

▶ 1st South East Aerials, 43 Old Mead, Southend-on-Sea, SS2 6SW Tel: (01702) 526555 Fax: (01702) 524622

A A R K Electrical Ltd, 4 Dolphin Square, Station Road, Bovey Tracey, Newton Abbot, Devon, TQ13 9AL Tel: (01626) 833703 Fax: (01626) 833475 E-mail: kevinmeldrum@aark-electrical.co.uk

▶ A & A Security, 17-25 Devon Place, Glasgow, G41 1RB Tel: 0141-778 6388

▶ A Andrews & Co. Ltd, Unit 1 Kimberley House, Stockport, Cheshire, SK6 3JG Tel: 0161-430 3996

▶ A B Electrical & Security Co. Ltd, 6 Haywood Way, Ivyhouse Lane Industrial Estate, Hastings, East Sussex, TN35 4PL Tel: (01424) 436385 Fax: (01424) 461538 E-mail: enquiries@abelec.co.uk

▶ A Burgoyne Electrical Contractors Ltd, 80 Fulbar Street, Renfrew, PA4 8PA Tel: 0141-886 5917 Fax: 0141-885 2558

A C Electrical Contractors, 7 Lynwood Avenue, Exeter, EX4 1EF Tel: (01392) 211109 Fax: (01392) 439494

▶ A C Electrical & Data Ltd, Ellerbeck House, Stokesley Industrial Estate, Stokesley, Middlesbrough, Cleveland, TS9 5JZ Tel: (01642) 712979

▶ A C G Installations Ltd, Elisabeth House, Willows Road, Walsall, WS1 2DR Tel: (01922) 648509 Fax: (01922) 648509

A C Webb Electrical, Mill Rise, Old Bury Road, Stanton, Bury St. Edmunds, Suffolk, IP31 2BX Tel: (01359) 250039 Fax: (01359) 250592 E-mail: acwebbelec@msn.com

A E Felgate Ltd, 59 George Street, Reading, RG1 7NP Tel: 0118-961 4141 Fax: 0118-967 7717 E-mail: aefelgate@piscarli.co.uk

A Finch & Co., 1-21 Bedminster Down Road, Bristol, BS13 7AB Tel: 0117-963 2763 Fax: 0117-963 2826

▶ A J Electrical, Unit 7, Back Grantley Street, Wakefield, West Yorkshire, WF1 4LG Tel: (01924) 362944 Fax: (01924) 362955

▶ A J K Services, Unit 3, Ordnance Road, Tidworth, Hampshire, SP9 7QD Tel: (01980) 846127 Fax: (01980) 846255

▶ A J Kramer, 77 Colvend Street, Glasgow, G40 4DU Tel: 0141-551 9333 Fax: 0141-551 9944

A L P Electrical Ltd, 70 St. Marks Road, Maidenhead, Berkshire, SL6 6DW Tel: (01628) 633998 Fax: (01628) 760981 E-mail: alp@alpelectrical.com

▶ A M Securities, Shore Road, Perth, PH2 8BD Tel: (01382) 623485 Fax: (01738) 639704

▶ A Morrison, 1 Rigs Road, Stornoway, Isle of Lewis, HS1 2RF Tel: (01851) 705700 Fax: (01851) 706700

A & S Electrical Services, 1 Carisbrooke Drive, Halesowen, West Midlands, B62 8SL Tel: 0121-550 2228 Fax: 0121-550 2228 E-mail: admin@niceic.org.uk

▶ A S Walter, 42 Chapel Avenue, Long Stratton, Norwich, NR15 2TE Tel: (01508) 532528 Fax: (01508) 532528 E-mail: enquiries@aswalter.co.uk

▶ A W Mackintosh Electrical Contractors, Shore Road, Perth, PH2 8BD Tel: (01738) 627172 Fax: (01738) 639704 E-mail: info@amsecurities.co.uk

A W Perry Electrical Co. Ltd, 35 Stroud Road, London, SE25 5DR Tel: (020) 8654 3122 Fax: (020) 8656 8806 E-mail: mail@perryelectrical.co.uk

▶ A W S Electrical Services, 30 Glenwood Place, Glasgow, G45 9UH Tel: 0141-631 2222 Fax: 0141-631 4400

A1 Electrical Installations Ltd, 120-122 Becontree Avenue, Dagenham, Essex, RM8 2TS Tel: (020) 8597 0953 Fax: (020) 8597 2556 E-mail: info@a1electrical.co.uk

Aardvark Electrical Repairs, 22 Commercial Street, Pontnewydd, Cwmbran, Gwent, NP44 1DZ Tel: (01633) 875381 Fax: (01633) 873101 E-mail: simon.ardvark@virgin.net

▶ Abacus Electrical Services Ltd, 6 High Street, Winterbourne, Bristol, BS36 1JN Tel: 0117-970 1688 Fax: (01454) 777567 E-mail: sales@abacuselectrical.co.uk

▶ Aberdeen Electrical Services Ltd, Unit 26 Frederick St Business Centre, Frederick Street, Aberdeen, AB24 5HY Tel: (01224) 649111 Fax: (01224) 649123

Acton Delta Ltd, Wombrook Business Centre, Giggetty Lane, Wombourne, Wolverhampton, WV5 8LZ Tel: (01902) 326563 Fax: (01902) 326564 E-mail: mail@actondelta.co.uk

▶ Advanced Access Ltd, Unit 1b Spinney View, Stone Circle Road, Round Spinney Industrial Estat, Northampton, NN3 8RF Tel: (01604) 647555 Fax: (01604) 647333

Advanced Maintenance Services Ltd, Alchorne Place, The Airport, Portsmouth, PO3 5QL Tel: (023) 9267 3333 Fax: (023) 9269 3319 E-mail: ams@zoom.co.uk

▶ Aegis Alarm Systems Ltd, 19 Bennetts Gate, Hemel Hempstead, Hertfordshire, HP3 8EW Tel: (01442) 240140 E-mail: admin@aegisalarms.co.uk

▶ Aerial Services (Edinburgh) Ltd, 86 Dalry Road, Edinburgh, EH11 2AX Tel: 0131-337 4421

▶ Aes, 8 Eden Court, Eden Way, Leighton Buzzard, Bedfordshire, LU7 4FY Tel: (01525) 217191 Fax: (01525) 381136

▶ Affleck Electrical, Unit 10 Oppenheimer Centre, Greenbridge Indust Estate, Greenbridge Industrial Estate, Swindon, SN3 3LS Tel: (01793) 533222 Fax: (01793) 533215

Airow Safe, Unit 14e Eleventh Avenue North, Team Valley Trading Estate, Gateshead, Tyne & Wear, NE11 0NJ Tel: 0191-491 4271 Fax: 0191-491 4272 E-mail: info@airowsafe.co.uk

Aish Electro, Unit 2b Cowley Road, Nuffield Industrial Estate, Poole, Dorset, BH17 0UJ Tel: (01202) 677100 Fax: (01202) 677233 E-mail: serbite@aishem.co.uk

▶ Alan Benfield Ltd, Sunny Bank Gardens, Belper, Derbyshire, DE56 1WD Tel: (01773) 821474 Fax: (01773) 828257

▶ Alan Boon Ltd, Unit 2, Stoneylands Road, Egham, Surrey, TW20 9QR Tel: (01784) 437999

▶ Alan R Cross & Son Ltd, 22a Station Road, Wymondham, Norfolk, NR18 0JX Tel: (01953) 603637 Fax: (01953) 602321 E-mail: enquiries@arcrosselectrical.co.uk

▶ Alan S Dickson, 11-13 Erskine Square, Hillington Industrial Estate, Glasgow, G52 4BJ Tel: 0141-883 3622 Fax: 0141-883 2129

▶ Alard Electrical, Unit 7, Cromwell Road, Bredbury, Stockport, Cheshire, SK6 2RF Tel: 0161-406 6600 Fax: 0161-430 8022

▶ Alarmfast Supervision Security Systems Ltd, 56 Ingram Street, Glasgow, G1 1EX Tel: 0141-564 4400 Fax: 0141-564 4409

Aleck J Shone, 16 High Street, Saltney, Chester, CH4 8SE Tel: (01244) 683531 Fax: (01244) 659770

▶ Alex Brewster, 32 Maxwell Place, Stirling, FK8 1JU Tel: (01786) 473851 Fax: (01786) 474825

Alfa Electric Ltd, 14 Burgess Road, Ivyhouse Industrial Estate, Hastings, East Sussex, TN35 4NR Tel: (01424) 424040 Fax: (01424) 424040 E-mail: sales@alfaelectric.co.uk

▶ Alfred Mcalpine Business Services Ltd, 1a Newquay Road, St. Columb Road, St. Columb, Cornwall, TR9 6PZ Tel: (01726) 860059 Fax: (01726) 860455

All Electrical Services Ltd, North Mace House, Viaduct Road, Cardiff, CF15 9XF Tel: (029) 2081 0274 Fax: (029) 2081 0282 E-mail: info@allelectricalserviceswales.com

▶ Allcare Facilities Management Ltd, 49 High Street, St. Mary Cray, Orpington, Kent, BR5 3NJ Tel: (01689) 820146

▶ Alliance Electrical Services Ltd, Auld Craichie Inn, Craichie, Forfar, Angus, DD8 2LU Tel: (01307) 819000 Fax: (01307) 819001 E-mail: info@alliance-electrical.co.uk

▶ Alpha Electrical, Unit 11 Kingsway, Norwich, NR2 4UE Tel: (01603) 662270 Fax: (01603) 633478 E-mail: info@alpha-electrical.co.uk

▶ Ambassador Electrical Services Ltd, 29 The Maples, Broadstairs, Kent, CT10 2PE Tel: (01843) 860258 Fax: (01843) 860258

▶ Amdon Electrical Ltd, 2 The Green, Westerham, Kent, TN16 1AS Tel: (01959) 565635 Fax: (01959) 565783

▶ Amec, Site Office, Longannet Power Station, Alloa, Clackmannanshire, FK10 4AA Tel: (01259) 730474

▶ Ampere Electrical Ltd, 27 St. Margaret Drive, Epsom, Surrey, KT18 7LB Tel: (0845) 8380825 Fax: (01372) 745580 E-mail: ampere@fsmail.net

▶ Andrew Mcrobb Ltd, Oldmill Road, Aberdeen, AB11 6EG Tel: (01224) 581327 Fax: (01224) 573828 E-mail: info@andrew-mcrobb.co.uk

Andross Electrics Ltd, Unit 12 Twyford Business Centre, London Road, Bishop's Stortford, Hertfordshire, CM23 3YT Tel: (01279) 657661 Fax: (01279) 506164 E-mail: sales@andross.net

▶ Anglia Electrical Services Ltd, Anglia House, Hamburg Way, North Lynn Industrial Estate, King's Lynn, Norfolk, PE30 2ND Tel: (01553) 773366 Fax: (01553) 771515

▶ APS Ltd, PO Box 12333, Birmingham, B43 6LL Tel: 0121-358 0581 Fax: 0121-358 1062 E-mail: pbenning@aradis.co.uk

Apt Electric Ltd, Unit 2 Hopton Indust Estate, Hopton Road, Devizes, Wiltshire, SN10 2DX Tel: (01380) 739837 Fax: (01380) 739839

Argent F M Ltd, Unit 8, Penarth Centre, London, SE15 1TW Tel: (0870) 8900399 Fax: (0870) 8900398 E-mail: info@argent.fm.co.uk

▶ Argus Electrical Services Ltd, 150 Avery Hill Road, London, SE9 2EY Tel: (020) 8850 9947 Fax: (020) 8859 8680 E-mail: arguselecservltd@aol.com

▶ Arktech UK Ltd, 11 Tower Road, Washington, Tyne & Wear, NE37 2SH Tel: 0191-419 3996 Fax: 0191-419 3096

▶ Arngrove Construction Services, 3 Easter Park, Teesside Industrial Estate, Stockton-on-Tees, Cleveland, TS17 9NT Tel: (01642) 800666 Fax: (01642) 800688

▶ Arrest Security Systems, Unit 2 142 Strathcona Drive, Glasgow, G13 1JQ Tel: 0141-958 1555 Fax: 0141-958 1558

▶ Arthur Mckay & Co. Ltd, 42 Dryden Road, Loanhead, Midlothian, EH20 9LZ Tel: 0131-440 6000 Fax: 0131-440 6001

▶ Asj Electrical Services, 6 Woodburn Road, Smethwick, West Midlands, B66 2PU Tel: 0121-555 8801 Fax: 0121-555 8803

▶ Aspull Electrical Services Ltd, 124-126 Frog Lane, Wigan, Lancashire, WN6 7DS Tel: (01942) 247459 Fax: (01942) 826367 E-mail: info@aspull-electrical.co.uk

▶ Associated Cooling Services, Unit 20 Metro Business Centre, Kangley Bridge Road, London, SE26 5BW Tel: (020) 8778 8668 Fax: (020) 8778 1221

Astelle Electrical Contractors Ltd, Mayflower House, 3 Chapel St, Billericay, Essex, CM12 9LT Tel: (01277) 651320 Fax: (01277) 630608

▶ Astra Electrical Services, Unit D16g Lakeside Park, Neptune Close, Medway City Estate, Rochester, Kent, ME2 4LT Tel: (01634) 291079 Fax: (01634) 291019

Atack Electrical Co. Ltd, 68 Churchbridge, Oldbury, West Midlands, B69 2AS Tel: 0121-552 3076 Fax: 0121-544 2697 E-mail: atack@atackelec.co.uk

▶ Atech Electrical, 269 Church Rd, Sheldon, Birmingham, B26 3YH Tel: 07967 305583 E-mail: atech.electrical@blueyonder.co.uk

Atlantas Co., 43c-43d Melbourne Place, North Berwick, East Lothian, EH39 4JS Tel: (01620) 893395 Fax: (01620) 894289

Austin Leisure, 153-154 Victoria Road, Swindon, SN1 3BU Tel: (01793) 528505 Fax: (01793) 613469 E-mail: office@austingroup.co.uk

▶ Automation Security Electrical Ltd, Bridge House, Dock Lane, Shipley, West Yorkshire, BD18 1BU Tel: (01274) 585222 Fax: (01274) 585444

▶ Aveat Heating Ltd, Lambert House, 7 Driberg Way, Braintree, Essex, CM7 1NB Tel: (01376) 325670 Fax: (01376) 551210 E-mail: aveat@btconnect.com

▶ Avocet Electrical Contractors Ltd, Units 2-2a, St. Johns Lane, Bewdley, Worcestershire, DY12 2QY Tel: (01299) 401501 Fax: (01299) 402828

▶ Aw Developments, 436 Queens Drive, West Derby, Liverpool, L13 0AR Tel: 0151-228 0001 Fax: 0151-252 1472

Axon Power & Control, 347 Pomeroy Road, Pomeroy, Dungannon, County Tyrone, BT70 3DT Tel: (028) 8775 8923 Fax: (028) 8775 8937

▶ Aztec Electrical Ltd, Cheney Manor Industrial Estate, Swindon, SN2 2PJ Tel: (01793) 484401 Fax: (01793) 484407

▶ B A Corry Ltd, 24 Whitelaw Road, Southampton, SO15 8LJ Tel: (023) 8077 2854 Fax: (023) 8078 7013 E-mail: office@bacorryltd.co.uk

B C Electrical, 8 Hurstleigh Heights, Thornton-Cleveleys, Lancashire, FY5 5NY Tel: (01253) 824781 E-mail: sales@bcelectrical.co.uk

B C Harper Ltd, 7-9 Vincent Street, Derby, DE23 8BT Tel: (01332) 773333 Fax: (01332) 773777

B J Cope (Electrical) Ltd, D6 Ivinghoe Bus Centre, Blackburn Road, Houghton Regis, Dunstable, Bedfordshire, LU5 5BQ Tel: (01582) 662434 Fax: (01582) 472753

▶ B J Electricians, 79 Charles Street, Glasgow, G21 2PS Tel: 0141-553 1133 Fax: 0141-552 5333

B J Forster Electrical Contractors, 16 Powys Close, Dinas Powys, South Glamorgan, CF64 4LQ Tel: (029) 2051 4326 Fax: (029) 2051 4326

▶ B Neale & Son Builders Ltd, 61 Weltmore Road, Luton, LU3 2TN Tel: (01582) 595541

▶ B Rogers, Unit 23 Mold Business Park, Wrexham Road, Mold, Clwyd, CH7 1XP Tel: (01352) 700096 Fax: (01352) 753100

B S P Electrics, 10 Horwood Court, Bletchley, Milton Keynes, MK1 1RD Tel: (01908) 645500 Fax: (01908) 647700

▶ B Tattersall, Unit 4a1 Strathspey Industrial Estate, Woodlands Terrace, Grantown-on-Spey, Morayshire, PH26 3NB Tel: (01479) 872184 Fax: (01479) 872184

▶ Bag Building Society Ltd, 10 Viscount''s Pend, Dundee, DD4 9RJ Tel: (01382) 509000

▶ Bailey, 5 South Gyle CR Lae, Edinburgh, EH12 9EG Tel: 0131-316 4443 Fax: 0131-316 4244

▶ Baineport Engineering Services, 4 The Dock, Ely, Cambridgeshire, CB7 4GS Tel: (0870) 2414806 Fax: (0870) 2417172

▶ Balfour Kilpatrick Ltd, Unit 2B, Bankhead Crossway South, Edinburgh, EH11 4TA Tel: 0131-453 4842

Balfour Kilpatrick Ltd, Glasgow Road, Deanside, Renfrew, PA4 8XZ Tel: 0141-885 4321 Fax: 0141-885 4480 E-mail: enquiry@balfourkilpatrick.com

Banks Dave Electric, 9 Harewood Road, Holymoorside, Chesterfield, Derbyshire, S42 7HT Tel: (01246) 567333 Fax: (01246) 567444

Barchem Construction Ltd, 3 Barton Court, 11-12 High Street, Highworth, Swindon, SN6 7AG Tel: (01793) 762380 Fax: (01793) 766005 E-mail: barchonpr@aol.com

▶ Bardra Building Services Ltd, 43 London Road, Brentwood, Essex, CM14 4NN Tel: (01277) 211609 Fax: (01277) 262726

J. Barker Electrical Services Ltd, The Old School Buildings, Churchill Street, Hull, HU9 1RR Tel: (01482) 588500 Fax: (01482) 594699 E-mail: enquiries@jbe1.com

Barlows Electrical, St.Josephs Bus Park, 3 St. Josephs Close, Hove, East Sussex, BN3 7EZ Tel: (01273) 710077 Fax: (01273) 710066 E-mail: office@barlowselectrical.co.uk

Barr Electrical Ltd, 1 Ladywell Road, Motherwell, Lanarkshire, ML1 3JA Tel: (01698) 263231 Fax: (01698) 263231

Barr R & T Electrical Ltd, 142-158 Pittencrieff Street, Dunfermline, Fife, KY12 8AN Tel: (01383) 722096 Fax: (01383) 739226 E-mail: rtbarr@hotmail.co.uk

Barrett Bros Electrical Ltd, 198 Hither Green Lane, London, SE13 6QB Tel: (020) 8852 4271 Fax: (020) 8852 0892 E-mail: barrettbros@btconnect.com

ELECTRICAL CONTRACTORS – *continued*

Barrett Electrical Contracts Ltd, Unit 29 Gortrush Industrial Estate, Omagh, County Tyrone, BT78 5EJ Tel: (028) 8224 9111 Fax: (028) 8224 6815 E-mail: barrett.electric@btconnect.com

Barry P Millard, 3 Underhill Lane, Lower Bourne, Farnham, Surrey, GU10 3NF Tel: (01252) 711002 Fax: (01252) 711002

▶ Bartram Walker, Bowburn North Industrial Estate, Bowburn, Durham, DH6 5PF Tel: 0191-377 4620 Fax: 0191-377 4621 E-mail: sales@bartramwalker.co.uk

Bartram Walker, Bowburn North Industrial Estate, Bowburn, Durham, DH6 5PF Tel: 0191-377 4620 Fax: 0191-377 4621 E-mail: sales@bartramwalker.co.uk

▶ Bartram Walker, Esh Burn, Burn Lane, Hexham, Northumberland, NE46 3HN Tel: (01434) 602441 Fax: (01434) 601975 E-mail: info@robsonwalker.co.uk

▶ Baudelaire Ltd, 7 Prospect Business Centre, Prospect Road, Alresford, Hampshire, SO24 9UH Tel: (0870) 7776380 Fax: (0870) 7776382

▶ Beale & Cole Ltd, 3 Limber Road, Lufton, Yeovil, Somerset, BA22 8RR Tel: (01935) 444660 Fax: (01935) 433523

Beaumont & Blackburn Ltd, 21 Wellington Road, Dewsbury, West Yorkshire, WF13 1HL Tel: (01924) 461067 Fax: (01924) 430971

▶ R.W. Bell Electrical Ltd, Atholl Road, Pitlochry, Perthshire, PH16 5BX Tel: (01796) 472263

Bennett & Dean Ltd, 9a Edison Road, Salisbury, SP2 7NU Tel: (01722) 413303 Fax: (01722) 414281

▶ Bernard Hunt (Electrical Contractors) Ltd, Northfield, Kilburn, Belper, Derbyshire, DE56 0LW Tel: (01332) 880665

▶ Berridge Electrical Services Ltd, Unit 2 38a Rosemary Lane, Blackwater, Camberley, Surrey, GU17 0LT Tel: (01276) 32707 Fax: (01276) 36538

▶ Betalec Ltd, Unit 29, Neath Abbey Business Park, Neath Abbey, Neath, West Glamorgan, SA10 7DR Tel: (01792) 324555

Beverley Electric Ltd, Annie Reed Road, Beverley, North Humberside, HU17 0LF Tel: (01482) 862379 Fax: (01482) 865811 E-mail: robkitchen@beverleyelectric.co.uk

Bilton & Johnson Co. Ltd, Chadwell Heath Industrial Park, Kemp Road, Dagenham, Essex, RM8 1SL Tel: (020) 8598 8088 Fax: (020) 8599 4311

▶ Bishopcraft Ltd, 7 Otley Road, Shipley, West Yorkshire, BD17 7DY Tel: (01274) 599466

▶ Blake Contractors Ltd, 10 Bircham Road, Southend-on-Sea, SS2 5DN Tel: (01702) 613641 Fax: (01702) 467002 E-mail: info@blakecontractors.co.uk

▶ BMS Electrical, Windmill Farm, Benenden Road, Rolvenden, Cranbrook, Kent, TN17 4PF Tel: (01580) 241841 Fax: (01580) 241873

Boler S E Ltd, 16-20 Princess Street, Sheffield, S4 7UW Tel: (0114) 272 0833 Fax: 0114-272 0838 E-mail: sales@boler-se.com

▶ Bonnells Electrical Contractors Ltd, 9 Long Drive, Ruislip, Middlesex, HA4 0HH Tel: (020) 8845 8455 Fax: (020) 8845 8745

▶ Boothright, Glaisdale Dr East, Nottingham, NG8 4GU Tel: 0115-942 8585 Fax: 0115-942 8586 E-mail: sales@boothright-electrical.co.uk

▶ Bootle Bros Ltd, 42B Banstead Road, Carshalton, Surrey, SM5 3NW Tel: (020) 8770 1347

▶ Borden Electrical Services Ltd, Riddles Road Off Borden Lane, Bredgar, Sittingbourne, Kent, ME9 8HP Tel: (01795) 410186 Fax: (01795) 410142

▶ Bore Electrical Services, 3 Venture Works, Charleywood Road, Knowsley Industrial Park, Liverpool, L33 7SG Tel: 0151-547 4447 Fax: 0151-547 4437

▶ Botes Maintenance, Harvey Road, Basildon, Essex, SS13 1EP Tel: (0800) 0730317

Boulting Group plc, Chapel Road, Penketh, Warrington, WA5 2PL Tel: (01925) 726661 Fax: (01925) 723508 E-mail: info@boulting.co.uk

Bowen Hopkins Ltd, 854 Carmarthen Road, Fforestfach, Swansea, SA5 8HS Tel: (01792) 581022 Fax: (01792) 583321

Bowshers Ltd, 19 Buckland Road, Pen Mill Trading Estate, Yeovil, Somerset, BA21 5HA Tel: (01935) 423926 Fax: (01935) 432865 E-mail: bowshers@bowshers-electrical.co.uk

T.A. Boxall & Co. Ltd, 20 Balcombe Road, Horley, Surrey, RH6 9HR Tel: (01293) 820133 Fax: (01293) 776139 E-mail: ronransley@taboxall.co.uk

▶ Bradley Electrical Services & Technicians Ltd, Hilton Trading Estate, Hilton Road, Lanesfield, Wolverhampton, WV4 6DW Tel: (01902) 493555 Fax: (01902) 493888 E-mail: sales@bradleyelectrical.co.uk

▶ Brady & Gallagher, 13 Cattle Street, St. Helier, Jersey, JE2 4WP Tel: (01534) 758267

▶ Brands Electronics, Faulds Park, Faulds Park Road, Gourock, Renfrewshire, PA19 1BN Tel: (01475) 657700

▶ Brenmar Electrical, Glen Eyre, Brickyard Road, Swanmore, Southampton, SO32 2PJ Tel: (01489) 891196 Fax: (01489) 891197

▶ Brentwood Electrical Contractors Ltd, 5 St. James Road, Brentwood, Essex, CM14 4LF Tel: (01277) 216121

▶ Brian Knight Electrical Ltd, 2 Summers Road, Godalming, Surrey, GU7 3BB Tel: (01483) 414477 Fax: (01483) 424300

▶ Brocol Pipe Work Ltd, 62a Thornes Lane, Wakefield, West Yorkshire, WF1 5RR Tel: (01924) 380048 Fax: (01924) 380588

Brook & Mayo Electrical, Acorn House, Lindum Business Park, Station Road, North Hykeham, Lincoln, LN6 3YL Tel: (01522) 686851 Fax: (01522) 686843 E-mail: nick@brookandmayo.co.uk

Bryan Powercom, 19 University Street, Belfast, BT7 1FY Tel: (028) 9032 6315 Fax: (028) 9032 3144 E-mail: bryanprcom@aol.com

▶ BSCL Ltd, Unit 1 Stoke View Business Park, Stoke View Road, Bristol, BS16 3AE Tel: 0117-958 3540 Fax: 0117-958 3539 E-mail: info@bscl.com

▶ Building Services Design, 5 Melbourne House Corby Gate Business Park, Priors Haw Road, Corby, Northamptonshire, NN17 5JG Tel: (01536) 403304 Fax: (01536) 403838

▶ Bull Electrical Services Westminster Ltd, 13-15 Johns Mews, London, WC1N 2PA Tel: (020) 7242 1282 Fax: (020) 7242 1909

Burgins News, 167 Wolverhampton Street, Dudley, West Midlands, DY1 3AH Tel: (01384) 255807

Ken Burrows Ltd, 40 Ogle Street, Hucknall, Nottingham, NG15 7FR Tel: 0115-963 2088 Fax: 0115-968 1737

▶ Butherway Electrical, Rhiw, Rosebush, Clynderwen, Dyfed, SA66 7RH Tel: (01437) 532511 Fax: (01437) 532964 E-mail: sales@butherwayelectrical.com

▶ Buzz Electrical Ltd, Cornmill Road, Evesham, Worcestershire, WR11 2LL Tel: (01386) 423600 Fax: (01386) 423900

▶ C A D E Electrical Contractors Ltd, 16 Evelyn Grove South, Grimsby, South Humberside, DN32 8LB Tel: (01472) 591713 Fax: (01472) 230576 E-mail: sales@cadeelectrical.co.uk

▶ C A Maddox, 150 Widemarsh Street, Hereford, HR4 9HN Tel: (01432) 267156 Fax: (01432) 267556 E-mail: ca.maddox@btconnect.com

C A Sothers Ltd, 156 Hockley Hill, Birmingham, B18 5AN Tel: 0121-554 2054 Fax: 0121-554 4090 E-mail: cas@sothers.com

C E C Engineering Services Ltd, 2 Cantelupe Mews, Cantelupe Road, East Grinstead, West Sussex, RH19 3BG Tel: (01342) 315935 Fax: (01342) 311526

▶ C E I Electrical Ltd, Unit 19 Mitchell Point, Ensign Way, Hamble, Southampton, SO31 4RF Tel: (023) 8045 4822 Fax: (023) 8045 6832 E-mail: email@dmelectrical.co.uk

C & F Electrics, Brookside Offices, Rassau Road, Rassau, Ebbw Vale, Gwent, NP23 5BL Tel: (01495) 350333 Fax: (01495) 305333

▶ C G J Building Services Ltd, 51 Station Road, Knowle, Solihull, West Midlands, B93 0HN Tel: (01564) 732000 Fax: (01564) 732001

▶ C I E International Ltd, Isle of Grain, Rochester, Kent, ME3 0EP Tel: (01634) 271601 Fax: (01634) 270723

C & M Electrical Contracts & Maintenance Ltd, 2f Vaughan Court, Stapylton Street, Middlesbrough, Cleveland, TS6 7BJ Tel: (01642) 440640 Fax: (01642) 460595 E-mail: jd@cmelec.co.uk

▶ C & M Group Ltd, 5-19 Holland Street, Aberdeen, AB25 3UJ Tel: (01224) 625928 Fax: (01224) 625914

▶ C M S Building Services, 30 St Dunstans Hill, Sutton, Surrey, SM1 2UD Tel: (020) 8641 5520 Fax: (020) 8641 1905

C M W Controls Ltd, Bryn Lane, Wrexham Industrial Estate, Wrexham, Clwyd, LL13 9UT Tel: (01978) 661516 Fax: (01978) 661626 E-mail: geoff.roberts@cmwcontrols.com

▶ C P L Engineering, 78 Main Street, Crumlin, County Antrim, BT29 4UU Tel: (028) 9445 3225

C R S Specialised Building Services Ltd, 45a Stoke Road, Gosport, Hampshire, PO12 1LS Tel: (023) 9258 3084 Fax: (023) 9258 3084 E-mail: enq@crsbuilders.co.uk

▶ C & S Electrical Engineering Services Ltd, Unit 30 Salford University BP, Winders Way, Salford, M6 6AR Tel: 0161-736 6486

C Y Electrical & Cranes Co. Ltd, Hayes Lane, Stourbridge, West Midlands, DY9 8QT Tel: (01384) 895570 Fax: (01384) 892877 E-mail: sales@cyequip.co.uk

Cable Jointing Services Ltd, Cedric Works, Cedric CR, Sunderland, SR2 7QP Tel: 0191-514 1165 Fax: 0191-564 0005 E-mail: sales@cablejointingservices.com

Cameras Stop Crime, Hillcrest, Roucan Road, Collin, Dumfries, DG1 4JF Tel: (01387) 750689 Fax: (01387) 750689

▶ Campbell & Mchardy Ltd, Unit 12 Linkwood Industrial Estate, Elgin, Morayshire, IV30 1XS Tel: (01343) 543516 Fax: (01343) 543516

Cannon Electrical Contractors (Manchester) Ltd, Unit 2 Derwent Street Industrial Estate, Odsall Lane, Salford, M5 4RE Tel: 0161-832 7320 Fax: 0161-839 4298 E-mail: cannonelectrical@btopenworld.com

▶ Capri Mechanical Services Ltd, 53-55 Cutlers Road, South Woodham Ferrers, Chelmsford, CM3 5WA Tel: (01245) 321144 E-mail: info@caprimechanical.co.uk

▶ Capstan Security Ltd, 127 East Barnet Road, Barnet, Hertfordshire, EN4 8RF Tel: (020) 8441 9700 Fax: (020) 8449 5319 E-mail: admin@capstansecurity.com

Caresafe Electrics, 15 Shorton Road, Paignton, Devon, TQ3 2NB Tel: (01803) 521003 Fax: (01803) 521003

Harry Carr Ltd, Armstrong Street, Grimsby, North East Lincolnshire, DN31 1LG Tel: (01472) 246600 Fax: (01472) 240466 E-mail: engineers@harrycarr.co.uk

▶ Cass Electric Co. Ltd, Unit 10-11, The Gateway Industrial Estate, Parkgate, Rotherham, South Yorkshire, S62 6JL Tel: (01709) 528822 Fax: (01709) 528882

Castles Shopfitters Limited, Bowland Street Works, Bowland Street, Bradford, West Yorkshire, BD1 3BW Tel: (01274) 724271 E-mail: mail@castle_shopfitters.co.uk

Causeway Electricial Services, Catherine Street, Warrington, WA5 0LH Tel: (01925) 633390 Fax: (01925) 243214

Cdi Group plc, 5-7 Melchett Road, Kings Norton Business Centre, Birmingham, B30 3HG Tel: 0121-458 4888 Fax: 0121-433 2800

Centra Controls Ltd, 14 Landywood Lane, Cheslyn Hay, Walsall, WS6 7AH Tel: (01922) 415510 Fax: (01922) 415510 E-mail: centra@tiscala.co.uk

Central Electrical Engineering Services Properties Ltd, 6-8 Edison Road, Rabans Lane Industrial Area, Aylesbury, Buckinghamshire, HP19 8TE Tel: (01296) 424561 Fax: (01296) 394907

▶ Central Electrical Installations Ltd, Bradley Mill, Bradley Lane, Newton Abbot, Devon, TQ12 1NF Tel: (01626) 330054 Fax: (01626) 331915 E-mail: devon@central-electrical.com

▶ Central Electrical Services Hinckley Ltd, 10a Ashby Road, Hinckley, Leicestershire, LE10 1SL Tel: (01455) 890860

▶ CFM Electrical Contractors, Elizabeth Terrace, Tower Road, St. Helier, Jersey, JE2 3HS Tel: (01534) 870722 Fax: (01534) 780757

▶ Chadwell Construction Ltd, Tralin House, Chesham Close, Romford, RM7 7PJ Tel: (01708) 767100 Fax: (01708) 759920 E-mail: info@chadwell.co.uk

Raymond Chalmers Electrical Contractor, 25A Kinloch Street, Ladybank, Cupar, Fife, KY15 7LF Tel: (01337) 831272 Fax: (01337) 831272 E-mail: rayspark1@aol.com

Chapman Ltd, Chapmans Corner, Reddal Hill Road, Cradley Heath, West Midlands, B64 5JG Tel: (01384) 569958 Fax: (01384) 413190

Charisma Sound & Light, 31e Redwood Drive, Brant Road Waddington, Lincoln, LN5 9BN Tel: (01522) 881212 Fax: (01522) 881515

Charlestown Electrical Co. Ltd, Collier Street, Glossop, Derbyshire, SK13 8LS Tel: (01457) 852134 Fax: (01457) 852134

▶ The Chiltern Lift Company Ltd, 8 Furlong Road, Bourne End, Buckinghamshire, SL8 5DG Tel: (01628) 529247 Fax: (01628) 810821

▶ Chris Bowker Ltd, Whitegate, White Lund Industrial Estate, Morecambe, Lancashire, LA3 3BS Tel: (01524) 36353 Fax: (01524) 841683

▶ Chubb Electronic Security Ltd, 120 Gower Road, Sketty, Swansea, SA2 9BT Tel: (0870) 2418680 Fax: (0870) 2418681

▶ Chubb Securities Ltd, 18 & 19 Lionel Street, Birmingham, B3 1AQ Tel: 0121-200 3311

▶ Cititec Building Services Ltd, Little Hyde Farm, Little Hyde Lane, Ingatestone, Essex, CM4 0DU Tel: (01277) 350730 Fax: (01277) 350731

▶ City Electrical Installations Cobridge Ltd, 36 Woodbank Street, Stoke-on-Trent, ST6 3BD Tel: (01782) 812217

City Guardian Electrical Ltd, Vision House, 182 Landells Road, London, SE22 9PP Tel: (020) 8299 5120 Fax: (020) 8299 5130 E-mail: reception@caivision.com

▶ City Renovations Ltd, 10 Bond Avenue Bletchley, Bletchley, Milton Keynes, MK1 1SW Tel: (01908) 366936

▶ Clarion Loss Prevention Ltd, Oak House, 103 Manchester Road, Audenshaw, Manchester, M34 5PY Tel: 0161-371 1888 Fax: (0870) 4448348

Clark Electrical Industries Ltd, 1e North Crescent, London, E16 4TG Tel: (020) 7474 7404 Fax: (020) 7473 1961 E-mail: enquries@ceiltd.co.uk

Clark Electrical Services, 78 Milnrow Road, Shaw, Oldham, OL2 8ER Tel: (01706) 290837 Fax: (01706) 290837 E-mail: electricalspurs@aol.com

▶ Clarkes Electrical Services, 127-128 Windmill Street, Gravesend, Kent, DA12 1BL Tel: (01474) 322948 Fax: (01474) 329988

Claud Hamilton Electrical Services Ltd, 24 Ellon Road, Bridge Of Don, Aberdeen, AB23 8BX Tel: (01224) 822685 Fax: (01224) 826200 E-mail: hq@ches-group.co.uk

▶ Claymore Lock & Alarm Co., 3 Hardgate, Haddington, East Lothian, EH41 3JW Tel: (01620) 829550 Fax: (01620) 829751

▶ CMB Fylde Engineering, 3 Skyways Commercial Campus, Amy Johnson Way, Blackpool, FY4 2RP Tel: (01253) 298366 Fax: (01253) 298377

▶ Cogent Electrical Services Ltd, Unit 16 Sulivan Enterprise Centre, Sulivan Road, London, SW6 3DJ Tel: (020) 7736 5666 Fax: (020) 7736 4666

Collinson & Grainger Ltd, 77 Dixons Green, Dudley, West Midlands, DY2 7DJ Tel: (01384) 230318 Fax: (01384) 457418

Combined Building Services Ltd, 7 Kennet Road, Dartford, DA1 4QN Tel: (01322) 520270 E-mail: combinedcbs@aol.com

▶ Combined Electrical Engineering Services, 12 Wyvern Buildings, Grove Trading Estate, Dorchester, Dorset, DT1 1ST Tel: (01305) 251177 Fax: (01305) 250552 E-mail: sales@ceesltd.co.uk

Commercial & Industrial Electrical Services Ltd, Unit 70, Gravelly Indust Park, Birmingham, B24 8TQ Tel: 0121-328 1780 Fax: 0121-327 7589

▶ Commertech Ltd, 55 High Street, Leatherhead, Surrey, KT22 8AG Tel: (01372) 376427

Complete Design Installations Ltd, 63 Austhorpe Road, Crossgates, Leeds, LS15 8EQ Tel: 0113-294 3909 Fax: 0113-294 3909

▶ Connections Properties Ltd, Phoenix House, 37 Palmer Street, Chippenham, Wiltshire, SN14 0DT Tel: (01249) 444715

▶ Contact Electrical, Rackheath Industrial Estate, Rackheath, Norwich, NR13 6LH Tel: (01603) 720401 Fax: (01603) 720070

Continental Appliance Services Midlands Ltd, 5 Showell Lane, Wolverhampton, WV4 4TZ Tel: (01902) 894433 Fax: (01902) 894433

Control Electrics Leicester Ltd, 30 Fowke Street, Rothley, Leicester, LE7 7PJ Tel: 0116-237 4233 E-mail: enquire@controlelectrics.co.uk

▶ Convert-E-Lite Ltd, Contech House, Rushington Business Park, Unit 2 Rushington Lane, Totton, Southampton, SO40 9LT Tel: (023) 8066 0987

Cooper Electrical Services, Unit 4e Wistaston Road Business Centre, Wistaston Road, Crewe, CW2 7RP Tel: (01270) 589879 Fax: (01270) 589191

Cooper & West, 101 Clarence Road, Fleet, Hampshire, GU51 3RS Tel: (01252) 617873 Fax: (01252) 617873

▶ Corwoods Electrical Contractors, Unit 28 King Street Trading Estate, Middlewich, Cheshire, CW10 9LF Tel: (01606) 737395

Cottrell Electrical Services Ltd, 276-278 Smithdown Road, Liverpool, L15 5AJ Tel: 0151-733 5100 Fax: 0151-734 4457 E-mail: sales@cottrellelectrical.co.uk

▶ Coxmoor Electrical Services Ltd, 14-16 Diamond Avenue, Kirkby-in-Ashfield, Nottingham, NG17 7GR Tel: (01623) 722366 Fax: (01623) 722365

▶ Craig Steven, 28 Mayburn Avenue, Loanhead, Midlothian, EH20 9EP Tel: 0131-440 0602 Fax: 0131 4400602 E-mail: info@sc-electrical-services.co.uk

▶ Craigs Electrical Co., 203 Kersey Crescent, Speen, Newbury, Berkshire, RG14 1SW Tel: (07876) 550331 Fax: (01635) 820308 E-mail: craig@youhirewewire.co.uk

▶ Cranbrook Loft Conversions Ltd, 732 Cranbrook Road, Ilford, Essex, IG6 1HU Tel: (0800) 525883 Fax: (020) 8551 1580 E-mail: admin@cranbrook.co.uk

Cranleigh Control Co., Unit 30 Hewitts Industrial Estate, Elmbridge Road, Cranleigh, Surrey, GU6 8LW Tel: (01483) 272663 Fax: (01483) 272663 E-mail: mail@cranleighcontrol.co.uk

▶ Crawt Simpkins Partnership, 71 Loudoun Road, London, NW8 0DQ Tel: (020) 7372 1881 Fax: (020) 7372 1991

▶ Creatside Ltd, 1 Dover Road, Northfleet, Gravesend, Kent, DA11 9PH Tel: (01474) 361230 Fax: (01474) 564380

▶ Cromb Electricians Crieff Ltd, Unit 7 Crioch Business Centre, Crioch Place, Crieff, Perthshire, PH7 3BW Tel: (01764) 653177

▶ Crosby Electrical Services Ltd, 5 Sovereign Business Centre, Stockingswater Lane, Enfield, Middlesex, EN3 7JX Tel: (020) 8443 1212 Fax: (020) 8804 3259 E-mail: info@crosbyelectrical.com

▶ Crown House Engineering, C/O N E C, Carnegie Road, Deans Industrial Estate, Deans, Livingston, West Lothian, EH54 8QX Tel: (01506) 410696

▶ Croztech Electrical Engineers, Unit 18 Botany Business Park, Macclesfield Road, Whaley Bridge, High Peak, Derbyshire, SK23 7DQ Tel: (01663) 719977 Fax: (01663) 719900

Cwmbran Electrical Services Ltd, Unit 34 Court Road Industrial Estate, Cwmbran, Gwent, NP44 3AS Tel: (01633) 483416 Fax: (01633) 874712

▶ Cybi Electrical Contracting, Cybi Buildings, St. Cybi Street, Holyhead, Gwynedd, LL65 1DS Tel: (01407) 762244 Fax: (01407) 762255

▶ D A Clarke, Highfields Farm, Huncote Road, Stoney Stanton, Leicester, LE9 4DJ Tel: (01455) 272214 Fax: (01455) 273302

D A Wright Ltd, 13 Lowman Units Lowman Way, Tiverton Business Park, Tiverton, Devon, EX16 6SR Tel: (01884) 254474 Fax: (01884) 256479 E-mail: info@dawright.co.uk

D B Brooks Electrical Engineers Ltd, Sinclair Close, Heanor, Derbyshire, DE75 7SP Tel: (01773) 763444 Fax: (01773) 530332 E-mail: admin@dbbrooks.co.uk

▶ D B Electrics, 3 Spartleton Place, Dundee, DD4 0UJ Tel: (01382) 739447 Fax: (01382) 739447 E-mail: dbelectrics@blueyonder.co.uk

▶ D B Installations, 4 Bridge Street, Newbridge, Midlothian, EH28 8SR Tel: (0800) 0377416 Fax: 0131-335 3770

▶ D B Mcintyre, Lochty Industrial Estate, Almondbank, Perth, PH1 3NP Tel: (01738) 582225 Fax: (01738) 582226

▶ D C Lighting Services Ltd, Unit 2a Keillor Buildings, 34 Mains Loan, Dundee, DD4 7BT Tel: (01382) 818222 Fax: (01382) 825028

D E I Electrical Services, Edison House, Dunslow Road, Eastfield, Scarborough, North Yorkshire, YO11 3UT Tel: (01723) 581515 Fax: (01723) 585247

D E P E Breaden Electrical Ltd, 396 Finchley Road, London, NW2 2HR Tel: (020) 7435 1304 Fax: (020) 7435 0194

▶ D Electrical, Valley Works, Bacup Road, Todmorden, Lancashire, OL14 7PJ Tel: (01706) 814854 Fax: (01706) 815023

D & G Electrical Controls, 7a Weller Drive, Finchampstead, Wokingham, Berkshire, RG40 4QZ Tel: 0118-973 7123 Fax: 0118-973 0071 E-mail: dg.electrical@virgin.net

▶ D & G Electrical Engineering Ltd, Unit Bs1 Junction 7 Business Park, Blackburn Road, Clayton le Moors, Accrington, Lancashire, BB5 5JW Tel: (01254) 398725 Fax: (01254) 398725

ELECTRICAL CONTRACTORS –

continued

▶ D H Electrical Services Ltd, Unit 2 Eversley Way, Thorpe Industrial Estate, Egham, Surrey, TW20 8RG Tel: (01784) 479400 Fax: (01784) 479300

▶ D H Marrion Ltd, 220 Sheffield Road, Barnsley, South Yorkshire, S70 4PF Tel: (01226) 282576 Fax: (01226) 248354

▶ D H Morris Group, Omega House, 37 Telford Street, Inverness, IV3 5LD Tel: (01463) 237667

▶ D H Morris Group (Edinburgh), 4 Trinity Crescent, Edinburgh, EH5 3ED Tel: 0131-552 7644

▶ D I S Electrical Contractors Ltd, Le Petit Catelet, La Route De St. Jean, St. John, Jersey, JE3 4EA Tel: (01534) 861488 Fax: (01534) 861487

▶ D J Electrical, Laramie, North Roskear Road, Tuckingmill, Camborne, Cornwall, TR14 8PX Tel: (01209) 711825 E-mail: dajo13496@lineone.net

▶ D J Robinson Electrical Ltd, Moat Mill, Brewerton Street, Knaresborough, North Yorkshire, HG5 8AZ Tel: (01423) 865129 Fax: (01423) 868412

D M Anderton Ltd, First Floor 19, Bark St East, Bolton, BL1 2BQ Tel: (01204) 532618 Fax: (01204) 532619 E-mail: dmanderton@btconnect.com

D & M Barthorpe, Oxford Street, Boston, Lincolnshire, PE21 8TW Tel: (01205) 367612 Fax: (01205) 357932

▶ D M Harris Ltd, 51 Eastmuir Street, Glasgow, G32 0HS Tel: 0141-763 2309 Fax: 0141-763 2373

▶ D & R Electrical, 6 Rayners Crescent, Northolt, Middlesex, UB5 6PB Tel: (020) 8841 2520 Fax: (020) 8723 3213 E-mail: sales@drelectricalservices.co.uk

▶ D & S Sloanes, 24 Alexandra Park, Sunderland, SR3 1XJ Tel: 0191-522 6610 Fax: 0191-549 1345 E-mail: dandasloanes@btconnect.com

▶ D Selby, Newcastle Street, Bulwell, Nottingham, NG6 8AW Tel: 0115-927 5103 Fax: 0115-927 4159

D Tec, Unit 2 Whitegate Business Center, Chadderton, Oldham, OL9 9QL Tel: 0161-627 3988 Fax: 0161-627 0194 E-mail: enquiries@dtec-elec.co.uk

D W Cassell & Co., The Belper, Dudley, West Midlands, DY1 3AH Tel: (01384) 234321

D & W Electrics West Bromwich, 29 Colshaw Road, Stourbridge, West Midlands, DY8 3AS Tel: (01384) 378289 Fax: (01384) 378289 E-mail: dw-electrics@blueyonder.co.uk

▶ D W Hargreaves Electrical Contractors, 92-94 Buttermarket Street, Warrington, WA1 2NZ Tel: (01925) 414884 Fax: (01925) 573748

▶ Dalmuri Community Concierge Service, 455 Dumbarton Road, Clydebank, Dunbartonshire, G81 4DT Tel: 0141-952 4666 Fax: 0141-952 5114

Darke & Taylor Ltd, Langford Locks, Kidlington, Oxfordshire, OX5 1LH Tel: (01865) 290000 Fax: (01865) 290029 E-mail: darke.taylor@btinternet.com

Dave Casey & Co., 1 Raeburn Street, Hartlepool, Cleveland, TS26 8PT Tel: (01429) 261510 Fax: (01429) 274950

▶ David Cruikshank, River View Business Park, Friarton Road, Perth, PH2 8BB Tel: (01738) 449944

▶ David Lowder Electrical Contractors Ltd, 55a Hercus Loan, Musselburgh, Midlothian, EH21 6AU Tel: 0131-665 7895 Fax: 0131-665 4577

▶ David Stagg & Associates Ltd, 49 Watchouse Road, Chelmsford, CM2 8PU Tel: (01245) 492491 Fax: 01245 269690 E-mail: brian@davidstagg.co.uk

▶ David Sykes (Whitley Bridge) Ltd, The Maltings Industrial Estate, Doncaster Road, Whitley Bridge, Goole, North Humberside, DN14 0HH Tel: (01977) 661351

Davis Hudson & Co. Ltd, 17 Bickford Road, Birmingham, B6 7EE Tel: 0121-327 0020 Fax: 0121-328 5649 E-mail: electricians@davishudson.co.uk

▶ Davison Electrical, 6c Ridley Road, Bournemouth, BH9 1LD Tel: (01202) 530260 Fax: (01202) 538341

▶ Dawson, Unit 1 Colquhoun Street, Stirling, FK7 7PX Tel: (01786) 446882 Fax: (01786) 446882

Dawson & Gibbond Ltd, 55 Red Lion St, Holborn, London, WC1R 4PD Tel: (020) 7242 6014 Fax: (020) 7242 2630 E-mail: admin@d-n-g.co.uk

Deeside Electrical Ltd, Central Point, Brunswick Road, Buckley, Clwyd, CH7 2EH Tel: (01244) 547707 Fax: (01244) 550616

▶ Delta Electrical Ltd, Queen Anne Battery, Plymouth, PL4 0LP Tel: (01752) 225225 Fax: (01752) 256357

▶ Dennis Cox Electrical Contractors, 5 Portland Business Centre, Manor House Lane, Datchet, Slough, SL3 9EG Tel: (01753) 580400 Fax: (01753) 549820

▶ Dennis Gordon Electrical, 68 High Street, Fraserburgh, Aberdeenshire, AB43 9HP Tel: (01346) 518561 Fax: (01346) 519229

Dennis Johns Electrical Ltd, 94a Rendlesham Road, London, E5 8PA Tel: (020) 8985 7668 Fax: (020) 8533 7356 E-mail: dennisjohns.elek@btconnect.com

▶ Dennis King, Unit 7 Middlethorpe Grange, Sim Balk Lane, Bishopthorpe, York, YO23 2UE Tel: (01904) 700334 Fax: (01904) 700390

▶ Derek Mitchell, 2 Station Yard Industrial Estate, Oakwell Road, Castle Douglas, Kirkcudbrightshire, DG7 1LA Tel: (01556) 503150 Fax: (01556) 504411

▶ Derek Smith Electrical Ltd, 5C Jefferson Avenue, Bournemouth, BH1 4NX Tel: (01202) 751508

Edward Dewhurst Ltd, Grierson House, Chain Call Way, Preston Riversway Docklands, Preston, PR2 2DG Tel: (01772) 761777 Fax: (01772) 761666 E-mail: pad@edewhurst.com

▶ DH Electrical, 1 Rosemary Crescent, Tiptree, Colchester, CO5 0XA Tel: (01621) 817827 E-mail: dh.electrical@btopenworld.com

Dicks Electrical Installation Ltd, Winnall Valley Road, Winchester, Hampshire, SO23 0LR Tel: (01962) 841441 Fax: (01962) 840730

Dimension Data Advanced Infrastructure, Thelwall Industrial Estate, Thelwall New Road, Warrington, WA4 2LY Tel: (01925) 602942 Fax: (01925) 267464 E-mail: sales@uk.didata.com

▶ Dodd Group, Unit 1 Rabone Lane, Smethwick, West Midlands, B66 3JH Tel: 0121-565 6000 Fax: 0121-565 6038

▶ Dodd Group South Western Ltd, 17-25 Hoopern Street, Exeter, EX4 4LU Tel: (01392) 426345 Fax: (01392) 426446

Doddgroup Eastern Ltd, Oldmedow Road, King's Lynn, Norfolk, PE30 4LB Tel: (01553) 772423 Fax: (01553) 691343 E-mail: kings-lynn@doddgroup.com

Dowds Electrical Ltd, 2-4 Milltown Road, Ballymoney, County Antrim, BT53 6LE Tel: (028) 2766 2789 Fax: (028) 2766 5905 E-mail: info@dowdselectrical.com

Downs Insulation & Electrical Ltd, Unit 16 Poulton Close, Dover, Kent, CT17 0HL Tel: (01304) 214473 Fax: (01304) 214473 E-mail: downselectrical@hotmail.com

▶ Dr Security & Electrical, De Beauvoir Road, London, N1 4EN Tel: (020) 7241 1001 E-mail: marketing@drsecurity.co.uk

Drakeset Ltd, 3 Tansey Green Road, Brierley Hill, West Midlands, DY5 4TL Tel: (01384) 79487 Fax: (01384) 70143 E-mail: drakeset@btconnect.com

▶ Drew & Co Electrical Contractors Ltd, Fellowes Court The Millfields, Plymouth, PL1 3JB Tel: (01752) 204415 Fax: (01752) 201684

▶ Dugdales, Skipton Auction Mart, Gargrave Road, Skipton, North Yorkshire, BD23 1UD Tel: (01756) 793530

Dugdales Electrical Engineers, Kirkgate, Settle, North Yorkshire, BD24 9DX Tel: (01729) 822337 Fax: (01729) 822785 E-mail: sales@dugdaleseuropean.com

Dunlop & Hamilton, 9 Prince Regent Road, Belfast, BT5 6SH Tel: (028) 9079 9399 Fax: (028) 9079 3251

▶ Dunsire Associates Electrical Ltd, Unit 10 Phoenix Lane, Dunfermline, Fife, KY12 9EB Tel: (01383) 723583 Fax: (01383) 621216

E B Mason & Son, 38 Breckhill Road, Woodthorpe, Nottingham, NG5 4GP Tel: 0115-926 4265 Fax: 0115-967 1537

E C Electricals Ltd, 16C Wincombe Business Park, Warminster Road, Shaftesbury, Dorset, SP7 9QJ Tel: (01747) 853861 Fax: (01747) 855274 E-mail: enquiries@ecelectricals.co.uk

▶ E C L Integrated Solutions, E Wrexham Road, Basildon, Essex, SS15 6PX Tel: (01268) 540926 Fax: (01268) 415326

▶ E C P S, 1 Clooney Road, Londonderry, BT47 6TB Tel: (028) 7186 1174 Fax: (028) 7186 1179

E E P Electrical, Crondal Road, Exhall, Coventry, CV7 9NH Tel: (024) 7636 3010 Fax: (024) 7636 5182

▶ E Fraser Electrical Orkney Ltd, The Store, Finstown, Orkney, KW17 2EL Tel: (01856) 761762

▶ E Fraser Electrical Orkney Ltd, The Store, Finstown, Orkney, KW17 2EL Tel: (01856) 761762 Fax: (01856) 761777

E H Humphries Norton Ltd, Great Western House, 35 Martindale, Cannock, Staffordshire, WS11 7XN Tel: (01543) 466766 Fax: (01543) 504845 E-mail: enquiries@ehhumphries.co.uk

▶ E I S Axon Ltd, Unit 2, Crusader Industrial Estate, Stirling Road, Cressex Business Park, High Wycombe, Buckinghamshire, HP12 3ST Tel: (01494) 511558 Fax: (01494) 449351 E-mail: paul@eis-axon.co.uk

▶ E I S (Midlands) Ltd, Canterbury Business Centre, Suit 5, 18 Ashchurch Road, Tewkesbury, Gloucestershire, GL20 8BT Tel: (0870) 1430023 Fax: (0870) 1430024

▶ E I S (North) Ltd, Block 7 Unit 2 Larkhall Indust Estate, Dunedin Road, Larkhall, Lanarkshire, ML9 2QS Tel: (01698) 884110 E-mail: enquiries@eisnorth.co.uk

▶ E I S (South) Ltd, Maxwelton Industrial Estate, Glasgow Road, Dumfries, DG2 0NW Tel: (01387) 255231

E I W H S, 69-72 High Street, Croydon, CR0 1PA Tel: (020) 8680 7071 Fax: (020) 8680 9818 E-mail: eiwhs@davishouse.co.uk

▶ E I W H S, Unit 23g The Avenues, Team Valley Trading Estate, Gateshead, Tyne & Wear, NE11 0JY Tel: 0191-487 9486 Fax: 0191-487 8048

▶ E J Ditton & Co., 41 Longfield Road, Dover, Kent, CT17 9QR Tel: (01304) 205141 Fax: (01304) 215047

E J Miller Nottingham Ltd, 539 Woodborough Road, Nottingham, NG3 5FR Tel: 0115-960 4232 Fax: 0115-955 2552

▶ E M C E Ltd, 133 Dean Road, Scarborough, North Yorkshire, YO12 7JH Tel: (01723) 364083 Fax: (01723) 364083 E-mail: quotes@emceltd.co.uk

▶ E P Electrical, Unit 1, Block 14, 82 Clydesmill Drive, Clydesmill Industrial Estate, Glasgow, G32 8RG Tel: 0141-646 2535

E S T Electrical Contractors Ltd, 18 Kenchester Close, Redditch, Worcestershire, B98 0BT Tel: (01527) 529050 Fax: (01527) 510550

▶ E Saunders Ltd, 241 Northdown Road, Margate, Kent, CT9 2PL Tel: (01843) 228546 Fax: (01843) 228290

East Finchley Electrical, 115 High Road, London, N2 8AG Tel: (020) 8883 9098 Fax: (020) 8444 3458 E-mail: dloizou@yahoo.co.uk

East Midlands Instrument Co. Ltd, Laughton Lane, Morton, Gainsborough, Lincolnshire, DN21 3ET Tel: (01427) 616721 Fax: (01427) 810804 E-mail: emi@eminst.co.uk

▶ Eastern Electric Scotland Ltd, 4 New Broompark, Edinburgh, EH5 1RS Tel: 0131-551 4100 Fax: 0131-551 4200

▶ Eastwood Electricial, 27 James Watt Place, East Kilbride, Glasgow, G74 5HG Tel: (01355) 228484 Fax: (01355) 228484

Ebdy Electrical, Acorn House, Acorn Close, Five Oak Green, Tonbridge, Kent, TN12 6RH Tel: (01892) 833000 Fax: (01892) 833311 E-mail: sales@ebdy.co.uk

Eca Contracts Ltd, 3 Fortnum Close, Kitts Green, Birmingham, B33 0LG Tel: 0121-785 4100 Fax: 0121-783 3596 E-mail: info@e-c-a.co.uk

▶ Edmundson Electrical Ltd, Hubert Road, Brentwood, Essex, CM14 4QQ Tel: (01277) 221338 Fax: (01277) 263531

Edmundson Rickards Electrical, 30 Garrett Road, Lynx Trading Estate, Yeovil, Somerset, BA20 2TJ Tel: (01935) 472727 Fax: (01935) 472010 E-mail: mail@spectrumelectrical.co.uk

▶ Edryd Jenkins, Units 43-44, Glan Yr Afon Industrial Estate, Llanbadarn Fawr, Aberystwyth, Dyfed, SY23 3JQ Tel: (01970) 626650 Fax: (01970) 611112

▶ EDS Global Field Services, D I A N House, 2 Aegean Road, Atlantic Street, Altrincham, Cheshire, WA14 5UW Tel: 0161-929 7889 Fax: (0870) 6067491

▶ Ehge, 58 Station Approach, South Ruislip, Ruislip, Middlesex, HA4 6SA Tel: (020) 8839 2640 Fax: (020) 8839 2641

Ei WHS, Staveley House, Fort Street, Blackburn, BB1 5EG Tel: (01254) 670261 Fax: (01254) 680832 E-mail: blackburn@eiwhs.co.uk

▶ Einw Ltd, 12a Leicester Road, Blaby, Leicester, LE8 4GQ Tel: 0116-278 7066 Fax: 0116-278 7355 E-mail: sales@einwltd.co.uk

Eiwhs, 1 London Road, Great Shelford, Cambridge, CB22 5DB Tel: (01223) 845776 Fax: (01223) 842910 E-mail: cambridge.eiwhs@staveley.co.uk

Eiwhs, 23 Dunlop Way, Queensway Industrial Estate, Scunthorpe, South Humberside, DN16 3RN Tel: (01724) 282328 Fax: (01724) 282321 E-mail: rchallis.eiwhs@staveley.co.uk

Eiwhs, Unit 10, President Buildings Savile St East, Sheffield, S4 7UQ Tel: 0114-275 0012 Fax: 0114-276 1402 E-mail: sheffield.eiwhs@staveley.co.uk

Eiwhs, 21 Allensway, Thornaby, Stockton-on-Tees, Cleveland, TS17 9HA Tel: (01642) 769085 Fax: (01642) 761137 E-mail: eiwhs.thornaby@staveley.co.uk

▶ Elecref Ltd, 20 Wilton Road, Humberston, Grimsby, South Humberside, DN36 4AW Tel: (01472) 211666 Fax: (01472) 810019

Electract, Walker Road, Bardon Hill, Coalville, Leicestershire, LE67 1TU Tel: (01530) 510011 Fax: (01530) 811224 E-mail: enquiries@electract.co.uk

▶ The Electric Man Ltd, Glascoed, Ger-y-Nant, Llangunnor, Carmarthen, SA31 2NY Tel: (07778) 463217 E-mail: gary@theelectricman.net

▶ Electrical Connections Ltd, Everik Business Centre, Prospect Way, Hutton, Brentwood, Essex, CM13 1XA Tel: (01277) 231414 Fax: (01277) 230617 E-mail: enquiries@electricalconnections.net

▶ Electrical Installations Ltd, Parker House, Suite 18, Parker Centre, Mansfield Road, Derby, DE21 4SZ Tel: (01332) 200166

Electrical Installations North West Ltd, Lawsons Road, Thornton-Cleveleys, Lancashire, FY5 4PW Tel: (01253) 822626 Fax: (01253) 827846 E-mail: sales@einw.co.uk

▶ Electrical Services (Cornwall) Ltd, Pargolla Road, Newquay, Cornwall, TR7 1RP Tel: (01637) 872700

Electrical Services (Nelson) Ltd, 43 Belgrave St., Nelson, Lancashire, BB9 9HS Tel: (01282) 696317 Fax: (01282) 611632 E-mail: david@electricialsales.co.uk

▶ Electrical Site Services, 111 Seaview Road, Wallasey, Merseyside, CH45 4NZ Tel: 0151-638 8444 Fax: 0151-639 5996

▶ Electricare Services, 33 The CR, Urmston, Manchester, M41 5QR Tel: 0161-202 9499 E-mail: office@electricareservices.co.uk

▶ Electronic Security Systems & Fire Protection Ltd, Roman Road, Kirkintilloch, Glasgow, G66 1DY Tel: 0141-776 0999 Fax: 0141-776 4225

▶ Electroplan Contracting Ltd, 2-4 St. James Road, Brentwood, Essex, CM14 4LF Tel: (01277) 210893 Fax: (01277) 849193

Elektrek Services Ltd, 19 Manning Road, Felixstowe, Suffolk, IP11 2AY Tel: (01394) 270777 Fax: (01394) 387177 E-mail: enquire@elektrek.com

▶ Elite Electrical Services Ltd, 2 Fieldings Road, Cheshunt, Waltham Cross, Hertfordshire, EN8 9TL Tel: (01992) 642000 Fax: (01992) 642959

▶ Ellis Electrical Ltd, Unit E6 Fareham Heights, Standard Way, Fareham, Hampshire, PO16 8XT Tel: (01329) 829333 Fax: (01329) 829555

▶ Elmec Systems Ltd, Bowbridge La, New Balderton, Newark, Nottinghamshire, NG24 3BY Tel: (01636) 676666 Fax: (01636) 676667

Emcor Facilities Services Ltd, 1 Thameside Centre, Kew Bridge Road, Brentford, Middlesex, TW8 0HF Tel: (020) 8380 6700 Fax: (020) 8380 6701

▶ Emeg Electrical Ltd, 3 Dunston Place, Dunston Road, Chesterfield, Derbyshire, S41 8NL Tel: (01246) 268678 Fax: (01246) 268679

▶ Emery Electrical Ltd, Riverside Business Park, Stoney Common Road, Stansted, Essex, CM24 8PL Tel: (01279) 647799

▶ Empress Electrical Ltd, 69 Plantation Street, Accrington, Lancashire, BB5 6RZ Tel: (01254) 871661

Emr North East Ltd, 5c Bowes Road, Middlesbrough, Cleveland, TS2 1LU Tel: (01642) 226096 Fax: (01642) 245471 E-mail: duncan.mcneill@onyxnet.co.uk

Engineering Service Co. Ltd, Albion Works, Bridgeman Street, Bolton, BL3 6BS Tel: (01204) 525647 Fax: (01204) 391705 E-mail: cad@eng-service.co.uk

▶ Enterprise Electrical Services Ltd, Unit 7 129 Western Road, Hockley, Birmingham, B18 7QD Tel: 0121-507 0602 Fax: 0121-507 0605

▶ Eric Boam, 20 Meadowbank, Passage Hill, Mylor, Falmouth, Cornwall, TR11 5SW Tel: (01326) 375915 Fax: (01326) 375915 E-mail: eric@electricianscornwall.co.uk

Eric Johnson Of Northwich Ltd, Ash House, Ash House Lane, Little Leigh, Northwich, Cheshire, CW8 4RG Tel: (01606) 892444 Fax: (01606) 892442 E-mail: irj@johnson42.fsnet.co.uk

▶ Erleback engineering ltd, Dixies Barns, High Street, Ashwell, Baldock, Hertfordshire, SG7 5NT Tel: (0870) 7407481 Fax: (0870) 7407482 E-mail: michael@erlebach.freeserve.co.uk

▶ ESI: Electrical Safety Inspections Ltd, Unit G32 Atlas Industrial Park, Rye Harbour Road, Rye, East Sussex, TN31 7TE Tel: (01797) 227741 Fax: (0870) 4860353 E-mail: rye@esi-team.co.uk

Ess, 12 Millcroft Road, Rutherglen, Glasgow, G73 1EN Tel: 0141-613 1714 Fax: 0141-613 1715

Estil Ltd, Charlotte Street, Dudley, West Midlands, DY1 1TD Tel: (01384) 243643 Fax: (01384) 243644E-mail: sales@estil.co.uk

▶ European Electrical Contractors UK Ltd, Unit 2, Sinfin Central Business Park, Derby, DE24 9HL Tel: (01332) 272225

Evans & Shea Ltd, 37 Collier Row Lane, Romford, RM5 3BD Tel: (01708) 741055 Fax: (01708) 764289

▶ Event & Electrical Services, 32 Southfields Rise, North Leverton, Retford, Nottinghamshire, DN22 0AY Tel: 01427 880802 E-mail: info@eventelectricalservices.co.uk

Russell Eves Electrical Ltd, Unit 7 Oxen Industrial Estate, Oxen Road, Luton, LU2 0DX Tel: (01582) 732766 Fax: (01582) 726147 E-mail: evesrussell@aol.com

▶ Evolution Electronic Security Systems, 1 Lancaster Court, Coronation Road, Cressex Business Park, High Wycombe, Buckinghamshire, HP12 3TD Tel: (01494) 539880 Fax: (01494) 539881 E-mail: rs@evolutionsecurity.com

▶ Express Security Systems, 88 Vallance Road, London, E1 5BW Tel: (020) 7377 6565 Fax: (020) 7900 1691 E-mail: marketing@etsuk.co.uk

▶ Eyre Colchester, Crown Business Centre, Old Ipswich Road, Ardleigh, Colchester, CO7 7QR Tel: (01206) 231870 Fax: (01206) 231325

▶ Eyre Electrical, C4 Castle Trading Estate, Snedshill, Telford, Shropshire, TF2 9NP Tel: (01743) 363650 Fax: (01952) 612715

▶ F B Ross & Co. Ltd, Rose Hill, 165 Lutterworth Road, Leicester, LE8 4DX Tel: 0116-277 1861 Fax: 0116-277 9986

F & C Electric Ltd, 45 Luff Close, Windsor, Berkshire, SL4 4NP Tel: (01753) 866944 Fax: (01753) 866944

▶ F J Lane & Sons Ltd, 38 Temple Road, Windsor, Berkshire, SL4 1HW Tel: (01753) 866430 Fax: (01753) 850903 E-mail: sales@fjlane.co.uk

F K B Electrical Ltd, Unit 10-12, Quakers Coppice, Crewe, CW1 6EW Tel: (01270) 501244 Fax: (01270) 251399 E-mail: fkb@fkb.co.uk

F K Electrical Services Ltd, Hyde Park Corner, Leeds, LS6 1AE Tel: 0113-275 9044 Fax: 0113-230 4631 E-mail: fkelectrical@fsmail.net

F W Marsh Electrical & Mechanical Ltd, Ryde Business Park, Nicholson Road, Ryde, Isle of Wight, PO33 1BF Tel: (01983) 562109 Fax: (01983) 615592

Fairburn Engineering Ltd, 73-79 Clarence Street, Hull, HU9 1DH Tel: (01482) 323352 Fax: (01482) 229873 E-mail: sales@fairburneng.co.uk

▶ Fairnote Ltd, Ivy House, 59 London Road, Bagshot, Surrey, GU19 5DT Tel: (01276) 451272 Fax: (01276) 451690

Farebrother Group Ltd, Ridgeway House, Progress Way, Denton, Manchester, M34 2GP Tel: 0161-320 0056 Fax: 0161-320 5010 E-mail: farebrother@farebrother.co.uk

ELECTRICAL CONTRACTORS – *continued*

▶ Farley Electrical, 18 Westway, Caterham, Surrey, CR3 5TP Tel: (01883) 343173 Fax: (01883) 340586
Farrant Electrical Ltd, 1 Homefield Road, Haverhill, Suffolk, CB9 8QP Tel: (01440) 703497 Fax: (01440) 704332
▶ Fawcett Electrical Ltd, 6 Station Road, Skelmanthorpe, Huddersfield, HD8 9AU Tel: (01484) 863769 Fax: (01484) 864972
▶ Findlay H & Sons Ltd, 52a Nutwell Lane, Armthorpe, Doncaster, South Yorkshire, DN3 3JF Tel: (01302) 830072 Fax: (01302) 830074
▶ Finlayson Ltd, 76 Northumberland Street, Edinburgh, EH3 6JG Tel: 0131-557 0779 Fax: 0131-557 9195 E-mail: mail@finlayson.org.uk
▶ Fits Ltd, Quarry Road, Chipping Sodbury, Bristol, BS37 6AX Tel: (01454) 312247 Fax: (01454) 312281
Fluorescent Lighting Services, Granville House, 181/187 Moseley Street, Birmingham, B12 0RT Tel: 0121-683 1515 Fax: 0121-683 1516 E-mail: sales@fls-lighting.co.uk
The Ford Group (Nottingham) Ltd, Park Lane Works, Old Basford, Nottingham, NG6 0EU Tel: 0115-977 0724 Fax: 0115-976 1041 E-mail: ford@fordgroup.co.uk
Fordham Electrical Contracting & Management Services Ltd, 7 Industrial Estate, Old Church Road, East Hanningfield, Chelmsford, CM3 8AB Tel: (01245) 400200 Fax: (01245) 400777 E-mail: info@fordhamelec.co.uk
Forest Electrical Services Ltd, Forest Farm, Windmill Hill, Ashill, Ilminster, Somerset, TA19 9LP Tel: (01823) 480905 Fax: (01823) 481042
▶ Forrest Electrical Ltd, 80-84 Ormskirk Business Park, New Court Way, Ormskirk, Lancashire, L39 2YT Tel: (01695) 573187 Fax: (01695) 577899
Fosse Electrical, White Gates, Goldcliff, Newport, Gwent, NP18 2AU Tel: (01633) 271420 Fax: (01633) 271420
▶ Foster & Done Ltd, 6 Priory Street, Birkenhead, Merseyside, CH41 5DX Tel: 0151-647 7336
Fox Electrical, 239 Queens Road, Beeston, Nottingham, NG9 2BP Tel: 0115-922 1005 Fax: 0115-922 1005
G.W. Franklin & Son Ltd, 4 Drakes Courtyard, 291 Kilburn High Road, London, NW6 7JR Tel: (020) 7328 6611 Fax: (020) 7328 4932
▶ Fraser Electrical Ltd, 37 West Street, Bexleyheath, Kent, DA7 4BE Tel: (020) 8303 6140 Fax: (020) 8301 4999 E-mail: info@fraserelectrical.co.uk
▶ Fraser Electrical, The Old School, Dewar Street, Dunfermline, Fife, KY12 8AB Tel: (01383) 720569 Fax: (01383) 720722
▶ Frederick Smith Electrical Ltd, 54 Nottingham Road, Leicester, LE5 4GH Tel: 0116-276 5755 Fax: 0116-276 8342
▶ Freedom Ltd, Woodlands Needham Road, Badley, Ipswich, IP6 8RS Tel: (01449) 675999 Fax: (01449) 745000 E-mail: admin@lanva.co.uk
Freeman & Co Installations Ltd, 152 High Street, Ongar, Essex, CM5 9JJ Tel: (0845) 6444354 Fax: (0845) 6444353 E-mail: sales@freemanandcompany.co.uk
▶ Freeway Lift Services Ltd, Dolphin Wharf, Rockingham Road, Uxbridge, Middlesex, UB8 2UB Tel: (01895) 811025 Fax: (01895) 811026
French Electrical Services, Chapel House, 25 Chapel Street, Loughborough, Leicestershire, LE12 9AF Tel: (01509) 502533 Fax: (01509) 505773 E-mail: wtfrench@btinternet.com
P.F. Friend & Son Ltd, 3 Rolle Cottages, Rolle Street, Barnstaple, Devon, EX31 1JL Tel: (01271) 343058 Fax: (01271) 325319 E-mail: pffriend@hotmail.co.uk
▶ G & A Barnie, 16 Carsegate Road South, Inverness, IV3 8LL Tel: (01463) 710826
G A Helmore, 2 Langlands Street, Dundee, DD4 6SZ Tel: (01382) 462154 Fax: (01382) 454004
▶ G D Chalmers Ltd, 101 Neilston Road, Paisley, Renfrewshire, PA2 6ES Tel: 0141-889 6233 Fax: 0141-889 7806
▶ G D X Technologies Ltd, 61-63 Back Sneddon Street, Paisley, Renfrewshire, PA3 2DD Tel: 0141-889 8800
▶ G E Energy Services, Badentoy Crescent, Badentoy Industrial Estate, Aberdeen, AB12 4YD Tel: (01224) 785100
G J Bess & Sons Electrical Contractors, Hayes, Salcombe Hill Road, Sidmouth, Devon, EX10 8JR Tel: (01395) 514662 Fax: (01395) 514662 E-mail: g.bess@virgin.net
G Leddington Electrical Ltd, 15 Church Parade, Telford, Shropshire, TF2 6EX Tel: (01952) 615958 Fax: (01952) 620473 E-mail: info@leddingtons.co.uk
▶ G M Lawrence Electrical Ltd, 43a Abbey Road, Far Cotton, Northampton, NN4 8EY Tel: (01604) 766511
▶ G R Bayley Electrical Contractors Ltd, 24 Brown Street, Macclesfield, Cheshire, SK11 6SA Tel: (01625) 423088 Fax: (01625) 669879
▶ G R Bradshaw & Co., 10a High Street, Neston, CH64 9TY Tel: 0151-336 1121 Fax: 0151-353 8385
▶ Gainsborough Electrical Services Ltd, Newholme Farm, Lark Hill Road, Canewdon, Rochford, Essex, SS4 3RX Tel: (01702) 257117 Fax: (01702) 258517
▶ Garndene Communications Systems Ltd, Hi-Pylon Works, Slades Road, Golcar, Huddersfield, HD7 4JS Tel: (01484) 658415 Fax: (01484) 656810
Garnham Switchgear Ltd, Unit 2 Olympus Close Business Park, Ipswich, IP1 5LJ Tel: (01473) 240407 Fax: (01473) 463730 E-mail: sales@garnhamswitchgear.co.uk
▶ Garrett J P Electrical Ltd, 104b Elm Grove, Brighton, BN2 3DB Tel: (01273) 625660 Fax: (01273) 625669
Gedye & Partners Ltd, 26 The Dean, Alresford, Hampshire, SO24 9AZ Tel: (01962) 734567 Fax: (01962) 734342
▶ Geoff Todd Electrical Ltd, Innisfree, West End, Queensbury, Bradford, West Yorkshire, BD13 2ES Tel: (01274) 883871 Fax: (01274) 815004
▶ Gerard E Gallagher (Electricalcontractors) Ltd, Cloonrane House, 21 Chorley Old Road, Bolton, BL1 3AD Tel: (01204) 387039
Gibbons Electrical Services, 18 Helford Close, Worcester, WR5 1NB Tel: (01905) 356061
Gibson Wight Ltd, 14-18 East Shaw Street, Kilmarnock, Ayrshire, KA1 4AN Tel: (01563) 523633 Fax: (01563) 536472 E-mail: charles.gibson@gibsonwight.co.uk
Gilbert & Creasey, 28 Margaret Drive, Boston, Lincolnshire, PE21 9AL Tel: (01205) 366584 Fax: (01205) 366584
Gilbert & Stamper, Drayton Road, Tonbridge, Kent, TN9 2BG Tel: (01732) 357372 Fax: (01732) 771058 E-mail: tunbridge@gilbertandstamper.com
▶ Gladwin & Co. Ltd, 204 Cheltenham Road, Bristol, BS6 5QZ Tel: 0117-924 1430
Glasswell & Last Ltd, 28 Eastern Way, Bury St. Edmunds, Suffolk, IP32 7AB Tel: (01284) 761528 Fax: (01284) 723528 E-mail: sales@glasswell-last.com
▶ Glendale Electrical Ltd, 1014 Cumbernauld Road, Glasgow, G33 2QR Tel: 0141-770 7191 Fax: 0141-770 9337 E-mail: info@glendale-electrical.co.uk
▶ Glendale Security Systems, Unit 3 62 Muirs, Kinross, KY13 8AU Tel: (01577) 863525 Fax: (01577) 863524
F.T. Gordon Building Services Ltd, Meridian Centre, Kings Street, Oldham, OL8 1EZ Tel: 0161-626 7667 Fax: 0161-627 5133 E-mail: info@ftguk.com
Gra Bern Electrical, Unit 26, Tweedale Court, Tweedale North Industrial Estate, Telford, Shropshire, TF7 4JZ Tel: (01952) 586038 Fax: (01952) 583365
▶ Graham Barber Electrical Services Ltd, Unit 12 The Dock, Ely, Cambridgeshire, CB7 4GS Tel: (01353) 666831 Fax: (01353) 668132
▶ Graham Robertson Electrical Ltd, 5 Fountain Road, Bridge of Allan, Stirling, FK9 4ET Tel: (01786) 832246 Fax: (01786) 834335
▶ Grant Dufftown Ltd, 33 Balvenie Street, Dufftown, Keith, Banffshire, AB55 4AS Tel: (01340) 820241 Fax: (01340) 820997
Gratte Brothers Ltd, 2 Regents Wharf, All Saints Street, London, N1 9RL Tel: (020) 7837 6433 Fax: (020) 7837 6779E-mail: info@gratte.com
Gray Electrics Stafford Ltd, Unit 1c Hollins Business Centre, 62 Rowley Street, Stafford, ST16 2RH Tel: (01785) 223010 Fax: (01785) 211360 E-mail: grayelectrics@aol.com
▶ Graybar Electrical Contractors, 10 Fleming Close, Park Farm Industrial Estate, Wellingborough, Northamptonshire, NN8 6UF Tel: (01933) 676700 Fax: (01933) 676800 E-mail: sales@graybar.co.uk
▶ Green, Welsh Road, Deeside, Clwyd, CH5 2LR Tel: (01244) 289751
▶ Greenhills Electric Ltd, 1a Puller Road, Hemel Hempstead, Hertfordshire, HP1 1QL Tel: (01442) 264126 Fax: (01442) 232193
▶ Greenwald & Gregory, 116 A Hallowell Road, Northwood, Middlesex, HA6 1DU Tel: (01923) 820974
▶ Greg & Co Ltd, Tent Street, London, E1 5DZ Tel: (020) 7481 0222 Fax: (020) 7481 3233 E-mail: info@gregandco.com
Gretton Ward Electrical Ltd, 112 Peckham Rye, London, SE15 4HA Tel: (020) 7639 3275 Fax: (020) 7358 1389 E-mail: grettonward@lineone.net
Groestar Ltd, 1 Morley Business Centre, Tonbridge, Kent, TN9 1RA Tel: (01732) 771121 Fax: (01732) 771124 E-mail: sales@groestar.co.uk
▶ H A Newall & Co Merseyside Ltd, 24 Dublin Street, Liverpool, L3 7DT Tel: 0151-298 1438 Fax: 0151-298 1469 E-mail: sales@hanewall.co.uk
▶ H C M Electrical Ltd, Market Place, Codnor, Ripley, Derbyshire, DE5 9QA Tel: (01773) 570596 Fax: (01773) 570933
▶ H & D Electrical, 1 Poulton Business Park, Poulton Close, Dover, Kent, CT17 0HL Tel: (01304) 226999 Fax: (01304) 226888
▶ H E C, Electric House, Blindustrial Lane, Todmorden, Lancashire, OL14 5HZ Tel: (01706) 814389
▶ H Goodman (Midway) Ltd, Unit 6, Ringway Business Park, Swadlincote, Derbyshire, DE11 8JL Tel: (01283) 217275
H & H Electrical Contractors, Suite 14 Stubbings House, Henley Road, Maidenhead, Berkshire, SL6 6QL Tel: (01628) 824131 Fax: (01628) 824131
▶ H J S Services, 75 Lifford Lane, Birmingham, B30 3JH Tel: 0121-486 1929 Fax: 0121-486 1930
H M Electrics, 95 Glen Road, Maghera, County Londonderry, BT46 5JG Tel: (028) 7964 2112 Fax: (028) 7964 3945 E-mail: enquiries@hmelectrics.com
▶ H Mills & Sons Ltd, Bleak Hill Sidings, Mansfield, Nottinghamshire, NG18 5EP Tel: (01623) 624015
H R Mann Ltd, Cape Road Industrial Estate, Cattell Road, Cape Industrial Estate, Warwick, CV34 4JN Tel: (01926) 492132 Fax: (01604) 750152
H S Harbon & Sons Ltd, Gordon Street, Doncaster, South Yorkshire, DN1 1RS Tel: (01302) 361140 Fax: (01302) 325745 E-mail: peter@harbon.co.uk
▶ H Smith (Electrical) Ltd, 1 Thompsons Yard, Westgate, Wakefield, West Yorkshire, WF1 2TP Tel: (01924) 372425
▶ H T Electrical Services, 17 Peasley Cross Lane, St. Helens, Merseyside, WA9 3BG Tel: (01744) 730099 Fax: (01744) 26610
H & T Mirage Ltd, 471 Kirkstall Road, Leeds, LS4 2QD Tel: 0113-263 0116 Fax: 0113-263 3770 E-mail: info@htmirage.co.uk
▶ H2 Plumbing Ltd, Unit L24 The Old Laboratories, 2 Michael Road, London, SW6 2AD Tel: (020) 7751 3344 E-mail: info@h2plumbing.co.uk
Haden Building Services Ltd, 44 Clarendon Road, Watford, WD17 1DR Tel: (01923) 232959 Fax: (01923) 295000 E-mail: headoffice@hadenyoung.co.uk
Halliday Electrical, Unit 31 Lynedoch Industrial Estate, Greenock, Renfrewshire, PA15 4AX Tel: (01475) 888440 Fax: (01475) 888220 E-mail: info@hallidayelectrical.co.uk
▶ John Halliday, 348 Lanark Road West, Currie, Midlothian, EH14 5RR Tel: 0131-538 8858 Fax: 0131-451 5072 E-mail: enquiries@jhalliday.co.uk
Halliwell Electrical Contractors, 16 Hartington Road, Bramhall, Stockport, Cheshire, SK7 2DZ Tel: 0161-439 7694 Fax: (01625) 850117
▶ Hamblemill Ltd, 13 A Harbey Crescent, Southampton, SO31 9TA Tel: (01489) 575161 Fax: (01489) 575161 E-mail: admin@hamblemill.com
Hampshire Electrical, 15 Park Lane, Old Basing, Basingstoke, Hampshire, RG24 7HF Tel: (01256) 359838 Fax: (01256) 364684
Hanson Support Services, Scotter Road South, Bottesford, Scunthorpe, South Humberside, DN17 2BU Tel: (01724) 842637 Fax: (01724) 282411 E-mail: enquiries@hanserve.com
Hardacre & Maltpress Ltd, Fernhill Road, Bootle, Merseyside, L20 9EA Tel: 0151-933 9592 Fax: 0151-922 1501 E-mail: hardmalt@liverpool1985.freeserve.co.uk
▶ Harper Electrical Contractors Ltd, 281 Vicarage Road, Kings Heath, Birmingham, B14 7NE Tel: 0121-441 2561 Fax: 0121-441 2993
▶ Harris, 30 Cecil Street, Rothwell, Kettering, Northamptonshire, NN14 6EZ Tel: (01536) 418899 Fax: (01536) 418877
Harrison & Cross Ltd, Unit 6 The Sidings Industrial Estate, Settle, North Yorkshire, BD24 9RP Tel: (01729) 823423 Fax: (01729) 823423
▶ Harrison Electrical Ltd, 1 Wyther Lane, Leeds, LS5 3BT Tel: 0113-278 2247
▶ Harry Sim & Sons Ltd, 115 Loch Street, Aberdeen, AB25 1DH Tel: (01224) 637904 Fax: (01224) 637904
▶ Hawk Systems London Ltd, Uplands Business Park, Blackhorse Lane, London, E17 5QJ Tel: (020) 8531 4473 Fax: (020) 8523 1403
▶ Head & Robins, 29 North Street, Pewsey, Wiltshire, SN9 5ES Tel: (01672) 562320 Fax: (01672) 562676
▶ John Heaney (Electrical) Ltd, Fairbairn Road, Howdenwest, Livingston, West Lothian, EH54 6TS Tel: (01506) 464000
▶ Heartlands Joint Managed Projects, 54-76 Bissell Street, Birmingham, B5 7HP Tel: 0121-666 6600 Fax: 0121-666 7700
▶ Hellesdon Park Electrical Co. Ltd, 98 Hellesdon Park Road, Drayton High Road, Norwich, NR6 5DR Tel: (01603) 407033 Fax: (01603) 409458
▶ Helmbalm Ltd, 12 Leeds Road, Mirfield, West Yorkshire, WF14 0ET Tel: (01924) 490803
Hendry Electrical Contractors, 2 Holton Business Park, Holton Court, Holton-le-Clay, Grimsby, South Humberside, DN36 5EE Tel: (01472) 825825 Fax: (01472) 825461
Hes Ltd, 43a Old Barn Road, Bournville, Birmingham, B30 1PX Tel: 0121-459 9646 Fax: 0121-628 1997
High Cross Electrical Ltd, 4A West Market Street, Newport, Gwent, NP20 2AU Tel: (01633) 216897 Fax: (01633) 214840 E-mail: enquires@highcrosselectrical.co.uk
High Voltage Maintenance Services, Littlebrook Business Centre, Littlebrook Manorway, Dartford, DA1 5PZ Tel: (01322) 273100 Fax: (01322) 294413 E-mail: enquiries@hvms.co.uk
▶ Hill Electrical Services, Unit 32 Blue Chalet Industrial Park, West Kingsdown, Sevenoaks, Kent, TN15 6BQ Tel: (01474) 855300 Fax: (01474) 855301
Hill & Priest Ltd, 187 Halesowen Rd, Cradley Heath, W. Midlands, B64 6HE Tel: (01384) 569747 Fax: (01384) 569747
▶ Hillgate Electrical Services, 480 Hale Road, Hale Barns, Altrincham, Cheshire, WA15 8XT Tel: 0161-904 0700 Fax: 0161-904 7878
▶ Hills Electrical & Mechanical plc, Unit 42 Vale Business Park, Llandow, Cowbridge, South Glamorgan, CF71 7PF Tel: (01446) 774002 Fax: (01446) 773002
▶ Hills Electrical & Mechanical plc, 106-114 Salkeld Street, Glasgow, G5 8HE Tel: 0141-429 6008 Fax: 0141-429 6009
▶ Hills Electrical & Mechanical plc, Tootal Grove, Salford, M6 8DN Tel: 0161-743 0400 Fax: 0161-743 0228
Hills Electrical & Mechanical plc, Green Lane, Walsall, WS2 8HB Tel: (01922) 721105 Fax: (01922) 721151 E-mail: admin@hillelec.plc.uk
Hio Tec Services Scotland Ltd, 62 Queen Street, Alva, Clackmannanshire, FK12 5EJ Tel: (01259) 760977 Fax: (01259) 769819 E-mail: hiotec@hiotec.plus.com
▶ Hirst & Danson Ltd, Butts Close, Thornton-Cleveleys, Lancashire, FY5 4HT Tel: (01253) 859262 Fax: (01253) 864953 E-mail: enquiries@hirstanddanson.co.uk
Hobbs Electrical Services, 121 High Street, Stony Stratford, Milton Keynes, MK11 1AT Tel: (01908) 565577 Fax: (01908) 261211 E-mail: hobbs.electrical@btinternet.com
▶ Holgate & French Shelford Ltd, 71a Newnham Street, Ely, Cambridgeshire, CB7 4PQ Tel: (01353) 668811 Fax: (01353) 668822
▶ Hollands & Long, Unit 6 Gilly Gabben Industrial Estate, Mawgan, Helston, Cornwall, TR12 6BL Tel: (01326) 221468 Fax: (01326) 221774
Hollisters Electrical Contractors Ltd, 54-56 Dover Road East, Gravesend, Kent, DA11 0RG Tel: (01474) 564088 Fax: (01474) 560455 E-mail: terry@hollisterselectrical.co.uk
▶ Hosie Electrical Ltd, 70 Market Place, Inverurie, Aberdeenshire, AB51 3XN Tel: (01467) 620831 Fax: (01467) 621255
Howard Electrical Services, Unit 19 Such Close, Letchworth Garden City, Hertfordshire, SG6 1JF Tel: (01462) 678915 Fax: (01462) 679815 E-mail: sales@howardelectricalservices.co.uk
HPW Electrical Installations, Zair Works, 111-119 Bishop Street, Birmingham, B5 6JL Tel: 0121-622 7111 Fax: 0121-622 7111 E-mail: sales@hpwelectrical.co.uk
▶ Hudson, 14 Jupiter Heights, Uxbridge, Middlesex, UB10 0TA Tel: (01895) 271457 Fax: (01895) 271460
▶ Hudson Engineering Ltd, 134 High Road, Benfleet, Essex, SS7 5LD Tel: (01268) 759575
▶ Humphreys Electrical Ltd, Unit 21 Shrivenham Hundred Business Park, Majors Road, Watchfield, Swindon, SN6 8TZ Tel: (01793) 783964 Fax: (01793) 783995
John G. Humphreys (Electrical) Ltd, 15 Burbeck Road, Caldicot, Gwent, NP26 4DX Tel: (01291) 421978 Fax: (01291) 420576 E-mail: ijhumphreys@aol.com
Hutcheon Services Ltd, Bowtree House, Minto Drive, Altens Industrial Estate, Aberdeen, AB12 3LW Tel: (01224) 874875 Fax: (01224) 895975 E-mail: info@hutcheon-services.ltd.uk
▶ Hyde Electrical Services, 5-7 Outram Road, Dukinfield, Cheshire, SK16 4XE Tel: 0161-214 8160 Fax: 0161-214 8161
Hyde Windings Ltd, Westbury Street, Hyde, Cheshire, SK14 4QP Tel: 0161-368 1468 Fax: 0161-367 9454
▶ Hyder Infrastructure Services, Wellhall Road, Hamilton, Lanarkshire, ML3 9BZ Tel: (01698) 422588
▶ I & A Crowhurst Ltd, Anker Bridge House, Bridge St, Polesworth, Tamworth, Staffordshire, B78 1DR Tel: (01827) 898527
▶ I C Electrical Ltd, Wetmore Road, Burton-on-Trent, Staffordshire, DE14 1SN Tel: (01283) 530666 Fax: (01283) 538666
▶ I Fraser & Sons, 42 High Street, Rothes, Aberlour, Banffshire, AB38 7AY Tel: (01340) 831302 Fax: (01340) 831351
I T S Projects Ltd, 42-44 Portman Road, Reading, RG30 1EA Tel: 0118-950 0225 Fax: 0118-950 3267 E-mail: info@itsprojects.co.uk
▶ Ian Milne Electrical Ltd, Newlands, Alyth, Blairgowrie, Perthshire, PH11 8HE Tel: (01828) 632893
Icel Group, Ashmill Bus Park, Ashford Road, Lenham, Maidstone, Kent, ME17 2GQ Tel: (01622) 858200 Fax: (01622) 850065 E-mail: sales@icel-group.co.uk
▶ Imtech Marine & Industry UK Ltd, 3 Belasis Court, Greenwood Road, Billingham, Cleveland, TS23 4AZ Tel: (01642) 567100 Fax: (01642) 567105
Industrial Belting International Ltd, Unit A1 The Sidings, Station Road, Ampthill, Bedford, MK45 2QY Tel: (01525) 840800 Fax: (01525) 840900 E-mail: sales@ibiuk.com
Industrial & Commercial Services Ltd, 38 Dunster Street, Northampton, NN1 3JY Tel: (01604) 636661 Fax: (01604) 629818 E-mail: mail@tinston.co.uk
▶ Industrial Electrical Services UK Ltd, 4b5 Unit, Blar Mhor Industrial Estate, Lochyside, Fort William, Inverness-Shire, PH33 7PT Tel: (01397) 703732 Fax: (01397) 703732
▶ Initial Electronic Security, 44 Colquhoun Avenue, Hillington Industrial Estate, Glasgow, G52 4BN Tel: 0141-882 1179 Fax: 0141-810 4957
▶ Ins Sudlows (Electrical) Ltd, Ducie Works, Hulme Hall Lane, Manchester, M40 8HH Tel: 0161-205 4900 E-mail: sales@inssudlows.com
Insight Services Southern Ltd, Rosebank, Hailsham Road, Polegate, East Sussex, BN26 6RE Tel: (01323) 489005 Fax: (01323) 489006 E-mail: enquiries@insightservices.co.uk
▶ Instelec Services, Project House, Well Street, Bolton, BL1 1TZ Tel: (01204) 364643 Fax: (01204) 363525
▶ Integral, 1290 Aztec West, Almondsbury, Bristol, BS32 4SG Tel: (01454) 278900 Fax: (01454) 201169

ELECTRICAL CONTRACTORS – *continued*

Integral, Broadoak Business Park, Ashburton Road West, Trafford Park, Manchester, M17 1RW Tel: 0161-872 7925 Fax: 0161-872 9508

▶ Integrated Building Management Ltd, West Atrium, Mercury Court, Tithebarn Street, Liverpool, L2 2QP Tel: 0151-236 8555

▶ Interface Contracts Ltd, Pennine House, Denton Lane, Chadderton, Oldham, OL9 8PU Tel: 0161-620 0698

Intergrated Electrical & Electronic Services, 11 Hutton Street, Boldon Colliery, Tyne & Wear, NE35 9LW Tel: 0191-519 0980 Fax: 0191-519 0705

Interphase Electrical Services, 67b High Street, Halstead, Essex, CO9 2JD Tel: (01787) 472222 Fax: (01787) 472222

Inviron Ltd, 17 Portman Road, Ipswich, IP1 2BP Tel: (01473) 219921 Fax: (01473) 231317

▶ Invisible Heating Systems Ltd, Morefield Industrial Estate, Ullapool, Ross-Shire, IV26 2SR Tel: (01854) 613161 Fax: (01854) 613160 E-mail: design@invisibleheating.co.uk

▶ J B Electrical Scotland Ltd, Grange Loan, Edinburgh, EH9 2NP Tel: (0870) 0469357

J Brand Ltd, 2 Margaret Street, London, W1W 8RD Tel: (020) 7636 8214 Fax: (020) 7436 0841 E-mail: enquiries@jbrand.co.uk

▶ J D Electrics, 115b Deepcut Bridge Road, Deepcut, Camberley, Surrey, GU16 6SD Tel: (01252) 838087 Fax: (01252) 834511

▶ J & D Shepherd, 7c Old Queens Head Yard, Morpeth, Northumberland, NE61 1PY Tel: (01670) 517459 Fax: (01670) 511763

▶ J D & T Johnson & Co. Ltd, Unit 6 Pilsworth Way, Bury, Lancashire, BL9 8RE Tel: 0161-796 3040 Fax: 0161-796 3040

J H Shouksmith & Sons Ltd, Murton Way, Osbaldwick, York, YO19 5GS Tel: (01904) 411261 Fax: (01904) 412038 E-mail: rps@shouksmiths.co.uk

▶ J & J Electricals Cumbria, 29 Oxford Street, Workington, Cumbria, CA14 2AL Tel: (01900) 871478 Fax: (01900) 63886

▶ J J Long Electrical Contractors Ltd, Killinghall Stone Quarry, Ripon Road, Killinghall, Harrogate, North Yorkshire, HG3 2BA Tel: (01423) 520720 Fax: (01423) 520720

▶ J M T Installations Ltd, 6 Waltham Court, Milley Lane, Hare Hatch, Reading, RG10 9AA Tel: 0118-940 1177 Fax: 0118-940 2344

J N Building Services Ltd, Cooper Yard, Old Cider Works, Abbotskerswell, Newton Abbot, Devon, TQ12 5NF Tel: (01626) 352056 Fax: (01626) 363599 E-mail: enquiries@jnbuildingservices.com

▶ J & N Electrics, 1373 Dumbarton Road, Glasgow, G14 9XT Tel: 0141-434 0434

J N G Construction & Engineering Ltd, 23 Hornsby Square, Southfields Industrial Park, Basildon, Essex, SS15 6SD Tel: (01268) 240888

▶ J Noble, Unit 3, Sherwood Industrial Estate, Bonnyrigg, Midlothian, EH19 3LW Tel: 0131-660 2275

J R Colston & Co., 119 Godstow Road, Wolvercote, Oxford, OX2 8PG Tel: (01865) 553483 Fax: (01865) 554043

▶ J R Livingstone & Co., Unit 6, Montgomery Place, Irvine, Ayrshire, KA12 8PN Tel: (01294) 275000

▶ J S Wilson, 23 Pitheavlis Terrace, Perth, PH2 0JZ Tel: (01738) 624704

J W Bowkett Electrical Installations Ltd, 2a Rugby Road, Newport, Gwent, NP19 0BS Tel: (01633) 254222 Fax: (01633) 213378 E-mail: jw.bowkett@virgin.net

▶ J W Jones & Son, 3-5 Bay View Road, Colwyn Bay, Clwyd, LL29 8DW Tel: (01492) 531414 Fax: (01492) 532336 E-mail: office@jwjones-son.co.uk

▶ J Wright Electrical, Quantas House, Rooley Lane, Bradford, West Yorkshire, BD4 7SJ Tel: (01274) 689696

Jackson Rich & Co., 9 Earn Avenue, Righead Industrial Estate, Bellshill, Lanarkshire, ML4 3LW Tel: (01698) 849661 Fax: (01698) 844036

Jackson Rich & Co. Ltd, Unit 4A, Faraday Court, Buckley Road Industrial Estate, Rochdale, Lancashire, OL12 9EF Tel: (01706) 650510 Fax: (01706) 647622 E-mail: mail@jackson-rich.com

Jarrards Ltd, The Old Cobblers, 52A Great North Road, Stanborough, Welwyn Garden City, Hertfordshire, AL8 7TL Tel: (01707) 323239 Fax: (01707) 336116 E-mail: jarrardsltd@aol.com

▶ Jary & Greensides, The Street, Framingham Pigot, Norwich, NR14 7QJ Tel: (01508) 493891 Fax: (01508) 495116

▶ Jaylec Electrical Contractors Ltd, 23 Burrowfield, Welwyn Garden City, Hertfordshire, AL7 4SS Tel: (01707) 333647 Fax: (01707) 391288

▶ JCM Electrical Services Ltd, 108 Yardley Road, Acocks Green, Birmingham, B27 6LG Tel: 0121-764 4911 Fax: 0121-707 4448

Jersey Electricity Co. Ltd, PO Box 45, Jersey, JE4 8NY Tel: (01534) 505000 Fax: (01534) 505011 E-mail: jec@jec.co.uk

Jeytec Services, 17 Silverwell Park, Modbury, Ivybridge, Devon, PL21 0RJ Tel: (01548) 830322 Fax: (01548) 830322

▶ JNV Security, 79 Stockiemuir Avenue, Bearsden, Glasgow, G61 3LL Tel: 0141-943 2174

▶ John G Macintosh, 20-22 Nelson Street, Edinburgh, EH3 6LJ Tel: 0131-557 2971

John Mcnicol & Co Electrical Engineers Ltd, 123 Elliot Street, Glasgow, G3 8EY Tel: 0141-221 0725 Fax: 0141-248 4569 E-mail: info@johnmcnicol.co.uk

John Perkins Bristol Ltd, 4 Ridgeway Industrial Centre, Chapel Lane, Clay Hill, Bristol, BS5 7EY Tel: 0117-965 3970 Fax: 0117-965 3980

▶ John Unwin Electrical Contractors Ltd, Contact House, 20 Jubilee Drive, Loughborough, Leicestershire, LE11 5XS Tel: (01509) 236313 Fax: (01509) 231862 E-mail: sales@john-unwin.com

Johnson & Cawley Ltd, Moston Road, Sandbach, Cheshire, CW11 3HL Tel: (01270) 765661 Fax: (01270) 766542 E-mail: philpeters@btconnect.com

Jones & Gough Electrical Ltd, 22 Horton Court, Hortonwood 50, Telford, Shropshire, TF1 7GY Tel: (01952) 606080 Fax: (01952) 608197

▶ JP Electrical Services Ltd, 10 Lovedean Lane, Waterlooville, Hampshire, PO8 8HH Tel: (023) 9257 1333 Fax: (023) 9257 1999 E-mail: sales@jpelec.co.uk

K C Hickson Ltd, 89-91 Rolfe Street, Smethwick, West Midlands, B66 2AY Tel: 0121-558 1884 Fax: 0121-558 0017 E-mail: kchickson@george-jones-engineering.co.uk

K D Electrical Co. Ltd, Lyde Green, Halesowen, West Midlands, B63 2PG Tel: (01384) 560333 Fax: (01384) 560423

▶ K Electrics, 20 Barnton Park Drive, Edinburgh, EH4 6HF Tel: 0131-336 3533

▶ K J Evans Electrical Ltd, 29 Spingate Close, Hornchurch, Essex, RM12 6SW Tel: (01708) 470570

▶ K J Pheysey, 1 Albert Street, Redditch, Worcestershire, B97 4DA Tel: (01527) 64404

▶ Kabel Management Services Ltd, Georges Row, Dinas Powys, South Glamorgan, CF64 4LF Tel: (029) 2051 1099 Fax: (029) 2051 1098

▶ Kayes & Co Electrical Contractors Ltd, 355 Bank Street, Coatbridge, Lanarkshire, ML5 1EJ Tel: (01236) 440882

Kaytu Systems Ltd, 6A & 6B Throckley Way, Middlefields Industrial Estate, South Shields, Tyne & Wear, NE34 0NU Tel: 0191-456 2046 Fax: 0191-456 1971 E-mail: kaytusystems@kaytu-systems.co.uk

Kelmat Ltd, Unit 13, Penarth Centre, Penarth Street, London, SE15 1TR Tel: (020) 7277 5167 Fax: (020) 7277 6601 E-mail: kelmet@btconnect.com

Kendall Electrical Services Telford Ltd, Stafford Park 6, Telford, Shropshire, TF3 3AT Tel: (01952) 290830 Fax: (01952) 291027 E-mail: sales@kendal-group.co.uk

▶ Kent P H K Ltd, Hermitage Way, Mansfield, Nottinghamshire, NG18 5ES Tel: (01623) 421202 Fax: (01623) 421302 E-mail: nottingham@kentphk.co.uk

▶ Kentec Building Services Ltd, 34 Nightingale Way, London, E6 5JR Tel: (020) 7474 4774 Fax: (020) 7474 4775

▶ Kenward Pullen Ltd, Head Office & Works, York Road, St. Leonards-on-Sea, East Sussex, TN37 6PU Tel: (01424) 435900 Fax: (01424) 422500

▶ Kestrel Electrical Systems Ltd, 85-86 High Street, Rowley Regis, West Midlands, B65 0EH Tel: 0121-559 2929 Fax: 0121-559 9933 E-mail: info@keslimited.co.uk

▶ Konect Electrical Services, 207 Bramhall Lane, Stockport, Cheshire, SK2 6JA Tel: 0161-456 1362 Fax: 0161-483 9473

▶ KW Electrics Southern Ltd, Rosedeane, Easthampstead Road, Wokingham, Berkshire, RG40 3AF Tel: 0118-979 2939 Fax: 0118-989 1174

L D H Plant Ltd, South Dock, Alexandra Docks, Newport, Gwent, NP20 2NQ Tel: (01633) 263936 Fax: (01633) 264013 E-mail: sales@ldhplant.co.uk

L E G Electrical Ltd, 83 High St South, London, E6 6EJ Tel: (020) 8471 8229 Fax: (020) 8472 1817

▶ L Harvey & Son Ltd, Binders Yard, Cryers Hill, High Wycombe, Buckinghamshire, HP15 6LJ Tel: (01494) 711925

L J Monks Process Ltd, Thorn Lane, Long Sandall, Doncaster, South Yorkshire, DN2 4NN Tel: (01302) 329090 Fax: (01302) 341399 E-mail: enquiries@ljmonks.co.uk

L Swanick, 9-11 Market Street, Uttoxeter, Staffordshire, ST14 8JA Tel: (01889) 569808 Fax: (01889) 566567 E-mail: swan@electrics.sagehost.co.uk

▶ Landalow P.L.C., Spectrum House, Inveralmond Place, Inveralmond Industrial Estate, Perth, PH1 3TS Tel: (01738) 633674

Landsdown & Angrove, 68 Llandaff Road, Cardiff, CF11 9NL Tel: (029) 2038 2034 Fax: (029) 2039 4377

▶ Laser Ltd, West House, 115 West Street, Faversham, Kent, ME13 7JB Tel: (01795) 590683 Fax: (01795) 533019

Laser Electrical Services, Rochester House, 275 Baddow Road, Chelmsford, CM2 7QA Tel: (01245) 492823

Lawmax Electrical Contractors Ltd, Lawmax House, 30-32 Nottingham Road, Stapleford, Nottingham, NG9 8AA Tel: 0115-939 4248 Fax: 0115-939 9412 E-mail: sales@lawmaxelec.co.uk

Leaf & Carver Electrical Services Ltd, 323 Kennington Road, London, SE11 4QE Tel: (020) 7735 8434 Fax: (020) 7735 0552 E-mail: leaf_carver@btconnect.com

Lee Beesley Ltd, 69 Sorby Street, Sheffield, S4 7LA Tel: 0114-272 8621 Fax: 0114-273 0586 E-mail: sfiddall@lbd.co.uk

▶ Leeward Properties Ltd, Brickwall House, Birch Road, Layer-de-la-Haye, Colchester, CO2 0EL Tel: 01206 734319 E-mail: nigel@sail-east.co.uk

▶ Legsun (W E Jeffreys) Ltd, 51 Springvale Industrial Estate, Cwmbran, Gwent, NP44 5BB Tel: (01633) 483073 Fax: (01633) 863560 E-mail: neil-jedd@legsun.fsbusiness.co.uk

Lektrix Installations Ltd, 820 Garratt Lane, London, SW17 0LZ Tel: (020) 8672 6945 Fax: (020) 8672 8118 E-mail: lektrix56@hotmail.com

Lewis & Beddows Ltd, Windsor Court, 9-13 Olton Road, Shirley, Solihull, West Midlands, B90 3NF Tel: 0121-733 1246 Fax: 0121-733 1245 E-mail: info@lewis-beddows.co.uk

▶ Lewis & King Electrical Services Ltd, Unit 14 Waterloo Industrial Estate, Waterloo Road, Bidford-on-Avon, Alcester, Warwickshire, B50 4JH Tel: (01789) 490049 Fax: (01789) 778490

▶ Lift Care, 3 Sutton Hall Cottages, Elton Head Road, St. Helens, Merseyside, WA9 5BN Tel: (01744) 817189 Fax: (01744) 850035

▶ Light House Electrical, Unit 19f Number One Industrial Estate, Consett, County Durham, DH8 6SY Tel: (01207) 500599 Fax: (01207) 508154

Lightfoot Bros Ltd, 32 Castle Street, Aylesbury, Buckinghamshire, HP20 2RA Tel: (01296) 482855 Fax: (01296) 482855

Lightline Electrical Services Ltd, 40a Dryden Avenue, Ashton-in-Makerfield, Wigan, Lancashire, WN4 0JZ Tel: (01942) 713394 Fax: (01942) 713394

▶ Lightmasters UK Ltd, 3 Little End Road, Eaton Socon, St. Neots, Cambridgeshire, PE19 8JH Tel: (01480) 407727 Fax: (01480) 407757

▶ Lightside Ltd, 2 Cardwell Terrace, Cardwell Road, London, N7 0NH Tel: (020) 7607 5640 Fax: (020) 7607 5240

Lilleker Bros Ltd, 30 Moorgate Road, Rotherham, South Yorkshire, S60 2AG Tel: (01709) 374073 Fax: (01709) 364517 E-mail: info@lillekerbros.com

▶ Lindars Electrical Contractors, 74-77 Magdalen Road, Oxford, OX4 1RE Tel: (01865) 794433 Fax: (01865) 203997

▶ Linton Electrical Contractors Kent Ltd, Arnold Businesss Park, Branbridges Road, East Peckham, Tonbridge, Kent, TN12 5HD Tel: (01622) 873333 Fax: (01622) 873344

▶ Lion Barn Electrical Ltd, Unit 3, Lion Lane, Ipswich, IP6 8NT Tel: (01449) 722221

▶ Loanhead Electrics, 111 The Loan, Loanhead, Midlothian, EH20 9AH Tel: 0131-440 0447 Fax: (01968) 670541

▶ Logie Building Services, Unit 4-5 Riverside Court, Mayo Avenue, Dundee, DD2 1XD Tel: (01382) 669669 Fax: (01382) 642111

Lomond Electrical Ltd, Poplar Road, Glenrothes, Fife, KY7 4AA Tel: (01592) 757176 Fax: (01592) 757210 E-mail: admin@cfelectricalservices.com

London Kbe, 562 Lordship Lane, London, N22 5BY Tel: (020) 8889 9709

▶ Lorne Stewart P.L.C., PO Box 7, Dumfries, DG2 8NE Tel: (01387) 254251

Lorne Stewart plc, Barley House, Duncan Road, Park Gate, Southampton, SO31 1ZT Tel: (01489) 885444 Fax: (01489) 885606 E-mail: soton@lornestewart.co.uk

▶ Lowestoft Electrical Co. Ltd, Service House, Wildes Street, Lowestoft, Suffolk, NR32 1XH Tel: (01502) 565484 Fax: (01502) 588933 E-mail: enquiries@lowestoftelectricalgroup.co.uk

Loxton Installations Ltd, Unit 14 Mill Hall Business Estate, Mill Hall, Aylesford, Kent, ME20 7JZ Tel: (01622) 716131 Fax: (01622) 719217 E-mail: info@loxtons.com

▶ Lucking & Holder, 33 Baker Close, Llantarnam Industrial Park, Cwmbran, Gwent, NP44 3AX Tel: (01633) 480408 Fax: (01633) 480407

Lumenglow Ltd, 335 Underhill Road, London, SE22 9EA Tel: (020) 8693 8919 Fax: (020) 8693 9847 E-mail: sole@lumenglow.co.uk

Lund Roberts Engineers Ltd, 1 Barbon Close, London, WC1N 3JX Tel: (020) 7405 8507 Fax: (020) 7831 7974 E-mail: engineers@lundroberts.co.uk

Lutterworth Electrical Services, 1a Market Street, Lutterworth, Leicestershire, LE17 4EJ Tel: (01455) 552511 Fax: (01455) 557812 E-mail: enquiries@lutterworthelectrical.co.uk

▶ Lyons Electrical, 7 Deacon Trading Centre, Knight Road, Rochester, Kent, ME2 2AU Tel: (01634) 290000 Fax: (01634) 290006

M A C Electrical & Heating Engineers Ltd, Sites, 6-7 Back O Hill Road Industrial Estate, Stirling, FK8 1SH Tel: (01786) 464782 Fax: (01786) 450658

M A C Services Ltd, 23 Blandford Street, London, W1U 3DL Tel: (020) 7486 9075 Fax: (020) 7224 1459 E-mail: mail@mac-services.co.uk

▶ M Albutt Electrical Contractors Ltd, 39a Birmingham Road, Blakedown, Kidderminster, Worcestershire, DY10 3JW Tel: (01562) 700242 Fax: (01562) 701242

▶ M C D Electrical Services Ltd, Unit 24b Chapelhall Industrial Estate, Chapelhall, Airdrie, Lanarkshire, ML6 8QH Tel: (01236) 771440 Fax: (01236) 771441

▶ M C I, Bridge Park, Merrow Lane, Guildford, Surrey, GU4 7BF Tel: (01483) 306500 Fax: (01483) 455378

▶ M E S L Group, Cordwallis House, Cordwallis Street, Maidenhead, Berkshire, SL6 7BG Tel: (01628) 771717 Fax: (01628) 770427

▶ M J N Colston, 9 Bridgend Business Park, Bennett Street, Bridgend Industrial Estate, Bridgend, Mid Glamorgan, CF31 3SH Tel: (01656) 661808 Fax: (01656) 660473 E-mail: bridgend@mjncolston.co.uk

▶ M J Quinn Integrated Services Ltd, Gormley House, Waxlow Road, London, NW10 7NU Tel: (020) 8453 0450 Fax: (020) 8453 0455

M K Site Services, Carillion Building, Loaninghill, Uphall, Broxburn, West Lothian, EH52 5NT Tel: (01506) 433435 Fax: (01506) 433438 E-mail: enquiries@mksiteservices.com

M M Electrical Services, 17 Reddicap Trading Estate, Sutton Coldfield, West Midlands, B75 7BU Tel: 0121-378 4565 Fax: 0121-378 3541 E-mail: info@mmelec.co.uk

▶ M & N Electrical & Mechanical Services Ltd, Unit 12, Southwell Business Park, Portland, Dorset, DT5 2JS Tel: (01305) 821142 Fax: (01305) 821268

▶ M R E Electrical Services, 21 Carnation Road, Farnworth, Bolton, BL4 0DT Tel: (01204) 709007 E-mail: mre_electrical@btinternet.com

▶ M W Cripwell Ltd, 6 Victoria Road, Burton-on-Trent, Staffordshire, DE14 2LU Tel: (01283) 564269 Fax: (01283) 569537 E-mail: info@mvcripwell.co.uk

▶ McAlpine Infrastructure Services, Palmer Mount Works, Kilmarnock Road, Dundonald, Kilmarnock, Ayrshire, KA2 9DR Tel: (01563) 850333

▶ Mcarthur, 12 Station Road, Kilsyth, Glasgow, G65 0AB Tel: (01236) 821480 Fax: (01236) 824480

▶ McArthurs Mechanical & Electrical Services Ltd, 55 Colvilles Place, Kelvin Industrial Estate, Glasgow, G75 0PZ Tel: (01355) 266630

▶ Mcauley, 26 Strawmore Road, Draperstown, Magherafelt, County Londonderry, BT45 7JE Tel: (028) 7962 8859 Fax: (028) 7962 7843

▶ Mcbean Contracts Ltd, 2a Gardenhall, East Kilbride, Glasgow, G75 8SP Tel: (01355) 248463 Fax: (01355) 241309

▶ Mccaig John Electric Contractors, 3 Old Farm Road, Ayr, KA8 9ST Tel: (01292) 283018

▶ Mccann, Albert House, Park Street, Motherwell, Lanarkshire, ML1 1PT Tel: (01698) 263625 Fax: (01698) 250238

▶ McCloud, Unit 4, Metro Business Centre, Kangley Bridge Road, London, SE26 5BW Tel: (020) 8778 4254 Fax: (020) 8776 9196

Mcdevitt Electrical Engineers, 212-218 Upper Newtownards Road, Belfast, BT4 3ET Tel: (028) 9047 2626 Fax: (028) 9047 3636 E-mail: info@vhmcdevitt.co.uk

Mcgill, Harrison Road, Dundee, DD2 3SN Tel: (01382) 884488 Fax: (01382) 828777 E-mail: sales@mcgill-electrical.co.uk

▶ Mcgoff & Vickers Ltd, 47 Canal Street, Bootle, Merseyside, L20 8AQ Tel: 0151-922 6441 Fax: 0151-944 1528

▶ McKinlay & Blair Ltd, Burnbank, Campbeltown, Argyll, PA28 6JD Tel: (01586) 552012

▶ Mackintosh Highland, Braeview Clava, Culloden Moor, Inverness, IV2 5EL Tel: (01463) 790779 Fax: (01463) 792290

▶ Mcnally Electrics, 19 Turnavall Road, Newry, County Down, BT34 1LZ Tel: (028) 3026 5760 Fax: (028) 3026 0881

▶ Maco Door & Window Hardware UK Ltd, Eurolink Industrial Centre, Castle Road, Sittingbourne, Kent, ME10 3LY Tel: (01795) 433900 Fax: (01795) 433901

▶ Mains Distribution Ltd, Union Street, Pendlebury, Swinton, Manchester, M27 4HL Tel: 0161-727 9996 Fax: 0161-727 9998

▶ Makein & Mcnab, Unit 3 Riverside Court, Cupar, Fife, KY15 5JY Tel: (01334) 654422 Fax: (01334) 656590

Malcolm Electrical Ltd, 657-661 High Road, London, E10 6RD Tel: (020) 8556 1838 Fax: (020) 8556 1352

▶ Manning & Norman Ltd, 11 Harvest Court, Harvest Drive, Lowestoft, Suffolk, NR33 7NB Tel: (01502) 572957

Mantells, A, 2 Holland Road, London, SE25 5RF Tel: (020) 8654 3163 Fax: (020) 8654 3163

Martel Electrical Contractors, Tamworth Business Centre, 23 Amber Close, Tamworth, Staffordshire, B77 4RP Tel: (01827) 316533 Fax: (01827) 316568

▶ Martin Rees, Brewery Field, Victoria CR, Llandovery, Dyfed, SA20 0YE Tel: (01550) 721198 Fax: (01550) 721180 E-mail: enquiries@martinrees.co.uk

▶ Masterplay Leisure Services Ltd, 16 Deanway Trading Estate, Wilmslow Road, Handforth, Wilmslow, Cheshire, SK9 3HW Tel: (01625) 533392 Fax: (01625) 524471

▶ Maurice Pierce Ltd, 1d The Maltings, Station Road, Sawbridgeworth, Hertfordshire, CM21 9JX Tel: (01279) 306633 Fax: (01279) 306644

Maval Ltd, Skippers Lane, Skippers Lane Industrial Estat, Middlesbrough, Cleveland, TS6 6HA Tel: (01642) 455101 Fax: (01642) 458507 E-mail: maval@talk21.com

▶ Mayflower Control Ltd, Mayflower House, Herbert Road, Stafford, ST17 9BH Tel: (01785) 245263 Fax: (01785) 245266

Wally Mays (Contractors) Ltd, 57 Spyvee Street, Hull, HU8 7JJ Tel: (01482) 324077 Fax: (01482) 589596 E-mail: info@wallymays.karoo.co.uk

Mechelec Building Services Ltd, Poulton Close, Dover, Kent, CT17 0HL Tel: (01304) 205559 Fax: (01304) 242068

Melcon (Hereford) Ltd, 8 St Martins St, Hereford, HR2 7RE Tel: (01432) 265195 Fax: (01432) 269623 E-mail: enquiries@melconltd.co.uk

▶ Menai Electrical Ltd, Station House, Treborth, Bangor, Gwynedd, LL57 2NX Tel: (01248) 353855 Fax: (01248) 361356

▶ Meridian Electrical (Eastern) Ltd, 775 Southchurch Road, Southend-On-Sea, SS1 2PP Tel: (01702) 466604

▶ indicates data change since last edition

ELECTRICAL CONTRACTORS - *continued*

▶ Merlin Electrical, 6 Border Place, Saltcoats, Ayrshire, KA21 5NL Tel: (01294) 468753 E-mail: merlinelectrical@sbmbroadband.com

Joseph Merritt Group P.L.C., Byron Ave, Lowmoor Business Park, Kirkby-in-Ashfield, Nottingham, NG17 7LA Tel: (01623) 759737 Fax: (01623) 758826 E-mail: enquiries@merrittgroupplc.co.uk

▶ Midall Stones, 443 Sheffield Road, Chesterfield, Derbyshire, S41 8LT Tel: (01246) 456466 Fax: (01246) 456922 E-mail: admin@midallstones.com

Mid-Essex Electrical Engineers Ltd, 37 Beehive Lane, Chelmsford, CM2 9TQ Tel: (01245) 262226 Fax: (01245) 495911 E-mail: midessex@aol.com

Midland Cable Jointing Co., 16 Gretton Road, Nottingham, NG3 5JT Tel: 0115-960 3413 Fax: 0115-960 3413

Midlands Electrical Installations Ltd, 51 Winpenny Road, Parkhouse Industrial Estate East, Newcastle, Staffordshire, ST5 7RH Tel: (01782) 566844 Fax: (01782) 566756

Midlands Electrical Specialists Ltd, 3 Ariane, Tamworth, Staffordshire, B79 7XF Tel: (01827) 63293 Fax: (01827) 55588

Walter Miles (Electrical Engineers) Ltd, 48 Hinckley Road, Leicester, LE3 0RB Tel: 0116-255 3131 Fax: 0116-254 9396 E-mail: office@waltermiles.co.uk

▶ Miller Electrics Ltd, Unit 5, Thistle Business Park North, Ayr Road, Cumnock, Ayrshire, KA18 1EQ Tel: (01290) 420202

▶ Millers Electrical & Building Services, 29 Portland Road, London, SE25 4UF Tel: (020) 8654 4440

▶ Mindgrade Ltd, 90 Plimsoll Road, London, N4 2EE Tel: (020) 7226 8004 Fax: (020) 7359 0434

▶ Moore Electrical Services Ltd, Unit 1 Ryder Court, Corby, Northamptonshire, NN18 9NX Tel: (01536) 461616 Fax: (01536) 461010

▶ Morayvale Ltd, 9 Terrace Road, Greenock, Renfrewshire, PA15 1DJ Tel: (01475) 786655

Morfitts Building Services, 16 St Michael's Lane, Leeds, LS6 3AJ Tel: 0113-275 8631 Fax: 0113-261 8701 E-mail: ajm@morfitts.co.uk

▶ Morland Electrical Ltd, 134 Park View Road, Welling, Kent, DA16 1SJ Tel: (020) 8303 3083

D. & H Morris Group Ltd, Cumbernold House, Cumbernold, Glasgow, G67 3JG Tel: (01236) 868000 Fax: (01236) 868111

▶ Morton Fairview Electrical Services Ltd, 349 London Road, Mitcham, Surrey, CR4 4SA Tel: (020) 8646 3989 Fax: (020) 8648 1705

Morwood Electrical Services Ltd, 27a Ullswater Road, Urmston, Manchester, M41 8SY Tel: 0161-613 8280 Fax: (07092) 391474

▶ Moyne UK Ltd, Building, 202d Elgin CR, London Heathrow Airport, Hounslow, TW6 2LS Tel: (020) 8759 1663 Fax: (020) 8759 1664 E-mail: admin@moyneuk.com

Multilec Electrical Contractors, 11 Golf Links Avenue, Hindhead, Surrey, GU26 6PQ Tel: (01428) 607222 Fax: (01428) 607444 E-mail: multilec@ukonline.co.uk

▶ Mulvey Building & Roofing Contractors Ltd, PO Box 2727, Glasgow, G61 2YB Tel: 0141-942 7788 Fax: 0141-942 7788

▶ Murley Electrical Ltd, 5 Lyon Road, Romford, RM1 2BA Tel: (01708) 722544 Fax: (01708) 728884

▶ N C D Electrical Ltd, 3 Grange Road, Batley, West Yorkshire, WF17 6LL Tel: (01924) 474765

▶ N G Bailey & Co. Ltd, Bairds Brae, Glasgow, G4 9SW Tel: 0141-332 8040 Fax: 0141-332 8272

▶ N G Bailey Ltd, Unit 8, Coulerdbank Industrial Estate, Lossiemouth, Morayshire, IV31 6NG Tel: (01343) 814807

▶ N & J Mcfarlane Ltd, Dunvegan Road, Portree, Isle of Skye, IV51 9HD Tel: (01478) 613613 Fax: (01478) 613614

▶ National Design Consultancy, Adam Ferguson House Eskmills Park, Station Road, Musselburgh, Midlothian, EH21 7PQ Tel: 0131-273 4343 Fax: 0131-273 4350

National Electric & Engineering Co B'Ham Ltd, The Cape Industrial Estate, Cattell Road, Warwick, CV34 4JQ Tel: (01926) 492132 Fax: (01926) 494891 E-mail: enquiries@nationalelectric.co.uk

Nationwide Maintenance Ltd, Nene House, Sopwith Way, Drayton Fields Industrial Estate, Daventry, Northamptonshire, NN11 8EA Tel: (01327) 311303 Fax: (01327) 300835 E-mail: accounts@nationmaint.co.uk

Naz Electric Ltd, 244 Melton Road, Leicester, LE4 7PG Tel: 0116-266 0940 Fax: 0116-266 0940

▶ Needham Electrical Ltd, Maitland Road, Lion Barn Industrial Estate, Needham Market, Ipswich, IP6 8NZ Tel: (01449) 722642 Fax: (01449) 722182

▶ Neil Hart Electrical Ltd, 33-35 Tryst Road, Stenhousemuir, Larbert, Stirlingshire, FK5 4QH Tel: (01324) 552799 Fax: (01324) 552819

▶ Neilson Adam Ltd, Old Causeway, Kinross, KY13 8EZ Tel: (01577) 862673 Fax: (01577) 864401

▶ Ness Engineering Ltd, Sumburgh Airport, Virkie, Shetland, ZE3 9JP Tel: (01950) 460714 Fax: (01950) 460378

New Century Systems Ltd, Ash Street, Bilston, West Midlands, WV14 8UP Tel: (01902) 405724 Fax: (01902) 353739

New Electrics Ltd, 90 Peasley Cross Lane, St. Helens, Merseyside, WA9 3BS Tel: (01744) 22244 Fax: (01744) 22264

▶ Newfield Electrical, Unit A5 Coombswood Way, Halesowen, West Midlands, B62 8BH Tel: 0121-561 6060 Fax: 0121-561 6066

▶ Newmark Security Products Ltd, 8 Cromwell Business Centre, Howard Way, Interchange Park, Newport Pagnell, Buckinghamshire, MK16 9QS Tel: (01908) 283590 Fax: (01908) 283599

▶ North Eastern Electrical PLC, Irwell House, 40-42 Frederick Road, Salford, M6 6NY Tel: 0870 4215735 Fax: 0870 4215736 E-mail: nee@neeplc.co.uk

▶ Northern Energy Services Ltd, 206 Askern Road, Bentley, Doncaster, South Yorkshire, DN5 0EU Tel: (01302) 820790 Fax: (01302) 873633

▶ Nurse Electrical Ltd, Harts Hill Road, Thatcham, Berkshire, RG18 4NX Tel: (01635) 865065 Fax: (01635) 877681

Nuttall Electrical Contractors, 15-17 Chatham Place, Liverpool, L7 3HD Tel: 0151-703 0212 Fax: 0151-707 2133 E-mail: glynnuttalllimited@btconnect.com

T.J. O'Connor, Unit 16, Derby Road Business Park, Derby Road, Burton-On-Trent, Staffordshire, DE14 1RW Tel: (01283) 515222

▶ Octopus Electrical Ltd, Battlefield Enterprise Park, Battlefield Enterprise Park, Shrewsbury, SY1 3JE Tel: (01743) 446347 Fax: (01743) 445777

▶ One Stop Security Services Ltd, Eighth Floor, Six Acre House, Town Square, Sale, Cheshire, M33 7WZ Tel: 0161-969 6262

▶ Orbis Property Protection plc, 7 Harmony Court, Loanbank Place, Glasgow, G51 3HN Tel: 0141-445 4338 Fax: 0141-445 1571

▶ Ormiston Electrical Services, 586a Blackpool Road, Ashton-on-Ribble, Preston, PR2 1JA Tel: (01772) 722512 Fax: (01772) 722507

▶ Orwin Electrical Ltd, Unit 7, Temple Normanton Business Park, Mansfield Road, Corbriggs, Chesterfield, Derbyshire, S41 0JS Tel: (01246) 202030

Osborn Electrical Services Ltd, 433 Park Road, Hockley, Birmingham, B18 5TE Tel: 0121-551 1184 Fax: 0121-523 7837 E-mail: mail@osbornelectricalservices.co.uk

Osborne & Collins Ltd, 133a Hersham Road, Walton-on-Thames, Surrey, KT12 1RW Tel: (01932) 224751 Fax: (01932) 254592 E-mail: info@osborneandcollins.co.uk

P A Electrical Ltd, Childerditch Industrial Park, Childerditch Hall Drive, Little Warley, Brentwood, Essex, CM13 3XU Tel: (01277) 812881 Fax: (01277) 812661 E-mail: cpettit55@aol.com

▶ P A Grant Electrical Contractors Ltd, 62 London Road, Canterbury, Kent, CT2 8JZ Tel: (01227) 472580 Fax: (01227) 763217

▶ P Branson & Co., Unit 14 Annwood Lodge, Arterial Road, Rayleigh, Essex, SS6 7UA Tel: (01268) 728220 Fax: (01268) 728221

▶ P & D, Unit 1-3, Allcoach Road, Tansley, Matlock, Derbyshire, DE4 5ND Tel: (01629) 581150 Fax: (01629) 581105 E-mail: sales@pjm-services.co.uk

P D Hunt Ltd, Lynwood Grange, Winsor Road, Winsor, Southampton, SO40 2HE Tel: (023) 8081 4348 Fax: (023) 8081 2911

▶ P E I Delta Ltd, Furness Drive, Poulton Industrial Estate, Poulton-le-Fylde, Lancashire, FY6 8JS Tel: (01253) 894411 Fax: (01253) 894422

▶ P J A Electrics Ltd, Carlton House, Arrow Road North, Redditch, Worcestershire, B98 8NN Tel: (01527) 596592 Fax: (01527) 596599

▶ P J Doyle (Electrical) Ltd, 78 Cumnor Road, Oxford, OX1 5JP Tel: (01865) 327222

▶ P Kent Ltd, 6 Howard Court, Nerston Industrial Estate, East Kilbride, Glasgow, G74 4QZ Tel: (01355) 230005 Fax: (01355) 230050 E-mail: sales@kentphk.co.uk

P M R Electrical, Lodge Lane, Langham, Colchester, CO4 5ND Tel: (01206) 231894 Fax: (01206) 231895 E-mail: tony@pmrelec.fsnet.co.uk

P O'Neill Electrical Ltd, 27 Salisbury Road, Luton, LU1 5AP Tel: (01582) 456361 Fax: (01582) 728637 E-mail: jean@ponmail.co.uk

▶ P & S Electrical Contractors, 427 Minster Road, Minster on Sea, Sheerness, Kent, ME12 3NS Tel: (01795) 871945 Fax: (01795) 871945

▶ Paktron Ltd, Unit 2D, Rink Road Industrial Estate, Ryde, Isle of Wight, PO33 2LT Tel: (01983) 611357 Fax: (01983) 563328 E-mail: contracting@paktron.co.uk

Pargenta Electrical Co. Ltd, Unit 1 Prospect Row, Dudley, West Midlands, DY2 8SG Tel: (01384) 232380 Fax: (01384) 230620 E-mail: micheal.trinder@btinternet.com

Parke Electrical, 7 Gate Lane, Sutton Coldfield, West Midlands, B73 5TR Tel: 0121-357 3532 Fax: 0121-354 2491 E-mail: parke.electrical@btopenworld.com

▶ Parkersell L & E Services Ltd, Unit E4, North Caldeen Road, Coatbridge, Lanarkshire, ML5 4EF Tel: (01236) 440310

▶ Parkersell Lighting & Electrical Services Ltd, 40 Old Glamis Road, Dundee, DD3 8JQ Tel: (01382) 832451 Fax: (01382) 813365

▶ Parkersell Lighting & Electrical Services Ltd, 10 Blackchapel Road, Edinburgh, EH15 3QU Tel: 0131-657 1232 Fax: 0131-657 4999

▶ Parkersell Lighting & Electrical Services Ltd, Unit 6 Bridge Industries, Fareham, Hampshire, PO16 8SX Tel: (01329) 231235 Fax: (01329) 288119

▶ Parkersell Lighting & Electrical Services Ltd, 17 Shield Drive, Wardley Industrial Estate, Worsley, Manchester, M28 2QB Tel: 0161-727 8205 Fax: 0161-727 7098

▶ Parkersell Lighting & Electrical Services Ltd, Unit 7 Hill La Industrial Estate, Markfield, Leicestershire, LE67 9PN Tel: (01530) 245360 Fax: (01530) 244586

▶ Parkersell (Lighting & Electrical) Services Ltd, 6 Moorview Court, Estover Close, Plymouth, PL6 7PL Tel: (01752) 733295 Fax: (01752) 695436

▶ Parkinsons Electrical, 18 Lealand Way, Boston, Lincolnshire, PE21 7SW Tel: (01205) 367376 Fax: (01205) 310807

▶ Part P electrical service, Arch 269 Cold Harbour Lane, London, SW9 8SE Tel: 0791 9802057 Fax: 0871 6618109

▶ Pas (UK) Ltd, Willow Park Business Centre, 14 Upton Lane, Stoke Golding, Nuneaton, Warwickshire, CV13 6EU Tel: (01455) 213344

Paul Earl Ltd, 1 Euro Business Park, New Road, Newhaven, East Sussex, BN9 0DQ Tel: (01273) 514356 Fax: (01273) 611036 E-mail: info@paulearl.co.uk

▶ Paul Frampton, 3 Glendinning Avenue, Weymouth, Dorset, DT4 7QF Tel: (01305) 779052

▶ Paul Hunt Electrical Installations Ltd, 3 Cherry Street, Warwick, CV34 4LR Tel: (01926) 496664

▶ Pegasus Power & Communications, Unit 2 Tollpark Road, Wardpark East, Cumbernauld, Glasgow, G68 0LW Tel: (01236) 452555

▶ Pegasus Systems Ltd, 127 Greenford Road, Harrow, Middlesex, HA1 3QN Tel: (020) 8423 1104 Fax: (020) 8423 9975 E-mail: pegasus@pegasus-systems.co.uk

▶ Penec UK Ltd, Unit 11 Prime Enterprise Park, Prime Park Way, Derby, DE1 3QB Tel: (01332) 224141 Fax: (01332) 224140

▶ Peninsula Solutions, Unit 10 Orchard Court, Heron Road, Sowton Industrial Estate, Exeter, EX2 7LL Tel: (01392) 444757 Fax: (01392) 444412 E-mail: sales@peninsula.co.uk

▶ Penney Electrical Ltd, Reynolds Road, Crawley, West Sussex, RH11 7HA Tel: (01293) 550800 Fax: (01293) 510700

▶ Perdune Ltd, Hayward Road Indust Estate, Hayward Road, Staple Hill, Bristol, BS16 4NY Tel: 0117-957 4499 Fax: 0117-957 6955

▶ Performance Electrical Ltd, 123 Radcliffe Road, Bury, Lancashire, BL9 9LD Tel: 0161-797 3476 Fax: 0161-764 2903 E-mail: sales@performanceelectrical.co.uk

Periam & Williamson Ltd, Norfolk Street, Boston, Lincolnshire, PE21 6PW Tel: (01205) 362281 Fax: (01205) 362281 E-mail: richard@p-wltd.totalserve.co.uk

▶ Peter Fowler Electrical Ltd, 6 Westfield Road, Hatfield, Doncaster, South Yorkshire, DN7 6PZ Tel: (01302) 842760 Fax: (01302) 351588

▶ Peter Robinson Electrical Ltd, 1 Broadfield Industrial Estate, Seymour Street, Heywood, Lancashire, OL10 3AJ Tel: (01706) 364046 Fax: (01706) 625916

▶ Peter Swales, Manchester Abattoir, Riverpark Road, Manchester, M40 2XP Tel: 0161-231 2041

▶ Peterhead Marine Electrics Ltd, 8 Bridge Street, Peterhead, Aberdeenshire, AB42 1DH Tel: (01779) 479461 Fax: (01779) 480106

▶ Philtech Installations Ltd, Bath Street, Walsall, WS1 3BZ Tel: (01922) 643805 Fax: (01922) 643845

Phoenix Electrical Co. Ltd, Yeoman House, 63 Croydon Road, London, SE20 7TS Tel: (020) 8778 9666 Fax: (020) 8659 9386 E-mail: davidrosedon@pheonixelectrical.co.uk

Pickering & Molloy Ltd, 86 Bank Street, Rossendale, Lancashire, BB4 8EG Tel: (01706) 213450 Fax: (01706) 216978

Pickup H Mechanical Electrical Services Ltd, Durham House, Lower Clark Street, Scarborough, North Yorkshire, YO12 7PW Tel: (01723) 369191 Fax: (01723) 362044 E-mail: pickup@hpickup.co.uk

▶ Piggott & Whitfield Ltd, Pishobury House, Pishiobury Drive, Sawbridgeworth, Hertfordshire, CM21 0AF Tel: (01279) 600940 Fax: (01279) 600540

▶ Pinnacle Heating Services Ltd, 1 Trinity Place Park Street, Aston, Birmingham, B6 5SH Tel: 0121-328 7800 Fax: 0121-773 3004

▶ Pirbright Electrical Contractors Ltd, Toad Hall, Vapery Lane, Pirbright, Woking, Surrey, GU24 0QD Tel: (01483) 474888 Fax: (01483) 489141

▶ Pirelli Construction Co. Ltd, Robslee Drive, Giffnock, Glasgow, G46 7QX Tel: 0141-638 1151

Pitts Wilson Electrical Ltd, Cutler House, Wakefield Road, Bradford, West Yorkshire, BD4 7LU Tel: (01274) 771100 Fax: (01274) 771188 E-mail: enquiries@pwe-elec.com

Playfords Ltd, Unit B1 Brookfields Centre, 20 Pents Road, Cambridge, CB24 8PS Tel: (01954) 251966 Fax: (01638) 661206 E-mail: office@playfords.co.uk

▶ Plummer Electrical Engineering, Shanklin, Plough Road, Great Bentley, Colchester, CO7 8LG Tel: (01206) 250158 Fax: (01206) 251169

Polarcool Refrigeration Ltd, Unit K1 Beckingham Business Park, Tolleshunt Major, Maldon, Essex, CM9 8LZ Tel: (01621) 868584 Fax: (01621) 868989 E-mail: sales@polarcool.co.uk

▶ Pollard Electrical Ltd, 39 Warwick Drive, Beverley, North Humberside, HU17 9TB Tel: (01482) 679434 E-mail: abarker@pollard-electrical.co.uk

▶ Positive Electrical Installations Ltd, Unit 1 Central Trading Estate, Stallings Lane, Kingswinford, West Midlands, DY6 7LJ Tel: (01384) 405320 Fax: (01384) 405321

Powell Electrical Ltd, 53 Churchfield Street, Dudley, West Midlands, DY2 8QN Tel: (01384) 259911 Fax: (01384) 211446 E-mail: john@powellelectrical.co.uk

▶ Power Installations Ltd, Southglade Business Park, Hucknall Road, Nottingham, NG5 9RA Tel: 0115-927 0483

Powerlight Engineering Co., 29 Alwinton Avenue, Stockport, Cheshire, SK4 3PU Tel: 0161-432 3195

Powermann Ltd, 16 Commercial Road, Poole, Dorset, BH14 0JW Tel: (01202) 722111 Fax: (01202) 722888 E-mail: sales@powermann.co.uk

▶ Powerstream Electrical & Building Services Ltd, Burbank Street, Hartlepool, Cleveland, TS24 7JW Tel: (01429) 277053 Fax: (01429) 865473 E-mail: sales@powerstream-ebs.com

Powersystems UK Ltd, Badminton Road Trading Estate, Badminton Road, Yate, Bristol, BS37 5GG Tel: (01454) 318000 Fax: (01454) 318111 E-mail: sales@powersystemsuk.co.uk

▶ Precision Construction Ltd, 44 Telford Road, Cumbernauld, Glasgow, G67 2AX Tel: (01236) 782600

▶ Premier Electrical (N I) Ltd, 87 Dromore Road, Ballynahinch, County Down, BT24 8HT Tel: (028) 9756 4046

Preston Electrical Ltd, Dalton Airfield Indutrial Estate, Dalton, Thirsk, North Yorkshire, YO7 3HE Tel: (01845) 577753 Fax: (01845) 578182 E-mail: enquiries@prestonelectrical.co.uk

▶ Princebuild Ltd, 18-19 Quarry Park Close, Moulton Park Industrial Estate, Northampton, NN3 6QB Tel: (01604) 645576 Fax: (01604) 643886

Procon Industrial Automation Ltd, Unit 5 Arclid Industrial Estate, Hemmingshaw Lane, Arclid, Sandbach, Cheshire, CW11 4SY Tel: (01270) 759708 Fax: (01270) 766350 E-mail: rn@proconuk.freeserve.co.uk

▶ Pro-Elec Ltd, 6 Willesborough Industrial Par, Willesborough, Ashford, Kent, TN24 0TD Tel: (01233) 611280

Prompt Maintenance Services, 358 Edgware Road, London, W2 1EB Tel: (020) 7724 7234 Fax: (020) 7224 9854 E-mail: contracts@caesarceramics.co.uk

▶ Property Protection, 80 Johnstone Avenue, Hillington Industrial Estate, Glasgow, G52 4NZ Tel: 0141-585 6710

▶ PTC Communication, 62 Pensby Road, Heswall, Wirral, Merseyside, CH60 7RE Tel: 0151-342 6288 Fax: 0151-342 6289 E-mail: sales@ptc-security.co.uk

▶ Pulsar Electrical Services Ltd, Great Maplestead, Halstead, Essex, CO9 2QT Tel: (01787) 462684 Fax: (01787) 461265

▶ Pulsar Management Services Ltd, 9 Concorde Road, Norwich, NR6 6BH Tel: (01603) 787676

▶ Q R T I (Scotland) Ltd, 156 Reid Street, Glasgow, G40 4PH Tel: 0141-551 8228 Fax: 0141-554 8474

Quantock Electric Co. Ltd, 70-72 St John Street, Bridgwater, Somerset, TA6 5HY Tel: (01278) 422530 Fax: (01278) 445843

▶ Quantum (UK) Ltd, Unit 5 Station Court, Station Approach, Borough Green, Sevenoaks, Kent, TN15 8AD Tel: (01732) 781133

Quartz Electrical & Mechanical Services Ltd, 2 Brighouse Business Village, Riverside Park, Middlesbrough, Cleveland, TS2 1RT Tel: (01642) 244411 Fax: (01642) 244499

▶ R A B Electrical Services Ltd, 6 Catheralls Industrial Estate, Brookhill Way, Buckley, Clwyd, CH7 3PS Tel: (01244) 544545 Fax: (01244) 543410

▶ R A S Crockett & Partners, 69-71 Scott Street, Dundee, DD2 2BA Tel: (01382) 669892 Fax: (01382) 669892

▶ R & B Electrical Skipton Ltd, 3-5 Bowers Wharf, Skipton, North Yorkshire, BD23 2PD Tel: (01756) 793039 Fax: (01756) 793945

R B Emerson, 8a Temple Farm Industrial Estate, Coopers Way, Temple Farm Industrial Estate, Southend-on-Sea, SS2 5TE Tel: (01702) 461999 Fax: (01702) 462001 E-mail: sales@emersons.uk.com

▶ R B Wilson Electrical Ltd, 14 Pittodrie Street, Aberdeen, AB24 5QL Tel: (01224) 630187 Fax: (01224) 640393

R D Brett Electrical Contractors Ltd, Lower Nursery, Sunningdale, Ascot, Berkshire, SL5 0PA Tel: (01344) 620444 Fax: (01344) 624873 E-mail: enquiries@rdbrett.co.uk

▶ R D Downie, 133 Shore Street, Fraserburgh, Aberdeenshire, AB43 9BP Tel: (01346) 518855 Fax: (01346) 515776

R D Jukes & Co. Ltd, Walsingham Works, 1 Walsingham Street, Walsall, WS1 2JZ Tel: (01922) 624222 Fax: (01922) 630587 E-mail: info@rdjukes.co.uk

R E S Services Ltd, Unit 16 Ilford Trading Estate, Paycocke Road, Basildon, Essex, SS14 3DR Tel: (01268) 531153 Fax: (01268) 525227 E-mail: janeryan@resservices.co.uk

▶ R E Wright (Bradford) Ltd, Cragg Works, Pannal Street, Great Horton, Bradford, West Yorkshire, BD7 4HG Tel: (01274) 502765

▶ R G & M F Sadler Electrical Ltd, 60 East Road, Oundle, Peterborough, PE8 4BZ Tel: (01832) 273677 Fax: (01832) 273677

▶ R H Electrical, 1a Stone Lane, Kinver, Stourbridge, West Midlands, DY7 6EQ Tel: (07836) 299206 Fax: (01384) 877874

R H Foster Ltd, 16 Essex Road, Basingstoke, Hampshire, RG21 7TD Tel: (01256) 465414 Fax: (01256) 841216

ELECTRICAL CONTRACTORS –

continued

R H K Davidson, 35 Bushmills Road, Coleraine, County Londonderry, BT52 2BP Tel: (028) 7034 2281 Fax: (020) 7035 7097 E-mail: rhkdavidson@btopenworld.com

R & I Electrical Services, 278 Philip Lane, London, N15 4AD Tel: (020) 8801 5771 Fax: (020) 8365 1800

▶ R J C Electrical Ltd, 34-36 Offerton Industrial Esta, Hempshaw Lane, Stockport, Cheshire, SK2 5TJ Tel: 0161-477 2244

▶ R J Pickford Electrical Ltd, Newbourne House, Bedford Grove, Nottingham, NG6 9DE Tel: 0115-976 4445 Fax: 0115-976 4440

R J S Electrical Contractors, Park House, Suckley, Worcester, WR6 5DJ Tel: (01886) 884000 Fax: (01886) 884777

▶ R J Wilson Electricians Ltd, A17 Washway Road, Fleet, Holbeach, Spalding, Lincolnshire, PE12 8LT Tel: (01406) 423331 Fax: (01406) 425533

▶ R K Electrical Bradford Ltd, Britannia Buildings, Reservoir Road, Halifax, West Yorkshire, HX2 0ET Tel: (01422) 364035 Fax: (01422) 348573

▶ R Levitt Ltd, 37 Low Street, Sherburn In Elmet, Leeds, LS25 6BB Tel: (01977) 682264

▶ R & M A Stewart Ltd, 349A Wandsworth Road, London, SW8 2JH Tel: (020) 7720 7810

▶ R S Merriman Ltd, Cairston Road, Stromness, Orkney, KW16 3JS Tel: (01856) 850105 Fax: (01856) 850632

▶ R & S Midland, 16 Primrose Meadow, Cannock, Staffordshire, WS11 7FN Tel: (01543) 274383 E-mail: richard.smith077@ntlworld.com

▶ R Sorley Electrical Services, 5 Pollock Walk, Dunfermline, Fife, KY12 9DA Tel: (01383) 736933 Fax: (01383) 736933

R T Harris & Son Electrical Contractors Ltd, Shotover Kilns, Shotover Hill, Headington, Oxford, OX3 8ST Tel: (01865) 742300 Fax: (01865) 741405 E-mail: office@rtharris.co.uk

▶ R Thomson Electrical Contractors Ltd, West Quay Road, Winwick Quay, Warrington, WA2 8TL Tel: (01925) 636773

▶ R W Curle Ltd, Wadd Lane, Snape, Saxmundham, Suffolk, IP17 1QN Tel: (01728) 688444 Fax: (01728) 688931

▶ R W Electrics, 16 Castle Douglas Road, Dumfries, DG2 7NX Tel: (01387) 250099 Fax: (01387) 250099

▶ R Williamson Ltd, 118 Duke Street, Glasgow, G4 0XW Tel: 0141-552 3654

Rae Electrical Services, 116a Blackstock Road, London, N4 2DR Tel: (020) 7226 2962 Fax: (020) 7359 3354 E-mail: raeelectrical@aol.com

▶ Railway Electrical Services Ltd, St.Bartholomews Church, Hallam Fields Road, Ilkeston, Derbyshire, DE7 4AZ Tel: 0115-944 4608 Fax: 0115-944 4988

▶ Rainbow Services Ltd, 369 Wellingborough Road, Northampton, NN1 4EU Tel: (01604) 627227 Fax: (01604) 627337

▶ Ramsay Electrical Co., 40 Ashley Terrace, Edinburgh, EH11 1RY Tel: 0131-346 7494

Randall & Daniels (Electrical) Ltd, Abbey Industrial Estate, Neath Abbey, Neath, West Glamorgan, SA10 7DR Tel: (01792) 813231 Fax: (01792) 321816 E-mail: sales@rd-electrical.com

Ravenscroft Cameras, 61 Grimsby Road, Cleethorpes, South Humberside, DN35 7AF Tel: (01472) 342007 Fax: (01472) 250504 E-mail: ravenscroftcameras@btinternet.com

▶ Reffold Electrical, 7 Hessle Road, Hull, HU3 2AA Tel: (01482) 320638 Fax: (01482) 586233

Reid Electrical & Computer Services, Elmsbrook, Lovacott, Newton Tracey, Barnstaple, Devon, EX31 3PU Tel: (01271) 858546 E-mail: info@reidelectrical.fsnet.co.uk

▶ Reiss Electrical Contractors, 5 Odeon Parade, Holloway Road, London, N7 6LS Tel: (020) 7272 5988

Renown Elec Co., 111 Bishops Road, London, SW6 7AU Tel: (020) 7731 1970

▶ Restoration & Renovation Scotland Ltd, South Street, Milnathort, Kinross, KY13 9XB Tel: (01577) 862919 Fax: (01577) 861409

Rex Campbell Properties Ltd, Phoenix Works, Steeley Lane, Chorley, Lancashire, PR6 0RJ Tel: (01257) 266521 Fax: (01257) 241362 E-mail: kim@rex-campbell.co.uk

▶ Rhedin Ltd, 73 Milford Road, Reading, RG1 8LG Tel: 0118-950 9541 Fax: 0118-957 2616

Rhodes Electrical, 77 St. Marys Road, Garston, Liverpool, L19 2NN Tel: 0151-427 6885 Fax: 0151-494 1535 E-mail: rhodeselectrical@onetel.com

Rigfone Electrics Ltd, 109-111 Bitterne Road West, Southampton, SO18 1AR Tel: (023) 8021 5100 Fax: (023) 8021 5101 E-mail: sales@rigfone.co.uk

▶ Ringready Ltd, 353-355 Old Durham Road, Gateshead, Tyne & Wear, NE9 5LA Tel: 0191-490 1494

Ringwood Company Builders, Unit 22 Brookvale Trading Estate, Moor Lane, Birmingham, B6 7AQ Tel: 0121-356 0157 Fax: 0121-344 4867

▶ Rivendell UK Ltd, Unit 21 Bonville Business Centre, Bonville Road, Bristol, BS4 5QR Tel: 0117-977 2550 Fax: 0117-977 2530

▶ RJS Ascot Ltd, 8 Beechwood Close, Ascot, Berkshire, SL5 8QJ Tel: (01344) 890442 Fax: (01344) 883685 E-mail: rjsascot@aol.com

▶ RMD Contracts, 4 Outram Road, Dukinfield, Cheshire, SK16 4XE Tel: 0161-339 9910 Fax: 0161-343 2015 E-mail: info@rmdcontracts.com

Robert Collins Electrical Ltd, 30 Wood End Gardens, Northolt, Middlesex, UB5 4QJ Tel: (020) 8864 6939 Fax: (020) 8423 3177 E-mail: johnwhittle7@aol.com

Robert Stewart, 52 Victoria Road, Dunoon, Argyll, PA23 7AE Tel: (01369) 702202 Fax: (01369) 704182

▶ Robertson Acom Ltd, 52 Kilnside Road, Paisley, Renfrewshire, PA1 1RN Tel: 0141-887 7878 Fax: 0141-887 5677 E-mail: sales@robertsonacom.fsbusiness.co.uk

Gus Robinson Developments Ltd, Stranton House, West View Road, Hartlepool, Cleveland, TS24 0BW Tel: (01429) 234221 Fax: (01429) 869822 E-mail: gus.hartlepool@gusrobinson.com

▶ Rock Special Projects, 131 Craighall Road, Glasgow, G4 9TN Tel: 0141-341 5055 Fax: 0141-341 5051

Rolcar Electrical Co. Ltd, Prospect Barn, Prospect Farm, Wedgenock, Warwick, CV35 7PX Tel: (01926) 493331 Fax: (01926) 493113 E-mail: info@rolcarelectrical.co.uk

Rolec, 14a Tickford Street, Newport Pagnell, Buckinghamshire, MK16 9AB Tel: (01908) 210679 Fax: (01908) 210678 E-mail: sales@rolec.co.uk

▶ Rosebery Group Ltd, Hastings House, 79-83 Station Road, Ellesmere Port, CH65 4BN Tel: 0151-357 1066 Fax: 0151-357 2066 E-mail: general@rosebery.co.uk

▶ Ross Fire Protection Ltd, 29 Deerdykes View, Cumbernauld, Glasgow, G68 9HN Tel: (01236) 738502 Fax: (01236) 727977

Rotary North West Ltd, Rotary House, Chantry Court, Chester West Employment Park, Chester, CH1 4QN Tel: (01244) 382233 Fax: (01244) 382458

Rotary Southern Ltd, Rotary House, Breakspear Road, Ruislip, Middlesex, HA4 7ST Tel: (01895) 674264 Fax: (01895) 630673 E-mail: info@rotarysouthern.co.uk

Rotary Yorkshire Ltd, 5 Buslingthorpe Green, Leeds, LS7 2HG Tel: 0113-262 0911 Fax: 0113-262 6342 E-mail: enquiries@rotary-yorkshire.co.uk

Routeco plc, Davy Avenue, Knowlhill, Milton Keynes, MK5 8HJ Tel: (01908) 666777 Fax: (01908) 666738

▶ Rowelec Ltd, Unit 2b Granada Trading Estate, Park Street, Oldbury, West Midlands, B69 4LH Tel: 0121-544 1117 Fax: 0121-544 2228 E-mail: rowelec@ic24.net

▶ Roy Dyke Electrical Contractors, 44 Poole Crescent, Bilston, West Midlands, WV14 8SU Tel: (01902) 492459 Fax: (01902) 493036

▶ S D M Building Contractors, 490 Calder Street, Glasgow, G42 0QD Tel: 0141-423 1444 Fax: 0141-423 7774 E-mail: sales@sdm-group.com

S.E.C. Electrical Ltd, 15 Stafford Place, Moulton Park Industrial Estate, Northampton, NN3 6NN Tel: (01604) 491101 Fax: (01604) 790542

S & F Electrics, Office5 Rope Walk, Littlehampton, West Sussex, BN17 5DH Tel: (01903) 723593 Fax: (01903) 723593

S & G Tate, 3 Pigot Road, Denbigh, Clwyd, LL16 3DG Tel: (01745) 814024 Fax: (01745) 814024

▶ S P S (Holdings) Ltd, 131 West Nile Street, Glasgow, G1 2RX Tel: 0141-332 9412

▶ S V Security Systems Ltd, Midway Offices, 68 Stone Road, Stoke-On-Trent, ST4 6SP Tel: (01782) 646455 Fax: (01782) 646564 E-mail: svelectrics@aol.com

▶ S Wade, Butterthwaite Lane, Ecclesfield, Sheffield, S35 9WA Tel: 0114-257 8190 Fax: 0114-257 8190

▶ Safecontrol Ltd, Tattershall Way, Fairfield Industrial Estate, Louth, Lincolnshire, LN11 0YZ Tel: (01507) 609944 Fax: (01507) 609579

Safety First Extinguishers, Safety First Ho, Hawthorn Rd, Bognor Regis, W. Sussex, PO21 2UW Tel: (01243) 822215 Fax: (01243) 822215 E-mail: mrpcampbell@safetyfirstextinguishers.freeserve.co.uk

Sandilands Electric Ltd, 151 Stroud Green Road, London, N4 3PZ Tel: (020) 7272 4084 Fax: (020) 7263 1037

Sapphire Contractors Ltd, 18 Gladstone Road, Croydon, CR0 2BQ Tel: (020) 8665 6226 Fax: (020) 8665 6282 E-mail: enquiries@sapphirecontractors.co.uk

▶ Satellite & Digital Services Ltd, Unit 5 Branhams Crescent, Roundswell, Barnstaple, Devon, EX31 3TD Tel: (01271) 325888 Fax: (01271) 329163

Scorahs Ltd, 699 Huddersfield Road, Ravensthorpe, Dewsbury, West Yorkshire, WF13 3LQ Tel: (01924) 493222 Fax: (01924) 493222

▶ Scotshield Ltd, Century House, Chapelhall Industrial Estate, Chapelhall, Airdrie, Lanarkshire, ML6 8QH Tel: (01236) 767788 Fax: (01236) 762233

▶ Scotshield Fire & Security Systems, 9 Lotland Street, Inverness, IV1 1ST Tel: (01463) 709637 Fax: (01463) 709638

▶ Scott & Foggon Ltd, 11 Exchange Street, Jedburgh, Roxburghshire, TD8 6BH Tel: (01835) 863357 Fax: (01835) 862143

SCS Building Services Ltd, 6 Middlefield Road, Falkirk, FK2 9AG Tel: (01324) 888000 Fax: 01324 888030 E-mail: enquiries@scsbuildingservices.co.uk

▶ SCS Installation Ltd, 30 St Catherine Street, Gloucester, GL1 2BX Tel: (01452) 310990 Fax: (01452) 310998

▶ Semple P.L.C., 15 Fullerton Court, Drumhead Place, Glasgow East Investment Park, Glasgow, G32 8EY Tel: 0141-646 5252

Serco Electrical Ltd, 93 Canwick Road, Lincoln, LN5 8HE Tel: (01522) 874874 Fax: (01522) 514732

Severn Electric Co. Ltd, 2 Lisle Avenue, Kidderminster, Worcestershire, DY11 7DN Tel: (01299) 877700 Fax: (01562) 865059 E-mail: sales@severnelectric.co.uk

Shaws Electrical, 349-353 Purley Way, Croydon, CR0 4NW Tel: (020) 8688 0491 Fax: (020) 8688 0492 E-mail: shawselectrical@compuserve.com

Sheplee Electrical Contractors Ltd, Unit 23, Jarman Way, Royston, Hertfordshire, SG8 5HW Tel: (01763) 243324

▶ Shetland Electrical Services, Rudda Park, Lerwick, Shetland, ZE1 0SD Tel: (01595) 692792 Fax: (01595) 695672

A.J. Sibthorpe & Co. Ltd, 22-42 Freshwater Road, Dagenham, Essex, RM8 1RY Tel: (020) 8597 7000 Fax: (020) 8597 7300

▶ Silenster Building Services Ltd, 33A Whiffler Road, Norwich, NR3 2AW Tel: (01603) 482300

Sinclair Decorators, Roscoe Street, Scarborough, North Yorkshire, YO12 7BY Tel: (01723) 367361 Fax: (01723) 370848 E-mail: admin@sinclair.co.uk

Sinclair Electrics, 130 Embankment Rd, Plymouth, PL4 9JF Tel: (01752) 268887 Fax: (01752) 268887

▶ Sinclair Scott Ltd, 6 Borthwick View, Pentland Industrial Estate, Loanhead, Midlothian, EH20 9QH Tel: 0131-448 0868 Fax: 0131-448 0869

▶ Skanska Rashleigh Weatherfoil Ltd, 160 Blackswarth Road, Bristol, BS5 8AG Tel: 0117-954 1175 Fax: 0117-955 1672

▶ Skanska Rashleigh Weatherfoil Ltd, 7 Colquhoun Avenue, Hillington Industrial Estate, Glasgow, G52 4BN Tel: 0141-810 1100 Fax: 0141-882 2200

Skanska Rashleigh Weatherfoil Ltd, West Lodge, Station Approach, West Byfleet, Surrey, KT14 6NG Tel: (01932) 791800 Fax: (01932) 791810 E-mail: krw.receptionist@skanska.co.uk

Skerritt Electrical Ltd, 1087 Kingsbury Road, Castle Vale, Birmingham, B35 6AJ Tel: 0121-776 5710 Fax: 0121-322 2216 E-mail: admin@skerrittelectrical.co.uk

▶ Skillbase, 106 Fintry Road, Dundee, DD4 9EZ Tel: (01382) 506676 Fax: (01382) 500884

▶ Sleetree Ltd, Edward House, Cores End Road, Bourne End, Buckinghamshire, SL8 5AL Tel: (01628) 529323 Fax: (01628) 850064 E-mail: enquiries@sleetree.co.uk

▶ Smith Property Maintenance, 129 Albany Road, Hornchurch, Essex, RM12 4AQ Tel: (01708) 477764 Fax: (01708) 442100 E-mail: lg_smiths@hotmail.com

▶ SMT Electrical Ltd, Great Lime Road, Newcastle upon Tyne, NE12 6RU Tel: 0191-268 5999 Fax: 0191-268 4440 E-mail: sales@smtelectrical.co.uk

Solent Electrical Ltd, Shepherds Road, Bartley, Southampton, SO40 2LH Tel: (023) 8081 4151 Fax: (023) 8081 3918

▶ Southern Electric, Hambridge Road, Newbury, Berkshire, RG14 5TP Tel: (01635) 572382 Fax: (01635) 572383

▶ Southern Electric, Benett Street, Ryde, Isle of Wight, PO33 2BJ Tel: (01983) 617000 Fax: (01983) 566324

Southern Heating Co., 272 South Coast Road, Peacehaven, East Sussex, BN10 7PD Tel: (01273) 588123 Fax: (01273) 588121 E-mail: southtg@fastnet.co.uk

▶ Sovereign Electrical Services, 22 Holifast Road, Sutton Coldfield, West Midlands, B72 1AP Tel: 0121-384 6285 Fax: 0121-350 1859

▶ Spaford Electro & Mechanic Services Ltd, Unit 7d, Beechcroft Industries, Chapelwood Road, Sevenoaks, Kent, TN15 7HX Tel: (01474) 879922

▶ Spain Building & Maintenance Ltd, 96 Keighley Road, Colne, Lancashire, BB8 0PH Tel: (01282) 866466

▶ Speyroc, 120 Strathmore Road, Balmour Industrial Estate, Glasgow, G22 7DW Tel: 0141-347 1033 Fax: 0141-347 1050

▶ Stafford & Coomber Electrical Contractors, 112 Lambrook Road, Taunton, Somerset, TA1 2AD Tel: (01823) 284620 Fax: (01823) 331283

Stannah Lift Service Ltd, Unit 6 Ambassador Industrial Estate, 9 Airfield Road, Christchurch, Dorset, BH23 3TG Tel: (01202) 476781

▶ Star Electrical Services, Unit 1a Motherwell Business Centre, Coursington Road, Motherwell, Lanarkshire, ML1 1PW Tel: (01698) 267865 Fax: (01698) 264354

▶ Star Electrics, 22 Mcgowan Street, Paisley, Renfrewshire, PA3 1QJ Tel: 0141-889 0947 Fax: 0141-887 2526

▶ Star Mechanical & Electrical, Fryern House, 125 Winchester Road, Chandler's Ford, Eastleigh, Hampshire, SO53 2DR Tel: (023) 8027 3050 Fax: (023) 8027 3051 E-mail: admin@dagenhammotors.co.uk

▶ Stark & Mccormick Ltd, 92 Liverpool Road North, Liverpool, L31 2HN Tel: 0151-531 8505 Fax: 0151-527 2233

▶ Steele Electrics Ltd, 3 Ambassador Industrial Estate, 9 Airfield Road, Christchurch, Dorset, BH23 3TG Tel: (01202) 487766 Fax: (01202) 490305 E-mail: info@steele-electrics.co.uk

▶ Stenson Laurencekirk Ltd, Station Road, Laurencekirk, Kincardineshire, AB30 1BE Tel: (01561) 377327 Fax: (01561) 378057

Sterling (Mechanical & Electrical) Contractors Ltd, 1 Queen Victoria Street, Bristol, BS2 0QR Tel: 0117-941 3111

▶ Stokes Clarkson Electrical Ltd, Unit D1 Admin Buildings, Admin Road, Knowsley Industrial Park, Liverpool, L33 7TX Tel: 0151-548 9377 Fax: 0151-548 6377

▶ Strongcastle Builders, 120 Whitehorse Road, Croydon, CR0 2JF Tel: (020) 8665 7129 Fax: (020) 8665 6907

Sturrock Power Installations Ltd, 15 Bankhead Drive, Edinburgh, EH11 4DW Tel: 0131-453 5050 Fax: 0131-458 5066

▶ Summit Engineering Services, 39 Glenburn Road, East Kilbride, Glasgow, G74 5BA Tel: (01355) 260200 Fax: (01355) 260456

▶ Sure Connects Systems, 1200 Rochdale Road, Manchester, M9 6FR Tel: 0161-795 6060 Fax: 0161-795 6161

▶ Swift Engineering Services Ltd, 4 Holgate Court, Western Road, Romford, RM1 3JS Tel: (01708) 764573

Switch Alarms, 8 Boothroyden Road, Middleton, Manchester, M24 4RY Tel: 0161-653 2541

Switchgear Engineering Services Ltd, Wright Street, Audenshaw, Manchester, M34 5TT Tel: 0161-371 0833 Fax: 0161-371 0834

▶ System Electrical Engineering Ltd, System House, Merthyr Tydfil Industrial Park, Pentrebach, Merthyr Tydfil, Mid Glamorgan, CF48 4DR Tel: (01443) 694030 Fax: (01443) 694039

T Clarke plc, Stanhope House, 116-118 Walworth Road, London, SE17 1JY Tel: (020) 7358 5000 Fax: (020) 7701 6265 E-mail: info@tclarke.co.uk

▶ T Darby Electrical Ltd, Clocktower Buildings, Shore Road, Warsash, Southampton, SO31 9GQ Tel: (01489) 559955 Fax: (01489) 559993

▶ T G Baker (Sound) Ltd, 173-175 Glasgow Road, Clydebank, Dunbartonshire, G81 1LQ Tel: 0141-941 3399 Fax: 0141-952 6003

T J Electrical Engineers & Contractors Ltd, Unit 3 Squirrels Lodge, Hards Lane, Peterborough, PE6 8RL Tel: (01778) 349680 Fax: (01778) 349683 E-mail: sales@tjelectrical.co.uk

▶ T K Drake, 30 London Street, Swaffham, Norfolk, PE37 7DG Tel: (01760) 725665 Fax: (01760) 720518 E-mail: contracting@tkdrake.co.uk

▶ T L O Electrical Contractors Ltd, Woodhouse Lane, Tamworth, Staffordshire, B77 3AE Tel: (01827) 52208 Fax: (01827) 60913

T M S Electrical Contractors, Guildford Road, Bucks Green, Rudgwick, Horsham, West Sussex, RH12 3JF Tel: (01403) 822266 Fax: (01403) 822890 E-mail: andywalder@tmselectrical.com

▶ T McNally Electricians Ltd, Unit 1 B, Motherwell Business Centre, Coursington Road, Motherwell, Lanarkshire, ML1 1PW Tel: (01698) 253046

▶ T Norman Price Dudley Ltd, 73 Dixons Green, Dudley, West Midlands, DY2 7DJ Tel: (01384) 253875 Fax: (01384) 211524

▶ T W Sampson & Co., Churchill House Lenton Lane, Nottingham, NG7 2NR Tel: 0115-986 8800 Fax: 0115-986 7909

▶ Tangent Electrical Ltd, Wheel Wright Yard, 2 The Street, Hatfield Peverel, Chelmsford, CM3 2EA Tel: (01245) 382552 Fax: (01245) 382135

Tappelectric Ltd, 2 Dragon Court, Crofts End Road, Bristol, BS5 7XX Tel: 0117-951 8274 Fax: 0117-951 3751 E-mail: info@tappelectric.co.uk

▶ Tarnwalk (U K) Ltd, 34 Hiltingbury Road, Chandlers Ford, Eastleigh, Hampshire, SO53 5SS Tel: (023) 8026 5912

▶ Tasc Digital Control Systems, 1280 Century Way, Thorpe Park, Leeds, LS15 8ZB Tel: 0113-201 8998 Fax: 0113-201 8999

▶ Taylor Building Services, 22 Cleveden Road, Glasgow, G12 0PX Tel: 0141-337 6588

F.A. Taylor & Co. Ltd, Faraday House, 17 Essendene Road, Caterham, Surrey, CR3 5PB Tel: (01883) 347016 Fax: (01883) 341499

Taylor J Electric Contractors Ltd, 590 Tonge Moor Road, Bolton, BL2 3BJ Tel: (01204) 592145 Fax: (01204) 598471 E-mail: jh@jtaylorelectrical.co.uk

▶ Taylor M.E. Ltd, Unit 3 Canal Court Business Centre, Infirmary Street, Carlisle, CA2 7AN Tel: (01228) 527584 E-mail: sales@taylor-me.co.uk

Team Services Ltd, Riverside Road, Pottington, Barnstaple, Devon, EX31 1TE Tel: (01271) 374019 Fax: (01271) 375977 E-mail: sales@teamservices.co.uk

Telecom Security N W Ltd, Rear of, 28 Bridge Street, Hindley, Wigan, Lancashire, WN2 3LQ Tel: (01942) 203891 Fax: (01942) 204880 E-mail: sales@telecomelectrical-uk.co.uk

▶ Terry Mark Ltd, 6 Brentfield Road, Dartford, DA1 1YJ Tel: (01322) 289700 Fax: (01322) 271548

Terry Rushton Associates, 49 Twyford Avenue, London, N2 9NR Tel: (020) 8442 1234 Fax: (020) 8442 1234E-mail: telrush@aol.com

▶ TFS Systems Ltd, Station Road Industrial Estate, Station Road, Clowne, Chesterfield, Derbyshire, S43 4AB Tel: (01246) 570870 Fax: (01246) 570704

▶ Thompson Electrical Cambridge Ltd, 15 Barnwell Business Park, Barnwell Drive, Cambridge, CB5 8UZ Tel: (01223) 212162 Fax: (01223) 242131

▶ Tilen Electrics Ltd, Eden Grove, Swallownest, Sheffield, S26 4TP Tel: 0114-287 2046 Fax: 0114-287 8613

▶ indicates data change since last edition

ELECTRICAL CONTRACTORS - *continued*

Geoff Till Electrical Contractors Ltd, 19 Sherwood Road, Aston Fields Industrial Estate, Bromsgrove, Worcestershire, B60 3DR Tel: (01527) 871123 Fax: (01527) 873075 E-mail: info@gtelec.co.uk

▶ Tioga Ltd, St. Thomas House, Mansfield Road, Derby, DE1 3TN Tel: (01332) 360884 Fax: (01332) 360885

Tjaden Ltd, 62a Chatsworth Road, London, E5 0LS Tel: (020) 8533 7234 Fax: (020) 8533 7234

Todd Herbert, Percys Lane, York, YO1 9TP Tel: (01904) 628676 Fax: (01904) 653328 E-mail: graham@htodd.co.uk

▶ Tom Croft Bolton Ltd, 6 Albert Street, Farnworth, Bolton, BL4 9HN Tel: (01204) 861368 Fax: (01204) 794391

▶ Total Electrical Ltd, Unit 7 Rose Way, Rochford, Essex, SS4 1LY Tel: (01702) 547744 Fax: (01702) 547741

▶ Total Security Installations Ltd, 3 Datapoint Business Centre, 6 South CR, London, E16 4TL Tel: (020) 7511 5555 Fax: (020) 7511 1384 E-mail: sales@tsi.uk.com

▶ Total Trade Services, Unit 1, Cefndy Road Employment Park, Cefndy Road, Rhyl, Clwyd, LL18 2HJ Tel: (01745) 360336

Traceman Fire Protection Consultants, 27 Leinster Road, Swinton, Manchester, M27 5YQ Tel: 0161-793 8448 Fax: 0161-794 2129 E-mail: enquiries@traceman.co.uk

▶ Trades Team Ltd, Greenlaw, Castle Douglas, Kirkcudbrightshire, DG7 2LH Tel: (01556) 504951

▶ Trattles & Rushforth Security Ltd, Faraday House, Sopwith Close, Preston Farm Industrial Estate, Stockton-on-Tees, Cleveland, TS18 3TT Tel: (01642) 604534 Fax: (01642) 677815 E-mail: ashleyday@trattles.com

Peter Tree Electrical Ltd, 79 Horley Road, Redhill, RH1 5AS Tel: (01737) 762168 Fax: (01737) 771435 E-mail: petertree@petertreeltd.co.uk

▶ Tremorfa Ltd, 5 Cyprus House, Pascal Close, St. Mellons, Cardiff, CF3 0LW Tel: (029) 2033 0000 Fax: (029) 2033 0029 E-mail: enquiries@tremorfar.com

Trilectric Ltd, 262-270 Field End Road, Ruislip, Middlesex, HA4 9NB Tel: (020) 8866 1611 Fax: (020) 8866 1655 E-mail: mainreception@trilectric.co.uk

▶ Trinity Electrical Services Ltd, St Johns House, Clyde Street, Bingley, West Yorkshire, BD16 4LD Tel: (01274) 551161

▶ Tucker Hammett Electrical, 4 Progress Way, Mid Suffolk Business Park, Eye, Suffolk, IP23 7HU Tel: (01379) 873009 Fax: (01379) 873179

Tyco, Jarrold Way, Bowthorpe Employment Area, Norwich, NR5 9JD Tel: (01603) 201201 Fax: (01603) 201333 E-mail: tycocontrolsystems.uk@tycoint.com

▶ Tyson L & Sons, Elland Road, Sowerby Bridge, West Yorkshire, HX6 4DB Tel: (01422) 823582 Fax: (01422) 823363

▶ Unit Two Security Ltd, 17 Hareleeshill Road, Larkhall, Lanarkshire, ML9 2EX Tel: (01698) 881885

▶ Unitech Electrical Ltd, Unit 4 Castlehill Industrial Estate, Carluke, Lanarkshire, ML8 5UF Tel: (01555) 752211 Fax: (01555) 772822

▶ Universal Security Systems Ltd, Mint Business Park, 41 Butchers Road, London, E16 1PW Tel: (020) 7511 8080

V G Willox & Building Contractor Ltd, Roadside Croft, Crimond, Fraserburgh, Aberdeenshire, AB43 8QD Tel: (01346) 532981 Fax: (01346) 532851

Vallectric Ltd, Sweet Street, Leeds, LS11 9DB Tel: 0113-242 3800 Fax: 0113-242 4960 E-mail: info@vallectric.co.uk

▶ Vallectric Hull Ltd, Unit 2, The Shine, St. Mark Street, Hull, HU8 7FB Tel: (01482) 324521 Fax: (01482) 587371

▶ Van Gaver Electrical Co. Ltd, 50 Bridgford Road, West Bridgford, Nottingham, NG2 6AP Tel: 0115-981 2820 Fax: 0115-945 5632 E-mail: mail@vangaverelectrical.co.uk

▶ Van Laun A E Ltd, 226 London Road, Portsmouth, PO2 9JQ Tel: (023) 9269 9081 Fax: (023) 9265 1798

▶ Victoria Electrical & Building Services Ltd, 82-84 Victoria Road, Glasgow, G42 7AA Tel: 0141-423 6122 Fax: 0141-422 1133

▶ Vivista Ltd, Methuen Park, Chippenham, Wiltshire, SN14 0TW Tel: (01249) 443777 Fax: (07002) 929999

B. Voles & Son Ltd, 279 Chiswick High Road, London, W4 4PU Tel: (020) 8994 0984 Fax: (020) 8747 8918 E-mail: mail@voles.co.uk

W C Martin & Co Ltd, Cumbernauld House, Cumbernauld, Glasgow, G67 3JG Tel: (01236) 868000 Fax: (01236) 868111

▶ W F Frost Services Ltd, Arundel Business Centre, 49 Station Road, Harold Wood, Romford, RM3 0BS Tel: (01708) 377002 Fax: (01708) 377149

W G Heath Electrical Services Ltd, 8 Pomphlett Farm Industrial Estate, Broxton Drive, Plymouth, PL9 7BG Tel: (01752) 480300 Fax: (01752) 480303 E-mail: heath@wgplymouth.ffnet.co.uk

W H K (Walton) Ltd, Walton Business Centre, 44-46 Terrace Road, Walton-on-Thames, Surrey, KT12 2SD Tel: (01932) 247979 Fax: (01932) 245948 E-mail: colin@whk.co.uk

▶ W J S Thomson, Riverside Industrial Estate, Newton Stewart, Wigtownshire, DG8 6EY Tel: (01671) 403467 Fax: (01671) 403642

▶ W K K Electrical Services, 35 The Cutts, Dunmurry, Belfast, BT17 9HN Tel: (028) 9030 8881 Fax: (028) 9030 8882

W L Sirman & Son Ltd, 145 Goldsworth Road, Woking, Surrey, GU21 6LS Tel: (01483) 768020 Fax: (01483) 740545

▶ W M B Installations Ltd, The Yard, Dorchester Road, Swinton, Manchester, M27 5NU Tel: 0161-793 6019 Fax: 0161-727 7067

▶ W Portsmouth & Co. Ltd, 69 Havelock Road, Luton, LU2 7PW Tel: (01582) 731517 Fax: (01582) 401920 E-mail: mail@wportsmouth.co.uk

▶ Walker Macleod Ltd, 8-36 Bulldale Street, Glasgow, G14 0NU Tel: 0141-954 0297 Fax: 0141-950 1351 E-mail: sales@walkermacleod.co.uk

▶ Walter J Parsons (Electrical Engineers) Ltd, 15 Heath Mill Lane, Birmingham, B9 4AE Tel: 0121-772 4524 Fax: 0121-766 8069 E-mail: dave@walterjparsons.com

C.T. Walters (Electrical) Ltd, Unit 4, Park End, Works Industrial Estate, Brackley, Northamptonshire, NN13 5LX Tel: (01869) 810047 Fax: (01869) 811103 E-mail: ctwalters@lineone.net

▶ Warmfloor Heating (Ireland) Ltd, Unit E11 Gortrush Industrial Estate, Great Northern Road, Omagh, County Tyrone, BT78 5LU Tel: (028) 8225 2288 Fax: (028) 8225 9515 E-mail: mail@warmfloor.ie

Warren F Electrical Ltd Electric Engineers, 10c6 Skerne Road Aycliffe Indust Estate, Aycliffe, Newton Aycliffe, County Durham, DL5 6EP Tel: (01325) 310322 Fax: (01325) 301075

▶ Waterman Gore Ltd, Cumbrae House, 15 Carlton Court, Glasgow, G5 9JP Tel: 0141-429 3386 Fax: 0141-429 6299

▶ Watson Electrical, Unit 1 Engine Shed Lane, Skipton, North Yorkshire, BD23 1UP Tel: (01756) 799661 Fax: (01756) 790332

Watson & May Ltd, 38b Pitshanger Lane, London, W5 1QY Tel: (020) 8997 3203 Fax: (020) 8997 3188 E-mail: wat.may@virgin.net

▶ Waveney Electrical Services, 115 Whapload Road, Lowestoft, Suffolk, NR32 1UL Tel: (01502) 561139 Fax: (01502) 560720

Weatherite Electrical Ltd, Weatherite House, Westgate Park, Tintagel Way, Aldridge, Walsall, WS9 8EX Tel: (01922) 741600 Fax: (01922) 741601 E-mail: sales@weatherite-electrical.com

▶ Weblight Lighting Contractors, 5 Central City Industrial Estate, Red Lane, Coventry, CV6 5RY Tel: (024) 7668 6620 Fax: (024) 7668 6080

▶ Weir & Mcquiston Scotland Ltd, 16 Netherdale Road, Netherton Industrial Estate, Wishaw, Lanarkshire, ML2 0ER Tel: (01698) 372113 Fax: (01698) 356924

▶ West Midlands Electrical, 17 High Street, West Bromwich, West Midlands, B70 6PP Tel: 0121-525 8919 Fax: 0121-553 1259

▶ Weston Electrical Services, Laurel House, 1 Station Road, Worle, Weston-super-Mare, Avon, BS22 6AR Tel: (01934) 516500 Fax: (01934) 516400

Wheeler's (Westbury) Ltd, 31D Link Road, West Wilts Trading Estate, Westbury, Wiltshire, BA13 4JB Tel: (01373) 823755 Fax: (01373) 858045 E-mail: info@wheelers-westbury.co.uk

Whesco Ltd, Aughton, Collingbourne Kingston, Marlborough, Wiltshire, SN8 3SA Tel: (01264) 850136 Fax: (01264) 850136 E-mail: mail@whesc-ltd.co.uk

▶ Whitecode Ltd, Highfield House, 2 West Hill, Dartford, DA1 2EW Tel: (01322) 289977 Fax: (01322) 289988

Whitehouse Electrical Ltd, Brickheath Road, Wolverhampton, WV1 2SR Tel: (01902) 451961 Fax: (01902) 870971 E-mail: peter@coswhielec.co.uk

Whittaker Bros Ltd, 31 Firs Street, Dudley, West Midlands, DY2 7DW Tel: (01384) 252112 Fax: (01384) 232541

Wholesale Lighting, 34-41 White Lion Street, London, N1 9PQ Tel: (020) 7278 8993 Fax: (020) 7833 4762 E-mail: sales@ryness.co.uk

▶ Wil Lec Electrical Contractors Ltd, 246 Corporation Road, Grimsby, South Humberside, DN31 2QB Tel: (01472) 241881 Fax: (01472) 241884

▶ Wildblood Electrical Contractors, Station Road, Heathfield, East Sussex, TN21 8LB Tel: (01435) 864655 Fax: (01435) 865772 E-mail: sales@wildblood.com

Willard Conservation, Leigh Road, Chichester, West Sussex, PO19 8TS Tel: (01243) 776928 Fax: (01243) 533845 E-mail: willard@willard.dial.iql.co.uk

▶ Williams Electrical Services Northern, 11 Gilpin Street, Sheffield, S6 3BL Tel: 0114-249 3012 Fax: 0114-249 3013 E-mail: business@williamselectrical.com

Williamson's Electrical Co. Ltd, 44b The Gardens, London, SE22 9PZ Tel: (020) 8693 1634 Fax: (020) 8693 5964

▶ Wilson Andrew H Electrical Ltd, Hatston Industrial Estate, Scotts Road, Kirkwall, Orkney, KW15 1RE Tel: (01856) 873015

Wilson Electrical Distributors Ltd, 2 Balfour Business Centre, Balfour Road, Southall, Middlesex, UB2 5BD Tel: (020) 8574 4218 Fax: (020) 8843 1048 E-mail: chris@lmob.co.uk

▶ Wingate Electrical plc, 70 Jessie Street, Glasgow, G42 0PG Tel: 0141-422 1800 Fax: 0141-422 1822

▶ Wingate Electrical plc, Unit C 25 Copperfield Street, London, SE1 0EN Tel: (020) 7401 3856 Fax: (020) 7928 1547

▶ Wood View Builders Ltd, 12 Carron Place, Kelvin Industrial Estate, East Kilbride, Glasgow, G75 0YL Tel: (01355) 612560

▶ Woodland Site Services Ltd, Unit 20 Optima Park, Thames Road, Dartford, DA1 4QX Tel: (01322) 555085 Fax: (01322) 520545 E-mail: enquiries@woodlands-ss.co.uk

Worster & Hounslow, 2 Oaklands Avenue, Watford, WD19 4LW Tel: (01923) 239762 Fax: (01923) 239762

▶ Worthing & District TV Ltd, 147 Tarring Road, Worthing, West Sussex, BN11 4HE Tel: (01903) 201925 Fax: (01903) 208420

Wright Guard Security Systems & Electrical, 2 Columbia Avenue, Mansfield, Nottinghamshire, NG18 3LD Tel: (01623) 645808

Michael Wright Ltd, PO Box 469, High Wycombe, Buckinghamshire, HP14 3GL Tel: (01491) 638274

▶ Wright & Owen Ec Ltd, 16 Watson Place, Plymouth, PL4 9QN Tel: (01752) 222133 Fax: (01752) 226909

▶ Wyre Electric, 31 Gilgal, Stourport-on-Severn, Worcestershire, DY13 9AJ Tel: (07973) 742085 Fax: (01299) 871765

▶ Zicam Intergrated Security Ltd, Cougar House, 4 Firs Street, Dudley, West Midlands, DY2 7DN Tel: (01384) 344999 Fax: (01384) 344998

ELECTRICAL CONTROL CABLES

Denmans Electrical Wholesalers Ltd, Unit 10 Pages Industrial Park, Eden Way, Leighton Buzzard, Bedfordshire, LU7 4TZ Tel: (01525) 374666 Fax: (01525) 852662 E-mail: denmans@theleightonbuzzard.freeserve.co.uk

Denmans Electrical Wholesalers Ltd, Hickman Avenue, Wolverhampton, WV1 2XD Tel: (01902) 453551 Fax: (01902) 456666 E-mail: wolverhampton@denmans.co.uk

Devondale Electrical Distributors, Unit 3 24 Marsh Green Road West, Marsh Barton Trading Estate, Exeter, EX2 8PN Tel: (01392) 667474 Fax: (01392) 420037 E-mail: sales@devondale.net

Electrical Supplies Bolton Ltd, 68 Chorley Old Road, Bolton, BL1 3AE Tel: (01204) 362959 Fax: (01204) 362503

Nexans Logistics, Llewellyn House, Chesney Wold, Bleak Hall, Milton Keynes, MK6 1NE Tel: (01908) 250850 Fax: (01908) 250851 E-mail: info@nexans.co.uk

ELECTRICAL CONTROL PANEL ASSEMBLY

Argosafe Ltd, Unit 11 Dawsons Lane, Barwell, Leicester, LE9 8BE Tel: (01455) 844801 Fax: (01455) 850280 E-mail: argosafe@btconnect.com

Ashtronics Ltd, 119 Meldreth Road, Whaddon, Royston, Hertfordshire, SG8 5RS Tel: (01223) 208308 Fax: (01223) 208308 E-mail: ashtronics@aol.com

▶ Customised Control panel Services, 3 York Close, Gillow Heath, Stoke-On-Trent, ST8 6SE Tel: 01782 523673 Fax: 01782 523673 E-mail: stuart.booth700@ntlworld.com

D Benson & Co. Ltd, Normanton Industrial Estate, Normanton, West Yorkshire, WF6 1QS Tel: (01924) 894162 Fax: (01924) 896518 E-mail: info@dbensoncontrols.co.uk

▶ E I S Axon Ltd, Unit 2, Crusader Industrial Estate, Stirling Road, Cressex Business Park, High Wycombe, Buckinghamshire, HP12 3ST Tel: (01494) 511558 Fax: (01494) 449351 E-mail: paul@eis-axon.co.uk

Fenton Industrial Ltd, 291 Edge Lane, Droylsden, Manchester, M43 6BS Tel: 0161-370 1568 Fax: 0161-370 9116 E-mail: info@fentonindustrial.co.uk

▶ Harnesscom, Unit 3 King Street Buildings, King Street, Enderby, Leicester, LE19 4NT Tel: 0116-284 1050 Fax: 0116-284 1048 E-mail: sales@harnesscom.co.uk

P.S. Higgins Electrical Services, Clarence House, 30 Queen Street, Market Drayton, Shropshire, TF9 1PS Tel: (01630) 655416 Fax: (01630) 658415 E-mail: info@pshiggins.co.uk

J K Control Systems Ltd, Unit 14 Kernick Industrial Estate, Penryn, Cornwall, TR10 9EP Tel: (01326) 378432 Fax: (01326) 378423 E-mail: info@jkcontrolsystems.co.uk

▶ P R Automation Ltd, Quality House, Fisher Street, Dudley Port, Tipton, West Midlands, DY4 8XE Tel: 0121-557 4311 Fax: 0121-557 4314

Pneutrol Ireland Ltd, 5 Caulside Drive, Antrim, BT41 2DU Tel: (028) 9448 1800 Fax: (028) 9448 1801 E-mail: info@pneutrol.com

▶ RJS Ascot Ltd, 8 Beechwood Close, Ascot, Berkshire, SL5 8QJ Tel: (01344) 890442 Fax: (01344) 883685 E-mail: rjsascot@aol.com

ELECTRICAL CONTROL PANELS TO SPECIFICATION

Ashtronics Ltd, 119 Meldreth Road, Whaddon, Royston, Hertfordshire, SG8 5RS Tel: (01223) 208308 Fax: (01223) 208308 E-mail: ashtronics@aol.com

Cord Controls Ltd, 29 Wigston Street, Countesthorpe, Leicester, LE8 5RP Tel: 0116-277 7396 Fax: 0116-277 7396 E-mail: cord.controls@btclick.com

Davies Control Systems, Unit 20 South Pontypool Industrial Park, Panteg Way, New Inn, Pontypool, Gwent, NP4 0LS Tel: (01495) 764094 Fax: (01495) 756237 E-mail: info@daviescontrolsystems.co.uk

Eddingbrook Ltd, Valley Works, Bacup Road, Todmorden, Lancashire, OL14 7PJ Tel: (01706) 814854 Fax: (01706) 815023 E-mail: info@eddingbrook.co.uk

Frostechnic, Power Park, Station Approach, Banbury, Oxfordshire, OX16 5AB Tel: (01295) 266500 Fax: (01295) 275434 E-mail: info@frostechnic.com

ELECTRICAL CONTROL SYSTEM COMPONENTS

Belmos Electrical Services Ltd, 19 Hagmill Road, East Shawhead Industrial Estate, Coatbridge, Lanarkshire, ML5 4XD Tel: (01236) 443382 Fax: (01236) 443384 E-mail: belmos@btconnect.com

ELECTRICAL DISCHARGE MACHINING (EDM) DRILLING

Electro-Discharge Ltd, Unit 14, Bagley Industrial Pk, Northfield Rd, Netherton, Dudley, West Midlands, DY2 9DY Tel: (01384) 238451 Fax: (01384) 245971 E-mail: ron@electro-discharge.co.uk

Precision 2000 Ltd, Princesway, Team Valley Trading Estate, Gateshead, Tyne & Wear, NE11 0TU Tel: 0191-420 0057 Fax: 0191-423 0100 E-mail: sales@precision2000.co.uk

ELECTRICAL DISCHARGE MACHINING (EDM) WIRE

▶ Primatec Edm Ltd, 6 Walkers Lane Lambourn, Hungerford, Berkshire, RG17 8YE Tel: (01488) 72766 Fax: (0870) 4602625 E-mail: m.schmitt@primatec-edm.de

ELECTRICAL DISCHARGE MACHINING (EDM)/SPECIALIST SERVICES

D R Case & Son, 5 Lady Bee Marina Industrial Units, Albion Street, Southwick, Brighton, BN42 4EG Tel: (01273) 870850 Fax: (01273) 870855 E-mail: colin.case@btconnect.com

Di-Spark Ltd, Unit 3B Wessex Gate, Portsmouth Road, Horndean, Waterlooville, Hampshire, PO8 9LP Tel: (023) 9259 6338 Fax: (023) 9259 4077 E-mail: sales@dispsrks.co.uk

ELECTRICAL DISTRIBUTION BOARDS

Britannic Engineering Co Ltd, The Old Bakery, Market St, Charlbury, Chipping Norton, Oxfordshire, OX7 3PH Tel: (01608) 810332 Fax: (01608) 811566 E-mail: office@britannickengineering.co.uk

Kane Engineering Ltd, Glenford Road, Newtownards, County Down, BT23 4AU Tel: (028) 9181 4465 Fax: (028) 9181 8900 E-mail: info@kane-engineering.co.uk

Mardix Automatic Controls Ltd, Westmorland Business Park, Gilthwaiterigg Lane, Kendal, Cumbria, LA9 6NS Tel: (01539) 720161 Fax: (01539) 724384 E-mail: switchgear@mardix.co.uk

Neesham Controls Ltd, Twerton Mill, Lower Bristol Road, Bath, BA2 1EW Tel: (01225) 402140 Fax: (01225) 448154

Protek Ltd, Phoenix House, Phoenix Road, Hawks Green, Cannock, Staffordshire, WS11 7LR Tel: (01543) 467575 Fax: (01543) 462370 E-mail: sales@protekuk.co.uk

ELECTRICAL DISTRIBUTION EQUIPMENT

▶ B D C Ltd, Marshall Stevens Way, Trafford Park, Manchester, M17 1PP Tel: 0161-848 9988

▶ I D E Systems, Unit 6, Swaffield Park Hyssop Close, Cannock, Staffordshire, WS11 7FU Tel: (01543) 574111 Fax: (01543) 571444 E-mail: sales@idesystems.co.uk

ELECTRICAL DISTRIBUTION EQUIPMENT EXPORT MERCHANTS OR AGENTS

B.E.S (Europe) Ltd, 3 Oriel Court, The Green, Twickenham, TW2 5AG Tel: (020) 8898 8396 Fax: (020) 8898 8494 E-mail: info@beseurope.com

ELECTRICAL DISTRIBUTION EQUIPMENT EXPORT MERCHANTS OR AGENTS – *continued*

Export Africa, 1 Terminus Industrial Estate, Durham Street, Portsmouth, PO1 1NR Tel: (023) 9282 3590 Fax: (023) 9281 2038 E-mail: sales@rundleholdings.co.uk

Powernets UK Ltd, 32 Eastlands, Stafford, ST17 9BB Tel: (01785) 242235 Fax: (01785) 612261 E-mail: gbr@powernets.com

Rabo Merchants Ltd, 267 Bearwood Road, Smethwick, West Midlands, B66 4NA Tel: (01386) 700193 Fax: 0121-429 4993 E-mail: reception@rabo.co.uk

ELECTRICAL DISTRIBUTION SYSTEM INSTALLATION

B P D Building Services, 7 Sunnyside Grove, Ashton-under-Lyne, Lancashire, OL6 6TN Tel: 0161-612 7514 E-mail: paul@bpd-ltd.com

ELECTRICAL DRIVES

A Davies & Sons Sales Ltd, Alpha Works, Old Moor Road, Bredbury, Stockport, Cheshire, SK6 2QF Tel: 0161-430 5297 Fax: 0161-494 2758

Gibbons Drive Systems Ltd, Woodrolfe Road, Tollesbury, Maldon, Essex, CM9 8RY Tel: (01621) 868138 Fax: (01621) 868188 E-mail: sales@gibbonsdrives.co.uk

Motech Control Ltd, Unit 14, Lloyds Court, Manor Royal, Crawley, West Sussex, RH10 9QX Tel: (01293) 440710 Fax: (01293) 440711 E-mail: sales@motech.co.uk

Parker Hannifin P.L.C., Arena Business Park, Holyrood Close, Poole, Dorset, BH17 7FJ Tel: (01202) 699000 Fax: (01202) 606301 E-mail: sales.digiplan@parker.com

ELECTRICAL EARTH LEAKAGE OR INSULATION MONITORING EQUIPMENT

Electrical Design & Manufacturing Co. Ltd, Station Street, Whetstone, Leicester, LE8 6JS Tel: 0116-286 2165

Megacon Controls Ltd, 21 Oldends Industrial Estate, Oldends, Stonehouse, Gloucestershire, GL10 3RQ Tel: (01453) 824471 Fax: (01453) 825234 E-mail: sales@megacon.co.uk

Spirol Industries Ltd, 17 Princewood Road, Earlstrees Industrial Estate, Corby, Northamptonshire, NN17 4ET Tel: (01536) 444800 Fax: (01536) 203415 E-mail: info@spirol.co.uk

Starkstrom (London) Ltd, 256 Field End Road, Eastcote, Ruislip, Middlesex, HA4 9UW Tel: (020) 8868 3732 Fax: (020) 8868 3736 E-mail: sales@starkstrom.com

ELECTRICAL EARTHING EQUIPMENT

A N Wallis, Greasley Street, Nottingham, NG6 8NG Tel: 0115-927 1721 Fax: 0115-875 6630 E-mail: info@an-wallis.com

Erico Europa GB Ltd, 52 Milford Road, Reading, RG1 8LJ Tel: 0118-958 8386 Fax: 0118-959 4856

W.J. Furse Ltd, Wilford Road, Nottingham, NG2 1EB Tel: 0115-964 3800 Fax: 0115-986 0538 E-mail: sales@furse.com

Megar Ltd, Archcliffe Road, Dover, Kent, CT17 9EN Tel: (01304) 502100 Fax: (01304) 241491 E-mail: uksales@megger.com

Tyco Electronics Ltd Bowthorpe Emp, Unit 8 A Freshfield Industrial Estate, Stevenson Road, Brighton, BN2 0DF Tel: (01273) 692591 Fax: (01273) 601741 E-mail: craig.sutton@bowthorpe-emp.com

ELECTRICAL EMERGENCY BREAKDOWN SERVICES

P.S. Higgins Electrical Services, Clarence House, 30 Queen Street, Market Drayton, Shropshire, TF9 1PS Tel: (01630) 655416 Fax: (01630) 658415 E-mail: info@pshiggins.co.uk

Ringwood Machinery Spares, 16 College Road, Ringwood, Hampshire, BH24 1NX Tel: (01425) 479459

ELECTRICAL ENERGY MONITORING EQUIPMENT

Socomec Ltd, Knowl Piece, Wilbury Way, Hitchin, Hertfordshire, SG4 0TY Tel: (01462) 440033 Fax: (01462) 431143 E-mail: sales@socomec.com

ELECTRICAL ENERGY SAVING EQUIPMENT

Enercom Ltd, 122 High Street, Earl Shilton, Leicester, LE9 7LQ Tel: (01455) 840100 Fax: (01455) 840200 E-mail: mike.garlick@enercom.co.uk

F E C Services Ltd, National Agricultural Centre, Stoneleigh Park, Kenilworth, Warwickshire, CV8 2LS Tel: (024) 7669 6512 Fax: (024) 7669 6360 E-mail: sales@farmenergy.com

▶ Ironteam Ltd, 20 Knightsbridge Drive, Nuthall, Nottingham, NG16 1RD Tel: 0115-975 1378 Fax: 0115-975 1378 E-mail: enquiries@ironteam.co.uk

▶ Phoenix Power, 323 Goring Road, Goring-by-Sea, Worthing, West Sussex, BN12 4NX Tel: (01903) 248999 Fax: (01903) 249555 E-mail: sales@phoenixpower.net

ELECTRICAL ENGINEERING DESIGN

Dowding & Mills Engineering Services Ltd, Colwall Street, Sheffield, S9 3WP Tel: 0114-244 6661 Fax: 0114-243 6782 E-mail: engineering.sheffield@dowdingandmills.com

▶ Nodal Engineering Ltd, Riverside House, Riverside Drive, Aberdeen, AB11 7LH Tel: 01224 224360 Fax: 01224 224301 E-mail: info@nodalengineering.com

▶ TTS, Celect House, 12a Fairbairn Road, Livingston, West Lothian, EH54 6TS Tel: (01506) 464448 Fax: (01506) 464430 E-mail: web@ttsce.co.uk

ELECTRICAL ENGINEERING RECRUITMENT

▶ Construction Consultancy Services Ltd, 3 Wellington Park, Belfast, BT9 6DJ Tel: (028) 9092 3360 Fax: (028) 9038 2451 E-mail: info@ccsni.com

▶ E T S Technical Sales, Phoenix House, Phoenix Way, Cirencester, Gloucestershire, GL7 1QG Tel: (0870) 0702246 E-mail: mark@ets-technical-sales.co.uk

▶ The Engineer, St Giles House, 50 Poland Street, London, W1F 7AX Tel: (020) 7970 4114 Fax: 0207 9704193 E-mail: matt.comley@centaur.co.uk

▶ Kelly Technical Services, 21 St Petersgate, Stockport, Cheshire, SK1 1EB Tel: 0161-429 9853 Fax: 0161-429 9867 E-mail: ker_manchester@kellyservices.co.uk

ELECTRICAL ENGINEERING TRAINING

Flite Electronics Ltd, Church House Farm, Clewer Hill, Waltham Chase, Southampton, SO32 2LN Tel: (01489) 892422 Fax: (01489) 897929 E-mail: sales@flite.co.uk

▶ Institute Of Applied Technology, Mitchelston Industrial Estate, Kirkcaldy, Fife, KY1 3LT Tel: (01592) 568500 Fax: (01592) 223601

▶ Prospects Business Training Ltd, Prospects House, 10 Fairfax Drive, Westcliff-on-Sea, Essex, SS0 9AR Tel: (01702) 214100 Fax: (01702) 390488 E-mail: jane_trent@prospectscollege.co.uk

Technique Training, Midland Court, Barlborough Links, Chesterfield, Derbyshire, S43 4UL Tel: (01246) 813703 Fax: (01246) 571090 E-mail: mark@techniquetraining.co.uk

ELECTRICAL ENGINEERS, INDUSTRIAL OR ENGINEERING SERVICES

A A Duncan Biggar Ltd, 16a Broughton Road, Biggar, Lanarkshire, ML12 6HA Tel: (01899) 220170 Fax: (01899) 220170

A L P Electrical Ltd, 70 St. Marks Road, Maidenhead, Berkshire, SL6 6DW Tel: (01628) 633998 Fax: (01628) 760981 E-mail: alp@alpelectrical.com

A L Technical Ltd, 2 Woodston Business Centre, Shrewsbury Avenue, Peterborough, PE2 7EF Tel: (01733) 390123 Fax: (01733) 394933 E-mail: altechnical@yahoo.co.uk

A S K Electrical Ltd, 10-14 Victoria Road, Bangor, County Down, BT20 5EX Tel: (028) 9127 0308 Fax: (028) 9145 8196 E-mail: info@askelectrical.com

Adair & Milliken Ltd, 1 Parkside Gardens, Belfast, BT15 3AW Tel: (028) 9074 8271 Fax: (028) 9075 1064 E-mail: adairandmilliken@btconnect.com

Advantech Controls Ltd, Hoggs Park House, Chilsworthy, Holsworthy, Devon, EX22 7BL Tel: (01409) 259254 Fax: (01409) 259253 E-mail: jorge@advantech-controls.co.uk

Alex Bonar & Co. Ltd, Pennybridge Industrial Estate, Ballymena, County Antrim, BT42 3HB Tel: (028) 2565 2449 Fax: (028) 2564 1838 E-mail: info@alexanderbonar.com

All Electrical Services Ltd, North Mace House, Viaduct Road, Cardiff, CF15 9XF Tel: (029) 2081 0274 Fax: (029) 2081 0282 E-mail: info@allelectricalserviceswales.com

Alpha Electrics Ltd, Unit 11, 158 Tithe St, Leicester, LE5 4BN Tel: 0116-276 8686 Fax: 0116-276 6776 E-mail: info@alphaelectrics.com

Alstom Combined Cycles International Ltd, Booths Hall, Chelford Road, Knutsford, Cheshire, WA16 8GE Tel: (01565) 758000 Fax: (01565) 758001

▶ Anstee Ware Ltd, Unit 59a Thornhill Industrial Estate, South Marston, Swindon, SN3 4TA Tel: (01793) 832828 Fax: (01793) 831955

Appliance Care Ltd, 1 Swallow Units, Alphinbrook Road, Marsh Barton Trading Estate, Exeter, EX2 8QF Tel: (0871) 2006625 Fax: (01392) 258302 E-mail: steve@appliancecare.tv

Astelle Electrical Contractors Ltd, Mayflower House, 3 Chapel St, Billericay, Essex, CM12 9LT Tel: (01277) 651320 Fax: (01277) 630608

Austick Construction Ltd, West Park View, Dudley, Cramlington, Northumberland, NE23 7AA Tel: 0191-250 2425 Fax: 0191-250 2450 E-mail: austickconstruction@hotmail.co.uk

R. Baker (Electrical) Ltd, Evans Road, Speke, Liverpool, L24 9PB Tel: 0151-486 6760 Fax: 0151-448 1225 E-mail: mail@rbaker.co.uk

Barr Electrical Ltd, 1 Ladywell Road, Motherwell, Lanarkshire, ML1 3JA Tel: (01698) 263231 Fax: (01698) 263231

Barr R & T Electrical Ltd, 142-158 Pittencrieff Street, Dunfermline, Fife, KY12 8AN Tel: (01383) 722096 Fax: (01383) 739226 E-mail: rtbarr@hotmail.co.uk

Beaven & Sons Ltd, 183 Westgate Street, Gloucester, GL1 2RN Tel: (01452) 314384 Fax: (01452) 300195

Blackbourne Electrical Co. Ltd, Springfarm Industrial Estate, Antrim, BT41 4NZ Tel: (028) 9446 4231 Fax: (028) 9446 7109 E-mail: bec@karl.co.uk

Blakley Electrics Ltd, 1 Thomas Road, Crayford, Dartford, DA1 4GA Tel: (0845) 0740084 Fax: (0845) 0740085 E-mail: sales@blakley.co.uk

▶ Bourne Gas Bournemouth Ltd, Unit 3 Broom Road Business Park, Broom Road, Poole, Dorset, BH12 4PA Tel: (01202) 716665 E-mail: gas@bournebg.ltd.uk

Bradmeres Engineering Ltd, Unit 42 Wilford Industrial Estate, Ruddington Lane, Wilford, Nottingham, NG11 7EP Tel: 0115-981 7814 Fax: 0115-981 9782 E-mail: bradmeres@btconnect.com

Buchanan & Curwen (Leatherhead) Ltd, Fairfield Works, Upper Fairfield Road, Leatherhead, Surrey, KT22 7HJ Tel: (01372) 373481 Fax: (01372) 377458 E-mail: buchanans@b-and-c.co.uk

▶ Building Environmental Services P.L.C., The Church House, Kneesworth Street, Royston, Hertfordshire, SG8 5AB Tel: (01763) 248752

C & M Electrical Contracts & Maintenance Ltd, 2f Vaughan Court, Stapylton Street, Middlesbrough, Cleveland, TS6 7BJ Tel: (01642) 440640 Fax: (01642) 460595 E-mail: jd@cmelec.co.uk

C P C Engineers Ltd, Adderley Road, Market Drayton, Shropshire, TF9 3SW Tel: (01630) 652904 Fax: (01630) 652904

Cannon Electrical Contractors (Manchester) Ltd, Unit 2 Derwent Street Industrial Estate, Odsall Lane, Salford, M5 4RE Tel: 0161-832 7320 Fax: 0161-839 4298 E-mail: cannonelectrical@btopenworld.com

Capelrig Ltd, Tern Place, Denmore Road, Bridge of Don, Aberdeen, AB23 8JX Tel: (01224) 702211 Fax: (01224) 702219 E-mail: sales@capelrig.co.uk

▶ Central Electrical Installations Ltd, Bradley Mill, Bradley Lane, Newton Abbot, Devon, TQ12 1NF Tel: (01626) 330054 Fax: (01626) 331915 E-mail: devon@central-electrical.com

Charles Andrews, The Corner House, Fourth Avenue, Trafford Park, Manchester, M17 1DB Tel: 0161-848 9955 Fax: 0161-848 9966 E-mail: info@charlesandrews.co.uk

Clark Electrical Industries Ltd, 1e North Crescent, London, E16 4TG Tel: (020) 7474 7404 Fax: (020) 7473 1961 E-mail: enquries@ceiltd.co.uk

Cleveland Electrical Co. Ltd, 50 Park Lane, Liverpool, L1 8HE Tel: 0151-709 6883 Fax: 0151-709 8861 E-mail: enquiries@cleveland-electrical.co.uk

Colchester Rewind & Repairs Ltd, Moss Road, Stanway, Colchester, CO3 0LE Tel: (01206) 768886 Fax: (01206) 768915 E-mail: sales@colchesterrewinds.co.uk

Control Electrics Leicester Ltd, 30 Fowke Street, Rothley, Leicester, LE7 7PJ Tel: 0116-237 4233 E-mail: enquire@controlelectrics.co.uk

Control System Supplies, Oaktrees, Croxton, Stafford, ST21 6PF Tel: (01630) 620355 Fax: (01630) 620377

Cottrell Electrical Services Ltd, 276-278 Smithdown Road, Liverpool, L15 5AJ Tel: 0151-733 5100 Fax: 0151-734 4457 E-mail: sales@cottrellelectrical.co.uk

Cranford Controls Systems Ltd, Unit 3 Pattenden La Buis Centre, Marden, Tonbridge, Kent, TN12 9QS Tel: (01622) 833300 Fax: (01622) 833311 E-mail: sales@cranfordcontrol.co.uk

Crosshall Engineering Ltd, 1 Wellington Street, Liverpool, L3 6JH Tel: 0151-207 4292 Fax: 0151-298 1447 E-mail: sales@crosshall.com

Crown House Technologies, Off Phoenix Way, Garngoch Industrial Estate, Gorseinon, Swansea, SA4 9WF Tel: (01792) 224100 Fax: (01792) 224101

Crusher Electrical Engineers, 120 Yapham Road, Pocklington, York, YO42 2DY Tel: (01759) 302652 Fax: (01759) 302680 E-mail: bruceluf c@aol.com

CSS Ltd, Road Three, Winsford Industrial Estate, Winsford, Cheshire, CW7 3PD Tel: (01606) 861809 Fax: (01606) 559337 E-mail: sales@chemicalsupport.co.uk

D B Brooks Electrical Engineers Ltd, Sinclair Close, Heanor, Derbyshire, DE75 7SP Tel: (01773) 763444 Fax: (01773) 530332 E-mail: admin@dbbrooks.co.uk

D B Controls Ltd, 9 Station Road, Adwick-Le-Street, Doncaster, South Yorkshire, DN6 7BE Tel: (01302) 330837 Fax: (01302) 724731 E-mail: sales@dbcontrols.co.uk

D E P E Breaden Electrical Ltd, 396 Finchley Road, London, NW2 2HR Tel: (020) 7435 1304 Fax: (020) 7435 0194

D H Morris & Co, Bellfield Street, Dundee, DD1 5DY Tel: (01382) 229691 Fax: (01382) 202621 E-mail: dhmorris@dhmdundee.fsnet.co.uk

Davis Hudson & Co. Ltd, 17 Bickford Road, Birmingham, B6 7EE Tel: 0121-327 0020 Fax: 0121-328 5649 E-mail: electricians@davishudson.co.uk

Daybury Electrical Services Ltd, Coppice Trading Estate, Kidderminster, Worcestershire, DY11 7QY Tel: (01299) 822070 Fax: (01562) 829747 E-mail: sales@daybury.co.uk

Deebridge Electrical Engineers, Craigshaw Road, West Tullos Industrial Estate, Aberdeen, AB12 3AR Tel: (01224) 871548 Fax: (01224) 899910 E-mail: info@deebridge.co.uk

Denray Cables & Controls, Edwards House, 327 Whapload Road, Lowestoft, Suffolk, NR32 1UL Tel: (01502) 516971 Fax: (01502) 537045

Design Installation Service Electrical Ltd, P O Box 137, Cheltenham, Gloucestershire, GL53 7ZF Tel: (01242) 533100 Fax: (01242) 221187

▶ Dodd Group, Unit 8-9 Gate Centre, Bredbury Park Way, Bredbury, Stockport, Cheshire, SK6 2SN Tel: 0161-406 1720 Fax: 0161-406 1729

Doddgroup Eastern Ltd, Oldmedow Road, King's Lynn, Norfolk, PE30 4LB Tel: (01553) 772423 Fax: (01553) 691343 E-mail: kings-lynn@doddgroup.com

Dowding & Mills Engineering Services Ltd, Colwall Street, Sheffield, S9 3WP Tel: 0114-244 6661 Fax: 0114-243 6782 E-mail: engineering.sheffield@dowdingandmills.com

Dowding & Mills Southern Ltd, 24-26 White Post Lane, London, E9 5EP Tel: (020) 8985 8351 Fax: (020) 8985 9615 E-mail: engineering.london@dowdingandmills.com

Dunham Engineering Services Ltd, The Burton Business Park, Hudson Road, Leeds, LS9 7DN Tel: 0113-248 4422 Fax: 0113-235 0809 E-mail: info@dunhamengineering.co.uk

E E P Electrical, Crondal Road, Exhall, Coventry, CV7 9NH Tel: (024) 7636 3010 Fax: (024) 7636 5182

E H Hornsby Electrical Engineers Ltd, Kings Hall Works, Kings Hall Road, Beckenham, Kent, BR3 1LN Tel: (020) 8778 7900 Fax: (020) 8778 4058 E-mail: ehhltd@btconnect.com

Edmundson Rickards Electrical, 30 Garrett Road, Lynx Trading Estate, Yeovil, Somerset, BA20 2TJ Tel: (01935) 472727 Fax: (01935) 472010 E-mail: mail@spectrumelectrical.co.uk

Edwards Engineering (Perth) Ltd, Glenearn Road, Perth, PH2 0NJ Tel: (01738) 627101 Fax: (01738) 630769 E-mail: mail@edwardsengineering.co.uk

Ergro Mechanical Services, Wallgrove House, Hooley Lane, Redhill, RH1 6DG Tel: (01737) 770001 Fax: (01737) 771900 E-mail: info@ergro.co.uk

Estil Ltd, Charlotte Street, Dudley, West Midlands, DY1 1TD Tel: (01384) 243643 Fax: (01384) 243644E-mail: sales@estil.co.uk

Evante Fitness Ltd, 71-73 High Street North, Dunstable, Bedfordshire, LU6 1JF Tel: (01582) 477600 Fax: (01582) 471366

Fire Systems Ltd, Station House, 5 Ridsdale Road, London, SE20 8AG Tel: (020) 8659 7235 Fax: (020) 8659 7237 E-mail: enquiries@firesystems.co.uk

Francis Chambers & Co., Taylors Lane, Parkgate, Rotherham, South Yorkshire, S62 6EE Tel: (01709) 522175 Fax: (01709) 522944 E-mail: fcco@freenetname.co.uk

Frank Bundy Electrical Engineers, 2 Darwin Crescent, Plymouth, PL3 6DX Tel: (01752) 667212 Fax: (01752) 667212

G E Oil & Gas, Badentoy Crescent, Badentoy Park, Aberdeen, AB12 4YD Tel: (01224) 785100 Fax: (01224) 785120

G K Littlemore Electrical Ltd, Contact House, Ditton Road, Widnes, Cheshire, WA8 0TH Tel: 0151-420 8022 Fax: 0151-420 4260 E-mail: gklittlemore@btconnect.com

Gemma Group Ltd, Grove Road, Cosham, Portsmouth, PO6 1LX Tel: (023) 9221 0015 Fax: (023) 9221 0058 E-mail: gemma@dial.pipex.com

Gibbons Electrical Services, 18 Helford Close, Worcester, WR5 1NB Tel: (01905) 356061

John Girvan & Sons Ltd, 26 Wellington Square, Ayr, KA7 1HH Tel: (01292) 267243 Fax: (01292) 611085 E-mail: enquiries@jgirvan.co.uk

GK Maintenance, Leamore Industrial Estate, 8 Wall End Close, Walsall, WS2 7PH Tel: (01922) 479462 Fax: (01922) 404842 E-mail: staff@gkmaintenance.co.uk

ELECTRICAL ENGINEERS, INDUSTRIAL OR ENGINEERING SERVICES – *continued*

John Godden, Forge Lane, Stoke-on-Trent, ST1 5NP Tel: (01782) 204224 Fax: (01782) 283502 E-mail: stoke@rexelsenate.co.uk

Gomer Electrical Ltd, Alfred Cook Building, Canal Parade, Cardiff, CF10 5RD Tel: (029) 2022 8384 Fax: (029) 2082 1000 E-mail: khill@gomer-electrical.co.uk

Goodmarriott & Hursthouse Ltd, Hooton Street, Nottingham, NG3 5GL Tel: 0115-950 5100 Fax: 0115-958 1200E-mail: mail@gandh.co.uk

H & L Sims, Unit 1-2 Business Park, Oldfield Lane, Wisbech, Cambridgeshire, PE13 2RJ Tel: (01945) 583682 Fax: (01945) 463754 E-mail: les4154s@aol.com

H S Harbon & Sons Ltd, Gordon Street, Doncaster, South Yorkshire, DN1 1RS Tel: (01302) 361140 Fax: (01302) 325745 E-mail: peter@harbon.co.uk

Haden Young Ltd, 11 Britannia Road, Patchway, Bristol, BS34 5TD Tel: 0117-969 3911 Fax: 0117-979 8711 E-mail: bristol@hadenyoung.co.uk

Heeley Installations Ltd, 202 Whitehall Road, Drighlington, Bradford, West Yorkshire, BD11 1AU Tel: 0113-285 2679 Fax: 0113-285 2762

Hilton Building Services Ltd, Waterway St West, Nottingham, NG2 3AD Tel: 0115-986 1221 Fax: 0115-986 6870 E-mail: sales@hiltons.co.uk

Hinton Electrical Services, 4 Trem Cinmel, Towyn, Abergele, Clwyd, LL22 9NJ Tel: (01745) 338019 Fax: (01745) 338088 E-mail: mail@hintons.co.uk

Humber Electrical Engineering Co. Ltd, 45-46 Portland Place, Hull, HU2 8QP Tel: (01482) 323042 Fax: (01482) 326811 E-mail: info@humberelectrical.com

Hyde Windings Ltd, Westbury Street, Hyde, Cheshire, SK14 4QP Tel: 0161-368 1468 Fax: 0161-367 9454

I D Howitt Ltd, Spring Hill Farm, 584 Doncaster Road, Crofton, Wakefield, West Yorkshire, WF4 1PR Tel: (01924) 862820 Fax: (01924) 865129

Industrial (Motor) Rewinds Ltd, Haut De L'Orme, Rue De Haut De L'Orme, Trinity, Jersey, JE3 5FP Tel: (01534) 865782 Fax: (01534) 865786 E-mail: rayimp@hotmail.com

▶ Industrial Switchgear Services, Unit 5A Corn Mill, Ravensfield Industrial Estate, Charles Street, Dukinfield, Cheshire, SK16 4SD Tel: 0161-344 1117

Itec Power Services Ltd, Itec House, 2 Berkeley Street, Ashton-under-Lyne, Lancashire, OL6 7DT Tel: 0161-343 1595 Fax: 0161-343 2341 E-mail: sales@itecpower.co.uk

Ivacroft Ltd, Old Guard House, Trimms Green, Sawbridgeworth, Hertfordshire, CM21 0LX Tel: (01279) 724946 Fax: (01279) 722673

▶ J E Nixon & Son, Northern Works, Bellingham, Hexham, Northumberland, NE48 2BS Tel: (01434) 220268 Fax: (01434) 220372

J R S Rewinds, 71 Halifax Road, Maidenhead, Berkshire, SL6 5ES Tel: (01628) 628964 Fax: (01628) 672333

Jarvis & Evered Ltd, Priorswood Industrial Estate, Taunton, Somerset, TA2 8DG Tel: (01823) 337141 Fax: (01823) 323475 E-mail: jon@jarvisevered.com

John Mcnicol & Co Electrical Engineers Ltd, 123 Elliot Street, Glasgow, G3 8EY Tel: 0141-221 0725 Fax: 0141-248 4569 E-mail: info@johnmcnicol.co.uk

Kerensa Systems Ltd, Unit 4, Mercers Road, Bury St. Edmunds, Suffolk, IP32 7HX Tel: (01284) 767334 Fax: (01284) 767335 E-mail: bsmith@kerensasystems.co.uk

Keynes Controls, PO Box 7828, Crowthorne, Berkshire, RG45 7NE Tel: (01344) 752036 Fax: (01344) 752233 E-mail: sales@keynes-controls.com

Lacegold Electrical & Mechanical Services, 1 Aerial House, School Aycliffe, Newton Aycliffe, County Durham, DL5 6QF Tel: (01325) 315316 Fax: (01325) 329940 E-mail: lacegoldems@upexgroup.co.uk

Lark Electrical Ltd, Woolpit Business Park, Windmill Avenue, Woolpit, Bury St. Edmunds, Suffolk, IP30 9UP Tel: (01359) 243500 Fax: (01359) 244405 E-mail: info@lark-technology.co.uk

Levern Engineering Ltd, 30 Cogan Street, Barrhead, Glasgow, G78 1EJ Tel: 0141-881 9101 Fax: 0141-881 1888 E-mail: service@leverneng.co.uk

Lilleker Bros Ltd, 30 Moorgate Road, Rotherham, South Yorkshire, S60 2AG Tel: (01709) 374073 Fax: (01709) 364517 E-mail: info@lillekerbros.com

Lilleson Engineering Ltd, Unit 12 Brookside Court, Parkgate, Rotherham, South Yorkshire, S62 6NX Tel: (01709) 371188 Fax: (01709) 378232 E-mail: sales@lilleson.co.uk

Lonco Retail Services Ltd, 168-170 Upminster Road, Upminster, Essex, RM14 2RB Tel: (01708) 462000 Fax: (01708) 462002 E-mail: enquiries@lisl.co.uk

Lorne Stewart plc, Phillips House, Sandgate Industrial Estate, Hartlepool, Cleveland, TS25 1UB Tel: (01429) 268116 Fax: (01429) 860244 E-mail: hartlepool@lornestewart.co.uk

M C R Electrical Services, 2 Factory Estate, English Street, Hull, HU3 2BE Tel: (01482) 589062 Fax: (01482) 589525 E-mail: mcr@unit2.fslife.co.uk

M J N Ltd, Davis House, 69-73 High Street, Croydon, CR9 1PY Tel: (020) 8686 5577 Fax: (020) 8681 3114 E-mail: jhipwell@mjncolston.co.uk

M M Electrical Services, 17 Reddicap Trading Estate, Sutton Coldfield, West Midlands, B75 7BU Tel: 0121-378 4565 Fax: 0121-378 3541 E-mail: info@mmelec.co.uk

Mcmillan & Co. (Electrical Engineers) Ltd, 49 Scrutton Street, London, EC2A 4XJ Tel: (020) 7729 1919 Fax: (020) 7729 0174 E-mail: rec@mcmh.clara.net

Melcon (Hereford) Ltd, 8 St Martins St, Hereford, HR2 7RE Tel: (01432) 265195 Fax: (01432) 269623 E-mail: enquiries@melconltd.co.uk

Joseph Merritt Group P.L.C., Byron Ave, Lowmoor Business Park, Kirkby-in-Ashfield, Nottingham, NG17 7LA Tel: (01623) 759737 Fax: (01623) 758826 E-mail: enquiries@merrittgroupplc.co.uk

Michael Brandon, 29 Royal Industrial Estate, Jarrow, Tyne & Wear, NE32 3HR Tel: 0191-428 6668 Fax: 0191-428 6066 E-mail: sales@brandonltd.co.uk

Midlands Electrical Installations Ltd, 51 Winpenny Road, Parkhouse Industrial Estate East, Newcastle, Staffordshire, ST5 7RH Tel: (01782) 566844 Fax: (01782) 566756

D. & H Morris Group Ltd, Cumbernold House, Cumbernold, Glasgow, G67 3JG Tel: (01236) 868000 Fax: (01236) 868111

Morson Projects Ltd, 37 Liverpool Road, Irlam, Manchester, M44 6TB Tel: 0161-777 4000 Fax: 0161-777 4001 E-mail: enquiries@morson-projects.co.uk

National Grid Co. P.L.C., Littlebrook Manorway, Dartford, DA1 5PS Tel: (01322) 295160 Fax: (01322) 295040 E-mail: robin.greaves@ngc.co.uk

Osborne & Collins Ltd, 133a Hersham Road, Walton-on-Thames, Surrey, KT12 1RW Tel: (01932) 224751 Fax: (01932) 254592 E-mail: info@osborneandcollins.co.uk

Owen & Palmer Ltd, Unit 12 Llandygai Industrial Estate, Llandygai, Bangor, Gwynedd, LL57 4YH Tel: (01248) 353515 Fax: (01248) 353736 E-mail: sales@owenandpalmer.co.uk

P D Hunt Ltd, Lynwood Grange, Winsor Road, Winsor, Southampton, SO40 2HE Tel: (023) 8081 4348 Fax: (023) 8081 2911

▶ P R S Plumbing & Heating Services Ltd, Premier House, Popham, Micheldever, Winchester, Hampshire, SO21 3BJ Tel: (01256) 398881 Fax: (01256) 398889

Power Panels Electrical Systems Ltd, Landywood Green, Cheslyn Hay, Walsall, WS6 7AL Tel: (01922) 419109 Fax: (01922) 418181 E-mail: sales@power-panels.co.uk

Powermann Ltd, 16 Commercial Road, Poole, Dorset, BH14 0JW Tel: (01202) 722111 Fax: (01202) 722888 E-mail: sales@powermann.co.uk

Powerminster Ltd, 20 Don Road, Sheffield, S9 2UB Tel: 0114-282 0220 Fax: 0114-282 0221 E-mail: info@powerminster.co.uk

Puposet Ltd, 121 Blackburn Road, Haslingden, Rossendale, Lancashire, BB4 5HL Tel: (01706) 229260 Fax: (01706) 213645 E-mail: popuset@tim-jackson.co.uk

▶ R & C Electrical Engineers Ltd, Cheshire House, Murhall Street, Stoke-on-Trent, ST6 4BL Tel: (01782) 824660 Fax: (01782) 825474

R D J, Unit 1 A, Cranmer Road, West Meadows Industrial Estate, Derby, DE21 6JL Tel: (01332) 345472 Fax: (01332) 293509

R D Jukes & Co. Ltd, Walsingham Works, 1 Walsingham Street, Walsall, WS1 2JZ Tel: (01922) 624222 Fax: (01922) 630587 E-mail: info@rdjukes.co.uk

▶ Reavey & Son, Unit 21 Mitchell Point, Ensign Way, Hamble, Southampton, SO31 4RF Tel: (023) 8045 4560 Fax: (023) 8045 4561

Rhodes Electrical, 77 St. Marys Road, Garston, Liverpool, L19 2NN Tel: 0151-427 6885 Fax: 0151-494 1535 E-mail: rhodeselectrical@onetel.com

Rigfone Electrics Ltd, 109-111 Bitterne Road West, Southampton, SO18 1AR Tel: (023) 8021 5100 Fax: (023) 8021 5101 E-mail: sales@rigfone.co.uk

RMR Control & Automation, 2 Denington Court, Denington Industrial Estate, Wellingborough, Northamptonshire, NN8 2QR Tel: (01933) 441110 Fax: (01933) 441130 E-mail: sales@rmr.co.uk

Robert Collins Electrical Ltd, 30 Wood End Gardens, Northolt, Middlesex, UB5 4QJ Tel: (020) 8864 6939 Fax: (020) 8423 3177 E-mail: johnwhittle7@aol.com

Robert Hill & Co. Ltd, 62 Strathblane Road, Milngavie, Glasgow, G62 8DJ Tel: 0141-956 2245 Fax: 0141-955 1011

Rosser & Russell Building Services Ltd, Orbit House, 1-6 Ritz Parade, London, W5 3RD Tel: (020) 8982 2222 Fax: (020) 8982 2331

▶ Rotating Machinery Services, 126 Fletcher Road, Stoke-on-Trent, ST4 4AJ Tel: (01782) 747580 Fax: (01782) 749647

Royle Jackson Ltd, 1 Granville Street, Southampton, SO14 5FQ Tel: (023) 8033 1288 Fax: (023) 8033 9022

RVT, 4 Halifax Place, Ryhope, Sunderland, SR2 0RD Tel: (07811) 207271 Fax: 0191-523 6333

S M L Ltd, 2 Red Rose Trading Estate, Lancaster Road, Barnet, Hertfordshire, EN4 8BZ Tel: (020) 8447 1199 Fax: (020) 8447 0880 E-mail: paulcarroll@sml.ltd.uk

Safety First Extinguishers, Safety First Ho, Hawthorn Rd, Bognor Regis, W. Sussex, PO21 2UW Tel: (01243) 822215 Fax: (01243) 822215 E-mail: mrpcampbell@safetyfirstextinguishers.freeserve.co.uk

Scatco Europa Ltd, Lowfield Road, Leeds, LS12 6BS Tel: 0113-243 5155 Fax: 0113-234 2170 E-mail: scatco@scatts.co.uk

Scomo (Heating & Ventilating) Ltd, Escon House, 8 Fieldings Road, Cheshunt, Waltham Cross, Hertfordshire, EN8 9TL Tel: (01992) 635515 Fax: (01992) 635168 E-mail: esl@8escon.fsnet.co.uk

Severn Electric Co. Ltd, 2 Lisle Avenue, Kidderminster, Worcestershire, DY11 7DN Tel: (01299) 877700 Fax: (01562) 865059 E-mail: sales@severnelectric.co.uk

Seymour & Castle Ltd, Tattershall Way, Fairfield Industrial Estate, Louth, Lincolnshire, LN11 0YZ Tel: (01507) 602491 Fax: (01507) 607717 E-mail: admin@seymour-castle.co.uk

Sinclair Electrics, 130 Embankment Rd, Plymouth, PL4 9JF Tel: (01752) 268887 Fax: (01752) 268887

Smith & Co Carlisle Ltd, Junction Street, Carlisle, CA2 5UQ Tel: (01228) 522213 Fax: (01228) 515388

Sotham Engineering Services Ltd, Home End, Fulbourn, Cambridge, CB21 5BS Tel: (01223) 881081 Fax: (01223) 880169 E-mail: info@sotham.co.uk

Southern & Redfern Ltd, Forward House, Mount Street, Bradford, West Yorkshire, BD3 9SR Tel: (01274) 733333 Fax: (01274) 731300 E-mail: bernard.davis@southern-redfern.co.uk

Specialised Electrical Services, 52 Belhaven Terrace, Wishaw, Lanarkshire, ML2 7AY Tel: (01698) 374718 Fax: (01698) 373984

R.J. Stearn & Sons (Luton) Ltd, Unit 9 Windmill Trading Estate, Thistle Road, Luton, LU1 3XJ Tel: (01582) 729458 Fax: (01582) 455582

Stemet Earthing Co. Ltd, 6 Downs View, Bow Brickhill, Milton Keynes, MK17 9JS Tel: (01908) 373907 Fax: (01908) 378658

Stockley Electrics Ltd, 154 Bedworth Road, Bulkington, Bedworth, Warwickshire, CV12 9LQ Tel: (024) 7631 2639 Fax: (024) 7631 2639

▶ Stonehenge Services Ltd, Faraday Road, Salisbury, SP2 7NR Tel: (01722) 414161 Fax: (01722) 335343 E-mail: stonehenge.serve@btconnect.com

Super Spares Ltd, Brookfield Industrial Estate, Peggys Loaning, Banbridge, County Down, BT32 3AP Tel: (028) 4066 2166 Fax: (028) 4062 6642 E-mail: info@super-spares.com

Surgecam Ltd, Cold Hesledon Industrial Estate, Cold Hesledon, Seaham, County Durham, SR7 8ST Tel: 0191-513 0666 Fax: 0191-513 0862 E-mail: david.watson@surgecam.co.uk

T A Ronan & Co., 2d Askew Road, London, W12 9BH Tel: (020) 8749 3051 Fax: (020) 8749 5618

▶ Taylor Jackson & Associates, Unit 2 Hepton Court, Leeds, LS9 6PW Tel: 0113 2489777

Team Services Ltd, Riverside Road, Pottington, Barnstaple, Devon, EX31 1TE Tel: (01271) 374019 Fax: (01271) 375977 E-mail: sales@teamservices.co.uk

▶ Thyson Technology Ltd, 264 Manchester Road, Warrington, WA1 3RB Tel: (01925) 575600 Fax: (01925) 575660

Transformotor Ltd, Unit 43 Coneygre Industrial Estate, Tipton, West Midlands, DY4 8XU Tel: 0121-557 4491 Fax: 0121-557 3175

▶ TTS, Celect House, 12a Fairbairn Road, Livingston, West Lothian, EH54 6TS Tel: (01506) 464448 Fax: (01506) 464430 E-mail: web@ttsce.co.uk

Twyver Ltd, Unit 9 Chancel Close, Gloucester, GL4 3SN Tel: (01452) 525096 Fax: (01452) 356555 E-mail: dslater@twyverswitchgear.co.uk

Vallectric Ltd, Sweet Street, Leeds, LS11 9DB Tel: 0113-242 3800 Fax: 0113-242 4960 E-mail: info@vallectric.co.uk

Varcol Electrical Services Ltd, Cornwall Street, Manchester, M11 2WQ Tel: 0161-223 9696 Fax: 0161-223 0976 E-mail: sales@varcol.co.uk

Vaughan Engineering Group Ltd, Aercon Works, 556 Antrim Road, Newtownabbey, County Antrim, BT36 4RF Tel: (028) 9083 7441 Fax: (028) 9034 2469 E-mail: info@vaughan-group.co.uk

Voltech Instruments Ltd, 148 Harwell International Business Centre, Harwell, Didcot, Oxfordshire, OX11 0RA Tel: (01235) 834555 Fax: (01235) 835016 E-mail: sales@voltech.co.uk

Walgrave Electrical Services Ltd, 13 North Portway Close, Round Spinney, Northampton, NN3 8RQ Tel: (01604) 490100 Fax: (01604) 490101 E-mail: walgrave@skynet.co.uk

Wardah Electrics Ltd, 207 Strathmartine Road, Dundee, DD3 8PH Tel: (01382) 815844 Fax: (01382) 810115 E-mail: sales@wardahelectrics.com

▶ Watson Norie Ltd, Wincomblee Road, Walker, Newcastle upon Tyne, NE6 3PL Tel: 0191-262 7411 Fax: 0191-263 0496 E-mail: headoffice@watsonnorie.co.uk

Weblight Lighting Contractors, Unit 14 Park Court, Sullivans Way, St. Helens, Merseyside, WA9 5GZ Tel: (01744) 455711 Fax: (01744) 455710 E-mail: sales@weblight.co.uk

Westwells Electrical Contractors, 311 Clipsley Lane, Haydock, St. Helens, Merseyside, WA11 0JG Tel: (01744) 23482 Fax: (01744) 28780 E-mail: george@westwells.co.uk

Woods Electromech Ltd, Unit 4 Parc Ty Glas, Llanishen, Cardiff, CF14 5DU Tel: (029) 2075 7071 Fax: (029) 2075 8934 E-mail: dawoods@btclick.com

Woodside Air Conditioning Ltd, 81 Woodside Business Park, Shore Road, Birkenhead, Merseyside, CH42 1EP Tel: 0151-650 2369 Fax: 0151-650 2375 E-mail: desau@merseymail.com

Michael Wright Ltd, PO Box 469, High Wycombe, Buckinghamshire, HP14 3GL Tel: (01491) 638274

Wycliff Services Ltd, Godwin Road, Earlstrees Industrial Estate, Corby, Northamptonshire, NN17 4DS Tel: (01536) 406500 Fax: (01536) 406800 E-mail: johnh@wycliff-services.co.uk

ELECTRICAL EQUIPMENT DESIGN

Hobbs Electrical Services, 121 High Street, Stony Stratford, Milton Keynes, MK11 1AT Tel: (01908) 565577 Fax: (01908) 261211 E-mail: hobbs.electrical@btinternet.com

March Designs & Measurements, 11 Alfred Street, Dunstable, Bedfordshire, LU5 4HZ Tel: (01582) 600016 Fax: (01582) 600016 E-mail: info@marchdesigns.com

Motivated Engineering Techniques Ltd, Roseville, Tongue End, Spalding, Lincolnshire, PE11 3JJ Tel: (01775) 670361 Fax: (01775) 670371

Ormskirk Microwaves & Kitchen Appliances, Ormskirk Market Hall, Moorgate, Ormskirk, Lancashire, L39 4RT Tel: (01695) 570277

Ventilation Gear Co. Ltd, 9 Morjon Drive, Birmingham, B43 6JH Tel: 0121-358 7592 Fax: 0121-358 2364

ELECTRICAL EQUIPMENT DISPOSAL

Webster-Wilkinson Ltd, Unit A, Halesfield 10, Telford, Shropshire, TF7 4QP Tel: (01952) 585701 Fax: (01952) 581901 E-mail: sales@webster-wilkinson.com

ELECTRICAL EQUIPMENT EUROPEAN STANDARD COMPLIANCE TESTING

▶ David Stagg & Associates Ltd, 49 Watchouse Road, Chelmsford, CM2 8PU Tel: (01245) 492491 Fax: 01245 269690 E-mail: brian@davidstagg.co.uk

▶ Ideal Pat Testing (West Midlands), 4 Brooklyn Grove, Coseley, Bilston, West Midlands, WV14 8YH Tel: 0121-557 5254 Fax: 0121-557 5254 E-mail: k-share_13@tiscali.co.uk

▶ Medway Portable Appliance Testing Ltd, 70 Ellison Way, Rainham, Gillingham, Kent, ME8 7PG Tel: (01634) 388966 Fax: (01634) 388966 E-mail: sales@medwaypattesting.co.uk

▶ Plugtest Ltd, 9 Mill Lane, Alwalton, Peterborough, PE7 3UZ Tel: (0870) 0630200 Fax: (0870) 0630201 E-mail: sales@plugtest.co.uk

ELECTRICAL EQUIPMENT MARK AND SEAL LABELS

Blue Code Labelling Technology, Great Central Way Industrial Estate, Great Central Way, Rugby, Warwickshire, CV21 3XH Tel: (01788) 576100 Fax: (01788) 578900 E-mail: sales@bluecode.co.uk

ELECTRICAL EQUIPMENT TESTING

Arbarr Electronics Ltd, 2 Kilgavanagh Road, Antrim, BT41 2LJ Tel: (028) 9442 9334 Fax: (028) 9442 9178 E-mail: enquiries@arbarr.co.uk

▶ Ashdale, 61 Manston CR, Leeds, LS15 8BN Tel: 0113-260 0527 Fax: 0113-260 0527 E-mail: ashdalepat@hotmail.co.uk

▶ Ballistic Research Ltd, PO Box 263, Romsey, Hampshire, SO51 7WY Tel: (01794) 521113 Fax: (01794) 521623 E-mail: info@ballisticresearch.co.uk

Era Technology Ltd, Cleeve Road, Leatherhead, Surrey, KT22 7SA Tel: (01372) 367000 Fax: (01372) 367099 E-mail: info@era.co.uk

▶ G J ELECTRICAL, 65 FAWNBRAKE AVENUE, HERNE HILL, LONDON, SE24 0BE Tel: 020 73264668E-mail: GJONAS4@HOTMAIL.COM

▶ Ideal Pat Testing (West Midlands), 4 Brooklyn Grove, Coseley, Bilston, West Midlands, WV14 8YH Tel: 0121-557 5254 Fax: 0121-557 5254 E-mail: k-share_13@tiscali.co.uk

▶ Medway Portable Appliance Testing Ltd, 70 Ellison Way, Rainham, Gillingham, Kent, ME8 7PG Tel: (01634) 388966 Fax: (01634) 388966 E-mail: sales@medwaypattesting.co.uk

Portable Appliance Safety Services Ltd, 1 Hunters Buildings, Bowesfield Lane, Stockton-on-Tees, Cleveland, TS18 3QZ Tel: (01642) 603039 Fax: (0870) 1431869 E-mail: info@pat-services.co.uk

Powermann Ltd, 16 Commercial Road, Poole, Dorset, BH14 0JW Tel: (01202) 722111 Fax: (01202) 722888 E-mail: sales@powermann.co.uk

ELECTRICAL EQUIPMENT TESTING
– *continued*

R U Safe Ltd, Aizlewoods Mill, Nursery Street, Sheffield, S3 8GG Tel: 0114-282 3498 Fax: 0114-282 3302 E-mail: rusafe@it-installations.co.uk

ELECTRICAL EQUIPMENT WEEE DIRECTIVE RECYCLING

WEEE Labels.com, Unit 4, City Estate,, Corngreaves Road, Cradley Heath, West Midlands, B64 7EP Tel: 0870 7773645 Fax: 0870 7773644 E-mail: sales@weeelabels.com

ELECTRICAL EQUIPMENT, WATERPROOF/ WEATHERPROOF

DS Developments, Unit 41a Hobbs Industrial Estate, Newchapel, Lingfield, Surrey, RH7 6HN Tel: (01342) 835444 Fax: (01342) 832277 E-mail: sales@dsdevelopments.co.uk

ELECTRICAL EXPLOSION PROTECTION EQUIPMENT

Schischek Ltd, 1 Saddlestones, New Road, Princes Risborough, Buckinghamshire, HP27 0JJ Tel: (01494) 794904 Fax: (01494) 794905 E-mail: schischek@msn.com

ELECTRICAL FIRE BARRIER EQUIPMENT

Macdonald Fire Equipment, 3 Building 24, Stevenston Industrial Estate, Stevenston, Ayrshire, KA20 3LR Tel: (01294) 601989 Fax: (01294) 602688

ELECTRICAL FIXED WIRE TESTING

▶ HMC Electrical Services Ltd, Maidstone Road, Nettlestead, Maidstone, Kent, ME18 5HP Tel: (01622) 870088 Fax: (01622) 870077 E-mail: hmcelectrical@btconnect.com

ELECTRICAL FOIL, *See Copper Foil etc*

ELECTRICAL GOODS (DOMESTIC) CERTIFYING AUTHORITIES

Elliott Electrical Supplies, 39 Margetts Road, Kempston, Bedford, MK42 8DT Tel: (01234) 857800 Fax: (01234) 857800

ELECTRICAL GOODS TESTING

E & C Engineering Services Ltd, Bargate House Woodside Park, Catteshall Lane, Godalming, Surrey, GU7 1LG Tel: (01483) 426766 Fax: (01483) 426708 E-mail: info@ecengineering.co.uk

E S T Electrical Contractors Ltd, 18 Kenchester Close, Redditch, Worcestershire, B98 0BT Tel: (01527) 529050 Fax: (01527) 510550

▶ Medway Portable Appliance Testing Ltd, 70 Ellison Way, Rainham, Gillingham, Kent, ME8 7PG Tel: (01634) 388966 Fax: (01634) 388966 E-mail: sales@medwaypattesting.co.uk

ELECTRICAL INDUSTRY ENGRAVERS

B.H.R. Precision Engraving, Units 215 Victory Business Centre, Somers Road North, Portsmouth, PO1 1PJ Tel: (023) 9281 6613 Fax: (023) 9281 6613

D B Sign & Engraving Co., Unit 4, Windmill Lane Industrial Estate, Denton, Manchester, M34 3RB Tel: 0161-320 0068 Fax: 0161-320 6829

Emslie Industrial Engraving Co., 62 West Harbour Road, Edinburgh, EH5 1PW Tel: 0131-552 9944 Fax: 0131-552 1093

G R C Engraving Ltd, 14 Darley Road, Ferndown, Dorset, BH22 8QX Tel: (01202) 861297 Fax: (01202) 861297

KD Engraving, 37 Boston Road, Leicester, LE4 1AW Tel: 0116-234 0131 Fax: 0116-234 0131

ELECTRICAL INSTALLATION CONNECTORS

▶ Electricare Services, 33 The CR, Urmston, Manchester, M41 5QR Tel: 0161-202 9499 E-mail: office@electricareservices.co.uk

I T W McMurdo Connectors, Norway Road, Hilsea, Portsmouth, PO3 5HT Tel: (023) 9269 4971 Fax: (023) 9265 3356 E-mail: itwswitch1@aol.com

ELECTRICAL INSTALLATION EQUIPMENT MANUFRS

▶ A S Walter, 42 Chapel Avenue, Long Stratton, Norwich, NR15 2TE Tel: (01508) 532528 Fax: (01508) 532528 E-mail: enquiries@aswalter.co.uk

Wilts Wholesale Electrical Co. Ltd, Kennet Way, Canal Road Industrial Estate, Trowbridge, Wiltshire, BA14 8BL Tel: (01225) 777300 Fax: (01225) 777001 E-mail: info@wilts.co.uk

ELECTRICAL INSTALLATION FIXINGS

Margin Services Ltd, Brookside Business Park, Brookside Avenue, Littlehampton, West Sussex, BN16 3LF Tel: (01903) 856123 Fax: (01903) 786062 E-mail: martin@marginservices.co.uk

ELECTRICAL INSTALLATION INSPECTION

B P D Building Services, 7 Sunnyside Grove, Ashton-under-Lyne, Lancashire, OL6 6TN Tel: 0161-612 7514 E-mail: paul@bpd-ltd.com

▶ Chaos Lighting, 36 Hollicondane Road, Ramsgate, Kent, CT11 7PH Tel: 01843 596997 Fax: 01843 596997 E-mail: russell@chaoslighting.co.uk

Electic, 40 Thorneyfields Lane, Stafford, ST17 9YS Tel: (01785) 229330 Fax: (01785) 229330

▶ Electrical & Electronic Services, 5 St Josephs Park, Downpatrick, County Down, BT30 7EN Tel: (028) 4484 1631 E-mail: aidenmoore@hotmail.com

▶ Grant Smith Electrical, 16 Hutcheson Drive, Largs, Ayrshire, KA30 8EE Tel: (07717) 734880 E-mail: enquiry@gselectrical.com

▶ Ideal Pat Testing, 200 Gorse Cover Road, Severn Beach, Bristol, BS35 4NT Tel: (01454) 631331 Fax: (01454) 631331 E-mail: idealhandling@tiscali.co.uk

▶ J R H Electrical Contractors Ltd, Unit A, Ashleigh Mews, Woodland Grove, Blackpool, FY3 9HD Tel: (01253) 390002 Fax: (01253) 390003 E-mail: info@jrh-electrical.com

▶ Midland Testing Services, 3 Hollis Meadow, East Leake, Loughborough, Leicestershire, LE12 6RU Tel: (01509) 854444 Fax: (01509) 854444 E-mail: kevinspencer@midlandstestingservices.co.uk

▶ Thermal Imaging & NICEIC Electrical Inspections, Riverside Mansions Flat 112, Milk Yard, London, E1W 3TA Tel: (0797) 1268030 Fax: (020) 7480 6578

▶ Wannells, Unit 1, Highfield Barns, Clyst Road, Topsham, Exeter, EX3 0BY Tel: (01392) 874281 Fax: E-mail: mail@wannells.com

ELECTRICAL INSTALLATION MOUNTING BOXES

▶ A S Walter, 42 Chapel Avenue, Long Stratton, Norwich, NR15 2TE Tel: (01508) 532528 Fax: (01508) 532528 E-mail: enquiries@aswalter.co.uk

ELECTRICAL INSTALLATION TESTING

E C Electricals Ltd, 16C Wincombe Business Park, Warminster Road, Shaftesbury, Dorset, SP7 9QJ Tel: (01747) 853861 Fax: (01747) 855274 E-mail: enquiries@ecelectricals.co.uk

Epsilon Test Services Ltd, Epsilon House, The Square, Gloucester Business Park, Gloucester, GL3 4AD Tel: (0845) 2336600 Fax: (0845) 2336633 E-mail: enquiries@epsilontsl.co.uk

▶ Glamorgan Electrical Ltd, Unit 3, Isaacs Place, Port Talbot, West Glamorgan, SA12 6NP Tel: (01639) 895217 E-mail: sales@glamorgan-electrical.com

R U Safe Ltd, Aizlewoods Mill, Nursery Street, Sheffield, S3 8GG Tel: 0114-282 3498 Fax: 0114-282 3302 E-mail: rusafe@it-installations.co.uk

ELECTRICAL INSULATING BOARDS

Whiteley Ltd, Pool In Wharfedale, Otley, West Yorkshire, LS21 1RP Tel: 0113-284 2121 Fax: 0113-284 2272

ELECTRICAL INSULATING MATERIALS

A & I Plastics Ltd, Unit 5, Boundary Road, Buckingham Road Industrial Estate, Brackley, Northamptonshire, NN13 7ES Tel: (01280) 840050 E-mail: sales@aiplastics.co.uk

CP Films Solutia UK Ltd, Chadwick Road, Astmoor Industrial Estate, Runcorn, Cheshire, WA7 1PW Tel: (01928) 580508 Fax: (01928) 580100 E-mail: sales.runcorn@cpfilms.co.uk

Esspee Fabrications Ltd, 149 Merton Bank Road, St. Helens, Merseyside, WA9 1DZ Tel: (01744) 28304 Fax: (01744) 28826 E-mail: sales@esspee.co.uk

Industrial Composites Ltd, Churchill Way, Nelson, Lancashire, BB9 6RT Tel: (01282) 619336 Fax: (01282) 619337 E-mail: info@indcomps.co.uk

Insulation & Machining Services Ltd, Russell Road, Southport, Merseyside, PR9 7SB Tel: (01704) 226878 Fax: (01704) 225857 E-mail: sales@ims-insulation.com

Jones Stroud Insulations, Queen Street, Longridge, Preston, PR3 3BS Tel: (01772) 783011 Fax: (01772) 784200 E-mail: info@krempel-group.com

Multiple Winding Co. Ltd, Taylor Lane, Denton, Manchester, M34 3NR Tel: 0161-336 6125 Fax: 0161-335 9134 E-mail: chris@multiplewinding.co.uk

Needs Ltd, 13 Queensway, Enfield, Middlesex, EN3 4SG Tel: (020) 8804 2281 Fax: (020) 8364 7113 E-mail: sales@needsplastics.co.uk

Rochling Materials Ltd, Waterwells Drive, Waterwells Business Park, Quedgeley, Gloucester, GL2 2AA Tel: (01452) 727900 Fax: (01452) 728056 E-mail: sales@roechling.co.uk

Tenmat Ltd, Ashburton Road West, Trafford Park, Manchester, M17 1RU Tel: 0161-872 2181 Fax: 0161-872 7596 E-mail: info@tenmat.com

Whiteley Ltd, Pool In Wharfedale, Otley, West Yorkshire, LS21 1RP Tel: 0113-284 2121 Fax: 0113-284 2272

J.J. Williams (Gaskets) Ltd, 1 Beresford Road, Whitstable, Kent, CT5 1JP Tel: (01227) 265522 Fax: (01227) 770146 E-mail: enquiries@jjwilliams.co.uk

ELECTRICAL INSULATING PAPER

▶ Bartec Paper & Packaging, Wincham Avenue, Wincham, Northwich, Cheshire, CW9 6GB Tel: (01606) 354664 Fax: (01606) 354665 E-mail: ute.cooper@good.co.uk

▶ U K P Ltd, Unit 12, Lawson Hunt Industrial Park, Guildford Road, Broadbridge Heath, Horsham, West Sussex, RH13 3JR Tel: (0870) 7707228 Fax: (0870) 7707229 E-mail: sales@ukp.co.uk

ELECTRICAL INSULATING RESINS

Bauder Ltd, Broughton House, 26 Broughton Road, Ipswich, IP1 3QR Tel: (01473) 257671 Fax: (01473) 230761 E-mail: marketing@bauder.co.uk

Sterling Technology Ltd, Europa Gate, Trafford Park, Manchester, M17 1DU Tel: 0161-848 8411 Fax: 0161-848 0966 E-mail: sales@sterling-tech.com

Trimite Ltd, Arundel Road, Uxbridge, Middlesex, UB8 2SD Tel: (01895) 251234 Fax: (01895) 256489 E-mail: info@trimite.com

ELECTRICAL INSULATING TAPES

▶ Trafford Rubber Products Ltd, Greengate Works, Broadoak Business Park, Ashburton Road West, Trafford Park, Manchester, M17 1RW Tel: 0161-873 7172 Fax: 0161-848 9762 E-mail: traffordrubber@beeb.net

ELECTRICAL INSULATING VARNISHES

Sterling Technology Ltd, Europa Gate, Trafford Park, Manchester, M17 1DU Tel: 0161-848 8411 Fax: 0161-848 0966 E-mail: sales@sterling-tech.com

Trimite Ltd, Arundel Road, Uxbridge, Middlesex, UB8 2SD Tel: (01895) 251234 Fax: (01895) 256489 E-mail: info@trimite.com

ELECTRICAL INSULATION ADHESIVE TAPES

▶ 24-7 Electrical Ltd, 167 Townfields Road, Winsford, Cheshire, CW7 4AX Tel: (01625) 266309 Fax: (01625) 266309 E-mail: mail@24-7group.co.uk

ELECTRICAL INSULATION CONTRACTORS, *See Electrical Contractors*

ELECTRICAL INSULATION TEST EQUIPMENT

Di-Log, Unit 28 Wheel Forge Way, Trafford Park, Manchester, M17 1EH Tel: 0161-877 0322 Fax: 0161-877 1614E-mail: sales@dilog.co.uk

T & M Supplies, Barton Street, North Tawton, Devon, EX20 2HL Tel: (01837) 82601 Fax: (01837) 89082 E-mail: tswhite@talk21.com

ELECTRICAL INVERTERS

Antares Europe Ltd, Chiltern Hill, Chalfont St. Peter, Gerrards Cross, Buckinghamshire, SL9 9UQ Tel: (01753) 890888 Fax: (01753) 891260 E-mail: info@antares.co.uk

B P C EMEA Ltd, B P C House, Romsey Industrial Estate, Greatbridge Road, Romsey, Hampshire, SO51 0HR Tel: (01794) 521200 Fax: (01794) 521400 E-mail: sales@bpc-ups.com

BPX Electro Mechanical Co, Unit 8 Decade Close, High Carr Business Park, Newcastle, Staffordshire, ST5 7UH Tel: (01782) 565500 Fax: (01782) 565500 E-mail: bpxstaffs@bpx.co.uk

C H Rewinds Ltd, Smithfold Lane, Worsley, Manchester, M28 0GP Tel: 0161-702 8737 Fax: 0161-702 8730 E-mail: sales@chrewinds.com

Data Systems & Solutions, Unit 14 Princes Park Princes Way, Team Valley Trading Estate, Gateshead, Tyne & Wear, NE11 0NF Tel: 0191-499 4000 Fax: 0191-499 4001 E-mail: tomsimpson@ds-s.com

Erskine Systems Ltd, Salter Road, Eastfield Industrial Estate, Scarborough, North Yorkshire, YO11 3DU Tel: (01723) 583511 Fax: (01723) 581231 E-mail: sales@erskine-systems.co.uk

M J Electronics Services (International) Ltd, Unit 19B, Sedgemount Industrial Park, Bristol Road, Bridgwater, Somerset, TA6 4AR Tel: (01278) 422882 Fax: (01278) 453331 E-mail: sales@mjelectronics.freeserve.co.uk

Mackwell Electronics Ltd, Hayward Industrial Park, Vigo Place, Walsall, WS9 8UG Tel: (01922) 458255 Fax: (01922) 451263 E-mail: sales@mackwell.com

Southern Industrial Controls, 118 Faulds Industrial Estate, Tutbury, Burton-on-Trent, Staffs, DE13 9HS Tel: (01283) 814488 Fax: (01283) 814480

ELECTRICAL JUNCTION BOXES

C Q R Security, 125 Pasture Road, Wirral, Merseyside, CH46 4TH Tel: 0151-606 9595 Fax: 0151-606 1122 E-mail: info@cqr.co.uk

Maxhunt Ltd, Yelverton Road, Bristol, BS4 5HP Tel: 0117-977 9001 Fax: 0117-971 5971 E-mail: sales@maxhunt.com

ELECTRICAL LAMINATES

Sudatek Ltd, 59 Barn Meadow Lane, Bookham, Leatherhead, Surrey, KT23 3EZ Tel: (01372) 450008 Fax: (01372) 450006 E-mail: sales@sudatek.com

ELECTRICAL MACHINE DESIGN

▶ Javelin Controls Ltd, 10 Warbleton Road, Chineham, Basingstoke, Hampshire, RG24 8RF Tel: 01256 812557 Fax: 01256 812557 E-mail: sales@javelin-controls.com

▶ R B Electronics, Unit 16 Jubilee Enterprise Centre, 15 Jubilee Close, Weymouth, Dorset, DT4 7BS Tel: (01305) 750555 Fax: (01305) 750555

ELECTRICAL MACHINERY CONDITION MONITORING

Dowding & Mills Calibration, The Service Centre Watchmoor Point, Watchmoor Road, Camberley, Surrey, GU15 3AD Tel: (01276) 701717 Fax: (01276) 700245 E-mail: calibration.camberley@dowdingandmills.com

▶ Macom Technologies Ltd, 17 Glasgow Road, Paisley, Renfrewshire, PA1 3QS Tel: 0141-849 6287 Fax: 0141-849 6497 E-mail: info@macomtech.net

ELECTRICAL MACHINERY CONDITION MONITORING – *continued*

Ramac Engineering, 142 Old Shoreham Road, Hove, East Sussex, BN3 7BD Tel: (01273) 622394 Fax: (01273) 202009 E-mail: nfo@whippendell-marine.co.uk

ELECTRICAL OR ELECTRONIC EQUIPMENT DIE CAST ENCLOSURES

A B Controls & Technology Ltd, Sanderson Street, Lower Don Valley, Sheffield, S9 2UA Tel: 0114-244 2424 Fax: 0114-243 4312 E-mail: info@ab-tech.co.uk

ELECTRICAL OR ELECTRONIC EQUIPMENT ENCLOSURES, *See also headings for type of material used*

A Davies & Sons Sales Ltd, Alpha Works, Old Moor Road, Bredbury, Stockport, Cheshire, SK6 2QF Tel: 0161-430 5297 Fax: 0161-494 2758

Beechcraft Ltd, First Avenue, Westfield Industrial Estate, Midsomer Norton, Radstock, BA3 4BS Tel: (01761) 416642 Fax: (01761) 419267 E-mail: info@beechcraft-ltd.com

Bernstein Ltd, Westgate Trading Estate, Westgate, Aldridge, Walsall, WS9 8EX Tel: (01922) 744999 Fax: (01922) 457555 E-mail: sales@bernstein-ltd.co.uk

Burgess & Co. Ltd, New North Road, Heckmondwike, West Yorkshire, WF16 9DP Tel: (01924) 402406 Fax: (01924) 410175 E-mail: info@cburgess.co.uk

Cholcroft Ltd, 7 Dane Drive, Ferndown, Dorset, BH22 8LX Tel: (01202) 874455 Fax: (01202) 874003 E-mail: trevor@cholcroft-ltd.freeserve.co.uk

D P Fabrications Ltd, Chantry Road, Woburn Road Industrial Estate, Kempston, Bedford, MK42 7HU Tel: (01234) 840156 Fax: (01234) 840177 E-mail: sales@dpfabs.co.uk

Elma Electronic UK Ltd, Premier Business Centre, Speedfields Park, Fareham, Hampshire, PO14 1TY Tel: (01329) 289100 Fax: (01329) 289101 E-mail: info@elma-electronic.co.uk

Hellermanntyton, Wharf Approach, Aldridge, Walsall, WS9 8BX Tel: (01922) 458151 Fax: (01922) 743237 E-mail: sales@hellermantyton.co.uk

John Hemy (Systems) Ltd, Dukesway, Teeside Industrial Estate, Stockton-On-Tees, Cleveland, TS17 9LT Tel: (01642) 769440 Fax: (01642) 763440 E-mail: info@johnhemysystems.co.uk

Lohmeier-Comat UK Ltd, 1 Dunston Pl, Dunston Rd, Chesterfield, Derbyshire, S41 8XA Tel: (01246) 264300 Fax: (01246) 264301 E-mail: sales@edlcomat.co.uk

Park Electrical Services, Crown Trading Centre, Clayton Road, Hayes, Middlesex, UB3 1DU Tel: (020) 8813 5889 Fax: (020) 8813 5946 E-mail: info@pes-group.co.uk

▶ Plastic Enclosures Ltd, Unit 24, Broughton Grounds, Broughton, Milton Keynes, Newport Pagnell, MK16 0HZ Tel: (01908) 676560 Fax: (01908) 200148 E-mail: info@evatron.com

S R S Products P.L.C., 19 Mead Industrial Park, River Way, Harlow, Essex, CM20 2SE Tel: (01279) 635500 Fax: (01279) 635282 E-mail: sales@srs-products.co.uk

Specialised Security Manufacturing Ltd, 5 David Wright Close, Great Dunmow, Dunmow, Essex, CM6 1DB Tel: (01371) 874600 Fax: (01371) 873006

Tadley Engineering Ltd, Oak Tree Works, Silchester Road, Tadley, Hampshire, RG26 3PX Tel: 0118-981 0621 Fax: 0118-981 0787 E-mail: info@tadleyengineering.co.uk

ELECTRICAL OR ELECTRONIC EQUIPMENT FIBREGLASS ENCLOSURES

Glasdon Manufacturing Ltd, Industrial Estate, Poulton Industrial Estate, Poulton-le-Fylde, Lancashire, FY6 8JW Tel: (01253) 891131 Fax: (01253) 891923 E-mail: sales@glasdon-manufacturing.co.uk

K N G Developments, North East Sector, Bournemouth Int Airport, Hurn, Christchurch, Dorset, BH23 6NE Tel: (07074) 581856 Fax: (01202) 581856 E-mail: keith.gilson@btinternet.com

P P S Glassfibre Ltd, Harlaw Way, Harlaw Road Industrial Estate, Inverurie, Aberdeenshire, AB51 4SG Tel: (01467) 621907 Fax: (01467) 620265 E-mail: ppsglassfibre@btconnect.com

Quinshield Ltd, Unit 27-28, Capel Hendre Industrial Estate, Ammanford, Dyfed, SA18 3SJ Tel: (01269) 832220 Fax: (01269) 832221 E-mail: info@quinshield.com

ELECTRICAL OR ELECTRONIC EQUIPMENT FLAMEPROOF ENCLOSURES

A B Controls & Technology Ltd, Sanderson Street, Lower Don Valley, Sheffield, S9 2UA Tel: 0114-244 2424 Fax: 0114-243 4312 E-mail: info@ab-tech.co.uk

Flameproof Electrical Enclosures Ltd, Units 1-1a St Martins Industrial Estate, Tat Bank Road, Oldbury, West Midlands, B69 4NP Tel: 0121-541 1315 Fax: 0121-552 0592 E-mail: flameproof@btinternet.com

Redapt Engineering Co. Ltd, Darlaston Central TRDG Estate, Salisbury Street, Wednesbury, West Midlands, WS10 8BQ Tel: 0121-526 7058

ELECTRICAL OR ELECTRONIC EQUIPMENT METAL ENCLOSURES

Ad Tek Products Ltd, 35 Broton Drive, Halstead, Essex, CO9 1HB Tel: (01787) 474470 Fax: (01787) 475880 E-mail: ad-tek@lineone.net

Akramatic Engineering Co. Ltd, Keys Road, Nix's Hill Industrial Estate, Alfreton, Derbyshire, DE55 7FQ Tel: (01773) 833223 Fax: (01773) 520595 E-mail: info@akramatic.com

B & Z, O2, Cherrycourt Way, Leighton Buzzard, Bedfordshire, LU7 4UH Tel: (01525) 373018 Fax: (01525) 851439 E-mail: enquiries@bandz.co.uk

Bridgwater Metalcraft Ltd, Brue Avenue, Bridgwater, Somerset, TA6 5LT Tel: (01278) 452867 Fax: (01278) 423167

Cadlow Enclosures, Bridge House, The Green, Redgrave, Diss, Norfolk, IP22 1RR Tel: (01379) 898810 Fax: (01379) 898812 E-mail: info@cadlow.co.uk

Cannon Technologies Europe Ltd, 13 Queensway, Stem Lane Industrial Estate, New Milton, Hampshire, BH25 5NU Tel: (01425) 638148 Fax: (01425) 619276 E-mail: sales@cannontech.co.uk

Carlton Controls Ltd, 3c Lea Road, Waltham Abbey, Essex, EN9 1AE Tel: (01992) 767609 Fax: (01992) 788446 E-mail: mail@carlton-controls.co.uk

Cooper B Line Ltd, Commerce Way, Highbridge, Somerset, TA9 4AQ Tel: (01278) 783371 Fax: (01278) 789037 E-mail: mwatts@cooperbline.co.uk

Dacon Fabrications Ltd, Dukesway, Team Valley Trading Estate, Gateshead, Tyne & Wear, NE11 0PZ Tel: 0191-482 5464 Fax: 0191-482 5463 E-mail: info@daconfab.co.uk

Data & Power Solutions, Unit 1 The Monarch Centre, Venture Way, Priorswood Industrial Estate, Taunton, Somerset, TA2 8DE Tel: (01823) 275100 Fax: (01823) 275002 E-mail: sales@dataandpower.com

Dataracks, Stagwood House, Beach Road, Cottenham, Cambridge, CB4 8FP Tel: (01954) 252229 Fax: (01954) 251461 E-mail: sales@dataracks.co.uk

E Farrington & Co. Ltd, Regent Engineering Works, Robert Street, Hyde, Cheshire, SK14 1BN Tel: 0161-368 1675 Fax: 0161-367 8868E-mail: info@farringtons.fsbusiness.co.uk

Eddingbrook Ltd, Valley Works, Bacup Road, Todmorden, Lancashire, OL14 7PJ Tel: (01706) 814854 Fax: (01706) 815023 E-mail: info@eddingbrook.co.uk

Eldon Electric Ltd, Rother Way, Hellaby, Rotherham, South Yorkshire, S66 8QN Tel: (01709) 701234 Fax: (01709) 701209 E-mail: info.uk@eldon.com

Electrical Cabinets (Bradford) Ltd, 2 Essex Street, Wakefield Road, Bradford, West Yorkshire, BD4 7PG Tel: (01274) 729076 Fax: (01274) 732297

Electropak Ltd, Bushell Street Mill, Bushell Street, Preston, PR1 2SP Tel: (01772) 251444 Fax: (01772) 251555 E-mail: info@electropak.net

Fife Fabrications Ltd, 29 Rutherford Road, Glenrothes, Fife, KY6 2RT Tel: (01592) 776700 Fax: (01592) 772101 E-mail: sales@fifab.co.uk

Flameproof Electrical Enclosures Ltd, Units 1-1a St Martins Industrial Estate, Tat Bank Road, Oldbury, West Midlands, B69 4NP Tel: 0121-541 1315 Fax: 0121-552 0592 E-mail: flameproof@btinternet.com

▶ Hawke Cable Glands Ltd, Oxford St West, Ashton-under-Lyne, Lancashire, OL7 0NA Tel: 0161-308 3611 Fax: 0161-830 6648 E-mail: sales@ehawke.com

K P Equipe Communications Ltd, 1-3 Faraday Close, Drayton Fields Industrial Estate, Daventry, Northamptonshire, NN11 8RD Tel: (01327) 871187 Fax: (01327) 871188

Kempston Ltd, Brunel Road, Bedford, MK41 9TG Tel: (01234) 341144 Fax: (01234) 348281

Logstrup (UK) Ltd, Units 3H & 4H Lyntown Trading Estate, Lynwell Road, Manchester, M30 9QG Tel: 0161-788 9811 Fax: 0161-789 0063 E-mail: sales@logstrupuk.co.uk

LPA Haswell Engineers Ltd, Oakwood Business Park, Stephenson Road West, Clacton-On-Sea, Essex, CO15 4TL Tel: (01255) 253900 Fax: (01255) 432963 E-mail: enquiries@lpa-haswell.com

Lund Bros & Co. Ltd, Brookside Avenue, Rustington, Littlehampton, West Sussex, BN16 3LF Tel: (01903) 784242 Fax: (01903) 787126 E-mail: sales@lunds.co.uk

M J Metalcraft Ltd, 32-34 Sampson Road North, Birmingham, B11 1BL Tel: 0121-771 3711 Fax: 0121-771 3766 E-mail: enquiries@mjmetalcraftltd.co.uk

Meade Bros Ltd, Eckersall Road, Birmingham, B38 8SS Tel: 0121-486 2291 Fax: 0121-486 2276 E-mail: meadebrothersltd@aol.com

P C D Products Ltd, Cleveland Road, Hemel Hempstead Industrial Estate, Hemel Hempstead, Hertfordshire, HP2 7EY Tel: (01442) 248565 Fax: (01442) 241033 E-mail: sales@pcdproducts.co.uk

Phoenix Mecano Ltd, 6-7 Faraday Road, Aylesbury, Buckinghamshire, HP19 8TX Tel: (01296) 619100 Fax: (01296) 398866 E-mail: info@phoenix-mecano.ltd.uk

Precision Components & Equipment Ltd, Railway Street, Heywood, Lancashire, OL10 1LX Tel: (01706) 621421 Fax: (01706) 621319 E-mail: mike-pce@johnbradleygroup.co.uk

Ritherdon & Co. Ltd, Lorne Street, Darwen, Lancashire, BB3 1QW Tel: (01254) 819100 Fax: (01254) 819101 E-mail: info@ritherdon.co.uk

Schroff UK Ltd, Maylands Avenue, Hemel Hempstead Industrial Estate, Hemel Hempstead, Hertfordshire, HP2 7DE Tel: (01442) 240471 Fax: (01442) 213508 E-mail: sales_uk@schroff.co.uk

Specialised Security Manufacturing Ltd, 5 David Wright Close, Great Dunmow, Dunmow, Essex, CM6 1DB Tel: (01371) 874600 Fax: (01371) 873006

▶ Stephen Clark Fabrication Ltd, Castle Street, Alloa, Clackmannanshire, FK10 1EU Tel: (01259) 729729 Fax: (01259) 210000 E-mail: sales@scfabs.com

Surestep Sheet Metal Ltd, Unit J2 Northfleet Industrial Estate, Lower Road, Northfleet, Gravesend, Kent, DA11 9BL Tel: (01474) 560511 Fax: (01474) 354396 E-mail: info@surestepsheetmetal.com

Tegrel Ltd, Tundry Way, Blaydon-on-Tyne, Tyne & Wear, NE21 5TT Tel: 0191-414 6111 Fax: 0191-414 0660 E-mail: sales@tegrel.co.uk

▶ Tempa Pano UK, Unit 5, Centre 21 Industrial Estate, Bridge Lane, Woolston, Warrington, WA1 4AW Tel: 0845 4941730 Fax: (01925) 810386 E-mail: info@tempapano.co.uk

Wedge Engineering Ltd, 16 Darlington Close, Sandy, Bedfordshire, SG19 1RW Tel: (01767) 683527 Fax: (01767) 683529 E-mail: wedgeeng@btconnect.com

Wheeler Fabrications Ltd, Orchard House, Sherbourne Road, Balsall Heath, Birmingham, B12 9DJ Tel: 0121-440 2345 Fax: 0121-440 4008 E-mail: wheelerfabs@btconnect.com

Woking Sheet Metal & Coachworks Ltd, 141 Goldsworth Road, Woking, Surrey, GU21 6LT Tel: (01483) 761898 Fax: (01483) 755605 E-mail: woking.sheetmetal@btinternet.com

Xixin Ltd, Hartington House, Bilton Way, Luton, LU1 1UU Tel: (01582) 400340 Fax: (01582) 481498 E-mail: sales@xixin.co.uk

Zero Cases (U K) Ltd, Alpha Park, Bevan Way, Smethwick, West Midlands, B66 1BZ Tel: 0121-558 2011 Fax: 0121-565 2115 E-mail: zero.cases.europe.sales@dial.pipex.com

ELECTRICAL OR ELECTRONIC EQUIPMENT STAINLESS STEEL ENCLOSURES

G & C Engineering plc, Cobham Road, Pershore, Worcestershire, WR10 2DL Tel: (01386) 553934 Fax: (01386) 555725 E-mail: sales@gandc.co.uk

Yellowpatter Sussex Ltd, Chantry Lane, Storrington, West Sussex, RH20 4TA Tel: (01903) 745741 Fax: (01903) 742668 E-mail: sales@yellowpatter.co.uk

ELECTRICAL OR ELECTRONIC INDUSTRY ADHESIVES

Anglo American Adhesives, Cg10 Warrington Business Park, Long Lane, Warrington, WA2 8TX Tel: (01925) 419111 Fax: (01925) 419222 E-mail: colin.fitz@virgin.net

Intertronics Electronic Equipment Component, 17a Station Field Industrial Estate, Kidlington, Oxfordshire, OX5 1JD Tel: (01865) 842842 Fax: (01865) 842172 E-mail: enquiries@intertronics.co.uk

ELECTRICAL OR ELECTRONICS FASTENERS

European Rivet Supplies, Uynit 4b Sovereign Park Industrial Estate, Market Harborough, Leicestershire, LE16 9EG Tel: (01858) 469191 Fax: (01858) 469190 E-mail: sales@eurorivet.co.uk

Everbright Stainless, Brimington Road North, Chesterfield, Derbyshire, S41 9BE Tel: (01246) 451600 Fax: (01246) 451611 E-mail: everbright.sales@infast.com

ELECTRICAL OR ELECTRONICS TAPES

Alba Self Adhesive Tape Supply Co. Ltd, 10 Rhynie Road, Broughty Ferry, Dundee, DD5 1RH Tel: (01382) 731100 Fax: (01382) 731100 E-mail: frank@albatapes.co.uk

Lewis Industrial Products, 25 Lichfield Close, New Arley, Coventry, Warwickshire, CV7 8PU Tel: (01676) 541792 Fax: (01676) 541184 E-mail: lewislip@aol.com

Venture Tape Europe, 5-6 Faraday Close, Drayton Fields Industrial Estate, Daventry, Northamptonshire, NN11 8RD Tel: (01327) 876555 Fax: (01327) 876444 E-mail: jaeanne@venturetape.co.uk

ELECTRICAL OR MECHANICAL INSULATION GASKETS

Premier Gaskets, Unit 16 Bell Farm Industrial Park, Nuthampstead, Royston, Hertfordshire, SG8 8ND Tel: (01763) 848849 Fax: (01763) 848848

ELECTRICAL OR SWITCHBOARD MATS

British Gaskets Ltd, Bulmer Road Industrial Estate, Bulmer Road, Sudbury, Suffolk, CO10 7HJ Tel: (01787) 881188 Fax: (01787) 880595

Dolman, 10 Rouse Mill Lane, Batley, West Yorkshire, WF17 5QB Tel: (01924) 445577 Fax: (01924) 443222 E-mail: sales@jamesdolman.co.uk

Kopak-Walker Ltd, PO Box 65, Hitchin, Hertfordshire, SG4 0TW Tel: (01462) 452487 Fax: (01462) 452249 E-mail: sales@kopak-walker.co.uk

Langdean Manufacturing Ltd, 3 Thames Industrial Estate, High St South, Dunstable, Bedfordshire, LU6 3HD Tel: (01582) 696369 Fax: (01582) 666658 E-mail: langdean@btconnect.com

ELECTRICAL PENETRATORS

Remote Marine Systems, Derwent Road, York Road Business Park, Malton, North Yorkshire, YO17 6YB Tel: (01653) 690001 Fax: (01653) 690002 E-mail: sales@rmsltd.com

ELECTRICAL PLUGS AND SOCKETS

Aphel Ltd, Wayside Business Park, Wilsons Lane, Coventry, CV6 6NY Tel: (0870) 7541880 Fax: (0870) 7541881 E-mail: sales@aphel.co.uk

Elco Europe, Exning Road, Newmarket, Suffolk, CB8 0AT Tel: (01638) 675000 Fax: (01638) 675001

F Walther Electrics Ltd, Cromwell Road, Bredbury, Stockport, Cheshire, SK6 2RF Tel: 0161-494 1233 Fax: 0161-494 5055 E-mail: mail@walther.demon.co.uk

Power Place The, 48a Kingsway, Stoke-on-Trent, ST4 1JH Tel: (01782) 744789 Fax: (01782) 744789

Vernon's Fuse Co, 22 Trinity Trading Estate, Tribune Drive, Sittingbourne, Kent, ME10 2PG Tel: (01795) 471234 Fax: (01795) 476996

ELECTRICAL POWER ENGINEERING

Britannic Engineering Co Ltd, The Old Bakery, Market St, Charlbury, Chipping Norton, Oxfordshire, OX7 3PH Tel: (01608) 810332 Fax: (01608) 811566 E-mail: office@britannickengineering.co.uk

Pickup H Mechanical Electrical Services Ltd, Durham House, Lower Clark Street, Scarborough, North Yorkshire, YO12 7PW Tel: (01723) 369191 Fax: (01723) 362044 E-mail: pickup@hpickup.co.uk

ELECTRICAL POWER EQUIPMENT

Curtis Holt Ltd, Longreach, Gallion Boulevard, Crossways Business Park, Dartford, DA2 6QE Tel: (01322) 321300 Fax: (01322) 383641 E-mail: sales@toolbank.com

Ultra Electronics Ltd, Armitage Road, Rugeley, Staffordshire, WS15 1DR Tel: (01889) 503300 Fax: (01889) 572929 E-mail: enquiries@pmes.com

ELECTRICAL POWER SUPPLIES

▶ Pentranic Group Ltd, 4 Michaelson Square, Kirkton Campus, Livingston, West Lothian, EH54 7DP Tel: (01506) 463300 Fax: (01506) 463320 E-mail: info@pentranic.com

▶ indicates data change since last edition

ELECTRICAL PROTECTIVE CLOTHING

Snickers Original Ltd, Unit N3 Meltham Mills Industrial Estate, Meltham, Holmfirth, HD9 4DS Tel: (01484) 854488 Fax: (01484) 854733

ELECTRICAL RAILWAY SIGNALLING SYSTEM DESIGN

Howells Group plc, Longley Lane, Sharston Industrial Area, Manchester, M22 4SS Tel: 0161-945 5567 Fax: 0161-945 5597 E-mail: j.dolan@howells-railway.co.uk

▶ Magnate Grey Box Ltd, Airport Business Centre, 10 Thornbury Road, Estover, Plymouth, PL6 7PP Tel: (0845) 0702490 Fax: (0845) 0702495 E-mail: enquires@mgbl.co.uk

ELECTRICAL RAILWAY SIGNALLING SYSTEMS

▶ Magnate Grey Box Ltd, Airport Business Centre, 10 Thornbury Road, Estover, Plymouth, PL6 7PP Tel: (0845) 0702490 Fax: (0845) 0702495 E-mail: enquires@mgbl.co.uk

Westinghouse Rail Systems Ltd, PO Box 79, Chippenham, Wiltshire, SN15 1JD Tel: (01249) 441441 Fax: (01249) 441442 E-mail: wrsl.marketing@invensys.com

ELECTRICAL RESIN BONDED PRODUCTS

Benring Ltd, Glebe Tail, Quarnford, Buxton, Derbyshire, SK17 0TG Tel: (01298) 74026 Fax: (01298) 72391

ELECTRICAL SAFETY EQUIPMENT OR AIDS

Clare Instruments, Dominion Way, Worthing, West Sussex, BN14 8NW Tel: (01903) 233314 Fax: (01903) 216089 E-mail: sales@clareinstruments.com

Diktron Developments Ltd, Griptight House Unit 19, Spitfire Road, Castle Bromwich, Birmingham, B24 9PR Tel: 0121-382 4938 Fax: 0121-747 3009 E-mail: diktron@btconnect.com

Electrical Safeguards, Charlwoods Road, East Grinstead, West Sussex, RH19 2HR Tel: (01342) 325100 Fax: (01342) 327115 E-mail: enquiries@insulatedtools.co.uk

Expo Technologies Ltd, Summer Road, Thames Ditton, Surrey, KT7 0RH Tel: (020) 8398 8011 Fax: (020) 8398 8014 E-mail: sales@expoworldwide.com

ELECTRICAL SAFETY TEST EQUIPMENT

Link Electrical Testing, Races Farm, Aston Street, Aston Tirrold, Didcot, Oxfordshire, OX11 9DJ Tel: (01235) 850813 Fax: (01235) 850672 E-mail: info@linktesting.co.uk

Martindale Electric Co. Ltd, Metrohm House, Penfold Trading Estate, Imperial Way, Watford, WD24 4YY Tel: (01923) 441717 Fax: (01923) 446900 E-mail: sales@martindale-electric.co.uk

Seaward Electronic Ltd, 11 Bracken Hill, South West Industrial Estate, Peterlee, County Durham, SR8 2LS Tel: 0191-586 3511 Fax: 0191-586 0227 E-mail: sales@seaward.co.uk

ELECTRICAL SECURITY FENCING

Calders & Grandidge, 194 London Road, Boston, Lincolnshire, PE21 7HJ Tel: (01205) 358866 Fax: (01205) 312400 E-mail: enquiries@caldersandgrandidge.com

Owl Security Services Ltd, 30C Cowbridge Road, Pontyclun, Mid Glamorgan, CF72 9EE Tel: (01443) 238600 Fax: (01443) 238600 E-mail: enquiries@owlsecurity.co.uk

ELECTRICAL SLIP RING ASSEMBLIES

Lambeth Commutators, Brassmill Lane Trading Estate, Bath, BA1 3JF Tel: (01225) 426250 Fax: (01225) 445372 E-mail: david.fearn@wyco.co.uk

ELECTRICAL SOCKET BOXES

Moreton Alarm Supplies, Unit 1, Soveriegn Way, Maritime Business Park, Dock Road, Birkenhead, Merseyside, CH41 1DG Tel: 0151-630 0000 Fax: 0151-670 9888 E-mail: save@mas-uk.co.uk

ELECTRICAL STEEL LAMINATIONS

Cogent Sankey Scott Laminations (Bilston), Bankfield Works, Greenway Road, Bilston, West Midlands, WV14 0TJ Tel: (01902) 401140 Fax: (01902) 409710 E-mail: sll@cogent-power.com

Euro Laminations Ltd, Cromwell Road, Ellesmere Port, CH65 4DT Tel: 0151-356 1791 Fax: 0151-356 1806 E-mail: gls@cogent-power.com

ELECTRICAL SUBCONTRACTORS

▶ A E S Associates, 48a Edith Avenue, Peacehaven, East Sussex, BN10 8JB Fax: (01342) 332102

Industrial (Motor) Rewinds Ltd, Haut De L'Orme, Rue De Haut De L'Orme, Trinity, Jersey, JE3 5FP Tel: (01534) 865782 Fax: (01534) 865786 E-mail: rayimp@hotmail.com

Parke Electrical, 7 Gate Lane, Sutton Coldfield, West Midlands, B73 5TR Tel: 0121-357 3532 Fax: 0121-354 2491 E-mail: parke.electrical@btopenworld.com

ELECTRICAL SYSTEM DESIGN

▶ Cim-Team UK Ltd, PO Box 133, Stockport, Cheshire, SK12 1NS Tel: (0870) 4211252 Fax: (0870) 4211253 E-mail: info@cim-team.co.uk

Ibex Geo-tech Ltd, Ibex House, Malt Mill Lane, Halesowen, W. Midlands, B62 8JJ Tel: 0121-559 3862 Fax: 0121-559 9404 E-mail: jane.palmer@ibexgeotech.com

ELECTRICAL TEST METERS

A M P Electrical Wholesalers, 28 Amhurst Road, London, E8 1JN Tel: (020) 8985 3013 Fax: (020) 8986 7971 E-mail: enquiries@ampelectrical.co.uk

ELECTRICAL TRACE HEATING SYSTEM OR INSTALLATION OR SERVICING

Infro Heat Ltd, 2 Landport Road, Wolverhampton, WV2 2QJ Tel: (01902) 351025 Fax: (01902) 352552 E-mail: sales@infroheat.co.uk

Loxton Installations Ltd, Unit 14 Mill Hall Business Estate, Mill Hall, Aylesford, Kent, ME20 7JZ Tel: (01622) 716131 Fax: (01622) 719217 E-mail: info@loxtons.com

Traceman Fire Protection Consultants, 27 Leinster Road, Swinton, Manchester, M27 5YQ Tel: 0161-793 8448 Fax: 0161-794 2129 E-mail: enquiries@traceman.co.uk

ELECTRICAL TRACE HEATING SYSTEMS

Boiswood Ltd, Unit A1 Spinnaker Park, Hempsted, Gloucester, GL2 5JA Tel: (01452) 330011 Fax: (01452) 330088 E-mail: ian.taylor@boiswood.co.uk

Delta T Trace Heating Ltd, 7 Alston Works, Alston Road, Barnet, Hertfordshire, EN5 4EL Tel: (020) 8441 9499 Fax: (020) 8441 4459 E-mail: enquiries@deltat.co.uk

Esh Trace Heating, A Station Road, Guiseley, Leeds, LS20 8BX Tel: (01943) 884044 Fax: (01943) 884041 E-mail: enquiries@eshltd.com

Express Electrical, Dunswell Road, Cottingham, North Humberside, HU16 4JG Tel: (01482) 846269 Fax: (01482) 876655 E-mail: sales@express-industrial-exports.co.uk

Global Trace Heating Ltd, Unit 4, Penkridge Industrial Estate, Penkridge, Stafford, ST19 5NZ Tel: (01785) 712211 Fax: (01785) 711168 E-mail: sales@globaltrace.co.uk

Netco Ltd, 27 Quail Green, Wolverhampton, WV6 8DF Tel: (01902) 763879 Fax: (01902) 763879 E-mail: mail@netcotraceheating.com

Surface Heating Systems Ltd, 1 Heath Mill Enterprise Park, Heath Mill Road, Wombourne, Wolverhampton, WV5 8AP Tel: (01902) 326062 Fax: (01902) 892866 E-mail: surfheat@aol.com

Thorne & Derrick, Units 9-10 Birchills Trading Estate, Emery Road, Bristol, BS4 5PF Tel: 0117-977 4647 Fax: 0117-977 5582 E-mail: southernsales@thorneandderrick.co.uk

Thorne & Derrick, Units 5 & 6 Gear House, Saltmeadows Road, Gateshead, Tyne & Wear, NE8 3AH Tel: 0191-490 1547 Fax: 0191-477 5371 E-mail: sales@thorneandderrick.co.uk

ELECTRICAL WHOLESALERS

▶ Factoryprice, Discounthouse, 3/7 Wyndham Street, Aldershot, Hampshire, GU12 4NY Tel: (01252) 312345 Fax: (01252) 680888 E-mail: m.ltd@ntlworld.com

▶ Faraday Fire & Security Supplies, Unit 26-31 Faraday Mill Business Park, Faraday Road, Plymouth, PL4 0ST Tel: (01752) 660156 Fax: (01752) 660162 E-mail: sales@grelectrical.co.uk

▶ Midland Electrial Supplies, 375 Tyburn Road, Birmingham, B24 8HJ Tel: 0121-328 6448 Fax: 0121-328 6448 E-mail: morris-i@btconnect.com

▶ Refrigeration Parts Wholesale Ltd, Unit 2 Vine Street, Aston, Birmingham, B6 5TS Tel: 0121-328 8388 Fax: 0121-327 7266

▶ St Helens Electrical Supplies Ltd, 17 Peasley Cross Lane, St. Helens, Merseyside, WA9 3BG Tel: (01744) 613333 Fax: (01744) 613216

▶ TLC Electrical Distributors Ltd, 9-11 South Street, Hucknall, Nottingham, NG15 7BS Tel: 0115-963 4794 Fax: 0115-964 2812 E-mail: sales@tlcelec.co.uk

ELECTRICAL WINDOW CONTROL SYSTEMS

B J P Window Controls Ltd, Unit 11 Springvale Industrial Park, Off Millfields Road, Bilston, West Midlands, WV14 0QL Tel: (01902) 409461 Fax: (01902) 494672 E-mail: sales@bjp-windowcontrols.co.uk

Ruskin Air Management Ltd, Stourbridge Road, Bridgnorth, Shropshire, WV15 5BB Tel: (01746) 761921 Fax: (01746) 766450 E-mail: sales@naco.co.uk

ELECTRICALLY CONDUCTIVE ADHESIVES

Henkel Ltd, Apollo Court, Bishops Square Business Park, Hatfield, Hertfordshire, AL10 9EY Tel: (01707) 635000 Fax: (01707) 635099 E-mail: ukcorp.communications@henkel.co.uk

Polymer Systems Technology Ltd, 6 Vernon Building, Westbourne Street, High Wycombe, Buckinghamshire, HP11 2PX Tel: (01494) 446610 Fax: (01494) 528611 E-mail: sales@silicone-polymers.co.uk

ELECTRICALLY CONDUCTIVE AGGREGATES

Maingrade Ltd, 9 Oakland Industrial Estate, Lower Road, Cannock, Staffordshire, WS12 2UZ Tel: (01543) 426155 Fax: (01543) 426155 E-mail: conductag@aol.com

ELECTRICALLY CONDUCTIVE FILLERS

Maingrade Ltd, 9 Oakland Industrial Estate, Lower Road, Cannock, Staffordshire, WS12 2UZ Tel: (01543) 426155 Fax: (01543) 426155 E-mail: conductag@aol.com

ELECTRICALLY OPERATED GARAGE DOORS

▶ Kay Garage Doors, Unit 1, Phoenix Industrial Estate, Kerse Road, Stirling, FK7 7SG Tel: (01786) 474709 Fax: (01786) 451540 E-mail: info@kaygaragedoors.co.uk

ELECTRICALLY OPERATED SMOKE CURTAINS

Bolton Gate Co. Ltd, Waterloo Street, Bolton, BL1 2SP Tel: (01204) 871000 Fax: (01204) 871049 E-mail: general@boltongate.co.uk

Smoke & Solar Controls Systems UK Ltd, PO Box 2143, Atherstone, Warwickshire, CV9 1YB Tel: (01827) 714513 Fax: (01827) 714513

ELECTRICALLY WELDED TUBES

Hayes Tubes Ltd, Balds Lane, Lye, Stourbridge, West Midlands, DY9 8NN Tel: (01384) 422373 Fax: (01384) 422877 E-mail: hayestubes@enterprise.net

▶ Marcegaglia UK Ltd, New Road, Dudley, West Midlands, DY2 8TA Tel: (01384) 242812 Fax: (01384) 242813 E-mail: uk@marcegaglia.com

ELECTRICIANS SAFETY GLOVES

Clydesdale Ltd, 3 Sunbeam Road, Woburn Road Industrial Estate, Kempston, Bedford, MK42 7BZ Tel: (01234) 855855 Fax: (01234) 856845 E-mail: david@clydesdale.ltd.uk

Marigold Industrial Ltd, B2 Vantage Park, Old Gloucester Road, Hambrook, Bristol, BS16 1GW Tel: (01454) 323633 Fax: (0845) 0753356 E-mail: sales@marigold-industrial.com

ELECTRICITY BROKERS

▶ Blackpool Utilities Independent Energy, 94 Newcastle Avenue, Blackpool, FY3 9DH Tel: (01253) 390441 Fax: (01253) 393548 E-mail: sales@blackpool-utilities.co.uk

Fargro Ltd, Toddington Lane, Wick, Littlehampton, West Sussex, BN17 7QR Tel: (01903) 721591 Fax: (01903) 730737 E-mail: sales@fargro.co.uk

▶ Phoenix Power, 323 Goring Road, Goring-by-Sea, Worthing, West Sussex, BN12 4NX Tel: (01903) 248999 Fax: (01903) 249555 E-mail: sales@phoenixpower.net

ELECTRICITY METER MAINTENANCE OR REPAIR

Emetco Lighting Ltd, 81 Ellingham Industrial Centre, Ellingham Way, Ashford, Kent, TN23 6JZ Tel: (01233) 663333 Fax: (01233) 663366 E-mail: sales@emetco.co.uk

Greenbrook, 62 West Road, Harlow, Essex, CM20 2BG Tel: (01803) 527524 Fax: (01803) 526789 E-mail: meters@rdluk.com

Stephen P Wales, The Old Brewery Works, Lower Ellacombe Church Road, Torquay, TQ1 1JH Tel: (01803) 295430 Fax: (01803) 212819 E-mail: steve@stephenpwales.co.uk

ELECTRICITY METER MANUFACTURERS

Actaris Metering Systems Ltd, Langer Road, Felixstowe, Suffolk, IP11 2ER Tel: (01394) 694000 Fax: (01394) 276030 E-mail: csaunders@actaris.co.uk

Greenbrook, 62 West Road, Harlow, Essex, CM20 2BG Tel: (01803) 527524 Fax: (01803) 526789 E-mail: meters@rdluk.com

Iskraemeco (UK) Ltd, Unit 15 Lenton Business Centre, Lenton Boulevard, Nottingham, NG7 2BY Tel: 0115-924 4511 Fax: 0115-924 4104 E-mail: sales@iskraemeco.co.uk

J W Instruments, 1 Church Lane, Normanton, West Yorkshire, WF6 2DE Tel: (01924) 891049 Fax: (01924) 220846 E-mail: j.wilson@jwinstruments.co.uk

ELECTRICITY METER TEST EQUIPMENT

Caltest Instruments Ltd, PO Box 7717, Lockerbie, Dumfriesshire, DG11 1YF Tel: (01387) 811910 Fax: (01387) 810195 E-mail: sales@caltest.co.uk

Omicron Electronics UK Ltd, Unit 9, Marconi Gate, Staffordshire Technology Park, Stafford, ST18 0FZ Tel: (01785) 251000 Fax: (01785) 252000 E-mail: info@uk.omicron.at

▶ Tecnisis Ltd, Unit 3 Martlesham Creek Industrial Estate, Sandy Lane, Martlesham, Woodbridge, Suffolk, IP12 4SD Tel: (01394) 389098 Fax: (01394) 389062 E-mail: sales@tecnisis.co.uk

ELECTRICITY METERING LATCHING MICRO CONTACTORS

Stephen P Wales, The Old Brewery Works, Lower Ellacombe Church Road, Torquay, TQ1 1JH Tel: (01803) 295430 Fax: (01803) 212819 E-mail: steve@stephenpwales.co.uk

ELECTRICITY METERS

Albar Associates, Meridian House, Road One, Winsford, Cheshire, CW7 3QG Tel: (01606) 861351 Fax: (01606) 861643 E-mail: albar@albar-energy.co.uk

Stephen P Wales, The Old Brewery Works, Lower Ellacombe Church Road, Torquay, TQ1 1JH Tel: (01803) 295430 Fax: (01803) 212819 E-mail: steve@stephenpwales.co.uk

Switch 2 Energy Solutions Ltd, High Mill, Mill Street, Cullingworth, Bradford, West Yorkshire, BD13 5HA Tel: (01535) 270266 Fax: (01535) 270282 E-mail: sales@switch2.com

Westwood Meters & Timers Ltd, Torre Station Yard, Newton Road, Torquay, TQ2 5DD Tel: (01803) 297179 Fax: (01803) 299080 E-mail: sales@electricmeters.co.uk

ELECTRICITY SUPPLY GENERATING EQUIPMENT

Powernets UK Ltd, 32 Eastlands, Stafford, ST17 9BB Tel: (01785) 242235 Fax: (01785) 612261 E-mail: gbr@powernets.com

ELECTRO OPTICAL EQUILPMENT

Coercive Group Ltd, Beta House, Laser Quay, Rochester, Kent, ME2 4HU Tel: (01634) 713053 Fax: (01634) 712541 E-mail: csl@coercive.com

Instro Precision Ltd, Hornet Close, Pysons Road Industrial Estate, Broadstairs, Kent, CT10 2YD Tel: (01843) 604455 Fax: (01843) 861032 E-mail: marketing@instro.com

ELECTRO ZINC COATED STEEL SHEET

Argent Independant Steel (UK) Ltd, Lake Road, Leeway Industrial Estate, Newport, Gwent, NP19 4WN Tel: (01633) 290260 Fax: (01633) 290911 E-mail: info@argentindependantsteel.ltd.uk

Cutler & Woolf (Steel) Ltd, Unit 32, Jubilee Trade Centre, Jubilee Road, Letchworth Garden City, Hertfordshire, SG6 1SP Tel: (01462) 480420 Fax: (01462) 480430 E-mail: sales@cutlerandwoolfe.co.uk

ELECTROCARDIOGRAPH (ECG) EQUIPMENT

Deltex Medical Ltd, Terminus Road, Chichester, West Sussex, PO19 8TX Tel: (01243) 774837 Fax: (01243) 532534 E-mail: info@deltexmedical.com

Ultramedic Ltd, Wavertree Boulevard South, Liverpool, L7 9PF Tel: 0151-228 0354 Fax: 0151-252 1673

ELECTROCARDIOGRAPH EQUIPMENT (ECG)

Cardionetics Ltd, Centaur House, Ancells Road, Fleet, Hampshire, GU51 2UJ Tel: (01252) 761040 Fax: (01252) 761117 E-mail: sales@cardionetics.com

ELECTROCHEMICAL DEPOSITION (ECD) PLATERS OR PLATING

Diesel Marine International Ltd, Gloucester Road, North Shields, Tyne & Wear, NE29 8RQ Tel: 0191-257 5577 Fax: 0191-258 6398 E-mail: david.murray@dmiuk.co.uk

John Stokes Ltd, 60 High Street, Princes End, Tipton, West Midlands, DY4 9HP Tel: 0121-520 6301 Fax: 0121-557 7191 E-mail: stokeschrome@hotmail.com

Poli Chrome Engineers Moulds Ltd, Adswood Road, Stockport, Cheshire, SK3 8HR Tel: 0161-477 7370 Fax: 0161-477 1020 E-mail: ianlusby1@hotmail.com

RCJ Metal Finishers Ltd, 3 Pindar Road, Hoddesdon, Hertfordshire, EN11 0BZ Tel: (01992) 467931 Fax: (01992) 471547 E-mail: john@rcjmf.co.uk

Rockrome, 156 Sandy Road, Liverpool, L21 1AQ Tel: 0151-928 0080 Fax: 0151-928 8388

R. Wilson & Co. (Platers) Ltd, Zachrome Works, Sheffield Road, Whittington Moor, Chesterfield, Derbyshire, S41 8NH Tel: (01246) 450387 Fax: (01246) 455875 E-mail: office@zachrome.com

ELECTROCHEMICAL ETCHING EQUIPMENT

Etch Mark Ltd, 5 Romford Road, Stafford, ST16 3DZ Tel: (01785) 253143 Fax: (01785) 223282 E-mail: info@etchmark.co.uk

ELECTROCHEMICAL INSTRUMENTATION

Sycopel Scientific Ltd, 15 Sedling Road, Wear Industrial Estate, Washington, Tyne & Wear, NE38 9BZ Tel: 0191-417 8788 Fax: 0191-417 6627 E-mail: sales@sycopel.com

Thermo Electron, Units 12-16, Sedgway Business Park, Common Road, Witchford, Ely, Cambridgeshire, CB6 2HY Tel: (01353) 666111 Fax: (01353) 666001

ELECTROCHEMICAL MACHINE TOOLS

Anotronic Ltd, Stewkley Road, Soulbury, Leighton Buzzard, Bedfordshire, LU7 0DF Tel: (01525) 270261 Fax: (01525) 270235 E-mail: sales@anotronic.co.uk

Electrochemical Machining Services Ltd, High Street, Oadby, Leicester, LE2 5DE Tel: 0116-271 8022 Fax: 0116-271 8023 E-mail: ivan@electrochemical.co.uk

ELECTROCHEMICAL MACHINING SERVICES

Electrochemical Machining Services Ltd, High Street, Oadby, Leicester, LE2 5DE Tel: 0116-271 8022 Fax: 0116-271 8023 E-mail: ivan@electrochemical.co.uk

ELECTROCHEMICAL PROCESSING CHEMICAL PRODUCTS

Metal Finishing Supplies Ltd, 99a North Street, Cannock, Staffordshire, WS11 0AZ Tel: (01543) 505771 Fax: (01543) 466011

ELECTROCHEMICAL SENSORS

Endress & Hauser Ltd, Floats Road, Roundthorn Industrial Estate, Manchester, M23 9NF Tel: 0161-286 5000 Fax: 0161-998 1841 E-mail: info@uk.endress.com

ELECTROCOATING RESINS

▶ Molecular Technologies, 2 Modular Court, Enterprise Drive, Four Ashes, Wolverhampton, WV10 7DF Tel: (01902) 797990 Fax: (01902) 798295

ELECTROFORMED TEXTILE PRINTING ROTARY SCREENS

Bond Trading GB Ltd, 2 Gillingham Green, Gillingham, Kent, ME7 1SS Tel: (01634) 580670 Fax: (01634) 855455 E-mail: bondtradingltd@aol.com

City Screen Printers (UK) Ltd, Unit 9, Earls Way, Earls Way Industrial Estate, Thurmaston, Leicester, LE4 8DL Tel: 0116-260 2484 Fax: 0116-264 0261 E-mail: info@cityscreen.fsnet.co.uk

ELECTROFORMING SERVICES

B J S Co. Ltd, 65 Bideford Avenue, Greenford, Middlesex, UB6 7PP Tel: (020) 8810 5779 Fax: (020) 8810 5883 E-mail: enquiries@bjsco.com

Hart Coating Technology, PO Box 10, Brierley Hill, West Midlands, DY5 2RQ Tel: (01902) 895446 Fax: (01902) 897469 E-mail: tony@hartcoating.demon.co.uk

Precision Micro, Vantage Way, Erdington, Birmingham, B24 9GZ Tel: 0121-380 0100 Fax: 0121-359 3313 E-mail: sales@precisionmicro.com

R A Chilton, Unit 5 Tarvin Sands, Barrow Lane, Tarvin, Chester, CH3 8JF Tel: (01829) 740992 Fax: (01829) 740629 E-mail: rob@chilton.u-net.com

Tecan Ltd, Tecan Way, Granby Industrial Estate, Weymouth, Dorset, DT4 9TU Tel: (01305) 765432 Fax: (01305) 780194 E-mail: info@tecan.co.uk

ELECTROHYDRAULIC ACTUATORS

Claverham Ltd, Bishops Road, Claverham, Bristol, BS49 4NF Tel: (01934) 835224 Fax: (01934) 835337 E-mail: reception@claverham.com

Kinetrol Ltd, Farnham Trading Estate, Farnham, Surrey, GU9 9NU Tel: (01252) 733838 Fax: (01252) 713042 E-mail: sales@kinetrol.com

Moog Controls Ltd, Ashchurch, Tewkesbury, Gloucestershire, GL20 8NA Tel: (01684) 296600 Fax: (01684) 296760 E-mail: sales@moog.co.uk

Valve Center, 2 Bold Business Centre, Bold Lane, St. Helens, Merseyside, WA9 4TX Tel: (01925) 290660 Fax: (01925) 227463 E-mail: sales@valvecenter.co.uk

ELECTROHYDRAULIC BRAKES

Johnson Elevanja Ltd, Bath Road, Bridgwater, Somerset, TA6 4YQ Tel: (01278) 456411 Fax: (01278) 429949 E-mail: sales@jbrakes.com

Witton Kramer Products, 72 Cakemore Road, Rowley Regis, West Midlands, B65 0QT Tel: 0121-698 3100 Fax: 0121-698 3241 E-mail: info@brookcrompton-blackheath.co.uk

ELECTROHYDRAULIC VALVES

Nord Hydraulic Ltd, Unit Lkr3 L & M Business Park, Norman Road, Altrincham, Cheshire, WA14 4ES Tel: 0161-928 1199 Fax: 0161-941 5667 E-mail: david@nordhydraulic.co.uk

ELECTROHYDRAULICALLY OPERATED BARRIERS

Simplex Security Systems, PO Box 33903, London, NW9 6ER Tel: (020) 8200 9991 Fax: (020) 8200 6598 E-mail: sales@simplex.org.uk

ELECTROHYDRAULICALLY OPERATED GATES

Faac Security Equipment, Unit 6 Hamilton Close, Basingstoke, Hampshire, RG21 6YT Tel: (01256) 318100 Fax: (01256) 318101 E-mail: sales@faac.co.uk

ELECTROLESS NICKEL PLATING

G.B. Hard Chrome Ltd, 23-25 Nobel Square, Burnt Mills, Basildon, Essex, SS13 1LP Tel: 0845 8550608 Fax: (01268) 727524 E-mail: dan.griffiths@gbhard-chrome.co.uk

K.L. Giddings Ltd, Lion Works, Station Road East, Whittlesford, Cambridge, CB22 4WL Tel: (01223) 832638 Fax: (01223) 832189 E-mail: enquires@klgiddings.co.uk

Levertech Metal Finishing Services, Green Lane, Eccles, Manchester, M30 8JJ Tel: 0161-787 7247 Fax: 0161-789 6411 E-mail: levertech@levertech.fsnet.co.uk

Modern Metal Finishes Ltd, Burstwick Industrial Estate, Ellifoot Lane, Burstwick, Hull, HU12 9EF Tel: (01964) 671040 Fax: (01964) 671040 E-mail: sales@mmfgold.co.uk

Niphos Metal Finishing Co. Ltd, 25 Hope Street, Crewe, CW2 7DR Tel: (01270) 214081 Fax: (01270) 214089

Nu-Pro Surface Treatments, Eagle Works, London Road, Thrupp, Stroud, Gloucestershire, GL5 2BA Tel: (01453) 883344 Fax: (01453) 731597 E-mail: sales@nu-pro.com

Poeton Cardiff Ltd, Penarth Road, Cardiff, CF11 8UL Tel: (029) 2038 8182 Fax: (029) 2038 8185 E-mail: cardiff@poeton.co.uk

Poeton Industries Ltd, Eastern Avenue, Gloucester, GL4 3DN Tel: (01452) 300500 Fax: (01452) 500400 E-mail: sales@poeton.co.uk

S M S Technologies Ltd, Elizabeth House, Elizabeth Way, Harlow, Essex, CM19 5TL Tel: (01279) 406000 Fax: (01279) 406001 E-mail: admin@smstl.com

S W S Metal Treatments Ltd, Second Avenue, Trafford Park, Manchester, M17 1EE Tel: 0161-872 3569 Fax: 0161-848 7356 E-mail: enquiries@swsmetaltreatments.co.uk

Silchrome Plating Ltd, Barras Garth Road, Leeds, LS12 4JW Tel: 0113-263 7808 Fax: 0113-263 2682 E-mail: sales@silchrome.co.uk

▶ Stotfold Plating Co. Ltd, Taylors Road, Stotfold, Hitchin, Hertfordshire, SG5 4AX Tel: (01462) 732158 Fax: (01462) 835330

Surface Technology plc, Godiva Place, Coventry, CV1 5PN Tel: (024) 7625 8444 Fax: (024) 7655 1402 E-mail: sales@ultraseal.co.uk

▶ Surface Technology plc, 15-17 Colvilles Place, Kelvin Industrial Estate, East Kilbride, Glasgow, G75 0PZ Tel: (01355) 248223 Fax: (01355) 237141 E-mail: ronald.ross@surface-technology.co.uk

▶ Surface Technology plc, Long Causeway, Leeds, LS9 0NY Tel: 0113-248 0555 Fax: 0113-235 0169 E-mail: sales@armourcote.co.uk

Dave Walch Ltd, 121 Percival Lane, Runcorn, Cheshire, WA7 4UY Tel: (01928) 574681 Fax: (01928) 577790 E-mail: dave@anodisersruncorn.com

Wear Cote 1980 Ltd, Unit 32 Cambridge Yard, Cambridge Road, London, W7 3UP Tel: (020) 8567 1911 Fax: (020) 8579 9185 E-mail: wearcote@hotmail.com

ELECTROLUMINESCENT (EL) INFORMATION DISPLAYS

Thermotor Ltd, Beacon House, Station Road, East Preston, Littlehampton, West Sussex, BN16 3AA Tel: (01903) 850650 Fax: (01903) 850428 E-mail: sales@thermotor.co.uk

ELECTROLUMINESCENT (EL) LAMPS

The Danielson Group Ltd, 29 Pembroke Road, Aylesbury, Buckinghamshire, HP20 1DB Tel: (01296) 319000 Fax: (01296) 392141 E-mail: sales@danielson.co.uk

ELECTROLYTIC ALUMINIUM CAPACITORS

Mushroom Components, 28 College Street, Kempston, Bedford, MK42 8LU Tel: (01234) 363611 Fax: (01234) 326611 E-mail: pv@mushroom.co.uk

Power Products International Ltd, Commerce Way, Edenbridge, Kent, TN8 6ED Tel: (01732) 866424 Fax: (01732) 866399 E-mail: sales@ppi-uk.com

ELECTROLYTIC ANTIFOULING SYSTEMS

Cathelco Ltd, 18 Hipper St South, Chesterfield, Derbyshire, S40 1SS Tel: (01246) 277656 Fax: (01246) 206519 E-mail: sales@cathelco.co.uk

ELECTROLYTIC CAPACITORS

Adex Technical Ltd, Unit 4 Canal Ironworks, Hope Mill Lane, London Road, Stroud, Gloucestershire, GL5 2SH Tel: (01453) 889202 Fax: (01453) 889203 E-mail: sales@adexltd.co.uk

ELECTROMAGNET MANUFRS

C R D Devices Ltd, 3 All Saints Industrial Estate, Darlington Road, Shildon, County Durham, DL4 2RD Tel: (01388) 778400 Fax: (01388) 778800 E-mail: sales@crd-devices.co.uk

Kendrion Binder Magnete (UK) Ltd, Huddersfield Road, Low Moor, Bradford, West Yorkshire, BD12 0TQ Tel: (01274) 601111 Fax: (01274) 691093 E-mail: sales@kendrion-binder.co.uk

Magnetic Component Engineering (U K) Ltd, 1 Union Street, Luton, LU1 3AN Tel: (01582) 735226 Fax: (01582) 734226 E-mail: eurosales@mceproducts.com

Magnetic Solutions, Unit B7, Crabtree Road, Thorpe Industrial Estate, Egham, Surrey, TW20 8RN Tel: (01784) 438666 Fax: (01784) 438777 E-mail: trushton@magsol.co.uk

Precision Magnetics Ltd, Mangham Road, Barbot Hall Industrial Estate, Rotherham, South Yorkshire, S61 4RJ Tel: (01709) 829783 Fax: (01709) 371506 E-mail: sales@precisionmagnetics.co.uk

Stephenson Gobin Engineering Ltd, South Road, High Etherley, Bishop Auckland, County Durham, DL14 0HY Tel: (01388) 830900 Fax: (01388) 834220 E-mail: sales@stephensongobin.com

Tesla Engineering Ltd, Water Lane, Storrington, Pulborough, West Sussex, RH20 3EA Tel: (01903) 743941 Fax: (01903) 745548 E-mail: tesla@tesla.co.uk

Valley Systems Ltd, 26 Moorfields Close, Staines, Middlesex, TW18 3LU Tel: (01784) 457645 Fax: (01784) 438777 E-mail: trushton@magsol.co.uk

ELECTROMAGNETIC BRAKES

J R Power Transmission Scotland Ltd, Faraday Street, Dryburgh Industrial Estate, Dundee, DD2 3QQ Tel: (01382) 813677 Fax: (01382) 833925 E-mail: info@jrpower.co.uk

Johnson Elevanja Ltd, Bath Road, Bridgwater, Somerset, TA6 4YQ Tel: (01278) 456411 Fax: (01278) 429949 E-mail: sales@jbrakes.com

Kendrion Binder Magnete (UK) Ltd, Huddersfield Road, Low Moor, Bradford, West Yorkshire, BD12 0TQ Tel: (01274) 601111 Fax: (01274) 691093 E-mail: sales@kendrion-binder.co.uk

Ortlinghaus (UK) Ltd, 19 Sugarbrook Rd, Aston Fields Industrial Estate, Bromsgrove, Worcestershire, B60 3DN Tel: (01527) 579123 Fax: (01527) 579077 E-mail: sales@ortlinghaus.co.uk

Stephenson Gobin Engineering Ltd, South Road, High Etherley, Bishop Auckland, County Durham, DL14 0HY Tel: (01388) 830900 Fax: (01388) 834220 E-mail: sales@stephensongobin.com

Stromag Ltd, 29 Wellingborough Road, Rushden, Northamptonshire, NN10 9YE Tel: (01933) 350407 Fax: (01933) 358692 E-mail: sales@stromag.com

Z F Great Britain Ltd, Abbeyfield Road, Nottingham, NG7 2SX Tel: 0115-986 9211 Fax: 0115-986 9261 E-mail: info@zf.com

ELECTROMAGNETIC CLUTCHES

Industrial Clutch Parts Ltd, Unit 11 Bingswood Trading Estate, Whaley Bridge, High Peak, Derbyshire, SK23 7LY Tel: (01663) 734627 Fax: (01663) 733023 E-mail: sales@icpltd.co.uk

J R Power Transmission Scotland Ltd, Faraday Street, Dryburgh Industrial Estate, Dundee, DD2 3QQ Tel: (01382) 813677 Fax: (01382) 833925 E-mail: info@jrpower.co.uk

Kendrion Binder Magnete (UK) Ltd, Huddersfield Road, Low Moor, Bradford, West Yorkshire, BD12 0TQ Tel: (01274) 601111 Fax: (01274) 691093 E-mail: sales@kendrion-binder.co.uk

ELECTROMAGNETIC CLUTCHES – *continued*

Peak Transmissions Ltd, Unit 8 Hardwick Court, Hardwick View Road, Holmewood, Chesterfield, Derbyshire, S42 5SA Tel: (01246) 856758 Fax: (01246) 856850 E-mail: sales@peakgroupltd.com

Stephenson Gobin Engineering Ltd, South Road, High Etherley, Bishop Auckland, County Durham, DL14 0HY Tel: (01388) 830900 Fax: (01388) 834220 E-mail: sales@stephensongobin.com

Z F Great Britain Ltd, Abbeyfield Road, Nottingham, NG7 2SX Tel: 0115-986 9211 Fax: 0115-986 9261 E-mail: info@zf.com

ELECTROMAGNETIC COMPATIBILITY (EMC) COMPLIANCE CONSULTANCY

T U V Product Service, Snitterfield Road, Bearley, Stratford-upon-Avon, Warwickshire, CV37 0EX Tel: (01789) 731155 Fax: (01789) 731264 E-mail: mbrain@tuvps.co.uk

ELECTROMAGNETIC COMPATIBILITY (EMC) COMPONENTS/EQUIPMENT

Astor Emc, Unit 1-2 Redlake Lane, Wokingham, Berkshire, RG40 3BF Tel: 0118-979 5909 Fax: 0118-979 5791 E-mail: oceangrove@hotmail.com

Murrelektronik Ltd, Albion Street, Pendlebury, Swinton, Manchester, M27 4FG Tel: 0161-728 3133 Fax: 0161-728 3130 E-mail: sales@murrelektronik.co.uk

T D K Electronics Europe Ltd, Confort House, 5-7 Queensway, Redhill, RH1 1YB Tel: (01737) 781372 Fax: (01737) 773810

ELECTROMAGNETIC COMPATIBILITY (EMC) CONSULTANTS

Cranage E M C Testing Ltd, Stable Court, Oakley Hall, Market Drayton, Shropshire, TF9 4AG Tel: (01630) 658568 Fax: (01630) 658921 E-mail: info@cranage.co.uk

Elmac Services, PO Box 111, Chichester, West Sussex, PO19 4ZS Tel: (01243) 533361 Fax: (01243) 790535

Era Technology Ltd, Cleeve Road, Leatherhead, Surrey, KT22 7SA Tel: (01372) 367000 Fax: (01372) 367099 E-mail: info@era.co.uk

Hursley Emc Services Ltd, Unit 16 Brickfield Lane, Chandler's Ford, Eastleigh, Hampshire, SO53 4DP Tel: (023) 8027 1111 Fax: (023) 8027 1144 E-mail: sales@hursley-emc.co.uk

Omega Research Ltd, 32 Wissey Way, Ely, Cambridgeshire, CB6 2WW Tel: (01353) 612520 Fax: (01353) 612520 E-mail: sales@omega-research.co.uk

R F Design Ltd, 27 Weelsby Way, Hessle, North Humberside, HU13 0JN Tel: (01482) 629270 Fax: (01482) 629270 E-mail: martyn@rfdesign.karoo.co.uk

ELECTROMAGNETIC COMPATIBILITY (EMC) DESIGN

R F Design Ltd, 27 Weelsby Way, Hessle, North Humberside, HU13 0JN Tel: (01482) 629270 Fax: (01482) 629270 E-mail: martyn@rfdesign.karoo.co.uk

ELECTROMAGNETIC COMPATIBILITY (EMC) (ENVIRONMENTAL ASSESSMENT) DESIGN CONSULTANTS

J.S. Chinn Project Engineering Ltd, Coventry Road, Exhall, Coventry, CV7 9FT Tel: 0117-958 4600 Fax: 0117-958 4601 E-mail: jschinn@internet-uk.net

▶ Phoenix Feng Shui, Climperwell Cottage, Climperwell, Brimpsfield, Gloucester, GL4 8LQ Tel: (01452) 863288 Fax: (0794) 1581202 E-mail: dee.ramage@phoenixfengshui.co.uk

ELECTROMAGNETIC COMPATIBILITY (EMC) FILTERS

Dialight B L P Ltd, Exning Road, Newmarket, Suffolk, CB8 0AX Tel: (01638) 665161 Fax: (01638) 660718 E-mail: sales@blpcomp.com

Spectrum Control GmbH, PO Box 34, Great Yarmouth, Norfolk, NR29 5RE Tel: (01692) 678041 Fax: (01692) 678042 E-mail: sales@spectrumcontrol.co.uk

Suppression Devices, Unit 8, York Street Business Centre, Clitheroe, Lancashire, BB7 2DL Tel: (01200) 444497 Fax: (01200) 444330 E-mail: sales@suppression-devices.com

ELECTROMAGNETIC COMPATIBILITY (EMC) RAW MATERIALS

Hart Coating Technology, PO Box 10, Brierley Hill, West Midlands, DY5 2RQ Tel: (01902) 895446 Fax: (01902) 897469 E-mail: tony@hartcoating.demon.co.uk

ELECTROMAGNETIC COMPATIBILITY (EMC) SHIELDING MANUFRS

Quality Plated Plastics, Shady Lane, Birmingham, B44 9ER Tel: 0121-366 7500 Fax: 0121-366 6436

ELECTROMAGNETIC COMPATIBILITY (EMC) SOFTWARE

Hursley Emc Services Ltd, Unit 16 Brickfield Lane, Chandler's Ford, Eastleigh, Hampshire, SO53 4DP Tel: (023) 8027 1111 Fax: (023) 8027 1144 E-mail: sales@hursley-emc.co.uk

Westbay Technology Ltd, Main Street, Baycliff, Ulverston, Cumbria, LA12 9RN Tel: (01229) 869108 Fax: (01229) 869108 E-mail: sales@westbay.ndirect.co.uk

ELECTROMAGNETIC COMPATIBILITY (EMC) TEST EQUIPMENT

Emc Partner UK Ltd, 1a Golf Link Villas, The Common, Downley, High Wycombe, Buckinghamshire, HP13 5YH Tel: (01494) 444255 Fax: (01494) 444277 E-mail: sales@emcpartner.co.uk

ELECTROMAGNETIC COMPATIBILITY (EMC) TESTING

3C Test Ltd, Technology Park, Silverstone Circuit, Silverstone, Towcester, Northamptonshire, NN12 8GX Tel: (01327) 857500 Fax: (01327) 857747 E-mail: sales@3ctest.co.uk

Building Research Establishment Ltd, Bucknalls Lane, Garston, Watford, WD25 9XX Tel: (01923) 664237 Fax: (01923) 664994 E-mail: enquiries@brecertification.com

Cranage E M C Testing Ltd, Stable Court, Oakley Hall, Market Drayton, Shropshire, TF9 4AG Tel: (01630) 658568 Fax: (01630) 658921 E-mail: info@cranage.co.uk

Daletech Electronics Ltd, Regency House, Valley Road, Pudsey, West Yorkshire, LS28 9EN Tel: 0113-239 4220 Fax: 0113-255 3583 E-mail: sales@daletech.co.uk

E M C Hire Ltd, Ivel Road, Shefford, Bedfordshire, SG17 5JU Tel: (01462) 817111 Fax: (01462) 817444 E-mail: sales@emchire.co.uk

Electromagnetic Testing Services, Pratts Field, Lubberhedges Lane, Stebbing, Dunmow, Essex, CM6 3BT Tel: (01371) 856061 Fax: (01371) 856144 E-mail: info@etsemc.co.uk

Hursley Emc Services Ltd, Unit 16 Brickfield Lane, Chandler's Ford, Eastleigh, Hampshire, SO53 4DP Tel: (023) 8027 1111 Fax: (023) 8027 1144 E-mail: sales@hursley-emc.co.uk

R F Shielding Ltd, Unit 16, Rising Sun Industrial Estate, Blaina, Abertillery, Gwent, NP13 3JW Tel: (01495) 292399 Fax: (01495) 292550 E-mail: info@rfshielding.co.uk

R N Electronics Ltd, Arnolds Farm Lane, Mountnessing, Brentwood, Essex, CM13 1UT Tel: (01277) 352219 Fax: (01277) 352968 E-mail: sales@rnelectronics.com

RFI Global Services Ltd, Ewhurst Park, Ramsdell, Tadley, Hampshire, RG26 5RQ Tel: (01256) 851193 Fax: (01256) 312001 E-mail: sales@rfi-global.com

T R W Automotive, Technical Centre, Stratford Road, Shirley, Solihull, West Midlands, B90 4GW Tel: 0121-627 4141 Fax: 0121-627 3584 E-mail: rob.miller@trw.com

Westinghouse Rail Systems Ltd, PO Box 79, Chippenham, Wiltshire, SN15 1JD Tel: (01249) 441441 Fax: (01249) 441442 E-mail: wrsl.marketing@invensys.com

ELECTROMAGNETIC COMPATIBILITY (EMC) TESTING ANTENNAS

T U V Product Service, Snitterfield Road, Bearley, Stratford-upon-Avon, Warwickshire, CV37 0EX Tel: (01789) 731155 Fax: (01789) 731264 E-mail: mbrain@tuvps.co.uk

ELECTROMAGNETIC COMPONENT/EQUIPMENT, *See also Contactor; Relay etc*

Redcliffe Magtronics, 19 Clothier Road, Brislington, Bristol, BS4 5PS Tel: 0117-972 9400 Fax: 0117-972 3013 E-mail: enquiries@redcliffe.biz

Spectrum Control GmbH, PO Box 34, Great Yarmouth, Norfolk, NR29 5RE Tel: (01692) 678041 Fax: (01692) 678042 E-mail: sales@spectrumcontrol.co.uk

ELECTROMAGNETIC CONTACTORS

ABB Ltd, Grovelands House, Longford Road, Coventry, CV7 9ND Tel: (024) 7636 8500 Fax: (024) 7636 4499 E-mail: info@gb.abb.com

Albright Engineers Ltd, 125 Red Lion Road, Surbiton, Surrey, KT6 7QS Tel: (020) 8390 5357 Fax: (020) 8390 1927 E-mail: sales@albright.co.uk

Mathew C Blythe & Son Ltd, The Green, Tredington, Shipston-on-Stour, Warwickshire, CV36 4NJ Tel: (01608) 662295 Fax: (01608) 662006 E-mail: sales@matthewcblythe.co.uk

ELECTROMAGNETIC DOOR LOCKS

▶ Abbey Locksmiths, 54 Halsey Park, London Colney, St. Albans, Hertfordshire, AL2 1BH Tel: (01727) 828048 Fax: (07092) 003147 E-mail: service@abbeylocks.co.uk

Access & Security 24Hr Locksmiths, Key House Coombe Rise, Oadby, Leicester, LE2 5TT Tel: 0116-271 9003 Fax: 0116-271 9229 E-mail: info@leicesterlocksmith.com

Adams Rite Europe Ltd, 6 Moreton Industrial Estate, London Road, Swanley, Kent, BR8 8TZ Tel: (01322) 668024 Fax: (01322) 660996 E-mail: info@adamsrite.co.uk

▶ Door-Tech Solutions Ltd, 4 Kean Close, Lichfield, Staffordshire, WS13 7EL Tel: (01543) 252374 Fax: (01543) 256845 E-mail: sales@doortechsolutions.co.uk

▶ GB Locking Systems Ltd, Redburn House, Redburn Road, Newcastle upon Tyne, NE5 1NB Tel: 0191-271 6344 Fax: 0191-271 3644 E-mail: sales@gblockingsystems.co.uk

Ross Manufacturers, Altbarn Industrial Estate Lordswood Industrial Estate, Revenge Road, Chatham, Kent, ME5 8UD Tel: (01634) 684808 Fax: (01634) 684831 E-mail: rossarch@btconnect.com

ELECTROMAGNETIC INTERFERENCE (EMI) AND RADIO FREQUENCY INTERFERENCE (RFI) ELECTRONIC ARTICLE SURVEILLANCE (EAS) EQUIPMENT

ProTag Retail Security, Units 2-3, Short Way, The Industrial Estate, Thornbury, Bristol, BS35 3UT Tel: (01454) 418500 Fax: (01454) 413708 E-mail: martin@touchpanels.co.uk

ELECTROMAGNETIC INTERFERENCE (EMI) APPLICATION SERVICES

J M K Ltd, Unit 9 Block 2, Vale of Leven Industrial Estate, Dumbarton, G82 3PW Tel: (01389) 751841 Fax: (01389) 751775 E-mail: jmkfilters@sol.co.uk

Leabank Coatings Ltd, Wycombe Road, Stokenchurch, High Wycombe, Buckinghamshire, HP14 3RJ Tel: (01494) 483737 Fax: (01494) 484239 E-mail: info@leabank.net

ELECTROMAGNETIC INTERFERENCE (EMI) POWER LINE FILTERS

▶ Esprit Solutions Ltd, 105 Boundary Street, Liverpool, L5 9YJ Tel: 0151-548 5900 Fax: (0870) 1417005 E-mail: sales@espritsolutions.info

ELECTROMAGNETIC INTERFERENCE SHIELDING (EMS) MATERIALS

C Brandauer & Co. Ltd, 235 Bridge Street West, Birmingham, B19 2YU Tel: 0121-359 2822 Fax: 0121-359 2836 E-mail: aedwards@brandauer.co.uk

Chomerics, Unit 6 Century Point, Cressex Business Park, High Wycombe, Buckinghamshire, HP12 3SL Tel: (01628) 404000 Fax: (01628) 404091 E-mail: chomerics_europe@parker.com

European Emc Products Ltd, Unit 8, Saffron Business Centre, Elizabeth Close, Saffron Walden, Essex, CB10 2BL Tel: (01799) 523073 Fax: (01799) 521191 E-mail: info@euro-emc.co.uk

P & P Technology Ltd, 1 Kestrel Park, Finch Drive, Springwood Industrial Estate, Braintree, Essex, CM7 2SF Tel: (01376) 550525 Fax: (01376) 552389 E-mail: info@p-p-t.co.uk

Precision Micro, Vantage Way, Erdington, Birmingham, B24 9GZ Tel: 0121-380 0100 Fax: 0121-359 3313 E-mail: sales@precisionmicro.com

R F I Seals & Gaskets Ltd, Unit 2, Saltash Business Park, Moorlands Trading Estate, Forge Lane, Saltash, Cornwall, PL12 6LX Tel: 01752 841051 Fax: 01752 847559 E-mail: sales@rfiseals.co.uk

R F I Shielding Ltd, Warner Drive, Springwood Industrial Estate, Braintree, Essex, CM7 2YW Tel: 01342 315044 Fax: (01376) 346442

Redcliffe Magtronics, 19 Clothier Road, Brislington, Bristol, BS4 5PS Tel: 0117-972 9400 Fax: 0117-972 3013 E-mail: enquiries@redcliffe.biz

Tecknit Europe Ltd, Swingbridge Road, Grantham, Lincolnshire, NG31 7XT Tel: (01476) 590600 Fax: (01476) 591600 E-mail: tecknit.sales@twp-europe.co.uk

ELECTROMAGNETIC TEST EQUIPMENT

E M C Hire Ltd, Ivel Road, Shefford, Bedfordshire, SG17 5JU Tel: (01462) 817111 Fax: (01462) 817444 E-mail: sales@emchire.co.uk

Seaward Electronic Ltd, 11 Bracken Hill, South West Industrial Estate, Peterlee, County Durham, SR8 2LS Tel: 0191-586 3511 Fax: 0191-586 0227 E-mail: sales@seaward.co.uk

ELECTROMECHANICAL ACTUATORS

Barnbrook Systems Ltd, 25 Fareham Park Road, Fareham, Hampshire, PO15 6LD Tel: (01329) 847722 Fax: (01329) 844132 E-mail: barnbrook@aol.co.uk

Claverham Ltd, Bishops Road, Claverham, Bristol, BS49 4NF Tel: (01934) 835224 Fax: (01934) 835337 E-mail: reception@claverham.com

Dewert Motorised Systems, Phoenix Mecano House, 1 Faraday Road, Aylesbury, Buckinghamshire, HP19 8TX Tel: (01296) 398855 Fax: (01296) 398866 E-mail: dewertgb@phoenix-mecano.com

LINAK UK Ltd, Actuation House, Crystal Drive, Sandwell Business Park, Smethwick, West Midlands, B66 1RJ Tel: 0121-544 2211 Fax: 0121-544 2552E-mail: sales@linak.co.uk

Muirhead Vactric Components Ltd, Oakfield Road, London, SE20 8EW Tel: (020) 8659 9090 Fax: (020) 8659 9906 E-mail: sales@muirheadaerospace.com

Power Jacks Ltd, South Harbour Road, Fraserburgh, Aberdeenshire, AB43 9BZ Tel: (01346) 513131 Fax: (01346) 516827 E-mail: sales@powerjacks.co.uk

S K F (U K) Ltd, Sundon Park Road, Luton, LU3 3BL Tel: (01582) 490049 Fax: (01582) 848091 E-mail: marketing.uk@skf.com

ELECTROMECHANICAL ASSEMBLY PRODUCTION OR SERVICES

Assembly Solutions Ltd, Units 4-8 Watermead Works, Slater Lane, Bolton, BL1 2TE Tel: (01204) 537621 Fax: (01204) 381007 E-mail: sales@assembly-solutions.com

Challenger Solutions Ltd, Unit 85 Haltwhistle Road, South Woodham Ferrers, Chelmsford, CM3 5ZA Tel: (01245) 325252 Fax: (01245) 325301 E-mail: jon@challengersolutions.com

Colbree Precision Ltd, Units 10-12 Beacon Court, Pitstone Green Business Park, Quarry Road, Pitstone, Leighton Buzzard, Bedfordshire, LU7 9GY Tel: (01296) 664200 Fax: (01296) 664201 E-mail: sales@colbree.com

Cyphermet Ltd, Bone Lane, Newbury, Berkshire, RG14 5SH Tel: (01635) 34099 Fax: (01635) 528623 E-mail: sales@cyphermet.co.uk

E R Edwards & Sons Ltd, Blatchford Road, Horsham, West Sussex, RH13 5QR Tel: (01403) 224400 Fax: (01403) 224401 E-mail: sales@eredwards.com

G I G Systems Ltd, Unit 9, 40 Wilton Road, Reading, RG30 2SS Tel: 0118-958 1115 Fax: 0118-958 1117 E-mail: gigssystems@btconnect.com

Grange Products Ltd, Unit 4 Station Road, Reddish, Stockport, Cheshire, SK5 6ND Tel: 0161-480 3318

Inoplas Technology Ltd, Uddens Trading Estate, Wimborne, Dorset, BH21 7LD Tel: (01202) 866000 Fax: (01202) 866016 E-mail: sales@inoplas.co.uk

▶ indicates data change since last edition

ELECTROMECHANICAL ASSEMBLY PRODUCTION OR SERVICES – *continued*

J J Electronics Ltd, 3a Telmere Industrial Estate, Albert Road, Luton, LU1 3QF Tel: (01582) 391156 Fax: (01582) 391896 E-mail: sales@jjelectronics.net
Manx Engineers Ltd, Wheel Hill, Laxey, Isle of Man, IM4 7NL Tel: (01624) 861362 Fax: (01624) 861914
Pandect Precision Components Ltd, Wellington Road, High Wycombe, Buckinghamshire, HP12 3PX Tel: (01494) 526303 Fax: (01494) 465557 E-mail: enquiries@pandect.demon.co.uk
Shakespeare Engineering, 91 Haltwhistle Road, South Woodham Ferrers, Chelmsford, CM3 5ZA Tel: (01245) 328118 Fax: (01245) 325696
Surgecam Ltd, Cold Hesledon Industrial Estate, Cold Hesledon, Seaham, County Durham, SR7 8ST Tel: 0191-513 0666 Fax: 0191-513 0862 E-mail: david.watson@surgecam.co.uk
Zonefollow Ltd, 2 Wilton Road, Haine Industrial Estate, Ramsgate, Kent, CT12 5HG Tel: (01843) 588087 Fax: (01843) 851313 E-mail: info@zonefollow.co.uk

ELECTROMECHANICAL ASSEMBLY TESTING

E R Edwards & Sons Ltd, Blatchford Road, Horsham, West Sussex, RH13 5QR Tel: (01403) 224400 Fax: (01403) 224401 E-mail: sales@eredwards.com
S K N Electronics Ltd, Armoury Road, Birmingham, B11 2PP Tel: 0121-773 6672 Fax: 0121-766 8457 E-mail: technical@sknelectronics.co.uk
Saygrove System & Technology, Units 9-10 Catheralls Industrial Estate, Brookhill Way, Buckley, Clwyd, CH7 3PS Tel: (01244) 550022 Fax: (01244) 549843 E-mail: info@saygrove.co.uk

ELECTROMECHANICAL COMPONENTS

Argo Electronic Components Ltd, Leyden Works, Station Road, Great Yarmouth, Norfolk, NR31 0HB Tel: (01493) 652752 Fax: (01493) 655433 E-mail: sales@norfolk-capacitors.com
Arrow Components, Unit 5 Mill Court, Spindle Way, Crawley, West Sussex, RH10 1TT Tel: (01293) 558900 Fax: (01293) 558901
Avnet Time, Avnet House, Rutherford Close, Stevenage, Hertfordshire, SG1 2EF Tel: (01438) 789789 E-mail: timeuk@avnet.com
ESD Ltd, 68 - 71 Chapel Street, Netherton, Dudley, West Midlands, DY2 9PN Tel: (01384) 572699 Fax: (01384) 572698 E-mail: sales@esdltd.com
Flint Ltd, Walker Road, Bardon Hill, Coalville, Leicestershire, LE67 1TU Tel: (01530) 510333 Fax: (01530) 510275 E-mail: info@flint.co.uk

ELECTROMECHANICAL CONNECTORS

Abacus Deltron, Deltron Emcon House, Hargreaves Way, Sawcliffe Industrial Park, Scunthorpe, South Humberside, DN15 8RF Tel: (01724) 273200 Fax: (01724) 270230 E-mail: info@abacus-deltron.co.uk

ELECTROMECHANICAL CONTROL SYSTEMS

Total Solutions Ltd, 11 Sealand Road, Sealand, Chester, CH1 6BS Tel: (01244) 881818 Fax: (01244) 881991 E-mail: totalsols@aol.com

ELECTROMECHANICAL ENGINEERS OR ENGINEERING

Almec E A S Ltd, Knowl Piece, Wilbury Way, Hitchin, Hertfordshire, SG4 0TY Tel: (01462) 436330 Fax: (01462) 437160 E-mail: enquiries@almec-eas.com
Amfax Ltd, 3 Clump Farm Industrial Estate, Blandford Heights, Blandford Forum, Dorset, DT11 7TE Tel: (01258) 480777 Fax: (01258) 480728 E-mail: sales@amfax.co.uk
Atec Hampshire Ltd, Peel Street, Southampton, SO14 5QT Tel: (023) 8063 1391 Fax: (023) 8033 8931 E-mail: sales@atec-hants.co.uk
Britannic Engineering Co Ltd, The Old Bakery, Market St, Charlbury, Chipping Norton, Oxfordshire, OX7 3PH Tel: (01608) 810332 Fax: (01608) 811566 E-mail: office@britannickengineering.co.uk
Levern Engineering Ltd, 30 Cogan Street, Barrhead, Glasgow, G78 1EJ Tel: 0141-881 9101 Fax: 0141-881 1888 E-mail: service@leverneng.co.uk
Radun Controls Ltd, Unit 42 Aberaman Industrial Estate, Aberaman, Aberdare, Mid Glamorgan, CF44 6UZ Tel: (01685) 887600 Fax: (01685) 887601 E-mail: general@radun.com
Zirkon Ltd, Butlers Leap, Rugby, Warwickshire, CV21 3RQ Tel: (01788) 534800 Fax: (01788) 569283 E-mail: info@zirkon.co.uk

ELECTROMECHANICAL EQUIPMENT/MACHINERY SPARE PARTS

James Dring Power Plant Ltd, 8 Eagle Road, Quarry Hill Industrial Estate, Ilkeston, Derbyshire, DE7 4RB Tel: 0115-944 0072 Fax: 0115-944 0235 E-mail: enquiries@jamesdring.co.uk

ELECTROMECHANICAL RELAYS

Argo Electronic Components Ltd, Leyden Works, Station Road, Great Yarmouth, Norfolk, NR31 0HB Tel: (01493) 652752 Fax: (01493) 655433 E-mail: sales@norfolk-capacitors.com
B C H Relays Ltd, Unit 15, Phoenix Business Park, Brindley Road, Dodwells Bridge Industrial Estate, Hinckley, Leicestershire, LE10 3BY Tel: (01455) 239675 Fax: (01455) 238795 E-mail: billpower@btconnect.com
Precision Relays Ltd, 3 Seafield Road, Inverness, IV1 1SG Tel: (01463) 233929 Fax: (01463) 712514 E-mail: sales@precisionrelays.co.uk

ELECTROMECHANICAL SWITCHES

Abacus Deltron, Deltron Emcon House, Hargreaves Way, Sawcliffe Industrial Park, Scunthorpe, South Humberside, DN15 8RF Tel: (01724) 273200 Fax: (01724) 270230 E-mail: info@abacus-deltron.co.uk

ELECTROMEDICAL EQUIPMENT MANUFRS

Dynamic Imaging Ltd, 9 Cochrane Square, Brucefield Industrial, Livingston, West Lothian, EH54 9DR Tel: (01506) 415282 Fax: (01506) 410603 E-mail: marketing@dynamicimaging.co.uk
E M E (Electro Medical Equipment) Ltd, 60 Gladstone Pl, Brighton, BN2 3QD Tel: (01273) 654100 Fax: (01273) 654101 E-mail: info@eme-med.co.uk
Ectron Ltd, Knap Close, Letchworth Garden City, Hertfordshire, SG6 1AQ Tel: (01462) 682124 Fax: (01462) 481463 E-mail: ectronltd@btconnect.com
Electro-Medical Supplies Greenham, Grove Street, Wantage, Oxfordshire, OX12 7AD Tel: (01235) 772272 Fax: (01235) 763518 E-mail: info@emslimited.co.uk
Huntleigh Healthcare Ltd, 310-312 Dallow Road, Luton, LU1 1TD Tel: (01582) 413104 Fax: (01582) 459100 E-mail: sales.admin@huntleigh-healthcare.com
Intercal, 99 Windmill Street, Gravesend, Kent, DA12 1LE Tel: (01474) 357479
Measurement Aids Ltd, 90-92 Tontine Street, Folkestone, Kent, CT20 1JW Tel: (01303) 850722 Fax: (01303) 220380
Nomeq Ltd, Unit 25-26 North St Industrial Estate, Droitwich, Worcestershire, WR9 8JB Tel: (01905) 795005 Fax: (01905) 796655 E-mail: info@nomeq.co.uk
S L E Ltd, Twin Bridges Business Park, 232 Selsdon Road, South Croydon, Surrey, CR2 6PL Tel: (020) 8681 1414 Fax: (020) 8649 8570 E-mail: admin@sle.co.uk

ELECTRON BEAM DRILLING

Fusion Technologies Ltd, 26 Avonbank Industrial Estate, West Town Road, Bristol, BS11 9DE Tel: 0117-982 6606 Fax: 0117-982 6616

ELECTRON BEAM WELDING

Bodycote Heating Treatment Ltd, 18 Westgate, Skelmersdale, Lancashire, WN8 8AZ Tel: (01695) 716500 Fax: (01695) 50105 E-mail: sales@bodycote.co.uk
Cambridge Electron Beam, 3 High Street, Toft, Cambridge, CB23 2RL Tel: (01223) 263588 Fax: (01223) 263391 E-mail: t.e.burns@talk21.com
Electron Beam Engineering, 49a Mill Corner, Soham, Ely, Cambridgeshire, CB7 5HT Tel: (01353) 624196 Fax: (01353) 624196 E-mail: ebengineering@btinternet.com

ELECTRON BEAM WELDING EQUIPMENT

Fusion Technologies Ltd, 26 Avonbank Industrial Estate, West Town Road, Bristol, BS11 9DE Tel: 0117-982 6606 Fax: 0117-982 6616

ELECTRON MICROSCOPE ACCESSORIES

Agar Scientific Ltd, 66a Cambridge Road, Stansted, Essex, CM24 8DA Tel: (01279) 813519 Fax: (01279) 815106 E-mail: sales@agarscientific.com
Deben UK, Brickfields Business Park, Old Stowmarket Road, Woolpit, Bury St. Edmunds, Suffolk, IP30 9QS Tel: (01359) 244870 Fax: (01359) 244879 E-mail: web@deben.co.uk
F E I, Philips House Cambridge Business Park, Cowley Road, Cambridge, CB4 0HF Tel: (01223) 468555 Fax: (01223) 468599
Gilder Grids, Unit 11 Withambrook Park Industrial Estate, Grantham, Lincolnshire, NG31 9ST Tel: (01476) 560052 Fax: (01476) 568165 E-mail: sales@gildergrids.co.uk
Micro-Analysis Consultants Ltd, Unit 19, Edison Road, St. Ives, Cambridgeshire, PE27 3LF Tel: (01480) 462626 Fax: (01480) 462901 E-mail: standards@dial.pipex.com
Obducat Camscan Ltd, Camscan House, Pembroke Avenue, Waterbeach, Cambridge, CB25 9PY Tel: (01223) 861066 Fax: (01223) 861077 E-mail: info@camscan.com

ELECTRON MICROSCOPE COMPONENTS

Obducat Camscan Ltd, Camscan House, Pembroke Avenue, Waterbeach, Cambridge, CB25 9PY Tel: (01223) 861066 Fax: (01223) 861077 E-mail: info@camscan.com

ELECTRON MICROSCOPE MANUFRS

Hitachi Hi-Technology Corporation, 7 Ivanhoe Road, Hogwood Industrial Estate, Finchampstead, Wokingham, Berkshire, RG40 4QQ Tel: 0118-932 8632 Fax: 0118-932 8779 E-mail: sales@hitachi-hitec-uk.com
I S S Group Ltd, Pellowe House, Francis Road, Withington, Manchester, M20 4XP Tel: 0161-445 5446 Fax: 0161-445 4914 E-mail: sales@iss-group.co.uk
Jeol UK Ltd, Silver Court, Watchmead, Welwyn Garden City, Hertfordshire, AL7 1LT Tel: (01707) 377117 Fax: (01707) 373254 E-mail: uk.sales@jeoleuro.com
Obducat Camscan Ltd, Camscan House, Pembroke Avenue, Waterbeach, Cambridge, CB25 9PY Tel: (01223) 861066 Fax: (01223) 861077 E-mail: info@camscan.com

ELECTRONIC ADJUSTABLE BEDS

And So To Bed Ltd, Pymore Mills, Pymore, Bridport, Dorset, DT6 5PJ Tel: (01308) 425252 Fax: (01308) 458811 E-mail: sales@andsotobed.co.uk
Brtitish Bed Exports, Lower Clough Mill, Pendle Street, Barrowford, Nelson, Lancashire, BB9 8PH Tel: (01282) 694777 Fax: (01282) 447777 E-mail: sales@silentnightexport.co.uk
Huntleigh Nesbit Evans Ltd, Woodsbank Trading Estate, Woden Road West, Wednesbury, West Midlands, WS10 7BL Tel: 0121-556 1511 Fax: 0121-502 2092 E-mail: sales@huntcare.co.uk
Tempur Mattress Mmanufacturers, Caxton Point, Printing House Lane, Hayes, Middlesex, UB3 1AP Tel: (020) 8589 7000 Fax: (020) 8589 7001

ELECTRONIC ARTICLE SURVEILLANCE (EAS) SYSTEMS

▶ Tag Company UK Ltd, Duval House, High Street Harmondsworth, Harmondsworth, West Drayton, Middlesex, UB7 0BT Tel: (020) 8283 4999 E-mail: info@tagcompany.com

ELECTRONIC ASSEMBLIES

Alpha Design, 1 Didcot Road, Nuffield Industrial Estate, Poole, Dorset, BH17 0GD Tel: (01202) 684248 Fax: (01202) 666190 E-mail: info@alphadesign-poole.co.uk
ESD Ltd, 68 - 71 Chapel Street, Netherton, Dudley, West Midlands, DY2 9PN Tel: (01384) 572699 Fax: (01384) 572698 E-mail: sales@esdltd.com
Link Cable Assemblers Ltd, North Caldeen Road, Coatbridge, Lanarkshire, ML5 4EF Tel: (01236) 423005 Fax: (01236) 449118 E-mail: sales@linkcableassemblies.co.uk
Martin Woolman Ltd, Unit 12 Martinfield Business Centre, Martinfield, Welwyn Garden City, Hertfordshire, AL7 1HG Tel: (01707) 373181 Fax: (01707) 373174 E-mail: sales@martinwoolman.co.uk
Pektron Group Ltd, Alfreton Road, Derby, DE21 4AP Tel: (01332) 832424 Fax: (01332) 833270 E-mail: info@pektron.co.uk

ELECTRONIC ASSEMBLY SERVICES, *See also headings for Electronic Contract Manufacturing etc*

A-Novo UK Ltd, Technology Centre, 5 Finlan Road, Middleton, Manchester, M24 2RW Tel: 0161-654 1400 Fax: 0161-654 1411
Bela Electronic Design Ltd, 12-14 Brooklands, Kempston, Bedford, MK42 7UH Tel: (01234) 840242 Fax: (01234) 843066 E-mail: sales@bela.co.uk
Briton EMS Ltd, 4 Shuttleworth Road, Elms Industrial Estate, Bedford, MK41 0EP Tel: (01234) 266300 Fax: (01234) 266488 E-mail: sales@britonems.co.uk
C Tech Electronics, Easting Close, Worthing, West Sussex, BN14 8HQ Tel: (01903) 524600 Fax: (01903) 524603 E-mail: sales@c-techelectronics.co.uk
Clamason Industries Ltd, Gibbons Industrial Park, Dudley Road, Kingswinford, West Midlands, DY6 8XG Tel: (01384) 400000 Fax: (01384) 400588 E-mail: sales@clamason.co.uk
Copper & Optic Terminations Ltd, 90 Town Road, Stoke-on-Trent, ST1 2LD Tel: (01782) 275810 Fax: (01782) 287820 E-mail: sales@copperandoptic.com
Crow-Electro Instruments Ltd, 9A Connors Yard, Crowborough Hill, Crowborough, East Sussex, TN6 2DA Tel: (01892) 662078 Fax: (01892) 663983 E-mail: crowelectro@fsbdial.co.uk
CT Production Ltd, 32-40 Harwell Road, Nuffield Industrial Estate, Poole, Dorset, BH17 0GE Tel: (01202) 687633 Fax: (01202) 680788 E-mail: sales@ctproduction.co.uk
Custom Keyboards Electronics Ltd, Unit 11, Claylands Road, Claylands Park, Bishops Waltham, Southampton, SO32 1BH Tel: (01489) 891851 Fax: (01489) 893708 E-mail: alancoppini@custom-keyboards.co.uk
Electrosembly Co., 35-37 Haviland Road, Ferndown Industrial Estate, Wimborne, Dorset, BH21 7SA Tel: (01202) 893392 Fax: (01202) 893378
G I G Systems Ltd, Unit 9, 40 Wilton Road, Reading, RG30 2SS Tel: 0118-958 1115 Fax: 0118-958 1117 E-mail: gigssystems@btconnect.com
G M Electronics, 7 Cyprus Avenue, Belfast, BT5 5NT Tel: (028) 9067 1876 Fax: (07092) 877376 E-mail: gme@gmelectronics.fsnet.co.uk
Gilbert Electronics, 35 Lower Road, Malvern, Worcestershire, WR14 4BX Tel: (01684) 576989 Fax: (01684) 576989
Hallmark Electronics Ltd, Hallmark House Loomer Road Industrial Estate, Loomer Road, Newcastle, Staffordshire, ST5 7LA Tel: (01782) 562255 Fax: (01782) 565684 E-mail: info@hallmarkelectronics.com
Holden Manufacturing Ltd, 4 Clarendon Drive, Wymbush, Milton Keynes, MK8 8DA Tel: (01908) 563636 Fax: (01908) 569778 E-mail: general@holdenmanufacturing.com
Intercole Sub-Contract Services Ltd, 3 Avenger Close, Chandlers Ford, Eastleigh, Hampshire, SO53 4YU Tel: (023) 8025 4727 Fax: (023) 8025 1090 E-mail: subcon@intercole.co.uk
J A M Ltd, 24 Farriers Way, Temple Farm Industrial Estate, Southend-on-Sea, SS2 5RY Tel: (01702) 602333 Fax: (01702) 602330 E-mail: sales@jam.uk.com
J N R Electronics Assemblies, 158 Wheatfield Road, Luton, LU4 0TD Tel: (01582) 471278 Fax: (01582) 600703E-mail: admin@jnr.org.uk
Kays Electronics Ltd, 85 Cavendish Street, Ipswich, IP3 8AX Tel: (01473) 214040 Fax: (01473) 214060 E-mail: enquiries@kayselectronics.com
LAM Electronics Ltd, Unit 6/A, Mercury House, Calleva Park, Aldermaston, Reading, RG7 8PN Tel: 0118-981 1717 Fax: 0118-981 7475 E-mail: almelecinfo@almelec.co.uk
N E M Co. Ltd, Stevenage Business Park, Wedgewood Way, Stevenage, Hertfordshire, SG1 4SX Tel: (01438) 346600 Fax: (01438) 346632 E-mail: sales@nemco.co.uk
Norcott Technologies Ltd, Brookfield House, Tarporley Road, Norcott Brook, Warrington, WA4 4EA Tel: (01925) 247600 Fax: (01925) 247610 E-mail: sales@norcott.co.uk
Pektron Group Ltd, Alfreton Road, Derby, DE21 4AP Tel: (01332) 832424 Fax: (01332) 833270 E-mail: info@pektron.co.uk
Power Solutions Ltd, 7 Copnor, Woolton Hill, Newbury, Berkshire, RG20 9UP Tel: (01635) 255570 Fax: (01635) 255560 E-mail: powersol@eclipse.co.uk
Precision Applications Ltd, Unit 19 Lodge Hill Industrial Estate, Station Road, Westbury sub Mendip, Wells, Somerset, BA5 1EY Tel: (01749) 870525 Fax: (01749) 870525 E-mail: sales@precisionapplications.co.uk
▶ R L Electronics, 16 Gurney Close, Bradford, West Yorkshire, BD5 9QR Tel: (01274) 229753 Fax: (01274) 229753 E-mail: rlad@rland.fsnet.co.uk
Raven Electronic Services Ltd, Unit 13, Little End Road, Eaton Socon, St. Neots, Cambridgeshire, PE19 8JH Tel: (01480) 407744 Fax: (01480) 470382 E-mail: dave@ravenelectronics.co.uk
▶ Remploy Ltd, Stone Court, Siskin Drive, Middlemarch Business Park, Coventry, CV3 4FJ Tel: (024) 7651 5800 Fax: (024) 7651 5860 E-mail: info@remploy.co.uk
Richard Kell, Blyth Valley Venture Workshops, Plessey Road, Blyth, Northumberland, NE24 4BN Tel: (01670) 363626 Fax: (01670) 363626

▶ indicates data change since last edition

ELECTRONIC ASSEMBLY SERVICES

– continued

S & G Cables Co. Ltd, Unit 2D, Chilton Industrial Estate, Chilton, Ferryhill, County Durham, DL17 0SZ Tel: (01388) 722255 Fax: (01388) 722266 E-mail: fgcables@btinternet.com

S K N Electronics Ltd, Armoury Road, Birmingham, B11 2PP Tel: 0121-773 6672 Fax: 0121-766 8457 E-mail: technical@sknelectronics.co.uk

Scrimsign Microelectronics Ltd, 8 Arkwright Way, North Newmoor Industrial Estate, Irvine, Ayrshire, KA11 4JU Tel: (01294) 216008 Fax: (01294) 219039 E-mail: sales@scrimsign.co.uk

Sign Trade Europe Ltd, Parker Street, Hucknall, Nottingham, NG15 7UF Tel: 0115-968 1000 Fax: 0115-968 1373 E-mail: email@signtrade.btconnect.com

Syntech Europe Ltd, 351 Wigan Road, Bolton, BL3 5QU Tel: (01204) 659899 Fax: (01204) 659941 E-mail: andrew@syntech-europe.com

Triangle Electronic Controls Ltd, Unit 3 Knowles Estate, Knowles Road, Clevedon, Avon, BS21 7XS Tel: (01275) 878770 Fax: (01275) 878771

Walkbury Electronics Ltd, 30 The Metro Centre, Peterborough, PE2 7UH Tel: (01733) 404830 Fax: (01733) 404839 E-mail: sales@walkbury.co.uk

Wildtrax Electronics Ltd, Unit 11A Southcourt Road, Worthing, West Sussex, BN14 7DF Tel: 0845 5314279 Fax: (01903) 212003 E-mail: howard@wildtrax.com

ELECTRONIC BANKING SYSTEMS

Co-Operative Systems, 18-20 Miles Street, London, SW8 1SD Tel: (020) 7793 0395 Fax: (020) 7735 6472 E-mail: team@coopsys.net

H Systems Ltd, 4 St Helens Cres, Hove, E. Sussex, BN3 8EP Tel: 01273 414011 Fax: 01273 414311

Software Integrators Ltd, New London Bridge House, 25 London Bridge Street, London, SE1 9SG Tel: (020) 7378 9309 Fax: (020) 7378 9310 E-mail: admin@software-integrators.co.uk

ELECTRONIC BAR CODE SCANNERS

Anchor Data Systems Ltd, Unit 36 North City Business Centre, 2 Duncairn Gardens, Belfast, BT15 2GG Tel: (028) 9074 0315 Fax: (028) 9035 1531 E-mail: info@anchordata.co.uk

Designwrights Ltd, Unit 18 Liss Business Centre, Station Road, Liss, Hampshire, GU33 7AW Tel: (01730) 890050 Fax: (01730) 890051 E-mail: info@designwrights.co.uk

ELECTRONIC BETTING SYSTEMS

▶ The Way2Lay Lay Betting Service, 16 Athol Street, Barrow-in-Furness, Cumbria, LA14 2QT Tel: (01229) 870079 E-mail: cleyden1@aol.com

ELECTRONIC BIRD REPELLENT SYSTEMS

Peter Cox Ltd, 53 Cuckoo Road, Birmingham, B7 5SY Tel: 0121-326 6434 Fax: 0121-326 7242 E-mail: petercox.birmingham@ecolab.com

▶ Peter Cox Ltd, Suite 5, Keynes House, Alfreton Road, Derby, DE21 4AS Tel: (01332) 299222 Fax: (01332) 200066

▶ Peter Cox Ltd, Unit 1, Marybank Lane, Dundee, DD2 3DY Tel: (01382) 400242 Fax: (01382) 400262 E-mail: petercox.dundee@ecolab.com

▶ Peter Cox Ltd, Unit M, Orchard Business Centre, St. Barnabas Close, Allington, Maidstone, Kent, ME16 0JZ Tel: (01622) 750081 Fax: (01622) 750083

Peter Cox Ltd, Unit 35, Viewforth Industrial Estate, The Loan, South Queensferry, West Lothian, EH30 9NS Tel: 0131-331 5030 Fax: 0131-319 1635 E-mail: peter.cox@ecolab.com

Peter Cox Ltd, Falcon House, Oakhurst Drive, Stockport, Cheshire, SK3 0XT Tel: 0161-491 3181 Fax: 0161-428 8138

Ecolab Ltd, Caerphilly Business Park, Caerphilly, Mid Glamorgan, CF83 3ED Tel: (029) 2085 2000 Fax: (029) 2086 5969

▶ Ecolab Pest Control Ltd, Falcon House, Lawnhurst Industrial Estate, Stockport, Cheshire, SK3 0XT Tel: 0161-491 3855 Fax: 0161 491 6088

▶ Ecolab Pest Prevention, Unit 47 Clifton Industrial Estate, Cherry Hinton Road, Cambridge, CB1 7ED Tel: (01223) 211303 Fax: (01223) 215151

Ecolab Pest Prevention, John O Gaunts Trading Estate, Leeds Road, Rothwell, Leeds, LS26 0JB Tel: 0113 288 7787 Fax: 0113 282 1298

▶ Ecolab Pest Prevention, Unit 5, Waterside Court, Bone Lane, Newbury, Berkshire, RG14 5SH Tel: (01635) 524780 Fax: (01635) 524761

▶ Ecolab Pest Prevention, 146 Moor Lane, Preston, PR1 1JR Tel: (01772) 563303 Fax: (01772) 561106

▶ Ecolab Services Ltd, Unit 11 Prideaux Close, Tamar View Industrial Estate, Saltash, Cornwall, PL12 6LD Tel: (01752) 841842 Fax: (01752) 840700

▶ Peter Cox Ltd, Unit 10, Avon Riverside Estate, Victoria Road, Avonmouth, Bristol, BS11 9DB Tel: 0117 938 7130 Fax: 0117 938 7137

Peter Cox Ltd, Unit 17, Engineer Park, Sandycroft, Deeside, Clwyd, CH5 2QB Tel: (01244) 538610 Fax: (01244) 534720

▶ Peter Cox, Unit 11d Station Approach, Team Valley Trading Estate, Gateshead, Tyne & Wear, NE11 0ZF Tel: 0191-487 2293 Fax: 0191-487 4804 E-mail: petercox.newcastle@ecolab.com

▶ Peter Cox Ltd, St. Andrews House, 385 Hillington Road, Hillington Industrial Estate, Glasgow, G52 4BL Tel: 0141 810 9100 Fax: 0141 810 9111

▶ Peter Cox Ltd, 103 Sadler Road, Lincoln, LN6 3RS Tel: (01522) 500214 Fax: (01522) 688838

▶ Peter Cox Ltd, 209 Century Buildings, Summers Road, Brunswick Business Park, Liverpool, L3 4BL Tel: 0151 709 1090 Fax: 0151 708 5304

▶ Peter Cox Ltd, 62h Lord Avenue, Thornaby, Stockton-on-Tees, Cleveland, TS17 9JX Tel: (01642) 769983 Fax: (01642) 769421

Scaringbirds.com Ltd, Lower Upton, Ludlow, Shropshire, SY8 4BB Tel: (01584) 711701 Fax: (01584) 711478 E-mail: info@scaringbirds.com

ELECTRONIC BUSINESS CARDS

▶ A D M Office Supplies Ltd, PO Box 1, Yateley, Hampshire, GU46 6WY Tel: (01252) 876494 Fax: (01252) 879505 E-mail: admin@admoffice.co.uk

▶ DiGi-Masters.Com, 24 Franche Road, Wolverley, Kidderminster, Worcestershire, DY11 5TP Tel: (01562) 636213 E-mail: info@digi-masters.com

Media Cards, 108 Davies Road, West Bridgford, Nottingham, NG2 5HY Tel: 0115-914 2369 E-mail: sales@media-cards.co.uk

▶ Online48 Ltd, 27 Seymour Terrace, Seymour Street, Liverpool, L3 5PE Tel: 0151-703 1065 Fax: 0151-703 1064 E-mail: enquiries@online48.co.uk

ELECTRONIC CABINET OR CONSOLE CONSULTANCY OR DESIGN

Spice Design Consultants, Hop Studios, 2 Jamaica Road, London, SE1 2BX Tel: (020) 7252 0808 Fax: (020) 7237 7199 E-mail: studio@spicehop.com

ELECTRONIC CABINETS AND CONSOLES

Archer Woodnutt Ltd, Pit Lane, Talke Pits, Stoke-on-Trent, ST7 1UH Tel: (01782) 785016 Fax: (01782) 776273 E-mail: info@archerwoodnutt.com

Armer Quality Components Ltd, Hope Mill, Greenacres Road, Oldham, OL4 2AB Tel: 0161-620 5203 Fax: 0161-627 5139 E-mail: mail@armerqc.co.uk

Beta Engineering Stotfold Ltd, Taylors Road, Stotfold, Hitchin, Hertfordshire, SG5 4AX Tel: (01462) 730910 Fax: (01462) 835325

Brighton Sheet Metal Ltd, The Hyde, Brighton, BN2 4JW Tel: (01273) 602216 Fax: (01273) 674153 E-mail: sales@brightonsheetmetal.co.uk

Cannon Technologies Europe Ltd, 13 Queensway, Stem Lane Industrial Estate, New Milton, Hampshire, BH25 5NU Tel: (01425) 638148 Fax: (01425) 619276 E-mail: sales@cannontech.co.uk

Carlton Controls Ltd, 3c Lea Road, Waltham Abbey, Essex, EN9 1AE Tel: (01992) 767609 Fax: (01992) 788446 E-mail: mail@carlton-controls.co.uk

Cooper B Line Ltd, Commerce Way, Highbridge, Somerset, TA9 4AQ Tel: (01278) 783371 Fax: (01278) 789037 E-mail: mwatts@cooperbline.co.uk

D R S Rugged Systems (Europe) Ltd, Lynwood House, The Trading Estate, Farnham, Surrey, GU9 9NN Tel: (01252) 734488 Fax: (01252) 730530

Eldon Electric Ltd, Rother Way, Hellaby, Rotherham, South Yorkshire, S66 8QN Tel: (01709) 701234 Fax: (01709) 701209 E-mail: info.uk@eldon.com

Knurr UK Ltd, Burrel Road, St. Ives, Cambridgeshire, PE27 3LE Tel: (01480) 496125 Fax: (01480) 496373 E-mail: knuerr.uk@knuerr.com

Lund Bros & Co. Ltd, Brookside Avenue, Rustington, Littlehampton, West Sussex, BN16 3LF Tel: (01903) 784242 Fax: (01903) 787126 E-mail: sales@lunds.co.uk

M J Metalcraft Ltd, 32-34 Sampson Road North, Birmingham, B11 1BL Tel: 0121-771 3711 Fax: 0121-771 3766 E-mail: enquiries@mjmetalcraftltd.co.uk

Metal Cabinets Sales Ltd, Moorfield Road Estate, Yeadon, Leeds, LS19 7BN Tel: 0113-250 8082 Fax: 0113-250 5138 E-mail: person@metalcabinets.co.uk

Midway Metalcraft, Ridgeway Court, Grovebury Rd, Leighton Buzzard, Bedfordshire, LU7 4SW Tel: (01525) 374861 Fax: (01525) 374082 E-mail: enquiries@midwaymetalcraft.com

Ritherdon & Co. Ltd, Lorne Street, Darwen, Lancashire, BB3 1QW Tel: (01254) 819100 Fax: (01254) 819101 E-mail: info@ritherdon.co.uk

Stevenage Sheet Metal Co. Ltd, Unit 1, Jubilee Trade Centre, Jubilee Road, Letchworth Garden City, Hertfordshire, SG6 1SP Tel: (01462) 674794 Fax: (01462) 481132 E-mail: richard@stevenagesheetmetal.com

Woking Sheet Metal & Coachworks Ltd, 141 Goldsworth Road, Woking, Surrey, GU21 6LT Tel: (01483) 761898 Fax: (01483) 755605 E-mail: woking.sheetmetal@btinternet.com

ELECTRONIC CABLE ASSEMBLIES OR HARNESSES

Abrae Technology Ltd, Park Hill Street, Bolton, BL1 4AR Tel: (01204) 361400 Fax: (0870) 3000693

Bancroft & Co., 5 Stairbridge Court, Stairbridge Lane, Bolney, Haywards Heath, West Sussex, RH17 5PA Tel: (01444) 248884 Fax: (01444) 242767 E-mail: sales@bancroft.co.uk

C & T Harnesses Ltd, Unit 2 Lanwades Business Park, Kennett, Newmarket, Suffolk, CB8 7PN Tel: (01638) 751511 Fax: (01638) 751965 E-mail: info@ctharnesses.com

Deval Ltd, Unit 6 Hamilton Way, New Milton, Hampshire, BH25 6TQ Tel: (01425) 620772 Fax: (01425) 638431 E-mail: sales@deval-ltd.co.uk

ESD Ltd, 68 - 71 Chapel Street, Netherton, Dudley, West Midlands, DY2 9PN Tel: (01384) 572699 Fax: (01384) 572698 E-mail: sales@esdltd.com

First Circuit Group, PO Box 7226, Redditch, Worcestershire, B98 7WR Tel: (01527) 503503 Fax: (01527) 456170 E-mail: info@1stcircuit.com

Grange Products Ltd, Unit 4 Station Road, Reddish, Stockport, Cheshire, SK5 6ND Tel: 0161-480 3318

Hawco Direct, 8 Cranfield Road, Lostock Industrial Estate, Lostock, Bolton, BL6 4SB Tel: (01204) 675000 Fax: (01204) 675010 E-mail: catalogue@hawcodirect.co.uk

Hawco Refridgeration, The Wharf, Abbey Mill Business Park, Lower Eashing, Godalming, Surrey, GU7 2QN Tel: (01483) 869070 Fax: (01483) 869001 E-mail: sales@hawco.co.uk

▶ Iubeo Europe Ltd, 82 Tenter Road, Moulton Park, Northampton, NN3 6AX Tel: +44 (01604) 646433 Fax: +44 (01604) 643737 E-mail: david@iubeo-europe.com

Jacarem Ltd, 78 Asheridge Road, Chesham, Buckinghamshire, HP5 2PY Tel: (01494) 791336 Fax: (01494) 792336 E-mail: sales@jacarem.co.uk

Manjet Electronics, Longmeadow Works, Ringwood Road, Three Legged Cross, Wimborne, Dorset, BH21 6RD Tel: (01202) 823013 Fax: (01202) 823013

Pageantry Electronic Systems, Unit 7 55 Weir Road Industrial Estate, London, SW19 8UG Tel: (020) 8947 3100 Fax: (020) 8879 0068 E-mail: sales@pageantry.co.uk

Primstone Electronics, 27a Whitehorse Street, Baldock, Hertfordshire, SG7 6QF Tel: (01462) 490594 Fax: (01462) 490595 E-mail: primstone@aol.com

Redileads Anglesey Ltd, Industrial Estate Road, Llangefni, Gwynedd, LL77 7JA Tel: (01248) 750280 Fax: (01248) 722031 E-mail: enquiries@redileads.co.uk

Rockford Group Ltd, Rockford House, Renalsham, Woodbridge, Suffolk, IP12 2GJ Tel: (01394) 420800 Fax: (01394) 420820 E-mail: sales@rockford.co.uk

Ruston Electronics Ltd, Unit 6, Sovereign Park, Laporte Way, Luton, LU4 8EL Tel: (01582) 506100 Fax: (01582) 506101 E-mail: sales@rustons.co.uk

Saffron Electronics Ltd, 3-04 St. Albans Road Industrial Estate, Stafford, ST16 3DR Tel: (0845) 1662314 Fax: (0845) 1662315 E-mail: sales@saffronelectronics.co.uk

Swansea Industrial Components Ltd, 66-70 Morfa Road, Swansea, SA1 2EF Tel: (01792) 458777 Fax: (01792) 456252

Walters Group, Walters House, 12 Merlin Centre, Lancaster Road, High Wycombe, Buckinghamshire, HP12 3TB Tel: (01494) 453700 Fax: (01494) 461107 E-mail: sales@waltersmicro.co.uk

ELECTRONIC CABLES

A W Perry Electrical Co. Ltd, 35 Stroud Road, London, SE25 5DR Tel: (020) 8654 3122 Fax: (020) 8656 8806 E-mail: mail@perryelectrical.co.uk

Belcom Cable & Wire Suppliers, Warish Hall, Warish Hall Road, Takeley, Bishop's Stortford, Hertfordshire, CM22 6NZ Tel: (01279) 871150 Fax: (01279) 871129 E-mail: dave@belcom.co.uk

Clarkin Electronics, 1 50 Lakes Road, Derwent Howe Industrial Estate, Workington, Cumbria, CA14 3YP Tel: (01900) 64576 Fax: (01900) 872475 E-mail: clarkin46@aol.com

Teledyne Reynolds Industries Ltd, Navigation House, Canal View Road, Newbury, Berkshire, RG14 5UR Tel: (01635) 262200 Fax: (01635) 30920 E-mail: trlsales@teledyne.com

Webb & Wells Ltd, 9 Chilford Court, Rayne Road, Braintree, Essex, CM7 2QS Tel: (01376) 550044 Fax: (01376) 550022 E-mail: sales@webbwells.co.uk

ELECTRONIC CHRONOMETERS

Sensors UK Ltd, 135-137 Hatfield Road, St. Albans, Hertfordshire, AL4 0DH Tel: (01727) 861110 Fax: (01727) 844272 E-mail: admin@sensorsuk.com

ELECTRONIC COMMERCE (ECOMMERCE) SOFTWARE

▶ Actinic Holdings Ltd, Globe House, Lavender Park Road, West Byfleet, Surrey, KT14 6ND Tel: (01932) 358340 Fax: (01932) 358341 E-mail: enquiries@actinic.co.uk

▶ Better 4 Business, 11 Brook Hey Avenue, Bolton, BL3 2EQ Tel: (0870) 8749500 E-mail: enquiries@better4business.co.uk

▶ Bright Lemon Ltd, Unit 12, Zeus House, London, N1 7NG Tel: (020) 7608 2838 E-mail: info@brightlemon.com

Davin Fowler, 15 Queens Square, Leeds, LS2 8AJ Tel: 0113 2255517 E-mail: info@giant-systems.co.uk

▶ Demopad Software Ltd, Midwest House, Canal Road, Timperley, Cheshire, WA14 1TF Tel: 08700 551100 Fax: 08707 062171 E-mail: sales@sentrypad.com

▶ Gempro Website Design and Development Services, 249 Beaver Lane, Ashford, Kent, TN23 5PA Tel: 01233 334069 E-mail: info@gempro.co.uk

▶ TrustSign UK Ltd, Unit 6, Nightingale Way, Alsager, Stoke-on-Trent, ST7 2GH Tel: (01270) 873942 Fax: (0870) 1300263 E-mail: sales@trustsign.co.uk

Wick Hill Ltd, Rivercourt, Albert Drive, Woking, Surrey, GU21 5RP Tel: (01483) 227600 Fax: (01483) 227700 E-mail: info@wickhill.co.uk

ELECTRONIC COMPONENT BAKING

Specific Components, Unit 23, Common Bank Industrial Estate, Ackhurst Road, Chorley, Lancashire, PR7 1NH Tel: (01257) 279944 Fax: (01257) 279922 E-mail: sales@specific-components.co.uk

ELECTRONIC COMPONENT BROKERS

Azigo Technology Services, Systems House, Wade Road, Basingstoke, Hampshire, RG24 8FL Tel: (01256) 811811 Fax: (01256) 811855 E-mail: niel-raggett@rtgh.com

Genalog Ltd, Gills Green Oast, Gills Green, Cranbrook, Kent, TN18 5ET Tel: (01580) 753754 Fax: (01580) 752979 E-mail: sales@genalog.com

Goldney Electronics UK, 6 Queen Anne's Gardens, Leatherhead, Surrey, KT22 7JE Tel: (01372) 378194 Fax: (01372) 375759 E-mail: purchasing@goldney.net

ELECTRONIC COMPONENT IMPORT/EXPORT MERCHANTS OR AGENTS

Amelec Ltd, 101 Moreton Street, Cannock, Staffordshire, WS11 5HN Tel: (01543) 466191 Fax: (01543) 467339 E-mail: info@amelec.co.uk

Chromalock Ltd, Beechwood House, Falkland Close, Charter Avenue Industrial Estate, Coventry, CV4 8HQ Tel: (024) 7646 6277 Fax: (024) 7646 5298 E-mail: admin@chromalock.com

D T I Action Hardware Ltd, West Farm, Popham, Micheldever, Winchester, Hampshire, SO21 3BH Tel: (01892) 511753 Fax: (01892) 530294 E-mail: action.hardware@virgin.net

Deltra Electronics Ltd, Deltra House, Heather Park Drive, Wembley, Middlesex, HA0 1SS Tel: (020) 8795 3000 Fax: (020) 8795 0700 E-mail: tony@deltra.co.uk

▶ DRY-OFF (UK) LTD, 23 Castalia Square, Docklands, London, UK, E14 3NG Tel: 0207 5441474 Fax: 0207 5441499 E-mail: EDWARD@DRY-OFF.COM

Empexion Ltd, Falcon House, 19 Deer Park Road, London, SW19 3UX Tel: (020) 8543 0911 Fax: (020) 8540 0034 E-mail: info@ctl-components.com

Goldney Electronics UK, 6 Queen Anne's Gardens, Leatherhead, Surrey, KT22 7JE Tel: (01372) 378194 Fax: (01372) 375759 E-mail: purchasing@goldney.net

ELECTRONIC COMPONENT IMPORT/EXPORT MERCHANTS OR AGENTS – *continued*

Mikay Distributors, Unit 17 River Road Business Park, 33 River Road, Barking, Essex, IG11 0DA Tel: (020) 8507 7665 Fax: (020) 8507 7670 E-mail: sales@mikay.co.uk
Mitsubishi Electric Finance Europe P.L.C., The Atrium, Uxbridge One, 1 Harefield Road, Uxbridge, Middlesex, UB8 1PH Tel: (01895) 276600 Fax: (01895) 276697
Pedoka Ltd, 4 The Old School, Church Street, Biggleswade, Bedfordshire, SG18 0JS Tel: (01767) 318318 Fax: (01767) 310960 E-mail: pedoka@pedoka.com
Semi Conductor Supplies International Ltd, 128-130 Carshalton Road, Sutton, Surrey, SM1 4TW Tel: (020) 8643 1126 Fax: (020) 8643 3937 E-mail: sales@ssi-uk.com
Vicsteels Ltd, Suite 20 London House, 266 Fulham Road, London, SW10 9EL Tel: (020) 7795 2345 Fax: (020) 7795 0460 E-mail: vicsteels@aol.com

ELECTRONIC COMPONENT KITTING SERVICES

Ace Components Ltd, 4 Priory Gardens, Scorton, Preston, PR3 1AQ Tel: (01524) 793893 Fax: (01524) 793894 E-mail: colinbabbs.ace@ukonline.co.uk
Anchor Components Ltd, 1 John Street, Biddulph, Stoke-on-Trent, ST8 6BB Tel: (01782) 522844 Fax: (01782) 522828 E-mail: sales@anchorcomponents.co.uk
Camtronics Ltd, The Walnut Tree, 38 High Street, Bluntisham, Huntingdon, Cambridgeshire, PE28 3LA Tel: (01487) 843278 Fax: (01487) 843280 E-mail: sales@camtronics.ltd.uk
Nitronics Ltd, Nitronics House, The Maltings Centre, Station Road, Sawbridgeworth, Hertfordshire, CM21 9JX Tel: (01279) 307555 Fax: (01279) 307700 E-mail: sales@nitronics.co.uk
Paragon Electronic Components plc, Wolseley Road, Kempston, Bedford, MK42 7UP Tel: (01234) 840101 Fax: (01234) 840707 E-mail: sales@paragon-plc.com

ELECTRONIC COMPONENT LEAD CUTTING SERVICES

J. & H. Humphrey, Unit 1, Fareham Enterprise Centre, Newgate Lane, Fareham, Hampshire, PO14 1TH Tel: (01329) 318463 Fax: (01329) 317342 E-mail: info@preforming.co.uk

ELECTRONIC COMPONENT LEAD CUTTING/BENDING MACHINES/TOOLS

Elite Engineering Ltd, 1 Davis Way, Fareham, Hampshire, PO14 1JF Tel: (01329) 231435 Fax: (01329) 822759 E-mail: sales@elite-eng.co.uk

ELECTRONIC COMPONENT PRECISION EXTRUDED AND DRAWN NON FERROUS WIRE

W G H Wire Drawers Ltd, Imperial Works, 217 Oxford Street, Bilston, West Midlands, WV14 7HY Tel: (01902) 354142 Fax: (01902) 354250

ELECTRONIC COMPONENT PREFORMING

J. & H. Humphrey, Unit 1, Fareham Enterprise Centre, Newgate Lane, Fareham, Hampshire, PO14 1TH Tel: (01329) 318463 Fax: (01329) 317342 E-mail: info@preforming.co.uk

ELECTRONIC COMPONENT PRESSINGS

Raven Manufacturing Ltd, Metcalf Drive, Altham Industrial Estate, Accrington, Lancashire, BB5 5TU Tel: (01282) 770000 Fax: (01282) 770022 E-mail: sales@raven.co.uk

ELECTRONIC COMPONENT SCRAP PRECIOUS METAL RECOVERY

▶ G R P (Electronic) Ltd, 2 Wham Cottages, Slackgate Lane, Denshaw, Oldham, OL3 5TZ Tel: (01457) 820864 Fax: (01457) 820864 E-mail: pollardgraham@talk21.com
M G H Reclaim Ltd, Unit 23 Common Bank Industrial Estate, Ackhurst Road, Chorley, Lancashire, PR7 1NH Tel: (01257) 279999 Fax: (01257) 279797 E-mail: neil@mgh-group.co.uk

ELECTRONIC COMPONENT SCRAP RECYCLING OR DISPOSAL OR PROCESSORS OR MERCHANTS

▶ Nextel Metals, 20 Woodlea Grove, Yeadon, Leeds, LS19 7YT Tel: (07946) 842491 Fax: 0113-250 4700 E-mail: nextelmetals@aol.com

ELECTRONIC COMPONENT (SURPLUS STOCK) BUYING AND PURCHASING

Greenweld, C/O Permex Ltd, Riverside House, Plumpton Road, Hoddesdon, Hertfordshire, EN11 0PA Tel: (01992) 452980 Fax: (01992) 452981 E-mail: bargains@greenweld.co.uk

ELECTRONIC COMPONENT TAPE/REELING SERVICES

Lewmax Programming, Unit 1, Fowke Street, Rothley, Leicester, LE7 7PJ Tel: 0116-212 2133 Fax: 0116-212 2136 E-mail: sales@lewmax.co.uk
M G H Reclaim Ltd, Unit 23 Common Bank Industrial Estate, Ackhurst Road, Chorley, Lancashire, PR7 1NH Tel: (01257) 279999 Fax: (01257) 279797 E-mail: neil@mgh-group.co.uk

ELECTRONIC COMPONENTS, *See also headings for particular types*

A B Electronic Ltd, Colbern House, Spring Gardens, Romford, RM7 9LP Tel: (01708) 762222 Fax: (01708) 762981 E-mail: info@abelectronic.com
A D I American Distributors Inc, Units 3-4 Peckworth Industrial Estate, Bedford Road, Lower Standon, Henlow, Bedfordshire, SG16 6EE Tel: (01462) 850804 Fax: (01462) 819596 E-mail: sales@americandistr.com
▶ A M G Electronics Ltd, Unit 1 & 5, Stephenson Court, Brindley Road, Stephenson Industrial Estate, Coalville, Leicestershire, LE67 3HG Tel: (01530) 836877 Fax: (01530) 836878
A Tec International Ltd, 109-111 St. Johns Hill, Sevenoaks, Kent, TN13 3PE Tel: (01732) 743737 Fax: (01732) 743838 E-mail: vic@a-tecuk.com
A V X Ltd, Admiral House, Harlington Way, Fleet, Hampshire, GU51 4BB Tel: (01252) 770000 Fax: (01252) 770001 E-mail: sales@flt.avxeur.com
Abacus Choice, Rooks Street, Cottenham, Cambridge, CB24 8QZ Tel: (01954) 287070 Fax: (01954) 252078
Abacus Eiger Northeast, Hall Mews, Clifford Road, Boston Spa, Wetherby, West Yorkshire, LS23 6DT Tel: (01937) 841312 Fax: (01937) 841062
Abacus Polar plc, Cherrycourt Way, Leighton Buzzard, Bedfordshire, LU7 4YY Tel: (01525) 858000 Fax: (01525) 858102 E-mail: sales@abacus.co.uk
Acal Technologies Ltd, 3 The Business Centre, Molly Millars Lane, Wokingham, Berkshire, RG41 2EY Tel: 0118-978 8878 Fax: 0118-977 6095 E-mail:
Acal Technology Ltd, 3 The Business Centre, Molly Millars Lane, Wokingham, Berkshire, RG41 2EY Tel: 0118-902 9702 Fax: 0118-902 9614 E-mail: admin@amega-group.com
▶ Advance Packaging Technology Of America, Howard Street, North Shields, Tyne & Wear, NE30 1AR Tel: 0191-258 6912 Fax: 0191-258 4554
Advent Electronics Ltd, 4 Forward Drive, Pennington, Lymington, Hampshire, SO41 8GA Tel: (023) 8028 2703 Fax: (023) 8028 3275 E-mail: mail@advent-elect.co.uk
Aero Dart Ltd, 5 Brook Road, Benfleet, Essex, SS7 5JB Tel: (01268) 566111 Fax: (01268) 565222 E-mail: direct@aerodart.ndirect.co.uk
Albol Electronic & Mechanical Products Ltd, Crown Buildings, Crown Street, London, SE5 0UR Tel: (020) 7703 2311 Fax: (020) 7703 3282 E-mail: sales@albol.co.uk
Alrad Instruments Ltd, Alder House, Turnpike Road Industrial Estate, Newbury, Berkshire, RG14 2NS Tel: (01635) 30345 Fax: (01635) 32630 E-mail: sales@alrad.co.uk
Amelec Ltd, 101 Moreton Street, Cannock, Staffordshire, WS11 5HN Tel: (01543) 466191 Fax: (01543) 467339 E-mail: info@amelec.co.uk
Anchor Components Ltd, 1 John Street, Biddulph, Stoke-on-Trent, ST8 6BB Tel: (01782) 522844 Fax: (01782) 522828 E-mail: sales@anchorcomponents.co.uk
Apache Electronics, Linc Business Park, Ofbolwick, York, YO10 3JB Tel: (01904) 436456 Fax: (01904) 436567 E-mail: sales@apache-electronics.com
Applied Research & Development Ltd, Newfield, Newfield Mains Road, Dundonald, Kilmarnock, Ayrshire, KA2 9AW Tel: (01563) 850180 Fax: 01563 850180
▶ Arc Electronics Ltd, Lower Ground Floor, 44 Bath Road, Swindon, SN1 4AY Tel: (01793) 549230 Fax: (01793) 549239 E-mail: enquiries@arcsales.co.uk
Artronics Manufacturing Ltd, Old School House, 6 Church Street, Somersham, Huntingdon, Cambridgeshire, PE28 3EG Tel: (01487) 740447 Fax: (01487) 740449 E-mail: sales@itonics.co.uk
Ashlea Components Ltd, 4 Shrivenham Hundred Business Park, Majors Road, Watchfield, Swindon, SN6 8TZ Tel: (01793) 783784 Fax: (01793) 783646 E-mail: sales@ashlea.co.uk
Astute Electronics Ltd, Church House, Church Street, Ware, Hertfordshire, SG12 9EN Tel: (01920) 483800 Fax: (01920) 486399 E-mail: insales@astute.co.uk
▶ Audioworkshop.Co.Uk, Unit 17 Lynderswood Farm, London Road, Black Notley, Braintree, Essex, CM77 8QN Tel: (01245) 361578 Fax: (01245) 361357 E-mail: sales@audio-workshop.co.uk
Avnet Time, Avnet House, Rutherford Close, Stevenage, Hertfordshire, SG1 2EF Tel: (01438) 789789 E-mail: timeuk@avnet.com
Azcon Components Solutions Ltd, Waterside Business Park, Eastways, Witham, Essex, CM8 3YQ Tel: (01376) 517642 Fax: (01376) 519333 E-mail: info@qualitycomponents.co.uk
Azigo Technology Services, Systems House, Wade Road, Basingstoke, Hampshire, RG24 8FL Tel: (01256) 811811 Fax: (01256) 811855 E-mail: niel-raggett@rtgh.com
B A L Broadcast, Unit 23 Croft Road Industrial Estate, Newcastle, Staffordshire, ST5 0TW Tel: (024) 7631 6500 Fax: (024) 7649 1117 E-mail: sales@bal.co.uk
B C L Distribution, Hornbeam Park, Hookstone Road, Harrogate, North Yorkshire, HG2 8QT Tel: (01423) 879787 Fax: (01423) 879030 E-mail: information@bcldistribution.com
B E C Distribution Ltd, Unit 5, Coronation Grove, Harrogate, North Yorkshire, HG2 8BU Tel: (0845) 4900405 Fax: (0845) 4900406 E-mail: sales@bec.co.uk
B F Components Ltd, Unit 6, Cobham Centre, Westmead Industrial Estate, Westlea, Swindon, SN5 7UJ Tel: (01793) 498020 Fax: (01793) 542019 E-mail: sales@bfgroup.co.uk
Basic Electronics Ltd, 5 Leapale Road, Guildford, Surrey, GU1 4JX Tel: (01483) 539984 Fax: (01483) 539984 E-mail: sales@basicelectronics.co.uk
Bonus Plug In Systems, Citadel Trading Park, Citadel Way, Hull, HU9 1TQ Tel: (01482) 313700 Fax: (01482) 588753
C J Harris Electronic Components, Rosebank, Chafford Lane, Fordcombe, Tunbridge Wells, Kent, TN3 0SH Tel: (01892) 740000 Fax: (01892) 740100 E-mail: chrisharris2@btconnect.com
▶ C P C, Component House, Faraday Drive, Fulwood, Preston, PR2 9PP Tel: (01772) 654455 Fax: (01772) 654466 E-mail: webadmin@cpc.co.uk
C S A Electronics, 59 High Street, Findon, Worthing, West Sussex, BN14 0ST Tel: (01903) 877781 Fax: (01903) 877781
Cambridge Capacitors Ltd, Budds Lane, Romsey, Hampshire, SO51 0ZQ Tel: (01794) 513481 Fax: (01794) 523940 E-mail: sales@camcap.co.uk
Campbell Collins Ltd, 162 High St, Stevenage, Hertfordshire, SG1 3LL Tel: (01438) 369466 Fax: (01438) 316465 E-mail: sales@camcol.co.uk
▶ Capss Electronic Component Distributors, Unit 8 Hotchkiss Way, Binley Industrial Estate, Coventry, CV3 2RL Tel: (024) 7644 4664 Fax: (024) 7644 4585
▶ Card Professionals Ltd, Sandhurst House, 297 Yorktown Road, College Town, Sandhurst, Berkshire, GU47 0QA Tel: (01276) 609777 Fax: (01276) 609888
Tony Chapman Electronics Ltd, Hayleys Manor, Epping Upland, Epping, Essex, CM16 6PQ Tel: (01992) 578231 Fax: (01992) 576139 E-mail: sales@tceltd.co.uk
Classic Components UK Ltd, Unit 1A, Stratford Court, Cranmore Boulevard, Shirley, Solihull, West Midlands, B90 4QT Tel: 0121-746 5300 Fax: 0121-746 5344 E-mail: sales@classicuk.co.uk
Component Forum Ltd, PO Box 20, Towcester, Northamptonshire, NN12 7XJ Tel: (01908) 543808 Fax: (01908) 543909 E-mail: enquiries@componentforum.co.uk
Components Electronic & Lighting Ltd, 93 Chilton Way, Hungerford, Berkshire, RG17 0JF Tel: (01488) 684625 Fax: 01488 683184 E-mail: celclive@btconnect.com
Comstock Electronics Ltd, Unit 6 Paycocke Road, Quatro Park, Basildon, Essex, SS14 3GH Tel: (01268) 295555 Fax: (01268) 523455 E-mail: celsales@comstock.co.uk
Connect Distibution, Connect Business Park, Bordesley Green Road, Birmingham, B9 4UA Tel: (0870) 4423700 Fax: 0121-766 7138
Contact Components Ltd, 5 Parkend, Harlow BSNS Park, Harlow, Essex, CM19 5QF Tel: (01279) 424211 Fax: (01279) 424213
Contact Electronics Ltd, Unit 4 Westmead House, 123 Westmead Road, Sutton, Surrey, SM1 4JH Tel: (020) 8643 3000 Fax: (020) 8643 5777 E-mail: contact@contact-electronics.co.uk
Cricklewood Electronics Ltd, 40-42 Cricklewood Broadway, London, NW2 3ET Tel: (020) 8452 0161 Fax: (020) 8208 1441 E-mail: sales@cricklewoodelectronics.com
D D C (U K) Ltd, Mill Reef House, 9-14 Cheap Street, Newbury, Berkshire, RG14 5DD Tel: (01635) 40158 Fax: (01635) 32264
D T I Action Hardware Ltd, West Farm, Popham, Micheldever, Winchester, Hampshire, SO21 3BH Tel: (01892) 511753 Fax: (01892) 530294 E-mail: action.hardware@virgin.net
Dau Components Ltd, 70-74 Barnham Road, Barnham, Bognor Regis, West Sussex, PO22 0ES Tel: (01243) 553031 Fax: (01243) 553860 E-mail: sales@dau-components.co.uk
▶ Decade Electronics Ltd, Ivy House Farm, Marston On Dove, Hilton, Derby, DE65 5GB Tel: (01283) 810044 Fax: (01283) 810077
Deltra Electronics Ltd, Deltra House, Heather Park Drive, Wembley, Middlesex, HA0 1SS Tel: (020) 8795 3000 Fax: (020) 8795 0700 E-mail: tony@deltra.co.uk
▶ Digiwave Technologies, 198 Slade Road, Birmingham, B23 7RJ Tel: 0121-386 4678
Distributed Technology Ltd, Howard House, Amy Road, Oxted, Surrey, RH8 0PW Tel: (01883) 716161 Fax: (01883) 716865 E-mail: mail@dtl-connectors.co.uk
E C M Electronics Ltd, Penmaen House, London Road, Ashington, Pulborough, West Sussex, RH20 3JR Tel: (01903) 892810 Fax: (01903) 892738 E-mail: ecm@ecmelectronics.co.uk
E Preston Electrical Ltd, Unit 28 Broadway, Globe Lane, Dukinfield, Cheshire, SK16 4UU Tel: 0161-339 5177 Fax: 0161-343 1935 E-mail: sales@epreston.co.uk
Eao Ltd, Albert Drive, Burgess Hill, West Sussex, RH15 9TN Tel: (01444) 236000 Fax: (01444) 236641 E-mail: sales.euk@eao.com
Easby Electronics Ltd, Mercury Road, Gallowfields Trading Estate, Richmond, North Yorkshire, DL10 4TQ Tel: (01748) 850555 Fax: (01748) 850556 E-mail: sales@easby.co.uk
Edmundson Electrical Ltd, 6 Springlakes Estate, Deadbrook Lane, Aldershot, Hampshire, GU12 4UH Tel: (01252) 343443 Fax: (01252) 328104
Electro Replacement Ltd, 1 Moor Park Industrial Centre, Tolpits Lane, Watford, WD18 9EU Tel: (01923) 255344 Fax: (01923) 255829
Electrocomponents U K Ltd, 5000 John Smith Drive, Oxford Business Park South, Oxford, OX4 2BH Tel: (01865) 204000 Fax: (01865) 207400E-mail: sales@electrocomponents.com
Electronics 2000 Ltd, Grafton House, Grafton Street, High Wycombe, Buckinghamshire, HP12 3AJ Tel: (01494) 444044 Fax: (01494) 470499 E-mail: sales@e2000.com
Electrovision Ltd, Lancots Lane, St. Helens, Merseyside, WA9 3EX Tel: (01744) 745000 Fax: (01744) 745001 E-mail: sales@electrovision.co.uk
Emc, Stevenage Business Park, Eastman Way, Stevenage, Hertfordshire, SG1 4SZ Tel: (01438) 748899 Fax: (01438) 728828 E-mail: sales@2k1.co.uk
Esr Electronic Components, Station Road, Cullercoats, North Shields, Tyne & Wear, NE30 4PQ Tel: 0191-251 4363 Fax: 0191-252 2296 E-mail: sales@esr.co.uk
Exfo Photonic Solutions, 2 Bank Place, Falmouth, Cornwall, TR11 4AT Tel: (01326) 311321
Farnell, Canal Road, Leeds, LS12 2TU Tel: (08447) 111111 Fax: (08447) 111112 E-mail: sales@farnell.com
Fastek Electronics Ltd, Palace House, Edinburgh Road, Linlithgow, West Lothian, EH49 6QS Tel: (01506) 848076 Fax: (01506) 848076 E-mail: fastekelectronice@hotmail.com
Felco Electronics Ltd, 2 Rivermead, Pipers Way, Thatcham, Berkshire, RG19 4EP Tel: (01635) 866940 Fax: (01635) 866951 E-mail: sales@felco.co.uk
▶ Ferro Electronic Component Distributors, 1 Lime Grove Estate, Falconer Road, Haverhill, Suffolk, CB9 7XU Tel: (01440) 711980 Fax: (01440) 711981
Flint Ltd, Walker Road, Bardon Hill, Coalville, Leicestershire, LE67 1TU Tel: (01530) 510333 Fax: (01530) 510275 E-mail: info@flint.co.uk
Future Electronics Ltd, 123 Renfrew Road, Paisley, Renfrewshire, PA3 4EA Tel: 0141-840 6500 Fax: 0141-849 6971
Genalog Ltd, Gills Green Oast, Gills Green, Cranbrook, Kent, TN18 5ET Tel: (01580) 753754 Fax: (01580) 752979 E-mail: sales@genalog.com
Goldney Electronics UK, 6 Queen Anne's Gardens, Leatherhead, Surrey, KT22 7JE Tel: (01372) 378194 Fax: (01372) 375759 E-mail: purchasing@goldney.net
Greenweld, C/O Permex Ltd, Riverside House, Plumpton Road, Hoddesdon, Hertfordshire, EN11 0PA Tel: (01992) 452980 Fax: (01992) 452981 E-mail: bargains@greenweld.co.uk
Harmon Precision Grinding, 55 Haviland Road, Ferndown Industrial Estate, Wimborne, Dorset, BH21 7PY Tel: (01202) 654198 Fax: (01202) 654199 E-mail: info@harmon.co.uk
Hills Components Ltd, Valley Park, Olds Approach, Watford, WD18 9TL Tel: (01923) 772773 Fax: (01923) 421421 E-mail: sales@hillscomponents.co.uk
▶ Hiltek Microwave Ltd, Newton House, Winch Road, Sittingbourne Research Centre, Sittingbourne, Kent, ME9 8EF Tel: (01795) 420998 Fax: (01795) 421998
I C Market, PO Box 20379, Henley-on-Thames, Oxfordshire, RG9 2BH Tel: (01491) 410719 Fax: (01491) 412912 E-mail: emma@icemktg.co.uk
In2connect Design & Marketing Ltd, Acton Grove, Long Eaton, Nottingham, NG10 1FY Tel: 0115-901 1100 Fax: 0115-901 1111 E-mail: info@in2connect.net

ELECTRONIC COMPONENTS – *continued*

Inelco Ltd, Unit 3 Theale Technology Centre, Station Raod, Theale, RG7 4XX Tel: (0870) 4203561 Fax: (0870) 4203563 E-mail: sales@inelco.co.uk

Interactive Components, 2A Patrick Way, Aylesbury, Buckinghamshire, HP21 9XH Tel: (01296) 425656 Fax: (01296) 395332 E-mail: interactive@bucksnet.co.uk

Iskra UK Ltd, Redlands, Coulsdon, Surrey, CR5 2HT Tel: (020) 8668 7141 Fax: (020) 8668 3108

J H Components, Unit 6 Europa Way, Britannia Enterprise Park, Lichfield, Staffordshire, WS14 9TZ Tel: (01543) 417471 Fax: (01543) 419001 E-mail: jhcdis@aol.com

Just Rams plc, 6 Iron Bridge Close, Great Central Way, London, NW10 0UF Tel: (020) 8451 8700 Fax: (020) 8459 6301 E-mail: sales@justrams.co.uk

Kestrel Electronic Components Ltd, 178 Brighton Road, Purley, Surrey, CR8 4HA Tel: (020) 8668 7522 Fax: (020) 8668 4190

Keytronics, 88 Hadham Road, Bishop's Stortford, Hertfordshire, CM23 2QT Tel: (01279) 505543 Fax: (01279) 757656 E-mail: pk@keytronics.co.uk

Lan Electronics, Unit 5 50, Rother Valley Way, Holbrook, Sheffield, S20 3RW Tel: 0114-251 1066 Fax: 0114-251 1067 E-mail: sales@lanelectronicsltd.co.uk

Langrex, Unit 4, Daux Road, Billingshurst, West Sussex, RH14 9SJ Tel: (01403) 785600 Fax: (01403) 785656E-mail: langrex@aol.com

Lasercare Bristol Ltd, 8 Bromley Heath Avenue, Bristol, BS16 6JS Tel: 0117-907 3463 Fax: 0117-907 7538 E-mail: sales@lasercarebristol.co.uk

▶ Lilco Ltd, Diamond House, Stenness, Stromness, Orkney, KW16 3JX Tel: (01856) 850179 Fax: (01856) 851291 E-mail: mail@lilco.co.uk

Livewire Electronic Components Ltd, CWM Farm Barn, Llantrisant, Usk, Gwent, NP15 1LG Tel: (01291) 673003 Fax: (01291) 671001 E-mail: info@livewire.uk.com

▶ Lumier Ltd, County Park Road, Barrow-in-Furness, Cumbria, LA14 4BQ Tel: (01229) 821104 Fax: (01229) 821104

Mainline Surplus Sales, Unit 1A, Cutters Close, Coventry Road, Harborough, Leicester, LE19 2FR Tel: (0116) 286 5303 Fax: (0116) 2867797 E-mail: sales@mainlinegroup.co.uk

Marathon Electronics Ltd, Sovereign Park, Cleveland Way, Hemel Hempstead, Hertfordshire, HP2 7DA Tel: (01442) 232324 Fax: (01442) 243656 E-mail: salse@marathonelectronics.couk

Marchwood Technologies Ltd, Unit 9, 7 Black Moor Road, Ebblake Industrial Estate, Verwood, Dorset, BH31 6AX Tel: (01202) 810770 Fax: (01202) 820770 E-mail: norma@marchwood.co.uk

Marlow Marketing, Electron House, Unit 2, Everglade Close, Longfield, Kent, DA3 7EZ Tel: (01474) 700121 Fax: (01474) 700122 E-mail: new.world@dial.pipex.com

Metron Technology (UK) Ltd, 2 Gregory Road, Livingston, West Lothian, EH54 7DR Tel: (01506) 403000 Fax: (01506) 403037

Micromark, Building 5, Waltham Road, White Waltham, Maidenhead, Berkshire, SL6 3TN Tel: (01628) 512900 Fax: (01628) 512999 E-mail: sales@micromark.net

Multicore Ltd, 2 Dorset Street, London, W1U 4EE Tel: (020) 7935 4022 Fax: (020) 7935 2687 E-mail: multicore@ntlworld.com

Multipulse Electronics Ltd, Unit 3 Goldsworth Park Trading Estate, Kestrel Way, Woking, Surrey, GU21 3BA Tel: (01483) 713600 Fax: (01483) 729851 E-mail: sales@multipulse.com

N C S Inc, 49 Parc-y-Felin, Creigiau, Cardiff, CF15 9PB Tel: (029) 2089 1515 Fax: (029) 2089 1694

N E C Electronics, Cygnus House, Sunrise Parkway, Linford Wood, Milton Keynes, MK14 6NP Tel: (01908) 691133 Fax: (01908) 670290 E-mail: receptioneuk@ee.nec.de

National Semi-Conductor (U K) Ltd, Milford House, Milford St, Swindon, SN1 1DW Tel: (01793) 614141 Fax: (01793) 427551 E-mail: elspethmurrin@nsc.com

New World Electronics, Unit A Cuters Close Industrial Estate, Cuters Close, Leicester, LE19 2FZ Tel: 0116-284 8785 Fax: 0116-286 7797 E-mail: new.world@dial.pipex.com

Nexus G B Ltd, Rushdene, Dodsley Grove, Easebourne, Midhurst, West Sussex, GU29 9BE Tel: (01730) 816502 Fax: (01730) 817393 E-mail: johncbarrett@msn.com

Nicera European Works Ltd, Unit 5 Yeoman Industrial Park, Test Lane, Southampton, SO16 9JX Tel: (023) 8066 7908 Fax: (023) 8066 3758 E-mail: sales@nicera-uk.com

Nikko Electronics Ltd, 358 Kingston Road, Epsom, Surrey, KT19 0DT Tel: (020) 8393 7774 Fax: (020) 8393 7395 E-mail: dalbani@nikko-electronics.co.uk

Nitronics Ltd, Nitronics House, The Maltings Centre, Station Road, Sawbridgeworth, Hertfordshire, CM21 9JX Tel: (01279) 307555 Fax: (01279) 307700 E-mail: sales@nitronics.co.uk

Nobel Electronics Ltd, Tudor Cottages, Footscray High Street, Sidcup, Kent, DA14 5HN Tel: (020) 8309 0500 Fax: (020) 8302 7901 E-mail: nicknoakes.nobel@idnetfreemail.co.uk

Northcott Electronics Ltd, 1 Marquis Business Centre, Royston Road, Baldock, Hertfordshire, SG7 6XL Tel: (01462) 490999 Fax: (01462) 490990 E-mail: info@northcott.co.uk

Northern Connectors Ltd, Abbotsfield Road, Reginald Road Industrial Estate, St. Helens, Merseyside, WA9 4HU Tel: (01744) 815001 Fax: (01744) 814040 E-mail: sales@northern-connectors.co.uk

Nywled Technology Ltd, Farmerie Road, Hundon, Sudbury, Suffolk, CO10 8HA Tel: (01440) 786611 Fax: (01440) 786800 E-mail: quote@forpcbs.com

P & B Metal Components Ltd, Tyler Way, Colewood Road, Whitstable, Kent, CT5 2RR Tel: (01227) 793456 Fax: (01227) 793597

P C Point Of Sale, Units 1-3 The Rutherford Centre, Rutherford Road, Basingstoke, Hants, RG24 8PB Tel: (01256) 356161 Fax: (01256) 356112

Pacer Components plc, Unit 4 Horseshoe Park, Pangbourne, Reading, RG8 7JW Tel: 0118-984 5280 Fax: 0118-984 5425 E-mail: pacer@pacer.co.uk

Panduit Europe Ltd, West World, Westgate, London, W5 1UD Tel: (020) 8601 7200 Fax: (020) 8601 7319

Partminer UK Ltd, 14 High Street, Leatherhead, Surrey, KT22 8AN Tel: (01372) 379930 Fax: (01372) 384998 E-mail: uk@partminer.com

Phoenix Electronics Ltd, Phoenix House, Carluke, Lanarkshire, ML8 5UF Tel: (01555) 751566 Fax: (01555) 751562 E-mail: sales@phoenix1.co.uk

Pickering Electronics Ltd, Stephenson Road, Clacton-on-Sea, Essex, CO15 4NL Tel: (01255) 428141 Fax: (01255) 475058 E-mail: sales@pickeringrelay.com

Pinewood Electronics Ltd, Riverside Business Park, Stoney Common Road, Stansted, Essex, CM24 8ND Tel: (01279) 816666 Fax: (01279) 816161 E-mail: info@pinewood.gb.com

▶ Programmed Logic Services, 59a Peach Street, Wokingham, Berkshire, RG40 1XP Tel: 0118-977 5855 Fax: 0118-979 2120 E-mail: microchips@btconnect.com

Region Services Ltd, Unit 3 Fullwood Close, Aldermans Green Industrial Estate, Coventry, CV2 2SS Tel: (024) 7661 8189 Fax: (024) 7662 2246 E-mail: info@rslkiosks.co.uk

▶ Resistance Wires Ltd, 110 Carnegie Road, Hillington Industrial Estate, Glasgow, G52 4JZ Tel: 0141-891 8881 Fax: 0141-891 8549 E-mail: sales@resistancewires.co.uk

Ridgeway Components Ltd, Unit 5, Prosperity Way, Middlewich, Cheshire, CW10 0GD Tel: (01606) 841010 Fax: (01606) 841011 E-mail: sales@ridgeway-components.co.uk

Roditi International Corp Ltd, Carrington House, 130 Regent Street, London, W1B 5SE Tel: (020) 7439 6142 Fax: (020) 7434 0896 E-mail: sales@roditi.com

Rombyte Ltd, Unit 6-7 Kingfisher Court, Newbury, Berkshire, RG14 5SJ Tel: (01635) 528006 Fax: (01635) 528115 E-mail: sales@rombyte.co.uk

Routeco, Unit 8, Spitfire Close, Coventry Business Park, Coventry, CV5 6UR Tel: (024) 7667 6513 Fax: (024) 7667 8490 E-mail: coventry@routeco.co.uk

S D Products, The Broadway, Mansfield, Nottinghamshire, NG18 2RL Tel: (01623) 655265 Fax: (01623) 420689 E-mail: sales@sdproducts.co.uk

St Davids Assemblies Co. Ltd, Glasfryn Road, St. Davids, Haverfordwest, Dyfed, SA62 6RY Tel: (01437) 720555 Fax: (01437) 725500 E-mail: sales@stdavidsassemblies.co.uk

Semi Conductor Supplies International Ltd, 128-130 Carshalton Road, Sutton, Surrey, SM1 4TW Tel: (020) 8643 1126 Fax: (020) 8643 3937 E-mail: sales@ssi-uk.com

Semiconductor Specialists (UK) Ltd, Lincoln Business Park, Osbaldwick, York, YO10 3JB Tel: (01904) 436450 Fax: (01904) 436550 E-mail: sales@semispecs.com

▶ Semikron, Skipton Road, Keighley, West Yorkshire, BD20 6DT Tel: (01535) 691795 Fax: (01535) 691795

▶ Sentry Systems, Britannia Enterprise Centre, Waterworks Road, Hastings, East Sussex, TN34 1RT Tel: (01424) 720600 Fax: (01424) 440092

Shaw Electronic Development Co., 7 Market Street, Church, Accrington, Lancashire, BB5 0DP Tel: (01254) 393878 Fax: (01254) 393878

▶ Silicon Sensor, 35 Orchard Close, Stanstead Abbotts, Ware, Hertfordshire, SG12 8AH Tel: (01920) 872090 E-mail: sales@silicon-sensor.de

Slencrest Ltd, Broad Oak House, Pheasant Lane, Maidstone, Kent, ME15 9QR Tel: (01622) 741122 Fax: (01622) 747722 E-mail: sales@slencrest.com

Solitek Ltd, Watermill House, Restmoor Way, Wallington, Surrey, SM6 7AH Tel: (020) 8669 6669 Fax: (020) 8669 6961 E-mail: sales@solitek.co.uk

Sovereign Rotating Electrics Ltd, Unit 1-2 Christie Place, Bognor Regis, West Sussex, PO22 9RT Tel: (01243) 833420 Fax: (01243) 833421 E-mail: sales@sovereignltd.co.uk

Spartan Europe Ltd, Unit A13 Railway Triangle, Walton Road, Portsmouth, PO6 1TN Tel: (023) 9221 0053 Fax: (023) 9221 0057 E-mail: sales@spartaneurope.com

Stanler Components Ltd, Crittal Court, Crittal Drive, Braintree, Essex, CM7 2SE Tel: (01376) 340902 Fax: (01376) 322510 E-mail: sales@stanler.co.uk

Steptronik UK Ltd, 1 & 2 Baird Close, District 12, Washington, Tyne & Wear, NE37 3HL Tel: 0191-417 8990 Fax: 0191-417 8202 E-mail: peter@steptronik.co.uk

Stewart Of Reading, 17 King Street, Mortimer Common, Reading, RG7 3RS Tel: 0118-933 1111 Fax: 0118-933 2375 E-mail: dwayn@stewart-of-reading.co.uk

Stotron Ltd, York Road Industrial Park, Derwent Road, Malton, North Yorkshire, YO17 6YB Tel: (01653) 600492 Fax: (01653) 690980

Surtech Distribution Ltd, Glenmore Business Park, Colebrook Way, Andover, Hampshire, SP10 3GZ Tel: (01264) 369991 Fax: (01264) 369992 E-mail: enquiries@surtechdist.co.uk

▶ Synapsys Solutions Ltd, 23 Cuckfield Road, Hurstpierpoint, Hassocks, West Sussex, BN6 9RW Tel: (01273) 831831 Fax: (01273) 831631E-mail: sales@synapsys-solutions.com

T S Industrial Products Ltd, 75 Somers Road, Rugby, Warwickshire, CV22 7DG Tel: (01788) 543387 Fax: (01788) 541311 E-mail: sales@tsindustrial.co.uk

Tarvet Electronics Ltd, 1 Ferry Toll Road, Rosyth, Dunfermline, Fife, KY11 2XF Tel: (01383) 414777 Fax: (01383) 415888

Techna International, Unit 1 Metro Centre, Dwight Road, Watford, WD18 9HG Tel: (01923) 222227 Fax: (01923) 219700 E-mail: sales@techna.co.uk

Thick Film Microcircuits Ltd, Unit 4 Wickford Way, London, E17 6JD Tel: (020) 8531 7226 Fax: (020) 8527 5521 E-mail: sales@thickfilm.co.uk

Toby Electronics Ltd, Beaumont Road, Banbury, Oxfordshire, OX16 1TU Tel: (01295) 271777 Fax: (01295) 271744 E-mail: info@toby.co.uk

Toko UK Ltd, Ward Royal Parade, Alma Road, Windsor, Berkshire, SL4 3HR Tel: (01753) 602222 Fax: (01753) 602255

Tomita (U K) Ltd, Fortway House, Banbury, Oxfordshire, OX16 4SP Tel: (01295) 277317 Fax: (01295) 278889 E-mail: sales@tomita.co.uk

Toshiba Electronics (Europe) Ltd, Riverside Way, Camberley, Surrey, GU15 3YA Tel: (01276) 694600 Fax: (01276) 694800 E-mail: infobox@teu.toshiba.co.uk

TTAB Connectors Ltd, Ynysboeth Industrial Estate, Abercynon, Mountain Ash, Mid Glamorgan, CF45 4SF Tel: (01443) 740331 Fax: (01443) 741676

Tyco Electronics, Head Office, Faraday Road, Swindon, SN3 5HH Tel: (01793) 528171 Fax: (01793) 572516 E-mail: passivesales@tycoelectronics.com

▶ U S I UK Ltd, 1 Steadman Place, Riverside Business Park, Irvine, Ayrshire, KA11 5DN Tel: (01294) 222444 Fax: (01294) 222456

▶ Vero Technologies Ltd, Unit 25 Solent Industrial Estate, Shamblehurst Lane, Hedge End, Southampton, SO30 2FY Tel: (01489) 776930 Fax: (01489) 776938 E-mail: sales@verotl.com

Vishay Ltd, Pallion Trading Estate, Sunderland, SR4 6SU Tel: 0191-514 4155 Fax: 0191-567 8662 E-mail: paul.robson@vishay.com

▶ Whistler Technology Xchange, Phoenix House, Oak Tree Lane, Mansfield, Nottinghamshire, NG18 4LF Tel: (01623) 425880 Fax: (01623) 425881

Yaskawa Electric UK Ltd, 1 Hunt Hill, Cumbernauld, Glasgow, G68 9LF Tel: (01236) 735000 Fax: (01236) 458182

ELECTRONIC CONNECTORS

2 E (UK) Ltd, Heyes Farm House, Grimshaw Road, Skelmersdale, Lancashire, WN8 6BH Tel: (01695) 50300 Fax: (01695) 50338 E-mail: sales@2euk.com

Abacus Choice, Rooks Street, Cottenham, Cambridge, CB24 8QZ Tel: (01954) 287070 Fax: (01954) 252078

Amphenol Ltd, Thanet Way, Whitstable, Kent, CT5 3JF Tel: (01227) 773200 Fax: (01227) 276571 E-mail: info@amphenol.co.uk

Cambridge Electronic Industries Ltd, Denny Industrial Centre, Denny End Road, Waterbeach, Cambridge, CB25 9PB Tel: (01223) 860041 Fax: (01223) 863625 E-mail: sales@cambridgeconnectors.com

Alex Everett Ltd, 34 Victoria Road, Writtle, Chelmsford, CM1 3PA Tel: (01245) 421198 Fax: (01245) 422433 E-mail: aelconnectors@btclick.com

Flint Ltd, Walker Road, Bardon Hill, Coalville, Leicestershire, LE67 1TU Tel: (01530) 510333 Fax: (01530) 510275 E-mail: info@flint.co.uk

Imperial Components, 7 Sutherland Court, Brownfields, Welwyn Garden City, Hertfordshire, AL7 1BJ Tel: (01707) 321122 Fax: (01707) 321121

Interconnect Products Ltd, Marlborough Road, Wootton Bassett, Swindon, SN4 7SA Tel: (01793) 849811 Fax: (01793) 849809 E-mail: sales@interconnect.demon.co.uk

Interplex PMP Ltd, Elliot Industrial Estate, Arbroath, Angus, DD11 2NN Tel: (01241) 873867 Fax: (01241) 879597 E-mail: pmp@pmp-interplex.co.uk

N C S Inc, 49 Parc-y-Felin, Creigiau, Cardiff, CF15 9PB Tel: (029) 2089 1515 Fax: (029) 2089 1694

T T I, 2 Cliveden Office Village, Lancaster Road, Cressex Business Park, High Wycombe, Buckinghamshire, HP12 3YZ Tel: (01494) 460000 Fax: (01494) 460090 E-mail: sales.london@uk.ttiinc.com

Tritech International Ltd, Peregrine Road, Westhill Business Park, Westhill, Aberdeenshire, AB32 6JL Tel: (01224) 744111 Fax: (01224) 741771 E-mail: sales@tritech.co.uk

ELECTRONIC CONSULTANTS OR DESIGNERS

4c Electronics Ltd, Diamond Court Douglas Close, Preston Farm Business Park, Preston Farm Industrial Estate, Stockton-on-Tees, Cleveland, TS18 3SB Tel: (01642) 616449 Fax: (01642) 605772 E-mail: sales@4celectronics.co.uk

A R M Electronics Ltd, 14 Kempson Cl, Gatehouse Way, Aylesbury, Bucks, HP19 8UQ Tel: (01296) 437021 Fax: (01296) 483463 E-mail: a2470580@infotrade.co.uk

A S P Electronic Design Ltd, 3a Warren House Road, Wokingham, Berkshire, RG40 5PN Tel: 0118-979 0825 Fax: 0118-977 1749 E-mail: enquiries@asp.uk.com

A1 Results Ltd, Jervaulx House, Station Road, Newton le Willows, Bedale, North Yorkshire, DL8 1TB Tel: (01677) 450665 Fax: (01677) 450665

Amfax Ltd, 3 Clump Farm Industrial Estate, Blandford Heights, Blandford Forum, Dorset, DT11 7TE Tel: (01258) 480777 Fax: (01258) 480728 E-mail: sales@amfax.co.uk

Arabesque, 2 Rodney Way, Guildford, Surrey, GU1 2NY Tel: (01483) 825949 E-mail: j_langridge@yahoo.co.uk

Arbarr Electronics Ltd, 2 Kilgavanagh Road, Antrim, BT41 2LJ Tel: (028) 9442 9334 Fax: (028) 9442 9178 E-mail: enquiries@arbarr.co.uk

Arrow Technical Services Ltd, 58 Nursery Street, Sheffield, S3 8GG Tel: 0114-281 2018 Fax: 0114-281 5404 E-mail: info@arrowtechnical.com

Audio Engine, 1 Lower Luton Road, Harpenden, Hertfordshire, AL5 5AF Tel: (01582) 768560 Fax: (01582) 469532 E-mail: phaudio@aol.com

Automated Entry Systems Ltd, Automation House, 61 East Street, Warminster, Wiltshire, BA12 9BZ Tel: (01985) 215827 Fax: (01985) 219299 E-mail: aeswinchcombe@aol.com

▶ Avanti Elektronik Ltd, 37 Forest Avenue, Aberdeen, AB15 4TU Tel: (01224) 319849

Axiomatic Design Services, 43 St. Marys Lane, Ecclesfield, Sheffield, S35 9YE Tel: 0114-246 0160 E-mail: james@axiomatic.biz

B D L Systems Ltd, 14 Denmark Lane, Poole, Dorset, BH15 2DG Tel: (01202) 669000 Fax: (01202) 682660

B & F Group Ltd, Sovereign Way, Chester West Employment Park, Chester, CH1 4QJ Tel: (01244) 390215 Fax: (01244) 382747

Beech Hill Electronics, Beechcroft, Beech Hill Road, Beech Hill, Reading, RG7 2AU Tel: 0118-988 4622 E-mail: sales@beech-hill.co.uk

Buswell Machine Electronics, Peel House, Peel Road, Skelmersdale, Lancashire, WN8 9PT Tel: (01695) 726518 Fax: (01695) 726518 E-mail: rbuswell@buswell.co.uk

Cambridge Micro Engineering Ltd, 83 High Street, Linton, Cambridge, CB21 4JT Tel: (01223) 893872 Fax: (01223) 891760 E-mail: enquiries@cme.co.uk

Chardec Consultants Ltd, 3 Hyde Close, The Street, Kingston, Lewes, East Sussex, BN7 3PA Tel: (01273) 483800 Fax: (01273) 483900 E-mail: rich@chardec.co.uk

Cherlyn Electronics Ltd, Brookmount Court, Kirkwood Road, Cambridge, CB4 2QH Tel: (01223) 424169 Fax: (01223) 426543 E-mail: mail@cherlyn.co.uk

Communications & Surveillance Systems Ltd, 3 Portman Square, London, W1H 6LB Tel: (020) 7486 3885 Fax: (020) 7486 2655 E-mail: sales@spymaster.co.uk

Components & Products, P O Box 2053, Hockley, Essex, SS5 4WA Tel: (01702) 207247 Fax: (01702) 207224

▶ Concise Electronic Engineering Ltd, Rhydybont Mill, Llanybydder, Dyfed, SA40 9QS Tel: (01570) 481344 Fax: (01570) 481495 E-mail: enquiries@concise-electronics.co.uk

D M Kent Electronics Ltd, 8 Hedge End Industrial Estate, Shuart Lane, St. Nicholas at Wade, Birchington, Kent, CT7 0NB Tel: (01843) 846755 Fax: (01843) 848008 E-mail: sales@dmkent.co.uk

▶ Design Interface Ltd, Thurston Grange, Thurston End, Hawkedon, Bury St. Edmunds, Suffolk, IP29 4LQ Tel: (01284) 789608 Fax: (01284) 789617 E-mail: enquiries@design-interface.com

Design International Ltd, Unit 8, Clwydfro Business Centre, Lon Parcwr Industrial Estate, Ruthin, Clwyd, LL15 1NJ Tel: (01824) 704327 Fax: (0871) 2215698 E-mail: sales@designinternational.ltd.uk

Digital Development, The Old School, East Baldwin, Isle Of Man, IM4 5EP Tel: (01624) 851482 Fax: (01624) 851482

Electronic Design Services Ltd, Stewart Street, Bury, Lancashire, BL8 1SP Tel: 0161-705 2117 Fax: 0161-763 6940

The Electronic Development Co. Ltd, 26 Beckett Road, Worcester, WR3 7NH Tel: (01905) 759609 Fax: (01905) 453273 E-mail: jonathan@the-electronic-development.co.uk

Eyebright Designs Ltd, 107 Leicester Road, Wolvey, Hinckley, Leicestershire, LE10 3HJ Tel: (01455) 220835 Fax: (01455) 220895 E-mail: info@eyebright.demon.co.uk

ELECTRONIC CONSULTANTS OR DESIGNERS – *continued*

Fisher Consultants Derbyshire Ltd, 8 Parkside, Belper, Derbyshire, DE56 1HY Tel: (0845) 3707760

Ford Electronics Ltd, Brewood Hall, Sparrows End Lane, Brewood, Stafford, ST19 9DB Tel: (01902) 455555 E-mail: sales@fordelectronics.co.uk

Frontline Electronics, 25 Laundry Road, Minster, Ramsgate, Kent, CT12 4HY Tel: (01843) 821512 Fax: (01843) 821603 E-mail: sales@frontlineelectronics.co.uk

Future Generation Services Ltd, A Future Court, George Summers Close, Medway City Estate, Rochester, Kent, ME2 4EL Tel: (01634) 718662 Fax: (01634) 718646 E-mail: services@bnol.co.uk

Gill Instruments Ltd, Saltmarsh Park, 67 Gosport Street, Lymington, Hampshire, SO41 9EG Tel: (01590) 613500 Fax: (01590) 613501 E-mail: gill@gill.co.uk

Harman Electronic Services, 1 Perth Street, Stoke-on-Trent, ST4 3PJ Tel: (01782) 598662 Fax: (01782) 598662

I M Design & Repair, 4 Hockley Lane, Ettington, Stratford-Upon-Avon, Warwickshire, CV37 7SS Tel: (01789) 740870 Fax: (01789) 740870 E-mail: ian@windowcontrols.com

Industrial Control & Communication Ltd, Unit 1 Manor Park, West End, Nailsea, Bristol, BS48 4DE Tel: (01275) 856552 Fax: (01275) 856593 E-mail: info@icc.win-uk.net

Industrial Electronics Consultants, 855 Holderness Road, Hull, HU8 9BA Tel: (01482) 374437 Fax: (01482) 796853 E-mail: ray@rayeldred.carouy.co.uk

Ingenion Design Ltd, 10 Kym Road, Kimbolton, Huntingdon, Cambridgeshire, PE28 0LW Tel: (01480) 860606 Fax: (01480) 861122 E-mail: sales@ingenion.co.uk

Jaltek Systems, Unit 13 Sundon Business Park, Dencora Way, Luton, LU3 3HP Tel: (01582) 578170 Fax: (01582) 578171 E-mail: marketing@jaltek.com

K C S Electronics Ltd, First Avenue, Crewe Gates Industrial Estate, Crewe, CW1 6BG Tel: (01270) 588733 Fax: (01270) 583472

K M C Electronics Ltd, Farcroft, Doley Gate, Gnosall, Stafford, ST20 0EH Tel: (01785) 822777

Katon Ingram Ltd, Vittlefields Industrial Estate, Forest Road, Newport, Isle of Wight, PO30 4LY Tel: (01983) 822180 Fax: (01983) 822181 E-mail: katoningram@aol.com

Kirby Devon Ltd, Elm Tree House, Yealmbury Hill, Yealmpton, Plymouth, PL8 2JH Tel: (01752) 881717 Fax: (01752) 881710 E-mail: sales@kirbydevon.freeserve.co.uk

▶ Lamerholn Electronics Ltd, Pixmore Centre, Pixmore Avenue, Letchworth Garden City, Hertfordshire, SG6 1JG Tel: (01462) 481396 Fax: (01462) 473942 E-mail: web@lamerholm.com

Macrodyne Electronics Ltd, The Birches, Birches Lane, Newent, Gloucestershire, GL18 1DN Tel: (01531) 828010 Fax: (01531) 821153 E-mail: mailbox@macrodyne.com

Marell Electronic Systems Ltd, Coldwell Street, Linthwaite, Huddersfield, HD7 5QN Tel: (01484) 843142 Fax: (01484) 843177 E-mail: info@marell.co.uk

Mason & Morton (Electronics) Ltd, 24 Ullswater Crescent, Ullswater Business Park, Coulsdon, Surrey, CR5 2HR Tel: (020) 8410 4610 Fax: (020) 8660 5469

Memotrace Controls, 13 The Avenue, Spinney Hill, Northampton, NN3 6BA Tel: (01604) 642808 Fax: (01604) 642808 E-mail: memotrace@lineone.net

MGN Electronics, Beaumont Enterprise Centre, Boston Road, Leicester, LE4 1HB Tel: 0116-235 4004 Fax: 0116-236 6584 E-mail: gush@mgnelect.co.uk

Monode Ltd, Celtic House, 44 Ballmoor, Buckingham Industrial Estate, Buckingham, MK18 1RQ Tel: (01280) 814171 Fax: (01280) 814169 E-mail: sales@monode.co.uk

MSR Electronics Ltd, Fernhill Court, Balsall Street, Balsall Common, Coventry, CV7 7FR Tel: (01676) 532468 Fax: (01676) 534247 E-mail: sales@msravionics.com

Mutech Ltd, Unit 25, Waters Edge Business Park, Modwen Road, Salford, M5 3EZ Tel: 0161-872 0400 E-mail: sales@mutech.co.uk

Neptune Radar Ltd, Gardiners Farmhouse, Sandhurst Lane, Sandhurst, Gloucester, GL2 9NW Tel: (01452) 730479 Fax: (01452) 731315 E-mail: seawaves@enterprise.net

Newbury Electronic Services Ltd, 1 Berwick Courtyard, Berwick St. Leonard, Salisbury, SP3 5UA Tel: (01747) 820615 E-mail: sales@nes-ltd.com

Norcott Technologies Ltd, Brookfield House, Tarporley Road, Norcott Brook, Warrington, WA4 4EA Tel: (01925) 247600 Fax: (01925) 247610 E-mail: sales@norcott.co.uk

Panther Design Services Ltd, Barleyfield, Hinckley, Leicestershire, LE10 1YE Tel: (01455) 890033 Fax: (01455) 890066 E-mail: sales@panther-designs.co.uk

Parallel Solutions Ltd, 62 Manor Lane, Sunbury-on-Thames, Middlesex, TW16 6JA Tel: (01932) 782759 Fax: (01932) 782759 E-mail: gerald.roberts@dial.pipex.com

Pathdale Systems Ltd, Unit L, Ringstones Indust Estate, Whaley Bridge, High Peak, Derbyshire, SK23 7RX Tel: (01663) 734462 Fax: (01663) 734462 E-mail: sales@pathdale.co.uk

Piercy Adams Computer & Electronic Systems Ltd, Cochrane House, Church Road, Bookham, Leatherhead, Surrey, KT23 3JP Tel: (01372) 459577 Fax: (01372) 459343

Project Electronics Ltd, Project House, Slade Green Road, Erith, Kent, DA8 2HX Tel: (01322) 350700 Fax: (01322) 351100 E-mail: mail@project-uk.com

Q M Systems Ltd, 4 Manor Park Estate, Wyndham Street, Aldershot, Hampshire, GU12 4NZ Tel: (01252) 336612 Fax: (01252) 343018 E-mail: sales@qm-systems.com

R F Insight Ltd, 47 Percival Road, Rugby, Warwickshire, CV22 5JU Tel: (01788) 541790 Fax: (01788) 541790E-mail: sales@vvlp.co.uk

R K W Associates, 22 Bishops Mead, Laverstock, Salisbury, SP1 1RU Tel: (01722) 502600 Fax: (01722) 337344

R N Electronics Ltd, Arnolds Farm Lane, Mountnessing, Brentwood, Essex, CM13 1UT Tel: (01277) 352219 Fax: (01277) 352968 E-mail: sales@rnelectronics.com

Radiometrix, 231 Kenton Lane, Harrow, Middlesex, HA3 8RP Tel: (020) 8909 9595 Fax: (020) 8909 2233 E-mail: info@radiometrix.co.uk

Reeset Electronics, 19 Ray Lea Road, Maidenhead, Berkshire, SL6 8QP Tel: (01628) 628146 Fax: (01628) 628146 E-mail: ed@reeset.com

Lindsay Ruddock Ltd, 34 Orchard Avenue, Castle Donington, Derby, DE74 2JZ Tel: (07785) 932272 E-mail: lindsayruddock@ntlworld.com

Rugby Electronics, 57 Somers Road, Rugby, Warwickshire, CV22 7DG Tel: (01788) 572492 Fax: (01788) 540005 E-mail: sales@rugbyelectronics.com

Ruston Electronics Ltd, Unit 6, Sovereign Park, Laporte Way, Luton, LU4 8EL Tel: (01582) 506100 Fax: (01582) 506101 E-mail: sales@rustons.co.uk

Sabre Technology (Hull) Ltd, 3a Newlands Science Park, Newlands Centre, Inglemire Lane, Hull, HU6 7TQ Tel: (01482) 801003 Fax: (01482) 801078 E-mail: info@sabretechnology.co.uk

Softronic Systems Ltd, Unit 2 & 3 Enterprise Estate, Station Road West, Ash Vale, Aldershot, Hampshire, GU12 5QJ Tel: (01252) 513884

Solution Product Systems Ltd, Unit 34, Walker Avenue, Wolverton Mill, Milton Keynes, MK12 5TW Tel: (01908) 682700 Fax: (01908) 682739 E-mail: sales@spslretail.com

▶ Sonardyne, Units 12-13, The Technology Centre, Claymore Drive, Bridge of Don, Aberdeen, AB23 8GD Tel: (01224) 707875 Fax: (01224) 707876

Storm Power, 13 Pendyffryn Road, Rhyl, Clwyd, LL18 4RU Tel: (01745) 354405 Fax: (01745) 361219 E-mail: sales@stormpower.co.uk

Surrey Management Consultants Ltd, Newmet House, Rue de St Lawrence, Waltham Abbey, Essex, EN9 1PF Tel: (01992) 703401 Fax: (01992) 768393 E-mail: materials@newmet.co.uk

Telectra Ltd, Units B3-B7, New Yatt Business Centre, New Yatt, Witney, Oxfordshire, OX29 6TJ Tel: (01993) 868866 Fax: (01993) 868894 E-mail: contact@telectra.com

Texcel Technology plc, Parkside Works, Thames Road, Crayford, Dartford, DA1 4SB Tel: (01322) 621700 Fax: (01322) 557733 E-mail: sales@texceltechnology.com

Trax Circuits, Unit 15a Ellough Industrial Estate, Ellough, Beccles, Suffolk, NR34 7TD Tel: (01502) 711626 Fax: (01502) 711626 E-mail: traxcircuits@electronicrepairs.co.uk

Valro Manufacturing Ltd, Units 2-4, The Grove, Parkgate Industrial Estate, Knutsford, Cheshire, WA16 8XP Tel: (01565) 650204 Fax: (01565) 650755 E-mail: enquiries@valro.co.uk

▶ Waddicor Associates, Beech House, Grasby Road, North Kelsey Moor, Market Rasen, Lincolnshire, LN7 6HJ Tel: (01652) 678321 Fax: (01652) 678317 E-mail: info@waddicor.com

Walter Group Ltd, Walters House, 12 Merlin Centre, Lancaster Road, High Wycombe, Buckinghamshire, HP12 3TB Tel: (01494) 795100 Fax: (01494) 461107 E-mail: terry@aquila-innovations.co.uk

Watchfront Electronics, 27 Charterhouse Close, Bracknell, Berkshire, RG12 0XF Tel: (020) 7517 4900 Fax: (020) 7517 4903 E-mail: sales@watchfront.co.uk

Wellgates, Unit 6 Junction 7 Business Park, Blackburn Road, Clayton Le Moors, Lancashire, BB5 5JW Tel: (01254) 395379 Fax: (01254) 395379

▶ Wild Insight Ltd, 5 Cambridge Road, Ely, Cambridgeshire, CB7 4HJ Tel: (01353) 665304 Fax: (01353) 610466 E-mail: enquiries@wildinsight.co.uk

▶ Wilkie Electronics, 16 Muirhall Terrace, Perth, PH2 7ES Tel: (01738) 621492

Zonefollow Ltd, 2 Wilton Road, Haine Industrial Estate, Ramsgate, Kent, CT12 5HG Tel: (01843) 588087 Fax: (01843) 851313 E-mail: info@zonefollow.co.uk

ELECTRONIC CONTRACT MANUFACTURING CONSULTANTS

A W Technology, West Street, Earl Shilton, Leicester, LE9 7EJ Tel: (01455) 841116 E-mail: hello@awtechnology.com

Apollo Electronics Co., Unit 1 Riverside Business Park, Wakefield Road, Scissett, Huddersfield, HD8 9HR Tel: (01484) 864940 Fax: (01484) 865830 E-mail: sales@apollo-electronics.com

DCC Electronics Ltd, 1 Newmarket Drive, Derby, DE24 8SW Tel: (01332) 757733 Fax: (01332) 572229 E-mail: reception@dcc-electronics.co.uk

Emma Services Ltd, 20 De Lisle Road, Bournemouth, BH3 7NF Tel: (01202) 522058 Fax: (01202) 522049 E-mail: sales@emmaservices.co.uk

ELECTRONIC CONTRACT MANUFACTURING PROTOTYPE SERVICES

B C F Technology Ltd, 3 Rutherford Square, Brucefield Industrial Estate, Livingston, West Lothian, EH54 9BU Tel: (01506) 460023 Fax: (01506) 460045 E-mail: office@bcftech.demon.co.uk

Buswell Machine Electronics, Peel House, Peel Road, Skelmersdale, Lancashire, WN8 9PT Tel: (01695) 726518 Fax: (01695) 726518 E-mail: rbuswell@buswell.co.uk

Coburn Electronics, A3 Faraday Road, Newbury, Berkshire, RG14 2AD Tel: (01635) 35133 Fax: (01635) 36350 E-mail: sandra@newstart-electronics.co.uk

Emma Services Ltd, 20 De Lisle Road, Bournemouth, BH3 7NF Tel: (01202) 522058 Fax: (01202) 522049 E-mail: sales@emmaservices.co.uk

J K Controls Ltd, 12a Rochester Airport Industrial Estate, Laker Road, Rochester, Kent, ME1 3QX Tel: (01634) 685858 Fax: (01634) 685850 E-mail: info@jkcontrols.co.uk

Lema Electronics, 1 Talisman Business Centre, Duncan Road, Park Gate, Southampton, SO31 7GA Tel: (01489) 572230 Fax: (01489) 578741 E-mail: sales@lemaelectronics.co.uk

MSH Electronics Ltd, Unit 1B, Stone Lane Industrial Estate, Wimborne, Dorset, BH21 1HB Tel: (01202) 881733 Fax: (01202) 881366 E-mail: sales@mshuk.com

R F Insight Ltd, 47 Percival Road, Rugby, Warwickshire, CV22 5JU Tel: (01788) 541790 Fax: (01788) 541790E-mail: sales@vvlp.co.uk

ELECTRONIC CONTRACT MANUFACTURING SERVICES

A B Cable & Wiring, 8 Walworth Enterprise Centre Duke Close, West Way, Andover, Hampshire, SP10 5AP Tel: (01264) 334076 Fax: (01264) 337721 E-mail: sales@abcableandwiring.com

A B I Electronics Ltd, Dodworth Business Park, Dodworth, Barnsley, South Yorkshire, S75 3SP Tel: (01226) 207420 Fax: (01226) 207620 E-mail: post@abielectronics.co.uk

Abrae Technology Ltd, Park Hill Street, Bolton, BL1 4AR Tel: (01204) 361400 Fax: (0870) 3000693

Aero Stanrew Ltd, Gratton Way, Roundswell Business Park, Barnstaple, Devon, EX31 3AR Tel: (01271) 341300 Fax: (01271) 341301 E-mail: sales@aerostanrew.co.uk

Allgood Technology, Unit 1 Horton Court, Hortonwood 50, Telford, Shropshire, TF1 7GY Tel: (01952) 677145 Fax: (01952) 677145 E-mail: info@allgoodsmt.com

Almec E A S Ltd, Knowl Piece, Wilbury Way, Hitchin, Hertfordshire, SG4 0TY Tel: (01462) 436330 Fax: (01462) 437160 E-mail: enquiries@almec-eas.com

Alpha Design, 1 Didcot Road, Nuffield Industrial Estate, Poole, Dorset, BH17 0GD Tel: (01202) 684248 Fax: (01202) 666190 E-mail: info@alphadesign-poole.co.uk

Altros Engineering Ltd, Birch House Commercial Square, Leigh Street, High Wycombe, Buckinghamshire, HP11 2QT Tel: (01494) 443082 Fax: (01494) 436186 E-mail: altros_uk@hotmail.com

Amos Electronics, 4 Little Balmer, Buckingham Industrial Estate, Buckingham, MK18 1TF Tel: (01280) 817877 Fax: (01280) 814140 E-mail: purchasing@paramountelectronics.co.uk

Apollo Electronics Co., Unit 1 Riverside Business Park, Wakefield Road, Scissett, Huddersfield, HD8 9HR Tel: (01484) 864940 Fax: (01484) 865830 E-mail: sales@apollo-electronics.com

Arrowvale Electronics, Shawbank Road, Redditch, Worcestershire, B98 8YN Tel: (01527) 514151 Fax: (01527) 514321 E-mail: info@arrowvale.co.uk

Asmec Electronics Solutions Ltd, 64-68 Wilbury Way, Hitchin, Hertfordshire, SG4 0TP Tel: (01462) 441155 Fax: (01462) 441150 E-mail: nashr@asmec.com

Axis Electronics, Manton Lane, Bedford, MK41 7NY Tel: (01234) 342932 Fax: (01234) 364941 E-mail: sales@axis-electronics.com

Axisclaim Ltd, 11 Leap Cross Small Business Centre, London Road, Hailsham, East Sussex, BN27 3PD Tel: (01323) 442717 Fax: (01323) 442717 E-mail: enquiries@axisclaimelectronics.co.uk

B N Precision Assemblies Ltd, Unit 10, Portsmouth Enterprise Centre, Quartremaine Road, Portsmouth, PO3 5QT Tel: (023) 9266 6444 Fax: (023) 9266 6444

Barric Ltd, Vinces Road, Diss, Norfolk, IP22 4WY Tel: (01379) 644202 Fax: (01379) 652361 E-mail: sales@barric.co.uk

Bela Electronic Design Ltd, 12-14 Brooklands, Kempston, Bedford, MK42 7UH Tel: (01234) 840242 Fax: (01234) 843066 E-mail: sales@bela.co.uk

Belix Services Ltd, 2 Hazel Business Park Sandwash Close, Rainford Industrial Estate, Rainford, St. Helens, Merseyside, WA11 8LY Tel: (01744) 885110 Fax: (01744) 885110 E-mail: belixservices@barclays.net

Brantham Engineering Ltd, 3l Moss Road, Witham, Essex, CM8 3UQ Tel: (01376) 518384 Fax: (01376) 518900 E-mail: mail@brantham.com

Brighton Electrical Assemblies Ltd, Cradle Hill Industrial Estate, Seaford, East Sussex, BN25 3JE Tel: (01323) 893295 Fax: (01323) 897429 E-mail: info@bealtd.co.uk

Briton EMS Ltd, 4 Shuttleworth Road, Elms Industrial Estate, Bedford, MK41 0EP Tel: (01234) 266300 Fax: (01234) 266488 E-mail: sales@britonems.co.uk

C D O Electronics Ltd, 17 Bowater Road, Westminster Industrial Estate, London, SE18 5TF Tel: (020) 8855 9508 Fax: (020) 8316 1892 E-mail: jim@cdo-electronics.com

C J Armstrong Manufacturing Co. Ltd, Unit 7-8 River Brent Business Park, Trumpers Way, London, W7 2QA Tel: (020) 8574 4602 Fax: (020) 8574 1078 E-mail: cjarmstrong@lycos.co.uk

Chemigraphic Ltd, 2 Fleming Centre, Fleming Way, Crawley, West Sussex, RH10 9NF Tel: (01293) 543517 Fax: (01293) 552859 E-mail: sales@chemigraphic.co.uk

Coburn Electronics, A3 Faraday Road, Newbury, Berkshire, RG14 2AD Tel: (01635) 35133 Fax: (01635) 36350 E-mail: sandra@newstart-electronics.co.uk

Cogent Technology Ltd, Dock Lane, Melton, Woodbridge, Suffolk, IP12 1PE Tel: (01394) 387444 Fax: (01394) 380604 E-mail: sales@cogent-technology.co.uk

Comtrol Europe, Unit 2, Stapleshurst Business Park, Howes Lane, Bicester, Oxfordshire, OX25 3QU Tel: (01869) 352740 Fax: (01869) 323211 E-mail: info@comtrol.co.uk

Copper & Optic Terminations Ltd, 90 Town Road, Stoke-on-Trent, ST1 2LD Tel: (01782) 275810 Fax: (01782) 287820 E-mail: sales@copperandoptic.com

CT Production Ltd, 32-40 Harwell Road, Nuffield Industrial Estate, Poole, Dorset, BH17 0GE Tel: (01202) 687633 Fax: (01202) 680788 E-mail: sales@ctproduction.co.uk

Custom Keyboards Electronics Ltd, Unit 11, Claylands Road, Claylands Park, Bishops Waltham, Southampton, SO32 1BH Tel: (01489) 891851 Fax: (01489) 893708 E-mail: alancoppini@custom-keyboards.co.uk

D & K Wiring Services Ltd, Unit 1 Urban Hive, Sundon Park Road, Luton, LU3 3QU Tel: (01582) 492033 Fax: (01582) 565944 E-mail: sales@dkwiring.co.uk

D M Kent Electronics Ltd, 8 Hedge End Industrial Estate, Shuart Lane, St. Nicholas at Wade, Birchington, Kent, CT7 0NB Tel: (01843) 846755 Fax: (01843) 848008 E-mail: sales@dmkent.co.uk

Daletech Electronics Ltd, Regency House, Valley Road, Pudsey, West Yorkshire, LS28 9EN Tel: 0113-239 4220 Fax: 0113-255 3583 E-mail: sales@daletech.co.uk

Dantom Production Solutions Ltd, 18 Cameron Court, Winwick Quay, Warrington, WA2 8RE Tel: (01925) 657400 Fax: (01925) 657006 E-mail: davecoyne@danton.freeserve.co.uk

David Maddox Ltd, 53-55 Gatwick Road, Crawley, West Sussex, RH10 9RD Tel: (01293) 452830 Fax: (01293) 452830 E-mail: david.maddox@virgin.net

Davlec Ltd, Unit 16, Severn Farm Industrial Estate, Welshpool, Powys, SY21 7DF Tel: (01938) 555791 Fax: (01938) 555792 E-mail: sales@davlec.com

DCC Electronics Ltd, 1 Newmarket Drive, Derby, DE24 8SW Tel: (01332) 757733 Fax: (01332) 572229 E-mail: reception@dcc-electronics.co.uk

Derdon Design & Development (Electronics) Ltd, Livingstone Road, Foleshill, Coventry, CV6 5AR Tel: (024) 7668 9302 Fax: (024) 7666 4146

Digitimer Ltd, 37 Hydeway, Welwyn Garden City, Hertfordshire, AL7 3BE Tel: (01707) 328347 Fax: (01707) 373153 E-mail: bcooper@digitimer.com

Electro Avionics, D Burnham Road, Dartford, DA1 5BN Tel: (01322) 288698 Fax: (01322) 277520 E-mail: colin@electroavionics.co.uk

Electronic Production Services, Lansbury Estate, 102 Lower Guildford Road, Knaphill, Woking, Surrey, GU21 2EP Tel: (01483) 487644 Fax: (01483) 486347 E-mail: epswoking@btconnect.com

Electrosembly Co., 35-37 Haviland Road, Ferndown Industrial Estate, Wimborne, Dorset, BH21 7SA Tel: (01202) 893392 Fax: (01202) 893378

Elite Electronic Systems Ltd, Lackaghboy Industrial Estate, Lackaghboy, Enniskillen, County Fermanagh, BT74 4RL Tel: (028) 6632 7172 Fax: (028) 6632 5668 E-mail: sales@elitees.com

Emma Services Ltd, 20 De Lisle Road, Bournemouth, BH3 7NF Tel: (01202) 522058 Fax: (01202) 522049 E-mail: sales@emmaservices.co.uk

Enham Garden Centre, Enham Alamein, Andover, Hampshire, SP11 6JS Tel: (01264) 345800 Fax: (01264) 333638 E-mail: info@enham.co.uk

ELECTRONIC CONTRACT MANUFACTURING SERVICES – *continued*

F D Electronics Ltd, Unit U1, Riverside Industrial Estate, Bridge Road, Littlehampton, West Sussex, BN17 5DF Tel: (01903) 734160 Fax: (01903) 734170 E-mail: info@fd-electronics.net

Fife Fabrications Ltd, 29 Rutherford Road, Glenrothes, Fife, KY6 2RT Tel: (01592) 776700 Fax: (01592) 772101 E-mail: sales@fifab.co.uk

G I G Systems Ltd, Unit 9, 40 Wilton Road, Reading, RG30 2SS Tel: 0118-958 1115 Fax: 0118-958 1117 E-mail: gigssystems@btconnect.com

G N Systems, Undershore Works, Brookside Road, Bolton, BL2 2SE Tel: (01204) 361533 Fax: (01204) 382879 E-mail: gnsystems@provider.co.uk

G S P K Electronics Ltd, GSPK Technology Park, Manse Lane, Knaresborough, North Yorkshire, HG5 8LF Tel: +44 (0) 1423 869151 Fax: +44 (0) 1423 869239 E-mail: mail@gspk-electronics.ltd.uk

Gilbert Electronics, 35 Lower Road, Malvern, Worcestershire, WR14 4BX Tel: (01684) 576989 Fax: (01684) 576989

Grange Products Ltd, Unit 4 Station Road, Reddish, Stockport, Cheshire, SK5 6ND Tel: 0161-480 3318

Hallmark Electronics Ltd, Hallmark House Loomer Road Industrial Estate, Loomer Road, Newcastle, Staffordshire, ST5 7LA Tel: (01782) 562255 Fax: (01782) 565684 E-mail: info@hallmarkelectronics.com

Hanbury Electronics Ltd, Blatchford Close, Blatchford Road Industrial Estate, Horsham, West Sussex, RH13 5RG Tel: (01403) 251300

Ingenion Design Ltd, 10 Kym Road, Kimbolton, Huntingdon, Cambridgeshire, PE28 0LW Tel: (01480) 860606 Fax: (01480) 861122 E-mail: sales@ingenion.co.uk

Integrated Technologies UK, 30 Coppice Road, Poynton, Stockport, Cheshire, SK12 1SL Tel: (01625) 877249 Fax: (01625) 858825 E-mail: cj.intech@btinternet.com

Intercole Sub-Contract Services Ltd, 3 Avenger Close, Chandlers Ford, Eastleigh, Hampshire, SO53 4YU Tel: (023) 8025 4727 Fax: (023) 8025 1090 E-mail: subcon@intercole.co.uk

Jaltek Systems, Unit 13 Sundon Business Park, Dencora Way, Luton, LU3 3HP Tel: (01582) 578170 Fax: (01582) 578171 E-mail: marketing@jaltek.com

JCD Electronics Ltd, 4a Oakwood Parade, Oakwood Hill, Loughton, Essex, IG10 3EL Tel: (020) 8508 3355 Fax: (020) 8508 3355

Jemtech Designs Ltd, 18 Invincible Road, Farnborough, Hampshire, GU14 7QU Tel: (01252) 513556 Fax: (01252) 376168 E-mail: jemtech@globalnet.co.uk

Joule Electronics Ltd, Bryn, Burn Lane, Newton Aycliffe, County Durham, DL5 4PG Tel: (01325) 310278

Kays Electronics Ltd, 85 Cavendish Street, Ipswich, IP3 8AX Tel: (01473) 214040 Fax: (01473) 214060 E-mail: enquiries@kayselectronics.com

Kinswood Electronic Services, 2 4 Josselin Court, Josselin Road, Burnt Mills Industrial Estate, Basildon, Essex, SS13 1QE Tel: (01268) 455100 Fax: (01268) 455103

LAM Electronics Ltd, Unit 6/A, Mercury House, Calleva Park, Aldermaston, Reading, RG7 8PN Tel: 0118-981 1717 Fax: 0118-981 7475 E-mail: almelecinfo@almelec.co.uk

Link Cable Assemblers Ltd, North Caldeen Road, Coatbridge, Lanarkshire, ML5 4EF Tel: (01236) 423005 Fax: (01236) 449118 E-mail: sales@linkcableassemblies.co.uk

M J P Electronics Ltd, Unit 1, Gore Cross Business Park, Corbin Way, Bradpole, Bridport, Dorset, DT6 3UX Tel: (01308) 425800 Fax: (01308) 455770 E-mail: murry@mjpelectronics.com

M K R Electronic Services, Unit 1 Havannah Street, Congleton, Cheshire, CW12 2AH Tel: (01260) 271553 Fax: (01260) 275750

Mpe Electronics Ltd, Brambleside, Bellbrook Industrial Estate, Uckfield, East Sussex, TN22 1QQ Tel: (01825) 764822 Fax: (01825) 765850 E-mail: k.chamberlain@mpe-electronics.co.uk

MSH Electronics Ltd, Unit 1B, Stone Lane Industrial Estate, Wimborne, Dorset, BH21 1HB Tel: (01202) 881733 Fax: (01202) 881366 E-mail: sales@mshuk.com

MSR Electronics Ltd, Fernhill Court, Balsall Street, Balsall Common, Coventry, CV7 7FR Tel: (01676) 532468 Fax: (01676) 534247 E-mail: sales@msravionics.com

N E L UK Ltd, 75 Burton Road, Carlton, Nottingham, NG4 3FP Tel: 0115-940 1894 Fax: 0115-987 0878E-mail: tony@nel-uk.co.uk

N E M Co. Ltd, Stevenage Business Park, Wedgewood Way, Stevenage, Hertfordshire, SG1 4SX Tel: (01438) 346600 Fax: (01438) 346632 E-mail: sales@nemco.co.uk

Neo Electronics Ltd, Compass House, Neville Street, Chadderton, Oldham, OL9 6LD Tel: 0161-633 2148 Fax: 0161-627 5324 E-mail: sales@neo.co.uk

Nortek Electronic Circuits Ltd, Bridge Mill, Royle Street, Congleton, Cheshire, CW12 1HR Tel: (01260) 276409 Fax: (01260) 299399 E-mail: mail@nortek.co.uk

Orb Systems, 2 Nelson House, 46 Station Road, Chertsey, Surrey, KT16 8BE Tel: (01932) 569100 Fax: (01932) 569100

P P V Electronics Ltd, Unit 1a, Bridge St Mills, Bridge St, Macclesfield, Cheshire, SK11 6QA Tel: (01625) 502062 Fax: (01625) 420507 E-mail: markhough@ppv-electronics.com

Pageantry Electronic Systems, Unit 7 55 Weir Road Industrial Estate, London, SW19 8UG Tel: (020) 8947 3100 Fax: (020) 8879 0068 E-mail: sales@pageantry.co.uk

Partnatech, Unit 6, 7 College Park Coldhams Lane, Cambridge, CB1 3HD Tel: (01223) 414419 Fax: (01223) 244177 E-mail: info@partnertech.co.uk

Partnertech Poole Ltd, Turnkey House, 31 Benson Road, Nuffield Industrial Estate, Poole, Dorset, BH17 0RY Tel: (01202) 674333 Fax: (01202) 678028 E-mail: info@hansatech.co.uk

Phase One Electronics, Orion Court, 2 Rodney Road, Southsea, Hampshire, PO4 8SZ Tel: (023) 9286 2394 Fax: (023) 9286 2396 E-mail: tonys@t1e.uk.com

Precision Electronics Assemblies Wingham, School Lane, Wingham, Canterbury, Kent, CT3 1BD Tel: (01227) 720360 Fax: (01227) 720360

Priheath Ltd, Unit 7 Shire Hill, Saffron Walden, Essex, CB11 3AQ Tel: (01799) 525982 Fax: (01799) 521686 E-mail: priheath@cambridgerapid.co.uk

Prima Electronic Services Ltd, 4 Harding Way, St. Ives, Cambridgeshire, PE27 3WR Tel: (01480) 498338 Fax: (01480) 495172 E-mail: sales@primagroup.co.uk

Primstone Electronics, 27a Whitehorse Street, Baldock, Hertfordshire, SG7 6QF Tel: (01462) 490594 Fax: (01462) 490595 E-mail: primstone@aol.com

Prism Electronics Ltd, Burrel Road, St. Ives, Cambridgeshire, PE27 3NF Tel: (01480) 462225 Fax: (01480) 494047 E-mail: sales@prism-electronics.com

▶ Programmed Logic Services, 59a Peach Street, Wokingham, Berkshire, RG40 1XP Tel: 0118-977 5855 Fax: 0118-979 2120 E-mail: microchips@btconnect.com

Project Electronics Ltd, Project House, Slade Green Road, Erith, Kent, DA8 2HX Tel: (01322) 350700 Fax: (01322) 351100 E-mail: mail@project-uk.com

Protech Electronic Services Ltd, 3 The Ringway Centre, Eddison Road, Basingstoke, Hampshire, RG21 6YH Tel: (01256) 818007 Fax: (01256) 819901 E-mail: bob@protech.freeuk.com

Quality Precision Electronics Ltd, 15 Faraday Road, Glenrothes, Fife, KY6 2RU Tel: (01592) 771455 Fax: (01592) 772944 E-mail: admin@qpe.co.uk

Quasson Ltd, Quasson House, Rennie Gate, Andover, Hampshire, SP10 3TU Tel: (01264) 332132 Fax: (01264) 334470 E-mail: sales@quasson.co.uk

▶ Ramar Electronics Services Ltd, Masons Road, Stratford-upon-Avon, Warwickshire, CV37 9NF Tel: (01789) 204879 Fax: (01789) 299727 E-mail: info@ramarpcb.co.uk

Raytheon Systems Ltd, Fullerton Road, Queensway Industrial Estate, Glenrothes, Fife, KY7 5PY Tel: (01592) 754311 Fax: (01592) 759775 E-mail: carol.fleming@raytheon.co.uk

Redcliffe Magtronics, 19 Clothier Road, Brislington, Bristol, BS4 5PS Tel: 0117-972 9400 Fax: 0117-972 3013 E-mail: enquiries@redcliffe.biz

▶ Remploy Ltd, Stone Court, Siskin Drive, Middlemarch Business Park, Coventry, CV3 4FJ Tel: (024) 7651 5800 Fax: (024) 7651 5860 E-mail: info@remploy.co.uk

Remploy Ltd, 13-6 South Gyle CR, Edinburgh, EH12 9EB Tel: 0131-334 2266 Fax: 0131-334 3167

Remploy Manufacturing Services, 79 Torrington Avenue, Coventry, CV4 9AQ Tel: (024) 7646 2715 Fax: (024) 7642 7064 E-mail: graham.howard-spink@remploy.co.uk

Remploy Recycle Ltd, Cymmer Road, Porth, Mid Glamorgan, CF39 9BW Tel: (01443) 497200 Fax: (01443) 497228 E-mail: mike.clarke@remploy.co.uk

Ruston Electronics Ltd, Unit 6, Sovereign Park, Laporte Way, Luton, LU4 8EL Tel: (01582) 506100 Fax: (01582) 506101 E-mail: sales@rustons.co.uk

Ryman Control Systems Ltd, 4 Faygate Business Centre, Faygate Lane, Faygate, Horsham, West Sussex, RH12 4DN Tel: (01293) 851865 Fax: (01293) 851866 E-mail: info@rymancontrol.co.uk

S K Electronics Ltd, Regent Street, Oldham, OL1 3TZ Tel: 0161-620 5414 Fax: 0161-627 3237 E-mail: sales@skelectronics.co.uk

S K N Electronics Ltd, Armoury Road, Birmingham, B11 2PP Tel: 0121-773 6672 Fax: 0121-766 8457 E-mail: technical@sknelectronics.co.uk

St Cross Electronics Ltd, 14 Mount Pleasant Industrial Estate, Mount Pleasant Road, Southampton, SO14 0SP Tel: (023) 8022 7636 Fax: (023) 8033 1769 E-mail: sales@st-cross-electronics.co.uk

Sascal Displays Ltd, Unit 1 Hayes Metro Centre, Springfield Road, Hayes, Middlesex, UB4 0LE Tel: (020) 8573 0303 Fax: (020) 8569 1515 E-mail: sales@sascal.com

Saygrove System & Technology, Units 9-10 Catheralls Industrial Estate, Brookhill Way, Buckley, Clwyd, CH7 3PS Tel: (01244) 550022 Fax: (01244) 549843 E-mail: info@saygrove.co.uk

Selectron Ltd, 1 Davis Way, Fareham, Hampshire, PO14 1JF Tel: (01329) 230525 Fax: (01329) 822759 E-mail: sales@solectron-ltd.co.uk

Shanoc Electronic Systems Ltd, 1-3 Pond Close, Walkern Road, Stevenage, Hertfordshire, SG1 3QP Tel: (01438) 727244 Fax: (01438) 726565 E-mail: info@shannock.co.uk

Sign Trade Europe Ltd, Parker Street, Hucknall, Nottingham, NG15 7UF Tel: 0115-968 1000 Fax: 0115-968 1373 E-mail: email@signtrade.btconnect.com

Spimin Development Ltd, Spimin House, Beacon Road, Poulton Industrial Estate, Poulton-Le-Fylde, Lancashire, FY6 8HD Tel: (01253) 881001 Fax: (01253) 881019 E-mail: sales@spimin.co.uk

Stylebord Ltd, 34 London Road, Great Shelford, Cambridge, CB22 5DD Tel: (01223) 843341

Systemation Euro Ltd, Mansion Close, Moulton Park Industrial Estate, Northampton, NN3 6RU Tel: (01604) 491107 Fax: (01604) 493931 E-mail: sales@systemationeuro.com

T F C Cable Assemblies Ltd, Excelsior Park, Wishaw, Lanarkshire, ML2 0ER Tel: (01698) 355017 Fax: (01698) 350559 E-mail: info@tfcasm.co.uk

Technology Services, W2 Warrington Business Park, Long Lane, Warrington, WA2 8TX Tel: (01925) 444621 Fax: (01925) 492221

Tek Associates Ltd, 23 Stephenson Road, St. Ives, Cambridgeshire, PE27 3WJ Tel: (01480) 495496 Fax: (01480) 496228 E-mail: lenscothfield@tekassociates.com

Tenkay Electronics Ltd, Lancing Business Park, Marlborough Road, Lancing, West Sussex, BN15 8TN Tel: (01903) 855455 Fax: (01903) 761942 E-mail: sue.brown@tenkay.co.uk

Tri-State Electronics, Unit 4, Bumpers Enterprise Centre, Bumpers Farm Industrial Estate, Chippenham, Wiltshire, SN14 6QA Tel: (01249) 464650 Fax: (01249) 445414 E-mail: mikenickless@msn.com

Walters Group, Walters House, 12 Merlin Centre, Lancaster Road, High Wycombe, Buckinghamshire, HP12 3TB Tel: (01494) 453700 Fax: (01494) 461107 E-mail: sales@waltersmicro.co.uk

Wayfarer Transit Systems Ltd, 10 Willis Way, Fleets Industrial Estate, Poole, Dorset, BH15 3SS Tel: (01202) 670671 Fax: (01202) 339369 E-mail: sales@wayfarer.co.uk

Whiteley Electronics Ltd, Grove Road, Cosham, Portsmouth, PO6 1LX Tel: (023) 9232 6223 Fax: (023) 9237 6327

Wilson Process Systems Ltd, Waterworks Road, Hastings, East Sussex, TN34 1RT Tel: (01424) 722222 Fax: (01424) 720730 E-mail: sales@wps.co.uk

Wire All Products, 42 New Road, Rochester, Kent, ME1 1DX Tel: (01634) 812984 Fax: 01634 409636 E-mail: sales@wireall.co.uk

Zeal Electronics Ltd, Vanguard Trading Estate, Britannia Road, Chesterfield, Derbyshire, S40 2TZ Tel: (01246) 209009 Fax: (01246) 232994 E-mail: sales@zeal-electronics.co.uk

Zeta Electronic Systems, Unit 4 Pandy Industrial Estate, Plas Acton Road, Wrexham, Clwyd, LL11 2UD Tel: (01978) 312427 Fax: (01978) 314062E-mail: enquiries@zeta-electronic.com

ELECTRONIC CONTRACT MANUFACTURING SYSTEMS

DCC Electronics Ltd, 1 Newmarket Drive, Derby, DE24 8SW Tel: (01332) 757733 Fax: (01332) 572229 E-mail: reception@dcc-electronics.co.uk

Elite Engineering Ltd, 1 Davis Way, Fareham, Hampshire, PO14 1JF Tel: (01329) 231435 Fax: (01329) 822759 E-mail: sales@elite-eng.co.uk

Kenton Research Ltd, Unit 19 Bourne Road Industrial Park, Bourne Road, Dartford, DA1 4BZ Tel: (01322) 552000 Fax: (01322) 552020 E-mail: info@kentonresearch.co.uk

Outsource Electronics, Unit 600 Nest Business Park, Martin Road, Havant, Hampshire, PO9 5TL Tel: (023) 9245 2222 Fax: (023) 9248 1922 E-mail: chrisc@outsourceelectronics.co.uk

Phase One Electronics, Orion Court, 2 Rodney Road, Southsea, Hampshire, PO4 8SZ Tel: (023) 9286 2394 Fax: (023) 9286 2396 E-mail: tonys@t1e.uk.com

S K Electronics Ltd, Regent Street, Oldham, OL1 3TZ Tel: 0161-620 5414 Fax: 0161-627 3237 E-mail: sales@skelectronics.co.uk

Stewart Technology Ltd, Tweedside Park, Tweedbank, Galashiels, Selkirkshire, TD1 3TE Tel: (01896) 668100 Fax: (01896) 668101 E-mail: sales@stewart-technology.co.uk

ELECTRONIC CONTRACT MANUFACTURING WORKBENCHES

Knurr UK Ltd, Burrel Road, St. Ives, Cambridgeshire, PE27 3LE Tel: (01480) 496125 Fax: (01480) 496373 E-mail: knuerr.uk@knuerr.com

ELECTRONIC CONTROL EQUIPMENT

Capricorn Controls, Thorpe Close, Banbury, Oxfordshire, OX16 4SW Tel: (01295) 272360 Fax: (01295) 264766 E-mail: sales@capricorn-controls.com

Chantec, Toddbrook House, 120 Padfield Main Road, Padfield, Glossop, Derbyshire, SK13 1ET Tel: (01457) 852376 Fax: (01457) 852376E-mail: sales@chantec.freeserve.co.uk

Dva Controls, 1 Sunningdale Grove, Colwyn Bay, Clwyd, LL29 6DG Tel: (01492) 534937 E-mail: info@dva-controls.co.uk

Tempatron Ltd, 5 Darwin Close, Reading, RG2 0TB Tel: 0118-931 4062 Fax: 0118-931 0175 E-mail: info@tempatron.co.uk

ELECTRONIC CONTROL EQUIPMENT DESIGN

M T H Ltd, 42 Queens Road, Farnborough, Hampshire, GU14 6DT Tel: (01252) 519251 Fax: (01252) 524494 E-mail: mthltd@nildram.co.uk

▶ Top Hex, 43 The Glades, Huntingdon, Cambridgeshire, PE29 6JS Tel: (01480) 456200 Fax: (01480) 456221 E-mail: info@tophex.co.uk

ELECTRONIC CONTROL SYSTEM COMPONENTS

Bradshaw Associates, P O Box 415, Maidstone, Kent, ME16 0LR Tel: (01622) 751747 Fax: (01622) 675050 E-mail: ivorbradshaw@cwcom.net

ELECTRONIC CONTROL SYSTEM MAINTENANCE OR REPAIR

C C Power Electronics Ltd, Unit 19, Haigh Park, Whitehill Industrial Estate, Stockport, Cheshire, SK4 1QR Tel: 0161-429 7923 Fax: 0161-474 1174 E-mail: info@ccpowerltd.co.uk

Centiflex Systems Ltd, PO Box 54, Saffron Walden, Essex, CB10 2AN Tel: (01799) 527602 Fax: (01799) 501961 E-mail: sales@centiflex.com

Coltan Electronics Ltd, Unit D16-17 Boston Industrial Centre, Norfolk Street, Boston, Lincolnshire, PE21 9HG Tel: (01205) 351027 Fax: (01205) 354296 E-mail: coltan@eletron.fsbusiness.co.uk

Electronic Repair Technology, Signal Works, Talbot Road, Wellingborough, Northants, NN8 1QH Tel: (01933) 228866 Fax: (01933) 443623 E-mail: dave@autocontrol.freeserve.co.uk

▶ Electrotech Solutions, Unit 2 Swan Park, Kettlebrook Road, Tamworth, Staffs, B77 1AG Tel: 01827 63989 Fax: 01827 64910 E-mail: mark@electrotech-solutions.co.uk

Meltek, 5 Spring Village, Horsehay, Telford, Shropshire, TF4 2LY Tel: (01952) 505207 E-mail: meltek@tesco.net

Microsys Controls Ltd, Fennels Way, Flackwell Heath, High Wycombe, Buckinghamshire, HP10 9BY Tel: (01628) 532195 Fax: (01628) 532196 E-mail: microsyscontrols@aol.com

▶ Newton Tesla (Electric Drives) Ltd, Unit G18 Warrington Business Park, Long Lane, Warrington, WA2 8TX Tel: (01925) 444773 Fax: (01925) 241477 E-mail: info@newton-tesla.com

SR Electromatics, 511 Fulbridge Road, Peterborough, PE4 6SB Tel: (01733) 579591 Fax: (01733) 571958

Trax Circuits, Unit 15a Ellough Industrial Estate, Ellough, Beccles, Suffolk, NR34 7TD Tel: (01502) 711626 Fax: (01502) 711626 E-mail: traxcircuits@electronicrepairs.co.uk

ELECTRONIC CONTROL SYSTEMS

Argosafe Ltd, Unit 11 Dawsons Lane, Barwell, Leicester, LE9 8BE Tel: (01455) 844801 Fax: (01455) 850280 E-mail: argosafe@btconnect.com

Argus Electronics, Frenches, Chew Valley Road, Greenfield, Oldham, OL3 7AE Tel: (01457) 876951 Fax: (01457) 876951

C J Controls Ltd, Crofty Industrial Estate, Penclawdd, Swansea, SA4 3RS Tel: (01792) 851083 Fax: (01792) 850442 E-mail: sales@cjcontrols.co.uk

C & W Electronics Ltd, Pool Street, Wolverhampton, WV2 4HN Tel: (01902) 426714 Fax: (01902) 422544

Camis Electronics Ltd, Platts Road, Amblecote, Stourbridge, West Midlands, DY8 4YR Tel: (01384) 441402 Fax: (01384) 370354 E-mail: sales@camis.demon.co.uk

Capricorn Controls, Thorpe Close, Banbury, Oxfordshire, OX16 4SW Tel: (01295) 272360 Fax: (01295) 264766 E-mail: sales@capricorn-controls.com

Central Southern Security Ltd, Station Street, Lymington, Hampshire, SO41 3BA Tel: (01590) 677366 Fax: (01590) 678024 E-mail: enquiries@central southern security.co.uk

Coltan Electronics Ltd, Unit D16-17 Boston Industrial Centre, Norfolk Street, Boston, Lincolnshire, PE21 9HG Tel: (01205) 351027 Fax: (01205) 354296 E-mail: coltan@eletron.fsbusiness.co.uk

▶ indicates data change since last edition

ELECTRONIC CONTROL SYSTEMS

– continued

Control Solutions Ltd, Avon House, 82 Wellington Street, Thame, Oxfordshire, OX9 3BN Tel: (01844) 216988 Fax: (01844) 261466 E-mail: mail@control-solutions.co.uk
Darpan Controls Ltd, Sandford Works, Cobden Street, Long Eaton, Nottingham, NG10 1BL Tel: 0115-973 2672 Fax: 0115-972 0682
Derdon Design & Development (Electronics) Ltd, Livingstone Road, Foleshill, Coventry, CV6 5AR Tel: (024) 7668 9302 Fax: (024) 7666 4146
Digitrol Ltd, Coronet Way, Swansea Enterprise Park, Swansea, SA6 8RH Tel: (01792) 796000 Fax: (01792) 701600E-mail: info@digitrol.com
Ditra Systems Ltd, Unit 14 Albury Close, Reading, RG30 1BD Tel: 0118-958 5489 Fax: 0118-959 6343 E-mail: info@ditra-systems.co.uk
E.D.C. International Ltd, Brook House Station Road, Pangbourne, Reading, RG8 7AN Tel: 0118-984 2040 Fax: 0118-984 5300 E-mail: sales@edcinternational.com
Elcontrol Ltd, 5 Regulus Works, 79 Lynch Lane, Weymouth, Dorset, DT4 9DW Tel: (01305) 773426 Fax: (01305) 760539 E-mail: sales@elcontrol.co.uk
Farm Energy & Control Services Ltd, Wyvols Court Farm, Basingstoke Road, Swallowfield, Reading, RG7 1WY Tel: 0118-988 9093 Fax: 0118-988 9658 E-mail: hugh@farmex.co.uk
Field Electronics Ltd, 23 Star Road, Star Trading Estate, Partridge Green, Horsham, West Sussex, RH13 8RA Tel: (01403) 713772 Fax: (0870) 0271033 E-mail: sales@fieldelectronics.com
G N Systems, Undershore Works, Brookside Road, Bolton, BL2 2SE Tel: (01204) 361533 Fax: (01204) 382879 E-mail: gnsystems@provider.co.uk
Geedev Ltd, 21 Barndale Drive, Arne, Wareham, Dorset, BH20 5BX Tel: (01929) 551122 Fax: (01929) 552936 E-mail: design@geedev.co.uk
Heber Ltd, Belvedere Mill, Chalford Industrial Estate, Chalford, Stroud, Gloucestershire, GL6 8NT Tel: (01453) 732300 Fax: (01453) 885013 E-mail: sales@heber.co.uk
Industrial Switchgear Ltd, 8 Howard Road, Park Farm Industrial Estate, Redditch, Worcestershire, B98 7SE Tel: (01527) 527346 Fax: (01527) 510186 E-mail: industrialswitch@btconnect.com
JCD Electronics Ltd, 4a Oakwood Parade, Oakwood Hill, Loughton, Essex, IG10 3EL Tel: (020) 8508 3355 Fax: (020) 8508 3355
Jenelec Ltd, Fuller Road, Harleston, Norfolk, IP20 9EA Tel: (01379) 853666 Fax: (01379) 854414 E-mail: sales@jenelec.co.uk
K P Electromech, Unit 3 Cross Hill, Codnor, Ripley, Derbyshire, DE5 9SQ Tel: (01773) 748270 Fax: (01773) 743612
K & S Engineering & Scientific Ltd, 18 Clifton Gardens, London, NW11 7EL Tel: (020) 8731 7461 Fax: (020) 8731 8604 E-mail: seedetails@www.kse-sci.com
Kongsberg Auto Motive, Christopher Martin Road, Basildon, Essex, SS14 3ES Tel: (01268) 522861 Fax: (01268) 282994 E-mail: m.dickason@morse-controls.co.uk
Lawtronic Ltd, Hamlin Way, King's Lynn, Norfolk, PE30 4NG Tel: (01553) 765247 Fax: (01553) 692147
Luma Automation, Technology House, Blackpole Trading Estate West, Worcester, WR3 8TJ Tel: (01905) 753700 Fax: (01905) 753701 E-mail: sales@rgautomation.co.uk
Mardix Automatic Controls Ltd, Westmorland Business Park, Gilthwaiterigg Lane, Kendal, Cumbria, LA9 6NS Tel: (01539) 720161 Fax: (01539) 724384 E-mail: switchgear@mardix.co.uk
Meltek, 5 Spring Village, Horsehay, Telford, Shropshire, TF4 2LY Tel: (01952) 505207 E-mail: meltek@tesco.net
Micromat International, Sanders Lodge Industrial Estate, Rushden, Northamptonshire, NN10 6BQ Tel: (01933) 313093 Fax: (01933) 319293 E-mail: sales@micromat.co.uk
Newton Controls Ltd, 26 Coltness Rd, Elburton, Plymouth, PL9 8HA Tel: (01752) 481528 Fax: (01752) 481972
▶ Oilgear European Holdings, 37 Burley Road, Leeds, LS3 1JT Tel: 0113-394 7300 Fax: 0113-394 7301 E-mail: enquiries@oilgear-towler.co.uk
Orange Instruments Ltd, Lower Farm Road, Moulton Park Industrial Estate, Northampton, NN3 6XF Tel: (01604) 790490 Fax: (01604) 790690 E-mail: alan@orangeinst.demon.co.uk
Ostcliffe Electronics Ltd, Barrowfield Road, Hoyland, Barnsley, South Yorkshire, S74 9TH Tel: (01226) 749233
P A V Electronics Ltd, Unit 7, Stirling Road Industrial Estate, Airdrie, Lanarkshire, ML6 7UD Tel: (01236) 764162 Fax: (01236) 747700 E-mail: rob@pavelectronics.co.uk
P M S Developments, Netherwood Road, Rotherwas Industrial Estate, Hereford, HR2 6JU Tel: (01432) 265768 Fax: (01432) 263782 E-mail: sales@pmssystems.com
PD Electronics Ltd, The Old Barn, Woods Lane, Potterspury, Towcester, Northamptonshire, NN12 7PT Tel: (01908) 543150 Fax: (01908) 543139
Pennine Machine Tools Ltd, Brookwoods Industrial Estate, Burrwood Way, Holywell Green, Halifax, West Yorkshire, HX4 9BH Tel: (01422) 370109 Fax: (01422) 371338 E-mail: sales@pennine.co.uk
Peterson Electronics Ltd, Academy Street, Forfar, Angus, DD8 2HA Tel: (01307) 462591 Fax: (01307) 462591
Protolink, 6 Zone B Chelmsford Road Industrial Estate, Chelmsford Road, Dunmow, Essex, CM6 1HD Tel: (01371) 875726 Fax: (01371) 876381 E-mail: sales@protolink.co.uk
Quinton Crane Electronics Ltd, Carnival Way, Castle Donington, Derby, DE74 2HP Tel: (01332) 810955 Fax: (01332) 810475 E-mail: info@systekcontrols.com
R F Electronics Controls Ltd, 8 Nazeing New Road, Broxbourne, Hertfordshire, EN10 6SU Tel: (01992) 460046 Fax: (01992) 442299 E-mail: sales@rfeltd.com
Robydome Ltd, Woodhall Business Park, Sudbury, Suffolk, CO10 1WH Tel: (01787) 310163 Fax: (01787) 880631 E-mail: peter@robydome.co.uk
Rolls Royce Marine Electrical Systems Ltd, Northarbour Road, Portsmouth, PO6 3TL Tel: (023) 9231 0000 Fax: (023) 9231 0001
Roomfoss Ltd, Larch Road, Saddlebow, King's Lynn, Norfolk, PE34 3HP Tel: (01553) 771413 Fax: (01553) 691184 E-mail: sales@roomfoss.co.uk
Rugby Electronics, 57 Somers Road, Rugby, Warwickshire, CV22 7DG Tel: (01788) 572492 Fax: (01788) 540005 E-mail: sales@rugbyelectronics.com
Sea Technik Ltd, Court House, 15 Glynne Way, Hawarden, Deeside, Clwyd, CH5 3NS Tel: (01244) 535787 Fax: (01244) 538908 E-mail: admin@seatechnik.com
Sencon (UK) Ltd, Unit P, Blackpole Trading Estate East, Worcester, WR3 8SG Tel: (01905) 755525 Fax: (01905) 456393 E-mail: sales@sencon.co.uk
Silicon Systems, 31-33 Park Hill, Swallownest, Sheffield, S26 4UN Tel: 0114-269 6311
▶ Superior Systems, 39 Deerhurst Road, Coventry, CV6 4EJ Tel: (024) 7666 3321 Fax: (024) 7666 3321 E-mail: sales@superior-systems.co.uk
Telesound Ltd, 31 Hall Green Close, Malvern, Worcestershire, WR14 3QY Tel: (01684) 572506 E-mail: sales@telesound.co.uk
Thames Valley Electrical Control Systems Ltd, Cannington Farm, Cannington Lane, Uplyme, Lyme Regis, Dorset, DT7 3SW Tel: (01297) 443172 Fax: (01297) 445005 E-mail: tvecs@aol.com
Thermomax Ltd, Balloo Industrial Estate, Bangor, County Down, BT19 7UP Tel: (028) 9127 0411 Fax: (028) 9127 0572 E-mail: sales@thermomax.com
Transmitton Ltd, Coalfield Way, Ashby-de-la-Zouch, Leicestershire, LE65 1JD Tel: (01530) 258000 Fax: (01530) 258008 E-mail: sales@transmitton.co.uk
Yokogawa Marex Ltd, 34 Medina Road, Cowes, Isle Of Wight, PO31 7DA Tel: (01983) 296011 Fax: (01983) 291776 E-mail: sales@ymx.yokogawa.com
Zener Designs Cheltenham Ltd, Exmouth Street, Cheltenham, Gloucestershire, GL53 7NS Tel: (01242) 527394 Fax: 01242 221871 E-mail: sales@zenerdesigns.com
Zirkon Ltd, Butlers Leap, Rugby, Warwickshire, CV21 3RQ Tel: (01788) 534800 Fax: (01788) 569283 E-mail: info@zirkon.co.uk

ELECTRONIC CONTROL TESTING MACHINES

Dynamotive Calibration Services, Whitwick Business Park, Stenson Road, Coalville, Leicestershire, LE67 4JP Tel: (01530) 277930 Fax: (01530) 277931 E-mail: sales@dynamotive.co.uk

ELECTRONIC CONTROL WELDING EQUIPMENT

Chiltern Electrical Services, 1 Shenstone Drive, Burnham, Slough, SL1 7HJ Tel: (01628) 665090 Fax: (01628) 665090 E-mail: miketerry@chilelecserv.freeserve.co.uk
Pyramid Engineering Services Co. Ltd, 4 Orchard Business Centre, Kangley Bridge Road, London, SE26 5AQ Tel: (020) 8776 5545 Fax: (020) 8768 7650 E-mail: enquiries@pyramideng.com
Redman Controls & Electronics Ltd, Brick Kiln Industrial Estate, Malders Lane, Maidenhead, Berkshire, SL6 6NQ Tel: (01628) 630514 Fax: (01628) 625254 E-mail: sales@redmancontrols.com

ELECTRONIC CONTROLLERS

Central Electrical Co., West Midland House, Gipsy Lane, Willenhall, West Midlands, WV13 2HA Tel: (01902) 482477 Fax: (01902) 482478 E-mail: sales@centralelec.co.uk
Thermomax Ltd, Balloo Industrial Estate, Bangor, County Down, BT19 7UP Tel: (028) 9127 0411 Fax: (028) 9127 0572 E-mail: sales@thermomax.com

ELECTRONIC COPYBOARDS

GBC UK Holdings Ltd, Rutherford Road, Basingstoke, Hampshire, RG24 8PD Tel: (01256) 842828 Fax: (01256) 842581 E-mail: sales@gbcuk.co.uk

ELECTRONIC COUNTERS

Autoswitch Electronics Ltd, 46 Lammas Way, Letchworth Garden City, Hertfordshire, SG6 4LW Tel: (01462) 677778 Fax: (01462) 480449
C D M, Central Boulevard, Blythe Valley Park, Solihull, West Midlands, B90 8AG Tel: (0870) 0116682 Fax: (01264) 711396 E-mail: cdmcontrol@aol.com
Data Track Process Instruments Ltd, 153 Somerford Road, Christchurch, Dorset, BH23 3TY Tel: (01425) 271900 Fax: (01425) 271978 E-mail: dtpi.sales@dtrack.com
Eagle Controls International Ltd, PO Box 42, Letchworth Garden City, Hertfordshire, SG6 1HQ Tel: (01462) 670566 Fax: (01462) 673992 E-mail: info@eaglecontrols.co.uk
Oval Automation Ltd, Lake Lane, Barnham, Bognor Regis, West Sussex, PO22 0AD Tel: (01243) 555885 Fax: (01243) 554846 E-mail: paul@oval.org.uk
Prism Europe Ltd, Abbey Gate One, 8 Whitewell Road, Colchester, CO2 7DE Tel: (01206) 761300 Fax: (01206) 719900 E-mail: sales@prism-uk.com
Rugby Electronics, 57 Somers Road, Rugby, Warwickshire, CV22 7DG Tel: (01788) 572492 Fax: (01788) 540005 E-mail: sales@rugbyelectronics.com
Seltec Automation, Subway Street, Hull, HU3 4EL Tel: (01482) 225297 Fax: (01482) 212470 E-mail: sales@seltec.co.uk
Synatel Instrumentation Ltd, Walsall Road, Norton Canes, Cannock, Staffordshire, WS11 9TB Tel: (01543) 277003 Fax: (01543) 271217 E-mail: sales@synatel.co.uk
Taylor Dynamic Controls, Unit W4 Blaby Industrial Park, Winchester Avenue, Blaby, Leicester, LE8 4GZ Tel: 0116-278 4100 Fax: 0116-278 4200 E-mail: sales@taylordynamics.com

ELECTRONIC DATA INTERCHANGE (EDI) SERVICES

Compliant Business Systems Ltd, PO Box 25, King's Lynn, Norfolk, PE30 4AR Tel: (01553) 660500 Fax: (01553) 660500 E-mail: mail@compliant.co.uk
Edimatrix Ltd, 411-413 High Road, Woodford Green, Essex, IG8 0XG Tel: (020) 8559 2454 Fax: (020) 8559 2497 E-mail: sales@edimatrix.co.uk
Freeway Commerce Ltd, Unit 12, Sceptre Court, Sceptre Way, Bamber Bridge, Preston, PR5 6AW Tel: (01772) 646000 Fax: (01772) 646001 E-mail: info@freewaycommece.co.uk
Saa Consultants Ltd, The Computer Complex, Somerset Place, Plymouth, PL3 4BB Tel: (01752) 606000 Fax: (01752) 606838 E-mail: sales@saaconsultants.com
Seeburger UK Ltd, Heathrow Boulevard 4, 280 Bath Road, West Drayton, Middlesex, UB7 0DQ Tel: (020) 8564 3914 E-mail: c.blomstedt@seeburger.co.uk

ELECTRONIC DELAY LINES

Bel Fuse Europe Ltd, G 7 Unit Preston Technology Centre, Marsh Lane, Preston, PR1 8UQ Tel: (01772) 556601 Fax: (01772) 883666 E-mail: bel_europe@belfuse.com
Faraday Technology Ltd, Units 22-26 Croft Road Indust Estate, Newcastle, Staffordshire, ST5 0TW Tel: (01782) 661501 Fax: (01782) 630101 E-mail: sales@faradaytech.co.uk
T D K Electronics Europe Ltd, Confort House, 5-7 Queensway, Redhill, RH1 1YB Tel: (01737) 781372 Fax: (01737) 773810
Xta Electronics Ltd, Riverside Business Centre, Worcester Road, Stourport-on-Severn, Worcestershire, DY13 9BZ Tel: (01299) 879977 Fax: (01299) 879969 E-mail: sales@xta.co.uk

ELECTRONIC DESIGN AUTOMATION (EDA)

▶ Coresys Ltd, Merlin Cottage, 23 Fore Street, Polruan, Fowey, Cornwall, PL23 1PQ Tel: (01726) 870775 E-mail: coresys@btinternet.com
▶ Northlogic Ltd, Newton Business Park, Talbot Road, Hyde, Cheshire, SK14 4UQ Tel: 0161-366 1002 Fax: 0161-366 1080

ELECTRONIC DESIGN AUTOMATION (EDA) SOFTWARE

▶ Coresys Ltd, Merlin Cottage, 23 Fore Street, Polruan, Fowey, Cornwall, PL23 1PQ Tel: (01726) 870775 E-mail: coresys@btinternet.com

ELECTRONIC DESIGN EQUIPMENT

▶ Grove Electronics Ltd, 26 Grove Court, Rampley Lane, Little Paxton, St. Neots, Cambridgeshire, PE19 6PQ Tel: (01480) 382909 Fax: (01480) 382909 E-mail: info@groveelectronics.co.uk
Imp Electronics Ltd, Rocol Building, 3 Glebe Road, Huntingdon, Cambridgeshire, PE29 7DL Tel: (01480) 411822 Fax: (01480) 411833
▶ Pax Designs, 23 Abbey Close, Tatworth, Chard, Somerset, TA20 2LD Tel: (01460) 220402 E-mail: derek@pax-designs.co.uk
▶ Scott Consulting, Perranporth, Truro, Cornwall, TR6 0HX Tel: 01872 572456 E-mail: martin_scott@dsl.pipex.com
▶ Top Hex, 43 The Glades, Huntingdon, Cambridgeshire, PE29 6JS Tel: (01480) 456200 Fax: (01480) 456221 E-mail: info@tophex.co.uk

ELECTRONIC DIRECT CURRENT (DC) CONVERTERS

Ablemail Electronics Ltd, Unit 17 Christie St Industrial Estate, Christie Street, Stockport, Cheshire, SK1 4LR Tel: 0161-480 6910 Fax: 0161-480 8686 E-mail: info@ablemail.co.uk
Davtrend Ltd, 7a Fitzherbert Spur, Farlington, Portsmouth, PO6 1TT Tel: (023) 9237 2004 Fax: (023) 9232 6307 E-mail: sales@davtrend.co.uk
K R P Power Source UK Ltd, 2 The Galloway Centre, Express Way, Newbury, Berkshire, RG14 5TL Tel: (01635) 32510 Fax: (01635) 32510 E-mail: sales@krp.co.uk

ELECTRONIC DIRECTORY EQUIPMENT

BTS Holdings plc, B T S House, 69-73 Manor Road, Wallington, Surrey, SM6 0DD Tel: (020) 8401 9000 Fax: (020) 8401 9101 E-mail: sales@bts.co.uk

ELECTRONIC DISTANCE MEASURING EQUIPMENT

Fernau Avionics Ltd, Unit C Airport Executive Park, President Way, Luton, LU2 9NY Tel: (01582) 483111 Fax: (01582) 484404 E-mail: info@fernau.com
Halda Ltd, Quay Business Centre, 12 Harvard Court, Winwick Quay, Warrington, WA2 8LT Tel: (01925) 629926 Fax: (01925) 629929 E-mail: haldauk@aol.com

ELECTRONIC DRUM KITS

▶ Drumland UK, Langney Road, Eastbourne, East Sussex, BN21 3JP Tel: (01323) 636142 Fax: (01323) 649100

ELECTRONIC ENCLOSURE AIR CONDITIONING (AC) EQUIPMENT

▶ T F L, Goland Road, Ballygawley, Dungannon, County Tyrone, BT70 2LA Tel: (07767) 640774 Fax: (028) 8556 7089 E-mail: hblake@tfl.eu.com

ELECTRONIC ENGINEERING

A D Developments Ltd, 5a London Road, Loughton, Milton Keynes, MK5 8AB Tel: (01908) 222606 E-mail: enquiries@addevelopments.com
Advanced Control Electronics, 98 Ashby Road, Loughborough, Leicestershire, LE11 3AF Tel: (01509) 211333 Fax: (01509) 211333 E-mail: ac.electronics@lycos.co.uk
Amcc Electronic Engineers, 15 Enterprise Industrial Estate, Station Road West, Ash Vale, Aldershot, Hampshire, GU12 5QJ Tel: (01252) 377723 Fax: (01252) 377724 E-mail: enquiries@amcc.co.uk
Apollo Electronics Co., Unit 1 Riverside Business Park, Wakefield Road, Scissett, Huddersfield, HD8 9HR Tel: (01484) 864940 Fax: (01484) 865830 E-mail: sales@apollo-electronics.com
Aquatec Electronics Ltd, High Street, Hartley Wintney, Hook, Hampshire, RG27 8NY Tel: (01252) 843072 Fax: (01252) 843074 E-mail: sales@aquatec.org.uk
Ashmond Electronics Ltd, 8 Gadwey House, Leigh Street, High Wycombe, Buckinghamshire, HP11 2QU Tel: (01494) 440925 Fax: (01494) 446795
B A W Precision Engineering Ltd, Cwmtawe Business Park, Alloy Industrial Estate, Pontardawe, Swansea, SA8 4EZ Tel: (01792) 862141 Fax: (01792) 865545 E-mail: peter@bawengineering.co.uk

ELECTRONIC ENGINEERING – *continued*

Becatech Ltd, The Olde Farm, Stone Allerton, Axbridge, Somerset, BS26 2NP Tel: (01934) 713608 Fax: (01934) 713737 E-mail: sales@becatech.com

Bereton Electronics Ltd, Unit 49 Kettley Business Park, Ketley, Telford, Shropshire, TF1 5JD Tel: (01952) 253222 Fax: (01952) 244445 E-mail: mail@bereton.co.uk

Brittons Ltd, Waterlip Works, Cranmore, Shepton Mallet, Somerset, BA4 4RW Tel: (01749) 880371 Fax: (01749) 880347 E-mail: sales@brittons-uk.com

Buckman Hardy Associates, The Old Bakehouse, Albert Road, Deal, Kent, CT14 9RD Tel: (01304) 365918 Fax: (01304) 369737 E-mail: sales@buckman-hardy.co.uk

C & T Harnesses Ltd, Unit 2 Lanwades Business Park, Kennett, Newmarket, Suffolk, CB8 7PN Tel: (01638) 751511 Fax: (01638) 751965 E-mail: info@ctharnesses.com

Caldwell Consulting Engineers, 8 Lorne Street, Belfast, BT9 7DU Tel: (028) 9066 9456 Fax: (028) 9066 2219 E-mail: admin@caldwellconsulting.net

Calpar Electronics, Calpar House, 1 Windermere Road, Beeston, Nottingham, NG9 3AS Tel: 0115-925 8335 Fax: 0115-925 8335 E-mail: keith@calpar-electronics

Ceema Technology, 4 The Omega Centre, Stratton Business Park, Biggleswade, Bedfordshire, SG18 8QB Tel: (01767) 319800 Fax: (01767) 317621 E-mail: reception@ceema.co.uk

Celtech UK Electronics Ltd, Unit 12 Barton Business Park, Cawdor Street, Eccles, Manchester, M30 0QR Tel: 0161-788 0267 Fax: 0161-787 8212 E-mail: celtech@celtech-uk.co.uk

J.S. Chinn Project Engineering Ltd, Coventry Road, Exhall, Coventry, CV7 9FT Tel: 0117-958 4600 Fax: 0117-958 4601 E-mail: jschinn@internet-uk.net

Chromalock Ltd, Beechwood House, Falkland Close, Charter Avenue Industrial Estate, Coventry, CV4 8HQ Tel: (024) 7646 6277 Fax: (024) 7646 5298 E-mail: admin@chromalock.com

Cogan & Shackleton, 35 Railway Road, Coleraine, County Londonderry, BT52 1PE Tel: (028) 7034 4036 Fax: (028) 7035 7028 E-mail: admin@coshack.co.uk

Connevans Ltd Equipment For The Deaf, 54 Albert Road North, Reigate, Surrey, RH2 9YR Tel: (01737) 247571 Fax: (01737) 223475 E-mail: mail@connevans.com

Contrive Ltd, 32 Beresford Road, London, E4 6EE Tel: (020) 8529 8425 Fax: (020) 8281 5980

Cooper Electronics, Tenlons Road, Nuneaton, Warwickshire, CV10 7HT Tel: (024) 7632 0585 Fax: (024) 7632 0564 E-mail: enquiries@cooper-electronics.com

D M Kent Electronics Ltd, 8 Hedge End Industrial Estate, Shuart Lane, St. Nicholas at Wade, Birchington, Kent, CT7 0NB Tel: (01843) 846755 Fax: (01843) 848008 E-mail: sales@dmkent.co.uk

Darpan Controls Ltd, Sandford Works, Cobden Street, Long Eaton, Nottingham, NG10 1BL Tel: 0115-973 2672 Fax: 0115-972 0682

Deva Electronic Controls Ltd, Unit 52 Woodside Business Park, Birkenhead, Merseyside, CH41 1EL Tel: 0151-647 3222 Fax: 0151-647 4511 E-mail: sales@deva.co.uk

Dowding & Mills Engineering Services Ltd, Unit 14 Maple Business Park, Walter Street, Birmingham, B7 5ET Tel: 0121-326 6306 Fax: 0121-326 9379 E-mail: electronics.birmingham@dowdingandmills.com

Drive Way Alarm, 15 West Street, Hothfield, Ashford, Kent, TN26 1ET Tel: (0870) 2240315 Fax: (0870) 7625903 E-mail: sales@drivewayalarm.co.uk

E I B M Electronics Ltd, Unit B2 Greengate Industrial Estate, Greenside Way, Middleton, Manchester, M24 1SW Tel: 0161-653 8181 Fax: 0161-653 8282 E-mail: jacki.eibm@boltblue.net

Electronic Modular Solutions Ltd, Kendal House, 20 Blaby Road, Wigston, Leicestershire, LE18 4SB Tel: 0116-277 5730 Fax: 0116-277 4973 E-mail: sales@video-captures.com

Enertron Ltd, 32 New Forest Enterprise Centre, Chapel La, Totton, Southampton, SO40 9LA Tel: (023) 8087 3522 Fax: (023) 8087 3522 E-mail: bob@enertronltd.co.uk

Eyebright Designs Ltd, 107 Leicester Road, Wolvey, Hinckley, Leicestershire, LE10 3HJ Tel: (01455) 220835 Fax: (01455) 220895 E-mail: info@eyebright.demon.co.uk

▶ Fenton Mcintosh, 3 Eastern Terrace Mews, Kemptown, Brighton, BN2 1EP Tel: (01273) 628700 E-mail: iain@fenton-mcintosh.co.uk

First Option Ltd, Signal House, Jacklyns Lane, Alresford, Hampshire, SO24 9JJ Tel: (01962) 738200 Fax: (01962) 738201 E-mail: mail@firstoption.net

Fisher Consultants Derbyshire Ltd, 8 Parkside, Belper, Derbyshire, DE56 1HY Tel: (0845) 3707760

Fraser & Macdonald Electric Motors Ltd, 176 Woodville Street, Glasgow, G51 2RN Tel: 0141-445 3874 Fax: 0141-425 1135 E-mail: frasmcd@aol.com

Frontline Electronics, 25 Laundry Road, Minster, Ramsgate, Kent, CT12 4HY Tel: (01843) 821512 Fax: (01843) 821603 E-mail: sales@frontlineelectronics.co.uk

G & T Computer Services, Brown Gables, Dyers End, Stambourne, Halstead, Essex, CO9 4NE Tel: (01440) 785596

▶ Griffin Electronics Ltd, Griffin House 5 Laura Avenue, Paignton, Devon, TQ3 2LS Tel: (01803) 523537 E-mail: info@griffinelectronics.co.uk

H Kuhnke, 21 Abbey Enterprise Centre, Premier Way, Romsey, Hampshire, SO51 9AQ Tel: (01794) 514445 Fax: (01794) 513514 E-mail: sales@kuhnke.co.uk

Halstead Auto Electrical, 3 Halstead Business Centre, Factory Lane West, Halstead, Essex, CO9 1EX Tel: (01787) 477474 Fax: (01787) 477474 E-mail: robbo@halautoelec.freeserve.co.uk

Holden Manufacturing Ltd, 4 Clarendon Drive, Wymbush, Milton Keynes, MK8 8DA Tel: (01908) 563636 Fax: (01908) 569778 E-mail: general@holdenmanufacturing.com

Holmes & Mann Associates Ltd, 465 Tachbrook Road, Leamington Spa, Warwickshire, CV31 3DQ Tel: (01926) 426854 Fax: (01926) 426854 E-mail: holmes@holmes-mann.com

I M Design & Repair, 4 Hockley Lane, Ettington, Stratford-Upon-Avon, Warwickshire, CV37 7SS Tel: (01789) 740870 Fax: (01789) 740870 E-mail: ian@windowcontrols.com

Industrial Calibration Ltd, Sunbeam Road, Kempston, Bedford, MK42 7BZ Tel: (01234) 857171 Fax: (01234) 840371 E-mail: clive@industrialcalibration.com

▶ Industrial Development Bangor (U W B) Ltd, Dean Street, Bangor, Gwynedd, LL57 1UT Tel: (01248) 382749 Fax: (01248) 372105 E-mail: info@idb-tech.com

Industrial Electronic Control By Design, Unit F5 Bersham Enterprise Centre, Colliery Road, Rhostyllen, Wrexham, Clwyd, LL14 4EG Tel: (01978) 368099 Fax: (01978) 354333 E-mail: sales@iecd.co.uk

▶ Iniveo Ltd, PO Box 2493, Leek, Staffordshire, ST13 5WZ Tel: (05511) 400146 E-mail: enquiries@iniveo.co.uk

▶ Inntact Electronic Systems Ltd, Inntact House, Rawson Green, Kilburn, Belper, Derbyshire, DE56 0LL Tel: (01332) 781199 Fax: (01332) 781188 E-mail: inntact@aol.com

Instrumentation & Control Services, Unit 3 The Old Forge, Peterchurch, Hereford, HR2 0SD Tel: (01981) 550011 Fax: (01981) 550955 E-mail: ics@ics-hereford.co.uk

Intelligent Control Systems Ltd, 29-31 Gabriels Hill, Maidstone, Kent, ME15 6HZ Tel: (01622) 683830 Fax: (01622) 683025

Item Ltd, 65 Bury Mead Road, Hitchin, Hertfordshire, SG5 1RT Tel: (01462) 453838 Fax: (01462) 453619 E-mail: item@co.com

J J Electronics Ltd, 3a Telmere Industrial Estate, Albert Road, Luton, LU1 3QF Tel: (01582) 391156 Fax: (01582) 391896 E-mail: sales@jjelectronics.net

Jaser Electronics Ltd, 1 Castle Mews, Rugby, Warwickshire, CV21 2XL Tel: (01788) 574796 Fax: (01788) 561352 E-mail: sales@jaser.co.uk

Jekyll Electronic Technology Ltd, Unit 3 Zephyr House, Calleva Park, Aldermaston, Reading, RG7 8JN Tel: 0118-981 7321 Fax: 0118-981 4743 E-mail: mail@jekyll-electronic.co.uk

Joyce-Loebl Ltd, 390 Princesway, Team Valley Trading Estate, Gateshead, Tyne & Wear, NE11 0TU Tel: 0191-420 3000 Fax: 0191-420 3030 E-mail: andy.kevins@joyce-loebel.com

▶ Lamerholn Electronics Ltd, Pixmore Centre, Pixmore Avenue, Letchworth Garden City, Hertfordshire, SG6 1JG Tel: (01462) 481396 Fax: (01462) 473942 E-mail: web@lamerholm.com

M J R Controls Ltd, Unit 85, Willows Court, Thornaby, Stockton-on-Tees, Cleveland, TS17 9PP Tel: (01642) 762151 Fax: (01642) 762502 E-mail: enquiries@mjrcontrols.com

Mendip Engineering Ltd, Mendip House, Pows Orchard, Midsomer Norton, Radstock, BA3 2HY Tel: (01761) 413698 Fax: (01761) 416172 E-mail: enquiries@mendipengineering.co.uk

D.E. Millwood, Queens Road, Malvern, Worcestershire, WR14 1RH Tel: (01684) 575002 Fax: (01684) 575002

Momentum Ltd, Clarkson Place, Dudley Road, Stourbridge, West Midlands, DY9 8EL Tel: (01384) 896879 Fax: (01384) 424691 E-mail: sales@hangar51.co.uk

Puposet Ltd, 121 Blackburn Road, Haslingden, Rossendale, Lancashire, BB4 5HL Tel: (01706) 229260 Fax: (01706) 213645 E-mail: popuset@tim-jackson.co.uk

R N Electronics Ltd, Arnolds Farm Lane, Mountnessing, Brentwood, Essex, CM13 1UT Tel: (01277) 352219 Fax: (01277) 352968 E-mail: sales@rnelectronics.com

R & S Installations, 54 Lowestoft Road, Carlton Colville, Lowestoft, Suffolk, NR33 8JB Tel: (01502) 572144 Fax: (01502) 572144 E-mail: sales@rsinstallations.co.uk

RH Industrial Electronics, Unit 11d Dabble Duck Industrial Estate, Shildon, County Durham, DL4 2RA Tel: (01388) 777823 Fax: (01388) 775902 E-mail: rhie@comp42.freeserve.co.uk

Richmond Electronics & Engineering International Ltd, Armtec Estate, North Lopham, Diss, Norfolk, IP22 2LR Tel: (01379) 686800 Fax: (01379) 688519 E-mail: info@richmondeei.co.uk

▶ Roke Manor Research, Roke Manor, Old Salisbury Lane, Romsey, Hampshire, SO51 0ZN Tel: (01794) 833000 Fax: (01794) 833433 E-mail: info@roke.co.uk

S T V S, Unit 8, 2 Perry Way, Witham, Essex, CM8 3SX Tel: (01376) 517333 Fax: (01376) 517333

Sargrove Automation, The Chestnuts, 11 Eastern Road, Havant, Hampshire, PO9 2JE Tel: (023) 9247 1981 Fax: (023) 9247 1981 E-mail: sargrove@btinternet.com

Secol Engineering Ltd, Unit 6-9 Cubitt Way, St. Leonards-on-Sea, East Sussex, TN38 9SU Tel: (01424) 855144 Fax: (01424) 855155 E-mail: gary@secolengineering.co.uk

Tech Ltd, The Granery, Leacon Farm, Leacon Lane, Charing, Ashford, Kent, TN27 0EN Tel: (01634) 290308 Fax: (01233) 714040 E-mail: johnbridges1@btconnect.com

Thurlaston Instrument Services, 5 Church Street, Thurlaston, Leicester, LE9 7TA Tel: (01455) 888484 E-mail: sales@thurlaston.com

Ultra Electronics Command & Control Systems, Knaves Beech Business Centre, Loudwater, High Wycombe, Buckinghamshire, HP10 9UT Tel: (01628) 530000 Fax: (01628) 524557 E-mail: info@ueccs.co.uk

Valro Manufacturing Ltd, Units 2-4, The Grove, Parkgate Industrial Estate, Knutsford, Cheshire, WA16 8XP Tel: (01565) 650204 Fax: (01565) 650755 E-mail: enquiries@valro.co.uk

Walkbury Electronics Ltd, 30 The Metro Centre, Peterborough, PE2 7UH Tel: (01733) 404830 Fax: (01733) 404839 E-mail: sales@walkbury.co.uk

ELECTRONIC ENGINEERING SOFTWARE

Control Technology International Ltd, Regal Chambers, 49-51 Bancroft, Hitchin, Hertfordshire, SG5 1LL Tel: (01462) 457700 Fax: (01462) 453377 E-mail: info@ctiweb.co.uk

Drive Technology Ltd, Bibsworth Lane, Broadway, Worcestershire, WR12 7LW Tel: (01386) 852089

▶ HeronSoft Ltd, 29 Chatteris Park, Sandymoor, Runcorn, Cheshire, WA7 1XE Tel: (01928) 571620 Fax: (01928) 571620 E-mail: heronsoft@aol.com

Puposet Ltd, 121 Blackburn Road, Haslingden, Rossendale, Lancashire, BB4 5HL Tel: (01706) 229260 Fax: (01706) 213645 E-mail: popuset@tim-jackson.co.uk

Teleca Ltd, 137 Barlow Moor Road, Manchester, M20 2PW Tel: 0161-447 6900 Fax: 0161-447 6901

Westbay Technology Ltd, Main Street, Baycliff, Ulverston, Cumbria, LA12 9RN Tel: (01229) 869108 Fax: (01229) 869108 E-mail: sales@westbay.ndirect.co.uk

ELECTRONIC EQUIPMENT BATTERIES

▶ M P S Ltd, 57 Woodroffe Drive, Basingstoke, Hampshire, RG22 6NH Tel: (01256) 817933 Fax: (08707) 625402 E-mail: sales@mpsintl.com

ELECTRONIC EQUIPMENT CONSULTANTS/DESIGNERS/ PRODUCTION SERVICES, CUSTOM BUILT

Abrae Technology Ltd, Park Hill Street, Bolton, BL1 4AR Tel: (01204) 361400 Fax: (0870) 3000693

Aish Technologies Ltd, Broom Road, Poole, Dorset, BH12 4NL Tel: (01202) 307007 Fax: (01202) 307000 E-mail: sales@aishtechnologies.com

Ajay Electronics Ltd, 4 Kimpton Trade Business Centre, 40 Kimpton Road, Sutton, Surrey, SM3 9QP Tel: (020) 8644 0534 Fax: (020) 8641 6558

ATE Ltd, Design Office, 56 Nodes Road, Northwood, Cowes, Isle of Wight, PO31 8AD Tel: (01983) 292052

Audio Partnership P.L.C., Units 3-4, Gallery Court, Hankey Place, London, SE1 4BB Tel: (020) 7940 2200 Fax: (020) 7940 2233

Axeon Ltd, Unit 1-2, Nobel Court, Nobel Road, West Gourdie Industrial Estate, Dundee, DD2 4UH Tel: (01382) 400040 Fax: (01382) 400044 E-mail: info@axeon.com

Axminster Electronics Ltd, Unit 1, Millwey Indust Estate, Axminster, Devon, EX13 5HU Tel: (01297) 32360 Fax: (01297) 35454 E-mail: mail@axminster-electronics.co.uk

Boyerman Ltd, Unit C Chesham Close, Romford, RM7 7PJ Tel: (01708) 742854 Fax: (01708) 737737 E-mail: sales@boyerman.co.uk

Buckman Hardy Associates, The Old Bakehouse, Albert Road, Deal, Kent, CT14 9RD Tel: (01304) 365918 Fax: (01304) 369737 E-mail: sales@buckman-hardy.co.uk

Chromalock Ltd, Beechwood House, Falkland Close, Charter Avenue Industrial Estate, Coventry, CV4 8HQ Tel: (024) 7646 6277 Fax: (024) 7646 5298 E-mail: admin@chromalock.com

Components & Products, P O Box 2053, Hockley, Essex, SS5 4WA Tel: (01702) 207247 Fax: (01702) 207224

Contronics Ltd, Greenfield Farm Industrial Estate, Congleton, Cheshire, CW12 4TU Tel: (01260) 298383 Fax: (01260) 298387 E-mail: sales@contronics.co.uk

Dalman Technical Services, Unit 36 Walworth Enterprise Centre Duke Close, West Way, Andover, Hampshire, SP10 5AP Tel: (01264) 357580 Fax: (01264) 351325 E-mail: sales@dalmants.co.uk

Designwrights Ltd, Unit 18 Liss Business Centre, Station Road, Liss, Hampshire, GU33 7AW Tel: (01730) 890050 Fax: (01730) 890051 E-mail: info@designwrights.co.uk

Double D Electronics Ltd, 6 Robins Wharf, Grove Road, Northfleet, Gravesend, Kent, DA11 9AX Tel: (01474) 333456 Fax: (01474) 333414 E-mail: sales@ddelec.co.uk

E M E Electrical & Mechanical Engineering Ltd, 25 The Mead Business Centre, Mead Lane, Hertford, SG13 7BJ Tel: (01992) 552151 E-mail: sales@emeltd.com

Heber Ltd, Belvedere Mill, Chalford Industrial Estate, Chalford, Stroud, Gloucestershire, GL6 8NT Tel: (01453) 732300 Fax: (01453) 885013 E-mail: sales@heber.co.uk

I C G Electronics, Unit 35 Second Drove Industrial Estate, Peterborough, PE1 5XA Tel: (01733) 557447 Fax: (01733) 314711

I M Design & Repair, 4 Hockley Lane, Ettington, Stratford-Upon-Avon, Warwickshire, CV37 7SS Tel: (01789) 740870 Fax: (01789) 740870 E-mail: ian@windowcontrols.com

Imp Electronics Ltd, Rocol Building, 3 Glebe Road, Huntingdon, Cambridgeshire, PE29 7DL Tel: (01480) 411822 Fax: (01480) 411833

Ingrid West Machinery Ltd, Unit 5L, Delta Drive, Tewkesbury Business Park, Tewkesbury, Gloucestershire, GL20 8HB Tel: (01684) 273164 Fax: (01684) 273171 E-mail: enquiries@ingridwest.co.uk

Integrated Electronic Services, 31 Church Street, Warrington, WA1 2SX Tel: (01925) 652065 Fax: (01925) 650565 E-mail: bjs@ies.ndirect.co.uk

Integrated Engineering Solutions Ltd, Millbrook Road West, Southampton, SO15 0HW Tel: (023) 8090 5020 Fax: (023) 8070 4073 E-mail: mail@iesl.co.uk

Intrinsyc Europe, Fountain House, Great Cornbow, Halesowen, West Midlands, B63 3BL Tel: 0121-501 6000 Fax: 0121-501 6035

J G Electronics, Wash Lane, Allostock, Knutsford, Cheshire, WA16 9JS Tel: (01565) 723334 Fax: (01565) 723334

▶ Jangi Electronics, 10 The Bramblings, Bicester, Oxfordshire, OX26 6SU Tel: (07851) 425703 E-mail: sales@jangielectronics.co.uk

Kaisertech, Unit 12, M3 Trade Park, Eastleigh, Hampshire, SO50 9YA Tel: (023) 8065 0065 Fax: (023) 8065 0060 E-mail: sales@kaisertech.co.uk

Lineplex Ltd, PO Box 590, Guildford, Surrey, GU5 9YL Tel: (01306) 731395 Fax: (01306) 731240 E-mail: lineplex@cix.co.uk

M S Instruments P.L.C., Unit 4, Ravens Quay Business Centre, Cray Avenue, Orpington, Kent, BR5 4BQ Tel: (01689) 883020 Fax: (01689) 871392 E-mail: sales@msinstruments.co.uk

M T H Ltd, 42 Queens Road, Farnborough, Hampshire, GU14 6DT Tel: (01252) 519251 Fax: (01252) 524494 E-mail: mthltd@nildram.co.uk

Mango Electronics, Mango House, 1 Buckhurst Road, Bexhill-On-Sea, East Sussex, TN40 1QF Tel: (01424) 731500 Fax: (01424) 731502E-mail: colin@mango-electronics.co.uk

Mantracourt Electronics Ltd, The Drive, Farringdon, Exeter, EX5 2JB Tel: (01395) 232020 Fax: (01395) 233190 E-mail: info@mantracourt.co.uk

Media Masters, Bernard Street, Uplands, Swansea, SA2 0HT Tel: (01792) 464441 Fax: (01792) 651356

Mowden Controls Ltd, Mount View, Standard Way Industrial Estate, Northallerton, North Yorkshire, DL6 2YD Tel: (01609) 779535 Fax: (01609) 779539 E-mail: enquiries@mowden.co.uk

Mutech Ltd, Unit 25, Waters Edge Business Park, Modwen Road, Salford, M5 3EZ Tel: 0161-872 0400 E-mail: sales@mutech.co.uk

Orange Instruments Ltd, Lower Farm Road, Moulton Park Industrial Estate, Northampton, NN3 6XF Tel: (01604) 790490 Fax: (01604) 790690 E-mail: alan@orangeinst.demon.co.uk

Project Electronics Ltd, Project House, Slade Green Road, Erith, Kent, DA8 2HX Tel: (01322) 350700 Fax: (01322) 351100 E-mail: mail@project-uk.com

Q M Systems Ltd, 4 Manor Park Estate, Wyndham Street, Aldershot, Hampshire, GU12 4NZ Tel: (01252) 336612 Fax: (01252) 343018 E-mail: sales@qm-systems.com

R Gorton & Associates Electronics Ltd, 308-310 Slade Lane, Manchester, M19 2BY Tel: 0161-224 5650 Fax: 0161-257 2761 E-mail: gortonelectronics@btinternet.com

Reeset Electronics, 19 Ray Lea Road, Maidenhead, Berkshire, SL6 8QP Tel: (01628) 628146 Fax: (01628) 628146 E-mail: ed@reeset.com

RGB Associates, 20 Newling Way, Worthing, West Sussex, BN13 3DG Tel: (01903) 694904 Fax: (01903) 260899 E-mail: sales@rgb.uk.com

Rhopoint Instrumentation, 12 Beeching Road, Bexhill-on-Sea, East Sussex, TN39 3LG Tel: (01424) 730600 Fax: (01424) 730600 E-mail: enquiries@rhopointinstruments.com

S R S Products P.L.C., 19 Mead Industrial Park, River Way, Harlow, Essex, CM20 2SE Tel: (01279) 635500 Fax: (01279) 635282 E-mail: sales@srs-products.co.uk

▶ indicates data change since last edition

ELECTRONIC EQUIPMENT CONSULTANTS/DESIGNERS/ PRODUCTION SERVICES, CUSTOM BUILT – *continued*

Satel Electronics, North East Suffolk Business Centre, Pinbush Road, Kessingland, Lowestoft, Suffolk, NR33 7NQ Tel: (01502) 513216 Fax: (01502) 513216 E-mail: satelelectronics@btclick.com
Silent Power Systems Ltd, Unit 9 Dain Street, Stoke-on-Trent, ST6 3LN Tel: (01782) 822402 Fax: (01782) 577262
Simutech Electronics Ltd, Unit 42 Louis Pearlman Centre, Goulton Street, Hull, HU3 4DL Tel: (01482) 212961 Fax: (01482) 585608 E-mail: simutechpt@compuserve.com
Slencrest Ltd, Broad Oak House, Pheasant Lane, Maidstone, Kent, ME15 9QR Tel: (01622) 741122 Fax: (01622) 747722 E-mail: sales@slencrest.com
Sloan Electronics Ltd, 241 Kells Lane, Gateshead, Tyne & Wear, NE9 5HU Tel: 0191-491 0191 Fax: 0191-482 6762 E-mail: info@sloanelectronics.co.uk
Softronic Systems Ltd, Unit 2 & 3 Enterprise Estate, Station Road West, Ash Vale, Aldershot, Hampshire, GU12 5QJ Tel: (01252) 513884
Soneck Electronics Ltd, 3A Cumberland Works, Wintersells Road, Byfleet, Byfleet, Surrey, KT14 7LF Tel: (01932) 355925 Fax: (01932) 336675 E-mail: soneck@tesco.net
Storm Power, 13 Pendyffryn Road, Rhyl, Clwyd, LL18 4RU Tel: (01745) 354405 Fax: (01745) 361219 E-mail: sales@stormpower.co.uk
Topline Electronics Ltd, 8a Ropemaker Park, Diplocks Way, Hailsham, East Sussex, BN27 3GU Tel: (01323) 440760 Fax: (01323) 844508 E-mail: toplineltd@compuserve.com
X B R Electronics Ltd, Campbell Road, Eastleigh, Hampshire, SO50 5AE Tel: (023) 8061 3211 Fax: (023) 8061 3215 E-mail: sales@xbrelectronics.com
Zeal Electronics Ltd, Vanguard Trading Estate, Britannia Road, Chesterfield, Derbyshire, S40 2TZ Tel: (01246) 209009 Fax: (01246) 232994 E-mail: sales@zeal-electronics.co.uk
Zeta Electronic Systems, Unit 4 Pandy Industrial Estate, Plas Acton Road, Wrexham, Clwyd, LL11 2UD Tel: (01978) 312427 Fax: (01978) 314062E-mail: enquiries@zeta-electronic.com
Zonefollow Ltd, 2 Wilton Road, Haine Industrial Estate, Ramsgate, Kent, CT12 5HG Tel: (01843) 588087 Fax: (01843) 851313 E-mail: info@zonefollow.co.uk

ELECTRONIC EQUIPMENT COOLING FANS

Comair Rotron Europe Ltd, 9 The I O Centre, Nash Road, Redditch, Worcestershire, B98 7AS Tel: (01527) 520525 Fax: (01527) 520565 E-mail: info@comairrotron.com
Dalroad Distribution Ltd, Bramingham Business Park, Enterprise Way, Luton, LU3 4BU Tel: (01582) 505252 Fax: (01582) 560060 E-mail: sales@dalroad.com
Ebm-Papst, The Barn, Sheepdown, East Ilsley, Newbury, Berkshire, RG20 7ND Tel: (0870) 7665170 Fax: (08707) 665180 E-mail: aanddsales@uk.ebmpapst.com

ELECTRONIC EQUIPMENT DEVELOPMENT

▶ Concise Electronic Engineering Ltd, Rhydybont Mill, Llanybydder, Dyfed, SA40 9QS Tel: (01570) 481344 Fax: (01570) 481495 E-mail: enquiries@concise-electronics.co.uk
Designwrights Ltd, Unit 18 Liss Business Centre, Station Road, Liss, Hampshire, GU33 7AW Tel: (01730) 890050 Fax: (01730) 890051 E-mail: info@designwrights.co.uk
Eyebright Designs Ltd, 107 Leicester Road, Wolvey, Hinckley, Leicestershire, LE10 3HJ Tel: (01455) 220835 Fax: (01455) 220895 E-mail: info@eyebright.demon.co.uk

ELECTRONIC EQUIPMENT (INDUSTRIAL) HIRE

Aughton Automation Ltd, 66 Brindley Road, Astmoor Industrial Estate, Runcorn, Cheshire, WA7 1PF Tel: (01928) 589606 Fax: (01928) 589601 E-mail: brian.duffy@aughtonuk.com
Office Electronics Centre UK Ltd, Electronics House Enterprise Court, Gapton Hall Road, Great Yarmouth, Norfolk, NR31 0ND Tel: (01493) 600500 Fax: (01493) 650398 E-mail: sales@oecuk.co.uk

ELECTRONIC EQUIPMENT MANUFACTURING TESTING

▶ Fluke (UK) Ltd, 52 Hurricane Way, Norwich, NR6 6JB Tel: (020) 7942 0700 Fax: (020) 7942 0701 E-mail: industrial@uk.fluke.nl
Oldham Controls, Middleton Road, Royton, Oldham, OL2 5LL Tel: 0161-624 1912 Fax: 0161-624 1912

▶ Tecnisis Ltd, Unit 3 Martlesham Creek Industrial Estate, Sandy Lane, Martlesham, Woodbridge, Suffolk, IP12 4SD Tel: (01394) 389098 Fax: (01394) 389062 E-mail: sales@tecnisis.co.uk

ELECTRONIC EQUIPMENT POWER VARIATION PROTECTION DEVICES

Tyco Electronics Ltd Bowthorpe Emp, Unit 8 A Freshfield Industrial Estate, Stevenson Road, Brighton, BN2 0DF Tel: (01273) 692591 Fax: (01273) 601741 E-mail: craig.sutton@bowthorpe-emp.com

ELECTRONIC EQUIPMENT WEEE DIRECTIVE RECYCLING

WEEE Labels.com, Unit 4, City Estate,, Corngreaves Road, Cradley Heath, West Midlands, B64 7EP Tel: 0870 7773645 Fax: 0870 7773644 E-mail: sales@weeelabels.com

ELECTRONIC EQUIPMENT, SUBSEA/UNDERWATER

Seatronics Ltd, 4 Denmore Industrial Estate, Denmore Road, Denmore Industrial Estate, Aberdeen, AB23 8JW Tel: (01224) 853100 Fax: (01224) 853101 E-mail: david.currie@seatronics-group.com

ELECTRONIC FLOOR COVERING STAPLERS

▶ Ace Flooring UK Ltd, 6 Warden Mill Close, Wateringbury, Maidstone, Kent, ME18 5DJ Tel: (01622) 815544 E-mail: aceflooring@btinternet.com

ELECTRONIC FUND TRANSFER (EFT) SYSTEMS

Dione P.L.C., Dione House, Oxford Road, Stokenchurch, High Wycombe, Buckinghamshire, HP14 3SX Tel: (01494) 486000 Fax: (01494) 486050 E-mail: info@dionecorp.com

ELECTRONIC FUND TRANSFER (EFT) TERMINALS

Dione P.L.C., Dione House, Oxford Road, Stokenchurch, High Wycombe, Buckinghamshire, HP14 3SX Tel: (01494) 486000 Fax: (01494) 486050 E-mail: info@dionecorp.com
Thales E Transactions Ltd, Unit 3-6 Milford Trading Estate, Blakey Road, Salisbury, SP1 2UD Tel: (01722) 332255 Fax: (01722) 322464 E-mail: sales@thales-e-transactions.com

ELECTRONIC GLASSWARE

Moores Evic Glassworks Ltd, Evic Works, 143 Hersham Road, Walton-on-Thames, Surrey, KT12 1RR Tel: (01932) 222314 Fax: (01932) 243330 E-mail: sales@moores-glass.co.uk

ELECTRONIC IMAGING

Qualitech Print Ltd, Bramhall Moor Industrial Park, Pepper Road, Stockport, Cheshire, SK7 5BW Tel: 0161-456 6866 Fax: 0161-487 1588 E-mail: sales@qualitech.co.uk
Schawk, Kingsway North, Team Valley Trading Estate, Gateshead, Tyne & Wear, NE11 0JH Tel: 0191-491 7777 Fax: 0191-487 6673

ELECTRONIC INCLINOMETERS

Tilt Measurement Ltd, Horizon House Baldock Industrial Estate, London Road, Baldock, Hertfordshire, SG7 6NG Tel: (01462) 894566 Fax: (01462) 895990 E-mail: sales@tilt-measurement.com

ELECTRONIC INFORMATION DISPLAY DEVICES

A A Electronique Services Ltd, Unit 5, Gtrove Park Business Estate, Waltham Road, White Waltham, Maidenhead, Berkshire, SL6 3LW Tel: (020) 8893 1907 Fax: (020) 8893 1908
Acord Electronics Ltd, Madeira Road, West Byfleet, Surrey, KT14 6DN Tel: (01932) 354565 Fax: (01932) 350140 E-mail: sales@acord.co.uk
Assign Technology, Unit 1 Wadsworth Business Centre, 21 Wadsworth Road, Greenford, Middlesex, UB6 7LQ Tel: (020) 8998 0806 Fax: (020) 8998 1272 E-mail: info@assigntechnology.com
C W Micro-Systems, 11 Mitchell Point, Ensign Way, Southampton, SO31 4RF Tel: (023) 8045 6888 Fax: (023) 8045 6542 E-mail: info@signblazer.com
E D C Technology, Suite 24, Mountbatten House, Hillcrest, Highgate, London, N6 4HJ Tel: (020) 8341 2689
Integrated Display Systems Ltd, Unit 15, Muarice Road, Wallsend, Tyne & Wear, NE28 6BY Tel: 0191-262 0091 Fax: 0191-262 0091 E-mail: sales@clavis.co.uk
M R G Systems Ltd, Willow Court, Beeches Green, Stroud, Gloucestershire, GL5 4BJ Tel: (01453) 751871 Fax: (01453) 753125 E-mail: sales@mrgsystems.co.uk
Melford Electronics Ltd, 14 Blenheim Road, Cresses Business Park, Cressex Business Park, High Wycombe, Buckinghamshire, HP12 3RS Tel: (01494) 638069 Fax: (01494) 463358 E-mail: sales@melford-elec.co.uk
Piers-Roger (Electronics) Ltd, Knights Court, Magellan Close, Walworth Industrial Estate, Andover, Hampshire, SP10 5NT Tel: (01264) 400800 Fax: (01264) 400900 E-mail: sales@polycomp.co.uk
Vision Options Ltd, York House, 22 Old Shoreham Road, Brighton, BN1 5DD Tel: (01273) 385000 Fax: (01273) 549549 E-mail: voptions@aol.com
Wasco Circuits, Wasco House, Willow Lane, Lancaster, LA1 5NA Tel: (01524) 69900 Fax: (01524) 67544 E-mail: front.office@nht.co.uk
Whiteley Electronics Ltd, Victoria Street, Mansfield, Nottinghamshire, NG18 5RW Tel: (01623) 415600 Fax: (01623) 420484 E-mail: e-mail@whiteleyelectronics.com

ELECTRONIC INSECT KILLERS

Arrow Guard, Byeways, Woodgate Road, Ryarsh, West Malling, Kent, ME19 5LH Tel: (01732) 820444 Fax: (01732) 820333

ELECTRONIC INSTRUMENT ENGINEERING

Industrial Calibration Ltd, Sunbeam Road, Kempston, Bedford, MK42 7BZ Tel: (01234) 857171 Fax: (01234) 840371 E-mail: clive@industrialcalibration.com
M K S Instruments UK, 10 Delta House, Carmondean Centre, Livingston, West Lothian, EH54 8PT Tel: (01506) 440004 Fax: (01506) 430004 E-mail: sales@mksinst.co.uk
Starr Pyrometers Ltd, 31 Spring Hill, Sheffield, S10 1ET Tel: (07973) 726785
▶ Watson Norie Ltd, Wincomblee Road, Walker, Newcastle upon Tyne, NE6 3PL Tel: 0191-262 7411 Fax: 0191-263 0496 E-mail: headoffice@watsonnorie.co.uk

ELECTRONIC INSTRUMENT MAINTENANCE OR REPAIR

C N Systems U K Ltd, Unit 1 Wellington St Workshops, Wellington Street, Warrington, WA1 2DB Tel: (01925) 445190 Fax: (01925) 445190 E-mail: info@c-nsystems.com
Celtech UK Electronics Ltd, Unit 12 Barton Business Park, Cawdor Street, Eccles, Manchester, M30 0QR Tel: 0161-788 0267 Fax: 0161-787 8212 E-mail: celtech@celtech-uk.co.uk
S R S Automation, Daneside House, Riverdane Road, Congleton, Cheshire, CW12 1UN Tel: (01260) 281432 Fax: (01260) 281831 E-mail: srsautomation@btinternet.com
S & S Electronics, Canal Works, Cadman Street, Sheffield, S4 7ZG Tel: 0114-275 8593 Fax: 0114-275 8593
Switzer Industrial Instruments, 14 Station Road, Lostock Gralam, Northwich, Cheshire, CW9 7PN Tel: (01606) 48950 Fax: (01606) 49581 E-mail: sswitzer1@aol.com

ELECTRONIC INSTRUMENT/ INSTRUMENTATION, *See also headings for particular types*

Aeroflex Ltd, 480 Bath Road, Slough, SL1 6BE Tel: (01628) 604455 Fax: (01628) 662017 E-mail: riws@aeroflex.com
Aeroflex, Burnham, 1 Progress House, Progress Business Centre, Whittle Parkway, Slough, SL1 6DQ Tel: (01628) 604455 Fax: (01628) 662017
Antec Instrumentation, Unit 1, 59 Queensway North, Team Valley Trading Estate, Gateshead, Tyne & Wear, NE11 0NX Tel: 0191-482 4241 Fax: 0191-487 8835
Bentley Instrument Co Ltd, 1 Block 2, Pennyburn Industrial Estate, Londonderry, BT48 0LU Tel: (028) 7126 1023 Fax: (028) 7126 6629 E-mail: sales@bentley-instruments.com
Bowden Bros Ltd, Brickworks House, Spook Hill, North Holmwood, Dorking, Surrey, RH5 4HR Tel: (01306) 743355 Fax: (01306) 876768 E-mail: info@bowdon-bros.com
C D M, Central Boulevard, Blythe Valley Park, Solihull, West Midlands, B90 8AG Tel: (0870) 0116682 Fax: (01264) 711396 E-mail: cdmcontrol@aol.com
C N Systems U K Ltd, Unit 1 Wellington St Workshops, Wellington Street, Warrington, WA1 2DB Tel: (01925) 445190 Fax: (01925) 445190 E-mail: info@c-nsystems.com
Caledonia Instrumentation Ltd, Unit 26 Dalsetter Avenue, Glasgow, G15 8TE Tel: 0141-949 0000 Fax: 0141-949 1154 E-mail: sales@cal-inst.com
Contral Instrument Services Ltd, 6 Abbotsinch Road, Grangemouth, Stirlingshire, FK3 9UX Tel: (01324) 484080 Fax: (01324) 483654 E-mail: info@contral.co.uk
Contronics Ltd, Greenfield Farm Industrial Estate, Congleton, Cheshire, CW12 4TU Tel: (01260) 298383 Fax: (01260) 298387 E-mail: sales@contronics.co.uk
Cooknell Electronics Ltd, 17 Cambridge Road, Granby Industrial Estate, Weymouth, Dorset, DT4 9TJ Tel: (01305) 773744 Fax: (01305) 779527 E-mail: admin@cooknell-electronics.co.uk
Electro-Flow Controls Ltd, Unit 3 Souter Head Industrial Centre, Souter Head Road, Altens, Aberdeen, AB12 3LF Tel: (01224) 249355 Fax: (01224) 249339 E-mail: efcltd@attglobal.net
Esr Electronic Components, Station Road, Cullercoats, North Shields, Tyne & Wear, NE30 4PQ Tel: 0191-251 4363 Fax: 0191-252 2296 E-mail: sales@esr.co.uk
G R C Electronics Systems Ltd, 157-159 West Street, Bedminster, Bristol, BS3 3PN Tel: 0117-963 9830 Fax: 0117-963 9567 E-mail: sales@grcelex.demon.co.uk
Hagemeyer Service Centre, Blaydon Banks Works, Blaydon-On-Tyne, Tyne & Wear, NE21 4AU Tel: 0191-414 5657 Fax: 0191-499 0153
▶ Industrial Development Bangor (U W B) Ltd, Dean Street, Bangor, Gwynedd, LL57 1UT Tel: (01248) 382749 Fax: (01248) 372105 E-mail: info@idb-tech.com
K D P Electronic Systems Ltd, Station Road, Gamlingay, Sandy, Bedfordshire, SG19 3HB Tel: (01767) 651058 Fax: (01767) 651144 E-mail: sales@kdpes.co.uk
Kemo Ltd, 3 Brook Co, Blakeney Road, Beckenham, Kent, BR3 1HG Tel: (020) 8658 3838 Fax: (020) 8658 4084 E-mail: technical@kemo.com
Lee-Dickens Ltd, Rushton Rd, Desborough, Kettering, Northamptonshire, NN14 2QW Tel: (01536) 760156 Fax: (01536) 762552 E-mail: sales@lee-dickens.co.uk
Levell Instruments, Four Hazels, Allard Way, Broxbourne, Hertfordshire, EN10 7ER Tel: (01992) 464248 Fax: (01992) 464248 E-mail: levellbcc@aol.com
Michael Brandon, 29 Royal Industrial Estate, Jarrow, Tyne & Wear, NE32 3HR Tel: 0191-428 6668 Fax: 0191-428 6066 E-mail: sales@brandonltd.co.uk
Nashcourt Ltd, 9 Penuel Road, Pentyrch, Cardiff, CF15 9QJ Tel: (029) 2089 1201 E-mail: nashcourtltd@aol.com
Oxford Scientific Products 2001, 74 Shakespeare Road, Eynsham, Witney, Oxfordshire, OX29 4PY Tel: (01865) 883211 Fax: (01865) 882232 E-mail: r.morton@ph.ox.ac.uk
Pentagon Instruments Ltd, Unit 4 Wayside, Commerce Way, Lancing, West Sussex, BN15 8SW Tel: (01903) 765225 Fax: (01903) 765547 E-mail: sales@pentagoninstruments.com
Prolec Ltd, Unit 5, Link 35, Nuffield Industrial Estate, Poole, Dorset, BH17 0GB Tel: (01202) 681190 Fax: (01202) 677909 E-mail: sales@prolec.co.uk
Protura, Unit 33 Loughborough Technology Centre, Epinal Way, Loughborough, Leics, LE11 3GE Tel: (01509) 269018 Fax: (01509) 269022 E-mail: sales@protura.co.uk
Pyrometer Systems Ltd, 20 Broadhurst Street, Stockport, Cheshire, SK3 8JH Tel: 0161-476 4994 Fax: 0161-476 2656 E-mail: sales@pyrometer.co.uk
R Gorton & Associates Electronics Ltd, 308-310 Slade Lane, Manchester, M19 2BY Tel: 0161-224 5650 Fax: 0161-257 2761 E-mail: gortonelectronics@btinternet.com
R & J Engineering, Gate House Cam Centre, Wilbury Way, Hitchin, Hertfordshire, SG4 0TW Tel: (01462) 620444 Fax: (01462) 620777
Rigserv Ltd, Unit 9 Wellheads Crescent, Wellheads Industrial Estate, Aberdeen, AB21 7GA Tel: (01224) 724212 Fax: (01224) 724282 E-mail: information@rigserv.com
Rohde & Schwarz UK Ltd, Ansells Bus Park, Fleet, Hampshire, GU51 2UZ Tel: (01252) 811377 Fax: (01252) 811447 E-mail: sales@rsuk.rohde-shwartz.com
Romotex Ltd, 22 London Road, Hazel Grove, Stockport, Cheshire, SK7 4AH Tel: 0161-419 9999 Fax: 0161-483 0101
Scotia Instrumentation Ltd, Unit 5c New York Way, New York Industrial Park, Newcastle upon Tyne, NE27 0QF Tel: 0191-296 3444 Fax: 0191-296 3555 E-mail: sales@scotia-instrumentation.com
Seltec Automation, Subway Street, Hull, HU3 4EL Tel: (01482) 225297 Fax: (01482) 212470 E-mail: sales@seltec.co.uk
Sentinel Instruments Ltd, Unit 20 Howe Moss Drive, Kirkhill Industrial Estate, Dyce, Aberdeen, AB21 0GG Tel: (01224) 775830 Fax: (01224) 775831
Siemens V D O Automotive Ltd, The Broadlands, 120 Holford Drive, Holford, Birmingham, B6 7UG Tel: 0121-344 2000 Fax: 0121-344 2072 E-mail: admin@vdodayton.com

ELECTRONIC INSTRUMENT/ INSTRUMENTATION – *continued*

Sky Electronic Systems Ltd, Unit D Cavendish Courtyard, Weldon North Industrial Estate, Corby, Northamptonshire, NN17 5DZ Tel: (01536) 267000 Fax: (01536) 267666 E-mail: ian@skyd.fsnet.co.uk

Switchgear & Instrumentation Ltd, Ripley Road, Bradford, West Yorkshire, BD4 7EH Tel: (01274) 734221 Fax: (01274) 731390 E-mail: sales@switchgear.co.uk

Triton Electronics Ltd, Bigods Hall, Bigods Lane, Dunmow, Essex, CM6 3BE Tel: (01371) 872812 Fax: (01371) 876065 E-mail: sales@tritonel.com

Williams Industrial Services Ltd, Unit 5, Hyde Park, Commercial Centre, Newtownabbey, County Antrim, BT36 4PY Tel: (028) 9083 8999 Fax: (028) 9084 2211 E-mail: sales@wis-ni.com

ELECTRONIC INSTRUMENT/ INSTRUMENTATION ASSEMBLERS TO THE TRADE

Beta Engineering Stotfold Ltd, Taylors Road, Stotfold, Hitchin, Hertfordshire, SG5 4AX Tel: (01462) 730910 Fax: (01462) 835325

Diamond Instrumentation Ltd, 46 Swan Road, Swan Industrial Estate, District 9, Washington, Tyne & Wear, NE38 8JJ Tel: 0191-417 8911 Fax: 0191-419 1426

Fourway Electronics Ltd, 3 Bone Lane, Newbury, Berkshire, RG14 5SH Tel: (01635) 45955 Fax: (01635) 551140 E-mail: 4wayelectronic@btclick.com

I T Telecoms Ltd, 34 Avenue Parade, Accrington, Lancashire, BB5 6PP Tel: (01254) 394608 Fax: (01254) 395649 E-mail: sales@it-telecoms.org

Instrument Solutions, The Laurels, The Square, Angmering, Littlehampton, West Sussex, BN16 4EA Tel: (01903) 856846 Fax: (01903) 856516 E-mail: info@instrumentsolutions.com

Romotex Ltd, 22 London Road, Hazel Grove, Stockport, Cheshire, SK7 4AH Tel: 0161-419 9999 Fax: 0161-483 0101

Saturn Engineering Ltd, 68 Wilbury Way, Hitchin, Hertfordshire, SG4 0TP Tel: (01462) 458511 Fax: (01462) 458515 E-mail: saturneng@hotmail.com

ELECTRONIC INSTRUMENT/ INSTRUMENTATION CASES/ CABINETS

Aish Technologies Ltd, Broom Road, Poole, Dorset, BH12 4NL Tel: (01202) 307007 Fax: (01202) 307000 E-mail: sales@aishtechnologies.com

Bullet Engineering Ltd, Vale Road, Spilsby, Lincolnshire, PE23 5HE Tel: (01790) 753320 Fax: (01790) 754530

C F Cases Ltd, 13 Consul Road, Rugby, Warwickshire, CV21 1PB Tel: (01788) 535484 Fax: (01788) 570933 E-mail: sales@cfcases.co.uk

JDR, 131 Grenfell Road, Maidenhead, Berkshire, SL6 1EX Tel: (01628) 629450 Fax: (01628) 625459 E-mail: ralph@jdrmhead.fsnet.co.uk

Zero Cases (U K) Ltd, Alpha Park, Bevan Way, Smethwick, West Midlands, B66 1BZ Tel: 0121-558 2011 Fax: 0121-565 2115 E-mail: zero.cases.europe.sales@dial.pipex.com

ELECTRONIC INSTRUMENT/ INSTRUMENTATION CHASSIS

Aeroflex Ltd, 480 Bath Road, Slough, SL1 6BE Tel: (01628) 604455 Fax: (01628) 662017 E-mail: riws@aeroflex.com

JDR, 131 Grenfell Road, Maidenhead, Berkshire, SL6 1EX Tel: (01628) 629450 Fax: (01628) 625459 E-mail: ralph@jdrmhead.fsnet.co.uk

Knurr UK Ltd, Burrel Road, St. Ives, Cambridgeshire, PE27 3LE Tel: (01480) 496125 Fax: (01480) 496373 E-mail: knuerr.uk@knuerr.com

ELECTRONIC INSTRUMENT/ INSTRUMENTATION DESIGNERS/CONSULTANTS

Buckman Hardy Associates, The Old Bakehouse, Albert Road, Deal, Kent, CT14 9RD Tel: (01304) 365918 Fax: (01304) 369737 E-mail: sales@buckman-hardy.co.uk

Cooknell Electronics Ltd, 17 Cambridge Road, Granby Industrial Estate, Weymouth, Dorset, DT4 9TJ Tel: (01305) 773744 Fax: (01305) 779527 E-mail: admin@cooknell-electronics.co.uk

The Electronic Development Co. Ltd, 26 Beckett Road, Worcester, WR3 7NH Tel: (01905) 759609 Fax: (01905) 453273 E-mail: jonathan@the-electronic-development.co.uk

I M Dempster Ltd, 15 Caesar Avenue, Carnoustie, Angus, DD7 6DR Tel: (01241) 852822 E-mail: imdempsterltd@aol.com

▶ Industrial Development Bangor (U W B) Ltd, Dean Street, Bangor, Gwynedd, LL57 1UT Tel: (01248) 382749 Fax: (01248) 372105 E-mail: info@idb-tech.com

Ingenion Design Ltd, 10 Kym Road, Kimbolton, Huntingdon, Cambridgeshire, PE28 0LW Tel: (01480) 860606 Fax: (01480) 861122 E-mail: sales@ingenion.co.uk

Instrument Solutions, The Laurels, The Square, Angmering, Littlehampton, West Sussex, BN16 4EA Tel: (01903) 856846 Fax: (01903) 856516 E-mail: info@instrumentsolutions.com

J K Controls Ltd, 12a Rochester Airport Industrial Estate, Laker Road, Rochester, Kent, ME1 3QX Tel: (01634) 685858 Fax: (01634) 685850 E-mail: info@jkcontrols.co.uk

Mantracourt Electronics Ltd, The Drive, Farringdon, Exeter, EX5 2JB Tel: (01395) 232020 Fax: (01395) 233190 E-mail: info@mantracourt.co.uk

March Designs & Measurements, 11 Alfred Street, Dunstable, Bedfordshire, LU5 4HZ Tel: (01582) 600016 Fax: (01582) 600016 E-mail: info@marchdesigns.com

Monode Ltd, Celtic House, 44 Ballmoor, Buckingham Industrial Estate, Buckingham, MK18 1RQ Tel: (01280) 814171 Fax: (01280) 814169 E-mail: sales@monode.co.uk

Technolog Group Ltd, Technolog House, Ravenstor Road, Matlock, Derbyshire, DE4 4FY Tel: (01629) 823611 Fax: (01629) 824283 E-mail: technolog@technolog.com

ELECTRONIC INSTRUMENT/ INSTRUMENTATION HIRE

Scotech International Services, Craigshaw Road, West Tullos Industrial Estate, Aberdeen, AB12 3AR Tel: (01224) 248450 Fax: (01224) 248023 E-mail: sales@scotech.co.uk

ELECTRONIC INSTRUMENT/ INSTRUMENTATION, EMERGENCY VEHICLES

▶ Hale Products Europe Ltd, Charles Street, Warwick, CV34 5LR Tel: (01926) 623614 Fax: (01926) 623689 E-mail: sales@haleeurope.com

ELECTRONIC INSTRUMENT/ INSTRUMENTATION, INDICATING

Protura, Unit 33 Loughborough Technology Centre, Epinal Way, Loughborough, Leics, LE11 3GE Tel: (01509) 269018 Fax: (01509) 269022 E-mail: sales@protura.co.uk

ELECTRONIC INSTRUMENT/ INSTRUMENTATION, INTRINSICALLY SAFE

Measurement Technology Ltd, 18 Power Court, Luton, LU1 3JJ Tel: (01582) 723633 Fax: (01582) 422283 E-mail: enquiry@mtl-inst.com

ELECTRONIC INSTRUMENT/ INSTRUMENTATION, USED

Microlease plc, Unit 6 Whitefriars Trading Estate, Tudor Road, Harrow, Middlesex, HA3 5SS Tel: (020) 8420 0200 Fax: (020) 8420 0299 E-mail: info@microlease.com

Telford Electronics, Hoo Farm, Hoo, Telford, Shropshire, TF6 6DJ Tel: (01952) 605451 Fax: (01952) 677978 E-mail: telfordelectronics@btinternet.com

ELECTRONIC KITCHEN SCALES

Homedics Group Ltd, 211 Vale Road, Tonbridge, Kent, TN9 1SU Tel: (01732) 354828 Fax: (01732) 358631 E-mail: uksales@homedics.co.uk

ELECTRONIC LABEL PRINTING MACHINES

Electro Graph Ltd, 177 Lower High Street, Stourbridge, West Midlands, DY8 1TG Tel: (01384) 378436 Fax: (01384) 392542 E-mail: sales@eguk.com

ELECTRONIC LABORATORY EQUIPMENT

Appleton Woods Ltd, Lindon House, Heeley Road, Selly Oak, Birmingham, B29 6EN Tel: 0121-472 7353 Fax: 0121-414 1075 E-mail: info@appletonwoods.co.uk

ELECTRONIC MAIL (EMAIL) MARKETING

▶ Pinpointworld, 24 Orton Enterprise Centre, Bakewell Road, Orton Southgate, Peterborough, PE2 6XU Tel: (01733) 233550 Fax: (01733) 233650 E-mail: contact@pinpointworld.com

▶ stream:20, Southbank house, Blackprince Road, London, SE1 7SJ Tel: 0207 7932450

ELECTRONIC MAIL (EMAIL) MOBILE TELEPHONE SUBSCRIPTION PROVIDERS

▶ Blue Mobiles, 6 Hampson Gardens, Edenthorpe, Doncaster, South Yorkshire, DN3 2TN Tel: 07921 996869 E-mail: bluemobiles@tiscali.co.uk

ELECTRONIC MAIL SERVICES/ BUREAU SERVICES

Information Technology Systems, Cygnet Lodge, Worcester Road, Worcester, WR8 0EA Tel: (01684) 311463 Fax: (01684) 311402 E-mail: sales@itsystems.co.uk

Teamtalk Satellite Ltd, Media House, Mann Island, Liverpool, L3 1DG Tel: 0151-236 4124 Fax: 0151-236 9907 E-mail: sue.henney@teamtalk.com

ELECTRONIC MAIL SYSTEMS

Creation Internet Services Ltd, 30 Broad Oak Way, Rayleigh, Essex, SS6 8JU Tel: (01268) 774415 Fax: (01268) 779159 E-mail: ian@creationinternet.co.uk

I T S L Net Ltd, 2 Marsh Lane, Birmingham, B23 6NX Tel: (0870) 7437780 Fax: (0870) 7437781 E-mail: sales@itslnet.com

Information Technology Systems, Cygnet Lodge, Worcester Road, Worcester, WR8 0EA Tel: (01684) 311463 Fax: (01684) 311402 E-mail: sales@itsystems.co.uk

Logo Systems, 8 Greenwich Quay, Clarence Road, London, SE8 3EY Tel: (020) 8469 2222 Fax: (020) 8469 2211 E-mail: service@logosystems.co.uk

▶ Timezone Digital Storage Ltd, Rivacre Business Centre, Mill Lane, Ellesmere Port, CH66 3TH Tel: 0151-339 2070 E-mail: info@timezonedigital.com

ELECTRONIC MEASURING INSTRUMENTS OR SYSTEMS

A W R Instruments Ltd, 1 Northpoint Business Estate, Enterprise Close, Rochester, Kent, ME2 4LX Tel: (01634) 290751 Fax: (01634) 290295 E-mail: info@awr-instruments.com

Alrian Industries Ltd, Unit 2D Lake Enterprise Park, Sandall Stones Road, Kirk Sandall, Doncaster, South Yorkshire, DN3 1QR Tel: (01302) 885851 Fax: (01302) 885851 E-mail: sales@alrian.idps.co.uk

Anritsu Ltd, 200 Capability Green, Luton, LU1 3LU Tel: (01582) 433200 Fax: (01582) 731303 E-mail: sales@anritsu.co.uk

Autonnic Research Ltd, Woodrolfe Road, Tollesbury, Maldon, Essex, CM9 8SE Tel: (01621) 869460 Fax: (01621) 868815 E-mail: info@autonnic.co.uk

Chauvin Arnoux UK Ltd, Waldeck House, Waldeck Road, Maidenhead, Berkshire, SL6 8BR Tel: (01628) 788888 Fax: (01628) 628099 E-mail: sales@chauvin-arnoux.co.uk

Comark Ltd, Comark House Gunnels Wood Park, Gunnels Wood Road, Stevenage, Hertfordshire, SG1 2TA Tel: (01438) 367367 Fax: (01438) 367400 E-mail: salesuk@comarkltd.com

Cropico Ltd, 15-18 Bracken Hill, South West Industrial Estate, Peterlee, County Durham, SR8 2SW Tel: 0191-586 3511 Fax: 0191-586 0227 E-mail: sales@seaward.co.uk

Diatest UK Ltd, 18 Avondale Avenue, Hinchley Wood, Esher, Surrey, KT10 0DA Tel: (020) 8398 1100 Fax: (020) 8398 9887 E-mail: sales@diatest.co.uk

Elcometer Instruments Ltd, Edge Lane, Droylsden, Manchester, M43 6BU Tel: 0161-371 6000 Fax: 0161-371 6010 E-mail: sale@elcometer.com

Fluke UK Ltd, 52 Hurricane Way, Norwich, NR6 6JB Tel: (01603) 256600 Fax: (01603) 483670 E-mail: sales@flukeprecision.co.uk

Fylde Electronic Laboratories Ltd, 49-51 Fylde Road, Preston, PR1 2XQ Tel: (01772) 257560 Fax: (01772) 821530E-mail: sales@fylde.com

Micro Movements Ltd, Eversley Centre, Hook, Hampshire, RG27 0NB Tel: 0118-973 0200 Fax: 0118-9328872 E-mail: info@micromovements.co.uk

Neutrik (UK) Ltd, Westridge Business Park, Ryde, Isle Of Wight, PO33 1QT Tel: (01983) 811441 Fax: (01983) 811439 E-mail: sales@neutrik.co.uk

Penny & Giles Controls Ltd, 15 Airfield Rd, Christchurch, Dorset, BH23 3TG Tel: (01202) 409409 Fax: (01202) 409475 E-mail: sales@pennyandgiles.com

Protronix Industrial Services, 3-15 Cross Street, Luton, LU2 0DP Tel: (01582) 418490 Fax: (01582) 486588 E-mail: sales@protronix.co.uk

Protura, Unit 33 Loughborough Technology Centre, Epinal Way, Loughborough, Leics, LE11 3GE Tel: (01509) 269018 Fax: (01509) 269022 E-mail: sales@protura.co.uk

Pullman Instruments (UK) Ltd, Chatsworth House, Chatsworth Terrace, Harrogate, North Yorkshire, HG1 5HT Tel: (01423) 720360 Fax: (01423) 720361 E-mail: info@pullman.co.uk

Pulsonic Technologies Ltd, Riverside House North Dean Business Park, Stainland Road, Greetland, Halifax, West Yorkshire, HX4 8LR Tel: (01422) 363462 Fax: (0870) 9224026 E-mail: sales@pulsonictechnologies.com

Richmond Measurement Services, Po Box 44, Derby, DE24 8ZT Tel: (01332) 364354 Fax: (01332) 362737

Rohde & Schwarz UK Ltd, Ansells Bus Park, Fleet, Hampshire, GU51 2UZ Tel: (01252) 811377 Fax: (01252) 811447 E-mail: sales@rsuk.rohde-shwartz.com

Sangamo Ltd, Auchenfoil Road, Port Glasgow, Renfrewshire, PA14 5XG Tel: (01475) 745131 Fax: (01475) 744567 E-mail: enquiries@sangamo.co.uk

Spea (UK) Ltd, Spea Ho, Sanford La, Wareham, Dorset, BH20 4DY Tel: (01929) 554444 Fax: (01929) 554446 E-mail: spea@spea.co.uk

Technolog Group Ltd, Technolog House, Ravenstor Road, Matlock, Derbyshire, DE4 4FY Tel: (01629) 823611 Fax: (01629) 824283 E-mail: technolog@technolog.com

Time Electronics Ltd, Unit 11, Sovereign Way, Tonbridge, Kent, TN9 1RH Tel: (01732) 355993 Fax: (01732) 770312 E-mail: mail@timeelectronics.co.uk

Warren Measurement Systems, 15 Berwick Way, Kettering, Northamptonshire, NN15 5XF Tel: (01536) 310722 Fax: (01536) 310722 E-mail: sales@warrenmeasurement.co.uk

Yokogawa Ltd, Stuart Road, Manor Park, Runcorn, Cheshire, WA7 1TR Tel: (01928) 597100 Fax: (01928) 597101 E-mail: info@uk.yokogawa.com

Zumbach Electronics, Unit 22 Cromwell Business Centre, Howard Way, Interchange Park, Newport Pagnell, Buckinghamshire, MK16 9QS Tel: (0870) 7743301 Fax: (0870) 7743302 E-mail: sales@zumbach.com

ELECTRONIC MEASURING INSTRUMENTS OR SYSTEMS HIRE

Express Instrument Hire Ltd, Express House, Church Road, Tarleton, Preston, PR4 6UP Tel: (01772) 815600 Fax: (01772) 815937 E-mail: sales@expresshire.net

I R Group, Forbes House, Whitefriars Estate, Tudor Road, Harrow, Middlesex, HA3 5SS Tel: (020) 8420 0211

Mayer International (UK) Ltd, 18 Monnach Way, Winchester, Hampshire, SO22 5QU Tel: (01962) 625618 E-mail: johnmayer@tunnel-lighting-control.com

ELECTRONIC METAL DETECTORS

Constant Instruments, Unit 8 Minster Court, Courtwick Lane, Wick, Littlehampton, West Sussex, BN17 7RN Tel: (01903) 739333 Fax: (01903) 739222 E-mail: sales@constant-ceia.com

ELECTRONIC MODULES, *See Electronic Module etc*

ELECTRONIC MOTION CONTROL EQUIPMENT

4 Q D Motor Control, 30 Reach Road, Burwell, Cambridge, CB25 0AH Tel: (01638) 741930 Fax: (01638) 744080E-mail: sales@4qd.co.uk

Chapmore Controls Ltd, 64 Junction Road, Northampton, NN2 7HS Tel: (01604) 714431 Fax: (01604) 714431 E-mail: info@chapmore.co.uk

ELECTRONIC NAVIGATIONAL INSTRUMENTS

Silva Ltd, Fleming Road, Kirkton Campus, Livingston, West Lothian, EH54 7BN Tel: (01506) 419555 Fax: (01506) 415906 E-mail: info@silva.ltd.uk

ELECTRONIC PERFORMANCE IMPROVEMENT AUTOMOTIVE COMPONENTS

▶ 1stautobulbs, Randstad House, Crowhall Road, Nelson Park, Cramlington, Northumberland, NE23 1WH Tel: 01670 706985 Fax: 01670 730820 E-mail: chrisclark@randstadltd.co.uk

ELECTRONIC POINT OF SALE (EPOS) ACCESSORIES

P C Cash Control Systems, 176 Tynemouth Road, North Shields, Tyne & Wear, NE30 1EG Tel: 0191-257 3738 E-mail: sales@pccash.co.uk

Posiflex International Ltd, Saddleworth Business Centre, Huddersfield Road, Delph, Oldham, OL3 5DF Tel: (01457) 877720 Fax: (01457) 877730

ELECTRONIC POINT OF SALE (EPOS) EQUIPMENT REPAIR

▶ a1shoppingchannel.com, Koloma House, Warren Avenue, Fakenham, Norfolk, NR21 8NP Tel: 0845 1665226 Fax: 0845 1665227 E-mail: sales@a1shoppingchannel.com

Electroversal Ltd, Units 4-9 Ribocon Way, Off Toddington Road, Luton, LU4 9UR Tel: (01582) 582023 Fax: (01582) 582087 E-mail: sales@electroversal.com

Impetus Technologies Ltd, Castle Farm, Cholmondeley, Malpas, Cheshire, SY14 8AQ Tel: (01829) 773200 Fax: (01829) 773208 E-mail: sales@impetusuk.net

Lincoln Equipment Ltd, Cash Register Centre, Moorland Way, Lincoln, LN6 7JW Tel: (01522) 814555 Fax: (01522) 814556 E-mail: enquiries@lsepos.co.uk

▶ S P C International, Unit 1-3, Station Road, Templecombe, Somerset, BA8 0JR Tel: (01963) 370504 Fax: (01963) 370101 E-mail: sales@spcint.com

ELECTRONIC POINT OF SALE (EPOS) EQUIPMENT TESTING OR APPROVAL CONSULTANCY

▶ a1shoppingchannel.com, Koloma House, Warren Avenue, Fakenham, Norfolk, NR21 8NP Tel: 0845 1665226 Fax: 0845 1665227 E-mail: sales@a1shoppingchannel.com

ELECTRONIC POSITIONING RAMS

Microdat Automation Co Uk Ltd, Unit2, Benyon Park Way, Leeds, LS12 6DP Tel: 0113-244 5225 Fax: 0113-244 5226 E-mail: info@microdat.co.uk

ELECTRONIC POWER ASSEMBLIES

Acrogen Ltd, 14A Cambridge Road, Granby Industrial Estate, Weymouth, Dorset, DT4 9TJ Tel: (01305) 769754 Fax: (01305) 784555 E-mail: acrogen@acrogen.com

Semikron UK Ltd, Martin House, 7 Fountain Drive, Hertford, SG13 7UB Tel: (01992) 584677 Fax: (01992) 554942 E-mail: sales.skuk@semikron.com

ELECTRONIC PRINTING EQUIPMENT

Able Systems Ltd, Denton Drive, Northwich, Cheshire, CW9 7TU Tel: (01606) 48621 Fax: (01606) 44903 E-mail: sales@able-systems.com

Litho Supplies, Flagship Square, Shaw Cross Business Park, Dewsbury, West Yorkshire, WF12 7TH Tel: (01924) 486130 Fax: (01924) 460502 E-mail: dewsbury@litho.co.uk

ELECTRONIC PROCUREMENT (EPROCUREMENT)

▶ Cutcost.Com, 200 Brook Drive, Reading, RG2 6UB Tel: (0870) 3518828 Fax: (0870) 3518829 E-mail: save@cutcost.com

Proactis Group Ltd, Holtby Manor, Stamford Bridge Road, Dunnington, York, YO19 5LL Tel: (01904) 481999 Fax: (01904) 481666

ELECTRONIC PROTOTYPE CONSULTANTS/DESIGNERS/ PRODUCTION SERVICES

Automated Entry Systems Ltd, Automation House, 61 East Street, Warminster, Wiltshire, BA12 9BZ Tel: (01985) 215827 Fax: (01985) 219299 E-mail: aeswinchcombe@aol.com

Buswell Machine Electronics, Peel House, Peel Road, Skelmersdale, Lancashire, WN8 9PT Tel: (01695) 726518 Fax: (01695) 726518 E-mail: rbuswell@buswell.co.uk

▶ Collingwood Consultancy, 20 Estcourt Road, Great Yarmouth, Norfolk, NR30 4JG Tel: (01493) 842022 Fax: (01493) 331955

Crown Hill Associates Ltd, Station House, Station Road, Wilburton, Ely, Cambridgeshire, CB6 3PZ Tel: (01353) 749990 Fax: (01353) 749991 E-mail: sales@crownhill.co.uk

Fourway Electronics Ltd, 3 Bone Lane, Newbury, Berkshire, RG14 5SH Tel: (01635) 45955 Fax: (01635) 551140 E-mail: 4wayelectronic@btclick.com

Frontline Electronics, 25 Laundry Road, Minster, Ramsgate, Kent, CT12 4HY Tel: (01843) 821512 Fax: (01843) 821603 E-mail: sales@frontlineelectronics.co.uk

Fuselodge Ltd, 267 Acton Lane, Chiswick, London, W4 5DG Tel: (020) 8994 6275 Fax: (020) 8994 6275 E-mail: fuse.lodge@virgin.net

Harman Electronic Services, 1 Perth Street, Stoke-on-Trent, ST4 3PJ Tel: (01782) 598662 Fax: (01782) 598662

Jana International Ltd, 4 Benson Road, Nuffield Industrial Estate, Poole, Dorset, BH17 0GB Tel: (01202) 673676 Fax: (01202) 675701 E-mail: janaint@btconnect.com

▶ Jangi Electronics, 10 The Bramblings, Bicester, Oxfordshire, OX26 6SU Tel: (07851) 425703 E-mail: sales@jangielectronics.co.uk

K D P Electronic Systems Ltd, Station Road, Gamlingay, Sandy, Bedfordshire, SG19 3HB Tel: (01767) 651058 Fax: (01767) 651144 E-mail: sales@kdpes.co.uk

Macrodyne Electronics Ltd, The Birches, Birches Lane, Newent, Gloucestershire, GL18 1DN Tel: (01531) 828010 Fax: (01531) 821153 E-mail: mailbox@macrodyne.com

MGN Electronics, Beaumont Enterprise Centre, Boston Road, Leicester, LE4 1HB Tel: 0116-235 4004 Fax: 0116-236 6584 E-mail: gush@mgnelect.co.uk

Monode Ltd, Celtic House, 44 Ballmoor, Buckingham Industrial Estate, Buckingham, MK18 1RQ Tel: (01280) 814171 Fax: (01280) 814169 E-mail: sales@monode.co.uk

Powerwise Consultant Engineering, Unit 4 Randswood Farm, The Common, West Wratting, Cambridge, CB21 5LR Tel: (01223) 291250 Fax: (01223) 291260 E-mail: powerwise@powerwise.co.uk

Reeset Electronics, 19 Ray Lea Road, Maidenhead, Berkshire, SL6 8QP Tel: (01628) 628146 Fax: (01628) 628146 E-mail: ed@reeset.com

▶ Scilutions, Trinafour, Abingdon Road, Marcham, Abingdon, Oxfordshire, OX13 6NU Tel: (01865) 391460 Fax: (01865) 391385 E-mail: kellysweb@scilutions.co.uk

Solution Product Systems Ltd, Unit 34, Walker Avenue, Wolverton Mill, Milton Keynes, MK12 5TW Tel: (01908) 682700 Fax: (01908) 682739 E-mail: sales@spslretail.com

ELECTRONIC PUBLISHING, *See also Desk Top Publishing etc*

▶ Bladonmore Ltd, 10-11 Percy Street, London, W1T 1DA Tel: (020) 7631 1155 Fax: (020) 7631 1444 E-mail: info@bladonmore.com

▶ Kingston Publishing Services, Broadway House, 105 Ferensway, Hull, HU1 3UN Tel: (01482) 602600 Fax: (01482) 216816 E-mail: sue.brightman@kcom.com

▶ Premedian.com, Ivy House, Main Street, Leyburn, North Yorkshire, DL8 4EX Tel: 01969 625674 E-mail: ttalbot@premedian.com

▶ Zoom Business Services Ltd, Suite 2, 131 Friargate, Preston, PR1 2EF Tel: 07888 813931 E-mail: info@editmywork.co.uk

ELECTRONIC REGULATORS

Chloride Power Ltd, Kempston Court, Manor Road, Kempston Hardwick, Bedford, MK43 9PQ Tel: (01234) 840282 Fax: (01234) 841156

ELECTRONIC REMOTE CONTROL SYSTEMS

Marell Electronic Systems Ltd, Coldwell Street, Linthwaite, Huddersfield, HD7 5QN Tel: (01484) 843142 Fax: (01484) 843177 E-mail: info@marell.co.uk

ELECTRONIC REMOTE UNDERGROUND SURVEY SERVICES

Aegis Survey Consultants Ltd, Ongar Road, Abridge, Romford, RM4 1AA Tel: (01708) 688050 Fax: (01708) 688045 E-mail: nt@aegissurveyconsultants.com

▶ Wide World Services, 16 Millers Yard, Mill Lane, Cambridge, CB2 1RQ Tel: (01223) 576044 E-mail: james_williams:wideworld.co.uk

ELECTRONIC REPAIR

Advanced Control Electronics, 98 Ashby Road, Loughborough, Leicestershire, LE11 3AF Tel: (01509) 211333 Fax: (01509) 211333 E-mail: ac.electronics@lycos.co.uk

▶ Antech Systems, Unit 3, Hackhurst Lane Industrial Estate, Lower Dicker, Hailsham, East Sussex, BN27 4BW Tel: (01323) 442035 E-mail: musicalfix@aol.com

Dowding & Mills Engineering Services Ltd, Unit 14 Maple Business Park, Walter Street, Birmingham, B7 5ET Tel: 0121-326 6306 Fax: 0121-326 9379 E-mail: electronics.birmingham@dowdingandmills.com

Eurotronix, 19, Telford, Shropshire, TF6 6HD Tel: (01952) 541873 Fax: (01952) 541874 E-mail: sales@eurotronixgb.co.uk

Field Engineering Services Ltd, West Park, Torryleith, Newmachar, Aberdeen, AB21 0QE Tel: (01651) 863321 Fax: (01651) 863411 E-mail: georgefieldeng@aol.com

Fletcher Moorland Ltd, Elenora Street, Stoke-On-Trent, ST4 1QG Tel: (01782) 411021 Fax: (01782) 744470 E-mail: info@fletchermoorland.co.uk

Hadfield CNC & Electronics Co. Ltd, 15 Retford Road, Worksop, Nottinghamshire, S80 2PT Tel: (01909) 500760 Fax: (01909) 542800 E-mail: service@hcnc.co.uk

Heasell Electromechanical Services Ltd, 9-11 Baldock Street, Royston, Hertfordshire, SG8 5AY Tel: (0871) 2227896 Fax: (01763) 248108 E-mail: gary@abrams-netlineuk.net

▶ Industrial Electronic Repairs, Unit 11 Business Centre West, Letchworth Business Centre, Aven, Letchworth Garden City, Hertfordshire, SG6 2HB Tel: (01462) 671001

▶ Industrial Electronics Ltd, 153 City Road, Stoke-on-Trent, ST4 4ND Tel: (01782) 415533 Fax: (01782) 747315 E-mail: info@industrialelectronicsltd.co.uk

Newfield Automation, Newfield House, Brook Lane, Astbury, Congleton, Cheshire, CW12 4TJ Tel: (01260) 282200 Fax: (01260) 282201 E-mail: team@newfieldautomation.com

O E Electronics Ltd, 6 Four Brooks Business Park, Stanier Road, Calne, Wiltshire, SN11 9PP Tel: (01249) 817370 Fax: (01249) 817346 E-mail: sales@pentagon-electronics.co.uk

Qaotek Northern Ltd, Unit 431 Thorp Arch Trading Estate, Thorp Arch, Wetherby, West Yorkshire, LS23 7BJ Tel: (01937) 849491 Fax: (01937) 849492 E-mail: wsales@findit-solutions.com

R D S South-West Ltd, 162 Chemical Road, West Wiltshire Trading Estate, Westbury, Wiltshire, BA13 4JN Tel: (01373) 864415 Fax: (01373) 825415

RGB Associates, 20 Newling Way, Worthing, West Sussex, BN13 3DG Tel: (01903) 694904 Fax: (01903) 260899 E-mail: sales@rgb.uk.com

S & S Electronics, Canal Works, Cadman Street, Sheffield, S4 7ZG Tel: 0114-275 8593 Fax: 0114-275 8593

Serco Integrated Services, Building 37, Second Avenue, Pensnett Trading Estate, Kingswinford, West Midlands, DY6 7UL Tel: (01384) 401515 Fax: (01384) 404543

Sontec Electronics Ltd, Sontec House, Concorde Road, Norwich, NR6 6BE Tel: (01603) 483675 Fax: (01603) 788937 E-mail: enquire@sontec.co.uk

SPC International Ltd, 106 Oxford Road, Uxbridge, Middlesex, UB8 1NA Tel: (01895) 454850 Fax: (01895) 454851 E-mail: sales@spcint.com

Steptronik UK Ltd, 1 & 2 Baird Close, District 12, Washington, Tyne & Wear, NE37 3HL Tel: 0191-417 8990 Fax: 0191-417 8202 E-mail: peter@steptronik.co.uk

Tech Ltd, The Granery, Leacon Farm, Leacon Lane, Charing, Ashford, Kent, TN27 0EN Tel: (01634) 290308 Fax: (01233) 714040 E-mail: johnbridges1@btconnect.com

Testlink Ltd, Poole, Dorset, BH16 5SJ Tel: (01202) 621100 Fax: (01202) 625577 E-mail: sales@testlink.co.uk

Trax Circuits, Unit 15a Ellough Industrial Estate, Ellough, Beccles, Suffolk, NR34 7TD Tel: (01502) 711626 Fax: (01502) 711626 E-mail: traxcircuits@electronicrepairs.co.uk

Valley Electronics, 15 Bridge End, Hebden Bridge, West Yorkshire, HX7 5DR Tel: (01422) 885088 Fax: (01422) 885088 E-mail: v.tronics@freeuk.com

X B R Electronics Ltd, Campbell Road, Eastleigh, Hampshire, SO50 5AE Tel: (023) 8061 3211 Fax: (023) 8061 3215 E-mail: sales@xbrelectronics.com

ELECTRONIC RESEARCH AND DEVELOPMENT ENGINEERS

Amcc Electronic Engineers, 15 Enterprise Industrial Estate, Station Road West, Ash Vale, Aldershot, Hampshire, GU12 5QJ Tel: (01252) 377723 Fax: (01252) 377724 E-mail: enquiries@amcc.co.uk

Bookham, Caswell, Towcester, Northamptonshire, NN12 8EQ Tel: (01327) 350581 Fax: (01327) 356775

Design Initiative Ltd, The Old Granary, The Street, Glynde, Lewes, East Sussex, BN8 6SX Tel: (01273) 858525 Fax: (01273) 858531 E-mail: info@designit.eu.com

Dolby Laboratories Inc, Interface Business Park, Binknoll Lane, Wootton Bassett, Swindon, SN4 8QJ Tel: (01793) 842100 Fax: (01793) 842101 E-mail: website@dolby.com

▶ Griffin Electronics Ltd, Griffin House 5 Laura Avenue, Paignton, Devon, TQ3 2LS Tel: (01803) 523537 E-mail: info@griffinelectronics.co.uk

Harman Electronic Services, 1 Perth Street, Stoke-on-Trent, ST4 3PJ Tel: (01782) 598662 Fax: (01782) 598662

Innovision Research & Technology P.L.C., Ash Court, 23 Rose Street, Wokingham, Berkshire, RG40 1XS Tel: 0118-979 2000 Fax: 0118-979 1500 E-mail: enquiries@innovision-group.com

ELECTRONIC SCAN EQUIPMENT

Kronology Ltd, Unit 20 Lochshot Place, Livingston, West Lothian, EH54 6SJ Tel: (07967) 136061

Tameside Scale Services, Winton Street, Ashton-under-Lyne, Lancashire, OL6 8NL Tel: 0161-339 6501 Fax: 0161-339 6501

Vision Assurance Systems, Basepoint Business & Innovation Centre, Caxton Close, Andover, Hampshire, SP10 3FG Tel: (01264) 326309 E-mail: sales@visionassurancesystems.com

ELECTRONIC SCANNING

A4 Plus Drawing Services Ltd, 11a Park Street, Chatteris, Cambridgeshire, PE16 6AB Tel: (01354) 691820 Fax: (01354) 691821 E-mail: enquiries@a4plus.co.uk

Asm Data Ltd, Unit 9-12, Faraday Park, Andover, Hampshire, SP10 3SA Tel: (01264) 336007 Fax: (01264) 336100 E-mail: admin@asmdata.co.uk

Claygate Digital Services Ltd, Airport House, Purley Way, Croydon, CR0 0XZ Tel: (020) 8288 3588 Fax: (020) 8288 3599 E-mail: sales@claygate.com

▶ Compact Data Management Ltd, 6 Leons Way, Tollgate Drive, Tollgate Industrial Estate, Stafford, ST16 3HS Tel: (01785) 220846 Fax: (01785) 220876 E-mail: sales@compact.uk.com

D X Imaging, Units 19 & 20, Watford Enterprise Centre, Watford, WD18 8EA Tel: (01923) 227644 Fax: (01923) 816896 E-mail: dximaging@dximaging.co.uk

Datascan Solutions Group Ltd, 424 Kingtson Road, Raynes Pk, London, SW20 8LL Tel: (020) 8542 5151 Fax: (020) 8544 0108 E-mail: enqiures@imagingandarchiving.co.uk

The Digital Printed Word Ltd, 19 Briset Street, London, EC1M 5NR Tel: (020) 7250 1404 Fax: (020) 7253 4675 E-mail: printedword@btconnect.com

E D M Group Ltd, Woden Road, Wolverhampton, WV10 0AY Tel: (01902) 459907 Fax: (01902) 351243 E-mail: docman@edm.co.uk

Effective Case Management Ltd, The Depository, Lewes Road, Lindfield, Haywards Heath, West Sussex, RH16 2LE Tel: (01444) 483968 Fax: (01444) 484852 E-mail: sales@casedocs.co.uk

▶ Mcpherson Document Solutions, 102-112 Main Road, Elderslie, Johnstone, Renfrewshire, PA5 9AX Tel: (01505) 331534 Fax: (01505) 328266 E-mail: sales@trmcpherson.co.uk

Optical Record Systems, Eagle Close, Chandler's Ford, Eastleigh, Hampshire, SO53 4NF Tel: (023) 8026 7755 Fax: (023) 8061 8861 E-mail: info@orsgroup.com

Stortext FM, Hikenield House, Icknield Way, Andover, Hampshire, SP10 5AH Tel: (01264) 360900 Fax: (01264) 360901 E-mail: richard.butler@stortextfm.com

▶ Timezone Digital Storage Ltd, Rivacre Business Centre, Mill Lane, Ellesmere Port, CH66 3TH Tel: 0151-339 2070 E-mail: info@timezonedigital.com

ELECTRONIC SCOREBOARDS

Contarnex Europe Ltd, 252 Martin Way, Morden, Surrey, SM4 4AW Tel: (020) 8540 1034 Fax: (020) 8543 3058 E-mail: enquiries@contarnex.com

F S L Electronics Ltd, Sandholes Road, Cookstown, County Tyrone, BT80 9AR Tel: (028) 8676 6131 Fax: (028) 8676 2414 E-mail: info@fslelectronics.com

ELECTRONIC SECURITY SYSTEMS OR EQUIPMENT

A R P Electrical, 31 Edwards Road, Halifax, West Yorkshire, HX2 7DG Tel: (01422) 353778 Fax: (01422) 353778
C I A 2000 Ltd, 72 High Street, Lees, Oldham, OL4 5AA Tel: 0161-624 8500 Fax: 0161-633 0479 E-mail: info@cialtd.com
Design International Ltd, Unit 8, Clwydfro Business Centre, Lon Parcwr Industrial Estate, Ruthin, Clwyd, LL15 1NJ Tel: (01824) 704327 Fax: (0871) 2215698 E-mail: sales@designinternational.ltd.uk
Ovation Systems Ltd, Springfield Barn, Milton Common, Thame, Oxfordshire, OX9 2JY Tel: (01844) 279638 Fax: (01844) 279071 E-mail: sales@ovation.co.uk
Telguard, 2 Ockley Court Farm Cottages, Coles Lane, Ockley, Dorking, Surrey, RH5 5LS Tel: (01306) 710120 Fax: (01306) 713769 E-mail: sales@telguard.co.uk

ELECTRONIC SEQUENCER CONTROLLERS

▶ Inntact Electronic Systems Ltd, Inntact House, Rawson Green, Kilburn, Belper, Derbyshire, DE56 0LL Tel: (01332) 781199 Fax: (01332) 781188 E-mail: inntact@aol.com

ELECTRONIC SIGNAL GENERATORS

Aeroflex Co. Ltd, Long Acres House, 6 Hills Way, Stevenage, Hertfordshire, SG1 2AN Tel: (01438) 742200 Fax: (01438) 727601 E-mail: deb.stockman@ifrsys.com
Masterswitch (UK) Ltd, 184 Walpole Rd, Tottenham, London, N17 6BW Tel: (020) 8881 3918 Fax: (020) 8881 3918 E-mail: pells@masterswich.prestel.co.uk

ELECTRONIC SIMULATORS

A M S, John Sutcliffe Building, Donibristle Industrial Park, Hillend, Dunfermline, Fife, KY11 9JX Tel: (01383) 821921 Fax: (01383) 824227
Mentor Graphic UK Ltd, Rivergate Newbury Business Park, London Road, Newbury, Berkshire, RG14 2QB Tel: (01635) 811411 Fax: (01635) 810108
Simtech Simulation Techniques, Westcott Venture Park, Westcott, Aylesbury, Buckinghamshire, HP18 0XB Tel: (01296) 655787 Fax: (01296) 651729 E-mail: info@simtech-simulation.com

ELECTRONIC SOFT STARTER SYSTEMS

John Martin Ltd, PO Box 28, Havant, Hampshire, PO9 2UB Tel: (023) 9249 2969 Fax: (023) 9249 2968 E-mail: jmelectronics@havant366.freeserve.co.uk

ELECTRONIC SORTING EQUIPMENT

E S M (U K) Ltd, PO Box 47, Bredbury, Cheshire, SK6 2FN Tel: 0161-406 3888 Fax: 0161-406 3889 E-mail: bshaw@satake-esm.co.uk
▶ Radix Systems Ltd, Unit D3-D4 The Premier Centre, Premier Way, Romsey, Hampshire, SO51 9DG Tel: (01794) 830240 Fax: (01794) 830143 E-mail: info@radixsystems.co.uk
Sortex Ltd, Pudding Mill Lane, London, E15 2PJ Tel: (020) 8519 0525 Fax: (020) 8519 5614 E-mail: sales@sortex.com

ELECTRONIC STARTER SYSTEMS

John Martin Ltd, PO Box 28, Havant, Hampshire, PO9 2UB Tel: (023) 9249 2969 Fax: (023) 9249 2968 E-mail: jmelectronics@havant366.freeserve.co.uk

ELECTRONIC SYSTEM DESIGN

▶ Trimerix Ltd, Unit 31 Lincoln Road, Cressex Business Park, High Wycombe, Buckinghamshire, HP12 3RL Tel: (01494) 447712 E-mail: info@trimerix.co.uk

ELECTRONIC SYSTEMS DESIGN

▶ Trimerix Ltd, Unit 31 Lincoln Road, Cressex Business Park, High Wycombe, Buckinghamshire, HP12 3RL Tel: (01494) 447712 E-mail: info@trimerix.co.uk

ELECTRONIC SYSTEMS TO SPECIFICATION

A1 Results Ltd, Jervaulx House, Station Road, Newton le Willows, Bedale, North Yorkshire, DL8 1TB Tel: (01677) 450665 Fax: (01677) 450665
Application Solutions Ltd, The Riverside Centre, Railway Lane, Lewes, East Sussex, BN7 2AQ Tel: (01273) 476608 Fax: (01273) 478888 E-mail: sales@aslnet.co.uk
Berwickshire Electronic Manufacturing Ltd, G Industrial Estate, Station Road, Duns, Berwickshire, TD11 3EJ Tel: (01361) 883888 Fax: (01361) 883888
Bonus Plug In Systems, Citadel Trading Park, Citadel Way, Hull, HU9 1TQ Tel: (01482) 313700 Fax: (01482) 588753
C-Matic Systems Ltd, Warren Court, Park Road, Crowborough, East Sussex, TN6 2QX Tel: (01892) 665688 Fax: (01892) 667515 E-mail: info@cmatic.co.uk
▶ Concise Electronic Engineering Ltd, Rhydybont Mill, Llanybydder, Dyfed, SA40 9QS Tel: (01570) 481344 Fax: (01570) 481495 E-mail: enquiries@concise-electronics.co.uk
D M G Control Systems Ltd, Unit 9, Bridgewater Road, Hertburn Industrial Estate, Washington, Tyne & Wear, NE37 2SG Tel: 0191-417 9888 Fax: 0191-415 1965 E-mail: sales@dmgcsl.co.uk
Rust Industries, Unit 6 Lyon Road, Broadheath, Altrincham, Cheshire, WA14 5DG Tel: 0161-929 7550 Fax: 0161-929 7551 E-mail: sales@rustelectronics.co.uk
Tri-State Electronics, Unit 4, Bumpers Enterprise Centre, Bumpers Farm Industrial Estate, Chippenham, Wiltshire, SN14 6QA Tel: (01249) 464650 Fax: (01249) 445414 E-mail: mikenickless@msn.com

ELECTRONIC TECHNICAL AUTHORING

▶ Continental Data Graphics Ltd, Gate House, Fretherne Road, Welwyn Garden City, Hertfordshire, AL8 6RD Tel: (01707) 392520 Fax: (01707) 371813 E-mail: sales@cdgl.com

ELECTRONIC TEMPERATURE CONTROLLERS

Eclipse Energy Controls Ltd, Unit 4, Wombourne Enterprise Park, Bridgnorth Road, Wombourne, Wolverhampton, WV5 0AL Tel: (01902) 897760 Fax: (01902) 897613 E-mail: sales@eclipse-energy.co.uk
F G H Instrument Services, 29 Oldmill Street, Stoke-on-Trent, ST4 2RP Tel: (01782) 414445 Fax: (01782) 414486 E-mail: sales@fghinst.fsbusiness.co.uk
Marlow Industries Europe, Aberdeen House, South Road, Haywards Heath, West Sussex, RH16 4NG Tel: (01444) 443404 Fax: (01444) 443334E-mail: support@marlow-europe.co.uk
Robydome Ltd, Woodhall Business Park, Sudbury, Suffolk, CO10 1WH Tel: (01787) 310163 Fax: (01787) 880631 E-mail: peter@robydome.co.uk

ELECTRONIC TEST EQUIPMENT

Abitec Products, Oak House, 50 Barton Drive, New Milton, Hampshire, BH25 7JJ Tel: (01425) 617852 Fax: (01425) 617852 E-mail: sales@abitec.co.uk
Caltest Instruments Ltd, PO Box 7717, Lockerbie, Dumfriesshire, DG11 1YF Tel: (01387) 811910 Fax: (01387) 810195 E-mail: sales@caltest.co.uk
▶ Isis Electronics Cheltentham Ltd, Building 66, Aston Down, Frampton Mansell, Stroud, Gloucestershire, GL6 8GA Tel: (01285) 760777 Fax: (01285) 760163 E-mail: sales@astondown.co.uk

ELECTRONIC THERMOMETERS

Edale Instruments (Cambridge) Ltd, Gresley House, Station Road, Longstanton, Cambridge, CB4 5DS Tel: (01954) 260853 Fax: (01954) 260894
James Hugh Group Ltd, 5 Hampstead West, 224 Iverson Road, London, NW6 2HL Tel: (020) 7328 3121 Fax: (020) 7328 5888
Quantum Production, Unit 25 Wornal Park, Menmarsh Road, Worminghall, Aylesbury, Buckinghamshire, HP18 9PH Tel: (01844) 339993 Fax: (01844) 339996 E-mail: info@quantumproduction.co.uk

ELECTRONIC TIMERS

Argus Electronics, Frenches, Chew Valley Road, Greenfield, Oldham, OL3 7AE Tel: (01457) 876951 Fax: (01457) 876951
Brodersen Control Systems, Unit 11 Canbury Business Park, Elm Cresent, Kingston upon Thames, Surrey, KT2 6HJ Tel: (020) 8546 4283 Fax: (020) 8547 3628 E-mail: bcs@brodersen.co.uk
Broyce Control Ltd, Pool St, Wolverhampton, WV2 4HN Tel: (01902) 773746 Fax: (01902) 420639 E-mail: sales@broycecontrol.com
Eagle Controls International Ltd, PO Box 42, Letchworth Garden City, Hertfordshire, SG6 1HQ Tel: (01462) 670566 Fax: (01462) 673992 E-mail: info@eaglecontrols.co.uk
Nortonics Ltd, Watts Street, Chadderton, Oldham, OL9 9LQ Tel: 0161-626 5316 Fax: 0161-627 0929
Oval Automation Ltd, Lake Lane, Barnham, Bognor Regis, West Sussex, PO22 0AD Tel: (01243) 555885 Fax: (01243) 554846 E-mail: paul@oval.org.uk
Westwood Meters & Timers Ltd, Torre Station Yard, Newton Road, Torquay, TQ2 5DD Tel: (01803) 297179 Fax: (01803) 299080 E-mail: sales@electricmeters.co.uk

ELECTRONIC TIMING RELAYS

Tele Control Ltd, Unit 21 Three Point Business Park, Charles Lane, Haslingden, Rossendale, Lancashire, BB4 5EH Tel: (01706) 226333 Fax: (01706) 226444 E-mail: sales@tele-control.co.uk

ELECTRONIC TRANSDUCERS

Components & Products, P O Box 2053, Hockley, Essex, SS5 4WA Tel: (01702) 207247 Fax: (01702) 207224
Kistler Instruments Ltd, Murrell Green Business Park, London Road, Hook, Hampshire, RG27 9GR Tel: (01256) 741550 Fax: (01256) 741551 E-mail: sales.uk@kistler.com
Kulite Sensors Ltd, Kulite House, Stroudley Road, Basingstoke, Hampshire, RG24 8UG Tel: (01256) 461646 Fax: (01256) 479510 E-mail: sales@kulite.co.uk
Multitek Ltd, Lancaster Way, Earls Colne, Colchester, CO6 2NS Tel: (01787) 223228 Fax: (01787) 223607 E-mail: chris@multitek-ltd.com
Pentagon Instruments Ltd, Unit 4 Wayside, Commerce Way, Lancing, West Sussex, BN15 8SW Tel: (01903) 765225 Fax: (01903) 765547 E-mail: sales@pentagoninstruments.com
Sailes Marketing Ltd, 15 Aintree Road, Keytec 7 Business Park, Pershore, Worcestershire, WR10 2JN Tel: (01386) 554210 Fax: (01386) 552461 E-mail: sales@sailesmarketing.com

ELECTRONIC TUBE MANUFRS

Acord Electronics Ltd, Madeira Road, West Byfleet, Surrey, KT14 6DN Tel: (01932) 354565 Fax: (01932) 350140 E-mail: sales@acord.co.uk
Billington Export Ltd, Units 1e-2e, Gilmans Industrial Estate, Billingshurst, West Sussex, RH14 9EZ Tel: (01403) 784961 Fax: (01403) 783519 E-mail: sales@bel-tubes.co.uk
Brimar Ltd, Greenside Way, Middleton, Manchester, M24 1SN Tel: 0161-681 7072 Fax: 0161-683 5978 E-mail: dave.eldridge@brimar.ltd.uk
Raedek Electronics, Unit 12 Avenue Fields Industrial Estate, Avenue Farm, Stratford-upon-Avon, Warwickshire, CV37 0HT Tel: (01789) 209294 Fax: (01789) 295757 E-mail: sales@raedek.com
TMD Technologies Ltd, Intercraft House, Swallowfield Way, Hayes, Middlesex, UB3 1AW Tel: (020) 8573 5555 Fax: (020) 8569 1839 E-mail: wecare@tmd.co.uk

ELECTRONIC VALVES

Aeroflex International, Ramsey Building Donibristle Industrial Estate, Muirton Way, Hillend, Dunfermline, Fife, KY11 9FZ Tel: (01383) 646464 Fax: (01383) 646468
▶ Arcadia (Engineering) Ltd, 22 & 23 Arcadia Avenue, London, N3 2JU Tel: (020) 8349 4816
▶ Astute Electronics, 2 Canyon Road, Netherton Industrial Estate, Wishaw, Lanarkshire, ML2 0EG Tel: (01698) 377450 Fax: (01698) 375860
Cookson Electronics, 3 Langlands Place, Kelvin South Business Park, East Kilbride, Glasgow, G75 0YF Tel: (01355) 276500 Fax: (01355) 264770
European Circuit Solutions Ltd, Impress House, Mansell Road, London, W3 7QH Tel: (020) 8743 8880 Fax: (020) 8740 4200 E-mail: sales@ecsamplifiers.co.uk
▶ F C I Ltd, Unit 1, Burnhead Road, Port Glasgow Industrial Estate, Port Glasgow, Port Of Glasgow, Renfrewshire, PA14 5XQ Tel: (01475) 742621
Force Components 89 Ltd, Suit 8 Grove Park Industrial Estate, Waltham Road, White Waltham, Maidenhead, Berkshire, SL6 3LW Tel: (01628) 820066 Fax: (01628) 825530 E-mail: sales@force89ltd.co.uk
▶ General Dynamics, Unit 3 Bryn Brithdir, Oakdale Business Park, Blackwood, Gwent, NP12 4AA Tel: (01495) 236300 Fax: (01495) 236400 E-mail: sales@generaldynamics.uk.com
▶ I M S Inovation Ltd, Fairykirk Road, Rosyth, Dunfermline, Fife, KY11 2QQ Tel: (01383) 410121
Langrex, Unit 4, Daux Road, Billingshurst, West Sussex, RH14 9SJ Tel: (01403) 785600 Fax: (01403) 785656E-mail: langrex@aol.com
▶ Mechshop Ltd, 9 Arden Business Centre, Arden Road, Alcester, Warwickshire, B49 6HW Tel: (01789) 763963 Fax: (01789) 400882
P M Components Ltd, Unit 17D, Eurolink Industrial Centre, Upper Field Road, Sittingbourne, Kent, ME10 3UP Tel: (01795) 419450 Fax: (01795) 430835 E-mail: sales@pmcomponents.co.uk
Raedek Electronics, Unit 12 Avenue Fields Industrial Estate, Avenue Farm, Stratford-upon-Avon, Warwickshire, CV37 0HT Tel: (01789) 209294 Fax: (01789) 295757 E-mail: sales@raedek.com
Renishaw plc, Heriot-Watt Research Park, Riccarton, Currie, Midlothian, EH14 4AP Tel: 0131-451 1616 Fax: 0131-451 1717
▶ S P Switchgear Ltd, The Courts, Western Access, Off Kestrel Road, Trafford Park, Manchester, M17 1SF Tel: 0161-872 4398 Fax: 0161-872 4550

ELECTRONIC VARIABLE SPEED POWER TRANSMISSION EQUIPMENT

Transdrive Engineering Services Ltd, Units 18-20, Moss Lane Indust Estate, Royton, Oldham, OL2 6HR Tel: (01706) 881940 Fax: (01706) 882436 E-mail: sales@transdrive.co.uk

ELECTRONIC VOTING SYSTEMS

▶ Answerback Ltd, 56a Hatton Garden, London, EC1N 8HP Tel: (020) 7251 9313 E-mail: paul.krisman@answerbackinteractive.com

ELECTRONIC WARFARE SIMULATORS

Stirling Solent Communications, 33 Portsmouth Enterprise Centre, Quartremaine Road, Portsmouth, PO3 5QT Tel: (0870) 7701702 Fax: (023) 9267 3518E-mail: csil@csil-uk.com

ELECTRONIC WATCHES

Casio Electronics Co. Ltd, 6 1000 North Circular Road, London, NW2 7JD Tel: (020) 8450 9131 Fax: (020) 8452 6323
L C Designs Co. Ltd, Sheldon Way, Larkfield, Aylesford, Kent, ME20 6SE Tel: (01622) 716000 Fax: (01622) 791119 E-mail: enquiries@londonclock.co.uk
Rotary Watches, Adia House 84-86 Regent Street, London, W1B 5RR Tel: (020) 7434 5500 Fax: (020) 7434 5548 E-mail: time@rotarywatches.com

ELECTRONICS INDUSTRY CERAMIC PRODUCTS

Advanced Ceramics Ltd, Castle Works, Stafford, ST16 2ET Tel: (01785) 241000 Fax: (01785) 214073 E-mail: mail@aclstafford.co.uk
C & T Fire, Stammerham Business Centre, Capel Road, Rusper, Horsham, West Sussex, RH12 4PZ Tel: (01306) 712421 Fax: (01306) 713225 E-mail: info@ctfire.co.uk
CBL Ceramics, Marble Hall Road, Milford Haven, Dyfed, SA73 2PP Tel: (01646) 697681 Fax: (01646) 690053
Coorstek, 64-66 Cavendish Way, Glenrothes, Fife, KY6 2SB Tel: (01592) 773743 Fax: (01592) 774925 E-mail: sales@coorstek.co.uk

ELECTRONICS INDUSTRY PERSONNEL RECRUITMENT AGENCIES OR CONSULTANTS

▶ Format Recruitment, 44 Rutland Road, Hove, East Sussex, BN3 5FF Tel: (01273) 772200 Fax: (01273) 748735 E-mail: nadina@formatrecruitment.com
Kinetic plc, Duckworth House, Talbot Road, Stretford, Manchester, M32 0FP Tel: 0161-872 2333 Fax: 0161-872 2444 E-mail: info@kinetic-plc.co.uk
Prime Recruitment Ltd, 37 Locks Heath Centre, Centre Way, Locks Heath, Southampton, SO31 6DX Tel: (01489) 559090 Fax: (01489) 559995 E-mail: enquiries@prime-recruitment.co.uk
Strongfield Technologies Ltd, Strongfield House, Unit 2 Inovation Park, 89 Manor Farm Road, Wembley, Middlesex, HA0 1BA Tel: (020) 8813 2684 Fax: (020) 8799 8901 E-mail: anu@strongfield.com

ELECTRONICS INDUSTRY SOFTWARE

Persys Consulting Ltd, 77 Bradvue Crescent, Bradville, Milton Keynes, MK13 7AH Tel: (01908) 319555 Fax: (07092) 104535

ELECTRONICS INDUSTRY SOFTWARE – *continued*

▶ Quantum Eds, Cefn Gwrgan Road, Margam, Port Talbot, West Glamorgan, SA13 2EZ Tel: (01639) 864646 Fax: (01639) 864676 E-mail: info@quantumeds.co.uk

Soft Sell Computers, 74 Darwen St, Blackburn, BB2 2BL Tel: (01254) 693593 Fax: (01254) 668975 E-mail: info@soft-sell.co.uk

Teleki, 20 Oxhay Court, Oxhay View, Newcastle, Staffordshire, ST5 0SA Tel: (01782) 662099 E-mail: info@teleki-electronics.co.uk

▶ Valutech Ltd, 79-80 Shrivenham Hundred Bus, Park, Watchfield, Swindon, SN6 8TZ Tel: (01793) 787080 Fax: (01793) 786683 E-mail: terry.pudwell@mikrolive.co.uk

ELECTRONICS INDUSTRY TEST EQUIPMENT, *See also headings for particular application*

A B I Electronics Ltd, Dodworth Business Park, Dodworth, Barnsley, South Yorkshire, S75 3SP Tel: (01226) 207420 Fax: (01226) 207620 E-mail: post@abielectronics.co.uk

Aeroflex, Burnham, 1 Progress House, Progress Business Centre, Whittle Parkway, Slough, SL1 6DQ Tel: (01628) 604455 Fax: (01628) 662017

ATE Ltd, Design Office, 56 Nodes Road, Northwood, Cowes, Isle of Wight, PO31 8AD Tel: (01983) 292052

▶ Cirris Solutions Ltd, 4 Commerce Way, Stanbridge Road, Leighton Buzzard, Bedfordshire, LU7 4RW Tel: (01525) 374466 Fax: (01525) 374468 E-mail: sales@cirris.co.uk

Cropico Ltd, 15-18 Bracken Hill, South West Industrial Estate, Peterlee, County Durham, SR8 2SW Tel: 0191-586 3511 Fax: 0191-586 0227 E-mail: sales@seaward.co.uk

Feedback Instruments Ltd, Park Road, Crowborough, East Sussex, TN6 2QR Tel: (01892) 653322 Fax: (01892) 663719 E-mail: feedback@fdbk.co.uk

Flite Electronics Ltd, Church House Farm, Clewer Hill, Waltham Chase, Southampton, SO32 2LN Tel: (01489) 892422 Fax: (01489) 897929 E-mail: sales@flite.co.uk

Genrad Holdings Ltd, Orion Business Park, Bird Hall Lane, Stockport, Cheshire, SK3 0XG Tel: (01483) 569933 Fax: 0161-491 9501

Hitachi Denshi UK, Windsor House, Britannia Road, Waltham Cross, Hertfordshire, EN8 7NX Tel: (01992) 704595 Fax: (0845) 1212180 E-mail: sales@hitachi-ke-eu.com

Integrex Ltd, Portwood Industrial Estate, Church Gresley, Swadlincote, Derbyshire, DE11 9PT Tel: (01283) 550880 Fax: (01283) 552028 E-mail: sales@integrex.co.uk

Ip Test Ltd, 15 The Pines Trading Estate, Broad Street, Guildford, Surrey, GU3 3BH Tel: (01483) 567218 Fax: (01483) 506054 E-mail: sales@iptest.com

Jdsu, Spinnaker House, Lime Tree Way, Chineham, Basingstoke, Hampshire, RG24 8GG Tel: (01256) 891400 Fax: (01256) 891439 E-mail: sales.uk@jdsu.com

▶ Lewis & Clark Ltd, 33 Coldstream Street, Blantyre, G72 0SR Tel: (0792) 1818223 Fax: (01698) 305302 E-mail: pmccreadie@lewis-clark.com

Nortech Management Ltd, Tadcaster House, Kempton Road, Pershore, Worcestershire, WR10 2TA Tel: (0870) 0111992 Fax: (0870) 0111993 E-mail: info@nortechonline.co.uk

Omiran Ltd, Units 1-2, James Carter Road, Mildenhall, Bury St. Edmunds, Suffolk, IP28 7DE Tel: (01638) 716748 Fax: (01638) 716779 E-mail: sales@omiran.co.uk

Pathdale Systems Ltd, Unit L, Ringstones Indust Estate, Whaley Bridge, High Peak, Derbyshire, SK23 7RX Tel: (01663) 734462 Fax: (01663) 734462 E-mail: sales@pathdale.co.uk

Peak Production Equipment Ltd, Peak House, Works Road, Letchworth Garden City, Hertfordshire, SG6 1GB Tel: (01462) 475605 Fax: (01462) 480294 E-mail: sales@thepeakgroup.com

Peak Test Services, 152a Front Street, Chester le Street, County Durham, DH3 3AY Tel: 0191-387 1923 Fax: 0191-387 1994 E-mail: peak.test@thepeakgroup.com

Satel Electronics, North East Suffolk Business Centre, Pinbush Road, Kessingland, Lowestoft, Suffolk, NR33 7NQ Tel: (01502) 513216 Fax: (01502) 513216 E-mail: satelelectronics@btclick.com

Sykes Pickervant Ltd, Lancaster House, Bowerhill Industrial Estate, Bowerhill, Melksham, Wiltshire, SN12 6TT Tel: (01225) 700750 Fax: (01225) 791845

Telford Electronics, Hoo Farm, Hoo, Telford, Shropshire, TF6 6DJ Tel: (01952) 605451 Fax: (01952) 677978 E-mail: telfordelectronics@btinternet.com

Telonic Instruments Ltd, Toutley Industrial Estate, Toutley Road, Wokingham, Berkshire, RG41 1QN Tel: 0118-978 6911 Fax: 0118-979 2338 E-mail: info@telonic.co.uk

Time Electronics Ltd, Unit 11, Sovereign Way, Tonbridge, Kent, TN9 1RH Tel: (01732) 355993 Fax: (01732) 770312 E-mail: mail@timeelectronics.co.uk

Wentworth Laboratories Ltd, 1 Gosforth Close, Sandy, Bedfordshire, SG19 1RB Tel: (01767) 681221 Fax: (01767) 691951

ELECTRONICS INDUSTRY TOOLS

Dyglen Engineering Ltd, 68 Cavendish Way, Glenrothes, Fife, KY6 2SB Tel: (01592) 774881 Fax: (01592) 774871 E-mail: admin@dyglen.co.uk

Electrocomponents U K Ltd, 5000 John Smith Drive, Oxford Business Park South, Oxford, OX4 2BH Tel: (01865) 204000 Fax: (01865) 207400E-mail: sales@electrocomponents.com

Q-Max (Electronics) Ltd, Bilton Road, Bletchley, Milton Keynes, MK1 1HW Tel: (01908) 368006 Fax: (01908) 270483

T W International Ltd, T W House, Oxford Road, Calne, Wiltshire, SN11 8RS Tel: (01249) 822100 Fax: (01249) 821919 E-mail: sales@twinternational.com

ELECTRONICS LACQUERS

Ici Paints plc T/As Dulux, Wexham Road, Slough, SL2 5DS Tel: (01753) 550000 Fax: (01753) 578218 E-mail: sales@dulux.com

ELECTRONICS MAGAZINES

Electronics Weekly, Quadrant House, The Quadrant, Sutton, Surrey, SM2 5AS Tel: (020) 8652 3500 Fax: (020) 8652 8938

ELECTRONICS SOLDERS

Henkel, Technologies House, Wood La End, Hemel Hempstead, Hertfordshire, HP2 4RQ Tel: (01442) 278000 Fax: (01442) 278071 E-mail: customer.enquiry@henkel.com

M B O (U K) Ltd, Mill End, Standon, Ware, Hertfordshire, SG11 1LR Tel: (01920) 823999 Fax: (01920) 823631 E-mail: sales@mbouk.co.uk

ELECTRONICS SPECIALIST ELECTROSTATIC DISCHARGE CONTROL SERVICES

Charleswater Ltd, Unit C, 4th Dimension, Fourth Avenue, Letchworth Garden City, Hertfordshire, SG6 2TD Tel: (01462) 672005 Fax: (01462) 670440 E-mail: sales@vermason.co.uk

S.J.M. Eurostat (U.K.) Ltd, Unit 4b, Bramhall Moor Industrial Park, Hazel Grove, Stockport, Cheshire, SK7 5BW Tel: 0161-456 6088 Fax: 0161-456 6089 E-mail: sjm@sjmeurostat.co.uk

ELECTRONICS SPUTTERING EQUIPMENT

Gencoa Ltd, Physics Road, Liverpool, L24 9HP Tel: 0151-486 4466 Fax: 0151-486 4488 E-mail: sales@gencoa.com

Oxford Instruments Plasma Technology Ltd, North End Road, Yatton, Bristol, BS49 4AP Tel: (01934) 837000 Fax: (01934) 837001 E-mail: plasma.technology@oxinst.co.uk

ELECTRONICS STAMPINGS

Batten & Allen Ltd, Bridge End, Cirencester, Gloucestershire, GL7 1NQ Tel: (01285) 655220 Fax: (01285) 652650 E-mail: admin@batten-allen.co.uk

Interplex PMP Ltd, Elliot Industrial Estate, Arbroath, Angus, DD11 2NN Tel: (01241) 873867 Fax: (01241) 879597 E-mail: pmp@pmp-interplex.co.uk

ELECTRONICS SWAB STICKS

Edson Electronics Ltd, Unit 2, Coquet Enterprise Park, Amble, Morpeth, Northumberland, NE65 0RB Tel: (01665) 710393 Fax: (01665) 711021 E-mail: sales@edsonelectronics.co.uk

ELECTROPAINTING SERVICES

▶ Matts & Jenkins Ltd, Garland Street, Birmingham, B9 4DE Tel: 0121-772 4718 Fax: 0121-773 0023 E-mail: sales@mattsandjenkins.co.uk

ELECTROPHORETIC PAINTING OR LACQUERING

Ecoat (Ireland) Ltd, Unit 13, Blaris Industrial Estate, Altona Road, Lisburn, County Antrim, BT27 5QB Tel: (028) 9260 4798 Fax: (028) 9260 4798 E-mail: info@ecoat.co.uk

Malcolm Enamellers Midlands Ltd, Lawley Middleway, Birmingham, B4 7XT Tel: 0121-359 7553 Fax: 0121-359 8309 E-mail: sales@malcolms.co.uk

Metokote U K Ltd, Hackwood Road, High March Industrial Estate, Daventry, Northamptonshire, NN11 4ES Tel: (01327) 703745 Fax: (01327) 300141

Webasto Roof Systems Ltd, Unit 7 Kingsbury Business Park, Kingsbury Road, Sutton Coldfield, West Midlands, B76 9DL Tel: 0121-313 5600 Fax: 0121-351 4905 E-mail: customer.service@webasto.co.uk

ELECTROPHORETIC PAINTING/ LACQUERING PLANT

Trulaw Fabs Ltd, 338 Summer Lane, Birmingham, B19 3QL Tel: 0121-359 1191 Fax: 0121-359 4855

ELECTROPHORETIC RESINS

▶ Molecular Technologies, 2 Modular Court, Enterprise Drive, Four Ashes, Wolverhampton, WV10 7DF Tel: (01902) 797990 Fax: (01902) 798295

ELECTROPHYSIOLOGICAL EQUIPMENT

S L E Ltd, Twin Bridges Business Park, 232 Selsdon Road, South Croydon, Surrey, CR2 6PL Tel: (020) 8681 1414 Fax: (020) 8649 8570 E-mail: admin@sle.co.uk

ELECTROPLATED DIAMOND TIPPED TOOLS

Astley Diamond Tools, Unit 10, Chancel Way, Witton Moor Lane Industrial Estate, Witton, Birmingham, B6 7AU Tel: 0121-356 8035 Fax: 0121-356 8035 E-mail: benorpeter@astley-diamontools.co.uk

ELECTROPLATING, *See also headings for particular types*

A & R Metal Finishers, Streetbridge Works, Royton, Oldham, OL2 5ZY Tel: 0161-627 0177 Fax: 0161-627 0177

A1 Plating, 36 Padgets Lane, Redditch, Worcestershire, B98 0RB Tel: (01527) 528852 Fax: (01527) 528852 E-mail: office@a1-plating.co.uk

Ace Electroplating Ltd, Wordsworth Road, Leicester, LE2 6EE Tel: 0116-270 8651 Fax: 0116-270 2593

Action EPC Ltd, Unit 14 Adam Business Centre, Cranes Farm Road, Basildon, Essex, SS14 3JF Tel: (01268) 288387 Fax: (01268) 288956 E-mail: actionplating@fsmail.net

Advanced Surface Treatments Ltd, Unit 11, Alpha Business Park, Deedmore Road, Coventry, CV2 1EQ Tel: (024) 7660 3232 Fax: (024) 7661 1776 E-mail: sales@astec-uk.com

Alderney Plating Ltd, Thrush Road, Poole, Dorset, BH12 4NP Tel: (01202) 744664 Fax: (01202) 733577

Alkemi M F Technologies, Clwyd Close, Manor Lane, Hawarden, Deeside, Clwyd, CH5 3PZ Tel: (01244) 536299 Fax: (01244) 520363 E-mail: simonn@alkemimetalfinishing.co.uk

Alkemi M F Technology, 15 Central Trade Park, Marley Way, Saltney, Chester, CH4 8SX Tel: (01244) 674800 Fax: (01244) 681063

Allenchrome Electroplating Ltd, Pocklington Industrial Estate, Pocklington, York, YO42 1NP Tel: (01759) 303788 Fax: (01759) 305776 E-mail: sales@allenchrome.co.uk

Almit Metal Finishing, Whinfield Drive, Aycliffe Industrial Estate, Aycliffe Industrial Park, Newton Aycliffe, County Durham, DL5 6AU Tel: (01325) 311777 Fax: (01325) 316472

Anochrome Technologies Ltd, Wood Lane, Wolverhampton, WV10 8HN Tel: (01902) 567567 Fax: (01902) 567777 E-mail: enquiries@anochrome-group.co.uk

Antique Renovating Co., 43 Bent Street, Manchester, M8 8NW Tel: 0161-834 8000

Ashton & Moore Ltd, 12 Smith Street, Hockley, Birmingham, B19 3EX Tel: 0845 618 8196 Fax: 0845 618 8197 E-mail: sales@ashton-moore.co.uk

Auric Metal Finishers Ltd, Herald Way, Binley Industrial Estate, Coventry, CV3 2RP Tel: (024) 7644 7431 Fax: (024) 7663 5719 E-mail: info@auric.co.uk

B J S Co. Ltd, 65 Bideford Avenue, Greenford, Middlesex, UB6 7PP Tel: (020) 8810 5779 Fax: (020) 8810 5883 E-mail: enquiries@bjsco.com

Baker Engineering Co., Unit 11 Paramount Industrial Estate, Sandown Road, Watford, WD24 7XA Tel: (01923) 229309 Fax: (01923) 801182 E-mail: sales@bakereng.co.uk

Beacon Metal Finishers Ltd, Unit 10 Sirhowy Industrial Estate, Thomas Ellis Way, Sirhowy, Tredegar, Gwent, NP22 4QZ Tel: (01495) 711383 Fax: (01495) 711383

Beckworth Technical Plating Ltd, 16 Caker Stream Road, Alton, Hampshire, GU34 2QF Tel: (01420) 80880 Fax: (01420) 80881 E-mail: admin@beckworth.net

BEP Surface Tecnologies, Eton Hill Road, Radcliffe, Manchester, M26 2XT Tel: 0161-724 9090 Fax: 0161-725 9539 E-mail: info@bepsurfacetecnologies.co.uk

Best Electroplating, 1 Columbia Works, Fleming Way, Crawley, West Sussex, RH10 9JU Tel: (01293) 532843 Fax: (01293) 523688 E-mail: mark@bestelectroplating.co.uk

Biggins Bros Ltd, 154 Arundel St, Sheffield, S1 4RE Tel: 0114-272 2612 Fax: 0114-275 6296

Bodycote Metallurgical Coatings Uxbridge Ltd, 5 Carleton House, 549 Eskdale Road, Uxbridge, Middlesex, UB8 2RT Tel: (01895) 252185 Fax: (01895) 810755

Braintree Electro Platers Ltd, 12-13 Springwood Drive, Braintree, Essex, CM7 2YN Tel: (01376) 344265 Fax: (01376) 328927

Brinksway Electro Plating Ltd, Unit 17 Latham Close, Bredbury Park Industrial Estate, Bredbury, Stockport, Cheshire, SK6 2SD Tel: 0161-494 6161 Fax: 0161-406 6447

British Electrometals Co, Netherward Works, Dens Road, Arbroath, Angus, DD11 1RU Tel: (01241) 875757 Fax: (01241) 874599 E-mail: bem@btconnect.com

C M L Group Ltd, Unit 5 Wheatland Business Park, Wheatland Lane, Wallasey, Merseyside, CH44 7ER Tel: 0151-631 5600 Fax: 0151-631 5601 E-mail: enquiries@cml-group.com

C S M Plating Ltd, Progress Works, Heath Mill La, Birmingham, B9 4AP Tel: 0121-772 2084 Fax: 0121-772 5190

Cambridge Electro Plating Ltd, 21 25 Union Lane, Cambridge, CB4 1PR Tel: (01223) 352464 Fax: (01223) 361085 E-mail: cep@btinternet.com

Clark Electro-Plating (Wrexham) Ltd, The Old Foundry, Hill Street, Rhostyllen, Wrexham, Clwyd, LL14 4AT Tel: (01978) 355803 Fax: (01978) 291321

Cresswell & Co Birmingham Ltd, 85 New Summer Street, Birmingham, B19 3TE Tel: 0121-359 6311 Fax: 0121-359 5736

Croydon Electroplaters Ltd, 2 Bridge Parade, Waddon Road, Croydon, CR0 4JH Tel: (020) 8688 4709

Davalow Metal Finishing Co. Ltd, Landport Road, Wolverhampton, WV2 2QJ Tel: (01902) 455562 Fax: (01902) 351268 E-mail: davalow@btopenworld.com

Davron Finishing Industries Ltd, 18 Tanners Drive, Blakelands, Milton Keynes, MK14 5BW Tel: (01908) 210799 Fax: (01908) 217211 E-mail: sales@davronfinsihing.co.uk

Deans Engineering Livingston Ltd, Royston Road, Deans Industrial Estate, Deans, Livingston, West Lothian, EH54 8AH Tel: (01506) 419797 Fax: (01506) 413849 E-mail: enquiries@deansengineering.com

Derby Plating Services Ltd, 148 Abbey Street, Derby, DE22 3SS Tel: (01332) 382408 Fax: (01332) 382408

The Diamond Metal Finishing Company Ltd, 6 Newfields Industrial Estate, High Street, Stoke-on-Trent, ST6 5PD Tel: (01782) 822442 Fax: (01782) 839125 E-mail: stevependo@aol.com

Diesel Marine International Ltd, Gloucester Road, North Shields, Tyne & Wear, NE29 8RQ Tel: 0191-257 5577 Fax: 0191-258 6398 E-mail: david.murray@dmiuk.co.uk

E C Williams Ltd, 17 Spencer Street, Birmingham, B18 6DN Tel: 0121-236 2524 Fax: 0121-233 4931 E-mail: plating@ecwilliams.co.uk

E Gilligan & Sons Ltd, 25 Allcock Street, Birmingham, B9 4DY Tel: 0121-766 7666 Fax: 0121-766 7601 E-mail: gilligan@btconnect.com

East Lancashire Platers Ltd, Oxford Mill, Oxford Road, Burnley, Lancashire, BB11 3BA Tel: (01282) 425621 Fax: (01282) 433618

Electro Plating Services Ltd, 22 Bates Road, Romford, RM3 0JH Tel: (01708) 342761 Fax: (01708) 381168 E-mail: epsessex@aol.com

Electrolytic Plating Co. Ltd, Crown Works, Wednesbury Road, Walsall, WS1 4JJ Tel: (01922) 627466 Fax: (01922) 723844 E-mail: sales@electrolytic.co.uk

Ellison Metal Finishing Ltd, 8 Acorn Business Park, Keighley Road, Skipton, North Yorkshire, BD23 2UE Tel: (01756) 796805 Fax: (01535) 630942 E-mail: sales@ellisonmf.co.uk

F H Lambert Ltd, Rembrandt House, King Georges Avenue, Watford, WD18 7PW Tel: (01923) 229444 Fax: (01923) 255717 E-mail: info@fhlambert.co.uk

Ferndown Finishing Ltd, 12 Cobham Road, Ferndown Industrial Estate, Wimborne, Dorset, BH21 7PS Tel: (01202) 877755 Fax: (01202) 877744

Flexiable Surface Tecnology Ltd, Nairn Road, Deans, Livingston, West Lothian, EH54 8AY Tel: (01506) 460515 Fax: (01506) 460510

Ford Electro Plating Ltd, Block B4 Ford Airfield Industrial Estate, Ford, Arundel, West Sussex, BN18 0HY Tel: (01903) 717424 Fax: (01903) 717424

G.B. Hard Chrome Ltd, 23-25 Nobel Square, Burnt Mills, Basildon, Essex, SS13 1LP Tel: 0845 8550608 Fax: (01268) 727524 E-mail: dan.griffiths@gbhard-chrome.co.uk

H D Simpson & Co Polishers Ltd, Downing Street Industrial Estate, Smethwick, West Midlands, B66 2JH Tel: 0121-558 3469 Fax: 0121-558 3469

H & M Plating Ltd, 37 Little Green Lane, Birmingham, B9 5AY Tel: 0121-773 6931 Fax: 0121-773 6931

H Reis Ltd, Powke Lane, Cradley Heath, West Midlands, B64 5QF Tel: (01384) 567727 Fax: (01384) 410317 E-mail: terry.reis@chromebar.co.uk

ELECTROPLATING - *continued*

Hampshire Electroplating Co Ltd, 69-75 Empress Road, Southampton, SO14 0JW Tel: (023) 8022 5639 Fax: (023) 8063 9874 E-mail: enquiries@hepcoltd.co.uk

Heer Platers Ltd, 9 Auster Industrial Estate, Silverdale Drive, Thurmaston, Leicester, LE4 8NG Tel: 0116-264 0931 Fax: 0116-264 0931

Hereford Metal Finishers, 10 Ramsden Road, Rotherwas Industrial Estate, Hereford, HR2 6LR Tel: (01432) 357630 Fax: (01432) 357630

▶ Hi Chrome (Europe) Ltd, Heathenford Industrial Estate, Widowhill Road, Burnley, Lancashire, BB10 2TT Tel: (01282) 418300 Fax: (01282) 418310 E-mail: sales@hycrome.com

Highland Electroplaters Ltd, Howemoss Drive, Kirkhill Industrial Estate, Aberdeen, AB21 0GL Tel: (01224) 725581 Fax: (01224) 725591 E-mail: enquires@hiplaters.co.uk

Hockley Enterprises Ltd, Grainger Road, Southend-on-Sea, SS2 5BZ Tel: (01702) 614067 Fax: (01702) 462163

Ingram & Glass Ltd, Catteshall Lane, Godalming, Surrey, GU7 1LB Tel: (01483) 415262 Fax: (01483) 426951 E-mail: patrick@ingram-glass.co.uk

Isleworth Polishing & Plating Ltd, 273 High Street, Brentford, Middlesex, TW8 0JL Tel: (020) 8560 7440 Fax: (020) 8560 7440

J.W.Rudge & Co.Limited, Anne Road, Smethwick, West Midlands, B66 2NZ Tel: 0121-558 5519 Fax: 0121-558 0053 E-mail: millssteve@btconnect.co.uk

John Stokes Ltd, 60 High Street, Princes End, Tipton, West Midlands, DY4 9HP Tel: 0121-520 6301 Fax: 0121-557 7191 E-mail: stokeschrome@hotmail.com

Kypol Ltd, Suven House, 55 Gosforth Close, Middlefield Industrial Estate, Sandy, Bedfordshire, SG19 1RB Tel: (01767) 682424 Fax: (01767) 681180 E-mail: info@kypol.co.uk

Lansdowne Cartmel Ltd, 3e West Way, Andover, Hampshire, SP10 5AS Tel: (01264) 353234 Fax: (01264) 359025 E-mail: lansdownecartmel@aol.com

Leicester Plating Co. Ltd, Wesley Street, Leicester, LE4 5QG Tel: 0116-266 1344 Fax: 0116-266 2716 E-mail: office@leicesterplating.co.uk

Levertech Metal Finishing Services, Green Lane, Eccles, Manchester, M30 8JJ Tel: 0161-787 7247 Fax: 0161-789 6411 E-mail: levertech@levertech.fsnet.co.uk

Lorlec Ltd, Horninglow Road North, Burton-on-Trent, Staffordshire, DE13 0SF Tel: (01283) 531191 Fax: (01283) 538113 E-mail: sales@lorlec.com

LWD Precision Engineering Co Ltd, 169 Elland Road, Leeds, LS11 8BY Tel: 0113-271 3097 Fax: 0113-271 8655 E-mail: sales@lwdeng.com

M A J Hi Spec Ltd, 1 Scott St, Keighley, West Yorkshire, BD21 2JJ Tel: (01535) 606524 Fax: (01535) 610255

M D Plating Ltd, 21 Wedgewood Gate Industrial Estate, Wedgewood Way, Stevenage, Hertfordshire, SG1 4SU Tel: (01438) 350527

M F S Electro Plating Co., Clifton Road, Huntingdon, Cambridgeshire, PE29 7EJ Tel: (01480) 459966

M S C Copperflow Ltd, 28 Hulme Street, Bolton, BL1 2SX Tel: (01204) 528206 Fax: (01204) 366877

Maidenhead Plating, 3 Martin Road, Maidenhead, Berkshire, SL6 7DE Tel: (01628) 783747 Fax: (01628) 778717

Merlin Electro-Plating Ltd, Newhouse Industrial Estate, Newhouse, Motherwell, Lanarkshire, ML1 5RX Tel: (01698) 734038 Fax: (01698) 834847 E-mail: info@merlinep.co.uk

Merthyr Electroplating Co. Ltd, Unit 23a Merthyr Tydfil Industrial Estate, Dowlais, Merthyr Tydfil, CF48 2SR Tel: (01685) 723677 Fax: (01685) 379343 E-mail: martin.sullivan@merthyrelectroplating.com

Metal Finishers Llandudno Ltd, Central Place, Llandudno, Gwynedd, LL30 2SZ Tel: (01492) 879183 Fax: (01492) 874695

Metal Finishing & Coatings Ltd, Sweet Street Foundry, Derwent View, Leeds, LS11 9TJ Tel: 0113-244 6686 Fax: 0113-234 0842 E-mail: coating@btconnect.com

Metex Engineering Ltd, 5 Holly Lane, Beeston, Nottingham, NG9 4AB Tel: 0115-943 0155 Fax: 0115-943 6365

Metreat Ltd t/a Applied Metal Finishers, Units 2-3, Prosper House, Padholme Road East, Peterborough, PE1 5XL Tel: (01733) 703030 Fax: (01733) 704040 E-mail: sales@appliedmetalfinishers.co.uk

Micrometics Ltd, 26 Hollands Rd, Haverhill, Suffolk, CB9 8PR Tel: (01440) 707010 Fax: (01440) 762116 E-mail: info@micrometics.co.uk

Midas Plating & Engineering Co. Ltd, Woodend Mills, Hartshead St, Oldham, OL4 5EE Tel: 0161-620 0939 Fax: 0161-678 8614

Midland Chromium Plating Co. Ltd, 116 Aldridge Road, Perry Barr, Birmingham, B42 2TP Tel: 0121-356 9431 Fax: 0121-356 5891 E-mail: info@midchrome.co.uk

Miller Plating Co., Unit 15 All Saints Industrial Estate, All Saints Street, Birmingham, B18 7RJ Tel: 0121-523 3348 Fax: 0121-515 3187

Modern Metal Finishes Ltd, Burstwick Industrial Estate, Ellifoot Lane, Burstwick, Hull, HU12 9EF Tel: (01964) 671040 Fax: (01964) 671040 E-mail: sales@mmfgold.co.uk

Newman Ltd, 219 Moseley Street, Birmingham, B5 6LE Tel: 0121-622 2884 Fax: 0121-622 1986 E-mail: singhsatnam@btconnect.com

Norcot Engineering Ltd, Richmond House, Hill Street, Ashton-under-Lyne, Lancashire, OL7 0PZ Tel: 0161-339 9361 Fax: 0161-343 3069

Northern Blacking Ltd, 47 Catley Road, Sheffield, S9 5JF Tel: 0114-244 5333 Fax: 0114-261 8891

Nottingham Platers Ltd, Southwark Street, Nottingham, NG6 0DB Tel: 0115-978 4637 Fax: 0115-978 9754 E-mail: martin@chrome-platers.com

Nottingham Zinc Group Ltd, Byron Avenue, Lowmoor Business Park, Kirkby-in-Ashfield, Nottingham, NG17 7LA Tel: (01623) 752107 Fax: (01623) 721453 E-mail: clive@nottinghamzinc.co.uk

P M D UK Ltd, Broad Lane, Coventry, CV5 7AY Tel: (024) 7646 6691 Fax: (024) 7647 3034 E-mail: sales@pmdgroup.co.uk

P Robinson, 10 London Road, Worcester, WR5 2DL Tel: (01905) 764077

Paramount Plating Ltd, South Stour Avenue, Ashford, Kent, TN23 7RS Tel: (01233) 626748 Fax: (01233) 641787 E-mail: home.supplies@virgin.net

Parker Finishing Ltd, The Basement, 31 Eyre St Hill, London, EC1R 5EW Tel: (020) 7713 5660 Fax: 0207 713 6366

Peacock & Trelfa Ltd, Barfillan Drive, Glasgow, G52 1BQ Tel: 0141-882 5424 Fax: 0141-882 5424 E-mail: john.peacock@btinternet.com

Perfection Electro Plating Ltd, Unit 2 Brunswick Industrial Centre, Hertford Street, Birmingham, B12 8NJ Tel: 0121-440 3173 Fax: 0121-440 2661

Peterborough Plating, 12 Maxwell Road, Peterborough, PE2 7HU Tel: (01733) 233250 Fax: (01733) 371411 E-mail: sales@peterboroughplating.co.uk

Pickersgill Electroplaters Ltd, Pepper Road, Leeds, LS10 2PP Tel: 0113-271 4909 Fax: 0113-276 0546E-mail: paul@pkaye.co.uk

Plating Company Ltd, The, Curriers Cl, Canley, Coventry, CV4 8AW Tel: (024) 7647 0545 Fax: (024) 7669 4120 E-mail: crplating@btconnect.com

Poli Chrome Engineers Moulds Ltd, Adswood Road, Stockport, Cheshire, SK3 8HR Tel: 0161-477 7370 Fax: 0161-477 1020 E-mail: ianlusby1@hotmail.com

Polish Inc, 4 Justin Business Park, Sandford Lane, Wareham, Dorset, BH20 4DY Tel: (01929) 554037 Fax: (01929) 555262

Poole Technical Plating Services Ltd, Unit 32-33 Dawkins Business Centre, Dawkins Road, Poole, Dorset, BH15 4JY Tel: (01202) 673640 Fax: (01202) 682414 E-mail: sales@ptpuk.com

Portsmouth Aviation Ltd, Airport Service Road, Portsmouth, PO3 5PF Tel: (023) 9266 2251 Fax: (023) 9267 3690 E-mail: info@portav.co.uk

Premier Plating Ltd, Lancaster Road, Cressex Business Park, High Wycombe, Buckinghamshire, HP12 3PY Tel: (01494) 533650 Fax: (01494) 473726 E-mail: gregmurray@premier-plating.co.uk

Premier Plating Works Walthamstow Ltd, 90 Shernhall Street, London, E17 9HP Tel: (020) 8520 5361 Fax: (020) 8520 5375 E-mail: sales@premierplatingworks.co.uk

Pro Plate Metal Finishing Co., 17 Manor Trading Estate, Armstrong Road, Benfleet, Essex, SS7 4PW Tel: (01268) 752037 Fax: (01268) 755862

Processed Light Alloys Ltd, 2 Astra Centre, Royle Barn Road, Rochdale, Lancashire, OL11 3DT Tel: (01706) 345551

Quality Electro Depositors Ltd, Shield House, Gatehouse Close, Gatehouse Industrial Area, Aylesbury, Buckinghamshire, HP19 8DE Tel: (01296) 426214 Fax: (01296) 487787 E-mail: wise.wise.owls@aol.com

Quality Plated Plastics, Shady Lane, Birmingham, B44 9ER Tel: 0121-366 7500 Fax: 0121-366 6436

R G Technofinish Ltd, Unit 5, Bilton Road, Hitchin, Hertfordshire, SG4 0SB Tel: (01462) 434002 Fax: (01462) 452556 E-mail: technofinish.ltd@virgin.net

Radleys Discovery Technologies Ltd, Shire Hill Industrial Estate, Shire Hill, Saffron Walden, Essex, CB11 3AZ Tel: (01799) 525381 Fax: (01799) 528066 E-mail: enquiries@sgatech.co.uk

Raycell Ltd, Unit 2 Sherwood Works, Brighton Road, Handcross, Haywards Heath, West Sussex, RH17 6BZ Tel: (01444) 400999 Fax: (01444) 400883 E-mail: raycell@mistral.co.uk

Reddish Electroplating, Mersey Street, Stockport, Cheshire, SK1 2HX Tel: 0161-480 7890 Fax: 0161-480 4383 E-mail: rep-sales@btconnect.com

Redditch Electro Plating Co. Ltd, Arrow Road North, Redditch, Worcestershire, B98 8NT Tel: (01527) 63858 Fax: (01527) 591504

Relion Broma Ltd, Avenue Industrial Estate, Gallows Corner, Romford, RM3 0BY Tel: (01708) 341177 Fax: (01708) 384999

Robert Stuart plc, 10-11 Edinburgh Wa, Harlow, Essex, CM20 2DH Tel: (01279) 442931 Fax: (01279) 626063 E-mail: sales@robertstuart.plc.uk

S G A Technologies Ltd, Shirehill Industrial Estate, Saffron Walden, Essex, CB11 3AQ Tel: (01799) 527264 Fax: (01799) 523064 E-mail: enquiries@sgatech.co.uk

S W S Metal Treatments Ltd, Second Avenue, Trafford Park, Manchester, M17 1EE Tel: 0161-872 3569 Fax: 0161-848 7356 E-mail: enquiries@swsmetaltreatments.co.uk

Satchrome Ltd, Unit 19 Birchills House Industrial Estate, Green Lane, Walsall, WS2 8LF Tel: (01922) 622721 Fax: (01922) 625353 E-mail: satchrome@yahoo.co.uk

Schleifring Systems Ltd, Abex Road, Newbury, Berkshire, RG14 5EY Tel: (01635) 36363 Fax: (01635) 582118 E-mail: sales@schleifring.co.uk

Selectrobuild Precision Plating Ltd, Meadowside, Cultercullen, Udny, Ellon, Aberdeenshire, AB41 6QQ Tel: (01651) 842533 Fax: (01651) 842533

Servex Ltd, Bellingdon Road, Chesham, Buckinghamshire, HP5 2NN Tel: (01494) 784501 Fax: (01494) 784086 E-mail: engineering@servexltd.co.uk

Silchrome Plating Ltd, Barras Garth Road, Leeds, LS12 4JW Tel: 0113-263 7808 Fax: 0113-263 2682 E-mail: sales@silchrome.co.uk

Small Batch Polishing & Plating, No 2 Arcade Workshops, Atlantic Trading Estate, Barry, S. Glam, CF63 3RF Tel: (01446) 720905

Snell & Prideaux Ltd, 6-9 Ernest Street, Birmingham, B1 1NS Tel: 0121-622 3824 Fax: 0121-666 6630

Stainless Plating Ltd, 24 Don Road, Sheffield, S9 2UB Tel: 0114-242 2000 Fax: 0114-242 2003 E-mail: brenda@stainlessplating.co.uk

▶ Stotfold Plating Co. Ltd, Taylors Road, Stotfold, Hitchin, Hertfordshire, SG5 4AX Tel: (01462) 732158 Fax: (01462) 835330

Talbot Plating Co. Ltd, Victoria Works, River Way, Barrowford, Nelson, Lancashire, BB9 6EL Tel: (01282) 618107 Fax: (01282) 692381

Tenn-elcon Ltd, Algernon Industrial Estate, Shiremoor, Newcastle Upon Tyne, NE27 0BL Tel: 0191-251 4065 Fax: 0191-252 3205

Tercet Precision Ltd, Millarston Industrial Estate, Paisley, Renfrewshire, PA1 2XR Tel: 0141-887 4153 Fax: 0141-887 4586 E-mail: sales@tercet.co.uk

Thomas H Gee & Co. Ltd, 271 Summer Lane, Birmingham, B19 2PX Tel: 0121-359 1279 Fax: 0121-359 7686 E-mail: sales@thomashgee.co.uk

Thomas HG & Co. Ltd, 78 Steward Street, Birmingham, B18 7AF Tel: 0121-454 0677 Fax: 0121-454 0677 E-mail: markf@thomashgee.co.uk

Total Finishing Solutions, 67-70 Mott Street, Birmingham, B19 3HE Tel: 0121-233 3505 Fax: 0121-233 9207 E-mail: wesley.jenkinson@totalfinishingsolutions.co.uk

Townhead Electroplating Services, Unit E3 Fieldhouse Industrial Estate, Fieldhouse Road, Rochdale, Lancashire, OL12 0AA Tel: (01706) 647802 E-mail: townheadelectroplating@yahoo.com

Townroe Ltd, 80 Rockingham Street, Sheffield, S1 4EB Tel: 0114-272 3361 Fax: 0114-275 7934

Turnbull (Electro Platers) Ltd, Factory BT 75-4, North Seaton Industrial Estate, Ashington, Northumberland, NE63 0YB Tel: (01670) 854383 Fax: (01670) 854593

Twickenham Plating Group Ltd, 12-13 Balena Close, Poole, Dorset, BH17 7DB Tel: (01202) 692416 Fax: (01202) 600628 E-mail: info@pender.co.uk

Twickenham Plating Group Ltd, 7-9 Edwin Road, Twickenham, TW1 4JJ Tel: (020) 8744 1800 Fax: (020) 8744 2001 E-mail: info@twickenham.co.uk

Unity Plating Co. Ltd, Mount Pleasant Street, Oldham, OL4 1HH Tel: 0161-287 8714 Fax: 0161-287 8715 E-mail: enquiries@unity.zuunet.co.uk

Verichrome Plating Services Ltd, Larkhall Industrial Estate, Larkhall, Lanarkshire, ML9 2PG Tel: (01698) 886060 Fax: (01698) 886060 E-mail: may@verichrome.com

W H Greaves & Son Electroplating Ltd, 2 Lock Street, Sheffield, S6 3BJ Tel: 0114-232 3272 Fax: 0114-232 3273

Dave Walch Ltd, 121 Percival Lane, Runcorn, Cheshire, WA7 4UY Tel: (01928) 574681 Fax: (01928) 577790 E-mail: dave@anodisersruncorn.com

Walton Plating Ltd, 118 Ashley Road, Walton-on-Thames, Surrey, KT12 1HN Tel: (01932) 221206 Fax: (01932) 246699 E-mail: enquiries@waltonplating.co.uk

▶ Watson & Lewis Ltd, 5 Cullen Way, London, NW10 6JZ Tel: (020) 8961 3000 Fax: (020) 8965 1990

Wellbrite Plating Co., 24 Lansdown Place Lane, Cheltenham, Gloucestershire, GL50 2LB Tel: (01242) 523790

West Bromwich Central Plating Co. Ltd, Great Bridge St, West Bromwich, West Midlands, B70 0DA Tel: 0121-557 5352

E. Williams Plating Ltd, Unit 3, The Dean, Alresford, Hampshire, SO24 9BQ Tel: (01962) 733199 Fax: (01962) 735146 E-mail: enquiries@ewp-hants.co.uk

Willochrome Ltd, Westside, Jackson Street, St. Helens, Merseyside, WA9 3AT Tel: (01744) 738488 Fax: (01744) 23039

Wolverhampton Electro Plating Ltd, Wood Lane, Wolverhampton, WV10 8HN Tel: (01902) 397333 Fax: (01902) 785372 E-mail: enquiries@anochrome-group.co.uk

XL Plating Co, 99-103 Ryecroft Street, Gloucester, GL1 4NB Tel: (01452) 525400

Y & B Plating Ltd, 6 Priestley Way, Crawley, West Sussex, RH10 9NT Tel: (01293) 528974 Fax: (01293) 552877

ELECTROPLATING BARRELS

Electrochemical Supplies Ltd, Chamberlain Road, Aylesbury, Buckinghamshire, HP19 8DY Tel: (01296) 428011 Fax: (01296) 392375 E-mail: info@echemsupplies.co.uk

Jacquet Weston Engineering, Tower Works, Membury Airfield Industrial Estate, Lambourn Woodlands, Hungerford, Berkshire, RG17 7TJ Tel: (01488) 674400 Fax: (01488) 674405 E-mail: sales@jweltd.com

Keronite Ltd, 26 Aintree Road, Keytec 7 Business Park, Pershore, Worcestershire, WR10 2JN Tel: (01386) 552032 Fax: (01386) 561261 E-mail: ics.systems@btconnect.com

Trulaw Fabs Ltd, 338 Summer Lane, Birmingham, B19 3QL Tel: 0121-359 1191 Fax: 0121-359 4855

ELECTROPLATING CHEMICAL PRODUCTS MANUFRS

Asbury Brodie & Co. Ltd, 1 Dover Street, Birmingham, B18 5HN Tel: 0121-554 7000 Fax: 0121-554 0242 E-mail: sales@asburybrodie.co.uk

Atotech UK Ltd, William Street, West Bromwich, West Midlands, B70 0BE Tel: 0121-606 7777 Fax: 0121-606 7200 E-mail: sales.uk@atotech.com

Cal Chem Ltd, Unit A3 Hortonwood 10, Telford, Shropshire, TF1 7ES Tel: (01952) 606220 Fax: (01952) 676278

MacDermid P.L.C., Palmer St, Bordesley, Birmingham, B9 4EU Tel: 0121-606 8100 Fax: 0121-606 8300 E-mail: cs@macdermid.com

P M D UK Ltd, Broad Lane, Coventry, CV5 7AY Tel: (024) 7646 6691 Fax: (024) 7647 3034 E-mail: sales@pmdgroup.co.uk

Schloetter Co. Ltd, Abbey Works, New Road, Pershore, Worcestershire, WR10 1BY Tel: (01386) 552331 Fax: (01386) 556864 E-mail: info@schloetter.co.uk

ELECTROPLATING CONTROL SYSTEMS

Keronite Ltd, 26 Aintree Road, Keytec 7 Business Park, Pershore, Worcestershire, WR10 2JN Tel: (01386) 552032 Fax: (01386) 561261 E-mail: ics.systems@btconnect.com

ELECTROPLATING EQUIPMENT, SELECTIVE

R. Palmer, Keynsham, Bristol, BS18 3ST Tel: (01225) 443206 E-mail: info@goldn.co.uk

ELECTROPLATING JIGS

A C Jigs, 10 Porters Way, Birmingham, B9 5RR Tel: 0121-753 0304 Fax: 0121-753 0304

Carrtech Ltd, Crossfield Road, Birmingham, B33 9HP Tel: 0121-683 2600 Fax: 0121-683 2601 E-mail: sales@carrtech.com

ELECTROPLATING PLANT AND EQUIPMENT MANUFRS

Electrical Power Ltd, PO Box 115, Bingley, West Yorkshire, BD16 1WQ Tel: (01274) 510970 Fax: (01274) 511109 E-mail: epsrec@hotmail.com

Electrochemical Supplies Ltd, Chamberlain Road, Aylesbury, Buckinghamshire, HP19 8DY Tel: (01296) 428011 Fax: (01296) 392375 E-mail: info@echemsupplies.co.uk

Hart Coating Technology, PO Box 10, Brierley Hill, West Midlands, DY5 2RQ Tel: (01902) 895446 Fax: (01902) 897469 E-mail: tony@hartcoating.demon.co.uk

Jacquet Weston Engineering, Tower Works, Membury Airfield Industrial Estate, Lambourn Woodlands, Hungerford, Berkshire, RG17 7TJ Tel: (01488) 674400 Fax: (01488) 674405 E-mail: sales@jweltd.com

Keronite Ltd, 26 Aintree Road, Keytec 7 Business Park, Pershore, Worcestershire, WR10 2JN Tel: (01386) 552032 Fax: (01386) 561261 E-mail: ics.systems@btconnect.com

Polytec Plastic Products, Ormrod Street, Bury, Lancashire, BL9 7HF Tel: 0161-705 1901 Fax: 0161-705 1935 E-mail: dmworsley@polytecpf.fsnet.co.uk

Premier Plating Jigs Ltd, 16 New Bartholomew Street, Birmingham, B5 5QS Tel: 0121-643 0727 Fax: 0121-633 3392

R J Faulkes, Unit C3 Guy Motors Industrial Park, Park Lane, Wolverhampton, WV10 9QF Tel: (01902) 306662 Fax: (01902) 306662

Riley Industries Ltd, 152 Wellhead Lane, Birmingham, B42 2SY Tel: 0121-356 2020 Fax: 0121-356 1117 E-mail: sales@rileyindustries.co.uk

Schloetter Co. Ltd, Abbey Works, New Road, Pershore, Worcestershire, WR10 1BY Tel: (01386) 552331 Fax: (01386) 556864 E-mail: info@schloetter.co.uk

ELECTROPLATING PLANT AND EQUIPMENT MANUFRS – *continued*

SIFCO Applied Surface Concepts (UK) Ltd, 38 Walkers Road, Moons Moat North, Moons Moat North Industrial Estate, Redditch, Worcestershire, B98 9HD Tel: (01527) 68008 Fax: (01527) 65924 E-mail: plating@sifco.co.uk

Trulaw Fabs Ltd, 338 Summer Lane, Birmingham, B19 3QL Tel: 0121-359 1191 Fax: 0121-359 4855

Ulster Electro Finishes Ltd, 78 Ballyrashane Road, Coleraine, County Londonderry, BT52 2LJ Tel: (028) 7034 3022 Fax: (028) 7035 5985 E-mail: uefltd@aol.com

ELECTROPLATING RECTIFIERS

Applied Power Techniques Ltd, 7 Maundrell Road, Calne, Wiltshire, SN11 9PU Tel: (01249) 811888 Fax: (01249) 811888

ELECTROPOLISHING

Metallics Metal Finishing Services, Unit 7 Sparkbrook Street, Coventry, CV1 5ST Tel: (024) 7663 3229 Fax: (024) 7625 2200

Poligrat (UK) Ltd, 2 Holder Road, Aldershot, Hampshire, GU12 4RH Tel: (01252) 336337 Fax: (01252) 322791 E-mail: info@poligratuk.co.uk

Polish Inc, 4 Justin Business Park, Sandford Lane, Wareham, Dorset, BH20 4DY Tel: (01929) 554037 Fax: (01929) 555262

ELECTROSTATIC CONSULTANTS

Chilworth Technology Ltd, Beta House Enterprise Road, Chilworth Science Park, Chilworth, Southampton, SO16 7NS Tel: (023) 8076 0722 Fax: (023) 8076 7866 E-mail: info@chilworth.co.uk

Electrostatic Solutions Ltd, 13 Redhill Crescent, Southampton, SO16 7BQ Tel: (023) 8090 5600 E-mail: jeremys@static-sol.com

ELECTROSTATIC DISCHARGE EQUIPMENT

D C A Elect, Unit 3D, Herald Industrial Estate, Hedge End, Southampton, SO30 2JW Tel: (01489) 799927 Fax: (01489) 798770 E-mail: sales@flocking.biz

Static Safe, 6 Timmis Road, Stourbridge, West Midlands, DY9 7BQ Tel: (01384) 898599 Fax: (01384) 898577 E-mail: sse@static-safe.demon.co.uk

ELECTROSTATIC DISCHARGE RESEARCH AND DEVELOPMENT CONSULTANTS

Electrostatic Solutions Ltd, 13 Redhill Crescent, Southampton, SO16 7BQ Tel: (023) 8090 5600 E-mail: jeremys@static-sol.com

ELECTROSTATIC FILTERS

UK Filters Ltd, 3b High Street, Cheshunt, Waltham Cross, Hertfordshire, EN8 0BX Tel: (01992) 468804

ELECTROSTATIC PAINT SPRAYING

Toricourt Ltd, 38 Westbury Road, Southampton, SO15 4JP Tel: (023) 8051 0982 Fax: (023) 8078 0363 E-mail: info@spectruminteriors.co.uk

ELECTROSTATIC PAINT SPRAYING EQUIPMENT MANUFRS

Exel Industrial UK Ltd, Unit 4 Lockflight Buildings, Wheatlea Industrial Estate, Wigan, Lancashire, WN3 6XR Tel: (01942) 829111 Fax: (01942) 820491 E-mail: enquiries@exel-uk.com

Nordson (UK) Ltd, Ashurst Drive, Cheadle Heath, Stockport, Cheshire, SK3 0RY Tel: 0161-495 4200 Fax: 0161-428 6716

ELECTROSTATIC PAPER COATERS/MANUFRS

Venex Technical Developments Ltd, Unit 3, Mount Pleasant Farm, Moorend Road, Yardley Gobion, Towcester, Northamptonshire, NN12 7UF Tel: (01908) 543158 Fax: (01908) 543052 E-mail: chris@venex.biz

ELECTROSTATIC POWDER COATING PLANT

▶ A G Servicing Ltd, 68 Wychall Drive, Bushbury, Wolverhampton, WV10 8UX Tel: (01902) 787121 Fax: (01902) 787121 E-mail: sales@agservicing.co.uk

Spray Art Ltd, Grove Farm, The Street, Crookham Village, Fleet, Hampshire, GU51 5SD Tel: (01202) 580942 Fax: (01252) 811796 E-mail: action@sprayart.co.uk

Three Spires Finishing Systems Ltd, 45 Lanes Close, Kings Bromley, Burton-on-Trent, Staffordshire, DE13 7JS Tel: (01543) 473069 Fax: (01543) 473069 E-mail: info@threespiresfinishing.co.uk

ELECTROSTATIC POWDER SPRAYING EQUIPMENT

D C A Elect, Unit 3D, Herald Industrial Estate, Hedge End, Southampton, SO30 2JW Tel: (01489) 799927 Fax: (01489) 798770 E-mail: sales@flocking.biz

Nordson (UK) Ltd, Ashurst Drive, Cheadle Heath, Stockport, Cheshire, SK3 0RY Tel: 0161-495 4200 Fax: 0161-428 6716

ELECTROSTATIC SPRAY EQUIPMENT, *See also headings for particular types*

KCS Herr-Voss UK Ltd, Glassworks House, Park Lane, Halesowen, West Midlands, B63 2QS Tel: (01384) 568114 Fax: (01384) 568115 E-mail: ukdrawingoffice@kcsherrvossuk.com

ELECTROTHERAPY INSTRUMENTS

Electro-Medical Supplies Greenham, Grove Street, Wantage, Oxfordshire, OX12 7AD Tel: (01235) 772272 Fax: (01235) 763518 E-mail: info@emslimited.co.uk

ELECTROTINNING, *See Tinning etc*

ELEVATOR BUCKETS

E C Y (Holdings) Ltd, Barley Castle Lane, Appleton, Warrington, WA4 4RB Tel: (01925) 860000 Fax: (01925) 861111 E-mail: sales@ecyltd.co.uk

R U D Chains Ltd, Units 10-14, John Wilson Business Park, Thanet Way, Whitstable, Kent, CT5 3QT Tel: (01227) 276611 Fax: (01227) 276586 E-mail: sales@rud.co.uk

EMAIL TO BRAILLE TRANSLATION SERVICES

▶ Braille Translations, 9 Wadham Gardens, Greenford, Middlesex, UB6 0BP Tel: (07005) 860169 Fax: (020) 8422 2237 E-mail: ghow@brailletranslations.co.uk

EMBEDDED COMPUTER CONTROLLERS

Blue Chip Technology Ltd, Chowley Oak, Chowley Oak Lane, Tattenhall, Chester, CH3 9EX Tel: (01829) 772000 Fax: (01829) 772001 E-mail: sales@bluechiptechnology.co.uk

H M Computing Ltd, Harmac House, Enigma Park, Malvern, Worcestershire, WR14 1GP Tel: (01684) 581850 Fax: (01684) 581851 E-mail: sales@hmcomputing.net

EMBEDDED COMPUTER SOFTWARE DESIGN

Absolute Software, Mount Pleasant, Chapel Hill, Porthtowan, Truro, Cornwall, TR4 8AS Tel: (01209) 891320 E-mail: info@absolute-software.co.uk

▶ Baker Automation, 3 Butternab Road, Huddersfield, HD4 7AH Tel: (07802) 495848 Fax: 0161-881 9376E-mail: john@ukelo.co.uk

Live Devices, Atlas House, Link Business Park, Osbaldwick, Link Road, York, YO10 3JB Tel: (01904) 562580 Fax: (01904) 562581

Selectactive Ltd, 67a Frimley Green Road, Frimley, Camberley, Surrey, GU16 8AL Tel: (01276) 683891 Fax: (01276) 683891 E-mail: alan@selectactive.co.uk

Tellima Technology Ltd, Unit 1g Denby Dale Industrial Park, Wakefield Road, Denby Dale, Huddersfield, HD8 8QH Tel: (01484) 866806 Fax: (01484) 866816 E-mail: sales@tellima.co.uk

EMBEDDED PERSONAL COMPUTERS (PC)

Clark Associates U.K, 57 Selby Lane, Keyworth, Nottingham, NG12 5AQ Tel: 0115-937 6136

EMBEDDED SOLUTION COMPUTER SYSTEMS

B F Group Ltd, Unit 6 Cobhan Centre, Westmead Industrial Estate, Westlea, Swindon, SN5 7UJ Tel: (01793) 498020 Fax: (01793) 542019 E-mail: sales@bfgroup.co.uk

Motorola Computer Group, 1 Oakwood Drive, Loughborough, Leicestershire, LE11 3NE Tel: (01509) 634444 Fax: (01509) 634333 E-mail: info@uk.europe.mcd.mct.com

EMBEDDED WIRELESS LOCAL AREA NETWORK (WLAN) SOLUTIONS

Bailey Telecom Ltd, 7 Brown Lane West, Leeds, LS12 6EH Tel: 0113-243 9921 Fax: (0845) 128128 E-mail: enquiries@baileyteswaine.co.uk

C S W Erlang Ltd, Unit 10, Green Farm, Fritwell, Bicester, Oxfordshire, OX27 7QU Tel: (01869) 345050 Fax: (01869) 345954 E-mail: mandy.jenkins@erlangcsw.co.uk

EMBLEMS/LOGOS

Davis Emblems, Unit 3 David Cuthbert Business Centre, Ashton Old Road, Manchester, M11 2NA Tel: 0161-231 7300 E-mail: davisembroidery@aol.com

Qasco UK Ltd, 43d Brecknock Road, London, N7 0BT Tel: (020) 7267 3079 Fax: (020) 7267 4212 E-mail: sales@qasco.co.uk

▶ SCENSION, 71 Bellegrove Road, Welling, Kent, DA16 3PG Tel: 0870 9914108 E-mail: enquiries@scension.co.uk

Zebra Studios, 52 Eldon St North, Barnsley, South Yorkshire, S71 1LG Tel: (01226) 299238 Fax: (01226) 299238 E-mail: sales@zebrastudios.co.uk

EMBLEMS/LOGOS, RESIN COATED

Polycrown Ltd, Unit 3 Smiths Forge, North End Road, Yatton, Bristol, BS49 4AU Tel: (01934) 876349 Fax: (01934) 835406 E-mail: sales@polycrown.com

EMBOSSED FOIL SEALS

Stephen Fossler Co. Inc., 24 The Business Village, Wexham Road, Slough, SL2 5HF Tel: (01753) 553413 Fax: (01753) 518532 E-mail: fossleruk@aol.com

EMBOSSED PAPER

Antalis Ltd, Unit 14, Avenue One, Witney, Oxfordshire, OX29 6XX Tel: (0870) 6073114 Fax: (01993) 779066

Elliott Baxter & Company Ltd, Central Way, North Feltham Trading Estate, Feltham, Middlesex, TW14 0RX Tel: (020) 8893 1144 Fax: (020) 8893 2167 E-mail: sales@ebbpaper.co.uk

North East Paper Co. Ltd, Benfield Road, Newcastle upon Tyne, NE6 4NT Tel: 0191-265 5000 Fax: 0191-224 0872 E-mail: sales@nep-uk.co.uk

EMBOSSING, *See also headings for particular types*

PDM Products, 104 Rushlake Road, Brighton, BN1 9AF Tel: (01273) 604691 Fax: (01273) 673238 E-mail: sales@pdmproducts.co.uk

EMBOSSING BRASS DIES

Falcontec Ltd, Falcon House, Mucklow Hill, Halesowen, West Midlands, B62 8DT Tel: 0121-550 1076 Fax: 0121-585 5126 E-mail: info@falcontec.co.uk

EMBOSSING DIES

Davidson & Co. Ltd, 92 Harwood Street, Sheffield, S2 4SE Tel: 0114-272 4584 Fax: 0114-279 7309

EMBOSSING PRESSES

▶ Brandtjen & Kluge, Inc. International, 5, Spring Mill Business Center, Avening Road, Nailsworth, Stroud, Gloucestershire, GL6 0BS Tel: (01453) 836522 Fax: (01453) 836009 E-mail: tandersen@kluge.biz

PDM Products, 104 Rushlake Road, Brighton, BN1 9AF Tel: (01273) 604691 Fax: (01273) 673238 E-mail: sales@pdmproducts.co.uk

EMBOSSING ROLLS/ROLLERS

David Bentley Ltd, Greengate, Salford, M3 7NS Tel: 0161-834 8851 Fax: 0161-835 3303 E-mail: sales@davidbentley.co.uk

EMBOSSING SERVICES TO THE PRINTING TRADE

Chapman & Mellor, 20 Hockley Hill, Birmingham, B18 5AQ Tel: 0121-554 3778 Fax: 0121-554 7931 E-mail: sales@foilprinters.co.uk

Chiltern Foil Printing Co., 6 Acorn Business Centre, Cublington Road, Wing, Leighton Buzzard, Bedfordshire, LU7 0LB Tel: (01296) 682299 Fax: (01296) 682299 E-mail: plucas@fsbdial.co.uk

Grays Foil Blockers, Unit 10 White Post Lane, London, E9 5EN Tel: (020) 8985 6518 Fax: (020) 8986 0396

Identisys Ltd, Unit S5, The Nene Centre, Freehold Street, Northampton, NN2 6EW Tel: 01604 710462 E-mail: sales@identisys.co.uk

EMBOSSING TOOLS

Borries, 28 Coalbrookdale Road, Clayhill Light Industrial Park, Neston, CH64 3UG Tel: 0151-336 3101 Fax: 0151-336 3217 E-mail: rob@borriesuk.fsnet.co.uk

C A Grant, Orgreave Crescent, Sheffield, S13 9NQ Tel: 0114-269 5498 Fax: 0114-269 5412 E-mail: sales@cagrant.co.uk

Craft Kits UK Ltd, Hounslow, TW3 4RE Tel: (020) 8814 2227 Fax: (020) 8814 1367

Engraving Tools Ltd, Unit 44 Stakehill Industrial Estate, Touchet Hall Road, Middleton, Manchester, M24 2FL Tel: 0161-653 8103 Fax: 0161-655 4061 E-mail: engrtools@aol.com

EMBROIDERED BADGES

A R Fabb Bros Ltd, 29-31 Risborough Road, Maidenhead, Berkshire, SL6 7BJ Tel: (01628) 623533 Fax: (01628) 622705 E-mail: sales@fabb.co.uk

Badge Design Ltd, Unit 4e Crofts End Industrial Estate, Crofts End Road, Bristol, BS5 7UW Tel: 0117-952 5856 Fax: 0117-952 5857 E-mail: badge.design@btconnect.com

Commando Knitwear Ltd, Countesthorpe Road, Wigston, Leicestershire, LE18 4PJ Tel: 0116-278 5288 E-mail: info@commando-knitwear.co.uk

Craigdon Business Gifts, Advertising House, Burghmuir Circle, Inverurie, Aberdeenshire, AB51 4FS Tel: (01467) 622943 Fax: (01467) 620286 E-mail: sales@craigdon.com

▶ Delta Labelling, Unit A Apollo Park Apollo, Litchfield Road Industrial, Lichfield Road Industrial Estate, Tamworth, Staffordshire, B79 7TA Tel: (01827) 302862 Fax: (01827) 300891E-mail: enquiries@delta-labelling.co.uk

Emblematic Embroiderers, Unit 26b North Tyne Industrial Estate, Whitley Road, Benton, Newcastle upon Tyne, NE12 9SZ Tel: 0191-270 1449 Fax: 0191-270 1449 E-mail: gmewett@emblematic.force9.co.uk

▶ Firmin & Sons P.L.C., Firmin House, 82-86 New Town Row, Birmingham, B6 4HU Tel: 0121-380 0800 Fax: 0121-359 3321 E-mail: sales@firmin.co.uk

Golden Finishes Ltd, 4 Malvern Drive, Llanishen, Cardiff, CF14 5DR Tel: (029) 2075 5733 Fax: (029) 2076 3993 E-mail: gfinishes@aol.com

Goldpress, 1 Lower Green Avenue, Scholes, Cleckheaton, West Yorkshire, BD19 6PB Tel: (01274) 878488 Fax: (01274) 878488 E-mail: davidkelly@goldpress.co.uk

I4c Publicity, 3 Broad Street, Coventry, CV6 5AX Tel: (024) 7666 7440 Fax: (024) 7666 3736 E-mail: sales@i4cpublicity.co.uk

J & A International Ltd, Vale Road, Spilsby, Lincolnshire, PE23 5HE Tel: (01790) 752757 Fax: (01790) 754132 E-mail: ja-int@ja-int.co.uk

Leisurelines Embroiderers, Unit 10 Staunton Court Business Park, Ledbury Road, Staunton, Gloucester, GL19 3QS Tel: (0800) 7318410

Logo Leisurewear, 111 Hubert Road, Birmingham, B29 6ET Tel: 0121-472 5300 Fax: 0121-472 8017 E-mail: peter@rsfarmah.freeserve.co.uk

Mark Handford & Co., 78 Coleswood Road, Harpenden, Hertfordshire, AL5 1EQ Tel: (01582) 762065 Fax: (01582) 623317

Marvelfairs Ltd, Suite 44-45, Level 7 Westec House, Westgate, Ealing, London, W5 1YY Tel: (020) 8998 9052 Fax: (020) 8991 0995 E-mail: general@marvelfairs.com

EMBROIDERED BADGES – *continued*

▶ militarybadges.co.uk, 27 Post House Wynd, Darlington, County Durham, DL3 7LP Tel: (01325) 489820 E-mail: diamondmerchants@btopenworld.com

N Schahid Ltd, Unit 3 Knoll Business Centre, Old Shoreham Road, Hove, East Sussex, BN3 7GS Tel: (01273) 424200 Fax: (01273) 424204 E-mail: nschahid@aol.com

The Neoknitting & Trim Ltd, Peter Pal House, Albion St, Leicester, LE2 5DE Tel: 0116-271 4923 Fax: 0116-271 4422 E-mail: sales@neotrims.com

Oak Hill Embroidery, 86 Bromley Road, Beckenham, Kent, BR3 5NP Tel: (020) 8650 6897 Fax: (020) 8663 3842

Pinpoint Badges & Promotions Ltd, Alma Road, Sidcup, Kent, DA14 4EA Tel: (020) 8302 8008 Fax: (020) 8302 4008 E-mail: sales@pinpointbadges.com

Practivewear, 47-49 Park Royal Road, London, NW10 7LQ Tel: (020) 8963 0888 Fax: (020) 8963 0343

Premier Badges, Unit 8 Little Hyde Farm, Ingatestone, Essex, CM4 0DU Tel: (01277) 355078 Fax: (01277) 355092 E-mail: sales@premierbadges.co.uk

Projected Image Products Ltd, Unit 8, Ynyschir Industrial Estate, Ynyschir, Porth, Mid Glamorgan, CF39 0HU Tel: (01443) 682196 Fax: (01443) 686840 E-mail: paul@projectimage.freeserve.co.uk

Sagittarian Embroidery, 27 Durham Road, Sacriston, Durham, DH7 6LN Tel: 0191-371 9371 Fax: 0191-371 2288 E-mail: sagittarianemb@clara.co.uk

Sports Crest, 8 Balloo Drive, Bangor, County Down, BT19 7QY Tel: (028) 9127 1131 Fax: (028) 9127 0799 E-mail: sales@sportscrest.net

EMBROIDERED CLOTHING

▶ Scot Crest, Concept House, Old Monkland Road, Coatbridge, Lanarkshire, ML5 5EU Tel: (01236) 606560 Fax: (01236) 627711

EMBROIDERY

▶ Ace Embroidery Ltd, 141 Tat Bank Road, Oldbury, West Midlands, B69 4NH Tel: 0121-544 7108 Fax: 0121-544 4965 E-mail: info@ace-embroidery.co.uk

▶ Amaya Sales UK Ltd, Trademark House, Ramshill, Petersfield, Hampshire, GU31 4AT Tel: (01730) 711151 Fax: (01730) 711141 E-mail: sales@amayauk.com

Amazon Promotions, Unit 126 Oystons Mill, Strand Road, Preston, PR1 8UR Tel: (01772) 722800 Fax: (01772) 722800 E-mail: maria.atherton@rediffmail.com

Animm Textiles Ltd, Mangochi House, 107-115 Gwendolen Road, Leicester, LE5 5FL Tel: 0116-212 1234 Fax: 0116-273 3396 E-mail: info@animm.com

Arthur Beesley, 7 Trotters Lane, Harlaxton, Grantham, Lincolnshire, NG32 1JQ Tel: (01476) 565386

▶ Richard Atkins, 132 Kingsley Park Terrace, Northampton, NN2 7HJ Tel: (01604) 710050 Fax: (01604) 710170 E-mail: sales@aps-promotions.com

Balmoral Knitwear (Scotland) Ltd, 16 Church Lane, Galston, Ayrshire, KA4 8HF Tel: (01563) 820213 Fax: (01563) 821740 E-mail: info@balmoralknitwear.co.uk

Benton & Johnson Ltd, Regalia House, Newtown Road, Bedworth, Warwickshire, CV12 8QR Tel: (024) 7684 8800 Fax: (024) 7664 3018 E-mail: bentonandjohnson@toye.com

Bradley Textiles Ltd, 6 Huss Row, Belfast, BT13 1EE Tel: (028) 9032 5434 Fax: (028) 9031 5350 E-mail: bradleytextiles@btopenworld.com

Brody International Ltd, Units 1-2, 18 Gillender Street, London, E3 3JW Tel: (020) 7538 5666 Fax: (020) 7510 1099 E-mail: sales@brody.co.uk

Busy Embroidery, 3 Village Farm Industrial Estate, Pyle, Bridgend, Mid Glamorgan, CF33 6ZR Tel: (01656) 741274 Fax: (01656) 741274 E-mail: sales@fusionembroidery.co.uk

Carousel Bridal Veils Ltd, 174-176 Carlton Road, Nottingham, NG3 2BB Tel: 0115-947 6205 E-mail: info@carouselveils.com

Castle Embroidering, Unit J Stonebridge Court, Nottingham, NG3 2GY Tel: 0115-947 2888 Fax: 0115-947 2888 E-mail: sales@castle-embroidery.co.uk

Charles Kirk & Co. Ltd, Horton Buildings, Goring Street, Goring-by-Sea, Worthing, West Sussex, BN12 5AD Tel: (01903) 244863 Fax: (01903) 700577 E-mail: sales@charleskirk.co.uk

▶ Cheerful Promotions Ltd, 38 Ferncroft Avenue, London, NW3 7PE Tel: (020) 7431 6293 Fax: (020) 7431 2060 E-mail: sales@cheerfulpromotions.co.uk

Constructiv Company Ltd, 1/St. Giles Business Park, Pool Road, Newtown, Powys, SY16 3AJ Tel: (01686) 610890 Fax: (01686) 610880 E-mail: enquiries@constructiv.co.uk

▶ Country Colonial Ltd, 82-86 Seymour Place, London, W1H 2NQ Tel: (020) 7723 0465 Fax: (020) 7723 4430 E-mail: textilediva@countrycolonial.co.uk

Crest Identity Ltd, Crest House, Stockton Road, Hartlepool, Cleveland, TS25 1TY Tel: (01429) 233533 Fax: (01429) 272400

Davmar Workwear, 1 Centenary Court, Earlsway, Team Valley Trading Estate, Gateshead, Tyne & Wear, NE11 0RQ Tel: 0191-487 2249 Fax: 0191-491 4237 E-mail: contact@davmarworkwear.com

▶ Dezigned4U Embroidery & Printing Services, 164 Newport Road, Caldicot, Monmouthshire, NP26 4AA Tel: (01291) 423724 Fax: (01291) 423724 E-mail: info@dezigned4u.com

▶ Dinsdale Embroideries, 13 Castle Close, Middleton St. George, Darlington, County Durham, DL2 1DE Tel: (01325) 332592 Fax: (01325) 335704 E-mail: info@dinsdaleembroideries.co.uk

Emblematic Embroiderers, Unit 26b North Tyne Industrial Estate, Whitley Road, Benton, Newcastle upon Tyne, NE12 9SZ Tel: 0191-270 1449 Fax: 0191-270 1449 E-mail: gmewett@emblematic.force9.co.uk

Excel Embroidery, 12 Argyll Road, Rosneath, Helensburgh, Dunbartonshire, G84 0RP Tel: (01436) 831850 Fax: (01436) 831028 E-mail: sales@excel-embroidery.com

Excel Laces & Fabrics Ltd, 13 Rancliffe Avenue, Keyworth, Nottingham, NG12 5HY Tel: 0115-937 5030 Fax: 0115-937 6619 E-mail: clive-johnson@lineone.net

Fewkes Ltd, Morley Avenue, Nottingham, NG3 5FW Tel: 0115-960 3561 Fax: 0115-969 2136

▶ Firstgear Clothing, The Croft, Lower Brand, Griffydam, Coalville, Leicestershire, LE67 8HE Tel: 01530 224474 Fax: 01530 224474 E-mail: info@firstgearclothing.co.uk

G S L Embroidery, 1 Berry Bank Lane, Holmfirth, HD9 7LA Tel: (01484) 683142 Fax: (01484) 685246 E-mail: sepiaemb@aol.com

▶ L Shailer, Hafod School House, Llanerfyl, Welshpool, Powys, SY21 0JH Tel: (01938) 820110 Fax: (01938) 820118 E-mail: info@lynshailer.co.uk

Logomotif Embroiderers, 2 Eagle Close, Arnold, Nottingham, NG5 7FJ Tel: 0115-920 0777 Fax: 0115-920 0888 E-mail: logomotif@aol.com

▶ M & M Embroidery, 39 Hutton Close, Crowther, Washington, Tyne & Wear, NE38 0AH Tel: 0191-415 3552 Fax: 0191-415 0514 E-mail: enquiries@mandm-embroidery.demon.co.uk

Meiklejohn Chef & Work Wear, 198 Swanston Street, Glasgow, G40 4HH Tel: 0141-554 2709 Fax: 0141-554 4645 E-mail: sales@meilkejohns.co.uk

Micheal Hope Sports, 7 High Street, Bathampton, Bath, BA2 6SY Tel: (01225) 464648 Fax: (01225) 464642 E-mail: sales@michaelhope.co.uk

Milliken White & Co. Ltd, 6 Huss Row, Belfast, BT13 1EE Tel: (028) 9032 2076 Fax: (028) 9031 5350 E-mail: millikenwhite@hotmail.co.uk

Projected Image Products Ltd, Unit 8, Ynyschir Industrial Estate, Ynyschir, Porth, Mid Glamorgan, CF39 0HU Tel: (01443) 682196 Fax: (01443) 686840 E-mail: paul@projectimage.freeserve.co.uk

R E Ashworth & Co. Ltd, 123 Mansfield Road, Daybrook, Nottingham, NG5 6HT Tel: 0115-967 0022 Fax: 0115-920 6875 E-mail: wendy@mirabeluk.com

R S Farmah & Sons, 111 Hubert Road, Birmingham, B29 6ET Tel: 0121-472 6672 Fax: 0121-472 8017 E-mail: peter@rsfarmah.freeserve.co.uk

▶ ReetPetite, The Cottage, Ragnall Lane, Walkley Wood, Nailsworth, Gloucestershire, GL6 0RX Tel: 01453 833996 E-mail: reet@reetpetite.biz

Strella Fabrics Ltd, Radford Boulevard, Nottingham, NG7 5QG Tel: 0115-955 4444 Fax: 0115-955 4500 E-mail: enquiries@strella-fabrics.ltd.uk

Surrey Embroidery Co. Ltd, 7 Linkfield Corner, Redhill, RH1 1BD Tel: (01737) 766691 Fax: (01737) 780666 E-mail: enquiries@surreyembroidery.co.uk

Terrane Promotions, Terrane House, Whisby Way Industrial Estate, Lincoln, LN6 3LQ Tel: (01522) 697000 Fax: (01522) 697154 E-mail: sales@terrane.co.uk

Walter Melville Ltd, Fanshaws Lane, Brickendon, Hertford, SG13 8PG Tel: (01992) 511285 Fax: (01992) 511286 E-mail: melville_trimmings@yahoo.co.uk

Wirral Textile Motifs Ltd, 117 Royden Road, Wirral, Merseyside, CH49 4LX Tel: 0151-678 6076 Fax: 0151-678 6076 E-mail: motifs@btopernworld.co.uk

EMBROIDERY DESIGN DIGITISING SERVICES

▶ A Campbell, Fernhurst Road, Milland, Liphook, Hampshire, GU30 7LU Tel: (01428) 741646 Fax: (01428) 741648

Busy Embroidery, 3 Village Farm Industrial Estate, Pyle, Bridgend, Mid Glamorgan, CF33 6ZR Tel: (01656) 741274 Fax: (01656) 741274 E-mail: sales@fusionembroidery.co.uk

▶ Dezigned4U Embroidery & Printing Services, 164 Newport Road, Caldicot, Monmouthshire, NP26 4AA Tel: (01291) 423724 Fax: (01291) 423724 E-mail: info@dezigned4u.com

▶ M & M Embroidery, 39 Hutton Close, Crowther, Washington, Tyne & Wear, NE38 0AH Tel: 0191-415 3552 Fax: 0191-415 0514 E-mail: enquiries@mandm-embroidery.demon.co.uk

▶ Motif Magic Ltd, 1 Davis Road, Brooklands, Weybridge, Surrey, KT13 0XH Tel: (01932) 830800 Fax: (0870) 7052851 E-mail: linda@motifmagic.co.uk

▶ Reynolds Embroidery & Sewing, 3 Bin Avenue, Cairnie, Huntly, Aberdeenshire, AB54 4TZ Tel: (07867) 957739

EMBROIDERY FRAMES

▶ Amaya Sales UK Ltd, Trademark House, Ramshill, Petersfield, Hampshire, GU31 4AT Tel: (01730) 711151 Fax: (01730) 711141 E-mail: sales@amayauk.com

Elbesee Products, Cotswold Works, London Road, Chalford, Stroud, Gloucestershire, GL6 8DT Tel: (01453) 883014 Fax: (01453) 882987

EMBROIDERY MACHINE MANUFRS

▶ Amaya Sales UK Ltd, Trademark House, Ramshill, Petersfield, Hampshire, GU31 4AT Tel: (01730) 711151 Fax: (01730) 711141 E-mail: sales@amayauk.com

EMBROIDERY TAPE

Castle Embroidering, Unit J Stonebridge Court, Nottingham, NG3 2GY Tel: 0115-947 2888 Fax: 0115-947 2888 E-mail: sales@castle-embroidery.co.uk

Geoffrey E. Macpherson Ltd, Unit 8, The Midway, Lenton, Nottingham, NG7 2TS Tel: 0115-986 8701 Fax: 0115-986 4430 E-mail: gem@macphersons.co.uk

EMBROIDERY THREAD

▶ Dinsdale Embroideries, 13 Castle Close, Middleton St. George, Darlington, County Durham, DL2 1DE Tel: (01325) 332592 Fax: (01325) 335704 E-mail: info@dinsdaleembroideries.co.uk

▶ ETC Embroidery, Enterprise House, 94 David Street, Bridgeton, Glasgow, G40 2UH Tel: 0141-550 1188 Fax: 0141-550 2999

New Line Promotions, 5 Wilbraham Road, Weaverham, Northwich, Cheshire, CW8 3JX Tel: (01606) 854600 Fax: (01606) 853527

EMERGENCY BOARDING UP GLAZING CONTRACTORS

▶ Christie's Emergency Glazing, 2 Trafalgar Road, Dartford, DA1 1NS Tel: (01322) 229874 Fax: (0845) 4309391 E-mail: john@glassforhome.com

▶ Jackson Glass, 25 Robinson Road, High Wycombe, Bucks, HP13 7BL Tel: 01494 812207 Fax: 0870 1367557 E-mail: enquiries@jacksonglass.co.uk

EMERGENCY COMMUNICATION SYSTEMS, *See also headings for particular types*

SELEX Communications, Green Park Business Centre, Sutton-On-Forest, York, YO61 1ET Tel: (01347) 811881 Fax: (01347) 811991 E-mail: davies.sales@selex-comms.com

Tyco Fire & Integrated Solutions, Molly Avenue, Mapperley, Nottingham, NG3 5FW Tel: 0115-955 1199 Fax: 0115-955 1919 E-mail: spectorlumunex.uk@tycoint.com

▶ David Webster Ltd, Field House, Station Approach, Harlow, Essex, CM20 2FB Tel: (01279) 645100 Fax: (01279) 645101 E-mail: info@dwltd.co.uk

EMERGENCY DOOR BOLT FIXTURES

Emexco Ltd, Unit 1, 46B Bulkington, Devizes, Wiltshire, SN10 1SL Tel: (01380) 828900 Fax: (01380) 828999 E-mail: sales@emexco.co.uk

Tindall Engineering Ltd, Abryll House, Oldham, OL1 3TF Tel: 0161 6200666

EMERGENCY FLOTATION EQUIPMENT

F P T Industries Ltd, Airport Service Road, Portsmouth, PO3 5PE Tel: (023) 9266 2391 Fax: (023) 9267 0899 E-mail: info@fptind.co.uk

EMERGENCY LIGHTING

A C D C Lighting Systems Ltd, Pasture Lane Works, Pasture Lane, Barrowford, Nelson, Lancashire, BB9 6ES Tel: (01282) 608400 Fax: (01282) 608401 E-mail: sales@acdclighting.co.uk

Airkool Projects Ltd, 10 Rotterdam Road, Hull, HU7 0XD Tel: (01482) 371888 Fax: (01482) 371889 E-mail: info@airkool.co.uk

Alsigns Self Luminous, Hilland Rise, Headley, Bordon, Hampshire, GU35 8LT Tel: (01536) 201525 Fax: (01780) 479032 E-mail: douglas@surelite.co.uk

Baravon Systems, Sanctus Street, Stratford-upon-Avon, Warwickshire, CV37 6DH Tel: (01789) 299668 Fax: (01789) 414230

Cluson Engineering Ltd, Unit 6, Bedford Road, Petersfield, Hampshire, GU32 3LJ Tel: (01730) 264672 Fax: (01730) 260475 E-mail: sales@clulite.co.uk

Cooper Lighting & Security, Wheatley Hall Road, Doncaster, South Yorkshire, DN2 4NB Tel: (01302) 321541 Fax: (01302) 303220 E-mail: sales@cooper-ls.com

D C Emergency Systems Ltd, Wharf Street, Dukinfield, Cheshire, SK16 4JG Tel: 0161-343 1189 Fax: 0161-343 2235 E-mail: sales@dc-emergency.com

Grainger Fire Protection, Unit 1a Newton Court, Wavertree Technology Park, Liverpool, L13 1EJ Tel: 0151-220 4068 Fax: 0151-259 4365E-mail: enquiries@graingersystems.co.uk

Hilclare Ltd, Unit 1 Bond Street Industrial Estate, Mancunian Way, Manchester, M12 6HW Tel: 0161-274 3626 Fax: 0161-274 3731 E-mail: sales@hilclare.com

Intram Barwell Ltd, Barwell Business Park, Leatherhead Road, Chessington, Surrey, KT9 2NY Tel: (020) 8391 7500 Fax: (020) 8974 1629 E-mail: enquiries@ibl.co.uk

Luminaire UK Ltd, 9-15 Henley Street, Birmingham, B11 1JB Tel: 0121-766 1490 Fax: 0121-766 1491 E-mail: sales@luminaireuk.com

Mattalex Lighting Ltd, Unit C, 13-2 The Acacia Buliding, Vantage Point Business Village, Mitcheldean, Gloucestershire, GL17 0DD Tel: (01594) 546368 Fax: (01594) 546373 E-mail: sales@mattalex.co.uk

Orbik Electronics Ltd, Orbik House, Northgate Way, Aldridge, Walsall, WS9 8TX Tel: (01922) 743515 Fax: (01922) 743173 E-mail: info@orbik.co.uk

Poselco Lighting, 1 Bristol Road, Greenford, Middlesex, UB6 8UW Tel: (020) 8813 0101 Fax: (020) 8813 0099 E-mail: sales@poselco.com

Premier Hazard Ltd, Moorfield Estate, Yeadon, Leeds, LS19 7BN Tel: 0113-239 1111 Fax: 0113-239 1131

Protec Fire Detection Export Ltd, Protec House, Churchill Way, Nelson, Lancashire, BB9 6RT Tel: (01282) 717171 Fax: (01282) 717273 E-mail: sales@protec.co.uk

Thomas & Betts Ltd, 5 Sheepcoats, Springfield Business Park, Chelmsford, CM2 5AE Tel: (01245) 453000 Fax: (01245) 453001 E-mail: enquiries@existalite.co.uk

▶ Trinity Protection Systems Ltd, Old Mill House, Oil Mill Lane, Clyst St. Mary, Exeter, EX5 1AG Tel: (01392) 874455 Fax: (01392) 875546 E-mail: info@trinityprotection.co.uk

Vitalighting Ltd, 4 Sutherland Court Moor Park Industrial Centre, Tolpits Lane, Watford, WD18 9NA Tel: (01923) 896476 Fax: (01923) 897741 E-mail: sales@vitalighting.com

Westman Systems Ltd, Unit 5-6 Thistle Park, Crossways Road, Bridgwater, Somerset, TA6 6LS Tel: (01278) 424717 Fax: (01278) 424718E-mail: westman.systems@lineone.net

Woodway Engineering Ltd, Lower Road, Barnacle, Shilton, Coventry, CV7 9LD Tel: (024) 7684 1750 Fax: (024) 7662 1796 E-mail: woodway@btconnect.com

EMERGENCY LIGHTING BATTERIES

Alcad, 1st Floor Unit 5 Astra Centre, Edinburgh Way, Harlow, Essex, CM20 2BN Tel: (01279) 772555 Fax: (01279) 420696 E-mail: carter.sarah@alcad.com

Bristol Batteries, Axis Business Centre, Westmead Trading Estate, Westmead, Swindon, SN5 7YS Tel: (01793) 616646 Fax: (01793) 490011 E-mail: sales@bristolbatteries.com

Celltech, Unit 3, Bldg 6 Tameside Bus Development Centre, Windmill Lane, Denton, Manchester, M34 3QS Tel: 0161-320 8096 Fax: 0161-320 3526 E-mail: sales@celltech-battery.co.uk

EMERGENCY LIGHTING MAINTENANCE OR TESTING SERVICES

Force Fire Consultants Ltd, 11 Gorse La Industrial Estate, Brunel Road, Clacton-on-Sea, Essex, CO15 4LU Tel: (01255) 221515 Fax: (01255) 222493 E-mail: info@forcefire.com

EMERGENCY LIGHTING SYSTEMS

▶ Icon Emergency Lighting Ltd, 9 Craven Way, Newmarket, Suffolk, CB8 0BW Tel: (01638) 561138 Fax: (01638) 561687 E-mail: sales@icon-emergencylighting.com

EMERGENCY OIL SPILLAGE STORAGE CONTAINERS

Fast Engineering Ltd, 5 Windmill Court, Antrim, BT41 2TX Tel: (028) 9442 8686 Fax: (028) 9442 9929 E-mail: info@fastank.com

G T Pollution Technology Ltd, 3 Medina Court, Arctic Road, Cowes, Isle Of Wight, PO31 7XD Tel: (01983) 280185 Fax: (01983) 280056 E-mail: info@lamor.com

EMERGENCY OR STANDBY GENERATOR SETS

Arun International (Power) Ltd, Unit F1, Dominion Way, Littlehampton, West Sussex, BN16 3HQ Tel: (01903) 850285 Fax: (01903) 850636 E-mail: sales@arunpower.co.uk

Bells Control Equipment Ltd, 49 Scrutton Street, London, EC2A 4XJ Tel: (020) 7729 1979 Fax: (020) 7729 3731 E-mail: bells@mcmh.clara.net

Eastleigh Power Plant, PO Box 199, Southampton, SO30 0WZ Tel: (023) 8040 7507 Fax: (01489) 780478 E-mail: epower@fpcad.com

International Power Generation, Unit 7c Carcroft Enterprise Park, Carcroft, Doncaster, South Yorkshire, DN6 8DD Tel: (01302) 722888 Fax: (01302) 721202 E-mail: sales@generator.co.uk

J Robinson Engineering Ltd, 12 Clarence Road, Fleet, Hampshire, GU51 3RZ Tel: (01252) 621312 Fax: (01252) 819100 E-mail: jim@jrobinsoneng.fsnet.co.uk

Musgrave Generators Ltd, 1 Enderby Road Industrial Estate, Whetstone, Leicester, LE8 6HZ Tel: 0116-286 1534 Fax: 0116-286 1559 E-mail: info@musgrave-generators.com

Sandhurst Manufacturing, Belchmire Lane, Gosberton, Spalding, Lincolnshire, PE11 4HG Tel: (01775) 840020 Fax: (01775) 843063 E-mail: info@sandhurst-mfg.com

T W Generators, 2 Long Marston Road, Marsworth, Tring, Hertfordshire, HP23 4NF Tel: (01296) 668420 Fax: (01296) 662064 E-mail: sales@twgenerators.co.uk

Wagenaar Generators Ltd, Gilfach-Y-Rhiw, Abergwili, Carmarthen, SA32 7ER Tel: (01267) 237078 Fax: (01267) 234113 E-mail: johndenver@amgenerators.com

Welland Engineering Ltd, 31a Cranmore Lane, Holbeach, Spalding, Lincolnshire, PE12 7HT Tel: (01406) 490660 Fax: (01406) 490444 E-mail: sales@generating-sets.com

EMERGENCY PROPERTY REINSTATEMENT, *See Property Reinstatement*

EMERGENCY REPAIR ROOFING CONTRACTORS

▶ Able, 10 Moretons Close, Whittlesey, Peterborough, PE7 1XP Tel: (01733) 208992 Fax: (01733) 208992 E-mail: ableroofing44@tiscali.co.uk

Accredited Roofing, 21 River Court, Minster Road, Coventry, CV1 3AT Tel: (024) 7625 6325 E-mail: enquires@accreditedroofing.co.uk

▶ Apex Roofing and building Maintenance, 28 Binley House, Highcliffe Drive, Roehampton, London, SW15 4PY Tel: 0208 392 9792 E-mail: masterson697@aol.com

▶ Edwards Roofing, 1 Jacksonville Farm, Towyn Way West, Towyn, Abergele, Clwyd, LL22 9LG Tel: (01745) 339411 Fax: (01745) 369232 E-mail: sales@edwards-roofing.co.uk

▶ Elevations Roofing Specialists (UK) Ltd, The Ridings, Biggin Hill, Westerham, Kent, TN16 3LE Tel: (0800) 5877765 Fax: (01959) 572462 E-mail: info@elevationsroofing.co.uk

EMERGENCY SHUTDOWN SYSTEMS

Arden Control Systems Ltd, Arden Street, New Mills, High Peak, Derbyshire, SK22 4NS Tel: (01663) 746060 Fax: (01663) 746189 E-mail: sales@ardencontrolsystems.co.uk

I C S Triplex, 10-14 Hall Road, Heybridge, Maldon, Essex, CM9 4LA Tel: (01621) 854444 Fax: (01621) 859221 E-mail: sales@icsplc.co.uk

Invensys Systems (UK) TLtd, 2 City Place, Beehive Ring Road, London Gatwick Airport, Gatwick, West Sussex, RH6 0PA Tel: (01293) 527777 Fax: (01293) 552640

Mge Ups Systems Ltd, Orion House, 171-177 High Street, Wealdstone, Harrow, Middlesex, HA3 5EA Tel: (020) 8861 4040 Fax: (020) 8861 2812 E-mail: jason.koffler@mgeups.com

Yokogawa UK Ltd, Solar House, Mercury Park, Wycombe Lane, Wooburn Green, High Wycombe, Buckinghamshire, HP10 0HH Tel: (01628) 535640 Fax: (0870) 2384342 E-mail: christine.amos@uk.yokogawa.co.uk

EMERGENCY WARNING SIRENS OR HOOTERS

Moflash Signalling, 18 Klaxon Tysley Industrial Estate, 751 Warwick Road, Tyseley, Birmingham, B11 2HA Tel: 0121-707 6681 Fax: 0121-707 8305 E-mail: uksales@moflash.co.uk

Premier Hazard Ltd, Moorfield Estate, Yeadon, Leeds, LS19 7BN Tel: 0113-239 1111 Fax: 0113-239 1131

S A Equipment Sales, Edison Point, Millmarsh Lane, Enfield, Middlesex, EN3 7QG Tel: (020) 8443 7420 Fax: (020) 8804 2655

Stirling Evp Ltd, 222 West Road, Westcliff-on-Sea, Essex, SS0 9DE Tel: (01702) 300999 Fax: (01702) 303039 E-mail: info@stirlingevp.com

Woodway Engineering Ltd, Lower Road, Barnacle, Shilton, Coventry, CV7 9LD Tel: (024) 7684 1750 Fax: (024) 7662 1796 E-mail: woodway@btconnect.com

EMOTIONAL INTELLIGENCE TRAINING

▶ Yogabuds Ltd, 47 Algers Road, Loughton, Essex, IG10 4NG Tel: 020 8508 3653

EMPLOYEE COMPENSATION CONSULTANCY

Organisation Resources Counsellors Inc, 127-131 Sloane Street, London, SW1X 9QP Tel: (020) 7591 5600 Fax: (020) 7591 5605 E-mail: sales@orcinc.co.uk

EMPLOYEE DEVELOPMENT CONSULTANCY

Collinson Grant, Ryecroft, Aviary Road, Worsley, Manchester, M28 2WF Tel: 0161-703 5600 Fax: 0161-790 9177 E-mail: postmaster@collinsongrant.com

▶ Effectivate Ltd., Brinkworth House, Brinkworth, Swindon, SN15 5DF Tel: 0870 1993867 Fax: 07005 801602 E-mail: info@effectivate.co.uk

FOCUS Eap, 1st Floor The Podium, Metropolitan House Darkes Lane, Potters Bar, Hertfordshire, EN6 1AG Tel: (01707) 661300 Fax: (01707) 661242 E-mail: info@focuseap.co.uk

Hay Group, Unit 2635 Kings Court, The Crescent, Birmingham Business Park, Birmingham, B37 7YE Tel: 0121-717 4600 Fax: 0121-717 4601

Mercuri International UK Ltd, 6 Olton Bridge, 245 Warwick Road, Solihull, West Midlands, B92 7AH Tel: 0121-706 3400 Fax: 0121-706 3900 E-mail: admin.london@mercuri.co.uk

Organisation Resources Counsellors Inc, 127-131 Sloane Street, London, SW1X 9QP Tel: (020) 7591 5600 Fax: (020) 7591 5605 E-mail: sales@orcinc.co.uk

EMPLOYEE INCENTIVE AWARDS

▶ Classic Motoring Ltd, Smilers Cottage, Brimpsfield, Gloucester, GL4 8LD Tel: (01452) 864050 E-mail: info@classicmotoring.co.uk

▶ Green Slate Trophies, 1 Derby Street, Burnley, Lancashire, BB11 1RL Tel: (01282) 411400 Fax: (01282) 432308

EMPLOYEE LIABILITY INSURANCE

▶ Goss & Co Insurance Brokers Ltd, Clarendon House, 59-75 Queen Road, Reading, RG1 4BN Tel: 0118-955 1800 Fax: 0118 955 1848 E-mail: insure@goss.co.uk

▶ Mike Robertson Associates, 3 Old Ladies Court, High Street, Battle, East Sussex, TN33 0AH Tel: (01424) 777156 Fax: (01424) 775668 E-mail: mike.robertson@mraltd.com

▶ Northern Counties Insurance Broker, NCi House, Lowreys Lane, Low Fell, Gateshead, Tyne & Wear, NE9 5JB Tel: 0191 482 1219 Fax: 0191 420 0097 E-mail: contactus@northerncounties.com

▶ Sandham Davies & Jones Ltd, 3 Park Square, Newport, Gwent, NP20 4EL Tel: (01633) 213063 Fax: (01633) 244316 E-mail: enquiries@sdandjones.co.uk

EMPLOYEE SCREENING CONSULTANCY

▶ Effectivate Ltd., Brinkworth House, Brinkworth, Swindon, SN15 5DF Tel: 0870 1993867 Fax: 07005 801602 E-mail: info@effectivate.co.uk

EMPLOYMENT AGENCIES, WORKING FROM HOME OR SECOND INCOME

▶ Bright Eyes Nanny Agency, 11 Gatley Drive, Guildford, Surrey, GU4 7JJ Tel: (01483) 506150 Fax: 01483 506150 E-mail: Brighteyesnannys@aol.com

▶ Playtime Nanny Agency, Burley, Bagshot Road, Knaphill, Woking, Surrey, GU21 2SG Tel: (01483) 488511 E-mail: sales@playtimenannies.co.uk

▶ UK Lottery Online, Unit 142 Roslyn Road, South Tottenham, London, N15 5JJ Tel: (020) 8800 7271 Fax: (020) 8800 7277 E-mail: info@uk-lotteryonline.co.uk

EMPLOYMENT MANAGEMENT SERVICES

1st Choice, 6 St. Ives Crescent, Sale, Cheshire, M33 3RU Tel: (07840) 344464 E-mail: firstchoicecvservices@ntlworld.com

▶ Nanny-Find Ltd Nanny Recruitment Agency, Bessemer Drive, Business & Technology Centre, Stevenage, Hertfordshire, SG1 2DX Tel: (0845) 6066162 E-mail: recruitment@nanny-find.co.uk

▶ Sickle Cell Network, 85 Raeburn Road, Northampton, NN2 7EP Tel: (0870) 8502271 E-mail: theokeclub@hotmail.com

EMPLOYMENT TRIBUNAL CONSULTANCY

▶ Steen & Co., Magdalen Centre, The Oxford Science Park, Oxford, OX4 4EA Tel: (01865) 784101 Fax: (01865) 784103 E-mail: mail@steenandco.co.uk

EMPTY TONER CARTRIDGES

▶ Laser Friend, Unit 14 15 Station Lane Industrial Estate, Station Lane, Old Whittington, Chesterfield, Derbyshire, S41 9QX Tel: (01246) 266010 Fax: (01246) 266011 E-mail: tony@laserfriend.com

▶ Speedbird Supplies, 15 Thistledown Drive, Ixworth, Bury St. Edmunds, Suffolk, IP31 2NH Tel: (01359) 235170 Fax: (01359) 232015 E-mail: sales@speedbird-supplies.co.uk

EMULSIFYING AGENTS

Danisco, Denington Road, Wellingborough, Northamptonshire, NN8 2QJ Tel: (01933) 304200 Fax: (01933) 304224

EMULSION PAINTS

C. Brewer & Sons Ltd, 81 Alston Drive, Bradwell Abbey, Milton Keynes, MK13 9HF Tel: (01908) 316719 Fax: (01908) 311423

Palatine Paints, Smallbrook Lane, Leigh, Lancashire, WN7 5PZ Tel: (01942) 884122 Fax: (01942) 887085

Plaspertex Paint Co. Ltd, 71 Mereside, Soham, Ely, Cambridgeshire, CB7 5EE Tel: (01353) 720796 Fax: (01353) 624327 E-mail: mail@plaspertex.co.uk

Resad Polymers Ltd, 53 Royce Close, West Portway Industrial Estate, Andover, Hampshire, SP10 3TS Tel: (01264) 334633 Fax: (01264) 332639 E-mail: sales@resad.co.uk

Teal & Mackrill Ltd, Lockwood Street, Hull, HU2 0HN Tel: (01482) 328053 Fax: (01482) 219266

ENAMELLED BADGES

Am Designer Logo Jewellers, Mount Pleasant, Barnet, Hertfordshire, EN4 9HH Tel: (020) 8441 3835 Fax: (020) 8440 7771 E-mail: info@promotionaljewellery.co.uk

Badgemans Recognition Express, 8 Hillside Industrial Estate, London Road, Horndean, Waterlooville, Hampshire, PO8 0BL Tel: (023) 9259 5509 Fax: (023) 9259 5528 E-mail: sales@re-southern.co.uk

Big Badge Co., Old School House, Victoria Avenue, London, N3 1GG Tel: (020) 8371 8752 Fax: (020) 8371 8751 E-mail: sales@theknightgroup.com

Diametric Technical Manufacturing Ltd, 26-28 Manners View, Newport, Isle of Wight, PO30 5FA Tel: (01983) 826611 Fax: (01983) 826622 E-mail: tad.james@diemetric-manufacturing.co.uk

Ernex Group, P O Box 53967, London, SW15 3UY Tel: (020) 7731 6707 Fax: (020) 7731 6703 E-mail: ties@ernex.co.uk

▶ Firmin & Sons P.L.C., Firmin House, 82-86 New Town Row, Birmingham, B6 4HU Tel: 0121-380 0800 Fax: 0121-359 3321 E-mail: sales@firmin.co.uk

Furnace End Fires, Ersthaus, Atherstone Road, Coleshill, Birmingham, B46 2LP Tel: (01675) 481653 E-mail: info@fefbadges.com

G L J Badges, Unit 10 Park Trading Estate, Park Road, Hockley, Birmingham, B18 5HB Tel: 0121-554 9869 Fax: 0121-523 9395 E-mail: sales@gijbadges.co.uk

Graphic Arts Coventry, 69-71 Hearsall Lane, Coventry, CV5 6HF Tel: (024) 7667 3415

▶ militarybadges.co.uk, 27 Post House Wynd, Darlington, County Durham, DL3 7LP Tel: (01325) 489820 E-mail: diamondmerchants@btopenworld.com

Pinpoint Badges & Promotions Ltd, Alma Road, Sidcup, Kent, DA14 4EA Tel: (020) 8302 8008 Fax: (020) 8302 4008 E-mail: sales@pinpointbadges.com

Rebus Badges & Regalia Ltd, Clayfields, Bodenham, Hereford, HR1 3LG Tel: (01568) 797401 Fax: (01568) 797402 E-mail: sales@e-badges.co.uk

S M T Associates Ltd, 17 Sandford Street, Lichfield, Staffordshire, WS13 6QA Tel: (01543) 250211 Fax: (01543) 257015 E-mail: sales@smtbadges.co.uk

▶ Selcraft Ltd, Leigh Sinton, Malvern, Worcestershire, WR13 5XS Tel: (01886) 834850 Fax: (01886) 834851 E-mail: info@selcraft.com

Shaw Munster Ltd, Winster Grove, Great Barr, Birmingham, B44 9EG Tel: 0121-360 4279 Fax: 0121-360 4265 E-mail: office@shawmunstergroup.co.uk

Stylex, 49 Berwick Street, London, W1F 8SH Tel: (020) 7437 2428 Fax: (020) 7437 0649 E-mail: sales@style-x.co.uk

Surrey Embroidery Co. Ltd, 7 Linkfield Corner, Redhill, RH1 1BD Tel: (01737) 766691 Fax: (01737) 780666 E-mail: enquiries@surreyembroidery.co.uk

Toye Kenning & Spencer Ltd, Regalia House, Newtown Road, Bedworth, Warwickshire, CV12 8QR Tel: (024) 7631 5634 Fax: (024) 7664 3018 E-mail: sales@toye.com

W Reeves Badges Ltd, 34-35 Tenby Street, Birmingham, B1 3EE Tel: 0121-236 3731 Fax: 0121-236 3731 E-mail: sales@reevesbadges.co.uk

West Country Marketing Advertising, Unit 1 Woodend Lane Industrial Estate, Stoke Lacy, Bromyard, Herefordshire, HR7 4HQ Tel: (01885) 490500 Fax: (01885) 490585 E-mail: sales@wcma.co.uk

ENAMELLED SIGNS

Harper Signs Ltd, 12-20 Diana Street, Newcastle upon Tyne, NE4 6DA Tel: 0191-232 4926 Fax: 0191-261 0676 E-mail: sales@harpersigns.co.uk

Sign Workshop, 8 The Ridgeway, Hitchin, Hertfordshire, SG5 2BT Tel: (01462) 442440 Fax: (01462) 442440 E-mail: sales@thesignworkshop.co.uk

Trico VE Ltd, 76 Windmill Hill, Colley Gate, Halesowen, West Midlands, B63 2BZ Tel: (01384) 569555 Fax: (01384) 565777 E-mail: anjella@trico-ve.co.uk

ENAMELLED WARE

Bilston & Battersea Enamels, 14-16 Barton Park, Mount Pleasant, Bilston, West Midlands, WV14 7LH Tel: (01902) 408440 Fax: (01902) 492162 E-mail: sales@bilstonandbattersea.com

▶ Crummles English Enamels, The Workshops, Weston Coyney Road, Stoke-on-Trent, ST3 5JT Tel: (01782) 599948 Fax: (01782) 599397 E-mail: sales@crummles.com

Lubkowski Saunders & Associates Designs & Exports Ltd, E Dolphin Estate, Windmill Road West, Sunbury-on-Thames, Middlesex, TW16 7HE Tel: (01932) 789721 Fax: (01932) 789793 E-mail: sales@lsa-international.co.uk

Nimbus Products (Sheffield) Ltd, Julian Way, Tyler Street Industrial Estate, Sheffield, S9 1GD Tel: 0114-243 2362 Fax: 0114-243 5046 E-mail: sales@nimbusproducts.co.uk

ENAMELS

Am Designer Logo Jewellers, Mount Pleasant, Barnet, Hertfordshire, EN4 9HH Tel: (020) 8441 3835 Fax: (020) 8440 7771 E-mail: info@promotionaljewellery.co.uk

▶ Diatherm & Ancillary Equipment, Gresham Works, Mornington Road, London, E4 7DR Tel: (020) 8524 9546 Fax: (020) 8524 9546 E-mail: diatherm@talk21.com

Intercoat Industrial Paints & Lacquers Ltd, Bridgeman Street, Walsall, WS2 9NW Tel: (01922) 638821 Fax: (01922) 722952

Kingstonian Paints Ltd, Sculcoates Lane, Hull, HU5 1DR Tel: (01482) 342216 Fax: (01482) 493096 E-mail: info@kpaints.co.uk

Trico VE Ltd, 76 Windmill Hill, Colley Gate, Halesowen, West Midlands, B63 2BZ Tel: (01384) 569555 Fax: (01384) 565777 E-mail: anjella@trico-ve.co.uk

ENCAPSULATED TRANSFORMERS

Carnhill Transformers Ltd, 4 Edison Road, St. Ives, Cambridgeshire, PE27 3LT Tel: (01480) 462978 Fax: (01480) 496196 E-mail: sales@carnhill.co.uk

ENCAPSULATED TRANSFORMERS – *continued*

Clairtronic Ltd, Shuttleworth Road, Elm Farm Industrial Estate, Bedford, MK41 0EP Tel: (01234) 330774 Fax: (01234) 330775 E-mail: sales@clairtronic.co.uk

ENCAPSULATING MACHINES/ SYSTEMS

D & K (Europe) Ltd, Unit 38-40, Crossgate Road, Park Farm Industrial Estate, Redditch, Worcestershire, B98 7SN Tel: (01527) 520073 Fax: (01527) 524056 E-mail: info@dkeurope.co.uk

Mouldex Automation Ltd, 6, William Lee Buildings, Nottingham Science & Technology Park, University Boulevard, Nottingham, NG7 2RQ Tel: (0845) 0453136 Fax: (07930) 361652 E-mail: michael.pickles@mouldexautomation.com

Tube Tec, Spurryhillock Industrial Estate, Broomhill Road, Stonehaven, Kincardineshire, AB39 2NH Tel: (01569) 762211 Fax: (01569) 768065 E-mail: sales@tubetec.co.uk

ENCAPSULATING MATERIALS

Bentley Chemicals Ltd, Unit 17 Hoo Farm Industrial Estate, Worcester Road, Kidderminster, Worcestershire, DY11 7RA Tel: (01562) 515121 Fax: (01562) 515847 E-mail: info@bentleychemicals.co.uk

R W Greeff, Tame Park, Vanguard, Wilnecote, Tamworth, Staffordshire, B77 5DY Tel: (01827) 255200 Fax: (01827) 255255 E-mail: rwgreeff@univareurope.com

ENCAPSULATING SHELLS

M W Encap Ltd, Oakbank Park Way, Mid Calder, Livingston, West Lothian, EH53 0TH Tel: (01506) 448080 Fax: (01506) 448081 E-mail: enquiries@encapdrugdelivery.com

ENCAPSULATION SERVICES TO THE ELECTRONICS INDUSTRY

Brookvine, Flitch Industrial Estate, Chelmsford Road, Dunmow, Essex, CM6 1XJ Tel: (01371) 875663 Fax: (01371) 875665 E-mail: brookvine@essex-x-ray.com

McKinlay Electrical Manufacturing Co. Ltd, 62 Weir Rd, Wimbledon, London, SW19 8UG Tel: (020) 8879 1141 Fax: (020) 8946 3047 E-mail: mckinlayelec@aol.com

Resin Technical Systems, 6 Alphage Road, Gosport, Hampshire, PO12 4DU Tel: (023) 9258 5899 Fax: (023) 9251 0306 E-mail: sales@resintek.co.uk

ENCAPSULATION SERVICES TO THE PRINT INDUSTRY

Ape Image Consultants, 36-40 Bloomfield Avenue, Luton, LU2 0PT Tel: (01582) 483718 Fax: (01582) 454518 E-mail: sales@apeimage.co.uk

Claymore Signs, 498 Knutsford Road, Warrington, WA4 1DX Tel: (01925) 573091 Fax: (01925) 630900 E-mail: claymoresigns@aol.com

Encapsulated Print Services, Unit 3a Prince William Way, Loughborough, Leicestershire, LE11 5DD Tel: (01509) 230892 Fax: (01509) 230877 E-mail: encapprintmids@aol.com

Encapsulating Co. Ltd, 3-11 Pensbury Place, London, SW8 4TP Tel: (020) 7498 6700 Fax: (020) 7498 6749 E-mail: admin@encapsulating.co.uk

Encore Encapsulation Ltd, Swallow Mill, Swallow Street, Stockport, Cheshire, SK1 3HJ Tel: 0161-476 2646 Fax: 0161-476 2646 E-mail: sales@encoreencapsulation.co.uk

Laminating East Midlands, 26 Low Farm Place, Moulton Park Industrial Estate, Northampton, NN3 6HY Tel: (01604) 642823 Fax: (01604) 790423 E-mail: postmaster@eml.uk.com

Libran Laminations Ltd, Coles Green Road, London, NW2 7HW Tel: (020) 8452 2006 Fax: (020) 8452 4456 E-mail: info@libranlaminations.co.uk

Plastic Art Company, Unit 7 Glover Way, Leeds, LS11 5JP Tel: 0113-271 7744 Fax: 0113-271 9590

Polymaps, 41 Truro Rd, St. Austell, Cornwall, PL25 5JE Tel: (01726) 66666 Fax: (01726) 64797

Thames Loose Leaf, 289 Kiln Road, Benfleet, Essex, SS7 1QS Tel: (01702) 551155 Fax: (01702) 559068 E-mail: sales@thameslooseleaf.co.uk

ENCLOSED SWITCHES

N S F Controls Ltd, Ingrow Bridge Works, Keighley, West Yorkshire, BD21 5EF Tel: (01535) 661144 Fax: (01535) 661474 E-mail: sales@nsfcontrols.co.uk

U K Solenoid Ltd, 115 London Road, Newbury, Berkshire, RG14 2AH Tel: (01635) 45991 Fax: (01635) 37807E-mail: sales@uksol.co.uk

ENCLOSURE CONSTRUCTION SYSTEMS

Edgar Engineering Co., Woods Way Industrial Estate, Goring-By-Sea, Worthing, West Sussex, BN12 4QY Tel: (01903) 505056 Fax: (01903) 506456 E-mail: edgareng@btconnect.com

ENCLOSURE CONSULTANTS OR DESIGNERS

Armagard Ltd, Unit 9 Fortnum Close, Birmingham, B33 0LG Tel: 0121-608 7210 Fax: 0121-608 4477 E-mail: sales@armagard.co.uk

Eurocraft Trustees Ltd, Cinderbank, Netherton, Dudley, West Midlands, DY2 9AE Tel: (01384) 230101 Fax: (01384) 256883 E-mail: sales@eurocraft.co.uk

Product Group, Unit 40a Colbourne CR, Nelson Park, Cramlington, Northumberland, NE23 1WB Tel: (01670) 730784 Fax: (01670) 734915 E-mail: product@theproductgroup.co.uk

ENCLOSURE ROBOT GUARDS

Industrial Machine Guards, 2 Dormston Trading Estate, Burton Road, Dudley, West Midlands, DY1 2UF Tel: (01902) 676485 Fax: (01902) 880987

ENCLOSURES FOR INDUSTRIAL APPLICATIONS

▶ 1A Enclosures, Unit 2 Highmoor Park, Clitheroe, Lancashire, BB7 1NP Tel: (07790) 633624 Fax: (07790) 633624 E-mail: grahamgallagher@environmentalenclosure.com

Sure Punch Precision Ltd, Tameside Mills, Park Road, Dukinfield, Cheshire, SK16 5PU Tel: 0161-343 7999 Fax: 0161-343 8999 E-mail: surepunch@surepunch.co.uk

ENCLOSURES TO SPECIFICATION

Armagard Ltd, Unit 9 Fortnum Close, Birmingham, B33 0LG Tel: 0121-608 7210 Fax: 0121-608 4477 E-mail: sales@armagard.co.uk

Halton Panelcraft Ltd, 2 Gavin Road, Widnes, Cheshire, WA8 8RE Tel: 0151-424 0022 Fax: 0151-424 2058 E-mail: panelcraft@lineone.net

Hitherbest Ltd, Heath Hill Court, Heath Hill Industrial Estate, Dawley, Telford, Shropshire, TF4 2RH Tel: (01952) 632100 Fax: (01952) 632109 E-mail: sales@hitherbest.co.uk

▶ Tempa Pano UK, Unit 5, Centre 21 Industrial Estate, Bridge Lane, Woolston, Warrington, WA1 4AW Tel: 0845 4941730 Fax: (01925) 810386 E-mail: info@tempapano.co.uk

ENCLOSURES, GLASS FIBRE OR FIBREGLASS, INSTRUMENTATION

A B Controls & Technology Ltd, Sanderson Street, Lower Don Valley, Sheffield, S9 2UA Tel: 0114-244 2424 Fax: 0114-243 4312 E-mail: info@ab-tech.co.uk

Intertec, Unit 5, Verwood Industrial Estate, Black Hill, Verwood, Dorset, BH31 6HA Tel: (01202) 822277 Fax: (01202) 821188 E-mail: sales@intertec-inst.co.uk

ENCLOSURES, MARINE, ELECTRICAL/ELECTRONIC EQUIPMENT

Furuno UK Ltd, Ocean House Parklands Business Park, Forest Road, Denmead, Waterlooville, Hampshire, PO7 6XP Tel: (023) 9223 0303 Fax: (023) 9223 0101 E-mail: denmead@furunouk.freeserve.co.uk

ENCLOSURES, RADIO FREQUENCY INTERFERENCE (RFI) AND ELECTROMAGNETIC INTERFERENCE (EMI)

▶ www.caelectrocomps.co.uk, 36 Park Lane, Bishop's Stortford, Hertfordshire, CM23 3NH Tel: (01279) 656051 Fax: (01279) 656051 E-mail: chris@caelectrocomps.co.uk

ENCODER MANUFRS, *See also headings for particular types under Encoders*

Crystal Structures Ltd, Crystal Park, Tunbridge Lane, Bottisham, Cambridge, CB25 9EA Tel: (01223) 811451 Fax: (01223) 811452 E-mail: sales@crystalstructures.co.uk

Heidenhain (GB) Ltd, 200 London Road, Burgess Hill, West Sussex, RH15 9RD Tel: (01444) 247711 Fax: (01444) 870024 E-mail: sales@heidenhain.co.uk

Hohner Automation Ltd, Unit 15 Whitegate Industrial Estate, Whitegate Road, Wrexham, Clwyd, LL13 8UG Tel: (01978) 363888 Fax: (01978) 364586 E-mail: uksales@hohner.com

Meridian Audio Ltd, Stonehill, Stukeley Meadows Industrial Es, Huntingdon, Cambridgeshire, PE29 6EX Tel: (01480) 445678 Fax: (01480) 445686

Screen Subtitling Systems Ltd, Old Rectory, Church Lane, Claydon, Ipswich, IP6 0EQ Tel: (01473) 831700 Fax: (01473) 830078 E-mail: sales@screen.subtitling.com

Siko Ltd, Unit 6, Cod Beck Estate, Dalton, Thirsk, North Yorkshire, YO7 3HR Tel: (01845) 578845 Fax: (01845) 577781 E-mail: sales@siko-uk.com

T R Controls Ltd, 12a Oak Industrial Park, Chelmsford Road, Dunmow, Essex, CM6 1XN Tel: (01371) 876187 Fax: (01371) 876287 E-mail: alan@trcontrols.co.uk

W + S Measuring Systems Ltd, Queens House, The Square, Corwen, Clwyd, LL21 0DG Tel: (01490) 413550 Fax: (01490) 413014 E-mail: info.uk@globalencoder.com

ENCYCLOPAEDIA PUBLISHERS

A1 Copying Systems & Supplies Ltd, 36 Church Street, Leighton Buzzard, Bedfordshire, LU7 1BT Tel: (01525) 371333 Fax: (01525) 371339 E-mail: a1copyingsys@btclick.com

Burrows Communications Ltd, 106 Stafford Road, Wallington, Surrey, SM6 9AY Tel: (020) 8773 3000 Fax: (020) 8773 8888 E-mail: generalservices@burrows.co.uk

END FEED PIPELINE FITTINGS

▶ just-endfeed, PO Box, 473, Harrogate, North Yorkshire, HG3 2ZL Tel: 0845 300060 Fax: 0845 300080 E-mail: sales@just-endfeed.co.uk

END FEED TUBE FITTINGS

▶ just-endfeed, PO Box, 473, Harrogate, North Yorkshire, HG3 2ZL Tel: 0845 300060 Fax: 0845 300080 E-mail: sales@just-endfeed.co.uk

ENDOSCOPES/INTROSCOPES

IntroVision, Units 6-7, The Glover Centre, 23-25 Bury Mead Road, Hitchin, Hertfordshire, SG4 1RP Tel: (01462) 459400 Fax: (01462) 459500 E-mail: introvision@ukonline.co.uk

Microscopix Medical Equipment Mnfrs, Unit 18 Impressapark, Pindar Road, Hoddesdon, Hertfordshire, EN11 0DL Tel: (01992) 469085 Fax: (01992) 470541 E-mail: atrh@mx-l.com

Ultrafine Technology Ltd, Unit 14 Brook Lane Business Centre, Brook Lane North, Brentford, Middlesex, TW8 0PP Tel: (020) 8569 9920 Fax: (020) 8569 9649 E-mail: sales@ultrafinetechnology.co.uk

ENERGY ABSORBING ELEMENTS

Plascore (UK), PO Box 2, Cheltenham, Gloucestershire, GL54 5YR Tel: (0871) 918 1525 Fax: (0871) 918 1525 E-mail: info@coretexgroup.co.uk

ENERGY BROKERS

Energy Solutions, 33 Kyle Crescent, Dunfermline, Fife, KY11 8GU Tel: (01383) 732088 Fax: (0870) 1341377 E-mail: info@energybrokers.co.uk

ENERGY CONSERVATION EQUIPMENT, *See also headings for particular types*

Allen Martin Conservation Ltd, 504 Dudley Road, Wolverhampton, WV2 3AA Tel: (01902) 560065 Fax: (01902) 560066 E-mail: support@allen-martin.co.uk

Thermwatch Ltd, 1 Bridge Court, Fishergate, Norwich, NR3 1UF Tel: (01603) 760255 Fax: (01603) 761276 E-mail: enquiries@thermwatch.co.uk

ENERGY CONSERVATION OR EFFICIENCY CONSULTANCY

Allen Martin Conservation Ltd, 504 Dudley Road, Wolverhampton, WV2 3AA Tel: (01902) 560065 Fax: (01902) 560066 E-mail: support@allen-martin.co.uk

The Bamford Group, Millgate, Market Street, Shawforth, Rochdale, Lancashire, OL12 8NX Tel: (01706) 897100 Fax: (01706) 897101 E-mail: bamford.group@virgin.net

Blezard Ltd, 44 Garstang Road, Preston, PR1 1NA Tel: (01772) 258511 Fax: (01772) 258265 E-mail: mail@blezard.co.uk

Ceramic Research Ltd, Queens Road, Stoke-on-Trent, ST4 7LQ Tel: (01782) 764444 Fax: (01782) 412331 E-mail: sales@ceram.co.uk

Charles Taylor Consulting, International House, 1 St.Katherines Way, London, E1W 1UT Tel: (020) 7759 4955 Fax: (020) 7481 9545 E-mail: info@charlestaylorconsulting.com

Consumers Utility Costs Ltd, C U C House, Crawley, West Sussex, RH11 9BN Tel: (01293) 516521 Fax: (01293) 512030 E-mail: sales@consumers-utility-cost.co.uk

Dalkia Utilities plc, Oakenshaw Lane, Crofton, Wakefield, West Yorkshire, WF4 1SE Tel: (01924) 258331 Fax: (01924) 259585

▶ Ecomiser, Cliftonville Chambers, 46 Billing Road, Northampton, NN1 5DB Tel: 01604 516750 Fax: 01604 516109 E-mail: info@ecomiser.co.uk

Ecotec Research & Consulting Ltd, 12-26 Albert Street, Birmingham, B4 7UD Tel: 0121-616 3600 Fax: 0121-616 3699 E-mail: welcome@ecotec.co.uk

▶ Energy Economisers Ltd, 1 Ewhurst Avenue, Birmingham, B29 6EY Tel: 0121-471 3038 Fax: 0121-471 3039 E-mail: sales@energyeconomisers.co.uk

▶ Entech Usb, 24/26 Aire Street, Leeds, LS1 4HT Tel: 0113-234 4048 Fax: 0113-234 3383 E-mail: info@entech.usb.co.uk

F E C Services Ltd, National Agricultural Centre, Stoneleigh Park, Kenilworth, Warwickshire, CV8 2LS Tel: (024) 7669 6512 Fax: (024) 7669 6360 E-mail: sales@farmenergy.com

Gardner Energy Management Ltd, 1 John Street, Bristol, BS1 Tel: 0117-917 7010 Fax: 0117-917 7011 E-mail: enq@gemtrap.co.uk

Heat Pump Technology, Woodlands, Brackendene Drive, Gateshead, Tyne & Wear, NE9 6DP Tel: 0191-482 3922 Fax: 0191-482 3922 E-mail: john@jweddle.freeserve.co.uk

Integrated Energy Systems Ltd, 11a Lune Street, Preston, PR1 2NL Tel: (01772) 250707 Fax: (01772) 258322 E-mail: admin@intergratedenergy.co.uk

John Hall Ltd, 9 Piries Place, Horsham, West Sussex, RH12 1EH Tel: (01403) 269430 Fax: (01403) 269451 E-mail: info@jhal.com

▶ JSH Energy Solutions Ltd, Ardennais House, 6 Sorrel Horse Mews, Grimwade Street, Ipswich, IP4 1LN Tel: 0845 050 5830 Fax: 01473 232137 E-mail: andrew.lashley@jshipswich.co.uk

Kyron, Oak Cottage, Benty Heath Lane, Willaston, Neston, CH64 1SB Tel: 0151-327 1957 Fax: 0151-327 7410 E-mail: john.hardman@kyron.co.uk

Mabbett & Associates Ltd, Mabbett House, 11 Sandyford Place, Glasgow, G3 7NB Tel: 0141-227 2300 Fax: 0141 227 2301 E-mail: bradley@mabbett.com

Mckiernan Group Ltd, Crown St Works, Crown Street, Accrington, Lancashire, BB5 0RW Tel: (01254) 398532 Fax: (01254) 392157 E-mail: design@themckiernangroup.co.uk

Northern Engineering Services, 16 Kew Gardens, Whitley Bay, Tyne & Wear, NE26 3LY Tel: 0191-253 4390 Fax: 0191-251 6674 E-mail: dshort@northeng.freeserve.co.uk

Novacroft Ltd, Harvest Barn Spring Hill, Harborough Road, Pitsford, Northampton, NN6 9AA Tel: (01604) 889500 Fax: (01604) 889508 E-mail: clivenotley@novacroft.com

Proto Associates, 26 Fox Lane, Hilltop, Bromsgrove, Worcestershire, B61 7NL Tel: (01527) 831567 Fax: (01527) 831567 E-mail: aturchyn@globalnet.co.uk

Redwood Energy Ltd, 68a High St, Ware, Herts, SG12 9DA Tel: (08700) 777999 Fax: (01920) 460071 E-mail: phil-coles@redwoodenergy.co.uk

Smart Cool Systems (UK) Ltd, Westgate, 104 High Street, Alton, Hampshire, GU34 1EN Tel: (01420) 544868 Fax: (01420) 544723 E-mail: enquries@smartcool.co.uk

Southern Heating Co., 272 South Coast Road, Peacehaven, East Sussex, BN10 7PD Tel: (01273) 588123 Fax: (01273) 588121 E-mail: southtg@fastnet.co.uk

▶ Stroma, Stroma Unit 4, Pioneer Way, Pioneer Business Park, Wakefield, West Yorkshire, WF10 5QU Tel: 0845 6211111 Fax: 0845 6211112 E-mail: info@stroma.com

Thermwatch Ltd, 1 Bridge Court, Fishergate, Norwich, NR3 1UF Tel: (01603) 760255 Fax: (01603) 761276 E-mail: enquiries@thermwatch.co.uk

ENERGY CONSERVATION SERVICES

▶ The Environment Shop Ltd, 25 Daggett Road, Cleethorpes, South Humberside, DN35 0EP Tel: (01472) 200023 E-mail: barrie_davis@hotmail.com

▶ indicates data change since last edition

ENERGY CONSERVATION TRAINING CONSULTANCY

Kyron, Oak Cottage, Benty Heath Lane, Willaston, Neston, CH64 1SB Tel: 0151-327 1957 Fax: 0151-327 7410 E-mail: john.hardman@kyron.co.uk

ENERGY CONSULTANCY

▶ Energyfactor, Chichester Way, Maldon, Essex, CM9 6YY Tel: (01621) 874801 E-mail: energyfactor@tiscali.co.uk

ENERGY CONTROL OR CONSERVATION SYSTEMS

CDS Meter Operatorrs, Little Wood Ho, Wheatley Rd, Sturton-le-steeple, Retford, Notts, DN22 9HU Tel: 01427 881551 Fax: 01427 881511

▶ ENERG P.L.C., ENER-G House, Daniel Adamson Road, Salford, M50 1DT Tel: 0161-745 7450 Fax: 0161-745 7457 E-mail: info@energ.co.uk

John Hall Ltd, 9 Piries Place, Horsham, West Sussex, RH12 1EH Tel: (01403) 269430 Fax: (01403) 269451 E-mail: info@jhal.com

Redwood Energy Ltd, 68a High St, Ware, Herts, SG12 9DA Tel: (08700) 777999 Fax: (01920) 460071 E-mail: phil-coles@redwoodenergy.co.uk

Thermwatch Ltd, 1 Bridge Court, Fishergate, Norwich, NR3 1UF Tel: (01603) 760255 Fax: (01603) 761276 E-mail: enquiries@thermwatch.co.uk

▶ Watersavers Water Treatment Equipment, Earl Road, Rackheath Industrial Estate, Rackheath, Norwich, NR13 6NT Tel: (01603) 720999 Fax: (01603) 721499 E-mail: sales@watersavers-norwich.co.uk

Western Regional Energy Agency Network, 1 Nugents Entry, Enniskillen, County Fermanagh, BT74 7DF Tel: (028) 6632 8269 Fax: (028) 6632 9771

ENERGY COST OR TARIFF CONSULTANCY

Argyle Energy, Stirling University Innovtn Park, Stirling, FK9 4NF Tel: (01786) 451030 Fax: (01786) 473688 E-mail: energy@argyleuk.com

Control Energy Costs Ltd, Tollers Farm, Drive Road, Coulsdon, Surrey, CR5 1BN Tel: (01737) 556631 Fax: (01737) 553601 E-mail: analysts@cec.uk.com

▶ The Energy Helpline, Unit 8, Great Guildford House, 30 Great Guildford Street, London, SE1 0HS Tel: (020) 74018943

▶ Entech Usb, 24/26 Aire Street, Leeds, LS1 4HT Tel: 0113-234 4048 Fax: 0113-234 3383 E-mail: info@entech.usb.co.uk

Inenco Group Ltd, Petros House, St. Andrews Road North, Lytham St. Annes, Lancashire, FY8 2NF Tel: (01253) 785000 Fax: (01253) 785001 E-mail: enquiries@inenco.com

Integrated Energy Systems Ltd, 11a Lune Street, Preston, PR1 2NL Tel: (01772) 250707 Fax: (01772) 258322 E-mail: admin@intergratedenergy.co.uk

Nus Consulting Group, Regent House, Queensway, Redhill, RH1 1QT Tel: (01737) 781200 Fax: (01737) 766799 E-mail: service@nusconsulting.co.uk

Utility Options, 78 Northgate Street, Chester, CH1 2HR Tel: (0800) 1950123 Fax: (01352) 781813 E-mail: enquiries@utility-options.co.uk

ENERGY EFFICIENT LIGHTING

Adv Lighting Ltd, 22 Electric Avenue, Harrogate, North Yorkshire, HG1 2BB Tel: (01423) 545493 Fax: (0845) 2801640 E-mail: advlighting@advlighting.co.uk

Ballast Tools (UK) Ltd, Unit 4 County Park Business Centre, Shrivenham Road, Swindon, SN1 2NR Tel: (01793) 697800 Fax: (01793) 527020 E-mail: btukltd@aol.com

Commercial Lighting Systems Ltd, Unit 16-17, Park Gate Business Centre, Chandlers Way, Park Gate, Southampton, SO31 1FQ Tel: (01489) 581002 Fax: (01489) 576262 E-mail: sales@commercial-lighting.co.uk

Llumarlite Ltd, Unit 30, Anglo Business Park, Smeaton Close, Aylesbury, Buckinghamshire, HP19 8UP Tel: (01296) 436666 Fax: (01296) 435533 E-mail: info@llumarlite.co.uk

ENERGY FROM WASTE SYSTEMS

▶ Ampliflaire Ltd, Off The Square Trade Centre, Bowmont Street, Kelso, Roxburghshire, TD5 7JH Tel: (01573) 225209 Fax: (01573) 225886

G E M Operations Ltd, Unit 20 Romsey Industrial Estate, Greatbridge Road, Romsey, Hampshire, SO51 0HR Tel: (01794) 519022 Fax: (01794) 516750 E-mail: sales@gem-ltd.co.uk

Lentjes UK Ltd, Dukes Court, Duke Street, Woking, Surrey, GU21 5BH Tel: (01483) 730044 Fax: (01483) 729595

ENERGY GIVING MEDICINES

▶ Touch Alternative Health, PO Box 4462, London, W1A 7NX Tel: 020 7935 2205 Fax: 020 7935 2008 E-mail: getintouch@londontouch.com

ENERGY MANAGEMENT CONTRACTORS OR INSTALLATION OR SERVICING

Allen Martin Conservation Ltd, 504 Dudley Road, Wolverhampton, WV2 3AA Tel: (01902) 560065 Fax: (01902) 560066 E-mail: support@allen-martin.co.uk

Associated Contract Energy Ltd, 73-75 Church Road, Redfield, Bristol, BS5 9JR Tel: 0117-939 4495 Fax: 0117-939 4496 E-mail: vivre21@hotmail.com

Consumers Utility Costs Ltd, C U C House, Crawley, West Sussex, RH11 9BN Tel: (01293) 516521 Fax: (01293) 512030 E-mail: sales@consumers-utility-cost.co.uk

Dalkia Utilities plc, Oakenshaw Lane, Crofton, Wakefield, West Yorkshire, WF4 1SE Tel: (01924) 258331 Fax: (01924) 259585

Dalkia Utilities Services plc, 12 London Road, Nottingham, NG2 3AB Tel: 0115-950 2816 Fax: 0115-953 6646

Elyo Services, Apian House, Selinas Lane, Dagenham, Essex, RM8 1TB Tel: (020) 8252 2929 Fax: (020) 8270 7379

▶ Mitsui Babcock Services Ltd, PO Box 8, Tipton, West Midlands, DY4 8YY Tel: 0121-557 3451

Mowlem Engineering Solutions, Bewley Court, Bylands Way, Belasis Hall Technology Park, Billingham, Cleveland, TS23 4EB Tel: (01642) 371313 Fax: (01642) 373101

Mowlem Water Engineering, Port Causeway, Bromborough, Wirral, Merseyside, CH62 4TP Tel: 0151-334 4990 Fax: 0151-334 9403

Parkersell Lighting, 4th Floor The Connect Centre, Kingstone Crescent, Portsmouth, PO2 8AD Tel: (023) 9262 3700 Fax: (023) 9262 3720 E-mail: enquiries@parkersell.com

▶ S T C Energy Management Ltd, STC House, 38 Croydon Road, Beckenham, Kent, BR3 4BJ Tel: (020) 8662 6500 Fax: (020) 8662 6501

Vickers Electronics Ltd, Alliance House, Westpoint Enterprise Park, Trafford Park, Manchester, M17 1QS Tel: (0870) 7420808 Fax: (0870) 7480808 E-mail: info@vickers-electronics.co.uk

ENERGY MANAGEMENT INSTRUMENTATION

Albar Associates, Meridian House, Road One, Winsford, Cheshire, CW7 3QG Tel: (01606) 861351 Fax: (01606) 861643 E-mail: albar@albar-energy.co.uk

Coster Environmental Controls Ltd, Unit 5 Sir Francis Ley Indust Park, Derby, DE23 8XA Tel: (01332) 200555 Fax: (01332) 204181

▶ D H P, Bracewell House, Broughton, Skipton, North Yorkshire, BD23 3AG Tel: (01756) 702480 Fax: (01756) 702489 E-mail: info@optimaenergy.net

Kane Group Ltd, Kane House, Swallowfield, Welwyn Garden City, Hertfordshire, AL7 1JG Tel: (01707) 375550 Fax: (01707) 393277 E-mail: sales@kane.co.uk

Marnic Technology Ltd, Station Road, Reddish, Stockport, Cheshire, SK5 6ND Tel: 0161-431 3662 E-mail: sales@marnict.demon.co.uk

Sauter Automations, Inova House Hampshire Int Business Park, Crockford Lane, Chineham, Basingstoke, Hampshire, RG24 8WH Tel: (01256) 374400 Fax: (01256) 374455 E-mail: info@uk.sauter-bc.com

ENERGY MANAGEMENT OR CONTROL OR REGULATOR SYSTEMS

Anglesey Geophysical Service Ltd, Unit 1, Mona Industrial Park, Gwalchmai, Holyhead, Gwynedd, LL65 4RJ Tel: (01407) 720333 Fax: (01248) 853874 E-mail: anglesey-geophysical@dial.tipex.com

C P Electronic Ltd, Unit 2 Abbey Manufacturing Estate, Wembley, Middlesex, HA0 1RR Tel: (020) 8900 0671 Fax: (020) 8900 0674 E-mail: enquiry@cpelectronics.co.uk

Celsius Energy Control Ltd, Systems House, 15 Station Road, High Wycombe, Buckinghamshire, HP13 6AD Tel: (01494) 688000 Fax: (01494) 688019 E-mail: general@celsisenergy.co.uk

Chalmor Ltd, 1 Telmere Industrial Estate, Albert Road, Luton, LU1 3QF Tel: (01582) 748700 Fax: (01582) 748748 E-mail: sales@chalmor.co.uk

Charter Tech Ltd, Leanne Business Centre, Sandford Lane, Wareham, Dorset, BH20 4DY Tel: (01929) 553000 Fax: (01929) 550022 E-mail: paul.burns@charter-tech.com

E C S Phillips Lighting Controls, Phillips Centre, Guildford Business Park, Guildford, Surrey, GU2 8XH Tel: (01483) 293235 Fax: (01483) 575534 E-mail: ecs.phillips@phillips.com

Elcomponent Ltd, Unit 5 Southmill Trading Centre, Southmill Road, Bishop's Stortford, Hertfordshire, CM23 3DY Tel: (01279) 503173 Fax: (01279) 654441 E-mail: sales@elcomponent.co.uk

Electronic & Technical Services Ltd, Unit 32, Price St Business Centre, Birkenhead, Merseyside, CH41 4JQ Tel: 0151-670 1897 Fax: 0151-652 9941

Electrotech Maintenance Services, Clarkswell House, Sugarswell Business Park, Shennington, Banbury, Oxon, OX15 6HW Tel: (01295) 688429 Fax: (01295) 680005 E-mail: admin@electrotech-cds.co.uk

▶ ENERG P.L.C., ENER-G House, Daniel Adamson Road, Salford, M50 1DT Tel: 0161-745 7450 Fax: 0161-745 7457 E-mail: info@energ.co.uk

Inenco Group Ltd, Petros House, St. Andrews Road North, Lytham St. Annes, Lancashire, FY8 2NF Tel: (01253) 785000 Fax: (01253) 785001 E-mail: enquiries@inenco.com

Keep Keen Controls Ltd, 8 Churchfield Croft, Rothwell, Leeds, LS26 0RX Tel: 0113-282 5387 Fax: 0113-288 0695 E-mail: john@keepkeen.co.uk

Metron Energy Management Ltd, PO Box 190, Winsford, Cheshire, CW7 9AH Tel: (01606) 882722 Fax: (01606) 889440 E-mail: enquiries@demmetron.co.uk

Northern Design Electronics Ltd, 228 Bolton Road, Bradford, West Yorkshire, BD3 0QW Tel: (01274) 729533 Fax: (01274) 721074 E-mail: sales@ndmeter.co.uk

Sauter Automations, Inova House Hampshire Int Business Park, Crockford Lane, Chineham, Basingstoke, Hampshire, RG24 8WH Tel: (01256) 374400 Fax: (01256) 374455 E-mail: info@uk.sauter-bc.com

Sundwell Solar Ltd, 7 Tower Road, Washington, Tyne & Wear, NE37 2SH Tel: 0191-416 3001 Fax: 0191-415 4297 E-mail: solar@sundwel.com

▶ Total Energy Saving Techniques, The Lodge, 18 Wakefield Road, Brighouse, West Yorkshire, HD6 1PE Tel: (01484) 717788 Fax: (01484) 717788

Vickers Electronics Ltd, Alliance House, Westpoint Enterprise Park, Trafford Park, Manchester, M17 1QS Tel: (0870) 7420808 Fax: (0870) 7480808 E-mail: info@vickers-electronics.co.uk

Wells Associates, Brundish Lodge, Brundish, Woodbridge, Suffolk, IP13 8BU Tel: (07768) 866958 Fax: (01986) 798731 E-mail: info@wells-associates.com

ENERGY METERING SYSTEMS

Sinergy Ltd, Station Road, Strines, Stockport, Cheshire, SK6 7GP Tel: (01663) 764833 Fax: (01663) 765885

ENERGY RISK MANAGEMENT

▶ The Finesse Organisation Ltd, The Barn, Green Farm Maidstone Road, Nettlestead, Maidstone, Kent, ME18 5HD Tel: (0870) 1900007 Fax: (0870) 1900008 E-mail: usave@thefinesseorg.com

ENERGY SAVING ELECTRIC MOTORS

Teco Electric Europe Ltd, Teco Building Centrepoint, Marshall Stevens Way, Trafford Park, Manchester, M17 1PP Tel: 0161-877 8025 Fax: 0161-877 8030 E-mail: enquiries@teco.co.uk

ENERGY SAVING LAMPS

▶ Ironteam Ltd, 20 Knightsbridge Drive, Nuthall, Nottingham, NG16 1RD Tel: 0115-975 1378 Fax: 0115-975 1378 E-mail: enquiries@ironteam.co.uk

ENERGY STORAGE SYSTEMS

URENCO (Capenhurst) Ltd, Capenhurst, Chester, CH1 6ER Tel: 0151-473 4000 Fax: 0151-473 4384 E-mail: cad@cap.urenco.co.uk

ENERGY SUPPLY CONSULTANCY OR DESIGN

The Ener G Group, Ener G House, Daniel Adamson Road, Salford, M50 2DT Tel: 0161-745 7450 Fax: 0161-745 7457 E-mail: sales@cpsl.co.uk

Energy Services Ltd, Utility Management Centre, Mucklow Hill, Halesowen, West Midlands, B62 8DR Tel: 0121-585 4000 Fax: 0121-585 4103 E-mail: simon.steed@energy-services.co.uk

Poten & Partners UK Ltd, 20 Balderton Street, London, W1K 6TL Tel: (020) 7493 7272 Fax: (020) 7629 7078E-mail: info@poten.com

Smith Rea, 78 Carden Place, Aberdeen, AB10 1UL Tel: (01224) 612400 Fax: (01224) 612401 E-mail: info@srel.co.uk

ENERGY UTILISATION CONSULTANCY

Consumers Utility Costs Ltd, C U C House, Crawley, West Sussex, RH11 9BN Tel: (01293) 516521 Fax: (01293) 512030 E-mail: sales@consumers-utility-cost.co.uk

Energy Advisers Ltd, Beech Hedges, 1 Wishing Stone Way, Matlock, Derbyshire, DE4 5LU Tel: (01629) 581400 Fax: (01629) 57313 E-mail: energy@breathe.co.uk

▶ Energy Efficiency Advice Centre, 20 George Hudson Street, York, YO1 6WR Tel: (01904) 554406 Fax: (01904) 554412 E-mail: owen@4sustainable-energy.co.uk

Energy Services Ltd, Utility Management Centre, Mucklow Hill, Halesowen, West Midlands, B62 8DR Tel: 0121-585 4000 Fax: 0121-585 4103 E-mail: simon.steed@energy-services.co.uk

Gas Tec At C R E Ltd, P O Box 279, Cheltenham, Gloucestershire, GL52 7ZJ Tel: (01242) 677877 Fax: (01242) 676506 E-mail: enquiries@gastecuk.com

Kyron, Oak Cottage, Benty Heath Lane, Willaston, Neston, CH64 1SB Tel: 0151-327 1957 Fax: 0151-327 7410 E-mail: john.hardman@kyron.co.uk

Northern Engineering Services, 16 Kew Gardens, Whitley Bay, Tyne & Wear, NE26 3LY Tel: 0191-253 4390 Fax: 0191-251 6674 E-mail: dshort@northeng.freeserve.co.uk

ENGAGEMENT RINGS, DIAMOND

▶ Cheshires Jewellers, 95 Spencer Street, Birmingham, B18 6DA Tel: 0121 5231124 Fax: 0121 523 1222 E-mail: info@cheshiresjewellers.co.uk

▶ Daniel Prince Of London, 24 Hatton Garden, London, EC1N 8BQ Tel: (0845) 1083684 Fax: (020) 8944 8418 E-mail: sales@danielprince.co.uk

▶ Maddison, 25 Hatton Garden, London, EC1N 8BQ Tel: (020) 7831 8122 Fax: (020) 7242 1988 E-mail: info@madisondiamondrings.co.uk

ENGINE BALANCING SERVICES

Bassett Down Balancing, Unit 19 Lower Bassett Down Workshops, Basset Down, Wroughton, Swindon, SN4 9QP Tel: (01793) 812331

Harlow Transmissions, Shenfield Court, Perry Road, Harlow, Essex, CM18 7LR Tel: (01279) 426943 E-mail: dom.daily@tesco.net

ENGINE DIAGNOSTIC EQUIPMENT

Alba Diagnostics Ltd, Unit 1 Bankhead Avenue, Glenrothes, Fife, KY7 6JG Tel: (01592) 774333 Fax: (01592) 774777 E-mail: marketing@brakefluidtester.com

ENGINE DRIVEN WELDING EQUIPMENT

Harrington Generators International Ltd, Ravenstor Road, Wirksworth, Matlock, Derbyshire, DE4 4FY Tel: (01629) 824284 Fax: (01629) 824613 E-mail: sales@harringtongen.co.uk

M R M International Generators Ltd, PO Box 78, Ipswich, IP9 2WZ Tel: (01473) 310000 Fax: (01473) 310011 E-mail: generators@mrmint.co.uk

ENGINE GOVERNORS

▶ Heinzmann UK Ltd, Durham Tees Valley Airport, Darlington, County Durham, DL2 1PD Tel: (01325) 332805 Fax: (01325) 333631 E-mail: info@heinzmannuk.com

Regulators Europa Ltd, Port Lane, Colchester, CO1 2NX Tel: (01206) 799556 Fax: (01206) 792685

ENGINE HEATERS

Nu-Heat (UK) Ltd, Heathpark House, Devonshire Road, Heathpark Industrial Estate, Honiton, Devon, EX14 1SD Tel: (01404) 549770 Fax: (01404) 549771 E-mail: info@nu-heat.co.uk

▶ indicates data change since last edition

ENGINE (INDUSTRIAL) COMPONENTS

Aktion Autormotive Ltd, Unit N3 Cardiff Bay Business Centre, Titan Road, Cardiff, CF24 5EJ Tel: (029) 2046 4668 Fax: (029) 2046 4669 E-mail: sales@aktionautomotive.co.uk

ENGINE (INDUSTRIAL) RECONDITIONING MACHINERY/ EQUIPMENT

Nu Line Engineering Ltd, George Street, Lincoln, LN5 8LG Tel: (01522) 544379 Fax: (01522) 544379 E-mail: nuline.ellis@tiscali.co.uk

Precision Engine Services (Inverness), Units 1-4, 48 Seafield Road, Inverness, IV1 1SG Tel: (01463) 235537 Fax: (01463) 712684

ENGINE (INDUSTRIAL) SPARE PARTS/WEARING PARTS

Chippindale Plant Hire & Sales Ltd, Gas Works Road, Keighley, West Yorkshire, BD21 4LY Tel: (01535) 606135 Fax: (01535) 690303 E-mail: general@chippindale-plant.co.uk

Endcape, Po Box 26, Pickering, North Yorkshire, YO18 7JL Tel: (01751) 476370 Fax: (01751) 474918 E-mail: sales@endcape.com

Engine & Truck (N I) Ltd, M2 Trade Centre, Duncrue Crescent, Belfast, BT3 9BW Tel: (028) 9077 1411 Fax: (028) 9077 5085 E-mail: sales@enginetruck.co.uk

F G Adamson & Son, Adamsons, Occupation Lane, Swanland, North Ferriby, North Humberside, HU14 3QZ Tel: (01482) 636200 Fax: (01482) 631672 E-mail: enquiry@buyamower.co.uk

Halesowen Engines Ltd, Bromsgrove Road, Halesowen, West Midlands, B63 3JG Tel: 0121-550 3211 Fax: 0121-550 4671 E-mail: sales.halesowen-engines@ssmail.net

Jennings Ltd, Unit 3 Sentry Lane, Newtownabbey, County Antrim, BT36 4XX Tel: (028) 9083 7799 Fax: (028) 9083 7762

▶ Geoff Matthews Engineers, Unit 17 Pavilion Workshops, Holmewood Industrial Park, Park Road, Holmewood, Chesterfield, Derbyshire, S42 5UY Tel: (01246) 851118 Fax: (01246) 855502 E-mail: enquiries@gmengineers.co.uk

Meetens Industrial Engines Ltd, Unit 2, Eclipse Trading Estate, 30 West Hill, Epsom, Surrey, KT19 8JD Tel: (08456) 340295 Fax: (08000) 150707 E-mail: sales@meetens.com

Phoenix Engines Ltd, Phoenix House, Railway Lane, Dimminsdale, Willenhall, West Midlands, WV13 2BE Tel: (01902) 601676 Fax: (01902) 601474 E-mail: david.scriven@phoenixengines.co.uk

Ses Engine Services Ltd, 5 Wealdstone Road, Sutton, Surrey, SM3 9QN Tel: (020) 8641 0252 Fax: (020) 8644 3983 E-mail: sales@sesengines.co.uk

ENGINE (INDUSTRIAL) TESTING

Bernard Hooper Engineering Ltd, PO Box 4155, Bridgnorth, Shropshire, WV15 5WY Tel: (01746) 761425 Fax: (01746) 761425 E-mail: bhe1@breathemail.net

ENGINE JOINTINGS, *See headings for particular types such as Hydraulic; also Steam etc*

ENGINE LUBRICATION PUMPS

E P Services, Unit 1, Central Industrial Estate, Cable Street, Wolverhampton, WV2 2RJ Tel: (01902) 452914 Fax: (01902) 871547 E-mail: enquiries@ep-services.co.uk

ENGINE MANAGEMENT SYSTEM COMPONENTS

Overdrive Auto Services, A 5 Dalton Street, Hull, HU8 8BB Tel: (01482) 222441 Fax: (01482) 222441 E-mail: paul@overdrive.karoo.co.uk

Zytek Systems Ltd, Fradley Distribution Park, Wood End Lane, Fradley, Lichfield, Staffordshire, WS13 8NE Tel: (01543) 412789

ENGINE MANUFACTURE, *See headings for particular types*

ENGINE (MOTOR VEHICLE) REBUILDERS/ RECONDITIONERS/SUPPLIERS

Caterpillar Remanufacturing Ltd, Sanders Lodge Industrial Estate, Rushden, Northamptonshire, NN10 6AZ Tel: (01933) 316622 Fax: (01933) 354601 E-mail: sales@wealdstone.co.uk

Classic Performance Ltd, 7 Trent Industrial Estate, Wetmore Road, Burton-on-Trent, Staffordshire, DE14 1QY Tel: (01283) 531122 Fax: (01283) 531328 E-mail: sales@classicperformance.co.uk

Component Distributors Ltd, Blackwater Road, Newtownabbey, County Antrim, BT36 4UA Tel: (028) 9034 1900 Fax: (028) 9034 1977 E-mail: mail@cd-group.com

Cotswold Engine Reconditioners, Gloucester Road, Cheltenham, Gloucestershire, GL51 8NL Tel: (01242) 244496 Fax: (01242) 244496 E-mail: mjm1@btconnect.com

Cranks & Bearings, 1A Rotherfield Road, Enfield, Middlesex, EN3 6AL Tel: (01992) 763279 Fax: (01992) 650840

D & R James Engineering Services Ltd, 16 Benson Road, Nuffield Industrial Estate, Poole, Dorset, BH17 0GB Tel: (01202) 678679

Dartford Rebore Ltd, 15 Overy Street, Dartford, DA1 1UP Tel: (01322) 220634 Fax: (01322) 220634

Datum Engine Services, Yard Mead, Egham, Surrey, TW20 0AB Tel: (01784) 470878

Engine Services (Croydon) Ltd, 173 Handcroft Road, Croydon, CR0 3LF Tel: (020) 8665 1952 Fax: (020) 8665 1952

Fields Engine Service Ltd, 2a Leslie Road, London, E11 4HG Tel: (020) 8539 5205 Fax: (020) 8539 7622

Green & Weatherly Ltd, 16 Bushey Hall Road, Bushey, WD23 2EA Tel: (01923) 228992 Fax: (01923) 241254

Bob Harman Performance Ltd, 101-107 Sutton Road, Watford, WD17 2QG Tel: (01923) 224303 Fax: (01923) 226596

▶ Hindle (Bradford), Nelson Street, Bradford, West Yorkshire, BD5 0EL Tel: (01274) 732284 Fax: (01274) 740237 E-mail: autos@hindle.co.uk

LCP Automotive Components, Prospect House, Broad Oak Road, Canterbury, Kent, CT2 7PX Tel: (01227) 766001 Fax: (01227) 769425

Lemar Engines Engine Reconditioners, Babbage Road, Totnes, Devon, TQ9 5JA Tel: (01803) 866548 Fax: (01803) 866548

Lyndale Engines Peterborough Ltd, Fengate, Peterborough, PE1 5XB Tel: (01733) 345256 Fax: (01733) 553920

▶ M K Engines Ltd, 6 Clarke Road, Bletchley, Milton Keynes, MK1 1LG Tel: (01908) 366566 Fax: (01908) 366566

Meldrum Motors Ltd, 3 Market Square, Oldmeldrum, Inverurie, Aberdeenshire, AB51 0AA Tel: (01651) 872247 Fax: (01651) 872247

Mitchell Cotts Transmissions, Winterstoke Road, Weston-super-Mare, Avon, BS24 9AT Tel: (01934) 428000 Fax: (01934) 428001 E-mail: andy.cook@gearboxes.com

Nu Line Engineering Ltd, George Street, Lincoln, LN5 8LG Tel: (01522) 544379 Fax: (01522) 544379 E-mail: nuline.ellis@tiscali.co.uk

Priestley Precision Engineering, 16 Leaside, Aycliffe Industrial Estate, Aycliffe Industrial Park, Newton Aycliffe, County Durham, DL5 6HX Tel: (01325) 316200 Fax: (01325) 310510

Rebore Service Sutton Ltd, 34 Lind Road, Sutton, Surrey, SM1 4PL Tel: (020) 8642 3419 Fax: (020) 8642 6119

Regal Engines, Unit B, 16 Juliet Way, Aveley, South Ockendon, Essex, RM15 4YD Tel: (01708) 868805 Fax: (01708) 868885 E-mail: info@engine-reconditioners.co.uk

Roe Engineering Fleet Ltd, 10 Kings Road, Fleet, Hampshire, GU51 3AD Tel: (01252) 613404 Fax: (01252) 612733 E-mail: g.s.roe@btinternet.com

Scholar Engines, Blue House, Norwich Road, Mendlesham, Stowmarket, Suffolk, IP14 5NH Tel: (01449) 767711 Fax: (01449) 767772 E-mail: adwsre@aol.com

Service Engineering Co Grimsby Ltd, 56 Roberts Street, Grimsby, South Humberside, DN32 8AP Tel: (01472) 358596 Fax: (01472) 267359

Thomas Hamlin & Co., 64 Monmouth Street, Bridgwater, Somerset, TA6 5EJ Tel: (01278) 422452 Fax: (01278) 424036

Tonge Fold Engineers Ltd, Ainsworth Lane, Bolton, BL2 2PP Tel: (01204) 521917 Fax: (01204) 521917

Towler Engineering Ltd, 34 Oxford Road, Clacton-on-Sea, Essex, CO15 3TB Tel: (01255) 423723 Fax: (01255) 434484

Urbanhurst UK Ltd, Twyford Business Centre, London Road, Bishop's Stortford, Hertfordshire, CM23 3YT Tel: (01279) 755590 Fax: (01279) 652644

W Drake Bradford Ltd, Bolling Road, Bradford, West Yorkshire, BD4 7BG Tel: (01274) 733541 Fax: (01274) 740892 E-mail: info@wdrake.co.uk

West Midland Engines, Saltley Road, Saltley, Birmingham, B7 4TD Tel: 0121-359 4402 Fax: 0121-359 7340

ENGINE PACKINGS, *See headings for particular types such as Hydraulic; also Steam etc*

ENGINE PISTONS

F J Engineering Ltd, 4 Keyhaven Road, Milford on Sea, Lymington, Hampshire, SO41 0QY Tel: (01590) 644644 Fax: (01590) 644644 E-mail: fjengineer@aol.com

MAHLE Power Train Ltd, Costin House, St. James Mill Road, Northampton, NN5 5TZ Tel: (0870) 1573000 Fax: (0870) 1573100 E-mail: sales@gb.mahle.com

Omega Pistons Ltd, Oak Barn Road, Halesowen, West Midlands, B62 9DW Tel: 0121-559 6778 Fax: 0121-559 6779 E-mail: info@omegapistons.com

ENGINE PROTECTION SYSTEMS, *See Diesel Engine Protection Systems etc*

ENGINE SECTIONALISING FOR EXHIBITION OR DISPLAY PURPOSES

Markfield Services, Trent Works, Felton Road, Nottingham, NG2 2EH Tel: 0115-985 0400 Fax: 0115-985 0252 E-mail: markfield@trentworks.demon.co.uk

ENGINE SPARE PARTS, *See also headings for particular types*

▶ Briggsbits.co.uk, Hutton Garden Centre, Banwell Road, Hutton, Weston-super-Mare, North Somerset, BS24 9UB Tel: (01934) 813261 Fax: (01934) 815356 E-mail: graham@westongm.eclipse.co.uk

D & L Diesel Ltd, 75 Scot Lane, Wigan, Lancashire, WN5 0TU Tel: (01942) 825545 Fax: (01942) 493890 E-mail: davidlong@dldiesels.co.uk

ENGINE STARTING SYSTEMS

Prestolite Electric Ltd, Larden Road, Acton, London, W3 7SX Tel: (020) 8735 4500 Fax: (020) 8735 4777

ENGINE TEST EQUIPMENT, *See also other headings for particular types*

A V L United Kingdom Ltd, Avon House, Hartlebury Trading Estate, Hartlebury, Kidderminster, Worcestershire, DY10 4JB Tel: (01299) 254600 Fax: (01299) 253734 E-mail: uk.sales@avl.com

Froude Hofmann, Blackpole Road, Worcester, WR3 8YB Tel: (01905) 856800 Fax: (01905) 856811 E-mail: sales@froude.fki-eng.com

ENGINE TESTING, *See also headings for particular types*

Bernard Hooper Engineering Ltd, PO Box 4155, Bridgnorth, Shropshire, WV15 5WY Tel: (01746) 761425 Fax: (01746) 761425 E-mail: bhe1@breathemail.net

Piper Test & Measurement Ltd, The Barn, Bilsington, Ashford, Kent, TN25 7JT Tel: (01233) 720130 Fax: (01233) 720140 E-mail: piper@piper-ltd.co.uk

ENGINE TUNING SERVICES, MOTORCYCLE

▶ Autosort, Pier Garage, Fairlie, Ayrshire, KA29 0AU Tel: (01475) 560088 E-mail: webmaster@autosort.co.uk

▶ GrinsBritishBikeSpares, Templehall, Kirkcaldy, Fife, KY2 6LT Tel: (01592) 262803 E-mail: grintriumph@blueyonder.co.uk

▶ Moto-Racing, 11 Pinewood Road, Matlock, Derbyshire, DE4 3HN Tel: (01629) 581552 Fax: (01629) 584394 E-mail: info@moto-racing.co.uk

ENGINE TUNING SERVICES, PERFORMANCE, MOTOR VEHICLE

▶ Alanco Motor Services Ltd, Goldmartin Garage, Sampys Mill, Mawnan Smith, Falmouth, Cornwall, TR11 5EW Tel: (01326) 250394 Fax: (01326) 250394 E-mail: info@alanco.co.uk

▶ American V8 Engines, 266 Orphanage Road, Erdington, Birmingham, B24 0BB Tel: 0121-350 1116 Fax: 0121-350 1116 E-mail: adrian@americanv8engines.co.uk

▶ Autosort, Pier Garage, Fairlie, Ayrshire, KA29 0AU Tel: (01475) 560088 E-mail: webmaster@autosort.co.uk

▶ Skater Motor Sport, 1 Flight Path Farm, Broadbridge Lane, Smallfield, Horley, Surrey, RH6 9RF Tel: (01342) 844077 Fax: (01342) 844887 E-mail: sales@skatermotorsport.co.uk

ENGINEER'S GAUGES

Piccadilly Precision Engineering Co. Ltd, Units H4 & H5, Halesfield 19, Telford, Shropshire, TF7 4QT Tel: (01952) 582113 Fax: (01952) 583239 E-mail: sales@piccadillyprecision.co.uk

Profile Gauge & Tool Co. Ltd, Mangham Way, Rotherham, South Yorkshire, S61 4RL Tel: (01709) 377184 Fax: (01709) 820281

ENGINEERED WOOD FLOORING

Holland & Welsh Ltd, Unit 13 Riverside Industrial Park, Treforest, Pontypridd, Mid Glamorgan, CF37 5TG Tel: (01443) 660255 Fax: (01443) 660651 E-mail: sales@hollandandwelsh.com

ENGINEERING ABRASION RESISTANT COATINGS

▶ Greenbank Group Inc, Hartshorne Road, Woodville, Swadlincote, Derbyshire, DE11 7GT Tel: (0870) 6078880 Fax: (0870) 6078889 E-mail: info@greenbank.tv

ENGINEERING ADHESIVES

Cromwell Ltd, Station Road, North Hykeham, Lincoln, LN6 9AL Tel: (01522) 500888 Fax: (01522) 500857 E-mail: sales@cromwell.co.uk

ENGINEERING ASSEMBLIES, PRECISION

▶ Armstrong omponents Limited, 57 Groveside, East Rudham, King's Lynn, Norfolk, PE31 8RL Tel: (01485) 529082 Fax: (01485) 529294 E-mail: dave@armstrongsales.f9.co.uk

▶ Geola Technologies Ltd, Sussex Innovation Centre, 10-13 Science Park Square, Falmer, Brighton, BN1 9SB Tel: (01273) 234644 Fax: (01273) 704477 E-mail: sales@geola.com

▶ Woodfield Engineering Services Ltd, Unit 2, Woodfield House, Gravel Lane, Banks, Southport, Merseyside, PR9 8BY Tel: (01704) 220729 Fax: (01704) 220515 E-mail: woodfieldservice@btconnect.com

ENGINEERING AUTOMATED GANTRIES

R B Engineering Services, Unit 43 College Street, Kempston, Bedford, MK42 8LU Tel: (01234) 211263 Fax: (01234) 328835

ENGINEERING BRICKS

Caradale Traditional Bricks Ltd, Goremire Road, Carluke, Lanarkshire, ML8 4PQ Tel: (01555) 771397 Fax: (01555) 771397

Carlton Main Brickworks Ltd, Grimethorpe, Barnsley, South Yorkshire, S72 7BG Tel: (01226) 711521 Fax: (01226) 780417 E-mail: office.admin@carltonbrick.co.uk

Ibstock Brick Ltd, Stourbridge Factory, Tansey Green Road, Kingswinford, West Midlands, DY6 7LS Tel: (01384) 294124 Fax: (01384) 274547

Ibstock Building Products Ltd, South Holmwood Factory, Newdigate Road, Beare Green, Dorking, Surrey, RH5 4QE Tel: (01306) 711223 Fax: (01306) 711466

A.F.G. Ray & Sons, The Old Coal Yard, Worcester Road, Kidderminster, Worcestershire, DY11 1HN Tel: (01562) 755585 Fax: (01562) 825218

ENGINEERING COMPONENT DIRECT LINE LOGISTIC SERVICES

C Lear & Sons Ltd, Unit 7-8 Rassbottom Industrial Estate, Stalybridge, Cheshire, SK15 1RH Tel: 0161-303 7410 Fax: 0161-338 4214 E-mail: learandsons@aol.com

Component Logistics Ltd, Milton Court Horsfield Way, Bredbury Park Industrial Estate, Bredbury, Stockport, Cheshire, SK6 2TD Tel: 0161-406 2800 Fax: 0161-406 2809 E-mail: cll@component-logistics.com

Ebbs & Dale Ltd, Unit 27 Austin Fields, King's Lynn, Norfolk, PE30 1PH Tel: (01553) 765554 Fax: (01553) 769140 E-mail: sales@ebbsanddale.com

ENGINEERING COMPUTER AIDED DESIGN (CAD)/SYSTEMS CONSULTANTS/SUPPLIERS

▶ ASK Innovation Limited, Suite 104b, Discovery Court, 551-553 Wallisdown Road, Poole, Dorset, BH12 5AG Tel: 01202 853221 Fax: 01202 853214 E-mail: enquiries@askinnovation.co.uk

Cambashi Ltd, 52 Mawson Road, Cambridge, CB1 2HY Tel: (01223) 460439 Fax: (01223) 461055 E-mail: info@cambashi.com

Complete Engineering Systems Ltd, The Lower Barn, Tilburstow Hill Road, South Godstone, Godstone, Surrey, RH9 8LY Tel: (01342) 893788 Fax: (01342) 893988

Femsys Ltd, 158 Upper New Walk, Leicester, LE1 7QA Tel: 0116-254 1475 Fax: 0116-255 8982 E-mail: info@senses.co.uk

Financial Management Systems (UK) P.L.C., 4 Hillbrow House, Linden Drive, Liss, Hampshire, GU33 7RJ Tel: (01730) 894789 Fax: (01730) 892387 E-mail: info@fmsuk.com

▶ Gellan Ltd, Faraday Road, Nottingham, NG7 2DU Tel: (0870) 4019955 Fax: (0870) 4019954 E-mail: info@cadwiseltd.co.uk

Haughton Design Ltd, Business Innovation Centre, Gates Court, Staffordshire Technology Park, Stafford, ST18 0AR Tel: (01785) 243767 Fax: (01785) 243768 E-mail: adm@haughtondesign.co.uk

The Mathworks Ltd, Matrix House 10 Cowley Park, Cowley Road, Cambridge, CB4 0HH Tel: (01223) 423200 Fax: (01223) 423289 E-mail: sales@mathworks.co.uk

▶ Mishi Ltd, 42 Harvest Way, Witney, Oxfordshire, OX28 1EG Tel: (01993) 708719 Fax: (01993) 708719 E-mail: mishi.ltd@tiscali.co.uk

Stirling Maynard & Partners Ltd, Stirling House, Rightwell, Bretton, Peterborough, PE3 8DJ Tel: (01733) 262319 Fax: (01733) 331527 E-mail: enquires@stirlingmaynard.com

Transcendata Europe Ltd, 4 Carlisbrooke Court, Buckingway Business Park, Anderson Road, Cambridge, CB24 4UQ Tel: (01954) 234300 Fax: (01954) 234349 E-mail: sales@transcendata.com

Wilde UK Ltd, Brindley Lodge, Adcroft Street, Stockport, Cheshire, SK1 3HZ Tel: 0161-474 7479 Fax: 0161-474 7492 E-mail: info@wildeandpartners.co.uk

ENGINEERING CONSULTANTS OR DESIGNERS, *See Consulting Engineers or Designers*

ENGINEERING CONTRACT MANUFACTURING SERVICES

▶ A & E Edm Ltd, 25 Mornington Road, Smethwick, West Midlands, B66 2JE Tel: 0121-558 8352 Fax: 0121-558 8350 E-mail: info@amedm.co.uk

▶ MMC Precision Engineering, Unit 7a Stanley Green Industrial Estate, Stanley Green Crescent, Poole, Dorset, BH15 3TH Tel: (01202) 667321 E-mail: mmc-eng@ntlworld.com

▶ Networks & Data Ltd, 2 Meadow Rise, Wadworth, Doncaster, South Yorkshire, DN11 9AP Tel: (01302) 854969 E-mail: dave@networksanddata.co.uk

▶ Peak Contracts Ltd, 7 Church Street, Hartshorne, Swadlincote, Derbyshire, DE11 7ER Tel: (08451) 566843 Fax: 08451 566843E-mail: enquiries@peakcontracts.co.uk

▶ R R Pullen, Frying Pan Farm, Melksham Lane, Broughton Gifford, Melksham, Wiltshire, SN12 8LL Tel: (01225) 702343 Fax: (01225) 793652 E-mail: rpbp@dsl.pipex.com

ENGINEERING DESIGN AND MANUFACTURING

▶ A V Steel Laser Services Ltd, 20a Mandervell Road, Oadby, Leicester, LE2 5LQ Tel: 0116-271 8080 Fax: 0116-271 1551 E-mail: sales@avsteel.co.uk

A2a Fabrications, Hill Farm, Tunnel Road, Galley Common, Ansley, Nuneaton, Warwickshire, CV10 9PE Tel: (024) 7639 7888 Fax: (024) 7639 7888 E-mail: a2afabrications@tiscali.co.uk

▶ Blackrow Engineering Co. Ltd, 7 Estate Road, South Humberside Industrial Estate, Grimsby, South Humberside, DN31 2TP Tel: (01472) 889200 Fax: (01472) 889201 E-mail: sales@blackrow.co.uk

▶ C G C Technology Ltd, E Grovebell Industrial Estate, Wrecclesham Road, Wrecclesham, Farnham, Surrey, GU10 4PL Tel: (01252) 724274 Fax: (01252) 722624 E-mail: enquiries@cgctech.com

D E E Services, Ael Y Bryn, Llandinam, Powys, SY17 5BT Tel: (01686) 688025 Fax: (01686) 688025 E-mail: info@dee-devices.co.uk

Fox Moving & Storage, Block C, Stourbridge Industrial Estate, Mill Race Lane, Stourbridge, West Midlands, DY8 1YL Tel: (01384) 395072 Fax: (01384) 440520 E-mail: stourbridge@fox-moving.com

▶ G M Design, Nightingale House, 8 Taylor Street, Liverpool, L5 5AD Tel: 0151-207 5595 Fax: 0151- 207 5601 E-mail: mattjack@agjengineering.co.uk

▶ Harpspring Designs Ltd, Bridge House, 3 Fleet Road, Farnborough, Hampshire, GU14 9RU Tel: 0118-375 7661 Fax: (07973) 856954 E-mail: harpspring.designs@ntlworld.com

▶ Christopher Hiett & Associates Ltd, 15 Oaklea Avenue, Chelmsford, CM2 6BY Tel: (01245) 283729 Fax: (01245) 600126 E-mail: chiett@christopherhiett.co.uk

K B Engineering Co. Ltd, Fowlswick Industrial Estate, Fowlswick Lane, Allington, Chippenham, Wiltshire, SN14 6QE Tel: (01249) 783186 Fax: (01249) 782603

▶ KJH - Solutions By Design, Holmlea, St Marys Road, Meare, Glastonbury, Somerset, BA6 9SS Tel: 07944 114235 E-mail: kevin@hann.freeserve.co.uk

M Donald, Unit A Kingmoor Park Heathlands Estate, Carlisle, CA6 4RE Tel: (01228) 672050 Fax: (01228) 672025 E-mail: sales@weldtech-uk.com

▶ Manufacturing Executive Ltd, Ivy House 90 Town Street, Lound, Retford, Nottinghamshire, DN22 8RX Tel: (01777) 818280 E-mail: info@manufacturingexecutive.com

▶ R S C Ltd, Unit 1a Horndon Business Park, West Horndon, Brentwood, Essex, CM13 3XL Tel: 01277 810111

▶ Resource Centre For Innovation & Design, Claremont Road, Newcastle upon Tyne, NE1 7RU Tel: 0191-222 5897 Fax: 0191-222 5833 E-mail: bf.dixon@ncl.ac.uk

Spirex Metal Products Ltd, Marsh Lane, Ware, Hertfordshire, SG12 9QQ Tel: (01920) 460516 Fax: (01920) 487028 E-mail: info@spirex.co.uk

Streamline Outsource Ltd, The Innovation Centre, Rennes Drive, University Of Exeter Campus, Exeter, EX4 4RN Tel: (07743) 845124 Fax: (0870) 4584046 E-mail: sales@streamlineoutsource.com

▶ W S Engineering Ltd, Park Works, Park Road, Leek, Staffordshire, ST13 8SA Tel: (01538) 373131 Fax: (01538) 384862 E-mail: info@wseng.co.uk

ENGINEERING DESIGN SOFTWARE

Aveva Engineering It Ltd, High Cross, Madingley Road, Cambridge, CB3 0HB Tel: (01223) 556655 Fax: (01223) 556666 E-mail: info@aveva.com

Beech Hill Electronics, Beechcroft, Beech Hill Road, Beech Hill, Reading, RG7 2AU Tel: 0118-988 4622 E-mail: sales@beech-hill.co.uk

House Builder XL Ltd, Citypoint, Temple Gate, Bristol, BS1 6PL Tel: (0870) 8502444 Fax: (0870) 8502555E-mail: sales@hbxl.co.uk

INBIS Ltd, Club Street, Bamber Bridge, Preston, PR5 6FN Tel: (01772) 645000 Fax: (01772) 645001 E-mail: mailbox@assystems.com

Inspection Software Ltd, 3 Brynau Drive, Mayals, Swansea, SA3 5EE Tel: (01792) 404235 E-mail: isl@inspection.co.uk

N A G Ltd, Wilkinson House Jordan Hill, Banbury Road, Oxford, OX2 8DR Tel: (01865) 311744 Fax: (01865) 310139 E-mail: info@nag.co.uk

Newbury Electronic Services Ltd, 1 Berwick Courtyard, Berwick St. Leonard, Salisbury, SP3 5UA Tel: (01747) 820615 E-mail: sales@nes-ltd.com

Pisces Engineering Services, 12 Loch Laxford, East Kilbride, Glasgow, G74 2DL Tel: (01355) 243220 Fax: (01355) 243220 E-mail: pisces@compuserve.com

Polyhedron Software Ltd, Linden House, 93 High Street, Witney, Oxfordshire, OX29 7RH Tel: (01865) 300579 Fax: (01865) 300232 E-mail: wwwsales@polyhedron.com

Xpertec Engineering Software Ltd, 19 Paddock End, Waterlooville, Hampshire, PO7 6UW Tel: (023) 9224 1546 Fax: (023) 9226 3770 E-mail: dbreach@xpertec.co.uk

ENGINEERING EQUIPMENT, *See also headings for particular types*

CDS Consultants, Bwlch Tocyn Farm, Bwlchtocyn, Pwllheli, Gwynedd, LL53 7BN Tel: (01758) 712245 Fax: (01758) 712014 E-mail: cdsconsultants@btinternet.com

Clipper Tech Ltd, 1 Oakley Industrial Estate, Carnock Road, Oakley, Dunfermline, Fife, KY12 9QB Tel: (01383) 851133 Fax: (01383) 851144 E-mail: sales@clippertech.co.uk

Robert Craig & Sons Ltd, Unit 10, Knock Moore Hill, Industrial Estate, Fergusion Drive, Lisburn, County Antrim, BT28 2OX Tel: (028) 9266 8500 Fax: (028) 9266 8550 E-mail: sales@craigs-products.co.uk

Cromwell Tools Ltd, Gorman House, James Street, Righead Industrial Estate, Bellshill, Lanarkshire, ML4 3LU Tel: (01698) 746974 Fax: (01698) 841988 E-mail: glasgow@cromwell-tools.co.uk

Cromwell Tools Ltd, Gibraltar Island Road, Old Mill Business Park, Leeds, LS10 1RJ Tel: 0113-277 7730 Fax: 0113-277 7724 E-mail: leeds@cromwell.co.uk

Dawson Bowman Ltd, 16 Flakefield, College Milton, East Kilbride, Glasgow, G74 1PF Tel: (01355) 229445 Fax: (01355) 264744 E-mail: sales@dawsonbowman.co.uk

Engineering Supply Co., 5 Block 3, Thornliebank Industrial Estate, Thornliebank, Glasgow, G46 8TU Tel: 0141-638 7905 Fax: 0141-638 9714 E-mail: sales@scottishtools.co.uk

FMB UK Ltd, P O Box 5222, Leicester, LE4 8ZE Tel: 0116-260 7744 Fax: 0116-260 7222 E-mail: sales@fmbuk.co.uk

Forth Engineering Services Ltd, 8 West Shore Bus Centre, Long Craig Rigg, Edinburgh, EH5 1QT Tel: 0131-551 5300 Fax: 0131-551 6610 E-mail: sales@forthengineering.co.uk

Henry R Ayton Ltd, 40 The Cutts, Dunmurry, Belfast, BT17 9HS Tel: (028) 9061 8511 Fax: (028) 9060 2436 E-mail: sales@hrayton.com

T. Hopkins, 112 Main Street, Woodhouse Eaves, Loughborough, Leicestershire, LE12 8RZ Tel: (01509) 891133 Fax: (01509) 891133

Morse Welding Supplies Ltd, Watercombe Lane, Lynx West Trading Estate, Yeovil, Somerset, BA20 2SU Tel: (01935) 426390 Fax: (01935) 420451 E-mail: info@morsewelding.com

Pennine Tools Ltd, PO Box B98, Huddersfield, HD2 1UR Tel: (01484) 519660 Fax: (01484) 420044 E-mail: toolsales@pennine-tools.co.uk

▶ Quality Tooling North East Ltd, 5 Back Norfolk Street, Sunderland, SR1 1EA Tel: 0191-514 5153 Fax: 0191-510 8485 E-mail: sales@quality-tooling.co.uk

Tom Smith Parts Ltd, Old Hakin Road, Walwyns Castle, Haverfordwest, Dyfed, SA62 3EL Tel: (01437) 890414 Fax: (01437) 890256 E-mail: sales@tomsmithparts.co.uk

Frank Warren Ltd, Terrace Street, Oldham, OL4 1HQ Tel: 0161-287 8118 Fax: 0161-287 5226 E-mail: sales@fwarren.co.uk

ENGINEERING EQUIPMENT IMPORT/EXPORT MERCHANTS OR AGENTS

B F S International, Willowbrook, 20 Bray Road, Bray, Maidenhead, Berkshire, SL6 1UE Tel: (01628) 671458 Fax: (01628) 784337 E-mail: sales@bfs-international.co.uk

Cambridge Overseas Trading Ltd, 13 Richmond Walk, St. Albans, Hertfordshire, AL4 9BA Tel: (01727) 833211 Fax: (01727) 810320 E-mail: cambost@aol.com

Central Computers Supplies, Washwood Heath Road, Birmingham, B8 2HQ Tel: (0870) 0434049 Fax: 0121-684 8885

Laltex & Co. Ltd, Leigh Commerce Park, Green Fold Way, Leigh, Lancashire, WN7 3XH Tel: (01942) 687000 Fax: (01942) 687070 E-mail: mail@laltex.com

Pritt & Co. Ltd, 23 Pembridge Square, London, W2 4DR Tel: (020) 7221 0909 Fax: (020) 7727 4837 E-mail: sales@pritt.co.uk

ENGINEERING FAILURE INVESTIGATION OR FORENSIC SERVICES

▶ Cadogan Consultants Ltd, 39 Cadogan Street, Glasgow, G2 7AB Tel: 0141-270 7060 Fax: 0141-270 7061 E-mail: enquiries@cadoganconsultants.co.uk

ENGINEERING FEASIBILITY STUDIES

Gravatom Engineering Systems Ltd, William Kelvin Building, Claylands Road, Bishops Waltham, Southampton, SO32 1BH Tel: (01489) 896010 Fax: (01489) 894382 E-mail: sales@gravatom.com

Hulbert Developments Ltd, 6 Grazebrook Industrial Park, Peartree Lane, Dudley, West Midlands, DY2 0XW Tel: (01384) 239019 Fax: (01384) 457280 E-mail: enq@hulbert-group.co.uk

ENGINEERING HAND TOOLS

Castle Tools Ltd, 33 Trent Street, Sheffield, S9 3XU Tel: 0114-261 7200 Fax: 0114-261 7370 E-mail: sales@castletools.co.uk

Chesterman Marketing Ltd, 3 Kenworthy Road, Stafford, ST16 3DY Tel: (01785) 250341 Fax: (01785) 250345 E-mail: enquiries@chestermanmarketing.com

Corbin & Frost Ltd, 3 Stepfield, Witham, Essex, CM8 3DP Tel: (01376) 572202 Fax: (01376) 513921 E-mail: corbin.frost@macunlimited.net

Power Rewind Ltd, 1 Conder Way, Colchester, CO2 8JN Tel: (01206) 791316 Fax: (01206) 792689

Sallco Tools Ltd, 3-4 Baddesley Park Industrial Estate, Botley Road, North Baddesley, Southampton, SO52 9NW Tel: (023) 8073 7355 Fax: (023) 8073 8647 E-mail: sales@sallcotools.co.uk

Sam Tooling Ltd, 60 Newland Street, Coleford, Gloucestershire, GL16 8AL Tel: (01594) 835542 Fax: (01594) 837293

ENGINEERING INDUSTRY TEST EQUIPMENT

Blacks Equipment Ltd, Barton La, Armthorpe, Doncaster, S. Yorkshire, DN3 3AA Tel: (01302) 834444 Fax: (01302) 831834 E-mail: sales@blacksequipment.com

E H P Technical Services Ltd, 6 Lincoln Road, Northborough, Peterborough, PE6 9BL Tel: (01733) 252428 Fax: (01733) 252674 E-mail: rayevans@ehpltd.freeserve.co.uk

T. & R. Test Equipment Ltd, 15-16 Woodbridge Meadows, Guilford, Guildford, Surrey, GU1 1BJ Tel: (01483) 207428 Fax: (01483) 235759 E-mail: sales@trtest.com

▶ Tees Valley Measurement, Cannon Street, Middlesbrough, Cleveland, TS1 5JJ Tel: (01642) 223535 Fax: (01642) 210317

ENGINEERING INSPECTION OR TESTING

Argos Inspection Co. Ltd, Tower Road, Washington, Tyne & Wear, NE37 2SH Tel: 0191-417 7707 Fax: 0191-415 4979 E-mail: ndt@argosinspection.com

▶ Cranetech (Bristol) Limited, 467 Bath Road, Brislington, Bristol, BS4 3JU Tel: 0778 995 3837 Fax: 0117 904 7142 E-mail: crane-tech@blueyonder.co.uk

Dimensional Inspection Services, Unit 19 Wombourne Enterprise Park, Bridgnorth Road, Wombourne, Wolverhampton, WV5 0AL Tel: (01902) 326225 Fax: (01902) 326225 E-mail: sales@diserv.free-online.co.uk

Lightning Protection Services, Cove Farm, Kirkpatrick Fleming, Lockerbie, Dumfriesshire, DG11 3AT Tel: (01461) 800323 Fax: (01461) 800269

P T S - Total Quality Management, Verulam Road, Stafford, ST16 3EA Tel: (01785) 250706 Fax: (01785) 250906

Sendt Ltd, Littlebrook Business Centre, Littlebrook Manorway, Dartford, DA1 5PZ Tel: (01322) 287347 Fax: (01322) 287493 E-mail: tony.blake@sendt.freeserve.co.uk

▶ Skypark Freight, 16 Owen Drive, Liverpool, L24 1YL Tel: 0151-448 0048 Fax: 0151-448 0007 E-mail: steve@skylog.freeserve.co.uk

Triple Engineering Yorkshire Ltd, Unit 7 Humberside Way, Barnsley, South Yorkshire, S71 3RN Tel: (01226) 770058 Fax: (01226) 731246

Tube Care Inspection Ltd, Bessemer Way, Harfreys Industrial Estate, Great Yarmouth, Norfolk, NR31 0LX Tel: (01493) 601548 Fax: (01493) 656097 E-mail: sales@tubecare.co.uk

ENGINEERING JOINTING MATERIALS

Evergreen, Clare Park, Unit 2, Farnham, Surrey, GU10 5DT Tel: (01252) 851849 Fax: (01252) 851849

ENGINEERING LUBRICANTS

Batoyle Freedom Group, Colne Vale Road, Milnsbridge, Huddersfield, HD3 4NT Tel: (01484) 653015 Fax: (01484) 460078 E-mail: bfgsales@aol.com

C P Lubricants, Drivers Wharf, Northam Road, Southampton, SO14 0YD Tel: (023) 8033 7800 Fax: (023) 8033 7801 E-mail: cp@cplubricants.co.uk

ENGINEERING MAINTENANCE

▶ Harlequin Electrical, Kings Close Cottage, South Walsham Road, North Burlingham, Norwich, NR13 4EJ Tel: (0800) 5118978 Fax: (01603) 270415 E-mail: info@harlequinelectrical.co.uk

▶ Mitie Engineering Maintenance, 22-30 Sturt Road, Frimley Green, Camberley, Surrey, GU16 6HY Tel: (01252) 836800 Fax: (01252) 832250 E-mail: phil.townsend@mitie.co.uk

Stevron Marine, 38 Farriers Way, Bootle, Merseyside, L30 4XL Tel: 0151-525 9555 Fax: 0151-521 7190 E-mail: sales@stevron.co.uk

ENGINEERING MODELS

A E Blanchard, 144 Station Road, Ratby, Leicester, LE6 0JP Tel: 0116-239 3831 Fax: 0116-239 3831

A P Woolrich, Canalside, Huntworth, Bridgwater, Somerset, TA7 0AJ Tel: (01278) 663020 Fax: (01278) 663913 E-mail: sales@ap-woolrich.co.uk

Amalgam Modelmakers Ltd, The Old Sorting Office, Eastfield Road, Cotham, Bristol, BS6 6AB Tel: 0117-924 9596 Fax: 0117-923 2727 E-mail: admin@amalgam-models.co.uk

Ambler Patterns, Riverside Works, Todmerton Rd, Littleborough, Lancs, OL15 9EG Tel: (01706) 378197 Fax: (01706) 377826 E-mail: sales@ambler-patterns.co.uk

▶ indicates data change since last edition

ENGINEERING MODELS – *continued*

Angell Patterns Ltd, 215a Fosse Road North, Leicester, LE3 5EZ Tel: 0116-253 1964 Fax: 0116-253 1964

Concept Creative Services Ltd, Unit 1, Baird House, Dudley Innovation Centre, Pensnett Trading Estate, Kingswinford, West Midlands, DY6 7YA Tel: (01384) 400161 Fax: (01384) 400190 E-mail: sales@concept-models.com

Confluence Creative, Unit 23, Merryhills Enterprise Park, Park Lane, Wolverhampton, WV10 9TJ Tel: (01902) 862601 Fax: (01902) 862602 E-mail: contact@confluencecreative.co.uk

Darrell Fieldhouse, Victoria Road, Rushden, Northamptonshire, NN10 0AS Tel: (01933) 410458

EDM Ltd, Brunel House, 1 Thorp Road, Newton Heath, Manchester, M40 5BJ Tel: 0161-203 3150 Fax: 0161-202 2500 E-mail: reception@edm.ltd.uk

Elkington Bros Ltd, 53-69 Baltimore Road, Birmingham, B42 1DD Tel: 0121-358 2431 Fax: 0121-358 7527 E-mail: lawrence.kelly@elkingtonbrothers.net

En Aid Design Workshop, Wassage Way, Hampton Lovett, Droitwich, Worcestershire, WR9 0NX Tel: (01905) 451501 Fax: (01905) 771771 E-mail: enaid@btclick.com

Forvm Designs, 8 Bucklers Close, Warden, Sheerness, Kent, ME12 4PT Tel: (01795) 511100 Fax: (01795) 511734 E-mail: forvmdesigns@aol.com

Hamlin Model Making Ltd, Old Tractor Shed, Welsh Road, Offchurch, Leamington Spa, Warwickshire, CV33 9BE Tel: (01926) 614147 Fax: (01926) 612899 E-mail: sales@hamlinrpd.co.uk

Irvine Ltd, Green Street, Enfield, Middlesex, EN3 7FJ Tel: (020) 8361 1123 Fax: (020) 8361 8684 E-mail: sales@irvineltd.com

▶ JSM Industrial Model Making, Unit 5 Home Farm House Works, Mildenhall, Marlborough, Wiltshire, SN8 2LR Tel: (01672) 512305 Fax: (01672) 512305 E-mail: studio@jsmmodelmakers.freeserve.co.uk

Lawson Model Makers, 21 Viking Way, Metheringham, Lincoln, LN4 3DW Tel: (01526) 321628 Fax: (01526) 322140 E-mail: john@jlawson.com

Lewis Ductwork, 43a Hayes Road, Bromley, BR2 9AF Tel: (020) 7737 4435

Model Engineering Supplies (Bexhill), Clifford Mews, Clifford Road, Bexhill-on-Sea, East Sussex, TN40 1QA Tel: (01424) 223702 Fax: (01424) 223702 E-mail: sales@model-engineering.co.uk

Model Technology Ltd, Unit 11 Speedgate Farm, Speedgate, Fawkham, Longfield, Kent, DA3 8NJ Tel: (01474) 879878 Fax: (01474) 874683

Malcolm Nicholls Ltd, Waterloo Road, Bidford-on-Avon, Alcester, Warwickshire, B50 4JH Tel: (01789) 490382 Fax: (01789) 490130 E-mail: rp@mnl.co.uk

Novo Designs, Church Farm, Eyeworth, Sandy, Bedfordshire, SG19 2HH Tel: (01767) 631117

Optimus Models, 115 Crosshall Road, Eaton Ford, St. Neots, Cambridgeshire, PE19 7AB Tel: (01480) 473831 Fax: (01480) 384098

Protechnol Precision Engineers, Unit 4, Christie Place, Bognor Regis, West Sussex, PO22 9RT Tel: (01243) 842233 Fax: (01243) 842233

Rainford Models Ltd, Bingswood Industrial Estate, Whaley Bridge, High Peak, Derbyshire, SK23 7LY Tel: (01663) 719119 Fax: (01663) 719109 E-mail: sales@rainfordmodels.co.uk

Reeves 2000, Appleby Hill, Austrey, Atherstone, Warwickshire, CV9 3ER Tel: (01827) 830894 Fax: (01827) 830631 E-mail: sales@ajreeves.com

Romford Models, 1b Bridge Close, Romford, RM7 0AU Tel: (01708) 743390 Fax: (01708) 743390

South Yorkshire Pattern Co. Ltd, Nimrod Works, Trinity Street, Sheffield, S3 7AJ Tel: 0114-272 1999 Fax: 0114-272 1999

Summit Patternmaking Co. Ltd, Paper Mill End Industrial Estate, Birmingham, B44 8NH Tel: 0121-344 3943 Fax: 0121-344 3944

ENGINEERING POWER TOOLS

Apex Industrial Ltd, 651 Eccles New Road, Salford, M50 1BA Tel: 0161-789 0909 Fax: 0161-787 7113

Power Tools Plus, 131 Gloucester Road, Bishopston, Bristol, BS7 8AX Tel: 0117-949 9700 Fax: 0117-914 7758

ENGINEERING RESEARCH CONSULTANCY

Adrian March, 5 The Paddock, Kings Worthy, Winchester, Hampshire, SO23 7QR Tel: (01962) 882277 E-mail: adrian@adrianmarch.com

▶ Cadogan Consultants Ltd, 39 Cadogan Street, Glasgow, G2 7AB Tel: 0141-270 7060 Fax: 0141-270 7061 E-mail: enquiries@cadoganconsultants.co.uk

ENGINEERING SERVICES, CONTROL PANEL

▶ Automated Building Controls, Wellesley House, 7 Clarence Parade, Cheltenham, Gloucestershire, GL50 3NY Tel: (01242) 265781 Fax: (01242) 265781 E-mail: mail@abc.uk.net

▶ J M G Systems Ltd, 68a Derry Road, Omagh, County Tyrone, BT78 5ED Tel: (028) 8224 4131 E-mail: info@jmgsystems.co.uk

ENGINEERING SOFTWARE

▶ ControlLoop, 14 St. Davids, Newtongrange, Midlothian, EH22 4LG Tel: (0131) 4540499

▶ Exact Designs Ltd, Neep Cottage, Pencaitland, East Lothian, EH34 5DE Tel: (01875) 340859

Ischus Ltd, 37 Water Meadows, Worksop, Nottinghamshire, S80 3DF Tel: (01909) 532288 E-mail: info@ischus.co.uk

Last Party, 7 Carlingnose Park, North Queensferry, Inverkeithing, Fife, KY11 1EX Tel: (01383) 415022 E-mail: sales@lastparty.co.uk

▶ LinuSoft, 10 Silfield Road, Wymondham, Norfolk, NR18 9AU Tel: (01953) 601294 E-mail: enquiries@linusoft.co.uk

Pca Engineers Ltd, Homer House, Sibthorp Street, Lincoln, LN5 7SL Tel: (01522) 530106 Fax: (01522) 511703 E-mail: sales@pcaeng.co.uk

Product Technology Partners Ltd, Barrington Road, Orwell, Royston, Cambridgeshire, SG8 5QP Tel: (01223) 208791 Fax: (01223) 208795 E-mail: frontdesk@ptpart.co.uk

▶ Smartdata, Abertechnium, Y Lanfa, Trefechan, Aberystwyth, Dyfed, SY23 1AS Tel: (0845) 6128061 Fax: (01970) 613480 E-mail: enquiries@smartdata.co.uk

ENGINEERING STEEL

Blanford Engineering, Forum Buildings, Main Road, Minsterworth, Gloucester, GL2 8JS Tel: (01452) 750510 Fax: (01452) 750553

Longhope Welding Engineers, Church Road, Longhope, Gloucestershire, GL17 0LA Tel: (01452) 830572 Fax: (01452) 830983

M L B Engineering, 1a Belle Eau Park, Bilsthorpe, Newark, Nottinghamshire, NG22 8TX Tel: (01623) 871991 Fax: (01623) 871991

W Spurr & Sons, 6 Wakefield Commercial Park, Bridge Road, Horbury, Wakefield, West Yorkshire, WF4 5NW Tel: (01924) 274746 Fax: (01924) 274746

ENGINEERING SUBCONTRACT SERVICES

▶ A & E Edm Ltd, 25 Mornington Road, Smethwick, West Midlands, B66 2JE Tel: 0121-558 8352 Fax: 0121-558 8350 E-mail: info@amedm.co.uk

A Kidman Engineering, Atlas Mill Road, Brighouse, West Yorkshire, HD6 1ES Tel: (01484) 720520 Fax: (01484) 401051

A & M Engineering, Briercliffe Business Centre, Burnley Road, Briercliffe, Burnley, Lancashire, BB10 2HG Tel: (01282) 412706 Fax: (01282) 424880

A & N Engineering Services Ltd, 4 Adam Business Centre, Henson Way, Telford Way Industrial Estate, Kettering, Northamptonshire, NN16 8PX Tel: (01536) 411182 Fax: (01536) 523317

A N Pecision Ltd, Salisbury Road, Hoddesdon, Hertfordshire, EN11 0HU Tel: (01992) 463666 Fax: (01992) 441730 E-mail: derek.heard@lineone.net

A R B Precision Engineers Ltd, Unit 69 Station Road Industrial Estate, Hailsham, East Sussex, BN27 2ES Tel: (01323) 846935 Fax: (01323) 846937 E-mail: keith@arbprecision.freeserve.co.uk

A1 Roper Ltd, Crown Works, Worth Way, Keighley, West Yorkshire, BD21 5LR Tel: (01535) 604215 Fax: (01535) 602689 E-mail: a1-roper@compuserve.com

Abbey Precision Ltd, 72 Alston Drive, Bradwell Abbey, Milton Keynes, MK13 9HG Tel: (01908) 225858 Fax: (01908) 225848 E-mail: sales@abbeyprecision.com

Abic Engineering Associates Ltd, 4 Lyon Close, Woburn Road Industrial Estate, Kempston, Bedford, MK42 7SB Tel: (01234) 852900 Fax: (01234) 304010 E-mail: info@abicengineering.co.uk

Ace Precision Engineers, 5 Tait Road, Croydon, CR0 2DT Tel: (020) 8683 0487 Fax: (020) 8684 4583E-mail: l.povada-ace@fsbdial.co.uk

Adaero Precision Components Ltd, Unit 6 Down End, Lords Meadow Industrial Estate, Crediton, Devon, EX17 1HN Tel: (01363) 778660 Fax: (01363) 773977 E-mail: enquiries@adaero.co.uk

Adage Co. Ltd, 1c Bridge Road, Camberley, Surrey, GU15 2QR Tel: (01276) 684922 Fax: (01276) 692025 E-mail: adage@eur-isp.com

Adrem Engineering Ltd, Unit 3, Murdock Rd, Bicester, Oxon, OX26 4PP Tel: (01869) 321365 Fax: (01869) 241764

Adroit, 1 Townsend Centre Blackburn Road, Townsend Industrial Estate, Houghton Regis, Dunstable, Bedfordshire, LU5 5BQ Tel: (01582) 672141 Fax: (01582) 672140 E-mail: mick.haron@btconnect.com

Advance Engineering Services Ltd, Unit 1, Farley Bank, Hastings, East Sussex, TN35 5QA Tel: (01424) 424720 Fax: (01424) 442924 E-mail: sales@advance-eng.co.uk

Advance Metal Components Ltd, Units 12-14, Minters Industrial Estate, Southwall Road, Deal, Kent, CT14 9PZ Tel: (01304) 380574 Fax: (01304) 380619 E-mail: sales@amc-uk.com

Aireworth Ltd, Parson Street, Keighley, West Yorkshire, BD21 3HD Tel: (01535) 662545 Fax: (01535) 611149 E-mail: aireworth@appelbe.com

▶ Aj Fabrications, Touch Wood, Dirty Lane, Fishlake, Doncaster, South Yorkshire, DN7 5LS Tel: (07855) 760620 Fax: (01302) 849769 E-mail: info@ajfabrications.net

Akd Engineering, Horn Hill, Lowestoft, Suffolk, NR33 0PX Tel: (01502) 527800 Fax: (01502) 527848 E-mail: info@akd-engineering.co.uk

Alex Morton, 43 Killysorrell Road, Dromore, County Down, BT25 1LB Tel: (028) 9269 3651 Fax: (028) 9269 3951 E-mail: amorton@domora43.fsnet.co.uk

Alfa Precision & General Engineering Co. Ltd, Solway Trading Estate, Maryport, Cumbria, CA15 8NF Tel: (01900) 815678 Fax: (01900) 814191 E-mail: alfaprecision@btclick.com

Allenfield Precision Engineering Ltd, Richs Sidings, Broadway, Didcot, Oxfordshire, OX11 8AG Tel: (01235) 816880 Fax: (01235) 811848 E-mail: trina@allenfield.co.uk

Alston Asset Management Services Ltd, Unit 27, 27 Roman Way Industrial Estate, Ribbleton, Preston, PR2 5BD Tel: (01772) 700590 Fax: (01772) 706510 E-mail: info@pre-applied.co.uk

Anglia Precision Engineering, 32 Stapledon Road, Orton Southgate, Peterborough, PE2 6TD Tel: (01733) 703230 Fax: (01733) 703231 E-mail: sales@angliaprecision.com

Anglian Pumping Services Ltd, APS House, The Drift, Nacton Road, Ipswich, IP3 9QR Tel: (01473) 719950 Fax: (01473) 719951 E-mail: info@anglianpumping.com

Apb Precision Engineers, Lakeside Business Park, Swan Lane, Sandhurst, Berkshire, GU47 9DN Tel: (01252) 890061 Fax: (01252) 890062

Archibald Young Ltd, Milton Road, Kirkintilloch, Glasgow, G66 1SY Tel: 0141-776 7701 Fax: 0141-775 1743 E-mail: sales@archibaldyoung.co.uk

Ardmore Construction Ltd, Bryne House, 54 Jeffreys Road, Enfield, Middlesex, EN3 7UB Tel: (020) 8805 0101 Fax: (020) 8364 7477 E-mail: millmarsh@mooregroup.co.uk

Argo Products Ltd, Viola Street, Bolton, BL1 8NG Tel: (01204) 595224 Fax: (01204) 307729

Ariel Machine Products Ltd, Yew Tree Lane, Caerleon, Newport, NP18 1LL Tel: (01633) 420405 Fax: (01633) 430072

Arrow Engineers, 6 Izons Lane Industrial Estate, West Bromwich, West Midlands, B70 9BY Tel: 0121-553 6559 Fax: 0121-553 5872

Ashley Precision (Parkstone) Ltd, 12 Broom Road, Parkstone, Poole, Dorset, BH12 4NL Tel: (01202) 744168 Fax: (01202) 744168

Aspec Precision Engineers, Unit P1 Dales Manor Business Park, Grove Road, Sawston, Cambridge, CB22 3TJ Tel: (01223) 836710 Fax: (01223) 836294 E-mail: info@aspec.co.uk

Atkinson Equipment Ltd, Moat Road, West Wilts Trading Estate, Westbury, Wiltshire, BA13 4JF Tel: (01373) 822220 Fax: (01373) 826996 E-mail: sales@atkinsonequipment.com

Atlantic Auto Engineering, Unit 7b Fernfield Farm, Little Horwood Road, Little Horwood, Milton Keynes, MK17 0PS Tel: (01908) 501904 Fax: (01908) 501904

Auto Engineering Supplies Ltd, Forties, Wilnecote, Tamworth, Staffordshire, B77 5DG Tel: (01827) 286161 Fax: (01827) 286042 E-mail: jmurphy@autoengsupplies.co.uk

Automatic Forming, 7 Kinwarton Farm Road, Kinwarton, Alcester, Warwickshire, B49 6EH Tel: (01789) 400567 Fax: (01789) 765213

Ayrshire Precision Engineering Ltd, Low Coylton, Coylton, Ayr, KA6 6LF Tel: (01292) 570450 Fax: (01292) 570891 E-mail: enquiries@ayrshire-precision.co.uk

Aztec Precision Engineering, Pixmore Avenue, Letchworth Garden City, Hertfordshire, SG6 1JG Tel: (01462) 677888 Fax: (01462) 677888

B D R Micro Instruments Ltd, The Bringey, Church Street, Great Baddow, Chelmsford, CM2 7JW Tel: (01245) 476777 Fax: (01245) 475761 E-mail: info@bdr-micro.co.uk

B O M Light Engineering Ltd, B O M Engineering Tools, Station Road, Morley, Leeds, LS27 8JT Tel: 0113-253 7544 Fax: 0113-252 7851 E-mail: sales@bomeng.co.uk

B P Newbould Ltd, 15 Hilltop Road, Hamilton, Leicester, LE5 1TT Tel: 0116-274 3303 Fax: 0116-274 3301 E-mail: sales@bpnewbould.co.uk

B R M Precision Engineers & Toolmakers Ltd, Unit 3, Brooks Street Business Centre, Brook Street, Colchester, CO1 2UZ Tel: (01206) 794617 Fax: (01206) 793839

B S P Engineering Ltd, Maitland Road, Lion Barn Industrial Estate, Needham Market, Ipswich, IP6 8NZ Tel: (01449) 722222 Fax: (01449) 721989 E-mail: sales@bspengineering.co.uk

Bardon Engineering, 9 Douglas Court, Eleventh Avenue, Team Valley Trading Estate, Gateshead, Tyne & Wear, NE11 0JY Tel: 0191-482 4407 Fax: 0191-482 4407

▶ Barrington Engineering Ltd, New Parkhall Industrial Estate, Parkhall Road, Stoke-on-Trent, ST3 5AT Tel: (01782) 370200

BDJ Engineering Worcester Ltd, A Carden Close, Worcester, WR1 2AR Tel: (01905) 23616 Fax: (01905) 22242 E-mail: brian@bdjengineering.wanadoo.co.uk

Belmar Engineering Services Ltd, Abbotswell Road, Aberdeen, AB12 3AJ Tel: (01224) 875038 Fax: (01224) 879125 E-mail: postmaster@belmar.co.uk

George Bethell Ltd, Unit 9 Rugby Park, Bletchley Road, Heaton Mersey, Stockport, Cheshire, SK4 3EJ Tel: 0161-442 8805 Fax: 0161-442 8818 E-mail: sales@bethell.com

BFS Sheet Metal & Engineering Ltd, 42 Woodham Lane, New Haw, Addlestone, Surrey, KT15 3NA Tel: (01932) 848142 Fax: (01932) 841937 E-mail: stephen@bfssheetmetal.co.uk

Billington Structures Ltd, Barnsley Road, Wombwell, Barnsley, South Yorkshire, S73 8DS Tel: (01226) 340666 Fax: (01226) 755947 E-mail: sales@billington-structures.co.uk

Bowden Precision Engineering Co. Ltd, Riverside, Market Harborough, Leicestershire, LE16 7PU Tel: (01858) 467508 Fax: (01858) 431656 E-mail: enquiries@bowdenprecision.co.uk

Boxall Engineering, Unit 50 Grace Business Centre, Willow Lane, Mitcham, Surrey, CR4 4TU Tel: (020) 8648 8468 Fax: (020) 8648 4162E-mail: info@boxall-industrial.co.uk

Brennan Tool & Engineering Co. Ltd, Unit 9-11 Brooke Trading Estate, Lyon Road, Romford, RM1 2AT Tel: (01708) 736600 Fax: (01708) 735500 E-mail: david.brennan@brennan-tools.co.uk

Britten Engineering Ltd, 12 Morris Road, Leicester, LE2 6BR Tel: 0116-270 0448 Fax: 0116-270 4998

Bromyard Engineering Company Ltd, 23 Rowberry Street, Bromyard, Herefordshire, HR7 4DT Tel: (01885) 483257 Fax: (01885) 488028 E-mail: linda@bromyard.com

Brooks Precision Engineering Ltd, 6 Chamberlain Road, Aylesbury, Buckinghamshire, HP19 8DY Tel: (01296) 393862 Fax: (01296) 421014

Bushell & Meadows Ltd, Northway Lane, Tewkesbury, Gloucestershire, GL20 8HG Tel: (01684) 292000 Fax: (01684) 855763 E-mail: info@bushell-meadows.co.uk

C H E Engineering, Unit 59, Bergen Way, North Lynn Industrial Estate, King's Lynn, Norfolk, PE30 2JL Tel: (01553) 691999 Fax: (01553) 691999

C J Engineering Ltd, 2 Faraday Place, Thetford, Norfolk, IP24 3RG Tel: (01842) 761726 Fax: (01842) 761119 E-mail: kevin@cjeng.co.uk

C P C Engineers Ltd, Adderley Road, Market Drayton, Shropshire, TF9 3SW Tel: (01630) 652904 Fax: (01630) 652904

C S Milne Engineering, Unit 2 Peckleton Lane Business Park, Peckleton Common, Elmesthorpe, Leicester, LE9 7SH Tel: (01455) 822569 Fax: (01455) 824012 E-mail: sales@cs-milne.co.uk

C & W Production Engineering Ltd, Unit 9 Vaughan St Industrial Estate, Manchester, M12 5BT Tel: 0161-223 9993 Fax: 0161-231 3113 E-mail: info@candwengineering.com

Callaghan Engineering, Pembroke Avenue, Waterbeach, Cambridge, CB25 9QP Tel: (01223) 863330 Fax: (01223) 863223

James Camden Engineering Ltd, Scar Bank, Warwick, CV34 5DB Tel: (01926) 491347 Fax: (01926) 411362 E-mail: jamescamden@btinternet.com

Campbell Engineering & Design, 67 Valley Business Centre, Church Road, Newtownabbey, County Antrim, BT36 7LS Tel: (028) 9055 1611 Fax: (028) 9055 1666 E-mail: mail@cednet.co.uk

Carron Tooling, 80 Shelley Road, Bournemouth, BH7 6HB Tel: (01202) 303811 Fax: (01202) 303811

Central Engineering Services Ltd, Star Works, Burton St, Leek, Staffordshire, ST13 8BX Tel: (01538) 398127 Fax: (01538) 373774 E-mail: inquire@cepltd.co.uk

Centralised Services, Piccadilly, Nottingham, NG6 9FN Tel: 0115-913 5000 Fax: 0115-977 0744 E-mail: centser@btconnect.com

Charter Precision Engineering, Unit 25-26, Enfield Industrial Estate, Redditch, Worcestershire, B97 6BY Tel: (01527) 584187 Fax: (01527) 584187

Chelburn Precision Ltd, 2 Plot 7-9 Trans Pennine Trading Estate, Gorrells Way, Rochdale, Lancashire, OL11 2PX Tel: (01706) 644538 Fax: (01706) 861733 E-mail: chelburn@zen.co.uk

Chiltern Thrust Bore Ltd, Unit 1 The Barn, Firs Farm, Stagsden, West End, Bedford, MK43 8TB Tel: (01234) 825948 Fax: (01234) 824147 E-mail: chiltern@onweb.co.uk

J.S. Chinn Project Engineering Ltd, Coventry Road, Exhall, Coventry, CV7 9FT Tel: 0117-958 4600 Fax: 0117-958 4601 E-mail: jschinn@internet-uk.net

Churchill Tool Co. Ltd, Empress Street, Old Trafford, Manchester, M16 9EN Tel: 0161-848 9539 Fax: 0161-872 9234 E-mail: info@churchill-grinders.co.uk

Clydeview Precision Engineering & Supplies Ltd, 197a Dumbarton Road, Clydebank, Dunbartonshire, G81 4XJ Tel: 0141-941 1873 Fax: 0141-951 1928

ENGINEERING SUBCONTRACT SERVICES – *continued*

Colin Mackenzie Engineering Ltd, 3 Murray Street, Paisley, Renfrewshire, PA3 1QG Tel: 0141-889 3031 Fax: 0141-889 3031

Colson Engineering, 8 Headlands Trading Estate, Swindon, SN2 7JQ Tel: (01793) 526660 Fax: (01793) 513294 E-mail: sales@colsonengineering.com

Computerised Engineering Co., Unit 2a High Pastures, Stortford Road, Hatfield Heath, Bishop's Stortford, Hertfordshire, CM22 7DL Tel: (01279) 739455 Fax: (01279) 739454 E-mail: james@computerisedengineering.com

Comwald Engineering, Unit 8 Bromag Industrial Estate, Minster Lovell, Witney, Oxfordshire, OX29 0SR Tel: (01993) 771478 Fax: (01993) 708220

Constant Precision, 5 Triumph Way, Woburn Road Industrial Estate, Kempston, Bedford, MK42 7QB Tel: (01234) 851131 Fax: (01234) 841265 E-mail: sales@constant-precision.co.uk

Coote & Hall Engineers Ltd, Spen Vale Street, Heckmondwike, West Yorkshire, WF16 0NQ Tel: (01924) 402854 Fax: (01924) 402854 E-mail: sales@coote-hall.co.uk

Cowfold Precision Engineering, Oakendene Industrial Estate, Bolney Road, Cowfold, Horsham, West Sussex, RH13 8AZ Tel: (01403) 864945 Fax: (01403) 864945 E-mail: cowfold.precision@blueyonder.co.uk

Creaton Engineering Ltd, 6 Merse Road, Moons Moat North Industrial Es, Redditch, Worcestershire, B98 9HL Tel: (01527) 582900 Fax: (01527) 582909 E-mail: enquiries@creaton-engineering.co.uk

Croft Engineering Co. Ltd, Unit 7A, Parnall Road, Fishponds, Bristol, BS16 3JH Tel: 0117-958 3286 Fax: 0117-958 4390

Cross Country Ltd, 4 Darby Gate, West Portway, Andover, Hampshire, SP10 3LF Tel: (01264) 351409 Fax: (01264) 333921

Custance & Thomson Blackheath Ltd, Meadowcourt Road, London, SE3 9DX Tel: (020) 8852 1545 Fax: (020) 8852 4352

D C E Holne Ltd, Mardle Way Industrial Estate, Buckfastleigh, Devon, TQ11 0NS Tel: (01364) 643862 Fax: (01364) 643025 E-mail: enquiries@dce-holne.co.uk

Datona Ltd, Unit 1A, Lawton Rd, Rushden, Northants, NN10 0DX Tel: (01933) 411616 Fax: (01933) 411873

Debanks Engineering, C3-C4 Unit, Grovelands Avenue Workshops, Winnersh, Wokingham, Berkshire, RG41 5LB Tel: 0118-977 3008 Fax: 0118-977 0903

Denley Engineering, Bayton Road, Exhall, Coventry, CV7 9EJ Tel: (024) 7636 1943 Fax: (024) 7664 4315

Dicol Co. Ltd, Colchester Road, Tendring, Clacton-on-Sea, Essex, CO16 9AA Tel: (01255) 830119 Fax: (01255) 831362 E-mail: sales@dicol.com

Die Max Engineering, 1-2 Mid Wynd, Dundee, DD1 4JG Tel: (01382) 224481 Fax: (01382) 224481

Dorcas Engineering Ltd, Howard Road, Eaton Socon, St. Neots, Cambridgeshire, PE19 8ET Tel: (01480) 213316 Fax: (01480) 216319

Dracup (UK) Ltd, Lane Close Mills, Bartle Lane, Bradford, West Yorkshire, BD7 4QQ Tel: (01274) 571071 Fax: (01274) 501209 E-mail: email@dracupuk.com

Dyke Engineering, Unit 4, Vastre Industrial Estate, Newtown, Powys, SY16 1DZ Tel: (01686) 624412 Fax: (01686) 623236 E-mail: dykeengineering@mid-wales.net

Eaves Engineering Hyde Ltd, Unit F Adamsons Industrial Estate, Hyde, Cheshire, SK14 1EF Tel: 0161-368 9828 Fax: 0161-367 8143 E-mail: stan-feerick@yahoo.com

Engineering Light Assembly Co., Unit 1 Lower Road Trading Estate, Ledbury, Herefordshire, HR8 2DJ Tel: (01531) 632547 Fax: (01531) 634790 E-mail: engineering-light@btconnect.com

Euroscot Engineering Ltd, 427 Hillington Road, Hillington Industrial Estate, Glasgow, G52 4UJ Tel: 0141-883 2218 Fax: 0141-883 8970 E-mail: office@euroscotengineering.co.uk

Ewart Engineering Ltd, Gretna Industrial Estate, Gretna, Dumfriesshire, DG16 5JN Tel: (01461) 337081 Fax: (01461) 337962 E-mail: info@ewart-eng.co.uk

Excel Precision Engineering Ltd, 32 High St, Drayton, Abingdon, Oxon, OX14 4JW Tel: (01235) 538333 Fax: (01235) 538303 E-mail: neiltyler@btconnect.com

Farge Engineering Stockport Ltd, 4 Greyhound Industrial Estate, Melford Road, Hazel Grove, Stockport, Cheshire, SK7 6DD Tel: 0161-456 8209 Fax: 0161-483 9738

First Engineering Services, Unit 1, Hare Street, Bilston, West Midlands, WV14 7DX Tel: (01902) 354735 Fax: (01902) 354805 E-mail: first.engineering@virgin.net

Flavell Precision Engineering Ltd, Moore Street, Wolverhampton, WV1 2HE Tel: (01902) 456583 Fax: (01902) 456583 E-mail: sales@precisionengineering.gbr.fm

Forrestford Engineering Ltd, Polo Grounds, New Inn, Pontypool, Gwent, NP4 0TW Tel: (01495) 756007 Fax: (01495) 750065 E-mail: darren@fford31.freeserve.co.uk

Fox VPS Ltd, Minekeep House, Bridge Road, Camberley, Surrey, GU15 2QR Tel: (01276) 683331 Fax: (01276) 683332 E-mail: sales@foxvps.co.uk

Fpe, 21 Blatchford Close, Horsham, West Sussex, RH13 5RG Tel: (01403) 269069 Fax: (01403) 211391

Furmanite International Ltd, Owens Road, Skippers Lane Industrial Estate, Middlesbrough, Cleveland, TS6 6HE Tel: (01642) 455111 Fax: (01642) 465692

G E Aviation, Wobaston Road, Wolverhampton, WV9 5EW Tel: (01902) 397700 Fax: (01902) 394394

G S Brown Precision Engineers Ltd, Beeches, Ladybank, Cupar, Fife, KY15 7LR Tel: (01337) 830264 Fax: (01337) 831269 E-mail: enquiries@gsbrown.com

Gilmour Tools Ltd, Baird Avenue, Strutherhill Industrial Estate, Larkhall, Lanarkshire, ML9 2PJ Tel: (01698) 884856 Fax: (01698) 886634 E-mail: info@gilmourtools.co.uk

Gravesend Engineering Co. Ltd, East Crescent Road, Gravesend, Kent, DA12 2AR Tel: (01474) 365475 Fax: (01474) 365475

H B Halstead & Sons Ltd, 247 Eldon Street, Ashton-on-Ribble, Preston, PR2 2BB Tel: (01772) 252820 Fax: (01772) 202609 E-mail: sales@hbhalstead.com

H C S Tools Ltd, Unit T, Millmeade Industrial Estate, Staines, Middlesex, TW18 4UK Tel: (01895) 257265 Fax: (01895) 235630 E-mail: alan@hcstools.fsnet.co.uk

H P C Engineering Plc, Victoria Gardens, Victoria Gardens Industrial Estate, Burgess Hill, West Sussex, RH15 9RQ Tel: (01444) 241671 Fax: (01444) 247587 E-mail: peterhowell@hpcplc.co.uk

H W Whiteley Engineering, Holmfield Industrial Estate, Holmfield, Halifax, West Yorkshire, HX2 9TN Tel: (01422) 244870 Fax: (01422) 248666 E-mail: gordonwhitaker@hwwhiteley.co.uk

Harrison & Hutchinson Ltd, Field Road, Heysham, Morecambe, Lancashire, LA3 2XU Tel: (01524) 850200 Fax: (01524) 850605 E-mail: harrison.hutchin@btconnect.com

Hart Automation Ltd, Icknield Road, Luton, LU3 2NY Tel: (01582) 599545 Fax: (01582) 579818

Hayneswood Engineering UK, Acorn Street, Lees, Oldham, OL4 3DE Tel: 0161-620 5337 Fax: 0161-621 5974 E-mail: engineering@hayneswood.co.uk

Helmrick Engineers Ltd, Ossett Lane, Dewsbury, West Yorkshire, WF12 8LS Tel: (01924) 462743 Fax: (01924) 430229 E-mail: helmrickuk@aol.com

Hollinwood Wood Precision Engineering Ltd, 8 Victoria Trading Estate, Drury Lane, Chadderton, Oldham, OL9 7PJ Tel: 0161-682 7900 Fax: 0161-681 4900 E-mail: sales@hollinwood.com

Holmes Engineering, Unit 2 Furtho Court, Towcester Road, Old Stratford, Milton Keynes, MK19 6AN Tel: (01908) 563169 Fax: (01908) 563169

International Engine Services, 6 Moss Road, Witham, Essex, CM8 3UQ Tel: (01376) 503115 Fax: (01376) 503118 E-mail: graham@iesracing.co.uk

J B D Tritec Ltd, 430 Helen Street, Glasgow, G51 3HR Tel: 0141-440 1292 Fax: 0141-440 1240

J & B Limmax, 22 Horsecroft Place, Harlow, Essex, CM19 5BX Tel: (01279) 444243 Fax: (01279) 450571 E-mail: sales@marksmanpaintball.com

J E A Engineering Components, 18-19 Whitehill Road, Glenrothes, Fife, KY6 2RW Tel: (01592) 771911 Fax: (01592) 771911

J P Forrest & Son Ltd, Claylands Avenue, Worksop, Nottinghamshire, S81 7DJ Tel: (01909) 472031 Fax: (01909) 530124 E-mail: sales@jpforrest.com

Jaybee Engineering Co Brighton Ltd, Avis Way, Newhaven, East Sussex, BN9 0DS Tel: (01273) 514623 Fax: (01273) 513702 E-mail: sales@jaybee-eng.co.uk

Jem Sheet Metal & Engineering Ltd, Borron Street, Portwood, Stockport, Cheshire, SK1 2JD Tel: 0161-480 2347 Fax: 0161-480 6210 E-mail: info.jem@btinternet.com

Jencol Engineering Ltd, 1 Somersham Road, St. Ives, Cambridgeshire, PE27 3LN Tel: (01480) 492922 Fax: (01480) 492926 E-mail: sales@jencolengineering.co.uk

Johnson's Engineering & Electrical Co., 61 High Street, Standlake, Witney, Oxfordshire, OX29 7RH Tel: (01865) 300270 Fax: (01865) 300911

K R G Industries Ltd, Russellcolt Street, Coatbridge, Lanarkshire, ML5 2BN Tel: (01236) 435659 Fax: (01236) 434812 E-mail: sales@krgindustries.com

Kaby Engineers Ltd, 14-16 Upper Charnwood Street, Leicester, LE2 0AU Tel: 0116-253 6353 Fax: 0116-251 5237 E-mail: kaby@kaby.co.uk

Kalstan Engineering Ltd, Cavendish Road, Stevenage, Hertfordshire, SG1 2ET Tel: (01438) 745588 Fax: (01438) 360579 E-mail: sjkalmar@kalstanengineering.co.uk

Kamech Engineering Services, 7 4-6 Abingdon Road, Nuffield Industrial Estate, Poole, Dorset, BH17 0UG Tel: (01202) 669452 Fax: (01202) 669453

Kayfern Tools, Manchester Road, Mossley, Ashton-under-Lyne, Lancashire, OL5 9AT Tel: (01457) 832747 Fax: (01457) 832747

Keegal Engineering Ltd, The Link Centre, Unit G Oldmixon CR, Weston-super-Mare, Avon, BS24 9AY Tel: (01934) 419659 Fax: (01934) 641185 E-mail: peter@keegal.co.uk

Kemmel Ltd, Unit 6, Cradle Hill Industrial Estate, Seaford, East Sussex, BN25 3JE Tel: (01323) 899024 Fax: (01323) 893149 E-mail: sales@kemmel.co.uk

King Engineering, Bell Farm, Royston, Hertfordshire, SG8 8ND Tel: (01763) 848899 Fax: (01763) 848899

Knight Engineering, Unit 22 Thruxton Industrial Estate, Thruxton, Andover, Hampshire, SP11 8PW Tel: (01264) 773291 Fax: (01264) 773075E-mail: sales@knightengineering.co.uk

Lazgill Ltd, 1 Vicarage Road, Hampton Wick, Kingston Upon Thames, Surrey, KT1 4EB Tel: (020) 8977 2125 Fax: (020) 8943 3248 E-mail: sales@lazgill.co.uk

Legend Engineering Ltd, Unit B1, Meadow Lane Industrial Estate, Alfreton, Derbyshire, DE55 7EZ Tel: (01773) 520192 Fax: (01773) 830267 E-mail: legend@fsbdial.co.uk

Lister Precision Components Ltd, 27 Benedict Square, Werrington, Peterborough, PE4 6GD Tel: (01733) 573700 Fax: (01733) 326224 E-mail: keith@listerprecision.co.uk

Loadpoint Ltd, Unit J Chelworth Industrial Estate, Chelworth Road, Cricklade, Swindon, SN6 6HE Tel: (01793) 751160 Fax: (01793) 750155 E-mail: sales@loadpoint.co.uk

Locke Engineering Egham, Unit 19, Eversley Way, Thorpe Industrial Estate, Egham, Surrey, TW20 8RG Tel: (01784) 438120 Fax: (01784) 438120

Longden Engineering, The Farriers, Annscroft, Shrewsbury, SY5 8AN Tel: (01743) 860131 Fax: (01743) 860315

Loughlin Engineering, 10a Woodham Lane, New Haw, Addlestone, Surrey, KT15 3NA Tel: (01932) 855250 Fax: (01932) 859623

Lymington Precision Engineers, Gosport Street, Lymington, Hampshire, SO41 9EE Tel: (01590) 677944 Fax: (01590) 647000

M F B Manufacturing Ltd, 7a The Stirling Centre, Market Deeping, Peterborough, PE6 8EQ Tel: 01778 343110

M F H Contract Engineering Services (Leicester) Ltd, Service Works, 2 Highmeres Road, Troon Industrial Estate, Leicester, LE4 7LZ Tel: 0116-276 3807 Fax: 0116-246 0198 E-mail: eng@mfhgroup.co.uk

M I C Engineering, 1a-B Unit, Dans Castle, Tow Law, Bishop Auckland, County Durham, DL13 4BB Tel: (01388) 731347 Fax: (01388) 731348 E-mail: info@mic-valves-eng.co.uk

M J B Engineering Ltd, 133 Barkers Lane, Bedford, MK41 9RX Tel: (01234) 358454 Fax: (01234) 273423 E-mail: sales@mjbengineering.co.uk

M J B Engineering (2000) Ltd, 20 Dodwells Bridge Industrial Estate, Jacknell Road, Hinckley, Leicestershire, LE10 3BS Tel: (01455) 615906 Fax: (01455) 633206 E-mail: m.j.bengltd@btconnect.com

M P Engineering Stalybridge Ltd, Park View Works, Park Street, Stalybridge, Cheshire, SK15 2BT Tel: 0161-303 9988 Fax: 0161-303 9988

Martin Aerospace Ltd, 2 Block 6, Caldwellside Industrial Estate, Lanark, ML11 7SR Tel: (01555) 664751 Fax: (01555) 665860 E-mail: sales@martinaerospace.com

Marvic Textiles Ltd, Chelsea Harbour Design Centre, London, SW10 0XE Tel: (020) 7352 3119 Fax: (020) 8879 3448

Maylan Engineering Co., Crucible Road, Corby, Northamptonshire, NN17 5TS Tel: (01536) 261798 Fax: (01536) 200957 E-mail: maylan@maylan.com

Colin Mealing Ironworks, Mealings Yard, 55 High Street, Westbury-on-Trym, Bristol, BS9 3ED Tel: 0117-950 6262

Metalfold Engineering Ltd, Riverside Works, London Road Terrace, Macclesfield, Cheshire, SK11 7RN Tel: (01625) 511598 Fax: (01625) 618838

▶ Microplus Engineering Ltd, Unit 12 Gainsborough Trad Estate, Rufford Road, Stourbridge, West Midlands, DY9 7ND Tel: (01384) 442991 Fax: (01384) 441164

Millbrook Engineering, Wesley Road, Cinderford, Gloucestershire, GL14 2JN Tel: (01594) 823822 Fax: (01594) 823222

Millturn Engineering, 17 Burrel Road, St. Ives, Cambridgeshire, PE27 3LE Tel: (01480) 469644 Fax: (01480) 469342

Mounsey Engineering Ltd, Unit 11 North Weylands Industrial Estate, Molesey Road, Walton-on-Thames, Surrey, KT12 3PL Tel: (01932) 888555 Fax: (01932) 225388 E-mail: mounseyengineering@tiscali.co.uk

Neisen Ltd, 8 West Newlands Industrial Park, St Ives Road, Somersham, Huntingdon, Cambridgeshire, PE28 3EB Tel: (01487) 840912 Fax: (01487) 843727

Newcom Precision Engineering Ltd, 1 Earith Business Park, Meadow Drove, Earith, Huntingdon, Cambridgeshire, PE28 3QF Tel: (01487) 840870 Fax: (01487) 740046 E-mail: info@newcom-engineering.co.uk

Newman Precision Engineering Ltd, 11-17 Steeple Street, Macclesfield, Cheshire, SK10 2QR Tel: (01625) 618627 Fax: (01625) 618627 E-mail: newmanprecision@aol.com

Newman Stallard Precision Engineers Ltd, 2 Westwood Court, Brunel Road, Totton, Southampton, SO40 3WX Tel: (023) 8086 4291 Fax: (023) 8042 8146

Nexus Precision Engineering Ltd, Badentoy Road, Badentoy Industrial Estate, Aberdeen, AB12 4YA Tel: (01224) 787300

North West Engineering Group Ltd, Mill Lane, Halton, Lancaster, LA2 6NF Tel: (01524) 811224 Fax: (01524) 811288 E-mail: sales@luneside.co.uk

O L D Engineering Co. Ltd, Unit 1 Sketchley Meadows, Hinckley, Leicestershire, LE10 3EN Tel: (01455) 612521 Fax: (01455) 635790 E-mail: m.topp@oldengineering.co.uk

Olympic Engineering, Unit F5 Charles House, Bridge Road, Southall, Middlesex, UB2 4BD Tel: (020) 8574 4406 Fax: (020) 8571 1556 E-mail: oloieng@aol.com

Ottaway Engineering Ltd, Renown Close, Chandlers Ford Industrial Estate, Chandler's Ford, Eastleigh, Hampshire, SO53 4HZ Tel: (023) 8026 9977 Fax: (023) 8027 0270 E-mail: info@otteng.co.uk

Oxford Network Support, 6 Colwell Drive, Abingdon, Oxfordshire, OX14 1AU Tel: (01235) 468530 Fax: (01235) 555581 E-mail: sales@oxfordnetworksupport.com

▶ P R Smith Engineering, Station Works, Lyndhurst Road, Ascot, Berkshire, SL5 9ED Tel: (01344) 874763 Fax: (01344) 875433 E-mail: topmut@themutznutz.com

Pattison Eurotech Engineering Ltd, Western Industrial Estate, Caerleon, Newport, NP18 3NN Tel: (01633) 420133 Fax: (01633) 430181 E-mail: office@patteuro.com

Paul Rhodes Precission Engineering, Walker Street, Scholes, Cleckheaton, West Yorkshire, BD19 6EQ Tel: (01274) 851225 Fax: (01274) 851270

PDQ Engineering Ltd, Industrial Road, Hertburn, Washington, Tyne & Wear, NE37 2SA Tel: 0191-417 2343 Fax: 0191-416 5518 E-mail: john@pdqengineering.com

▶ Peak Contracts Ltd, 7 Church Street, Hartshorne, Swadlincote, Derbyshire, DE11 7ER Tel: (08451) 566843 Fax: 08451 566843E-mail: enquiries@peakcontracts.co.uk

Phoenix Tavinor Engineering, Lichfield Road Industrial Estate, Apollo, Tamworth, Staffordshire, B79 7TA Tel: (01827) 58704 Fax: (01827) 311443

Premier Engineering Co. Ltd, 59a Virginia Street, Southport, Merseyside, PR8 6SJ Tel: (01704) 535955 Fax: (01704) 535955

Presto Engineering, Unit 11 Lakeside Industrial Estate, Stanton Harcourt, Witney, Oxfordshire, OX29 5SL Tel: (01865) 883508 Fax: (01865) 881228

Priority Technical Services Ltd, Suite 7 Thorn Office Centre, Thorn Business Park, Rotherwas, Hereford, HR2 6JT Tel: (01432) 271080 Fax: (01432) 271137

Priory Engineering Co Christchurch Ltd, 60 Purewell, Christchurch, Dorset, BH23 1ES Tel: (01202) 486538 Fax: (01202) 473740 E-mail: enquire@prioryengineering.co.uk

Quick Edge Engineering, Grosvenor Works, Windmill Lane, Denton, Manchester, M34 3LA Tel: 0161-335 0331 Fax: 0161-335 0332 E-mail: keith@quickedge.co.uk

R G D Engineering Co. Ltd, Stonecross Industrial Estate, Downham Market, Norfolk, PE38 0AD Tel: (01366) 382962 Fax: (01366) 384938 E-mail: rgdengineering@btconnect.com

R H G Stone Engineering, 121 Main Street, Walton, Street, Somerset, BA16 9QL Tel: (01458) 442167 Fax: (01458) 447252 E-mail: info@rhgstone.co.uk

R J B Engineering Ltd, Unit 5 Oak Industrial Park, Chelmsford Road, Dunmow, Essex, CM6 1XN Tel: (01371) 876377 Fax: (01371) 876378 E-mail: rbrown7571@aol.com

▶ R J Lift & Testing Services Ltd, Suite 210. Astra House, Arklow Road, London, SE14 6EB Tel: (020) 8691 5920 Fax: (020) 8691 5921 E-mail: mail@rjliftandtestingservices.co.uk

▶ R K Engineering, 40 Fourways, Atherstone, Warwickshire, CV9 1LG Tel: (01827) 715041 Fax: (01827) 718135

R & K Metal Components, Unit 37 Claro Court Business Centre, Claro Road, Harrogate, North Yorkshire, HG1 4BA Tel: (01423) 523139 Fax: (01423) 523139

R & L Enterprises Ltd, Swinnow View, Leeds, LS13 4NA Tel: 0113-257 4208 Fax: 0113-256 0876 E-mail: subcon@rexaloy.co.uk

R M W Witney Ltd, Unit 10br Bromag Industrial Estate, Burford Road, Minster Lovell, Witney, Oxfordshire, OX29 0SR Tel: (01993) 702505 Fax: (01993) 774103 E-mail: sales@rmwwitneyltd.co.uk

R O C Engineering, 13 Melton Road, Queniborough, Leicester, LE7 3FP Tel: 0116-269 6801 Fax: 0116-269 6807 E-mail: rocengi@btconnect.com

Renoco Engineering Ltd, Unit 36, Station Lane Industrial Estate, Old Whittington, Chesterfield, Derbyshire, S41 9QX Tel: (01246) 454725 Fax: (01246) 454599 E-mail: renocoeng@aol.com

Rodwell Engineering Group Ltd, 199-209 Hornchurch Road, Hornchurch, Essex, RM12 4TJ Tel: (01708) 448877 Fax: (01708) 700007

Roton Precision Engineering Ltd, The Old Ambulance, Stansfield Road, Todmorden, Lancashire, OL14 5DL Tel: (01706) 813399 Fax: (01706) 813399

S M Engineering, 14 Courtyard Workshops, Bath Street, Market Harborough, Leicestershire, LE16 9PW Tel: (01858) 432211 Fax: (01858) 410305

Salford Engineering Ltd, Unit 9 Seaford Industrial Estate, Seaford Road, Salford, M6 6AQ Tel: 0161-737 7670 Fax: 0161-745 9224

Sawford Engineering Ltd, B1 Priors Haw Road, Corby, Northamptonshire, NN17 5JG Tel: (01536) 263211 Fax: (01536) 406266 E-mail: sales@sawfordengineering.co.uk

Saxon Engineering, Unit 1, Bredgar Road, Gillingham, Kent, ME8 6PL Tel: (01634) 370023 Fax: (01634) 263250 E-mail: saxoneng@aol.com

Secol Engineering Ltd, Unit 6-9 Cubitt Way, St. Leonards-on-Sea, East Sussex, TN38 9SU Tel: (01424) 855144 Fax: (01424) 855155 E-mail: gary@secolengineering.co.uk

Select Engineering, Broad Ground Road, Redditch, Worcestershire, B98 8YP Tel: (01527) 517157 Fax: (01527) 517145 E-mail: info@select-engineering.co.uk

▶ indicates data change since last edition

ENGINEERING SUBCONTRACT SERVICES – *continued*

Shield Engineering, Wenlock Way, Leicester, LE4 9HU Tel: 0116-246 0660 Fax: 0116-246 1551 E-mail: shield@shield.eng.co.uk
Sign Trade Europe Ltd, Parker Street, Hucknall, Nottingham, NG15 7UF Tel: 0115-968 1000 Fax: 0115-968 1373 E-mail: email@signtrade.btconnect.com
SLK Engineering & Manufacturing Services Ltd, 4 Castle Road, Ellon, Aberdeenshire, AB41 9EY Tel: (01358) 724002 Fax: (01358) 720166 E-mail: sales@sltengineering.co.uk
▶ Solution Rail Ltd, 4 Raleigh Close, Pinner, Middlesex, HA5 1NR Tel: (07951) 361723 Fax: (0871) 9895700 E-mail: enquiries@solutionrail.co.uk
Southern J G & Tool Ltd, Edge Lane, Henley-in-Arden, West Midlands, B95 5DT Tel: (01564) 792651 Fax: (01564) 794403
Speed Bird Engineering, 21 Cunliffe Drive Industrial Estate, Cunliffe Drive, Kettering, Northamptonshire, NN16 8LD Tel: (01536) 524240 Fax: (01536) 520689 E-mail: nitulpanchal@speedbird-engineering.com
Sportsmatch UK Ltd, 16 Summer Street, Leighton Buzzard, Bedfordshire, LU7 1HT Tel: (01525) 381638 Fax: (01525) 851236 E-mail: info@sportsmatch-uk.com
Springwood Engineering, Bunces Lane, Burghfield Common, Reading, RG7 3DH Tel: 0118-983 2411 Fax: 0118-983 4731 E-mail: springwood.eng@btopenworld.com
Sprite Engineering Ltd, 10 Lenziemill Road, Cumbernauld, Glasgow, G67 2RL Tel: (01236) 457970 Fax: (01236) 457970
Standish Engineering Co. Ltd, Mayflower Works, Bradley Lane, Standish, Wigan, Lancashire, WN6 0XF Tel: (01257) 422838 Fax: (01257) 422381 E-mail: enquiries@cnc-machining.co.uk
Stelex Construction Equipment Ltd, Prees Industrial Estate, Shrewsbury Rd, Prees, Whitchurch, Shropshire, SY13 2DJ Tel: (01948) 840840 Fax: (01948) 841147 E-mail: info@stelex.co.uk
George Sumner Ltd, Bridge Street, Oldham, OL1 1EB Tel: 0161-678 6111 Fax: 0161-624 7773 E-mail: terry@georgesumner.co.uk
Swift, Unit 13 Glover Centre, Egmont Street, Mossley, Ashton-under-Lyne, Lancashire, OL5 9PY Tel: (01457) 834005 Fax: (01457) 836617 E-mail: enquiries@swiftengineering.co.uk
T G Sussex, Ivy Arch Road, Worthing, West Sussex, BN14 8BX Tel: (01903) 215515 Fax: (01903) 215211
T P Cooke, 1 Kym Road, Bicton Industrial Park, Kimbolton, Huntingdon, Cambridgeshire, PE28 0LW Tel: (01480) 860138 Fax: (01480) 860138 E-mail: tpcookeengineering@btinternet.com
T R Precision Engineering Co. Ltd, 1 Wattville Road, Smethwick, West Midlands, B66 2NT Tel: 0121-565 1384 Fax: 0121-565 2946 E-mail: trprecision@btconnect.com
Thorne Engineers Ltd, Millfield Industrial Estate, York, YO19 6NA Tel: 01904 448890
Tilling Engineering Ltd, 1 Dale House, Craven Road, Broadheath, Altrincham, Cheshire, WA14 5HJ Tel: 0161-926 9995 Fax: 0161-926 9995 E-mail: clive.tilling@tillingeng.co.uk
Timac, Unit 8 Stratton Business Park, Edworth, Biggleswade, Bedfordshire, SG18 8QB Tel: (01767) 312849 Fax: (01767) 601388 E-mail: timac.engineering@freenet.co.uk
Tracel Ltd, Sand Road Industrial Site, Great Gransden, Sandy, Bedfordshire, SG19 3AJ Tel: (01767) 677521 Fax: (01767) 677952
Tri Development Ltd, Loomer Road, Newcastle, Staffordshire, ST5 7LB Tel: (01782) 561526 Fax: (01782) 561584 E-mail: tridevltd@btconnect.com
Trutorq Actuators, 1 The Anchorage, Gosport, Hampshire, PO12 1LY Tel: (023) 9251 1123 Fax: (023) 9250 2272 E-mail: leon@trutorq-actuators.com
Tryst Engineering Ltd, Fairfield Works, West Wycombe Road, High Wycombe, Buckinghamshire, HP11 2LR Tel: (01494) 442497 Fax: (01494) 465829 E-mail: tryst@ndirect.co.uk
Tuke & Bell, Galaxy Point, Patent Drive Moorcroft Park, Wednesbury, West Midlands, WS10 7XD Tel: 0121-506 7330 Fax: 0121-506 7333 E-mail: reception@tukeandbell.co.uk
Tyckam Engineering Ltd, 18 Levellers Lane, Eynesbury, St. Neots, Cambridgeshire, PE19 2JL Tel: (01480) 218282 Fax: (01480) 218282
V I Precision Grinders Ltd, Pingemead Farm, Pingewood, Reading, RG30 3UR Tel: 0118 9866546
Victoria Production Engineering Ltd, Oldham Street, Denton, Manchester, M34 3SA Tel: 0161-320 1800 Fax: 0161-320 1810 E-mail: sales@victoriaproduction.co.uk
Vordale Ltd, Irthlingborough Road, Little Addington, Kettering, Northamptonshire, NN14 4AS Tel: (01933) 652330 Fax: (01933) 651592
W R Clark & Co Engineers Ltd, Bridge St Industrial Estate, Bridge Street, Clay Cross, Chesterfield, Derbyshire, S45 9NU Tel: (01246) 862325 Fax: (01246) 250033
Waldham Precision Engineering Ltd, 2 Lennox Road, Bilton Industrial Estate, Basingstoke, Hampshire, RG22 4AP Tel: (01256) 359898 Fax: (01256) 844043 E-mail: sales@waldhamprecision.co.uk
David Walker Engineering Services, St Lawrence Industrial Estate, Manston Road, Ramsgate, Kent, CT11 0QZ Tel: (01843) 589954 Fax: (01843) 589954
Warren Engineering, 18A Station Close, Potters Bar, Hertfordshire, EN6 1TL Tel: (01707) 642870 Fax: (01707) 642870
Weaver Mabbs Engineering Ltd, 31a North Street, Emsworth, Hampshire, PO10 7DA Tel: (01243) 371416 Fax: (01243) 376343 E-mail: sales@weavermabbs.co.uk
West Surrey Engineering Ltd, Enterprise House, Ashford Road, Ashford, Middlesex, TW15 1XG Tel: (01784) 254085 Fax: (01784) 247785 E-mail: sales@wse.co.uk
Westcombe Industries Ltd, Royce Road, Peterborough, PE1 5YB Tel: (01733) 746300 Fax: (01733) 746310
Westwell Developments Ltd, Whitewall Road, Frindsbury, Rochester, Kent, ME2 4DZ Tel: (01634) 726148 Fax: (01634) 727081 E-mail: info@westwelldevelopments.fsnet.com
Whittlesey Engineering Co. Ltd, Fenland District Industrial Estate, Station Road, Whittlesey, Peterborough, PE7 2EY Tel: (01733) 203766 Fax: (01733) 350808
Willcocks Engineering Avon Ltd, Pizey Avenue, Clevedon, Avon, BS21 7TS Tel: (01275) 873035 Fax: (01275) 870209 E-mail: willcocksavon@btconnect.com
Wilson & Sons (Engineering) Ltd, Morley Road, Staple Hill, Bristol, BS16 4QB Tel: 0117-956 9769 Fax: 0117-957 1670 E-mail: admin@wilsons-engineering.co.uk
Wragg Bros Engineering Ltd, Keys Road, Nixs Hill Industrial Estate, Alfreton, Derbyshire, DE55 7FQ Tel: (01773) 832288 Fax: (01773) 520776
Wroughton Developments, 14 Barcelona Cresent, Wroughton, Swindon, SN4 9EE Tel: (01793) 812292 Fax: (01793) 812292
Xavier Engineering Ltd, Fleetwood Road, Lune Street, Padiham, Burnley, Lancashire, BB12 8DG Tel: (01282) 680000 Fax: (01282) 680888 E-mail: sales@xavier-eng.co.uk
XM Services, Baldovie Road, Dundee, DD4 8UQ Tel: (01382) 734488 Fax: (01382) 734489 E-mail: sales@xmservices.co.uk
York Assemblies Ltd, 374 Thurmaston BLVD, Leicester, LE4 9LE Tel: 0116-246 3240

ENGINEERING TECHNICAL SERVICES

▶ Asmet Engineering & Technical Services Ltd, 27 Highcroft Crescent, Leamington Spa, Warwickshire, CV32 6BN Tel: (01926) 314536 Fax: 0871 2439203E-mail: asmet@clara.co.uk
Graham Leonard Ltd, Alexander House, Ringtail Place, Burscough Industrial Estate, Ormskirk, Lancashire, L40 8LA Tel: (01704) 895421 Fax: (01704) 895471
Instrumatics I & E Ltd, Unit 7 Ash Holt Industrial Estat, Bank End Road Finningley, Finningley, Doncaster, South Yorkshire, DN9 3NT Tel: (01302) 772999 Fax: (01302) 770000 E-mail: instrufabb@btconnect.com
Maineport Ltd, Rossmore Industrial Estate, Ellesmere Port, CH65 3BS Tel: 0151-355 0111 Fax: 0151-356 1093 E-mail: sales@uecnet.co.uk
Numerate Technology Ltd, 4 Ashley Gardens, Tunbridge Wells, Kent, TN4 8TY Tel: (01892) 545049
Shaw Design Services, Moorfield Mills, Chapel Lane, Heckmondwike, West Yorkshire, WF16 9JU Tel: (01924) 410938 Fax: (01924) 410178
Taylor Bros Holdings Ltd, Taylor Building, 247 Crompton Ware, Bolton, BL2 2RY Tel: (01204) 380726 Fax: (01204) 380724 E-mail: info@taylorbros-uk.com

ENGINEERING THERMOPLASTIC (ETP) COMPONENTS

Glossop Thermoplastics Ltd, Brookfield Industrial Estate, Glossop, Derbyshire, SK13 6JF Tel: (01457) 866111 Fax: (01457) 861802 E-mail: sales@gt-uk.com

ENGINEERING TRAINING

Aylesbury Training Group, Gatehouse Close, Gatehouse Industrial Area, Aylesbury, Buckinghamshire, HP19 8DN Tel: (01296) 481818 Fax: (01296) 437391 E-mail: training@atg-training.co.uk
Fortec T A Ltd, 5 Upminster Trading Park, Warley Street, Upminster, Essex, RM14 3PJ Tel: (01708) 224713 Fax: (01708) 641029 E-mail: kp@fortectraining.co.uk
Gas Tec At C R E Ltd, P O Box 279, Cheltenham, Gloucestershire, GL52 7ZJ Tel: (01242) 677877 Fax: (01242) 676506 E-mail: enquiries@gastecuk.com
In Comm Business Services Ltd, Unit 12 Hayward Industrial Park, Vigo Place, Walsall, WS9 8UG Tel: (01922) 457686 Fax: (01922) 453211 E-mail: info@in-comm.co.uk
Leeds Training Trust, Mitchell House, 139 Richardshaw Lane, Stanningley, Pudsey, West Yorkshire, LS28 6AA Tel: 0113-255 2417 Fax: 0113-236 1004 E-mail: admin@ltt.co.uk
Oak Cad Training Ltd, 18 Cubitts Close, Digswell, Welwyn, Hertfordshire, AL6 0DZ Tel: (01438) 712258 Fax: (01438) 712258 E-mail: alan@oakcad.co.uk
Oakcad Ltd, 116 Whalley Drive, Bletchley, Milton Keynes, MK3 6HU Tel: (01908) 365781 Fax: (01908) 365811 E-mail: alan@oakcad.co.uk
Otc, Lees Road, Oldham, OL4 1JP Tel: 0161-624 5360 Fax: 0161-627 0560 E-mail: info@otctraining.co.uk
Semta Centre, 14 Upton Road, Watford, WD18 0JT Tel: (01923) 238441 Fax: (01642) 566124 E-mail: infodesk@senta.org.uk
Smallpiece Enterprises, 27 Newbold Terrace, Leamington Spa, Warwickshire, CV32 4ES Tel: (01926) 336423 Fax: (01926) 450679 E-mail: train@smallpeice.co.uk
Stockport Engineering Training Association Ltd, Hammond Avenue, Stockport, Cheshire, SK4 1PQ Tel: 0161-480 9822 Fax: 0161-477 4720 E-mail: julie-burns@lineone.net
Tracs International Ltd, Falcon House, Union Grove Lane, Aberdeen, AB10 6XU Tel: (01224) 321213 Fax: (01224) 321214
XM Services, Baldovie Road, Dundee, DD4 8UQ Tel: (01382) 734488 Fax: (01382) 734489 E-mail: sales@xmservices.co.uk

ENGINEERING TRAINING/ TEACHING EQUIPMENT

Norwood Instruments Ltd, New Mill Road, Honley, Holmfirth, HD9 6QD Tel: (01484) 661318 Fax: (01484) 661319 E-mail: gpc@norwood.cc
Otc, Lees Road, Oldham, OL4 1JP Tel: 0161-624 5360 Fax: 0161-627 0560 E-mail: info@otctraining.co.uk

ENGINEERING, HIGH PRECISION

▶ Alan Grinding, Unit 2H, Alverdiscott Road Industrial Estate, Bideford, Devon, EX39 4LQ Tel: (01237) 477458 Fax: (01237) 477458 E-mail: alan@alangrinding.co.uk
▶ L S S International Ltd, E 206 Manchester Road, Mossley, Ashton-under-Lyne, Lancashire, OL5 9AY Tel: (01457) 833170 Fax: (01457) 834087
▶ P K Engineering, Windsor Avenue, Darton, Barnsley, South Yorkshire, S75 5LN Tel: (01226) 230411 E-mail: dimwits.daft1@blueyonder.co.uk
▶ Woodfield Engineering Services Ltd, Unit 2, Woodfield House, Gravel Lane, Banks, Southport, Merseyside, PR9 8BY Tel: (01704) 220729 Fax: (01704) 220515 E-mail: woodfieldservice@btconnect.com

ENGINEERS CLAMPS

A M Designs Powergrip, 45 Tyler Hill Road, Blean, Canterbury, Kent, CT2 9HU Tel: (01227) 472203 Fax: (01227) 454749 E-mail: am@powergrip.co.uk
Emuge (UK) Ltd, 2 Claire Court, Rawmarsh Road, Rotherham, South Yorkshire, S60 1RU Tel: (01709) 364494 Fax: (01709) 364540 E-mail: sales@emuge-uk.co.uk
Kee Systems Ltd, 11 Thornsett Road, London, SW18 4EW Tel: (020) 8874 6566 Fax: (020) 8874 5726 E-mail: sales@keesystems.com
Lindapter International, Brackenbeck Road, Bradford, West Yorkshire, BD7 2NF Tel: (01274) 521444 Fax: (01274) 521130 E-mail: enquiries@lindapter.com
Rollrite Manufacturing (Sales) Ltd, 20 Regent Parade, Birmingham, B1 3NS Tel: (0121) 236 1643 Fax: (0121) 212 1550
Staveley Tools, Bailey Drive, Norwood Industrial Estate, Killamarsh, Sheffield, S21 2JF Tel: 0114-247 3367

ENGINEERS GAUGE RECALIBRATION

Access Instrumentation Ltd, Reading Road, Eversley, Hook, Hampshire, RG27 0RP Tel: 0118-973 4702 Fax: 0118-973 1177 E-mail: sales@accessinstrumentation.co.uk

ENGINEERS IRON CASTINGS

Cast Metal Repairs Ltd, High Street Mills, High St, Heckmondwike, W. Yorkshire, WF16 0DL Tel: (01924) 403444 Fax: (01924) 410164 E-mail: tranter@rhodesengineering.co.uk
Derwent Castings Ltd, Derwent Foundry, Derby Road, Whatstandwell, Matlock, Derbyshire, DE4 5HG Tel: (01773) 852173 Fax: (01773) 856632 E-mail: info@derwent-foundry.co.uk

ENGINEERS VICES

Irwin Industrial Tool Co. Ltd, Parkway Works, Kettlebridge Road, Sheffield, S9 3BL Tel: 0114-244 9066 Fax: 0114-256 1788 E-mail: nroshier@recordtools.co.uk
Paramo Tools Group Ltd, Bailey St, Sheffield, S1 3BS Tel: 0114-249 0880 Fax: 0114-249 0881

ENGINEERS WATER FITTINGS

A & J Gummers Ltd, Unit H Redfern Park Way, Birmingham, B11 2DN Tel: 0121-706 2241 Fax: 0121-706 2960 E-mail: sales@gummers.co.uk
Avilion, Gateway X111 Industrial Estate, Ferry Lane, Rainham, Essex, RM13 9YH Tel: (01708) 526361 Fax: (01708) 550220 E-mail: sales@avilion.co.uk
Grohe Ltd, Blays House, Wick Road, Englefield Green, Egham, Surrey, TW20 0HJ Tel: (0871) 2003414 Fax: (020) 8594 8898 E-mail: info@grohe.co.uk
Polypipe Bathroom & Kitchen Products Ltd, Edlington Lane, Warmsworth, Doncaster, South Yorkshire, DN4 9LS Tel: (01302) 310666 Fax: (01302) 856421
Shavrin Levatap Co. Ltd, 32 Watersides, Kings Langley, Hertfordshire, WD4 8HH Tel: (01923) 267678 Fax: (01923) 265050 E-mail: sales@shavinlevatap.co.uk
Springlynn, Manor Road, Woodley, Stockport, Cheshire, SK6 1RT Tel: 0161-430 6719 Fax: 0161-406 6193 E-mail: david@springlynn.fsbusiness.co.uk
World Of Water, West Street, Coggeshall, Colchester, CO6 1NT Tel: (01376) 563836 Fax: (01376) 563598 E-mail: sales@worldofwater.com

ENGINEERS' AGENTS/ REPRESENTATIVES

Cromwell Tools Ltd, Gorman House, James Street, Righead Industrial Estate, Bellshill, Lanarkshire, ML4 3LU Tel: (01698) 746974 Fax: (01698) 841988 E-mail: glasgow@cromwell-tools.co.uk
Dawcul Ltd, 42 West St, Marlow, Buckinghamshire, SL7 2NB Tel: (01628) 472737 Fax: (01628) 890055 E-mail: sales@dawcul.co.uk
Samuel Hodge Ltd, 2 Bluecoats Avenue, Hertford, SG14 1PB Tel: (01992) 558675 Fax: (01992) 581881
Intellect, Russell Square House, 10-12 Russell Square, London, WC1B 5EE Tel: (020) 7331 2000 Fax: (020) 7331 2040 E-mail: info@intellectuk.org
B.J. Male & Son Ltd, Uints 4-10, Ellis Square, Selsey, Chichester, West Sussex, PO20 0AY Tel: (01243) 602231 Fax: (01243) 602770
Mito Construction & Engineering Ltd, Adams Wharf, 19 Yeoman Street, London, SE8 5DT Tel: (020) 7231 0918 Fax: (020) 7231 6307 E-mail: mitocons@aol.com
R & M Sutcliffe, Clifton Warehouse, Lower Clifton Street, Sowerby Bridge, West Yorkshire, HX6 2BY Tel: (01422) 831038 Fax: (01422) 839841 E-mail: pml@bbn.co.uk

ENGINEERS' MAGNETIC BASE STANDS

Linear Tools Ltd, 1 Clock Tower Road, Isleworth, Middlesex, TW7 6DT Tel: (020) 8400 2020 Fax: (020) 8400 2021 E-mail: sales@lineartools.co.uk

ENGINEERS' PATTERN MAKERS

A P Patterns Ltd, Unit 7-8 Clarendon Industrial Estate, Hyde, Cheshire, SK14 2EW Tel: 0161-368 6389 Fax: 0161-367 9669 E-mail: appatterns@btconnect.com
Abbey Products Norfolk Ltd, Ayton Road, Wymondham, Norfolk, NR18 0QH Tel: (01953) 602627 Fax: (01953) 601428 E-mail: info@abbey4pu.com
Accuvac Prototypes Ltd, Unit F2 Watlington Industrial Estate, Cuxham Road, Watlington, Oxfordshire, OX49 5LU Tel: (01491) 613161 Fax: (01491) 613161 E-mail: enquiries@accuvac.co.uk
Allwick Patterns, The Shipyard, Upper Brents, Faversham, Kent, ME13 7LB Tel: (01795) 532580 Fax: (01795) 533707 E-mail: allwickpatterns@btconnect.com
Alma Patterns, Pondfield, Church Lane, Sheering, Bishop's Stortford, Hertfordshire, CM22 7NR Tel: (01279) 734079 Fax: (01279) 734079
Alpha Pattern Co., Grove Road, Northfleet, Gravesend, Kent, DA11 9AX Tel: (01474) 568669 Fax: (01474) 568669
Ambler Patterns, Riverside Works, Todmerton Rd, Littleborough, Lancs, OL15 9EG Tel: (01706) 378197 Fax: (01706) 377826 E-mail: sales@ambler-patterns.co.uk
Angell Patterns Ltd, 215a Fosse Road North, Leicester, LE3 5EZ Tel: 0116-253 1964 Fax: 0116-253 1964
Anthony D Roberts, Westminster Industrial Estate, Station Road, North Hykeham, Lincoln, LN6 3QY Tel: (01522) 689199 Fax: (01522) 689199
Apc Group Ltd, Crown Street, Thornton Road, Bradford, West Yorkshire, BD1 2LA Tel: (01274) 306970 Fax: (01274) 730900 E-mail: info@a-p-c.biz
Apex Patterns, Unit 10 Redland Indust Estate, Station Hill St.Georges, Madeley, Telford, Shropshire, TF7 5EF Tel: (01952) 614337 Fax: (01952) 614337 E-mail: apexpatterns1@btclick.com

▶ indicates data change since last edition

ENGINEERS' PATTERN MAKERS - *continued*

Astral Pattern Co. Ltd, Roway La, Oldbury, W. Midlands, B69 3EJ Tel: 0121-552 3507 Fax: 0121-544 2471

Barron-Clark Castings Ltd, Royce Road, Peterborough, PE1 5YB Tel: (01733) 551141 Fax: (01733) 896004 E-mail: info@barronclark-castings.co.uk

Briggs Trading Co Southern Ltd, Ebblake Industrial Estate, 21 Blackmoor Road, Verwood, Dorset, BH31 6AX Tel: (01202) 825555 Fax: (01202) 823980 E-mail: enquiries@briggsproducts.com

C & L Patterns, Unit 5 Field Gate, Walsall, WS1 3DJ Tel: (01922) 628377 Fax: (01922) 628377

C & S Tooling Ltd, 103 Nathan Way, London, SE28 0AQ Tel: (020) 8854 0888 Fax: (020) 8854 0888

Cambtec Pattern & Model Making, Unit 3, Nene Road, Bicton Industrial Park, Kimbolton, Huntingdon, Cambridgeshire, PE28 0LF Tel: (01480) 860240 Fax: (01480) 860240

Cheltenham Patterns 1983 Ltd, Gloucestershire Airport, Staverton, Cheltenham, Gloucestershire, GL51 6SP Tel: (01452) 713037 Fax: (01452) 713270 E-mail: mike@cheltpatts.fsnet.co.uk

Cooke Group, West Avenue, Wigston, Leicestershire, LE18 2FB Tel: 0116-288 1234 Fax: 0116-288 1238 E-mail: cookejohn@hotmail.com

Crawley Patterns Ltd, Unit 17, Blackhouse Farm, Blackhouse Road, Colgate, Horsham, West Sussex, RH13 6HS Tel: (01293) 852744

▶ Cromaston Ltd, 17 Swan Street, Sileby, Loughborough, Leicestershire, LE12 7NN Tel: (01509) 812840 Fax: (01509) 813494

Darrell Fieldhouse, Victoria Road, Rushden, Northamptonshire, NN10 0AS Tel: (01933) 410458

Dawson's Pattern Works Ltd, Westland Square, Leeds, LS11 5SS Tel: 0113-270 5142 Fax: 0113-276 1335

Dekton Components Leicester Ltd, All Saints Road, Leicester, LE3 5AB Tel: 0116-251 8387 Fax: 0116-253 2824 E-mail: mouldmakers@dekton.co.uk

Delta Pattern & Tool Co. Ltd, Unit 32, Llantarnum Industrial Estate Park, Cwmbran, Gwent, NP44 3AX Tel: (01633) 838108 Fax: (01633) 838108 E-mail: carl@deltapattern.fsnet.co.uk

Derwent Patterns & Models Ltd, Sandown Road, Derby, DE24 8SR Tel: (01332) 349555 Fax: (01332) 349555

Design Pattern & Tool Co. Ltd, Unit 31A, Central Industrial Estate, Cable Street, Wolverhampton, WV2 2RL Tel: (01902) 872777 Fax: (01902) 872778 E-mail: sales@designpattern.co.uk

Dial Patterns Ltd, 5 Bridge Road Business Centre, Bridge Road, Ashford, Kent, TN23 1BB Tel: (01233) 663073 Fax: (01233) 643775 E-mail: sales@dialpatterns.co.uk

Elkington Bros Ltd, 53-69 Baltimore Road, Birmingham, B42 1DD Tel: 0121-358 2431 Fax: 0121-358 7527 E-mail: lawrence.kelly@elkingtonbrothers.net

Elliott Musgrave Ltd, Jackson Street, Bradford, West Yorkshire, BD3 9SJ Tel: (01274) 731115 Fax: (01274) 722691 E-mail: sales@elliott-musgrave.co.uk

Engineering Patterns, Salford Trading Estate, Salford Street, Birmingham, B6 7SH Tel: 0121-327 0226 Fax: 0121-327 0226

F A Simpson Ltd, 186 Solly Street, Sheffield, S1 4BB Tel: 0114-272 5561 Fax: 0114-276 1500

F Bullett & Co., Island Farm Road, West Molesey, Surrey, KT8 2UU Tel: (020) 8979 1573 Fax: (020) 8941 7352 E-mail: nickbullet@fbullet.com

F & H Pattern Makers, 7 Canal Street, Bootle, Merseyside, L20 8AB Tel: 0151-922 1349 Fax: 0151-922 1349

Farnell (Pattern Makers), Abbot St, Arbroath, Angus, DD11 1HH Tel: (01241) 872548 Fax: (01241) 872548

Forward Pattern Co. Ltd, 4 Long Acre Trading Estate, Long Acre, Birmingham, B7 5JD Tel: 0121-328 8228 Fax: 0121-328 8228 E-mail: roger@forward15.freeserve.co.uk

G Parker Engineering Ltd, Grange Lane, Accrington, Lancashire, BB5 1HX Tel: (01254) 384235 Fax: (01254) 872584 E-mail: info@parkereng.com

Grainger & Worrall Ltd, Unit 1-4 Stanmore Industrial Estate, Bridgnorth, Shropshire, WV15 5HP Tel: (01746) 768250 Fax: (01746) 768251 E-mail: sales@gwcast.co.uk

Greenbank Patterns, Southwell Lane, Kirkby-in-Ashfield, Nottingham, NG17 8FN Tel: (01623) 759919 Fax: (01623) 755834 E-mail: sales@greenbankpatterns.com

H & H Patterns, 18 Monument Way West, Woking, Surrey, GU21 5EN Tel: (01483) 769101 Fax: (01483) 740848 E-mail: sales@hhpaytterns.co.uk

Harvey Manchester Ltd, Oldham Street, Denton, Manchester, M34 3SW Tel: 0161-336 3951 Fax: 0161-336 3936 E-mail: sales@harveymanchester.com

Hockley Pattern & Tool Company Ltd, Lodgefield Road, Halesowen, West Midlands, B62 8AR Tel: 0121-561 4665 Fax: 0121-525 0595 E-mail: sales@hockleypattern.co.uk

Inca Tooling Ltd, Unit 9 Northbrook Close, Worcester, WR3 8BP Tel: (01905) 26937 Fax: (01905) 23593 E-mail: sales@incatooling.co.uk

J & H Busby Ltd, Leicester Road, Lutterworth, Leicestershire, LE17 4NJ Tel: (01455) 552309 Fax: (01455) 552309

J M Shutt Pattern Makers Ltd, The Old Engine House Duke, Street Fenton, Stoke-on-Trent, ST4 3BJ Tel: (01782) 316214 Fax: (01782) 599410

J Miller (Patternmakers) Ltd, 22 Beardmore Way, Clydebank Industrial Estate, Dalmuir, Clydebank, Dunbartonshire, G81 4HT Tel: 0141-952 5930 Fax: 0141-952 5930

Arthur Jackson & Co. Ltd, Rastrick Common, Brighouse, West Yorkshire, HD6 3DR Tel: (01484) 713345 Fax: (01484) 718150 E-mail: aj@ajack.demon.co.uk

John Burn & Co Birmingham Ltd, 74 Albert Road, Stechford, Birmingham, B33 9AJ Tel: 0121-508 4144 Fax: 0121-508 4145 E-mail: info@johnburn.co.uk

JTH Patternmakers Ltd, Players Foundry, Clydach, Swansea, SA6 5BQ Tel: (01792) 842363 Fax: (01792) 845275 E-mail: enquiries@jthpatternmakers.co.uk

Leonard Hall Patterns Ltd, 352 Loxley Road, Sheffield, S6 4TJ Tel: 0114-234 3571 Fax: 0114-234 3571

M & M Patterns, Unit 11 Park Farm Buildings, Cranfield Road, Wavendon, Milton Keynes, MK17 8HA Tel: (01908) 585164 Fax: (01908) 585164

Main Line Patterns, Unit 20b, Alliance Industrial Estate Dodsworth Street, Darlington, County Durham, DL1 2NS Tel: (01325) 483462 Fax: (01325) 483462

Matrix Moulds & Models Ltd, Glover Street, St. Helens, Merseyside, WA10 3LF Tel: (01744) 24333 Fax: (01744) 27999 E-mail: mmm@rapid.co.uk

Micra Pattern Co. Ltd, 91 Sorby Street, Sheffield, S4 7LA Tel: 0114 2720724

John Mills & Sons (Newcastle) Ltd, 509 Shields Road, Walkergate, Newcastle upon Tyne, NE6 4PX Tel: 0191-265 6550 Fax: 0191-265 1002 E-mail: sales@johnmillsnewcastleltd.co.uk

Narvik Developments Ltd, Clay Lane, Oldbury, West Midlands, B69 4TH Tel: 0121-552 3429 Fax: 0121-552 6162

Novo Designs, Church Farm, Eyeworth, Sandy, Bedfordshire, SG19 2HH Tel: 01767 631117

Park Patterns, Overend Road, Corngreaves Trading Estate, Cradley Heath, West Midlands, B64 7DD Tel: (01384) 569962 Fax: (01384) 569962

Pattern Equipment Co Ltd, 24 Mandervell Road, Oadby, Leicester, LE2 5LQ Tel: 0116-271 3254 Fax: 0116-271 3645 E-mail: sales@pattequip.demon.co.uk

Pattern Shop, 27 Offerton Industrial Estate, Hempshaw Lane, Stockport, Cheshire, SK2 5TH Tel: 0161-480 5670 Fax: 0161-480 4565

Patterns Ltd, Darley Abbey Mills, Darley Abbey, Derby, DE22 1DZ Tel: (01332) 342127 Fax: (01332) 298242 E-mail: enquiries@patternsderby.co.uk

Patterns & Dies Ltd, Bute Street, Stoke-on-Trent, ST4 3PW Tel: (01782) 343700 Fax: (01782) 343800 E-mail: sales@patterns-dies.co.uk

Peak Pattern Co. Ltd, 31 Staniforth Road, Sheffield, S9 3HB Tel: 0114-244 1812 Fax: 0114-242 6685

Pitt & Dickson Ltd, 140 Bridgeman Street, Walsall, WS2 9NW Tel: (01922) 623048 Fax: (01922) 620261 E-mail: pitt.dickson@virgin.net

Potter & Upton, 4 St Martins Industrial Estate, Tat Bank Road, Oldbury, West Midlands, B69 4NP Tel: 0121-544 8400 Fax: 0121-544 4050

Premier Pattern Leicester Co. Ltd, 79 Coleman Road, Leicester, LE5 4LE Tel: 0116-276 6094 Fax: 0116-276 5371

R J Stoddart & Co., 96 Orbiston Street, Motherwell, Lanarkshire, ML1 1PX Tel: (01698) 263333 Fax: (01698) 263333

R Woodhead & J Fisher, Unit 2 Oak St Trading Estate, Oak Street, Quarry Bank, Brierley Hill, West Midlands, DY5 2JQ Tel: (01384) 261189 Fax: (01384) 261189

Retrac Productions Ltd, 3-5 Bramble Road, Techno Trading Estate, Swindon, SN2 8HB Tel: (01793) 524616 Fax: (01793) 511899 E-mail: andycarter@retrac-group.com

Rhodes & Kimberley, Bell Place, Blakenhall, Wolverhampton, WV2 4LY Tel: (01902) 458085 Fax: (01902) 458085

Rhodes Nicholson Ltd, Emerald Ironworks, Emerald Street, Huddersfield, HD1 6BY Tel: (01484) 537383 Fax: (01484) 542931 E-mail: gerry@rhodes-nicholson.co.uk

Richard Wilkinson & Co., Devonshire Yard, Pitt Street, Keighley, West Yorkshire, BD21 4PF Tel: (01535) 602512 Fax: (01535) 602713 E-mail: sales@wilktool.co.uk

Rojac Patterns Ltd, Automotive Components Park, Hallens Drive, Wednesbury, West Midlands, WS10 7DD Tel: 0121-556 0909 Fax: 0121-556 4343 E-mail: sales@rojac.com

S Bateman & Sons Ltd, Hart Street, Blackburn, BB1 1HW Tel: (01254 56153 Fax: (01254) 664416

S P C Patterns Ltd, 191 Vincent Road, Sheffield, S7 1BZ Tel: 0114-255 0040 Fax: 0114-255 8023

Seymour Patterns & Castings, Oak St Trading Estate, Oak Street, Quarry Bank, Brierley Hill, West Midlands, DY5 2JQ Tel: (01384) 78768 Fax: (01384) 79138 E-mail: john.elwell@yesit.co.uk

Shenstone Pattern & Crafts Ltd, Little Cornbow, Halesowen, West Midlands, B63 3AJ Tel: 0121-503 0362 Fax: 0121-585 7440

Simmons (Patternmakers) Ltd, Station Street West Business Park, Coventry, CV6 5BP Tel: (024) 7663 7028 Fax: (024) 7663 7030 E-mail: sales@epoxyworktops.com

South Lincs Patterns, Ivanhoe, Spalding Common, Spalding, Lincolnshire, PE11 3AS Tel: (01775) 722988 Fax: (01775) 760386 E-mail: sales@southlincsfoundry.co.uk

South Yorkshire Pattern Co. Ltd, Nimrod Works, Trinity Street, Sheffield, S3 7AJ Tel: 0114-272 1999 Fax: 0114-272 1999

Summit Patternmaking Co. Ltd, Paper Mill End Industrial Estate, Birmingham, B44 8NH Tel: 0121-344 3943 Fax: 0121-344 3944

Sussex Pattern Co. Ltd, 70 Victoria Road, Burgess Hill, West Sussex, RH15 9LY Tel: (01444) 245292 Fax: (01444) 247168 E-mail: info@sussexpattern.co.uk

Thomas Bros Leeds Ltd, Stanningley Field Close, Leeds, LS13 4QG Tel: 0113-256 7210 Fax: 0113-256 9199E-mail: info@tbleeds.com

Traffco Engineers Pattern Co, Midland Road, Scunthorpe, South Humberside, DN16 1DQ Tel: (01724) 842753 Fax: (01724) 865569

Tremelling Pattern Co., 3 Lisle Road, High Wycombe, Buckinghamshire, HP13 5SH Tel: (01494) 533897 Fax: (01494) 472777

Turnstyle Wood Turners, Leicester Street, Melton Mowbray, Leicestershire, LE13 0PP Tel: (01664) 562460 Fax: (01664) 562460

W F Flavell (Patternmakers), Avon Industrial Estate, Rugby, Warwickshire, CV21 3UY Tel: (01788) 575967 Fax: (01788) 575967

W J Evans Precision Ltd, Lint House, Linthouse Lane, Wednesfield, Wolverhampton, WV11 3EA Tel: (01902) 731116

Wallop Woodcrafts (Master Pattern Makers), Unit 3, Hollom Down Road, Lopcombe Corner, Salisbury, SP5 1BP Tel: (01264) 781766 Fax: (01264) 782793 E-mail: nick@wallopwoodcrafts.co.uk

Westward Mouldings Ltd, The New Factory, Delaware Road, Gunnislake, Cornwall, PL18 9AS Tel: (01822) 832120 Fax: (01822) 833938 E-mail: enquiry@fleetscale.co.uk

Wilstead Patterns & Castings, Brickyard House, Mill Lane, Arlesey, Bedfordshire, SG15 6RF Tel: (01462) 835559

R. Winter Tooling, 7 Stirling Park, Laker Road, Rochester, Kent, ME1 3QR Tel: 01634 666627 Fax: 01634 666637 E-mail: focus@rwintertooling.com

Wombourne Patterns Ltd, Heath Mill Close, Wombourne, Wolverhampton, WV5 8EX Tel: (01902) 893415 Fax: (01902) 324011

Wood & Loines Ltd, Unit 5 Portersfield Road, Cradley Heath, West Midlands, B64 7BN Tel: (01384) 411581 Fax: (01384) 413660 E-mail: sales@wood-loines.com

Woodcrafts, 25 Bayton Road Industrial Estate, Bayton Road, Exhall, Coventry, CV7 9EL Tel: (024) 7636 1022 Fax: (024) 7664 4299 E-mail: pdl@btconnect.com

Woodtec, 38 Festival Drive, Loughborough, Leicestershire, LE11 5XJ Tel: (01509) 219246 Fax: (01509) 260117 E-mail: sales@woodtec2.co.uk

Zeus Pattern & Tool Co. Ltd, Sunrise Business Park, High Street Wooliston, Stourbridge, West Midlands, DY8 4ZZ Tel: (01384) 482222 Fax: (01384) 446446

ENGINEERS' PATTERN MAKING MACHINERY

Ajay Patterns, 236 Berwick Avenue, Slough, SL1 4QT Tel: (01753) 525505 Fax: (01753) 825411

ENGINEERS' PATTERN MAKING MATERIALS

John Burn & Co Birmingham Ltd, 74 Albert Road, Stechford, Birmingham, B33 9AJ Tel: 0121-508 4144 Fax: 0121-508 4145 E-mail: info@johnburn.co.uk

ENGINEERS' SUPPLIES

A T Engineering Supplies Ltd, Garstang Road, Claughton-on-Brock, Preston, PR3 0RB Tel: (01995) 640058 Fax: (01995) 640031

A T Tool Centre Ltd, 26-27 Buckingham Trade Park, Buckingham Avenue, Slough, SL1 4QA Tel: 01753 536811 Fax: 01753 532709 E-mail: slough@at-toolcentre.co.uk

A W V Turner & Co. Ltd, Rex Works, Harvest Lane, Sheffield, S3 8EB Tel: 0114-272 4162 Fax: 0114-276 9284 E-mail: awvturner@awvturner.f9.co.uk

A Winston & Sons, 461 Paisley Road, Glasgow, G5 8RJ Tel: 0141-429 4278 Fax: 0141-429 0577 E-mail: bryanwinston@hotmail.co.uk

Adams Ironmongers Sutton Coldfield Ltd, 112 Holland Road, Sutton Coldfield, West Midlands, B72 1RE Tel: 0121-354 4822 Fax: 0121-355 6968 E-mail: sales@adamsindustrial.co.uk

Allcap Ltd, Unit 24c Morelands Trading Estate, Bristol Road, Gloucester, GL1 5RZ Tel: (01452) 525800 Fax: (01452) 331125 E-mail: sales@allcap.co.uk

Anglo Eastern Ship Management UK Ltd, The Parks, 107-115 Milton Street, Glasgow, G4 0DN Tel: 0141-353 1020 Fax: 0141-353 2366 E-mail: supplies@tandh.co.uk

Annasbrook Supply Co. Ltd, Gapton Hall Road, Great Yarmouth, Norfolk, NR31 0HX Tel: (01493) 668721 Fax: (01493) 440250 E-mail: sales@annasbrook.com

Antron Engineers Supplies, Unit 11 Broomers Hill Par, Broomers Hill Lane, Pulborough, West Sussex, RH20 2RY Tel: (01798) 872720 E-mail: sales@antroneng.co.uk

A-T Tool Centre Ltd, 19 Alston Drive, Bradwell Abbey, Milton Keynes, MK13 9HA Tel: 01908 310707 Fax: 01908 220695 E-mail: miltonkeynes@at-toolcentre.co.uk

At Toolcentre Ltd, Studland Road, Kingsthorpe, Northampton, NN2 6RL Tel: (01604) 711711 Fax: (01604) 711111 E-mail: northampton@at-toolcentre.co.uk

Avenue Tools Ltd, 3 David Road, Colnbrook, Slough, SL3 0TW Tel: (01753) 685921 Fax: (01753) 685922 E-mail: avenue@avenue-group.co.uk

Avery Knight & Bowlers Engineering Ltd, 33-35 James St West, Bath, BA1 2BT Tel: (01225) 425894 Fax: (01225) 445753 E-mail: sales@averyknight.co.uk

Avon Fastenings & Industrial Supplies Ltd, Unit 10, Western Road Industrial Estate, Stratford-Upon-Avon, Warwickshire, CV37 0AH Tel: (01789) 269661 Fax: (01789) 267051 E-mail: avonfastenings@aol.com

Barry & Son Ltd, 37 Bute Street, Salford, M50 1DU Tel: 0161-737 6888 Fax: 0161-745 8159 E-mail: sales@barryandson.co.uk

Binney & Son Ltd, Unit H Spring Hill Industrial Park, Steward Street, Birmingham, B18 7AF Tel: 0121-454 4545 Fax: 0121-454 1145 E-mail: binney.eng@btconnect.com

Binneys Coventry, Unit 1 Challenge Business Park, Challenge Close, Coventry, CV1 5JG Tel: (024) 7622 0228 Fax: (024) 7652 5342 E-mail: info@binneys.co.uk

Bolt & Nut Supplies Ltd, 35-37 Chapeltown, Pudsey, West Yorkshire, LS28 7RZ Tel: 0113-255 6336 Fax: 0113-256 9242

Brabbin & Rudd Ltd, Walker Street, Bolton, BL1 4TB Tel: (01204) 521171 Fax: (01204) 364972E-mail: sales@brabbin-and-rudd.co.uk

Brian S Pope Ltd, 200 Manchester Road, Stockport, Cheshire, SK4 1NN Tel: 0161-480 8322 Fax: 0161-474 1406 E-mail: sales@brianpope.com

Buck & Hickman Ltd, 4 Block A Hareness Park, Hareness Circle, Altens Industrial Estate, Aberdeen, AB12 3QY Tel: (01224) 895272 Fax: (01224) 895248 E-mail: aberdeen@buckhickmaninone.com

Buck & Hickman Ltd, 5 Mod Department, Spitfire Road, Birmingham, B24 9PR Tel: 0121-386 8000 Fax: 0121-386 8011 E-mail: manchester@buckhickman.co.uk

Buck & Hickman Ltd, 203 Longmead Road, Emersons Green, Bristol, BS16 7FG Tel: 0117-957 9797 Fax: 0117-957 9799 E-mail: bristol@buckhickmaninone.com

Buck & Hickman Ltd, R Kingsville Road, Kingsditch Trading Estate, Cheltenham, Gloucestershire, GL51 9NZ Tel: (01242) 519665 Fax: (01242) 224097 E-mail: cheltenham@buckhickmaninone.co.uk

Buck & Hickman Ltd, Unit 16 Gatwick Int Distribution Centre, Cobham Way, Crawley, West Sussex, RH10 9RX Tel: (01293) 561651 Fax: (01293) 561637 E-mail: crawley@buckhickmaninone.com

Buck & Hickman Ltd, Rosswood Road, Rossmore Industrial Estate, Ellesmere Port, CH65 3BU Tel: 0151-356 2160 Fax: 0151-357 2019 E-mail: ellesmere@buckhickmaninone.com

Buck & Hickman Ltd, Unit 19 Ringway Industrial Estate, Beck Road, Huddersfield, HD1 5DG Tel: (01484) 426611 Fax: (01484) 435368 E-mail: huddersfield@buckhickman.co.uk

Buck & Hickman Ltd, Unit 9a, Finway, Dallow Road, Luton, LU1 1TR Tel: (01582) 419887 Fax: (01582) 425824 E-mail: luton@buckhickmaninone.co.uk

Buck & Hickman Ltd, 7 Cannon Park Way, Cannon Park Industrial Estate, Middlesbrough, Cleveland, TS1 5JU Tel: (01642) 240116 Fax: (01642) 245299 E-mail: middlesbrough@buckhickmaninone.com

Buck & Hickman Ltd, A Hambridge Road, Newbury, Berkshire, RG14 5SS Tel: (01635) 521747 Fax: (01635) 32605 E-mail: newbury@buckhickmaninone.com

Buck & Hickman Ltd, Hamar Close, Tyne Tunnel Trading Estate, North Shields, Tyne & Wear, NE29 7UY Tel: 0191-296 0333 Fax: 0191-296 0335 E-mail: newcastle@buckhickman.co.uk

Buck & Hickman Ltd, Unit 2 Longwall Avenue, Queens Drive Industrial Estate, Nottingham, NG2 1NA Tel: 0115-986 8282 Fax: 0115-986 8486 E-mail: nottingham@buckhickmaninone.com

Buck & Hickman Ltd, Unit 2a Treelyn Park, Welbeck Way Woodston, Peterborough, PE2 7WH Tel: (01733) 371737 Fax: (01733) 232245 E-mail: peterborough@buckhickmaninone.co.uk

Buck & Hickman Ltd, 4 Phoenix Business Park, Estover Road, Plymouth, PL6 7PY Tel: (01752) 692700 Fax: (01752) 692701 E-mail: plymouth@buckhickmaninone.com

Buck & Hickman Ltd, Unit 12, Riverside Court, Don Road, Sheffield, S9 2TJ Tel: 0114-244 1012 Fax: 0114-244 5372 E-mail: sheffield@buckhickman.co.uk

Buck & Hickman Ltd, Building 110 Nursling Industrial Estate, Mauretania Road, Nursling, Southampton, SO16 0YS Tel: (023) 8074 2300 Fax: (023) 8074 2301 E-mail: southampton@buckhickmaninone.com

ENGINEERS' SUPPLIES – *continued*

Buck & Hickman Ltd, Lyme Vale Court, Parklands Business Park, Parklands, Stoke-on-Trent, ST4 6NW Tel: (01782) 279927 Fax: (01782) 286355 E-mail: stoke@buckhickman.co.uk

Buck & Hickman Ltd, Unit 12 Ferryboat Close, Enterprise Park, Swansea Enterprise Park, Swansea, SA6 8QN Tel: (01792) 799998 Fax: (01792) 700678 E-mail: swansea@buckhickman.co.uk

Buck & Hickman Ltd, 103-109 Waldegrave Road, Teddington, Middlesex, TW11 8LL Tel: (020) 8977 8844 Fax: (020) 8943 2826 E-mail: teddington@buckhickman.co.uk

Buck Hickman In One Ltd, 70 Lancefield Street, Glasgow, G3 8JD Tel: 0141-221 7174 Fax: 0141-221 8877 E-mail: glasgow@buckhickman.co.uk

Buck In Hickman, Neptune Point, Vanguard Way, Ocean Park, Cardiff, CF24 5PG Tel: (029) 2030 6000 Fax: (029) 2030 6030 E-mail: cardiff@buckhickmaninone.co.uk

Buckhickman Ltd, Castleton Road, Armley, Leeds, LS12 2EN Tel: 0113-246 0911 Fax: 0113-244 6888 E-mail: sales@buckhickmaninone.com

BuckHickman InOne, Unit 2, Chartergate, Moulton Park, Northampton, NN3 6QF Tel: (01604) 797400 Fax: (01604) 797401 E-mail: northampton@buckhickmaninone.co.uk

C A Baldwin & Co. Ltd, 146-154 Wells Way, London, SE5 7SY Tel: (020) 7703 2138 Fax: (020) 7701 8436 E-mail: info@baldwin.co.uk

C H Morgan & Co. Ltd, 1 Clifton Business Park, Chamberlain Road, Aylesbury, Buckinghamshire, HP19 8DY Tel: (01296) 434878 Fax: (01296) 338520

C W W Engineers Supply Co. Ltd, 7 Stanlake Mews, London, W12 7HA Tel: (020) 8743 0651 Fax: (020) 8740 7731 E-mail: sales@cww.uk

Cassells Industrial Products, 60 Littleworth, Mansfield, Nottinghamshire, NG18 2SH Tel: (01623) 622439 Fax: (01623) 420134 E-mail: enquiries@cip-ltd.co.uk

Caswells, Lagonda Road, Cowpen Lane Industrial Estate, Billingham, Cleveland, TS23 4JA Tel: (01642) 379600 Fax: (01642) 562978 E-mail: sales@caswellsgroup.com

Clwyd Welding Services Ltd, Clwyd Close, Hawarden Industrial Park, Hawarden, Deeside, Clwyd, CH5 3PZ Tel: (01244) 531667 Fax: (01244) 531842 E-mail: clwydweld@aol.com

Coventry Grinders Ltd, 7 Alpha Business Park, Deedmore Road, Coventry, CV2 1EQ Tel: (024) 7660 4377 Fax: (024) 7660 4975 E-mail: info@coventry-grinders.co.uk

Cromwell Basingstoke, Unit 5, Sherrington Way, Basingstoke, Hampshire, RG22 4DQ Tel: (01256) 355966 Fax: (01256) 477230 E-mail: info@cromwell.co.uk

Cromwell (Birmingham), 217 Chester Street, Aston, Birmingham, B6 4AE Tel: 0121-380 1700 Fax: 0121-380 1710 E-mail: birmingham@cromwell.co.uk

Cromwell Bristol Ltd, Unit E St. Vincents Trading Estate, Bristol, BS2 0UY Tel: 0117-972 1127 Fax: 0117-972 4287 E-mail: bristol@cromwell.co.uk

Cromwell Group Ltd, B Great Fenton Business Park, Grove Road, Stoke-on-Trent, ST4 4LZ Tel: (01782) 746746 Fax: (01782) 414414 E-mail: stoke@cromwell.co.uk

Cromwell Industrial Supplies, Unit 2-3 Anthonys Way, Medway City Estate, Rochester, Kent, ME2 4DN Tel: (01634) 290586 Fax: (01634) 290589 E-mail: rochester@cromwell.co.uk

Cromwell Manchester Ltd, 2 Brent Road, Green Lane Trading Estate, Stockport, Cheshire, SK4 2LD Tel: 0161-476 6666 Fax: 0161-476 4444 E-mail: cromwell@manchester.co.uk

Cromwell (Portsmouth), Unit 15, Admirals Park, Williams Road, Portsmouth, PO3 5NJ Tel: (023) 9266 8512 Fax: (023) 9269 9179 E-mail: portsmouth@cromwell-tools.co.uk

Cromwell (Smethwick), Middlemore Road, Smethwick, West Midlands, B66 2DR Tel: 0121-558 1133 Fax: 0121-565 3530 E-mail: smethwick@cromwell.co.uk

Cromwell Tools Ltd, 2 Murcar Industrial Estate, Denmore Road, Bridge of Don, Aberdeen, AB23 8JW Tel: (01224) 820851 Fax: (01224) 820877 E-mail: sales@kennedy-tools.co.uk

Cromwell Tools Ltd, 3-4 Tollgate Close, Cardiff, CF11 8TN Tel: (029) 2034 5888 Fax: (029) 2034 5777 E-mail: cardiff@cromwell.co.uk

Cromwell Tools Ltd, 27 Endemere Road, Coventry, CV6 5PY Tel: (024) 7666 4614 Fax: (024) 7666 6667 E-mail: coventry@cromwell-tools.co.uk

▶ Cromwell Tools Ltd, Thirsk Place, Derby, DE24 8JJ Tel: (01332) 360660 Fax: (01332) 204239 E-mail: derby@cromwell.co.uk

Cromwell Tools Ltd, Shaw Lane Industrial Estate, Ogden Road, Doncaster, South Yorkshire, DN2 4SQ Tel: (01302) 366600 Fax: (01302) 327556 E-mail: doncaster@cromwell-tools.co.uk

Cromwell Tools Ltd, St. James Street, Hull, HU3 2DH Tel: (01482) 326999 Fax: (01482) 213089 E-mail: hull@cromwell-tools.co.uk

Cromwell Tools Ltd, Unit D 7 Bilton Way, Luton, LU1 1UU Tel: (01582) 484666 Fax: (01582) 726167 E-mail: luton@cromwell-tools.co.uk

Cromwell Tools Ltd, The Tool Centre, 75 St James Mill Road, Northampton, NN5 5JP Tel: (01604) 752488 Fax: (01604) 753815 E-mail: northampton@cromwell-tools.co.uk

Cromwell Tools Ltd, 19 Concorde Road, Norwich, NR6 6BJ Tel: (01603) 410939 Fax: (01603) 410939 E-mail: norwich@cromwell-tools.co.uk

Cromwell Tools Ltd, 131 Queens Road, Beeston, Nottingham, NG9 2FE Tel: 0115-922 3311 Fax: 0115-925 1342 E-mail: nottingham@cromwell-tools.co.uk

Cromwell Tools Ltd, Westcombe Square, Royce Road, Peterborough, PE1 5YB Tel: (01733) 555524 Fax: (01733) 311103 E-mail: peterborough@cromwell-tools.co.uk

Cromwell Tools Ltd, 770 Buckingham Avenue, Slough, SL1 4NL Tel: (01753) 696000 Fax: (01753) 696966 E-mail: slough@cromwell-tools.co.uk

Cromwell Tools Ltd, Ark Grove Industrial Estate, Ross Road, Stockton-on-Tees, Cleveland, TS18 2NH Tel: (01642) 673605 Fax: (01642) 671479 E-mail: stockton@cromwell.co.uk

Cromwell Tools Ltd, Kirkby Folly Road, Sutton-in-Ashfield, Nottinghamshire, NG17 5HN Tel: (01623) 551616 Fax: (01623) 552007 E-mail: mansfield@cromwell-tools.co.uk

Cromwells, Waverley House, Effingham Road, Sheffield, S4 7YR Tel: 0114-275 0631 Fax: 0114-275 4447 E-mail: sheffield@cromwell.co.uk

Cromwells Fife, Unit 4 Woodgate Way South, Glenrothes, Fife, KY7 4PF Tel: (01592) 631632 Fax: (01592) 631641 E-mail: fife@cromwell.co.uk

Crossford Oil & Tool Supplies Ltd, Unit 94 Springvale Industrial Estate, Cwmbran, Gwent, NP44 5BH Tel: (01633) 873612 Fax: (01633) 864884 E-mail: sales@crossfords.co.uk

Crossling Ltd, Coast Road, Heaton, Newcastle upon Tyne, NE6 5TP Tel: 0191-265 4166 Fax: 0191-276 4839 E-mail: marketing@crossling.co.uk

D G Jackson Industrial Supplies Ltd, Dukeries Way, Worksop, Nottinghamshire, S81 7DW Tel: (01909) 474085 Fax: (01909) 477201

D H S Tool Supply Co. Ltd, 61 St Modwen Road, Park Way Industrial Estate, Marsh Mills, Plymouth, PL6 8LH Tel: (01752) 223536 Fax: (01752) 222706

D L Skerrett Ltd, 14-14a Unit, Palmerston Street, Joiners Square Industrial Estate, Stoke-on-Trent, ST1 3EU Tel: (01782) 281471 Fax: (01782) 202357 E-mail: sales@dlskerrett.co.uk

D & V Engineering, 17 Browning Avenue, Sutton, Surrey, SM1 3QU Tel: (020) 8642 5127 Fax: (020) 8770 1992

Dagar Tools Ltd, 6 Providence Industrial Estate, Providence Street, Stourbridge, West Midlands, DY9 8HQ Tel: (01384) 893344 Fax: (01384) 422996

Diverse Products (Scotland) Ltd, Unit 34 Govan Workspace, 6 Harmony Row, Glasgow, G51 3BA Tel: 0141-445 3263 Fax: 0141-445 4668 E-mail: sales@diverseproducts.com

Dixon Hall & Co. Ltd, Grafton Street, Batley, West Yorkshire, WF17 6AR Tel: (01924) 476166 Fax: (01924) 471667 E-mail: sales@dixonhall.co.uk

Diytools Com Ltd, 20 Market Street, Watford, WD18 0PD Tel: (01923) 250295 Fax: (01923) 818219 E-mail: mur@diytools.com

Energas Ltd, Westmorland Street, Hull, HU2 0HX Tel: (01482) 329333 Fax: (01482) 212335 E-mail: sales@energas.co.uk

Engineering Supply Co., 5 Block 3, Thornliebank Industrial Estate, Thornliebank, Glasgow, G46 8TU Tel: 0141-638 7905 Fax: 0141-638 9714 E-mail: sales@scottishtools.co.uk

ERIKS UK, Industrial Distribution Service Centre, Greenwell Place, East Tullos, Aberdeen, AB12 3AY Tel: (01224) 877523 Fax: (01224) 879645 E-mail: mcw.aberdeen@wyko.co.uk

F P Tools Ltd, Tyseley Lane, Birmingham, B11 3PX Tel: 0121-707 3838 Fax: 0121-707 3097 E-mail: sales@fptools.co.uk

F R Smith & Co Newton Heath Ltd, Daisy Bank Mill, Terence Street, Manchester, M40 1GD Tel: 0161-681 1313 Fax: 0161-683 4763

F W B Southwest, Threemilestone Industrial Estate, Threemilestone, Truro, Cornwall, TR4 9LD Tel: (01872) 243520 Fax: (01872) 222191 E-mail: enquiries@fwbsw.co.uk

F W Sibley 1980 Ltd, 36 Goldcroft Works, Yeovil, Somerset, BA21 4DH Tel: (01935) 423671 Fax: (01935) 433407 E-mail: dillonharris@tiscali.co.uk

Joseph Firth, 10 Pepper Road, Leeds, LS10 2EU Tel: 0113-271 1148 Fax: 0113-270 3101 E-mail: sales@josephfirth.co.uk

Forth Engineering Services Ltd, 8 West Shore Bus Centre, Long Craig Rigg, Edinburgh, EH5 1QT Tel: 0131-551 5300 Fax: 0131-551 6610 E-mail: sales@forthengineering.co.uk

Frank Bailey Machine Tools Ltd, 1 Hadfield Street, Globe Square, Dukinfield, Cheshire, SK16 4RL Tel: 0161-330 4738 Fax: 0161-343 4365

Frazer, Station Road, Hebburn, Tyne & Wear, NE31 1BD Tel: 0191-428 7801 Fax: 0191-483 3628 E-mail: sales.northern@ashworth-frazer.co.uk

Fred Blake (Tools) Ltd, 143a Balaam Street, London, E13 8AF Tel: (020) 8552 1221 Fax: (020) 8471 8909

FWB Keithley, C Gresley Road, Keighley, West Yorkshire, BD21 5JG Tel: (01535) 687300 Fax: (01535) 687301 E-mail: sales@fwbkeighley.co.uk

Fyfe & Mcgrouther, 218-254 Kennedy Street, Glasgow, G4 0BS Tel: 0141-552 4966 Fax: 0141-552 7917

G & M Tools, Mill Lane, Ashington, Pulborough, West Sussex, RH20 3BX Tel: (01903) 892510 Fax: (01903) 892221 E-mail: sales@gandmtools.co.uk

G T S S Engineers, Hotchkiss Way, Binley Industrial Estate, Binley Industrial Estate, Coventry, CV3 2RL Tel: (024) 7645 9654 Fax: (024) 7645 7006 E-mail: sales@gtssltd.co.uk

G W Metals & Tools, Unit O & Q Newtown Road Trading Estate, Newtown Road, Worcester, WR5 1HA Tel: (01905) 612342 Fax: (01905) 25544

Gauge Service & Supply Co (Leamington) Ltd, 3 Park Street, Leamington Spa, Warwickshire, CV32 4QN Tel: (01926) 336137 Fax: (01926) 450636 E-mail: sales@gss.co.uk

General Engineers Supply Co. Ltd, 555-557 High Road Leytonstone, London, E11 4PD Tel: (020) 8556 0201 Fax: (020) 8558 9305 E-mail: gens@engineers555.freeserve.co.uk

Greenwoods (Coleshill) Ltd, Unit 28, Roman Way, Coleshill, Birmingham, B46 1HQ Tel: (01675) 464280 Fax: (01675) 467160 E-mail: sales@greenwoodtools.demon.co.uk

Gregory Pank, 86-87 Digbeth, Birmingham, B5 6DY Tel: 0121-643 3008 Fax: 0121-643 3360

Guildford Tool Supplies Ltd, A Victoria Farm, Brunswick Road, Brookwood, Woking, Surrey, GU24 0AQ Tel: (01483) 480000 Fax: (01483) 486886 E-mail: sales@guildfordtools.co.uk

H & H Industrial Fasteners Midlands Ltd, The Paddocks, Somersal Herbert, Ashbourne, Derbyshire, DE6 5PD Tel: (01283) 585473 Fax: (01283) 585625 E-mail: john@h-hfasteners.com

H M Brand, 28 Trades Lane, Dundee, DD1 3ET Tel: (01382) 226576 Fax: (01382) 225971 E-mail: harrymbrand@aol.com

H Rothwell & Co. Ltd, Duke Street, Rochdale, Lancashire, OL12 0LS Tel: (01706) 649231 Fax: (01706) 647906 E-mail: sales@rothwells.co.uk

Heap & Partners Ltd, Britannia House, Newton Road, Hoylake, Wirral, Merseyside, CH47 3DG Tel: 0151-632 3393 Fax: 0151-632 4453 E-mail: info@heaps.co.uk

Hereford Industrial Supply Co. Ltd, Units 18-20, Three Elms Trading Estate, Hereford, HR4 9PU Tel: (01432) 353232 Fax: (01432) 352505E-mail: sales@herefordindustrial.co.uk

Heward & Dean Ltd, Spurling Works, Pindar Road, Hoddesdon, Hertfordshire, EN11 0DB Tel: (01992) 467557 Fax: (01992) 467477 E-mail: sales@hewardanddean.co.uk

Hopkins & Bryant Small Tools Ltd, Phillips Street Industrial Estate, 103 Phillips Street, Birmingham, B6 4PT Tel: 0121-359 2195 Fax: 0121-359 1843

House Of Hastings Ltd, 181-182 Queens Road, Hastings, East Sussex, TN34 1RQ Tel: (01424) 423072 Fax: (01424) 431501 E-mail: enquiries@houseofhastings.com

Hughes & Holmes, Unit F, Key Industrial Park, Fernside Road, Willenhall, West Midlands, WV13 3YA Tel: (01902) 728888 Fax: (01902) 727111 E-mail: willenhall@lister.co.uk

Industrial Fixing Systems Ltd, 16 & 17 North Leith Sands, Industrial Estate, Edinburgh, EH6 4ER Tel: 0131-553 6323 Fax: 0131-555 0161

J J Engineers Supplies Ltd, 35 Valley Road, Banbury, Oxfordshire, OX16 9BH Tel: (01295) 253168 Fax: (01295) 252843 E-mail: sales@jjengineerssupplies.co.uk

J L Leach & Co. Ltd, Etruscan Street, Stoke-on-Trent, ST1 5SE Tel: (01782) 202001 Fax: (01782) 286868 E-mail: sales@jlleech.com

J R Webster, Unit 1 Prince William Avenue, Sandycroft, Deeside, Clwyd, CH5 2QZ Tel: (01244) 534747 Fax: (01244) 535866 E-mail: kwalker.jrw@cuk.com

Jackdaw Tools Ltd, Leveson Street, Willenhall, West Midlands, WV13 1DB Tel: (01902) 366551 Fax: (01902) 634983 E-mail: jackd@ukindustry.co.uk

James Gibb & Co. Ltd, Royston Works, Royston Avenue, Southend-on-Sea, SS2 5JY Tel: (01702) 614927 Fax: (01702) 601382

James Lister, 2 Miller Street, Birmingham, B6 4NF Tel: 0121-359 3774 Fax: 0121-333 3021 E-mail: birmingham@lister.co.uk

The Jemma Tools Group Ltd, Bell Lane, Bayton Road Industrial Estate, Uckfield, East Sussex, TN22 1QL Tel: (01825) 761711 Fax: (01825) 767568 E-mail: info@jemmatools.co.uk

Jigtools Supplies Ltd, Unit A1, Trecenydd Industrial Estate, Caerphilly, Mid Glamorgan, CF83 2RZ Tel: (029) 2088 3066 Fax: (029) 2088 9763 E-mail: info@jigtools.co.uk

John Young, 7 Cranbrook Court, Avenue Two, Witney, Oxfordshire, OX28 4YP Tel: (01993) 700337 Fax: (01993) 778123 E-mail: john-young1@btconnect.com

Johnston & Bulman Ltd, Lancaster Street, Carlisle, CA1 1TD Tel: (01228) 534131 Fax: (01228) 548188 E-mail: sales@johnstonbulman.co.uk

JSL Bearbreak Ltd, Arcown House, Peartree Lane, Dudley, West Midlands, DY2 0XR Tel: (01384) 455777 Fax: (01384) 456184 E-mail: dudley@bearbreak.co.uk

K Supplies Ltd, Hill End Lane, Rossendale, Lancashire, BB4 7PP Tel: (01706) 217441 Fax: (01706) 831772 E-mail: sales@ksupplies.co.uk

Kennedy & Morrison Ltd, Boucher Road, Belfast, BT12 6QF Tel: (028) 9087 0870 Fax: (028) 9087 0871 E-mail: sales@kandm.co.uk

Francis Kirk & Son Ltd, Denton Hall Farm Road, Denton, Manchester, M34 2QN Tel: 0161-336 2631 Fax: 0161-335 0043 E-mail: sales@franciskirk.com

KL Nuts & Bolts, 4 Oldmedow Road, King's Lynn, Norfolk, PE30 4JL Tel: (01553) 763487 Fax: (01553) 774097

H.I.S. Lawson Ltd, 84-88 Millbrook Road East, Southampton, SO15 1BG Tel: (023) 8063 2927 Fax: (023) 8033 9878 E-mail: enquiries@lawson-his.co.uk

Lawson Products Ltd, 300 Quadrant, Ash Ridge Road, Bradley Stoke, Bristol, BS32 4QA Tel: (01454) 202223 Fax: (01454) 618510

Lawton Tools Ltd, Manor Street, Stoke-on-Trent, ST4 2UF Tel: (01782) 747007 Fax: (01782) 413983 E-mail: sales@lawtontools.co.uk

Leck Curphey Ltd, 6 Gloucester Road, Anfield, Liverpool, L6 4DS Tel: 0151-260 0096

Lugg Facilities Ltd, 99-107 Hill Top, West Bromwich, West Midlands, B70 0RY Tel: 0121-556 1551 Fax: 0121-556 1552 E-mail: sales@lugg-tools.co.uk

M C Mills & Co. Ltd, Lower Castlereagh St, Barnsley, South Yorkshire, S70 1AR Tel: (01226) 732566 Fax: (01226) 285446 E-mail: mc.mills@virgin.net

M D S Wedgloking Services, Unit 6, Alpha Business Park, Deedmore Road, Coventry, CV2 1EQ Tel: (024) 7661 4577 Fax: (024) 7660 4975

Metalocast Ltd, 58-60 Duncrue Street, Belfast, BT3 9AR Tel: (028) 9074 7433 Fax: (028) 9074 8017 E-mail: metalocast@aol.com

Midway Tools Ltd, 9a Walsall Street, West Bromwich, West Midlands, B70 7NX Tel: 0121-553 3819 Fax: 0121-500 5453 E-mail: sales@midwaytools.co.uk

Miltools Engineering Supplies, The Sanderson Centre, Lees Lane, Gosport, Hampshire, PO12 3UL Tel: (023) 9252 6551 Fax: (023) 9252 2559

Modern Machinery Supplies Ltd, Rathdown Road, Lissue Industrial Estate West, Lisburn, County Antrim, BT28 2RE Tel: (028) 9262 2011 Fax: (028) 9262 2181 E-mail: sales@modernmachinerysupplies.co.uk

Monks & Crane Ltd, Seawall Road, Cardiff, CF24 5XG Tel: (029) 2043 6400 Fax: (029) 2048 9910 E-mail: mcinfo@mcrane.co.uk

Monochic Ltd, Canalside Unit, Staly Industrial Estate, Knowle Street, Stalybridge, Cheshire, SK15 3AJ Tel: 0161-338 8888 Fax: 0161-303 0970

Nortech Services Ltd, Drypool Way, Hull, HU9 1NL Tel: (01482) 327791 Fax: (01482) 320550 E-mail: sales@nortech.co.uk

North British Tapes Ltd, Unit 5 Locomotion Way, Camperdown Industrial Estate, Newcastle upon Tyne, NE12 5US Tel: 0191-268 6272 Fax: 0191-268 7400

Norton, Works Road, Letchworth Garden City, Hertfordshire, SG6 1LP Tel: (01462) 676944 Fax: (01462) 677192 E-mail: nif-ltd@btconnect.com

Nu Tools Machinery Sales, Rockingham Way, Redhouse Interchange, Adwick-le-Street, Doncaster, South Yorkshire, DN6 7FB Tel: (01302) 721791 Fax: (01302) 728317 E-mail: sales@nutool.co.uk

Orbital Fasteners, Olds Approach, Tolpits Lane, Watford, WD18 9XT Tel: (01923) 777777 Fax: (01923) 779169 E-mail: sales@orbitalfasteners.co.uk

P C M Engineering Services Ltd, Castleblair Works, Castle Blair Lane, Dunfermline, Fife, KY12 9DP Tel: (01383) 733334 Fax: (01383) 739496

P V R Direct Ltd, 8 St. Stephens Business Centre, Poplar Road, Warmley, Bristol, BS30 5HT Tel: 0117-967 5115 Fax: 0117-935 2399 E-mail: vivrooker@aol.com

Phoenix Saxton Ltd, Thornton Industrial Trading Estate, Milford Haven, Dyfed, SA73 2RR Tel: (01646) 690588 Fax: (01646) 690570

Phoenix-Saxton Ltd, Pomeroy Works, Clarence Road, Cardiff Bay, Cardiff, CF10 5FA Tel: (029) 2048 7848 Fax: (029) 2049 3493 E-mail: sales@phoenix-saxton.com

Pipeline Centre, Shails Lane, Trowbridge, Wiltshire, BA14 8LQ Tel: (01225) 762331 Fax: (01225) 777370 E-mail: sales@pipeline.centre.co.uk

Profast Holdings Ltd, 26-30 Rydalmere Street, Belfast, BT12 6GF Tel: (028) 9024 3215 Fax: (028) 9033 3301 E-mail: sales@profast.co.uk

R H Bruce Co Ltd, 4 The Idas, Pontefract Road, Leeds, LS10 1SP Tel: 0113-271 5533 Fax: 0113-271 8833

R J Pryce & Co. Ltd, Trinity Road, Lowestoft, Suffolk, NR32 1XJ Tel: (01502) 574141 Fax: (01502) 501213 E-mail: sales@rjpryce.co.uk

Gordon Richards Tools (Birmingham), Unit 28, Roman Way, Coles Hill, Birmingham, B46 1HQ Tel: 0121-328 5454 Fax: 0121-322 2148

Richmonds Of London Ltd, 66 Weir Road, London, SW19 8UG Tel: (020) 8879 3500 Fax: (020) 8879 3563 E-mail: sales@richmondsoflondon.co.uk

Riverside Hardware & Engineers Supplies, North Road, Bridgend Industrial Estate, Bridgend, Mid Glamorgan, CF31 3TP Tel: (01656) 662449 Fax: (01656) 768375

Robert Samuel & Co. Ltd, 7 Court Parade, Wembley, Middlesex, HA0 3JA Tel: (020) 8904 1144 Fax: (020) 8904 6349

Ronco Engineering Ltd, 3a-3b Unit Alderman Wood Road, Tanfield Lea Industrial Estate South, Tanfield Lea, Stanley, County Durham, DH9 9XF Tel: (01207) 284848 Fax: (01207) 290306 E-mail: enquires@ronco-engineering.co.uk

S J Andrew & Sons, South Turnpike, Redruth, Cornwall, TR15 2LZ Tel: (01209) 213171 Fax: (01209) 219459 E-mail: nathan@sjandrew.com

ENGINEERS' SUPPLIES – *continued*

S K S Plant & Equipment Ltd, 11 Redehall Road, Smallfield, Horley, Surrey, RH6 9PY Tel: (01342) 843688 Fax: (01342) 842236 E-mail: jpeters@sks-group.co.uk
Samuel Fields & Co., Croft Street, Willenhall, West Midlands, WV13 2NU Tel: (01902) 607177 Fax: (01902) 606582
Selectequip Ltd, Unit 7, Brittannia Way, Brittania Enterprise Park, Lichfield, Staffordshire, WS14 9UY Tel: (01543) 416641 Fax: (01543) 416083 E-mail: sales@selectequip.co.uk
Ses Scarborough Ltd, Melrose Street, Scarborough, North Yorkshire, YO12 7SH Tel: (01723) 367341 Fax: (01723) 375758 E-mail: sales@s-e-s-ltd.co.uk
Springfields Supplies, 11 Bangor Road, Overton, Wrexham, Clwyd, LL13 0HB Tel: (01978) 710291 Fax: (01978) 710292 E-mail: sales@springfieldsupplies.co.uk
Standaparts Ltd, 7A South Bank, Thames Ditton, Surrey, KT7 0UD Tel: (020) 8398 7812 Fax: (020) 8398 7813 E-mail: standaparts@btclick.com
Super Spares Ltd, Brookfield Industrial Estate, Peggys Loaning, Banbridge, County Down, BT32 3AP Tel: (028) 4066 2166 Fax: (028) 4062 6642 E-mail: info@super-spares.com
Swansea Fastners, Unit 8, Horizon Park, Swansea Enterprise Park, Swansea, SA6 8RG Tel: (01792) 310284 Fax: (01792) 310291 E-mail: sales@swanseafasteners.com
T E Hughes & Son Warrington Ltd, Crossley Street, Warrington, WA1 2PF Tel: (01925) 634348 Fax: (01925) 234405
T I S Tooling, Unit 16 Abbey Court, Corporation Road, Leicester, LE4 5PW Tel: 0116-261 1220 Fax: 0116-261 2224 E-mail: sales@tistooling.co.uk
Taylor Lowestoft Ltd, Newcombe Road, Lowestoft, Suffolk, NR32 1XA Tel: (01502) 572753 Fax: (01502) 572753
Till & Whitehead Ltd, Ellesmere Street, Manchester, M15 4JX Tel: 0161-827 3901 Fax: 0161-827 3915E-mail: sales@tillwite.com
Till & Whitehead, 65 Brindley Road, Astmoor Industrial Estate, Runcorn, Cheshire, WA7 1PF Tel: (01928) 581200 Fax: (01928) 580859 E-mail: info@tillwite.com
Toolcom Supplies Ltd, Pitreavie Business Park, Pitreavie Business Park, Dunfermline, Fife, KY11 8UQ Tel: (01383) 728970 Fax: (01383) 620079 E-mail: sales@toolcom.co.uk
Tooltek Supplies Ltd, Spyvee Street, Hull, HU8 7JJ Tel: (01482) 229628 Fax: (01482) 229630 E-mail: info@tooltek.co.uk
Toy Trading Ltd, 7 North St Industrial Estate, Droitwich, Worcestershire, WR9 8JB Tel: (01905) 794979 Fax: (01905) 774503 E-mail: sales@toytrading.net
▶ William Twigg (Matlock) Ltd, 26 Bakewell Road, Matlock, Derbyshire, DE4 3AX Tel: (01629) 56651 Fax: (01629) 56123 E-mail: sales@twiggs.co.uk
Valentine Tools, 6 Royce Road, Crawley, West Sussex, RH10 9NX Tel: (01293) 428555 Fax: (01293) 428559 E-mail: sales@valentinetools.co.uk
W H Povoas Ltd, Radnor Street, Stretford, Manchester, M32 8LP Tel: 0161-865 1086 Fax: 0161-864 3584 E-mail: sales@whpovoas.co.uk
Walker & Howell Ltd, Forge Road, Whaley Bridge, High Peak, Derbyshire, SK23 7HY Tel: (01663) 732471 Fax: (01663) 733927 E-mail: sales@walkerandhowell.co.uk
Warwick Industrial Supplies, Emscote Mill, Wharf Street, Warwick, CV34 5LB Tel: (01926) 497350 Fax: (01926) 403777 E-mail: sales@warwicksupplies.com
Washington & Riley Ltd, 1 William Clowes Street, Stoke-on-Trent, ST6 3AR Tel: (01782) 834363 Fax: (01782) 834366 E-mail: info@washingtonandriley.ltd.uk
Waverly Cutting Tools, 55 Abbotswell Road, Aberdeen, AB12 3AD Tel: (01224) 879714 Fax: (01224) 872385
Williams Distributors, 108-110 Burghley Road, Peterborough, PE1 2QE Tel: (01733) 564252 Fax: (01733) 555275
James Wilson & Sons, 33 Brown Street, Glasgow, G2 8PF Tel: 0141-221 3590 Fax: 0141-248 3673
Wrexham Power Tool Services, Five Fords Gate, Bridge Road, Wrexham Industrial Estate, Wrexham, Clwyd, LL13 9PS Tel: (01978) 660011 Fax: (01978) 664644
▶ Wwe Solutions, Erskine Square, Hillington Industrial Estate, Glasgow, G52 4BJ Tel: 0141-585 9255 Fax: 0141-585 9254 E-mail: sales@wwesol.co.uk

ENGINEERS' TOOL/TOOLING IMPORT/EXPORT MERCHANTS OR AGENTS

Group Components Ltd, The Potteries, Woodgreen Road, Waltham Abbey, Essex, EN9 3TN Tel: (01992) 715900 Fax: (01992) 711993E-mail: sales@groupcomponents.co.uk
Nuts, Cowling Brow Industrial Estate, Cowling Brow, Chorley, Lancashire, PR6 0QG Tel: (01257) 264040 Fax: (01257) 273782 E-mail: sales@nutsofchorley.co.uk
S K S Plant & Equipment Ltd, 11 Redehall Road, Smallfield, Horley, Surrey, RH6 9PY Tel: (01342) 843688 Fax: (01342) 842140 E-mail: export@fks-group.co.uk

ENGINEERS' TOOLS/TOOLING

A T Tool Centre Ltd, 26-27 Buckingham Trade Park, Buckingham Avenue, Slough, SL1 4QA Tel: 01753 536811 Fax: 01753 532709 E-mail: slough@at-toolcentre.co.uk
Alan Gordon, George Street, Chorley, Lancashire, PR7 2BE Tel: (01257) 274723 Fax: (01257) 241342 E-mail: sales@alangordoneng.co.uk
Andover Precision Ltd, Marriott Road, Dudley, West Midlands, DY2 0JZ Tel: (01384) 212655 Fax: (01384) 235863 E-mail: dave.andover@btconnect.com
Artisan Tools Ltd, Edison Courtyard, Brunel Road, Earlstrees Industrial Estate, Corby, Northamptonshire, NN17 4LS Tel: (01536) 201000 Fax: (01536) 201389 E-mail: sales@artisan-tools.co.uk
A-T Tool Centre Ltd, 19 Alston Drive, Bradwell Abbey, Milton Keynes, MK13 9HA Tel: 01908 310707 Fax: 01908 220695 E-mail: miltonkeynes@at-toolcentre.co.uk
Avenue Tools Ltd, 3 David Road, Colnbrook, Slough, SL3 0TW Tel: (01753) 685921 Fax: (01753) 685922 E-mail: avenue@avenue-group.co.uk
B A Engineering, 4a Tulnacross Road, Cookstown, County Tyrone, BT80 9NH Tel: (028) 8675 1117 Fax: (028) 8675 1017
Belton & Slade, 84 Wandsworth High Street, London, SW18 4LB Tel: (020) 8871 1000 Fax: (020) 8874 3117 E-mail: sales@beltonandslade.co.uk
Bescol Ltd, Unit 8a Number One Industrial Estate, Consett, County Durham, DH8 6SS Tel: (01207) 582555 Fax: (01207) 583951 E-mail: name@btconnect.com
Bestalinks Engineers Ltd, 2 Wood Street, Dukinfield, Cheshire, SK16 4UT Tel: 0161-330 8515 Fax: 0161-343 2228 E-mail: bestlink@aol.com
Bonnell Engineering Ltd, 28-33 Stewart Street, Wolverhampton, WV2 4JW Tel: (01902) 712855 Fax: (01902) 712855
Brookfield Engineering Co., James Street, Littleborough, Lancashire, OL15 8LT Tel: (01706) 378042 Fax: (01706) 378042
C B Powell Ltd, 10 St Josephs Close, Hove, East Sussex, BN3 7ES Tel: (01273) 771144 Fax: (01273) 726966 E-mail: cbpowel@btconnect.com
C W Fasteners, Unit 60 Sandy Way, Amington Industrial Estate, Tamworth, Staffordshire, B77 4DS Tel: (01827) 67091 Fax: (01827) 61552E-mail: cwdfasteners@btopenworld.com
Cambridge Tool Supplies Ltd, Unit 1 Brookfield Business Centre, Twentypence Road, Cottenham, Cambridge, CB4 8PS Tel: (01954) 251862 Fax: (01954) 251073 E-mail: camtool@btconnect.com
Castle Tools Ltd, 33 Trent Street, Sheffield, S9 3XU Tel: 0114-261 7200 Fax: 0114-261 7370 E-mail: sales@castletools.co.uk
▶ Cottenden Ltd, 1 Oakfield Business Corner, Works Road, Letchworth Garden City, Hertfordshire, SG6 1FB Tel: (01462) 672179 E-mail: terry@cottenden.co.uk
Cromwell Manchester Ltd, 2 Brent Road, Green Lane Trading Estate, Stockport, Cheshire, SK4 2LD Tel: 0161-476 6666 Fax: 0161-476 4444 E-mail: cromwell@manchester.co.uk
Cromwell Tools Ltd, Estate Road 6, South Humberside Industrial Estate, Grimsby, South Humberside, DN31 2TG Tel: (01472) 358741 Fax: (01472) 241433 E-mail: grimsby@cromwell-tools.co.uk
Cromwell Tools Ltd, Unit D 7 Bilton Way, Luton, LU1 1UU Tel: (01582) 484666 Fax: (01582) 726167 E-mail: luton@cromwell-tools.co.uk
Cromwell Tools Ltd, 770 Buckingham Avenue, Slough, SL1 4NL Tel: (01753) 696000 Fax: (01753) 696966 E-mail: slough@cromwell-tools.co.uk
Cromwell Tools Ltd, Kirkby Folly Road, Sutton-in-Ashfield, Nottinghamshire, NG17 5HN Tel: (01623) 551616 Fax: (01623) 552007 E-mail: mansfield@cromwell-tools.co.uk
Curtis Holt Southampton Ltd, Westwood Business Park, Nutwood Way, Totton, Southampton, SO40 3WW Tel: (023) 8086 1991 Fax: (023) 8066 4505 E-mail: sales@tallbank.com
Curtis Holt Southampton Ltd, Westwood Business Park, Nutwood Way, Totton, Southampton, SO40 3WW Tel: (023) 8086 1991 Fax: (023) 8066 4555 E-mail: sales@tallbank.com
Curtis Holt (St. Albans), Unit 10B Brick Knoll Park, Ashley Road, St. Albans, Hertfordshire, AL1 5UG Tel: (01727) 845095 Fax: (01727) 845082 E-mail: stalbons.sales@torbank.com
D S W Engineering Co. Ltd, 6 Chester Hall Lane, Basildon, Essex, SS14 3BG Tel: (01268) 523185 Fax: (01268) 534325 E-mail: admin@dsw.biz
Dagar Tools Ltd, 6 Providence Industrial Estate, Providence Street, Stourbridge, West Midlands, DY9 8HQ Tel: (01384) 893344 Fax: (01384) 422996
Denebank Engineering UK Ltd, 108 Windmill Road, Sunbury-on-Thames, Middlesex, TW16 7HB Tel: (01932) 788180 Fax: (01932) 788150 E-mail: paulgoldthorpe@denebank.co.uk
Dimill Engineering Ltd, Doric Works, Church Street, Studley, Warwickshire, B80 7LG Tel: (01527) 854672 Fax: (01527) 853683 E-mail: info@dimill.co.uk
Diset Engineering, Units 46-48 Hotchkiss Way, Binley Indust Estate, Coventry, CV3 2RL Tel: (024) 7644 9607
DMS Systems, Ivel Road, Shefford, Bedfordshire, SG17 5JU Tel: (01462) 857955 Fax: (01462) 819168
Donart Engineering Co., Station Street, Bromsgrove, Worcestershire, B60 2BS Tel: (01527) 879722 Fax: (01527) 879722
Engineering Supply Co., 5 Block 3, Thornliebank Industrial Estate, Thornliebank, Glasgow, G46 8TU Tel: 0141-638 7905 Fax: 0141-638 9714 E-mail: sales@scottishtools.co.uk
Fast Tools Holdings Ltd, Llanthony Road, Hempsted, Gloucester, GL2 5HL Tel: (01452) 529671 Fax: (01452) 307992 E-mail: sales@fasttoolsltd.co.uk
Fenn Tool Ltd, 44 Spring Wood Drive, Springwood Industrial Estate, Braintree, Essex, CM7 2YN Tel: (01376) 347566 Fax: (01376) 550827 E-mail: enquiries@fenntool.co.uk
Fenton Engineering Ltd, Finedon Sidings, Station Road, Finedon, Wellingborough, Northamptonshire, NN9 5NY Tel: (01536) 723488 Fax: (01536) 726642 E-mail: sales@fentonprecision.co.uk
Frio UK Ltd, Whitleys, Wolfscastle, Haverfordwest, Dyfed, SA62 5DY Tel: (01437) 741755 Fax: (01437) 741781 E-mail: frio@btinternet.com
FSG, Newtown Industrial Estate, Llantwit Fardre, Pontypridd, Mid Glamorgan, CF38 2EE Tel: (01443) 202281 Fax: (01443) 205747 E-mail: admin@fsgtoolanddie.co.uk
G C Banks & Son Ltd, 5 Harolds Road, Harlow, Essex, CM19 5BJ Tel: (01279) 424019 Fax: (01279) 452203
Gauge Service & Supply Co (Leamington) Ltd, 3 Park Street, Leamington Spa, Warwickshire, CV32 4QN Tel: (01926) 336137 Fax: (01926) 450636 E-mail: sales@gss.co.uk
▶ Gibbs & Dandy, PO Box 17, Luton, LU1 1YB Tel: (01582) 798798 Fax: (01582) 798799 E-mail: mail@gibbsanddandy.com
Gilmour Tools Ltd, Baird Avenue, Strutherhill Industrial Estate, Larkhall, Lanarkshire, ML9 2PJ Tel: (01698) 884856 Fax: (01698) 886634 E-mail: info@gilmourtools.co.uk
Grasam Samson Ltd, Doulton Trading Estate, Doulton Road, Rowley Regis, West Midlands, B65 8JQ Tel: (01384) 634162 Fax: (01384) 568051 E-mail: grasamsamson@aol.com
Gregory Pank, 86-87 Digbeth, Birmingham, B5 6DY Tel: 0121-643 3008 Fax: 0121-643 3360
H Fisher Distributors & Factors Fareham Ltd, 9-10 Highbury Buildings, Portsmouth Road, Portsmouth, PO6 2SN Tel: (023) 9237 2111 Fax: (023) 9238 0243 E-mail: sales@hfishertools.co.uk
Harthill Developments Ltd, Mansfield Road, Aston, Sheffield, S26 5PQ Tel: 0114-287 4522 Fax: 0114-287 6397 E-mail: sales@harthill.com
Harvey Manchester Ltd, Oldham Street, Denton, Manchester, M34 3SW Tel: 0161-336 3951 Fax: 0161-336 3936 E-mail: sales@harveymanchester.com
Curtis Holt (North West), Toolbank House, Appleton Thorn Trading Estate, Lyncastle Way, Appleton, Warrington, WA4 4ST Tel: (01925) 261333 Fax: (01925) 604478
Hopkins & Bryant Small Tools Ltd, Phillips Street Industrial Estate, 103 Phillips Street, Birmingham, B6 4PT Tel: 0121-359 2195 Fax: 0121-359 1843
Inca Tooling Ltd, Unit 9 Northbrook Close, Worcester, WR3 8BP Tel: (01905) 26937 Fax: (01905) 23593 E-mail: sales@incatooling.co.uk
Inter City Machine Tools (High Wycombe) Ltd, High Wycombe, Buckinghamshire, HP14 3WZ Tel: (01494) 485701 Fax: (01494) 485716 E-mail: sales@intercmt.co.uk
James Gibb & Co. Ltd, Royston Works, Royston Avenue, Southend-on-Sea, SS2 5JY Tel: (01702) 614927 Fax: (01702) 601382
James & Maja Ltd, 1a Rydens Grove, Walton-on-Thames, Surrey, KT12 5RX Tel: (01932) 228301 Fax: (01932) 228301
The Jemma Tools Group Ltd, Bell Lane, Bayton Road Industrial Estate, Uckfield, East Sussex, TN22 1QL Tel: (01825) 761711 Fax: (01825) 767568 E-mail: info@jemmatools.co.uk
Jigs & Fixtures, Station Yard, Rigg Street, Stewarton, Kilmarnock, Ayrshire, KA3 5AG Tel: (01560) 483512 Fax: (01560) 485160 E-mail: sales@jigsandfixtures.uk.com
Jigtools Supplies Ltd, Unit A1, Trecenydd Industrial Estate, Caerphilly, Mid Glamorgan, CF83 2RZ Tel: (029) 2088 3066 Fax: (029) 2088 9763 E-mail: info@jigtools.co.uk
Kerswell Tooling Services Ltd, Britannic Lodge, Britannic Way, Llandarcy, Neath, West Glamorgan, SA10 6EL Tel: (01792) 812101 Fax: (01792) 814575 E-mail: sales@kerswelltoolingservices.com
Lafarge Roofing Technical Centers Ltd, Sussex Manor Business Park, Gatwick Road, Crawley, West Sussex, RH10 9NZ Tel: (01293) 618418 Fax: (01293) 614548
Langstone Engineering Ltd, Units 1-3 Beaver Industrial Est., Southmoor Lane, Havant, Hampshire, PO9 1JW Tel: (023) 9245 2430 Fax: (023) 9245 2440 E-mail: corporate@langstone-engineering.co.uk
Lawson Distributors Ltd, Scotshaw Brook House, Scotshaw Brook Estate, Lower Darwen, Darwen, Lancashire, BB3 0PR Tel: (01254) 677121 Fax: (01254) 665922 E-mail: sales@johnlawsondist.co.uk
Leck Curphey Ltd, 6 Gloucester Road, Anfield, Liverpool, L6 4DS Tel: 0151-260 0096
James Lister & Sons Ltd, Spon La South, Smethwick, West Midlands, B66 1QJ Tel: 0121-553 2949 Fax: 0121-525 6116 E-mail: tools@lister.co.uk
Ludlow, 6 Prospect View, Rock Lane, Ludlow, Shropshire, SY8 1ST Tel: (01584) 875096
D.R. Markey & Sons, Adcroft Street, Higher Hillgate, Stockport, Cheshire, SK1 3HZ Tel: 0161-480 1440 Fax: 0161-480 6164
Marshall Drills Ltd, Metrology House, Dukinfield Road, Hyde, Cheshire, SK14 4SD Tel: 0161-882 9618 Fax: 0161-366 9800 E-mail: sales@marshalldrills.co.uk
Mayes & Warwick Ltd, 5 Mount Road, Burntwood Industrial Estate, Burntwood, Staffordshire, WS7 0AJ Tel: (01543) 682561 Fax: (01543) 686232E-mail: sales@mayesandwarwick.com
Mercian Toolmaking Co Tamworth Ltd, 6 Felspar Road, Amington Industrial Estate, Tamworth, Staffordshire, B77 4DP Tel: (01827) 69484 Fax: (01827) 310153 E-mail: sales@merciancut.co.uk
Mercury Thread Gauges, 182-186 Fletchamstead Highway Industrial Estate, Fletchamstead Highway, Coventry, CV4 7BB Tel: (024) 7671 4185 Fax: (024) 7669 1234 E-mail: sales@mercurygauges.co.uk
Mill Hill Supplies, Unit 37 Broton Trading Estate, Broton Drive, Halstead, Essex, CO9 1HB Tel: (01787) 472236 Fax: (01787) 477797 E-mail: mail@millhillsupplies.co.uk
Miltools Engineering Supplies, The Sanderson Centre, Lees Lane, Gosport, Hampshire, PO12 3UL Tel: (023) 9252 6551 Fax: (023) 9252 2559
Cyril Minns Engineering Ltd, Gladstone Road, Kingswood, Bristol, BS15 1SW Tel: 0117-967 1834 Fax: 0117-961 8638 E-mail: cyrilminns@dial.pipex.com
Monks & Crane Holdings plc, Unit 2 Atlantic Way, Black Country New Road, Wednesbury, West Midlands, WS10 7WW Tel: 0121-506 4000 Fax: 0121-500 5001 E-mail: info@monks-crane.com
Monochic Ltd, Canalside Unit, Staly Industrial Estate, Knowle Street, Stalybridge, Cheshire, SK15 3AJ Tel: 0161-338 8888 Fax: 0161-303 0970
Narvik Developments Ltd, Clay Lane, Oldbury, West Midlands, B69 4TH Tel: 0121-552 3429 Fax: 0121-552 6162
Northern Tools & Accessories Ltd, PO Box 5, Newcastle upon Tyne, NE6 5XB Tel: 0191-265 2821 Fax: 0191-276 2668 E-mail: marketing@crossling.co.uk
Nu Tools Machinery Sales, Rockingham Way, Redhouse Interchange, Adwick-le-Street, Doncaster, South Yorkshire, DN6 7FB Tel: (01302) 721791 Fax: (01302) 728317 E-mail: sales@nutool.co.uk
Oceaneering International Services Ltd, Pitmedden Road, Dyce, Aberdeen, AB21 0DP Tel: (01224) 770444 Fax: (01224) 771583
Timothy Ormerod Ltd, Bryngwyn Manor, Wormelow, Hereford, HR2 8EH Tel: (01981) 540476 Fax: (01981) 540846 E-mail: matormerod@hotmail.com
P & B Engineering, Factory Estate College Road, Unit 7, Perry Barr, Birmingham, B42 8BS Tel: 0121-356 5490 Fax: 0121-356 4295
P & C Tools Ltd, 80 Cato Street North, Birmingham, B7 5AN Tel: 0121-333 7772 Fax: 0121-333 7776 E-mail: pctoolsltd@yahoo.co.uk
P M Tools & Fasteners Ltd, 7 Phoenix Road Industrial Estate, Phoenix Road, Wolverhampton, WV11 3PX Tel: (01902) 727959 Fax: (01902) 738558 E-mail: info@pmtools.co.uk
Parlec Engineers, E Syston Centre, Station Road, Kingswood, Bristol, BS15 4GQ Tel: 0117-967 4881 Fax: 0117-960 3800 E-mail: sales@parlec.com
Peak Precision Engineering Ltd, Alexandra Works, St Annes Road, Manchester, M34 3DY Tel: 0161-303 4800 Fax: 0161-303 4801
Preformtools Ltd, First Avenue, Bletchley, Milton Keynes, MK1 1DY Tel: (01908) 370788 Fax: (01908) 362802 E-mail: sales@preformtools.co.uk
R A Atkins, Hunts Hill House, Hunts Hill, Normandy, Guildford, Surrey, GU3 2AH Tel: (01483) 811146 Fax: (01483) 811243
Rapid Tool Rec Ltd, Unit 2 Armoury Road Trading, Estate Armoury Road, Small Heath, Birmingham, B11 2RG Tel: 0121-771 1555 Fax: 0121-706 2479 E-mail: sales@rapidtool-rec.co.uk
S D Tooling UK Ltd, Manor Lodge, Tabors Hill, Great Baddow, Chelmsford, CM2 7BP Tel: (01245) 471807 Fax: (01245) 475884
Salt Engineering (Midlands) Ltd, Unit 4, Macefield Close, Aldermans Green, Coventry, CV2 2PJ Tel: (024) 7661 6595 Fax: (024) 7660 2165 E-mail: vaughan@saltengineering.co.uk
Southend Total Engineering & Fabrication, 14 Terminal Close, Shoeburyness, Southend-on-Sea, SS3 9BN Tel: (01702) 299499 Fax: (01702) 299561
Startrite Designs Ltd, Courteney Road, Hoath Way, Gillingham, Kent, ME8 0RZ Tel: (01634) 233216 Fax: (01634) 373516 E-mail: startritedesigns@btinternet.com
Steelcraft Precision, Unit A Mortimer Road, Narborough, Leicester, LE19 2GA Tel: 0116-284 1025 Fax: 0116-286 9781 E-mail: info@steelcraft.co.uk
Summit Patternmaking Co. Ltd, Paper Mill End Industrial Estate, Birmingham, B44 8NH Tel: 0121-344 3943 Fax: 0121-344 3944

ENGINEERS' TOOLS/TOOLING – *continued*

T F Keller & Sons Ltd, 24 Cattle Market St, Norwich, NR1 3DY Tel: (01603) 624681 Fax: (01603) 663790 E-mail: info@modelmarque.com
Tate Engineering, Tate Estate, Kingsdown Road, Swindon, SN25 6SF Tel: (01793) 820503 Fax: (01793) 820504 E-mail: tate.engineering@virgin.net
Toolmatic Tool Design, 36 Hall Street, Birmingham, B18 6BS Tel: 0121-236 1417 Fax: 0121-233 9240
Turner Tools Ltd, 15 Armstrong Close, St. Leonards-on-Sea, East Sussex, TN38 9ST Tel: (01424) 853055 Fax: (01424) 851085 E-mail: turnertools@turnertools.com
Universal Tool (Gloucester) Co. Ltd, Unit 16-18, Bamfurlong Industrial Park, Staverton, Cheltenham, Gloucestershire, GL51 6SX Tel: (01452) 712597 Fax: (01452) 857540 E-mail: mike@inona-uk.com
W A Carr Engineering Ltd, 60 Broad Oaks, Sheffield, S9 3HJ Tel: 0114-256 2222 Fax: 0114-256 2474
Walsall Die & Tool Co. Ltd, Unit 2 Woodall Street, Walsall, WS3 3HG Tel: (01922) 492989 Fax: (01922) 492989
Warwick Industrial Supplies, Emscote Mill, Wharf Street, Warwick, CV34 5LB Tel: (01926) 497350 Fax: (01926) 403777 E-mail: sales@warwicksupplies.com
Waverly Cutting Tools, 55 Abbotswell Road, Aberdeen, AB12 3AD Tel: (01224) 879714 Fax: (01224) 872385
Webbro Ltd, Whinfield Drive, Aycliffe Industrial Estate, Aycliffe Industrial Park, Newton Aycliffe, County Durham, DL5 6AU Tel: (01325) 313781 Fax: (01325) 300762
West Suffolk Tool & Gauge Ltd, 63d Gorse Industrial Estate, Barnham, Thetford, Norfolk, IP24 2PH Tel: (01842) 890278 Fax: (01842) 890632
Whiton Tools Ltd, Parsonage Street, Oldbury, West Midlands, B69 4PH Tel: 0121-552 6065 Fax: 0121-544 7684
Whittingham Design & Manufacturing Co. Ltd, Chapel Works, Chapel Green, Willenhall, West Midlands, WV13 1QY Tel: (01902) 607272 Fax: (01902) 637884
R. Winter Tooling, 7 Stirling Park, Laker Road, Rochester, Kent, ME1 3QR Tel: 01634 666627 Fax: 01634 666637 E-mail: focus@rwintertooling.com

ENGINES, IRRIGATION

▶ Aqua-Light, 21 Favourite Road, Whitstable, Kent, CT5 4UB Tel: (01227) 282130 E-mail: info@aqua-light.co.uk

ENGINES, MARINE, DIESEL

A L D Engineering (UK) Ltd, Les Searle Plant Yard, Parsonage Way, Horsham, West Sussex, RH12 4AL Tel: (01403) 271964 Fax: (01403) 271965
Cummins Engine Co. Ltd, Royal Oak Way South, Royal Oak Industrial Estate, Daventry, Northamptonshire, NN11 8NU Tel: (01327) 886000 Fax: (01327) 886100
D B Marine, Cookham Bridge, Cookham On Thames, Cookham, Maidenhead, Berkshire, SL6 9SN Tel: (01628) 526032 Fax: (01628) 520564 E-mail: sales@dbmarine.co.uk
Foxwood Boring & Grinding Ltd, 17 Whitting Valley Road, Old Whittington, Chesterfield, Derbyshire, S41 9EY Tel: (01246) 260199 Fax: (01246) 455274 E-mail: ken@foxwooddiesel.com

ENGINES, PROTOTYPE/ EXPERIMENTAL

Eaton Socon Engineering, Renhold Road, Ravensden, Bedford, MK44 2RH Tel: (01234) 772145 Fax: (01234) 771881 E-mail: eaton-socon@tiscali.co.uk

ENGLISH TIMBER MERCHANTS

Denis Brown & Son (Nailsworth) Ltd, Broadmead, Bath Road, Woodchester, Stroud, Gloucestershire, GL5 5EG Tel: (01453) 873516 Fax: (01453) 873333
G E Collis & Sons Ltd, Queen St Industrial Estate, Queens Drive, Burntwood, Staffordshire, WS7 4QF Tel: (01543) 686370 Fax: (01543) 675221 E-mail: sales@collissheds.co.uk
George Barker & Sons Ltd, Backbarrow, Ulverston, Cumbria, LA12 8TA Tel: (01539) 531236 Fax: (01539) 530801 E-mail: sales@gbsltd.sagehost.co.uk
Jewson Ltd, 25 Bakewell Road, Loughborough, Leicestershire, LE11 5QY Tel: (01509) 212121 Fax: (01509) 610218
Nidd Valley Saw Mills Ltd, Dacre Banks, Harrogate, North Yorkshire, HG3 4EA Tel: (01423) 780220 Fax: (01423) 780220
R Thorne & Sons, Mannington Sawmills, Holt Road, Three Legged Cross, Wimborne, Dorset, BH21 6SE Tel: (01202) 822204 Fax: (01202) 824410 E-mail: robertthorne@fsbdial.co.uk
Stormleaf Ltd, Unit 7 Premier House Midland Business Units, Finedon Road, Wellingborough, Northamptonshire, NN8 4AD Tel: (01933) 274499 Fax: (01933) 277794
Sykes Timber, Carlyon Road, Atherstone, Warwickshire, CV9 1JD Tel: (01827) 718951 Fax: (01827) 714257 E-mail: wood@sykestimber.co.uk
Thomson Sawmills, The Sawmill, Holt Road, Felthorpe, Norwich, NR10 4DB Tel: (01603) 754442 Fax: (01603) 755409 E-mail: ENQUIRIES@THOMSON-SAWMILLS.CO.UK
Timber Centre, Hatches Lane, Salisbury, SP1 2NZ Tel: (01722) 414900 Fax: (01722) 414909
▶ Treviscoe Builders Merchants, The Old Cooperage, Little Treviscoe, St. Austell, Cornwall, PL26 7QP Tel: (01726) 822388 Fax: (01726) 823383 E-mail: sales@treviscoe.com
W Howkins & Co., 65-67 Newnham Avenue, Bedford, MK41 9QJ Tel: (01234) 261143 E-mail: sales@whowkins.co.uk
W Metcalfe Leamington Ltd, Rugby Road, Cubbington, Leamington Spa, Warwickshire, CV32 7NU Tel: (01926) 335175 Fax: (01926) 337623

ENGLISH TO WELSH TRANSLATION

▶ Wolfestone Translation, Metropole Chambers, Salubrious Passage, Swansea, SA1 3RT Tel: (0845) 0000083 Fax: 0845 000 0083 E-mail: sales@wolfestone.co.uk

ENGRAVED LABELS

Alamode Engraving & Sign Co. Ltd, 3 Reform Street, Hull, HU2 8EF Tel: (01482) 323704 Fax: (01482) 216403 E-mail: sales@alamode.freeserve.co.uk
Computerised Engraving, 10 Waterloo Road, Widnes, Cheshire, WA8 0PY Tel: 0151-420 4590 Fax: 0151-495 1132 E-mail: info@computerisedengraving.com
Identilabel Ltd, Unit 2a The Gattinetts, Hadleigh Road, East Bergholt, Colchester, CO7 6QT Tel: (01206) 299777 Fax: (01206) 299007 E-mail: sales@identilabel.co.uk
Laser Techniques Ltd, Unit 11 Shaw Crescent, Hutton, Brentwood, Essex, CM13 1JD Tel: (01277) 228194 Fax: (01277) 232840 E-mail: sales@laser-techniques.com
Paragon Signs & Labels Ltd, Paragon House, Homefield Road, Haverhill, Suffolk, CB9 8QP Tel: (01440) 761405 Fax: (01440) 712147 E-mail: sales@paragon-signs.co.uk
Plastics W Graham Ltd, 114 Cowgate, Dundee, DD1 2JU Tel: (01382) 223734 Fax: (01382) 201799 E-mail: sales@pwgsigns.com
R C Perry & Co. Ltd, Unit 4 Worthington Way, Wigan, Lancashire, WN3 6XE Tel: (01942) 494012 Fax: (01942) 494021 E-mail: inquiries@rcperry.co.uk

ENGRAVED NAMEPLATES

W.R. Anderton Group, Maltings Lane, Castleton, Rochdale, Lancs, OL11 2UY Tel: (01706) 631277 Fax: (01706) 358201 E-mail: info@andertongroup.com
Bolsons Ltd, The Gatehouse, Cooks Road, London, E15 2PW Tel: (020) 8555 7137 Fax: (020) 8519 6641 E-mail: info@bolsons.co.uk
Class 1 Signs Ltd, 69 Breck Road, Anfield, Liverpool, L4 2QS Tel: 0151-264 0003 Fax: 0151-263 5996 E-mail: sales@class1signs.co.uk
Grant's Sign Shop, 76 Croydon Road, Elmers End, Beckenham, Kent, BR3 4DF Tel: (020) 8658 7578 Fax: (020) 8663 3780
Graphic Engineering Northern Ltd, Sheaf Bank Business Park, Prospect Road, Heeley, Sheffield, S2 3EN Tel: 0114-250 0151 Fax: 0114-255 5161 E-mail: sales@graphicengineering.co.uk
KD Engraving, 37 Boston Road, Leicester, LE4 1AW Tel: 0116-234 0131 Fax: 0116-234 0131
W E Services Ltd, 1 Shillingford Close, Appleton, Warrington, WA4 5QB Tel: (01925) 263490 Fax: (07092) 304593 E-mail: wayne@weservices.wanado.com

ENGRAVED SIGNS

Acorn Engraving Co., 4 Pump Lane, Regent Business Centre, Hayes, Middlesex, UB3 3NP Tel: (020) 8848 7367 Fax: (020) 8756 1028
AES Science Ltd, The Old Laundry, 15 Barratt Street, Easton, Bristol, BS5 6DE Tel: 0117-951 0234 Fax: 0117-952 0234 E-mail: aes@aessigns.co.uk
Allsigns, 122 Connaught Road, Brookwood, Woking, Surrey, GU24 0AS Tel: (01483) 799100 Fax: (01483) 799188
Autograph, The Malthouse, 139-141 Eastgate, Worksop, Nottinghamshire, S80 1QS Tel: (01909) 488500 Fax: (01909) 482687 E-mail: autographsigns.uk@btconnect.com
Avonmouth Shipping & Salvage, Chittening Industrial Estate, Chittening, Bristol, BS11 0YB Tel: 0117-982 9608 Fax: 0117-982 9559 E-mail: avonmouthsigns@btconnect.com
Briggs Priestley Ltd, 1-3 Lord Street, Halifax, West Yorkshire, HX1 5AE Tel: (01422) 354565 Fax: (01422) 356687 E-mail: dan@briggspriestley.ndo.co.uk
Brite Technology, Unit C Radford Business Centre, Radford Way, Billericay, Essex, CM12 0DP Tel: (01277) 655922 Fax: (01277) 655949 E-mail: j.creek@britetec.com
Butterfield Signs Ltd, 174 Sunbridge Road, Bradford, West Yorkshire, BD1 2RZ Tel: (01274) 722244 Fax: (01274) 848998 E-mail: general@butterfield-signs.co.uk
Central Signs & Graphics, 6 Saltley Industrial Centre, Adderley Road, Birmingham, B8 1AW Tel: 0121-326 7744 Fax: 0121-326 8123 E-mail: reginold1@aol.com
Class 1 Signs Ltd, 69 Breck Road, Anfield, Liverpool, L4 2QS Tel: 0151-264 0003 Fax: 0151-263 5996 E-mail: sales@class1signs.co.uk
Deco Bishop Auckland Ltd, Roman Way Industrial Estate, Bishop Auckland, County Durham, DL14 9AW Tel: (01388) 604590 Fax: (01388) 604590
East Herts Signs & Engraving, 3 Old Cross, Hertford, SG14 1HX Tel: (01992) 553004 Fax: (01992) 501165
Entech Precision Engraving, 4 Old Forge Cottage, Pearson Road, Sonning, Reading, RG4 6UH Tel: 0118-927 2499 Fax: 0118-927 2499 E-mail: ejak@btclick.com
Global Signs & Engraving Ltd, Admiralty Road, Great Yarmouth, Norfolk, NR30 3PU Tel: (01493) 843300 Fax: (01493) 843340 E-mail: globalsigns@ukonline.co.uk
Grant's Sign Shop, 76 Croydon Road, Elmers End, Beckenham, Kent, BR3 4DF Tel: (020) 8658 7578 Fax: (020) 8663 3780
Horsham Engraving Ltd, Foundry Lane, Horsham, West Sussex, RH13 5PX Tel: (01403) 260729 Fax: (01403) 210057 E-mail: horshamengraving@aol.com
Ihkos Digital Ltd, Coventry, CV2 3WB Tel: (024) 7626 7622 Fax: (024) 7672 9855 E-mail: info@ihkos.co.uk
Industrial Signs Ltd, 8 Astor Park, Padholme Road, Peterborough, PE1 5XL Tel: (01733) 555153 Fax: (01733) 555157 E-mail: isignsltd@compuserve.com
Jenter Engraving Ltd, Unit 4F, Lansbury Estate, 102 Lower Guildford Road, Knaphill, Woking, Surrey, GU21 2EP Tel: (01483) 289100 Fax: (01483) 289200
Labels 'N' Signs, 254 Rake Lane, Wallasey, Merseyside, CH45 1JR Tel: 0151-630 2337 Fax: 0151-691 2001 E-mail: sales@labelsnsigns.co.uk
Leek Signs & Graphics, Unit 10 Town Yard Industrial Estate, Station Street, Leek, Staffordshire, ST13 8BF Tel: (01538) 385262 Fax: (01538) 385262
Liskeard Signs & Trophies, 8 Pike Street, Liskeard, Cornwall, PL14 3JE Tel: (01579) 347098 Fax: (01579) 347098
M K Marking Systems Ltd, 22 Carters Lane, Kiln Farm Industrial Estate, Kiln Farm, Milton Keynes, MK11 3HL Tel: (01908) 561676 Fax: (01908) 562551 E-mail: sales@mkmarking.co.uk
▶ Mersey Signs, Unit 24, Junction 8 Business Park, Ross Cliffe Road, Ellesmere Port, CH65 3AS Tel: 0151-355 0478 Fax: 0151-356 5352 E-mail: info@merseysigns.co.uk
Opal Signs Ltd, Stirling Way, Borehamwood, Hertfordshire, WD6 2HP Tel: (020) 8236 0103 Fax: (020) 8953 7984 E-mail: sales@opalsigns.com
Oxton Signs & Printers, Enfield Terrace, Prenton, Merseyside, CH43 4UB Tel: 0151-670 1779 Fax: 0151-652 6642
S K Signs & Labels Ltd, The Brookside Centre, Sumpters Way, Southend-on-Sea, SS2 5RR Tel: (01702) 462401 Fax: (01702) 662404 E-mail: info@sksigns.co.uk
Sign It, Beehive Works, Beehive Lane, Chelmsford, CM2 9JY Tel: (01245) 492294 Fax: (01245) 262147 E-mail: sales@sign-it.co.uk
Sign Workshop, 8 The Ridgeway, Hitchin, Hertfordshire, SG5 2BT Tel: (01462) 442440 Fax: (01462) 442440 E-mail: sales@thesignworkshop.co.uk
Signs Of The Times, Unit 6, 3 Campsie Rosd, Kirkintilloch, Glasgow, G66 1SL Tel: 0141-775 0456 Fax: 0141-776 3322 E-mail: signsofthetimes@aol.com
Snell Signs & Supplies Ltd, 243-245 Cleethorpe Road, Grimsby, South Humberside, DN31 3BE Tel: (01472) 342000 Fax: (01472) 240027
Town & Country Signs Ltd, 125 Poplar High Street, London, E14 0AE Tel: (020) 7515 8383 Fax: (020) 7538 8657 E-mail: info@tcsigns.co.uk
Valley Engraving Ltd, 91-92 High Street, Clydach, Swansea, SA6 5LN Tel: (01792) 842374 Fax: (01792) 846130
Vital Signs, 1-15 Union Street, Cookstown, County Tyrone, BT80 8NN Tel: (028) 8676 5551 E-mail: sales@vitalsigns.org.uk
W E Services Ltd, 1 Shillingford Close, Appleton, Warrington, WA4 5QB Tel: (01925) 263490 Fax: (07092) 304593 E-mail: wayne@weservices.wanado.com
West Riding Engravers Ltd, 60 Wellington Street, Leeds, LS1 2EE Tel: 0113-243 9156 Fax: 0113-246 0787 E-mail: sales@wre-ltd.com

ENGRAVED TEXTILE PRINTING ROTARY SCREENS

Laserflex Ltd, J Balthane Industrial Estate, Balthane, Ballasalla, Isle of Man, IM9 2AG Tel: (01624) 822155 Fax: (01624) 824573 E-mail: sales@laserflex.co.uk
John Spencer (Hazelhurst) Ltd, Hazelhurst Engraving Works, 258 Bolton Road West, Ramsbottom, Bury, Lancashire, BL0 9PX Tel: (01706) 823244 Fax: (01706) 828529 E-mail: jshlaser@compuserve.com

ENGRAVERS' BOXWOOD BLOCKS

J S Drew, 856 Plymouth Road, Slough, SL1 4LP Tel: (01753) 568181 Fax: (01753) 568121 E-mail: jsdrewengravers@aol.com
T N Lawrence & Sons Ltd, 208 Portland Road, Hove, East Sussex, BN3 5QT Tel: (01273) 260260 Fax: (01273) 260270 E-mail: artbox@lawrence.co.uk

ENGRAVERS, GRAVURE

Decorflair Ltd, Chaddock Lane, Worsley, Manchester, M28 1DL Tel: 0161-790 2551 Fax: 0161-702 8665 E-mail: sales@decorflair.co.uk
Keating Gravure Systems (U K) Ltd, Unit 4, Bromfield Industrial Estate, Mold, Clwyd, CH7 1HE Tel: (01352) 755800 Fax: (01352) 756757
Mipa (UK) Ltd, 25 Robin Ride, Brackley, Northamptonshire, NN13 6PU Tel: (01280) 841190 Fax: (01280) 841191 E-mail: mipauk@aol.com

ENGRAVING

Don Browning Trophies, 4 St. Georges Street, Cheltenham, Gloucestershire, GL50 4AF Tel: (01242) 690314 Fax: (01242) 690313 E-mail: richard@dbtrophies.co.uk
▶ Green Slate Trophies, 1 Derby Street, Burnley, Lancashire, BB11 1RL Tel: (01282) 411400 Fax: (01282) 432308
H W Mclean, 1-5 George Place, Paisley, Renfrewshire, PA1 2HZ Tel: 0141-889 9268 Fax: 0141-889 9268
K & E K Sports Trophies, 16 Holderness Road, Hull, HU9 1EG Tel: (01482) 212138 Fax: (01482) 212138
▶ One to One Engravers Ltd, 3 Cirrus Park, Lower Farm Road, Moulton Park Industrial Estate, Northampton, NN3 6UR Tel: (01606) 644604 Fax: (01604) 644755 E-mail: info@otoel.com
▶ Timpson Engraving, Unit 4 Sutton Oak Drive, St. Helens, Merseyside, WA9 3PH Tel: (01744) 815350 Fax: (01744) 815671
Trophies Of Radstock, Unit 15 Old Mills Industrial Estate, Old Mills, Paulton, Bristol, BS39 7SU Tel: (01761) 418488 Fax: (01761) 418488
Bill Upsall Ltd, Charlotte Street, South Shields, Tyne & Wear, NE33 1PX Tel: 0191-455 6305 Fax: 0191-455 6305 E-mail: phil@billupsalltrophies.fslife.co.uk

ENGRAVING MACHINE MANUFRS

H K Technologies Ltd, Unit 7 Hadrians Way, Glebe Farm Industrial Estate, Rugby, Warwickshire, CV21 1ST Tel: (01788) 577288 Fax: (01788) 562808 E-mail: admin@hktechnologies.com
Micom Engineering Ltd, 7 Industrial Estate, The St, Heybridge, Maldon, Essex, CM9 4XB Tel: (01621) 856324 Fax: (01621) 858778 E-mail: sales@micomltd.co.uk

ENGRAVING MATERIALS, LAMINATES

Eglen Engravers Ltd, 12 Lord Street, Halifax, West Yorkshire, HX1 5AE Tel: (01422) 365556 Fax: (01422) 365564 E-mail: sales@eglenengravers.co.uk

ENGRAVING TRADE SUPPLIES

Denny Engraving, 1 Manse Place, Falkirk, FK1 1JN Tel: (01324) 634900 Fax: (01324) 634900
England Signs, The Malthouse, Main St, Offenham, Evesham, Worcs, WR11 8QD Tel: (01386) 442712 Fax: (01386) 442977
H W Mclean, 1-5 George Place, Paisley, Renfrewshire, PA1 2HZ Tel: 0141-889 9268 Fax: 0141-889 9268
J S Trophies, 2 Rood Hill, Congleton, Cheshire, CW12 1LG Tel: (01260) 272505 Fax: (01260) 272505 E-mail: jstrophies@tiscali.co.uk

ENROBING CHOCOLATES

Casemir Chocolates UK Ltd, 5a Tetherdown, London, N10 1ND Tel: (020) 8365 2132 E-mail: info@casemirchocolates.co.uk

ENSUITE BATHROOM CONSULTANCY

▶ Ensuite Solutions, 34-41 High Street, Newmarket, Suffolk, CB8 8NA Tel: (01638) 560566

ENTERPRISE RESOURCE PLANNING (ERP) SOFTWARE

Mainframe Data Ltd, 7 Oakwood Court, 122 Bromley Road, Beckenham, Kent, BR3 6PD Tel: (020) 8658 3928 E-mail: support@londondatabases.com

ENTERTAINER HIRE

▶ A R C Entertainments, 10 Church Lane, Redmarshall, Stockton-on-Tees, Cleveland, TS21 1EP Tel: (01740) 631292 E-mail: arcents@aol.com
▶ Ace of Face, 5 Manstead Gardens, Rainham, Essex, RM13 9HL Tel: 01708 738802 E-mail: sarahjane.mcdonald@aon.co.uk
▶ In 2 Faces, 6 The Ball, Bratton, Westbury, Wiltshire, BA13 4SB Tel: 01380 830772 E-mail: becky@in2faces.co.uk
▶ Powwow Face Painting, 76 Delves Crescent, Walsall, WS5 4LT Tel: (01922) 440261 Fax: 01922 440261 E-mail: powwowfp@btopenworld.com
▶ Professor Reg E Mental, 64 Wrangleden Road, Maidstone, Kent, ME15 9LJ Tel: (01622) 674643 E-mail: info@regemental.co.uk
▶ Unique Fun Casino, 57 Kilmiston Drive, Fareham, Hampshire, PO16 8EG Tel: (01329) 513624 Fax: (01329) 513624 E-mail: debraann.foxell@btconnect.com

ENTERTAINERS AGENCIES

▶ A R C Entertainments, 10 Church Lane, Redmarshall, Stockton-on-Tees, Cleveland, TS21 1EP Tel: (01740) 631292 E-mail: arcents@aol.com
▶ Ace of Face, 5 Manstead Gardens, Rainham, Essex, RM13 9HL Tel: 01708 738802 E-mail: sarahjane.mcdonald@aon.co.uk
Global Entertainments, PO Box 6945, ILKESTON, Derbyshire, DE7 5TG Tel: 0115-917 2767 Fax: 0115-917 4458 E-mail: global.ents@ntlworld.com
▶ Nick Levi - Close Up Magic, 2 North Park Avenue, Norwich, NR4 7EG Tel: (07962) 252949 E-mail: nick@levimagic.com

ENTERTAINMENT AGENTS

▶ Balloon Print, 22 Hammond Road, Woking, Surrey, GU21 4TQ Tel: (01483) 722229 Fax: (01483) 722229 E-mail: balloons.partyworld@ntlworld.com
▶ Carousel Entertainments, 18 Westbury Lodge Close, Pinner, Middlesex, HA5 3FG Tel: (0870) 7518688 Fax: (0870) 7518668 E-mail: sales@carouselentertainments.co.uk
▶ Encore Entertainment Ltd, 44 Churchfield Road, Walton-on-Thames, Surrey, KT12 2SY Tel: 01932 253273 E-mail: Encore_info@yahoo.co.uk
▶ Eventurous, The Water front, West Midlands Water Ski centre, Tamworth, Staffordshire, B78 2DL Tel: (0870) 6071258 E-mail: sales@eventurous.co.uk
Gekko Entertainments, 42 Theobalds Road, London, WC1X 8NW Tel: (020) 7404 1252 Fax: (020) 7242 1691 E-mail: info@gekkoentertainments.com
Global Entertainments, PO Box 6945, ILKESTON, Derbyshire, DE7 5TG Tel: 0115-917 2767 Fax: 0115-917 4458 E-mail: global.ents@ntlworld.com
▶ HFBC Events, 33 St. Michaels Road, Kirkham, Preston, PR4 2TQ Tel: (01772) 687455 E-mail: info@hfbc-events.co.uk
▶ J B Entertainments, 125 Boxley Drive, West Bridgford, Nottingham, NG2 7GN Tel: 0115-923 5747 Fax: 0115-923 5747 E-mail: info@jbentertainments.com
▶ Andy James Roadshows, The Ashes, Chargrove, Bristol, BS30 5NT Tel: 0117-960 6738 E-mail: info@andyjames.co.uk
▶ Parties Galore, Catriona Crescent, Arnold, Nottingham, NG5 8EN Tel: 0115-956 9143 E-mail: info@partiesgalore.co.uk
Protolog Sound Ltd, 49 Beech Road, Alresford, Hampshire, SO24 9JS Tel: (01962) 734545 Fax: (01962) 733849
▶ Silver Dog Music, Chorlton, Manchester, M21 0AT Tel: 0161 8617182 E-mail: info@silverdogmusic.co.uk

ENTERTAINMENT AGENTS, BALLOON MODELLERS

▶ Aplus Entertainment, Calshot Road, Birmingham, B42 2BY Tel: 0800 9168762 E-mail: sales@aplusentertainment.co.uk
▶ Changing Faces.Biz, 1 Courtney Road, Rushden, Northamptonshire, NN10 9FL Tel: (01933) 419910 E-mail: info@changingfaces.biz
Will Gray, The Magic Castle, 88 Church Lane, Whitwick, Coalville, Leicestershire, LE67 5DJ Tel: (01530) 457465 Fax: (0871) 7333318 E-mail: magic@willgray.co.uk

ENTERTAINMENT AGENTS, BELLY DANCERS

▶ Aplus Entertainment, Calshot Road, Birmingham, B42 2BY Tel: 0800 9168762 E-mail: sales@aplusentertainment.co.uk

ENTERTAINMENT AGENTS, BODY PAINTERS

▶ Changing Faces.Biz, 1 Courtney Road, Rushden, Northamptonshire, NN10 9FL Tel: (01933) 419910 E-mail: info@changingfaces.biz

ENTERTAINMENT AGENTS, CARICATURISTS

▶ Aplus Entertainment, Calshot Road, Birmingham, B42 2BY Tel: 0800 9168762 E-mail: sales@aplusentertainment.co.uk
▶ ianart.co.uk, Egremont, Arterial Road, Basildon, Essex, SS14 3JN Tel: (01268) 520899 Fax: (01268) 520899 E-mail: ian@ianart.co.uk

ENTERTAINMENT AGENTS, COSTUME CHARACTERS

▶ The Booking Agency, 152 Malpas Road, Newport, NP20 5PN Tel: (01633) 671498 Fax: (0871) 6612184 E-mail: info@thebookingagency.co.uk

ENTERTAINMENT AGENTS, DIGITAL PHOTOGRAPHERS

▶ Chris Hanley, 2 Wellfield Road, Stockport, Cheshire, SK2 6AS Tel: 0161-487 1217 E-mail: info@chrishanleyphotography.co.uk
▶ Funkie World Entertainments Ltd, 7 Trevarrick Court, Horwich, Bolton, BL6 6TF Tel: (07005) 981782 E-mail: aquatane@aquatane.co.uk
Saban Photography, Charwell House, Wilsom Road, Alton, Hampshire, GU34 2PP Tel: (01420) 540227 E-mail: martin@saban.co.uk
▶ Shannon Fine Art Photography, Norseman Studio Unit 8, Tedco Business Centre, Viking Industrial Park, Jarrow, Tyne & Wear, NE32 3DT Tel: 0191-428 3517

ENTERTAINMENT AGENTS, DISC JOCKEYS

▶ Sapphire Sounds, 68 Lancaster Avenue, Accrington, Lancs, BB5 4BH Tel: (01254) 235868 E-mail: sapphire_sounds2003@yahoo.co.uk
▶ Soundbarrier Systems, 4 Knowsley Crescent, Portsmouth, PO6 2PJ Tel: (07709) 815242 E-mail: simon@soundbarriersystems.com
▶ Top Class Disco's, 1 Salisbury Terrace, Stockton-on-Tees, Cleveland, TS20 2DS Tel: (01642) 863851

ENTERTAINMENT AGENTS, DRIVE IN SHOWS, SCHOOL PARTIES

▶ Hunsbury School of Motoring, 32 Barn Owl Close, East Hunsbury, Northampton, NN4 0UA Tel: (01604) 702808 E-mail: hsmdrive@aol.com

ENTERTAINMENT AGENTS, EVENT HOSTING

▶ Casino-To-Go, Unit 3 Foulswick Business Park, Fowlswick Lane, Allington, Chippenham, Wiltshire, SN14 6QE Tel: (01793) 686402 E-mail: info@casino-to-go.co.uk
▶ London Canal Museum, 12-13 New Wharf Road, London, N1 9RT Tel: (020) 7713 0836 Fax: (020) 7689 6679 E-mail: hire@canalmuseum.org.uk

ENTERTAINMENT AGENTS, GAMES EVENTS

▶ Funkie World Entertainments Ltd, 7 Trevarrick Court, Horwich, Bolton, BL6 6TF Tel: (07005) 981782 E-mail: aquatane@aquatane.co.uk
▶ Knights Templar Events, PO Box 740, Warrington, WA4 2WT Tel: (01925) 267658 Fax: (01925) 267658 E-mail: info@knightstemplarevents.co.uk
▶ Star Quality Entertainment Agency UK, 10 Park Meadow Avenue, Bilston, West Midlands, WV14 6HA Tel: (01902) 578959 E-mail: info@starqualityentertainment.net
▶ TDB Events, The Laurels, Comberton, Ludlow, Shropshire, SY8 4HE Tel: 01584 831215 Fax: 01584 831215 E-mail: drive@f1-simulator.co.uk
▶ Tickets To See.com, Lockheed House, Green Lane Business Park, London, SE9 3TL Tel: 0870 199 9742 E-mail: ken.peach@ticketstosee.com

ENTERTAINMENT AGENTS, HENNA TATTOOISTS

▶ In 2 Faces, 6 The Ball, Bratton, Westbury, Wiltshire, BA13 4SB Tel: 01380 830772 E-mail: becky@in2faces.co.uk
▶ Tiger-Designs, Boundary House, Pipers Lane, Northchapel, Petworth, West Sussex, GU28 9JA Tel: 0870 4460310 Fax: 0870 1349048 E-mail: sales@boundarygroup.com

ENTERTAINMENT AGENTS, MAGICIANS

▶ Phil Jay, 12 Gower Rise, Gowerton, Swansea, SA4 3DZ Tel: (01792) 875523 Fax: (01792) 875523 E-mail: phil@philjaymagic.com
Will Gray, The Magic Castle, 88 Church Lane, Whitwick, Coalville, Leicestershire, LE67 5DJ Tel: (01530) 457465 Fax: (0871) 7333318 E-mail: magic@willgray.co.uk

ENTERTAINMENT AGENTS, MUSIC

▶ AffordaBand, 275 Rotherhithe Street, London, SE16 5EY Tel: (020) 7237 7886
▶ The Booking Agency, 152 Malpas Road, Newport, NP20 5PN Tel: (01633) 671498 Fax: (0871) 6612184 E-mail: info@thebookingagency.co.uk
Campbell Murray Guitar Tutor - Scotland, 3 Cedar Gardens, Newarthill, Motherwell, Lanarkshire, ML1 5TP Tel: 01698 290525 E-mail: guitartutor@fsmail.net
Counties Barn Dance Agency, Derby Close, Broughton Astley, Leicester, LE9 6NF Tel: (0870) 240 1214 Fax: (0870) 240 1214 E-mail: countiesfolkagency@hotmail.com
▶ Creme22 Entertainments, Hockers Farm House, Hockers Lane, Detling, Maidstone, Kent, ME14 3JN Tel: 0845 607 6642 E-mail: info@creme22.com
▶ Fairy Management, 38 Mount Pleasant, Bryntirion, Bridgend, CF31 4EF Tel: (08701) 464871E-mail: sarah@fairymanagement.co.uk
▶ J B Entertainments, 125 Boxley Drive, West Bridgford, Nottingham, NG2 7GN Tel: 0115-923 5747 Fax: 0115-923 5747 E-mail: info@jbentertainments.com
▶ Manor House Music String Quartet, 6 Goose Acre, Cheddington, Leighton Buzzard, Bedfordshire, LU7 0SR Tel: (01296) 663744 E-mail: info@manorhousemusic.co.uk
▶ Professor Paradox, 42 St. James Street, St. James, South Petherton, Somerset, TA13 5BN Tel: 01460 242549 E-mail: mike@wisefool.co.uk
▶ Quintessential Music, 72 Southview Rd, London, N8 7LS Tel: 020 8340 9870 E-mail: carmen@quintessentialmusic.com
▶ Star Quality Entertainment Agency UK, 10 Park Meadow Avenue, Bilston, West Midlands, WV14 6HA Tel: (01902) 578959 E-mail: info@starqualityentertainment.net
▶ Sunrise Music Group, 11 Redstock Close, Westhoughton, Bolton, BL5 3UX Tel: 01942-810 820 E-mail: sales@sunrisemusicgroup.co.uk
▶ Ventura (Jazz Band), Seafire Close, York, YO30 4UU Tel: (0776) 9504794 E-mail: yorkjazz@fmail.co.uk

ENTERTAINMENT AGENTS, PERFORMING ACTS

▶ 1st Class Corporate Entertainment, 4 Porchester Court, Bournemouth, BH8 8JE Tel: (01202) 467970 E-mail: funcasino@msn.com
▶ Professor Paradox, 42 St. James Street, St. James, South Petherton, Somerset, TA13 5BN Tel: 01460 242549 E-mail: mike@wisefool.co.uk

ENTERTAINMENT AGENTS, TRIBUTE BANDS

▶ AffordaBand, 275 Rotherhithe Street, London, SE16 5EY Tel: (020) 7237 7886

ENTERTAINMENT CONSOLES

Barnet Leisure 2000, 28a Westerham Avenue, London, N9 9BU Tel: (020) 8807 3598
Childrens Entertainment Service, Brookview, Knights Road, Oxford, OX4 6DQ Tel: (01865) 775906 Fax: 01865775906
Dick Ropa, Carrstone Lodge, Pullover Road, Tilney All Saints, King's Lynn, Norfolk, PE34 4SG Tel: (01553) 692035 E-mail: info@dickropa.com
DJ Supplies Sound & Lighting, 149 Greatfield Road, Kidderminster, Worcestershire, DY11 6PP Tel: (01562) 865353 Fax: (01562) 865353 E-mail: sales@djsupplies.co.uk
M D M Leisure Ltd, 7 Battisford Park, Plympton, Plymouth, PL7 5AT Tel: (01752) 342589 Fax: (01752) 342589
Nostalgia Amusements, 22 Greenwood Close, Thames Ditton, Surrey, KT7 0BG Tel: (020) 8398 2141 Fax: (020) 8398 4343 E-mail: bdavey@globalnet.co.uk
Simply The Best Entertainments, 1 Claypool Court, South Shields, Tyne & Wear, NE34 0XD Tel: 0191-456 6023 E-mail: elgood@hotmail.com

ENTERTAINMENT LIGHTING COLOUR CHANGERS

K C Hickson Ltd, 89-91 Rolfe Street, Smethwick, West Midlands, B66 2AY Tel: 0121-558 1884 Fax: 0121-558 0017 E-mail: kchickson@george-jones-engineering.co.uk
Mango Electronics, Mango House, 1 Buckhurst Road, Bexhill-On-Sea, East Sussex, TN40 1QF Tel: (01424) 731500 Fax: (01424) 731502E-mail: colin@mango-electronics.co.uk

ENTERTAINMENTS AGENT, AFTER DINNER SPEAKERS

Global Entertainments, PO Box 6945, ILKESTON, Derbyshire, DE7 5TG Tel: 0115-917 2767 Fax: 0115-917 4458 E-mail: global.ents@ntlworld.com

ENTERTAINMENTS AGENT, DANCE INSTRUCTORS

▶ First Dance UK, 11 Thorn Road, Wrecclesham, Farnham, Surrey, GU10 4TU Tel: (01252) 792078 E-mail: adam@firstdanceuk.co.uk
▶ Tango Mercado, 16 Church Lane, Dingley, Market Harborough, Leicestershire, LE16 8PG Tel: (01858) 535319 E-mail: dcturner2@aol.com

ENTRANCE MATS

Jaymart Rubber & Plastics Ltd, Woodlands Trading Estate, Eden Vale Road, Westbury, Wiltshire, BA13 3QS Tel: (01373) 864926 Fax: (01373) 858454 E-mail: matting@jaymart.net

ENVELOPE BLANK CUTTERS

Newart, Mandervell Road, Oadby, Leicester, LE2 5LQ Tel: (0870) 7591650 Fax: (0870) 7591651 E-mail: sales@newartltd.com

ENVELOPE MACHINERY

Polygraphica Equipment Ltd, 1 Benton Office Park, Horbury, Wakefield, West Yorkshire, WF4 5RA Tel: (01924) 200444 Fax: (01924) 363714 E-mail: sales@polygraphica.com

ENVELOPE PRINTERS/ OVERPRINTING SERVICES

▶ Ad3 Envelope Printers Ltd, Unit 143 Aireplace Mills, Kirkstall Road, Leeds, LS3 1JL Tel: 0113-244 3700 Fax: 0113-244 9400 E-mail: andy.martin@ad3envelope.co.uk
Eagle Envelopes Ltd, Bloxwich Road, Walsall, WS2 7BD Tel: (01922) 613888 Fax: (01922) 613999 E-mail: walsall@eagle-envelopes.com
Envoprint, Penry Avenue, Cadishead, Manchester, M44 5ZE Tel: 0161-775 7272 Fax: 0161-776 0067
Flaps Envelopes Ltd, 70 Summer Lane, Birmingham, B19 3NG Tel: 0121-693 7377 Fax: 0121-693 0354

ENVELOPE PRINTERS/ OVERPRINTING SERVICES – *continued*

Hot Metal Press, Museum Works Elscar Workshops, Wath Road, Elsecar, Barnsley, South Yorkshire, S74 8HJ Tel: (01226) 740498 Fax: (01226) 350201 E-mail: info@hotmetalpress.co.uk

▶ Keith Day, Unit 51 Van Alloys Industrial Estate, Busgrove Lane, Stoke Row, Henley-on-Thames, Oxfordshire, RG9 5QW Tel: (01491) 680040 Fax: (01491) 682123 E-mail: keithdayprinters@btinternet.com

▶ Opt Complete Print Solutions Ltd, 58 Coulsdon Road, Coulsdon, Surrey, CR5 2LA Tel: (020) 8405 9386 Fax: (020) 8405 9386 E-mail: sales@optlimited.co.uk

Rapid Envelopes, Potters Bar, Herts, EN6 4SP Tel: (01707) 878783

S & K Envelopes Ltd, Greatfield Farm, Single Street, Berrys Green, Westerham, Kent, TN16 3AA Tel: (01959) 575755 Fax: (01959) 574554

Toplix Envelopes, 20-22 Benson Road, Poole, Dorset, BH17 0GB Tel: (01202) 684685 Fax: (01202) 666182 E-mail: wessex@multiplex.co.uk

Versapak International, The Versapak Centre, Centurion Way, Erith, Kent, DA18 4AF Tel: (020) 8333 5353 Fax: (020) 8312 2051 E-mail: catsales@versapak.co.uk

West Midland Office Supplies, Cherry Tree Walk, Farrier Street, Worcester, WR1 3BH Tel: (0870) 3330933 Fax: (0870) 9001449

ENVELOPES, *See also headings for particular types*

▶ 1st Class Post Ltd, 3 Silver Royd Business Park, Silver Royd Hill, Leeds, LS12 4QQ Tel: 0113-263 8684 Fax: 0113-263 7347

▶ Ad3 Envelope Printers Ltd, Unit 143 Aireplace Mills, Kirkstall Road, Leeds, LS3 1JL Tel: 0113-244 3700 Fax: 0113-244 9400 E-mail: andy.martin@ad3envelope.co.uk

Bingo Office Supplies Ltd, PO Box 845, Halifax, West Yorkshire, HX3 6YR Tel: (0800) 0424646 Fax: (0800) 0424329 E-mail: sales@bingo-office.co.uk

▶ Commercial Envelopes, 158 Lichfield Road, Sandhills, Walsall, WS9 9PF Tel: (01543) 452326 Fax: (01543) 821509 E-mail: denise@commercialenvelopes.co.uk

Corners Direct Ltd, Hillam Road, Bradford, West Yorkshire, BD2 1QL Tel: (01274) 733213 Fax: (01274) 721128 E-mail: peterwright@cornersdirect.co.uk

The Ex Mill Envelope & Paper Company Ltd, 5-9 City Garden Row, London, N1 8DW Tel: (020) 7253 8312 Fax: (020) 7251 5336 E-mail: sales@exmill.co.uk

Intermart International Ltd, 29 Victoria Road, Horwich, Bolton, BL6 5NA Tel: (01204) 460600 Fax: (01204) 460666

Mailtime Services Ltd, 490 Gorton Road, Reddish, Stockport, Cheshire, SK5 6PP Tel: 0161-223 0044 Fax: 0161-223 0055

Meldrum Mailing Ltd, Units 1-2 Hainault Works, Hainault Road, Little Heath, Romford, RM6 5NF Tel: (020) 8597 3218 Fax: (0845) 6445675

Paper Tigers, 77 Greenfield Road, London, E1 1EJ Tel: (020) 7377 0070 Fax: (01732) 362429

▶ Post Safe, Unit B3 Thanet Reach BSNS Park, Millennium Way, Broadstairs, Kent, CT10 2LA Tel: (01843) 860212 Fax: (01843) 864393 E-mail: sales@postsafe.co.uk

Rajapack, Unit 1, Marston Gate, Bridgemont, Bedford, MK43 0YL Tel: (0800) 5424428 Fax: (0800) 5424429 E-mail: sales@rajapack.co.uk

Smith Anderson Envelopes Ltd, Whiteside Industrial Estate, Bathgate, West Lothian, EH48 2RX Tel: (01506) 634463 Fax: (01506) 634366 E-mail: sales@eagle-envelopes.com

W G Office Supplies Ltd, Unit 3 Crayford Industrial Estate, Swaisland Drive, Crayford, Dartford, DA1 4HS Tel: (01322) 526527 Fax: (01322) 556249E-mail: sales@wgo.co.uk

ENVELOPES, CARDBOARD, MAILING

▶ Board Envelopes, Unit 15 Newark Storage Industrial Estate, Bowbridge Road, Newark, Nottinghamshire, NG24 4EQ Tel: (01636) 700611 Fax: (01636) 700084 E-mail: sales@boardenvelopes.com

Cummins & Papyrus Ltd, Canal Road, Bradford, West Yorkshire, BD2 1AJ Tel: (01274) 533555 Fax: (01274) 533666 E-mail: sales@cummingspapyrus.co.uk

Davies Envelope, Foxwood Industrial Park, Chesterfield, Derbyshire, S41 9RN Tel: (020) 8368 4236 Fax: (01246) 572270

ENVELOPES, TO CUSTOMER SPECIFICATION

Ace Envelopes Ltd, Hillside House, 2-6 Friern Park, London, N12 9BT Tel: (020) 8445 0123 Fax: (020) 8446 9423 E-mail: sales@ace-envelopes.co.uk

Eagle Envelopes Ltd, Bloxwich Road, Walsall, WS2 7BD Tel: (01922) 613888 Fax: (01922) 613999 E-mail: walsall@eagle-envelopes.com

Flaps Envelopes Ltd, 70 Summer Lane, Birmingham, B19 3NG Tel: 0121-693 7377 Fax: 0121-693 0354

Hugh Imlay & Co. Ltd, 3 Duff St, Aberdeen, AB24 5LF Tel: (01224) 640151 Fax: (01224) 647399 E-mail: info@hughimlay.co.uk

Impress Printers Ltd, 54 Burners Lane, Kiln Farm, Milton Keynes, MK11 3HD Tel: (01908) 262111 Fax: (01908) 262555 E-mail: carol@impress-envelopes.co.uk

ENVIRONMENTAL ACOUSTIC FENCING CONTRACTORS

▶ Kirkaldy Fencing & Dyking, 64 Feus, Auchterarder, Perthshire, PH3 1DG Tel: (01764) 663115 E-mail: kirkaldyfencinganddyking@msn.com

ENVIRONMENTAL BUNDED TANKS

▶ James Blake & Co. (Engineers) Ltd, 30-32 South Fort Street, Leith, Edinburgh, EH6 5NU Tel: 0131-554 1646 Fax: 0131-553 4128 E-mail: info@blakegroup.co.uk

ENVIRONMENTAL CHAMBER HIRE

Climatic Services Ltd, 41 Cavendish Way, Glenrothes, Fife, KY6 2SB Tel: (01592) 771254 Fax: (01592) 775626 E-mail: webmail@climaticservices.co.uk

Refrigerated Transport Information Society, 140 Newmarket Road, Cambridge, CB5 8HE Tel: (01223) 461352 Fax: (01223) 461522 E-mail: crt@crtech.demon.co.uk

ENVIRONMENTAL CHAMBER MAINTENANCE OR REFURBISHMENT OR SERVICE

Climatic Services Ltd, 41 Cavendish Way, Glenrothes, Fife, KY6 2SB Tel: (01592) 771254 Fax: (01592) 775626 E-mail: webmail@climaticservices.co.uk

Satalight Videography, Parkside Studio, Gotham Road, East Leake, Loughborough, Leicestershire, LE12 6JG Tel: (01509) 854004 Fax: (01509) 853111 E-mail: sales@satalight.co.uk

ENVIRONMENTAL CHAMBER MANUFRS

Alphatech Ltd, Green House, Homefield Road, Haverhill, Suffolk, CB9 8QP Tel: (01440) 714709 Fax: (01440) 714706 E-mail: info@alphatech.eu.com

Cee Tel, Unit 8 Manners View, Northumberland Rd, Newport, Isle of Wight, PO30 5SA Tel: (01983) 537171 Fax: (01983) 882444

Climatec Ltd, Unit 23 Empire Centre Imperial Way, Watford, WD24 4YH Tel: (01923) 237178 Fax: (01923) 237403 E-mail: robert_livingstone@talk21.com

James Technical Services, 3 Talgarth Business Park, Trefecca Road, Talgarth, Brecon, Powys, LD3 0PQ Tel: (01874) 711209 Fax: (01874) 712010E-mail: sales@jts-test-chambers.co.uk

Satalight Videography, Parkside Studio, Gotham Road, East Leake, Loughborough, Leicestershire, LE12 6JG Tel: (01509) 854004 Fax: (01509) 853111 E-mail: sales@satalight.co.uk

Sharetree Ltd, Unit 3 Meadow Mill Eastington Trading Estate, Churchend, Eastington, Stonehouse, Gloucestershire, GL10 3RZ Tel: (01453) 828642 Fax: (01453) 828076 E-mail: sales@sharetree.com

Temperature Applied Sciences Ltd, Unit 15 Martlets Way, Goring-by-Sea, Worthing, West Sussex, BN12 4HF Tel: (01903) 506903 Fax: (01903) 506911

ENVIRONMENTAL CHAMBER TESTING

Alphatech Ltd, Green House, Homefield Road, Haverhill, Suffolk, CB9 8QP Tel: (01440) 714709 Fax: (01440) 714706 E-mail: info@alphatech.eu.com

ENVIRONMENTAL CLEAN ROOMS

A A F-Mcquay UK Ltd, Bassington Lane, Cramlington, Northumberland, NE23 8AF Tel: (01670) 713477 Fax: (01670) 714370

Ardmac Performance Contracting Ltd, Annesborough Industrial Area, 15 Annesborough Road, Lurgan, Craigavon, County Armagh, BT67 9JD Tel: (028) 3834 7093 Fax: (028) 3834 1604 E-mail: info@ardmac.com

Bassaire Ltd, Duncan Road, Park Gate, Southampton, SO31 1ZS Tel: (01489) 885111 Fax: (01489) 885211 E-mail: sales@bassaire.co.uk

Clestra Cleanrooms, Hamilton House, 3 North Street, Carshalton, Surrey, SM5 2HZ Tel: (020) 8773 2121 Fax: (020) 8260 6814

Envair Ltd, Envair House, York Avenue, Haslingden, Rossendale, Lancashire, BB4 4HX Tel: (01706) 228416 Fax: (01706) 229577 E-mail: sales@envair.co.uk

M S S Clean Technology, Castle House, The Industrial Estate, York Road, York, YO60 6RZ Tel: (01347) 878877 Fax: (01347) 878878 E-mail: postbox@mss-ct.co.uk

Scientific Lesser Ltd, Hanworth Lane, Chertsey, Surrey, KT16 9JX Tel: (01932) 568122 Fax: (01932) 560818 E-mail: sllairskil@aol.com

Thermal Transfer (Northern) Ltd, Thermal Transfer House, 2 Railway Street, Glossop, Derbyshire, SK13 7AG Tel: (01457) 854341 Fax: (01457) 868357 E-mail: ttglossop@compuserve.co.uk

ENVIRONMENTAL CONSULTANCY OR TESTING

Alderley plc, Alderley House, Arnolds Field Estate, Wotton-under-Edge, Gloucestershire, GL12 8JD Tel: (01454) 299888 Fax: (01454) 299720 E-mail: marketing@alderley.com

Asbestos Analysis Services Ltd, 8 Tower Quays, Tower Road, Birkenhead, Merseyside, CH41 1BP Tel: 0151-649 0541 Fax: 0151-649 0547

Aztec Upvc Specialists, Unit 29-30, Colliery Close, Dinnington, Sheffield, S25 3QX Tel: (01909) 564946 Fax: (01909) 550418 E-mail: northfibre@aol.co.uk

B M T Cordah Ltd, Scotstown Road, Bridge of Don, Aberdeen, AB23 8HG Tel: (01224) 414200 Fax: (01224) 414250 E-mail: main@cordah.co.uk

The Bamford Group, Millgate, Market Street, Shawforth, Rochdale, Lancashire, OL12 8NX Tel: (01706) 897100 Fax: (01706) 897101 E-mail: bamford.group@virgin.net

Barton Willmore Partnership, 35 Kings Hill Avenue, Kings Hill, West Malling, Kent, ME19 4BW Tel: (01732) 845845 Fax: (01732) 223808 E-mail: architects@eastern.bartonwillmore.co.uk

Bodycote Materials Testing Ltd, 4 Bleasdale Court, 2 South Avenue, Clydebank Business Park, Clydebank, Dunbartonshire, G81 2LE Tel: 0141-941 2022 Fax: 0141-952 7099 E-mail: analytical@bodycote.com

Briggs Environmental Services Ltd, Leading Light Building, 142 Sinclair Road, Aberdeen, AB11 9PR Tel: (01224) 898666 Fax: (01224) 896950 E-mail: marketing@briggsmarine.com

Bristol Scientific Services, 7 Redcross Street, Bristol, BS2 0BA Tel: 0117-903 8666 Fax: 0117-903 8667 E-mail: labmail@sciserv.demon.co.uk

Bullen Consultants Ltd, Copthall House, Station Square, Coventry, CV1 2GT Tel: (024) 7663 2299 Fax: (024) 7663 2221 E-mail: coventry@bullen.co.uk

M.J. Carter Associates, Baddesley Colliery Offices, Main Road, Baxterley, Atherstone, Warwickshire, CV9 2LE Tel: (01827) 717891 Fax: (01827) 718507 E-mail: mailbox@mjca.co.uk

Casella Hazmat, 10-17 Seven Ways Parade, Woodford Avenue, Ilford, Essex, IG2 6JX Tel: (020) 8551 6195 Fax: (020) 8551 3554 E-mail: admin@casellagroup.com

Ch2m Hill, Avon House, Avonmore Road, London, W14 8TS Tel: (020) 7471 6100 Fax: (020) 7471 6101

Civil Engineering Dynamics Ltd, 11 Oak Walk, Wallington, Surrey, SM6 7DE Tel: (020) 8647 1908 Fax: (020) 8395 1556 E-mail: sales@environmental.co.uk

Crowther Clayton Associates, 31 Tennyson Road, London, NW7 4AB Tel: (020) 8959 7376 Fax: (020) 8959 6880 E-mail: info@crowther-clayton.com

D T S Raeburn Ltd, Moor Lane, Witton, Birmingham, B6 7HG Tel: 0121-344 3826 Fax: 0121-344 4754 E-mail: enquiries@dts-raeburn.co.uk

Dpus Plus Ltd, Flotta Oil Terminal, Flotta, Stromness, Orkney, KW16 3NP Tel: (01856) 702000 Fax: (01856) 701473 E-mail: admin@opusplus.co.uk

E R M Risks, 8 Cavendish Square, London, W1G OER Tel: (020) 7465 7349 Fax: (020) 7465 7270 E-mail: tawg@ermuk.com

ENSR UK, Portwall Place, Portwall Lane, Bristol, BS1 6NB Tel: (0845) 8630880 Fax: (0845) 8630880 E-mail: bgordon@ensr.aecom.com

Enstec Services, 141 Queen Ediths Way, Cambridge, CB1 8PT Tel: (01223) 566471 Fax: (01223) 413800 E-mail: ss_ens@netcomuk.co.uk

Environmental Engineering Ltd, Floor 3 Aspen Building, Vantage Point Business Village, Mitcheldean, Gloucestershire, GL17 0DD Tel: (01594) 546334 Fax: (01594) 546342

Environmental & Remediation Services, Unit 11 12 Mercia Business Village, Torwood Close, Westwood Business Park, Coventry, CV4 8HX Tel: (024) 7642 6600 Fax: (024) 7642 6610 E-mail: ears@cel-international.com

Enviros, Shrewsbury Business Park, Shrewsbury, SY2 6LG Tel: (01743) 284800 Fax: (01743) 245558 E-mail: marketing@enviros.com

Enviros Consulting Group, Waterfront Quay, Salford, M50 3XW Tel: 0161-874 3600 Fax: 0161-848 0181 E-mail: paul.bromley@enviros.com

Aaron Evans Architects Ltd, 3 Argyle Street, Bath, BA2 4BA Tel: (01225) 466234 Fax: (01225) 444364 E-mail: aea@aearchitects.co.uk

▶ Ewan Associates Ltd, 8 Boleyn Court, Manor Park, Runcorn, Cheshire, WA7 1SR Tel: (01928) 571025 Fax: (01928) 571026

▶ Fibrecount U K Ltd, Thomas Ho, 88-90 Goodmayes Rd, Goodmayes, Ilford, Essex, IG3 9UU Tel: (020) 8597 8785 Fax: (020) 8597 5605 E-mail: info@fibrecount.co.uk

Flow Science Ltd, Goldstein Laboratory, Liverpool Road, Eccles, Manchester, M30 7RU Tel: 0161-787 8749 Fax: 0161-787 8749 E-mail: flowsci@fs1.ae.man.ac.uk

Golder Associates (UK) Ltd, Clyde House, Reform Road, Maidenhead, Berkshire, SL6 8BY Tel: (01628) 771731 Fax: (01628) 770699 E-mail: golder_uk@golder.com

Ground Solutions Group Ltd, Cobbs Wood Industrial Estate, Hanover Close, Ashford, Kent, TN23 1EJ Tel: (01233) 658270 Fax: (01233) 658299 E-mail: gsg@groundsolutions.co.uk

H R Wallingford Ltd, Howbery Park, Wallingford, Oxfordshire, OX10 8BA Tel: (01491) 835381 Fax: (01491) 832233 E-mail: info@hrwallingford.co.uk

John W. Hannay & Co. Ltd, Linwood Avenue, East Kilbride, Glasgow, G74 5NE Tel: (01355) 225455 Fax: (01355) 231463 E-mail: sales@hannay.co.uk

Health & Safety Technology & Management Ltd, The Old Bakehouse, Fullbridge, Maldon, Essex, CM9 4LE Tel: (01621) 854111 Fax: (01621) 851756 E-mail: hastam@hastam.co.uk

Integral Geotechnique Ltd, West End House, Blackfriars Road, Nailsea, Bristol, BS48 4DJ Tel: (01275) 810580 Fax: (01275) 810581

Isoquest Environmental Consultants, 10 Fontmell Park, Ashford, Middlesex, TW15 2NW Tel: (01784) 252275 E-mail: info@isoquest.co.uk

M E L Research, 8 Holt Court North, Heneage St West, Birmingham, B7 4AX Tel: 0121-604 4664 Fax: 0121-604 6776 E-mail: info@m-e-l.co.uk

Midland Environmental Laboratories, Unit D17 Forge Lane, Minworth Industrial Park, Minworth, Sutton Coldfield, West Midlands, B76 1AH Tel: 0121-351 6469 Fax: 0121-351 6469

Brian Milligan Associates, 57 Wensley Road, Salford, M7 3GJ Tel: 0845 5314073 Fax: 0161-792 2269 E-mail: brian@brian-milligan.co.uk

Mouchel Parkman plc, West Hall, Parvis Road, West Byfleet, Surrey, KT14 6EZ Tel: (01932) 337000 Fax: (01932) 340673 E-mail: info@mouchelparkman.com

Nalco, 5 Riverside Business Park, Dogflud Way, Farnham, Surrey, GU9 7SS Tel: (01252) 735454 Fax: (01252) 734430 E-mail: enquiries@ondeo-nalco.com

Nalco, 20-22 Albion Way, Kelvin Industrial Estate, East Kilbride, Glasgow, G75 0YN Tel: (01355) 573900 Fax: (01355) 263660

Nalco Ltd, Weavergate Works, P O Box 11, Winnington Avenue, Northwich, Cheshire, CW8 4DX Tel: (01606) 74488 Fax: 01606 79557

NSG Enviromental Ltd, Scientia House Matrix Park, Western Avenue, Buckshaw Village, Chorley, Lancashire, PR7 7NB Tel: (01772) 458818 Fax: (01772) 458819 E-mail: mailbox@nsgenvironmental.co.uk

P W M Environmental Group, Bassett Road, Halesowen, West Midlands, B63 2RE Tel: (01384) 564866 Fax: (01384) 560945 E-mail: info@pwmills.co.uk

Pattinson Scientific Services, Scott House, Penn Street, Newcastle upon Tyne, NE4 7BG Tel: 0191-226 1300 Fax: 0191-226 1266 E-mail: pattinsonscientic@btconnect.com

Quality Assurance Advisors Ltd, 68 Ferryhill Road, Aberdeen, AB11 6RR Tel: (01224) 588885 Fax: (01224) 588885 E-mail: qaa@dial.pipex.com

R P S Consultants Ltd, Executive Freight Building, Kirkhill Drive, Kirkhill Industrial Estate, Aberdeen, AB21 0EU Tel: (01224) 773734 Fax: (01224) 724220 E-mail: rpsad@rpsplc.co.uk

R P S Laboratories Ltd, Unit 12 Waters Edge Business Park, Modwen Road, Salford, M5 3EZ Tel: 0161-872 2443 Fax: 0161-877 3959 E-mail: rpsma@rpsplc.co.uk

RPS Health, Safety and Environment, 185 Park Street, London, SE1 9DY Tel: (020) 7928 0999 Fax: (020) 7928 0708 E-mail: rpslo@rpsgroup.com

RSK E N S R Ltd, 16 Frogmore Road Industrial Estate, Frogmore Road, Hemel Hempstead, Hertfordshire, HP3 9RW Tel: (01442) 437500 Fax: (01442) 437550 E-mail: info@rsk.co.uk

Sound Research Laboratories Ltd, Holbrook House, Holbrook Hall Park, Little Waldingfield, Sudbury, Suffolk, CO10 0TH Tel: (01787) 247595 Fax: (01787) 248420 E-mail: srl@soundresearch.co.uk

Sypol Ltd, Elsinore House, Buckingham Street, Aylesbury, Buckinghamshire, HP20 2NQ Tel: (01296) 415715 Fax: (01296) 397106 E-mail: helpme@sypol.com

T P S Consultants, Centre Tower, Whitgift Centre, Croydon, CR9 0AU Tel: (020) 8256 4000 Fax: (020) 8256 4116 E-mail: sales@tpsconsult.ltd.uk

ENVIRONMENTAL CONSULTANCY OR TESTING – *continued*

T R W Automotive, Technical Centre, Stratford Road, Shirley, Solihull, West Midlands, B90 4GW Tel: 0121-627 4141 Fax: 0121-627 3584 E-mail: rob.miller@trw.com

Vintec Laboratories, Bucknalls Lane, Watford, WD25 9XX Tel: (01923) 661144 Fax: (01923) 661115 E-mail: vinteclabs@aol.com

Viridian Envirosolutions Ltd, Unit 81, Thomas Way, Lakesview International Business Park, Hersden, Canterbury, Kent, CT3 4JZ Tel: (01227) 713999 Fax: (01227) 713607 E-mail: info@viridian.biz

Webs Ltd, Ashborne House Waterperry Court, Middleton Road, Banbury, Oxfordshire, OX16 4QG Tel: (01295) 277272 Fax: (01295) 264070 E-mail: enquiries@websint.com

White Young Green Consulting, Family House, 4 Bedford Business Park, Croydon, CR0 2AP Tel: (020) 8649 6600 Fax: (020) 8649 6629 E-mail: londoncroydon@wyg.com

WRC plc, Frankland Road, Blagrove, Swindon, SN5 8YF Tel: (01793) 865000 Fax: (01793) 865001 E-mail: solutions@wrcplc.co.uk

ENVIRONMENTAL CONTROL SYSTEM INSTALLATION OR SERVICING

Air Pollution Services, Suite 6 Chiltern House, Leys Road, Brierley Hill, West Midlands, DY5 3UP Tel: (01384) 78094 Fax: (01384) 480940 E-mail: martinwil@msn.com

C F Whaler Ltd, Bridge Works, Horncastle Road, Wragby, Market Rasen, Lincolnshire, LN8 5RB Tel: (01673) 857575 Fax: (01673) 857788 E-mail: mail@cfwhaler.co.uk

Climatec Systems Ltd, Unit 6 Dymock Road Indust Estate, Dymock Road, Parkway, Ledbury, Herefordshire, HR8 2JQ Tel: (01531) 631161 Fax: (01531) 631165 E-mail: climatec@climatec.co.uk

Micronair, Unit 17, Bradwell Works, Davenport Street, Stoke-on-Trent, ST6 4LL Tel: (01782) 816300 Fax: (01782) 790767 E-mail: kp@filter.co.uk

Radco Services Ltd, Little Limekilns, Middle Lypiatt, Stroud, Gloucestershire, GL6 7LR Tel: (01453) 883746 Fax: (01453) 884211

ENVIRONMENTAL CONTROL SYSTEMS

Adcock Refrigeration & Air Conditioning Ltd, 5 Industrial Estate, London Road, Pampisford, Cambridge, CB22 3XX Tel: (01223) 834189 Fax: (01223) 837116 E-mail: enquiries@adcock.co.uk

Air Handling Equipment Ltd, 23 Cotton Street, Liverpool, L3 7DY Tel: 0151-236 2910 Fax: 0151-236 2910 E-mail: sales@ahe.co.uk

Airology Systems Ltd, Brickyard Lane, Studley, Warwickshire, B80 7EE Tel: (01527) 850717 Fax: (01527) 850737 E-mail: aircon@airology.freeserve.co.uk

C F Whaler Ltd, Bridge Works, Horncastle Road, Wragby, Market Rasen, Lincolnshire, LN8 5RB Tel: (01673) 857575 Fax: (01673) 857788 E-mail: mail@cfwhaler.co.uk

Climatec Systems Ltd, Unit 6 Dymock Road Indust Estate, Dymock Road, Parkway, Ledbury, Herefordshire, HR8 2JQ Tel: (01531) 631161 Fax: (01531) 631165 E-mail: climatec@climatec.co.uk

Electrotech Maintenance Services, Clarkswell House, Sugarswell Business Park, Shennington, Banbury, Oxon, OX15 6HW Tel: (01295) 688429 Fax: (01295) 680005 E-mail: admin@electrotech-cds.co.uk

Ferrob Ltd, Regency House, Kingsclere Park, Kingsclere, Newbury, Berkshire, RG20 4SW Tel: (01635) 299266 Fax: (01635) 299277 E-mail: sales@ferrob.co.uk

Griffin Cardwell Ltd, 87 Fleet Road, Fleet, Hampshire, GU51 3PJ Tel: (01252) 365500 Fax: (01252) 612875 E-mail: sales@griffincardwell.com

Hevantac Control Services Ltd, Unit 3 125 Park Road, Beckenham, Kent, BR3 1QJ Tel: (020) 8658 7218 Fax: (020) 8650 1243 E-mail: barry@aimteq.co.uk

Ies Pca Ltd, The Millcourt Centre, Pleasley Vale, Mansfield, Nottinghamshire, NG19 8RL Tel: (01623) 819319 Fax: (01623) 819329 E-mail: info@iespca.com

ENVIRONMENTAL ENGINEERING

Arch Henderson & Partners, 26 Rubislaw Terrace, Aberdeen, AB10 1XE Tel: (01224) 631122 Fax: (01224) 632233 E-mail: headoffice@arch-henderson.co.uk

ENSR UK, Portwall Place, Portwall Lane, Bristol, BS1 6NB Tel: (0845) 8630880 Fax: (0845) 8630880 E-mail: bgordon@ensr.aecom.com

Environment Measures, East Forest Byre, Morpeth, Northumberland, NE61 3ET Tel: (01670) 786079 Fax: (01670) 786079 E-mail: info@enviromentmeasure.co.uk

Environmental Maintenance Services, Hyde Pk, London, W2 2UH Tel: 020 74021510 Fax: 020 74021510

Rda, Unit 1 Plot 7 River Way Industrial Estate, Newport, Isle of Wight, PO30 5UX Tel: (01983) 821189 Fax: (01983) 821149 E-mail: sales@rda-eng.com

ENVIRONMENTAL IMPACT ASSESSMENT CONSULTANCY

A M S Acoustics, Rayleigh House, 21 Queen Annes Place, Enfield, Middlesex, EN1 2QB Tel: (020) 8886 4060 Fax: (020) 8360 2640 E-mail: info@amsacoustics.co.uk

Acoustics Noise & Vibration, Hastings House, Auckland Park, Bletchley, Milton Keynes, MK1 1BU Tel: (01908) 642811 Fax: (01908) 642800 E-mail: info@anv.uk.com

B M T Cordah Ltd, Scotstown Road, Bridge of Don, Aberdeen, AB23 8HG Tel: (01224) 414200 Fax: (01224) 414250 E-mail: main@cordah.co.uk

Broadway Malyan, 3 Weybridge Business Park, Addlestone Road, Addlestone, Surrey, KT15 2BW Tel: (01932) 845599 Fax: (01932) 856206 E-mail: man@broadwaymalyan.com

Burau Verater Ltd, 91 Winchester Road, Chandlers Ford, Eastleigh, Hampshire, SO53 2GG Tel: (023) 8024 2300 Fax: (023) 8024 2399

M.J. Carter Associates, Baddesley Colliery Offices, Main Road, Baxterley, Atherstone, Warwickshire, CV9 2LE Tel: (01827) 717891 Fax: (01827) 718507 E-mail: mailbox@mjca.co.uk

The Countryside Agency, John Dower House, Crescent Place, Cheltenham, Gloucestershire, GL50 3RA Tel: (01242) 521381 Fax: (01242) 584270 E-mail: info@countryside.gov.uk

ENSR UK, Portwall Place, Portwall Lane, Bristol, BS1 6NB Tel: (0845) 8630880 Fax: (0845) 8630880 E-mail: bgordon@ensr.aecom.com

▶ Environmental Practice At Work Ltd, 10 Mayville Road, Brierfield, Nelson, Lancashire, BB9 5RP Tel: (01282) 602829 E-mail: info@epaw.co.uk

Enviros, Shrewsbury Business Park, Shrewsbury, SY2 6LG Tel: (01743) 284800 Fax: (01743) 245558 E-mail: marketing@enviros.com

Ground Restoration Ltd, Unit 15 Ingoldmells Court, Edinburgh Way, Corsham, Wiltshire, SN13 9XN Tel: (01225) 810818 Fax: (01225) 811030 E-mail: grla1cad@aol.com

H R Wallingford Ltd, Howbery Park, Wallingford, Oxfordshire, OX10 8BA Tel: (01491) 835381 Fax: (01491) 832233 E-mail: info@hrwallingford.co.uk

Hepworth Acoustics Ltd, 5 Bankside, Crosfield Street, Warrington, WA1 1UP Tel: (01925) 579100 Fax: (01925) 579150 E-mail: enquiries@hepworth-acoustics.co.uk

Land Use Consultants, 43 Chalton Street, London, NW1 1JD Tel: (020) 7383 5784 Fax: (020) 7383 4798

Pauline Roscoe & Associates Ltd, 183 Town Lane, Whittle-le-Woods, Chorley, Lancashire, PR6 8AG Tel: (01257) 260157 Fax: (01257) 260157 E-mail: pr@pauline-roscoe.co.uk

RSK E N S R Ltd, 16 Frogmore Road Industrial Estate, Frogmore Road, Hemel Hempstead, Hertfordshire, HP3 9RW Tel: (01442) 437500 Fax: (01442) 437550 E-mail: info@rsk.co.uk

ENVIRONMENTAL IMPACT PLANNING APPLICATION CONSULTANCY

▶ Contract Ecology and Landscapes, 84 Tulketh Crescent, Ashton-On-Ribble, Preston, PR2 2RJ Tel: 01772 731404 E-mail: enquiries@contractecology.co.uk

▶ R Walker, 41 The Pastures, Lower Bullingham, Hereford, HR2 6EU Tel: (01432) 341636 E-mail: enquires@rwalker-plans.co.uk

Turley Associates Ltd, 43 Park Place, Leeds, LS1 2RY Tel: 0113-386 3800 Fax: 0113-244 3650 E-mail: leeds@rta.co.uk

ENVIRONMENTAL MANAGEMENT CONSULTANCY

▶ Onset Management Ltd, Nelson House (HF), 58 Wimbledon Hill Road, London, SW19 7PA Tel: 07803 901631 E-mail: info@onsetmanagement.co.uk

ENVIRONMENTAL MANAGEMENT SERVICES

▶ A F Crudden Associates, 209 High Street, Elgin, Morayshire, IV30 1DJ Tel: (01343) 550500 Fax: (01343) 550886

▶ AMP (GB) Ltd, Horton Corner, Small Dole, Henfield, West Sussex, BN5 9XJ Tel: (01903) 817004 Fax: (01903) 817114 E-mail: mphippf@amp.com

▶ Consultants In Quality Assurance Ltd, 215 Staines Road, Lauham, Staines, Middlesex, TW18 2RS Tel: (01784) 460563 E-mail: rhoweles@ciqa.co.uk

Enviromental Research Institute, Castle Street, Thurso, Caithness, KW14 7JD Tel: (01847) 889589 Fax: (01847) 890014

▶ Environmental Practice At Work Ltd, 10 Mayville Road, Brierfield, Nelson, Lancashire, BB9 5RP Tel: (01282) 602829 E-mail: info@epaw.co.uk

Excel Partnership, 25 Silverthorn Drive, Hemel Hempstead, Hertfordshire, HP3 8BX Tel: (01442) 242929 Fax: (01442) 216057 E-mail: training@excellpartnership.co.uk

▶ Infrastructure Associates Ltd, Weir Bank, Monkey Island Lane, Bray, Maidenhead, Berkshire, SL6 2ED Tel: (01628) 762730 Fax: (01628) 762730 E-mail: scherry@infrastructureassociates.com

▶ J S C International Ltd, Simpson House 11 Windsor Court, Clarence Drive, Harrogate, North Yorkshire, HG1 2PE Tel: (01423) 520245 Fax: (01423) 520297 E-mail: enquires@jsci.co.uk

Kramba Associates Ltd, 6 Lynwood Close, Darwen, Lancashire, BB3 0JY Tel: (01254) 776616 Fax: (01254) 776616 E-mail: kramba@tiscali.co.uk

▶ Landmark Environmental Ltd, Myerscough Hall, St. Michaels Road, Bilsborrow, Preston, PR3 0RY Tel: (01995) 642109 Fax: (01995) 642108 E-mail: info@land-mark.co.uk

▶ Mab Environment & Ecology Ltd, The Old Chapel, Knayton, Thirsk, North Yorkshire, YO7 4AZ Tel: (01845) 537845 E-mail: Giles@mab.uk.com

Mars Hall Consultancy & Training, Cheshire House, 164 Main Road, Goostrey, Crewe, CW4 8JP Tel: (01477) 534209 Fax: (01477) 537170 E-mail: enquiries@techsafeconsultants.co.uk

Rda, Unit 1 Plot 7 River Way Industrial Estate, Newport, Isle of Wight, PO30 5UX Tel: (01983) 821189 Fax: (01983) 821149 E-mail: sales@rda-eng.com

▶ Renaissance Regeneration Ltd, 33 St. Andrews Street North, Bury St. Edmunds, Suffolk, IP33 1SZ Tel: (01284) 765563 Fax: 01284 777445 E-mail: magnus.willatts@renreg.co.uk

▶ S L R Consulting Ltd, No. 4 The Roundal, Roddinglaw Business Park, Gogar, Edinburgh, EH12 9DB Tel: 0131-335 6830 Fax: 0131-335 6831

Sayvol Chemicals Ltd, 111 Laurence Leyland Complex, Irthlingborough Road, Wellingborough, Northamptonshire, NN8 1RT Tel: (01933) 442069 Fax: (01933) 442070 E-mail: enquiries@sayvol.com

▶ Tayreed Co., Airfield Industrial Estate, Errol, PH2 7TB Tel: (01821) 642466 Fax: (01821) 642827

▶ U K A E A, Dounreay, Thurso, Caithness, KW14 7TZ Tel: (01847) 802121

Willacy Oil Services Ltd, Whittle Close, Engineer Park, Deeside, Clwyd, CH5 2QE Tel: (01244) 520122 Fax: (01244) 520283 E-mail: sales@willacyoil.com

ENVIRONMENTAL MONITORING

Ad-Qual Group, 28 Mirfield Road, Solihull, West Midlands, B91 1JD Tel: 0121- 711 8785 Fax: 0121- 711 8785 E-mail: castech@blueyonder.co.uk

C A Clase (UK) Ltd, 20 Woolmer Way, Bordon, Hampshire, GU35 9QF Tel: (01420) 488422 Fax: (01420) 488522 E-mail: sales@caclase.co.uk

E P I Service Ltd, Witan Park, Avenue Two, Station Lane, Witney, Oxfordshire, OX28 4FH Tel: (01993) 708855 Fax: (01993) 708850 E-mail: admin@epi-uk.com

▶ Enitial, Enterprise Drive, Four Ashes, Wolverhampton, WV10 7DF Tel: (01902) 798798 Fax: (01902) 798711

▶ Fibrecount U K Ltd, Thomas Ho, 88-90 Goodmayes Rd, Goodmayes, Ilford, Essex, IG3 9UU Tel: (020) 8597 8785 Fax: (020) 8597 5605 E-mail: info@fibrecount.co.uk

Harwell Scientifics, 551 South Becquerel Avenue, Didcot, Oxfordshire, OX11 0TB Tel: (01235) 841970 Fax: (01235) 832287 E-mail: sales@scientifics.com

Brian Milligan Associates, 57 Wensley Road, Salford, M7 3GJ Tel: 0845 5314073 Fax: 0161-792 2269 E-mail: brian@brian-milligan.co.uk

▶ Partrac - Science for Sediment Management, 141 St. James Road, Glasgow, G4 0LT Tel: 0141-303 8255 E-mail: info@partrac.com

▶ S L R Consulting Ltd, No. 4 The Roundal, Roddinglaw Business Park, Gogar, Edinburgh, EH12 9DB Tel: 0131-335 6830 Fax: 0131-335 6831

Web Fabrications Ltd, Gledholt Business Park, Allen Row, Paddock, Huddersfield, HD1 4SB Tel: (01484) 545333 Fax: (01484) 422194

ENVIRONMENTAL MONITORING EQUIPMENT/SYSTEMS DESIGN ENGINEERS

Civil Engineering Dynamics Ltd, 11 Oak Walk, Wallington, Surrey, SM6 7DE Tel: (020) 8647 1908 Fax: (020) 8395 1556 E-mail: sales@environmental.co.uk

E P I Service Ltd, Witan Park, Avenue Two, Station Lane, Witney, Oxfordshire, OX28 4FH Tel: (01993) 708855 Fax: (01993) 708850 E-mail: admin@epi-uk.com

Horiba Instruments Ltd, Kyoto Close, Summerhouse Road, Moulton Park, Northampton, NN3 6FL Tel: (01604) 542500 Fax: (01604) 542699

ENVIRONMENTAL MONITORING EQUIPMENT/SYSTEMS HIRE

▶ Partrac - Science for Sediment Management, 141 St. James Road, Glasgow, G4 0LT Tel: 0141-303 8255 E-mail: info@partrac.com

ENVIRONMENTAL MONITORING EQUIPMENT/SYSTEMS MANUFRS

C A Clase (UK) Ltd, 20 Woolmer Way, Bordon, Hampshire, GU35 9QF Tel: (01420) 488422 Fax: (01420) 488522 E-mail: sales@caclase.co.uk

C F Whaler Ltd, Bridge Works, Horncastle Road, Wragby, Market Rasen, Lincolnshire, LN8 5RB Tel: (01673) 857575 Fax: (01673) 857788 E-mail: mail@cfwhaler.co.uk

C S I P Ltd, Unit 11 Granby Court, Surrey Close, Granby Industrial Estate, Weymouth, Dorset, DT4 9XB Tel: (01305) 779020 Fax: (01305) 778095 E-mail: sales@csip.co.uk

▶ Casp Products Ltd, W.H.S. Building, Harcourt Road, Harrogate, North Yorkshire, HG1 5NL Tel: (01423) 525206 Fax: (01423) 536500 E-mail: sales@casp-products.com

Elcomponent Ltd, Unit 5 Southmill Trading Centre, Southmill Road, Bishop's Stortford, Hertfordshire, CM23 3DY Tel: (01279) 503173 Fax: (01279) 654441 E-mail: sales@elcomponent.co.uk

Ele International, Chartmoor Road, Leighton Buzzard, Bedfordshire, LU7 4WG Tel: (01525) 249200 Fax: (01525) 249249 E-mail: ele@eleint.co.uk

European Spectrometry Systems, Genesis House, Denton Drive, Northwich, Cheshire, CW9 7LU Tel: (01606) 49400 Fax: (01606) 330937 E-mail: service@essco.u-net.com

F W Parrett Ltd, 65 Ridefield Road, London, SE9 2RA Tel: (020) 8859 3254 Fax: (020) 7504 3536 E-mail: fparrett@aol.com

G D S Technologies, Swillington Lane, Swillington, Leeds, LS26 8BZ Tel: 0113-286 0166 Fax: 0113-286 4073 E-mail: sales@gds-technologies.co.uk

Horiba Instruments Ltd, Kyoto Close, Summerhouse Road, Moulton Park, Northampton, NN3 6FL Tel: (01604) 542500 Fax: (01604) 542699

K A D Detection Systems Ltd, Units 4-5, Barrmill Road, Galston, Ayrshire, KA4 8HH Tel: (01563) 820148 Fax: (01563) 820163 E-mail: sales@kad-detection.com

▶ Met Engineering Ltd, Unit 3, Mode Wheel Road, Salford, M5 5DQ Tel: 0161-737 2627 Fax: 0161-737 2628 E-mail: info@metenguk.com

▶ Met-Check Ltd, 9 Churchfield Road, Chilton Industrial Estate, Sudbury, Suffolk, CO10 2YA Tel: (01787) 883138 Fax: (01787) 883139 E-mail: sales@met-check.co.uk

Quantitech Ltd, 3 Old Wolverton Road, Old Wolverton, Milton Keynes, MK12 5NP Tel: (01908) 227722 Fax: (01908) 227733 E-mail: quant@quantitech.co.uk

Read Scientific Ltd, 32 Brancaster Way, Swaffham, Norfolk, PE37 7RY Tel: (01760) 724546 Fax: (01760) 724340 E-mail: bill.read@ntlworld.com

S K C Ltd, Unit 11, Sunrise Park, Higher Shaftesbury Road, Blandford Forum, Dorset, DT11 8ST Tel: (01258) 480188 Fax: (01258) 480184 E-mail: info@skcltd.com

Scientifics Ltd, 52 Offerton Industrial Estate, Hempshaw Lane, Stockport, Cheshire, SK2 5TJ Tel: 0161-477 3004 Fax: 0161-480 4642

Turnkey Instruments Ltd, Units 1-2 Dalby Court, Gadbrook Business Centre, Rudheath, Northwich, Cheshire, CW9 7TN Tel: (01606) 44520 Fax: (01606) 331526 E-mail: shop@turnkey-instruments.com

Weltech International Ltd, 10 Bramley Road, St. Ives, Cambridgeshire, PE27 3WS Tel: (01480) 461611 Fax: (01480) 301010

Westmid Fans, Zephyr House, Mucklow Hill, Halesowen, West Midlands, B62 8DN Tel: 0121-550 0315 Fax: 0121-585 5185 E-mail: westmidfunds@btconnect.com

ENVIRONMENTAL MONITORING OR MAINTENANCE CONSULTANCY

Broadway Group, 136 Stanwell Road, Ashford, Middlesex, TW15 3QP Tel: (0845) 6019006 Fax: (0845) 6019007 E-mail: ppstechnical@yahoo.co.uk

Land Use Consultants, 43 Chalton Street, London, NW1 1JD Tel: (020) 7383 5784 Fax: (020) 7383 4798

RSK E N S R Ltd, 16 Frogmore Road Industrial Estate, Frogmore Road, Hemel Hempstead, Hertfordshire, HP3 9RW Tel: (01442) 437500 Fax: (01442) 437550 E-mail: info@rsk.co.uk

Viridian Envirosolutions Ltd, Unit 81, Thomas Way, Lakesview International Business Park, Hersden, Canterbury, Kent, CT3 4JZ Tel: (01227) 713999 Fax: (01227) 713607 E-mail: info@viridian.biz

ENVIRONMENTAL MONITORING, INDUSTRIAL

▶ Advanced Noise Solutions Ltd, 13 Boissy Close, St Albans, St. Albans, Hertfordshire, AL4 0UE Tel: (01727) 864667
▶ Andrew Josephs, 16 South Terrace, Sowerby, Thirsk, North Yorkshire, YO7 1RH Tel: (01743) 343322 E-mail: ritaw18@hotmail.com

ENVIRONMENTAL QUALITY MANAGEMENT CONSULTANCY

▶ Auriga Business Solutions Ltd, Soldon Cross Farm Soldon Cross, Holsworthy, Devon, EX22 7PH Tel: (01409) 241060 E-mail: sales@aurigasolutions.co.uk
▶ Bridge Consultants, 19 Beck Ford, Teal Farm, Washington, Tyne & Wear, NE38 8TP Tel: (07967) 383105 Fax: (0870) 1692863 E-mail: enquiries@bridgeconsultants.co.uk
▶ Cookprior Associates Ltd, 6 High Street, Sutton-in-Craven, Keighley, West Yorkshire, BD20 7NX Tel: (01535) 635128 Fax: (0870) 0529845 E-mail: enquiries@cookprior.co.uk
▶ Environmental Practice At Work Ltd, 10 Mayville Road, Brierfield, Nelson, Lancashire, BB9 5RP Tel: (01282) 602829 E-mail: info@epaw.co.uk
▶ Imsys Ltd, 15 Dawlish Close, Blackburn, BB2 4NS Tel: (01254) 692077 Fax: (01254) 671539 E-mail: abw@imsys.biz
Isoquest Environmental Consultants, 10 Fontmell Park, Ashford, Middlesex, TW15 2NW Tel: (01784) 252275 E-mail: info@isoquest.co.uk
▶ K. Marshall & Associates, School House, Rushall, Pewsey, Wiltshire, SN9 6EN Tel: (01980) 630688 Fax: (01980) 630549 E-mail: kma@consult.screaming.net
▶ Polaris Training & Development Systems, Awford House, 43-45 Rectory Grove, Leigh-on-Sea, Essex, SS9 2HA Tel: (01702) 474499 Fax: (01702) 474018 E-mail: systems@gedgilligan.co.uk
▶ Proprove Ltd, 2 New Road Langtoft, Peterborough, PE6 9LE Tel: (01778) 345990 Fax: (01778) 345990 E-mail: jim.yates@lycos.co.uk

ENVIRONMENTAL REMEDIATION CONTRACTORS

Clovemead, Stephenson House, Howley Lane, Warrington, WA1 2DN Tel: (01925) 411221 Fax: (01925) 418496 E-mail: clovemead@brunelhouse.u-net.com
Cobban Environmental Development & Remediation Ltd, 93 Clifton Street Roath, Cardiff, CF24 1LT Tel: (029) 2040 7330 Fax: (029) 2040 7330
Geodelft Environmental, 18 Victoria Avenue, Newtownards, County Down, BT23 7EB Tel: (028) 9182 0061 Fax: (028) 9181 6634

ENVIRONMENTAL RESEARCH CONSULTANCY

Building Research Establishment Ltd, Bucknalls Lane, Garston, Watford, WD25 9XX Tel: (01923) 664000 Fax: (01923) 664010 E-mail: enquiries@bre.co.uk
Ecotec Research & Consulting Ltd, 12-26 Albert Street, Birmingham, B4 7UD Tel: 0121-616 3600 Fax: 0121-616 3699 E-mail: welcome@ecotec.co.uk
H R Wallingford Ltd, Howbery Park, Wallingford, Oxfordshire, OX10 8BA Tel: (01491) 835381 Fax: (01491) 832233 E-mail: info@hrwallingford.co.uk
Mayer Enviromental Ltd, Transport Avenue, Brentford, Middlesex, TW8 9HA Tel: (020) 8847 3637 Fax: (020) 8847 3638 E-mail: info@mayer-enviro.com
UK Centre For Economic & Environmental Development, 48 Broadway, Peterborough, PE1 1SB Tel: (01733) 311644 Fax: (01733) 312782 E-mail: info@ukceed.org

ENVIRONMENTAL SERVICES OR RECOVERY CONTRACTORS

Arundelle Industrial Services Ltd, 250 High Street, Cranleigh, Surrey, GU6 8RL Tel: (01483) 277801 Fax: (01483) 277802 E-mail: sales@arundelle.co.uk
Aztec Upvc Specialists, Unit 29-30, Colliery Close, Dinnington, Sheffield, S25 3QX Tel: (01909) 564946 Fax: (01909) 550418 E-mail: northfibre@aol.co.uk
Birmingham City Laboratories, Phoenix House, Valepits Road, Garretts Green, Birmingham, B33 0TD Tel: 0121-303 9300 Fax: 0121-303 9301 E-mail: trevor_box@birmingham.gov.uk
Ch2m Hill, Avon House, Avonmore Road, London, W14 8TS Tel: (020) 7471 6100 Fax: (020) 7471 6101
Cleansing Service Group Ltd, Botley Road, Hedge End, Southampton, SO30 2HE Tel: (01489) 785856 Fax: (01489) 789821 E-mail: enquiries@csgwasteman.co.uk
Clearway Disposals Ltd, 41 Dobbin Road, Portadown, Craigavon, County Armagh, BT62 4EY Tel: (028) 3833 7333 Fax: (028) 3833 6716 E-mail: info@clearwaypordesign.ffs.uk
Downham Components, Church Lane, Whittington, King's Lynn, Norfolk, PE33 9TG Tel: (01366) 500737 Fax: (01366) 501156
Enba NI Ltd, The Old Mill, Drumaness, Ballynahinch, County Down, BT24 8LS Tel: (028) 9756 1574 Fax: (028) 9756 1576 E-mail: sales@enbani.com
Swiftclean (UK) Ltd, Aviation Way, Southend-On-Sea, SS2 6UN Tel: (01702) 531221 Fax: (01702) 531220 E-mail: info@swiftclean.co.uk
W L Straughan & Son Ltd, Bedlington Lane Farm, Bedlington, Northumberland, NE22 6AA Tel: (01670) 823042 Fax: (01670) 827230 E-mail: enqs@wlstrayghan.co.uk

ENVIRONMENTAL SPILLAGE CONTAINMENT PRODUCTS

▶ Bpi Packaging, Brook Road, Buckhurst Hill, Essex, IG9 5TU Tel: (020) 8504 9151 Fax: (020) 8506 1892 E-mail: salesessex@bpipoly.com
▶ Safestore UK Limited, 1 Parkway Avenue, Sheffield, S9 4WA Tel: 01142 728181 Fax: 01142 728191 E-mail: sales@safestoreuk.co.uk

ENVIRONMENTAL TEST CHAMBER EQUIPMENT

James Technical Services, 3 Talgarth Business Park, Trefecca Road, Talgarth, Brecon, Powys, LD3 0PQ Tel: (01874) 711209 Fax: (01874) 712010E-mail: sales@jts-test-chambers.co.uk

ENVIRONMENTAL TEST CHAMBERS, TEMPERATURE, BENCHTOP

Satalight Videography, Parkside Studio, Gotham Road, East Leake, Loughborough, Leicestershire, LE12 6JG Tel: (01509) 854004 Fax: (01509) 853111 E-mail: sales@satalight.co.uk

ENVIRONMENTAL TEST EQUIPMENT

Palintest Ltd, Kingsway, Team Valley Trading Estate, Gateshead, Tyne & Wear, NE11 0NS Tel: 0191-491 0808 Fax: 0191-482 5372 E-mail: sales@palintest.com

ENVIRONMENTALLY FRIENDLY CLEANING PRODUCTS

St Margarets Mill Retreats, St. Margarets Mill, Caister Road, Acle, Norwich, NR13 3AX Tel: (01493) 752288

ENVIRONMENTALLY FRIENDLY PAPER

Cellande Cleaning Materials, Cellande House, 118 Gristhorpe Road, Birmingham, B29 7SL Tel: 0121-472 2903 Fax: 0121-246 7446 E-mail: e-mail@cellande.co.uk
Fenner Paper Co. Ltd, Unit 15 Orchard Business Centre, Vale Rd, Tonbridge, Kent, TN9 1QF Tel: (01732) 771100 Fax: (01732) 771103 E-mail: info@fennerpaper.co.uk

ENZYMES

Biocatalysts Ltd, Cefn Coed, Nantgarw, Cardiff, CF15 7QQ Tel: (01443) 843712 Fax: (01443) 846500 E-mail: sales@biocats.com
Biozyme Holdings Ltd, Tnit 6 Gilchrist Thomas Estate, Bleanavon, Pontypool, Gwent, NP4 9RL Tel: (01495) 790678 Fax: (01495) 791780 E-mail: sales@biozyme.co.uk
Danisco, Denington Road, Wellingborough, Northamptonshire, NN8 2QJ Tel: (01933) 304200 Fax: (01933) 304224
▶ Enzyme Process UK, 4 Broadgate House, Westlode Street, Spalding, Lincolnshire, PE11 2AF Tel: (01775) 761927 Fax: (01775) 761104 E-mail: enquiries@enzymepro.com
Forum Bioscience Holdings Ltd, 41-51 Brighton Road, Redhill, RH1 6YS Tel: (01737) 773711 Fax: (01737) 770053

EPICYCLIC GEARBOXES

Adan Ltd, Nursery Road Industrial Estate, Boston, Lincolnshire, PE21 7TN Tel: (01205) 311500 Fax: (01205) 358013 E-mail: sales@adanltd.co.uk
Allen Gears, Atlas Works, Station Road, Pershore, Worcestershire, WR10 2BZ Tel: (01386) 552211 Fax: (01386) 554491 E-mail: sales@allengears.com
Bonfiglioli UK Ltd, 3-5 Grosvenor Grange, Woolston, Warrington, WA1 4SF Tel: (01925) 852667 Fax: (01925) 852668 E-mail: sales@bonfiglioliuk.co.uk

EPILATION NEEDLES

Sterex Electrolysis International Ltd, 174 Kings Road, Tyseley, Birmingham, B11 2AP Tel: 0121-708 2404 Fax: 0121-707 0028 E-mail: info@sterex.demon.co.uk

EPOXY PAINTS

Industrial Paint Services S W Ltd, 1 Lyte Building, Wern Trading Estate, Rogerstone, Newport, Gwent, NP10 9FQ Tel: (01633) 897766 Fax: (01633) 897716
▶ Skippers, Manor Lane, Rochester, Kent, ME1 3JN Tel: (01634) 815522 Fax: (01634) 815533

EPOXY POWDER COATING PROCESSORS OR SERVICES

Alw, Tweedale Industrial Estate, Madeley, Telford, Shropshire, TF7 4JR Tel: (01952) 684100 Fax: (01952) 581611 E-mail: bruce@alws.freeserve.co.uk
Atlas Coating Ltd, Unit 15a Hixon Airfield Estate, New Road, Hixon, Stafford, ST18 0PF Tel: (01889) 271002 Fax: (01889) 271178 E-mail: mail@atlascoating.co.uk
Circuit Coatings Ltd, Marlow Street, Walsall, WS2 8AQ Tel: (01922) 635589 Fax: (01922) 638444 E-mail: mail@circuit-coating.co.uk
Coatapart Ltd, 58 Arthur Street, Redditch, Worcestershire, B98 8JY Tel: (01527) 528851 Fax: (01527) 517186
Coventry Powder Coating, Unit 5-7 Bilton Industrial Estate, Humber Avenue, Coventry, CV3 1JL Tel: (024) 7645 4694 Fax: (024) 7645 4476 E-mail: info@cpc.co.uk
Kate Crown Ltd, Trinity Way, West Bromwich, West Midlands, B70 6NU Tel: 0121-500 6348 Fax: 0121-580 0749 E-mail: katecrown@fsmail.net
Darrenpalm Ltd, 33 Highmeres Road, Leicester, LE4 9LZ Tel: 0116-276 9872
Ercon Powder Coating Ltd, Unit 16-17, Spring Vale Business Park, Bilston, West Midlands, WV14 0QL Tel: (01902) 491011 Fax: (01902) 492032
Express Metal Finishers, Manchester Road, Mossley, Ashton-under-Lyne, Lancashire, OL5 9QN Tel: (01457) 837718 Fax: (01457) 835801
Felspar Finishings Ltd, C Phoenix Works, Windsor Road, Redditch, Worcestershire, B97 6DJ Tel: (01527) 585878 Fax: (01527) 63167 E-mail: felsparfinish@aol.com
Powder Coatings Ltd, 215 Tyburn Road, Birmingham, B24 8NB Tel: 0121-250 2145 Fax: 0121-250 2154 E-mail: roger@abbeyland.co.uk
R A Peatey & Sons Ltd, Green Lane, Yeadon, Leeds, LS19 7BY Tel: 0113-250 1046 Fax: 0113-250 7364
Scruse & Crossland Ltd, 2 Wingate Road, Gosport, Hampshire, PO12 4DR Tel: (023) 9250 2403 Fax: (023) 9251 1728 E-mail: sales@scruse.co.uk

EPOXY POWDER COATINGS

C T C & Co. (Essex) Ltd, Benbridge Indust Estate, The Square, Heybridge, Maldon, Essex, CM9 4LT Tel: (01621) 841100 Fax: (01621) 842233 E-mail: sales@ctcandcompany-essex.co.uk
▶ DPC Ltd, Unit 29, Spring Road Industrial Estate, Lanesfield Drive, Wolverhampton, WV4 6UB Tel: (0845) 8380801 Fax: 0121-559 6688 E-mail: sales@custom-finish.com
Ferro (G B) Ltd, Westgate, Aldridge, Walsall, WS9 8YH Tel: (01922) 741300 Fax: (01922) 741327
Thermaset Ltd, Apollo, Lichfield Road Industrial Estate, Tamworth, Staffordshire, B79 7TA Tel: (01827 55777 Fax: (01827 53713

EPOXY PUTTY REPAIR COMPOUNDS

Kalimex Ltd, Unit 3, Plumpton Green Studios, St. Helena Lane, Plumpton Green, Lewes, East Sussex, BN7 3DQ Tel: (01273) 891162 Fax: (01273) 890704 E-mail: enquiries@kalimex.co.uk

EPOXY RESIN COATING PROCESSORS OR SERVICES

Interfax Acuflow Ltd, 2b Reddicap Heath Road, Sutton Coldfield, West Midlands, B75 7DU Tel: 0121-378 2626 Fax: 0121-378 2223 E-mail: sales@acuflow.co.uk

EPOXY RESIN CURING AGENTS

Air Products (Chemicals) P.L.C., Clayton Lane, Clayton, Manchester, M11 4SR Tel: 0161-230 4230 Fax: 0161-223 5488 E-mail: epoxybox@airproducts.com
Alchemie Ltd, Warwick Road, Kineton, Warwick, CV35 0HU Tel: (01926) 640600 Fax: (01926) 641698 E-mail: sales@alchemie.com
Industrial Copolymers Ltd, Iotech House, Miller Street, Preston, PR1 1EA Tel: (01772) 201964 Fax: (01772) 255194 E-mail: info@incorez.com
Kinder Marketing, Unit D Roe Cross Indust Park, Old Road, Mottram, Hyde, Cheshire, SK14 6LG Tel: (01457) 762758 Fax: (01457) 776547

EPOXY RESIN MIXING MACHINES

2KM UK Ltd, 11 Sherwood House, Sherwood Road, Aston Fields Trading Estate, Bromsgrove, Worcestershire, B60 3DR Tel: (01527) 834720 Fax: (01527) 834729 E-mail: sales@2km.co.uk
Interfax Acuflow Ltd, 2b Reddicap Heath Road, Sutton Coldfield, West Midlands, B75 7DU Tel: 0121-378 2626 Fax: 0121-378 2223 E-mail: sales@acuflow.co.uk

EPOXY RESINS

Alton Chemicals, 4 Bollinbarn Drive, Macclesfield, Cheshire, SK10 3DN Tel: (01625) 425694 Fax: (01625) 610405
Benring Ltd, Glebe Tail, Quarnford, Buxton, Derbyshire, SK17 0TG Tel: (01298) 74026 Fax: (01298) 72391
Delta Resin Products Ltd, 77 Torkington Road, Hazel Grove, Stockport, Cheshire, SK7 6NR Tel: 0161-483 4513 Fax: 0161-426 0329 E-mail: info@deltaresins.co.uk
EMS-CHEMIE (UK) Ltd, Darfin House, Priestly Court, Stafford Technology Park, Stafford, ST18 0AR Tel: (01785) 283739 Fax: (01785) 283722 E-mail: welcome@uk.emsgrivory.com
Formulated Resins Ltd, Greg Street, Stockport, Cheshire, SK5 7LY Tel: 0161-480 2121 Fax: 0161-480 4445 E-mail: info@formulatedresins.com
G R P Ltd, Robin Hood Industrial Estate, Alfred St South, Nottingham, NG3 1GE Tel: 0115-924 3244 Fax: 0115-924 3236
Hi Bond Chemicals Ltd, 32 Bryn Street, Ince, Wigan, Lancashire, WN3 4RX Tel: (01942) 615800 Fax: (01942) 615801 E-mail: info@hibond.fsnet.co.uk
Maresco Ltd, 2 The Alcorns, Cambridge Road, Stansted, Essex, CM24 8DF Tel: (01279) 817333 Fax: (01279) 817334
Plastic Technology Service Ltd, Flamstone Street, Bishopstone, Salisbury, SP5 4BZ Tel: (01722) 781088 Fax: (01722) 781071 E-mail: info@ptsuk.com
Resdev Ni Ltd, 4 22 Duncrue Road, Belfast, BT3 9BP Tel: (028) 9077 6882 Fax: (028) 9077 8492 E-mail: info@resindevelopment.com
Sika Ltd, Watchmead, Welwyn Garden City, Hertfordshire, AL7 1BQ Tel: (01707) 394444 Fax: (01707) 329129 E-mail: info@sika.com
Sterling Technology Ltd, Europa Gate, Trafford Park, Manchester, M17 1DU Tel: 0161-848 8411 Fax: 0161-848 0966 E-mail: sales@sterling-tech.com
Techsil Ltd, Unit 30 Bidavon Industrial Estate, Waterloo Road, Bidford-on-Avon, Alcester, Warwickshire, B50 4JN Tel: (01789) 773232 Fax: (01789) 774239 E-mail: sales@techsil.co.uk
Wessex Resins & Adhesives Ltd, Cupernham Lane, Romsey, Hampshire, SO51 7LF Tel: (01794) 521111 Fax: (01870) 7701032 E-mail: info@wessex-resins.com

EPSOM SALTS

Harris Hart & Co. Ltd, Gregge Street Works, Gregge Street, Heywood, Lancashire, OL10 2EJ Tel: (01706) 625355 Fax: (01706) 360570 E-mail: sales@epsom-salts.com

EQUESTRIAN CLOTHING

Bailey Textiles, 9-10 The Warren, East Goscote, Leicester, LE7 3XA Tel: 0116-269 4694 Fax: 0116-269 3956 E-mail: sales@baileysdirect.plus.com
Bridle Way At Gauntleys, Mill House, Laneham Road, Dunham-on-Trent, Newark, Nottinghamshire, NG22 0UW Tel: (01777) 228040 Fax: (01777) 228977
Colne Saddlery, The Barn, Tewkesbury Road, Norton, Gloucester, GL2 9LH Tel: (01452) 731456 Fax: (01452) 731456 E-mail: sales@colnesaddlery.co.uk
▶ Equestrian Originals, 57 Severn Way, Bletchley, Milton Keynes, MK3 7QG Tel: (01908) 647555 E-mail: info@equestrian-originals.co.uk
▶ Falmouth Horsewise, 9 West End Industrial Estate, West End, Penryn, Cornwall, TR10 8RT Tel: (01326) 378828 Fax: (01326) 378828 E-mail: info@falmouthhorsewise.co.uk

EQUESTRIAN CLOTHING – *continued*

Hoof Aloof, 29 Oakwood Drive, Ravenshead, Nottingham, NG15 9DP Tel: (01623) 795628 Fax: (01623) 795628 E-mail: sales@hoofaloof.co.uk
Jonathan Dean Textiles Ltd, The Old Coach House, Wharncliffe Road, Loughborough, Leicestershire, LE11 1SN Tel: (01509) 235251 Fax: (01509) 611121 E-mail: jonathan.dean@yahoo.co.uk
▶ Polly Products, Home Farm Barn, Winkburn, Newark, Nottinghamshire, NG22 8PQ Tel: (01636) 636135 Fax: (01636) 636643 E-mail: sales@pollyproducts.co.uk
B.S. Suthi & Brothers Ltd, Unit H1, 80 Rolfe Street, Smethwick, West Midlands, B66 2AR Tel: 0121-558 2420 Fax: 0121-555 5319 E-mail: info@bsssuthi.com
J. Wood & Son Ltd, Kirkby Mills Industrial Estate, Kirby Mills, Kirkbymoorside, York, YO62 6NL Tel: (01751) 433434 Fax: (01751) 433094 E-mail: sales@johnwoods.co.uk

EQUESTRIAN EQUIPMENT

Abbey Saddlery Ltd, Camden Street, Walsall, WS4 2AX Tel: (01565) 650343 Fax: (01565) 633825
▶ Acre House Equestrian, 2 Spencer Trading Estate, Rhyl Road, Denbigh, Clwyd, LL16 5TQ Tel: (01745) 816628 Fax: (01745) 816628
Aerborn Equestrian Ltd, 198 Sneinton Dale, Nottingham, NG2 4HJ Tel: 0115-941 4040 Fax: 0115-948 3273 E-mail: sales@aerborn.co.uk
B Jenkinson & Sons, 5 Wellington Road East, Dewsbury, West Yorkshire, WF13 1HF Tel: (01924) 454681 Fax: (01924) 458696 E-mail: sales@elico.co.uk
Rose Bank Stores & Saddlery, Middle Lane, Kings Norton, Birmingham, B38 0DX Tel: (01564) 822112 Fax: (01564) 822112
Bob Langrish, The Old Court House, High Street, Bisley, Stroud, Gloucestershire, GL6 7AA Tel: (01452) 770140 Fax: (01452) 770146
Bridle Way At Gauntleys, Mill House, Laneham Road, Dunham-on-Trent, Newark, Nottinghamshire, NG22 0UW Tel: (01777) 228040 Fax: (01777) 228977
▶ Bridoon, Heywood Equestrian Centre, Westbury, Wiltshire, BA13 4LP Tel: (01985) 848485
Buxactic Ltd, Sedgwick Lane, Horsham, West Sussex, RH13 6QE Tel: (01403) 218880 Fax: (01403) 274111 E-mail: chris@buxatic.co.uk
Calcutt & Sons Ltd, Bullington Lane, Sutton Scotney, Winchester, Hampshire, SO21 3RA Tel: (01962) 760210 Fax: (01962) 760702 E-mail: calcutts@msn.com
Cannon & Reading Ltd, A 9 Oakendene Industrial Estate, Bolney Road, Cowfold, Horsham, West Sussex, RH13 8AZ Tel: (01403) 865947 Fax: (01403) 865950
Countryside Fencing, Capel Grove, Capel St. Mary, Ipswich, IP9 2JS Tel: (01473) 314230 Fax: (01473) 314052 E-mail: sales@countryside-gates.co.uk
Crocket Equestrian & Outdoor, 3 Old Bridge Road, Ayr, KA8 9SX Tel: (01292) 286377 Fax: (01292) 610444
Deboiz Equestrian Supplies, Roman Castle Barn, Pickhill, Thirsk, North Yorkshire, YO7 4JR Tel: (01845) 567840 Fax: (01845) 567840 E-mail: sales@deboiz.com
Designer Browbands, Great Dunham, King's Lynn, Norfolk, PE32 2FE Tel: (01328) 700808 Fax: (01328) 700505 E-mail: sales@seignewrbrowbands.co.uk
Earlswood Supplies, Thatchems Farm, Williamscot, Banbury, Oxfordshire, OX16 3JR Tel: (01295) 758734 Fax: (01295) 758011 E-mail: sales@earlswoodsupplies.com
Eclipse, Long Rock, Penzance, Cornwall, TR20 8LD Tel: (01736) 719170 Fax: (01736) 710872
Efi Ltd, Little Park Farm, Wootton Bassett, Swindon, SN4 7QW Tel: (01793) 852185 Fax: (01793) 848580 E-mail: sales@jumpershorseline.com
Elizabeth Greenwood Equestrian Products Ltd, Unit 1-3 Stoney Spring Mill, Stoney Spring, Luddendenfoot, Halifax, West Yorkshire, HX2 6HP Tel: (01422) 884866 Fax: (01422) 885796
Jack Ellis, Marshall House, West Street, Glenfield, Leicester, LE3 8DT Tel: 0116-232 0022 Fax: 0116-232 0032 E-mail: admin@jackellis.co.uk
▶ Equicentric Ltd, Tower Road, Little Downham, Ely, Cambridgeshire, CB6 2TD Tel: (01353) 699909 Fax: (01353) 699910 E-mail: sales@equicentric.com
Equicraft, 42 Rodney Road, Backwell, Bristol, BS48 3HW Tel: (01275) 463933 Fax: (01275) 794414
Equifor, Barton House, Oake, Taunton, Somerset, TA4 1DR Tel: (01823) 400123 Fax: (01823) 400126
▶ Equine, Hawes Hill Court, Drift Road, Winkfield, Windsor, Berks, SL4 4QQ Tel: (01344) 891695
Equine Affairs, Orchard Close, Gravenhurst, Bedford, MK45 4JF Tel: (01462) 713849 Fax: (01462) 713848
▶ Falmouth Horsewise, 9 West End Industrial Estate, West End, Penryn, Cornwall, TR10 8RT Tel: (01326) 378828 Fax: (01326) 378828 E-mail: info@falmouthhorsewise.co.uk
Farm & Stable Supplies, Sutton Court Farm, Sutton Lane, Slough, SL3 8AR Tel: (01753) 595022 Fax: (01753) 591395
Fieldguard Ltd, Horsham Road, Cranleigh, Surrey, GU6 8EH Tel: (01483) 275182 Fax: (01483) 275341
Fieldhouse Riding Equipment Ltd, Green Lane, Birchills, Walsall, WS2 8LE Tel: (01922) 638094 Fax: (01922) 622921 E-mail: sales@fieldhouse.co.uk
Fine English Bridals, Unit 2 Mayfield Workshops, 19 Wednesbury Rd, Walsall, WS1 3RU Tel: 01922 722033
Fyna Lite, Wixford Lodge Farm, Georges Elm Lane, Bidford-on-Avon, Alcester, Warwickshire, B50 4JT Tel: (01789) 773320 Fax: (01789) 490326 E-mail: sales@fynalite.co.uk
▶ Galopeur Equestrian Supplies Ltd, Whitebridge Lane, Stone, Staffordshire, ST15 8LQ Tel: (01785) 816969
George Schumacher, Unit 1 R A C Estate, Parks Road, Faringdon, Oxfordshire, SN7 8LA Tel: (01367) 244697 Fax: (01367) 242819
Griffin Nuu Med, Pipers Farm, Berhill, Ashcott, Bridgwater, Somerset, TA7 9QN Tel: (01458) 210324 Fax: (01458) 210396 E-mail: info@numnah.co.uk
▶ H Zone Clothing, Unit 15 Ladford Covert Industrial Park, Seighford, Stafford, ST18 9QL Tel: (01785) 282821 Fax: (01785) 282822 E-mail: info@hzoneuk.com
▶ Horse Box, 3 Shifnal Shopping Centre, Bradford Street, Shifnal, Shropshire, TF11 8AU Tel: (01952) 460976 E-mail: beckyhorsebox@yahoo.co.uk
▶ James Howard, Carrs Industrial Estate, Commerce Street, Haslingden, Rossendale, Lancashire, BB4 5JT Tel: (01706) 833511 Fax: (01706) 833550 E-mail: sales@james-howard.co.uk
Hows Racesafe, 9 Carlton Road, Wilbarston, Market Harborough, Leicestershire, LE16 8QD Tel: (01536) 771051 Fax: (01536) 779144
▶ J S W & Son (Coachbuilders), Northallerton Business Park, Thurston Rd, Northallerton, North Yorkshire, DL6 2NA Tel: (01609) 772449 Fax: (01609) 777995 E-mail: info@jswhorseboxes.co.uk
▶ KingswoodSaddlery.co.uk, Barleycorn Cottage, Babylon Lane, Lower Kingswood, Tadworth, Surrey, KT20 6XD Tel: (01737) 249121 Fax: (01737) 249121 E-mail: sales@kingswoodsaddlery.co.uk
▶ Mobile Racing & Equestrian Supplies, Nortons Piece, Bristol Road, Hardwicke, Gloucester, GL2 4RF Tel: (01452) 886398 E-mail: richardwardle@btinternet.com
Modern Saddlery Ltd, Leamore Lane, Walsall, WS2 7NT Tel: (01922) 476166 Fax: (01922) 497958 E-mail: enquries@modernsaddlery.com
Nu Direct, Knowle Fields Industrial Estate, Alcester Road, Inkberrow, Worcester, WR7 4HR Tel: (01386) 793339 Fax: (01386) 792030 E-mail: sales@jump4joy.co.uk
▶ Overland Marketing Ltd, The Barn, Parsonage Farm Lane, Woodditton, Newmarket, Suffolk, CB8 9RZ Tel: (01638) 730700 Fax: (01638) 730200
Plas Equestrian, Plas Y Mista Farm, Rhydargaeau Road, Rhydargaeau, Carmarthen, Dyfed, SA32 7JJ Tel: (01267) 253251 Fax: (01267) 253251 E-mail: sales@plasequestrian.co.uk
▶ Polly Products, Home Farm Barn, Winkburn, Newark, Nottinghamshire, NG22 8PQ Tel: (01636) 636135 Fax: (01636) 636643 E-mail: sales@pollyproducts.co.uk
R & R Country, Hull Road, Hemingbrough, Selby, North Yorkshire, YO8 6QJ Tel: (01757) 638555 Fax: (01757) 630770 E-mail: randrcountry@btconnect.com
▶ Riders, Longlands Lane, Brodsworth, Doncaster, South Yorkshire, DN5 7XB Tel: (01302) 722255 Fax: (01302) 722255 E-mail: info@riders-equestrian.co.uk
S E Gear Ltd, 19 Wenhill Heights, Calne, Wilts, SN11 0JZ Tel: 01249 811000 Fax: 01249 811000
Stanneylands Livery, Stanneylands Road, Wilmslow, Cheshire, SK9 4ER Tel: (01625) 533250
Stockfarm Equestrian Supplies, 38 Upton Lane, Upton, Chester, CH2 1EE Tel: (0800) 0899020
▶ Stoney Brook, The Maltings, Main Road, Narborough, King's Lynn, Norfolk, PE32 1TE Tel: (01760) 339469 Fax: (0871) 4310456 E-mail: rachael@stoneybrook.co.uk
▶ T Frost (Bawtry), Home Farm Barn, Winkburn, Newark, Nottinghamshire, NG22 8PQ Tel: (01636) 636981 Fax: (01636) 636643 E-mail: sales@tfrost.co.uk
▶ Tack Rack, Unit 17 Midland Mills, Station Road, Cross Hills, Keighley, West Yorkshire, BD20 7DT Tel: (01535) 631100 Fax: (01535) 631100
Westgate Group Ltd, Newchurch, Romney Marsh, Kent, TN29 0DZ Tel: (01303) 872277 Fax: (01303) 874801E-mail: sales@wefi.co.uk
Whitakers Equestrian Services Ltd, 3 Hikers Way, Drakes Drive, Long Crendon, Aylesbury, Buckinghamshire, HP18 9RW Tel: (01844) 202151 Fax: (01844) 202152 E-mail: sales@polyjumps.com

EQUESTRIAN EQUIPMENT CATALOGUES

▶ Wentworth Equine Travel - Self Drive Horseboxes, Elm Villas, Crazies Hill, Wargrave, RG10 8LU Tel: 07946 451629 E-mail: sales@wentworthequinetravel.co.uk

EQUIPMENT PROTECTION ALARM SYSTEMS

Concept Smoke Screens, North End, Swineshead, Swineshead, Boston, Lincolnshire, PE20 3LR Tel: (01205) 821111 Fax: (01205) 820316 E-mail: info@smoke-screen.co.uk

EQUIPMENT RELIABILITY TESTING

▶ Reliability Plus, 5 High Street, South Woodchester, Stroud, Gloucestershire, GL5 5EL Tel: 01453 878540 Fax: 01453 878595 E-mail: bob.page@environmental.org.uk

ERBIUM DOPED FIBRES

▶ Optosci Ltd, Engineering Application Centre, 141 St James Road, Glasgow, G4 0LT Tel: 0141-552 7020 Fax: 0141-552 3886

ERGONOMIC ASSEMBLY TOOLING

D S W Engineering Co. Ltd, 6 Chester Hall Lane, Basildon, Essex, SS14 3BG Tel: (01268) 523185 Fax: (01268) 534325 E-mail: admin@dsw.biz

ERGONOMICS CONSULTANTS

▶ ACS Ergonomics, 1-2 Redbrick Cottages, Main Street, Southwick, Peterborough, PE8 5BL Tel: 01832 272958
Aquarius Back Care, The Old Dairy, Broom Hill, Bristol, BS16 1DN Tel: 0117-965 8555 Fax: 0117-965 8444 E-mail: info@backcare.co.uk
Ergonomos Ltd, 11 St. Johns Road, Richmond, Surrey, TW9 2PE Tel: (020) 8940 7939 Fax: (020) 8940 7939 E-mail: info@ergonomos.co.uk

EROSION CONTROL SERVICES

A G A Group, Crawfold Farm, Balls Cross, Petworth, West Sussex, GU28 9JT Tel: (01403) 820999 Fax: (01403) 820011 E-mail: info@agagroup.org.uk
RMB Hydroseeding, Lower Wick Farm, Lower Wick, Dursley, Gloucestershire, GL11 6DD Tel: (01453) 511365 Fax: (01453) 511364 E-mail: info@hydroseeding.co.uk

ESCALATOR INSTALLATION OR SERVICING

Thyssenkrupp Elevator UK Ltd, Traffic Street, Nottingham, NG2 1NF Tel: 0115-986 8213 Fax: 0115-986 1549
Thyssenkrupp Elevator UK Ltd, 183-185 Lower Richmond Road, Richmond, Surrey, TW9 4LN Tel: (020) 8487 1445 Fax: (020) 8487 9494 E-mail: twickenham.office@tke-uk-thyssenkrupp.com

ESCALATORS

▶ Britain China Trading Co. Ltd, Cinnabar Wharf, East Block, 26 Wapping High Street, London, E1W 1NG Tel: (020) 7680 8032 Fax: (020) 7680 8001 E-mail: mars@buj.co.uk
▶ Northern Istallations Ltd, Lumbrook Mills, Westercroft Lane, Halifax, West Yorkshire, HX3 7TY Tel: (01422) 202777 Fax: (01422) 202888 E-mail: info@northerninstallations.co.uk
Otis Ltd, 187 Twyford Abbey Road, London, NW10 7DG Tel: (020) 8955 3000 Fax: (020) 8955 3001
Thyssen Lifts & Esculators Ltd, 4Th Floor Maple House, High Street, Potters Bar, Hertfordshire, EN6 5BS Tel: (01707) 672000 Fax: (01707) 672011

ESPRESSO MACHINE MAINTENANCE

▶ Espressocare, 12 Gordon Street, Colne, Lancashire, BB8 0NE Tel: 01282 710651 Fax: 01282 710651 E-mail: sales@espressocare.co.uk

ESSENTIAL OIL DISTILLERS OR PRODUCERS

Adrian Essential Oils Ltd, 1 Essence House, Crabtree Road, Thorpe Industrial Estate, Egham, Surrey, TW20 8RN Tel: (01784) 485600 Fax: (01784) 472255 E-mail: uksales@adrian.fr
Carvansons LLP, Hollins Vale Works, Hollins Village, Bury, Lancashire, BL9 8QG Tel: 0161-766 3768 Fax: 0161-767 9437 E-mail: enquiries@carvansons.demon.co.uk
Castle Care Cosmetics Ltd, Invincible Road, Farnborough, Hampshire, GU14 7QP Tel: (01252) 548887 Fax: (01252) 548880 E-mail: sales@castlecare.co.uk
F D Copeland & Sons Ltd, 5 Westfield Street, London, SE18 5TL Tel: (020) 8854 8101 Fax: (020) 8854 1077 E-mail: sales@copelandoil.co.uk
Frutarom UK Ltd, Belasis Avenue, Billingham, Cleveland, TS23 1LQ Tel: (01642) 379900 Fax: (01642) 379901 E-mail: sales@frutarom.com
Frutarom UK Ltd, 3 Kingsthorne Park, Henson Way, Telford Way Industrial Estate, Kettering, Northamptonshire, NN16 8PX Tel: (01536) 532300 Fax: (01536) 532301 E-mail: sales@frutarom.co.uk
Givaudan UK Ltd, Chippenham Drive, Kingston, Milton Keynes, MK10 0AE Tel: (01908) 242424 Fax: (01908) 282232
F. Gutkind & Co. Ltd, Suite F8, Oxford Centre For Innovation, Mill Street, Oxford, OX2 0JX Tel: (01865) 812031 Fax: (01865) 249261 E-mail: info@fgutkind.com
Lionel Hitchen (Essential Oils) Ltd, Gravel Lane, Barton Stacey, Winchester, Hampshire, SO21 3RQ Tel: (01962) 760815 Fax: (01962) 760072 E-mail: info@lhn.co.uk
J C Buck Ltd, 8 The Stafford Estate, Hillman Close, Hornchurch, Essex, RM11 2SJ Tel: (01708) 437099 Fax: (01708) 456761 E-mail: sales@jcbuck.co.uk
N. & G. Rich, 2 Coval Gardens, London, SW14 7DG Tel: (020) 8878 2976 Fax: (020) 8392 8653
S R S Aromatics Ltd, Boldero Road, Moreton Hall Industrial Estate, Bury St. Edmunds, Suffolk, IP32 7BS Tel: (01284) 760818 Fax: (01284) 750224
Ungerer Ltd, Sealand Road, Chester, CH1 4LP Tel: (01244) 371711 Fax: (01244) 380185 E-mail: ungereruk@ungerer.co.uk
Wilson & Mansfield Ltd, Headley House, Headley Road, Grayshott, Surrey, GU26 6TU Tel: (01428) 601140 Fax: (01428) 607851 E-mail: david@wmjuice.co.uk

ESSENTIAL OILS, NATURAL

▶ Scent-Ible Solutions, 10 Sorrento Grove, Stoke-on-Trent, ST3 5XZ Tel: (01782) 594862 Fax: (01782) 599189 E-mail: Helen@scentsiblesolutions.co.uk

ESTATE AGENCY TRAINING

Endaim, 3rd Floor Phoenix House, Christopher Martin Road, Basildon, Essex, SS14 3HG Tel: (01268) 270022 Fax: (01268) 285050 E-mail: sandie.lorkins@headoffice.endaim.com

ESTATE AGENT APPLICATION SERVICE PROVIDERS (ASP)

▶ Daniel Sims, 2 Cheriton High Street, Folkestone, Kent, CT19 4ER Tel: (01303) 277211 Fax: (01303) 270370 E-mail: sales@danielsims.co.uk
▶ dream4avilla, 11 Underwood Road, Southampton, SO16 7BZ Tel: (023) 8058 1520 Fax: (023) 8058 1520 E-mail: info@dream4avilla.com
▶ Goldschmidt & Howland, 47 Maida Vale, London, W9 1SH Tel: (020) 7289 6633 Fax: (020) 7289 6646 E-mail: lvs@g-h.co.uk
▶ My Home Bulgaria Ltd, 129 Wellington Road, London, london, E6 6EB Tel: (020) 8552 5920 Fax: (0870) 7622839 E-mail: zaur@pochta.ws
▶ Romanian Properties Ltd, 6 Hearne Court, Chalfont St. Giles, Buckinghamshire, HP8 4PW Tel: (07879) 604710
▶ Secondhome Ltd, 2 Beech Lane, Spofforth, Harrogate, North Yorkshire, HG3 1AN Tel: 01423 590574 Fax: 01423 590574 E-mail: peter.shackleton@secondhomeagency.com
▶ Sell My House Now, 20 Fairfield Avenue, Peverell, Plymouth, PL2 3QF Tel: 0800 0272393 E-mail: enquiries@sellmyhousenow.co.uk
▶ Turkey Property Search, 11 St. Davids Crescent, Penarth, South Glamorgan, CF64 3LZ Tel: (029) 2071 1898 E-mail: s.burston1@ntlworld.com
▶ Wilkinson Estates, 1 High Street, Maidenhead, Berkshire, SL6 1JN Tel: (01628) 777075 Fax: (01628) 788007 E-mail: post@wilkinsons.co.uk

ESTATE AGENT CLEANING SERVICES

Anthony Jackson, Unit C2 Sheaf Bank Business Park, Prospect Road, Heeley, Sheffield, S2 3EN Tel: 0114-258 9889 Fax: 0114-258 5255 E-mail: info@jacksoncleaning.com
▶ Domestic Perfection, 4 Speldhurst Road, Tunbridge Wells, Kent, TN4 0DP Tel: (07743) 933171 E-mail: d.perfection@btinternet.com

ESTATE AGENT CLEANING SERVICES – *continued*

▶ Magic Bean & Cow Ltd., 93-97 Gowe Street, London, WC1E 6AD Tel: 07841 841319 Fax: 0207 9169686 E-mail: info@magicbeanandcow.co.uk

▶ Party Supplies, North Kelsey Road, Caistor, Market Rasen, Lincolnshire, LN7 6SF Tel: (01472) 851430 E-mail: info@partysupplies-for-u.co.uk

▶ Romanian Properties Ltd, 6 Hearne Court, Chalfont St. Giles, Buckinghamshire, HP8 4PW Tel: (07879) 604710

▶ Surf4apropety, Leeds, LS17 1BX Tel: 0113-266 9639 Fax: 0113-266 9639 E-mail: info@surf4aproperty.com

▶ WILSON CLEANING SERVICES, 20 RISHWORTH CLOSE, Stockport, Cheshire, SK2 5NG Tel: 0161 483 0571

ESTATE AGENT OR AGENCY SOFTWARE

▶ Breeze Media Ltd, Gleann Cottage, 1 The Terrace, Glenlomond, Kinross, KY13 9HF Tel: (01592) 840640 E-mail: info@breezemedia.co.uk

ESTATE AGENTS, OVERSEAS

▶ Amazing Spanish Villas, 14 Denham Road, Sheffield, S11 8NE Tel: 0114 2756784

▶ TeamAbroad Avon, 1 The Cloisters, Church Lane, Glastonbury, Somerset, BA6 9NL Tel: (01458) 834195 E-mail: info@TeamAbroad-Avon.com

ETCHING, PRINTING TRADE, *See Process Engravers etc*

ETHERNET INPUT OUTPUT (IO) SYSTEMS

System Devices Ltd Automation Di, 17 Beeston Court, Stuart Road, Manor Park, Runcorn, Cheshire, WA7 1SS Tel: (01928) 571977 Fax: (01928) 571988 E-mail: sales@systemdevices.co.uk

ETHYL SILICATES

Morrison Hydraulics Ltd, 331-337 Derby Road, Bootle, Merseyside, L20 8LQ Tel: 0151-933 0044 Fax: 0151-944 1302 E-mail: chemicals@morrisonsgrp.co.uk

ETHYLENE PROPYLENE DIENE MONOMER (EPDM) EXTRUSIONS

Fabprene Ltd, Broadway, Globe Lane Industrial Estate, Dukinfield, Cheshire, SK16 4UU Tel: 0161-342 6902 Fax: 0161-342 6903 E-mail: sales@fabprene.co.uk

ETHYLENE PROPYLENE DIENE MONOMER (EPDM) POND LINERS

▶ Flexible Lining Products Ltd, Vantage Point Business Village, Mitcheldean, Gloucestershire, GL17 0DD Tel: (0845) 2262478 Fax: (0845) 2269697 E-mail: info@flexibleliningproducts.co.uk

ETHYLENE PROPYLENE DIENE MONOMER (EPDM) SPONGE RUBBER SHEETING

Atlantic Rubber & Plastic Ltd, 6 St. Annes Road, Willenhall, West Midlands, WV13 1ED Tel: (01902) 634400 Fax: 01902 634413 E-mail: hintons@blueyonder.co.uk

ETHYLENE VINYL ACETATE (EVA) GRADE POLYETHYLENE (PE)

Horn UK Ltd, Townfoot Industrial Estate, Brampton, Cumbria, CA8 1SW Tel: (01697) 741080 Fax: (01697) 741022 E-mail: eng@cumbrian.co.uk

EVACUATION CHAIRS

Enable Access Disabled Access Equipement, 16 Plantagenet Road, Barnet, Hertfordshire, EN5 5JG Tel: (020) 8275 0375 Fax: (020) 8449 0326

EVAPORATOR PROCESS EQUIPMENT

H T G Trading Ltd, Hillview, Church Road, Otley, Ipswich, IP6 9NP Tel: (01473) 890522 Fax: (01473) 890758 E-mail: info@hubbard.co.uk

EVENING WEAR, LADIES

▶ Eshenda Moda Ltd, Unit 23, Cygnus Business Centre,, Dalmeyer Road, London, NW10 2XA Tel: (020) 8200 3560 Fax: (020) 8200 6623 E-mail: shinyi_j@yahoo.co.uk

▶ Funktees, 51 Edgeworth, Yate, Bristol, BS37 8YN Tel: (0778) 6653999 E-mail: funktees@hotmail.co.uk

▶ Princess Stores, Latteridge House, Latteridge Green, Bristol, BS37 9TS Tel: 0870 1995481 E-mail: sales@princessstores.co.uk

EVENT MANAGEMENT

▶ The Angels Communcations Limited, The Round Foundry Media Centre, Foundry Street, Leeds, LS11 5QP Tel: 0870 4202442 Fax: 0870 4202444 E-mail: info@the-angels.com

▶ Crossan Communications, 37 Bernard Street, Edinburgh, EH6 6SH Tel: 0131-553 1872 Fax: 0131-555 4255 E-mail: info@crossancom.co.uk

Elite Promotions Personnel Ltd, 6 Park Lane, Whitefield, Manchester, M45 7PB Tel: 0161-272 1400 Fax: 0161-272 1401 E-mail: sales@elitepromo.co.uk

▶ Event Energy, Russet Knowle, Wild Duck Lane, Cleasby, Darlington, County Durham, DL2 2RB Tel: (01325) 467684

▶ Fairy Management, 38 Mount Pleasant, Bryntirion, Bridgend, CF31 4EF Tel: (08701) 464871E-mail: sarah@fairymanagement.co.uk

▶ Lightning Connection.biz, 35 Underbank Lane, Moulton, Northampton, NN3 7HH Tel: (0776) 2771290 E-mail: info@lightningconnection.biz

▶ Music For London, 122 Wigmore Street, London, W1U 3RX Tel: (0845) 2262971 Fax: (0845) 2262972 E-mail: info@musicforlondon.co.uk

▶ Occasions Caterers Ltd, Unit 22 Bow Triangle Business, Centre Eleanor Street, London, E3 4UR Tel: (020) 8980 2770

▶ River Communications, 9 The Terrace, Woodford Green, Essex, IG8 0XS Tel: (020) 8504 4009 Fax: (020) 8504 4454 E-mail: info@river-communications.com

▶ Talk Events UK Ltd, Unit 6, 229 Torrington Avenue, Coventry, CV4 9HN Tel: (024) 7646 2444 Fax: (0845) 6126013 E-mail: info@talkevents.com

▶ Top Banana Team Ltd, The Old Castle, Farleigh Hungerford, Bath, BA2 7RW Tel: (01225) 752445 E-mail: info@topbananateam.com

▶ Unicorn Events Ltd, Unicorn House, 5 Russell Grove, Westbury Park, Bristol, BS6 7UD Tel: 0117-942 9151 Fax: (0845) 2805151 E-mail: info@unicornevents.com

▶ Venue Reservations, 13 Bishopsgate, London, EC2N 3BA Tel: (020) 7334 3922 Fax: (020) 7334 3911 E-mail: enquiries@venuereservations.co.uk

▶ Weddings Abroad, 15 High Street, Chasetown, Burntwood, Staffordshire, WS7 3XE Tel: (01543) 686884 Fax: 01543 686884 E-mail: helen@perfect-weddings.net

EVENT ORGANISING OR CONSULTANCY

A Touch Of Taste, Unit 15 Monument Business Park, Warpsgrove Lane, Chalgrove, Oxford, OX44 7RW Tel: (01865) 400968 Fax: (01865) 400970 E-mail: admin@atouchoftaste.co.uk

Airflare Bouncy Castle Hire, Quarry Cottage, 94 Worlebury Hill Road, Weston-super-Mare, Avon, BS22 9TG Tel: (01934) 414286 Fax: (01934) 414286

▶ Arrange It Lifestyle Management, 23 Redstart Avenue, Kidderminster, Worcestershire, DY10 4JR Tel: 01562 631682 E-mail: annehope@arrangeitlifestylemanagement.co.uk

▶ At Your Service, Clarendon House, 52 Cornmarket Street, Oxford, OX1 3HJ Tel: (0870) 4130424 Fax: (0870) 4130425 E-mail: oxford@ays.co.uk

B & B Event Hire, Lyon Road, Walton-on-Thames, Surrey, KT12 3PU Tel: (01932) 253253 Fax: (01932) 254976

Big Fun Casino Co., Crackley Lane, Kenilworth, Warwickshire, CV8 2JT Tel: (01926) 863090 Fax: (01926) 511533 E-mail: sales@bigindoorgames.co.uk

Brocket Hall Ltd, Brocket Hall, Brocket Park, Lemsford, Welwyn Garden City, Hertfordshire, AL8 7XG Tel: (01707) 335241 Fax: (01707) 375166 E-mail: mail@brocket-hall.co.uk

Bryce Curdy Productions, PO Box 400, Ayr, KA7 4NB Tel: (01292) 443398 Fax: (01292) 443398 E-mail: mail@bryce-curdy.com

Castle Ashby House, Castle Ashby, Northampton, NN7 1LQ Tel: (01604) 696696 Fax: (01604) 696516 E-mail: admin@castleashby.co.uk

Central Display Production, B Gresham Way Industrial Estate, Gresham Way, London, SW19 8ED Tel: (020) 8944 5156 Fax: (020) 8944 5950 E-mail: dudley@centraldisplay.com

Complete Support Group Ltd, The Garden House, Castle Bromwich, Chester Road, Birmingham, B36 9DE Tel: 0121-776 7766 Fax: 0121-776 7666 E-mail: enquiries@completesupport.co.uk

Conference Contacts Ltd, 16a College Avenue, Maidenhead, Berkshire, SL6 6AX Tel: (01628) 773300 Fax: (01628) 621033 E-mail: enquiries@c-contacts.com

Consilium, The Old Stables, Onehouse Hall, Lower Road, Onehouse, Stowmarket, Suffolk, IP14 3BY Tel: (01449) 676435 Fax: (01449) 676436 E-mail: sb@exclusiveheritagevenues.co.uk

Dial Marketing Ltd, 68 Dial Hill Road, Clevedon, Avon, BS21 7EW Tel: (01275) 875876 Fax: (01275) 340899 E-mail: dialmarketing@btconnect.com

D'Vision Ltd, Market Place, Chipping Norton, Oxfordshire, OX7 5NA Tel: (01608) 648948 Fax: (01608) 648949 E-mail: info@d-vision.co.uk

▶ Edinburgh Event Production Services, 5/6 Broughton Place Lane, Edinburgh, EH1 3RS Tel: 0131-558 3824 E-mail: eeps@warpro.co.uk

Expotel Barton Ltd, Kingsgate House, Kingsgate Place, London, NW6 4TA Tel: (020) 7328 9841 Fax: (020) 7328 8021 E-mail: lores@expotel.com

Expotel Hotel Reservations Ltd, Albert Chambers, 13 Bath Street, Glasgow, G2 1HY Tel: 0141-331 1771 Fax: 0141-331 1117 E-mail: events@expotel.co.uk

Expotel Hotel Reservations Ltd, Leeds Bridge House, Hunslet Road, Leeds, LS10 1JN Tel: 0113-242 3434 Fax: 0113-234 2781 E-mail: info@expotel.co.uk

Forest Fireworks, 97-99 Shipston Road, Stratford-upon-Avon, Warwickshire, CV37 7LW Tel: (01789) 295563 Fax: (01789) 295563

H2 Organisation, Hop Farm Country Park, Maidstone Road, Paddock Wood, Tonbridge, Kent, TN12 6PY Tel: (01622) 872123 E-mail: sales@h2organisation.co.uk

Heart Of England Promotions, Old Hall, Wallhill Road, Fillongley, Coventry, CV7 8DX Tel: (01676) 540333 Fax: (01676) 540365 E-mail: sales@heartofengland.co.uk

Hopkinson White, 46 Brook Street, Aston Clinton, Aylesbury, Buckinghamshire, HP22 5ES Tel: (01296) 631898 Fax: (01296) 630321 E-mail: info@hopkinson-white.co.uk

Impress Event Management Ltd, The Annex, 8 Kelsey Way, Beckenham, Kent, BR3 3LL Tel: (020) 8663 6647 Fax: (020) 8663 3195 E-mail: matthew@impressevents.co.uk

▶ IN GEAR EVENT SUPPORT, Unit 7 Coppen Road, Dagenham, Essex, RM8 1HJ Tel: 020 8593 0550 Fax: 020 8593 0552 E-mail: Glenn@ingearevents.fsbusiness.co.uk

KDM Events Ltd, Crowcrofts Road, Barlaston, Stoke-on-Trent, ST12 9BA Tel: (01782) 646300 Fax: (01782) 646060 E-mail: info@kdmevents.co.uk

Mimicks Face Painting, 5 Corinthian Road, Chandler's Ford, Eastleigh, Hampshire, SO53 2BA Tel: (023) 8025 5894 E-mail: mimicks@ntlworld.com

Mithril Racing Ltd, Goodwood Airfield, Goodwood, Chichester, West Sussex, PO18 0PH Tel: (01243) 528815 Fax: (01243) 771522 E-mail: chris@mithril.co.uk

Mr Bounce, Y-Jays, London Rd, Flimwell, Wadhurst, E. Sussex, TN5 7PL Tel: (01892) 540324 Fax: (01580) 879707

Olympia Conference Centre, Hammersmith Road, Kensington, London, W14 8UX Tel: (020) 7370 8532 Fax: (020) 7370 8144 E-mail: conferences@eco.co.uk

Paramount Marine Hotel, 8 Crosbie Road, Troon, Ayrshire, KA10 6HE Tel: (01292) 314444 Fax: (01292) 316922 E-mail: marine@paramount-hotels.co.uk

Payne & Gunter Ltd, Twickenham Stadium, Rugby Road, Twickenham, TW1 1DS Tel: (020) 8744 9997 Fax: (020) 8831 7990 E-mail: twickenhamexperience@rfu.com

Phoenix Fireworks Ltd, The Garth, Hill Park Farm, Wrotham Hill Road, Wrotham, Sevenoaks, Kent, TN15 7PX Tel: (0800) 781 1747 Fax: (01732) 823916 E-mail: info@phoenixfireworks.co.uk

Regency Banqueting Suite, 113 Bruce Grove, London, N17 6UR Tel: (020) 8885 2490 Fax: (020) 8885 1739 E-mail: enquiries@regencybanqueting.com

Shropshire & West Midlands Agricultural Society, Berwick Road, Shrewsbury, SY1 2PF Tel: (01743) 289831 Fax: (01743) 289920 E-mail: mail@west-mid-show.org.uk

Silver Leaf Productions, 253 Lavender Hill, London, SW11 1JW Tel: (020) 7924 6544 Fax: (020) 7801 3105 E-mail: sales@silverleafp.co.uk

T B A P.L.C., 174-178 North Gower Street, London, NW1 2NB Tel: (020) 7380 0953 Fax: (020) 7387 9004 E-mail: gen@tbaplc.co.uk

Theme Traders Ltd, The Stadium, Oaklands Road, London, NW2 6DL Tel: (020) 8452 8518 Fax: (020) 8450 7322 E-mail: mailroom@themetraders.com

Travel Lines Ltd, 3 Church Street, Shoreham-By-Sea, West Sussex, BN43 5DQ Tel: (01273) 464662 Fax: (01273) 464693 E-mail: info@travel-lines.co.uk

Turk Launches Ltd, Town End Pier, 68 High Street, Kingston Upon Thames, Surrey, KT1 1HN Tel: (020) 8546 2434 Fax: (020) 8546 5775 E-mail: operations@turks.co.uk

▶ Weddings Abroad, 15 High Street, Chasetown, Burntwood, Staffordshire, WS7 3XE Tel: (01543) 686884 Fax: 01543 686884 E-mail: helen@perfect-weddings.net

William Martin Ltd, The Studio, Tubney Warren Barn, Tubney, Abingdon, Oxfordshire, OX13 5QJ Tel: (01865) 390258 Fax: (01865) 390234 E-mail: info@wmproductions.co.uk

Your Wish Is My Command Limited, 2nd Floor, Westminster House, 188 Stratford Road, Shirley, Solihull, West Midlands, B90 3AQ Tel: 0845 8380548 E-mail: genie@yourwishismycommand.co.uk

Zibrant, 2 Prospect Place, Pride Park, Derby, DE24 8HG Tel: (01332) 285577 Fax: (01332) 294964 E-mail: enquiries@zibrant.co.uk

EVENT ORGANISING, GAMBLING NIGHTS

▶ Casino-To-Go, Unit 3 Foulswick Business Park, Fowlswick Lane, Allington, Chippenham, Wiltshire, SN14 6QE Tel: (01793) 686402 E-mail: info@casino-to-go.co.uk

▶ Poker Shop, Unit 2, Fletchers Square, Southend-on-Sea, SS2 5RN Tel: (0870) 8712007 Fax: (0870) 8736007 E-mail: srush@poker-shop.co.uk

▶ Poker Store Ltd, 10 Rutland Avenue, Southend On Sea, Southend-on-Sea, SS1 2XH Tel: (01702) 615413 E-mail: katy@poker-store.co.uk

EVENT SECURITY SERVICES

▶ Alamo Security Services, Channelsea House, Canning Road, Stratford, London, E15 3ND Tel: (020) 8519 8866 Fax: (020) 8519 1191 E-mail: info@alamosecurity.co.uk

▶ Nemesis Security & Training Ltd, Unit 15, Belmont Business Centre, East Hoathly, Lewes, East Sussex, BN8 6QL Tel: (0845) 3653768 E-mail: nemesissecurityltd@hotmail.com

EVENTS VENUE FINDING CONSULTANCY

▶ Organza Events, 72 Clarence Road, London, E12 5BH Tel: (020) 8553 5523 Fax: 0208 553 5523 E-mail: info@organzaevents.com

▶ Pendleton Events Ltd, Pendleton House 37 Horseshoe, Close Pound Hill, Crawley, West Sussex, RH10 7YS Tel: (07984) 510856 Fax: 0845 330 7263 E-mail: info@pendletonevents.co.uk

▶ Silver Fern Venues, 81 Westbury Road, Brentwood, Essex, CM14 4JS Tel: (01277) 222546 E-mail: greg@silverfernvenues.com

▶ Venue Reservations, 13 Bishopsgate, London, EC2N 3BA Tel: (020) 7334 3922 Fax: (020) 7334 3911 E-mail: enquiries@venuereservations.co.uk

▶ WonderWorks, Redemption House, 53 Theobald Street, Borehamwood, Herts, WD6 4RT Tel: 020 8953 7733 Fax: 020 8953 3388 E-mail: info@wworks.co.uk

EVICTION CONSULTANCY

▶ Land Sheriffs, The Yard, PO Box 5854, Harlow, Essex, CM18 7FB Tel: 07921 100100 E-mail: info@landsheriffs.co.uk

EXAM PAPERS

▶ Lords College Ltd, 53 Manchester Road, Bolton, BL2 1ES Tel: (01204) 523731 Fax: (0870) 4299706 E-mail: principal@lordscollege.co.uk

EXCAVATION CONTRACTORS

A R B Contractors, Pepper Hill Farm, Pepper Hill, Halifax, West Yorkshire, HX3 7TH Tel: (01274) 674055 Fax: (01274) 693506 E-mail: sales@arbcontractors.co.uk

Active Groundworks, C Polglaze Barton Farm, Liskey Hill, Perranporth, Cornwall, TR6 0BB Tel: (01872) 573222

B J Crowther & Sons, Windsor House, Windsor Street, Oldham, OL1 4AE Tel: 0161-652 0505 Fax: 0161-628 5187

B Line L, Channel View, Cilonen, Three Crosses, Swansea, SA4 3UR Tel: (01792) 874449 Fax: (01792) 874449

B Shelsher & Son, Bridge Cottage, The Druce, Clavering, Saffron Walden, Essex, CB11 4QP Tel: (01799) 550350 Fax: (01799) 550135

EXCAVATION CONTRACTORS – *continued*

Baram Ltd, Unit 1 Station Hill, Curdridge, Southampton, SO30 2DN Tel: (01489) 785086 Fax: (01489) 785929 E-mail: baramltd@aol.com

▶ Dennis Barnfield Ltd, Main Bye Pass Road, Bolton le Sands, Carnforth, Lancashire, LA5 8JA Tel: (01524) 823156 Fax: (01524) 823156

Basover Construction Ltd, Gweedore, Newnham Lane, Old Basing, Basingstoke, Hampshire, RG24 7AT Tel: (01256) 461949

▶ Braithwaite Excavations Ltd, Claycliffe Road, Barnsley, South Yorkshire, S75 1HS Tel: (01226) 779527 Fax: (01226) 203080

Briggs Land Drainage & Excavations Ltd, Liley Lane, Mirfield, West Yorkshire, WF14 8EB Tel: (01924) 492588 Fax: (01924) 491545

Britom Contractors Ltd, Valley Ind Est, Valley Rd, Earlswood, Solihull, W. Midlands, B94 6AA Tel: 01564 703366

D.J. Broady Ltd, Foster Street, Kingston Upon Hull, East Yorkshire, Hull, HU8 8BT Tel: (01482) 585985 Fax: (01482) 585995

Buckle & Davies Construction Ltd, 4 Little Langlands, East Hagbourne, Didcot, Oxfordshire, OX11 9TA Tel: (01235) 819586 Fax: (01235) 819586

Buxted Construction Ltd, Lower Lowlands Farm, Shepherds Hill, Buxted, Uckfield, East Sussex, TN22 4PX Tel: (01825) 890091 Fax: (01825) 890181

Carmac, Burton Road, Finedon, Wellingborough, Northamptonshire, NN9 5HX Tel: (01933) 682345 Fax: (01933) 682555 E-mail: admin@carmac.co.uk

▶ CC Groundworks, 49 Bridge Street, Usk, Gwent, NP15 1BQ Tel: (01291) 671116

M.J. Conway, Woodleigh, Stoke Row, Henley-On-Thames, Oxfordshire, RG9 5RB Tel: (01491) 681220 Fax: (01491) 681220

▶ D J Groundworkers Ltd, Robins Barn, Church Lane, Frampton, Dorchester, Dorset, DT2 9NL Tel: (01300) 320118 Fax: (01300) 321611

▶ D & L Contractors, Manchester Road, Mossley, Ashton-under-Lyne, Lancashire, OL5 9AY Tel: (0870) 2422892 Fax: (0870) 2422893

Dale R Contractors, 2 Mereside Avenue, Congleton, Cheshire, CW12 4JZ Tel: (01260) 270776 Fax: (01260) 270776

Delaney Plant, Beckside Works, Old Corn Mill Lane, Bradford, West Yorkshire, BD7 2LB Tel: (01274) 579224 Fax: (01274) 503372

DNS Midlands Ltd, 1 Bridge Street, Derby, DE1 3HZ Tel: (01332) 363187 Fax: (01332) 371615 E-mail: enquiries@dnsmidlands.co.uk

▶ Doodle & Construct, Port Medway Marina, Station Road, Cuxton, Rochester, Kent, ME2 1AB Tel: (01634) 727599 Fax: (01634) 295070E-mail: info@fastracconstruction.co.uk

▶ Dow Group Ltd, 23 Lenziemill Road, Cumbernauld, Glasgow, G67 2RL Tel: (01236) 730730 Fax: (01236) 730555 E-mail: sales@wmdow.com

Downland Contractors, The Old Poorhouse, Graffham, Petworth, West Sussex, GU28 0NS Tel: (01798) 867297 Fax: (01798) 867297

E & M Brennan Plant Hire Ltd, Unit 3, Crossley Industrial Estate, Manchester, M18 8BA Tel: 0161-231 2583 Fax: 0161-231 2792 E-mail: embrennan@btconnect.com

Edwards Excavations Ltd, 6 Woodman Works, South Lane, Elland, West Yorkshire, HX5 0PA Tel: (01422) 377829 Fax: (01422) 310082

F J C Excavations, 8 Acorn Way, Bootle, Merseyside, L20 6QA Tel: 0151-922 7788 Fax: 0151-922 7889

Fenton Hadley Contracts Ltd, Arrowhead Road, Theale, Reading, RG7 4AE Tel: 0118-988 3266 Fax: 0118-988 4538 E-mail: waste@hadley.co.uk

G B Plant Hire & Groundwork, 40 Bramley Shaw, Waltham Abbey, Essex, EN9 3NN Tel: (01992) 761307 Fax: (01992) 761307 E-mail: gbbg20@hotmail.com

G & K Groundworks, 30 Manor Trading Estate, Brunel Road, Benfleet, Essex, SS7 4PS Tel: (01268) 752298 Fax: (01268) 795529

George Beattie & Sons Ltd, Auchinvole Castle, Kilsyth, Glasgow, G65 0SA Tel: (01236) 823160 Fax: (01236) 823201 E-mail: info@beattie-demolition.com

▶ Grabby Hire Ltd, Tewkesbury Road, Upton-upon-Severn, Worcester, WR8 0PW Tel: (01684) 592654

▶ Ground Works And Plant Hire, 19, Bentinck Street, Kilmarnock, Ayrshire, KA1 4AW Tel: (01563) 570285 Fax: (01563) 541052

Grundy & Co. Excavations Ltd, The Liver Yard, Ditton Road, Widnes, Cheshire, WA8 0TH Tel: 0151-257 8816 Fax: 0151-424 4153

Hunt & Merriman Ltd, Gas Works Site, Liverpool Street, Salford, M5 4DG Tel: 0161-745 7272 Fax: 0161-743 9920

J H Mason & Sons, The Old Barn, Chester Road, Penyffordd, Chester, CH4 0JZ Tel: (01244) 548944 Fax: (01244) 548944

J M Geggus & Sons, 50 Ferniefields, High Wycombe, Buckinghamshire, HP12 4SL Tel: (01494) 439926 Fax: (01494) 439926

J White & Co Tde Ltd, Meadow Bank Road, Rotherham, South Yorkshire, S61 2NF Tel: (01709) 740099 Fax: (01709) 740438 E-mail: jwhite-tde@jwhite-tde.co.uk

John B Akroyd Excavation Ltd, Albion Business Centre, 4 Albion Street, Halifax, West Yorkshire, HX1 1DU Tel: (01422) 381471 Fax: (01422) 321594 E-mail: enquires@jba-excavations.com

John Jones Excavation Ltd, Norjon House, Newby Road, Stockport, Cheshire, SK7 5DU Tel: 0161-483 9316 Fax: 0161-483 8006

Keltbray Ltd, Wentworth House, Dormay Street, London, SW18 1EY Tel: (020) 7643 1000 Fax: (020) 7643 1001 E-mail: office@keltbray.com

Paul King, Keepers Cottage, Tilmanstone, Tilmanstone, Deal, Kent, CT14 0JN Tel: (01304) 832545 Fax: (01304) 830370

▶ L F Nugent Ltd, High Street, Handcross, Haywards Heath, West Sussex, RH17 6BN Tel: (01444) 401097 Fax: (01444) 401103 E-mail: info@lfnugentgroup.co.uk

Land Technology Ltd, Playing Fields, Gunters La, Bexhill-on-Sea, E. Sussex, TN39 4EN Tel: (01424) 214082 Fax: (01424) 214082

▶ Lugsys Plant, Bridge Meadow Stadium, Bridge Meadow Lane, Haverfordwest, Dyfed, SA61 2EX Tel: (01437) 779427

M G Mathews, Homefield, Westlands Road, Lacey Green, Princes Risborough, Buckinghamshire, HP27 0QP Tel: (07768) 574573 Fax: (01844) 344819

M & J Evans Construction, 44 Hall Lane, Walsall Wood, Walsall, WS9 9BB Tel: (01543) 373766 Fax: (01543) 379018

M S Quirke, 171 St Agnells Lane, Hemel Hempstead, Hertfordshire, HP2 6LH Tel: (01442) 244603

▶ McCann Groundworks Ltd, Rear Office, 2 London Road, East Grinstead, West Sussex, RH19 1AQ Tel: (01342) 312519 Fax: (01342) 312535

Martello Plant Hire Ltd, Potts Marsh Industrial Estate, Westham, Pevensey, East Sussex, BN24 5NA Tel: (01323) 761887 Fax: (01323) 461933

Meaden Civil Engineering, 71 Micheldever Road, Whitchurch, Hampshire, RG28 7JH Tel: (01256) 893270

Minster Lovell Construction Ltd, 57 Brize Norton Road, Minster Lovell, Witney, Oxfordshire, OX29 0SG Tel: (01993) 775355 Fax: (01993) 775409

▶ Mitchell & Struthers, Unit 6, Royal Elizabeth Yard, Kirkliston, West Lothian, EH29 9EN Tel: 0131-331 4971 Fax: 0131-331 4971

Oshea J Sons Ltd, Orchard Street, Salford, M6 6FL Tel: 0161-925 9800 Fax: 0161-925 9801 E-mail: info@josheagroup.com

P & M Thornton, Blackheath Farm, Milton-under-Wychwood, Chipping Norton, Oxfordshire, OX7 6HX Tel: (01993) 823365 Fax: (01933) 823365

R H Mawdsley Ltd, 39 Gorsey Lane, Mawdesley, Ormskirk, Lancashire, L40 3TE Tel: (01704) 822204 Fax: (01704) 822204

R M George & Son, 6 Firs Road, Firsdown, Salisbury, SP5 1SF Tel: (01980) 862267

▶ R S Deacon, 74 Station Road, Teynham, Sittingbourne, Kent, ME9 9SN Tel: (01795) 520963 Fax: (01795) 520716 E-mail: rsdeconltd@hotmail.com

Randalls (Groundworks) Ltd, Monmouth House, Northgate, Park Road, Abergavenny, Gwent, NP7 5TT Tel: (01873) 851656 Fax: (01873) 851667

Reid F Contractor, Crewe Park Road, Glenavy, Crumlin, County Antrim, BT29 4NJ Tel: (028) 9442 2486

S J Maguire Groundwork, 20 Moseley Road, Naphill, High Wycombe, Buckinghamshire, HP14 4SQ Tel: (01494) 563056

Sinclair Horticulture & Leisure Ltd, Moss Lock Road, Ravenstruther, Lanark, ML11 8NP Tel: (01555) 870780 Fax: (01555) 870552

▶ SLS Construction, Orchard Lodge, Brinsea, Bristol, BS49 5JP Tel: 01934 853331

Smith & Sons (Bletchington) Ltd, Enslow, Kidlington, Oxfordshire, OX5 3AY Tel: (01869) 331281 Fax: (01869) 331734

Stanley Land Drainage Ltd, Crow Royd Farm, North Moor Lane, Huddersfield, HD5 0PZ Tel: (01924) 497283 Fax: (01924) 493481

Edwin Storey Builders Ltd, 1a Haslemere Road, Thornton Heath, Surrey, CR7 7BF Tel: (020) 8664 8277 Fax: (020) 8664 8279

▶ Trenchco Ltd, 400 Edgware Road, London, NW2 6ND Tel: (020) 8208 3234 Fax: (020) 8450 9958

Trodell Plant Ltd, Ightham Sandpit, Borough Green Road, Ightham, Sevenoaks, Kent, TN15 9JB Tel: (01732) 882662 Fax: (01732) 885675

W J Ginniff, 161 Ballygowan Road, Banbridge, County Down, BT32 3QS Tel: (028) 4066 2285 Fax: (028) 4066 2285

Wilson Construction Ltd, Saltcoats House, Cutlers Road, South Woodham Ferrers, Chelmsford, CM3 5WA Tel: (01245) 428282 Fax: (01245) 428283 E-mail: info@wilson-construction.com

EXCAVATOR BUCKETS

Anross Ltd, Leadgate Industrial Estate, Lope Hill Road, Consett, County Durham, DH8 7RN Tel: (01207) 509448 Fax: (01207) 592158 E-mail: sales@anross.co.uk

▶ Hill Engineering Ltd, 1 Sandy Road, Newry, County Down, BT34 2LB Tel: (028) 3025 2555 Fax: (028) 3026 4020 E-mail: sales@hillengineeringltd.com

Lemac Engineering, Pentrebach Road, Pontypridd, Mid Glamorgan, CF37 4BW Tel: (01443) 407777 Fax: (01443) 401720 E-mail: lemac.eng@btinternet.com

Plantforce Ltd, The Hatchery, Hawthorn, Crick, Caldicot, Gwent, NP26 5UT Tel: (01291) 431111 Fax: (01291) 424803

Strickland Direct Ltd, 5 Main Road, Cropthorne, Pershore, Worcestershire, WR10 3NE Tel: (01386) 860349 Fax: (01386) 860057 E-mail: sales@stricklanduk.com

United Parts, Station Farm, Station Road, Kirton Lindsey, Gainsborough, Lincolnshire, DN21 4BD Tel: (01652) 648931 Fax: (01652) 640769 E-mail: jimg@unitedparts.co.uk

EXCAVATOR HIRE

Addscan Hire Centre, 221 Edleston Road, Crewe, CW2 7HT Tel: (01270) 211061 Fax: (01270) 211353 E-mail: lynne_smith@btconnect.com

Arrowhead Hire, Unit 5 Kennet Weir Bussiness Park, Arrowhead Road, Theale, Reading, RG7 4AD Tel: 0118-930 3703 Fax: 0118-930 4160

Briggs & Partner Ltd, The Storth, Huddersfield Road, Elland, West Yorkshire, HX5 9JR Tel: (01422) 372515 Fax: (01422) 311093 E-mail: briggs@zen.co.uk

Brooks Haulage, Redcliffe Street, Sutton-in-Ashfield, Nottinghamshire, NG17 4ES Tel: (01623) 441255

▶ Claude Fenton (Plant Hire) Ltd, Unit 1 Kennet Weir Business Park, Arrowhead Road, Theale, Reading, RG7 4AE Tel: 0118-930 3066 Fax: 0118-930 3041 E-mail: reading@fentonplant.co.uk

▶ Crescent Plant Hire, South Street, Braintree, Essex, CM7 3QQ Tel: (01376) 344871

Curle M J Ltd, Sunnymead Farm, Naird Lane, Shifnal, Shropshire, TF11 9PJ Tel: (01952) 460382 Fax: (01952) 463238 E-mail: mjcurle@netscapeonline.co.uk

Danbury Plant Hire, 2 Maldon Road, Danbury, Chelmsford, CM3 4QJ Tel: (01245) 223483 Fax: (01245) 226067 E-mail: danburyplanthire@aol.com

Delver Construction, Queens Road, Barnet, Hertfordshire, EN5 4HE Tel: (020) 8440 1993

Dynamic Construction Ltd, Rose Cottage, 73 Main Road, Kempsey, Worcester, WR5 3NB Tel: (01684) 594763 Fax: 01905 821858 E-mail: hayley.southall@virgin.net

H S S Lift & Shift, 6 Colville Court, Winwick Quay, Warrington, WA2 8QT Tel: (01925) 231262 Fax: (01925) 231219

Hewden Hire Centres Ltd, Main Road, Long Hanborough, Witney, Oxfordshire, OX29 8SY Tel: (01993) 883939 Fax: (01993) 882877

Hewden Plant Hire, 119 Hamilton Road, Mount Vernon, Glasgow, G32 9QW Tel: (0141) 762 4076 Fax: (0141) 764 0578

Hewden Plant Hire Ltd, Vicarage Farm Road, Peterborough, PE1 5TN Tel: (01733) 564378 Fax: (01733) 566480

R W Almond & Co. Ltd, Heysham Road, Bootle, Merseyside, L30 6UA Tel: 0151-521 5454 Fax: 0151-525 0115 E-mail: sales@rwalmond.co.uk

▶ J Webb Plant Hire, 14 Cripps Avenue, Peacehaven, East Sussex, BN10 8AL Tel: (01273) 582459 Fax: (01273) 587080 E-mail: info@jwebbplanthire.co.uk

EXCAVATOR MAINTENANCE OR REPAIR SPECIALIST SERVICES

▶ City Plant Services Ltd, 12 Craigmore Road, Newry, County Down, BT35 6PL Tel: (028) 3082 5522 Fax: 02830 825533 E-mail: sales@cpsnewry.com

Dunham Engineering, 48-49 Greenhey Place, Skelmersdale, Lancashire, WN8 9SA Tel: (01695) 729031 Fax: (01695) 555876 E-mail: alan@dunhameng.com

Incomestyle Ltd, 1 Wayfarers, Newton-le-Willows, Merseyside, WA12 8DF Tel: (01925) 221931 Fax: (01925) 221931 E-mail: james@incomestyleltd.wanadoo.co.uk

EXCAVATOR MOUNTED HYDRAULIC HAMMERS

▶ Sandhurst Equipment Rental, Thames House, College Road, Northfleet, Gravesend, Kent, DA11 9AU Tel: (0845) 120 6622 Fax: (01474) 567611 E-mail: info@sandhurst-rent.co.uk

EXCAVATOR SPARE PARTS OR WEARING PARTS

Anross Ltd, Leadgate Industrial Estate, Lope Hill Road, Consett, County Durham, DH8 7RN Tel: (01207) 509448 Fax: (01207) 592158 E-mail: sales@anross.co.uk

Capital Plant Services Ltd, Elys Estate, Angel Road, London, N18 3BH Tel: (020) 8807 1672 Fax: (020) 8807 1639

▶ City Plant Services Ltd, 12 Craigmore Road, Newry, County Down, BT35 6PL Tel: (028) 3082 5522 Fax: 02830 825533 E-mail: sales@cpsnewry.com

Massey Engineering Ltd, Ludlow Business Park, Orleton Road, Ludlow Business Park, Ludlow, Shropshire, SY8 1XF Tel: (01584) 875210 Fax: (01584) 874089

Partex Service Ltd, Station Road, Pershore, Worcestershire, WR10 2DB Tel: (01386) 554838 Fax: (01386) 556895 E-mail: partexservice@aol.com

United Parts, Station Farm, Station Road, Kirton Lindsey, Gainsborough, Lincolnshire, DN21 4BD Tel: (01652) 648931 Fax: (01652) 640769 E-mail: jimg@unitedparts.co.uk

EXCAVATORS

Arnold Plant Hire Ltd, Bredbury Park Way, Bredbury Park Industrial Estate, Bredbury, Stockport, Cheshire, SK6 2SN Tel: 0161-406 8734 Fax: 0161-406 8804 E-mail: hire@arnold-plant.co.uk

Butler Reynolds Ltd, Loughborough Road, Costock, Loughborough, Leicestershire, LE12 6XB Tel: (01509) 854144 Fax: (01509) 854199 E-mail: sales@butlerreynolds.co.uk

Caterpillar UK Ltd, Peckleton Lane, Desford, Leicester, LE9 9JU Tel: (01455) 826826 Fax: (01455) 826900

Gunn J C B Ltd, Atlantic Street, Broadheath, Altrincham, Cheshire, WA14 5DN Tel: 0161-941 2631 Fax: 0161-942 3399 E-mail: enguireies@gunn-jcb.co.uk

H M Plant Ltd, Monkton Business Park North, Hebburn, Tyne & Wear, NE31 2JZ Tel: 0191-430 8400 Fax: 0191-430 8500 E-mail: info@hmplantltd.uk

H M Plant Ltd, 964 Weston Road, Slough Trading Estate, Slough, SL1 4HR Tel: (01753) 213900 Fax: (01753) 213901 E-mail: info@hmplant.ltd.uk

Hurst Plant Sales Ltd, Station Yard Station Road, Haxey Junction, Doncaster, South Yorkshire, DN9 2NL Tel: (01427) 753030 Fax: (01427) 752030 E-mail: sales@hurstplantsales.co.uk

J C B Landpower Ltd, Lakeside Works, Denstone Road, Rocester, Uttoxeter, Staffordshire, ST14 5JP Tel: (01889) 590312 Fax: (01889) 590588 E-mail: enq@jcbinfo.co.uk

Lewis Equipment Ltd, Waterloo Road, Bidford-on-Avon, Alcester, Warwickshire, B50 4JH Tel: (01789) 773044 Fax: (01789) 490379 E-mail: sales@lewis-equipment.co.uk

▶ McGarvey Construction, 86 Clark Street, Paisley, Renfrewshire, PA3 1RB Tel: 0141-848 7555

Manitowoc Potain Ltd, Unit 2c Tomo Industrial Estate, Packet Boat Lane, Uxbridge, Middlesex, UB8 2JP Tel: (01895) 430053 Fax: (01895) 459500

R B Cranes Ltd, Thrumpton Lane, Retford, Nottinghamshire, DN22 7AN Tel: (01777) 700039 Fax: (01777) 713192 E-mail: info@jnd.co.uk

▶ Sandhurst Plant, The Whitewall Centre, Whitewall Road, Medway City Estate, Rochester, Kent, ME2 4DZ Tel: (01634) 739590 Fax: (0845) 1206644 E-mail: info@sandhurst.co.uk

Takeuchi Mfg (UK) Ltd, Unit E2B, John Boyd Dunlop Drive, Kingsway Business Park, Rochdale, Lancashire, OL16 4NG Tel: 01706 657722 E-mail: sales@takeuchi-mfg.co.uk

EXECUTIVE AIRCRAFT

Flightplan Ltd, PO Box 1159, Farnborough, Hampshire, GU14 6XA Tel: (01252) 52 62 82 Fax: (01252) 52 62 89 E-mail: info@flightplan.org.uk

Glasgow Airport Ltd, St. Andrews Drive, Glasgow Airport, Abbotsinch, Paisley, Renfrewshire, PA3 2ST Tel: 0141-887 1111 Fax: (0870) 7511004 E-mail: info@first-travel.co.uk

EXECUTIVE CASES

Japinda Products Ltd, Constellation Works, Fernhurst Street, Chadderton, Oldham, OL1 2RN Tel: 0161-620 4231 Fax: 0161-627 0914 E-mail: sales@japinda.co.uk

EXECUTIVE COACHING

▶ Enteleki Change Consultants Ltd, 37 Marston Street, Oxford, OX4 1JU Tel: (01865) 247003 E-mail: hazeldouglas@enteleki.co.uk

▶ Eskhill & Co., Eskhill House, 15 Inveresk Village, Musselburgh, Midlothian, EH21 7TD Tel: 0131-271 4000 Fax: 0131-271 7000

▶ Fort Chapard Ltd, Prospect House, 32 Sovereign Street, Leeds, LS1 4BJ Tel: 0113-389 1085 Fax: 0113-389 1190 E-mail: info@fortchapard.com

▶ Jigsaw Executive Ltd, Regus House, Herald Way, Pegasus Business Park, Castle Donington, DE74 2TZ Tel: 01332 638046 Fax: 01332 638001 E-mail: info@JigsawExecutive.com

▶ K D Partnership, 12-16 Clerkenwell Road, London, EC1M 5PQ Tel: (020) 7324 6343 E-mail: info@kdpartnership.co.uk

▶ Sheppard Moscow Scotland Ltd, 57 Melville Street, Edinburgh, EH3 7HL Tel: 0131-226 3399 Fax: 0131-226 3344

EXECUTIVE OFFICE FURNITURE

▶ Woodman Construction Management Ltd, 50 Victoria Road, Burgess Hill, West Sussex, RH15 9LH Tel: 01444 233413 Fax: 01444 871231 E-mail: clientservices@woodman.co.uk

EXECUTIVE SEARCH CONSULTANTS

Adamson & Partners Ltd, 10 Lisbon Square, Leeds, LS1 4LY Tel: 0113-245 1212 Fax: 0113-242 0802 E-mail: stuart.adamson@adamsons.com

▶ Alexander James Executive Search Ltd, Winslow House, 16 Rumford Court, Rumford Place, Liverpool, L3 9DG Tel: 0151 236 1875 Fax: 0151 258 2018 E-mail: info@alexanderjamesltd.co.uk

Deven Anderson Ltd, George House, 121 High Street, Henley-in-Arden, West Midlands, B95 5AU Tel: (01564) 795565 Fax: (01564) 795122 E-mail: headhunt@devenanderson.co.uk

▶ Anova Communications Group, 41 Market Place, Henley-on-Thames, Oxfordshire, RG9 2AA Tel: (01491) 636300 Fax: (0870) 1336271 E-mail: info@futureincoms.com

▶ Baldock Advanced Motorcycle Training, 31 Bush Spring, Baldock, Hertfordshire, SG7 6QT Tel: (01462) 641775 Fax: (0871) 4335485 E-mail: tclarke@evprecruit.com

▶ Barnett Consulting Services Ltd, Providence House, River Street, Windsor, Berkshire, SL4 1QT Tel: (01753) 856723 Fax: (01753) 866297 E-mail: barnettgp@aol.com

Connaught Partners Ltd, 111 Hagley Road, Birmingham, B16 8LB Tel: 0121-452 5117 Fax: 0121-452 5118 E-mail: sales@connaughtpartners.com

Davis Co. Ltd, 45-49 Mortimer Street, London, W1W 8HL Tel: (020) 7323 6696 Fax: (020) 7323 6697 E-mail: marketing@davisrecruitment.co.uk

E G Recruitment Ltd, 56 Meldon Terrace, Newbiggin-by-the-Sea, Northumberland, NE64 6XH Tel: (01670) 858834 Fax: (01865) 400166 E-mail: eddie@egrecruitment.co.uk

Edward Drummond & Co Ltd., Westpoint 78 Queens Road, Clifton, Bristol, BS8 1QX Tel: 0117 9858755 E-mail: info@edwarddrummond.com

▶ Hillcote Partnership, 32 London Road, Guildford, Surrey, GU1 2AB Tel: (01483) 230310

Hudson Global Resources Ltd, Grosvenor House, 14 Bennetts Hill, Birmingham, B2 5RS Tel: 0121-633 0010 Fax: 0121-633 0862

Macmillan Davies Consultants Ltd, Salisbury House, Bluecoats Avenue, Hertford, SG14 1PU Tel: (01992) 552552 Fax: (01992) 514101 E-mail: contact@hodes.co.uk

▶ Ortus Professional Search, 5a The Courtyard, 707 Warwick Road, Solihull, West Midlands, B91 3DA Tel: 0121 7127820

▶ Ping Executive Search, PO Box 841, St. Albans, Hertfordshire, AL3 6BG Tel: (01727) 840850 E-mail: info@pingexecsearch.co.uk

▶ Pitch Perfect (UK) Ltd., Communications House, 26 York Street, London, W1U 6PZ Tel: 0845 351 0615 E-mail: info@pitchperfect.biz

Rose Partnership, 12 Copthall Avenue, London, EC2R 7DH Tel: (020) 7466 6000 Fax: (020) 7466 6058

Russell Reynolds Associates Inc, 24 St James's Square, London, SW1Y 4HZ Tel: (020) 7839 7788 Fax: (020) 7839 9295

Sciteb Ltd, 18 Newton Man, Queens Club Gardens, London, W14 9RR Tel: (020) 7381 1481 Fax: (020) 7499 9253 E-mail: nicholas.beale@sciteb.com

▶ Skills UK, 17 Britannia Road, Burbage, Hinckley, Leics, LE10 2HE Tel: 01455 617776 E-mail: ted@skills.uk.com

▶ Stephens Associates, 14 Buckingham Street, London, WC2N 6DF Tel: (020) 7925 0200 Fax: (020) 7925 0235 E-mail: stephens@stephens.co.uk

Tek Personnel Consultants Ltd, Bells Square, Sheffield, S1 2FY Tel: 0114-252 5730 Fax: 0114-252 5731 E-mail: enquiries@tekpersonel.co.uk

Tyzack Associates Ltd, Medius House, 2 Sheraton Street, London, W1F 8BH Tel: (020) 7758 4000 Fax: (020) 7758 4001 E-mail: info@tyzackassociates.com

▶ Wilson Alexander, Queen Caroline House, 3 High, Windsor, Berkshire, SL4 1LD Tel: (01753) 850540 Fax: 01753 850490 E-mail: info@wilsonalexander.com

EXECUTIVE TRAINING QUALIFICATIONS

▶ Executive Coaching & Mentoring Ltd, 67 Hampton Road, Southport, Merseyside, PR8 6QA Tel: (01704) 530821 E-mail: info@ecam.nu

▶ Lasa Development UK Ltd, Little Manor, Itlay, Daglingworth, Cirencester, Gloucestershire, GL7 7HZ Tel: (01285) 643469 E-mail: info@lasadev.com

Paul Temple Associates Ltd, Laurel Cottage, 15a Hillside Road, Haslemere, Surrey, GU27 3RL Tel: (01428) 656150 Fax: (01428) 642676 E-mail: paul@paultempleassociates.com

▶ Up Front Security Ltd, 307 West George Street, Glasgow, G2 4LF Tel: 0141-221 5448 Fax: 0141-221 5449

EXHAUST EMISSION CONTROL SYSTEMS

▶ Blackthorn Enviromental Ltd, Forum House, Stirling Road, Chichester, West Sussex, PO19 7DN Tel: (0870) 0101800 Fax: (0870) 0101811 E-mail: contact@blackthorn.eu.com

EXHAUST FANS

G T Fan Services & Repairs Ltd, Unit D Leona Industrial Estate, Nimmings Road, Halesowen, West Midlands, B62 9JQ Tel: 0121-559 1824 Fax: 0121-561 2153

Hydor Ltd, Unit 8, Parkers Close, Downton Industrial Estate, Salisbury, SP5 3RB Tel: (01725) 511422 Fax: (01725) 512637 E-mail: info@hydor.co.uk

Manrose Manufacturing Ltd, Albion House, Albion Close, Slough, SL2 5DT Tel: (01753) 691399 Fax: (01753) 692294 E-mail: sales@manrose.com

Vent Axia Ltd, Fleming Way, Crawley, West Sussex, RH10 9YX Tel: (01293) 526062 Fax: (01293) 551188 E-mail: info@vent-axia.com

EXHAUST GAS BOILERS

London Essential Maintenance Ltd, 62 Rainham Road, London, NW10 5DJ Tel: (0800) 0191363 Fax: (0870) 7621371 E-mail: sales@londonessential.co.uk

EXHAUST SILENCERS

Arvinmeritor, Squires Gate Lane, Blackpool, FY4 3RN Tel: (01253) 345591 Fax: (01253) 402012 E-mail: info@arvin.com

Bernard L Haywood Sales Ltd, 89-91 New Town Row, Birmingham, B6 4HG Tel: 0121-333 6656 Fax: 0121-359 1530 E-mail: sales@hbl.co.uk

▶ Bosal UK Ltd, Unit 330 Four Oaks Road, Walton Summit Centre, Bamber Bridge, Preston, PR5 8AP Tel: (01772) 771000 Fax: (01772) 312750 E-mail: marketing@eur.bosal.com

Burgess Architectural Products Ltd, Brookfield Road, Burbage, Hinckley, Leicestershire, LE10 2LL Tel: (01455) 618787 Fax: (01455) 251061 E-mail: sales@fleetguard.com

Franklin Silencers Ltd, 1 Grafton Place, Grafton Street Industrial Estate, Northampton, NN1 2PS Tel: (01604) 626266 Fax: (01604) 233757 E-mail: sales@franklinsilencers.co.uk

Futaba Tenneco UK Ltd, Liverpool Road, Burnley, Lancashire, BB12 6HJ Tel: (01282) 433171 Fax: (01282) 450778

P D Gough Co. Ltd, Old Foundry, Common Lane, Watnall, Nottingham, NG16 1HD Tel: 0115-938 2241 Fax: 0115-945 9162 E-mail: info@pdgough.com

TG Silencers, Lower Sherriff Street, Rochdale, Lancashire, OL12 6TG Tel: (01706) 646144 Fax: (01706) 759947

EXHAUST SYSTEM CLAMPS

▶ Cats Direct, 70-72 Acton Road, Long Eaton, Nottingham, NG10 1FR Tel: 0115-983 5280 Fax: 0115-972 1112 E-mail: mail@cats-direct.com

EXHAUST SYSTEM COMPONENTS

C E S UK Ltd, Knutsford Way, Sealand Industrial Estate, Chester, CH1 4NS Tel: (01244) 372555 Fax: (01244) 371248 E-mail: sales@cesuk.com

Exhausts By Design, West Well Farm, West Well Lane, Tingewick, Buckingham, MK18 4BD Tel: (01280) 847756 Fax: (01280) 847759 E-mail: grahamf@ukonline.co.uk

Shelley (Halesowen) Ltd, 39 The Old Woodyard, Hagley Hall Hagley, Hagley, Stourbridge, West Midlands, DY9 9LQ Tel: (01562) 885905 Fax: (01562) 884941

EXHAUST SYSTEM FITTINGS

Mr Exhaust Supercentres, 18 London Road, Reigate, Surrey, RH2 9HY Tel: (01737) 243900 Fax: (01737) 224705

Vegem Ltd, PO Box 9, Leeds, LS27 0QN Tel: 0113-253 0451 Fax: 0113-252 1161 E-mail: enquiries@vegem.co.uk

EXHAUST SYSTEMS MANUFRS

A T S Euromaster Ltd, Vantage Point, 20 Upper Portland Street, Aston, Birmingham, B6 5TW Tel: 0121-325 7300 Fax: 0121-325 7333 E-mail: info@atseuromaster.co.uk

A T S Exhausts & Tyres (Edenbridge) Ltd, Unit 1 Monza House, Fircroft Way, Edenbridge, Kent, TN8 6EJ Tel: (01732) 867746 Fax: (01732) 868274

Allen Bros Southsea Ltd, Albert Road, Southsea, Hampshire, PO5 2SG Tel: (023) 9282 8432 E-mail: sales@allen-bros.co.uk

Arvin Replacement Products, New Haden Road, Cheadle, Stoke-on-Trent, ST10 1UF Tel: (01538) 752561 Fax: (01538) 752202

Arvin Replacment Products, Squires Gate Industrial Estate, Squires Gate Lane, Blackpool, FY4 3RN Tel: (01253) 400400 Fax: (01253) 406475

Ashley Competition Exhausts, 1 New Street, Walsall, WS1 3DF Tel: (01922) 720767 Fax: (01922) 721354 E-mail: sales@ashleycompetitionexhausts.com

Auto Tyre & Battery Co., Southern Avenue, Leominster, Herefordshire, HR6 0QF Tel: (01568) 615680

Benson Components Ltd, Saxon Works, South St, Openshaw, Manchester, M11 2FY Tel: (0845) 1300000 Fax: 0161-231 6866 E-mail: sales@bensonexhausts.com

▶ Bosal UK Ltd, Unit 330 Four Oaks Road, Walton Summit Centre, Bamber Bridge, Preston, PR5 8AP Tel: (01772) 771000 Fax: (01772) 312750 E-mail: marketing@eur.bosal.com

BTB Exhausts Ltd, 3-5 The Beaver Centre, Great Central Way, Woodford Halse, Daventry, Northamptonshire, NN11 3DP Tel: (01327) 261797 Fax: (01327) 263577

Budget Tyre & Auto Service, 95 Orbiston Street, Motherwell, Lanarkshire, ML1 1PY Tel: (01698) 275070 Fax: (01698) 276667

Burgess Architectural Products Ltd, Brookfield Road, Burbage, Hinckley, Leicestershire, LE10 2LL Tel: (01455) 618787 Fax: (01455) 251061 E-mail: sales@fleetguard.com

Calsonic Automotive Products Ltd, 5 Bentall Business Park, Washington, Tyne & Wear, NE37 3JD Tel: 0191-417 0084 Fax: 0191-417 0184

▶ Clampco, Unit 6, Hammond Avenue, Stockport, Cheshire, SK4 1PQ Tel: 0161-476 3600 Fax: 0161-476 3600 E-mail: sales@Clampcouk.ltd.uk

CLF Technologies Ltd, Sawpit Lane, Tibshelf, Alfreton, Derbyshire, DE55 5NH Tel: (01773) 876333 Fax: (01773) 876301 E-mail: info@clf.co.uk

Clives Tyre & Exhaust Co. Ltd, Unit1 Hampers Common, Petworth, West Sussex, GU28 9NN Tel: (01798) 343441 Fax: (01798) 343441

D & K Specialist Exhaust Centre Ltd, Unit 19 Halifax Industrial Centre, Marshway, Halifax, West Yorkshire, HX1 5RW Tel: (01422) 322141 Fax: (01422) 322939

Eminox Ltd, Brick Kiln Lane, Stoke-On-Trent, ST4 7BS Tel: (01782) 206300 Fax: (01782) 283800 E-mail: dawn.day@eminox.com

Exhausts By Design, West Well Farm, West Well Lane, Tingewick, Buckingham, MK18 4BD Tel: (01280) 847756 Fax: (01280) 847759 E-mail: grahamf@ukonline.co.uk

Fossitt & Thorne UK Ltd, 46 Fydell Street, Boston, Lincolnshire, PE21 8LF Tel: (01205) 319960 Fax: (01205) 319972 E-mail: fossitt.thorne@virgin.net

G T Exhausts, Ledra Works, Northgate, Aldridge, Walsall, WS9 8TH Tel: (01922) 745800 Fax: (01922) 745566 E-mail: sales2@gtexhausts.co.uk

Guaranteed Exhaust Systems Ltd, Unit 4-5 Willand Industrial Estate, Willand, Cullompton, Devon, EX15 2QW Tel: (01884) 821237 Fax: (01884) 820631 E-mail: enquiries@stainlesssteelexhausts.net

▶ Hamp Products Ltd, 2F, Everite Road Industrial Estate, Westgate, Widnes, Cheshire, WA8 8RA Tel: 0151-422 0123

Kipling Motorist Centre, 76 Ifield Road, Crawley, West Sussex, RH11 7BQ Tel: (01293) 612211 Fax: (01293) 612444

Lathom Motorcraft, 15 Briars Lane, Lathom, Ormskirk, Lancashire, L40 5TG Tel: (01704) 893284 Fax: (01704) 893284 E-mail: enquiries@catchup2000.com

▶ Longlife Exhausts, 7 Denvale Trade Park, Galdames Place, Cardiff, CF24 5PF Tel: (029) 2048 9657 Fax: (029) 2048 6812

Maniflow Exhaust Centre, Mitchell Road, Salisbury, SP2 7PY Tel: (01722) 335378 Fax: (01722) 320834 E-mail: maniflow@lineone.net

Mr Exhaust Supercentres, 18 London Road, Reigate, Surrey, RH2 9HY Tel: (01737) 243900 Fax: (01737) 224705

National Tyre Service Ltd, Regent House, Heaton Lane, Stockport, Cheshire, SK4 1BS Tel: 0161-480 7461 Fax: 0161-475 3540

P D Gough Co. Ltd, Old Foundry, Common Lane, Watnall, Nottingham, NG16 1HD Tel: 0115-938 2241 Fax: 0115-945 9162 E-mail: info@pdgough.com

▶ Predator Exhaust System, 84 Tewin Road, Welwyn Garden City, Hertfordshire, AL7 1BD Tel: (01707) 334050 Fax: (01707) 339009 E-mail: sales@predatormotorsport.co.uk

▶ Pro Speed Exhausts, Rear of, 113 City Road, Cardiff, CF24 3BN Tel: (029) 2046 1444 Fax: (029) 2046 1444

R M S Engineering Prestwick Ltd, 5 Glenburn Industrial Estate, Shawfarm Road, Prestwick, Ayrshire, KA9 2NS Tel: (01292) 671160 Fax: (01292) 671404 E-mail: info@rmstainlesssteelexhausts.com

Renegade Products, Unit 2-3 Clearways Industrial Estate, London Road, West Kingsdown, Sevenoaks, Kent, TN15 6ES Tel: (01474) 852255 Fax: (01474) 852999

Southern Exhaust Supplies, Unit 22, Phase 2, Fairfax Road, Heathfield Industrial Estate, Heathfield, Newton Abbot, Devon, TQ12 6TT Tel: (01626) 833300 Fax: (01626) 835814

Stapleton's Commercial & Agricultural Depot, Fourth Avenue, Letchworth Garden City, Hertfordshire, SG6 2TT Tel: (01462) 488844 Fax: (01462) 488845 E-mail: admin@stapletons-tyres.co.uk

Tenneco Automotive UK Ltd, Wharfdale Road, Tyseley, Birmingham, B11 2DF Tel: 0121-707 8000 Fax: 0121-609 3035 E-mail: sales@tenneco.com

▶ Tma, Unit 9 Shepley Industrial Estate North, Audenshaw, Manchester, M34 5DR Tel: 0161-320 4050 Fax: 0161-320 7001

Top Gear St Albans Ltd, 152 London Road, St. Albans, Hertfordshire, AL1 1PQ Tel: (01727) 850537 Fax: (01727) 856557 E-mail: info@topgear.co.uk

Tuberex Exhausts Systems Ltd, Airfield Industrial Estate, Hixon, Stafford, ST18 0PF Tel: (01889) 271212 Fax: (01889) 272112

EXHIBITION AUDIO/VISUAL EQUIPMENT HIRE

Carpenter Communications Group Ltd, Old Greenfield House, Greenfield, Christmas Common, Watlington, Oxfordshire, OX49 5HF Tel: (01491) 614144 Fax: (01491) 613416 E-mail: sales@carpentercomms.co.uk

Charlesworth & Valentine, 34 Bridgnorth Road, Aqueduct Village, Telford, Shropshire, TF3 1BZ Tel: (01952) 592012 Fax: (01952) 270121

Dorset Merc, 851 Wimborne Road, Bournemouth, BH9 2BG Tel: (01202) 775566 E-mail: david.bridgewater@dorset-merc.net

▶ J N M Electrical Services, 23 Claro Court Business Centre, Claro Road, Harrogate, North Yorkshire, HG1 4BA Tel: (01423) 817187 Fax: (01423) 552512 E-mail: info@jnmonline.co.uk

Lightsource Data Presentations, Fox Studio, King Street, Much Wenlock, Shropshire, TF13 6BL Tel: (01952) 727715 Fax: (0870) 4204316 E-mail: lights@lightsource.co.uk

Spyx Audio Equipment, 36 Shaftesbury Road, Coventry, CV5 6FN Tel: (024) 7667 7896 Fax: (024) 7667 7896 E-mail: spyx@btinternet.com

Time Ltd, 6 Brook St Mill, Brook Street, Macclesfield, Cheshire, SK11 7AW Tel: (01625) 615768 Fax: (01625) 614605 E-mail: ron@timesccv.co.uk

EXHIBITION CASES

Fibre Box Co. Ltd, Victoria Works, Barton Road, Dukinfield, Cheshire, SK16 4US Tel: 0161-308 4856 Fax: 0161-339 1666 E-mail: dalesmanu@hotmail.co.uk

Nomadic Display, The Nomadic House, 71 St Johns Road, Isleworth, Middlesex, TW7 6XQ Tel: 0121-333 4956 Fax: (020) 8326 5522 E-mail: hqsales@nomadicdisplay.co.uk

EXHIBITION CENTRES/ GALLERIES/HALLS AVAILABLE FOR HIRE

Brighton Centre, Kings Road, Brighton, BN1 2GR Tel: (01273) 290131 Fax: (01273) 779980 E-mail: info@brightoncentre.co.uk

Connect Wall Systems, 26 Westcott Crescent, London, W7 1PA Tel: (020) 8578 2437 Fax: (020) 8578 2450

Earls Court & Olympia Group Ltd, Exhibition Centre, Warwick Road, London, SW5 9TA Tel: (020) 7370 8078 Fax: (020) 7370 8390 E-mail: sales@eco.co.uk

Fire & Iron Ltd, Rowhurst Forge, Oxshott Road, Leatherhead, Surrey, KT22 0EN Tel: (01372) 386453 Fax: (01372) 386516 E-mail: sales@fireandiron.co.uk

Mall Galleries, 17 Carlton House Terrace, London, SW1Y 5BD Tel: (020) 7930 6844 Fax: (020) 7839 7830 E-mail: info@mallgalleries.com

The National Exhibition Centre Ltd, National Exhibition Centre, Birmingham, B40 1NT Tel: 0121-780 4141 Fax: 0121-767 3815 E-mail: nec-exhibitions@necgroup.co.uk

Regency Banqueting Suite, 113 Bruce Grove, London, N17 6UR Tel: (020) 8885 2490 Fax: (020) 8885 1739 E-mail: enquiries@regencybanqueting.com

Scottish Conference Centre Ltd, Exhibition Way, Glasgow, G3 8YW Tel: 0141-248 3000 Fax: 0141-226 3423 E-mail: info@secc.co.uk

EXHIBITION CONTRACTORS,

See Exhibition Stand etc

EXHIBITION DISPLAY DESIGNERS/PRODUCERS/ SERVICES

A M Photographic, St. Johns Innovation Centre, Cowley Road, Cambridge, CB4 0WS Tel: (0870) 1635192 E-mail: tony@amphotographic.co.uk

EXHIBITION DISPLAY DESIGNERS/ PRODUCERS/SERVICES – *continued*

Abbey Design Ltd, Lakeside Trading Centre, Beoley Road East, Redditch, Worcestershire, B98 8PE Tel: (01527) 585888 Fax: (01527) 596334 E-mail: sales@systematicdisplays.co.uk

Advertising Constructions Ltd, Engineering Centre, Brick Kiln Lane, Stoke-on-Trent, ST4 7BS Tel: (01782) 213444 Fax: (01782) 266555 E-mail: adcons@adcons.co.uk

Advertising Design & Photography, 16-20 Little Patrick Street, Belfast, BT15 1BA Tel: (028) 9032 2605 Fax: (028) 9023 1235 E-mail: adesphot@yahoo.co.uk

Alfa Display & Design Ltd, Unit 4 Sandleheath Industrial Estate, Sandleheath, Fordingbridge, Hampshire, SP6 1PA Tel: (01425) 653943 Fax: (01425) 657075 E-mail: info@alfadisplay.co.uk

Antone Displays Ltd, Wanstead Road, Leicester, LE3 1TR Tel: 0116-232 4700 Fax: 0116-287 8012

Ardan Exhibition, Unit 7 North Medburn Farm, Watling Street, Elstree, Hertfordshire, WD6 3AA Tel: (020) 8207 4957 Fax: (020) 8207 3040 E-mail: info@ardan.co.uk

Artful Dodgers, Burrs Hill, Staplehurst Rd, Marden, Tonbridge, Kent, TN12 9BS Tel: 01622 831800 Fax: 01622 831800

▶ Artisan Ltd, Dean Court, Great Western Business Park, Yate, Bristol, BS37 5NJ Tel: (01454) 321212 Fax: (01454) 313471

Assignment Signs & Nameplates, 26 Brindley Road, Dodwells Bridge Industrial Estate, Hinckley, Leicestershire, LE10 3BY Tel: (01455) 891200 Fax: (01455) 619426

Aston Display Ltd, 30 Brewery Street, Aston, Birmingham, B6 4JB Tel: 0121-333 6768 Fax: 0121-333 6769 E-mail: info@astondisplay.com

Bryan & Clark Ltd, Ground Floor, West Cumberland House, 80 Scrubs Lane, London, NW10 6RF Tel: (020) 8969 9933 Fax: (020) 8960 7430E-mail: sales@bryanandclark.co.uk

Checkland Kindleysides Ltd, Charnwood Edge, Syston Road, Cossington, Leicester, LE7 4UZ Tel: 0116-264 4700 Fax: 0116-264 4701 E-mail: info@checkind.com

Classic Design & Build (UK) Ltd, Lode Lane Industrial Estate, Vulcan Road, Solihull, West Midlands, B91 2JY Tel: 0121-709 2040 Fax: 0121-709 2044 E-mail: info@classicdb.co.uk

Clip Ltd, Athena, 210 Bristol Business Park, The Close, Bristol, BS16 1FJ Tel: 0117-937 5700 Fax: 0117-931 4561 E-mail: info@clipdisplay.com

Contemporary Design Unit, Arlington Wharf, 12 Arlington Square, London, N1 7DR Tel: (020) 7226 2077 Fax: (020) 7359 7032 E-mail: info@cdu.co.uk

Crown Exhibitions & Displays, 3 Partons Road, Kings Heath, Birmingham, B14 6TA Tel: 0121-441 2822 Fax: 0121-441 2772 E-mail: info@crownexhibition.co.uk

Cube Arts Ltd, 14-18 Abbotsbury Road, Morden, Surrey, SM4 5LQ Tel: (020) 8685 9108 Fax: (020) 8085 9089 E-mail: info@cubearts.com

▶ Cubed Creative, The London Business Innovation Centre 28 Innova Business Par, Enfield, Middlesex, EN3 7XU Tel: (020) 8350 1289 Fax: (020) 8350 1351 E-mail: sales@cubedcreative.co.uk

D E Signs, Cartref, Chelmsford Road, Barnston, Dunmow, Essex, CM6 1LS Tel: (01371) 874011 Fax: (01371) 874011 E-mail: tim@de-signs.co.uk

The D P Design Co. Ltd, 31 Warwick Row, Coventry, CV1 1EY Tel: (024) 7622 3390 Fax: (024) 7622 0740

David Wilson's Trailers, Hillsdown Farm, Birch Grove, Horsted Keynes, Haywards Heath, West Sussex, RH17 7DH Tel: (01825) 740696 Fax: (01825) 740260 E-mail: info@dwt-exhibitions.co.uk

Dayman Display Ltd, Sidney House, 262 Aylestone Lane, Wigston, Leicestershire, LE18 1BD Tel: 0116-288 3338 E-mail: sales@daymandisplay.fsnet.co.uk

Deeleys Ltd, Unit 43 Belgrave Industrial Estate, Highgate Place, Birmingham, B12 0DD Tel: 0121-693 0740 Fax: 0121-693 0741 E-mail: info@deeleysdisplays.co.uk

Design Built Exhibitions Ltd, 46 Enfield Industrial Estate, Redditch, Worcestershire, B97 6DE Tel: (01527) 69132 Fax: (01527) 65692

Ltd Design Consultants, 54 Warwick Square, London, SW1V 2AJ Tel: (020) 7931 7607 Fax: (020) 7931 7608 E-mail: enquiries@ltddesign.co.uk

Design Group, 2nd Floor Quay House, 7 The Quay, Poole, Dorset, BH15 1HA Tel: (01202) 669090 Fax: (01202) 669930 E-mail: sales@designgroup.co.uk

Devonshire House Associates Ltd, Gainsborough Trading Estate, Rufford Road, Stourbridge, West Midlands, DY9 7ND Tel: (01384) 442322 Fax: (01384) 440949

Displaysia Exhibitions Ltd, Unit 49 Longshot Industrial Estate, Longshot Lane, Bracknell, Berkshire, RG12 1RL Tel: (01344) 487220 Fax: (01344) 487221

Displex Display & Exhibition Ltd, Graphex House, Adcroft Street, Stockport, Cheshire, SK1 3HZ Tel: 0161-480 4626 Fax: 0161-474 1875 E-mail: sales@displex.co.uk

▶ Andy Dixon, PO Box 164, Hertford, SG13 7ZJ Tel: (0845) 3308770 Fax: (0870) 6611554 E-mail: andy@scene2.co.uk

Driscoll Bros Group Ltd, 59 Grasmere Road, Gatley, Cheadle, Cheshire, SK8 4RS Tel: 0161-428 2109 Fax: (01625) 548466 E-mail: glynn@driscollbros.co.uk

Dunns Imaging Group Ltd, Chester Road, Cradley Heath, West Midlands, B64 6AA Tel: (01384) 564770 Fax: (01384) 637165 E-mail: enquiries@dunns.co.uk

E S L Displays & Graphics, Units 3-5 Hillside Mews, Riding Barn Hill, Wick, Bristol, BS30 5PA Tel: 0117-937 4777 Fax: 0117-937 4550 E-mail: info@eslgroupuk.co.uk

Ec Display Associates Ltd, Unit 1 Winsor, 50 Windsor Avenue, London, SW19 2TJ Tel: (020) 8545 0505 Fax: (020) 8545 0042 E-mail: info@ecdisplay.com

Equinox Design Ltd, Equinox Park, 100 Jack Lane, Leeds, LS10 1BW Tel: 0113-244 1300 Fax: 0113-242 4533 E-mail: equinoxdesign@compuserve.com

▶ Excalibur Exhibitions Ltd, 4 Stowe Close, Buckingham, MK18 1HY Tel: (01280) 815093 Fax: (01280) 822022 E-mail: info@excaliburexhibitions.com

▶ Exhibit Design UK, Rudry, Withybed Corner, Walton on the Hill, Tadworth, Surrey, KT20 7UH Tel: (07710) 413896 E-mail: studio@exhibit-design.co.uk

Exhibition Department Ltd, South March, Long March Industrial Estate, Daventry, Northamptonshire, NN11 4PH Tel: (024) 7636 8474 Fax: (01327) 704488 E-mail: sales@theexhibitiondepartment.co.uk

The Exhibition & Interiors Co. Ltd, Station Road, Irthlingborough, Wellingborough, Northamptonshire, NN9 5QE Tel: (01933) 650222 Fax: (01933) 655688 E-mail: sales@exhibitionandinteriors.co.uk

Exhibition Works Ltd, 42 Lanchester Way, Royal Oak Industrial Estate, Daventry, Northamptonshire, NN11 8PH Tel: (01327) 705250 Fax: (01327) 705199 E-mail: sales@exhibitionworks.co.uk

Expo Display Service Ltd, 84a High Street, Stony Stratford, Milton Keynes, MK11 1AH Tel: (01908) 263656 Fax: (01908) 263616 E-mail: info@expo-display-service.com

Eyelevel Displays, 18 Market Square, Bishops Castle, Shropshire, SY9 5BN Tel: (01588) 630200 Fax: (01588) 630559 E-mail: info@eyelevel-displays.co.uk

Fastlane Displays Ltd, 19 Arkwright Court, Astmoor Industrial Estate, Runcorn, Cheshire, WA7 1NX Tel: (01928) 569846 Fax: (01928) 569846

Finesse Group, Cobbswood Industrial Estate, Brunswick Road, Ashford, Kent, TN23 1EH Tel: (01233) 663399 Fax: (01233) 665599 E-mail: info@finessegroup.com

Focal Design Ltd, The Old Bakery, Albion Road, New Mills, High Peak, Derbyshire, SK22 3EX Tel: (01663) 746100 Fax: (01663) 746920 E-mail: sales@focaldesign.co.uk

Frank Layton (Display), 9 Broadway Place, London, SW19 3TP Tel: (020) 8946 5041 Fax: (020) 8944 7324

G H Display, 4-5 Papyrus Road, Peterborough, PE4 5BH Tel: (01733) 571222 Fax: (01733) 320665 E-mail: mail@ghdisplay.co.uk

GDC Themed Events Ltd, 38-42 Fife Road, Kingston Upon Thames, Surrey, KT1 1SU Tel: (020) 8547 3682 Fax: (020) 8546 8461 E-mail: tim@gdc-events.co.uk

George Gidden Graphics Ltd, 14 Park Street, Guildford, Surrey, GU1 4XB Tel: (01483) 303040 Fax: (01483) 303222 E-mail: paul@giddenplace.com

Graphic Services UK Ltd, 26 Eastcott Hill, Swindon, SN1 3JG Tel: (01793) 542678 Fax: (01793) 430788

Gratel Signs & Nameplates, 4 Blatchford Close, Horsham, West Sussex, RH13 5RG Tel: (01403) 210385 Fax: (01403) 218282

HBM Ltd, H B House, 31 Chalfont Road, Beaconsfield, Buckinghamshire, HP9 2QP Tel: (01494) 671246 Fax: (01494) 678112 E-mail: sales@hbm.co.uk

Highfield International Exhibition Services Ltd, Unit 1A, Worcester Trading Estate, Blackpole Rd, Worcester, WR3 8HR Tel: (01905) 754158 Fax: (01905) 456218

I D Design, 48 Broadway Avenue, Harlow, Essex, CM17 0AG Tel: (01279) 415548 Fax: (01279) 415548 E-mail: iddesign@dial.pipex.com

The Image Projections Co. Ltd, Wickhurst Studios, Wickhurst Lane, Broadbridge Heath, Horsham, West Sussex, RH12 3LA Tel: (01403) 211110 E-mail: support@imageprojections.co.uk

Independent Design & Display, Independent, 275 Meanwood Road, Leeds, LS7 2JD Tel: 0113-242 9944 Fax: 0113-242 9669 E-mail: info@independentdesign.co.uk

▶ Innov-8 Ltd, Clayfield Industrial Estate, Tickhill Road, Doncaster, South Yorkshire, DN4 8QG Tel: (01302) 310888 Fax: (01302) 855060

International Exhibition Design Services Ltd, 62A High Street, Hampton Hill, Hampton, Middlesex, TW12 1PD Tel: (020) 8977 5129 Fax: (020) 8977 0036 E-mail: design@ieds-ltd.com

Jacee Contracts Ltd, 2 Station Road, Cottingham, North Humberside, HU16 4LL Tel: (01482) 840167 Fax: (01482) 875467 E-mail: paul@jc.fsnet.co.uk

John Adams, 8 Granville Road, Ilford, Essex, IG1 4JY Tel: (020) 8554 8019 Fax: (020) 4784 7927 E-mail: jadamsdesign@aol.com

Limelight, 107 George Lane, London, E18 1AN Tel: (020) 8989 6106 Fax: (020) 8989 7163 E-mail: contact@limelightdesign.co.uk

▶ M C Squared Ltd, Old Kings Head Court, 11 High Street, Dorking, Surrey, RH4 1AR Tel: (01306) 876505 Fax: (01306) 877508 E-mail: studio@mvsquared.co.uk

Madden Construction & Display Ltd, Unit 26-27 Watery La Industrial Estate, Watery Lane, Willenhall, West Midlands, WV13 3SU Tel: (01902) 366234 Fax: (01902) 366500

Joe Manby Ltd, Hook Stone Park, Harrogate, North Yorkshire, HG2 7DB Tel: (01423) 814730 Fax: (01423) 814760 E-mail: info@joemanby.co.uk

Martin Hopkins Partnership, 31 The Parade, Roath, Cardiff, CF24 3AD Tel: (029) 2046 1233 Fax: (029) 2049 7208 E-mail: info@martinhopkins.co.uk

Mayridge Ltd, Atherstone Hill Farm, Atherstone on Stour, Stratford-upon-Avon, Warwickshire, CV37 8NF Tel: (01789) 450898 Fax: (01789) 450855 E-mail: info@mayridge.com

Mobex Ltd, Unit 6 Rigestate Industrial Estate, Station Road, Berkeley, Gloucestershire, GL13 9RL Tel: (01453) 511210 Fax: (01453) 511226 E-mail: info@mobex.co.uk

Moonlight Photographic Services, 80 Wollaston Way, Burnt Mills Industrial Estate, Basildon, Essex, SS13 1DJ Tel: (01268) 727789 Fax: (01268) 725777 E-mail: info@moonlight-uk.com

Coleman Moore Partner Agency Network Ltd, 53A Main Road, Duston, Northampton, NN5 6JN Tel: (01604) 598989 Fax: (01604) 598979 E-mail: info@colemanmoore.com

Guy Morgan Design, 87 Maunsell Way, Wroughton, Swindon, SN4 9JF Tel: (01793) 814300 Fax: E-mail: guy@gmdesign.co.uk

Nebrak Ltd, 1 Ipplepen Business Park, Edgelands Lane, Ipplepen, Newton Abbot, Devon, TQ12 5UG Tel: (01803) 813900 Fax: (01803) 812300 E-mail: sales@nebrak.com

Normalite Ltd, Kingsley Street, Leicester, LE2 6DY Tel: 0116-270 0893 Fax: 0116-270 1221 E-mail: sales@normalite.fsnet.co.uk

Nortex Ltd, 73 Arthur Street, Lakeside, Redditch, Worcestershire, B98 8JY Tel: (01527) 500742 Fax: (01527) 502999 E-mail: nortex.exhibitions@virgin.net

▶ Palm Signs Systems, 35a Greenfield Business Park, Bagillt Road, Greenfield, Holywell, Clwyd, CH8 7HJ Tel: (01352) 712222 Fax: (01352) 712255 E-mail: info@palmsigns.co.uk

Peco Signs, Unit 5, Arrow Road North, Lakeside, Redditch, Worcestershire, B98 8NT Tel: (01527) 595364 Fax: (01527) 595366 E-mail: info@pecostudios.com

Pennine Arts International Ltd, Long Lea Works, Halifax Road, Elland, West Yorkshire, HX5 0SH Tel: (01422) 378123 Fax: (01422) 370879 E-mail: sales@pennine-arts.co.uk

Pentagram Design Ltd, 11 Needham Road, London, W11 2RP Tel: (020) 7229 3477 Fax: (020) 7727 9932 E-mail: email@pentagram.co.uk

Perton Signs, 3 Roslin Road, London, W3 8DH Tel: (020) 8992 5775 Fax: (020) 8992 5885 E-mail: sales@pertonsigns.com

Plastengrave Ltd, Unit 29 77-87 Trafalgar Business Centre, River Road, Barking, Essex, IG11 0JU Tel: (020) 8591 2595 Fax: (020) 8594 0459 E-mail: sales@plastengrave.co.uk

Print Express, 4 Sunnyside Terrace, London, NW9 5DL Tel: (020) 8200 0600 Fax: (020) 8200 6866 E-mail: printexpress@btclick.com

▶ Pro-Stage Europe Ltd, The Stables, Watersplash Farm Ford Bridge Roa, Sunbury-on-Thames, Middlesex, TW16 6AU Tel: (01932) 779399 Fax: (01932) 779399 E-mail: info@prostageeurope.com

Quadrant Displays Ltd, 14 Woodham Road, Barry Dock, Barry, South Glamorgan, CF63 4JE Tel: (01446) 747142 Fax: (01446) 749696

Rapiergroup, Rapier House, Crane Mead, Ware, Hertfordshire, SG12 9PW Tel: (0870) 9007782 Fax: (0870) 9007783 E-mail: info@rapiergroup.com

Redwood Photographic, 7 Brunel Court, Brunel Way, Severalls Industrial Park, Colchester, CO4 9XW Tel: (01206) 751241 Fax: (01206) 855134 E-mail: info@redwoodphoto.com

Roy John Design, 117 Christchurch Road, Ringwood, Hampshire, BH24 3AQ Tel: (01425) 477644 Fax: (01425) 480254 E-mail: enquiries@royjohndesign.co.uk

Sasex International, Sasex House, Haverhill Road, Horseheath, Cambridge, CB21 4QR Tel: (01223) 892319 Fax: (01223) 891535 E-mail: sales@sasex.co.uk

Scanachrome, 49 Glebe Road, Skelmersdale, Lancashire, WN8 9JP Tel: (01695) 725486 Fax: (01695) 722695 E-mail: sales@scanachrome.com

SD Displays Ltd, 157 Boyn Valley Road, Maidenhead, Berkshire, SL6 4EG Tel: (01628) 673864 Fax: (01628) 674803 E-mail: sales@sd-displays.co.uk

SDD Exhibitions, Marlborough House, 4 Marlborough Road, Sheffield, S10 1DD Tel: 0114-268 6040 Fax: 0114-266 2572 E-mail: sddex@sdd.co.uk

Service Graphics Ltd, 1 Sarum Business Park, The Portway, Salisbury, SP4 6EA Tel: (01722) 321736 Fax: (01722) 330041

Showprint Photographics Ltd, 29 High Street, Hampton Wick, Kingston Upon Thames, Surrey, KT1 4DA Tel: (020) 8943 9572 Fax: (020) 8943 5372

Sign Nature Ltd, Monks Heath Hall Workshop, Chelford Road, Nether Alderley, Macclesfield, Cheshire, SK10 4SY Tel: (01625) 860921 Fax: (01625) 890255 E-mail: tim@sign-nature.co.uk

Signshopuk.Com, 12 Crescent Road, Windermere, Cumbria, LA23 1EA Tel: (01539) 448884 Fax: (01539) 488884 E-mail: sales@signshopuk.com

Silverwood Exhibitions Ltd, 14 The Avenue, York, YO30 6AS Tel: (01904) 672700 Fax: (01904) 655800 E-mail: sales@silverwoodexhibitions.co.uk

Small Back Room, 88 Camberwell Road, London, SE5 0EG Tel: (020) 7701 4227 Fax: (020) 7703 3474 E-mail: sbr@smallbackroom.co.uk

Springboard Design, Unit4 Point 2, The Paint Works, Bath Road, Bristol, BS4 3EH Tel: 0117-958 8500 Fax: 0117-958 8501 E-mail: info@springboard-design.co.uk

Sprint Graphics, Station Road, Irthlingborough, Wellingborough, Northamptonshire, NN9 5QE Tel: (01933) 651908 Fax: (01933) 655688 E-mail: sales@sprintgraphics.co.uk

Stewart Furneaux, 16E Portland Road, Holland Park, London, W11 4LA Tel: (020) 7792 9000 Fax: (020) 7792 9270

▶ Sticky Letter Co., 35 Bridgefield, Farnham, Surrey, GU9 8AW Tel: (01252) 713683 Fax: (01252) 713683 E-mail: ideas@stickyletter.co.uk

▶ Still Works Ltd, 76 Wells Street, Cardiff, CF11 6DY Tel: (029) 2035 3940 Fax: (029) 2035 3941 E-mail: info@stillsdesign.com

Studio 2, 101 Lockhurst Lane, Coventry, CV6 5SF Tel: (024) 7663 8144 Fax: (024) 7666 1457 E-mail: sales@studio2exhibitions.co.uk

T A G Brand, The Barn, 13-17 Margett Street, Cottenham, Cambridge, CB24 8QY Tel: (01954) 250100 Fax: (01954) 250200 E-mail: info@tagbrand.co.uk

▶ Topdraw Visual Services, 12 Clinton Close, Grange Park, Swindon, SN5 6BP Tel: (01793) 877034 E-mail: info@topdrawvs.co.uk

United Business Media GP No 3 Ltd, Ludgate House, 245 Blackfriars Road, London, SE1 9UY Tel: (020) 7921 5000 Fax: (020) 7528 2772

Webb Display Services Ltd, Canalside Harris Business Park, Hanbury Road, Stoke Prior, Bromsgrove, Worcestershire, B60 4DJ Tel: (01527) 837306 Fax: (01527) 575230 E-mail: graphics@webbdisplay.co.uk

EXHIBITION DISPLAY GRAPHIC DESIGN

▶ About Turn Creative, Somerford Business Court, Holmes Chapel Road, Somerford, Congleton, Cheshire, CW12 4SN Tel: (01260) 281431 Fax: (01260) 289362 E-mail: info@aboutturncreative.co.uk

▶ Blinding Web Site Design, 8 Dalkeith Street, Barrow-in-Furness, Cumbria, LA14 1SP Tel: (01229) 828028 E-mail: info@blindingwebdesign.co.uk

▶ Blue Cube Design, 6 Keble Park North, Bishopthorpe, York, YO23 2SX Tel: (01904) 778222 Fax: (01904) 708828 E-mail: admin@bluecubedesign.com

▶ Brand Creative, Slackcote Lane, Delph, Oldham, OL3 5TP Tel: (01457) 874016 Fax: (01457) 874016 E-mail: design@brand-creative.co.uk

Clip Ltd, Athena, 210 Bristol Business Park, The Close, Bristol, BS16 1FJ Tel: 0117-937 5700 Fax: 0117-931 4561 E-mail: info@clipdisplay.com

▶ D C Group, Corsley, Corsley, Warminster, Wiltshire, BA12 7QH Tel: (01373) 832288 Fax: (01373) 832589 E-mail: stefen@dcgroup.uk.net

▶ Definitive Consulting, Parkfield Business Centre, Park Street, Stafford, ST17 4AL Tel: (01785) 226430 Fax: (01785) 222217 E-mail: info@definitiveuk.com

▶ Envisage Design Ltd, Brick Kiln Lane, Basford, Stoke-on-Trent, ST4 7BS Tel: (01782) 219922 Fax: (01782) 289580E-mail: info@enviz.co.uk

▶ Evolve, 35 Townfield Road, Mobberley, Knutsford, Cheshire, WA16 7HG Tel: (01565) 872683 Fax: (01565) 872534

▶ Exhibit Design UK, Rudry, Withybed Corner, Walton on the Hill, Tadworth, Surrey, KT20 7UH Tel: (07710) 413896 E-mail: studio@exhibit-design.co.uk

▶ Eye For Design, PO BOX 4657, Shrewsbury, SY1 9AD Tel: 01743 353536 E-mail: sales@eyefor.co.uk

▶ Fernleigh Design Ltd, Unit 5 Parc Ty Glas, Llanishen, Cardiff, CF11 7BF Tel: 02920 763524 Fax: 02920 763525 E-mail: amanda@fernleighdesign.co.uk

Five Fish Ltd, 77 Richmond Road, Twickenham, TW1 3AW Tel: (020) 8538 9277 Fax: (020) 8538 9270 E-mail: info@fivefish.co.uk

▶ Fli Backward Ltd, 557 Wilmslow Road, Manchester, M20 4GJ Tel: 0161-445 0273

▶ G D Sign, 62 West Street, Gorseinon, Swansea, SA4 4AF Tel: (01792) 549172 E-mail: sales@gdsign.co.uk

▶ G3 Creative Solutions, 7 Woodside Crescent, Glasgow, G3 7UL Tel: (01389) 875889 Fax: 0141-332 2233 E-mail: mail@g3creative.co.uk

Giant, 36 Queen Square, Bristol, BS1 4QS Tel: 0117 9086666 Fax: 0117 9085566 E-mail: info@gianteffect.co.uk

▶ High Kite, Fordham, Linden Avenue, Odiham, Hook, Hampshire, RG29 1AW Tel: (01256) 704876 E-mail: info@highkite.co.uk

▶ Image Directors, Power House, Powerscroft Road, Sidcup, Kent, DA14 5EA Tel: (0870) 4584475 Fax: (0870) 4584476 E-mail: steve@imagedirectors.co.uk

EXHIBITION DISPLAY GRAPHIC DESIGN – *continued*

▶ Irphoto, Burn Cottage, Southwick, Dumfries, DG2 8AN Tel: (01387) 780635 E-mail: mackay@irphoto.co.uk

▶ Jamie Ambler Studio, 34 Headlands, Kettering, Northamptonshire, NN15 7HP Tel: (01536) 525467 Fax: 01536 312535 E-mail: sales@bluemoonstudios.uk.com

Kiosk, No. 2, 43 High Street, Leamington Spa, Warwickshire, CV31 1LN Tel: (01926) 776282

▶ Knew Image Ltd, 33 Hampton Road, Twickenham, TW2 5QE Tel: (020) 8893 9661 Fax: (020) 8893 9662 E-mail: sales@knewimage.co.uk

▶ Kreative Juice, 24 Martholme Close, Blackburn, BB6 7TZ Tel: (01254) 884917 E-mail: info@kreativejuice.co.uk

▶ M C Squared Ltd, Old Kings Head Court, 11 High Street, Dorking, Surrey, RH4 1AR Tel: (01306) 876505 Fax: (01306) 877508 E-mail: studio@mvsquared.co.uk

▶ McHardy Media Ltd, The Media Centre, 6 North Isla Street, Dundee, DD3 7JQ Tel: (01382) 423248 E-mail: sales@mchardymedia.co.uk

Origin One UK Ltd, Dukes Yard Shakespeare Industrial Estate, Acme Road, Watford, WD24 5AL Tel: (01923) 246116 Fax: (01923) 246113 E-mail: info@origin-1.co.uk

▶ Profile Design, 10 West Pallant, Chichester, West Sussex, PO19 1TF Tel: (01243) 537444 Fax: (01243) 537440 E-mail: sales@profiledesign.net

▶ Remote New Media, 17 Lower Down, Lydbury North, Shropshire, SY7 8BB Tel: (01588) 680480 E-mail: info@remote.uk.com

▶ RT Media Ltd, Allen House, 2a East Borough, Wimborne, Dorset, BH21 1PF Tel: (01202) 888192 Fax: (01202) 888192 E-mail: info@rtmedia.com

▶ Rye Design, 107-109 High Street, Rochester, Kent, ME1 1JS Tel: (01634) 818168 Fax: (01634) 818178 E-mail: sales@ryedesign.co.uk

Sapio Solutions, New Brook House, 385 Alfreton Road, Nottingham, NG7 5LR Tel: 0115-875 8837 Fax: 0115-875 9900 E-mail: info@wowdesignsolutions.com

▶ SM Creative Ltd, 4 Raven Close, Chorley, Lancashire, PR7 2RE Tel: (01257) 232392 Fax: (01257) 232392 E-mail: design@smcreative.co.uk

▶ Stik-Chik Agency, Old Straw Barn, 5 Greenacre Drive, Rushden, Northamptonshire, NN10 0TQ Tel: (07866) 718132 E-mail: enquiries@ntlworld.co.uk

▶ Topdraw Visual Services, 12 Clinton Close, Grange Park, Swindon, SN5 6BP Tel: (01793) 877034 E-mail: info@topdrawvs.co.uk

Toucan Graphic Design Ltd, 25 Southernhay East, Exeter, EX1 1NS Tel: (01392) 438463 Fax: (01392) 495415 E-mail: designers@toucandesign.co.uk

▶ The Vector Studio, 44 High Oakham Close, Sutton-in-Ashfield, Nottinghamshire, NG17 4JS Tel: (07931) 934479 E-mail: thevectorstudio@hotmail.com

▶ VMAL, Unit B3 Connaught Business Centre, London, NW9 6JL Tel: (0845) 1082356 Fax: (0845) 1082357 E-mail: info@vmal.co.uk

EXHIBITION DISPLAY HIRE

Displex Display & Exhibition Ltd, Graphex House, Adcroft Street, Stockport, Cheshire, SK1 3HZ Tel: 0161-480 4626 Fax: 0161-474 1875 E-mail: sales@displex.co.uk

Image Design, Hangar SE38, Gloucestershire Airport, Staverton, Cheltenham, Gloucestershire, GL51 6SP Tel: (01452) 712000 Fax: (01452) 857785 E-mail: info@imagedesignuk.com

Indusfoto Ltd, 39-41 Margravine Road, London, W6 8LL Tel: (020) 7385 7618 Fax: (020) 7381 0047 E-mail: mark@indusfoto.co.uk

Merit Display, 8-10 Maudslay Road, Coventry, CV5 8EL Tel: (024) 7667 6700

Guy Morgan Design, 87 Maunsell Way, Wroughton, Swindon, SN4 9JF Tel: (01793) 814300 Fax: E-mail: guy@gmdesign.co.uk

MPD, Bitham Brook House, Gibbs Close, Westbury, Wiltshire, BA13 3DT Tel: (01373) 827111 Fax: (01373) 827222 E-mail: sales@ukmpd.com

Piers-Roger (Electronics) Ltd, Knights Court, Magellan Close, Walworth Industrial Estate, Andover, Hampshire, SP10 5NT Tel: (01264) 400800 Fax: (01264) 400900 E-mail: sales@polycomp.co.uk

Silverwood Exhibitions Ltd, 14 The Avenue, York, YO30 6AS Tel: (01904) 672700 Fax: (01904) 655800 E-mail: sales@silverwoodexhibitions.co.uk

Technik Exhibit Solutions Ltd, Unit 14 Boxted Farm Business Park, Berkhamsted Road, Hemel Hempstead, Hertfordshire, HP1 2SG Tel: (01442) 220130 Fax: (01442) 251412 E-mail: sales@techniksolutions.co.uk

EXHIBITION DISPLAY MATERIALS

▶ Credes Solutions, 326 Molesey Road, Walton-on-Thames, Surrey, KT12 3PD Tel: (01932) 244599 Fax: (01932) 244955 E-mail: sales@credes.co.uk

▶ Dijon Exhibition Design Co., 1 Castle Farm, Clifton Road, Deddington, Banbury, Oxfordshire, OX15 0TP Tel: (01869) 337311 Fax: (01869) 337322 E-mail: sales@dijondesigns.com

▶ Eventous, Unit 26B, 8-10 Glasgow Road, Kirkintilloch, Glasgow, G66 1SH Tel: (0845) 1679565 E-mail: info@eventous.com

▶ Inter-Expo, 15 Stonebridge, Peterborough, PE2 5NF Tel: 01733 237988 Fax: 01733 237988 E-mail: info@ExpoA1.com

Newshield Enterprises Ltd, Unit 2h Northlands Business Park, Bognor Road, Warnham, Horsham, West Sussex, RH12 3SH Tel: (01306) 627087 Fax: (01306) 627119 E-mail: sales@newshield.co.uk

Saw See Displays Ltd, 6 Speckled Wood, Hastings, East Sussex, TN35 5AH Tel: (0870) 1997726 Fax: (01424) 200521 E-mail: info@sawsee.net

EXHIBITION DISPLAY PANELS

▶ 4Max Visual Impact, The Stables, Claverdon Oaks, Henley Road, Claverdon, Warwick, CV35 8PS Tel: (0870) 2364163 Fax: (0870) 2364164 E-mail: john.blakey@4max.co.uk

▶ Denby Display Ltd, Unit 9, Stewart Close, Penarth Road, Cardiff, CF11 8QF Tel: (029) 2022 3446 E-mail: t.tribe@sky-hook.com

EXHIBITION DISPLAY SYSTEMS, PORTABLE

▶ 4Max Visual Impact, The Stables, Claverdon Oaks, Henley Road, Claverdon, Warwick, CV35 8PS Tel: (0870) 2364163 Fax: (0870) 2364164 E-mail: john.blakey@4max.co.uk

▶ Denby Display Ltd, Unit 9, Stewart Close, Penarth Road, Cardiff, CF11 8QF Tel: (029) 2022 3446 E-mail: t.tribe@sky-hook.com

▶ Displaymania, Back Grove Farm Estate, Bulls Lane, Wishaw, Sutton Coldfield, West Midlands, B76 9QN Tel: 0121-313 1313 Fax: 0121-313 1212 E-mail: sales@displaymania.co.uk

EXHIBITION DISPLAYS, SPACE FRAME/DOME

Advertising Constructions Ltd, Engineering Centre, Brick Kiln Lane, Stoke-on-Trent, ST4 7BS Tel: (01782) 213444 Fax: (01782) 266555 E-mail: adcons@adcons.co.uk

▶ Arena Display Ltd, 3 Scotch George Lane, Knaresborough, North Yorkshire, HG5 9EH Tel: (01423) 770900 Fax: (01423) 770400 E-mail: steve@arenadisplay.co.uk

Eyelevel Displays, 18 Market Square, Bishops Castle, Shropshire, SY9 5BN Tel: (01588) 630200 Fax: (01588) 630559 E-mail: info@eyelevel-displays.co.uk

EXHIBITION DISPLAYS, STANDS, CUSTOM

▶ Astro Exhibitions Ltd, Unit 3, Ensor Trading Estate, Ensor Way, New Mills, New Mills, High Peak, Derbyshire, SK22 4NQ Tel: 01663 744868 Fax: 01663 747950 E-mail: info@astroexhibitions.co.uk

▶ Compass Inc Ltd, Regus House, Fairbourne Drive, Atterbury, Milton Keynes, MK10 9RG Tel: (01908) 487509 Fax: (01908) 787501 E-mail: info@compassinc.co.uk

▶ Graphic Pavement Signs Ltd, Letchworth Garden City, Hertfordshire, SG6 3XH Tel: (01462) 673831 Fax: (01462) 481703 E-mail: mail@posterholders.fsnet.co.uk

EXHIBITION ELECTRICAL CONTRACTORS

Illumination, Unit 7, North Medburn Farm, Watling Street, Elstree, Borehamwood, Hertfordshire, WD6 3AA Tel: (020) 8953 1414 Fax: (020) 8207 3040 E-mail: info@illumelec.co.uk

Joe Manby Ltd, Hook Stone Park, Harrogate, North Yorkshire, HG2 7DB Tel: (01423) 814730 Fax: (01423) 814760 E-mail: info@joemanby.co.uk

Richard Norman Electrics Ltd, Clasford Farm Units 5-9, Aldershot Road, Guildford, Surrey, GU3 3HQ Tel: (01483) 233900 Fax: (01483) 236500 E-mail: sales@rne.co.uk

▶ Scenic Effect, Eyreswood Farm, Astwood Road, Cranfield, Bedford, MK43 0AU Tel: (01234) 750777 Fax: (01234) 752172 E-mail: martin@sceniceffects.com

S. Seymour (Electrics) Ltd, 50 Glentham Road, London, SW13 9JJ Tel: (020) 8748 7788 Fax: (020) 8741 0720 E-mail: seymourelectrics@aol.com

EXHIBITION ENGINEERING

Helm Exhibitions Ltd, 27-29 Speedwell Road, Haymills, Birmingham, B25 8HU Tel: 0121-766 6755 Fax: 0121-766 6752 E-mail: enquiries@helmx.co.uk

Markfield Services, Trent Works, Felton Road, Nottingham, NG2 2EH Tel: 0115-985 0400 Fax: 0115-985 0252 E-mail: markfield@trentworks.demon.co.uk

▶ Science Projects Ltd, 20 St. James Street, London, W6 9RW Tel: (020) 8741 2306 Fax: (020) 8741 2307 E-mail: info@science-projects.org

EXHIBITION GRAPHICS DESIGN

▶ Exhibit Design UK, Rudry, Withybed Corner, Walton on the Hill, Tadworth, Surrey, KT20 7UH Tel: (07710) 413896 E-mail: studio@exhibit-design.co.uk

▶ Idealogic, Focal Point, 88 Coronation Avenue, Bath, BA2 2JP Tel: 01225 483322 Fax: 01225 483322 E-mail: kirstie@idealogicuk.com

▶ Studio K, The Lodge, 145 Westgate, Cleckheaton, West Yorkshire, BD19 5EJ Tel: 01274 861433 E-mail: imelda@studiok.fsbusiness.co.uk

▶ Westgate Design, 37 The Drive, Sevenoaks, Kent, TN13 3AD Tel: (01732) 454588 Fax: (01732) 779087 E-mail: shaun@westgatedesign.co.uk

Ziggurat Design, Hall Farm Barn, Carleton Forehoe, Norwich, NR9 4AL Tel: (01603) 757600 E-mail: info@zigguratdesign.co.uk

EXHIBITION HIRE FURNISHERS

Camden Hire Ltd, Unit C, 125 Brantwood Road, Tottenham, London, N17 0DX Tel: (020) 8961 6161 Fax: (020) 8961 6162 E-mail: contact@thorns.co.uk

Connect Wall Systems, 26 Westcott Crescent, London, W7 1PA Tel: (020) 8578 2437 Fax: (020) 8578 2450

Exoplan International Ltd, Unit 13, Industrial Estate, National Exhibition Centre, Birmingham, B40 1PJ Tel: 0121-780 4513 Fax: 0121-780 4810 E-mail: sales@exoplan.co.uk

Milton Furniture Ltd, Touriment Building, Smifby Road, Ashby-de-la-Zouch, Leicestershire, LE65 2UR Tel: (01530) 564287 Fax: (01530) 564723 E-mail: mfh@thefurniturehirepeople.com

Technik Exhibit Solutions Ltd, Unit 14 Boxted Farm Business Park, Berkhamsted Road, Hemel Hempstead, Hertfordshire, HP1 2SG Tel: (01442) 220130 Fax: (01442) 251412 E-mail: sales@techniksolutions.co.uk

EXHIBITION LIFTING CONTRACTORS

▶ Scenic Effect, Eyreswood Farm, Astwood Road, Cranfield, Bedford, MK43 0AU Tel: (01234) 750777 Fax: (01234) 752172 E-mail: martin@sceniceffects.com

Yorkshire Exhibtion Services, Unit 17 Industrial Estate, National Exhibition Centre, Birmingham, B40 1PJ Tel: 0121-782 4626 Fax: 0121-782 4680 E-mail: horst@yes-exh.com

EXHIBITION MARQUEES

▶ Apna Marquee.com, 6 Copinger Walk, Edgware, Middlesex, HA8 0AH Tel: (07956) 895677 E-mail: info@ApnaMarquee.com

▶ Dijon Exhibition Design Co., 1 Castle Farm, Clifton Road, Deddington, Banbury, Oxfordshire, OX15 0TP Tel: (01869) 337311 Fax: (01869) 337322 E-mail: sales@dijondesigns.com

▶ Hoecker Structures UK Ltd, Robinson Way, Telford Way Industrial Estate, Kettering, Northamptonshire, NN16 8PT Tel: (01536) 316970 Fax: (01536) 316979 E-mail: sales@hoecker.plus.com

Newshield Enterprises Ltd, Unit 2h Northlands Business Park, Bognor Road, Warnham, Horsham, West Sussex, RH12 3SH Tel: (01306) 627087 Fax: (01306) 627119 E-mail: sales@newshield.co.uk

EXHIBITION (MOBILE) TRANSPORT MANAGEMENT

CPM Mobile Marketing, Unit 3 Newby Road Industrial Estate, Levens Road, Hazel Grove, Stockport, Cheshire, SK7 5DA Tel: 0161-483 5319 Fax: 0161-483 5375 E-mail: enquiries@mmcpm.co.uk

▶ European International, Unit 5 6 Skitts Manor Farm, Moor Lane, Marsh Green, Edenbridge, Kent, TN8 5RA Tel: (01732) 860330 Fax: (01732) 860331 E-mail: info@european-intl.com

▶ MDB Group, Cavendish House, Cavendish Rd, Stevenage, Hertfordshire, SG1 2EQ Tel: 01438 365451 E-mail: sales@mdbgroup.co.uk

Pro Ex Group Ltd, Hamilton House, Rackery Lane, Llay, Wrexham, Clwyd, LL12 0PB Tel: (01978) 855622 Fax: (01978) 855151 E-mail: enquiries@pro-ex.co.uk

Torton Bodies Ltd, Pilot Works, Holyhead Road, Oakengates, Telford, Shropshire, TF2 6BB Tel: (01952) 612648 Fax: (01952) 620373 E-mail: sales@torton.com

Worldwide Exhibition Specialists Ltd, 1 York House, Langston Road, Loughton, Essex, IG10 3TQ Tel: (020) 8508 2224 Fax: (020) 8502 4969 E-mail: info@worldwidexpo.co.uk

EXHIBITION (MOBILE) UNIT HIRE

A T F Services, 60 Brick Kiln Lane, Parkhouse Industrial Estate West, Newcastle, Staffordshire, ST5 7AS Tel: (01782) 561095 Fax: (01782) 566444

David Wilson's Trailers, Hillsdown Farm, Birch Grove, Horsted Keynes, Haywards Heath, West Sussex, RH17 7DH Tel: (01825) 740696 Fax: (01825) 740260 E-mail: info@dwt-exhibitions.co.uk

Pro Ex Group Ltd, Hamilton House, Rackery Lane, Llay, Wrexham, Clwyd, LL12 0PB Tel: (01978) 855622 Fax: (01978) 855151 E-mail: enquiries@pro-ex.co.uk

Sienna Exhibitions Ltd, Unit 1r, Membury Business Park, Lambourn Woodlands, Hungerford, Berkshire, RG17 7TJ Tel: (01488) 73720 Fax: (01488) 73721 E-mail: sales@sienna-indigo.com

Torton Bodies Ltd, Pilot Works, Holyhead Road, Oakengates, Telford, Shropshire, TF2 6BB Tel: (01952) 612648 Fax: (01952) 620373 E-mail: sales@torton.com

EXHIBITION (MOBILE) UNIT REFURBISHMENT

Central Display Production, B Gresham Way Industrial Estate, Gresham Way, London, SW19 8ED Tel: (020) 8944 5156 Fax: (020) 8944 5950 E-mail: dudley@centraldisplay.com

Torton Bodies Ltd, Pilot Works, Holyhead Road, Oakengates, Telford, Shropshire, TF2 6BB Tel: (01952) 612648 Fax: (01952) 620373 E-mail: sales@torton.com

EXHIBITION (MOBILE) UNITS

Bank Farm Trailers Ltd, Robeston Wathen, Narberth, Dyfed, SA67 8EN Tel: (01834) 860605 Fax: (01834) 861498 E-mail: sales@bankfarm-trailers.co.uk

Connect Wall Systems, 26 Westcott Crescent, London, W7 1PA Tel: (020) 8578 2437 Fax: (020) 8578 2450

CPM Mobile Marketing, Unit 3 Newby Road Industrial Estate, Levens Road, Hazel Grove, Stockport, Cheshire, SK7 5DA Tel: 0161-483 5319 Fax: 0161-483 5375 E-mail: enquiries@mmcpm.co.uk

Lynton Trailers UK Ltd, Constable Street, Manchester, M18 8GJ Tel: 0161-223 8211 Fax: 0161-223 0933 E-mail: lyntonmail@aol.com

Myers John Associates, Park Street, Parkfield Business Centre, Stafford, ST17 4AL Tel: (01785) 224134 Fax: (01785) 246654 E-mail: jma@onetel.net.uk

Pro Ex Group Ltd, Hamilton House, Rackery Lane, Llay, Wrexham, Clwyd, LL12 0PB Tel: (01978) 855622 Fax: (01978) 855151 E-mail: enquiries@pro-ex.co.uk

EXHIBITION MODELS

Confluence Creative, Unit 23, Merryhills Enterprise Park, Park Lane, Wolverhampton, WV10 9TJ Tel: (01902) 862601 Fax: (01902) 862602 E-mail: contact@confluencecreative.co.uk

▶ JSM Industrial Model Making, Unit 5 Home Farm House Works, Mildenhall, Marlborough, Wiltshire, SN8 2LR Tel: (01672) 512305 Fax: (01672) 512305 E-mail: studio@jsmmodelmakers.freeserve.co.uk

EXHIBITION (MODULAR) DISPLAY SYSTEMS MANUFRS

Abbey Design Ltd, Lakeside Trading Centre, Beoley Road East, Redditch, Worcestershire, B98 8PE Tel: (01527) 585888 Fax: (01527) 596334 E-mail: sales@systematicdisplays.co.uk

Adams Exhibitions, 6 Rose Green Road, Bristol, BS5 7XE Tel: 0117-952 1000 Fax: 0117-952 2000 E-mail: joe@adams-exhibitions.co.uk

Aspect Exhibitions Ltd, 1 Ashton Lodge Farm, Hartwell Road, Ashton, Northampton, NN7 2JT Tel: (01604) 864999 Fax: (01604) 864888 E-mail: sales@aspectexhib.co.uk

City Self Drive, Swallowdale Lane, Hemel Hempstead Industrial Estate, Hemel Hempstead Industrial Estate, Hemel Hempstead, Hertfordshire, HP2 7EA Tel: (01442) 419419 Fax: (01442) 419201 E-mail: info@citygroup.com

Classic Design & Build (UK) Ltd, Lode Lane Industrial Estate, Vulcan Road, Solihull, West Midlands, B91 2JY Tel: 0121-709 2040 Fax: 0121-709 2044 E-mail: info@classicdb.co.uk

Cobb Group Exhibition Services Ltd, PO Box 37, Luton, LU1 1YW Tel: (01582) 453308 Fax: (01582) 417528 E-mail: info@cobbgroup.co.uk

EXHIBITION (MODULAR) DISPLAY SYSTEMS MANUFRS – *continued*

The D P Design Co. Ltd, 31 Warwick Row, Coventry, CV1 1EY Tel: (024) 7622 3390 Fax: (024) 7622 0740
Display Services International, Unit 3 Victoria Wharf Victoria Industrial Park, Victoria Road, Dartford, DA1 5AJ Tel: (01322) 222474 Fax: (01322) 276328 E-mail: info@handsie-display.co.uk
Exhibition Services Ltd, 6 271 Merton Road, London, SW18 5JS Tel: (020) 8874 1787 Fax: (020) 8874 1587 E-mail: info@exhibitionservices.com
Exhibition Works Ltd, 42 Lanchester Way, Royal Oak Industrial Estate, Daventry, Northamptonshire, NN11 8PH Tel: (01327) 705250 Fax: (01327) 705199 E-mail: sales@exhibitionworks.co.uk
Expo Display Service Ltd, 84a High Street, Stony Stratford, Milton Keynes, MK11 1AH Tel: (01908) 263656 Fax: (01908) 263616 E-mail: info@expo-display-service.com
Moonlight Photographic Services, 80 Wollaston Way, Burnt Mills Industrial Estate, Basildon, Essex, SS13 1DJ Tel: (01268) 727789 Fax: (01268) 725777 E-mail: info@moonlight-uk.com
Guy Morgan Design, 87 Maunsell Way, Wroughton, Swindon, SN4 9JF Tel: (01793) 814300 Fax: E-mail: guy@gmdesign.co.uk
Nomadic Display, The Nomadic House, 71 St Johns Road, Isleworth, Middlesex, TW7 6XQ Tel: 0121-333 4956 Fax: (020) 8326 5522 E-mail: hqsales@nomadicdisplay.co.uk
The Production House, Old Customs House Studios, 1 West Harbour Road, Edinburgh, EH5 1PH Tel: 0131-551 1301 Fax: 0131-551 2473 E-mail: productionhouse1@aol.com
Roy John Design, 117 Christchurch Road, Ringwood, Hampshire, BH24 3AQ Tel: (01425) 477644 Fax: (01425) 480254 E-mail: enquiries@royjohndesign.co.uk
Supertube, Darby House, Darby Way, Narborough, Leicester, LE19 2GP Tel: 0116-286 6611 Fax: 0116-275 0216

EXHIBITION ORGANISERS AND MANAGEMENT

Air Displays (International) Ltd, Building 509, Churchill Way, Biggin Hill Airport, Westerham, Kent, TN16 3BN Tel: (01959) 572277 Fax: (01959) 575969 E-mail: sales@airdisplaysint.co.uk
▶ Binsted Group plc, Attwood House Mansfield Business Park, Lymington Bottom Road, Medstead, Alton, Hampshire, GU34 5PZ Tel: (01420) 568900 Fax: (01420) 565994 E-mail: info@binstedgroup.com
Brintex Ltd, 32 Vauxhall Bridge Road, London, SW1V 2SS Tel: (020) 7973 6404 Fax: (020) 7233 5054 E-mail: sales@brintex.com
Britihsh Marine Federation, Marine House, Thorpe Lea Road, Egham, Surrey, TW20 8BF Tel: (01784) 473377 Fax: (01784) 439678 E-mail: enquiries@bmif.co.uk
Cardiff International Arena, Mary Ann Street, Cardiff, CF10 2EQ Tel: (029) 2022 4488 Fax: (029) 2023 4501 E-mail: cia.sales@clearchannel.co.uk
Design Built Exhibitions Ltd, 46 Enfield Industrial Estate, Redditch, Worcestershire, B97 6DE Tel: (01527) 69132 Fax: (01527) 65692
DMG World Media, Equitable House, Lyon Road, Harrow, Middlesex, HA1 2EW Tel: (020) 8515 2000 Fax: (020) 8515 2080 E-mail: sales@dmgworldmedia.com
Emap TPS Ltd, 19Th Floor Leon House, 233 High Street, Croydon, CR0 9XT Tel: (020) 8277 5000 Fax: (020) 8277 5887 E-mail: info@emap.com
European Trade & Exhibition Services Ltd, 9-11 High Street, Staines, Middlesex, TW18 4QY Tel: (01784) 880890 Fax: (01784) 880892 E-mail: enquiries@etes.co.uk
Exhibition Department Ltd, South March, Long March Industrial Estate, Daventry, Northamptonshire, NN11 4PH Tel: (024) 7636 8474 Fax: (01327) 704488 E-mail: sales@theexhibitiondepartment.co.uk
Exhibitions International Ltd, Clearwater Indust Estate, Wolverhampton, WV2 2JP Tel: (01902) 450040 Fax: (01902) 450567 E-mail: sales@exhibitionsinternational.co.uk
Fairs & Exhibitions (1992) Ltd, Manor House, 1 The Crescent, Leatherhead, Surrey, KT22 8DH Tel: (020) 8391 0999 Fax: (020) 8391 0220 E-mail: info@fairs-exhibs.com
Hannover Associates, 4 Hurst View Road, South Croydon, Surrey, CR2 7AG Tel: (020) 8688 9541 Fax: (020) 8681 0069 E-mail: sales@hannoverfairs.co.uk
Inside Communications Ltd, Bank House, 23 Warwick Road, Coventry, CV1 2EW Tel: (024) 7657 1000 Fax: (024) 7625 2241
The John Mills Group, 11 Hope Street, Liverpool, L1 9BJ Tel: 0151-709 9822 Fax: 0151-709 6585 E-mail: sales@johnmillsgroup.com
Mayridge Ltd, Atherstone Hill Farm, Atherstone on Stour, Stratford-upon-Avon, Warwickshire, CV37 8NF Tel: (01789) 450898 Fax: (01789) 450855 E-mail: info@mayridge.com
Audry Montgomery Ltd, 9 Manchester Square, London, W1U 9PL Tel: (020) 7886 3000 Fax: (020) 7886 3001 E-mail: mel@montex.co.uk
Olympia Conference Centre, Hammersmith Road, Kensington, London, W14 8UX Tel: (020) 7370 8532 Fax: (020) 7370 8144 E-mail: conferences@eco.co.uk
Photosound Communications Ltd, Stansted Road, Birchanger, Bishop's Stortford, Hertfordshire, CM23 5PT Tel: (01279) 818400 Fax: (01279) 647746
Picon Ltd, St. Christophers House, Holloway Hill, Godalming, Surrey, GU7 1QZ Tel: (01483) 412000 Fax: (01483) 412001 E-mail: info@picon.co.uk
Reed Exhibition's Ltd, Oriel House, 26 The Quadrant, Richmond, Surrey, TW9 1DL Tel: (020) 8910 7910 Fax: (020) 8940 2171 E-mail: rxinfo@reedexpo.co.uk
Silver Leaf Productions, 253 Lavender Hill, London, SW11 1JW Tel: (020) 7924 6544 Fax: (020) 7801 3105 E-mail: sales@silverleafp.co.uk
Spoken Image Ltd, The Design Centre, 44 Canal St, Manchester, M1 3WD Tel: 0161-236 7522 Fax: 0161-236 3386 E-mail: multimedia@spoken-image.com
Supotco Design Ltd, 3-5 Valentine Place, London, SE1 8QH Tel: (020) 7928 5474 Fax: (020) 7928 6082 E-mail: info@supotco.co.uk
Tarsus Group plc, Commonwealth House, Chalkhill Road, London, W6 8DW Tel: (020) 8846 2700 Fax: (020) 8846 2801 E-mail: sales@tarsus-exhibitions.com
Trident Exhibitions Ltd, West Devon Business Park, Brook Lane, Tavistock, Devon, PL19 9DP Tel: (01822) 614671 Fax: (01822) 614818 E-mail: info@trident-exhibition.co.uk
World's Fair Ltd, Albert Mill, Albert Street, Oldham, OL8 3QL Tel: 0161-683 8000 Fax: 0161-683 8001 E-mail: wfair@worldsfair.co.uk
Xmark Media Ltd, Old Village Hall, The Street, Effingham, Leatherhead, Surrey, KT24 5JS Tel: (01372) 750555 Fax: (01372) 750666 E-mail: mobilex@zetnet.co.uk

EXHIBITION SECURITY SERVICES

▶ Diamond Event Security Ltd, 60 Heol Collen, Cardiff, CF5 5TX Tel: (029) 2059 1340 Fax: (029) 2059 6091 E-mail: info@diamondeventsecurity.co.uk
Grenadier Guards Security Services, Grenadier House, Condover, Shrewsbury, SY5 7BG Tel: 08450 539198 E-mail: info@grenadiersecurity.co.uk
Grenadier Security Nationwide, Quarry House, Telford, Shropshire, TF6 6NP Tel: (0845) 0539198 E-mail: info@grenadiersecurity.co.uk
Securitas Group, 203-205 Lower Richmond Road, Richmond, Surrey, TW9 4LN Tel: 0845 5314061 Fax: (020) 8876 4650 E-mail: jenny.campbell@securitas.uk.com

EXHIBITION SERVICES

▶ Absolute Audio Visual Solutions, Cheney Lodge, 81 Station Road, Odsey, Baldock, Hertfordshire, SG7 5RP Tel: (01462) 743003 E-mail: enquiry@absoluteavs.co.uk
▶ ACT, F1 Capital Point, Capital Business Park, Parkway, Cardiff, CF3 2PY Tel: (0845) 074 0100 Fax: (0845) 074 0120 E-mail: ian@actrepro.co.uk
▶ Bigger Scene Ltd, 172 Monks Wood, North Shields, Tyne & Wear, NE30 2UB Tel: 0191-272 8998
▶ Elevation Rigging Ltd, 3 Duchess Place, Edgbaston House, Birmingham, B16 8NH Tel: 0121 456 7949 Fax: 0121 789 6190 E-mail: mail@elevationrigging.com
▶ Event-tech Exhibition Services Ltd, Drybridge Park, Shewalton Road, Drybridge, Irvine, Ayrshire, KA11 5AL Tel: (01294) 312537 Fax: (01294) 273691
▶ Expositionists International, 62 Bridge Road East, Welwyn Garden City, Hertfordshire, AL7 1JU Tel: (01707) 390122 Fax: (01707) 390061 E-mail: info@expositionists.co.uk
▶ Jigsaw Confex Ltd, Events Office - Raincliffe Manor, Lady Ediths Drive, Scarborough, North Yorkshire, YO12 5RJ Tel: (07951) 164820 Fax: (07092) 399780 E-mail: office@jigsaw-confex.co.uk
Showtech Sound & Light Design, Unit 23 Hammond Business Centre, Hammond Close, Attleborough Fields Ind Estate, Nuneaton, Warwickshire, CV11 6RY Tel: (024) 7634 8890 Fax: (024) 7634 8890 E-mail: enquiries@ssld.co.uk
Sound Services, Button Street, Swanley, Kent, BR8 8DX Tel: (01322) 667709 Fax: 0208-196 2387 E-mail: mail@sound-services.co.uk

EXHIBITION SIGNS

1st Call Mercury Signs, Highfield View, Park Lane, Stokenchurch, Buckinghamshire, HP14 3TQ Tel: (01494) 482288 Fax: (01494) 483152 E-mail: mcgillsign@aol.com
Active Signs Ltd, 24 Leigh Road, Haine Industrial Estate, Ramsgate, Kent, CT12 5EU Tel: (01843) 850800 Fax: (01843) 852830
Alpha Signs (Northampton) Ltd, Clarence Avenue, Northampton, NN2 6NY Tel: (01604) 712233 Fax: (01604) 717131
▶ Bigger Scene Ltd, 172 Monks Wood, North Shields, Tyne & Wear, NE30 2UB Tel: 0191-272 8998
Clarks Signs Ltd, Alchorn Place, Portsmouth, PO3 5QL Tel: (023) 9282 6411 Fax: (023) 9266 9991 E-mail: sales@clarks-signs.co.uk
Design of Walton, 3 Lyln Road, Hersham Trading Estate, Walton-on-Thames, Surrey, KT12 3PU Tel: (01932) 240376 Fax: (01932) 241110 E-mail: signs@designofwalton.co.uk
The Holiday Inn, Junction 18 M1, Crick, Northampton, NN6 7XR Tel: (0870) 4009059 Fax: (01788) 823955 E-mail: reservations-rugby@6c.com
Jupiter Signs, 20 Singer Way, Kempston, Bedford, MK42 7AE Tel: (01234) 854577 Fax: (01234) 841401 E-mail: sales@jupitersigns.com
Macdonald Bower Hotel, Hollinwood Avenue, Chadderton, Oldham, OL9 8DE Tel: 0161-682 7254 Fax: 0161-683 4605 E-mail: admin@macdonaldhotels.co.uk
Mcquillan Signs, Cleves, Keymer Road, Burgess Hill, West Sussex, RH15 0AP Tel: (01444) 471847 Fax: (01444) 248592 E-mail: johntmcquillan@fsnet.co.uk
Nicol & Moon Ltd, 7 Wimbledon Stadium Business Centre, Riverside Road, London, SW17 0BA Tel: (020) 8879 6000 Fax: (020) 8879 6111 E-mail: info@nicolandmoon.ltd.uk
Smithbrewer Ltd, Sunnyside Road North, Weston-super-Mare, Avon, BS23 3PZ Tel: (01934) 642642 Fax: (01934) 642646 E-mail: sales@smithbrewer.co.uk
▶ Sticky Letter Co., 35 Bridgefield, Farnham, Surrey, GU9 8AW Tel: (01252) 713683 Fax: (01252) 713683 E-mail: ideas@stickyletter.co.uk
Trafford Signs Ltd, First Avenue, Trafford Park, Manchester, M17 1TS Tel: 0161-872 7103 Fax: 0161-848 8565 E-mail: traffordsigns@btconnect.com

EXHIBITION SOFT FURNISHINGS

D Donovan & Sons Carpet Services Ltd, 112 Blythe Road, London, W14 0HD Tel: (020) 7603 4161 Fax: (020) 7602 9929
Omega Drapes, Unit 17 Riverside Industrial Estate, Thames Road, Barking, Essex, IG11 0ND Tel: (020) 8591 4945 Fax: (020) 8591 4139 E-mail: sales@omegadrapes.fsnet.co.uk
Performance Sails, Victoria Loft, Hill Furze, Pershore, Worcestershire, WR10 2NB Tel: (01386) 861161 Fax: (01386) 861253 E-mail: performancesails@hotmail.com
Sidhu Textile Co. Ltd, 85-87 The Broadway, Southall, Middlesex, UB1 1LA Tel: (020) 8574 3385 Fax: (020) 8843 9229 E-mail: s_sidhu100@hotmail.com

EXHIBITION STAND BANNER LIGHTING

▶ Banner & Flag Co., 9 Lubnaig Gardens, Bearsden, Glasgow, G61 4QX Tel: 0141-577 9141 Fax: 0141-563 7147 E-mail: graphics@bf-c.co.uk

EXHIBITION STAND CONTRACTORS OR DESIGNERS OR FABRICATORS

A B C Graphics Ltd, 12 Ossory Road, London, SE1 5AN Tel: (020) 7231 5588 Fax: (020) 7231 6128
Abbey Design Ltd, Lakeside Trading Centre, Beoley Road East, Redditch, Worcestershire, B98 8PE Tel: (01527) 585888 Fax: (01527) 596334 E-mail: sales@systematicdisplays.co.uk
Adams Exhibitions, 6 Rose Green Road, Bristol, BS5 7XE Tel: 0117-952 1000 Fax: 0117-952 2000 E-mail: joe@adams-exhibitions.co.uk
Advertising Constructions Ltd, Engineering Centre, Brick Kiln Lane, Stoke-on-Trent, ST4 7BS Tel: (01782) 213444 Fax: (01782) 266555 E-mail: adcons@adcons.co.uk
Antone Displays Ltd, Wanstead Road, Leicester, LE3 1TR Tel: 0116-232 4700 Fax: 0116-287 8012
Ardan Exhibition, Unit 7 North Medburn Farm, Watling Street, Elstree, Hertfordshire, WD6 3AA Tel: (020) 8207 4957 Fax: (020) 8207 3040 E-mail: info@ardan.co.uk
▶ Arena Display Ltd, 3 Scotch George Lane, Knaresborough, North Yorkshire, HG5 9EH Tel: (01423) 770900 Fax: (01423) 770400 E-mail: steve@arenadisplay.co.uk
▶ Artisan Ltd, Dean Court, Great Western Business Park, Yate, Bristol, BS37 5NJ Tel: (01454) 321212 Fax: (01454) 313471
Aspect Exhibitions Ltd, 1 Ashton Lodge Farm, Hartwell Road, Ashton, Northampton, NN7 2JT Tel: (01604) 864999 Fax: (01604) 864888 E-mail: sales@aspectexhib.co.uk
Aston Display Ltd, 30 Brewery Street, Aston, Birmingham, B6 4JB Tel: 0121-333 6768 Fax: 0121-333 6769 E-mail: info@astondisplay.com
▶ Astro Exhibitions Ltd, Unit 3, Ensor Trading Estate, Ensor Way, New Mills, New Mills, High Peak, Derbyshire, SK22 4NQ Tel: 01663 744868 Fax: 01663 747950 E-mail: info@astroexhibitions.co.uk
Blackfriars Scenery Ltd, Blackfriars Studio, 33 Bear Lane, London, SE1 0UH Tel: (020) 7928 6413 Fax: (020) 7261 1994 E-mail: staging@compuserve.com
C D L Co. Ltd, 29 Grafton Road, Croydon, CR0 3RP Tel: (020) 8680 3077 Fax: (020) 8686 9225 E-mail: annaaustin@cdlco.fsnet.co.uk
Carpenter Communications Group Ltd, Old Greenfield House, Greenfield, Christmas Common, Watlington, Oxfordshire, OX49 5HF Tel: (01491) 614144 Fax: (01491) 613416 E-mail: sales@carpentercomms.co.uk
Charlesworth & Valentine, 34 Bridgnorth Road, Aqueduct Village, Telford, Shropshire, TF3 1BZ Tel: (01952) 592012 Fax: (01952) 270121
Classic Design & Build (UK) Ltd, Lode Lane Industrial Estate, Vulcan Road, Solihull, West Midlands, B91 2JY Tel: 0121-709 2040 Fax: 0121-709 2044 E-mail: info@classicdb.co.uk
Clements & Street Ltd, Hanbury Road, Stoke Prior, Bromsgrove, Worcestershire, B60 4AA Tel: (01527) 835777 Fax: (01527) 873061 E-mail: sales@clementsandstreet.co.uk
Cobb Group Exhibition Services Ltd, PO Box 37, Luton, LU1 1YW Tel: (01582) 453308 Fax: (01582) 417528 E-mail: info@cobbgroup.co.uk
Corner House, Laverstock, Uttoxeter Road, Foston, Derby, DE65 5PX Tel: (01283) 812848 Fax: (01283) 814542 E-mail: sales@cornerhouse.uk.com
CPM Mobile Marketing, Unit 3 Newby Road Industrial Estate, Levens Road, Hazel Grove, Stockport, Cheshire, SK7 5DA Tel: 0161-483 5319 Fax: 0161-483 5375 E-mail: enquiries@mmcpm.co.uk
Crown Exhibitions & Displays, 3 Partons Road, Kings Heath, Birmingham, B14 6TA Tel: 0121-441 2822 Fax: 0121-441 2772 E-mail: info@crownexhibition.co.uk
The D P Design Co. Ltd, 31 Warwick Row, Coventry, CV1 1EY Tel: (024) 7622 3390 Fax: (024) 7622 0740
Devonshire House Associates Ltd, Gainsborough Trading Estate, Rufford Road, Stourbridge, West Midlands, DY9 7ND Tel: (01384) 442322 Fax: (01384) 440949
Digital Print Factory, 12-12a Rosebery Avenue, London, EC1R 4TD Tel: (020) 7837 8666 Fax: (020) 7404 4762 E-mail: t.harding@colyer.co.uk
Display Maintenance Ltd, Old Bank Mills, Old Bank Road, Earlsheaton, Dewsbury, West Yorkshire, WF12 7AA Tel: (01924) 469664 Fax: (0870) 8508511 E-mail: enquiries@displaymaintenance.co.uk
Display Matrix, Unit 14, Dixon Business Centre Dixon Road, Bristol, BS4 5QW Tel: 0117-300 9925 Fax: 0117-977 2457 E-mail: info@displaymatrix.co.uk
▶ Displayer, 30 Rosedale Way, Forest Town, Mansfield, Nottinghamshire, NG19 0QR Tel: (01623) 628309 Fax: 01623 628309 E-mail: alanmarshall@displayer.co.uk
Displaysia Exhibitions Ltd, Unit 49 Longshot Industrial Estate, Longshot Lane, Bracknell, Berkshire, RG12 1RL Tel: (01344) 487220 Fax: (01344) 487221
Displex Display & Exhibition Ltd, Graphex House, Adcroft Street, Stockport, Cheshire, SK1 3HZ Tel: 0161-480 4626 Fax: 0161-474 1875 E-mail: sales@displex.co.uk
Domic Welding Services, Unit 8, Victor Business Centre, Arthur St, Redditch, Worcestershire, B98 8JY Tel: (01527) 510041 Fax: (01527) 510403 E-mail: paul@pjwelding.fsnet.co.uk
Durleigh Display Systems, 6 Symons Way, Bridgwater, Somerset, TA6 4DR Tel: (01278) 447447 Fax: (01278) 456376
Ec Display Associates Ltd, Unit 1 Winsor, 50 Windsor Avenue, London, SW19 2TJ Tel: (020) 8545 0505 Fax: (020) 8545 0042 E-mail: info@ecdisplay.com
Eclipse Displays, Unit 20 Portland Business Park, 130 Richmond Park Road, Sheffield, S13 8HS Tel: 0114-242 2601 Fax: 0114-242 2629 E-mail: sales@eclipsedisplays.co.uk
Encore Of Gloucester Ltd, 5 Francis Woodcock Trading Estate, 277 Barton Street, Gloucester, GL1 4JE Tel: (01452) 503079 Fax: (01452) 310177 E-mail: j-mckee@btconnect.com
Equinox Design Ltd, Equinox Park, 100 Jack Lane, Leeds, LS10 1BW Tel: 0113-244 1300 Fax: 0113-242 4533 E-mail: equinoxdesign@compuserve.com
Exhibition House, Exhibition House, 7 Davis Road, Chessington, Surrey, KT9 1TT Tel: (020) 8974 1781 Fax: (020) 8397 1736 E-mail: exhibit@mems.co.uk
Exhibition Works Ltd, 42 Lanchester Way, Royal Oak Industrial Estate, Daventry, Northamptonshire, NN11 8PH Tel: (01327) 705250 Fax: (01327) 705199 E-mail: sales@exhibitionworks.co.uk
Exoplan International Ltd, Unit 13, Industrial Estate, National Exhibition Centre, Birmingham, B40 1PJ Tel: 0121-780 4513 Fax: 0121-780 4810 E-mail: sales@exoplan.co.uk
▶ Fernleigh Design Ltd, Unit 5 Parc Ty Glas, Llanishen, Cardiff, CF11 7BF Tel: 02920 763524 Fax: 02920 763525 E-mail: amanda@fernleighdesign.co.uk
Finesse Group, Cobbswood Industrial Estate, Brunswick Road, Ashford, Kent, TN23 1EH Tel: (01233) 663399 Fax: (01233) 665599 E-mail: info@finessegroup.com
Focal Design Ltd, The Old Bakery, Albion Road, New Mills, High Peak, Derbyshire, SK22 3EX Tel: (01663) 746100 Fax: (01663) 746920 E-mail: sales@focaldesign.co.uk

EXHIBITION STAND CONTRACTORS OR DESIGNERS OR FABRICATORS

– *continued*

Ford & Barley Exhibitions Ltd, Unit 2 Fulwood Road South, Sutton-in-Ashfield, Nottinghamshire, NG17 2JZ Tel: (01623) 551120 Fax: (01623) 440063 E-mail: ford.barley@btconnect.com
Global Displays Ltd, Global House, Berry Hill, Berry Hill Industrial Estate, Droitwich, Worcestershire, WR9 9RB Tel: (01905) 797978 Fax: (01905) 797919 E-mail: sales@globaldisplays.co.uk
Graham Toms Displays, 13 Lindsay Street, Kettering, Northamptonshire, NN16 8RG Tel: (01536) 510858 Fax: (01536) 510858 E-mail: info@grahamtoms.co.uk
Gray Audio Visual, 34-36 Bickerton Road, London, N19 5JS Tel: (020) 7263 9561 Fax: (020) 7272 0146 E-mail: office@gray-av.co.uk
Harlequin Colour Laboratories, 6 Newlands End, Basildon, Essex, SS15 6DU Tel: (01268) 540932 Fax: (01268) 541633 E-mail: harlequincolour@aol.com
HBM Ltd, H B House, 31 Chalfont Road, Beaconsfield, Buckinghamshire, HP9 2QP Tel: (01494) 671246 Fax: (01494) 678112 E-mail: sales@hbm.co.uk
Highfield International Exhibition Services Ltd, Unit 1A, Worcester Trading Estate, Blackpole Rd, Worcester, WR3 8HR Tel: (01905) 754158 Fax: (01905) 456218
Hytner Exhibitions Ltd, Bullock Road, Washingley, Peterborough, PE7 3SJ Tel: (01733) 246950 Fax: (01733) 246951 E-mail: exhibits@hytner.co.uk
Independent Design & Display, Independent, 275 Meanwood Road, Leeds, LS7 2JD Tel: 0113-242 9944 Fax: 0113-242 9669 E-mail: info@independentdesign.co.uk
▶ Innov-8 Ltd, Clayfield Industrial Estate, Tickhill Road, Doncaster, South Yorkshire, DN4 8QG Tel: (01302) 310888 Fax: (01302) 855060
Interlink Design & Display Ltd, Unit 2-4 Station Road Industrial Estate, Station Road, Coleshill, Birmingham, B46 1HT Tel: (01675) 467870 Fax: (01675) 467871 E-mail: enquiries@interlinkdesign.co.uk
John Adams, 8 Granville Road, Ilford, Essex, IG1 4JY Tel: (020) 8554 8019 Fax: (020) 4784 7927 E-mail: jadamsdesign@aol.com
Kirk John Design, 18 Hayhill, Barrow upon Soar, Loughborough, Leicestershire, LE12 8LD Tel: (01509) 817100 Fax: (01509) 817101 E-mail: accounts@johnkirkdesign.co.uk
Lawson Model Makers, 21 Viking Way, Metheringham, Lincoln, LN4 3DW Tel: (01526) 321628 Fax: (01526) 322140 E-mail: john@jlawson.com
Madden Construction & Display Ltd, Unit 26-27 Watery La Industrial Estate, Watery Lane, Willenhall, West Midlands, WV13 3SU Tel: (01902) 366234 Fax: (01902) 366500
Joe Manby Ltd, Hook Stone Park, Harrogate, North Yorkshire, HG2 7DB Tel: (01423) 814730 Fax: (01423) 814760 E-mail: info@joemanby.co.uk
Markfield Services, Trent Works, Felton Road, Nottingham, NG2 2EH Tel: 0115-985 0400 Fax: 0115-985 0252 E-mail: markfield@trentworks.demon.co.uk
Mayridge Ltd, Atherstone Hill Farm, Atherstone on Stour, Stratford-upon-Avon, Warwickshire, CV37 8NF Tel: (01789) 450898 Fax: (01789) 450855 E-mail: info@mayridge.com
Myers John Associates, Park Street, Parkfield Business Centre, Stafford, ST17 4AL Tel: (01785) 224134 Fax: (01785) 246654 E-mail: jma@onetel.net.uk
New Dimension Exhibitions Ltd, 1 Woodfield Road, Welwyn Garden City, Hertfordshire, AL7 1JQ Tel: (01707) 323244 Fax: (01707) 323366 E-mail: exhibit@newdimension.co.uk
Nomadic Display, The Nomadic House, 71 St Johns Road, Isleworth, Middlesex, TW7 6XQ Tel: 0121-333 4956 Fax: (020) 8326 5522 E-mail: hqsales@nomadicdisplay.co.uk
Nortex Ltd, 73 Arthur Street, Lakeside, Redditch, Worcestershire, B98 8JY Tel: (01527) 500742 Fax: (01527) 502999 E-mail: nortex.exhibitions@virgin.net
Oakmace Exhibitions Ltd, Aimes Green Farm, Galley Hill, Waltham Abbey, Essex, EN9 2AU Tel: (01992) 893768 Fax: (01992) 893981 E-mail: display@oakmace.com
Opex, Exhibition Centre, Warwick Road, London, SW5 9TA Tel: (020) 7370 8145 Fax: (020) 7370 8084 E-mail: enquiries@opex.co.uk
P P L Graphex, 241a Selbourne Road, Luton, LU4 8NP Tel: (01582) 599529 Fax: (01582) 583366 E-mail: bgale@pplgraphex.com
Park Display plc, 10 Telford Road, Bicester, Oxfordshire, OX26 4LD Tel: (01869) 245703 Fax: (01869) 249675 E-mail: sales@parkdisplay.co.uk
Trevor Peters Design, Unit 18 Portway Business Centre, Old Sarum, Salisbury, SP4 6QX Tel: (01722) 412227 Fax: (01722) 414179 E-mail: tpd@tpdesign.co.uk
▶ Premier Display Ltd, 1 Mill Lane Industrial Estate, The Mill Lane, Glenfield, Leicester, LE3 8DX Tel: 0116-231 3335 Fax: 0116-232 0015 E-mail: sales@premdisp.co.uk
Prestech Exhibition Services, Unit 14 Belgrave Industrial Estate, Belgrave Road, Southampton, SO17 3EA Tel: (023) 8055 0557 Fax: (023) 8055 2452 E-mail: prestech@prestech.co.uk
Prima International, Abeles Way, Holly Lane Industrial Estate, Atherstone, Warwickshire, CV9 2QZ Tel: (01827) 715479 Fax: (01827) 715479
Pyramid Displays, Unit 1, Navigation Road, Diglis Trading Estate, Worcester, WR5 3DE Tel: (01905) 358488 Fax: (01905) 358473
R E L Interexpo, 4 West House, West Avenue, Wigston, Leicestershire, LE18 2FB Tel: 0116-288 6622 Fax: 0116-281 3983 E-mail: info@interexpo.co.uk
R M Display Systems Ltd, 44 Murrell Green Business Park, Hook, Hampshire, RG27 9GR Tel: (01256) 740211 Fax: (01256) 740201 E-mail: info@rmdisplay.co.uk
Realistic Digital Graphics, Stafford Studios, 129a Stafford Road, Wallington, Surrey, SM6 9BN Tel: (020) 8669 4900 Fax: (020) 8773 0129 E-mail: info@realistic-digital.com
Redwood Photographic, 7 Brunel Court, Brunel Way, Severalls Industrial Park, Colchester, CO4 9XW Tel: (01206) 751241 Fax: (01206) 855134 E-mail: info@redwoodphoto.com
Sheetfabs (Nottingham) Ltd, Nottingham Road, Attenborough, Beeston, Nottingham, NG9 6DR Tel: 0115-925 8101 Fax: 0115-943 0872 E-mail: sheetfabs@sheetfabs.co.uk
Sienna Exhibitions Ltd, Unit 1r, Membury Business Park, Lambourn Woodlands, Hungerford, Berkshire, RG17 7TJ Tel: (01488) 73720 Fax: (01488) 73721 E-mail: sales@sienna-indigo.com
Silverwood Exhibitions Ltd, 14 The Avenue, York, YO30 6AS Tel: (01904) 672700 Fax: (01904) 655800 E-mail: sales@silverwoodexhibitions.co.uk
Stanco Exhibitions Ltd, 4 Tregwilym Industrial Estate, Tregwilym Road, Rogerstone, Newport, Gwent, NP10 9DQ Tel: (01633) 890300 Fax: (01633) 890301 E-mail: reception@stanco.co.uk
Standpoint Ltd, Unit 22A, Park Avenue Estate, Sundon Park, Luton, LU3 3BP Tel: (01582) 561754 Fax: (01582) 563296 E-mail: info@standpoint.uk.com
Stylographics Ltd, 134 St Albans Road, Watford, WD24 4AE Tel: (01923) 800666 Fax: (01923) 800777 E-mail: admin@stylographics.co.uk
T D S Exhibition Design, 29 Grosvenor Way, Droitwich, Worcestershire, WR9 7SR Tel: (01905) 778379 Fax: (01905) 778379
Technik Exhibit Solutions Ltd, Unit 14 Boxted Farm Business Park, Berkhamsted Road, Hemel Hempstead, Hertfordshire, HP1 2SG Tel: (01442) 220130 Fax: (01442) 251412 E-mail: sales@techniksolutions.co.uk
Time Ltd, 6 Brook St Mill, Brook Street, Macclesfield, Cheshire, SK11 7AW Tel: (01625) 615768 Fax: (01625) 614605 E-mail: ron@timescctv.co.uk
R. & S. Tonks, Boothen Green, Campbell Road, Stoke-On-Trent, ST4 4BJ Tel: (01782) 848235 Fax: (01782) 747049 E-mail: headoffice@rstonks.co.uk
Whitecroft Designs Ltd, 53 High Street, Stourbridge, West Midlands, DY8 1DE Tel: (01384) 443644 Fax: (01384) 443696 E-mail: acutler@btconnect.com
Wup Doodle, The Street, Hepworth, Diss, Norfolk, IP22 2PS Tel: (01359) 254001 Fax: (01953) 688378 E-mail: info@wupdoodle.com

EXHIBITION STANDS

A F Electrics, Millbank Street, Stoke-on-Trent, ST3 1AE Tel: (01782) 332276 Fax: (01782) 341036 E-mail: arnot@audemex.co.uk
Clip Ltd, Athena, 210 Bristol Business Park, The Close, Bristol, BS16 1FJ Tel: 0117-937 5700 Fax: 0117-931 4561 E-mail: info@clipdisplay.com
▶ E S M Ltd, Unit C5, Imperial Business Estate, Westmill, Gravesend, Kent, DA11 0DL Tel: (01474) 536360

EXHIBITION SUPPLY SERVICES

▶ Elevation Rigging Ltd, 3 Duchess Place, Edgbaston House, Birmingham, B16 8NH Tel: 0121 456 7949 Fax: 0121 789 6190 E-mail: mail@elevationrigging.com
▶ Science Projects Ltd, 20 St. James Street, London, W6 9RW Tel: (020) 8741 2306 Fax: (020) 8741 2307 E-mail: info@science-projects.org

EXOTHERMIC WELDING EQUIPMENT

Thermit Welding GB Ltd, 87 Ferry Lane, Rainham, Essex, RM13 9YH Tel: (01708) 522626 Fax: (01708) 553806

EXOTIC METAL BOLTS AND NUTS

TR Fastenings, Trifast House, Bolton Close, Bellbrook Industrial Estate, Uckfield, East Sussex, TN22 1QW Tel: (01825) 764711 Fax: (01256) 461281

EXOTIC METAL FABRICATORS

Imi Components, Nobel Way, Witton, Birmingham, B6 7ES Tel: 0121-344 5800 Fax: 0121-344 3056

EXOTIC METAL MACHINING

Bowater Cordell Ltd, Dukesway, Teesside Industrial Estate, Thornaby, Stockton-On-Tees, Cleveland, TS17 9LT Tel: (01642) 750303 Fax: (01642) 750164 E-mail: bowater@cordellgroup.com

EXOTIC METAL SPINNING

Ashford Metal Spinners Ltd, Unit E, Chilmington Works, Chilmington Green, Great Chart, Ashford, Kent, TN23 3DR Tel: (01233) 610404 E-mail: ams@ashfordmetalspinning.co.uk
Metspin Ltd, Clovelly Road, Southbourne, Emsworth, Hampshire, PO10 8PF Tel: (01243) 378401 Fax: (01243) 374219 E-mail: sales@metspin.com

EXOTIC METALS

British Refractory Metals, 27 Nobel Square, Burnt Mills Industrial Estate, Basildon, Essex, SS13 1LP Tel: (01268) 591386 Fax: (01268) 591389 E-mail: pcurtisbrm@aol.com

EXOTIC TIMBER MERCHANTS

Craft Supplies Ltd, Newburgh Works, Netherside, Bradwell, Hope Valley, Derbyshire, S33 9NT Tel: (01433) 622550 Fax: (01433) 622552 E-mail: sales@craft-supplies.co.uk
Hardwood Dimensions Ltd, Trafford Park Road, Trafford Park, Manchester, M17 1WH Tel: 0161-872 5111 Fax: 0161-873 7004 E-mail: sales@hardwooddimensions.ltd.uk

EXPANDED METAL PRODUCTS MANUFRS

A & F Supplies, Railway Road, Adlington, Chorley, Lancashire, PR6 9RF Tel: (01257) 480500 Fax: (01257) 483338 E-mail: sales@a-f-supplies.co.uk
C & T Metals Ltd, 10 Carlyle Avenue, Hillington Industrial Estate, Glasgow, G52 4JJ Tel: 0141-810 4411 Fax: 0141-810 4414 E-mail: information@ctmetals.com
▶ Catnic, Pontygwindy Industrial Estate, Caerphilly, Mid Glamorgan, CF83 2WJ Tel: (029) 2033 7900 Fax: (029) 2086 3178 E-mail: sali.morris@corusgroup.com
Cornercare Ltd, Unit 3-4 Walter Nash Road West, Birchen Coppice Trading Estate, Kidderminster, Worcestershire, DY11 7QY Tel: (01562) 515200 Fax: (01562) 864063 E-mail: cornercare@compuserve.com
Dramex Expanded Metal Ltd, Unit 24-26, Crossgate Road, Park Farm Industrial Estate, Redditch, Worcestershire, B98 7SN Tel: (0800) 1804454 Fax: (01527) 501725 E-mail: uksales@dramex.com
The Expanded Metal Company, PO Box 14, Hartlepool, Cleveland, TS25 1PR Tel: (01429) 867388 Fax: (01429) 866795 E-mail: sales@expamet.co.uk
▶ Fine Mesh Metals, Unit 10, Wallows Industrial Estate, Wallows Road, Brierley Hill, West Midlands, DY5 1QA Tel: (01384) 263268 Fax: (01902) 898179 E-mail: sales@finemeshmetals.co.uk
Leckmill Ltd, 3 Norman Road, Rochdale, Lancashire, OL11 4HS Tel: (01706) 353737 Fax: (01706) 358577
Longar Industries Ltd, Unit 25 Glenmore Business Park, Colebrook Way, Andover, Hampshire, SP10 3GZ Tel: (01264) 332993 Fax: (01264) 332994 E-mail: sales@longar.co.uk
Siddall & Hilton Mesh Ltd, Birds Royd Lane, Brighouse, West Yorkshire, HD6 1LT Tel: (01484) 401610 Fax: (01484) 721028 E-mail: sales@shmesh.com

EXPANDED POLYPROPYLENE (EPP) MOULDING MACHINERY

B A Thorne Ltd, Eagle Road, Moons Moat North Industrial Es, Redditch, Worcestershire, B98 9HF Tel: (01527) 584714 Fax: (01527) 584784 E-mail: bat@bathorne.co.uk

EXPANDED POLYSTYRENE (EPS) PRODUCTS, *See also headings under Polystyrene (PS)*

E P S Products Ltd, Units 5-6, Govan Road, Fenton Industrial Estate, Stoke-on-Trent, ST4 2RS Tel: (01782) 749662 Fax: (01782) 749757
Jubilee Plastics, Regency Mews, 219 Willesden High Road, London, NW10 2SA Tel: (020) 8459 2065 Fax: (020) 8459 0832
K B Packaging & Insulation, The Warehouse, Foggathorpe, Selby, North Yorkshire, YO8 6PR Tel: (01757) 289131 Fax: (01757) 289142 E-mail: enquiries@kbpackagingandinsulation.co.uk
Kay-Metzeler Ltd, Brook Street, Chelmsford, CM1 1UQ Tel: (01245) 342100 Fax: (01245) 342123 E-mail: epssales@kay-metzeler.co.uk
Kirkstons Packaging Insulation(E Midlands) Ltd, Unit 16, Corringham Road Industrial Estate, Gainsborough, Lincolnshire, DN21 1QB Tel: (01427) 612007 Fax: (01427) 810952 E-mail: kirkston@packaging.fsworld.co.uk
Linpac Moulded Foams, Unit 4 Dinas Isaf Industrial Estate, Williamstown, Tonypandy, Mid Glamorgan, CF40 1NY Tel: (01443) 441491 Fax: (01443) 441453
Polyscot Polystyrene, 4 Craigluscar Road, Dunfermline, Fife, KY12 9JA Tel: (01383) 732296 Fax: (01383) 620365 E-mail: eps@polyscot.co.uk
S & B E P S Ltd, Dudley, Cramlington, Northumberland, NE23 7PY Tel: 0191-250 0818 Fax: 0191-250 0548 E-mail: company@sandbeps.com
St Vincents Insulation Ltd, 19 St Vincents Road, Dartford, DA1 1XF Tel: (01322) 225174 Fax: (01322) 221474 E-mail: sales@stvincents.co.uk
Solo Europe, Tower Close, Huntingdon, Cambridgeshire, PE29 7BZ Tel: (01480) 459413 Fax: (01480) 459274 E-mail: sales@soloeurope.co.uk
Springvale Eps Ltd, 75 Springvale Road, Doagh, Ballyclare, County Antrim, BT39 0SS Tel: (028) 9334 0203 Fax: (028) 9334 1159 E-mail: sales@springvale.com
Springvale EPS Ltd, Hazlerigg, Newcastle Upon Tyne, NE13 7AP Tel: 0191-217 1144 Fax: 0191-217 1212 E-mail: sales@springvale.com
Springvale Eps Ltd (Glossop Division), Dinting Vale Business Park, Glossop, Derbyshire, SK13 6LG Tel: (01457) 863211 Fax: (01457) 869269
Styropack UK Ltd, Craigshaw Road, West Tullos Industrial Estate, Aberdeen, AB12 3AS Tel: (01224) 873166 Fax: (01224) 873361 E-mail: aberdeen@styropack.co.uk
Styropack UK Ltd, Unit A Rudford Industrial Estate, Ford Road, Ford, Arundel, West Sussex, BN18 0BD Tel: (01903) 725282 Fax: (01903) 731628 E-mail: ford@styropack.co.uk
Sundolitt Ltd, 8 Broomfield Road, Montrose, Angus, DD10 8SY Tel: (01674) 676006 Fax: (01674) 676686
Sundolitt, Mirren Court (Three), 123 Renfrew Road, Paisley, Renfrewshire, PA3 4EA Tel: 0141-887 1123 Fax: 0141-889 9878 E-mail: enquiries@sundolitt.co.uk

EXPANDED POLYSTYRENE (EPS) PROTECTIVE PACKAGING

▶ Styro Park (UK), Aberamon Park Industrial Estate, Aberdare, Mid Glamorgan, CF44 6DA Tel: (01685) 881022 Fax: (01685) 871515

EXPANDING MANDRELS

P W T, Park Works, Lister Lane, Halifax, West Yorkshire, HX1 5JH Tel: (01422) 358361 Fax: (01422) 359379
Precision Products, 2a Penner Road, Havant, Hampshire, PO9 1QH Tel: (023) 9248 1848 Fax: (023) 9245 5024 E-mail: salesppp@aol.com

EXPANSION JOINT/BELLOWS/ CONNECTOR MANUFRS, *See also headings for particular types*

▶ FlexEJ, 28 Hadcroft Grange, Stourbridge, West Midlands, DY9 7EP Tel: (0845) 0204323 Fax: (01384) 896875 E-mail: sales@flexej.co.uk
Keith Lealand Services, 50 Village Farm Road, Village Farm Industrial Estate, Pyle, Bridgend, Mid Glamorgan, CF33 6BN Tel: (01656) 742555 Fax: (01656) 744261

EXPANSION JOINTS/BELLOWS/ CONNECTORS, FABRIC

Barlow Blinds Ltd, 54 Uppingham Road, Leicester, LE5 0QE Tel: 0116-276 9771 Fax: 0116-246 0490 E-mail: brian@barlow-bellows.co.uk

EXPANSION JOINTS/BELLOWS/ CONNECTORS, METAL

▶ Eurospan Engineering Ltd, 5 Wheatmoor Rise, Sutton Coldfield, West Midlands, B75 6AW Tel: 0121-378 1596 Fax: 0121-329 2542 E-mail: eurospan@blueyonder.co.uk
J & P Supplies Ltd, Junction Road, Audnam, Stourbridge, West Midlands, DY8 4YH Tel: (01384) 393329 Fax: (01384) 440212 E-mail: info@jpsupplies.co.uk

▶ indicates data change since last edition

EXPANSION JOINTS/BELLOWS/ CONNECTORS, METAL – *continued*

Munro & Miller Fittings Ltd, 3 Westerton Road, East Mains Industrial Estate, Broxburn, West Lothian, EH52 5AU Tel: (01506) 853531 Fax: (01506) 856628 E-mail: sales@munro-miller.co.uk

Senior Aerospace Bird Bellows, Radnor Park Industrial Estate, Congleton, Cheshire, CW12 4UQ Tel: (01260) 271411 Fax: (01260) 270910 E-mail: info@bird-bellows.co.uk

Teddington Engineered Solutions, Heol Cropin, Dafen, Llanelli, Dyfed, SA14 8QW Tel: (01554) 744500 Fax: (01792) 885843 E-mail: sales@tes.uk.com

Thermosel Solutions Ltd, Calico Lane, Furness Vale, High Peak, Derbyshire, SK23 7SW Tel: (01663) 748220 Fax: (01663) 741685

EXPANSION JOINTS/BELLOWS/ CONNECTORS, RUBBER

Engineering Appliances Ltd, 11 Brooklands Close, Sunbury-on-Thames, Middlesex, TW16 7DX Tel: (01932) 788888 Fax: (01932) 761263 E-mail: info@engineering-appliances.com

J & P Supplies Ltd, Junction Road, Audnam, Stourbridge, West Midlands, DY8 4YH Tel: (01384) 393329 Fax: (01384) 440212 E-mail: info@jpsupplies.co.uk

Radflex Contract Services Ltd, Unit 35 Wilks Avenue, Questor, Dartford, DA1 1JS Tel: (01322) 276363 Fax: (01322) 270606 E-mail: expjoint@radflex.co.uk

EXPERT WITNESSES

A J M Consultants, Bradstones, Hewshott Lane, Liphook, Hampshire, GU30 7SU Tel: (01428) 723030 Fax: (01428) 727232 E-mail: ajm.consultants@farmline.com

John Ashworth & Partners Ltd, PO Box 160, Bacup, Lancashire, OL13 0BW Tel: (01706) 879544 Fax: (01706) 647767 E-mail: johnashworth.paint@virgin.net

Byrom Clark Roberts Ltd, Maclaren House, Talbot Road, Stretford, Manchester, M32 0FP Tel: 0161-875 0600 Fax: 0161-875 0601 E-mail: bcrmcr@bcr.uk.com

▶ Cadogan Consultants Ltd, 39 Cadogan Street, Glasgow, G2 7AB Tel: 0141-270 7060 Fax: 0141-270 7061 E-mail: enquiries@cadoganconsultants.co.uk

Gibson Consulting Ltd, 3 The Quadrant, Coventry, CV1 2DY Tel: (024) 7624 3607 Fax: (024) 7624 3608 E-mail: mark.gibson@gibsonconsulting.co.uk

▶ Hooper Safety, 25 Honey Lane, Buntingford, Hertfordshire, SG9 9BQ Tel: (01763) 271051 Fax: (01763) 271051 E-mail: ian@hoopersafety.net

▶ Reckon LLP, 20 Theobalds Road, London, WC1X 8PF Tel: (020) 7841 5850 Fax: (020) 7841 5850 E-mail: feedback@reckon.co.uk

Refrigerated Transport Information Society, 140 Newmarket Road, Cambridge, CB5 8HE Tel: (01223) 461352 Fax: (01223) 461522 E-mail: crt@crtech.demon.co.uk

▶ University Of Leeds Farms Ltd, Financial Services, 11-84 Ec Stoner Building, Leeds, LS2 9JT Tel: 0113-234 0206 Fax: 0113-343 4058 E-mail: consulting@leeds.ac.uk

Owen Williams Ltd, 41 Whitcomb Street, London, WC2H 7DT Tel: (020) 7839 1072 Fax: (020) 7827 2439

Withnall Design Consultants, Trinity House, Church Lane, Croughton, Brackley, Northamptonshire, NN13 5LS Tel: (01869) 810590 Fax: (01869) 810590 E-mail: withnall@btopenworld.com

EXPLODERS, EXPLOSIVES DETONATION

Arbra Instruments, Advance Park, Park Road, Rhosymedre, Wrexham, Clwyd, LL14 3YR Tel: (01978) 823900 Fax: (01978) 822913 E-mail: sales@aslgroup.uk

EXPLOSION PROOF ALARM SYSTEMS

J C E (Europe) Ltd, East Way, Lee Mill Industrial Estate, Ivybridge, Devon, PL21 9LL Tel: (01752) 690530 Fax: (01752) 690531 E-mail: info.euro@jcegroup.com

S A Equipment Sales, Edison Point, Millmarsh Lane, Enfield, Middlesex, EN3 7QG Tel: (020) 8443 7420 Fax: (020) 8804 2655

EXPLOSION PROOF CABLE GLANDS

C M P Products, 36 Nelson Way, Nelson Park East, Cramlington, Northumberland, NE23 1WH Tel: 0191 2657411 Fax: 0191 2650581 E-mail: cmp@cmp-products.com

▶ Hawke Cable Glands Ltd, Oxford St West, Ashton-under-Lyne, Lancashire, OL7 0NA Tel: 0161-308 3611 Fax: 0161-830 6648 E-mail: sales@ehawke.com

EXPLOSION PROOF CONNECTORS

▶ Hydro Bond Engineering Ltd, 2b Woodside Road, Bridge of Don Industrial Estate, Aberdeen, AB23 8EF Tel: (01224) 822996 Fax: (01224) 825142 E-mail: sales@hydrohouse.co.uk

EXPLOSION PROOF ELECTRIC MOTORS

Heasell Electromechanical Services Ltd, 9-11 Baldock Street, Royston, Hertfordshire, SG8 5AY Tel: (0871) 2227896 Fax: (01763) 248108 E-mail: gary@abrams-netlineuk.net

J C E (Europe) Ltd, East Way, Lee Mill Industrial Estate, Ivybridge, Devon, PL21 9LL Tel: (01752) 690530 Fax: (01752) 690531 E-mail: info.euro@jcegroup.com

Powertronic Drive Systems Ltd, Treetops House, Gillotts Lane, Henley-On-Thames, Oxfordshire, RG9 1PT Tel: (01491) 579118 Fax: (01491) 412211 E-mail: sales@powertronic.co.uk

EXPLOSION PROOF (ELECTRICAL) (HAZARDOUS AREA) EQUIPMENT MANUFRS

Bernstein Ltd, Westgate Trading Estate, Westgate, Aldridge, Walsall, WS9 8EX Tel: (01922) 744999 Fax: (01922) 457555 E-mail: sales@bernstein-ltd.co.uk

Expo Technologies Ltd, Summer Road, Thames Ditton, Surrey, KT7 0RH Tel: (020) 8398 8011 Fax: (020) 8398 8014 E-mail: sales@expoworldwide.com

J B Systems Ltd, 8 Bridgegate Business Park, Gatehouse Way, Gatehouse Industrial Area, Aylesbury, Buckinghamshire, HP19 8XN Tel: (01296) 489967 Fax: (01296) 393515 E-mail: info@jbsystems.co.uk

Medc Ltd, Colliery Road, Pinxton, Nottingham, NG16 6JF Tel: (01773) 864111 Fax: (01773) 582800 E-mail: sales@medc.com

Orga, A1 Kingsway Business Park, Oldfield Road, Hampton, Middlesex, TW12 2HD Tel: (0870) 6092452 Fax: (020) 8941 6683 E-mail: sales@orga.nl

Redapt Engineering Co. Ltd, Darlaston Central TRDG Estate, Salisbury Street, Wednesbury, West Midlands, WS10 8BQ Tel: 0121-526 7058

Schischek Ltd, 1 Saddlestones, New Road, Princes Risborough, Buckinghamshire, HP27 0JJ Tel: (01494) 794904 Fax: (01494) 794905 E-mail: schischek@msn.com

The Wolf Safety Lamp Co. Ltd, Saxon Road Works, Heeley, Sheffield, S8 0YA Tel: 0114-255 1051 Fax: 0114-255 7988 E-mail: info@wolf-safety.co.uk

EXPLOSION PROOF PROXIMITY SWITCHES

Longvale Ltd, The Grain Warehouse, Derby Street, Burton-On-Trent, Staffordshire, DE14 2JJ Tel: (01283) 510108 Fax: (01283) 510910 E-mail: rdear@longvale.co.uk

EXPLOSION PROOF SLIP RINGS

Schleifring Systems Ltd, Abex Road, Newbury, Berkshire, RG14 5EY Tel: (01635) 36363 Fax: (01635) 582118 E-mail: sales@schleifring.co.uk

EXPLOSION PROTECTED HAZARDOUS WARNING LAMPS

D G Controls Ltd, Cadley Hill Road, Swadlincote, Derbyshire, DE11 9TB Tel: (01283) 550850 Fax: (01283) 550776 E-mail: mail@beaconlamps.com

EXPLOSION PROTECTED LIGHTING

P F P Electrical Products Ltd, 22 Fortnum Close, Mackadown Lane, Kitts Green, Birmingham, B33 0LB Tel: 0121-783 7161 Fax: 0121-783 5717 E-mail: sales@pfp-elec.co.uk

The Wolf Safety Lamp Co. Ltd, Saxon Road Works, Heeley, Sheffield, S8 0YA Tel: 0114-255 1051 Fax: 0114-255 7988 E-mail: info@wolf-safety.co.uk

EXPLOSION PROTECTION ENGINEERING

Stuvex Safety Systems Ltd, 48 Church Street, Weybridge, Surrey, KT13 8DP Tel: (01932) 849602 Fax: (01932) 852171 E-mail: sales@stuvex.com

EXPLOSION RESISTING DOORS

Trans-Global Engineering Ltd, Camlock Works, 13-15 Bridlington Road, Hunmanby, Filey, North Yorkshire, YO14 0LR Tel: (01723) 892122 Fax: (01723) 891554 E-mail: trans@beckgroup.co.uk

EXPLOSION SUPPRESSION EQUIPMENT

Intronics Fire Protection Consultants, 122 Broadmead, Tunbridge Wells, Kent, TN2 5RW Tel: (01892) 516366 Fax: (01892) 512212 E-mail: sales@intronics.co.uk

Stuvex Safety Systems Ltd, 48 Church Street, Weybridge, Surrey, KT13 8DP Tel: (01932) 849602 Fax: (01932) 852171 E-mail: sales@stuvex.com

EXPLOSIVE ENGINEERING

Explosive Developments Ltd, The Airfield, Full Sutton, York, YO41 1HS Tel: (01759) 305568 Fax: (01759) 304873

Macc International, Unit Q, Camilla Court, Nacton, Ipswich, IP10 0EU Tel: (01473) 655127 Fax: (01473) 655098 E-mail: macc@macc-eod.com

Robinson & Birdsell, Audby House, Audby Lane, Wetherby, West Yorkshire, LS22 7FD Tel: (01937) 548800 Fax: (01937) 548801 E-mail: r-b@robinson-birdsell.co.uk

EXPLOSIVE OR BOMB DISPOSAL

▶ TerraDat Geophysics Ltd, Unit 2, Ocean Ho, Hunter St, Cardiff, CF10 5FR Tel: (0870) 7303050 Fax: (0870) 7303051 E-mail: info@terradat.co.uk

▶ UXB (UK) Ltd, Challacombe Close, Landkey, Barnstaple, Devon, EX32 0NG Tel: (01271) 831439 Fax: (01271) 831442 E-mail: pjh@uxb.com

EXPLOSIVES

Exchem Explosives, PO Box 4, Alfreton, Derbyshire, DE55 7AB Tel: (01773) 832253 Fax: (01773) 520723

Explosive Developments Ltd, The Airfield, Full Sutton, York, YO41 1HS Tel: (01759) 305568 Fax: (01759) 304873

P W Defence Ltd, Wilne Mill, Draycott, Derby, DE72 3QJ Tel: (01332) 872475 Fax: (01332) 873046

Ulster Industrial Explosives Ltd, Unit 1 Kilroot Park, Carrickfergus, County Antrim, BT38 7PR Tel: (028) 9335 1444 Fax: (028) 9335 1474 E-mail: info@uielimited.com

EXPLOSIVES DETECTORS

SDS Group Ltd, 3 Courtlands Farm, Turnden Road, Cranbrook, Kent, TN17 2QL Tel: (01580) 715038 Fax: (01580) 712056 E-mail: sales@sdsgroupltd.co.uk

EXPLOSIVES STORES

J G Turnbull Ltd, Station Approach, East Boldon, Tyne & Wear, NE36 0AD Tel: 0191-536 2090 Fax: 0191-519 0218 E-mail: office@jgturnballltd.co.uk

EXPLOSIVES/BOMB DISPOSAL EQUIPMENT

N I C Instruments Ltd, Gladstone Road, Folkestone, Kent, CT19 5NF Tel: (01303) 851022 Fax: (01303) 850155 E-mail: sales@nicltd.co.uk

Richmond Electronics & Engineering International Ltd, Armtec Estate, North Lopham, Diss, Norfolk, IP22 2LR Tel: (01379) 686800 Fax: (01379) 688519 E-mail: info@richmondeei.co.uk

▶ Vestguard UK Ltd, Sevenacres, Barnhall Road, Tolleshunt Knights, Maldon, Essex, CM9 8HD Tel: (0845) 6016660 Fax: (01621) 814316 E-mail: info@vestguard.com

EXPORT BUYING AGENTS, *See Buying/Purchasing etc*

EXPORT CREDIT INSURANCE

▶ CIFF - Credit Insurance, Factoring & Finance., Cliff House, 75 Hill Top, Bolsover, Derbyshire, S44 6NJ Tel: 01246 241002 Fax: 0845 127 4385 E-mail: ciff1@holroydr.plus.com

Euler Hermes UK plc, 1 Canada Square, London, E14 5DX Tel: (0800) 0565452 Fax: (0207) 8602455 E-mail: creditinfo@eulerhermes.com

Export Credits Guarantee Department, PO Box 2200, London, E14 9GS Tel: (020) 7512 7000 Fax: (020) 7512 7649 E-mail: help@ecgd.gsi.gov.uk

Rycroft Associates LLP, 16 Queens Avenue, Shirley, Solihull, West Midlands, B90 2NT Tel: 0121 7458978 Fax: 0121 7443562 E-mail: mikestott@rycroftassociates.com

EXPORT FINANCE

British Arab Commercial Bank Ltd, 8-10 Manson House Place, London, EC4N 8BJ Tel: (020) 7648 7777 Fax: (020) 7600 3318

Brown Shipley Asset Management Ltd, Founders Court, Lothbury, London, EC2R 7HE Tel: (020) 7606 9833 Fax: (020) 7606 6657

The F D A, Boston House, Little Green, Richmond, Surrey, TW9 1QE Tel: (020) 8332 9955 Fax: (020) 8332 2585 E-mail: nicola.breeze@thefda.org.uk

Ghana International Bank Plc, PO Box 77, London, EC2P 2BB Tel: (020) 7248 2384 Fax: (020) 7489 9058 E-mail: info@ghanabank.co.uk

Kirans London Ltd, 69 St. John Street, London, EC1M 4AN Tel: (020) 7608 0299 Fax: (020) 7608 3150 E-mail: info@kiranlondon.co.uk

EXPORT FINANCE CONSULTANTS

Factoring UK Ltd, Gildredge Road, Eastbourne, East Sussex, BN21 4SA Tel: (01323) 411770 Fax: (01323) 430014 E-mail: info@factoringuk.com

EXPORT MANAGEMENT/ MARKETING/DEVELOPMENT CONSULTANTS OR SERVICES

Mark Cansick & Co., 44a Highgate High Street, London, N6 5JE Tel: (020) 8340 0094 Fax: (020) 8340 0096 E-mail: markcansick@btconnect.com

▶ Creative Pod Ltd, Basepoint Business & Innovation Centre, Metcalf Way, Crawley, West Sussex, RH11 7XX Tel: (01293) 817228 Fax: (01293) 518201 E-mail: ideas@creative-pod.com

D T I (Department of Trade and Industry), 1 Victoria Street, London, SW1H 0ET Tel: (020) 7215 5000 Fax: (020) 7215 3529 E-mail: dti.enquiries@dti.gsi.gov.uk

David Franks & Co., PO Box 33, Newmarket, Suffolk, CB8 8SH Tel: (01638) 751132 Fax: (01638) 750933

Anthony Goldsmith, 17 Wentworth Hill, Wembley, Middlesex, HA9 9SF Tel: (020) 8908 6296 Fax: (020) 8908 9296 E-mail: agolex.went@virgin.net

Peter Hall Export Services, Flaunden Lane, Bovingdon, Hemel Hempstead, Hertfordshire, HP3 0QA Tel: (01442) 833241 Fax: (01442) 834142 E-mail: peter@exportservices.co.uk

M F R Consultancy Services Ltd, Dunelm Ho, 33 Greenfields Rise, Whitchurch, Shropshire, SY13 1EP Tel: (01948) 666778 Fax: (01948) 666775 E-mail: mfrose@mfrcsl.co.uk

Singapore Economic Development Board, 30 Charles Ii Street, London, SW1Y 4AE Tel: (020) 7839 6688 Fax: (020) 7839 6162 E-mail: edbln@edb.gov.sg

Watpower International Ltd, PO Box 1389, London, W5 1JJ Tel: (020) 8810 9148 Fax: (020) 8810 5509 E-mail: info@watpower.co.uk

EXPORT MERCHANTS OR AGENTS, *See also General Merchants etc*

Ace International, Wedge Street, Walsall, WS1 2HQ Tel: (01922) 746454 Fax: (01922) 638484 E-mail: ace@aceinternationaluk.com

Adnan UK Ltd, 25 Friar Mews, West Norwood, London, SE27 0PU Tel: (020) 8766 0262 Fax: (020) 8766 6260

Aero Dart Ltd, 5 Brook Road, Benfleet, Essex, SS7 5JB Tel: (01268) 566111 Fax: (01268) 565222 E-mail: direct@aerodart.ndirect.co.uk

Agremimpex Trading House Ltd, Trafalgar House, 11 Waterloo Place, London, SW1Y 4AU Tel: (020) 7839 2887 Fax: (020) 7930 0465 E-mail: isclon@msn.com

Allcord Ltd, Ilford Road, Newcastle upon Tyne, NE2 3NX Tel: 0191-284 8444 Fax: 0191-284 1550 E-mail: enquiries@allcord.co.uk

Alma Steels Ltd, Steetley Industrial Estate, Bean Road, Bilston, West Midlands, WV14 9EE Tel: (01902) 880726 Fax: (01902) 880726

Apex Agencies International Ltd, Sportrite House, 155 Tame Road, Witton, Birmingham, B6 7DG Tel: 0121-328 9190 Fax: 0121-328 4175 E-mail: info@apex-world.com

Arcon Overseas Ltd, 12 Relton Mews, London, SW7 1ET Tel: (020) 7225 1411 Fax: (020) 7225 1811 E-mail: sales@arcon-london.co.uk

Automec Equipment & Parts Ltd, 36 Ballmoor, Buckingham, MK18 1RQ Tel: (01280) 822818 Fax: (01280) 823140 E-mail: info@automec.co.uk

▶ indicates data change since last edition

EXPORT MERCHANTS OR AGENTS

– continued

Autorise Ltd, Maspro House, Chadwick Road, Astmoor Industrial Estate, Runcorn, Cheshire, WA7 1PW Tel: (01928) 561552 Fax: (01928) 591531

Babylon Health Ltd, 57 Uxbridge Road, Shepherds Bush, London, W12 8NR Tel: (020) 8749 0037 Fax: (020) 8749 5628 E-mail: merrell@globalnet.co.uk

Bailey & Davidson Ltd, The Street, Bishop's Cannings, Devizes, Wiltshire, SN10 2LD Tel: (01380) 860386 Fax: (01380) 860897 E-mail: nbailey@kwikbuild.com

Bargate International Ltd, 6 Premier Court, Boarden Close, Moulton Park Industrial Estate, Northampton, NN3 6LF Tel: (01604) 679500 Fax: (01604) 495919 E-mail: sales@bargateinternational.com

BFL Trading Ltd, 314 Regents Park Road, London, N3 2LT Tel: (020) 8371 6000 Fax: (020) 8371 6010 E-mail: info@bfl.com

Blackwell UK Ltd, Beaver House, Hythe Bridge Street, Oxford, OX1 2ET Tel: (01865) 792792 Fax: (01865) 791438 E-mail: enquries@blackwell.co.uk

Bridgewater Europe Ltd, 132 Windmill Rd, Gillingham, Kent, ME7 5PD Tel: (01634) 311717 Fax: (01634) 310632 E-mail: riaz@zoom.co.uk

Busi & Stephenson Ltd, 101 Bold Street, Liverpool, L1 4HL Tel: 0151-709 8998 Fax: 0151-709 8919 E-mail: busico@boldst.demon.co.uk

C J Penn Sales Ltd, 49 Hardwick Road, Sutton Coldfield, West Midlands, B74 3DN Tel: 0121-580 9099 Fax: 0121-580 9088

Canecrown Ltd, 34 London Road, Croydon, CR0 2TA Tel: (020) 8649 8349 Fax: (020) 8649 8349 E-mail: tilcluk@aol.com

Mark Cansick & Co., 44a Highgate High Street, London, N6 5JE Tel: (020) 8340 0094 Fax: (020) 8340 0096 E-mail: markcansick@btconnect.com

Cedar Supplies Ltd, PO Box 59, Crowborough, East Sussex, TN6 3NQ Tel: (01892) 853389 Fax: (01892) 853411 E-mail: sales@cedarsupplies.com

Chesterfield Plastics, 61 Foljambe Avenue, Chesterfield, Derbyshire, S40 3EY Tel: (01246) 540670 Fax: (01246) 540106 E-mail: clive.cooper1@virgin.net

Complex Ltd, 1st Floor, 199 Cumberland Road, Stanmore, Middlesex, HA7 1EL Tel: (020) 8206 2067 Fax: (020) 8204 2294 E-mail: complex@jayaar.com

Contitrades Ltd, 348a Jersey Road, Isleworth, Middlesex, TW7 5PL Tel: (020) 8847 4411 Fax: (020) 8568 8239 E-mail: info@contitrade.com

Coronation Travel & Tours Ltd, 108 Aldersgate Street, London, EC1A 4JQ Tel: (020) 7253 6666 Fax: (020) 7251 8240 E-mail: info@coronation-group.com

Coursamis Ltd, Unit 3 11 Tait Road, Croydon, CR0 2DP Tel: (020) 8684 7973 Fax: (020) 8684 6532 E-mail: sgv@csgroup.fsnet.co.uk

D & J Export Ltd, 33 Valkyrie Road, Westcliff-on-Sea, Essex, SS0 8BY Tel: (01702) 348340 Fax: (01702) 331080 E-mail: don@d-jexports.com

Daltrade P.L.C., 16 Devonshire Street, London, W1G 7AF Tel: (020) 7436 5454 Fax: (020) 7436 1445 E-mail: info@daltrade.co.uk

Data Loop Ltd, Beare Green Court, Dorking, Surrey, RH5 4SL Tel: +44 (0) 1306 711088 Fax: +44 (0) 1306 713108 E-mail: sales@data-loop.co.uk

Deltra Electronics Ltd, Deltra House, Heather Park Drive, Wembley, Middlesex, HA0 1SS Tel: (020) 8795 3000 Fax: (020) 8795 0700 E-mail: tony@deltra.co.uk

C.P. Demetriades & Son, 7 Beech Close, Ollerton, Knutsford, Cheshire, WA16 8TD Tel: (01565) 652488 Fax: (01565) 652588

Diak Technical Export Ltd, Diak House, Romsey, Hampshire, SO51 6AE Tel: (01794) 518808 Fax: (01794) 519960 E-mail: sales@diak.com

Dolphin Movers, Unit 2 Haslemere Business Centre, Lincoln Way, Enfield, Middlesex, EN1 1DX Tel: (020) 8804 7700 Fax: (020) 8804 3232 E-mail: sales@dolphinmovers.com

Elbee Traders, 839 Harrow Road, London, NW10 5NH Tel: (020) 8969 9423 Fax: (020) 8969 2611 E-mail: sales@elbee-traders.co.uk

Entec International Ltd, B Belfont Trading Estate, Mucklow Hill, Halesowen, West Midlands, B62 8DR Tel: 0121-585 8800 Fax: 0121-585 8899 E-mail: info@entec-int.com

Ess Tee United Traders London Ltd, Northumberland House 11 The Pavement, Popes Lane, London, W5 4NG Tel: (020) 8566 3636 Fax: (020) 8566 1831

Eurolink Corporation Ltd, The Annexe Feildings, 11 Rosken Grove, Farnham Royal, Slough, SL2 3DZ Tel: (01753) 642500 Fax: (01753) 642999 E-mail: info@eurolinkcorp.com

Evolution Automotive Components Ltd, 17 Lythalls Lane, Coventry, CV6 6FN Tel: (024) 7663 7337 Fax: (024) 7663 7351 E-mail: sales@eacparts.com

Export Africa, 1 Terminus Industrial Estate, Durham Street, Portsmouth, PO1 1NR Tel: (023) 9282 3590 Fax: (023) 9281 2038 E-mail: sales@rundleholdings.co.uk

Expotec Ltd, 10 Harles Arces, Hickling, Melton Mowbray, Leicestershire, LE14 3AF Tel: (01664) 822725 Fax: (01664) 822725 E-mail: tony.fox2@ntlworld.com

Exvenda Export & Import Agents, 52 Eastwood Road, Manchester, M40 3TF Tel: 0161-688 0647 Fax: 0161-688 4182 E-mail: enquiries@expenda.com

F S M Enterprises Ltd, 2 Adams Close, London, NW9 8PT Tel: (020) 8200 7736 Fax: (020) 8200 6112 E-mail: fmalik1541@aol.com

Far East Mercantile Co., Central House, 7-8 Ritz Parade, London, W5 3RA Tel: (020) 8998 8885 Fax: (020) 8566 8672 E-mail: mail@fareastuk.com

Forbes Campbell Ltd, Forbes House, 9 Artillery Lane, London, E1 7LP Tel: (020) 7377 8484 Fax: (020) 7377 0032 E-mail: rcompton@casley.co.uk

Gathercrest Ltd, Lynton House, 304 Bensham Lane, Thornton Heath, Surrey, CR7 7EQ Tel: (020) 8683 0494 Fax: (020) 8689 8155

Genesis Trading (UK) Corp, 32 Woodhall Drive, Pinner, Middlesex, HA5 4TQ Tel: (020) 8420 1177 Fax: (020) 8420 1155 E-mail: gentauk@hotmail.com

Gia International Ltd, PO Box 4274, Poole, Dorset, BH14 0LL Tel: (01202) 730535 Fax: (01202) 730535 E-mail: mail@griffininternational.co.uk

Anthony Goldsmith, 17 Wentworth Hill, Wembley, Middlesex, HA9 9SF Tel: (020) 8908 6296 Fax: (020) 8908 9296 E-mail: agolex.went@virgin.net

James Greaves & Co., Brazennose House, Manchester, M60 2JA Tel: 0161-834 0991 Fax: 0161-832 0753 E-mail: jamesgreavesco@btinternet.com

Gunter Haas Export Marketing Ltd, 20 Goonwartha Road, Looe, Cornwall, PL13 2PJ Tel: (01503) 265601 Fax: (01503) 265607 E-mail: sales@gunta-sport.com

Guralp Systems Ltd, 3 Midas House, Calleva Park, Reading, RG7 8QZ Tel: 0118-981 9056 Fax: 0118-981 9943 E-mail: guralp@guralp.com

Harvey Scruton, North Lane, Huntington, York, YO32 9SU Tel: (01904) 400878 Fax: (01904) 400120

Hesley Trading London Ltd, 37 Emperors Gate, London, SW7 4HJ Tel: (020) 7370 5933 Fax: (020) 7244 8214 E-mail: kenhes@tiscali.co.uk

Hira Company Ltd The, Elizabeth House, Elizabeth Street, Manchester, M8 8JJ Tel: 0161-834 2868 Fax: 0161-832 4566 E-mail: info@texet.com

Hotbray Ltd, 16 Jubilee Way, London, SW19 3GZ Tel: (020) 8545 0011 Fax: (020) 8545 0020 E-mail: sales@hotbray.co.uk

Inprojex International UK Ltd, 58 Uxbridge Road, London, W5 2ST Tel: (020) 8567 9680 Fax: (020) 8579 5241 E-mail: inprojex@inprojex.co.uk

Itl Impex Ltd, Commercial House, 19 Station Road, Bognor Regis, West Sussex, PO21 1QD Tel: (01243) 841734 Fax: (01243) 841734 E-mail: itl@hopcbroadband.com

J & J B Traders Ltd, Hamilton House, 1 Temple Avenue, London, EC4Y 0HA Tel: (020) 7353 2123 Fax: (020) 7583 8823 E-mail: jjbtl@btinternet.com

Jackdaw Tools Ltd, Leveson Street, Willenhall, West Midlands, WV13 1DB Tel: (01902) 366551 Fax: (01902) 634983 E-mail: jackd@ukindustry.co.uk

James Bruce & Co London Ltd, Great Oddynes, Cinder Hill Lane, Horsted Keynes, Haywards Heath, West Sussex, RH17 7BA Tel: (01825) 791123 Fax: (01825) 791411 E-mail:

Richard James International Ltd, 48 Davis Street, Bristol, BS11 9JW Tel: 0117-982 8575 Fax: 0117-982 6361 E-mail: mail@richard-james.co.uk

Kanematsu Europe plc, Dashwood House, 69 Old Broad Street, London, EC2M 1NS Tel: (020) 7456 6300 Fax: (020) 7256 2850

Karimjee Jivanjee & Co UK Ltd, Hanging Sword House, 21 Whitefriars Street, London, EC4Y 8JJ Tel: (020) 7583 3768 Fax: (020) 7583 3916 E-mail: carol@karimjee.com

Kolon Imperial Graphics plc, Erico House, 93/99 Upper Richmond Road, London, SW15 2TG Tel: (020) 8780 1585 Fax: (020) 8785 7004 E-mail: junelee21@kolonuk.net

KPC Engineering Company Ltd, KPC House, Coventry Road, Yardley, Birmingham, B26 1DD Tel: 0121-707 0004 Fax: 0121-706 0065 E-mail: kpcengineering@btclick.com

L A D Fish Exporters, Dales Industrial Estate, Peterhead, Aberdeenshire, AB42 3JF Tel: (01779) 479327 Fax: (01779) 474891 E-mail: rafael@ladfish.freeserve.co.uk

L G International (U K) Ltd, Profile West, 950 Great West Road, Brentford, Middlesex, TW8 9ES Tel: (020) 8326 1400 Fax: (020) 8560 5601 E-mail: bmsuh@lgi.co.kr

L & M Phoenix Luggage UK Ltd, Middlesex House, 29-45 High Street, Edgware, Middlesex, HA8 7UU Tel: (020) 8905 6678 Fax: (020) 8905 6644 E-mail: sales@phoenixint.net

Laltex & Co. Ltd, Leigh Commerce Park, Green Fold Way, Leigh, Lancashire, WN7 3XH Tel: (01942) 687000 Fax: (01942) 687070 E-mail: mail@laltex.com

Laxbrin Ltd, York House, Empire Way, Wembley, Middlesex, HA9 0QL Tel: (020) 8900 0243 Fax: (020) 8900 1804E-mail: laxbrin@aol.com

Leventis Overseas Ltd, West Africa House, Ashbourne Road, London, W5 3QP Tel: (020) 8997 6651 Fax: (020) 8997 2621 E-mail: leventis@overseas.com

Liaison & Consultant Services (U K) Ltd, PO Box 56, Woking, Surrey, GU21 2PP Tel: (01483) 799322 Fax: (01483) 799311 E-mail: rclcsuk@aol.com

Lixmere Ltd, Lixmere House, 211 Kenton Road, Harrow, Middlesex, HA3 0HD Tel: (020) 8907 1177 Fax: (020) 8909 2777 E-mail: enquiries@lixmere.co.uk

London & Overseas Supplies, Unit G, Crackley Way, Peartree Lane, Dudley, West Midlands, DY2 0UW Tel: (01384) 246230 Fax: (01384) 246240 E-mail: landos@wyko.co.uk

M R S Scientific Ltd, Brocks BSNS Park, Hodgson Way, Wickford, Essex, SS11 8YN Tel: (01268) 730777 Fax: (01268) 560241 E-mail: sales@mrs-scientific.com

Mead Grove Export Ltd, 25 Curzon Street, London, W1J 7TG Tel: (020) 7629 5886 Fax: (020) 7408 0849 E-mail: info@meadoil.com

Mechagryl Ltd, Unit 7, London Group Business Park, 715 North Circular Road, London, NW2 7AQ Tel: (020) 8208 4677 Fax: (020) 8903 2802 E-mail: mechagryl@btclick.com

Midland Mercantile Export Company, 2 The Avenue, Bedford Park, London, W4 1HT Tel: (020) 8994 8111 Fax: (020) 8994 6856

Mitsubishi Corporation (UK) P.L.C., Mid City Place, 71 High Holborn, London, WC1V 6BA Tel: (020) 7025 3000 Fax: (020) 7025 3499

Mitsukoshi, Dorland House, 14-20 Regent Street, London, SW1Y 4PH Tel: (020) 7930 0317 Fax: (020) 7839 1167

Nash Management, 7 The Chenies, Petts Wood, Orpington, Kent, BR6 0ED Tel: (01689) 820751 Fax: (01689) 875467 E-mail: nash@datel.ssworld.co.uk

Co Ordinated Engineering Ltd, 2 Cantelupe Mews, Cantelupe Road, East Grinstead, West Sussex, RH19 3BG Tel: (01342) 410130 Fax: (01342) 410125 E-mail: info@cecgroup.org.uk

Perhome Ltd, 23 Old Court House, 24 Old Court Place, London, W8 4PD Tel: (020) 7938 4099 Fax: (020) 7938 2409

Pintorex Ltd, Unit 16 The Royal London Estate, 33 West Road, London, N17 0XL Tel: (020) 8808 0882 Fax: (020) 8801 9846 E-mail: pintorex@pintorex.co.uk

Portman Hill & Co. Ltd, P.O. Box 10, Middlesbrough, Cleveland, TS2 1HH Tel: (01642) 218538 Fax: (01642) 245775 E-mail: exports@parson-crosland.demon.co.uk

R J B Engineering, Westminster Industrial Estate, Station Road, North Hykeham, Lincoln, LN6 3QY Tel: (01522) 690491 Fax: (01522) 697543 E-mail: info@sje-engineering.co.uk

R M Supplies Inverkeithing Ltd, Cruickness Road, Ferryhills Road, Inverkeithing, Fife, KY11 1HL Tel: (01383) 418901 Fax: (01383) 418198

Redreef Ltd, 8 Vale Road, Bromley, BR1 2AL Tel: (020) 8467 3445 Fax: (020) 8467 4108 E-mail: redreef@compuserve.com

Seafin Export & Import Agents, 52 Four Oaks Road, Sutton Coldfield, West Midlands, B74 2XX Tel: 0121-308 8340 Fax: 0121-308 8340 E-mail: seafin@totalise.co.uk

Sealand General Exporters, 78 New Oxford Street, London, WC1A 1HB Tel: (020) 7580 8663 Fax: (020) 7580 8662 E-mail: sales@sealand.co.uk

Sherbrook International Ltd, Unit 3, Upper Keys Business Park, Keys Park Road, Hednesford, Cannock, Staffordshire, WS12 2GE Tel: (01543) 495555 E-mail: export@sherbrook.co.uk

Sojitz P.L.C., Old Change House, 128 Queen Victoria Street, London, EC4V 4HR Tel: (020) 7886 7000 Fax: (020) 7634 0490

Star Services UK Ltd, 108 Riverbank House, 1 Putney Bridge Approach, London, SW6 3JD Tel: (020) 7731 2361 Fax: (020) 7384 2213 E-mail: janstarren@msn.com

Sumitomo Corporation Europe Holding Ltd, Vintners Place, 68 Upper Thames Street, London, EC4V 3BJ Tel: (020) 7246 3600 Fax: (020) 7246 3925 E-mail: info@sumitomocorp.co.uk

Sunag Corporation Europe Ltd, Middlesex House, 29-45 High Street, Edgware, Middlesex, HA8 7UU Tel: (020) 8381 1232 Fax: (020) 8381 1632

Tashglen Ltd, 3 Mountington Park Close, Harrow, Middlesex, HA3 0NW Tel: (020) 8907 9428 Fax: 020) 8909 1661 E-mail: tashglen@compuserve.com

Tata Ltd, 18 Grosvenor Place, London, SW1X 7HS Tel: (020) 7235 8281 Fax: (020) 7235 8727 E-mail: tata@tata.co.uk

Team Overseas Ltd, Meridian House, Nazeing Glass Works Estate, Nazeing New Road, Broxbourne, Hertfordshire, EN10 6SX Tel: +44 (01992) 788233 Fax: +44 (01992) 788695 E-mail: sales@teamoverseas.com

Tecapet Ltd, Unitec House, Albert Place, London, N3 1QB Tel: (020) 8349 4299 Fax: (020) 8349 0252 E-mail: tecapet@aol.com

Tower Hill Merchants plc, 92-94 Tooley Street, London, SE1 2TH Tel: (020) 7407 8161 Fax: (020) 7407 2949 E-mail: thm@towerhillmchts.co.uk

Toyota Motor Marketing Europe, Alexandra Dock North, Grimsby, South Humberside, DN31 3TD Tel: (01472) 347477 Fax: (01472) 348426

Trade-Link (EC) Ltd, 5 Carlton Gardens, Ealing, London, W5 2AN Tel: (020) 8998 1090 Fax: (020) 8810 5871 E-mail: tradelinkec@clara.net

Trading Transactions Ltd, Shepherds Hill, London, N6 5RG Tel: (020) 8341 3474 Fax: (020) 8347 8552

Tri Med Services Ltd, 1-2 Ossian Mews, London, N4 4DT Tel: (020) 8348 4666 Fax: (020) 8348 5666 E-mail: london@tri-med.com

Typhoon Ltd, K Colindale Business Park, Carlisle Road, London, NW9 0HN Tel: (020) 8200 5688 Fax: (020) 8205 5088

U S I Group Ltd, The Tube, 86 North Street, Manchester, M8 8RA Tel: (0845) 3734200 Fax: (0845) 3734300E-mail: sales@usiltd.com

Unimatco Ltd, Bulstrode, Oxford Road, Gerrards Cross, Buckinghamshire, SL9 8SZ Tel: (01753) 886105 Fax: (01753) 889378 E-mail: sales@unimatco.co.uk

Union Veneers, 20 Rigg Approach, London, E10 7QN Tel: (020) 8556 8866 Fax: (020) 8539 1382

United Trade & Services Ltd, 256 Water Road, Wembley, Middlesex, HA0 1HX Tel: (020) 8810 6444 Fax: (020) 8810 6455 E-mail: united.trade@btinternet.com

Robert Vanderpump & Co. Ltd, Clarks Farm Road, Danbury, Chelmsford, CM3 4PH Tel: (01245) 225966 Fax: (01245) 225866 E-mail: vanderpump@btconnect.com

View Pulse, 6 Tarranbrae, Willesden Lane, London, NW6 7PL Tel: (020) 7372 7595 Fax: (020) 7372 4067

Vital Pharmaceuticals Ltd, 68 Wellington Court, 55-67 Wellington Road, St. Johns Wood, London, NW8 9TA Tel: (020) 7586 7070 Fax: (020) 7586 5757 E-mail: vitalpharm@aol.com

Windlelm Ltd, 130 Western Road, Hove, East Sussex, BN3 1DA Tel: (01273) 770681 Fax: (01273) 321387

Windmill Buying Services Ltd, 4 Derby Street, Norwich, NR2 4PU Tel: (01603) 632008 Fax: (01603) 612236 E-mail: wwindmill@compuserve.com

EXPORT PACKERS/SPECIALIST PACKING

▶ A & L Movers, 87 Burnell Avenue, Welling, Kent, DA16 3HP Tel: (020) 8309 8005 E-mail: sales@aandlmovers.co.uk

Abels Moving Services Ltd, Wimbledon Avenue, Brandon, Suffolk, IP27 0NZ Tel: (01842) 816600 Fax: (01842) 813613 E-mail: enquiries@abels.co.uk

Abingdon Freight Fowarding, Park 34, Collett, Didcot, Oxfordshire, OX11 7WB Tel: (01235) 813471 Fax: (01235) 750040 E-mail: info@affa.co.uk

Air Sea Packing Group Ltd, Air Sea House, Third Cross Road, Twickenham, TW2 5EB Tel: (020) 8893 3303 Fax: (020) 8893 3068 E-mail: sales@airseapacking.com

Anchor Export Services Ltd, Unit D 1, Gildersome Spur Estate, Wakefield Road, Leeds, LS27 7JZ Tel: 0113-252 6544 Fax: 0113-238 0028

Bampton Packaging Holdings Ltd, Lenton Lane, Nottingham, NG7 2NR Tel: 0115-986 8601 Fax: 0115-986 2984 E-mail: sales@bamtonpacking.co.uk

Basingstoke Packaging, 24 London Road, Thatcham, Berkshire, RG18 4LQ Tel: (01635) 863783 Fax: (01635) 861675

Bestworld Packing Ltd, Spur Road, Feltham, Middlesex, TW14 0SL Tel: (020) 8893 2930 Fax: (020) 8893 2476 E-mail: gcecil@bestworldpacking.com

Breydon Enterprises Ltd, Fenner Road, Unit 1, Great Yarmouth, Norfolk, NR30 3PS Tel: (01493) 331411 Fax: (01493) 331411 E-mail: breydonenterprises@fsmail.net

Con-Lloyd Ltd, Chapter Street, Manchester, M40 2AY Tel: 0161-203 4660 Fax: 0161-205 4518 E-mail: info@con-lloyd.com

Container Products Ltd, Unit 7C, Castle Mill Works, Bimingham New Road, Dudley, West Midlands, DY1 4DA Tel: 01384 251391 Fax: 01384 251390 E-mail: info@containerproducts.co.uk

Conway Packing Services Ltd, Central Works, Groveland Road, Tipton, West Midlands, DY4 7UD Tel: 0121-520 1144 Fax: 0121-520 2670 E-mail: admin@conwaypack.co.uk

Crown Worldwide Ltd, Cullen Square, Deans Road, Deans Industrial Estate, Livingston, West Lothian, EH54 8SJ Tel: (01506) 468150 Fax: (01506) 468151 E-mail: general.gblob@crownworldwide.com

D L Packing Ltd, Unit 4 Lawrence Trading Estate, Blackwell Lane, Greenwich, London, SE10 0AR Tel: (020) 8858 3713 Fax: (020) 8293 4578 E-mail: dlpacking@btconnect.com

Dolphin Movers, Unit 2 Haslemere Business Centre, Lincoln Way, Enfield, Middlesex, EN1 1DX Tel: (020) 8804 7700 Fax: (020) 8804 3232 E-mail: sales@dolphinmovers.com

E W Hoe Export Packers Ltd, Violet Road, London, E3 3QH Tel: (020) 7987 2444 Fax: (020) 7987 0497 E-mail: sales@ewhoe.co.uk

Eastside Freight Services Ltd, Stratford St North, Birmingham, B11 1BY Tel: 0121-766 8333 Fax: 0121-766 8361 E-mail: efs.services@virgin.net

Expack Packers, 6 King St Industrial Estate, Langtoft, Peterborough, PE6 9NF Tel: (01778) 560381 Fax: (01778) 561118

Export & General Packing Co. Ltd, Chapter Street, Manchester, M40 2AY Tel: 0161-205 8948 Fax: 0161-205 4518

Fleet Shipping International Ltd, 41-47 Blue Anchor Lane, London, SE16 3UL Tel: (020) 7232 0777 Fax: (020) 7232 2600 E-mail: sales@fwwshipping.com

Hamnett Machinery Removals, Gibbet Street, Halifax, West Yorkshire, HX2 0AR Tel: (01422) 345571 Fax: (01422) 346766 E-mail: hamnett@btinternet.com

Harrow Green Removals Ltd, Unit Q1, Queen Elizabeth Distribution Park, Purfleet, Essex, RM19 1TT Tel: (020) 8551 3555 Fax: (020) 8551 9199 E-mail: sales@harrowgreen.com

EXPORT PACKERS/SPECIALIST PACKING – *continued*

Havas Packing & Shipping Ltd, Little Parrock Farm, Shepherds Hill, Colemans Hatch, Hartfield, East Sussex, TN7 4HP Tel: (01342) 824388 Fax: (01342) 825541 E-mail: enquiries@havas.co.uk

▶ Heathrow Packing, Unit 4, Poyle Tech Center, Willow Road, Colnbrook, Slough, SL3 0DP Tel: (01753) 730081 Fax: (01753) 730082 E-mail: chris@atlaspacking.co.uk

Involvement Packing Ltd, Overthorpe Road, Banbury, Oxfordshire, OX16 4SY Tel: (01295) 258059 Fax: (01295) 265817 E-mail: ipl@ipl-involvement.co.uk

J K Francis & Son Ltd, 16 Fortnum Close, Birmingham, B33 0JY Tel: 0121-783 7568 Fax: 0121-789 7140

John Pipe Ltd, 380 Ringwood Road, Poole, Dorset, BH12 3LT Tel: (01202) 715888 Fax: (01202) 743707 E-mail: david.pipe@johnpipe.co.uk

Charles Kendall Freight Ltd, Spur Road, Feltham, Middlesex, TW14 0SL Tel: (020) 8384 9494 Fax: (020) 8384 9403 E-mail: ckf@charleskendallfreight.com

Kidd Services (Yorkshire), International House, Cliff Road, Hornsea, North Humberside, HU18 1JB Tel: (01964) 537000 Fax: (01964) 537111 E-mail: user@kidds.co.uk

M E P Services Ltd, 3 Catsash Rd, Langstone, Newport, Gwent, NP18 2LZ Tel: (01633) 211995 Fax: (01633) 213131 E-mail: enq@mepfreight.com

M G Cases Ltd, Unit 8 Neills Road, Bold Industrial Park, St. Helens, Merseyside, WA9 4TU Tel: (01744) 821630 Fax: (01744) 821630

Mcwiltons Ltd, 4 Basin Road North, Portslade, Brighton, BN41 1WA Tel: (01273) 423733 Fax: (01273) 430836

Monmouthshire Timber Supplies Ltd, PO Box 20, Newport, Gwent, NP20 2YQ Tel: (01633) 213268 Fax: (01633) 257088 E-mail: mts@montimber.co.uk

Neal Bros, Queens Buildings, Hastings Road, Leicester, LE5 0LJ Tel: 0116-274 0005 Fax: 0116-274 2028 E-mail: sales@nealbrothers.co.uk

Neil Smith Export Services Ltd, 44 Hurricane Way, Norwich, NR6 6JB Tel: (01603) 409771 Fax: (01603) 788157 E-mail: sales@neilsmithexports.co.uk

P B O Ltd, Unit 18 Shepperton Business Park, Govett Avenue, Shepperton, Middlesex, TW17 8BA Tel: (01932) 232233 Fax: (01932) 243516 E-mail: paul@pbologistics.com

P & D Case Making, Unit 12 Ventura Place, Poole, Dorset, BH16 5SW Tel: (01202) 632181 Fax: (01202) 621041

P K Marine Freight Services Ltd, 1 Perimeter Road, Knowsley Industrial Park, Liverpool, L33 3AY Tel: 0151-547 3822 Fax: 0151-548 0884 E-mail: sales@pkmarine.co.uk

P & M (Packing) Ltd, Unit 11, Alstam Complex, Campbell Road, Eastleigh, Hampshire, SO50 5AD Tel: (023) 8049 0400 Fax: (023) 8049 0444 E-mail: naomi@pmpacking.com

Paksafe Crates & Packing Cases, 1 Tewin Court, Welwyn Garden City, Hertfordshire, AL7 1AU Tel: (01707) 391939 Fax: (01707) 390989 E-mail: jag.1@virgin.net

Power Packing Export Services Ltd, Pinhoe Trading Estate, Venny Bridge, Exeter, EX4 8JN Tel: (01392) 468088 Fax: (01392) 467987 E-mail: mail@powerpacking.co.uk

R H Export Packers Ltd, Lenton Freight Terminal, Lenton Lane, Nottingham, NG7 2NR Tel: 0115-943 8034 Fax: 0115-943 8045 E-mail: sales@rhep.co.uk

Radius Shipping Ltd, 886 Old Kent Road, London, SE15 1NQ Tel: (020) 7639 2048 Fax: (020) 7639 7313 E-mail: office@radius.uk.net

Robert Claire & Co. Ltd, Unit 5-6 Discovery Business Park, St James's Road, London, SE16 4RA Tel: (020) 7231 9000 Fax: (020) 7231 5657

Rosewood Maufacturing Co. Ltd, Bede Trading Estate, Jarrow, Tyne & Wear, NE32 3EN Tel: 0191-428 1214 Fax: 0191-428 1021 E-mail: sales@rosewoodpackaging.co.uk

Roshview International Ltd, 3-11 Stean Street, London, E8 4ED Tel: (020) 7254 4836 Fax: (020) 7249 9886

RSF Commercial Services Ltd, Unit 24 Walkers Road, Moons Moat North Industrial Estate, Redditch, Worcestershire, B98 9HE Tel: (01527) 598777 Fax: (01527) 598538 E-mail: office@rsfonline.co.uk

S C A, Riverbank Works, Riverford Road, Glasgow, G43 1RP Tel: 0141-632 0999 Fax: 0141-632 8111

S D V UK Ltd, Building 673, Spur Road, Feltham, Middlesex, TW14 0SL Tel: (020) 8831 4900 Fax: (020) 8890 1111 E-mail: sdvlhr@sdv.co.uk

Salmon Poachers Ltd, Unit 1-4 Salisbury Road Business Park, Salisbury Road, Pewsey, Wiltshire, SN9 5PZ Tel: (01672) 562786 Fax: (01672) 564286 E-mail: sales@salmonpoachers.co.uk

▶ Scott Walker Perfumery, Carlton Buildings, Nangreaves Street, Leigh, Lancashire, WN7 4TN Tel: (01942) 676969 Fax: (01942) 676986

Sheffield Packaging Services Ltd, Sheffield Road, Woodhouse Mill, Sheffield, S13 9WH Tel: 0114-269 3977 Fax: 0114-269 3980 E-mail: sheffpack@btopenworld.com

Showell Packing Ltd, Showell Road, Wolverhampton, WV10 9JY Tel: (01902) 725895 Fax: (01902) 862962 E-mail: peterhoward@hoship.com

Slough International Freight & Packing Ltd, 820 Yeovil Road, Slough, SL1 4JA Tel: (01753) 691011 Fax: (01753) 825669 E-mail: sloughinter@btconnect.com

Smith Packaging Services, Lochlands Industrial Estate, Larbert, Stirlingshire, FK5 3NS Tel: (01324) 555521 Fax: (01324) 555988 E-mail: smith.packaging@btinternet.com

▶ Spanish Removals, Hellman House, Lakeside Estate, Colnbrook, Slough, SL3 0EL Tel: (0870) 4202950 Fax: (08704) 202951 E-mail: info@spanishremovals.com

▶ Stadium, Hannington Works, Longrigg, Swalwell, Newcastle upon Tyne, NE16 3AS Tel: 0191-496 1321 Fax: 0191-488 4127 E-mail: sales-gh@stadium-packing.co.uk

Surfair Freight Services Ltd, Wilson Road, Wigston, Leicestershire, LE18 4TQ Tel: 0116-278 6206 Fax: 0116-277 7784 E-mail: transport@surfair.co.uk

Henry Sutcliffe Ltd, Hulme Street, Salford, M5 4PX Tel: 0161-736 1337 Fax: 0161-745 7724 E-mail: sales@hsltd.co.uk

T S International Packing Ltd, Unit C1 Halesfield 19, Telford, Shropshire, TF7 4QT Tel: (01952) 586820 Fax: (01952) 585958 E-mail: connect@tsipacking.co.uk

Thompson Shipping Ltd, 66 Totternhoe Road, Eaton Bray, Dunstable, Bedfordshire, LU6 2BD Tel: (01525) 223071 Fax: (01525) 851482 E-mail: jim@fahawkins.com

Total Logistics, Leigh Park, Fulflood Road, Havant, Hampshire, PO9 5AX Tel: (023) 9247 4123 Fax: (023) 9247 0467 E-mail: sales@appliedlogistics.co.uk

Tuplin Ltd, Unit 7-8 Bridge Industrial Estate, Balcombe Road, Horley, Surrey, RH6 9HU Tel: (01293) 433433 Fax: (01293) 433438 E-mail: sales@tuplin.co.uk

Tuplin Stansted Ltd, Unit 4 Birchanger Industrial Estate, Stansted Road, Bishop's Stortford, Hertfordshire, CM23 2TH Tel: (01279) 656461 Fax: (01279) 652520

Universal Packing Specialists Ltd, Unit 7 Space Waye, Feltham, Middlesex, TW14 0TH Tel: (020) 8893 1180 Fax: (020) 8893 2214 E-mail: sales@universalpacking.co.uk

Walker Holding Ltd, 33-34 Liliput Road, Brackmills Industrial Estate, Northampton, NN4 7DT Tel: (01604) 760529 Fax: (01604) 675641 E-mail: sales@walkerpack.co.uk

Wasp Joinery & Construction Ltd, Eastington Trading Estate, Eastington, Stonehouse, Gloucestershire, GL10 3RZ Tel: (01453) 824289 Fax: (01453) 824289

Wells & Root Ltd, Parker Drive, Leicester, LE4 0JP Tel: 0116-235 3535 Fax: 0116-235 3910 E-mail: enquiries@wellsandroot.co.uk

EXPORT PACKING CASE FITTINGS

E E Olley & Sons Ltd, Dartford Trade Park, Dartford, DA1 1PE Tel: (01322) 227681 Fax: (01322) 289724 E-mail: sales@eeolley.co.uk

▶ Woodland Export Packaging UK, 52 Cobden Street, Salford, M6 6WF Tel: 0161-736 2032 Fax: 0161-736 1733 E-mail: sales@woodlandsxp.com

EXPORT PACKING CASES

▶ A & L Movers, 87 Burnell Avenue, Welling, Kent, DA16 3HP Tel: (020) 8309 8005 E-mail: sales@aandlmovers.co.uk

Abbey Case Co. Ltd, Britannia Road, Waltham Cross, Hertfordshire, EN8 7NZ Tel: (01992) 715996 Fax: (01992) 719852 E-mail: sales@abbeycase.co.uk

Anchor Export Services Ltd, Unit D 1, Gildersome Spur Estate, Wakefield Road, Leeds, LS27 7JZ Tel: 0113-252 6544 Fax: 0113-238 0028

Breydon Enterprises Ltd, Fenner Road, Unit 1, Great Yarmouth, Norfolk, NR30 3PS Tel: (01493) 331411 Fax: (01493) 331411 E-mail: breydonenterprises@fsmail.net

Brookley Case Co. Ltd, Shaw Road, Dudley, West Midlands, DY2 8TP Tel: (01384) 259908 Fax: (01384) 241624 E-mail: brookley.case@btinternet.com

Cargo Packing Services Ltd, Portland Works, Hill Street, Ashton-under-Lyne, Lancashire, OL7 0PZ Tel: 0161-343 4737 Fax: 0161-343 4738

Coleshill Freight Services Ltd, Coleshill Freight Terminal, Station Road, Coleshill, Birmingham, B46 1JJ Tel: (01675) 463869 Fax: (01675) 465727 E-mail: john@coleshillfreight.com

Container Products Ltd, Unit 7C, Castle Mill Works, Bimingham New Road, Dudley, West Midlands, DY1 4DA Tel: 01384 251391 Fax: 01384 251390 E-mail: info@containerproducts.co.uk

E W Turner & Co. Ltd, Tame Street, West Bromwich, West Midlands, B70 0QP Tel: 0121-556 1141 Fax: 0121-556 3911 E-mail: accounts@ewturner.co.uk

Geddes Packaging, Dumblederry Lane, Walsall, WS9 0DH Tel: (01922) 455988 Fax: (01922) 454988E-mail: sales@geddespackaging.co.uk

Glen Pac Southern Ltd, 11 The Forty, Cricklade, Swindon, SN6 6HW Tel: (01793) 751527 Fax: (01793) 750551 E-mail: sales@glenpac.com

Good Packing Co. Ltd, Mariner, Lichfield Road Industrial Estate, Tamworth, Staffordshire, B79 7TJ Tel: (01827) 65911 Fax: (01827) 59310 E-mail: info@goodpackaging.co.uk

Invicta Borough Saw Mills, Unit 14, Invicta Buisiness Park, Gillingham, Kent, ME8 6TT Tel: (01732) 882012 E-mail: enquiries@invictabgs.co.uk

John Pipe Ltd, 380 Ringwood Road, Poole, Dorset, BH12 3LT Tel: (01202) 715888 Fax: (01202) 743707 E-mail: david.pipe@johnpipe.co.uk

M G Cases Ltd, Unit 8 Neills Road, Bold Industrial Park, St. Helens, Merseyside, WA9 4TU Tel: (01744) 821630 Fax: (01744) 821630

Mersey Forwarding Co Shipping Services Ltd, Mersey House, 1 Church Street, Bootle, Merseyside, L20 1AF Tel: 0151-933 2000 Fax: 0151-933 0883 E-mail: tlennonmfss@btconnect.com

N & R Manufacturing Ltd, Lawrence House Apollo, Lichfield Road Industrial Estate, Tamworth, Staffordshire, B79 7TA Tel: (01827) 57218 Fax: (01827) 60289

Neil Smith Export Services Ltd, 44 Hurricane Way, Norwich, NR6 6JB Tel: (01603) 409771 Fax: (01603) 788157 E-mail: sales@neilsmithexports.co.uk

Packaging Industries Ltd, Beaumont Way, Aycliffe Industrial Pk, Newton Aycliffe, Co. Durham, DL5 6SN Tel: (01325) 313444 Fax: (01325) 300246 E-mail: sales@pi-box.co.uk

Radius Shipping Ltd, 886 Old Kent Road, London, SE15 1NQ Tel: (020) 7639 2048 Fax: (020) 7639 7313 E-mail: office@radius.uk.net

Sheffield Packaging Services Ltd, Sheffield Road, Woodhouse Mill, Sheffield, S13 9WH Tel: 0114-269 3977 Fax: 0114-269 3980 E-mail: sheffpack@btopenworld.com

Showell Packing Ltd, Showell Road, Wolverhampton, WV10 9JY Tel: (01902) 725895 Fax: (01902) 862962 E-mail: peterhoward@hoship.com

▶ Stadium, Hannington Works, Longrigg, Swalwell, Newcastle upon Tyne, NE16 3AS Tel: 0191-496 1321 Fax: 0191-488 4127 E-mail: sales-gh@stadium-packing.co.uk

Star Pac Ltd, 23 Fernwood Close, Redditch, Worcestershire, B98 7TN Tel: (01527) 850022 Fax: (01527) 850033 E-mail: sales@starpac.co.uk

Henry Sutcliffe Ltd, Hulme Street, Salford, M5 4PX Tel: 0161-736 1337 Fax: 0161-745 7724 E-mail: sales@hsltd.co.uk

Thompson Shipping Ltd, 66 Totternhoe Road, Eaton Bray, Dunstable, Bedfordshire, LU6 2BD Tel: (01525) 223071 Fax: (01525) 851482 E-mail: jim@fahawkins.com

Tuplin Stansted Ltd, Unit 4 Birchanger Industrial Estate, Stansted Road, Bishop's Stortford, Hertfordshire, CM23 2TH Tel: (01279) 656461 Fax: (01279) 652520

Wasp Joinery & Construction Ltd, Eastington Trading Estate, Eastington, Stonehouse, Gloucestershire, GL10 3RZ Tel: (01453) 824289 Fax: (01453) 824289

Whirlowdale Trading Co. Ltd, Canklow Meadows Industrial Estate, West Bawtry Road, Rotherham, South Yorkshire, S60 2XL Tel: (01709) 829061 Fax: (01709) 378947 E-mail: sales@whirlowdale.com

▶ Woodland Export Packaging UK, 52 Cobden Street, Salford, M6 6WF Tel: 0161-736 2032 Fax: 0161-736 1733 E-mail: sales@woodlandsxp.com

EXPORT SERVICES TO THE ENGINEERING INDUSTRY

Express Electrical, Dunswell Road, Cottingham, North Humberside, HU16 4JG Tel: (01482) 846269 Fax: (01482) 876655 E-mail: sales@express-industrial-exports.co.uk

London & Overseas Supplies, Unit G, Crackley Way, Peartree Lane, Dudley, West Midlands, DY2 0UW Tel: (01384) 246230 Fax: (01384) 246240 E-mail: landos@wyko.co.uk

Sunag Corporation Europe Ltd, Middlesex House, 29-45 High Street, Edgware, Middlesex, HA8 7UU Tel: (020) 8381 1232 Fax: (020) 8381 1632

EXPORT/IMPORT DOCUMENTATION/ INFORMATION CONSULTANTS OR SERVICES

Airocean Freight Ltd, 6-9 Spring Road, Smethwick, West Midlands, B66 1PE Tel: 0121-580 6730 Fax: 0121-525 5296 E-mail: info@airoceanfreight.co.uk

Autorise Ltd, Maspro House, Chadwick Road, Astmoor Industrial Estate, Runcorn, Cheshire, WA7 1PW Tel: (01928) 561552 Fax: (01928) 591531

Birmingham Chamber Training Ltd, 75 Harbourne Road, Edgbaston, Birmingham, B15 3DH Tel: 0121-454 1999 Fax: 0121-455 8700 E-mail: enquiries@birminghamchamber.org.uk

Brooklands International Freight Services Ltd, Airport House Redhill Aerodrome, Kings Mill Lane, Redhill, RH1 5JY Tel: (01737) 823575 Fax: (01737) 823634 E-mail: sales@bifs.net

Central & West Lancashire Chamber Of Commerce & Industry, Unit 9-10 Eastway Business Village, Olivers Place, Fulwood, Preston, PR2 9WT Tel: (01772) 653000 Fax: (01772) 655544 E-mail: info@lancschamber.co.uk

Chamber Of Commerce & Business Link West Mercia, Severn House, Prescott Drive, Worcester, WR4 9NE Tel: (0845) 6414641 Fax: (0845) 6414641 E-mail: enquiries@hwchamber.co.uk

Chamber Of Commerce Trade & Industry, Commerce House, Fenton Street, Lancaster, LA1 1AB Tel: (01524) 381331 Fax: (01524) 389505 E-mail: sales@lancaster-chamber.org.uk

Doncaster Chamber, Enterprise House, White Rose Way, Hyde Park 45, Doncaster, South Yorkshire, DN4 5ND Tel: (01302) 341000 Fax: (01302) 328382 E-mail: chamber@doncaster-chamber.co.uk

IES Ltd, 1 Portview Road, Bristol, BS11 9LS Tel: 0117-938 0600 Fax: 0117-938 0900 E-mail: info@ies.co.uk

Institute Of Export Ltd, Export House, Minerva Business Park, Lynch Wood, Peterborough, PE2 6FT Tel: (01733) 404400 Fax: (01733) 404444 E-mail: institute@export.org.uk

Jersey Chamber of Commerce & Industry Inc., Chamber House, 25 Pier Road, St. Helier, Jersey, JE1 4HF Tel: (01534) 724536 Fax: (01534) 734942 E-mail: admin@jerseychamber.com

K M B Shipping Ltd, Lower Church Lane, Tipton, West Midlands, DY4 7PH Tel: 0121-557 3352 Fax: 0121-520 0936 E-mail: info@onestopshipping.co.uk

Leicestershire Chamber Of Commerce & Industry, 5 New Walk, Leicester, LE1 6TE Tel: 0116-247 1800 Fax: 0116-247 0430 E-mail: info@chamberofcommerce.co.uk

Liaison & Consultant Services (U K) Ltd, PO Box 56, Woking, Surrey, GU21 2PP Tel: (01483) 799322 Fax: (01483) 799311 E-mail: rclcsuk@aol.com

Liverpool Chamber Of Commerce & Industry, 1 Old Hall Street, Liverpool, L3 9HG Tel: 0151-227 1233 Fax: 0151-236 0121 E-mail: info@liverpoolchamber.org.uk

Nash Management, 7 The Chenies, Petts Wood, Orpington, Kent, BR6 0ED Tel: (01689) 820751 Fax: (01689) 875467 E-mail: nash@datel.ssworld.co.uk

Newman White Ltd, 36 Blind Lane, Southwick, Trowbridge, Wiltshire, BA14 9PJ Tel: (01225) 762337

P & H Export Services Ltd, 212 Katherine Street, Ashton-under-Lyne, Lancashire, OL6 7AS Tel: 0161-343 8558 Fax: 0161-343 2492 E-mail: info@phexports.co.uk

Surrey Chamber Of Commerce Ltd, 5th Floor Hollywood House, Church Street East, Woking, Surrey, GU21 6HJ Tel: (01483) 726655 Fax: (01483) 740217 E-mail: info@surrey_chambers.co.uk

Teknoserv (U.K.) Ltd, Culford House Unit 7, 1/7 Orsman Road, London, N1 5RA Tel: (020) 7729 3676 Fax: (020) 7729 5184 E-mail: sorab@teknoserv.freeserve.co.uk

Watford & West Herts Chamber Of Commerce, The Business Centre, Colne Way, Watford, WD24 7AA Tel: (01923) 442442 Fax: (01923) 445050 E-mail: sales@watford-chamber.co.uk

EXPRESS FREIGHT ROAD TRANSPORT AND HAULAGE

▶ Crowfoot Carriers Ltd, Gosforth Rd, Ascot Drive, Derby, DE24 8HU Tel: (01332) 372621 Fax: (01332) 346171

▶ Crowfoots Carriers (Manchester) Ltd, Park Street, Stalybridge, Cheshire, SK15 2BT Tel: 0161-303 7133 Fax: 0161-304 8226

Kent Link Transport & Storage, Unit 18 Henwood Business Centre, Henwood, Ashford, Kent, TN24 8DH Tel: (01233) 638889 Fax: (01233) 635869 E-mail: sales@kentlink.com

EXPRESS PARCEL DELIVERY SERVICES

A Cars Express Despatch Ltd, Unit 14 Langley Terrace Industrial Park, Latimer Road, Luton, LU1 3XQ Tel: (01582) 731900 Fax: (0870) 2330612 E-mail: acars@acars.co.uk

A N C Harlow Ltd, 5 Edinburgh Place, Edinburgh Way, Harlow, Essex, CM20 2DJ Tel: (01279) 442031 Fax: (01279) 428753 E-mail: operations0023@anc.co.uk

▶ Anc North Yorkshire Ltd, York Road, Flaxby, Knaresborough, North Yorkshire, HG5 0RP Tel: (01423) 869696 Fax: (01423) 862922

Cargo Forwarding, Transit 1, West Bank Way, Belfast, BT3 9LB Tel: (028) 9037 3700 Fax: (028) 9037 3736 E-mail: sales@cargo-forwarding.co.uk

City Air Express Ni Ltd, West Bank Drive, Belfast, BT3 9LA Tel: (028) 9078 1878 Fax: (028) 9078 1788 E-mail: sales@cityairexpress.com

Connection Delivery Service Ltd, 6 Domingo Street, London, EC1Y 0TA Tel: (020) 7253 2211 Fax: (020) 7251 3381

Cooper Carriers Ltd, Tir Llwyd Industrial Estate, Kinmel Bay, Rhyl, Clwyd, LL18 5JA Tel: (01745) 362800 Fax: (01745) 362801

Dale Express Transport Ltd, Dale House, 232 Selsdon Road, Croydon, CR2 6PL Tel: (020) 8760 5000 Fax: (020) 8760 0202 E-mail: service@daleexpress.co.uk

EXPRESS PARCEL DELIVERY SERVICES – *continued*

Double M Transport Ltd, The Courtyard, Warkworth, Banbury, Oxfordshire, OX17 2AG Tel: (01295) 712828 Fax: (01295) 711886 E-mail: stuartdoublem@aol.com

E J Masters Ltd, Railway Terrace, Kings Langley, Hertfordshire, WD4 8JA Tel: (01923) 265757 Fax: (01923) 267827

▶ Easy Parcel Worldwide, Mercury House, Russell Gardens, Wickford, Essex, SS11 8BH Tel: (0800) 180 4995 Fax: (01268) 570621 E-mail: sales@easyparcel.net

Fastway Flyers Ltd, 78 Rivington Street, London, EC2A 3AY Tel: (020) 7729 3333 Fax: (020) 7729 3806 E-mail: fastwayflyers@1tel.net.uk

Gills Northern Ltd, North CR, Seaham, County Durham, SR7 8RD Tel: 0191-581 3853 Fax: 0191-513 0266

Grand Prix Express, Swan Road, Mochdre Business Park, Mochdre, Colwyn Bay, Clwyd, LL28 5HB Tel: (01492) 545293 Fax: (01492) 546241 E-mail: john@grandprixexpress.com

Haul Small Ltd, Unit 2 Knightwood Court, Edison Way, Gapton Hall Industrial Estate, Great Yarmouth, Norfolk, NR31 0NG Tel: (01493) 604691 Fax: (01493) 604692

Highwayman Couriers, 31 Firs St, Dudley, West Midlands, DY2 7DW Tel: (01384) 456976 Fax: (01384) 457146 E-mail: enquiries@hiwaymancouriers.co.uk

Initial City Link Ltd, Wellington House, 61-73 Staines Road West, Sunbury-On-Thames, Middlesex, TW16 7AH Tel: (01932) 822622 Fax: (01932) 785560 E-mail: enquiries@city-link.co.uk

Interfreight Ltd, 8 The Felbridge Centre, The Birches Industrial Estate, Imberhorne Lane, East Grinstead, West Sussex, RH19 1XP Tel: (01342) 410454 Fax: (01342) 327237 E-mail: interfreight@lineone.net

Interlink Express Parcels Ltd, Earlesfield Lane, Grantham, Lincolnshire, NG31 7NT Tel: (01476) 570263 Fax: (01476) 570268 E-mail: depot634@interlinkexpress.com

Lynx Express Ltd, Pentland Industrial Estate, Loanhead, Midlothian, EH20 9QH Tel: 0131-448 2625 Fax: 0131-448 2621

▶ M & S Carriers, Unit 24, Charnley Fold Industrial Estat, School Lane, Bamber Bridge, Preston, PR5 6PS Tel: (01772) 696555

Nationwide Express Parcels, Unit 4b Surrey Street, Glossop, Derbyshire, SK13 7AJ Tel: (01457) 860826 Fax: (01457) 855652

Nightfreight (GB) Ltd, Imberhorne Way, East Grinstead, West Sussex, RH19 1RL Tel: (01342) 316221 Fax: (01342) 316134 E-mail: info@nightfreight.co.uk

Olympic Express Ltd, Head Office, 90-91 Moseley Street, Birmingham, B12 0RT Tel: (08451) 255505 Fax: 0121-666 7541

Parceline Ltd, Roebuck Lane, Smethwick, West Midlands, B66 1BY Tel: (0845) 9505505 Fax: 0121-500 2646 E-mail: info@parceline.com

Point To Point Couriers Ltd, Eve Road, Woking, Surrey, GU21 5JS Tel: (01483) 723511 Fax: (01483) 750427

Quick Tripper Transport, 63 Wyrley Road, Birmingham, B6 7BT Tel: 0121-327 0925 Fax: 0121-327 1136

Ripponden Carriers Ltd, Oldham Road, Ripponden, Sowerby Bridge, West Yorkshire, HX6 4ED Tel: (01422) 822266 Fax: (01422) 823882 E-mail: info@rippondencarriers.co.uk

Roseville Taxis, Stanier Street, Newcastle, Staffordshire, ST5 2SY Tel: (01782) 631234 Fax: (01782) 634800

S P D S Ltd, 20 Singer Road, Kelvin Industrial Estate, East Kilbride, Glasgow, G75 0XS Tel: (01355) 234807 Fax: (01355) 260525 E-mail: admin@spds.co.uk

Southern Express, Express House, 832 Yeovil Road, Slough, SL1 4JG Tel: (01753) 820022 Fax: (01753) 691276 E-mail: sales@palletforce.com

Special Delivery Ltd, 531 Kings Road, London, SW10 0TZ Tel: (020) 7351 5133 Fax: (020) 7351 6076

T N T Express, Abeles Way, Atherstone, Warwickshire, CV9 2RY Tel: (01827) 303030 Fax: (01827) 301301 E-mail: steve.doig@tnt.co.uk

T N T Express, Abeles Way, Atherstone, Warwickshire, CV9 2RY Tel: (01827) 303030 Fax: (01827) 301301

T N T Express, Hall Road, Aylesford, Kent, ME20 7TR Tel: (01622) 716601 Fax: (01622) 716040

▶ T N T Express, Unit 5 12 Cromwell Road Industrial Estate, Bredbury, Stockport, Cheshire, SK6 2RF Tel: (0800) 777222 Fax: 0161-406 8788

Target Worldwide Express Ltd, 6 Woodlands Park, Ashton Road, Newton-le-Willows, Merseyside, WA12 0HF Tel: (01925) 247000 Fax: (01925) 575700 E-mail: enquiries@targetexpress.co.uk

▶ Topclass Executive Private Hire, 1st Floor Co-op Stores, The Street, Woolpit, Bury St. Edmunds, Suffolk, IP30 9RU Tel: (07949) 372949 E-mail: info@topclass-executive.co.uk

Tornado Express, Suite 220, London, E15 2SP Tel: (020) 8519 7800 Fax: (020) 8519 0603

Tuffnells Parcel Express Ltd, P Yew Tree Trading Estate, Kilbuck Lane, Haydock, St. Helens, Merseyside, WA11 9UX Tel: (01942) 721313 Fax: (01942) 721498

▶ Tuffnells Parcels Express Ltd, Azalea Road, Rogerstone, Newport, Gwent, NP10 9SA Tel: (01633) 891010 Fax: (01633) 891044 E-mail: nick.walters@tuffnells.co.uk

United Parcels Service (UPS) Ltd, Gresham Road, Nuneaton, Warwickshire, CV10 7QR Tel: (0845) 7877877 Fax: (024) 7664 2188 E-mail: callcentre@europe.ups.com

West One Carriers, 99 North Street, London, SW4 0HF Tel: (020) 7720 0056

World's End Couriers, Unit 6b Farm Lane Trading Estate, Farm Lane, London, SW6 1QJ Tel: (020) 7381 8991 Fax: (020) 7385 4468

EXTENDED LIFE LIGHT BULBS

▶ Ebulbshop Lighting Retailers, 42 44 High Street, Hythe, Kent, CT21 5AT Tel: (01303) 264400 Fax: (01303) 264664 E-mail: andrew@ebulbshop.com

▶ First Light Direct, 4 Bentsbrook Road, North Holmwood, Dorking, Surrey, RH5 4HW Tel: (01306) 881314 E-mail: sales@firstlightdirect.com

▶ Rock Electronics, 113 Glasgow Road, Dumbarton, G82 1RG Tel: (01389) 841473 Fax: (01389) 730300 E-mail: rockelectronics@fsbdial.co.uk

EXTENSIBLE BELTING

Bond-a-Band Transmissions Ltd, Vale Mills, Oakworth, Keighley, West Yorkshire, BD22 0EB Tel: 01535 643123 Fax: 01535 646795 E-mail: sales@bondaband.com

EXTENSION SPRINGS

Harris Springs Ltd, Ruscombe Works Tavistock Industrial Estate, Ruscombe Lane, Ruscombe, Reading, RG10 9LR Tel: 0118-934 0024 Fax: 0118-934 1365 E-mail: sales@harris-springs.com

Springcoil Spring Distributors, 2 Woodbourn Hill, Sheffield, S9 3NE Tel: 0114-273 1111 Fax: 0114-273 0222 E-mail: enquiries@springcoil.co.uk

EXTERIOR IRRIGATION SYSTEMS

▶ Aqua-Light, 21 Favourite Road, Whitstable, Kent, CT5 4UB Tel: (01227) 282130 E-mail: info@aqua-light.co.uk

EXTERIOR SIGN ILLUMINATION LIGHTING

Bernlite Ltd, 3 Brookside, Colne Way, Watford, WD24 7QJ Tel: (01923) 200160 Fax: (01923) 246057

D W Windsor Ltd, Pindar Road, Hoddesdon, Hertfordshire, EN11 0DX Tel: (01992) 474600 Fax: (01992) 474601 E-mail: sales@dwwindsor.co.uk

Sondia Lighting Ltd, 45 Portland Place, Hull, HU2 8QP Tel: (01482) 223353 Fax: (01482) 225681 E-mail: sales@sondialighting.com

EXTERIOR SUNBLINDS

Agp Blinds & Curtains, 1 Exhibition Way, Pinhoe Trading Estate, Exeter, EX4 8JD Tel: (01392) 462767 Fax: (01392) 205147 E-mail: agp.astrablinds@hotmail.co.uk

Awnings & Blinds By Morco, Riverside, Lombard Wall, London, SE7 7SG Tel: (020) 8858 2083 Fax: (020) 8305 2431 E-mail: sales@morcoblinds.co.uk

Claxton Blinds Ltd, Beaumont Works, Sutton Road, St. Albans, Hertfordshire, AL1 5HH Tel: (01727) 840001 Fax: (01727) 840004 E-mail: claxton-blinds@btconnect.com

Douglas Knight Sunblinds Ltd, 31b Station Road, Park Gate, Southampton, SO31 7GJ Tel: (01489) 575507 Fax: (01489) 575507

Eclipse Blind Systems Ltd, 10 Fountain Crescent, Inchinnan Business Park, Renfrew, PA4 9RE Tel: 0141-812 3322 Fax: 0141-812 5253 E-mail: orrd@eclipseblinds.co.uk

G Stanley, 5 Wyke Street, Hull, HU9 1PA Tel: (01482) 225590 Fax: (01482) 588764 E-mail: sales@gstanleys.co.uk

Hall, 11 Back Avondale Road East, Heysham, Morecambe, Lancashire, LA3 1SW Tel: (01524) 414638 Fax: (01229) 466462

Jordans Sunblinds Ltd, York St, Hull, HU2 0QW Tel: (01482) 326657 Fax: (01482) 212486 E-mail: enquiries@jordansofhull.co.uk

Levolux A T Ltd, Levolux House 24 Eastville Close, Eastern Avenue, Gloucester, GL4 3SJ Tel: (01452) 500007 Fax: (01452) 527496 E-mail: info@levolux.com

Malvern Blinds, The Old Fire Station, Howsell Road, Malvern, Worcestershire, WR14 1TF Tel: (01684) 574047 Fax: (01684) 892729 E-mail: info@malvernblinds.co.uk

North West Sunblinds, 19 Kilburn Close, Heald Green, Cheadle, Cheshire, SK8 3LP Tel: 0161-437 6808 Fax: 0161-437 6808 E-mail: nwblinds@aol.com

Parasol Blinds, 134 Magdalen Street, Norwich, NR3 1JD Tel: (01603) 666008 Fax: (01603) 410333

Putney Blinds, 4 Thornsett Road, London, SW18 4EN Tel: (020) 8874 6001 Fax: (020) 8874 6229 E-mail: sales@putneyblinds.co.uk

Rogers Blinds & Awnings Ltd, Unit 6 Castle Buildings, Gilston Road, Saltash, Cornwall, PL12 6TW Tel: (01752) 840616 Fax: (01752) 840571 E-mail: rogersblinds@supanet.com

Shackleton Mortimer & Sons Ltd, 25 Pitcliffe Way, Bradford, West Yorkshire, BD5 7SG Tel: (01274) 726890 Fax: (01274) 390384

Shadewell Blinds Ltd, St Margarets Lane, Fareham, Hampshire, PO14 4BG Tel: (01329) 841199 Fax: (01329) 842299 E-mail: info@shadewell.co.uk

Solaris Sunblinds Ltd, 48 Victoria Road, Woolston, Southampton, SO19 9DX Tel: (023) 8043 1739 Fax: (023) 8043 7531 E-mail: info@solarissunblinds.co.uk

Sunshade Blinds, 592 Kingstanding Road, Birmingham, B44 9SH Tel: 0121-373 1919 Fax: 0121-373 1919

SW Blinds & Interiors Ltd, Unit 60-61 Faraday Mill Business Park, Faraday Road, Plymouth, PL4 0ST Tel: (01752) 663517 Fax: (01752) 226150 E-mail: info@swblinds.com

Turner Sunblinds, Forrest Street, Blackburn, BB1 3BB Tel: (01254) 57763 Fax: (01254) 272101

Wessex Blinds Covers Ltd, Belvedere Trading Estate, Taunton, Somerset, TA1 1BH Tel: (01823) 366060 Fax: (01823) 366063

EXTERNAL DOORS

Cashmores Joinery Ltd, 86-88 Essex Road, Leicester, LE4 9EG Tel: 0116-276 9948 Fax: 0116-276 9948

▶ S E A Windows & Doors, Unit 1a North Street, Reading, RG1 7DA Tel: 0118-957 3976 Fax: 0118-939 3610

▶ Woodcraft Supplies, 163-165 Deanston Drive, Glasgow, G41 3LP Tel: 0141-649 3838 Fax: 0141-649 9181 E-mail: info@woodcraftsupplies.co.uk

EXTERNAL GLASS DOORS

▶ Woodcraft Supplies, 163-165 Deanston Drive, Glasgow, G41 3LP Tel: 0141-649 3838 Fax: 0141-649 9181 E-mail: info@woodcraftsupplies.co.uk

EXTERNAL OR INTERNAL LINE MARKING CONTRACTORS

▶ Amark Safety Markings, 78 Shawfield Road, Ash, Aldershot, Hampshire, GU12 6RB Tel: (01252) 320325 Fax: (01252) 320325 E-mail: rjwright2005@yahoo.co.uk

EXTERNAL WALL INSULATION BEADS

Dyson Insulations Ltd, Unit 16H, Sollingsby Park, Gateshead, Tyne & Wear, NE10 8YF Tel: 0191-416 5969 Fax: 0191-417 3817

Structherm Ltd, Bent Ley Road, Meltham, Holmfirth, HD9 4AP Tel: (01484) 850098 Fax: (01484) 851388 E-mail: sales@structherm.co.uk

EXTRA LARGE INDUSTRIAL DOORS

Kaba Door Systems Ltd, Crow Arch La Industrial Estate, Crow Arch Lane, Ringwood, Hampshire, BH24 1PD Tel: (0870) 0005225 Fax: (0870) 0005226

EXTRACTION TECHNOLOGY KNOW HOW EQUIPMENT, PROCESS CONTAINMENT

Total Ventilation Solutions Ltd, Unit 10, Midland Oak Trading Estate, Marlissa Drive, Coventry, CV6 6HQ Tel: (024) 7666 2255 Fax: (024) 7666 2255

EXTRACTS, NATURAL PRODUCTS

▶ RIS Products Ltd, Prospect Place, Welwyn, Hertfordshire, AL6 9EW Tel: (01438) 840135 Fax: (01438) 716067 E-mail: sales@risproducts.co.uk

EXTRUDED METAL PRODUCTS, *See also headings for particular types*

Ashfield Extrusion Ltd, B Field Industrial Estate, Clover Street, Kirkby-in-Ashfield, Nottingham, NG17 7LH Tel: (01623) 757333 Fax: (01623) 751771 E-mail: ashfield.sales@btconnect.com

▶ Cold Formed Products Ltd, 24 St. Mary's Road, London, E13 9AD Tel: (020) 8471 2727 Fax: (020) 8470 1706 E-mail: sales@cfp.biz

Floform Ltd, Henfaes Lane, Welshpool, Powys, SY21 7BJ Tel: (01938) 552611 Fax: (01938) 555339 E-mail: sales@floform.co.uk

G K N Hardy Spicer Ltd-Birfield Extrusions, Station Works, Old Walsall Rd, Great Barr, Birmingham, B42 1DZ Tel: 0121-623 8818 Fax: 0121-358 4033

Holzer Ltd, Neachells Lane, Wednesfield, Wolverhampton, WV11 3QG Tel: (01902) 866355 Fax: (01902) 734073 E-mail: admin2@holzerltd-metalldyne.fsnet.co.uk

Hydro Aluminium Extrusion, Durham Road, Birtley, Chester le Street, County Durham, DH3 2AH Tel: 0191-301 1200 Fax: 0191-301 1234 E-mail: sales@hydro.com

Munro & Miller Fittings Ltd, 3 Westerton Road, East Mains Industrial Estate, Broxburn, West Lothian, EH52 5AU Tel: (01506) 853531 Fax: (01506) 856628 E-mail: sales@munro-miller.co.uk

Osborn Steel Extrusions Ltd, Brighouse Road, Low Moor, Bradford, West Yorkshire, BD12 0QL Tel: (01274) 677331 Fax: (01274) 607858 E-mail: extrusion@osbornbujon.com

EXTRUDER/EXTRUSION MACHINE ANCILLARY EQUIPMENT

N R Seal & Son, Main Street, Wick, Pershore, Worcestershire, WR10 3NU Tel: (01386) 555706 Fax: (01386) 555707 E-mail: nrsandson@tiscali.co.uk

Plasplant Ltd, Unit 4 Oakhanger Farm, Oakhanger, Bordon, Hampshire, GU35 9JA Tel: (01420) 473013 Fax: (01420) 475152 E-mail: sales@plasplant.com

EXTRUDER/EXTRUSION MACHINE COMPONENTS/TOOLS

Frisby Extrusion Services Ltd, Unit F Tyson Courtyard, Weldon South Industrial Estate, Corby, Northamptonshire, NN18 8AZ Tel: (01536) 263545 Fax: (01536) 205184 E-mail: welcome@fes-ltd.com

H B Halstead & Sons Ltd, 247 Eldon Street, Ashton-on-Ribble, Preston, PR2 2BB Tel: (01772) 252820 Fax: (01772) 202609 E-mail: sales@hbhalstead.com

Independent Tool Consultants Ltd, Unit 7, Bamfurlong Industrial Park, Staverton, Cheltenham, Gloucestershire, GL51 6SX Tel: (01452) 712519 Fax: (01452) 714786 E-mail: intoco.extrusion@virgin.net

Industrial Plastics Ltd, Unit 13 Canterbury Industrial Park, 297 Ilderton Road, London, SE15 1NP Tel: (020) 7252 9600 Fax: (020) 7252 9601 E-mail: sales@ipl-london.co.uk

Stanley Vickers Ltd, Snowdon Road, Middlesbrough, Cleveland, TS2 1LG Tel: (01642) 247353 Fax: (01642) 231571 E-mail: info@sv-ltd.co.uk

T J Avent, Unit 14a Innsworth Technology Park, Innsworth Lane, Gloucester, GL3 1DL Tel: (01452) 530041 Fax: (01452) 530040

EXTRUDER/EXTRUSION MACHINE MAINTENANCE/ REPAIR/RECONDITIONING SERVICES

N R Seal & Son, Main Street, Wick, Pershore, Worcestershire, WR10 3NU Tel: (01386) 555706 Fax: (01386) 555707 E-mail: nrsandson@tiscali.co.uk

EXTRUDER/EXTRUSION MACHINES, *See also headings for particular types*

Boston Matthews Machinery Ltd, Navigation Road, Diglis, Worcester, WR5 3DE Tel: (01905) 763100 Fax: (01905) 763101 E-mail: info@bostonmatthews.co.uk

N G C Consultancy Ltd, Unit 1A, The Mayfields, Southcrest, Redditch, Worcestershire, B98 7DU Tel: (01527) 404739 Fax: (01527) 404739

Regis Machinery Sales Ltd, 9b Arun Business Park, Bognor Regis, West Sussex, PO22 9SX Tel: (01243) 825661 Fax: (01243) 829364 E-mail: sales@regismachinery.co.uk

EXTRUDER/EXTRUSION MACHINES, ALUMINIUM

Holton Conform Ltd, Albany House, Elliott Road, Bournemouth, BH11 8JH Tel: (01202) 581881 Fax: (01202) 581789 E-mail: enquiries@holton-conform.com

EXTRUDER/EXTRUSION MACHINES, BLOWN FILM

Wittey Machinery Ltd, Unit 17 Haddenham Aerodrome Industrial Estate, Dollicott, Haddenham, Aylesbury, Buckinghamshire, HP17 8LJ Tel: (01844) 344723 Fax: (01844) 342004

EXTRUDER/EXTRUSION MACHINES, METAL/ALLOY

Holton Conform Ltd, Albany House, Elliott Road, Bournemouth, BH11 8JH Tel: (01202) 581881 Fax: (01202) 581789 E-mail: enquiries@holton-conform.com

EXTRUDER/EXTRUSION MACHINES, PLASTIC/ SYNTHETIC MATERIALS

B A Thorne Ltd, Eagle Road, Moons Moat North Industrial Es, Redditch, Worcestershire, B98 9HF Tel: (01527) 584714 Fax: (01527) 584784 E-mail: bat@bathorne.co.uk
Coperion Ltd, Victoria House, 19-21 Ack Lane East, Bramhall, Stockport, Cheshire, SK7 2BE Tel: 0161-925 6910 Fax: 0161-925 6911 E-mail: sandra.wyatt@coperion.com
▶ Gatfield Systems, Surrey Saw Mills, 70 Wrecclesham Hill, Wrecclesham, Farnham, Surrey, GU10 4JX Tel: (01252) 737357 Fax: (01252) 737358 E-mail: info@gatfield-systems.co.uk
John Madeley Machinery Ltd, Firs Industrial Estate, Kidderminster, Worcestershire, DY11 7QN Tel: (01562) 69955 Fax: (01562) 746304 E-mail: madeleyj@aol.com
Kween B Ltd, 29 Dalkeith Road, Sutton Coldfield, West Midlands, B73 6PW Tel: 0121-355 2662 E-mail: info@kweenb.co.uk
Mapex UK Ltd, Unit 9 Pulloxhill Business Pk, Greenfield Rd, Pulloxhill, Bedford, MK45 5EU Tel: (01525) 719979 Fax: (01525) 719339 E-mail: info@mapex.demon.co.uk
Metaltech, Bonsall Street, Mill Hill, Blackburn, BB2 4DD Tel: (01254) 691488
N R Seal & Son, Main Street, Wick, Pershore, Worcestershire, WR10 3NU Tel: (01386) 555706 Fax: (01386) 555707 E-mail: nrsandson@tiscali.co.uk

EXTRUDER/EXTRUSION MACHINES, RUBBER/NATURAL MATERIALS

Farrel Ltd, PO Box 27, Rochdale, Lancashire, OL11 2PF Tel: (01706) 647434 Fax: (01706) 638982 E-mail: farreluk@farrel.com

EXTRUDERS, FORMING, FOOD INDUSTRY

▶ Food Forming Machines Ltd, 15 Gosditch Street, Cirencester, Gloucestershire, GL7 2AG Tel: (01285) 658995 Fax: (01285) 659099 E-mail: mail@foodformingmachines.com

EXTRUSION COATED PAPER

Walki Ltd, Ray Lane, Barnacre, Preston, PR3 1GG Tel: (01995) 604227 Fax: (01995) 605222 E-mail: wawgar@upm-kymmene.com

EXTRUSION COATING SERVICES

Walki Ltd, Ray Lane, Barnacre, Preston, PR3 1GG Tel: (01995) 604227 Fax: (01995) 605222 E-mail: wawgar@upm-kymmene.com

EXTRUSION TOOLING

Interlink Import Export Ltd, The Rodings, Lancaster Lane, Parbold, Wigan, Lancashire, WN8 7HQ Tel: (01257) 463211 Fax: (01257) 464220 E-mail: peter@interlink.uk.com

EYE OR RING BOLTS

A W Precision Ltd, Cosford Lane, Rugby, Warwickshire, CV21 1QN Tel: (01788) 542271 Fax: (01788) 561256 E-mail: sales@awp-ltd.com
Brooks Forgings Ltd, Doulton Road, Cradley Heath, West Midlands, B64 5QJ Tel: (01384) 566772 Fax: (01384) 637380 E-mail: sales@brooksforgings.co.uk

EYELETS

W.J. Cons & Co., 20 Queensway, Enfield, Middlesex, EN3 4SA Tel: (020) 8443 4001 Fax: (020) 8804 0805E-mail: info@berbo.com
▶ Curtain Genius, Eallisaid, Corsock, Castle Douglas, Kirkcudbrightshire, DG7 3DW Tel: (01644) 440264 Fax: (01644) 440253 E-mail: info@curtaingenius.co.uk
D.T.P. Supplies, 242 Whitworth Rd, Rochdale, Lancashire, OL12 0SA Tel: 0845 8550605 Fax: (01706) 648180 E-mail: jon@dtpsupplies.com
Rivfast Ltd, Unit 23 Bordesley Trading Estate, Bordesley Green Road, Birmingham, B8 1BZ Tel: 0121-359 4500 Fax: 0121-359 4501 E-mail: mark@rivfast.co.uk

EYELETTING MACHINES

W.J. Cons & Co., 20 Queensway, Enfield, Middlesex, EN3 4SA Tel: (020) 8443 4001 Fax: (020) 8804 0805E-mail: info@berbo.com
D.T.P. Supplies, 242 Whitworth Rd, Rochdale, Lancashire, OL12 0SA Tel: 0845 8550605 Fax: (01706) 648180 E-mail: jon@dtpsupplies.com
Sas Machine, Watton Road, Ware, Hertfordshire, SG12 0AE Tel: (01920) 465281 Fax: (01920) 465285 E-mail: sales@sasmachines.co.uk

EYELETTING SERVICES

Eyetag Ltd, Albert Works, Melville Street, Bradford, West Yorkshire, BD7 1JD Tel: (01274) 721332 Fax: (01274) 740196

FABRIC COLLARS

Webster Bros, Walworth Enterprise Centre, Duke Close West Way, Andover, Hampshire, SP10 5AR Tel: (01264) 323842

FABRIC CONCRETE FORMWORK

Conserve Ltd, 80 Priory Road, Kenilworth, Warwickshire, CV8 1LQ Tel: (01926) 512006 Fax: (01926) 864569 E-mail: martin@proserveltd.co.uk

FABRIC DUSTERS

Brencliffe Ltd, Rossendale Road, Burnley, Lancashire, BB11 5HD Tel: (01282) 435226 Fax: (01282) 436147 E-mail: sales@brencliffe.com

FABRIC EXHIBITION GRAPHICS

Flying Monk Graphics, 9 Malmesbury Business Park, Beuttell Way, Malmesbury, Wiltshire, SN16 9JU Tel: (01666) 829228 Fax: (01666) 829229 E-mail: sales@flyingmonkgraphics.co.uk

FABRIC FILTER CLOTHS

Andrew Webron Ltd, Hareholme Mill, Bacup Road, Rawtenstall, Rossendale, Lancashire, BB4 7JL Tel: (01706) 214001 Fax: (01706) 830003 E-mail: info@andrewwebron.com
Custom Filter Co., Bretfield Court, Bretton Street Industrial Estate, Dewsbury, West Yorkshire, WF12 9BG Tel: (01924) 468272 Fax: (01924) 464240 E-mail: sales@customfilter.co.uk
Heath Filtration Ltd, PO Box 1, Stoke-on-Trent, ST6 4SH Tel: (01782) 838591 Fax: (01782) 835508 E-mail: info@heathfiltration.com
Hollingsworth & Vose Air Filtration Ltd, Waterford Bridge, Kentmere, Kendal, Cumbria, LA8 9JJ Tel: (01539) 825200 Fax: (01539) 825201 E-mail: sales@hvaf.co.uk
A. Holt & Sons Ltd, 115 Whitecross Street, London, EC1Y 8JQ Tel: (020) 7256 2222 Fax: (020) 7638 3578 E-mail: sales@aholt.co.uk
J P Filtration Ltd, 133-135 High Street, Stratford, London, E15 2RB Tel: (020) 8534 7431 Fax: (020) 8519 8768
Madison Filter, Knowsley Road Industrial Estate, Haslingden, Rossendale, Lancashire, BB4 4EJ Tel: (01706) 213421 Fax: (01706) 221916 E-mail: info@madisonfilter.com
Mitchell Interflex Ltd, County Brook Mill, County Brook Lane, Foulridge, Colne, Lancashire, BB8 7LT Tel: (01282) 813221 Fax: (01282) 813633 E-mail: sales@mitchell-interflex.co.uk
Multiple Fabric Co. Ltd, Vulcan Mills, William Street, Tong, Bradford, West Yorkshire, BD4 9QX Tel: (01274) 682323 Fax: (01274) 651341 E-mail: info@multiplefabric.co.uk
Pyrotek Engineering Materials Ltd, Garamonde Drive, Wymbush, Milton Keynes, MK8 8LN Tel: (01908) 561155 Fax: (01908) 560473 E-mail: petwin@pyrotek-inc.com
Sefar Ltd, Bury Business Centre, Kay Street, Bury, Lancashire, BL9 6BU Tel: 0161-705 1878 Fax: 0161-763 1382 E-mail: sales@sefar.co.uk

FABRIC FOLDING MACHINES

H J Weir Engineering Co. Ltd, Bulwark Industrial Estate, Bulwark, Chepstow, Gwent, NP16 5QZ Tel: (01291) 622036 Fax: (01291) 627350 E-mail: sales@hjweir.co.uk

FABRIC GARMENT BELTS

Be That Body, Christs Hospital Sports Centre, Christs Hospital, Horsham, West Sussex, RH13 0YP Tel: (023) 8025 1125 E-mail: enquiries@bethatbody.com
Stylex, 49 Berwick Street, London, W1F 8SH Tel: (020) 7437 2428 Fax: (020) 7437 0649 E-mail: sales@style-x.co.uk

FABRIC LABELS

Bell Woven Brake, New Market Street, Colne, Lancashire, BB8 9DA Tel: (01282) 864000 Fax: (01282) 864325 E-mail: info@bellwoven.co.uk
Genel 86 Ltd, Kent House, 9 Beech Street, Leicester, LE5 0DF Tel: 0116-251 5156 Fax: 0116-251 5159 E-mail: genel86sales@aol.com
Hallmark Labels, 10 Oakwood Hill Industrial Estate, Oakwood Hill, Loughton, Essex, IG10 3TZ Tel: (020) 8532 0620 Fax: (020) 8532 0621 E-mail: hallmark@hallmarklabels.demon.co.uk
Inotec UK, Unit 1, Viking Close, Hull, HU10 6DZ Tel: (01482) 654466 Fax: (01482) 655004
K R Snoxell & Sons Ltd, 24-26 Clarendon Road, Luton, LU2 7PQ Tel: (01582) 724704 Fax: (01582) 452928 E-mail: snoxell-headwear@lineone.net
Nelsons Labels MCR Ltd, Unit 3 Waterside, Trafford Park, Manchester, M17 1WD Tel: 0161-873 4500 Fax: 0161-873 4505 E-mail: sales@nelsons-labels.co.uk
Partners in Print, Venture Place, 45 Lord Street, Birmingham, B7 4DQ Tel: 0121-359 0202 Fax: 0121-359 5550 E-mail: mail@partnersinprint.co.uk
Willeringhaus & Co. Ltd, The Mill, 23 Saunders Copse, Mayford, Woking, Surrey, GU22 0NS Tel: (01483) 723158 Fax: (01483) 723158 E-mail: willeringhaus.co@talk21.com

FABRIC LAUNDRY BAGS

Standard Laundry (N I) Ltd, 213 Donegall Avenue, Belfast, BT12 6LU Tel: (028) 9032 7295 Fax: (028) 9031 4026

FABRIC OR TEXTILE WALLCOVERINGS

John Boyd Textiles Ltd, Higher Flax Mills, Castle Cary, Somerset, BA7 7DY Tel: (01963) 350451 Fax: (01963) 351078 E-mail: enquiries@johnboydtextiles.co.uk
Crowson Fabrics, Crowson House, Bellbrook Industrial Estate, Uckfield, East Sussex, TN22 1QZ Tel: (01825) 761044 Fax: (01825) 764283 E-mail: sales@crowsonfabrics.com
Morland Profiles Ltd, Henfaes Lane, Welshpool, Powys, SY21 7BE Tel: (01938) 554020 Fax: (01938) 554285
Muraspec Ltd, 74-78 Wood Lane End, Hemel Hempstead, Hertfordshire, HP2 4RF Tel: (01442) 268890 Fax: (0870) 5329020 E-mail: customerservices@muraspec.com
Tektura Wallcoverings, One Heron Quay, London, E14 4JA Tel: (020) 7536 3300 Fax: (020) 7536 3322 E-mail: sales@tektura.com

FABRIC RAINWEAR

Burberry, 18-22 Haymarket, London, SW1Y 4DQ Tel: (020) 7930 3343 Fax: (020) 7839 6691 E-mail: sales@burberry.com
Cooper & Stolbrand Ltd, Cottenham House, 1 Cottenham Lane, Salford, M3 7LJ Tel: 0161-834 3062 Fax: 0161-834 7586 E-mail: mail@cooperstollbrand.co.uk
Macintosh Ltd, Unit 10a Blairlinn Industrial Estate, Cumbernauld, Glasgow, G67 2TW Tel: (01422) 846953 Fax: (01236) 723924 E-mail: sales@mackintosh-scotland.com

FABRIC TAPES

Bowmer Bond Narrow Fabrics Ltd, Hanging Bridge Mills, Ashbourne, Derbyshire, DE6 2EA Tel: (01335) 342244 Fax: (01335) 300651 E-mail: sales@bowmerbond.co.uk
Cheshire Ribbon Manufacturing Co., Kingston Mills, Manchester Road, Hyde, Cheshire, SK14 2BZ Tel: 0161-368 2048 Fax: 0161-367 8193 E-mail: sales@cheshirerib.co.uk
Hattersley Aladdin UK, Greengate, Keighley, West Yorkshire, BD21 5JL Tel: (01639) 730997 Fax: (01535) 610195 E-mail: info@hattersley.co.uk
Nottingham Narrow Fabrics, Block A Harrington Mills, Leopold Street, Long Eaton, Nottingham, NG10 4QG Tel: 0115-946 8883 Fax: 0115-946 8652
Rykneld Tean Ltd, Hansard Gate, West Meadows Industrial Estate, Derby, DE21 6RR Tel: (01332) 542700 Fax: (01332) 542710 E-mail: sales@rykneldtean.co.uk

FABRIC TESTING EQUIPMENT

Abbey Spares & Supplies, 16g Top Barn Business Centre, Worcester Road, Holt Heath, Worcester, WR6 6NH Tel: (01905) 621666

FABRICATED CONSTRUCTION SWIMMING POOL ENCLOSURES

Ardep UK Ltd, Unit 34, Spring Vale Industrial Estate, Cwmbran, Gwent, NP44 5BD Tel: (01633) 480496 Fax: (01633) 480497 E-mail: sales@ardep.com
Clearwater Swimming Pools Ltd, The Studio, 81 Langley Close, Headington, Oxford, OX3 7DB Tel: (01865) 766112 Fax: (01865) 741373 E-mail: sales@clearwater-pools.co.uk
Hartley Botanic Ltd, Wellington Road, Greenfield, Oldham, OL3 7AG Tel: (0870) 7770320 Fax: (0870) 7770323 E-mail: info@hartleybotanic.co.uk
Intermark Leisure Ltd, Winnington Avenue, Winnington, Northwich, Cheshire, CW8 4EE Tel: (01606) 871831 Fax: (01606) 782241 E-mail: sales@intermarkleisure.ltd.uk
Mcgregor Polytunnels Ltd, Winton Farm, Petersfield Road, Monkwood, Alresford, Hampshire, SO24 0HB Tel: (01962) 772368 Fax: (01962) 772471 E-mail: sales@mcgregorpolytunnels.co.uk

FABRICATED PRESSINGS

Birmingham Stopper, 235 Icknield Street, Hockley, Birmingham, B18 6QU Tel: 0121-551 7781 Fax: 0121-554 4567 E-mail: robertp@birminghamstopper.co.uk
Dockdale Ltd, 30 Lower Dartmouth Street, Birmingham, B9 4LG Tel: 0121-771 4681 Fax: 0121-773 7783
P F C Industries, 1 Livingstone Road, Sheffield, S9 3XX Tel: 0114-256 1508 Fax: 0114-256 1485
Shire Pressings Ltd, Doubak Works, Barton Industrial Estate, Bilston, West Midlands, WV14 7LH Tel: (01902) 490155 Fax: (01902) 490155
Stowfledge Ltd, Mill Works, Mountsorrel Lane, Sileby, Loughborough, Leicestershire, LE12 7NF Tel: (01509) 812915 Fax: (01509) 816648
Wolverhampton Pressings Co. Ltd, Whetstone House, Fordhouse Road, Wolverhampton, WV10 9EA Tel: (01902) 307799 Fax: (01902) 721026 E-mail: sales@ralphmartindale.com
Woodseats Engineering, 3 Canal Works, Cadman Street, Sheffield, S4 7ZG Tel: 0114-279 6143 Fax: 0114-279 6143 E-mail: sales@woodseatsengineering.com
Wye Valley Engineering Ltd, Unit 260 Netherwood Road Rotherwas Indust Estate, Rotherwas Industrial Estate, Hereford, HR2 6JU Tel: (01432) 266507 Fax: (01432) 341645 E-mail: enquries@durabase.co.uk

FABRICATING MACHINERY

International Business Networks, Brigade House, Brigade Close, Harrow, Middlesex, HA2 0LQ Tel: (020) 8515 9000 Fax: (020) 8515 9001 E-mail: info@ibnetworks.com
J Stevens, Hull Road, Eastrington, Goole, North Humberside, DN14 7XL Tel: (01430) 410333 Fax: (01430) 410354 E-mail: gdae@uk2.net
Q Mac Engineering, 161 Ballymaguire Road, Stewartstown, Dungannon, County Tyrone, BT71 5NN Tel: (028) 8673 7312
T R W Fabrication & Welding, 1 Milnthorpe Road, Holme, Carnforth, Lancashire, LA6 1PS Tel: (01524) 782647

FABRICATING SERVICES

Able Engineering, Cadley Hill Road, Swadlincote, Derbyshire, DE11 9EQ Tel: (01283) 227160 Fax: (01283) 222375 E-mail: dave@able-engineering.co.uk
Mirlyn Ltd, 57 Coleridge Street, Hove, East Sussex, BN3 5AB Tel: (01273) 733404 Fax: (01273) 703330
T M Engineers Midlands Ltd, Oak Lane, Kingswinford, West Midlands, DY6 7JW Tel: (01384) 400212 Fax: (01384) 296019 E-mail: sales@tmengineers.co.uk

FABRICATION MACHINING SERVICES

P A Brenchley & Sons, Clergy Farm Sutton Road, Four Gotes, Tydd, Wisbech, Cambridgeshire, PE13 5PH Tel: (01945) 420738 Fax: (01945) 420788

FABRICATORS, LIGHT/NON FERROUS METAL

Aluminium Copper & Stainless Co. Ltd, 22-24 Crittall Road, Witham, Essex, CM8 3DR Tel: (01376) 513419 Fax: (01376) 511615

FABRICATORS, LIGHT/NON FERROUS METAL – *continued*

Anglosax Ltd, 3 Pomeroy Drive, Oadby Industrial Estate, Oadby, Leicester, LE2 5NE Tel: 0116-271 1005

Ark Site Fabrications, Unit 7b Greenhill Mills, Grange Road, Batley, West Yorkshire, WF17 6LH Tel: (01924) 420874 Fax: (01924) 359744 E-mail: brian@arksite.co.uk

Bambury Metal Fabrications, Short Street, Bristol, BS2 0SW Tel: 0117-971 9216 Fax: 0117-971 1898

Brady Fabrications, Units 20& 22, Wedgewood Road, Bicester, Oxfordshire, OX26 4UL Tel: (01869) 252750 Fax: (01869) 247394 E-mail: bradyfabs@btopenworld.com

C H Jones & Son, 1 The Square, North Tawton, Devon, EX20 2EW Tel: (01837) 82237 Fax: (01837) 82526 E-mail: chjengineers@aol.com

C.W. (Industrial) Fans Ltd, Unit 25, Thornleigh Trading Estate, Dudley, West Midlands, DY2 8UB Tel: (01384) 211010 Fax: (01384) 238086

Calder Engineering Ltd, Unit 15 Ormlie Industrial Estate, Thurso, Caithness, KW14 7QU Tel: (01847) 892122 Fax: (01847) 892345 E-mail: admin@calderengineering.co.uk

Crown Metal Fabrications, 24-26 Albert St West, Failsworth, Manchester, M35 0JN Tel: 0161-688 7571 Fax: 0161-688 7546

D L I Precision Engineering Ltd, Trimdon Grange Industrial Estate, Trimdon Grange, Trimdon Station, County Durham, TS29 6PA Tel: (01429) 880454 Fax: (01429) 880369 E-mail: info@dlipe.plus.com

D M D Electronic Engineers Ltd, 2 Nags Head Road, Enfield, Middlesex, EN3 7AJ Tel: (020) 8805 5056 Fax: (020) 8443 4160

Denall Engineering Co. Ltd, 55 Bridgewater Street, Little Hulton, Manchester, M38 9ND Tel: 0161-799 2600 Fax: 0161-703 8342

Droitwich Road Aquatics, Droitwich Road, Claines, Worcester, WR3 7SW Tel: (01905) 757376 Fax: (01905) 452242

Dual Brown, Ross Road, Stockton-on-Tees, Cleveland, TS18 2NH Tel: (01642) 602226 Fax: (01642) 602227

Durham Sheet Metal Works Ltd, Progress House, Templetown, South Shields, Tyne & Wear, NE33 5TE Tel: 0191-455 3558 Fax: 0191-456 8837 E-mail: paul@durhamsheetmetal.co.uk

Foster Laws & Co. Ltd, 9 D Park View West Industrial Estate, Hartlepool, Cleveland, TS25 1PE Tel: (01429) 275541 Fax: (01429) 869177

Furniss & White Foundries Ltd, Unit 17 Abbey Way, North Anston Trading Estate, North Anston, Sheffield, S25 4JL Tel: (01909) 568831 Fax: (01909) 569322 E-mail: upgrading@f-w-f.co.uk

Halifax Fabrications & Engineering Ltd, Grantham Works, Grantham Road, Halifax, West Yorkshire, HX3 6PL Tel: (01422) 364163 Fax: (01422) 254135 E-mail: hfe-ltd@dsl.pipex.com

J.A. Harvey (Bassingham) Ltd, The Old Dairy, Navenby Lane, Bassingham, Lincoln, LN5 9JF Tel: (01522) 788111 Fax: (01522) 788195 E-mail: ja.harvey@btconnect.com

Heatherside Engineering Ltd, Old Oak Close Industrial Estate, Old Oak Close, Arlesey, Bedfordshire, SG15 6XD Tel: (01462) 731575 Fax: (01462) 731575 E-mail: heatherside@btconnect.com

Interplan Panel Systems Ltd, 7-11 Glentanar Road, Glasgow, G22 7XS Tel: 0141-336 4040 Fax: 0141-336 4433

J D Fabrications Leicester Ltd, 38 Boston Road, Gorse Hill Industrial Estate, Beaumont Leys, Leicester, LE4 1AU Tel: 0116-236 8622 Fax: 0116-235 6220 E-mail: jdfabsleicesltd@aol.com

J E Jenkins, 7 Eye Green Industries, Crowland Road, Eye, Peterborough, PE6 7SZ Tel: (01733) 223650 Fax: (01733) 223650

Jolibar Metal Works Ltd, Howe Moss Drive, Dyce, Aberdeen, AB21 0GL Tel: (01224) 770445 Fax: (01224) 770019 E-mail: sales@jolibarmetalworks.co.uk

Kendal Metal Works Ltd, Mintsfeet Road, Kendal, Cumbria, LA9 6NN Tel: (01539) 722050 Fax: (01539) 741190

Lodge Sheet Metal Ltd, Commerce Street, Haslingden, Rossendale, Lancashire, BB4 5JT Tel: (01706) 212606 Fax: (01706) 831417

Lowther Manufacturing Ltd, Nest Road, Felling, Gateshead, Tyne & Wear, NE10 0ES Tel: 0191-438 6936 Fax: 0191-495 0428

M P L Fabrications, Dutton Road, Aldermans Green Industrial Estate, Coventry, CV2 2LE Tel: (024) 7661 0778 Fax: (024) 7661 9499 E-mail: sales@mplfabrications.com

M P Welding Fabrications, Wareley Road, Peterborough, PE2 9PF Tel: (01733) 344455 Fax: (01733) 561628

M R M Engineering Ltd, Units 15-16, Enterprise Drive, Westhill Industrial Estate, Westhill, Aberdeenshire, AB32 6TQ Tel: (01224) 742383 Fax: (01224) 742326 E-mail: sales@mrmengineering.co.uk

M Tech Engineering, Plot 16 Tufthorn Industrial Estate, Stepbridge Road, Coleford, Gloucestershire, GL16 8PJ Tel: (01594) 837172 Fax: (01594) 832999

Mainframe Fabrications Hereford Ltd, Unit 6A Thorn Business Park, Rotherwas, Hereford, HR2 6JT Tel: (01432) 353703 Fax: (01432) 340588

Mechanical & Ferrous Ltd, 1 Church Road, Erith, Kent, DA8 1PG Tel: (01322) 447714 Fax: (01322) 436228 E-mail: mechferrous@aol.com

Metcraft Engineering Ltd, Unit 10 Fenn FLD Indust Estate, Homefield Road, Haverhill, Suffolk, CB9 8QP Tel: (01440) 712227 Fax: (01440) 712274

MGL Van Hire, Unit 8, Trench Lock Industrial Estate, Telford, Shropshire, TF1 5SW Tel: (01952) 252396

Michael L Shaw Fabrications Ltd, 257 Hollin Lane, Middleton, Manchester, M24 5LU Tel: 0161-653 1081 Fax: 0161-655 4326 E-mail: m4@mlshawfabs.com

Mitchell Engineering Ltd, 10 Bridge Street, Cambuslang, Glasgow, G72 7ED Tel: 0141-641 2177 Fax: 0141-641 5185

Mitchell Engineering Ltd, 10 Bridge Street, Cambuslang, Glasgow, G72 7ED Tel: 0141-641 2177 Fax: 0141-641 5185 E-mail: mail@mitchellengineering.co.uk

N F F Precision Ltd, 4 Enterprise Way Aviation Park, Bournemouth Int Airp, Hurn, Christchurch, Dorset, BH23 6EW Tel: (01202) 583000 Fax: (01202) 583058 E-mail: sales@nff.uk.com

Permoid Industries Ltd, Horndale Avenue, Aycliffe Industrial Estate, Aycliffe Industrial Park, Newton Aycliffe, County Durham, DL5 6DW Tel: (01325) 300767 Fax: (01325) 312186

Plan It, 13 Palacecraig Street, Coatbridge, Lanarkshire, ML5 4SB Tel: (01236) 421082 Fax: (01236) 424311 E-mail: peryslick@gmail.com

Professional Welding Services Ltd, 80-82 Cobham Road, Ferndown Industrial Estate, Wimborne, Dorset, BH21 7RW Tel: (01202) 895080 Fax: (01202) 861463 E-mail: sales@prowelding.co.uk

Rank Engineering, Unit 4b Barton Hill Trading Estate, Herapath Street, Bristol, BS5 9RD Tel: 0117-955 1298 Fax: 0117-955 6528

Rednal Polishing & Spraying Co. Ltd, Station Works, 17-19 Station Road, Northfield, Birmingham, B31 3TE Tel: 0121-475 4826 Fax: 0121-475 2712

Shelley Engineering Redhill Ltd, Unit 31-33 Grace Business Centre, 23 Willow Lane, Mitcham, Surrey, CR4 4TU Tel: (020) 8685 0302 Fax: (020) 8687 0572 E-mail: mail@shelleyengineering.co.uk

Squires Metal Fabrications Ltd, 6 Burgess Road, Hastings, East Sussex, TN35 4NR Tel: (01424) 428794 Fax: (01424) 431567 E-mail: squires@squiresmetal.freeserve.co.uk

Technicraft Anglia Ltd, Wilford Bridge Road, Melton, Woodbridge, Suffolk, IP12 1RB Tel: (01394) 385213 Fax: (01394) 387914 E-mail: technicraft@technicraft.co.uk

Terry Gregory Metal Fabrications Ltd, 599 Kingston Road, London, SW20 8SA Tel: (020) 8542 9941 Fax: (020) 8543 6091 E-mail: metal@terrygregory.freeserve.co.uk

Thomfab Engineering Services, Unit 1 Blackhill Industrial Estate, Findon, Aberdeen, AB12 4RL Tel: (01224) 781615 Fax: (01224) 781615 E-mail: duncan@thomfab.com

W H Dale Ltd, Main Street, Thornton Curtis, Ulceby, South Humberside, DN39 6XW Tel: (01469) 531229 Fax: (01469) 530611 E-mail: sales@whdale.co.uk

Western Metalcraft, 79d Grove Road, Fishponds, Bristol, BS16 2BP Tel: 0117-965 3865 Fax: 0117-965 3865

Westman Engineering Ltd, Units 15-18 Block 3, Old Mill Parkindustial Estate, Mansfield Woodhouse, Nottinghamshire, NG19 9BG Tel: (01623) 648740 Fax: (01623) 420376

Westwhite Engineering Services, 32 Boston Road, Gorse Hill Industrial Estate, Leicester, LE4 1AU Tel: 0116-235 7522 Fax: 0116-235 7522

Wilman Equipment Ltd, Baker Street, Bradford, West Yorkshire, BD2 4NX Tel: (01274) 636977 Fax: (01274) 636714

Winstanley Metal Fabrications Ltd, 501 Old York Road, London, SW18 1TF Tel: (020) 8874 9043 Fax: (020) 8874 9044

Wren Industrial & Marine Fabrications Ltd, 24 Sandon Way, Liverpool, L5 9YN Tel: 0151-207 0023 Fax: 0151-207 3916

Wrought Art, 7 Gordon Road, Derby, DE23 6WR Tel: (01332) 340563 Fax: (01332) 200234

FABRICATORS, STEEL

A D Fabrications Telford Ltd, Unit B5 Dawley Bank Industrial Estate, Cemetery Road, Dawley Bank, Telford, Shropshire, TF4 2BS Tel: (01952) 505525 Fax: (01952) 505489

Ellrod Engineering, 6A Stone Road, Coal Aston, Dronfield, Derbyshire, S18 3AH Tel: (01246) 415436 Fax: (01246) 416494

FABRICS, BATIK

▶ Artworkshops, 43 Broomleaf Road, Farnham, Surrey, GU9 8DQ Tel: 01252 714221

FABRICS, PRE-IMPREGNATED

Calzeat & Co. Ltd, 16 Maddox Street, London, W1S 1PH Tel: (020) 7493 1866

CP Films Solutia UK Ltd, Chadwick Road, Astmoor Industrial Estate, Runcorn, Cheshire, WA7 1PW Tel: (01928) 580508 Fax: (01928) 580100 E-mail: sales.runcorn@cpfilms.co.uk

Lees Newsome Ltd, Ashley Mill, Ashley Street, Oldham, OL9 6LS Tel: 0161-652 1321 Fax: 0161-627 3362 E-mail: sales@leesnewsome.co.uk

Penn Nyla Ltd, Acton Road, Long Eaton, Nottingham, NG10 1FX Tel: 0115-973 4441 Fax: 0115-946 1085 E-mail: sales@penn-nyla.com

Primco Ltd, Grimshaw Lane, Middleton, Manchester, M24 2AE Tel: 0161-653 4876 Fax: 0161-655 3673 E-mail: sales@northwesternblanks.co.uk

Tantalize Ltd, 186 Seven Sisters Road, London, N7 7PX Tel: (020) 7263 2404 Fax: (020) 7263 2559

Texon Nonwoven Ltd, Skelton Industrial Estate, Skelton-in-Cleveland, Saltburn-by-the-Sea, Cleveland, TS12 2LH Tel: (01287) 650551 Fax: (01287) 650788 E-mail: enquiries@texon.com

FABRICS, TEXTILE, *See headings under Textile*

FACILITATION

▶ I Change Ltd, Birchwood, South Munstead Lane, Godalming, Surrey, GU8 4AG Tel: (01483) 208505 Fax: (01483) 208505 E-mail: info@i-change.biz

▶ NLP Solutions, Alsa Wood House, Stansted, Essex, CM24 8SU Tel: 01279 817976 E-mail: sian@nlpsolutions.com

▶ Stephen Quinn Associates Ltd, 4 Fitzroy Place, Glasgow, G3 7RH Tel: 0141-221 6611 Fax: 0141-882 5192

FACILITIES MAINTENANCE

▶ Mercury Facilities Management (UK) Ltd, 17 Camp Road, Rutherglen, Glasgow, G73 1EU Tel: 0141-613 6132 Fax: 0141-613 3411 E-mail: enqiries@mercuryfacilities.co.uk

▶ Parker Contract Cleaning, 141 Banbury Road, Kidlington, Oxfordshire, OX5 1AJ Tel: (01865) 376655 E-mail: benb40@hotmail.com

▶ Total Services - Grounds Maintenance, Mercian Park, Felspar Road, Amington, Tamworth, Staffordshire, B77 4DP Tel: (01827) 723806 Fax: (01827) 723816 E-mail: info@total-services.co.uk

FACILITIES MANAGEMENT

Aberdeen Catering, 38 Upperkirkgate, Aberdeen, AB10 1BA Tel: (01224) 658588 Fax: (01224) 658588

▶ All Property Care, 7 Highfield Close, Danbury, Chelmsford, CM3 4EG Tel: (01245) 222320 E-mail: admin@allpropertycare.co.uk

Bay Management Services Ltd, Applegarth House, Heversham, Milnthorpe, Cumbria, LA7 7FD Tel: (01539) 564642

Bowman Group Ltd, 1200 Century Way, Thorpe Park Business Park, Leeds, LS15 8ZB Tel: (01422) 322211 Fax: (01325) 151100 E-mail: info@bowman-group.co.uk

Castle View Services Ltd, Steuart Road, Bridge of Allan, Stirling, FK9 4JX Tel: (01786) 834060 Fax: (01786) 832658 E-mail: enquiries@castleview.co.uk

Claremont Business Environment, Design Studio 2 Quay Side Commerce Centre, Lower Quay, Fareham, Hampshire, PO16 0XR Tel: (01329) 220123 Fax: (01329) 221322 E-mail: info@claremontgi.com

▶ Coleman F M Ltd, PO Box 2088, Rayleigh, Essex, SS6 8WB Tel: (0845) 2261756 Fax: (0845) 2261757

Commando Security Services Ltd, Black Friars House, West Street, Warwick, CV34 6AN Tel: (01926) 499495 Fax: (01926) 499802

Dalkia, The Connect Centre, Kingston CR, Portsmouth, PO2 8AD Tel: (0800) 0853208 Fax: (023) 9262 9656 E-mail: enquiries@dalkia.co.uk

Document Control Services Ltd, 10 Stapledon Road, Orton Southgate, Peterborough, PE2 6TB Tel: (01733) 366800 Fax: (01733) 366801 E-mail: dcs@sapasolutions.co.uk

Drake & Scull Engineering Ltd, Drake Scull Ho, 86 Talbot Rd, Old Trafford, Manchester, M16 0QD Tel: 0161-874 4800 Fax: 0161-874 4900

Emcor Facilities Services Ltd, 1 Thameside Centre, Kew Bridge Road, Brentford, Middlesex, TW8 0HF Tel: (020) 8380 6700 Fax: (020) 8380 6701

H B S Facilities Management Ltd, Ireland House, 150 New Bond Street, London, W1S 2TU Tel: (020) 7317 4800 Fax: (020) 7317 4801 E-mail: enquiries@hbsf.com

Harris & Porter, 49 Whitehall, London, SW1A 2BX Tel: (020) 7839 6064 Fax: (020) 7839 3876 E-mail: handp@nnpland.demon.co.uk

▶ Health Management, Scottish Health Service Centre, Crewe Road South, Edinburgh, EH4 2LF Tel: 0131-623 2535 Fax: 0131-315 2369

Holbrow Brookes & Partners, Pinewood, Bell Heath Way, Birmingham, B32 3BZ Tel: 0121-423 4000 Fax: 0121-423 4230 E-mail: info@holbrowbrookes.co.uk

Ikon Office Solutions plc, James House, 55 Welford Road, Leicester, LE2 7AP Tel: 0116-254 0999 Fax: 0116-285 4812 E-mail: sales@ikon.com

Ikon Office Solutions plc, 160 Edinburgh Avenue, Slough, SL1 4UE Tel: (01753) 771000 Fax: (01753) 696045

Interserve Holdings plc, Tilbury House, Ruscombe Park, Reading, RG10 9JU Tel: 0118-932 0123 Fax: 0118-932 0206 E-mail: info@interserveplc.co.uk

Kier Managed Services Ltd, Conway House, St. Mellons Business Park, Fortran Road, Cardiff, CF3 0EY Tel: (029) 2036 1616 Fax: (029) 2036 2303 E-mail: enquiries@kier.co.uk

LB Ford Ltd, Park Lane, Nottingham, NG6 0DT Tel: 0115-927 2821 Fax: 0115-976 1041 E-mail: lb@ford.co.uk

Mcdonald Insulation & Maintenance Ltd, 7 Eastbury Road, London, E6 6LP Tel: (020) 7511 8899 Fax: (020) 7473 1133 E-mail: info@mcdonaldbrownltd.co.uk

MacLellan International Ltd, 110 Birmingham Road, West Bromwich, West Midlands, B70 6RP Tel: 0121-500 5000 Fax: 0121-524 8815 E-mail: enquiries@maclellan-int.com

Norec Ltd, Norec House, Fall Bank Industrial Estate, Dodworth, Barnsley, South Yorkshire, S75 3LS Tel: (01226) 730440 Fax: (01226) 730688 E-mail: sales@norec.ltd.uk

▶ PITHON Limited, Ground Floor, 74 Markland Avenue, Uckfield, East Sussex, TN22 2DG Tel: 01825 767669 E-mail: info@pithon.co.uk

Promanex Ltd, The Stables Hurley Hall Barns Industrial Estate, Atherstone L, Hurley, Atherstone, Warwickshire, CV9 2HT Tel: (01827) 874567 Fax: (01827) 871030 E-mail: enquiries@promanex.co.uk

Serco Group P.L.C., Serco House, 16 Bartley Wood, Business Park, Hook, Hampshire, RG27 9UY Tel: (01256) 745900 Fax: (01256) 744111

Skanska Rashleigh Weatherfoil Ltd, West Lodge, Station Approach, West Byfleet, Surrey, KT14 6NG Tel: (01932) 791800 Fax: (01932) 791810 E-mail: krw.receptionist@skanska.co.uk

Sodexho Ltd, Buchanan Tower Buchanan Business Park, Cumbernauld Road, Stepps, Glasgow, G33 6HZ Tel: 0141-779 8200 Fax: 0141-779 8201

Stiell Ltd, Cannock Side Park, Uddingston, Glasgow, G71 5PW Tel: (01698) 805100 Fax: (01698) 805111 E-mail: ho@stiell.co.uk

▶ T R G Recruitment Services Ltd, 5th Floor, 4 St. Pauls Churchyard, London, EC4M 8AY Tel: (020) 7236 8844 Fax: (020) 7236 8181 E-mail: cv@thetrggroup.co.uk

Warings Construction Group Holdings Ltd, Gatcombe House, Hilsea, Portsmouth, PO2 0TU Tel: (023) 9269 4900 Fax: (023) 9269 4948

▶ Young Consultants, The Old Mill, Inverichnie, Banff, AB45 3LL Tel: (01261) 821473

FACING BRICKS

Bovingdon Brickworks Ltd, Pudds Cross, Bovingdon, Hemel Hempstead, Hertfordshire, HP3 0NW Tel: (01442) 833176 Fax: (01442) 834539 E-mail: info@bovingdonbrickworks.co.uk

Carlton Main Brickworks Ltd, Grimethorpe, Barnsley, South Yorkshire, S72 7BG Tel: (01226) 711521 Fax: (01226) 780417 E-mail: office.admin@carltonbrick.co.uk

Chelwood Brick Ltd, Eurolink Industrial Estate, Castle Road, Sittingbourne, Kent, ME10 3TN Tel: (01795) 421651 Fax: (01795) 426489

Hanson Aggregates Ltd, Ashby Road East, Shepshed, Loughborough, Leicestershire, LE12 9BU Tel: (01509) 507050 Fax: (01509) 504120

Ibstock Brick Ltd, Dorket Head Factory, Lime Lane, Arnold, Nottingham, NG5 8PZ Tel: 0115-926 0441 Fax: 0115-967 0121

Ibstock Building Products Ltd, Funton Factory, Sheerness Road, Lower Halstow, Sittingbourne, Kent, ME9 7EG Tel: (01795) 842551 Fax: (01795) 845387

Ibstock Building Products Ltd, Ravenhead Factory, Chequer Lane, Upholland, Skelmersdale, Lancashire, WN8 0DD Tel: (01695) 625511 Fax: (01695) 624287 E-mail: w.lord@ibstock.co.uk

Ibstock Building Products Ltd, Brickyard Road, Aldridge, Walsall, WS9 8TB Tel: (01922) 741400 Fax: (01922) 743086

W.T. Lamb & Sons Ltd, Nyewood Court, Brookers Road, Billingshurst, West Sussex, RH14 9RZ Tel: (01403) 785141 Fax: (01403) 784663 E-mail: sales@lambsbricks.com

Northcot Brick Ltd, Blockley, Moreton-In-Marsh, Gloucestershire, GL56 9LH Tel: (01386) 700551 Fax: (01386) 700852 E-mail: info@northcotbrick.co.uk

Red Bank Manufacturing Co. Ltd, Atherstone Road, Measham, Swadlincote, Derbyshire, DE12 7EL Tel: (01530) 270333 Fax: (01530) 270542 E-mail: info@redbank-manufacturing.co.uk

Shaws Of Darwen, Waterside, Darwen, Lancashire, BB3 3NX Tel: (01254) 771086 Fax: (01254) 873462 E-mail: sales@shaws-of-darwen.co.uk

Tyrone Brick Ltd, Coalisland Road, Dungannon, County Tyrone, BT71 6LA Tel: (028) 8772 3421 Fax: (028) 8772 7193 E-mail: sales@tyrone-brick.co.uk

W H Collier Ltd, Brick Works, Church Lane, Marks Tey, Colchester, CO6 1LN Tel: (01206) 210301 Fax: (01206) 212540

FACSIMILE STATIONERY MANUFRS

▶ Cartridge Swop Shop, 201 Hoylake Road, Wirral, Merseyside, CH46 0SJ Tel: 0151-606 1435 Fax: 0151-606 0763 E-mail: Mark@cartridgeswopshop.com
Clarity Copiers Cornwall & Co, Unit 5d 5d Carminnow Road Industrial Estate, Bodmin, Cornwall, PL31 1EP Tel: (01208) 78201 Fax: (01208) 75916
Dominion Business Supplies Ltd, Dominion House, Medway City Industrial Estate, Medway City Estate, Rochester, Kent, ME2 4DU Tel: (01634) 716666 Fax: (01634) 290620 E-mail: sales@dominion-group.com
Hertsmere Group Services, 2 Chartmoor Road, Leighton Buzzard, Bedfordshire, LU7 4WG Tel: (01525) 219227 Fax: (01525) 219220 E-mail: sales@hgs-uk.com
Lynbrook Reprographic Ltd, Unit 15A, Boxer Place, Leyland, PR26 7QL Tel: (01772) 452125 Fax: (01772) 622304 E-mail: sales@lynbrookreprographic.co.uk

FACSIMILE TRANSMITTING/ RECEIVING EQUIPMENT

A Kelly Ltd, Mita House, Wester Gourdie Industrial Estate, West Gourdie Industrial Estate, Dundee, DD2 4UH Tel: (01382) 623311 Fax: (01382) 611910 E-mail: admin@kellyscopiers.co.uk
A M F Business Systems Ltd, New Malden, Surrey, KT3 5WN Tel: (020) 8605 1111 Fax: (020) 8605 1105
Alpha Telecommunications Ltd, 359a Hagley Rd, Edgbaston, Birmingham, B17 8DL Tel: 0121-434 4003 Fax: 0121-434 4043
Beta Electronics Ltd, 11 Indescon Court, Docklands, London, E14 9TN Tel: (020) 7531 2828 Fax: (020) 7531 2929
Bleepers, PO Box 71, Barnet, Hertfordshire, EN4 0QD Tel: (07000) 253373 Fax: (020) 8440 8024 E-mail: sales@bleepers.co.uk
Blythe Business Equipment Ltd, 161-165 Newcastle Street, Stoke-on-Trent, ST6 3QJ Tel: (01782) 817121 Fax: (01782) 575087 E-mail: sales@blythebusiness.co.uk
Club Copying Co. Ltd, 10-18 Sandgate Street, London, SE15 1LE Tel: (020) 7635 5252 Fax: (020) 7635 5714 E-mail: jacquidalton@clubcopying.co.uk
Complete Imaging plc, 62 Ravenhurst Street, Birmingham, B12 0EL Tel: 0121-766 2000 Fax: 0121-766 5404 E-mail: sales@completeplc.co.uk
Copier Maintenance Co. Ltd, 642 Warwick Road, Tyseley, Birmingham, B11 2HJ Tel: 0121-624 8484 Fax: 0121-708 2406 E-mail: sales@printersforbusiness.com
Corporate Business Technology, Tileyard Road, Unit 31, London, N7 9AH Tel: (020) 7503 3000 Fax: (020) 7503 3072 E-mail: sales@corporategroup.co.uk
Dataline Northern Ltd, 160-162 Cross Street, Sale, Cheshire, M33 7AQ Tel: 0161-905 1200 Fax: 0161-905 3001 E-mail: dataline@btconnect.com
Document Co. Xerox Ltd, Bridge House, Oxford Road, Uxbridge, Middlesex, UB8 1HS Tel: (01895) 251133 Fax: (01895) 254095
Fax (UK) Ltd, Timber House, Standford Place, Church Stretton, Shropshire, SY6 6DY Tel: (01694) 722333 Fax: (0870) 3665760 E-mail: sales@shopuk.co.uk
Fujitsu U K Ltd, Hayes Park Central Building, Hayes End Road, Hayes, Middlesex, UB4 8FE Tel: (020) 8573 4444 Fax: (020) 8573 2643 E-mail: sales@uk.fujitsu.com
H A Office Supplies, 25 Pittfield Street, London, N1 6HB Tel: (020) 7608 3670 Fax: (020) 7608 3670
▶ Insite Systems, Unit 2, Invicta Business Park, London Road, Wrotham, Sevenoaks, Kent, TN15 7RJ Tel: (01732) 887457 Fax: (01732) 886492
London Business Equipment, 529 High Road Leytonstone, London, E11 4PB Tel: (020) 8558 0024 Fax: (020) 8556 4865 E-mail: sales@1ondonbusinessequipment.com
Muratec (UK) Ltd, Unit 23, Hewitts Industrial Estate, Elm Bridge Road, Cranleigh, Surrey, GU6 8LW Tel: (0870) 6086084 Fax: (0870) 2408725
Office Electronics Centre UK Ltd, Electronics House Enterprise Court, Gapton Hall Road, Great Yarmouth, Norfolk, NR31 0ND Tel: (01493) 600500 Fax: (01493) 650398 E-mail: sales@oecuk.co.uk
Platt Office Equipment Ltd, 65 Minchenden Crescent, London, N14 7EP Tel: (020) 8886 9632 Fax: (020) 8886 2142 E-mail: melvyn@plattoffice.co.uk
Ricoh UK Ltd, 1 Plane Tree Crescent, Feltham, Middlesex, TW13 7HG Tel: (020) 8261 4000 Fax: (020) 8261 4004E-mail: info@ricoh.co.uk
Rocom Ltd, Thorp Arch Trading Estate, Thorp Arch, Wetherby, West Yorkshire, LS23 7RR Tel: (01937) 847777 Fax: (01937) 847788 E-mail: sales@rocon.co.uk
Toshiba Information Systems (UK) Ltd, Toshiba Court, Weybridge Business Park, Addlestone Road, Weybridge, Surrey, KT15 2UL Tel: (01932) 841600 Fax: (01932) 852455 E-mail: contact@toshiba-tiu.co.uk
Uniter Group Ltd, Unit 3, Uniter House, Radford Way, Billericay, Essex, CM12 0DX Tel: (0845) 8112000 Fax: (0845) 8112001
Dan Wood Scotland, Grampian House, Virginia Street, Aberdeen, AB11 5AU Tel: (01224) 211900 Fax: (01224) 212828 E-mail: reception.aberdeen@sctland.co.uk

FACSIMILE TRANSMITTING/ RECEIVING EQUIPMENT MAINTENANCE AND REPAIR

A M F Business Systems Ltd, New Malden, Surrey, KT3 5WN Tel: (020) 8605 1111 Fax: (020) 8605 1105
Anly Office Services, 1191 Middleton Road, Chadderton, Oldham, OL9 0NN Tel: 0161-627 5870 Fax: 0161-287 3945 E-mail: enquiry@anly.co.uk
Best Office Services Sussex, Five Ash Down, Uckfield, East Sussex, TN22 3AP Tel: (01825) 732020 Fax: (01825) 733506 E-mail: bos.s@virgin.net
Charlwood Copiers, 60 The Street, Charlwood, Horley, Surrey, RH6 0DF Tel: (01293) 862743 Fax: (0870) 8032291 E-mail: info@charlwoodcopiers.co.uk
Clark Office Electronics, 18 Willoughby Road, Tamworth, Staffordshire, B79 8NH Tel: (01827) 53520 Fax: (01827) 58557 E-mail: clark.office@ntlworld.com
Datasharp Independent Solutions, The Old Stockyard, Farleigh Road, Cliddesden, Basingstoke, Hampshire, RG25 2JS Tel: (01256) 811519 Fax: (01256) 818211 E-mail: sales@datasharp.uk.com
▶ Exiserv Ltd, 1 Page Heath Lane, Bromley, BR1 2DR Tel: (07931) 970900 Fax: (01474) 873589 E-mail: sales@exiserv.com
Fax Typewriter Service, Greenlands, Danes Green, Claines, Worcester, WR3 7RU Tel: (01905) 456705 Fax: (01905) 456705
Hendry Ferguson Company, 6 Blackwood Road, Milngavie, Glasgow, G62 7LA Tel: 0141-955 0041 Fax: 0141-955 1541 E-mail: sales@hfco.sol.co.uk
Sebserv Business Machine Repairs, Ramsay House, 18 Vera Avenue, London, N21 1RA Tel: (020) 8360 8845 Fax: (020) 8360 6688 E-mail: info@sebserv.com
Teffont Business Systems Ltd, 9 Falcons Gate, Dean Road, Yate, Bristol, BS37 5NH Tel: (01454) 318128 Fax: (01454) 321686 E-mail: sales@teffont.co.uk

FACSIMILE TRANSMITTING/ RECEIVING/BUREAU SERVICES

Copy Centre, 70 Park Lane, London, N17 0JR Tel: (020) 8808 7275 Fax: (020) 8365 1430
Copyright Office Furniture & Equipment, 150 Conway Road, Colwyn Bay, Clwyd, LL29 7LR Tel: (01492) 534807 Fax: (01492) 534807 E-mail: sales@copyrite.net
▶ Nettmedia Ltd, Unit 3, Red Cow Yard, Knutsford, Cheshire, WA16 6DG Tel: (01565) 652300 Fax: (01565) 654211 E-mail: info@nettmedia.co.uk
Qualitext Business Services Ltd, 1 Howard Road, Reigate, Surrey, RH2 7JE Tel: (01737) 242999 Fax: (01737) 248117 E-mail: hialje@qualitext.freeserve.co.uk
Swiftnet Ltd, Britannia House, 958-964 High Road, London, N12 9RY Tel: (020) 8446 9494 Fax: (020) 8446 7010 E-mail: sales@swiftnet.co.uk
Torplan Ltd, 216 Heaton Moor Road, Stockport, Cheshire, SK4 4DU Tel: 0161-443 1881 Fax: 0161-431 0786 E-mail: sales@torplan.co.uk

FACTORY AGENTS OR PROPERTY CONSULTANCY

American Appraisal (UK) Ltd, Portland Buildings, 127-129 Portland Street, Manchester, M1 4PZ Tel: 0161-237 9907 Fax: 0161-237 9908
James Andrew International Ltd, 72-75 Marylebone High Street, London, W1U 5JW Tel: (020) 7224 4436 Fax: (020) 7486 5277 E-mail: hms@jamesandrew.co.uk
Bond Estates Ltd, Bond Avenue, Bletchley, Milton Keynes, MK1 1JJ Tel: (01908) 270900 Fax: (01908) 270052 E-mail: info@terrapin-ltd.co.uk
C A P Furnaces, 2 Upper Interfields, Leigh Sinton Road, Malvern, Worcestershire, WR14 1UT Tel: (01886) 833663 Fax: (01886) 833663 E-mail: cap@furnaces.fsn.co.uk
▶ dream4avilla, 11 Underwood Road, Southampton, SO16 7BZ Tel: (023) 8058 1520 Fax: (023) 8058 1520 E-mail: info@dream4avilla.com
Robert Irving & Burns, 23-24 Margaret St, London, W1W 8LF Tel: (020) 7637 0821 Fax: (020) 7637 8827E-mail: props@rib.co.uk
Nai Gooch Webster, 4 Albemarle Street, London, W1S 4BW Tel: (020) 7409 5100 Fax: (020) 7409 5199
Teacher Marks Ltd, 23 Princes Street, London, W1B 2LX Tel: (020) 7493 4422 Fax: (020) 7497 7773 E-mail: offices@teachermarks.co.uk
Daniel Watney, 25 Hosier Lane, London, EC1A 9DW Tel: (020) 7246 5000 Fax: (020) 7248 7001 E-mail: info@danwat.com

FACTORY CLEANING CONTRACTORS

Envirotec Support Services, Cornwall House, London Road, Purfleet, Essex, RM19 1PS Tel: (01708) 685230 Fax: (01708) 861862
Green Bros Ltd, 44 High Street, Corby, Northamptonshire, NN17 1UU Tel: (01536) 265754 Fax: (01536) 206460 E-mail: enquiries@greenbros.co.uk
L & M Window Cleaning Co. Ltd, 7-9 Summer Hill Terrace, Birmingham, B1 3RA Tel: 0121-236 1448 Fax: 0121-233 0037 E-mail: info@londonandmidland.co.uk
Progress Cleaning Services White Plume Ltd, 19 Middle Street, Southampton, SO14 6GH Tel: (023) 8022 5181 Fax: (023) 8063 0622 E-mail: sales@progresscleaningservices.co.uk
Service Systems UK Ltd, Chester Road, Sandycroft, Deeside, Clwyd, CH5 2QW Tel: (01244) 535095 Fax: (01244) 538987 E-mail: service@servicesystems.co.uk
▶ Smart Cleanings UK Ltd, 66 Queen"s Park, Aylesbury, Buckinghamshire, HP21 7RT Tel: 08448 442548 Fax: 01296 580632 E-mail: admin@smart-cleanings.co.uk
Trustclean Ltd, Queens Court, Doncaster, South Yorkshire, DN5 9QH Tel: (01302) 783193 Fax: (01302) 781556 E-mail: info@trustclean.co.uk

FACTORY FLOOR DATA COLLECTION SYSTEMS

▶ D Lo UK Ltd, Select House, Popes Lane, Oldbury, West Midlands, B69 4PA Tel: 0121-544 6256 Fax: 0121-541 4264 E-mail: info@dlog.co.uk

FACTORY FURNISHERS/ EQUIPMENT SUPPLIERS, *See Mill/Factory etc*

FACTORY INSTALLATION ENVIRONMENTAL GAS MONITORING SYSTEMS

Air Liquide Ltd, Johnsons Bridge Road, West Bromwich, West Midlands, B71 1LG Tel: 0121-500 1000 Fax: 0121-500 1111 E-mail: trevor.longley@uk.linde-gas.com

FACTORY LINE MARKING EQUIPMENT OR MATERIALS

▶ Amark Safety Markings, 78 Shawfield Road, Ash, Aldershot, Hampshire, GU12 6RB Tel: (01252) 320325 Fax: (01252) 320325 E-mail: rjwright2005@yahoo.co.uk

FACTORY MADE SOFT FURNISHING GOODS, *See headings for particular types*

FACTORY MAINTENANCE

Ellis Engineering & Welding Services, Salmon Road, Great Yarmouth, Norfolk, NR30 3QS Tel: (01493) 842690 Fax: (01493) 842690 E-mail: ellisengineering@btconnect.com
M & W Contractors (Pensnett) Ltd, Morgan House, Folkes Road, Lye, Stourbridge, West Midlands, DY9 8RG Tel: (01384) 424411 Fax: (01384) 892425 E-mail: david@mwcontractors.co.uk

FACTORY PRODUCTION WORKER RECRUITMENT AGENCIES

Direct Specialist Recruitment, 8-10 North Street, Barking, Essex, IG11 8AW Tel: (020) 8591 6787 Fax: (020) 8591 6787 E-mail: info@dsrecruitment.com

FACTORY REMOVAL OR RELOCATION CONTRACTORS

Ainscough Vanguard, William Thorpe Industrial Park, Park Road, Holmwood, Chesterfield, Derbyshire, S42 5UY Tel: (01246) 854644 Fax: (01246) 854161
B & W Machinery Installations Ltd, Eagle Iron Works, Tame Street, Stalybridge, Cheshire, SK15 1ST Tel: 0161-338 6588 Fax: 0161-338 6385
Commercial Trading Co. Ltd, Unit D6 Sandown Industrial Park, Mill Road, Esher, Surrey, KT10 8BL Tel: (01372) 468383 Fax: (01372) 468576 E-mail: admin@ctc.co.uk
Crown Worldwide Movers Ltd, 1 Ninian Park, Ninian Way, Wilnecote, Tamworth, Staffordshire, B77 5ES Tel: (01827) 264100 Fax: (01827) 264101 E-mail: general@crownrelo.com
▶ DMMI, 745 Antrim Road, Templepatrick, Ballyclare, County Antrim, BT39 0AP Tel: (028) 9443 9449 Fax: (028) 9443 9446 E-mail: info@dmmi.co.uk
Factory Plant Removals UK, European Business Park, Taylors Lane, Oldbury, West Midlands, B69 2BN Tel: 0121-544 4774 Fax: 0121-552 2018 E-mail: barry.jones@factory-plant-removals.co.uk
Garrards Removals & Storage, Unit 9b Mill Lane Trading Estate, Mill Lane, Croydon, CR0 4AA Tel: (020) 8688 4979 Fax: (020) 8686 4140
Hanlon & Wright Ltd, Tudor House, Park Road, Dukinfield, Cheshire, SK16 5LX Tel: 0161-330 7631 Fax: 0161-330 0436 E-mail: sales@hanlonandwright.co.uk
J Exley Ltd, Park Works, 644 Bradford Road, Batley, West Yorkshire, WF17 8HG Tel: (01924) 472353 Fax: (01924) 440007 E-mail: greg@jexley.co.uk
J Kool, Acre Holdings, Little Weighton Road, Skidby, Cottingham, North Humberside, HU16 5TP Tel: (01482) 875747 Fax: (01482) 845024 E-mail: sales@jkoo1-engineers.co.uk
M F H Engineering Holdings Ltd, Charlotte House, 500 Charlotte Road, Sheffield, S2 4ER Tel: 0114-279 9999 Fax: 0114-279 7501 E-mail: eng@mfhgroup.co.uk
Machinery Installations (Birmingham) Ltd, Unit 12A, Middlemore Lane West, Aldridge, Walsall, WS9 8BG Tel: (01922) 743187 Fax: (01922) 743206 E-mail: mibham@aol.com
Mechanical Services (Luton) Ltd, 158A Beechwood Road, Luton, LU4 9RY Tel: (01582) 494747 Fax: (01582) 494749 E-mail: mechservluton@aol.com
Midland Plant Installations Ltd, Curriers Cl, Charter Avenue Industrial Estate, Coventry, CV4 8AW Tel: (024) 7646 1225 Fax: (024) 7669 4261 E-mail: info@mpi-uk.com
Smethwick Maintenance Co. Ltd, 336 Spon Lane South, West Bromwich, West Midlands, B70 6AZ Tel: 0121-553 3941 Fax: 0121-553 5371 E-mail: sales@sis-group.co.uk
Vic Haines, Racecourse Road, Pershore, Worcestershire, WR10 2EY Tel: (01386) 553288 Fax: (01386) 554615

FACTORY REMOVAL/LOAD MOVING EQUIPMENT

Ainscough Engineering Services Ltd, Farington Business Park, Leyland, PR25 3GG Tel: (01772) 622116 Fax: (01772) 622210 E-mail: a.keith@ainscoughengineering.co.uk

FACTORY TURNKEY CONTRACTORS OR SERVICES

Westside Engineering Site Services Ltd, Westside House, Pontugwindy Industrial Estate, Caerphilly, Mid Glamorgan, CF83 3HU Tel: (029) 2086 0123 Fax: (029) 2085 1122

FAILSAFE BRAKES

Adan Ltd, Nursery Road Industrial Estate, Boston, Lincolnshire, PE21 7TN Tel: (01205) 311500 Fax: (01205) 358013 E-mail: sales@adanltd.co.uk
Stromag Ltd, 29 Wellingborough Road, Rushden, Northamptonshire, NN10 9YE Tel: (01933) 350407 Fax: (01933) 358692 E-mail: sales@stromag.com

FALL ARREST DEVICES

Capital Safety Group Ltd, 7 Christleton Court, Manor Park, Runcorn, Cheshire, WA7 1ST Tel: (01928) 571324 Fax: (01928) 571325 E-mail: csgne@csgne.co.uk
▶ F & L Accessories Ltd, 4 5 Chosen View Road, Cheltenham, Gloucestershire, GL51 9LT Tel: (01242) 571409 Fax: (01242) 574240 E-mail: sales@flacc.co.uk
▶ Highwire Ltd, 4 Fairfield Avenue, Fairfield Wells, Droylsden, Manchester, M43 6ED Tel: 0161-612 7633 Fax: 0161-612 2105 E-mail: sales@highwire.info

FALL ARREST SAFETY LIFELINES

Gecko Safety Systems Ltd, Unit M5 Cherrycourt Way, Leighton Buzzard, Bedfordshire, LU7 4UH Tel: (01525) 382040 Fax: (01525) 378956 E-mail: info@geckosafety.co.uk
Total Access UK Ltd, Units 5b/C, Raleigh Hall Indust Estate, Eccleshall, Stafford, ST21 6JL Tel: (01785) 850333 Fax: (01785) 850339 E-mail: sales@totalaccess.co.uk

FALL ARREST SAFETY NETS

▶ R W P Scaffolding & Safety Netting Services, 1 Pelton Walk, Monsall, Manchester, M40 8QY Tel: 0161-277 9704 Fax: 0161-205 5981 E-mail: rwpscaffolding@aol.com

▶ Response Safety Netting Ltd, RSN Units, Purbrook Raod, Wolverhampton, WV1 2EJ Tel: (01902) 451812 Fax: (01902) 871297

FALLING BALL AUTOMATIC VISCOMETERS

Benson Viscometers Ltd, Croft Quarry, West Williamston, Kilgetty, Dyfed, SA68 0TN Tel: (01646) 650065

FAN ACCESSORIES

Pacet Manufacturing Ltd, Wyebridge, Cores End Road, Bourne End, Buckinghamshire, SL8 5HH Tel: (01628) 526754 Fax: (01628) 810080 E-mail: enquiries@pacet.co.uk

FAN ASSISTED VARIABLE AIR VOLUME (VAV) UNITS

Energy Technique plc, 47 Central Avenue, West Molesey, Surrey, KT8 2QZ Tel: (020) 8941 2199 Fax: (020) 8783 0140 E-mail: sales@energytechniqueplc.co.uk

FAN BELTS

Arntz Belting Co. Ltd, Pennyburn Passage, Londonderry, BT48 0AE Tel: (028) 7126 1221 Fax: (028) 7126 3386 E-mail: abcderry@globalnet.co.uk

O E S Ltd, Unit S1 Didcot Enterprise Centre, Southmead Industrial Pk, Hawksworth, Didcot, Oxon, OX11 7PH Tel: (01235) 511922 Fax: (01235) 511822

FAN COILS

Biddle Air Curtains Ltd, St Mary's Road, Nuneaton, Warwickshire, CV11 5AU Tel: (024) 7638 4233 Fax: (024) 7637 3621 E-mail: info@biddle-air.co.uk

Energy Technique plc, 47 Central Avenue, West Molesey, Surrey, KT8 2QZ Tel: (020) 8941 2199 Fax: (020) 8783 0140 E-mail: sales@energytechniqueplc.co.uk

S I C Equipment Ltd, 5 St. Thomas Road, Belvedere, Kent, DA17 6AG Tel: (020) 8311 7081 Fax: (020) 8311 7082

FAN IMPELLERS

Fral Products Ltd, 15 Dukes Close, Earls Way Industrial Estate, Thurmaston, Leicester, LE4 8EY Tel: 0116-260 1062 Fax: 0116-293 8013 E-mail: sales@multi-wing.co.uk

Standard & Pochin Ltd, 6-7 Westminster Road, Wareham, Dorset, BH20 4SP Tel: 0845 1306660 Fax: (01929) 556726 E-mail: sales@standard-pochin.co.uk

FANCY BOXES/DRUMS/ CYLINDERS, CARDBOARD/ PAPERBOARD

Arden Box Ltd, Unit, Tything Road East, Kinwarton, Alcester, Warwickshire, B49 6ES Tel: (01527) 545635 Fax: (01527) 540299 E-mail: ardenbox@hotmail.com

Bosworth Wright, Express Works, Hollow Road, Anstey, Leicester, LE7 7FP Tel: 0116-236 2231 Fax: 0116-235 2230 E-mail: bosworthwright@hotmail.com

Burton Box Co. Ltd, Burton Road Works, Burton-On-Trent, Staffordshire, DE14 3DH Tel: (01283) 540023 Fax: (01283) 565985

E.B. Crowhurst & Co. Ltd, Building 50, Pensnett Trading Estate, Kingswinford, West Midlands, DY6 7XD Tel: (01384) 400100 Fax: (01384) 400455 E-mail: sales@crowhurst.cio.uk

M. Fish (Packaging) Ltd, 7 Faraday Close, Oakwood Business Park, Clacton-On-Sea, Essex, CO15 4TR Tel: (01255) 475964 Fax: (01255) 221125 E-mail: sales@m-fish.co.uk

▶ Pandora's Hat Boxes, Althorpe Lodge, Main Street, Althorpe, Scunthorpe, North Lincolnshire, DN17 3HJ Tel: (01724) 784493 E-mail: giuseppina@pandorashatboxes.co.uk

Simpkin & Icke Holdings Ltd, Glaisdale Works, Glaisdale Drive, Nottingham, NG8 4JU Tel: 0115-929 2106 Fax: 0115-929 0446 E-mail: boxes@simpkin-and-icke.co.uk

Thomas Norman, Unit 1 Moreton Industrial Estate, London Road, Swanley, Kent, BR8 8DE Tel: (01322) 611600 Fax: (01322) 611609 E-mail: info@thomasnorman.co.uk

W Maccarthy & Sons Ltd, Unit 1 Block 1, Woolwich Dockyard Industrial Estate, Woolwich Church St, London, SE18 5PQ Tel: (020) 8316 4321 Fax: (020) 8316 5566 E-mail: box.maccarthy@virgin.net

FANCY BRASSWARE MANUFRS

Direct Manufacturing Supply Co., 19 Anne Road, Smethwick, West Midlands, B66 2PJ Tel: 0121-558 4591 Fax: 0121-565 7513 E-mail: admin@slemcka.co.uk

Samuel Heath & Sons P.L.C., Cobden Works, Leopold Street, Birmingham, B12 0UJ Tel: 0121-772 2303 Fax: 0121-772 3334 E-mail: info@samuel-heath.com

J & M Parker Ltd, 9 New Summer Street, Birmingham, B19 3QN Tel: 0121-359 8897 Fax: 0121-359 4497 E-mail: enquiries@parker.co.uk

Valsan UK Ltd, 1-3 Durban Park, Bognor Regis, West Sussex, PO22 9RJ Tel: (01243) 833500 Fax: (01243) 833503 E-mail: sales@valsanuk.com

W J Fish, 47 Brearley Street, Hockley, Birmingham, B19 3NS Tel: 0121-359 2252 Fax: 0121-359 2252

FANCY COPPERWARE

Direct Manufacturing Supply Co., 19 Anne Road, Smethwick, West Midlands, B66 2PJ Tel: 0121-558 4591 Fax: 0121-565 7513 E-mail: admin@slemcka.co.uk

FANCY CORDS

Stribbons Ltd, 99 Sanders Road, Finedon Road Industrial Estate, Wellingborough, Northamptonshire, NN8 4NL Tel: (01933) 443446 Fax: (01933) 443435 E-mail: info@stribbons.co.uk

FANCY DRESS COSTUMES

▶ Enchanted Heaven Fancy Dress & Party Supplies, 111 Cornwall Road, Herne Bay, Kent, CT6 7SZ Tel: (01227) 283933 E-mail: enchantedheaven1@yahoo.co.uk

The Fancy Fox, Dunroamin, Back Lane, Ilchester, Yeovil, Somerset, BA22 8LZ Tel: (01935) 840481 E-mail: sales@thefancyfox.com

▶ The Passion Store, 25 Sunart Way, Hawthorn Common, Nuneaton, Warwickshire, CV10 9TB Tel: 0800 6121069 Fax: 0800 6121068 E-mail: sales@thepassionstore.co.uk

▶ The Tutu Shop, 2-4 Pendarves Street, Beacon, Camborne, Cornwall, TR14 7SQ Tel: (01209) 716833 E-mail: sales@thetutushop.co.uk

FANCY DRESS HIRE

The Fancy Fox, Dunroamin, Back Lane, Ilchester, Yeovil, Somerset, BA22 8LZ Tel: (01935) 840481 E-mail: sales@thefancyfox.com

FANCY FEATHER GOODS

▶ Draytords Of Chesterfield, 4 Shap Close, Chesterfield, Derbyshire, S40 4NB Tel: (01246) 205914

FANCY GOODS, *See also heading for particulat types*

Branded Bargains, Ilford House, 6-12 Audley Street, Liverpool, L3 8LB Tel: 0151-207 2797 Fax: 0151-207 1433 E-mail: info@taylorsuperstore.co.uk

Britannic Warehouse, 142 Sand Pits, Birmingham, B1 3RJ Tel: 0121-236 7271 Fax: 0121-236 8266 E-mail: sales@britannicwarehouse.co.uk

Davies Products Liverpool Ltd, Alsol House, Laburnum Place, Bootle, Merseyside, L20 3NE Tel: 0151-922 4246 Fax: 0151-944 1901

Draper Party Products, 30 Comberton Hill, Kidderminster, Worcestershire, DY10 1QN Tel: (01562) 754973

Elgate Products, Unit 1 Patricia Way, Pysons Road Industrial Estate, Broadstairs, Kent, CT10 2LF Tel: (01843) 609200 Fax: (01843) 866234 E-mail: sales@elgate.co.uk

Fanfare Productions Ltd, 2 Wrentham Avenue, London, NW10 3HB Tel: (020) 8969 6994 Fax: (020) 8969 6994

Hooty's Supplies (Wholesale) Ltd, Longacre, Willenhall, West Midlands, WV13 2JX Tel: (01902) 369900 Fax: (01902) 636713 E-mail: hootyssuperstore@aol.com

Lesser & Pavey Ltd, Leonardo House Fawkes Avenue, Dartford Trade Park, Dartford, DA1 1JQ Tel: (01322) 279225 Fax: (01322) 279586 E-mail: sales@leonardo.co.uk

Marshall Group Ltd, Cader House, Cader Avenue, Kinmel Bay, Rhyl, Clwyd, LL18 5HU Tel: (01745) 343131 Fax: (01745) 345223 E-mail: mmar@dialstart.net

George Mitchell & Co. (Newcastle) Ltd, 8 Malmo Close, Tyne Tunnel Trading Estate, North Shields, Tyne & Wear, NE29 7SX Tel: 0191-296 3434 Fax: 0191-296 2978

P H D Import & Export Ltd, 1st Floor, 44-45 Great Hampston Street, Hockley, Birmingham, B18 6EL Tel: 0121-554 2822 Fax: 0121-554 8978 E-mail: sjhutti2000@yahoo.co.uk

Prestons (Cash & Carry) Ltd, 110 Oldham Road, Manchester, M4 6AG Tel: 0161-236 9258 Fax: 0161-236 7760

Sampson Souvenirs Ltd, 77 Vanguard Way, Shoeburyness, Southend-on-Sea, SS3 9QY Tel: (01702) 296488 Fax: (01702) 293437 E-mail: csh@sampsonsouvenirs.ltd.uk

Shonn Bros Manchester Ltd, Emperor House, 151 Great Ducie Street, Manchester, M3 1FB Tel: 0161-834 1394 Fax: 0161-832 1875 E-mail: shonnbros@yahoo.co.uk

W J Fish, 47 Brearley Street, Hockley, Birmingham, B19 3NS Tel: 0121-359 2252 Fax: 0121-359 2252

Woolbro (Distributors) Ltd, Prospect Ho, Victoria Rd, Morley, Leeds, LS27 9DB Tel: 0113-252 4349 Fax: 0113-238 0142

FANCY GOODS IMPORT/ EXPORT MERCHANTS OR AGENTS

Radmore Agencies Ltd, Perry House, Torton, Kidderminster, Worcestershire, DY10 4HY Tel: (01299) 250621 Fax: (01299) 251444

Stax Trade Centre, Brades Road, Oldbury, West Midlands, B69 2HN Tel: 0121-569 7000 Fax: 0121-569 7010

Stonegalleon plc, The SPS Building, Burnaby Road, Coventry, CV6 4AE Tel: (024) 7658 4584 Fax: (024) 7657 4585 E-mail: stonegalleon@plc.com

Jennifer Ulisse Ltd, Warwick House, Monument Way West, Woking, Surrey, GU21 5ET Tel: (01483) 721614 Fax: (01483) 770644 E-mail: sales@jenniferulisse.com

FANCY GOODS, WHOLESALE

▶ Vast Trading, Titus House, 29 Saltaire Road, Shipley, West Yorkshire, BD18 3HH Tel: 01274 609609 Fax: 01274 531966 E-mail: mark@vasttrading.co.uk

FANCY LEATHER GOODS

Acorn Hip Flasks Ltd, Reliance Works, 62 Northwood Street, Birmingham, B3 1TT Tel: (0777) 9724408 Fax: 0121-233 4336 E-mail: peter@hipflasks.co.uk

Cathian Leather Goods, Compstall Mills Estate, Andrew Street, Compstall, Stockport, Cheshire, SK6 5HN Tel: 0161-427 4871 Fax: 0161-427 4871 E-mail: cathian@ukonline.co.uk

Champion Saddlery, 3 Singers Yard, Torquay Road, Paignton, Devon, TQ3 2AH Tel: (01803) 521704

Eurobelts.com, 8 Stuart Close, Darwen, Lancashire, BB3 1DP Tel: (01254) 704395 Fax: (01254) 704395 E-mail: roy@eurobelts.com

G Aldridge & Son, 90 Friar Street, Reading, RG1 1EN Tel: 0118-957 2383 Fax: 0118-957 2383 E-mail: info@aldridges.co.uk

G Ettinger Ltd, 215 Putney Bridge Road, London, SW15 2NY Tel: (020) 8877 1616 Fax: (020) 8877 1146 E-mail: info@ettinger.co.uk

Lissan Harper International Ltd, Unit B4 Stafford Park 4, Telford, Shropshire, TF3 3BA Tel: (01952) 292408 Fax: (01952) 292419 E-mail: info@lissan-harper.co.uk

▶ Offshore Select, 116 Weddington Road, Weddington, Nuneaton, Warwickshire, CV10 0AL Tel: (024) 7632 7582 E-mail: suedeandleather@hotmail.co.uk

Printform Direct Ltd, 8 Longbridge, Willesborough, Ashford, Kent, TN24 0TA Tel: (01233) 639898 Fax: (01233) 636866 E-mail: sales@printform.co.uk

Tricorne Leather, 13 Bell Lane, London, NW4 2BP Tel: (020) 8203 6774 Fax: (020) 8203 6145

Wheeler & Oliver, 22 Cooperage Green, Royal Clarence Marina, Gosport, Hampshire, PO12 1FY Tel: (023) 9252 0091 Fax: (023) 9252 0189E-mail: info@wheelerandoliver.com

FANCY METAL GOODS

FGH Products, 68 Hunters Vale, Birmingham, B19 2XH Tel: 0121-554 4329 Fax: 0121-554 1857 E-mail: fghsilver@btconnect.com

Grants Of Dalvey Ltd, Unit 6 Dailnanrocas, Teaninich Industrial Estate, Alness, Ross-Shire, IV17 0XT Tel: (01349) 884111 Fax: (01349) 884100 E-mail: sales@dalvey.com

Royal Selangor Pewter UK Ltd, 2 Eastbury Road, London, E6 6LP Tel: (020) 7474 5511 Fax: (020) 7474 5522 E-mail: sales@royalselangor.com

Unique Concepts Licensing Ltd, Regus House, Falcon Drive, Cardiff, CF10 4RU Tel: (029) 2050 4029 Fax: (029) 2050 4129

FANCY PAPER

Brown Brothers Group Ltd, 168/170 South Street, Dorking, Surrey, RH4 2ES Tel: (01306) 742611 Fax: (01306) 742601 E-mail: duncan@brownbros.co.uk

Hallons Display Fixtures, Riverside Works, Forde Road, Newton Abbot, Devon, TQ12 4AD Tel: (01626) 358700 Fax: (01626) 358701 E-mail: sales@hallons.co.uk

T N Lawrence & Sons Ltd, 208 Portland Road, Hove, East Sussex, BN3 5QT Tel: (01273) 260260 Fax: (01273) 260270 E-mail: artbox@lawrence.co.uk

FANCY PLASTER

Southern Drylining, 32 North Poulner Road, Ringwood, Hampshire, BH24 1SP Tel: (07739) 605060 Fax: (0781) 2245583 E-mail: info@southerndrylining.co.uk

FANCY PLASTIC GOODS

Sampson Souvenirs Ltd, 77 Vanguard Way, Shoeburyness, Southend-on-Sea, SS3 9QY Tel: (01702) 296488 Fax: (01702) 293437 E-mail: csh@sampsonsouvenirs.ltd.uk

FANCY TEXTILE GOODS

▶ TD Textiles Direct, Wilson Road, Huyton, Liverpool, L36 6JG Tel: 0151-489 2121

FANCY WOODEN GOODS

Birmingham Woodcrafts, Units 9-10 All Saints Industrial Estate, Hockley, Birmingham, B18 7RJ Tel: 0121-523 8007 Fax: 0121-507 0685

Grange Hill Products Ltd, 124 Countesthorpe Road, Wigston, Leicestershire, LE18 4PG Tel: 0116-277 6255 Fax: 0116-277 6255

FANCY YARN

Copley Marshall, Tunbridge Mills, Quay Street, Huddersfield, HD1 6QX Tel: (01484) 345320 Fax: (01404) 345321 E-mail: yarns@wm-white-hudd.co.uk

John L Brierley Ltd, Turnbridge Mills, Huddersfield, HD1 6QT Tel: (01484) 435555 Fax: (01484) 435159 E-mail: sales@johnlbrierley.com

k1 Yarns Knitting Boutique, 6 Queen Margaret Drive, Glasgow, G20 8NY Tel: 0141 576 0113 E-mail: info@k1yarns.com

FANS AND BLOWERS, *See also headings under Fans*

Domus Ventilation Ltd, Bearwalden Industrial Park, Royston Road, Wendens Ambo, Saffron Walden, Essex, CB11 4JX Tel: (01799) 541175 Fax: (01799) 541143 E-mail: info@domusventilation.co.uk

▶ Fan Horn, 12, Clifftown Parade, Southend-on-Sea, SS1 1DP Tel: (01702) 341727 Fax: (01702) 390790

▶ Fischbach Fans, 17 Siddeley Way, Royal Oak Industrial Estate, Daventry, Northamptonshire, NN11 8PA Tel: (01327) 315012 Fax: (01327) 315013 E-mail: fischbachacv@aol.com

▶ Howden Industrial, Braehead Industrial Estate, Old Govan Road, Renfrew, PA4 8XJ Tel: 0141-885 7500 Fax: 0141-886 1963 E-mail: marketing@howden.com

Lojer Products Ltd, 56 The Broadway, Thatcham, Berkshire, RG19 3HP Tel: (01635) 865882 Fax: (01635) 871087 E-mail: sales@lojerproducts.co.uk

▶ The Long Eaton Fan Co., 152, Newthorpe Common, Newthorpe, Nottingham, NG16 2EN Tel: (01773) 768343 Fax: (01773) 771083

S K (Sales) Ltd, Unit C1, Sapphire Way, Rhombus Business Park, Norwich, NR6 6NN Tel: (01603) 417522 Fax: (01603) 417524 E-mail: orders@sksales.co.uk

Standard & Pochin Ltd, 6-7 Westminster Road, Wareham, Dorset, BH20 4SP Tel: 0845 1306660 Fax: (01929) 556726 E-mail: sales@standard-pochin.co.uk

Stockbridge Airco Ltd, Blossom Street Works, Ancoats, Manchester, M4 6AE Tel: 0161-236 9314 Fax: 0161-228 0009 E-mail: mark@stockbridge-airco.com

FANS TO CUSTOMER SPECIFICATION

Elta Fans, 17 Barnes Wallis Road, Fareham, Hampshire, PO15 5TT Tel: (01489) 583044 Fax: (01489) 566555 E-mail: mailbox@eltafans.co.uk

Servebrow Ltd, Bay 11 Central Works, Peartree Lane, Dudley, West Midlands, DY2 0XG Tel: (01384) 351453 Fax: (01384) 74948

FANS, COOLING, POWER SUPPLY SYSTEM

▶ Clever Air Conditioning Sales Ltd, 26 York Street, London, W1U 6PZ Tel: (0845) 0573097 Fax: (020) 7206 9432 E-mail: sales@cleverengineering.co.uk

FARE COLLECTION SYSTEMS

Cubic Transportation Systems Ltd, Honeycrock Lane, Redhill, RH1 5LA Tel: (01737) 782200 Fax: (01737) 789759 E-mail: cubicafc@cts-ltd.co.uk
ERG Transit Systems (UK) Ltd, Unit 1 Riverside, Waters Meeting Road, The Valley, Bolton, BL1 8TT Tel: (01204) 384709 Fax: (01204) 384806

FARM BASED ENERGY RECOVERY BIOGAS INSTALLATIONS

▶ JSH Energy Solutions Ltd, Ardennais House, 6 Sorrel Horse Mews, Grimwade Street, Ipswich, IP4 1LN Tel: 0845 050 5830 Fax: 01473 232137 E-mail: andrew.lashley@jshipswich.co.uk

FARM MANAGEMENT

George Briggs & Son, Wirswall, Whitchurch, Shropshire, SY13 4LF Tel: (01948) 663733
▶ M G Sutton, Grendon House Farm, Warton Lane, Grendon, Atherstone, Warwickshire, CV9 3DT Tel: (01827) 892295 Fax: (01827) 892432 E-mail: lee.sutton@btinternet.com

FARMERS MARKET ORGANISERS

▶ Local Farmers Markets, 29 Compton Street, Chesterfield, Derbyshire, S40 4TA Tel: 01246 230302

FARRIERS TOOLS

A J Pledger & Co Metals Ltd, West Street, Stamford, Lincolnshire, PE9 2PN Tel: (01780) 762245 Fax: (01780) 754531 E-mail: sales@pledger.co.uk
Atlantic Equine Ltd, Calcutt House, Flecknoe, Rugby, Warwickshire, CV23 8AU Tel: (01788) 891406 Fax: (01788) 890793 E-mail: sales@atlantic-equine.co.uk
Arthur Cottam & Co., Carrwood Road, Chesterfield, Derbyshire, S41 9QB Tel: (01246) 453672 Fax: (01246) 260274 E-mail: sales@cottamhorseshoes.com
S.W. Eakins, Ravensbank Stables, Icknield Street, Redditch, Worcestershire, B98 9AD Tel: (01527) 597354
Farriers Equipment Ltd, The Forge, Windsor Road, Chobham, Woking, Surrey, GU24 8QS Tel: (01276) 858416 Fax: (01276) 858416 E-mail: graham@farriersequipment.com
G K E Sampson & Sons, 22 Paddock Road, Newbury, Berkshire, RG14 7DG Tel: (01635) 43204
J & A Ferrie, The Smithy, High Street, Newmilns, Ayrshire, KA16 9EE Tel: (01560) 323002 Fax: (01560) 322382 E-mail: enquiries@j-aferrie.co.uk
J Henty, 21a Lower Road, Eastbourne, East Sussex, BN21 1QE Tel: (01323) 721938
P W Knight, Silverdale Park, Perranwell Station, Truro, Cornwall, TR3 7LW Tel: (01872) 862395
Phillips Bros Farriers, Lillingstone House, Lillingstone Dayrell, Buckingham, MK18 5AG Tel: (01280) 860334 Fax: (01280) 860150
T R Vowden Farrier, The Forge, Luton, Chudleigh, Newton Abbot, Devon, TQ13 0BW Tel: (01626) 865484

FASCIA PANELS

Bedford Dials Ltd, Corn Exchange, Teme Street, Tenbury Wells, Worcestershire, WR15 8BB Tel: (01584) 810345 Fax: (01584) 810683 E-mail: info@bedforddials.co.uk
Chequers UK Ltd, 78 Ponders End Industrial Estate, East Duck Lees Lane, Enfield, Middlesex, EN3 7SR Tel: (020) 8805 8855 Fax: (020) 8805 9318
GPS Developments Ltd, 14 Darlington Close, Sandy, Bedfordshire, SG19 1RW Tel: (01767) 681560 Fax: (01767) 691685 E-mail: sales@gpsdevelopments.co.uk
Kedon Industrial Supplies, Oaklands Farm Industrial Estate, Goatsmoor Lane, Stock, Ingatestone, Essex, CM4 9RS Tel: (01277) 636346 Fax: (01277) 636356 E-mail: enquiries@kedonengravers.com
Letters & Logos Ltd, Crow La Bus Park, Crow, Ringwood, Hampshire, BH24 3EA Tel: (01425) 477281 Fax: (01425) 480094 E-mail: team@lettersandlogos.co.uk
Sign Studios Ltd, 16 Broomhills Industrial Estate, Rayne Road, Braintree, Essex, CM7 2RG Tel: (01376) 349529 Fax: (01376) 552635 E-mail: sign.studios@btinternet.com

FASHION ACCESSORIES

Harper- Little Ltd, 50 Brunswick Square, Hove, East Sussex, BN3 1EF Tel: (020) 7993 4087 Fax: (0870) 6220607

FASHION CLOTHING, MENS

▶ A S Fashions Ltd, Imperial Typewriter Buildings, East Park Road, Leicester, LE5 4QD Tel: 0116-276 2780 Fax: 0116-276 2780
▶ High Demand Clothing, PO BOX 58, Longfield, Kent, DA3 7YQ Tel: (020) 8123 4985 E-mail: info@hdclothing.co.uk
necktiesonline.co.uk Ltd, Daymer, Ashmore Green Road, Ashmore Green, Thatcham, Berkshire, RG18 9ER Tel: (01635) 872499 E-mail: sales@necktiesonline.co.uk
▶ NICK SMITH NEW YORK, Somerset House, 40-49 Price Street, Birmingham, B4 6LZ Tel: 0870 486 7021 Fax: 0870 4324196 E-mail: info@nsny.co.uk
▶ Phormium Ltd, Braehead Cottage, Finavon, Forfar, Angus, DD8 3PX Tel: (01307) 850715 Fax: (01307) 850756 E-mail: p.s.ingham@btinternet.com
▶ Sun-Togs, Litton House, Saville Road, Peterborough, PE3 7PR Tel: (01733) 765030 Fax: (01733) 765210 E-mail: sales@sun-togs.co.uk
▶ Z 2 Clothing, Conduit Lane, Bridgnorth, Shropshire, WV16 5BW Tel: 01746 762467 Fax: 01746 762467 E-mail: info@z2clothing.com

FASHION FABRICS

Arcadia Group Ltd, Hudson Road, Leeds, LS9 7DN Tel: 0113-249 4949 Fax: 0113-380 6282
▶ Atlas Quality Fashion Fabrics (Europe), 9 Maidwell Close, Wigston, Leicestershire, LE18 3WU Tel: 0116-292 9685 E-mail: m.kennell@ntlworld.com
Exsa UK Ltd, 29 Marylebone Road, London, NW1 5JX Tel: (020) 7487 3989 Fax: (020) 7487 5179
K G Christys & Co. Ltd, Helmet Street, Manchester, M1 2NT Tel: 0161-274 4339 Fax: 0161-274 4322 E-mail: sales@kgchristys.co.uk

FASHION PHOTOGRAPHY

Beedle & Cooper Photograpy, Orchard Studio, 8 Beech Lane, Kislingbury, Northampton, NN7 4AL Tel: (01604) 832555 E-mail: beedle.cooper@btinternet.com
▶ Beverley Foster Wedding Photographer, 14 Moorfields, Leek, Staffordshire, ST13 5LU Tel: (01538) 386403 E-mail: admin@weddingstorybook.co.uk
▶ Dorchester Ledbetter Photographers Ltd, The Studio, 54 North Street, Leeds, LS2 7PN Tel: 0113-245 1718 Fax: 0113-245 0737 E-mail: simon@hyltonphotography.co.uk
▶ Nottingham Girls Model Agency, 49 Penrhyn Cresent, Nottingham, NG9 5PA Tel: 0115 841 9685 E-mail: agency@nottinghamgirls.co.uk
▶ Paul Harness, 41 Pondfields Drive, Kippax, Leeds, LS25 7HJ Tel: 0113-286 0909 E-mail: sales@paulharness.freeserve.co.uk
▶ Photo Models UK, 1 Burford, Brookside, Telford, Shropshire, TF3 1LJ Tel: 01952 279110 E-mail: info@photomodelsuk.co.uk
▶ Shutter Point Photography, Milford Place, High Street, Kings Heath, Birmingham, B14 7LF Tel: (07759) 057549 E-mail: steve@shutterpoint.co.uk
▶ Spotstudio, 70-72 Kingsland Road, Shoreditch, London, E2 8DP Tel: (020) 8459 4301 E-mail: info@spotstudio.net

FASHION WORKWEAR

Carrington Career & Workwear Ltd, Market Street, Adlington, Chorley, Lancashire, PR7 4HE Tel: (01257) 476850 Fax: (01257) 476852 E-mail: info@carrington.uk.com
Debonair, Anchor House, 4 Bridgeman Street, Walsall, WS2 9NW Tel: (01922) 649399 Fax: (01922) 648091 E-mail: salesdebonair@aol.com
Dub Clothing Mnfrs, Thurland Chambers, 4-6 Thurland Street, Nottingham, NG1 3DR Tel: 0115-924 3166 Fax: 0115-924 3166 E-mail: sales@dubclothing.com
Excel London, 6-16 Arbutus Street, London, E8 4DT Tel: (020) 7241 2100 Fax: (020) 7923 0098 E-mail: info@excellondon.co.uk
Fashion Fair Ltd, Unit 2 Benson Street, Leicester, LE5 4HB Tel: 0116-273 0107 Fax: 0116-273 3837 E-mail: fashionfairltd@yahoo.co.uk
Nalestar Ltd, Melton House, Melton Place, Leyland, Preston, PR25 4XU Tel: (01772) 431226 Fax: (01772) 622497 E-mail: sales@nalestar.co.uk
Orbit International P.L.C., Orbit House, 5 Dugdale Street, Birmingham, B18 4JA Tel: 0121-558 8444 Fax: 0121-565 0385 E-mail: sales@orbit-int.co.uk
R F M Workwear Ltd, 36 Glenburn Road, College Milton North, East Kilbride, Glasgow, G74 5BA Tel: (01355) 238161 Fax: (01355) 263682 E-mail: sales@corstonsinclair.com
Florence Roby, Caddick Road, Knowsley Business Park, Prescot, Merseyside, L34 9HP Tel: 0151-548 2228 Fax: 0151-549 2011 E-mail: froby@uniformcollection.com

FAST ACTING INDUSTRIAL DOORS

▶ A S R Shutters, 2 Woodseats Road, Woodseats, Sheffield, S8 0PJ Tel: (0800) 9230016
Welding Engineers (Hertford) Ltd, Unit 1, Lower Road, Great Amwell, Ware, Hertfordshire, SG12 9TA Tel: (01920) 468634 Fax: (01920) 487463 E-mail: hertford@weldingengineers.co.uk

FAST MOVING CONSUMER GOODS (FMCG) EXPORT AGENTS

▶ GM Commercial Ltd, PO Box 14, Worcester, WR8 0YD Tel: (01684) 592836 Fax: (07050) 500152 E-mail: gmai@gmcommercial.co.uk

FAST MOVING CONSUMER GOODS (FMCG) EXPORT CONSULTANCY

▶ GM Commercial Ltd, PO Box 14, Worcester, WR8 0YD Tel: (01684) 592836 Fax: (07050) 500152 E-mail: gmai@gmcommercial.co.uk

FASTENER KITS

Brenmark Holdings Ltd, 1 Newbridge Road, St Annes, Bristol, BS4 4GH Tel: 0117-971 3121 Fax: 0117-971 3428 E-mail: info@brenmark.co.uk
Gilbert Laurence Ltd, 1 Union Buildings, Wallingford Road, Uxbridge, Middlesex, UB8 2FR Tel: (01895) 455980 Fax: (01895) 455999 E-mail: sales@gilbertlaurence.co.uk
R P S Trading Ltd, Unit 2, S D H Industrial Estate, Asquith Bottom Mill, Sowerby Bridge, Halifax, West Yorkshire, HX6 3BT Tel: (01422) 839303 Fax: (01422) 836800

FASTENER MAKING MACHINE MAINTENANCE/REPAIR SERVICES

HCH Engineering Ltd, Unit 4 Charlton Drive, Corngreaves Trading Estate, Cradley Heath, West Midlands, B64 7BJ Tel: (01384) 413233 Fax: (01384) 633637 E-mail: hch@ntlbusiness.com
Metalform Inc Ltd, Stratford St North, Birmingham, B11 1BP Tel: 0121-771 4432 Fax: 0121-766 6911

FASTENER MAKING MACHINE MANUFRS

Earlsdon Technology Properties Ltd, Unit 11 Spitfire Close, Coventry Business Park, Coventry, CV5 6UR Tel: (024) 7671 7062 Fax: (024) 7671 7062 E-mail: sales@e-tech.co.uk
Johnson Machine & Tool, Westbourne Road, Wednesbury, West Midlands, WS10 8BJ Tel: 0121-568 8013 Fax: 0121-526 4984 E-mail: jmt@johnson-group.co.uk
Rex Crystal Fixings, Commercial St, Wakefield, West Yorkshire, WF1 5RN Tel: (01924) 374099 Fax: (01924) 370045 E-mail: sales@rexcrystal.co.uk
Wafios-Metoma Ltd, 21 Colemeadow Road, North Moons Moat, Redditch, Worcestershire, B98 9PB Tel: (01527) 65396 Fax: (01527) 67570 E-mail: sales@wafios-metoma.com

FASTENER MICROENCAPSULATION

P S M International plc, Longacre, Willenhall, West Midlands, WV13 2JS Tel: (01902) 600000 Fax: (01902) 600073 E-mail: tlspsm@compuserve.com

FASTENER THREADLOCKING OR SEALING CONVERSION SERVICES

Alston Asset Management Services Ltd, Unit 27, 27 Roman Way Industrial Estate, Ribbleton, Preston, PR2 5BD Tel: (01772) 700590 Fax: (01772) 706510 E-mail: info@pre-applied.co.uk
Inlex Locking Ltd, Wood Lane, Wolverhampton, WV10 8HN Tel: (01902) 397300 Fax: (01902) 785372 E-mail: enquiries@anochrome-group.co.uk
Kerb Konus, Unit B5 Hortonwood 10, Telford, Shropshire, TF1 7ES Tel: (01952) 677388 Fax: (01952) 677488E-mail: kkuk@pipex.com

FASTENER TOOLING MANUFRS

Canterbury Tools & Fasteners, 16 Herne Bay Road, Whitstable, Kent, CT5 2LJ Tel: (0845) 4264015 Fax: (01227) 266841 E-mail: normanctf@hotmail.com
Dyer Fastners, 31 Rodway Close, Brierley Hill, West Midlands, DY5 2NA Tel: (01384) 895588 Fax: (01384) 836032 E-mail: gilldyer@blueyonder.co.uk
Frank Howard, Unit 11 Lakes Industrial Park, Lower Chapel Hill, Braintree, Essex, CM7 3RU Tel: (01376) 327454 Fax: (01376) 552025
Johnson Machine & Tool, Westbourne Road, Wednesbury, West Midlands, WS10 8BJ Tel: 0121-568 8013 Fax: 0121-526 4984 E-mail: jmt@johnson-group.co.uk
R.T.C Engineering, 39 Kiltyclogher Road, Cookstown, County Tyrone, BT80 9BZ Tel: (028) 8676 5218 Fax: (01687) 65218 E-mail: sales@rtcubolts.com
Rocfast, Unit 20, Worton Hall Industrial Estate, Worton Road, Isleworth, Middlesex, TW7 6ER Tel: (020) 8568 1616 Fax: (020) 8568 5656 E-mail: Info@rocfast.co.uk
Tooling International Ltd, Unit 8 Speedwell Trading Estate, Kings Road, Tyseley, Birmingham, B11 2AT Tel: 0121-771 0611 Fax: 0121-773 6588 E-mail: til@enterprise.net

FASTENER WEDGE LOCKING

M D S Wedgloking Services, Unit 6, Alpha Business Park, Deedmore Road, Coventry, CV2 1EQ Tel: (024) 7661 4577 Fax: (024) 7660 4975

FASTENERS

▶ 1st Fix Systems, Hobson Industrial Estate, Hobson, Newcastle upon Tyne, NE16 6EA Tel: (01207) 271777 Fax: (01207) 271777
Abec Fixings Ltd, Unit 22 Small Heath Trading Estate, Armoury Road, Birmingham, B11 2RJ Tel: 0121-683 0061 Fax: 0121-683 0064 E-mail: sales@abecfixings.co.uk
Alfran Fasteners Ltd, Central Ironworks, Parson Street, Keighley, West Yorkshire, BD21 3HD Tel: (01535) 664993 Fax: (01535) 664994 E-mail: sales@alfranfasteners.co.uk
Amfast Fasteners & Fixing Devices, Clifton House Southdown Industrial Estate, Southdown Road, Harpenden, Hertfordshire, AL5 1PW Tel: (01582) 715150 Fax: (01582) 712120 E-mail: ritagill@am-fast.co.uk
▶ Anixter Industrial - Barrow, Unit 2D Ashburner Way, Walney Road Industrial Estate, Barrow-In-Furness, Cumbria, LA14 5UZ Tel: (01229) 825871 Fax: (01229) 827442
Anixter Industrial - Chesterfield, Brimington Road North, Chesterfield, Derbyshire, S41 9BE Tel: (01246) 452188 Fax: (01246) 455778 E-mail: chesterfield.sales@alistairindustrial.com
Beardshaw Bolts & Fixings, Stalham Road, Hoveton, Norwich, NR12 8DU Tel: (01603) 783811 Fax: (01603) 783859 E-mail: sales@beardshaw.co.uk
Binneys Coventry, Unit 1 Challenge Business Park, Challenge Close, Coventry, CV1 5JG Tel: (024) 7622 0228 Fax: (024) 7652 5342 E-mail: info@binneys.co.uk
▶ Eta Fixing Systems Ltd, Fixings House, Crowcroft, Leigh Sinton, Malvern, Worcestershire, WR13 5ED Tel: (01886) 833600 Fax: (01886) 833477
▶ Fasteq Ltd, 3 Fairbairn Road, Livingston, West Lothian, EH54 6TS Tel: (01506) 460888 Fax: (01506) 461144 E-mail: sales@fasteq.co.uk
▶ Fixings Direct, Castle Court, Bodmin Road, Coventry, CV2 5DB Tel: (024) 7660 4406 Fax: (024) 7661 2545
▶ Fixings Warehouse, Old Printworks, Medway Street, Maidstone, Kent, ME14 1JS Tel: (01622) 766321 Fax: (01622) 664011
Icon, Unit 2-3 Beldray Park, Beldray Road, Bilston, West Midlands, WV14 7NH Tel: (01902) 491122 Fax: (01902) 404044 E-mail: icon@icon-fasteners.co.uk
Industrial Contract Supplies, Unit 10, Swan Lane Industrial Estate, Swan Lane, West Bromwich, West Midlands, B70 0NU Tel: 0121-553 4505 Fax: 0121-553 4505
Industrial Fasteners Ltd, Chilcott Avenue, Brynmenyn Industrial Estate, Brynmenyn, Bridgend, CF32 9RQ Tel: (01656) 724775 Fax: (01656) 729612

FASTENERS – *continued*

▶ Industrial Fasteners Ltd, Unit 10 Sundon Business Park, Dencora Way, Luton, LU3 3HP Tel: (01582) 563100 Fax: (01582) 563040 E-mail: sales@anixterfasteners.com

▶ Industrial Fasteners Ltd, 7 Bell Park Bell Close, Newnham Industrial Estate, Plympton, Plymouth, PL7 4TA Tel: (01752) 341100 Fax: (01752) 346012

▶ Industrial Fasteners Ltd, 6 Station Road, Thatcham, Berkshire, RG19 4RB Tel: (01635) 865885 Fax: (01635) 871511

Julius Cee, 65-69 County Street, London, SE1 4AD Tel: (020) 7407 7273 Fax: (020) 7923 1794 E-mail: juliuscee@btconnect.com

Lamberts.Co.Uk Industrial Distributor, Whiffler Road, Norwich, NR3 2AY Tel: (01603) 422100 Fax: (01603) 422130 E-mail: nr.sales@lamberts.co.uk

M G H Industries Ltd, Lancaster House, Old Wellington Road, Eccles, Manchester, M30 9QG Tel: 0161-707 7690 Fax: 0161-707 7701 E-mail: sales@nultz-boltz.co.uk

▶ Nedschroef Fasteners, Road Transport Workshop, 7000 Alec Issigonis Way, Oxford Business Park North, Oxford, OX4 2ZY Tel: (01865) 713030 Fax: (01865) 401274

Scot-Nail Ltd, Pit Road, Kirkintilloch, Glasgow, G66 3ND Tel: 0141-777 6388 Fax: 0141-776 2581

Specialist Fastener Systems Ltd, 5 The Forward Industrial Estate, Talbot Road, Leyland, PR25 2ZJ Tel: (01772) 622194 Fax: (01772) 623189 E-mail: info@specialistfastenersystems.co.uk

▶ The Stedifix, Unit 12 Marbury House Farm, Bentleys Farm Lane, Higher Whitley, Warrington, WA4 4QW Tel: (01925) 730938 Fax: (0845) 0092670 E-mail: stedifix@tiscali.co.uk

▶ Walters Hexagon, 4 Grange Park, Newtownabbey, County Antrim, BT36 4LA Tel: (028) 9083 8924 Fax: (028) 9083 8924 E-mail: admin@waltershexagon.com

White Milne & Co., Baird Avenue, Dundee, DD2 3XG Tel: (01382) 814822 Fax: (01382) 813751 E-mail: sales@whitemilne.co.uk

FASTENERS TO SPECIFICATION

Anglian Fasteners Ltd, 16 Millbrook Close, Northampton, NN5 5JF Tel: (01604) 758585 Fax: (01604) 758565 E-mail: anglianf@micromat.net

Boltworthy Ltd, Unit I1 Cowlairs, Nottingham, NG5 9RA Tel: 0115-977 0432 Fax: 0115-977 0424

Bright Screw Co. Ltd, Bagley Lane, Rodley, Leeds, LS13 1JB Tel: 0113-256 4166 Fax: 0113-239 3480 E-mail: sales@brightscrew.co.uk

Canmec Global Ltd, 7 Dawley Brook Road, Kingswinford, West Midlands, DY6 7BD Tel: (01384) 271203 Fax: (01384) 400179 E-mail: sales@canmecglobal.com

Fisco Fasteners Ltd, Sirdar Road, Rayleigh, Essex, SS6 7XF Tel: (01268) 745421 Fax: (01268) 745467 E-mail: sales@fisco-fasteners.co.uk

Icon, Unit 2-3 Beldray Park, Beldray Road, Bilston, West Midlands, WV14 7NH Tel: (01902) 491122 Fax: (01902) 404044 E-mail: icon@icon-fasteners.co.uk

L A Sarb Engineering, Unit 6b, George Street, West Bromwich, West Midlands, B70 6NH Tel: 0121-525 2569 Fax: 0121-525 2459

Lokfast Special Fasteners Ltd, Audley Street, Mossley, Ashton-under-Lyne, Lancashire, OL5 9NH Tel: (01457) 837514 Fax: (01457) 832213 E-mail: lockfast@aol.com

M & C Engineering, Unit 12 West Bowhouse Workshops, Girdle Toll, Irvine, Ayrshire, KA11 1BU Tel: (01294) 215986 Fax: (01294) 215986

M P T Products, 14 Malmesbury Road, Kingsditch Trading Estate, Cheltenham, Gloucestershire, GL51 9PL Tel: (01594) 825438 Fax: (01242) 227071 E-mail: tom@mptproducts.demon.co.uk

Maxwell Engineering Co. Ltd, Waterloo Road, Llandrindod Wells, Powys, LD1 6BH Tel: (01597) 822414 Fax: (01597) 823067 E-mail: sales@maxwell-engineering.co.uk

Shellbourne Manufacturing Co. Ltd, Bolton Bus Centre, 44-49 Lower Bridgeman St, Bolton, BL2 1DG Tel: (01204) 546410 Fax: (01925) 740062 E-mail: sales@shellbourne.co.uk

Specialist Fastener Systems Ltd, 5 The Forward Industrial Estate, Talbot Road, Leyland, PR25 2ZJ Tel: (01772) 622194 Fax: (01772) 623189 E-mail: info@specialistfastenersystems.co.uk

Tigges UK Ltd, Unit 13, Road 32, Telford, Shropshire, TF1 7EU Tel: (01952) 670173 Fax: (01952) 670190 E-mail: tigges@icom-web.com

Wirth Engineering, Birch House, Fraser Road, Erith, Kent, DA8 1QX Tel: (01322) 434345 Fax: (01322) 434346

FASTENERS, AEROSPACE, METRIC

▶ Swift Aerospace Ltd, Metro Centre, Ronsons Way, St. Albans, Hertfordshire, AL4 9QT Tel: (01727) 868293 Fax: (01727) 868292 E-mail: sales@swiftaero.com

FASTENERS, AIRCRAFT/ AEROSPACE INDUSTRY, MANUFRS

A F Aerospace Ltd, Unit 2 Chariot Way, Glebe Farm Industrial Estate, Rugby, Warwickshire, CV21 1DA Tel: (01788) 578431 Fax: (01788) 540268 E-mail: sales@lentern.co.uk

Alcoa Fastening Systems Ltd, Stafford Park 7, Telford, Shropshire, TF3 3BQ Tel: (01952) 290011 Fax: (01952) 290459 E-mail: info@huck.co.uk

B A S Components Ltd, 2 Cramptons Road, Sevenoaks, Kent, TN14 5EF Tel: (01732) 450011 Fax: (01732) 455884 E-mail: info@bas-airospace.co.uk

Elmor Supplies Ltd, 104 Branbridges Road, East Peckham, Tonbridge, Kent, TN12 5HH Tel: (01622) 871870 Fax: (01622) 872024

▶ Engineering Services Fasteners Ltd, Parson Street, Keighley, West Yorkshire, BD21 3HD Tel: (01535) 665414 Fax: (01535) 608377 E-mail: sales@engservfast.co.uk

Galbraith Aerospace Fasteners Ltd, 54b Lilford Road, Camberwell, London, SE5 9HY Tel: (020) 7733 0118 Fax: (020) 7733 0118

J P Aero-Com Engineering Company Ltd, Station Approach, Cherry Tree Rise, Buckhurst Hill, Essex, IG9 6EY Tel: (020) 8504 8833 Fax: (020) 8505 0697 E-mail: sales@jpaero-com-eng.co.uk

Linread Northbridge, Crossgate Road, Redditch, Worcestershire, B98 7TD Tel: (01527) 525719 Fax: (01527) 526881 E-mail: info@linreadnorthbridge.co.uk

Linread Northbridge, Viking Road, Wigston, Leicestershire, LE18 2BL Tel: 0116-288 1192 Fax: 0116-257 2901

Morton & Crowder Ltd, 14 Fortnum Close, Birmingham, B33 0JX Tel: 0121-783 7571 Fax: 0121-783 1327 E-mail: morcro@aol.com

Precision Aerospace Component Engineering Ltd, Blackwell Drive, Braintree, Essex, CM7 2QJ Tel: (01376) 340000 Fax: (01376) 552210 E-mail: sales@pace-ltd.co.uk

Satair Hardware Ltd, Shoreham Airport, Shoreham-by-Sea, West Sussex, BN43 5FF Tel: (01273) 441149 Fax: (01273) 464577 E-mail: enquiries@satair.com

SPS Technologies Ltd, Troon Industrial Area, 191 Barkby Road, Leicester, LE4 9HX Tel: 0116-276 8261 Fax: 0116-274 0243

Stainless Steel Centre Ltd, Renown Close, Chandler's Ford, Eastleigh, Hampshire, SO53 4HZ Tel: (023) 8027 1155 Fax: (023) 8027 1110 E-mail: sales@stainlesssteelcentre.co.uk

▶ Swift Aerospace Ltd, Metro Centre, Ronsons Way, St. Albans, Hertfordshire, AL4 9QT Tel: (01727) 868293 Fax: (01727) 868292 E-mail: sales@swiftaero.com

Swift Fasteners Ltd, Unit 20 Oldends Industrial Estate, Oldends, Stonehouse, Gloucestershire, GL10 3RQ Tel: (01453) 825222 Fax: (01453) 827824E-mail: sales@swift-fasteners-ltd.co.uk

W T I Fasteners Ltd, Unit 10 Huntingdon Court, Westminster Industrial Estate, Measham, Swadlincote, Derbyshire, DE12 7DS Tel: (01530) 273100 Fax: (01530) 273007 E-mail: admin@wireinserts.com

FASTENERS, BUILDING/ STRUCTURAL, *See Fixing etc*

FASTENERS, GARMENT, MANUFRS

Avery Dennison UK Ltd, Business Media Division Thomas Road, Wooburn Industrial Park, Wooburn Green, High Wycombe, Buckinghamshire, HP10 0PE Tel: (01628) 859500 Fax: (01628) 859599 E-mail: sales@averydennison.com

Euro Screws, 16 Whitchurch Lane, Edgware, Middlesex, HA8 6JZ Tel: (020) 8381 2675 Fax: (020) 8381 2674

Thomas Walker Pensions Trust Ltd, 39 St Paul's Square, Birmingham, B3 1QY Tel: 0121-236 5565 Fax: 0121-236 6725 E-mail: sales@thomaswalker.co.uk

▶ Zipex UK Ltd, 15 Abbey Gate, Leicester, LE4 0AA Tel: 0116-262 4988 Fax: 0116-251 3745 E-mail: sales@zipex.co.uk

FASTENERS, HOOK AND LOOP, MANUFRS

▶ Capatex Ltd, 127 North Gate, Nottingham, NG7 7FZ Tel: 0115-978 6111 Fax: 0115-978 6222 E-mail: info@capatex.com

Dawk Trimmers, Crown Mill, 1 Crown Street, Salford, M3 7DH Tel: 0161-832 3262 Fax: 0161-834 4704E-mail: fpinetex@aol.com

Indigo Industrial Supplies Ltd, Unit 3B, Sopwith Crescent, Wickford Business Park, Wickford, Essex, SS11 8YU Tel: (01268) 768768 Fax: (01268) 768764 E-mail: sales@indigoshop.co.uk

Mansam Products Ltd, 49-51 Broughton Lane, Manchester, M8 9UE Tel: 0161-834 1356 Fax: 0161-835 1024 E-mail: sales@mansam.co.uk

MPD, Bitham Brook House, Gibbs Close, Westbury, Wiltshire, BA13 3DT Tel: (01373) 827111 Fax: (01373) 827222 E-mail: sales@ukmpd.com

Frank Pine Ltd, Crown Mill, 1 Crown Street, Salford, M3 7DH Tel: 0161-834 0456 Fax: 0161-832 0385E-mail: fpinetex@aol.com

Velcro Ltd, 1 Aston Way, Middlewich, Cheshire, CW10 0HS Tel: 01606 738806 Fax: 01606 738814 E-mail: uksales@velcro.co.uk

FASTENERS, OVER CENTRE

Southco Manufacturing Co., Shire Business Park, Wainwright Road, Worcester, WR4 9FA Tel: (01905) 751000 Fax: (01905) 751090 E-mail: info@southco.com

FASTENERS, PLASTIC, MANUFRS

Allthread Plastics Ltd, Ridley Road, Burnt Mills Industrial Estate, Basildon, Essex, SS13 1EG Tel: (01268) 726559 Fax: (01268) 725287 E-mail: sales@allthread.co.uk

Amberlea Plastics Ltd, 26 Palmerston Business Park, Palmerston Drive, Fareham, Hampshire, PO14 1DJ Tel: (01329) 231031 Fax: (01329) 239995 E-mail: sales@amberlea.co.uk

Micro Plastics (International) Ltd, Unit 2, Henley Industrial Park, Henley Road, Coventry, CV2 1SR Tel: (024) 7661 4320 Fax: (024) 7661 4831 E-mail: microplas@aol.com

▶ Montravia Fasteners & Fixing Devices, Unit 10 St. Augustines Business Park, Estuary Close, Whitstable, Kent, CT5 2QJ Tel: (01227) 791790 Fax: (01227) 791789 E-mail: robknight@sky.com

Scarborough Fixings & Tool Hire, Lower William Street, Scarborough, North Yorkshire, YO12 7PL Tel: (01723) 360326 Fax: (01723) 374184 E-mail: sales@scarboroughfixings.co.uk

Southco Europe, Farnham Trading Estate, Farnham, Surrey, GU9 9PL Tel: (01252) 714422 Fax: (01252) 712738 E-mail: info@dzus.com

FATIGUE MONITORING SPECIALIST SERVICES

Incotest, Holmer Road, Hereford, HR4 9SL Tel: (01432) 352230 Fax: (01432) 353545 E-mail: info@incotest.co.uk

Integrated Computer Services (Scotland) Ltd, 105a Shore Rd, Innellan, Dunoon, Argyll, PA23 7SR Tel: (01369) 830647 Fax: (01369) 830783 E-mail: ics_ltd@netcomuk.co.uk

FATTY ACIDS

Chema UK Ltd, Station Road, Cheddleton, Leek, Staffordshire, ST13 7EF Tel: (01538) 369000 Fax: (01538) 361330 E-mail:

Croda Chemicals Europe Ltd, Oak Road, Hull, HU6 7PH Tel: (01482) 443181 Fax: (01482) 341792

H. Foster & Co. Ltd, 103 Kirkstall Road, Leeds, LS3 1JL Tel: 0113-243 9016 Fax: 0113-242 2418 E-mail: sales@hfoster.co.uk

Oleotec Ltd, Rossfield Road, Ellesmere Port, CH65 3BS Tel: 0151-357 1778 Fax: 0151-357 1857 E-mail: sales@oleotec.com

▶ The Scottish Crop Research Institute, Invergowrie, Dundee, DD2 5DA Tel: (01382) 562731 Fax: (01382) 562426

Tennants Distribution, Gelderd Road, Birstall, Batley, West Yorkshire, WF17 9LY Tel: (01924) 474447 Fax: (01924) 477842 E-mail: sales.leeds@tennantsdistribution.com

Uniqema, Pool Lane, Bromborough Pool, Wirral, Merseyside, CH62 4UF Tel: 0151-643 3200 Fax: 0151-645 9197

FATTY ESTERS

Chema UK Ltd, Station Road, Cheddleton, Leek, Staffordshire, ST13 7EF Tel: (01538) 369000 Fax: (01538) 361330 E-mail:

Uniqema, Pool Lane, Bromborough Pool, Wirral, Merseyside, CH62 4UF Tel: 0151-643 3200 Fax: 0151-645 9197

FEATURE TELEPHONES

Enabling Communications Group Ltd, Unit 3 Wareley Yard, Wareley Road, Peterborough, PE2 9PF Tel: (01733) 892031 Fax: (01733) 891197 E-mail: sales@ecgcomms.co.uk

FEED/FEEDER SYSTEMS, SURFACE MOUNTED TECHNOLOGY (SMT)

Assembleon (UK) Ltd, Philips Ho, Cambridge Business Pk, Cowley Rd, Cambridge, CB4 0HE Tel: (01223) 468268 Fax: (01223) 468269 E-mail: louise.hartley@philips.com

FEET (ADJUSTABLE) (PLASTIC) MANUFRS

Banbury Plastic Fittings Ltd, Unit 13, Overfield, Thorpe Way Industrial Estate, Banbury, Oxfordshire, OX16 4XR Tel: (01295) 264800 Fax: (01295) 264901 E-mail: sales@bpfittings.co.uk

FELT, *See also headings for particular types*

Bryan & Clark Ltd, Ground Floor, West Cumberland House, 80 Scrubs Lane, London, NW10 6RF Tel: (020) 8969 9933 Fax: (020) 8960 7430E-mail: sales@bryanandclark.co.uk

FELT CARPET UNDERLAY

▶ Automobile Trimmings Co., Stonebridge Works, Cumberland Road, Stanmore, Middlesex, HA7 1EL Tel: (020) 8204 8242 Fax: (020) 8204 0255 E-mail: sales@automobiletrim.com

LCW, 56 Norfolk Street, Liverpool, L1 0BE Tel: 0151-709 7034 Fax: 0151-708 6022

Underlay Direct, 1 Woodlea Gardens, Sauchie, Alloa, Clackmannanshire, FK10 3BD Tel: (07768) 588714 Fax: (01259) 218097 E-mail: sales@underlaydirectscotland.co.uk

FELT COMPONENT MANUFRS

Anglo Felt Industries Ltd, Bridge End Mills, Tong Lane, Whitworth, Rochdale, Lancashire, OL12 8BG Tel: (01706) 853513 Fax: (01706) 853625 E-mail: enquiries@anglofelt.com

Baxter Hart & Abraham Ltd, 141 New Bedford Road, Luton, LU3 1LF Tel: (01582) 721381 Fax: (01582) 451033 E-mail: hornbha@aol.com

Hardy & Hanson Ltd, Summit Works, Longlands Road, Staincliffe, Dewsbury, West Yorkshire, WF13 4AB Tel: (01924) 462353 Fax: (01924) 457883E-mail: enquiries@hardy-hanson.co.uk

Naish Felts Ltd, Crow Lane, Wilton, Salisbury, SP2 0HD Tel: (01722) 743505 Fax: (01722) 744048 E-mail: sales@naishfelts.co.uk

FELT GASKETS

Gilca Manufacturing Ltd, 853 Wolverhampton Road, Oldbury, West Midlands, B69 4RU Tel: 0121-544 1929 Fax: 0121-544 6301 E-mail: info@gilca.biz

Whitby & Chandler Ltd, Green Road, Penistone, Sheffield, S36 6PH Tel: (01226) 370380 Fax: (01226) 767138 E-mail: enquiries@whitby-chandler.co.uk

FELT ROOFING CONTRACTORS

▶ A & D Joinery Ltd, Unit 14, Bolton Road Mill, Bolton Road, Bolton, BL5 3JG Tel: (01942) 814501 Fax: (01942) 810468 E-mail: john@aanddjoinery

A E S Roofing Contractors Ltd, Lingens Bungalow, Sledgemoor, Broadwas, Worcester, WR6 5NR Tel: (01905) 333697 Fax: (01905) 333650 E-mail: info@aesroofing.co.uk

Alpha Roofing Ltd, Unit 9 Crompton Mrne Industria, Est Victoria Rd, Oulton Broad, Lowestoft, Suffolk, NR33 9NQ Tel: (01502) 569847 Fax: (01502) 567573 E-mail: info@alpharoof.co.uk

Apex Asphalt & Paving Co. Ltd, 60 Cato Street, Nechells, Birmingham, B7 4TS Tel: 0121-359 8447 Fax: 0121-359 5418 E-mail: apex@apex-asphalt.co.uk

Atkin John Construction Ltd, Viking Place, Cardiff, CF10 4UU Tel: (029) 2044 2060 Fax: (029) 2044 2065 E-mail: atkintrade@atkingroup.co.uk

Canonbury Asphalte Co. Ltd, The Street, Sheering, Bishop's Stortford, Hertfordshire, CM22 7LY Tel: (01279) 734077 Fax: (01279) 734568 E-mail: canonburyasphalt@aol.com

Matthew Charlton & Sons (Slaters) Ltd, Chareway Lane, Hexham, Northumberland, NE46 3HW Tel: (01434) 606177 Fax: (01434) 601679 E-mail: slaters@matthewcharlton.com

Clonshall Ltd, Whiteacre House, 97 Whiteacre Road, Ashton-under-Lyne, Lancashire, OL6 9PJ Tel: 0161-339 9637 Fax: 0161-343 1036 E-mail: adrian.young@clonshall.co.uk

Geetee Investments Ltd, Plant Street, Wordsley, Stourbridge, West Midlands, DY8 5SY Tel: (01384) 79761 Fax: (01384) 480427 E-mail: monarchroofing@btclick.com

The General Asphalte Company Ltd, La Brea House, Coventry Street, Birmingham, B5 5NJ Tel: 0121-643 1846 Fax: 0121-643 7134 E-mail: gacltd@talk21.com

Granflex (Roofing) Ltd, Brick Kiln Lane, Basford, Stoke-On-Trent, ST4 7BT Tel: (01782) 202208 Fax: (01782) 273601 E-mail: sales@granflexroofing.co.uk

▶ Hi Spek Roofing Ltd, Hi-Spek House, Pitsford Road, Moulton, Northampton, NN3 7RS Tel: (01604) 492999 Fax: (01604) 492666 E-mail: info@hispekroofing.co.uk

FELT ROOFING CONTRACTORS - *continued*

Hyflex Roofing, Halfords Lane, Smethwick, West Midlands, B66 1BJ Tel: 0121-555 6464 Fax: 0121-555 5862 E-mail: smethwick@hyflex.co.uk

Midland Felt Roofing Ltd, Green Lane, Woodstock, Oxfordshire, OX20 1JP Tel: (01993) 811543 Fax: (01993) 813418

Midland Properties, Reeves Street, Walsall, WS3 2DL Tel: (01922) 404148 Fax: (01922) 400212

Pickles Bros Slaters Ltd, 2 323 Burley Road, Leeds, LS4 2HY Tel: 0113-275 2620 Fax: 0113-275 2620 E-mail: sales@picklesbros.co.uk

Roofdec Ltd, Braithwell Way, Hellaby, Rotherham, South Yorkshire, S66 8QY Tel: (01709) 546421 Fax: (01709) 701409

Roofproof Ltd, The Reach, Remenham, Henley-on-Thames, Oxfordshire, RG9 3DD Tel: (01491) 572966 Fax: (01491) 572967 E-mail: sales@roofproof.co.uk

W G Walker & Co Ayr Ltd, Hawkhill Works, Somerset Road, Ayr, KA8 9NF Tel: (01292) 263122 Fax: (01292) 611691 E-mail: enquiries@wgwalker.co.uk

Woodhull Roofing Ltd, Unit S3 Olton Wharf, Richmond Road, Solihull, West Midlands, B92 7RN Tel: 0121-707 3111 Fax: 0121-708 1222 E-mail: woodhull.roofing@ic24.net

Woodstock Felt Roofing Ltd, 1 Elmsfield House, Worcester Road, Chipping Norton, Oxfordshire, OX7 5XS Tel: (01608) 644644 Fax: (01608) 646658 E-mail: wfr001@aol.com

FELT SEWING NEEDLES

Foster Needle Ltd, Groz-Beckert House, 139 Gloucester Crescent, Wigston, Leicestershire, LE18 4YL Tel: 0116-258 1570 Fax: 0116-258 1579 E-mail: sales@fosterneedle.co.uk

FELT TIP MARKERS

Pentech Moulding Co. Ltd, Pump Lane Industrial Estate, Silverdale Road, Hayes, Middlesex, UB3 3BN Tel: (020) 8569 3439 Fax: (020) 8569 1219 E-mail: rapidpartner@gmail.com

FELT WASHERS

Anglo Felt Industries Ltd, Bridge End Mills, Tong Lane, Whitworth, Rochdale, Lancashire, OL12 8BG Tel: (01706) 853513 Fax: (01706) 853625 E-mail: enquiries@anglofelt.com

FEMININE CARE PRODUCTS

▶ Millennium Hygiene Services, Unit 20 Longton Business Park, Station Road, Little Hoole, Preston, PR4 5LE Tel: (0870) 7669119 Fax: (0870) 7665119 E-mail: office@mhsuk.com

FENCING, *See also headings for particular materials*

A E Cox & Sons, Caretakers Caravan, North Street, Winterton, Scunthorpe, South Humberside, DN15 9QN Tel: (01724) 732676 Fax: (01724) 732676

A M J Fencing, Unit 7 Arden Street, Swindles Yard, Stockport, Cheshire, SK12 4NS Tel: (01663) 744560 Fax: (01663) 744560

A & T A Payne, Stretch Hill, Fittleworth, Pulborough, West Sussex, RH20 1JJ Tel: (01798) 865642

Abbey Fencing, 4 Foxholes Road, Leicester, LE3 1TH Tel: 0116-287 7795

Allen Engineering Rotherham Ltd, North Street, Rotherham, South Yorkshire, S60 1LG Tel: (01709) 836800 Fax: (01709) 830300 E-mail: sales@alleneng.co.uk

Arc Services Ltd, Unit 1-2 Andrews Road Industrial Estate, Andrews Road, Cardiff, CF14 2JP Tel: (029) 2055 1919 Fax: (029) 2055 2777

Ashvale Sawmills Ltd, East Shalford Lane, Shalford, Guildford, Surrey, GU4 8AS Tel: (01483) 537505 Fax: (01483) 451298

Ashwood Garden Services & Crafts, Blendworth, Waterlooville, Hampshire, PO8 0QG Tel: (07071) 229946 Fax: (023) 9257 1700

B B F Fencing, Victoria Street Sawmills, Stoke-on-Trent, ST4 6HD Tel: (01782) 717757 Fax: (01782) 712565 E-mail: trentwoodtimber@talktalkbusiness.net

B & M Fencing Centre Ltd, Reading Road, Rotherwick, Hook, Hampshire, RG27 9DB Tel: (01256) 762739 Fax: (01256) 766891

Barkers Engineering, Etna Works, Duke Street, Stoke-on-Trent, ST4 3NS Tel: (01782) 319264 Fax: (01782) 599724 E-mail: sales.enquiries@churchill.com

Barlows & Sons Hermitage Ltd, Red Shute Hill Industrial Estate, Red Shute Hill, Hermitage, Thatcham, Berkshire, RG18 9QL Tel: (01635) 200253 Fax: (01635) 201092

▶ Perry Barr Fencing, 72 Walsall Road, Perry Barr, Birmingham, B42 1TX Tel: 0121-356 9405

Barriers International Ltd, PO Box 999, Malmesbury, Wiltshire, SN16 0JJ Tel: (01666) 829100 Fax: (01666) 823800 E-mail: admin@barriersint.com

Bentleys Fabrications, Gatesland, Stafford Road, Huntington, Cannock, Staffordshire, WS12 4NQ Tel: (01543) 570911 Fax: (01543) 570911

Bouchier Fencing Ltd, Goring Road, Woodcote, Reading, RG8 0QD Tel: (01491) 681265 Fax: (01491) 681737

British Gates & Timber Ltd, Biddenden, Ashford, Kent, TN27 8DN Tel: (01580) 291555 Fax: (01580) 292011 E-mail: sales@britishgates.co.uk

Bromyard Timber & Fencing Ltd, Station Road, Bromyard, Herefordshire, HR7 4NT Tel: (01885) 482443 Fax: (01885) 489053

D. Brookes & Son (Timber) Ltd, Oldfields, Corngreaves Road, Cradley Heath, West Midlands, B64 6BS Tel: (01384) 568821

William Burns & Sons, 1 School Road, Millisle, Newtownards, County Down, BT22 2DZ Tel: (028) 9048 4140 Fax: (028) 9048 4140

C A Palmer & Sons, Clayford Cottages, Clayford, Wimborne, Dorset, BH21 7BJ Tel: (01202) 893467 Fax: (01202) 893467

C L D Fencing Systems Suppliers, Unit 11, Springvale Business Centre, Millbuck Way, Sandbach, Cheshire, CW11 3HY Tel: (01270) 764751

Challenge Fencing Contractors Ltd, The Sawyard, Downside Road, Downside, Cobham, Surrey, KT11 3LY Tel: (01932) 860101 Fax: (01932) 866445 E-mail: sales@challengefencing.com

Cheltenham Fencing & Landscaping Supplies, Hayden Road, Cheltenham, Gloucestershire, GL51 0SN Tel: (01242) 526946 Fax: (01242) 526480E-mail: info@cheltenhamfencing.co.uk

Chettle Timber Impregnation Co., Chettle House, Chettle, Blandford Forum, Dorset, DT11 8DB Tel: (01258) 830380 Fax: (01258) 830380

Clear Hedge Forestry, Chiddingly Road, Horam, Heathfield, East Sussex, TN21 0JJ Tel: (01435) 812202 Fax: (01435) 812202

Cocklestorm Fencing Co., Cross Lane, Radcliffe, Manchester, M26 2RF Tel: 0161-724 9595 Fax: 0161-724 9595 E-mail: sales@cocklestorm.co.uk

J.A. Connelly Fencing Ltd, Town Foot, Acre Lane, Preesall, Poulton-Le-Fylde, Lancashire, FY6 0HW Tel: (01253) 700017 Fax: (01253) 700017

Construction Products & Services Ltd, 40 Rannoch Drive, Cardiff, CF23 6LQ Tel: (029) 2076 1176 Fax: (029) 2075 6179 E-mail: john.lowder@conprod.co.uk

Coolings Nurseries Ltd, Rushmore Hill Nurseries, Rushmore Hill, Knockholt, Sevenoaks, Kent, TN14 7NJ Tel: (01959) 532269 Fax: (01959) 534092

▶ Corner Post Fencing & Sheds, 1b Raynor Road, Wolverhampton, WV10 9QY Tel: (01902) 736444 Fax: (01902) 736444

Country Forge, Kidderminster Road, Dodford, Bromsgrove, Worcestershire, B61 9DU Tel: (01527) 575765 Fax: (01527) 575761 E-mail: sales@metalartproducts.co.uk

Countryside Fencing, Capel Grove, Capel St. Mary, Ipswich, IP9 2JS Tel: (01473) 314230 Fax: (01473) 314052 E-mail: sales@countryside-gates.co.uk

Coventry Fencing, Castle Wynd, Auchterarder, Perthshire, PH3 1DA Tel: (01764) 662911 Fax: (01764) 664291 E-mail: c4fencing@aol.com

Coventry Fencing, Carnwath Road, Carstairs Junction, Lanark, ML11 8RW Tel: (01555) 870494 Fax: (01555) 870941

Coventry For Fencing, Station Yard, Oxton, Lauder, Berwickshire, TD2 6PR Tel: (01578) 750666 Fax: (01578) 750612

Crestala Fencing Ltd, South Farm, Broom Lane, Langton Green, Tunbridge Wells, Kent, TN3 9JN Tel: (01892) 864366 Fax: (01892) 864366

Crowthorne Fencing Systems Ltd, Weston Road, Bretforton, Evesham, Worcestershire, WR11 7QA Tel: (01386) 831450 Fax: (01386) 831475

Crowthorne Fencing & Timber Supplies, Cambridge Road, Bedford, MK42 0LH Tel: (01234) 273077 Fax: (01234) 217130 E-mail: sales@crowthornefencing.com

D A Ramsay, Auchentoshan Estate, Clydebank, Dunbartonshire, G81 4SP Tel: (01389) 873391 Fax: (01389) 872287

D Stewart, Brocks Way, East Mains Industrial Estate, Broxburn, West Lothian, EH52 5NB Tel: (01506) 858282 Fax: (01506) 858465

D W W Fencing Ltd, Gorseinon Road, Penllergaer, Swansea, SA4 1GE Tel: (01792) 874222 Fax: (01792) 874222

Direct Fencing Supplies, 58 Gateford Road, Worksop, Nottinghamshire, S80 1EB Tel: (01909) 475928 Fax: (01909) 475928

▶ Discount Sheds, Bowdell Farm, Brenzett, Romney Marsh, Kent, TN29 9RP Tel: (01797) 343991

Dobson Welding, 69 Carlisle Street, Leicester, LE3 6AH Tel: 0116-254 1675 Fax: 0116-254 1675

Drayton Fencing, 93 Park View Road, Uxbridge, Middlesex, UB8 3LN Tel: (01895) 444727 Fax: (01895) 431054

Drivall Ltd, Narrow Lane, Halesowen, West Midlands, B62 9PA Tel: 0121-423 1122 Fax: 0121-422 9498E-mail: sales@drivall.com

E F C Fencing, Estate Yard, Lawnhead, Stafford, ST20 0JQ Tel: (01785) 284477 Fax: (01785) 284825 E-mail: andy@efcfencing.com

Easeserve Ltd, 3 The Mill, Durham Street, Droylsden, Manchester, M43 6DT Tel: 0161-370 9580 Fax: 0161-370 6746

English Hurdle, Curload, Stoke St. Gregory, Taunton, Somerset, TA3 6JD Tel: (01823) 698418 Fax: (01823) 698859 E-mail: hurdle@enterprise.net

The Expanded Metal Company, PO Box 14, Hartlepool, Cleveland, TS25 1PR Tel: (01429) 867388 Fax: (01429) 866795 E-mail: sales@expamet.co.uk

Fabrinos, 22 Station Road, Thurnscoe, Rotherham, South Yorkshire, S63 8AB Tel: (01709) 881432 Fax: (01709) 898116

Farm Fencing Ltd, 105-125 Ashurst Road, Tadworth, Surrey, KT20 5PX Tel: (01737) 812124 Fax: (01737) 812108 E-mail: info@farmfencingltd.co.uk

Farm Supplies Dorking Ltd, Ansell Road, Dorking, Surrey, RH4 1QW Tel: (01306) 880456 Fax: (01306) 876869

Fawns Recreational Services Ltd, Woodcot Court, 2a Woodcot Gardens, Farnborough, Hampshire, GU14 9RD Tel: (01252) 515199 Fax: (01252) 515858 E-mail: sales@fawns.co.uk

Fenceco Ltd, Unit 15-16 Weaver Park Estate, Mill Lane, Frodsham, WA6 7JA Tel: (01928) 735243 Fax: (01928) 735493

Fencing, 238 Gateford Road, Worksop, Nottinghamshire, S81 7AS Tel: (01909) 501176

Fencing Centre, Chapel Lane, Parley, Christchurch, Dorset, BH23 6BG Tel: (01202) 579539 Fax: (01202) 579792 E-mail: sales@fencingcentre.co.uk

Fencing Centre, Higher Farm Industrial Estate, Preston Road, Yeovil, Somerset, BA20 2ET Tel: (01935) 412241 Fax: (01935) 412741 E-mail: info@fencingcentre.co.uk

Fernlow Fencing, Hall Farm, School Lane, East Stoke, Newark, Nottinghamshire, NG23 5QL Tel: (01636) 525966 Fax: (01636) 525966

Forest Craft, 3 West Shore Road, Edinburgh, EH5 1QB Tel: 0131-552 8287 Fax: 0131-552 6367

Forestry Products Kent, Sharsted Avenue, Newnham, Sittingbourne, Kent, ME9 0JX Tel: (01795) 890683 Fax: (01795) 890895

▶ Fortress, Next To Darnley Auto Works, Cuxton Road, Rochester, Kent, ME2 2JA Tel: (01634) 405056 Fax: (01634) 714425

G A Collinson Fencing Co Ltd, Stannetts, Laindon, Basildon, Essex, SS15 6DN Tel: (01268) 411671 Fax: (01268) 541134 E-mail: info@collinsonfencing.co.uk

G & M B Manning Ltd, Hog Lane, Ashley Green, Chesham, Buckinghamshire, HP5 3PS Tel: (01442) 866264 Fax: (01442) 877105

G S A Engineering Co., Mushroom Street, Leeds, LS9 7NB Tel: 0113-244 4010 Fax: 0113-244 4010

▶ Garden Fencing, Shipyard Estate, Brightlingsea, Colchester, CO7 0AR Tel: (01206) 308900 Fax: (01206) 308623

S.R. Garrad, Stoke Road, Aylesbury, Buckinghamshire, HP21 7TE Tel: (01296) 331555 Fax: (01296) 428438 E-mail: info@srgarrad.co.uk

Gatewrights Fence Suppliers, 45 Hawkwood Road, Sible Hedingham, Halstead, Essex, CO9 3JR Tel: (01787) 461500 Fax: (01787) 460880

Gill & Punter Racing Supplies, The Barn, Shere Road, Albury, Guildford, Surrey, GU5 9BW Tel: (01483) 203044 Fax: (01483) 203338

Glasfryn Fencing and Sawmill, Llanaelhaearn Road, Y Ffor, Pwllheli, Gwynedd, LL53 6RN Tel: (01758) 750623 Fax: (01758) 750624

Golden Larch Fencing, Ringwood Road, Bartley, Southampton, SO40 7LT Tel: (023) 8081 3157 Fax: (023) 8081 2774 E-mail: sales@rfgiddings.com

Golden Soney Agri Fencing, The Gables, Golden Soney, Tockholes, Darwen, Lancashire, BB3 0NL Tel: (01254) 773648

Grangewood Fencing Supplies, Grangewood, Netherseal, Swadlincote, Derbyshire, DE12 8BG Tel: (01283) 762662 Fax: (01283) 762642

Guardwise & Co., 18 Jamaica St, Liverpool, L1 0AF Tel: 0151-708 0241 Fax: 0151-708 0241

H G Froud & Son, 24 Newtown Road, Verwood, Dorset, BH31 6EJ Tel: (01202) 822444

H W J Fencing, 85 Belmont St, Swadlincote, Derbyshire, DE11 8JZ Tel: (01283) 550262

H W Morgan & Sons, 12 Sufton Rise, Mordiford, Hereford, HR1 4EN Tel: (01432) 850436 Fax: (01432) 850792 E-mail: julie5557@hotmail.co.uk

Hampton Steel & Wire, London Road, Wellingborough, Northamptonshire, NN8 2DJ Tel: (01933) 233333 Fax: (01933) 442701 E-mail: sales@hamptonsteel.co.uk

Hazelwood Products Wattle Hurdles, Golden Dell, Golden Dell, Herriard, Basingstoke, Hants, RG25 2PE Tel: (01256) 381266

Heras UK Fencing Systems, Herons Way, Balby, Doncaster, South Yorkshire, DN4 8WA Tel: (01302) 364551 Fax: (01302) 322401 E-mail: heras.sales@heras.co.uk

▶ Hodges & Lawrence Ltd, Baccabox Lane, Hollywood, Birmingham, B47 5DD Tel: (01564) 823049 Fax: (01564) 826599 E-mail: enquiries@hnl-fencing.co.uk

J Arthurton, Stonycroft, Heath Road, Hockering, Dereham, Norfolk, NR20 3JB Tel: (01603) 880690

J & W Fencing Ltd, Pecks Hill, Nazeing, Waltham Abbey, Essex, EN9 2NY Tel: (01992) 893352 Fax: (01992) 893324

Jacob Fencing & Garden Supplies, 6 New Park Road, Ashford, Middlesex, TW15 1EG Tel: (01784) 256930

▶ JT (Fencing) Services Ltd, Beech House, Gosditch, Ashton Keynes, Swindon, SN6 6NZ Tel: (01285) 861710

Jupp & Sons, Fattings Hovel, Ditchling Road, Haywards Heath, West Sussex, RH17 7RE Tel: (01444) 471102 Fax: (01444) 471152

Kensworth Sawmills Ltd, Dovehouse Lane, Kensworth, Dunstable, Bedfordshire, LU6 2PQ Tel: (01582) 873124 Fax: (01582) 873024 E-mail: kensworthsawmillsltd@hotmail.com

▶ Krazy Bobs, Chester Road, Heswall, Wirral, Merseyside, CH60 3SE Tel: 0151-342 4700

Lee Fencing, Lidsey Road, Woodgate, Chichester, West Sussex, PO20 3SU Tel: (01243) 542345 Fax: (01243) 542345

Lewmar Fencing Co., 11 Sutherland Street, Swinton, Manchester, M27 6AT Tel: 0161-793 7630 Fax: 0161-793 7630 E-mail: sales@lewmarfencing.co.uk

Lincoln Timber & Fencing, Unit 3 Great Northern Way, Lincoln, LN5 8XF Tel: (01522) 514448 Fax: (01522) 514448

Linnell Bros Ltd, Silverstone Fields Farm, Silverstone, Towcester, Northamptonshire, NN12 8TB Tel: (01327) 354422 Fax: (01327) 355840 E-mail: info@linnellbros.co.uk

M & B Fencing Supplies Ltd, Unit 49, Boughton Industrial Estate, Boughton, Newark, Nottinghamshire, NG22 9LD Tel: (01623) 861184 Fax: (01623) 862820 E-mail: sales@mbfence.co.uk

M G A Fencing, 8 Bottomley Yard, Bottomley Street, Nelson, Lancashire, BB9 9SW Tel: (01282) 449100 Fax: (01282) 449100

M J & H J Mills, 53 Livesey Street, Wateringbury, Maidstone, Kent, ME18 5BQ Tel: (01622) 812204

Mcarthur Group Ltd, 27 Perimeter Road, Pinefield Industrial Estate, Elgin, Morayshire, IV30 6AF Tel: (01343) 548694 Fax: (01343) 541688 E-mail: marketing@mcarthur-group.com

Mcveigh Parker & Co Ltd, Southend Road, Southend, Reading, RG7 6HA Tel: (0845) 1207755 Fax: 0118-974 4123 E-mail: sales@mcveighparker.co.uk

Main Line Timber Ltd, Station Yard Caravan, Station Road, Woodford Halse, Daventry, Northamptonshire, NN11 3RB Tel: (01327) 262124

▶ The Mayfield Group UK Ltd, Bournemouth, BH1 9GR Tel: (01202) 233959 Fax: (01202) 732853 E-mail: enquiries@themayfieldgroup.co.uk

▶ Merseyside & North Wales Fencing, Mold Road, Alltami, Mold, Clwyd, CH7 6LG Tel: (01352) 780373 Fax: (01244) 548184

Michael R Hawes, 18 Clovelly Road, Hayling Island, Hampshire, PO11 0SD Tel: (023) 9246 4470 Fax: (023) 9246 9472 E-mail: michael.hawes6@btinternet.com

Morework Fabrications, 4 Heath Road, Hounslow, TW3 2NH Tel: (020) 8577 5027 Fax: (020) 8572 5396

Mount Trading Co. Ltd, Glan Yr Afon Industrial Estate, Llanbadarn Fawr, Aberystwyth, Dyfed, SY23 3JQ Tel: (01970) 611919 Fax: (01970) 627062

New Forest Fencing Ltd, Mill Lane, Nursling, Southampton, SO16 0YE Tel: (023) 8073 3442 Fax: (023) 8074 0181

▶ Newick Fencing, 31 Hamsland, Horsted Keynes, Haywards Heath, West Sussex, RH17 7DS Tel: (01825) 790990 E-mail: barry@newickfencing.com

Norbury (Pallets) Ltd, Unit 28, Marshgate Drive, Hertford, SG13 7AJ Tel: (01992) 504236 Fax: (01992) 584978 E-mail: sales@norburypallets.com

▶ North West Fencing, 55 Lacrosse Avenue, Oldham, OL8 4LU Tel: 0161-633 2426

P Hartwell Timber, Timber Yard, Weston-Subedge, Chipping Campden, Gloucestershire, GL55 6QH Tel: (01386) 840373 Fax: (01386) 841370 E-mail: info@hartwellfencing.co.uk

P & J Webster Gate Manufacturers, 251 Wakefield Road, Dewsbury, West Yorkshire, WF12 8ET Tel: (01924) 452720 Fax: (01924) 452720

Jim Packman, Uplees Cottages, Uplees Road, Oare, Faversham, Kent, ME13 0QR Tel: (01795) 533741

Piper Fabrication & Fencing Supplies Ltd, 214 Northwood Road, Harefield, Uxbridge, Middlesex, UB9 6PT Tel: (01895) 824372 Fax: (01895) 824372

Post Anchor Co., Halesfield 21, Telford, Shropshire, TF7 4PA Tel: 0121-522 4585

Premier Fencing (Yorkshire) Ltd, Unit 4, Strafford Industrial Park, Gilroyd Lane, Dodworth, Barnsley, South Yorkshire, S75 3EJ Tel: (01226) 285333

Premier Sheds & Fencing, Streatham Common, Station Approach, London, SW16 5NR Tel: (020) 8677 0459 Fax: (020) 8677 3778 E-mail: premiershedsresponse@btconnect.com

Presto Fencing, Unit 1b, The Old Forge, Main Rd, Huntley, Gloucester, GL19 3DZ Tel: 01452 831 466 Fax: 01452 831 516

Protech Systems Northern Ltd, Woodside House, Woodside Lane, Sheffield, S3 9PB Tel: 0114-272 2705 Fax: 0114-272 2706

R F Giddings & Co. Ltd, 28 Sharlands Road, Fareham, Hampshire, PO14 1RD Tel: (01329) 234670 Fax: (01329) 234670

R J Sharples, Riverside Sawmill, Fishwick Bottoms, Preston, PR2 5AU Tel: (01772) 556019 Fax: (01772) 250708 E-mail: info@rjsharples.co.uk

FENCING – *continued*

Rainworth Fencing Manufacturers, Helmsley Road, Rainworth, Mansfield, Nottinghamshire, NG21 0DG Tel: (01623) 795066 Fax: (01623) 797543 E-mail: sales@rainworthfencing.com

▶ RFB Engineering, Unit 9, London Road Business Park, Retford, Nottinghamshire, DN22 6HG Tel: (01777) 860000 Fax: (01777) 860000

Richards & Hewitt Sales Ltd, Dorset Way, Byfleet, West Byfleet, Surrey, KT14 7LB Tel: (01932) 346025 Fax: (01932) 348517

Rutland Electric Fencing Co. Ltd, Unit 11 Brechin Bus Park, West Road, Brechin, Angus, DD9 6RJ Tel: (01356) 624109 Fax: (01356) 624109 E-mail: refscotsales@btclick.com

The Scotia Fencing Company Ltd, Howe Road, Kilsyth, Glasgow, G65 0TA Tel: (01236) 823339 Fax: (01236) 826434

Somerlap Forest Products, Wells Road, Mark, Highbridge, Somerset, TA9 4NR Tel: (01278) 641671 Fax: (01278) 641629 E-mail: admin@somerlap.net

South West Fencing & Sheds, Unit 1A Plum Lane, Dunwear, Bridgwater, Somerset, TA6 5HL Tel: (01278) 447031

Southill Saw Mills Ltd, Southill Park, Southill, Biggleswade, Bedfordshire, SG18 9LJ Tel: (01462) 819173 Fax: (01462) 851873

Sparkford Sawmills Ltd, Sparkford, Yeovil, Somerset, BA22 7LH Tel: (01963) 440414 Fax: (01963) 440982 E-mail: enquiries@sparkford.com

Stansted Sawmill Ltd, Stansted Park, Rowland's Castle, Hampshire, PO9 6DU Tel: (023) 9241 2445 Fax: (023) 9241 3434

Stevenage Fencing Co., 105 Mobbsbury Way, Stevenage, Hertfordshire, SG2 0HZ Tel: (01438) 725918 Fax: (01438) 235081 E-mail: stevefencing@aol.com

Stow Agricultural Services, Lower Swell Road, Stow on the Wold, Cheltenham, Gloucestershire, GL54 1LD Tel: (01451) 830400

Sunbeam Timber Products, 119 Bristol Road, Frampton Cotterell, Bristol, BS36 2AU Tel: (01454) 273300 Fax: (01454) 273300

Sussex Fencing & Construction Co., 1 Beaconsfield Road, Portslade, Brighton, BN41 1XA Tel: (01273) 418878 Fax: (01273) 881858

▶ Tate Fencing Ltd, 1 Chase Wood Works, Frant Road, Frant, Tunbridge Wells, Kent, TN3 9HG Tel: (01892) 750230 Fax: (01892) 750130 E-mail: sales@tate-fencing.co.uk

Edward Thomas & Son Ltd, Usk Sawmills, Sennybridge, Brecon, Powys, LD3 8RS Tel: (01874) 636321

Timber Line DIY, 1 Nicholson Buildings, South Shields, Tyne & Wear, NE33 5BD Tel: 0191-428 6645 Fax: 0191-428 0789 E-mail: sales@timberline.co.uk

Top Marks Fencing, 7 Leas Road, Mansfield Woodhouse, Mansfield, Nottinghamshire, NG19 8JH Tel: (01623) 636635

Top Security Fencing UK Ltd, 55 High Street, Bridgnorth, Shropshire, WV16 4DX Tel: (01746) 763299 Fax: (01746) 766374 E-mail: topsec@btconnect.com

Tornado Wire Ltd, 4b Waterloo Road, Bidford-on-Avon, Alcester, Warwickshire, B50 4JH Tel: (01789) 778766 Fax: (01789) 490508 E-mail: sales@tornadowire.co.uk

Tornado Wire Ltd, Unit 4 Devonshire Road, Millom, Cumbria, LA18 4JF Tel: (01229) 774572 Fax: (01229) 775145

U R S A Automatic Gates & Traffic Barriers Ltd, Unit 24 Howard Court, Nerston Industrial Estate, East Kilbride, Glasgow, G74 4QZ Tel: (0845) 4300800 Fax: (01355) 234617 E-mail: sales@ursagates.co.uk

▶ Uniwire Ltd, Unit 21 Glan Yr Afon Industrial Estate, Llanbadarn Fawr, Aberystwyth, Dyfed, SY23 3JQ Tel: (01970) 611326 Fax: (01970) 615868

Valedene, 12 Lillington Avenue, Leamington Spa, Warwickshire, CV32 5UJ Tel: (01926) 339707 Fax: (01926) 316071

W G Dodds & Son, The Sawmill Bowesfield Industrial Estate, Bowesfield Lane, Stockton-on-Tees, Cleveland, TS18 3HJ Tel: (01642) 674827 Fax: (01642) 644809 E-mail: sales@wgdodds.co.uk

W Howkins & Co., 65-67 Newnham Avenue, Bedford, MK41 9QJ Tel: (01234) 261143 E-mail: sales@whowkins.co.uk

Watt Fences, Broken Brea Farm, Easby, Richmond, North Yorkshire, DL10 7EY Tel: (01748) 822666 Fax: (01748) 822666

Weavo Fencing Products Ltd, Station Works, Hatch Beauchamp, Taunton, Somerset, TA3 6SH Tel: (01823) 480571 Fax: (01823) 480175 E-mail: sales@weavo.co.uk

Wharton Landscapes, Esh Winning, Durham, DH7 9PT Tel: 0191-373 3213 Fax: 0191-373 4975

Wideacre Metal Gates Ltd, 15 Buttress Way, Smethwick, West Midlands, B66 3DL Tel: 0121-558 4263 Fax: 0121-558 5735 E-mail: gailkaren@msn.com

Willowcrete Manufacturing Co., Deptford Terrace, Sunderland, SR4 6DF Tel: 0191-565 9528 Fax: 0191-564 0934 E-mail: jeff.broomfield@willowcrete.com

FENCING ACCESSORIES OR EQUIPMENT

Abbey Fencing, 4 Foxholes Road, Leicester, LE3 1TH Tel: 0116-287 7795

Banbury Environmental Products Ltd, Yorke Street, Mansfield Woodhouse, Mansfield, Nottinghamshire, NG19 9NX Tel: (01623) 662002 Fax: (01623) 640864

Birkdale Sales, Granville House Lees Parade, Uxbridge Road, Uxbridge, Middlesex, UB10 0PQ Tel: (01895) 272112

Bridle Way At Gauntleys, Mill House, Laneham Road, Dunham-on-Trent, Newark, Nottinghamshire, NG22 0UW Tel: (01777) 228040 Fax: (01777) 228977

Britannia Fasteners, 4/6 Auckland Street, Hot Lane Industrial Estate, Stoke-on-Trent, ST6 2AT Tel: (01782) 833233 Fax: (01782) 833255E-mail: sales@britanniafasteners.co.uk

British Gates & Timber Ltd, Biddenden, Ashford, Kent, TN27 8DN Tel: (01580) 291555 Fax: (01580) 292011 E-mail: sales@britishgates.co.uk

Cambrian Fencing, Rhydlydan Yard, Llywernog, Ponterwyd, Aberystwyth, Dyfed, SY23 3AB Tel: (01970) 890502 Fax: (01970) 890502

Chase Timber Products Ltd, Twickenham Avenue, Brandon, Suffolk, IP27 0PD Tel: (01842) 810690 Fax: (01842) 812987 E-mail: mail@chasetimberproducts.co.uk

Clear Hedge Forestry, Chiddingly Road, Horam, Heathfield, East Sussex, TN21 0JJ Tel: (01435) 812202 Fax: (01435) 812202

D J Price, Sleap, Harmer Hill, Shrewsbury, SY4 3HE Tel: (01939) 290894 Fax: (01939) 290894 E-mail: sales@davidjprice.co.uk

Deeleys Fencing, The Stables, Ford Lane, Chorley, Lichfield, Staffordshire, WS13 8BY Tel: (01543) 682361

Downend Fencing, Cuckoo Lane, Winterbourne Down, Bristol, BS36 1AG Tel: 0117-951 8582

Fenceco Ltd, Unit 15-16 Weaver Park Estate, Mill Lane, Frodsham, WA6 7JA Tel: (01928) 735243 Fax: (01928) 735493

G & R Leigh, Nunsfield Farm, Fairfield, Buxton, Derbyshire, SK17 7HN Tel: (01298) 22725 Fax: (01298) 25138

Hamilton & Kinneil Ltd, Riccarton Sawmill, Hamilton, Lanarkshire, ML3 7UE Tel: (01698) 282452 Fax: (01698) 283884

Hoist & Co., Bonnyacre Farm, Wrotham Road, Meopham, Gravesend, Kent, DA13 0RF Tel: (01732) 823826 Fax: (01732) 823826

J & H Rosenheim & Co. Ltd, Lancaster Fields, Crewe, CW1 6FF Tel: (01270) 585959 Fax: (01270) 586611 E-mail: enquiries@rosenheim.co.uk

Logmasters Fence Suppliers, Mystycroft, Burtons Green, Halstead, Essex, CO9 1RH Tel: (01787) 473450 Fax: (01787) 472299

M G A Fencing, 8 Bottomley Yard, Bottomley Street, Nelson, Lancashire, BB9 9SW Tel: (01282) 449100 Fax: (01282) 449100

Mcarthur Group Ltd, Brunswick Indust Estate, Brunswick Village, Hazlerigg, Newcastle upon Tyne, NE13 7DX Tel: 0191-236 5911 Fax: 0191-217 0581 E-mail: marketing@mcarthur-group.com

Marks Tey Products, Church Lane, Marks Tey, Colchester, CO6 1LN Tel: (01206) 210744 Fax: (01206) 210744

MJM Fencing, Halebank Road, Widnes, Cheshire, WA8 8NA Tel: 0151-495 3948 Fax: 0151-495 3948

Northpoint Ltd, Globe Lane, Dukinfield, Cheshire, SK16 4UY Tel: 0161-330 4551 Fax: 0161-339 7169 E-mail: sales@northpoint.ltd.uk

Phoenix Fencing Supplies, The Chalk Hole, Harbour Farm, Molash, Canterbury, Kent, CT4 8HN Tel: (01233) 740004

Stix & Stones Garden Products Ltd, The Yard, Colchester Main Road, Alresford, Colchester, CO7 8DD Tel: (01206) 826835 Fax: (01206) 827655

Stockfield Fencing Products Ltd, Stockfield Road, Chadderton, Oldham, OL9 9HD Tel: 0161-620 4034 Fax: 0161-620 4034

Tango Rail, Bilport Lane, Wednesbury, West Midlands, WS10 0NT Tel: 0121-502 6600 Fax: 0121-502 0303

Taylor Fencing, 4 Coton Carriage Works, Heath End Road, Nuneaton, Warwickshire, CV10 7JB Tel: (024) 7635 3313 Fax: (024) 7635 3313

FENCING CONTRACTORS

1st Aid 4 Fencing, 2 Cornbrash Rise, Hilperton, Trowbridge, Wiltshire, BA14 7TT Tel: 0800 611 8344 E-mail: info@1staid4fencing.com

A & R Fencing Ltd, Paxton Street, Stoke-on-Trent, ST1 3SD Tel: (01782) 215419 Fax: (01782) 208516 E-mail: ian@aandrfencing.co.uk

Abram Fencing, 59 Old Park Lane, Southport, Merseyside, PR9 7BQ Tel: (01704) 224923 Fax: (01704) 224923 E-mail: john@abramfencing.co.uk

▶ Advance Supplies Eastern Ltd, Victoria Stables, South Road, Bourne, Lincolnshire, PE10 9JZ Tel: (01778) 426633 Fax: (01778) 426899 E-mail: sales@advancesupplies.co.uk

Allen Engineering Rotherham Ltd, North Street, Rotherham, South Yorkshire, S60 1LG Tel: (01709) 836800 Fax: (01709) 830300 E-mail: sales@alleneng.co.uk

Allen Groundcare Ltd, 3 Home Close, Greens Norton, Towcester, Northamptonshire, NN12 8AY Tel: (01327) 354789 Fax: (01327) 354053 E-mail: steve@allengroundcare.co.uk

Alltype Fencing Co. Ltd, Howgare Road, Broad Chalke, Salisbury, SP5 5DR Tel: (01722) 780563 Fax: (01722) 780138 E-mail: sales@alltypefencing.fsnet.co.uk

Ashvale Timber Industries, 62-68 Birling Road, Ashford, Kent, TN24 8BB Tel: (01233) 623592 Fax: (01233) 712611

B B Fencing Ltd, Foxley Farm, Draycote Water, Kytes Hardwick, Rugby, Warwickshire, CV23 8AB Tel: (01788) 812800 Fax: (01788) 812500

B & M Fencing Centre Ltd, Reading Road, Rotherwick, Hook, Hampshire, RG27 9DB Tel: (01256) 762739 Fax: (01256) 766891

Banfield Fencing, 2 Alexander Way, Yatton, Bristol, BS49 4HE Tel: (01934) 838885 Fax: (01934) 838885

Bedford Fencing Co. Ltd, 8 Sargeant Turner Trading Estate, Bromley Street, Stourbridge, West Midlands, DY9 8HZ Tel: (01384) 422688 Fax: (01384) 422688

Blackford Fencing Contractors, 92 Blackford Road, Shirley, Solihull, West Midlands, B90 4BX Tel: 0121-745 6691 Fax: 0121-745 6691

Bradmore Garden Centres, Pendock Lane, Bradmore, Nottingham, NG11 6PQ Tel: 0115-984 7990 Fax: 0115-940 6175

Brads Fencing Co. Ltd, 22 Hare Lane, Godalming, Surrey, GU7 3EE Tel: (01483) 414745 Fax: (01483) 419394

Bruno Timber Products, Weston Court, Holton Road, Barry, South Glamorgan, CF63 4JD Tel: (01446) 732693 Fax: (01446) 732693

Capel Security Solutions Ltd, 22 Sychem Lane, Five Oak Green, Tonbridge, Kent, TN12 6TR Tel: (01892) 836036 Fax: (01892) 834844 E-mail: info@capelfencing.co.uk

Carters Gate & Fencing Specialists, 12 Sea Road, East Preston, Littlehampton, West Sussex, BN16 1JP Tel: (01903) 785324 Fax: (01903) 783580

▶ Chafford Landscapes, 14 St. James Avenue East, Stanford-le-Hope, Essex, SS17 7BQ Tel: (01375) 676003 E-mail: ianholloway@btconnect.com

Chestnut Products Ltd, Unit 15 Gaza Trading Estate, Scabharbour Road, Hildenborough, Tonbridge, Kent, TN11 8PL Tel: (01732) 463777 Fax: (01732) 454636 E-mail: sales@chestnutproducts.fsnet.co.uk

Claytons, 28 Main Street, Whittington, Lichfield, Staffordshire, WS14 9JS Tel: (01543) 433038

Coates Fencing Ltd, Unit 3 Barham Close, Bridgwater, Somerset, TA6 4DS Tel: (01278) 423577 Fax: (01278) 427760 E-mail: info@coatesfencing.co.uk

Crestala Fencing Ltd, South Farm, Broom Lane, Langton Green, Tunbridge Wells, Kent, TN3 9JN Tel: (01892) 864366 Fax: (01892) 864366

D E Fencing Ltd, Forthill Avenue, Jedburgh, Roxburghshire, TD8 6HJ Tel: (01835) 863623 Fax: (01835) 862113

Dale Fencing Ltd, 834 London Road, North Cheam, Sutton, Surrey, SM3 9BJ Tel: (020) 8641 2367 Fax: (020) 8641 1838 E-mail: dale@fences.fsbusiness.co.uk

Darfen Durafencing, Herons Way, Carr Hill, Doncaster, South Yorkshire, DN4 8WA Tel: (01302) 360242 Fax: (01302) 364359 E-mail: mail@darfen.co.uk

Deeleys Fencing, The Stables, Ford Lane, Chorley, Lichfield, Staffordshire, WS13 8BY Tel: (01543) 682361

Demo Fences, 4 Garden Close, London, SW15 3TH Tel: (020) 8785 1078

E G Hingston & Son, Wilburton Farm, Ivybridge, Devon, PL21 9LB Tel: (01752) 880416

Elmwood Fencing Ltd, 10 Sheen Lane, London, SW14 8LL Tel: (020) 8878 0993 Fax: (020) 8878 2332

Fellwood Products, Cherryfields, Fullers Road, Rowledge, Farnham, Surrey, GU10 4DF Tel: (01252) 793807

Fencing Products Ltd, 10 King Street Lane, Winnersh, Wokingham, Berkshire, RG41 5AS Tel: 0118-978 5162 Fax: 0118-977 6422 E-mail: j.a.o.@btinternet.com

Fernden Construction Winchester Ltd, Barfield Close, Winchester, Hampshire, SO23 9SQ Tel: (01962) 866400 Fax: (01962) 864139 E-mail: sales@ferndenwin.co.uk

G A Collinson Fencing Co Ltd, Stannetts, Laindon, Basildon, Essex, SS15 6DN Tel: (01268) 411671 Fax: (01268) 541134 E-mail: info@collinsonfencing.co.uk

G B G Fences Ltd, 25 Barns Lane, Walsall, WS4 1HQ Tel: (01922) 623207 Fax: (01922) 722110 E-mail: enquiries@gbgfences.co.uk

G & H Fencing Contractors, 69 Maple Leaf Drive, Birmingham, B37 7JB Tel: 0121-770 0105 Fax: 0121-770 1751

G Ross Contractors, Camps Industrial Estate, Kirknewton, Midlothian, EH27 8DF Tel: (01506) 880569 Fax: (01506) 883728 E-mail: billy@rosscontractors.fsnet.co.uk

▶ Gracelands Landscapes Ltd, The Yard, Bramshill Close, Arborfield Cross, Reading, RG2 9PT Tel: 0118-976 0660 Fax: 0118-976 0990 E-mail: info@gracelands-landscapes.co.uk

Hadley's Fencing Contractors Ltd, Kiln House Saw Mill, Pottery Road, Bovey Tracey, Newton Abbot, Devon, TQ13 9DS Tel: (01626) 835726 Fax: (01626) 834860 E-mail: sales@hadleysfencing.co.uk

Hassett Fencing Ltd, Old Quarry Field, Harborough Road, Pitsford, Northampton, NN6 9RU Tel: (01604) 820902 Fax: (01604) 820899

Havering Fencing Co, 237 Chase Cross Road, Romford, RM5 3XS Tel: (01708) 747855 Fax: (01708) 721010 E-mail: enquiries@haveringfencing.com

Heras UK Fencing Systems, Herons Way, Balby, Doncaster, South Yorkshire, DN4 8WA Tel: (01302) 364551 Fax: (01302) 322401 E-mail: heras.sales@heras.co.uk

Hortech Landscape, The Nurseries, Moddershall, Stone, Staffordshire, ST15 8TQ Tel: (01785) 818080 Fax: (01785) 285452 E-mail: enquiries@hortech.co.uk

▶ Id Fencing, 24 Hayle Avenue, Warwick, CV34 5TW Tel: (01926) 496753 Fax: (01926) 496753 E-mail: info@idfencing.co.uk

Job Earnshaw & Bros.Limited, Main Offices Stocksmoor Road, Midgley, Wakefield, West Yorkshire, WF4 4JG Tel: (01924) 830099 Fax: (01924) 830080 E-mail: john@job-earnshaw.co.uk

▶ Kidderminster Fencing, 9 mayfield close, kidderminster, Worcestershire, DY11 5NG Tel: 01562 745427 E-mail: kidderminsterfencing@yahoo.co.uk

Kingsforth Landscape & Construction Ltd, Mangham Way, Rotherham, South Yorkshire, S61 4RL Tel: (01709) 378977 Fax: (01709) 838992 E-mail: enquiries@kingsforthfencing.co.uk

Lewbuild Fence Products, Ashton Rd, Bardsley, Oldham, OL8 3HT Tel: 0161-633 2301 Fax: 0161-624 7525

▶ Lowrey Contractors Ltd, 200 South Liberty Lane, Bristol, BS3 2TY Tel: 0117-963 7111 Fax: 0117-963 7111

▶ M D G Property Services, 60 Sandholme Drive, Bradford, West Yorkshire, BD10 8EY Tel: (01274) 200078 E-mail: mikegreasley@blueyonder.co.uk

▶ M & G Sheds & Fencing, Unit J9 Dudley Trading Estate, Shaw Road, Dudley, West Midlands, DY2 8QX Tel: (01384) 240956 Fax: (01384) 255741

Mcewan Bros Kirkintilloch Ltd, The Smithy House, Old Duntiblae Road, Glasgow, G66 3LG Tel: 0141-776 1880 Fax: 0141-776 1040 E-mail: mcewansfencing@aol.com

May Gurney Ltd, Ringland Lane, Costessey, Norwich, NR8 5BG Tel: (01603) 744440 Fax: (01603) 747310

Melvin Bros, Unit 3 Baird Avenue, Strutherhill Industrial Estate, Larkhall, Lanarkshire, ML9 2PJ Tel: (01698) 887605 Fax: (01698) 884871 E-mail: melvinbrothers@aol.com

Montgomerie Steel & Co. Ltd, Glen Works, 4 Paisley Road, Barrhead, Glasgow, G78 1ND Tel: 0141-881 4500 Fax: 0141-881 8275 E-mail: info@montgomeriesteele.co.uk

N K Fencing, 40 Trailcock Road, Carrickfergus, County Antrim, BT38 7NU Tel: (028) 9335 1172 Fax: (028) 9333 6433 E-mail: sales@nkfencing.com

▶ Newick Fencing, 31 Hamsland, Horsted Keynes, Haywards Heath, West Sussex, RH17 7DS Tel: (01825) 790990 E-mail: barry@newickfencing.com

Norcroft Equestrian Development, 1 Norton Road, Loddon, Norwich, NR14 6JN Tel: (01508) 520743 Fax: (01508) 528879

Oakdale Fencing Ltd, Bedworth Road, Bulkington, Bedworth, Warwickshire, CV12 9LG Tel: (024) 7664 0120 Fax: (024) 7664 0120 E-mail: enquiries@oakdalefencing.co.uk

P Hartwell Timber, Timber Yard, Weston-Subedge, Chipping Campden, Gloucestershire, GL55 6QH Tel: (01386) 840373 Fax: (01386) 841370 E-mail: info@hartwellfencing.co.uk

Pembury Fencing, Unit, Church Farm, Collier Street, Tonbridge, Kent, TN12 9RT Tel: (0870) 2423707 Fax: (0870) 2423708 E-mail: pemburyfencing@tiscali.co.uk

Protek Fencing Ltd, Coney Park, Harrogate Road, Yeadon, Leeds, LS19 7XS Tel: 0113-250 0995 Fax: 0113-250 1899 E-mail: contact@protek-fencing.co.uk

▶ R & C Landscapes, 82 Groveside Close, Carshalton, Surrey, SM5 2ET Tel: (020) 8773 8296 E-mail: robertgibbs364@hotmail.com

R & S Fencing, 31 Kingsland Close, Portsmouth, PO6 4AL Tel: (023) 9221 0365

R Y Thomson & Son, 15 Ash Street, Dundee, DD1 5AR Tel: (01382) 221460 Fax: (01382) 907005 E-mail: rythomson@btconnect.com

Rasburn Fence Suppliers, 699 Crankwood Road, Leigh, Lancashire, WN7 4PP Tel: (01942) 605604 Fax: (01942) 861188

Rees David Fencing Construction, The Grove, Clarbeston Road, Dyfed, SA63 4SP Tel: (01437) 731308 Fax: (01437) 731551 E-mail: davidreesfencing@lineone.net

Robert Ballantine & Son, East End, Star, Glenrothes, Fife, KY7 6LQ Tel: (01592) 758542 Fax: (01592) 610707

▶ Rushmere Fencing, 65 Linksfield, Rushmere St Andrew, Ipswich, IP5 1BA Tel: (01473) 623248 Fax: (01473) 623248 E-mail: will@forascape.co.uk

Sampson & Partners Fencing, Aubrey Works, 15 Aubrey Ave, London Colney, St. Albans, Herts, AL2 1NE Tel: (01727) 822222 Fax: (01727) 826307 E-mail: primasampson@compuserve.com

South Staffordshire Fencing Co. Ltd, Unit 12, Brookfield Drive, Cannock, Staffordshire, WS11 0JN Tel: (01543) 462008 Fax: (01543) 462341

Stockfield Fencing Products Ltd, Stockfield Road, Chadderton, Oldham, OL9 9HD Tel: 0161-620 4034 Fax: 0161-620 4034

Stockton Fencing, Park Farm, Riseley Road, Bletsoe, Bedford, MK44 1QU Tel: (01234) 708318 Fax: (01234) 709917 E-mail: sales@stocktonfencing.co.uk

FENCING CONTRACTORS – *continued*

Tilbrooks Landscape Ltd, 3 High Street, Tuddenham, Bury St. Edmunds, Suffolk, IP28 6SQ Tel: (01638) 712766 Fax: (01638) 715362 E-mail: info@tilbrooks.co.uk

Tonbridge Fencing Ltd, Court Lane Farm, Court Lane, Hadlow, Tonbridge, Kent, TN11 0DP Tel: (01732) 852596 Fax: (01732) 852593 E-mail: info@tonbridgefencing.co.uk

▶ Voyager Site Services, Ashton Clough Road, Liversedge, West Yorkshire, WF15 6JX Tel: (07870) 588297 E-mail: voyagersiteservices@aol.com

W A Skinner & Co UK Ltd, Dorset Way, Byfleet, West Byfleet, Surrey, KT14 7LB Tel: (01932) 344228 Fax: (01932) 348517

▶ W J Wicks & Sons, Bigadon Lane, Buckfastleigh, Devon, TQ11 0DT Tel: (01364) 643237 Fax: (01364) 642054

W L West & Sons Ltd, Selham, Petworth, West Sussex, GU28 0PJ Tel: (01798) 861611 Fax: (01798) 861633

Warefence Ltd, Clare Terrace, Carterton, Oxfordshire, OX18 3ES Tel: (01993) 847227 Fax: (01993) 840551 E-mail: info@warefence.co.uk

W.H. Wesson (Fencing) Ltd, 126 Connaught Road, Brookwood, Woking, Surrey, GU24 0AS Tel: (01483) 472124 Fax: (01483) 472115

Chris Wheeler Construction Ltd, Church Farm, Burbage, Marlborough, Wiltshire, SN8 3AT Tel: (01672) 810315 Fax: (01672) 810309 E-mail: cw.cw@btinternet.com

White & Etherington Ltd, New Farm Road, Alresford, Hampshire, SO24 9QE Tel: (01962) 732783 Fax: (01962) 735422

Wideacre Metal Gates Ltd, 15 Buttress Way, Smethwick, West Midlands, B66 3DL Tel: 0121-558 4263 Fax: 0121-558 5735 E-mail: gailkaren@msn.com

Willowcrete Manufacturing Co., Deptford Terrace, Sunderland, SR4 6DF Tel: 0191-565 9528 Fax: 0191-564 0934 E-mail: jeff.broomfield@willowcrete.com

Winterborne Zelston Fencing Ltd, Bridge Cottage, Winterborne Zelston, Blandford Forum, Dorset, DT11 9EU Tel: (01929) 459245 Fax: (01929) 459011 E-mail: rbower@wzfencing.fsnet.co.uk

FENCING POST BRACKETS

▶ Woodcraft Fencing, Mold Road, Cefn-y-Bedd, Wrexham, Clwyd, LL12 9YG Tel: (01978) 769330 Fax: (01978) 756490 E-mail: woodcraft_fencing@yahoo.co.uk

FENDER SYSTEMS

▶ Fendequip, Unit 12, Lawerance Hill Business Centre, Wincanton, Somerset, BA9 9RT Tel: (01963) 33322 Fax: (01963) 33344 E-mail: info@fendequip.com

▶ Metso Minerals (UK) Ltd, Parkfield Road, Rugby, Warwickshire, CV21 1QJ Tel: (01788) 532100 Fax: (01788) 560442 E-mail: ukenquiries@metso.com

FENDERS, BOAT/SHIP/YACHT

▶ Fendequip, Unit 12, Lawerance Hill Business Centre, Wincanton, Somerset, BA9 9RT Tel: (01963) 33322 Fax: (01963) 33344 E-mail: info@fendequip.com

Marine Equipment Supply, Enterprise House, Harveys Lane, Seething, Norwich, NR15 1EN Tel: (01508) 483703 Fax: (01508) 482710 E-mail: sales@fendercare.com

Soverign Rubber, Hillgate Industrial Estate, Carrington Field St, Stockport, Cheshire, SK1 3JN Tel: 0161-429 8787 Fax: 0161-480 3573E-mail: salessov@sovereign-rubber.co.uk

Wilks (Rubber Plastics Manufacturing) Co. Ltd, Woodrolfe Road, Tollesbury, Maldon, Essex, CM9 8RY Tel: (01621) 869609 Fax: (01621) 868863 E-mail: sales@wilks.co.uk

FENT/TEXTILE REMNANTS

L Littlewood & Son Exports Ltd, 3 Edwin Road, Beswick, Manchester, M11 3ER Tel: 0161-273 1344 Fax: 0161-273 3013 E-mail: l-littlewood@btconnect.com

FERMENTATION PLANT/ EQUIPMENT, INDUSTRIAL

Brighton Systems Ltd, Unit 24 Euro Business Park, New Road, Newhaven, East Sussex, BN9 0DQ Tel: (01273) 515563 Fax: (01273) 611533 E-mail: sales@brightonsystems.co.uk

Electrolab Ltd, Unit E2 Northway Trading Estate, Northway Lane, Tewkesbury, Gloucestershire, GL20 8JH Tel: (01684) 291007 Fax: (01684) 291006 E-mail: sales@electrolab.co.uk

Meura (Brewery Equipment) Ltd, 1 Park Farm, Buntingford, Hertfordshire, SG9 9AZ Tel: (01763) 272680 Fax: (01763) 272321 E-mail: info@meura.co.uk

FERMENTATION VESSELS, BIOLOGICAL/PHARMACEUTICAL

New Brunswick Scientific UK Ltd, 17 Alban Park, Hatfield Road, St. Albans, Hertfordshire, AL4 0JJ Tel: (01727) 853855 Fax: (01727) 835666 E-mail: sales@nbsuk.co.uk

Suncombe Ltd, Jade House, Lockfield Avenue, Brimsdown, Enfield, Middlesex, EN3 7JY Tel: (020) 8443 3454 Fax: (020) 8443 3969 E-mail: sales@suncombe.com

FERRITE COMPONENTS

Ace Wound Products Ltd, 1g Skillion Business Park, Thames Road, Barking, Essex, IG11 0JP Tel: (020) 8507 2330 Fax: (020) 8507 8981 E-mail: mac@acewound.com

Steward Ltd, 5 Cochrane Square, Brucefield Industrial Estate, Livingston, West Lothian, EH54 9DR Tel: (01506) 414200 Fax: (01506) 410694 E-mail: europe@steward.com

Trak Microwave Ltd, Dunsinane Avenue, Dunsinane Industrial Estate, Dundee, DD2 3QF Tel: (01382) 833411 Fax: (01382) 833599

FERRITE CORES, *See also headings for particular types*

Power Magnetics Ltd, Pace House, 15 Little Balmer, Buckingham Industrial Estate, Buckingham, MK18 1TF Tel: (01280) 817243 Fax: (01280) 823167 E-mail: sales@powermagnetics.co.uk

FERRITE TRANSFORMERS

A G W Electronics Ltd, Hayford Way, Staveley, Chesterfield, Derbyshire, S43 3JR Tel: (01246) 473086 Fax: (01246) 280082 E-mail: sales@agw.co.uk

Carnhill Transformers Ltd, 68 Sandford Lane, Kennington, Oxford, OX1 5RW Tel: (01865) 327843 Fax: (01865) 736538 E-mail: sales@carnhill.co.uk

Carnhill Transformers Ltd, 4 Edison Road, St. Ives, Cambridgeshire, PE27 3LT Tel: (01480) 462978 Fax: (01480) 496196 E-mail: sales@carnhill.co.uk

Custom Transformers Ltd, Unit 23, Whitewalls, Easton Grey, Malmesbury, Wiltshire, SN16 0RD Tel: (01666) 824411 Fax: (01666) 824413 E-mail: sales@custom-transformers.co.uk

Isomatic UK Ltd, 9 Pimms Close, Guildford, Surrey, GU4 7YG Tel: (01483) 534634 Fax: (01483) 573624 E-mail: peter.burton@isomatics.biz

Walsall Transformers Ltd, 246 Green Lane, Walsall, WS2 8HS Tel: (01922) 722933 Fax: (01922) 721222 E-mail: sales@walsall-transformers.co.uk

FERRO ALLOYS

Aetc Ltd, Victoria Avenue, Yeadon, Leeds, LS19 7AW Tel: 0113-250 5151 Fax: 0113-238 6006

Axis Alloys FP Ltd, 4 Popes Lane, Oldbury, West Midlands, B69 4PN Tel: 0121-552 7733 Fax: 0121-552 3682 E-mail: axisalloys@aol.com

Richard Cooke Engineering Steels Ltd, 38 Moorgate Road, Rotherham, South Yorkshire, S60 2AG Tel: (01709) 830214 Fax: (01709) 830216 E-mail: sales@rces.co.uk

F E Mottram Ltd, Oakes Green, Stevenson Road, Sheffield, S9 3XG Tel: 0114-244 6723 Fax: 0114-242 5344 E-mail: ferrometals@femottram.co.uk

SMP Metallurgical Ltd, Surrey Street, Glossop, Derbyshire, SK13 7AL Tel: (01457) 852333 Fax: (01457) 855655 E-mail: sales@smp-metallurgical.com

Transition International Ltd, Hi-Temp Works, 480 Penistone Road, Sheffield, S6 2FU Tel: 0114-244 7447 Fax: 0114-233 3071 E-mail: david@transition-international.com

FERRO MOLYBDENUM

Axis Alloys FP Ltd, 4 Popes Lane, Oldbury, West Midlands, B69 4PN Tel: 0121-552 7733 Fax: 0121-552 3682 E-mail: axisalloys@aol.com

Climax Molybdenum UK Ltd, Needham Road, Stowmarket, Suffolk, IP14 2AE Tel: (01449) 674431 Fax: (01449) 675972 E-mail: climax@phelpsdodge.com

FERRO TITANIUM

Wogen Group Ltd, 4 The Sanctuary, Westminster, London, SW1P 3JS Tel: (020) 7222 2171 Fax: (020) 7222 5862 E-mail: wogen@wogen.co.uk

FERROUS ALLOYS

A E Burgess & Sons Ltd, Ulverscroft Road, Leicester, LE4 6BY Tel: 0116-262 0065 Fax: 0116-251 0501

Universal Alloys & Metals Ltd, Lowe House, 1 Ranmoor CR, Sheffield, S10 3GU Tel: 0114-230 8855

FERROUS CASTINGS

Intercast UK Ltd, 73 Ringstead Crescent, Crosspool, Sheffield, S10 5SH Tel: 0114-266 6873 Fax: (08704)287885 E-mail: sales@intercastuk.com

Technicast Moulds, Unit 1 Garnett Close, Watford, WD24 7GN Tel: (01923) 246530 Fax: (01923) 255983 E-mail: isoo4e2893@blueyonder.co.uk

FERROUS METALS

▶ Christie & Son (Metal Merchants) Ltd, Lobnitz Dock, Meadowside Street, Renfrew, PA4 8SY Tel: 0141-885 1253 Fax: 0141-885 1937 E-mail: info@christieandson.com

FERROUS SULPHATE

▶ Craig Generics Ltd, Thistle Building, 9 Cairn Court, East Kilbride, Glasgow, G74 4NB Tel: (01355) 576500 Fax: (01355) 576510

FERROUS WIRE MESH

Multi Weldmesh Ltd, Heasandford Industrial Estate, Widow Hill Road, Burnley, Lancashire, BB10 2TJ Tel: (01282) 425300 Fax: (01282) 422204

FERRULE FITTINGS

Fluid Controls Ltd, 4 Minerva House, Calleva Park, Aldermaston, Reading, RG7 8NA Tel: 0118-981 1004 Fax: 0118-981 0775 E-mail: sales@fluidcontrols.co.uk

FERRY SERVICES

▶ Albion Service, 9 Silverwood Way, Up Hatherley, Cheltenham, Gloucestershire, GL51 3TW Tel: (01242) 254771 Fax: (01242) 254771 E-mail: albionservice@btopenworld.com

▶ Cremyll Ferry, 1 Cremyll Quay Penhellis, Maker Lane, Cremyll, Torpoint, Cornwall, PL10 1HX Tel: (01752) 822105

▶ Portsea Harbour Company Ltd, South Street, Gosport, Hampshire, PO12 1ZZ Tel: (023) 9252 4551

FERTILISER PRODUCTION PLANT

Bradley Pulverizer Co., 15 Kennet Road, Crayford, Crayford, Dartford, DA1 4QN Tel: (01322) 559106 Fax: (01322) 528690 E-mail: bradley.pulverizer@btinternet.com

FERTILISER SPRAY EQUIPMENT

S. Lappin, 191 Granemore Road, Tassagh, Armagh, BT60 2RD Tel: (028) 3753 8634 Fax: (028) 3753 8634

Sisis Equipment Macclesfield Ltd, Hurdsfield Industrial Estate, Macclesfield, Cheshire, SK10 2LZ Tel: (01625) 503030 Fax: (01625) 427426 E-mail: info@sisis.com

FERTILISER SPREADERS

John Bownes Ltd, Courthouse Farm, Swanlow Lane, Darnhall, Winsford, Cheshire, CW7 4BS Tel: (01606) 592639 Fax: (01606) 861410 E-mail: sales@jbownes.co.uk

Shelbourne Reynolds Engineering Ltd, Shepherds Grove Industrial Estate, Stanton, Bury St. Edmunds, Suffolk, IP31 2AR Tel: (01359) 250415 Fax: (01359) 250464 E-mail: info@shelbourne.com

FERTILISERS, *See also headings under Fertilisers*

Agrimark Europe Agricultural Merchants, Folly Lane, Bell Royd Farm, Thurlstone, Sheffield, S36 7QF Tel: (01226) 370013 Fax: (01226) 370178

Agritek Sales & Service Ltd, Upgate Road, Seething, Norwich, NR15 1EL Tel: (01508) 483200 Fax: (01508) 483201 E-mail: info@agritek.co.uk

▶ Angus Fertilizers Ltd, River Street, Montrose, Angus, DD10 8DL Tel: (01674) 678400 Fax: (01674) 671318 E-mail: info@cars-feltilizer.co.uk

Bartholomews (Chichester) Ltd, Mullaney Business Park, Deanland Road, Golden Cross, Hailsham, East Sussex, BN27 3RP Tel: (01825) 872697 Fax: (01825) 872850 E-mail: goldencross@bartholomews.fsnet.co.uk

J. & H. Bunn Ltd, South Beach Parade, Great Yarmouth, Norfolk, NR30 3QA Tel: (01493) 744700 Fax: (01493) 744701 E-mail: info@jhbunn.co.uk

Carrs Fertilisers, Inverbreakie Industrial Estate, Invergordon, Ross-Shire, IV18 0QR Tel: (01349) 853745 Fax: (01349) 854066 E-mail: enquiries@carrs-fertiliser.co.uk

Carrs Fertilisers Ltd, Wath, Silloth, Wigton, Cumbria, CA7 4PH Tel: (01697) 332333 Fax: (01697) 332279

Chempak Products, Unit 40 Hillgrove Business Park, Nazeing Road, Nazeing, Waltham Abbey, Essex, EN9 2BB Tel: (01992) 890770 Fax: (01992) 890660

Contract Fertiliser & Storage Ltd, Spaldington Airfield, Bubwith Road, Spaldington, Goole, East Yorkshire, DN14 7NG Tel: (01430) 431511 Fax: (01430) 432070 E-mail: cfs@jhbunn.co.uk

▶ Dxui Ltd, Unit 5 Autumn Park Industrial Estate, Dysart Road, Grantham, Lincolnshire, NG31 7DD Tel: (01476) 564387 Fax: (01476) 564448 E-mail: admin@dxui.net

Eden Park Ltd, Crown Quay Lane, Sittingbourne, Kent, ME10 3JJ Tel: (01795) 471583 Fax: (01795) 428011 E-mail: sales@edenpark.co.uk

Thomas Elliott Ltd, Oakley Road, Bromley, BR2 8HG Tel: (01732) 866566 Fax: (020) 8462 5599

Farmway Machinery Ltd, Cock Lane, Piercebridge, Darlington, County Durham, DL2 3TJ Tel: (01325) 374000 Fax: (01325) 374094 E-mail: csd@farmway.co.uk

▶ Fertecon, The Pantiles, Tunbridge Wells, Kent, TN2 5TE Tel: (01892) 701710 Fax: (01892) 701711

Forizo Co., Walker Street, Higher Tranmere, Birkenhead, Merseyside, CH42 0LY Tel: 0151-652 2275

▶ Garden Wizard, Hoghton Road, Leyland, PR25 1XX Tel: (01772) 454724

▶ Glasson Fertillisers, Greens Farm Depot, Park Lane, Winmarleigh, Preston, PR3 0JU Tel: (01524) 752200 Fax: (01524) 753601 E-mail: info@glassongrain.co.uk

Growmoor Horticulture Ltd, 207 Derrylee Road, Dungannon, County Tyrone, BT71 6NY Tel: (028) 3885 2346 Fax: (028) 3885 1050 E-mail: info@growmoor.co.uk

▶ Harrington & Jessop Ltd, Priest Lane, West End, Woking, Surrey, GU24 9NA Tel: (01483) 472423

Helm Fertilizer Great Britain, The Exchange, Station Parade, Harrogate, North Yorkshire, HG1 1PL Tel: (01423) 527799 Fax: (01423) 527799 E-mail: info@helmag.com

I A W F, Rushenden Road, Queenborough, Kent, ME11 5HH Tel: (01795) 580365 Fax: (01795) 580649 E-mail: sales@sheppyfertilisers.co.uk

I A W S Ltd, North Side North Dock, Alexandra Dock, Newport, Gwent, NP20 2NP Tel: (01633) 255999 Fax: (01633) 250999

I A W S Fertilisers UK Ltd, Maxwell Road, Plymouth, PL4 0SN Tel: (01752) 601124 Fax: (01752) 223758

John Hall Ltd, Selby Place, Stanley Industrial Estate, Skelmersdale, Lancashire, WN8 8EF Tel: (01695) 51875 Fax: (01695) 51863 E-mail: johnhall@enta.net

Kenira, Ince Marshes, Ince, Chester, CH2 4LB Tel: 0151-357 1010 Fax: 0151-357 1755

P.B. Kent & Co. Ltd, Alexandra Road South, Immingham Dock, Immingham, North East Lincolnshire, DN40 2QW Tel: (01469) 563980 Fax: (01469) 571444 E-mail: michael.dickinson@pbkent.co.uk

M Forker, 8 Maghery Road, Portadown, Craigavon, County Armagh, BT62 1SZ Tel: (028) 3885 1268 Fax: (028) 3885 1017

Maxicrop (UK) Ltd, Corby, Northamptonshire, NN17 1ZH Tel: (08700) 115117 Fax: (08700) 115118 E-mail: info@maxicrop.co.uk

▶ Joseph Metcalf Ltd, Nook Lane, Lower Green, Astley, Manchester, M29 7LW Tel: (01942) 896668 Fax: (01942) 897485 E-mail: rgrice@gemweb.co.uk

Keith Mount Liming Ltd, Rougham Industrial Estate, Rougham, Bury St. Edmunds, Suffolk, IP30 9ND Tel: (01359) 271033 Fax: (01359) 271151 E-mail: keith@mountliming.co.uk

▶ Neat Crown Corwen Ltd, Station Yard Industrial Estate, Corwen, Clwyd, LL21 0EE Tel: (01490) 413121 Fax: (01490) 412177

Omex Environmental Ltd, Riverside Industrial Estate, King's Lynn, Norfolk, PE30 2HH Tel: (01553) 770092 Fax: (01553) 776547 E-mail: enquire@omex.com

▶ Payne Bros East Anglia Ltd, Helhoughton Road, Hempton, Fakenham, Norfolk, NR21 7DY Tel: (01328) 864864 Fax: (01328) 856900

The Scotts Co. (UK) Ltd, Howden Dyke, Goole, North Humberside, DN14 7UF Tel: (01430) 433300 Fax: (01430) 431658

Sheppy Ltd, Rushenden Road, Queenborough, Kent, ME11 5HH Tel: (01795) 580181 Fax: (01795) 580649 E-mail: sales@sheppy.ltd.uk

Soil Fertility Dunns Ltd, North Harbour Street, Ayr, KA8 8AH Tel: (01292) 611622 Fax: (01292) 619990

FERTILISERS – *continued*

▶ Syngenta Ltd, PO Box A38, Huddersfield, HD2 1FF Tel: (01484) 537456 Fax: (01484) 517067

Terra Nitrogen UK Ltd, Florence House, Radcliffe CR, Thornaby, Stockton-on-Tees, Cleveland, TS17 6BS Tel: (01642) 637000 Fax: (01642) 637104 E-mail: webmasteruk@uk.terraindusties.com

Terralift UK Ltd, 18 The Grove, Market Deeping, Peterborough, PE6 8AW Tel: (01778) 380005 Fax: (01778) 348835 E-mail: sales@terralift.ie

Thompson Fertiliser Sales, Cornfield Cottage, Thorpe Bassett, Malton, North Yorkshire, YO17 8LU Tel: (01944) 758091 Fax: (01944) 758621 E-mail: thom-fert@supanet.com

Timac UK Ltd, Bath Road Industrial Estate, Bath Road, Chippenham, Wiltshire, SN14 0AB Tel: (01249) 467100 Fax: (01249) 660232

Vitagrow Fertilisers Ltd, PO Box 161, Southport, Merseyside, PR9 8GH Tel: (01704) 507777 Fax: (01704) 507222 E-mail: sales@vitagrow.co.uk

W L Dingley & Co, Buckle Street, Honeybourne, Evesham, Worcestershire, WR11 7QE Tel: (01386) 830242 Fax: (01386) 833541

Wild Park Leisure Ltd, Wild Park Brailsford, Brailsford, Ashbourne, DE6 3BN Tel: (01335) 360485 Fax: (01335) 361019 E-mail: enquiries@wildparkleisure.com

William Sinclair Holdings Public Ltd Company, Firth Road, Lincoln, LN6 7AH Tel: (01522) 537561 Fax: (01522) 560648 E-mail: info@william-sinclair.co.uk

FERTILISERS, COMPOST

▶ Joseph Metcalf Ltd, Nook Lane, Lower Green, Astley, Manchester, M29 7LW Tel: (01942) 896668 Fax: (01942) 897485 E-mail: rgrice@gemweb.co.uk

▶ Seramis Hydroponics, Unit 11, Pentood Enterprise Park, Cardigan, Dyfed, SA43 3AG Tel: (0870) 0271980 Fax: (0870) 0271985 E-mail: sales@seramishydroponics.com

FERTILISERS, LIME

▶ Michael Williams Agricultural Merchant, PO Box 1, Uttoxeter, Staffordshire, ST14 7SB Tel: (0870) 4324626 E-mail: agbiz@michaelwilliams.biz

FESTOON LIGHTING

Electrosite UK Ltd, Easton Lane, Bozeat, Wellingborough, Northamptonshire, NN29 7NN Tel: (01933) 665022 Fax: (01933) 665520 E-mail: electrosite@kbnet.net

FESTOON OR ROMAN OR DECORATIVE OR DOMESTIC BLINDS

Apollo Blinds Ltd, 8 Lorne Arcade, Ayr, KA7 1SB Tel: (01292) 261838 Fax: (01292) 261838

▶ Apollo Blinds Ltd, 64 Main Street, Rutherglen, Glasgow, G73 2HY Tel: 0141-647 0341 Fax: 0141-647 0341

▶ Apollo Blinds Ltd, 73 South Methven Street, Perth, PH1 5NX Tel: (01738) 622366 Fax: (01738) 622366

Apollo Blinds Ltd, 6 Senator Industrial Estate, College Close, Sandown, Isle of Wight, PO36 8EH Tel: (01983) 407395 Fax: (01983) 407395 E-mail: apolloexpiowltd@skelly.co.uk

Appeal Conservatory Blinds Ltd, Unit 6 Vale Lane, Bristol, BS3 5SD Tel: 0117-963 7734 Fax: 0117-966 6216 E-mail: sales@appealblinds.com

Blinds, Bremilham House, Bremilham Road, Malmesbury, Wiltshire, SN16 0DQ Tel: (01666) 822680

Blinds By Elizabeth, 352 Southchurch Road, Southend-on-Sea, SS1 2QB Tel: (01702) 603659 Fax: (01702) 522657

Stephen Butler Blinds, The Street, Walberton, Arundel, West Sussex, BN18 0PF Tel: (01243) 555222 Fax: (01243) 555222 E-mail: sales@stephenbutlerblinds.co.uk

C F M Blindmaker Supplies Ltd, 18 20 James Road, Tyseley, Birmingham, B11 2BA Tel: (0870) 7702965 Fax: (0871) 4332309 E-mail: sales@cfmblinds.co.uk

Capital Blinds, Factory Place, Docklands, London, E14 3AN Tel: (0800) 0433442

▶ Curtain Blinds: Custom Curtain Blinds, Redhouse Road, Moulton Park, Northampton, NN3 6AQ Tel: (01604) 497994 Fax: (01604) 497994 E-mail: blinds@saster.fsnet.co.uk

D & S Blinds, 177 Stamford St Central, Ashton-under-Lyne, Lancashire, OL6 7PS Tel: 0161-339 5755 Fax: 0161-339 5755 E-mail: sales@kcblinds.co.uk

Discount Blind Centre, 11 Centurion Street, Belfast, BT13 3AS Tel: (028) 9033 3606 Fax: (028) 9024 5724

Euro Blinds UK, King Street, Newton Abbot, Devon, TQ12 2LG Tel: (01392) 824225 Fax: (01626) 369005 E-mail: info@euroblindsdevon.co.uk

▶ Finavon Fabrics, 128 Murray Street, Montrose, Angus, DD10 8JG Tel: (01674) 676141

Florida Blinds, 16 Noran Cresent, Troon, Ayrshire, KA10 7JF Tel: (01292) 318203 Fax: (01292) 318203

G & C Blinds, Unit 4 Green Street, Lane Business Park Green St Lane, Ayr, KA8 8BE Tel: (01292) 260993 Fax: (01292) 260993

Highbury Design, 3 Catton Road, Arnold, Nottingham, NG5 7JD Tel: 0115-967 1188 E-mail: info@highburyblinds.co.uk

Jamieson's Blinds, 54 Exley Lane, Elland, West Yorkshire, HX5 0SW Tel: (01484) 402299 Fax: (01422) 377363

Jayem Blinds, 3 Scotter Road, Bournemouth, BH7 6LY Tel: (01202) 422525 Fax: (01202) 422525 E-mail: sales@jayemblinds.co.uk

▶ K W Curtain Designs, 59 Holt Drive, Loughborough, Leicestershire, LE11 3HZ Tel: (01509) 210585 E-mail: kwalmsley@kwdesigns.fsnet.co.uk

Macdougalls Blinds, 4 Wisteria Drive, Healing, Grimsby, South Humberside, DN41 7JB Tel: (01472) 887049 Fax: (01472) 887049

Manor Park Blinds Ltd, The Spinney, 5A Rectory Lane, Castle Bromwich, Birmingham, B36 9DH Tel: 0121-748 6900 Fax: 0121-747 9254

Prestige Conservatory Blinds, Unit 20 Birchbrook Industrial Park, Lynn Lane, Shenstone, Lichfield, Staffordshire, WS14 0DJ Tel: (01543) 483780 Fax: (01543) 483784

Regal Sterling Blinds, 16 Thirlmere, Great Ashby, Stevenage, Hertfordshire, SG1 6AH Tel: (01438) 238650 E-mail: gary@regalsterling.com

See More Blinds, 24 Church Square, Midsomer Norton, Radstock, BA3 2HX Tel: (01761) 411063 Fax: (01761) 411063 E-mail: seemoreblinds@yahoo.com

Shade Solutions Ltd, Oatley Trading Estate, Seymour Road, Kingswood, Bristol, BS15 1SD Tel: 0117-373 0599 Fax: 0117-330 9342 E-mail: sales@shadesolutions.co.uk

Sunset Blinds, Rugby House, Hinckley Road, Sapcote, Leicester, LE9 4FS Tel: (01455) 274927 Fax: (01455) 274948

Taylor Maid Blinds, The Engine House, The Close, Ardington, Wantage, Oxfordshire, OX12 8PT Tel: (01235) 831599 Fax: (01235) 831599

Trade Blinds, 104 Oak Road, Sittingbourne, Kent, ME10 3PR Tel: (01795) 428793

FIBRE BACKED ABRASIVE PRODUCTS

Ipc Fixings, 1 National Road, Hunslet Business Park, Leeds, LS10 1TD Tel: 0113-277 9444 Fax: 0113-277 9555

FIBRE BONDED CARPETS

Heckmondwike F B Ltd, PO Box 7, Liversedge, West Yorkshire, WF15 7XA Tel: (01924) 406161 Fax: (01924) 413613 E-mail: sales@heckmondwike-fb.co.uk

Rawson Carpets Ltd, Castlebank Mills, Portobello Road, Wakefield, West Yorkshire, WF1 5PS Tel: (01924) 382860 Fax: (01924) 290334 E-mail: sales@rawsoncarpets.co.uk

FIBRE CHANNEL CABLES

Amphenol Spectrastrip Ltd, Unit 21-23 Romsey Industrial Estate, Greatbridge Road, Romsey, Hampshire, SO51 0HR Tel: (01794) 517575 Fax: (01794) 516246 E-mail: info@spectra-strip.com

FIBRE CONCRETE REINFORCING

▶ Propex Concrete Systems, No. 9, Royal Court, Basil Close, Chesterfield, Derbyshire, S41 7SL Tel: 0845 5314078 Fax: (01246) 564201 E-mail: trevor.atkinson@propexinc.co.uk

FIBRE DRUMS

Fibre Drums Ltd, Abbeyway South, Vista Road, Haydock, St. Helens, Merseyside, WA11 0RW Tel: (01942) 722299 Fax: (01942) 271325 E-mail: sales@fdlgroup.co.uk

Fibrestar Drums Ltd, Redhouse Lane, Disley, Stockport, Cheshire, SK12 2NW Tel: (01663) 764141 Fax: (01633) 762967 E-mail: sales@fibrestar.co.uk

FIBRE FOAM OFFICE FURNITURE

New Concept Upholsterer, 70 Thomas Street, Tamworth, Staffordshire, B77 3PR Tel: (01827) 51414

White Grove Group plc, Central House, Halesfield 19, Telford, Shropshire, TF7 4QT Tel: (01952) 685300 Fax: (01952) 581612 E-mail: sales@whitegrove.co.uk

FIBRE GASKETS

Whitby & Chandler Ltd, Green Road, Penistone, Sheffield, S36 6PH Tel: (01226) 370380 Fax: (01226) 767138 E-mail: enquiries@whitby-chandler.co.uk

FIBRE OPTIC ASSEMBLY SERVICES

Laser 2000 UK Ltd, Britannia House, Denford Road, Ringstead, Kettering, Northamptonshire, NN14 4DF Tel: (01933) 461666 Fax: (01933) 461699 E-mail: sales@laser2000.co.uk

Servicepower Ltd, Rosse Works, Moorhead Lane, Shipley, West Yorkshire, BD18 4JH Tel: (01274) 785500 Fax: (01274) 785544 E-mail: sales@servicepower.ltd.uk

FIBRE OPTIC CABLE CONNECTIONS

Molex Premise Networks Ltd, Network House, Concorde Way, Fareham, Hampshire, PO15 5RL Tel: (01489) 572111 Fax: (01489) 559106 E-mail: sales@molexpn.co.uk

▶ Structured Lan, The Garage, Crag Lane, Beckwithshaw, Harrogate, North Yorkshire, HG3 1QA Tel: (01423) 508011 Fax: (01423) 508011 E-mail: structuredlan@btconnect.com

FIBRE OPTIC CABLE INSTALLATION CONTRACTORS

C M W Controls Ltd, Bryn Lane, Wrexham Industrial Estate, Wrexham, Clwyd, LL13 9UT Tel: (01978) 661516 Fax: (01978) 661626 E-mail: geoff.roberts@cmwcontrols.com

Electrical Installations North West Ltd, Lawsons Road, Thornton-Cleveleys, Lancashire, FY5 4PW Tel: (01253) 822626 Fax: (01253) 827846 E-mail: sales@einw.co.uk

Fibrecomm Solutions, 12 Devonshire Avenue, Long Eaton, Nottingham, NG10 2EP Tel: 0115-946 5777 Fax: 0115-946 5888 E-mail: enquiries@fibrecomm.co.uk

Lineartron Cabling Systems Ltd, Unit 5 Slader Business Park, Witney Road, Nuffield Industerial Estate, Poole, Dorset, BH17 0GP Tel: (01202) 672689 Fax: (01202) 672457 E-mail: sales@lineartron.co.uk

Pedler Robin, Empire Buildings, 47-49 Church Street, Stoke-on-Trent, ST4 1DQ Tel: (01782) 749749 Fax: (01782) 747840 E-mail: sales@sgbworldservice.com

Phoenix Optics UK Ltd, Unit B The Grange, Colesden, Bedford, MK44 3DB Tel: (01234) 376120 Fax: (01234) 376122 E-mail: sales@phoenixoptics.com

FIBRE OPTIC CABLE SPLICE PROTECTORS

Finish-Adapt Ltd, Unit 8 Hillmead Industrial Estate, Marshall Road, Swindon, SN5 5FZ Tel: (01793) 758720 Fax: (01793) 876059 E-mail: sales@finishadapt.com

FIBRE OPTIC CABLES

Abbey Surgical Repairs, Silver Wing Industrial Estate, Horatius Way, Croydon, CR0 4RU Tel: (020) 8688 8555 Fax: (020) 8688 8557 E-mail: info@abbeysurgical.com

Absolute Action Ltd, 6 Tonbridge Road, Maidstone, Kent, ME16 8RP Tel: (01622) 351000 Fax: (01622) 351001 E-mail: enquiries@absolute-action.com

Alker Optical Equipment Ltd, Alker House, 190 North Gate, New Basford, Nottingham, NG7 7FT Tel: 0115-942 0290 Fax: 0115-978 8190 E-mail: sales@alker.co.uk

B K A Solutions, Unit 13 Headley Park Area Ten, Woodley, Reading, RG5 4SW Tel: (0870) 2403586 Fax: (0870) 2403587 E-mail: sales@bka.co.uk

Brand Rex Ltd, Viewfield Industrial Estate, Glenrothes, Fife, KY6 2RS Tel: (01592) 772124 Fax: (01592) 775314 E-mail: loswald@brand-rex.com

Dunasfern Cable & Wire Suppliers, 24 Peverel Drive, Bletchley, Milton Keynes, MK1 1NW Tel: (01908) 647144 Fax: (01908) 270106 E-mail: dunasfern.sales@virgin.net

Hagemeyer Group, Unit 34 Minworth Industrial Park, Forge Lane, Sutton Coldfield, West Midlands, B76 1AH Tel: 0121-351 5222 Fax: 0121-351 4851 E-mail: sales@hageneyer.com

Mainframe Communications Ltd, Network House, Journeymans Way, Temple Farm Industrial Estate, Southend-On-Sea, SS2 5TF Tel: (01702) 443800 Fax: (01702) 443801 E-mail: sales@mainframecomms.co.uk

▶ Qing Cables Ltd, Malmesbury Road, Kingsditch Trading Estate, Cheltenham, Gloucestershire, GL51 9PL Tel: (01242) 224141 Fax: (01242) 224134 E-mail: enquire@qingcables.co.uk

FIBRE OPTIC CABLING EQUIPMENT

Metals Research Ltd, Newton Hall, Town Street, Newton, Cambridge, CB2 5PE Tel: (01223) 872822 Fax: (01223) 872983 E-mail: info@newtonhall.co.uk

FIBRE OPTIC CONNECTORS

Aci Solutions (Europe) Ltd, Boundary Road, Sturmer, Haverhill, Suffolk, CB9 7YH Tel: (01440) 712525 Fax: (01440) 718801 E-mail: sales@aci-solutions.net

Lemo U K Ltd, 12 North Street, Worthing, West Sussex, BN11 1DU Tel: (01903) 234543 Fax: (01903) 206231 E-mail: uk.office.services@lemo.com

Sumitomo Electric Europe Ltd, Unit 220 Centennial Park, Elstree, Hertfordshire, WD6 3SL Tel: (020) 8953 4489 Fax: (020) 8207 5950 E-mail: a.bayram@sumielectric.com

FIBRE OPTIC DATA TRANSMISSION DEVICES

▶ C Mac Microcircuits Ltd, South Denes, Great Yarmouth, Norfolk, NR30 3PX Tel: (01493) 856122 Fax: (01493) 858536 E-mail: KenTurrell@cmac.com

Greenwich Instruments, Meridian House, Park Road, Swanley, Kent, BR8 8AH Tel: (0870) 0505404 Fax: (0870) 0505405 E-mail: sales@greenwichinst.co.uk

FIBRE OPTIC FUSION SPLICERS

▶ Vytran UK Ltd, 8 Kew Court Pynes Hill, Rydon Lane, Exeter, EX2 5AZ Tel: (01392) 445777 Fax: (01392) 445009

FIBRE OPTIC INSPECTION

Cooknell Optronics Ltd, 48 Lynch Lane, Weymouth, Dorset, DT4 9DN Tel: (01305) 781567 Fax: (01305) 759648 E-mail: sales@cooknelloptronics.co.uk

FIBRE OPTIC LIGHT GUIDES

Image Optics Components, Harvey Road, Basildon, Essex, SS13 1ES Tel: (01268) 728477 Fax: (01268) 590445 E-mail: sales@image-optics.fsnet.co.uk

Par Opti Projects Ltd, 67 Stirling Road, London, W3 8DJ Tel: (020) 8896 2588 Fax: (020) 8896 2599 E-mail: paropti@aol.com

Ultrafine Technology Ltd, Unit 14 Brook Lane Business Centre, Brook Lane North, Brentford, Middlesex, TW8 0PP Tel: (020) 8569 9920 Fax: (020) 8569 9649 E-mail: sales@ultrafinetechnology.co.uk

Universal Fibre Optics (Old Co) Ltd, 6 Home Place, Coldstream, Berwickshire, TD12 4DT Tel: (01890) 883416 Fax: (01890) 883062 E-mail: info@universal-fibre-optics.com

FIBRE OPTIC LIGHT SOURCES

Absolute Action Ltd, 6 Tonbridge Road, Maidstone, Kent, ME16 8RP Tel: (01622) 351000 Fax: (01622) 351001 E-mail: enquiries@absolute-action.com

Fibre Optic Systems Ltd, Unit 127 Whitehall Industrial Estate, Whitehall Road, Leeds, LS12 5JB Tel: 0113-263 0633 Fax: 0113-263 8868 E-mail: sales@fibreopticsystems.co.uk

FIBRE OPTIC LIGHTING

Absolute Action Ltd, 6 Tonbridge Road, Maidstone, Kent, ME16 8RP Tel: (01622) 351000 Fax: (01622) 351001 E-mail: enquiries@absolute-action.com

Fibre Optic Systems Ltd, Unit 127 Whitehall Industrial Estate, Whitehall Road, Leeds, LS12 5JB Tel: 0113-263 0633 Fax: 0113-263 8868 E-mail: sales@fibreopticsystems.co.uk

Green Island Ltd, The Lighthouse, Eastwood Road, Penryn, Cornwall, TR10 8LA Tel: (01326) 377775 Fax: (01326) 377773 E-mail: ianbibby@greenisland.co.uk

Par Opti Projects Ltd, 67 Stirling Road, London, W3 8DJ Tel: (020) 8896 2588 Fax: (020) 8896 2599 E-mail: paropti@aol.com

▶ Starscape, 7 Main Street, Lowick, Berwick-upon-Tweed, TD15 2UD Tel: (01289) 388399 E-mail: info@starceiling.co.uk

FIBRE OPTIC NETWORKS

Advance Communications, Business Development Centre, Main Avenue, Treforest Indust Estate, Pontypridd, Mid Glamorgan, CF37 5UR Tel: (01443) 843555 Fax: (01443) 841449

FIBRE OPTIC PULLING EQUIPMENT

Metals Research Ltd, Newton Hall, Town Street, Newton, Cambridge, CB2 5PE Tel: (01223) 872822 Fax: (01223) 872983 E-mail: info@newtonhall.co.uk

FIBRE OPTIC ROTARY JOINTS

Metals Research Ltd, Newton Hall, Town Street, Newton, Cambridge, CB2 5PE Tel: (01223) 872822 Fax: (01223) 872983 E-mail: info@newtonhall.co.uk

FIBRE OPTIC SENSORS

Computer Optical Products, 45 Leaver Road, Henley-On-Thames, Oxfordshire, RG9 1UW Tel: (01491) 412055 Fax: (01491) 413006 E-mail: sales@sensortronic.co.uk
Sensa, Gamma House, Enterprise Road, Chilworth Science Park, Southampton, SO16 7NS Tel: (023) 8076 5500 Fax: (023) 8076 5501
Sensopart UK Ltd, Unit G8 The Arch, 48-52 Floodgate Street, Birmingham, B5 5SL Tel: 0121-772 5104 Fax: 0121-772 5126 E-mail: info@sensopart.com
▶ Vydas International Marketing, Swan House, Passfield Business Centre, Lynchborough Road, Passfield, Liphook, Hampshire, GU30 7SB Tel: (01428) 751822 Fax: (01428) 751833 E-mail: info@vydas.co.uk
Wenglor Sensoric, Suite B Secondfloor Aspen House, 15 Medlicott Close, Corby, Northamptonshire, NN18 9NF Tel: (01536) 747299 Fax: (01536) 742301 E-mail: info.uk@wenglor.de

FIBRE OPTIC TEST EQUIPMENT

Anritsu Ltd, 200 Capability Green, Luton, LU1 3LU Tel: (01582) 433200 Fax: (01582) 731303 E-mail: sales@anritsu.co.uk
G C H Test & Computer Services Ltd, I S C House 5 Progress Business Centre, Whittle Parkway, Slough, SL1 6DQ Tel: (01628) 559980 Fax: (01628) 559990 E-mail: sales@gch-services.com

FIBRE OPTICS COMMUNICATION SYSTEMS

Barkers International Communication Ltd, Barkers Lane, Bedford, MK41 9TR Tel: (01234) 327772 Fax: (01234) 325526 E-mail: richard@barkers-int.co.uk
Black Box Network Services Ltd, 464 Basingstoke Road, Reading, RG2 0BG Tel: 0118-965 5000 Fax: 0118-965 5001 E-mail: info@blackbox.co.uk
Cablepoint Ltd, Phoenix House, Amsterdam Road, Sutton Fields Industrial Estate, Hull, HU7 0XP Tel: (01482) 837400 Fax: (01482) 839651 E-mail: sales@cablepoint.co.uk
Nessco Services Ltd, Discovery House Arnhall Business, Park, Westhill, Aberdeenshire, AB32 6FG Tel: (01355) 266900 Fax: (01224) 428401 E-mail: sales@nessco.co.uk
Optilan, Common Lane Industrial Estate, Kenilworth, Warwickshire, CV8 2EL Tel: (01926) 864999 Fax: (01926) 851818
Preformed Line Products GB Ltd, East Portway, Andover, Hampshire, SP10 3LH Tel: (01264) 366234 Fax: (01264) 356714 E-mail: sales@preformed.com
Splice (UK) Ltd, The Coach House, Whitehall Road, Drighlington, Bradford, West Yorkshire, BD11 1LN Tel: 0113-285 2536 Fax: 0113-285 2741 E-mail: info@spliceuk.com

FIBRE OPTICS COMMUNICATION SYSTEMS CONSULTANTS OR DESIGNERS

▶ Lucid Optical Services Ltd, Lucid Training Centre, Garsdale, Sedbergh, Cumbria, LA10 5PE Tel: (01539) 621219 Fax: (01539) 621205 E-mail: annette@lucidos.co.uk
M C I, Reading International Business Park, Reading, RG2 6DA Tel: 0118-905 5000 Fax: 0118-905 5711
Mainframe Communications Ltd, Network House, Journeymans Way, Temple Farm Industrial Estate, Southend-On-Sea, SS2 5TF Tel: (01702) 443800 Fax: (01702) 443801 E-mail: sales@mainframecomms.co.uk

FIBRE OPTICS COMPONENT/ EQUIPMENT/INSTRUMENT DISTRIBUTORS OR AGENTS

▶ Auriga Europe plc, Davy Avenue, Knowlhill, Milton Keynes, MK5 8ND Tel: (0870) 1219990 Fax: (0870) 1219991 E-mail: sales@aurigaeurope.com
B F I Optilas Ltd, Mill Square, Featherstone Road, Wolverton Mill, Milton Keynes, MK12 5ZY Tel: (01908) 326326 Fax: (01908) 221110 E-mail: info.uk@bfioptilas.com
Communication Centre (International) Ltd, 60 Riverside I I I, Sir Thomas Longley Road, Strood, Rochester, Kent, ME2 4BH Tel: (01634) 295295 Fax: (01634) 723895 E-mail: enquiries@commscentre.com

FIBRE OPTICS COMPONENT/ EQUIPMENT/INSTRUMENT MANUFRS

Aci Solutions (Europe) Ltd, Boundary Road, Sturmer, Haverhill, Suffolk, CB9 7YH Tel: (01440) 712525 Fax: (01440) 718801 E-mail: sales@aci-solutions.net
ADC Communications (UK) Ltd, Runnings Road, Kingsditch Trading Estate, Cheltenham, Gloucestershire, GL51 9NQ Tel: (01242) 264400 Fax: (01242) 264488 E-mail: christianname.surname@adckrone.com
Atlantic Fibre Optics, Lynch Green, Hethersett, Norwich, NR9 3JU Tel: (01603) 811994 Fax: (01603) 810395 E-mail: info@atlanticfo.co.uk
Finish-Adapt Ltd, Unit 8 Hillmead Industrial Estate, Marshall Road, Swindon, SN5 5FZ Tel: (01793) 758720 Fax: (01793) 876059 E-mail: sales@finishadapt.com
Image Optics Components, Harvey Road, Basildon, Essex, SS13 1ES Tel: (01268) 728477 Fax: (01268) 590445 E-mail: sales@image-optics.fsnet.co.uk
Keymed Ltd, Keymed House, Stock Road, Southend-on-Sea, SS2 5QH Tel: (01702) 616333 Fax: (01702) 465677 E-mail: keymed@keymed.co.uk
Lambda Photometrics Ltd, Lambda House, Batford Mill, Lower Luton Road, Harpenden, Hertfordshire, AL5 5BZ Tel: (01582) 764334 Fax: (01582) 712084 E-mail: info@lambdaphoto.co.uk
Majortek Components Ltd, Netley Firs, Kanes Hill, Southampton, SO19 6AJ Tel: (023) 8040 5276 Fax: (023) 8040 2873 E-mail: sales@majortek.co.uk
Perkin Elmer, Sorbus House, Mulberry Business Park, Wokingham, Berkshire, RG41 2GY Tel: 0118-977 3003 Fax: 0118-977 3493 E-mail: sales@perkinelmer.com
Tech Optics Ltd, 6 Tannery Road, Tonbridge, Kent, TN9 1RF Tel: (01732) 770466 Fax: (01732) 770476 E-mail: sales@techoptics.com

FIBRE OPTICS PATCHCORDS/ PIGTAILS

Alker Optical Equipment Ltd, Alker House, 190 North Gate, New Basford, Nottingham, NG7 7FT Tel: 0115-942 0290 Fax: 0115-978 8190 E-mail: sales@alker.co.uk
Cooknell Optronics Ltd, 48 Lynch Lane, Weymouth, Dorset, DT4 9DN Tel: (01305) 781567 Fax: (01305) 759648 E-mail: sales@cooknelloptronics.co.uk

FIBRE OPTICS SPLICING ENCLOSURES/ACCESSORIES

Finish-Adapt Ltd, Unit 8 Hillmead Industrial Estate, Marshall Road, Swindon, SN5 5FZ Tel: (01793) 758720 Fax: (01793) 876059 E-mail: sales@finishadapt.com

FIBRE OPTICS SYSTEMS MANUFRS

L B Technologies Ltd, 42 Medley Road, Rayne, Braintree, Essex, CM77 6TQ Tel: (01376) 345041 E-mail: bullimores@aol.com
MOOG Components Group Ltd, 30 Suttons Park Avenue, Suttons Business Park, Reading, RG6 1AW Tel: 0118-966 6044 Fax: 0118-966 6524 E-mail: mcg@moog.com
Point Source Ltd, Mitchell Point, Ensign Way, Hamble, Southampton, SO31 4RF Tel: (023) 8074 4500 Fax: (023) 8074 4501 E-mail: sales@point-source.com
Sanmor Communications Ltd, 37 The Drive, Ilford, Essex, IG1 3HA Tel: (020) 8554 7773 Fax: (020) 8554 7787

FIBRE OR COIR OR COCONUT MATS

Designer Logo Matting, 56 Southbury Road, Enfield, Middlesex, EN1 1YB Tel: (020) 8342 2020 Fax: (020) 8342 2021

FIBRE OR FIBROUS CEMENT BUILDING PRODUCTS

Fibre Technology Ltd, Brookhill Road, Pinxton, Nottingham, NG16 6NT Tel: (01773) 864205 Fax: (01773) 580287 E-mail: sales@fibretech.com
Hodkin & Jones (Sheffield) Ltd, Callywhite Lane, Dronfield, Derbyshire, S18 2XP Tel: (01246) 290890 Fax: (01246) 290292

FIBRE TIP PENS

Kuretake UK Ltd, 14 Broad Ground Road, Redditch, Worcestershire, B98 8YP Tel: (01527) 523799 Fax: (01527) 523815 E-mail: zig33uk@kuretake.ne.jp

FIBRE WASTE, TEXTILE, *See Textile Waste etc*

FIBREBOARD

Diamond Corrugated Cases Ltd, 12-13 Pennyburn Industrial Estate, Londonderry, BT48 0LU Tel: (028) 7126 2957 Fax: (028) 7126 7094 E-mail: mail@diamondcorr.com
Europanel UK Ltd, 1 Gerrards Place, East Gillibrands, Skelmersdale, Lancashire, WN8 9SU Tel: (01695) 731033 Fax: (01695) 727489 E-mail: europaneluk@btconnect.co.uk
Montague L Meyer (Pension Trustee) Ltd, Rippleway Wharf, Barking, Essex, IG11 0DU Tel: (020) 8477 8000 Fax: (020) 8594 8255 E-mail: info@mlmuk.com

FIBREBOARD BOXES/CASES/ CONTAINERS

▶ Armstrong Packaging Ltd, Baden-Powell Road, Kirkton Industrial Estate, Arbroath, Angus, DD11 3LS Tel: (01241) 430000 Fax: (01241) 431122 E-mail: admin@apbox.co.uk
▶ Bourne Fibre Manufacturing Ltd, The Chapel, The Street, Brockdish, Diss, Norfolk, IP21 4JY Tel: (01379) 668743 Fax: (01379) 669032 E-mail: hopeatthechapel@aol.com
Clifford Packaging Ltd, Bradbourne Drive, Tilbrook, Milton Keynes, MK7 8AQ Tel: (0870) 1226333 Fax: (01908) 270429 E-mail: enquiries@cliffordpackaging.com
D S Smith, Fordham Road, Newmarket, Suffolk, CB8 7TX Tel: (01638) 722100 Fax: (01638) 722101
Excelsior Rotational Moulding Ltd, Ferngrove Mills, Rochdale Old Road, Bury, Lancashire, BL9 7LS Tel: 0161-797 0855 Fax: 0161-763 1614 E-mail: sales@excelsior-ltd.co.uk
Gough Packaging Ltd, 49 Whiffler Road, Norwich, NR3 2AW Tel: (01603) 423860 Fax: (01603) 485000 E-mail: leshgough@aol.com
Kappa Corrugated UK, London Road, Purfleet, Essex, RM19 1QY Tel: (01708) 861776 Fax: (01708) 861910
Northern Box & Packaging Co. Ltd, Moss Bridge Mill, Blackburn Road, Darwen, Lancashire, BB3 0AJ Tel: (01254) 702375 Fax: (01254) 873709
▶ Trench Ltd, Unit 5, C M T Industrial Estate, Broadwell Road, Oldbury, West Midlands, B69 4BQ Tel: 0121-544 7011 Fax: 0121-544 7721

FIBREBOARD BOXES/CASES/ CONTAINERS, VULCANISED

▶ Bourne Fibre Manufacturing Ltd, The Chapel, The Street, Brockdish, Diss, Norfolk, IP21 4JY Tel: (01379) 668743 Fax: (01379) 669032 E-mail: hopeatthechapel@aol.com

FIBREBOARD DRUMS

F D L Packaging Group, Abbeyway South, Vista Road, Haydock, St. Helens, Merseyside, WA11 0RW Tel: (01942) 722299 Fax: (01942) 271325 E-mail: sales@fdlgroup.co.uk
Fibre Drums Ltd, Abbeyway South, Vista Road, Haydock, St. Helens, Merseyside, WA11 0RW Tel: (01942) 722299 Fax: (01942) 271325 E-mail: sales@fdlgroup.co.uk
Fibrestar Drums Ltd, Redhouse Lane, Disley, Stockport, Cheshire, SK12 2NW Tel: (01663) 764141 Fax: (01633) 762967 E-mail: sales@fibrestar.co.uk

FIBREBOARD OR HARDBOARD VARNISHING

Stock Associates Print Finishers Ltd, Unit 2-3, Perry Way, Witham, Essex, CM8 3SX Tel: (01376) 500123 Fax: (01376) 501744 E-mail: sales@stock.uk.com

FIBREGLASS ACCESS CHAMBER COVERS

Danetech Glass Fibre Mnfrs, 2b The CR, Witney, Oxfordshire, OX28 2EL Tel: (01327) 311011 Fax: (01327) 300216 E-mail: sales@danetech.co.uk

FIBREGLASS BUILDING OR INDUSTRIAL HOUSING

1st Choice Superseal Ltd, 688 Aldridge Road, Great Barr, Birmingham, B44 8NJ Tel: 0121-366 6782 Fax: 0121-366 6624
▶ Arbory Group Ltd, Holker Business Centre, Burnley Road, Colne, Lancashire, BB8 8EG Tel: (0870) 0802322 Fax: (0870) 0802325 E-mail: sales@arborygroup.co.uk
Image Composites Ltd, Govan Road, Fenton Industrial Estate, Fenton, Stoke-on-Trent, ST4 2RS Tel: (01782) 411611 Fax: (01782) 411888 E-mail: info@imageplastics.co.uk
Octaveward Ltd, Balle Street Mill, Balle Street, Darwen, Lancashire, BB3 2AZ Tel: (01254) 773300 Fax: (01254) 773950 E-mail: info@octaveward.com
Prima Plastics & Associates Ltd, London Road, Bagshot, Surrey, GU19 5HZ Tel: (01276) 453849 Fax: (01276) 453849 E-mail: sales@primaplastics.co.uk
Quinshield Ltd, Unit 27-28, Capel Hendre Industrial Estate, Ammanford, Dyfed, SA18 3SJ Tel: (01269) 832220 Fax: (01269) 832221 E-mail: info@quinshield.com
Somersham G R P Mouldings, Somersham Road, Little Blakenham, Ipswich, IP8 4NF Tel: (01473) 831333 Fax: (01473) 832466
Tamworth Glass Fibre, Pooley Lane, Pooley Hall Farmhouse, Polesworth, Tamworth, Staffordshire, B78 1JA Tel: (01827) 331010 Fax: (01827) 330027 E-mail: m.hopkins267@ntlworld.com

FIBREGLASS BUILDING OR STRUCTURAL PRODUCTS

1st Choice Superseal Ltd, 688 Aldridge Road, Great Barr, Birmingham, B44 8NJ Tel: 0121-366 6782 Fax: 0121-366 6624
▶ B & N Plastics, Unit 5-6 Haslam Business Centre, Haslam Street, Bolton, BL3 6LB Tel: (01204) 529112 Fax: (01204) 529112 E-mail: sales@bnplastics.co.uk
Castle Mouldings, 1 Dew Farm, Church Lane, Peasmarsh, Rye, East Sussex, TN31 6XD Tel: (01797) 230734 E-mail: castlemouldings@hotmail.com
Croy Glass Fibre Products, 3 Lower Dartmouth Street, Birmingham, B9 4LG Tel: 0121-773 8714 Fax: 0121-773 8714
W.L. Cunliffe (Southport) Ltd, Gratton Place, Skelmersdale, Lancashire, WN8 9UE Tel: (01695) 711800 Fax: (01695) 711811 E-mail: sales@wlcunliffe.com
Euroresins UK Ltd, 2 First Avenue, Halstead, Essex, CO9 2EX Tel: (01787) 472300 Fax: (01787) 473686
Fibre Glass Technology, Wellington House, Pollard St East, Manchester, M40 7FS Tel: 0161-273 1273 Fax: 0161-273 1273
Insulation Ltd, 6 Kerse Road, Stirling, FK7 7RW Tel: (01786) 451170 Fax: (01786) 451245
Logical Ltd, Unit 5 Avis Way, Newhaven, East Sussex, BN9 0DS Tel: (01273) 514146 Fax: (01273) 514146 E-mail: enquiries@logical-grp.co.uk
Neptune Glassfibre Mouldings, Old Ice Factory, Rolle Street, Barnstaple, Devon, EX31 1JP Tel: (01271) 374722 Fax: (01271) 371339
Neptune Glassfibre Mouldings, Old Ice Factory, Rolle Street, Barnstaple, Devon, EX31 1JP Tel: (01271) 374722 Fax: (01271) 371339
Octaveward Ltd, Balle Street Mill, Balle Street, Darwen, Lancashire, BB3 2AZ Tel: (01254) 773300 Fax: (01254) 773950 E-mail: info@octaveward.com
Quinshield Ltd, Unit 27-28, Capel Hendre Industrial Estate, Ammanford, Dyfed, SA18 3SJ Tel: (01269) 832220 Fax: (01269) 832221 E-mail: info@quinshield.com
Ralph Plastics, Unit 12b Macmerry Industrial Estate, Tranent, East Lothian, EH33 1RD Tel: (01875) 615247 Fax: (01875) 615247 E-mail: trishralph@aol.com

FIBREGLASS CANOPIES

▶ B & N Plastics, Unit 5-6 Haslam Business Centre, Haslam Street, Bolton, BL3 6LB Tel: (01204) 529112 Fax: (01204) 529112 E-mail: sales@bnplastics.co.uk
Metafab Solutions, Marine Shed, Cu Lighting Estate, Broadwell, Coleford, Gloucestershire, GL16 7EG Tel: (01594) 839220 Fax: (01594) 827878 E-mail: sales@metafabs.com
Multitex G R P, Unit 5 Dolphin Industrial Estate, Salisbury, SP1 2NB Tel: (01722) 332139 Fax: (01722) 338458 E-mail: sales@multitex.co.uk
Stuart Pease Fibreglass Ltd, Unit 1 Taylors Close, Parkgate, Rotherham, South Yorkshire, S62 6NW Tel: (01709) 527761 Fax: (01709) 522147 E-mail: stuartpeaseltd@btinternet.com

FIBREGLASS DOOR CANOPY MOULDINGS

▶ B & N Plastics, Unit 5-6 Haslam Business Centre, Haslam Street, Bolton, BL3 6LB Tel: (01204) 529112 Fax: (01204) 529112 E-mail: sales@bnplastics.co.uk

FIBREGLASS DOOR CANOPY MOULDINGS – *continued*

▶ Hurst Plastics Ltd, 1 Kingston Int Business Park, Somerden Road, Hull, HU9 5PE Tel: (01482) 790790 Fax: (01482) 790690 E-mail: sales@hurst-plastics.co.uk

Morrison Glass Fibre, Rose Hill Works, Rose Hill, Denton, Manchester, M34 3ZA Tel: 0161-336 0632 Fax: 0161-335 9852

FIBREGLASS FIRE BLANKETS OR CURTAINS

▶ C P Covers Ltd, 18 Hanson Close, Middleton, Manchester, M24 2HD Tel: 0161-654 9396 Fax: 0161-654 6017 E-mail: cpcovers@btopenworld.com

Culimetea Saveguard Ltd, Tame Valley Mill, Wainwright Street, Dukinfield, Cheshire, SK16 5NB Tel: 0161-344 2484 Fax: 0161-344 2486E-mail: sales@culimetea-saveguard.com

Ic International Ltd, Gower Street Trading Estate, St. Georges, Telford, Shropshire, TF2 9HW Tel: (01952) 620206 Fax: (01952) 620456 E-mail: sales@ic-international.com

Sheffield Ceilings S E Ltd, 165 Bow Road, Wateringbury, Maidstone, Kent, ME18 5EA Tel: (01622) 814477 Fax: (01622) 813555 E-mail: sheffield.ceilings@btinternet.com

Westford Plastics & Engineering Ltd, Westford, Wellington, Somerset, TA21 0DU Tel: (01823) 662377 Fax: (01823) 663238 E-mail: l_cross@msn.com

FIBREGLASS FLAT ROOFING MATERIALS

Elliott Bros Ltd, Millbank Wharf, Northam, Southampton, SO14 5AG Tel: (023) 8022 6852 Fax: (023) 8023 2041 E-mail: donnac@elliott-brothers.co.uk

▶ Stormcheck, 26a Bondgate Green, Ripon, North Yorkshire, HG4 1QW Tel: 01765 692053 Fax: 01765 692053 E-mail: sales@stormcheck.co.uk

FIBREGLASS INSULATION, *See headings under Insulating*

FIBREGLASS LADDERS

▶ LFI Ladder & Fencing Industries (Newent) Ltd, Horsefair Lane, Newent, Glos, GL18 1RP Tel: (01531) 820541 Fax: (01531) 821161 E-mail: sales@lfi-ladders.co.uk

Lyte Ladders & Towers, Wind Road, Ystradgynlais, Swansea, SA9 1AF Tel: (01639) 846816 Fax: (01639) 841541 E-mail: sales@lyteladders.co.uk

FIBREGLASS MOULDINGS, *See also headings for particular types*

A B Terratec Ltd, Units 2-2a, Phoebe La Industrial Estate, Halifax, West Yorkshire, HX3 9EX Tel: (01422) 354469 Fax: (01422) 354460 E-mail: sales@plantpots.co.uk

A C Plastic Industries Ltd, Armstrong Road, Basingstoke, Hampshire, RG24 8NU Tel: (01256) 329334 Fax: (01256) 817862 E-mail: sales@ac-plastics.com

A V E Composites, Compstall Mill, Compstall, Stockport, Cheshire, SK6 5HN Tel: 0161-427 1552 Fax: 0161-426 0016 E-mail: sales@avecomposites.co.uk

Ace Fibreglass Mouldings Repairs, Castletown Way, Sherborne, Dorset, DT9 4EA Tel: (01935) 816437 E-mail: sales@fibreglass.com

▶ Amman Mouldings, Dinefwr House, Pantyffynnon Road, Ammanford, Dyfed, SA18 3HL Tel: (01269) 851603 Fax: (01269) 851603

▶ Andream Car Component Mnfrs, 12 Griston Road, Watton, Thetford, Norfolk, IP25 6DL Tel: (01953) 884176 Fax: (01953) 884176 E-mail: admin@addream.co.uk

Anglian Developments Ltd, School Lane, Neatishead, Norwich, NR12 8BU Tel: (01692) 630808 Fax: (01692) 631591 E-mail: angdev@paston.co.uk

Aquafibre Mouldings Ltd, Wendover Road, Rackheath Industrial Estate, Rackheath, Norwich, NR13 6LH Tel: (01603) 720651 Fax: (01603) 720654 E-mail: info@aquafibre.co.uk

Artistic Solutions Ltd, Coventry Road, Burbage, Hinckley, Leicestershire, LE10 2HL Tel: (01455) 634742 Fax: (01455) 633543

Austin Roberts, Tarran Way South, Tarran Industrial Estate, Wirral, Merseyside, CH46 4UB Tel: 0151-678 6088 Fax: 0151-678 9448 E-mail: austin.roberts@virgin.net

Aviation Enterprises Ltd, Membury Airfield, Lambourn, Hungerford, Berkshire, RG17 7TJ Tel: (01488) 72224 Fax: (01488) 72224 E-mail: sales@aviationenterprises.co.uk

B B Beresford, Goods Road, Belper, Derbyshire, DE56 1UU Tel: (01773) 825959 Fax: (01773) 821213 E-mail: beresford@btconnect.com

B P Marine, 11 Durham Road, Basildon, Essex, SS15 6PH Tel: (01268) 541737 Fax: (01268) 541737 E-mail: bpmarine@blueyonder.co.uk

B S Fibre Glass Moulding, 1 Carloggas, St. Columb Major Industrial Estate, St. Columb, Cornwall, TR9 6SF Tel: (01637) 880700 Fax: (01637) 880056 E-mail: enquiries@bspanelvanconversions.gbr.fm

Birmingham Glass Fibre Mouldings, 5 Weston Works, Weston Lane, Birmingham, B11 3RP Tel: 0121-708 1400 Fax: 0121-707 5312 E-mail: info@birminghamglassfibre.co.uk

Broadfield Plastics Ltd, Foxcroft Street, Littleborough, Lancashire, OL15 8LB Tel: (01706) 378636 Fax: (01706) 377131 E-mail: sales@broadfieldplastics.co.uk

Broadwater Mouldings Ltd, Denham Site, Horham Road, Denham, Eye, Suffolk, IP21 5DQ Tel: (01379) 384145 Fax: (01379) 384150 E-mail: info@broadwater.co.uk

Camellia Contracts, Unit 3 & 10, Walronds Park, Isle Brewers, Taunton, Somerset, TA3 6QP Tel: (01460) 281848 Fax: (01460) 281868

Capvond Plastics Ltd, 32 Welbeck Road, Glasgow, G53 7SD Tel: 0141-876 9000 Fax: 0141-876 4123 E-mail: office@capvond.co.uk

Cheltenham Laminating Company Ltd, Unit 10, Bamfurlong Indust Park, Staverton, Cheltenham, Gloucestershire, GL51 6SX Tel: (01452) 713098 Fax: 01452 715114 E-mail: murray.derek@sky.com

Christian Day, 2 Phoenix Building, Rushock Trading Estate, Rushock, Droitwich, Worcestershire, WR9 0NR Tel: (01299) 250385 Fax: (01299) 250335 E-mail: sales@christianday.co.uk

Clarke & Spears International Ltd, Knaphill Nursery, Barrs Lane, Knaphill, Woking, Surrey, GU21 2JW Tel: (01483) 485800 Fax: (01483) 485801 E-mail: sales@clarkandspears.co.uk

Cobham Composites Ltd, Davey House, Gelders Ha, Shepshed, Loughborough, Leicestershire, LE12 9NH Tel: (01509) 504541 Fax: (01509) 507563

Conbury Consultants Ltd, Bowcombe Business Park, Bowcombe Road, Newport, Isle Of Wight, PO30 3HZ Tel: (01983) 532727 Fax: (01983) 532727

Consort Glass Fibre, Brooke End Farm Buildings, Portleys Lane, Drayton Bassett, Tamworth, Staffordshire, B78 2AD Tel: (01827) 283775 Fax: (01827) 283775

Croy Glass Fibre Products, 3 Lower Dartmouth Street, Birmingham, B9 4LG Tel: 0121-773 8714 Fax: 0121-773 8714

Curley Specialised Mouldings In Group, Weald House, Pattenden Lane, Marden, Tonbridge, Kent, TN12 9QJ Tel: (01622) 833181 E-mail: info@curleyuk.com

Custom Mouldings Ltd, Woodside House, Plaistow Road Dunsfold, Godalming, Surrey, GU8 4PG Tel: (01483) 200492 Fax: 01483 200504

D J Sportscars International Ltd, 2 Edinburgh Place, Harlow, Essex, CM20 2DJ Tel: (01279) 442661 Fax: (01279) 434956 E-mail: post@daxcars.co.uk

Darjon Mouldings, 7 Dock Road, Tilbury, Essex, RM18 7DB Tel: (01375) 857505 Fax: (01375) 857505 E-mail: info@darjon-mouldings.co.uk

Davand Plastics Ltd, Units 33/34, Mill St East, Dewsbury, West Yorkshire, WF12 9AH Tel: (01924) 466248 Fax: (01924) 430148

Derby Laminates, 1 The Old Boatyard, Church Broughton Lane, Foston, Derby, DE65 5PW Tel: (01283) 521183 Fax: (01283) 521183

▶ Droitwich Glass Fibre Mouldings Ltd, Hangar 5, Long Lane, Throckmorton, Pershore, Worcestershire, WR10 2JH Tel: (01386) 555787 Fax: (01386) 555748 E-mail: glassfibres@btconnect.com

E & F Composites Ltd, Graythorp Industrial Estate, Hartlepool, Cleveland, TS25 2DF Tel: (01429) 272356 Fax: (01429) 861571 E-mail: sales@eandf-composites.co.uk

Eiger (UK) Ltd, Unit 12, Landsdown Industrial Estate, Cheltenham, Gloucestershire, GL51 8PL Tel: (01242) 245678 Fax: (01242) 224643 E-mail: valform@aol.com

Enalon Ltd, Vale Rise, Tonbridge, Kent, TN9 1RR Tel: (01732) 358500 Fax: (01732) 770463 E-mail: office@enalon.co.uk

Express Composites Group Ltd, 8 Beccles Road, Loddon, Norwich, NR14 6JQ Tel: (01508) 528000 Fax: (01508) 528764 E-mail: sales@ex-pressplastics.com

Fibaform Products Ltd, 22a Caton Road, Lansil Industrial Estate, Lancaster, LA1 3PQ Tel: (01524) 60182 Fax: (01524) 389829 E-mail: info@fibaform.co.uk

Fibre Glass Specialists, 31 Ringstead Road, London, SE6 2BU Tel: (020) 8461 0146 Fax: (020) 8698 8639 E-mail: patriciabroug@aol.com

▶ Fibreon, Unit 2 Dadsford Bridge Industrial Estate, Plant Street, Stourbridge, West Midlands, DY8 5SY Tel: (01384) 262211 Fax: (01384) 262211

Fibretex Mouldings, Waterloo Road, Pudsey, West Yorkshire, LS28 8DQ Tel: 0113-236 1094 Fax: 0113-255 5345

Fi-Glass Developments Ltd, Station Road, Edenbridge, Kent, TN8 6EB Tel: (01732) 863465 Fax: (01732) 867287 E-mail: sales@fi-glass.co.uk

G Helson Patterns Ltd, Riverside Works, South Street, Sherborne, Dorset, DT9 3NH Tel: (01935) 813246 Fax: (01935) 813246

G R P Fabrications, Unit 12 Jubilee Industrial Estate, Ashington, Northumberland, NE63 8UB Tel: (01670) 811800 Fax: (01670) 811800 E-mail: info@grpfabrications.com

G R P Mouldings (Brightlingsea), Tower Street, Brightlingsea, Colchester, CO7 0AW Tel: (01206) 302387

G & T Plastics, Unit 37 Lythalls La Industrial Estate, Lythalls Lane, Coventry, CV6 6FL Tel: (024) 7663 7983 Fax: (024) 7663 7983

Galloway Boats & Mouldings Ltd, Culdoach Road, Tongland, Kirkcudbright, DG6 4LU Tel: (01557) 331973 Fax: (01557) 331978 E-mail: ian.carsen@talk21.com

Glasmaster Ltd, 20 Enterprise Park, Piddlehinton, Dorchester, Dorset, DT2 7UA Tel: (01305) 848758 Fax: (01305) 848942 E-mail: dickgain@aol.com

Grantura Plastics Ltd, Unit 10 Hoo Hill Industrial Estate, Bispham Road, Blackpool, FY3 7HJ Tel: (01253) 392058 Fax: (01253) 302207

▶ Haven Industries Ltd, 5 Allington Lane, Fair Oak, Eastleigh, Hampshire, SO50 7DA Tel: (023) 8069 5544 Fax: 01489 89090 E-mail: ralphybruce.@hotmail.com

Hepworth Composites, Pollard Moor, Padiham, Burnley, Lancashire, BB12 7JR Tel: (01282) 683444 Fax: (01282) 683445 E-mail: ann.booth@hepworth.co.uk

Hippo Composites Ltd, Maserati House, Gelderd Road, Leeds, LS12 1AS Tel: 0113-279 4144 Fax: 0113-279 7935 E-mail: sales@widdsigns.co.uk

Hodkin & Jones (Sheffield) Ltd, Callywhite Lane, Dronfield, Derbyshire, S18 2XP Tel: (01246) 290890 Fax: (01246) 290292 E-mail: info@hodkin-jones.co.uk

▶ Innovation Mouldings, Unit 2 Axis Park, Fort Fareham Industrial Site, Fareham, Hampshire, PO14 1FD Tel: (01329) 234848 Fax: (01329) 234848 E-mail: innovationmouldings@tiscali.co.uk

Jetmarine Ltd, 1 National Trading Estate, Bramhall Moor Lane, Hazel Grove, Stockport, Cheshire, SK7 5AA Tel: 0161-487 1648 Fax: 0161-483 7820 E-mail: sales@jetmarine.co.uk

K N G Developments, North East Sector, Bournemouth Int Airport, Hurn, Christchurch, Dorset, BH23 6NE Tel: (07074) 581856 Fax: (01202) 581856 E-mail: keith.gilson@btinternet.com

▶ Kinpars Industrial Plastics Ltd, Whitlaw Indust Estate, Lauder, Berwickshire, TD2 6QA Tel: (01578) 718855 Fax: (01578) 718844 E-mail: admin@kinpars.co.uk

Lam Plas Durham Ltd, Pont Factory, Pont Lane, Leadgate, Consett, County Durham, DH8 6LA Tel: (01207) 502474 Fax: (01207) 500407 E-mail: jimdeath@lamplas.co.uk

Latches Ltd, 24 Hebden Road, Scunthorpe, South Humberside, DN15 8DT Tel: (01724) 270660 Fax: (01724) 271750

Logical Ltd, Unit 5 Avis Way, Newhaven, East Sussex, BN9 0DS Tel: (01273) 514146 Fax: (01273) 514146 E-mail: enquiries@logical-grp.co.uk

M J Fry Ltd, 1-2 Allens Lane, Poole, Dorset, BH16 5DA Tel: (01202) 622863 Fax: (01202) 624127

Marchant Manufacturing Co. Ltd, Piperell Way, Haverhill, Suffolk, CB9 8QW Tel: (01440) 705351 Fax: (01440) 762593 E-mail: sales@marchant.co.uk

Marine & Industrial Plastics Ltd, Unit D/1, Segensworth Business Centre, Segensworth Road, Fareham, Hampshire, PO15 5RQ Tel: (01329) 847443 Fax: (01329) 847451 E-mail: sales@mipltd.co.uk

▶ Martek Composites, Park Works, Park Road, Crosland Moor, Huddersfield, HD4 5DD Tel: (01484) 431527 Fax: (01484) 431522 E-mail: enquiries@martek-composites.co.uk

Medway Fibre-Glass Ltd, 8 Trinity Trading Estate, Tribune Drive, Sittingbourne, Kent, ME10 2PG Tel: (01795) 435535 E-mail: medwayfibreglass@btconnect.com

Mega International Group, Block C4, Ford Airfield Industrial Estate, Ford, Arundel, West Sussex, BN18 0HY Tel: (01903) 717150 Fax: (01903) 717150 E-mail: info@mega-kayaks.co.uk

Metro Leisure Developments Ltd, 13 Hylton Street, North Shields, Tyne & Wear, NE29 6SQ Tel: 0191-258 3677 Fax: 0191-295 4926 E-mail: johnkelly@metroleisure.co.uk

T.P. Millen Co. Ltd, 4 Stuart Way, East Grinstead, West Sussex, RH19 4RS Tel: (0787) 6658207 Fax: (01342) 335747 E-mail: tmillen@vodafone.net

Millfield F R P Ltd, Newburn Industrial Estate, Shelley Road, Newcastle upon Tyne, NE15 9RT Tel: 0191-264 8541 Fax: 0191-264 6962 E-mail: mail@millfield-group.co.uk

Minster Composite Products, Minster House, Private Road 2, Colwick Industrial Estate, Nottingham, NG4 2JR Tel: 0115-940 0644 Fax: 0115-940 0655 E-mail: minster@btclick.com

▶ Moorland Compound, 2 Power Wash Trading Estate, Tunstall Road, Knypersley, Stoke-on-Trent, ST8 7BE Tel: (01782) 515522 Fax: (01782) 515522 E-mail: miked@moorlandcompounds.co.uk

Morris & Rosam Group Mouldings, The Sanderson Centre, Lees Lane, Gosport, Hampshire, PO12 3UL Tel: (023) 9252 5448 Fax: (023) 9251 3999 E-mail: w1lfs@yahoo.com

Morrison Glass Fibre, Rose Hill Works, Rose Hill, Denton, Manchester, M34 3ZA Tel: 0161-336 0632 Fax: 0161-335 9852

Oasis Fibreglass Ltd, Froxton Whitstone, Holsworthy, Devon, EX22 6TP Tel: (01288) 341628 Fax: (01288) 341565

Orkney Boats Ltd, Unit 1 Ford La Business Park, Ford, Arundel, West Sussex, BN18 0UZ Tel: (01243) 551456 Fax: (01243) 551914 E-mail: enquiries@orkneyboatsltd.co.uk

Oyster Products Ltd, Unit 3 Stonestile Farm, Stone Stile Farm, Selling, Faversham, Kent, ME13 9SD Tel: (01227) 732345 Fax: (01227) 738850 E-mail: oysterproducts@hotmail.com

▶ Paramount Industries, Arowry House, Hanmer, Whitchurch, Shropshire, SY13 3EQ Tel: (01948) 830641 Fax: (01948) 830605

Parglas Ltd, Barton Manor, Bristol, BS2 0RP Tel: 0117-955 2325 Fax: 0117-941 1806 E-mail: parglas@btclick.com

Parton Fibreglass Ltd, P F G House, Claymore, Tame Valley Industrial Estate, Tamworth, Staffordshire, B77 5DQ Tel: (01827) 261771 Fax: (01827) 261390 E-mail: sales@pfg-tanks.com

Patterns & Moulds Ltd, Unit D2 Wymeswold Industrial Park, Wymeswold Road, Burton-on-the-Wolds, Loughborough, Leicestershire, LE12 5TY Tel: (01509) 881581 Fax: (01509) 881681 E-mail: info@patternsandmoulds.com

Pentam Composites, 9 Martin Court, Bleneim Industrial Estate, Nottingham, NG6 8US Tel: 0115-979 4494 Fax: 0115-979 4495

Production Glassfibre, Myregormie Place, Mitchelston Industrial Estate, Kirkcaldy, Fife, KY1 3NA Tel: (01592) 650444 Fax: (01592) 652444 E-mail: sales@productionglassfibre.co.uk

Quadplas Ltd, Mulberry Trading Estate, Foundry Lane, Horsham, West Sussex, RH13 5PX Tel: (01403) 241533 Fax: (01403) 268234 E-mail: steve.botting@quadplas.co.uk

Quality Mouldings, 3 Culverin Square, Limberline Road, Hilsea, Portsmouth, PO3 5BU Tel: (023) 9267 9704 Fax: (023) 9267 8531

R B F Fibreglass Ltd, Far Lane, Normanton on Soar, Loughborough, Leicestershire, LE12 5HA Tel: (01509) 646560 Fax: (01509) 646669 E-mail: rbffibreglass@aol.co.uk

R M J Mouldings, 4B Centurion Park, Kendel Road, Shrewsbury, SY1 4EH Tel: (01743) 450470 Fax: (01743) 351584

Ralph Plastics, Unit 12b Macmerry Industrial Estate, Tranent, East Lothian, EH33 1RD Tel: (01875) 615247 Fax: (01875) 615247 E-mail: trishralph@aol.com

Renaissance Period Mouldings, 262 Handsworth Road, Sheffield, S13 9BS Tel: 0114-244 6622 Fax: 0114-261 0472

Robby Tanks Ltd, Cruwys Morchard, Tiverton, Devon, EX16 8LY Tel: (01363) 866310 Fax: (01363) 866310

▶ RPD Mouldings, 1c Market Street, Shipdham, Thetford, Norfolk, IP25 7LY Tel: (01362) 821211 Fax: (01362) 821211 E-mail: relement@aol.com

S & D Plastics, 14 Huntspill Road, Highbridge, Somerset, TA9 3DD Tel: (01278) 781853 Fax: (01278) 782834

S J Rolls Ltd, Plot 7, Wimbledon Avenue, Brandon, Suffolk, IP27 0NZ Tel: (01842) 811918 Fax: (01842) 811693

S P Fibreglass, Station Road, Northiam, Rye, East Sussex, TN31 6QA Tel: (01797) 252476 Fax: (01797) 253093

Sculpture Studios, 3 Hornsby Square, Southfields Industrial Park, Laindon, Basildon, Essex, SS15 6SD Tel: (01268) 418837 E-mail: aden.hynes@virgin.net

Smith & Deakin Plastics, 75 Blackpole Trading Estate West, Worcester, WR3 8TJ Tel: (01905) 458886 Fax: (01905) 458889 E-mail: sales@smithanddeakin.co.uk

Sutton Mouldings Ltd, Brook Road Industrial Estate, Totman Cresent, Rayleigh, Essex, SS6 7UY Tel: (01268) 779655 Fax: (01268) 779633

Tamworth Glass Fibre, Pooley Lane, Pooley Hall Farmhouse, Polesworth, Tamworth, Staffordshire, B78 1JA Tel: (01827) 331010 Fax: (01827) 330027 E-mail: m.hopkins267@ntlworld.com

▶ Thames Group, Green Lane, Burghfield Bridge, Burghfield, Reading, RG30 3XN Tel: 0118-958 4499 Fax: 0118-959 6442 E-mail: sales@thamesgrp.com

Thistle Special Beltings, Bridge of Mondynes, Fordoun, Laurencekirk, Kincardineshire, AB30 1LD Tel: (01569) 740204 Fax: (01569) 740322 E-mail: mail@thistle.uk.com

Trevor K Deakin, Unit 11 High Street Industrial Estate, Long Lane, High Street, St. Austell, Cornwall, PL26 7SU Tel: (01726) 824616 Fax: (01726) 822101

Valance Glass Fibre Co. Ltd, Unit 8 Netherwood Indsl Estate, Atherstone, Warwickshire, CV9 1JA Tel: (01827) 715619 Fax: (01827) 715619

Valley Canoe Products Ltd, Private Road 4, Colwick Industrial Estate, Nottingham, NG4 2JT Tel: 0115-961 4995 Fax: 0115-961 4970 E-mail: ceakayak@globalnet.co.uk

Victoria Mouldings, 8 Emley Moor Business Park, Leys Lane, Emley, Huddersfield, HD8 9QY Tel: (01924) 840611 Fax: (01924) 840611

W A Simpson Marine Ltd, 1 Logie Avenue, Dundee, DD2 2AS Tel: (01382) 566670 Fax: (01382) 668661 E-mail: admin@wasimpsonmarine.com

Wessex Garage Doors Ltd, Bessemer Close, Ebblake Industrial Estate, Verwood, Dorset, BH31 6AZ Tel: (01202) 825451 Fax: (01202) 823242 E-mail: sales@wessexdoors.co.uk

Westford Plastics & Engineering Ltd, Westford, Wellington, Somerset, TA21 0DU Tel: (01823) 662377 Fax: (01823) 663238 E-mail: l_cross@msn.com

FIBREGLASS OR GLASS FIBRE MOTOR VEHICLE BODY PANELS, CUSTOM MADE, *See also headings under Glass Fibre*

Quantum Mouldings Ltd, Emville Street, Stourbridge, West Midlands, DY8 3TD Tel: (01384) 834422 Fax: (01384) 443743 E-mail: sales@quantummouldings.co.uk

FIBREGLASS ROOFING CONTRACTORS

Salty Yacht Productions Ltd, Victoria Wharf, River Bank, Old Town Dock, Newport, Gwent, NP20 2BS Tel: (01633) 250652 Fax: (01633) 842267 E-mail: sales@saltyyachts.com

FIBREGLASS ROOFING MATERIALS

Hambleside Danelaw Ltd, 2-8 Bentley Way, Royal Oak Industrial Estate, Daventry, Northamptonshire, NN11 8QH Tel: (01327) 701900 Fax: (01327) 701909 E-mail: marketing@hambleside-danelaw.co.uk
Heys-Shawl Ltd, Waterloo House, Langham Street Industrial Estate, Ashton-Under-Lyne, Lancashire, OL7 9AX Tel: 0161-343 2060 Fax: 0161-343 1542

FIBREGLASS SHEETS

Hambleside Danelaw Ltd, 2-8 Bentley Way, Royal Oak Industrial Estate, Daventry, Northamptonshire, NN11 8QH Tel: (01327) 701900 Fax: (01327) 701909 E-mail: marketing@hambleside-danelaw.co.uk

FIBREGLASS TUBES

Exel Ltd, Fairoak Lane, Whitehouse, Runcorn, Cheshire, WA7 3DU Tel: (01928) 701515 Fax: (01928) 713572 E-mail: sales@exel.net
Fibrerod Pultrusions, Wemco House 477, Whippendell Road, Watford, WD18 7PS Tel: (01923) 221255 Fax: (01923) 221255 E-mail: sales@fibrerodpultrusions.co.uk
M B Plastics Ltd, Bridge Lane, Woolston, Warrington, WA1 4BA Tel: (01925) 822811 Fax: (01925) 818907 E-mail: sales@mbplastics.co.uk
Plasticon, 7 Dunlop Way, Queensway Industrial Estate, Scunthorpe, South Humberside, DN16 3RN Tel: (01724) 855036 Fax: (01724) 872526 E-mail: sales@plasticon.co.uk

FIBREGLASS WALLCOVERINGS

Johns Manville, Unit 4 Roundwood Drive, Sherdley Road Industrial Estate, St. Helens, Merseyside, WA9 5JD Tel: (01744) 762500 Fax: (01744) 451076 E-mail: jeff.nash@jm.com
▶ Property Network Services Ltd., 29 Woodlands Crescent, Johnstone, Renfrewshire, PA5 0AZ Tel: 01505 320281

FIBRES, *See also headings for particular types*

Du Pont UK Ltd, Wedgewood Way, Stevenage, Hertfordshire, SG1 4QN Tel: (01438) 734000 Fax: (01438) 734836 E-mail: enquiries@dupontpharma.com
Fibreline Yorkshire Ltd, Victoria Park Mills, Hard Ings Road, Keighley, West Yorkshire, BD21 3ND Tel: (01535) 681218 Fax: (01535) 611265 E-mail: sales@fibreline-ltd.co.uk
Forum Bioscience Holdings Ltd, 41-51 Brighton Road, Redhill, RH1 6YS Tel: (01737) 773711 Fax: (01737) 770053
H Dawson Sons & Co (Wool) Ltd, Mercury House, Essex St, Bradford, West Yorkshire, BD4 7PG Tel: (01274) 727464 Fax: (01274) 723326 E-mail: info@h-dawson-wool.com
Richkeen Chemicals Ltd, 33 Chapmans Cresent, Chesham, Buckinghamshire, HP5 2QT Tel: (01494) 786669 Fax: (01494) 786503 E-mail: richkeenc@aol.com
Sapt Textile Products Co. Ltd, Bluepits Mills, Queensway, Castleton, Rochdale, Lancashire, OL11 2PG Tel: (01706) 632931 Fax: (01706) 640878 E-mail: sapt.uk@btclick.com
Sparkford Chemicals Ltd, Sparkfrod House, 58 The Avenue, Southampton, SO17 1XS Tel: (023) 8022 8747 Fax: (023) 8021 0240 E-mail: info@sparkford.co.uk
Stevensons Of Norwich Ltd, Roundtree Way, Norwich, NR7 8SQ Tel: (01603) 400824 Fax: (01603) 405113 E-mail: sales@stevensons-of-norwich.co.uk
Wigglesworth Company.Ltd International Merchants, 69 Southwark Bridge Road, Wigglesworth House, London, SE1 0NG Tel: (020) 7403 1919 Fax: (020) 7403 3232 E-mail: enquiries@wigglesworthfibres.com

FIBROUS PLASTER

John Andrews Studio, Rear Of Cranham Farm, The Chase, Upminster, Essex, RM14 3YB Tel: 01708 224040 Fax: 01708 641 206
H. & F. Badcock (Fibrous & Solid Plastering) Ltd, Unit 9, 57 Sandgate Street, Old Kent Road, London, SE15 1LE Tel: (020) 7639 0304 Fax: (020) 7358 1239 E-mail: info@hf-badcock.co.uk
Clancast Contracts Ltd, 48 Shaw Street, Glasgow, G51 3BL Tel: 0141-440 2345 Fax: 0141-440 2488 E-mail: info@clancast.co.uk
Clark & Fenn Skanska Ltd, Unit 19 Mitcham Industrial Estate, Streatham Road, Mitcham, Surrey, CR4 2AP Tel: (020) 8685 5000 Fax: (020) 8640 1986 E-mail: clark.and.fenn@skanska.co.uk
E J Harmer & Co. Ltd, 19a Birkbeck Hill, London, SE21 8JS Tel: (020) 8670 1017 Fax: (020) 8766 6026 E-mail: info@ejharmer.co.uk
Hodkin & Jones (Sheffield) Ltd, Callywhite Lane, Dronfield, Derbyshire, S18 2XP Tel: (01246) 290890 Fax: (01246) 290292 E-mail: info@hodkin-jones.co.uk
Kingston Ornate Plaster, 23 Saner Street, Hull, HU3 2TR Tel: (01482) 320536 Fax: (01482) 320536
Steads Fibrous Plasterers, Victoria Plaster Works, Victoria Road, Bradford, West Yorkshire, BD2 2DJ Tel: (01274) 637222 Fax: (01274) 637222 E-mail: enquiries@steadsplasterers.co.uk
Studio Four Regency Design, Dormston Trading Estate, Burton Road, Dudley, West Midlands, DY1 2UF Tel: (01902) 663913
Thomas & Wilson Ltd, 903 Fulham Road, London, SW6 5HU Tel: (020) 7384 0111 Fax: (020) 7384 0222 E-mail: sales@thomasandwilson.com
Troika Contracting Ltd, 850 Herries Road, Sheffield, S6 1QW Tel: 0114-269 0900 Fax: 0114-234 4885 E-mail: sales@troikaam.co.uk
W G Crotch Ornamental Plaster Work, 10 Tuddenham Avenue, Ipswich, IP4 2HE Tel: (01473) 250349 Fax: (01473) 213180 E-mail: annetaylorwgcrtch@yahoo.co.uk

FIBROUS PLASTER CONTRACTORS

▶ Border Plastering Services, 33 Elizabeth Road,, Kington, Herefordshire, HR5 3DB Tel: 01544 230099 E-mail: terry@townsend33.fsworld.co.uk
Butcher Plasterworks Ltd, 8 Fitzroy Road, Primrose Hill, London, NW1 8TX Tel: (020) 7722 9771 Fax: (020) 7586 2953
Clark & Fenn Skanska Ltd, Unit 19 Mitcham Industrial Estate, Streatham Road, Mitcham, Surrey, CR4 2AP Tel: (020) 8685 5000 Fax: (020) 8640 1986 E-mail: clark.and.fenn@skanska.co.uk
Cornwall Bros Ltd, 2a Tovil Hill, Maidstone, Kent, ME15 6QS Tel: (01622) 755066 Fax: (01622) 755066
Hollywood Plasterers, Woodhouse, Packhorse Lane, Kings Norton, Birmingham, B38 0DN Tel: (01564) 824100 Fax: (01564) 823447
▶ J O'Donnell, 17 Barmouth Grove, Biddulph, Stoke-on-Trent, ST8 7QE Tel: (01782) 511042 E-mail: jodonnell.plastering@hotmail.co.uk
London Plastercraft Ltd, 314 Wandsworth Bridge Road, London, SW6 2UA Tel: (020) 7736 5146 Fax: (020) 7736 7190 E-mail: info@londonplastercraft.com
Southern Drylining, 32 North Poulner Road, Ringwood, Hampshire, BH24 1SP Tel: (07739) 605060 Fax: (0781) 2245583 E-mail: info@southerndrylining.co.uk

FIELD MARKETING COMPANIES/ SERVICES

▶ Dalepak, Caswell Road, Brackmills Industrial Estate, Northampton, NN4 7PW Tel: (01604) 676246 Fax: (01604) 767606 E-mail: sales@dalepak.ltd.uk
F D S Ltd, F D S House, 94-104 John Wilson Busn Park, Chestfield, Whitstable, Kent, CT5 3QZ Tel: (01227) 741111 Fax: (0845) 0741112 E-mail: info@fds-uk.com
▶ The Farmyard, 5 Samuel Court, Templecombe, Somerset, BA8 0JN Tel: (01963) 370841 E-mail: info@the-farmyard.com
▶ GfK NOP, Ludgate House, 245 Blackfriars Road, London, SE1 9UL Tel: 020 7890 9000 Fax: 020 7890 9001 E-mail: ukinfo@gfk.com
Ims, Ten Pound Walk, Doncaster, South Yorkshire, DN4 5HX Tel: (01302) 554996 Fax: (01302) 554996 E-mail: sales@ukims.co.uk
▶ Spark Promotions Ltd, Building 3.1 Power Road Studio, Power Road, London, W4 5PY Tel: (020) 8742 5920 E-mail: spriestman@blackjack.co.uk

FIELD SPORTS CLOTHING

Abbtex Sports, 215 Galton Road, Smethwick, West Midlands, B67 5JH Tel: 0121-429 8830 Fax: 0121-247 5772 E-mail: admin@abbtexsports.co.uk
Albert Martin & Co. Ltd, Kirkby Road, Sutton-in-Ashfield, Nottinghamshire, NG17 1GP Tel: (01623) 441122 Fax: (01623) 551037
Arabesque, 302-304 Westborough Road, Westcliff-on-Sea, Essex, SS0 9PX Tel: (01702) 333244 Fax: (01702) 331066
B H E Sports Ltd, Units 4-5 Sharbrook Trading Estate, Mullineux Street, Manchester, M28 3DZ Tel: 0161-790 5071 Fax: 0161-703 7324
City Styles Leicester Ltd, 150 St Nicholas Circle, Leicester, LE1 4JJ Tel: 0116-251 5411
Conquest Clothing Ltd, The Old Farm House, Amport, Andover, Hampshire, SP11 8JB Tel: (01264) 889566 Fax: (01264) 889371 E-mail: bob@conquestclothing.co.uk
Godfrey Sports, Abbeyfield Road, Nottingham, NG7 2SZ Tel: 0115-986 4600 Fax: 0115-986 2018 E-mail: sales@godfrey.co.uk
Grays International Ltd, Station Road, Robertsbridge, East Sussex, TN32 5DH Tel: (0845) 0661823 Fax: (01580) 881156 E-mail: sales@grays-hockey.co.uk
Gymphlex Ltd, Boston Road, Horncastle, Lincolnshire, LN9 6HU Tel: (01507) 523243 Fax: (01507) 524421 E-mail: sales@gymphlex.co.uk
Jacetts Ltd, 18 Hope Road, Deal, Kent, CT14 7DF Tel: (01304) 381990 Fax: (01304) 381991 E-mail: sales@jacetts.co.uk
▶ Leisurewear-actecs, 6 Penhill Industrail Park, Beaumont Road, Banbury, Oxon, OX16 1RW Tel: (01295) 703165 Fax: (01295) 255059 E-mail: sales@actecs.co.uk
P E Sports, Portland Mill, Portland St South, Ashton-under-Lyne, Lancashire, OL6 7SX Tel: 0161-330 4075 Fax: 0161-304 7692 E-mail: pesports@btconnect.com
Peveril Manufacturing Co Sportswear Ltd, 1 Campbell Street, Darvel, Ayrshire, KA17 0DL Tel: (01560) 321965 Fax: (01560) 322016
Pro Star, PO Box 20, Wakefield, West Yorkshire, WF2 7AY Tel: (01924) 291441 Fax: (01924) 364411 E-mail: info@prostar.co.uk
Ruggerbug Leisure Island Embroidery, Unit 39 Dyffryn Business Park, Ystrad Mynach, Hengoed, Mid Glamorgan, CF82 7RJ Tel: (01443) 862067 Fax: (01443) 862067 E-mail: contact@ruggerbug.com
Teritex Sportswear, Teritex Factory, Boughton, Newark, Nottinghamshire, NG22 9ZD Tel: (01623) 861381 Fax: (01623) 835301 E-mail: info@teritex.com
W Powell & Son Ltd, 35-37 Carrs Lane, Birmingham, B4 7SX Tel: 0121-643 0689 Fax: 0121-631 3504 E-mail: sales@william-powell.co.uk

FIFTH WHEEL SHUNTING TRACTORS

▶ A M T Logistics Ltd, Hill Business Park, Iddesleigh, Winkleigh, Devon, EX19 8SW Tel: (01837) 811144 Fax: (01837) 811166 E-mail: office@amtlogistics.co.uk

FILING (OFFICE) SYSTEMS MANUFRS

Acco Eastlight Ltd, Ashton Road, Denton, Manchester, M34 3LR Tel: 0161-336 9431 Fax: 0161-320 8012 E-mail: mark.winstanley@acco-eastlight.co.uk
Avery Dennison UK Ltd, P O Box 16, Oldbury, West Midlands, B69 4LU Tel: 0121-511 2500 Fax: 0121-511 2525
Flexiform Business Furniture Ltd, The Office Furniture Centre, 1392 Leeds Road, Bradford, West Yorkshire, BD3 7AE Tel: (01274) 656013 Fax: (01274) 665760 E-mail: sales@flexiform.co.uk
Gilmex International Ltd, 78 Conington Road, London, SE13 7LH Tel: (020) 8318 3921 Fax: (020) 8463 0565 E-mail: sales@gilmex.com
Helix Group plc, Lye, Engine Lane, Stourbridge, West Midlands, DY9 7AJ Tel: (01384) 424441 Fax: (01384) 892617 E-mail: info@helixhq.com
Kardex Systems UK Ltd, Kestrel House Falconry Court, Bakers Lane, Epping, Essex, CM16 5LL Tel: (0870) 2422224 Fax: (0870) 2400420 E-mail: moreinfo@kardex.co.uk
Knoll International, 1 Lindsey Street, London Central Markets, London, EC1A 9PQ Tel: (020) 7236 6655 Fax: (020) 7248 1744
The Maine Group, Home Park Industrial Estate, Station Road, Kings Langley, Hertfordshire, WD4 8LZ Tel: (01923) 260411 Fax: (01923) 267136 E-mail: sales@maine.co.uk
▶ Production Lines Northern Ltd, 14 Pleasant Row, Queensbury, Bradford, West Yorkshire, BD13 2BW Tel: (01274) 812035 E-mail: philip@productionlines.co.uk
Railex Systems Ltd, Station Road, Lawford, Manningtree, Essex, CO11 1DZ Tel: (08706) 006664 Fax: (01206) 391465 E-mail: info@railex.co.uk
Railex Systems Ltd, Crossens Way, Marine Drive, Southport, Merseyside, PR9 9LY Tel: (01704) 226866 Fax: (01704) 225814 E-mail: info@railex.co.uk
Rotadex Systems Ltd, Sytems House, Central Business Park, Mackadown Lane, Birmingham, B33 0JL Tel: 0121-783 7411 Fax: 0121-783 1876 E-mail: cathi.croton@rotadex.co.uk
Sabell & Co., Saxon Way, Birmingham, B37 5AX Tel: 0121-770 1389 Fax: 0121-788 1970
Setten & Durward Ltd, Ixl House, Waterloo Road, Llandrindod Wells, Powys, LD1 6BH Tel: (01597) 827800 Fax: (01597) 827847 E-mail: sales@ixl.uk.com
TBS (South Wales) Ltd, Triumph Works, The Willows, Merthyr Tydfil, Mid Glamorgan, CF48 1YH Tel: (01685) 384041 Fax: (01685) 352202 E-mail: sales@triumph-tbs.com

FILLED CUSHIONS

Cheshire Drapes Ltd, Chichister Road, Romley, Stockport, Cheshire, SK6 4BL Tel: 0161-430 4110 Fax: 0161-406 6327
Christine's Cane Furniture, 2a Watson Road, Worksop, Nottinghamshire, S80 2BB Tel: (01909) 483790 Fax: (01909) 483790 E-mail: christinestevens30@virgin.com
Cush In Co., Heald House Road, Leyland, PR25 4JA Tel: (01772) 621804
Fibreline Yorkshire Ltd, Victoria Park Mills, Hard Ings Road, Keighley, West Yorkshire, BD21 3ND Tel: (01535) 681218 Fax: (01535) 611265 E-mail: sales@fibreline-ltd.co.uk
Fleur De Lis Furnishings Ltd, Collingwood House, Coach Lane, North Shields, Tyne & Wear, NE29 6TN Tel: 0191-258 1531 Fax: 0191-259 1318 E-mail: sales@fleur-de-lis.co.uk
▶ Foam Wizards Ltd, 3 Canal Street, Stourbridge, West Midlands, DY8 4LU Tel: (01384) 377018 Fax: (01384) 376757 E-mail: knettleford@aol.com
Thomas French Ltd, James Street, Bury, Lancashire, BL9 7EG Tel: 0161-764 5356 Fax: 0161-764 6416 E-mail: peter.owen@thomasfrench.com
Fuda International Trading Co. Ltd, Middle Engine Lane, North Shields, Tyne & Wear, NE29 8HG Tel: 0191-258 2233 Fax: 0191-258 2267
Fullwith Textiles Ltd, Sunnybank Mills, Town Street, Farsley, Pudsey, West Yorkshire, LS28 5UJ Tel: 0113-257 9811 Fax: 0113-257 7064
Gale Furs Ltd, Unit 7 Plough Yard, London, EC2A 3LP Tel: (020) 7247 2014 Fax: (020) 7377 6792
Inva Care Ltd, M S S House, Taffs Fall Road, Treforest Industrial Estate, Pontypridd, Mid Glamorgan, CF37 5TT Tel: (01443) 849222 Fax: (01656) 649016 E-mail: uk@inva-care.com
James Harvey UK Ltd, 2 The Lane, 1121 Cathcart Road, Glasgow, G42 9BD Tel: 0141-636 5514 Fax: 0141-636 5518
▶ Mr Pole, Unit 9B 38-40 Upper Clapton, London, E5 8BQ Tel: (020) 7923 4441 Fax: (020) 7254 7117 E-mail: feathersdeluxe@yahoo.com
Norfolk Feather Co. Ltd, Park Road, Diss, Norfolk, IP22 4AS Tel: (01379) 643187 Fax: (01379) 650413 E-mail: sales@norfolkfeathercompany.co.uk
Spenco Healthcare International, Brian Royd Mills, Saddleworth Road, Greetland, Halifax, West Yorkshire, HX4 8NF Tel: (01422) 378569 Fax: (01422) 376064 E-mail: sales@spenco-healthcare.co.uk
United Fillings Ltd, 27 Vine Street, Billingborough, Sleaford, Lincolnshire, NG34 0QE Tel: (01529) 240207 Fax: (01529) 240204 E-mail: cushions@unitedfillings.co.uk

FILLED PILLOWS

Bedcrest Ltd, Old Hall Street, Middleton, Manchester, M24 1AG Tel: (0870) 7662324
Downland Bedding Co. Ltd, 23 Blackstock Street, Liverpool, L3 6ER Tel: 0151-236 7166 Fax: 0151-236 0062 E-mail: sales@downlandbedding.co.uk
James Harvey UK Ltd, 2 The Lane, 1121 Cathcart Road, Glasgow, G42 9BD Tel: 0141-636 5514 Fax: 0141-636 5518
Norfolk Feather Co. Ltd, Park Road, Diss, Norfolk, IP22 4AS Tel: (01379) 643187 Fax: (01379) 650413 E-mail: sales@norfolkfeathercompany.co.uk
Platt & Hill Ltd, Belgrave Mill, Fitton Hill Road, Oldham, OL8 2LZ Tel: 0161-621 4400 Fax: 0161-621 4408 E-mail: sales@phfillings.co.uk
Trendsetter Home Furnishings Ltd, Brook Mill, Hollins Road, Oldham, OL8 4JY Tel: 0161-627 4458 Fax: 0161-627 0649
William S Graham & Sons Dewsbury Ltd, Ravens Ing Mills, Ravensthorpe, Dewsbury, West Yorkshire, WF13 3JF Tel: (01924) 462456 Fax: (01924) 457985

FILLERS, FOR PAINT INDUSTRY

Imerys Minerals Ltd, Par Moor Centre, Par Moor Road, Par, Cornwall, PL24 2SQ Tel: (01726) 818000 Fax: (01726) 811200 E-mail: perfmins@imerys.com

FILLERS, FOR PLASTIC INDUSTRY

Goonvean Fibres Ltd, Ottery Moor Lane, Honiton, Devon, EX14 1BW Tel: (01404) 44194 Fax: (01404) 45102 E-mail: office@goonveanfibres.co.uk

FILLERS, FOR PLASTIC INDUSTRY

– continued

Trelleborg Fillite Ltd, Goddard Road, Astmoor Industrial Estate, Runcorn, Cheshire, WA7 1QF Tel: (01928) 566661 Fax: (01928) 572380 E-mail: enquiries@fillite.com
W T L International, Tunstall Road, Bosley, Macclesfield, Cheshire, SK11 0PE Tel: (01260) 223284 Fax: (01260) 223589 E-mail: sales@wtl-int.com

FILLERS, FOR RESIN INDUSTRY

W T L International, Tunstall Road, Bosley, Macclesfield, Cheshire, SK11 0PE Tel: (01260) 223284 Fax: (01260) 223589 E-mail: sales@wtl-int.com

FILLERS, FOR RUBBER INDUSTRY

Trelleborg Fillite Ltd, Goddard Road, Astmoor Industrial Estate, Runcorn, Cheshire, WA7 1QF Tel: (01928) 566661 Fax: (01928) 572380 E-mail: enquiries@fillite.com

FILLERS, FOR TEXTILE INDUSTRY

Portways, Sedgley Road East, Tipton, West Midlands, DY4 7UY Tel: 0121-557 7641 Fax: 0121-522 2012 E-mail: sales@vitafibres.com
Trelleborg Fillite Ltd, Goddard Road, Astmoor Industrial Estate, Runcorn, Cheshire, WA7 1QF Tel: (01928) 566661 Fax: (01928) 572380 E-mail: enquiries@fillite.com

FILLING MACHINE MANUFRS,

See also headings for particular types

A B A Alite Ltd, 4 Fen End, Stotfold, Hitchin, Hertfordshire, SG5 4BA Tel: (01462) 732777 Fax: (01462) 732999
A T Sack Fillers, Unit 26 Highlode Industrial Estate, Stocking Fen Road, Ramsey, Huntingdon, Cambridgeshire, PE26 2RB Tel: (01487) 814002 Fax: (01487) 814002 E-mail: sales@simplafillsystems.co.uk
Accrapak Systems Ltd, Burtonwood Industrial Centre, Burtonwood, Warrington, WA5 4HX Tel: (01925) 222926 Fax: (01925) 220137 E-mail: enquiries@accrapak.co.uk
▶ Aerofill, 33-35 Clayton Road, Hayes, Middlesex, UB3 1RU Tel: (020) 8848 4501 Fax: (020) 8561 3308 E-mail: sales@aerofill.com
Albro Dyco Gravfil, Henwood Industrial Estate, Ashford, Kent, TN24 8DH Tel: (01233) 629161 Fax: (01233) 639560 E-mail: ashfordsales@bradmanlake.com
All Fill Ltd, 5 Gateshead Close, Sandy, Bedfordshire, SG19 1RS Tel: (01767) 691100 Fax: (01767) 681406 E-mail: info@allfill.co.uk
Apple Engineering Ltd, Unit 23 Gothenburg Way, Hull, HU7 0YG Tel: (01482) 824200 Fax: (01482) 824196 E-mail: sales@appleng.co.uk
Barry Wehmiller Europe Ltd, 16 Roman Way, Thetford, Norfolk, IP24 1XB Tel: (01842) 754171 Fax: (01842) 755318 E-mail: info@hayssen.co.uk
Elopak UK, Meadway, Rutherford Close, Stevenage, Hertfordshire, SG1 2PR Tel: (01438) 847400 Fax: (01438) 741324 E-mail: elopak.hq@elopak.com
Elopak UK, Meadway, Rutherford Close, Stevenage, Hertfordshire, SG1 2PR Tel: (01438) 847400 Fax: (01438) 741324 E-mail: elopak.hq@elopak.no
Eurofill Ltd, Unit 1 Old Allen Barn, Old Allen Road, Bradford, West Yorkshire, BD13 3RY Tel: (01535) 270590 Fax: (01535) 270590 E-mail: eurofill@btopenworld.com
Farason Ltd, Low Hall Road, Horsforth, Leeds, LS18 4EF Tel: 0113-258 6538 Fax: 0113-258 7149 E-mail: kdmcinnes@aol.com
Handtmann Ltd, 23-24 North Luton Industrial Estate, Sedgewick Road, Luton, LU4 9DT Tel: (01582) 576116 Fax: (01582) 597164 E-mail: enquiries@handtmann.co.uk
Huhtamaki (UK) Ltd, Rowner Road, Gosport, Hants, PO13 0PR Tel: (023) 9251 2434 Fax: (023) 9251 2330 E-mail: sales@gb.huhtamaki.com
Johnston Lightning Filler Ltd, K Prescot Trade Centre, Oliver Lyme Road, Prescot, Merseyside, L34 2SH Tel: 0151-430 0900 Fax: 0151-430 7350 E-mail: sales@jlf-packaging.co.uk
Kemwall Engineering Co., 52 Bensham Grove, Thornton Heath, Surrey, CR7 8DA Tel: (020) 8653 7111 Fax: (020) 8653 9669 E-mail: sales@kemwall.co.uk
M & P (Engineering) Ltd, Wharfside Way, Trafford Park, Manchester, M17 1AN Tel: 0161-872 8378 Fax: 0161-872 9250 E-mail: info@mp-engineering.co.uk
Masterfil Ltd, Olympus House, Mill Green Road, Haywards Heath, West Sussex, RH16 1XQ Tel: 01444 472300 Fax: 01444 472329 E-mail: sales@masterfil.com
Norden UK Ltd, Church Street, Baldock, Hertfordshire, SG7 5AF Tel: (01462) 895245 Fax: (01462) 895683 E-mail: enquiries@norden.co.uk
R C S Filling Machines Ltd, Unit 1 Brand Street, Nottingham, NG2 3GW Tel: 0115-985 1717 Fax: 0115-985 1948 E-mail: sales@rcsfilling.com
Turbo Systems, 1 Gillett Street, Hull, HU3 4JA Tel: (01482) 325651 Fax: (01482) 211434 E-mail: mmoss@turbo-systems.com

FILLINGS, NATURAL FIBRE, FOR SOFT FURNISHINGS ETC

▶ Aston Carpets, 7 Polmorla Walk, Wadebridge, Cornwall, PL27 7NS Tel: (01208) 812184 Fax: (01208) 816137 E-mail: enquiries@astons-online.co.uk
H Dawson Sons & Co (Wool) Ltd, Mercury House, Essex St, Bradford, West Yorkshire, BD4 7PG Tel: (01274) 727464 Fax: (01274) 723326 E-mail: info@h-dawson-wool.com
Peter Cook International, Aneal Business Centre, Cross Green Approach, Leeds, LS9 0SG Tel: 0113-235 1111 Fax: 0113-235 0034 E-mail: sales@petercookint.com
Sidhu Textile Co. Ltd, 85-87 The Broadway, Southall, Middlesex, UB1 1LA Tel: (020) 8574 3385 Fax: (020) 8843 9229 E-mail: s_sidhu100@hotmail.com
W E Rawson Ltd, Castlebank Mills, Portobello Road, Wakefield, West Yorkshire, WF1 5PS Tel: (01924) 373421 Fax: (01924) 290334

FILM AND TELEVISION GRIP EQUIPMENT

▶ Square Sail Ship Yard Ltd, Charlestown Harbour, St. Austell, Cornwall, PL25 3NJ Tel: (01726) 70241 Fax: (01726) 61839 E-mail: info@square-sail.com

FILM AND VIDEO LIBRARY SERVICES

▶ Activity Media Ltd, 7 Conway Drive, Flitwick, Bedford, MK45 1DE Tel: (01525) 759047
▶ Clouds Hill Imaging Ltd., Rock House, Curland, Taunton, Somerset, TA3 5SB Tel: 01823 481894 E-mail: david@cloudshillimaging.co.uk

FILM LAMINATING MACHINES

D & K (Europe) Ltd, Unit 38-40, Crossgate Road, Park Farm Industrial Estate, Redditch, Worcestershire, B98 7SN Tel: (01527) 520073 Fax: (01527) 524056 E-mail: info@dkeurope.co.uk
Securit World Ltd, Spectrum House, Hillview Gardens, London, NW4 2JQ Tel: (020) 8266 3300 Fax: (020) 8203 1027 E-mail: support@securitworld.com

FILM OR TELEVISION OR PHOTOGRAPHIC LAMPS

Artseens.com Picture Library, 45 Avondale Court, Avondale Road, London, E16 4PU Tel: (020) 7476 0215 E-mail: info@artseens.com
Specialist Lighting Co. Ltd, 49 The Broadway, Cheam, Sutton, Surrey, SM3 8BL Tel: (020) 8643 3110 Fax: (020) 8770 1911 E-mail: sic-@hotmail.com
Specialist Lighting Co. Ltd, 49 The Broadway, Cheam, Sutton, Surrey, SM3 8BL Tel: (020) 8643 3110 Fax: (020) 8770 1911 E-mail: elc-ltd@hotmail.com

FILM OR TELEVISION PROP HIRE

Arckiv Vintage Eyewear, Unit 87a, The Stables Market, London, NW1 8AH Tel: (07790) 102204 Fax: (020) 7428 0123 E-mail: info@arckiv.net
▶ Classic Motoring Ltd, Smilers Cottage, Brimpsfield, Gloucester, GL4 8LD Tel: (01452) 864050 E-mail: info@classicmotoring.co.uk

FILM OR TELEVISION PROPS

Arckiv Vintage Eyewear, Unit 87a, The Stables Market, London, NW1 8AH Tel: (07790) 102204 Fax: (020) 7428 0123 E-mail: info@arckiv.net

FILM OR TELEVISION STORY BOARD SERVICES

▶ Cathartic Designs, 20 Albert Mews, Lockside, London, E14 8EH Tel: (07976) 718081 E-mail: info@cathartic.co.uk

FILM PRODUCTION LIGHTING

Lightfactor Sales, 20 Greenhill Crescent, Watford Business Park, Watford, WD18 8JA Tel: (01923) 698090 Fax: (01923) 698081 E-mail: info@lightfactor.co.uk

FILM STUDIO FACILITIES

The Studio, 21 Cabul Road, London, SW11 2PR Tel: (020) 7228 5228 Fax: (020) 7228 9975

FILM TO FILM LAMINATING SERVICES

Chamberlain Plastics Ltd, Bury Close, Higham Ferrers, Rushden, Northamptonshire, NN10 8HQ Tel: (01933) 353875 Fax: (01933) 410206 E-mail: sales@chamberlain-plastics.co.uk
Duraseal, 7 27 Black Moor Road, Ebblake Industrial Estate, Verwood, Dorset, BH31 6BE Tel: (01202) 826911 Fax: (01202) 813811
G T Laminators, Rear of 60 Great Norbury Street, Hyde, Cheshire, SK14 1HY Tel: (07979) 286187 Fax: 0161-366 0856
Printpack Ltd, Bridge Hall Mills, Bridge Hall Lane, Bury, Lancashire, BL9 7PA Tel: 0161-764 5441 Fax: 0161-705 1624 E-mail: bbleasdale@printpack.com

FILM TO FILM PACKAGING LAMINATES

Amcore Flexibles, Hawkfield Way, Hawkfield Business Park, Bristol, BS14 0BD Tel: 0117-975 3200 Fax: 0117-975 3311 E-mail: sales@amcore.com
▶ Sudpack UK Ltd, 40 High Park Drive, Wolverton Mill, Milton Keynes, MK12 5TT Tel: (01908) 525720 Fax: (01908) 525721 E-mail: info@suedpack.com

FILM/TELEVISION INDUSTRY BADGES/STICKERS

North & South Labels Ltd, Unit 1, 56A Bensham Grove, Thornton Heath, Surrey, CR7 8DA Tel: (020) 8653 4477 Fax: (020) 8653 5666 E-mail: sales@nslabels.co.uk
Tyrell Corporation Ltd, 17-19 Foley Street, London, W1W 6DW Tel: (020) 7343 5500 E-mail: sales@tyrell.co.uk

FILTER BAG CAGES

Dyson Ltd, Tetbury Hill, Malmesbury, Wiltshire, SN16 0RP Tel: (01666) 827200 Fax: (01666) 827299 E-mail: james.ross-smith@dyson.com
Hilson, Acre House, Shentonfield Road, Sharston Industrial Area, Manchester, M22 4RW Tel: 0161-491 7800 Fax: 0161-428 1179 E-mail: sales@hilson.co.uk
Porter Environmental Supplies Ltd, 18 Montpelier Avenue, Bexley, Kent, DA5 3AL Tel: (020) 8298 1919 Fax: (020) 8298 7737

FILTER BAG/SLEEVE ACCESSORIES

Filter Specialists International Ltd, Unit H1 Taylor Business Park, Warrington, WA3 6BL Tel: (01925) 762576 Fax: (01925) 763875 E-mail: info@fsiltd.demon.co.uk

FILTER BAGS, MULTI POCKET

▶ Fabric Filter Services Ltd, 6 Springfield Commercial Centre, Bagley Lane, Farsley, Pudsey, West Yorkshire, LS28 5LY Tel: 0113-256 6964 Fax: 0113-255 0432 E-mail: sales@fabricfilters.co.uk

FILTER BAGS/SLEEVES

A & I Holmes & Co. Ltd, Unit 8c Kayley Industrial Estate, Richmond Street, Ashton-under-Lyne, Lancashire, OL7 0AU Tel: 0161-343 1911 Fax: 0161-343 2959 E-mail: aiholmes@btconnect.com
Allied Filter Systems Ltd, Huntsman Drive, Northbank Industrial Park, Irlam, Manchester, M44 5EG Tel: 0161-777 9505 Fax: 0161-777 9506 E-mail: sales@alliedfilter.com
Andrew Webron Ltd, Hareholme Mill, Bacup Road, Rawtenstall, Rossendale, Lancashire, BB4 7JL Tel: (01706) 214001 Fax: (01706) 830003 E-mail: info@andrewwebron.com
Custom Filter Co., Bretfield Court, Bretton Street Industrial Estate, Dewsbury, West Yorkshire, WF12 9BG Tel: (01924) 468272 Fax: (01924) 464240 E-mail: sales@customfilter.co.uk
Ductwork Accessories Ltd, Haldon House, 385 Brettell Lane, Brierley Hill, West Midlands, DY5 3LQ Tel: (01384) 571767 Fax: (01384) 571767
▶ Fabric Filter Services Ltd, 6 Springfield Commercial Centre, Bagley Lane, Farsley, Pudsey, West Yorkshire, LS28 5LY Tel: 0113-256 6964 Fax: 0113-255 0432 E-mail: sales@fabricfilters.co.uk
Filter & Press Cloth Co. Ltd, 26 Town Road, Hillchurch Street, Stoke-on-Trent, ST1 2EX Tel: (01782) 281819 Fax: (01782) 281819
Filter Specialists International Ltd, Unit H1 Taylor Business Park, Warrington, WA3 6BL Tel: (01925) 762576 Fax: (01925) 763875 E-mail: info@fsiltd.demon.co.uk
Filter Technology, Unit 11 Boundary Business Centre, Boundary Way, Woking, Surrey, GU21 5DH Tel: (01483) 776649 Fax: (01483) 740588 E-mail: dennis@filtertechnology.co.uk
H R Filtration & Co., The Green Barn Complex, The Scarr, Newent, Gloucestershire, GL18 1DQ Tel: (01531) 820320 Fax: (01531) 822253 E-mail: sales@hrfiltration.com
Heath Filtration Ltd, PO Box 1, Stoke-on-Trent, ST6 4SH Tel: (01782) 838591 Fax: (01782) 835508 E-mail: info@heathfiltration.com
G. Hunt Filtration Ltd, Portland Mill, Portland Street South, Ashton-Under-Lyne, Lancashire, OL6 7SX Tel: 0161-330 7337 Fax: 0161-343 2365 E-mail: sales@hunt-filtration.co.uk
J P Filtration Ltd, 133-135 High Street, Stratford, London, E15 2RB Tel: (020) 8534 7431 Fax: (020) 8519 8768
Multiple Fabric Co. Ltd, Vulcan Mills, William Street, Tong, Bradford, West Yorkshire, BD4 9QX Tel: (01274) 682323 Fax: (01274) 651341 E-mail: info@multiplefabric.co.uk
Oberlin Filter Ltd, 6 Thames Centre, Aycliffe Industrial Park, Newton Aycliffe, County Durham, DL5 6UJ Tel: 01325 317900
Porter Environmental Supplies Ltd, 18 Montpelier Avenue, Bexley, Kent, DA5 3AL Tel: (020) 8298 1919 Fax: (020) 8298 7737
R & B Industrial Ltd, 41 Charlton Road, Andover, Hampshire, SP10 3JH Tel: (01264) 351844 Fax: (01264) 354191 E-mail: info@rbindustrial.co.uk
R Cadisch & Sons, Unit 1, 879 High Road, London, N12 8QA Tel: (020) 8492 0444 Fax: (020) 8492 0333 E-mail: info@cadisch.com
Scottex Precision Textiles Ltd, Bolholt Industrial Park, Walshaw Road, Bury, Lancashire, BL8 1PL Tel: 0161-763 6550 Fax: 0161-764 1365 E-mail: sales@scottex-filters.com
Sefar Ltd, Bury Business Centre, Kay Street, Bury, Lancashire, BL9 6BU Tel: 0161-705 1878 Fax: 0161-763 1382 E-mail: sales@sefar.co.uk
Simpson Thomson Filtration, Virginia Mills, 187 Higher Hillgate, Stockport, Cheshire, SK1 3JG Tel: 0161-480 8991 Fax: 0161-429 8413
Tyne-Tees Filtration Ltd, Blue House Point Road, Portrack Industrial Estate, Stockton-On-Tees, Cleveland, TS18 2QL Tel: (01642) 617401 Fax: (01642) 617404 E-mail: enquiries@ttf-uk.com
Sam Weller & Sons Ltd, Pickwick Mill, Thongsbridge, Holmfirth, HD9 3JL Tel: (01484) 683201 Fax: (01484) 689700 E-mail: info@samwellerltd.co.uk
Wolf Filtration Ltd, 81 Burlington Street, Ashton-under-Lyne, Lancashire, OL6 7HJ Tel: 0161-339 1604 Fax: 0161-343 1434 E-mail: sales@wolffiltration.co.uk

FILTER BED MEDIA

A M T Systems, West Stockwith Park, Stockwith Road, Misterton, Doncaster, South Yorkshire, DN10 4ES Tel: (01427) 890022 Fax: (01427) 890063 E-mail: graham@amt-systems.co.uk
Bucbricks Ardleigh Sands, Martells Industrial Estate, Slough Lane, Ardleigh, Colchester, CO7 7RU Tel: (01206) 230310 Fax: (01206) 231057 E-mail: sands@bucbricks.co.uk
Day Group Ltd, Transport Avenue, Great West Road, Brentford, Middlesex, TW8 9HF Tel: (01483) 725100 Fax: (020) 8380 9700 E-mail: email@daygroup.co.uk
Madison Filter, Knowsley Road Industrial Estate, Haslingden, Rossendale, Lancashire, BB4 4EJ Tel: (01706) 213421 Fax: (01706) 221916 E-mail: info@madisonfilter.com
▶ Peak Machine Tools, 19 Hallam Grange Crescent, Sheffield, S10 4BA Tel: 0114-230 7122 E-mail: rod@peakmachinetools.co.uk
Progenitive Filtration Ltd, Hampson Street, Horwich, Bolton, BL6 7JH Tel: (01204) 478210 Fax: (01204) 478211 E-mail: sales@pflfiltermedia.com
Scottex Precision Textiles Ltd, Bolholt Industrial Park, Walshaw Road, Bury, Lancashire, BL8 1PL Tel: 0161-763 6550 Fax: 0161-764 1365 E-mail: sales@scottex-filters.com

FILTER BELTS

Micronics Filtration, Sandbach Road, Stoke-on-Trent, ST6 2DR Tel: (01782) 284385 Fax: (01782) 284987 E-mail: info@micronicsinc.com

FILTER CLEANING AND DEGREASING

B&M Longworth (Edgworth) Ltd, Sett End Road North, Shadsworth Business Park, Blackburn, BB1 2QG Tel: (01254) 680501 Fax: (01254) 54041 E-mail: enquiries@bmlongworth.com

FILTER CONNECTORS

Conec Electronic Equipment Component, Ringway House, Kelvin Road, Newbury, Berkshire, RG14 2DB Tel: (01635) 36929 Fax: (01635) 36925 E-mail: conec@conec.co.uk

FILTER DRYERS

Powder Systems Ltd, Estuary Business Park, Speke, Liverpool, L24 8RG Tel: 0151-448 7700 Fax: 0151-448 7702 E-mail: sales@p-s-l.com

FILTER ELEMENTS

British Filters Ltd, 11-12 Porsham Close, Roborough, Plymouth, PL6 7DB Tel: (01752) 703900 Fax: (01752) 703901 E-mail: pdenyer@britishfilters.co.uk
Custom Filter Co., Bretfield Court, Bretton Street Industrial Estate, Dewsbury, West Yorkshire, WF12 9BG Tel: (01924) 468272 Fax: (01924) 464240 E-mail: sales@customfilter.co.uk
Dingbro Ltd, Unit 7 Whitemyres Avenue, Aberdeen, AB16 6HQ Tel: (01224) 692842 Fax: (01224) 693881 E-mail: filter@dingbro.com
Power Utilities Ltd, Queen Street, Premier Business Park, Walsall, WS2 9QE Tel: (01922) 720561 Fax: (01922) 720461 E-mail: filters@power-utilities.com
Walker Filtration Ltd, Spire Road, Glover East, Washington, Tyne & Wear, NE37 3ES Tel: 0191-417 7816 Fax: 0191-415 3748 E-mail: sales@walkerfiltration.co.uk

FILTER FOAM

Beldam Burgmann Ltd, Neachells Lane, Wednesfield, Wolverhampton, WV11 3QG Tel: (01902) 307711 Fax: (01902) 305201 E-mail: sales@beldamburgmann.com
Ian Cook & Son, Tremoddrett Farm, Roche, St. Austell, Cornwall, PL26 8LP Tel: (01726) 890206 Fax: (01726) 890899
Custom Foams, Deans Rd, Wolverton Industry, Milton Keynes, MK12 5NA Tel: (01908) 312331 Fax: (01908) 220715 E-mail: sales@customfoams.co.uk
Foam Techniques Ltd, 39 Booth Drive, Park Farm South, Wellingborough, Northamptonshire, NN8 6GR Tel: (01933) 400096 Fax: (01933) 400095 E-mail: sales@foamtechniques.co.uk

FILTER LEAF

Plastok Associates Ltd, 79 Market Street, Birkenhead, Merseyside, CH41 6AN Tel: 0151-666 2056 Fax: 0151-650 0073 E-mail: sales@plastok.co.uk

FILTER MAINTENANCE AND REPAIR

Scottex Precision Textiles Ltd, Bolholt Industrial Park, Walshaw Road, Bury, Lancashire, BL8 1PL Tel: 0161-763 6550 Fax: 0161-764 1365 E-mail: sales@scottex-filters.com

FILTER MANUFRS, *See also headings under Filters*

Air Safety Ltd, Vickers Industrial Estate, Mellishaw Lane, Morecambe, Lancashire, LA3 3EN Tel: (01524) 388696 Fax: (01524) 33386 E-mail: sales@airsafetymedical.com
▶ Airpel Filtration, Hambridge Road, Newbury, Berkshire, RG14 5TR Tel: +44 (0) 1635 263915 Fax: +44 (0) 1635 36006 E-mail: airpel@spx.com
Amazon Filters Ltd, Albany Park, Frimley Road, Camberley, Surrey, GU15 2RA Tel: (01276) 670600 Fax: (01276) 670101 E-mail: sales@amazonfilters.co.uk
▶ Avery Hardoll, Holland Way, Blandford Forum, Dorset, DT11 7BJ Tel: (01258) 486600 Fax: (01258) 486601 E-mail: sales@meggittfuelling.com
B E C Global Ltd, Gore Road Industrial Estate, New Milton, Hampshire, BH25 6SA Tel: (01425) 613131 Fax: (01425) 616551 E-mail: info@becgroup.com
B S C (Contracts) Ltd, Unit 4 Inoic Park, Birmingham New Road, Dudley, West Midlands, DY1 4SJ Tel: 0121-557 4651 Fax: 0121-557 7375 E-mail: sales@bsc-contracts.co.uk
Barton Firtop Engineering, Stoke Heath Works, Hanbury Road, Stoke Heath, Bromsgrove, Worcestershire, B60 4LT Tel: (01527) 831664 Fax: (01527) 832638 E-mail: sales@bartonfirtop.co.uk
Broadway Group, 136 Stanwell Road, Ashford, Middlesex, TW15 3QP Tel: (0845) 6019006 Fax: (0845) 6019007 E-mail: ppstechnical@yahoo.co.uk
Caldwell Filtration Ltd, Unit 3d, Lyncastle Way, Barley Castle Trading Estate, Warrington, WA4 4ST Tel: (01925) 267111 Fax: (01925) 267744 E-mail: info@caldwellfiltration.co.uk
Camfil Ltd, Knowsley Road, Haslingden, Rossendale, Lancashire, BB4 4EG Tel: (01706) 238000 Fax: (01706) 226736 E-mail: info@camfil.com
Carlson Filtration Ltd, The Buttmill, Barnoldswick, Lancashire, BB18 5HP Tel: (01282) 811000 Fax: (01282) 811001 E-mail: sales@carlson.co.uk
Cauthery Reid, Kingfisher House, 2 Barry Close, Braunstone, Leicester, LE3 3TP Tel: 0116-239 4022 Fax: 0116-238 8330 E-mail: sales@cautheryreid.co.uk
Culligan International UK Ltd, Daimler Drive, Cowpen Lane Industrial Estate, Billingham, Cleveland, TS23 4JD Tel: (01642) 373500 Fax: (01642) 373575 E-mail: brianaire@culligan.co.uk
Davis Industrial (Filters) Ltd, 21d Holmethorpe Avenue, Redhill, RH1 2NB Tel: (0845) 2735025 Fax: (0845) 2735026 E-mail: sales@davisfilters.co.uk
Delkor Ltd, Unit C, First Avenue, Midsomer Norton, Radstock, BA3 4BS Tel: (01761) 417079 Fax: (01761) 414435
Donaldson Filter Components Ltd, Oslo Road, Hull, HU7 0YN Tel: (01482) 835213 Fax: (01482) 835411 E-mail: info@donaldson.com
Donaldson Filtration (GB) Ltd, Humberstone Lane, Thurmaston, Leicester, LE4 8HP Tel: 0116-269 6161 Fax: 0116-269 3028 E-mail: peter.cowing@emea.donaldson.com
Durham Filtration Engineers Ltd, Victoria Industrial Estate, Victoria Road West, Hebburn, Tyne & Wear, NE31 1UB Tel: 0191-428 4111 Fax: 0191-428 4226 E-mail: sales@durhamfiltration.co.uk
Emcel Filters Ltd, Blatchford Road, Horsham, West Sussex, RH13 5RA Tel: (01403) 253215 Fax: (01403) 259881 E-mail: filtration@emcelfilters.co.uk
Endecotts Ltd, 9 Lombard Road, London, SW19 3UP Tel: (020) 8542 8121 Fax: (020) 8543 6629 E-mail: sales@endecotts.com
Euro Filter, Hare Park Mills, 46 Hare Park Lane, Liversedge, West Yorkshire, WF15 8EP Tel: (01623) 412412 Fax: (01623) 412455 E-mail: sales@eurofilter.co.uk
Eurotech Filtration Ltd, 15 Furlong Lane, Stoke-on-Trent, ST6 3LE Tel: (01782) 836667 Fax: (01782) 834830
▶ Facet Industrial UK Ltd, Unit G4, Treforest Industrial Estate, Pontypridd, Mid Glamorgan, CF37 5YL Tel: (01443) 844141 Fax: (01443) 844282E-mail: uksales@facetinternational.net
Fan-Master Environmental Products Ltd, Unit 2 Lever Bridge Mills, Radcliffe Road, Bolton, BL3 1RU Tel: (01204) 523556 Fax: (01204) 557951 E-mail: sales@smethurst-security.co.uk
Fenchurch Environmental Group Ltd, Dennow Farm, Firs Lane, Appleton, Warrington, WA4 5LF Tel: (01925) 269111 Fax: (01925) 269444 E-mail: sales@fengroup.com
Fileder Filter Systems Ltd, St. Leonards Road, Allington, Maidstone, Kent, ME16 0LS Tel: (01622) 691886 Fax: (01622) 621932 E-mail: office@fileder.co.uk
Filtair Ltd, 9 Brookvale Trading Estate, Moor Lane, Birmingham, B6 7AQ Tel: 0121-356 9595 Fax: 0121-356 9538
Filter Services (UK) Ltd, Units 6/7/8, Broombank Park, Sheepbridge, Chesterfield, Derbyshire, S41 9RT Tel: (01246) 455481 Fax: (01246) 455346 E-mail: sales@filter-services.co.uk
Filter Technology, Unit 11 Boundary Business Centre, Boundary Way, Woking, Surrey, GU21 5DH Tel: (01483) 776649 Fax: (01483) 740588 E-mail: dennis@filtertechnology.co.uk
Filtermist International Ltd, Faraday Drive, Bridgnorth, Shropshire, WV15 5BA Tel: (01746) 765361 Fax: (01746) 766882 E-mail: sales@filtermist.com
Filters For Industry, 12c Queensway, New Milton, Hampshire, BH25 5NN Tel: (01425) 628533 Fax: (01425) 621767 E-mail: sales@porvairfiltration.com
Filtrex Environmental, Unit 18 Burnt Mill Industrial Estate, Elizabeth Way, Harlow, Essex, CM20 2HS Tel: (01279) 457590 Fax: (01279) 457591
First Line Ltd, Bessemer Close, Bicester, Oxfordshire, OX26 6QE Tel: (01869) 248484 Fax: (01869) 240472 E-mail: sales@firstline.co.uk
Foam Techniques Ltd, 39 Booth Drive, Park Farm South, Wellingborough, Northamptonshire, NN8 6GR Tel: (01933) 400096 Fax: (01933) 400095 E-mail: sales@foamtechniques.co.uk
G F S A Ltd, 4 West Court, Buntsford Park Road, Bromsgrove, Worcestershire, B60 3DX Tel: (01527) 831037 Fax: (01527) 836333 E-mail: enquiries@gfsa.co.uk
Gilbeyco Ltd, 32 Edison Road, Rabans Lane Industrial Area, Aylesbury, Buckinghamshire, HP19 8TE Tel: (01296) 414966 Fax: (01296) 414969 E-mail: enquiries@gilbeyco.com
Gilroy Filtration Ltd, 44 Stranmillis Embankment, Belfast, BT9 5FL Tel: (028) 9080 3888 Fax: (028) 9080 3889 E-mail: custserv@gilroys.com
Greyfriars Filters, 6 Douglas Road Industrial Park, Douglas Road, Kingswood, Bristol, BS15 8PD Tel: 0117-960 4249 Fax: 0117-947 5729
Hiross, Thame Valley Industrial Estate, 1 Claymore, Wilnecote, Tamworth, Staffordshire, B77 5DQ Tel: (01827) 260056 Fax: (01827) 261196 E-mail: sales@zanderuk.com
Hydro Pneumatic Services, Bastion House, Harlequin Avenue, Brentford, Middlesex, TW8 9EW Tel: (020) 8560 4968 Fax: (020) 8560 4958
Industrial Pneumatic Services Liverpool Ltd, 13 Dunnings Bridge Road, Bootle, Merseyside, L30 6TE Tel: 0151-525 9381 Fax: 0151-525 1982
Industrial Purification Systems Ltd, Unit 10 Lea Green Business Park, St. Helens, Merseyside, WA9 4TR Tel: (01744) 811652 Fax: (01744) 833687 E-mail: info@industrial-purification.co.uk
▶ Jad Filters, Unit 6, 1-3 Fairfield, Christchurch, Dorset, BH23 1QX Tel: (01202) 487618 Fax: (01202) 484786
Jasun Filtration plc, Riverside House, Parrett Way, Bridgwater, Somerset, TA6 5LB Tel: (01278) 452277 Fax: (01278) 450873 E-mail: info@jfilters.com
Knitwire Products, Dalton Court, Chadwick Road, Runcorn, Cheshire, WA7 1PU Tel: (01928) 566996 Fax: (01928) 566996 E-mail: sales@knitwire.com
Leyland Filtration Ltd, Yarrow Road, Chorley, Lancashire, PR6 0LP Tel: (01257) 269292 Fax: (01257) 261056 E-mail: layland.filtration@talk21.com
Longar Industries Ltd, Unit 25 Glenmore Business Park, Colebrook Way, Andover, Hampshire, SP10 3GZ Tel: (01264) 332993 Fax: (01264) 332994 E-mail: enquires@longar.co.uk
M C Air Filtration Ltd, Motney Hill Road, Gillingham, Kent, ME8 7TZ Tel: (01634) 388333 Fax: (01634) 379384 E-mail: sales@mcaf.co.uk
M I F Filter Systems Ltd, M I F Ho, Waterfall Lane Trading Estate, Cradley Heath, West Midlands, B64 6PU Tel: 0121-561 5380 Fax: 0121-561 3711 E-mail: sales@mif-filters.com
Micrafilter, Lake Road, Unit 4, Quarry Wood, Aylesford, Kent, ME20 7TQ Tel: (01622) 716616 Fax: (01622) 716606 E-mail: rod.fletcher@micrafilter.co.uk
Microelectronics, Europa House, Havant Street, Portsmouth, PO1 3PD Tel: (023) 9230 3303 Fax: (023) 9230 2506 E-mail: processuk@pall.com
Microtech Filters Ltd, The Lodge Factory, Kirkby Lane, Pinxton, Nottingham, NG16 6HW Tel: (01773) 862345 Fax: (01773) 863111 E-mail: info@microtechfilters.co.uk
John Morfield Ltd, 10 Teal Court, Strathclyde Business Park, Bellshill, Lanarkshire, ML4 3NN Tel: (01698) 840888 Fax: (01698) 840234
Nationwide Filter Co. Ltd, Unit 16 First Quarter, Blenheim Road, Epsom, Surrey, KT19 9QN Tel: (01372) 728548 Fax: (01372) 742831
Oberlin Filter Ltd, 6 Thames Centre, Aycliffe Industrial Park, Newton Aycliffe, County Durham, DL5 6UJ Tel: 01325 317900
▶ Orrell Filtration Ltd, Caroline House, 2b High Street, Stalybridge, Cheshire, SK15 1SE Tel: 0161-303 2344 Fax: 0161-304 7573
P S B Group Ltd, Williamson Street, Stoke-on-Trent, ST6 6AS Tel: (01782) 837644 Fax: (01782) 837378 E-mail: psb@psbgroup.co.uk
Pall Life Sciences, Walton Road, Farlinton, Portsmouth, PO6 1TD Tel: (023) 9230 2600 Fax: (023) 9230 2601
▶ Peak Machine Tools, 19 Hallam Grange Crescent, Sheffield, S10 4BA Tel: 0114-230 7122 E-mail: rod@peakmachinetools.co.uk
Plenty Filters, Plenty House, Hambridge Road, Newbury, Berkshire, RG14 5TR Tel: +44 (0) 1635 42363 Fax: +44 (0) 1635 49758 E-mail: filters@plenty.co.uk
▶ Polyfilters (UK) Ltd, PO Box 18, Mirfield, West Yorkshire, WF14 0NL Tel: (01924) 496584 Fax: (01924) 496249 E-mail: info@polyfilters.com
Pressure Tech Ltd, Unit 6, Graphite Way, Hadfield, Glossop, Derbyshire, SK13 1QG Tel: (01457) 899307 Fax: (01457) 899308 E-mail: steve@pressure-tech.com
Pti Technologies UK Ltd, Orgreave Lane, Handsworth, Sheffield, S13 9NZ Tel: 0114-269 3999 Fax: 0114-269 1409 E-mail: filters@ptitechnologies.co.uk
Quantum Air Technology, Unit 1 Victoria Way, Rawtenstall, Rossendale, Lancashire, BB4 7NY Tel: (01706) 835135 Fax: (01706) 836100 E-mail: graham@quantumairtech.com
Rafmi Electronics, Morrison Road, Stanley, County Durham, DH9 7RX Tel: (01207) 291300 Fax: (01207) 291304 E-mail: accounts@rasmi.com
Russell Finex Ltd, Russell House, Browells Lane, Feltham, Middlesex, TW13 7EW Tel: (020) 8818 2000 Fax: (020) 8818 2060 E-mail: enquiries@russellfinexinc.com
S P X Air Treatment Ltd, Hazleton Interchange, Lakesmere Road, Horndean, Waterlooville, Hampshire, PO8 9JU Tel: (023) 9257 2820 Fax: (023) 9257 2830 E-mail: enquiries@airtreatment.spx.com
Serfilco Europe Ltd, Broadoak Business Park, Ashburton Road West, Trafford Park, Manchester, M17 1RW Tel: 0161-872 1317 Fax: 0161-873 8027 E-mail: sales@serfilco-europe.com
Sintamesh Ltd, Unit 2, Bentinck Workshops, Park Lane, Kirkby-in-Ashfield, Nottingham, NG17 9LE Tel: (01623) 753401 Fax: (01623) 753408 E-mail: sinta@btconnect.com
Sogefi Filtration Ltd, Llantrisant Industrial Estate, Llantrisant, Pontyclun, Mid Glamorgan, CF72 8YU Tel: (01443) 223000 Fax: (01443) 225459 E-mail: stuart.hobbs@sogefifiltration.com
Talbot Components, Unit 1 Talbot Way, Shavington Park, Market Drayton, Shropshire, TF9 3SJ Tel: (01630) 653551 Fax: (01630) 654425 E-mail: sales@talbotcomp.co.uk
Technical Filtration Systems Ltd, Croft House, Sandbeck Way, Wetherby, West Yorkshire, LS22 7DP Tel: (01937) 588222 Fax: (01937) 588345 E-mail: mail@tfs-ltd.co.uk
UK Filters Ltd, 3b High Street, Cheshunt, Waltham Cross, Hertfordshire, EN8 0BX Tel: (01992) 468804
Usk Valley Fluid Power, Unit 16 Mill Street Industrial Estate, Mill Street, Abergavenny, Gwent, NP7 5HE Tel: (01873) 857225 Fax: (01873) 858790 E-mail: sales@uskvalleyfp.co.uk
Vee Bee Ltd, Old Wharf Road, Stourbridge, West Midlands, DY8 4LS Tel: (01384) 378884 Fax: (01384) 374179 E-mail: veebee-filtration@veebee.co.uk
Vokes Ltd, Henley Park, Normandy, Guildford, Surrey, GU3 2AF Tel: (01483) 569971 Fax: (01483) 235384 E-mail: sales@vokes.com
Walker Filtration Ltd, Spire Road, Glover East, Washington, Tyne & Wear, NE37 3ES Tel: 0191-417 7816 Fax: 0191-415 3748 E-mail: sales@walkerfiltration.co.uk
Webron Marling Ltd, Hareholme Mill, Bacup Road, Rawtenstall, Rossendale, Lancashire, BB4 7JL Tel: (01706) 214001 Fax: (01706) 830003 E-mail: sales@andrewwebron.com
Wolf Filtration Ltd, 81 Burlington Street, Ashton-under-Lyne, Lancashire, OL6 7HJ Tel: 0161-339 1604 Fax: 0161-343 1434 E-mail: sales@wolffiltration.co.uk

FILTER MEDIA MANUFRS, *See also headings for particular types*

Anderman & Co. Ltd, 145 London Road, Kingston Upon Thames, Surrey, KT2 6NH Tel: (020) 8541 0035 Fax: (020) 8549 1617 E-mail: enquiries@earthwaterfire.com
Carlson Filtration Ltd, The Buttmill, Barnoldswick, Lancashire, BB18 5HP Tel: (01282) 811000 Fax: (01282) 811001 E-mail: sales@carlson.co.uk
Custom Foams, Deans Rd, Wolverton Industry, Milton Keynes, MK12 5NA Tel: (01908) 312331 Fax: (01908) 220715 E-mail: sales@customfoams.co.uk
Durham Filtration Engineers Ltd, Victoria Industrial Estate, Victoria Road West, Hebburn, Tyne & Wear, NE31 1UB Tel: 0191-428 4111 Fax: 0191-428 4226 E-mail: sales@durhamfiltration.co.uk
Madison Filter, Knowsley Road Industrial Estate, Haslingden, Rossendale, Lancashire, BB4 4EJ Tel: (01706) 213421 Fax: (01706) 221916 E-mail: info@madisonfilter.com
Oberlin Filter Ltd, 6 Thames Centre, Aycliffe Industrial Park, Newton Aycliffe, County Durham, DL5 6UJ Tel: 01325 317900
Porvair Technology Ltd, Clywedog Road South, Wrexham Industrial Estate, Wrexham, Clwyd, LL13 9XS Tel: (01978) 661144 Fax: (01978) 664554E-mail: enquiries@porvairfiltration.com
R J Faulkes, Unit C3 Guy Motors Industrial Park, Park Lane, Wolverhampton, WV10 9QF Tel: (01902) 306662 Fax: (01902) 306662

FILTER MEDIA, FIBRE/WOVEN

Allied Filter Systems Ltd, Huntsman Drive, Northbank Industrial Park, Irlam, Manchester, M44 5EG Tel: 0161-777 9505 Fax: 0161-777 9506 E-mail: sales@alliedfilter.com
Durham Filtration Engineers Ltd, Victoria Industrial Estate, Victoria Road West, Hebburn, Tyne & Wear, NE31 1UB Tel: 0191-428 4111 Fax: 0191-428 4226 E-mail: sales@durhamfiltration.co.uk
Micronics Filtration, Sandbach Road, Stoke-on-Trent, ST6 2DR Tel: (01782) 284385 Fax: (01782) 284987 E-mail: info@micronicsinc.com
P G Lawton, Caldene Business Park, Burnley Road, Mytholmroyd, Hebden Bridge, West Yorkshire, HX7 5QJ Tel: (01422) 883903 Fax: (01422) 884278 E-mail: pg.lawton@uk.sglcarbon.de
Purification Products Ltd, Reliance Works, Saltaire Road, Shipley, West Yorkshire, BD18 3HL Tel: (01274) 530155 Fax: (01274) 580453 E-mail: sales@purification.co.uk

FILTER PANELS

Airclean Ltd, PO Box 147, Maidstone, Kent, ME14 2LA Tel: (01622) 832777 Fax: (01622) 832507 E-mail: info@airclean.co.uk

FILTER PAPER

▶ Ahlstrom Chirnside Ltd, Chirnside, Duns, Berwickshire, TD11 3JW Tel: (01890) 818303 Fax: (01890) 818256 E-mail: karen.renton@ahlstrom.com
Filtration Service Engineering Ltd, Unit 15 Oldington Trading Estate, Kidderminster, Worcestershire, DY11 7QP Tel: (01562) 60233 Fax: (01562) 748387 E-mail: info@fse.co.uk
J R Crompton U S A Ltd, 12th Floor, Sunlight House, Manchester, M3 3JZ Tel: 0161-817 6500 Fax: 0161-817 6506 E-mail: info@crompton.co.uk
▶ Peak Machine Tools, 19 Hallam Grange Crescent, Sheffield, S10 4BA Tel: 0114-230 7122 E-mail: rod@peakmachinetools.co.uk

FILTER PAPER – *continued*

Thomas & Green Ltd/Konos Gmbh, 81 Orchard Way, Burmell, Cambridge, CB25 0EQ Tel: 07768 682210 Fax: 01638 605146 E-mail: richard.start@ntlworld.com

FILTER PLATES

Lenser (UK) Ltd, Winton House, Stoke Road, Stoke-On-Trent, ST4 2RW Tel: (01782) 415414 Fax: (01782) 415757 E-mail: lenseruk@aol.com

FILTER PRESS REFURBISHMENT OR MAINTENANCE OR REPAIR

C D Bissell Engineering Services Ltd, Unit 28, Moorfields Industrial Estate, Cotes Heath, Stafford, ST21 6QY Tel: (01782) 791711 Fax: (01782) 791511 E-mail: mick@cdbissell.com

FILTER PRESSES

Andritz Ltd, R & B Technology Centre, Speedwell Road, Parkhouse East Industrial Estate, Newcastle, Staffordshire, ST5 7RG Tel: (01782) 565656 Fax: (01782) 566130 E-mail: welcome@andritzltd.com

Ashbrook Simon-Hartley Ltd, 10/11 Brindley Court, Dalewood Road, Lymedale Business Park, Newcastle-under-Lyme, Staffordshire, ST5 9QH Tel: (01782) 578650 Fax: (01782) 260534 E-mail: enquiries@as-h.com

G L M & I S I International Ltd, 143 Woburn Tower, Broomcroft Avenue, Northolt, Middlesex, UB5 6HU Tel: (07956) 877690 Fax: (020) 8845 1010 E-mail: hawigeorge@hotmail.com

Latham International Ltd, Rowhurst Close, Rowhurst Industrial Estate, Newcastle, Staffordshire, ST5 6BD Tel: (01782) 565364 Fax: (01782) 564886 E-mail: info@lathaminternational.com

Lenser (UK) Ltd, Winton House, Stoke Road, Stoke-On-Trent, ST4 2RW Tel: (01782) 415414 Fax: (01782) 415757 E-mail: lenseruk@aol.com

FILTER PRODUCTION MACHINERY

North East Secure Electronics Ltd, North East Innovation Centre, Neilson Road, Gateshead, Tyne & Wear, NE10 0EW Tel: 0191-477 9235 Fax: 0191-478 3639 E-mail: g.ord@neic.co.uk

FILTERING STRAINERS

Cadar Ltd, Unit 3 The Point, Market Harborough, Leicestershire, LE16 7QU Tel: (01858) 410101 Fax: (01858) 433934 E-mail: sales@cadar.ltd.uk

Filter Fabrications, 2 Pound Lane Industrial Estate, Maypole Fields, Halesowen, West Midlands, B63 2QB Tel: (01384) 635630 Fax: (01384) 566884 E-mail: info@filterfabs.co.uk

FILTERS TO SPECIFICATION

Airlec Truck & Bus Parts, Unit 24 Tomlinson Business Park, Tomlinson Road, Leyland, PR25 2DY Tel: (01772) 433564 Fax: (01772) 433568 E-mail: sales@airlec.co.uk

Induction Technology Group Ltd, Unit B Quinn Close, Coventry, CV3 4LH Tel: (024) 7630 5386 Fax: (024) 7630 7999 E-mail: sales@itgairfilters.com

FILTERS, AIR, PRE-CLEANER

Agrie Mach Ltd, Wayfarers, Domewood, Copthorne, Crawley, West Sussex, RH10 3HD Tel: (01342) 713743 Fax: (01342) 719181 E-mail: info@agriemach.com

FILTERS, CLOTH/FABRIC

Micronics Filtration, Sandbach Road, Stoke-on-Trent, ST6 2DR Tel: (01782) 284385 Fax: (01782) 284987 E-mail: info@micronicsinc.com

P G Lawton, Caldene Business Park, Burnley Road, Mytholmroyd, Hebden Bridge, West Yorkshire, HX7 5QJ Tel: (01422) 883903 Fax: (01422) 884278 E-mail: pg.lawton@uk.sglcarbon.de

Webron Marling Ltd, Hareholme Mill, Bacup Road, Rawtenstall, Rossendale, Lancashire, BB4 7JL Tel: (01706) 214001 Fax: (01706) 830003 E-mail: sales@andrewwebron.com

FILTERS, GAUZE (METALLIC)

Filter Fabrications, 2 Pound Lane Industrial Estate, Maypole Fields, Halesowen, West Midlands, B63 2QB Tel: (01384) 635630 Fax: (01384) 566884 E-mail: info@filterfabs.co.uk

Incamesh Filtration Ltd, Dingle Lane, Appleton, Warrington, WA4 3HR Tel: (01925) 261900 Fax: (01925) 860568 E-mail: sales@incamesh.co.uk

FILTERS, GLASS FIBRE OR FIBREGLASS ELEMENT

Airclean Ltd, PO Box 147, Maidstone, Kent, ME14 2LA Tel: (01622) 832777 Fax: (01622) 832507 E-mail: info@airclean.co.uk

FILTERS, WIRE WOUND

Set Square Fabrications, 19 Willow Road, Colnbrook, Slough, SL3 0BS Tel: (01753) 686212 Fax: (01753) 686212

FILTRATION BY-PASS SYSTEMS, HYDRAULIC EQUIPMENT

Hamilton Machinery Sales Ltd, Hamilton House, Broadfields, Bicester Road, Aylesbury, Bucks, HP19 8BU Tel: (01296) 318222 Fax: (01296) 397005 E-mail: john.hat@hamac.co.uk

Hydrotechnik UK Ltd, Unit 10, Easter Park, Lenton Lane, Nottingham, NG7 2PX Tel: 0115-900 3550 Fax: 0115-970 5597 E-mail: sales@hydrotechnik.co.uk

FILTRATION EQUIPMENT

Capital Water Treatment Ltd, 79a Lansdowne Road, Croydon, CR0 2BF Tel: (020) 8649 9503 Fax: (020) 8649 9504 E-mail: sales@capitalwater.co.uk

Eastfield Engineering Ltd, PO Box 232, Stafford, ST19 5QY Tel: (01785) 714794 Fax: (01785) 711373 E-mail: sales@eastfield-engineering.com

Hydac Technology Ltd, Woodstock Road, Charlbury, Charlbury, Chipping Norton, Oxfordshire, OX7 3ES Tel: (01608) 811211 Fax: (01608) 811259E-mail: info@hydac.co.uk

Hydrotechnik UK Ltd, Unit 10, Easter Park, Lenton Lane, Nottingham, NG7 2PX Tel: 0115-900 3550 Fax: 0115-970 5597 E-mail: sales@hydrotechnik.co.uk

Lenser (UK) Ltd, Winton House, Stoke Road, Stoke-On-Trent, ST4 2RW Tel: (01782) 415414 Fax: (01782) 415757 E-mail: lenseruk@aol.com

FILTRATION PLANT

Amafiltergroup Ltd, Navigation Road, Stoke-on-Trent, ST6 3RU Tel: (01782) 575611 Fax: (01782) 577001 E-mail: salesuk@amafilter.com

Arboga Darenth Ltd, Darenth Works, Ray Lamb Way, Erith, Kent, DA8 2LA Tel: (01322) 342533 Fax: (01322) 331226 E-mail: info@arbogadarenth.co.uk

Filterall Ltd, PO Box 29, Daventry, Northamptonshire, NN11 1AQ Tel: (01327) 877624 Fax: (01327) 705749 E-mail: filterall@btconnect.com

Industrial Purification Systems Ltd, Unit 10 Lea Green Business Park, St. Helens, Merseyside, WA9 4TR Tel: (01744) 811652 Fax: (01744) 833687 E-mail: info@industrial-purification.co.uk

Koch Membrane Systems, The Granary, Telegraph Street, Stafford, ST17 4AT Tel: (01785) 272500 Fax: (01785) 223149

Latham International Ltd, Rowhurst Close, Rowhurst Industrial Estate, Newcastle, Staffordshire, ST5 6BD Tel: (01782) 565364 Fax: (01782) 564886 E-mail: info@lathaminternational.com

FILTRATION PLANT, WATER, *See Water etc*

FILTRATION SPECIALIST SERVICES

British Filters Ltd, 11-12 Porsham Close, Roborough, Plymouth, PL6 7DB Tel: (01752) 703900 Fax: (01752) 703901 E-mail: pdenyer@britishfilters.co.uk

Photo Gen Ic Ltd, Unit 4 Parc Industrial Estate, Llanidloes, Powys, SY18 6RB Tel: (01686) 413292 Fax: (01686) 413425 E-mail: sales@photogenic.co.uk

FILTRATION SYSTEMS CONTRACTORS OR DESIGNERS

Arboga Darenth Ltd, Darenth Works, Ray Lamb Way, Erith, Kent, DA8 2LA Tel: (01322) 342533 Fax: (01322) 331226 E-mail: info@arbogadarenth.co.uk

Carter Environmental Engineers Ltd, 2 Lawley Middleway, Birmingham, B4 7XL Tel: 0121-250 1000 Fax: 0121-250 1400 E-mail: sales@cee.co.uk

Chainings Ltd, Pomona Works, Newent Business Park, Newent, Gloucestershire, GL18 1DZ Tel: (01531) 822244 Fax: (01531) 821555 E-mail: sales@chainings.com

Filtech 2000 Ltd, East Market Street, Newport, Gwent, NP20 2AY Tel: (01633) 253878 Fax: (01633) 267914 E-mail: bc.hydraulics@btinternet.com

Pool Filtration Ltd, 76 Stafford Road, Wallington, Surrey, SM6 9AY Tel: (020) 8669 0657 Fax: (020) 8773 0647 E-mail: poolfiltrationltd@tiscali.co.uk

▶ R S E Associates Ltd, Seascape, Main Road, Trevone, Padstow, Cornwall, PL28 8QX Tel: (01841) 520915 Fax: (01841) 520833

Spray-Trac Systems Ltd, Legram Lane, Marton-Cum-Grafton, Boroughbridge, York, YO51 9PS Tel: (01423) 322377 Fax: (01423) 324678 E-mail: sales@spraytrac.com

Sussex Water Treatment Systems, 17 Harefield Road, Bognor Regis, West Sussex, PO22 6EE Tel: (01243) 587928 Fax: (01243) 587928

T P Pumps Ltd, Pathfields Business Park, South Molton, Devon, EX36 3LH Tel: (01769) 579487 Fax: (01769) 574600 E-mail: sales@tppumps.co.uk

FINANCE BROKERS

A S C Partnership plc, 3 Park Road, London, NW1 6AS Tel: (020) 7616 6628 Fax: (020) 7616 6634 E-mail: central@asc.co.uk

▶ Allegiance Finance, 12 Royal Cresent, Cheltenham, Gloucestershire, GL50 3DA Tel: (01242) 260557 Fax: (01242) 269874 E-mail: enquiries@allegiance-finance.co.uk

▶ ASC Berkshire & Oxfordshire, Suite 7, Stubbings House, Henley Road, Maidenhead, Berkshire, SL6 6QL Tel: 01628 828220

Bedrock Business Finance Ltd, 29/30 Fleet Street, Torquay, TQ1 1BB Tel: 01803 217917 Fax: 01803 217916 E-mail: finance@bedrock.uk.com

▶ Business Engineering Ltd, 15 The Maples, Banstead, Surrey, SM7 3QZ Tel: (01737) 373121 Fax: (01737) 211837 E-mail: peter@business-engineering.co.uk

C L P Structured Finance Ltd, 131 Baker Street, London, W1U 6SE Tel: (020) 7486 0655 Fax: (020) 7935 5489 E-mail: mail@cpl.uk.com

▶ Chandler & Co., Red Hill, Wateringbury, Maidstone, Kent, ME18 5NN Tel: (01622) 817484 Fax: (01622) 817152 E-mail: info@chandlerandco.co.uk

Chase De Vere Mortgage Management Ltd, St James House, 23 Kings Street, London, SW1Y 6QY Tel: (020) 7930 7242 Fax: (020) 7930 3691 E-mail: simon.tyler@cdvmm.co.uk

▶ Commercial Factoring Ltd, Belle Grove House, Manor Court, Rogiet, Caldicot, Gwent, NP26 3TU Tel: (0845) 1235696 E-mail: admin@factoringadvice.com

Ernst & Young Ltd, George House, 50 George Square, Glasgow, G2 1RR Tel: 0141-626 5000 Fax: 0141-626 5001

▶ First Capital Finance Ltd, 360 Charminster Road, Bournemouth, BH8 9RX Tel: 01202 512233 Fax: 01202 510011 E-mail: jon.wedge@firstcapitalfinance.co.uk

▶ Haughtons Business Sales, Gladstone Street, Kibworth, Leicester, LE8 0HL Tel: 0116-279 2509 Fax: 0116-279 2509 E-mail: alan@hbsales.co.uk

Mealey Horgan plc, 16 Park Street, London, W1K 2HZ Tel: (020) 7499 4902 Fax: (020) 7499 4903 E-mail: mealyhorgan@btclick.com

Redleaf Vehicle Leasing, 28-29 Westhampnett Road, Chichester, West Sussex, PO19 7HH Tel: (08457) 669988 Fax: (01243) 780750

▶ SLJ Commercial Finance, 72 Manor Avenue South, Kidderminster, Worcestershire, DY11 6DG Tel: (01562) 744300 Fax: (01562) 744300 E-mail: admin@sljcf.co.uk

▶ Smaart Associates, 1 Farnham Road, Guildford, Surrey, GU2 4RG Tel: (01483) 549815 Fax: (01483) 549115 E-mail: info@smaart.info

Tullett Liberty Number 3 Ltd, Cable House, 54-62 New Broad Street, London, EC2M 1JJ Tel: (020) 7827 2520 Fax: (020) 7827 2859 E-mail: enquiries@tullett.com

Wilson Insurance Broking Group Ltd, Wilson House, 1-3 Waverley Street, Nottingham, NG7 4HG Tel: 0115-942 0111 Fax: 0115-942 0459 E-mail: info@wilorg.co.uk

FINANCE COMPANIES, LEASING

▶ The Accruals Bureau & Credithouse P.L.C., Spectrum House, Dunstable Road, Redbourn, St. Albans, Hertfordshire, AL3 7PR Tel: (0870) 4441753 Fax: (01582) 791203 E-mail: info@abandc.co.uk

Anglo Group Ltd, Capital House, Bond Street, Bristol, BS1 3LA Tel: (0870) 5673631 Fax: (0870) 5673649

Barclays Mercantile Business Finance Ltd, Churchill Plaza, Churchill Way, Basingstoke, Hampshire, RG21 7GP Tel: (01256) 314108 Fax: (01256) 791850 E-mail: bassf@barclays.co.uk

Calando Finance Ltd, 115a St. Johns Hill, Sevenoaks, Kent, TN13 3PE Tel: (01732) 743400 Fax: (01732) 743335 E-mail: broughfame@yahoo.com

▶ Commercial Factoring Ltd, Belle Grove House, Manor Court, Rogiet, Caldicot, Gwent, NP26 3TU Tel: (0845) 1235696 E-mail: admin@factoringadvice.com

Concord Motor Contracts Ltd, 10 Cambridge Road, Stansted, Essex, CM24 8BZ Tel: (01279) 813608 Fax: (01279) 813594 E-mail: sales@motorcontracts.com

Countrywide Fleet Services UK Ltd, West Mill House, 114 Carisbrooke Road, Newport, Isle of Wight, PO30 1DF Tel: (0870) 6080858 Fax: (0870) 6080859 E-mail: sales@countrywide-fleet.co.uk

Finova Capital P.L.C., 11 Albemarle St, London, W1S 4HH Tel: (020) 7493 5518 Fax: (020) 7493 3521

HSBC P.L.C., 12 Calthorpe Road, Edgbaston, Birmingham, B15 1QZ Tel: 0121-455 3255 Fax: 0121-455 3244

HSBC Equipment Finance (UK) Ltd, 12 Calthorpe Road, Edge Baston, Birmingham, B15 1HT Tel: 0121-450 1515 Fax: (0845) 6076067

Humberclyde Farm Finance, Northern Cross, Basing View, Basingstoke, Hampshire, RG21 4HL Tel: (0845) 2267378 Fax: (0845) 2267379 E-mail: enquiries@humberclyde.co.uk

Lombard Facilities Ltd, 3 Princess Way, Redhill, RH1 1NP Tel: (01737) 774111 Fax: (01737) 760031

Marylebone Commercial Finance Ltd, Sovereign House, P O Box 302, Manchester, M60 4AL Tel: 0161-833 2222 Fax: 0161-953 3333

▶ New Car Discount.com Ltd, Unit 7A, Kayley Industrial Estate, Richmond Street, Ashton-under-Lyne, Lancashire, OL7 0AU Tel: (08703) 500144 Fax: (08703) 500244 E-mail: sales@new-car-discount.com

State Securities plc, Jellicoe House, Grange Drive, Hedge End, Southampton, SO30 2AF Tel: (01489) 775600 Fax: (01489) 775601 E-mail: jmacklin@statesecurities.plc.uk

Tokyo Leasing UK plc, 6th Floor, Valiant House, London, EC3A 5DQ Tel: (020) 7283 6100 Fax: (020) 7283 6102

FINANCE COMPANIES, OVERSEAS PROJECT OR INTERNATIONAL TRADE

British Arab Commercial Bank Ltd, 8-10 Manson House Place, London, EC4N 8BJ Tel: (020) 7648 7777 Fax: (020) 7600 3318

Dashwood Finance Co. Ltd, Georgian House, 63 Coleman Street, London, EC2R 5BB Tel: (020) 7588 3215 Fax: (020) 7588 4818 E-mail: dashwood.group@virgin.net

▶ Factoring Partners, The Cottage, Bearley Road, Snitterfield, Stratford-upon-Avon, Warwickshire, CV37 0JH Tel: (01789) 730137 Fax: (01789) 730137 E-mail: julian@factor-broker.co.uk

Pritt & Co. Ltd, 23 Pembridge Square, London, W2 4DR Tel: (020) 7221 0909 Fax: (020) 7727 4837 E-mail: sales@pritt.co.uk

FINANCE COMPANIES/AGENTS/ FINANCIAL SERVICES, *See also other nearby headings for particular types*

1st Contact, Clydesdale Bank House, 33 Regent Street, London, SW1Y 4ZT Tel: (0800) 0393082 Fax: (020) 7494 4334 E-mail: info@1st-contact.co.uk

Agricultural Mortgage Corporation Plc, Charlton Place, Charlton Road, Andover, Hampshire, SP10 1RE Tel: (01264) 334747 Fax: (01264) 334614 E-mail: info@amconline.co.uk

Air & General Finance Ltd, Tolworth Tower, Ewell Road, Surbiton, Surrey, KT6 7EL Tel: (020) 8390 9444 Fax: (020) 8390 8211 E-mail: office@airandgeneral.com

Anglo Irish Asset Finance plc, Town Centre House, Southam Road, Banbury, Oxfordshire, OX16 2EN Tel: (01295) 755500 Fax: (01295) 755100

Anglo Irish Bank, 10 Old Jewry, London, EC2R 8DN Tel: (020) 7710 7000 Fax: (020) 7710 7050 E-mail: enquiries@angloirishbank.co.uk

Aon Ltd, 145 St Vincent Street, Glasgow, G2 5JF Tel: 0141-222 7000 Fax: 0141-222 3345

British Markitex Ltd, PO Box 52, Waltham Cross, Hertfordshire, EN8 7AF Tel: (01992) 650455 Fax: (01992) 700319 E-mail: markitex@compuserve.com

Capita Financial Ltd, Beaufort House, 15 St. Botolph Street, London, EC3A 7HH Tel: (020) 7556 8800 Fax: (020) 7556 8850

Capita Hartshead, Castle House, Park Road, Banstead, Surrey, SM7 3BX Tel: (01737) 357272 Fax: (01737) 363106 E-mail: enquires@captia.co.uk

Carlton Corporate Finance Ltd, 38 Berkeley Square, London, W1J 5AE Tel: (020) 7355 2211 Fax: (020) 7355 1633 E-mail: ccf@carltoncf.com

FINANCE COMPANIES/AGENTS/ FINANCIAL SERVICES – *continued*

Cattles plc, Kingston House Centre 27 Business Park, Woodhead Road, Birstall, Batley, West Yorkshire, WF17 9TD Tel: (01924) 444466 Fax: (01924) 442255

▶ Charterhouse Group International Plc, 2nd Floor, 37 Lombard Street, London, United Kingdom, EC3V 9BQ Tel: 0800 634 4848 Fax: 0800 634 4849 E-mail: sales@charterhouseplc.com

Co-Operative Society Ltd, 189 Hamilton Road, Felixstowe, Suffolk, IP11 7DT Tel: (01394) 283085 Fax: (01394) 279629

Countrywide Principal Services, Sovereign House, Hockliffe Street, Leighton Buzzard, Bedfordshire, LU7 1GT Tel: (01525) 383084 Fax: (01525) 850285

Dalbeattie Finance Co. Ltd, Maxwell Street, Dalbeattie, Kirkcudbrightshire, DG5 4AJ Tel: (01556) 610243 Fax: (01556) 611717 E-mail: info@dalbeattiefinance.co.uk

▶ Finesco Financial Services Ltd, 6 Woodside Cresent, Glasgow, G3 7UL Tel: 0141-332 3113 Fax: 0141-331 2039 E-mail: sales@finesco.co.uk

Fortis Bank, 5 Aldermanbury Square, London, EC2V 7HR Tel: (020) 7444 8000 Fax: (020) 7444 8888

G E Commercial Finance Ltd, 24 Bennetts Hill, Birmingham, B2 5QP Tel: 0121-616 3400 Fax: 0121-616 3418

Garban Intercapital, Park House, Finsbury Circus, London, EC2M 7UR Tel: (020) 7638 7592 Fax: (020) 7374 6743

Gmac Commercial Finance Plc, Sovereign House, Church St, Brighton, BN1 3WX Tel: (01273) 864069 Fax: (01273) 771501 E-mail: info@gmaccf.co.uk

GML International Ltd, Knighton House, 56 Mortimer Street, London, W1W 7RT Tel: (020) 7580 8588 Fax: (020) 7580 8688 E-mail: info@gml.net

HFC Bank Ltd, North Street, Winkfield, Windsor, Berkshire, SL4 4TD Tel: (01344) 890000 Fax: (01344) 890014

▶ HLB International, 21 Ebury Street, London, SW1W 0LD Tel: (020) 7881 1100 Fax: (020) 7881 1109 E-mail: mailbox@hlbi.com

HSBC P.L.C., 12 Calthorpe Road, Edgbaston, Birmingham, B15 1QZ Tel: 0121-455 3255 Fax: 0121-455 3244

HSBC Invoice Finance, 12 Calthorpe Road, Edgbaston, Birmingham, B15 1RA Tel: 0121-455 2611 Fax: 0121-455 2190 E-mail: sales@invoicefinance.hsbc.co.uk

Intrum Justitia Group, Warwick House, Birmingham Road, Stratford-Upon-Avon, Warwickshire, CV37 0BP Tel: (01789) 415181 Fax: (01789) 412072

Invesco Asset Management Ltd, 30 Finsbury Square, London, EC2A 1AG Tel: (020) 7065 4000 Fax: (020) 7638 0752 E-mail: enquiry@invescoperpetual.co.uk

Investors Planning Associates Ltd, Mimosa House, 12 Princes Street, Hanover Square, London, W1B 2LL Tel: (020) 7499 0325 Fax: (020) 7408 0640

J M Marriott & Co, Storey House White Cross, South Road, Lancaster, LA1 4XF Tel: (01524) 845611 Fax: (01524) 845612 E-mail: jmt@jmmarriott.co.uk

▶ Ledingham Chalmers, Critchton House, Critchton Close, Edinburgh, EH8 8DT Tel: 0131-200 1000 Fax: 0131-200 1080

Lewis Group Plc, Lawrence House, Riverside Drive, Cleckheaton, West Yorkshire, BD19 4DH Tel: (01274) 852000 Fax: (01274) 862602

Lloyds T S B, St. William House, Tresillian Terrace, Cardiff, CF10 5BH Tel: (029) 2029 6000 Fax: (0870) 8503105

Lloyds T S B Development Capital Ltd, 45 Old Bond Street, London, W1S 4QT Tel: (020) 7499 1500 Fax: (020) 7647 2000 E-mail: info@ldc.co.uk

Lombard Facilities Ltd, 3 Princess Way, Redhill, RH1 1NP Tel: (01737) 774111 Fax: (01737) 760031

London Financial Group, 19 Hillcroft Crescent, Ealing, London, W5 2SG Tel: (020) 8810 8801 Fax: (020) 8663 9087 E-mail: info@londonfinancial.co.uk

▶ M G T Ltd, P O Box 200, Kirkcaldy, Fife, KY2 6WD Tel: (0870) 8407000 Fax: (0870) 8407001

M M & K Ltd, 1 Bengal Court, London, EC3V 9DD Tel: (020) 7283 7200 Fax: (020) 7283 4119 E-mail: info@mm-k.com

▶ Macfarlane Gray Group, 15 Gladstone Place, Stirling, FK8 2NX Tel: (01786) 451745 Fax: (01786) 472528

▶ Melville Craig, Harbourside House, Ocean Square, 110 Commercial Street, Edinburgh, EH6 6NF Tel: 0131-555 4321 Fax: 0131-555 4224

▶ Millnet Financial Ltd, Stapleton House, 29-33 Scrutton Street, London, EC2A 4HU Tel: (020) 7375 2300 Fax: (020) 7422 8888 E-mail: help@efinancialcareers.com

Mortgage Shop Ltd, King Georges Chambers, 1 St. James Square, Bacup, Lancashire, OL13 9AA Tel: (01706) 875746 Fax: (01706) 875122 E-mail: mortgageshopltd@btconnect.com

N I I B Group Ltd, 26-32 Central Avenue, Bangor, County Down, BT20 3AS Tel: (028) 9146 9415 Fax: (028) 9147 4455 E-mail: support@boiuk.co.uk

Quayle Munro Ltd, 8 Charlotte Square, Edinburgh, EH2 4DR Tel: 0131-226 4421 Fax: 0131-225 3391

Quester Capital Management Ltd, 29 Queen Annes Gate, London, SW1H 9BU Tel: (020) 7222 5472 Fax: (020) 7222 5250 E-mail: sales@quester.co.uk

Rathbone Brothers plc, 159 New Bond Street, London, W1S 2UD Tel: (020) 7399 0000 Fax: (020) 7399 0011 E-mail: marketing@rathbones.com

The Results Corporation Ltd, Pendragon House, 170 Merton High Street, London, SW19 1AY Tel: (0870) 2201748 Fax: (020) 8241 3333 E-mail: gds@gordonsknight.co.uk

▶ T B Dunn & Co., Albert House, 308 Albert Drive, Glasgow, G41 5RS Tel: 0141-429 1700 Fax: 0141-420 1397

United Trade & Services Ltd, 256 Water Road, Wembley, Middlesex, HA0 1HX Tel: (020) 8810 6444 Fax: (020) 8810 6455 E-mail: united.trade@btinternet.com

Uswitch.Com, Portland House, Stag Place, London, SW1E 5BH Tel: (0800) 0930607 Fax: (020) 7233 5933 E-mail: sales@uswitch.com

FINANCE CONSULTANTS, *See also Independent Financial Advisers*

A W D Chase Devere P.L.C., 10 Paternoster Square, London, EC4M 7DY Tel: (020) 7828 9297 Fax: (020) 7248 7742 E-mail: enquiries@awdplc.com

Anchor Trust Co. Ltd, PO Box 496, Jersey, JE4 5TD Tel: (01534) 887211 Fax: (01534) 887212 E-mail: anchor@jerseyoffice.com

Anglo Irish Bank, 10 Old Jewry, London, EC2R 8DN Tel: (020) 7710 7000 Fax: (020) 7710 7050 E-mail: enquiries@angloirishbank.co.uk

Carlton Corporate Finance Ltd, 38 Berkeley Square, London, W1J 5AE Tel: (020) 7355 2211 Fax: (020) 7355 1633 E-mail: ccf@carltoncf.com

Chase De Vere Mortgage Management Ltd, St James House, 23 Kings Street, London, SW1Y 6QY Tel: (020) 7930 7242 Fax: (020) 7930 3691 E-mail: simon.tyler@cdvmm.co.uk

Countrywide Principal Services, Sovereign House, Hockliffe Street, Leighton Buzzard, Bedfordshire, LU7 1GT Tel: (01525) 383084 Fax: (01525) 850285

D F C Ltd, 141-143 Drury Lane, London, WC2B 5TB Tel: (020) 7836 3424 Fax: (020) 7379 4931 E-mail: london@thedfcgroup.com

Davis International Banking Consultants (UK) Ltd, 42 Brook Street, London, W1K 5DB Tel: (020) 7958 9008 Fax: (020) 7958 9275 E-mail: dibc@dibc.co.uk

Douglas Deakin Young Ltd, 22-25a Sackville Street, London, W1S 3HQ Tel: (020) 7439 3344 Fax: (020) 7439 3402 E-mail: enquiries@ddy.co.uk

▶ Eastside Consulting, 91 Brick Lane, London, E1 6QL Tel: 020 77706144 E-mail: trevor@eastsideconsulting.co.uk

Facts & Figures Scotland Ltd, 4 Polwarth Gardens, Edinburgh, EH11 1LW Tel: 0131-221 0330 Fax: 0131-221 0770

G E Commercial Finance Ltd, 24 Bennetts Hill, Birmingham, B2 5QP Tel: 0121-616 3400 Fax: 0121-616 3418

Harris Kafton, 54-58 High Street, Edgware, Middlesex, HA8 7EJ Tel: (020) 8381 3770 Fax: (020) 8381 3470

Charles Hurst Group, 62 Boucher Road, Belfast, BT12 6LR Tel: (028) 9038 1721 Fax: (028) 9066 4688

Ibcc, 9 Ferndown Close, Bristol, BS11 0UP Tel: 0117-968 2691 Fax: 0117-962 6500 E-mail: ibcc@btinternet.com

Michael Kennedy, 43 Hillbeck Crescent, Nottingham, NG8 2EZ Tel: 0115-913 8167 Fax: (0870) 7120591 E-mail: kennedy@grantsuk.fsbusiness.co.uk

Mason & Ball & Associates Ltd, Bourn House, Park Street, Bagshot, Surrey, GU19 5AQ Tel: (01276) 472774 Fax: (01276) 451520 E-mail: mail@mba-uk.co.uk

Planmaster Systems Ltd, York House, Wycombe End, Beaconsfield, Buckinghamshire, HP9 1XA Tel: (01494) 672184 Fax: (01494) 670218 E-mail: sales@planmaster.co.uk

R M Walkden & Co. Ltd, 14 Pensioners Court The Charterhouse, Charterhouse Square, London, EC1M 6AU Tel: (020) 7253 6677 Fax: (020) 7253 2154

Siemens Financial Services Ltd, Townsend House, 160 Northolt Road, Harrow, Middlesex, HA2 0PG Tel: (020) 8422 7101 Fax: (020) 8422 4402 E-mail: enquiries.leasing@sfs-uk.com

Stonehage Ltd, 21 Dartmouth Street, London, SW1H 9BP Tel: (020) 7799 3159 Fax: (020) 7799 3236

FINANCE FACTORING SERVICES

▶ The Accruals Bureau & Credithouse P.L.C., Spectrum House, Dunstable Road, Redbourn, St. Albans, Hertfordshire, AL3 7PR Tel: (0870) 4441753 Fax: (01582) 791203 E-mail: info@abandc.co.uk

▶ ASC Berkshire & Oxfordshire, Suite 7, Stubbings House, Henley Road, Maidenhead, Berkshire, SL6 6QL Tel: 01628 828220

B C R Publishing Ltd, 3 Cobden Court, Wimpole Close, Bromley, BR2 9JF Tel: (020) 8466 6987 Fax: (020) 8466 0654 E-mail: bcr@bcrpub.co.uk

The Boss Corporation, 31 Wren Gardens, Alderholt, Fordingbridge, Hampshire, SP6 3PJ Tel: (0845) 2574685 Fax: (0871) 4332393 E-mail: sales@thebosscorporation.co.uk

▶ Cattles Invoice Finance Ltd, St. James House, Charlotte Street, Manchester, M1 4DZ Tel: 0161-237 1483 Fax: (0870) 0438333 E-mail: hotline@cattlesif.co.uk

Close Invoice Finance Ltd, 25 Bartholomew Street, Newbury, Berkshire, RG14 5LL Tel: (01635) 31517 Fax: (01635) 521180 E-mail: sales@closeinvoice.co.uk

The F D A, Boston House, Little Green, Richmond, Surrey, TW9 1QE Tel: (020) 8332 9955 Fax: (020) 8332 2585 E-mail: nicola.breeze@thefda.org.uk

▶ Factoring Partners, The Cottage, Bearley Road, Snitterfield, Stratford-upon-Avon, Warwickshire, CV37 0JH Tel: (01789) 730137 Fax: (01789) 730137 E-mail: julian@factor-broker.co.uk

Factoring UK Ltd, Gildredge Road, Eastbourne, East Sussex, BN21 4SA Tel: (01323) 411770 Fax: (01323) 430014 E-mail: info@factoringuk.com

G E Commercial Finance, Enterprise House, Bancroft Road, Reigate, Surrey, RH2 7RT Tel: (01737) 841200 Fax: (01737) 841357

Gmac Commercial Finance Plc, Sovereign House, Church St, Brighton, BN1 3WX Tel: (01273) 864069 Fax: (01273) 771501 E-mail: info@gmaccf.co.uk

HSBC Bank plc, 21 Farncombe Road, Worthing, West Sussex, BN11 2BW Tel: (0800) 343435 Fax: (01903) 214101 E-mail: info@invoicefinance.hsbc.co.uk

▶ Invoice Finance Ltd, Highfield Close, Kenilworth, Warwickshire, CV8 1QR Tel: (01926) 512876 Fax: (01926) 512876 E-mail: brianbwood@aol.com

Irons Bros Ltd, Factory, St. Breock, Wadebridge, Cornwall, PL27 7JP Tel: (01208) 812635 Fax: (01208) 814884 E-mail: sales@ironsbrothers.com

Lloys TSB Commercial Finance, 1 Brookhill Way, Banbury, Oxfordshire, OX16 3EL Tel: (01295) 272272 Fax: (01295) 272246 E-mail: sue.baker@ltsbcf.co.uk

▶ Mortgage Advice Co., 111 Union Street, Glasgow, G1 3TA Tel: 0141-204 5770 Fax: 0141-221 4055 E-mail: sales@mortgageadvicecompany.co.uk

▶ Regency Factors plc, 2 Regency Chambers, Jubilee Way, Bury, Lancashire, BL9 0JW Tel: 0161-761 4017 Fax: 0161-761 4018 E-mail: info@regencyfactors.com

Silverburn Finance UK Ltd, 76 Winter Hey Lane, Horwich, Bolton, BL6 7PQ Tel: (01204) 432369 Fax: (01204) 693471

Ulster Factors Ltd, 7 North Street, Belfast, BT1 1NH Tel: (028) 9032 4522 Fax: (028) 9023 0336 E-mail: wjm@ulsterfactors.com

FINANCE PLANNING CONSULTANTS, PERSONAL

Bradford & Bingley plc, PO Box 88, Bingley, West Yorkshire, BD16 2UA Tel: (01274) 555555 Fax: (01274) 554422 E-mail: enquiries@bbg.co.uk

First National, First National House, 15 College Road, Harrow, Middlesex, HA1 1BY Tel: (020) 8909 4646

▶ I Need That Mortgage.com, 129 High St, Watton at Stone, Hertford, SG14 3SB Tel: 0870 991 7255 Fax: 07005 931146 E-mail: salesinformation@ineedthatmortgage.com

FINANCE SOFTWARE

Advice By Telephone Ltd, 306 St. Marys Lane, Upminster, Essex, RM14 3HL Tel: (01708) 640110 Fax: (01708) 224802 E-mail: admin@advice.uk.com

Ansty Computer Systems, 1 North Cottages, Cuckfield Road, Ansty, Haywards Heath, West Sussex, RH17 5AG Tel: (01444) 455760 Fax: (01444) 458067 E-mail: peterhutchinson@lineone.net

Apak Group plc, Apak House Badminton Court, Station Road, Yate, Bristol, BS37 5HZ Tel: (01454) 871000 Fax: (01454) 871199 E-mail: enquiries@apakgroup.com

Blem Information Management Ltd, Fox House, 135 High Street, Bromley, BR1 1JF Tel: (020) 8313 1616 Fax: (020) 8313 1919 E-mail: info@blem.com

Boot Computers Ltd, Stapeley House, London Road, Stapeley, Nantwich, Cheshire, CW5 7JW Tel: (01270) 611299 Fax: (01270) 611302

Cing Technologies Ltd, 3 Malt House Cottages, 31 Byfield Road, Chipping Warden, Banbury, Oxfordshire, OX17 1LE Tel: (01295) 660682 E-mail: nigel.galletly@cingtech.com

Codis Ltd, 38-44 St Anns Road, Harrow, Middlesex, HA1 1LA Tel: (020) 8861 0610 Fax: (020) 8515 7049 E-mail: codis@codis.co.uk

Comverse Kenan UK, 1a Stoke Road, Slough, SL2 5AA Tel: (01753) 745300 Fax: (01753) 745304

Dancerace plc, 2 Brock Street, Bath, BA1 2LN Tel: (0870) 7773033 Fax: (0870) 7772022 E-mail: info@dancerace.com

Dataday Computer Services, Chalfont House, Hampden Road, Chalfont St. Peter, Gerrards Cross, Buckinghamshire, SL9 9RY Tel: (01753) 892112 Fax: (01753) 892113

Derivity Ltd, Chiltern House, 45 Station Road, Henley-on-Thames, Oxfordshire, RG9 1AT Tel: (01491) 845345 Fax: (01491) 845501 E-mail: info@derivity.com

Diamond Management Services Ltd, Diamond House, 149 Frimley Road, Camberley, Surrey, GU15 2PS Tel: (01276) 691415 Fax: (01276) 692903 E-mail: info@dms-management.com

Econintel Treasury Systems Ltd, The Octagon, 27 Middleborough, Colchester, CO1 1TG Tel: (01206) 760033 Fax: (01206) 760133 E-mail: colchester@econintel.com

Filenet Ltd, Waterside House 4 Cowley Business Park, High Street, Cowley, Uxbridge, Middlesex, UB8 2FN Tel: (01895) 207300 Fax: (01895) 207365

Functionpoint Ltd, Newlands Cottage, Weedon Hill, Hyde Heath, Amersham, Buckinghamshire, HP6 5RN Tel: (01494) 791995 Fax: (01494) 792014 E-mail: alan@functionpoint.co.uk

General Systems Ltd, Stockport Road, Cheadle, Cheshire, SK8 2AA Tel: 0161-495 6700 Fax: 0161-495 6701

H P D Software Ltd, Aspley House, 176 Upper Richmond Road, London, SW15 2SH Tel: (020) 8780 6800 Fax: (020) 8780 6801 E-mail: sales@hpdsoftware.com

I P L Information Processing Ltd, Eveleigh House, Grove Street, Bath, BA1 5LR Tel: (01225) 475000 Fax: (01225) 444400 E-mail: sales@iplbath.com

Information Systems For Business Ltd, 80 Buttermarket Street, Warrington, WA1 2NN Tel: (01925) 240240 Fax: (01925) 240250 E-mail: sales@isbl.co.uk

Interface D C B Technolgy Ltd, Tyler Close, Normanton Industrial Estate, Normanton, West Yorkshire, WF6 1RL Tel: (01924) 224929 Fax: (01924) 224939 E-mail: general@interf.co.uk

Justcroft International Ltd, Justcroft House, High Street, Staplehurst, Tonbridge, Kent, TN12 0AH Tel: (01580) 893333 Fax: (01580) 893399 E-mail: sales@justcroft.com

Kaniko Computing, 23 Edward Road, Harrow, Middlesex, HA2 6QB Tel: (020) 8861 6543 Fax: (020) 8861 6543 E-mail: kanikoc@aol.com

Kramer Lee & Associates Ltd, Vermont House, Chrisy Close, Southfields Business Park, Basildon, Essex, SS15 6EA Tel: (01268) 494500 Fax: (01268) 494555 E-mail: info@kramerlee.com

Lake Financial Systems, Stable Mews Beechwoods Estate, Elmete Lane, Leeds, LS8 2LQ Tel: 0113-273 7788 Fax: 0113-273 9300 E-mail: info@lake.co.uk

Lawson Software, Building C Trinity Court, Wokingham Road, Bracknell, Berkshire, RG42 1PL Tel: (01344) 360273 Fax: (01344) 868351

Lynx Ltd, 269 Banbury Road, Oxford, OX2 7JF Tel: (01865) 310150 Fax: (01865) 310499

Macdonald Associates Ltd, 6 Cecil Aldin Drive, Tilehurst, Reading, RG31 6YP Tel: 0118-945 2862 Fax: 0118-962 4854 E-mail: info@macd.com

Misys P.L.C., Burleigh House, Chapel Oak, Salford Priors, Evesham, Worcestershire, WR11 8SP Tel: (01386) 871373 Fax: (01386) 871045

Qubix International Ltd, Highclere House, 5 High Street, Knaphill, Woking, Surrey, GU21 2PG Tel: (01483) 480222 Fax: (01483) 473050 E-mail: sales@qubixinternational.com

Risk Factor Solutions Ltd, Units B-C Kemps Farm, London Road, Balcombe, Haywards Heath, West Sussex, RH17 6JH Tel: (01444) 819460 Fax: (01444) 819461 E-mail: info@riskfactor-solutions.com

Ritz Software Ltd, 139 High Sreet, Farnborough, Orpington, Kent, BR6 7AZ Tel: (01689) 860444 Fax: (01689) 856234 E-mail: sales@ritzaccounts.co.uk

Rockport Software Ltd, 551 Fairlie Road, Slough, SL1 4PY Tel: (01753) 577201 Fax: (01753) 577202 E-mail: info@rockportsoft.com

Synergy Financial Systems Ltd, 8-9 Edison Village, Nottingham Science Technology Park, Nottingham, NG7 2RF Tel: 0115-967 7933 Fax: 0115-967 7933 E-mail: info@synergy-sf.com

▶ VeriSIM Ltd, Forsyth House, Rosyth Europarc, Rosyth, Dunfermline, Fife, KY11 2UU Tel: (01383) 428059 Fax: (01383) 428060

Web Applications, Hollinwood Business Centre, Albert Street, Oldham, OL8 3QL Tel: 0161-682 6565 Fax: 0161-682 6969 E-mail: kamal@webappuk.com

Welcom Software Ltd, The Exchange, Station Parade, Harrogate, North Yorkshire, HG1 1TS Tel: (0845) 4565859 Fax: E-mail: info@welcom.co.uk

David Winrow Marketing, PO Box 9, Northwich, Cheshire, CW9 7TP Tel: (01606) 41241 Fax: (01606) 47847 E-mail: sales@winrow.co.uk

X K O Group P.L.C., Clyde House, 16 Milburn Avenue, Oldbrook, Milton Keynes, MK6 2WA Tel: (01908) 295400 Fax: (01908) 393633

X-GL Systems Ltd, 24 Hunters Reach, Waltham Cross, Hertfordshire, EN7 6HQ Tel: (01992) 638763 Fax: (0870) 0521734 E-mail: sales@xgl.com

Zipzap Ltd, Unit 18 Exchange Road, Lincoln, LN6 3JZ Tel: (01522) 684705 Fax: (01522) 684627 E-mail: sales@zipzap.co.uk

FINANCIAL ADVICE

▶ Anglia Financial Services, 106 Hellesdon Park Road, Drayton High Road, Norwich, NR6 5DR Tel: (01603) 418320 Fax: (01603) 418320 E-mail: sales@anglia.demon.co.uk

▶ Barrie Scott & Co., 16-18 Weir Street, Falkirk, FK1 1RA Tel: (01324) 637654 Fax: (01324) 635678

▶ Bevington Evans & Associates, 53 Harrowby Street, Cardiff, CF10 5GA Tel: (029) 2048 5221 Fax: (029) 2048 5231 E-mail: cbevev@ntlbusiness.com

Brewin Dolphin Securities, 1 Courthouse Square, Dundee, DD1 1NH Tel: (01382) 317200 Fax: (01382) 317201 E-mail: david.chalmers@blw.co.uk

▶ Chamberlain Corporate Advisors, Gatsby Court, 1 Holliday Street, Birmingham, B1 1TJ Tel: 0121-248 5400 Fax: 0121-551 9606 E-mail: james@thechamberlaingroup.com

▶ Corporate Turnaround Services, 30 Nicholds Close, Bilston, West Midlands, WV14 9JS Tel: (07813) 102014 Fax: (0870) 1681652 E-mail: paul_brindley@talk21.com

▶ Emenex (Financial) Ltd, Fen Drayton House, Park Lane, Fen Drayton, Cambridge, CB4 5SW Tel: (01954) 232078 E-mail: julianredman@emenex.com

▶ First Spread Bet Ltd, 87 Boclair Road Milngavie, Glasgow, G62 6EP Tel: 013606 20745 E-mail: list@financial-spread-betting.com

Liverpool Victoria Financial Advice Services Ltd, County Gates, Bournemouth, BH1 2NF Tel: (0845) 6020690 Fax: (01202) 292253 E-mail: sales@liverpoolvictoria.co.uk

▶ Magellan Capital, 51 Lowther Road, London, SW13 9NT Tel: (07976) 878417 Fax: (020) 8741 7702 E-mail: info@magellan-capital.com

Morses Club Ltd, 1 Watery Lane, St. Johns, Worcester, WR2 5UA Tel: (01905) 425051 Fax: (01905) 615443

▶ Mortgage Port Ltd, 6 St John's Hill, Shrewsbury, SY1 1JD Tel: (0870) 9509600 E-mail: oneport@shawsolutions.co.uk

▶ Origin Financial Solutions, 3 Parkgate Croft, Mosborough, Sheffield, S20 5DX Tel: 0114-248 8844 Fax: (0871) 2423782 E-mail: seanlee@thinkpositive.co.uk

▶ Surrex Financial Management, 2 Paddock Road, Ashford, Kent, TN23 5WH Tel: (01233) 665812 Fax: (01903) 261550 E-mail: walterb@surrexfm.com

▶ Taxcafe, 214 High Street, Kirkcaldy, Fife, KY1 1JT Tel: (01592) 560081

▶ Think Smart Finance Ltd, 778 High Road, London, N12 9QR Tel: (020) 8445 5428

Wilson Insurance Broking Group Ltd, Wilson House, 1-3 Waverley Street, Nottingham, NG7 4HG Tel: 0115-942 0111 Fax: 0115-942 0459 E-mail: info@wilorg.co.uk

FINANCIAL CUSTOMER SERVICES

▶ Magellan Capital, 51 Lowther Road, London, SW13 9NT Tel: (07976) 878417 Fax: (020) 8741 7702 E-mail: info@magellan-capital.com

FINANCIAL FUTURES BROKERS/ DEALERS

Chicago Mercantile Exchange Inc, Mark Douglas Blundell, Chicago Mercantile Exchange Inc., London, EC3R 8HN Tel: (020) 7623 2550 Fax: (020) 7623 2565 E-mail: cme@cmeurope.co.uk

FINANCIAL HUMAN RESOURCES (HR) CONSULTANCY

▶ Indigo HR Consulting Ltd, Oxford Cottage, 22 Conisboro Avenue Caversham, Reading, RG4 7JB Tel: (07949) 552403 E-mail: louise@indigohr.com

FINANCIAL HUMAN RESOURCES (HR) SERVICES

▶ Indigo HR Consulting Ltd, Oxford Cottage, 22 Conisboro Avenue Caversham, Reading, RG4 7JB Tel: (07949) 552403 E-mail: louise@indigohr.com

FINANCIAL INFORMATION SERVICES

C A F (Charities Aid Foundation), 25 Kings Hill Avenue, West Malling, Kent, ME19 4TA Tel: (01732) 520000 Fax: (01732) 520001 E-mail: enquiries@cafonline.org

Calkin Pattinson & Co. Ltd, 40 Piccadilly, London, W1J 0HR Tel: (020) 7734 2176 Fax: (020) 7437 0604 E-mail: info@calkin.org

Ember J D Insurance, Belhaven House, 67 Walton Road, East Molesey, Surrey, KT8 0DP Tel: (020) 8941 2204 Fax: (020) 8979 9796 E-mail: ember1970@hotmail.com

Interactive Data, Fitzroy House, 13/17 Epworth Street, London, EC2A 4DL Tel: (020) 7825 8000 Fax: (020) 7251 2725 E-mail: investorrelations@interactivedatercorp.com

Jammal Trust Bank, 80 Berkeley Court, London, NW1 5ND Tel: (020) 7486 1314 Fax: (020) 7486 1315

▶ Magellan Capital, 51 Lowther Road, London, SW13 9NT Tel: (07976) 878417 Fax: (020) 8741 7702 E-mail: info@magellan-capital.com

▶ Stephens Associates, 14 Buckingham Street, London, WC2N 6DF Tel: (020) 7925 0200 Fax: (020) 7925 0235 E-mail: stephens@stephens.co.uk

FINANCIAL INFORMATION SERVICES, MARKET DATA

▶ Project Finance International, Aldgate House, 33 Aldgate High Street, London, EC3N 1DL Tel: 020 73697454 Fax: 020 73697333 E-mail: marketing@tfn.com

FINANCIAL PRINTING

Burrups Ltd, St. Ives House, Lavington Street, London, SE1 0NX Tel: (020) 7928 8844 Fax: (020) 7902 6572 E-mail: london@burrups.com

C & R, Bruce House, Warren Park Way, Enderby, LE19 4ZW Tel: 0116-284 7464 Fax: 0116-284 7440 E-mail: info@candr.co.uk

Cgi Europe, Unit C3 Enterprise Business Park, Millharbour, London, E14 9TE Tel: (020) 7531 0500 Fax: (020) 7531 0531

Fisherprint Ltd, Padholme Road, Peterborough, PE1 5UL Tel: (01733) 341444 Fax: (01733) 349416 E-mail: enquiries@fisherprint.co.uk

Jones & Palmer Ltd, 95 Carver Street, Birmingham, B1 3AR Tel: 0121-236 9007 Fax: 0121-236 5513 E-mail: info@jonesandpalmer.co.uk

▶ Menzies Nunn Ltd, The Wallows Industrial Estate, Fens Pool Avenue, Brierley Hill, West Midlands, DY5 1QA Tel: (01384) 262148 Fax: (01384) 265136 E-mail: sales@menzies-nunn.co.uk

FINANCIAL SERVICES, BLOCK DISCOUNTING, CONSTRUCTION INDUSTRY

▶ Saracen Finance, The Old Barn, Hall Farm, Main Street, Kirklington, Newark, Nottinghamshire, NG22 8NN Tel: (01636) 815685 Fax: (01636) 817859 E-mail: vstrachan@saracenfinance.com

FINANCIAL SERVICES, HIRE PURCHASE, CONSTRUCTION INDUSTRY

▶ Saracen Finance, The Old Barn, Hall Farm, Main Street, Kirklington, Newark, Nottinghamshire, NG22 8NN Tel: (01636) 815685 Fax: (01636) 817859 E-mail: vstrachan@saracenfinance.com

FINANCIAL SERVICES, RETAIL

▶ Handscombe Financial Planning Ltd, Telford House, 102 Collingdon Street, Luton, LU1 1RX Tel: (01582) 400202 Fax: (01582) 400951 E-mail: advice@handscombes.com

FINANCIAL STAFF RECRUITMENT AGENCIES

Accountancy Support Reading Ltd, 8 Hencroft St North, Slough, SL1 1RD Tel: (01753) 533006 Fax: (01753) 533002 E-mail: andy@accountancysupport.co.uk

The Aristotle Corporation, Blenheim House, 56 Old Steine, Brighton, BN1 1NH Tel: (01273) 222400 Fax: (01273) 778464 E-mail: candidates@aristotlecorp.com

Badenoch & Clark, 16-18 New Bridge Street, London, EC4V 6HU Tel: (020) 7583 0073 Fax: (020) 7353 3908 E-mail: corp.comms@badenochandclark.com

▶ Byron Finance, 41 London Road, Reigate, Surrey, RH2 9QE Tel: (01737) 228777 Fax: (01737) 735200 E-mail: recruitment@byronfinance.com

E G Recruitment Ltd, 56 Meldon Terrace, Newbiggin-by-the-Sea, Northumberland, NE64 6XH Tel: (01670) 858834 Fax: (01865) 400166 E-mail: eddie@egrecruitment.co.uk

Great Fleet P.L.C., 85 Gracechurch Street, London, EC3V 0AA Tel: (0845) 8810700 Fax: (0845) 8810723 E-mail: info@greatfleet.co.uk

Kotschy Pauline Associates, 83 Mansel Street, Swansea, SA1 5TY Tel: (01792) 472725 Fax: (01792) 479828 E-mail: info@paulinek.com

▶ Grant Lawson Ltd, Albany House, 14 Shute End, Wokingham, Berkshire, RG40 1BJ Tel: 0118-979 6023 Fax: (07092) 382965

Martin Ward Anderson Ltd, 7 Savoy Court, The Strand, London, WC2R 0EL Tel: (020) 7240 2233 Fax: (020) 7240 8818 E-mail: info@martinwardanderson.com

People Agenda Ltd, 167 Watling St West, Towcester, Northamptonshire, NN12 6BX Tel: (01327) 354871 Fax: (01327) 358799 E-mail: sales@peopleagenda.com

Robert Half International, 1st Floor, 2 Thames Avenue, Windsor, Berkshire, SL4 1QP Tel: (01753) 835900 Fax: (01753) 835901 E-mail: windsor@roberthalf.co.uk

FINANCIAL SYSTEMS SERVICES

C A F (Charities Aid Foundation), 25 Kings Hill Avenue, West Malling, Kent, ME19 4TA Tel: (01732) 520000 Fax: (01732) 520001 E-mail: enquiries@cafonline.org

Electronic Payments & Commerce Ltd, 139 Tankerton Road, Whitstable, Kent, CT5 2AW Tel: (01227) 273000 E-mail: epaycom@compuserve.com

Planmaster Systems Ltd, York House, Wycombe End, Beaconsfield, Buckinghamshire, HP9 1XA Tel: (01494) 672184 Fax: (01494) 670218 E-mail: sales@planmaster.co.uk

FINE ART CONSULTANCY

Christies International P.L.C., 8 King Street, St. James's, London, SW1Y 6QT Tel: (020) 7839 9060 Fax: (020) 7839 1611 E-mail: info@christies.com

▶ Jiq Jaq Gallery, 112 Heath Street, London, NW3 1DR Tel: (020) 7435 9300 Fax: E-mail: gallery@jiqjaq.com

▶ Metropolis Modern Art, 29 Compton Street, Chesterfield, Derbyshire, S40 4TA Tel: (01246) 233568

▶ www.emmalove.com, Bridle Lane, Streetly, Sutton Coldfield, West Midlands, B74 3PT Tel: (0797) 1425195 E-mail: design@interiorlove.co.uk

FINE ART HIRE

▶ Jiq Jaq Gallery, 112 Heath Street, London, NW3 1DR Tel: (020) 7435 9300 Fax: E-mail: gallery@jiqjaq.com

▶ Andrew McIntosh, Craggan Cottage, Grantown-on-Spey, Morayshire, PH26 3NT Tel: (01479) 872489 E-mail: andmcandtosh@hotmail.com

▶ Metropolis Modern Art, 29 Compton Street, Chesterfield, Derbyshire, S40 4TA Tel: (01246) 233568

Whites Ltd, 4 Bond Gate Chambers, Bond Gate, Nuneaton, Warwickshire, CV11 4AL Tel: (024) 7635 0909 Fax: (024) 7635 0909 E-mail: knight@pipemedia.co.uk

FINE ART PRINTS

▶ contemporaryart4all.co.uk, 14 West Park Crescent, Inverbervie, Montrose, Angus, DD10 0TX Tel: 01561 362902 E-mail: ros@contemporaryart4all.co.uk

▶ Knotweed Creations, 6 High Street, Bluntisham, Huntingdon, Cambridgeshire, PE28 3LD Tel: (01487) 842033 E-mail: andrea@knotweedcreations.co.uk

▶ Andrew McIntosh, Craggan Cottage, Grantown-on-Spey, Morayshire, PH26 3NT Tel: (01479) 872489 E-mail: andmcandtosh@hotmail.com

▶ Neil Hipkiss Fine Art Studio, PO Box 781, Worcester, WR4 4BQ Tel: (01886) 888658 E-mail: neil.hipkiss@blueyonder.co.uk

▶ Photolatitude.com, 67 North Drive, TROON, Ayrshire, KA10 7DL Tel: 01292 318028 Fax: 01292 318037 E-mail: info@photolatitude.com

▶ Van Renselar, 1 Rydal Drive, West Wickham, Kent, BR4 9QH Tel: (020) 8462 1022 E-mail: art@van-renselar.com

▶ www.emmalove.com, Bridle Lane, Streetly, Sutton Coldfield, West Midlands, B74 3PT Tel: (0797) 1425195 E-mail: design@interiorlove.co.uk

FINE BLANKING PRESSWORKERS

Able Production, 77 Arthur Street, Redditch, Worcestershire, B98 8JY Tel: (01527) 510899 Fax: (01527) 514234

Bacol Fine Blanking Ltd, Tramway, Oldbury Road, Smethwick, West Midlands, B66 1NY Tel: (01527) 874205 Fax: (01527) 833761 E-mail: info@bacolfineblanking.co.uk

William Mitchell Ltd, Tram Way, Oldbury Road, Smethwick, West Midlands, B66 1NY Tel: 0121-558 2694 Fax: 0121-558 4239 E-mail: phil.bytheway@virgin.net

FINE CHEMICALS

Chemquest Ltd, Springfield House, Water Lane, Wilmslow, Cheshire, SK9 5BG Tel: (01625) 528808 Fax: (01625) 527557 E-mail: enquiries@chemquest.co.uk

Chemtura Manaufacturing UK Ltd, Tenax Road, Trafford Park, Manchester, M17 1WT Tel: (01407) 830451 Fax: (01407) 830001 E-mail:

Cognis Performance Chemicals Ltd, Hardley, Hythe, Southampton, SO45 3ZG Tel: (023) 8089 4666 Fax: (023) 8024 3113 E-mail:

Collinda Investments Ltd, 25 Ottways Lane, Ashtead, Surrey, KT21 2PL Tel: (01372) 278416 Fax: (01372) 278559 E-mail: info@collinda.co.uk

Environmental & Remediation Services, Unit 11 12 Mercia Business Village, Torwood Close, Westwood Business Park, Coventry, CV4 8HX Tel: (024) 7642 6600 Fax: (024) 7642 6610 E-mail: ears@cel-international.com

Excelsyn Ltd, Mostyn Road, Holywell, Flintshire, CH8 9DN Tel: (01352) 717100 Fax: (01352) 717171 E-mail: info@excelsyn.com

Ferro Metal & Chemical Corporation Ltd, 179 Kings Road, Reading, RG1 4EX Tel: 0118-960 4700 Fax: 0118-950 9216 E-mail: sales@phibrochem.com

Genzyme Vehicle Leasing Ltd, Hollands Road, Haverhill, Suffolk, CB9 8PU Tel: (01440) 703522 Fax: (01440) 716269

Lambson Ltd, Avenue D, 603 Thorp Arch Estate, Wetherby, Leeds, LS23 7FS Tel: (01937) 840150 Fax: (01937) 840171 E-mail: sales@lambson.com

Oxford Chemicals Ltd, Zinc Works Road, Seaton Carew, Hartlepool, Cleveland, TS25 2DT Tel: (01429) 863222 Fax: (01429) 867567 E-mail: sales@oxfordchemicals.com

Peboc Division of Eastman Co. (UK) Ltd, Industrial Estate, Llangefni, Gwynedd, LL77 7YQ Tel: (01248) 750724 Fax: (01248) 723890

Rhodia Pharma Solutions, Dudley Lane, Dudley, Cramlington, Northumberland, NE23 7QG Tel: 0191-250 0471 Fax: 0191-250 1514 E-mail: john.lindley@eu.rhodia.com

Robinson Brothers Ltd, Phoenix Street, West Bromwich, West Midlands, B70 0AH Tel: 0121-553 2451 Fax: 0121-500 5183 E-mail: sales@robinsonbrothers.ltd.uk

Seal Sands Chemicals Ltd, Seal Sands Road, Seal Sands, Middlesbrough, Cleveland, TS2 1UB Tel: (01642) 546546 Fax: (01642) 546068 E-mail: george.christopherson@cambrex.com

Tessenderlo Fine Chemicals Ltd, Macclesfield Road, Leek, Staffordshire, ST13 8LD Tel: (01538) 399100 Fax: (01538) 399025 E-mail: sales@tessenderlofinechemicals.com

V W R International Ltd, Hunter Boulevard, Magna Park, Lutterworth, Leicestershire, LE17 4XN Tel: (01455) 558600 Fax: (01455) 558586 E-mail: uk.sales@uk.vwr.com

Wilfrid Smith Group plc, Elm House, Medlicott Close, Corby, Northamptonshire, NN18 9NF Tel: (01536) 460020 Fax: (01536) 462400 E-mail: info@wilfrid-smith.co.uk

FINE GRAIN STEEL PLATE

Universal Steel, 9 Lindholme Gardens, Owlthorpe, Sheffield, S20 6TD Tel: (07870) 575523 Fax: 0114-248 4139 E-mail: peterjwatters@tiscali.co.uk

FINE PAPER

Donald Murray, 211 Maclellan Street, Glasgow, G41 1RR Tel: 0141-427 1271 Fax: 0141-427 6999 E-mail: sales@donald-murray-paper.co.uk

Elliott Baxter & Company Ltd, Central Way, North Feltham Trading Estate, Feltham, Middlesex, TW14 0RX Tel: (020) 8893 1144 Fax: (020) 8893 2167 E-mail: sales@ebbpaper.co.uk

G S Smith Ltd, Lockwood Street, Hull, HU2 0HL Tel: (01482) 323503 Fax: (01482) 223174 E-mail: sales@gssmith.com

FINE PITCH GEARS

Biddle & Mumford Gears Ltd, 8-18 Kings Place, Buckhurst Hill, Essex, IG9 5EA Tel: (020) 8505 4615 Fax: (020) 8505 3718 E-mail: sales@biddleandmumford.co.uk

FINE PRESSINGS

William Mitchell Ltd, Tram Way, Oldbury Road, Smethwick, West Midlands, B66 1NY Tel: 0121-558 2694 Fax: 0121-558 4239 E-mail: phil.bytheway@virgin.net

FINE STRUCTURED HIGH DENSITY POLYETHYLENE (HDPE) NETS

Alan Roberts Midlands Ltd, Alan Roberts Midlands Ltd, Barton Dock Road, Stretford, Manchester, M32 0YL Tel: (01384) 263266 Fax: (01384) 265830 E-mail: jaspemal@aol.com

FINE WIRE

▶ Carrington Wire, P O Box 56, Cardiff, CF24 2WR Tel: (029) 2025 6100 Fax: (029) 2025 6101
E-mail: sales@carringtonwiregroup.co.uk

FINISHED PRESSINGS

Doughty Pressings Ltd, Stewart Street, Wolverhampton, WV2 4JW Tel: (01902) 426264 Fax: (01902) 772245
E-mail: info@doughty.uk.com

FINISHES, AUTOMOTIVE/MOTOR VEHICLE

Component Distributors Ltd, Blackwater Road, Newtownabbey, County Antrim, BT36 4UA Tel: (028) 9034 1900 Fax: (028) 9034 1977
E-mail: mail@cd-group.com

FINISHING CONSULTANTS AND ADVISORY SERVICES

Ad-Qual Group, 28 Mirfield Road, Solihull, West Midlands, B91 1JD Tel: 0121- 711 8785 Fax: 0121- 711 8785
E-mail: castech@blueyonder.co.uk

FINISHING EMBROIDERERS

Badge Design Ltd, Unit 4e Crofts End Industrial Estate, Crofts End Road, Bristol, BS5 7UW Tel: 0117-952 5856 Fax: 0117-952 5857
E-mail: badge.design@btconnect.com

Cookson Ltd, 16 Morris Road, Clarendon Industrial Estate, Leicester, LE2 6BR Tel: 0116-270 6288 Fax: 0116-270 6882

D P S Birmingham Ltd, 46 Hallam Street, Birmingham, B12 9PS Tel: 0121-440 3203 Fax: 0121-440 5220

Edinburgh Embroidery Services, Unit 11 North Peffer Place, Edinburgh, EH16 4UZ Tel: 0131-621 7222 Fax: 0131-539 7374
E-mail: embroidery@forthsector.org.uk

Emblematic Embroiderers, Unit 26b North Tyne Industrial Estate, Whitley Road, Benton, Newcastle upon Tyne, NE12 9SZ Tel: 0191-270 1449 Fax: 0191-270 1449
E-mail: gmewett@emblematic.force9.co.uk

Fewkes Ltd, Morley Avenue, Nottingham, NG3 5FW Tel: 0115-960 3561 Fax: 0115-969 2136

G S L Embroidery, 1 Berry Bank Lane, Holmfirth, HD9 7LA Tel: (01484) 683142 Fax: (01484) 685246 E-mail: sepiaemb@aol.com

▶ Hand & Lock, 86 Margaret Street, London, W1W 8TE Tel: (020) 7580 7488 Fax: (020) 7580 7499
E-mail: enquiries@handembroidery.com

Monsoon Ruggur Farm & Country Clothing Ltd, 63 Teignmouth Road, Clevedon, Avon, BS21 6DL Tel: (01275) 870220 Fax: (01275) 342272 E-mail: sales@monmark.co.uk

Personal Touch, Stag House, Western Way, Exeter, EX1 2DE Tel: (01392) 410260 Fax: (01392) 421235
E-mail: sales@personaltouch-emb.co.uk

Quickstitch Embroiderers, Willows Lane, Accrington, Lancashire, BB5 0SS Tel: (01254) 394538 Fax: (01254) 875335

Sagittarian Embroidery, 27 Durham Road, Sacriston, Durham, DH7 6LN Tel: 0191-371 9371 Fax: 0191-371 2288
E-mail: sagittarianemb@clara.co.uk

Turgelplan Ltd, 38-39 Somerset House, Somerset Road, London, SW19 5JA Tel: (020) 8947 8655 Fax: (020) 8947 8382

Wovina Woven Labels, 1 & 3 Omaha Road, Bodmin, Cornwall, PL31 1ER Tel: (01208) 73484 Fax: (01208) 78158
E-mail: sales@wovina.com

FINISHING MACHINES

Finishing Techniques Ltd, Halter Inn Works, Holcombe Brook, Ramsbottom, Bury, Lancashire, BL0 9SA Tel: (01706) 825819 Fax: (01706) 825748
E-mail: sales@fintek.co.uk

Permat Machines Ltd, Station Road, Coleshill, Birmingham, B46 1JG Tel: (01675) 463351 Fax: (01675) 465816
E-mail: sales@permat.com

FINISHING, AUTOMOTIVE COMPONENTS

Spyder Engineering Ltd, Fenland District Industrial Estate, Station Road, Whittlesey, Peterborough, PE7 2EY Tel: (01733) 203986 Fax: (01733) 350662

FINITE ELEMENT ANALYSIS SERVICES

Finite Element Analysis Consultant, 11 Ullswater Close, Dronfield Woodhouse, Dronfield, Derbyshire, S18 8NW Tel: (01246) 290638 Fax: (01246) 290638
E-mail: samir-mizban@bee.net

M G Bennett & Associates Ltd, Bennett House, Pleasley Road, Whiston, Rotherham, South Yorkshire, S60 4HQ Tel: (01709) 373782 Fax: (01709) 363730
E-mail: mgb@bennettmg.co.uk

Wilde UK Ltd, Brindley Lodge, Adcroft Street, Stockport, Cheshire, SK1 3HZ Tel: 0161-474 7479 Fax: 0161-474 7492
E-mail: info@wildeandpartners.co.uk

FIRE ALARM ASSEMBLY EQUIPMENT

Safetech Systems Ltd, 97 Firs Drive, Hounslow, TW5 9TB Tel: (020) 8897 3317 Fax: (020) 8384 1660

Tees Fire Systems, 8 Stonehouse Street, Middlesbrough, Cleveland, TS5 6HR Tel: (01642) 800006 Fax: (01642) 800007
E-mail: sales@teesfire.co.uk

FIRE ALARM CALL POINTS

FaelSafe Fire & Safety, 15 Moorside Vale, Drighlington, Bradford, West Yorkshire, BD11 1DW Tel: 0113-287 9999 Fax: 0113-287 9999 E-mail: andrew@faelsafe.co.uk

▶ Fire Fault Ltd, Bedfont House, Holywell Lane, Upchurch, Sittingbourne, Kent, ME9 7HN Tel: (01634) 262860 Fax: (01634) 262798
E-mail: enquiries@firefault.co.uk

FIRE ALARM CONTRACTORS OR INSTALLATION OR HIRE OR SERVICE

A & B Fire Prevention Wales, Mayfield, Chester Road, Buckley, Clwyd, CH7 3AH Tel: (01244) 543171 Fax: (01244) 544310

Abercolwyn Fire & Security, Fron Deg, Gilfach Road, Penmaenmawr, Gwynedd, LL34 6EY Tel: (01492) 623650 Fax: (01492) 623650

Alarmtec Ltd, 49 Fore Street, Bradninch, Exeter, EX5 4NN Tel: (01392) 881620 Fax: (01392) 882016 E-mail: alarmtec@alarmtec.co.uk

Aztek Services Ltd, Unit 8 Hall Barn Industrial Estate, Isleham, Ely, Cambridgeshire, CB7 5RB Tel: (01638) 781799 Fax: (01638) 781768 E-mail: sales@aztekservices.co.uk

Buchanan & Curwen (Leatherhead) Ltd, Fairfield Works, Upper Fairfield Road, Leatherhead, Surrey, KT22 7HJ Tel: (01372) 373481 Fax: (01372) 377458
E-mail: buchanans@b-and-c.co.uk

C Q Alarms 1982 Ltd, 1a Dora Road, Birmingham, B10 9RF Tel: 0121-772 1566 Fax: 0121-766 8231

C & T Fire, Stammerham Business Centre, Capel Road, Rusper, Horsham, West Sussex, RH12 4PZ Tel: (01306) 712421 Fax: (01306) 713225 E-mail: info@ctfire.co.uk

Castle Alarms, Millennium House, Boundary Bank, Kendal, Cumbria, LA9 5RR Tel: (01539) 731394 Fax: (01539) 735367
E-mail: sales@fp.castlealarms.f9.co.uk

Challenge Alarm Services, Unit 1a, Grange Hill Industrial Estate, Bratton Fleming, Barnstaple, Devon, EX31 4UH Tel: (01598) 710853 Fax: (01598) 710500

Chris Lewis, Faraday House, 38 Poole Road, Bournemouth, BH4 9DW Tel: (01202) 751599 Fax: (01202) 759500
E-mail: sales@chrislewissecurity.co.uk

Cuerdale Fire Protection Systems Ltd, Chorley Road, Walton Le Dale, Preston, PR5 4JA Tel: (01772) 566210 Fax: (01772) 558165
E-mail: enquiries@cuerdalefire.co.uk

D & G Electrical Controls, 7a Weller Drive, Finchampstead, Wokingham, Berkshire, RG40 4QZ Tel: 0118-973 7123 Fax: 0118-973 0071 E-mail: dg.electrical@virgin.net

Daemon Fire & Security Ltd, 41-42 Albert Road, Tamworth, Staffordshire, B79 7JS Tel: (01827) 69266 Fax: (01827) 53584
E-mail: sales@daemonfire.co.uk

Darlington Alarm Centre, 78 Heathfield Park, Middleton St. George, Darlington, County Durham, DL2 1LW Tel: (01325) 354500
E-mail: sales@darlingtonalarmcentre.co.uk

Davenheath, Unit 3 Kingfisher House, Trinity Business Park, London, E4 8TD Tel: (020) 8531 2003 Fax: (020) 8531 9105

Defensor Fire Detection Systems, 11-15 Kingsley Street, Leicester, LE2 6DY Tel: 0116-244 8689 Fax: 0116-244 8884

Erif UK Ltd, Prospect House, 6 Archipelago, Lyon Way, Frimley, Camberley, Surrey, GU16 7ER Tel: (0845) 8877999 Fax: (01276) 601337
E-mail: tim@erif.co.uk

Eurofire UK, 12 Fontwell Drive, Alton, Hampshire, GU34 2TN Tel: (01420) 542424 Fax: (01420) 82287

Evasafe Products Ltd, Farren Court, Cowfold, Horsham, West Sussex, RH13 8BP Tel: (01403) 864486 Fax: (01403) 864873
E-mail: info@evasafe.co.uk

F K B Electrical Ltd, Unit 10-12, Quakers Coppice, Crewe, CW1 6EW Tel: (01270) 501244 Fax: (01270) 251399
E-mail: fkb@fkb.co.uk

F R F Alarms Ltd, 136 Mackintosh Place, Cardiff, CF24 4RS Tel: (029) 2075 5799 Fax: (029) 2075 5799 E-mail: frfcardiff@aol.com

Fire Equipment Services Ltd, 269-271 Billinge Road, Wigan, Lancashire, WN5 8DF Tel: (01942) 228170 Fax: (01942) 228170
E-mail: info@fire-equipmentuk.com

Fire Protection Services Se, 215 London Road, Ewell, Epsom, Surrey, KT17 2BU Tel: (020) 8393 2897 Fax: (020) 8786 8793

▶ Firehawk Ltd, Unit 6-14, Peele Street, Manchester, M35 0UF Tel: 0161-683 5424 Fax: 0161-682 2233
E-mail: info@firehawk.ltd.uk

Fireplan Installations Ltd, Tuesnoad Grange, Bethersden, Ashford, Kent, TN26 3EH Tel: 01233 820292

Fixfire, Mayflower House, Bodmin Road, Coventry, CV2 5DB Tel: (024) 7661 6699 Fax: (024) 7662 1990

Fourway Communication Ltd, Delamare Road, Cheshunt, Waltham Cross, Hertfordshire, EN8 9SH Tel: (01992) 629182 Fax: (01992) 639227 E-mail: info@fourway.co.uk

P.F. Friend & Son Ltd, 3 Rolle Cottages, Rolle Street, Barnstaple, Devon, EX31 1JL Tel: (01271) 343058 Fax: (01271) 325319
E-mail: pffriend@hotmail.co.uk

G B Alarms Ltd, High St, Donington, Spalding, Lincolnshire, PE11 4TA Tel: (01775) 821100 Fax: (01775) 821395
E-mail: admin@gbalarms.com

G C S Alarms, Essex House, Stephenson Road, Clacton-on-Sea, Essex, CO15 4XA Tel: (01255) 220316 Fax: (01255) 479122
E-mail: sales@gcsalarms.co.uk

Gilmark Fire Protection, 2 Lonsdale Avenue, Portsmouth, PO6 2PX Tel: (023) 9220 1504 Fax: (023) 9232 1983

Grainger Fire Protection, Unit 1a Newton Court, Wavertree Technology Park, Liverpool, L13 1EJ Tel: 0151-220 4068 Fax: 0151-259 4365E-mail: enquiries@graingersystems.co.uk

Home County Fire Protection, 31 Fern Towers, Harestone Hill, Caterham, Surrey, CR3 6SL Tel: (01883) 341634 Fax: (01883) 342540

Hornchurch Electronics, 251 Goodwood Avenue, Hornchurch, Essex, RM12 6DD Tel: (01708) 441224 Fax: (01708) 620060

▶ Knight Systems, 43 Thornbury Drive, Uphill, Weston-Super-Mare, Avon, BS23 4YA Tel: (01934) 625089
E-mail: info@knightsystems.org

Lightfoot Bros Ltd, 32 Castle Street, Aylesbury, Buckinghamshire, HP20 2RA Tel: (01296) 482855 Fax: (01296) 482855

M K Fire Ltd, 65-69 Queens Road, High Wycombe, Buckinghamshire, HP13 6AH Tel: (01494) 769774 Fax: (01494) 465378
E-mail: info@mkfire.co.uk

N K M Fire Protection Ltd, Broadford Oast, Goudhurst Road, Tonbridge, Kent, TN12 8ET Tel: (01892) 724242 Fax: (01892) 723242

Nimrod Fire Protection Ltd, Unit 1, Lower Soldridge Business Park, Soldridge Road, Medstead, Alton, Hampshire, GU34 5JF Tel: (01420) 561117 Fax: (01420) 561131

Olympian Fire Protection Ltd, Charwell House Ash Farm, Ash Lane, Hale, Altrincham, Cheshire, WA15 8PH Tel: 0161-903 9941 Fax: 0161-904 7514

Passive Systems Ltd, Unit 8, Caburn Enterprise Park The Broyle, Ringmer, Lewes, East Sussex, BN8 5NP Tel: (01273) 813505 Fax: (01273) 813259

Patol Ltd, Rectory Road, Padworth Common, Reading, RG7 4JD Tel: 0118-970 1701 Fax: 0118-970 1458E-mail: sales@patol.co.uk

Peerless Maintenance Services Ltd, Coppins Yard, Grove Green Lane, Weavering, Maidstone, Kent, ME14 5JW Tel: (01622) 631444 Fax: (01622) 631222

Phoenix Fire Protection Midlands Ltd, Mountfield House, High Street, Kingswinford, West Midlands, DY6 8AL Tel: (01384) 295529 Fax: (01384) 271391
E-mail: sales@phoenix-fire.co.uk

Prestige Fire Protection, 14 Malvern Road, Southampton, SO16 6QA Tel: (023) 8077 3231 Fax: (023) 8052 8393
E-mail: prestige@rfwebb..co.uk

▶ Pyrotec Services Ltd, The Old Forge, Main Road, Fyfield, Abingdon, Oxfordshire, OX13 5LN Tel: (01865) 390190 Fax: (01865) 390088 E-mail: mail@pyrotec-systems.co.uk

R H Foster Ltd, 16 Essex Road, Basingstoke, Hampshire, RG21 7TD Tel: (01256) 465414 Fax: (01256) 841216

Secure It All Ltd, 25 Howley Grange Road, Halesowen, West Midlands, B62 0HW Tel: 0121-423 1119 Fax: 0121-423 3393
E-mail: sales@secureitall.co.uk

Securexe Security Systems, 24 Park Lane, Exmouth, Devon, EX8 1TH Tel: (01395) 227337 Fax: (01395) 260260

Securitel Fire Alarm Systems, 94 Warren Road, Brighton, BN2 6BA Tel: (01273) 888326 Fax: (01273) 887427
E-mail: info@securitel.co.uk

Shires Fire & Safety Ltd, Unit F3 Oswestry Service Centre, Bank Top Industrial Estate, St. Martins, Oswestry, Shropshire, SY10 7BB Tel: (01743) 741741 Fax: (01691) 773144
E-mail: info@sfas.co.uk

Shires Fire & Safety Ltd, Units 16-18 Business Development Centre, Stafford Park 4, Telford, Shropshire, TF3 3BA Tel: (01952) 292488 Fax: (01952) 292222 E-mail: info@ssaf.co.uk

Sightguard I O W Ltd, 39 High Street, Wootton Bridge, Ryde, Isle of Wight, PO33 4LU Tel: (01983) 884000 Fax: (01983) 884000

Sinclair Electrics, 130 Embankment Rd, Plymouth, PL4 9JF Tel: (01752) 268887 Fax: (01752) 268887

Squirealarms Ltd, 165-171 Humberstone Road, Leicester, LE5 3AF Tel: 0116-262 3916
E-mail: info@squirealarms.co.uk

Stafford Automatic Systems Ltd, Stafford House, Freeman Street, Stafford, ST16 3HY Tel: (01785) 251045 Fax: (01785) 212152

T H White Installation Ltd, 3 Nursteed Road Trading Estate, William Road, Devizes, Wiltshire, SN10 3EW Tel: (01380) 726656 Fax: (01380) 725707
E-mail: thwhite@bigwig.net

T L Fire Security Systems, 59 Hawthorn Road, Birmingham, B44 8QT Tel: 0121-384 1557 Fax: 0121-384 1557

Team Technology (South West) Ltd, Riverside Road, Pottington Business Park, Barnstaple, Devon, EX31 1TE Tel: (01271) 370420 Fax: (01271) 375977
E-mail: sales@teamtechnologysw.co.uk

Tranter Fire & Security Systems Ltd, 118 Bull Head Street, Wigston, Leicestershire, LE18 1PB Tel: 0116-288 8555 Fax: 0116-288 8855

Uni Fire Seurities, 9 Moor St Trading Estate, Brierley Hill, West Midlands, DY5 3SS Tel: (01432) 353400 Fax: (0800) 0723868
E-mail: admin@uni-fire.co.uk

▶ Westmorland Fire & Security Ltd, Beezon Chambers, Sandes Avenue, Kendal, Cumbria, LA9 6BL Tel: (01539) 724919 Fax: (01539) 740589
E-mail: service@westmorlandsecurity.co.uk

Westronics Ltd, 11-12 Marcus Close, Tilehurst, Reading, RG30 4EA Tel: 0118-942 6726 Fax: 0118-945 1481
E-mail: sales@westronics.co.uk

Whirlwind Fire Extinguisher Maintenance, Whirlwind Rise, Dudmoor Lane, Christchurch, Dorset, BH23 6BQ Tel: (01202) 475255 Fax: (01202) 475255

FIRE ALARM MAINTENANCE OR REPAIR

▶ Alpha Peerless Fire Systems Ltd, Wiltshire House, Tovil Green, Maidstone, Kent, ME15 6RJ Tel: (01622) 693869 Fax: (01622) 756675

Aylesbury Fire Systems Ltd, Queens Park, Aylesbury, Buckinghamshire, HP21 7SG Tel: (01296) 399994 Fax: (01296) 394692
E-mail: jane@aylesburyfire.co.uk

Chameleon Systems Ltd, Great Central House, Great Central Avenue, Ruislip, Middlesex, HA4 6TS Tel: (020) 8839 8526 Fax: (020) 8839 8527
E-mail: sales@chameleonsystems.co.uk

Channel Safety Systems Ltd, 9 Petersfield Business Park, Bedford Road, Petersfield, Hampshire, GU32 3QA Tel: (01730) 268231 Fax: (01730) 265552
E-mail: sales@channelsafety.co.uk

Daemon Fire & Security Ltd, 41-42 Albert Road, Tamworth, Staffordshire, B79 7JS Tel: (01827) 69266 Fax: (01827) 53584
E-mail: sales@daemonfire.co.uk

Davenheath, Unit 3 Kingfisher House, Trinity Business Park, London, E4 8TD Tel: (020) 8531 2003 Fax: (020) 8531 9105

Erif UK Ltd, Prospect House, 6 Archipelago, Lyon Way, Frimley, Camberley, Surrey, GU16 7ER Tel: (0845) 8877999 Fax: (01276) 601337
E-mail: tim@erif.co.uk

Euro Fire Guard Ltd, PO Box 95, Cirencester, Gloucestershire, GL7 5YX Tel: (01285) 850720 Fax: (01285) 850605
E-mail: carol@euro-fire-guard.co.uk

Fire Alarm Services, 71 Burfield Road, Old Windsor, Windsor, Berkshire, SL4 2LN Tel: (01753) 841140 Fax: (01753) 856717
E-mail: sales@firealarmservices.co.uk

Firesolve Ltd, Unit 2a Skelmanthorpe Technology Park, Station Road, Skelmanthorpe, Huddersfield, HD8 9GA Tel: (01484) 866614 Fax: (01484) 864466
E-mail: sales@fireslove.co.uk

G S Fire Protection, 46 Gotham Road, Birmingham, B26 1LB Tel: 0121-244 4747 Fax: 0121-693 3883
E-mail: info@gsfireprotection.co.uk

Haes Systems Ltd, Columbia House Tomo Industrial Estate, Packet Boat Lane, Uxbridge, Middlesex, UB8 2JP Tel: (01895) 422066 Fax: (01895) 420603
E-mail: enquiries@haes-systems.co.uk

Hopton Fire Prevention Services, Camp Road, Lowestoft, Suffolk, NR32 2LL Tel: (01502) 572564 Fax: (07802) 573023

Kidde Fire Protection Services Ltd, PO Box 318, Sunbury-on-Thames, Middlesex, TW16 7YX Tel: (0845) 6003909 Fax: (01582) 402339
E-mail: kiddefps@kiddefps.co.uk

M K Fire Ltd, 65-69 Queens Road, High Wycombe, Buckinghamshire, HP13 6AH Tel: (01494) 769774 Fax: (01494) 465378
E-mail: info@mkfire.co.uk

R H Foster Ltd, 16 Essex Road, Basingstoke, Hampshire, RG21 7TD Tel: (01256) 465414 Fax: (01256) 841216

Russell Fire Ltd, 25-26 Second Drove Industrial Estate, Peterborough, PE1 5XA Tel: (01733) 310469 Fax: (01733) 897510
E-mail: sales@russellfire.co.uk

Total Fire Protection, 73 Greenham, Bretton, Peterborough, PE3 9YS Tel: (01733) 700722

FIRE ALARM OR DETECTION SYSTEMS

Apollo Fire Detectors Ltd, 36 Brookside Road, Havant, Hampshire, PO9 1JR Tel: (023) 9249 2412 Fax: (023) 9249 2754 E-mail: sales@apollo-fire.co.uk

Haes Systems Ltd, Columbia House Tomo Industrial Estate, Packet Boat Lane, Uxbridge, Middlesex, UB8 2JP Tel: (01895) 422066 Fax: (01895) 420603 E-mail: enquiries@haes-systems.co.uk

Halma P.L.C., Misbourne Court, Rectory Way, Amersham, Buckinghamshire, HP7 0DE Tel: (01494) 721111 Fax: (01494) 728032 E-mail: halma@halma.com

Kidde Fire Protection Services Ltd, PO Box 318, Sunbury-on-Thames, Middlesex, TW16 7YX Tel: (0845) 6003909 Fax: (01582) 402339 E-mail: kiddefps@kiddefps.co.uk

Patol Ltd, Rectory Road, Padworth Common, Reading, RG7 4JD Tel: 0118-970 1701 Fax: 0118-970 1458E-mail: sales@patol.co.uk

Peripheral Support Services Ltd, Unit 14 Enterprise Court, Rankine Road, Basingstoke, Hampshire, RG24 8GE Tel: (01256) 844685 Fax: (01256) 810082 E-mail: sales@pss-firequest.co.uk

Ventec Systems Ltd, Units D1-D4 St. Catherines Business Complex, Broad Lane, Leeds, LS13 2TD Tel: 0113-239 4170 Fax: 0113-239 4190 E-mail: admin@ventec.co.uk

FIRE ALARM SYSTEMS

A B C Fire Ltd, Unit 14 Heath Hill Industrial Estate, Dawley, Telford, Shropshire, TF4 2RH Tel: (01952) 505098 Fax: (01952) 505098

A F S Systems Ltd, 9 Tamworth Road, Lichfield, Staffordshire, WS14 9EY Tel: (01543) 264034 Fax: (01543) 414367 E-mail: enquiries@arrowfire.co.uk

A G S Security Systems Ltd, Field Way, Denbigh Road, Mold, Flintshire, CH7 1BP Tel: (01244) 812222 Fax: (01352) 707889 E-mail: info@ags-security.co.uk

▶ A P I Fire & Safety Ltd, Unit 7, Vulcan Way, Eaton Socon, St. Neots, Cambridgeshire, PE19 8TS Tel: (01480) 217774 Fax: (01480) 217775

▶ Advanced Electronics, Unit 34 Moorland Way, Nelson Park, Cramlington, Northumberland, NE23 1WE Tel: (01670) 707111 Fax: (01670) 707222

Alarm Radio Monitoring Ltd, Southern Avenue, Leominster, Herefordshire, HR6 0QF Tel: (01568) 610016 Fax: (01568) 615511

Anglia Industrial Fire Ltd, 21 Old Court, Long Melford, Sudbury, Suffolk, CO10 9HA Tel: (01787) 883437

▶ Apex Fire Ltd, Broadfieds, Headstone Lane, Harrow, Middlesex, HA2 6NN Tel: (020) 8421 2228 Fax: (020) 8421 5257

Apollo Fire Detectors Ltd, 36 Brookside Road, Havant, Hampshire, PO9 1JR Tel: (023) 9249 2412 Fax: (023) 9249 2754 E-mail: sales@apollo-fire.co.uk

Assured Fire & Safety, 59 Florist Street, Stockport, Cheshire, SK3 8DW Tel: 0161-666 0204 Fax: 0161-666 0204 E-mail: paul@assuredfireandsafety.fsnet.co.uk

B L Acoustics Ltd, 152 Enterprise Court, Eastways, Witham, Essex, CM8 3YS Tel: (01376) 521525 Fax: (01376) 521526 E-mail: male@blacoustics.net

Baravon Systems, Sanctus Street, Stratford-upon-Avon, Warwickshire, CV37 6DH Tel: (01789) 299668 Fax: (01789) 414230

▶ CAMS Fire & Security P.L.C., 6 Wedgwood Court, Wedgwood Way, Stevenage, Hertfordshire, SG1 4QR Tel: (01438) 740840 Fax: (01438) 737969 E-mail: info@camssecurity.co.uk

Christie Intruder Alarms Ltd, Security House, 212-218 London Road, Waterlooville, Hampshire, PO7 7AJ Tel: (023) 9226 5111 Fax: (023) 9226 5112 E-mail: enquiries@ciaalarms.co.uk

Cirrus Communication Systems Ltd, Hampton Lovett Industrial Estate, Lovett Road, Hampton Lovett, Droitwich, Worcestershire, WR9 0QG Tel: (01905) 827252 Fax: (01905) 827253 E-mail: info@coltronic.co.uk

Cooper Lighting & Security, Wheatley Hall Road, Doncaster, South Yorkshire, DN2 4NB Tel: (01302) 321541 Fax: (01302) 303220 E-mail: sales@cooper-ls.com

▶ Dante Fire & Security, Houghton Enterprise Centre, Lake Road, Houghton Le Spring, Tyne & Wear, DH5 8BJ Tel: (0870) 4447073 Fax: (0870) 4447078

E M S Radio, Fire & Systems Ltd, Unit 11, Herne Bay West Trading Estate, Herne Bay, Kent, CT6 8JZ Tel: (01227) 369570 Fax: (01227) 740041 E-mail: sales@emsgroup.co.uk

F A C E Schamu, The Stables, The Dean Estate, Wickham Road, Fareham, Hampshire, PO17 5BN Tel: (01329) 282049 Fax: (01329) 221707 E-mail: enquiries@schamu.co.uk

Fire Ltd, 97A Rochdale Road, Bury, Lancashire, BL9 7BA Tel: 0161-764 8999 Fax: 0161-764 8979

▶ Fire Defence plc, Pathfields Indust Estate, South Molton, Devon, EX36 3DW Tel: (01769) 574070 Fax: (01769) 574079 E-mail: fds@fire-defence.com

Fire Rite, Unit G1 Caerphilly Business Park, Caerphilly, Mid Glamorgan, CF83 3ED Tel: (029) 2086 7222 Fax: (029) 2086 7333 E-mail: sales@firerite.com

Firetec Ltd, Wessex House, Great Western Road, Gloucester, GL1 3NG Tel: (01452) 530142 Fax: (01452) 380791 E-mail: paul@firetecltd.btconnect.co.uk

▶ Fowler Fire Alarms, 3 Hermitage Walk, London, E18 2BP Tel: (020) 8530 8005 Fax: (020) 8530 8281

G S Fire Protection, 46 Gotham Road, Birmingham, B26 1LB Tel: 0121-244 4747 Fax: 0121-693 3883 E-mail: info@gsfireprotection.co.uk

Global Fire Equipment Ltd, Unit A4, Spectrum Business Estate, Anthonys Way, Medway City Estate, Rochester, Kent, ME2 4NP Tel: (01634) 716882 Fax: (01634) 711557 E-mail: martin@global-fire.co.uk

Grainger Fire Protection, Unit 1a Newton Court, Wavertree Technology Park, Liverpool, L13 1EJ Tel: 0151-220 4068 Fax: 0151-259 4365E-mail: enquiries@graingersystems.co.uk

Haes Systems Ltd, Columbia House Tomo Industrial Estate, Packet Boat Lane, Uxbridge, Middlesex, UB8 2JP Tel: (01895) 422066 Fax: (01895) 420603 E-mail: enquiries@haes-systems.co.uk

▶ Initial Electronic Security Systems Ltd, Sunley House, Olds Approach, Watford, WD18 9TB Tel: (01923) 775099 Fax: (01923) 770616 E-mail: watfordfire@ifs.com

▶ J B Fire Systems, 54 Glebe Way, West Wickham, Kent, BR4 0RL Tel: (020) 8402 1847 Fax: (020) 8402 1848 E-mail: sales@jbfiresystems.co.uk

Kidde Fire Protection Services Ltd, 400 Dallow Road, Luton, LU1 1UR Tel: (01582) 413694 Fax: (01582) 402339 E-mail: kiddefps@kiddefps.com

Kidde Products, Unit 2, Blair Way, Dawdon, Seaham, County Durham, SR7 7PP Tel: 0191-513 6100 Fax: 0191-513 6102

Link Systems Ltd, 15 Greenfields, Adstock, Buckingham, MK18 2JA Tel: (0800) 7311450 Fax: (01296) 714664

▶ Midland Fire & Safety, Summerwood, Symonds Yat, Ross-on-Wye, Herefordshire, HR9 6BP Tel: (01600) 891338 Fax: (01600) 891380 E-mail: info@morganrose.co.uk

Nittan (UK) Ltd, Hipley Street, Woking, Surrey, GU22 9LQ Tel: (01483) 769555 Fax: (01483) 756686 E-mail: sales@nittan.co.uk

Notifier Ltd, Charles Avenue, Burgess Hill, West Sussex, RH15 9UF Tel: (01444) 230300 Fax: (01444) 230888 E-mail: sales@notifierfiresystems.co.uk

▶ Orchard Fire & Security Ltd, Eckington Business Park, Rotherside Road, Eckington, Sheffield, S21 4HL Tel: (01246) 432788 Fax: (01246) 432799

Peripheral Support Services Ltd, Unit 14 Enterprise Court, Rankine Road, Basingstoke, Hampshire, RG24 8GE Tel: (01256) 844685 Fax: (01256) 810082 E-mail: sales@pss-firequest.co.uk

Phoenix Fire Alarms, Phoenix House, Gollburne Street, Keighley, West Yorkshire, BD21 1YR Tel: (01535) 600200 Fax: (01535) 600200

Protector Alarms UK Ltd, 20-22 Gipsy Hill, London, SE19 1NL Tel: (020) 8761 3771 Fax: (020) 8670 9441 E-mail: sales@protectoralarms.com

Pyramid Fire Protection Ltd, 132 Rutland Road, Sheffield, S3 9PP Tel: 0114-272 8921 Fax: 0114-272 7631 E-mail: sales@pyramid-fire.co.uk

Reliable Fire Sprinkler Ltd, Unit A2 Epsom Business Park, Kiln Lane, Epsom, Surrey, KT17 1JF Tel: (01372) 728899 Fax: (01372) 724461 E-mail: rfsl@reliablesprinkler.com

▶ Safyre Ltd, Unit 10 Tait Road Industrial Estate, Tait Road, Croydon, CR0 2DP Tel: (020) 8684 3080 Fax: (020) 8684 2634 E-mail: sales@safyre.co.uk

Sapphire Detection Systems Ltd, 263 Boundary Road, Loudwater, High Wycombe, Buckinghamshire, HP10 9QN Tel: (01628) 532830

Siemans Building Technologies Ltd, Hawthorne Road, Staines, Middlesex, TW18 3AY Tel: (01784) 461616 Fax: (01784) 464646

Tate Fire & Security Protection, 3 Cheddar Business Park, Wedmore Road, Cheddar, Somerset, BS27 3EB Tel: (01934) 744111 Fax: (01934) 744304 E-mail: sales@tatefire.co.uk

Total Fire Protection, 73 Greenham, Bretton, Peterborough, PE3 9YS Tel: (01733) 700722

Traceman Fire Protection Consultants, 27 Leinster Road, Swinton, Manchester, M27 5YQ Tel: 0161-793 8448 Fax: 0161-794 2129 E-mail: enquiries@traceman.co.uk

▶ Trident Fire Alarm Systems Ltd, Unit GM Wilsons Park, Monsall Road, Manchester, M40 8WN Tel: 0161-205 1661 Fax: 0161-205 1771

Wormald Lintott, Hewett Road, Great Yarmouth, Norfolk, NR31 0NN Tel: (01493) 440500 Fax: (01493) 442639 E-mail: wormaldsafetyandservice.uk@tycoint.com

FIRE ALARM SYSTEMS TO SPECIFICATION

▶ Access Audio Ltd, Unit 32-35,, Hardengreen Business Park, Dalhousie Road, Eskbank, Dalkeith, Midlothian, EH22 3NX Tel: 0131-663 0777 Fax: 0131-660 9777 E-mail: info@accessaudio.co.uk

Notifier Ltd, Charles Avenue, Burgess Hill, West Sussex, RH15 9UF Tel: (01444) 230300 Fax: (01444) 230888 E-mail: sales@notifierfiresystems.co.uk

Peripheral Support Services Ltd, Unit 14 Enterprise Court, Rankine Road, Basingstoke, Hampshire, RG24 8GE Tel: (01256) 844685 Fax: (01256) 810082 E-mail: sales@pss-firequest.co.uk

FIRE ALARMS, *See also headings for particular types*

A H Fire Prevention, 233a Golders Green Road, London, NW11 9ES Tel: (020) 8458 0448 Fax: (020) 8458 0338

▶ Ablaze Building Solutions Ltd, Wesley House, 24 Grosvenor Road, Aldershot, Hampshire, GU11 1DP Tel: (01252) 401030 Fax: (01252) 310864 E-mail: sales@ablaze.co.uk

Ace Fire Ltd, 14 Concorde Road, Norwich, NR6 6BW Tel: (01603) 787333 Fax: (01603) 787332 E-mail: info@acefire.co.uk

▶ Advance Intergrated Systems, Unit 1A, Spa Fields Industrial Estate, New Street, Slaithwaite, Huddersfield, HD7 5BB Tel: (01484) 844433 Fax: (01484) 845533

▶ Advanced Fire & Security Services Ltd, 18 Acorn Industrial Park, Crayford Road, Dartford, DA1 4AL Tel: (01322) 557755 Fax: (01322) 557507

▶ Alerts Security/Installations Ltd, 1a Jubilee Terrace, Ryton, Tyne & Wear, NE40 4HL Tel: 0191-413 9090 Fax: 0191-413 9090

Banham Security Ltd, 10 Pascal Street, London, SW8 4SH Tel: (020) 7622 5151 Fax: (020) 7498 2461 E-mail: security@banham.com

▶ Blake Contractors Ltd, 10 Bircham Road, Southend-on-Sea, SS2 5DN Tel: (01702) 613641 Fax: (01702) 467002 E-mail: info@blakecontractors.co.uk

▶ CAMS Fire & Security P.L.C., 6 Wedgwood Court, Wedgwood Way, Stevenage, Hertfordshire, SG1 4QR Tel: (01438) 740840 Fax: (01438) 737969 E-mail: info@camssecurity.co.uk

Chameleon Systems Ltd, Great Central House, Great Central Avenue, Ruislip, Middlesex, HA4 6TS Tel: (020) 8839 8526 Fax: (020) 8839 8527 E-mail: sales@chameleonsystems.co.uk

Channel Safety Systems Ltd, 9 Petersfield Business Park, Bedford Road, Petersfield, Hampshire, GU32 3QA Tel: (01730) 268231 Fax: (01730) 265552 E-mail: sales@channelsafety.co.uk

Contract Distributors, 7 Tansley Road, North Wingfield, Chesterfield, Derbyshire, S42 5JZ Tel: (01246) 859257 Fax: (01246) 853787 E-mail: somedayuk2000@yahoo.co.uk

D A Security Systems Ltd, 5 Cornfield Road, Lee-On-The-Solent, Hampshire, PO13 8HZ Tel: (023) 9255 0627

Dart Fire Protection Ltd, Dart Fire Protection Centre, Plymouth Road, Totnes, Devon, TQ9 5PH Tel: (01803) 862416 Fax: (01803) 867183 E-mail: sales@dartfire.co.uk

Deta Electrical Co. Ltd, Kingsway House, Laporte Way, Luton, LU4 8RJ Tel: (01582) 544544 Fax: (01582) 544501 E-mail: sales@detaelectrical.co.uk

Duchy Alarms, Silverwell, Blackwater, Truro, Cornwall, TR4 8JG Tel: (01872) 560560 Fax: (01872) 560041 E-mail: irg@duchyalarms.co.uk

Euro Fire Guard Ltd, PO Box 95, Cirencester, Gloucestershire, GL7 5YX Tel: (01285) 850720 Fax: (01285) 850605 E-mail: carol@euro-fire-guard.co.uk

F E S C O, 201 Wylds Lane, Worcester, WR5 1EL Tel: (01905) 351058 Fax: (01905) 351058

▶ Facilities System Design & Service Ltd, 9 Station Road, Stoke Mandeville, Aylesbury, Buckinghamshire, HP22 5UL Tel: (07000) 373773 Fax: (07000) 373775 E-mail: info@firealarms.gb.com

Fire Ltd, 97A Rochdale Road, Bury, Lancashire, BL9 7BA Tel: 0161-764 8999 Fax: 0161-764 8979

Firemaster Alarms Ltd, Unit 11 Wedgewood Court, Wedgewood Way, Stevenage, Hertfordshire, SG1 4QR Tel: (01438) 737900

Fireplan Installations Ltd, Tuesnoad Grange, Bethersden, Ashford, Kent, TN26 3EH Tel: 01233 820292

G M C Fire & Security-Protection, Service, 14 Railway St, Malton, North Yorkshire, YO17 7NR Tel: (01653) 697917 Fax: (01653) 697836

Global Fire Systems Ltd, Global House, 15 The Triangle, NG2 Business Park, Queen's Drive, Nottingham, NG2 1AE Tel: (0870) 2208211 Fax: (0115) 9438999 E-mail: sales@globalfire.co.uk

M & E Alarms Ltd, Lower Charlecott, Tawstock, Barnstaple, Devon, EX31 3JY Tel: (01271) 858550 Fax: (01271) 858423 E-mail: sales@m-and-e.co.uk

Notifier Ltd, Charles Avenue, Burgess Hill, West Sussex, RH15 9UF Tel: (01444) 230300 Fax: (01444) 230888 E-mail: sales@notifierfiresystems.co.uk

Olympian Fire Protection Ltd, Charwell House Ash Farm, Ash Lane, Hale, Altrincham, Cheshire, WA15 8PH Tel: 0161-903 9941 Fax: 0161-904 7514

P F D S Ltd, 1st Floor 2 Stakes Hill Road, Waterlooville, Hampshire, PO7 7HY Tel: (023) 9225 6366 Fax: (023) 9225 6371 E-mail: sales@pfds.co.uk

Patol Ltd, Rectory Road, Padworth Common, Reading, RG7 4JD Tel: 0118-970 1701 Fax: 0118-970 1458E-mail: sales@patol.co.uk

▶ PRW Group Ltd, D Second Avenue, Westfield Industrial Estate, Midsomer Norton, Radstock, BA3 4BH Tel: (01761) 416885 Fax: (01761) 419381 E-mail: business@trwgroup.co.uk

▶ Receptor Ltd, Elizabeth House, 73 High Street, Syston, Leicester, LE7 1GQ Tel: 0116-260 2500 Fax: 0116-260 5656 E-mail: graham@firefirefire.co.uk

S S Systems, Sorby House, The Point, Rotherham, South Yorkshire, S60 1BP Tel: (01709) 362999 Fax: (0845) 4023789

Sensotec Europe Ltd, Unit 7 Industrial Estate, Bala, Gwynedd, LL23 7NL Tel: (01678) 520022 Fax: (0870) 0740000 E-mail: technical@sensotec.co.uk

Sensotec Europe Ltd, 6 Lumb Lane, Liversedge, West Yorkshire, WF15 7QH Tel: (01924) 412859 Fax: (0870) 0720000 E-mail: sales@sensotec.co.uk

▶ Siemens Building Technologies, Unit C19-C20, Poplar Business Park, 10 Prestons Road, London, E14 9RL Tel: (020) 7537 2888 Fax: (020) 7538 4118

Sovereign Security Services Ltd, 28 Station Road, Shirehampton, Bristol, BS11 9TX Tel: 0117-982 6618

Specialised Security Systems Ltd, Carmichael House, Village Green, Inkberrow, Worcester, WR7 4DZ Tel: (01386) 792522 Fax: (01386) 792729 E-mail: info@specialisedsecurity.co.uk

Star Security (UK) Ltd, Somerset House, School Lane, East Harling, Norwich, NR16 2LU Tel: (01953) 718600 Fax: (01953) 718662 E-mail: steve@starsecurity.co.uk

▶ Trity Protection Systems, Unit C15B Holly Farm Business Park, Honiley, Kenilworth, Warwickshire, CV8 1NP Tel: (01926) 485080 Fax: (01926) 485090

Unifire & Security, Unit 3 Station Yard, Bromfield, Ludlow, Shropshire, SY8 2BT Tel: (01584) 856868 Fax: (020) 7754 9148 E-mail: peter@uni-fire.co.uk

Ventec Systems Ltd, Units D1-D4 St. Catherines Business Complex, Broad Lane, Leeds, LS13 2TD Tel: 0113-239 4170 Fax: 0113-239 4190 E-mail: admin@ventec.co.uk

▶ Wessex Fire & Security Ltd, Wessex House, Wincombe Lane, Shaftesbury, Dorset, SP7 8PJ Tel: (01747) 851661 Fax: (01747) 858860 E-mail: fire@wessex.org

FIRE AND GAS DETECTION SYSTEMS

Halma P.L.C., Misbourne Court, Rectory Way, Amersham, Buckinghamshire, HP7 0DE Tel: (01494) 721111 Fax: (01494) 728032 E-mail: halma@halma.com

FIRE BARRIER CONSTRUCTORS OR CONTRACTORS

Checkfire, Unit 12, Pontygwindy Industrial Estate, Caerphilly, Mid Glamorgan, CF83 3HU Tel: (029) 2086 8333 Fax: (029) 2085 0627 E-mail: sales@checkfire.co.uk

FIRE BARRIER SYSTEMS

Premier Fire Protection Northumberland Ltd, 5 Farm Court, Druridge Bay, Morpeth, Northumberland, NE61 5EG Tel: (01670) 862088 Fax: (01670) 862088 E-mail: tony_pfp@msn.com

FIRE BLANKETS OR CURTAINS

▶ C P Covers Ltd, 18 Hanson Close, Middleton, Manchester, M24 2HD Tel: 0161-654 9396 Fax: 0161-654 6017 E-mail: cpcovers@btopenworld.com

Chubb Fire Ltd, Chubb House, Staines Road West, Sunbury-on-Thames, Middlesex, TW16 7AR Tel: (01932) 785588 Fax: (01932) 776673 E-mail: info@chubb.co.uk

Commercial Body Fittings, 80 Bridge Road East, Welwyn Garden City, Hertfordshire, AL7 1JY Tel: (01707) 371161 Fax: (01707) 372603 E-mail: sales@cbf.uk.com

Cowley Fire, 29 Arkwright Court, Blackpool & Fylde Industrial Estate, Blackpool, FY4 5DR Tel: (01253) 769666 Fax: (01253) 769888 E-mail: info@cowleyfire.co.uk

Culimetea Saveguard Ltd, Tame Valley Mill, Wainwright Street, Dukinfield, Cheshire, SK16 5NB Tel: 0161-344 2484 Fax: 0161-344 2486E-mail: sales@culimetea-saveguard.com

F E S C O, 201 Wylds Lane, Worcester, WR5 1EL Tel: (01905) 351058 Fax: (01905) 351058

Fire Extinguisher Rental, Alfred Works, Woodhill Street, Bury, Lancashire, BL8 1AT Tel: 0161-764 1434 Fax: 0161-764 1434

Hoyles Fire & Safety Ltd, Sandwash Close, Rainford Industrial Estate, Rainford, St. Helens, Merseyside, WA11 8LY Tel: (01744) 885161 Fax: (01744) 882410 E-mail: customer.service@hoyles.co.uk

Lewis's Medical Supplies, Broadoak House, Coronation Street, Stockport, Cheshire, SK5 7PG Tel: 0161-480 6797 Fax: 0161 -480 4587 E-mail: sales@lewis-plast.co.uk

Warwickshire Fire Protection, 17 Sanders Road, Coventry, CV6 6DH Tel: (024) 7636 4729 Fax: (024) 7636 4729

FIRE BLANKETS OR CURTAINS – *continued*

Wormald Lintott, Hewett Road, Great Yarmouth, Norfolk, NR31 0NN Tel: (01493) 440500 Fax: (01493) 442639 E-mail: wormaldsafetyandservice.uk@tycoint.com

FIRE BRICKS

Charnwood Forest Brick Ltd, Old Station Close, Shepshed, Loughborough, Leicestershire, LE12 9NJ Tel: (01509) 503203 Fax: (01509) 507566 E-mail: sales@charnwoodforest.com

▶ Dyson Industries Ltd, Griffs Works, Stopes Road, Stannington, Sheffield, S6 6BW Tel: 0114-234 8663 Fax: 0114-232 2519 E-mail: enq@dyson-holloware.com

R E Knowles Ltd, Buxton Road, Furness Vale, High Peak, Derbyshire, SK23 7PJ Tel: (01663) 744127 Fax: (01663) 741562

FIRE CEMENT

Fortafix Ltd, First Drove, Fengate, Peterborough, PE1 5BJ Tel: (01733) 566136 Fax: (01733) 315393 E-mail: sales@fortafix.com

Jay's Refractory Specialists Ltd, Callywhite Lane, Dronfield, Derbyshire, S18 2XR Tel: (01246) 410241 Fax: (01246) 290221 E-mail: info@jrsuk.com

Vitcas Ltd, 16 Clothier Road, Brislington, Bristol, BS4 5PS Tel: 0117 9117895 Fax: 0117 9711152 E-mail: info@vitcas.com

FIRE CONTROL SYSTEMS

Central Fire Curtains, 80 Blackmore Drive, Leicester, LE3 1LP Tel: 0116-247 0247 E-mail: firecurtains@lycos.com

FIRE DAMPERS

▶ Blocker Products Ltd, Pals Haven, Hook Lane, Aldingbourne, Chichester, West Sussex, PO20 3TE Tel: (01243) 545465 Fax: (01243) 545475 E-mail: millerbrian@btconnect.com

Duct Engineering Luton Ltd, Cradock Industrial Estate, Cradock Road, Luton, LU4 0JF Tel: (01582) 562626 Fax: (01582) 583046 E-mail: ductengineering@aol.com

Flamgard Engineering Ltd, Unit 2-3 Pontnewynydd Industrial Estate, Pontnewynydd, Pontypool, Gwent, NP4 6YW Tel: (01495) 757347 Fax: (01495) 755443 E-mail: sales@flamgard.co.uk

Halton Products Ltd, 5 Waterside Business Park, Eastways, Witham, Essex, CM8 3YQ Tel: (01376) 503040 Fax: (01376) 503060 E-mail: enquiries@haltongroup.com

Mann Mcgowan Fabrications Ltd, 4 The Brook Trading Estate, Deadbrook Lane, Aldershot, Hampshire, GU12 4XB Tel: (01252) 333601 Fax: (01252) 322724 E-mail: sales@mannmcgowan.co.uk

S G L Systems Ltd, Milton Industrial Estate, Lesmahagow, Lanark, ML11 0JN Tel: (01555) 894449 Fax: (01555) 894227

FIRE DETECTION SYSTEM DESIGN WITH VOICE ALARM

A M S Acoustics, Rayleigh House, 21 Queen Annes Place, Enfield, Middlesex, EN1 2QB Tel: (020) 8886 4060 Fax: (020) 8360 2640 E-mail: info@amsacoustics.co.uk

FIRE DETECTOR AND EXTINGUISHING SYSTEMS

Ace Fire Ltd, 14 Concorde Road, Norwich, NR6 6BW Tel: (01603) 787333 Fax: (01603) 787332 E-mail: info@acefire.co.uk

Ace Fire Midlands Ltd, 15 Lichfield Lane, Mansfield, Nottinghamshire, NG18 4RA Tel: (01623) 662805

Autoquench Ltd, 132 Priory Road, Hall Green, Birmingham, B28 0TB Tel: 0121-693 6888 Fax: 0121-430 6007 E-mail: mail@autoquench.co.uk

Complete Fire Protection Ltd, Unit 32, Moor Park Industrial Centre, Tolpits Lane, Watford, WD18 9SP Tel: (01923) 251446 Fax: (01923) 801170 E-mail: cfirep@tiscali.co.uk

J S Fire Protection Ltd, 4 Mews Road, St. Leonards-on-Sea, East Sussex, TN38 0EA Tel: (01424) 428174

Lyontech Engineering Ltd, Unit 16 Manor Industrial Estate, Flint, Clwyd, CH6 5UY Tel: (01352) 730710 Fax: (01352) 730320

Macron Safety Systems UK Ltd, Woodlands Road, Guildford, Surrey, GU1 1RN Tel: (01483) 572222 Fax: (01483) 302180 E-mail: info@macron-safety.com

FIRE DETECTOR SYSTEMS

Apollo Fire Detectors Ltd, 36 Brookside Road, Havant, Hampshire, PO9 1JR Tel: (023) 9249 2412 Fax: (023) 9249 2754 E-mail: sales@apollo-fire.co.uk

Autronica Industrial Ltd, 11 Dudley Bank, Edinburgh, EH6 4HH Tel: 0131-555 1013 Fax: 0131-467 0712

Bristol Fire, Covert End, Westleigh Close, Yate, Bristol, BS37 4PR Tel: (01793) 480040 Fax: (01454) 273312 E-mail: sales@bristolfire.com

Control Equipment Ltd, Tyco Park, Grimshaw Lane, Newton Heath, Manchester, M40 2WL Tel: 0161-455 4232 Fax: 0161-455 4441 E-mail: tycocontrolsystems.uk@tycoint.com

Detection Instruments (Northern) Ltd, Unit 5-6 Bonnyton Industrial Estate, Munro Place, Kilmarnock, Ayrshire, KA1 2NP Tel: (01563) 525525 Fax: (01563) 542350 E-mail: info@di-northern.com

Exco Fire & Safety Control Ltd, 46 St Gluvias Street, Penryn, Cornwall, TR10 8BJ Tel: (01326) 372878 Fax: (01326) 377135 E-mail: jack@excotec.co.uk

Fire Fighting Enterprises, 9 Hunting Gate, Hitchin, Hertfordshire, SG4 0TJ Tel: (01462) 444740 Fax: (0845) 4024201 E-mail: sales@ffeuk.com

Icam Ltd, Unit 2, Spring Gardens, Washington, Pulborough, West Sussex, RH20 3BS Tel: (01903) 892222 Fax: (01903) 892277 E-mail: icam@icam.ltd.uk

K A D Detection Systems Ltd, Units 4-5, Barrmill Road, Galston, Ayrshire, KA4 8HH Tel: (01563) 820148 Fax: (01563) 820163 E-mail: sales@kad-detection.com

Micropack Engineering Ltd, Fir Training Centre, Portlethen, Aberdeen, AB12 4RR Tel: (01224) 784055 Fax: (01224) 784056 E-mail: info@micropack.co.uk

Nittan (UK) Ltd, Hipley Street, Woking, Surrey, GU22 9LQ Tel: (01483) 769555 Fax: (01483) 756686 E-mail: sales@nittan.co.uk

No Climb Products, 163 Dixons Hill Road, North Mymms, Hatfield, Hertfordshire, AL9 7JE Tel: (01707) 282760 Fax: (01707) 282777 E-mail: info@noclimb.com

Talentum Development Ltd, Beal Lane, Shaw, Oldham, OL2 8PF Tel: (01706) 844714 Fax: (01706) 882612 E-mail: info@talentum.co.uk

Tynetec Ltd, Cowley Road, Blyth Industrial Estate, Blyth, Northumberland, NE24 5TF Tel: (01670) 352371 Fax: (01670) 362807 E-mail: sales@tynetec.co.uk

Ulster Fire Extinguishers Service, 58 Greystone Road, Antrim, BT41 1JZ Tel: (028) 9446 1524 Fax: (028) 9442 9515

FIRE DETECTOR SYSTEMS CONTRACTORS

Eagle Fire Systems, 100 Liverpool Street, Salford, M5 4LP Tel: 0161-745 9578 Fax: 0161-745 9578 E-mail: eaglfirsys@aol.com

Evasafe Products Ltd, Farren Court, Cowfold, Horsham, West Sussex, RH13 8BP Tel: (01403) 864486 Fax: (01403) 864873 E-mail: info@evasafe.co.uk

FIRE DOOR CLOSERS

▶ Door-Tech Solutions Ltd, 4 Kean Close, Lichfield, Staffordshire, WS13 7EL Tel: (01543) 252374 Fax: (01543) 256845 E-mail: sales@doortechsolutions.co.uk

FIRE DOOR CONTROL OR MONITORING SYSTEMS

Electrical Control Systems, 89 Queslett Road East, Sutton Coldfield, West Midlands, B74 2AH Tel: 0121-353 1231 E-mail: info@ecscontrol.co.uk

Hoyles Fire & Safety Ltd, Sandwash Close, Rainford Industrial Estate, Rainford, St. Helens, Merseyside, WA11 8LY Tel: (01744) 885161 Fax: (01744) 882410 E-mail: customer.service@hoyles.co.uk

FIRE DOOR INSTALLATION CONTRACTORS

Booth Industries, PO Box 50, Bolton, BL3 2RW Tel: (01204) 366333 Fax: (01204) 380888 E-mail: sales@booth-industries.co.uk

FIRE DOOR MAINTENANCE OR REPAIR

James Aiken (Offshore) Ltd, Horizons Ho, 81 Waterloo Quay, Aberdeen, AB11 5DE Tel: (01224) 573322 Fax: (01224) 572666 E-mail: sales@aikenoffshore.com

FIRE DOOR RETAINERS

▶ GB Locking Systems Ltd, Redburn House, Redburn Road, Newcastle upon Tyne, NE5 1NB Tel: 0191-271 6344 Fax: 0191-271 3644 E-mail: sales@gblockingsystems.co.uk

▶ Security Matters, 1 Wellingborough Road, Broughton, Kettering, Northamptonshire, NN14 1PD Tel: (01536) 790999 Fax: (01536) 790710

FIRE DOORS OR COMPONENTS

Bespoke Services (Manchester) Ltd, Whitehill Industrial Estate, Whitehill Street, Reddish, Stockport, Cheshire, SK5 7LW Tel: 0161-476 3522 Fax: 0161-476 0522 E-mail: info@bespoke-services.co.uk

C R F Sections Ltd, Hale Trading Estate, Lower Church Lane, Tipton, West Midlands, DY4 7PQ Tel: 0121-557 1234 Fax: 0121-522 3003

Door Maintenance Co. Ltd, Unit 8, Curran Industrial Estate, Curran Road, Cardiff, CF10 5DF Tel: (029) 2066 5539 Fax: (029) 2066 8207E-mail: rpickford@harlechdoors.net

F.R. Shadbolt & Sons, Ltd, 7 Springwood Drive, Braintree, Essex, CM7 2YN Tel: (01376) 333376 Fax: (020) 8523 2774 E-mail: sales@shadbolt.co.uk

Fitzpatrick Doors Ltd, Rushey Lane, Birmingham, B11 2BL Tel: 0121-706 6363 Fax: 0121-708 2250 E-mail: fitzuk1@aol.com

Humphrey & Stretton (Properties) Ltd, Stretton House, 20 Pindar Road, Hoddesdon, Hertfordshire, EN11 0EU Tel: (01992) 462965 Fax: (01992) 463996 E-mail: sales@humphreystretton.com

Mcgeoch Marine Ltd, 38 Loanbank Quadrant, Glasgow, G51 3HZ Tel: 0141-445 5353 Fax: 0141-445 5164E-mail: sales@m-m-l.com

Meridian Doors Ltd, The Croft, High Street, Whetstone, Leicester, LE8 6LQ Tel: 0116-275 0666 Fax: 0116-275 0606 E-mail: meridiandoors@webleicester.co.uk

Midland Veneers Ltd, 3 The Hayes Trading Estate, Folkes Road, Stourbridge, West Midlands, DY9 8RG Tel: (01384) 424924 Fax: (01384) 424929 E-mail: sales@mid-ven.co.uk

Noberne Doors Ltd, Lupton Street, Leeds, LS10 2QP Tel: 0113-277 8577 Fax: 0113-277 2049 E-mail: nobernedoors@cs.com

Northern Doors (UK) Ltd, Kingsforth Road, Thurcroft, Rotherham, South Yorkshire, S66 9HU Tel: (01709) 545999 Fax: (01709) 545341 E-mail: mail@northerndoors.co.uk

Premdor Crosby Ltd, Huddersfield Road, Darton, Barnsley, South Yorkshire, S75 5JS Tel: (01226) 383434 Fax: (01226) 388808 E-mail: ukmarketing@premdor.com

Profile Ltd, Sir Frank Whittle Road, Derby, DE21 4XE Tel: 01332 366900 Fax: (01332) 369613 E-mail: mail@profileuk.com

Ranford Doors, Unit 6 Sterling Industrial Estate, Rainham Road South, Dagenham, Essex, RM10 8TX Tel: (0800) 037 9133 Fax: (020) 8984 0378 E-mail: sales@lbsgroup.co.uk

Sunray Engineering Ltd, Wotton Road, Ashford, Kent, TN23 6LL Tel: (01233) 639039 Fax: (01233) 625137 E-mail: sales@sunraydoors.co.uk

Syston Rolling Shutters Ltd, 33 Albert Street, Syston, Leicester, LE7 2JB Tel: 0116-260 8841 Fax: 0116-264 0846 E-mail: sales@syston.com

Vista-Brunswick Ltd, 105 Glenfrome Road, Bristol, BS2 9XA Tel: 0117 9551491

W Button & Co. Ltd, Larchfield Works, Larchfield Road, Leeds, LS10 1QP Tel: 0113-270 4287 Fax: 0113-277 6975 E-mail: wbuttonco@aol.com

Watson Bros Ltd, 30-34 Wilson Place, East Kilbride, Glasgow, G74 4QD Tel: (01355) 233144 Fax: (01355) 233850 E-mail: colin@turnersrollerdoors.com

FIRE ENGINE COMPONENTS/ SPARE PARTS

Emergency One UK Ltd, Block 4, Caponacre Industrial Estate, Cumnock, Ayrshire, KA18 1SH Tel: (01290) 424200 Fax: (01290) 423834 E-mail: mmadsen@emergencyone.co.uk

John Dennis Coach Builders Ltd, Westfield Road, Slyfield Industrial Estate, Guildford, Surrey, GU1 1RR Tel: (01483) 506678 Fax: (01483) 579488 E-mail: sales@jdcfire.co.uk

FIRE ENGINES

John Dennis Coach Builders Ltd, Westfield Road, Slyfield Industrial Estate, Guildford, Surrey, GU1 1RR Tel: (01483) 506678 Fax: (01483) 579488 E-mail: sales@jdcfire.co.uk

Reynolds Boughton (Devon) Ltd, Winkleigh Airfield, Winkleigh, Devon, EX19 8DR Tel: (01837) 83555 Fax: (01837) 83768 E-mail: sales@boughton.co.uk

FIRE ESCAPE DOORS

Bolton Gate Co. Ltd, Waterloo Street, Bolton, BL1 2SP Tel: (01204) 871000 Fax: (01204) 871049 E-mail: general@boltongate.co.uk

▶ Voyager Site Services, Ashton Clough Road, Liversedge, West Yorkshire, WF15 6JX Tel: (07870) 588297 E-mail: voyagersiteservices@aol.com

FIRE ESCAPE FABRICATORS

Alloy Fabweld Ltd, 5 Zone C Chelmsford Road Industrial Estate, Chelmsford Road, Dunmow, Essex, CM6 1HD Tel: (01371) 859544 Fax: (01371) 878608

The Fire Escape Specialist, Unit 6 Barton Road Industrial Units, Barton Road, Torquay, TQ2 7NS Tel: (01803) 322299 Fax: (01803) 322299

W. & G.W. Garratt Ltd, Upper Allen Street Works, Upper Allen Street, Sheffield, S3 7HA Tel: 0114-272 7094 Fax: 0114-272 0115 E-mail: enquiries@garrattsonline.com

Luton Fabrications Ltd, Tring Road, Dunstable, Bedfordshire, LU6 2JX Tel: (01582) 663330 Fax: (01582) 662333

Myatt & Degville Fabrications Ltd, Selborne Street, Walsall, WS1 2JN Tel: (01922) 648222 Fax: (01922) 613565

Premier Fabrications, St 1, 54-76 Bissell Street, Birmingham, B5 7HP Tel: 0121-693 9059 Fax: 0121-693 9058

Whitwell & Sons, 1 Laycock Gate, Blackpool, FY3 8AT Tel: (01253) 395172 Fax: (01253) 395176

FIRE ESCAPE INSTALLATION CONTRACTORS OR FABRICATORS

Deplynn Engineering Ltd, 3 Thornham Grove, London, E15 1DN Tel: (020) 8519 6028 Fax: (020) 8519 6028

Dormar Fabrications Bilston Ltd, Jubilee House, Halesfield 2, Telford, Shropshire, TF7 4QH Tel: (01952) 585736 Fax: (01952) 684526

Hawthorne Engineering Ltd, Unit 5 Hexthorpe Trading Park, Littlewood Street, Hexthorpe, Doncaster, South Yorkshire, DN4 0EJ Tel: (01302) 321990 Fax: (01302) 349939 E-mail: sales@hawthorneengineeringltd.co.uk

Scorpio Welding & Fabrications, 1 Old Wharf, Old Birchills, Walsall, WS2 8QD Tel: (01922) 643000 Fax: (01922) 643000

Steel Craft, Greenhill Mills, Grange Road, Batley, West Yorkshire, WF17 6LH Tel: (01924) 441770 Fax: (01924) 441770

Wood & Son, 3 Barrack Road, Guildford, Surrey, GU2 9RU Tel: (01483) 504012 Fax: (01483) 504012

FIRE ESCAPE STAIRCASES

Allslade plc, Dundas Lane, Portsmouth, PO3 5SD Tel: (023) 9266 7531 Fax: (023) 9267 9818 E-mail: accounts@allslade.co.uk

Amber Valley Engineering Ltd, Pye Bridge Industrial Estate, Pye Bridge, Alfreton, Derbyshire, DE55 4NX Tel: (01773) 604753 Fax: (01773) 540136 E-mail: ambervalleyeng@hotmail.com

Andrew Young & Son (Engineers) Ltd, 45 Midwharf Street, Glasgow, G4 0LD Tel: (0141) 332 1165 Fax: (0141) 331 2690

Chatsworth Forge Ltd, Woods Way, Goring-by-Sea, Worthing, West Sussex, BN12 4RE Tel: (01903) 502221 Fax: (01903) 700002 E-mail: sales@chatsworthforge.co.uk

Craven & Nicholas Engineering Ltd, St Johns Road, Boston, Lincolnshire, PE21 6BG Tel: (01205) 364004 Fax: (01205) 310798 E-mail: info@carven-nicholas.co.uk

Tony Craze Welding & Fabrication, 13 United Downs Industrial Park, St. Day, Redruth, Cornwall, TR16 5HY Tel: (01209) 821166 Fax: (01209) 821864 E-mail: steel@tonycraze.net

Dormar Fabrications Bilston Ltd, Jubilee House, Halesfield 2, Telford, Shropshire, TF7 4QH Tel: (01952) 585736 Fax: (01952) 684526

Down & Francis Industrial Products Ltd, Ardath Road, Kings Norton, Birmingham, B38 9PN Tel: 0121-433 3300 Fax: 0121-433 3325 E-mail: reception@downandfrancis.co.uk

Edwin Clarke, Francis House, George Street, Lincoln, LN5 8LG Tel: (01522) 530912 Fax: (01522) 510929

Escape-net UK, Hexham, Northumberland, NE46 3YP Tel: (01434) 603938 E-mail: hexham666@aol.com

Fab Vent Engineering, North Road, Stoke-on-Trent, ST6 2BZ Tel: (01782) 219995 Fax: (01782) 219995

Fire Escapes Unlimited, Unit 2 Atlas Trading Estate, Colebrook Road, Birmingham, B11 2NT Tel: 0121-772 4443 Fax: 0121-753 4222 E-mail: feunlimited@aol.com

Forge Fabrications Ltd, The Street, Lyng, Norwich, NR9 5QZ Tel: (01603) 872088 Fax: (01603) 872744 E-mail: enquiries@forgefabrications.co.uk

G & B Fabrications Services, Unit 20 Newfields Industrial Estate, High Street, Stoke-on-Trent, ST6 5PD Tel: (01782) 824600 Fax: (01782) 824700

FIRE ESCAPE STAIRCASES - *continued*

Hough Engineering, 138A High Street, Silverdale, Newcastle, Staffordshire, ST5 6LX Tel: (01782) 633984 Fax: (01782) 715987 E-mail: houghengineering@supnet.com
Ivanhoe Forge Ltd, Station Road, Seaton Delaval, Whitley Bay, Tyne & Wear, NE25 0QB Tel: 0191-237 0676 Fax: 0191-237 6887
J P Fabrications, C 4 Belcon Industrial Estate, Geddings Road, Hoddesdon, Hertfordshire, EN11 0NT Tel: (01992) 444428 Fax: (01992) 444428 E-mail: jpfabs@aol.com
Mecright Contractors Ltd, Unit 10 Prospect Business Park, Longford Road, Cannock, Staffordshire, WS11 0LG Tel: (01543) 469222 Fax: (01543) 469444 E-mail: patrick@mecright.co.uk
Midas Technologies, Unit A Roundhouse Close, Fengate, Peterborough, PE1 5TA Tel: (01733) 342600 Fax: (01733) 346672 E-mail: sales@midastech.co.uk
Norris Adams Fabrications, Unit 6, Upcott Avenue, Pottington Business Park, Barnstaple, Devon, EX31 1HN Tel: (01271) 322969 Fax: (01271) 322969
Northend Construction, Maypole Crescent, Wallhouse Road, Erith, Kent, DA8 2JZ Tel: (01322) 333441 Fax: (01322) 333441
Oadby Wrought Iron, Chapel Street, Oadby, Leicester, LE2 5AD Tel: 0116-271 5040
P & M Decorative Metal Work Ltd, Unit 1, Park Street, Oldbury, West Midlands, B69 4LQ Tel: 0121-544 8880 Fax: 0121-544 4617 E-mail: pmdeco@aol.com
Peter Marshall Ltd, Gelderd Road, Morley, Leeds, LS27 7LL Tel: 0113-307 6730 Fax: 0113-307 5968
Plymouth Metal Fabrications, 13 Porsham Close, Roborough, Plymouth, PL6 7DB Tel: (01752) 788883 Fax: (01752) 788228
R Ekin, Claylands Avenue, Worksop, Nottinghamshire, S81 7BE Tel: (01909) 472638 Fax: (01909) 472638
Safety Stairways Ltd, Unit 45 Owen Road Industrial Estate, Willenhall, West Midlands, WV13 2PX Tel: 0121-526 3133 Fax: 0121-526 2833 E-mail: info@safety-stairways.com
Shrub Hill Fabrications, Unit 3 British Rail Industrial Estate, Tolladine Road, Worcester, WR4 9PT Tel: (01905) 20644 Fax: (01905) 20644
South East Steel Fabrication & Engineering, Legge Street, London, SE13 6NP Tel: (020) 8690 6229 Fax: (020) 8690 6229
Southern Staircases, 81 Dudley Road, Brighton, BN1 7GL Tel: (01273) 551556
Stonaco Fabrications Ltd, Wilton Road, Haine Industrial Estate, Ramsgate, Kent, CT12 5HG Tel: (01843) 596448 Fax: (01843) 593548
Sussex Ironcraft South Eastern Ltd, 31b Avis Way, Newhaven, East Sussex, BN9 0DJ Tel: (01273) 515931 Fax: (01273) 513811
Sutcliffe Bros Bradford Ltd, Paradise Works, 164 Sunbridge Road, Bradford, West Yorkshire, BD1 2HF Tel: (01274) 733063 Fax: (01274) 304434 E-mail: sutbros@aol.com
Taylor & Russell Ltd, Stonebridge Mill, Preston Road, Longridge, Preston, PR3 3AN Tel: (01772) 782295 Fax: (01772) 785341
Thanet-Ware Kent Ltd, Ellington Works, Princes Road, Ramsgate, Kent, CT11 7RZ Tel: (01843) 591076 Fax: (01843) 586198
W & G Metalwork Ltd, Sugarbrook Mill, Buntsford Hill, Stoke Pound, Bromsgrove, Worcestershire, B60 3AR Tel: (01527) 870752 Fax: (01527) 579930
Walker Metalwork (Elland) Ltd, Castle Mills, Elland, West Yorkshire, HX5 0RY Tel: 01422 310011

FIRE EVACUATION RESCUE EQUIPMENT

Enable Access Disabled Access Equipement, 16 Plantagenet Road, Barnet, Hertfordshire, EN5 5JG Tel: (020) 8275 0375 Fax: (020) 8449 0326
Luminose Escape Routes, 75 Birkmyre Road, Glasgow, G51 3JH Tel: 0141-445 6655 Fax: 0141-425 1511
▶ Specialist Training Consultants Ltd, The Sycamores, 7 Rugby Close, Seaford, East Sussex, BN25 3PQ Tel: (01323) 873043 Fax: (01323) 872308 E-mail: pgwilliam@aol.com

FIRE EXIT LOCKS

Surelock Mcgill Ltd, 26 The Business Centre, Molly Millars Lane, Wokingham, Berkshire, RG41 2QY Tel: 0118-977 2525 Fax: 0118-977 1913 E-mail: info@surelock.co.uk

FIRE EXTINGUISHER REFILLS

Approved Fire Appliances Ltd, Spinney Hill Road, Leicester, LE5 3GG Tel: 0116-276 8991 Fax: 0116-253 8017 E-mail: sales@approvedfire.co.uk
Central Service Fire Protection, Central House, Vivars Way, Canal Road, Selby, North Yorkshire, YO8 8BE Tel: (01757) 213360 Fax: (01757) 210022 E-mail: csfp@btconnect.com
Checkfire, Unit 12, Pontygwindy Industrial Estate, Caerphilly, Mid Glamorgan, CF83 3HU Tel: (029) 2086 8333 Fax: (029) 2085 0627 E-mail: sales@checkfire.co.uk
▶ F P S Fire Protection Ltd, Friemark House, Pioneer Park, Bristol, BS4 3QB Tel: 0117-971 7050 Fax: 0117-935 1605 E-mail: sales@firemarkext.co.uk
Fire Safety Express, Tesla Court, Innovation Way, Lynch Wood, Peterborough, PE2 6FL Tel: (01733) 234504 Fax: (01733) 234504 E-mail: enquiries@firesafetyexpress.co.uk
Lifeline Fire & Safety Systems Ltd, Burnsall Road Industrial Estate, Burnsall Road, Coventry, CV5 6BU Tel: (024) 7671 2999 Fax: (024) 7671 2998 E-mail: sales@lifeline-fire.co.uk
Pendle Nu Tech, Old School House, School Lane, Laneshawbridge, Colne, Lancashire, BB8 7EQ Tel: (01282) 861111 Fax: (01282) 871113

FIRE EXTINGUISHER SPRINKLER SYSTEM MAINTENANCE

▶ Taylor Robinson Ltd, Fire Protection House, Woolley Colliery Road, Darton, Barnsley, South Yorkshire, S75 5JA Tel: 0161-764 8674 Fax: (01226) 388206

FIRE EXTINGUISHER SUPPLY OR REFILL OR MAINTENANCE

1st Quote Fire, 49 Forthview Walk, Tranent, East Lothian, EH33 1FE Tel: 0131-448 0723 Fax: 0131-448 0723
A A Fire Security, 69 Rawson Road, Bolton, BL1 4JQ Tel: (01204) 497305 Fax: (01294) 849181
A S D Fire Protection, Fisher Street, Newcastle upon Tyne, NE6 4LT Tel: (01698) 356444 Fax: (01698) 356678 E-mail: asdfire@btconnect.com
Admiral Fire Extinguishers, 19 Flude Road, Coventry, CV7 9AQ Tel: (024) 7636 5157 Fax: (024) 7636 2815 E-mail: admiralfire@btopenworld.com
AIS Fire Tech Tech, Unit 12 Riverside Business Park, 33 River Road, Barking, Essex, IG11 0DA Tel: (020) 8591 3433 Fax: (020) 8594 1226 E-mail: enquiries@firetech.co.uk
Alarmtec Ltd, 49 Fore Street, Bradninch, Exeter, EX5 4NN Tel: (01392) 881620 Fax: (01392) 882016 E-mail: alarmtec@alarmtec.co.uk
▶ Alert Fire Ltd, Unit 18, Britannia Court, Burnt Mills Industrial Estate, Basildon, Essex, SS13 3EU Tel: (01268) 726999 Fax: (01268) 725292 E-mail: info@alert-fire.co.uk
Approved Fire Appliances Ltd, Spinney Hill Road, Leicester, LE5 3GG Tel: 0116-276 8991 Fax: 0116-253 8017 E-mail: sales@approvedfire.co.uk
Approved Services, 180 Long Chaulden, Hemel Hempstead, Hertfordshire, HP1 2JL Tel: (01442) 255081 Fax: (01442) 211185
ARM Fire Extinguisher Services, 12 Vicarage Way, Arksey, Doncaster, South Yorkshire, DN5 0TG Tel: (01302) 873379 Fax: (01302) 873379
Atlas Fire & Security Ltd, Unit 8A Lansil Industrial Estate, Caton Road, Lancaster, LA1 3PQ Tel: (01524) 69488 Fax: (01524) 842972
Avon Extinguishers, Hanham Business Park, Memorial Road, Hanham, Bristol, BS15 3JE Tel: 0117-960 2266 Fax: 0117-960 2233 E-mail: avon-extinguish@btconnect.com
B M Hire & Sales, 203 Askern Road, Bentley, Doncaster, South Yorkshire, DN5 0JR Tel: (01302) 876225 Fax: (01302) 876225
Berks Extinguisher Services, 48 Ardingly, Bracknell, Berkshire, RG12 8XR Tel: (01344) 425015 Fax: (01344) 304924 E-mail: enquiries@berksext.co.uk
BFSS Ltd, 2 Strawberry Lane, Tiptree, Colchester, CO5 0RX Tel: (01621) 810500 Fax: (01621) 810500 E-mail: sales@blackwaterfss.co.uk
Border Offset Printers, Church Street, Caldewgate, Carlisle, CA2 5TJ Tel: (01228) 526675 Fax: (01228) 515245
C & C Fire Extinguisher Service Ltd, 39 Pencricket Lane, Oldbury, West Midlands, B68 8LX Tel: 0121-559 6611 Fax: 0121-559 3399
Canon Fire Protection, The Wharf, Midhurst, West Sussex, GU29 9PX Tel: (01730) 815209 Fax: (01730) 816377 E-mail: cfp@canonfire.co.uk
Castle Fire Ltd, Ghyll Mill, Beehive Lane, New Hutton, Kendal, Cumbria, LA8 0AJ Tel: (01539) 722500 Fax: (01539) 741044
Coastal Fire, 799 Foxhall Road, Ipswich, IP4 5TJ Tel: (01473) 714708 Fax: (01473) 714708
Cormeton Fire Protection Ltd, Unit 12 Delaval Trading Estate, Seaton Delaval, Whitley Bay, Tyne & Wear, NE25 0QT Tel: 0191-237 0790 Fax: 0191-237 5143 E-mail: sales@cormeton.co.uk
Cotswold Fire Ltd, Cotswold House, Coldpool Lane Badgeworth, Cheltenham, Gloucestershire, GL51 4UP Tel: (01452) 713272 Fax: (01242) 227765
T.A. Cowap & Co. Ltd, Hazel Grove Works, Guy Edge, Linthwaite, Huddersfield, HD7 5TQ Tel: (01484) 851177 Fax: (01484) 648798 E-mail: lisa@tacowap.com
Crawley Fire Protection, Hazelwick Mill Lane, Crawley, West Sussex, RH10 1SU Tel: (01293) 547654 Fax: (01293) 440295
Cross Fire Protection, 413 Chichester Road, Bognor Regis, West Sussex, PO21 5BU Tel: (01243) 827168 Fax: (01243) 827168
Cuerdale Fire Protection Systems Ltd, Chorley Road, Walton Le Dale, Preston, PR5 4JA Tel: (01772) 566210 Fax: (01772) 558165 E-mail: enquiries@cuerdalefire.co.uk
Delta Fire Systems Ltd, Jews Lane, Dudley, West Midlands, DY3 2AV Tel: (01902) 664181 Fax: (01902) 665538
Direct Fire Protection, 52 Watling Street, Gillingham, Kent, ME7 2YN Tel: (01634) 855600 Fax: (01634) 570571
E & J Fire Protection, 5 Rice Bridge Industrial Estate, Station Road, Thorpe-le-Soken, Clacton-on-Sea, Essex, CO16 0HH Tel: (01255) 860645 Fax: (01255) 860156 E-mail: julie@ejfire.co.uk
Econogard Services Ltd, Econogard House, 1 Halifax Road, Cambridge, CB4 3QB Tel: (01763) 261970 Fax: (01223) 352494
Enfield Safety Supplies, 40 Queensway, Enfield, Middlesex, EN3 4SP Tel: (020) 8805 1015 Fax: (0870) 3800077
Eurofire UK, 12 Fontwell Drive, Alton, Hampshire, GU34 2TN Tel: (01420) 542424 Fax: (01420) 82287
Express Fire Equipment Ltd, Unit 4 Mersey Road Industrial Estate, Mersey Road North, Failsworth, Manchester, M35 9LU Tel: 0161-688 5050 Fax: 0161-688 5151 E-mail: john@xpressfire.co.uk
Extinguisher Rental Service, 29-31 Bayes Street, Kettering, Northamptonshire, NN16 8EH Tel: (01536) 417231 Fax: (01536) 411484
Fire Check Services, 34 Gibbons Grove, Wolverhampton, WV6 0JF Tel: (01902) 746842 Fax: (01902) 836556 E-mail: sales@firecheckservives.co.uk
Fire Protection Services, Unit B7, Imperial Business Estate, West Mill, Gravesend, Kent, DA11 0DL Tel: (0800) 317195 Fax: (01474) 535111 E-mail: info@fire-protection-services.co.uk
Fire Rite, Unit G1 Caerphilly Business Park, Caerphilly, Mid Glamorgan, CF83 3ED Tel: (029) 2086 7222 Fax: (029) 2086 7333 E-mail: sales@firerite.com
Firepoint Services Ltd, 134 Great Lime Road, Newcastle Upon Tyne, NE12 7NJ Tel: 0191-268 6854 Fax: 0191-268 6854
Firesafe, PO Box 1350, Harlow, Essex, CM20 2BQ Tel: (01279) 626000 Fax: (01279) 730505
Fireshields Extinguisher Services Ltd, 7 Princes Gardens, Whitley Bay, Tyne & Wear, NE25 8EA Tel: 0191-291 0444 Fax: 0191-252 2340
Firesolve Ltd, Unit 2a Skelmanthorpe Technology Park, Station Road, Skelmanthorpe, Huddersfield, HD8 9GA Tel: (01484) 866614 Fax: (01484) 864466 E-mail: sales@fireslove.co.uk
Fixfire, Mayflower House, Bodmin Road, Coventry, CV2 5DB Tel: (024) 7661 6699 Fax: (024) 7662 1990
Gatwick Fire Protection, 44 Prince Albert Square, Redhill, RH1 5AW Tel: (0800) 9562006 Fax: (01737) 773949 E-mail: sales@gatwickfire.co.uk
Gilmark Fire Protection, 2 Lonsdale Avenue, Portsmouth, PO6 2PX Tel: (023) 9220 1504 Fax: (023) 9232 1983
Gloria UK, Parkfield House, Manchester Old Road, Middleton, Manchester, M24 4DY Tel: 0161-654 2216 Fax: 0161-654 2253 E-mail: sales@gloria.co.uk
Griffin & General Fire Services Ltd, 7 Willow Street, London, EC2A 4BH Tel: (020) 7251 9379 Fax: (020) 7729 5652 E-mail: headoffice@griffinfire.co.uk
H E Woolley Ltd, Newport Works, Forty Foot Road, Middlesbrough, Cleveland, TS2 1HG Tel: (01642) 247337 Fax: (01642) 250188 E-mail: info@he-woolley.co.uk
Home County Fire Protection, 31 Fern Towers, Harestone Hill, Caterham, Surrey, CR3 6SL Tel: (01883) 341634 Fax: (01883) 342540
Home & Office Fire Extinguishers Ltd, Unit 6, Saffron Business Centre, Elizabeth Close, Saffron Walden, Essex, CB10 2NL Tel: (01799) 513360 Fax: (01799) 513713 E-mail: fire@pslink.co.uk
Hoyles Fire & Safety Ltd, Sandwash Close, Rainford Industrial Estate, Rainford, St. Helens, Merseyside, WA11 8LY Tel: (01744) 885161 Fax: (01744) 882410 E-mail: customer.service@hoyles.co.uk
Kidde Fire Protection Services Ltd, PO Box 318, Sunbury-on-Thames, Middlesex, TW16 7YX Tel: (0845) 6003909 Fax: (01582) 402339 E-mail: kiddefps@kiddefps.co.uk
KP Fire, 283 Dinas, Newtown, Powys, SY16 1NW Tel: (01686) 626312 Fax: (01686) 626312
L W Safety Ltd, Unit 12, Derby Road, Greenford, Middlesex, UB6 8UJ Tel: (020) 8575 9000 Fax: (020) 8575 0600
M K Fire Ltd, 65-69 Queens Road, High Wycombe, Buckinghamshire, HP13 6AH Tel: (01494) 769774 Fax: (01494) 465378 E-mail: info@mkfire.co.uk
Marbco Fire & Safety, Barrington Industrial Estate, Bedlington, Northumberland, NE22 7DQ Tel: (01670) 828488 Fax: (01670) 828315
Midland Fire, Lido House, Sansome Road, Shirley, Solihull, West Midlands, B90 2BJ Tel: 0121-745 8444 Fax: 0121-745 4115
Morgantic Ltd, 71 Harehills Road, Harehills, Leeds, LS8 5HS Tel: (0845) 3000440 Fax: (0845) 3000441
N F S Fire Protection Ltd, Morton Street, Middleton, Manchester, M24 6AN Tel: 0161-643 9338 Fax: 0161-655 3878
Nationwide Fire Protection Associates, Southcote Mill, Southcote Farm Lane, Reading, RG30 3DZ Tel: 0118-951 1799 Fax: 0118-951 1799
Nimrod Fire Protection Ltd, Unit 1, Lower Soldridge Business Park, Soldridge Road, Medstead, Alton, Hampshire, GU34 5JF Tel: (01420) 561117 Fax: (01420) 561131
North West Fire Ltd, Glan Llyn Road, Bradley, Wrexham, Clwyd, LL11 4BB Tel: (01978) 720999 Fax: (01978) 751646
North West Fire Protection, 110 Pleasington Close, Blackburn, BB2 1TU Tel: (01254) 278555 Fax: (01254) 278666
P S P Safety Products Ltd, 9 Aintree Road, Keytech 7 Business Park, Keytec 7 Business Park, Pershore, Worcestershire, WR10 2JN Tel: (01386) 552555 Fax: (01386) 552592
Pendle Nu Tech, Old School House, School Lane, Laneshawbridge, Colne, Lancashire, BB8 7EQ Tel: (01282) 861111 Fax: (01282) 871113
Pennine Fire Extinguisher Services, Pleasington Street, Blackburn, BB2 1UF Tel: (01254) 263378 Fax: (01254) 278898 E-mail: info@penninefire.co.uk
Phoenix Fire Extinguishing Services, 32 Bullar Road, Southampton, SO18 1GS Tel: (023) 8055 8638 Fax: (023) 8034 9121
Pyrotec Fire Detection Ltd, 8 Caburn Enterprise Park, The Broyle, Ringmer, Lewes, East Sussex, BN8 5NP Tel: (01273) 813505 Fax: (01273) 813259 E-mail: sales@pyrotec.co.uk
R S M Refko Installations Ltd, 8 Capstan Centre, Thurrock Park Way, Tilbury, Essex, RM18 7HH Tel: (01375) 855500 Fax: (01375) 855533
Regis Plastic Signs, Providence Street, Stourbridge, West Midlands, DY9 8HN Tel: (01384) 892366 Fax: (01384) 892367
Russell Fire Ltd, 25-26 Second Drove Industrial Estate, Peterborough, PE1 5XA Tel: (01733) 310469 Fax: (01733) 897510 E-mail: sales@russellfire.co.uk
S S Oakes Fire Protection Ltd, Fourth Street, Bolton, BL1 7NW Tel: (01204) 845876 Fax: (01204) 845876
Saxon Fire, 8 Newlands, Rushbrooke Lane, Bury St. Edmunds, Suffolk, IP33 2RS Tel: (01284) 704400
Shires Fire & Safety Ltd, Unit F3 Oswestry Service Centre, Bank Top Industrial Estate, St. Martins, Oswestry, Shropshire, SY10 7BB Tel: (01743) 741741 Fax: (01691) 773144 E-mail: info@sfas.co.uk
Shires Fire & Safety Ltd, Units 16-18 Business Development Centre, Stafford Park 4, Telford, Shropshire, TF3 3BA Tel: (01952) 292488 Fax: (01952) 292222 E-mail: info@ssaf.co.uk
Stockport Fire Extinguishers, Unit 14 Haigh Park, Haigh Avenue, Stockport, Cheshire, SK4 1QR Tel: 0161-476 2004 Fax: 0161-429 7239
Stockport Fire Protection, 14 Hade Park, White Hill Industrial Estate, Stockport, Cheshire, SK4 1QR Tel: 0161-477 0061 Fax: 0161-429 7239 E-mail: safe@globalnet.co.uk
Trinity Fire Ltd, Unit 8 Caburn Enterprise Park, The Broyle, Ringmer, Lewes, East Sussex, BN8 5NP Tel: (01273) 812208 Fax: (01273) 813259
Uni Fire Seurities, 9 Moor St Trading Estate, Brierley Hill, West Midlands, DY5 3SS Tel: (01432) 353400 Fax: (0800) 0723868 E-mail: admin@uni-fire.co.uk
Virage, Cambridge Business Park, Cowley Road, Cambridge, CB4 0WZ Tel: (01223) 488540 Fax: (01223) 488541 E-mail: info@virage.com
Wessex Fire & Safety Ltd, 8 St. Martins Avenue, Shanklin, Isle of Wight, PO37 6HB Tel: (01983) 862765 Fax: (01983) 867326 E-mail: sales@wessexfire.com

FIRE EXTINGUISHER TRAINING

Citrus Training Ltd, 16 Bentley Court, Finedon Road Industrial Estate, Wellingborough, Northamptonshire, NN8 4BQ Tel: (0870) 8503505 Fax: (01933) 228876 E-mail: develop@citrustraining.com
▶ Commercial Training, Training & Development Centre, Longfield, Hitchin Road, Stevenage, Herts, SG1 4AE Tel: 01438 847321 Fax: 01438 314031 E-mail: commercial.training@hertscc.gov.uk
▶ Fire Defence, 6 Listullycurran Road, Dromore, County Down, BT25 1RB Tel: (028) 9269 8710 Fax: (028) 9269 8710 E-mail: info@firedefenceni.co.uk
▶ Fire Solutions, Units 1 & 2 The Great Barn, Earls Croome, Worcester, WR8 9DF Tel: (01905) 371321 Fax: E-mail: info@firesolutions.co.uk
First Choice Training & Development Ltd, 37 Langdale Crescent Eston, Grange Middlesbrough, Middlesbrough, Cleveland, TS6 7RB Tel: (01642) 511877 E-mail: firstchoicetraining@ntlwolrd.com
▶ Jupiter Safety Management Ltd, 36 Shelley Road, Reddish, Stockport, Cheshire, Stockport, Cheshire, SK5 6JG Tel: 0161 442 4359 Fax: 0161 442 4359 E-mail: ccork-jupitersafety@fsmail.net
▶ Nefco Ltd, Unit 8 Derwentdale Industrial Estate, Consett, County Durham, DH8 8PZ Tel: (01207) 593623 E-mail: info@nefco.co.uk

FIRE EXTINGUISHER TRAINING - *continued*

▶ Nordal Fire Protection Services Ltd, Nordalmere House, 46 Midland Road, Raunds, Northamptonshire, NN9 6JF Tel: (01933) 625407 Fax: (01933) 626939 E-mail: sales@nordal.co.uk
▶ Pyramid Training (UK) Ltd, Beechwood House, 34 Beechwood Avenue, Bradford, West Yorkshire, BD6 3AF Tel: (01274) 677776 E-mail: info@pyramid2000.fsnet.co.uk
▶ Risk Assessment & Training, Fire House, 205 West Lake Avenue, Hampton Vale, Peterborough, PE7 8LN Tel: (01733) 247172 Fax: (01733) 247172 E-mail: angliafiresafety@btinternet.com
▶ Unique Fire Safety Solutions, Suite 39, 792 Wilmslow Road, Didsbury, Manchester, M20 6UG Tel: (07969) 664105 E-mail: sales@uniquefiresafety.com

FIRE EXTINGUISHERS

Advance Fire Services, 21-23 Lawrence Street, York, YO10 3BP Tel: (01904) 634036 Fax: (01904) 634036 E-mail: sales@advancefireyork.co.uk
Amerex Fire International Ltd, Unit 54 Springvale Industrial Estate, Cwmbran, Gwent, NP44 5BD Tel: (01633) 627000 Fax: (01633) 627005 E-mail: sales@amerexfire.eu
Approved Fire Appliances Ltd, Spinney Hill Road, Leicester, LE5 3GG Tel: 0116-276 8991 Fax: 0116-253 8017 E-mail: sales@approvedfire.co.uk
Assured Fire & Safety, 59 Florist Street, Stockport, Cheshire, SK3 8DW Tel: 0161-666 0204 Fax: 0161-666 0204 E-mail: paul@assuredfireandsafety.fsnet.co.uk
BFSS Ltd, 2 Strawberry Lane, Tiptree, Colchester, CO5 0RX Tel: (01621) 810500 Fax: (01621) 810500 E-mail: sales@blackwaterfss.co.uk
▶ CAMS Fire & Security P.L.C., 6 Wedgwood Court, Wedgwood Way, Stevenage, Hertfordshire, SG1 4QR Tel: (01438) 740840 Fax: (01438) 737969 E-mail: info@camssecurity.co.uk
Cwmbran Fire Protection (SW) Ltd, Unit 13, Oldbury Business Centre, Cwmbran, Gwent, NP44 3JU Tel: (01633) 863895 Fax: (01633) 869552 E-mail: rod@cfirep.co.uk
Express Fire Equipment Ltd, Unit 4 Mersey Road Industrial Estate, Mersey Road North, Failsworth, Manchester, M35 9LU Tel: 0161-688 5050 Fax: 0161-688 5151 E-mail: john@xpressfire.co.uk
The Fire Extinguisher Supply Company Ltd, 40 Barncroft Road, Chell Heath, Stoke-on-Trent, ST6 6QF Tel: (01782) 814590 Fax: (01782) 814590
▶ Fire Extinguisher Valve Co. Ltd, Unit 10, Ford Lane Business Park, Ford, Arundel, West Sussex, BN18 0UZ Tel: (01243) 555566 Fax: (01243) 555660 E-mail: sales@f-e-v.co.uk
Fire Fighting Equipment, Unit 20, Tait Road Industrial Estate, Croydon, CR0 2DP Tel: (020) 8665 4120 Fax: (020) 8665 4125 E-mail: tonyc@ffe.co.uk
Firecare Ltd, 72 Tartnakilly Road, Limavady, County Londonderry, BT49 9NA Tel: (028) 7776 4002 E-mail: sales@fire-care.co.uk
Fireguard Services, Unit 1 Milton Business Centre Wick Drive, New Milton, Hampshire, BH25 6RH Tel: (01425) 616139 Fax: (01425) 616139E-mail: office@fireguardservices.co.uk
Gloria UK, Parkfield House, Manchester Old Road, Middleton, Manchester, M24 4DY Tel: 0161-654 2216 Fax: 0161-654 2253 E-mail: sales@gloria.co.uk
Group 2, Chilton, Ferryhill, County Durham, DL17 0SZ Tel: (01388) 720741 Fax: (01388) 721741
Guardian Fire Ltd, Hurricane Way, Norwich, NR6 6EY Tel: (01603) 787679 Fax: (01603) 787996 E-mail: guardfire@aol.com
Guardian Security, 1 North Lane, Sandgate, Folkestone, Kent, CT20 3AS Tel: (01303) 226452 Fax: (01303) 248399 E-mail:
▶ Hireman (London) Ltd, Unit 4, Apex Industrial Estate, 22 Hythe Road, London, NW10 6RT Tel: (020) 8964 2464 Fax: (020) 8964 1343
Kidde Fire Protection Services Ltd, 400 Dallow Road, Luton, LU1 1UR Tel: (01582) 413694 Fax: (01582) 402339 E-mail: kiddefps@kiddefps.com
Lewis's Medical Supplies, Broadoak House, Coronation Street, Stockport, Cheshire, SK5 7PG Tel: 0161-480 6797 Fax: 0161 4804787 E-mail: sales@lewis-plast.co.uk
Lifeline Fire & Safety Systems Ltd, Burnsall Road Industrial Estate, Burnsall Road, Coventry, CV5 6BU Tel: (024) 7671 2999 Fax: (024) 7671 2998 E-mail: sales@lifeline-fire.co.uk
▶ Millwood Servicing Ltd, 102 Stafford Road, Wallington, Surrey, SM6 9AY Tel: (020) 8669 0080 Fax: (020) 8669 2727 E-mail: tracey@millwood.co.uk
P S P Safety Products Ltd, 9 Aintree Road, Keytech 7 Business Park, Keytec 7 Business Park, Pershore, Worcestershire, WR10 2JN Tel: (01386) 552555 Fax: (01386) 552592
Premium Fire Protection Ltd, 68 Edwin Street, Daybrook, Nottingham, NG5 6AY Tel: 0115-926 7736 Fax: 0115-919 0111
▶ Protect Fire Equipment, 3a The Pound, Coate, Devizes, Wiltshire, SN10 3LG Tel: (01380) 860022 Fax: (01380) 860022 E-mail: mail@protect-fire.co.uk
Safeguard Fire & Industrial, Silver Street, Gastard, Corsham, Wiltshire, SN13 9PY Tel: (01249) 715999 Fax: (01249) 715966 E-mail: sales@safeguardfireind.co.uk
Specialist Equipment, 18 Derwent Road, Honley, Holmfirth, HD9 6HS Tel: (01484) 661962 Fax: (01484) 329468 E-mail: sales@specialistequipment.com
Total Fire Protection, 73 Greenham, Bretton, Peterborough, PE3 9YS Tel: (01733) 700722
W Gordon Scott & Co., Unit 14 Ies Centre, Horndale Avenue, Aycliffe Industrial Park, Newton Aycliffe, County Durham, DL5 6DS Tel: (01325) 300643 Fax: (01325) 300643
Warwickshire Fire Protection, 17 Sanders Road, Coventry, CV6 6DH Tel: (024) 7636 4729 Fax: (024) 7636 4729
Whirlwind Fire Extinguisher Maintenance, Whirlwind Rise, Dudmoor Lane, Christchurch, Dorset, BH23 6BQ Tel: (01202) 475255 Fax: (01202) 475255

FIRE EXTINGUISHING SPRINKLER, *See Sprinkler etc*

FIRE FIGHTING CHEMICAL FOAM COMPOUNDS

▶ Abc Macintosh Ltd, Bleak Hall Farm Bleak Lane, Hoscar Moss, Lathom, Ormskirk, Lancashire, L40 4BP Tel: (01704) 896677 E-mail: enquires@abcmacintosh.com
Central Fire Security, 9 Gateworth Industrial Estate, Barnard Street, Warrington, WA5 1DD Tel: (01925) 230071 Fax: (01925) 652201
▶ Fire Logistics, 4 Union Street, Newcastle upon Tyne, NE2 1AH Tel: 0191-230 3647 Fax: 0191-230 3650 E-mail: sales@firelogistics.co.uk
Kerr Fire Fighting Chemicals Ltd, Ashcroft Road, Knowsley Industrial Park, Kirkby, Liverpool, L33 7TS Tel: 0151-548 6424 Fax: 0151-548 7263 E-mail: info@kfp.co.uk

FIRE FIGHTING CLOTHING

Bristol Uniforms Ltd, Victoria Street, Staple Hill, Bristol, BS16 5LL Tel: 0117-956 3101 Fax: 0117-956 5927 E-mail: enquiries@bristoluniforms.co.uk
O C A S Ltd, PO Box 228, Maidenhead, Berkshire, SL6 6PQ Tel: (01628) 510260 Fax: (01628) 510261 E-mail: ocas@vossnet.co.uk
Trelleborg Beadle, Unit 30 Bergen Way, Hull, HU7 0YQ Tel: (01482) 839119 Fax: (01482) 879418 E-mail: lesley.kidd@trelleborg.com

FIRE FIGHTING FOAM

Kerr Fire Fighting Chemicals Ltd, Ashcroft Road, Knowsley Industrial Park, Kirkby, Liverpool, L33 7TS Tel: 0151-548 6424 Fax: 0151-548 7263 E-mail: info@kfp.co.uk

FIRE FIGHTING POWDER

Kerr Fire Fighting Chemicals Ltd, Ashcroft Road, Knowsley Industrial Park, Kirkby, Liverpool, L33 7TS Tel: 0151-548 6424 Fax: 0151-548 7263 E-mail: info@kfp.co.uk

FIRE HOSE REELS

Firecare Ltd, 72 Tartnakilly Road, Limavady, County Londonderry, BT49 9NA Tel: (028) 7776 4002 E-mail: sales@fire-care.co.uk
H R Fire & Safety Ltd, Forge House, Whitehall Industrial Estate, Whitehall Road, Leeds, LS12 5JB Tel: 0113-279 4078 Fax: 0113-279 4768 E-mail: darren@hrfireandsafety.co.uk
Haselden Manufacturing Co., PO Box 349A, Surbiton, Surrey, KT5 9YG Tel: (020) 8337 7284 Fax: (020) 8337 7284

FIRE HOSE REPAIR EQUIPMENT

Anchor Fire Protection Ltd, 11 Elkin Road, Morecambe, Lancashire, LA4 5RN Tel: (01524) 832238 Fax: 01524 832238
Safe & Sure Fire Protection Ltd, Mill Road, Langley Moor, Durham, DH7 8HE Tel: 0191-378 1153 Fax: 0191-378 9297 E-mail: info@safeandsurefire.com

FIRE HOSES

A S D Fire Protection, Fisher Street, Newcastle upon Tyne, NE6 4LT Tel: (01698) 356444 Fax: (01698) 356678 E-mail: asdfire@btconnect.com
Angus Fire, Thame Park Road, Thame, Oxfordshire, OX9 3RT Tel: (01844) 214545 Fax: (01844) 265156 E-mail: general.enquiries@kiddeuk.co.uk

FIRE OR FLOOD EMERGENCY PROPERTY REINSTATEMENT

Property Repair Ltd, 52 Montrose Terrace, Edinburgh, EH7 5DL Tel: 0131-478 3391 E-mail: info@www.propertyrepairltd.co.uk

FIRE OR RADIATOR GUARDS

C Aiano & Sons Ltd, 64-70 Chrisp Street, London, E14 6LR Tel: (020) 7987 1184 Fax: (020) 7538 2786 E-mail: caianoandson@aol.com
Davies Bros (Metal Finishers), 123-127 Western Road, Hockley, Birmingham, B18 7QD Tel: 0121-554 3148 Fax: 0121-554 3148 E-mail: sales@british-fireside.co.uk

FIRE OR SECURITY ALARM CONTROL EQUIPMENT

A K Security, 12 Hailsham Close, Mickleover, Derby, DE3 0PE Tel: (01332) 518070
Metaform Ltd, 12 Trading Estate Road, London, NW10 7LU Tel: (020) 8961 0999 Fax: (020) 8965 3319
Sectorguard plc, Gainsborough House, Sheering Lower Road, Sawbridgeworth, Hertfordshire, CM21 9RG Tel: (01279) 724777 Fax: (01279) 723977 E-mail: collette@sectorguard.plc.uk

FIRE POINT EXTINGUISHER BOXES OR ENCLOSURES

Canon Fire Protection, The Wharf, Midhurst, West Sussex, GU29 9PX Tel: (01730) 815209 Fax: (01730) 816377 E-mail: cfp@canonfire.co.uk
Cowley Fire, 29 Arkwright Court, Blackpool & Fylde Industrial Estate, Blackpool, FY4 5DR Tel: (01253) 769666 Fax: (01253) 769888 E-mail: info@cowleyfire.co.uk
▶ F P S Fire Protection Ltd, Friemark House, Pioneer Park, Bristol, BS4 3QB Tel: 0117-971 7050 Fax: 0117-935 1605 E-mail: sales@firemarkext.co.uk

FIRE PROOFING SERVICES, *See also Fire Protection etc*

Thermal Designs UK Ltd, Broadway, Market Lavington, Devizes, Wiltshire, SN10 5RQ Tel: (01380) 816079 Fax: (01380) 813394 E-mail: sales@tdiuk.com

FIRE PROTECTION COATING SERVICES

Mitie Mccartney Fire Protection Ltd, 8 Lawmoor Place, Glasgow, G5 0XW Tel: 0141-429 4646 Fax: 0141-429 4442 E-mail: charlesa@mccartney.co.uk
▶ Mitie Mccartney Fire Protection Ltd, 3 Abbey Mead Industrial Park, Brooker Road, Waltham Abbey, Essex, EN9 1HU Tel: (01992) 761666 Fax: (01992) 761777 E-mail: paulas.waide@mitie.co.uk

FIRE PROTECTION COATINGS

Cafco International, Bluebell Close, Clover Nook Industrial Park, Somercotes, Alfreton, Derbyshire, DE55 4RA Tel: (01773) 837900 Fax: (01773) 836710 E-mail: info@cafcoimtl.com
Firetex, Tower Works, Kestor Street, Bolton, BL2 2AL Tel: (01204) 521771 Fax: (01204) 381826 E-mail: enquiries@leighspaints.co.uk
Pyricon Ltd, PO Box 4641, London, SE11 4XE Tel: (020) 7735 8777
Quelfire Ltd, PO Box 35, Altrincham, Cheshire, WA14 5QA Tel: 0161-928 7308 Fax: 0161-924 1340
Thermal Designs UK Ltd, Broadway, Market Lavington, Devizes, Wiltshire, SN10 5RQ Tel: (01380) 816079 Fax: (01380) 813394 E-mail: sales@tdiuk.com

FIRE PROTECTION CONSULTANCY

Airedale Fire Protection Services, Howden Grange, Holden Lane, Silsden, Keighley, West Yorkshire, BD20 0LS Tel: (01535) 652069 Fax: (01535) 652069
AIS Fire Tech Tech, Unit 12 Riverside Business Park, 33 River Road, Barking, Essex, IG11 0DA Tel: (020) 8591 3433 Fax: (020) 8594 1226 E-mail: enquiries@firetech.co.uk
Argus Fire Protection Co, Hendglade House, 46 New Road, Stourbridge, West Midlands, DY8 1PA Tel: (01384) 376256 Fax: (01384) 393955 E-mail: sales@argusfire.co.uk
Belfor Relectronic UK Ltd, Imbach House, Gerard, Tamworth, Staffordshire, B79 7UW Tel: (01827) 310100 Fax: (01827) 310200 E-mail: tamworth@uk.belfor.com
Brimset Ltd, 2 Stocks Lane, Rawmarsh, Rotherham, South Yorkshire, S62 6NL Tel: (01709) 522270 Fax: (01709) 527240 E-mail: contracts@brimset.f9.co.uk
Butler & Young Associates, 54-62 Station Road East, Oxted, Surrey, RH8 0PG Tel: (01883) 717172 Fax: (01883) 717174 E-mail: enquiries@bya.co.uk
Eurofire Firefighting Equipment, Mallusk Enterprise Park, Mallusk Drive, Newtownabbey, County Antrim, BT36 4GN Tel: (028) 9034 2991 Fax: (028) 9084 3414 E-mail: info@eurofire-ni.com
Fire Check Services, 61 Beechdale Avenue, Great Barr, Birmingham, B44 9DJ Tel: 0121-605 7049 Fax: 0121-605 7049
Fire Equipment Services Ltd, 269-271 Billinge Road, Wigan, Lancashire, WN5 8DF Tel: (01942) 228170 Fax: (01942) 228170 E-mail: info@fire-equipmentuk.com
Fire Industry Confederation, 55 Eden Street, Kingston Upon Thames, Surrey, KT1 1BW Tel: (020) 8549 8839 Fax: (020) 8547 1564 E-mail: fic@abft.org.uk
Fire Proof Ltd, Unit 14 Matrix House, Constitution Hill, Leicester, LE1 1PL Tel: 0116-248 9555 Fax: 0116-248 9555
Fire Rite, Unit G1 Caerphilly Business Park, Caerphilly, Mid Glamorgan, CF83 3ED Tel: (029) 2086 7222 Fax: (029) 2086 7333 E-mail: sales@firerite.com
Firetex, Tower Works, Kestor Street, Bolton, BL2 2AL Tel: (01204) 521771 Fax: (01204) 381826 E-mail: enquiries@leighspaints.co.uk
Flamex Firefighting Equipment, Sir Frank Whittle Business Centre, Great Central Way, Rugby, Warwickshire, CV21 3XH Tel: (01788) 577977 Fax: (01788) 577977 E-mail: phuddlestone@tiscalli.co.uk
Force Fire Consultants Ltd, 11 Gorse La Industrial Estate, Brunel Road, Clacton-on-Sea, Essex, CO15 4LU Tel: (01255) 221515 Fax: (01255) 222493 E-mail: info@forcefire.com
Jordan Marine, High Bank, Moorland Road, Birch Vale, High Peak, Derbyshire, SK22 1BS Tel: (01663) 743885 Fax: (01663) 743885
M & G Fire Protection, Colchester Road, Maldon, Essex, CM9 4NN Tel: (01621) 840999 Fax: (01621) 842322 E-mail: mgfireessex@aol.com
Mitie Mccartney Fire Protection Ltd, 8 Lawmoor Place, Glasgow, G5 0XW Tel: 0141-429 4646 Fax: 0141-429 4442 E-mail: charlesa@mccartney.co.uk
▶ Mitie Mccartney Fire Protection Ltd, 3 Abbey Mead Industrial Park, Brooker Road, Waltham Abbey, Essex, EN9 1HU Tel: (01992) 761666 Fax: (01992) 761777 E-mail: paulas.waide@mitie.co.uk
▶ Monitor Fire, 92 Hopewell Drive, Chatham, Kent, ME5 7PY Tel: (01634) 827127 Fax: (01634) 827128 E-mail: monfire@designsmartuk.com
Specialist Coatings UK Ltd, 5 Tramsheds Industrial Estate, Coomber Way, Croydon, CR0 4TQ Tel: (020) 8665 5888 Fax: (020) 8665 6888 E-mail: info@specialistcoatingsuk.com
Specialist Equipment, 18 Derwent Road, Honley, Holmfirth, HD9 6HS Tel: (01484) 661962 Fax: (01484) 329468 E-mail: sales@specialistequipment.com
Surrey Fire & Rescue Service, Wray Park Centre, 70 Wray Park Road, Reigate, Surrey, RH2 0EJ Tel: (01737) 224024 Fax: (01737) 224092 E-mail: wraypark@surreycc.gov.uk
T Dunwoody & Partners, Dunwoody House, 396 Kenton Road, Harrow, Middlesex, HA3 9DH Tel: (020) 8621 2100 Fax: (020) 8621 2111 E-mail: admin@dunwoody.uk.com
T V F plc, 59-69 Queens Road, High Wycombe, Buckinghamshire, HP13 6AH Tel: (01494) 450641 Fax: (01494) 465378
▶ Venture Fire Consultancy, Windowplan House, Knight Road, Rochester, Kent, ME2 2AH Tel: (01634) 719025 Fax: (01634) 719025 E-mail: office@venturefire.co.uk
Warringtonfire Global Safety, Holmesfield Road, Warrington, WA1 2DS Tel: (01925) 655116 Fax: (01925) 655419 E-mail: info@wfrc.co.uk

FIRE PROTECTION CONTRACTORS

▶ MSF, M S F House, Charlwood Road, Lowfield Heath, Crawley, West Sussex, RH11 0PT Tel: (01293) 543333 Fax: (01293) 597590 E-mail: sales@msf-fire.co.uk
▶ Swift, Matthew Elliott House, 64 Broadway, Salford, M50 2TS Tel: 0161-872 6262 Fax: 0161-877 2424 E-mail: info@swiftsecurity.com
▶ TASC Fire Protection Services Ltd, 24B Orgreave Crescent, Dore House Industrial Estate, Sheffield, S13 9NQ Tel: (0870) 7705130 Fax: (0870) 7705131 E-mail: enquiries@tasc-groupltd.co.uk

FIRE PROTECTION EQUIPMENT OR SYSTEMS

A F S Systems Ltd, 9 Tamworth Road, Lichfield, Staffordshire, WS14 9EY Tel: (01543) 264034 Fax: (01543) 414367 E-mail: enquiries@arrowfire.co.uk
Angus Fire, Thame Park Road, Thame, Oxfordshire, OX9 3RT Tel: (01844) 214545 Fax: (01844) 265156 E-mail: general.enquiries@kiddeuk.co.uk

FIRE PROTECTION EQUIPMENT OR SYSTEMS – *continued*

▶ Argyll & Highland Fire Services, Ben Nevis Drive, Ben Nevis Industrial Estate, Fort William, Inverness-Shire, PH33 6RU Tel: (01397) 700234 Fax: (01397) 705377

Autoquench Ltd, 132 Priory Road, Hall Green, Birmingham, B28 0TB Tel: 0121-693 6888 Fax: 0121-430 6007 E-mail: mail@autoquench.co.uk

B M Hire & Sales, 203 Askern Road, Bentley, Doncaster, South Yorkshire, DN5 0JR Tel: (01302) 876225 Fax: (01302) 876225

Besseges Ltd, Riverside, Dukinfield, Cheshire, SK16 4HE Tel: 0161-308 3252 Fax: 0161-339 5003 E-mail: sales@besseges.co.uk

Chubb Fire Scotland Ltd, South Deeside Road, Maryculter, Aberdeen, AB12 5GB Tel: (01224) 735605 Fax: (01224) 735604 E-mail: gfp.limited@btinternet.com

Darchem Engineering Ltd, Iron Masters Way, Stillington, Stockton-on-Tees, Cleveland, TS21 1LB Tel: (01740) 630461 Fax: (01740) 630529 E-mail: sales@darchem.co.uk

Dawn Fire Engineers Ltd, 26 Wooburn Industrial Park, Wooburn Green, High Wycombe, Buckinghamshire, HP10 0PF Tel: (01628) 526531 Fax: (01628) 526634 E-mail: sales@dawnfire.co.uk

Richard Edwards Fabrications Ltd, 15 Broadfield Close, Croydon, CR0 4XR Tel: (020) 8686 8616 Fax: (020) 8686 5313

Exco Fire & Safety Control Ltd, 46 St Gluvias Street, Penryn, Cornwall, TR10 8BJ Tel: (01326) 372878 Fax: (01326) 377135 E-mail: jack@excotec.co.uk

F G F Ltd, Fernhurst Road, Bristol, BS5 7XN Tel: 0117-951 7755 Fax: 0117-935 4231 E-mail: sales@fgfltd.co.uk

F G F Ltd, West Quay Road, Southampton, SO15 1GZ Tel: (023) 8021 2121 Fax: (023) 8022 3274 E-mail: southampton@fgflimited.co.uk

Firetex, Tower Works, Kestor Street, Bolton, BL2 2AL Tel: (01204) 521771 Fax: (01204) 381826 E-mail: enquiries@leighspaints.co.uk

David Hughes Enterprises Ltd, New Cottage, Oulton, Norbury, Stafford, ST20 0PG Tel: (01785) 284410 Fax: (01785) 284410

I C S Triplex, 10-14 Hall Road, Heybridge, Maldon, Essex, CM9 4LA Tel: (01621) 854444 Fax: (01621) 859221 E-mail: sales@icsplc.co.uk

Interlink Systems, 15 Greenacres Avenue, Winnersh, Wokingham, Berkshire, RG41 5SX Tel: 0118-962 9900 Fax: 0118-962 9955 E-mail: interlinksystems@btinternet.com

Kidde Fire Protection Services Ltd, Unit 12 Llwyn' Y' Graig, Garngoth Industrial Estate, Gorsenion, Swansea, SA4 9WG Tel: (01792) 898884 Fax: (01792) 891808 E-mail: kfpfswansea@kiddefps.com

Macron Safety Systems UK Ltd, Woodlands Road, Guildford, Surrey, GU1 1RN Tel: (01483) 572222 Fax: (01483) 302180 E-mail: info@macron-safety.com

Mann Mcgowan Fabrications Ltd, 4 The Brook Trading Estate, Deadbrook Lane, Aldershot, Hampshire, GU12 4XB Tel: (01252) 333601 Fax: (01252) 322724 E-mail: sales@mannmcgowan.co.uk

Midland Fire Protection Services Ltd, Unit 17 Courtaulds Industrial Estate, Foleshill Road, Coventry, CV6 5AY Tel: (024) 7668 5252 Fax: (024) 7663 7575 E-mail: info@midlandfire.co.uk

▶ MSF, M S F House, Charlwood Road, Lowfield Heath, Crawley, West Sussex, RH11 0PT Tel: (01293) 543333 Fax: (01293) 597590 E-mail: sales@msf-fire.co.uk

N F S Fire Protection Ltd, Morton Street, Middleton, Manchester, M24 6AN Tel: 0161-643 9338 Fax: 0161-655 3878

Nationwide Fire Protection Associates, Southcote Mill, Southcote Farm Lane, Reading, RG30 3DZ Tel: 0118-951 1799 Fax: 0118-951 1799

Nittan (UK) Ltd, Hipley Street, Woking, Surrey, GU22 9LQ Tel: (01483) 769555 Fax: (01483) 756686 E-mail: sales@nittan.co.uk

Pegasus Fire Protection, 8 Southedge Close, Hipperholme, Halifax, West Yorkshire, HX3 8DW Tel: (01422) 206076 Fax: (01422) 206076

Pennine Fire Extinguisher Services, Pleasington Street, Blackburn, BB2 1UF Tel: (01254) 263378 Fax: (01254) 278898 E-mail: info@penninefire.co.uk

Pyramid Fire Protection Ltd, 132 Rutland Road, Sheffield, S3 9PP Tel: 0114-272 8921 Fax: 0114-272 7631 E-mail: sales@pyramid-fire.co.uk

Reading Extinguisher Services, 139b Caversham Road, Reading, RG1 8AU Tel: (0800) 7310727 Fax: 0118-959 1167 E-mail: sales@extinguishers.co.uk

Redbox Fire Control, 7 South View Road, Southampton, SO15 5JD Tel: (023) 8077 6131 Fax: (023) 8077 6131 E-mail: enquiries@redboxfire.co.uk

Rochdale Fire Sprinklers Ltd, Unit 13, Rochdale Industrial Centre, Albion Road, Rochdale, Lancashire, OL11 4HQ Tel: (01706) 527177 Fax: (01706) 527179 E-mail: rochdalefire@btconnect.com

Salford Fire & Safety Co. Ltd, 11 Vestris Drive, Salford, M6 8EL Tel: 0161-789 5550

Sargom Fire, 6 Station Terrace, London, NW10 5RT Tel: (020) 8964 0808 Fax: (020) 8960 2113 E-mail: sales@sargom.com

Southern Fire Security Ltd, 4 The Old Saw Mill Industrial Estate, The Street, Broughton Gifford, Melksham, Wiltshire, SN12 8PY Tel: (01225) 782020 Fax: (01225) 782007

Talentum Development Ltd, Beal Lane, Shaw, Oldham, OL2 8PF Tel: (01706) 844714 Fax: (01706) 882612 E-mail: info@talentum.co.uk

Telegan Protection Ltd, 3-5 Holmethorpe Avenue, Redhill, RH1 2LZ Tel: (01737) 763800 Fax: (01737) 782727 E-mail: sales@teleganprotection.com

Trident Fire Protection Company Ltd, Henfold Lane, Newdigate, Dorking, Surrey, RH5 5AF Tel: (01306) 886166 Fax: (01306) 631430 E-mail: cbta@arabact.co.uk

UK Fire International Ltd, The Safety Centre, Mountergate, Norwich, NR1 1PY Tel: (01603) 727000 Fax: (01603) 727073 E-mail: norwich@ukfire.co.uk

UK Fire Protection Rentals Ltd, Alscott Mill, Alscott, Telford, Shropshire, TF6 5EE Tel: (01952) 250750 Fax: 0121-270 6575 E-mail: enquiries@ukfireprotection.com

Vipond Fire Protection Ltd, 10 Glenfield Road, Kelvin Industrial Estate, East Kilbride, Glasgow, G75 0RA Tel: (01355) 237588 Fax: (01355) 263399 E-mail: admin.uk@vipondltd.co.uk

Wardfire, 6 The Galloway Centre, Hambridge Lane, Newbury, Berkshire, RG14 5TL Tel: (01635) 552999 Fax: (01635) 552566 E-mail: sales@wardfire.co.uk

X R Fasteners Ltd, Unit 85 86 Imperial Trading Estate, Lambs La North, Rainham, Essex, RM13 9XL Tel: (01708) 526274 Fax: (01708) 525981

FIRE PROTECTION INSTALLATION OR SERVICING

A F S Systems Ltd, 9 Tamworth Road, Lichfield, Staffordshire, WS14 9EY Tel: (01543) 264034 Fax: (01543) 414367 E-mail: enquiries@arrowfire.co.uk

A & F Sprinklers Ltd, Atrium House, 574 Manchester Road, Bury, Lancashire, BL9 9SW Tel: 0161-796 5397 Fax: 0161-796 6057 E-mail: lhill@afsprinklers.co.uk

A H Fire Prevention, 233a Golders Green Road, London, NW11 9ES Tel: (020) 8458 0448 Fax: (020) 8458 0338

A L Technical Ltd, 2 Woodston Business Centre, Shrewsbury Avenue, Peterborough, PE2 7EF Tel: (01733) 390123 Fax: (01733) 394933 E-mail: altechnical@yahoo.co.uk

Anglian Energy Services, 23 Windrush Road, Kesgrave, Ipswich, IP5 2NZ Tel: (01473) 614446 Fax: (01473) 620443 E-mail: aessprinklers@aol.com

Argus Fire Protection Co, Hendglade House, 46 New Road, Stourbridge, West Midlands, DY8 1PA Tel: (01384) 376256 Fax: (01384) 393955 E-mail: sales@argusfire.co.uk

Besseges Ltd, Riverside, Dukinfield, Cheshire, SK16 4HE Tel: 0161-308 3252 Fax: 0161-339 5003 E-mail: sales@besseges.co.uk

▶ Cannon Fire Protection, 1 Industrial Estate, Hallcroft Road, Retford, Nottinghamshire, DN22 7SS Tel: (01777) 710975 Fax: (01777) 719628

Ceasefire, 4 Reedmace, Tamworth, Staffordshire, B77 1BH Tel: (01827) 56556 Fax: (01827) 54364

Central Fire Protection, 5 Bewsey Road, Warrington, WA2 7LN Tel: (01925) 414464 Fax: (01925) 244298 E-mail: cfp.warrington@central-fire.co.uk

Central Service Fire Protection, Central House, Vivars Way, Canal Road, Selby, North Yorkshire, YO8 8BE Tel: (01757) 213360 Fax: (01757) 210022 E-mail: csfp@btconnect.com

▶ Checkmate Passive Fire Protection Ltd, B Honley Business Centre, New Mill Road, Honley, Holmfirth, HD9 6QB Tel: (01484) 664028 Fax: (01484) 665320

Cormeton Fire Protection Ltd, Unit 12 Delaval Trading Estate, Seaton Delaval, Whitley Bay, Tyne & Wear, NE25 0QT Tel: 0191-237 0790 Fax: 0191-237 5143 E-mail: sales@cormeton.co.uk

Crawley Fire Protection, Hazelwick Mill Lane, Crawley, West Sussex, RH10 1SU Tel: (01293) 547654 Fax: (01293) 440295

▶ D H H Sprinklers, 123 Front Road, Drumbo, Lisburn, County Antrim, BT27 5JY Tel: (028) 9082 7008 Fax: (028) 9082 7012 E-mail:

Dalkia, The Connect Centre, Kingston CR, Portsmouth, PO2 8AD Tel: (0800) 0853208 Fax: (023) 9262 9656 E-mail: enquiries@dalkia.co.uk

Dawn Fire Engineers Ltd, 26 Wooburn Industrial Park, Wooburn Green, High Wycombe, Buckinghamshire, HP10 0PF Tel: (01628) 526531 Fax: (01628) 526634 E-mail: sales@dawnfire.co.uk

Deborah Services Ltd, Thornes Moor Road, Wakefield, West Yorkshire, WF2 8PT Tel: (01924) 378222 Fax: (01924) 366250 E-mail: enquiries@deborahservices.co.uk

Direction Fire Ltd, 5 First Quarter, Blenheim Road, Epsom, Surrey, KT19 9QN Tel: (01372) 744499 Fax: (01372) 741188 E-mail: angellinaw@directionfire.co.uk

Econogard Services Ltd, Econogard House, 1 Halifax Road, Cambridge, CB4 3QB Tel: (01763) 261970 Fax: (01223) 352494

Express Fire Equipment Ltd, Unit 4 Mersey Road Industrial Estate, Mersey Road North, Failsworth, Manchester, M35 9LU Tel: 0161-688 5050 Fax: 0161-688 5151 E-mail: john@xpressfire.co.uk

Fire Protection Services, 4 Churchill Avenue, Haverhill, Suffolk, CB9 0AA Tel: (01440) 708833

Firefill International, Trocell House, Wakening Road, Barking, Essex, IG11 8PD Tel: (020) 8594 9599 Fax: (020) 8594 1933 E-mail: info@firefill.co.uk

▶ Firth Fire Protection Servicing Co. Ltd, Stony Lane, Christchurch, Dorset, BH23 7LQ Tel: (01202) 476902 Fax: (01202) 479493

Fixfire, Mayflower House, Bodmin Road, Coventry, CV2 5DB Tel: (024) 7661 6699 Fax: (024) 7662 1990

Gradwood Ltd, Lansdown House, 85 Buxton Road, Stockport, Cheshire, SK2 6LR Tel: 0161-480 9629 Fax: 0161-474 7433 E-mail: sales@gradwood.co.uk

Haden Young Ltd, 11 Britannia Road, Patchway, Bristol, BS34 5TD Tel: 0117-969 3911 Fax: 0117-979 8711 E-mail: bristol@hadenyoung.co.uk

Herefordshire Fire Protection Services, Unit A2, Holmer Trading Estate, College Rd, Hereford, HR1 1JS Tel: (01432) 269094 Fax: (01432) 344095

J & J Services, Gowan Avenue, Falkirk, FK2 7HL Tel: (01324) 620204 Fax: (01324) 885914 E-mail: jr@jjfirepro.co.uk

Jordan Marine, High Bank, Moorland Road, Birch Vale, High Peak, Derbyshire, SK22 1BS Tel: (01663) 743885 Fax: (01663) 743885

Knebworth Fire Protection, 22 Doncaster Close, Stevenage, Hertfordshire, SG1 5RY Tel: (01438) 712642 Fax: (01438) 861759

L & S Fire Protection Systems Ltd, 7a Rathbone Square, 28 Tanfield Road, Croydon, CR0 1AL Tel: (020) 8240 4456 Fax: (020) 8240 4457 E-mail: landsfire@ssbdial.co.uk

Linkester Fire Protection, 4-6 Cross Street, Macclesfield, Cheshire, SK11 7PG Tel: (01625) 511272 Fax: (01625) 511272

Macron Safety Systems UK Ltd, Woodlands Road, Guildford, Surrey, GU1 1RN Tel: (01483) 572222 Fax: (01483) 302180 E-mail: info@macron-safety.com

Marbco Fire & Safety, Barrington Industrial Estate, Bedlington, Northumberland, NE22 7DQ Tel: (01670) 828488 Fax: (01670) 828315

MB Fire Protection, Unit 22 Bourne Road Industrial Park, Bourne Road, Dartford, DA1 4BZ Tel: (01322) 523399 Fax: (01322) 528883

▶ Monitor Fire, 92 Hopewell Drive, Chatham, Kent, ME5 7PY Tel: (01634) 827127 Fax: (01634) 827128 E-mail: monfire@designsmartuk.com

Morgantic Ltd, 71 Harehills Road, Harehills, Leeds, LS8 5HS Tel: (0845) 3000440 Fax: (0845) 3000441

Ozone Fire Protection Ltd, Havyatt Manor, Havyatt, Glastonbury, Somerset, BA6 8LF Tel: (0800) 006900

Pegasus Fire Protection, 8 Southedge Close, Hipperholme, Halifax, West Yorkshire, HX3 8DW Tel: (01422) 206076 Fax: (01422) 206076

Phoenix Fire Services Ltd, Homes Court House, 29a Bridge Street, Kenilworth, Warwickshire, CV8 1BP Tel: (01926) 855991 Fax: (01926) 855338 E-mail: paul@phoenixfireservices.co.uk

Quantock Ceilings Southern Ltd, Unit 27 Hamp Industrial Estate, Old Taunton Road, Bridgwater, Somerset, TA6 3NT Tel: (01278) 446611 Fax: (01278) 446612 E-mail: sales@quantockceilings.co.uk

R S M Refko Installations Ltd, 8 Capstan Centre, Thurrock Park Way, Tilbury, Essex, RM18 7HH Tel: (01375) 855500 Fax: (01375) 855533

Redditch Fire Protection, Bliss Gate House, Edgioake Lane, Astwood Bank, Redditch, Worcestershire, B96 6BG Tel: (01527) 893336 Fax: (01527) 893336 E-mail: brogers@redditchfire.co.uk

Regis Plastic Signs, Providence Street, Stourbridge, West Midlands, DY9 8HN Tel: (01384) 892366 Fax: (01384) 892367

Richmond Fire Engineers, 30 Firby Road, Gallowfields Trading Estate, Richmond, North Yorkshire, DL10 4ST Tel: (01748) 825612 Fax: (01748) 825935 E-mail: sprinklers@richmondfire.co.uk

Rochdale Fire Sprinklers Ltd, Unit 13, Rochdale Industrial Centre, Albion Road, Rochdale, Lancashire, OL11 4HQ Tel: (01706) 527177 Fax: (01706) 527179 E-mail: rochdalefire@btconnect.com

S S Oakes Fire Protection Ltd, Fourth Street, Bolton, BL1 7NW Tel: (01204) 845876 Fax: (01204) 845876

St Andrews Fire Equipment, 3 St Williams Way, Norwich, NR7 0AH Tel: (01603) 431122 Fax: (01603) 448640

Salamis International Ltd, 3 Greenhole Place, Bridge of Don Industrial Estate, Aberdeen, AB23 8EU Tel: (01224) 246001 Fax: (01224) 246100

Siemans Building Technologies Ltd, Hawthorne Road, Staines, Middlesex, TW18 3AY Tel: (01784) 461616 Fax: (01784) 464646

Strebor Fire Protection (Intl) Ltd, 20 Brook Road, Wimborne, Dorset, BH21 2BH Tel: (01202) 886797 Fax: (01202) 889329 E-mail: sales@streborfire.com

Structural Space Ltd, Trident House, Neptune Business Estate, Dolphin Way, Purfleet, Essex, RM19 1NZ Tel: (01708) 683041 Fax: (01708) 683068 E-mail: info@structuralspace.co.uk

Supablast Nationwide Ltd, 11 Gorsey Lane, Coleshill, Birmingham, B46 1JU Tel: (01675) 464446 Fax: (01675) 464447 E-mail: enquiries@supablast.co.uk

T H White Installation Ltd, 3 Nursteed Road Trading Estate, William Road, Devizes, Wiltshire, SN10 3EW Tel: (01380) 726656 Fax: (01380) 725707 E-mail: thwhite@bigwig.net

Telegan Protection Ltd, 3-5 Holmethorpe Avenue, Redhill, RH1 2LZ Tel: (01737) 763800 Fax: (01737) 782727 E-mail: sales@teleganprotection.com

Trident Fire Protection Company Ltd, Henfold Lane, Newdigate, Dorking, Surrey, RH5 5AF Tel: (01306) 886166 Fax: (01306) 631430 E-mail: cbta@arabact.co.uk

▶ Trinity Protection Systems Ltd, Old Mill House, Oil Mill Lane, Clyst St. Mary, Exeter, EX5 1AG Tel: (01392) 874455 Fax: (01392) 875546 E-mail: info@trinityprotection.co.uk

UK Fire International Ltd, The Safety Centre, Mountergate, Norwich, NR1 1PY Tel: (01603) 727000 Fax: (01603) 727073 E-mail: norwich@ukfire.co.uk

Vipond Fire Protection Ltd, 10 Glenfield Road, Kelvin Industrial Estate, East Kilbride, Glasgow, G75 0RA Tel: (01355) 237588 Fax: (01355) 263399 E-mail: admin.uk@vipondltd.co.uk

Walker Fire, 10 The Quad, Mercury Court, Chester, CH1 4QP Tel: (01244) 371345 Fax: (01244) 370396 E-mail: uk@walkerfire.com

Warren Insulation, Blackthorne Road, Colnbrook, Slough, SL3 0DU Tel: (01753) 687272 Fax: (01753) 681623 E-mail: heathrow@warren.co.uk

FIRE PROTECTION MATERIALS

Ace Fire Ltd, 14 Concorde Road, Norwich, NR6 6BW Tel: (01603) 787333 Fax: (01603) 787332 E-mail: info@acefire.co.uk

▶ C P Covers Ltd, 18 Hanson Close, Middleton, Manchester, M24 2HD Tel: 0161-654 9396 Fax: 0161-654 6017 E-mail: cpcovers@btopenworld.com

Culimetea Saveguard Ltd, Tame Valley Mill, Wainwright Street, Dukinfield, Cheshire, SK16 5NB Tel: 0161-344 2484 Fax: 0161-344 2486E-mail: sales@culimetea-saveguard.com

E S B Environmental, 126 Hillcroft Crescent, Watford, WD19 4NZ Tel: (01923) 800852 Fax: (01923) 229003 E-mail: jbird@moose.co.uk

Intellect Computers, 12 Scarsdale Place, Buxton, Derbyshire, SK17 6EF Tel: (01298) 70055 Fax: (01298) 70066 E-mail: enquiries@oxin.net

Rockwool Rockpanel B V, Pencoed, Bridgend, Mid Glamorgan, CF35 6NY Tel: (01656) 862621 Fax: (01656) 862302 E-mail: info@rockwool.co.uk

Tenmat Ltd, Ashburton Road West, Trafford Park, Manchester, M17 1RU Tel: 0161-872 2181 Fax: 0161-872 7596 E-mail: info@tenmat.com

Three Counties Fire Protection, 43 Station Road, Foxton, Cambridge, CB22 6SA Tel: (01223) 510878 Fax: 01223 510878

UK Prevention (Nottingham) Ltd, 53 York Dr, Princes Meadows, Nottingham, NG8 6PP Tel: 0115-942 5999

FIRE RATED WINDOWS

▶ North West Timber Products Ltd, Unit 11B, Newhaven Business Park, Barton Lane, Eccles, Manchester, M30 0HH Tel: 0161-7073797 Fax: 0161-7079717 E-mail: sales@nwtimberproducts.co.uk

▶ Plus Windows & Doors Ltd, Units 16 & 18 Moor Park Industrial Centre, Tolpits Lane, Watford, WD18 9SP Tel: (01923) 225855 Fax: (01923) 256106 E-mail: sales@apluswindows.co.uk

FIRE RESISTANT (FR) BUILDING BOARD

F G F Ltd, West Quay Road, Southampton, SO15 1GZ Tel: (023) 8021 2121 Fax: (023) 8022 3274 E-mail: southampton@fgflimited.co.uk

FIRE RESISTANT (FR) CABLES

BCD Cables Ltd, The E-Tech Centre, Boundary Road, Great Yarmouth, Norfolk, NR31 0LY Tel: (01493) 604604 Fax: (01493) 604606 E-mail: john.milne@etechcentre.com

Haani Cables Ltd, Tofts Farm Industrial Estate East, Brenda Road, Hartlepool, Cleveland, TS25 2BS Tel: (01429) 221184 Fax: (01429) 272714 E-mail: info@haanicables.co.uk

Rexel Senate Electrical Wholesalers Ltd, Senate House, 6-16 Southgate Road, Potters Bar, Hertfordshire, EN6 5DS Tel: (01707) 640000 Fax: (01707) 640111

FIRE RESISTANT (FR) GLAZING SYSTEMS

Apex Security Engineering Ltd, Flint Road, Letchworth Garden City, Hertfordshire, SG6 1HJ Tel: (01462) 673431 Fax: (01462) 671518 E-mail: sales@apexsecuritiesfurniture.com

Lorient Holdings Ltd, Fairfax Road, Heathfield Industrial Estate, Newton Abbot, Devon, TQ12 6UD Tel: (01626) 834252 Fax: (01626) 833166 E-mail: admin@lorient.co.uk

▶ Multi Fabricated Systems Ltd, Finchwood Farm, Copse Lane, Hayling Island, Hampshire, PO11 0QB Tel: (023) 9246 1211 Fax: (023) 9246 1800 E-mail: info@multifirescreens.com

FIRE RESISTANT (FR) OFFICE CABINETS AND FILES

Fbh-Fichet Ltd, 7/8 Amor Way, Letchworth Garden City, Hertfordshire, SG6 1UG Tel: (01462) 472900 Fax: (01462) 472901 E-mail: sales@fbh-fichet.com

Kardex Systems UK Ltd, Kestrel House Falconry Court, Bakers Lane, Epping, Essex, CM16 5LL Tel: (0870) 2422224 Fax: (0870) 2400420 E-mail: moreinfo@kardex.co.uk

Safe Security, 29 New Hall Lane, Preston, PR1 5NX Tel: (01772) 793792 Fax: (01772) 651886 E-mail: info@thesafeshop.co.uk

Safetyworks GB Limited, P.O. Box 753, Aylesbury, Buckinghamshire, HP22 9BJ Tel: (01296) 655506 Fax: (01296) 655503 E-mail: david@safety-works.co.uk

Withy Grove Stores Ltd, 35-39 Withy Grove, Manchester, M4 2BJ Tel: 0161-834 0044

FIRE RESISTANT (FR) OR LOW SMOKE EMISSION FLOORING

Industrial Latex Compounds Ltd, Burns Mill, Manchester Street, Heywood, Lancashire, OL10 1DN Tel: (01706) 366161 Fax: (01706) 625664 E-mail: enquiries@indlatex.co.uk

North Offshore Ltd, Saltire House, Blackness Avenue, Altens Industrial Estate, Aberdeen, AB12 3PG Tel: (01224) 871906 Fax: (01224) 878828 E-mail: northoffshore@northgroup.co.uk

FIRE RESISTANT (FR) PANELLING OR ENCLOSURES

British Mica Co. Ltd, 123 Barkers Lane, Bedford, MK41 9RR Tel: (01234) 327977 Fax: (01234) 352016 E-mail: info@britishmica.co.uk

FIRE RESISTANT (FR) PARTITION OR WALL INSTALLATION CONTRACTORS

Welin Fire Insulation, Unit 14a Millpark Industrial Estate, Cannock, Staffordshire, WS11 7XU Tel: (01543) 469220 Fax: (01543) 468129

FIRE RESISTANT (FR) PARTITIONS OR WALLS

Bridge Ceilings Ltd, Interiors House, Samson Road, Coalville, Leicestershire, LE67 3FP Tel: (01530) 834777 Fax: (01530) 813388 E-mail: info@bridgeinteriors.co.uk

C P Supplies Ltd, 1-3 Brixton Road, London, SW9 6DE Tel: (020) 7582 2911 Fax: (020) 7582 0271 E-mail: bmkennington@cpsupplies.co.uk

FIRE RESISTANT (FR) ROLLER SHUTTERS

Amber Doors Ltd, Mason Way, Platts Common Industrial Estate Hoyland, Barnsley, South Yorkshire, S74 9TG Tel: (01226) 351135 Fax: (01226) 350176 E-mail: sales@amberdoors.co.uk

CNC Doors, Premier Partnership Estate, Leys Road, Brierley Hill, West Midlands, DY5 3UP Tel: (01384) 78833 Fax: (01384) 78867 E-mail: cncdoors@btconnect.com

Meridian Doors Ltd, The Croft, High Street, Whetstone, Leicester, LE8 6LQ Tel: 0116-275 0666 Fax: 0116-275 0606 E-mail: meridiandoors@webleicester.co.uk

R N B Industrial Door Service Ltd, 6 Davenport Centre, Renwick Road, Barking, Essex, IG11 0SH Tel: (020) 8595 1242 Fax: (020) 8595 3849

FIRE RESISTANT (FR) SAFES

Dudley Safes Ltd, Unit 17 Deepdale Works, Deepdale Lane, Upper Gornal, Dudley, West Midlands, DY3 2AF Tel: (01384) 239991 Fax: (01384) 455129 E-mail: sales@dudleysafes.com

Safetyworks GB Limited, P.O. Box 753, Aylesbury, Buckinghamshire, HP22 9BJ Tel: (01296) 655506 Fax: (01296) 655503 E-mail: david@safety-works.co.uk

FIRE RESISTANT (FR) VENTILATORS

Lorient Holdings Ltd, Fairfax Road, Heathfield Industrial Estate, Newton Abbot, Devon, TQ12 6UD Tel: (01626) 834252 Fax: (01626) 833166 E-mail: admin@lorient.co.uk

FIRE RISK ASSESSMENT

▶ Rushbrook Consultants Ltd, 216 West George Street, Glasgow, G2 2PQ Tel: (01357) 300633

▶ Safety Simply, 23 Cock Close Road, Yaxley, Peterborough, PE7 3HJ Tel: (0845) 2600710 Fax: (0845) 2600711 E-mail: info@safetysimplifield.co.uk

▶ Tme Training Ltd, 5 Lower Actis, Glastonbury, Somerset, BA6 8DP Tel: (01458) 832607

▶ Venture Fire Consultancy, Windowplan House, Knight Road, Rochester, Kent, ME2 2AH Tel: (01634) 719025 Fax: (01634) 719025 E-mail: office@venturefire.co.uk

▶ www.firesafetyconsultants.co.uk, 5 Pardovan Holdings, Philpstoun, Linlithgow, West Lothian, EH49 6QZ Tel: (01506) 671707 Fax: (0700) 6313561 E-mail: sbrooker@firesafetyconsultants.co.uk

FIRE SAFE HALOGEN LIGHTING

Electro Technik Ltd, 10-12 Shaw Lane, Stoke Prior, Bromsgrove, Worcestershire, B60 4DT Tel: (01527) 831794 Fax: (01527) 574470 E-mail: electro.technik@virgin.net

FIRE SAFETY AUDITS

▶ Btatraining Ltd, 32 Cornwall Crescent, Brighouse, West Yorkshire, HD6 4DS Tel: (01484) 718218 E-mail: stuart@btatraining.co.uk

FIRE SAFETY CONSULTANCY,

See also Fire Protection etc

BDS Consultants, 4 Cumberland Road, Urmston, Manchester, M41 9HS Tel: 0161-748 2712 Fax: 0161-748 2378 E-mail: info@bds-consultants.co.uk

Coselt Kenmore, Unit G3 Narvik Way, Tyne Tunnel Trading Estate, North Shields, Tyne & Wear, NE29 7XJ Tel: 0191-259 6644 Fax: 0191-258 6363 E-mail: sales@cosaltkenmore.co.uk

▶ Derek C Miles Fire & Safety Consultants, 502 Fulwood Road, Sheffield, S10 3QD Tel: 0114-230 2200 Fax: 0114-230 7700 E-mail: info@dcmfiresafe.co.uk

▶ ESI: Electrical Safety Inspections Ltd, 5 Chulkhurst, Sissinghurst Road, Biddenden, Ashford, Kent, TN27 8DG Tel: (0870) 4860351 Fax: (0870) 4860353 E-mail: jamie@esielectrical.co.uk

Extinguisher Rental Service, 29-31 Bayes Street, Kettering, Northamptonshire, NN16 8EH Tel: (01536) 417231 Fax: (01536) 411484

▶ Fire Maintenance Services, Unit 26 Swan Road, Swan Industrial Estate, Washington, Tyne & Wear, NE38 8JJ Tel: 0191-497 2929 Fax: 0191-415 0061 E-mail: fms@whfc.net

Force Fire Consultants Ltd, 11 Gorse La Industrial Estate, Brunel Road, Clacton-on-Sea, Essex, CO15 4LU Tel: (01255) 221515 Fax: (01255) 222493 E-mail: info@forcefire.com

▶ Hooper Safety, 25 Honey Lane, Buntingford, Hertfordshire, SG9 9BQ Tel: (01763) 271051 Fax: (01763) 271051 E-mail: ian@hoopersafety.net

Morgan Fire Protection Ltd, Hillgrove Business Park, Nazeing Road, Nazeing, Waltham Abbey, Essex, EN9 2HB Tel: (01992) 893498 Fax: (01992) 892098 E-mail: info@totalprotectionservices.co.uk

▶ Solutions Fire Safety Ltd, PO Box 5963, Basildon, Essex, SS14 3GW Tel: 0845 6012632 Fax: 0845 6012659 E-mail: sales@solutionsfiresafety.co.uk

Richard Thorpe Fire Safety Services, Melbreak, Hazel Road, Ash Green, Aldershot, Hampshire, GU12 6HR Tel: (01252) 316330 E-mail: sales@richardthorpefire.co.uk

Warringtonfire Global Safety, Holmesfield Road, Warrington, WA1 2DS Tel: (01925) 655116 Fax: (01925) 655419 E-mail: info@wfrc.co.uk

FIRE SAFETY EQUIPMENT

Sling & Tackle, Unit 57, Third Avenue, Bletchley, Milton Keynes, MK1 1DR Tel: (01908) 449300 Fax: (01908) 449301 E-mail: sales@slingandtackle.co.uk

▶ Taf Tyre Products, Littleton House, Littleton Road, Ashford, Middlesex, TW15 1UU Tel: (01784) 420505 Fax: (01784) 259707 E-mail: tas@tas-tyreproducts.com

FIRE SAFETY TRAINING

▶ Btatraining Ltd, 32 Cornwall Crescent, Brighouse, West Yorkshire, HD6 4DS Tel: (01484) 718218 E-mail: stuart@btatraining.co.uk

FIRE SCREENS

Richard Quinnell Ltd, Rowhurst Forge, Oxshott Road, Leatherhead, Surrey, KT22 0EN Tel: (01372) 375148 Fax: (01372) 386516 E-mail: rjquinnell@aol.com

Spectrum Fire Protection Ltd, Middlemore Lane, Walsall, WS9 8SP Tel: (01922) 744466 Fax: (01922) 744477 E-mail: sales@spectrumfire.co.uk

FIRE SCREENS, GLASS

▶ Essex Safety Glass Ltd, Moss Road, Witham, Essex, CM8 3UQ Tel: (01376) 520061 Fax: (01376) 521176 E-mail: graeme.brouder@essexsafetyglass.co.uk

▶ Glass Studio, 180 John Wilson Business Park, Chestfield, Whitstable, Kent, CT5 3RB Tel: (01227) 770613 Fax: (01227) 770613 E-mail: sales@theglassstudio.co.uk

FIRE STOPPING MATERIALS

Celltex Fabrications Ltd, Unit 9a Barnfield Trading Estate, Ramsey Road, Tipton, West Midlands, DY4 9DU Tel: 0121-520 3443 Fax: 0121-520 1772 E-mail: sales@celltex.co.uk

Newmor Group Ltd, Madoc Works, Henfaes Lane, Welshpool, Powys, SY21 7BE Tel: (01938) 552671 Fax: (01938) 554285 E-mail: enquiries@newmor.com

Rhodia Sealants Ltd, 4 Pomeroy Drive, Oadby, Leicester, LE2 5NE Tel: 0116-206 3400 Fax: 0116-206 3460 E-mail: rhodia.sealants@eu.rohodia.com

S P C, Unit 1, Chalford Industrial Estate, Chalford, Stroud, Glos, GL6 8NT Tel: (01453) 885929 Fax: (01453) 731044

FIRE TESTING LABORATORY AND CERTIFICATION BODY

Warrington Fire Research Centre, 101 Marsh Gate La, Stratford, London, E15 2NQ Tel: (020) 8519 8297 Fax: (020) 8519 3029

Warringtonfire Global Safety, Holmesfield Road, Warrington, WA1 2DS Tel: (01925) 655116 Fax: (01925) 655419 E-mail: info@wfrc.co.uk

FIRE WATER MONITORS AND NOZZLES

P N R UK Ltd, 13 16 Sugarbrook Road, Bromsgrove, Worcestershire, B60 3DW Tel: (01527) 579066 Fax: (01527) 579067 E-mail: sales@pnr.co.uk

Strebor Fire Protection (Intl) Ltd, 20 Brook Road, Wimborne, Dorset, BH21 2BH Tel: (01202) 886797 Fax: (01202) 889329 E-mail: sales@streborfire.com

FIRECLAY PRODUCTS OR FIRECLAY

R E Knowles Ltd, Buxton Road, Furness Vale, High Peak, Derbyshire, SK23 7PJ Tel: (01663) 744127 Fax: (01663) 741562

FIRED HEATERS

Flaretec Alloys & Equipment Ltd, Hardwick View Road, Holmewood, Chesterfield, Derbyshire, S42 5SA Tel: (01246) 853522 Fax: (01246) 852415 E-mail: contact@flaretec.com

FIREFIGHTING EQUIPMENT

A F E Comber, 2-2a Brownlow Street, Comber, Newtownards, County Down, BT23 5ER Tel: (028) 9187 8088 Fax: (028) 9187 3290

A F S Fire & Security, Unit 5d Mullacott Cross Indust Estate, Two Potts, Ilfracombe, Devon, EX34 8PL Tel: (01271) 864754 Fax: (01271) 864754

Abbey Fire, 22 Willow Court, West Quay Road, Winwick, Warrington, WA2 8UF Tel: (0870) 2099920 Fax: (01925) 423735 E-mail: sales@abbeyfireuk.co.uk

Ace Fire Midlands Ltd, 15 Lichfield Lane, Mansfield, Nottinghamshire, NG18 4RA Tel: (01623) 662805

Allfire Protection Services Ltd, Leigh Court, Leigh St, High Wycombe, Buckinghamshire, HP11 2RH Tel: (01494) 446646 Fax: (0114) 944 6646

Alpha Fire Protection, Unit 30 East Belfast Enterprise Park, Albertbridge Road, Belfast, BT5 4GX Tel: (028) 9046 1681 Fax: (028) 9045 7376

Angus Fire, Station Road, High Bentham, Lancaster, LA2 7NA Tel: (01524) 261611 Fax: (01524) 264180

Autronica Industrial Ltd, 11 Dudley Bank, Edinburgh, EH6 4HH Tel: 0131-555 1013 Fax: 0131-467 0712

B P Fire Protection Services, 37 Emerson Road, Poole, Dorset, BH15 1QS Tel: (01202) 665506 Fax: (01202) 669990

▶ B W Fire Engineering, Moorgreen Industrial Park, Engine Lane, Newthorpe, Nottingham, NG16 3QU Tel: (01773) 715978

Barber Bros, Unit 1-6 Clifton Road Industrial Estate, Clifton Road, Balsall Heath, Birmingham, B12 8SX Tel: 0121-440 4737 Fax: 0121-440 2480

Bath & West Fire & Safety, 61 Winsley Road, Bradford-on-Avon, Wiltshire, BA15 1NX Tel: (01225) 868199 Fax: (01225) 868118

Bristol Fire, Covert End, Westleigh Close, Yate, Bristol, BS37 4PR Tel: (01793) 480040 Fax: (01454) 273312 E-mail: sales@bristolfire.com

C & C Fire Extinguisher Service Ltd, 39 Pencricket Lane, Oldbury, West Midlands, B68 8LX Tel: 0121-559 6611 Fax: 0121-559 3399

Camfire Protection, 10 Hythe Close, Burwell, Cambridge, CB25 0EZ Tel: (01638) 741894 Fax: (01638) 741895 E-mail: sales@camfire.co.uk

Canon Fire Protection, The Wharf, Midhurst, West Sussex, GU29 9PX Tel: (01730) 815209 Fax: (01730) 816377 E-mail: cfp@canonfire.co.uk

Commercial & Industrial Gauges, Unit 7 Coed Aben Road, Wrexham Industrial Estate, Wrexham, Clwyd, LL13 9UH Tel: (01978) 661704 Fax: (01978) 660321 E-mail: info@cigltd.co.uk

D A B Engineering Co Ltd, 157 Dukes Road, London, W3 0SL Tel: (020) 8993 1771 Fax: (020) 8993 9048

Delta Fire Ltd, 8 Mission Road, Rackheath Industrial Estate, Rackheath, Norwich, NR13 6PL Tel: (01603) 735000 Fax: (01603) 735009 E-mail: sales@deltafire.co.uk

Diktron Developments Ltd, Griptight House Unit 19, Spitfire Road, Castle Bromwich, Birmingham, B24 9PR Tel: 0121-382 4938 Fax: 0121-747 3009 E-mail: diktron@btconnect.com

▶ Dry Riser Services, Ashdown House, Well Hill Lane, Orpington, Kent, BR6 7QJ Tel: (01959) 533838 Fax: (01959) 534848

E S Safety Supplies, Unit 33, 10 Barley Mow Pass, London, W4 4PH Tel: (020) 8575 8127 Fax: (020) 8944 1533

Eagle Fire Systems, 100 Liverpool Street, Salford, M5 4LP Tel: 0161-745 9578 Fax: 0161-745 9578 E-mail: eaglfirsys@aol.com

William Eagles Ltd, 100 Liverpool Street, Salford, M5 4LP Tel: 0161-736 1661 Fax: 0161-745 7765 E-mail: sales@william-eagles.co.uk

Eurofire UK, 12 Fontwell Drive, Alton, Hampshire, GU34 2TN Tel: (01420) 542424 Fax: (01420) 82287

▶ Expressfire Co. UK, Duck Farm Workshops, Bockhampton, Dorchester, Dorset, DT2 8QL Tel: 01305 848222 Fax: 01305 848222 E-mail: sales@expresfire.co.uk

F I R E Fire Industry Recources Equipment Ltd, Unit 19 Enterprise House, 44-46 Terrace Road, Walton-On-Thames, Surrey, KT12 2SD Tel: (01932) 222010 Fax: (01932) 226201 E-mail: office@firecontingency.com

Fire Appliance Components Ltd, Penallta Industrial Estate, Hengoed, Mid Glamorgan, CF82 7QZ Tel: (01443) 813959 Fax: (01443) 812545

Fire Appliance Industries (Dundee) Ltd, 38 Brown Street, Dundee, DD1 5DT Tel: (01382) 322410 Fax: (01382) 322410 E-mail: fireahendo@aol.com

Fire Fogging Systems Ltd, 1 Church Lane, Newmains, Wishaw, Lanarkshire, ML2 9BF Tel: (01698) 386444 Fax: (01698) 386869 E-mail: sales@scotkleen.co.uk

Fire Protection Services, Unit B7, Imperial Business Estate, West Mill, Gravesend, Kent, DA11 0DL Tel: (0800) 317195 Fax: (01474) 535111 E-mail: info@fire-protection-services.co.uk

Fire Protection Services Se, 215 London Road, Ewell, Epsom, Surrey, KT17 2BU Tel: (020) 8393 2897 Fax: (020) 8786 8793

Fire Queen Ltd, 23-37 Broadstone Road, Stockport, Cheshire, SK5 7AR Tel: 0161-442 5500 Fax: 0161-442 2664

Firepoint Scotland Ltd, 13 London Street, Larkhall, Lanarkshire, ML9 1AQ Tel: (01698) 881775 Fax: (01698) 307077

Firepro Fire Protection Consultants, J7 Business Park, Blackburn Road, Clayton le Moors, Accrington, Lancashire, BB5 5JW Tel: (01254) 600002 Fax: (01254) 392955 E-mail: firepro@ntlworld.com

FIREFIGHTING EQUIPMENT – *continued*

Fireshields Extinguisher Services Ltd, 7 Princes Gardens, Whitley Bay, Tyne & Wear, NE25 8EA Tel: 0191-291 0444 Fax: 0191-252 2340

Firesolve Ltd, Unit 2a Skelmanthorpe Technology Park, Station Road, Skelmanthorpe, Huddersfield, HD8 9GA Tel: (01484) 866614 Fax: (01484) 864466 E-mail: sales@fireslove.co.uk

Flameskill Ltd, Unit 1 R & A Development, Great Yarmouth, Norfolk, NR31 0LT Tel: (01493) 440464 Fax: (01493) 440581 E-mail: admin@flameskill.co.uk

Walter Frank & Sons Ltd, PO Box 16, Hightown Road, Cleckheaton, West Yorkshire, BD19 5JT Tel: (01226) 201771 Fax: (01226) 284218 E-mail: it@walterfrank.co.uk

G F A Premier Fire Ltd, Whistons Lane, Elland, West Yorkshire, HX5 9DS Tel: (01422) 377521 Fax: (01422) 379569 E-mail: customer.service@nuswift.co.uk

Galena (Fire Engineering) Ltd, Studland Street, London, W6 0JX Tel: (020) 8748 6154 Fax: (020) 8748 9885 E-mail: sales@galena.sagehost.co.uk

Griffin & General Fire Services Ltd, 7 Willow Street, London, EC2A 4BH Tel: (020) 7251 9379 Fax: (020) 7729 5652 E-mail: headoffice@griffinfire.co.uk

H E Woolley Ltd, Newport Works, Forty Foot Road, Middlesbrough, Cleveland, TS2 1HG Tel: (01642) 247337 Fax: (01642) 250188 E-mail: info@he-woolley.co.uk

H R Fire & Safety Ltd, Forge House, Whitehall Industrial Estate, Whitehall Road, Leeds, LS12 5JB Tel: 0113-279 4078 Fax: 0113-279 4768 E-mail: darren@hrfireandsafety.co.uk

▶ Hale Products Europe Ltd, Charles Street, Warwick, CV34 5LR Tel: (01926) 623614 Fax: (01926) 623689 E-mail: sales@haleeurope.com

Home & Office Fire Extinguishers Ltd, Unit 6, Saffron Business Centre, Elizabeth Close, Saffron Walden, Essex, CB10 2NL Tel: (01799) 513360 Fax: (01799) 513713 E-mail: fire@pslink.co.uk

▶ Hopton Fire Prevention Services, Camp Road, Lowestoft, Suffolk, NR32 2LL Tel: (01502) 572564 Fax: (07802) 573023

▶ I S E Fire Products & Services Ltd, 4 Duke Street, Burton Latimer, Kettering, Northamptonshire, NN15 5SG Tel: (01536) 420333 Fax: (01536) 420444 E-mail: sales@isefireproducts.co.uk

J D Fire Ltd, Wren Metals, Russell Street, Chadderton, Oldham, OL9 9LD Tel: 0161-652 2655 Fax: 0161-624 8303 E-mail: sales@jdfire.co.uk

L W Vass Holdings Ltd, Station Road, Ampthill, Bedford, MK45 2RB Tel: (01525) 403255 Fax: (01525) 404194 E-mail: sales@vass.co.uk

London Fire & Pump Co. Ltd, 11 Bridle Road, Pinner, Middlesex, HA5 2SL Tel: (020) 8866 6342 Fax: (020) 8866 6342

M F Fire & Safety Equipment, The Safety Centre, 198 Cator Lane, Beeston, Nottingham, NG9 4BE Tel: 0115-925 2261

M & G Fire Protection, Colchester Road, Maldon, Essex, CM9 4NN Tel: (01621) 840999 Fax: (01621) 842322 E-mail: mgfireessex@aol.com

M & S Fire Protection Glasgow Ltd, 50 Waddell Street, Glasgow, G5 0LU Tel: 0141-429 7991 Fax: 0141-429 2958

Morgan Fire Protection Ltd, Hillgrove Business Park, Nazeing Road, Nazeing, Waltham Abbey, Essex, EN9 2HB Tel: (01992) 893498 Fax: (01992) 892098

Northern Fire & Safety Co, Lodge House, Morton Street, Middleton, Manchester, M24 6AN Tel: 0161-643 9338 Fax: 0161-655 3878 E-mail: info@fireandsafety.co.uk

Northway Fire Protection & Marine Services, Farset Enterprise Park, 638 Springfield Road, Belfast, BT12 7DY Tel: (028) 9024 1700 Fax: (028) 9024 1901

Nu Swift International Ltd, PO Box 10, Elland, West Yorkshire, HX5 9DS Tel: (01422) 372852 Fax: (01422) 379569 E-mail: customer.service@nuswift.co.uk

Ocean Safety Ltd, Saxon Wharf, Lower York Street, Southampton, SO14 5QF Tel: (023) 8072 0800 Fax: (023) 8072 0801

P S P Safety Products Ltd, 9 Aintree Road, Keytech 7 Business Park, Keytec 7 Business Park, Pershore, Worcestershire, WR10 2JN Tel: (01386) 552555 Fax: (01386) 552592

Pacific Scientific, Howarth Road, Maidenhead, Berkshire, SL6 1AP Tel: (01628) 682200 Fax: (01628) 682250 E-mail: custadmin@pacscieurope.com

Rayner Firefighting Equipment Ltd, 71 Harehills Road, Leeds, LS8 5HS Tel: (0845) 3000440 Fax: 0113-293 0493

Redi Fire Ltd, 15 Evesham Road, Redditch, Worcestershire, B97 4JU Tel: (01527) 542369

Reliable Fire Sprinkler Ltd, Unit A2 Epsom Business Park, Kiln Lane, Epsom, Surrey, KT17 1JF Tel: (01372) 728899 Fax: (01372) 724461 E-mail: rfsl@reliablesprinkler.com

Safefire Protection Ltd, 14 Kendal Way, Leigh-on-Sea, Essex, SS9 5QS Tel: (01702) 522183E-mail: sales@safefireprotection.co.uk

Salford Fire & Safety Co. Ltd, 11 Vestris Drive, Salford, M6 8EL Tel: 0161-789 5550

Scarff Fire Safety UK Ltd, Unit 10 Cae FFWT Business Park, Pendraw'R Llan, Glan Conwy, Colwyn Bay, Clwyd, LL28 5SP Tel: (01492) 572992 Fax: (01492) 572992

Southern Fire Security Ltd, 4 The Old Saw Mill Industrial Estate, The Street, Broughton Gifford, Melksham, Wiltshire, SN12 8PY Tel: (01225) 782020 Fax: (01225) 782007

T & J Fire Ltd, 5 Martinfield Business Centre, Martinfield, Welwyn Garden City, Hertfordshire, AL7 1HG Tel: (01707) 326093 Fax: (01707) 376280 E-mail: sales@tjfire.co.uk

Tees Valley Fire Protection Ltd, Unit 11 Nestfield Industrial Estate, Darlington, County Durham, DL1 2NW Tel: (01325) 365555 Fax: (01325) 365555

Triangle Fire Protection Ltd, White Cliffs Business Park, Honeywood Road, Whitfield, Dover, Kent, CT16 3EH Tel: (01304) 828182 Fax: (01304) 829000

UK Fire International Ltd, PO Box 7708, Market Harborough, Leicestershire, LE16 8ZR Tel: (01536) 772261 Fax:

UK Fire Protection Rentals Ltd, Alscott Mill, Alscott, Telford, Shropshire, TF6 5EE Tel: (01952) 250750 Fax: 0121-270 6575 E-mail: enquiries@ukfireprotection.com

Unifire & Security, Unit 3 Station Yard, Bromfield, Ludlow, Shropshire, SY8 2BT Tel: (01584) 856868 Fax: (020) 7754 9148 E-mail: peter@uni-fire.co.uk

Virage, Cambridge Business Park, Cowley Road, Cambridge, CB4 0WZ Tel: (01223) 488540 Fax: (01223) 488541 E-mail: info@virage.com

Walker Fire, Unit 1 Brock House, Brocks Way, East Mains Industrial Estate, Broxburn, West Lothian, EH52 5NB Tel: (01506) 858108 Fax: (01506) 858002 E-mail: uk@walkerfire.com

Walker Fire, 2 Roman Way, Longridge Road, Ribbleton, Preston, PR2 5BB Tel: (01772) 693777 Fax: (01772) 693760 E-mail: uk@walkerfire.com

FIREFIGHTING EQUIPMENT CABINETS

J D Fire Ltd, Wren Metals, Russell Street, Chadderton, Oldham, OL9 9LD Tel: 0161-652 2655 Fax: 0161-624 8303 E-mail: sales@jdfire.co.uk

FIREFIGHTING EQUIPMENT FOAM SYSTEMS

Angus Fire, Thame Park Road, Thame, Oxfordshire, OX9 3RT Tel: (01844) 214545 Fax: (01844) 265156 E-mail: general.enquiries@kiddeuk.co.uk

FIREFIGHTING HOSE REELS

MB Fire Protection, Unit 22 Bourne Road Industrial Park, Bourne Road, Dartford, DA1 4BZ Tel: (01322) 523399 Fax: (01322) 528883

FIREPLACE ACCESSORIES

▶ Ahika Ltd, Unit 13, 2 Lansdowne Drive, London, E8 3EZ Tel: (0870) 4440650 E-mail: info@ahikaflame.com

▶ Cast Iron Fires.Com, Grove Mill, Commerce Street, Carrs Industrial Estate, Haslingden, Lancashire, BB4 5JT Tel: 0845 230 1991 E-mail: enquiries@castironfires.com

FIREPLACE CONTEMPORARY DESIGN

▶ Ahika Ltd, Unit 13, 2 Lansdowne Drive, London, E8 3EZ Tel: (0870) 4440650 E-mail: info@ahikaflame.com

▶ Embers Fireplaces, 221 Frimley Green Road, Frimley Green, Camberley, Surrey, GU16 6LA Tel: (01252) 837837 Fax: (01252) 837837 E-mail: steve@fireplaces.co.uk

FIREPLACE INSTALLATION

▶ B & J Swindells Masonry Ltd, 9-11 Mill Lane, Macclesfield, Cheshire, SK11 7NN Tel: (01625) 420221

FIREPLACE SPARK CURTAINS

A & M Energy Fires, Pool House, Main Road, Huntley, Gloucester, GL19 3DZ Tel: (01452) 830662 Fax: (01452) 830891 E-mail: am@energy fires.co.uk

J Day Stoneworks, Church Lane, Colney Heath, St. Albans, Hertfordshire, AL4 0NH Tel: (01727) 823326 Fax: (01727) 827710 E-mail: jdaystoneworks@btinternet.com

FIREPLACES

▶ A & H Interiors Ltd, Unit 40 Minerva Works, Crossley Lane, Huddersfield, HD5 9SA Tel: (01484) 432422 Fax: (01484) 426228

▶ Adams Fireplaces, 117 London Road, King's Lynn, Norfolk, PE30 5ES Tel: (01553) 760541

▶ Artisan, Phoenix Mills, Phoenix Street, Brighouse, West Yorkshire, HD6 1PD Tel: (01484) 723717 Fax: (01484) 723184

Fires4U, PO Box 6843, Swadlincote, Derbyshire, DE12 7XX Tel: (0845) 6120001 E-mail: sales@fires4u.co.uk

J. Hutchinson (Fuels) Ltd, 74 Church Street, Leatherhead, Surrey, KT22 8EN Tel: (01372) 372084 Fax: (01372) 360188

▶ New Forest Woodburning Centre Ltd, The Old School House, Church Lane, Sway, Lymington, Hampshire, SO41 6AD Tel: (01590) 683585 Fax: (01590) 683587 E-mail: sales@woodburners.com

▶ The Tetbury Stone Company Ltd, Week Farm, Combe Hay, Bath, BA2 8RF Tel: (01225) 836149 Fax: 01225 836149 E-mail: luke.pearce@tetburystone.co.uk

▶ Wessex Mantles Ltd, 16 Airfield Road, Christchurch, Dorset, BH23 3TG Tel: (01202) 481555 Fax: (01202) 481555

FIREWORK DISPLAY CONTRACTORS

▶ Pyroartistry, PO Box 3, Broughton-in-Furness, Cumbria, LA20 6GB Tel: (01229) 716700 Fax: (01229) 716700 E-mail: sales@pyroartistry.co.uk

FIREWORKS

1st Galaxy Fireworks Ltd, The Pyro Plot, Nottingham Road, Ravenshead, Nottingham, NG15 9HP Tel: (01623) 792121 Fax: (0870) 4430211 E-mail: sales@1stgalaxy.co.uk

Absolutely Fabulous Fireworks, 4 Park Parade, Gunnersbury Avenue, London, W3 9BD Tel: (01753) 524648 E-mail: info@fireworks-uk.com

▶ All Stars Fireworks, 379c Gloucester Road, Horfield, Bristol, BS7 8TN Tel: 0117-944 4880 E-mail: sales@allstarsfireworks.co.uk

Alpha Fireworks Ltd, Marlie Farm, The Broyle Shortgate, Lewes, East Sussex, BN8 6PH Tel: (01825) 840818 Fax: (01825) 840818 E-mail: sales@sussexfireworks.co.uk

Aurora Fireworks Ltd, Kiln Industries, Fittleworth Road, Wisborough Green, Billingshurst, West Sussex, RH14 0ES Tel: (0800) 9756573 Fax: (01403) 701085 E-mail: sales@aurorafireworks.co.uk

Big Bang Productions Ltd, 45 Oakleys Road, Long Eaton, Nottingham, NG10 1FQ Tel: 0115-973 0435 Fax: 0115-946 3937 E-mail: bb.fireworks@virgin.net

Bracknell Fireworks Ltd, 2 Bullbrook Row, Bracknell, Berkshire, RG12 2NL Tel: (01344) 425321 Fax: (01344) 861006 E-mail: sales@bracknell-fireworks.co.uk

Devco Fireworks Ltd, 8 Fauconberg Road, London, W4 3JY Tel: (020) 8994 0714 Fax: (020) 8994 6305 E-mail: info@devecofireworks.co.uk

Essex Pyrotechnics Ltd, 6 Wicken Road, Newport, Saffron Walden, Essex, CB11 3QG Tel: (01799) 541414 Fax: (01799) 541415

Fireking Ltd, Sefton Lodge, Rough Road, Woking, Surrey, GU22 0RB Tel: (020) 8786 8100 Fax: (01483) 476024

▶ Firework Events, 5 Hanover Road, Scarborough, North Yorkshire, YO11 1LS Tel: (01723) 507357 E-mail: jmevents4@aol.com

Firework Factors Ltd, Pegs Farm, Staplow, Ledbury, Herefordshire, HR8 1NQ Tel: (01531) 640441 Fax: (01531) 640004 E-mail: info@fireworkfactors.com

Flamebursт Effects, Grassmere, Dinton, Salisbury, SP3 5EG Tel: (01722) 716434 Fax: (01722) 716515

FTF Worldwide, 15 Mill Lane, Campton, Shefford, Bedfordshire, SG17 5NX Tel: (0870) 2643010 Fax: (0870) 2643020 E-mail: info@ftfworldwide.net

▶ G S Pyrotechnics, Woodlands Ways, Birmingham, B37 6RN Tel: 0121-243 7120 Fax: 0121-779 3622 E-mail: gspyrotechnics@blueyonder.co.uk

▶ Global Fireworks Ltd, The Cross, Kirkgate, Sherburn in Elmet, Leeds, LS25 6BH Tel: (0870) 7668253 Fax: (0870) 7668291 E-mail: info@globalfireworks.co.uk

Kimbolton Fireworks (Displays) Ltd, 7 High Street, Kimbolton, Huntingdon, Cambridgeshire, PE28 0HB Tel: (01480) 860988 Fax: (01480) 861277 E-mail: info@kimboltonfireworks.co.uk

Merlin Fireworks Ltd, Sunnyside View, Stockbridge Road, Kings Somborne, Stockbridge, Hampshire, SO20 6PH Tel: (01794) 389111 Fax: (01794) 389051

Midland Fireworks, 89 High Street, Burton-on-Trent, Staffordshire, DE14 1LJ Tel: (01332) 294043 Fax: (01332) 364206

▶ Mr McMichael, 37 Widnes Road, Widnes, Cheshire, WA8 6AZ Tel: 0151-424 3000 Fax: 0151-220 4020

Parallel House Ltd, 70 The Green, Christian Malford, Chippenham, Wiltshire, SN15 4BQ Tel: (0870) 0762538 Fax: (0870) 0762538 Fax: (0870) 2262262

Pendragon Fireworks & Pyrotechnics, 125 Newport Road, Cwmcarn/Cross Keys, Cross Keys, Newport, Gwent, NP11 7LZ Tel: (01633) 482626 E-mail: sales@pendragonfireworks.com

▶ Rocket Box, 2 Nelson Place East, Bath, BA1 5DA Tel: (01225) 463911 Fax: (01722) 716901

Sandling Fireworks, Building Se16, Gloucestershire Airport, Staverton, Cheltenham, Gloucestershire, GL51 6SP Tel: (01452) 855915 Fax: (01452) 855917 E-mail: sundlingsfireworks@aol.com

Shellscape Pyrotechnics Ltd, Butchers Lane, White Walthem, Maidenhead, Berkshire, SL6 3SD Tel: (01628) 829401

Skyburst Illuminations Ltd, 16 Chestnut Drive, Claverham, Bristol, BS49 4LN Tel: (01934) 877359 E-mail: info@skyburst..co.uk

▶ Josh Smith, 1St Galaxy Fireworks, Pyro Plot, Nottingham Road, Ravenshead, Nottingham, NG15 9HP Tel: (0870) 4430210

Sonic Party Time, 2a North Street, Heavitree, Exeter, EX1 2RH Tel: (01392) 848785

Sonning Fireworks Ltd, The Old Cottage, Sonning Eye, Reading, RG4 6TN Tel: (0800) 0743140 E-mail: enquiries@sonningfireworks.co.uk

▶ Starlight, 5 Gateway Trading Estate, Hythe Road, London, NW10 6RJ Tel: (020) 8960 6078 Fax: (020) 8960 7991

▶ Supreme Fireworks, Tree Tops, Golden Ball Lane, Maidenhead, Berkshire, SL6 6NW Tel: (01628) 625261 Fax: (01628) 625261 E-mail: sales@supremefireworks.com

TNT Fireworks (UK) Ltd, Dinton Woods Storage Site, Catherine Ford Road, Dinton, Salisbury, SP3 5HB Tel: (01722) 716900 Fax: (01722) 716901

FIRST AID DRESSINGS

Cuxson Gerrard & Co., 125 Broadwell Road, Oldbury, West Midlands, B69 4BF Tel: 0121-544 7117 Fax: 0121-544 8616 E-mail: sales@cuxsongerrard.com

▶ Firstaid4sport.co.uk, 6A Exchange Close, North Hykeham, Lincoln, LN6 3TR Tel: (01522) 883344 Fax: (01522) 875253 E-mail: gemma.newlove@firstaid4sport.co.uk

Steroplast, Alpha Point, Bradnor Road, Sharston Industrial Area, Manchester, M22 4TE Tel: 0161-902 3030 Fax: 0161-902 3040 E-mail: sales@steroplast.co.uk

FIRST AID OUTFITS

Lewis's Medical Supplies, Broadoak House, Coronation Street, Stockport, Cheshire, SK5 7PG Tel: 0161-480 6797 Fax: 0161 4804787 E-mail: sales@lewis-plast.co.uk

St. John Supplies, PO Box 707A, London, EC1V 7NE Tel: (020) 7278 7888 Fax: (020) 7278 0314 E-mail: customer-services@stjohnsupplies.co.uk

FIRST AID SUPPLY SERVICES

B C B International Ltd, Units 7-8, Clydesmuir Road Industrial Estate, Cardiff, CF24 2QS Tel: (029) 2043 3700 Fax: (029) 2043 3701 E-mail: info@bcbin.com

Beaver Healthcare Equipment, Beaver House, 1 Vale Rise, Tonbridge, Kent, TN9 1TB Tel: (01732) 367777

▶ Bell Stretchers, Unit 1B, Boundary Bank, Underbarrow Road, Kendal, Cumbria, LA9 5RR Tel: (01539) 732281 E-mail: info@bellstretchers.co.uk

Day Lewis Medical Supplies, 54 Springfield Road, Gorleston, Great Yarmouth, Norfolk, NR31 6AD Tel: (01493) 602673 Fax: (01493) 651106 E-mail: albanoffshore@daylewisplc.com

First Aid Supplies & Training Wales, 305 Gladstone Road, Barry, South Glamorgan, CF63 1NL Tel: (01446) 735680 Fax: (01446) 735680

First In Safety Ltd, Unit 71 Campbell Street, Brierley Hill, West Midlands, DY5 3YG Tel: (01384) 346858 Fax: (01384) 346861

Lion Safety Products, Jackson Avenue, Grangemouth, Stirlingshire, FK3 8JU Tel: (01324) 474744

Morsafe Supplies, 192 Monkmoor Road, Shrewsbury, SY2 5BH Tel: (01743) 356319 Fax: (01743) 350875

Oak Industrial Supplies, Hamilton Road, Sutton-in-Ashfield, Nottinghamshire, NG17 5LN Tel: (01623) 442222 Fax: (01623) 441234 E-mail: sales@oakis.co.uk

Phoenix Healthcare Distribution Ltd, Eddison Road, Hamshall Distribution Park, Coleshill, Birmingham, B46 1DA Tel: (01675) 436500 Fax: (01675) 436502

S A F A Group Ltd, 59 Hill Street, Liverpool, L8 5SB Tel: 0151-708 0397 E-mail: sales@safa.co.uk

St. John Supplies, PO Box 707A, London, EC1V 7NE Tel: (020) 7278 7888 Fax: (020) 7278 0314 E-mail: customer-services@stjohnsupplies.co.uk

Frank Sammeroff Ltd, 131 Woodhead Road, Glasgow, G53 7NN Tel: 0141-881 5701 Fax: 0141-881 4919 E-mail: info@sammeroff.co.uk

Stalwart Signs & Industrial Supplies Ltd, Anglian House Admiralty Road, Great Yarmouth, Norfolk, NR30 3DY Tel: (01493) 857410 Fax: (01493) 852383 E-mail: stalwartsafety@dsl.pipex.com

Sweeney First Aid Supplies Ltd, 13 Scar Bank, Warwick, CV34 5DB Tel: (01926) 497108 Fax: (01926) 497109 E-mail: sales@sweeneyfirstaid.co.uk

FIRST AID SUPPLY SERVICES – *continued*

Wallace, Cameron & Co. Ltd, 26 Netherhall Road, Netherton Industrial Estate, Wishaw, Lanarkshire, ML2 0JG Tel: (01698) 354600 Fax: (01698) 354700 E-mail: sales@wallacecameron.com
D.M. Wood Medical Ltd, Units 6-7, 1 Kirkhill Place, Kirkhill Industrial Estate, Dyce, Aberdeen, AB21 0GU Tel: (01224) 723388 Fax: (01224) 770670 E-mail: admin@dmwood-medical.com

FISH

Thistle Seafood Ltd, The Harbour, Harbour Street, Boddam, Peterhead, Aberdeenshire, AB42 3AU Tel: (01779) 478991 Fax: (01779) 471014 E-mail: mail@thistleseafoods.com
▶ White Water Charters, Penarth Marina, Penarth, Vale of Glamorgan, CF64 1TZ Tel: (07970) 936443 E-mail: info@whitewatercharters.co.uk

FISH EXPORT

The Coral Bazaar Aquatic Centre, Queens Close, Chequers Lane, Walton On The Hill, Tadworth, Surrey, KT20 7SU Tel: (01737) 812475 Fax: (01737) 812722
L A D Fish Exporters, Dales Industrial Estate, Peterhead, Aberdeenshire, AB42 3JF Tel: (01779) 479327 Fax: (01779) 474891 E-mail: rafael@ladfish.freeserve.co.uk

FISH FARM EQUIPMENT

▶ Koiman Enterprises, 10 Main Road, Duston, Northampton, NN5 6JB Tel: (01604) 581074 E-mail: koiman.geff@btinternet.com
Purewell Fish Farming Equipment, Units 13-14 Wicormarine, Cranleigh Road, Portchester, Fareham, Hampshire, PO16 9DR Tel: (01329) 829100 Fax: (01329) 829100

FISH FARM NETS

House & Co., 6 Gordleton Industrial Estate, Hannah Way, Pennington, Lymington, Hampshire, SO41 8JD Tel: (01590) 682285 Fax: (01590) 683553 E-mail: saleshouseandco@aol.com

FISH FEED

Sea Pet Centre Ltd, 21 Beardmore Park, Martlesham Heath, Ipswich, IP5 3RX Tel: (01473) 610969 Fax: (01473) 610265 E-mail: sales@seapets.co.uk

FISH FOOD PRODUCTS

Alvechurch Fisheries, Little Stannalls, Bittell Road, Barnt Green, Birmingham, B45 8LT Tel: 0121-445 4274 Fax: 0121-447 7117
Berwick Salmon Co. Ltd, 1 Main Street, Spittal, Berwick-upon-Tweed, TD15 1QY Tel: (01289) 307474 Fax: (01289) 305913
Bloomsbury International Ltd, Hoghton Street, Southport, Merseyside, PR9 0PA Tel: (01704) 514646 Fax: (01704) 514848
C Fish, 11 Main Road, Portavogie, Newtownards, County Down, BT22 1EL Tel: (028) 4277 1560 Fax: (028) 4277 2345
Cheshire Water Life, Blakemere Craft Centre, Chester Road, Sandiway, Northwich, Cheshire, CW8 2EB Tel: (01606) 882223 Fax: (01606) 889964E-mail: sales@cheshire-waterlife.co.uk
Coldwater Seafood UK Ltd, Estate Road 2, South Humberside Industrial Estate, Grimsby, South Humberside, DN31 2TG Tel: (01472) 321100 Fax: (01472) 321220 E-mail: reception@coldwater-seafood.co.uk
Cornish Cuisine, The Smoke House, Islington Wharf, Penryn, Cornwall, TR10 8AT Tel: (01326) 376244 Fax: (01326) 376244
Dalziel Ltd, Unit 11 Hunslet Trading Estate, Low Road, Leeds, LS10 1QR Tel: 0113-277 7662 Fax: 0113-271 4954
Derwent Koi & Tropicals, Hope Road, Bamford, Hope Valley, Derbyshire, S33 0AL Tel: (01433) 650029 Fax: (01433) 650029
East Fresh & Frozen, Trimmers Court, Broad Street, Portsmouth, PO1 2EE Tel: (023) 9282 9696 Fax: (023) 9287 3236
The Edinburgh Smoked Salmon Company 1992 Ltd, 1 Strath View, Dingwall Business Park, Dingwall, Ross-Shire, IV15 9XD Tel: (01349) 860600 Fax: (01349) 840606 E-mail: essco@jwsaefoods.co.uk
Ewos Ltd, Westfields, Westfield, Bathgate, West Lothian, EH48 3BP Tel: (01506) 633966 Fax: (01506) 632730 E-mail: ian.carr@ewos.com
Exciting Foods Ltd, 127 Cleethorpe Road, Grimsby, South Humberside, DN31 3EW Tel: (01472) 311955 Fax: (01472) 342436 E-mail: sales@excitingfoods.co.uk
Five Star Fish Ltd, Great Grimsby Business Park, Sargon Way, Great Coates, Grimsby, South Humberside, DN37 9SY Tel: (01472) 344962 Fax: (01472) 250113 E-mail: info@fivestarfish.co.uk
Fortunes Fish Smokers, 22 Henrietta Street, Whitby, North Yorkshire, YO22 4DW Tel: (01947) 601659
Galloway Smokehouse, Carsluith, Newton Stewart, Wigtownshire, DG8 7DN Tel: (01671) 820354 Fax: (01671) 820545
Inshore Fish & Frozen Foods, Unit 3 Princes Way, The Old Filling Station, Leasgill, Milnthorpe, Cumbria, LA7 7ET Tel: 015395 64748 Fax: 015395 64110
J Lawrie & Sons, The Pier, Mallaig, Inverness-Shire, PH41 4QD Tel: (01687) 462224 Fax: (01687) 462871
King Salmon Co., 54 Kinloch Drive, London, NW9 7LH Tel: (020) 8205 1550 Fax: (020) 8205 1550
L W Waller & Son Ltd, Waller Building, Fish Market, Lowestoft, Suffolk, NR32 1BU Tel: (01502) 573236
D. Macalister, Chruch Hill Quarry Stores, Tarbert, Argyll, PA29 6YA Tel: (01880) 820845
Manx Seafoods Ltd, Mill Road, Peel, Isle of Man, IM5 1TA Tel: (01624) 842415 Fax: (01624) 842342 E-mail: manxseafoods@manx.net
Martin Mathew & Co. Ltd, Riverdene House, 140 High Street, Cheshunt, Waltham Cross, Hertfordshire, EN8 0AW Tel: (01992) 641641 Fax: (01992) 641888 E-mail: sales@martinmathew.co.uk
Melingey Smoked Fish & Trout Farm, St. Issey, Wadebridge, Cornwall, PL27 7QU Tel: (01841) 540551 Fax: (01841) 540476
R & A Grantham, Keynor Lane, Sidlesham, Chichester, West Sussex, PO20 7NL Tel: (01243) 641678 Fax: (01243) 641808
R & P Macdonald, South Esplanade East, Aberdeen, AB11 9PB Tel: (01224) 879402 Fax: (01224) 896958
S & L Fish, The Fish Market, The Quay, East Looe, Looe, Cornwall, PL13 1DT Tel: (01503) 262140 Fax: (01503) 263832
Shetland Smoked Salmon Ltd, Easterdale, Hamnavoe, Shetland, ZE2 9LB Tel: (01595) 859464 Fax: (01595) 859464
United Fish Industries (U K) Ltd, Gilbey Road, Grimsby, South Humberside, DN31 2SL Tel: (01472) 263333 Fax: (01472) 263451
W G & P D Gilson, 8 Burdett Road, Southend-on-Sea, SS1 2TN Tel: (01702) 467030 Fax: (01702) 467030
Youngs Blue Quest Ltd, Liverpool Street, Hull, HU3 4XT Tel: (01482) 327997 Fax: (01482) 216513

FISH FRYING RANGES

Ellidge & Fairley, New Line Industrial Estate, The Sidings, Bacup, Lancashire, OL13 9RW Tel: (01706) 875175 Fax: (01706) 875120 E-mail: info@ellidgefairley.co.uk
Mallinson's Of Oldham Ltd, Trent Industrial Estate, Duchess Street, Shaw, Oldham, OL2 7UT Tel: (01706) 299000 Fax: (01706) 299700
Martin Edwards, 16a Limerick Road, Redcar, Cleveland, TS10 5JU Tel: (01642) 494688 Fax: (01642) 494688 E-mail: dave.atkinson@me-ff.com
Preston & Thomas Ltd, Woodville Engineering Works, Heron Road, Rumney, Cardiff, CF3 3JE Tel: (029) 2079 3331 Fax: (029) 2077 9195 E-mail: info@prestonandthomas.co.uk
Rangetek Catering Equipment, Unit 1a Crabtree Close, Gravesend Road, Wrotham, Sevenoaks, Kent, TN15 7JL Tel: (01732) 822477 Fax: (01732) 822477 E-mail: sales@rangetek.co.uk

FISH HANDLING EQUIPMENT

▶ Murray Aquatics, 1 Houston Place, Glasgow, G5 8SG Tel: 0141-420 1020 Fax: 0141-420 1040 E-mail: sales@murrayaquatics.co.uk

FISH HATCHERY EQUIPMENT

Koi Joy, 14 Norwich Road, Lowestoft, Suffolk, NR32 2BW Tel: (01502) 564479 Fax: (01502) 564479
Purewell Fish Farming Equipment, Units 13-14 Wicormarine, Cranleigh Road, Portchester, Fareham, Hampshire, PO16 9DR Tel: (01329) 829100 Fax: (01329) 829100

FISH POND HEATING EQUIPMENT

Aquatic Discount Centre, 1a Haydock Street, Newton-le-Willows, Merseyside, WA12 9AB Tel: (01925) 291439 Fax: (01925) 291439
Bristol Waterworld, Wyevale Garden Centre, Hicks Gate, Keynsham, Bristol, BS31 2AD Tel: 0117-977 2955 Fax: 0117-977 2956 E-mail: sales@fishkeeper.com
Thermalec Products Ltd, Kingsley Close, Lee Mill Industrial Estate, Ivybridge, Devon, PL21 9GD Tel: (01752) 313343 Fax: (01752) 313353 E-mail: sales@thermalec.com

FISH PROCESSING MACHINES

AFOS (NSE) Ltd, Kingston House,, Saxon Way, Priory Park West, Hessle, East Yorkshire, HU13 9PB Tel: (01482) 372100 Fax: (01482) 372150 E-mail: info@afosgroup.com
E Anderson, 29 South Esplanade West, Aberdeen, AB11 9AA Tel: (01224) 877609
Falcon Food Equipment Ltd, Unit 3 The Old Station, Wells Road, Hallatrow, Bristol, BS39 6EN Tel: (01761) 453010 Fax: (01761) 452975 E-mail: sales@falconfoodequipment.com
Seafin Export & Import Agents, 52 Four Oaks Road, Sutton Coldfield, West Midlands, B74 2XX Tel: 0121-308 8340 Fax: 0121-308 8340 E-mail: seafin@totalise.co.uk

FISH PRODUCT BINDING AGENTS

▶ Troutline Fishing Supplies, 80 Stoneybeck, Bishop Middleham, Ferryhill, County Durham, DL17 9BN Tel: (07917) 016359 E-mail: sales@troutline.co.uk

FISH SMOKERS

Cookequip Ltd, Unit 4, Sumner Place, Addlestone, Surrey, KT15 1QD Tel: (01932) 841171 E-mail: sales@cookequip.co.uk

FISH TRANSPORT, *See Refrigerated Transport etc*

FISHBURGERS

Maidenhead Aquatic Centre, Bourne End Garden Centre, Hedsor Road, Bourne End, Buckinghamshire, SL8 5EE Tel: (01628) 528882 Fax: (01628) 850429

FISHERY CONSULTANCY

▶ Stellar Environmental Solutions Ltd, 1 Main Street, Ayston, Oakham, Rutland, LE15 9AE Tel: (07747) 125780
▶ The Willows, Hessay, York, YO26 8JU Tel: (01904) 738206 Fax: (01904) 738206 E-mail: info@willowsfishery.co.uk

FISHERY SERVICES

▶ Stellar Environmental Solutions Ltd, 1 Main Street, Ayston, Oakham, Rutland, LE15 9AE Tel: (07747) 125780

FISHING BAITS

▶ Bang on Baits, 273 Senwick Drive, Wellingborough, Northamptonshire, NN8 1SD Tel: (01933) 274968 E-mail: bangonbaits@yahoo.co.uk
Megabaits, 16 Brue Avenue, Bridgwater, Somerset, TA6 5LT Tel: (01278) 424614 Fax: (01278) 424615
Seabait Ltd, Woodhorn Village, Ashington, Northumberland, NE63 9NW Tel: (01670) 814102 Fax: (01670) 814102 E-mail: sales@seabait.co.uk
Turner's Tackle & Bait, 4a Station Road, Faringdon, Oxfordshire, SN7 7BN Tel: (01367) 241044

FISHING BOAT BUILDERS

Cleethorpes Angling Centre, 291 Brereton Avenue, Cleethorpes, South Humberside, DN35 7QX Tel: (01472) 602002 Fax: (01472) 602002
Cygnus Marine Ltd, 6 Annear Road, Penryn, Cornwall, TR10 9ER Tel: (01326) 372970 Fax: (01326) 374585 E-mail: info@cygnusmarine.co.uk
J & K Tackle, 62-64 Sheep Street, Bicester, Oxfordshire, OX26 6LG Tel: (01869) 242589 Fax: (01869) 320821
▶ MiTi Co, Ford Mill farm, Woolsery, Bideford, Devon, EX39 5RF Tel: (01409) 241289 E-mail: mikeivory@miticompany.co.uk

FISHING LANDING NETS

Brentwood Angling, 118 Warley Hill, Warley, Brentwood, Essex, CM14 5HB Tel: (01277) 225585 Fax: (01277) 219500 E-mail: enquiries@brentwoodangling.co.uk
▶ Rods & Reels, 6 Chapel Street, Barwell, Leicester, LE9 8DD Tel: 01455 842450 Fax: 01455 842451 E-mail: fishingebay@yahoo.co.uk

FISHING LINE, FLY

▶ World Wide Fishing Flies, 5 Gillfoot Avenue, Smithfield, Egremont, Cumbria, CA22 2QE Tel: (01946) 820593 Fax: (01946) 820593 E-mail: mark@worldwidefishingflies.co.uk

FISHING RODS

Brentwood Angling, 118 Warley Hill, Warley, Brentwood, Essex, CM14 5HB Tel: (01277) 225585 Fax: (01277) 219500 E-mail: enquiries@brentwoodangling.co.uk
Conoflex Ltd, 9 Sybron Way, Crowborough, East Sussex, TN6 3DZ Tel: (01892) 664388 Fax: (01892) 664178 E-mail: sales@conoflex.co.uk
Custom Built Rods, 1c Valebridge Road, Burgess Hill, West Sussex, RH15 0RA Tel: (01444) 250930 Fax: 01444 250930
Daiwa Sports Ltd, Netherton Industrial Estate, Wishaw, Lanarkshire, ML2 0EY Tel: (01698) 355723 Fax: (01698) 372505 E-mail: info@diawasports.co.uk
Estate & Country Sports Equipment Ltd, 25 Five Acres Cl, Lindford, Bordon, Hants, GU35 0SJ Tel: (01420) 473395 Fax: (01420) 473395
▶ The Fly Factory, Unit 325, Vale Enterprise Centre, Hayes Road, Sully, Penarth, South Glamorgan, CF64 5SY Tel: (01446) 700401 Fax: (01446) 404646 E-mail: sales@theflyfactory.co.uk
Greys Of Alnwick, Station Yard, Alnwick, Northumberland, NE66 2NP Tel: (01665) 510020 Fax: (01665) 604530 E-mail: info@hardycomposites.co.uk
Judds Of Ruislip, 524-526 Victoria Road, Ruislip, Middlesex, HA4 0HD Tel: (020) 8841 7194 Fax: (020) 8841 7195
North Western Blanks Ltd, Grimshaw Lane, Middleton, Manchester, M24 2AA Tel: 0161-653 3500 Fax: 0161-655 3673 E-mail: sales@northwesternblanks.co.uk
▶ Rugby Tackle, 155a Bilton Road, Rugby, Warwickshire, CV22 7DS Tel: (01788) 544913 Fax: (01788) 570645 E-mail: sales@rugbytackle.co.uk
Specialist Tackle Ltd, 93 Chase Cross Road, Romford, RM5 3RP Tel: (01708) 752277 Fax: (01708) 754714 E-mail: info@specialist-tackle.co.uk
William Boyer & Sons Transport Ltd, Trout Road, West Drayton, Middlesex, UB7 7SN Tel: (01895) 445141 Fax: (01895) 442027

FISHING TACKLE

476 Sprowston Road, 277 Aylsham, Norwich, NR3 2RE Tel: (01603) 400757 Fax: (01603) 406927 E-mail: info@anglingdirect.co.uk
A M Hobbs Ltd, The Island, Midsomer Norton, Radstock, BA3 2HQ Tel: (01761) 413961 Fax: (01761) 413961 E-mail: sales@amhobbsfirearms.co.uk
A R Tackle, 8 Castle Street, Hastings, East Sussex, TN34 3DY Tel: (01424) 422094
Abbey Angling & Aquatic Centre, 54b High Street, Hanham, Bristol, BS15 3DR Tel: 0117-985 5448 Fax: 0117-908 1130
All Seasons Angling Centre, 8 Dunton Street, Wigston, Leicestershire, LE18 4PU Tel: 0116-278 2440
Angler Craft, Greenbogue, Torthorwald, Dumfries, DG1 3QG Tel: (01387) 750247 Fax: (01387) 750247
Anglers Corner, 80 Station Road, Llanelli, Dyfed, SA15 1AN Tel: (01554) 773981 Fax: (01554) 773981
▶ Anglers Den, 26a High Street, Haverfordwest, Dyfed, SA61 2DA Tel: (01437) 760045
The Anglers Emporium, 64 Cadzow Street, Hamilton, Lanarkshire, ML3 6DS Tel: (01698) 283903 E-mail: info@anglersemporium.co.uk
▶ Anglers Peg, 4 Ashworth House, Cannock Road, Cannock, Staffordshire, WS11 5DZ Tel: (01543) 466946 E-mail: sales@anglerspeg.com
Anglers Stop, 161 Rose Avenue, Worcester, WR4 9QN Tel: (01905) 619803
▶ Angling Centre, 3 Forrest Street, Airdrie, Lanarkshire, ML6 7BA Tel: (01236) 750288
Angling Centre, 85 St Leonards Road, Northampton, NN4 8DN Tel: (01604) 764847
▶ Angling & Out Door Center, 121/122 Ennerdale Road, Cleator Moor, Cumbria, CA25 5LP Tel: (01946) 810377 E-mail: sales@angleingandoutdoor.co.uk
▶ Angling Supplies, 49 Retford Road, Worksop, Nottinghamshire, S80 2PU Tel: (01909) 482974 Fax: (01909) 482974
Aspinall's Angling Supplies, 36 Cross Street, Barry, South Glamorgan, CF63 4LU Tel: (01446) 742645 Fax: (01446) 742645 E-mail: aspinallangling@aol.com
Albert Atkins, 71 Coleraine Road, Garvagh, Coleraine, County Londonderry, BT51 5HR Tel: (028) 2955 7691 Fax: (028) 9255 7692
▶ Bait & Tackle Supplies, 692 Bolton Road, Pendlebury, Swinton, Manchester, M27 6EL Tel: 0161-728 4400
Bakewell Fly Fishing, 3a Hebden Court, Matlock Street, Bakewell, Derbyshire, DE45 1EE Tel: (01629) 813531 Fax: (01629) 813531
Banks & Burr, 25 Claremont Road, Rugby, Warwickshire, CV21 3NA Tel: (01788) 576782 Fax: (01788) 560774 E-mail: sales@tackleup.com

FISHING TACKLE – *continued*

▶ Bayview Angling, 12 Greenfield Road, Colwyn Bay, Clwyd, LL29 8EL Tel: (01492) 535888
▶ Bennetts Angling Stores Ltd, 9 Market Place, Mountsorrel, Loughborough, Leicestershire, LE12 7BA Tel: 0116-230 2818 Fax: 0116-237 4333 E-mail: fishing@bennettsangling.com
Bennington Bait, The Bait Factory, Valley Lane, Long Bennington, Newark, Nottinghamshire, NG23 5EE Tel: (01400) 281525
▶ Bernie's Bait & Tackle, Snuff Court, Snuff Street, Devizes, Wiltshire, SN10 1HU Tel: (01380) 730712
Bevan Carp Tackle, 3 Havengore, Chelmsford, CM1 6JP Tel: (01245) 266833 Fax: (01245) 344249 E-mail: sales@bevancarptackle.co.uk
Billing Aquadrome Ltd, Crow Lane, Little Billing, Northampton, NN3 9DA Tel: (01604) 408181 Fax: (01604) 784412 E-mail: brochures@aquadrome.co.uk
▶ Bilston Angling Centre, 48 Church Street, Bilston, West Midlands, WV14 0AH Tel: (01902) 495366
Bonefish Adventure Ltd, 75 Bargates, Christchurch, Dorset, BH23 1QE Tel: 01202 474343 E-mail: info@bonefishadventure.com
▶ Bournemouth Fishing Lodge, 904 Wimborne Road, Bournemouth, BH9 2DW Tel: (01202) 514345 Fax: (01202) 514345
Breakaway Tackle Development Co. Ltd, 376 Bramford Road, Ipswich, IP1 5AY Tel: (01473) 741393 Fax: (01473) 462482
▶ Bristol Angling Centre, 12-16 Doncaster Road, Bristol, BS10 5PL Tel: 0117-950 0201 Fax: 0117-959 2799 E-mail: admin@bristolangling.co.uk
Brown Hills Tackle, 5 Silvercourt, Walsall, WS8 6HA Tel: (01543) 372395
Bude Angling Supplies, 6 Queen Street, Bude, Cornwall, EX23 8BB Tel: (01288) 353396 Fax: (01288) 353396 E-mail: petsgalorebude@aol.com
Castaline Angling Equipment, 18-20 Upgate, Louth, Lincolnshire, LN11 9ET Tel: (01507) 602149 Fax: (01507) 603163
▶ Chapman's, 21-29 Beechway, Scunthorpe, South Humberside, DN16 2HF Tel: (01724) 862585 Fax: (01724) 270096
▶ Claudy Tackle & Sports, 630 Baranailt Road, Claudy, Londonderry, BT47 4EA Tel: (028) 7133 7323
Cliff Madden Angling, 5 Church Street, Staveley, Chesterfield, Derbyshire, S43 3TL Tel: (01246) 472410
▶ Codnor Angling, 21 Market Place, Codnor, Ripley, Derbyshire, DE5 9QA Tel: (01773) 743411
Colchester Bait & Tackle, 243a Harwich Road, Colchester, CO4 3DQ Tel: (01206) 860649 Fax: (01206) 860649
Country Lines, 4 Alexandria Terrace, Bridge Street, Brigg, South Humberside, DN20 8NW Tel: (01652) 651650 Fax: (01652) 651650 E-mail: sales@gpmgroup.com
▶ Coxs Tackle, Unit 120, 122 The Commercial Centre, Picket Piece, Andover, Hampshire, SP11 6LU Tel: (01264) 333170 Fax: (01264) 333170
Craftye Fisherman, 13 Montagu Terrace, Edinburgh, EH3 5QX Tel: 0131-551 1224 Fax: 0131-551 1226
▶ Crewes Carp'In Centre, 122 West Street, Crewe, CW1 3HG Tel: (01270) 588466 Fax: (01270) 258825
D & A Tackle, 242-244 Woodhouse Road, London, N12 0RU Tel: (020) 8368 8799 Fax: (020) 8368 8799
▶ D C Angling, 292 Charter Avenue, Coventry, CV4 8DA Tel: (024) 7647 1526 Fax: (024) 7647 4053
D Kiddy, 28 Barton Road, Torquay, TQ1 4DP Tel: (01803) 293999 Fax: (01803) 201326
Daves Peg, Corner Shop, 1 London Road, Sleaford, Lincolnshire, NG34 7LF Tel: (01529) 415896
Davis Fishing Tackle, 75 Bargates, Christchurch, Dorset, BH23 1QE Tel: (01202) 485169 Fax: (01202) 474261 E-mail: mail@davistackle.co.uk
▶ Deals On Wheels, 22 Bruce Street, Dunfermline, Fife, KY12 7AG Tel: (01383) 728108 Fax: (01383) 730077 E-mail: info@premierfrenchparts.com
Deltaflash Angling Equipment, 40 Broom Road, Ferryhill, County Durham, DL17 8AF Tel: (01740) 652360 Fax: (01740) 652360
Dinsmores Ltd, Westgate, Aldridge, Walsall, WS9 8EX Tel: (01922) 456421 Fax: (01922) 455791 E-mail: dinsmoresmft@aol.com
Esher Angling Centre, Pond House, Weston Green, Thames Ditton, Surrey, KT7 0JX Tel: (020) 8398 2405
Eurobait, Pte Road No 4, Colwick Industrial Estate, Nottingham, NG4 2JT Tel: 0115-987 4888 Fax: (0115) 9875553
Everetts, 691 Holderness Road, Hull, HU8 9AN Tel: (01482) 374201 Fax: (01482) 788801
Exchange Angling, 184 Elfredton Road, Nottingham, NG7 3PE Tel: 0115-942 4941 Fax: 0115-978 4158
F J & F J Farrington, 2-4 Ferry Lane, Cambridge, CB4 1NT Tel: (01223) 461361
Fish & Field, 60 Broad Street, Chipping Sodbury, Bristol, BS37 6AG Tel: (01454) 314034 Fax: (01454) 314034
Fishermans Cove Angling Centre, 60 Milton Road, Ellesmere Port, CH65 5DD Tel: 0151-356 9030 Fax: 0151-356 9030 E-mail: sales@fishermanscove.co.uk
Fishermans Friends, 194-196 Jamaica Road, London, SE16 4RT Tel: (020) 7237 7702 Fax: (020) 7237 7702
Fishermans Knockout, 1118 Stratford Road, Hall Green, Birmingham, B28 8AE Tel: 0121-777 0307
Fishermans Tacklebox Wirral, 36 Downham Drive, Heswall, Wirral, Merseyside, CH60 5RF Tel: 0151-342 5207 Fax: 0151-342 5207 E-mail: paullynnemeadows@hotmail.com
▶ Fishermate, Belsize Avenue, Peterborough, PE2 9JA Tel: (01733) 314868
Fishing Shop, 293 Ings Road, Hull, HU8 0NB Tel: (01482) 781926 Fax: (01482) 781926
▶ Flack Tackle, Veitchii Barn, New Barn Road, Swanley, Kent, BR8 7PW Tel: (01322) 660770 Fax: (01322) 660790 E-mail: sales@flacktackle.co.uk
▶ Floaters, 10 Estcourt Road, Great Yarmouth, Norfolk, NR30 4JG Tel: (01493) 853700 Fax: (01493) 721171
Foxon's Ltd, Foxon'S Tackle, Lower Denbigh Road, St. Asaph, Clwyd, LL17 0ED Tel: (01745) 583583 Fax: (01745) 583175 E-mail: info@foxons.co.uk
Gallaway Aquatics & Water Gardens, Bladnoch, Wigtown, Newton Stewart, Wigtownshire, DG8 9AB Tel: (01988) 403363 Fax: (01671) 401333
George's Fishing Tackle, 15 Frog Lane, Wigan, Lancashire, WN6 7DE Tel: (01942) 241932
Gerry's Of Nottingham, Radford Boulevard, Nottingham, NG7 3BN Tel: 0115-978 8723 Fax: 0115-979 1989
Gilders Northampton Ltd, 32 Montagu Street, Kettering, Northamptonshire, NN16 8RU Tel: (01536) 514509 Fax: (01536) 525252
Hackney Angling Centre, 28 Broadway Market, London, E8 4QJ Tel: 020 72750059
Hastings Angling Centre, 33 The Bourne, Hastings, East Sussex, TN34 3AY Tel: (01424) 432178
Henry Monk Gunmaker Ltd, 8 Queen Street, Chester, CH1 3LG Tel: (01244) 320988 Fax: (01244) 320988
Holt's Fishing Tackle, 122 Marston Road, Stafford, ST16 3BX Tel: (01785) 251073
▶ Hooked In Scotland, 1028 Shettleston Road, Glasgow, G32 7PP Tel: 0141-778 6600 Fax: 0141-778 6600
Hounslow Angling Centre, 265-267 Bath Road, Hounslow, TW3 3DA Tel: (020) 8570 6156 Fax: (020) 8570 8885
Ibstock Gun & Tackle Ltd, 61 Chapel Street, Ibstock, Leicestershire, LE67 6HF Tel: (01530) 260901 Fax: (01530) 260901
J B Angling Centre, 37 Eastside, Kirkintilloch, Glasgow, G66 1QA Tel: 0141-775 0083 Fax: 0141-775 0083
J & S Tackle, 59 West Street, Arnold, Nottingham, NG5 7DB Tel: 0115-926 2644
▶ Johns Of Essex, 86 High Street, Earls Colne, Colchester, CO6 2QX Tel: (01787) 221940 Fax: (01787) 221940 E-mail: nicholspongo@aol.com
Joseph Braddell & Sons, 11 North Street, Belfast, BT1 1NA Tel: (028) 9032 0525 Fax: (028) 9032 2657 E-mail: fishing@braddells.fsnet.co.uk
Judds Of Hillingdon Ltd, 3 Westbourne Parade, Uxbridge Road, Hillingdon, Uxbridge, Middlesex, UB10 0NY Tel: (020) 8573 0196 Fax: (020) 8756 1766
Judds Of Ruislip, 524-526 Victoria Road, Ruislip, Middlesex, HA4 0HD Tel: (020) 8841 7194 Fax: (020) 8841 7195
K F T Ltd, Baliscate, Tobermory, Isle of Mull, PA75 6QA Tel: (01688) 302113 Fax: (01688) 302113
K & L Tackle, Farfield House, 127 North Street, Keighley, West Yorkshire, BD21 3AB Tel: (01535) 667574 Fax: (01535) 661805
K O Imports, 78 Cadogan Avenue, West Horndon, Brentwood, Essex, CM13 3TX Tel: (01277) 810870 Fax: (01277) 810772
Kingfisher Angling Centre, 9 New Street, Shrewsbury, SY3 8JN Tel: (01743) 240602 Fax: (01743) 240602
L M D Farms, Kirton Road, Blyton, Gainsborough, Lincolnshire, DN21 3PE Tel: (01427) 628059
Lakeside Leisure Park, Trunch Lane, Chapel St. Leonards, Skegness, Lincolnshire, PE24 5TU Tel: (01754) 872631 Fax: (01754) 872631
Leegem Angling Centre, 81 Sheffield Road, Chesterfield, Derbyshire, S41 7LT Tel: (01246) 559480 Fax: (01246) 559420
Linsley Bros Established 1780 Ltd, 55 Tower Street, Harrogate, North Yorkshire, HG1 1HS Tel: (01423) 505677 Fax: (01423) 563673
Liveline Fishing Tackle & Guns, 41 West Main Street, Armadale, Bathgate, West Lothian, EH48 3PZ Tel: (01501) 733150 Fax: (01501) 733150
Lostock Tackle Box, 16 Watkin Lane, Lostock Hall, Preston, PR5 5RD Tel: (01772) 626585 Fax: (01772) 626585
▶ Maggot Inn, 193 Upminster Road South, Rainham, Essex, RM13 9BB Tel: (01708) 526652
Megabaits, 16 Brue Avenue, Bridgwater, Somerset, TA6 5LT Tel: (01278) 424614 Fax: (01278) 424615
Metcalfe J.J Fishing Tackle, 15 Newgate Street, Walton on the Naze, Essex, CO14 8DT Tel: (01255) 675680 Fax: (01255) 675680
Mevagissey Shark & Angling Centre, West Wharf, Mevagissey, St. Austell, Cornwall, PL26 6UJ Tel: (01726) 843430 Fax: (01726) 843430 E-mail: sales@skua.org.uk
▶ Moorland Tackle, 32a Russell Street, Leek, Staffordshire, ST13 5JF Tel: (01538) 372288
Newtown Angling Centre, Newtown, Germoe, Penzance, Cornwall, TR20 9AQ Tel: (01736) 763721
Nine Oaks, Craigfryn, Oakford, Llanarth, Dyfed, SA47 0RW Tel: (01545) 580482
Oakleys, 161-163 Northfield Road, Sheffield, S10 1QQ Tel: 0114-268 1723 Fax: 0114-268 1723
Orvis Shop, Bridge House, High Street, Stockbridge, Hampshire, SO20 6HB Tel: (01264) 810017 Fax: (01264) 810504 E-mail: admin@orvis.co.uk
Paige's Fishing Tackle, 36 Station Road, Hayling Island, Hampshire, PO11 0EQ Tel: (023) 9246 3500
Peacehaven Angler, 135 South Coast Road, Peacehaven, East Sussex, BN10 8PA Tel: (01273) 586000
Penn Fishing Tackle Europe, Cartside Avenue, Inchinnan, Renfrew, PA4 9RX Tel: 0141-814 6565 Fax: 0141-814 6560 E-mail: sales@pennfishing.com
▶ Planet Carp, Alfreton Road, Nottingham, NG7 3PE Tel: 0115-942 4941 Fax: 0115-978 4158 E-mail: sales@carpfishingonline.com
Porthcawl Angling Centre, 10 Dock Street, Porthcawl, Mid Glamorgan, CF36 3BL Tel: (01656) 772404 Fax: (01656) 772404
Purbeck Angling, 28 South Street, Wareham, Dorset, BH20 4LU Tel: (01929) 550770 Fax: (01929) 550770
Reels & Deals, 61b St. Thomas Street, Weymouth, Dorset, DT4 8EQ Tel: (01305) 787848 Fax: (01305) 787783
Reid Fishing Tackle & Sports, 33 Hope Street, Crook, County Durham, DL15 9HU Tel: (01388) 763867 Fax: (01388) 763867
Retford Angling Centre, Northfield Way, Retford, Nottinghamshire, DN22 7LR Tel: (01777) 706168 Fax: (01777) 709779
Dave Richards, 73 Church Road, Newport, Gwent, NP19 7EH Tel: (01633) 254910
Roaches 4 Tackle, Bridge Hill, Stainforth, Doncaster, South Yorkshire, DN7 5JE Tel: (01302) 844688
▶ Rod Rest, 149 York Street, Heywood, Lancashire, OL10 4NX Tel: (01706) 622340 Fax: (01706) 622340
▶ Rods & Reels, King Street, Builth Wells, Powys, LD2 3DP Tel: (01982) 551706 Fax: (01982) 551706
Roger's Tackle, Pilot House Wharf, Swansea, SA1 1UN Tel: (01792) 469999 Fax: (01792) 469999
Roxy Angling Supplies, 171 Queens Road, Ashton-under-Lyne, Lancashire, OL6 8EW Tel: 0161-339 1799 Fax: 0161-830 0162
▶ Rugby Tackle, 155a Bilton Road, Rugby, Warwickshire, CV22 7DS Tel: (01788) 544913 Fax: (01788) 570645 E-mail: sales@rugbytackle.co.uk
The Salmons Leap, Salmon Leap, Cenarth, Newcastle Emlyn, Dyfed, SA38 9JP Tel: (01239) 711242
Sheltons Of Peterborough Ltd, 67 South Street, Stanground, Peterborough, PE2 8EX Tel: (01733) 565287 Fax: (01733) 560186
Shorrock's Bros, 210-212 Albert Road, Farnworth, Bolton, BL4 9JB Tel: (01204) 571386
Six Am Tackle & Bait Ltd, 82 Worksop Road, Swallownest, Sheffield, S26 4WD Tel: 0114-287 3070 Fax: 0114-287 3070
Southwold Angling Centre, 9 Station Road, Southwold, Suffolk, IP18 6AX Tel: (01502) 722085 Fax: (01502) 722085
Specialist Tackle Ltd, 93 Chase Cross Road, Romford, RM5 3RP Tel: (01708) 752277 Fax: (01708) 754714 E-mail: info@specialist-tackle.co.uk
Sportfish Ltd, Winforton, Hereford, HR3 6SP Tel: (01544) 327111 Fax: (01544) 327093 E-mail: orders@sportfish.co.uk
▶ Spotty Dog Tackle, 15 Yarm Lane, Stockton-on-Tees, Cleveland, TS18 3DR Tel: (01642) 601171 Fax: (01642) 601172 E-mail: sales@spottydogtackle.com
Stephen J Fawcett, 7 Great John Street, Lancaster, LA1 1NQ Tel: (01524) 32033 Fax: (01524) 843470 E-mail: sales@fawcettonline.com
Stocks Fly Fishery, Bank House Lancaster Road, Caton, Lancaster, LA2 9HX Tel: (01524) 770412 Fax: (01524) 770412
▶ Streamline Fishing, Forest Road, New Ollerton, Newark, Nottinghamshire, NG22 9QT Tel: (01623) 869363 Fax: (01623) 869363
▶ Stretford Angling Centre, 854 Chester Road, Stretford, Manchester, M32 0QJ Tel: 0161-865 2646
▶ Studley Fish & Tackle, 10 High Street, Studley, Warwickshire, B80 7HJ Tel: 01527 854244
▶ Alan Tackle, 10 Bridge Road, Southampton, SO19 7GQ Tel: (023) 8044 6222
Tackle & Gun, 3 East Well, High Street, Tenterden, Kent, TN30 6AH Tel: (01580) 764851
Terminal Tackle UK Ltd, 4 Friday Street, Leighton Buzzard, Bedfordshire, LU7 1AN Tel: (01525) 370779 Fax: (01525) 370779 E-mail: terminal4takle@hotmail.com
▶ Thames Fishing Tackle Ltd, Unit 11 Bartleet Road, Redditch, Worcestershire, B98 0DQ Tel: (01527) 501633 Fax: (01527) 501744
Thatcham Angling Centre, 4 Sagecroft Road, Thatcham, Berkshire, RG18 3DZ Tel: (01635) 871450
Thompson Tackle, 2b Hitchin Road, Arlesey, Bedfordshire, SG15 6RP Tel: (01462) 835269
Tom C Saville Ltd, 9 Nottingham Road, Trowell, Nottingham, NG9 3PA Tel: 0115-930 8800 Fax: 0115-930 3336
Tonbridge Rod & Line, 17a Priory Road, Tonbridge, Kent, TN9 2AQ Tel: (01732) 352450 Fax: (01732) 352450
Tony's Tackle Shop, 211 Seaside, Eastbourne, East Sussex, BN22 7NP Tel: (01323) 731388 Fax: (01323) 647247 E-mail: tonytackle@aol.com
▶ Top Tack, Unit 23 Rope Walk Shopping Centre, Rope Walk, Rye, East Sussex, TN31 7NA Tel: (01797) 222333
Turner's Tackle & Bait, 4a Station Road, Faringdon, Oxfordshire, SN7 7BN Tel: (01367) 241044
Two Guys, 27a Burnaby Close, Basingstoke, Hampshire, RG22 6UJ Tel: (01256) 464981 Fax: (01256) 464356
▶ uksaltwaterflies.com, 15 Bay View Terrace, Porthleven, Helston, Cornwall, TR13 9JQ Tel: (01326) 562753 E-mail: sales@uksaltwaterflies.com
▶ Ultimate Angling Centre, 118 Cambridge Road, Hitchin, Hertfordshire, SG4 0JN Tel: (01462) 440600 Fax: (01462) 434500
Vanguard Fishing Tackle, 25 Widebar Gate, Boston, Lincolnshire, PE21 6SR Tel: (01205) 369994 Fax: (01205) 359327
W R Hardy, 153 East High Street, Forfar, Angus, DD8 2EQ Tel: (01307) 466635 Fax: (01307) 468820
▶ Wac Tackle, 5 Anstice Square, Madeley, Telford, Shropshire, TF7 5BD Tel: (01952) 586786 Fax: (01952) 620497
▶ Walkers Of Shrewsbury Ltd, 51 Mardol, Shrewsbury, SY1 1PP Tel: (01743) 241411
Wayahead Tackle Ltd, Off Back Market Street, Hindley, Wigan, Lancashire, WN2 3AD Tel: (01942) 525868 Fax: (01942) 525860
▶ Wellington Angling Centre, 18 High Street, Wellington, Somerset, TA21 8RA Tel: (01823) 666343 Fax: (01823) 666343
West Bay Water Sports Ltd, 10A West Bay, Bridport, Dorset, DT6 4EL Tel: (01308) 421800 Fax: (01308) 421800 E-mail: steve@anglianmailorder.com
Whitby Angling Supplies, 65 Haggersgate, Whitby, North Yorkshire, YO21 3PP Tel: (01947) 603855
Wickersley Angling Centre, Unit 3 Denby Way, Maltby, Rotherham, South Yorkshire, S66 8HR Tel: (01709) 540998 Fax: (01709) 540998
William Boyer & Sons Transport Ltd, Trout Road, West Drayton, Middlesex, UB7 7SN Tel: (01895) 445141 Fax: (01895) 442027
▶ Willis Tackle Products, The Rye, Eaton Bray, Dunstable, Bedfordshire, LU6 2BQ Tel: (01525) 221968
Wolverhampton Mobility, 210 Newhampton Road West, Wolverhampton, WV6 0RW Tel: (01902) 744824 E-mail: info@wolverhamptonmobility.co.uk
▶ Wrigmers Baits, Unit 3 Exeter Street, Teignmouth, Devon, TQ14 8JJ Tel: (01626) 777302

FISHING TACKLE HOOKS

▶ Rods & Reels, 6 Chapel Street, Barwell, Leicester, LE9 8DD Tel: 01455 842450 Fax: 01455 842451 E-mail: fishingebay@yahoo.co.uk

FISHING TACKLE LUGGAGE

Flambeau Europlast Ltd, Manston Road, Ramsgate, Kent, CT12 6HW Tel: (01843) 854000 Fax: (01843) 854010 E-mail: sales@flambeaueuro.com
Hambry's Angling Equipment, 8 Tamworth Road, Polesworth, Tamworth, Staffordshire, B78 1JH Tel: (01827) 895011
J Graham & Co., 37-39 Castle Street, Inverness, IV2 3DU Tel: (01463) 233178 Fax: (01463) 710287 E-mail: william@johngrahamandco.co.uk
John R Gow Ltd, 12 Union Street, Dundee, DD1 4BH Tel: (01382) 225427 Fax: (01382) 225427 E-mail: sales@scotland-fishing.co.uk
Reel Thing, 17 Royal Opera Arcade, London, SW1Y 4UY Tel: (020) 7976 1830 Fax: (020) 7976 1850
▶ Rods & Reels, 6 Chapel Street, Barwell, Leicester, LE9 8DD Tel: 01455 842450 Fax: 01455 842451 E-mail: fishingebay@yahoo.co.uk
Tight Lines, 164 Milnrow Road, Shaw, Oldham, OL2 8AY Tel: (01706) 881459 Fax: (01706) 881459
▶ uksaltwaterflies.com, 15 Bay View Terrace, Porthleven, Helston, Cornwall, TR13 9JQ Tel: (01326) 562753 E-mail: sales@uksaltwaterflies.com

FITTED BATHROOM FURNITURE

▶ BG Properties, 15 Palgrave Road, London, W12 9NB Tel: 07968 034592 Fax: 07092 038898
▶ Sam Brown Furniture, Unit 12 Berlin Bank, North London Freight Depot, York Way, London, N1 0UZ Tel: (07778) 615980 E-mail: sam@sambrownfurniture.co.uk
▶ Flat Pack Man Ltd, 53 Warwick Road, Cliftonville, Margate, Kent, CT9 2JU Tel: (0800) 0407744 E-mail: whirlyweston1@hotmail.com
▶ Lochaber Kitchens, Unit 12e, Annat Industrial Estate, Fort William, Inverness-shire, PH33 7HR Tel: (01397) 702710 E-mail: info@lochaberkitchens.co.uk

FITTED BATHROOM FURNITURE – *continued*

▶ Jon Riley Furniture, Moores Farmhouse, Corse Lawn, Gloucester, GL19 4LY Tel: (01452) 781074 E-mail: enquiries@jon-riley.co.uk
▶ West Window Interiors, 2 Straw House Cottage, Kirkby Road, Ripon, North Yorkshire, HG4 3JU Tel: (01765) 608609 E-mail: sales@westwindowinteriors.co.uk

FITTED BEDROOM FURNITURE

▶ 1st Choice Fitted Bedrooms, Unit A, Springvale Business Park, Darwen, Lancashire, BB3 2EP Tel: (01254) 873173 Fax: (01254) 873787 E-mail: 1stchoicebedrooms@tiscali.co.uk
▶ Barwoods Bedrooms Ltd, 34 Market Street, Mottram, Hyde, Cheshire, SK14 6JG Tel: (01457) 763355 Fax: (01457) 763355 E-mail: mbardsley@barwoods.com
▶ Bedbugz Bedding & Blankets, 243-245 Dewsbury Road, Leeds, LS11 5HZ Tel: 0113-277 7753 Fax: 0113-277 7753
▶ Bespoke Bedrooms, 68 Huntingdon Road, Chatteris, Cambridgeshire, PE16 6ED Tel: (01354) 693392 Fax: (01354) 696807 E-mail: sales@bespokebedroomfurniture.co.uk
▶ Sam Brown Furniture, Unit 12 Berlin Bank, North London Freight Depot, York Way, London, N1 0UZ Tel: (07778) 615980 E-mail: sam@sambrownfurniture.co.uk
Cole, 24 Station Parade, Hornchurch, Essex, RM12 5AB Tel: (01708) 444279 Fax: (01708) 705003
▶ David Collier Fitted Furniture, Unit 5 Stirling Industrial Estate, Off Chorley New Road, Horwich, Bolton, BL6 6DU Tel: (01204) 668899 Fax: (01204) 668899 E-mail: info@davidcollier.co.uk
▶ Exclusiv Fitted Interiors, 16a Longfield Road, Eglinton, Londonderry, BT47 3PY Tel: (028) 7181 1114 Fax: (028) 7181 4916
▶ Fitted Bedroom Co., Block 5, Inveresk Industrial Estate, Musselburgh, Midlothian, EH21 7UL Tel: 0131-665 1990 Fax: 0131-665 1770
▶ Flat Pack Amigos Ltd, Alpine House, 28 Church Road, Rainford, St. Helens, Merseyside, WA11 8HE Tel: (01744) 886670 E-mail: info@flatpackamigos.co.uk
Greenheart Design Ltd, The Tall House, Harberton, Totnes, Devon, TQ9 7SQ Tel: (01803) 868685 Fax: (01803) 866694
▶ Integrated Cinema Experience, 11 Chatteris Close, Stoke-on-Trent, ST3 7TX Tel: 01782 399317 Fax: 01782 399317 E-mail: icexperience@yahoo.com
▶ Prestige Bedrooms, 99 Blackshaw Lane, Royton, Oldham, OL2 6NT Tel: (01706) 845691
▶ Jon Riley Furniture, Moores Farmhouse, Corse Lawn, Gloucester, GL19 4LY Tel: (01452) 781074 E-mail: enquiries@jon-riley.co.uk
▶ Sliding Door Wardrobes Ltd, Unit H2-H3, Cowlairs, Nottingham, NG5 9RA Tel: 0115-928 3987 E-mail: slidingwardrobe@aol.com
Spacemaker Bedrooms Ltd, 160-162 Hornchurch Road, Hornchurch, Essex, RM11 1QH Tel: (01708) 473020
▶ Woodstock Designs Ltd, Manor House, Ryehill, Hull, HU12 9NH Tel: (01964) 621100

FITTED FURNITURE DOORS

Panel Projects, Portview Road, Avonmouth, Bristol, BS11 9LQ Tel: 0117-316 7020 Fax: 0117-316 7001 E-mail: sales@panelprojects.com
Sharps Bedrooms Ltd, Unit 11 Grahamston Retail Park, Grahams Road, Falkirk, FK1 1LW Tel: (01324) 626403

FITTED KITCHEN WORKTOPS

BTM Ltd, 1 Nagi Business Centre, Marsh Road, Wembley, Middlesex, HA0 1ES Tel: (020) 8566 8866 Fax: (020) 8566 8188 E-mail: sales@btmltd.co.uk
F & K Electrical & Refrigeration Ltd, High Street Village, St. Austell, Cornwall, PL26 7SR Tel: (01726) 822288 E-mail: info@fk-ltd.co.uk
▶ Lochaber Kitchens, Unit 12e, Annat Industrial Estate, Fort William, Inverness-shire, PH33 7HR Tel: (01397) 702710 E-mail: info@lochaberkitchens.co.uk
▶ Plasticlad Double Glazing Installers, 20 Bracken Close, Huntington, York, YO32 9NZ Tel: (01904) 763907 Fax: (01904) 763907 E-mail: plasticlad@btinternet.com
▶ R Austin, 35 Searle Way, Eight Ash Green, Colchester, CO6 3QS Tel: (01206) 572217 Fax: (01206) 572217
▶ Redwood Kitchens, 81 Tamar Way, Wokingham, Berkshire, RG41 3UB Tel: 0118-977 2233 Fax: (0845) 2265658 E-mail: sales@redwoodkitchens.co.uk
▶ Replacement Kitchen Door Co., 1 Hollow Cottages, London Road, Purfleet, Essex, RM19 1QP Tel: (01708) 865386 Fax: (01708) 890595 E-mail: sales@replacementkitchendoor.co.uk
▶ Stone Mine Ltd, 22 Blackfriars Street, Facing Travelodge, City Centre, Manchester, M3 5BQ Tel: 0161-833 2333 Fax: 0161-870 6340 E-mail: alex@stonemine.co.uk
▶ Universal Worktops, Prospect Road, Crook, County Durham, DL15 8JN Tel: (01388) 768500 Fax: (01388) 768703 E-mail: sales@universalworktops.com

FIXED GRATE BOILERS

Bib Cochran Ltd, Newbie Works, Annan, Dumfriesshire, DG12 5QU Tel: (01522) 510510 Fax: (01461) 205511 E-mail: enquiries@bibcochran.com

FIXED HOLIDAY CARAVANS

B K Bluebird Ltd, Mannings Heath Road, Parkstone, Poole, Dorset, BH12 4NF Tel: (01202) 740182 Fax: (01202) 715545 E-mail: uksales@bkbluebird.co.uk
Brentmere Leisure, 18 Mallard Close, Earls Barton, Northampton, NN6 0JF Tel: (01604) 810700 Fax: (01604) 812497
▶ Chloes Caravan Holidays, 31 Templars Field, Canley, Coventry, CV4 8FR Tel: (024) 7647 3580 E-mail: frank@leach60.fsnet.co.uk
Cosalt Holiday Homes Ltd, Stoneferry, Hull, HU8 8EH Tel: (01482) 227203 Fax: (01482) 210481 E-mail: info@coshomes.co.uk
Homeseeker Homes Ltd, Shipton Way Express Business Park, Rushden, Northamptonshire, NN10 6GL Tel: (01933) 651644 Fax: (01933) 652601 E-mail: sales@homeseekerhomes.com
Manor Park Homes Ltd, Finedon Sidings Industrial Estate, Furnace Lane, Finedon, Wellingborough, Northamptonshire, NN9 5NY Tel: (01536) 726009 Fax: (01536) 726203 E-mail: manorparkhomes@lineone.net
Omar Homes Ltd, London Road, Brandon, Suffolk, IP27 0NE Tel: (01842) 810673 Fax: (01842) 814328 E-mail: sales@omar.co.uk
Pemberton Leisure Homes Ltd, Woodhouse Lane, Wigan, Lancashire, WN6 7NF Tel: (01942) 321221 Fax: (01942) 234150 E-mail: info@pembertonlh.co.uk
Swift Holdings Ltd, Dunswell Road, Cottingham, North Humberside, HU16 4JX Tel: (01482) 847332 Fax: (01482) 876335 E-mail: enquire@swiftleisure.co.uk
Wessex Homes Group Ltd, Shillingstone Lane, Okeford Fitzpaine, Blandford Forum, Dorset, DT11 0RB Tel: (01258) 860455 Fax: (01258) 861436 E-mail: info@wessexparkhomes.co.uk

FIXED MULTILAYER CERAMIC CAPACITORS

Syfer Technology Ltd, Old Stoke Road, Arminghall, Norwich, NR14 8SQ Tel: (01603) 629721 Fax: (01603) 665001 E-mail: sales@syfer.co.uk
V T M U K Ltd, 8 Corinium Centre, Raans Road, Amersham, Buckinghamshire, HP6 6JQ Tel: (01494) 738600 Fax: (01494) 738610 E-mail: admin@vtm.co.uk

FIXED OR PORTABLE FLAMEPROOF LIGHTING

Chalmit Lighting, 388 Hillington Road, Hillington Industrial Estate, Glasgow, G52 4BL Tel: 0141-882 5555 Fax: 0141-883 3704 E-mail: sales@chalmit.com

FIXINGS

▶ 1st Fix Systems, Hobson Industrial Estate, Hobson, Newcastle upon Tyne, NE16 6EA Tel: (01207) 271777 Fax: (01207) 271777
Alpha Fasteners, Unit 13 Ffrwdgrech Industrial Estate, Ffrwdgrech Road, Brecon, Powys, LD3 8LA Tel: (01874) 625631 Fax: (01874) 625326 E-mail: sales@alphafasteners.co.uk
Anglia Fixing Supplies, Anglia House, Grange Avenue, Mayland, Chelmsford, CM3 6BG Tel: (01621) 744490 Fax: (01621) 744821
Capstan Screws & Fastenings Ltd, Unit 4 Evingar Trading Estate, Ardglen Road, Whitchurch, Hampshire, RG28 7BB Tel: (01256) 895245 Fax: (01256) 892440
D Fix Bridgend Ltd, Newton Yard, Cemetery Road, Bridgend, Mid Glamorgan, CF31 1NA Tel: (01656) 669609 Fax: (01656) 767584 E-mail: mikecoleman@datapowertool.co.uk
▶ Grampian Fastners, Grampian House, Pitmedden Road, Dyce, Aberdeen, AB21 0DP Tel: (01224) 772777 Fax: (01224) 772778 E-mail: sales@grampianfasteners.com
Harrison Matthews & Co. Ltd, 28 College Road, Sutton Coldfield, West Midlands, B73 5DJ Tel: 0121-355 4760 Fax: 0121-243 1104
Infix Holdings Ltd, 85 87 Stapleton Road, Bristol, BS5 0QF Tel: 0117-955 3987 Fax: 0117-955 9833 E-mail: enquiries@infix.co.uk
Jo-El Electric Ltd, Stafford Park 5, Telford, Shropshire, TF3 3AS Tel: (01952) 209001 Fax: (01952) 209645 E-mail: info@jo-el.com
▶ Swiftfix, 18 Newtown Road, Southampton, SO19 9HQ Tel: (023) 8044 8444 Fax: (023) 8044 8444 E-mail: sales@swiftfix.co.uk

FLAGS

A1 Plymol Flagstaff Co., Unit 6 Carr Lane Business Park, Carr Lane, Hoylake, Wirral, Merseyside, CH47 4AZ Tel: 0151-632 1354 Fax: 0151-632 4912 E-mail: sales@flagstaffs.co.uk
Aaask Innobative Solutions, The Gap, Hafod Moor, Gwernaffield, Mold, Clwyd, CH7 5ET Tel: 0141-616 3333 Fax: 0141-639 5895 E-mail: sales@aaask.com
Amazing Bunting Co., Units 1-7, 22 Pleydell Road, Northampton, NN4 8NL Tel: (01604) 675556 Fax: (01604) 675557 E-mail: sales@amazingbunting.co.uk
Autosigns Ltd, North Mills, Frog Island, Leicester, LE3 5DH Tel: 0116-262 9526 Fax: 0116-251 2889 E-mail: enquiries@autosigns.co.uk
Banner Warehouse, Unit 4 & 5 Knowle Business Centre, Wadhurst Road, Frant, Tunbridge Wells, Kent, TN3 9EJ Tel: (0800) 0523659 Fax: (0800) 0523658 E-mail: regencysigns@btclick.com
▶ Bigger Scene Ltd, 172 Monks Wood, North Shields, Tyne & Wear, NE30 2UB Tel: 0191-272 8998
Daniel Boyle & Son, 1 Carruthers Street, Liverpool, L3 6BY Tel: 0151-255 0055 Fax: 0151-255 0011 E-mail: sales@titherleys.co.uk
Byte Systems, 50 Hoskyn Close, Rugby, Warwickshire, CV21 4LA Tel: (01788) 331495 Fax: (0870) 941027 E-mail: sales@byte-solutions.co.uk
▶ C & S Banners, 244 North Lane, Aldershot, Hampshire, GU12 4TJ Tel: (01252) 317701 Fax: (01252) 324375
Concorde Nottingham & Leicester Flag Co., 48 School Lane, Woodhouse, Loughborough, Leicestershire, LE12 8UJ Tel: (01509) 891078 Fax: (01509) 891281 E-mail: sales@concordeflag.co.uk
Delta Flags Ltd, 37 Weathercock Lane, Woburn Sands, Milton Keynes, MK17 8NP Tel: (01908) 582883 Fax: (01908) 582552 E-mail: info@deltaflags.co.uk
Ensign Flag, 42 Dunes Way, Liverpool, L5 9RJ Tel: 0151-298 1007 Fax: 0151-298 1006 E-mail: enquiries@ensignflags.com
Flag Services & Supply Co., 302 Westbourne Grove, Westcliff-on-Sea, Essex, SS0 0PT Tel: (01702) 333343 Fax: (01702) 343330
Flagmaker Ltd, 20 Clarion Court, Clarion Close, The Enterprise Park, Llansamlet, Swansea, SA6 8RF Tel: (01792) 700795 Fax: (0845) 0613915 E-mail: support@mrflag.com
Flags & Banners Ltd, Springfield Industrial Estate, Burnham-on-Crouch, Essex, CM0 8TE Tel: (01621) 783221 Fax: (01621) 783532 E-mail: sales@flags-banners.co.uk
Flying Colours, Unit 5-6 Orchard Court, Iles Lane, Knaresborough, North Yorkshire, HG5 8PP Tel: (01423) 860007 Fax: (01423) 861858 E-mail: sales@flag-makers.co.uk
Halton Print & Promotional, High Street, Knutton, Newcastle, Staffordshire, ST5 6BX Tel: (01782) 712909 Fax: (01782) 713626 E-mail: info@haltonpromotional.co.uk
Harrison Flagpoles, Borough Road, Darlington, County Durham, DL1 1SW Tel: (01325) 355433 Fax: (01325) 461726 E-mail: sales@flagpoles.co.uk
Heaton Paper Co. Ltd, Eldon Street, Gateshead, Tyne & Wear, NE8 3ND Tel: 0191-477 3783 Fax: 0191-490 0247 E-mail: sales@heatonpaper.co.uk
Icon Display, 130-136 Maidstone Road, Sidcup, Kent, DA14 5HS Tel: (020) 8302 4921 Fax: (020) 8302 3971 E-mail: icondisplay@cix.co.uk
Id Signs Scotland Ltd, 200 Swniton Road, Baillieston, Glasgow, G69 6DB Tel: 0141-773 3666 Fax: 0141-773 1690
J & D Wilkie Ltd, Gairie Works, Bellies Brae, Kirriemuir, Angus, DD8 4BL Tel: (01575) 572502 Fax: (01575) 574564 E-mail: sales@jdwilkie.co.uk
J W Plant & Co. Ltd, 39 Ashley Road, Leeds, LS9 7AJ Tel: 0113-248 0454 Fax: 0113-235 0118 E-mail: sales@jwplant.co.uk
Newton Newton, Bishop Tozers Chapel, Middlemarsh Road, Burgh le Marsh, Skegness, Lincolnshire, PE24 5AD Tel: (01754) 768401 Fax: (01754) 610612 E-mail: info@newtonnewtonflags.com
Northern Flags Ltd, Unit 1 5 Matrix Court, Leeds, LS11 5WB Tel: 0113-205 5180 Fax: 0113-205 5181 E-mail: info@northernflags.com
Porter Bros Ltd, King's Dock Mill, Tabley Street, Liverpool, L1 8JH Tel: 0151-709 5155 Fax: 0151-709 6637 E-mail: sales@flagsbyporters.co.uk
Purvis Marquee Hire, East Mains Holdings, Ingliston, Newbridge, Midlothian, EH28 8NB Tel: 0131-335 3685 Fax: 0131-335 0294 E-mail: sales@purvis-maquees.co.uk
Speedings Flags Poles & Masts, 4 Carrmere Road, Leechmere Industrial Estate, Sunderland, SR2 9TW Tel: 0191-523 9933 Fax: 0191-523 9955 E-mail: speedingsltd@btconnect.com
James Stevenson Flags Ltd, 75 Westmoreland Street, Glasgow, G42 8LH Tel: 0141-423 5757 Fax: 0141-946 3741 E-mail: john@stevensonflags.com
▶ Techno Associates, 382, Sykes Road, Slough, SL1 4SP Tel: (01753) 572800 Fax: (01753) 572800
Thames Valley Textiles, Oddington Grange, Weston-on-the-Green, Bicester, Oxfordshire, OX25 3QW Tel: (01865) 331009 Fax: (01865) 331721 E-mail: info@tvt1.co.uk
TLC Signs, Fairfax House, Deeping St.James Road, Deeping Gate, Peterborough, PE6 9AP Tel: (01778) 349282 E-mail: sales@tlcsigns.co.uk
Trounce Ltd, New St Marks Works, St Marks Lane, Manchester, M8 4FW Tel: 0161-740 2159 Fax: 0161-721 4768 E-mail: sales@trounce.co.uk
Turtle & Pearce Ltd, 30 Borough High Street, London, SE1 1XU Tel: (020) 7407 1301 Fax: (020) 7378 0267 E-mail: sales@flags-turtle.co.uk
George Tutill Ltd, 9 Higham Road, Chesham, Buckinghamshire, HP5 2AF Tel: (01494) 783938 Fax: (01494) 791241 E-mail: info@flags-tutill.co.uk
Union Industries, Whitehouse Street, Leeds, LS10 1AD Tel: 0113-244 8393 Fax: 0113-242 1307 E-mail: sales@unionindustries.co.uk
United Flags & Flagstaffs Ltd, Boarshaw Road, Middleton, Manchester, M24 2WH Tel: 0161-653 6381 Fax: 0161-655 3383 E-mail: sales@unitedflags.co.uk
Up The Pole Ltd, 56 Meadow Road, Catshill, Bromsgrove, Worcestershire, B61 0JL Tel: (01527) 833873 Fax: (01527) 836578

FLAGSTAFFS

A1 Plymol Flagstaff Co., Unit 6 Carr Lane Business Park, Carr Lane, Hoylake, Wirral, Merseyside, CH47 4AZ Tel: 0151-632 1354 Fax: 0151-632 4912 E-mail: sales@flagstaffs.co.uk
Aboval & Co. Ltd, 24 Firtrees Close, Rothershide, London, SE16 5NG Tel: (07774) 852505 Fax: (020) 7252 3793
Delta Flags Ltd, 37 Weathercock Lane, Woburn Sands, Milton Keynes, MK17 8NP Tel: (01908) 582883 Fax: (01908) 582552 E-mail: info@deltaflags.co.uk
Flags Flags Poles & Masts, 10 Monton Green, Eccles, Manchester, M30 9LW Tel: 0161-788 0131 Fax: 0161-788 0131
Harrison Flagpoles, Borough Road, Darlington, County Durham, DL1 1SW Tel: (01325) 355433 Fax: (01325) 461726 E-mail: sales@flagpoles.co.uk
Houston's Of Cupar Ltd, Station House, Station Road, Cupar, Fife, KY15 5HX Tel: (01334) 655331 Fax: (01334) 656437 E-mail: sales@houstons.co.uk
Northern Flags Ltd, Unit 1 5 Matrix Court, Leeds, LS11 5WB Tel: 0113-205 5180 Fax: 0113-205 5181 E-mail: info@northernflags.com
James Stevenson Flags Ltd, 75 Westmoreland Street, Glasgow, G42 8LH Tel: 0141-423 5757 Fax: 0141-946 3741 E-mail: john@stevensonflags.com
TLC Signs, Fairfax House, Deeping St.James Road, Deeping Gate, Peterborough, PE6 9AP Tel: (01778) 349282 E-mail: sales@tlcsigns.co.uk
Turtle & Pearce Ltd, 30 Borough High Street, London, SE1 1XU Tel: (020) 7407 1301 Fax: (020) 7378 0267 E-mail: sales@flags-turtle.co.uk
George Tutill Ltd, 9 Higham Road, Chesham, Buckinghamshire, HP5 2AF Tel: (01494) 783938 Fax: (01494) 791241 E-mail: info@flags-tutill.co.uk
United Flags & Flagstaffs Ltd, Boarshaw Road, Middleton, Manchester, M24 2WH Tel: 0161-653 6381 Fax: 0161-655 3383 E-mail: sales@unitedflags.co.uk
W E Harrison Sheffield Ltd, 33 Regent Terrace, Sheffield, S3 7QA Tel: 0114-272 0561 Fax: 0114-272 0564 E-mail: weh@quista.net
▶ The Wooden Flagpole Co., The Croft, West Street, Wiveliscombe, Somerset, TA4 2JP Tel: 01984 624794 Fax: 01984 624532 E-mail: mark.stoddart@btconnect.com

FLAME ARRESTERS

A F S Associates, 1 The Paddock, Much Wenlock, Shropshire, TF13 6LT Tel: (01952) 728188 Fax: (01952) 728174 E-mail: sales@afsassociates.co.uk
G F S A Ltd, 4 West Court, Buntsford Park Road, Bromsgrove, Worcestershire, B60 3DX Tel: (01527) 831037 Fax: (01527) 836333 E-mail: enquiries@gfsa.co.uk
Johnson Hall Services Ltd, 93 Gorof Road, Ystradgynlais, Lower Cwmtwrch, Swansea, SA9 1DS Tel: (01639) 849564 Fax: (01639) 845348
Motherwell Control Systems Ltd, 1 St Michaels Road, St. Helens, Merseyside, WA9 4WZ Tel: (01744) 815211 Fax: (01744) 814497 E-mail: sales@motherwellcs.com
Servais Silencers, 409 Harlestone Road, Northampton, NN5 6PB Tel: (01604) 754888 Fax: (01604) 759548

FLAME CUT STEEL BLANKS

Elston Profiles and Compnents Ltd, St. Annes Road, Cradley Heath, West Midlands, B64 5BH Tel: (01384) 566919 Fax: (01384) 569684
Strata Flame Cutting & Fabrications, 101 York Road, Hall Green, Birmingham, B28 8LH Tel: 0121-778 5022 Fax: 0121-777 8241

FLAME CUTTING

Ajs Profiles, Unit 12a Parkrose Industrial Estate, Middlemore Road, Smethwick, West Midlands, B66 2DZ Tel: 0121-565 5379 Fax: 0121-565 5379 E-mail: ajsprofiles.ltd@virgin.net
Elston Profiles Ltd, Unit G2 Bullock Street, West Bromwich, West Midlands, B70 7HE Tel: 0121-553 6292 Fax: 0121-553 6707
▶ J L Steel Services, Unit 101, Bandeath Industrial Estate, Stirling, FK7 7NP Tel: (01786) 817081 Fax: (01786) 810981
John Eccles & Co Blackheath Ltd, Holt Road, Halesowen, West Midlands, B62 9HQ Tel: 0121-559 1753 Fax: 0121-559 1753
▶ Keiton Engineering Ltd, 2 William Burton Works, St. James Street, Wednesbury, West Midlands, WS10 7DY Tel: 0121-556 9919 Fax: 0121-556 1398
Lynrose Engineering, Unit 12 Shrub Hill Industrial Estate, Worcester, WR4 9EL Tel: (01905) 729795 Fax: (01905) 729798 E-mail: mhlynrosesales@aol.com
North East Profiling & Engineering Co. Ltd, Bellway Industrial Estate, Whitley Road, Longbenton, Newcastle upon Tyne, NE12 9SW Tel: 0191-266 4521 Fax: 0191-270 0983 E-mail: sales@northeastprofiling.com
Pegasus Profiles Southern Ltd, Unit 12 Hopkinson Way, Telford Gate, Andover, Hampshire, SP10 3SF Tel: (01264) 358525 Fax: (01264) 366319 E-mail: info@pegpro.co.uk
Abram Pulman & Sons Ltd, Walton Street, Sowerby Bridge, West Yorkshire, HX6 1AN Tel: (01422) 833993 Fax: (01422) 834100 E-mail: sales@pulmans.co.uk
Springfield Stainless, Springfield Works, Stocks Lane, Batley, West Yorkshire, WF17 8PA Tel: (01924) 420303 Fax: (01924) 423333 E-mail: info@springfield-stainless.co.uk
Taylor Metals, 244 Bernard Street, Glasgow, G40 3NX Tel: 0141-556 1903 Fax: 0141-556 1903

FLAME CUTTING EQUIPMENT MANUFRS

Goodwin Air Plasma Ltd, Unit 18 Kernan Drive, Loughborough, Leicestershire, LE11 5JF Tel: (01509) 237369 Fax: (01509) 234942 E-mail: goodwinplasma@aol.com

FLAME DETECTORS

Hamworthy Combustion Engineering Ltd, Fleets Corner, Poole, Dorset, BH17 0LA Tel: (01202) 662700 Fax: (01202) 669875 E-mail: info@hamworthy-combustion.com
Intronics Fire Protection Consultants, 122 Broadmead, Tunbridge Wells, Kent, TN2 5RW Tel: (01892) 516366 Fax: (01892) 512212 E-mail: sales@intronics.co.uk
Spectrex Inc, 6 Applecross Road, Kirkintilloch, Glasgow, G66 3TJ Tel: 0141-578 0693 Fax: 0141-578 9689 E-mail: ian@spectrex-inc.com

FLAME GUNS

Sheen Equipment, Greasley Street, Nottingham, NG6 8NH Tel: 0115-927 2321 Fax: 0115-977 0671

FLAME HARDENING EQUIPMENT

Multijet Hardening Ltd, 8 West Don Street, Sheffield, S6 3BH Tel: 0114-234 5592 Fax: 0114-231 4772

FLAME RETARDANT (FR) ADDITIVE/CHEMICAL PRODUCTS

I M C D UK Ltd, Times House, Throwley Way, Sutton, Surrey, SM1 4AF Tel: (020) 8770 7090 Fax: (020) 8770 7295 E-mail:

FLAME RETARDANT (FR) ADDITIVE/CHEMICAL PRODUCTS, INDUSTRIAL

Liquid Plastics Ltd, PO Box 7, Preston, PR1 1EA Tel: (01772) 255017 Fax: (01772) 255671 E-mail: info@liquidplastics.co.uk

FLAME RETARDANT (FR) ADDITIVE/CHEMICAL PRODUCTS, TEXTILE

Rudolf Chemicals Ltd, Keys Road, Nixs Hill Industrial Estate, Alfreton, Derbyshire, DE55 7FQ Tel: (01773) 832703 Fax: (01773) 520092 E-mail: rudolf@rudolfchemicals.freeserve.co.uk

FLAME RETARDANT (FR) CLOTHING/GARMENTS

P G Products Ltd, Folgate Road, North Walsham, Norfolk, NR28 0AJ Tel: (01692) 500390 Fax: (01692) 402863 E-mail: sales@pgproducts.com
Pioner Fristads (UK) Ltd, 7 Wensum Mount Business Centre, Low Road, Hellesdon, Norwich, NR6 5AQ Tel: (01603) 786160 Fax: (01603) 414540 E-mail: enquiries@fristads-co.com
Watts & Stone, Castle Balfour Demesne, Lisnaskea, Enniskillen, County Fermanagh, BT92 0LT Tel: (028) 6772 1282 Fax: (028) 6772 1106E-mail: sales@wattsandstone.co.uk
Wenaas UK Ltd, Wenaas Buildings, Hareness Circle, Altens Industrial Estate, Aberdeen, AB12 3LY Tel: (01224) 894000 Fax: (01224) 878789 E-mail: sales@wenaas.co.uk

FLAME RETARDANT (FR) COATINGS FOR CERAMIC OR FIBREGLASS

Fireprotect Chester Ltd, Factory Road, Sandycroft, Deeside, Clwyd, CH5 2QJ Tel: (01244) 536595 Fax: (01244) 533592 E-mail: sales@fireprotect.co.uk
Liquid Plastics Ltd, PO Box 7, Preston, PR1 1EA Tel: (01772) 255017 Fax: (01772) 255671 E-mail: info@liquidplastics.co.uk

FLAME RETARDANT (FR) COMPOUNDS

Americhem Ltd, Cawdor Street, Eccles, Manchester, M30 0QF Tel: 0161-789 7832 Fax: 0161-787 7832
J Storey & Co. Ltd, Heron Chemical Works, Moor Lane, Lancaster, LA1 1QQ Tel: (01524) 63252 Fax: (01524) 381805 E-mail: sales@samuelbanner.co.uk
Vita Liquid Polymers Ltd, Harling Road, Wythenshawe, Manchester, M22 4SZ Tel: 0161-998 3226 Fax: 0161-946 0118 E-mail: sales@vita-liquid.co.uk

FLAME RETARDANT (FR) CURTAIN FABRICS

Thomas French Ltd, James Street, Bury, Lancashire, BL9 7EG Tel: 0161-764 5356 Fax: 0161-764 6416 E-mail: peter.owen@thomasfrench.com

FLAME RETARDANT (FR) FABRIC, FURNISHING

Denholme Velvets Ltd, Halifax Rd, Denholme, Bradford, West Yorkshire, BD13 4EZ Tel: (01274) 832185 Fax: (01274) 832646 E-mail: sales@denholme-velvets.co.uk

FLAME RETARDANT (FR) FABRIC, THEATRICAL

J D Mcdougall Ltd, 4 Mcgrath Road, London, E15 4JP Tel: (020) 8534 2921 Fax: (020) 8519 8423 E-mail: sales@mcdougall.co.uk

FLAME RETARDANT (FR) FABRICS

Anthan Engineering Ltd, Watford, WD19 4EZ Tel: (01923) 249474 Fax: (01923) 249477 E-mail: anthan@anthan.co.uk
Cowens Ltd, Ellers Mill, Dalston, Carlisle, CA5 7QJ Tel: (01228) 710205 Fax: (01228) 710331 E-mail: info@cowens.co.uk
J.T. Inglis & Sons Ltd, Riverside Works, Carolina Port, Dundee, DD1 3LU Tel: (01382) 462131 Fax: (01382) 462846
Rubitex Protective Clothing, 52 Lord Street, Manchester, M3 1HN Tel: 0161-834 3340 Fax: 0161-834 3326 E-mail: info@rubitex.co.uk
S M D Textiles Ltd, Pittman Way, Fulwood, Preston, PR2 9ZD Tel: (01772) 651199 Fax: (01772) 654034 E-mail: enquiries@swatchbox.co.uk
Universal Carbon Fibres Ltd, Station Mills, Station Road, Wyke, Bradford, West Yorkshire, BD12 8LA Tel: (01274) 600600 Fax: (01274) 711666 E-mail: info@ucfltd.co.uk

FLAME RETARDANT (FR) PAINTS OR VARNISHES OR COATINGS

Technical Paint Services, 27 Southcote Road, Bournemouth, BH1 3SH Tel: (01202) 295570 Fax: (0845) 2301255 E-mail: sales@technicalpaintservices.com

FLAME RETARDANT (FR) PLASTIC MATERIALS

Vpe, 7 Verwood Industrial Estate, Blackhill, Verwood, Dorset, BH31 6HA Tel: (01202) 827205 Fax: (01202) 827207 E-mail: sales@vpeltd.co.uk

FLAME RETARDANT (FR) WALLCOVERINGS

Muraspec Ltd, 74-78 Wood Lane End, Hemel Hempstead, Hertfordshire, HP2 4RF Tel: (01442) 268890 Fax: (0870) 5329020 E-mail: customerservices@muraspec.com

FLAME TREATMENT SYSTEMS

Nordsea Ltd, Captain Clarke Road, Hyde, Cheshire, SK14 4QG Tel: 0161-366 3010 Fax: 0161-366 3011 E-mail: nordsea@compuserve.com
▶ Rapidflame Ltd, Brian Royd Mills, Saddleworth Road, Greetland, Halifax, West Yorkshire, HX4 8NF Tel: (01422) 311232 Fax: (01422) 311248 E-mail: sales@rapidflame.com

FLAMEPROOF ELECTRIC HEATERS

Chemtec UK Ltd, PO Box 3, Beith, Ayrshire, KA15 1JQ Tel: (01505) 502206 Fax: (01505) 502545 E-mail: sales@chemtecuklimted.co.uk
Heatrae Industrial, Duncombe Road, Bradford, West Yorkshire, BD8 9TB Tel: (01274) 362798 Fax: (01274) 493580 E-mail: sales@heatrae-industrial.com

FLAMEPROOF ELECTRIC MOTORS

A S K Rewinds Ltd, Unit 5 Laneside, Metcalf Drive, Altham Industrial Estate, Accrington, Lancashire, BB5 5TU Tel: (01282) 776475 Fax: (01282) 779438 E-mail: sales@ask-rewinds-ltd.co.uk
Micro Clutch Developments Ltd, Unit 8-9 Kiln Park Industrial Estate, Searle CR, Weston-super-Mare, Avon, BS23 3XP Tel: (01934) 415606 Fax: (01934) 636658 E-mail: sales@microclutch.com
The Morley Electrical Engineering Co. Ltd, Bradford Road, Stanningley, Pudsey, West Yorkshire, LS28 6QB Tel: 0113-257 1734 Fax: 0113-257 0751 E-mail: sales@morleymotors.com
Powertronic Drive Systems Ltd, Treetops House, Gillotts Lane, Henley-On-Thames, Oxfordshire, RG9 1PT Tel: (01491) 579118 Fax: (01491) 412211 E-mail: sales@powertronic.co.uk

FLAMEPROOF SWITCHES

H N L Engineering Ltd, Dukesway, Teesside Industrial Estate, Stockton-On-Tees, Cleveland, TS17 9LT Tel: (01642) 765553 Fax: (01642) 762899 E-mail: sales@hnl-uk.com
Pyropress Engineering Co. Ltd, Bell Close, Newnham Industrial Estate, Plympton, Plymouth, PL7 4JH Tel: (01752) 339866 Fax: (01752) 336681 E-mail: pyromail@pyropress.com
Sirco Controls Ltd, Swaines Industrial Estate, Ashingdon Road, Rochford, Essex, SS4 1RQ Tel: (01702) 545125 Fax: (01702) 546873 E-mail: sales@sirco-controls.co.uk

FLAMEPROOF SWITCHGEARS

Hawker Siddeley Switchgear Ltd, Newport Road, Pontllanfraith, Blackwood, Gwent, NP12 2XH Tel: (01495) 223001 Fax: (01495) 225674 E-mail: sales@hss-ltd.com

FLAMEPROOF TEXTILES, *See headings under Flame Retardant*

FLAMEPROOF/ FLAMEPROOFING, *See Flame Retardant etc*

FLAMEPROOFED THERMOSTATS

▶ Cross Electrical Nottingham Ltd, Trace Works, Debdale Lane, Keyworth, Nottingham, NG12 5HN Tel: 0115-937 5121 Fax: 0115-937 5116 E-mail: heat@cross-electrical.co.uk

FLANGE COVERS

Dbi Plastics, Cottage La Industrial Estate, Broughton Astley, Leicester, LE9 6PD Tel: (01455) 283380 Fax: (01455) 283384 E-mail: info@dbiplastics.com
Furmanite Engineering Ltd, 7 Colville Court, Winwick Quay, Warrington, WA2 8QT Tel: (01925) 418858 Fax: (01925) 418863 E-mail: enquiries@furmanite.com
Plastic Parts Centre, Unit 4, Harelaw Industrial Estate, Annfield Plain, Stanley, County Durham, DH9 8HN Tel: (01207) 290599 Fax: (01207) 299718 E-mail: newcastlesales@plastic-parts.co.uk
Protec The Cap Company Ltd, Princes Park Princesway, Team Valley Trading Estate, Gateshead, Tyne & Wear, NE11 0NF Tel: 0191-442 4242 Fax: 0191-442 4222 E-mail: sales@protecplastics.com

FLANGE FASTENERS

Fairways Fasteners Ltd, Unit 6 Starvale Road Industrial Estate, Lye, Stourbridge, West Midlands, DY9 8PP Tel: (01384) 897535 Fax: (01384) 423611 E-mail: sales@screwsandbolts.co.uk

FLANGE FITTINGS MANUFRS

Evenort Ltd, Houghton Road, North Anston, Sheffield, S25 4JJ Tel: (01909) 569361 Fax: (01909) 550631 E-mail: sales@evenort.co.uk
Full Supply Ltd, Unit 29a Dawley Trading Estate, Stallings Lane, Kingswinford, West Midlands, DY6 7AP Tel: (01384) 402101 Fax: (01384) 402501 E-mail: sales@fullsupply.co.uk
Ogley Bros Ltd, Smithfield, Sheffield, S3 7AS Tel: 0114-276 8948 Fax: 0114-275 5105 E-mail: ogleybrothers@btconnect.com

FLANGE MANUFRS, *See also headings for particular types under Flanges*

Anson Ltd, Team Valley Trading Estate, Seventh Avenue, Gateshead, Tyne & Wear, NE11 0JW Tel: 0191-482 0022 Fax: 0191-487 8835 E-mail: anson-gateshead@anson.co.uk
B D Profiles Ltd, PO Box 65, Cradley Heath, West Midlands, B64 5PP Tel: 0121-559 5136 Fax: 0121-561 4265 E-mail: syoung@bdprofiles.co.uk
C M L Alloys Ltd, Units 44-45 Stretford Motorway Estate, Barton Dock Road, Trafford Park, Manchester, M32 0ZH Tel: 0161-864 5001 Fax: 0161-865 5751 E-mail: sales@cmlimited.com
Carbern Pipes & Fittings, Unit 3 Bevan Industrial Estate, Brierley Hill, West Midlands, DY5 3TF Tel: (01384) 76111 Fax: (01384) 262309 E-mail: sales@carbern.co.uk
Chemipetro Ltd, Plant A Peartree Indust Park, Pear Tree Lane, Dudley, West Midlands, DY2 0UW Tel: (01384) 239441 Fax: (01384) 238430 E-mail: sales@chemipetro.com
Clydeview Precision Engineering & Supplies Ltd, 197a Dumbarton Road, Clydebank, Dunbartonshire, G81 4XJ Tel: 0141-941 1873 Fax: 0141-951 1928
Deans Engineering Supplies, E M S House, Rossfield Road, Ellesmere Port, CH65 3BS Tel: 0151-357 1030 Fax: 0151-357 1990
Destec Engineering Ltd, Five Mile Lane, Washingborough, Lincoln, LN4 1AF Tel: (01522) 791721 Fax: (01522) 790033 E-mail: sales@destec.co.uk
Essex Partners Flange, 73 Park Lane, Liverpool, L1 5EX Tel: 0151-709 6636 Fax: 0151-709 2109
Fithandel (Scotland) Ltd, 1 Woodside Road, Bridge of Don Industrial Estate, Aberdeen, AB23 8EF Tel: (01224) 704964 Fax: (01224) 825421 E-mail: sales@fithandle.com
Flanges Ltd, Portrack Trading Estate, Stockton-on-Tees, Cleveland, TS18 2PL Tel: (01642) 672626 Fax: (01642) 617574 E-mail: sales@flanges-ltd.co.uk
Folglade Pipe & Fittings Ltd, Penlake Industrial Estate, Reginald Road, Sutton, St. Helens, Merseyside, WA9 4JA Tel: (01744) 820119 Fax: (01744) 811412 E-mail: sales@folglade.co.uk
Forged Flanges & Fittings Ltd, Castle House, Station Road, New Barnet, Hertfordshire, EN5 1PE Tel: (020) 8440 6541 Fax: (020) 8441 6911 E-mail: franklissauer@iraco.co.uk
Formula One Pipelines Ltd, Unit 20, Delph Road, Delph Road Industrial Estate, Brierley Hill, West Midlands, DY5 2TW Tel: (01384) 482211 Fax: (01384) 482223
Glamal Engineering Ltd, Pegasus House, Wynyard Avenue, Wynyard, Billingham, Cleveland, TS22 5TB Tel: (01740) 645040 Fax: (01642) 565831 E-mail: sales@glamal.co.uk
H P F Energy Services, 1 Links Place, Aberdeen, AB11 5DY Tel: (01224) 584588 Fax: (01224) 211938 E-mail: sales@hpf-energy.com
H P F Energy Services, 3 Kinwarton Farm Road, Arden Forest Industrial Estate, Alcester, Warwickshire, B49 6EH Tel: (01789) 761212 Fax: (01789) 761222 E-mail: alcester@hpf-energy.com

FLANGE MANUFRS – *continued*

HPF Energy Services, 5 Hoyer Industrial Estate, Bridges Road, Ellesmere Port, CH65 4LB Tel: 0151-357 3322 Fax: 0151-357 1334 E-mail: ellesmere@hpf-energy.com

John Crossley, Tan Yard Road, Catterall, Preston, PR3 0HP Tel: (01995) 606058 Fax: (01995) 606058 E-mail: sharonhenriques@btconnect.com

John D Dunlop, 3 Kyle Road, Irvine Industrial Estate, Irvine, Ayrshire, KA12 8JF Tel: (01294) 273475 Fax: (01294) 274297 E-mail: kdylanalexander@btconnect.com

L F F Scotland Ltd, Peregrine Road, Westhill Business Park, Westhill, Aberdeen, AB32 6JL Tel: (01224) 747636 Fax: (01224) 747637 E-mail: a.mitchell@aberdeen.lff.co.uk

Leo Fittings Ltd, Lakes Road, Braintree, Essex, CM7 3QS Tel: (01376) 341616 Fax: (01376) 349427 E-mail: info@leofittings.co.uk

Linvic Engineering Ltd, Hickman Avenue, Wolverhampton, WV1 2DW Tel: (01902) 456333 Fax: (01902) 455856 E-mail: sales@linvic.co.uk

Marla Tube Fittings Ltd, Units 1-2, Kinwarton Farm Road, Kinwarton, Alcester, Warwickshire, B49 6EH Tel: (01789) 761234 Fax: (01789) 761205 E-mail: alcester@hpf-energy.com

Mechalloy Ltd, 4 Orgreave Cresent, Sheffield, S13 9NQ Tel: 0114-269 3945 Fax: 0114-269 8099

Ogley Bros Ltd, Smithfield, Sheffield, S3 7AS Tel: 0114-276 8948 Fax: 0114-275 5105 E-mail: ogleybrothers@btconnect.com

Park Lane Flanges & Fittings Ltd, Unit 12A Bluebird Industrial Estate, Park Lane, Wolverhampton, WV10 9QG Tel: (01902) 728400 Fax: (01902) 728600 E-mail: parklaneltd@hotmail.com

Priory Woodfield Engineering Ltd, Millbrook Works, Lower Horseley Field, Wolverhampton, WV1 3DZ Tel: (01902) 351530 Fax: (01902) 351290 E-mail: sales@priorywoodfield.com

Scanfit International Ltd, 11-14 Burton Close, Norwich, NR6 6AZ Tel: (01603) 480400 Fax: (01603) 424547 E-mail: mark@scanfit.co.uk

Special Piping Materials Ltd, Broadway, Dukinfield, Cheshire, SK16 4UU Tel: 0161-343 7005 Fax: 0161-343 7011 E-mail: sales@spm.co.uk

Stainless & Alloy (Aberdeen) Ltd, 1 Crombie Road, Aberdeen, AB11 9QQ Tel: (01224) 874666 Fax: (01224) 874699 E-mail: sales@stainlessandalloy.co.uk

Unisant (Holdings) Ltd, PO Box 65, Cradley Heath, West Midlands, B64 5PP Tel: 0121-559 5136 Fax: 0121-561 4265 E-mail: syoung@bdprofiles.co.uk

▶ Welding Units UK Ltd, Mill Lane, Rainford, St. Helens, Merseyside, WA11 8LR Tel: (01744) 884881 Fax: (01744) 883302 E-mail: sales@weldingunits.com

FLANGED OR ANGLE RINGS

B Saxton & Co. Ltd, Unit 6a Arrow Trading Estate, Corporation Road, Audenshaw, Manchester, M34 5LR Tel: 0161-320 1444 Fax: 0161-320 1555 E-mail: sales@banshaws.com

Doncasters Blaenavon Ltd, Forge Side, Blaenavon, Pontypool, Gwent, NP4 9XG Tel: (01495) 790345 Fax: (01495) 791565 E-mail: rhudson@doncasters.com

JMR Section Benders Ltd, Unit 8 Sterling Industrial Estate, Rainham Road South, Dagenham, Essex, RM10 8TX Tel: (020) 8593 7324 Fax: (020) 8595 6139 E-mail: sales@jmrsectionbenders.co.uk

John Crossley, Tan Yard Road, Catterall, Preston, PR3 0HP Tel: (01995) 606058 Fax: (01995) 606058 E-mail: sharonhenriques@btconnect.com

T H E Section Bending Co. Ltd, Houghton Road, North Anston Trading Estate, North Anston, Sheffield, S25 4JJ Tel: (01909) 550080 Fax: (01909) 550114 E-mail: sales@thebending.co.uk

White Cross Ring Co. Ltd, Battye Street, Bradford, West Yorkshire, BD4 8AG Tel: (01274) 669933 Fax: (01274) 660137 E-mail: jason@whitecrossring.co.uk

FLAPJACKS

▶ Baking Solutions Ltd, Avenue Two, Witney, Oxfordshire, OX28 4YQ Tel: (01993) 864777 Fax: (01993) 777440 E-mail: info@bakingsolutions.co.uk

FLARESTACK IGNITION SYSTEMS

▶ G B A Flare Systems, Burnham House, 93 High Street, Burnham, Slough, SL1 7JZ Tel: (01628) 610100 Fax: (01628) 610170 E-mail: mark.swann@gba-flares.com

FLARESTACK IGNITION SYSTEMS, PETROLEUM REFINERY

Hamworthy Combustion Engineering Ltd, Fleets Corner, Poole, Dorset, BH17 0LA Tel: (01202) 662700 Fax: (01202) 669875 E-mail: info@hamworthy-combustion.com

FLASH BUTT RESISTANCE WELDING EQUIPMENT

Donald Engineering Services Ltd, 131 Walmley Road, Sutton Coldfield, West Midlands, B76 1QL Tel: 0121-351 4057 E-mail: donaldengser@aol.com

FLASH BUTT WELDING

Donald Engineering Services Ltd, 131 Walmley Road, Sutton Coldfield, West Midlands, B76 1QL Tel: 0121-351 4057 E-mail: donaldengser@aol.com

FLASH WEBSITE DESIGN

▶ Phase 2, 1 Wheeler Grove, Wells, Somerset, BA5 2GB Tel: (01749) 674458 Fax: (01749) 671319 E-mail: info@phase2.org.uk

▶ Wing-Graphics.com, P.O. BOX 61, Leighton Buzzard, Bedfordshire, LU7 0UW Tel: 01296 682445 Fax: 01296 682445 E-mail: jason@wing-graphics.com

FLASH WELDED RINGS

Doncasters Blaenavon Ltd, Forge Side, Blaenavon, Pontypool, Gwent, NP4 9XG Tel: (01495) 790345 Fax: (01495) 791565 E-mail: rhudson@doncasters.com

A.K. Orme & Son, 114-122 Arundel Street, Sheffield, S1 4RE Tel: 0114-272 2409 Fax: 0114-272 2409 E-mail: ormerings@aol.com

FLASHING BEACONS

Premier Hazard Ltd, Moorfield Estate, Yeadon, Leeds, LS19 7BN Tel: 0113-239 1111 Fax: 0113-239 1131

FLASHING LED BEACONS

STL INTERNATIONAL LTD, Hill Farm, Linton Hill, Linton, Maidstone, Kent, ME17 4AL Tel: 01622 749633 Fax: 01622 746800 E-mail: solutions@stl-int.co.uk

FLAT BOTTOM HOOK BOLTS

John Howard & Sons Ltd, Mullineux Street, Worsley, Manchester, M28 3DZ Tel: 0161-790 2149 Fax: 0161-703 8253

FLAT GLASS HANDLING EQUIPMENT

Bohle, Unit 7 Fifth Avenue, Dukinfield, Cheshire, SK16 4PP Tel: 0161-342 1100 Fax: 0161-344 0111 E-mail: bohleuk@bohle.de

▶ mh design, 6 Willand Court, Retford, Retford, Nottinghamshire, DN22 7GD Tel: 01777 704967 Fax: 01777 719517 E-mail: sales@mhdesign.co.uk

▶ S R Burke Engineering Ltd, Derwent Way, Wath-upon-Dearne, Rotherham, South Yorkshire, S63 6EX Tel: (01709) 877888 Fax: (01709) 877888 E-mail: info@srburke.co.uk

Solaglas Ltd, Guild House, Cradley Road, Dudley, West Midlands, DY2 9TH Tel: (01384) 411511 Fax: (01384) 411234 E-mail: midlandsales@solaglass.co.uk

Alan E. Wheeler & Son, Unit 90, Condover Industrial Estate, Condover, Shrewsbury, SY5 7NH Tel: (01743) 718426 Fax: (01743) 718224 E-mail: sales@vacuumlifting.com

FLAT OR RIBBON CABLE ASSEMBLY CONNECTORS

Amphenol Ltd, Thanet Way, Whitstable, Kent, CT5 3JF Tel: (01227) 773200 Fax: (01227) 276571 E-mail: info@amphenol.co.uk

Clipper Components Ltd, 3 Ministry Wharf, Wycombe Road, Saunderton, High Wycombe, Buckinghamshire, HP14 4HW Tel: (01296) 432067 Fax: (01296) 487272 E-mail: ccompo6494@aol.com

Elco Europe, Exning Road, Newmarket, Suffolk, CB8 0AT Tel: (01638) 675000 Fax: (01638) 675001

Glenair UK Ltd, 40 Lower Oakham Way, Mansfield, Nottinghamshire, NG18 5BY Tel: (01623) 638100 Fax: (01623) 638111 E-mail: enquiries@glenair.co.uk

Imperial Components, 7 Sutherland Court, Brownfields, Welwyn Garden City, Hertfordshire, AL7 1BJ Tel: (01707) 321122 Fax: (01707) 321121

FLAT PACK FURNITURE

▶ Konteaki Furniture Importers, Unit C Aisecome Way, Weston-super-Mare, Avon, BS22 8NA Tel: (01934) 425050 Fax: (01934) 425050 E-mail: steve@hattrick-furniture.co.uk

▶ The Urban Decor Shop, PO Box 245, Barnstaple, Devon, EX32 9WZ Tel: (01271) 323634 E-mail: info@theurbandecorshop.com

FLAT RINGS, EQUESTRIAN, STAINLESS STEEL

▶ Discount Equestrian Ltd, 197/199 Barnsley Road, Wombwell, Barnsley, South Yorkshire, S73 8DR Tel: 01226 270555 E-mail: sales@discountequestrian.co.uk

FLAT ROOF FLASHING

▶ 1aaa Torquay Roofing, 43 Hoxton Road, Torquay, TQ1 1NY Tel: (01803) 290549 Fax: (01803) 290549 E-mail: sales@torquayroofing.co.uk

▶ Copper Ridges Systems Ltd, 154 Larne Road, Carrickfergus, County Antrim, BT38 7NL Tel: (028) 9335 1767 E-mail: info@copperridges.com

Elliott Bros Ltd, Millbank Wharf, Northam, Southampton, SO14 5AG Tel: (023) 8022 6852 Fax: (023) 8023 2041 E-mail: donnac@elliott-brothers.co.uk

FLAT ROOF WINDOWS

▶ 1aaa Torquay Roofing, 43 Hoxton Road, Torquay, TQ1 1NY Tel: (01803) 290549 Fax: (01803) 290549 E-mail: sales@torquayroofing.co.uk

Elliott Bros Ltd, Millbank Wharf, Northam, Southampton, SO14 5AG Tel: (023) 8022 6852 Fax: (023) 8023 2041 E-mail: donnac@elliott-brothers.co.uk

▶ Fletcher Roofing Ltd, 11 Ash Furlong Close, Balsall Common, Coventry, CV7 7QA Tel: (01676) 530373 E-mail: fletcher_roofing@yahoo.co.uk

▶ Pinnacle Services, 22 Carnoustie, Bolton, BL3 4TF Tel: (01204) 61043 E-mail: info@oneroof.co.uk

FLAT SCREEN MONITORS

▶ BF Interactive, 128 Frankwell, Shrewsbury, SY3 8JX Tel: (01743) 270444 Fax: (01743) 368381 E-mail: mitch@bfgroup.co.uk

FLAT SPRINGS

All Spring Ltd, C/O Multistroke Ltd, King Street, Old Hill, Cradley Heath, West Midlands, B64 6JJ Tel: (01384) 567773 Fax: (01304) 566589 E-mail: allspringltd@btconnect.com

Claridge Presswork Co. Ltd, 11 Bolton Road, Reading, RG2 0NH Tel: 0118-986 0114 Fax: 0118-931 3842 E-mail: sales@springsandwireforms.co.uk

F I S Loveday Ltd, 16-18 Princip Street, Birmingham, B4 6LE Tel: 0121-359 3176 Fax: 0121-359 1098 E-mail: fisloveday@aol.com

S D Precision, 3 Stevenage Enterprise Centre, Orchard Road, Stevenage, Hertfordshire, SG1 3HH Tel: (01438) 361587 Fax: (01438) 721217 E-mail: sales@sdprecision.co.uk

Springco (N I) Ltd, Tavanagh Factory, Armagh Road, Craigavon, County Armagh, BT62 3EG Tel: (028) 3833 3482 Fax: (028) 3833 8721 E-mail: sales@springco.co.uk

FLAT SURFACE GRINDING

Enterprise Grinding Ltd, 58 Sapcote Trading Centre, Powke Lane, Cradley Heath, West Midlands, B64 5QX Tel: (01384) 413598 Fax: (01384) 413599

FLAT SURFACE GRINDING MACHINES

Exe Engineering Co. Ltd, 64 Alphington Road, Exeter, EX2 8HX Tel: (01392) 275186 Fax: (01392) 260336 E-mail: sales@exeengineering.co.uk

Jones & Shipman Precision Ltd, Murrayfield Road, Braunstone Frith Industrial Estate, Leicester, LE3 1UW Tel: 0116-201 3000 Fax: 0116-201 3002 E-mail: sales@jonesshipman.com

Peter Walters (U K) Ltd, Brindley Road, Dodwells Bridge Industrial Estate, Hinckley, Leicestershire, LE10 3BY Tel: (01455) 631707 Fax: (01455) 611360 E-mail: pwuk@peter-wolters.com

FLAT TO PITCHED CONVERTING ROOFING SYSTEMS

▶ Rubbershield EPDM Flat Roofing Material Suppliers, 529 Leeds Road, Bradford, West Yorkshire, BD10 8PA Tel: 0845 838 5312 Fax: 01274 617045 E-mail: info@rubbershield.co.uk

FLAT WEBBING SLINGS

Damar Webbing Products Ltd, Unit 3 Cobnar Wood Close, Chesterfield, Derbyshire, S41 9RQ Tel: (01246) 269969 Fax: (01246) 269946 E-mail: sales@damarwebbingproducts.com

Trans-Web Ltd, Manchester Street, Oldham, OL9 6EF Tel: 0161 6270022

FLATS, BRASS

Metal Supermarkets, 1 Overland Trading Estate Gelderd Road, Gildersome, Morley, Leeds, LS27 7JN Tel: 0113-238 0900 Fax: 0113-238 0060 E-mail: headoffice@metalsupermarkets.com

FLAW DETECTION SERVICES

Bodycote Metallurgical Coatings Ltd, Harrison Way, Brunswick Business Park, Liverpool, L3 4BG Tel: 0151-709 8411 Fax: 0151-709 2622 E-mail: info@aerogistics.com

FLAX GOODS, MADE-UP, *See Canvas etc*

FLEET VEHICLE MANAGEMENT SPECIALISTS/CONSULTANTS

C F C Sollutions, 1310 Solihull Parkway, Birmingham Business Park, Birmingham, B37 7YB Tel: 0121-717 7040 Fax: 0121-717 7011 E-mail: enquiries@cfcsolutions.co.uk

C L M Fleet Management plc, Corporate House, Jenna Way, Interchange Park, Newport Pagnell, Buckinghamshire, MK16 9QB Tel: (01908) 210100 Fax: (01908) 210102 E-mail: clm@clm.co.uk

▶ John Grose Group Ltd, Beveridge Way, Hardwick Narrows, King's Lynn, Norfolk, PE30 4NB Tel: (01553) 770060 Fax: (01553) 778226

Inchcape Fleet Solutions, Haven House, Compass Road, Portsmouth, PO6 4RP Tel: (0870) 1914444 Fax: (0870) 1914455 E-mail: rental@ifs.inchcape.co.uk

▶ Intelligent Fleet Ltd, Eden House, 101A Marsland Road, Sale, Cheshire, M33 3HS Tel: (0870) 2856125 Fax: (0870) 2856126 E-mail: mail@intelligentfleet.co.uk

Lease Products Ltd, 165 Bath Road, Slough, SL1 4AA Tel: (01753) 802000 Fax: (01753) 791447 E-mail: marketing.lpgb@leaseplan.co.uk

M I S Fuel Monitoring Ltd, Horseley Works, Walsall Street, Wolverhampton, WV1 3LN Tel: (01902) 870037 Fax: (01902) 871661 E-mail: info@merridale.co.uk

Neva Consultants P.L.C., Neva House, Piltdown, Uckfield, East Sussex, TN22 3XL Tel: (0870) 4445725 Fax: (0870) 4445724 E-mail: sales@nevaplc.com

Pendragon Contracts Ltd, Sir Frank Whittle Road, Derby, DE21 4AZ Tel: (01332) 292777 Fax: (01332) 364270 E-mail: info@pendragon-contracts.co.uk

Preston Hall BMW, Concorde House, Concorde Way, Preston Farm Industrial Estate, Stockton-on-Tees, Cleveland, TS18 3RB Tel: (01642) 618618 Fax: (01642) 608613 E-mail: info@prestonhallbmw.co.uk

Transflo Instruments Ltd, Station Road, Staplehurst, Tonbridge, Kent, TN12 0QD Tel: (01580) 895000 Fax: (01580) 895050

FLEXI RIGID PRINTED CIRCUITS

Circuit Dynamics Ltd, 112 Beckenham Road, Beckenham, Kent, BR3 4RH Tel: (020) 8650 0723 Fax: (020) 8650 0921 E-mail: circuitdynamics@businessserve.co.uk

Flex Ability Ltd, Prospect Way, Park View West Industrial Estate, Hartlepool, Cleveland, TS25 1UD Tel: (01429) 860233 Fax: (01429) 869696 E-mail: sales@flex-ability.co.uk

Invotec Circuits Tamworth Ltd, 2-28 Hedging Lane, Wilnecote, Tamworth, Staffordshire, B77 5EP Tel: (01827) 263000 Fax: (01827) 263230 E-mail: firstname.surname@invertechgroup.com

FLEXI RIGID PRINTED CIRCUITS – *continued*

Samtec Europe Ltd, 117 Deerdykes View, Cumbernauld, Glasgow, G68 9HN Tel: (01236) 739292 Fax: (01236) 727113 E-mail: sales@samtec.com
Teknoflex Ltd, Quarry Lane Industrial Estate, Quarry Lane, Chichester, West Sussex, PO19 8PE Tel: (01243) 784516 Fax: (01243) 832832 E-mail: sales@teknoflex.com
Yeovil Circuits Ltd, 1 Armoury Road, Lufton Trading Estate, Lufton, Yeovil, Somerset, BA22 8RL Tel: (01935) 428313 Fax: (01935) 431446 E-mail: yeovil.circuits@eclipse.co.uk

FLEXIBLE ASSEMBLY HYDRAULIC HOSES

J P Miles, Sophurst Wood Lane, Matfield, Tonbridge, Kent, TN12 7LH Tel: (01892) 724315 Fax: (01892) 724319 E-mail: jpmiles@seedersti.co.uk
Moss Hydraulics, Mount Pleasant Farm, Icknield Street, Kings Norton, Birmingham, B38 0EH Tel: (01564) 822254 Fax: (01564) 822254 E-mail: robinmoss@blackgraves.freeserve.co.uk

FLEXIBLE BULK LIQUID CONTAINERS

S C A Industrial, Dodwells Road, Hinckley, Leicestershire, LE10 3BX Tel: (01455) 251400 Fax: (01455) 251404 E-mail: info.industrial@sca.com

FLEXIBLE BUSBARS

S M L, 3 Little Common, Stanmore, Middlesex, HA7 3BZ Tel: (020) 8954 7302 Fax: (020) 8954 1703 E-mail: punches@sml.co.uk

FLEXIBLE CABLE CONDUITS

Dyson Products, Moor St Industrial Estate, Moor Street, Brierley Hill, West Midlands, DY5 3ST Tel: (01384) 77833 Fax: (01384) 263724
T N Robinson Ltd, 5 Priestley Business Centre, Priestley Street, Warrington, WA5 1TF Tel: (01925) 650501 Fax: (01925) 418614 E-mail: sales@tnr.com
▶ Thomas & Betts Holdings UK, Wilford Road, Nottingham, NG2 1EB Tel: 0115-964 3837 Fax: 0115-986 0538 E-mail: martin.critchley@tnb.com

FLEXIBLE CABLE HIRE

FLD Pumps And Power, 2 Ness Road, Erith, Kent, DA8 2LD Tel: (01322) 350088 Fax: (01322) 350066 E-mail: erith@fldpumpspowerpowerent.co.uk

FLEXIBLE CABLES

A C A Cable Distributors, Unit 7 Coegnant Close, Brackla Industrial Estate, Bridgend, Mid Glamorgan, CF31 2AY Tel: (01656) 766060 Fax: (01656) 664123 E-mail: sales@acacables.co.uk
Autac Products Ltd, Bollin Cable Works, London Road, Macclesfield, Cheshire, SK11 7RN Tel: (01625) 619277 Fax: (01625) 619366 E-mail: info@autac.co.uk
C & M Corporation, Dunfermline, Fife, KY12 9YX Tel: (01383) 621225 Fax: (01383) 623455 E-mail: sales@cmcorporation.co.uk
Capital Cables, D 20 Frogmore Industrial Estate, Motherwell Way, Grays, Essex, RM20 3XD Tel: (01708) 864464 Fax: (01708) 865385
Central Cables, Unit 15 Brindley Business Park, Chaseside Drive, Hednesford, Cannock, Staffordshire, WS11 7GD Tel: (01543) 422477 Fax: (01543) 422420 E-mail: sales@centralcables.co.uk
Concordia Co. Ltd, Derwent Street, Long Eaton, Nottingham, NG10 3LP Tel: 0115-946 7400 Fax: 0115-946 1026
J D Cables Ltd, Park House, Greenhill Cresent, Watford, WD18 8PH Tel: (01923) 222600 Fax: (01923) 222608 E-mail: sales@jdcables.com
Mayflex Middle East Ltd, Excel House, Junction Six Industrial Park, Birmingham, B6 7JJ Tel: 0121-326 7557 Fax: (0800) 3892270 E-mail: sales@mayflex.com
S E I Interconnect Products Ltd, 10 Axis Court, Mallard Way, Riverside Business Park, Swansea, SA7 0AJ Tel: (01639) 822806 Fax: (01792) 794357 E-mail: nperkins@sumi-electric.com
▶ Sellec Special Cables Ltd, Dukeries Way, Worksop, Nottinghamshire, S81 7DW Tel: (01909) 483539 Fax: (01909) 500181 E-mail: sales@sellec.com
UK Cables Ltd, London Distribution Centre, Westlands Industrial Estate, Millington Road, Hayes, Middlesex, UB3 4AZ Tel: (020) 8561 9111 Fax: (020) 8561 6777
Wessel Energy Cables, Aghafad, Longford, County Longford, Tel: 0161-763 7474 Fax: 0161-763 7373 E-mail: abbcablesale.ie@abb.com

FLEXIBLE CABLES, CONTROL

Capro Europe, Building 54, Second Avenue, Pensnett Trading Estate, Kingswinford, West Midlands, DY6 7XJ Tel: (01384) 276300 Fax: (01384) 402010
Catton Control Cables Ltd, 33-35 Kings Road, Yardley, Birmingham, B25 8JB Tel: 0121-772 4297 Fax: 0121-766 6075 E-mail: nick@catton.co.uk
Crown Surveillance, 11 Huss's Lane, Long Eaton, Nottingham, NG10 1GS Tel: 0115-946 5422 Fax: 0115-946 5433 E-mail: info@crown-cctv.co.uk
Gills Cables, 25 Apollo, Lichfield Road Industrial Estate, Tamworth, Staffordshire, B79 7TA Tel: (01827) 304777 Fax: (01827) 314568 E-mail: kevinhatton@gillscables.com
T F X Automotive Ltd, St. Clements Road, Nechells, Birmingham, B7 5AE Tel: 0121-322 2500 Fax: 0121-322 2501
Tuthill Controls Group, Diplocks Way, Hailsham, East Sussex, BN27 3JS Tel: (01323) 841510 Fax: (01323) 845848
Venhill Engineering Ltd, 21 Ranmore Road, Dorking, Surrey, RH4 1HE Tel: (01306) 885111 Fax: (01306) 740535 E-mail: info@venhill.co.uk
Wicks & Martin Ltd, Bromyard Industrial Estate, Bromyard, Herefordshire, HR7 4HT Tel: (01885) 483636 Fax: (01885) 483692 E-mail: mike@wicksandmartin.co.uk

FLEXIBLE CONVEYOR SYSTEMS

Caljan Rite Hite Ltd, Moorbridge Road, Bingham, Nottingham, NG13 8GG Tel: (01949) 838850 Fax: (01949) 836953 E-mail: caljanritehite@caljanritehite.co.uk
Joy Mining Machinery Ltd, Meco Works, Bromyard Road, Worcester, WR2 5EG Tel: (01905) 422291 Fax: (0870) 2521888 E-mail: worcester@joy.co.uk
Owens Conveyor, Westgate House, Westgate, Aldridge, Walsall, WS9 8EX Tel: (01922) 452333 Fax: (01922) 458777 E-mail: msullivan@ocon.co.uk
Van Der Lande Industries, 59 Marsh Lane, Hampton-in-Arden, Solihull, West Midlands, B92 0AJ Tel: (01675) 443801 Fax: (01675) 443169 E-mail: roger.peart@vanderlande.co.uk

FLEXIBLE COUPLINGS

Bibby Tranmissions Ltd, Cannon Way, Dewsbury, West Yorkshire, WF13 1EH Tel: (01924) 460801 Fax: (01924) 457668 E-mail: sales@bibbytransmissions.co.uk
British Autogard Ltd, Siddington, Cirencester, Gloucestershire, GL7 6EU Tel: (01285) 640333 Fax: (01285) 659476 E-mail: sales@autogard.co.uk
Derbyshire Hose & Fittings Ltd, Calow Lane, Hasland, Chesterfield, Derbyshire, S41 0AL Tel: (01246) 477707 Fax: (01246) 222251 E-mail: dhfhyds@aol.com
Francis and Francis Ltd (Schmidt, Poggi & KBK), The Stables Works, Station Road, Kenley, Surrey, CR8 5JA Tel: (020) 8668 9792 Fax: (020) 8668 9793 E-mail: sales@powertransmissions.co.uk
K T R Couplings Ltd, Robert House Unit 7, Acorn Business Park, Woodseats Close, Sheffield, S8 0TB Tel: 0114-258 7757 Fax: 0114-258 7740 E-mail: ktr-uk@ktr.com
Leyden Transmissions Ltd, Roberttown Lane, Liversedge, West Yorkshire, WF15 7LQ Tel: (01924) 402820 Fax: (01924) 411350 E-mail: info@leyden-ptc.co.uk
Naylor Concrete Products Ltd, Clough Green, Cawthorne, Barnsley, South Yorkshire, S75 4AD Tel: (01226) 790591 Fax: (01226) 790531 E-mail: info@naylor.co.uk
Renold High Tech Couplings, 112 Parkinson Lane, Halifax, West Yorkshire, HX1 3QH Tel: (01422) 255000 Fax: (01422) 320273 E-mail: sales@hitec.renold.com
▶ S S White Technologies UK Ltd, 19 Heathfield, Stacey Bushes, Milton Keynes, MK12 6HP Tel: (01908) 525124 Fax: (01908) 319967 E-mail: insales@sswhite.co.uk
Vulkan Industries Ltd, Archer Road, Armytage Road Industrial Estate, Brighouse, West Yorkshire, HD6 1XF Tel: (01484) 712273 Fax: (01484) 721376 E-mail: sales@vulkan.co.uk

FLEXIBLE DRIVES

Dematic Ltd, Sir William Siemens House, Princess Road, Manchester, M20 2UR Tel: 0161-446 5292 Fax: 0161-446 5214 E-mail: sfmpost@plcman.siemens.co.uk

FLEXIBLE DUCTING

C C L Veloduct Ltd, 10 Redburn Industrial Estate, Woodall Road, Enfield, Middlesex, EN3 4LE Tel: (020) 8805 3656 Fax: (020) 8805 0558 E-mail: sales@cclveloduct.co.uk
CCL Veloduct, 1-3 Dean Road, Lincoln, LN2 4DR Tel: (01522) 567087 Fax: (01522) 563525
Circuit Hydraulics Ltd, Unit 16 Kensington Industrial Park, Kensington Road, Southport, Merseyside, PR9 0RY Tel: (01704) 546288 Fax: (01704) 546313 E-mail: circuit.hyd@btinternet.com
James Dawson & Son Ltd, Tritton Road, Lincoln, LN6 7AF Tel: (01522) 531821 Fax: (01522) 510029 E-mail: sales@james-dawson.co.uk
Duct Products, 2 Greenway, Conlig, Newtownards, County Down, BT23 7SU Tel: (028) 9147 1121 Fax: (028) 9147 9252 E-mail: postbox@ductproducts.com
Dy-rect Services Ltd, Unit 8 Hikers Way, Crendon Industrial Park, Long Crendon, Aylesbury, Buckinghamshire, HP18 9RW Tel: (01844) 202233 Fax: (01844) 208748 E-mail: info@dy-rect.co.uk
Ernest Morrison & Co., Unit 13 Loughside Industrial Estate, Dargan CR, Belfast, BT3 9JP Tel: (028) 9077 7093 Fax: (028) 9077 6299
Flexible Ducting Ltd, Cloberfield Industrial Estate, Milngavie, Glasgow, G62 7LW Tel: 0141-956 4551 Fax: 0141-956 4847 E-mail: sales@flexibleducting.co.uk
Flexible Hose Supplies Ltd, 12 Osyth Close, Brackmills Industrial Estate, Northampton, NN4 7DY Tel: (01604) 762175 Fax: (01604) 769915 E-mail: sales@fhsn.co.uk
Interlock Flexible Products Ltd, 1 Burbidge Road, Birmingham, B9 4US Tel: 0121-766 7766 Fax: 0121-766 7799 E-mail: sales@interlockflex.com
Masterflex Technical Hoses Ltd, Unit G & H Prince Of Wales, Vulcan St, Oldham, OL1 4ER Tel: 0161 6268066
Oakbray Ltd, Whieldon Industrial Estate, Whieldon Road, Stoke-on-Trent, ST4 4JP Tel: (01782) 744555 Fax: (01782) 414244 E-mail: sales@oakbray.co.uk
P & J Dust Extraction Ltd, Otterham Quay, Gillingham, Kent, ME8 8NA Tel: 01634 233933

FLEXIBLE DUCTING FABRICATING MACHINE

Interlock Flexible Products Ltd, 1 Burbidge Road, Birmingham, B9 4US Tel: 0121-766 7766 Fax: 0121-766 7799 E-mail: sales@interlockflex.com

FLEXIBLE ELECTRICAL CONNECTORS

Head Braiding Ltd, Armstrong Works, Raynham Rd, Bishop's Stortford, Herts, CM23 5PB Tel: (01279) 658271 Fax: (01279) 503566
P T M UK Ltd, Haigh Avenue, Stockport, Cheshire, SK4 1NZ Tel: 0161-477 6486 Fax: 0161-480 4624 E-mail: sales@ptmuk.co.uk
Process Link Ltd, Tilemans Lane, Shipston-on-Stour, Warwickshire, CV36 4QZ Tel: (01608) 662878 Fax: (01608) 662968 E-mail: info@processlink.co.uk

FLEXIBLE FAN COIL CONNECTORS

Biddle Air Curtains Ltd, St Mary's Road, Nuneaton, Warwickshire, CV11 5AU Tel: (024) 7638 4233 Fax: (024) 7637 3621 E-mail: info@biddle-air.co.uk

FLEXIBLE (FPC) PRINTED CIRCUITS

Circuit Dynamics Ltd, 112 Beckenham Road, Beckenham, Kent, BR3 4RH Tel: (020) 8650 0723 Fax: (020) 8650 0921 E-mail: cirtcuitdynamics@businessserve.co.uk
Image Management Technology, 16 The Oakwood Centre, Downley Road, Havant, Hampshire, PO9 2NP Tel: (023) 9245 6564 Fax: (023) 9236 7050 E-mail: wcteurope@worldcircuit.com
Printech Circuit Laboratories Ltd, 31-35 Haltwhistle Road, South Woodham Ferrers, Chelmsford, CM3 5ZA Tel: (01245) 323244 Fax: (01245) 329472 E-mail: sales@pcll.co.uk
Stevenage Circuits Ltd, Caxton Way, Stevenage, Hertfordshire, SG1 2DF Tel: (01438) 751800 Fax: (01438) 728103 E-mail: sales@stevenagecircuits.co.uk
Tru-Lon Printed Circuits (Royston) Ltd, Newark Close, York Way Industrial Estate, Royston, Hertfordshire, SG8 5HL Tel: (01763) 248922 Fax: (01763) 249281 E-mail: info@tru-lon.co.uk

FLEXIBLE FUEL CELLS

F P T Industries Ltd, Airport Service Road, Portsmouth, PO3 5PE Tel: (023) 9266 2391 Fax: (023) 9267 0899 E-mail: info@fptind.co.uk

FLEXIBLE FUEL TANKS

▶ Dunlop G R G Holdings Ltd, Unit 62, Touchet Hall Road, Stakehill Industrial Estate, Middleton, Manchester, M24 2RW Tel: 0161-653 5964 Fax: 0161-643 0184 E-mail: sales@dunlopgrg.co.uk

FLEXIBLE INDUSTRIAL DOORS

▶ A S R Shutters, 2 Woodseats Road, Woodseats, Sheffield, S8 0PJ Tel: (0800) 9230016
Central Doors, 3 Arleston Drive, Nottingham, NG8 2FR Tel: 0115-913 0071 Fax: 0115-928 2814
Doorco Ltd, Phoenix Works, Whitefield Road, Bredbury, Stockport, Cheshire, SK6 2QR Tel: 0161-406 8660 Fax: 0161-406 8433 E-mail: info@doorco.co.uk
The Garage Door Centre, 6-8 Meadow Close, Wellingborough, Northamptonshire, NN8 4BH Tel: (01933) 229135 Fax: (01933) 442676

FLEXIBLE INTERMEDIATE BULK CONTAINER (FIBC) FILLING AND EMPTYING MACHINES

Entecon UK Ltd, Stanhope Road, Yorktown Industrial Estate, Camberley, Surrey, GU15 3BW Tel: (01276) 414540 Fax: (01276) 414544 E-mail: enquiries@entecon.co.uk
Humber Europe Ltd, Shorten Brook Drive, Altham Business Park, Altham, Accrington, Lancashire, BB5 5YH Tel: (01282) 770333 Fax: (01282) 776888 E-mail: info@humberbigbag.com
Matcon Group Ltd, Matcon House, London Road, Moreton-in-Marsh, Gloucestershire, GL56 0HJ Tel: (01608) 651666 Fax: (01608) 651635 E-mail: matcon@matcon.co.uk

FLEXIBLE INTERMEDIATE BULK CONTAINERS (FIBC)

Ady, Antrim Road, Warrington, WA2 8JT Tel: (01925) 419933 Fax: (01925) 419944 E-mail: sales@bulkbags.co.uk
Bulkbag Ltd, Block 20, Kilspindie Road, Dunsinane Industrial Estate, Dundee, DD2 3QH Tel: (01382) 833111 Fax: (01382) 832272 E-mail: sales@bulkbuy.co.uk
Humber Europe Ltd, Shorten Brook Drive, Altham Business Park, Altham, Accrington, Lancashire, BB5 5YH Tel: (01282) 770333 Fax: (01282) 776888 E-mail: info@humberbigbag.com
J M J Bulk Packaging Ltd, Earlstrees Road, Earlstrees Industrial Estate, Corby, Northamptonshire, NN17 4AZ Tel: (01536) 274400 Fax: (01536) 261180 E-mail: sales@packaging.uk.com
John Lee Sacks Ltd, Old Wharf Road, Grantham, Lincolnshire, NG31 7AA Tel: (01476) 565501 Fax: (01476) 590580 E-mail:
Liverpool Bulk Bags, 35a Seaforth Vale North, Liverpool, L21 3TR Tel: 0151-920 2280 Fax: 0151-922 4076 E-mail: info@bulkbagsuk.com
M I P Ltd, Park Lane, Halesowen, West Midlands, B63 2RE Tel: (01384) 637711 Fax: (01384) 410104
Mason & Jones Packaging, Unit 7, Aston Road, Aston Fields Industrial Estate, Bromsgrove, Worcestershire, B60 3EX Tel: (01527) 577123 Fax: (01527) 577248 E-mail: sales@masonandjones.com
Mulox Ltd, 2 High Carr Network Centre, Millennium Way, High Carr Business Park, Newcastle, Staffordshire, ST5 7XE Tel: (01782) 565659 Fax: (01782) 565252 E-mail: andrew.reardon@mulox.co.uk
Structure-Flex Ltd, Peacock Way, Melton Constable, Norfolk, NR24 2AZ Tel: (01263) 863100 Fax: (01263) 863120 E-mail: enquiries@structure-flex.co.uk
▶ Tyler Packaging Ltd, Fosse Way, Chesterton, Leamington Spa, Warwickshire, CV33 9JY Tel: (01926) 651451 Fax: (01926) 651691 E-mail: info@tylerpackaging.co.uk
Warwick Container Systems (UK) ltd, Stoneleigh Visual Centre, Queensway, Leamington Spa, Warwickshire, CV31 3JT Tel: (01926) 314120 Fax: (01926) 885719 E-mail: post@warwickcontainer.demon.co.uk
Wessex Rope & Packaging, 6 20 Abingdon Road, Nuffield Industrial Estate, Poole, Dorset, BH17 0UG Tel: (01202) 661066 Fax: (01202) 661077 E-mail: sales@wrp-poole.co.uk

FLEXIBLE LAMINATED PLASTIC

Chamberlain Plastics Ltd, Bury Close, Higham Ferrers, Rushden, Northamptonshire, NN10 8HQ Tel: (01933) 353875 Fax: (01933) 410206 E-mail: sales@chamberlain-plastics.co.uk
G T S Flexible Materials Ltd, G T S House, 3 Wellington Business Park, Dukes Ride, Crowthorne, Berkshire, RG45 6LS Tel: (01344) 762376 Fax: (01344) 761615 E-mail: mail@gts-flexible.co.uk

FLEXIBLE LAMINATED PLASTIC – *continued*

Isola Werke UK Ltd, 2 Dunlop Square, Deans, Livingston, West Lothian, EH54 8SB Tel: (01506) 412812 Fax: (01506) 410571

FLEXIBLE MANUFACTURING SYSTEMS

Heller Machine Tools, Acanthus Road, Ravensbank Business Park, Redditch, Worcestershire, B98 9EX Tel: 0121-275 3300 Fax: 0121-275 3340 E-mail: sales@heller.co.uk

Manufacturing Technology Partnership Ltd, 1b Millennium Way, Belfast, BT12 7AL Tel: (028) 9027 9860 Fax: (028) 9027 9869 E-mail: sales@mtpltd.com

FLEXIBLE MANUFACTURING SYSTEMS DESIGN/ INSTALLATION ENGINEERS, CENTRAL COMPUTER ROBOT CONTROL

Concept Technical Services Ltd, Unit 8, Peartree Industrial Park, Dudley, West Midlands, DY2 0UW Tel: (01384) 241600 Fax: (01384) 243657

FLEXIBLE METALLIC HOSES OR TUBING

Aflex Hose Ltd, Spring Bank Industrial Estate, Watson Mill Lane, Sowerby Bridge, West Yorkshire, HX6 3BW Tel: (01422) 317200 Fax: (01422) 836000 E-mail: sales@aflex-hose.co.uk

Amnitec Ltd, Abercanaid, Merthyr Tydfil, Mid Glamorgan, CF48 1UX Tel: (01685) 385641 Fax: (01685) 389683 E-mail: sales@amnitec.co.uk

Arnold Hose Ltd, 2 Rothersthorpe Avenue, Rothersthorpe Avenue Industrial Estate, Northampton, NN4 8JH Tel: (01604) 706570 Fax: (01604) 661170 E-mail: ahl@arnoldhose.demon.co.uk

▶ Bowbros Ltd, Newby Road Industrial Estate, Newby Road, Hazel Grove, Stockport, Cheshire, SK7 5DD Tel: (01656) 661224 Fax: (01656) 660009

Ferschl Hose & Hydraulics Ltd, Dukesway, Team Valley Trading Estate, Gateshead, Tyne & Wear, NE11 0PZ Tel: 0191-482 2511 Fax: 0191-491 0604 E-mail: info@jferschl.co.uk

Filton Ltd, Caswell Rd, Sydenham Industrial Estate, Leamington Spa, Warwickshire, CV31 1QF Tel: (01926) 423191 Fax: (01926) 450610 E-mail: sales@filtonltd.co.uk

Flexible Hose Supplies Ltd, 12 Osyth Close, Brackmills Industrial Estate, Northampton, NN4 7DY Tel: (01604) 762175 Fax: (01604) 769915 E-mail: sales@fhsn.co.uk

Hose Tech Ltd, 3 Wheatlea Industrial Estate, Wheatlea Road, Wigan, Lancashire, WN3 6XP Tel: (01942) 233036 Fax: (01942) 322915 E-mail: sales@hose-tech.co.uk

Metalflex Industrial Supplies Ltd, Unit 9 Adlington Court, Birchwood, Warrington, WA3 6PL Tel: (01925) 814999 Fax: (01925) 838999 E-mail: john.milsom@metalflex.co.uk

Test Valley Engineers Ltd, Stoneymarsh, Michelmersh, Romsey, Hampshire, SO51 0LB Tel: (01794) 368308 Fax: (01794) 368693 E-mail: sales@test-valley.co.uk

Venhill Engineering Ltd, 21 Ranmore Road, Dorking, Surrey, RH4 1HE Tel: (01306) 885111 Fax: (01306) 740535 E-mail: info@venhill.co.uk

Witzenmann UK Ltd, Righead Industrial Estate, Bellshill, Lanarkshire, ML4 3LW Tel: (01698) 749660 Fax: (01698) 740774

FLEXIBLE MIRROR GLASS

Opals (Mirror-Flex) Co. Ltd, Unit 3 B Seaden Court, Steveson Road, Gorse Lane Industrial Estate, Clacton-On-Sea, Essex, CO15 4XN Tel: (01255) 423927 Fax: (01255) 221117 E-mail: sales@mirrorflex.co.uk

FLEXIBLE MOTOR VEHICLE EXHAUST COUPLINGS

Senior Automotive Products Division, 1 Oakwood Close, Pen-Y-Fan Industrial Estate, Crumlin, Newport, Gwent, NP11 3HY Tel: (01495) 241500 Fax: (01495) 241501

Unipart Eberspacher Exhaust Systems, Durbar Avenue, Coventry, CV6 5LZ Tel: (024) 7663 8663 Fax: (024) 7666 1084 E-mail: enquiries@unipart.co.uk

FLEXIBLE PACKAGING LAMINATING SERVICES

Ferrisgate Coating Ltd, Ferrisgate House, Burrell Way, Thetford, Norfolk, IP24 3RA Tel: (01842) 766308 Fax: (01842) 754438 E-mail: ferriscoatings@aol.com

Mipa (UK) Ltd, 25 Robin Ride, Brackley, Northamptonshire, NN13 6PU Tel: (01280) 841190 Fax: (01280) 841191 E-mail: mipauk@aol.com

FLEXIBLE PAPER TUBES

Caraustar Industrial & Consumer Products Group Ltd, 86 Bison Place, Moss Side, Leyland, PR26 7QR Tel: (01772) 621562 Fax: (01772) 622263 E-mail: david.dredge@caraustar.com

FLEXIBLE PIPELINE FITTINGS

Pipeline Centre, 2 Hartburn Close, Crow Lane Industrial Estate, Northampton, NN3 9UE Tel: (01604) 410888 Fax: (01604) 410777 E-mail: bv.northhampton@wolsley.co.uk

FLEXIBLE POLYURETHANE (PU) FOAM

B I Composites Ltd, Green Lane, Cannock, Staffordshire, WS11 0JW Tel: (01543) 466021 Fax: (01543) 574157 E-mail: firstname.lastname@bi-composites.co.uk

Borderfoam Ltd, Lingen Road, Ludlow Business Park, Ludlow, Shropshire, SY8 1XD Tel: (01584) 877107 Fax: (01584) 874073

Kay Metzeler Ltd, Wellington Road, Bollington, Macclesfield, Cheshire, SK10 5JJ Tel: (01625) 573366 Fax: (01625) 574075 E-mail: info@kay-metzeler.co.uk

Martin's Rubber Co. Ltd, Orchard Place, Southampton, SO14 3PE Tel: (023) 8022 6330 Fax: (023) 8063 1577 E-mail: sales@martins-rubber.co.uk

Vita Cortex Ni Ltd, Dunmurry Industrial Estate, Dunmurry, Belfast, BT17 9HU Tel: (028) 9061 8625 Fax: (028) 9061 9479 E-mail: info@vitacortex.com

FLEXIBLE PRINTED CIRCUIT (FPC) BOARD (PCB) LASER CUTTING SERVICES

▶ Flexible Technology, 23 Wolverstone Drive, Brighton, BN1 7FB Tel: (01273) 566922 Fax: (01273) 566922 E-mail: kb-ftl@netpointproject.net

FLEXIBLE PVC WINDOWS

Crown Windows Hull Ltd, New Cleveland Street, Hull, HU8 7HA Tel: (01482) 329043 Fax: (01482) 39043

FLEXIBLE SCREW CONVEYOR SYSTEMS

Collinson Ernest & Co. Ltd, Riverside Industrial Park, Tan Yard Road, Catterall, Preston, PR3 0HP Tel: (01995) 606451 Fax: (01995) 605503 E-mail: agri.sales@collinson.co.uk

FLEXIBLE SHAFT DRIVE EQUIPMENT OR MACHINES

Finishing Aids & Tools, Unit 25 Woolfold Industrial Estate, Mitchell Street, Bury, Lancashire, BL8 1SF Tel: 0161-705 1300 Fax: 0161-763 1959

Flextol Ltd, 20 Swannington Road, Cottage Lane Industrial Estate, Broughton Astley, Leicester, LE9 6TU Tel: (01455) 285333 Fax: (01455) 285238 E-mail: sales@flextol.co.uk

▶ S S White Technologies UK Ltd, 19 Heathfield, Stacey Bushes, Milton Keynes, MK12 6HP Tel: (01908) 525124 Fax: (01908) 319967 E-mail: insales@sswhite.co.uk

FLEXIBLE SHAFTING

Rotatools UK Ltd, Brookfield Drive, Liverpool, L9 7EG Tel: 0151-525 8611 Fax: 0151-525 4868 E-mail: richard_dearn@hotmail.com

▶ S S White Technologies UK Ltd, 19 Heathfield, Stacey Bushes, Milton Keynes, MK12 6HP Tel: (01908) 525124 Fax: (01908) 319967 E-mail: insales@sswhite.co.uk

FLEXIBLE STRANDED COPPER WIRE

▶ Pirelli Cables Ltd, Carr Lane, Prescot, Merseyside, L34 1PD Tel: 0151-430 4300 Fax: 0151-430 4390 E-mail: neil.bootman@pirelli.com

FLEXIBLE STRIP DOOR CURTAINS

G B R Industries Ltd, Galebreaker House, New Mills Industrial Estate, Ledbury, Herefordshire, HR8 2SS Tel: (01531) 637900 Fax: (01531) 637901 E-mail: jps@galebreaker.co.uk

Mainline Screens, 19 Medway Drive, Chandler's Ford, Eastleigh, Hampshire, SO53 4SR Tel: (023) 8026 7846 Fax: (023) 8026 7869 E-mail: info@mainlinescreens.co.uk

FLEXIBLE TANKS

▶ Dunlop G R G Holdings Ltd, Unit 62, Touchet, Hall Road, Stakehill Industrial Estate, Middleton, Manchester, M24 2RW Tel: 0161-653 5964 Fax: 0161-643 0184 E-mail: sales@dunlopgrg.co.uk

Hovercraft Consultants, Unit 43 South Hampshire Industrial Park, Totton, Southampton, SO40 3SA Tel: (023) 8087 1188 Fax: (023) 8087 1799 E-mail: enquiries@duratank.com

Structure-Flex Ltd, Peacock Way, Melton Constable, Norfolk, NR24 2AZ Tel: (01263) 863100 Fax: (01263) 863120 E-mail: enquiries@structure-flex.co.uk

FLEXIBLE TUBING OR HOSE OR CONDUIT OVERBRAIDING SERVICES

Head Braiding Ltd, Armstrong Works, Raynham Rd, Bishop's Stortford, Herts, CM23 5PB Tel: (01279) 658271 Fax: (01279) 503566

FLEXIBLE TUBING OR HOSE OR CONDUITS

Adaptaflex Ltd, Station Road Industrial Estate, Station Road, Coleshill, Birmingham, B46 1HT Tel: (01675) 468200 Fax: (01675) 462090 E-mail: sales@adaptaflex.co.uk

Arnold Hose Ltd, 2 Rothersthorpe Avenue, Rothersthorpe Avenue Industrial Estate, Northampton, NN4 8JH Tel: (01604) 706570 Fax: (01604) 661170 E-mail: ahl@arnoldhose.demon.co.uk

▶ Bowbros Ltd, Newby Road Industrial Estate, Newby Road, Hazel Grove, Stockport, Cheshire, SK7 5DD Tel: (01656) 661224 Fax: (01656) 660009

Bowden Bros & Co. (Manchester) Ltd, Newby Road Industrial Estate, Hazel Grove, Stockport, Cheshire, SK7 5DD Tel: 0161-483 9311 Fax: 0161-483 1080 E-mail: sales@bowbros.co.uk

Britannia Enterprises Ltd, Unit 14 Canal Industrial Park, Canal Road, Gravesend, Kent, DA12 2PA Tel: (01474) 328051 Fax: (01474) 320564

Cougar Flex, 59 Rixon Road, Wellingborough, Northamptonshire, NN8 4BA Tel: (01933) 223354 Fax: (01933) 224522 E-mail: salescougarflex@btconnect.com

Designation Ltd, Newark Road, Peterborough, PE1 5YD Tel: (01733) 893333 Fax: (01733) 314889 E-mail: sales@desihose.com

F T L Co. Ltd, Howley Park Road, Morley, Leeds, LS27 0QS Tel: 0113-253 0331 Fax: 0113-289 7748

Fans & Spares Ltd, 72 Cheston Road, Aston, Birmingham, B7 5EE Tel: 0121-322 0200 Fax: 0121-322 0201 E-mail: hq@fansandspares.co.uk

Flexbore, Pontygwindy Industrial Estate, Caerphilly, Mid Glamorgan, CF83 3HU Tel: (029) 2088 3552 Fax: (029) 2086 6410

Harnessflex Ltd, PO Box 7690, Birmingham, B46 1HT Tel: (01675) 468200 Fax: (01675) 464930 E-mail: sales@harnessflex.co.uk

Hopespare Ltd, Units 2, East Burrowfields, Welwyn Garden City, Hertfordshire, AL7 4TB Tel: (01707) 321212 Fax: (01707) 371717 E-mail: darrene@hopespare.com

Hydraulic Equipment Supply Co. Ltd, 419 New Kings Road, London, SW6 4RN Tel: (020) 7736 7391 Fax: (020) 7736 7019

King Industrial Products Ltd, Unit 12, Techno Trading Estate, Brambell Road, Swindon, SN2 8HB Tel: (01793) 491606 Fax: (01793) 530461 E-mail: sales@kingindustrial.co.uk

Masterflex Technical Hoses Ltd, Unit G & H Prince Of Wales, Vulcan St, Oldham, OL1 4ER Tel: 0161 6268066

P C Hydraulics (Northern) Ltd, 6-8 Hillkirk Street, Beswick, Manchester, M11 3EZ Tel: 0161-273 1660 Fax: 0161-273 5002 E-mail: enquiries@pc-hydraulics.co.uk

Parkland Engineering Ltd, 72 Dykehead Street, Glasgow, G33 4AQ Tel: 0141-774 6200 Fax: 0141-774 0034 E-mail: glasgowsales@parkland-eng.co.uk

Plastiflex UK Ltd, Ripley Close, Normanton Industrial Estate, Normanton, West Yorkshire, WF6 1TB Tel: (01924) 783600 Fax: (01924) 896715 E-mail: info@plastiflex.co.uk

Plymouth Rubber Hose & Hydraulics, Drill Hall, Rocky Hill, Tavistock, Devon, PL19 0DZ Tel: (01822) 616061 Fax: (01822) 617755 E-mail: sales@hoseandhydraulicsgroup.co.uk

Swagelock London, Unit 11, Kingley Park, Station Road, Kings Langley, Hertfordshire, WD4 8GW Tel: (020) 8200 1677 Fax: (020) 8200 9819 E-mail: info@london.swagelock.com

Witzenmann UK Ltd, Righead Industrial Estate, Bellshill, Lanarkshire, ML4 3LW Tel: (01698) 749660 Fax: (01698) 740774

FLEXIBLE TUBING/HOSE/ CONDUIT ASSEMBLIES, AUTOMOTIVE

▶ T I Group Automotive Systems UK Ltd, Halesfield 9, Telford, Shropshire, TF7 4ET Tel: (01952) 651000 Fax: (01952) 651166 E-mail: mdebono@uk.tiauto.com

FLEXIBLE TUBING/HOSE/ CONDUIT, VACUUM CLEANER

Dyson Ltd, Tetbury Hill, Malmesbury, Wiltshire, SN16 0RP Tel: (01666) 827200 Fax: (01666) 827299 E-mail: james.ross-smith@dyson.com

FLEXIBLE WEB GUILLOTINES

Dixon, Unit C, 3 Fen End, Astwick Road, Stotfold, Hitchin, Hertfordshire, SG5 4BA Tel: (01462) 834911 Fax: (01462) 834911 E-mail: sales@dixontechnologies.com

FLEXIBLE WORKING HOUR TIME RECORDERS

Aberdeen Time Recorder Co., 66 Morningside Road, Aberdeen, AB10 7NT Tel: (01224) 322400 Fax: (01224) 322400 E-mail: sales@aberdeentimerecorder.co.uk

Anglia Time Recorders Ltd, 3 Cox Close, Kesgrave, Ipswich, IP5 2DW Tel: (01353) 778518 Fax: (01487) 823862 E-mail: sales@angliatime.co.uk

Autoclock Systems Ltd, 93-97 Second Avenue, Newcastle upon Tyne, NE6 5XT Tel: 0191-276 1611 Fax: 0191-265 0586 E-mail: sales@autoclocksystems.co.uk

Cotswold Recording Systems, 12 Rodbourne Road, Swindon, SN2 2AG Tel: (01793) 618874 Fax: (01793) 511874 E-mail: rodger@clockingmachine.co.uk

Custom Micro Products Ltd, 450 Blandford Road, Poole, Dorset, BH16 5BN Tel: (01202) 631733 Fax: (01202) 632036 E-mail: sales@custom-micro.com

H F X Ltd, The Clock House, Green Street, Elsenham, Bishop's Stortford, Hertfordshire, CM22 6DS Tel: (01279) 647474 Fax: (01279) 647700 E-mail: info@hfx.co.uk

Ontime Systems Ltd, Unit 3 Bessemer Crescent, Aylesbury, Buckinghamshire, HP19 8TF Tel: 0800 975 0960 Fax: (01296) 395787 E-mail: ontime-sales@btconnect.com

FLEXOGRAPHIC LABEL PRINTING MACHINES

Wood Machines Ltd, 1 Galley Hill Industrial Estate, London Road, Swanscombe, Kent, DA10 0AA Tel: (01322) 385566 Fax: (01322) 384449 E-mail: mail@uemcoltd.com

FLEXOGRAPHIC PAPER PRINTING

Hovat, Westmead, New Hythe Lane, Larkfield, Aylesford, Kent, ME20 6XJ Tel: (01622) 791193 Fax: (01622) 791192 E-mail: executive.hovat@btinternet.com

Roberts,Mart & Co.Limited, Aire Valley House, Thornes Farm Way, Leeds, LS9 0AN Tel: 0113-202 6500 Fax: 0113-202 6550 E-mail: info@roberts-mart.co.uk

FLEXOGRAPHIC PRINTING, *See also Specific Services*

Clifton Packaging Group P.L.C., Maridian Business Park, Centurion Way, Leicester, LE19 1WH Tel: 0116-289 3355 Fax: 0116-289 1113 E-mail: info@cliftonpackaging.co.uk

V.C. Crow & Co. Ltd, Unit F, Halesfield 19, Telford, Shropshire, TF7 4QT Tel: (01952) 686888 Fax: (01952) 686889 E-mail: info@cropac.co.uk

D S Smith, Mareham Road, Horncastle, Lincolnshire, LN9 6NG Tel: (01507) 523434 Fax: (01507) 523431

FLEXOGRAPHIC PRINTING – *continued*

▶ Europrint Games Ltd, Unit 9-10 Laneside Metcalf Drive, Altham Industrial Estate, Accrington, Lancashire, BB5 5TU Tel: (01282) 774333 Fax: (01282) 688701

J.M. Heaford Ltd, Unit 9 Century Park, Pacific Road, Altrincham, Cheshire, WA14 5BJ Tel: 0161-928 5679 Fax: 0161-927 7517 E-mail: sales@jmheaford.co.uk

▶ John White Printers Ltd, Station Road, Alford, Lincolnshire, LN13 9JA Tel: (01507) 466892 Fax: (01507) 463374

Killyleagh Box Co. Ltd, 39 Shrigley Road, Killyleagh, Downpatrick, County Down, BT30 9SR Tel: (028) 4482 8708 Fax: (028) 4482 1222 E-mail: sales@killyleaghbox.co.uk

FLEXOGRAPHIC PRINTING EQUIPMENT MANUFRS

Chiltern Colour Services, Unit 23 Titan Court, Laporte Way, Luton, LU4 8EF Tel: (01525) 385184 Fax: (01582) 482888

Cooper Printing Machinery Ltd, 42 Coldharbour Lane, Harpenden, Hertfordshire, AL5 4UN Tel: (01582) 764431 Fax: (01582) 768608 E-mail: sales@cooperprint.co.uk

Croft Printing, Label House, Wilford Road, Ruddington, Nottingham, NG11 6ES Tel: 0115-945 6065 Fax: 0115-945 6067 E-mail: info@croftprinting.co.uk

Ident Machines Ltd, Stapleton Lane, Barwell, Leicester, LE9 8HE Tel: (01455) 840056 Fax: (01455) 848070 E-mail: ident.machines@talk21.com

K2 International Trading Ltd, The Kdo Business Park, Little Witley, Little Witley, Worcester, WR6 6LR Tel: (01299) 896959 Fax: (01299) 896965 E-mail: info@kdo.co.uk

Litho Supplies Scotland Ltd, 8 Elphinstone Square, Deans Industrial Estate, Deans, Livingston, West Lothian, EH54 8RG Tel: (01506) 462555 Fax: (01506) 465678 E-mail: scotland@litho.co.uk

Plastotype Ltd, Crustable Close, Mushep Industrial Park, Coleford, Gloucestershire, GL16 8RE Tel: (01594) 837474 Fax: (01594) 837312 E-mail: info@plastotype.com

FLEXOGRAPHIC PRINTING INKS

Intercolor Ltd, 795 London Road, Grays, Essex, RM20 3LH Tel: (01708) 899091 Fax: (01708) 899092 E-mail: sales@intercolor-ink.com

Luminescence Incorporated, The Fairway, Bush Fair, Harlow, Essex, CM18 6NG Tel: (01279) 453711 Fax: (01279) 421142 E-mail: sales@luminescence.co.uk

FLEXOGRAPHIC PRINTING PLATE DESIGN

Acorn Graphics, Mercia Way, Foxhills Industrial Estate, Scunthorpe, South Humberside, DN15 8RE Tel: (01724) 280368 Fax: (01724) 271988 E-mail: sales@acorn-graphics.co.uk

▶ Swift Inline, 123 Walkern Road, Stevenage, Hertfordshire, SG1 3RE Tel: (01438) 244721 Fax: (01438) 244698 E-mail: scott@swiftinline.co.uk

FLEXOGRAPHIC PRINTING PLATE ENGRAVERS/MANUFRS

Acorn Graphics, Mercia Way, Foxhills Industrial Estate, Scunthorpe, South Humberside, DN15 8RE Tel: (01724) 280368 Fax: (01724) 271988 E-mail: sales@acorn-graphics.co.uk

Pamarco Europe Ltd, New Cut Lane, Woolston, Warrington, WA1 4AQ Tel: (01925) 456789 Fax: (01925) 456778 E-mail: sales-roll@pamarco.co.uk

Promopack Ltd, Heanor Gate Road, Heanor, Derbyshire, DE75 7RG Tel: (01773) 533600 Fax: (01773) 710963

Pulse Media Ltd, 32-42 Station Road, Heaton Mersey, Stockport, Cheshire, SK4 3QT Tel: 0161-432 2225 Fax: 0161-442 9096

Regal Engravers, Polsole Bridge Works, Hamlin Lane, Exeter, EX1 2RY Tel: (01392) 278790 Fax: (01392) 278790 E-mail: regalengravers@yahoo.com

Schawk Ltd, Boston Court, Kansas Avenue, Salford, M50 2GN Tel: 0161-872 9449 Fax: 0161-848 8441

▶ Swift Inline, 123 Walkern Road, Stevenage, Hertfordshire, SG1 3RE Tel: (01438) 244721 Fax: (01438) 244698 E-mail: scott@swiftinline.co.uk

FLEXOGRAPHIC PRINTING ROLLER CLEANING SYSTEMS

Ultrasonic Cleaning Services UK Ltd, 10 Pepper Road, Leeds, LS10 2EU Tel: 0113-271 5807 Fax: 0113-271 5722 E-mail: sales@ucs-uk-ltd.co.uk

FLEXOGRAPHIC PRINTING, FILM/FOIL

Arteb Printing Ltd, Unit 13 Lyon Industrial Estate, Brindley Road, Reginald Road Industrial Estate, St. Helens, Merseyside, WA9 4HY Tel: (01744) 820933 Fax: (01744) 815154 E-mail: info@arteb.co.uk

Hovat, Westmead, New Hythe Lane, Larkfield, Aylesford, Kent, ME20 6XJ Tel: (01622) 791193 Fax: (01622) 791192 E-mail: executive.hovat@btinternet.com

Polyprint Mailing Films Ltd, Mackintosh Road, Rackheath Industrial Estate, Rackheath, Norwich, NR13 6LJ Tel: (01603) 721807 Fax: (01603) 721813 E-mail: jneville@polyprint.co.uk

R & R Flexo Ltd, Concorde Road, Norwich, NR6 6BW Tel: (01603) 485707 Fax: (01603) 408363 E-mail: andy@mailingfilms.co.uk

Roberts,Mart & Co.Limited, Aire Valley House, Thornes Farm Way, Leeds, LS9 0AN Tel: 0113-202 6500 Fax: 0113-202 6550 E-mail: info@roberts-mart.co.uk

FLICKER METER REPAIR

Dowding & Mills plc, Camp Hill, Birmingham, B12 0JJ Tel: 0121-766 6161 Fax: 0121-773 2345 E-mail: group.birmingham@dowdingandmills.com

FLIGHT CASE FITTINGS

A B S Cases, 2 Pylon Trading Estate, Cody Road, London, E16 4SP Tel: (020) 7474 0333 Fax: (020) 7473 2548 E-mail: sales@abscases.co.uk

Clubsafe Case Mnfrs, 1 Spinners End Industrial Estate Oldfields, Corngreaves, Cradley Heath, West Midlands, B64 6BS Tel: (01384) 411311 Fax: (01384) 411311 E-mail: enquiries@cslclubsafe.co.uk

Adam Hall Ltd, 3 The Cordwainers, Temple Farm Industrial Estate, Southend-on-Sea, SS2 5RU Tel: (01702) 613922 Fax: (01702) 617168 E-mail: sales@adamhall.co.uk

FLIGHT CASES

A B S Cases, 2 Pylon Trading Estate, Cody Road, London, E16 4SP Tel: (020) 7474 0333 Fax: (020) 7473 2548 E-mail: sales@abscases.co.uk

Clubsafe Case Mnfrs, 1 Spinners End Industrial Estate Oldfields, Corngreaves, Cradley Heath, West Midlands, B64 6BS Tel: (01384) 411311 Fax: (01384) 411311 E-mail: enquiries@cslclubsafe.co.uk

Dynamic Packaging Ltd, 18-20 Cater Road, Bishopworth, Bristol, BS13 7TW Tel: 0117-978 1222 Fax: (0117) 978 1333 E-mail: sales@dymanicpackaging.co.uk

Gothard Flight Cases, 322 Beverley Road, Hull, HU5 1BA Tel: (07831) 421751 Fax: (01977) 680271 E-mail: info@gothardflightcases.co.uk

Jit Pak, Unit 14 Pages Industrial Park, Eden Way, Leighton Buzzard, Bedfordshire, LU7 4TZ Tel: (01525) 374412 Fax: (01525) 374416 E-mail: info@jitpak.co.uk

Justin Case Co., 23 Water Street, Edinburgh, EH6 6SU Tel: 0131-555 4466 Fax: 0131-555 9601

M A J Electronics, Stallings Lane, Kingswinford, West Midlands, DY6 7HU Tel: (01384) 278646 Fax: (01384) 298877 E-mail: sales@majelectronic.co.uk

Nomad plc, Rockingham Road, Market Harborough, Leicestershire, LE16 7QE Tel: (01858) 464878 Fax: (01858) 410175 E-mail: nomadsolutions@aol.com

Oakleigh Cases Ltd, 10 The Summit Centre, Summit Road, Potters Bar, Hertfordshire, EN6 3JN Tel: (01707) 655011 Fax: (01707) 646447 E-mail: sales@oakleighcases.com

Protechnic Ltd, Unit 109 Central Park, Petherton Road, Bristol, BS14 9BZ Tel: (01275) 833779 Fax: (01275) 835560 E-mail: sales@protechnic.com

Record Dimensions Co., Kelvedon House, Hall Lane, Knutsford, Cheshire, WA16 7AE Tel: (01565) 873300 Fax: (01565) 873000 E-mail: sales@rdco.co.uk

Savill Cases, Units 14-17, Willow Farm Business Park, Rickinghall, Diss, Norfolk, IP22 1LQ Tel: (01379) 898898 Fax: (01379) 898466 E-mail: savillcases@aol.com

Topper Cases Ltd, St. Peter's Hill, Huntingdon, Cambridgeshire, PE29 7DX Tel: (01480) 457251 Fax: (01480) 452107 E-mail: sales@toppercases.co.uk

Triflite Cases, 14 The Studio, Oldbury Business Centre, Cwmbran, Gwent, NP44 3JU Tel: (01633) 869142 Fax: (01633) 869155 E-mail: brad@triflite-cases.co.uk

FLIGHT SIMULATORS

C A E UK plc, Innovation Drive, York Road, Burgess Hill, West Sussex, RH15 9TW Tel: (01444) 247535 Fax: (01444) 244895 E-mail: cae_plc@cae.co.uk

Cuesim Ltd, 2-4 Highfield Park, Highfield Road, Oakley, Bedford, MK43 7TA Tel: (01234) 828000 Fax: (01234) 828001 E-mail: sales@cuesim.com

Quadrant Systems Ltd, Victoria Gardens, Burgess Hill, West Sussex, RH15 9NB Tel: (01444) 246226 Fax: (01444) 870172 E-mail: pmasters@quadrant-systems.co.uk

Tector Visual Systems, Woodhill Road, Collingham, Newark, Nottinghamshire, NG23 7NR Tel: (01636) 892246 Fax: (01636) 893317 E-mail: sales@graffelectronics.co.uk

FLOAT SWITCHES

Able Instruments & Controls Ltd, Danehill, Lower Earley, Reading, RG6 4UT Tel: 0118-931 1188 Fax: 0118-931 2161 E-mail: sales@able.co.uk

Applications Engineering Ltd, 5 Horsted Square, Bellbrook Industrial Estate, Uckfield, East Sussex, TN22 1QG Tel: (01825) 764737 Fax: (01825) 768330 E-mail: info@appeng.co.uk

K S R Kuebler (UK) Level Measurement & Control Ltd, 43 Cherry Orchard Rd, West Molesey, Surrey, KT8 1QZ Tel: (020) 8941 3075 Fax: (020) 8979 4386 E-mail: ksruk@ksr-kuebler.com

Sor Europe Ltd, Farren Court, The Street, Cowfold, Horsham, West Sussex, RH13 8BP Tel: (01403) 864000 Fax: (01403) 710177 E-mail: sales@soreur.co.uk

Triton Controls Ltd, 2 Randolph Industrial Estate, Evenwood, Bishop Auckland, County Durham, DL14 9SJ Tel: (01388) 833000 Fax: (01388) 833680 E-mail: info@tritoncontrols.co.uk

FLOAT VALVES

Opella Ltd, Twyford Road, Rotherwas Industrial Estate, Hereford, HR2 6JR Tel: (01432) 357331 Fax: (01432) 264014 E-mail: sales@opella.co.uk

FLOATING CRANES

Humber Workboats Ltd, North Killingholme, Immingham, South Humberside, DN40 3LX Tel: (01469) 540156 Fax: (01469) 540303 E-mail: elliotmorton@humberworkboats.co.uk

FLOATS

J L Float Ltd, Westgate, Aldridge, Walsall, WS9 8UF Tel: (01922) 455677 Fax: (01922) 743193 E-mail: info@jlfloat.com

FLOCK COATED FABRIC/ FLOCKED FABRIC

Hiva Products, Disraeli Street, Leicester, LE2 8LX Tel: 0116-283 6977 Fax: 0116-283 5265 E-mail: info@hiva.co.uk

FLOCK COATING SERVICES

Electroflock Ltd, Unit 7-8 Building 33, Second Avenue, Pensnett Trading Estate, Kingswinford, West Midlands, DY6 7UG Tel: (01384) 402660 Fax: (01384) 402662 E-mail: electroflock@btinternet.com

Flock Development & Research Co. Ltd, Clarence Mill, Clarence Street, Stalybridge, Cheshire, SK15 1QF Tel: 0161-339 4946 Fax: 0161-343 2045 E-mail: flock@flockdev.co.uk

Hiva Products, Disraeli Street, Leicester, LE2 8LX Tel: 0116-283 6977 Fax: 0116-283 5265 E-mail: info@hiva.co.uk

FLOCK FILLINGS, BEDDING/ UPHOLSTERY

▶ Henderson Alan & Sons, Unit 6 Morgan Drive, Guisborough, Cleveland, TS14 7DH Tel: (01287) 619191 Fax: (01287) 619191 E-mail: upholstery@ntlworld.com

Natural Feather UK Ltd, 31 Berkeley Road, London, N15 6HH Tel: (020) 8800 3355 Fax: (020) 8800 0101

FLOCK TRANSFERS

Technographics UK, Polymark House, Abbeydale Road, Wembley, Middlesex, HA0 1LQ Tel: (020) 8991 0011 Fax: (020) 8998 8080 E-mail: sales@technographics.co.uk

FLOOD WELDING

Dielife Actheron, 30 Commercial Street, Middlesbrough, Cleveland, TS2 1JW Tel: (01642) 241516 Fax: (01642) 245171

FLOODLIGHTING CONTRACTORS OR SUPPLIERS

Floodlighting & Electrical Services Ltd, Unit 22-23 Woodlands Workshops, Coedcae Lane, Pontyclun, Mid Glamorgan, CF72 9DW Tel: (01443) 226009 Fax: (01443) 225481 E-mail: info@floodlighting-electrical.co.uk

G J Bess & Sons Electrical Contractors, Hayes, Salcombe Hill Road, Sidmouth, Devon, EX10 8JR Tel: (01395) 514662 Fax: (01395) 514662 E-mail: g.bess@virgin.net

▶ GVA Grimley Ltd, 211-213 West George Street, Glasgow, G2 2LW Tel: 0141-225 5729

FLOODLIGHTING TOWERS OR COLUMNS

Brimotor Ltd, 10-12 Culverden Down, Tunbridge Wells, Kent, TN4 9SA Tel: (01892) 537588 Fax: (01892) 527724 E-mail: info@brimotor.co.uk

C U Lighting Ltd, 35 Westgate, Cleckheaton, West Yorkshire, BD19 5LE Tel: (01274) 876887 Fax: (01274) 876888 E-mail: sales@cuphosco.co.uk

Christy Lighting Ltd, 8 Northumberland Court, Chelmsford, CM2 6UW Tel: (01245) 451212 Fax: (01245) 451818

Floodlighting & Electrical Services Ltd, Unit 22-23 Woodlands Workshops, Coedcae Lane, Pontyclun, Mid Glamorgan, CF72 9DW Tel: (01443) 226009 Fax: (01443) 225481 E-mail: info@floodlighting-electrical.co.uk

Swann Engineering Group Ltd, Springwood Drive, Braintree, Essex, CM7 2YN Tel: (01376) 320100 Fax: (01376) 347995

Tower Structures Marketing Ltd, 44 Westbourne Terrace, London, W2 3UH Tel: (020) 7402 4452 Fax: (020) 7706 8643

Towermaster Ltd, Braintree Enterprise Centre, 46 Springwood Drive, Braintree, Essex, CM7 2YN Tel: (01376) 324809 Fax: (01376) 552296 E-mail: sales@towermaster.co.uk

FLOODLIGHTS

Albion Electric Stores Ltd, South Accommodation Road, Leeds, LS10 1PR Tel: 0113-245 0196 Fax: 0113-234 1408 E-mail: sales@albionelectric.co.uk

C U Lighting Ltd, 35 Westgate, Cleckheaton, West Yorkshire, BD19 5LE Tel: (01274) 876887 Fax: (01274) 876888 E-mail: sales@cuphosco.co.uk

C U Thosco Lighting Ltd, Charles House, Furlong, Ware, Hertfordshire, SG12 9TA Tel: (01920) 462272 Fax: (01920) 485915 E-mail: export@cuphosco.co.uk

Christy Lighting Ltd, 8 Northumberland Court, Chelmsford, CM2 6UW Tel: (01245) 451212 Fax: (01245) 451818

Deeco Lighting, Highfield, Bryn Awelon, Mold, Clwyd, CH7 1LT Tel: (01352) 700380 Fax: (01352) 700380

J C C Lighting Products, Southern Cross Trading Estate, Lamplighter House, Bognor Regis, West Sussex, PO22 9TS Tel: (01243) 829040 Fax: (01243) 829051 E-mail: sales@jcc-lighting.co.uk

Lightways (Contractors) Ltd, Lochlands Industrial Estate, Larbert, Stirlingshire, FK5 3NS Tel: (01324) 553025 Fax: (01324) 557870 E-mail: head.office@lightways.co.uk

Luckswitch Ltd, Unit 1b St Columbe Industrial Estate, St. Columb Road, St. Columb, Cornwall, TR9 6PZ Tel: (01726) 862994 Fax: (01726) 862995

Thorlux Lighting P.L.C., Merse Road, North Moons Moat, Redditch, Worcestershire, B98 9HH Tel: (01527) 583200 Fax: (01527) 584177 E-mail: marketing@thorlux.co.uk

FLOOR CLEANING CHEMICAL PRODUCTS

Addagrip Surface Treatments UK Ltd, Addagrip House, Bell Lane Industrial Estate, Uckfield, East Sussex, TN22 1QL Tel: (01825) 761333 Fax: (01825) 768566 E-mail: sales@addagrip.co.uk

Bio Natura Ltd, PO Box 2, Ilkley, West Yorkshire, LS29 8AS Tel: (01943) 816816 Fax: (01943) 816818 E-mail: sales@bionutura.co.uk

F Moxham & Son, 43 Higher Market Street, Farnworth, Bolton, BL4 8HQ Tel: (01204) 573342 Fax: (01204) 573342

Fleetfield Chemical Co. Ltd, Norfolk Barocks, 76-136 Edmund Road(Clough Road Entrance), Sheffield, S2 4EE Tel: 0114-273 8999 Fax: 0114-243 3739

▶ Uniteg Overseas Solvents Ltd, Business & Technology Centre, Bessemer Drive, Stevenage, Hertfordshire, SG1 2DX Tel: (01438) 310037 Fax: (01438) 310001 E-mail: uniteg@btopenworld.com

FLOOR CLEANING CONTRACTORS

▶ B & M Industrial Floor Cleaning Machinery, 6 Town Lane, Denton, Manchester, M34 6LE Tel: 0161-320 4291 Fax: 0161-320 4291

FLOOR CLEANING CONTRACTORS

– *continued*

▶ Browns Associated Cleaners, Tamarind House, 41 Marshall Avenue, Bridlington, North Humberside, YO15 2DT Tel: (01262) 606779 E-mail: brownscleaners@btinternet.com
Clandrex Cleaning Ltd, PO Box 14, Grantham, Lincolnshire, NG31 9BL Tel: (01476) 577972 Fax: (01476) 590862
D & R Services, 36 Eastfield Road, Wellingborough, Northamptonshire, NN8 1QU Tel: (01933) 278921 Fax: (01933) 278921
Green Bros Ltd, 44 High Street, Corby, Northamptonshire, NN17 1UU Tel: (01536) 265754 Fax: (01536) 206460 E-mail: enquiries@greenbros.co.uk
O'Neill Floor Preparation & Shotblasting Contractors, 28 Cherry Avenue, Bury, Lancashire, BL9 7NA Tel: 0161-763 9349 E-mail: oneillfloorprep@hotmail.co.uk
R E L Contracts, Springfield, Brumstead Road, Stalham, Norwich, NR12 9DE Tel: (01692) 582238

FLOOR CLEANING MACHINE OR EQUIPMENT HIRE

▶ B & M Industrial Floor Cleaning Machinery, 6 Town Lane, Denton, Manchester, M34 6LE Tel: 0161-320 4291 Fax: 0161-320 4291
Cleaning Machinery K E W Ltd, Whiteball Garage, Whiteball, Wellington, Somerset, TA21 0LT Tel: (01823) 672069 Fax: (01823) 672200 E-mail: kew.cleaning@virgin.net

FLOOR CLEANING MACHINES OR EQUIPMENT

Allbrite Cleaning Services Ltd, Darleydale Road, Corby, Northamptonshire, NN17 2DF Tel: (01536) 202295 Fax: (01536) 266246
Clandrex Cleaning Ltd, PO Box 14, Grantham, Lincolnshire, NG31 9BL Tel: (01476) 577972 Fax: (01476) 590862
Clean Solutions, Unit 1 Kenwood Road, Stockport, Cheshire, SK5 6PH Tel: 0161-947 9947 Fax: 0161-947 9940 E-mail: enquiries@cleansolutions.co.uk
HPSC Moxons Ltd, Courtney Street, Hull, HU8 7QF Tel: (01482) 229016 Fax: (01482) 589562 E-mail: info@hpcsltd.co.uk
▶ Keystone, 204 Duggins Lane, Coventry, CV4 9GP Tel: (024) 7642 2580
▶ Kleanstone Floor Maintenance Equipment, 204 Duggins Lane, Coventry, CV4 9GP Tel: (024) 7642 2609 Fax: (024) 7669 5794
Nilfisk-ALTO, Bowerbank Way, Penrith, Cumbria, CA11 9BQ Tel: (01768) 868995 Fax: (01768) 864713 E-mail: sales.uk@nilfisk-alto.com
Panda Cleaning Machines Ltd, 18 Thomas Flawn Road, Irthlingborough, Wellingborough, Northamptonshire, NN9 5PA Tel: (01933) 653545 Fax: (01933) 653545
Phoenix Floor Maintenance Equipment Ltd, Unit 7, Padgets Lane, South Moons Moat, Redditch, Worcestershire, B98 0RA Tel: (01527) 517161 Fax: (01527) 520765 E-mail: sales@jangro.co.uk
▶ Refina Ltd, Unit 7 Upton Industrial Estate, Factory Road, Poole, Dorset, BH16 5SL Tel: (01202) 632270 Fax: (01202) 632432 E-mail: sales@refina.co.uk
T D C Services, T D C House, Ferry Hill, Ewloe, Deeside, Clwyd, CH5 3AW Tel: (01244) 534521 Fax: (01244) 533562 E-mail: sales@tdcservices.co.uk
T G B Cleaning Supplies Ltd, 370 Northolt Road, Harrow, Middlesex, HA2 8ES Tel: (020) 8423 2155 Fax: (020) 8423 6409 E-mail: tgb@tgb.co.uk
Tennant UK Ltd, Gladstone Road, Northampton, NN5 7RX Tel: (01604) 583191 Fax: (01604) 751517 E-mail: europe@tennantco.com

FLOOR CLEANING PADS

▶ Freudenberg Household Products, 2 Chichester Street, Rochdale, Lancashire, OL16 2AX Tel: (01706) 759597 Fax: (01706) 350143 E-mail: steve.barber@fhp.com
▶ Kleanstone Floor Maintenance Equipment, 204 Duggins Lane, Coventry, CV4 9GP Tel: (024) 7642 2609 Fax: (024) 7669 5794
M A P A Spontex UK Ltd, Berkeley Business Park Berkeley Business Park, Wainwright Road, Worcester, WR4 9ZS Tel: (01905) 450300 Fax: (01905) 450350
Tecserv, Unit 7, Parsons Green Estate, Boulton Road, Stevenage, Hertfordshire, SG1 4QG Tel: (01438) 750905 Fax: (01438) 315270 E-mail: macserv-fcm@btconnect.com

FLOOR CLEANING PRODUCTS

▶ Allan Environmental Solutions, Hewitt House, Winstanley Road, Billinge, Wigan, Lancashire, WN5 7XA Tel: (01695) 682010 Fax: (01695) 682011 E-mail: info@cleantechuk.com
Nilfisk Northern Ireland Ltd, Unit 9, 48 Duncrue Street, Belfast, BT3 9AR Tel: (028) 9074 1444 Fax: (028) 9075 4555 E-mail: sales@nilfix.co.uk

FLOOR COVERING ADHESIVES

Cadonmain Ltd, 3 Aspen Court, Lancing, West Sussex, BN15 8UN Tel: (01903) 750522 Fax: (01903) 851111
His Contracts, 24-28 Pritchards Road, London, E2 9AP Tel: (020) 7739 1455 Fax: (020) 7729 9438 E-mail: info@hiscontracts.co.uk
John Abbott Flooring Contractors Ltd, Wallshaw House, Wallshaw Street, Oldham, OL1 3XD Tel: 0161-624 8246 Fax: 0161-627 1779 E-mail: sales@johnabbottflooring.co.uk
Laybond Products Ltd, Riverside, Chester, CH4 8RS Tel: (01244) 674774 Fax: (01244) 682218 E-mail: sales-info@laybond.com
Lee Floorstok Ltd, Unit B1 The Dresser Centre, Whitworth Street, Openshaw, Manchester, M11 2NE Tel: 0161-231 8080 Fax: 0161-231 8787 E-mail: leefloor@aol.com
▶ M D Flooring, Tenterfield Road, Ossett, West Yorkshire, WF5 0RU Tel: (07876) 350823 E-mail: mdflooring@fsmail.net

FLOOR COVERING CONTRACTORS OR SPECIALIST LAYING SERVICES

A Evans & Son Ltd, 35 Wyle Cop, Shrewsbury, SY1 1XF Tel: (01743) 343078 Fax: (01743) 357141
A. J. B. Floor Coverings Ltd, Unit 1 Bulay Commercial Park, St Thomas Road Longroyd Bridge, Huddersfield, HD1 3LG Tel: (01484) 537255 Fax: (01484) 549328 E-mail: info@ajbflooring.co.uk
▶ All Floors 'N' Rugs, 14 Limes Walk, Oakengates, Telford, Shropshire, TF2 6EP Tel: (01952) 618191 Fax: (01952) 222151 E-mail: sales@floorsnrugs.co.uk
B & K Ceilings Ltd, Unit B8 Manor Development Centre, 40 Alison Crescent, Sheffield, S2 1AS Tel: 0114-253 1620 Fax: 0114-239 4976
▶ B U Interiors Ltd, Unit 15 Nonsuch Industrial Estate, Kiln Lane, Epsom, Surrey, KT17 1DH Tel: (01372) 747677 Fax: (01372) 747706 E-mail: sales@buinteriors.co.uk
Baker Flooring Ltd, Unit D2-D4 Guy Motors Industrial Park, Park Lane, Wolverhampton, WV10 9QG Tel: (01902) 730990 Fax: (01902) 722012 E-mail: mail@bakerflooringltd.co.uk
Bryan & Clark Ltd, Ground Floor, West Cumberland House, 80 Scrubs Lane, London, NW10 6RF Tel: (020) 8969 9933 Fax: (020) 8960 7430E-mail: sales@bryanandclark.co.uk
G W Brooks Flooring Ltd, Unit 19 Waterside Industrial Estate, Ettingshall Road, Wolverhampton, WV2 2RH Tel: (01902) 498213 Fax: (01902) 495707 E-mail: sales@brooksflooring.co.uk
Gateway Ceramics Ltd, School Lane, Chandler's Ford, Eastleigh, Hampshire, SO53 4DG Tel: (023) 8026 0290 Fax: (023) 8025 1049
Industrial Flooring Services Ltd, Sankey Valley Industrial Estate, Newton-le-Willows, Merseyside, WA12 8DN Tel: (01925) 220000 Fax: (01925) 220011 E-mail: info@industrial-flooring.co.uk
▶ Iona Flooring Services Ltd, 109 Langside Drive, Glasgow, G43 2SX Tel: 0141-637 7444 Fax: 0141 6375026 E-mail: ionaflooring@aol.com
J & J Floorings (Watford) Ltd, 18 Caxton Way, Watford Business Park, Watford, WD18 8UA Tel: (01923) 231644 Fax: (01923) 818946
▶ Justkarndean, 85 Blewitt Street, Brierley Hill, West Midlands, DY5 4AL Tel: (07981) 878863 E-mail: justkarndean@blueyonder.co.uk
The London Floor Spring Co., PO Box 6888, London, N1 8EX Tel: (020) 7253 2538 Fax: (01268) 514940
Peter Newman Flooring Ltd, Unit 27 Newtown Business Park, Albion Close, Parkstone, Poole, Dorset, BH12 3LL Tel: (01202) 747175 Fax: (01202) 723421 E-mail: info@peternewmanflooring.com
P M N Aviation Ltd, Unit B, Crawford Street, Rochdale, Lancashire, OL16 5NU Tel: (01706) 655134 Fax: (01706) 631561 E-mail: info@pegasusaviation.co.uk

FLOOR COVERINGS, *See also headings for particular types*

Baileys Carpets Of Bristol Ltd, Broadmead Lane, Keynsham, Bristol, BS31 1ST Tel: 0117-986 8431 Fax: (0800) 212701 E-mail: baileybristol@mcd.co.uk
Beds Flooring Distributors, Cambridge Road, Bedford, MK42 0LH Tel: (01234) 342444 Fax: (01234) 364925 E-mail: sales@bedsflooring.co.uk
Betrex Flooring Supplies, 3 Dollman Street, Birmingham, B7 4RP Tel: 0121-333 3432 Fax: 0121-333 3436 E-mail: sales@floorwise.co.uk
Concept Flooring Suppliers Ltd, Unit 1, Corner Of Roebuck Lane, Dartmouth Road, Smethwick, West Midlands, B66 1BY Tel: 0121-580 1300 Fax: 0121-580 1180
D J Hann Ltd, Aylesford Way, Thatcham, Berkshire, RG19 4NW Tel: (01494) 524422 Fax: (01494) 461670 E-mail: sales@djhann.com
Faithfull Floor Coverings, Lady La Industrial Estate, Hadleigh, Ipswich, IP7 6AU Tel: (01473) 822686 Fax: (01473) 829737 E-mail: faithfulls@headlam.co.uk
▶ Floorboy, 9 Malpas drive, Northampton, NN5 6XL Tel: (01604) 461142 E-mail: floorboy@hotmail.com
Florco, Aylesford Way, Thatcham, Berkshire, RG19 4NW Tel: (01635) 863456 Fax: (01635) 871024 E-mail: info@florco-sales.co.uk
Garrod Bros London Ltd, 50 Aden Road, Enfield, Middlesex, EN3 7SY Tel: (020) 8805 6767 Fax: (020) 8805 9810 E-mail: sales@garrodbros.fsnet.co.uk
J De Bruyn Ltd, Units 4 & 6-7, Simonds Road, London, E10 7BN Tel: (020) 8558 4726 Fax: (020) 8539 7050 E-mail: enquiries@de-bruyne.co.uk
Junckers Ltd, Wheaton Court Commercial Centr, Wheaton Road, Witham, Essex, CM8 3UJ Tel: (01376) 517512 Fax: (01376) 514401 E-mail: sales@junckers.co.uk
▶ Justkarndean, 85 Blewitt Street, Brierley Hill, West Midlands, DY5 4AL Tel: (07981) 878863 E-mail: justkarndean@blueyonder.co.uk
Kellars Ltd, Unit 14, Rugby Park, Bletchley Road, Stockport, Cheshire, SK4 3EJ Tel: 0161-443 0970 Fax: 0161-432 7453 E-mail: tonybates@aol.com
Lee Floorstok Ltd, Unit B1 The Dresser Centre, Whitworth Street, Openshaw, Manchester, M11 2NE Tel: 0161-231 8080 Fax: 0161-231 8787 E-mail: leefloor@aol.com
Planners Services & Sundries Ltd, 8-9 Brandon Road, London, N7 9AA Tel: (020) 7609 8321 Fax: (020) 7700 2010
Potts & Ward Woodcocks Ltd, Lion House, Crowhurst Road, Brighton, BN1 8AF Tel: (01273) 557211 Fax: (01273) 557093
R P S Flooring Ltd, Old Mill Lane Industrial Estate, Mansfield Woodhouse, Mansfield, Nottinghamshire, NG19 9BG Tel: (01623) 624198 Fax: (01623) 620931
Sheffield Wholesale Linoleum & Carpet Co. Ltd, 137 West Bar, Sheffield, S3 8PU Tel: 0114-272 8116 Fax: 0114-272 6558 E-mail: salesswlltd@btconnect.com
Veitchi (Scotland) Ltd, Unit 7, Hareness Circle, Altens Industrial Estate, Aberdeen, AB12 3LY Tel: (01224) 896333 Fax: (01224) 890354 E-mail: aberdeen@veitchi.com

FLOOR FINISHING PREPARATIONS

Boston Chemical Co. Ltd, 48 Millbeck Green, Collingham, Wetherby, West Yorkshire, LS22 5AJ Tel: (01937) 579522 Fax: (01937) 907473 E-mail: bccinfo@bostonchemicals.co.uk
O'Neill Floor Preparation & Shotblasting Contractors, 28 Cherry Avenue, Bury, Lancashire, BL9 7NA Tel: 0161-763 9349 E-mail: oneillfloorprep@hotmail.co.uk

FLOOR GRAPHICS SYSTEMS

Call Print 16 Ltd, 201 Shenley Road, Borehamwood, Hertfordshire, WD6 1AT Tel: (020) 8207 1188 Fax: (020) 8207 0193 E-mail: bwood@callprint.co.uk
Macdermot Autotype Ltd, Grove Road, Wantage, Oxfordshire, OX12 7BZ Tel: (01235) 771111 Fax: (01235) 771196 E-mail: feedback@autotype.com

FLOOR LACQUERS

▶ Ace Flooring UK Ltd, 6 Warden Mill Close, Wateringbury, Maidstone, Kent, ME18 5DJ Tel: (01622) 815544 E-mail: aceflooring@btinternet.com
Marrs Cross & Wilfrid Fairbairns Ltd, Hardwood House, 1 Oglander Road, London, SE15 4EH Tel: (020) 7639 5106 Fax: (020) 7639 5106 E-mail: mxf@ukgateway.net

FLOOR LEVELLING COMPOUNDS

Boston Chemical Co. Ltd, 48 Millbeck Green, Collingham, Wetherby, West Yorkshire, LS22 5AJ Tel: (01937) 579522 Fax: (01937) 907473 E-mail: bccinfo@bostonchemicals.co.uk
F Ball & Co. Ltd, Churnetside Business Park, Station Road, Cheddleton, Leek, Staffordshire, ST13 7RS Tel: (01538) 361633 Fax: (01538) 361622 E-mail: webmaster@f-ball.co.uk

FLOOR MAINTENANCE AND REFURBISHMENT

South Western Flooring Services, 145-147 Park Lane, Frampton Cotterell, Bristol, BS36 2ES Tel: (01454) 880982 Fax: (01454) 880982 E-mail: swflooring@blueyonda.co.uk

FLOOR MAINTENANCE SUPPLY SERVICES

Epoxy Products, 7 Haviland Road, Ferndown Industrial Estate, Wimborne, Dorset, BH21 7RZ Tel: (01202) 891899 Fax: (01202) 896983 E-mail: sales@epoxyproducts.co.uk

FLOOR MOUNTED MOTORCYCLE SECURITY EQUIPMENT

▶ Y anchor, 19 Earsdon Terrace, West Allotment, Newcastle Upon Tyne, NE27 0DY Tel: 0191 2159738

FLOOR OR FLOORING MATERIALS

Airology Systems Ltd, Brickyard Lane, Studley, Warwickshire, B80 7EE Tel: (01527) 850717 Fax: (01527) 850737 E-mail: aircon@airology.freeserve.co.uk
▶ Carpetright plc, Unit 2c Northwich Retail Park, Manchester Road, Northwich, Cheshire, CW9 5LY Tel: (01606) 47585 Fax: (01606) 47285
▶ Decorative Flooring Services, 1501 Nitshill Road, Thornliebank, Glasgow, G46 8QG Tel: 0141-621 2990 Fax: 0141-621 2991 E-mail: sales@decorativeflooringservices.co.uk
Fired Earth Ltd, 1-3 Twyford Mill, Oxford Road, Adderbury, Banbury, Oxfordshire, OX17 3SX Tel: (01295) 812088 Fax: (01295) 810832 E-mail: info@firedearth.com
▶ Fraser Bruce, Millhall, Stirling, FK7 7LT Tel: (01786) 448822 Fax: (01786) 451192 E-mail: info@fraser-bruce.com
Hall's Carpets Ltd, 80-82 Pretoria Road, Edmonton, London, N18 1SP Tel: (020) 8803 1400 Fax: (020) 8803 8904 E-mail: sales@hallsfloorings.co.uk
▶ Industrial Floor Treatments Ltd, 10 Lithgow Place, College Milton, East Kilbride, Glasgow, G74 1PW Tel: (01355) 233600 Fax: (01355) 225777 E-mail: contoact@ift.co.uk
▶ Lerwick Building Centre Ltd, 5d Gremista Industrial Estate, Gremista, Lerwick, Shetland, ZE1 0PX Tel: (01595) 696373 Fax: (01595) 692802 E-mail: billy@lerwickbuildingcentre.co.uk
Red Rose Distribution, Parliament Street, Burnley, Lancashire, BB11 3JT Tel: (01282) 724600 Fax: (01282) 724644
▶ S D Flooring, 30 Guildford Road, Worthing, West Sussex, BN14 7LL Tel: (01903) 538201 E-mail: sales@sdflooring.co.uk
Tile Supply Solutions Ltd, Thornescroft, West Street, Wiveliscombe, Taunton, Somerset, TA4 2JP Tel: (01984) 624757 Fax: (0845) 2800105 E-mail: simon@tilesupplysolutions.com
Whitten Timber Ltd, Eagle Wharf, Peckham Hill Street, London, SE15 5JT Tel: (020) 7732 3804 Fax: (020) 7635 3555

FLOOR OR PAVING TILES

▶ A T Knott & Sons, Cornelian Cottages, 76a Manor Road, Wallington, Surrey, SM6 0AB Tel: (020) 8669 5208 Fax: (020) 8669 5150
Brick Specialists (Midlands) Ltd, 2 Cottage Terrace, The Rope Walk, Nottingham, NG1 5DX Tel: 0115-985 9100 Fax: 0115-947 8960 E-mail: rgb@bricks99.freserve.co.uk
Ceramodo Tiles, 236 Easterly Road, Leeds, LS8 3ES Tel: 0113-249 0041 Fax: 0113-248 5665 E-mail: sales@ceramodotiles.co.uk
Michelmersh Brick & Tile Co. Ltd, Hill View Road, Michelmersh, Romsey, Hampshire, SO51 0NN Tel: (01794) 368506 Fax: (01794) 368845 E-mail: sales@michelmersh.co.uk
Milton Pipes Ltd, Cooks Lane, Sittingbourne, Kent, ME10 2QF Tel: (01795) 425191 Fax: (01795) 420360 E-mail: sales@miltonpipes.com
Stocks Bros Ltd, Blocks, 5 Ninelands Lane, Garforth, Leeds, LS25 1NT Tel: 0113-232 0022 Fax: 0113-287 0839 E-mail: sales@stocks-blocks.co.uk
Thames Valley Tiles, Bagshot Road, Bracknell, Berkshire, RG12 9SE Tel: (01344) 420585 Fax: (01344) 420585

FLOOR OR ROOF DRAIN UNITS OR PRODUCTS

Alumasc Exterior Building Products, White House Works, Bold Road, Sutton, St. Helens, Merseyside, WA9 4JG Tel: 01744 648400 Fax: 01744 648401 E-mail: info@alumasc-exteriors.co.uk

FLOOR POLISH

Cambridge Traditional Products, Millfield, Cottenham, Cambridge, CB4 8RE Tel: (01954) 251380 Fax: (01954) 251387 E-mail: info@bees-wax.co.uk
R B Polishes Ltd, 579 London Road, Isleworth, Middlesex, TW7 4EJ Tel: (020) 8560 6348 Fax: (020) 8568 1253

FLOOR POLISHING MACHINES

Eureka Products, 35 Norfolk Street, Nelson, Lancashire, BB9 7SY Tel: (01282) 615661 Fax: (01282) 699542

▶ indicates data change since last edition

FLOOR POLISHING MACHINES - *continued*

Phoenix Floor Maintenance Equipment Ltd, Unit 7, Padgets Lane, South Moons Moat, Redditch, Worcestershire, B98 0RA Tel: (01527) 517161 Fax: (01527) 520765 E-mail: sales@jangro.co.uk

FLOOR PROTECTION PRODUCTS

▶ Filmtape Ltd, PO Box 400, Southampton, SO30 3XN Tel: (023) 8047 1922 E-mail: sales@filmtape.co.uk

P H S Mat Services Ltd, Unit 5 Transport Avenue, Brentford, Middlesex, TW8 9HF Tel: (020) 8568 1005 Fax: (020) 8568 7425

FLOOR SANDING CONTRACTORS

▶ Atkinson Sanding, 97 Replingham Road, Southfields, London, SW18 5LU Tel: (0770) 4571080E-mail: tom@atkinsondsanding.co.uk

Peter Dorrell & Co., PO Box 14, Malvern, Worcestershire, WR13 5AS Tel: (01684) 567504 Fax: (01684) 563101 E-mail: sales@peterdorrell.freeserve.co.uk

Interstrip, 127 Downham Road, Tranmere, Birkenhead, Merseyside, CH42 6PA Tel: 01766 830141 E-mail: popsaw19@talktalk.com

▶ interstrip.co.uk, 127 Downham road, Tranmere, Birkenhead, Merseyside, CH42 6PA Tel: 0151-641 9925 E-mail: interstrip@talktalk.net

Parkett Borse Ltd, 81 Bolton Street, Chorley, Lancashire, PR7 3AG Tel: (01257) 270148 Fax: (01257) 270147 E-mail: info@parkettborse.com

FLOOR SANDING MACHINES

Eureka Products, 35 Norfolk Street, Nelson, Lancashire, BB9 7SY Tel: (01282) 615661 Fax: (01282) 699542

Hire Technicians Group, Chalk Hill House, 8 Chalk Hill, Watford, WD19 4BH Tel: (0845) 2303340 Fax: (0845) 2303345 E-mail: sales@hiretech.biz

FLOOR SCREED OR SCREEDING

▶ A.D.H Flooring Ltd, 1a Shepherds Avenue, Worksop, Nottinghamshire, S81 0JD Tel: (01909) 489915 Fax: 01909 470094 E-mail: antonyharper@btinternet.com

C S C Screeding Ltd, Chancery Court, Lincolns Inn, Lincoln Road, High Wycombe, Buckinghamshire, HP12 3RE Tel: (0845) 500 4055 Fax: (0845) 500 4056 E-mail: info@cscscreeding.co.uk

▶ Level Best Screeders, 17 Swallows Green Drive, Durrington, Worthing, West Sussex, BN13 2TS Tel: 01903 830126 Fax: 01903 261574 E-mail: floorscreeder@aol.com

Metamix Concrete, Purdy Road, Bilston, West Midlands, WV14 8UB Tel: (01902) 493626 Fax: (01902) 497418

Resdev Ltd, Puma Floor House, Ainley Industrial Estate, Elland, West Yorkshire, HX5 9JP Tel: (01422) 379131 Fax: (01422) 370943 E-mail: info@resdev.co.uk

Support Site P.L.C., Pedmore Road, Dudley, West Midlands, DY2 0RN Tel: (01384) 472250 Fax: (01384) 472251 E-mail: birmingham@supportsite.co.uk

FLOOR SCREED OR SCREEDING CONTRACTORS

▶ A.D.H Flooring Ltd, 1a Shepherds Avenue, Worksop, Nottinghamshire, S81 0JD Tel: (01909) 489915 Fax: 01909 470094 E-mail: antonyharper@btinternet.com

C S C Screeding Ltd, Chancery Court, Lincolns Inn, Lincoln Road, High Wycombe, Buckinghamshire, HP12 3RE Tel: (0845) 500 4055 Fax: (0845) 500 4056 E-mail: info@cscscreeding.co.uk

Castlework Contractors Ltd, 98 College Street, Kempston, Bedford, MK42 8LU Tel: (01234) 217941 Fax: (01234) 357232 E-mail: sales@castlework-contractors.co.uk

▶ Level Best Screeders, 17 Swallows Green Drive, Durrington, Worthing, West Sussex, BN13 2TS Tel: 01903 830126 Fax: 01903 261574 E-mail: floorscreeder@aol.com

▶ PC Flooring (Southern) Ltd, Lake House, Waltham Business Park, Brickyard Road, Swanmore, Southampton, SO32 2SA Tel: (01489) 894332 Fax: (01489) 891392 E-mail: pcf@pc-group.co.uk

FLOOR SCRUBBING MACHINERY

Barloworld Vacuum Technology P.L.C, Harbour Road, Gosport, Hampshire, PO12 1BG Tel: (0870) 0107666 Fax: (0870) 0106916 E-mail: marketing@barloworldvt.com

Finning UK Ltd, Units 1, 3 & 5, Delphwood Drive, Sherdley Park Industrial Estate, Sherdley Road, St. Helens, Merseyside, WA9 5JE Tel: (01744) 451075 Fax: (01744) 451767 E-mail: lisad@birchwood-mechanical.co.uk

Micro Precision Instruments Ltd, The Welsh Mill, Park Hill Drive, Frome, Somerset, BA11 2LE Tel: (01373) 461057 Fax: (01373) 451835

Tennant UK Ltd, Gladstone Road, Northampton, NN5 7RX Tel: (01604) 583191 Fax: (01604) 751517 E-mail: europe@tennantco.com

FLOOR SEALING COMPOUNDS

Bondaglass Voss Ltd, 158 Ravenscroft Road, Beckenham, Kent, BR3 4TW Tel: (020) 8778 0071 Fax: (020) 8659 5297 E-mail: bondaglass@btconnect.com

Everlac (GB) Ltd, Hawthorn House, Helions Bumpstead Road, Haverhill, Suffolk, CB9 7AA Tel: (01440) 766360 Fax: (01440) 768897 E-mail: admin@everlac.co.uk

I R L Group Ltd, C1 Swingbridge Road, Loughborough, Leicestershire, LE11 5JD Tel: (01509) 217101 Fax: (01509) 611004 E-mail: info@irlgroup.com

FLOOR STABILISATION

▶ Uretek UK Ltd, Peel House, Peel Rd, Skelmersdale, Lancs, WN8 9PT Tel: (01695) 50525 Fax: (01695) 555212 E-mail: sales@uretek.co.uk

FLOOR SURFACING CONTRACTORS

Floor Maintenance Services Ltd, 215 Melton Road, Edwalton, Nottingham, NG12 4AF Tel: 0115-945 2186 Fax: 0115-974 7656 E-mail: sonia.mabbott@ntlworld.com

Flooring & Blinds, 20 Chester Street, Mold, Clwyd, CH7 1EG Tel: (01352) 750874 Fax: (01352) 750872

FLOOR TREATMENT PRODUCTS

Corroless Northern Ltd, Regent House, Regent Street, Oldham, OL1 3TZ Tel: 0161-624 4941 Fax: 0161-627 5072 E-mail: sales@kenyon-group.co.uk

Regal Paints Ltd, Meadow Lane Indust Estate, Meadow Lane, Alfreton, Derbyshire, DE55 7EZ Tel: (01773) 830700 Fax: (01773) 832652 E-mail: regalpaintslimited@tiscali.co.uk

FLOORING INSTALLATION

▶ KBC Wood Floors Ltd, 135 Banbury Road, Brackley, Northamptonshire, NN13 6AX Tel: (01280) 700305 Fax: (01280) 700305 E-mail: kev@kbcwoodfloors.com

Renovate Contracts Ltd, 91 Park Road, Earl Shilton, Leicester, LE9 7ZY Tel: 01455 851900 Fax: 01455 851900 E-mail: duncan@renovatecontracts.wanadoo.co.uk

FLOORING JOISTS

Pace Timber Engineering Ltd, Bleak Hall, Milton Keynes, MK6 1LA Tel: (01908) 302880 Fax: (01908) 397881 E-mail: enquiries@pacete.com

FLOORING OR GRATING OR WALKWAYS

A1 Roper Ltd, Crown Works, Worth Way, Keighley, West Yorkshire, BD21 5LR Tel: (01535) 604215 Fax: (01535) 602689 E-mail: a1-roper@compuserve.com

Arco Redman Ltd, The Boardroom Suite, Lingley House, Commissioners Road, Strood, Rochester, Kent, ME2 4EE Tel: (01634) 723372 Fax: (01634) 725572 E-mail: mail@arcoredman.co.uk

Dramex Expanded Metal Ltd, Unit 24-26, Crossgate Road, Park Farm Industrial Estate, Redditch, Worcestershire, B98 7SN Tel: (0800) 1804454 Fax: (01527) 501725 E-mail: uksales@dramex.com

Eurogrid (Incorp) B I E Ltd, Halesfield 18, Telford, Shropshire, TF7 4JS Tel: (01952) 581988 Fax: (01952) 586285 E-mail: sales@eurogrid.co.uk

Fibergrate Composite Structures Ltd, Wass Way, Eaglescliffe, Stockton-on-Tees, Cleveland, TS16 0RG Tel: (01642) 784747 Fax: (01642) 784748 E-mail: info@fibergrate.co.uk

Lothian Steel Services Ltd, Whitburn Road, Bathgate, West Lothian, EH48 2HR Tel: (01506) 633500 Fax: (01506) 633648 E-mail: sales@lothiansteels.co.uk

Orsogril UK, 4 Pentland Road, Edinburgh, EH13 0JA Tel: 0131-441 1255 Fax: 0131-441 4161 E-mail: sales@orsogril.co.uk

Tri Development Ltd, Loomer Road, Newcastle, Staffordshire, ST5 7LB Tel: (01782) 561526 Fax: (01782) 561584 E-mail: tridevltd@btconnect.com

Weland Ltd, Hardley Industrial Estate, Hardley, Southampton, SO45 3NQ Tel: (023) 8084 9747 Fax: (023) 8084 9054 E-mail: info@weland.co.uk

FLOPPY DISCS, COMPUTER

Eurotec Distribution Ltd, Church Croft House, Station Road, Rugeley, Staffordshire, WS15 2HE Tel: (01889) 503100 Fax: (01889) 503101 E-mail: sales@media-resources.co.uk

FLORAL DESIGN

▶ claire gray floral designs, 57 Clement Way, Upminster, Essex, RM14 2NX Tel: 07800 918615 E-mail: claire.gray57@ntlworld.com

▶ Florabundance.Co.Uk, 73 London Road, East Grinstead, West Sussex, RH19 1EQ Tel: (01342) 311478 Fax: (01342) 311542 E-mail: sales@florabundance.co.uk

▶ Flower Shop, 29 Foxhall Road, Ipswich, IP3 8JU Tel: (01473) 255970 Fax: (01473) 255970 E-mail: sheila.bloom@intamail.com

FLORAL DISPLAY CONTRACTORS, *See also headings beginning with Plant*

Babylon Hanging Gardens, 11 Stirling Crescent, Horsforth, Leeds, LS18 5SJ Tel: 0113-239 0909 Fax: 0113-239 0909

Botanica Nurseries, Crown Lane, Farnham Royal, Slough, SL2 3SG Tel: (01753) 647476 Fax: (01753) 647476

M. & C. Brown Ltd, Maryland, Highfield Road, Sunbury-on-Thames, Middlesex, TW16 6DL Tel: (01932) 787332

Business Plants, 34D St. Phillips Avenue, Worcester Park, Surrey, KT4 8JT Tel: (01424) 777452

Camden Plant Display Ltd, 116 Eversholt Street, London, NW1 1BP Tel: (020) 7387 7019 Fax: (020) 7387 7824

Cannon Horticulture, Unit 21 22 Pelham Court, Pelham Place, Crawley, West Sussex, RH11 9SH Tel: (01293) 562068 Fax: (01293) 562788

Creative Flowers, 28 Highwalls Avenue, Dinas Powys, South Glamorgan, CF64 4AP Tel: (029) 2051 4754 Fax: (029) 2051 4754 E-mail: creflow@aol.com

Delphi Floral Display Hire, Studio 4, The Business Village, Broomhill Road, London, SW18 4JQ Tel: (020) 8871 5146 Fax: (020) 8871 5079 E-mail: studio@freshflower.co.uk

E Lodge, Catherine House, 1 Albert Drive, Gateshead, Tyne & Wear, NE9 6EH Tel: 0191-482 6392 Fax: 0191-482 6392 E-mail: simplyimpressive@aol.com

Flower Bowl Of Mayfair, 91 Edgware Road, London, W2 2HX Tel: (020) 7723 0153 Fax: (020) 7723 8559 E-mail: sales@flowerbowl.biz

Foxmoor Nurserys, Haywards Lane, Wellington, Somerset, TA21 9PH Tel: (01823) 662188 Fax: (01823) 665605 E-mail: foxmooruk@aol.con

Garden Scene, Potter La, Higher Walton, Preston, PR5 4EN Tel: 01772 877441

Greener Interior Landscaping, Three Acres, The Avenue, Medburn, Newcastle upon Tyne, NE20 0JD Tel: (01661) 825238 Fax: (01661) 825522 E-mail: sales@greenerinteriors.com

Greengrace Floral & Plant Displays, 129 Elmbridge Avenue, Surbiton, Surrey, KT5 9HE Tel: (020) 8399 8174 Fax: (020) 8390 1871

Hanging Gardens, The Laurels, Wildmoor Lane, Sherfield-on-Loddon, Hook, Hampshire, RG27 0JD Tel: (01256) 880647 Fax: (01256) 880651 E-mail: sales@hanginggarden.co.uk

Hydroplan Interior Landscapes Ltd, Cassidy Court, Kansas Avenue, Salford, M50 2QW Tel: 0161-873 7349 Fax: 0161-872 0254 E-mail: hdryoplanltd@aol.com

Indoor Garden Design Ltd, Woodside Works, Summersby Road, London, N6 5UH Tel: (020) 8444 1414 Fax: (020) 8444 3414 E-mail: office@igd.uk.com

Interior One, 4 Alton Holdings, Milton Of Campsie, Glasgow, G66 8AD Tel: 0141-776 3024 Fax: 0141-776 2471 E-mail: ted@mcbrides.fsbusiness.co.uk

Interior Planting Features, Upshire House, Greenways, Lambourn, Hungerford, Berkshire, RG17 7LE Tel: (01488) 71614 Fax: (01488) 72058

Jane Packer Ltd, 32-34 New Cavendish Street, London, W1G 8UE Tel: (020) 7486 1300 E-mail: sales@janepacker.com

Leaflike Floral & Plant Displays, Wallingford Road, Uxbridge, Middlesex, UB8 2RW Tel: (01895) 810910 Fax: (01895) 233609

Oasis Interior Landscaping, Towers Yard Farm, Towers Road, Poynton, Stockport, Cheshire, SK12 1DE Tel: (01625) 859195 Fax: (01625) 859898

Office Plant Displays, 9 Gables Close, Chalfont St. Peter, Gerrards Cross, Buckinghamshire, SL9 0PR Tel: (01494) 872573

Pheeco Horticulture Ltd, The Seed Bed Centre, Shadow Brook Lane, Hampton-In-Arden, Solihull, West Midlands, B92 0DL Tel: (0845) 4570800 Fax: (0870) 0601620 E-mail: info@pheeco.co.uk

Plant Displays Plus, 38 Park Road, Ashford, Middlesex, TW15 1EY Tel: (01784) 888000 Fax: (01784) 888001 E-mail: sales@plantdisplaysplus.com

Plant Plan, Lyon Close, Wigston, Leicestershire, LE18 2BJ Tel: 0116-281 1933 Fax: 0116-288 6973

Plant & Planters, Bow Wharf, 221 Grove Road, London, E3 5SN Tel: (0845) 6123663 Fax: (020) 8981 9568 E-mail: sales@tropical-plants.co.uk

Plantrite, Woodside Nursery, Long Wittenham, Abingdon, Oxfordshire, OX14 4PT Tel: (01865) 407337 Fax: (0870) 6094684

Plantscape, The Dower House, Decker Hill, Shifnal, Shropshire, TF11 8QL Tel: (01952) 462582

Prospect Plant Display, Botanic House, 4 Aston Mount, Leeds, LS13 2BY Tel: 0113-255 7533 Fax: (0870) 2432270

Rent A Plant Ltd, 245 Cathedral Road, Cardiff, CF11 9PP Tel: (029) 2089 2825 Fax: (029) 2023 3044

Rentokil Tropical Plants, Pipehouse Nursery, Pipehouse, Freshford, Bath, BA2 7UJ Tel: (01225) 722655 Fax: (01225) 722725

Rentokil Tropical Plants, York Road, Leeds, LS15 4NF Tel: 0113-265 0050 Fax: 0113-265 0788 E-mail: enquiries@rentokil-tps.co.uk

S J Floral Displays, 29 Newton Avenue, Tonbridge, Kent, TN10 4RR Tel: (01732) 356447 Fax: (01732) 356447

Silks Of Northampton, 52 Tenter Road, Moulton Park Industrial Estate, Northampton, NN3 6AX Tel: (01604) 644488 Fax: (01604) 644488

Silwood Park Nurseries Ltd, Cheapside Road, Ascot, Berkshire, SL5 7QY Tel: (01344) 621354 Fax: (01344) 872740

Superplants Ltd, Chart House, Shaftesbury Lane, Stoke Trister, Wincanton, Somerset, BA9 9PL Tel: (01963) 34842 Fax: (01963) 34673 E-mail: info@superplants.co.uk

Tropical Interior Landscapes, 2 The Old Fire Station, Albion Street, Birmingham, B1 3EA Tel: 0121-233 9804 Fax: 0121-233 9802

Veronica Preserved Plants, 131 Ballysnod Road, Larne, County Antrim, BT40 3NP Tel: (028) 2827 4016 Fax: (028) 2827 4016

West End Plant Display, Manor Nursery, Kilham Lane, Winchester, Hampshire, SO22 5QD Tel: (01962) 852844

FLORAL SUPPLIES, FLOWER POTS, PLASTIC

▶ Meadowcraft Flowers Of Scotland Ltd, Clettyden, Woodhead, Turriff, Aberdeenshire, AB53 8PL Tel: (01651) 891799 Fax: (01651) 891799 E-mail: sales@flowersofscotland.com

▶ Promoseeds UK, White Hart Hill, Guestling, Hastings, East Sussex, TN35 4LP Tel: (01424) 813572 Fax: (01424) 814631 E-mail: tony@promoseeds.co.uk

FLORAL SUPPLIES, ORCHIDS

▶ Growlighting.co.uk, Unit 19 Chatsworth Green, Basingstoke, Hampshire, RG22 4QA Tel: (01256) 320350 Fax: (01256) 320350 E-mail: rob@growlighting.co.uk

FLORISTS' TRADE SUNDRIES

Britannia Nurseries, 103 Eleanor Cross Road, Waltham Cross, Hertfordshire, EN8 7NS Tel: (01992) 713696

▶ Kensington Flowers, 3 Launceston Place, London, W8 5RL Tel: (020) 7937 0268 Fax: 020 7937 0268 E-mail: info@kensingtonflowers.co.uk

Silks Of Northampton, 52 Tenter Road, Moulton Park Industrial Estate, Northampton, NN3 6AX Tel: (01604) 644488 Fax: (01604) 644488

Tidmas Townsend Ltd, 208-210 Seaside, Eastbourne, East Sussex, BN22 7QS Tel: (01323) 734240 Fax: (01323) 416894

Wards Of Helston, 27 Meneage Street, Helston, Cornwall, TR13 8AA Tel: (01326) 572244 Fax: (01326) 572243

Wentus Ltd, 2 Business Centre, Osbournby, Sleaford, Lincolnshire, NG34 0DH Tel: 01529 455695

The Wire House, Unit 13, 72 Farm Lane, London, SW6 1QA Tel: (020) 7385 5490 Fax: (020) 7385 5490

FLOUR HANDLING EQUIPMENT

Romar Process Engineering Ltd, 12 Faraday Road, Leigh-on-Sea, Essex, SS9 5JU Tel: (01702) 523351 Fax: (01702) 421402 E-mail: info@romar.uk.net

FLOUR MILLING MACHINERY

Springhill Mills, 12 Harts Road, Haddenham, Aylesbury, Buckinghamshire, HP17 8HJ Tel: (01844) 299406 Fax: (01844) 299406 E-mail: gbsmr521@attgolbal.net

FLOUR, BREAD MAKING

▶ Warburtons Ltd, 3 Christleton Court, Manor Park, Runcorn, Cheshire, WA7 1ST Tel: (01928) 579088 Fax: (01928) 579089

FLOW CONTROL CONSULTANTS/DESIGNERS

Cham Ltd, 40 High St Wimbledon, London, SW19 5AU Tel: (020) 8947 7651 Fax: (020) 8879 3497 E-mail: phoenics@cham.co.uk

Hydraulic Analysis Ltd, Mill House, Hawksworth Road, Horsforth, Leeds, LS18 4JP Tel: 0113-258 1622 Fax: 0113-259 0863 E-mail: sales@hydraulic-analysis.com

FLOW CONTROL VALVES

Akro Valves Co., 2 Chaucer Industrial Estate, Dittons Road, Polegate, East Sussex, BN26 6JF Tel: (01323) 485272 Fax: (01323) 485273 E-mail: info@akrovalve.co.uk

Bifold Fluidpower Ltd, Greenside Way, Middleton, Manchester, M24 1SW Tel: 0161-345 4777 Fax: 0161-345 4780 E-mail: sales@bifold-fluidpower.co.uk

Dereve Flow Control Ltd, Park Lane, Handsworth, Birmingham, B21 8LE Tel: 0121-553 7021 Fax: 0121-525 5664 E-mail: dc.controls@btinternet.com

Drainage Center Ltd, 116 London Road, Hailsham, East Sussex, BN27 3AL Tel: (01323) 442333 Fax: (01323) 847488 E-mail: sales@drainagecenter.co.uk

Fort Vale Engineering Ltd, Parkfield Works, Brunswick Street, Nelson, Lancashire, BB9 0SG Tel: (01282) 440000 Fax: (01282) 440046 E-mail: sales@fortvale.com

Pipeline Products Ltd, Units 15-16 Five C Business Centre, Concorde Drive, Clevedon, Avon, BS21 6UH Tel: (01275) 873103 Fax: (01275) 873801 E-mail: info@pipelineproducts.ltd.uk

Reliance Water Controls Ltd, Worcester Road, Evesham, Worcestershire, WR11 4RA Tel: (01386) 47148 Fax: (01386) 47028 E-mail: sales@rwc.co.uk

FLOW CONTROLLERS

John Guest, Horton Road, West Drayton, Middlesex, UB7 8JL Tel: (01895) 449233 Fax: (01895) 420321 E-mail: sales@johnguest.co.uk

FLOW DETECTORS

Furness Controls Ltd, Beeching Road, Bexhill-on-Sea, East Sussex, TN39 3LJ Tel: (01424) 730316 Fax: (01424) 730317 E-mail: sales@furness-controls.com

Powelectrics Ltd, 46 Kepler, Tamworth, Staffordshire, B79 7XE Tel: (01827) 310666 Fax: (01827) 310999 E-mail: sales@powelectrics.co.uk

FLOW DIGITAL TOTALISER

Flowdata Systems, PO Box 71, Newbury, Berks, RG20 0YN Tel: (01488) 668810 Fax: (01488) 668883 E-mail: sales@flowdatasystems.co.uk

FLOW INDICATORS

Data Track Process Instruments Ltd, 153 Somerford Road, Christchurch, Dorset, BH23 3TY Tel: (01425) 271900 Fax: (01425) 271978 E-mail: dtpi.sales@dtrack.com

Flowdata Systems, PO Box 71, Newbury, Berks, RG20 0YN Tel: (01488) 668810 Fax: (01488) 668883 E-mail: sales@flowdatasystems.co.uk

GlasTechnik, Sagana Lodge, Scotton Rd, Scotter, Gainsborough, Lincs, DN21 3SB Tel: (01724) 761172 Fax: (01724) 764352 E-mail: sightglasses@aol.com

Titan Enterprises Ltd, Unit 2 5a Coldharbour Business Park, Sherborne, Dorset, DT9 4JW Tel: (01935) 812790 Fax: (01935) 812890 E-mail: sales@flowmeters.co.uk

▶ West Controls Ltd, 14 Manstone Mead, Sidmouth, Devon, EX10 9RX Tel: 01395 512816 Fax: 01395 513532 E-mail: sales@westcontrols.co.uk

FLOW MEASUREMENT CONSULTANTS/DESIGNERS

Tyco Fire & Intigrated Solutions, Unit 1A Howemoss Drive, Kirkhill Industrial Estate, Dyce, Aberdeen, AB21 0GL Tel: (01224) 255900 Fax: (01224) 255905

FLOW MEASUREMENT ENGINEERS, INSTALLATION OR SERVICE

GB Engineering Services, 6 Town House Farm, Alsager Road, Audley, Stoke-on-Trent, ST7 8JQ Tel: (01782) 723666 Fax: (01782) 723777

J E Cockayne Ltd, The Exchange, Scottish Enterprise Technology Park, East Kilbride, Glasgow, G75 0QU Tel: (01355) 272305 Fax: (01355) 272306 E-mail: ian.cockayne@cockayne.co.uk

FLOW MEASUREMENT SYSTEMS MANUFRS

A B B Ltd, Howard Road, St. Neots, Cambridgeshire, PE19 8EU Tel: (01480) 475321 Fax: (01480) 217948 E-mail: automationltd.sales@gb.abb.com

Aqua Data Services Ltd, Unit 1 Townsend Court, Poulshot, Devizes, Wiltshire, SN10 1SD Tel: (01380) 828971 Fax: (01380) 828971 E-mail: sales@aqua-data.com

Baker Hughes Production Quest, Rowan Court, North Leigh Business Park, Woodstock Road, North Leigh, Witney, Oxfordshire, OX29 6SW Tel: (01993) 883366 Fax: (01993) 881123 E-mail: baker@hughes.com

Barton Instrument Systems Ltd, 3 Steyning Way, Southern Cross Trading Estate, Bognor Regis, West Sussex, PO22 9TT Tel: (01243) 826741 Fax: (01243) 860263 E-mail: bartonuk@nuflotech.com

Dantec Dynamics Ltd, Unit 16 Garonor Way, Portbury, Bristol, BS20 7XE Tel: (01275) 375333 Fax: (01275) 375336 E-mail: scientific@dantecdynamics.com

Emerson Process Management, Horsfield Way, Bredbury, Stockport, Cheshire, SK6 2SU Tel: 0161-430 7100 Fax: (0870) 2404389

Filton Process Control Engineering, 5a Boltro Road, Haywards Heath, West Sussex, RH16 1BP Tel: (01444) 417880 Fax: (01444) 417668 E-mail: sales@filton.com

▶ Flowquip Ltd, Riverside, Canal Road, Sowerby Bridge, W. Yorkshire, HX6 2AY Tel: (01422) 829920 Fax: (01422) 829921 E-mail: sales@flowquip.co.uk

GB Engineering Services, 6 Town House Farm, Alsager Road, Audley, Stoke-on-Trent, ST7 8JQ Tel: (01782) 723666 Fax: (01782) 723777

Kigass Aero Components Ltd, Montague Road, Warwick, CV34 5LW Tel: (01926) 493833 Fax: (01926) 401456 E-mail: enquiries@kigassaero.co.uk

Metering Systems UK Ltd, Cross Edge, Oswaldtwistle, Accrington, Lancashire, BB5 3SD Tel: (01254) 395651 Fax: (01254) 237349 E-mail: john@meteringsystems.co.uk

Thermo Fisher Sceientific, Unit A2, Swift Park, Old Leicester Road, Rugby, Warwickshire, CV21 1DZ Tel: (01788) 820319 Fax: (01788) 820301 E-mail: saleswiuk@thermofisher.com

Titan Enterprises Ltd, Unit 2 5a Coldharbour Business Park, Sherborne, Dorset, DT9 4JW Tel: (01935) 812790 Fax: (01935) 812890 E-mail: sales@flowmeters.co.uk

Tyco Fire & Intigrated Solutions, Unit 1A Howemoss Drive, Kirkhill Industrial Estate, Dyce, Aberdeen, AB21 0GL Tel: (01224) 255900 Fax: (01224) 255905

FLOW METER DISTRIBUTORS OR AGENTS

▶ J.W. Fairbairn Process Solutions Ltd, 120 Woodneuk Road, Darnley Industrial Estate, Glasgow, G53 7QS Tel: 0141-880 7455 Fax: 0141-880 5290 E-mail: sales@jwfltd.com

Fine Controls UK Ltd, Bassendale Road, Bromborough, Wirral, Merseyside, CH62 3QL Tel: 0151-343 9966 Fax: 0151-343 0062 E-mail: sales@finecontrols.com

Flotech Solutions Ltd, Stuart Road, Bredbury Park Industrial Estate, Bredbury, Stockport, Cheshire, SK6 2SR Tel: 0161-406 2200 Fax: 0161-406 9196 E-mail: enquiries@flotech.co.uk

Hach Langer Ltd, 5 Pacific Way, Salford, M50 1DL Tel: 0161-872 1487 Fax: 0161-848 7324 E-mail: info@hach-lange.co.uk

J E Cockayne Ltd, The Exchange, Scottish Enterprise Technology Park, East Kilbride, Glasgow, G75 0QU Tel: (01355) 272305 Fax: (01355) 272306 E-mail: ian.cockayne@cockayne.co.uk

K T Hydraulic Ltd, Hope Hall Mill, Union Street South, Halifax, West Yorkshire, HX1 2LA Tel: (01422) 358885 Fax: (01422) 359512

Loader Fluid Engineering, Unit 4 2 Willis Way, Poole, Dorset, BH15 3SS Tel: (01202) 675220 Fax: (01202) 666890 E-mail: sales@loadereng.co.uk

Premier Control Technologies Ltd, 1 Highland Close, St. Helens Way, Thetford, Norfolk, IP24 1HG Tel: (01842) 753456 Fax: (01842) 752424 E-mail: sales@pctflow.com

FLOW METER HIRE

Filton Process Control Engineering, 5a Boltro Road, Haywards Heath, West Sussex, RH16 1BP Tel: (01444) 417880 Fax: (01444) 417668 E-mail: sales@filton.com

Flowhire Hire Centres, Riverside, Canal Road, Sowerby Bridge, West Yorkshire, HX6 2AY Tel: (0800) 0356944 Fax: (07000) 356944 E-mail: sales@flowhire.co.uk

Micronics Ltd, Knaves Beech Business Centre, Davies Way, Loudwater, High Wycombe, Buckinghamshire, HP10 9QR Tel: (01628) 810456 Fax: (01628) 531540 E-mail: sales@micronicsltd.co.uk

FLOW METER MAINTENANCE, REPAIR AND REFURBISHMENT

Pulsonic Technologies Ltd, Riverside House North Dean Business Park, Stainland Road, Greetland, Halifax, West Yorkshire, HX4 8LR Tel: (01422) 363462 Fax: (0870) 9224026 E-mail: sales@pulsonictechnologies.com

FLOW METER MANUFRS, *See also headings under Flow Meters*

Able Instruments & Controls Ltd, Danehill, Lower Earley, Reading, RG6 4UT Tel: 0118-931 1188 Fax: 0118-931 2161 E-mail: sales@able.co.uk

▶ AMP (GB) Ltd, Horton Corner, Small Dole, Henfield, West Sussex, BN5 9XJ Tel: (01903) 817004 Fax: (01903) 817114 E-mail: mphippf@amp.com

Aqua Data Services Ltd, Unit 1 Townsend Court, Poulshot, Devizes, Wiltshire, SN10 1SD Tel: (01380) 828971 Fax: (01380) 828971 E-mail: sales@aqua-data.com

Atkinson Equipment Ltd, Moat Road, West Wilts Trading Estate, Westbury, Wiltshire, BA13 4JF Tel: (01373) 822220 Fax: (01373) 826996 E-mail: sales@atkinsonequipment.com

BMS Group, 3 Faversham Road, Challock, Ashford, Kent, TN25 4BQ Tel: (01233) 740134 Fax: (01233) 740943 E-mail: sales@bms-ltd.com

DMS Flow Measurement & Control Ltd, The Lodge, 9 Mansfield Rd, Eastwood, Nottingham, NG16 3AQ Tel: (01773) 534555 Fax: (01773) 534666 E-mail: sales@dmsltd.com

Emerson Process Management, Horsfield Way, Bredbury, Stockport, Cheshire, SK6 2SU Tel: 0161-430 7100 Fax: (0870) 2404389

▶ Eurospan Engineering Ltd, 5 Wheatmoor Rise, Sutton Coldfield, West Midlands, B75 6AW Tel: 0121-378 1596 Fax: 0121-329 2542 E-mail: eurospan@blueyonder.co.uk

Filton Process Control Engineering, 5a Boltro Road, Haywards Heath, West Sussex, RH16 1BP Tel: (01444) 417880 Fax: (01444) 417668 E-mail: sales@filton.com

Flowdata Systems, PO Box 71, Newbury, Berks, RG20 0YN Tel: (01488) 668810 Fax: (01488) 668883 E-mail: sales@flowdatasystems.co.uk

G L Flow Ltd, Hanson Park, Hanson Close, Middleton, Manchester, M24 2QZ Tel: 0161-643 9833 Fax: 0161-643 9835 E-mail: info@glflow.co.uk

Hydrotechnik UK Ltd, Unit 10, Easter Park, Lenton Lane, Nottingham, NG7 2PX Tel: 0115-900 3550 Fax: 0115-970 5597 E-mail: sales@hydrotechnik.co.uk

Industrial Flow Control Ltd, Unit 1, Askews Farm Lane, Grays, Essex, RM17 5XR Tel: (01375) 387155 Fax: (01375) 387420 E-mail: sales@inflow.co.uk

JPS, 7 Radway Industrial Estate, Radway Road, Shirley, Solihull, West Midlands, B90 4NR Tel: 0121-711 2115 Fax: 0121-711 2584 E-mail: soltaujpsengineering@btinternet.com

KDG Instruments, Crompton Way, Crawley, West Sussex, RH10 9YZ Tel: (01293) 525151 Fax: (01293) 533095 E-mail: sales@mobrey.com

Krohne Ltd, Rutherford Drive, Park Farm Industrial Estate, Wellingborough, Northamptonshire, NN8 6AE Tel: (01933) 408500 Fax: (01933) 408501 E-mail: info@krohne.co.uk

Litre Meter Ltd, Unit 50 Rabans Close, Rabans Lane Industrial Area, Aylesbury, Buckinghamshire, HP19 8RS Tel: (01296) 420341 Fax: (01296) 436446 E-mail: sales@litremeter.com

M P B Industries Ltd, Unit 1, Branbridges Industrial Estate, East Peckham, Tonbridge, Kent, TN12 5HF Tel: (01622) 872401 Fax: (01622) 871294 E-mail: mail@mpbflowmeters.com

Meller Flowtrans Ltd, 12 Millersdale Close, Euroway Industrial Estate, Bradford, West Yorkshire, BD4 6RX Tel: (01274) 687687 Fax: (01274) 687744 E-mail: info@mellerflowtrans.co.uk

Micronics Ltd, Knaves Beech Business Centre, Davies Way, Loudwater, High Wycombe, Buckinghamshire, HP10 9QR Tel: (01628) 810456 Fax: (01628) 531540 E-mail: sales@micronicsltd.co.uk

Pulsonic Technologies Ltd, Riverside House North Dean Business Park, Stainland Road, Greetland, Halifax, West Yorkshire, HX4 8LR Tel: (01422) 363462 Fax: (0870) 9224026 E-mail: sales@pulsonictechnologies.com

Sandhurst Instruments Ltd, 30 Sudley Road, Bognor Regis, West Sussex, PO21 1ER Tel: (01243) 820200 Fax: (01243) 860111 E-mail: sandhurst.instruments@freenet.co.uk

▶ Solartron Mobrey Ltd, 158 Edinburgh Avenue, Slough, SL1 4UE Tel: (01753) 756600 Fax: (01753) 823589

Titan Enterprises Ltd, Unit 2 5a Coldharbour Business Park, Sherborne, Dorset, DT9 4JW Tel: (01935) 812790 Fax: (01935) 812890 E-mail: sales@flowmeters.co.uk

Webtec Products Ltd, Nuffield Road, St. Ives, Cambridgeshire, PE27 3LZ Tel: (01480) 397444 Fax: (01480) 466555 E-mail: sales@webtec.co.uk

FLOW METERS, AIR

Ateq UK Ltd, Unit 71 Heming Road, The Washford Industrial Estate, Redditch, Worcestershire, B98 0EA Tel: (01527) 520011 Fax: (01527) 520022 E-mail: info@ateq.co.uk

Flowhire Hire Centres, Riverside, Canal Road, Sowerby Bridge, West Yorkshire, HX6 2AY Tel: (0800) 0356944 Fax: (07000) 356944 E-mail: sales@flowhire.co.uk

FLOW METERS, BATCH CONTROL

Litre Meter Ltd, Unit 50 Rabans Close, Rabans Lane Industrial Area, Aylesbury, Buckinghamshire, HP19 8RS Tel: (01296) 420341 Fax: (01296) 436446 E-mail: sales@litremeter.com

FLOW METERS, BIO-GAS

Litre Meter Ltd, Unit 50 Rabans Close, Rabans Lane Industrial Area, Aylesbury, Buckinghamshire, HP19 8RS Tel: (01296) 420341 Fax: (01296) 436446 E-mail: sales@litremeter.com

FLOW METERS, ELECTROMAGNETIC

Aqua Data Services Ltd, Unit 1 Townsend Court, Poulshot, Devizes, Wiltshire, SN10 1SD Tel: (01380) 828971 Fax: (01380) 828971 E-mail: sales@aqua-data.com

Flowline Manufacturing Ltd, 11a Shenley Road, Borehamwood, Hertfordshire, WD6 1AD Tel: (020) 8207 6565 Fax: (020) 8207 3082 E-mail: sales@flowline.co.uk

FLOW METERS, FOOD INDUSTRY

Access Instrumentation Ltd, Reading Road, Eversley, Hook, Hampshire, RG27 0RP Tel: 0118-973 4702 Fax: 0118-973 1177 E-mail: sales@accessinstrumentation.co.uk

Metering Systems UK Ltd, Cross Edge, Oswaldtwistle, Accrington, Lancashire, BB5 3SD Tel: (01254) 395651 Fax: (01254) 237349 E-mail: john@meteringsystems.co.uk

FLOW METERS, GAS FLOW

Access Instrumentation Ltd, Reading Road, Eversley, Hook, Hampshire, RG27 0RP Tel: 0118-973 4702 Fax: 0118-973 1177 E-mail: sales@accessinstrumentation.co.uk

C K Gas Products Ltd, Unit 3, Murrell Green Business Park, London Road, Hook, Hampshire, RG27 9GR Tel: (01256) 766633 Fax: (01256) 766630 E-mail: sales@ckgas.com

Flowline Manufacturing Ltd, 11a Shenley Road, Borehamwood, Hertfordshire, WD6 1AD Tel: (020) 8207 6565 Fax: (020) 8207 3082 E-mail: sales@flowline.co.uk

G L Flow Ltd, Hanson Park, Hanson Close, Middleton, Manchester, M24 2QZ Tel: 0161-643 9833 Fax: 0161-643 9835 E-mail: info@glflow.co.uk

M P B Industries Ltd, Unit 1, Branbridges Industrial Estate, East Peckham, Tonbridge, Kent, TN12 5HF Tel: (01622) 872401 Fax: (01622) 871294 E-mail: mail@mpbflowmeters.com

Roxar Ltd, Heritage Gate, Sandy Lane West, Littlemore, Oxford, OX4 6LB Tel: (01865) 712828 Fax: (01865) 712829

Ultramedic Ltd, Wavertree Boulevard South, Liverpool, L7 9PF Tel: 0151-228 0354 Fax: 0151-252 1673

FLOW METERS, OPEN CHANNEL

Flowline Manufacturing Ltd, 11a Shenley Road, Borehamwood, Hertfordshire, WD6 1AD Tel: (020) 8207 6565 Fax: (020) 8207 3082 E-mail: sales@flowline.co.uk

FLOW METERS, PITOT TUBE

Able Instruments & Controls Ltd, Danehill, Lower Earley, Reading, RG6 4UT Tel: 0118-931 1188 Fax: 0118-931 2161 E-mail: sales@able.co.uk

Micronics Ltd, Knaves Beech Business Centre, Davies Way, Loudwater, High Wycombe, Buckinghamshire, HP10 9QR Tel: (01628) 810456 Fax: (01628) 531540 E-mail: sales@micronicsltd.co.uk

FLOW METERS, STEAM

Flowhire Hire Centres, Riverside, Canal Road, Sowerby Bridge, West Yorkshire, HX6 2AY Tel: (0800) 0356944 Fax: (07000) 356944 E-mail: sales@flowhire.co.uk

▶ Flowquip Ltd, Riverside, Canal Road, Sowerby Bridge, W. Yorkshire, HX6 2AY Tel: (01422) 829920 Fax: (01422) 829921 E-mail: sales@flowquip.co.uk

FLOW METERS, TURBINE

▶ Flowquip Ltd, Riverside, Canal Road, Sowerby Bridge, W. Yorkshire, HX6 2AY Tel: (01422) 829920 Fax: (01422) 829921 E-mail: sales@flowquip.co.uk

FLOW METERS, ULTRASONIC

Able Instruments & Controls Ltd, Danehill, Lower Earley, Reading, RG6 4UT Tel: 0118-931 1188 Fax: 0118-931 2161 E-mail: sales@able.co.uk

Siemens Process Instruments, Century House, Bridgwater Road, Worcester, WR4 9ZQ Tel: (01905) 450500 Fax: (01905) 450501

FLOW METERS, VARIABLE AREA

Flotech Solutions Ltd, Stuart Road, Bredbury Park Industrial Estate, Bredbury, Stockport, Cheshire, SK6 2SR Tel: 0161-406 2200 Fax: 0161-406 9196 E-mail: enquiries@flotech.co.uk

M P B Industries Ltd, Unit 1, Branbridges Industrial Estate, East Peckham, Tonbridge, Kent, TN12 5HF Tel: (01622) 872401 Fax: (01622) 871294 E-mail: mail@mpbflowmeters.com

FLOW REGULATORS

S G E (Europe) Ltd, 1 Potters Lane, Kiln Farm, Milton Keynes, MK11 3LA Tel: (01908) 568844 Fax: (01908) 566790 E-mail: uk@sge.com

FLOW SIMULATION SOFTWARE CONSULTANTS

Resource Management Systems, Mexborough Business Centre, College Road, Mexborough, South Yorkshire, S64 9JP Tel: (01709) 578300 Fax: (01709) 578010 E-mail: sales@rmsuk.co.uk

FLOW SWITCH MANUFRS

Burford Controls Ltd, Unit 18 Applins Park, Farrington, Blandford Forum, Dorset, DT11 8RA Tel: (01747) 811173 Fax: (01747) 811171 E-mail: information@burfordcontrols.co.uk

▶ Alexander Cardew Ltd, Unit 27 Chelsea Wharf, 15 Lots Road, London, SW10 0QJ Tel: (020) 7235 3785 Fax: (020) 7352 4635 E-mail: sales@cardew.com

Gems Sensors Pension Trustees Ltd, Lennox Road, Basingstoke, Hampshire, RG22 4AW Tel: (01256) 320244 Fax: (01256) 473680 E-mail: sales@gems-sensors.co.uk

Magnetrol International UK Ltd, 1 Regent Business Centre, Jubilee Road, Burgess Hill, West Sussex, RH15 9TL Tel: (01444) 871313 Fax: (01444) 871317 E-mail: sales@magnetrol.co.uk

FLOW WRAPPING

▶ Record Packaging Systems Ltd, Unit 41 Stretford Motorway Estate, Stretford, Manchester, M32 0ZH Tel: 0161-864 3971 Fax: 0161-864 1390 E-mail: sales@recordpackaging.com

FLOW WRAPPING MACHINERY

Rose Forgrove, 101 Lilac Grove, Beeston, Nottingham, NG9 1PF Tel: 0115-967 8787 Fax: 0115-967 8707 E-mail: sales@rose-forgrove.co.uk

FLOWER ARRANGING SERVICES

▶ claire gray floral designs, 57 Clement Way, Upminster, Essex, RM14 2NX Tel: 07800 918615 E-mail: claire.gray57@ntlworld.com

▶ Covent Garden Flower Emporium Ltd, 5 Thornhill Road, Cardiff, CF14 6PD Tel: (029) 2075 0750 Fax: (029) 2075 0757 E-mail: coventgardenfloweremporium@btconnect.com

▶ Florabundance.Co.Uk, 73 London Road, East Grinstead, West Sussex, RH19 1EQ Tel: (01342) 311478 Fax: (01342) 311542 E-mail: sales@florabundance.co.uk

▶ Flower Shop, 29 Foxhall Road, Ipswich, IP3 8JU Tel: (01473) 255970 Fax: (01473) 255970 E-mail: sheila.bloom@intamail.com

▶ Flowerworks Florists, 15 Windsor Street, Uxbridge, Middlesex, UB8 1AB Tel: (01895) 810885 Fax: (01895) 810008 E-mail: sales@actionflowers.com

▶ Mayhew Flowers, 6 Cockpit Hill, Cullompton, Devon, EX15 1DF Tel: (01884) 839826 Fax: 01884 839826 E-mail: info@mayhewflowers.co.uk

▶ Oak Floral Design, Manor Farm, Main Street, Shangton, Leicester, LE8 0PG Tel: (07754) 07122

▶ Sonning Flowers, 2 The Old Forge, Pearson Road, Sonning, Reading, RG4 6UH Tel: 0118-944 8400 E-mail: info05@sonningflowers.com

▶ Zara Flora Service Ltd, 1 Old Stone Link, Ship Street, East Grinstead, West Sussex, RH19 4EF Tel: (01342) 300500 Fax: (01342) 300111 E-mail: flowers@zaraflora.com

FLOWER BOUQUETS

▶ Covent Garden Flower Emporium Ltd, 5 Thornhill Road, Cardiff, CF14 6PD Tel: (029) 2075 0750 Fax: (029) 2075 0757 E-mail: coventgardenfloweremporium@btconnect.com

▶ Flowerworks Florists, 15 Windsor Street, Uxbridge, Middlesex, UB8 1AB Tel: (01895) 810885 Fax: (01895) 810008 E-mail: sales@actionflowers.com

Lavendersblue Florists, 4 York Street, Ramsgate, Kent, CT11 9DS Tel: (01843) 595953 E-mail: lavenders36@aol.com

▶ Sonning Flowers, 2 The Old Forge, Pearson Road, Sonning, Reading, RG4 6UH Tel: 0118-944 8400 E-mail: info05@sonningflowers.com

▶ Zara Flora Service Ltd, 1 Old Stone Link, Ship Street, East Grinstead, West Sussex, RH19 4EF Tel: (01342) 300500 Fax: (01342) 300111 E-mail: flowers@zaraflora.com

FLOWERS

▶ Covent Garden Flower Emporium Ltd, 5 Thornhill Road, Cardiff, CF14 6PD Tel: (029) 2075 0750 Fax: (029) 2075 0757 E-mail: coventgardenfloweremporium@btconnect.com

Creative Works UK Ltd, Unit 1 The Stable Block, Brewer Street Bletchingley, Bletchingley, Redhill, RH1 4QP Tel: (01883) 742999 E-mail: info@ckworks.net

Lavendersblue Florists, 4 York Street, Ramsgate, Kent, CT11 9DS Tel: (01843) 595953 E-mail: lavenders36@aol.com

Party Time Ltd, 37 Cartergate, Newark, Nottinghamshire, NG24 1UA Tel: (01636) 611669 Fax: (01636) 615669 E-mail: enquiries@zillionsofchuckles.com

▶ Zara Flora Service Ltd, 1 Old Stone Link, Ship Street, East Grinstead, West Sussex, RH19 4EF Tel: (01342) 300500 Fax: (01342) 300111 E-mail: flowers@zaraflora.com

FLOWMETERS, BUBBLE

▶ English MeterCo, 9 Atherton Lane, Rastrick, Brighouse, West Yorkshire, HD6 3TJ Tel: (01484) 710073 Fax: (01484) 710073 E-mail: Geoff.English@Blueyonder.co.uk

FLOWMETERS, COMPRESSED AIR

▶ English MeterCo, 9 Atherton Lane, Rastrick, Brighouse, West Yorkshire, HD6 3TJ Tel: (01484) 710073 Fax: (01484) 710073 E-mail: Geoff.English@Blueyonder.co.uk

FLOWMETERS, OVAL GEAR

▶ English MeterCo, 9 Atherton Lane, Rastrick, Brighouse, West Yorkshire, HD6 3TJ Tel: (01484) 710073 Fax: (01484) 710073 E-mail: Geoff.English@Blueyonder.co.uk

▶ KEM Kueppers UK, 2 Highfield Drive, Ickenham, Uxbridge, Middlesex, UB10 8AL Tel: (01895) 233552 Fax: (01895) 230312 E-mail: service@kueppers.co.uk

FLOWMETERS, TURBINE, LIQUID

▶ Flowmetersdirect.co.uk, Unit E1, Hanson Park, Hanson Close, Middleton, Manchester, M24 2QZ Tel: 0161-643 9802 Fax: 0161-643 9835 E-mail: info@flowmetersdirect.co.uk

FLUE GAS ANALYSERS

Afriso Eurogauge Ltd, Imberhorne Lane, East Grinstead, West Sussex, RH19 1RF Tel: (01342) 323641 Fax: (01342) 315513 E-mail: sales@eurogauge.co.uk

Energy Technology & Control Ltd, 25 North Street, Lewes, East Sussex, BN7 2PE Tel: (01273) 480667 Fax: (01273) 480652 E-mail: sales@energytechnologycontrol.com

▶ Enotec UK Ltd, PO Box 9026, Dumfries, DG1 3YH Tel: (0870) 3500102 Fax: (0870) 3500302 E-mail: enotec.uk@enotec.com

Sabre Systems (Heating) Ltd, Unit 9, Ruxley Corner Industrial Estate, Edgington Way, Sidcup, Kent, DA14 5BL Tel: (020) 8308 0708 Fax: (020) 8309 6727 E-mail: sales@sabresystems.co.uk

Servomex Group Ltd, Crowborough Hill, Jarvis Brook, Crowborough, East Sussex, TN6 3DU Tel: (01892) 652181 Fax: (01892) 662253 E-mail: info@servomex.com

FLUE LININGS

Countrylife Stoves, Coopers Orchard, Brook Street, North Newton, Bridgwater, Somerset, TA7 0BL Tel: (01278) 662449 Fax: (01278) 662449

Schiedel Right Vent Ltd, Crowther Road, Crowther Industrial Estate, Washington, Tyne & Wear, NE38 0AQ Tel: 0191-416 1150

Shropshire Flue & Duct Services, Unit 84, Condover Industrial Estate, Dorrington, Shrewsbury, SY5 7NH Tel: (01743) 718844 Fax: (01743) 718874

Turner & Wilson Ltd, Road Three, Winsford Industrial Estate, Winsford, Cheshire, CW7 3PD Tel: (01606) 861191 Fax: (01606) 861231 E-mail: sales@turnerwilson.com

FLUE PIPES

A 1 Sheetmetal Flues Ltd, Maun Way, Boughton Industrial Estate, Newark, Nottinghamshire, NG22 9ZD Tel: (01623) 860578 Fax: (0870) 1602281 E-mail: info@a1flues.co.uk

Charlestown Engineering Services Ltd, Rayner House, Bayley Street, Stalybridge, Cheshire, SK15 1PZ Tel: 0161-338 7300 Fax: 0161-338 4884 E-mail: sales@charlestown1.com

Countrylife Stoves, Coopers Orchard, Brook Street, North Newton, Bridgwater, Somerset, TA7 0BL Tel: (01278) 662449 Fax: (01278) 662449

County Enterprises Sheltered Workshop, St Pauls Street, Worcester, WR1 2BA Tel: (01905) 23819 Fax: (01905) 27832 E-mail: countyenteprises@worcestershire.gov.uk

Flamco Ltd, 4 St. Michaels Road, St. Helens, Merseyside, WA9 4WZ Tel: (01744) 818100 Fax: (01744) 830400 E-mail: info@flamco.co.uk

Flues & Flashings Ltd, Unit 246 Ikon Industrial Estate, Droitwich Road, Hartlebury, Kidderminster, Worcestershire, DY10 4EU Tel: (01299) 250049 Fax: (01299) 250947 E-mail: info@fluesandflashings.co.uk

H Docherty Ltd, Red Shute Hill Industrial Estate, Red Shute Hill, Hermitage, Thatcham, Berkshire, RG18 9QL Tel: (01635) 200145 Fax: (01635) 201737 E-mail: info@docherty.co.uk

M M F Ltd, 55 Woodburn Road, Smethwick, West Midlands, B66 2PU Tel: 0121-555 6555 Fax: 0121-555 6816 E-mail: sales@fluepipes.com

Pennine Systems Ltd, Crossley Works, Stockfield Mount, Off Peel Street, Chadderton, Oldham, OL9 9LR Tel: 0161 678 2998 Fax: 0161 678 2997 E-mail: sales@penninesystems.co.uk

FLUE TRADE SUPPLIES

Docherty Chimney Group, 15 Alfred St South, Nottingham, NG3 2AD Tel: 0115-958 4734 Fax: 0115-950 2899 E-mail: sales@docherty.co.uk

FLUID BED DRYERS

I M A (UK) Ltd, 3 Arden Road, Alcester, Warwickshire, B49 6HN Tel: (01789) 400880 Fax: (01789) 400880 E-mail: hotdesk@imauk.co.uk

Kason Corporation Europe, Unit 12-13 Parkhall Business Village, Parkhall Road, Stoke-on-Trent, ST3 5XA Tel: (01782) 597540 Fax: (01782) 597549 E-mail: sales@kasoneurope.co.uk

Arthur White Dryers Ltd, 16 Upper Brook Street, Oswestry, Shropshire, SY11 2TB Tel: (01691) 657960 Fax: (01691) 670462 E-mail: awdryers@moulson-chemplant.co.uk

FLUID COUPLINGS

Bibby Tranmissions Ltd, Cannon Way, Dewsbury, West Yorkshire, WF13 1EH Tel: (01924) 460801 Fax: (01924) 457668 E-mail: sales@bibbytransmissions.co.uk

FLUID POWER CONSULTANTS

Hydraulic & Pneumatic Supplies Ltd, Unit 39, Second Drove Industrial Estate, Fengate, Peterborough, PE1 5XA Tel: (01733) 894500 Fax: (01733) 894892 E-mail: sales@hps-ltd.co.uk

FLUID POWER EQUIPMENT MANUFRS

Agramkow Fluid Systems Ltd, Windmill House Industrial Estate, Sutton Road, Wigginton, York, YO32 2RA Tel: (01904) 750320 Fax: (01904) 750321 E-mail: agramkow@agramkow.co.uk

British Engineering Productions Ltd, 19 Arnside Road, Waterlooville, Hampshire, PO7 7UP Tel: (023) 9226 8733 Fax: (023) 9225 1104 E-mail: sales@bep-manifolds.com

FLUID TRANSFER SYSTEMS

Ernest H Hill Ltd, Unit 10-12, Meadowbrook Park, Halfway, Sheffield, S20 3PJ Tel: 0114-248 4882 Fax: 0114-248 9142 E-mail: sales@hillpumps.com

FLUIDIC MANAGEMENT COMPONENTS, DRUG DISCOVERY OR PROTEOMICS

▶ Starbridge Systems Ltd, Techneum 2, Kings Road, The Docks, Swansea, SA1 8PJ Tel: (01792) 485530 Fax: (01792) 485531 E-mail: info@labstar.co.uk

FLUMES, STAINLESS STEEL

▶ Aqua-Leisure Internatinal Ltd, The Tannery, Queen Street, Gomshall, Surrey, GU5 9LY Tel: (0870) 4050600 Fax: (0870) 4050601 E-mail: info@aqua-leisure.co.uk

FLUORESCENT LAMP OR TUBE RECYCLING

▶ Envirolite Ltd, Shore Road, Perth, PH2 8BH Tel: (01738) 630731 Fax: (01738) 637150

FLUORESCENT LAMPS OR TUBES

▶ Envirolite Ltd, Shore Road, Perth, PH2 8BH Tel: (01738) 630731 Fax: (01738) 637150

Intram Barwell Ltd, Barwell Business Park, Leatherhead Road, Chessington, Surrey, KT9 2NY Tel: (020) 8391 7500 Fax: (020) 8974 1629 E-mail: enquiries@ibl.co.uk

Mccroft Lighting, 54a Woods Lane, Derby, DE22 3UD Tel: (01332) 299100 Fax: (01332) 200365

FLUORESCENT LIGHT FITTINGS

▶ Anglepoise Ltd, 6 Stratfield Park, Elettra Avenue, Waterlooville, Hampshire, PO7 7XN Tel: (023) 9225 0934 Fax: (023) 9225 0696 E-mail: sales@anglepoise.co.uk

Bookham Technology Ltd, Brixham Road, Paignton, Devon, TQ4 7BE Tel: (01803) 662000 Fax: (01803) 559218

Designed Architectural Lighting Ltd, 6 Conqueror Court, Spilsby Road, Harold Hill, Romford, RM3 8SB Tel: (01708) 381999 Fax: (01708) 381585

EncapSulite International Ltd, 17 Chartwell Business Park, Chartmoor Road, Leighton Buzzard, Bedfordshire, LU7 4WG Tel: (01525) 376974 Fax: (01525) 850306 E-mail: reply@encapsulite.co.uk

FLUORESCENT LIGHT FITTINGS – *continued*

Fastlight.co.uk, Unit 19 Chatsworth Green, Basingstoke, Hampshire, RG22 4QA Tel: (0870) 7601420 Fax: (0870) 7601421 E-mail: rob@fastlight.co.uk
Gilbey Electrical Ltd, 55-59 Spear Street, Manchester, M1 1DF Tel: 0161-236 5079 Fax: 0161-228 2155 E-mail: sales@gilbeyelectrical.co.uk
Horsell Electrics Ltd, 30 Hollingdean Road, Brighton, BN2 4AA Tel: (01273) 694124 Fax: (01273) 603361 E-mail: horsell@globalnet.co.uk
J & G Coughtrie Ltd, Montrose Avenue, Hillington, Glasgow, G52 4LZ Tel: 0141-810 4516 Fax: 0141-882 0191 E-mail: sales@coughtree.com
Luminaire UK Ltd, 9-15 Henley Street, Birmingham, B11 1JB Tel: 0121-766 1490 Fax: 0121-766 1491 E-mail: sales@luminaireuk.com
Lumitron Ltd, Park House, 15-23 Greenhill Crescent, Watford Business Park, Watford, WD18 8PH Tel: (01923) 226222 Fax: (01923) 211300 E-mail: sales@lumitron.co.uk
Poselco Lighting, 1 Bristol Road, Greenford, Middlesex, UB6 8UW Tel: (020) 8813 0101 Fax: (020) 8813 0099 E-mail: sales@poselco.com
Frank Rigg Ltd, 489 Edenfield Road, Rochdale, Lancashire, OL11 5XR Tel: (01706) 644509 Fax: (01706) 643910
Thorlux Lighting P.L.C., Merse Road, North Moons Moat, Redditch, Worcestershire, B98 9HH Tel: (01527) 583200 Fax: (01527) 584177 E-mail: marketing@thorlux.co.uk

FLUORESCENT LIGHTING

EncapSulite International Ltd, 17 Chartwell Business Park, Chartmoor Road, Leighton Buzzard, Bedfordshire, LU7 4WG Tel: (01525) 376974 Fax: (01525) 850306 E-mail: reply@encapsulite.co.uk
▶ GVA Grimley Ltd, 211-213 West George Street, Glasgow, G2 2LW Tel: 0141-225 5729
Rex Electrical Wholesale, 231 London Road, Staines, Middlesex, TW18 4HR Tel: (01784) 463366 Fax: (01784) 449781

FLUORESCENT LIGHTING CONTROL GEAR

Arlen Electrical Ltd, Unit 1, High Point Business Village, Henwood Industrial Estate, Ashford, Kent, TN24 8DH Tel: (01233) 668041 Fax: (01233) 668042 E-mail: efasales@arlen.co.uk
B G Electrical Accessories, Unit 1 Highpoint Business Village, Henwood, Ashford, Kent, TN24 8DH Tel: (01233) 668000 Fax: (01233) 668100 E-mail: efasales@arlen.co.uk
H & T Mirage Ltd, 471 Kirkstall Road, Leeds, LS4 2QD Tel: 0113-263 0116 Fax: 0113-263 3770 E-mail: info@htmirage.co.uk
Tridonic Ltd, Thomas House Hampshire International Business Park, Crockford L, Chineham, Basingstoke, Hampshire, RG24 8LB Tel: (01256) 374300 Fax: (01256) 374200 E-mail: enquiries@uk.tridonic.co.uk

FLUORESCENT LIGHTING STARTER SWITCHES

B G Electrical Accessories, Unit 1 Highpoint Business Village, Henwood, Ashford, Kent, TN24 8DH Tel: (01233) 668000 Fax: (01233) 668100 E-mail: efasales@arlen.co.uk
John Martin Ltd, PO Box 28, Havant, Hampshire, PO9 2UB Tel: (023) 9249 2969 Fax: (023) 9249 2968 E-mail: jmelectronics@havant366.freeserve.co.uk

FLUORESCENT PAPER/BOARDS

Slater Harrison & Co. Ltd, Lowerhouse Mills, Bollington, Macclesfield, Cheshire, SK10 5HW Tel: (01625) 578900 Fax: (01625) 578972 E-mail: l.preston@slater-harrison.co.uk

FLUORESCENT PIGMENTS

Swada London, High Street, London, E15 2PP Tel: (020) 8534 7171 Fax: (020) 8519 2818

FLUORESCENT SIGNS

W A Ellwood Signs, 1 Ferry Lane, Rainham, Essex, RM13 9YH Tel: (01708) 521703 Fax: (01708) 521703

FLUORESCENT TUBE CLIPS

F T Pressings Ltd, Eagle Works, New Road, Studley, Warwickshire, B80 7LY Tel: (01527) 854925 Fax: (01527) 854925

FLUORESCENT TUBE DISPOSAL

▶ Karraway Waste Paper Ltd, 1 Folly Close, Radlett, Hertfordshire, WD7 8DR Tel: (020) 8236 0108 Fax: (01753) 279301 E-mail: info@karraway.demon.co.uk

FLUORINATED PRINTED CIRCUIT BOARD (PCB) COATINGS

Acota Ltd, Unit B1 Centrepoint Stafford Drive, Battlefield, Shrewsbury, SY1 3BF Tel: (01743) 466392 Fax: (01743) 466555 E-mail: admin@acota.co.uk

FLUOROCARBON COATING PROCESSORS OR SERVICES

Edlon, Riverside, Leven, Fife, KY8 4RT Tel: (01333) 426222 Fax: (01333) 426314 E-mail: sales@edlon.co.uk
Fluoro Precision Coatings, Units 19-20 Hewitts Industrial Estate, Elmbridge Road, Cranleigh, Surrey, GU6 8LW Tel: (01483) 276887 Fax: (01483) 276130 E-mail: gs@fluoroprecision.co.uk
Fluorocarbon Coatings (Sheffield Division) Ltd, Burlyvale Avenue, Sheffield, S12 2AX Tel: 0114-253 0353 Fax: 0114-253 0355 E-mail: info@fluorocarbon.co.uk
Fluorotech Dispersions Ltd, 11 Hampers Common Industrial Estate, Petworth, West Sussex, GU28 9NR Tel: (01798) 343586 Fax: (01798) 343586

FLUOROELASTOMER LIQUID COATINGS

J-Flex Rubber Products Ltd, Unit 1, London Road Business Park, Retford, Nottinghamshire, DN22 6HG Tel: (01777) 712400 Fax: (01777) 712409 E-mail: john@j-flex.co.uk

FLUOROELASTOMER SEALANTS

J-Flex Rubber Products Ltd, Unit 1, London Road Business Park, Retford, Nottinghamshire, DN22 6HG Tel: (01777) 712400 Fax: (01777) 712409 E-mail: john@j-flex.co.uk

FLUOROPOLYMER COATED GRAPHITE BURSTING DISCS

Elfab Ltd, Alder Road, North Shields, Tyne & Wear, NE29 8SD Tel: 0191-293 1269 Fax: 0191-293 1200 E-mail: sales@elfab.com

FLUOROPOLYMER COATINGS

Whitford Plastics Ltd, Christleton Court, Manor Park, Runcorn, Cheshire, WA7 1ST Tel: (01928) 571000 Fax: (01928) 571010 E-mail: sales@whitfordww.co.uk

FLUOROPOLYMER INJECTION MOULDINGS

D W Precision Engineering, 9 Sopwith CR, Hurricane Way, Wickford, Essex, SS11 8YU Tel: (01268) 571616 Fax: (01268) 571626 E-mail: dwp@netcomuk.co.uk

FLUOROPOLYMER MOULDINGS

D T Industries Ltd, Unit 10, Coulman Road Industrial Estate, Doncaster, South Yorkshire, DN8 5JU Tel: (01405) 740313 Fax: (01405) 817903 E-mail: sales@dtindustries.co.uk

FLUSH DOORS

F.R. Shadbolt & Sons, Ltd, 7 Springwood Drive, Braintree, Essex, CM7 2YN Tel: (01376) 333376 Fax: (020) 8523 2774 E-mail: sales@shadbolt.co.uk
Humphrey & Stretton (Properties) Ltd, Stretton House, 20 Pindar Road, Hoddesdon, Hertfordshire, EN11 0EU Tel: (01992) 462965 Fax: (01992) 463996 E-mail: sales@humphreystretton.com
Manor Doors Ltd, Manor House, 6-8 Creek Road, Barking, Essex, IG11 0TA Tel: (020) 8591 3300 Fax: (020) 8591 3338 E-mail: enquiries@manordoors.com
Midland Veneers Ltd, 3 The Hayes Trading Estate, Folkes Road, Stourbridge, West Midlands, DY9 8RG Tel: (01384) 424924 Fax: (01384) 424929 E-mail: sales@mid-ven.co.uk
Young's Doors, 24 City Road, Norwich, NR1 3AN Tel: (01603) 629889 Fax: (01603) 764650 E-mail: mail@youngs-doors.co.uk

FLUSH DOORS TO SPECIFICATION

Young's Doors, 24 City Road, Norwich, NR1 3AN Tel: (01603) 629889 Fax: (01603) 764650 E-mail: mail@youngs-doors.co.uk

FLUX, *See also headings for particular types*

Grosvenor Electronic Supplies, Priory Tec Park Saxon Way, Priory Park, Hessle, North Humberside, HU13 9PB Tel: (01482) 627327 Fax: (01482) 627328 E-mail: sales@grosvenor-group.com
Johnson Matthey Plc, York Way, Royston, Hertfordshire, SG8 5HJ Tel: (01763) 253200 Fax: (01763) 253168 E-mail: webbp@matthey.com
Ramsell-Naber Ltd, Vigo Place, Aldridge, Walsall, WS9 8YB Tel: (01922) 455521 Fax: (01922) 455277 E-mail: info@ramsell-naber.co.uk
Spanesi Automotive Mechanic Ltd, 33-37 Second Avenue Ind Estate, Chatham, Kent, ME4 5AY Tel: (01634) 845580 Fax: (01634) 401515

FLUX CORED WELDING WIRES

Metrode Products Ltd, Hanworth Lane, Chertsey, Surrey, KT16 9LL Tel: (01932) 566721 Fax: (01932) 565168 E-mail: info@metrode.com

FLUXGATES

Pandect Instrument Laboratories Ltd, Wellington Road, Cressex Business Park, High Wycombe, Buckinghamshire, HP12 3PX Tel: (01494) 526301 Fax: (01494) 464503 E-mail: enquiries@pandect.demon.co.uk

FLUXING MACHINES

Surface Engineering Process Equipment Ltd, Bennetts Field Trading Estate, Bennetts Field, Wincanton, Somerset, BA9 9DT Tel: (01963) 31274 Fax: (01963) 31288

FLUXMETERS

Hirst Magnetic Instruments Ltd, Pesla House, Tregoniggie Industrial Estate, Falmouth, Cornwall, TR11 4SN Tel: (01326) 372734 Fax: (01326) 378069 E-mail: dudding@hirst-magnetics.com

FLY CONTROL PRODUCTS

▶ UK Fly Control, Parkwood Estate, East Somerset Way, Wells, Somerset, BA5 1UT Tel: (01749) 673688 Fax: (01749) 673681 E-mail: candy@arkayltd.co.uk

FLY HYDRAULIC PRESS CONVERSION

Wescombe Maurice B, Silverdale Road, Hayes, Middlesex, UB3 3BN Tel: (020) 8561 0862 Fax: (020) 8561 7007

FLY KILLERS

▶ Pest Control Products UK, PO Box 50758, London, NW6 9AN Tel: 020 7993 4640 E-mail: neil@pestcontrolproducts.co.uk

FLY PRESS TOOLS

▶ Hunton - R M T - Gabro Machines, Cobbs Wood Industrial Estate, Hilton Road, Ashford, Kent, TN23 1EW Tel: (01233) 628976 Fax: (01233) 664909 E-mail: sales@mjallen.co.uk

FLY SCREEN DOORS

Exclusive Screens Ltd, PO Box 183,, Bishop Auckland, County Durham, DL15 8WW Tel: 01388 762377 Fax: 01388 762377 E-mail: info@exclusivescreens.co.uk

FLY SCREENING SYSTEMS

A & M Energy Fires, Pool House, Main Road, Huntley, Gloucester, GL19 3DZ Tel: (01452) 830662 Fax: (01452) 830891 E-mail: am@energy fires.co.uk
Exclusive Screens Ltd, PO Box 183,, Bishop Auckland, County Durham, DL15 8WW Tel: 01388 762377 Fax: 01388 762377 E-mail: info@exclusivescreens.co.uk
Plastok Associates Ltd, 79 Market Street, Birkenhead, Merseyside, CH41 6AN Tel: 0151-666 2056 Fax: 0151-650 0073 E-mail: sales@plastok.co.uk

FLY SCREENS

B D X Insect Screen Sales, The Onsite Building, Stephenson Way, Crawley, West Sussex, RH10 1TN Tel: (01293) 744426
Better Blind Co., Wych Fold, Hyde, Cheshire, SK14 5ED Tel: (0800) 1693765 Fax: 0161-367 9318 E-mail: info@newblinds.co.uk
BPC (Anglia) Ltd, Unit 1, 22-24 Brunel Way, Thetford, Norfolk, IP24 1HP Tel: (01603) 721197 Fax: (01603) 721197
Flydor Ltd, Unit 3 Priory Works, Newton Street, Newton St. Faith, Norwich, NR10 3AD Tel: (01603) 897799 Fax: (01603) 897280 E-mail: sales@flydor.co.uk
Mainline Screens, 19 Medway Drive, Chandler's Ford, Eastleigh, Hampshire, SO53 4SR Tel: (023) 8026 7846 Fax: (023) 8026 7869 E-mail: info@mainlinescreens.co.uk
Maximesh Ltd, Unit 6A, Morelands Trading Estate, Bristol Road, Gloucester, GL1 5RZ Tel: (01452) 561156 Fax: (01452) 544005 E-mail: sales@maximesh.co.uk
Midge & Flyscreen Co., Clearwater House, Glenuig, Lochailort, Inverness-Shire, PH38 4NB Tel: (01687) 470318 Fax: (01687) 470318
▶ Pest Control Products UK, PO Box 50758, London, NW6 9AN Tel: 020 7993 4640 E-mail: neil@pestcontrolproducts.co.uk
Synektics Ltd, 4 Brinksway, Fleet, Hampshire, GU51 3LZ Tel: (01252) 815281 Fax: (01252) 624433 E-mail: sales@synektics.co.uk
Vincents Shopfitters Ltd, Priory Works, Newton Street, Newton Saint Faith, Norwich, NR10 3AD Tel: (01603) 891050 Fax: (01603) 890689 E-mail: post@vincents.co.uk
▶ Windowscreens UK, PO Box 181, Upminster, Essex, RM14 1GX Tel: (01708) 222273 Fax: (01708) 641898 E-mail: info@flyscreensuk.co.uk
Woodland Flyscreen & Bird Exclusion Products, 73a Kennel Ride, Ascot, Berkshire, SL5 7NU Tel: (01344) 886459 Fax: (01344) 886459

FOAM, *See also headings for particular types and materials*

British Seals & Rubber Mouldings Ltd, Unit 7 Childerditch Indust Park, Childerditch Hall Drive, Brentwood, Essex, CM13 3HD Tel: (01277) 815300 Fax: (01277) 815350 E-mail: seals@british-gaskets.co.uk
Ian Cook & Son, Tremoddrett Farm, Roche, St. Austell, Cornwall, PL26 8LP Tel: (01726) 890206 Fax: (01726) 890899
Derby Foam & Upholstery Supplies, 10 Becket Street, Derby, DE1 1HT Tel: (01332) 345059
Foam Centre, 29 Howard Street, Glasgow, G1 4BA Tel: 0141-221 7578 Fax: 0141-221 7578 E-mail: sales@foamcentre.co.uk
Glasplies Ltd, 2 Crowland Street, Southport, Merseyside, PR9 7RZ Tel: (01704) 540626 Fax: (01704) 537322 E-mail: office@glasplies.co.uk
Herberts Foam & Textiles, 108 Victoria Road, Aldershot, Hampshire, GU11 1JX Tel: (01252) 332838 Fax: (01252) 345002
Interfoam Ltd, 16 Ronald Close, Woburn Road Industrial Estate, Bedford, MK42 7SH Tel: (01234) 855355 Fax: (01234) 855665 E-mail: sales@interfoam.co.uk
Kewell Converters Ltd, 60 Holmethorpe Avenue, Redhill, RH1 2NL Tel: (01737) 771710 Fax: (01737) 769732 E-mail: sales@kewell-converters.co.uk
Local Trading Co., 207 London Road, Sheffield, S2 4LJ Tel: 0114-255 1953 Fax: 0114-255 1953
M G R Foamtex Ltd, 10 Jefferson Way, Thame, Oxfordshire, OX9 3SZ Tel: (01844) 260005 Fax: (01844) 260157 E-mail: sales@mgrfoamtex.co.uk
Polyfoam Foam Products, 380c Ringwood Road, Poole, Dorset, BH12 3LT Tel: (01202) 736353 Fax: (01202) 736023 E-mail: peterthompson@polyfoam.sagehost.co.uk
Prima Foam, Caxton Road, Elm Farm Industrial Estate, Bedford, MK41 0ZW Tel: (01234) 213121 Fax: (01234) 340119
Quality Foam Products, 70-72 Sussex St, Norwich, NR3 3DE Tel: (01603) 622730 Fax: (01603) 622730
S M Upholstery Ltd, 212a Whitchurch Road, Cardiff, CF14 3NB Tel: (029) 2061 9813 Fax: (029) 2061 7579 E-mail: sales@smfoam.co.uk
Wales Foam, Unit 3 Rocky Park, Tenby, Dyfed, SA70 7LH Tel: (01834) 844333 Fax: (01834) 844346 E-mail: info@walesfoam.com

FOAM CUTTING

Polyfoam Foam Products, 380c Ringwood Road, Poole, Dorset, BH12 3LT Tel: (01202) 736353 Fax: (01202) 736023 E-mail: peterthompson@polyfoam.sagehost.co.uk

FOAM CUTTING MACHINERY

CGB Engineering Services Ltd, 2 Britannia House, Gorton Road, Manchester, M11 2DA Tel: 0161-231 7347 Fax: 0161-231 7077 E-mail: cgbservices@aol.com

Homag UK Ltd, 10c Sills Road, Castle Donington, Derby, DE74 2US Tel: (0870) 2433244 Fax: (01332) 856400 E-mail: sales@homag-uk.co.uk

A. Tarr Ltd, Meadow Business Centre, Uckfield Road, Ringmer, Lewes, East Sussex, BN8 5RW Tel: (01273) 814131 Fax: (01825) 762154 E-mail: sales@atarr.co.uk

FOAM DRESSINGS

▶ Smith & Nephew Extruded Films Ltd, Gateway To Humberside Trading Estate, Gilberdyke, Brough, North Humberside, HU15 2TD Tel: (01430) 440757 Fax: (01430) 440211 E-mail: phil.redshaw@smith-nephew.com

FOAM FILLED CUSHIONS

Aerofoam Ltd, 30 Dalston Gardens, Stanmore, Middlesex, HA7 1BY Tel: (020) 8204 8411 Fax: (020) 8204 7072

Fleur De Lis Furnishings Ltd, Collingwood House, Coach Lane, North Shields, Tyne & Wear, NE29 6TN Tel: 0191-258 1531 Fax: 0191-259 1318 E-mail: sales@fleur-de-lis.co.uk

▶ Foam Wizards Ltd, 3 Canal Street, Stourbridge, West Midlands, DY8 4LU Tel: (01384) 377018 Fax: (01384) 376757 E-mail: knettleford@aol.com

Herberts Foam & Textiles, 108 Victoria Road, Aldershot, Hampshire, GU11 1JX Tel: (01252) 332838 Fax: (01252) 345002

▶ London Foam, Unit 14 38-40 Upper Clapton Road, London, E5 8BQ Tel: (020) 8442 9327 Fax: (020) 8806 6188 E-mail: sales@cutfoam.co.uk

MSS, Taffs Fall Road, Treforest Industrial Estate, Pontypridd, Mid Glamorgan, CF37 5TT Tel: (01443) 849200 Fax: (01443) 843377 E-mail: info@medsys.co.uk

Spenco Healthcare International, Brian Royd Mills, Saddleworth Road, Greetland, Halifax, West Yorkshire, HX4 8NF Tel: (01422) 378569 Fax: (01422) 376064 E-mail: sales@spenco-healthcare.co.uk

FOAM GENERATION/SPRAYING EQUIPMENT

Hingerose Ltd, 5 Ryder Court, Corby, Northamptonshire, NN18 9NX Tel: (01536) 461441 Fax: (01536) 461600 E-mail: info@hingerose.co.uk

FOAM IN PLACE GASKETING MACHINERY

2KM UK Ltd, 11 Sherwood House, Sherwood Road, Aston Fields Trading Estate, Bromsgrove, Worcestershire, B60 3DR Tel: (01527) 834720 Fax: (01527) 834729 E-mail: sales@2km.co.uk

FOAM INERTING SERVICES

B J Services Co (U K) Ltd, Marine Base, Southtown Road, Great Yarmouth, Norfolk, NR31 0JJ Tel: (01493) 680680 Fax: (01493) 680780

Meek The Furnishers, 13-14 Market Place, Penzance, Cornwall, TR18 2JL Tel: (01736) 367890 Fax: (01736) 363071

FOAM MATTRESSES

▶ Abberley Ltd, Unit 7, Roach View, Millhead Way, Rochford, Essex, SS4 1LB Tel: (01702) 533761 Fax: (01702) 533760

B & A Quilting Co. Ltd, Oxford Mill, Oxford Street East, Ashton-under-Lyne, Lancashire, OL7 0LT Tel: 0161-330 5030 Fax: 0161-339 0418 E-mail: info@ba-quilting.co.uk

Blindcraft, 2 Peffer Place, Edinburgh, EH16 4BB Tel: 0131-661 1205 Fax: 0131-652 2095 E-mail: sales@blindcraft.co.uk

Burgess Bedding Ltd, 123 Pollard Street, Manchester, M4 7JB Tel: 0161-273 5528 Fax: 0161-273 5563

Recticel Midlands, Unit 3, Azalea Close, Clover Nook Industrial Park, Alfreton, Derbyshire, DE55 4QX Tel: (01773) 520242 Fax: (01773) 520513 E-mail: recticel@midlands.co.uk

Theraposture Ltd, Unit 11 Warminster Business Park, Furnax Lane, Warminster, Wiltshire, BA12 8PE Tel: (01985) 847788 Fax: (01985) 847700

FOAM NOVELTY HANDS

Imagineers Ltd, Abercromby Avenue, High Wycombe, Buckinghamshire, HP12 3BW Tel: (01494) 473861 Fax: (01494) 473863 E-mail: enquiries@imagineersltd.co.uk

FOAM PACKAGING

Alsamex Products Ltd, 1 Protea Way, Pixmore Avenue, Letchworth Garden City, Hertfordshire, SG6 1JT Tel: (01462) 672951 Fax: (01462) 480660 E-mail: sales@alsamex.co.uk

Functional Foam Beacons Products, Efi Industrial Estate, Brecon Road, Merthyr Tydfil, Mid Glamorgan, CF47 8RB Tel: (01685) 350011 Fax: (01685) 388396 E-mail: sales@beaconsproducts.co.uk

Turner Packaging Ltd, Horndon Business Park, West Horndon, Brentwood, Essex, CM13 3HW Tel: (01277) 810846 Fax: (01277) 810191 E-mail: service@turnerpack.co.uk

FOAM (PLASTIC) PRODUCTION MACHINERY AND EQUIPMENT MANUFRS

Drury Adams Ltd, New Hey Mill, Newchurch Road, Bacup, Lancashire, OL13 0BH Tel: (01706) 874000 Fax: (01706) 874747 E-mail: sales@druryadams.co.uk

Edulan Ltd, Unit M North Stage, 92 Broadway, Salford, M50 2UW Tel: 0161-876 8040 Fax: 0161-876 8041 E-mail: sales@edulan.com

H Y M A (UK) Ltd, Units 2-3, Westpoint Industrial Estate, Hargreaves Street, Oldham, OL9 9ND Tel: 0161-620 4137 Fax: 0161-627 0713

FOAM PRODUCTS

A & S Rubber & Plastics, Unit 10c Old Park Industrial Estate, Old Park Road, Wednesbury, West Midlands, WS10 9LR Tel: 0121-556 4415 Fax: 0121-556 2414 E-mail: info@asrubber.com

Brighton Foam Shop, 99 North Road, Brighton, BN1 1YE Tel: (01273) 606291 Fax: (01273) 606291

Peter Dewson, Chequers Hill, Doddington, Sittingbourne, Kent, ME9 0BN Tel: (01795) 886869 Fax: (01795) 886426

H M Foam Distributors Ltd, Shelburne Road, Calne, Wiltshire, SN11 8ER Tel: (01249) 816686 Fax: (01249) 817199 E-mail: h_m_foam@lineone.net

Pentonville Rubber Products Ltd, 104-106 Pentonville Road, London, N1 9JB Tel: (020) 7837 4582 Fax: (020) 7278 7392 E-mail: enquiries@pentonvillerubber.co.uk

Proceeds U.L.P. (UK) Ltd, Unit A, Stakehill Industrial Estate, Middleton, Manchester, M24 2SJ Tel: 0161-654 2500 Fax: 0161-655 4433

Rainbow Group, 15-17 Stanley Street, Manchester, M8 8SH Tel: 0161-834 8435 Fax: 0161-834 8435

Recticel Pendle, Dale Mill, Hallam Road, Nelson, Lancashire, BB9 8AN Tel: (01282) 697528 Fax: (01282) 694766

Rubber Products Leeds Ltd, Ingram Road, Leeds, LS11 9RQ Tel: 0113-243 4358 Fax: 0113-245 4945

Tekfoam Foam Products, 3 Bleach Works, Whitebirk Road, Blackburn, BB1 3HY Tel: (01254) 663839 Fax: (01254) 663839

Val Spicer, The Sugar Mill, Harford Bridge, Tavistock, Devon, PL19 9LR Tel: (01822) 617610 Fax: (01822) 617610

FOAM PRODUCTS, LATEX/ RUBBER

Aerofoam Ltd, 30 Dalston Gardens, Stanmore, Middlesex, HA7 1BY Tel: (020) 8204 8411 Fax: (020) 8204 7072

G N G Foam Converters Lancs Ltd, Todmorden Road, Littleborough, Lancashire, OL15 9EG Tel: (01706) 372222 Fax: (01706) 377991 E-mail: info@gngfoam.com

FOAM ROLLERS

Longs Ltd, Hanworth Lane Business Park, Chertsey, Surrey, KT16 9LZ Tel: (01932) 561241 Fax: (01932) 567391 E-mail: sales@longs.co.uk

FOAM RUBBER GASKETS

A & S Rubber & Plastics, Unit 10c Old Park Industrial Estate, Old Park Road, Wednesbury, West Midlands, WS10 9LR Tel: 0121-556 4415 Fax: 0121-556 2414 E-mail: info@asrubber.com

Bluemay Weston, Cooks Cross, South Molton, Devon, EX36 4AW Tel: (01769) 574574 Fax: (01769) 512944 E-mail: sales@bluemayweston.co.uk

FOAM, HIGH PERFORMANCE

▶ Foam Forge, 6 Rempstone Barns, Rempstone, Corfe Castle, Wareham, Dorset, BH20 5JH Tel: (01929) 480600 Fax: (01929) 480600 E-mail: sales@foamforge.co.uk

FOAM, POLYURETHANE (PU), RIGID/SEMIRIGID

Borderfoam Ltd, Lingen Road, Ludlow Business Park, Ludlow, Shropshire, SY8 1XD Tel: (01584) 877107 Fax: (01584) 874073

Boston Chemical Co. Ltd, 48 Millbeck Green, Collingham, Wetherby, West Yorkshire, LS22 5AJ Tel: (01937) 579522 Fax: (01937) 907473 E-mail: bccinfo@bostonchemicals.co.uk

Cellular Mouldings Ltd, 2 Pytchley Lodge Industrial Estate, Pytchley Lodge Road, Kettering, Northamptonshire, NN15 6JQ Tel: (01536) 513452 Fax: (01536) 411206 E-mail: sales@cellularmouldings.co.uk

Combass Ltd, Rotherham Close, Norwood Industrial Estate, Sheffield, S21 2JU Tel: 0114-248 0616 Fax: 0114-248 2684 E-mail: irmackie@aol.com

Martin's Rubber Co. Ltd, Orchard Place, Southampton, SO14 3PE Tel: (023) 8022 6330 Fax: (023) 8063 1577 E-mail: sales@martins-rubber.co.uk

Oakleaf Reproductions Ltd, Ling Bob Mill, Main St, Wilsden, Bradford, West Yorkshire, BD15 0JP Tel: (01535) 272878 Fax: (01535) 275748 E-mail: sales@oakleaf.co.uk

Orion Industries Ltd, Syma House, Halifax Road, Cressex Business Park, High Wycombe, Buckinghamshire, HP12 3SN Tel: (01494) 453800 Fax: (01494) 442762 E-mail: terry@aquila-innovations.co.uk

Rim Plastics Technology Ltd, 1 Wollaston Way, Burnt Mills Industrial Estate, Basildon, Essex, SS13 1DJ Tel: (01268) 729679 Fax: (01268) 729031 E-mail: sales@rimplas.co.uk

Vita Cortex Ni Ltd, Dunmurry Industrial Estate, Dunmurry, Belfast, BT17 9HU Tel: (028) 9061 8625 Fax: (028) 9061 9479 E-mail: info@vitacortex.com

FOAMING AGENTS

E A B Associates, 3 Craven Court, Craven Road, Broadheath, Altrincham, Cheshire, WA14 5DY Tel: 0161-926 9077 Fax: 0161-927 7718 E-mail: eaball@eabassoc.co.uk

Industrial Latex Compounds Ltd, Burns Mill, Manchester Street, Heywood, Lancashire, OL10 1DN Tel: (01706) 366161 Fax: (01706) 625664 E-mail: enquiries@indlatex.co.uk

FOIL BLOCKING SERVICES

Chiltern Foil Printing Co., 6 Acorn Business Centre, Cublington Road, Wing, Leighton Buzzard, Bedfordshire, LU7 0LB Tel: (01296) 682299 Fax: (01296) 682299 E-mail: plucas@fsbdial.co.uk

Foil Ribbon & Impact Printing Scotland Ltd, 4 Rutherford Court, 15 North Avenue, Clydebank Business Park, Clydebank, Dunbartonshire, G81 2QP Tel: 0141-952 5525 Fax: 0141-952 5524 E-mail: scotland@foilribbon.com

Grays Foil Blockers, Unit 10 White Post Lane, London, E9 5EN Tel: (020) 8985 6518 Fax: (020) 8986 0396

Impressions, 31 Shannon Way, Canvey Island, Essex, SS8 0PD Tel: (01268) 694175 Fax: (01268) 682000

Jenkinson Marshall & Co. Ltd, 103 Neepsend Lane, Sheffield, S3 8AT Tel: 0114-272 1311 Fax: 0114-276 6240

Kingfob, 4 John Street, Walsall, WS2 8AF Tel: (01922) 722561 Fax: (01922) 722442 E-mail: artwork@keyfob.co.uk

Parkins of Aylesbury Ltd, Unit 15, Park Street Industrial Estate, Aylesbury, Buckinghamshire, HP20 1EB Tel: (020) 8539 7559 Fax: (01296) 483018 E-mail: orders@postglow.co.uk

FOIL BLOCKING TOOLS

R E Bowers & Freeman Ltd, 15 Saffron Road, Wigston, Leicestershire, LE18 4TG Tel: 0116-278 5311 Fax: 0116-277 9544 E-mail: info@bowersfreeman.co.uk

FOIL HEATING ELEMENTS

Kanthal Ltd, Canal Arm, Festival Way, Stoke-on-Trent, ST1 5UR Tel: (01782) 224800 Fax: (01782) 224820 E-mail: info.uk@kanthal.se

Vulcan Refractories Ltd, Brookhouse Industrial Estate, Cheadle, Stoke-on-Trent, ST10 1PN Tel: (01538) 752238 Fax: (01538) 753349 E-mail: sales@vulcan-refractories.co.uk

FOIL STAMPING, *See Hot Foil etc*

FOLDED CARTONS

Barrows Cartons Ltd, Unit 1a Squires Mill, Micklehurst Road, Mossley, Ashton-under-Lyne, Lancashire, OL5 9JL Tel: (01457) 835253 Fax: (01457) 835898 E-mail: kel.b@btinternet.com

Box Wise Ltd, Rayne House, 3 The Street, Rayne, Braintree, Essex, CM77 6RH Tel: (01376) 551166 Fax: (01376) 551429 E-mail: sales@boxwise.ltd.uk

Boxes G H Ltd, Palatine Mill, Meadow Street, Great Harwood, Blackburn, BB6 7EJ Tel: (01254) 888151 Fax: (01254) 889569 E-mail: carton@boxesgh.co.uk

Bridger Packaging, Avenue One, Letchworth Garden City, Hertfordshire, SG6 2WP Tel: (01462) 636465 Fax: (01462) 636433 E-mail: postmaster@bridger.co.uk

Colourpass Cartons Ltd, 52 Cressex Enterprise Centre, Lincoln Road, Cressex Business Park, High Wycombe, Buckinghamshire, HP12 3RL Tel: (01494) 452527 Fax: (01494) 463815 E-mail: mikewillard2211@aol.com

Firstan Ltd, Trafalgar Way, Bar Hill, Cambridge, CB3 8SQ Tel: (01954) 201010 Fax: (01954) 782923 E-mail: sales@firstan.co.uk

KMD Investors Ltd, 140 Queens Road, Leicester, LE2 3FX Tel: 0116-270 9221 Fax: 0116-270 2334 E-mail: steve@kmd-company.co.uk

Landor Cartons Ltd, Church Manorway, Erith, Kent, DA8 1NP Tel: (01322) 435426 Fax: (01322) 445830 E-mail: erithsales@landorcartons.co.uk

PSW Packaging Ltd, 1 Creslands, Oldmixon CR, Weston-super-Mare, Avon, BS24 9AX Tel: (01934) 418183 Fax: (01934) 626953 E-mail: pswpackagingltd@fsbdial.co.uk

Springfield Cartons Ltd, Cottenham Lane, Salford, M7 1TW Tel: 0161-833 9857 Fax: 0161-832 1831

Tams Packaging Ltd, Sopers Road, Cuffley, Potters Bar, Hertfordshire, EN6 4TP Tel: (01707) 876777 Fax: (01707) 872233 E-mail: tams.packaging@talk21.com

FOLDERS, FILING, PAPER/ BOARD

Acco Eastlight Ltd, Ashton Road, Denton, Manchester, M34 3LR Tel: 0161-336 9431 Fax: 0161-320 8012 E-mail: mark.winstanley@acco-eastlight.co.uk

Dayfold Ltd, Unit 4-6 27 Black Moor Road, Ebblake Industrial Estate, Verwood, Dorset, BH31 6BE Tel: 01202 827401 Fax: (01202) 825841 E-mail: enquiries@dayfold.com

New Town Printers Redditch Ltd, Brickyard Lane, Studley, Warwickshire, B80 7EE Tel: (01527) 850011 Fax: (01527) 850055 E-mail: info@newtownprinters.co.uk

FOLDING ACCESS RAMPS

▶ Robin Ramps, The Courtyard, Durham Way North, Aycliffe Industrial Park, Newton Aycliffe, County Durham, DL5 6HP Tel: (01325) 304070 Fax: (01325) 304088 E-mail: info@robinproducts.com

FOLDING AND INSERTING MACHINES

▶ Flowline Mailing Systems, The Seedbed Centre, Langston Road, Loughton, Essex, IG10 3TQ Tel: (020) 8787 7122 Fax: (01268) 493031 E-mail: info@flowlineservice.co.uk

FOLDING BLINDS

▶ Natural Blinds, PO Box 2082, Gloucester, GL3 3WX Tel: 0845 056 4415 Fax: 0845 056 4415 E-mail: info@naturalblinds.co.uk

FOLDING CARDBOARD BOXES/ CASES/CONTAINERS

A S C Cartons Ltd, Hillside Works, Leeds Road, Shipley, West Yorkshire, BD18 1DZ Tel: (01274) 599842 Fax: (01274) 592225 E-mail: sales@asc-cartons.co.uk

Bosworth Wright, Express Works, Hollow Road, Anstey, Leicester, LE7 7FP Tel: 0116-236 2231 Fax: 0116-235 2230 E-mail: bosworthwright@hotmail.com

Contact Print & Packaging Ltd, Haigh Avenue, Stockport, Cheshire, SK4 1NU Tel: 0161-480 3568 Fax: 0161-480 8185

Field Group Ltd, Misbourne House Badminton Court, Church Street, Amersham, Buckinghamshire, HP7 0DD Tel: (01494) 720200 Fax: (01494) 431138 E-mail: marketing@fieldgroup.com

Maxdean, PO Box 19, Manchester, M25 9JP Tel: 0161-796 6696 Fax: 0161-796 6400 E-mail: maxdean@uk2.net

Melpack Ltd, 79 Huddersfield Road, Meltham, Holmfirth, HD9 4AF Tel: (01484) 850940 Fax: (01484) 850940

T Leighton & Sons, Unit 1a Albion Trading Estate, Mossley Road, Ashton-under-Lyne, Lancashire, OL6 6NQ Tel: 0161-330 4933 Fax: 0161-343 7025 E-mail: tlsbox@aol.com

Tylex Bropad Ltd, Ballingdon Hill Industrial Estate, Ballingdon Hill, Sudbury, Suffolk, CO10 2DX Tel: (01787) 371158 Fax: (01787) 311044 E-mail: tylex.polystyrene@btinternet.com

FOLDING MACHINES, METAL/ SHEET METAL

C M Z Machinery Ltd, Fullers End, Elsenham, Bishop's Stortford, Hertfordshire, CM22 6DU Tel: (01279) 814491 Fax: (01279) 814541 E-mail: info@cmzweb.co.uk

R M T-Gabro Ltd, Hilton Road, Cobbs Wood Industrial Estate, Ashford, Kent, TN23 1EW Tel: (01233) 628976 Fax: (01233) 631888 E-mail: sales@mjallen.co.uk

Waltons Of Radcliffe Sales Ltd, Unit 14 Bradley Fold Trading Estate, Radcliffe Moor Road, Bradley Fold, Bolton, BL2 6RT Tel: (01204) 393633 Fax: (01204) 363196 E-mail: sales@waltons-of-radcliffe.com

FOLDING MACHINES, METAL/ SHEET METAL, HAND OPERATED

C M Z Machinery Ltd, Fullers End, Elsenham, Bishop's Stortford, Hertfordshire, CM22 6DU Tel: (01279) 814491 Fax: (01279) 814541 E-mail: info@cmzweb.co.uk

FOLDING MACHINES, PAPER/ BOARD

Heidelberg Graphic Equipment Ltd, Intercity Way, Leeds, LS13 4LX Tel: 0113-224 8300 Fax: 0113-239 3118

Packaging Craftsman Ltd, Units 1a-1b, Park Mill Way, Clayton West, Huddersfield, HD8 9XJ Tel: (01484) 865680 Fax: (01484) 865681 E-mail: sales@packagingcraftsman.co.uk

Printaply Printers' Services, Highfield Lane, Sheffield, S13 9NA Tel: 0114-269 3322 Fax: (0845) 0850077 E-mail: printaply@yahoo.co.uk

FOLDING METAL BEDSTEADS

Beds & Furniture Superstore, 280 Oxlow Lane, Dagenham, Essex, RM10 8LP Tel: (020) 8593 7776 Fax: (020) 8593 7776

Jay Be Ltd, Spen Lane, Gomersal, Cleckheaton, West Yorkshire, BD19 4PN Tel: (01924) 517820 Fax: (01924) 517910 E-mail: sales@jaybe.co.uk

To Catch A Dream Ltd, The Ginnel, Harrogate, North Yorkshire, HG1 2RB Tel: (01423) 503060 Fax: (01423) 528111 E-mail: info@tocatchadream.net

FOLDING OR SLIDING PARTITIONING

Acoustic Products Ltd, 167 Tankerton Road, Whitstable, Kent, CT5 2AR Tel: (01227) 281140 Fax: (01227) 281141 E-mail: admin@acoustic-products.co.uk

Alco Beldan Ltd, Accordial House, 35 Watford Metro Centre, Watford, WD18 9XN Tel: (01923) 246600 Fax: (01923) 245654 E-mail: enquiries@alcobeldan.com

Becker Sliding Partitions Ltd, Wemco House, 477 Whippendell Road, Watford, WD18 7QY Tel: (01923) 236906 Fax: (01923) 230149 E-mail: sales@becker.uk.com

Flexiwall Co. Ltd, 15 Iliad Street, Liverpool, L5 3LU Tel: 0151-207 1103 Fax: 0151-207 1588

Hillaldam Coburn Ltd, 6 Wyvern Estate, Beverley Way, New Malden, Surrey, KT3 4PH Tel: (020) 8336 1515 Fax: (020) 8336 1414 E-mail: sales@hillaldam.co.uk

Kaba Hufcor Operable Partitions, Trent Lane, Castle Donington, Derby, DE74 2NP Tel: (0870) 0005250 Fax: (01332) 811059 E-mail: hufcoruk@dial.pipex.com

L H Safety Ltd, Greenbridge Works, Fallbarn Road, Rossendale, Lancashire, BB4 7NX Tel: (01706) 235100 Fax: (01706) 235150 E-mail: enquiries@lhsafety.co.uk

Leyton Engineering Services Ltd, Unit 8 Horndon Industrial Park, Station Road, West Horndon, Brentwood, Essex, CM13 3XL Tel: (01277) 812404 Fax: (01277) 810853 E-mail: sales@leytongroup.com

Masters Choice Ltd, 4 Carrive Road, Silverbridge, Newry, County Down, BT35 9LJ Tel: (028) 3086 1032 Fax: (028) 3086 1693 E-mail: chenjian80515@163.com

Monowa Ltd, Gable House, 16 Lower Plantation, Loudwater, Rickmansworth, Hertfordshire, WD3 4PQ Tel: (01923) 897779 Fax: (01923) 897780 E-mail: sales@monowa.co.uk

Pellfold Parthos Ltd, 1 The Quadrant, Howarth Road, Maidenhead, Berkshire, SL6 1AP Tel: (01628) 773353 Fax: (01628) 773363 E-mail: sales@pellfoldparthos.co.uk

Surefold Partitions, Cavendish House Cavendish Avenue, Birchwood Park, Birchwood, Warrington, WA3 6BU Tel: (01925) 810022 Fax: (01925) 818050

Westgate Factory Dividers, PO Box 21, Stafford, ST16 3DD Tel: (01785) 242171

FOLDING SECURITY SHUTTERS

Access & Security Systems Ltd, 7 Bacchus House, Calleva Park, Aldermaston, Reading, RG7 8EN Tel: 0118-981 7300 Fax: 0118-982 0455 E-mail: info@securityrollershutters.co.uk

Security Shutter Systems, 49 Torquay Crescent, Stevenage, Hertfordshire, SG1 2RQ Tel: 0870 6092324 Fax: (01462) 638729 E-mail: cjanecolwill@aol.com

FOLDING SERVICES, METAL/ SHEET METAL, CNC

Boydell Pipeworks & Fabrications, Poplar Street, Leigh, Lancashire, WN7 4HL Tel: (01942) 672951 Fax: (01942) 262042 E-mail: info@boydellfab.com

Curbridge Motor Co. Ltd, Unit 8a Bury Farm, Botley, Southampton, SO30 2HB Tel: (01489) 780782 Fax: (01489) 783982 E-mail: ian@curbridge-engineering.fsnet.co.uk

Hydram Engineering Ltd, Avenue Two, Chilton Industrial Estate, Chilton, Ferryhill, County Durham, DL17 0SG Tel: (01388) 720222 Fax: (01388) 721025 E-mail: hydram@hydram.co.uk

J S J Precision, Milburn Road, Stoke-on-Trent, ST6 2QF Tel: (01782) 269694 Fax: (01782) 279138

Niche Operable Systems Ltd, The Studio, Rear Of 18, Bath Street, Bolton, BL1 2DJ Tel: (01204) 381552 Fax: (01204) 381556 E-mail: enquiries@folding-partitions.co.uk

FOLDING STEP STOOLS

Malroy Products Dudley Ltd, Shaw Road, Dudley, West Midlands, DY2 8TR Tel: (01384) 254178 Fax: (01384) 230126 E-mail: info@malroy.co.freeserve.co.uk

FOOD BLENDING OR MIXING

▶ UK Blending Ltd, 9 Davy Road, Clacton-on-Sea, Essex, CO15 4XD Tel: (01255) 225002 Fax: (01255) 225003 E-mail: sales@uk-blending.com

FOOD CANS

Barplas Ltd, Barplas Industrial Park, Raymond Street, Bradford, West Yorkshire, BD5 8DG Tel: (01274) 727111 Fax: (01274) 726111 E-mail: ken@barplas.com

Carnaud Metalbox P.L.C., Perry Wood Walk, Worcester, WR5 1EG Tel: (01905) 762000 Fax: (01905) 762357

FOOD CHEMICALS

▶ Albion Chemicals Ltd, Union Mills, Oxford Road, Gomersal, Cleckheaton, West Yorkshire, BD19 4JW Tel: (01274) 850300 Fax: (01274) 851252 E-mail: enquiries@albionchemicals.co.uk

Apex Industrial Chemicals Ltd, Peterseat Drive, Altens Industrial Estate, Aberdeen, AB12 3HT Tel: (01224) 878420 Fax: (01224) 871195 E-mail: sales@apex-chemical.co.uk

Brotherton Speciality Products Ltd, Calder Vale Road, Wakefield, West Yorkshire, WF1 5PH Tel: (01924) 371919 Fax: (01924) 290408 E-mail: info@brotherton.co.uk

Cayley Chemical Corporation Ltd, 10 Manor Park Business Centre, Mackenzie Way, Swindon Village, Cheltenham, Gloucestershire, GL51 9TX Tel: (01242) 222971 Fax: (01242) 227634 E-mail: cayley@btinternet.com

Honeywill & Stein Ltd, Times House, Throwley Way, Sutton, Surrey, SM1 4AF Tel: (020) 8770 3455 Fax: (020) 8770 3464 E-mail: schuelerm@honeywill.co.uk

Northern Dairy Supplies Ltd, Lea Road, Lea Town, Preston, PR4 0RA Tel: (01772) 720358 Fax: (01772) 726489 E-mail: admin@dairyhygiene.co.uk

Peter Whiting Chemicals Ltd, 8 Barb Mews, London, W6 7PA Tel: (020) 8741 4025 Fax: (020) 8741 1737 E-mail: sales@whiting-cemicals.co.uk

Purac Biochem UK Ltd, 50-54 St. Pauls Square, Birmingham, B3 1QS Tel: 0121-236 1828 Fax: 0121-236 1401 E-mail: puk@purac.com

Safechem Ltd, Drum Industrial Estate, Drum Industrial Estate, Chester le Street, County Durham, DH2 1SR Tel: 0191-410 8668 Fax: 0191-410 2934 E-mail: enquiries@safechem.co.uk

Univar Ltd, International House, Zenith, Paycocke Road, Basildon, Essex, SS14 3DW Tel: (01268) 594400 Fax: (01268) 594482 E-mail: exports@univareurope.com

FOOD COATING/ENROBING EQUIPMENT

D F Dickens Ltd, Little Tennis Street South, Nottingham, NG2 4EU Tel: 0115-950 4084 Fax: 0115-950 8425

J.W. Durman, Greenway Farm, Moon Lane, North Petherton, Bridgwater, Somerset, TA7 0DS Tel: (01278) 662656

Laston Partnership, Laston House, Barnstaple Road, Ilfracombe, Devon, EX34 9NT Tel: (01271) 866557 Fax: (01271) 867754

Nutrition Point Ltd, 13 Taurus Park, Europa Boulevard, Westbrook, Warrington, WA5 7ZT Tel: (01925) 258000 Fax: (01925) 258001

Synergy Flavours, Synergy House, 2 Hillbottom Road, Sands Industrial Estate, High Wycombe, Buckinghamshire, HP12 4HJ Tel: (01494) 492222 Fax: (01494) 492111 E-mail: info@synergyflavours.com

FOOD COLOURING ADDITIVES

▶ Blends Ltd, Units 14-18 Manor Complex, Kirkby Bank Road, Knowsley Industrial Park, Liverpool, L33 7SY Tel: 0151-548 3000 Fax: 0151-548 3111 E-mail: sales@blendsltd.co.uk

British Salt Ltd, Cledford Lane, Middlewich, Cheshire, CW10 0JP Tel: (01606) 832881 Fax: (01606) 835999 E-mail: sales@british-salt.co.uk

Chr. Hansen (UK) Ltd, 2 Tealgate, Charnham Park, Hungerford, Berkshire, RG17 0YT Tel: (01488) 689800 Fax: (01488) 685436 E-mail: contactus-gb@gb.chr-hansen.com

▶ Dera Food Technology Ltd, Derby Road Business Park, Clay Cross, Chesterfield, Derbyshire, S45 9AG Tel: (01246) 250626 Fax: (01246) 250638 E-mail: callygreen@foodology.co.uk

T.M. Duche & Sons Ltd, 16A Hall Road, Wilmslow, Cheshire, SK9 5BN Tel: (01625) 538530 Fax: (01625) 538540 E-mail: info@tmduche.com

Flavormatic UK Ltd, The Heath Business & Technical Park, Runcorn, Cheshire, WA7 4QX Tel: (0870) 7579300

Islander International Ltd, The Old Vicarage, Somerset Square, Nailsea, Bristol, BS48 1RN Tel: (01275) 810194 Fax: (01275) 851752 E-mail: sales@islander.co.uk

Overseal Natural Ingredients Ltd, Swains Park Indust Estate, Swadlincote, Derbyshire, DE12 6JS Tel: (01283) 224221 Fax: (01283) 222006 E-mail: colours@overseal.co.uk

Regency Mowbray Co. Ltd, Hixon Industrial Estate, Hixon, Stafford, ST18 0PY Tel: (01889) 270554 Fax: (01889) 270927 E-mail: sales@regencymowbray.co.uk

Sensient Colors Ltd, Old Meadow Road, King's Lynn, Norfolk, PE30 4LA Tel: (01553) 669444 Fax: (01553) 770707

S.J. Taylor, Longmeadow Farm, Wappenham Rd, Syresham, Brackley, Northants, NN13 5HQ Tel: 01280 850084

Unbar Rothon Ltd, 2 Radford Crescent, Billericay, Essex, CM12 0DR Tel: (01277) 632211 Fax: (01277) 630151 E-mail: prothon@unbarrothon.co.uk

FOOD CONVEYOR BELTING

C P T Enterprises, 143 White Hart Lane, Portchester, Fareham, Hampshire, PO16 9BB Tel: (023) 9238 9521 Fax: (023) 9237 5181 E-mail: info@cptenterprises.co.uk

Charles Walker Ltd, 22-24 John Brannan Way, Bellshill, Lanarkshire, ML4 3HD Tel: (01698) 327600 Fax: (01698) 327602 E-mail: se.scotland@charleswalker.co.uk

Icon Engineering, Europa Way, Wisbech, Wisbech, Cambridgeshire, PE13 2TZ Tel: (01945) 474411 Fax: (01945) 474144 E-mail: paul@icon-eng.co.uk

FOOD CONVEYOR SYSTEMS

Asmech Systems Ltd, Units 108-111, Old Mill Lane Industrial Estate, Mansfield Woodhouse, Mansfield, Nottinghamshire, NG19 9BG Tel: (01623) 424442 Fax: (01623) 424433 E-mail: sales@asmechsystems.co.uk

CKF Systems Ltd, Unit 10 St Albans Road, Empire Way, Gloucester, GL2 5FW Tel: (01452) 424565 Fax: (01452) 423477 E-mail: sales@ckf.co.uk

Deighton Manufacturing UK Ltd, Gibson Street, Bradford, West Yorkshire, BD3 9TR Tel: (01274) 668771 Fax: (01274) 665214 E-mail: sales@deightonmanufacturing.co.uk

Driver Southall Ltd, Unit 18 Maybrook Industrial Estate, Maybrook Road, Walsall, WS8 7DG Tel: (01543) 375566 Fax: (01543) 375979 E-mail: email@driversouthall.co.uk

Geppert Conveyors UK, Camberley, Surrey, GU17 0RP Tel: (01252) 875871 Fax: (01252) 878804 E-mail: gwilliams@geppert-band.de

Kensal Handling Systems Ltd, Kensal House, President Way, Luton, LU2 9NR Tel: (01582) 425777 Fax: (01582) 425776 E-mail: sales@kensal.com

McConnell Equipment Ltd, 16 Ballycraigy Road, Antrim, BT41 1PL Tel: (028) 9446 3921 Fax: (028) 9446 7102 E-mail: macquip@btinternet.com

Newsmith Stainless Ltd, Fountain Works, Child Lane, Liversedge, West Yorkshire, WF15 7PH Tel: (01924) 405988 Fax: (01924) 403304 E-mail: sales@newsmiths.co.uk

PJH Engineering Ltd, Unit 15e Bergen Way, Sutton Fields Industrial Estate, Hull, HU7 0YQ Tel: (01482) 370375 Fax: (01482) 370385

Protech Fabrications Ltd, Rushden Road, Milton Ernest, Bedford, MK44 1RU Tel: (01234) 826233 Fax: (01234) 822762 E-mail: info@protech-food-systems.co.uk

Pulling, Sweetlands Way, Gosberton, Spalding, Lincolnshire, PE11 4HH Tel: (01775) 841070 Fax: (01775) 840167 E-mail: info@andypullingengineering.co.uk

Quality Conveyors Ltd, 10 Elland Lane, Elland, West Yorkshire, HX5 9DU Tel: (01422) 377166 Fax: (01422) 377238 E-mail: qconveyor@aol.com

Romech Spiral Systems Ltd, Carnaby Industrial Estate, Lancaster Road, Carnaby, Bridlington, North Humberside, YO15 3QY Tel: (01262) 601128 Fax: (01262) 671905 E-mail: sales@romech.co.uk

Stewart Gill Conveyor Ltd, 2 Christy Estate, Ivy Road, Aldershot, Hampshire, GU12 4TX Tel: (01252) 332221 Fax: (01252) 334387 E-mail: info@stewart-gill.co.uk

West Engineering Services Ltd, Unit 1a Abbey Mill Business Centre, Paisley, Renfrewshire, PA1 1TJ Tel: 0141-889 2331 Fax: 0141-887 9564

FOOD COOKERS

Double D Bakery Engineering Ltd, 6 Simpson Road, East Mains Industrial Estate, Broxburn, West Lothian, EH52 5NP Tel: (01506) 857112 Fax: (01506) 852232 E-mail: sales@double-d.co.uk

FOOD COOLERS

The Alumasc Group Plc, Station Road, Burton Latimer, Kettering, Northamptonshire, NN15 5JP Tel: (01536) 383848 Fax: (01536) 420147 E-mail: info@alumascprecision.co.uk

Centre Bar Concepts, Willow House, New Road, Droitwich, Worcestershire, WR9 0PQ Tel: (01299) 851649 Fax: (01299) 851550 E-mail: centrebarconcept@aol.com

FOOD DELIVERY BAGS

Flying Pizza Co., 5 Barnwell Business Park, Barnwell Drive, Cambridge, CB5 8UX Tel: (01223) 244875

▶ London's Flying Chef, 38 Great Suffolk Street, London, SE1 0UE Tel: (020) 7633 0099 Fax: (020) 7633 0999 E-mail: sales@flyingchef.co.uk

▶ Nymfoodmaniacs Ltd, 15 Harefield Road, Uxbridge, Middlesex, UB8 1PH Tel: 01895 234456 Fax: 01895 234456 E-mail: pat@nymfoodmaniacs.co.uk

FOOD DEPOSITING MACHINES

Dexmore Co Ltd, Hartshill Road, Stoke-on-Trent, ST4 7NF Tel: (01782) 846376 Fax: (01782) 414769 E-mail: sales@dexmore.co.uk

Winyard Engineering Ltd, 2-3 Cresswell Close, Pinchbeck, Spalding, Lincolnshire, PE11 3TY Tel: (01775) 725285 Fax: (01775) 710620 E-mail: sales@wfpe.co.uk

FOOD DISTRIBUTORS/AGENTS/ PACKERS

5 Star Meats, 95 Redlam, Blackburn, BB2 1UN Tel: (01254) 698781 Fax: (01254) 698781

Anglian Caterers, 4 Hurricane Way, Norwich, NR6 6EN Tel: (01603) 485273 Fax: (01603) 418679

▶ Atlas Foods, 11a Grove Street, Salford, M7 2YZ Tel: 0161-792 3000 Fax: 0161-792 3000

Baselica Ltd, 3 Somers Place, London, SW2 2AL Tel: (020) 8671 6622 Fax: (020) 8678 6151 E-mail: enquires@fineitalianfood.co.uk

Bernard Matthews plc, Upper Holton, Halesworth, Suffolk, IP19 8NJ Tel: (01986) 872262 Fax: (01986) 872188

Brake Logistics, Queensway, Rochdale, Lancashire, OL11 2RG Tel: (01706) 525211 Fax: (01706) 525213

British & Brazilian Produce Co. Ltd, Silvertown House, Orion Avenue, Great Blakenham, Ipswich, IP6 0LW Tel: (01473) 835640 Fax: (01473) 835657 E-mail: mail@produceworld.co.uk

J.L. Brooks (Provisions) Ltd, Unit 16, Waterloo Mills, Waterloo Road, Pudsey, West Yorkshire, LS28 8DQ Tel: 0113-257 0975

Brookside Products Co. Ltd, Harbour View, Glasson Industrial Estate, Maryport, Cumbria, CA15 8NT Tel: (01900) 815757 Fax: (01900) 814606 E-mail: brooksideproducts.co.uk@onetel.net.uk

▶ Castell Howell Foods, Unit 2 Merthyr Tydfil Industrial Park, Pentrebach, Merthyr Tydfil, Mid Glamorgan, CF48 4DR Tel: (01443) 693491 Fax: (01443) 620938

Charvo Finishing Ltd, Snaygill Industrial Estate, Keighley Road, Skipton, North Yorkshire, BD23 2QR Tel: (01756) 795028 Fax: (01756) 798473 E-mail: sales@charvo.co.uk

Christian Salvesen plc, Easton, Grantham, Lincolnshire, NG33 5AU Tel: (01476) 515000 Fax: (01476) 515011

FOOD DISTRIBUTORS/AGENTS/ PACKERS – *continued*

Continental Ltd, 229 East Street, London, SE17 2SS Tel: (020) 7703 6705 Fax: (020) 7701 6433

▶ Dial A Roti, 582 Great Horton Road, Bradford, West Yorkshire, BD7 3EU Tel: (01274) 522722

Eric Twigg Foods Ltd, 33-43 Aldwarke Road, Parkgate, Rotherham, South Yorkshire, S62 6BZ Tel: (01709) 523333 Fax: (01709) 523537 E-mail: info@erictwiggfoods.com

F D H (Lisnaskea) Ltd, Main Street, Lisnaskea, Enniskillen, County Fermanagh, BT92 0JE Tel: (028) 6772 1697 Fax: (028) 6672 2468

Fish-house Ltd, Dean Feld Way, Link 59 Business Park, Clitheroe, Lancashire, BB7 1QU Tel: (01200) 427527 Fax: (01200) 427027 E-mail: john@fish-house.co.uk

Five Star Edible Products Ltd, Phoenix Works, Avery Hill Road, London, SE9 2BD Tel: (020) 7538 4448 Fax: (020) 7538 4495 E-mail: enquiries@gandhi5star.co.uk

Food Partners Kilmarnock Ltd, Rowallan Business Park, Southcraig Avenue, Kilmarnock, Ayrshire, KA3 6BQ Tel: (01563) 556000 Fax: (01563) 570040

Galtee Meats (U K), 45 St Peters Street, Canterbury, Kent, CT1 2BG Tel: (01227) 787900

Golden Wonder Snack Services, Unit 4 Nelson Industrial Park, Herald Road, Hedge End, Southampton, SO30 2JH Tel: (01489) 789077 Fax: (01489) 789272 E-mail: mathewblake@walkers.co.uk

Hereford Catering Supplies, 9 Gruneisen Street, Hereford, HR4 0DX Tel: (01432) 357028

Holcrofts Catering Suppliers, Coldwell Burn Farm, Haswell, Durham, DH6 2XS Tel: 0191-517 0414 Fax: 0191-517 0162

Holdsworths, 91-93 St. James Mill Road, St. James Business Park, Northampton, NN5 5JP Tel: (01604) 581411 Fax: (01604) 581864

▶ J W Munro, 18 Bogmoor Place, Glasgow, G51 4TQ Tel: 0141-445 4339 Fax: 0141-445 5511

Kassero Edible Oils Ltd, 6-8 Albert Road, St. Philips, Bristol, BS2 0XA Tel: 0117-971 4331 Fax: 0117-972 4183 E-mail: sales@kassero.co.uk

▶ Kerry Foods Ltd, Horsfield Way, Bredbury Park Industrial Estate, Bredbury, Stockport, Cheshire, SK6 2TE Tel: 0161-406 4500 Fax: 0161-406 4515

Kilbrandon Oysters, Cuan Road, Oban, Argyll, PA34 4RB Tel: (01852) 300586 Fax: (01852) 300584 E-mail: scott.glen@kilbrandon-oysters.co.uk

Larousse Foods Ltd, 24 Finaghy Road South, Belfast, BT10 0DR Tel: (028) 9043 2522 Fax: (028) 9062 3492 E-mail: sales@laroussefoods.co.uk

Lowrie Foods Ltd, 153 Brinkburn Street, Newcastle upon Tyne, NE6 2BU Tel: 0191-265 9161 Fax: 0191-224 0019 E-mail: sales@lowriefoods.co.uk

M & J Seafoods Wholesale Ltd, 1 Crescent Wharf, North Woolwich Road, London, E16 2BG Tel: (020) 7540 4800 Fax: (020) 7540 4809

▶ Mccue's Food Packers, Pelham Road, Cleethorpes, South Humberside, DN35 7JZ Tel: (01472) 291999 Fax: (01472) 291999

Manchester Toiletries & Food Wholesale, 173-175 Cheetham Hill Road, Manchester, M8 8LG Tel: (0161) 839 7086 Fax: (0161) 839 7084 E-mail: zabarimports@aol.com

Manoucher Food & Co UK Ltd, 4 Wilton Mews, London, SW1X 7AR Tel: (020) 7823 2345 Fax: (020) 7245 1202 E-mail: sales@manoucher.com

Moy Park Ltd, Screevagh, Lisnaskea, Enniskillen, County Fermanagh, BT92 0FA Tel: (028) 6772 1999 Fax: (028) 6772 2442 E-mail: fernefoods@btinternet.com

Mr Crisp Ltd, 1 Decoy Road, Worthing, West Sussex, BN14 8ND Tel: (01903) 877422 Fax: (01903) 877422

Musgrave Retail Partners, Waldrist Way, Erith, Kent, DA18 4AG Tel: (020) 8320 9200 Fax: (020) 8312 9126

▶ Norton Logistics, Fengate Road, West Pinchbeck, Spalding, Lincolnshire, PE11 3NE Tel: (01775) 641000 E-mail: info@nortonholgate.com

Parkway Fine Foods, 44 High Street, Pinner, Middlesex, HA5 5PW Tel: (020) 8421 5452 Fax: (020) 8421 5452 E-mail: emporiodomani@aol.com

Pauleys Ltd, Sondes Road, Willowbrook East Industrial Estate, Corby, Northamptonshire, NN17 5XP Tel: (01536) 207200 Fax: (01536) 207201 E-mail: sales@pauleys.co.uk

Pourshins plc, The Lodge, Harmondsworth Lane, West Drayton, Middlesex, UB7 0AB Tel: (020) 8917 5777 Fax: (020) 8917 5791 E-mail: info@pourshins.com

Premium Oil Co., Brunel Way, Minehead, Somerset, TA24 5BY Tel: (01643) 706951 Fax: (01643) 706956 E-mail: sales@oilco.co.uk

Ritter Courivaud Ltd, Unit 4 Westlinks, Alperton Lane, Wembley, Middlesex, HA0 1ER Tel: (020) 8991 4350 Fax: (020) 8991 4383 E-mail: sales@rittercourivaud.co.uk

Simply Fresh Foods Ltd, Chaddock Lane, Worsley, Manchester, M28 1DR Tel: 0161-703 7023 Fax: 0161-703 7025

Spa Vending, Bona Vista, Kirkby Malzeard, Ripon, North Yorkshire, HG4 3RY Tel: (01765) 658113 Fax: (01765) 658219

Sunrise Fine Foods, Unit 5 The Business Centre, Morgans Vale Road, Redlynch, Salisbury, SP5 2HA Tel: (01725) 513122 Fax: (01725) 513322 E-mail: admin@wiltonwholefoods.co.uk

Supply Direct Ltd, 8 Priory House, Cloisters Business Park, 8 Battersea Park Road, London, SW8 4BH Tel: (020) 7622 9119 Fax: (020) 7622 0567 E-mail: info@supplydirect.com

Tekno Fuel Sports Drinks, Crest Complex, Courteney Road, Gillingham, Kent, ME8 0RX Tel: (01634) 233272 E-mail: graham@teknofuel.co.uk

3663, Hickling Road, Kingswood Lakeside, Cannock, Staffordshire, WS11 8JH Tel: (0870) 3663461 Fax: (01543) 405503

3663, Lee Mill Industrial Estate, Central Avenue, Ivybridge, Devon, PL21 9EW Tel: (0870) 3663601 Fax: (01752) 632 036

Veggie World Co. Ltd, 150-152 Queen's Way, Bletchley, Milton Keynes, MK2 2RS Tel: (0870) 7449976 Fax: (0870) 7449978 E-mail: sales@veggie-world.com

Victoria Foods (Bristol) Ltd, 39 Marsh Common Road, Pilning, Bristol, BS35 4JY Tel: (01454) 618618 Fax: (01454) 202713 E-mail: victoria.foods@virgin.net

▶ Violet Farm Foods Ltd, Units 10-11, Uddens Trading Estate, Wimborne, Dorset, BH21 7LQ Tel: (01202) 891006 Fax: (01202) 896281 E-mail: sales@vff.co.uk

Walkers Snack Foods Ltd, Leacroft Road, Birchwood, Warrington, WA3 6WA Tel: (01925) 283500 Fax: (01925) 283555 E-mail: nrdc.reception@intl.pepsico.com

West Country Fine Food Ltd, East Farm, Church Lane, Codford, Warminster, Wiltshire, BA12 0PJ Tel: (01985) 850524 Fax: (01985) 850690

Westham Food Supplies, 9 Gordon Row, Weymouth, Dorset, DT4 8LL Tel: (01305) 783608

Harris Winsford, Wharton Rd, Wharton Bridge, Winsford, Cheshire, CW7 3BB Tel: (01606) 557321 Fax: (01606) 559115

Worldwide Catering Ltd, 8 Failsworth Industrial Estate, Morton Street, Failsworth, Manchester, M35 0BN Tel: 0161-684 7774 Fax: 0161-684 7343

FOOD DRYERS

C C Process Engineering Ltd, Unit 44 Carlisle Enterprise Centre, James Street, Carlisle, CA2 5BB Tel: (01228) 819550 Fax: (01228) 819551 E-mail: sales@ccprocessengineering.com

Europrocessing Ltd, Euro Vent Ltd, Govan Road Fenton Industrial, Fenton Industrial Estate, Stoke-on-Trent, ST4 2RS Tel: (01782) 744242 Fax: (01782) 744475 E-mail: sales@eurovent.com

Mitchinson Engineering, Airfield, Kirkbride, Wigton, Cumbria, CA7 5LF Tel: (01697) 351925 Fax: (01697) 352060

Petrie Technologies Ltd, Common Bank Industrial Estate, Ackhurst Road, Chorley, Lancashire, PR7 1NH Tel: (01257) 241206 Fax: (01257) 267562 E-mail: sales@petrieltd.com

R Simon Dryers Ltd, Private Road No 3 Colwick Industrial Estate, Colwick Industrial Estate, Nottingham, NG4 2BD Tel: 0115-961 6276 Fax: 0115-961 6351 E-mail: sales@simon-dryers.co.uk

Spray Processes Ltd, 49A Bromham Road, Bedford, MK40 2AA Tel: (01234) 273922 Fax: (01234) 269436 E-mail: sales@spraypro.com

Telford Process Engineering Ltd, Business Development Centre, Stafford Park 4, Telford, Shropshire, TF3 3BA Tel: (01952) 293231 Fax: (01952) 201246 E-mail: dryers.ovens@tpe.co.uk

FOOD ELEVATORS

Peter Cox Marketing Ltd, High Street, Wrestlingworth, Sandy, Bedfordshire, SG19 2EN Tel: (01767) 631733 Fax: (01767) 631722 E-mail: info@petercoxmarketing.co.uk

FOOD FLAVOURS

Belmay Ltd, Turnells Mill Lane, Denington Industrial Estate, Wellingborough, Northamptonshire, NN8 2RN Tel: (01933) 440343 Fax: (01933) 274414 E-mail: postmaster@belmay.co.uk

Cargill Flavor Systems UK Ltd, Old Trafford Essence Distillery, 416 Chester Road, Manchester, M16 9HJ Tel: 0161-872 0225 Fax: 0161-848 7331 E-mail: sales_enquiries@cargi.com

Danisco, Denington Road, Wellingborough, Northamptonshire, NN8 2QJ Tel: (01933) 304200 Fax: (01933) 304224

Forrester Wood & Co. Ltd, Heron Street, Hawksley Industrial Estate, Oldham, OL8 4UJ Tel: 0161-620 4124 Fax: 0161-627 1050 E-mail: info@forresterwood.com

Frutarom UK Ltd, 3 Kingsthorne Park, Henson Way, Telford Way Industrial Estate, Kettering, Northamptonshire, NN16 8PX Tel: (01536) 532300 Fax: (01536) 532301 E-mail: sales@frutarom.co.uk

Givaudan UK Ltd, Chippenham Drive, Kingston, Milton Keynes, MK10 0AE Tel: (01908) 242424 Fax: (01908) 282232

Lionel Hitchen (Essential Oils) Ltd, Gravel Lane, Barton Stacey, Winchester, Hampshire, SO21 3RQ Tel: (01962) 760815 Fax: (01962) 760072 E-mail: info@lhn.co.uk

Industrial Proteins Ltd, 97 Burbage Road, London, SE24 9HD Tel: (020) 7501 9145 Fax: (020) 7737 1739

International Flavours & Fragrances (I F F) (GB) Ltd, Duddery Hill, Haverhill, Suffolk, CB9 8LG Tel: (01440) 715000 Fax: (01440) 762199 E-mail: iff.uk@iff.com

R D Campbell & Co. Ltd, Unit 14 Mill Farm Business Park, Millfield Road, Hounslow, TW4 5PY Tel: (020) 8898 6611 Fax: (020) 8898 6622

Rayner & Co. Ltd, 4 Bull Lane, Edmonton, London, N18 1TQ Tel: (020) 8807 3080 Fax: (020) 8807 9205 E-mail: info@rayner.co.uk

Regency Mowbray Co. Ltd, Hixon Industrial Estate, Hixon, Stafford, ST18 0PY Tel: (01889) 270554 Fax: (01889) 270927 E-mail: sales@regencymowbray.co.uk

H.E. Stringer Ltd, Icknield Way, Tring, Hertfordshire, HP23 4JZ Tel: (01442) 822621 Fax: (01442) 822727 E-mail: info@stringer-flavour.com

Unbar Rothon Ltd, 2 Radford Crescent, Billericay, Essex, CM12 0DR Tel: (01277) 632211 Fax: (01277) 630151 E-mail: prothon@unbarrothon.co.uk

Ungerer Ltd, Sealand Road, Chester, CH1 4LP Tel: (01244) 371711 Fax: (01244) 380185 E-mail: ungereruk@ungerer.co.uk

FOOD GIFT SETS

▶ Annie's Hampers, Bar Farm, Market Weighton Road, Holme-on-Spalding-Moor, York, YO43 4ED Tel: (01430) 860339 E-mail: enquires@annieshampers.com

▶ French Flavour Ltd, PO Box 2192, Wrexham, Clwyd, LL14 2TB Tel: (01978) 844378 Fax: (01978) 844378 E-mail: info@frenchflavour.co.uk

▶ The Gourmet House, Market Place, Durham, DH1 3NJ Tel: 0191-375 7511 E-mail: info@thegourmethouse.co.uk

FOOD GRADE COCONUT OIL

▶ Coconut Island, 43 Enys Road, Eastbourne, East Sussex, BN21 2DH Tel: (01323) 641757 E-mail: smaas@btinternet.com

▶ fresh-coconut organic virgin coconut oil, 145A Wembley Park Drive, Wembley, Middx, HA9 8HQ Tel: 07950 606390

FOOD GRADE GUM ACACIA

Agri Products, Finchley Road, London, NW3 6JG Tel: (020) 7483 2737 Fax: (020) 7586 7338 E-mail: gtitchener@agriproducts.com

FOOD GRADE LUBRICANTS

Caswells, Lagonda Road, Cowpen Lane Industrial Estate, Billingham, Cleveland, TS23 4JA Tel: (01642) 379600 Fax: (01642) 562978 E-mail: sales@caswellsgroup.com

Dynamics, Berwicks Trading Estate, Terling Hall Road, Hatfield Peverell, Chelmsford, CM3 2EY Tel: 0870 1620130 Fax: 0870 1688707 E-mail: sales@dynospill-dynamics.com

Lubrication Engineers UK Ltd, Latton Bush Business Ctr, Southern Way, Harlow, Essex, CM18 7BH Tel: (01763) 274253 Fax: (01763) 274253 E-mail: sales@le-lubricants.co.uk

Mobil Oil Co. Ltd, ExxonMobil House, Ermyn Way, Leatherhead, Surrey, KT22 8UX Tel: (01372) 222000 Fax: (01372) 222556

Sovereign Lubricants UK Ltd, Sovereign House, Crowtrees Lane, Brighouse, West Yorkshire, HD6 3LZ Tel: (01484) 718674 Fax: (01484) 400164 E-mail: schesters@btconnect.com

Trachem Fluid Solutions, 10 Victoria Road, Adwick-le-Street, Doncaster, South Yorkshire, DN6 7AZ Tel: (01302) 723111 Fax: (01302) 727744 E-mail: sales@oil-store.co.uk

FOOD HEALTH AND SAFETY CONSULTANCY

▶ Abergavenny Consultancy Ltd, Elephant House, Clifton Road, Abergavenny, Gwent, NP7 6AG Tel: (01873) 850534 Fax: (01873) 850534 E-mail: info@aberfood.com

▶ RMS Technical Services, 8 Sandwick Close, Fulwood, Preston, PR2 9RZ Tel: 01772 721310 E-mail: info@rmstechnical.co.uk

FOOD HYGIENE LEGISLATION CONSULTANCY

▶ Abergavenny Consultancy Ltd, Elephant House, Clifton Road, Abergavenny, Gwent, NP7 6AG Tel: (01873) 850534 Fax: (01873) 850534 E-mail: info@aberfood.com

I H C Ltd, The Innovation Centre, Vienna Court, Kirkleatham Business Park, Redcar, Cleveland, TS10 5SH Tel: (01642) 777733 Fax: (01642) 777744 E-mail: enquiries@qai.co.uk

FOOD IMPORT OR EXPORT

Allied Meat Importers, Stuart House, Britannia Road, Queens Gate, Waltham Cross, Hertfordshire, EN8 7TF Tel: (01992) 807950 Fax: (01992) 807951 E-mail: amiuk@alliedmeats.com

General Dietary Ltd, PO Box 38, Kingston upon Thames, Surrey, KT2 7YP Tel: (020) 8336 2323 Fax: (020) 8942 8274 E-mail: greareal.dietary@vigin.net

▶ Gerald McDonald & Co. Ltd, Cranes Farm Road, Basildon, Essex, SS14 3GT Tel: (01268) 244900

▶ S D Par Food Co. Ltd, Barlow Drive, Woodford Park Industrial Estat, Winsford, Cheshire, CW7 2RB Tel: (01606) 592299

FOOD INDUSTRY BELTING

Ammeraal Beltech Ltd, John Tate Road, Foxholes Business Park, Hertford, SG13 7QE Tel: (01992) 500550 Fax: (01992) 553010 E-mail: sales@ammeraalbeltech.co.uk

Ammeraal Beltech Ltd, Parkwood Street, Keighley, West Yorkshire, BD21 4PL Tel: (01535) 667015 Fax: (01535) 610250 E-mail: keighley@ammeraalbeltech.co.uk

Anaconda Belting Co., 2 Ashwood Place, Bean, Dartford, DA2 8BD Tel: (01474) 709784 Fax: (01474) 709896 E-mail: info@anacondabelting.co.uk

Belt Technologies Europe, Pennine House, Washington, Tyne & Wear, NE37 1LY Tel: 0191-415 3010 Fax: 0191-415 0333 E-mail: sales@bte.co.uk

Benson Beltings Ltd, Spenvale Works, Balme Road, Cleckheaton, West Yorkshire, BD19 4EW Tel: (01274) 851600 Fax: (01274) 851620 E-mail: sales@benson-beltings.co.uk

Chiorino UK, Phoenix Avenue, Featherstone, Pontefract, West Yorkshire, WF7 6EP Tel: (01977) 691880 Fax: (0870) 6065061 E-mail: sales@chiorino.co.uk

Davies Woven Wire Ltd, Unit 38 Cradley Heath Factory Centre, Woods Lane, Cradley Heath, West Midlands, B64 7AQ Tel: (01384) 411991 Fax: (01384) 410999 E-mail: sales@davieswovenwire.co.uk

Habasit Rossi Ltd, Habegger House, Keighley Road, Silsden, Keighley, West Yorkshire, BD20 0EA Tel: (0870) 8359555 Fax: (0870) 8359777 E-mail: info@habasitrossi.com

JD Vulcanising Services Ltd, Apple Orchard House, Skelton-in-Cleveland, Saltburn-by-the-Sea, Cleveland, TS12 2AZ Tel: (01287) 651194 Fax: (01287) 651194

R S Richardson Belting Co. Ltd, Crown Works, Staincliffe Road, Dewsbury, West Yorkshire, WF13 4SB Tel: (01924) 468191 Fax: (01924) 458065 E-mail: mail@diepress-richardson.co.uk

Red Box Supplies, Unit 19d, Bergen Way, Hull, HU7 0YQ Tel: (01482) 321713 Fax: (01482) 321714 E-mail: sales@redboxsupplies.co.uk

Siegling Ltd, Unit 4, Fifth Avenue, Tameside Park, Dukinfield, Cheshire, SK16 4PP Tel: 0161-331 3412 Fax: 0161-308 4385 E-mail: info@siegling.co.uk

FOOD INDUSTRY HYGIENIC EQUIPMENT/PRODUCTS

A & M Associates, Unit 2, Stuart Street, Off Fishwick Street, Rochdale, Lancashire, OL16 5NB Tel: (01706) 710747 Fax: (01706) 710746 E-mail: amasso@zen.co.uk

Chloroxy-Tech Ltd, Powke Lane Industrial Estate, Powke La, Blackheath, Birmingham, B65 0AH Tel: 0121-559 4141 Fax: 0121-559 2503 E-mail: chloroxy.tech@virgin.net

Global Hygiene Ltd, Unit 18, Ladford Fields Industrial Park, Seigford, Stafford, ST18 9QE Tel: (01785) 282900 Fax: (01785) 282222

I F M Services Ltd, Unit 14 Lodge Hill Industrial Estate, Station Road, Wells, Somerset, BA5 1EY Tel: (01749) 870942 Fax: (01749) 870087

Icp Claning Supplies, Unit 1, Fernie Road, Market Harborough, Leicestershire, LE16 7PH Tel: (01858) 462338 Fax: (01858) 433367 E-mail: icpcleaning@btconnect.com

Spot On Supplies Industrial Consumables Ltd, Willand Industrial Estate, Willand, Cullompton, Devon, EX15 2QW Tel: (01884) 821169 Fax: (01884) 821276 E-mail: admin@spotonsupplies.com

FOOD INDUSTRY OVENS

AFOS (NSE) Ltd, Kingston House,, Saxon Way, Priory Park West, Hessle, East Yorkshire, HU13 9PB Tel: (01482) 372100 Fax: (01482) 372150 E-mail: info@afosgroup.com

Double D Bakery Engineering Ltd, 6 Simpson Road, East Mains Industrial Estate, Broxburn, West Lothian, EH52 5NP Tel: (01506) 857112 Fax: (01506) 852232 E-mail: sales@double-d.co.uk

Frederick Bone & Co Ltd, Masterbaker Works, 53 Whytecliffe Road South, Purley, Surrey, CR8 2AZ Tel: (020) 8668 2234

FOOD INDUSTRY PIPEWORK

Ferrier Pumps Ltd, Burlington Street, Leith, Edinburgh, EH6 5JL Tel: 0131-554 1200 Fax: 0131-553 1272 E-mail: edinburgh@ferrierpumps.co.uk

FOOD INGREDIENT PRODUCTS

Agglomeration Technology Ltd, 7 Manse Lane, Monkswell Park, Knaresborough, North Yorkshire, HG5 8NQ Tel: (01423) 868411 Fax: (01423) 868410 E-mail: sales@aggtech.co.uk

Albion Chemicals Ltd, 46-50 Sydney Street West, Belfast, BT13 3GX Tel: (028) 9078 7450 Fax: (028) 9075 2500 E-mail: sales@albionchemicals.co.uk

Allchem (International) Ltd, Broadway House, 21 Broadway, Maidenhead, Berkshire, SL6 1NJ Tel: (01753) 443331 Fax: (01753) 443323 E-mail: info@allchem.co.uk

Authentic Indian Co., 1 Glebe Farm, Dennis Street, Hugglescote, Coalville, Leicestershire, LE67 2FP Tel: (01530) 830308 Fax: (01530) 838978 E-mail: sales@authenticindian.co.uk

Broste Ltd, Unit 8 North Lynn Business Village, Bergen Way, North Lynn Industrial Estate, King's Lynn, Norfolk, PE30 2JG Tel: (01553) 776066 Fax: (01553) 767319 E-mail: broste.uk@broste.com

John Butler (Hatfield) Ltd, 1 Bury Road, Hatfield, Hertfordshire, AL10 8BQ Tel: (01707) 262257 Fax: (01707) 251929

Chicken Joes, Empire Industrial Estate, Brickyard Road, Aldridge, Walsall, WS9 8UR Tel: (0870) 0601240 E-mail: mail@chickenjoes.net

Compass Group plc, Compass House, Guilford Street, Chertsey, Surrey, KT16 9BQ Tel: 0121-457 5555 Fax: (01932) 569956

Confoco International Ltd, Duncan House, High Street, Ripley, Woking, Surrey, GU23 6AY Tel: (01483) 211288 Fax: (01483) 211388 E-mail: info@confoco-food.com

Corcoran Chemicals Ltd, Oak House, Oak Close, Wilmslow, Cheshire, SK9 6DF Tel: (01625) 532731 Fax: (01625) 539096 E-mail: info@corcoranchemicals.com

Dalziel Packaging, Unit C3 Drumhead Road, Chorley North Business Park, Chorley, Lancashire, PR6 7DE Tel: (01257) 226010 Fax: (01257) 226019 E-mail: chorley@dalziel.co.uk

Dietary Foods Ltd, Cumberland House, Brook Street, Soham, Ely, Cambridgeshire, CB7 5BA Tel: (01353) 720791 Fax: (01353) 721705 E-mail: info@dietaryfoods.co.uk

Far East Food Products, Sheffield Road, Conisbrough, Doncaster, South Yorkshire, DN12 2BU Tel: (01709) 860800 Fax: (01709) 860881

▶ Fayrefield FoodTec Ltd, Gateway, Crewe Gates Industrial Estate, Crewe, CW1 6XA Tel: (01270) 211294 Fax: (01270) 580605

Flowfood Ltd, South Street, Ashton-under-Lyne, Lancashire, OL7 0PH Tel: 0161-330 0411 Fax: 0161-343 2193 E-mail: sales@flowfood.co.uk

Fountain Foods Ltd, New Road, Upwell, Wisbech, Cambridgeshire, PE14 9AB Tel: (01945) 773333 Fax: (01945) 772174 E-mail: fountainfoods@supernet.com

Fresh Farm Catering, Unit 2 96 White Post Lane, London, E9 5EN Tel: (020) 8525 0809 Fax: (020) 8525 6729

G Alderson, 11a Clarke Road, Bletchley, Milton Keynes, MK1 1UA Tel: (01908) 641680 Fax: (01908) 643517

Glanbia Cheese Ltd, Glanhwfa Road, Llangefni, Gwynedd, LL77 7TT Tel: (01248) 750351 Fax: (01248) 750566

H P Foods Ltd, 253 Tower Rd, Birmingham, B6 5AB Tel: 0121-359 4911 Fax: 0121 3595452

Harding's Oriental Food Supplies, Parlas, 3-5 Stanhope, South Shields, Tyne & Wear, NE33 4BA Tel: 0191-454 2000 Fax: 0191-454 2005 E-mail: hofs@perlas.co.uk

Alexander Harley Seeds Ltd, Thomanean, Milnathort, Kinross, KY13 0RF Tel: (01577) 862586 Fax: (01577) 862823 E-mail: petermclellan@harleys.co.uk

I M O (Marketing) Ltd, Whynscar House, The Ring, Bracknell, Berkshire, RG12 1BP Tel: (01344) 319770 Fax: (01344) 460112

Imarco, Beech House, The Covert, Ascot, Berkshire, SL5 9JS Tel: (01344) 845858 Fax: (01344) 626088

Kerry Ingredients Ltd, Portbury Way, Royal Portbury Dock, Portbury, Bristol, BS20 7XN Tel: (01275) 378500 Fax: (01275) 378555

Kerry Ingredients UK Ltd, Equinox South, Great Park Road, Bradley Stoke, Bristol, BS32 4QL Tel: (01454) 201666 Fax: (01454) 620711 E-mail: info@kerry-ingredients.co.uk

Kerry Ingredients UK Ltd, Carr Lane, Gainsborough, Lincolnshire, DN21 1LG Tel: (01427) 613927 Fax: (01427) 811805

Martin Mathew & Co. Ltd, Riverdene House, 140 High Street, Cheshunt, Waltham Cross, Hertfordshire, EN8 0AW Tel: (01992) 641641 Fax: (01992) 641888 E-mail: sales@martinmathew.co.uk

Nestle UK Ltd, Sarsons Works, Mills Hill Rd, Middleton, Manchester, M24 2ED Tel: 0161-653 4005 Fax: 01457 890164

Pettigrews Of Kelso, Pinnaclehill Industrial Estate, Kelso, Roxburghshire, TD5 8DW Tel: (01573) 224234 Fax: (01573) 223717 E-mail: sales@pettigrews.com

Robinson Brothers Ltd, Phoenix Street, West Bromwich, West Midlands, B70 0AH Tel: 0121-553 2451 Fax: 0121-500 5183 E-mail: sales@robinsonbrothers.ltd.uk

Sansol Foods Ltd, 101 Perth Road, Scone, Perth, PH2 6JL Tel: (01738) 567168 Fax: (01738) 567168

Sensine Flavors Ltd, Felinfach, Lampeter, Dyfed, SA48 8AG Tel: (01570) 470277 Fax: (01570) 470958

Sweet Success, Unit 7 Gauntley Court, Ward Street, Nottingham, NG7 5HD Tel: 0115-845 0660 Fax: 0115-845 0661 E-mail: info@sweetsuccess.uk.com

T R S International Foods Ltd, Argall Avenue, London, E10 7AS Tel: (020) 8556 2117 Fax: (020) 8556 6151

▶ UK Blending Ltd, 9 Davy Road, Clacton-on-Sea, Essex, CO15 4XD Tel: (01255) 225002 Fax: (01255) 225003 E-mail: sales@uk-blending.com

FOOD INSPECTION EQUIPMENT

E S M (U K) Ltd, PO Box 47, Bredbury, Cheshire, SK6 2FN Tel: 0161-406 3888 Fax: 0161-406 3889 E-mail: bshaw@satake-esm.co.uk

David James, Grove Cottage, Blounts Court Road, Peppard Common, Henley-on-Thames, Oxfordshire, RG9 5EU Tel: 0118-972 4945 Fax: 0118-972 4946

▶ Radix Systems Ltd, Unit D3-D4 The Premier Centre, Premier Way, Romsey, Hampshire, SO51 9DG Tel: (01794) 830240 Fax: (01794) 830143 E-mail: info@radixsystems.co.uk

FOOD INSULATED CONTAINERS

Bakkavor, 86 Carver Street, Birmingham, B1 3AL Tel: 0121-236 6464 Fax: 0121-233 2711 E-mail: info@bakkavor-bham.co.uk

Delphi Food Products Ltd, 14 Grenville Road, London, N19 4EH Tel: (020) 7281 2206 Fax: (020) 7281 4390

Metaltex UK Ltd, Brunleys, Kiln Farm, Milton Keynes, MK11 3HR Tel: (01908) 262062 Fax: (01908) 262162 E-mail: info@metaltex.com

FOOD LABELS

Aztec Labels, Kidderminster Industrial Estate, Spennells Valley Road, Kidderminster, Worcestershire, DY10 1XS Tel: (01562) 66518 Fax: (01562) 69802 E-mail: sales@azteclabel.co.uk

Briddon Baker Labels, Monkham Wood, Purley Ford, Luxborough, Watchet, Somerset, TA23 0SA Tel: (01984) 640084 Fax: (01984) 640521 E-mail: briddon.baker@virgin.net

Labelpower Ltd, 6 Kingsbury Trading Estate, Church Lane, London, NW9 8AU Tel: (020) 8205 8255 Fax: (020) 8200 1769 E-mail: sales@labelpower.co.uk

Premier Labels & Name Plates, Harrow Lane, Farncombe Street, Godalming, Surrey, GU7 3LD Tel: (01483) 423424

Skanem Cardiff, Bedwas House Industrial Estate, Bedwas, Caerphilly, Mid Glamorgan, CF83 8DW Tel: (029) 2086 5567 Fax: (029) 2086 5543 E-mail: gavin.braddon@selabelimage.co.uk

FOOD MACHINERY BLADES

The Jewel Blade Co. Ltd, 442 Penistone Road, Sheffield, S6 2FU Tel: 0114-234 3533 Fax: 0114-285 2473 E-mail: sales@jewelblade.co.uk

M G Knife Services, 8 Avon Business Park, Lodge Causeway, Bristol, BS16 3JP Tel: 0117-958 3974 Fax: 0117-958 3997

FOOD MANUFACTURERS

Saxby Brothers Ltd, PO Box 15, Wellingborough, Northamptonshire, NN8 1LH Tel: (01933) 221700 Fax: (01933) 221702 E-mail: info@saxbys.co.uk

FOOD MANUFACTURING INDUSTRY RECRUITMENT

▶ Goose Recruit, Walnut Tree Cottage, Main Road, Theberton, Leiston, Suffolk, IP16 4RU Tel: (01728) 833502 Fax: (01728) 833502 E-mail: rlapage@gooserecruit.co.uk

▶ Ridings Food Brokers Ltd, Unit 7 8 & 9, Linthwaite Business Centre, Manchester Road, Huddersfield, HD7 5QS Tel: (01484) 841920

FOOD PACKAGING MACHINES

Autarky Co. Ltd, Charlwoods Industrial Estate, Charlwoods Place, East Grinstead, West Sussex, RH19 2HY Tel: (01342) 311388 Fax: (01342) 323733 E-mail: sales@autarky.co.uk

G's Fresh Beetroot, Hostmoor Avenue, March Industrial Estate, March, Cambridgeshire, PE15 0AX Tel: (01354) 652659 Fax: (01354) 658292

Multivac UK, Multivac House, Rivermead Drive, Swindon, SN5 7UY Tel: (01793) 425800 Fax: (01793) 616219 E-mail: sales@multivac.co.uk

Original Pretzel Co. Ltd, 8 Temple Farm Industrial Estate, Sutton Road, Southend-On-Sea, SS2 5RN Tel: (01702) 461116 Fax: (01702) 461544

Packaging Automation Ltd, 1 Montgomery Close, Parkgate Industrial Estate, Knutsford, Cheshire, WA16 8XW Tel: (01565) 755000 Fax: (01565) 751015 E-mail: sales@pal.co.uk

Wipak UK Ltd, Unit 3 Buttington Cross Enterprise Park, Buttington, Welshpool, Powys, SY21 8SL Tel: (01938) 555255 Fax: (01938) 555277 E-mail: sales@wipak.com

FOOD PACKAGING MATERIALS MANUFRS

Alma Products Ltd, 51-53 Brindley Road, Astmoor Industrial Estate, Runcorn, Cheshire, WA7 1PF Tel: (01928) 580595 Fax: (01928) 581022

Amcor Ltd, Denmark House, Brick Close, Kiln Farm, Milton Keynes, MK11 3DP Tel: (01908) 261333 Fax: (01908) 261334

Amcore Flexibles, Hawkfield Way, Hawkfield Business Park, Bristol, BS14 0BD Tel: 0117-975 3200 Fax: 0117-975 3311 E-mail: sales@amcore.com

Britton Gelplas Ltd, Venture House, 5th Avenue, Letchworth Garden City, Herts, SG6 1JT Tel: (01462) 480808 Fax: (01462) 481398 E-mail: roger.young@britton-group.com

Buckingham Foods Ltd, Wimblington Drive, Redmoor, Milton Keynes, MK6 4AH Tel: (01908) 838900 Fax: (01908) 838920

Henry Colbeck Ltd, Seventh Avenue, Team Valley Trading Estate, Gateshead, Tyne & Wear, NE11 0HG Tel: 0191-482 4242 Fax: 0191-491 0357 E-mail: sales@colbeck.co.uk

Convenience Food Systems, Interchange Park, Newport Pagnell, Buckinghamshire, MK16 9PS Tel: (01908) 513500 Fax: (01908) 513555

Crimped Paper Works(M/C) Ltd, Bowden Park, Chapel-En-Le-Frith, High Peak, Derbyshire, SK23 0JX Tel: (01298) 812181 Fax: (01298) 815905 E-mail: sales@crimpedpaper.co.uk

Dalziel Ltd, 100 New Greenham Park, Greenham, Thatcham, Berkshire, RG19 6HN Tel: (01635) 265160 Fax: (01635) 38559

Dempson Packaging, Hermitage Mills, Hermitage Lane, Maidstone, Kent, ME16 9NP Tel: (01622) 727027 Fax: (01622) 720768 E-mail: sales@dempson.co.uk

Fispak Ltd, Marsmount Road, Shawfarm Industrial Estate, Prestwick, Ayrshire, KA9 2TQ Tel: (01292) 474455 Fax: (01292) 474022 E-mail: lehodge@msn.com

Frith's Flexible Packaging Ltd, 1 The Forum Coopers Way, Temple Farm Industrial Estate, Southend-on-Sea, SS2 5TE Tel: (01702) 462605 Fax: (01702) 616954 E-mail: sales@friths.co.uk

Gpi UK Ltd, Unit 6 Merlin Way, North Weald, Epping, Essex, CM16 6HR Tel: (01992) 524439 Fax: (01992) 524522

Grampian Country Pork Ashton, Mackeson Road, Ashton-under-Lyne, Lancashire, OL6 8HZ Tel: 0161-344 5601 Fax: 0161-339 2644

Harrison Europac Ltd, Stayton House, 93 Stayton Road, Sutton, Surrey, SM1 2PS Tel: (020) 8254 2300 Fax: (020) 8254 2301 E-mail: hep@harrison-europac.co.uk

M A P Systems, Unit 51, Bergen Way, North Lynn Industrial Estate, King's Lynn, Norfolk, PE30 2JG Tel: (01553) 764314 Fax: (01553) 769388 E-mail: eng@mapsystems.co.uk

Nicholas Packaging Ltd, Ham Lane, Kingswinford, West Midlands, DY6 7JJ Tel: (01384) 400500 Fax: (01384) 270943 E-mail: sales@nicholaspackaging.com

Nicholl Food Packaging Ltd, Bowdenhay Mill, Bowden Lane, Chapel-en-le-Frith, High Peak, Derbyshire, SK23 0JQ Tel: (01298) 812357 Fax: (01298) 815210 E-mail: sales@nichollfoodpackaging.co.uk

Co Ordinated Packaging Ltd, 3-4 Robert Way, Wickford, Essex, SS11 8DD Tel: (01268) 570551 Fax: (01268) 570611

▶ Plasware, Plasware House, Westmoreland Road, Kingsbury, London, NW9 9RN Tel: (020) 8621 2611 E-mail: info@plaswareuk.com

Rillatech Ltd, Callywhite Lane, Dronfield, Derbyshire, S18 2XP Tel: (01246) 291488 Fax: (01246) 291227

Tranfood Meat Co. Ltd, 1 Abbey Street, Birkenhead, Merseyside, CH41 5JG Tel: 0151-666 1660 Fax: 0151-647 4172

Wrap Film Systems Ltd, Hortonwood 45, Telford, Shropshire, TF1 7FA Tel: (01952) 678800 Fax: (01952) 678801 E-mail: sales@wrapfilm.com

FOOD PACKAGING, FRUIT AND VEGETABLES

▶ NNZ Ltd, 37 Market Place, Long Eaton, Nottingham, NG10 1JL Tel: 0115-972 7021 Fax: 0115-946 1375 E-mail: info@nnzuk.co.uk

FOOD PHOTOGRAPHERS

▶ Creative Photo Shop & Portrait Studio, Unit 16, 34 Gerard Street, Ashton-In-Makerfield, Wigan, Lancashire, WN4 9AE Tel: (01942) 725847 E-mail: info@creativephotoshop.co.uk

▶ Matthew Noble, Yew Grange, Wykeham, Scarborough, North Yorkshire, YO13 9QP Tel: (01723) 865384 E-mail: matthew@matthewnoble.co.uk

▶ Photo Express, 7 Melville Terrace, Edinburgh, EH9 1ND Tel: 0131-667 2164 Fax: 0131-667 2164 E-mail: info@photo-express-edinburgh.co.uk

▶ Pixeleyes Photography, 3rd floor, 21 perseverance works, 38 kingsland road, London, London, E2 8DA Tel: 020 7739 7239 Fax: 020 7739 7377 E-mail: studio@pixeleyesphotography.co.uk

▶ Terry Trott, The Studio, 24 School Lane, Bapchild, Sittingbourne, Kent, ME9 9NL Tel: (01795) 472833 Fax: (01795) 475941 E-mail: info@terrytrottphotography.co.uk

▶ Vision Photographic Ltd, Unit 1 Slader Business Park, Witney Road, Nuffield Industrial Estate, Poole, Dorset, BH17 0GP Tel: (01202) 667670 Fax: (01202) 668670 E-mail: info@visionphoto.co.uk

FOOD PREPARATION (CATERING) EQUIPMENT MANUFRS

B C E Scotland Ltd, 4 119 Cambuslang Road, Rutherglen, Glasgow, G73 1BW Tel: 0141-613 1850 Fax: 0141-613 1850

Caterers Equipment World, 121 Avenue Street, Parkhead, Glasgow, G40 3SA Tel: 0141 5565740 Fax: 0141 5565740 E-mail: enquiries@cew-soltan.co.uk

Chicken Joes, Empire Industrial Estate, Brickyard Road, Aldridge, Walsall, WS9 8UR Tel: (0870) 0601240 E-mail: mail@chickenjoes.net

Confoco International Ltd, Duncan House, High Street, Ripley, Woking, Surrey, GU23 6AY Tel: (01483) 211288 Fax: (01483) 211388 E-mail: info@confoco-food.com

Crawford Precision Engineering, Cross Court Industrial Estate, Kettering, Northamptonshire, NN16 9BN Tel: (01536) 417140 Fax: (01536) 524059 E-mail: cpeng@globalnet.co.uk

Dean Foods Ltd, Stocks Lane, Duckmanton, Chesterfield, Derbyshire, S44 5HZ Tel: (01246) 822161 Fax: (01246) 826717

▶ Dorset Cottage Foods, Gallop Cottages, Spetisbury, Blandford Forum, Dorset, DT11 9ED Tel: (01258) 857300 E-mail: jdwwatt@aol.com

Gilberts Food Equipment Ltd, Gilbert House, 1 Warwick Place, Borehamwood, Hertfordshire, WD6 1UA Tel: (0845) 2300681 Fax: (0845) 2300682 E-mail: info@topgourmet.co.uk

H Kilburn Ltd, 18 The Arcade, New Market Hall, Huddersfield, HD1 2UJ Tel: (01484) 423565 Fax: (01484) 423565

Hygienic Valves & Fittings Ltd, Huffwood Trading Estate, Partridge Green, Horsham, West Sussex, RH13 8AU Tel: (01403) 710255 Fax: (01403) 710338

Jasons Food Trade Supplies, 1a Edward Street, Stone, Staffordshire, ST15 8HN Tel: (01785) 819317 Fax: (01785) 811278

Kiremko Food Processing Equipment UK Ltd, Armstrong House, First Avenue, Doncaster Finningley Airport, Doncaster, South Yorkshire, DN9 3GA Tel: (01302) 772929 Fax: (01302) 770548 E-mail: sales@kiremko.com

A. Midgley & Co., Unit 2 Heritage Acres, Wakefield Road, Fitzwilliam, Pontefract, West Yorkshire, WF9 5BP Tel: (01977) 613426 Fax: (01977) 616532 E-mail: david@amfoodmachinery.fsnet.co.uk

3663, Unit 12, Severnbridge Industrial Estate, Symondscliffe Way, Caldicot, Gwent, NP26 5YA Tel: (0870) 3663661 Fax: (0870) 3663669

Unitech Engineering Ltd, Prospect Road, Burntwood, Staffordshire, WS7 0AL Tel: (01543) 675800 Fax: (01543) 687070 E-mail: info@unitech.uk.com

X Tech Stainless Steel Fabrications Ltd, Unit A2 Trecenydd Industrial Estate, Caerphilly, Mid Glamorgan, CF83 2RZ Tel: 029 20886639

FOOD PROCESS SCREENS/ SIEVES

D B Prepared Vegetables, Bedford Street, Stoke-on-Trent, ST1 4PZ Tel: (01782) 207266

Interfish Ltd, Wallsend Industrial Estate, Cattedown Wharves, Plymouth, PL4 0RW Tel: (01752) 267261 Fax: (01752) 224252

Russell Finex Ltd, Russell House, Browells Lane, Feltham, Middlesex, TW13 7EW Tel: (020) 8818 2000 Fax: (020) 8818 2060 E-mail: enquiries@russellfinexinc.com

Strathaird Salmon Ltd, 21-23 Longman Drive, Inverness, IV1 1SU Tel: (01463) 715123 Fax: (01463) 230867 E-mail: reception@strathaird.com

FOOD PROCESSING EQUIPMENT, USED

▶ Prins Packaging Solutions, Unit 140 Hartlebury Trading Estate, Hartlebury, Kidderminster, Worcestershire, DY10 4JB Tel: (01299) 251400 Fax: (01299) 251800 E-mail: sales@prinsuk.com
V Power Ltd, Hollins Mill, Rochdale Road, Todmorden, Lancashire, OL14 6SA Tel: (01706) 815008

FOOD PROCESSING METAL DETECTORS

Allcontrols Ltd, 20 Halifax Road, Cambridge, CB4 3PX Tel: (01223) 366164 Fax: (0870) 4580314 E-mail: info@allcontrols.co.uk
Cintex Ltd, Featherstone Road, Wolverton Mill, Milton Keynes, MK12 5TH Tel: (01908) 629200 Fax: (01908) 579824
Lock Inspection Group Ltd, Lock House, Neville Street, Oldham, OL9 6LF Tel: 0161-624 0333 Fax: 0161-624 5181 E-mail: marketing@lockinspection.co.uk
Mettler Toledo Safeline Ltd, Montford Street, Salford, M50 2XD Tel: 0161-848 8636 Fax: 0161-848 8595

FOOD PROCESSING MIXERS

John R Boone Ltd, 18 Silk Street, Congleton, Cheshire, CW12 4DH Tel: (01260) 272894 Fax: (01260) 281128 E-mail: sales@jrboone.com

FOOD PROCESSING PLANT AND MACHINERY ACCESSORIES

Armor Inox, Fairways Woodlands View, New Rhosrobin, Rhosrobin, Wrexham, Clwyd, LL11 4PT Tel: (01978) 263482 Fax: (01978) 263488
Silgan White Cap UK Ltd, 1 Thames Side, Windsor, Berkshire, SL4 1QN Tel: (01753) 832828 Fax: (01753) 620825

FOOD PROCESSING PLANT AND MACHINERY IMPORT/ EXPORT MERCHANTS AGENTS

Cambridge Overseas Trading Ltd, 13 Richmond Walk, St. Albans, Hertfordshire, AL4 9BA Tel: (01727) 833211 Fax: (01727) 810320 E-mail: cambost@aol.com
Weiler Beehive Europe Ltd, Unit 60 Beeches Industrial Estate, Waverley Road, Yate, Bristol, BS37 5QR Tel: (01454) 320900 Fax: (01454) 326262 E-mail: sales@weilerinc.co.uk

FOOD PROCESSING PLANT AND MACHINERY INSTALLATION

A L Technical Ltd, 2 Woodston Business Centre, Shrewsbury Avenue, Peterborough, PE2 7EF Tel: (01733) 390123 Fax: (01733) 394933 E-mail: altechnical@yahoo.co.uk
▶ Abergavenny Consultancy Ltd, Elephant House, Clifton Road, Abergavenny, Gwent, NP7 6AG Tel: (01873) 850534 Fax: (01873) 850534 E-mail: info@aberfood.com
D & T Engineering, Unit 12d Thorn Business Park, Rotherwas, Hereford, HR2 6JT Tel: (01432) 355433 Fax: (01432) 355519 E-mail: d.t.eng@btopenworld.com
Ferguson Engineering Northern Ltd, 2 Coulton Road, Brierfield, Nelson, Lancashire, BB9 5ST Tel: (01282) 447500 Fax: (01282) 447600 E-mail: sales@f-e-n.com

FOOD PROCESSING PLANT AND MACHINERY MANUFRS

A M C Food Machinery Ltd, 55-57 Waverley Road, Yate, Bristol, BS37 5QR Tel: (01454) 322315 Fax: (01454) 323144 E-mail: sales@amcfoodmachinery.com
Abacus Aquameter Ltd, 8 Woodlands Drive, Hoddesdon, Hertfordshire, EN11 8AZ Tel: (01992) 442861 Fax: (01992) 467919 E-mail: info@abacusaquameter.com
Advanced Food Technology, 3a Wenman Road, Thame, Oxfordshire, OX9 3UF Tel: (01844) 217303 Fax: (01844) 212341 E-mail: info@appliedfood.co.uk
Apple Engineering Ltd, Unit 23 Gothenburg Way, Hull, HU7 0YG Tel: (01482) 824200 Fax: (01482) 824196 E-mail: sales@appleng.co.uk
Aquarius Engineering Ltd, 52 Bergen Way, North Lynn Industrial Estate, King's Lynn, Norfolk, PE30 2JG Tel: (01553) 771716 Fax: (01553) 765164 E-mail: aquarius.eng@easynet.co.uk
Arcall plc, Westminster Road, Wareham, Dorset, BH20 4SR Tel: (01929) 554884 Fax: (01929) 554466 E-mail: email@arcall.co.uk
Automatic Peeler Co., Premier House, 146 Field Lane, Burton-on-Trent, Staffordshire, DE13 0NN Tel: (01283) 565819 Fax: (01283) 565819 E-mail: sales@autopeel.com
Base Handling Products Ltd, Unit 20 Barleyfield Industrial Estate, Barleyfield Way, Nantyglo, Ebbw Vale, Gwent, NP23 4LU Tel: (01495) 312172 Fax: (01495) 312089 E-mail: info@baseproducts.co.uk
Bell Perkins Ltd, Channing Houidses, Mart Road, Minehead, Somerset, TA24 5BJ Tel: (01643) 704541 Fax: (07643) 705646 E-mail: info@brookfood.co.uk
Benson Engineering Ltd, Units 14-16, Houghton Road, Sheffield, S25 4JJ Tel: (01909) 563551 Fax: (01909) 569953 E-mail: bensons@heh.co.uk
Bizerba UK Ltd, Eastman Way, Hemel Hempstead Industrial Estate, Hemel Hempstead, Hertfordshire, HP2 7DU Tel: (01442) 240751 Fax: (01442) 231328 E-mail: info@bizerba.co.uk
Boyd Food Machinery, Ramas, Buckie, Banffshire, AB56 4BA Tel: (01542) 835885 Fax: (01542) 835080 E-mail: boyd@boydfood.com
Briggs Holdings Ltd, Briggs House, Derby Street, Burton-on-Trent, Staffordshire, DE14 2LH Tel: (01283) 566661 Fax: (01283) 545978
▶ Camwheat Pie Machine Co. Ltd, Adelaide Street, Halifax, West Yorkshire, HX1 4LY Tel: (01422) 323202 Fax: (01422) 321113
▶ Carruthers Ltd, Staunton Court Business Park Ledbury Road, Unit 17c, Staunton, Gloucester, GL19 3QS Tel: (01452) 849099 E-mail: info@carruthers-equipment.com
CDK Engineering Services Ltd, 30 The Avenue, Stoke-Sub-Hamdon, Somerset, TA14 6QB Tel: 01935 825592 Fax: 01823 261066 E-mail: sales@cdkengineering.com
▶ Chard Ltd, Hurtham Farm, Chilson Common, South Chard, Chard, Somerset, TA20 2NT Tel: (01460) 221399 Fax: (01460) 221399
Chemtech International Ltd, 448 Basingstoke Road, Reading, RG2 0LP Tel: 0118-986 1222 Fax: 0118-986 0028 E-mail: sales@chemtechinternational.com
The Colston Manufacturing Engineering Company Ltd, Brunel Park, Vincients Road, Bumpers Farm, Chippenham, Wiltshire, SN14 6NQ Tel: (01249) 652652 Fax: (01249) 444684 E-mail: sales@colstonltd.co.uk
Clifford Coupe Ltd, 1 Royal Close, Worcester Park, Surrey, KT4 7JS Tel: (020) 8330 0660 Fax: (020) 8330 0660
Cox & Plant Products Ltd, Monument Works, Balds Lane, Stourbridge, West Midlands, DY9 8SE Tel: (01384) 895121 Fax: (01384) 893611 E-mail: convey@cox-plant.com
Cranford International Ltd, 10 Beech Waye, Gerrards Cross, Buckinghamshire, SL9 8BL Tel: (01753) 889831 Fax: (01753) 890892 E-mail: cranfd@aol.com
D C Norris & Co Engineering Ltd, Sand Road Industrial Estate, Sand Road, Great Gransden, Sandy, Bedfordshire, SG19 3AH Tel: (01767) 677515 Fax: (01767) 677956 E-mail: mail@dcnorris.co.uk
Dairy Pipe Lines Ltd, Commercial Centre, Ashdon Road, Saffron Walden, Essex, CB10 2NH Tel: (01799) 520188 Fax: (01799) 520183 E-mail: dairypipelines@dpluk.co.uk
Dantech UK Ltd, Burlington House, Crosby Road North, Liverpool, L22 0LG Tel: 0151-920 9080 Fax: 0151-920 9083 E-mail: sales@dantech.info
Deighton Manufacturing UK Ltd, Gibson Street, Bradford, West Yorkshire, BD3 9TR Tel: (01274) 668771 Fax: (01274) 665214 E-mail: sales@deightonmanufacturing.co.uk
Dunelm Supplies Ltd, Netherset Lane, Madeley, Crewe, CW3 9PF Tel: (01782) 750884 Fax: (01782) 751305 E-mail: dunelmpete@aol.co.uk
E S M (U K) Ltd, PO Box 47, Bredbury, Cheshire, SK6 2FN Tel: 0161-406 3888 Fax: 0161-406 3889 E-mail: bshaw@satake-esm.co.uk
▶ Emperor Leisure Services Ltd, Lavenham Business Centre, Parsons Street, Oldham, OL9 7AN Tel: 0161-652 6048 E-mail: sales@empreor.co.uk
Eric Kinder, 66 Mallusk Enterprise Park, Mallusk Drive, Newtownabbey, County Antrim, BT36 4GN Tel: (028) 9034 2454 Fax: (028) 9034 2454
Euro Food Machinery Ltd, Station Road Industrial Estate, Elmswell, Bury St. Edmunds, Suffolk, IP30 9HR Tel: (01359) 241971 Fax: (01359) 242092 E-mail: info@eurofood.co.uk
Fay Engineering Ltd, 5 Audley Court, Fison Way, Thetford, Norfolk, IP24 1HT Tel: (01842) 763622 Fax: (01842) 763622
Fountain Foods Ltd, New Road, Upwell, Wisbech, Cambridgeshire, PE14 9AB Tel: (01945) 773333 Fax: (01945) 772174 E-mail: fountainfoods@supernet.com
Fresh-pak Chilled Foods Ltd, 21-22 Kernan Drive, Loughborough, Leicestershire, LE11 5JT Tel: (01509) 233327 Fax: (01509) 269468 E-mail: info@fresh-pak.co.uk
▶ Globetech Cellar Services Ltd, 20a Wilson Street, Bristol, BS2 9HH Tel: 0117-924 8444 Fax: 0117-924 8555
H & K (Rugby) Ltd, 1 Crosford Lane, Swift Valley, Rugby, Warwickshire, CV21 1QN Tel: (01788) 554000
Haith-Tickhill Group, Cowhouse Lane, Armthorpe, Doncaster, South Yorkshire, DN3 3EE Tel: (01302) 831911 Fax: (01302) 300173 E-mail: sales@haith.co.uk
Handtmann Ltd, 23-24 North Luton Industrial Estate, Sedgewick Road, Luton, LU4 9DT Tel: (01582) 576116 Fax: (01582) 597164 E-mail: enquiries@handtmann.co.uk
Handyman, Unit 4 Lower Rectory Farm, Great Brickhill, Milton Keynes, MK17 9AF Tel: (01908) 366228 Fax: (01908) 366661
Hiley Engineering (Halifax) Co. Ltd, Station Road, Shay Lane, Holmfield, Halifax, West Yorkshire, HX2 9AY Tel: (01422) 248327 Fax: (01422) 240610 E-mail: hileyeng@hileyeng.co.uk
▶ Hong Wans, Unit 39 Enterprise Industrial Estate, Bolina Road, London, SE16 3LF Tel: (020) 7231 1628
Jackson Engineering Stoke On Trent Ltd, Scott Lidgett Road, Stoke-on-Trent, ST6 4LX Tel: (01782) 812139 Fax: (01782) 824374 E-mail: sales@jacksonengineering.co.uk
K B Engineering Co. Ltd, Fowlswick Industrial Estate, Fowlswick Lane, Allington, Chippenham, Wiltshire, SN14 6QE Tel: (01249) 783186 Fax: (01249) 782603
▶ Keemlaw Catering, 755 London Road, Larkfield, Aylesford, Kent, ME20 6DE Tel: (01732) 522419 Fax: (01622) 790348 E-mail: info@keemlaw.co.uk
▶ L S C Services Ltd, Unit 7, Brampton Centre, Brampton Road, Wath-Upon-Dearne, Rotherham, South Yorkshire, S63 6BB Tel: (01709) 879555
▶ Raymond Lydiard Engineering Services, Industrial Estate, 16 Willow Road, Yaxley, Peterborough, PE7 3HT Tel: (01733) 245532 Fax: (01733) 245534
Lynnmoore Engineering Co. Ltd, Horsleys Fields, King's Lynn, Norfolk, PE30 5DD Tel: (01553) 771122 Fax: (01553) 777105 E-mail: tech@lynnmooreeng.co.uk
M P E Systems Ltd, 1 Manor Farm, Culham, Abingdon, Oxfordshire, OX14 4NP Tel: (01235) 554771 Fax: (01235) 550656
M & P (Engineering) Ltd, Wharfside Way, Trafford Park, Manchester, M17 1AN Tel: 0161-872 8378 Fax: 0161-872 9250 E-mail: info@mp-engineering.co.uk
Mateline Engineering Ltd, 42 Walkers Road, Moons Moat North Industrial Estate, Redditch, Worcestershire, B98 9HD Tel: (01527) 63213 Fax: (01527) 584530 E-mail: mateline.engineering@tiscali.co.uk
Micronizing (UK) Co. Ltd, Charnwood Mill, Framlingham, Woodbridge, Suffolk, IP13 9PT Tel: (01728) 723435 Fax: (01728) 724359 E-mail: newton@micronizing.com
Moody plc, West Carr Road Industrial Estate, Retford, Nottinghamshire, DN22 7SN Tel: (01777) 701141 Fax: (01777) 709086 E-mail: paul.gregory@moodyplc.com
Morep Food Process Systems Ltd, 223a King Cross Road, Halifax, West Yorkshire, HX1 3JL Tel: (01422) 884761 Fax: (01422) 885140 E-mail: morepltd@aol.com
▶ Norbake Services Ltd, 8 Lady Ann Business Park, Lady Ann Road, Batley, West Yorkshire, WF17 0PS Tel: (01924) 442662 Fax: (01924) 420087 E-mail: sales@norbake.co.uk
Orbiter Food Machinery, Private Road 7, Colwick Industrial Estate, Nottingham, NG4 2JW Tel: 0115-940 0372 Fax: 0115-961 8741 E-mail: enquiries@orbiterfoodmachinery.co.uk
Pandet Ltd, 1 Premier Drum Works, Canal Street, Wigston, Leicestershire, LE18 4PL Tel: 0116-277 2372 Fax: 0116-277 2672 E-mail: sales@kuroma.com
Polar Systems Ltd, Austin Fields, King's Lynn, Norfolk, PE30 1PH Tel: (01553) 691472 Fax: (01553) 691473 E-mail: sales@polar-systems.co.uk
Pulling, Sweetlands Way, Gosberton, Spalding, Lincolnshire, PE11 4HH Tel: (01775) 841070 Fax: (01775) 840167 E-mail: info@andypullingengineering.co.uk
R Wright & Son Marine Engineers Ltd, Church Broughton Road, Foston, Derby, DE65 5PW Tel: (01283) 812177 Fax: (01283) 812052
Raymond Travel, 192 High Street, Dorking, Surrey, RH4 1QR Tel: (01306) 743780 Fax: (01306) 743764 E-mail: info@raymondtravel.co.uk
Riley Product Handling Ltd, Unit 2b, Meteor Business Park Mansfield Ro, Derby, DE21 4ST Tel: (01332) 866000 Fax: (01332) 866127 E-mail: paolo.graziani@rileyproducthandling.com
Selo UK Ltd, Mulberry Road, Rock Ferry, Birkenhead, Merseyside, CH42 3YA Tel: 0151-644 9393 Fax: 0151-645 2202 E-mail: info@selo.co.uk
▶ Shobwood Engineering (Burton) Ltd, Crown Industrial Estate, Anglesey Road, Burton-on-Trent, Staffordshire, DE14 3NX Tel: 01283 516730
Signs 2000, Unit 4 Kenworthy Road, Stafford, ST16 3DY Tel: (01785) 220561 Fax: (01785) 220969 E-mail: admin@signs2k.co.uk
SPC International Food Ltd, 35 Pinfold Lane, Grimsby, South Humberside, DN33 2EW Tel: (01472) 505080 Fax: (01472) 505088
Sugden Ltd, Pasture Lane, Barrowford, Nelson, Lancashire, BB9 6ES Tel: (01282) 611199 Fax: (01282) 613373 E-mail: sales@sugden.ltd.uk
▶ Tetra Pak Processing UK Ltd, Swan House Peregrine Business Park, Gomm Road, High Wycombe, Buckinghamshire, HP13 7DL Tel: (0870) 4426400 Fax: (0870) 4426401 E-mail: processing.uk@tetrapack.com
Thornton Industries (UK) Ltd, Thornton Ho, Dock La, Shipley, W. Yorkshire, BD17 7BE Tel: (01274) 598694 Fax: (01274) 531577 E-mail: sales@tiukltd.net
Trelrapak Cheese & Powder Systems Ltd, Coldharbour Business Park, Sherborne, Dorset, DT9 4JW Tel: (01935) 818800 Fax: (01935) 818818
Turbo Systems, 1 Gillett Street, Hull, HU3 4JA Tel: (01482) 325651 Fax: (01482) 211434 E-mail: mmoss@turbo-systems.com
Unifab Engineering Ltd, Pelham Road, Cleethorpes, South Humberside, DN35 7JT Tel: (01472) 230149 Fax: (01472) 230149
Urschel International Ltd, Tiber Way, Meridian Business Park, Leicester, LE19 1QP Tel: 0116-263 4321 Fax: 0116-263 4300 E-mail: international@urschel.com
Windsor Food Machinery, Units 1-6 Mountain Farm, Marsh Road, Hamstreet, Ashford, Kent, TN26 2JD Tel: (01233) 733737 Fax: (01233) 733392 E-mail: sales@windsorfoodmachinery.com
Winyard Engineering Ltd, 2-3 Cresswell Close, Pinchbeck, Spalding, Lincolnshire, PE11 3TY Tel: (01775) 725285 Fax: (01775) 710620 E-mail: sales@wfpe.co.uk
▶ Wymbs Engineering Ltd, Clarence Road, Bollington, Macclesfield, Cheshire, SK10 5JZ Tel: (01625) 575154 Fax: (01625) 573109 E-mail: info@wymbsengineering.com

FOOD PROCESSING PLANT CONTRACTORS OR DESIGNERS

Automatic Peeler Co., Premier House, 146 Field Lane, Burton-on-Trent, Staffordshire, DE13 0NN Tel: (01283) 565819 Fax: (01283) 565819 E-mail: sales@autopeel.com
Birotech Food Machinery, 34 Beveridge Road, Kirkcaldy, Fife, KY1 1UY Tel: (01592) 260288 Fax: (01592) 644150 E-mail: biro.tech@virgin.net
Coates Engineering International Ltd, Millfold, Whitworth, Rochdale, Lancashire, OL12 8DN Tel: (01706) 852122 Fax: (01706) 853629 E-mail: info@bchltd.com
Code-A-Weld, Units 5-10, Bessemer Way, Harfreys Industrial Estate, Great Yarmouth, Norfolk, NR31 0LX Tel: (01493) 602844 Fax: (01493) 653331 E-mail: codeaweld@btinternet.com
Fenmarc Ltd, Moor Lane, Swinderby, Lincoln, LN6 9LX Tel: (01522) 868484 Fax: (01522) 868835
Kerry Foods Ltd, Rookery Farm, Attleborough Road, Little Ellingham, Attleborough, Norfolk, NR17 1JH Tel: (01953) 851076 Fax: (01953) 851441
Micronizing (UK) Co. Ltd, Charnwood Mill, Framlingham, Woodbridge, Suffolk, IP13 9PT Tel: (01728) 723435 Fax: (01728) 724359 E-mail: newton@micronizing.com
Polar Systems Ltd, Austin Fields, King's Lynn, Norfolk, PE30 1PH Tel: (01553) 691472 Fax: (01553) 691473 E-mail: sales@polar-systems.co.uk
Thermax Construction, Unit 3 Dover Court, Dover Road, Latchford, Warrington, WA4 1NW Tel: (01925) 242450 Fax: (01925) 242455 E-mail: malcolmferguson@parflothermax.co.uk
Vincent Processes Ltd, Turnpike Industrial Estate, Turnpike Road, Newbury, Berkshire, RG14 2NT Tel: (01635) 40295 Fax: (01635) 37680 E-mail: carlsmith@vincentprocesses.co.uk

FOOD PROCESSORS/ PRODUCTS, *See also headings for particular types*

▶ Aba Foods, 6 Morrison Yard, 551a High Road, London, N17 6SB Tel: (020) 8885 2710 Fax: (020) 8959 6062
▶ Accolade Food Manufacturers Ltd, North Wall, Grimsby, South Humberside, DN31 3SY Tel: (01472) 349762 Fax: (01472) 349769
Active Health Ltd, Unit 12 Lakeside Business Park, Swan Lane, Sandhurst, Berkshire, GU47 9DN Tel: (01252) 861666 Fax: (01252) 861455
Adams Pork Products Ltd, 1 Viscount Way, Woodley, Reading, RG5 4DZ Tel: 0118-921 9227 Fax: 0118-944 8756
Aeron Bacon Supplies, Unit 1 Felin Fach Industrial Estate, Felinfach, Lampeter, Dyfed, SA48 8AE Tel: (01570) 471065
All Fresh, ABC House, Lakeside Industrial Park, Cotswold Dene, Standlake, Witney, Oxfordshire, OX29 7PJ Tel: (01865) 300900 Fax: (01865) 300879
Almaz Food Co Ltd, 2 Raeburn Crescent, Kirkcaldy, Fife, KY2 5QQ Tel: (01592) 646414 Fax: (01592) 646414
Aloe Vera Health Products & Information Service, 55 Amity Grove, London, SW20 0LQ Tel: (020) 8947 6528 Fax: (020) 8947 1463
Amko Foods Ltd, Shiffnal Street, Bolton, BL2 1BZ Tel: (01204) 388801 E-mail: sales@amko.fsnet.co.uk
Ancient Recipes, Empire Way, Gretna, Dumfriesshire, DG16 5BN Tel: (01461) 338117 Fax: (01461) 338436 E-mail: mail@solwayveg.co.uk
▶ Anila's Authentic Sauces, Walton-On-Thames, Surrey, KT12 3WS Tel: (020) 8577 6162 Fax: (020) 8577 6162 E-mail: info@anilassauces.com
Ansteys Of Worcester Traditional Cheese Makers, Broomhall Lane, Broomhall, Worcester, WR5 2NT Tel: (01905) 820232 Fax: (01905) 828032 E-mail: gifts@ansteys.com

FOOD PROCESSORS/PRODUCTS - *continued*

Applejacks, Unit 28 The Mall, The Stratford Centre, London, E15 1XD Tel: (020) 8519 5809 Fax: (020) 8519 1099 E-mail: robert@applejacks.co.uk

▶ Atlas Foods, 11a Grove Street, Salford, M7 2YZ Tel: 0161-792 3000 Fax: 0161-792 3000

Authentic Asian Snacks, 24-26 Cedar Road, Newcastle upon Tyne, NE4 9XX Tel: 0191-273 4715 Fax: 0191-273 4715 E-mail: rehmansweetcentre@hotmail.com

Axgro Foods Ltd, 39 West Street, West Butterwick, Scunthorpe, South Humberside, DN17 3JZ Tel: (01724) 783214 Fax: (01724) 782198E-mail: admin@axgrofoods.fsnet.co.uk

B I Ltd, 2 Robinson Road, Leicester, LE5 4NS Tel: 0116-276 6344 Fax: 0116-276 6187 E-mail: info@biltd.com

Bar & Restaurant Foods Ltd, Nine Mile Point Industrial Estate, Newport, Gwent, NP11 7HZ Tel: (01495) 202100 Fax: (01495) 200869 E-mail: sales@barfoods.com

Basmati Rice UK Ltd, Pari House, Stambourne Road, Great Yeldham, Halstead, Essex, CO9 4RB Tel: (01787) 237173 Fax: (01787) 237318 E-mail: admin@basmatiriceukltd.co.uk

Baxters Food Group, Baxters Of Speyside, Fochabers, Morayshire, IV32 7LD Tel: (01343) 820393 Fax: (01343) 820286 E-mail: info@baxters.co.uk

▶ Bayford Foods Ltd, Unit 24, Wynford Farm Industrial Estate, Belbins, Romsey, Hampshire, SO51 0PW Tel: (01794) 367567

Beanfeast Wholefoods, 2 The Arcade, Fore Street, Okehampton, Devon, EX20 1EX Tel: (01837) 52387

Big Bite, Rowles House, Weston-on-the-Green, Bicester, Oxfordshire, OX25 3QQ Tel: (01869) 351383 Fax: (01869) 351383

▶ BN Pork Products Ltd, Unit 23-24-25 Riverside, Power Station Road, Rugeley, Staffordshire, WS15 2YR Tel: (01889) 570088 Fax: (01889) 583550 E-mail: raygrey@btconnect.com

Bourne Salads, Spalding Road, Bourne, Lincolnshire, PE10 0AT Tel: (01778) 393222 Fax: (01778) 393001

Brakes Ltd, Enterprise House Nicholas Road, Eureka Science Park, Ashford, Kent, TN25 4AG Tel: (01233) 206206 Fax: (01223) 206035E-mail: customer.service@brake.co.uk

Brand Partnership Ltd, Southfork Industrial Estate, Dartmouth Way, Leeds, LS11 5JL Tel: 0113-270 6061 Fax: 0113-277 5319 E-mail: patrick.barrow@brandpartnership.co.uk

The Brecks Co. Ltd, Breighton Airfield, Breighton, Selby, North Yorkshire, YO8 7DH Tel: (01757) 288943 Fax: (01757) 289119

▶ C A Treble, 88-90 Hatton Garden, London, EC1N 8PN Tel: (020) 7405 5556 Fax: (020) 7405 5556

Calder Foods, Unit 20, Harrison Way, Carlisle, CA1 2SS Tel: (01228) 514518 Fax: (01228) 514518

Campbells Grocery Products Ltd, Batchelors Factory, Kennington Road, Willesborough, Ashford, Kent, TN24 0LU Tel: (01233) 644111 Fax: (01233) 644203

Campbells Grocery Products Ltd, Hardwick Road, King's Lynn, Norfolk, PE30 4HS Tel: (01553) 615000 Fax: (01553) 615501 E-mail: enquiries@homepride.co.uk

Carley & Webb, 52 The Thoroughfare, Woodbridge, Suffolk, IP12 1AL Tel: (01394) 385650 Fax: (01394) 388984

Cavaghan & Gray Group Ltd, Brunel House, Brunel Way, Durranhill Industrial Estate, Carlisle, CA1 3NQ Tel: (01228) 518200 Fax: (01228) 518215 E-mail: enquiries@northern-foods.co.uk

Chandra Enterprises, 3 Lower Place Business Centre, Steele Road, London, NW10 7AT Tel: (020) 8453 1990 Fax: (020) 8838 4649

Chapman Foods, 57 Battlehill Road, Portadown, Craigavon, County Armagh, BT62 4ES Tel: (028) 3887 1225 Fax: (028) 3887 0088

Christian Salvesen plc, Easton, Grantham, Lincolnshire, NG33 5AU Tel: (01476) 515000 Fax: (01476) 515011

Christian Salvesen plc, Salvesen Buildings, Ladysmith Road, Grimsby, South Humberside, DN32 9SL Tel: (01472) 327200 Fax: (01472) 327210

Churchills Handmade Sandwich Co Ltd, 2-3 Robin Hood Industrial Estate, Alfred St South, Nottingham, NG3 1GE Tel: 0115-941 9789

Circadia, 4 Deer Park Road, London, SW19 3GY Tel: (020) 8254 3100 Fax: (020) 8540 7430 E-mail: circadia@compass-group.co.uk

City Wholefoods, 67 Magdalen Road, Exeter, EX2 4TA Tel: (01392) 252295

Claybrook Mill, Frolesworth La, Claybrooke Magna, Lutterworth, Leics, LE17 5DB Tel: (01455) 202443 Fax: (01455) 202443 E-mail: claybrookmill@yahoo.co.uk

Coldwater (Aberdeen) Ltd, Craigshaw Street, West Tullos Industrial Estate, Aberdeen, AB12 3AE Tel: (01224) 878099 Fax: (01224) 878438

Coles Traditional Foods Ltd, London Road, Great Chesterford, Saffron Walden, Essex, CB10 1PG Tel: (01799) 531053 Fax: (01799) 531140 E-mail: sales@colestrad.co.uk

Continental Meat Products, 241 Radford Road, Nottingham, NG7 5GU Tel: 0115-978 4129 Fax: 0115-978 4129

Continental Pasta Ltd, Units 1-2, Locksbrook Court, Locksbrook Road, Bath, BA1 3EN Tel: (01225) 312300 Fax: (01225) 460343 E-mail: enquiries@cpastas.co.uk

Crazy Products Ltd, P O Box 170, Northwood, Middx, HA6 3SS Tel: (01923) 842222 Fax: (01923) 842233

Cromwell Packers, 53A Milton Rd, Warley, Brentwood, Essex, CM14 5DS Tel: (01277) 213290

Daniel Chilled Food, Biddenden Road, Headcorn, Ashford, Kent, TN27 9LW Tel: (01622) 892800 Fax: (01622) 892829

Danisco Beaminster, 6 North Street, Beaminster, Dorset, DT8 3DZ Tel: (01308) 862216 Fax: (01308) 863630

DBC Foodservice Ltd, Denmark House, Parkway, Welwyn Garden City, Hertfordshire, AL8 6JN Tel: (01707) 323421 Fax: (01707) 320143 E-mail: info@dbc.foodservice.co.uk

Deans Foods Ltd, The Moor, Bilsthorpe, Newark, Nottinghamshire, NG22 8TS Tel: (01623) 870384 Fax: (01623) 870657

▶ Deli Solutions, Salt Hill Industrial Estate, Salthill Road, Clitheroe, Lancashire, BB7 1NU Tel: (01200) 420790 Fax: (01200) 427782

Dietary Foods Ltd, Cumberland House, Brook Street, Soham, Ely, Cambridgeshire, CB7 5BA Tel: (01353) 720791 Fax: (01353) 721705 E-mail: info@dietaryfoods.co.uk

Dobbindale Foods, Armagh Business Centre, Loughgall Road, Armagh, BT61 7NH Tel: (028) 3751 0501 Fax: (028) 3751 0501

Down To Earth, 406 Sharrow Vale Road, Sheffield, S11 8ZP Tel: 0114-268 5220

Ecopac Power, Unit 7 Field End, Crendon Industrial Area, Long Crendon, Aylesbury, Buckinghamshire, HP18 9EJ Tel: (01844) 204420 Fax: (01844) 204421

Elsenham Quality Foods Ltd, Elsenham, Bishop's Stortford, Hertfordshire, CM22 6DT Tel: (01279) 818307 Fax: (01279) 812715

English Village Cellars Ltd, Camblesforth Grange, Brigg Lane, Camblesforth, Selby, North Yorkshire, YO8 8ND Tel: (01757) 618084 Fax: (01757) 614159

▶ Essential Dressings Ltd, 21 Eston Avenue, Malvern, Worcestershire, WR14 2SR Tel: (01684) 576150 E-mail: mail@essentialdressings.co.uk

Ethnic Cuisine Ltd, Viking Way, Winch Wen Industrial Estate, Winch Wen, Swansea, SA1 7DE Tel: (01792) 772064 Fax: (01792) 773334

European Foods plc, Venton Orchard, Weare Giffard, Bideford, Devon, EX39 4QY Tel: (01237) 422000 Fax: (01237) 422111 E-mail: sales@europeanfoods.co.uk

Fane Valley Co-Operative Society Ltd, Alexander Road, Armagh, BT61 7JJ Tel: (028) 3752 2344 Fax: (028) 3752 7876 E-mail: contact@fanevalley.co.uk

Far East Food Products, Sheffield Road, Conisbrough, Doncaster, South Yorkshire, DN12 2BU Tel: (01709) 860800 Fax: (01709) 860881

Fayrefield Foodtec Ltd, Avoca House, Molivers Lane, Bromham, Bedford, MK43 8JT Tel: (01234) 825704 Fax: (01234) 825705 E-mail: paulc@fayrefield.com

Fen Fruits Ltd, Eastfield Farm, Chapel Road, Tilney Fen End, Wisbech, Cambridgeshire, PE14 8JL Tel: (01945) 880380 Fax: (01945) 880308

First Choice Expedition Foods, Heads Road, Stape, Pickering, North Yorkshire, YO18 8HX Tel: (01751) 473330 E-mail: info@expeditionfoods.com

First Farm Foods Ltd, South Hams Business Pk, Churchstow, Kingsbridge, Devon, TQ7 3QR Tel: 01548 856565

Fjord Seafoods, Unit 1 Marybank Industrial Estate, Marybank, Isle of Lewis, HS2 0DB Tel: (01851) 707600 Fax: (01851) 704834

Fold Hill Foods Ltd, Reg Office, Fold Hill, Stickney, Boston, Lincolnshire, PE22 8HQ Tel: (01205) 270500 Fax: (01205) 270596 E-mail: info@foldhillfoods.fsnet.co.uk

▶ Food Chain, 2 Steppingley Road, Flitwick, Bedford, MK45 1AJ Tel: (01525) 718766 Fax: (01525) 717319

Fountain Foods Ltd, New Road, Upwell, Wisbech, Cambridgeshire, PE14 9AB Tel: (01945) 773333 Fax: (01945) 772174 E-mail: fountainfoods@supernet.com

Framar Health Foods, 391 Ormeau Road, Belfast, BT7 3GP Tel: (028) 9069 4210 Fax: (028) 9066 3891

Frank Dale Foods Ltd, Station Road, Tivetshall St. Margaret, Norwich, NR15 2ED Tel: (01379) 677273 Fax: (01379) 674443 E-mail: sales@frankdalefoods.co.uk

Fresh Bacon Co., Ty Verlon Industrial Estate, Cardiff Road, Barry, South Glamorgan, CF63 2BE Tel: (01446) 700900

Freshtime UK Ltd, Marsh Lane, Boston, Lincolnshire, PE21 7RJ Tel: (01205) 312010 Fax: (01205) 357838 E-mail: sales@freshtime.co.uk

Fullwell Mill Ltd, Unit 5d Southwick Industrial Estate, Sunderland, SR5 3TX Tel: 0191-548 0050 Fax: 0191-516 9946 E-mail: info@fmfoods.co.uk

G E Seafoods, Unit 8 March Road Industrial Estate, Buckie, Banffshire, AB56 4BY Tel: (01542) 834987 Fax: (01542) 834987

G & P Trading Co. Ltd, 20 Binns Way, Binns Road Industrial Estate, Liverpool, L13 1EF Tel: 0151-259 6604 Fax: 0151-259 0374

G W Trading Ltd, Cottage Beck Road, Scunthorpe, South Humberside, DN16 1TT Tel: (01724) 281222 Fax: (01724) 292704

Gabriels Foods Ltd, Higher Poleo, Praze, Camborne, Cornwall, TR14 9PG Tel: (01209) 831284 Fax: (01209) 831228 E-mail: gabrielsfoods@btinternet.com

Galloway Lodge Preserves, 24-28 High Street, Gatehouse of Fleet, Castle Douglas, Kirkcudbrightshire, DG7 2HP Tel: (01557) 814357 Fax: (01557) 814046

Geest Mariner, Athenian Way, Great Coates, Grimsby, South Humberside, DN37 9SY Tel: (01472) 254100 Fax: (01472) 254129 E-mail: geest@co.uk

Geest Normanby Food UK, Park Farm Road, Foxhills Industrial Estate, Scunthorpe, North Lincolnshire, DN15 8QP Tel: (01724) 749291 Fax: (01724) 749291

Gilberts Foods, Middleton Business Park, Middleton Road, Middleton, Morecambe, Lancashire, LA3 3PW Tel: (01524) 852378 Fax: (01524) 852378 E-mail: andrew@gibertsfoods.com

Ginsters Ltd, 81 Tavistock Road, Callington, Cornwall, PL17 7XG Tel: (01579) 386200 Fax: (01579) 386387 E-mail: info@ginsters.co.uk

Ginsters Ltd, 6 Castings Court, Falkirk, FK2 7BA Tel: (01324) 621157 Fax: (01324) 621150

Glen Fresh Foods, 6 Berryhill Road, Donemana Enterprise Park, Dunamanagh, Strabane, County Tyrone, BT82 0NR Tel: (028) 7139 7969 Fax: (028) 7139 7969

Golden West Foods Ltd, Hareshill Road, Heywood, Lancashire, OL10 2TN Tel: (01706) 620580 Fax: (01706) 620572 E-mail: sales@goldenwest.co.uk

Golden Wonder Ltd, Edinburgh House, Abbey Street, Market Harborough, Leicestershire, LE16 9AA Tel: (01858) 410410 Fax: (01858) 414110 E-mail: talktous@golden-wonder.co.uk

Goldenfry Foods Ltd, Sandbeck Way, Wetherby, West Yorkshire, LS22 7DW Tel: (01937) 583631 Fax: (01937) 580024

L. Goldstein, 32 Alderney Rd, London, E1 4EG Tel: 020 77904144 Fax: 02077028166

Gorno's Speciality Foods Ltd, 3 Fairfield Industrial Estate, Pentyrch Road, Gwaelod-y-Garth, Cardiff, CF15 8LA Tel: (029) 2081 1225 Fax: (029) 2081 1299 E-mail: gornos.foods@virgin.net

Grampian Country Pork Ashton, Mackeson Road, Ashton-under-Lyne, Lancashire, OL6 8HZ Tel: 0161-344 5601 Fax: 0161-339 2644

Grampian Country Pork Case, Sandy's Moor, Wiveliscombe, Taunton, Somerset, TA4 2TU Tel: (01984) 624642 Fax: (01984) 624353

Grampian Country Pork Suffolk Ltd, Little Wratting, Haverhill, Suffolk, CB9 7TD Tel: (01440) 704444 Fax: (01440) 762120 E-mail: grampian@gcfg.com

Grampian Country Porks Ltd, Mile Bank, Whitchurch, Shropshire, SY13 4JX Tel: (01948) 662367 Fax: (01948) 662369

▶ Granny Kearneys, 10 Down Business Centre Down Business Park, 46 Belfast Road, Downpatrick, County Down, BT30 9UP Tel: (028) 4483 8883 Fax: (028) 4483 8883

Granny S Kitchen Ltd, St Catherines Mill, Broad Lane, Leeds, LS13 2TD Tel: 0113-255 3884 Fax: 0113-239 3694

Julian Graves Ltd, 1 The Podium, Northgate Street, Bath, BA1 5AL Tel: (01225) 448404 Fax: (01225) 448404

Green Cuisine Food Products Ltd, Unit 3 Threxton Industrial Estate, Watton, Thetford, Norfolk, IP25 6NG Tel: (01953) 882991 Fax: (01953) 885401 E-mail: greencuisine@btinternet.com

Green Top Snack Foods Ltd, Gagarin, Litchfield Road, Tamworth, Staffordshire, B79 7TA Tel: (01827) 60008 Fax: (01827) 60007 E-mail: enquiries@gts-ltd.com

H J Heinz Co. Ltd, South Building, Hayes Park, Hayes, Middlesex, UB4 8AL Tel: (020) 8573 7757 Fax: (020) 8848 2325 E-mail: enquiries@heinz.co.uk

H S Fishing 2000 Ltd, Sutton Road, Great Yarmouth, Norfolk, NR30 3NA Tel: (01493) 858118 Fax: (01493) 859517 E-mail: hsfishing@gy2000.fsnet.co.uk

▶ Haggetts Original Pies, 4-5 Alansway, Finnimore Industrial Estate, Ottery St. Mary, Devon, EX11 1NR Tel: (01404) 814401 Fax: (01404) 814401

Hakens Meat Wholesale, 2 Third Avenue, Greasley Street, Nottingham, NG6 8ND Tel: 0115-976 2995 Fax: 0115-979 5733

Harding's Oriental Food Supplies, Parlas, 3-5 Stanhope, South Shields, Tyne & Wear, NE33 4BA Tel: 0191-454 2000 Fax: 0191-454 2005 E-mail: hofs@perlas.co.uk

Harvest Natural Foods Ltd, 37 Walcot Street, Bath, BA1 5BN Tel: (01225) 465519 Fax: (01225) 401143

Harveys Pickled Products, 2 Court Barton, Crewkerne, Somerset, TA18 7HW Tel: (01460) 72384

Health Leads UK Ltd, 2 St. Clears Business Park, Tenby Road, St. Clears, Carmarthen, SA33 4JW Tel: (01994) 231940 Fax: (01994) 231941 E-mail: mail@healthleadsuk.com

Hedon Salads Ltd, Main Road, Newport, Brough, North Humberside, HU15 2PR Tel: (01430) 441552 Fax: (01430) 441720

Hendra Health Store, 8 Lemon Street, Truro, Cornwall, TR1 2LQ Tel: (01872) 223799 Fax: (01872) 273031

▶ Hewitts Fine Foods Ltd, 38 Manor Industrial Estate, Flint, Clwyd, CH6 5UY Tel: (01352) 730488 Fax: (01352) 730489

Hicks Casings, 11 Inswell Court, Tavistock, Devon, PL19 8LS Tel: (01822) 613312

Highland Fine Cheese Ltd, Blarliath Farm, Tain, Ross-Shire, IV19 1EB Tel: (01862) 892034 Fax: (01862) 894289

Highland Fish Products, 31 Sinclair Road, Aberdeen, AB11 9PL Tel: (01224) 875401

Highland Smoked Salmon (Scotland) Ltd, Blar Mhor Industrial Estate, Lochyside, Fort William, Inverness-Shire, PH33 7PT Tel: (01397) 703649 Fax: (01397) 705632 E-mail: sales@highlandsmokedsalmon.com

Highland Truffle Co., 16 Pinefield Parade, Elgin, Morayshire, IV30 6AG Tel: (01343) 552200 Fax: (01343) 552200 E-mail: sales@highlandtruffles.co.uk

HK Food Products, 2-3 Helmsley Place, London, E8 3SB Tel: (020) 7249 4130 Fax: (020) 7249 4137 E-mail: hkfood@btinternet.com

Holdsworth Chocolate Ltd, Station Road, Bakewell, Derbyshire, DE45 1GE Tel: (01629) 813573 Fax: (01629) 813850 E-mail: info@holdsworthchocolates.co.uk

Holland & Barrett Ltd, 54-55 The Pallasades, Birmingham, B2 4XH Tel: 0121-633 0104

Holland & Barrett Ltd, 14 St Marys Way, Thornbury, Bristol, BS35 2BH Tel: (01454) 417201

Holland & Barrett Ltd, 39 High Street, Nantwich, Cheshire, CW5 5DB Tel: (01270) 610041

Walter Holland & Sons, Blackburn Road, Accrington, Lancashire, BB5 2SA Tel: (01706) 213591 Fax: (01706) 228044 E-mail: enquiries@hollands-pies.co.uk

Human Nature, 13 Malvern Road, London, NW6 5PS Tel: (020) 7328 5452

Humber Quality Foods Ltd, Brigg Road, Scunthorpe, South Humberside, DN15 6TZ Tel: (01724) 270306 Fax: (01724) 270345 E-mail: john@hqf.co.uk

▶ Hunter Biltong Ltd, 2 Lyon Business Park, River Road, Barking, Essex, IG11 0JS Tel: (020) 8591 8221 Fax: (020) 8591 8224

Inverawe Smokehouses, Inverawe, Inverawe, Taynuilt, Argyll, PA35 1HU Tel: (01866) 822777 Fax: (01866) 822274 E-mail: info@inverawe.co.uk

Ivthing Vale Quality Foods Ltd, Berlin Street, Carlisle, CA1 2NL Tel: (01228) 595373 Fax: (01228) 533288

J C Morris & Sons, Unit 2e Netherton Industrial Estate, St. Monans, Anstruther, Fife, KY10 2DW Tel: (01333) 730658 Fax: (01333) 730658 E-mail: sales@ru-an-fhodar.co.uk

J C Rennie, 62 Stair Street, Drummore, Stranraer, Wigtownshire, DG9 9PT Tel: (01776) 840332 Fax: 01776 840 332

J Fulton & Co., 19a Rainey Street, Magherafelt, County Londonderry, BT45 5DA Tel: (028) 7963 2329 Fax: (028) 7963 4264 E-mail: meal@fultonandco.com

J Parker & Son Ltd, The Weind, Great Eccleston, Preston, PR3 0ZU Tel: (01995) 670173 Fax: (01995) 671325

Jay Shah, 56 Portland Cres, Stanmore, Middx, HA7 1NB Tel: (020) 8954 9441 Fax: (020) 8357 8391 E-mail: jayshah2002@hotmail.com

Jenkins & Hustwit Ltd, 3b Laurel Way, Bishop Auckland, County Durham, DL14 7NF Tel: (01388) 605005 Fax: (01388) 605005

▶ JK Seafoods, Fish Market Building, The Harbour, Kilkeel, Newry, County Down, BT34 4AX Tel: (07754) 462654 Fax: (028) 4176 1110 E-mail: kierantrimble@mfn.com

▶ Just Good Food Ltd, Ouseley Farm House, Hinxhill, Ashford, Kent, TN25 5NP Tel: (01233) 624886 Fax: (01233) 636367

K M Allerfeldt, Chapple Farm, Chapple Road, Bovey Tracey, Newton Abbot, Devon, TQ13 9JX Tel: (01626) 832284 Fax: (01626) 832284

K P Foods, Macklin Avenue, Cowpen Lane Industrial Estate, Billingham, Cleveland, TS23 4DU Tel: (01642) 373600 Fax: (01642) 561590

D. Kane Bacon, 493 Huddersfield Road, Oldham, OL4 2JG Tel: 0161-626 8464 Fax: 0161-626 4387

Keddie Saucemasters Ltd, Prince of Wales Industrial Estate, Abercarn, Newport, Gwent, NP11 5AR Tel: (01495) 244721 Fax: (01495) 244626

Kensey Foods, Pennygillam Industrial Estate, Launceston, Cornwall, PL15 7AF Tel: (01566) 778300 Fax: (01566) 778333

Kerry Foods Ltd, Corinium Industrial Estate, Raans Road, Amersham, Buckinghamshire, HP6 6HU Tel: (01494) 721552 Fax: (01494) 432394

Kerry Foodservice, Gatehouse Road, Gatehouse Industrial Area, Aylesbury, Buckinghamshire, HP19 8HH Tel: (01296) 318000 Fax: (01296) 338425 E-mail: info@kerry-foodservice.co.uk

Kerry Holdings UK Ltd, Thorpe Lea Manor, Thorpe Lea Road, Egham, Surrey, TW20 8HY Tel: (01784) 430777 Fax: (01784) 479597 E-mail: enquiries@kerryfoods.co.uk

Kilhallon Quality Meats Ltd, The Abattoir, Kilhallon, Par, Cornwall, PL24 2RL Tel: (01726) 814926 Fax: (01726) 812800 E-mail: info@kittowsbutchers.co.uk

▶ Mrs Elizabeth King Ltd, 30 High Hazles Road, Cotgrave, Nottingham, NG12 3GZ Tel: 0115-989 4101 Fax: 0115-989 4101

Kinnoull Bacon Co. Ltd, 32 Main Street, Almondbank, Perth, PH1 3NJ Tel: (01738) 583292 Fax: (01738) 583292 E-mail: jharty@fsnet.com

▶ Kiren Foods, 3 Smallbridge Industrial Park, Riverside Drive, Rochdale, Lancashire, OL16 2SH Tel: (01706) 526732 Fax: (01706) 869749 E-mail: enquiries@kirenfoods.com

▶ Kiren Foods, 3 Smallbridge Industrial Park, Riverside Drive, Rochdale, Lancashire, OL16 2SH Tel: (01706) 526732 Fax: (01706) 869749

Korker Sausages Ltd, High Street, Rolvenden, Cranbrook, Kent, TN17 4LN Tel: (01580) 241307 Fax: (01580) 240092 E-mail: enquiries@korker-sausages.co.uk

FOOD PROCESSORS/PRODUCTS - *continued*

▶ Krispy Kreme UK Ltd, Albany Park, Camberley, Surrey, GU16 7PQ Tel: (01276) 601170 Fax: (01276) 601180 E-mail: office@krispykreme.co.uk

Kwik Snax Ltd, John Hillhouse Ind Est, Cambuslang Rd, Cambuslang, Glasgow, G72 7TS Tel: 0141-643 2111 Fax: 0141 647 5614

La Tea Doh Ltd, 136 Nithsdale Road, Glasgow, G41 5RB Tel: 0141-424 3224 Fax: 0141-424 3224 E-mail: info@lateadoh.co.uk

Linpharma Ltd, PO Box 13511, Linlithgow, West Lothian, EH49 7YH Tel: (01506) 848649 Fax: (01506) 848775 E-mail: info@linpharma.com

Llangloffan Cheese Ltd, Prendergast, Castle Morris, Haverfordwest, Dyfed, SA62 5ET Tel: (01348) 891241 Fax: (0870) 0561043 E-mail: sales@welshcheese.co.uk

Lo's Noodle Co. Ltd, 6 Dansey Place, London, W1D 6EZ Tel: (020) 7734 3885

Mackay Bros, Culag Square, Lochinver, Lairg, Sutherland, IV27 4LE Tel: (01571) 844298 Fax: (01571) 844598

Macphie of Glenbervie Ltd, Glenbervie, Stonehaven, Kincardineshire, AB39 3YG Tel: (01569) 740641 Fax: (01569) 740677 E-mail: cservice@macphie.com

Mcvities Cake Co., Kingston Mills, Hopwood Lane, Halifax, West Yorkshire, HX1 4EY Tel: (01422) 360697 Fax: (01422) 330284

▶ Mahan Fod, 21 Dragor Road, London, NW10 6JN Tel: (020) 8963 0012 Fax: (020) 8963 0090

Manor Bakeries Ltd, Fish Dam Lane, Barnsley, South Yorkshire, S71 3HQ Tel: (01226) 286191 Fax: (01226) 291003

▶ Markus Products, Murray Way, Wincanton Business Park, Wincanton, Somerset, BA9 9RX Tel: (01963) 435270 Fax: (01963) 435271 E-mail: info@markusproducts.co.uk

Masterfoods, Hansa Road, King's Lynn, Norfolk, PE30 4JE Tel: (01553) 692222 Fax: (01553) 697920 E-mail: sales@unclebens.co.uk

Menallack Farm, Treverva, Penryn, Cornwall, TR10 9BP Tel: (01326) 340333

Midland Snacks Ltd, 6 Park Village Industrial Estate, Bridge Street, Park Village, Wolverhampton, WV10 9DX Tel: (01902) 728394 Fax: (01902) 863335 E-mail: sales@midlandsnacks.co.uk

Mogerley's Food Products, 49 Friars Vennel, Dumfries, DG1 2RQ Tel: (01387) 253590

Mondo Foods Ltd, Station Road, Winslow, Buckingham, MK18 3DD Tel: (01296) 715007 Fax: (01296) 712575

Morco Fish Merchants, Cormorant House, 9 Raik Road, Aberdeen, AB11 5QL Tel: (01224) 594366 Fax: (01224) 588123

Mount Tai Foods, 38 Eastdown Park, London, SE13 5HS Tel: (020) 8318 3818 Fax: (020) 8463 0302E-mail: sales@mounttaifoods.co.uk

National Starch & Chemical, James Street, Goole, North Humberside, DN14 5TG Tel: (01405) 762641 Fax: (01405) 760031

▶ Nature's Free Foods Ltd, 1400-1500 Blueprint, Dundas Spur, Portsmouth, PO3 5RW Tel: (023) 9265 5541 Fax: (023) 9265 5563

Natures Way, 305 Upper Newtownards Road, Belfast, BT4 3JH Tel: (028) 9047 1333 Fax: (028) 9065 6694

John Naylor & Son, Redhall Road, Dudley, West Midlands, DY3 2NL Tel: (01384) 256346 Fax: (01384) 240486

Nestle Cereal Partners, Bridge Road East, Welwyn Garden City, Hertfordshire, AL7 1RR Tel: (01707) 824400 Fax: (01707) 824401

Nestle Holdings UK plc, St George's House, Park Lane, Croydon, CR9 1NR Tel: (020) 8686 3333 Fax: (020) 8686 6072

Nestle UK Ltd, Wheldon Road, Castleford, West Yorkshire, WF10 2JN Tel: (01422) 862100 Fax: (01422) 862101

Network Seafoods Ltd, Quarry Road, Newhaven, East Sussex, BN9 9DB Tel: (01273) 513884 Fax: (01273) 517884 E-mail: sales@networkseafoods.co.uk

New Covent Garden Soup Co. Ltd, Westwood Farm, Bretton Gate, Westwood, Peterborough, PE3 9UP Tel: (01733) 262601 Fax: (01733) 261201

▶ Neya Taste, 36 Hastings Road, Leicester, LE5 0HL Tel: 0116-276 7767 Fax: 0116-276 7767

Novus Foods Ltd, Suite 31 Salford University Business Park, Leslie Hough Way, Salford, M6 6AJ Tel: 0161-736 8180 Fax: 0161-736 8190 E-mail: novusfoods@supanet.com

▶ Ny Snacks & Confectionery, 14 Hemmons Road, Manchester, M12 5ST Tel: 0161-256 0080 Fax: 0161-256 0080

▶ OceanC Ltd, Kitling Road, Knowsley Business Park, Prescot, Merseyside, L34 9JA Tel: 0151-546 2727 Fax: 0151-547 2603 E-mail: info@oceanc.co.uk

▶ O'Kane Irish Foods, 8-9 Quad Road, East Lane, Wembley, Middlesex, HA9 7NE Tel: (020) 8385 1771 Fax: (020) 8385 1991 E-mail: sales@okaneirishfoods.co.uk

Oldfields Quality Foods, Twelvetrees CR, London, E3 3JH Tel: (020) 7536 8000 Fax: (020) 7538 8316

Olivien Craft Centre, 126 Burton Road, Manchester, M20 1JQ Tel: 0161-434 5444

Omar Foods, 123 Upwell Street, Sheffield, S4 8AN Tel: 0114-261 0052 Fax: 0114-258 0491

Only Natural, 48 Westfield Street, St. Helens, Merseyside, WA10 1QF Tel: (01744) 759797

Orchidwood Mushrooms Ltd, Hobbs Lane, Beckley, Rye, East Sussex, TN31 6TS Tel: (01797) 260411 Fax: (01797) 260603 E-mail: info@orchidwood.co.uk

Original Pretzel Co. Ltd, 8 Temple Farm Industrial Estate, Sutton Road, Southend-On-Sea, SS2 5RN Tel: (01702) 461116 Fax: (01702) 461544

P S Thurtle, Great Horton Road, Bradford, West Yorkshire, BD7 4DU Tel: (01274) 502754

Pantry Frans, 1A Key Street, Lostwithiel, Cornwall, PL22 0BS Tel: (01208) 872407

Park Tonks Ltd, 48 North Road, Great Abington, Cambridge, CB21 6AS Tel: (01223) 891721 Fax: (01223) 893571 E-mail: mail@parktonks.co.uk

Parker Foods Ltd, Cams Alders, Redlands Lane, Fareham, Hampshire, PO16 0QH Tel: (01329) 823777 Fax: (01329) 823888

▶ Parry Scragg Ltd, 25-33 Dalrymple Street, Liverpool, L5 5HB Tel: 0151-207 5867 Fax: 0151-207 5868 E-mail: dprawcliffe@msn.com

Partingtons Pies, 294 Manchester Road, Bolton, BL3 2QS Tel: (01204) 521488

Pasta Foods Ltd, Pasteur Road, Great Yarmouth, Norfolk, NR31 0DW Tel: (01493) 656071 Fax: (01493) 653346 E-mail: enquiries@pastafoods.com

Peppercorn 84, 11 Railway Street, Pocklington, York, YO42 2QR Tel: (01759) 303275 Fax: (01759) 303275

Pharaos Foods, 271 Upper Brook Street, Manchester, M13 0HR Tel: 0161-272 6340 Fax: 0161-272 6341

Phoenix Foods Ltd, Brakey Road, Weldon North Industrial Estate, Corby, Northamptonshire, NN17 5LU Tel: (01536) 200101 Fax: (01536) 202218 E-mail: sales@phoenixfoods.co.uk

Pork Farms Bowyers Ltd, Dartmouth Rd, Smethwick, W. Midlands, B66 1AS Tel: 0121-558 6672 Fax: 0121-555 6310

Portobello Wholefoods, 266 Portobello Road, London, W10 5TY Tel: (020) 8968 9133 Fax: (020) 8560 1840

Pot Ready Processing, Lisnaskea, Enniskillen, County Fermanagh, BT92 0AW Tel: (028) 6772 3272 Fax: (028) 6772 3272

Premier Foods, Batchelors Factory, Claylands Avenue, Worksop, Nottinghamshire, S81 7AY Tel: (01909) 475522 Fax: (01909) 530381

Premier International Foods, Lynn Road, Wisbech, Cambridgeshire, PE13 3DG Tel: (01945) 585161 Fax: (01945) 464968

Prinsen UK Ltd, Mayfair House, 11 Lurke Street, Bedford, MK40 3HZ Tel: (01234) 345066 Fax: (01234) 355640

Procters Cheeses Ltd, The Cheese Warehouse, Saunders Raike, Chipping, Preston, PR3 2QR Tel: (01995) 61626 Fax: (01995) 61077 E-mail: sales@procterscheeses.co.uk

Puglisi Pasta (UK) Ltd, 1 Glendale Drive, London, SW19 7BG Tel: (020) 8947 7036 Fax: (020) 8946 7987 E-mail: info@puglisi.co.uk

Ramsay Of Carluke Ltd, 22 Mount Stewart Street, Carluke, Lanarkshire, ML8 5ED Tel: (01555) 772277 Fax: (01555) 750686 E-mail: sales@ramsayofcarluke.co.uk

Red Mill Snack Foods Ltd, Globe Street, Wednesbury, West Midlands, WS10 0NN Tel: 0121-505 1500 Fax: 0121-505 2424 E-mail: info@redmill.co.uk

Redmill Snack Foods Ltd, Great Bank Road, Wingates Industrial Estate, Westhoughton, Bolton, BL5 3XU Tel: (01942) 815543 Fax: (01942) 810614 E-mail: enquiries@redmill.co.uk

Revital, 154 High Street, Hounslow, TW3 1LR Tel: (020) 8570 4560 Fax: (020) 8572 0310

Rezet & Son, 491 Hornsey Road, London, N19 3QL Tel: (020) 7272 2788 Fax: (01763) 262459

RHM Brands, Booth Lane, Middlewich, Cheshire, CW10 0HD Tel: (01606) 834747 Fax: (01606) 737590

Ripon Select Foods Ltd, Dallamires Way North, Ripon, North Yorkshire, HG4 1TL Tel: (01765) 601711 Fax: (01765) 607481 E-mail: ingredients@rsf.co.uk

Riverfarm Smokery Shop, Wilbraham Road, Bottisham, Cambridge, CB25 9BU Tel: (01223) 812577 Fax: (01223) 812319

Riverside Smoked Foods Ltd, Frizington Industrial Estate, Frizington, Cumbria, CA26 3QY Tel: (01946) 817000 Fax: (01946) 818939 E-mail: sales@riverside-smoked-foods.co.uk

Robertson, Unit 5 Hardengreen Industrial Estate, Dalkeith, Midlothian, EH22 3NX Tel: 0131-663 6666 Fax: 0131-663 6664

Rotor Motion Midland Ltd, 3 Mandervell Road, Oadby, Leicester, LE2 5LQ Tel: 0116-271 0666 Fax: 0116-271 0333 E-mail: sales@plastic-and-rubber-engineer.ltd.uk

▶ Royale Cuisine, Mill Mead Industrial Centre, Mill Mead Road, London, N17 9QU Tel: (020) 8808 3316

▶ Rye Valley, 1 Garretts Green Industrial Estate, Granby Avenue, Birmingham, B33 0SU Tel: 0121-786 1664 Fax: 0121-786 1684

Ryvita Co., Ashton Road, Bredbury, Stockport, Cheshire, SK6 2SA Tel: 0161-494 5125 Fax: 0161-406 3288

Saccenda Group Ltd, High Street, Okeford Fitzpaine, Blandford Forum, Dorset, DT11 0RQ Tel: (01258) 860304 Fax: (01258) 861208

Salmon Poachers Ltd, Unit 1-4 Salisbury Road Business Park, Salisbury Road, Pewsey, Wiltshire, SN9 5PZ Tel: (01672) 562786 Fax: (01672) 564286 E-mail: sales@salmonpoachers.co.uk

▶ Sandwich Fillers, Unit D1 East Dorset Trade Park, Nimrod Way, Wimborne, Dorset, BH21 7SH Tel: (01202) 854774

Sandwich Fillings Ltd, Unit 22 Village Court, Village Farm Industrial Estate, Pyle, Bridgend, Mid Glamorgan, CF33 6BX Tel: (01656) 744944 Fax: (01656) 745454

▶ Sandwich King, Enfield Street, Leeds, LS7 1RF Tel: 0113-242 6031 Fax: 0113-234 2047 E-mail: enquires@sandwichkinguk.com

▶ Sarahvee Gluten Free Foods Ltd, Unit 7, Sittingbourne Industrial Park, Crown Quay Lane, Sittingbourne, Kent, ME10 3JH Tel: (01795) 428417

Sayers Confectioners Ltd, Lorenzo Drive, Liverpool, L11 1BJ Tel: 0151-287 8700 Fax: 0151-270 2030

Scandic Foods, Beaufront Castle Flats, Hexham, Northumberland, NE46 4LT Tel: (01434) 608220 Fax: (01434) 608221 E-mail: sales@scandicfoods.com

▶ Scotprime, Murray Street, Grimsby, South Humberside, DN31 3RD Tel: (01472) 358100 Fax: (01472) 350328 E-mail: admin@scotprime.co.uk

Scotprime Seafoods Ltd, 11 Whitfield Drive, Heathfield Industrial Estate, Ayr, KA8 9RX Tel: (01292) 611161 Fax: (01292) 611039 E-mail: sales@scotprime.com

Seaford Health Store, 26 Church Street, Seaford, East Sussex, BN25 1LD Tel: (01323) 893473 Fax: (01323) 893473

Sekhon Savouries, 619 Foleshill Road, Coventry, CV6 5JR Tel: (024) 7666 7722

Selsea Fish & Lobster Co. Ltd, Lagoon Cottage, Kingsway, Selsey, Chichester, West Sussex, PO20 0SY Tel: (01243) 607444 Fax: (01243) 607333

Severn & Wye Smokery Ltd, The Smoke House, Chaxhill, Westbury-on-Severn, Gloucestershire, GL14 1QW Tel: (01452) 760190 Fax: (01452) 760193 E-mail: info@severnandwye.co.uk

Silver Spoon Co., Silver Way, Bury St. Edmunds, Suffolk, IP32 7BZ Tel: (01284) 701621 Fax: (01284) 731200

Simply Organic, Units 19-21, Dryden Vale, Bilston Glen, Loanhead, Midlothian, EH20 9HN Tel: 0131-448 0440 Fax: 0131-448 0441 E-mail: info@simplyorganic.co.uk

Siop Newydd, 50 High Street, Criccieth, Gwynedd, LL52 0EY Tel: (01766) 522737

▶ Sona Jewellers, 1 Morris Street, Oldham, OL4 1EL Tel: 0161-620 7049 E-mail: sales@hannahjewellers.co.uk

▶ Spanks Foods, Mead Lane, Saltford, Bristol, BS31 3ER Tel: (01225) 874466 Fax: (01225) 874466

Sullis Health, The Hollies, Mill Hill, Wellow, Bath, BA2 8QJ Tel: (01225) 833150 Fax: (01225) 833150 E-mail: sullis-health@sullis-health.co.uk

Sunrider Europe Incorporated, 14-20 Shand Street, Shand House, London, SE1 2ES Tel: (020) 7940 8000 Fax: (020) 7940 8040 E-mail: info@sunrider.co.uk

Sunrise Fine Foods, Unit 5 The Business Centre, Morgans Vale Road, Redlynch, Salisbury, SP5 2HA Tel: (01725) 513122 Fax: (01725) 513322 E-mail: admin@wiltonwholefoods.co.uk

▶ Supreme Food Ingredients, 5 Moor Close, Holmewood Industrial Park, Holmewood, Chesterfield, Derbyshire, S42 5UX Tel: (01246) 855552 Fax: (01246) 855664

▶ Surrey Downs Food, Units 79-80, Dunsfold Park, Stovolds Hill, Cranleigh, Surrey, GU6 8TB Tel: (01483) 273000 Fax: (01483) 273022 E-mail: info@surreydownsfoods.com

Sustainable Life, 12 Catherine Street, St. Davids, Haverfordwest, Dyfed, SA62 6RJ Tel: (01437) 721849 Fax: (01437) 721849 E-mail: sales@sustlife.com

Sylvasprings Watercress Ltd, Manor Farm, Southbrook, Bere Regis, Wareham, Dorset, BH20 7LH Tel: (01929) 471381

T M I Foods Ltd, Lodge Way, Lodge Farm Industrial Estate, Northampton, NN5 7US Tel: (01604) 583421 Fax: (01604) 587392 E-mail: sales@tmifoods.co.uk

T S & M E Darlington & Daughters, 47a Lancaster Fields, Crewe, CW1 6FF Tel: (01270) 250710 Fax: (01270) 250710 E-mail: sales@mrsdarlingtons.com

Tastees Food Products, 20 Victoria Industrial Estate, Victoria Road, London, W3 6UU Tel: (020) 8993 1289 Fax: (020) 8993 1579 E-mail: tast33s@aol.com

Tayto Ni Ltd, Tandragee Castle, Tandragee, Craigavon, County Armagh, BT62 2AB Tel: (028) 3884 0249 Fax: (028) 3884 0085 E-mail: sales@tayto.com

Tayto (NI) Ltd, 6 Pit Hey Place, West Pimbo, Skelmersdale, Lancashire, WN8 9PS Tel: (01695) 726228 Fax: (01695) 50197 E-mail: maurice@rowanfsbusiness.co.uk

Tillery Valley Foods, Unit 2-3 Cwmtillery Industrial Estate, Cwmtillery, Abertillery, Gwent, NP13 1LZ Tel: (01495) 211555 Fax: (01495) 212935 E-mail: info@tvf-online.co.uk

Trebor Bassett, Brimington Road, Chesterfield, Derbyshire, S41 7UN Tel: 0114-250 3358 Fax: (01246) 233820

Trinity Fish Products Ltd, 4 Trinity Street, Grimsby, North East Lincolnshire, DN31 3AN Tel: (01472) 354963 Fax: (01472) 361320 E-mail: trinityfp@hotmail.com

Trinity Wholefoods, 3 Trinity Street, Hastings, East Sussex, TN34 1HG Tel: (01424) 430473 E-mail: trintywholesales@phonecoop.coop

Tommy Tucker Ltd, Barnham House, Aurillac Way, Hallcroft Industrial Estate, Retford, Nottinghamshire, DN22 7PX Tel: (01777) 705141 Fax: (01777) 860859 E-mail: sales@mgagency.demon.co.uk

Turners Fine Foods, Spelmonden Farm, Spelmonden Road, Goudhurst, Cranbrook, Kent, TN17 1HE Tel: (01580) 212818 Fax: (01580) 212241

▶ U G Foods UK Ltd, Unit B 10 Aladdin Workspace, Long Drive, Greenford, Middlesex, UB6 8UH Tel: (020) 8575 6353 Fax: (020) 8578 6354

▶ Uncle Roy's, 2 Holm Street, Moffat, Dumfriesshire, DG10 9EB Tel: (01683) 221076 Fax: (01683) 221076

Uni Lever, Carrow Works, Bracondale, Norwich, NR1 2DD Tel: (01603) 660166 Fax: (01603) 692099 E-mail: sales@unilever.com

Unilever Bestfoods UK Ltd, Croespenmaen Industrial Estate, Kendon, Crumlin, Newport, Gwent, NP11 3AG Tel: (01495) 248555 Fax: (01495) 247657 E-mail: enquiries@ubfoodsuk.com

Unilever Frozen Food & Ice Cream, Martin Score, Lowestoft, Suffolk, NR32 1JG Tel: (01502) 573131 Fax: (01502) 504840

Uniq plc, 1 Chalfont Park, Gerrards Cross, Buckinghamshire, SL9 0UN Tel: (01753) 276000 Fax: (01753) 276071 E-mail: info@uniqplc.com

Uniq Prepared Foods Smedleys, Wardentree Lane, Pinchbeck, Spalding, Lincolnshire, PE11 3UY Tel: (01775) 710789 Fax: (01775) 710504 E-mail: enquiries@uniq.com

United Biscuits UK Ltd, Crossley Road, Manchester, M19 2SD Tel: 0161-432 0202 Fax: 0161-443 1896

V M G Bakeries Ltd, 90-94 Glentanar Road, Glasgow, G22 7XA Tel: 0141-336 6999 Fax: 0141-336 6191

Valley Farm Foods Ltd, Zenith House, North Holme Road, Louth, Lincolnshire, LN11 0HQ Tel: (01507) 600976 Fax: (01507) 607839 E-mail: sales@valleyfarmfoods.com

Veggie World Co. Ltd, 150-152 Queen's Way, Bletchley, Milton Keynes, MK2 2RS Tel: (0870) 7449976 Fax: (0870) 7449978 E-mail: sales@veggie-world.com

▶ Voakes Of Whixley, Whixley Grange, Boroughbridge Road, Whixley, York, YO26 8AY Tel: (01423) 339988 E-mail: enquiries@voakespies.co.uk

W & P Food Service Ltd, Tannochside Drive, Uddingston, Glasgow, G71 5PD Tel: (01698) 803000 Fax: 01698 803031

Weetabix Ltd, Factory 1, Earlstree Industrial Estate, Earlstree Road, Corby, Northamptonshire, NN17 4AZ Tel: (01536) 722181 Fax: (01536) 401532

Welsh Lady Preserves Ltd, Bryn, Y Ffor, Pwllheli, Gwynedd, LL53 6RL Tel: (01766) 810496 Fax: (01766) 810067 E-mail: info@welshladypreserves.com

Wessex Fine Foods, 148 Tuckton Road, Bournemouth, BH6 3JX Tel: (01202) 429267

West Wales Bacon, 5 Carmarthen Road, Cross Hands, Llanelli, Dyfed, SA14 6SP Tel: (01269) 842148 Fax: (01269) 842148

Westbury Country Foods Ltd, Unit 1 Lodge Hill Industrial Estate, Station Road, Westbury Sub Mendip, Wells, Somerset, BA5 1EY Tel: (01749) 870122 Fax: (01749) 870177

▶ Western Foods, Units 3-4 Bridge Court, Imerington Road, Ivybridge, Devon, PL21 9EY Tel: (01752) 690371 Fax: (01752) 690371

Whit Products Ltd, Factory Road, Tipton, West Midlands, DY4 9DJ Tel: 0121-557 7651 Fax: 0121-557 5334

Whitworths Ltd, Orchard House, Irthlingborough, Wellingborough, Northamptonshire, NN9 5DB Tel: (01933) 653000 Fax: (01933) 652525 E-mail: sales@whitworths.co.uk

Wholefoods Bedford, 1 Thurlow Street, Bedford, MK40 1LR Tel: (01234) 219618 Fax: (01234) 213929

Wild Thymes, 2 Hughenden Yard, High Street, Marlborough, Wiltshire, SN8 1LT Tel: (01672) 516373 Fax: (01672) 516373

K.D. Winkle, 46-47 Retreat Street, Wolverhampton, WV3 0JT Tel: (01902) 428738

Winning Blend Ltd (T/U Welsh Pantry), Unit 1 Riverside Industrial Park, Treforest Industrial Estate, Treforest, Pontypridd, Mid Glamorgan, CF37 5TG Tel: (01443) 843587 Fax: (01443) 842304 E-mail: sales@welshpantry.com

Wise Weigh, 33-34 Retail Market, Coventry, CV1 3HT Tel: (024) 7652 5034 E-mail: berylbrozj3@supernet.co.uk

Wok Master Foods Ltd, 14 Birch Lane, Manchester, M13 0NN Tel: 0161-225 3072 Fax: 0161-248 0989

Woldsway Foods Ltd, Ashby-by-Partney, Spilsby, Lincolnshire, PE23 5RG Tel: (01754) 890641 Fax: (01754) 890444 E-mail: sales@woldsway.co.uk

FOOD PRODUCT TESTING/ RESEARCH SERVICES

Due Diligence Advice Ltd, 83 Heavitree Road, Exeter, EX1 2ND Tel: (01392) 431222 Fax: (01392) 422691

Global Analysis, Tappers Building, Huddersfield Road, Mirfield, West Yorkshire, WF14 9DQ Tel: (01924) 499776 Fax: (01924) 499325 E-mail: user@globalanalysis.co.uk

▶ indicates data change since last edition

FOOD PRODUCT TESTING/ RESEARCH SERVICES – *continued*

R H M Technology Ltd, Lord Rank Centre, Lincoln Road, High Wycombe, Buckinghamshire, HP12 3QR Tel: (01494) 526191 Fax: (01494) 428080 E-mail: enquiries@rhmtech.co.uk

FOOD PRODUCTION STABILISERS

Cesalpinia UK Ltd, Mare House, 1 Bilton Way, Luton, LU1 1UU Tel: (01582) 811900 Fax: (01582) 811901 E-mail: sales@cesalpinia.co.uk

Regency Mowbray Co. Ltd, Hixon Industrial Estate, Hixon, Stafford, ST18 0PY Tel: (01889) 270554 Fax: (01889) 270927 E-mail: sales@regencymowbray.co.uk

FOOD QUALITY CONTROL SYSTEMS

▶ RMS Technical Services, 8 Sandwick Close, Fulwood, Preston, PR2 9RZ Tel: 01772 721310 E-mail: info@rmstechnical.co.uk

FOOD SAFE HYGIENIC FLOORING

Altro Ltd, Works Road, Letchworth Garden City, Hertfordshire, SG6 1NW Tel: (01462) 707604 Fax: (01462) 707504 E-mail: leisure@altro.co.uk

Lasercroft Ltd, 9 Hedon Road, Hull, HU9 1LL Tel: (01482) 229119 Fax: (01482) 223077 E-mail: info@lasercroft.com

Specialist Environmental Flooring Ltd, 38 Fowler Avenue, Spondon, Derby, DE21 7GR Tel: (01332) 669353 Fax: (01332) 669011

FOOD SAFETY CONSULTANCY

R A G, The Malthouse, Old Bexley Heath Business Park, 19 Bourne Road, Bexley, Kent, DA5 1LR Tel: (0800) 0431416 Fax: (0870) 850 1417 E-mail: info@ragcomms.com

FOOD SAFETY LABELS

▶ RMS Technical Services, 8 Sandwick Close, Fulwood, Preston, PR2 9RZ Tel: 01772 721310 E-mail: info@rmstechnical.co.uk

FOOD SEASONINGS

▶ A French Touch, 20 Lewis Street, Eccles, Manchester, M30 0PX Tel: 0774 2641509 Fax: 0161 7079145 E-mail: sales@finestfrench.com

Glenco Food Trade Supplies, 30 Pancake Lane, Hemel Hempstead, Hertfordshire, HP2 4NQ Tel: (01442) 267172 Fax: (01442) 267172 E-mail: graeme.north@ntlworld.com

Griffith Laboratories Ltd, Cotes Park Estate, Somercotes, Alfreton, Derbyshire, DE55 4NN Tel: (01773) 837000 Fax: (01773) 837001

Kerry Foodservice, Gatehouse Road, Gatehouse Industrial Area, Aylesbury, Buckinghamshire, HP19 8HH Tel: (01296) 318000 Fax: (01296) 338425 E-mail: info@kerry-foodservice.co.uk

Newly Weds Foods Europe Ltd, Owl Lane, Ossett, West Yorkshire, WF5 9AX Tel: (01924) 280444 Fax: (01924) 281042

FOOD SHELF LIFE TESTING

▶ Direct Laboratories, Woodthorne, Wergs Road, Wolverhampton, WV6 8TQ Tel: (01902) 743222 Fax: (01902) 746183 E-mail: angeliki.chrevatidis@directlabs.co.uk

FOOD SLICER BLADES

▶ incisive edge-industrial machine knives, 12 carson mount, Sheffield, S12 3GA Tel: 07901 835190 Fax: 01142 654946 E-mail: dniks@tiscali.co.uk

FOOD STORAGE BUILDINGS

▶ Celsius First Ltd, High Meads, Temple Mill Lane, London, E15 2EW Tel: (020) 8534 5577 Fax: (020) 8519 0263

FOOD SUPPLEMENTS

▶ Gymking, 67 Belvedere Avenue, Ilford, Essex, IG5 0UH Tel: 0208 5512285 E-mail: gymking1@hotmail.co.uk

FOOD SWEETENERS

Danisco Beaminster, 6 North Street, Beaminster, Dorset, DT8 3DZ Tel: (01308) 862216 Fax: (01308) 863630

FOOD TECHNOLOGY CONSULTANTS

A F S, Shelwick Farm, Shelwick, Hereford, HR1 3AL Tel: (01432) 341131 Fax: (01432) 264190

▶ Adele Addams Accociates, 71 Keighley Road, Skipton, North Yorkshire, BD23 2LX Tel: (01756) 797444 Fax: (01756) 799506

Bodycote Health Sciences, 121 Shady Lane, Great Barr, Birmingham, B44 9ET Tel: 0121-206 4100 Fax: 0121-251 4040 E-mail: healthsciences@bodycote.com

Cranford International Ltd, 10 Beech Waye, Gerrards Cross, Buckinghamshire, SL9 8BL Tel: (01753) 889831 Fax: (01753) 890892 E-mail: cranfd@aol.com

▶ Diotte Consulting & Technology Ltd, The Conifers 36 Bishops Wood, Nantwich, Cheshire, CW5 7QD Tel: (01270) 627129 Fax: 01270 610358 E-mail: ranj@diotte.co.uk

F J B Systems, 11 Claremont Road, Claygate, Esher, Surrey, KT10 0PL Tel: (01372) 468839 Fax: (01372) 471056 E-mail: sales@fjb.co.uk

▶ Food Business Ltd, St. Georges House, 50 Adelaide Street, St. Albans, Hertfordshire, AL3 5BG Tel: (01727) 832834 Fax: (01727) 832836 E-mail: sally@thefoodbusiness.co.uk

Food Business Development Consultancy, 68 Park Street, St. Albans, Hertfordshire, AL2 2PW Tel: (01727) 873303 Fax: (01727) 874063 E-mail: susan@fbdc.co.uk

Food Centre Wales, Horeb, Llandysul, Dyfed, SA44 4JG Tel: (01559) 362230 Fax: (01559) 362086 E-mail: jen@foodcentrewales.org.uk

▶ Food Diligence Systems Ltd, Tamerton House, Furzefield Avenue, Speldhurst, Tunbridge Wells, Kent, TN3 0LD Tel: (01892) 861074 Fax: (01892) 861078

FSC, Cheddar Business Park, Wedmore Road, Cheddar, Somerset, BS27 3EB Tel: (01934) 745600 Fax: (01934) 745631 E-mail: sales@foodservicecentre.co.uk

Kurt Hafner Associates, 24 Robin Hill Drive, Camberley, Surrey, GU15 1EG Tel: (01276) 682247 Fax: (01276) 683381

Natural Food Co., 37a Mansfield Road, Nottingham, NG1 3FB Tel: (01949) 876483 Fax: 0115-955 9914 E-mail: info@naturalfoodcompany.net

▶ Practical Solutions International Ltd, Spencers Wood, Reading, RG7 1YF Tel: 0118-988 8033 Fax: 0118-988 8033

Product Assurance Ltd, 10 Castle Street, Buckingham, MK18 1EQ Tel: (01280) 817346 Fax: (01280) 817932

R H M Technology Ltd, Lord Rank Centre, Lincoln Road, High Wycombe, Buckinghamshire, HP12 3QR Tel: (01494) 526191 Fax: (01494) 428080 E-mail: enquiries@rhmtech.co.uk

▶ Spriegel Associates, 27 Downs Way, Tadworth, Surrey, KT20 5DH Tel: (01737) 817799 Fax: (01737) 817799

Wickham Laboratories, Winchester Road, Wickham, Fareham, Hampshire, PO17 5EU Tel: (01329) 832511 Fax: (01329) 834262 E-mail: mail@wickhamlabs.co.uk

FOOD USE BY DATE SAFETY LABELS

Rhinopac Ltd, Tri-Star House, Unit 4, The Arena, Mollison Avenue, Enfield, Middlesex, EN3 7NL Tel: (020) 8443 9100 Fax: (020) 8443 9118 E-mail: sales@rhinopac.com

FOOD USE CASINGS

Hicks Casings, 11 Inswell Court, Tavistock, Devon, PL19 8LS Tel: (01822) 613312

FOOD VENDING MACHINES

▶ Allied Machine Sales, 23 Saxton Lane, Saxton, Tadcaster, North Yorkshire, LS24 9QD Tel: (01937) 558560 Fax: (01937) 558642 E-mail: info@alliedmachines.co.uk

Betttavend Ltd, 5 Speedwell Close, Chandlers Ford Industrial Estate, Eastleigh, Hampshire, SO53 4BT Tel: (023) 8025 5222 Fax: (023) 8027 6644 E-mail: enquiries@bettavend.co.uk

Bunzl Vending Services Ltd, 19 Aintree Road, Greenford, Middlesex, UB6 7LG Tel: (020) 8998 2828 Fax: (020) 8998 0704 E-mail: enquiries@bunzlvend.com

Care Vending Services Ltd, Unit 16 Gunnels Wood Park, Gunnels Wood Road, Stevenage, Hertfordshire, SG1 2BH Tel: (01438) 760600 Fax: (01438) 760602 E-mail: sales@carevending.co.uk

▶ Corporate Food Co. Ltd, Unit 6 Queensferry Industrial Estate, Chester Road, Pentre, Deeside, Flintshire, CH5 2DJ Tel: (01244) 536273 Fax: (01244) 537999 E-mail: info@cfccaterers.co.uk

▶ Eurocup, 7 Paddock Road, Skelmersdale, Lancashire, WN8 9PL Tel: (01695) 550820 Fax: (01695) 558550 E-mail: sales@eurocup.co.uk

Manchester Vending Services Ltd, Alpha Point, Bradnor Road, Manchester, M22 4TE Tel: 0161-945 2030 E-mail: info@manvend.com

Precision Vending Machines Ltd, Unit 2, Avonside Industrial Estate, Feeder Road, St. Philips, Bristol, BS2 0UB Tel: 0117-972 3232 Fax: 0117-972 3887

Westomatic Vending Systems Ltd, Shaldon Road, Newton Abbot, Devon, TQ12 4TZ Tel: (01626) 323100 Fax: (01626) 332828 E-mail: mailbox@westomatic.com

FOOD WASHING EQUIPMENT

Central Hygiene Ltd, Unit 4e Brymau Three Trading Estate, River Lane, Saltney, Chester, CH4 8RQ Tel: (01244) 675066 Fax: (01244) 680129 E-mail: sales@central-hygiene.co.uk

FOOD WASTE COMPOSTING

▶ Fast Fermentation Ltd, Eastbank House, 19 Woodside Road, Northwood, Middlesex, HA6 3QE Tel: (07946) 512551 E-mail: stephen.herman@fastfermentation.co.uk

FOOD X RAY INSPECTION EQUIPMENT

Advanced Inspection Services (AIS) Ltd, 43 Booth Drive, Park Farm South, Wellingborough, Northamptonshire, NN8 6GR Tel: (01933) 674030 Fax: (01933) 674858 E-mail: sales@aisxray.co.uk

FOODS, ORGANIC

▶ Local Farmers Markets, 29 Compton Street, Chesterfield, Derbyshire, S40 4TA Tel: 01246 230302

▶ The Olive Oil Store, 1 Saffron Road, Chafford Hundred, Grays, Essex, RM16 6NA Tel: 01375 483863 E-mail: sales@oliveoilstore.co.uk

FOODS, VENDING

▶ Vendsafe Ltd, 19 Elim Court Gardens, Crowborough, East Sussex, TN6 1BS Tel: (01892) 655752 E-mail: vendsafe@fsmail.net

FOODSERVICE EQUIPMENT

Deighton Manufacturing UK Ltd, Gibson Street, Bradford, West Yorkshire, BD3 9TR Tel: (01274) 668771 Fax: (01274) 665214 E-mail: sales@deightonmanufacturing.co.uk

Foodmek Ltd, 17 Shanwell Road, Tayport, Fife, DD6 9EA Tel: (01382) 553577 Fax: (01382) 552173 E-mail: enquiries@foodmek.co.uk

▶ Forthcare, Unit 7, Hardengreen Industrial Estate, Dalkeith, Midlothian, EH22 3NX Tel: 0131-663 7175 Fax: 0131-663 7175

Hamden System Sales Ltd, Granville Way, Bicester, Oxfordshire, OX26 4JT Tel: (01869) 324944 Fax: (01869) 242979 E-mail: enquiries@hamden.co.uk

Kason Hardware (UK) Ltd, Unit 3, Monmore Park Industrial Estate, Ettingshall Road, Wolverhampton, WV2 2LQ Tel: (01902) 409431 Fax: (01902) 353939 E-mail: kasonukltd@tiscali.co.uk

M S A Ltd, Wassalls Hall, Bishops Wood Road, Wickham, Hampshire, PO17 5AT Tel: (01329) 835440 Fax: (01329) 835430 E-mail: sales@msaltd.com

Prima Catering Supplies, 2 Whitworth Industrial Estate, Tilton Road, Birmingham, B9 4PP Tel: 0121-771 3116 Fax: 0121-772 2616 E-mail: primacatering@hotmail.com

FOODSTUFF PUMPS

Ferrier Pumps Ltd, Burlington Street, Leith, Edinburgh, EH6 5JL Tel: 0131-554 1200 Fax: 0131-553 1272 E-mail: edinburgh@ferrierpumps.co.uk

FOOTCARE PRODUCTS

▶ Elmbronze Ltd, PO Box 8361, Largs, Ayrshire, KA30 8YA Tel: (01475) 689274

FOOTWEAR, *See also headings for particular types*

Charles Ager Ltd, 20-26 Corporation Street, Coventry, CV1 1GF Tel: (024) 7622 1619 Fax: (024) 7663 2684 E-mail: sales@charlesager.co.uk

Airwair International Ltd, Cobbs Lane, Wollaston, Wellingborough, Northamptonshire, NN29 7SW Tel: (01933) 663281 Fax: (01933) 663848

Alexon Group plc, 40-48 Guildford Street, Luton, LU1 2PB Tel: (01582) 723131 Fax: (01582) 724158

▶ B T C Euro Ltd, Bond Street, Nuneaton, Warwickshire, CV11 4BX Tel: (024) 7632 8104 Fax: (024) 7664 1948 E-mail: sales@btceuro.co.uk

Casson & Co. Ltd, 117 Huddersfield Road, Oldham, OL1 3NY Tel: 0161-624 2227 Fax: 0161-627 5231

▶ Chancery Footwear Ltd, 86 Bunting Road, Northampton, NN2 6EE Tel: (01604) 712159 Fax: (01604) 722397

Clarkes International, Natland Road, Kendal, Cumbria, LA9 7LS Tel: (01539) 815021 Fax: (01539) 815139 E-mail: john.keery@clarkes.com

▶ Dane Crafts, Havyatt Farm, Glastonbury, Somerset, BA6 8LF Tel: (01458) 835105 Fax: (01458) 832627

Florentine Shoes, European Cargo Centre, Motherwell Way, Grays, Essex, RM20 3XD Tel: (01708) 867111 Fax: (01708) 862110 E-mail: mikeluff@florentineshoes.freeserve.co.uk

The Florida Group Ltd, Dibden Road, Norwich, NR3 4RR Tel: (01603) 426341 Fax: (01603) 424354 E-mail: mailroom@floridagroup.co.uk

The Garage Street Shoes, Unit 13 St. Johns Centre, Leeds, LS2 8LQ Tel: 0113-273 9700 Fax: 0113-232 9221 E-mail: waynesshoes@aol.com

Gardiner Bros & Co. (Leathers) Ltd, 1 Alvin Street, Gloucester, GL1 3EJ Tel: (01452) 422001 Fax: (01452) 307220 E-mail: sales@gardinerbros.co.uk

Gilbert & Mellish Ltd, 3 Lightning Way, Birmingham, B31 3PH Tel: 0121-475 1101 Fax: 0121-478 0163 E-mail: sales@gilbert-mellish.co.uk

Goodwear Shoes 2001 Ltd, 5 Dudlow Drive, Liverpool, L18 2HB Tel: 0151-280 3049 Fax: 0151-280 3049 E-mail: trevordh@blueyonder.co.uk

▶ Harrier Shoes Ltd, Kenmuir Road, Finedon, Wellingborough, Northamptonshire, NN9 5LS Tel: (01933) 681401

J B I Ltd, Riverside, Bacup, Lancashire, OL13 0DT Tel: (01706) 873355 Fax: (01706) 874047 E-mail: enquires@j-b-i.co.uk

▶ Ken Hall, Newman Street, Kettering, Northamptonshire, NN16 0TG Tel: (01536) 522468 Fax: (01536) 410373 E-mail: enquiries@kenhall.co.uk

▶ Lotus Ltd, Gambrel Road, Westgate Industrial Estate, Northampton, NN5 5BB Tel: (01604) 755211 Fax: (01604) 759061

▶ M W T International Ltd, Great North Way, York, YO26 6RB Tel: (01904) 789880 Fax: (01904) 693192 E-mail: sales@mwtsafestyle.co.uk

Macksons London Ltd, 270 Kilburn High Road, London, NW6 2BY Tel: (020) 7624 7133 Fax: (020) 7625 6091 E-mail: enquiries@macksons.co.uk

Marlborough Leathers, Unit A Bury Close, Higham Ferrers, Rushden, Northamptonshire, NN10 8HQ Tel: (01933) 411314 Fax: (01604) 790946 E-mail: ml@witmore-bacon.co.uk

Nikwax Ltd, Unit B, Durgates Industrial Estate, Wadhurst, East Sussex, TN5 6DF Tel: (01892) 786400 Fax: (01892) 783748 E-mail: sales@nikwax.co.uk

Northampton Footwear Distributors Ltd, Summerhouse Road, Moulton Park Industrial Estate, Northampton, NN3 6WD Tel: (01604) 790828 Fax: (01604) 790577 E-mail: footwear@n-f-d.fsnet.co.uk

▶ Now Shoes UK Ltd, 232 Leicester Road, Markfield, Leicestershire, LE67 9RG Tel: (01530) 242727 Fax: (01530) 242475

Pacific Brands (UK) Ltd, Unit 1 Stretton Green Distribution Park, Langford Way, Barleycastle Lane, Appleton, Warrington, WA4 4TQ Tel: (01925) 212212 Fax: (01925) 212222

▶ Plus in Boots Ltd, 150 Magna Road, Poole, Dorset, BH11 9NB Tel: 01202 581566

Prescription Footwear Associates Ltd, P F A House, Lake Lane, Barnham, Bognor Regis, West Sussex, PO22 0JB Tel: (01243) 554407 Fax: (01243) 554407 E-mail: sales@pfa.sageweb.co.uk

▶ QS Discount Outlets, ENA MILL, Flapper fold lane, Atherton, M46 0HB Tel: 01942 879349 E-mail: sales@dsdiscount.com

Savvas Georgiou, 207-209 Langham Road, London, N15 3LH Tel: (020) 8889 7999 Fax: (020) 8888 8927

Shico (UK) Industrial Footwear Ltd, 35 Morris Road, Leicester, LE2 6BR Tel: (01933) 273800 Fax: (01933) 228179 E-mail: shico@shico.co.uk

▶ Skechers Usa Ltd, Katherine House Darkes Lane, 9 - 11 Wyllyotts Place, Potters Bar, Hertfordshire, EN6 2JD Tel: (01707) 655955 Fax: (01707) 647986

▶ The Slipper . Com, Brantwood Lodge, Coniston, Cumbria, LA21 8AD Tel: 015394 41997 Fax: 015394 41998 E-mail: lasts@theslipper.com

▶ Smart Upper Closes, 8a, North Way, Claverings Industrial Estate, London, N9 0AD Tel: (020) 8803 1116 Fax: (020) 8803 1116

▶ Somerset Footwear Ltd, Unit 15 Canvin Court, Bancombe Road, Somerton, Somerset, TA11 6SB Tel: (01458) 273997 Fax: (01458) 274483

FOOTWEAR – *continued*

▶ Star Child, Unit 18 The Oak Business Centre, 79-93 Ratcliffe Road, Sileby, Loughborough, Leicestershire, LE12 7PU Tel: (01509) 817601 Fax: (01509) 817602 E-mail: info@starchildshoes.co.uk
▶ Topline Dance Shoes Ltd, Havers Road, Norwich, NR3 2DU Tel: (01603) 788359 Fax: (01603) 400144
Tutte & Thomas, J 1 Liners Industrial Estate, Pitt Road, Southampton, SO15 3FQ Tel: (023) 8022 5343 Fax: (023) 8023 3446 E-mail: tutte.thomas@virgin.net
UK Distributors Footwear Ltd, Churchill Way, Fleckney, Leicester, LE8 8UD Tel: 0116-240 3485 Fax: 0116-240 2762 E-mail: footwear@ukdistributors.co.uk
▶ William James Shoes Ltd, Sartoris Road, Rushden, Northamptonshire, NN10 9TL Tel: (01933) 317497
▶ William Paton Ltd, West Avenue, Phoenix Retail Park, Paisley, Renfrewshire, PA1 2FB Tel: 0141-840 6040
William Smith Ltd, 7 Faraday Street, Dryburgh Industrial Estate, Dundee, DD2 3QQ Tel: (01382) 813814 Fax: (01382) 814222 E-mail: info@smithshoes.co.uk

FOOTWEAR ACCESSORIES OR COMPONENTS, *See also headings for particular types*

Best Boots, Nettleton, Chippenham, Wiltshire, SN14 7NS Tel: (01249) 783530 Fax: (01249) 782058 E-mail: info@bestboots.co.uk
▶ Haddon Costello Ltd, 34 Percy Road, Leicester, LE2 8FP Tel: 0116-233 8858 Fax: 0116-233 8857

FOOTWEAR IMPORT/EXPORT MERCHANTS OR AGENTS

Brevitt Rieker Ltd, 37 Tenter Road, Moulton Park Industrial Estate, Northampton, NN3 6AX Tel: (01604) 491222 Fax: (01604) 499512 E-mail: sales@rieker.net
Britorion Ltd, PO Box 98, Alton, Hampshire, GU34 4YL Tel: (01420) 22134 Fax: (01420) 520345 E-mail: britorion@aol.com
Fabrianne Collection Ltd, Danielle House, Southmoor Road, Wythenshawe, Manchester, M23 9GP Tel: 0161-945 8001 Fax: 0161-947 8843
Goodwear Shoes 2001 Ltd, 5 Dudlow Drive, Liverpool, L18 2HB Tel: 0151-280 3049 Fax: 0151-280 3049 E-mail: trevordh@blueyonder.co.uk
Nathan's Wastesavers Ltd, Unit 13 Winchester Avenue, Denny, Stirlingshire, FK6 6QE Tel: (01324) 826888 Fax: (01324) 826555
Newmans Footwear Ltd, Garden Street, Blackburn, BB2 1TZ Tel: (01254) 56211 Fax: (01254) 680545 E-mail: newmans@nfw.co.uk

FOOTWEAR INDUSTRIAL CLEANING MACHINES

Shooshyne, 481 Meanwood Road, Leeds, LS6 2BH Tel: 0113-275 2283 Fax: 0113-275 2362 E-mail: shoeshine@compuserve.com

FOOTWEAR PRODUCTION LEATHER

▶ Cambridge Interiors Ltd, 71 Nelson Street, Kettering, Northamptonshire, NN16 9QL Tel: (01536) 481586 Fax: (01536) 481586
Loake Bros Ltd, Wood Street, Kettering, Northamptonshire, NN16 9SN Tel: (01536) 415411 Fax: (01536) 410190 E-mail: enquiries@loake.co.uk

FOOTWEAR PRODUCTION PLANT, MACHINERY OR EQUIPMENT

Charles Birch (Essex) Ltd, Units 7-8, Fleet Hall Road, Purdeys Industrial, Rochford, Essex, SS4 1NF Tel: (01702) 530656 Fax: (01702) 531417 E-mail: info@charlesbirch.com
Livingston & Doughty Ltd, 17 Mandervell Road, Oadby, Leicester, LE2 5LR Tel: 0116-271 4221 Fax: 0116-271 6977 E-mail: orders@shoenet.co.uk
Sas Machine, Watton Road, Ware, Hertfordshire, SG12 0AE Tel: (01920) 465281 Fax: (01920) 465285 E-mail: sales@sasmachines.co.uk

FOOTWEAR WATERPROOFING PRODUCTS

Grangers International Ltd, Grange Close, Clover Nook Industrial Park, Somercotes, Alfreton, Derbyshire, DE55 4QT Tel: (01773) 521521 Fax: (01773) 521262 E-mail: grangers@grangers.co.uk
Nikwax Ltd, Unit B, Durgates Industrial Estate, Wadhurst, East Sussex, TN5 6DF Tel: (01892) 786400 Fax: (01892) 783748 E-mail: sales@nikwax.co.uk

FOOTWEAR, PLASTIC/ SYNTHETIC

Ronaldsway Shoe Co. Ltd, Ballasalla, Isle Of Man, IM9 2RS Tel: (01624) 823011 Fax: (01624) 822441

FORCE MEASUREMENT TRANSDUCERS

Interface Force Measurements Ltd, Ground Floor, Unit 19 Wellington Business Park, Duke Ride, Crowthorne, Berkshire, RG45 6LS Tel: 0845 4941748 Fax: (01344) 774765 E-mail: info@interface.uk.com
Kistler Instruments Ltd, Murrell Green Business Park, London Road, Hook, Hampshire, RG27 9GR Tel: (01256) 741550 Fax: (01256) 741551 E-mail: sales.uk@kistler.com
Procter & Chester (Measurements) Ltd, Dalehouse Lane, Kenilworth, Warwickshire, CV8 2UE Tel: (01926) 864444 Fax: (01926) 864888 E-mail: info@pcm-uk.com
Thames Side-Maywood Ltd, 2 Collumbers Drive, Summet Avenue, Southwood, Farnborough, Hampshire, GU14 0NZ Tel: (01252) 555811 Fax: (01252) 375394 E-mail: sales@thames-side.co.uk
Vishay Measurements Group UK Ltd, 1 Cartel Units, Stroudley Road, Basingstoke, Hampshire, RG24 8FW Tel: (01256) 462131 Fax: (01256) 471441 E-mail: email@measurementsgroup.co.uk

FORCE SENSORS

Data Harvest Group Ltd, 1 Eden Court, Eden Way, Leighton Buzzard, Bedfordshire, LU7 4FY Tel: (01525) 373666 Fax: (01525) 851638 E-mail: sales@data-harvest.co.uk
Procter & Chester (Measurements) Ltd, Dalehouse Lane, Kenilworth, Warwickshire, CV8 2UE Tel: (01926) 864444 Fax: (01926) 864888 E-mail: info@pcm-uk.com

FORENSIC SCIENTIST DOCUMENT EXAMINATION

Global, PO Box 101, Northampton, NN1 4BS Tel: (01604) 636531 Fax: (01604) 760656 E-mail: info@globalintelligence.ltd.uk

FORENSIC SECURITY DYES

Synnex Information Technology Ltd, Synnex House, Nedge Hill, Telford, Shropshire, TF3 3AH Tel: (01952) 207200 E-mail: enquiries@smartwater.com

FORESTRY CONSULTANCY

▶ Capita, The Capita Building, Kingmoor Business Park, Carlisle, CA6 4SJ Tel: (01228) 673000 Fax: (01228) 673111
▶ Tree Tops Forestry, The Old School House, Coniston Cold, Skipton, North Yorkshire, BD23 4EA Tel: (01756) 749626 Fax: (01756) 749626 E-mail: jonathan@treetopsforestry.fsbusiness.co.uk

FORESTRY EQUIPMENT

Blount UK, Unit 3 Arianda Warwhouses, Steinhoff Business Park, Tewkesbury, Gloucestershire, GL20 8GY Tel: (01684) 297600 Fax: (01684) 855497 E-mail: sales@blount.co.uk
D H Jones, Unit 10 Industrial Estate, Llanuwchllyn, Bala, Gwynedd, LL23 7NL Tel: (01678) 520666 Fax: (01678) 520666
Eurogreen Machinery, The Tythe Barn, North Barn Farm, Titnore Lane, Worthing, West Sussex, BN12 6NZ Tel: (01903) 700678 Fax: (01903) 247585 E-mail: admin@eurogreenuk.com
Green Mech Ltd, The Mill Industrial Park, Kings Coughton, Alcester, Warwickshire, B49 5QG Tel: (01789) 400044 Fax: (01789) 400167 E-mail: sales@greenmech.co.uk
▶ GreenwayDirect, The Barn, Oaklands Home Farm, Church Street, Barrowford, Nelson, Lancashire, BB9 6EB Tel: (01282) 693661 E-mail: peter.maltby@greenwaydirect.com
Honey Bros, New Pond Road, Peasmarsh, Guildford, Surrey, GU3 1JR Tel: (01483) 575098 Fax: (01483) 535608 E-mail: sales@honeybros.co.uk
Husqvarna Outdoor Products Ltd, Oldends Lane Industrial Estate, Stonedale Road, Stonehouse, Gloucestershire, GL10 3SY Tel: (01453) 820300 Fax: (01453) 826936 E-mail: info.husqvarna@husqvarna.co.uk
Hydrocut Ltd, PO Box 2926, Colchester, CO6 2QP Tel: (01787) 222266 Fax: (01787) 222210 E-mail: sales@hydrocut.co.uk
John H Thomson, Merlwood, Kirkgunzeon, Dumfries, DG2 8JR Tel: (01387) 760270 Fax: (01387) 760655
Longleat Forestry, Picket Post, Warminster, Wiltshire, BA12 7JS Tel: (01985) 213507 Fax: (01985) 847438
M I Edwards Engineers, Mundford Road, Weeting, Brandon, Suffolk, IP27 0PL Tel: (01842) 813555 Fax: (01842) 811595
Sibert Technology, 2a Merrow Business Centre, Merrow Lane, Guildford, Surrey, GU4 7WA Tel: (01483) 440724 Fax: (01483) 440727 E-mail: NDT@sibtec.com

FORESTRY LAND AGENTS

Amcort Ltd, Field House, McMichaels Way, Hurst Green, Etchingham, East Sussex, TN19 7HJ Tel: (01580) 860500 Fax: (01580) 860171 E-mail: info@amcort.com

FORGED STEEL PIPELINE FITTINGS

F W B Cymru Co. Ltd, Five Crosses Industrial Estate, Ruthin Road, Minera, Wrexham, Clwyd, LL11 3RD Tel: (01978) 720720 Fax: (01978) 720721 E-mail: sales@fwbcymru.co.uk
H P F Energy Services, 3 Kinwarton Farm Road, Arden Forest Industrial Estate, Alcester, Warwickshire, B49 6EH Tel: (01789) 761212 Fax: (01789) 761222 E-mail: alcester@hpf-energy.com

FORGED STEEL ROLLMAKERS

Akers UK Ltd, Suite 14, Shire Hall Complex, Pentonville, Newport, Gwent, NP20 5HB Tel: (01633) 265544 E-mail: sales@akersuk.com

FORGED STEEL VALVES

G & S Valves Ltd, Catteshall Lane, Godalming, Surrey, GU7 1JS Tel: (01483) 415444 Fax: (01483) 426891 E-mail: gsvalves@aol.com

FORGERY DETECTORS

Aco Electronics Ltd, Unit 3 Manor Farm Business Park, Shingay cum Wendy, Royston, Hertfordshire, SG8 0HW Tel: (01223) 208222 Fax: (01223) 208150 E-mail: sales@acoelectronics.com

FORGING DIES/TOOLS

A F M Precision Die & Tool Co. Ltd, Froysell St, Willenhall, West Midlands, WV13 1QH Tel: (01902) 607640 Fax: (01902) 634505

FORGING HEAT TREATMENT

Alloy Heat Treatment, Block 6 Grazebrook Industrial Park, Peartree Lane, Dudley, West Midlands, DY2 0XW Tel: (01384) 456777 Fax: (01384) 453900 E-mail: sales@alloyheat.co.uk

FORGING MACHINISTS

Slater Yendall Ltd, Howard Road, Park Farm North, Redditch, Worcestershire, B98 7SE Tel: (01527) 529069 Fax: (01527) 510359

FORGING PLANT

Forge Tech Services Ltd, Gatefield Works, Whitelands Road, Ashton-under-Lyne, Lancashire, OL6 6UG Tel: 0161-339 1120 Fax: 0161-343 2257 E-mail: info@forgetechservices.com

FORGING STEELS

Boswell & Co. (Steels) Ltd, Bassett Road, Park Lane Industrial Estate, Cradley, Halesowen, West Midlands, B63 2RE Tel: (01384) 637375 Fax: (01384) 410103 E-mail: boswellsteel@aol.com
Finkl UK Ltd, Langley Green Road, Oldbury, West Midlands, B69 4TR Tel: 0121-544 4506 Fax: 0121-544 1706 E-mail: sales@finkl-uk.co.uk

FORGINGS, *See also headings under Forgings, when method is described, or under metal used eg: Steel*

▶ B & A Metal Finishers Ltd, Unit 4, Ellingham Way Industrial Estate, Ashford, Kent, TN23 6NF Tel: (01233) 661652 Fax: (01333) 624500 E-mail: julie@kmd.co.uk
Barzillai Hingley & Sons Ltd, Lion Chain Works, Providence Street, Cradley Heath, West Midlands, B64 5DT Tel: (01384) 569141 Fax: (01384) 639177 E-mail: sales@barzillai.com
▶ C D Topp, Lyndhurst, Carlton Husthwaite, Thirsk, North Yorkshire, YO7 2BJ Tel: (01845) 501415 Fax: (01845) 501072 E-mail: enquiries@christopp.co.uk
▶ C & H Howe Ltd, Progress Drive, Cannock, Staffordshire, WS11 0JE Tel: (01543) 577575 Fax: (01543) 504289
▶ C R F Coatings Ltd, Unit 1 Bullock Street, West Bromwich, West Midlands, B70 7HE Tel: 0121-525 1888 Fax: 0121-525 0888
Clydesdale Forge Co., Marriott Road, Dudley, West Midlands, DY2 0LA Tel: (01384) 252587 Fax: (01384) 231005 E-mail: sales@clydesdale-forge.co.uk
Dyform Jenkins Dunn Ltd, Moland Forge, Central Trading Estate, Shaw Road, Dudley, West Midlands, DY2 8QX Tel: (01384) 232844 Fax: (01384) 455628
▶ L Blackstock, Threeply Farm, Torr Road, Bridge of Weir, Renfrewshire, PA11 3RT Tel: (01505) 612375 Fax: (01505) 612425
Langley Alloys Ltd, Campbell Rd, Stoke-on-Trent, ST4 4ER Tel: (01782) 847474 Fax: (01782) 847476 E-mail: chris@meighs.co.uk
Stephen D. Lowe, The Forge, 49 Claverham Road, Yatton, Bristol, BS49 4LD Tel: (01934) 834907 Fax: (01934) 876568
Parker Hannifin plc, Triton Works, Woods Lane, Cradley Heath, West Midlands, B64 7AS Tel: (01384) 566592 Fax: (01384) 567275
▶ Profile 7000 Ltd, Station St West Business Park, Coventry, CV6 5BP Tel: 024 76683366
▶ Spectrum Architectural Coatings, High Street, Princes End, Tipton, West Midlands, DY4 9HG Tel: 0121-522 2244 Fax: 0121-522 2243
▶ T P Powder Coating Ltd, Unit 318 Fauld Industrial Estate, Fauld, Tutbury, Burton-on-Trent, Staffordshire, DE13 9HS Tel: (01283) 520548 Fax: (01283) 520549 E-mail: sales@tppowder.co.uk

FORGINGS, DROP, DEFENCE STANDARDS

Eyres Forgings Ltd, Lord North Street, Miles Platting, Manchester, M40 8HT Tel: 0161-205 1090 Fax: 0161-203 4513

FORK LIFT TRUCK OPERATOR INSTRUCTOR TRAINING

▶ Pinkerton Forklift Training, Bryn Hyfred, Garth Farm, Llangwstenin, Llandudno Junction, Conwy, LL31 9JF Tel: (01492) 540521 Fax: (01492) 540521 E-mail: wendy.brown10@virgin.net
▶ Tag Training Services, 20 Leyland Drive, Kingsthorpe, Northampton, NN2 8QA Tel: 07974 972913 Fax: 0870 1351199

FORK LIFT TRUCK OPERATOR TRAINING, NARROW AISLE

▶ Tag Training Services, 20 Leyland Drive, Kingsthorpe, Northampton, NN2 8QA Tel: 07974 972913 Fax: 0870 1351199

FORK LIFT TRUCK OPERATOR TRAINING, ROUGH TERRAIN

Advance Onsite Training, 10 Knutsford Road, Holmes Chapel, Crewe, CW4 7DE Tel: 07929 575197 Fax: 01297 631671 E-mail: andrew@advance-onsite-training.co.uk
▶ Safety-Train UK, 7 Belgravia Court, Oakthorpe Drive, Kingshurst, Birmingham, B37 6HY Tel: 0121-605 0598 E-mail: info@safety-trainuk.co.uk

FORKLIFT TRUCK ACCESS PLATFORMS

▶ D A C Handling Solutions Ltd, Oxford Street Industrial Park, Vulcan Road, Bilston, West Midlands, WV14 7JG Tel: (0845) 6013529 Fax: (0870) 1662904 E-mail: drock@dac-handling.co.uk
Dac Handling Solutions, 10 Kestrel Park, Tallon Road, Hutton, Brentwood, Essex, CM13 1TN Tel: (01277) 223055 Fax: (01277) 222472 E-mail: info@dac-handling.co.uk
HSS Lift & Shift, Sotherby Road, Middlesbrough, Cleveland, TS3 8BS Tel: (01642) 246015 Fax: (01642) 251411
▶ Max Lift Trucks, Tumbletrees, Cannock, Staffordshire, WS12 4DX Tel: 01543 279879
Nationwide Access Ltd, 15 Midland Court, Central Park, Lutterworth, Leicestershire, LE17 4PN Tel: (01455) 558874 Fax: (01455) 550974 E-mail: sales@nationwideaccess.co.uk
Pallet Trucks Direct, 61 Greenways, Fleet, Hampshire, GU52 7XF Tel: 01252 617028 Fax: 01252 615096 E-mail: pallettrucksdirect@btopenworld.com

FORKLIFT TRUCK ARMS

Amdec Fork Lift Truck, Globe Lane Industrial Estate, Broadway, Dukinfield, Cheshire, SK16 4UU Tel: 0161-330 5151 Fax: 0161-338 8002

▶ Dab Handling, 42-50 Tannoch Drive, Cumbernauld, Glasgow, G67 2XX Tel: (01236) 453331 Fax: (01236) 452653 E-mail: arthur@dabhandling.co.uk

Delta Equipment Ltd, Laurel Street, Bradford, West Yorkshire, BD3 9TP Tel: (01274) 778855 Fax: (01274) 666028 E-mail: sales-hire-del@btconnect.com

FORKLIFT TRUCK ATTACHMENTS

▶ Abbey Attachments Ltd, Unit 7, Croft Lane Industrial Estate, Pilsworth, Bury, Lancashire, BL9 8QG Tel: 0161-766 8885 Fax: 0161-767 9017 E-mail: sales@abbey-attachments.co.uk

Attachments Ltd, 6 Peterborough Road, Crowland, Peterborough, PE6 0BA Tel: (01733) 210611 Fax: (01733) 211345 E-mail: sales@attachments.ltd.uk

B & B Attachments Ltd, Unit 39 Colbourne Cresent, Nelson Park, Cramlington, Northumberland, NE23 1WB Tel: (01670) 737373 Fax: (01670) 736286

B & B Attachments Ltd, Guildgate House, Pelican Lane, Newbury, Berkshire, RG14 1NX Tel: (01635) 232000 Fax: (01635) 237444 E-mail: info@bandbattachments.com

Bakers, 2 Hainge Road, Tividale, Oldbury, West Midlands, B69 2NH Tel: 0121-557 1935 Fax: 0121-557 4245 E-mail: sales@bfsltd.co.uk

Bolzoni Auramo Ltd, Unit 10 Taurus Park, Europa Boulevard, Westbrook, Warrington, WA5 7ZT Tel: (01925) 624570 Fax: (01925) 624578 E-mail: admin@bolzoni-auramo.com

Bridge Engineering Ltd, Station Road, Thorney, Peterborough, PE6 0QE Tel: (01733) 270308 Fax: (01733) 270985 E-mail: bridgeeng@btopenworld.com

Cascade (UK) Ltd, Unit 5, Eden Close, Hellaby Industrial Estate, Hellaby, Rotherham, South Yorkshire, S66 8RW Tel: (01709) 704500 Fax: (01709) 704501 E-mail: uk-sales@cascorp.com

Contact Attachments, Unit E, Mochdre Industrial Estate, Newtown, Powys, SY16 4LE Tel: (01686) 611200 Fax: (01686) 611201 E-mail: sales@forklift-attachments.co.uk

Dawson Rentals Ltd, Aberford Road, Garforth, Leeds, LS25 2ET Tel: 0113-287 4874 Fax: 0113-286 9158 E-mail: info@dawsongroup.co.uk

Electric Lift Truck Services, 6 Village Way, Farndon, Newark, Nottinghamshire, NG24 4SX Tel: (01636) 701573

▶ Elf Forktrucks, Alder Street, Huddersfield, HD1 6JY Tel: (01484) 511101 Fax: (01484) 432764 E-mail: sales@elfforktrucks.co.uk

Fabcon Engineering, 41 Gortlenaghan Road, Dungannon, County Tyrone, BT70 3AJ Tel: (028) 8776 1116 Fax: (028) 8776 1799

Hallam Materials Handling Ltd, 232-234 Woodbourn Road, Sheffield, S9 3LQ Tel: 0114-275 3000 Fax: 0114-275 3222 E-mail: hallam-mh@btconnect.com

▶ Hoperole Ltd, 4 Norman Way Indust Estate, Over, Cambridge, CB24 5LY Tel: (01954) 230900 Fax: (01954) 230990

Invicta Forks & Attachments, Westland Square, Dewsbury Road, Leeds, LS11 5SS Tel: 0113-277 1222 Fax: 0113-271 6860 E-mail: sales@invictaforks.co.uk

Jungheinrich (G B) Ltd, Orpen Park, Ash Ridge Road, Almondsbury, Bristol, BS32 4QD Tel: (01454) 616898 Fax: (01454) 616206 E-mail: trevorw@jungheinrich.co.uk

Liftomatic International Ltd, 9 Farriers Way, Bootle, Merseyside, L30 4XL Tel: 0151-524 3066 Fax: 0151-524 3075 E-mail: liftomatic.ltd@btconnect.com

M S I Forks Ltd, Carr Hill, Doncaster, South Yorkshire, DN4 8DH Tel: (01302) 366961 Fax: (01302) 340663

Quicklift Ltd, 636 Birmingham Road, Lydiate Ash, Bromsgrove, Worcestershire, B61 0QB Tel: 0121-457 8995 Fax: 0121-457 8935

Roy Fabrications Ltd, 2 Chancel Way Industrial Estate, Birmingham, B6 7AU Tel: 0121 3444082

S M C Euro Clamps Ltd, Demmings Road, Cheadle, Cheshire, SK8 2PP Tel: 0161-428 8323 Fax: 0161-428 4513 E-mail: purchasing@smceuroclamps.com

Strimech Engineering Ltd, Longmore Avenue, Walsall, WS2 0BW Tel: (01922) 649700 Fax: (01922) 649802 E-mail: info@strimech.com

Vacuum Lifting, Rowallan, Kilmarnock, Ayrshire, KA3 2LW Tel: (01563) 540400 Fax: (01563) 520139 E-mail: sales@vacuumliftinguk.co.uk

FORKLIFT TRUCK CHAINS

Chaintec Ltd, Unit 43, Westbrook Trading Estate, Westbrook Road, Trafford Park, Manchester, M17 1AY Tel: 0161-877 7373 Fax: 0161-876 0365 E-mail: info@chaintec.co.uk

▶ Chaintech Northern Ltd, 22 Ganners Lane, Leeds, LS13 2NX Tel: (07767) 307497 Fax: 0113-256 2379 E-mail: keith@chaintech.fsbusiness.co.uk

▶ Sundown Services, Unit 29 Carcroft Enterprise Park, Carcroft, Doncaster, South Yorkshire, DN6 8DD Tel: (01302) 729436 Fax: (01302) 725635E-mail: sales@sundownservices.co.uk

FORKLIFT TRUCK DELIVERY AND COLLECTION

Chapman Fork Lift Services Ltd, Wood Lane Industrial Estate, Wood End, Marston Moretaine, Bedford, MK43 0NZ Tel: (01234) 766855 Fax: (01234) 766855

Devon Forklift Services, Merribrocke, Station Road, Broadclyst, Exeter, EX5 3AR Tel: (01392) 462754 Fax: 01392 462754

FORKLIFT TRUCK ELECTRICAL SPARE PARTS

Machine Electrics Ltd, Unit 6 The Timberyard, East Moors Road, Cardiff, CF24 5ES Tel: (029) 2049 8840 Fax: (029) 2048 0469

FORKLIFT TRUCK FORK ATTACHMENTS

Bolzoni Auramo Ltd, Unit 10 Taurus Park, Europa Boulevard, Westbrook, Warrington, WA5 7ZT Tel: (01925) 624570 Fax: (01925) 624578 E-mail: admin@bolzoni-auramo.com

Cascade (UK) Ltd, Unit 5, Eden Close, Hellaby Industrial Estate, Hellaby, Rotherham, South Yorkshire, S66 8RW Tel: (01709) 704500 Fax: (01709) 704501 E-mail: uk-sales@cascorp.com

▶ Hoperole Ltd, 4 Norman Way Indust Estate, Over, Cambridge, CB24 5LY Tel: (01954) 230900 Fax: (01954) 230990

FORKLIFT TRUCK FORKS

Cascade Kenhar Ltd, 3 Kelbrook Road, Manchester, M11 2DD Tel: 0161-230 7472 Fax: 0161-230 7879

Invicta Forks & Attachments, Westland Square, Dewsbury Road, Leeds, LS11 5SS Tel: 0113-277 1222 Fax: 0113-271 6860 E-mail: sales@invictaforks.co.uk

Langside Linde Servernside Ltd, 4 Britannia Road, Patchway, Bristol, BS34 5TA Tel: 0117-906 3000 Fax: 0117-906 3001 E-mail: enquiries@linde.severnside.co.uk

Lift West Nissan Ltd, New Road, Seavington St Michael, Ilminster, Somerset, TA19 0QQ Tel: (01460) 242400 Fax: (01460) 240020 E-mail: info@liftwest.com

Rossendale Fork Trucks Ltd, 18 Thirlmere Avenue, Haslingden, Rossendale, Lancashire, BB4 6LU Tel: 01706 228583

United Fork Trucks 1992 Ltd, 1 Eurolink Commercial Park, Symmonds Drive, Sittingbourne, Kent, ME10 3SY Tel: (01795) 472498 Fax: (01795) 429730 E-mail: sittingbourne@unitedforktrucks.co.uk

FORKLIFT TRUCK HIRE

1st Class Fork Truck Services, Unit 1, Oaks Green, Sheffield, S9 3WR Tel: 0114-261 9495

A B Equipment, Unit 13a Owen O'Cork Mills, 288 Beersbridge Road, Belfast, BT5 5DX Tel: (028) 9045 5520 Fax: (028) 9045 5520 E-mail: ab_equipment@yahoo.co.uk

A D Cragg, Whisperings, Osborne Road, Pitsea, Basildon, Essex, SS13 2LG Tel: (01268) 726737 Fax: (01268) 727668

A F L Trucks Ltd, 8 Factory Road, Poole, Dorset, BH16 5HT Tel: (01202) 621212 Fax: (01202) 621111 E-mail: sales@afltrucks.co.uk

A I M S Ltd, Unit 3, Parkwater Industrial Estate, Forest Road, Newport, Isle Of Wight, PO30 4LY Tel: (01983) 520526 Fax: (01983) 520298 E-mail: aims@forkliftrucks.eu.com

A J Mechanical Handling Services Ltd, Bridge Works, 2 North End Road, Yatton, Bristol, BS49 4AL Tel: (01934) 835835 Fax: (01934) 838999

A & L Stronach, Unit 16 17 Camiestone Road, Kemnay, Inverurie, Aberdeenshire, AB51 5GT Tel: (01467) 624655 Fax: (01467) 624629

Ability Handling Ltd, Mangham Way, Rotherham, South Yorkshire, S61 4RL Tel: (01709) 821821 Fax: (01709) 821421 E-mail: sales@abilityhandlingltd.co.uk

Access Mechanical Handling Ltd, 11 Sholto Cresent, Righead Industrial Estate, Bellshill, Lanarkshire, ML4 3LX Tel: (01698) 745859 Fax: (01698) 740869 E-mail: sales@forktrucks-scotland.co.uk

Active Handling (Sales) Ltd, Unit 10, Pipers Lane Trading Estate, Pipers Lane, Thatcham, Berkshire, RG19 4NA Tel: (01635) 872972 Fax: (01635) 872909 E-mail: sales@stacatruc.co.uk

Advanced Fork Lift Service Midlands Ltd, Chapel Street, Handsworth, Birmingham, B21 0PA Tel: 0121-554 8811 Fax: 0121-554 4812 E-mail: info@advancedforklift.co.uk

Amvar Ltd, Unit 2 Mucklow Hill Trading Estate, Mucklow Hill, Halesowen, West Midlands, B62 8DF Tel: (0800) 5424512 Fax: 0121-550 7222 E-mail: amvar@forklift-trucks.uk.com

Apollo Plant Holdings Ltd, Redstone Industrial Estate, Boston, Lincolnshire, PE21 8AL Tel: (01205) 351722 Fax: (01205) 360432 E-mail: enquiries@apollo-plant.co.uk

Approved Welding Supplies, Hill Top Farm, 22 Main Street, South Croxton, Leicester, LE7 3RJ Tel: (01664) 840098 Fax: (01664) 840527

Arrow Lift Trucks Ltd, 9 Kepler, Tamworth, Staffordshire, B79 7XE Tel: (01827) 313335 Fax: (01827) 313336 E-mail: sales@arrowlifttrucks.co.uk

B & J Material Handling Ltd, 3 Hardy Drive, Hardingstone, Northampton, NN4 6UX Tel: (01604) 769977 Fax: (01604) 708151

Barloworld, 2 Brook Office Park, Emersons Green, Bristol, BS16 7FL Tel: 0117-970 9450 Fax: 0117-982 1465 E-mail: marketing@handling.barloworld.co.uk

Barloworld Handling Ltd, Unit 1 Minto Drive, Altens Industrial Estate, Aberdeen, AB12 3LW Tel: (01224) 878959 Fax: (01224) 896226 E-mail: aberdeen@handling.barloworld.co.uk

Barloworld Handling Ltd, Portobello Road, Birtley, Chester Le Street, County Durham, DH3 2RZ Tel: 0191-410 6221 Fax: 0191-410 5795 E-mail: birtley@handling.barloworld.co.uk

Barloworld Handling Ltd, 6 Rutherford Road, Dryburgh Industrial Estate, Dundee, DD2 3XH Tel: (01382) 811523 Fax: (01382) 858640 E-mail: sales@barlow.co.uk

Barloworld Handling Ltd, Unit G Cumbernauld Business Park, Wardlaw Road, Cumbernauld, Glasgow, G67 3JZ Tel: (01236) 725061 Fax: (01236) 736212 E-mail: cumbernauld@handling.barloworld.co.uk

Barloworld Handling Ltd, Farthing Road Indust Estate, Ipswich, IP1 5BL Tel: (01473) 740241 Fax: (01473) 740903

Barloworld Handling Ltd, Barlow House, Howley Park Road East, Morley, Leeds, LS27 0SW Tel: 0113-252 1711 Fax: 0113-253 4339

Barloworld Handling Ltd, Unit 4, Vitruvius Way, Meridian Business Park, Leicester, LE19 1WA Tel: 0116-282 7500 Fax: 0116-282 3888

Barloworld Handling Ltd, Unit 5 Burrington Way, Plymouth, PL5 3LR Tel: (01752) 782540 Fax: (01752) 768467 E-mail: plymouth@handling.barloworld.co.uk

Barloworld Handling Ltd, Barlow House, Dolphin Way, Purfleet, Essex, RM19 1NZ Tel: (01708) 257300 Fax: (01708) 257310 E-mail: haydock@handling.barloworld.co.uk

Barloworld Handling Ltd, Unit 1 30 Stevenston Industrial Estate, Stevenston, Ayrshire, KA20 3LR Tel: (01294) 463350 Fax: (01294) 462410 E-mail: knelson@handling.barloworld.co.uk

Barloworld Handling Ltd, Barlow House, Yew Tree Way, Golborne, Warrington, WA3 3JD Tel: (01942) 721111 Fax: (01942) 408100 E-mail: warrington@handling.barloworld.co.uk

Barloworld Handling Ltd, 2 Cygnus Way, West Bromwich, West Midlands, B70 0XB Tel: 0121-521 2500 Fax: 0121-521 2550 E-mail: birmingham@barlow.co.uk

Barloworld Handling Ltd, 104 Coed Aben, Wrexham, Clwyd, LL13 9NY Tel: (01978) 661333 Fax: (01978) 664234 E-mail: wrexham@handling.barloworld.co.uk

Bendigo Mitchell Ltd, 104 Windy Arbour, Kenilworth, Warwickshire, CV8 2BH Tel: (01926) 857626 Fax: (01926) 850609 E-mail: sales@bendigomitchell.com

Bolne Materials Handling, Unit 2 Stoken Place, Steventon, Basingstoke, Hampshire, RG25 3BD Tel: (01256) 398585 Fax: (01256) 398484 E-mail: sales@bolne.co.uk

Brindley Lift Truck Services Ltd, Unit 4, Aston Lane, Sharnford, Hinckley, Leicestershire, LE10 3PA Tel: (01455) 272800 Fax: (01455) 274712 E-mail: rhayes@lift-truck.co.uk

▶ Bristol Forklifts, The Grove Industrial Estate, Gloucester Road, Patchway, Bristol, BS34 5BB Tel: 0117-969 4141 Fax: 0117-969 1211 E-mail: info@bristolforklifts.co.uk

C S M Services Ltd, Bradley Hall Trading Estate, Bradley Lane, Standish, Wigan, Lancashire, WN6 0XQ Tel: (01257) 424548 Fax: (01257) 424548

Capital Lift Trucks Ltd, Reading Road, Sherdon House, Sherfield-On-Loddon, Hook, Hampshire, RG27 0EX Tel: (01256) 882047 Fax: (01256) 811876

Carryduff Forklift, 5 Cadger Road, Carryduff, Belfast, BT8 8AU Tel: (028) 9081 2864 Fax: (028) 9081 4532 E-mail: sales@carryduff.co.uk.

Carrylift Materials Handling Ltd, Peel Road, Skelmersdale, Lancashire, WN8 9PT Tel: (01695) 455000 Fax: (01695) 455099 E-mail: info@carryliftgroup.com

Carville Engineering, Unit 11 Seymour Hill Industrial Estate, Dunmurry, Belfast, BT17 9PH Tel: (028) 9062 6999 Fax: (028) 9062 7300 E-mail: carvilleng@btconnect.com

Classic Fork Trucks Ltd, 1 Durbar Avenue Industrial Estate, Durbar Avenue, Coventry, CV6 5QF Tel: (024) 7663 7467 Fax: (024) 7663 7600

CMS Lift Trucks Ltd, 9 Michelin Road, Newtownabbey, County Antrim, BT36 4PT Tel: (028) 9084 2537 Fax: (028) 9084 2947 E-mail: colin@cmslifttrucks.com

Crown Lift Trucks Ltd, Tollbridge House, 135 Windmill Road, Sunbury-on-Thames, Middlesex, TW16 7EF Tel: (01932) 777500 Fax: (0845) 8509277 E-mail: info@crown.com

Davison Fork Lift, Ablow Street, Wolverhampton, WV2 4ER Tel: (01902) 420123 Fax: (01902) 429013

Dawson Rentals Ltd, Aberford Road, Garforth, Leeds, LS25 2ET Tel: 0113-287 4874 Fax: 0113-286 9158 E-mail: info@dawsongroup.co.uk

Deca Materials Handling Ltd, 13 Adkin Way, Wantage, Oxfordshire, OX12 9HN Tel: (01235) 770022 Fax: (01235) 770027 E-mail: sales@deca-mh.co.uk

Delta Equipment Ltd, Laurel Street, Bradford, West Yorkshire, BD3 9TP Tel: (01274) 778855 Fax: (01274) 666028 E-mail: sales@deltaforktrucks.co.uk

Dyson Fork Truck Services, Unit 1 Lawn Court, Lawn Road Industrial Estate, Carlton-in-Lindrick, Worksop, Nottinghamshire, S81 9ED Tel: (01909) 732040 Fax: (01909) 732073

E H Roberts & Co Southend Ltd, 251-255 Church Road, Benfleet, Essex, SS7 4QP Tel: (01268) 752811 Fax: (01268) 793416

E & S Forklift Sales, Malting Lane, Donington, Spalding, Lincolnshire, PE11 4XA Tel: (01775) 822022 Fax: (01775) 822009 E-mail: info@e-s-forklifts.co.uk

Electroserve Mechanical Handling Equipment, 8 Lemmington Way, Horsham, West Sussex, RH12 5JG Tel: (01403) 273335 Fax: (01403) 249803

Euro Forklifts Ltd, St. Michaels Road, Sittingbourne, Kent, ME10 3DN Tel: (01795) 425536 Fax: (01795) 476192

▶ Fairway Forklifts Ltd, 8 Watt Road, Hillington Industrial Estate, Glasgow, G52 4RY Tel: 0141-882 6242 Fax: 0141-882 7426 E-mail: admin@fairwayforklifts.co.uk

Fenton Plant Hire, A Culverlands Industrial Estate, Winchester Road, Shedfield, Southampton, SO32 2JF Tel: (01329) 830011 Fax: (01329) 833683 E-mail: sales@fentonplant.co.uk

Finning UK Ltd, Units 1, 3 & 5, Delphwood Drive, Sherdley Park Industrial Estate, Sherdley Road, St. Helens, Merseyside, WA9 5JE Tel: (01744) 451075 Fax: (01744) 451767 E-mail: lisad@birchwood-mechanical.co.uk

▶ Fork Lift Mechanical Services Ltd, East Hermiston Farm, Currie, Midlothian, EH14 4AJ Tel: 0131-442 2002 Fax: 0131-442 2662 E-mail: gus@forkliftserviceslimited.co.uk

Fork Truck Direct, Unit 5, Redhills Road, South Woodham Ferrers, Chelmsford, CM3 5UL Tel: (01245) 322252 Fax: (01245) 322227 E-mail: forktruck.direct@virgin.net

Fork Truck Maintenance, Units 1-2 Ewenny Industrial Estate, Bridgend, Mid Glamorgan, CF31 3EX Tel: (01656) 766200 Fax: (01656) 767976 E-mail: barryr@ftmbridgend.co.uk

Fork Truck Service Ltd, Derby Road, Wingerworth, Chesterfield, Derbyshire, S42 6NB Tel: (01246) 209632 Fax: (01246) 206633 E-mail: enquiries@forktruckbreakers.com

Fork Truck Services Aberdeen Ltd, Silverburn Crescent, Bridge of Don Industrial Estate, Aberdeen, AB23 8EW Tel: (01224) 703366 Fax: (01224) 828533

Forklift (Midlands), Unit 4, Balds Lane, Jubilee Business Park, Lye, Stourbridge, West Midlands, DY9 8SH Tel: (01384) 898984 Fax: (01384) 897590 E-mail: enquiries@clarkliftmidland.co.uk

Forklift Services, Site 4 The Old Airfield, Crabtree Lane, High Ercall, Telford, Shropshire, TF6 6AP Tel: (01952) 771166 Fax: (01952) 771177

Forkway Group Ltd, Unit 7 Corinium Industrial Estate, Raans Road, Amersham, Buckinghamshire, HP6 6JQ Tel: (01494) 723456 Fax: (01494) 723724 E-mail: sales@forkway.co.uk

Forward Forklifts & Engineering, Forward House Future Court, George Summers Close, Medway City Estate, Rochester, Kent, ME2 4EL Tel: (01634) 730200 Fax: (01634) 730193 E-mail: enquiries@forwardforklifts.co.uk

G B Fork Lifts, Unit K1 Innsworth Technology Park, Innsworth Lane, Gloucester, GL3 1DL Tel: (01452) 731350 Fax: (01452) 731373 E-mail: sales@gbforklifts.co.uk

G B Lift Trucks Ltd, C Building The Depot Pinnacle Storage Park, Cat & Fiddle Lane, West Hallam, Ilkeston, Derbyshire, DE7 6HE Tel: 0115-930 7901 Fax: 0115-930 8414

G E Plant Services Ltd, 10a Dawkins Road, Poole, Dorset, BH15 4JD Tel: (01202) 676463 Fax: (01202) 665725 E-mail: geplant@btinternet.com

Gaylee Ltd, Pope Street, Smethwick, West Midlands, B66 2JP Tel: 0121-558 2027 Fax: 0121-558 2029

Gerald Hamill & Sons, 114 Obin Street, Portadown, Craigavon, County Armagh, BT62 1BP Tel: (028) 3833 2297 Fax: (028) 3839 3377

H F T Forklift Ltd, Unit A, Ramsden Road, Rotherwas Industrial Estate, Hereford, HR2 6NP Tel: (01432) 277180 Fax: (01432) 352249 E-mail: info@hftforklifts.com

▶ Hoots Lift Trucks, Atlas House, 15 Bell Street, West Bromwich, West Midlands, B70 7BT Tel: 0121-500 5885 Fax: (07980) 701827 E-mail: info@hoots4forklifts.co.uk

J S T Forklifts Ltd, 5 Higham Ferrers Road, Chelveston, Wellingborough, Northamptonshire, NN9 6AN Tel: (01933) 624215 Fax: (01933) 622393 E-mail: sales@jst-forktrucks.co.uk

Jungheinrich GB Ltd, 620 Europa Boulevard, Westbrook, Warrington, WA5 7TX Tel: (01925) 625400 Fax: (01925) 230891 E-mail: info@jungheinrich.co.uk

FORKLIFT TRUCK HIRE – *continued*

K O S Lift Trucks, Unit 2, Shuttleworth Court, Shuttleworth Road, Bedford, MK41 0EN Tel: (01234) 216993

▶ Knightsbridge Mechanical Handling Ltd, Newby Road Industrial Estate, Newby Road, Hazel Grove, Stockport, Cheshire, SK7 5DA Tel: 0161-456 0123 Fax: 0161-456 8683 E-mail: knightsbridgemechanical@btconnect.com

Kridan Forklifts Garth House, Scarborough Road, East Heslerton, Malton, North Yorkshire, YO17 8RW Tel: (01944) 728301 Fax: (01944) 728301

Lektro Mechanical Handling, Shear House, Petersfield Avenue, Slough, SL2 5DY Tel: (0800) 0854245 Fax: (01753) 497859 E-mail: info@lektro.co.uk

Len Griffiths Fork Lift Services, Units 24-26 Station Industrial Estate, Worcester Road, Leominster, Herefordshire, HR6 8AR Tel: (01568) 611773 Fax: (01568) 615400 E-mail: lgfs27@aol.com

Lincolnshire Fork Lifts, Fen Farm, Stickney, Boston, Lincolnshire, PE22 8BJ Tel: (01205) 480336 Fax: (01205) 366408

Linde Jewsbury's Ltd, Units 5-7 Deans Trading Estate, Deans Road, Swinton, M27 0RD Tel: 0161-794 6101 Fax: 0161-794 1592 E-mail: enquiries@linde-jewsburys.co.uk

Linde Material Handling East Ltd, Unit 1 Charlton Mead Lane, Hoddesdon, Hertfordshire, EN11 0DJ Tel: (01992) 443121 Fax: (01992) 468050

Linde Material Handling UK Ltd, Kingsclere Road, Basingstoke, Hampshire, RG21 6XJ Tel: (01256) 342000 Fax: (01256) 342921 E-mail: sales@lansinglinde.co.uk

Lothian Mechanical Handling Ltd, 8 Mosshall Industrial Estate, Blackburn, Bathgate, West Lothian, EH47 7LY Tel: (01506) 655535 Fax: (01506) 634799 E-mail: lmh@lothianmechanicalhandling.co.uk

M & S Lift Trucks, 1240 Dewsbury Road, Tingley, Wakefield, West Yorkshire, WF3 1LX Tel: 0113-259 7909 Fax: 0113-252 9072

M T Mechanical Handling, Unit B6 Chasewater Estate, High Street, Burntwood Business Park, Burntwood, Staffordshire, WS7 3XD Tel: (01543) 675573 Fax: (01543) 674590 E-mail: sales@mtmechanical.co.uk

Mcleman Forklift Services Ltd, 15 Andover Street, Birmingham, B5 5RG Tel: 0121-643 1788 Fax: 0121-631 3725 E-mail: dgillespie@mclemanforklifts.co.uk

Meadows Lift Trucks, Ridley Road, Burnt Mills Industrial Estate, Basildon, Essex, SS13 1EG Tel: (01268) 724422 Fax: (01268) 725282

D A T Mechanical Services, 19 Waldorf Heights, Blackwater, Camberley, Surrey, GU17 9JQ Tel: (01276) 35801 Fax: (01276) 36515 E-mail: datforktrucks@aol.com

Mexmast Ltd, 2 Jubilee Road, Victoria Industrial Estate, Burgess Hill, West Sussex, RH15 9TL Tel: (01444) 247198 Fax: (01444) 246431 E-mail: sales@mexmast.co.uk

Midland Fork Lifts Ltd, Orion Way, Kettering Business Park, Kettering, Northamptonshire, NN15 6NL Tel: (01536) 482561 Fax: (01536) 511559 E-mail: sales@midlandforklifts.co.uk

Midland Materials Handling Co. Ltd, Reeves Street, Walsall, WS3 2DL Tel: (01922) 409887 Fax: (01922) 710253 E-mail: midlandmh@aol.com

Midwest Forklift Services Ltd, Blackheath Trading Estate, Cakemore Road, Rowley Regis, West Midlands, B65 0QN Tel: 0121-561 2141 Fax: 0121-561 5931

Mobile Pallet Truck Services, The Watermill, Barton Mill Lane, Faldo Road, Barton-le-Clay, Bedford, MK45 4RF Tel: (01582) 769971 Fax: (01582) 763665

Multilift Fork Trucks, 4 Burma Road, Blidworth, Mansfield, Nottinghamshire, NG21 0RT Tel: (01623) 794094 Fax: (01623) 795095 E-mail: sales@mlift.co.uk

▶ Nacco Materials Handling Group Ltd, Flagship House, Reading Road North, Fleet, Hampshire, GU51 4WD Tel: (01252) 810264 Fax: (01922) 742469 E-mail: yaleinfo@nmhg.com

Newbury Fork Truck Centre Ltd, Unit 12 Bone Lane, Newbury, Berkshire, RG14 5SH Tel: (01635) 41635 Fax: (01635) 35388

North Hants Forklift Services Ltd, 2 Berry Court, Little London, Tadley, Hampshire, RG26 5AT Tel: 01256 850959

Northern Fork Lifts, 22 Ballybrakes Road, Ballymoney, County Antrim, BT53 6LQ Tel: (028) 2766 3030 Fax: (028) 2766 9191 E-mail: sales@northernforklifts.com

P L P Lift Trucks Ltd, 3 Monksbridge Business Park, Monksbridge Road, Dinnington, Sheffield, S25 3QS Tel: (01909) 564257 Fax: (01909) 567818 E-mail: plpalifttrucks@msn.com

P R Firman Fork Trucks Ltd, Unit 8, Roudham Road, Harling Road, Norwich, NR16 2QN Tel: (01953) 717770 Fax: (01953) 717770 E-mail: info@firmanforktrucks.co.uk

Pec Forklifts Ltd, Bridge Farm, Besthorpe Road, North Scarle, Lincoln, LN6 9EZ Tel: (01522) 778894 Fax: (01522) 778895 E-mail: pecforklifts@aol.com

Peter Evans Ltd, Wickwar Road, Chipping Sodbury, Bristol, BS37 6BQ Tel: (01278) 793339 Fax: (01278) 793251 E-mail: mail@peforktrucks.co.uk

Qa Liftrucks Ltd, 111 Pritchett Street, Aston Birmingham, Birmingham, B6 4ES Tel: 0121-333 3597 Fax: 0121-359 6291 E-mail: sales@qaliftrucks.com

R B Lewis & Co., Wherley Rough Garage, Lower Heath, Prees, Whitchurch, Shropshire, SY13 2BH Tel: (01948) 840886 Fax: (01948) 840109

Rushlift Mechanical Handling, Longfield Road, South Church Enterprise Park, Bishop Auckland, County Durham, DL14 6XB Tel: (01388) 777494 Fax: (01388) 770725 E-mail: sales@rushlift.co.uk

S R B E Ltd, Stewkley Road, Soulbury, Leighton Buzzard, Bedfordshire, LU7 0DF Tel: (01525) 270591 Fax: (01525) 270727 E-mail: sales@srbe.co.uk

Second City Storage Systems Ltd, 108-110 Wood Lane, Erdington, Birmingham, B24 9QL Tel: 0121-382 7878 Fax: 0121-377 7758

Servatruc Ltd, Church Street, Old Basford, Nottingham, NG6 0GA Tel: 0115-978 5504 Fax: 0115-942 2001 E-mail: sales@servatruc.co.uk

Shad Fork Lifts, Faverdale Industrial Estate, Darlington, County Durham, DL3 0QQ Tel: (01325) 353894 Fax: (01325) 353894

Solent Forklift Trucks Ltd, Paultons Park, Ower, Romsey, Hampshire, SO51 6AL Tel: (023) 8081 4545 Fax: (023) 8081 3935 E-mail: solents@forkway.co.uk

Stephensons Enterprise Fork Trucks, Unit 1, Great Bank Road, Westhoughton, Bolton, BL5 3XU Tel: (01942) 276711 Fax: (01942) 276728 E-mail: enterpriseforktruck@lineone.net

Still Materials Handling, Aston Way, Moss Side Industrial Estate, Leyland, PR26 7UX Tel: (01772) 644300 Fax: (01772) 454668 E-mail: sales@still.co.uk

T A G Forklift Trucks, Barlow Street, Worsley, Manchester, M28 3BQ Tel: 0161-799 6507 Fax: 0161-799 9010

Truckmasters Handling Ltd, Boston Road, Wainfleet St. Mary, Skegness, Lincolnshire, PE24 4HA Tel: (01754) 880481 Fax: (01754) 880601 E-mail: mail@truckmasters.co.uk

West Mercia Fork Truck Services Ltd, 23 Hainge Road, Tividale, Oldbury, West Midlands, B69 2NR Tel: 0121-522 2211 Fax: 0121-557 2665 E-mail: sales@westmercia.co.uk

Willard Handling Systems Ltd, Eagle Iron Works, Bromley Street, Hull, HU2 0PQ Tel: (01482) 223746 Fax: (01482) 213404 E-mail: user@whs.co.uk

Windsor Engineering Ltd, Unit 10 Eastgate Park, Arkwright Way, Scunthorpe, South Humberside, DN16 1AE Tel: (01724) 867418 Fax: (01724) 281708 E-mail: scunthorpesales@windsorkomatsu.co.uk

Yale Materials Handling UK, Unit 2 Red Rooster Industrial Estate, Tintagel Way, Aldridge, Walsall, WS9 8ER Tel: (01922) 742460 Fax: (01922) 742469 E-mail: sales@yale-uk.com

Yale UK, 143 Rimrose Road, Bootle, Merseyside, L20 4XQ Tel: 0151-933 8300 Fax: 0151-933 5465

FORKLIFT TRUCK HOODS

B M B Weatherproof Canopies, Arrowe Brook Road, Wirral, Merseyside, CH49 1SX Tel: 0151-678 7888 Fax: 0151-678 7999 E-mail: sales@bmb-weatherproofcanopies.co.uk

Covertech Plastics, Springfield Commerical Centre, Bagley Lane, Farsley, Pudsey, West Yorkshire, LS28 5LY Tel: 0113-255 2288 Fax: 0113-255 2381 E-mail: enquiries@cover-techleeds.co.uk

Weatherwise Canopies & Covers, Thorpe Lane, Banbury, Oxfordshire, OX16 4UT Tel: (01295) 253097 Fax: (01295) 253097 E-mail: weatherwise@fsbdial.co.uk

FORKLIFT TRUCK MAINTENANCE OR REPAIR

▶ Compass Lift Truck Services Ltd, Unit 15b, Lowley Road, Pennygillam Industrial Estate, Launceston, Cornwall, PL15 7PY Tel: (01566) 777750 Fax: (01566) 777746 E-mail: info@compasslifttrucks.co.uk

FORKLIFT TRUCK OPERATOR TRAINING SCHOOLS

A D Tech, 4 Bowmont Place, East Kilbride, Glasgow, G75 8YG Tel: (01355) 242432 Fax: (01355) 242432

A S T Fork Truck Training Ltd, PO Box 2218, Redditch, Worcestershire, B98 8SZ Tel: (01527) 595946 Fax: (01527) 595931

▶ Abacus Safety Training, 7 Pennywort Grove, Harrogate, North Yorkshire, HG3 2XJ Tel: (01423) 550413 Fax: (01423) 552355 E-mail: info@abacussafetytraining.com

Ace Training Services, Glebe Farm, Church Lane, Winterbourne, Bristol, BS36 1SG Tel: (01454) 250073 Fax: (01454) 250073 E-mail: sue@ace-training-services.freeserve.co.uk

Amvar Ltd, Unit 2 Mucklow Hill Trading Estate, Mucklow Hill, Halesowen, West Midlands, B62 8DF Tel: (0800) 5424512 Fax: 0121-550 7222 E-mail: amvar@forklift-trucks.uk.com

Beacon Training Co., 21 Thetford Road, Birmingham, B42 2JA Tel: 0121-357 2992 Fax: 0121-357 2992

D S C Associates, Chester Court Chester Park, Alfreton Road, Derby, DE21 4AB Tel: (01332) 204144 Fax: (01332) 200344 E-mail: info@derwentsafetycentre.co.uk

▶ Driver Training (Central Scotland) Limited, Fir Park, Tillicoultry, Clackmannanshire, FK13 6PL Tel: (01259) 753600 Fax: (01259) 753600 E-mail: driver.training.ltd@hotmail.co.uk

▶ Employee Development Forum, Unit 11a Lyons Farm Estate, Lyons Road, Slinfold, Horsham, West Sussex, RH13 0QP Tel: (01403) 791292 Fax: (01403) 791293 E-mail: sales@theedf.com

Employee Management, Stone Cross Place, Stone Cross La North, Lowton, Warrington, WA3 2SH Tel: (01942) 727200 Fax: (01942) 727225 E-mail: sales@employeemanagement.co.uk

G B Fork Lifts, Unit K1 Innsworth Technology Park, Innsworth Lane, Gloucester, GL3 1DL Tel: (01452) 731350 Fax: (01452) 731373 E-mail: sales@gbforklifts.co.uk

Gallant Training Services, Brook Works, Main Street, Frodsham, WA6 7AY Tel: (01928) 734300 Fax: (01928) 734300 E-mail: gallanttrngserv@aol.com

H F T Forklift Ltd, Unit A, Ramsden Road, Rotherwas Industrial Estate, Hereford, HR2 6NP Tel: (01432) 277180 Fax: (01432) 352249 E-mail: info@hftforklifts.com

Hitec Lift Trucks Ltd, 12 Bradfield Road, Finedon Road Industrial Estate, Wellingborough, Northamptonshire, NN8 4HB Tel: (01234) 350404 Fax: (01933) 440296 E-mail: sales@askhitec.co.uk

▶ Hitss Safety Training Ltd, Foxgloves, Millers Lane, Hornton, Banbury, Oxfordshire, OX15 6BS Tel: (01295) 678200 Fax: (01295) 670252 E-mail: sales@hitss.co.uk

I T S (UK) Ltd, PO Box 335, Cardiff, CF23 7YQ Tel: (029) 2073 6080 Fax: (029) 2073 6080 E-mail: training@itsukltd.com

Manchester Training Ltd, Greengate, Middleton, Manchester, M24 1RU Tel: (0800) 3895283 Fax: 0161-653 3536 E-mail: mail@manchestertraining.com

Mexmast Ltd, 2 Jubilee Road, Victoria Industrial Estate, Burgess Hill, West Sussex, RH15 9TL Tel: (01444) 247198 Fax: (01444) 246431 E-mail: sales@mexmast.co.uk

North Warwickshire & Hinkley College, The Bermuda Pk Innovation Ctr, St Davids Way, Bermuda Park Indust Est, Nuneaton, Warwickshire, CV10 7SD Tel: 024 76322928 Fax: 024 76322923

P R Firman Fork Trucks Ltd, Unit 8, Roudham Road, Harling Road, Norwich, NR16 2QN Tel: (01953) 717770 Fax: (01953) 717770 E-mail: info@firmanforktrucks.co.uk

Robinson Fork Trucks, Brookside Works, Wigton, Cumbria, CA7 9AW Tel: (01697) 342328 Fax: (01697) 345055

Rushlift Mechanical Handling, Longfield Road, South Church Enterprise Park, Bishop Auckland, County Durham, DL14 6XB Tel: (01388) 777494 Fax: (01388) 770725 E-mail: sales@rushlift.co.uk

Safe Handling, Unit 7-8 Pennine View Industrial Estate, of Shepley Lane, Marple, Stockport, Cheshire, SK6 7JW Tel: 0161-427 0639 Fax: 0161-427 0012

▶ Safety-Train UK, 7 Belgravia Court, Oakthorpe Drive, Kingshurst, Birmingham, B37 6HY Tel: 0121-605 0598 E-mail: info@safety-trainuk.co.uk

Sigma Studies Training, 121 Corringham Road, Stanford-le-Hope, Essex, SS17 0BA Tel: (01375) 671111 Fax: (07092) 380757 E-mail: info@sigmastudies.co.uk

▶ Steve Robertson Training Services, Peamore Truck Centre, Alphington, Exeter, EX2 9SL Tel: 01392 833369 E-mail: lorrydrivertraining@tiscali.co.uk

Train A Lift Ltd, Tal Centre, Charter Avenue, Coventry, CV4 8AF Tel: (024) 7646 9027 Fax: (024) 7646 2005 E-mail: sales@train-a-lift.co.uk

Transport Training Services, 16 Whitburn Drive, Bury, Lancashire, BL8 1EH Tel: 0161-764 3949 Fax: 0161-763 5690 E-mail: sales@transporttraining.co.uk

United Fork Trucks (1992) Ltd, Unit 30, Malmesbury Road, Kingsditch Trading Estate, Cheltenham, Gloucestershire, GL51 9PL Tel: (01242) 577092 Fax: (01242) 577092 E-mail: cheltenham@unitedforktrucks.co.uk

FORKLIFT TRUCK SAFETY OR OVERLOAD PROTECTION SYSTEMS

▶ Log-It Systems Ltd, 12 Sycamore Close, Retford, Nottinghamshire, DN22 7JP Tel: (0800) 7834625 Fax: (0800) 3281240 E-mail: sales@logitsystems.com

FORKLIFT TRUCK SAFETY TRAINING

Advance Onsite Training, 10 Knutsford Road, Holmes Chapel, Crewe, CW4 7DE Tel: 07929 575197 Fax: 01297 631671 E-mail: andrew@advance-onsite-training.co.uk

▶ AES Training Services, 1 Lower Bar, Newport, Shropshire, TF10 7BE Tel: (01952) 812535 Fax: (01952) 272233 E-mail: safety@aes-training.com

Andover Fork Truck Services, Fluens Yard, Picket Piece, Andover, Hampshire, SP11 6LU Tel: (01264) 324055 Fax: (01264) 334735 E-mail: info@andoverforktruckservices.co.uk

Keith Cook Training Services, Madonna Villa, Oaks Road, Coalville, Leicestershire, LE67 5UN Tel: (01509) 506913 Fax: 01509 506913 E-mail: admin@kcts.me.uk

Gallant Training Services, Brook Works, Main Street, Frodsham, WA6 7AY Tel: (01928) 734300 Fax: (01928) 734300 E-mail: gallanttrngserv@aol.com

▶ Global Training Ltd, 15 Ripley Crescent, Urmston, Manchester, M41 8PH Tel: (0800) 0730818 E-mail: infoman@globaltrainingltd.com

▶ Global Training Ltd, 6 Hillside Avenue, Queenborough, Kent, ME11 5LE Tel: (0800) 0730818 E-mail: info@globaltrainingltd.com

▶ Independent Handling & Driver Training Ltd, Wilsher Barn, Haldon Hill, Kennford, Exeter, EX6 7XU Tel: (07787) 795508 Fax: E-mail: fwilliams@independenthandling.co.uk

▶ JH Training Services Ltd, 7 Baron Court, Peterborough, PE4 7ZE Tel: (07752) 847195

▶ Liftec Training Services, 66 Romford Road, Aveley, South Ockendon, Essex, RM15 4PP Tel: (07905) 426975

Mid Counties Handling Ltd, Unit 11 Haywoods Court, Garretts Green Trading Estate, Valepits Road, Birmingham, B33 0TD Tel: 0121-784 0704 Fax: 0121-789 7054 E-mail: sales@midcountieshandling.co.uk

▶ Redditch Lift Truck Training Services, 19 Goodrich Close, Redditch, Worcestershire, B98 0NE Tel: (01527) 502632 Fax: 01527 502632 E-mail: Info@rltts.freeserve.co.uk

▶ Safety-Train UK, 7 Belgravia Court, Oakthorpe Drive, Kingshurst, Birmingham, B37 6HY Tel: 0121-605 0598 E-mail: info@safety-trainuk.co.uk

▶ Tag Training Services, 20 Leyland Drive, Kingsthorpe, Northampton, NN2 8QA Tel: 07974 972913 Fax: 0870 1351199

▶ Trans Plant Mastertrain, Schovella, Cliff Road, Gorran Haven, St. Austell, Cornwall, PL26 6JN Tel: (01392) 426242 Fax: (01392) 205006 E-mail: geoff_fox@hotmail.com

WotWot.com, Armstrong House, 4-6 First Avenue, Doncaster Finningley Airport, Hayfield Lane, Doncaster, South Yorkshire, DN9 3GA Tel: (0870) 1657305 Fax: (0870) 1657319 E-mail: enquiries@envico-online.com

FORKLIFT TRUCK SEATS

Milsco Manufacturing Ltd, Harrington Way, Bermuda Park, Nuneaton, Warwickshire, CV10 7SH Tel: (024) 7658 0400 Fax: (024) 7658 0401 E-mail: info@milsco.co.uk

FORKLIFT TRUCK SERVICING OR MAINTENANCE OR REPAIR OR TEST SERVICES

1st Class, 13 Osbert Rd, Rotherham, South Yorkshire, S60 3LD Tel: 01709 531782 Fax: 01709 518458

1st Class Fork Truck Services, Unit 1, Oaks Green, Sheffield, S9 3WR Tel: 0114-261 9495

A D Cragg, Whisperings, Osborne Road, Pitsea, Basildon, Essex, SS13 2LG Tel: (01268) 726737 Fax: (01268) 727668

A F L Trucks Ltd, 8 Factory Road, Poole, Dorset, BH16 5HT Tel: (01202) 621212 Fax: (01202) 621111 E-mail: sales@afltrucks.co.uk

A J Mechanical Handling Services Ltd, Bridge Works, 2 North End Road, Yatton, Bristol, BS49 4AL Tel: (01934) 835835 Fax: (01934) 838999

Aclaim Handling Ltd, Woodbastwick, Norwich, NR13 6AG Tel: (01603) 721208 Fax: (01603) 721235

Advanced Fork Lift Service Midlands Ltd, Chapel Street, Handsworth, Birmingham, B21 0PA Tel: 0121-554 8811 Fax: 0121-554 4812 E-mail: info@advancedforklift.co.uk

Apollo Plant Holdings Ltd, Redstone Industrial Estate, Boston, Lincolnshire, PE21 8AL Tel: (01205) 351722 Fax: (01205) 360432 E-mail: enquiries@apollo-plant.co.uk

Approved Welding Supplies, Hill Top Farm, 22 Main Street, South Croxton, Leicester, LE7 3RJ Tel: (01664) 840098 Fax: (01664) 840527

Arnold Lift Trucks, 161 Ramsey Drive, Arnold, Nottingham, NG5 6SB Tel: 0115-926 2884 Fax: 0115-926 2884

Arrow Lift Trucks Ltd, 9 Kepler, Tamworth, Staffordshire, B79 7XE Tel: (01827) 313335 Fax: (01827) 313336 E-mail: sales@arrowlifttrucks.co.uk

B Conway Mechanical Handling Ltd, Hamilton Street, Oldham, OL4 1DA Tel: 0161-624 6621 Fax: 0161-627 2419 E-mail: admin@bconway.co.uk

Babbis Ltd, Deopham Road, Great Ellingham, Attleborough, Norfolk, NR17 1LJ Tel: (01953) 455422 Fax: (01953) 456491

C C Power Electronics Ltd, Unit 19, Haigh Park, Whitehill Industrial Estate, Stockport, Cheshire, SK4 1QR Tel: 0161-429 7923 Fax: 0161-474 1174 E-mail: info@ccpowerltd.co.uk

C S M Services Ltd, Bradley Hall Trading Estate, Bradley Lane, Standish, Wigan, Lancashire, WN6 0XQ Tel: (01257) 424548 Fax: (01257) 424548

FORKLIFT TRUCK SERVICING OR MAINTENANCE OR REPAIR OR TEST SERVICES – *continued*

Carrylift Materials Handling Ltd, Peel Road, Skelmersdale, Lancashire, WN8 9PT Tel: (01695) 455000 Fax: (01695) 455099 E-mail: info@carryliftgroup.com

Carville Engineering, Unit 11 Seymour Hill Industrial Estate, Dunmurry, Belfast, BT17 9PH Tel: (028) 9062 6999 Fax: (028) 9062 7300 E-mail: carvilleng@btconnect.com

D D Forklift Services, 318 Main Road, Walters Ash, High Wycombe, Buckinghamshire, HP14 4TH Tel: (01494) 563150 Fax: (01494) 563150

D J S Forktruck, Crowthers Crossing, Worcester Road, Summerfield, Kidderminster, Worcestershire, DY11 7RB Tel: (01299) 251182 Fax: (01562) 744888

D J S Forktruck, Crowthers Crossing, Worcester Road, Summerfield, Kidderminster, Worcestershire, DY11 7RB Tel: (01299) 251182 Fax: (01562) 744888

Dac Handling Solutions, 7 Eldon Way, Bristol, BS4 3PZ Tel: (01264) 772012 Fax: (01264) 771083 E-mail: drock@dac-handling.co.uk

Deca Materials Handling Ltd, 13 Adkin Way, Wantage, Oxfordshire, OX12 9HN Tel: (01235) 770022 Fax: (01235) 770027 E-mail: sales@deca-mh.co.uk

Dorset Mechanical Services, 28 Gravel Hill, Wimborne, Dorset, BH21 1RR Tel: (01202) 841241

Edge Independent, Bridge Works, Fontley Road, Titchfield, Fareham, Hampshire, PO15 6QZ Tel: (01329) 842029 Fax: (01329) 842029

▶ Elf Forktrucks, Alder Street, Huddersfield, HD1 6JY Tel: (01484) 511101 Fax: (01484) 432764 E-mail: sales@elfforktrucks.co.uk

Ets UK Ltd, Northside Industrial Park, Whitley Bridge, Goole, North Humberside, DN14 0GH Tel: (01977) 662910 Fax: (01977) 661797 E-mail: sales@ets-uk.co.uk

Fork Truck Direct, Unit 5, Redhills Road, South Woodham Ferrers, Chelmsford, CM3 5UL Tel: (01245) 322252 Fax: (01245) 322227 E-mail: forktruck.direct@virgin.net

Fork Truck Service Ltd, Derby Road, Wingerworth, Chesterfield, Derbyshire, S42 6NB Tel: (01246) 209632 Fax: (01246) 206633 E-mail: enquiries@forktruckbreakers.com

Forklift Services, Site 4 The Old Airfield, Crabtree Lane, High Ercall, Telford, Shropshire, TF6 6AP Tel: (01952) 771166 Fax: (01952) 771177

Forkway Group Ltd, Unit 7 Corinium Industrial Estate, Raans Road, Amersham, Buckinghamshire, HP6 6JQ Tel: (01494) 723456 Fax: (01494) 723724 E-mail: sales@forkway.co.uk

Forward Forklifts & Engineering, Forward House Future Court, George Summers Close, Medway City Estate, Rochester, Kent, ME2 4EL Tel: (01634) 730200 Fax: (01634) 730193 E-mail: enquiries@forwardforklifts.co.uk

Ful Ton Fork Lifts, Argyle Crescent, Hillhouse Industrial Estate, Hamilton, Lanarkshire, ML3 9BH Tel: (01698) 286490 Fax: (01698) 429531 E-mail: sales@ful-ton-forklifts.com

Gaylee Ltd, Pope Street, Smethwick, West Midlands, B66 2JP Tel: 0121-558 2027 Fax: 0121-558 2029

Grant Handling Ltd, Unit 8 Alma Place, Rochester, Kent, ME2 2AE Tel: (01634) 714142 Fax: (01634) 290512 E-mail: sales@forktrucks.co.uk

H F T Forklift Ltd, Unit A, Ramsden Road, Rotherwas Industrial Estate, Hereford, HR2 6NP Tel: (01432) 277180 Fax: (01432) 352249 E-mail: info@hftforklifts.com

Handling Truck Services Ltd, 28-34 Latimer Road, Luton, LU1 3UZ Tel: (01582) 458405 Fax: (01582) 722655 E-mail: sales@handlingtruck.com

▶ Hannaman Engineering, 38 Drome Road, Deeside Industrial Park, Deeside, Clwyd, CH5 2NY Tel: (01244) 288652 Fax: (01244) 280038 E-mail: d.hannamanengltd@btinternet.com

Hitec Lift Trucks Ltd, 12 Bradfield Road, Finedon Road Industrial Estate, Wellingborough, Northamptonshire, NN8 4HB Tel: (01234) 350404 Fax: (01933) 440296 E-mail: sales@askhitec.co.uk

Jofson Ltd, 25 Enterprise Drive, Sutton Coldfield, West Midlands, B74 2DY Tel: 0121-353 2721 Fax: 0121-353 6573 E-mail: info@jofson.com

Jungheinrich GB Ltd, 620 Europa Boulevard, Westbrook, Warrington, WA5 7TX Tel: (01925) 625400 Fax: (01925) 230891 E-mail: info@jungheinrich.co.uk

K O S Lift Trucks, Unit 2, Shuttleworth Court, Shuttleworth Road, Bedford, MK41 0EN Tel: (01234) 216993

Kontact Engineering Services, Court Lodge Farm, Kenward Road, Yalding, Maidstone, Kent, ME18 6JP Tel: (01622) 817966

Kridan Forklifts Garth House, Scarborough Road, East Heslerton, Malton, North Yorkshire, YO17 8RW Tel: (01944) 728301 Fax: (01944) 728301

Len Griffiths Fork Lift Services, Units 24-26 Station Industrial Estate, Worcester Road, Leominster, Herefordshire, HR6 8AR Tel: (01568) 611773 Fax: (01568) 615400 E-mail: lgfs27@aol.com

Lincolnshire Fork Lifts, Fen Farm, Stickney, Boston, Lincolnshire, PE22 8BJ Tel: (01205) 480336 Fax: (01205) 366408

Linde Castle Ltd, Linde Way, Aycliffe Industrial Park, Newton Aycliffe, County Durham, DL5 6HR Tel: (01325) 311526 Fax: (01325) 315860 E-mail: castle@lansinglinde.co.uk

Linde Jewsbury's Ltd, Units 5-7 Deans Trading Estate, Deans Road, Swinton, M27 0RD Tel: 0161-794 6101 Fax: 0161-794 1592 E-mail: enquiries@linde-jewsburys.co.uk

Linde Material Handeling (Scotland) Ltd, Unit 9, Riverside Drive, Dundee, DD2 1UH Tel: (01382) 644301 Fax: (01382) 644243

Linde Material Handling East Ltd, Unit 1 Charlton Mead Lane, Hoddesdon, Hertfordshire, EN11 0DJ Tel: (01992) 443121 Fax: (01992) 468050

Linde Material Handling (South East) Ltd, Affinity Point, Glebeland Road, Camberley, Surrey, GU15 3DB Tel: (01276) 403400 Fax: (01276) 403499

Lothian Mechanical Handling Ltd, 8 Mosshall Industrial Estate, Blackburn, Bathgate, West Lothian, EH47 7LY Tel: (01506) 655535 Fax: (01506) 634799 E-mail: lmh@lothianmechanicalhandling.co.uk

M M Fork Truck Services, Greenhill Farm, Dunstable Road, Tilsworth, Leighton Buzzard, Bedfordshire, LU7 9PU Tel: (01525) 210605 Fax: (01525) 384864

M T Mechanical Handling, Unit B6 Chasewater Estate, High Street, Burntwood Business Park, Burntwood, Staffordshire, WS7 3XD Tel: (01543) 675573 Fax: (01543) 674590 E-mail: sales@mtmechanical.co.uk

M & W Toyota Handling, The Luther Challis Business Centre, Barnwood Road, Gloucester, GL4 3HX Tel: (01452) 523490 Fax: (01452) 523491

Macbrown Fork Truck Services Ltd, 95 Wakefield Road Ossett, Wakefield, Ossett, West Yorkshire, WF5 9JY Tel: (01924) 278609 Fax: (01924) 261220 E-mail: info@macbrown.co.uk

Mcleman Forklift Services Ltd, 15 Andover Street, Birmingham, B5 5RG Tel: 0121-643 1788 Fax: 0121-631 3725 E-mail: dgillespie@mclemanforklifts.co.uk

Manor Forklift Services, 18 Harvesters Road, Willenhall, West Midlands, WV12 4AG Tel: (01902) 633390 Fax: (01902) 633390

Meadows Lift Trucks, Ridley Road, Burnt Mills Industrial Estate, Basildon, Essex, SS13 1EG Tel: (01268) 724422 Fax: (01268) 725282

D A T Mechanical Services, 19 Waldorf Heights, Blackwater, Camberley, Surrey, GU17 9JQ Tel: (01276) 35801 Fax: (01276) 36515 E-mail: datforktrucks@aol.com

Mega U K, Wheldon Road, Castleford, West Yorkshire, WF10 2SE Tel: (01977) 556531 Fax: (01977) 519980

Midland Fork Lifts Ltd, Orion Way, Kettering Business Park, Kettering, Northamptonshire, NN15 6NL Tel: (01536) 482561 Fax: (01536) 511559 E-mail: sales@midlandforklifts.co.uk

Midland Materials Handling Co. Ltd, Reeves Street, Walsall, WS3 2DL Tel: (01922) 409887 Fax: (01922) 710253 E-mail: midlandmh@aol.com

Midwest Forklift Services Ltd, Blackheath Trading Estate, Cakemore Road, Rowley Regis, West Midlands, B65 0QN Tel: 0121-561 2141 Fax: 0121-561 5931

Moores Forklifts Ltd, Baythorne House, St. Luke's Square, London, E16 1HT Tel: (020) 7511 8696 Fax: (020) 7511 7636

Motherwell Fork Truck Services, 141 North Orchard Street, Motherwell, Lanarkshire, ML1 3JL Tel: (01698) 265667 Fax: (01698) 254088 E-mail: mftservices@btconnect.com

North Hants Forklift Services Ltd, 2 Berry Court, Little London, Tadley, Hampshire, RG26 5AT Tel: 01256 850959

Northern Fork Lifts, 22 Ballybrakes Road, Ballymoney, County Antrim, BT53 6LQ Tel: (028) 2766 3030 Fax: (028) 2766 9191 E-mail: sales@northernforklifts.com

P L P Lift Trucks Ltd, 3 Monksbridge Business Park, Monksbridge Road, Dinnington, Sheffield, S25 3QS Tel: (01909) 564257 Fax: (01909) 567818 E-mail: plplifttrucks@msn.com

P R Firman Fork Trucks Ltd, Unit 8, Roudham Road, Harling Road, Norwich, NR16 2QN Tel: (01953) 717770 Fax: (01953) 717770 E-mail: info@firmanforktrucks.co.uk

Pallet Truck Services, 3 Blackgates Court, Tingley, Wakefield, West Yorkshire, WF3 1TH Tel: 0113-252 7852 Fax: 0113-252 7852

Pareco Fork Trucks Service Ltd, Unit 13 Park Road Industrial Estate, Park Road, Swanley, Kent, BR8 8AH Tel: (01322) 613222 Fax: (01322) 615028 E-mail: sales@pareco.co.uk

Permatt Fork Lift Trucks, Unit 7c Mylord CR, Camperdown Industrial Estate, Newcastle upon Tyne, NE12 5UJ Tel: (0870) 1451450 Fax: (0870) 1451451

Peter Evans Ltd, Wickwar Road, Chipping Sodbury, Bristol, BS37 6BQ Tel: (01278) 793339 Fax: (01278) 793251 E-mail: mail@peforktrucks.co.uk

R J Rudd & Co., Westwood Farm, Highcross Road, Southfleet, Gravesend, Kent, DA13 9PH Tel: (01474) 833899 Fax: (01474) 833799

R Moss Fork Lifts, White House, Staithes Road, Preston, Hull, HU12 8TH Tel: (01482) 896524 Fax: (01482) 896524

R & S Fork Trucks, 6 Ardmore Road, South Ockendon, Essex, RM15 5TH Tel: (01708) 851444 Fax: (01708) 557076 E-mail: randsforklifts@aveley.fsnet.co.uk

Robert Walker Haulage Ltd, Hall Lane, Woodley, Stockport, Cheshire, SK6 1PR Tel: 0161-430 2618 Fax: 0161-430 3154 E-mail: john@rwalkers.co.uk

Robin Martin, 2a Lough Road, Ballinderry Upper, Lisburn, County Antrim, BT28 2PJ Tel: (028) 9264 8616 Fax: (028) 9264 8881

Robinson Fork Trucks, Brookside Works, Wigton, Cumbria, CA7 9AW Tel: (01697) 342328 Fax: (01697) 345055

Second City Storage Systems Ltd, 108-110 Wood Lane, Erdington, Birmingham, B24 9QL Tel: 0121-382 7878 Fax: 0121-377 7758

▶ Selkirk Mechanical Handling Ltd, Dairycoates Industrial Estate, Wiltshire Road, Hull, HU4 6PA Tel: (01482) 502010 Fax: (01482) 502011 E-mail: selkirk.mh@virgin.co.uk

Servatruc Ltd, Church Street, Old Basford, Nottingham, NG6 0GA Tel: 0115-978 5504 Fax: 0115-942 2001 E-mail: sales@servatruc.co.uk

Shad Fork Lifts, Faverdale Industrial Estate, Darlington, County Durham, DL3 0QQ Tel: (01325) 353894 Fax: (01325) 353894

Solent Forklift Trucks Ltd, Paultons Park, Ower, Romsey, Hampshire, SO51 6AL Tel: (023) 8081 4545 Fax: (023) 8081 3935 E-mail: solents@forkway.co.uk

Stephensons Enterprise Fork Trucks, Unit 1, Great Bank Road, Westhoughton, Bolton, BL5 3XU Tel: (01942) 276711 Fax: (01942) 276728 E-mail: enterpriseforktruck@lineone.net

Thurrock Fork Lift Trucks, 43 King Edwards Road, South Woodham Ferrers, Chelmsford, CM3 5PQ Tel: (01245) 323256

United Fork Trucks (1992) Ltd, Unit 30, Malmesbury Road, Kingsditch Trading Estate, Cheltenham, Gloucestershire, GL51 9PL Tel: (01242) 577092 Fax: (01242) 577092 E-mail: cheltenham@unitedforktrucks.co.uk

Waveney Fork Trucks Ltd, Whapload Road, Lowestoft, Suffolk, NR32 1UL Tel: (01502) 569106 Fax: (01502) 508273 E-mail: info@waveneylifttrucks.co.uk

Willard Handling Systems Ltd, Eagle Iron Works, Bromley Street, Hull, HU2 0PQ Tel: (01482) 223746 Fax: (01482) 213404 E-mail: user@whs.co.uk

Yale UK, 143 Rimrose Road, Bootle, Merseyside, L20 4XQ Tel: 0151-933 8300 Fax: 0151-933 5465

FORKLIFT TRUCK SPARE PARTS

Adr Forktruck Components, Leeds Road, Wakefield, West Yorkshire, WF1 2DT Tel: (01924) 873101 Fax: (01924) 873103 E-mail: adrian@forktruckcomopents.com

Barloworld, 2 Brook Office Park, Emersons Green, Bristol, BS16 7FL Tel: 0117-970 9450 Fax: 0117-982 1465 E-mail: marketing@handling.barloworld.co.uk

Barloworld Handling Ltd, Unit 1 Minto Drive, Altens Industrial Estate, Aberdeen, AB12 3LW Tel: (01224) 878959 Fax: (01224) 896226 E-mail: aberdeen@handling.barloworld.co.uk

Barloworld Handling Ltd, Portobello Road, Birtley, Chester Le Street, County Durham, DH3 2RZ Tel: 0191-410 6221 Fax: 0191-410 5795 E-mail: birtley@handling.barloworld.co.uk

Barloworld Handling Ltd, 6 Rutherford Road, Dryburgh Industrial Estate, Dundee, DD2 3XH Tel: (01382) 811523 Fax: (01382) 858640 E-mail: sales@barlow.co.uk

Barloworld Handling Ltd, Unit G Cumbernauld Business Park, Wardlaw Road, Cumbernauld, Glasgow, G67 3JZ Tel: (01236) 725061 Fax: (01236) 736212 E-mail: cumbernauld@handling.barloworld.co.uk

Barloworld Handling Ltd, Farthing Road Indust Estate, Ipswich, IP1 5BL Tel: (01473) 740241 Fax: (01473) 740903

Barloworld Handling Ltd, Barlow House, Howley Park Road East, Morley, Leeds, LS27 0SW Tel: 0113-252 1711 Fax: 0113-253 4339

Barloworld Handling Ltd, Unit 4, Vitruvius Way, Meridian Business Park, Leicester, LE19 1WA Tel: 0116-282 7500 Fax: 0116-282 3888

Barloworld Handling Ltd, Unit 5 Burrington Way, Plymouth, PL5 3LR Tel: (01752) 782540 Fax: (01752) 768467 E-mail: plymouth@handling.barloworld.co.uk

Barloworld Handling Ltd, Barlow House, Dolphin Way, Purfleet, Essex, RM19 1NZ Tel: (01708) 257300 Fax: (01708) 257310 E-mail: haydock@handling.barloworld.co.uk

Barloworld Handling Ltd, Unit 1 30 Stevenston Industrial Estate, Stevenston, Ayrshire, KA20 3LR Tel: (01294) 463350 Fax: (01294) 462410 E-mail: knelson@handling.barloworld.co.uk

Barloworld Handling Ltd, Barlow House, Yew Tree Way, Golborne, Warrington, WA3 3JD Tel: (01942) 721111 Fax: (01942) 408100 E-mail: warrington@handling.barloworld.co.uk

Barloworld Handling Ltd, 2 Cygnus Way, West Bromwich, West Midlands, B70 0XB Tel: 0121-521 2500 Fax: 0121-521 2550 E-mail: birmingham@barlow.co.uk

Dorset Mechanical Services, 28 Gravel Hill, Wimborne, Dorset, BH21 1RR Tel: (01202) 841241

Ful Ton Fork Lifts, Argyle Crescent, Hillhouse Industrial Estate, Hamilton, Lanarkshire, ML3 9BH Tel: (01698) 286490 Fax: (01698) 429531 E-mail: sales@ful-ton-forklifts.com

Handling Logistics Ltd, Unit 45, Oakhill Trading Estate, Devonshire Road, Worsley, Manchester, M28 3PT Tel: (07818) 000968 Fax: (01204) 570350 E-mail: sales@handlinglogistics.co.uk

Handling Truck Services Ltd, 28-34 Latimer Road, Luton, LU1 3UZ Tel: (01582) 458405 Fax: (01582) 722655 E-mail: sales@handlingtruck.com

▶ Hannaman Engineering, 38 Drome Road, Deeside Industrial Park, Deeside, Clwyd, CH5 2NY Tel: (01244) 288652 Fax: (01244) 280038 E-mail: d.hannamanengltd@btinternet.com

Ifp Engineering Ltd, 23 Cuttlers Road, South Woodham Ferrers, Chelmsford, CM3 5WA Tel: (01245) 328391 Fax: (01245) 329330 E-mail: ted@hazledine.com

Krane Ltd, Unit 9 Broomers Hill Park, Broomers Hill Lane, Pulborough, West Sussex, RH20 2RY Tel: 0845 4941750 Fax: (01798) 872100 E-mail: kraneltd@aol.com

M & W Toyota Handling, The Luther Challis Business Centre, Barnwood Road, Gloucester, GL4 3HX Tel: (01452) 523490 Fax: (01452) 523491

Machine Electrics Ltd, Unit 6 The Timberyard, East Moors Road, Cardiff, CF24 5ES Tel: (029) 2049 8840 Fax: (029) 2048 0469

Machine Electrics Ltd, Whitefield Road, Bredbury, Stockport, Cheshire, SK6 2RW Tel: 0161-430 6825 Fax: 0161-494 8954 E-mail: sales@machineelectrics.com

P P Lift Chains Ltd, 14 Williams Road, Radford Semele, Leamington Spa, Warwickshire, CV31 1UR Tel: (01926) 313218 Fax: (01926) 313218

R B Lewis & Co., Wherley Rough Garage, Lower Heath, Prees, Whitchurch, Shropshire, SY13 2BH Tel: (01948) 840886 Fax: (01948) 840109

FORKLIFT TRUCK WEIGHER OR WEIGHING SYSTEMS

Palway Ltd, 6 Macadam Close, Drayton Fields Industrial Estate, Daventry, Northamptonshire, NN11 8RX Tel: (01327) 876387 Fax: (01327) 872615 E-mail: sales@palway.com

FORKLIFT TRUCKS, *See also headings for particular types*

1st Class, 13 Osbert Rd, Rotherham, South Yorkshire, S60 3LD Tel: 01709 531782 Fax: 01709 518458

A A Fork Truck & Engineering Ltd, 98-104 Vauxhall Road, Liverpool, L3 6EZ Tel: 0151-236 7421 Fax: 0151-236 2767 E-mail: sales@evcuk.com

▶ A A Material Handling Ltd, 5 Telford Place, South Newmoor Industrial Estate, Irvine, Ayrshire, KA11 4HW Tel: (01294) 221133 Fax: (01294) 221136 E-mail: enquiries@aamaterialhandlingltd.co.uk

A B Equipment, Unit 13a Owen O'Cork Mills, 288 Beersbridge Road, Belfast, BT5 5DX Tel: (028) 9045 5520 Fax: (028) 9045 5520 E-mail: ab_equipment@yahoo.co.uk

A I M S Ltd, Unit 3, Parkwater Industrial Estate, Forest Road, Newport, Isle Of Wight, PO30 4LY Tel: (01983) 520526 Fax: (01983) 520298 E-mail: aims@forklifttrucks.eu.com

Active Handling (Sales) Ltd, Unit 10, Pipers Lane Trading Estate, Pipers Lane, Thatcham, Berkshire, RG19 4NA Tel: (01635) 872972 Fax: (01635) 872909 E-mail: sales@stacatruc.co.uk

Allied Material Handling, Unit 24 Philadelphia Complex, Philadelphia, Houghton le Spring, Tyne & Wear, DH4 4UG Tel: 0191-584 7617 Fax: 0191-584 9797 E-mail: joe@alliedmaterialhandling.fsnet.co.uk

Amvar Ltd, Unit 2 Mucklow Hill Trading Estate, Mucklow Hill, Halesowen, West Midlands, B62 8DF Tel: (0800) 5424512 Fax: 0121-550 7222 E-mail: amvar@forklift-trucks.uk.com

Apollo Plant Holdings Ltd, Redstone Industrial Estate, Boston, Lincolnshire, PE21 8AL Tel: (01205) 351722 Fax: (01205) 360432 E-mail: enquiries@apollo-plant.co.uk

Approved Welding Supplies, Hill Top Farm, 22 Main Street, South Croxton, Leicester, LE7 3RJ Tel: (01664) 840098 Fax: (01664) 840527

▶ Association Of Industrial Truck Trainers, The Springboard Centre, Mantle Lane, Coalville, Leicestershire, LE67 3DW Tel: (01530) 277857 Fax: (01530) 810231

▶ Atlas Handling Ltd, Unit 15, Bondor Business Centre, London Road, Baldock, Hertfordshire, SG7 6HP Tel: (01462) 491700 Fax: (01462) 491666 E-mail: john.p.johnson@btconnect.com

B Conway Mechanical Handling Ltd, Hamilton Street, Oldham, OL4 1DA Tel: 0161-624 6621 Fax: 0161-627 2419 E-mail: admin@bconway.co.uk

Barloworld, 2 Brook Office Park, Emersons Green, Bristol, BS16 7FL Tel: 0117-970 9450 Fax: 0117-982 1465 E-mail: marketing@handling.barloworld.co.uk

Barloworld Handling Ltd, Unit 1 Minto Drive, Altens Industrial Estate, Aberdeen, AB12 3LW Tel: (01224) 878959 Fax: (01224) 896226 E-mail: aberdeen@handling.barloworld.co.uk

Barloworld Handling Ltd, 6 Rutherford Road, Dryburgh Industrial Estate, Dundee, DD2 3XH Tel: (01382) 811523 Fax: (01382) 858640 E-mail: sales@barlow.co.uk

FORKLIFT TRUCKS – *continued*

Barloworld Handling Ltd, Unit G Cumbernauld Business Park, Wardlaw Road, Cumbernauld, Glasgow, G67 3JZ Tel: (01236) 725061 Fax: (01236) 736212 E-mail: cumbernauld@handling.barloworld.co.uk

Barloworld Handling Ltd, Farthing Road Indust Estate, Ipswich, IP1 5BL Tel: (01473) 740241 Fax: (01473) 740903

Barloworld Handling Ltd, Barlow House, Howley Park Road East, Morley, Leeds, LS27 0SW Tel: 0113-252 1711 Fax: 0113-253 4339

Barloworld Handling Ltd, Unit 4, Vitruvius Way, Meridian Business Park, Leicester, LE19 1WA Tel: 0116-282 7500 Fax: 0116-282 3888

Barloworld Handling Ltd, Unit 5 Burrington Way, Plymouth, PL5 3LR Tel: (01752) 782540 Fax: (01752) 768467 E-mail: plymouth@handling.barloworld.co.uk

Barloworld Handling Ltd, Barlow House, Dolphin Way, Purfleet, Essex, RM19 1NZ Tel: (01708) 257300 Fax: (01708) 257310 E-mail: haydock@handling.barloworld.co.uk

Barloworld Handling Ltd, Unit 1 30 Stevenston Industrial Estate, Stevenston, Ayrshire, KA20 3LR Tel: (01294) 463350 Fax: (01294) 462410 E-mail: knelson@handling.barloworld.co.uk

Barloworld Handling Ltd, Barlow House, Yew Tree Way, Golborne, Warrington, WA3 3JD Tel: (01942) 721111 Fax: (01942) 408100 E-mail: warrington@handling.barloworld.co.uk

Barloworld Handling Ltd, 2 Cygnus Way, West Bromwich, West Midlands, B70 0XB Tel: 0121-521 2500 Fax: 0121-521 2550 E-mail: birmingham@barlow.co.uk

Barloworld Handling Ltd, 104 Coed Aben, Wrexham, Clwyd, LL13 9NY Tel: (01978) 661333 Fax: (01978) 664234 E-mail: wrexham@handling.barloworld.co.uk

Bronze Mechanical Ltd, Trading Estate, Motherwell Way, Grays, Essex, RM20 3XD Tel: (01708) 862444 Fax: (01708) 867890 E-mail: bronze@machanicalhandling.freeserve.com

BT International Ltd, Regatta House, 67-71 High Street, Marlow, Buckinghamshire, SL7 1AB Tel: (01628) 470040 Fax: (01628) 470041 E-mail: info@bt-international.com

C & D Fork Truck Services, Drapers Yard, Warrenwood Industrial Estate, Stapleford, Hertford, SG14 3NU Tel: (01992) 503463 Fax: (01992) 501584

C S M Services Ltd, Bradley Hall Trading Estate, Bradley Lane, Standish, Wigan, Lancashire, WN6 0XQ Tel: (01257) 424548 Fax: (01257) 424548

Capital Lift Trucks Ltd, Reading Road, Sherdon House, Sherfield-On-Loddon, Hook, Hampshire, RG27 0EX Tel: (01256) 882047 Fax: (01256) 811876

Carrylift Materials Handling Ltd, Peel Road, Skelmersdale, Lancashire, WN8 9PT Tel: (01695) 455000 Fax: (01695) 455099 E-mail: info@carryliftgroup.com

Cesab Ltd, Unit 10 Regent Park, Booth Drive Park Farm South, Park Farm Industrial Estate, Wellingborough, Northamptonshire, NN8 6GR Tel: (01933) 670460 Fax: (01933) 679854 E-mail: sales@cesab.net

Classic Fork Trucks Ltd, 1 Durbar Avenue Industrial Estate, Durbar Avenue, Coventry, CV6 5QF Tel: (024) 7663 7467 Fax: (024) 7663 7600

▶ Compass Lift Truck Services Ltd, Unit 15b, Lowley Road, Pennygillam Industrial Estate, Launceston, Cornwall, PL15 7PY Tel: (01566) 777750 Fax: (01566) 777746 E-mail: info@compasslifttrucks.co.uk

Crown Lift Trucks Ltd, Stirling Road, South Marston Park, Swindon, SN3 4TS Tel: (01793) 821090 Fax: (0845) 8509271

Crown Lift Trucks Ltd, Tollbridge House, 135 Windmill Road, Sunbury-on-Thames, Middlesex, TW16 7EF Tel: (01932) 777500 Fax: (0845) 8509277 E-mail: info@crown.com

D A C Handling, Unit 1 Douglas Mill, Bradley Lane, Standish, Wigan, Lancashire, WN6 0XF Tel: (01257) 425050 Fax: (01257) 422080

Dac Handling Solutions, 7 Eldon Way, Bristol, BS4 3PZ Tel: (01264) 772012 Fax: (01264) 771083 E-mail: drock@dac-handling.co.uk

Electroserve Mechanical Handling Equipment, 8 Lemmington Way, Horsham, West Sussex, RH12 5JG Tel: (01403) 273335 Fax: (01403) 249803

▶ Euro Trucks Direct Ltd, Terminus Road, Chichester, West Sussex, PO19 8TX Tel: (01243) 788415 Fax: (01243) 839436 E-mail: enquiries@eurotrucksdirect.co.uk

European Handling Equipment Ltd, 43 Steward Street, Birmingham, B18 7AE Tel: 0121-585 7333 Fax: 0121-585 7444 E-mail: enquiries@european-handling.com

Express Forklift Services, Unit 14 Bell Farm Industrial Park, Nuthampstead, Royston, Hertfordshire, SG8 8ND Tel: (01223) 207964 Fax: (01223) 208664

Finning UK Ltd, Orbital 7, Orbital Way, Cannock, Staffordshire, WS11 8XW Tel: (01543) 465165 Fax: (01543) 437801

Finning UK Ltd, Orbital 7, Orbital Way, Cannock, Staffordshire, WS11 8XW Tel: (01543) 465165 Fax: (01543) 437801

Finning UK Ltd, Units 1, 3 & 5, Delphwood Drive, Sherdley Park Industrial Estate, Sherdley Road, St. Helens, Merseyside, WA9 5JE Tel: (01744) 451075 Fax: (01744) 451767 E-mail: lisad@birchwood-mechanical.co.uk

▶ Fork Lift Mechanical Services Ltd, East Hermiston Farm, Currie, Midlothian, EH14 4AJ Tel: 0131-442 2002 Fax: 0131-442 2662 E-mail: gus@forkliftservicesltd.co.uk

Fork Lift Repairers, Bryn CWR Industrial Estate, Gwalchmai, Holyhead, Gwynedd, LL65 4PU Tel: (01407) 720944

Fork Truck Direct, Unit 5, Redhills Road, South Woodham Ferrers, Chelmsford, CM3 5UL Tel: (01245) 322252 Fax: (01245) 322227 E-mail: forktruck.direct@virgin.net

Fork Truck Service Ltd, Derby Road, Wingerworth, Chesterfield, Derbyshire, S42 6NB Tel: (01246) 209632 Fax: (01246) 206633 E-mail: enquiries@forktruckbreakers.com

Forklift Services, Site 4 The Old Airfield, Crabtree Lane, High Ercall, Telford, Shropshire, TF6 6AP Tel: (01952) 771166 Fax: (01952) 771177

Forkway Ltd, Shaw Cross Court, Horace Waller V C Parade, Shaw Cross Business Park, Dewsbury, West Yorkshire, WF12 7RF Tel: (01924) 465999 Fax: (01924) 465888 E-mail: dewsbury@forkway.co.uk

Forkway Group Ltd, Unit 7 Corinium Industrial Estate, Raans Road, Amersham, Buckinghamshire, HP6 6JQ Tel: (01494) 723456 Fax: (01494) 723724 E-mail: sales@forkway.co.uk

Forward Forklifts & Engineering, Forward House Future Court, George Summers Close, Medway City Estate, Rochester, Kent, ME2 4EL Tel: (01634) 730200 Fax: (01634) 730193 E-mail: enquiries@forwardforklifts.co.uk

G B Fork Lifts, Unit K1 Innsworth Technology Park, Innsworth Lane, Gloucester, GL3 1DL Tel: (01452) 731350 Fax: (01452) 731373 E-mail: sales@gbforklifts.co.uk

G Reekie Group Ltd, Ruthvenfield Road, Inveralmond Industrial Estate, Perth, PH1 3EE Tel: (01738) 622471 Fax: (01738) 639613 E-mail: info@reekiegroup.wannadoo.co.uk

▶ Glosrose Engineering Ltd, 33 Westcott Venture Park, Westcott, Aylesbury, Buckinghamshire, HP18 0XB Tel: (01296) 655969 Fax: (01296) 655859

▶ Grant Handling Ltd, 1 Rosse Close, Washington, Tyne & Wear, NE37 1ET Tel: 0191-417 6660 Fax: 0191-417 6661 E-mail: newcastle@forktrucks.co.uk

▶ Hannaman Engineering, 38 Drome Road, Deeside Industrial Park, Deeside, Clwyd, CH5 2NY Tel: (01244) 288652 Fax: (01244) 280038 E-mail: d.hannamanengltd@btinternet.com

Hitec Lift Trucks Ltd, 12 Bradfield Road, Finedon Road Industrial Estate, Wellingborough, Northamptonshire, NN8 4HB Tel: (01234) 350404 Fax: (01933) 440296 E-mail: sales@askhitec.co.uk

Hyster Europe, Flagship House, Reading Road North, Fleet, Hampshire, GU51 4WD Tel: (01252) 810261 Fax: (01252) 770702 E-mail: sales@hyster.co.uk

▶ I T M S, Unit 1, Great Bridge Industrial Estate, Tipton, West Midlands, DY4 0HR Tel: 0121-522 3622 Fax: 0121-522 3822

J & J Forktrucks, Farholme Mill, Farholme Lane, Bacup, Lancashire, OL13 0EZ Tel: (01706) 879769 Fax: (01706) 875286

Jofson Ltd, 25 Enterprise Drive, Sutton Coldfield, West Midlands, B74 2DY Tel: 0121-353 2721 Fax: 0121-353 6573 E-mail: info@jofson.com

▶ K W Training Services Ltd, High Street, Alfriston, Polegate, East Sussex, BN26 5SZ Tel: (01323) 870392 Fax: (01323) 870392

Kalmar Ltd, Siskin Drive, Middlemarch Business Park, Coventry, CV3 4FJ Tel: (024) 7683 4500 Fax: (024) 7683 4523 E-mail: sales@kalmarind.com

Kridan Forklifts Garth House, Scarborough Road, East Heslerton, Malton, North Yorkshire, YO17 8RW Tel: (01944) 728301 Fax: (01944) 728301

L T Industrial Training, 99 Desborough Road, Rothwell, Kettering, Northamptonshire, NN14 6JQ Tel: (01536) 711183 Fax: (01536) 711961

Lincolnshire Fork Lifts, Fen Farm, Stickney, Boston, Lincolnshire, PE22 8BJ Tel: (01205) 480336 Fax: (01205) 366408

Linde Castle Ltd, Linde Way, Aycliffe Industrial Park, Newton Aycliffe, County Durham, DL5 6HR Tel: (01325) 311526 Fax: (01325) 315860 E-mail: castle@lansinglinde.co.uk

Linde Jewsbury's Ltd, Units 5-7 Deans Trading Estate, Deans Road, Swinton, M27 0RD Tel: 0161-794 6101 Fax: 0161-794 1592 E-mail: enquiries@linde-jewsburys.co.uk

Linde Material Handling East Ltd, Unit 1 Charlton Mead Lane, Hoddesdon, Hertfordshire, EN11 0DJ Tel: (01992) 443121 Fax: (01992) 468050

Linde Material Handling Scotland, Unit 11 Barrett Trading Estate, Denmore Road, Bridge of Don, Aberdeen, AB23 8JW Tel: (01224) 707020 Fax: (01224) 707066 E-mail: enquiries@linde-mh-scotland.co.uk

▶ Linde Material Handling (South East) Ltd, Affinity Point, Glebeland Road, Camberley, Surrey, GU15 3DB Tel: (01276) 403400 Fax: (01276) 403499

Linde Material Handling UK Ltd, Kingsclere Road, Basingstoke, Hampshire, RG21 6XJ Tel: (01256) 342000 Fax: (01256) 342921 E-mail: sales@lansinglinde.co.uk

Lothian Mechanical Handling Ltd, 8 Mosshall Industrial Estate, Blackburn, Bathgate, West Lothian, EH47 7LY Tel: (01506) 655535 Fax: (01506) 634799 E-mail: lmh@lothianmechanicalhandling.co.uk

LS Forklifts, 12 Clonmakate Road, Portadown, Craigavon, County Armagh, BT62 1LR Tel: (028) 3885 1728 Fax: (028) 3885 1234 E-mail: sales@lsforklifts.co.uk

M M Fork Truck Services, Greenhill Farm, Dunstable Road, Tilsworth, Leighton Buzzard, Bedfordshire, LU7 9PU Tel: (01525) 210605 Fax: (01525) 384864

M & W Toyota Handling, The Luther Challis Business Centre, Barnwood Road, Gloucester, GL4 3HX Tel: (01452) 523490 Fax: (01452) 523491

Malcolm West Fork Lifts Immingham Ltd, Bridge House, Goulton Street, Hull, HU3 4DD Tel: (01482) 327681 Fax: (01482) 226116 E-mail: info@malcolmwest-nissan.co.uk

MEB Equipment Ltd, Broadwater Lane, Harefield, Uxbridge, Middlesex, UB9 6AH Tel: (01895) 821002 Fax: (01895) 824845 E-mail: sales@mebequipment.co.uk

Mexmast Ltd, 2 Jubilee Road, Victoria Industrial Estate, Burgess Hill, West Sussex, RH15 9TL Tel: (01444) 247198 Fax: (01444) 246431 E-mail: sales@mexmast.co.uk

Midland Materials Handling Co. Ltd, Reeves Street, Walsall, WS3 2DL Tel: (01922) 409887 Fax: (01922) 710253 E-mail: midlandmh@aol.com

Midwest Forklift Services Ltd, Blackheath Trading Estate, Cakemore Road, Rowley Regis, West Midlands, B65 0QN Tel: 0121-561 2141 Fax: 0121-561 5931

Multilift Fork Trucks, 4 Burma Road, Blidworth, Mansfield, Nottinghamshire, NG21 0RT Tel: (01623) 794094 Fax: (01623) 795095 E-mail: sales@mlift.co.uk

Newbury Fork Truck Centre Ltd, Unit 12 Bone Lane, Newbury, Berkshire, RG14 5SH Tel: (01635) 41635 Fax: (01635) 35388

▶ Northern County Forklift Ltd, 15 The Avenue, Rainford, St. Helens, Merseyside, WA11 8DR Tel: (01744) 883959

Pegasus Fork Truck Services Ltd, 3-4 Quarry Farm, Row of Ashes Lane, Redhill, Bristol, BS40 5TU Tel: (01934) 863781 Fax: (01934) 863782

▶ Powertech, Unit 5, 35 Catley Road, Sheffield, S9 5JF Tel: 0114-244 2404 Fax: 0114-244 2404

Powertruck Services, 18 Main Rd, Springside, Irvine, Ayrshire, KA11 3AN Tel: 01294 211745 Fax: 01294 211745

R B Lewis & Co., Wherley Rough Garage, Lower Heath, Prees, Whitchurch, Shropshire, SY13 2BH Tel: (01948) 840886 Fax: (01948) 840109

R & S Fork Trucks, 6 Ardmore Road, South Ockendon, Essex, RM15 5TH Tel: (01708) 851444 Fax: (01708) 557076 E-mail: randsforklifts@aveley.fsnet.co.uk

Rack-N-Stak Ltd, Aston Way, Moss Side, Leyland, PR26 7UX Tel: (01772) 644300

Rushlift Mechanical Handling, Longfield Road, South Church Enterprise Park, Bishop Auckland, County Durham, DL14 6XB Tel: (01388) 777494 Fax: (01388) 770725 E-mail: sales@rushlift.co.uk

Rushlift Mechanical Handling, Longfield Road, South Church Enterprise Park, Bishop Auckland, County Durham, DL14 6XB Tel: (01388) 777494 Fax: (01388) 770725 E-mail: sales@rushlift.co.uk

SAMUK Lift Trucks Ltd, Park Road, Toddington, Dunstable, Bedfordshire, LU5 6HJ Tel: (01525) 877700 Fax: (01525) 874555 E-mail: admin@samuk.net

Second City Storage Systems Ltd, 108-110 Wood Lane, Erdington, Birmingham, B24 9QL Tel: 0121-382 7878 Fax: 0121-377 7758

Servatruc Ltd, Church Street, Old Basford, Nottingham, NG6 0GA Tel: 0115-978 5504 Fax: 0115-942 2001 E-mail: sales@servatruc.co.uk

Sev, 356d Dukesway Court, Gateshead, Tyne & Wear, NE11 0BH Tel: 0191-487 1311 Fax: 0191-482 0243 E-mail: sales@sev.co.uk

South Wales Fork Trucks, Oaktree Workshops, Main Road, Crynant, Neath, West Glamorgan, SA10 8PF Tel: (01639) 750161 Fax: (01639) 750612 E-mail: admin@southwalesforktrucks.co.uk

Still Materials Handling, Aston Way, Moss Side Industrial Estate, Leyland, PR26 7UX Tel: (01772) 644300 Fax: (01772) 454668 E-mail: sales@still.co.uk

Stourbridge Fork Lift Co. Ltd, Knoll Hill, Belbroughton Road, Blakedown, Kidderminster, Worcestershire, DY10 3LN Tel: (01562) 700099 Fax: (01562) 700915

▶ Sundown Services, Unit 29 Carcroft Enterprise Park, Carcroft, Doncaster, South Yorkshire, DN6 8DD Tel: (01302) 729436 Fax: (01302) 725635E-mail: sales@sundownservices.co.uk

Toyota Industrial Equipment Northern Ltd, Pioneer Way, Castleford, West Yorkshire, WF10 5QG Tel: (01977) 712000 Fax: (01977) 712001 E-mail: we.deliver@uk.toyota-industries.eu

Toyota Material Handling UK, Unit 1-5, Sheetglass Road, Culler Drive, Queenborough, Kent, ME11 5JS Tel: 0870 850 1400

Truckmasters Handling Ltd, Boston Road, Wainfleet St. Mary, Skegness, Lincolnshire, PE24 4HA Tel: (01754) 880481 Fax: (01754) 880601 E-mail: mail@truckmasters.co.uk

United Fork Trucks (1992) Ltd, Unit 30, Malmesbury Road, Kingsditch Trading Estate, Cheltenham, Gloucestershire, GL51 9PL Tel: (01242) 577092 Fax: (01242) 577092 E-mail: cheltenham@unitedforktrucks.co.uk

United Lift Trucks London, Old London Road, Copdock, Ipswich, IP8 3JF Tel: (01279) 417155

Used Fork Lifts, 107 Perry Street, Billericay, Essex, CM12 0NH Tel: (01277) 624608 Fax: (01277) 656108

▶ Valmec Lift Trucks Ltd, Units 16-17, Pontcynon Industrial Estate, Abercynon, Mountain Ash, Mid Glamorgan, CF45 4EP Tel: (01443) 740488 Fax: (01443) 742736

W Hall Ltd, Hydepark Industrial Estate, Cloughmore Road, Newtownabbey, County Antrim, BT36 4WW Tel: (028) 9084 1444 Fax: (028) 9034 2466 E-mail: sales@whall.co.uk

Waveney Fork Trucks Ltd, Whapload Road, Lowestoft, Suffolk, NR32 1UL Tel: (01502) 569106 Fax: (01502) 508273 E-mail: info@waveneylifttrucks.co.uk

West Mercia Fork Truck Services Ltd, 23 Hainge Road, Tividale, Oldbury, West Midlands, B69 2NR Tel: 0121-522 2211 Fax: 0121-557 2665 E-mail: sales@westmercia.co.uk

Willard Handling Systems Ltd, Eagle Iron Works, Bromley Street, Hull, HU2 0PQ Tel: (01482) 223746 Fax: (01482) 213404 E-mail: user@whs.co.uk

Yale Europe, Flagship House, Reading Road North, Fleet, Hampshire, GU51 4WD Tel: (01252) 770700 Fax: (01252) 770890

FORKLIFT TRUCKS, SIDE LOADER

Hoist Mec Ltd, Brook Farm, Drayton Road, Newton Longville, Milton Keynes, MK17 0BH Tel: (01908) 641949 Fax: (01908) 641988

Lektro Mechanical Handling, Shear House, Petersfield Avenue, Slough, SL2 5DY Tel: (0800) 0854245 Fax: (01753) 497859 E-mail: info@lektro.co.uk

Specialised Sideloader Products Ltd, Units 2-4 Wilton Court Industrial Estate, 851 Bradford Road, Batley, West Yorkshire, WF17 8NN Tel: (01924) 477499 Fax: (01924) 473220 E-mail: sales@sspsideloaders.com

FORM FILL AND SEAL BAGGING MACHINERY

P F M Packaging Machinery Ltd, P F M House, 2 Pilgrim Way, Stanningley, Pudsey, West Yorkshire, LS28 6LU Tel: 0113-239 3401 Fax: 0113-239 3402 E-mail: pfm@pfm-ltd.co.uk

Sandiacre Packaging Machinery Ltd, 101 Lilac Grove, Beeston, Nottingham, NG9 1PF Tel: 0115-967 8787 Fax: 0115-967 8707 E-mail: sandiacre.uk@molins.com

FORM HANDLING EQUIPMENT, BUSINESS/OFFICE

P F E International Ltd, P F E International House, Oakwood Hill Industrial Estate, Oakwood Hill, Loughton, Essex, IG10 3TZ Tel: (020) 8502 1011 Fax: (020) 8502 4187 E-mail: marketing@pfe.co.uk

FORM RELIEVED MILLING CUTTERS

Acedes Gear Tools, 2-4 Fleming Road, Newbury, Berkshire, RG14 2DE Tel: (01635) 524252 Fax: (01635) 521085 E-mail: sales@acedes.co.uk

FORM TOOLS

A S A P Tooling Ltd, Crondal Road, Exhall, Coventry, CV7 9NH Tel: (024) 7664 4555 Fax: (024) 7636 7019 E-mail: asaptooling@btconnect.com

Argyle Engineering Ltd, 21-29 Regent Street, Liverpool, L3 7BW Tel: 0151-236 0777 Fax: 0151-236 8073

Coventry Form Tools Ltd, 10 Cashs Lane, Coventry, CV1 4DS Tel: (024) 7622 2440 Fax: (024) 7622 8778 E-mail: coventryformtools@hotmail.co.uk

L M Form Tools Precision Grinding, Unit 18 Canalside Industrial Estate, Brettell Lane, Brierley Hill, West Midlands, DY5 3JU Tel: (01384) 78738 Fax: (01384) 78738 E-mail: sales@formtools.co.uk

Maydown International Tours Ltd, Mercury Park, Amber Close, Tamworth, Staffordshire, B77 4RP Tel: (01827) 309700 Fax: (01827) 309719

Mor Brock Tool & Gauge Co., Maldon Road, Romford, RM7 0JB Tel: (01708) 706606 Fax: (01708) 740906

N E C Grinding Services, 61b Shaw Heath, Stockport, Cheshire, SK3 8WH Tel: 0161-480 1899 Fax: 0161-480 1899

O P G Precision Engineering Ltd, Station Road, Rowley Regis, West Midlands, B65 0LD Tel: 0121-559 4121 Fax: 0121-559 3661 E-mail: sales@opg-ltd.co.uk

P & C Tools Ltd, 80 Cato Street North, Birmingham, B7 5AN Tel: 0121-333 7772 Fax: 0121-333 7776 E-mail: pctoolsltd@yahoo.co.uk

FORM TOOLS – *continued*

Pharon S & R Ltd, 228 Lythalls Lane, Foleshill, Coventry, CV6 6GF Tel: (024) 7668 7235 Fax: (024) 7666 4397 E-mail: skelcher&rowe@pipemedia.co.uk
Projax Tools (1989) Ltd, Arthur St, Redditch, Worcestershire, B98 8DZ Tel: 01527 523734
Rapid Grinding Services Ltd, 3 Bilston Key Industrial Estate, Oxford Street, Bilston, West Midlands, WV14 7DW Tel: (01902) 354040 Fax: (01902) 354055
S P C Tools, Unit B, Lyttleton Road, Northampton, NN5 7ET Tel: (01604) 583411 Fax: (01604) 758567 E-mail: spc001@hotmail.co.uk

FORMAL WEAR, EVENING

▶ Eshenda Moda Ltd, Unit 23, Cygnus Business Centre,, Dalmeyer Road, London, NW10 2XA Tel: (020) 8200 3560 Fax: (020) 8200 6623 E-mail: shinyi_j@yahoo.co.uk
▶ Princess Stores, Latteridge House, Latteridge Green, Bristol, BS37 9TS Tel: 0870 1995481 E-mail: sales@princessstores.co.uk

FORMALDEHYDE

Synthite Ltd, Alyn Works, Denbigh Road, Mold, Clwyd, CH7 1BT Tel: (01352) 752521 Fax: (01352) 700182

FORMS, BUSINESS/OFFICE

Adare Halcyon Ltd, Park Mill, Clayton West, Huddersfield, HD8 9QQ Tel: (01484) 863411 Fax: (01484) 862355 E-mail: info@adare.com
Adare Pillings Ltd, Elland Lane, Elland, West Yorkshire, HX5 9DZ Tel: (01422) 379711 Fax: (01422) 377503 E-mail: info@adarepillings.com
Albert Taylor & Sons,Limited, Thames House, Thames Street, Rotherham, South Yorkshire, S60 1LU Tel: (01709) 515131 Fax: (01709) 515135 E-mail: info@taylorsprint.com
Albert E. Bailey & Sons Ltd, 25 Holywell Row, London, EC2A 4XE Tel: (020) 7729 1442 E-mail: baileyprintgroup@talk21.com
Blackburns Of Bolton, Unit H, Lecturers Close, Bolton, BL3 6DG Tel: (01204) 532121 Fax: (01204) 396670 E-mail: sales@blackburns.co.uk
Business Link East, 4 Bishops Square Business Park, Hatfield, Hertfordshire, AL10 9NE Tel: (0845) 7171615 Fax: (0845) 6076117 E-mail: info@businesslinkeast.org.uk
Centreprint Graphics Ltd, Units 1-2, Lanesfield Drive, Ettingshall, Wolverhampton, WV4 6UA Tel: (01902) 402693 Fax: (01902) 491794 E-mail: sales@centreprint.co.uk
Colorscope Printers Ltd, Charlwoods Road, East Grinstead, West Sussex, RH19 2HF Tel: (01342) 311821 Fax: (01342) 315358 E-mail: sales@colorscope.co.uk
Computer Press, 1 Rowles Way, Kidlington, Oxfordshire, OX5 1LA Tel: (01865) 849158 Fax: (01865) 374007 E-mail: sales@cpdirect.co.uk
Darley Ltd, Wellington Road, Burton-on-Trent, Staffordshire, DE14 2AD Tel: (01283) 564936 Fax: (01283) 545688 E-mail: mailbox@darley.co.uk
David Richards Ltd, 1-2 The Deacon Estate, Cabinet Way, London, E4 8QF Tel: (020) 8523 2051 Fax: (020) 8523 2746 E-mail: enquiries@davidrichards.co.uk
Deanson Wilkes Forms & Systems Ltd, 1 Cramp Hill, Wednesbury, West Midlands, WS10 8ES Tel: 0121-568 7123 Fax: 0121-568 7122 E-mail: sales@deansonwilkes.co.uk
Duffields Business Forms Ltd, 4 Nunn Brook Road, Huthwaite, Sutton-in-Ashfield, Nottinghamshire, NG17 2HU Tel: (01623) 440140 Fax: (01623) 440124
Etrinsic, 473 Stratford Road, Shirley, Solihull, West Midlands, B90 4AD Tel: (0870) 4646131 Fax: (0870) 4646040
Eximedia UK Ltd, 4 Black Swan Yard, London, SE1 3XW Tel: (020) 7403 1555 Fax: (020) 7403 8524 E-mail: info@eximedia.co.uk
Formula Business Form, 5 Block 5 Shenstone Trading Estate, Bromsgrove Road, Halesowen, West Midlands, B63 3XB Tel: 0121-585 6333 Fax: 0121-585 5620 E-mail: sales@formulabusinessforms.co.uk
Foxe Graphics Ltd, Enterprise Road, Golf Road Industrial Estate, Mablethorpe, Lincolnshire, LN12 1NB Tel: (01507) 477748 Fax: (01507) 473128 E-mail: alex@foxe.co.uk
H N Cooper, 353-355 High Street, West Bromwich, West Midlands, B70 9QG Tel: 0121-553 0836 Fax: 0121-553 0836
Jaguar Business Forms, 9-17 Crompton Way, Crawley, West Sussex, RH10 9QG Tel: (01293) 512688 Fax: (01293) 551703 E-mail: sales@jagforms.co.uk
Jones & Brooks Ltd, Duchess Street Industrial Estate, Shaw, Oldham, OL2 7UX Tel: (01706) 843121 Fax: (01706) 882985 E-mail: sales@jones-brooks.co.uk
Lion F P G Ltd, Oldbury Road, West Bromwich, West Midlands, B70 9DQ Tel: 0121-585 0000 Fax: 0121-503 0419 E-mail: sales@lionfpg.co.uk
Merchants Systems, 11 Paul Street, Liverpool, L3 6DX Tel: 0151-236 2253 Fax: 0151-236 0861 E-mail: sales@merchants-systems.co.uk
Moores of London Ltd, Third Floor, Elizabeth House, 54-58 High Street, Edgware, Middlesex, HA8 7EJ Tel: (020) 8731 2120 Fax: (020) 8731 2121 E-mail: sales@mooreslondon.co.uk
Multiple Press Ltd, C Chiltern Trading Estate, Grovebury Road, Leighton Buzzard, Bedfordshire, LU7 4TU Tel: (01525) 380800 Fax: (01525) 380802 E-mail: sales@multiplepress.co.uk
Multisets Ltd, Suite 2B, Second Floor, Eastheath House, Eastheath Avenue, Wokingham, Berkshire, RG41 2PR Tel: 0118-936 7600 Fax: 0118-936 7601 E-mail: info@multisets.co.uk
Nova Press Printing, 3 The Old Mill, 61 Reading Road, Pangbourne, Reading, RG8 7HY Tel: 0118-984 5370 Fax: 0118-984 5370 E-mail: trevor@novapress.freeserve.co.uk
Office Depot UK, Guilbert House, Greenwich Way, Andover, Hampshire, SP10 4JZ Tel: (0870) 7556611 Fax: (0870) 4114735 E-mail: name@officedepot.com
Orchestra Wotton Group Ltd, Walk Mills, Kingswood, Wotton-under-Edge, Gloucestershire, GL12 8JT Tel: (01453) 845019 Fax: (01453) 845019 E-mail: enquiries@orchestrawotton.co.uk
Paragon Ltd, Park Road, Castleford, West Yorkshire, WF10 4RR Tel: (01977) 669700 Fax: (01977) 603036 E-mail: sales@paragon-castleford.com
Polestar Digital Labels Ltd, 501 Dewsbury Road, Leeds, LS11 5LL Tel: 0113-201 6600 Fax: 0113-276 2552 E-mail: leeds.direct@polestar-group.com
Pregem Computing Ltd, 9 Oriel Business Park, Omega Park, Alton, Hampshire, GU34 2YT Tel: (01420) 544514 Fax: (01420) 544599 E-mail: sales@pregem.com
R P Business Forms Ltd, Unit 17 Fallings Park Industrial Estate, Park Lane, Wolverhampton, WV10 9QB Tel: (01902) 723500 Fax: (01902) 723116 E-mail: rpbusinessforms@btinternet.com
The Rather Nice Co. Ltd, Quill House, 91 High Street, Markyate, St. Albans, Hertfordshire, AL3 8JG Tel: (01582) 842107 Fax: (01582) 842113
Smith & Ouzman Ltd, 45 Brampton Road, Eastbourne, East Sussex, BN22 9AH Tel: (01323) 524000 Fax: (01323) 524024 E-mail: print@smith-ouzman.com
Tate Fastforms Ltd, Wingate House, Wingate Road, Luton, LU4 8PU Tel: (01582) 586700 Fax: (01582) 586725 E-mail: enquiries@tateconsumables.co.uk
Trade Set Forms Ltd, Unit 1, Building 329, Rushock Trading Estate, Droitwich Road, Rushock, Droitwich, Worcestershire, WR9 0NR Tel: (01299) 251076 Fax: (01299) 251077 E-mail: info@tradesetforms.com
Trendell's Print Ltd, Critchmere Lane, Haslemere, Surrey, GU27 1PR Tel: (01428) 643269 Fax: (01428) 656057 E-mail: john@trendells.co.uk
Trilogybrookes Printing, Ashbourne Way, Shirley, Solihull, West Midlands, B90 4QU Tel: 0121-745 9600 Fax: 0121-745 6200 E-mail: tkeatet@trilogymediagroup.com
Tungate Forms & Labels Ltd, Brookhouse Way, Cheadle, Stoke-on-Trent, ST10 1SR Tel: (01538) 755755 Fax: (01538) 756062
Wentworth Business Services, Pennine View, Birstall, Batley, West Yorkshire, WF17 9NF Tel: (01924) 444501 Fax: (01924) 444266 E-mail: sales@wentworthbs.co.uk
Weston Business Forms, Unit 23-24 Solent Industrial Estate, Shamblehurst Lane, Hedge End, Southampton, SO30 2FY Tel: (01489) 780707 Fax: (01489) 780200 E-mail: sales@westonbusinessforms.co.uk

FORMWORK AND SHUTTERING

A & J Civil Engineering, 25 Croyland Road, Edmonton Green, London, N9 7BA Tel: 078 1649 2523 Fax: (020) 8807 9553 E-mail: joegallagher25@hotmail.com
Special Formwork Ltd, Stubbers Green Road, Aldridge, Walsall, WS9 8BN Tel: (01922) 451909 Fax: (01922) 454520 E-mail: info@formwork.co.uk

FOUNDATION BOLTS

Arthur Black General Smiths Ltd, Clay Lane, Oldbury, West Midlands, B69 4TH Tel: 0121-552 4212 Fax: 0121-552 2208 E-mail: info@arthurblack.com
Bolt & Nut Manufacturing, White Lee Road, Swinton, Mexborough, South Yorkshire, S64 8BH Tel: (01709) 570212 Fax: (01709) 584125 E-mail: sales@tachart.com
Fussey Piling Ltd, Lancaster Approach, North Killingholme, Immingham, South Humberside, DN40 3JZ Tel: (01469) 540644 Fax: (01469) 540849 E-mail: info@fusseyengineering.com
Liebig Bolts Ltd, Silica Road, Amington Industrial Estate, Tamworth, Staffordshire, B77 4DT Tel: (01827) 50547 Fax: (01827) 310524 E-mail: sales@liebigbolts.co.uk
Triton Boat Fitters, Eliza Ann Street, Eccles, Manchester, M30 0GL Tel: 0161-787 9200 Fax: 0161-787 8225 E-mail: sales@tritonboatfitters.co.uk
Universal Boltforgers, Unit 28 Dudley Road West, Tividale, Oldbury, West Midlands, B69 2PJ Tel: 0121-522 5950 Fax: 0121-520 5333 E-mail: office@universal-boltforgers.co.uk

FOUNDATION GARMENTS

Filma Ltd, Clarke Street, Derby, DE1 2BU Tel: (01332) 347571 Fax: (01332) 294960
Naturana Ltd, Eastern Avenue, Lichfield, Staffordshire, WS13 6RT Tel: (01543) 257333 Fax: (01543) 250230 E-mail: naturana.uk@btinternet.com
Playtex Ltd, Unit D Park Indust Estate, Gareloch Road, Port Glasgow, Renfrewshire, PA14 5XH Tel: (01475) 741631 Fax: (01475) 743119 E-mail: enquiries@playtex.co.uk
Triumph International Ltd, Arkwright Road, Groundwell Industrial Estate, Swindon, SN25 5BE Tel: (01793) 722200 Fax: (01793) 728341

FOUNDATION SHEETING PILING

▶ Volker Stevin Ltd, 152-154 Coles Green Road, London, NW2 7HD Tel: (020) 8438 6380 Fax: (020) 8438 6414 E-mail: info.london@volkerstevin.co.uk

FOUNDRY ACCESSORIES

Delphorge 83 Ltd, Overend Road, Corngreaves Trading Estate, Cradley Heath, West Midlands, B64 7DD Tel: (01384) 636279 Fax: (01384) 636279
Foseco FS Ltd, Coleshill Road, Tamworth, Staffordshire, B78 3TL Tel: (01827) 289999 Fax: (01827) 250806 E-mail: enquiries@foseco.com
C.M. Hartshorne & Co. Ltd, Hawke Street, Sheffield, S9 2SU Tel: 0114-249 5408 Fax: 0114-249 5407 E-mail: cmhartshorne@aol.com
Morganite Crucible Ltd, Woodbury Lane, Norton, Worcester, WR5 2PU Tel: (01905) 728200 Fax: (01905) 767877 E-mail: marketing@morganitecrucible.com

FOUNDRY BLACKING

James Durrans & Sons Ltd, Phoenix Works, Thurlstone, Sheffield, S36 9QU Tel: (01226) 370000 Fax: (01226) 370336 E-mail: enquiries@durrans.co.uk

FOUNDRY CONSULTANTS

Apc Group Ltd, Crown Street, Thornton Road, Bradford, West Yorkshire, BD1 2LA Tel: (01274) 306970 Fax: (01274) 730900 E-mail: info@a-p-c.biz

FOUNDRY CORE SHOOTERS

Selus Supplies & Equipment Ltd, Copper Beech, Black Hill, Lindfield, Haywards Heath, West Sussex, RH16 2HF Tel: (01444) 452390 Fax: (01444) 450654 E-mail: selus.supplies@btconnect.com

FOUNDRY EQUIPMENT/PLANT MANUFRS

Acetarc Welding & Engineering Co. Ltd, Atley Works, Dalton Lane, Keighley, West Yorkshire, BD21 4HT Tel: (01535) 607323 Fax: (01535) 602522 E-mail: sales@acetarc.co.uk
Datech Scientific Ltd, Unit 13 Step Business Centre, Wortley Road, Deepcar, Sheffield, S36 2UH Tel: (0870) 7469810 Fax: (0870) 7469811E-mail: sales@datech-scientific.co.uk
Developlant Ltd, Unit 37, Clocktower Business Centre, Works Road, Hollingwood, Chesterfield, Derbyshire, S43 2PE Tel: (01246) 471982 Fax: (01246) 471886 E-mail: sales@developlant.co.uk
Eildon Refractories Ltd, 26 Abbotsford Terrace, Darnick, Melrose, Roxburghshire, TD6 9AD Tel: (01896) 823853 Fax: (01896) 823880
Electrogenerators Ltd, 14 Australia Road, Slough, SL1 1SA Tel: (01753) 522877 Fax: (01753) 824653
F T L Foundry Equipment, 6-11 Riley Street, Willenhall, West Midlands, WV13 1RH Tel: (01902) 630222 Fax: 01902 636593 E-mail: ftl_foundry@compuserve.co.uk
Fulworth Engineering 1991 Ltd, Atley Works, Dalton Lane, Keighley, West Yorkshire, BD21 4HT Tel: (01535) 665188 Fax: (01535) 610186 E-mail: sales@fulworth.co.uk
General Kinematics Ltd, Dawley Brook Works, Kingswinford, West Midlands, DY6 7BB Tel: (01384) 273303 Fax: (01384) 273404 E-mail: mail@generalkinematics.co.uk
George Green (Keighley) Ltd, Parkwood Works, Parkwood Street, Keighley, West Yorkshire, BD21 4PN Tel: (01535) 603728 Fax: (01535) 610340 E-mail: enquiries@georgegreen-uk.com
Guest Foundry Machines Ltd, Unit 14 Berry Hill, Droitwich, Worcestershire, WR9 9AB Tel: (01905) 776242 Fax: (01905) 776318 E-mail: gfmfoundrymach@btconnect.com
C.M. Hartshorne & Co. Ltd, Hawke Street, Sheffield, S9 2SU Tel: 0114-249 5408 Fax: 0114-249 5407 E-mail: cmhartshorne@aol.com
Ladco, Sir William Smith Road, Kirkton Industrial Estate, Arbroath, Angus, DD11 3RD Tel: (01241) 434444 Fax: (01241) 434411 E-mail: enquiries@macintyre.co.uk
Manor Industries Sa, Westwood, Dobbin Lane, Barlow, Dronfield, Derbyshire, S18 7SU Tel: 0114-289 1305 Fax: 0114-289 9264 E-mail: manoiruk@globlenet.co.uk
Mechatherm International Ltd, Hampshire House, High Street, Kingswinford, West Midlands, DY6 8AW Tel: (01384) 279132 Fax: (01384) 291211 E-mail: milcom@mechatherm.co.uk
Omega Foundry Machinery Ltd, 8 Stapledon Road, Orton Southgate, Peterborough, PE2 6TB Tel: (01733) 232231 Fax: (01733) 237012 E-mail: sales@omegafoundrymachinery.com
Pangborn UK Ltd, Riverside House Brymau Three Trading Estate, River Lane, Saltney, Chester, CH4 8RQ Tel: (01244) 659852 Fax: (01244) 659853 E-mail: sales@pangborn.co.uk
Pangborn (UK) Ltd, Orgreave Drive, Sheffield, S13 9NR Tel: 0114-288 0786 Fax: 0114-288 0791 E-mail: panguk@aol.com
Pattern Equipment Co Ltd, 24 Mandervell Road, Oadby, Leicester, LE2 5LQ Tel: 0116-271 3254 Fax: 0116-271 3645 E-mail: sales@pattequip.demon.co.uk
Towerip Ltd, Unit 1-2 162 Leabrook Road, Tipton, West Midlands, DY4 0DY Tel: 0121 5020469
Vulcan Europe, 9 New Star Road, Leicester, LE4 9JD Tel: 0116-246 0055 Fax: 0116-246 1142 E-mail: sales@vulcaneurope.com
John Winter & Co. Ltd, Washer Lane Works, Halifax, West Yorkshire, HX2 7DP Tel: (01422) 364213 Fax: (01422) 330493 E-mail: sales@johnwinter.co.uk

FOUNDRY POURING UNITS

Brightcross Insulation Ltd, Shaftesbury Street, Derby, DE23 8XA Tel: (01332) 331808 Fax: (01332) 292697 E-mail: sales@brightcross.co.uk

FOUNDRY SAND

Bardon Concrete Ltd, Lichfield Road, Barton under Needwood, Burton-on-Trent, Staffordshire, DE13 8EF Tel: (01283) 712677 Fax: (01283) 716598 E-mail: general@aggregate.com
Stanley Evans Ltd, Sandy Lane, Wildmoor, Bromsgrove, Worcestershire, B61 0QT Tel: 0121-366 7300 Fax: 0121-460 1397
Ingram Foundry Industries Ltd, Unit E1 Dudley Central Trading Estate, Shaw Road, Dudley, West Midlands, DY2 8QX Tel: (01384) 253022 Fax: (01384) 213339 E-mail: sales@ingram-industries.com
Peter D Stirling Ltd, Reema Road, Bellshill, Lanarkshire, ML4 1RR Tel: (01698) 749555 Fax: (01698) 740569
Wild Moor Quarry Products, Cinetic Quarries, Sandy Lane, Wildmoor, Bromsgrove, Worcestershire, B61 0QR Tel: 0121-453 3121 Fax: 0121-457 8558 E-mail: jwcineticsands@aol.com

FOUNDRY SAND RECLAMATION EQUIPMENT

Vulcan Europe, 9 New Star Road, Leicester, LE4 9JD Tel: 0116-246 0055 Fax: 0116-246 1142 E-mail: sales@vulcaneurope.com

FOUNDRY SUPPLY SERVICES OR AGENTS

Ashland Foundry Products, Vale Industrial Estate, Kidderminster, Worcestershire, DY11 7QU Tel: (01562) 821300 Fax: (01562) 740785
Axis Alloys FP Ltd, 4 Popes Lane, Oldbury, West Midlands, B69 4PN Tel: 0121-552 7733 Fax: 0121-552 3682 E-mail: axisalloys@aol.com
Beecroft & Partners Ltd, Northfield Road, Rotherham, South Yorkshire, S60 1RR Tel: (01709) 377881 Fax: (01709) 369264 E-mail: sales@beecroft-science.co.uk
D J K Machinery Supplies Ltd, 20 Midhurst Close, Northside, Sunderland, SR3 2QD Tel: 0191-528 6923 Fax: 0191-528 6936 E-mail: d.sirey@btopenworld.com
William Foxall Ltd, Balds Lane, Stourbridge, West Midlands, DY9 8SG Tel: (01384) 422727 Fax: (01384) 892309
Huttenes Albertus UK Ltd, Blackbrook Road, Dudley, West Midlands, DY2 0QR Tel: (01384) 77377 Fax: (01384) 261519 E-mail: info@huttenes-albertus.co.uk
Ingram Foundry Industries Ltd, Unit E1 Dudley Central Trading Estate, Shaw Road, Dudley, West Midlands, DY2 8QX Tel: (01384) 253022 Fax: (01384) 213339 E-mail: sales@ingram-industries.com
Johnson Porter Industrial Services, Attwood Street, Stourbridge, West Midlands, DY9 8RY Tel: (01384) 897080 Fax: (01384) 897170
Lawday Engineering Ltd, Grafton Road, West Bromwich, West Midlands, B71 4EH Tel: 0121-553 4892 Fax: 0121-500 5842 E-mail: sales@lawday.co.uk

FOUNDRY SUPPLY SERVICES OR AGENTS – *continued*

Mark Metals Ltd, Seven Stars Road, Oldbury, West Midlands, B69 4JR Tel: 0121-552 7479 Fax: 0121-552 9088

Morrison Hydraulics Ltd, 331-337 Derby Road, Bootle, Merseyside, L20 8LQ Tel: 0151-933 0044 Fax: 0151-944 1302 E-mail: chemicals@morrisongrp.co.uk

Myriad Services Ltd, 111 Woods Lane, Derby, DE22 3UE Tel: (01332) 380763 Fax: (01332) 380763

Nicholl & Wood Ltd, Netherton Works, Holmfield, Halifax, West Yorkshire, HX3 6ST Tel: (01422) 244484 Fax: (01422) 248777 E-mail: sales@niwood.co.uk

North East Foundry Supplies Ltd, Batts Works, Wolsingham, Bishop Auckland, County Durham, DL13 3BD Tel: (01388) 527299 Fax: (01388) 527593

Phoenix Metals, Firs Industrial Estate, Kidderminster, Worcestershire, DY11 7QN Tel: (01562) 822777 Fax: (01562) 822477

Sandpiper Formulations Ltd, Harriott Drive, Heathcote Industrial Estate, Warwick, CV34 6TJ Tel: (01926) 334900 Fax: (01926) 334926 E-mail: mep.sandpiperformulationsltd@hotmail.co.uk

Stapak Services, Bankside, Youlgrave, Bakewell, Derbyshire, DE45 1WD Tel: (01629) 636855 Fax: (01629) 636187 E-mail: stapakservices@aol.com

West Brook Resources Ltd, West Brook House, Wreakes Lane, Dronfield, Derbyshire, S18 1LY Tel: (01246) 290545 Fax: (01246) 292293

FOUNDRY TEST EQUIPMENT

Vitabiotics Health Foods, 1 Apsley Way, London, NW2 7HF Tel: (020) 8955 2600 Fax: (020) 8955 2601

FOUNDRY ZINC ALUMINIUM ALLOY CASTINGS

Halifax Castings Brass Founders, Clarence House, Akeds Road, Halifax, West Yorkshire, HX1 2TR Tel: (01422) 365760

FOUNTAIN CONSULTANCY OR DESIGN OR EQUIPMENT SUPPLIERS, WATER DISPLAY

Aquascapes, 153 Cardinal Avenue, Morden, Surrey, SM4 4ST Tel: (020) 8337 9880 Fax: (020) 8330 1069

Fountains Direct Ltd, 41 Dartnell Park Road, West Byfleet, Surrey, KT14 6PR Tel: (01932) 336338 Fax: (01932) 353223 E-mail: sales@fountains-direct.co.uk

▶ Greenhouse Water Gardens, 87 Chase Cross Road, Romford, RM5 3RP Tel: (01708) 726726 Fax: (01708) 780557 E-mail: goosegreenn114@aol.com

Ritchie MacKenzie & Co. Ltd, Broomhill Industrial Estate, Kirkintilloch, Glasgow, G66 1TQ Tel: 0141-776 6274 Fax: 0141-776 0285 E-mail: sales@ritmac.co.uk

Simon Moore Water Services, Unit 2, Poundbury West Industrial Estate, Dorchester, Dorset, DT1 2PG Tel: (01305) 251551 Fax: (01305) 257107

Ustigate Ltd, Unit 4, Norfolk Road Industrial Estate, Gravesend, Kent, DA12 2PS Tel: (01474) 363012 Fax: (01474) 359046 E-mail: sales@ustigate.co.uk

Water Techniques Maintenance Ltd, 5 Devoil Close, Guildford, Surrey, GU4 7FG Tel: (01483) 565544 Fax: (01483) 454400 E-mail: sales@watertechniques.co.uk

West Dorset Aquatics, Littlemoor Road, Weymouth, Dorset, DT3 6AD Tel: (01305) 835250 Fax: (01305) 835250

FOUNTAIN (DRINKING) MANUFRS

Acrokool Ltd, 1 Veerman Park, Thaxted Road, Saffron Walden, Essex, CB10 2UP Tel: (01799) 513631 Fax: (01799) 513635 E-mail: sales@acrokool.co.uk

Maestro International Ltd, 11-17 Powerscroft Road, Sidcup, Kent, DA14 5NH Tel: (020) 8302 4035 Fax: (020) 8302 8933 E-mail: info@maestrointl.co.uk

Pressure Coolers Ltd, 11-17 Powerscroft Road, Sidcup, Kent, DA14 5NH Tel: (020) 8300 8080 Fax: (020) 8309 0912 E-mail: office@pressurecoolers.co.uk

Watercoolers (UK) Ltd, Unit 4 Brickfields Industrial Estate, Finway Road, Hemel Hempstead, Hertfordshire, HP2 7QA Tel: (01442) 211121 Fax: (01442) 211171 E-mail: sales@mainlinewater.co.uk

FOUNTAIN PENS

A T Cross Ltd, Windmill Trading Estate, Thistle Road, Luton, LU1 3XJ Tel: (01582) 422793 Fax: (01582) 456097 E-mail: crossuk@cross.com

Manuscript Pen Co. Ltd, New Road, Highley, Bridgnorth, Shropshire, WV16 6NN Tel: (01746) 861236 Fax: (01746) 862737 E-mail: manuscript@calligraphy.co.uk

Sanford Europe Parker Pen Co., 52 Railway Road, Newhaven, East Sussex, BN9 0AU Tel: (01273) 513233 Fax: (01273) 514773 E-mail: enquiries@parkerpen.co.uk

Sheaffer Pen (UK) Ltd, Chaplin House, Widewater Place, Harefield, Middlesex, UB9 6NF Tel: (01895) 827100 Fax: (01895) 827101

Staedler (UK) Ltd, Cowbridge Road, Pontyclun, Mid Glamorgan, CF72 8YJ Tel: (01443) 235011 Fax: (01443) 237668 E-mail: terry.james@uk.staedler.com

FOUNTAIN SCULPTURES

▶ Two & A Half, 9 Queens Road, Enfield, Middlesex, EN1 1NE Tel: (020) 8363 6709 Fax: (020) 8363 6709 E-mail: enquiries@twoandahalf.co.uk

FOUR AXIS STAND ALONE MOTION CONTROLLERS

Europtronic Group, 5 Kerry Avenue, Stanmore, Middlesex, HA7 4NJ Tel: (020) 8954 9798 Fax: (020) 8954 8918 E-mail: evelina.huang@europtronic.com

FOUR COLOUR PROCESS LABELS

Denny Brothers Ltd, Kempson Way, Bury St. Edmunds, Suffolk, IP32 7AR Tel: (01284) 701381 Fax: (01284) 705575 E-mail: denny.bros@dennybros.com

Labels Plus Ltd, Unit 3, River Side Industrial Estate, Bordercot Lane, Wickham Market, Woodbridge, Suffolk, IP13 0TA Tel: (0870) 7705161 Fax: (01728) 745385

FOUR DIRECTIONAL FORKLIFT TRUCKS

Translift Holdings plc, 22 Padgets Lane, Redditch, Worcestershire, B98 0RB Tel: (01527) 527411 Fax: (01527) 510177 E-mail: sales@translift.co.uk

FOUR WHEEL DRIVE (4WD) VEHICLES

E.T. & A. Beynon, Bryncelyn, Blaenpennal, Aberystwyth, Dyfed, SY23 4TL Tel: (01974) 251294 Fax: (01974) 251294 E-mail: bryncelyn@supanet.com

Bucklands Independent Land Rover, Court Farm Workshops, Huntley Road, Tibberton, Gloucester, GL19 3AF Tel: (01452) 790788

FRACTIONAL HORSEPOWER ELECTRIC MOTORS

A O Smith Electrical Products Ltd, Heapham Road Industrial Estate, Gainsborough, Lincolnshire, DN21 1XU Tel: (01427) 614141 Fax: (01427) 617513 E-mail: d.heatlie@aosmith.net

Cooper Control Ltd, 20 Greenhill Crescent, Watford Business Park, Watford, WD18 8XG Tel: (01923) 495495 Fax: (01923) 800190 E-mail: nelco@polaron-group.co.uk

Halolux Electric Motors, 606 Romford Road, London, E12 5AF Tel: (020) 8478 8262 Fax: (020) 8478 1686

Johnson Engineering Co., 319 Kennington Road, London, SE11 4QE Tel: (020) 7735 1412 Fax: (020) 7582 1161

LEMAC Ltd, Hospital Road, Haddington, East Lothian, EH41 3PD Tel: (01620) 828700 Fax: (01620) 828730 E-mail: info@lemac.com

Mondside Ltd, Unit 22 Jubilee Trade Centre, Jubilee Road, Letchworth Garden City, Hertfordshire, SG6 1SP Tel: (01462) 682875 Fax: (01462) 686698 E-mail: mail@monside.com

Parvalux Electric Motors Ltd, 490-492 Wallisdown Road, Bournemouth, BH11 8PU Tel: (01202) 512575 Fax: (01202) 530885 E-mail: sales@parvalux.co.uk

Tyco Networks (UK) Ltd, Wheatley Hall Road, Doncaster, South Yorkshire, DN2 4NB Tel: (01302) 812712 Fax: (01302) 364738

Wynnstruments Ltd, Wynn House, Lansdown Estate, Cheltenham, Gloucestershire, GL51 8PL Tel: (01242) 232266 Fax: (01242) 231131 E-mail: sales@wynn.co.uk

FRAMED PICTURES

▶ Aesthetic Frames & Pictures, 33 Northfield Crescent, Driffield, East Yorkshire, YO25 5ES Tel: (01377) 256243 E-mail: mick@pictureframing-uk.com

Fisher & De Domenici, 10 Church Road, Wimbledon Village, London, SW19 5DL Tel: (020) 8946 9781 Fax: (020) 8946 9781

Glass Style, 9a Stone Cross La North, Lowton, Warrington, WA3 2SA Tel: (01942) 717226 Fax: (01942) 717249

▶ Gleeson Framers, 587c Kingston Road, London, SW20 8SA Tel: (020) 8542 5005 Fax: (020) 8542 5005 E-mail: sales@gleesonframers.co.uk

Manuscript Holdings Ltd, Moorswater, Moorswater, Liskeard, Cornwall, PL14 4LG Tel: (01579) 340340 Fax: (01579) 340341 E-mail: sales@manuscript.co.uk

Midland Framing, 988 Tyburn Road, Birmingham, B24 0TL Tel: 0121-384 4831 Fax: 0121-384 4831

▶ N H Picture Frames, 57 Brongwinau, Comins Coch, Aberystwyth, Dyfed, SY23 3BQ Tel: (01970) 615512 E-mail: kyleireland@hotmail.com

Newgate Gallery, 6a The Bank, Barnard Castle, County Durham, DL12 8PQ Tel: (01833) 695201 Fax: (01833) 695201 E-mail: sales@newgategallery.co.uk

FRAMELESS ELECTRIC MOTORS

Zeitlauf, Treetops House, Gillotts Lane, Henley-On-Thames, Oxfordshire, RG9 1PT Tel: (01491) 579118 Fax: (01491) 412211 E-mail: sales@acdcsystems.com

FREE STANDING TIMBER SHEDS

▶ Ecclesall Woods Saw Mill, Abbey Lane, Sheffield, S7 2QZ Tel: 0114-262 0025 Fax: 0114-262 1470 E-mail: sales@logga.co.uk

▶ Mercury Architectural Projects Ltd, 2 Shrike Close Clayton Heights, Bradford, West Yorkshire, BD6 3YG Tel: (0800) 695 7595 E-mail: info@mercurygardens.co.uk

▶ Russell's Garden Buildings, Gelsmoor Road, Coleorton, Coalville, Leicestershire, LE67 8JF Tel: (01530) 222295 E-mail: shedsrus@hotmail.co.uk

▶ Tele-Sheds, Shelton Drive, Southport, Merseyside, PR8 2TE Tel: (01704) 571215 E-mail: sales@telesheds.co.uk

FREE SWING CONCRETE CRUSHERS

▶ A & S Crushing Services Ltd, Theedhams Farm, Steeple Road, Southminster, Essex, CM0 7BD Tel: 01621 772620

▶ R K Bell Ltd, Dunwear Depot, Dunwear, Bridgwater, Somerset, TA7 0AA Tel: (01278) 424883 Fax: 01278 425944 E-mail: jerome@rkbell.com

FREELANCE BUSINESS CONSULTANCY

▶ Nick Owens, Broadwood, Holford, Bridgwater, Somerset, TA5 1DU Tel: (0845) 1235899 Fax: (0870) 0515953

▶ Proficio Solutions Ltd, 2 Cleaver Cottages Appleshaw, Andover, Hampshire, SP11 9AD Tel: (01264) 772047 Fax: (01264) 772047 E-mail: info@proficiosolutions.co.uk

FREELANCE ILLUSTRATOR RECRUITMENT AGENCIES

▶ Cathartic Designs, 20 Albert Mews, Lockside, London, E14 8EH Tel: (07976) 718081 E-mail: info@cathartic.co.uk

FREELANCE PHOTOGRAPHER RECRUITMENT

Artis Studios Ltd, The Studio 56a High Street, Sunninghill, Ascot, Berkshire, SL5 9NF Tel: (01344) 870033 E-mail: kat@artisstudios.com

▶ Aurora Imaging, Delfan, Cas-Mael, Haverfordwest, Pembrokeshire, SA62 5RJ Tel: 01348 881444 E-mail: info@photowales.com

▶ Karina Hoskyns Photography, Hareshaw, The Platt, Dormansland, Lingfield, Surrey, RH7 6QX Tel: (07778) 599146 Fax: (01342) 836987 E-mail: enquiries@karinahoskynsphotos.co.uk

▶ Paul Harness, 41 Pondfields Drive, Kippax, Leeds, LS25 7HJ Tel: 0113-286 0909 E-mail: sales@paulharness.freeserve.co.uk

▶ Ian Phillips-McLaren Photographers, Orchard End, Watling Lane, Thaxted, Essex, CM6 2QY Tel: (07889) 861654 E-mail: ian@ianphillips-mclaren.com

R.P.L.Photography, Liverpool, L1 1EB Tel: (07947) 543764 E-mail: r.p.l.photography@mac.com

▶ Robert Irving Photography, 36 Parkway, Dorking, Surrey, RH4 1EU Tel: (01306) 879853 E-mail: info@robirvingphotography.com

▶ S D M Images, 16 Blenheim Close, Chandler's Ford, Eastleigh, Hampshire, SO53 4LD Tel: (023) 8027 6828 E-mail: info@sdmimages.co.uk

▶ Sharp Photography, 14 Devonshire Place, Brighton, BN2 1QA Tel: (07775) 895477 E-mail: info@janesharp.com

FREELANCE STAFF RECRUITMENT AGENCIES

▶ Agency Staff Ltd, PO Box 8315, Birmingham, B31 2AL Tel: 0121-476 8337 Fax: 0121-476 8337 E-mail: agency.staff@virgin.net

▶ D I Recruitment, 8 Dig Street, Ashbourne, Derbyshire, DE6 1GF Tel: (01335) 342354 Fax: (01335) 300179 E-mail: info@direcruitment.co.uk

FREELANCE TELEVISION OR FILM CAMERA OPERATOR HIRE

▶ Filmscape Media UK, 6 Stammerham Business Centre, Capel Road, Rusper, Horsham, West Sussex, RH12 4PZ Tel: (01306) 710144 E-mail: info@filmscapemedia.com

FREEZE DRYERS

Frozen In Time Ltd, The Industrial Estate, York Road, Sheriff Hutton, York, YO60 6RZ Tel: (01347) 878158 Fax: (01347) 878303 E-mail: info@freezedriers.com

FREEZERS

Armultra Ltd, Armultra House, Hewett Road, Great Yarmouth, Norfolk, NR31 0RB Tel: (01493) 652150 Fax: (01493) 652842 E-mail: sales@armultra.co.uk

Eurotek Engineering Ltd, Eurotek House, Aylsham, Norwich, NR11 6RR Tel: (01263) 733499 Fax: (01263) 733899 E-mail: sales@eurotek-eng.co.uk

▶ Freezing Systems, 5 Highland Close, St Helen's Way, Thetford, Norfolk, IP24 1HG Tel: (01842) 762511 Fax: (01842) 763322 E-mail: enquiries@jackstonefreezing.co.uk

Hoover Candy Group, New Chester Road, Bromborough, Wirral, Merseyside, CH62 3PE Tel: 0151-334 2781 Fax: 0151-334 0185

Kiremko Food Processing Equipment UK Ltd, Armstrong House, First Avenue, Doncaster Finningley Airport, Doncaster, South Yorkshire, DN9 3GA Tel: (01302) 772929 Fax: (01302) 770548 E-mail: sales@kiremko.com

Starfrost UK Ltd, Starfrost House, Newcombe Road, Lowestoft, Suffolk, NR32 1XA Tel: (01502) 562206 Fax: (01502) 584104 E-mail: info@starfrost.co.uk

FREEZERS, ULTRA LOW TEMPERATURE

Jepson Bolton & Co. Ltd, Suite 1, 186 St Albans Road, Watford, WD24 4AS Tel: (020) 8386 6853 Fax: (020) 8386 5130 E-mail: sales@jepbol.com

FREEZING/CHILLING SYSTEMS, AUTOMATED

Starfrost UK Ltd, Starfrost House, Newcombe Road, Lowestoft, Suffolk, NR32 1XA Tel: (01502) 562206 Fax: (01502) 584104 E-mail: info@starfrost.co.uk

FREIGHT BROKERS

Ariel Maritime (UK) Ltd, Unit 26, Waters Edge Business Park, Salford, M5 3EZ Tel: 0161-848 9009 Fax: 0161-848 9511 E-mail: manchester@arielmaritime.co.uk

Spatial Air Brokers & Forwarders Ltd, Unit 7c Willow Farm Business Park, Castle Donington, Derby, DE74 2TW Tel: (01332) 850925 Fax: (01332) 812427 E-mail: sales@the-spatial-group.com

▶ indicates data change since last edition

FREIGHT CONTAINER CONVERSION SERVICES

D C V Container Conversions, Mardyke Works, St Marys Lane, North Ockendon, Upminster, Essex, RM14 3PA Tel: (01708) 641169 Fax: (01708) 641192 E-mail: derek@containerconversions.freeserve.co.uk
Northern Containers Ltd, Haigh Park Road, Leeds, LS10 1RT Tel: 0113-270 8515 Fax: 0113-271 9687 E-mail: mailing@norcon.co.uk

FREIGHT CONTAINER HIRE

Bootle Containers Ltd, 72 St Johns Road, Bootle, Merseyside, L20 8BH Tel: 0151-922 0610 Fax: 0151-944 1280 E-mail: sales@bootlecontainers.co.uk
C T C Container Trading (U.K.) Ltd, Hillview Base, Hillview Rd, East Tullos, Aberdeen, AB12 3HB Tel: (01224) 879111 Fax: (01224) 879015 E-mail: information@ctccontainers.com
Cronos Containers Ltd, The Ice House, Dean Street, Marlow, Buckinghamshire, SL7 3AB Tel: (01628) 405580 Fax: (01628) 405650 E-mail: bjp@cronos.com
Ferguson Seacabs Ltd, Denmore Road, Bridge of Don, Aberdeen, AB23 8JW Tel: (01224) 706464 Fax: (01224) 706455 E-mail: info@fergusonseacabs.com
Leavesley Container Services, Lichfield Rd, Branston, Burton-on-Trent, Staffordshire, DE14 3HD Tel: (01283) 537382 Fax: (01283) 511740 E-mail: sales@leavesley-containers.com
Northern Containers Ltd, Haigh Park Road, Leeds, LS10 1RT Tel: 0113-270 8515 Fax: 0113-271 9687 E-mail: mailing@norcon.co.uk
Sea Containers Railway Services Ltd, Containers House, 20 Upper Ground, London, SE1 9PF Tel: (020) 7805 5000 Fax: (020) 7805 5908 E-mail: info@seacontainers.com
Swire Oil Field Services, Swire House, Souter Head Road, Altens Industrial Estate, Aberdeen, AB12 3LF Tel: (01224) 872707 Fax: (01224) 874516 E-mail: jlucas@swireos.com
Transmit Containers Ltd, Bessemer Way, Harfreys Industrial Estate, Great Yarmouth, Norfolk, NR31 0LX Tel: (01493) 650792 Fax: (01493) 443500
Universal Container Services Ltd, Boundary Trading Park, Liverpool Road, Irlam, Manchester, M44 6QJ Tel: 0845 4941757 Fax: 0161-775 9079 E-mail: sales@universal-containers.com
Wallminster Ltd, 24 Charles II Street, St. James's, London, SW1Y 4QU Tel: (020) 7976 1840 Fax: (020) 7976 1850 E-mail: info@tankcontainers.co.uk

FREIGHT CONTAINER MAINTENANCE/REPAIR/ STORAGE/TEST SERVICES

Containercare Ltd, Dock Road, Liverpool, L19 2JW Tel: 0151-427 1771 Fax: 0151-427 1772 E-mail: sales@concare.co.uk
Eldapoint Ltd, Charleywood Road, Knowsley Industrial Park, Liverpool, L33 7SG Tel: 0151-548 9838 Fax: 0151-548 7357 E-mail: control.liverpool@eldapoint.co.uk
Seaborne Container Services & Supplies Ltd, Oliver Road, Grays, Essex, RM20 3ED Tel: (01708) 863388 Fax: (01708) 866779 E-mail: sales@bcsltd.co.uk

FREIGHT CONTAINER OPERATORS OR SERVICES

Binoray Ltd, Elm Grove, London, SW19 4HL Tel: (020) 8946 5157 Fax: (020) 8944 1476 E-mail: sales@binoray.co.uk
Brooklands International Freight Services Ltd, Airport House Redhill Aerodrome, Kings Mill Lane, Redhill, RH1 5JY Tel: (01737) 823575 Fax: (01737) 823634 E-mail: sales@bifs.net
Currie European Transport Ltd, Heathhall, Dumfries, DG1 3NX Tel: (01387) 267333 Fax: (01387) 267339 E-mail: info@currie-european.com
Damco Sea & Air Ltd, Suite 20 Orwell House, Ferry Lane, Felixstowe, Suffolk, IP11 3QP Tel: (01394) 675989 Fax: (01394) 674208 E-mail: sales@damcomar.com
Davies Turner & Co. Ltd, Unit C16 Taylors Court, Parkgate, Rotherham, South Yorkshire, S62 6NU Tel: (01709) 529709 Fax: (01709) 529710E-mail: paulknight@daviesturner.co.uk
Davis Freight Forwarding Ltd, Manby Road Bypass, Immingham, South Humberside, DN40 2DW Tel: (01469) 572556 Fax: (01469) 571287
Eagle Global Logistics, 20 Leacroft Road, Birchwood, Warrington, WA3 6PJ Tel: (01925) 250500 Fax: (01925) 250585
Finnlines UK Ltd, 8 Heron Quay, London, E14 4JB Tel: (020) 7519 7300 Fax: (020) 7536 0255 E-mail: info@finnlines.co.uk
▶ Gracechurch Container Line Ltd, 1stFloor, Port Of Liverpool, Building Pier Head, Liverpool, L3 1BY Tel: 0151-231 1144
▶ Graylaw Freight Group, Graylaw Freight Terminal, Gillibrands Road, Skelmersdale, Lancashire, WN8 9TA Tel: (01695) 729101 Fax: (01695) 729125
Huktra UK Ltd, Pickerings Road, Halebank, Widnes, Cheshire, WA8 8XW Tel: 0151-420 3443 Fax: 0151-423 5427 E-mail: sales@huktratanks.com
Maersk Line (UK), 58 Robertson Street, Glasgow, G2 8DU Tel: 0141-275 6380 Fax: 0141-248 3496
Orchid Logistics Ltd, Unit C14, Holly Farm Business Park, Honiley, Kenilworth, Warwickshire, CV8 1NP Tel: (01926) 484088 Fax: (01926) 484478
P C Howard Ltd, West Hay, Kings Cliffe, Peterborough, PE8 6XX Tel: (01780) 444444 Fax: (01780) 444744
Pinnacle International Freight Ltd, C Mortimer Road, Narborough, Leicester, LE19 2GA Tel: 0116-286 6566 Fax: 0116-286 7928 E-mail: lecmail@pif.co.uk
▶ PoundSpinner Ltd, 194 Soho Road, Birmingham, B21 9LR Tel: 0121 5519000 Fax: 0121 5540533 E-mail: www.poundspinner@hotmail.com

FREIGHT CONTAINER OR CONSOLIDATION OR GROUPAGE TERMINAL OPERATORS

▶ Great Yarmouth Port Co., 20-21 South Quay, Great Yarmouth, Norfolk, NR30 2RE Tel: (01493) 335500 Fax: (01493) 852480 E-mail: gypa@gypa.co.uk
The Maersk Company UK Ltd, Maersk House, Brayham Street, London, E1 8EP Tel: (020) 7441 1439 Fax: (020) 7712 5100 E-mail: gbrmkt@maersk.com
Maliksons Logistics, Building B, South Road, Trafford Park, Manchester, M17 1PY Tel: 0161- 872 6565 Fax: 0161- 872 6566 E-mail: sales@maliksons.co.uk
Nightfreight (GB) Ltd, Imberhorne Way, East Grinstead, West Sussex, RH19 1RL Tel: (01342) 316221 Fax: (01342) 316134 E-mail: info@nightfreight.co.uk
P & O Developments Ltd, 4 Carlton Gardens, Pall Mall, London, SW1Y 5AB Tel: (020) 7839 5611 Fax: (020) 7930 2098
Portsmouth Handling Services Ltd, Britney Centre, Wharf Road, Portsmouth, PO2 8RU Tel: (023) 9287 0087 Fax: (023) 9287 0104 E-mail: trevorphs@tiscali.co.uk
Roadways, Barton Dock Road, Urmston, Manchester, M41 7BQ Tel: 0161-911 5300 Fax: 0161-911 5239
Roadways Container Logistics Ltd, Gartsherrie Road, Coatbridge, Lanarkshire, ML5 2DS Tel: (01236) 504700 Fax: (01236) 504730
Roadways Container Logistics, Valley Farm Way, Leeds, LS10 1SE Tel: 0113-296 8400 Fax: 0113-296 8322
Elliott Sargeant Ltd, 4 Rushington Business Park, Rushington Lane, Totton, Southampton, SO40 9AH Tel: (023) 8066 1666 Fax: (023) 8066 1567

FREIGHT CONTAINER SURVEYORS

BMT Murray Fenton Ltd, 70 Newcomen Street, London, SE1 1YT Tel: (020) 7234 9160 Fax: (020) 7234 9161 E-mail: enquiries@bmtmarcon.com

FREIGHT CONTAINERS

▶ APL Ltd, Eagle Court, 9 Vine Street, Uxbridge, Middlesex, UB8 1QE Tel: (01895) 202600 Fax: (01895) 202698
Bootle Containers Ltd, 72 St Johns Road, Bootle, Merseyside, L20 8BH Tel: 0151-922 0610 Fax: 0151-944 1280 E-mail: sales@bootlecontainers.co.uk
Currie European Transport Ltd, Heathhall, Dumfries, DG1 3NX Tel: (01387) 267333 Fax: (01387) 267339 E-mail: info@currie-european.com
D C V Container Conversions, Mardyke Works, St Marys Lane, North Ockendon, Upminster, Essex, RM14 3PA Tel: (01708) 641169 Fax: (01708) 641192 E-mail: derek@containerconversions.freeserve.co.uk
Damco Sea & Air Ltd, Suite 20 Orwell House, Ferry Lane, Felixstowe, Suffolk, IP11 3QP Tel: (01394) 675989 Fax: (01394) 674208 E-mail: sales@damcomar.com
Foremost International Ltd, Unit C Mill Mead, Staines, Middlesex, TW18 4UQ Tel: (01784) 464319 Fax: (01784) 466418 E-mail: ops@foremost-worldcargo.co.uk
▶ Graylaw Freight Group, Graylaw Freight Terminal, Gillibrands Road, Skelmersdale, Lancashire, WN8 9TA Tel: (01695) 729101 Fax: (01695) 729125
Maersk Line (UK), 58 Robertson Street, Glasgow, G2 8DU Tel: 0141-275 6380 Fax: 0141-248 3496
Maersk Sealand (UK), Silkhouse Court, Tithebarn Street, Liverpool, L2 2LZ Tel: (08703) 330804 Fax: 0151-236 4199 E-mail: lplmng@maersk.com
Mayfly Containers Ltd, Bridge St Industrial Estate, Bridge Street, Clay Cross, Chesterfield, Derbyshire, S45 9NU Tel: (01246) 862456 Fax: (01246) 862711
Montracon Ltd, Carr Hill, Doncaster, S. Yorkshire, DN4 8DE Tel: (01302) 739292 Fax: (01302) 730660 E-mail: enquiries@montracon.com
P R Gibson Refridgerated Container Sales, Little Tennis St South, Nottingham, NG2 4EU Tel: 0115-950 6298 Fax: 0115-950 6299
Sea Containers Railway Services Ltd, Containers House, 20 Upper Ground, London, SE1 9PF Tel: (020) 7805 5000 Fax: (020) 7805 5908 E-mail: info@seacontainers.com
W H Davis Ltd, Langwith Road, Langwith Junction, Mansfield, Nottinghamshire, NG20 9SA Tel: (01623) 742621 Fax: (01623) 744474 E-mail: management@whdavis.co.uk
The Yorkshire Bed Company, Belprin Road Swinemoor Lane, Beverley, North Humberside, HU17 0LN Tel: (01482) 304340 Fax: (01482) 870319 E-mail: sales@containers.com

FREIGHT FORWARDERS/ FORWARDING AGENTS

A B P H, Manby Road, Immingham, South Humberside, DN40 3EG Tel: (01469) 551308 Fax: (01469) 571588
A Hartrodt UK Ltd, Unit 2 Pump Lane Industrial Estate, Hayes, Middlesex, UB3 3NB Tel: (020) 8848 3545 Fax: (020) 8561 0940 E-mail: london@hartrodt.co.uk
A P S Freight Ltd, Lord Warden House, Lord Warden Square, Dover, Kent, CT17 9EQ Tel: (01304) 225600 Fax: (01304) 225601 E-mail: office@apsfreight.com
Abbey Forwarding Ltd, 50 Purland Road, Nathan Way, London, SE28 0AT Tel: (020) 8311 4222 Fax: (020) 8310 1859 E-mail: admin@abbeyforwarding.co.uk
Abels Moving Services Ltd, Wimbledon Avenue, Brandon, Suffolk, IP27 0NZ Tel: (01842) 816600 Fax: (01842) 813613 E-mail: enquiries@abels.co.uk
Abingdon Freight Fowarding, Park 34, Collett, Didcot, Oxfordshire, OX11 7WB Tel: (01235) 813471 Fax: (01235) 750040 E-mail: info@affa.co.uk
Henry Abram & Sons Ltd, 17 Sandyford Place, Glasgow, G3 7NB Tel: 0141-221 3075 Fax: 0141-226 5501 E-mail: shipping@henryabram.co.uk
Access Shipping Ltd, Rainham House Rainham Trading Estate, New Road, Rainham, Essex, RM13 8RA Tel: (01708) 521113 Fax: (01708) 521151 E-mail: access-shipping@cnsmail.co.uk
Active International Movements Ltd, 380 Ringwood Road, Poole, Dorset, BH12 3LT Tel: (01202) 307349 Fax: (01202) 743707 E-mail: sales@activefreight.co.uk
Adeptstar Shipping Ltd, Estate House, Marsh Way, Fairview Industrial Park, Rainham, Essex, RM13 8UH Tel: (01708) 550909 Fax: (01708) 551945 E-mail: adeptstar@shipping-ltd.fsnet.co.uk
Air Menzies International Ltd, 5 The Enterprise Centre, Kelvin Lane, Crawley, West Sussex, RH10 9PT Tel: (01293) 658000 Fax: (01293) 551114 E-mail: info@airmenzies.com
Air Sea Packing Group Ltd, Air Sea House, Third Cross Road, Twickenham, TW2 5EB Tel: (020) 8893 3303 Fax: (020) 8893 3068 E-mail: sales@airseapacking.com
Aircargo & Container Services Ltd, Unit H President Way, Luton, LU2 9NL Tel: (01582) 456700 Fax: (01582) 401646 E-mail: chris@accs.co.uk
Airocean Freight Ltd, 6-9 Spring Road, Smethwick, West Midlands, B66 1PE Tel: 0121-580 6730 Fax: 0121-525 5296 E-mail: info@airoceanfreight.co.uk
Airworld International, 2 The Faraday Centre, Faraday Road, Crawley, West Sussex, RH10 9PX Tel: (01293) 510007 Fax: (01293) 521361 E-mail: airsales@allport.co.uk
Allport Ltd, 2 The Faraday Centre, Faraday Road, Crawley, West Sussex, RH10 9PX Tel: (01293) 510246 Fax: (01293) 562044 E-mail: info@allport.co.uk
Allport Ltd, 26 Chase Road, Park Royale, London, NW10 6QA Tel: (020) 8965 0678 Fax: (020) 8965 1340 E-mail: info@allport.co.uk
Allport Overland, Allport House, Thurrock Park Way, Tilbury, Essex, RM18 7HZ Tel: (01375) 487800 Fax: (01375) 487890 E-mail: info@allport.co.uk
Amba Forwarding Ltd, 6 Trafalgar Business Centre, River Road, Barking, Essex, IG11 0JU Tel: (020) 8591 1600 Fax: (020) 8591 1700 E-mail: info@ambaforwarding.com
Anglia Forwarding Group Ltd, The Anglian Centre, Blackwater Close, Rainham, Essex, RM13 8UA Tel: (01708) 527000 Fax: (01708) 524881 E-mail: london@anglia-forwarding.co.uk
Anoca Ltd, 24 Roman Way, Thetford, Norfolk, IP24 1XB Tel: (01842) 766131 Fax: (01842) 762929 E-mail: sales@anoca.co.uk
Arbuckle Smith & Co., 106 Abercorn Street, Paisley, Renfrewshire, PA3 4AY Tel: (0141) 887 5252 Fax: (0141) 887 4461 E-mail: craig_hodgson@zieglergroup.com
Archfield (Shipping) Ltd, Factory Road, London, E16 2HD Tel: (020) 7476 4386 Fax: (020) 7511 2238 E-mail: sales@archfield.co.uk
Arends International Ltd, Sankey Valley Industrial Estate, Anglezarke Road, Newton-le-Willows, Merseyside, WA12 8DJ Tel: (01925) 223323 Fax: (01925) 229800 E-mail: sales@arends.co.uk
Ariel Maritime (UK) Ltd, Unit 26, Waters Edge Business Park, Salford, M5 3EZ Tel: 0161-848 9009 Fax: 0161-848 9511 E-mail: manchester@arielmaritime.co.uk
Arrowfreight Ltd, Unit D3, Crossgate Drive, Queens Drive Industrial Estate, Nottingham, NG2 1LW Tel: 0115-986 8031 Fax: 0115-986 0607 E-mail: info@arrowfreight.com
Atco Development, 42 Albemarle Street, London, W1S 4JH Tel: (020) 7491 3664 Fax: (020) 7629 1120 E-mail: liam@atcolondon.com
Atkinson & Prickett, Crowle House, Hull, HU1 1RJ Tel: (01482) 324191 Fax: (01482) 224914 E-mail: hull@kettlewell.com
Atlantis Forwarding Ltd, 1607 Pershore Road, Stirchley, Birmingham, B30 2JF Tel: 0121-451 1588 Fax: 0121-433 4034 E-mail: enquiries@atlantisltd.co.uk
Axa Couriers Ltd, Axa House, Blandford Road, Southall, Middlesex, UB2 4JY Tel: (020) 8571 4747 Fax: (020) 8574 5697
B K International Freight Ltd, Unit 13 Maguire Industrial Estate, 219 Torrington Avenue, Coventry, CV4 9HN Tel: (024) 7646 4983 Fax: (024) 7669 4184 E-mail: admin@bkfreight.co.uk
Bahr Forwarding, Suite 16b Unit 4 Orwell House, Ferry Lane, Felixstowe, Suffolk, IP11 3QR Tel: (01394) 675686 Fax: (01394) 674232 E-mail: admin@bahrforwarding.co.uk
Balkan & Black Sea Shipping Co. Ltd, Black Sea House, 72 Wilson Street, London, EC2A 2DH Tel: (020) 7684 2800 Fax: (020) 7684 2790 E-mail: enquiries@bbss.uk
Bargate International Ltd, 6 Premier Court, Boarden Close, Moulton Park Industrial Estate, Northampton, NN3 6LF Tel: (01604) 679500 Fax: (01604) 495919 E-mail: sales@bargateinternational.com
Belgrave Shipping Co. Ltd, Fishers Way, Belvedere, Kent, DA17 6BS Tel: (020) 8310 1890 Fax: (020) 8312 3505 E-mail: belgrave@ukfraite.co.uk
Bernard Group Ltd, Bernard House 52-54 Peregrine Road, Hainault, Ilford, Essex, IG6 3SZ Tel: (020) 8501 2599 Fax: (020) 8559 9922 E-mail: corporate@bernardgroup.plc.uk
F.H. Bertling Ltd, York House, Empire Way, Wembley, Middlesex, HA9 0PA Tel: (020) 8900 2060 Fax: (020) 8900 1248 E-mail: sales@bertling.com
Bidcorp P.L.C., 6 Stratton Street, London, W1J 8LD Tel: (020) 7408 0123 Fax: (020) 7495 8284
Binoray Ltd, Elm Grove, London, SW19 4HL Tel: (020) 8946 5157 Fax: (020) 8944 1476 E-mail: sales@binoray.co.uk
Birds Groupage Services Ltd, Tat Bank Road, Oldbury, West Midlands, B69 4NQ Tel: 0121-543 6400 Fax: 0121-544 4928 E-mail: ken@birds.co.uk
Bonded Services, Unit 1, Aerodrome Way, Cranford Lane, Hounslow, TW5 9QB Tel: (020) 8990 9192 Fax: (020) 8990 9028 E-mail: sales@ftsbonded.com
Bower Green Ltd, Dryden Street, Bradford, West Yorkshire, BD1 5ND Tel: (01274) 733537 Fax: (01274) 393511 E-mail: info@bowergreen.co.uk
Bower Green Ltd, Station Road, Norwood Green, Halifax, West Yorkshire, HX3 8QD Tel: (01274) 672450 Fax: (01274) 693136 E-mail: norwood@bowergreen.co.uk
Brooklands International Freight Services Ltd, Airport House Redhill Aerodrome, Kings Mill Lane, Redhill, RH1 5JY Tel: (01737) 823575 Fax: (01737) 823634 E-mail: sales@bifs.net
T.H. Brown Ltd, Estate Road No. 1, South Humberside Industal Estate, Grimsby, North East Lincolnshire, DN31 2TA Tel: (01472) 362603 Fax: (01472) 360112 E-mail: admin@thbrown.co.uk
Cargo Forwarding, Transit 1, West Bank Way, Belfast, BT3 9LB Tel: (028) 9037 3700 Fax: (028) 9037 3736 E-mail: sales@cargo-forwarding.co.uk
Carrifreight International Ltd, 35 Knighton Rd, Romford, RM7 9BU Tel: (01708) 508603 Fax: (01708) 505981
Casper Shipping Ltd, 1 Cleveland Business Centre, Watson Street, Middlesbrough, Cleveland, TS1 2RQ Tel: (01642) 243662 Fax: (01642) 243936
Ceva Logistics, Tunnel Estate, Easton Avenue, Grays, Essex, RM20 3LW Tel: (01708) 258200 Fax: (01708) 258299
Chambers & Cook Ltd, European House, Perrywell Road, Witton, Birmingham, B6 7AT Tel: 0121-356 1441 Fax: 0121-356 7880 E-mail: admin@chambers-and-cook.co.uk
Chiltern Airfreight, Poyle Road, Colnbrook, Slough, SL3 0AY Tel: (01753) 680845 Fax: 01753 681094
Chiltern Cargo Services Ltd, Willen Works, Willen Road, Newport Pagnell, Bucks, MK16 0DG Tel: (01908) 611222 Fax: (01908) 612221 E-mail: admin@chiltern.cargo.co.uk
Cmaine Shipping Ltd, 22 Ruther Park, Haverfordwest, Dyfed, SA61 1DH Tel: (01437) 769922 Fax: (01437) 766797 E-mail: cmaine@btinternet.com
Coleshill Freight Services Ltd, Coleshill Freight Terminal, Station Road, Coleshill, Birmingham, B46 1JJ Tel: (01675) 463869 Fax: (01675) 465727 E-mail: john@coleshillfreight.com
Consolidated Laser Line Ltd, Fawcett House, Record Street, Ruthin, Clwyd, LL15 1DS Tel: (01824) 705807 Fax: (01824) 705816 E-mail: ruthincll@btconnect.com

▶ indicates data change since last edition

FREIGHT FORWARDERS/ FORWARDING AGENTS – *continued*

Continental Airlines, Beulah Court, Albert Road, Horley, Surrey, RH6 7HP Tel: (0845) 6076760 Fax: (01293) 773726

Continental Freight Forwarding Ltd, PO Box 11438, Ellon, Aberdeenshire, AB41 9NU Tel: (01358) 723418 Fax: (01358) 723613 E-mail: fgb@continental-freight.co.uk

Cooper Carriers Ltd, Tir Llwyd Industrial Estate, Kinmel Bay, Rhyl, Clwyd, LL18 5JA Tel: (01745) 362800 Fax: (01745) 362801

Cory Bros Shipping Ltd, The Deep Business Centre, Tower Street, Hull, HU1 4BG Tel: (01482) 382840 Fax: (01482) 382841 E-mail: coryhull@cory.co.uk

Cory Logistics Ltd, 90 Giles Street, Leith, Edinburgh, EH6 6BZ Tel: 0131-554 6631 Fax: 0131-554 8504 E-mail: info@cory.co.uk

Cotrans International Ltd, Strathallen House, 197 Winchester Road, Chandlers Ford, Eastleigh, Hampshire, SO53 2DU Tel: (023) 8027 3222 Fax: (023) 8027 3244 E-mail: gary_m_turner@hotmail.co.uk

Cranleigh Freight Services Ltd, Building 68 Dunsfold Park, Stovolds Hill, Cranleigh, Surrey, GU6 8TB Tel: (01483) 201330 Fax: (01483) 272124 E-mail: info@cranleigh.co.uk

Crest Freight Forwarding Ltd, 76 High Street, Stony Stratford, Milton Keynes, MK11 1AH Tel: (01908) 307655 Fax: (01908) 307656 E-mail: sales@crestfreight.co.uk

Crete Shipping, 42 Battersea Rise, London, SW11 1EE Tel: (020) 7223 1244 Fax: (020) 7924 3895 E-mail: sales@creteshipping.co.uk

Cromac Smith Ltd, 34-40 Warwick Road, Kenilworth, Warwickshire, CV8 1HE Tel: (01926) 865800 Fax: (01926) 865808 E-mail: albatros@cromacsmith.com

Cutler Freight Forwarding Ltd, Car Shipping House, 2a South Gipsy Road, Welling, Kent, DA16 1JB Tel: (020) 8301 6626 Fax: (020) 8301 2580 E-mail: info@cutlerfreight.co.uk

D F D S, Enterprise Point, Altrincham Road, Manchester, M22 4NY Tel: 0161-947 6592 Fax: 0161-947 6588

D F D S Transport Ltd, Third Way, Avonmouth, Bristol, BS11 9HL Tel: 0117-982 2288 Fax: 0117-938 6793 E-mail: transport@dfdstransport.co.uk

D F D S Transport Ltd, Kingsbury Link, Trinity Road, Piccadilly, Tamworth, Staffordshire, B78 2EX Tel: (01827) 871200 Fax: (01827) 871212 E-mail: transport@dfdstransport.co.uk

D J G Exhibition Freight Services Ltd, Unit 34 Grace Business Centre, Willow Lane, Mitcham, Surrey, CR4 4TQ Tel: (020) 8646 4200 Fax: (020) 8646 6090 E-mail: d.j.g.efsl@btinternet.com

Dachser Transport UK Ltd, Oxwich Close, Brackmills Industrial Estate, Northampton, NN4 7BH Tel: (01604) 666222 Fax: (01604) 666239 E-mail: dachser.northampton@dachser.com

▶ Dando Drilling International Ltd, Old Customs House, Wharf Road, Littlehampton, West Sussex, BN17 5DD Tel: (01903) 731312 Fax: (01903) 730305 E-mail: info@dando.co.uk

Danzas AEI Intercontinental, 18-32 London Road, Staines, Middlesex, TW18 4BP Tel: (01784) 871118 Fax: (01784) 871158 E-mail: mark.oxtoby@gb.danzas.com

Davies Turner & Co. Ltd, Dartford Freight Terminal, Edison's Park, Dartford, DA2 6QJ Tel: (01322) 277558 Fax: (01322) 289063 E-mail: webmaster@daviesturner.co.uk

Davies Turner & Co. Ltd, Unit C16 Taylors Court, Parkgate, Rotherham, South Yorkshire, S62 6NU Tel: (01709) 529709 Fax: (01709) 529710E-mail: paulknight@daviesturner.co.uk

Davies Turner & Co. Ltd, 184 Portswood Road, Southampton, SO17 2NJ Tel: (023) 8055 5955 Fax: (023) 8055 5644 E-mail: mikerees@davisturner.co.uk

Davies Turner & Co. Ltd, London House, Hide Street, Stoke-on-Trent, ST4 1NF Tel: (01782) 413617 Fax: (01782) 744063

Davis Freight Forwarding Ltd, Manby Road Bypass, Immingham, South Humberside, DN40 2DW Tel: (01469) 572556 Fax: (01469) 571287

Davis Shipping Ltd, Enterprise Industrial Estate, Bolina Road, London, SE16 3LF Tel: (020) 7231 9340 Fax: (020) 7231 1120 E-mail: bevan@davis-se1.freeserve.co.uk

Delivered On Time, 4 Mercury Centre, Central Way, Feltham, Middlesex, TW14 0RN Tel: (020) 8890 5511 Fax: (020) 8890 5533 E-mail: sales@shand.co.uk

Deltamove Ltd, Clare Terrace, Carterton, Oxfordshire, OX18 3ES Tel: (01993) 845020 Fax: (01993) 843023 E-mail: andy@deltamove.co.uk

Denholm Forwarding Ltd, 1 First Way, Avonmouth, Bristol, BS11 9EF Tel: 0117-982 5313 Fax: 0117-982 5885

The Dundee Perth & London Shipping Company Ltd, 26 East Dock Street, Dundee, DD1 9HY Tel: (01382) 203111 Fax: (01382) 200575 E-mail: agency@dpandl.co.uk

E L Sibbles Ltd, Woolbloch House, Bolling Road, Bradford, West Yorkshire, BD4 7BT Tel: (01274) 729433 Fax: (01274) 370611 E-mail: sales@elsibbles.com

E M S Cargo Ltd, Unit 5, Ringway Trading Estate, Manchester, M22 5LH Tel: 0161-499 1344 Fax: 0161-499 0847 E-mail: man@ems-cargo.co.uk

E W Taylor & Co Forwarding Ltd, Dunbar House Eurolink Industrial Centre, Castle Road, Sittingbourne, Kent, ME10 3RN Tel: (01795) 410110 Fax: (01795) 410111 E-mail: sharonlambert@ewtaylorgroup.com

Eagle Global Logistics, 20 Leacroft Road, Birchwood, Warrington, WA3 6PJ Tel: (01925) 250500 Fax: (01925) 250585

Eastside Freight Services Ltd, Stratford St North, Birmingham, B11 1BY Tel: 0121-766 8333 Fax: 0121-766 8361 E-mail: efs.services@virgin.net

Eimskip UK Ltd, Middleplatt Road, Immingham, South Humberside, DN40 1AH Tel: (01469) 550200 Fax: (01469) 550394 E-mail: info@eimskip-uk.co.uk

Enterprise Liner Agencies Ltd, Unit 20 Trafalgar Business Centre, River Road, Barking, Essex, IG11 0JU Tel: (020) 8591 8787 Fax: (020) 8591 1502 E-mail: elaltd@elaltd.demon.co.uk

Eurocontinental Logistics Ltd, Unit 7, Everitt Close, Denington Industrial Estate, Wellingborough, Northamptonshire, NN8 2QE Tel: (01933) 223851 Fax: (01933) 272630 E-mail: info@eurocontinental-logistics.co.uk

Eurogate International Forwarding Co. Ltd, Garret Green Freight Depot, Bannerley Road, Birmingham, B33 0SL Tel: 0121-785 0270 Fax: 0121-785 0271 E-mail: birmingham@eurogate.co.uk

Europa Express Freight, Second Avenue, Trafford Park, Manchester, M17 1EE Tel: 0161-872 8094 Fax: 0161-873 8258 E-mail: manchester@europa-worldwide.co.uk

▶ Europa Worldwide, Unit 2 Building 110, Castle Donington, Derby, DE74 2SA Tel: (01332) 815900 Fax: (01332) 815909 E-mail: sales@europa-worldwide.co.uk

Europa Worldwide Logistics, Europa House, 68 Hailey Rd, Erith, Kent, DA18 4AU Tel: (020) 8311 5000 Fax: (020) 8310 4805 E-mail: sales@europa-worldwide.co.uk

▶ Europa Worldwide Services, Europa House, 46 Tilton Road, Birmingham, B9 4PP Tel: 0121-766 8000 Fax: 0121-771 4669 E-mail: sales@europa-worldwide.co.uk

Europa Worldwide Services, Europa House Unit 3 Severnside Trading Estate, St. Andrews Road, Avonmouth, Bristol, BS11 9AG Tel: 0117-982 1000 Fax: 0117-923 5741 E-mail: bristol@europa-worldwide.co.uk

▶ Euroship Logistics Ltd, PO Box 515, Grimsby, South Humberside, DN37 9QD Tel: (01472) 353333 Fax: (01472) 595695 E-mail: dchristie@euroshiplogistics.co.uk

Euroxpress Delivery Services, 6e Arndale Road, Wick, Littlehampton, West Sussex, BN17 7HD Tel: (01903) 732733 Fax: (01903) 732734 E-mail: sales@euro-xpress.com

Exel, McKinney Industrial Estate, Mallusk, Newtownabbey, County Antrim, BT36 8YZ Tel: (028) 9084 3481 Fax: (028) 9083 3153 E-mail: pam.millar@dhl.co.uk

Exel Freight Management UK Ltd, Great South West Road, Feltham, Middlesex, TW14 8NE Tel: (020) 8750 7000 Fax: (020) 8890 8444

Exel Freight Management UK Ltd, Great South West Road, Feltham, Middlesex, TW14 8NE Tel: (020) 8750 7000 Fax: (020) 8890 8444 E-mail: derrick.froom@exel.com

Export Centre, Unit 72 Wimbledon Stadium Business Centre, Rosemary Road, London, SW17 0BA Tel: (020) 8947 6767 Fax: (020) 8944 1414 E-mail: info@london-frieght.co.uk

Express 2000 Ltd, Pembley Green, Copthorne Common, Copthorne, Crawley, West Sussex, RH10 3LF Tel: (01342) 713500 Fax: (01342) 713520 E-mail: sales@express2000.co.uk

Express Export Services Ltd, Arlette House, 143 Wardour Street, London, W1F 8WA Tel: (020) 7734 8356 Fax: (020) 7734 3729 E-mail: expressexportservices@ukbusiness.com

Express Forwarders Ltd, 9 Meadowbrook Industrial Centre, Crawley, West Sussex, RH10 9SA Tel: (01293) 551642 Fax: (01293) 553375 E-mail: sales@expressforwarders.co.uk

F F G Hillebrand, Dissigna House, Weston Avenue, West Thurrock, Grays, Essex, RM20 3ZP Tel: (01708) 689000 Fax: (01708) 689001 E-mail: sales@ffg-hil.com

F F G International Manchester Ltd, 24-26 Brook Street, Chadderton, Oldham, OL9 6NN Tel: 0161-626 8686 Fax: 0161-678 8407 E-mail: sales@ffg.co.uk

Fabine Investments Ltd, Unit 3 Pilot Trading Estate, West Wycombe Road, High Wycombe, Buckinghamshire, HP12 3AH Tel: (01494) 462749 Fax: (01494) 522325 E-mail: pilot@pilotgroup.co.uk

Fleet Removals Of Liverpool, Fleet House, Stretton Way, Liverpool, L36 6JF Tel: 0151-489 7990 Fax: 0151-480 6277 E-mail: malf@fleetremovals.co.uk

Fleet Shipping International Ltd, 41-47 Blue Anchor Lane, London, SE16 3UL Tel: (020) 7232 0777 Fax: (020) 7232 2600 E-mail: sales@fwwshipping.com

Flixborough Wharf Ltd, Trent Port House, Flixborough, Scunthorpe, North Lincolnshire, DN15 8RS Tel: (01724) 867691 Fax: (01724) 851207 E-mail: info@flixboroughwharf.co.uk

Foremost International Ltd, Unit C Mill Mead, Staines, Middlesex, TW18 4UQ Tel: (01784) 464319 Fax: (01784) 466418 E-mail: ops@foremost-worldcargo.co.uk

Frans Maas (U K) Ltd, 36 North Quay, Great Yarmouth, Norfolk, NR30 1JE Tel: (01493) 336600 Fax: (01493) 858730 E-mail: sales@fmaas.co.uk

Freight Clearance Ltd, New Bridge House, New Bridge, Dover, Kent, CT16 1JS Tel: (01304) 211020 Fax: (01304) 209753

Freight Co. International Ltd, Unit 5 Howe Moss Drive, Dyce, Aberdeen, AB21 0GL Tel: (01224) 771881 Fax: (01224) 770730 E-mail: info@freightco-group.co.uk

Freight Transport Ltd, C3-C5 Unit, Railway Triangle, Walton Road, Portsmouth, PO6 1TW Tel: (023) 9232 4213 Fax: (023) 9221 0324 E-mail: sales@freighttransport.co.uk

Freightlocators, The Sidings, Windmill La, Ringwood, Hants, BH24 2DQ Tel: (01425) 478861 E-mail: freightlocators@aol.com

Future Forwarding Co. Ltd, Building 305, World Freight Terminal, Manchester Airport, Manchester, M90 5PY Tel: 0161-436 8181 Fax: 0161-499 0654 E-mail: andreadelves@futureforwarding.com

▶ G B Shipping & Forwarding Ltd, Meridian House, Alexandra Dock North, Grimsby, North East Lincolnshire, DN31 3UA Tel: (01472) 345551 Fax: (01472) 346927 E-mail: shipping@gbagroup.com

G K N Freight Services Ltd, Equity House, 128-136 High St, Edgware, Middlesex, HA8 7EL Tel: (020) 8905 6688 Fax: (020) 8905 6951 E-mail: info.fsl@gkndriveline.com

G T Stone & Son, Dudnance Lane, Pool, Redruth, Cornwall, TR15 3QZ Tel: (01736) 763777 Fax: (01209) 710285

GAC Benair Ltd, Building 301 World Freight Terminal, Manchester Airport, Manchester, M90 5BF Tel: 0161-954 3300 Fax: 0161-436 1670 E-mail: manchester@gacworld.com

Gardner Freight International Ltd, Mersey Chambers, Covent Garden, Liverpool, L2 8XT Tel: 0151-236 7366 Fax: 0151-243 3463 E-mail: harrisons@liverpool.co.uk

Garrick Freight International Ltd, 6-8 Furrow La, London, E9 6JS Tel: (020) 8985 2789 Fax: (020) 8985 4961

Geologistics Ltd, Royal Court, 81 Tweedy Road, Bromley, BR1 1TW Tel: (020) 8460 5050 Fax: (020) 8461 8884 E-mail: prandall@geo-logistics.com

Geologistics Ltd, Unit 12 The Brunel Centre, Newton Road, Crawley, West Sussex, RH10 9TU Tel: (01293) 652900 Fax: (01293) 652901 E-mail: gatwick@geo-logistics.com

Geologistics Expo Services Ltd, Unit 18 National Exhibition Centre, Third Exhibition Avenue, Birmingham, B40 1PJ Tel: 0121-780 2627 Fax: 0121-780 2329

Glennfreight Services Ltd, 9 Enterprise Court, Metcalf Way, Crawley, West Sussex, RH11 7RW Tel: (01293) 437770 Fax: (01293) 437775 E-mail: info@glennfreight.co.uk

Global Logistics Systems Ltd, 448 Oakshot Place, Bamber Bridge, Preston, PR5 8AT Tel: (01772) 626400 Fax: (01772) 627251

Globe Freight Ltd, 119 Turnpike Lane, London, N8 0DU Tel: (020) 8340 4395 Fax: (020) 8348 8036

Golding, Hoptroff & Co. Ltd, Unit 8 Aintree Buildings, Aintree Way, Retail & Business Park, Liverpool, L9 5AQ Tel: 0151-525 2381 Fax: 0151-530 1351 E-mail: sales@goldinghop.demon.co.uk

Gondrand U.K., Gondrand House, 2 Oriental Road, London, E16 2BZ Tel: (020) 7540 2000 Fax: (020) 7540 2001 E-mail: info@gondrand.co.uk

John Good Shipping Ltd, Craven Gate, Lorne Road, Warley, Brentwood, Essex, CM14 5HH Tel: (0845) 2582050 Fax: (01277) 202758 E-mail: london@johngood.co.uk

Goodrem Nicholson, Export House, Rowley Road, Coventry, CV3 4FR Tel: (024) 7630 5601 Fax: (024) 7630 4663 E-mail: colin@goodrem.co.uk

Grampian International Freight Ltd, Grampian House, Hewett Road, Gaptus Hall Industrial Estate, Great Yarmouth, Norfolk, NR31 0NN Tel: (01493) 441212 Fax: (01493) 440391 E-mail: gtyarmouth@gif.co.uk

▶ Graylaw Freight Group, Graylaw Freight Terminal, Gillibrands Road, Skelmersdale, Lancashire, WN8 9TA Tel: (01695) 729101 Fax: (01695) 729125

Graysons Freight Services Ltd, Border Freight Terminal, 4 Hollands Road, Haverhill, Suffolk, CB9 8PP Tel: (01440) 762558 Fax: (01440) 707119 E-mail: sales@graysons.net

Greenshields, Cowie & Co. Ltd, Greenshields House, Perimeter Road, Knowsley Industrial Park North, Liverpool, L33 3BA Tel: 0151-546 2044 Fax: 0151-546 1967

Groupage Shipping Services Ltd, Ten Acres, Station Road, Rushall, Walsall, WS4 1ET Tel: (01922) 638711 Fax: (01922) 722883

Guernsey Freight Services, Airport Complex, Forest, Guernsey, GY8 0DJ Tel: (01481) 238180 Fax: (01481) 235479

Gwynedd Shipping Ltd, Chapel Yard, London Road, Holyhead, Gwynedd, LL65 2PB Tel: (01407) 760232 Fax: (01407) 765344 E-mail: info@gwyneddshipping.com

Hales, Hammond Road, Knowsley Industrial Park, Liverpool, L33 7UL Tel: 0151-546 5249 Fax: 0151-545 1010 E-mail: deb@halestrans.u-net.com

Hales Freight Ltd, Horseshoe Farm, London Road, Harlow, Essex, CM17 9LH Tel: (01279) 421122 Fax: (01279) 439144 E-mail: philipveltom@halesfreight.com

Hamilton Shipping Ltd, 14 Clarendon Road, Belfast, BT1 3BG Tel: (028) 9053 3200 Fax: (028) 9053 3222 E-mail: containers@hamiltonshipping.com

Hart Bros & Co., Office Suite 14, Tower Building 22 Water Street, Liverpool, L3 1BA Tel: 0151-236 1786 Fax: 0151-236 3969

Hauser Ltd, Unit 2 Westpoint Enterprise Park, Clarence Ave, Trafford Park, Manchester, M17 1QS Tel: 0161-877 3317 Fax: 0161-872 0293 E-mail: enquiries@hauser.co.uk

▶ Hauser Ltd, Heighington Lane, Aycliffe Industrial Park, Newton Aycliffe, County Durham, DL5 6UE Tel: (01325) 300855 Fax: (01325) 300844 E-mail: northeast@hauser.co.uk

▶ Hauser Sheffield Ltd, Alliance House, Roman Ridge Road, Sheffield, S9 1GB Tel: 0114-244 9977 Fax: 0114-242 3481 E-mail: sheffield@hauser.co.uk

Havas Packing & Shipping Ltd, Little Parrock Farm, Shepherds Hill, Colemans Hatch, Hartfield, East Sussex, TN7 4HP Tel: (01342) 824388 Fax: (01342) 825541 E-mail: enquiries@havas.co.uk

HDS Freight Services Ltd, 12 Saxon Way, West Drayton, Middlesex, UB7 0LW Tel: (020) 8564 9955 Fax: (020) 8564 7060 E-mail: operations@hdsfreight.co.uk

Hellmann Worldwide Logistics Ltd, Hellmann House Lakeside Industrial Estate, Colnbrook By Passage, Colnbrook, Slough, SL3 0EL Tel: (01753) 688500 Fax: (01753) 684771

Howard Shipping Services Ltd, Showell Road, Wolverhampton, WV10 9JY Tel: (01902) 738838 Fax: (01902) 862962 E-mail: peterhoward@hoship.com

Howard Tenens Associates Ltd, Kingfisher Business Park, London Road, Thrupp, Stroud, Gloucestershire, GL5 2BY Tel: (01453) 885087 Fax: (01453) 886145 E-mail: enquiries@tenens.com

IES Ltd, 1 Portview Road, Bristol, BS11 9LS Tel: 0117-938 0600 Fax: 0117-938 0900 E-mail: info@ies.co.uk

Ifs Global Logistics Ltd, I F S Logistics Park, Seven Mile Straight, Muckamore, Antrim, BT41 4QE Tel: (028) 9446 4211 Fax: (028) 9446 7723 E-mail: sales@antrim.ifsgroup.com

Immediate Transportation Co. Ltd, First Floor, St Nicholas House, Chappel St, Liverpool, L2 8TX Tel: 0151-227 4521 Fax: 0151-236 8036 E-mail: itcolhr@itcolhr.co.uk

Import My Vehicle Ltd, Currie House, Herbert Walker Avenue, Western Docks, Southampton, SO15 1HJ Tel: (023) 8033 6635 Fax: (023) 8033 8833E-mail: info@importmyvehicle.co.uk

Incare International Ltd, Headlands Business Park, Salisbury Road, Blashford, Ringwood, Hampshire, BH24 3PB Tel: (01425) 479932 Fax: (01425) 471146 E-mail: freight@incare.co.uk

Inchcape P.L.C, 22a St James Square, London, SW1Y 5LP Tel: (020) 7546 0022 Fax: (020) 7546 0010

Inchcape Shipping Services UK Ltd, Berth 2 Forest Products Terminal Gordano Quay, Royal Portbury, Portbury, Bristol, BS20 7XF Tel: (01275) 375868 Fax: (01275) 375380

Inchcape Shipping Services UK Ltd, North Side Albert Dock, Leith Docks, Edinburgh, EH6 7DN Tel: 0131-553 5969 Fax: (01324) 478803

Inchcape Shipping Services UK Ltd, Unit 53 Evans Business Centre, Earls Road, Grangemouth, Stirlingshire, FK3 8XE Tel: (01324) 492777 Fax: (01324) 492776 E-mail: gbgrg@iss-shipping.com

Inchcape Shipping Services UK Ltd, East Side Locks, Immingham Dock, Immingham, South Humberside, DN40 2LZ Tel: (01469) 571400 Fax: (01469) 571309

Inchcape Shipping Services UK Ltd, Portland Port, Castletown, Portland, Dorset, DT5 1PP Tel: (01305) 822775 Fax: (01305) 822623 E-mail: gbptl@iss-shipping.com

▶ Independent Freight Solutions Ltd, 91 Chaytor Drive, Chapel End, Nuneaton, Warwickshire, CV10 9SU Tel: (024) 7639 8663 Fax: (024) 7639 2757 E-mail: ifsltd@btconnect.com

Intersped Logistics UK Ltd, Unit 9 Gatesway Business Centre, Tom Cribb Road, London, SE28 0EZ Tel: (020) 8316 4300 Fax: (020) 8316 1210 E-mail: logistics@intersped.co.uk

Irish Ferries, Salt Island, Holyhead, Gwynedd, LL65 1DR Tel: (0870) 5329129 Fax: (01407) 760340

Irish Ferries, Custom House, The Dockyard, Pembroke Dock, Dyfed, SA72 6TW Tel: (0870) 5329543 Fax: (01646) 621125 E-mail: ifpembroke@btinternet.com

▶ J D Freight Ltd, Unit 3, Hurricane Way, Slough, SL3 8AG Tel: (01753) 545556 Fax: 01753 545557 E-mail: lee.tuppen@jdfreight.co.uk

J P Knight Ltd, Admirals Offices Main Gate Road, The Historic Dockyard, Chatham, Kent, ME4 4TZ Tel: (01634) 826633 Fax: (01634) 829093 E-mail: info@jpknight.com

James W Parsons Ltd, 5 Printing House Yard, Hackney Road, London, E2 7PR Tel: (020) 7739 0768 Fax: (020) 7739 1258 E-mail: jamesw@parsonslimited.fsnet.co.uk

Jaymar Freight Services Ltd, Container Base Box Lane, Renwick Road, Barking, Essex, IG11 0SQ Tel: (020) 8984 8030 Fax: (020) 8984 7379 E-mail: shipping@jaymarfreight.co.uk

John C Wheeler International Ltd, Fishers Way, Belvedere, Kent, DA17 6BS Tel: (020) 8310 2032 Fax: (020) 8312 1913 E-mail: info@johncwheeler.co.uk

John Gardiner Airfreight Ltd, 14 Mount Road, Feltham, Middlesex, TW13 6AR Tel: (020) 8894 3537 Fax: (020) 8894 3542 E-mail: john@johngardinerfreight.com

John Good & Sons London Ltd, Northfleet Hope House Site 41, Tilbury Docks, Tilbury, Essex, RM18 7HX Tel: (01375) 859841 Fax: (01375) 850343 E-mail: tilbury@johngood.co.uk

John S Braid & Co. Ltd, Maritime House, 143 Woodville Street, Glasgow, G51 2RQ Tel: 0141-445 2525 Fax: 0141-440 1238 E-mail: ddarroch@braidco.com

▶ indicates data change since last edition

FREIGHT FORWARDERS/ FORWARDING AGENTS – *continued*

John Sutcliffe & Son Grimsby Ltd, Alexandra Chambers, Flour Square, Grimsby, South Humberside, DN31 3LS Tel: (01472) 359101 Fax: (01472) 241935 E-mail: admin@jsutcliffe.co.uk

John Jolly, P O Box 2, Kirkwall, Orkney, KW15 1HS Tel: (01856) 872268 Fax: (01856) 875002 E-mail: operations@johnjolly.co.uk

Simon Jones Superfreight Ltd, 1-2 Grant Road, London, SW11 2NU Tel: (020) 7924 3933 Fax: (020) 7223 1293 E-mail: simonjones@superfreight.fsnet.co.uk

K M B Shipping Ltd, Lower Church Lane, Tipton, West Midlands, DY4 7PH Tel: 0121-557 3352 Fax: 0121-520 0936 E-mail: info@onestopshipping.co.uk

Karman Shipping Ltd, Timber Lodge, Plantation Road, Leighton Buzzard, Bedfordshire, LU7 3JB Tel: (01525) 851545 Fax: (01525) 850996 E-mail: sales@karmanshipping.com

Kay Oneill Ltd, Unit 6, Horton Road, Colnbrook, Slough, SL3 0AT Tel: (01753) 684606 Fax: (01753) 682241 E-mail: lhr@kayoneill.com

Keller Bryant & Co. Ltd, Swan Centre, Fishers Lane, London, W4 1RX Tel: (020) 8996 9525 E-mail: mail@keller-bryant.co.uk

Kelly Freight, C Cedars Transport Depot, Church Manorway, Erith, Kent, DA8 1DE Tel: (01322) 430231 Fax: (01322) 463446 E-mail: upn55scott@aol.com

Kelly Freight, C Cedars Transport Depot, Church Manorway, Erith, Kent, DA8 1DE Tel: (01322) 430231 Fax: (01322) 463446 E-mail: upn55scott@aol.com

Charles Kendall Freight Ltd, Spur Road, Feltham, Middlesex, TW14 0SL Tel: (020) 8384 9494 Fax: (020) 8384 9403 E-mail: ckf@charleskendallfreight.com

Kinnes Shipping Ltd, Fish Dock Road, Dundee, DD1 3LZ Tel: (01382) 462858 Fax: (01382) 462870E-mail: general@kinnes-shipping.co.uk

Kuehne & Nagel Ltd, Building 317, World Freight Terminal, Manchester Airport, Manchester, M90 5NA Tel: 0161-436 9400 Fax: 0161-436 9429 E-mail: manfa@kuehne-nagel.com

Kuehne & Nagel UK Ltd, Old Bath Road, Colnbrook, Slough, SL3 0NW Tel: (01895) 552000 Fax: (01753) 762401

L B Freight Ltd, 36 Prescott Street, Halifax, West Yorkshire, HX1 2QW Tel: (01422) 351217 Fax: (01422) 330209 E-mail: sales@lbfreight.co.uk

L V Shipping Ltd, Walton Avenue, Felixstowe, Suffolk, IP11 3AL Tel: (01394) 278784 Fax: (01394) 284498 E-mail: felixstowe@lvshipping.com

Laser Transport International Ltd, Lympne Industrial Estate, Lympne, Hythe, Kent, CT21 4LR Tel: (01303) 260471 Fax: (01303) 264851 E-mail: sales@laserint.co.uk

Laser Vision, 52 North Street, Bedminster, Bristol, BS3 1HJ Tel: 0117-963 2963 E-mail: laservisioncouk@aol.com

Leafe & Hawkes Ltd, 5 Merrick Street, Hull, HU9 1NF Tel: (01482) 325951 Fax: (01482) 225406E-mail: s.leafe@leafeandhawkes.co.uk

Harry Leeks Freight Ltd, St. Leonard's Street, Bedford, MK42 9BS Tel: (01234) 359402 Fax: (01234) 348891

Leman Ltd, New Works Road, Low Moor, Bradford, West Yorkshire, BD12 0QN Tel: (01274) 693231 Fax: (01274) 693190 E-mail: bradford@leman.co.uk

Little Whiting & Tedford Ltd, Princes Dock, 14 Clarendon Road, Belfast, BT1 3BG Tel: (028) 9053 3302 Fax: (028) 9053 3222 E-mail: agency@hamiltonshipping.com

Locker Freight Ltd, Wilson Rd, Huyton, Liverpool, L36 6AN Tel: 0151-480 8922 Fax: 0151-480 3744 E-mail: general@locker-freight.co.uk

Lockson Services Ltd, Heath Park Industrial Estate, Freshwater Road, Dagenham, Essex, RM8 1RX Tel: (020) 8597 2889 Fax: (020) 8597 5265 E-mail: enquiries@lockson.co.uk

Lombard Shipping & Forwarding Ltd, Lombard Centre, Link Road, Huyton, Liverpool, L36 6AP Tel: 0151-449 3535 Fax: 0151-489 1229 E-mail: sales@1ombardshipping.co.uk

M E P Services Ltd, 3 Catsash Rd, Langstone, Newport, Gwent, NP18 2LZ Tel: (01633) 211995 Fax: (01633) 213131 E-mail: enq@mepfreight.com

M M D (Shipping Services) Ltd, Flathouse Quay, Prospect Road, Portsmouth, PO2 7SP Tel: (023) 9282 6351 Fax: (023) 9229 1910

M M K Express Ltd, 4 Antrim Business Park, Sentry Lane, Newtownabbey, County Antrim, BT36 4XX Tel: (028) 9083 8388 Fax: (028) 9084 8822 E-mail: sales@mmkexpress.co.uk

M & S Shipping International Ltd, Enterprise House, 34 Faringdon Avenue, Romford, RM3 8SU Tel: (01708) 340034 Fax: (01708) 373787 E-mail: logistics2000@msshipping.com

Mcgruther & Marshall Shipping, Shore Road, Invergordon, Ross-Shire, IV18 0ER Tel: (01349) 853073 Fax: (01349) 853678 E-mail: dave@mmagency.co.uk

Maersk Logistics, Unit 6 Orwell House, Ferry Lane, Felixstowe, Suffolk, IP11 3AQ Tel: (01394) 614600 Fax: (01394) 614636

Maina Freight Forwarders plc, 5 Featherstone Industrial Estate, Dominion Road, Southall, Middlesex, UB2 5DP Tel: (020) 8843 1977 Fax: (020) 8571 5628E-mail: info@maina.com

Mann & Son London Ltd, The Navel House, Kings Quay Street, Harwich, Essex, CO12 3JJ Tel: (01255) 245200 Fax: (01255) 245219 E-mail: enquiries@manngroup.co.uk

Martells Of Sutton Ltd, Unit 3, 4, Charlwoods Road, East Grinstead, West Sussex, RH19 2HG Tel: (01342) 321303 Fax: (01342) 302145 E-mail: removals@martells.co.uk

Meadows Wye Container Groupage, Castlebank House, Oak Road, Leatherhead, Surrey, KT22 7PG Tel: (01372) 370066 Fax: (01372) 370077

Menlow Worldwide, Unit 19 Airlinks Industrial Estate, Spitfire Way, Heston, Hounslow, TW5 9NR Tel: (020) 8260 6000 Fax: (020) 8260 6170 E-mail: stewartinnes@menlowworldwide.com

Metro Shipping Ltd, 50 Cliveland Street, Birmingham, B19 3SH Tel: 0121-333 4455 Fax: 0121-333 4021 E-mail: enquiries@metroshipping.co.uk

Michel Hurel, Manor Farm, Church Street, Appleford, Abingdon, Oxfordshire, OX14 4PA Tel: (01235) 847200 Fax: (01235) 847888 E-mail: sales@michel-hurel.co.uk

Mis Shipping Ltd, 34 The Mall, London, W5 3TJ Tel: (020) 8567 4456 Fax: (020) 8567 5890 E-mail: misshipping@msn.com

Mistley Quay & Forwarding, High Street, Mistley, Manningtree, Essex, CO11 1HB Tel: (01206) 394431 Fax: (01206) 393882 E-mail: enquiries@twlogistics.co.uk

▶ MJ Freight Solutions Ltd, 7 Bristol Close, Rayleigh, Essex, SS6 9RZ Tel: 01268 780637 Fax: 01268 780653 E-mail: Jo@mjfreightsolutions.co.uk

▶ MMK Solutions, 8 De Mandeville Road, Elsenham, Bishop's Stortford, Hertfordshire, CM22 6LR Tel: (01279) 816230 Fax: (01279) 816030 E-mail: sales@mmksolutions.co.uk

Montgomery Tank Services, 50 Trench Road, Newtownabbey, County Antrim, BT36 4TY Tel: (028) 9084 3723 Fax: (028) 9084 9111 E-mail: sales@montgomerytankservices.co.uk

Moonbridge Air Project S A Freight Ltd, Unit 9, Ascot Road, Bedfont, Feltham, Middlesex, TW14 8QH Tel: (01784) 259555 Fax: (01784) 259599 E-mail: administrator@moonbridge.co.uk

Allan Morris Transport Ltd, Factory Road, Sandycroft, Deeside, Flintshire, CH5 2QJ Tel: (01244) 533320 Fax: (01244) 533766 E-mail: enq@allanmorris.co.uk

Mostyn Maritime Services Ltd, Mostyn Docks Mostyn, Mostyn, Holywell, Clwyd, CH8 9HE Tel: (01745) 560335 Fax: (01745) 560324 E-mail: portofmostyn@aol.com

Multiserv Group Ltd, Strawberry Lane, Willenhall, West Midlands, WV13 3RS Tel: (01902) 636381 Fax: (01902) 636186 E-mail: info@multiserv.com

N Y K Logistics, Common Road, Huthwaite, Sutton-in-Ashfield, Nottinghamshire, NG17 2JY Tel: (01623) 510510 Fax: (01623) 518612 E-mail:

Neal Bros, Queens Buildings, Hastings Road, Leicester, LE5 0LJ Tel: 0116-274 0005 Fax: 0116-274 2028 E-mail: sales@nealbrothers.co.uk

Neill & Brown Global Logistics Group Ltd, Overseas House, Livingstone Road, Hessle, North Humberside, HU13 0AW Tel: (01482) 644287 Fax: (01482) 644284 E-mail: whin@neillbrown.com

New Alliance Services Ltd, 403A Trelawny House, The Dock, Felixstowe, Suffolk, IP11 3EQ Tel: (01394) 676212 Fax: (01394) 676423

Norman Global Logistics Ltd, 1 Griffin Centre, Staines Road, Feltham, Middlesex, TW14 0HS Tel: (020) 8893 2999 Fax: (020) 8893 1770 E-mail: pob@norman.co.uk

▶ NTS International Express Ltd, 3 Capel Close, Leacon Road, Ashford, Kent, TN23 4GY Tel: (01233) 637722 Fax: (01233) 637733 E-mail: ashford@nts-express.co.uk

O B C Shipping Ltd, Osprey House, Richmond Road, Pembroke Dock, Dyfed, SA72 6TS Tel: (01646) 622220 Fax: (01646) 622221 E-mail: pembroke.agency@obcgroup.com

O R T Forwarding Ltd, Unit 24 Bourne Road Industrial Park, Bourne Road, Dartford, DA1 4BZ Tel: (01322) 555486 Fax: (01322) 528528 E-mail: enquiries@ort.co.uk

Obc Shipping Ltd, 2a Gateway Business Park, Beancross Road, Grangemouth, Stirlingshire, FK3 8WX Tel: (01324) 482811 Fax: (01324) 665197 E-mail: grangemouth.agency@obcgroup.com

▶ On-Line Shipping Ltd, Unit 3 Argonaut Park, Galleymead Road, Colnbrook, Slough, SL3 0EN Tel: (01753) 687702 Fax: (01753) 684404 E-mail: paul@onlineshippingltd.co.uk

Orbit Import Export, Ferry Terminal, Ramsgate, Kent, CT11 9FT Tel: (01843) 588899 Fax: (01843) 850278

P B O Ltd, Unit 18 Shepperton Business Park, Govett Avenue, Shepperton, Middlesex, TW17 8BA Tel: (01932) 232233 Fax: (01932) 243516 E-mail: paul@pbologistics.com

P C Howard Ltd, West Hay, Kings Cliffe, Peterborough, PE8 6XX Tel: (01780) 444444 Fax: (01780) 444744

P D Logistics, Cowpen Lane, Billingham, Cleveland, TS23 4DB Tel: (01642) 560456 Fax: (01642) 564061 E-mail: durhams@thpal.co.uk

P K Marine Freight Services Ltd, 1 Perimeter Road, Knowsley Industrial Park, Liverpool, L33 3AY Tel: 0151-547 3822 Fax: 0151-548 0884 E-mail: sales@pkmarine.co.uk

P S A Transport Ltd, 16 Devonshire Street, London, W1G 7AF Tel: (020) 7637 3271 Fax: (020) 7255 2229 E-mail: sales@psatransport.co.uk

P T S UK Ltd, 10 Cliff Road, Ipswich, IP3 0AY Tel: (01473) 282600 Fax: (01473) 287521 E-mail: sales@ptsukltd.co.uk

Paksafe Crates & Packing Cases, 1 Tewin Court, Welwyn Garden City, Hertfordshire, AL7 1AU Tel: (01707) 391939 Fax: (01707) 390989 E-mail: jag.1@virgin.net

Panalpina World Transport Ltd, Great South West Road, Feltham, Middlesex, TW14 8NE Tel: (020) 8587 9000 Fax: (020) 8587 9200

Pentagon Freight Services plc, Pentagon House, Unit 102 Crayfield Industrial Park, Orpington, Kent, BR5 3HP Tel: (01689) 877777 Fax: (01689) 878477 E-mail: operations@pfsheadoffice.co.uk

▶ Peters & May Ltd, Prysmian House, Dew Lane, Eastleigh, Hampshire, SO50 9PX Tel: (023) 8048 0501 Fax: (01752) 775699 E-mail: enquiriesplh@petersandmay.com

Porter & Laker, Dissegna House, Weston Avenue, West Thurrock, Grays, Essex, RM20 3ZP Tel: (01708) 689400 Fax: (01708) 689401

Power Packing Export Services Ltd, Pinhoe Trading Estate, Venny Bridge, Exeter, EX4 8JN Tel: (01392) 468088 Fax: (01392) 467987 E-mail: mail@powerpacking.co.uk

▶ Premier, 24 Brunel Way, Fareham, Hampshire, PO15 5SD Tel: (01489) 565577 Fax: (01489) 565588 E-mail: sales@psap.co.uk

Princia Shipping Ltd, Unit C1a Purfleet Industrial Park, London Road, Aveley, South Ockendon, Essex, RM15 4YA Tel: (01708) 860848 Fax: (01708) 867765 E-mail: princia@princia.fsnet.co.uk

PSL Freight Ltd, Quayside Park Indust Estate, Bates Road, Maldon (Essex), Maldon, Essex, CM9 4RS Tel: (01621) 854451 Fax: (01621) 854452 E-mail: sales@pslgroup.net

Quality Freight (UK) Ltd, 1st Floor Port Office, Manisty Wharf, Ellesmere Port, CH65 1AF Tel: 0151-355 6006 Fax: 0151-355 3273 E-mail: info@quality-freight.co.uk

R E L Freight Ltd, 346 Garratt Lane, London, SW18 4ES Tel: (020) 8874 2435 Fax: (020) 8874 7344

R J J Freight Ltd, R J J House, Haven Exchange South, Felixstowe, Suffolk, IP11 2QE Tel: (01394) 695560 Fax: (01394) 673031 E-mail: sales@rjjfreight.co.uk

R & T Shipping Ltd, 2nd Floor, Holegate House, Holegate Court, Western Road, Romford, RM1 3JS Tel: (0870) 7745612 Fax: (0870) 7745602

Radius Shipping Ltd, 886 Old Kent Road, London, SE15 1NQ Tel: (020) 7639 2048 Fax: (020) 7639 7313 E-mail: office@radius.uk.net

Raker Freight, 100 Ellingham Industrial Centre, Ellingham Way, Ashford, Kent, TN23 6LZ Tel: (01233) 651660 Fax: (01233) 651661 E-mail: info@rakerfreight.co.uk

Read & Sutcliffe Ltd, St. Johns Road, Boston, Lincolnshire, PE21 6HG Tel: (01205) 310444 Fax: (01205) 310500 E-mail: info@rsboston.com

Redbourn International Forwarding Ltd, 43A Adelaide Street, Luton, LU1 5BD Tel: (01582) 425611 Fax: (01582) 405705 E-mail: office@redbourninternational.co.uk

Redfern Transports Ltd, Mount Street Mill, Mount Street, Bradford, West Yorkshire, BD3 9RJ Tel: (01274) 392721 Fax: (01274) 370851 E-mail: sales@redferntransports.co.uk

Regency Forwarding Ltd, Unit 6 Moorfield Road Estate, Yeadon, Leeds, LS19 7BN Tel: 0113-250 7714 Fax: 0113-250 8391 E-mail: sales@regencyforwarding.com

Regional Freight Services Ltd, Airport Business Centre, Regional House, Norwich, NR6 6BS Tel: (01603) 414125 Fax: (01603) 402542 E-mail: rfs@regfrt.co.uk

Rewood Shipping Ltd, 149-151 High Road, Chadwell Heath, Romford, RM6 6BJ Tel: (020) 8597 3382 Fax: (020) 8478 0310 E-mail: mervyn@rewood.co.uk

Rhenus Hauser Ltd, Bowden House, Luckyn Lane, Basildon, Essex, SS14 3AX Tel: (01268) 592180 Fax: (01268) 592181 E-mail: london@uk.rhenus.com

Roadferry Ltd, Carr Lane, Leyland, Leyland, PR25 3RD Tel: (01772) 455338 Fax: (01772) 422311

Roshview International Ltd, 3-11 Stean Street, London, E8 4ED Tel: (020) 7254 4836 Fax: (020) 7249 9886

Royfreight Ltd, 2 Queen Annes Place, Enfield, Middlesex, EN1 2PX Tel: (020) 8360 3060 Fax: (020) 8360 0440 E-mail: enquires@royfrieght.co.uk

RSF Commercial Services Ltd, Unit 24 Walkers Road, Moons Moat North Industrial Estate, Redditch, Worcestershire, B98 9HE Tel: (01527) 598777 Fax: (01527) 598538 E-mail: office@rsfonline.co.uk

Rumsey & Sons, Market House, Market Road, Richmond, Surrey, TW9 4LZ Tel: (020) 8892 1896 Fax: (020) 8876 9969 E-mail: removals@rumseyandson.com

Rycon Shipping & Forwarding Ltd, Rycon Warehouse, Rye Harbour Road, Rye, East Sussex, TN31 7TE Tel: (01797) 222747 Fax: (01797) 224535 E-mail: ryecon@btconnect.com

S H E Maritime Services Ltd, Unit 2 Town Quay Wharf, Abbey Road, Barking, Essex, IG11 7BZ Tel: (020) 8594 9325 Fax: (020) 8591 8369 E-mail: sales@she-maritime.com

S T S Eurolink, Andes Road, Nursling, Southampton, SO16 0YZ Tel: (023) 8073 0816 Fax: (023) 8073 0819 E-mail: stseurolink@dial.pipex.com

S & T Shipping Ltd, 5 St. Annes Fort, King's Lynn, Norfolk, PE30 1QS Tel: (01553) 772661 Fax: (01553) 691074 E-mail: sandt01@aol.com

Samfreight Ltd, Bath Road, West Drayton, Middlesex, UB7 0DB Tel: (020) 8750 2300 Fax: (020) 8750 2301 E-mail: lee.george@samfreight.co.uk

Schenkers Ltd, Schenkers House, Great South West Road, Feltham, Middlesex, TW14 8NT Tel: (020) 8890 8899 Fax: (020) 8751 0141 E-mail: enquires@schenker.com

SDV Bernard Ltd, Convent Drive, Waterbeach, Cambridge, CB25 9QT Tel: (01223) 861460 Fax: (01223) 860985 E-mail: eastanglia@sdvbernard.co.uk

▶ Sea Wing Cargo Services Ltd, Unit 1, Lakeside Industrial Estate, Colnbrook By Pass, Colnbrook, Slough, SL3 0ED Tel: (01753) 763488 Fax: (01753) 763489 E-mail: admin@seawing.co.uk

Seabourne Group P.L.C., Unit 13, Saxon Way Trading Centre, Saxon Way, Harmondsworth, West Drayton, Middlesex, UB7 0LW Tel: (020) 7536 6360 Fax: (020) 7987 9889

Seacon Shipping Ltd, Tower Warf, North Fleet, Gravesend, Kent, DA11 9BD Tel: (01474) 320000 Fax: (01474) 329946 E-mail: ships@seacon.co.uk

Sealand General Exporters, 78 New Oxford Street, London, WC1A 1HB Tel: (020) 7580 8663 Fax: (020) 7580 8662 E-mail: sales@sealand.co.uk

Sealandair Transport Co., 101 Stephenson Street, London, E16 4SA Tel: (020) 7511 2288 Fax: (020) 7511 1466 E-mail: frt@sealandair.com

Shea International Ltd, 31 King Street, Stanford-le-Hope, Essex, SS17 0HJ Tel: (01375) 642626 Fax: (01375) 361304 E-mail: sheaint@btconnect.com

Slough International Freight & Packing Ltd, 820 Yeovil Road, Slough, SL1 4JA Tel: (01753) 691011 Fax: (01753) 825669 E-mail: sloughinter@btconnect.com

Small & Co. Shipping Ltd, Europa House, 40 South Quay, Great Yarmouth, Norfolk, NR30 2RL Tel: (01502) 572301 Fax: (01493) 857533 E-mail: smallandcoshipping@halcyonshipping.com

Smith, Hogg & Co. Ltd, Dock Offices, Cleveland Road, Hartlepool, Cleveland, TS24 0UZ Tel: (01429) 273157 Fax: (01429) 270693

Solar Marine Services, 4 Barratt Industrial Park, Gillender Street, London, E3 3JX Tel: (020) 7987 2244 Fax: (020) 7987 0242

Special Carrier, Express House, Kedlestone Road, Whitfield, Dover, Kent, CT16 3NX Tel: (01304) 820999 Fax: (01304) 820990 E-mail: info@specialcarrier.co.uk

Spedition Services, 32 Anyards Road, Cobham, Surrey, KT11 2LA Tel: (01932) 584458 Fax: (01932) 584459 E-mail: info@spedition.co.uk

Spicer Global Systems Ltd, Elmdon House, Airport Cargo, Birmingham International Airport, Birmingham, B26 3QN Tel: 0121-782 2882 Fax: 0121-782 2103 E-mail: spicerg@spicer-global.co.uk

Staley Radford & Co. Ltd, Blackburn House, 22-26 Eastern Road, Romford, RM1 3PJ Tel: (01708) 737333 Fax: (01708) 737334

Standard Freight Forwarders Ltd, 73 Maltings Place, London, SW6 2BY Tel: (020) 7384 1212 Fax: (020) 7384 1030 E-mail: exports@standardfreight.com

Stephen Morris, Unit 4 Brent Trading Centre, 390 North Circular Road, London, NW10 0JF Tel: (020) 8830 1919 Fax: (020) 8830 1999 E-mail: enquiries@shipsms.co.uk

Strowmar Ltd, Scottish Mutual House, North Street, Hornchurch, Essex, RM11 1RS Tel: (01708) 446253 Fax: (020) 8534 0652 E-mail: martine@strowmar.co.uk

Surfair Freight Services Ltd, Wilson Road, Wigston, Leicestershire, LE18 4TQ Tel: 0116-278 6206 Fax: 0116-277 7784 E-mail: transport@surfair.co.uk

Sussex Port Forwarding Ltd, Shoreham Port, Harbour Office, 84-86 Albion Street, Southwick, Brighton, BN42 4ED Tel: (01273) 598100 Fax: (01273) 592492 E-mail: info@shoreham-port.co.uk

Sutch & Searle Shipping Ltd, Highwood Road, Writtle, Chelmsford, CM1 3PT Tel: (01245) 421770 Fax: (01245) 422734 E-mail: keith.davis@sutchanddsearle.com

Swift Forwarders (Midlands) Ltd, Unit 7 Greets Green Industrial Estate, Greets Green Road, West Bromwich, West Midlands, B70 9EW Tel: 0121-522 4499 Fax: 0121-522 4490 E-mail: info@swiftforwarders.freeserve.co.uk

T Rogers, 1a Broughton Street, London, SW8 3QJ Tel: (020) 7720 2789 Fax: (020) 7627 3318 E-mail: trogersco@aol.com

T S International Freight Forwarders Ltd, Halesfield 19, Telford, Shropshire, TF7 4QT Tel: (01952) 586467 Fax: (01952) 680048 E-mail: info@tsinternational.com

T Ward Shipping Ltd, 3 Johns Place, Leith, Edinburgh, EH6 7EL Tel: 0131-554 1231 Fax: 0131-553 3631 E-mail: shipping@tward.co.uk

Teamsped Ltd, Unit 4 Waterfall La Trading Estate, Cradley Heath, West Midlands, B64 6PU Tel: 0121-561 3886 Fax: 0121-561 3959 E-mail: john@teamsped.co.uk

Thompson Shipping Ltd, 66 Totternhoe Road, Eaton Bray, Dunstable, Bedfordshire, LU6 2BD Tel: (01525) 223071 Fax: (01525) 851482 E-mail: jim@fahawkins.com

TNT Freight Management, Unit 5 & 6 Park Way Trading Estate, Cranford Lane, Hounslow, TW5 9QA Tel: (020) 8814 7000 Fax: (020) 8814 7078 E-mail: info@uk.tntfreight.com

▶ indicates data change since last edition

FREIGHT FORWARDERS/ FORWARDING AGENTS – *continued*

Trans European Trailer Services Holbeach, 2a Avenue Road, Grantham, Lincolnshire, NG31 6TA Tel: (01476) 570077 Fax: (01476) 577799
Trans World Shipping, Thurrock Park Way, Tilbury, Essex, RM18 7HW Tel: (01375) 488222 Fax: (01375) 488233 E-mail: tws@bernardgroup.plc.co.uk
Transglobal Air, 11 Skyways Business Park, Exeter Airport, Silverton, Exeter, EX5 4HX Tel: (01392) 362122 Fax: (01392) 362092 E-mail: exeter@transglobalgroup.com
Transport Distribution Ltd, Dock Gate 2, Felixstowe, Suffolk, IP11 3SW Tel: (01394) 675601 Fax: (01394) 674278
TricoInternational (Shipping) Ltd, Unit 4, Building C Woodgreen Business Centre, Clarendon Road, London, N22 6TP Tel: (020) 8888 8787 Fax: (020) 8889 5445 E-mail: trico@tricoshipping.com
Tricon Freight Services, Shuttleworth Close, Great Yarmouth, Norfolk, NR31 0NQ Tel: (01493) 659311 Fax: (01493) 653657 E-mail: triconfrt@aol.com
Tryus Transport Ltd, 1 Delph Industrial Estate, Delph Road, Brierley Hill, West Midlands, DY5 2UA Tel: (01384) 265237 Fax: (01384) 262474
Tuplin Stansted Ltd, Unit 4 Birchanger Industrial Estate, Stansted Road, Bishop's Stortford, Hertfordshire, CM23 2TH Tel: (01279) 656461 Fax: (01279) 652520
U T I Ltd, Skyway 14, Calder Way, Colnbrook, Slough, SL3 0BQ Tel: (01753) 681212 Fax: (01753) 764450
Uniex Freight Services, Lodge Way, Thetford, Norfolk, IP24 1HE Tel: (01842) 751751 Fax: (01842) 751665 E-mail: freight@uniex.co.uk
Union Transport Group plc, Imperial House, 21-25 North Street, Bromley, BR1 1SJ Tel: (020) 8290 1234 Fax: (020) 8402 7770 E-mail: utg.plc@uniontransport.co.uk
Unitrans International Ltd, Woodfield House, Hatmill Lane, Brenchley, Tonbridge, Kent, TN12 7AE Tel: (01892) 723270 Fax: (01892) 724188 E-mail: robert-fogg@unitrans.fsnet.co.uk
Universal Express Ltd, 139-141 Hamilton Road, Felixstowe, Suffolk, IP11 7BL Tel: (01394) 282867 Fax: (01394) 286767 E-mail: info@universalexpress.co.uk
Universal Forwarding, Freight Village, Newcastle Int Airport, Woolsington, Newcastle upon Tyne, NE13 8BH Tel: 0191-214 0800 Fax: 0191-214 0811 E-mail: info@universal-forwarding.co.uk
Vanstead, Unit 6 Manor Farm Road, Birmingham, B11 2HT Tel: 0121-707 4929 Fax: 0121-707 2155 E-mail: office@vanstead.com
Viking Shipping Services Ltd, Ousegate, Selby, North Yorkshire, YO8 8BL Tel: (01757) 702688 Fax: (01757) 701601 E-mail: sales@vikingshipping.co.uk
W E Deane Ltd, Mayesbrook House, River Road, Barking, Essex, IG11 0EU Tel: (020) 8532 6400 Fax: (020) 8532 6497 E-mail: info@deanefreight.com
W H B Logistics Ltd, Old Wolverton Road, Milton Keynes, MK12 5NL Tel: (01908) 222121 Fax: (01908) 222929 E-mail: sp@whb-international.com
Wainwright Bros & Co. Ltd, Lambourn House, 7 Western Road, Romford, RM1 3LD Tel: (01708) 756622 Fax: (01708) 756633 E-mail: freight@wainwrightgroup.com
Walker Freight Services Ltd, 8-9 Blackthorne Cresent, Colnbrook, Slough, SL3 0QR Tel: (01753) 683288 Fax: (01753) 681917 E-mail: sales@walker-freight.com
Herbert Watson Freight Services Ltd, Mirwell House, Carrington Lane, Sale, Cheshire, M33 5NL Tel: 0161-905 0410 Fax: 0161-905 0420 E-mail: phil@herbertwatson.co.uk
Gerry Webb Transport Services Ltd, 4 Shelson Parade, Ashford Road, Feltham, Middlesex, TW13 4QZ Tel: (020) 8867 0000 Fax: (020) 8867 0088 E-mail: gerrywebbtpt@talk21.com
Wells & Root Ltd, Parker Drive, Leicester, LE4 0JP Tel: 0116-235 3535 Fax: 0116-235 3910 E-mail: enquiries@wellsandroot.co.uk
Wentmore Shipping & Haulage Ltd, The Lodge Barrington Hall, Dunmow Road, Hatfield Broad Oak, Bishop's Stortford, Hertfordshire, CM22 7JL Tel: (01279) 718711 Fax: (01279) 718510 E-mail: wentmore@globalnet.co.uk
Wessex Compressor Services, B1 46 Holton Road, Holton Heath Trading Park, Poole, Dorset, BH16 6LT Tel: (01202) 624877 Fax: (01202) 625827 E-mail: office@wessexcompressors.co.uk
Westfield Truro Cornwall Ltd, Kerley Paddock, Chacewater, Truro, Cornwall, TR4 8JY Tel: (01872) 560860 Fax: (01872) 561056 E-mail: info@westfieldtransport.com
C. Oliver Whitby & Sons Ltd, Hospital Fields, Fulford Road, York, YO10 4FS Tel: (01904) 655106 Fax: (01904) 627663 E-mail: wcoliver@aol.com
Woodland International Transport, Anglia Cargo Terminal, Priors Way, Coggeshall, Colchester, CO6 1TL Tel: (01376) 565100 Fax: (01376) 565101 E-mail: info@woodlanduk.com
World Transport Agency Ltd, 19-21 Schneider Close, Felixstowe, Suffolk, IP11 3BQ Tel: (01394) 673247 Fax: (01394) 673721 E-mail: arb@wta.co.uk
World Transport Agency Ltd, Thameside House Kingsway Business Park, Oldfield Road, Hampton, Middlesex, TW12 2HD Tel: (020) 8941 7373 Fax: (020) 8941 8138
Zim UK, Suite 249 2nd Floor, India Buildings Water Street, Liverpool, L2 0QD Tel: 0151-258 1118 Fax: 0151-258 1117 E-mail: sales@zim.uk.com

FREIGHT SERVICES, *See also Road Transport and Haulage Services etc*

Brian Harris Ltd, Pottery Road, Bovey Tracey, Newton Abbot, Devon, TQ13 9DS Tel: (01626) 833371 Fax: (01626) 834680
▶ Dalepak, Caswell Road, Brackmills Industrial Estate, Northampton, NN4 7PW Tel: (01604) 676246 Fax: (01604) 767606 E-mail: sales@dalepak.ltd.uk
Eurgent Ecspress, Unit 1b, Charnwood Park, Bridgend, Mid Glamorgan, CF31 3PL Tel: (01656) 645555 Fax: (01656) 656534 E-mail: enq@eurgent.co.uk
▶ Europa Worldwide, Unit 2 Building 110, Castle Donington, Derby, DE74 2SA Tel: (01332) 815900 Fax: (01332) 815909 E-mail: sales@europa-worldwide.co.uk
▶ Jaguar Freight Services Ltd, The Linen House, 253 Kilburn Lane, London, W10 4BQ Tel: (020) 8964 2621 Fax: (020) 8964 1055 E-mail: sales@jaguarfreight.com
▶ James Cargo Services Ltd, 9 Galleymead Road, Colnbrook, Slough, SL3 0EN Tel: (01753) 687722 Fax: (01753) 687723

FREIGHT SERVICES, AIR, EXPRESS

▶ Audit Logistics UK, Apex House, 72 Peghouse Rise, Uplands, Stroud, Gloucestershire, GL5 1UR Tel: (01453) 750740 Fax: (01453) 750786 E-mail: contact@auditlogistics.co.uk
▶ Euroship Logistics Ltd, PO Box 515, Grimsby, South Humberside, DN37 9QD Tel: (01472) 353333 Fax: (01472) 595695 E-mail: dchristie@euroshiplogistics.co.uk
▶ G S G Cargo Ltd, Unit 14 Northbrook Business Park, Northbrook Road, Worthing, West Sussex, BN14 8PQ Tel: (01903) 204666 Fax: (01903) 212966 E-mail: sales@gsgcargo.com
▶ Same-day Dispatch Services, International House, 226 Seven Sisters Road, London, N4 3GG Tel: 0845 226 2994 E-mail: admin@samedaydispatch.uk.com
▶ Sea Wing Cargo, Unit, 1 Beta Way, Thorpe Industrial Park, Egham, Surrey, TW20 8RE Tel: (01784) 435111 Fax: (01784) 439444
Smith's Solutions, 27 Kiln Lane, Hope, Wrexham, Clwyd, LL12 9PH Tel: (01978) 769090 Fax: 01978 769173 E-mail: sales@smiths-solutions.co.uk
▶ Viamaster International Ltd, Valley Farm Way, Leeds, LS10 1SE Tel: 0113-270 0033 Fax: 0113 270 0065 E-mail: mail@viamaster-intl.com

FRENCH CHALK

Water Of Ayr, Dalmore, Stair, Mauchline, Ayrshire, KA5 5PA Tel: (01292) 591204

FRENCH DOORS

Glorywood Ltd, 401 Footscray Road, New Eltham, London, SE9 2DP Tel: (020) 8317 0429 Fax: (020) 8331 6509 E-mail: info@glorywood.com

FRENCH POLISH

Fiddes & Son Ltd, Florence Works, Brindley Road, Cardiff, CF11 8TX Tel: (029) 2034 0323 Fax: (029) 2034 3235 E-mail: finishes@fiddes.co.uk
Foxell & James, 57 Farringdon Road, London, EC1M 3JB Tel: (020) 7405 0152 Fax: (020) 7405 3631 E-mail: sales@foxellandjames.co.uk
Myland's Paints & Woodfinishes, 80 Norwood High Street, London, SE27 9NW Tel: (020) 8761 5197 Fax: (020) 8761 5700 E-mail: sales@mylands.co.uk
Smith & Rodger Ltd, 34 Elliott Street, Glasgow, G3 8EA Tel: 0141-248 6341 Fax: 0141-248 6475 E-mail: info@smithandrodger.co.uk
W S Jenkins & Co. Ltd, Tariff Road, London, N17 0EN Tel: (020) 8808 2336 Fax: (020) 8365 1534 E-mail: sales@wsjenkins.co.uk

FRENCH POLISHING

A.H. French Polishers, 4 Hunters Grove, Orpington, Kent, BR6 7TW Tel: (01689) 859853 Fax: (01689) 859853
Beckwith & Son, St. Nicholas Hall, 43 St. Andrew Street, Hertford, SG14 1HZ Tel: (01992) 582079 Fax: (01992) 581009 E-mail: sales@beckwithandsonantiques.co.uk
Brockinwood French Polishing, Unit 16 Admington Lane, Admington, Shipston-on-Stour, Warwickshire, CV36 4JJ Tel: (01789) 450914
▶ Carey B Restoration, Units 2-3, 63A Westcote Road, London, SW16 6BN Tel: (020) 8696 7555 E-mail: info@antiquerestoration.co.uk
F Bennett & Son Ltd, 9 Chester Square Mews, London, SW1W 9DS Tel: (020) 7730 6546 Fax: (020) 7823 4864 E-mail: info@fbennettandson.co.uk
M. Fine & Co., 4 Hoghill Road, Collier Row, Romford, RM5 2DH Tel: (01708) 741489 Fax: (01708) 741489
▶ Furniture Diamond, 198 Newlands Road, Glasgow, G44 4EY Tel: 0141-633 0414 Fax: 0141-633 0414 E-mail: furniturediamond@hotmail.co.uk
Glew & Whittaker, Eagle House, Cleveland Street, Hull, HU8 7AU Tel: (01482) 224202 Fax: (01482) 219644
I & P Clark, Granville Street, Willenhall, West Midlands, WV13 1DN Tel: (01902) 636957
Peter S Toms & Co., Charlton Mead Lane, Hoddesdon, Hertfordshire, EN11 0DJ Tel: (01992) 464436 Fax: (01992) 448433
Price Bros (Ascot) Ltd, Unit 1 Peter James Business Centre, Pump Lane, Hayes, Middlesex, UB3 3NT Tel: (020) 8569 2251 Fax: (020) 8569 2458 E-mail: info@pricebrothersascot.co.uk
▶ SJM French Polishers Ltd, 30 Marion CR, Orpington, Kent, BR5 2DD Tel: (01689) 897210 Fax: (01689) 890119 E-mail: sales@sjmltd.co.uk
▶ Theocus, Mitton Manor Garage, Bredon Road, Tewkesbury, Gloucestershire, GL20 5DA Tel: (01684) 298400 Fax: (01684) 298400 E-mail: Theocus@hotmail.co.uk

FRENCH PROPERTY ESTATE AGENTS

▶ Allegiance Finance, 12 Royal Cresent, Cheltenham, Gloucestershire, GL50 3DA Tel: (01242) 260557 Fax: (01242) 269874 E-mail: enquiries@allegiance-developments.co.uk
▶ Angel Property Services, Silton Road, Bourton, Gillingham, Dorset, SP8 5DD Tel: (08712) 715128 E-mail: rennie@angelpropertyservices.net
▶ First Contact, Romford Road, London, E12 5JG Tel: (020) 8911 8787 Fax: (020) 8553 4440 E-mail: Faisal@FirstContactUk.net
▶ Leapfrog Properties, Sutton Court Road, Chiswick, London, W4 4NN Tel: (0845) 6066919 Fax: (020) 8742 1170 E-mail: info@leapfrog-properties.com
▶ Propertystorm, The Coach House, Edstone, Wootton Wawen, Henley-in-Arden, West Midlands, B95 6DD Tel: (07971) 095664 E-mail: propertystorm@btinternet.com
▶ Rosefame Properties, West Cottage, Church Street, Ticehurst, Wadhurst, East Sussex, TN5 7DL Tel: (01580) 201319 Fax: (01580) 201604 E-mail: info@rosefame.co.uk

FRENCH SPECIALIST FOOD

Teesdale Trenchman, The Lendings, Barnard Castle, County Durham, DL12 9AB Tel: (01833) 638370 Fax: (01833) 631439 E-mail: orders@trenchermen.co.uk

FREQUENCY CONVERTER HIRE

Powerplant Stamford Ltd, Wackerley Works, Bourne Road, Essendine, Stamford, Lincolnshire, PE9 4LT Tel: (01780) 766017 Fax: (01780) 750910 E-mail: sales@powerplantstamford.co.uk

FREQUENCY CONVERTERS, ROTARY/DYNAMIC/MOTOR GENERATOR

BEVI Group UK, 62 Alleyn Park, London, SE21 8SF Tel: (020) 8670 0806 Fax: (0870) 4601131 E-mail: sales@bevi.co.uk
Powerco (International) Ltd, 1 Strawberry Vale, Twickenham, TW1 4RY Tel: (0208) 831 6634 Fax: (0208) 891 6435 E-mail: radin.powerco@virgin.net

FREQUENCY INVERTERS

Danfoss Bauer, Unit 1, Natlane Business Park, Winsford, Cheshire, CW7 3BS Tel: (01606) 868600 Fax: (01606) 868603 E-mail: sales@danfoss.com
▶ Inntact Electronic Systems Ltd, Inntact House, Rawson Green, Kilburn, Belper, Derbyshire, DE56 0LL Tel: (01332) 781199 Fax: (01332) 781188 E-mail: inntact@aol.com

FRESH HERBS

▶ Freshwashed Herbs Ltd, Chestnuts Farm, Langton Green, Eye, Suffolk, IP23 7HL Tel: (01379) 871410 Fax: (01379) 873322 E-mail: info@freshwashedherbs.co.uk
▶ R & G, Lucas Green Nurseries, Lucas Green Road, West End, Woking, Surrey, GU24 9LY Tel: (01483) 474041 Fax: (01483) 476371 E-mail: enquiries@freshherbsolutions.com

FRESH VEGETABLES

▶ Riverford Home Delivery, 20 Deepdene Road, London, SE5 8EG Tel: (020) 7738 5076 Fax: (020) 7738 5076

FRESH WATER CONTRACTORS

Farm Services Ltd, Chesterton Estate Yard, Banbury Road, Lighthorne, Warwick, CV35 0AF Tel: (01926) 651540 Fax: (01926) 651540 E-mail: info@sportsdrainage.co.uk
Godlingston Manor Springs Ltd, Godlingston Manor, Washpond Lane, Swanage, Dorset, BH19 3DJ Tel: (01929) 422910 Fax: (01929) 427974
▶ Hydrosave Water Engineers, Swallow Court, Kettering Parkway, Kettering, Northamptonshire, NN15 6XX Tel: (01536) 515110 Fax: (01536) 515119 E-mail: sales@hydrosave.co.uk

FRICTION BRAKES

Federal Mogul Friction Products Ltd, Hayfield Road, Chapel-en-le-Frith, High Peak, Derbyshire, SK23 0JP Tel: (01298) 811300 Fax: (01298) 811319 E-mail: info@ferodo.co.uk
J Motor Components Ltd, 1-5 Crimea Road Winton, Bournemouth, BH9 1AR Tel: (01202) 711177 Fax: (01202) 535777
Matrix Engineered Systems Ltd, Eastmill Road, Brechin, Angus, DD9 7EP Tel: (01356) 602000 Fax: (01356) 602060 E-mail: sales@matrix-international.com
W R P Construction, Southway House, Southway Drive, Bristol, BS30 5LW Tel: 0117-961 9111 Fax: 0117-961 9222 E-mail: sales@frictionservices.co.uk
Wichita Co. Ltd, Ampthill Road, Bedford, MK42 9RD Tel: (01234) 350311 Fax: (01234) 350317 E-mail: clutch@wichita.co.uk

FRICTION CLUTCHES

Eaton Clutch Transmission, Norfolk Street, Worsley Estate North, Worsley, Manchester, M28 3GJ Tel: (01204) 797077 Fax: (01204) 797090
Luk UK Ltd, Waleswood Road, Wales Bar, Sheffield, S26 5PN Tel: (01909) 510500 Fax: (01909) 515151 E-mail: info@luk.co.uk
Matrix Engineered Systems Ltd, Eastmill Road, Brechin, Angus, DD9 7EP Tel: (01356) 602000 Fax: (01356) 602060 E-mail: sales@matrix-international.com
Raybestos G B F Ltd, Unit 1 Preserve Works, Jubilee Way, Thackley Old Rd, Shipley, W. Yorkshire, BD18 1QB Tel: (01274) 597332 Fax: (01274) 597357 E-mail: info@raybestosgbf.freeserve.co.uk
Van Der Graaf UK Ltd, 23 The Metro Centre, Peterborough, PE2 7UH Tel: (01733) 391777 Fax: (01733) 391044 E-mail: paul@vandergraaf.co.uk

FRICTION MATERIALS MANUFRS

Bonding & Reline Services Co. Ltd, Unit 4, Carls Way, Thurmaston, Leicester, LE4 8DL Tel: 0116-260 1717 Fax: 0116-260 1958
Double Glazing Supplies Group plc, Sycamore Road, Castle Donington, Derby, DE74 2NW Tel: (01332) 811611 Fax: (01332) 812650 E-mail: reception@dgsgroup.co.uk
European Friction Industries, 6-7 Bonville Road, Bristol, BS4 5NZ Tel: 0117-977 7859 Fax: 0117-971 0573 E-mail: sales@efi.compulink.co.uk
Federal Mogul Friction Products Ltd, Hayfield Road, Chapel-en-le-Frith, High Peak, Derbyshire, SK23 0JP Tel: (01298) 811300 Fax: (01298) 811319 E-mail: info@ferodo.co.uk
H Kimber Friction Ltd, Printing Trades House, Bond Street, Southampton, SO14 5QA Tel: (023) 8022 6577 Fax: (023) 8063 1154 E-mail: pscott.hkimber@auto-net.co.uk
Jim Jack, 16-18 Tannoch Place, Cumbernauld, Glasgow, G67 2XU Tel: (01236) 738484 Fax: (01236) 725597 E-mail: ind_friction@cqm.co.uk
Newton Friction Ltd, Unit A, 20 Mearns Street, Aberdeen, AB11 5AT Tel: (01224) 589336 Fax: (01224) 583389 E-mail: info@newtonfriction.co.uk
Roadlink International Ltd, Strawberry Lane, Willenhall, West Midlands, WV13 3RL Tel: (01902) 606210 Fax: (01902) 606604 E-mail: j.darwin@roadlink-international.co.uk
Saftek Brakes, 1 Rawfolds Industrial Estate, Bradford Road, Rawfolds, Cleckheaton, West Yorkshire, BD19 5LT Tel: (01274) 862666 Fax: (01274) 862444
Savilles Motor Factors Ltd, 15 Elders Street, Scarborough, North Yorkshire, YO11 1DZ Tel: (01723) 375010 Fax: (01723) 353798
Trimat Ltd, Narrowboat Way, Hurst Business Pk, Brierley Hill, W. Midlands, DY5 1UF Tel: (01384) 473400 Fax: (01384) 261010 E-mail: sales@trimat.co.uk

FRICTION WELDING

Blair Engineering Ltd, Balmoral Road, Rattray, Blairgowrie, Perthshire, PH10 7AH Tel: (01250) 872244 Fax: (01250) 872244 E-mail: sales@blairengineering.co.uk
Phillips Welding, Sedgedale Cottage, Killingworth Village, Newcastle upon Tyne, NE12 6BL Tel: 0191-268 6741 Fax: 0191-268 6741
Thompson Friction Welding Ltd, Hereward Rise, Halesowen, West Midlands, B62 8AN Tel: 0121-585 0888 Fax: 0121-585 0810 E-mail: sales@thompson-friction-welding.co.uk

FRICTION WELDING EQUIPMENT

Friction Welding Products, Castle Mill Works, Birmingham New Road, Dudley, West Midlands, DY1 4DA Tel: (01384) 236961 Fax: (01384) 236982 E-mail: adv102@gbfederal.co.uk
Thompson Friction Welding Ltd, Hereward Rise, Halesowen, West Midlands, B62 8AN Tel: 0121-585 0888 Fax: 0121-585 0810 E-mail: sales@thompson-friction-welding.co.uk

FRINGES

A Attenborough & Co Ltd, Nuart Road, Beeston, Nottingham, NG9 2NH Tel: 0115-925 8185 Fax: 0115-922 7445 E-mail: a.attenborough@btinternet.com

FROZEN DESSERTS

▶ Classic Desserts, Unit 10, Blencathra Business Centre, Threlkeld, Keswick, Cumbria, CA12 4TR Tel: (01768) 779043

FROZEN ETHNIC FOOD

▶ Scheelite Ltd, 2-3 Cursitor Street, London, EC4A 1NE Tel: (020) 7748 4408 E-mail: mail@scheelite.co.uk

FROZEN FOODS

A D M UK Ltd, Pondswood Industrial Estate, Drury Lane, St. Leonards-on-Sea, East Sussex, TN38 9XL Tel: (01424) 456900 Fax: (01424) 426483
A T Hunter, Blacksness, Scalloway, Shetland, ZE1 0TQ Tel: (01595) 880388 Fax: (01595) 880733 E-mail: hgibbie@aol.com
Alexander Buchan Ltd, East Quay, Peterhead, Aberdeenshire, AB42 1JF Tel: 0131-554 9400 Fax: (01779) 471910
Andy Race Ltd, The Harbour, Mallaig, Inverness-Shire, PH41 4PX Tel: (01687) 462626 Fax: (01687) 462060 E-mail: sales@andyrace.co.uk
Apetito Ltd, Canal Road, Trowbridge, Wiltshire, BA14 8RJ Tel: (01225) 753636 Fax: (01225) 777084 E-mail: sales@apetito.co.uk
Aqua Blue Seafoods Ltd, Brookfield, Brook Lane, Westbury, Wiltshire, BA13 4EN Tel: (01373) 824242 Fax: (01373) 825566 E-mail: sales@aquablue.co.uk
Bernard Matthews plc, Upper Holton, Halesworth, Suffolk, IP19 8NJ Tel: (01986) 872262 Fax: (01986) 872188
Brakes Ltd, Enterprise House Nicholas Road, Eureka Science Park, Ashford, Kent, TN25 4AG Tel: (01233) 206206 Fax: (01223) 206035E-mail: customer.service@brake.co.uk
Calbourne Classics, Three Gates Farm, Yarmouth Road, Shalfleet, Newport, Isle of Wight, PO30 4NA Tel: (01983) 531204 Fax: (01983) 555065 E-mail: sales@calbourneclassics.co.uk
Caley Fisheries Ltd, Castle Street, Peterhead, Aberdeenshire, AB42 1EN Tel: (01779) 479121 Fax: (01779) 474813
Cherry Valley Farms Ltd, Rothwell, Market Rasen, Lincolnshire, LN7 6BJ Tel: (01472) 371271 Fax: (01472) 362422 E-mail: admin@cherryvalley.co.uk
Christian Salvesen plc, Easton, Grantham, Lincolnshire, NG33 5AU Tel: (01476) 515000 Fax: (01476) 515011
Andrew Christie Junior Ltd, 3 Riverside Business Centre, North Esplanade West, Aberdeen, AB11 5RJ Tel: (01224) 590327 Fax: (01224) 580763 E-mail: office@achristiejnr.com
Coffee Bay, 67A Holly Rd, Twickenham, TW1 4HF Tel: 020 87442363 Fax: 020 88928110
Coldwater Seafood UK Ltd, Estate Road 2, South Humberside Industrial Estate, Grimsby, South Humberside, DN31 2TG Tel: (01472) 321100 Fax: (01472) 321220 E-mail: reception@coldwater-seafood.co.uk
Cooperative Retail Logistics Ltd, Unit 24, Raleigh Hall Industrial Estate, Eccleshall, Stafford, ST21 6JL Tel: (01785) 850831 Fax: (01785) 851850
Croan Seafoods Ltd, Units 5-10 Albert Street, Peterhead, Aberdeenshire, AB42 1ZW Tel: (01779) 471621 Fax: (01779) 472916
D B C Food Services Ltd, Industrial Road, Hertburn Estate, Washington, Tyne & Wear, NE37 2SD Tel: 0191-416 2571 Fax: 0191-415 5739
D M Welsh, West Quay, Gourdon, Montrose, Angus, DD10 0PQ Tel: (01561) 361454 Fax: (01561) 361441
Dalziel Ltd, Unit 11 Hunslet Trading Estate, Low Road, Leeds, LS10 1QR Tel: 0113-277 7662 Fax: 0113-271 4954
Dalziel Packaging, Unit C3 Drumhead Road, Chorley North Business Park, Chorley, Lancashire, PR6 7DE Tel: (01257) 226010 Fax: (01257) 226019 E-mail: chorley@dalziel.co.uk
Daniel's Sweet Herring, Achnagonlin Industrial Estate, Grantown-on-Spey, Morayshire, PH26 3TA Tel: (01479) 870072 Fax: (01479) 870074
Dawn Foods Ltd, Worcester Road, Evesham, Worcestershire, WR11 4QU Tel: (01386) 760800 Fax: (01386) 443608 E-mail: uk@dawnfoods.com
Dawnfresh Projects Ltd, Bothwell Park Industrial Estate, Uddingston, Glasgow, G71 6LS Tel: (01698) 810008 Fax: (01698) 810088 E-mail: sales@dawnfresh.co.uk
Deal Bros, 5 East Street, Leigh-on-Sea, Essex, SS9 1QF Tel: (01702) 710983 Fax: (01702) 472620
Deans Foods Ltd, The Moor, Bilsthorpe, Newark, Nottinghamshire, NG22 8TS Tel: (01623) 870384 Fax: (01623) 870657
Devon Desserts Ltd, Minerva Way, Brunel Rd, Newton Abbot, Devon, TQ12 4PJ Tel: 01626 366166 Fax: 01626 361400
A Divers JNR, 6 Russell Road, Aberdeen, AB11 5RB Tel: (01224) 580830 Fax: (01224) 580830
E G Jenkinson, West Road, Filey, North Yorkshire, YO14 9HA Tel: (01723) 512039 Fax: (01723) 341665
Euro Norfolk Foods Ltd, 34 Surrey Street, Norwich, NR1 3NY Tel: (01603) 760123 Fax: (01603) 760124
Faithlie Ice Co. Ltd, Harbour Road, Fraserburgh, Aberdeenshire, AB43 9TB Tel: (01346) 515010 Fax: (01346) 517025
Fish-house Ltd, Dean Feld Way, Link 59 Business Park, Clitheroe, Lancashire, BB7 1QU Tel: (01200) 427527 Fax: (01200) 427027 E-mail: john@fish-house.co.uk
Flowfood Ltd, South Street, Ashton-under-Lyne, Lancashire, OL7 0PH Tel: 0161-330 0411 Fax: 0161-343 2193 E-mail: sales@flowfood.co.uk
Colin Fraser, Unit 2 Raik Road, Aberdeen, AB11 5QL Tel: (01224) 593132 Fax: (01224) 591772
Fraserburgh Ice Co. (1988) Ltd, Portacabin, Saltoun Jetty, Fraserburgh, Aberdeenshire, AB43 9RY Tel: (01346) 514048 Fax: (01346) 510511
Global Group plc, Park Lane, Wolverhampton, WV10 9QD Tel: (01902) 865714 Fax: (01902) 866316
Good Life Foods Ltd, 34 Tatton Court, Kingsland Grange, Woolston, Warrington, WA1 4FF Tel: (01925) 837810 Fax: (01925) 838648 E-mail: enquiry@goodlife.co.uk
Gorsis Indian Frozen Foods, Hamer Street, Radcliffe, Manchester, M26 2RS Tel: 0161-723 4536 Fax: 0161-723 1395
Gourmet Food Co. Ltd, Taylor Street, Bury, Lancashire, BL9 6DW Tel: 0161-797 8600 Fax: 0161-763 1116
H & H Fish, Poynernook Road, Aberdeen, AB11 5QX Tel: (01224) 212094 Fax: (01224) 212429
Harlequin Foods Ltd, Harlequin Avenue, Great West Road, Brentford, Middlesex, TW8 9EQ Tel: (020) 8560 3211 Fax: (020) 8326 1530
Hazelwood Foods Ltd, Mansfield Road, Wales Bar, Sheffield, S26 5PF Tel: (01909) 770861 Fax: (01909) 772797 E-mail: info@hwpm.com
Heinz Foodservice, South Building, Hayes Park, Hayes, Middlesex, UB4 8AL Tel: (0800) 575755 E-mail: foodservice.enquiry@uk.hjheinz.com
Heron Frozen Foods Ltd, Station Road, Worstead, North Walsham, Norfolk, NR28 9RY Tel: (01692) 403211 Fax: (01692) 405911
Holdsworths, 91-93 St. James Mill Road, St. James Business Park, Northampton, NN5 5JP Tel: (01604) 581411 Fax: (01604) 581864
Walter Holland & Sons, Blackburn Road, Accrington, Lancashire, BB5 2SA Tel: (01706) 213591 Fax: (01706) 228044 E-mail: enquiries@hollands-pies.co.uk
Homestead Foods Ltd, 108 High Street, Godalming, Surrey, GU7 1DW Tel: (01483) 860006 Fax: (01483) 429837 E-mail: enquiries@homestead-foods.co.uk
Hunts Frozen Foods Bristol Ltd, Unit 3 Pucklechurch Trading Estate, Pucklechurch, Bristol, BS16 9QH Tel: 0117-937 2341 Fax: 0117-937 4160 E-mail: sales@hunts-food-service.co.uk
Interlink Food, Shadsworth Bakery, Sett End Road, Shadsworth Business Park, Blackburn, BB1 2PT Tel: (01254) 55495 Fax: (01254) 663602 E-mail: sales@interlinkfoods.co.uk
William Jackson & Son Ltd, 40 Derringham Street, Hull, HU3 1EW Tel: (01482) 224939 Fax: (01482) 588237 E-mail: sales@wjs.co.uk
Jawads Frozen Foods, 51 Ayres Road, Manchester, M16 9NH Tel: 0161-227 1786 Fax: 0161-227 1786
Joe Smokes Ribs, 50 Monier Road, London, E3 2ND Tel: (020) 8533 3373 Fax: (020) 8533 3833
M. Johnston, Killard Sq, Ballyhornan, Downpatrick, Co. Down, BT30 7PW Tel: (028) 4484 1196 Fax: (028) 4484 2228
Kim's Food, 284-288 Western Road, London, SW19 2QA Tel: (020) 8640 4018 Fax: (020) 8640 4018 E-mail: kimsfood@yahoo.com
Kitchen Range Foods Ltd, Kingfisher Way, Hinchingbrooke Business Park, Huntingdon, Cambridgeshire, PE29 6FJ Tel: (01480) 445900 Fax: (01480) 453555 E-mail: krf@kitchenrangefoods.co.uk
L Doble Ltd, Newdowns, West Polberro, St. Agnes, Cornwall, TR5 0ST Tel: (01872) 552121 Fax: (01872) 553797 E-mail: sales@doble.foods.co.uk
L & M Food Group Ltd, Trelawney House, 454-456 Larkshall Road, Highams Park, London, E4 9HH Tel: (020) 8531 7631 Fax: (020) 8531 8607
Lochinver Fish Selling Co., Culag Square, Lochinver, Lairg, Sutherland, IV27 4LG Tel: (01571) 844228 Fax: (01571) 844344
Lossie Seafoods Ltd, 2 March Road Industrial Estate, Buckie, Banffshire, AB56 4BY Tel: (01542) 831000 Fax: (01542) 833300 E-mail: tracy@lossieseafoods.demon.co.uk
Lowrie Foods Ltd, 153 Brinkburn Street, Newcastle upon Tyne, NE6 2BU Tel: 0191-265 9161 Fax: 0191-224 0019 E-mail: sales@lowriefoods.co.uk
Lyons Seafoods Ltd, 3 Fairfield Road, Warminster, Wiltshire, BA12 9DA Tel: (01985) 217214 Fax: (01985) 847117 E-mail: info@lyons-seafoods.com
M K G Food Products Ltd, Westgate, Aldridge, Walsall, WS9 8DE Tel: (01922) 459311 Fax: (01922) 743077 E-mail: sales@mkgfoods.co.uk
Mccain Foods G B Ltd, Havers Hill, Eastfield, Scarborough, North Yorkshire, YO11 3BS Tel: (01723) 584141 Fax: (01723) 581230 E-mail: info@mccain.com
Mccain Foods GB Ltd, Heath Mill Road, Wombourne, Wolverhampton, WV5 8AE Tel: (01902) 894022 Fax: (01902) 897998
McLay Ltd, Glentanar Road, The Balmore Industrial Estate, Glasgow, G22 7XS Tel: 0141-336 6543 Fax: 0141-336 4857 E-mail: meat@mclay.co.uk
Marine Harvest Scotland Ltd, Ratho Park, 88 Glasgow Road, Newbridge, Midlothian, EH28 8PP Tel: (01397) 701550 Fax: 0131-336 1199
Bernard Matthews Foods Ltd, Great Witchingham Hall, Norwich, NR9 5QD Tel: (01603) 872611 Fax: (01603) 871118
Ministry of Cake Ltd, Frobisher Way, Bindon Road, Taunton, Somerset, TA2 6AB Tel: (01823) 257922 Fax: (01823) 333328 E-mail: commercials@ministryofcake.co.uk
Pataks Foods Ltd, Kiribati Way, Leigh, Lancashire, WN7 5RS Tel: (01942) 267000 Fax: (01942) 267070 E-mail: info.dept@pataksfoods.co.uk
Peterhead Ice Co., Model Jetty, Seagate, Peterhead, Aberdeenshire, AB42 1JP Tel: (01779) 478681 Fax: (01779) 470018
Pioneer Ltd, Birley Street, Blackburn, BB1 5DN Tel: (01254) 678642 Fax: (01254) 678645
Pioneer Food Service, PO Box 30, Carlisle, CA1 2RR Tel: (01228) 523474 Fax: (01228) 512906 E-mail: sales@pioneerfoodservice.co.uk
Prima Products, 72 Leicester Road, Manchester, M7 4AR Tel: 0161-708 9090 Fax: 0161-792 0098 E-mail: prima@leisurego.co.uk
Pyrol Frozen Foods Ltd, Warehouse Unit, Park Street, Nuneaton, Warwickshire, CV11 4NS Tel: (024) 7664 2255 Fax: (024) 7637 5755 E-mail: sales@pyrol.com
R Bedford & Sons Cooked Meats, Cunliffe Road, Blackburn, BB1 5SU Tel: (01254) 52553 Fax: (01254) 583701
Raja Frozen Foods, Doris Road, Bordesley Green, Birmingham, B9 4SJ Tel: 0121-771 0039 Fax: 0121-771 0030
Regent Seafoods Ltd, 388 (Rear Of) Yorktown Road, College Town, Sandhurst, Berkshire, GU47 0PU Tel: (01276) 32622 Fax: (01276) 35509
Roach Bros Ltd, Havelock Street, Hull, HU3 4JH Tel: (01482) 324838 Fax: (01482) 219050 E-mail: roachbrosltd@yhoo.co.uk
Roberts Of Port Dinorwic Ltd, Griffiths Crossing Industrial Estate, Griffiths Crossing, Caernarfon, Gwynedd, LL55 1TS Tel: (01286) 676111 Fax: (01286) 677669 E-mail: sales@innkeepers-selection.com
S T B Foods Ltd, Ettingshall Road, Wolverhampton, WV2 2RB Tel: (01902) 490514 Fax: (01902) 354172
▶ Scheelite Ltd, 2-3 Cursitor Street, London, EC4A 1NE Tel: (020) 7748 4408 E-mail: mail@scheelite.co.uk
Scofish Ltd, Broadfold Road, Bridge-Of-Don, Aberdeen, AB23 8EE Tel: (01224) 222089 Fax: (01224) 222098
Sea Fayre Cuisine, Unit 5 Marsh Lane, Hayle, Cornwall, TR27 4PS Tel: (01736) 755961 Fax: (01736) 755961
Seafish UK, 45-55 Wassand Street, Hull, HU3 4AN Tel: (01482) 223648 Fax: (01482) 216230 E-mail: keith@sheltie.co.uk
Seagull Foods Ltd, Little Forge Road, Redditch, Worcestershire, B98 7SF Tel: (01527) 525154 Fax: (01527) 838100
Shetland Seafish Ltd, 4a North Ness, Lerwick, Shetland, ZE1 0LZ Tel: (01595) 696949 Fax: (01595) 696929 E-mail: info@shetland-seafish.co.uk
F. Smales & Son Ltd, 30 West Dock Street, Hull, HU3 4HL Tel: (01482) 324997 Fax: (01482) 323765 E-mail: info@smales.co.uk
Solway Sea Foods, Bladnoch Bridge Industrial Estatae, Bladnoch, Wigtown, Newton Stewart, Wigtownshire, DG8 9AB Tel: (01988) 402661 Fax: (01988) 402662 E-mail: enquiries@solwayseafoods.co.uk
Sous Vide, 48-50 Edison Road, Rabans Lane Industrial Area, Aylesbury, Buckinghamshire, HP19 8TE Tel: (0845) 1212213 Fax: (01296) 431133 E-mail: lucy@sous-vide.co.uk
Spey Fish Ltd, 6 March Lane, Buckie, Banffshire, AB56 4BB Tel: (01542) 834524 Fax: (01542) 834970
Stateside Foods Ltd, 31-32 Great Bank Road, Wingate South, Bolton, BL5 3XU Tel: (01942) 841200 Fax: (01942) 841201 E-mail: sales@stateside-foods.co.uk
T D G Novacold, South View Road, Willand, Cullompton, Devon, EX15 2RU Tel: (01884) 820008 Fax: (01884) 821372
Taylor Catering Foods, Exeter Road, Ottery St. Mary, Devon, EX11 1LH Tel: (01404) 814312
3663, Langdon Road, Prince Of Wales Dock, Swansea, SA1 8QY Tel: (0870) 3663231 Fax: (0870) 3663239
Top Frost International Ltd, 35 Malden Way, New Malden, Surrey, KT3 6EB Tel: (020) 8942 9424 Fax: (020) 8336 1214 E-mail: info@topfrost.co.uk
Trawlpac Sea Foods Ltd, Craigshaw Place, West Tullos Industrial Estate, Aberdeen, AB12 3AH Tel: (01224) 871093 Fax: (01224) 872266 E-mail: trawlpac@aol.com
W.A. Turner Ltd, Broadwater Lane, Tunbridge Wells, Kent, TN2 5RD Tel: (01892) 515215 Fax: (01892) 510028 E-mail: sales@waturner.co.uk
Unilever UK Walls's Ltd, Station Avenue, Walton-On-Thames, Surrey, KT12 1NT Tel: (01932) 263000 Fax: (01932) 263152
▶ Violet Farm Foods Ltd, Units 10-11, Uddens Trading Estate, Wimborne, Dorset, BH21 7LQ Tel: (01202) 891006 Fax: (01202) 896281 E-mail: sales@vff.co.uk
▶ Wiltshire Farm Foods, Unit 3, 147 Stockton Street, Middlesbrough, Cleveland, TS2 1BU Tel: (01642) 643999 Fax: (01642) 648017
Wok Master Foods Ltd, 14 Birch Lane, Manchester, M13 0NN Tel: 0161-225 3072 Fax: 0161-248 0989
Woodwards Food Service, Craigshaw Drive, West Tullos Industrial Estate, Aberdeen, AB12 3AN Tel: (01224) 291744 Fax: (01224) 291765

FROZEN HALAL FOODS

Cater Direct Ltd, Unit 6 Pasadena Close, Hayes, Middlesex, UB3 3NQ Tel: (020) 8561 7706 Fax: (020) 8561 7748 E-mail: info@caterdirect.co.uk
▶ Scheelite Ltd, 2-3 Cursitor Street, London, EC4A 1NE Tel: (020) 7748 4408 E-mail: mail@scheelite.co.uk

FROZEN VEGETARIAN FOODS

Bran Tub Ltd, 20 Lavant Street, Petersfield, Hampshire, GU32 3EW Tel: (01730) 267043 Fax: (01730) 267043
Good Life Foods Ltd, 34 Tatton Court, Kingsland Grange, Woolston, Warrington, WA1 4FF Tel: (01925) 837810 Fax: (01925) 838648 E-mail: enquiry@goodlife.co.uk

FRUIT BOWLS

▶ Rod Page Woodturning, 11 Southmead Crescent, Crewkerne, Somerset, TA18 8DH Tel: (01460) 271426 Fax: E-mail: rod@rodpage-woodturner.co.uk

FRUIT CAGES

Knowle Nets Ltd, 20 East Road, Bridport, Dorset, DT6 4NX Tel: (01308) 424342 Fax: (01308) 458186 E-mail: sales@knowlenets.co.uk

FRUIT JUICE

▶ A1 Fruit, 12 Berrington Road, Leamington Spa, Warwickshire, CV31 1NB Tel: (01926) 312222
Aspall, The Cider House, Aspall Hall, Debenham, Stowmarket, Suffolk, IP14 6PD Tel: (01728) 860510 Fax: (01728) 861031 E-mail: barry@aspall.co.uk
Britannia Soft Drinks Ltd, Britvic House, Broomfield Road, Chelmsford, CM1 1TU Tel: (01245) 261871 Fax: (01245) 267147 E-mail: forename.surname@britvic.co.uk
Coca-Cola Enterprises Europe Ltd, Charter Place, Vine Street, Uxbridge, Middlesex, UB8 1EZ Tel: (01895) 231313
Dayla Liquid Packing Ltd, Netherton Road, Overross Industrial Estate, Ross-on-Wye, Herefordshire, HR9 7QQ Tel: (01989) 760400 Fax: (01989) 760414 E-mail: dayla@dayla.co.uk
Del Monte Europe Ltd, Del Monte House, London Road, Staines, Middlesex, TW18 4JD Tel: (01784) 447400 Fax: (01784) 465301
Exotic Planet Juices Ltd, 17 Westpark, Eaton Rise, London, W5 2HH Tel: (020) 8723 7000 Fax: (020) 8723 7000 E-mail: exoticplanet@breathemail.net

FRUIT JUICE – *continued*

Gerber Juice Company Ltd, 78 Wembdon Road, Bridgwater, Somerset, TA6 7QR Tel: (01278) 441600 Fax: (01278) 441777 E-mail: enquiries@gerberfoods.com

Pan European Foods Ltd, Units 9-10, Brailwood Close, Bilsthorpe, Newark, Nottinghamshire, NG22 8UG Tel: (01623) 411488 Fax: (01623) 411420

Pride Oil plc, Crown Road, Enfield, Middlesex, EN1 1DZ Tel: (020) 8345 8100 Fax: (020) 8804 9977 E-mail: info@pride-oils.co.uk

Princes Soft Drinks Division, Lord North Street, Manchester, M40 2HJ Tel: 0161-202 1044 Fax: 0161-205 7741

R D A Organic, 118 Putney Bridge Road, London, SW15 2NQ Tel: (020) 8875 9740 Fax: (020) 8875 0370 E-mail: info@rdaorganic.com

Wilson & Mansfield Ltd, Headley House, Headley Road, Grayshott, Surrey, GU26 6TU Tel: (01428) 601140 Fax: (01428) 607851 E-mail: david@wmjuice.co.uk

FRUIT MACHINES

B & M Automatics Ltd, The Dingle, 56a New Penkridge Road, Cannock, Staffordshire, WS11 1HW Tel: (01543) 468138

FRUIT PROCESSING

Ainsworth & Burgess Ltd, The Forstal, Lenham Heath, Maidstone, Kent, ME17 2JB Tel: (01622) 858343 Fax: (01622) 850664 E-mail: mail@ainsworthburgess.plus.com

FRUIT TREES

▶ www.saundersallotment.co.uk, 88 Dunkeld Road, Gosport, Hampshire, PO12 4NJ Tel: (023) 92 586619 E-mail: berylsau@saundersallotment.co.uk

FUEL CONVERSION BOILERS

Bib Cochran Ltd, Newbie Works, Annan, Dumfriesshire, DG12 5QU Tel: (01522) 510510 Fax: (01461) 205511 E-mail: enquiries@bibcochran.com

FUEL DISPENSERS

Centaur Fuel Management, 251 Manchester Road, Walkden, Manchester, M28 3HE Tel: (0870) 7576323 Fax: 0161-794 8031 E-mail: mc@centauronline.co.uk

Pumptronics Europe Ltd, Folgate Road, North Walsham, Norfolk, NR28 0AJ Tel: (01692) 500640 Fax: (01692) 406710 E-mail: sales@pumptronics.co.uk

Transflo Instruments Ltd, Station Road, Staplehurst, Tonbridge, Kent, TN12 0QD Tel: (01580) 895000 Fax: (01580) 895050

FUEL FILLER CAPS

▶ Stant Ltd, Skewfields, New Inn, Pontypool, Gwent, NP4 0XZ Tel: (01495) 757555 Fax: (01495) 757609

FUEL FLOW MONITORING SYSTEMS MANUFRS

C I Automation Ltd, Shaftesbury Centre, Percy Street, Swindon, SN2 2AZ Tel: (01793) 530063 Fax: (01793) 530064

M I S Fuel Monitoring Ltd, Horseley Works, Walsall Street, Wolverhampton, WV1 3LN Tel: (01902) 870037 Fax: (01902) 871661 E-mail: info@merridale.co.uk

Transflo Instruments Ltd, Station Road, Staplehurst, Tonbridge, Kent, TN12 0QD Tel: (01580) 895000 Fax: (01580) 895050

FUEL INJECTION ENGINEERING SERVICES

A P Diesel Ltd, 25 Victoria Street, Englefield Green, Egham, Surrey, TW20 0QY Tel: (01784) 433832 Fax: (01784) 430690 E-mail: apdiesel@mcmail.com

A.B. Butt Ltd, Frog Island, Leicester, LE3 5AZ Tel: 0116-251 3344 Fax: 0116-253 6377 E-mail: sales@abbutt.co.uk

C A E Diesel Ltd, 49a Chingford Mount Road, London, E4 8LU Tel: (020) 8527 8077

C C S Fuel Injection, Industrial Estate, Hallcroft Road, Retford, Nottinghamshire, DN22 7SS Tel: (01777) 711715 Fax: (01777) 711719

C J Diesel Injection, 6 Wood Lane, Isleworth, Middlesex, TW7 5ER Tel: (020) 8560 2297 Fax: (020) 8560 1282 E-mail: sales@cjdiesel.com

Commercial Injection Services, 2 Flowers Industrial Estate, Latimer Road, Luton, LU1 3XA Tel: (01582) 724072 Fax: (01582) 728043

Diesel Injector Services, 8 Staveley Way, Brixworth Industrial Estate, Brixworth, Northampton, NN6 9EU Tel: (01604) 880546 Fax: (01604) 880704 E-mail: info@dieselinjectors.co.uk

Eres Ltd, 264 Maybank Road, London, E18 1ES Tel: (020) 8504 1188 Fax: (020) 8504 1192

First Diesel Injection (Croydon) Ltd, 240 Thornton Road, Croydon, CR0 3EU Tel: (020) 8689 1806 Fax: (020) 8684 8060 E-mail: service@firstdieselinjection.co.uk

G W Dale Diesel Engineer Ltd, 139 Newcastle Street, Stoke-on-Trent, ST6 3QJ Tel: (01782) 837824 Fax: (01782) 839550

Gosling Of Kidderminster, Unit 208 Foley Industrial Estate, Kidderminster, Worcestershire, DY11 7DH Tel: (01562) 68427 Fax: (01562) 68427 E-mail: sales@goslings.co.uk

H W Richmond & Sons, Swanston Road, Great Yarmouth, Norfolk, NR30 3NQ Tel: (01493) 842066

J R D Engineers Ltd, 5 Willow Road, Poyle Trading Estate, Colnbrook, Slough, SL3 0BU Tel: (01753) 682665 Fax: (01753) 681475

Kmi Petrol Injection Engineers, Unit 2a Farm La Trading Estate, Farm Lane, London, SW6 1QJ Tel: (020) 7385 7138 Fax: (020) 7610 0884

M & B Diesel Glasgow Ltd, 31 Queensferry Street, Glasgow, G5 0XR Tel: 0141-429 2000 Fax: 0141-429 3130 E-mail: mbdiesel@btconnect.com

M & B Fuel Injection Service Ltd, Unit 22 Parham Drive, Eastleigh, Hampshire, SO50 4NU Tel: (023) 8061 9655 Fax: (023) 8062 9524

Motortune, 41 Carrhill Road, Mossley, Ashton-under-Lyne, Lancashire, OL5 0SE Tel: (01457) 832798 Fax: (01457) 831500

P & G Engineering Ltd, Unit 19 Bow Triangle Business Centre, Eleanor Street, London, E3 4NP Tel: (020) 8980 2387 Fax: (020) 8980 6680

Power Line, Power House, Station Road, Shipley, West Yorkshire, BD18 2JL Tel: (01274) 582721 Fax: (01274) 581495 E-mail: injection@power-line.co.uk

Powerdrive Diesel Fuel Injection Specialists, Unit 7, Dundas Spur, Portsmouth, PO3 5NX Tel: (023) 9265 0404 Fax: (023) 9265 5158

Precision Engine Services (Inverness), Units 1-4, 48 Seafield Road, Inverness, IV1 1SG Tel: (01463) 235537 Fax: (01463) 712684

Richards Brothers, Cardrew Industrial Estate, Redruth, Cornwall, TR15 1SS Tel: (01209) 212234 Fax: (01209) 219464

Roncol Services Ltd, Plas Celyn, Bangor Road, Penmaenmawr, Gwynedd, LL34 6LD Tel: (01492) 623787 Fax: (01492) 622086 E-mail: sales@roncol.co.uk

Stoneycroft Diesels Ltd, 9 Empress Road, Anfield, Liverpool, L6 0BX Tel: 0151-260 9066 Fax: 0151-260 9066

T A Flavell & Son Ltd, 11 Mandale Road, Thornaby, Stockton-on-Tees, Cleveland, TS17 6AW Tel: (01642) 674536 Fax: (01642) 618249 E-mail: dave@taflavell.co.uk

T P S Automotives, Hoobrook Trading Estate, Worcester Road, Kidderminster, Worcestershire, DY10 1HY Tel: (01562) 744492 Fax: (01562) 746442 E-mail: tps.auto@lineone.net

Transport & Plant Services, Hoobrook Trading Estate, Worcester Road, Kidderminster, Worcestershire, DY10 1HY Tel: (01562) 822446 Fax: (01562) 746442

▶ James Troop, 4 Davy Road, Astmoor Industrial Estate, Runcorn, Cheshire, WA7 1PZ Tel: (01928) 566170 Fax: (01928) 577314 E-mail: sales@jamestroop.co.uk

Tyne Electro Diesel Ltd, Units 5-7, Noble St Industrial Estate, Newcastle upon Tyne, NE4 7PD Tel: 0191-226 1286 Fax: 0191-226 1438 E-mail: sales@tyneelectrodiesel.co.uk

Watson Diesel Ltd, Elm Grove, London, SW19 4HE Tel: (020) 8879 3854 Fax: (0870) 4441386 E-mail: sales@watsondiesel.com

FUEL INJECTION EQUIPMENT

A P Diesel Ltd, 25 Victoria Street, Englefield Green, Egham, Surrey, TW20 0QY Tel: (01784) 433832 Fax: (01784) 430690 E-mail: apdiesel@mcmail.com

Burlen Fuel Systems Ltd, Spitfire Hous, Castle Road, Salisbury, SP1 3SA Tel: (01722) 412500 Fax: (01722) 334221 E-mail: info@burlen.co.uk

Carwood Motor Units Ltd, Herald Way, Binley Industrial Estate, Coventry, CV3 2RQ Tel: (024) 7644 9533 Fax: (024) 7645 2074 E-mail: carwood@carwood.co.uk

Central Diesel, Unit 15 Hawksley Industrial Estate, Hawksley Street, Oldham, OL8 4PQ Tel: 0161-620 7070 Fax: 0161-620 6007 E-mail: steve.kay@central-diesel.co.uk

Colchester Fuel Injection Ltd, Haven Road, Colchester, CO2 8HT Tel: (01206) 862049 Fax: (01206) 861771 E-mail: info@colchesterfuelinjection.co.uk

Delphi Diesel Systems, Courteney Road, Gillingham, Kent, ME8 0RU Tel: (01634) 224000 Fax: (01634) 374725 E-mail: paul.turner@dds.delphiauto.com

Euro Diesel, Vulcan Road South, Norwich, NR6 6AF Tel: (01603) 406525 Fax: (01603) 484046 E-mail: rayradford@btconnect.com

Helptoday Ltd, 8 Farrier Road, Lincoln Industrial Park, Lincoln, LN6 3RU Tel: (01522) 501001 Fax: (01522) 500099 E-mail: gary.cheshire@helptoday.co.uk

Ladenall Ltd, Diesel House 5 Humber Trading Estate, Humber Road, London, NW2 6DW Tel: (020) 8452 1552 Fax: (020) 8452 8471 E-mail: enquiries@ladenall.com

Macpower Ltd, 167 Cheviot Gardens, London, NW2 1PY Tel: (020) 8458 2793 Fax: (020) 8458 8484

Monark Diesel & Electrical Products UK Ltd, 19 Hanley Workshops, Hanley Swan, Worcester, WR8 0DX Tel: (01684) 311031 Fax: (01684) 311009 E-mail: sales@monarkdiesel.co.uk

SSAB Swedish Steel UK (Dobel), Unit 17 Narrowboat Way, Hurst Business Park, Brierley Hill, West Midlands, DY5 1UF Tel: (01384) 74660 Fax: (01384) 77575 E-mail: sales@dobel.co.uk

Unison Engine Components, 1 Bentley Wood Way, Network 65 Business Park, Hapton, Burnley, Lancashire, BB11 5TG Tel: (01282) 831199 Fax: (01282) 422989

Welham Diesel Injection Co. Ltd, Hawarden Avenue, Coleman Road, Leicester, LE5 4NL Tel: 0116-276 6831 Fax: 0116-246 0635

FUEL INJECTION EQUIPMENT COMPONENTS

▶ ADEPT Precision Ltd, Unit 7 Deacon Trading Estate, 203 Vale Road, Tonbridge, Kent, TN9 1SU Tel: 01732 773777 Fax: 01732 771115 E-mail: sales@adeptprecision.com

FUEL INJECTION EQUIPMENT MAINTENANCE AND REPAIR

A P Diesel Ltd, 25 Victoria Street, Englefield Green, Egham, Surrey, TW20 0QY Tel: (01784) 433832 Fax: (01784) 430690 E-mail: apdiesel@mcmail.com

Commercial Injection Services, 2 Flowers Industrial Estate, Latimer Road, Luton, LU1 3XA Tel: (01582) 724072 Fax: (01582) 728043

Richards Brothers, Cardrew Industrial Estate, Redruth, Cornwall, TR15 1SS Tel: (01209) 212234 Fax: (01209) 219464

Unison Engine Components, 1 Bentley Wood Way, Network 65 Business Park, Hapton, Burnley, Lancashire, BB11 5TG Tel: (01282) 831199 Fax: (01282) 422989

FUEL INJECTION PUMPS

Ladenall Ltd, Diesel House 5 Humber Trading Estate, Humber Road, London, NW2 6DW Tel: (020) 8452 1552 Fax: (020) 8452 8471 E-mail: enquiries@ladenall.com

FUEL INJECTION TEST EQUIPMENT

Commercial Injection Services, 2 Flowers Industrial Estate, Latimer Road, Luton, LU1 3XA Tel: (01582) 724072 Fax: (01582) 728043

Merlin Diesel Systems Ltd, Unit 3-4 Lincoln Place, Walton Summit Centre, Bamber Bridge, Preston, PR5 8NA Tel: (01772) 627676 Fax: (01772) 626220 E-mail: sales@merlindiesel.com

FUEL NOZZLES

Elaflex Ltd, Riverside House, Plumpton Road, Hoddesdon, Hertfordshire, EN11 0PA Tel: (01992) 452950 Fax: (01992) 452911 E-mail: info@elaflex.co.uk

FUEL OIL ADDITIVES

Highspeed Lubricants Ltd, 1 Newbridge Industrial Estate, Pitt Street, Keighley, West Yorkshire, BD21 4PQ Tel: (01535) 611103 Fax: (01535) 611546 E-mail: info@highspeed.co.uk

FUEL OIL FILTERS

B S C (Contracts) Ltd, Unit 4 Inoic Park, Birmingham New Road, Dudley, West Midlands, DY1 4SJ Tel: 0121-557 4651 Fax: 0121-557 7375 E-mail: sales@bsc-contracts.co.uk

Chainings Ltd, Pomona Works, Newent Business Park, Newent, Gloucestershire, GL18 1DZ Tel: (01531) 822244 Fax: (01531) 821555 E-mail: sales@chainings.com

Sogefi Filtration Ltd, Llantrisant Industrial Estate, Llantrisant, Pontyclun, Mid Glamorgan, CF72 8YU Tel: (01443) 223000 Fax: (01443) 225459 E-mail: stuart.hobbs@sogefifiltration.com

FUEL OIL HEATERS

A K Waugh Ltd, 49 Dalsetter Avenue, Glasgow, G15 8TE Tel: 0141-944 3303 Fax: 0141-944 4750 E-mail: sales@akwaugh.com

Eberspacher UK Ltd, Unit 10 Headlands Business Park, Salisbury Road, Blashford, Ringwood, Hampshire, BH24 3PB Tel: (01425) 480151 Fax: (01425) 480152 E-mail: enquiries@eberspacher.com

Metal Developments Ltd, The Workshop, Wheatcroft Farm, Cullompton, Devon, EX15 1RA Tel: (01884) 35806 Fax: (01884) 35505

TP Fay Ltd, 57 Admin Road, Knowsley Industrial Park, Liverpool, L33 7TX Tel: (0870) 3505058 Fax: (0870) 3505059 E-mail: sales@tpfay.co.uk

FUEL OIL TANKS

Adler & Allan Ltd, 22-42 Livingstone Road, London, E15 2LJ Tel: (020) 8555 7111 Fax: (020) 8519 3090 E-mail: sales@adlerandallan.co.uk

B I Engineering Ltd, Crane Close, Denington Industrial Estate, Wellingborough, Northamptonshire, NN8 2QG Tel: (01933) 228012 Fax: (01933) 441935 E-mail: biengineering@btconnect.com

Balmoral Tanks Ltd, Wellington Road, Aberdeen, AB12 3GY Tel: (01224) 859100 Fax: (01224) 859123 E-mail: tanks@balmoral.co.uk

Central Welding, 50 Creagh Road, Toomebridge, Antrim, BT41 3SE Tel: (028) 7965 0841 Fax: (028) 7965 9772 E-mail: info@centralwelding.co.uk

Southern Tank Services Ltd, Deptford Field Barn, Deptford Farm, Wylye, Warminster, Wiltshire, BA12 0QQ Tel: (01985) 248555

Taylor Fuel Control, Unit 4a New England Estate, Off Pindar Road, Hoddesdon, Hertfordshire, EN11 0BZ Tel: (01992) 451101 Fax: (01992) 444954

Trailer Engineering, Central Avenue, Cradley Heath, West Midlands, B64 7BY Tel: (01384) 564765 Fax: (01384) 410782 E-mail: info@trailerengineering.co.uk

FUEL OILS

A1 Service From Wynnstay Fuels, Saighton Lane, Waverton, Chester, CH3 7PD Tel: (01244) 332055 Fax: (01244) 355482 E-mail: wynnstayfuels@btconnect.com

Accent Fuels Ltd, Barracks Road, Sandy La Industrial Estate, Stourport-on-Severn, Worcestershire, DY13 9QB Tel: (01299) 822690 Fax: (01299) 877351

Adler & Allan Ltd, 22-42 Livingstone Road, London, E15 2LJ Tel: (020) 8555 7111 Fax: (020) 8519 3090 E-mail: sales@adlerandallan.co.uk

Andrew Gray & Co Fuels Ltd, Portland Depot, London Road, Kilmarnock, Ayrshire, KA3 7DD Tel: (01563) 525215 Fax: (01563) 541146 E-mail: andrew@graysfuels.freeserve.co.uk

Apollo Fuels Ltd, Templeborough Depot, Sheffield Road, Tinsley, Sheffield, S9 1RT Tel: 0114-243 6814 Fax: 0114-242 3362

Barton Petroleum Ltd, 6-7 Vaux Road, Finedon Road Industrial Estate, Wellingborough, Northamptonshire, NN8 4TG Tel: (01933) 224317 Fax: (01933) 441039 E-mail: enquiries@bartonpetroleum.co.uk

Bayford & Co. Ltd, Bowcliffe Hall, Bramham, Wetherby, West Yorkshire, LS23 6LP Tel: (01937) 541111 Fax: (01937) 841465 E-mail: sales@bayford.co.uk

Bayford Cambria, Tir Llwyd Enterprise Park, Kinmel Bay, Rhyl, Clwyd, LL18 5JH Tel: (01745) 332121 Fax: (01745) 332122 E-mail: sales@BAYFORDCAMBRIA.co.uk

Beesley Fuel Services Ltd, Whitehall Road, Greatbridge, Tipton, West Midlands, DY4 7JT Tel: 0121-557 4239 Fax: 0121-520 4536

Billericay Farm Services Ltd, School Road, Downham, Billericay, Essex, CM11 1QU Tel: (01268) 710237 Fax: (01268) 711040 E-mail: sales@bfs.uk.com

Browns Of Burwell Ltd, 7 North Street, Burwell, Whittlesford, Cambridge, CB4 3QW Tel: (01638) 741306 Fax: (01638) 743497 E-mail: sales@brownsofburwell.co.uk

C P L Petroleum Ltd, Prince Regent Way, Diss, Norfolk, IP22 4GW Tel: (01379) 652235 Fax: (01379) 643529 E-mail: diss@cplpetroleum.co.uk

C P L Petroleum, 22 Hawbank Road, East Kilbride, Glasgow, G74 5HA Tel: (01355) 249077 Fax: (01355) 264043 E-mail: eastkilbride@cplpetroleum.co.uk

Direct Fuel Services Ltd, Sandy Lane, Titton, Stourport-on-Severn, Worcestershire, DY13 9PN Tel: (01299) 828449 Fax: (01299) 828435E-mail: sales@directfuelservices.co.uk

Emo Oils Ni Ltd, Airport Road West, Belfast, BT3 9ED Tel: (028) 9045 4555 Fax: (028) 9046 0921 E-mail: enquiries@emooil.com

Fuel Oils London, Swedish Wharf, Townmead Road, London, SW6 2SN Tel: (020) 7731 3456 Fax: (020) 7731 0281

Fuel Services, Airport Road West, Belfast, BT3 9ED Tel: (028) 9045 3333 Fax: (028) 9045 0243 E-mail: sales@fuelservicesoil.com

H & J Transport Ltd, Blakeley Hall Road, Oldbury, West Midlands, B69 4ET Tel: 0121-552 1078 Fax: 0121-544 8872

Heltor Warehouses, Heltor Business Park, Old Newton Road, Heathfield, Newton Abbot, Devon, TQ12 6RW Tel: (01626) 832516 Fax: (01626) 834373 E-mail: admin@heltor.co.uk

FUEL OILS – *continued*

Henderson Fuels Domestic Industrial Agricultural, 36 Cranagh Road, Coleraine, County Londonderry, BT51 3NN Tel: (028) 7035 5980 Fax: (028) 7035 5980

Kelly Fuels, Railway Yard, Railway Street, Ballymena, County Antrim, BT42 2AF Tel: (028) 2564 9811 Fax: (028) 2564 0099

Laurence Industrial Oil Services Ltd, Gardner & Son, Bowerland Lane, Lingfield, Surrey, RH7 6DF Tel: (01342) 836143 Fax: (01342) 836375

McAlonan Oils, 3 Mill Street, Ballycastle, County Antrim, BT54 6ES Tel: (028) 2076 2233 Fax: (028) 2076 8939

Noble Fuels, Hutton Rudby, Skutterskelfe, Yarm, Cleveland, TS15 0JR Tel: (01642) 711401 Fax: (01642) 711547 E-mail: sales@noblefuels.sagehost.co.uk

Oakley Fuel Oils Ltd, Halesfield 19, Telford, Shropshire, TF7 4QT Tel: (01952) 684600 Fax: (01952) 684577 E-mail: enquiries@oakleysfueloils.co.uk

Ormskirk Oils Ltd, Hardacre Street, Ormskirk, Lancashire, L39 2XD Tel: (01695) 578120 Fax: (01695) 578126 E-mail: sales@ormskirk-oils.co.uk

Q8 Fuel Care, Estuary Road, King's Lynn, Norfolk, PE30 2HH Tel: (01553) 614800 Fax: (01553) 614835 E-mail: enquiries@q8fuelcare.co.uk

Q8 Fuels Care, 10 Midurst Road, Fernhurst, Haslemere, Surrey, GU27 3EE Tel: (01428) 652218 Fax: (01428) 652250

Shelford Energy, 2 Station Road, Great Shelford, Cambridge, CB22 5LT Tel: (01223) 846846 Fax: (01223) 551161 E-mail: sales@shelford.co.uk

Southdown Oil Supplies Ltd, Pound Lane, Thatcham, Berkshire, RG19 3TQ Tel: (01635) 877456 Fax: (01635) 861352

Total Butler, Farnham Road, Bishop's Stortford, Hertfordshire, CM23 1TB Tel: (01279) 467646 Fax: (01279) 504303

Upton Oil Co. Ltd, Blandford Road North, Upton, Poole, Dorset, BH16 6AA Tel: (01202) 622257 Fax: (01202) 632578 E-mail: uptonoil.co@btinternet.com

▶ W C F Fuels North West, Station Goods Yard, Warton Road, Carnforth, Lancashire, LA5 9EU Tel: (01524) 733669 Fax: (01524) 720077 E-mail: sales@wcfnorthwest.co.uk

Watson Petroleum Ltd, Vector House, Sileby Road, Barrow upon Soar, Loughborough, Leicestershire, LE12 8LX Tel: (01509) 815777 Fax: (01509) 816363

Watson Petroleum Ltd, Hunters Lane, Rugby, Warwickshire, CV21 1EA Tel: (01788) 572401 Fax: (01788) 540010

FUEL PUMPS

A R Ellis Ltd, The Green, Horton Road, Horton, Slough, SL3 9NU Tel: (01753) 685333 Fax: (01753) 680749E-mail: tony@arellis.com

Chappell & Tibbert Ltd, 50 Stamford Road, Easton on the Hill, Stamford, Lincolnshire, PE9 3PA Tel: (01780) 751014 Fax: (01780) 751014

CTS, 41 Forge Lane, Minworth Industrial Park, Minworth, Sutton Coldfield, West Midlands, B76 1AH Tel: 0121-351 4445 Fax: 0121-351 4442 E-mail: sales@centretank.com

M I S Fuel Monitoring Ltd, Horseley Works, Walsall Street, Wolverhampton, WV1 3LN Tel: (01902) 870037 Fax: (01902) 871661 E-mail: info@merridale.co.uk

Purolator Products Automotive, Glenco Ho, Drake Ave, Staines, Middx, TW18 2AW Tel: (01784) 493555

Stamford International Export Ltd, Jack Haws Lane, Barnack, Stamford, Lincolnshire, PE9 3DY Tel: (01780) 740400 Fax: (01780) 740460 E-mail: sales@stamfordint.demon.co.uk

FUEL STORAGE TANKS

C I Automation Ltd, Shaftesbury Centre, Percy Street, Swindon, SN2 2AZ Tel: (01793) 530063 Fax: (01793) 530064

Centaur Fuel Management, 251 Manchester Road, Walkden, Manchester, M28 3HE Tel: (0870) 7576323 Fax: 0161-794 8031 E-mail: mc@centauronline.co.uk

FUEL TANKS

▶ LCH Generators, 13 Main Street, Milngavie, Glasgow, G62 6BJ Tel: 0141-956 7111 Fax: 0141-956 7222 E-mail: headoffice@speedygenerators.co.uk

FUEL TANKS, PLASTIC

▶ Ribble Fuel Oils, Unit 281 Carrfield Place, Walton Summit Centre, Bamber Bridge, Preston, PR5 8AN Tel: (01772) 337367 Fax: (01772) 620094 E-mail: info@ribblefueloils.co.uk

FUEL WASTE RECYCLING CONTRACTORS OR PROCESSORS

Onyx Environmental Group P.L.C., 154A Pentonville Road, London, N1 9PE Tel: (020) 7812 5000 Fax: (020) 7812 5001

FULFILMENT HOUSE SERVICES

20-20 Direct Mail, Unit 49 The Washford Industrial Estate, Heming Road, Redditch, Worcestershire, B98 0EA Tel: (01527) 510444 Fax: (01527) 510006 E-mail: sales@2020dml.com

Alpha Media Direct Marketing, 38 Second Drove, Peterborough, PE1 5XA Tel: (01733) 898023 Fax: (01733) 898324 E-mail: sales@alphamedia.co.uk

Ark H Handling Ltd, 1 Wilstead Industrial Park, Kenneth Way, Wilstead, Bedford, MK45 3PD Tel: (01234) 742777 Fax: (01234) 742999 E-mail: sales@ark-h.co.uk

▶ C Y Logistics Ltd, Deanland Road, Golden Cross, Hailsham, East Sussex, BN27 5 GT Tel: 01825 873333 Fax: 01825 873311 E-mail: yvonne@cylogistics.co.uk

▶ Cavalier Mailing Services Ltd, Mackintosh Road, Rackheath Industrial Estate, Norwich, NR13 6LJ Tel: (01603) 720303 Fax: (01603) 721247 E-mail: a.kerridge@cavaliermailing.com

Challoner Marketing Ltd, Quill Hall Lane, Amersham, Buckinghamshire, HP6 6LL Tel: (01494) 431163 Fax: (01494) 725732 E-mail: challonermarketing@compuserve.com

Dawson Marketing P.L.C., The Arena, Stafferton Way, Maidenhead, Berkshire, SL6 1AY Tel: (01628) 628777 Fax: (01628) 789634 E-mail: sales@dawsonmarketing.co.uk

Elsdon Mailing Ltd, Unit 16 Nonsuch Industrial Estate, Kiln Lane, Epsom, Surrey, KT17 1DH Tel: (01372) 720613 E-mail: elsdonmailing@lineone.net

▶ Fulfilment House, Unit 4, Beaver Industrial Estate, 8 Airfield Road, Christchurch, Dorset, BH23 3TG Tel: 0800 0195139 E-mail: info@fulfilmenthouse.co.uk

Innovative Marketing International Ltd, 21 Dorset Square, London, NW1 6QE Tel: (020) 7723 7228 Fax: (020) 7723 1192 E-mail: enquiries@innovativemarketing.co.uk

Mailshot Services, 21 Upper Priory Street, Grafton Street Industrial Estate, Northampton, NN1 2PT Tel: (01604) 622290 Fax: (01604) 622290

Mando Brand Assurance Ltd, 27-28 Faraday Road, Rabans La Industrial Area, Aylesbury, Buckinghamshire, HP19 8TY Tel: (01296) 717900 Fax: (01296) 394273

Rocket Mailing Ltd, 13 Lea Road, Waltham Abbey, Essex, EN9 1AS Tel: (01992) 788881 Fax: (01992) 788882 E-mail: sales@rocketmailing.co.uk

FULLY FLATTENED STEEL SHEET

John Tainton, Hoo Farm Industrial Estate, Worcester Road, Kidderminster, Worcestershire, DY11 7RA Tel: (01562) 740477 Fax: (01562) 68765 E-mail: jtsales@johntainton.co.uk

FUME CUPBOARDS/CABINETS,

See also headings for particular types

Cityarch Ltd, 3 Potters Lane, Kiln Farm, Milton Keynes, MK11 3HE Tel: (01908) 265557 Fax: (01908) 265400 E-mail: cityarch.limited@virgin.net

H F H Fumecupboards, 9a Aire Place Mills, 103 Kirkstall Road, Leeds, LS3 1JL Tel: 0113-245 4111 Fax: 0113-246 9964 E-mail: hfhmail@yahoo.co.uk

H M Stainless Fabrications Ltd, 227 Bradford Road, Batley, West Yorkshire, WF17 6JL Tel: (01924) 266422 Fax: (01924) 266423 E-mail: david.keylorson@btconnect.com

Mach Aire Ltd, Bridge Street, Horwich, Bolton, BL6 7BT Tel: (01204) 668905 Fax: (01204) 668906 E-mail: sales@machaire.co.uk

Plastic Tanks & Fabrications Ltd, Unit 5, Stone Lane Industrial Estate, Wimborne, Dorset, BH21 1HD Tel: (01202) 888133 Fax: (01202) 886288 E-mail: ptf@avnet.co.uk

FUME CUPBOARDS/CABINETS, LABORATORY

A S P Electronic Design Ltd, 3a Warren House Road, Wokingham, Berkshire, RG40 5PN Tel: 0118-979 0825 Fax: 0118-977 1749 E-mail: enquiries@asp.uk.com

Associated Joinery Techniques Ltd, Marks Hall, Marks Hall Lane, Margaret Roding, Dunmow, Essex, CM6 1QT Tel: (01245) 231881 Fax: (01245) 231818 E-mail: ajt.ltd@btinternet.com

Batchit Ltd, 204 Halesowen Road, Dudley, West Midlands, DY2 9FD Tel: (01384) 633900 Fax: (01384) 566941 E-mail: info@batchit.co.uk

Envair Ltd, Envair House, York Avenue, Haslingden, Rossendale, Lancashire, BB4 4HX Tel: (01706) 228416 Fax: (01706) 229577 E-mail: sales@envair.co.uk

Howorth Airtech Ltd, Victoria Works, Lorne Street, Farnworth, Bolton, BL4 7LZ Tel: (01204) 700900 Fax: (01204) 862378 E-mail: info@howorthairtech.co.uk

Lab Furnishings Group, Unit 2 Malmo Park, Stockholm Road, Sutton Fields Industrial Estate, Hull, HU7 0XW Tel: (01482) 827999 Fax: (01482) 827995 E-mail: p.moran@lfplc.co.uk

Lab Systems Furniture Ltd, Rotary House, Bontoft Avenue, Hull, HU5 4HF Tel: (01482) 444650 Fax: (01482) 444730 E-mail: office@lab-systems.co.uk

Mach Aire Ltd, Bridge Street, Horwich, Bolton, BL6 7BT Tel: (01204) 668905 Fax: (01204) 668906 E-mail: sales@machaire.co.uk

Regal Fans Ltd, Ventris House, Lakes Road, Braintree, Essex, CM7 3SS Tel: (01376) 342914 Fax: (01376) 348208 E-mail: tim@regalfans.co.uk

Robinson & Gronnow Ltd, 3 Mackenzie Industrial Estate, Bird Hall Lane, Stockport, Cheshire, SK3 0SB Tel: 0161-428 1199 Fax: 0161-428 0635 E-mail: info@robinson-gronnow.co.uk

Safelab Systems Ltd, Unit 29, Lynx Crescent, Weston-super-Mare, Avon, BS24 9DJ Tel: (01934) 421340 Fax: (0870) 2402274 E-mail: sales@safelab.co.uk

Simmons (Patternmakers) Ltd, Station Street West Business Park, Coventry, CV6 5BP Tel: (024) 7663 7028 Fax: (024) 7663 7030 E-mail: sales@epoxyworktops.com

Temperature Electronics Ltd, 388-400 Manchester Road, Rochdale, Lancashire, OL11 4NW Tel: (01706) 633438 Fax: (01706) 524609 E-mail: sales@tel-uk.com

FUME EXTRACTION

Air Plants Environmental Control Systems, 295 Aylestone Road, Leicester, LE2 7PB Tel: 0116-283 7800 Fax: 0116-283 7311 E-mail: sales@airplants.co.uk

Fumex Ltd, 411 Effingham Rd, Sheffield, S9 3QD Tel: 0114-243 0538 Fax: 0114-243 2394 E-mail: enquiries@fumex.co.uk

FUME EXTRACTION FANS

Apmg Ltd, Mount Skip Lane, Little Hulton, Manchester, M38 9AL Tel: 0161-799 2200 Fax: 0161-799 2220 E-mail: enquiries@apmg.co.uk

B W Fabrications Ltd, 3 Market Side, Albert Road, St. Philips, Bristol, BS2 0XS Tel: 0117-972 4002 Fax: 0117-972 3094 E-mail: bwfabrications@hotmail.com

Environmental Supply Co. Ltd, Unit 1, 10 Prince Regent Road, Belfast, BT5 6QR Tel: (028) 9040 2100 Fax: (028) 9040 2123 E-mail: environmental@btconnect.com

Enviroplas Services, Unit 2 Shepherd Cross St Industrial Estate, Bolton, BL1 3DE Tel: (01204) 844744 Fax: (01204) 841500 E-mail: sales@enviroplas.co.uk

M Y Fans Ltd, Westend Street, Oldham, OL9 6AJ Tel: 0161-628 3337 Fax: 0161-627 4153 E-mail: m.y.fans@mmp-ltd.co.uk

FUME EXTRACTION INSTALLATION OR SERVICING

Airflow Engineering Services Heating Ventilation Air Conditioning, Drift Road, Kymba House, Whitehill, Bordon, Hampshire, GU35 9DZ Tel: (01420) 473401 Fax: (01420) 489955

Airtec Filtration Ltd, Manor Street, St. Helens, Merseyside, WA9 3AX Tel: (01744) 733211 Fax: (01744) 730917 E-mail: sales@airtecfiltration.com

Apmg Ltd, Mount Skip Lane, Little Hulton, Manchester, M38 9AL Tel: 0161-799 2200 Fax: 0161-799 2220 E-mail: enquiries@apmg.co.uk

Associated Joinery Techniques Ltd, Marks Hall, Marks Hall Lane, Margaret Roding, Dunmow, Essex, CM6 1QT Tel: (01245) 231881 Fax: (01245) 231818 E-mail: ajt.ltd@btinternet.com

Auto Extract Systems, Brearley House, Burnley Road, Halifax, West Yorkshire, HX2 6NB Tel: (01422) 888144 Fax: (01422) 888145

Cityarch Ltd, 3 Potters Lane, Kiln Farm, Milton Keynes, MK11 3HE Tel: (01908) 265557 Fax: (01908) 265400 E-mail: cityarch.limited@virgin.net

Cliftonair Ltd, 48 High Street, Newport Pagnell, Buckinghamshire, MK16 8AQ Tel: (01908) 216416 Fax: (01908) 616732 E-mail: brian@cliftonair.co.uk

Commark Air, Oaktrees, Little Warley Hall La, Little Warley, Brentwood, Essex, CM13 3EX Tel: (01277) 200309

Crawley Welding Supplies Ltd, Royce Road, Crawley, West Sussex, RH10 9NX Tel: (01293) 529761 Fax: (01293) 545081 E-mail: crawleywelding@btclick.co.uk

Crown Engineering Co., Unit 9 Hedgend Industrial Estate, Shuart Lane, St. Nicholas at Wade, Birchington, Kent, CT7 0NB Tel: (01843) 845300 Fax: (01843) 848352 E-mail: enquiries@crownengineering.co.uk

Enviroplas Services, Unit 2 Shepherd Cross St Industrial Estate, Bolton, BL1 3DE Tel: (01204) 844744 Fax: (01204) 841500 E-mail: sales@enviroplas.co.uk

Glenair Ltd, 171-177 Hessle Road, Hull, HU3 4AA Tel: (01482) 223313 Fax: (01482) 229962 E-mail: info@glenair.ltd.uk

▶ Jamieson (Environmental Services) Ltd, 142 Busby RF, Clarkston, Glasgow, G76 8BG Tel: 0141-644 5191 Fax: 0141-644 1696 E-mail: sales@jamiesonenvironmental.co.uk

Maine Engineering Services Ltd, West Line Industrial Estate, Birtley, Chester le Street, County Durham, DH2 1AU Tel: 0191-410 0004 Fax: 0191-410 2053 E-mail: mick.main@dsl.pipex.com

Marcol Fabrications Ltd, Unit 10 Southfield Road Trading Estate, Nailsea, Bristol, BS48 1JJ Tel: (01275) 810022 Fax: (01275) 810033 E-mail: sales@marcolplastics.co.uk

Premier Lab Serve Ltd, Gethceln House, Dawley Road, Hayes, Middlesex, UB3 1EH Tel: (020) 8581 4055 Fax: (020) 8581 4056 E-mail: info@premierlabserve.co.uk

Regal Fans Ltd, Ventris House, Lakes Road, Braintree, Essex, CM7 3SS Tel: (01376) 342914 Fax: (01376) 348208 E-mail: tim@regalfans.co.uk

Techshare Ventilation Systems, 39 Leapfish, Washington, Tyne & Wear, NE38 0RB Tel: 0191-417 2424 Fax: 0191-415 1686 E-mail: sales@techshare.co.uk

Temperature Electronics Ltd, 388-400 Manchester Road, Rochdale, Lancashire, OL11 4NW Tel: (01706) 633438 Fax: (01706) 524609 E-mail: sales@tel-uk.com

Vented Services Telford Ltd, Unit A6 Hortonwood 10, Telford, Shropshire, TF1 7ES Tel: (01952) 677788 Fax: (01952) 677789 E-mail: addessee@vented-services.co.uk

FUME EXTRACTION PLANT AND EQUIPMENT MANUFRS

A K L Sheet Metal Co., 7 Embassy Industrial Estate, Attwood Street, Stourbridge, West Midlands, DY9 8RY Tel: (01384) 892361 Fax: (01384) 892361

Apmg Ltd, Mount Skip Lane, Little Hulton, Manchester, M38 9AL Tel: 0161-799 2200 Fax: 0161-799 2220 E-mail: enquiries@apmg.co.uk

Auto Extract Systems, Brearley House, Burnley Road, Halifax, West Yorkshire, HX2 6NB Tel: (01422) 888144 Fax: (01422) 888145

C C P Gransden Bi-Chem, 17 Moss Road, Ballygowan, Newtownards, County Down, BT23 6JQ Tel: (028) 9752 8501 Fax: (028) 9752 1024 E-mail: info@ccp-gransden.com

Cliftonair Ltd, 48 High Street, Newport Pagnell, Buckinghamshire, MK16 8AQ Tel: (01908) 216416 Fax: (01908) 616732 E-mail: brian@cliftonair.co.uk

Dolphin Enterprises, 4 Eddington Drive, Newton Mearns, Glasgow, G77 5AX Tel: 0141-639 4551 Fax: 0141-639 4551 E-mail: dolphinenterprizes@btconnect.com

Donaldson Filtration (GB) Ltd, Humberstone Lane, Thurmaston, Leicester, LE4 8HP Tel: 0116-269 6161 Fax: 0116-269 3028 E-mail: peter.cowing@emea.donaldson.com

Durnbury Ltd, 30 First Avenue, Halstead, Essex, CO9 2EX Tel: (01787) 475351 Fax: (01787) 477821 E-mail: durnburyltd@aol.com

Dust Control, 1b Pury Business Park, Alderton Road, Paulerspury, Towcester, Northamptonshire, NN12 7LS Tel: (01327) 811510 Fax: (01327) 811413 E-mail: sales@dustcontrol.co.uk

Dustraction Ltd, Mandervell Road, Oadby, Leicester, LE2 5ND Tel: 0116-271 3212 Fax: 0116-271 3215 E-mail: steve.matuska@dustraction.co.uk

Engineering Systems Ltd, Lifford Way, Binley Industrial Estate, Binley Industrial Estate, Coventry, CV3 2RN Tel: (024) 7645 7555 Fax: (024) 7645 7888 E-mail: engsysltd@tiscali.co.uk

Flextraction Ltd, 10 Digby Drive, Leicester Road Industrial Estate, Melton Mowbray, Leicestershire, LE13 0RQ Tel: (01664) 410641 Fax: (01664) 480244 E-mail: sales@flextraction.co.uk

Form Fabrications, 21-25 The Crescent, Hockley, Birmingham, B18 5LU Tel: 0121-551 3561 Fax: 0121-551 6258 E-mail: enquiries@formfabs.com

Luhrfilter Ltd, 58a Thornhill Road, Sutton Coldfield, West Midlands, B74 3EN Tel: 0121-353 8703 Fax: 0121-353 4066 E-mail: sales@luhrgb.demon.co.uk

Mardon Engineering Co. Ltd, Ditton Priors Trading Estate, Station Road, Ditton Priors, Bridgnorth, Shropshire, WV16 6SS Tel: (01746) 712616 Fax: (01746) 712349

Marlborough Constructional Engineers Ltd, Winston Avenue, Croft, Leicester, LE9 3GQ Tel: (01455) 283500 Fax: (01455) 285147 E-mail: enquiries@marlboroughltd.com

Modus Air Ltd, 75 Lifford Lane, Birmingham, B30 3JH Tel: 0121-459 3060 Fax: 0121-459 6417 E-mail: modusair@btinternet.com

Molyneux Dust Control Ltd, 7 Leicester Avenue, Alsager, Stoke-on-Trent, ST7 2BS Tel: (01270) 879359 Fax: (01270) 879355 E-mail: johnmolydust@aol.com

Nederman Ltd, PO Box 503, Preston, PR5 8AF Tel: (01772) 334721 Fax: (01772) 315273

Plastic Fabrications (1991), Unit 10, Bickford Road, Aston, Birmingham, B6 7EE Tel: (0121) 327 1013 Fax: (0121) 326 6139

FUME EXTRACTION PLANT AND EQUIPMENT MANUFRS – *continued*

Plastic Facilities, Fen End, Stotfold, Hitchin, Hertfordshire, SG5 4BA Tel: (01462) 832832 Fax: (01462) 832830 E-mail: sales@plasticfacilities.co.uk
R J Plastics, 83-84 Buckingham Street, Birmingham, B19 3HU Tel: 0121-233 1077 Fax: 0121-236 6355
Raven Engineering Developments, Raven Engineering Developments, 291 Watling Street, DARTFORD, DA2 6EP Tel: 01322 421290 Fax: 0870 8900064
Sangre Engineering Ltd, Unit 32c The Washford Industrial Estate, Heming Road, Redditch, Worcestershire, B98 0DH Tel: (01527) 524782 Fax: (01527) 510323 E-mail: sales@sangre.co.uk
Scot Vent Ltd, 18-20 Boswell Square, Hillington Industrial Estate, Glasgow, G52 4BQ Tel: 0141-882 3243 Fax: 0141-810 5100
Seabrook Welding Supplies Ltd, 4-6 Cannock Street, Leicester, LE4 9HR Tel: 0116-276 4091 Fax: 0116-246 0492
Techshare Ventilation Systems, 39 Leaplish, Washington, Tyne & Wear, NE38 0RB Tel: 0191-417 2424 Fax: 0191-415 1686 E-mail: sales@techshare.co.uk
Versaduct Sheet Metal Ltd, Edwin Avenue, Hoo Farm Industrial Estate, Kidderminster, Worcestershire, DY11 7RA Tel: (01562) 824913 Fax: (01562) 823809
West Bromwich Sheet Metal Ltd, Unit 43n Siddons Factory Estate, Howard Street, West Bromwich, West Midlands, B70 0SU Tel: 0121-556 9120 Fax: 0121-556 9120
Wilson Bros Sheffield Ltd, 35 Kirk Street, Sheffield, S4 7JX Tel: 0114-272 6179 Fax: 0114-276 5889
Worcester Ventilation Systems Ltd, PO Box 190, Droitwich, Worcestershire, WR9 7DE Tel: (01905) 794422 Fax: (01905) 794488 E-mail: mail@worcester-vent.co.uk

FUME EXTRACTION SYSTEMS

Broen Valves Ltd, 7 Cleton Street Business Park, Cleton Street, Tipton, West Midlands, DY4 7TR Tel: 0121-522 4505 Fax: 0121-522 4535 E-mail: broenvalves@broen.com

FUME INCINERATORS

Sly Filters Europe Ltd, 16 The Warren, East Goscote, Leicester, LE7 3XA Tel: 0116-260 8187 Fax: 0116-264 0543 E-mail: sly@ridgep.fsbusiness.co.uk

FUMIGATION CONTRACTORS

Best Pest, 4 Waterloo Place, Duncombe Street, Kingsbridge, Devon, TQ7 1LX Tel: (01548) 854353 Fax: (01548) 857256

FUNCTIONAL FLUIDS TO SPECIFICATION

Flowsolve Ltd, 130 Arthur Road, London, SW19 8AA Tel: (020) 8944 0940 Fax: (020) 8944 1218 E-mail: cfd@flowsolve.com

FUNDING CONSULTANTS, BUSINESS

Axa Investment Managers Ltd, 7 Newgate Street, London, EC1A 7NX Tel: (020) 7645 1000 Fax: (020) 7575 8585
▶ Development Capital Exchange, PO Box 75, Leominster, Herefordshire, HR6 8RG Tel: 01568 611196 E-mail: dcxworld@aol.com
▶ Redarch Associates Ltd, Unit 1 42 Feering Hill, Feering, Colchester, CO5 9NH Tel: (01376) 573767 Fax: (01376) 573900 E-mail: enquiry@redarch.co.uk
▶ vision40 finance, 7 Whymark Avenue, Woodgreen, London, N22 6DJ Tel: (07958) 630576 Fax: (020) 8352 3472 E-mail: tanwa@vision40finance.com

FUNDRAISING PRODUCTS

Fund it UK Ltd, The Rectory, Babworth, Retford, Nottinghamshire, DN22 8ET Tel: (0845) 2011787 Fax: (0845) 2011786 E-mail: info@fundit.co.uk

FUNERAL FLORAL SUPPLIES

F J Luxton & Son, 21 Tip Hill, Ottery St. Mary, Devon, EX11 1BE Tel: (01404) 812646
▶ Mayhew Flowers, 6 Cockpit Hill, Cullompton, Devon, EX15 1DF Tel: (01884) 839826 Fax: 01884 839826 E-mail: info@mayhewflowers.co.uk
T & I Stockman Ltd, 19 Holwell Road, Brixham, Devon, TQ5 9NE Tel: (01803) 882385 E-mail: info@stockmanfuneralservice.co.uk

FUNGICIDAL PAINTS

▶ Renotex Ltd, Pollard Street, Lofthouse, Wakefield, West Yorkshire, WF3 3HG Tel: (01924) 820003 Fax: (01924) 829529 E-mail: sales@renotex.co.uk

FUNGICIDES

Certis, The Crown Business Park, Old Dalby, Melton Mowbray, Leicestershire, LE14 3NQ Tel: (01664) 820052 Fax: (01664) 820216 E-mail: enquiry@luxan.co.uk

FUR GARMENTS, FURRIERS

S. Burland & Son Ltd, 19-29 Redchurch Street, London, E2 7DJ Tel: (020) 7739 6366 Fax: (020) 7729 5041
Furs of Mayfair Ltd, 47 South Molton Street, London, W1K 5RY Tel: (020) 7437 6276 Fax: (020) 7629 6324
Gale Furs Ltd, Unit 7 Plough Yard, London, EC2A 3LP Tel: (020) 7247 2014 Fax: (020) 7377 6792
Glyns Collections, 26 Blackfriars Street, Salford, M3 5BQ Tel: 0161-834 7581 Fax: 0161-834 7581 E-mail: martcgg@aol.com
Noble Furs Regent Street Ltd, 3 New Burlington Place, London, W1S 2HR Tel: (020) 8734 6394 Fax: (020) 7734 6396 E-mail: enquiries@noblefurs.com
Paul & Deanfield, 47 South Molton Street, London, W1K 5RY Tel: (020) 7629 6324 Fax: (020) 7629 6324

FURNACE BRAZING

Intoto Furniture, 46-48 Barbourne Road, Worcester, WR1 1HU Tel: (01905) 24760 Fax: (01905) 726003 E-mail: worcester@intoto.co.uk

FURNACE CHARGING EQUIPMENT

Furnace Engineering, Unit 1d Hownsgill Industrial Park, Knitsley Lane, Consett, County Durham, DH8 7NU Tel: (01207) 590121 Fax: (01207) 505762 E-mail: sales@furnaceengineering.co.uk

FURNACE CONSULTANCY OR DESIGN

C A P Furnaces, 2 Upper Interfields, Leigh Sinton Road, Malvern, Worcestershire, WR14 1UT Tel: (01886) 833663 Fax: (01886) 833663 E-mail: cap@furnaces.fsn.co.uk
Efco Group Ltd, 29 Avro Way, Brooklands Business Park, Weybridge, Surrey, KT13 0YZ Tel: (01932) 350534 Fax: (01932) 350543
Eurofusion Ltd, Ituri, Darcy Rise, Little Baddow, Chelmsford, CM3 4SN Tel: (01245) 221235 Fax: (0870) 4296791 E-mail: glass@eurofusion.co.uk
Furnace Construction Co. Ltd, Newton Moor Industrial Estate, Hyde, Cheshire, SK14 4LF Tel: 0161-368 8419 Fax: 0161-368 3813 E-mail: sales@furnace-construction.co.uk
Hendrick Industrial Equipment Ltd, Unit 32d The Washford Industrial Estate, Heming Road, Redditch, Worcestershire, B98 0DH Tel: (01527) 523712 Fax: (01527) 514545 E-mail: heat@hendrick.co.uk
Stinchcombe Furnaces Ltd, Unit 9 Mount Road Industrial Estate, Mount Road, Burntwood, Staffs, WS7 9QF Tel: 01543 674031 Fax: 01543 683846 E-mail: stinchcombeltd@aol.com
TECO Europe Ltd, 60 Savile Street East, Sheffield, S4 7UQ Tel: 0114-275 9020 Fax: 0114-270 0875 E-mail: sales@tecoglas.com
Vacua Therm Sales Ltd, 5 Parkburn Court, Parkburn Industrial Estate, Hamilton, Lanarkshire, ML3 0QQ Tel: (01698) 825169 Fax: (01698) 824265
Walsall Furnace Construction Services Ltd, 272 West Bromwich Road, Walsall, WS5 4NN Tel: (01922) 637388 Fax: (01922) 637388

FURNACE FITTINGS AND AUXILIARY EQUIPMENT

Assistance Teknica Ltd, York House, Borough Road, Middlesbrough, Cleveland, TS1 2HJ Tel: (01642) 224545 Fax: (01642) 243514 E-mail: enquiries@teknica.co.uk
Lisland Ltd, St. Chads, Fisher Street, Brindley Ford, Stoke-on-Trent, ST8 7QJ Tel: (01782) 522544 Fax: (01782) 522255
Taylormade Induction Ltd, Unit 6 Station Road, Bakewell, Derbyshire, DE45 1GE Tel: (01629) 815122 Fax: (01629) 814776 E-mail: sales@ihstaylormade.com

FURNACE INSTALLATION OR SERVICING

Advanced Furnace Technology Ltd, 65 Church End, Cambridge, CB1 3LF Tel: (01223) 245033 Fax: (01223) 410267
Bar Refractories Ltd, Moorfield Rd, Alcester, Warwickshire, B49 5DA Tel: (01789) 764448 Fax: (01527) 821238
C A P Furnaces, 2 Upper Interfields, Leigh Sinton Road, Malvern, Worcestershire, WR14 1UT Tel: (01886) 833663 Fax: (01886) 833663 E-mail: cap@furnaces.fsn.co.uk
Fabwell Ltd, Unti J Balds Lane, Stourbridge, West Midlands, DY9 8TE Tel: (01384) 898288 Fax: (01384) 898289 E-mail: sales@fabwell.co.uk
Furnace Engineering, Unit 1d Hownsgill Industrial Park, Knitsley Lane, Consett, County Durham, DH8 7NU Tel: (01207) 590121 Fax: (01207) 505762 E-mail: sales@furnaceengineering.co.uk
Furnace Maintenance Co., 20 Swanbourne Road, Sheffield, S5 7TL Tel: 0114-245 6842 Fax: 0114-245 6842
▶ Hotwork Combustion Technology Ltd, Bretton Street, Savile Town, Dewsbury, West Yorkshire, WF12 9DB Tel: (01924) 506506 Fax: (01924) 506311 E-mail: engineering@hotworkct.com
M & W Contractors (Pensnett) Ltd, Morgan House, Folkes Road, Lye, Stourbridge, West Midlands, DY9 8RG Tel: (01384) 424411 Fax: (01384) 892425 E-mail: david@mwcontractors.co.uk
Meltech Ltd, 185 Cannock Road, Westcroft, Wolverhampton, WV10 8QL Tel: (01902) 722588 Fax: (01902) 730142 E-mail: steve@induction-furnaces.co.uk
▶ Phoenix Site Services, Unit 4b Gateway Close, Parkgate, Rotherham, South Yorkshire, S62 6LJ Tel: (01709) 529951 Fax: (01709) 529549 E-mail: paul.phoenixservices@btopenworld.com
R J T Furnaces Ltd, Unit 10 Holland Park, Bentley Road South, Wednesbury, West Midlands, WS10 8LN Tel: 0121-568 6474 Fax: 0121-568 6269
Refractory Installation Services, 27 Park Lane, Rothwell, Leeds, LS10 3BA Tel: 0113-282 2258 E-mail: paul.harvey@ris-leeds.co.uk
Robert Lickley Ltd, Dudley, West Midlands, DY1 2RL Tel: (01902) 880123 Fax: (01902) 880019 E-mail: admin@robertlickley.co.uk
S G Blair & Co. Ltd, Davy Road, Astmoor Industrial Estate, Runcorn, Cheshire, WA7 1SL Tel: (01928) 503200 Fax: (01928) 715200 E-mail: sales@sgblair.com
Tynok Ltd, Midland Ho, Vicarage Road West, Woodsetton, Dudley, W. Midlands, DY1 4NP Tel: (01902) 887270 Fax: (01902) 880428
Vacua Therm Sales Ltd, 5 Parkburn Court, Parkburn Industrial Estate, Hamilton, Lanarkshire, ML3 0QQ Tel: (01698) 825169 Fax: (01698) 824265
York Linings International Ltd, Millfield Industrial Estate, Wheldrake, York, YO19 6NA Tel: (01904) 449777 Fax: (01904) 449888 E-mail: yorkhq@yli-ltd.demon.co.uk

FURNACE LININGS

▶ Densit Wear Protection UK Ltd, Oasis Building, 17 Lisle Avenue, Kidderminster, Worcestershire, DY11 7DE Tel: (01562) 515195 Fax: (01562) 515094 E-mail: enquiries@densit.co.uk
Designcode Ltd, 5 Merseyton Road, Ellesmere Port, CH65 2JE Tel: 0151-355 9172 Fax: 0151-357 2868 E-mail: designcode@tinyworld.co.uk

FURNACE MAINTENANCE OR REPAIR

Advanced Furnace Technology, 18 Cheddars Lane, Cambridge, CB5 8LD Tel: (01223) 461321 Fax: (01223) 362318
Designcode Ltd, 5 Merseyton Road, Ellesmere Port, CH65 2JE Tel: 0151-355 9172 Fax: 0151-357 2868 E-mail: designcode@tinyworld.co.uk
Essex Refractory Ltd, Unit 1 Middleton Hall, Brentwood, Essex, CM13 3LX Tel: (01277) 812282 Fax: (01277) 811185
Furnace Engineering, Unit 1d Hownsgill Industrial Park, Knitsley Lane, Consett, County Durham, DH8 7NU Tel: (01207) 590121 Fax: (01207) 505762 E-mail: sales@furnaceengineering.co.uk
Induction Services Ltd, 16 Wharfedale Cresent, Droitwich, Worcestershire, WR9 8TU Tel: (01905) 771669 Fax: (01905) 797609 E-mail: sales@inductionservices.co.uk
Otto Junker (U K) Ltd, Kingsbury Road, Curdworth, Sutton Coldfield, West Midlands, B76 9EE Tel: (01675) 470551 Fax: (01675) 470645 E-mail: sales@otto-junker.co.uk

FURNACE OR BOILER OR REFRACTORY INSTALLATION BRICKWORK CONTRACTORS

Boden Clark Ltd, George Henry Rd, Greatbridge, Tipton, W. Midlands, DY4 7BZ Tel: 0121-557 1700 Fax: 0121-557 3788
John Morris Developments Ltd, Stanton House, 6 Eastham Village Road, Eastham, Wirral, Merseyside, CH62 0DE Tel: 0151-326 2275 Fax: 0151-326 2276E-mail: i.lee@tiscali.co.uk

FURNACE SETTING/LINING, *See Furnace Engineers etc*

FURNACE VALVES

G R Controls, 19 109 Sydenham Road, Birmingham, B11 1DG Tel: 0121-773 8007 Fax: 0121-773 8007 E-mail: grcontrols1@yahoo.co.uk

FURNACES, *See also headings for particular types*

B T U (Europe) Ltd, Unit 14 Armstrong Mall, Southwood Business Park, Farnborough, Hampshire, GU14 0NR Tel: (01252) 660010 Fax: (01252) 660011 E-mail: sales@btu.co.uk
Boustead International Heaters Ltd, Southwick Square, Southwick, Brighton, BN42 4UA Tel: (01273) 596868 Fax: (01273) 596860 E-mail: sales@bihl.com
▶ Coils & Cables Ltd, Unit 29, Siddons Factory Estate, Howard Street, West Bromwich, West Midlands, B70 0SU Tel: 0121-556 0500 Fax: 0121-556 0600
▶ Furntech Services, Unit 13 Smestow Bridge Industrial Estate, Bridgnorth Road, Wombourne, Wolverhampton, WV5 8AY Tel: (01902) 326030 Fax: (01902) 326030
Hasco-Thermic Ltd, 134 Birchfield Lane, Oldbury, West Midlands, B69 2AY Tel: 0121-552 4911 Fax: 0121-544 8143E-mail: mail@hasco.co.uk
▶ Stein Atkinson Stordy Ltd, Heath Mill House, Heath Mill Road, Wombourne, Wolverhampton, WV5 8AP Tel: (01902) 892388 Fax: (01902) 894880 E-mail: chris.baldwin@sas-eng.com
▶ Thermetal Furnaces, 1 Building 38, Thornleigh Trading Estate, Dudley, West Midlands, DY2 8UB Tel: (01384) 214888 Fax: (01384) 214778

FURNACES, FLUIDIZED BED

Clayton Thermal Processes Ltd, 2 Summerton Road, Oldbury, West Midlands, B69 2EL Tel: 0121-511 1203 Fax: 0121-511 1192 E-mail: claytonthermal@claytonholdings.com

FURNACES, GLASS MELTING/ ANNEALING

A F T UK Ltd, Industrial Estate, Hallcroft Road, Retford, Nottinghamshire, DN22 7SS Tel: (01777) 700722 Fax: (01777) 860335 E-mail: sales@aft-glass.co.uk
Abbeville Instrument Control Ltd, Bridge Street, Derby, DE1 3LA Tel: (01332) 371138 Fax: (01332) 291668 E-mail: sales@aicderby.co.uk
Electroglass Ltd, 4 Brunel Road, Manor Trading Estate, Benfleet, Essex, SS7 4PS Tel: (01268) 565577 Fax: (01268) 565594 E-mail: info@electroglass.co.uk
Leerco Engineering Ltd, Full Sutton Industrial Estate, Stamford Bridge, York, YO41 1HS Tel: (01759) 371128 Fax: (01759) 371034 E-mail: leercoeng@aol.com

FURNACES, SMELTING/ REFINING

▶ Northern Combustion Systems Ltd, 64 Battye Street, Dewsbury, West Yorkshire, WF13 1NX Tel: (01924) 457300 Fax: (01924) 459487 E-mail: sales@ncsltd.co.uk

FURNISHING FABRIC IMPORT/ EXPORT MERCHANTS OR AGENTS

High Style Furnishings, Saxon Way, Melbourn, Royston, Hertfordshire, SG8 6DN Tel: (01763) 261837 Fax: (01763) 262489 E-mail: enq@highstyle.co.uk
Lloyd Furnishings, Albert Close Trading Estate, Whitefield, Manchester, M45 8EH Tel: 0161-796 1920 Fax: 0161-796 1921 E-mail: sales@curtains.co.uk
▶ Marrakesh Trading, 14a Pottergate, Norwich, NR2 1DS Tel: (01603) 610092 E-mail: thetinmine@hotmail.com

FURNISHING FABRIC IMPORT/ EXPORT MERCHANTS OR AGENTS

– continued

H.A. Percheron Ltd, 202 The Chambers, Chelsea Harbour, London, SW10 0XF Tel: (020) 7349 1590 Fax: (020) 7349 1595
E-mail: info@hapercheron.co.uk

Selhide, Vulcan Works, Pollard Street, Manchester, M4 7AN Tel: 0161-273 1772
Fax: 0161-273 2437

FURNISHING FABRICS

Albert Jones Textiles Ltd, 51-53 Richmond Street, Manchester, M1 3WB Tel: 0161-236 4043
Fax: 0161-236 0434

G.P.& J. Baker, Po Box 30, London, SW10 0XE
Tel: (020) 7351 7760 Fax: (020) 7351 7752
E-mail: sales@gpjbaker.co.uk

Barracks Fabrics Printing Co. Ltd, Caton Road, Lancaster, LA1 3PA Tel: (01524) 389308
Fax: (01524) 381057

Edmund Bell & Co. Ltd, Belfry House, Roydsdale Way, Euroway Industrial Estate, Bradford, West Yorkshire, BD4 6SU Tel: (01274) 680000
Fax: (01274) 680699
E-mail: sales@edmundbell.co.uk

John Boyd Textiles Ltd, Higher Flax Mills, Castle Cary, Somerset, BA7 7DY Tel: (01963) 350451
Fax: (01963) 351078
E-mail: enquiries@johnboydtextiles.co.uk

DMF Ltd, Deighton Mills, Leeds Road, Huddersfield, HD2 1TY Tel: (01484) 429889
Fax: (01484) 420445

Donald Bros, Arrol Road, West Gourdie Industrial Estate, Dundee, DD2 4TH Tel: (01382) 618488 Fax: (01382) 618488
E-mail: sales@donald-bros.com

Anna French Ltd, 36 Hinton Road, London, SE24 0HJ Tel: (020) 7737 6555
E-mail: info@annafrench.co.uk

Gainsborough Silk Weaving Co. Ltd, Alexandra Road, Sudbury, Suffolk, CO10 2XH
Tel: (01787) 372081 Fax: (01787) 881785
E-mail: sales@gainsborough.co.uk

Hallis Hudson Group Ltd, Unit B1, Redscar Business Park, Longridge Road, Preston, PR2 5NJ Tel: (01772) 909500 Fax: (01772) 909599 E-mail: info@hallishudson.com

Hardy Fabrics Ltd, 565 Blandford Road, Poole, Dorset, BH16 5BW Tel: (01202) 631637
Fax: (01202) 632918
E-mail: sales@hardyfabrics.com

James Hare Ltd, PO Box 72, Leeds, LS1 1LX
Tel: 0113-243 1204 Fax: 0113-234 7648
E-mail: sales@jameshare silks.co.uk

High Style Furnishings, Saxon Way, Melbourn, Royston, Hertfordshire, SG8 6DN Tel: (01763) 261837 Fax: (01763) 262489
E-mail: enq@highstyle.co.uk

Charles Holliday & Co., Railway Station, Green Road, Newmarket, Suffolk, CB8 9WT
Tel: (01638) 661603 Fax: (01638) 665124
E-mail: brookefairbairn@btconnect.com

J Brooke Fairbairn & Co., Railway Station, Green Road, Newmarket, Suffolk, CB8 9WT
Tel: (01638) 666476 Fax: (01638) 665124
E-mail: brookefairbairn@btconnect.com

Jade Cushions, Gisburn Road, Barrowford, Nelson, Lancashire, BB9 6JD Tel: (01282) 615780

Jaftextil Ltd, Unit 18, Hillgate Business Centre, Swallow Street, Higher Hillgate, Stockport, Cheshire, SK1 3AU Tel: 0161-480 2342
Fax: 0161-480 2397
E-mail: info@jaftextil.co.uk

Krams Ugo Ltd, 18 Deans Drive, Edgware, Middlesex, HA8 9NU Tel: (020) 8906 8656
Fax: (020) 8906 8822
E-mail: enquiries@kramsugo.co.uk

J. Lewis & Co. (Manchester) Ltd, Vulcan Works, Pollard Street, Manchester, M4 7AN
Tel: 0161-273 3077 Fax: 0161-273 2044
E-mail: avijlewis@aol.com

Listers, 3 Gloddaeth Street, Llandudno, Gwynedd, LL30 2DD Tel: (01492) 871940

Maisonneuve & Co., 29 Newman Street, London, W1T 1PS Tel: (020) 7636 9686 Fax: (020) 7436 0770 E-mail: enq@maisonneuve.co.uk

Orchid Soft Furnishing, 86 High Street, Earls Colne, Colchester, CO6 2QX Tel: (01787) 223030 Fax: 01787 223030

H.A. Percheron Ltd, 202 The Chambers, Chelsea Harbour, London, SW10 0XF Tel: (020) 7349 1590 Fax: (020) 7349 1595
E-mail: info@hapercheron.co.uk

Peter Greig & Co., Victoria Linen Works, 147-151 St Clair Street, Kirkcaldy, Fife, KY1 2BU
Tel: (01592) 651901 Fax: (01592) 655596
E-mail: rosie@petergreig.co.uk

Pinewood Drapilux UK Ltd, Albert Street, Leek, Staffordshire, ST13 8AH Tel: (01538) 399153
Fax: (01538) 373235
E-mail: sales@pinewood-fabrics.com

R C Kennedy Ltd, 1 North Street, Manchester, M8 8RE Tel: 0161-832 6182 Fax: 0161-834 3053

Ross Fabrics, Manor Mill Lane, Leeds, LS11 8LQ
Tel: 0113-385 2200 Fax: 0113-277 8855
E-mail: sales@rossfabrics.co.uk

S M D Textiles Ltd, Pittman Way, Fulwood, Preston, PR2 9ZD Tel: (01772) 651199
Fax: (01772) 654034
E-mail: enquiries@swatchbox.co.uk

Sanderson, Sanderson House, Oxford Road, Denham, Uxbridge, Middlesex, UB9 4DX
Tel: (01895) 830000 Fax: (01895) 830055

Sekers Fabrics Ltd, Unit 7A, Nobel Road, West Gourdie Industrial Estate, Dundee, DD2 4UH
Tel: (01946) 517500 Fax: (01946) 517503
E-mail: sales@sekers.co.uk

Selhide, Vulcan Works, Pollard Street, Manchester, M4 7AN Tel: 0161-273 1772
Fax: 0161-273 2437

John Sellars & Co, 4 Broadgate La, Deeping St James, Peterborough, PE6 8NW Tel: 01778 342608 Fax: 01788 341663

Shawe Hall Textiles, 85 North Western Street, Manchester, M12 6DY Tel: 0161-273 6006
Fax: 0161-273 6006

Today Interiors Holdings Ltd, Hollis Road, Grantham, Lincolnshire, NG31 7QH
Tel: (01476) 574401 Fax: (01476) 590208
E-mail: info@today-interiors.co.uk

▶ Zenick Group Ltd, 184 Stanley Green Road, Poole, Dorset, BH15 3AH Tel: (01202) 673744
Fax: (01202) 678798
E-mail: jane@zenickgroup.fsnet.co.uk

FURNISHING TRIMMINGS

British Trimmings Ltd, Coronation Street, Stockport, Cheshire, SK5 7PJ Tel: 0161-480 6122 Fax: 0161-477 1789
E-mail: uk.sales@btrim.co.uk

Goodwear Holdings Ltd, Samros House, 1A Finsbury Park Road, London, N4 2LA
Tel: (020) 7359 6341 Fax: (020) 7359 5678
E-mail: sales@goodwear.co.uk

FURNITURE, *See also headings for particular types*

A H Distributors, 53 Donaldson Street, Kirkintilloch, Glasgow, G66 1XG Tel: 0141-776 2844 Fax: 0141-776 6099

Adept Design & Construction Ltd, Unit D7 Cowdray Centre, Cowdray Avenue, Colchester, CO1 1BW Tel: (01206) 762126
Fax: (01206) 763557

Ananas & Dansk, The Old Coachworks, Rotterdam Road, Lowestoft, Suffolk, NR32 2EX Tel: (01502) 514848 Fax: (01502) 514828 E-mail: sales@ananasanddansk.com

Abercraft Furniture, 315 Princes Road, Stoke-on-Trent, ST4 7JS Tel: (01782) 413719
Fax: (01782) 749156

Ancient Barn Ltd, Coxford Abbey Farm, Coxford, King's Lynn, Norfolk, PE31 6TB Tel: (01485) 528860

Arlington Interiors, 3 Damgate Lane, Acle, Norwich, NR13 3DH Tel: (01493) 751628

Ashcraft Furniture Ltd, Unit 1, Orchard Industrial Estate, Toddington, Cheltenham, Gloucestershire, GL54 5EB Tel: (01242) 620731 Fax: (01242) 621939

Ashwood Designs Ltd, Robertstown House, Aberdare Business Park, Aberdare, Mid Glamorgan, CF44 8ER Tel: (01685) 883388
Fax: (01685) 883399

Atmosphere Ltd, 14 Suffolk Avenue, Westgate-on-Sea, Kent, CT8 8JG Tel: (01843) 833818 Fax: (01843) 833518
E-mail: info@lexterten.com

B A Beds & Pine, 4 Joyce Dawson Way, London, SE28 8RA Tel: (020) 8310 0200 Fax: (020) 8312 1208

Barlis Pine Ltd, 5-6 Tentercroft Street Industrial Estate, Lincoln, LN5 7ED Tel: (01522) 567745
Fax: (01522) 544336
E-mail: barlispine@hotmail.com

The Barn, 48 Walcott Road, Billinghay, Lincoln, LN4 4EH Tel: (01526) 861881 Fax: (01526) 861881

Barton Products Ltd, Barton Road, Long Eaton, Nottingham, NG10 2FN Tel: 0115-972 5134
Fax: 0115-946 1370
E-mail: sales@barton-products.co.uk

Bates Furniture, 21 Newton Road, Rushden, Northamptonshire, NN10 0PS Tel: (01933) 358295 Fax: (01933) 358295

Beaumont Beds Ltd, 5-31 Eastmoor St, London, SE7 8LX Tel: (020) 8853 1155 Fax: (020) 853 2337

Bed Bedroom, 124-126 Walsgrave Road, Coventry, CV2 4AX Tel: (024) 7645 3924
Fax: (024) 7645 3924

Bed & Pine Centre, 20 Wallsgreen Road, Cardenden, Lochgelly, Fife, KY5 0JF
Tel: (01592) 720373 Fax: (01592) 721665

Bed Post, 4-5 Elm Parade, Main Road, Sidcup, Kent, DA14 6NF Tel: (020) 8309 6016
Fax: (020) 8309 6017

Bed Shed, 135 King Street, Kilmarnock, Ayrshire, KA1 1QJ Tel: (01563) 522151 Fax: (01563) 522151

Beds Direct From Sleepers, 4 Boxer Trading Estate, Ponthir Road, Caerleon, Newport, NP18 3NY Tel: (01633) 430022 Fax: (01633) 430011

Bensons Bed Centres Ltd, Unit 4 Alexandra Centre, Park Road, Oldham, OL8 1DB
Tel: 0161-624 8893

John K. Bone, 404 Cremer Business Centre, Cremer Street, London, E2 8HD Tel: (020) 7739 2470 Fax: (020) 7739 2470
E-mail: terryberry321@hotmail.com

Michael Bysouth & Son, The Barn Trueloves, Trueloves Lane, Ingatestone, Essex, CM4 0NQ Tel: (01277) 355315 Fax: (01277) 355315

C W Burrows Ltd, 4 Roydenbury Industrial Estate, Horsecroft Road, Harlow, Essex, CM19 5BZ Tel: (01279) 426558

Camborne Mattress & Bed Centre, 85 Pendarves Street, Tuckingmill, Camborne, Cornwall, TR14 8NP Tel: (01209) 718029

Cambridge Country Furniture, Main Hall Farm, Conington, Cambridge, CB3 8LR Tel: 01954 267156 Fax: 01954 267156

Castle Pine Trading Co., Burcroft Hill, Conisbrough, Doncaster, South Yorkshire, DN12 3EF Tel: (01709) 865999 Fax: (01709) 865999

Centurion Furniture plc, Centurion Building, Farington Road, Farington Moss, Leyland, PR26 6JW Tel: (01772) 450111 Fax: (01772) 453511 E-mail: sales@centurion.telme.com

Chamberlains Falkirk Bed Centre, 54 Cow Wynd, Falkirk, FK1 1PU Tel: (01324) 670060
Fax: (01324) 670060
E-mail: sales@bedsscotland.co.uk

▶ Changing Wood Ltd, Unit 2, Manor Farm, Risborough Road, Aylesbury, Buckinghamshire, HP17 8LU Tel: (01844) 290899 Fax: (01844) 291448
E-mail: andy@changingwood.co.uk

Chistlehurst Bar Seating, 1 Redhill, Chislehurst, Kent, BR7 6DB Tel: (020) 8467 7138
Fax: (020) 8467 7138

Cobweb Furniture, The Old Chapel Workshop, West Street, West Butterwick, Scunthorpe, South Humberside, DN17 3JZ Tel: (01724) 783888

Cobwebs Pine, The Quadrant, St. Ives, Cambridgeshire, PE27 5PE Tel: (01480) 386187 Fax: (01480) 386187

Country Corner, Unit 15 Taverham Craft Centre, Fir Covert Road, Taverham, Norwich, NR8 6HT Tel: (01603) 261745

Country Pine, Hayton, Retford, Nottinghamshire, DN22 9LG Tel: (01777) 710001 Fax: (01777) 706967

Countryside Cabinet Maker, 8 Wellsway Works, Wells Road, Radstock, BA3 3RZ Tel: (0781) 2688101 Fax: (01225) 840864
E-mail: scott.joyce@virgin.net

Crocks Emporium, 63 Longrow, Campbeltown, Argyll, PA28 6ER Tel: (01586) 551344
Fax: (01586) 551277

D P Furniture Express, 15 King Street, Blackburn, BB2 2DH Tel: (01254) 691004
Fax: (01254) 691106

Dalewood Designs, Skirlaugh Road, Old Ellerby, Hull, HU11 5AN Tel: (01964) 563242
Fax: (01964) 563242

▶ Dams International, 29-35 Great Portland Street, London, W1W 8QF Tel: (020) 7637 9520 Fax: (020) 7436 8696

Keith De La Plain Ltd, The Street, Smarden, Ashford, Kent, TN27 8NA Tel: (01233) 770555
Fax: (01233) 770666

Dove Interious, Unit 6, Fairfield Road, Downham Market, Norfolk, PE38 9ET Tel: (01366) 383684 Fax: (01366) 387429
E-mail: simon@doveinteriers.com

Dream Merchants, Canal Mill, Botany Bay, Chorley, Lancashire, PR6 9AF Tel: (01257) 270172 Fax: (01257) 270172

Drew Forsyth & Co. Ltd, Beehive Mills, Hebble End, Hebden Bridge, West Yorkshire, HX7 6HJ Tel: (01422) 842206 Fax: (01422) 844828 E-mail: info@drewforsyth.co.uk

E L Schofield & Son, 49 New Street, Pudsey, West Yorkshire, LS28 8PE Tel: 0113-256 5308
Fax: 0113-255 0052
E-mail: schofieldandson@aol.com

Eight By Four Ltd, Eight By Four, 6A Kings Yard, Carpenters Road, London, E15 2HD Tel: (020) 8985 6001 Fax: (020) 8533 5372
E-mail: sales@eightbyfour.co.uk

Ellis Furniture, Dormers, Main Road, Ashbocking, Ipswich, IP6 9JX Tel: (01473) 890309
Fax: (01473) 890309
E-mail: iroko@tinyonline.co.uk

Elva Wholesale Ltd, 406 Long St, London, E2 8HG Tel: (020) 7739 5622 Fax: (020) 7739 8128 E-mail: elvawholesale@ukbusiness.com

F & S Factory Seconds, Church Bridge House, Church Bridge Park, Bridge Street, Cannock, Staffordshire, WS11 3DQ Tel: (01543) 468797

Farmhill Fitted Furniture, 36 Farmhill Road, Omagh, County Tyrone, BT79 0PY Tel: (028) 8225 2151 Fax: (028) 8225 2151

▶ Firth's Furnishings, 103 Commercial Street, Batley, West Yorkshire, WF17 5DQ
Tel: (01924) 478294

Floor To Ceiling Fitted Bedrooms, 4 Far Field Road, Edenthorpe, Doncaster, South Yorkshire, DN3 2NS Tel: (01302) 886074
Fax: (01302) 886074

Fourposters Ltd, 127 London Rd, Hurst Green, Etchingham, E. Sussex, TN19 7PN
Tel: (01580) 860252 Fax: (01580) 860252

Furniture Wise, 40 Edderthorpe Street, Bradford, West Yorkshire, BD3 9JX Tel: (01274) 306918
Fax: (01274) 306918

G & P Furniture Ltd, Tofts Farm Industrial Estate East, Brenda Road, Hartlepool, Cleveland, TS25 2BS Tel: (01429) 280200 Fax: (01429) 280010 E-mail: sales@gandpfurniture.com

G R Joinery, Abernant Workshops, Pontardawe Rd, Rhydyfro/pontardawe, Swansea, SA8 4SX
Tel: 01269 820000

Gattzbee Kitchens, Darley Street, Darley Abbey, Derby, DE22 1DX Tel: (01332) 556699
Fax: (01332) 556699

George F Knowles Ltd, 50 St Anne Street, Liverpool, L3 3EA Tel: 0151-207 1311
Fax: 0151-298 2008

Gerald Weir, 1 Deben Road, Woodbridge, Suffolk, IP12 1AZ Tel: (01394) 610900
Fax: (01394) 610901
E-mail: geraldweirantiques@btinternet.com

Stuart Groves Furniture, Folly Works, 8 Dashwood Avenue, High Wycombe, Buckinghamshire, HP12 3DN Tel: (01494) 446460 Fax: (01494) 446461

Gullane Leisure Furniture Ltd, 22 Bowlers Croft, Basildon, Essex, SS14 3EE Tel: (01268) 274140 Fax: (01268) 274180

H J Contracts General Woodworkers Ltd, 43b Hardingham Road, Hingham, Norwich, NR9 4LX Tel: (01953) 851448 Fax: (01953) 851443

▶ Habitat U.K. Ltd, 196 Tottenham Court Road, London, W1T 7LG Tel: (020) 7631 3880
Fax: (020) 7614 5209
E-mail: store.tcr@habitat.co.uk

Halstock Cabinets Makers Ltd, Higher Halstock Leigh, Yeovil, Somerset, BA22 9QZ
Tel: (01935) 891762 Fax: (01935) 891967
E-mail: andy@halstock-designs.co.uk

Hamilton Frazer Seatstore Ltd, 7 Ravenstone Road, Camberley, Surrey, GU15 1SN
Tel: (01276) 23903 Fax: (01276) 683799
E-mail: info@hamiltonfrazer.co.uk

Hancock & Lant, 164-170 Queens Road, Sheffield, S2 4DH Tel: 0114-272 2176
Fax: 0114-270 0289

▶ Harling Collection, The Old Greyhound Barn, Bury Road, Hopton, Diss, Norfolk, IP22 2NU
Tel: (01953) 688352 Fax: (01953) 688352

Harvey Williams Associates, Unit 3-4 Hurstfold Workshop, Fernhurst, Haslemere, Surrey, GU27 3JG Tel: (01483) 831619 Fax: (01428) 658237 E-mail: simon@harvey-williams.com

Harveys Furnishing Ltd, Amberley House, New Road, Rainham, Essex, RM13 8QN
Tel: (01708) 521177 Fax: (01708) 521514

Haselbech Oak & Country Furniture, Haselbech Hill, Haselbech, Northampton, NN6 9LL
Tel: (01604) 686360 Fax: (01604) 686360
E-mail: enquiries@haselbechoak.co.uk

Heathfield Pine, Heathfield Farm Cottage, 30 Manor Road, Hatfield, Doncaster, South Yorkshire, DN7 6SD Tel: (01302) 846781

Hillside Kitchens Bedrooms & Bathrooms, 302 Liverpool Road, Southport, Merseyside, PR8 4PW Tel: (01704) 560758 Fax: (01704) 560716 E-mail: sales@hillsidekitchens.com

Austin Hinkley Furniture Ltd, Wilson Way, Redruth, Cornwall, TR15 3RS Tel: (01209) 310910 Fax: (01209) 212045

Holders Fine Furniture, 169-173 Malden Road, London, NW5 4HT Tel: (020) 7485 2741
Fax: (020) 7916 9259
E-mail: sales@holders-pine.co.uk

House Hold Furniture Stores Ltd, Unit 11, Lake Business Centre, Tariff Road, London, N17 0YX Tel: (020) 8374 9691 Fax: (020) 8374 8106
E-mail: kelly@furnituredomesticdirect.com

Ideal Upholstery Ltd, 319 Railway Street, Nelson, Lancashire, BB9 0JD Tel: (01282) 697769
Fax: (01282) 698869
E-mail: enquiries@ideal-upholstery.co.uk

Indaux UK Ltd, Mga House, Ray Mill Road East, Maidenhead, Berkshire, SL6 8ST Tel: (01628) 780250 Fax: (01628) 780251
E-mail: sales@indaux.com

▶ Inner Space Furniture Ltd, The Old Dairy Church Farm, South Harting, Petersfield, Hampshire, GU31 5QG Tel: (01730) 826633
Fax: (01730) 826644
E-mail: info@innserspacefurniture.co.uk

J & P Furniture Ltd, 5-8 Fenn Field Units, Homefield Road, Haverhill, Suffolk, CB9 8QU
Tel: (01440) 702592 Fax: (01440) 707079
E-mail: sales@jpfurniture.co.uk

E.S. Jackson, The Dees, Doddington, Lincoln, LN6 4RR Tel: (01522) 692921 Fax: (01522) 696314 E-mail: info@jacksonpine.co.uk

Geoffrey Jackson, Elizabeth Buildings, Langley-on-Tyne, Hexham, Northumberland, NE47 5LA Tel: (01434) 688977 Fax: (01434) 684487

John Nicholas Reproduction, Emblem House, Manor Hall Road, Southwick, Brighton, BN42 4NH Tel: (01273) 424876 Fax: (01273) 424876
E-mail: jnicholasreproductions@mistral.co.uk

K K Beds & Pine, 72-75 Lower Bristol Road, Bath, BA2 3HB Tel: (01225) 481818
Fax: (01225) 481818

▶ K M Furniture Ltd, Newton House, Pottery La West, Chesterfield, Derbyshire, S41 9BN
Tel: (01246) 260123 Fax: (01246) 260221
E-mail: sales@efmchesterfield.co.uk

Karva Furniture, Widdrington, Morpeth, Northumberland, NE61 5DW Tel: (01670) 790325 Fax: (01670) 790325

▶ KOI Furniture, PO Box 449, Harpenden, Herts, AL5 9AF Tel: 0845 2268271 Fax: 0870 7626151 E-mail: enquiries@koifurniture.co.uk

Larkswood Ltd, Care Of Courts, Orchard Retail Pk, London Rd, Coventry, CV3 4EU Tel: 024 76303020

La-z-Boy, Centurion Building, Lancashire Enterprises Business Park, Leyland, PR26 6JW Tel: (01772) 450100 Fax: (01772) 453511 E-mail: sales@centurion.tellme.com

Leyland Furniture Frames, Altcar Lane, Leyland, PR25 1LE Tel: (01772) 434090 Fax: (01772) 434090

Linford Furniture, Mill Lane, Stony Stratford, Milton Keynes, MK11 1EW Tel: (01908) 261521

Linton Handcrafts, 213 Milton Road, Weston-super-Mare, Avon, BS22 8EG
Tel: (01934) 642849 Fax: (01934) 642849
E-mail: sales@lintonhandcrafts.co.uk

Living In Style, Unit 1, 162 Coles Green Road, London, NW2 7HW Tel: (020) 8450 9555
Fax: (020) 8450 7565
E-mail: sales@livinginstyle.co.uk

Longpre Furniture Ltd, Station Road, Bruton, Somerset, BA10 0EH Tel: (01749) 813966
Fax: (01749) 813977
E-mail: furniture@longpre.co.uk

G. Lusty Ltd, Hoo Lane, Chipping Campden, Gloucestershire, GL55 6AU Tel: (01386) 841333 Fax: (01386) 841322
E-mail: geoffreylusty@aol.com

FURNITURE – *continued*

M A Platt Ltd, St. James Street, Accrington, Lancashire, BB5 1NU Tel: (01254) 234743 Fax: (01254) 238884
M F Furnishings, 5 Richmond St, Walsall, WS1 2JX Tel: 01922 624040 Fax: 01902 368282
Mccollin Furniture, 39 Urlwin Street, London, SE5 0NF Tel: (020) 7703 2262 Fax: (020) 7703 2262 E-mail: mccollinbryan@aol.com
Mardec Joinery Distributors Sussex Ltd, Unit 16 Swan Barn Business Centre, Old Swan Lane, Hailsham, East Sussex, BN27 2BY Tel: (01323) 449028 Fax: (01323) 449024
Mark Brazier Jones, Hyde Hall Barn, Sandon, Buntingford, Hertfordshire, SG9 0RU Tel: (01763) 273599 Fax: (01763) 273410 E-mail: studio@braizer-jones.com
Mark Wilkinson (Furniture) Ltd, Overton House, High St, Bromham, Chippenham, Wiltshire, SN15 2HA Tel: (01380) 850004 Fax: (01380) 850184 E-mail: info@mws.com
Julian Masters, Newbridge House, Chew Road, Winford, Bristol, BS40 8HL Tel: (01275) 331080 Fax: (01275) 331080 E-mail: info@newbridgefurniture.com
Charles Matts, Manor Farm, Thurgarton, Norwich, NR11 7PG Tel: (01263) 761422 Fax: (01263) 768748
Herman Miller Ltd, 61 Aldwych, London, WC2B 4AE Tel: (0845) 226 7202 Fax: (0845) 430 9260 E-mail: info_uk@hermanmiller.com
Mother Hubbard's, Old Church, Craigour Road, Torphins, Banchory, Kincardineshire, AB31 4HE Tel: (01339) 882756 Fax: (01339) 882797 E-mail: sales@motherhubbardspine.com
Moy Antique Pine, 12 The Square, Moy, Dungannon, County Tyrone, BT71 7SG Tel: (028) 8778 9909 Fax: (028) 8778 4895
Multiyork Furniture Ltd, 15 Piccadilly, York, YO1 9PB Tel: (01904) 674050 Fax: (01904) 674030 E-mail: york@multiyork.co.uk
Mumbles Pine Co., 42 The Grove, Mumbles, Swansea, SA2 0QR Tel: (01792) 472764 Fax: (01792) 360749
▶ Lawrence Neal, 22 High Street, Stockton, Southam, Warwickshire, CV47 8JZ Tel: (01926) 811998 E-mail: sales@lawrencenealchairs.co.uk
▶ Nick Hodder, 74 St James's Street, London, E17 7PE Tel: (020) 8520 7082 Fax: (020) 8520 7082
Oakridge Direct Ltd, Maerdy Industrial Estate, Rhymney, Tredegar, Gwent, NP22 5YD Tel: (01685) 844000 Fax: (01685) 844911
Oakwood Traditional Furniture Ltd, Crewe Hill, Crewe Hill Lane, Farndon, Chester, CH3 6PD Tel: (01829) 270704 Fax: (01829) 271709 E-mail: enquiries@oakwoodfurniture.co.uk
Oblique, Stamford Works, Gillett Street, London, N16 8JH Tel: (020) 7249 7363 Fax: (020) 7275 7495
P H Chandler Leyland Ltd, 5 The Forward Industrial Estate, Talbot Road, Leyland, PR25 2ZJ Tel: (01772) 421651 Fax: (01772) 621493 E-mail: carolw@phchandler.co.uk
Paint & Timber Workshop, The Kennels The Oak Tree, Ellenbrook Lane, Hatfield, Hertfordshire, AL10 9NT Tel: (01707) 258727 Fax: (01707) 258727 E-mail: workshop@paintimber.fsnet.co.uk
Papworth Furniture Ltd, Unit 4 Stirling Way, Papworth Everard, Cambridge, CB23 3GX Tel: (0845) 1308300 Fax: (01480) 830516 E-mail: sales@papworth-furniture.co.uk
Park Interiors, 49 Purdeys Industrial Estate, Purdeys Way, Rochford, Essex, SS4 1ND Tel: (01702) 549424 Fax: (01702) 542199 E-mail: paul@parkinteriors.co.uk
Patrick Baxter Furniture, Girdwoodend Farm, Auchengray, Carnwath, Lanark, ML11 8LL Tel: (01501) 785460 Fax: (01501) 785450
Peppercorn Pine, 25 High Street, Headcorn, Ashford, Kent, TN27 9NH Tel: (01622) 891773 Fax: (01622) 891773
Peter Pine, 123 Outram Street, Sutton-in-Ashfield, Nottinghamshire, NG17 4BG Tel: (01623) 555744
Berwyn Phillips, Unit 5 St James Street, Blue Bridge, Milton Keynes, MK13 0BW Tel: (01908) 221885 Fax: (01908) 221885
Pine Factory, Nortonthorpe Mill, Wakefield Road, Scissett, Huddersfield, HD8 9JL Tel: (01484) 865042 Fax: (01484) 866289 E-mail: sales@the-pinefactory.co.uk
Pine Warehouse Ltd, 21 Osborne Street, Hull, HU1 2NL Tel: (01482) 224583 Fax: (01482) 224583 E-mail: pwarehousehull@hotmail.com
Pine Warehouse, Unit 4 Portrack Retail Park, Holme House Road, Stockton-on-Tees, Cleveland, TS18 1BT Tel: (01642) 670222 Fax: (01642) 670444
The Pinewood Studio, The Lays Farm, Charlton Road, Keynsham, Bristol, BS31 2SE Tel: 0117-986 3950
Pineworld, Timworth Green, Timworth, Bury St. Edmunds, Suffolk, IP31 1HS Tel: (01284) 728621 Fax: (01284) 728191 E-mail: sales@pineworlduk.com
Poldark Cabinet Makers, Woodbine Cottage, Gerrards Cross Road, Stoke Poges, Slough, SL2 4EL Tel: (01753) 662920 Fax: (01753) 662920
Harry Powell, 1 Hill Road, Clevedon, Avon, BS21 7LN Tel: (01275) 875907 Fax: (01275) 349237 E-mail: sales@harrypowell.com
Prittlewell Interiors, Rear of, 275 Victoria Avenue, Southend-on-Sea, SS2 6NE Tel: (01702) 330865 Fax: (01702) 392034
Quainton Cottage Furniture, Brixton Buildings, Station Road, Quainton, Aylesbury, Buckinghamshire, HP22 4BX Tel: (01296) 655726 Fax: (0870) 516601 E-mail: jeff@qcf.uk.com
R K Furniture Ltd, The Airfield, Tholthorpe, York, YO61 1ST Tel: (01347) 838182 Fax: (01347) 838330 E-mail: enquiries@rkfurniture.co.uk
Raleigh Workshop Ltd, 1a Saltoun Road, London, SW2 1EN Tel: (020) 7733 8110 Fax: (020) 7733 8778
Remploy Furniture Group Ltd, 15-16 Fall Bank Industrial Estate, Dodworth, Barnsley, South Yorkshire, S75 3LS Tel: (01226) 284064 Fax: (01226) 720131
Restall Brown & Clennell Ltd, 21 North Street, Lewes, East Sussex, BN7 2PE Tel: (01273) 473612 Fax: 01273 477783 E-mail: sales@rbc-furniture.co.uk
Richardson Bros, 39 Leg Street, Oswestry, Shropshire, SY11 2NN Tel: (01691) 656980 Fax: (01691) 656980
Roberts Contract Furniture Ltd, 1-2 Badby Park, Heartlands Business Park, Daventry, Northamptonshire, NN11 8YT Tel: (01327) 311446 Fax: (01327) 300867 E-mail: chris@robertscontracts.com
▶ Rogeroger, 24 Clonbrock Road, London, N16 8RR Tel: (020) 7254 7706 Fax: (020) 7254 7706 E-mail: info@rogeroger.co.uk
Rooms, 98 Drumcroon Road, Blackhill, Coleraine, County Londonderry, BT51 4ER Tel: (028) 7086 8689 E-mail: wcollins@btconnect.com
Rothwell & Thomas, 7 Knowsley Street, Manchester, M8 8QN Tel: 0161-832 9100 Fax: 0161-839 4963 E-mail: tomrat@globalnet.co.uk
Royal Oak Furniture Co., Moor Lane, Grassington, Skipton, North Yorkshire, BD23 5BD Tel: (01756) 753378 Fax: (01756) 752865 E-mail: sales@royaloakfurniture.com
Royal Strathclyde Blindcraft Industries, 6 Candleriggs, Glasgow, G1 1LD Tel: 0141-553 2005 Fax: 0141-553 2060
Rustic Leather Co., 3 Penllwyngwent Industrial Estate, Saville Road, Ogmore Vale, Bridgend, Mid Glamorgan, CF32 7AX Tel: (01656) 842832 Fax: (01656) 841144 E-mail: sales@therusticleathercompany.co.uk
Samuel Bruce, 1-7 Corstorphine Road, Edinburgh, EH12 6DD Tel: 0131-313 3760 Fax: 0131-313 3721
Scartop Pine Villages, Moor Lodge, Oldfield, Keighley, West Yorkshire, BD22 0JL Tel: (01535) 642585 Fax: (01535) 644655
Sebel Furniture Ltd, 7 Canon Harnett Court, Wolverton Mill, Milton Keynes, MK12 5NF Tel: (01908) 317766 Fax: (01908) 317788 E-mail: sales@sebel.com.au
Selector Office Furniture, Harley Street, Todmorden, Lancashire, OL14 5JE Tel: (01706) 818821 Fax: (01706) 812099 E-mail: info@selectoroffice.co.uk
Sharps Bedrooms Ltd, Inside Allied Carpets, Barnstaple Retail Pk Station Rd, Sticklepath, Barnstaple, Devon, EX31 2AU Tel: 01271 321713
Sharps Bedrooms Ltd, Homebase, St Andrews Avenue, Colchester, CO4 3BG Tel: (01206) 861821
Sharps Bedrooms Ltd, Madford Business Park, Mansfield Road, Daybrook, Nottingham, NG5 6AD Tel: 0115-967 1311
Sharps Bedrooms, Inside Home Base, Horspath Driftway, Eastern Bypass, Headington, Oxford, OX3 7JN Tel: (01865) 777170
Sharps Bedrooms Ltd, Unit 9 Thorp Arch Trading Estate, Thorp Arch, Wetherby, West Yorkshire, LS23 7BJ Tel: (01937) 843245
Sharps Moben & Dolphin, The Royals, Haygate Avenue, Southend-on-Sea, SS1 1DQ Tel: (01702) 464722
▶ Silly Billys, Knightsbridge Place, 3 Nottingham Road, Ripley, Derbyshire, DE5 3DJ Tel: (01773) 741222
Silver Lining Workshops, Unit 5 Castle Farm, Cholmondeley, Malpas, Cheshire, SY14 8AQ Tel: (01948) 822150 Fax: (01948) 822151 E-mail: info@silverliningfurniture.com
Sleepmasters Ltd, 25 Gravel Street, Leicester, LE1 3AG Tel: 0116-253 2523 Fax: 0116-251 3684
Sleepmasters Ltd, 27 Loire Drive, Robin Park, Wigan, Lancashire, WN5 0UH Tel: (01942) 218800 Fax: (01942) 218800
Sole Bay Pine Co., Red House Farm, Hinton, Saxmundham, Suffolk, IP17 3RF Tel: (01502) 478077 Fax: (01502) 478006
Somerdell Furniture, 98 Radstock Road, Midsomer Norton, Radstock, BA3 2AU Tel: (01761) 418969 Fax: (01761) 418969 E-mail: somerdell@aol.com
Sonnet Furniture, Units 1-5, Blackfriars Road, Nailsea, Bristol, BS48 4DJ Tel: (01275) 858131 Fax: (01275) 811834
Sonnet Furniture, Units 1-5, Blackfriars Road, Nailsea, Bristol, BS48 4DJ Tel: (01275) 858131 Fax: (01275) 811834
Stenco Furniture, Harvest Works, Vale Road, London, N4 1PL Tel: (020) 8800 2277 Fax: (020) 8809 5612
Stevana Ltd, Leverton Buildings, Leverton, Hungerford, Berkshire, RG17 0TA Tel: (01488) 684444 Fax: (01488) 684444 E-mail: mail@stevana.co.uk
▶ Stewart George Upholstery Ltd, Stanhope Mill, Stanhope Street, Long Eaton, Nottingham, NG10 4QN Tel: 0115-946 4818
Stratton Woodcraft, Foxcote House, Broad Lane, East Chinnock, Yeovil, Somerset, BA22 9ES Tel: (01935) 862776 Fax: (01935) 862776
Table Makers, 155 St. John's Hill, London, SW11 1TQ Tel: (020) 7223 2075 Fax: (020) 7223 7296 E-mail: sales@tablemakers.co.uk
Target Furniture Ltd, 1 Ardington Road, Northampton, NN1 5LP Tel: (01604) 622405 Fax: (01604) 628578
Touchwood, Sluice Farm, Sandy Lane, Martlesham, Woodbridge, Suffolk, IP12 4SD Tel: (01394) 385522 Fax: (01394) 389555 E-mail: touchwood@zoom.co.uk
Town Head Farm Cottages, Town Head Farm, Great Asby, Appleby-in-Westmorland, Cumbria, CA16 6EX Tel: (01768) 351499 Fax: (01768) 353771 E-mail: sales@westmorlandfurniture.co.uk
Town Joinery, Garth Road, Morden, Surrey, SM4 4NJ Tel: (020) 8330 7451 Fax: (020) 8330 7336 E-mail: sales@townjoinery.co.uk
Traesko Furniture, 89-91 Joel Street, Northwood, Middlesex, HA6 1LU Tel: (01923) 820341 Fax: (01923) 826711
Treasko, Centurion House, 136-142 London Road, St. Albans, Hertfordshire, AL1 1PQ Tel: (01727) 837773 Fax: (01727) 836562
Treske Ltd, Station Works, Thirsk, North Yorkshire, YO7 4NY Tel: (01845) 522770 Fax: (01845) 522692 E-mail: info@treske.co.uk
True Craft Furniture Ltd, Bath Lane, Leeds, LS13 3BB Tel: 0113-236 1100 Fax: 0113-236 0301 E-mail: furniture@true-craft.freeserve.co.uk
Alan Turrell Furniture, Ffrwdy Drain, Llandeilo, Dyfed, SA19 6SA Tel: (01558) 822383 Fax: (01558) 822383
Darren Tyson Furniture, 10 Lane End Road, High Wycombe, Buckinghamshire, HP12 4JF Tel: (01494) 445090
Vale Furniture Warehouse, 83 Laurelvale Road, Tandragee, Craigavon, County Armagh, BT62 2LE Tel: (028) 3884 9921 Fax: (028) 3884 9921
W S D S Business Systems Ltd, 5 Chapel Road, Portslade, Brighton, BN41 1PF Tel: (01273) 420011 Fax: (01273) 420022 E-mail: sales@wsds-works.co.uk
Roy Walker Pine, Lindens Farm, North Road, Newark, Nottinghamshire, NG23 6QL Tel: (01636) 822173 Fax: (01636) 822229 E-mail: sale@roywalkerpine.com
Webbs Woodwork Ltd, 1 Queens Passage, Chislehurst, Kent, BR7 5AP Tel: (020) 8467 7900 Fax: (020) 8467 7900
Winch, Tony, Chapel Farm, Chapel Lane, Westhumble, Dorking, Surrey, RH5 6AY Tel: (01306) 742373
Wingates Ltd, Unit 3 East Way, Rivergreen Industrial Estate, Sunderland, SR4 6AD Tel: 0191-510 1717 Fax: 0191-510 1188 E-mail: info@wingatesltd.co.uk
Wood, 2 Sea View Road, Colwyn Bay, Clwyd, LL29 8DG Tel: (01492) 534000
Woodcraft & Design, 202 High Street, London Colney, St. Albans, Hertfordshire, AL2 1JQ Tel: (01727) 823154 Fax: (01727) 823154 E-mail: info@woodcraftdesign.co.uk
▶ Wooden Heart Designs, Chapel Barn Yard, Deptford, Wylye, Warminster, Wilts, BA12 0QQ Tel: (01985) 248286 Fax: (01985) 248286
Wooden Workshop Ltd, 454 Hornsey Road, London, N19 4EE Tel: (020) 7263 8070 Fax: (020) 7272 1668 E-mail: enquiries@wwltd.freeserve.co.uk
Woodentops, 26 High Street, Dereham, Norfolk, NR19 1DR Tel: (01362) 699656 Fax: (01362) 699656
Woodentops, 31 Norfolk Street, King's Lynn, Norfolk, PE30 1AL Tel: (01553) 765928 Fax: (01553) 765928
Woodrich Design Ltd, Shaw Barn, Whitesmith, Lewes, East Sussex, BN8 6JD Tel: (01825) 872066 Fax: (01825) 872894
Woodstock Interiors 2000, Garth Works, Taffs Well, Cardiff, CF15 7YF Tel: (029) 2081 0363 Fax: (029) 2081 0363 E-mail: derick.kingston@ntlworld.com
Woodstock Leabank Office Furniture, Corrie Way, Bredbury, Stockport, Cheshire, SK6 2ST Tel: 0161-494 1242 Fax: 0161-494 4409 E-mail: sales@woodstockleabank.co.uk
Woody's Pine Emporium, 34-40 Derby Road, Ipswich, IP3 8DN Tel: (01473) 717064 Fax: (01473) 713480 E-mail: info@woodyspine.co.uk
Wreake Valley Craftsmen Ltd, Rearsby Road, Thrussington, Leicester, LE7 4UD Tel: (01664) 424380 Fax: (01664) 424287 E-mail: info@wreakevalley.com

FURNITURE CASTORS

Colson Castors Ltd, Golds Green Works, Bagnall Street, Hill Top, West Bromwich, West Midlands, B70 0TZ Tel: 0121-556 7221 Fax: 0121-502 2658
Colson Castors Ltd, Golds Green Works, Bagnall Street, West Bromwich, West Midlands, B70 0TS Tel: 0121-556 7221 Fax: 0121-502 6258 E-mail: info@colson-castors.co.uk
H Varley Ltd, Unit 5, Century Park, Unit 5, Pacific Road, Altrincham, Cheshire, WA14 5BJ Tel: 0161-928 9617 Fax: 0161-928 7824 E-mail: sales@varley.co.uk
Page Castor Ltd, Blakemore Road, West Bromwich, West Midlands, B70 8JF Tel: 0121-553 1710 Fax: 0121-525 0631

FURNITURE DESIGNERS OR CONSULTANTS

▶ A World of Old, The Barns, Wingrave Road, Aston Abbotts, Aylesbury, Buckinghamshire, HP22 4LU Tel: (01296) 680406 Fax: (01296) 680437
Adept Design & Construction Ltd, Unit D7 Cowdray Centre, Cowdray Avenue, Colchester, CO1 1BW Tel: (01206) 762126 Fax: (01206) 763557
Alan Johnson Cabinet Maker, Kingsgate Workshops, 110-116 Kingsgate Road, London, NW6 2JG Tel: (020) 7372 6736 Fax: (020) 7328 7878
Atton Furniture, Church Lane, Church Walk, Little Dalby, Melton Mowbray, Leicestershire, LE14 2UQ Tel: (01664) 454553 Fax: (01664) 454553
Belvedere Manufacturing Co. Ltd, The Old Printing Works, Waterloo Road, Radstock, BA3 3EP Tel: (01761) 437621 Fax: (01761) 436616 E-mail: belvederemfg@aol.com
Boss Design Ltd, Boss Drive, Dudley, West Midlands, DY2 8SZ Tel: (01384) 455570 Fax: (01384) 241628 E-mail: sales@boss-design.co.uk
Box Products Ltd, The Lodge 3 Russell House, Cambridge Street, London, SW1V 4EQ Tel: (020) 7976 6791 Fax: (020) 7828 7133 E-mail: boxproducts@btinternet.com
Bridge Ceilings Ltd, Interiors House, Samson Road, Coalville, Leicestershire, LE67 3FP Tel: (01530) 834777 Fax: (01530) 813388 E-mail: info@bridgeinteriors.co.uk
Cerdan Ltd, Silver Street Workshops, 37 Silver Street, Ashwell, Baldock, Hertfordshire, SG7 5QH Tel: (01462) 742837 Fax: (01462) 743130 E-mail: info@cerdan.co.uk
Ron Cox, 24 Shoebury Road, Great Wakering, Southend-on-Sea, SS3 0BW Tel: (01702) 218418
David Barnett Associates, The Studio, 84 Park Street, St. Albans, Hertfordshire, AL2 2JR Tel: (01727) 872481 Fax: (01727) 875587 E-mail: design@dbassociate.co.uk
▶ Stephen J. Davies, 43 Curtis Avenue, Abingdon, Oxfordshire, OX14 3UL Tel: (01235) 200869
Design For Modern Living, 43 High St, Wing, Leighton Buzzard, Bedfordshire, LU7 0NS Tel: (01296) 682994 Fax: (01296) 682995 E-mail: graham@mancha.demon.co.uk
Detail Design, 2d Metropolitan Wharf, Wapping Wall, London, E1W 3SS Tel: (020) 7488 1669 Fax: (020) 7488 2524 E-mail: gorden@detail.co.uk
Dream Design, Hinton Old Sawmill, A35 Lyndhurst Road, Hinton, Christchurch, Dorset, BH23 7DU Tel: (01425) 279525 Fax: (01425) 273550
▶ Fish Contemporary, North Quay Road, Newhaven, East Sussex, BN9 0AB Tel: (01273) 513611 E-mail: info@fishcontemporaryfurniture.com
Floor To Ceiling Fitted Bedrooms, 4 Far Field Road, Edenthorpe, Doncaster, South Yorkshire, DN3 2NS Tel: (01302) 886074 Fax: (01302) 886074
▶ David Fox Design, Briars Lane, Stainforth, Doncaster, South Yorkshire, DN7 5AZ Tel: (01302) 849299 Fax: (01302) 849299 E-mail: info@davidfoxdesign.com
Fray Design Ltd, Ghyll Way Airedale Business Centre, Keighley Road, Skipton, North Yorkshire, BD23 2TZ Tel: (01756) 704040 Fax: (01756) 704041 E-mail: sales@fraydesign.co.uk
Fredrose Furniture, 17 Rutland Gardens, Sandy, Bedfordshire, SG19 1JG Tel: (01767) 681923 Fax: (01767) 691931
Gilbert & Sons, Sharrow Vale Road, Sheffield, S11 8XD Tel: 0114-267 0634 Fax: 0114-267 0634
Godfrey Syrett Ltd, Littleburn Industrial Estate, Langley Moor, Durham, DH7 8HE Tel: 0191-268 1010 Fax: 0191-378 1660 E-mail: sales@godfreysyrett.co.uk
H N T Creative, 70-74 Stewarts Road, London, SW8 4DE Tel: (020) 7720 0223 Fax: (020) 7622 3666
Peter Hall & Son, Danes Road, Staveley, Kendal, Cumbria, LA8 9PR Tel: (01539) 821633 Fax: (01539) 821905 E-mail: info@peter-hall.co.uk
Hayloft Woodwork Ltd, 3 Bond Street, Chiswick, London, W4 1QZ Tel: (020) 8747 3510 Fax: (020) 8742 1860
Knightsbridge Reproduction, Unit 14 Greenside Trading Centre, Greenside Lane, Droylsden, Manchester, M43 7AJ Tel: 0161-370 2999 Fax: 0161-371 1991
Linford Furniture, Mill Lane, Stony Stratford, Milton Keynes, MK11 1EW Tel: (01908) 261521
Mccarthy Design, Ladygrove Court, Preston, Hitchin, Hertfordshire, SG4 7SA Tel: (01462) 440957 Fax: (01462) 440961 E-mail: peter@mccarthydesign.co.uk
Mark Brazier Jones, Hyde Hall Barn, Sandon, Buntingford, Hertfordshire, SG9 0RU Tel: (01763) 273599 Fax: (01763) 273410 E-mail: studio@braizer-jones.com
Wayne Maxwell Designs, Unit6, Resolution Way, Deptford, London, SE8 4NT Tel: (020) 8691 3000 E-mail: designs@waynemaxwell.com
Millwood Cabinet Makers, Bates Farm, Wittersham, Tenterden, Kent, TN30 7PL Tel: (01797) 270170 Fax: (01797) 270505

FURNITURE DESIGNERS OR CONSULTANTS – *continued*

Noble Russell Furniture Ltd, Station Road, Uppingham, Rutland, Leicestershire, LE15 9TX Tel: (01572) 821591 Fax: (01572) 823434 E-mail: sales@noblerussell.co.uk
Simon Thomas Pirie, Slepe Farm Workshop, Dorchester Road, Lytchett Minster, Poole, Dorset, BH16 6HT Tel: (01202) 625725 Fax: (01202) 625725 E-mail: sales@simonthomaspirie.co.uk
Praxis Farm Ltd, Hoe Lane, Flansham, Bognor Regis, West Sussex, PO22 8NN Tel: (01243) 587354 Fax: (01243) 587353
▶ Prestwood Interiors, 24 Orchard Lane, Prestwood, Great Missenden, Buckinghamshire, HP16 0NN Tel: (0800) 1694615 Fax: (01494) 890607 E-mail: asheri1234@aol.com
Raleigh Workshop Ltd, 1a Saltoun Road, London, SW2 1EN Tel: (020) 7733 8110 Fax: (020) 7733 8778
▶ Response Furniture Systems Ltd, 52 Tanners Drive, Blakelands, Milton Keynes, MK14 5BW Tel: (01908) 216466 Fax: (01908) 216467 E-mail: sales@responsefurnituresystems.co.uk
Richard Williams, 7 28 Plantation Road, Amersham, Buckinghamshire, HP6 6HL Tel: (01494) 729026 Fax: (01494) 721169 E-mail: r@richardwilliamsfurniture.com
▶ Neil Robinson, Goyt Mill, Upper Hibbert Lane, Marple, Stockport, Cheshire, SK6 7HX Tel: 0161-449 5444 Fax: 0161-449 5444
▶ Rogeroger, 24 Clonbrock Road, London, N16 8RR Tel: (020) 7254 7706 Fax: (020) 7254 7706 E-mail: info@rogeroger.co.uk
Rustic Leather Co., 3 Penllwyngwent Industrial Estate, Saville Road, Ogmore Vale, Bridgend, Mid Glamorgan, CF32 7AX Tel: (01656) 842832 Fax: (01656) 841144 E-mail: sales@therusticleathercompany.co.uk
Sean Feeney Furniture, The Old School House, Preston on Stour, Stratford-upon-Avon, Warwickshire, CV37 8NG Tel: (01789) 450519 E-mail: sales@seanfeeneyfurniture.co.uk
Serota Furniture, 92 Hilliard Road, Northwood, Middlesex, HA6 1SW Tel: (01923) 840697 E-mail: michael@serota.co.uk
Shire Business Interiors, Snowdown, PO Box 123 Dough Bank, Ombersley, Droitwich, Worcestershire, WR9 0HN Tel: (01905) 621691 Fax: (01905) 621345 E-mail: sales@shirebusinessinteriors.co.uk
Tiger Moth Designs, Greenfields Studios, Halnaker, Chichester, W. Sussex, PO18 0NQ Tel: 01243 528508
Timack NW Ltd, Premier Mill, Begonia Street, Darwen, Lancashire, BB3 2DP Tel: (01254) 775401 Fax: (01254) 703318 E-mail: sales@timack.co.uk
Trojan Woodworking, Bourne Road, Pode Hole, Spalding, Lincolnshire, PE11 3LW Tel: (01775) 767786 Fax: (01775) 767786
Darren Tyson Furniture, 10 Lane End Road, High Wycombe, Buckinghamshire, HP12 4JF Tel: (01494) 445090
John Warren Furniture Ltd, 4-6 New Inn, Broadway, London, EC2A 3PZ Tel: (020) 8986 3366 Fax: (020) 7729 8770 E-mail: sales@jwfltd.co.uk

FURNITURE FASTENERS

B G B Services & Supply Ltd, Unit 52, Sovereign Road, Kings Norton Business Centre, Birmingham, B30 3HN Tel: 0121-458 5424 Fax: 0121-459 4756 E-mail: ian@bgbservices.co.uk
Haroby Ltd, Unit 139 Bradley Hall Trading Estate, Bradley Lane, Standish, Wigan, Lancashire, WN6 0XQ Tel: (01257) 478100 Fax: (01257) 478109 E-mail: fasteners@haroby.co.uk
Quicksharp Services, 20 Old Mill Road, Kings Langley, Hertfordshire, WD4 8QT Tel: (01923) 262054 Fax: (01923) 261150
R P S Trading Ltd, Unit 2, S D H Industrial Estate, Asquith Bottom Mill, Sowerby Bridge, Halifax, West Yorkshire, HX6 3BT Tel: (01422) 839303 Fax: (01422) 836800
Walls Pre Pack Ltd, 37 Avenue Road, Bilston, West Midlands, WV14 9DJ Tel: (01902) 883333

FURNITURE FITTINGS, *See also headings for particular material*

A C Sissling Specialist Ironmongers Ltd, 20 Fitzwilliam Street, Bradford, West Yorkshire, BD4 7BL Tel: (01274) 200320 Fax: (01274) 220330 E-mail: sales@sissling-group.co.uk
Agostino Ferrari UK Ltd, Units H & L Strawberry Street Industrial Estate, Strawberry Street, Hull, HU9 1EN Tel: (01482) 594450 Fax: (01482) 594455 E-mail: info@aferrariuk.com
Alexander Fitted Furniture, 25 Beech Grove, Bedlington, Northumberland, NE22 5DA Tel: (01670) 820200 Fax: (01670) 820200
Beaumont Structural Consultants, Goose Green Marsh, La Rue Du Craslin, St. Peter, Jersey, JE3 7BU Tel: (01534) 822888 Fax: (01534) 822889
Boscombe Beds & Suites, 40 Ashley Road, Bournemouth, BH1 4LJ Tel: (01202) 300909 Fax: (01202) 720888 E-mail: sales@boscombebeds.com
▶ Brophy Castings, Building 15 Soho Mills, Wooburn Green, High Wycombe, Buckinghamshire, HP10 0PF Tel: (01628) 525068 Fax: (01628) 525129 E-mail: info@brophycastings.co.uk
Conisborough Furniture Components Ltd, Denaby Lane Industrial Estate, Denaby Main, Doncaster, South Yorkshire, DN12 4JS Tel: (01709) 863122 Fax: (01709) 865068 E-mail: components@conisborough.com
Crofts & Assinder, Standard Brass Works, Lombard Street, Deritend, Birmingham, B12 0QX Tel: 0121-622 1074 Fax: 0121-622 1074 E-mail: general@crofts.co.uk
East Coast Fittings, Gaddesby Lane, Rearsby, Leicester, LE7 4YH Tel: (01664) 424288 Fax: (01664) 424243 E-mail: sales@eastcoastfittings.co.uk
Fenton Bed Warehouse, 267 City Road, Stoke-on-Trent, ST4 2QA Tel: (01782) 415649 Fax: (01782) 415649 E-mail: sales@fentonbeds.co.uk
Hammonds Furniture Ltd, Great Bridge Road, Bilston, West Midlands, WV14 8LB Tel: (01902) 490133 Fax: (01902) 494936
Hardex Fittings, Shilton Industrial Estate, Bulkington Road, Coventry, CV7 9JY Tel: (024) 7658 7600 Fax: (024) 7658 7606 E-mail: enquiries@hardex.co.uk
Hiatt Hardware Ltd, Hiatt Industrial Estate, Baltimore Road, Great Barr, Birmingham, B42 1HZ Tel: 0121-358 4970 Fax: 0121-357 6033 E-mail: sales@hiatt-hardware.com
J Shiner & Sons Ltd, 8 Windmill Street, London, W1T 2JE Tel: (020) 7636 0740 Fax: (020) 7580 0740 E-mail: info@j-shiner.co.uk
K J Bridgewater, 6 Jarvis Close, Hinckley, Leicestershire, LE10 1PG Tel: (01455) 635363 Fax: (01455) 635363
Knaggs Furniture Fittings, Ash Industrial Estate, Flex Meadow, Harlow, Essex, CM19 5TJ Tel: (01279) 641199 Fax: (01279) 641133 E-mail: enquiries@knaggs4fittings.co.uk
M S Midlands Ltd, Unit 9, Oak Street Trading Estate, Quarry Bank, Brierley Hill, West Midlands, DY5 2JQ Tel: (01384) 262252 Fax: (01384) 484951
P.G. Perry, Summerfield House, Watling Street, Muckley Corner, Lichfield, Staffordshire, WS14 0BD Tel: (01543) 375695
Pine Emporium, Piccotts End, Hemel Hempstead, Hertfordshire, HP1 3BA Tel: (01442) 244644 Fax: (01442) 246181
The Pinery, 233 Oakbrook Road, Sheffield, S11 7EB Tel: 0114-230 2635 Fax: 0114-230 2635 E-mail: mail@pinery.co.uk
Plastic Parts Centre, Unit 12 Old Forge Trading Estate, Dudley Road, Stourbridge, West Midlands, DY9 8EL Tel: (01384) 424248 Fax: (01384) 424348 E-mail: sales@mossplastics.co.uk
R P S Trading Ltd, Unit 2, S D H Industrial Estate, Asquith Bottom Mill, Sowerby Bridge, Halifax, West Yorkshire, HX6 3BT Tel: (01422) 839303 Fax: (01422) 836800
▶ Rycroft Distribution, Blackmore Road, Hill Barton Business Park, Clyst St. Mary, Exeter, EX5 1SA Tel: (01395) 233603
S C F Hardware Ltd, 3 Brook Park Estate, 27 Brook Road, Wimborne, Dorset, BH21 2BH Tel: (01202) 857140 Fax: (01202) 884419 E-mail: sales@scfhardware.com
Scunthorpe Interior Design, 242 Ashby High Street, Scunthorpe, South Humberside, DN16 2SE Tel: (01724) 289556 Fax: (01724) 289556
Sharps Bedrooms Ltd, 58-60 High Street, Banstead, Surrey, SM7 2LX Tel: (01737) 370321
Sharps Bedrooms Ltd, C/o, Portfield Way, Chichester, W. Sussex, PO19 7YH Tel: 01243 530936
Sleepmasters Ltd, Unit 7 Great Eastern Way, Parkgate, Rotherham, South Yorkshire, S62 6JD Tel: (01709) 780802 Fax: (01709) 780802
Sycamore Products Ltd, Unit 6a Astra Park, Parkside Lane, Leeds, LS11 5SZ Tel: 0113-271 3200 Fax: 0113-276 1195
Titus International plc, Ridgeway Industrial Estate, Iver, Buckinghamshire, SL0 9HW Tel: (01753) 654680 Fax: (01753) 655385 E-mail: ryanhammond@titusint.com
Woodfit Ltd, Kem Mill, Kem Mill Lane, Whittle-le-Woods, Chorley, Lancashire, PR6 7EA Tel: (01257) 266421 Fax: (01257) 264271 E-mail: sales@woodfit.com

FURNITURE FRAMES

A & A Furnishings Ltd, Farington, Leyland, PR25 4GU Tel: (01772) 457836 Fax: (01772) 436188
E Hughes, 28 Old Moy Road, Dungannon, County Tyrone, BT71 6RY Tel: (028) 8775 2030 Fax: (028) 8772 2060
R G B Products, Unit 2 Gilmans Industrial Estate, Billingshurst, West Sussex, RH14 9EZ Tel: (01403) 783670 Fax: (01403) 783670
▶ P Shipston & Sons, Victoria Mill, Watt Street, Sabden, Clitheroe, Lancashire, BB7 9ED Tel: (01282) 770225 Fax: (01282) 777146
Technic Wood Products Ltd, Cambrian Industrial Estate East Side, Coedcae Lane, Pontyclun, Mid Glamorgan, CF72 9EW Tel: (01443) 222110
Traditional Woodworking Co. Ltd, Unit 11 North St Trading Estate, Brierley Hill, West Midlands, DY5 3QF Tel: (01384) 262405 Fax: (01384) 483707
Watchwise Ltd, 20 North River Road, Great Yarmouth, Norfolk, NR30 1SG Tel: (01493) 842216 Fax: (01493) 857703 E-mail: ngraver@watchwise.co.uk

FURNITURE HIRE

Camden Hire Ltd, Unit C, 125 Brantwood Road, Tottenham, London, N17 0DX Tel: (020) 8961 6161 Fax: (020) 8961 6162 E-mail: contact@thorns.co.uk
Cater Hire Ltd, Unit J Gregorys Bank, Worcester, WR3 8AB Tel: (01905) 23260 Fax: (01905) 23152 E-mail: info@cater-hire.co.uk
Chichester Canvas, Chichester Road, Sidlesham Common, Chichester, West Sussex, PO20 7PY Tel: (01243) 641164 Fax: (01243) 641888 E-mail: sales@chicanvas.co.uk
Dover Marquee Co. Ltd, 30 Mayfield Avenue, Dover, Kent, CT16 2PL Tel: (01304) 215315 Fax: (01304) 202086 E-mail: sales@dover-marquee.co.uk
Event Hire, Stuart Road, Bredbury Park Industrial Estate, Bredbury, Stockport, Cheshire, SK6 2SR Tel: 0161-494 5213 Fax: 0161-494 5213 E-mail: info@mcmeventhire.co.uk
Exoplan International Ltd, Unit 13, Industrial Estate, National Exhibition Centre, Birmingham, B40 1PJ Tel: 0121-780 4513 Fax: 0121-780 4810 E-mail: sales@exoplan.co.uk
Hart & Co Windsor, 151 St Leonards Road, Windsor, Berkshire, SL4 3DW Tel: (01753) 864075 Fax: (01753) 830251 E-mail: sales@hartstents.co.uk
Johnson Hospitality Services Ltd, Unit 5, Martinbridge Trading Estate, Lincoln Road, Enfield, Middlesex, EN1 1QL Tel: (020) 8443 3333 Fax: (020) 8805 8710
Markham Marquees, Morrow House, Morrow Lane, Ardleigh, Colchester, CO7 7NG Tel: (01206) 231084 Fax: (01206) 230713 E-mail: info@markham-marquees.co.uk
Regency Marquees Ltd, Bilsington Road, Willow Court, Ruckinge, Ashford, Kent, TN26 2PB Tel: (01233) 732130 Fax: (01233) 733757 E-mail: info@regencymarquees.co.uk

FURNITURE IMPORT/EXPORT MERCHANTS OR AGENTS

Artedi (U K) Ltd, Unit D, Everitt Road, London, NW10 6PL Tel: (020) 8961 6555 Fax: (020) 8961 9996
Bedstead Collection, 1 & 2 Montpellier Walk, The Ginnel, Harrogate, North Yorkshire, HG1 2RB Tel: (01423) 528111 Fax: (01423) 538321
Bruton Classic Furniture Ltd, Riverside, Station Road, Bruton, Somerset, BA10 0EH Tel: (01749) 813266 Fax: (01749) 813266 E-mail: sales@brutonclassic.co.uk
Earsham Hall Pine, 6 St Benedicts Street, Norwich, NR2 4AG Tel: (01603) 615710 Fax: (01603) 615710 E-mail: sales@earshamhallpine.co.uk
Febland Group Ltd, Ashworth Road, Marton, Blackpool, FY4 4UN Tel: (01253) 600600 Fax: (01253) 792211 E-mail: info@febland.co.uk
▶ International Furniture Exporters, Old Cement Works, South Heighton, Newhaven, East Sussex, BN9 0HS Tel: (01273) 611251 Fax: (01273) 611574
Jacobs Young & Westbury, Bridge Road, Haywards Heath, West Sussex, RH16 1UA Tel: (01444) 412411 Fax: (01444) 457662 E-mail: sales@jyw-uk.com
Oomers Ltd, 8 St. Andrew's Road, London, E17 6BD Tel: (020) 8527 8388 Fax: (020) 8527 8288 E-mail: sales@oomers.co.uk
Quitmann Furniture, Unit 1, Avonmouth Way West, Bristol, BS11 9EX Tel: 0117-982 2004 Fax: 0117-982 2009 E-mail: info@quitmannfurniture.co.uk
Scarthingwell Replicas, Scarthingwell Centre Scarthingwell, Barkston Ash, Tadcaster, North Yorkshire, LS24 9Pf Tel: (01937) 557877 Fax: (01937) 558084 E-mail: sales@scarthingwell.co.uk
Sharps Bedrooms Ltd, Enterprise Way, Luton, LU3 4BW Tel: (01582) 561345
Wilkinsons Furniture, Adlington Industrial Estate, Adlington, Macclesfield, Cheshire, SK10 4NL Tel: (01625) 870070 Fax: (01625) 870070

FURNITURE INTERIOR DESIGN CONSULTANCY

▶ 1:50, 15 Silver Birch Close, Sholing, Southampton, SO19 8FY Tel: (0845) 2262817 E-mail: info@1-50.co.uk
▶ Amber Radiator Covers, 14 Freemans Way, Harrogate, North Yorkshire, HG3 1DH Tel: (01423) 883386 Fax: (01423) 883386 E-mail: sales@amberradiatorcovers.co.uk
▶ Chantilly, Reading Road, Cholsey, Wallingford, Oxon, OX10 9HL Tel: 01491 652848 Fax: 07889 644848 E-mail: susiegsmith@btinernet.com
Clear Water Interiors, 69 Anglesmede Crescent, Pinner, Middlesex, HA5 5ST Tel: (020) 8863 1732
▶ Interior Solutions, 57 Comiston View, Edinburgh, EH10 6LT Tel: 0131-445 2200 Fax: 0131-466 1516 E-mail: mail@interiorsolutionsedinburgh.com
Interiors By Design, 37 The Spinney, Pulborough, West Sussex, RH20 2AP Tel: (01798) 874969 E-mail: interiorsbydesign@ukonline.co.uk
▶ Kelson Interiors, Topcliffe Lane, Morley, Leeds, LS27 0HW Tel: 0113-252 7900 Fax: 0113-252 7977 E-mail: info@kelson.co.uk
▶ Christina Lees, Cocoa Court, 21a Pillory Street, Nantwich, Cheshire, CW5 5BZ Tel: (01270) 611142 Fax: (01270) 842822
▶ Lemon Tree Interiors, 5 Cambridge Road, Ely, Cambridgeshire, CB7 4HJ Tel: (01353) 610585 Fax: (01353) 610466 E-mail: Design@LemonTreeInteriors.Co.Uk
Wayne Maxwell Designs, Unit6, Resolution Way, Deptford, London, SE8 4NT Tel: (020) 8691 3000 E-mail: designs@waynemaxwell.com
▶ Sally Treloar, Southview, Whiteoak Green, Hailey, Witney, Oxfordshire, OX29 9XP Tel: 01993 869119 E-mail: support@firstideas.co.uk
▶ Visual Communications, 209 Lynchford Road, Farnborough, Hampshire, GU14 6HF Tel: (01252) 540044 Fax: (01252) 516616 E-mail: tara@vis-com.net

FURNITURE POLISH

Cambridge Traditional Products, Millfield, Cottenham, Cambridge, CB4 8RE Tel: (01954) 251380 Fax: (01954) 251387 E-mail: info@bees-wax.co.uk
Fiddes & Son Ltd, Florence Works, Brindley Road, Cardiff, CF11 8TX Tel: (029) 2034 0323 Fax: (029) 2034 3235 E-mail: finishes@fiddes.co.uk
Regency Gold Ltd, Unit 4 Minafon Yard, Betws Yn Rhos, Abergele, Clwyd, LL22 8AW Tel: (01492) 680440 Fax: (01492) 680633 E-mail: support@regencygold.co.uk

FURNITURE REPAIR SUPPLIES

▶ Gilletts Upholstrey, 15 Cranbrook Terrace, Cranleigh, Surrey, GU6 7ES Tel: (01483) 274897E-mail: gillettsupholstrey@yahoo.co.uk

FURNITURE RESTORATION OR REPAIR SPECIALIST SERVICES

All Pine, 97 Dymchurch Road, Hythe, Kent, CT21 6JN Tel: (01303) 262373 Fax: (01303) 262373
Beckwith & Son, St. Nicholas Hall, 43 St. Andrew Street, Hertford, SG14 1HZ Tel: (01992) 582079 Fax: (01992) 581009 E-mail: sales@beckwithandsonantiques.co.uk
Bloxwich Co., Park Road, Bloxwich, Walsall, WS3 3SS Tel: (01922) 710588 Fax: (01922) 710588
Boswell & Davis, 1 Sunbury Workshops, Swanfield Street, London, E2 7LF Tel: (020) 7739 5738
Brights Of Nettlebed, The Old Gaol, The Strand, Topsham, Exeter, EX3 0JB Tel: (01392) 877443 Fax: (01392) 877633
Brockinwood French Polishing, Unit 16 Admington Lane, Admington, Shipston-on-Stour, Warwickshire, CV36 4JJ Tel: (01789) 450914
Browns, 2 Hallam Mill, Hallam Street, Stockport, Cheshire, SK2 6PT Tel: (01925) 759740 Fax: 0161-476 4533
C T Finishings (Services) (Manufacturing), Unit 29 Enterprise House, Balloo Industrial Estate, Bangor, County Down, BT19 7QT Tel: (028) 9127 1525 Fax: (028) 9127 0080
Cane Workshop, The Gospel Hall, Westport, Langport, Somerset, TA10 0BH Tel: (01460) 281636
▶ Carey B Restoration, Units 2-3, 63A Westcote Road, London, SW16 6BN Tel: (020) 8696 7555 E-mail: info@antiquerestoration.co.uk
Castle Reproductions Skipton Ltd, 26-27 North Street, Ripon, North Yorkshire, HG4 1HJ Tel: (01765) 690307 Fax: (01423) 712116
Church Lane Restorations, 1 Church La, Teddington, Middx, TW11 8PA Tel: (020) 8977 2526
Corwell Cabinet Makers, Unit 6 Amners Farm, Burghfield, Reading, RG30 3UE Tel: 0118-983 3404 Fax: 0118-983 3404 E-mail: info@corwell.co.uk
Dashdoctor Plastic & Leather Repair, 112 Dukes Brow, Blackburn, BB2 6DJ Tel: 01254 698783 Fax: 01254 698783
▶ Stephen J. Davies, 43 Curtis Avenue, Abingdon, Oxfordshire, OX14 3UL Tel: (01235) 200869
▶ DND, 25 Ackworth Road, Portsmouth, PO3 5NS Tel: (023) 9265 2866 Fax: 023 92652866 E-mail: enquiries@dnd.co.uk
E & A Wates Ltd, 82-84 Mitcham Lane, London, SW16 6NR Tel: (020) 8769 2205 Fax: (020) 8677 4766 E-mail: sales@eandawates.co.uk
▶ East Anglia Leather, Rushmere Cottage, The Green, Wickham Skeith, Eye, Suffolk, IP23 8LX Tel: (01449) 766722 Fax: (01449) 766722 E-mail: sales@leather-furniture-repairs.com
Ellis Furniture, Dormers, Main Road, Ashbocking, Ipswich, IP6 9JX Tel: (01473) 890309 Fax: (01473) 890309 E-mail: iroko@tinyonline.co.uk
Fenbrook Kitchen & Antique Pine Furniture, 103 Sidbury, Worcester, WR1 2HU Tel: (01905) 767537

▶ indicates data change since last edition

FURNITURE RESTORATION OR REPAIR SPECIALIST SERVICES – *continued*

Fernyhough Restoration, Hall End Farm, Watling Street, Dordon, Tamworth, Staffordshire, B78 1SZ Tel: (01827) 330944

Gatts Ltd, 11-13 Balmoral Terrace, Aberdeen, AB10 6HH Tel: (01224) 582288 Fax: (01224) 582299 E-mail: gatts@chessgroup.co.uk

▶ Gilletts Upholstrey, 15 Cranbrook Terrace, Cranleigh, Surrey, GU6 7ES Tel: (01483) 274897E-mail: gillettsupholstrey@yahoo.co.uk

E & S Gott, Priestley Butts, Whitby Road, Pickering, North Yorkshire, YO18 7HL Tel: (01751) 472009

I & P Clark, Granville Street, Willenhall, West Midlands, WV13 1DN Tel: (01902) 636957

Alf McKay, Manor Barn, Crewkerne, Somerset, TA18 8QT Tel: (01460) 78916 Fax: (01460) 78916

▶ Magic Man Ltd, Gordon House, 15 Gordon Road, Portslade, Brighton, BN41 1GL Tel: (01273) 417110 Fax: (0845) 4581011 E-mail: info@magicman.ltd.uk

Michael Figgitt Upholstery Upholstery, Orleans Close, Unit 3, Four Pools Industrial Estate, Evesham, Worcestershire, WR11 2FP Tel: (01386) 45120 Fax: (01386) 45264 E-mail: sales@figgittupholstery.co.uk

Millbrook Furnishings Industries, Stephenson Road, Calmore Industrial Estate, Totton, Southampton, SO40 3RY Tel: (023) 8066 2221 Fax: (023) 8066 2264E-mail: sales@mfil.co.uk

Office Principles, 472 Basingstoke Road, Reading, RG2 0QN Tel: 0118-986 9860 Fax: 0118-967 2283

Overton Cabinet Makers, 85 Milestone Road, Carterton, Oxfordshire, OX18 3RL Tel: (01993) 843376 E-mail: info@thecraftsman.co.uk

▶ Prestwood Interiors, 24 Orchard Lane, Prestwood, Great Missenden, Buckinghamshire, HP16 0NN Tel: (0800) 1694615 Fax: (01494) 890607 E-mail: asheri1234@aol.com

Servi-Sew, 38 The Chase, Stroud, Gloucestershire, GL5 4SB Tel: (01453) 757617

Supreme Seating & Desking Ltd, 4 40 Wilton Road, Reading, RG30 2SS Tel: 0118-959 5535 Fax: 0118-950 3271 E-mail: info@supremeseating.com

▶ Suretech Services Ltd, 12 Florence Road, Codsall, Wolverhampton, WV8 1JD Tel: (01902) 840684 Fax: (01902) 847088 E-mail: info@suretechservices.co.uk

W T Parkes Upholstery, Regency Works, 1a Shakleton Road, Coventry, CV5 6HT Tel: (024) 7669 1199

FURNITURE RETAILER SOFTWARE

Global Technology Resource, 741 Oldham Road, Rochdale, Lancashire, OL16 4RH Tel: (01706) 651222

FURNITURE WHOLESALERS

▶ Ambient Lounge, Elm Road, Kingston Upon Thames, Surrey, KT2 6HT Tel: (0870) 2851619 Fax: (0870) 2851613 E-mail: info@ambientlounge.com

▶ Brown & Biggs, Continental House, Avis Way, Newhaven, East Sussex, BN9 0DH Tel: (01273) 515919 Fax: (01273) 515939

Decking (NI) Ltd, 75 Coole Road, Dungannon, County Tyrone, BT71 5DR Tel: (028) 8774 1199 Fax: (028) 87749140

▶ Harris Office Furniture Ltd, 41 Grove Street, Edinburgh, EH3 8AF Tel: 0131-229 3180 Fax: 0131-228 3767

▶ ImagineHowe, Rennadal House, Firth, Orkney, KW17 2NY Tel: (07786) 578000

▶ Konteaki Furniture Importers, Unit C Aisecome Way, Weston-super-Mare, Avon, BS22 8NA Tel: (01934) 425050 Fax: (01934) 425050 E-mail: steve@hattrick-furniture.co.uk

Old Time, Dairy Hall, 2a John Street, Newtownards, County Down, BT23 4LZ Tel: (028) 9181 7417 Fax: (028) 9181 7169 E-mail: amacrory@aol.com

▶ The Urban Decor Shop, PO Box 245, Barnstaple, Devon, EX32 9WZ Tel: (01271) 323634 E-mail: info@theurbandecorshop.com

V J Imports Ltd, Unit 14,, Welch Hill St, Leigh, Lancs, WN7 4DU Tel: 01942 673281 E-mail: vjimports@fsmail.net

▶ Victoria Jones Ltd, Wandsworth Bridge Road, London, SW6 2UH Tel: (020) 7610 6969 Fax: (020) 7610 9191 E-mail: info@vjones.com

FURNITURE WIPES

▶ Saraco Industries, PO Box 190, Bolton, BL1 8AH Tel: (01204) 381990 Fax: (01204) 525190 E-mail: info@saraco-industries.com

FURNITURE, CATERING

Band International, Woodlands, Middleton, Freshwater, Isle of Wight, PO40 9RW Tel: (01983) 755858 Fax: (01983) 756273 E-mail: will@band.co.uk

FURNITURE, HEALTH CARE

▶ Bradma Furniture, Unit 12 Suprema Business Park, Suprema Avenue, Edington, Bridgwater, Somerset, TA7 9LF Tel: (01278) 723467 Fax: (01278) 723129

Huntleigh Renray, Huntleigh Renray Ltd, Road Five, Winsford Industrial Estate, Winsford, Cheshire, CW7 3RB Tel: (01606) 593456 Fax: (01606) 861354 E-mail: sales@renraydavidbaker.co.uk

FURNITURE, HOTEL, *See Hotel etc*

FURNITURE, INDUSTRIAL, *See also headings for particular types*

Fine Line Interiors, Surrex Farm, Colchester Road, Coggeshall, Colchester, CO6 1RR Tel: (01376) 561611 Fax: (01376) 561110

▶ Fish Contemporary, North Quay Road, Newhaven, East Sussex, BN9 0AB Tel: (01273) 513611 E-mail: info@fishcontemporaryfurniture.com

Hov & Dokka UK Ltd, 9 Green Hill Road, Camberley, Surrey, GU15 1PF Tel: (01276) 22599 Fax: (01276) 25333

Interfocus Design Ltd, Unit 4 Molesworth Business Estate, Molesworth, Huntingdon, Cambridgeshire, PE28 0QG Tel: (01832) 710647 Fax: (01832) 710142

Litton Furniture, Bonslea House, White Lane Close, Sturminster Newton, Dorset, DT10 1EJ Tel: (01258) 472359 Fax: (01258) 473512

Nortek Educational Furniture & Equipment Ltd, Vale Works, Priesty Fields Industrial Estate, Congleton, Cheshire, CW12 4AQ Tel: (01260) 298321 Fax: (01260) 298169 E-mail: sales@nortekgroup.co.uk

Quantum Industries Ltd, D Frenbury Estate, Drayton High Road, Norwich, NR6 5DP Tel: (01603) 789000 Fax: (01603) 405476 E-mail: enquiries@selbix.co.uk

Remploy Furniture Group, Cwmgarw Road, Upper Brynamman, Ammanford, Dyfed, SA18 1DG Tel: (01269) 822141 Fax: (01269) 826188 E-mail: anna.davies@remploy.co.uk

FURNITURE, OUTDOOR

Branson Leisure Ltd, Fosters Croft, Foster Street, Harlow, Essex, CM17 9HS Tel: (01279) 432151 Fax: (01279) 450542 E-mail: sales@bransonleisure.co.uk

Fire Island, Southdowns, Redruth, Cornwall, TR15 2NW Tel: (01209) 314448 Fax: (01209) 313191 E-mail: sales@fireisland.co.uk

Mode Lifestyle, Winsham, Chard, Somerset, TA20 4BZ Tel: (0870) 2403606 E-mail: e@mode.co.uk

Orchard Street Furniture, 119 The Street, Crowmarsh Gifford, Wallingford, Oxfordshire, OX10 8EF Tel: (01491) 826100 Fax: (01491) 642126 E-mail: sales@orchardstreet.co.uk

FURNITURE, RATTAN

Birds Baskets, The Old School House, Butt Lane, Burgh Castle, Great Yarmouth, Norfolk, NR31 9QE Tel: (01493) 843392 Fax: (01493) 843392 E-mail: basketsbirds@aol.com

FURNITURE, TO SPECIFICATION/CUSTOM MADE

A Beswetherick, Venn Farm, Launcells, Bude, Cornwall, EX23 9LL Tel: (01288) 321472

Alan Johnson Cabinet Maker, Kingsgate Workshops, 110-116 Kingsgate Road, London, NW6 2JG Tel: (020) 7372 6736 Fax: (020) 7328 7878

Andrew Paul Bulmer, Mill House, Mill Lane, Topcliffe, Thirsk, North Yorkshire, YO7 3RZ Tel: (01845) 578172 Fax: (01845) 578172

Barratt & Swann, Hardigate Road, Cropwell Butler, Nottingham, NG12 3AH Tel: 0115-933 2642 Fax: 0115-933 3957 E-mail: info@barrattandswan.co.uk

Bedroom Options, 13 Wychwood Avenue, Edgware, Middlesex, HA8 6TL Tel: (020) 8952 3200 Fax: (020) 8952 3200

Bee Line Fitted Bedrooms, 71 Station Road, Flitwick, Bedford, MK45 1JU Tel: (01525) 712090 Fax: (01525) 712090

Bespoke Services (Manchester) Ltd, Whitehill Industrial Estate, Whitehill Street, Reddish, Stockport, Cheshire, SK5 7LW Tel: 0161-476 3522 Fax: 0161-476 0522 E-mail: info@bespoke-services.co.uk

Broxted Furniture, Chickney Hall Farm, Chickney, Broxted, Dunmow, Essex, CM6 2BY Tel: (01279) 850733

C D S Interiors, 26 Westover Road, Fleet, Hampshire, GU51 3DG Tel: (01252) 623047

▶ Carthouse Furniture, Glebe Farm, Carlton Miniott, Thirsk, North Yorkshire, YO7 4NJ Tel: (01845) 525110 Fax: (01845) 574326 E-mail: enquire@carthousefurniture.com

Donal Channer & Co., 50-52 Tower Hill, Dilton Marsh, Westbury, Wiltshire, BA13 4DA Tel: (01373) 824895 Fax: (01373) 824895

Cobweb Crafts, The Old School, Cadney Road, Howsham, Market Rasen, Lincolnshire, LN7 6LA Tel: (01652) 678761 Fax: (01652) 678710

Countryside Cabinet Maker, 8 Wellsway Works, Wells Road, Radstock, BA3 3RZ Tel: (0781) 2688101 Fax: (01225) 840864 E-mail: scott.joyce@virgin.net

David Colwell, Llawr-Y-Glyn, Llawr-y-Glyn, Caersws, Powys, SY17 5RH Tel: (01686) 430434 E-mail: info@davidcolwell.com

Davison Highley Ltd, Old Oxford Road, Piddington, High Wycombe, Buckinghamshire, HP14 3BE Tel: (01494) 883862 Fax: (01494) 881572 E-mail: magic@davisonhighley.co.uk

Delcor Furniture Ltd, Double Row, Seaton Delaval, Whitley Bay, Tyne & Wear, NE25 0PR Tel: 0191-237 2395 Fax: 0191-237 6892

Design Line, G/3, Unit Joseph Adamson Industrial Estate Croft Street, Hyde, Cheshire, SK14 1EE Tel: 0161-368 0713 Fax: 0161-368 0713 E-mail: vbirley@hotmail.com

Dreams plc, Lonsdale House, 7-11 High Street, Reigate, Surrey, RH2 9AA Tel: (01737) 242451 Fax: (01737) 242452

E C Hodge MF Ltd, Norton Road, Stevenage, Hertfordshire, SG1 2BB Tel: (01438) 357341 Fax: (01438) 361408 E-mail: echodgemflimited@aol.com

Fox Country Furniture, Reapsmoor, Longnor, Buxton, Derbyshire, SK17 0LG Tel: (01298) 84467 Fax: 01298 84467

Foxglove Kitchens, 56-58 High Street, Swavesey, Cambridge, CB4 5QU Tel: (01954) 230263 Fax: (01954) 230263

Greenheart Design Ltd, The Tall House, Harberton, Totnes, Devon, TQ9 7SQ Tel: (01803) 868685 Fax: (01803) 866694

H N D UK Ltd, Unit 15 Shrub Hill Industrial Estate, Worcester, WR4 9EL Tel: (01905) 29294 E-mail: info@hnd-uk.com

Hawk Furniture Ltd, Holme Industrial Estate, Skiff Lane, Holme-on-Spalding-Moor, York, YO43 4BB Tel: (01430) 861229 Fax: (01430) 861225E-mail: enquiries@hawkfurniture.co.uk

Hayloft Woodwork Ltd, 3 Bond Street, Chiswick, London, W4 1QZ Tel: (020) 8747 3510 Fax: (020) 8742 1860

Interior Bedding Centre, 9-10 Station Road, Sunderland, SR6 9AA Tel: 0191-549 9998 Fax: 0191-297 0999

Iron Awe, Unit 24 Lansil Walk, Lansil Industrial Estate, Lancaster, LA1 3PQ Tel: (01524) 845511 Fax: (01524) 845511 E-mail: petersmalley@ironawe.com

J R Spalding, 55 Mill Street, Kingston upon Thames, Surrey, KT1 2RG Tel: (020) 8546 0363 Fax: (020) 8546 0363 E-mail: jrspalding.joinery@amserve.net

▶ K M Furniture Ltd, Newton House, Pottery La West, Chesterfield, Derbyshire, S41 9BN Tel: (01246) 260123 Fax: (01246) 260221

Kay & Stemmer, Stamford Works, Gillett Street, London, N16 8JH Tel: (020) 7503 2105 Fax: (020) 7275 7495

Kingcome Sofas Ltd, 24 Old Newton Road, Heathfield Industrial Estate, Heathfield, Newton Abbot, Devon, TQ12 6RA Tel: (01626) 834800 Fax: (01626) 835866 E-mail: sales@kingcomesofas.co.uk

Kirton Healthcare Group Ltd, 23 Rookwood Way, Haverhill, Suffolk, CB9 8PB Tel: (01440) 705352 Fax: (01440) 706199 E-mail: info@kirtonhealthcare.demon.co.uk

L M D Frames Ltd, Unit 45 Burton Indust Est, Petford St, Cradley Heath, Cradley Heath, West Midlands, B64 6DJ Tel: 01384 410909 Fax: 01384 634344

Latter's Pine Furniture, 18 Crescent Road, London, N22 7RS Tel: (020) 8888 7477

Andrew Lawton Furniture, Goatscliff Workshops, Grindleford, Hope Valley, Derbyshire, S32 2HG Tel: (01433) 631754 Fax: (01433) 631754 E-mail: andrewlawton@btinternet.com

Linford Furniture, Mill Lane, Stony Stratford, Milton Keynes, MK11 1EW Tel: (01908) 261521

M A Culshaw, School Farm, Back La East, Mawdesley, Ormskirk, Lancashire, L40 3TA Tel: (01704) 821076 Fax: (01704) 821986 E-mail: sales@furniture-bespoke.co.uk

Max E Ott Ltd, 1a Southcote Road, London, N19 5BJ Tel: (020) 7607 1384 Fax: (020) 7607 3506

Mitre Woodcraft, The Workshops, Market Street, Wells, Somerset, BA5 2DS Tel: (01749) 671266 Fax: (01749) 671266

Old Mill Furniture, Balk, Thirsk, North Yorkshire, YO7 2AH Tel: (01845) 597227 E-mail: theoldmill@btinternet.com

Orior By Design, Unit 12 Greenbank Industrial Estate, Rampart Road, Newry, County Down, BT34 2QU Tel: (028) 3026 2620 Fax: (028) 3026 3810 E-mail: oriorbydesign@btconnect.com

Osborne Cabinet Makers, 10 Mowbray Gardens, Dorking, Surrey, RH4 1LL Tel: (01306) 713007 Fax: (01306) 644999

P Bastow, Silver Street, Reeth, Richmond, North Yorkshire, DL11 6SP Tel: (01748) 884555 Fax: (01748) 884181

Page Lacquer Co. Ltd, 3 Ferrier Industrial Estate, Ferrier Street, London, SW18 1SN Tel: (020) 8871 1235 Fax: (020) 8874 8167 E-mail: info@pagelacquer.co.uk

Priory Fitted Furniture, Sporehams Lane, Danbury, Chelmsford, CM3 4AJ Tel: (01245) 227330 Fax: (01245) 227331

Quainton Cottage Furniture, Brixton Buildings, Station Road, Quainton, Aylesbury, Buckinghamshire, HP22 4BX Tel: (01296) 655726 Fax: (0870) 516601 E-mail: jeff@qcf.uk.com

R & J Pine, Harmers Yard, Hall La, Walton on the Naze, Essex, CO14 8HW Tel: (01255) 673124 Fax: (01255) 673124

Robins Cabinet Makers, Lodge Farm Bungalow, Kineton, Warwick, CV35 0JH Tel: (01926) 640151 Fax: (01926) 640151

Sawle & Vaughan, School House Farm, Littleham, Bideford, Devon, EX39 5HR Tel: (01237) 477181 Fax: (01237) 477181 E-mail: sales@sawleandvaughan.co.uk

Stewart Linford Chair Maker Ltd, Kitchener Works, Kitchener Road, High Wycombe, Buckinghamshire, HP11 2SJ Tel: (01494) 440408 Fax: (01494) 451555

Style Seating Ltd, Algores Way, Wisbech, Cambridgeshire, PE13 2TQ Tel: (01945) 580099 Fax: (01945) 580127 E-mail: sales@styleseating.co.uk

Tudor Thomas Design, 1a Fawe Street, London, E14 6PD Tel: (020) 7987 8145 Fax: (020) 7515 4970 E-mail: tudor@tudorthomas.com

Tough Furniture, Stokewood Road, Craven Arms Business Park, Craven Arms, Shropshire, SY7 8NR Tel: (01588) 674340 Fax: (01588) 674341

Tubewise Furniture, The Roundhouse, Harbour Road, Par, Cornwall, PL24 2BB Tel: (01726) 817625 Fax: (01726) 816405

Wilfred Hutchinson & Son, Husthwaite, York, YO61 4PB Tel: (01347) 868352

FURNITURE, TUBULAR, *See Tubular etc*

FUSE CARRIERS OR HOLDERS OR BASES

Cooper UK Ltd, Melton Road, Burton-on-the-Wolds, Loughborough, Leicestershire, LE12 5TH Tel: (01509) 882600 Fax: (01509) 882786 E-mail: eurosales@bussmann.co.uk

Dialight B L P Ltd, Exning Road, Newmarket, Suffolk, CB8 0AX Tel: (01638) 665161 Fax: (01638) 660718 E-mail: sales@blpcomp.com

Lawson Fuses Ltd, Meadowfield, Ponteland, Newcastle upon Tyne, NE20 9SW Tel: (01661) 823232 Fax: (01661) 824213 E-mail: sales@lawson-fuses.co.uk

Volex, Butts Mill, Butts Street, Leigh, Lancashire, WN7 3AD Tel: (01942) 672393 Fax: (01942) 677395 E-mail: sales@volexwiring.com

FUSE SWITCHES

Cooper UK Ltd, Melton Road, Burton-on-the-Wolds, Loughborough, Leicestershire, LE12 5TH Tel: (01509) 882600 Fax: (01509) 882786 E-mail: eurosales@bussmann.co.uk

FUSED QUARTZ PRODUCTS

Enterprise Q Ltd, 1 Tallow Way, Fairhills Industrial Park, Irlam, Manchester, M44 6RJ Tel: 0161-777 4888 Fax: 0161-777 4899 E-mail: info@enterprise-q.co.uk

▶ Saint-Gobain Quartz P.L.C, PO Box 6, Wallsend, Tyne & Wear, NE28 6DG Tel: 0191-262 5311 Fax: 0191-263 8040 E-mail: quartz.sales@saint-gobain.com

FUSED SILICA ELECTRICAL COMPONENTS

A W Intruder Alarms, Wycherley, Llanvihangel Crucorney, Abergavenny, Gwent, NP7 7LB Tel: (01873) 890272 Fax: (01873) 890272

Industrial Applied Elements, 10 Bronte Drive, Kidderminster, Worcestershire, DY10 3YU Tel: (01562) 755490 Fax: (01562) 755490

FUSED SILICA PRODUCTS

Enterprise Q Ltd, 1 Tallow Way, Fairhills Industrial Park, Irlam, Manchester, M44 6RJ Tel: 0161-777 4888 Fax: 0161-777 4899 E-mail: info@enterprise-q.co.uk

FUSES

Alex Nangle Electrical Ltd, Unit 3 Oakbank Park Way, Mid Calder, Livingston, West Lothian, EH53 0TH Tel: (01506) 449400 Fax: (01506) 449404 E-mail: info@nangle.co.uk

Bel Fuse Europe Ltd, G 7 Unit Preston Technology Centre, Marsh Lane, Preston, PR1 8UQ Tel: (01772) 556601 Fax: (01772) 883666 E-mail: bel_europe@belfuse.com

Comstock Electronics Ltd, Unit 6 Paycocke Road, Quatro Park, Basildon, Essex, SS14 3GH Tel: (01268) 295555 Fax: (01268) 523455 E-mail: celsales@comstock.co.uk

Electro Replacement Ltd, 1 Moor Park Industrial Centre, Tolpits Lane, Watford, WD18 9EU Tel: (01923) 255344 Fax: (01923) 255829

FUSES – *continued*

Kempston Controls, Shirley Road, Rushden, Northamptonshire, NN10 6BZ Tel: (01933) 414500 Fax: (01933) 410211 E-mail: sales@kempstoncontrols.co.uk
L C Switchgear Ltd, Unit 2, Hove Technology Centre, St Josephs Close, Hove, East Sussex, BN3 7ES Tel: (01273) 770540 Fax: (01273) 770547

FUSIBLE ALLOYS

Lowden Metals Ltd, 7 Harvey Works Industrial Estate, Shelah Road, Halesowen, West Midlands, B63 3PG Tel: 0121-501 3596 Fax: 0121-585 5162 E-mail: enquiries@metals26.freeserve.co.uk
Mining & Chemical Products Ltd, 1-4 Nielson Road, Finedon Road Industrial Estate, Wellingborough, Northamptonshire, NN8 4PE Tel: (01933) 225766 Fax: (01933) 227814 E-mail: info@mcp-group.co.uk

FUSIBLE INTERLININGS

Colletex Ltd, Whitebirk Road, Blackburn, BB1 3JA Tel: (01254) 261768 Fax: (01254) 665425 E-mail: sales@colletex.co.uk
Vilene Interlinings, PO Box 3, Elland, West Yorkshire, HX5 9DX Tel: (01422) 327900 Fax: (01422) 327999 E-mail: vilenesales@freudenberg-nw.com

GABIONS

Maccaferri Ltd, 7600 The Quorum, Oxford Business Park North, Garsington Road, Oxford, OX4 2JZ Tel: (01865) 770555 Fax: (01865) 774550 E-mail: oxford@maccaferri.co.uk
▶ P C Construction Ltd, Chorlton Lane, Chorlton-by-Backford, Chester, CH2 4DD Tel: (01244) 851875 Fax: (01244) 851874 E-mail: pcconstruction@btopenworld.com

GALLIUM

Mining & Chemical Products Ltd, 1-4 Nielson Road, Finedon Road Industrial Estate, Wellingborough, Northamptonshire, NN8 4PE Tel: (01933) 225766 Fax: (01933) 227814 E-mail: info@mcp-group.co.uk

GALVANISED ARCHITECTURAL METALWORK

A M P Metalworks, 837-839 Consort Road, London, SE15 2PR Tel: (020) 7277 5569 Fax: (020) 7635 6001 E-mail: sales@apmetalworks.co.uk
Hubbard Architectural Metalwork Ltd, 3 Hurricane Way, Norwich, NR6 6HS Tel: (01603) 424817 Fax: (01603) 487158 E-mail: tony.hubbard@hubbardsmetalwork.co.uk
▶ Titchmarsh Engineering, Primrose Cottage, East Cottingwith, York, YO42 4TH Tel: (01759) 319222

GALVANISED BOLTS AND NUTS

TLW Fasteners Ltd, 115 Lodgefield Road, Halesowen, West Midlands, B62 8AX Tel: 0121-602 4040 Fax: 0121-602 4040

GALVANISED BUCKETS AND PAILS

Brettell & Shaw, Allfor House, Hayes Lane, Stourbridge, West Midlands, DY9 8QT Tel: (01384) 898911 Fax: (01384) 899100 E-mail: jpc@bretshaweltex.com
Main Line Products Richards, Attwood Street, Stourbridge, West Midlands, DY9 8SL Tel: (01384) 422661 Fax: (01384) 423163

GALVANISED OR PREFORMED ARCH FRAMES

Allmat East Surrey Ltd, The Kenley Waterworks, Godstone Road, Kenley, Surrey, CR8 5AE Tel: (020) 8668 6666 Fax: (020) 8763 2110 E-mail: info@allmat.co.uk
Barton Industrial Services Ltd, 6 Longlands Avenue, Newtownabbey, County Antrim, BT36 7NE Tel: (028) 9085 4535 Fax: (028) 9036 5133 E-mail: mail@barton-industrial.com

GALVANISED STEEL ROOF TRUSS CLIPS

Mitek Industries Ltd, Grazebrook Industrial Park, Peartree Lane, Dudley, West Midlands, DY2 0XW Tel: (01384) 451400 Fax: (01384) 451411 E-mail: sales@mitek.co.uk

GALVANISED STEEL SHEET

Carter Steel Ltd, Yarm Road, Stockton-on-Tees, Cleveland, TS18 3SA Tel: (01642) 679831 Fax: (01642) 670346
Hereford Galvanisers Ltd, Grandstand Road, Hereford, HR4 9NS Tel: (01432) 267664 Fax: (01432) 352735 E-mail: zink@hereford.galvanizers.co.uk

GALVANISERS OR GALVANISING PROCESSORS OR SERVICES

Acrow Galvanising Ltd, 4 Commercial Centre, Ashdon Road, Saffron Walden, Essex, CB10 2NH Tel: (01799) 522219 Fax: (01799) 522447 E-mail: acrow@wedge-galv.co.uk
Arkinstall Galvanizers, Ebro Works, Dudley Road West, Tividale, Oldbury, West Midlands, B69 2PF Tel: 0121-557 1851 Fax: 0121-522 3991 E-mail: arkinstall@galvanizing.co.uk
Arkinstall Galvanizing Ltd, 38 Coventry Street, Birmingham, B5 5NQ Tel: 0121-643 6455 Fax: 0121-643 0192 E-mail: info@galvanizing.co.uk
B E Wedge Holdings Ltd, Stafford Street, Willenhall, West Midlands, WV13 1RZ Tel: (01902) 630311 Fax: (01902) 366353 E-mail: wedge.holdings@wedge-galv.co.uk
Birtley Building Products Ltd, Mary Avenue, Birtley, Chester le Street, County Durham, DH3 1JF Tel: 0191-492 1059 Fax: 0191-410 0650 E-mail: info@birtley-building.co.uk
British Metal Treatments Ltd, 40 Battery Road, Great Yarmouth, Norfolk, NR30 3NN Tel: (01493) 844153 Fax: (01493) 330303 E-mail: sales@bmtgalv.co.uk
Clydeside Galvanizers Ltd, 96 Eastvale Place, Glasgow, G3 8QG Tel: 0141-334 9678 Fax: 0141-337 1830 E-mail: sales@clydegalv.co.uk
W. Corbett & Co. (Galvanizing) Ltd, New Alexandra Works, Haldane Halesfield 1, Telford, Shropshire, TF7 4QQ Tel: (01952) 412777 Fax: (01952) 412888 E-mail: corbetthotdip@aol.com
East Anglian Galvanising Ltd, Wareley Road, Peterborough, PE2 9PF Tel: (01733) 346664 Fax: (01733) 310663 E-mail: east.anglian@wedge-galv.co.uk
East Anglian Galvanising Ltd, Wareley Road, Peterborough, PE2 9PF Tel: (01733) 346664 Fax: (01733) 310663
Frank Hand Ltd, Private Road No 7, Colwick Industrial Estate, Nottingham, NG4 2AD Tel: 0115-987 0508 Fax: 0115-940 0793 E-mail: info@trentshot.com
Hereford Galvanisers Ltd, Grandstand Road, Hereford, HR4 9NS Tel: (01432) 267664 Fax: (01432) 352735 E-mail: zink@hereford.galvanizers.co.uk
Edward Howell Galvanizers Ltd, Watery Lane, Willenhall, West Midlands, WV13 3SU Tel: (01902) 637463 Fax: (01902) 630923 E-mail: edward.howell@wedge-galv.co.uk
Joseph Ash, Mortimer Road, Hereford, HR4 9SY Tel: (01432) 277722 Fax: (01432) 359091
Joseph Ash, Stafford Park 6, Telford, Shropshire, TF3 3AT Tel: (01952) 290201 Fax: (01952) 290113 E-mail: telford@josephash.co.uk
Joseph Ash Galvanising, Seven Stars Road, Oldbury, West Midlands, B69 4JS Tel: 0121-552 1682 Fax: 0121-511 1125 E-mail: albion@josephash.co.uk
Joseph Ash London, Glaucus Works, Leven Road, London, E14 0LP Tel: (020) 7987 5070 Fax: (020) 7515 7498 E-mail: enquiries@josephash.co.uk
Joseph Ash Walsall, Briteon Street Off Pleck Road, Walsall, WS2 9HW Tel: (01922) 628141 Fax: (01922) 623451 E-mail: walsall@josephash.co.uk
Lancaster & Co. (Bow) Ltd, Hancock Road, London, E3 3DF Tel: (020) 8980 2827 Fax: (020) 8981 7815 E-mail: info.grahamwelding@btconnect.com
Merseyside Galvanising Ltd, Weaver Industrial Estate, Blackburne Street, Liverpool, L19 8JA Tel: 0151-427 1449 Fax: 0151-427 2690 E-mail: merseyside@wedge-galv.co.uk
Metaltreat Ltd, 359 Canal Road, Bradford, West Yorkshire, BD2 1AN Tel: (01274) 221500 Fax: (01274) 221520 E-mail: metaltreat@wedge-galv.co.uk
Metnor Galvanising Ltd, Hardwick View Road, Holmewood, Chesterfield, Derbyshire, S42 5SA Tel: (01246) 854650 Fax: (01246) 850086
N K Coatings Ltd, 4 Michelin Road, Newtownabbey, County Antrim, BT36 4PT Tel: (028) 9083 3725 Fax: (028) 9083 7433 E-mail: mail@nkcoatings.com
▶ Newport Galvanisers Ltd, Whitehead Works, Mendalgief Road, Newport, Gwent, NP20 2NF Tel: (01633) 241100 Fax: (01633) 841352 E-mail: geoff.bulger@wedge-galv.co.uk
Newport Galvanisers Ltd., Llanwern Works, Newport, Gwent, NP19 4QX Tel: (01633) 277400 Fax: (01633) 277997
Parkes Galvanizing Ltd, Marshgate Lane, London, E15 2NQ Tel: (020) 8555 9051 Fax: (020) 8519 8151 E-mail: parkes@wedge-galv.co.uk
Pillar Spin Galvanizing Ltd, Metaltreat House, Canal Road, Bradford, West Yorkshire, BD2 1AN Tel: (01274) 221500 Fax: (01274) 221520 E-mail: pillar.spin@wedge-galv.co.uk
Pillar Wedge Ltd, Green Lane, Heywood, Lancashire, OL10 2DY Tel: (01706) 366191 Fax: (01706) 625939 E-mail: pillar-wedge@wedge-galv.co.uk
Precedent Industrial Products UK Ltd, PO Box 2668, Poole, Dorset, BH17 0RT Tel: (01202) 673339 Fax: (01202) 673339 E-mail: sales@galvtech.com
Rayleigh Galvanizers Ltd, 6 Rawreth Industrial Estate, Rawreth Lane, Rayleigh, Essex, SS6 9RL Tel: (01268) 784456 Fax: (01268) 784456
Roebuck & Clarke Galvanising Ltd, Charles Work, Meadow Bank Road, Rotherham, South Yorkshire, S61 2NF Tel: (01709) 560888 Fax: (01709) 554277 E-mail: enquiries@roebuckandclarke.co.uk
Roften Galvanising Ltd, North Road, Ellesmere Port, CH65 1AB Tel: 0151-355 4257 Fax: 0151-355 0753 E-mail: creditacc_roften@yahoo.co.uk
Scottish Galvanisers Ltd, Maclellan Street, Glasgow, G41 1RR Tel: 0141-427 3041 Fax: 0141-427 4981 E-mail: scottish@wedge-galv.co.uk
▶ South East Galvanizers Ltd, Weston Industrial Estate, Crittall Road, Witham, Essex, CM8 3AW Tel: (01376) 501501 Fax: (01376) 513410 E-mail: lionel.bell@wedge-galv.co.uk
South West Galvanizers Ltd, Marsh End, Lords Meadow Industrial Estate, Crediton, Devon, EX17 1DN Tel: (01363) 774574 Fax: (01363) 775070 E-mail: south.west@wedge-galv.co.uk
Stoke Galvanising Ltd, Nevada Lane, Hot Lane, Hot Lane Industrial Estate, Stoke-on-Trent, ST6 2BN Tel: (01782) 811226 Fax: (01782) 836686
Technocover, Whittington Road, Oswestry, Shropshire, SY11 1HZ Tel: (01691) 653251 Fax: (01691) 658222 E-mail: sales@jonesofoswestry.com
Warley Galvanizers, Station Street, Cradley Heath, West Midlands, B64 6AJ Tel: (01384) 566548 Fax: (01384) 566624
Wedge Group Galvanising Ltd, 359 Canal Road, Bradford, West Yorkshire, BD2 1AN Tel: (01274) 221555 Fax: (01274) 221566
Wessex Galvanisers Ltd, Tower Industrial Estate, Tower Lane, Eastleigh, Hampshire, SO50 6NZ Tel: (023) 8062 9952 Fax: (023) 8065 0289 E-mail: wessex@wedge-galv.co.uk
Worksop Galvanizing Ltd, Claylands Avenue, Worksop, Nottinghamshire, S81 7BQ Tel: (01909) 486384 Fax: (01909) 482540 E-mail: worksop@wedge-galv.co.uk

GALVANIZED HOLLOW-WARE

Bird Stevens & Co. Ltd, Sun Street, Brierley Hill, West Midlands, DY5 2JE Tel: (01384) 567381 Fax: (01384) 637357 E-mail: sales@birdstevens.co.uk
Brettell & Shaw, Allfor House, Hayes Lane, Stourbridge, West Midlands, DY9 8QT Tel: (01384) 898911 Fax: (01384) 899100 E-mail: jpc@bretshaweltex.com
Garrods of Barking Ltd, Abbey Wharf, Kings Bridge Road, Barking, Essex, IG11 0BD Tel: (020) 8594 0224 Fax: (020) 8594 0225 E-mail: info@garrods.com
H & E Knowles (Lye) Ltd, Britannia Works, Talbots Lane, Brierley Hill, West Midlands, DY5 2YX Tel: (01384) 78877 Fax: (01384) 79012 E-mail: sales@heknowles.freeserves.co.uk
Main Line Products Richards, Attwood Street, Stourbridge, West Midlands, DY9 8SL Tel: (01384) 422661 Fax: (01384) 423163

GALVANIZED STEEL MANUFRS

Alexander Stirling & Co., Meadowforth Road, Stirling, FK7 7SA Tel: (01786) 473333 Fax: (01786) 450408 E-mail: sales@alexanderstirling.co.uk
Armstrong Glen Metals, 14 Palacecraig Street, Coatbridge, Lanarkshire, ML5 4RY Tel: (01236) 424396 Fax: (01236) 433330 E-mail: glenmetals@asdmetalservices.co.uk
C J Upton & Sons Ltd, 7 Stamford Square, Ashton-under-Lyne, Lancashire, OL6 6QU Tel: 0161-339 3330 Fax: 0161-339 3304 E-mail: sales@cjupton.com
Frank Hughes & Son Ltd, Lunts Heath Road, Widnes, Cheshire, WA8 5SG Tel: 0151-424 5731 Fax: 0151-495 2063 E-mail: sales@frankhughes.co.uk

GALVANIZED TANKS

Balmoral Tanks Ltd, Wellington Road, Aberdeen, AB12 3GY Tel: (01224) 859100 Fax: (01224) 859123 E-mail: tanks@balmoral.co.uk
Midland Tank & Ironplate Co. Ltd, 241-243 Heneage Street, Birmingham, B7 4LY Tel: 0121-359 0298 Fax: 0121-333 3035 E-mail: sales@mti.uk.com

GALVANIZED WIRE

▶ Rope Assemblies Ltd, Aurillac Way, Retford, Nottinghamshire, DN22 7PX Tel: (01777) 700714 Fax: (01777) 860719 E-mail: siobhan@ropeasseblies.co.uk
Webster & Horsfall Ltd, Fordrough, Birmingham, B25 8DW Tel: 0121-772 2555 Fax: 0121-772 0762 E-mail: sales@websterandhorsfall.co.uk
The Willing Wire Company Ltd, Middlemore Lane, Walsall, WS9 8SP Tel: (01922) 452814 Fax: (01922) 743248 E-mail: mail@willing-wire.com

GAME COMPONENTS

John Jaques & Sons Ltd, House of Jaques, 1 Fircroft Way, Edenbridge, Kent, TN8 6EL Tel: (01732) 500200 Fax: (01732) 500111 E-mail: gameon@jaques.co.uk
Plastics For Games Ltd, Riverside View, Wickham Market, Woodbridge, Suffolk, IP13 0TA Tel: (01728) 745300 Fax: (01728) 745309 E-mail: sales@plasticsforgames.co.uk

GAME DICE

Plastics For Games Ltd, Riverside View, Wickham Market, Woodbridge, Suffolk, IP13 0TA Tel: (01728) 745300 Fax: (01728) 745309 E-mail: sales@plasticsforgames.co.uk

GAME (EDIBLE) FOOD PRODUCTS

Fish-house Ltd, Dean Feld Way, Link 59 Business Park, Clitheroe, Lancashire, BB7 1QU Tel: (01200) 427527 Fax: (01200) 427027 E-mail: john@fish-house.co.uk

GAME REARING NETS

Deben Group Industries Ltd, Gore Cross Business Park, Corbin Way, Bradpole, Bridport, Dorset, DT6 3UX Tel: (01308) 423576 Fax: (01308) 425912 E-mail: johnp@deben.com

GAMES

John Adams Trading Co. Ltd, The Barn, 3 Deanes Close, Steventon, Abingdon, Oxfordshire, OX13 6SZ Tel: (01235) 833066 Fax: (01235) 861116 E-mail: trading@johnadams.co.uk
Atari Ltd, Landmark House, Hammersmith Bridge Road, London, W6 9EJ Tel: (020) 8222 9700 Fax: (020) 8222 9870
Bounceabouts Leisure Ltd, Asfare Business Park, Hinckley Road, Wolvey, Hinckley, Leicestershire, LE10 3HQ Tel: (01455) 220886 Fax: (01455) 220988 E-mail: sales@bounceabouts.co.uk
▶ Chiltern Games & Puzzles, PO Box 5, Llanfyllin, Powys, SY22 5WD Tel: (01691) 648864
Code Masters Software Co. Ltd, Lower Farm, Stoneythorpe, Southam, Warwickshire, CV47 2DL Tel: (01926) 814132 Fax: (01926) 817595 E-mail: enquiries@codemasters.com
Flights Of Fancy, 15 New Street, Leamington Spa, Warwickshire, CV31 1HP Tel: (01926) 423436 Fax: (01926) 311925 E-mail: mail@flightsoffancy.co.uk
Greyhound Ltd, Duckfield Barn, Bakers Road, Belchamp St. Paul, Sudbury, Suffolk, CO10 7DG Tel: (01787) 277372 Fax: (01787) 278787
House Of Marbles Ltd, Pottery Road, Bovey Tracey, Newton Abbot, Devon, TQ13 9DS Tel: (01626) 835358 Fax: (01626) 835315 E-mail: sales@houseofmarbles.com
Irregular Miniatures, 41 Lesley Avenue, York, YO10 4JR Tel: (01904) 671101 Fax: (01904) 671101E-mail: email@irregularmin.fsnet.co.uk
▶ Iweave Ltd, 4 Brentham Crescent, Stirling, FK8 2AZ Tel: (01786) 450606 Fax: (01786) 462876
Jolly Roger (Amusement Rides) Ltd, College View Works, Manby Road, Grimoldby, Louth, Lincolnshire, LN11 8HE Tel: (01507) 328856 Fax: (01507) 327060 E-mail: roger@jolly-roger.co.uk
Teign Valley Glass, The Old Pottery, Pottery Road, Bovey Tracey, Newton Abbot, Devon, TQ13 9DS Tel: (01626) 835285 Fax: (01626) 835315 E-mail: info@houseofmarbles.com

GAMES, VIDEO/TELEVISION, COIN OPERATED, *See Amusement Machines etc*

GAMING MACHINE MANUFRS OR CONCESSIONAIRES

▶ Bellmatic Leisure Ltd, 10-12 Boswell Square, Hillington Industrial Estate, Glasgow, G52 4BQ Tel: 0141-882 8320 Fax: 0141-810 4098 E-mail: carrigan@bellmatic.com
Eurotek Designs Ltd, 9-10 Bessemer Close, Cardiff, CF11 8DL Tel: (029) 2066 6550 Fax: (029) 2066 7399 E-mail: eudeltd@aol.com
Reel Control, Woodlands, Draycott-in-the-Clay, Ashbourne, Derbyshire, DE6 5GZ Tel: (01283) 821128 Fax: (01283) 821228 E-mail: enquiries@reelcontrol.com

GAMING MACHINE MANUFRS OR CONCESSIONAIRES – *continued*

Rex Leisure (Scotland) Ltd, 105 Bothwell Road, Hamilton, Lanarkshire, ML3 0DW Tel: (01698) 283283 Fax: (01698) 201290 E-mail: info@rexleisure.co.uk

Sterling Plastics, 5 Crocus Place, Crocus Street, Nottingham, NG2 3DE Tel: 0115-985 1101 Fax: 0115-985 1101

Technical Casino Services Ltd, Unit 9 Mulberry Business Centre, Quebec Way, Rotherhithe, London, SE16 7LE Tel: (020) 7394 4000 Fax: (020) 7231 7414 E-mail: tcsuk@tcsgroup.com

W & D, Belmont House, Coopers Lane, Christchurch, Coleford, Gloucestershire, GL16 7AL Tel: (01594) 835839 Fax: (01594) 835839

Wearside Electronics, 32 Wilson Street North, Sheepfolds Industrial Estate, Sunderland, SR5 1BB Tel: 0191-514 4199 Fax: 0191-514 1324 E-mail: jimjohnson@edward-thompson.com

GAMMA RAY STERILISATION SERVICES

Swann-Morton Europe Ltd, Owlerton Green, Sheffield, S6 2BJ Tel: 0114-234 4231 Fax: 0114-231 4966 E-mail: services@swann-morton.com

GANTRY CRANES

Morris Material Handling, Lodge Way, Thetford, Norfolk, IP24 1HE Tel: (01842) 750252 Fax: (01842) 750909

GAP SENSORS

Capacitec, PO Box 4022, Reading, RG8 8HG Tel: 0118-984 5351 Fax: 0118-984 3979 E-mail: sales@sensortronic.co.uk

GARAGE AIR COMPRESSORS

D M F Ltd, 2 Dewsbury Road, Wakefield, West Yorkshire, WF2 9BS Tel: (01924) 370685 Fax: (01924) 364160 E-mail: sales@dmfwakefield.ltd.uk

Garage Equipment Services, Unit 2100, The Crescent, Solihull Parkway, Birmingham Business Park, Birmingham, B37 7YE Tel: 0121-329 1154 Fax: 0121-329 1190 E-mail: ges@unipart.co.uk

GARAGE DOOR ACCESSORIES

Dave Cox, 43 Ingrave Road, Brentwood, Essex, CM15 8AZ Tel: (01277) 228240 Fax: (01277) 228240

Garador Enquiries, Bunford Lane, Yeovil, Somerset, BA20 2EJ Tel: (0800) 706670 Fax: (01935) 443744 E-mail: enquiries@garador.co.uk

Kingsley Garage Doors, Unit 3 Eastman Way, Hemel Hempstead Industrial Est, Hemel Hempstead, Hertfordshire, HP2 7DU Tel: (01442) 257111 Fax: (01442) 257111 E-mail: jason@swrgaragedoors.com

Seip UK Ltd, Unit 11 Monument Business Park, Warpsgrove Lane, Chalgrove, Oxford, OX44 7RW Tel: (01865) 400469 Fax: (01865) 400217

GARAGE DOOR LOCKS

Access & Security 24Hr Locksmiths, Key House Coombe Rise, Oadby, Leicester, LE2 5TT Tel: 0116-271 9003 Fax: 0116-271 9229 E-mail: info@leicesterlocksmith.com

▶ The Key Shop Lutterworth Ltd, 14 High Street, Lutterworth, Leicestershire, LE17 4AD Tel: (01455) 554999 Fax: (01455) 554999 E-mail: ian@thekeyshop.co.uk

GARAGE DOOR REPAIR

1st Stop Door Shop, 13 Tavistock Close, Northampton, NN3 5DQ Tel: (0800) 0435341 E-mail: info@1ststopdoorshop.co.uk

▶ The Garage Door & Gate Automation Co., Unit 7 Block D, Isle of Man Business Park, Isle of Man, IM2 2QY Tel: (01624) 624122 Fax: (01624) 623877 E-mail: info@manxgaragedoors.com

▶ Instant Access Garage Doors, Caenant House, Mill Road, Caerphilly, Mid Glamorgan, CF83 3FE Tel: (029) 2088 4622 E-mail: info@autogateswales.co.uk

▶ JM Fabrications Electrical, 18 Green Hill Holt, Leeds, LS12 4HY Tel: 0113-263 1924 E-mail: jason@jmfabrications.co.uk

▶ Kay Garage Doors, Unit 1, Phoenix Industrial Estate, Kerse Road, Stirling, FK7 7SG Tel: (01786) 474709 Fax: (01786) 451540 E-mail: info@kaygaragedoors.co.uk

GARAGE FLOORING

▶ Garage Wizards, 4 Cambridge Terrace, St James Road, Brackley, Northamptonshire, NN13 7XY Tel: 01280 700563 Fax: 01280 700444 E-mail: info@garagewizards.com

GARAGE FORECOURT EQUIPMENT

▶ CSC Forecourt Services Ltd, 6 Timon View, Heathcote, Warwick, CV34 6ES Tel: (01926) 882377 Fax: (01926) 882377 E-mail: info@cscspec.com

Htec Ltd, Unit H George Curl Way, Southampton, SO18 2RX Tel: (023) 8068 9200 Fax: (023) 8068 9201 E-mail: sstocks@htec.co.uk

Purfleet Commercials Ltd, 520 London Road, Grays, Essex, RM20 3BE Tel: (01708) 863931 Fax: (01708) 868226 E-mail: tmason@harris-group.co.uk

Wright Engineering Co. Ltd, Masons Road, Stratford-upon-Avon, Warwickshire, CV37 9JA Tel: (01789) 292939 Fax: (01789) 297458 E-mail: sales@wright-eng.co.uk

GARAGE HYDRAULIC EQUIPMENT MAINTENANCE OR REPAIR

Ksa, Tippons Strawberry Gardens, Mill Hill Lane, Tavistock, Devon, PL19 8NH Tel: (01822) 614894 Fax: (01822) 614800

GARAGE LUBRICATING EQUIPMENT

Garage Equipment Services, Unit 2100, The Crescent, Solihull Parkway, Birmingham Business Park, Birmingham, B37 7YE Tel: 0121-329 1154 Fax: 0121-329 1190 E-mail: ges@unipart.co.uk

GARAGE SERVICE EQUIPMENT, USED

Prosol UK, 18-24 Gleadless Road, Sheffield, S2 3AB Tel: 0114-255 7700 Fax: 0114-255 7171

GARAGE SERVICE EQUIPMENT/ TOOL INSTALLATION SERVICES

Bruntech Equipment, Easthills, Laurencekirk, Kincardineshire, AB30 1EJ Tel: (01561) 378866 Fax: (01561) 378877 E-mail: robin@bruntech.com

Calibration & Repair Services Ltd, Cars House, 137a Inkerman Street, Ashton-on-Ribble, Preston, PR2 2HN Tel: (01772) 728233 Fax: (01772) 768031 E-mail: sales@carslimited.co.uk

D & H Equipment & Service, Unit 3, Linstock Way, Atherton, Manchester, M46 0RS Tel: (01942) 887557 Fax: (01942) 889800

▶ Eastwick Engineering Services, 1 Gladwin Industrial Prk, Charles Street, Kilnhurst, Mexborough, South Yorkshire, S64 5TG Tel: (01709) 589044 Fax: (01709) 591752 E-mail: sales@eastwickengineeringservices.co.uk

Gemco 2000 Ltd, 3 Export Drive, Huthwaite, Sutton-in-Ashfield, Nottinghamshire, NG17 6AF Tel: (01623) 551818 Fax: (01623) 551717

Ksa, Tippons Strawberry Gardens, Mill Hill Lane, Tavistock, Devon, PL19 8NH Tel: (01822) 614894 Fax: (01822) 614800

Trojan Garage Equipment Services Ltd, 3 Orchard Court, Armstrong Way, Yate, Bristol, BS37 5GW Tel: (01454) 326161 Fax: (01454) 326363 E-mail: trojanges@btconnect.com

GARAGE SERVICE EQUIPMENT/ TOOL MAINTENANCE/REPAIR SERVICES

Allspeed Clutches & Brakes, Unit 14c Birches Industrial Estate, East Grinstead, West Sussex, RH19 1XZ Tel: (01342) 322829 Fax: (01342) 300464

Almac Sales & Service Ltd, Capelrig Lane, Newton Mearns, Glasgow, G77 6XZ Tel: 0141-639 2578 Fax: 0141-639 2578

B.N.B Vehicle Lifting Equipment, 17 Grasmere Park, Carrickfergus, County Antrim, BT38 7TP Tel: (028) 9336 5677

Barry Air Service, Hafod Lon, Port Road West, Barry, South Glamorgan, CF62 3BA Tel: (01446) 734153 Fax: (01446) 734153

Calibration & Repair Services Ltd, Cars House, 137a Inkerman Street, Ashton-on-Ribble, Preston, PR2 2HN Tel: (01772) 728233 Fax: (01772) 768031 E-mail: sales@carslimited.co.uk

▶ David Taylor Garages (Filling Stations) 2000 Ltd, Granada Park Motors, Llangattock, Crickhowell, Powys, NP8 1HW Tel: (01873) 810304 Fax: (01873) 811320 E-mail: davidtaylorgarages@compuserve.co.uk

Eastern Garage Equipment, 24 Orchard Bank, Drayton, Norwich, NR8 6RN Tel: (01603) 262523 Fax: (01603) 262523

▶ Eastwick Engineering Services, 1 Gladwin Industrial Prk, Charles Street, Kilnhurst, Mexborough, South Yorkshire, S64 5TG Tel: (01709) 589044 Fax: (01709) 591752 E-mail: sales@eastwickengineeringservices.co.uk

Enterprise Motors, Dean Street, Bedford, MK40 3EQ Tel: (01234) 302230 Fax: (01234) 302230 E-mail: colindm@hotmail.com

▶ Ever Cal, Citadel Trading Park, Citadel Way, Hull, HU9 1TQ Tel: (01482) 610601 Fax: (01482) 610602 E-mail: sales@ever-cal.com

Garage Equipment Maintenance Co. Ltd, 153-165 Bridge Street, Northampton, NN1 1QG Tel: (01604) 828500 Fax: (01604) 232995 E-mail: sales@gemco.co.uk

Gemco Equipment Ltd, Unit B1 Fortwilliam Court, 24 Duncrue CR, Belfast, BT3 9BW Tel: (028) 9077 2666 Fax: (028) 9077 9251 E-mail: sales@allenengineering.co.uk

Hi Q Ltd, Southdownview Way, Worthing, West Sussex, BN14 8NL Tel: (01903) 236734

Ksa, Tippons Strawberry Gardens, Mill Hill Lane, Tavistock, Devon, PL19 8NH Tel: (01822) 614894 Fax: (01822) 614800

Lakshmi Collison Care, 290a Ampthill Road, Bedford, MK42 9QL Tel: (01234) 261930 Fax: (01234) 353372

Albert Littlewood Garage Equipment Ltd, 1 Westfield Lane, Barlborough, Chesterfield, Derbyshire, S43 4TP Tel: (01246) 811268 Fax: (01246) 811268

Meldrum Motors Ltd, 3 Market Square, Oldmeldrum, Inverurie, Aberdeenshire, AB51 0AA Tel: (01651) 872247 Fax: (01651) 872247

Mersh Brothers Lewisham Ltd, 16a Algernon Road, London, SE13 7AT Tel: (020) 8692 2844 Fax: (020) 8692 2804 E-mail: sales@mershbros.co.uk

No 1 Garage Equipment Ltd, Canon Pyon Road, Hereford, HR4 7RB Tel: (01432) 272594 Fax: (01432) 343534

Rand Equipment Europe Ltd, Unit 8 Commonwealth Close, Leigh, Lancashire, WN7 3BD Tel: (01942) 606062 Fax: (01942) 606087

South Eastern Tools, Old Odiham Road, Alton, Hampshire, GU34 4BU Tel: (01420) 89555 Fax: (01420) 84463

T R Bullworthy, Gatehouse Farm, High Street, Culworth, Banbury, Oxfordshire, OX17 2BG Tel: (01295) 768373 Fax: (01295) 768351 E-mail: bullworthy@btconnect.com

Wilsons Hydraulic Services Ltd, 142 Clydeholm Road, Clydeside Industrial Estate, Glasgow, G14 0QQ Tel: 0141-569 1066 Fax: 0141-954 3986 E-mail: sales@wilsonhydraulics.co.uk

GARAGE SERVICE EQUIPMENT/ TOOLS

▶ A T Garage Equipment Services Ltd, Unit 5-8 Swan La Industrial Estate, Swan Lane, West Bromwich, West Midlands, B70 0NU Tel: 0121-553 2278 Fax: (01902) 338339

Advance Tools (Oxford), 7 Links Road, Kennington, Oxford, OX1 5RU Tel: (01865) 739739 Fax: (01865) 739755 E-mail: advancetools@ic24.net

Ashton Engineering Co. Ltd, Floodgate Street, Birmingham, B5 5SS Tel: 0121-643 5134 Fax: 0121-643 4212 E-mail: sales@ashtonengineering.co.uk

▶ Autocal Ltd, Unit 2 Feldspar Close, Enderby, Leicester, LE19 4SD Tel: 0116-286 2444 Fax: 0116-286 3444 E-mail: sales@autocal.co.uk

Autocraft Equipment Ltd, Higher Street, Norton sub Hamdon, Stoke-sub-Hamdon, Somerset, TA14 6SN Tel: (01935) 881848 Fax: (01935) 881793

Autocraft Equipment Ltd, Higher Street, Norton sub Hamdon, Stoke-sub-Hamdon, Somerset, TA14 6SN Tel: (01935) 881848 Fax: (01935) 881793 E-mail: sales@autocraftequipment.co.uk

▶ Automotive Test Equipment, Unit 2 Feldspar Close, Enderby, Leicester, LE19 4SD Tel: 0116-286 5959 Fax: 0116-286 3444 E-mail: sales@automotivetestequipment.co.uk

Automotive Tools & Supplies Ltd, Old Smithy, Hambledon View, Read, Burnley, Lancashire, BB12 7PD Tel: (01282) 771432 Fax: (01282) 774944 E-mail: sales@auto-tools.co.uk

Autoparts Ecosse Garage Equipment Services, 175 Castlebank Street, Glasgow, G11 6DP Tel: 0141-271 7400 Fax: 0141-334 0022 E-mail: garage.equipment@arnoldclark.co.uk

Barry Air Service, Hafod Lon, Port Road West, Barry, South Glamorgan, CF62 3BA Tel: (01446) 734153 Fax: (01446) 734153

Bond Engineering Ltd, Harrowbrook Road, Hinckley, Leicestershire, LE10 3DJ Tel: (01455) 632775 Fax: (01455) 632738 E-mail: bondeng31@aol.com

Bristol Workshop Services, St. Francis Road, Bristol, BS3 2AN Tel: 0117-953 0381 Fax: 0117-953 7353 E-mail: bwsequip@aol.com

Calibration & Repair Services Ltd, Cars House, 137a Inkerman Street, Ashton-on-Ribble, Preston, PR2 2HN Tel: (01772) 728233 Fax: (01772) 768031 E-mail: sales@carslimited.co.uk

Carlton Downs Holdings Ltd, Hulley Road, Hurdsfield, Macclesfield, Cheshire, SK10 2LZ Tel: (01625) 616570 Fax: (01625) 427427 E-mail: enquiries@carltondowns.co.uk

Cascos UK Ltd, Unit 2 Conyer Farm Estate, Conyer, Sittingbourne, Kent, ME9 9HH Tel: (01795) 522201 Fax: (01795) 522281 E-mail: sales@cascos.uk.com

Celtech UK Electronics Ltd, Unit 12 Barton Business Park, Cawdor Street, Eccles, Manchester, M30 0QR Tel: 0161-788 0267 Fax: 0161-787 8212 E-mail: celtech@celtech-uk.co.uk

Clean Machine Garage & Industrial Services Ltd, Bridge Industrial Centre, Wharf Road, Tovil, Maidstone, Kent, ME15 6RR Tel: (01622) 688115 Fax: (01622) 688054 E-mail: sales@clean-machine.com

Codi International Ltd, Abbey Lodge, Tintern, Chepstow, Gwent, NP16 6SF Tel: (01291) 689427 Fax: (01291) 689999 E-mail: info@codi-international.com

Craig Specialist Services Ltd, Unit 3 Preston Enterprise Ctr, Salter St, Preston, PR1 1NT Tel: 01772 828585 Fax: 01772 827307

Diamond Distributors, 2 Loughgall Road, Armagh, BT61 7NH Tel: (07802) 903300 Fax: (028) 3752 6464 E-mail: sales@automaintain.co.uk

Durnbury Ltd, 30 First Avenue, Halstead, Essex, CO9 2EX Tel: (01787) 475351 Fax: (01787) 477821 E-mail: durnburyltd@aol.com

E R P Power Products Ltd, Cannon House, Reform Street, Hull, HU2 8EF Tel: (01482) 227479 Fax: (01482) 588556 E-mail: enquries@erpuk.com

E R Varney (Tools) Ltd, Botsford Street, Sheffield, S3 9PF Tel: 0114-272 7650 Fax: 0114-272 7030

▶ Eastwick Engineering Services, 1 Gladwin Industrial Prk, Charles Street, Kilnhurst, Mexborough, South Yorkshire, S64 5TG Tel: (01709) 589044 Fax: (01709) 591752 E-mail: sales@eastwickengineeringservices.co.uk

F.F. Franklin & Co. Ltd, Platt Street, Sheffield, S3 8BQ Tel: 0114-272 1429 Fax: 0114-272 7030 E-mail: sales@franklin-tools.co.uk

Garafit Services Ltd, Willis House, Flowers Hill, Bristol, BS4 5JJ Tel: 0117-971 1451 Fax: 0117-977 8022 E-mail: garafit.info@garafit.com

Kent Hydraulic & Garage Eqt, The Range, Clement Street, Swanley, Kent, BR8 7PQ Tel: (01322) 666432 Fax: (01322) 666532

Kudos U K, Dimension House, Cundell Drive, Cottenham, Cambridge, CB24 8RU Tel: (01954) 252000 Fax: (01954) 250956

Lancashire & Cheshire Garage Equipment Services, Progress House, 7 Longshut Lane West, Stockport, Cheshire, SK2 6RX Tel: 0161-477 6715 Fax: 0161-477 6151 E-mail: enquiries@garageequipment.biz

Lions Equipment Ltd, 1 Little Balmer, Buckingham Industrial Estate, Buckingham, MK18 1TF Tel: (01280) 822655 Fax: (01280) 822656 E-mail: lionsequipment@aol.com

Lumatic Ga Ltd, Theaklen Drive, St. Leonards-on-Sea, East Sussex, TN38 9AZ Tel: (01424) 436343 Fax: (01424) 429926 E-mail: sales@lumatic.co.uk

M A C Tools, Gowerton Road, BlackMills, Northampton, NN4 7BW Tel: (01604) 827351 Fax: (01604) 661654

M J Garage Equipment Services Ltd, The Meadows, Bristol, BS15 3PB Tel: (07957) 855505 Fax: 0117-967 2994

Machine Mart Ltd, 71-73 Manchester Road, Altrincham, Cheshire, WA14 4RJ Tel: 0161-941 2666

Machine Mart Ltd, 211 Lower Parliament Street, Nottingham, NG1 1GN Tel: (0870) 7707830 Fax: (0870) 7707811 E-mail: sales@machinemart.co.uk

Marathon Equipment, PO Box 102, Bexhill-on-Sea, East Sussex, TN40 2ZT Tel: (01424) 223700 Fax: (01424) 223800

Maywood Equipment Group Ltd, Larkfield Trading Estate, Larkfield, Aylesford, Kent, ME20 6SW Tel: 01622 718044

Mbe Fabrications Ltd, 1 Town Drove, Quadring, Spalding, Lincolnshire, PE11 4PU Tel: (01775) 821222 Fax: (01775) 820914 E-mail: sales@mbefabs.com

Thomas Meldrum Ltd, Freedom Works, John Street, Sheffield, S2 4QT Tel: 0114-272 5156 Fax: 0114-272 6409 E-mail: sales@thomasmeldrumltd.co.uk

Microplus Solutions Ltd, 7 66 Fazeley Road, Tamworth, Staffordshire, B78 3JN Tel: (01827) 68080 Fax: (01827) 64620 E-mail: info@mpsl.co.uk

Midland Garage Services, Stourport House, Stourport Road, Kidderminster, Worcestershire, DY11 7QL Tel: (01562) 752458 Fax: (01562) 752548

Morelli Central Ltd, 414 Stoney Stanton Road, Coventry, CV6 5DG Tel: (024) 7668 1143 Fax: (024) 7663 7464 E-mail: headoffice@morelli.co.uk

Multiquip Supplies Ltd, Unit 1, Glenmore Business Park, Bumpers Farm Industrial Estate, Chippenham, Wiltshire, SN14 6BB Tel: (01249) 654945 Fax: (01249) 654255 E-mail: sales@multiquip.uk.com

P W Group Ltd, 2 Wedgwood Road, Bicester, Oxfordshire, OX26 4UL Tel: (01869) 253688 Fax: (01869) 240249 E-mail: sales@portablewelders.ltd.uk

GARAGE SERVICE EQUIPMENT/ TOOLS – *continued*

Pneumatic Components Ltd, Holbrook Rise, Holbrook Industrial Estate, Sheffield, S20 3GE Tel: 0114-248 2712 Fax: 0114-247 8342 E-mail: info@pclairtechnology.com

▶ R S Workshop Equipment, Unit 28 Barnwell Manor Estate, Barnwell, Peterborough, PE8 5PL Tel: (01832) 741007 Fax: (01832) 741008 E-mail: sales@rsworkshopequipment.co.uk

Ratcliffe Service Tools, Wilmore Lane, Byrkley, Rangemore, Burton-on-Trent, Staffordshire, DE13 9RD Tel: (01283) 711400 Fax: (01283) 711900

▶ S E S Quicktrak, 7 Longport Enterprise Centre, Scott Lidgett Road, Stoke-on-Trent, ST6 4NQ Tel: (01782) 826800 Fax: (01782) 813641

▶ S T Sheldon, Unit 31, Wren Court, Strathclyde Business Park, Bellshill, Lanarkshire, ML4 3NQ Tel: (01698) 747470 Fax: (01698) 747174 E-mail: enquiry@stsheldon.co.uk

Southern Supplies Ltd, Eastern Industrial Estate, South Woodham Ferrers, Chelmsford, CM3 5UF Tel: (01245) 321451 Fax: (01245) 329465

Sun Diagnostic, Unit 12 Horsleys Fields, King's Lynn, Norfolk, PE30 5DD Tel: (01553) 692422 Fax: (01553) 691844 E-mail: uksales@snapon.com

Supplie Direct UK Ltd, Unit 5, Commondale Way, Euroway Industrial Estate, Bradford, West Yorkshire, BD4 6SF Tel: (01274) 652000 Fax: (01274) 685632

Tecalemit Garage Equipment Co. Ltd, Eagle Road, Plympton, Plymouth, PL7 5JY Tel: (01752) 219111 Fax: (01752) 219128 E-mail: sales@tecalemit.co.uk

Total Equipment, 140 Bell Hill Road, Bristol, BS5 7NF Tel: 0117-967 3333 Fax: (01275) 852121

Trans Pennine Garage Equipment, 11 Twitch Hill, Horbury, Wakefield, West Yorkshire, WF4 6NA Tel: (01924) 266355 Fax: (01924) 263572

Trojan Garage Equipment Services Ltd, 3 Orchard Court, Armstrong Way, Yate, Bristol, BS37 5GW Tel: (01454) 326161 Fax: (01454) 326363 E-mail: trojanges@btconnect.com

Wielander & Schill UK Ltd, Unit 13 Hurricane Close, Old Sarum, Salisbury, SP4 6LG Tel: (01722) 422270 Fax: (01722) 410511 E-mail: info@wielanderschill.co.uk

Wilsons Hydraulic Services Ltd, 142 Clydeholm Road, Clydeside Industrial Estate, Glasgow, G14 0QQ Tel: 0141-569 1066 Fax: 0141-954 3986 E-mail: sales@wilsonhydraulics.co.uk

GARAGE TEST EQUIPMENT

Hartridge, Tingewick Road, Buckingham, MK18 1EF Tel: (01280) 825600 Fax: (01280) 825601 E-mail: sales@hartridge.co.uk

Lions Equipment Ltd, 1 Little Balmer, Buckingham Industrial Estate, Buckingham, MK18 1TF Tel: (01280) 822655 Fax: (01280) 822656 E-mail: lionsequipment@aol.com

▶ Wessco Ltd, 26 Botley Road, Hedge End, Southampton, SO30 2HE Tel: (01489) 790099 Fax: (01489) 795799 E-mail: sales@wessco.co.uk

GARDEN ACCESSORIES

Farmers Cottage Lamps, Castle Lane, Coleshill, Birmingham, B46 2RA Tel: (01675) 464705 Fax: (01675) 462857

▶ Online Gravel, Online Gravel, Mickering Lane, Ormskirk, Lancashire, L39 6SR Tel: 01695 422144 E-mail: kellysearch@onlinegravel.co.uk

▶ Timber & Garden Supplies Scotland Ltd, Cally Industrial Estate, Blairgowrie Road, Dunkeld, Perthshire, PH8 0EP Tel: (01350) 727070 Fax: (01350) 727647

▶ Wooden Garden, 9 Moffathill, Airdrie, Lanarkshire, ML6 8PY Tel: (01236) 602715

GARDEN BUILDINGS TO SPECIFICATION

▶ Garden Offices Limited, 4 Fareham Road, Gosport, Hampshire, PO13 9AX Tel: 01329 285563 Fax: 01329 237056 E-mail: sales@garden-offices.co.uk

▶ treehousebuilders.co.uk, 60 Court Leet, Coventry, CV3 2JR Tel: (07879) 224260 E-mail: chris@treehousebuilders.co.uk

GARDEN COMPOST, *See also headings for particular types*

▶ Harrington & Jessop Ltd, Priest Lane, West End, Woking, Surrey, GU24 9NA Tel: (01483) 472423

GARDEN DESIGN

External Bliss, Calder House, Spring Lane, Colne, Lancashire, BB8 9BD Tel: (01282) 857188 E-mail: info@externalbliss.co.uk

▶ Graham Fox Garden Design and Landscaping, Clover Cottage, 75 Compton Bassett, Calne, Wiltshire, SN11 8SN Tel: 07796 654775 Fax: 01249 760460 E-mail: gbl.fox@btinternet.com

▶ Helen Lowrie, 40 Roxborough Road, Harrow, Middlesex, HA1 1PA Tel: (020) 8427 2674 E-mail: info@helenlowrie.co.uk

▶ Hind Garden Design, 2 St Clair Road, Otley, West Yorkshire, LS21 1DE Tel: 01943 464986

▶ Ian McBain Garden Design, Tythorne Lodge, Oasby, Grantham, Lincolnshire, NG32 3NA Tel: 01529 455755 E-mail: mail@ianmcbain.co.uk

▶ J & B Landscape Services Ltd, Serenity House 12 Waters Edge, Handsacre, Rugeley, Staffordshire, WS15 4HP Tel: (08000) 112) 114 Fax: 08700 802 329 E-mail: info@jblandscapes.co.uk

▶ Mossspace Landscape Design, 36a Bird in Bush Road, Peckham, London, SE15 6RW Tel: (020) 7639 2475 E-mail: sue@mossspace.co.uk

R & J Watson Gardening Landscape, 6 Charter Road, Slough, SL1 5JE Tel: (07730) 434118

▶ Real Oasis, 19 Station Road, Weaverham, Northwich, Cheshire, CW8 3PY Tel: (01606) 851740 E-mail: enquiries@realoasis.com

▶ Sam Mcgowan, 26 Dunrobin Place, Edinburgh, EH3 5HZ Tel: 0131-343 6536 Fax: 0131-343 6086

GARDEN EQUIPMENT MAINTENANCE OR REPAIR

▶ Farm Machinery Ltd, The Livestock & Auction Centre, Wenlock Road, Bridgnorth, Shropshire, WV16 4QR Tel: (01746) 769812 Fax: (01746) 769813 E-mail: sales@farm-garden.co.uk

▶ J & B Landscape Services Ltd, Serenity House 12 Waters Edge, Handsacre, Rugeley, Staffordshire, WS15 4HP Tel: (08000) 112) 114 Fax: 08700 802 329 E-mail: info@jblandscapes.co.uk

GARDEN FERTILISERS

W L Dingley & Co, Buckle Street, Honeybourne, Evesham, Worcestershire, WR11 7QE Tel: (01386) 830242 Fax: (01386) 833541

GARDEN FOUNTAIN OR POOL PUMPS

Bradshaws Direct Ltd, James Nicolson Link, Clifton Moore, York, YO30 4XX Tel: (01904) 691169 Fax: (01904) 691133 E-mail: ferrey@aol.com

Crystalclear Leisure, Woodside Centre, Southend Arterial Road, Rayleigh, Essex, SS6 7TR Tel: (01268) 776690 Fax: (01268) 775842 E-mail: accleisure@aol.com

Fountains Direct Ltd, 41 Dartnell Park Road, West Byfleet, Surrey, KT14 6PR Tel: (01932) 336338 Fax: (01932) 353223 E-mail: sales@fountains-direct.co.uk

Pond Liners Direct Ltd, 8 Millbrook Business Park, Hoe Lane, Nazeing, Waltham Abbey, Essex, EN9 2RJ Tel: (01992) 890901 Fax: (01992) 893393 E-mail: info@e-pond.co.uk

GARDEN FOUNTAINS

▶ Dar Interiors, 11 Arches, Miles Street, London, SW8 1RZ Tel: (020) 7720 9678 Fax: (020) 7627 5129E-mail: enquiries@darinteriors.com

▶ Two & A Half, 9 Queens Road, Enfield, Middlesex, EN1 1NE Tel: (020) 8363 6709 Fax: (020) 8363 6709 E-mail: enquiries@twoandahalf.co.uk

GARDEN FURNITURE, *See also headings for different materials*

▶ Absolutely Lights, Shedfield House Dairy, Sandy Lane, Shedfield, Southampton, SO32 2HQ Tel: (01329) 835999 Fax: (01329) 835999

Acorn Woodcraft, Northcote Workshop, Burrington, Umberleigh, Devon, EX37 9NF Tel: (01769) 560108 Fax: (01769) 560555

Balgownie Machine Centre Ltd, 78a Powis Terrace, Aberdeen, AB25 3PQ Tel: (01224) 485291 Fax: (01224) 482344 E-mail: sales@balgownie.co.uk

▶ Caribee Garden Furniture, Chartwell Court, Fort Fareham, Fareham, Hampshire, PO14 1AH Tel: (01329) 825205 Fax: (01329) 825207

Castle Hardware Company Ltd The, Park Road, Hockley, Birmingham, B18 5JA Tel: 0121-551 6021 Fax: 0121-554 7507

▶ Custom Creations, 1 Plot 120 Village Farm Road, Village Farm Industrial Estate, Pyle, Bridgend, Mid Glamorgan, CF33 6BL Tel: (01656) 749855 Fax: (01656) 749855 E-mail: customc@tiscali.co.uk

▶ D G S, Unit 3, Block 1, Watson Terrace, Drongan, Ayr, KA6 7AA Tel: (01292) 592266 Fax: (01292) 592266

▶ Express Garden Furniture, 12-13 Lower Cherwell Street, Banbury, Oxfordshire, OX16 5AY Tel: (01295) 220430 Fax: (01295) 220431

▶ Gandalf's Garden, Manchester House, Bridge Street, Cardigan, Dyfed, SA43 1HY Tel: (01239) 621107 Fax: (01239) 621107

▶ Garden Iron, Four Oaks, Newent, Gloucestershire, GL18 1LU Tel: (01531) 890123 Fax: (01531) 890136 E-mail: info@gardeniron.co.uk

Garden Leisure Furniture Ltd, Unit 12 Hartlebury Trading Estate, Hartlebury, Kidderminster, Worcestershire, DY10 4JB Tel: (01299) 251883 Fax: (01299) 251563

Glencrest Seatex Ltd, Heron Avenue, Wickford, Essex, SS11 8DL Tel: (01268) 769641 Fax: (01268) 562950 E-mail: sales@glencrestseatex.com

Hailey Wood Sawmill Ltd, Stroud Road, Coates, Cirencester, Gloucestershire, GL7 6LA Tel: (01285) 652191 Fax: (01285) 654649

Harvington Lesiure, Kimberley Cottage, Worcester Road, Harvington, Kidderminster, Worcestershire, DY10 4LJ Tel: (01562) 777255

Holloways Furniture, 1 Lower Court, Church Lane, Suckley, Worcester, WR6 5DE Tel: (01886) 884665 Fax: (01886) 884796 E-mail: enquires@holloways.co.uk

Hyacinth, The Rickyard, Eashing Lane, Godalming, Surrey, GU7 2QA Tel: (01483) 417851 Fax: (01483) 417906 E-mail: sales@hyacinth.uk.com

▶ In Focus Interiors, Oxenwood, Westhill Road South, South Wonston, Winchester, Hampshire, SO21 3HP Tel: (01962) 883092 Fax: (01962) 885144

Kettler (GB) Ltd, Merse Road, North Moons Moat, Redditch, Worcestershire, B98 9HL Tel: (01527) 591901 Fax: (01527) 62423 E-mail: sales@kettler.co.uk

Lifestyle Products Direct, London Road, Osbournby, Sleaford, Lincolnshire, NG34 0DG Tel: (01529) 455666 Fax: (01529) 455646 E-mail: sales@lifestyleproductsdirect.com

▶ Lilo Leisure Products Ltd, Cupola Way, Scunthorpe, South Humberside, DN15 9YJ Tel: (01724) 872202 Fax: (01724) 270041

Lockharts Of Canterbury Ltd, Woodside House, Upper Harbledown, Canterbury, Kent, CT2 9AX Tel: (01227) 454990 Fax: (01227) 780940

▶ Lucra Garden & Leisure, Culver Garden Centre, Cattlegate Road, Enfield, Middlesex, EN2 9DS Tel: (020) 8363 2628

▶ Mayantex Garden Furniture, Trenton House, 4-5 Imperial Way, Croydon, CR0 4RR Tel: (020) 8686 2144

Meadow Designs Ltd, Church Farm Rural Workshops, Stanton Lacy, Ludlow, Shropshire, SY8 2AE Tel: (01584) 856562

Modus Furniture Ltd, Unit 12-14, Rose Mills Industrial Estate, Hort Bridge, Ilminster, Somerset, TA19 9PS Tel: (01460) 57465 Fax: (01460) 57004 E-mail: sales@modusfurniture.co.uk

Pathway Workshop, Dunnock Way, Blackbird Leys, Oxford, OX4 7EX Tel: (01865) 714111 Fax: (01865) 715111

▶ Pepe Garden Furniture, Unit 2b Honeybourne Airfield Trading Estate, Honeybourne, Evesham, Worcestershire, WR11 7QF Tel: (01386) 833211 Fax: (01386) 833269 E-mail: info@pepegarden.co.uk

▶ Regent Garden Collection Ltd, Unit 16 Bordon Trading Estate, Old Station Way, Bordon, Hampshire, GU35 9HH Tel: (01420) 478888 Fax: (01420) 478999

▶ Rustic Gardens, Wade Road, Clacton-on-Sea, Essex, CO15 4LT Tel: (01255) 434676

▶ Sarkan Gardens, Vicarage Lane, Hessle, North Humberside, HU13 9LQ Tel: (01482) 649825

▶ Scenes Easy, Bath Road, Hare Hatch, Reading, RG10 9SB Tel: 0118-940 1700

▶ Sevenoaks, 3 The Mall, Bromley, BR1 1TR Tel: (020) 8313 1511 Fax: (020) 8466 5670

▶ Simply Stone Ltd, 48 King Street, Larbert, Stirlingshire, FK5 4HD Tel: (01324) 579700

▶ Smartwood Lesiure Products, Belle Vue Barn, Mansergh, Carnforth, Lancashire, LA6 2EJ Tel: (01524) 273333 Fax: (01524) 273303

Solus Garden & Leisure Ltd, Bluebird Park, Bromsgrove Road, Hunnington, Halesowen, West Midlands, B62 0EW Tel: 0121-504 2700 Fax: 0121-585 5971 E-mail: sales@solusgl.com

South West Fencing & Sheds, Unit 1A Plum Lane, Dunwear, Bridgwater, Somerset, TA6 5HL Tel: (01278) 447031

▶ TFC The Furniture Co. Ltd, Swingbridge Road, Grantham, Lincolnshire, NG31 7XT Tel: (01476) 577760 Fax: (01476) 575199

▶ The Topiary Organisation, 42, The Briars, Foxholes, Hertford, SG13 7TR Tel: 01992 419426 Fax: 01992 419426 E-mail: info@topiary.org.uk

▶ World of Garden Leisure, 30 Broadway, Sheerness, Kent, ME12 1TP Tel: (01795) 663444

▶ Your Home Furniture, 145 West Street, Banbury, Oxfordshire, OX16 3HE Tel: (0871) 2006251 Fax: (0871) 2006251 E-mail: enquiries@yourhomefurniture.co.uk

GARDEN FURNITURE COVERS

▶ Kingshall Furniture, 5 Millennium Point, Broadfields, Aylesbury, Buckinghamshire, HP19 8ZU Tel: (01296) 339925 Fax: (01296) 392900 E-mail: info@kingshallfurniture.com

▶ Odd Ltd, Oxford, OX7 6WZ Tel: (01993) 830674 Fax: (01993) 832474 E-mail: mail@oddlimited.com

GARDEN FURNITURE CUSHIONS

▶ Bakers & Larners Of Holt, 10 Market Place, Holt, Norfolk, NR25 6BW Tel: (01263) 712323 Fax: (01263) 712720 E-mail: sales@bakersandlarners.com

▶ Garden Furniture Online, Thorp Arch, Wetherby, West Yorkshire, LS23 7RR Tel: 0800 931 7777 Fax: 0870 7776665 E-mail: sales@gardenfurnitureonline.com

GARDEN FURNITURE HIRE

Lace Hire Altrincham Ltd, 203 Woodhouse La East, Timperley, Altrincham, Cheshire, WA15 6AS Tel: 0161-905 1652 Fax: 0161-905 1652 E-mail: altcaterhire@tisacali.co.uk

▶ The Topiary Organisation, 42, The Briars, Foxholes, Hertford, SG13 7TR Tel: 01992 419426 Fax: 01992 419426 E-mail: info@topiary.org.uk

GARDEN HOSE CONNECTORS

▶ Jackson's Online Garden Centre, Jackson's Nurseries, Bagnall, Stoke-on-Trent, ST9 9LD Tel: (01782) 504931 Fax: (01782) 504931 E-mail: luke@jacksonsnurseries.co.uk

GARDEN MACHINERY

D M Chainsaws, Walberton Place Farm, Yapton Lane, Walberton, Arundel, West Sussex, BN18 0AS Tel: (01243) 554065 Fax: (01243) 554065

▶ Easy Life GM Ltd, Dairy House Farm, Chester Road, Oakmere, Northwich, Cheshire, CW8 2HB Tel: (01606) 889833 Fax: (01606) 882090

▶ Farm Machinery Ltd, The Livestock & Auction Centre, Wenlock Road, Bridgnorth, Shropshire, WV16 4QR Tel: (01746) 769812 Fax: (01746) 769813 E-mail: sales@farm-garden.co.uk

▶ J B Backhouse, 107 High Street, Airmyn, Goole, North Humberside, DN14 8LD Tel: (01405) 762876 Fax: (01405) 766412 E-mail: sales@honda-uk.com

▶ Jack Stock Essex Fencing, The Old Bakery, Hawk Lane, Battlesbridge, Wickford, Essex, SS11 7RL Tel: (01268) 732184 Fax: (01268) 761675

Midland Power Machinery Distributors Ltd, Farrell House, Orchard Street, Worcester, WR5 3DW Tel: (01905) 763027 Fax: (01905) 354241 E-mail: info@midlandpower.co.uk

R A & M D Butler, Murrays Service Station, Ashford Hill, Thatcham, Berkshire, RG19 8BQ Tel: 0118-981 3646 Fax: 0118-981 9139 E-mail: info@butlersgarage.co.uk

Trenchex Garden Machinery, Dove Fields Industrial Estate, Uttoxeter, Staffordshire, ST14 8ER Tel: (01889) 565155 Fax: (01889) 563140 E-mail: enquiries@trenchax.com

GARDEN NURSERY EQUIPMENT

▶ Growlighting.co.uk, Unit 19 Chatsworth Green, Basingstoke, Hampshire, RG22 4QA Tel: (01256) 320350 Fax: (01256) 320350 E-mail: rob@growlighting.co.uk

▶ Playways, Maiden Green, Upottery, Honiton, Devon, EX14 9QT Tel: (01404) 861379 Fax: (01404) 861379 E-mail: enquiries@playways.co.uk

▶ Wilkinson, Unit 1 28 St. Johns Walk, Colchester, CO2 7AL Tel: (01206) 767662

GARDEN ORNAMENTS

Farringdon Garden Stone, Sandshill, Faringdon, Oxfordshire, SN7 7PQ Tel: (01367) 240774 Fax: (01367) 242980 E-mail: rogers.gardenstone@btinternet.com

Flambeau Europlast Ltd, Manston Road, Ramsgate, Kent, CT12 6HW Tel: (01843) 854000 Fax: (01843) 854010 E-mail: sales@flambeaueuro.com

Four Seasons, 59 High Street, Barwell, Leicester, LE9 8DS Tel: (01455) 844991

Griffin Stone Ltd, Brookmede, Halstead Road, Fordham, Colchester, CO6 3LW Tel: (01206) 240318

Holloways Furniture, 1 Lower Court, Church Lane, Suckley, Worcester, WR6 5DE Tel: (01886) 884665 Fax: (01886) 884796 E-mail: enquires@holloways.co.uk

Millstone Studios Ltd, Works Road, Hollingwood, Chesterfield, Derbyshire, S43 2PE Tel: (01246) 477516 Fax: (01246) 281666 E-mail: millstone@lineone.net

Minsterstone Ltd, Harts Close, Ilminster, Somerset, TA19 9DJ Tel: (01460) 52277 Fax: (01460) 57865 E-mail: varyl@minsterstone.ltd.uk

Rockways Aquarium & Pond Supplies, Unit 23-25 Crosby Sarek Works, Station Road, Sible Hedingham, Halstead, Essex, CO9 3QA Tel: (01787) 461616 Fax: (01787) 463020

GARDEN ORNAMENTS – *continued*

▶ Stancombe Stone Ltd, The Camp, Stroud, Gloucestershire, GL6 7EW Tel: (01285) 821839 Fax: (01285) 821841

Sundial Workshop, Valley Farm, Bix, Henley-on-Thames, Oxfordshire, RG9 6BW Tel: (01491) 576956 Fax: (01491) 413524 E-mail: enquiry@sundial-workshop.com

Weston Sawmill & Nursery, Hatch Lane, Weston Under Lizard, Shifnal, Shropshire, TF11 8JU Tel: (01952) 850383 Fax: (01952) 850372

GARDEN RETAIL OUTLET CENTRE STRUCTURES

Alpa Garden Centre, 142-144 Swallow Street, Iver, Buckinghamshire, SL0 0HR Tel: (01753) 654101 Fax: (01753) 652641

Clovis Lande Associates, 104 Branbridges Road, East Peckham, Tonbridge, Kent, TN12 5HH Tel: (01622) 872581 Fax: (01622) 873903 E-mail: sales@clovis.co.uk

▶ Concrete Gardens Patio & Garden Centre, Flour Square, Grimsby, South Humberside, DN31 3LS Tel: (01472) 352022

Country Lanes Garden Centre Ltd, Country Lanes Garden Centre, Exeter Road, Stockley, Okehampton, Devon, EX20 1QH Tel: (01837) 52489 Fax: (01837) 52489

G S G Buildings Ltd, Frank Street, Preston, PR1 1PB Tel: (01772) 824953 Fax: (01772) 882606

Horley Garden Centre, Station Approach, Horley, Surrey, RH6 9HQ Tel: (07866) 433473

Moss Lodge Fish Farm & Water Garden Centre, Moss Road, Moss, Doncaster, South Yorkshire, DN6 0HF Tel: (01302) 700959 Fax: (01302) 707171

National Polytunnels Ltd, 258 Station Road, Bamber Bridge, Preston, PR5 6EA Tel: (01772) 799200 Fax: (01772) 799250 E-mail: sales@nationalalpolytunnels.co.uk

Roydon Hamlet Water Garden Centre, Tylers Road, Roydon, Harlow, Essex, CM19 5LJ Tel: (01279) 792235 Fax: (01279) 792803

Wilkinson, 81 High Street, Redcar, Cleveland, TS10 3DE Tel: (01642) 492471 E-mail: enquiries@wilko.co.uk

GARDEN SCULPTURES

▶ Snowdrop Gardening & Design Services, 3 Stapeley Farm Cottages, Odiham, Hampshire, RG29 1JE Tel: (01256) 862020 E-mail: info@snowdropgardening.co.uk

GARDEN SERVICES

Active Groundworks, C Polglaze Barton Farm, Liskey Hill, Perranporth, Cornwall, TR6 0BB Tel: (01872) 573222

▶ Ashbourne Property Services, 75 Ashford Avenue, Hayes, Middlesex, UB4 0NB Tel: (020) 8581 2415 Fax: 020 85812415 E-mail: mrdbryn@yahoo.co.uk

Central Window Cleaners Ltd, 21 Sussex Close, Nuneaton, Warwickshire, CV10 8JZ Tel: (024) 7675 7615 Fax: E-mail: enquires@centralwindowcleaners.co.uk

Direct Garden Services, 23 Orched Road, South Croydon, CROYDON, CR2 9LY Tel: (07900) 687013 E-mail: sales@directgardenservices.co.uk

▶ The Garden Design Co., 109 Brewery Road, Pampisford, Cambridge, CB22 3EW Tel: (01223) 835889 Fax: (01223) 835889 E-mail: gardendesignco@btinternet.com

▶ GS Gardening Services, 36 Japonica Way, Havant, Hampshire, PO9 2FN Tel: (023) 9261 0279 E-mail: george.stew@ntlworld.com

▶ Hawthorn Gardening Services, The Hawthorns, Ewell, Epsom, Surrey, KT17 2QA Tel: 07929 196344 E-mail: jon@hawthorn-gardening.com

▶ Howes Garden Services, 4 Charleston Court, Basildon, Essex, SS13 1TA Tel: (01268) 724213

▶ Lawncraft Ltd, 17 Holywell Hill, St. Albans, Herts, AL1 1DT Tel: 01727 856777 Fax: 01727 830087 E-mail: info@lawncraft.co.uk

Stump Co - Tree Stump Removal Services, 6 Holt Park Approach, Leeds, LS16 7PW Tel: 0113-293 7510 E-mail: sales@stumpco.co.uk

▶ T&K Summerson, stockgill close, Gamston, Nottingham, NG2 6SA Tel: 0115-981 5153 E-mail: info@tkgardenservices.co.uk

▶ The Vigilante Gardener, 149 Pavilion Road, Worthing, West Sussex, BN14 7EG Tel: (01903) 200853 E-mail: stuart@tvglandscaping.co.uk

▶ Wilkinson Hardware Stores Ltd, 14-18 Nutter Road, Thornton-Cleveleys, Lancashire, FY5 1BG Tel: (01253) 859326

GARDEN SHEDS

▶ Burtenshaw Garden Buildings Ltd, c/o Notcutts Garden Centre, Tonbridge Road,, Pembury, Tunbridge Wells, Kent, TN2 4QN Tel: (01892) 825338 E-mail: enquiries@burtenshawgardenbuildings.co.uk

▶ Chafford Landscapes, 14 St. James Avenue East, Stanford-le-Hope, Essex, SS17 7BQ Tel: (01375) 676003 E-mail: ianholloway@btconnect.com

▶ Flourish Gardens Ltd, 47 St. Johns Road, Tunbridge Wells, Kent, TN4 9TP Tel: (01892) 547146 Fax: (01892) 546525 E-mail: diana.segal@flourishgardens.co.uk

Horley Garden Centre, Station Approach, Horley, Surrey, RH6 9HQ Tel: (07866) 433473

▶ Horns Garden Sheds, 1 Winchester Drive, South West Industrial Estate, Peterlee, County Durham, SR8 2RJ Tel: 0191-518 1098 Fax: 0191-518 1098

▶ Mercury Architectural Projects Ltd, 2 Shrike Close Clayton Heights, Bradford, West Yorkshire, BD6 3YG Tel: (0800) 695 7595 E-mail: info@mercurygardens.co.uk

Rayners Buildings Ltd, Meadrow, Godalming, Surrey, GU7 3HR Tel: (01483) 416242 Fax: (01483) 419378

▶ Russell's Garden Buildings, Gelsmoor Road, Coleorton, Coalville, Leicestershire, LE67 8JF Tel: (01530) 222295 E-mail: shedsrus@hotmail.co.uk

▶ Sheds & Chalets, Llanelli Enterprise Workshops, Lower Trostre Road, Llanelli, Dyfed, SA15 2EA Tel: (01554) 759472 Fax: (01554) 775022 E-mail: sales@shedsnchalets.co.uk

▶ Sheds & Shelters, Pilgrims Way, Hollingbourne, Maidstone, Kent, ME17 1UT Tel: (01622) 880031 Fax: (01622) 880031

▶ Sticks & Stones, Colchester Main Road, Alresford, Colchester, CO7 8DD Tel: (01206) 826835 Fax: (01206) 827655 E-mail: info@stixandstones.co.uk

▶ Tele-Sheds, Shelton Drive, Southport, Merseyside, PR8 2TE Tel: (01704) 571215 E-mail: sales@telesheds.co.uk

Whites Conservatories & Garden Buildings, Reigate Road, Buckland, Reigate, Surrey, RH2 9RE Tel: (01737) 240579 Fax: (01737) 240579 E-mail: sales@whitesconservatories.co.uk

GARDEN SPRAY EQUIPMENT

Allman Sprayers Ltd, Birdham Business Park, Birdham Road, Chichester, West Sussex, PO20 7BT Tel: (01243) 512511 Fax: (01243) 511171 E-mail: sales@allman-sprayers.co.uk

Claxton Engineering Co., 1 Buckminster Lane, Skillington, Grantham, Lincolnshire, NG33 5EY Tel: (01476) 860870 Fax: (01476) 861681 E-mail: claxtonsprayers@lineone.net

GARDEN TOOLS, *See also headings for particular types*

Damar Industrial Machinery Ltd, Clipper Road, Troon Industrial Estate, Leicester, LE4 9JE Tel: 0116-276 4144 Fax: 0116-246 0663 E-mail: sales@damar.biz

▶ Darlac Ltd, Deseronto TRDG Estate, Slough, SL3 7WW Tel: (01753) 547790 Fax: (01753) 580524 E-mail: sales@darlac.com

▶ Dxui Ltd, Unit 5 Autumn Park Industrial Estate, Dysart Road, Grantham, Lincolnshire, NG31 7DD Tel: (01476) 564387 Fax: (01476) 564448 E-mail: admin@dxui.net

Elegant, Estate House, 143 Connaught Avenue, Frinton-on-Sea, Essex, CO13 9AB Tel: (01255) 679559 Fax: (01255) 679825 E-mail: elegantltd@btconnect.com

Emak UK Ltd, Unit A1 Chasewater Industrial Estate, Burntwood Business Park, Burntwood, Staffordshire, WS7 3XD Tel: (01543) 687660 Fax: (01543) 670721 E-mail: sales@emak.co.uk

F & M Garden Machinery Ltd, The White House, Bentley Heath, Barnet, Hertfordshire, EN5 4RY Tel: (020) 8440 6165 Fax: (020) 8447 0670 E-mail: sales@fmgardenmachinery.com

Henton & Chattell Ltd, London Road, Nottingham, NG2 3HW Tel: 0115-986 6646 Fax: 0115-986 6169 E-mail: info@hentonandchattell.co.uk

▶ HSS Hire, Wimbledon Builders Merchants, Gap Road, London, SW19 8JA Tel: (020) 8879 6100 Fax: (020) 8879 6200

Husqvarna Outdoor Products Ltd, Oldends Lane Industrial Estate, Stonedale Road, Stonehouse, Gloucestershire, GL10 3SY Tel: (01453) 820300 Fax: (01453) 826936 E-mail: info.husqvarna@husqvarna.co.uk

▶ K & M Mowers, Poolbank Lane, Welton, Brough, North Humberside, HU15 1PX Tel: (01482) 667004 Fax: (01482) 666520 E-mail: mlowe@kmmowers.co.uk

Mincost Trading, 15a High Street, Lydney, Gloucestershire, GL15 5DP Tel: (01594) 841014 Fax: (01594) 843341 E-mail: sales@mincost.co.uk

Power Equipment Services Ltd, Oldington Trading Estate, Kidderminster, Worcestershire, DY11 7QP Tel: (01562) 742400 Fax: (01562) 865826

▶ Promoseeds UK, White Hart Hill, Guestling, Hastings, East Sussex, TN35 4LP Tel: (01424) 813572 Fax: (01424) 814631 E-mail: tony@promoseeds.co.uk

The Scotts Co. (UK) Ltd, Howden Dyke, Goole, North Humberside, DN14 7UF Tel: (01430) 433300 Fax: (01430) 431658

Simbles Ltd, 76 Queens Road, Watford, WD17 2LD Tel: (01923) 226052 Fax: (01923) 817526 E-mail: sales@simbles.com

Spear & Jackson Ltd, St Pauls Road, Wednesbury, West Midlands, WS10 9RA Tel: 0121 5561414

GARDEN TOYS

Spinnaker Products Ltd, Unit 15, Rylands Farm Industrial Estate, Bagley Road, Rockwell Grove, Wellington, Somerset, TA21 9PZ Tel: (01823) 400969 Fax: (01823) 665268

GARDEN UMBRELLAS

Formlo Leisure Products Ltd, Cleadon House, Church Lane, Tibberton, Droitwich, Worcestershire, WR9 7NW Tel: (01905) 345496 Fax: (01905) 345827 E-mail: formlo.leisure@virgin.net

Glencrest Seatex Ltd, Heron Avenue, Wickford, Essex, SS11 8DL Tel: (01268) 769641 Fax: (01268) 562950 E-mail: sales@glencrestseatex.com

Hoyland Fox Ltd, Manchester Road, Millhouse Green, Sheffield, S36 9NR Tel: (01226) 762244 Fax: (01226) 370022 E-mail: hfsales@hoylandfox.com

Stephens Umbrellas, Sandall Stones Road, Kirk Sandall Industrial Estate, Kirk Sandall, Doncaster, South Yorkshire, DN3 1QR Tel: (01302) 790790 Fax: (01302) 790088 E-mail: sue@oasisleisure.ltd.uk

Walter Phillips Materials Ltd, Unit 3 Ratcliffe Street, Stockport, Cheshire, SK1 3ES Tel: 0161-429 0309 Fax: 0161-477 7884 E-mail: brolly@clara.net

GARDEN WATERING SYSTEMS

▶ Celtic Water Management Ltd, Dolfedwen, Tresaith, Cardigan, Ceredigion, SA43 2JG Tel: (01239) 811465 Fax: (01239) 811918 E-mail: info@celticwater.co.uk

▶ Scenic Blue, 13 Ferndene, Bradley Stoke, Bristol, BS32 9DG Tel: (0800) 7833428 Fax: E-mail: tracy_graham@scenicblue.co.uk

GARDENING CONTAINERS

▶ Groundforce Gardening, 94 Church Road, Emneth, Wisbech, Cambridgeshire, PE14 8AF Tel: (01945) 466555 Fax: (01945) 466192 E-mail: graham.brindley@groundforcegardening.net

Link-A-Bord, The Colliery Industrial Estate, Main Road, Morton, Alfreton, Derbyshire, DE55 6HL Tel: (01773) 590566 Fax: (01773) 590681 E-mail: sales@link-a-bord.co.uk

▶ Shademakers, 171 Cottonmill Lane, St. Albans, Hertfordshire, AL1 2EX Tel: (0800) 0851558 Fax: (0870) 4214097 E-mail: mike@shademakers.co.uk

GARMENT ACCESSORIES/ COMPONENTS, *See also headings for particular materials*

▶ Bahi Group, 68 Pullman Road, Wigston, Leicestershire, LE18 2DB Tel: 0116-281 3111

Balgownie Machine Centre Ltd, 78a Powis Terrace, Aberdeen, AB25 3PQ Tel: (01224) 485291 Fax: (01224) 482344 E-mail: sales@balgownie.co.uk

▶ Highland Dress Hire, 246 Brown Royd Avenue, Dalton, Huddersfield, HD5 9NW Tel: (01484) 546915 Fax: (01484) 432589 E-mail: laurie@highlandhire.co.uk

Holland & Holland Holdings Ltd, 31-33 Bruton Street, London, W1J 6HH Tel: (020) 7499 4411 Fax: (020) 7499 4544

J2G Ltd, Unit 16, Robjohns House, Navigation Road, Chelmsford, CM2 6ND Tel: (01245) 346290 Fax: (01245) 280800

▶ Morrison Sporrans, Ruthvenfield Way, Inveralmond Industrial Estate, Perth, PH1 3UF Tel: (01738) 630103 Fax: (01738) 63105

The Neoknitting & Trim Ltd, Peter Pal House, Albion St, Leicester, LE2 5DE Tel: 0116-271 4923 Fax: 0116-271 4422 E-mail: sales@neotrims.com

Rayflex Ltd, Unit 6-9, 35 River Road, Barking, Essex, IG11 0DA Tel: (020) 8591 9418 Fax: (020) 8591 9419 E-mail: info@rayflexltd.co.uk

Slik Fasteners Ltd, Units B2-B3 The Dresser Centre, Whitworth Street, Openshaw, Manchester, M11 2NE Tel: 0161-230 6878 Fax: 0161-230 7636 E-mail: info@slik.co.uk

Totes Isotoner UK Ltd, Eastman House, Radford Cresent, Billericay, Essex, CM12 0DN Tel: (01277) 630277 Fax: (01277) 630276

GARMENT ACCESSORIES/ COMPONENTS, METAL

Foam 4 U Army & Navy Stores, 21 Chestergate, Macclesfield, Cheshire, SK11 6BX Tel: (01625) 425164

Industrial Protective & Safetywear, Unit 4-8, Reginald Street, Stoke-on-Trent, ST6 1DU Tel: (01782) 821923 Fax: (01782) 575011 E-mail: ipstoke@hotmail.com

John O Groats Crafts Ltd, John O' Groats, John O' Groats, Wick, Caithness, KW1 4YR Tel: (01955) 611371 Fax: (01955) 611326

Mothercare P.L.C., Cherry Tree Road, Watford, WD24 6SH Tel: (01923) 241000 Fax: (01923) 241000

Mountain Warehouse Ltd, The Great Western Desnr Village, Kemble Drive, Cheney Manor Industrial Estate, Swindon, SN2 2DZ Tel: (01793) 538273 Fax: (01793) 538273

Nottingham Design Studio, Queen Elizabeth Way, Ilkeston, Derbyshire, DE7 4NU Tel: 0115-944 1944 Fax: 0115-944 1944

Two Star Fashions Ltd, 53 Hatter Street, Manchester, M4 5FU Tel: 0161-832 5318 Fax: 0161-839 9779

GARMENT ACCESSORIES/ COMPONENTS, PLASTIC

Concept Covers Ltd, 1 Monarch Works, Balds Lane, Stourbridge, West Midlands, DY9 8TE Tel: (01384) 897101 Fax: (01384) 891171 E-mail: concept-covers@supanet.com

K B Packaging Ltd, Merlin Way, Quarry Hill Industrial Estate, Ilkeston, Derbyshire, DE7 4RA Tel: 0115-944 1600 Fax: 0115-932 7460 E-mail: enquiries@totalboxpack.co.uk

Nikita Clothing Co. Ltd, 1 Kamloops Cresent, Leicester, LE1 2HX Tel: 0116-262 3438 Fax: 0116-253 1939 E-mail: info@nikita.co.uk

GARMENT BAGS

Braitrim Group Ltd, Braitrim House, 98 Victoria Road, London, NW10 6NB Tel: (020) 8723 3000 Fax: (020) 8723 3001 E-mail: service@braitrim.com

▶ First Source Ltd, Elmdon Grange, Elmdon Park, Solihull, West Midlands, B92 9EL Tel: 0121-722 3900 Fax: 0121-743 4794 E-mail: firstsource@orange.net

▶ Terfware All Terrain Mountain Boarding Apparel, 4 Lopes Road, Dousland, Yelverton, Devon, PL20 6NX Tel: (01822) 854354

GARMENT HANDLING EQUIPMENT

Polymark (G B) Ltd, Unit 14, Sopwith Way, Drayton Field Industrial Estate, Daventry, Northamptonshire, NN11 8PB Tel: (01327) 308600 Fax: (01327) 308611 E-mail: polymark.sales@polymark.co.uk

GARMENT RAILS

Kee Systems Ltd, 11 Thornsett Road, London, SW18 4EW Tel: (020) 8874 6566 Fax: (020) 8874 5726 E-mail: sales@keesystems.com

Metallon Ltd, Unit D Lea Road Trading Estate, Lea Road, Waltham Abbey, Essex, EN9 1AE Tel: (01992) 715737 Fax: (01992) 767607 E-mail: sales@metallon.co.uk

Richardson & Co. Ltd, Smithfold Lane, Worsley, Manchester, M28 0GP Tel: 0161-702 7002

V D M Sales, Unit 22 Mackley Industrial Estate, Henfield Road, Small Dole, Henfield, West Sussex, BN5 9XR Tel: (01273) 494066 Fax: (01273) 494147

GARMENT SWING TICKETS

Icon Labels Ltd, 1 Lower Oakham Way, Oakham Business Park, Mansfield, Nottinghamshire, NG18 5BU Tel: (01623) 421241 Fax: (01623) 421251 E-mail: sales@iconlabels.co.uk

Kalamazoo Secure Solutions Ltd, Northfield, Birmingham, B31 2NY Tel: 0121-256 2222 Fax: 0121-256 2249 E-mail: kalamazoo@ksp.co.uk

▶ Paxar Apparel Group Ltd, Private Road No 1, Colwick Industrial Estate, Nottingham, NG4 2JQ Tel: 0115-989 6500 Fax: 0115-989 6622 E-mail: info@paxar-emea.com

GAS ALARM OR DETECTION SYSTEMS

▶ Nereus Alarms Ltd, 9 Britannia Road, Lower Parkstone, Poole, Dorset, BH14 8AZ Tel: (01202) 731886 Fax: (01202) 739060 E-mail: info@nereusalarms.co.uk

GAS ANALYSERS

▶ A & R Designs Ltd, Unit 21, Stevenston Industrial Estate, Stevenston, Ayrshire, KA20 3LR Tel: (01294) 601042 Fax: (01294) 601400 E-mail: ardgas@aol.com

Cambridge Sensotec Ltd, Unit 8, Royce Court, Burrel Road, St. Ives, Cambridgeshire, PE27 3NE Tel: 0845 5314235 Fax: (01480) 466032 E-mail: sales@cambridge-sensotec.co.uk

CBISS Ltd, 11 Ark Royal Way, Lairdside Technology Park, Tranmere, Birkenhead, Merseyside, CH41 9HT Tel: 0151-666 8300 Fax: 0151-666 8329 E-mail: sales@cbiss.com

GAS ANALYSERS – *continued*

Colwick Instruments Ltd, PO Box 8268, Nottingham, NG3 6AJ Tel: 0115-962 2999 Fax: 0115-961 4582 E-mail: enquires@colwickinstruments.co.uk

Emerson Process Management, Meridian East, Leicester, LE19 1UX Tel: 0116-282 2822 Fax: 0116-289 2896

Emmerson Process Management Ltd, Heath Place, Bognor Regis, West Sussex, PO22 9SH Tel: (01243) 867554 Fax: (01243) 867554

Hiden Analytical Ltd, 420 Europa Boulevard, Westbrook, Warrington, WA5 7UN Tel: (01925) 445225 Fax: (01925) 416518 E-mail: info@hiden.co.uk

Horiba Instruments Ltd, Kyoto Close, Summerhouse Road, Moulton Park, Northampton, NN3 6FL Tel: (01604) 542500 Fax: (01604) 542699

Icam Ltd, Unit 2, Spring Gardens, Washington, Pulborough, West Sussex, RH20 3BS Tel: (01903) 892222 Fax: (01903) 892277 E-mail: icam@icam.ltd.uk

IMA Ltd, Parkwell House, Otley Rd, Guiseley, Leeds, LS20 8BH Tel: 0845 4941692 Fax: (01943) 879988E-mail: sales@ima.co.uk

Instromet, Charlotte Street, Melton Mowbray, Leicestershire, LE13 1NA Tel: (01664) 567797 Fax: (01664) 410254 E-mail: sales@instrometuk.co.uk

Onix Process Analysis, Ion Path, Road Three, Winsford Industrial Estate, Winsford, Cheshire, CW7 3GA Tel: (01606) 548704 Fax: (01606) 548711 E-mail: glewis@onixpa.com

Procal Analytics Ltd, 5 Maxwell Road, Peterborough, PE2 7HU Tel: (01733) 232495 Fax: (01733) 235255 E-mail: post@procalanalytics.com

Sabre Systems (Heating) Ltd, Unit 9, Ruxley Corner Industrial Estate, Edgington Way, Sidcup, Kent, DA14 5BL Tel: (020) 8308 0708 Fax: (020) 8309 6727 E-mail: sales@sabresystems.co.uk

Saes Getters (GB) Ltd, Heritage House, Vicker Lane, Daventry, Northamptonshire, NN11 5AA Tel: (01327) 310777 Fax: (01327) 310555 E-mail: saes-gb@saes-group.com

Servomex Group Ltd, Crowborough Hill, Jarvis Brook, Crowborough, East Sussex, TN6 3DU Tel: (01892) 652181 Fax: (01892) 662253 E-mail: info@servomex.com

Siemens Process Instruments, Century House, Bridgwater Road, Worcester, WR4 9ZQ Tel: (01905) 450500 Fax: (01905) 450501

Signal Group Ltd, Standards House, 12 Doman Road, Camberley, Surrey, GU15 3DF Tel: (01276) 682841 Fax: (01276) 691302 E-mail: instruments@signal-group.com

Specialty Gases Ltd, Buiding 940 Kent Science Park, Sittingbourne, Kent, ME9 8PS Tel: (01795) 599099 Fax: (01795) 411525 E-mail: sales@specialty-gases.com

Spectra Sensortech Ltd, Cowley Way, Crewe, CW1 6AG Tel: (01270) 250150 Fax: (01270) 251939

Thermo Onix Ltd, Factory 1, Ion Path, Road Three, Winsford, Cheshire, CW7 3GA Tel: (01606) 548700 Fax: (01606) 548711 E-mail: eurosales@thermoonix.com

GAS APPLIANCES

Advanced Gas, 40 Station Road, Erdington, Birmingham, B23 6UE Tel: 0121-377 7387

B.K. Gas Supplies, 35 Kings Road, West Drayton, Middlesex, UB7 9EF Tel: (01895) 446115 Fax: (01895) 446115

Cowley Components Ltd, Masons Road, Stratford-upon-Avon, Warwickshire, CV37 9NF Tel: 0117-963 7142 Fax: (01789) 415623

Edinburgh Sensors Ltd, 2 Bain Square, Livingston, West Lothian, EH54 7DQ Tel: (01506) 425300 Fax: (01506) 425320 E-mail: sales@edinst.com

G T C Ltd, Woolpit Business Park, Bury Road, Woolpit, Bury St. Edmunds, Suffolk, IP30 9UP Tel: (01359) 240363 Fax: (01359) 244045

Gas Appliance Distributors Ltd, Junction Two Industrial Estate, Demuth Way, Oldbury, West Midlands, B69 4LT Tel: 0121-544 5566 Fax: 0121-544 7437

Instagas Boston Ltd, Industrial Estate, Hamilton Way, Boston, Lincolnshire, PE21 8TT Tel: (01205) 368622 Fax: (01205) 351807 E-mail: enquiries@instagas.co.uk

Rangemaster Leisure, Clarence Street, Leamington Spa, Warwickshire, CV31 2AD Tel: (01926) 427027 Fax: (01926) 450526 E-mail: consumers@leisurecp.co.uk

Robinson Willey Ltd, Mill Lane, Old Swan, Liverpool, L13 4AJ Tel: 0151-228 9111 Fax: 0151-228 6661 E-mail: info@robinson-willey.com

Sirocco 2000 Ltd, Imperial Mill, Liverpool Road, Burnley, Lancashire, BB12 6HH Tel: (01282) 441771 Fax: (01282) 441770

Valor Heating, Wood Lane, Erdington, Birmingham, B24 9QP Tel: 0121-373 8111 Fax: 0121-373 8181E-mail: sales@valor.co.uk

Verine Ltd, 52 Broton Drive Trad Estate, Halstead, Essex, CO9 1HB Tel: (01787) 472551 Fax: (01787) 476589 E-mail: sales@verine.co.uk

GAS BOILER MAINTENANCE OR REPAIR

▶ M R Gas Services, 6 Elm Grove, Plympton, Plymouth, PL7 2BW Tel: (01752) 346482 Fax:

GAS BOOSTER COMPRESSORS

Bowman Power Group Ltd, Ocean Quay, Belvidere Road, Southampton, SO14 5QY Tel: (023) 8023 6700 Fax: (023) 8035 2565 E-mail: sales@bowmanpower.co.uk

GAS BOOSTERS, *See also headings for particular types*

Air & Gas Blowers, 22 Hitch Lowes, Chelford, Macclesfield, Cheshire, SK11 9SR Tel: (01625) 860146 Fax: (01625) 860147

Clarke Energy Ltd, C Senator Point, South Boundary Road, Knowsley Industrial Park, Liverpool, L33 7RR Tel: 0151-546 4446 Fax: 0151-546 4447 E-mail: info@clarke-energy.com

Fans & Blowers Ltd, Walrow Industrial Estate, Commerce Way, Highbridge, Somerset, TA9 4AG Tel: (01278) 784004 Fax: (01278) 792848 E-mail: fab-sales@btconnect.com

Haskel Energy Systems Ltd, North Hylton Road, Sunderland, SR5 3JD Tel: 0191-549 1212 Fax: 0191-549 0911 E-mail: sales@haskel.co.uk

GAS BOTTLE STORAGE CAGES

Carlton Downs Holdings Ltd, Hulley Road, Hurdsfield, Macclesfield, Cheshire, SK10 2LZ Tel: (01625) 616570 Fax: (01625) 427427 E-mail: enquiries@carltondowns.co.uk

GAS BOTTLES

Electro Hire & Supply LLP, The Paddock, Off Wharf Road, Biddulph, Stoke-On-Trent, ST8 6AL Tel: (01782) 518322 Fax: (01782) 515960 E-mail: sales@ehireandsupply.co.uk

GAS BURNER CONTROLS

Kromschroder UK Ltd, Unit 15a Frederick Road, Hoo Farm Industrial Estate, Kidderminster, Worcestershire, DY11 7RA Tel: (01562) 747756 Fax: (01562) 744129

Thermaco Ltd, Unit 5, Spring Lane North, Malvern, Worcestershire, WR14 1BU Tel: (01684) 566163 Fax: (01684) 892356 E-mail: sales@thermaco.co.uk

GAS BURNER INSTALLATION OR SERVICING

Elyo Services, Apian House, Selinas Lane, Dagenham, Essex, RM8 1TB Tel: (020) 8252 2929 Fax: (020) 8270 7379

High-Fire Ltd, 37a Cyprus Rd, Leicester, LE2 8QP Tel: 0116-232 7980

Maval Ltd, Skippers Lane, Skippers Lane Industrial Estat, Middlesbrough, Cleveland, TS6 6HA Tel: (01642) 455101 Fax: (01642) 458507 E-mail: maval@talk21.com

S & S Burner Services Ltd, Unit 14 193 The Garth Road Industrial Centre, Garth Road, Morden, Surrey, SM4 4LZ Tel: (020) 8330 7992 Fax: (020) 8330 7993

GAS BURNER PILOT OXYGEN DEPLETION SYSTEMS

Seagas Industries Ltd, 152 Abbey Lane, Leicester, LE4 0DA Tel: 0116-266 9988 Fax: 0116-268 2557E-mail: sales@seagas.net

GAS BURNERS, *See also headings for particular types*

Aeromatix Ltd, Denby Works, Ripley, Derbyshire, DE5 8JH Tel: (01773) 744925 Fax: (01773) 570170 E-mail: info@aeromatix.com

Comtherm Ltd, Comenco Works, Union Lane, Droitwich, Worcestershire, WR9 9AZ Tel: (01905) 775783 Fax: (01905) 794195 E-mail: sales@comtherm.co.uk

Consultant Gas Engineers, Peel Road, West Pimbo, Skelmersdale, Lancashire, WN8 9PT Tel: (01695) 727441 Fax: (01695) 729466 E-mail: sales@cgekilns.co.uk

E O G B Energy Products Ltd, Howard Road, Eaton Socon, St. Neots, Cambridgeshire, PE19 8ET Tel: (01480) 477066 Fax: (01480) 477022 E-mail: sales@eogb.co.uk

Eurograde Plant Ltd, 3 Viscount Industrial Estate, Horton Road, Colnbrook, Slough, SL3 0DF Tel: (020) 8606 0420 Fax: (01753) 681452 E-mail: david@eurograde.com

▶ Hotwork Combustion Technology Ltd, Bretton Street, Savile Town, Dewsbury, West Yorkshire, WF12 9DB Tel: (01924) 506506 Fax: (01924) 506311 E-mail: engineering@hotworkct.com

J P Burners Ltd, 14 Monks Crescent, Leicester, LE4 2WA Tel: 0116-246 0400 Fax: 0116-235 8411 E-mail: sales@jpburners.co.uk

Nordsea Ltd, Captain Clarke Road, Hyde, Cheshire, SK14 4QG Tel: 0161-366 3010 Fax: 0161-366 3011 E-mail: nordsea@compuserve.com

Nu Way Ltd, PO Box 1, Droitwich, Worcestershire, WR9 8NA Tel: (01905) 794331 Fax: (01905) 794017 E-mail: info@nu-way.co.uk

Proctor Process Plant Ltd, Taylor Holme House, Baldwin Street, Bacup, Lancashire, OL13 0LT Tel: (01706) 874444 Fax: (01706) 879686 E-mail: info@ppp-ltd.co.uk

Viessmann Ltd, Hortonwood 30, Telford, Shropshire, TF1 7YP Tel: (01952) 675000 Fax: (01952) 675040 E-mail: info-uk@viessmann.com

Weishaupt UK Ltd, Stoke Gardens, Slough, SL1 3QD Tel: (01753) 512345 Fax: (01753) 512585 E-mail: sales@weishaupt.idps.co.uk

Whites Burners Ltd, 9 Ilfracombe Gardens, Whitley Bay, Tyne & Wear, NE26 3ND Tel: 0191-252 9933 Fax: 0191-252 9955

GAS CATERING EQUIPMENT HIRE

Catering Equipment Engineers Ltd, Kildrum Indust Estate, Kildrum Road, Shankbridge, Ballymena, County Antrim, BT42 3EY Tel: (028) 2589 2122 Fax: (028) 2589 8208 E-mail: info@cee-group.com

GAS CLEANING/SCRUBBING PLANT AND EQUIPMENT

Axsia Mozley, 370 Bristol Road, Gloucester, GL2 5DH Tel: (01452) 833800 Fax: (01209) 211068 E-mail: asbl@axsia.com

▶ Hygrade Industrial Plastics Ltd, Hunters Lane, Rugby, Warwickshire, CV21 1EA Tel: (01788) 571316 Fax: (01788) 541184 E-mail: techsales@hygradeplastics.com

Resinfab & Associates, 6 Imex Business Park, Kings Road, Tyseley, Birmingham, B11 2AL Tel: 0121-706 1848 Fax: 0121-706 1848 E-mail: tech@resinfab.co.uk

Techtrol Ltd, Gregson Road, Stockport, Cheshire, SK5 7SS Tel: 0161-476 6955 Fax: 0161-476 2674 E-mail: mailbox@techtrol.co.uk

Van Tongeren International Ltd, Van Tongeren House, 84a High Street, Godalming, Surrey, GU7 1DU Tel: (01483) 428082 Fax: (01483) 417741 E-mail: van-tong@netcomuk.co.uk

GAS COMPRESSION SPRING STRUTS/SUPPORTS

Stabilus, Unit 4 Canada Close, Banbury, Oxfordshire, OX16 2RT Tel: (01295) 700100 Fax: (01295) 700106 E-mail: info@uk.stabilus.com

GAS COMPRESSORS

Belliss & Morcom Ltd, Chequers Bridge, Gloucester, GL1 4LL Tel: (01452) 338338 Fax: (01452) 338307 E-mail: indsales@gardnerdenver.co.uk

Dresser Roots-Holmes Operations, PO Box B7, Huddersfield, HD1 6RB Tel: (01484) 422222 Fax: (01484) 422668 E-mail: dmd_roots@dresser.co.uk

Gas Compressors Ltd, Star Farm, Golden Green, Tonbridge, Kent, TN11 0BE Tel: (01732) 852048 Fax: (01732) 852376 E-mail: sales@gascompressors.co.uk

Nash Elmo UK Ltd, Road One, Winsford Industrial Estate, Winsford, Cheshire, CW7 3PL Tel: (01606) 542400 Fax: (01606) 542434 E-mail: sales@nasheng.com

Peter Brotherhood Holdings Ltd, Werrington Park Way, Peterborough, PE4 5HG Tel: (01733) 292200 Fax: (01733) 292300 E-mail: sales@peterbrotherhood.co.uk

Rolls Royce Power Enginering P.L.C., Atlantic Park, Dunnings Bridge Road, Bootle, Merseyside, L30 4UZ Tel: 0151-524 6555 Fax: 0151-524 6557 E-mail: m.morgan@ces.com

GAS CONSULTANCY OR CONSULTING ENGINEERS

CHN Gas Services & Maintenance, Paper Mill End Industrial Estate, Birmingham, B44 8NH Tel: 0121-344 4789

▶ Enterprise Manage Services, Unit 12 Ashville Way, Whetstone, Leicester, LE8 6NU Tel: 0116-284 8005 Fax: 0116-284 1512

Harley Haddow Partnership, 8 Coates Crescent, Edinburgh, EH3 7BY Tel: 0131-226 3331 Fax: 0131-226 2563 E-mail: edin@harleyhaddow.com

Instromet, Charlotte Street, Melton Mowbray, Leicestershire, LE13 1NA Tel: (01664) 567797 Fax: (01664) 410254 E-mail: sales@instrometuk.co.uk

Proteus Developments, West Lynne, 16 The Crescent, Northwich, Cheshire, CW9 8AD Tel: (01606) 350614 Fax: (01606) 350614

T M Services Ltd, 5 Charterhouse Square, London, EC1M 6PX Tel: (020) 7867 8600 Fax: (020) 7867 8787 E-mail: tmservices@tmworldwide.co.uk

GAS CONTRACTING ENGINEERS

▶ Brenden Fern Heating & Plumbing, 27 Paradise Street, Stoke-on-Trent, ST6 5AG Tel: (01782) 818577 Fax: (01782) 818578 E-mail: info@bfplum.co.uk

C O P Autogas Ltd, Somersall Mill, Grove Lane, Doveridge, Ashbourne, Derbyshire, DE6 5PB Tel: (01283) 585240 Fax: (01283) 585738

Gas Service Agents Ltd, 39-43 Harrison Road, Southampton, SO17 3TL Tel: (023) 8051 6611 Fax: (023) 8067 1968 E-mail: info@gascare.com

S G Ray & Co. Ltd, Sheerlands House, Sheerlands Road, Finchampstead, Wokingham, Berkshire, RG40 4QX Tel: 0118-973 2515

GAS CONTROL EQUIPMENT MANUFRS

Gas Arc Group Ltd, Vinces Road, Diss, Norfolk, IP22 4WW Tel: (01379) 652263 Fax: (01379) 644235 E-mail: mail@gas-arc.co.uk

Parts Center Commercial, Unit 14, Harp Road, Off Guinness Road, Trafford Park, Manchester, M17 1SR Tel: 0161-848 0546 Fax: 0161-872 0265

GAS CONTROLS, DOMESTIC APPLIANCE

▶ Peerless Gas Controls Ltd, Unit 11 Maple Business Park, Walter Street, Aston, Birmingham, B7 5ET Tel: 0121-327 6777 Fax: 0121-327 4555 E-mail: info@peerlesscontrols.com

GAS COOKER COMPONENTS

▶ Glem Gas Spares Ltd, 150 Tarbock Road, Hyton, Huyton, Liverpool, L36 5TJ Tel: (07729) 729129 E-mail: glemgasspares@btinternet.com

GAS COOKERS

A B C Catering Equipment, 196 Edgeware Bury Lane, Edgware, Middlesex, HA8 8QW Tel: (020) 8958 1958 Fax: (020) 8958 1958 E-mail: sales@abccatering.co.uk

Aga Factory Shop, Station Road, Ketley, Telford, Shropshire, TF1 5AQ Tel: (01952) 642024 Fax: (01952) 243138 E-mail: info@aga-web.co.uk

Cater Hire Ltd, Unit J Gregorys Bank, Worcester, WR3 8AB Tel: (01905) 23260 Fax: (01905) 23152 E-mail: info@cater-hire.co.uk

Walter Dix & Co., 1 Stirling Court, Team Valley Trading Estate, Gateshead, Tyne & Wear, NE11 0JF Tel: 0191-482 0033 Fax: 0191-491 1488 E-mail: sales@wdix.co.uk

Electrolux, Merrington Lane Trading Estate, Spennymoor, County Durham, DL16 7UU Tel: (01388) 814141 Fax: (01388) 812753 E-mail: graham.metcalfe@electrolux.co.uk

▶ Glebe Radio & Television Ltd, 33 Glebe Farm Road, Birmingham, B33 9LY Tel: 0121-783 3352 Fax: 0121-783 1498 E-mail: glebetv@freedomnames.co.uk

Glen Dimplex Cooking Ltd, Stoney Lane, Whiston, Prescot, Merseyside, L35 2XW Tel: 0151-426 6551 Fax: 0151-426 3261

Johnson & Johnson Furniture plc, Unit 12-19 Guinness Road Trading Estate, Guinness Road, Trafford Park, Manchester, M17 1SB Tel: 0161-872 7041 Fax: 0161-872 7351 E-mail: mail@jjff.co.uk

Rangemaster, Meadow Lane, Long Eaton, Nottingham, NG10 2AT Tel: 0115-946 4000 Fax: 0115-946 0374 E-mail: sales@rangemaster.co.uk

GAS CYLINDERS, HELIUM

▶ Partyrama, 73 Garamonde Drive, Wymbush, Milton Keynes, MK8 8DD Tel: (0870) 0420173 Fax: (0870) 0420173 E-mail: admin@partyrama.co.uk

GAS DETECTION AND ANALYSIS

Adc Gas Analysis Ltd, Hoddesdon Industrial Centre, Pindar Road, Hoddesdon, Hertfordshire, EN11 0FF Tel: (01992) 478600 Fax: (01992) 478938 E-mail: sales@adc-analysers.com

GAS DETECTION AND ANALYSIS - *continued*

CBISS Ltd, 11 Ark Royal Way, Lairdside Technology Park, Tranmere, Birkenhead, Merseyside, CH41 9HT Tel: 0151-666 8300 Fax: 0151-666 8329 E-mail: sales@cbiss.com
City Technology Ltd, City Technology Centre, Walton Road, Portsmouth, PO6 1SZ Tel: (023) 9232 5511 Fax: (023) 9238 6611 E-mail: sensors@citytech.co.uk
▶ Pal Technologies, 141 St. James Road, Glasgow, G4 0LT Tel: 0141-552 6085 Fax: 0141-552 6085 E-mail: sales@paltechnologies.com
Servomex Group Ltd, Crowborough Hill, Jarvis Brook, Crowborough, East Sussex, TN6 3DU Tel: (01892) 652181 Fax: (01892) 662253 E-mail: info@servomex.com
T Q Environmental P.L.C., Unit 10, Flanshaw Way, Wakefield, West Yorkshire, WF2 9LP Tel: (01924) 380700 Fax: (01924) 361700 E-mail: sales@tqplc.com

GAS DETECTION EQUIPMENT OR SYSTEM MAINTENANCE OR REPAIR

Gas & Environmental Services Ltd, Unit 9, Little Ridge, Welwyn Garden City, Hertfordshire, AL7 2BH Tel: (01707) 373751 Fax: (01707) 373752 E-mail: kevin.mileson@btinternet.com

GAS DETECTION EQUIPMENT/ SYSTEMS HIRE

Eim Northern Ltd, 1 Adcroft Street, Off Higher Hillgate, Stockport, Cheshire, SK1 3HZ Tel: 0161-476 3303 Fax: 0161-476 4010 E-mail: sales@eimnorthern.co.uk

GAS DETECTION EQUIPMENT/ SYSTEMS MANUFRS

A T M I (UK), Kingsland House, 512 Wimborne Road East, Ferndown, Dorset, BH22 9NG Tel: (01202) 875753 Fax: (01202) 875763 E-mail: info/europe@atmi.com
ATAC Ltd, 6 Redlands Centre, Redlands, Coulsdon, Surrey, CR5 2HT Tel: (020) 8763 9494 Fax: (020) 8763 9540 E-mail: atac@atacuk.com
Blakell Europlacer Ltd, 30 Factory Road, Poole, Dorset, BH16 5SL Tel: (01202) 266500 Fax: (01202) 266599 E-mail: gas@europlacer.co.uk
CBISS Ltd, 11 Ark Royal Way, Lairdside Technology Park, Tranmere, Birkenhead, Merseyside, CH41 9HT Tel: 0151-666 8300 Fax: 0151-666 8329 E-mail: sales@cbiss.com
City Technology Ltd, City Technology Centre, Walton Road, Portsmouth, PO6 1SZ Tel: (023) 9232 5511 Fax: (023) 9238 6611 E-mail: sensors@citytech.co.uk
Detection Instruments (Northern) Ltd, Unit 5-6 Bonnyton Industrial Estate, Munro Place, Kilmarnock, Ayrshire, KA1 2NP Tel: (01563) 525525 Fax: (01563) 542350 E-mail: info@di-northern.com
Eim Northern Ltd, 1 Adcroft Street, Off Higher Hillgate, Stockport, Cheshire, SK1 3HZ Tel: 0161-476 3303 Fax: 0161-476 4010 E-mail: sales@eimnorthern.co.uk
G D S Technologies, Swillington Lane, Swillington, Leeds, LS26 8BZ Tel: 0113-286 0166 Fax: 0113-286 4073 E-mail: sales@gds-technologies.co.uk
Gas & Environmental Services Ltd, Unit 9, Little Ridge, Welwyn Garden City, Hertfordshire, AL7 2BH Tel: (01707) 373751 Fax: (01707) 373752 E-mail: kevin.mileson@btinternet.com
General Monitors UK Ltd, 1 Heather Close, Lyme Green Business Park, Macclesfield, Cheshire, SK11 0LR Tel: (01625) 619583 Fax: (01625) 619098 E-mail: info@generalmonitors.co.uk
Geotechnical Instruments (UK) Ltd, Sovereign House, Queensway, Leamington Spa, Warwickshire, CV31 3JR Tel: (01926) 338111 Fax: (01926) 338110 E-mail: sales@geotech.co.uk
Honeywell Analytics Ltd, Hatch Pond House, 4 Stinsford Road, Nuffield Estate, Poole, Dorset, BH17 0RZ Tel: (01202) 676161 Fax: (01202) 678011 E-mail: tracy.dawe@honeywell.com
Icam Ltd, Unit 2, Spring Gardens, Washington, Pulborough, West Sussex, RH20 3BS Tel: (01903) 892222 Fax: (01903) 892277 E-mail: icam@icam.ltd.uk
K A D Detection Systems Ltd, Units 4-5, Barrmill Road, Galston, Ayrshire, KA4 8HH Tel: (01563) 820148 Fax: (01563) 820163 E-mail: sales@kad-detection.com
M S A Britain Ltd, Shawhead Industrial Estate, Coatbridge, Lanarkshire, ML5 4TD Tel: (01236) 424966 Fax: (01236) 440881 E-mail: sales@msabritain.co.uk
S F Detection Ltd, Hatch Pond House, 4 Stinsford Road, Nuffield Estate, Poole, Dorset, BH17 0RZ Tel: (01202) 645577 Fax: (01202) 665331 E-mail: sales@sfdetection.com
Scotsafe Testing Ltd, 17 Woodlands Drive, Kirkhill Industrial Estate, Aberdeen, AB21 0GW Tel: (01224) 771200 Fax: (01224) 725511 E-mail: adrian@scotsafe.co.uk
Signal Group Ltd, Standards House, 12 Doman Road, Camberley, Surrey, GU15 3DF Tel: (01276) 682841 Fax: (01276) 691302 E-mail: instruments@signal-group.com
Status Scientific Controls, Hermitage Lane Inudst Estate, Kings Mill Way, Mansfield, Nottinghamshire, NG18 5ER Tel: (01623) 651381 Fax: (01623) 421063 E-mail: sales@status-scientific.com
T Q Environmental P.L.C., Unit 10, Flanshaw Way, Wakefield, West Yorkshire, WF2 9LP Tel: (01924) 380700 Fax: (01924) 361700 E-mail: sales@tqplc.com

GAS DETECTION SERVICES

G D S Technologies, Swillington Lane, Swillington, Leeds, LS26 8BZ Tel: 0113-286 0166 Fax: 0113-286 4073 E-mail: sales@gds-technologies.co.uk
Sure Safe Ltd, College Farm Business Centre, North End, Meldreth, Royston, Hertfordshire, SG8 6NT Tel: (01763) 262649 Fax: (01763) 263134 E-mail: henrik@sure-safe.com
T C W Services Controls Ltd, Bradshaw Works, Bradshaw Road, Honley, Holmfirth, HD9 6DT Tel: (01484) 662865 Fax: (01484) 667574 E-mail: sales@tcw-services.co.uk

GAS DISCHARGE TUBES

Surgetech Ltd, Durlston House, North Street, Westbourne, Emsworth, Hampshire, PO10 8SN Tel: (01243) 379613 Fax: (01243) 370003 E-mail: bill.jones@surgetech.co.uk

GAS DRIVEN GENERATOR SETS

Alstom Power Generation Ltd, Silverlink Business Park, Silverlink, Wallsend, Tyne & Wear, NE28 9ND Tel: 0191-295 2000 Fax: 0191-295 2011
Beaver Power Ltd, Goat Mill Road, Dowlais, Merthyr Tydfil, CF48 3TF Tel: (01685) 353270 Fax: (01685) 353271 E-mail: sales@beaverpower.co.uk
International Power Generation, Unit 7c Carcroft Enterprise Park, Carcroft, Doncaster, South Yorkshire, DN6 8DD Tel: (01302) 722888 Fax: (01302) 721202 E-mail: sales@generator.co.uk

GAS DRYING PLANT

Axsia Mozley, 370 Bristol Road, Gloucester, GL2 5DH Tel: (01452) 833800 Fax: (01209) 211068 E-mail: asbl@axsia.com

GAS ENGINE DRIVEN GENERATOR SETS

Dale Power Solutions Ltd, Salter Road, Eastfield, Scarborough, North Yorkshire, YO11 3DU Tel: (01723) 583511 Fax: (01723) 581231 E-mail: sales@dalepowersolutions.com

GAS ENGINE MANUFRS

Deutz AG - UK, Willow Park, Burdock Close, Cannock, Staffordshire, WS11 7FQ Tel: (01543) 438900 Fax: (01543) 438932
Perkins Engines Co. Ltd, Frank Perkins Way, Eastfield, Peterborough, PE1 5NA Tel: (01733) 583000 Fax: (01733) 582240 E-mail: purdy_claire@perkins.com
Tilsley & Lovatt Ltd, Newstead Industrial Trading Estate, Stoke-on-Trent, ST4 8HT Tel: (01782) 657331 Fax: (01782) 644600 E-mail: sales@tilsleyandlovatt.co.uk

GAS FILTERS

Donaldson Filtration (GB) Ltd, Humberstone Lane, Thurmaston, Leicester, LE4 8HP Tel: 0116-269 6161 Fax: 0116-269 3028 E-mail: peter.cowing@emea.donaldson.com
Headline Filters Ltd, Mill Hall Business Estate, Mill Hall, Aylesford, Kent, ME20 7JZ Tel: (01622) 718927 Fax: (01622) 882448 E-mail: sales@headlinefilters.com
M F & T, 22 Dawkins Road Industrial Estate, Hamworthy, Poole, Dorset, BH15 4JY Tel: (01202) 666456 Fax: (01202) 685545 E-mail: steve.hunt@porvairfilteration.com
John Morfield Ltd, 10 Teal Court, Strathclyde Business Park, Bellshill, Lanarkshire, ML4 3NN Tel: (01698) 840888 Fax: (01698) 840234

GAS FILTRATION/SEPARATION EQUIPMENT

Natco Group, C/O Axsia Howmar Ltd, Albany Park Estate, Frimley Road, Camberley, Surrey, GU16 7QQ Tel: (01276) 681101 Fax: (01276) 681107 E-mail: ahl@axsia.com

GAS FIRE RADIANTS

Instagas Boston Ltd, Industrial Estate, Hamilton Way, Boston, Lincolnshire, PE21 8TT Tel: (01205) 368622 Fax: (01205) 351807 E-mail: enquiries@instagas.co.uk
Space-Ray UK, 4-6 Chapel Lane, Claydon, Ipswich, IP6 0JL Tel: (01473) 830551 Fax: (01473) 832055 E-mail: info@spaceray.co.uk

GAS FIRED AIR CONDITIONING (AC) EQUIPMENT

Stewart Anthony, Data House, 2 Waldeck Road, Dartford, DA1 1UA Tel: (01322) 293005 Fax: (01322) 293879 E-mail: peterdavison@stewartanthony.co.uk

GAS FIRED AIR HEATERS

Bering Heating Supplies Ltd, Unit 9 Station Industrial Estate, Oxford Road, Wokingham, Berkshire, RG41 2YQ Tel: 0118-978 9886 Fax: 0118-978 7460
Comtherm Ltd, Comenco Works, Union Lane, Droitwich, Worcestershire, WR9 9AZ Tel: (01905) 775783 Fax: (01905) 794195 E-mail: sales@comtherm.co.uk
▶ Hot Fires & Heating, 33 West Auckland Road, Darlington, County Durham, DL3 9EL Tel: (01325) 351351 Fax: (01325) 351351 E-mail: hotfires@btconnect.com
William May Ltd, Cavendish Street, Ashton-under-Lyne, Lancashire, OL6 7QW Tel: 0161-330 3838 Fax: 0161-339 1097 E-mail: mwm@william-may.com
Roberts-Gordon, Oxford Street, Bilston, West Midlands, WV14 7EG Tel: (01902) 494425 Fax: (01902) 403200 E-mail: uksales@rg-inc.com

GAS FIRED APPLIANCES, *See headings for particular types*

GAS FIRED BOILER COMPONENTS

▶ M R Gas Services, 6 Elm Grove, Plympton, Plymouth, PL7 2BW Tel: (01752) 346482 Fax:

GAS FIRED BOILERS

▶ Abtap, 326B St Albans Road, Watford, WD24 6PQ Tel: (01923) 630022 Fax: (01923) 630011 E-mail: abtap@btconnect.com
Atlantic 2000, PO Box 11, Ashton-under-Lyne, Lancashire, OL6 7TR Tel: 0161-621 5960 Fax: 0161-621 5966 E-mail: info@atlanticboilers.com
Clyde Energy Solutions Ltd, Unit 10, Lion Park Avenue, Chessington, Surrey, KT9 1ST Tel: (020) 8391 2020 Fax: (020) 8397 4598 E-mail: info@clyde-nrg.com
Crossling, 2 Kingstown Broadway, Kingstown Industrial Estate, Carlisle, CA3 0HA Tel: (01228) 541101 Fax: (01228) 539288 E-mail: marketing@crossling.co.uk
Halstead Boilers Ltd, 16-22 First Avenue, Halstead, Essex, CO9 2EX Tel: (01787) 475557 Fax: (01787) 474588 E-mail: sales@halsteadboilers.co.uk
Heatcall Group Services, Nottingham Road, Belper, Derbyshire, DE56 1JT Tel: (01773) 828100 Fax: (01773) 828123
▶ Hot Fires & Heating, 33 West Auckland Road, Darlington, County Durham, DL3 9EL Tel: (01325) 351351 Fax: (01325) 351351 E-mail: hotfires@btconnect.com
Malvern Boilers Ltd, Spring Lane North, Malvern, Worcestershire, WR14 1BW Tel: (01684) 893777 Fax: (01684) 893776 E-mail: sales@malvernboilers.co.uk
Travis Perkins plc, Sydenham Wharf, Lower Bristol Road, Bath, BA2 3EE Tel: (01225) 446110 Fax: (01225) 442796 E-mail: bath@travisperkins.co.uk
Vaillant Ltd, Vaillant House, Trident Close, Medway City Estate, Rochester, Kent, ME2 4EZ Tel: (01634) 292300 Fax: (01634) 290166

GAS FIRED WARM AIR APPLIANCES

Benson Heating, Ludlow Road, Knighton, Powys, LD7 1LP Tel: (01547) 529245 Fax: (01547) 520399 E-mail: information@bensonheating.co.uk

GAS FIREPLACE FRONTS

▶ Feature Fire, 1 2 Warne Park, Warne Road, Weston-super-Mare, Avon, BS23 3TP Tel: (01934) 628142 Fax: (01934) 645625 E-mail: sales@feature-fireplaces.co.uk
▶ Gas Style, 374 Blackpool Road, Ashton-on-Ribble, Preston, PR2 2DS Tel: (01772) 761006 Fax: (01772) 761006
Gas-Fire Com, 15-17 High Street, Rishton, Blackburn, BB1 4JZ Tel: (0800) 0281936 Fax: (01254) 887569 E-mail: sales@gas-fire.com
▶ Pendragon Fireplaces, 12 Market Street, Stourbridge, West Midlands, DY8 1AD Tel: 01384 376441 Fax: 01384 376441 E-mail: pendragongifts@hotmail.com
Stylecharm Fireplaces, 14 Bowlers Croft, Basildon, Essex, SS14 3EE Tel: (01268) 287673 Fax: (01268) 287710 E-mail: carl@beeb.net
Wyvern Marlborough Ltd, Wyvern Buildings, 1 Grove Trading Estate, Dorchester, Dorset, DT1 1SU Tel: (01305) 268981 Fax: (01305) 264717

GAS FIRES

▶ Casterbridge Fires, Unit 15 Casterbridge Industrial Estate, London Road, Dorchester, Dorset, DT1 1PL Tel: (01305) 262829 Fax: (01305) 257483
▶ Gibson and Gould, 1-3 Scotland Street, Glasgow, G5 8LS Tel: (01292) 268478
▶ Multiglow Fires, Canterbury Road, St. Nicholas at Wade, Birchington, Kent, CT7 0PQ Tel: (01843) 847575 Fax: (01843) 848300

GAS FITTINGS, *See also also Plumbers' headings etc*

Bowden Bros & Co. (Manchester) Ltd, Newby Road Industrial Estate, Hazel Grove, Stockport, Cheshire, SK7 5DD Tel: 0161-483 9311 Fax: 0161-483 1080 E-mail: sales@bowbros.co.uk
Brass Fittings & Supplies Ltd, Hawkshead Mill, Hope Street, Glossop, Derbyshire, SK13 7SS Tel: (01457) 854415 Fax: (01457) 855403 E-mail: b.f.s@btconnect.com
Scotland Gas Networks, 11 West Shore Road, Edinburgh, EH5 1RH Tel: 0131-559 6000 Fax: 0131-559 6000
James Southerton Ltd, Unit 24A, Reddicap Trading Estate, Sutton Coldfield, West Midlands, B75 7BU Tel: 0121-378 0194 Fax: 0121-378 3438 E-mail: rjsd@southertons.com

GAS FLOW METERS

Advanced Energy Industries UK Ltd, 5 Minton Place, Victoria Road, Bicester, Oxfordshire, OX26 6QB Tel: (01869) 320022 Fax: (01869) 325004

GAS FURNACES

Boustead International Heaters Ltd, Southwick Square, Southwick, Brighton, BN42 4UA Tel: (01273) 596868 Fax: (01273) 596860 E-mail: sales@bihl.com
Can-Eng Furnaces UK Ltd, Unit 8, Ninian Park, Ninian Way, Wilnecote, Tamworth, Staffordshire, B77 5ES Tel: (01827) 262601 Fax: (01827) 262602 E-mail: can-enguk@mcmail.com
Eurofusion Ltd, Ituri, Darcy Rise, Little Baddow, Chelmsford, CM3 4SN Tel: (01245) 221235 Fax: (0870) 4296791 E-mail: glass@eurofusion.co.uk
J G Shelton & Co. Ltd, The Warren, Ashtead, Surrey, KT21 2SH Tel: (01372) 278422 Fax: (01372) 279338 E-mail: mail@jg-shelton.co.uk
Swan Portaforge, Units 1 & 2 Gamma, Orchard Trading Estate, Toddington, Cheltenham, Gloucestershire, GL54 5EB Tel: (01242) 621590 Fax: (01242) 621591 E-mail: swan@swan-portaforge.co.uk

GAS GOVERNORS

Kromschroder UK Ltd, Unit 15a Frederick Road, Hoo Farm Industrial Estate, Kidderminster, Worcestershire, DY11 7RA Tel: (01562) 747756 Fax: (01562) 744129

GAS HIGH PRESSURE VALVES

Dynamic Controls Ltd, Union Street, Royton, Oldham, OL2 5JD Tel: 0161-633 3933 Fax: 0161-633 4113 E-mail: sales@dynamiccontrols.co.uk
Hale Hamilton Ltd, Cowley Road, Uxbridge, Middlesex, UB8 2AF Tel: (01895) 236525 Fax: (01895) 231407 E-mail: enquiries@halehamilton.com

GAS HOLDERS

MB Engineering Services, Midland Road, Leeds, LS10 2RP Tel: (01924) 877860 Fax: 0113-276 0372 E-mail: sales@clayton-walker.co.uk

GAS IGNITERS, INDUSTRIAL/ WELDING SYSTEMS, *See Ignition etc*

GAS INJECTORS

Stereomatics Ltd, Seven Stars Industrial Estate, Wheler Road, Coventry, CV3 4LB Tel: (024) 7630 4000 Fax: (024) 7630 4455 E-mail: sales@stereomatic.co.uk

GAS INSTALLATION TRAINING

▶ MGM Petrogas, 29 Hazeldown Road, TEIGNMOUTH, Devon, TQ14 8QR Tel: 01626 775803 Fax: 01626 775803 E-mail: mgmpetrogas@btinternet.com

GAS INSULATED ELECTRICAL LINES

Procare GB Ltd, 1 Burcott Road, Purley, Surrey, CR8 4AD Tel: (020) 8763 8444 Fax: (020) 8668 8399

GAS LEAK SEARCHER BARS

Peter Wood & Co. Ltd, Riverside House, Weedon Street, Sheffield, S9 2FT Tel: 0114-244 0000 Fax: 0114-244 4646

GAS LIGHTING FITTINGS OR SYSTEMS OR EQUIPMENT

Sugg Lighting Ltd, Sussex Manor Business Park, Gatwick Road, Crawley, West Sussex, RH10 9GD Tel: (01293) 540111 Fax: (01293) 540114 E-mail: admin@sugglighting.co.uk

GAS MEASUREMENT EQUIPMENT/SYSTEMS

Invensys Metering Systems Ltd, Unit 11 The Quadrangle, Premier Way, Romsey, Hampshire, SO51 9DL Tel: (01794) 526100 Fax: (01794) 526101 E-mail: romseysales@invensys.com

Skeltonhall Systems Ltd, 70 Carwood Road, Sheffield, S4 7SD Tel: 0114-243 1332 Fax: 0114-244 9579 E-mail: info@skeltonhall-systems.com

GAS METER FITTINGS

Brass Fittings & Supplies Ltd, Hawkshead Mill, Hope Street, Glossop, Derbyshire, SK13 7SS Tel: (01457) 854415 Fax: (01457) 855403 E-mail: b.f.s@btconnect.com

GAS METER MAINTENANCE OR REPAIR

George Wilson Industries Ltd, 1 First Avenue, Minworth, Sutton Coldfield, West Midlands, B76 1BA Tel: 0121-313 7000 Fax: 0121-313 7001 E-mail: malcolm.w@gwi-ltd.co.uk

GAS METERS

Actaris Metering Systems Ltd, Langer Road, Felixstowe, Suffolk, IP11 2ER Tel: (01394) 694000 Fax: (01394) 276030 E-mail: csaunders@actaris.co.uk

Instromet, Charlotte Street, Melton Mowbray, Leicestershire, LE13 1NA Tel: (01664) 567797 Fax: (01664) 410254 E-mail: sales@instrometuk.co.uk

Invensys Metering Systems Ltd, Unit 11 The Quadrangle, Premier Way, Romsey, Hampshire, SO51 9DL Tel: (01794) 526100 Fax: (01794) 526101 E-mail: romseysales@invensys.com

Switch 2 Energy Solutions Ltd, High Mill, Mill Street, Cullingworth, Bradford, West Yorkshire, BD13 5HA Tel: (01535) 270266 Fax: (01535) 270282 E-mail: sales@switch2.com

George Wilson Industries Ltd, 1 First Avenue, Minworth, Sutton Coldfield, West Midlands, B76 1BA Tel: 0121-313 7000 Fax: 0121-313 7001 E-mail: malcolm.w@gwi-ltd.co.uk

GAS MIXTURES, CALIBRATION/ INSTRUMENTATION

C K Gas Products Ltd, Unit 3, Murrell Green Business Park, London Road, Hook, Hampshire, RG27 9GR Tel: (01256) 766633 Fax: (01256) 766630 E-mail: sales@ckgas.com

▶ Scientific & Technical Gases Ltd, 1 Speedwell Road, Parkhouse Industrial Estate East, Newcastle, Staffordshire, ST5 7RG Tel: (01782) 564906 Fax: (01782) 564906 E-mail: info@stgas.eu

Spantech Products Ltd, Spantech House, Lagham Road, South Godstone, Godstone, Surrey, RH9 8HB Tel: (01342) 893239 Fax: (01342) 892584 E-mail: spantech-acd@tiscali.co.uk

GAS MONITORS/GAS ALARMS, PERSONAL

▶ Nereus Alarms Ltd, 9 Britannia Road, Lower Parkstone, Poole, Dorset, BH14 8AZ Tel: (01202) 731886 Fax: (01202) 739060 E-mail: info@nereusalarms.co.uk

GAS (NATURAL) ANALYSIS AND CALIBRATION CONSULTANTS

Effectech Ltd, Dovefields Road, Dovefields Industrial Estate, Uttoxeter, Staffordshire, ST14 8HU Tel: (01889) 569220 Fax: (01889) 569220 E-mail: sharon.foster@effectech.co.uk

GAS (NATURAL) QUALITY MEASURING SYSTEMS AUDITING AND COMMISSIONING CONSULTANTS

Effectech Ltd, Dovefields Road, Dovefields Industrial Estate, Uttoxeter, Staffordshire, ST14 8HU Tel: (01889) 569220 Fax: (01889) 569220 E-mail: sharon.foster@effectech.co.uk

GAS OPERATED SPRINGS

Ace Controls International, 1 Belvedere Road, Newton-le-Willows, Merseyside, WA12 0JJ Tel: (01925) 227171 Fax: (01925) 229323 E-mail: sales@ace-controls.co.uk

Draco Gas Springs, 26 Waterloo Park, Bidford-on-Avon, Alcester, Warwickshire, B50 4JG Tel: (01789) 490030 Fax: (01789) 490904

Metrol Springs Ltd, 75 Tenter Road, Moulton Park Industrial Estate, Northampton, NN3 6AX Tel: (01604) 499332 Fax: (01604) 493390 E-mail: sales@metrol.com

GAS OR AIR DAMPERS

Flowrite Industrial Dampers Ltd, The Glasshouse Kings Lane, Norwich, NR1 3PS Tel: (01603) 633163 Fax: (01603) 633763 E-mail: sales@industrialdampers.com

GAS OR OIL BOILER IGNITION SYSTEMS

Igniters Combustion Engineering Ltd, Unit 6 Prospect Drive, Britannia Enterprise Park, Lichfield, Staffordshire, WS14 9UX Tel: (01543) 251478 Fax: (01543) 257850 E-mail: renglish@igniters.co.uk

GAS OR OIL OR WATER PIPELINE COUPLINGS

Drain Centre, Heron Works, Heron Road, Sowton Industrial Estate, Exeter, EX2 7LL Tel: (01392) 445588 Fax: (01392) 445599

Dril-Quip (Europe) Ltd, Stoneywood Park, Stoneywood Road, Dyce, Aberdeen, AB21 7DZ Tel: (01224) 727000 Fax: (01224) 727070

Ham Baker Hartley, Garner Street, Etruria, Stoke-on-Trent, ST4 7BH Tel: (01782) 202300 Fax: (01782) 203639 E-mail: enquiries@hambaker.co.uk

Naylor Concrete Products Ltd, Clough Green, Cawthorne, Barnsley, South Yorkshire, S75 4AD Tel: (01226) 790591 Fax: (01226) 790531 E-mail: info@naylor.co.uk

Philmac (U K) Ltd, Diplocks Way, Hailsham, East Sussex, BN27 3JF Tel: (01323) 847323 Fax: (01323) 844775 E-mail: philmacorders@philmac.co.uk

Pipeline Centre, Millmarsh Lane, Enfield, Middlesex, EN3 7QG Tel: (020) 8805 9588 Fax: (020) 8805 2297

Pipeline Centre, Ingram Road, Leeds, LS11 9BB Tel: 0113-242 8280 Fax: 0113-242 8283 E-mail: sales@pipeline.com

GAS PIPELINE INSTALLATION OR SERVICING

Frazer, Station Road, Hebburn, Tyne & Wear, NE31 1BD Tel: 0191-428 7801 Fax: 0191-483 3628 E-mail: sales.northern@ashworth-frazer.co.uk

Goldace Industries, Unit 17 Harmill Industrial Estate, Grovebury Road, Leighton Buzzard, Bedfordshire, LU7 4FF Tel: (01525) 851815 Fax: (01525) 852484 E-mail: info@goldaceindustries.com

▶ Steve Wall Plumbing & Heating Ltd, Furlong Road, Stoke-on-Trent, ST6 5UN Tel: (01782) 821730 Fax: (01782) 812155

GAS PURIFICATION SYSTEMS

Axsia Mozley, 370 Bristol Road, Gloucester, GL2 5DH Tel: (01452) 833800 Fax: (01209) 211068 E-mail: asbl@axsia.com

Saes Getters (GB) Ltd, Heritage House, Vicker Lane, Daventry, Northamptonshire, NN11 5AA Tel: (01327) 310777 Fax: (01327) 310555 E-mail: saes-gb@saes-group.com

GAS RECOVERY SYSTEMS

▶ Hi Lo Flare Systems & Services UK Ltd, Fairewell House, Yarmouth Road, Ormesby, Great Yarmouth, Norfolk, NR29 3QB Tel: (01493) 730095 Fax: (01493) 731043 E-mail: hi-lo@hi-loflare.co.uk

GAS REFRIGERANT LEAK DETECTION EQUIPMENT/ SYSTEMS

T Q Environmental P.L.C., Unit 10, Flanshaw Way, Wakefield, West Yorkshire, WF2 9LP Tel: (01924) 380700 Fax: (01924) 361700 E-mail: sales@tqplc.com

GAS REGULATOR MAINTENANCE OR REPAIR

M W Polymer Products Ltd, The Old Brewery, Duffield Road, Little Eaton, Derby, DE21 5DS Tel: (01332) 835001 Fax: (01332) 835051

GAS REGULATOR MANUFRS

Bryan Donkin Ltd, Enterprise Drive, Holmewood, Chesterfield, Derbyshire, S42 5UZ Tel: (01246) 501501 Fax: (01246) 501500 E-mail: sales@bdrmg.co.uk

Gas Arc Group Ltd, Vinces Road, Diss, Norfolk, IP22 4WW Tel: (01379) 652263 Fax: (01379) 644235 E-mail: mail@gas-arc.co.uk

Gas Control Equipment Ltd, Yew Tree Way, Golborne, Warrington, WA3 3JD Tel: (01942) 292950 Fax: (01942) 292951 E-mail: sales@gceuk.com

Keller UK Ltd, Winfrith Technology Centre, Winfrith Newburgh, Dorchester, Dorset, DT2 8ZB Tel: (01929) 401200 Fax: (07000) 329535 E-mail: sales@keller-pressure.co.uk

Pressure Tech Ltd, Unit 6, Graphite Way, Hadfield, Glossop, Derbyshire, SK13 1QG Tel: (01457) 899307 Fax: (01457) 899308 E-mail: steve@pressure-tech.com

George Wilson Industries Ltd, 1 First Avenue, Minworth, Sutton Coldfield, West Midlands, B76 1BA Tel: 0121-313 7000 Fax: 0121-313 7001 E-mail: malcolm.w@gwi-ltd.co.uk

GAS SAFETY EQUIPMENT

T C W Services Controls Ltd, Bradshaw Works, Bradshaw Road, Honley, Holmfirth, HD9 6DT Tel: (01484) 662865 Fax: (01484) 667574 E-mail: sales@tcw-services.co.uk

GAS SAFETY INSPECTION SERVICES

Electic, 40 Thorneyfields Lane, Stafford, ST17 9YS Tel: (01785) 229330 Fax: (01785) 229330

GAS SAFETY VALVES

Magne-Flo Excess Flow Valves Ltd, Alcester Road, Portway, Birmingham, B48 7HX Tel: (01564) 822383 Fax: (01564) 824712 E-mail: enquiries@magne-flo.co.uk

GAS SEALING MATERIALS

PLCS Ltd, Wartell Bank, Kingswinford, West Midlands, DY6 7QJ Tel: (01384) 298000 Fax: (01384) 400845 E-mail: sales@pressleakage.com

GAS SENSORS

Alphasense Ltd, 3 Oak Industrial Park, Chelmsford Road, Dunmow, Essex, CM6 1XN Tel: (01371) 878048 Fax: (01371) 878066 E-mail: sensors@alphasense.com

Analox Sensor Technology Ltd, 15 Ellerbeck Court, Stokesley Business Park, Stokesley, Middlesbrough, Cleveland, TS9 5PT Tel: (01642) 711400 Fax: (01642) 713900 E-mail: admin@analox.net

City Technology Ltd, City Technology Centre, Walton Road, Portsmouth, PO6 1SZ Tel: (023) 9232 5511 Fax: (023) 9238 6611 E-mail: sensors@citytech.co.uk

GAS SEPARATION PLANT

Cougar Industries Ltd, 1 Riverpark, Billet Lane, Berkhamsted, Hertfordshire, HP4 1HL Tel: (01442) 860000 Fax: (01442) 864686 E-mail: sales@cougar-industries.co.uk

GAS SOLDERING IRONS

E Partridge & Sons Ltd, Maypole Fields, Halesowen, West Midlands, B63 2QH Tel: (01384) 566667 Fax: (01384) 410211

GAS SOLENOID VALVES

▶ Younique Products, South Avenue, Blantyre Industrial Estate, Blantyre, Glasgow, G72 0XB Tel: (01698) 723330 Fax: (01698) 327066

GAS STRUTS/DAMPERS

Stabilus, Unit 4 Canada Close, Banbury, Oxfordshire, OX16 2RT Tel: (01295) 700100 Fax: (01295) 700106 E-mail: info@uk.stabilus.com

GAS SUPPLY SYSTEMS

Biogas Technology Ltd, Brookside Industrial Estate, Sawtry, Huntingdon, Cambridgeshire, PE28 5SB Tel: (01487) 831701 Fax: (01487) 830962 E-mail: info@biogas.co.uk

Imgas Ltd, Sansom House, Portland Street, Daybrook, Nottingham, NG5 6BL Tel: 0115-966 7030 Fax: 0115-966 7031 E-mail: sales@imgas.co.uk

GAS TOOLING SPRINGS

Metrol Springs Ltd, 75 Tenter Road, Moulton Park Industrial Estate, Northampton, NN3 6AX Tel: (01604) 499332 Fax: (01604) 493390 E-mail: sales@metrol.com

GAS TURBINE DRIVEN ELECTRIC GENERATOR SETS

Combustion Energy & Steam Specialists Ltd, 77-79 John Street, Stromness, Orkney, KW16 3AD Tel: (01856) 851177 Fax: (01856) 851199 E-mail: enquiries@cess.co.uk

GAS TURBINE HEAT EXCHANGERS

Bowman Power Group Ltd, Ocean Quay, Belvidere Road, Southampton, SO14 5QY Tel: (023) 8023 6700 Fax: (023) 8035 2565 E-mail: sales@bowmanpower.co.uk

GAS TURBINES

Aetc Ltd, Victoria Avenue, Yeadon, Leeds, LS19 7AW Tel: 0113-250 5151 Fax: 0113-238 6006

Alstom Power Generation Ltd, Silverlink Business Park, Silverlink, Wallsend, Tyne & Wear, NE28 9ND Tel: 0191-295 2000 Fax: 0191-295 2011

Cooper Energy Services, Mondial House, 5 Mondial Way, Hayes, Middlesex, UB3 5AR Tel: (020) 8990 1900 Fax: (020) 8990 1911

Microturbo Ltd, Concorde Way, Fareham, Hampshire, PO15 5RL Tel: (01489) 564848 Fax: (01489) 563905 E-mail: sales@microturbo.co.uk

Rolls Royce Ltd, Ansty, Coventry, CV7 9JR Tel: (024) 7662 4000 Fax: (024) 7662 4666 E-mail: sales@sourcerer-online.com

Rolls Royce Power Engineering P.L.C., Atlantic Park, Dunnings Bridge Road, Bootle, Merseyside, L30 4UZ Tel: 0151-524 6555 Fax: 0151-524 6557 E-mail: m.morgan@ces.com

Solar Turbines Europe Sa, Suite H Centennial Court, Easthampstead Road, Bracknell, Berkshire, RG12 1YQ Tel: (01344) 782920 Fax: (01344) 782930

GAS VEHICLE REFUELLING STATIONS

Comainwells Ltd, Harfreys Road, Great Yarmouth, Norfolk, NR31 0LS Tel: (01493) 656444 Fax: (01493) 656444 E-mail: comwell@hotmail.co.uk

GAS VENTILATORS

Airflow (Nicoll Ventilators) Ltd, Queensway, New Milton, Hampshire, BH25 5NN Tel: (01425) 611547 Fax: (01425) 638912 E-mail: sales@airflow-vent.co.uk

GAS WATER HEATERS

▶ Aqua Heat State Sales, 61-67 Commercial Road, Southampton, SO15 1GG Tel: (023) 8057 1107 Fax: (023) 8057 7965 E-mail: enquiries@state-waterheaters.co.uk

Crown Water Heaters Ltd, Sunbeam Studios, Sunbeam Street, Wolverhampton, WV2 4PF Tel: (01902) 310678 Fax: (01902) 425707 E-mail: sales@crownheat.force9.co.uk

Hamworthy Heating Ltd, Fleets Corner, Poole, Dorset, BH17 0HH Tel: (01202) 662500 Fax: (01202) 662550 E-mail: sales@hamworthy-heating.com

Johnson & Starley Ltd, Brackmills Indust Estate, Brackmills Industrial Estate, Northampton, NN4 7HR Tel: (01604) 762881 Fax: (01604) 767408 E-mail: sales@johnsonandstarley.co.uk

Nordsea Ltd, Captain Clarke Road, Hyde, Cheshire, SK14 4QG Tel: 0161-366 3010 Fax: 0161-366 3011 E-mail: nordsea@compuserve.com

GAS WORK PLANT

B G E UK Ltd, Brighouse Bay Compressor Station, Borgue, Kirkcudbright, DG6 4TR Tel: (01557) 870349 Fax: (01557) 870292

GASKET COMPRESSION FASTENERS

Southco Manufacturing Co., Shire Business Park, Wainwright Road, Worcester, WR4 9FA Tel: (01905) 751000 Fax: (01905) 751090 E-mail: info@southco.com

GASKET MANUFRS

A G C Gasket Co., 1 30 Albert Road, St. Philips, Bristol, BS2 0XA Tel: 0117-972 1410 Fax: 0117-972 3896 E-mail: agcgaskets@onetel.com

A M S (Burnham) Fluid Sealing, 30-32 Dropmore Road, Burnham, Slough, SL1 8BE Tel: (01628) 603311 Fax: (01628) 660040

Advanced Seals & Gaskets, Polymer Works, Hope Street, Dudley, West Midlands, DY2 8RS Tel: (01384) 252555 Fax: (01384) 252373 E-mail: kate@advancedseals.co.uk

All Marque, Unit 5 Block F, St. Michaels Industrial Estate, Widnes, Cheshire, WA8 8TL Tel: 0151-424 1984 Fax: 0151-420 3144 E-mail: sales@allmarque.co.uk

Allseal Insulation Products Ltd, Phoenix Works Industrial Estate, Richards Street, Wednesbury, West Midlands, WS10 8BZ Tel: 0121-526 4241 Fax: 0121-568 8177

Amorim UK Ltd, Suite 1a Bishops Weald House, Albion Way, Horsham, West Sussex, RH12 1AH Tel: (01403) 710001 Fax: (01403) 710003 E-mail: sales@wicanders.co.uk

Arco Ltd, Tenax Circle, Trafford Park, Manchester, M17 1EZ Tel: 0161-869 5800 Fax: 0161-869 5858 E-mail: traffordpark.branch@arco.co.uk

Arco East Scotland, Avon Mill Industrial Estate, Mill Road, Linlithgow Bridge, Linlithgow, West Lothian, EH49 7QY Tel: (01506) 844661 Fax: (01506) 847816 E-mail: arco.eastscotland@arco.co.uk

Arco Glasgow, 210 Edmiston Drive, Glasgow, G51 2YY Tel: 0141-419 3200 Fax: 0141-419 3232 E-mail: arco-glasgow@arco.com

Arco South East, Cray Avenue, Orpington, Kent, BR5 3QB Tel: (01689) 875411 Fax: (01689) 876538 E-mail: orpington.branch@arco.co.uk

Arco Tyne & Wear Ltd, PO Box 8, Blaydon-on-Tyne, Tyne & Wear, NE21 5TP Tel: 0191-414 7721 Fax: 0191-414 0258 E-mail: arco.tynewear@arco.co.uk

Atlantic Rubber Company Ltd, Castleton Works, Atlantic Street, Altrincham, Cheshire, WA14 5BX Tel: 0161-928 3727 Fax: 0161-926 9755 E-mail: info@atlanticgb.co.uk

Avon Group Manufacturing Ltd, 30 Vale Lane, Bristol, BS3 5RU Tel: 0117-904 3355 Fax: 0117-904 3366 E-mail: admin@avon-group.co.uk

Beldam Lascar Seals Ltd, Lascar Works, Staines Road, Hounslow, TW3 3JL Tel: (020) 8570 7722 Fax: (020) 8570 4438 E-mail: enquiries@beldamlascargroup.com

Bluemay Weston, Cooks Cross, South Molton, Devon, EX36 4AW Tel: (01769) 574574 Fax: (01769) 512944 E-mail: sales@bluemayweston.co.uk

Boreflex Ltd, Unit 9 Gateway Court, Parkgate, Rotherham, South Yorkshire, S62 6LH Tel: (01709) 522333 Fax: (01709) 522663 E-mail: sales@boreflex.co.uk

Bradford Rubber Services Ltd, 25 Annison Street, Garnet Street, Bradford, West Yorkshire, BD3 9HJ Tel: (01274) 307030 Fax: (01274) 305699 E-mail: sales@bradfordrubber.co.uk

British Gaskets Ltd, Bulmer Road Industrial Estate, Bulmer Road, Sudbury, Suffolk, CO10 7HJ Tel: (01787) 881188 Fax: (01787) 880595 E-mail: sales@british-gaskets.co.uk

Chemical Reactor Services, Unit 5 Lyon Road Industrial Estate, Kearsley, Bolton, BL4 8TG Tel: (01204) 862777 Fax: (01204) 577484

Cheshire Leathers UK Ltd, 3 Cobden Industrial Centre, Quakers Coppice, Crewe, CW1 6FA Tel: (01270) 251556 Fax: (01270) 251557 E-mail: cheshireleather@aol.com

▶ CL Automotive, Unit 111 B M K Industrial Estate, Wakefield Road, Liversedge, West Yorkshire, WF15 6BS Tel: (01924) 404040 Fax: (01924) 404050

Clifton Rubber Co. Ltd, 5 Edison Road, St. Ives, Cambridgeshire, PE27 3FF Tel: (01480) 496161 Fax: (01480) 484700 E-mail: sales@cliftonrubber.co.uk

Alexander Comrie & Sons Ltd, Unit 8, Second Avenue Business Park, Millbrook, Southampton, SO15 0LP Tel: (023) 8070 2911 Fax: (023) 8070 2617

Gilbert Curry Industrial Plastics Co. Ltd, 16 Bayton Road, Exhall, Coventry, CV7 9EJ Tel: (024) 7664 4645 Fax: (024) 7658 8389 E-mail: k-sales@gcip.co.uk

D E L Industrial Fastenings Ltd, Elvetham Bridge, Fleet, Hampshire, GU51 1AE Tel: (01252) 626425 Fax: (01252) 811741 E-mail: info@delindustrial.co.uk

Dantec Ltd, Tarran Way, Tarran Industrial Estate, Wirral, Merseyside, CH46 4TL Tel: 0151-678 2222 Fax: 0151-606 0188 E-mail: sales@dantec.ltd.uk

Dolman, 10 Rouse Mill Lane, Batley, West Yorkshire, WF17 5QB Tel: (01924) 445577 Fax: (01924) 443222 E-mail: sales@jamesdolman.co.uk

Dowty Engineered Seals Ltd, Ashchurch, Tewkesbury, Gloucestershire, GL20 8JS Tel: (01684) 299111 Fax: (01684) 852210

E Dobson & Co Gaskets Ltd, Oakworth Road, Keighley, West Yorkshire, BD21 1QQ Tel: (01535) 607257 Fax: (01535) 608171 E-mail: sales@dobsongasket.com

East Anglian Sealing Co. Ltd, Units 4 & 5, Goldingham Hall, Bulmer, Sudbury, Suffolk, CO10 7ER Tel: (01787) 880433 Fax: (0871) 4338858 E-mail: sales@easeals.co.uk

Ernest Platt Bury Ltd, Whalley Road, Ramsbottom, Bury, Lancashire, BL0 0DE Tel: (01706) 282200 Fax: (01706) 821464

First Line Ltd, Bessemer Close, Bicester, Oxfordshire, OX26 6QE Tel: (01869) 248484 Fax: (01869) 240472 E-mail: sales@firstline.co.uk

Flexible Connections Ltd, King Street Trading Estate, Middlewich, Cheshire, CW10 9LF Tel: (01606) 836024 Fax: (01606) 836241 E-mail: flexibles@talk21.com

Flexitallic Ltd, PO Box 3, Cleckheaton, West Yorkshire, BD19 5BT Tel: (01274) 851273 Fax: (01274) 851386 E-mail: ukmarketing@flexitallic.com

Flowseal Ltd, 34h Aston Road, Waterlooville, Hampshire, PO7 7XQ Tel: (023) 9226 5031 Fax: (023) 9224 0382 E-mail: sales@flowseal.co.uk

▶ G & H Engineering Services Ltd, 31 Carlyle Avenue, Hillington Industrial Estate, Glasgow, G52 4XX Tel: 0141-810 1160 Fax: 0141-892 0843 E-mail: sales@gh-eng.co.uk

▶ GD Gaskets & Seals, Unit 1 Mapplewell Business Park, Staincross, Barnsley, South Yorkshire, S75 6BP Tel: (01226) 381666 Fax: (01226) 381222 E-mail: garydavis1@btconnect.com

GKN Sinter Metals Ltd, PO Box 3, Lichfield, Staffordshire, WS13 6HB Tel: (01543) 403000 Fax: (01543) 403001 E-mail: info@gknsintermetals.co.uk

GMS, 175 Booth Street, Birmingham, B21 0NU Tel: 0121-551 5440 Fax: 0121-554 5344 E-mail: enquiries@gmspolymer.co.uk

Godfrey Insulations Ltd, Siddons Factory Estate, Howard Street, West Bromwich, West Midlands, B70 0SZ Tel: 0121-556 0011 Fax: 0121-556 9553

Grange Gaskets (Bradford) Ltd, Carnarvon Works, Bolton Lane, Bradford, West Yorkshire, BD2 1AE Tel: (01274) 734238 Fax: (01274) 306594

Harrison, J.A. & Co. Ltd, Britain Works, Sherborne Street, Manchester, M8 8HP Tel: 0161-832 2282 Fax: 0161-832 3263 E-mail: enquiries@jaharrison.co.uk

Hayne Ingleby Ltd, 895 High Road, Chadwell Heath, Romford, RM6 4HL Tel: (020) 8590 6232 Fax: (020) 8590 6568

Interseals Engineers' Merchants, Lowlands Industrial Estate, Braye Road, Vale, Guernsey, GY3 5XG Tel: (01481) 246364 Fax: (01481) 248235 E-mail: sales@interseals.co.uk

J.A. Harrison & Co (Manchester) Limited, Britain Works, Sherborne St, Manchester, M8 8HP Tel: 0161 832 2282 Fax: 0161 832 3263 E-mail: ben@alliancegaskets.co.uk

J M C Washers & Gaskets, Unit 3 Hartlebury Trading Estate, Hartlebury, Kidderminster, Worcestershire, DY10 4JB Tel: (01299) 251339 Fax: (01299) 251008

William Johnston & Company Ltd, 9 Spiersbridge Terrace, Thornliebank Industrial Estate, Glasgow, G46 8JH Tel: 0141-620 1666 Fax: 0141-620 1888 E-mail: sales@williamjohnston.co.uk

Joseph Dixon Tool Company Ltd, Unit 2 Charles Street, Town Wharf Business Park, Walsall, WS2 9LZ Tel: (01922) 622051 Fax: (01922) 721168 E-mail: sales@josephdixon.co.uk

K B Engineering Supplies Ltd, 7 Bloomfield Road, Tipton, West Midlands, DY4 9EU Tel: 0121-520 0003 Fax: 0121-520 5554 E-mail: frank.kendrick@ukonline.co.uk

Kewell Converters Ltd, 60 Holmethorpe Avenue, Redhill, RH1 2NL Tel: (01737) 771710 Fax: (01737) 769732 E-mail: sales@kewell-converters.co.uk

Klinger Ltd, Klinger Building, Wharfedale Road, Euroway Industrial Estate, Bradford, West Yorkshire, BD4 6SG Tel: (01274) 688222 Fax: (01274) 688962 E-mail: enquiries@klingeruk.co.uk

Kopak-Walker Ltd, PO Box 65, Hitchin, Hertfordshire, SG4 0TW Tel: (01462) 452487 Fax: (01462) 452249 E-mail: sales@kopak-walker.co.uk

L S P Ltd, 168 Blackfen Road, Hawthorn Terrace, Sidcup, Kent, DA15 8PT Tel: (020) 8859 8877 Fax: (020) 8859 8787 E-mail: sales@lspuk.com

Langstone Safetywear Ltd, 1 St. Johns Court, Upper Forest Way, Swansea Enterprise Park, Swansea, SA6 8QR Tel: (01792) 535500 Fax: (01792) 535509 E-mail: info@langstone.co.uk

Linear Ltd, Coatham Avenue, Aycliffe Industrial Park, Newton Aycliffe, County Durham, DL5 6DB Tel: (01325) 310151 Fax: (01325) 307200 E-mail: enquiries@linear-ltd.com

▶ Main Train Transmissions LTD, 143 Coppermill Lane, Walthamstow, London, E17 7HD Tel: 0845 8380599 E-mail: sales@maintrainltd.com

Martin's Rubber Co. Ltd, Orchard Place, Southampton, SO14 3PE Tel: (023) 8022 6330 Fax: (023) 8063 1577 E-mail: sales@martins-rubber.co.uk

Meadex Mouldings Ltd, Units 1-2, Tanyard Lane, Ross-On-Wye, Herefordshire, HR9 7BH Tel: (01989) 567999 Fax: (01989) 768022 E-mail: sales@meadex.co.uk

Metflex, Queen Street, Great Harwood, Blackburn, BB6 7AU Tel: (01254) 884171 Fax: (01254) 887753 E-mail: sales@metlex.co.uk

Moyer Manufacturing Co. Ltd, Vansittart Estate, Duke Street, Windsor, Berkshire, SL4 1SG Tel: (01753) 830088 Fax: (01753) 818793 E-mail: moyer@tcom.co.uk

Naish Felts Ltd, Crow Lane, Wilton, Salisbury, SP2 0HD Tel: (01722) 743505 Fax: (01722) 744048 E-mail: sales@naishfelts.co.uk

Northern Engineering Sheffield Ltd, Haigh Moor Drive, Dinnington, Sheffield, S25 2JY Tel: (01909) 560203 Fax: (01909) 560184 E-mail: sales@northerneng.co.uk

Northern Gaskets & Mouldings Ltd, Unit 1 Norquest Industrial Park, Birstall, Batley, West Yorkshire, WF17 9NE Tel: (01924) 422233 Fax: (01924) 422244 E-mail: sales@northerngaskets.com

Novus Sealing, Hunsworth Lane, Cleckheaton, West Yorkshire, BD19 4EJ Tel: (01274) 852543 Fax: (01274) 862588 E-mail: mailbox@novussealing.com

R.H. Nuttall Ltd, Century Works, Great Brook Street, Nechells Green, Birmingham, B7 4EN Tel: 0121-359 2484 Fax: 0121-359 4439 E-mail: sales@rhnuttall.co.uk

P A R (Preston) Ltd, Club Street, Bamber Bridge, Preston, PR5 6FN Tel: (01772) 322114 Fax: (01772) 627524

P T M UK Ltd, Haigh Avenue, Stockport, Cheshire, SK4 1NZ Tel: 0161-477 6486 Fax: 0161-480 4624 E-mail: sales@ptmuk.co.uk

Pipeline Seal & Insulator Co. Ltd, Unit 1A, Colmworth Business Park, St. Neots, Cambridgeshire, PE19 8YH Tel: (01480) 404661 Fax: (01480) 404662 E-mail: sales@pipelineseal.co.uk

Plastic Shims & Gaskets Co. Ltd, 49-53 Glengall Road, Peckham, London, SE15 6NF Tel: (020) 7740 9705 Fax: (020) 7635 9791 E-mail: sales@psggroup.co.uk

Portmere Rubber Ltd, Victoria Street, Northam, Southampton, SO14 5QZ Tel: (023) 8022 3628 Fax: (023) 8022 3250

Precision Cut Rubber Co. Ltd, Leafield Industrial Estate, Leafield Way, Corsham, Wiltshire, SN13 9RU Tel: (01225) 816300 Fax: (01225) 816327 E-mail: sales@pcrltd.co.uk

Premier Gaskets, Unit 16 Bell Farm Industrial Park, Nuthampstead, Royston, Hertfordshire, SG8 8ND Tel: (01763) 848849 Fax: (01763) 848848

R F I Seals & Gaskets Ltd, Unit 2, Saltash Business Park, Moorlands Trading Estate, Forge Lane, Saltash, Cornwall, PL12 6LX Tel: 01752 841051 Fax: 01752 847559 E-mail: sales@rfiseals.co.uk

Rafseal Ltd, Millers Avenue, Brynmenyn Industrial Estate, Brynmenyn, Bridgend, Mid Glamorgan, CF32 9TD Tel: (01656) 725118 Fax: (01656) 724520 E-mail: rafseal@btclick.com

Ram Gasket Solutions Ltd, Unit 14, Cardrew Indust Estate, Redruth, Cornwall, TR15 1SS Tel: (01209) 314700 Fax: (01209) 314900 E-mail: mailbox@ramgasket.co.uk

Ramsay Rubber Ltd, Units 5 & 6, Speed Road, Barnfield Industrial Estate, Tipton, West Midlands, DY4 9DX Tel: (01384) 453160 Fax: (01384) 254955 E-mail: sales@ramson.com

Rocon Foam Products Ltd, 14 Shrub Hill, Worcester, WR4 9EL Tel: (01905) 26616 Fax: (01905) 612319 E-mail: sales@roconfoam.co.uk

RSS International Ltd, Carr Mills, Bradford Road, Birstall, Batley, West Yorkshire, WF17 9JY Tel: (01924) 443553 Fax: (01924) 443320

S B A Ltd, Freemens Common Road, Leicester, LE2 7SQ Tel: 0116-257 6595 Fax: 0116-247 0072 E-mail: sales@sba.co.uk

S J Gaskets Ltd, Tything Park, Tything Road East, Kinwarton, Alcester, Warwickshire, B49 6ES Tel: (01789) 763721 Fax: (01789) 764070 E-mail: sjgaskets@thesjgroup.com

Sampson Gaskets Ltd, Unit 22, Leigh Road, Ramsgate, Kent, CT12 5EU Tel: (01843) 854800 Fax: (01843) 854801 E-mail: uksales@sampsons.co.uk

Scandura, St. James Road, Corby, Northamptonshire, NN18 8AW Tel: (01536) 267121 Fax: (01536) 266392 E-mail: sales@scandura.co.uk

Sealtight Gaskets Ltd, Unit 15 Calow Brook Drive, Hasland, Chesterfield, Derbyshire, S41 0DR Tel: (01246) 222400 Fax: (01246) 222401 E-mail: harveyslack@supernet.com

▶ SKF Economos U.K. Ltd, Unit 20 Avonbank Industrial Estate, West Town Rd, Bristol, BS11 9DE Tel: 0117-982 5729 Fax: 0117-982 5730 E-mail: bristol@economos.com

▶ SKF Economos U.K. Ltd, Unit B2, Connaught Business Centre, 22 Willow Lane, Mitcham, Surrey, CR4 4NA Tel: (020) 8648 0252 Fax: (020) 8648 0248 E-mail: mitcham@economos.com

▶ SKF Economos U.K. Ltd, Unit 32, Stirling Close, Pattinson South Industrial Estate, Washington, Tyne & Wear, NE38 3QD Tel: 0191-417 1094 Fax: 0191-417 1118 E-mail: washington@economos.com

▶ SKF Economos UK Ltd, Unit 5-6, Armley Link, Armley Road, Leeds, LS12 2QN Tel: 0113-231 0303 Fax: 0113-231 0395 E-mail: leeds@economos.com

▶ SKF Economos UK Ltd, 83 Buckingham Avenue, Trading Estate, Slough, SL1 4PN Tel: (01753) 696565 Fax: (01753) 696181 E-mail: uk.sales@economos.com

Specialised Engineering Products, Unit C3-7 The Premier Centre, Premier Way, Romsey, Hampshire, SO51 9DG Tel: (01794) 830757 Fax: (01794) 830736 E-mail: sales@specialisedengineering.co.uk

SRM Gaskets Ltd, Station Road, Hatton, Derby, DE65 5EL Tel: (01283) 812946 Fax: (01283) 813172

Synthotech Elastomers Ltd, Mangham Road, Barbot Hall Industrial Estate, Rotherham, South Yorkshire, S61 4RJ Tel: (01709) 363705 Fax: (01709) 369165 E-mail: info@synthotech-rubber.co.uk

Veker Extrusions Ltd, Shaftmoor Lane, Hall Green, Birmingham, B28 8SP Tel: 0121-777 5000 Fax: 0121-777 5015 E-mail: enquiries@vekex.com

Vulcan Industrial Fasteners Ltd, Unit 6, Emerald Way, Stone Business Park, Stone, Staffordshire, ST15 0SR Tel: (01785) 818494 Fax: (01785) 818399 E-mail: sales@vulcanfasteners.co.uk

W C Munsch & Co., Unit Ag2 3 Clarence Business Park, Clarence Road, Bollington, Macclesfield, Cheshire, SK10 5JZ Tel: (01625) 573971 Fax: (01625) 573250 E-mail: sales@wcmunsch.co.uk

Waterjet Profiles Ltd, Units 9, Ryder Way, Basildon, Essex, SS13 1QH Tel: (01268) 591491 Fax: (01268) 729726 E-mail: sales@waterjet-profiles.co.uk

Whitby & Chandler Ltd, Green Road, Penistone, Sheffield, S36 6PH Tel: (01226) 370380 Fax: (01226) 767138 E-mail: enquiries@whitby-chandler.co.uk

D.P. White & Co., 58 Hackenden Cl, East Grinstead, West Sussex, RH19 3DS Fax: (01342) 335747

J.J. Williams (Gaskets) Ltd, 1 Beresford Road, Whitstable, Kent, CT5 1JP Tel: (01227) 265522 Fax: (01227) 770146 E-mail: enquiries@jjwilliams.co.uk

Woodley Engineering Stockport Ltd, Whitefield Road, Bredbury, Stockport, Cheshire, SK6 2QR Tel: 0161-430 7488 Fax: 0161-406 6061

X-Cel GB Ltd, Barbara House, Cross Green Approach, Leeds, LS9 0SG Tel: 0113-391 8230 Fax: 0113-391 8239 E-mail: sales@x-cel.com

GASKET MATERIAL, ELECTROMAGNETIC INTERFERENCE (EMI) AND RADIO FREQUENCY (RF) SHIELDING

Tecknit Europe Ltd, Swingbridge Road, Grantham, Lincolnshire, NG31 7XT Tel: (01476) 590600 Fax: (01476) 591600 E-mail: tecknit.sales@twp-europe.co.uk

GASKET MATERIALS

FDE Factdate Engineering (UK) Ltd, Premier Business Centre, 47-49 Park Royal Road, London, NW10 7LQ Tel: 020 8838 4755 Fax: 020 8181 4515 E-mail: info@fdeuk.com

Dr D. Mueller (UK) Ltd, Unit 7 Silver End Business Park, Brettell Lane, Brierley Hill, West Midlands, DY5 3LG Tel: (01384) 482806 Fax: (01384) 482808 E-mail: info.uk@mueller-ahlhorn.com

▶ indicates data change since last edition

GASKETS TO SPECIFICATION

RSS International Ltd, Carr Mills, Bradford Road, Birstall, Batley, West Yorkshire, WF17 9JY Tel: (01924) 443553 Fax: (01924) 443320

GASKETS, CAMPROFILE

Flexitallic Ltd, PO Box 3, Cleckheaton, West Yorkshire, BD19 5BT Tel: (01274) 851273 Fax: (01274) 851386 E-mail: ukmarketing@flexitallic.com

GASKETS, ELECTROMAGNETIC INTERFERENCE (EMI) AND RADIO FREQUENCY (RF) SHIELDING

Barfield UK Ltd, 3A Parker Road, Bournemouth, BH9 1AX Tel: (01202) 515132 Fax: (01202) 515133 E-mail: sales@barfielduk.com
Border Precision Ltd, Pinnaclehill Industrial Estate, Kelso, Roxburghshire, TD5 8DW Tel: (01573) 224941 Fax: (01573) 225220 E-mail: sales@borderprecision.com
Chomerics, Unit 6 Century Point, Cressex Business Park, High Wycombe, Buckinghamshire, HP12 3SL Tel: (01628) 404000 Fax: (01628) 404091 E-mail: chomerics_europe@parker.com
R F I Seals & Gaskets Ltd, Unit 2, Saltash Business Park, Moorlands Trading Estate, Forge Lane, Saltash, Cornwall, PL12 6LX Tel: 01752 841051 Fax: 01752 847559 E-mail: sales@rfiseals.co.uk
R F I Shielding Ltd, Warner Drive, Springwood Industrial Estate, Braintree, Essex, CM7 2YW Tel: 01342 315044 Fax: (01376) 346442
Tecknit Europe Ltd, Swingbridge Road, Grantham, Lincolnshire, NG31 7XT Tel: (01476) 590600 Fax: (01476) 591600 E-mail: tecknit.sales@twp-europe.co.uk

GATE AUTOMATION SYSTEMS

▶ L & L Welding, Unit E 1, St. Davids Industrial Estate, Pengam, Blackwood, Gwent, NP12 3SW Tel: (01443) 832000 Fax: (01443) 832000 E-mail: marklewiswales@yahoo.co.uk

GATE CATCHES

▶ Cotswold Forge, 2 Exmouth Street, Cheltenham, Gloucestershire, GL53 7NS Tel: (01242) 242754 Fax: (01242) 242754 E-mail: sales@cotswoldforge.com

GATE VALVES

Aquaflow Ltd, Onneley Works, Newcastle Road, Woore, Crewe, CW3 9RU Tel: (01630) 647111 Fax: (01630) 647734 E-mail: response@aquaflowvalves.com
Brassware Sales Ltd, Unit 5 Junction 6 Industrial Park, 66 Electric Avenue, Witton, Birmingham, B6 7JJ Tel: 0121-327 1234 Fax: 0121-327 4066
Flow Control Co. Ltd, Cooper Drive, Springwood Industrial Estate, Braintree, Essex, CM7 2RF Tel: (01376) 321211 Fax: (01376) 321222 E-mail: flowcontrolco@lineone.net
GBH Technical Ltd, Blackness Avenue, Altens Industrial Estate, Altens Industrial Estate, Aberdeen, AB12 3PG Tel: (01224) 879000 Fax: (01224) 899898 E-mail: sales@gbhtechnical.com
Hattersley Newman Hender Ltd, 2 Burscough Road, Ormskirk, Lancashire, L39 2XG Tel: (01695) 577199 Fax: (01695) 578775 E-mail: uksales@hattersley.com
Transmark FCX Ltd, Heaton House, Riverside Drive, Hunsworth Lane, Bradford, West Yorkshire, BD19 4DH Tel: (01274) 700000 Fax: (01274) 700152 E-mail: jhill@heaton-valves.co.uk
Wolstenholmes Valves, Ainsworth Vale Mill, Vale Street, Bolton, BL2 6QF Tel: (01204) 528609 Fax: (01204) 361964 E-mail: sales@wolstenholmes-valves.co.uk
Yorkshire Fittings Ltd, P O Box 166, Leeds, LS10 1NA Tel: 0113-270 6945 Fax: 0113-271 5275 E-mail: info@yorkshirefittings.co.uk

GATES

▶ A C Forge, 12 Roseberry Grove, Tranmere, Birkenhead, Merseyside, CH42 9PR Tel: 0151-652 7033
Brough & Horner Ltd, Station Road, Loftus, Saltburn-by-the-Sea, Cleveland, TS13 4QB Tel: (01287) 640374
Fabco, 33a Groganstown, Dunmurry, Belfast, BT17 0NR Tel: (028) 9062 6666 Fax: (028) 9062 6666
▶ Felixstowe Ironworks, Lodge Farm, Kirton, Ipswich, IP10 0QE Tel: (01394) 448669 Fax: (01394) 448669
Gatewrights Fence Suppliers, 45 Hawkwood Road, Sible Hedingham, Halstead, Essex, CO9 3JR Tel: (01787) 461500 Fax: (01787) 460880
▶ Liverpool Gate Co., 73, Henry Street, Liverpool, L1 5BS Tel: 0151-709 7172 Fax: 0151-709 7172
Stansted All-Steel Ltd, Unit 1 Parsonage Farm Industrial Estate, Forest Hall Road, Stansted, Essex, CM24 8TY Tel: (01279) 817801 Fax: (01279) 815704
T J Blackburn & Son, Victoria, Ableton Lane, Severn Beach, Bristol, BS35 4PR Tel: (01454) 632905 Fax: (01454) 632905
Titan Forge Ltd, 3 Shaftesbury Road, London, E10 7DA Tel: (020) 8558 9000 Fax: (020) 8558 8614
▶ Whitten Ltd, Unit 4, 39 Willow Lane, Mitcham, Surrey, CR4 4NA Tel: (020) 8640 3888 E-mail: whittenmetalworks@btconnect.com

GAUGE BLANKS

Yorkshire Precision Gauges Ltd, Cuckoo Lane, Hatfield, Doncaster, South Yorkshire, DN7 6QF Tel: (01302) 840303 Fax: (01302) 843570 E-mail: gauges@ypg.co.uk

GAUGE GLASS

GlasTechnik, Sagana Lodge, Scotton Rd, Scotter, Gainsborough, Lincs, DN21 3SB Tel: (01724) 761172 Fax: (01724) 764352 E-mail: sightglasses@aol.com
Monax Glass Ltd, 22 Charles Jarvis Court, Cupar, Fife, KY15 5EJ Tel: (01334) 657800 Fax: (01334) 657857 E-mail: monax@sol.co.uk
Nu Gauge, 38 Hoyland Road, Sheffield, S3 8AB Tel: 0114-275 4006 Fax: 0114-275 4006 E-mail: sales@nu-gauge.co.uk

GAUGE MAINTENANCE/REPAIR SERVICES

Abbey Gauge Co. Ltd, 139-141 Becontree Avenue, Dagenham, Essex, RM8 2UL Tel: (020) 8590 3233 Fax: (020) 8590 5082 E-mail: sales@abbeygauge.co.uk
Aspland Gauge Co Ltd, Broadway, Hyde, Cheshire, SK14 4QF Tel: 0161-368 3432 Fax: 0161-367 8426 E-mail: sales@aspland.co.uk
Gauge Developments Ltd, Langham Street, Ashton-under-Lyne, Lancashire, OL7 9AX Tel: 0161-343 3020 Fax: 0161-343 2969 E-mail: gdev@btconnect.com
Industrial & Technical Services Co., Victoria House, 28 Borneo Street, Walsall, WS4 2HY Tel: (01922) 644239 Fax: (01922) 644239
Instruments To Industry Ltd, Woodward Road, Knowsley Industrial Park North, Knowsley Industrial Park, Liverpool, L33 7UZ Tel: 0151-546 4943 Fax: 0151-548 6262 E-mail: sales@itiuk.com
Pressure Gauges Ltd, Park Street, Oldbury, West Midlands, B69 4LE Tel: 0121-544 4408 Fax: 0121-544 7332 E-mail: enquiries@pressure-gauges-ltd.com
Saunders & Weeks Bristol Ltd, 265-267 Church Road, Redfield, Bristol, BS5 9HU Tel: 0117-955 7142 Fax: 0117-955 6064 E-mail: sales@saundersweeks.co.uk

GAUGE TEST EQUIPMENT

Rubert & Co. Ltd, Acru Works, Demmings Road, Cheadle, Cheshire, SK8 2PG Tel: 0161-428 5855 Fax: 0161-428 1146 E-mail: info@rubert.co.uk

GAUGES, *See also headings for particular types*

Broomfield Carbide Gauges Ltd, Unit 7 Crossley Mills, New Mill Road Honley, Honley, Holmfirth, HD9 6PL Tel: (01484) 664982 Fax: (01484) 664982 E-mail: info@broomfieldgauges.com
Charnwood Instrumentation Services, 81 Park Road, Coalville, Leicestershire, LE67 3AF Tel: (01530) 510615 Fax: (01530) 510950 E-mail: graham@instrumentationservices.net
Checkmate Products Ltd, 64 Lindsell Road, West Timperley, Altrincham, Cheshire, WA14 5NX Tel: 0161-928 0046 Fax: 0161-286 3729 E-mail: checkprod@aol.com
▶ J.W. Fairbairn Process Solutions Ltd, 120 Woodneuk Road, Darnley Industrial Estate, Glasgow, G53 7QS Tel: 0141-880 7455 Fax: 0141-880 5290 E-mail: sales@jwfltd.com
Flucon Pumps Ltd, 1 High Street, St. Asaph, Clwyd, LL17 0RG Tel: (01745) 584772 Fax: (01745) 582096 E-mail: info@flucon.co.uk
Humberside Instruments Ltd, 13-15 Barkhouse Lane, Cleethorpes, South Humberside, DN35 8RA Tel: (01472) 691157 Fax: (01472) 692585 E-mail: sales@humbrsideinstruments.co.uk
Nottingham Gauge & Thermometer Co., Unit C, Thornfield Industrial Estate, Off Hooton Street, Carlton, Nottingham, NG3 2NJ Tel: 0115-950 7213 Fax: 0115-950 7227
Pressure Gauges Ltd, Park Street, Oldbury, West Midlands, B69 4LE Tel: 0121-544 4408 Fax: 0121-544 7332 E-mail: enquiries@pressure-gauges-ltd.com
Profile Gauge & Tool Co. Ltd, Mangham Way, Rotherham, South Yorkshire, S61 4RL Tel: (01709) 377184 Fax: (01709) 820281
RÖHM (Great Britain) Ltd, 12 Ashway Centre, Elm Crescent, Kingston Upon Thames, Surrey, KT2 6HH Tel: (020) 8549 6647 Fax: (020) 8541 1783 E-mail: sales@rohmgb.co.uk
▶ Select Gauges & Calibration Ltd, Select Works, Trevol Business Park, Torpoint, Cornwall, PL11 2PN Tel: (01752) 812147 Fax: (01752) 814892
Thermo Fisher Scientific, Shepherd Road, Gloucester, GL2 5HF Tel: (01452) 337800 Fax: (01452) 415156
W B J Ltd, Metrology House, Dukinfield Road, Hyde, Cheshire, SK14 4SD Tel: 0161-367 9898 Fax: 0161-367 9700 E-mail: admin@wbj.co.uk
Zodiac Screw Gauge Ltd, 15-17 Fortnum Close, Birmingham, B33 0LG Tel: 0121-784 0474 Fax: 0121-789 7210 E-mail: sales@zodiacscrewgauge.co.uk

GAUGES, AIR/PNEUMATIC OPERATED

Hydramatics Ltd, Unit 2b The Quantum, Marshfield Bank Industrial Estate, Crewe, CW2 8UY Tel: (01270) 584348 Fax: (01270) 584348 E-mail: hydramatics@aol.com

GAUGES, PLUG/RING

Armson-Boult Ltd, 144b George Street, Coventry, CV1 4HE Tel: (024) 7622 6817 Fax: (024) 7622 6817
Nu Gauge, 38 Hoyland Road, Sheffield, S3 8AB Tel: 0114-275 4006 Fax: 0114-275 4006 E-mail: sales@nu-gauge.co.uk
Threadmaster Gauges Ltd, Princes Dr Industrial Estate, Coventry Road, Kenilworth, Warwickshire, CV8 2FD Tel: (01926) 852428 Fax: (01926) 850047 E-mail: sales@threadmastergauges.co.uk
Tru-Thread Ltd, Station Road, Coleshill, Birmingham, B46 1HT Tel: (01675) 462193 Fax: (01675) 462841 E-mail: admin@tru-thread.co.uk
Yorkshire Precision Gauges Ltd, Cuckoo Lane, Hatfield, Doncaster, South Yorkshire, DN7 6QF Tel: (01302) 840303 Fax: (01302) 843570 E-mail: gauges@ypg.co.uk

GAUGES, PRECISION INSPECTION/MEASUREMENT

Armson-Boult Ltd, 144b George Street, Coventry, CV1 4HE Tel: (024) 7622 6817 Fax: (024) 7622 6817
Baty International, Victoria Road, Burgess Hill, West Sussex, RH15 9LB Tel: (01444) 235621 Fax: (01444) 246985E-mail: sales@baty.co.uk
Conway Precision Engineering Group Ltd, 106 Tame Road, Birmingham, B6 7EZ Tel: 0121-327 8037 Fax: 0121-328 4885 E-mail: design@gauges.co.uk
Dimensional Inspection Services, Unit 19 Wombourne Enterprise Park, Bridgnorth Road, Wombourne, Wolverhampton, WV5 0AL Tel: (01902) 326225 Fax: (01902) 326225 E-mail: sales@diserv.free-online.co.uk
Gaugemaster Co. Ltd, 93 Leopold Street, Birmingham, B12 0UD Tel: 0121-773 6331 Fax: 0121-772 4046 E-mail: enquiries@gaugemaster.net
Hammond & Co. Ltd, Finway Road, Hemel Hempstead Industrial Estate, Hemel Hempstead, Hertfordshire, HP2 7PT Tel: (01442) 212211 Fax: (01442) 252003 E-mail: sales@hammco.com
Intra Ltd, 27 Wilbury Way, Hitchin, Hertfordshire, SG4 0TS Tel: (01462) 422111 Fax: (01462) 453667 E-mail: info@intra-corp.co.uk
Longbridge Tool & Gauge Ltd, Unit 74, Heming Road, Washford Industrial Estate, Redditch, Worcestershire, B98 0EA Tel: (01527) 520706 Fax: (01527) 510170
Malken Gauge & Tool Co. Ltd, 260 Summer Lane, New Town, Birmingham, B19 2PX Tel: 0121-333 3808 Fax: 0121-333 3617 E-mail: enquiries@malkengauge.co.uk
Marposs Ltd, Leofric Business Park, Progress Way, Binley Industrial Estate, Coventry, CV3 2TJ Tel: (024) 7688 4950 Fax: (024) 7663 6622 E-mail: sales@uk.marposs.com
Mercury Thread Gauges, 182-186 Fletchamstead Highway Industrial Estate, Fletchamstead Highway, Coventry, CV4 7BB Tel: (024) 7671 4185 Fax: (024) 7669 1234 E-mail: sales@mercurygauges.co.uk
Metris UK Ltd, Argosy Road, Nottingham EMA, Castle Donnington, Derby, DE74 2SA Tel: (01332) 811349 Fax: (01332) 850149 E-mail: sales@lkuk.co.uk
Micron Gauges Ltd, 1-3 Keyford Court, Manor Furlong, Frome, Somerset, BA11 4BD Tel: (01373) 461584 Fax: (01373) 461585 E-mail: sales@microngauges.co.uk
Moore & Wright, Unit 15 Bordon Trading Estate, Old Station Way, Bordon, Hampshire, GU35 9HH Tel: 0114-225 0400 Fax: 0114-225 0410 E-mail: sales@moore-and-wright.com
Nu Gauge, 38 Hoyland Road, Sheffield, S3 8AB Tel: 0114-275 4006 Fax: 0114-275 4006 E-mail: sales@nu-gauge.co.uk
Perry Pearson Engineering Co. Ltd, Unit 6 219 Torrington Avenue, Coventry, CV4 9HN Tel: 024 76460339
Salt Engineering (Midlands) Ltd, Unit 4, Macefield Close, Aldermans Green, Coventry, CV2 2PJ Tel: (024) 7661 6595 Fax: (024) 7660 2165 E-mail: vaughan@saltengineering.co.uk
Startrite Designs Ltd, Courteney Road, Hoath Way, Gillingham, Kent, ME8 0RZ Tel: (01634) 233216 Fax: (01634) 373516 E-mail: startritedesigns@btinternet.com

GAUGES, THREAD/SCREW THREAD

Piccadilly Precision Engineering Co. Ltd, Units H4 & H5, Halesfield 19, Telford, Shropshire, TF7 4QT Tel: (01952) 582113 Fax: (01952) 583239 E-mail: sales@piccadillyprecision.co.uk
Telford Threadgauge Ltd, Unit 1 Halesfield 18, Telford, Shropshire, TF7 4PP Tel: (01952) 588858 Fax: (01952) 588616
Threadmaster Gauges Ltd, Princes Dr Industrial Estate, Coventry Road, Kenilworth, Warwickshire, CV8 2FD Tel: (01926) 852428 Fax: (01926) 850047 E-mail: sales@threadmastergauges.co.uk
Tru-Thread Ltd, Station Road, Coleshill, Birmingham, B46 1HT Tel: (01675) 462193 Fax: (01675) 462841 E-mail: admin@tru-thread.co.uk

GAUGING ELECTRONIC INSPECTION/MEASUREMENT EQUIPMENT/SYSTEMS

J.H. Barclay & Co., 53 Burnfield Road, Giffnock, Glasgow, G46 7PY Tel: 0141-638 9382 Fax: 0141-638 9848 E-mail: solutions@jhbarclay.co.uk
Beta Lasermike Ltd, Stirling Road, Cressex Business Park, High Wycombe, Buckinghamshire, HP12 3RT Tel: (01494) 894400 Fax: (01494) 894401 E-mail: sales@uk.betalasermike.com
E G S Gauging Ltd, The Atrium, 18-21 Church Gate, Thatcham, Berkshire, RG19 3PN Tel: (01635) 861117 Fax: (01635) 273249 E-mail: info@egsgauging.com
Hexagon Metrology, Halesfield 13, Telford, Shropshire, TF7 4PL Tel: (01952) 681300 Fax: (01952) 681311 E-mail: enquiry@hexmet.co.uk
Innovative Measurement Technology, 49 Christchurch Crescent, Bognor Regis, West Sussex, PO21 5SL Tel: (01243) 824506 Fax: (01243) 826340 E-mail: sales@imeasure.co.uk
Intra Ltd, 27 Wilbury Way, Hitchin, Hertfordshire, SG4 0TS Tel: (01462) 422111 Fax: (01462) 453667 E-mail: info@intra-corp.co.uk
C.E. Johansson Ltd, Metrology House, Halesfield 13, Telford, Shropshire, TF7 4PL Tel: 0870 4462667 Fax: 0870 4462668 E-mail: enquiry@hexmet.co.uk
Marposs Ltd, Leofric Business Park, Progress Way, Binley Industrial Estate, Coventry, CV3 2TJ Tel: (024) 7688 4950 Fax: (024) 7663 6622 E-mail: sales@uk.marposs.com
Metris UK Ltd, Argosy Road, Nottingham EMA, Castle Donnington, Derby, DE74 2SA Tel: (01332) 811349 Fax: (01332) 850149 E-mail: sales@lkuk.co.uk
Micron Gauges Ltd, 1-3 Keyford Court, Manor Furlong, Frome, Somerset, BA11 4BD Tel: (01373) 461584 Fax: (01373) 461585 E-mail: sales@microngauges.co.uk
Thermo Fisher Scientific, Shepherd Road, Gloucester, GL2 5HF Tel: (01452) 337800 Fax: (01452) 415156
Zumbach Electronics, Unit 22 Cromwell Business Centre, Howard Way, Interchange Park, Newport Pagnell, Buckinghamshire, MK16 9QS Tel: (0870) 7743301 Fax: (0870) 7743302 E-mail: sales@zumbach.com

GAUGING TRANSDUCERS

▶ Solartron Metrology Ltd, 1 Steyning Way, Bognor Regis, West Sussex, PO22 9ST Tel: (01243) 833300 Fax: (01243) 861244

GAZEBOS

MARINA SPA, 40 Portsmouth Road, Camberley, Surrey, GU15 1JU Tel: 01276 686682 Fax: 01276 686682 E-mail: info@marinaspa.co.uk

GEAR CHANGE CONTROL CABLES

Kongsberg Auto Motive, Christopher Martin Road, Basildon, Essex, SS14 3ES Tel: (01268) 522861 Fax: (01268) 282994 E-mail: m.dickason@morse-controls.co.uk
Tuthill Controls Group, Diplocks Way, Hailsham, East Sussex, BN27 3JS Tel: (01323) 841510 Fax: (01323) 845848

GEAR CUTTING

▶ D G Steel & Son Engineering Ltd, Gear Works, Brook Street, Bury, Lancashire, BL9 6AF Tel: 0161-764 4862

GEAR CUTTING MACHINES OR TOOLS

Broad Oak Gears Ltd, Old Warburton Bakery, Jacob Street, Accrington, Lancashire, BB5 1HU Tel: (01254) 397489 Fax: (01254) 390550 E-mail: bogears@aol.com
D Midgley & Sons Ltd, Holmfield Industrial Estate, Holdsworth Road, Holmfield, Halifax, West Yorkshire, HX2 9TN Tel: (01422) 247185 Fax: (01422) 247234 E-mail: dmidleyandsons@aol.com
Gear Technology Ltd, 228 Lythalls Lane, Coventry, CV6 6GF Tel: (024) 7666 2556 Fax: (024) 7666 6355 E-mail: geartec@skelcher-rowe.co.uk
Micro Precision Ltd, Duxons Turn, Hemel Hempstead, Hertfordshire, HP2 4SB Tel: (01442) 241027 Fax: (01442) 268074 E-mail: enquiries@microprecision.co.uk
Samputensili (UK) Ltd, Rotherham, S. Yorkshire, S66 8XX Tel: (01709) 703707 Fax: (01709) 703232E-mail: postbox@geartec.demon.co.uk

GEAR CUTTING, WORMWHEEL

M&B, Blaby Industrial Park, Winchester Avenue, Blaby, Leicester, LE8 4GZ Tel: 0116-277 6363 Fax: 0116-278 7871 E-mail: enquiries@mbgears.co.uk

GEAR DISTRIBUTORS OR AGENTS

Autoglide Garage Services, Birkett House, Wellington Road, Bollington, Macclesfield, Cheshire, SK10 5HT Tel: (01625) 574126 Fax: (01625) 574126
Davall Stock Gears, Travellers Lane, North Mymms, Hatfield, Hertfordshire, AL9 7JB Tel: (01707) 283100 Fax: (01707) 283111 E-mail: dsg@davall.co.uk
HPC Gears Ltd, Unit 14, Foxwood Industrial Park, Foxwood Road, Chesterfield, Derbyshire, S41 9RN Tel: (01246) 268080 Fax: (01246) 260003 E-mail: sales@hpcgears.com
R.W Gear Ltd, Stargate Industrial Estate, Bailey House, Ryton, Tyne & Wear, NE40 3DG Tel: 0191-413 2244 Fax: 0191-413 1133 E-mail: rwryton@rwtransmissions.com
Shropshire Bearing Services, 6 Beveley Road, Oakengates, Telford, Shropshire, TF2 6AT Tel: (01952) 610157 Fax: (01952) 619669 E-mail: shropshirebearings@hotmail.com

GEAR GRINDING MACHINES

H K Technologies Ltd, Unit 7 Hadrians Way, Glebe Farm Industrial Estate, Rugby, Warwickshire, CV21 1ST Tel: (01788) 577288 Fax: (01788) 562808 E-mail: admin@hktechnologies.com
▶ Takisawa Ltd, Meir Road, Redditch, Worcestershire, B98 7SY Tel: (01527) 522211 Fax: (01527) 510728 E-mail: sales@takisawa.com

GEAR GRINDING SERVICES

Colledge & Morley (Gears) Ltd, Curriers Close, Charter Avenue, Canley, Coventry, CV4 8AW Tel: (024) 7646 2328 Fax: (024) 7669 4008
DePe Gear Co. Ltd, Unit 1 Grove Road Industrial Estate, Grove Road, Fenton, Stoke-On-Trent, ST4 4LG Tel: (01782) 594114 Fax: (01782) 594115 E-mail: sales@depe.co.uk
Emr Brackley Ltd, County Road, Buckingham Road Industrial Estate, Brackley, Northamptonshire, NN13 7AX Tel: (01280) 701321 Fax: (01280) 701327 E-mail: sales@emreng.co.uk
Gibbs Gears Precision Engineers Ltd, 58 B Western Road, Tring, Hertfordshire, HP23 4BB Tel: (01442) 828898 Fax: (01422) 828020 E-mail: sales@gibbsgears.com
Ground Form Gears Ltd, Unit 4-5 Abeles Way, Holly Lane Industrial Estate, Atherstone, Warwickshire, CV9 2QZ Tel: (01827) 718555 Fax: (01827) 718789 E-mail: gearsground@yahoo.co.uk
Jackson Precision Gear Services Ltd, Elmtree Street, Belle Vue, Wakefield, West Yorkshire, WF1 5EQ Tel: (01924) 299866 Fax: (01924) 299338 E-mail: j.s.j@btinternet.com
Multispline Gear Cutters, Unit 66 Coleshill Industrial Estate, Station Road, Coleshill, Birmingham, B46 1JT Tel: (01675) 462253 Fax: (01675) 463485 E-mail: sales@multispline.co.uk
Sprint Industrial Sales Ltd, 1 Rosehill, Willenhall, West Midlands, WV13 2AR Tel: (01902) 636106 Fax: (01902) 636137 E-mail: sprint@btclick.com

GEAR HOBS

Acedes Gear Tools, 2-4 Fleming Road, Newbury, Berkshire, RG14 2DE Tel: (01635) 524252 Fax: (01635) 521085 E-mail: sales@acedes.co.uk

GEAR MANUFRS/CUTTERS, *See also headings under Gears*

Albion Automotive Ltd, Lancashire Enterprises Business Park, Centurian Way, Leyland, PR26 6TZ Tel: (01772) 831400 Fax: (01772) 831401
All Gear Services 1990 Ltd, 8 Hogwood Farm, Sheerlands Road, Finchampstead, Wokingham, Berkshire, RG40 4QY Tel: 0118-973 0053 Fax: 0118-973 4722 E-mail: linda.rapley@btinternet.com
Alpenbury Ltd, 11 Gateway Industrial Estate, Parkgate, Rotherham, South Yorkshire, S62 6JL Tel: (01709) 528186 Fax: (01709) 528287 E-mail: enquiries@alpenbury.co.uk
Bedford Transmissions Ltd, Unit 26-27, Raynham Road, Bishop's Stortford, Hertfordshire, CM23 5PE Tel: (01279) 461397 Fax: (01279) 659017 E-mail: enquires@btlgears.co.uk
Bell Gears Ltd, Frestan Works, Carwood Road, Sheffield, S4 7SE Tel: 0114-243 1938 Fax: 0114-243 2428 E-mail: sales@bell-gears.co.uk
Carford Transmissions Ltd, 68 Rea Street South, Birmingham, B5 6LB Tel: 0121-622 7060 Fax: 0121-622 4060 E-mail: admin@carford.com
M. Clarke Engineering, 566 Attercliffe Road, Sheffield, S9 3QP Tel: 0114-244 7234 Fax: 0114-244 7234
Colledge & Morley (Gears) Ltd, Curriers Close, Charter Avenue, Canley, Coventry, CV4 8AW Tel: (024) 7646 2328 Fax: (024) 7669 4008
Colsalake Ltd, 6 Eldon Road Industrial Estate, Attenborough, Beeston, Nottingham, NG9 6DZ Tel: 0115-943 1558 Fax: 0115-925 0990 E-mail: coleslakeltd@aol.com
Comma Tech Ltd, Carlyon Road, Atherstone, Warwickshire, CV9 1LW Tel: (01827) 714741 Fax: (01827) 718943 E-mail: sales@commatech.co.uk
Cornish Engineering Ltd, Popham Street, Nottingham, NG1 7JD Tel: 0115-950 4944 Fax: 0115-950 4215
E S L Engineers (Basildon) Ltd, Woolaston Way, Basildon, Essex, SS13 1DJ Tel: (01268) 727777 Fax: (01268) 728866 E-mail: sales@eslengineers.co.uk
Emr Brackley Ltd, County Road, Buckingham Road Industrial Estate, Brackley, Northamptonshire, NN13 7AX Tel: (01280) 701321 Fax: (01280) 701327 E-mail: sales@emreng.co.uk
▶ Freedom Engineering Co. Ltd, 34 Springfield Way, Anlaby, Hull, HU10 6RJ Tel: (01482) 565566 Fax: (01482) 500826 E-mail: mike@freedomgears.fsnet.co.uk
Gear Service, Oxford Road, Pen Mill Trading Estate, Yeovil, Somerset, BA21 5HR Tel: (01935) 428473 Fax: (01935) 432765 E-mail: yeovilgears@btconnect.com
Gears in Motion, Unit 66 Rovex Business Park, Hy Hall Road, Tyseley, Birmingham, B11 2AQ Tel: 0121-706 8821 Fax: 0121-708 0512 E-mail: info@gearsinmotion.co.uk
Gould Pulleys & Drives Ltd, Unit 19, Worcester Road Industrial Estate, Chipping Norton, Oxfordshire, OX7 5XW Tel: (01608) 643311 Fax: (01608) 643050 E-mail: sales@gouldpulleys.com
Greenwood Gears Ltd, Digital House, Royd Way, Keighley, West Yorkshire, BD21 3LG Tel: (01535) 604393 Fax: (01535) 680587 E-mail: sales@hewitt-topham.co.uk
Guest Gear Services, Higham Mead, Higham Road, Chesham, Buckinghamshire, HP5 2AF Tel: (01494) 794667 Fax: (01494) 794668 E-mail: guestgears@yahoo.com
Hargreaves Hamilton Gears Ltd, Nelson Mill Gaskell Street, Bolton, BL1 2QE Tel: (01204) 456190 Fax: (01204) 371355
Hilsea Engineering Ltd, 3 St Georges Indust Estate, Rodney Road, Southsea, Hampshire, PO4 8SS Tel: (023) 9273 1676 Fax: (023) 9282 7801 E-mail: hilseaeng@fsbdial.co.uk
Hindle Gears, Caledonia Street, Bradford, West Yorkshire, BD5 0EL Tel: (01274) 727234 Fax: (01274) 737343 E-mail: gears@hindle.co.uk
Humberside Gear Co. Ltd, Thrunscoe House, Thrunscoe Road, Cleethorpes, South Humberside, DN35 8TA Tel: (01472) 601111 Fax: (01472) 602143 E-mail: humberside.gears@virgin.net
Hunter Gears Ltd, Addison Works, Haugh Lane, Blaydon-on-Tyne, Tyne & Wear, NE21 4SB Tel: 0191-414 4545 Fax: 0191-414 0135
Jackson Precision Gear Services Ltd, Elmtree Street, Belle Vue, Wakefield, West Yorkshire, WF1 5EQ Tel: (01924) 299866 Fax: (01924) 299338 E-mail: j.s.j@btinternet.com
Jubilee Engineering Ltd, Unit 10b, Miry Lane Industrial Estate, Wigan, Lancashire, WN6 7TG Tel: (01942) 247111 Fax: (01942) 247333
Kelston Precisions Gears Ltd, Crews Hole Road, Bristol, BS5 8BB Tel: 0117-955 8671 Fax: 0117-935 0023 E-mail: sales@kelstongears.co.uk
Kenward Precision & Gear, Unit 1b & 13 Perseverance Mills, Lockwood Scar, Huddersfield, HD4 6BW Tel: (01484) 512355 Fax: (01484) 420793 E-mail: kenward@mywebpage.net
Kingsway Engineering Ltd., Hanham Road, Bristol, BS15 8PX Tel: 0117-961 3168 Fax: 0117-960 4718 E-mail: sales@kingswayengineering.co.uk
Lamond & Murray Ltd, Burnside, Inverkeithing, Fife, KY11 1HT Tel: (01383) 413541 Fax: (01383) 414548 E-mail: gears@lamondandmurray.co.uk
Charles Leek & Sons Ltd, Springfield Works, Ashbourne Road, Leek, Staffordshire, ST13 5AY Tel: (01538) 382066 Fax: (01538) 373153 E-mail: sales@leekgears.co.uk
Linco Engineering Co. Ltd, 108 Park Street, Motherwell, Lanarkshire, ML1 1PF Tel: (01698) 254541 Fax: (01698) 276178
Longford Gear Cutting Co Ltd, Bayton Road Industrial Estate, Bayton Road, Exhall, Coventry, CV7 9EL Tel: (024) 7636 5777 Fax: (024) 7636 5727 E-mail: sales@longford-gear.co.uk
M&B, Blaby Industrial Park, Winchester Avenue, Blaby, Leicester, LE8 4GZ Tel: 0116-277 6363 Fax: 0116-278 7871 E-mail: enquiries@mbgears.co.uk
Martec Engineering, Grange Road, Tipree, Colchester, CO5 0QQ Tel: (01621) 819673 Fax: (01621) 817297 E-mail: marteng@aol.com
Meldon Gears 1967 Ltd, Lees Road, Knowsley Industrial Park, Liverpool, L33 7XP Tel: 0151-546 9787 Fax: 0151-546 2861 E-mail: sales@meldongears.co.uk
Metalite Ltd, 121 Barkby Road, Leicester, LE4 9LU Tel: 0116-276 7874 Fax: 0116-233 0337
Northern Tool & Gear Co. Ltd, John St West, Arbroath, Angus, DD11 1RT Tel: (01241) 872626 Fax: (01241) 870040 E-mail: general@ntgear.co.uk
P V S Engineers Ltd, 1-2 Murrills Estate, Fareham, Hampshire, PO16 9RD Tel: (023) 9237 9495 Fax: (023) 9238 8801 E-mail: rec@pvsengineers.co.uk
▶ Paddock Gear Engineering Ltd, 2 Kingsbury Link, Trinity Road, Piccadilly, Tamworth, Staffordshire, B78 2EX Tel: (01827) 875566 Fax: (01827) 875880
Pentag Gears & Oilfield Equipment Ltd, 5 John Street, Sheffield, S2 4QR Tel: 0114-258 3473 Fax: 0114-258 4264 E-mail: meril@pentage-gears.com
Planet Gears Ltd, 2 Maguire Industrial Estate, Coventry, CV4 9HN Tel: 024 76474213
Precision Powertrain UK Ltd, Catto Drive, Peterhead, Aberdeenshire, AB42 1RL Tel: (01779) 473161 Fax: (01779) 477424
R A Howarth Engineering Ltd, Earl Road, Rackheath Industrial Estate, Rackheath, Norwich, NR13 6NT Tel: (01603) 721155 Fax: (01603) 721648
R.W Gear Ltd, Stargate Industrial Estate, Bailey House, Ryton, Tyne & Wear, NE40 3DG Tel: 0191-413 2244 Fax: 0191-413 1133 E-mail: rwryton@rwtransmissions.com
Reliance Precision Mechatronics LLP, Rowley Mills, Penistone Road, Lepton, Huddersfield, HD8 0LE Tel: (01484) 601000 Fax: (01484) 601001 E-mail: sales@reliance.co.uk
Renold Gears, Station Road, Milnrow, Rochdale, Lancashire, OL16 3LS Tel: (01706) 751000 Fax: (01706) 751001 E-mail: gears.sales@renold.com
Roundwood Engineering Works, 15 Carrigs Road, Newcastle, County Down, BT33 0JZ Tel: (028) 4372 3550 Fax: (028) 4372 6636
S Z Gears Ltd, Pontymister Industrial Estate, Risca, Newport, Gwent, NP11 6NP Tel: (01633) 612071 Fax: (01633) 612626
Shaw Gears, Unit 5 Duchess St Industrial Estate, Shaw, Oldham, OL2 7UX Tel: (01706) 847220 Fax: (01706) 847220
South East Power Transmissions Ltd, Network House, Perry Road, Harlow, Essex, CM18 7ND Tel: (01279) 418300 Fax: (01279) 418100 E-mail: stransltd@aol.com
Super Gear Co. Ltd, Unit 2 Nine Trees Trading Estate, Morthen Road, Thurcroft, Rotherham, South Yorkshire, S66 9JG Tel: (01709) 702320 Fax: (01709) 700733
Sutton Gears Ltd, Unit 2 Lifford Way, Binley Industrial Estate, Binley Industrial Estate, Coventry, CV3 2RN Tel: (024) 7643 1331 Fax: (024) 7665 1000
T B Engineering Ltd, Network House, Perry Road, Harlow, Essex, CM18 7NS Tel: (01279) 418300 Fax: (01279) 418100
T K Engineering & Gear Cutting Ltd, Forest Mills, Denman Street East, Nottingham, NG7 3PZ Tel: 0115-970 0978 Fax: 0115-942 2928
Tradex Instruments Ltd, C Davis Road, Chessington, Surrey, KT9 1TY Tel: (020) 8391 0136 Fax: (020) 8397 1924 E-mail: info@tradexinstruments.com
Trent Valley Bearings & Pneumatics Ltd, Transmission House, 1 South Street, Long Eaton, Nottingham, NG10 1ER Tel: 0115-973 2234 Fax: 0115-946 0817 E-mail: sales@trent-valley.co.uk
Village Gears Ltd, Duke Street, Wednesfield, Wolverhampton, WV11 1TH Tel: (01902) 725565 Fax: (01902) 727313
W K W Precision Engineering Co. Ltd, Shaw Royd Works, Shaw Lane, Halifax, West Yorkshire, HX3 9HD Tel: (01422) 351720 Fax: (01422) 330017 E-mail: sales@wkw-eng.co.uk
R.L. Walsh & Sons (Coventry) Ltd, 17 Lythalls Lane, Coventry, CV6 6FN Tel: (024) 7668 7241 Fax: (024) 7666 2870 E-mail: office@rlwalsh.co.uk
▶ Walton Clutch, 2a Beech Road, Walton, Liverpool, L4 5UU Tel: 0151-525 5505 Fax: 0151-525 5505
Williams & Co Southampton Ltd, Victoria Street, Southampton, SO14 5QZ Tel: (023) 8022 0490 Fax: (023) 8063 8930 E-mail: sales@williams-eng.co.uk
Winfield Gears Ltd, 80a Windsor Road, Bexhill-on-Sea, East Sussex, TN39 3PE Tel: 01424 733599
Woollacott Gears Ltd, Llay Hall Industrial Estate, Cefn-Y-Bedd, Wrexham, Clwyd, LL12 9YG Tel: (01978) 761848 Fax: (01978) 762340

GEAR PRODUCTION MACHINERY

Sumitomo Drive Technologies SM Cyclo (UK) Ltd, Unit 29, Bergen Way, Hull, HU7 0YQ Tel: (01482) 790340 Fax: (01482) 790321 E-mail: marketing@sumitomoeurope.com

GEAR PUMPS

Albany Standard Pumps, Richter Works, Garnett Street, Bradford, West Yorkshire, BD3 9HB Tel: (01274) 725351 Fax: (01274) 742467 E-mail: sales@albany-pumps.co.uk
Camera One Ltd, 1275 Stratford Road, Hall Green, Birmingham, B28 9AJ Tel: 0121-733 1999
K T Hydraulic Ltd, Hope Hall Mill, Union Street South, Halifax, West Yorkshire, HX1 2LA Tel: (01422) 358885 Fax: (01422) 359512
Sauer-Danfoss Ltd, Cheney Manor, Swindon, SN2 2PZ Tel: (01793) 530101 Fax: (01793) 481925
Selwood Pump Co. Ltd, 188 Robin Hood Lane, Birmingham, B28 0LG Tel: 0121-777 5631 Fax: 0121-702 2195 E-mail: graham.gallon@selwood-pumps.com
Varley Pumps Ltd, 1 Kimpton Road, Luton, LU1 3LD Tel: (01582) 731144 Fax: (01582) 402563E-mail: varleysales@haywardtyler.com

GEAR RACKS

HPC Gears Ltd, Unit 14, Foxwood Industrial Park, Foxwood Road, Chesterfield, Derbyshire, S41 9RN Tel: (01246) 268080 Fax: (01246) 260003 E-mail: sales@hpcgears.com
Kingsway Engineering Ltd., Hanham Road, Bristol, BS15 8PX Tel: 0117-961 3168 Fax: 0117-960 4718 E-mail: sales@kingswayengineering.co.uk

GEAR RECONDITIONING SERVICES

A & R Transmissions, Pridham Lane, Plymouth, PL2 3PH Tel: (01752) 770777 Fax: (01752) 777716
Bell Gears Ltd, Frestan Works, Carwood Road, Sheffield, S4 7SE Tel: 0114-243 1938 Fax: 0114-243 2428 E-mail: sales@bell-gears.co.uk
Cartmell Transmissions, 4 Lytham Road, Warton, Preston, PR4 1XD Tel: (01772) 631679
Christopher Howard Cars, Forge Engineering Works, Pye Corner, Ulcombe, Maidstone, Kent, ME17 1EH Tel: (01622) 851140
Kent Transmissions Centre, Unit 1 Skein Enterprise Park, Hodsoll Street, Sevenoaks, Kent, TN15 7LB Tel: (01732) 824618
Overdrive Repair Services, 50 Rother Valley Way, Holbrook, Sheffield, S20 3RW Tel: 0114-248 2632 Fax: 0114-248 2786 E-mail: sales@overdrive-repairs.co.uk
Transfix Gearboxes, 8 The Maple Industrial Estate, Wentworth Road, Mapplewell, Barnsley, South Yorkshire, S75 6DT Tel: (01226) 381000 Fax: (01226) 381000

GEAR SHAPER CUTTERS

Acedes Gear Tools, 2-4 Fleming Road, Newbury, Berkshire, RG14 2DE Tel: (01635) 524252 Fax: (01635) 521085 E-mail: sales@acedes.co.uk
Dathan Tool & Gauge Co. Ltd, Mean Lane, Meltham, Holmfirth, HD9 5RU Tel: (01484) 851207 Fax: (01484) 852271 E-mail: sales@dathan.co.uk

GEAR SHAVING CUTTERS

Dathan Tool & Gauge Co. Ltd, Mean Lane, Meltham, Holmfirth, HD9 5RU Tel: (01484) 851207 Fax: (01484) 852271 E-mail: sales@dathan.co.uk

GEAR TEST EQUIPMENT

Edgerton Gears Ltd, Park Square, Ossett, West Yorkshire, WF5 0JS Tel: (01924) 273193 Fax: (01924) 275560

GEAR TESTING CHART RECORDERS

Roger's Machine Tools, Unit 21 Two Gates Trading Estate, Watling Street, Two Gates, Tamworth, Staffordshire, B77 5AE Tel: (01827) 283247 Fax: (01827) 262049 E-mail: rmtools@btopenworld.com

GEAR TOOTH COUPLINGS

Matrix Engineered Systems Ltd, Eastmill Road, Brechin, Angus, DD9 7EP Tel: (01356) 602000 Fax: (01356) 602060 E-mail: sales@matrix-international.com

Planet Gears Ltd, 2 Maguire Industrial Estate, Coventry, CV4 9HN Tel: 024 76474213

GEARBOX DISTRIBUTORS OR AGENTS

▶ A J Transmissions, 4 Stanhope Close, Wilmslow, Cheshire, SK9 2NN Tel: (01625) 533466 Fax: (01625) 533466 E-mail: tomatajt@aol.co.uk

A & M Drive Systems, 16 Bayfield Avenue, Frimley, Camberley, Surrey, GU16 8TU Tel: (01276) 26651 Fax: (01276) 685193

▶ A & M Gearboxes Automatic & Manual, Lorien, The Shrave, Four Marks, Alton, Hampshire, GU34 5BH Tel: (07901) 661065

Alliance Automatic Co., Unit 3 The Pilton Estate, Pitlake, Croydon, CR0 3RY Tel: (020) 8688 1866 Fax: (020) 8686 3381

Bristol Transmissions, Unit 4, Strachan & Henshaw Building, Foundry Lane, Fishponds, Bristol, BS5 7UF Tel: 0117-952 4920 Fax: 0117-951 4982 E-mail: service@bristoltransmissions.co.uk

Combidrive Ltd, Unit 6, Parc Menter, Meadows Bridge, Cross Hands, Llanelli, Carmarthenshire, SA14 6RA Tel: (01269) 834848 Fax: (01269) 834850 E-mail: sales@combidrive.com

ERIKS UK, Industrial Distribution Service Centre, Unit 12 Robin Hood Industrial Estate, Alfred Street South, Nottingham, NG3 1GE Tel: 0115-958 1312 Fax: 0115-958 1279 E-mail: nottingham@eriks.co.uk

M T S (Sales) Ltd, Midland House, Hayes Lane, Lye, Stourbridge, West Midlands, DY9 8RD Tel: (01384) 424823 Fax: (01384) 422819 E-mail: sales@gearbox-mts.com

Micro Clutch Developments Ltd, Unit 8-9 Kiln Park Industrial Estate, Searle CR, Weston-super-Mare, Avon, BS23 3XP Tel: (01934) 415606 Fax: (01934) 636658 E-mail: sales@microclutch.com

Motor Technology Ltd, Motec House, Chadkirk Business Park, Stockport, Cheshire, SK6 3NE Tel: 0161-217 7100 Fax: 0161-217 7101 E-mail: sales@motec.co.uk

R G Automatics, 7 Spa Road, Hockley, Essex, SS5 4AZ Tel: (01702) 205251

R G C Transmission Services Ltd, Unit 26 Westend Estate, Bruntcliffe Road, Morley, Leeds, LS27 0LJ Tel: 0113-252 3520

S B T Engineering Services Ltd, Empress Street, Old Trafford, Manchester, M16 9EN Tel: 0161-877 7755 Fax: 0161-848 9225 E-mail: info@sbtengineering.co.uk

S.I.S. Industrial Automation Ltd, 8 Amphion Court Hale Trading Estate, Lower Church Lane, Tipton, West Midlands, DY4 7HN Tel: 0121-520 7211 Fax: 0121-557 8146

GEARBOX MAINTENANCE OR REPAIR

Allen Gears, Atlas Works, Station Road, Pershore, Worcestershire, WR10 2BZ Tel: (01386) 552211 Fax: (01386) 554491 E-mail: sales@allengears.com

▶ Black Diamond Ltd, Units 2-7 Guardian St Industrial Estate, Guardian Street, Warrington, WA5 1SJ Tel: (01925) 416619 Fax: (01925) 230472

DePe Gear Co. Ltd, Unit 1 Grove Road Industrial Estate, Grove Road, Fenton, Stoke-On-Trent, ST4 4LG Tel: (01782) 594114 Fax: (01782) 594115 E-mail: sales@depe.co.uk

Exeeco Ltd, Regina House, Ring Road, Bramley, Leeds, LS13 4ET Tel: 0113-256 7922 Fax: 0113-236 3310 E-mail: sales@exeeco.co.uk

Harlow Transmissions, Shenfield Court, Perry Road, Harlow, Essex, CM18 7LR Tel: (01279) 426943 E-mail: dom.daily@tesco.net

M & E James, Unit 2 Hare Street, Bilston, West Midlands, WV14 7DX Tel: (01902) 408030 Fax: (01902) 490166 E-mail: saws@supanet.com

▶ M K Engines Ltd, 6 Clarke Road, Bletchley, Milton Keynes, MK1 1LG Tel: (01908) 366566 Fax: (01908) 366566

▶ S H I Cyclo Drive Europe Ltd, Marfleet, Hull, HU9 5RA Tel: (01482) 788022

▶ Sheffield Transmission Developments, Highfield Lane, Sheffield, S13 9NA Tel: 0114-288 9440 Fax: 0114-288 0319 E-mail: sales@sheffield-transmission.com

GEARBOX MODIFICATION

Harlow Transmissions, Shenfield Court, Perry Road, Harlow, Essex, CM18 7LR Tel: (01279) 426943 E-mail: dom.daily@tesco.net

GEARBOX RECONDITIONING

Thornford Transmissions, Unit 4 Station Approach, Yetminster, Sherborne, Dorset, DT9 6LH Tel: (01935) 872500 Fax: (01935) 872779

GEARBOX REPAIR, VARIABLE SPEED

Nottingham Engineering Services Ltd, Mount Street, New Basford, Nottingham, NG7 7HX Tel: 0115 9780080

GEARBOX/UNIT MANUFRS, *See also headings for particular types under Gearboxes, etc*

▶ Advantiv Ltd, 46-47 Centerprise House, New Greenham Park, Greenham, Newbury, Berkshire, RG19 6HP Tel: (01635) 817371 Fax: (01635) 817471 E-mail: sales@advantiv.co.uk

Amir Power Transmission Ltd, Amir House, Maxted Road, Hemel Hempstead Industrial Estate, Hemel Hempstead, Hertfordshire, HP2 7DX Tel: (01442) 212671 Fax: (01442) 246640 E-mail: amirpower@amirpower.co.uk

▶ Antifriction Components Ltd, Unit 3 Pearce Way, Gloucester, GL2 5YD Tel: (01452) 529669 Fax: (01452) 423873 E-mail: gloucestersales@afc-uk.com

▶ Automatic Man Ltd, 64 Davis Road, London, W3 7SG Tel: (020) 8740 1020 E-mail: automaticman.ltd@virgin.net

Bonfiglioli UK Ltd, 3-5 Grosvenor Grange, Woolston, Warrington, WA1 4SF Tel: (01925) 852667 Fax: (01925) 852668 E-mail: sales@bonfiglioliuk.co.uk

Bosch Rexroth Ltd, Cromwell Road, St. Neots, Cambridgeshire, PE19 2ES Tel: (01480) 223200 Fax: (01480) 219052 E-mail: info@boschrexroth.co.uk

David Brown Engineering Ltd, Park Works, Park Road, Huddersfield, HD4 5DD Tel: (01484) 465500 Fax: (01484) 465586 E-mail: sales@davidbrown.textron.com

Cornwall & Devon Transmissions Ltd, Old Ambulance Station, Pentewan Road, St. Austell, Cornwall, PL25 5BU Tel: (01726) 63666 Fax: (01726) 68898

Desmi Ltd, Unit 6A, Rosevale Business Park, Parkhouse Industrial Estate West, Newcastle, Staffordshire, ST5 7UB Tel: (01782) 566900 Fax: (01782) 563666 E-mail: desmi_ltd@desmi.com

East London Transmissions, Billet Road, London, E17 5DL Tel: (020) 8531 8390 Fax: (020) 8503 2182

Exeeco Ltd, Regina House, Ring Road, Bramley, Leeds, LS13 4ET Tel: 0113-256 7922 Fax: 0113-236 3310 E-mail: sales@exeeco.co.uk

Exeter Gearbox Centre, Grace Road Central, Marsh Barton Trading Estate, Exeter, EX2 8QA Tel: (01392) 434049 Fax: (01392) 437131 E-mail: info@gearboxcentre.com

▶ G D K Engineering Co. Ltd, Unit 65 Blackpole Trading Estate West, Worcester, WR3 8TJ Tel: (01905) 454261 Fax: (01905) 454231 E-mail: sales@gdk-engineering.co.uk

Garmendale Engineering Ltd, Dale Works, Manners Industrial Estate, Ilkeston, Derbyshire, DE7 8EF Tel: 0115-932 7082 Fax: 0115-930 9391 E-mail: garmendale@enquiries.com

Heynau, Unit 43, Britannia Way, Enterprise Industrial Park, Lichfield, Staffordshire, WS14 9UY Tel: (01543) 255995 Fax: (01543) 250316 E-mail: acdcpowerdrives@aol.com

▶ Hi-Ton (International) Ltd, Montgomery Street, Sparkbrook, Birmingham, B11 1DY Tel: 0121-772 2711

▶ Main Train Transmissions LTD, 143 Coppermill Lane, Walthamstow, London, E17 7HD Tel: 0845 8380599 E-mail: sales@maintrainltd.com

Midland Transmissions Ltd, 887 Melton Road, Thurmaston, Leicester, LE4 8EF Tel: 0116-260 6200 Fax: 0116-260 2548 E-mail: fosse.bearings@btinternet.com

Newbrook Engineering Co. Ltd, Church Street, Donington, Spalding, Lincolnshire, PE11 4UA Tel: (01775) 820583 Fax: (01775) 820487 E-mail: newbrook.eng@virgin.net

Nord Gear Ltd, 11 Barton Lane, Abingdon, Oxfordshire, OX14 3NB Tel: (01235) 534404 Fax: (01235) 534414 E-mail: info@nord.uk.com

Nottingham Electrical Transmissions, Northern Court, Nottingham, NG6 0BJ Tel: 0115-975 3655 Fax: 0115-977 0366 E-mail: info@net-eng.co.uk

▶ Piv Drive, Posiva Works 8 Skipping Dale Industrial Estate, Exmoor Avenue, Scunthorpe, South Humberside, DN15 8NJ Tel: (01724) 281868 Fax: (01724) 282808

Power Jacks Ltd, South Harbour Road, Fraserburgh, Aberdeenshire, AB43 9BZ Tel: (01346) 513131 Fax: (01346) 516827 E-mail: sales@powerjacks.co.uk

R.W Gear Ltd, Stargate Industrial Estate, Bailey House, Ryton, Tyne & Wear, NE40 3DG Tel: 0191-413 2244 Fax: 0191-413 1133 E-mail: rwryton@rwtransmissions.com

Rosendale Gearboxes, Railway Arch 879, Rosendale Road, London, SE24 9EH Tel: (020) 8671 5074

Rossi Gearmotors Ltd, Unit 8-9 Phoenix Park, Bayton Road Industrial Estate, Coventry, CV7 9QN Tel: (024) 7664 4646 Fax: (024) 7664 4535 E-mail: sales@rossigears.com

S E W Eurodrive Ltd, Beckbridge Road, Normanton Industrial Estate, Normanton, West Yorkshire, WF6 1QR Tel: (01924) 893855 Fax: (01924) 893702 E-mail: sales@sew-eurodrive.co.uk

S & R Transmissions Ltd, Old Stafford Road, Slade Heath, Wolverhampton, WV10 7PH Tel: (01902) 798877 Fax: (01902) 798088 E-mail: sales@transmissionunits.com

▶ Standel Dawman Ltd, Pasture Lane Works, Factory La, Barrowford, Nelson, Lancs, BB9 6ES Tel: (01282) 613175 Fax: (01282) 615429E-mail: sales@standeldawman.uk.com

Target Transmission, Kilby's Yard, 25-27 Bacon Lane, Edgware, Middlesex, HA8 5AR Tel: (020) 8381 2863 Fax: (020) 8381 2863

Technidrive Solutions, 89 Moy Road, Armagh, BT61 8DR Tel: (028) 3751 8111 Fax: (028) 3752 8181 E-mail: sales@technidrive.co.uk

Time Engineers Ltd, Unit 3, Manor Way, Rainham, Essex, RM13 8RH Tel: (01708) 555464 Fax: (01708) 555765

Transmission Components Ltd, 2 Jubilee Trading Centre, Jubilee Road, Letchworth Garden City, Hertfordshire, SG6 1NE Tel: (01462) 672222 Fax: (01462) 480001 E-mail: gwhite@transmissioncomponents.com

Turner Power Train Systems Ltd, Racecourse Road, Wolverhampton, WV6 0QT Tel: (01902) 833000 Fax: (01902) 833750 E-mail: page_kevin_g@cat.com

Unigears Ashford Ltd, Unit 8 Henwood Business Centre, Henwood Industrial Estate, Ashford, Kent, TN24 8DH Tel: (01233) 642798 Fax: (01233) 650725 E-mail: sales@unigears.co.uk

Webster Drives Ltd, Folds Road, Bolton, BL1 2SE Tel: (01204) 382121 Fax: (01204) 386100

Z F Great Britain Ltd, Abbeyfield Road, Nottingham, NG7 2SX Tel: 0115-986 9211 Fax: 0115-986 9261 E-mail: info@zf.com

GEARBOXES TO SPECIFICATION

Garmendale Engineering Ltd, Dale Works, Manners Industrial Estate, Ilkeston, Derbyshire, DE7 8EF Tel: 0115-932 7082 Fax: 0115-930 9391 E-mail: garmendale@enquiries.com

GEARBOXES, AUTOMOTIVE

Automatic Transmissions Ltd, 201 Fulwich Road, Dartford, DA1 1UW Tel: (01322) 222608 Fax: (01322) 222608

Automotive Technology Ltd, 3 Morton Street, Leamington Spa, Warwickshire, CV32 5SY Tel: (01926) 882201 Fax: (01926) 420934 E-mail: sidaway@atl-uk.com

BRT Bearings Ltd, 9 Common Bank Industrial Estate, Ackhurst Road, Chorley, Lancashire, PR7 1NH Tel: (01257) 264266 Fax: (01257) 274698

Car Transmissions, 122 Elmton Road, Creswell, Worksop, Nottinghamshire, S80 4DE Tel: (01909) 721437 Fax: (01909) 721437

Kluber Lubrication, Bradford Road, Halifax, West Yorkshire, HX3 7BN Tel: (01422) 319149 Fax: (01422) 206073 E-mail: info@uk.klueber.com

GEARBOXES, INDUSTRIAL

Allen Gears, Atlas Works, Station Road, Pershore, Worcestershire, WR10 2BZ Tel: (01386) 552211 Fax: (01386) 554491 E-mail: sales@allengears.com

DePe Gear Co. Ltd, Unit 1 Grove Road Industrial Estate, Grove Road, Fenton, Stoke-On-Trent, ST4 4LG Tel: (01782) 594114 Fax: (01782) 594115 E-mail: sales@depe.co.uk

J & J Industrial, Barnbrook Boiler Works, Brook Street, Bury, Lancashire, BL9 6AF Tel: 0161-763 6520 Fax: 0161-763 6519

S B T Engineering Services Ltd, Empress Street, Old Trafford, Manchester, M16 9EN Tel: 0161-877 7755 Fax: 0161-848 9225 E-mail: info@sbtengineering.co.uk

GEARBOXES, MARINE

▶ European Marine & Machinery Agencies, Nutsey House, Nutsey Lane, Totton, Southampton, SO40 3NB Tel: (023) 8058 0020 Fax: (023) 8058 0021 E-mail: sales@europeanmarine.co.uk

GEARBOXES, MOTOR CAR, AUTOMATIC

Automatic Gearboxes Leigh Ltd, Unit 3, Victoria Industrial Estate, Leigh, Lancashire, WN7 5SE Tel: (01942) 677800 Fax: (01942) 677800

K Motors LTD, K Motors Ltd, 9f Centurion Court, Farington, Leyland, PR25 3UQ Tel: (01772) 613329 Fax: (0870) 4601296 E-mail: enquiries@kmotors.co.uk

Magel Engineering Ltd, Headley Road East, Woodley, Reading, RG5 4SN Tel: 0118-969 2351 Fax: 0118-927 2307

Mechanical Workshop, 45 Station Road, Littlethorpe, Leicester, LE19 2HS Tel: 0116-286 3896 Fax: 0116-286 3962

GEARED MOTORS, *See also headings for particular types*

Anstee & Ware Gloucester Ltd, Bonds Mill, Bristol Road, Stonehouse, Gloucestershire, GL10 3RF Tel: (01453) 826433 Fax: (01453) 827653 E-mail: awglass@aol.com

Dynatork Air Motors Ltd, Merchant Drive, Hertford, SG13 7BL Tel: (01992) 501900 Fax: (01992) 509890 E-mail: dynatork@huco.com

Kaba Garog, 9 Eagle Park Drive, Warrington, WA2 8JA Tel: (01925) 401555 Fax: (01925) 401551 E-mail: sales@kgw.kaba.co.uk

M G C Systems Ltd, Power Transmission House, Redcliffe Road, Mansfield, Nottinghamshire, NG18 2QH Tel: (01623) 635150 Fax: (01623) 635125 E-mail: sales@mgcsystems.com

R M B Engineering Services Ltd, Union Street, West Bromwich, West Midlands, B70 6BP Tel: 0121-500 1940 Fax: 0121-500 1941 E-mail: sales@rmbderitend.co.uk

Leroy Somer Ltd, Heathrow Interchange, Bullsbrook Road, Hayes, Middlesex, UB4 0JR Tel: (020) 8756 7000 Fax: (020) 8756 7028 E-mail: leroy-somer@leroy.somer.co.uk

STM Power Transmission Ltd, Unit 10 Hartford Business Centre, Chester Road, Hartford, Northwich, Cheshire, CW8 2AB Tel: (01606) 557200 Fax: (01606) 301260 E-mail: info@stmuk.co.uk

Transdrive Engineering Services Ltd, Units 18-20, Moss Lane Indust Estate, Royton, Oldham, OL2 6HR Tel: (01706) 881940 Fax: (01706) 882436 E-mail: sales@transdrive.co.uk

GELATIN/GELATINE

Chemcolloids Ltd, Tunstall Road, Bosley, Macclesfield, Cheshire, SK11 0PE Tel: (01260) 223284 Fax: (01260) 223589 E-mail: dennis.quinn@chemcolloids.com

Landauer Ltd, 25 Beaufort Court, Admirals Way, London, E14 9XL Tel: (020) 7538 5383 Fax: (020) 7538 2007 E-mail: trading@landauerseafood.com

PB Gelatins UK, Severn Road, Treforest Industrial Estate, Pontypridd, Mid Glamorgan, CF37 5SQ Tel: (01443) 849300 Fax: (01443) 844209

GEMMOLOGISTS' INSTRUMENTS

The Gemmological Association & Laboratory Of Great Britain, 27 Greville Street, London, EC1N 8TN Tel: (020) 7404 3334 Fax: (020) 7404 8843 E-mail: sales@gem-a.info

GEMSTONES

Bezalel Gems Ltd, St Georges House, 44 Hatton Garden, London, EC1N 8ER Tel: (020) 7405 5923 Fax: (020) 7405 2201

Chas Mathews Lapidaries Ltd, 5 Hatton Garden, London, EC1N 8AA Tel: (020) 7405 7333 Fax: (020) 7405 3827

Cultured Pearl Co. Ltd, 27 Hatton Garden, London, EC1N 8BR Tel: (020) 7405 3339 Fax: (020) 7405 5936 E-mail: info@theculturedpearl.co.uk

G F Williams & Co., 46 Hatton Garden, London, EC1N 8EX Tel: (020) 7405 5477 Fax: (020) 7831 4063 E-mail: jason@gfwilliams.co.uk

George Lindley & Co Export Ltd, 3-5 Bleeding Heart Yard, London, EC1N 8NJ Tel: (020) 7242 5772 Fax: (020) 7242 7779

J Rosenfeld & Sons, 11 Hatton Garden, London, EC1N 8AH Tel: (020) 7831 3470 Fax: (020) 7430 1137

L A Overseas Co., 50 Northampton St, Hockley, Birmingham, B18 6DX Tel: 0121 2366671 Fax: 0121 2334513 E-mail: laoverseas1@yahoo.co.uk

Levy Gems Co., Minerva House, 26-27 Hatton Garden, London, EC1N 8BR Tel: (020) 7242 4547 Fax: (020) 7831 0102 E-mail: levey.gems@virgin.net

Shipton & Co. Ltd, 27-33 Spencer Street, Birmingham, B18 6DL Tel: 0121-236 2427 Fax: 0121-212 0591

Sterling Enterprises Precious Stone Merchants, 26-27 Hatton Garden, Minerva House, London, EC1N 8BR Tel: (020) 7405 5255 Fax: (020) 7405 5255

GEMSTONES – *continued*

William Stead, 67-68 Hatton Garden, London, EC1N 8JY Tel: (020) 7242 5330 Fax: (020) 7242 6160

GENERAL BRUSHES

Amos Swift Co. Ltd, Boathouse Lane, Stockton-on-Tees, Cleveland, TS18 3AW Tel: (01642) 675241 Fax: (01642) 675241 E-mail: john.hingley@ntlworld.com

Bee Gee Brushes Ltd, Unit 3c Saxon Business Park, Hanbury Road, Stoke Prior, Bromsgrove, Worcestershire, B60 4AD Tel: (01527) 837001 Fax: (01527) 837001 E-mail: mar_r_goddard@hotmail.com

Bell Brush Co., 286 Alma Road, Enfield, Middlesex, EN3 7BB Tel: (020) 8804 4144 Fax: (020) 8804 4235 E-mail: sales@bellbrush.com

Bromley Brush Co Kent Ltd, 1 Pembroke Road, Bromley, BR1 2TJ Tel: (020) 8464 1707 Fax: (020) 8313 3494

Brushes North West Ltd, 16 Offerton Industrial Estate, Hempshaw Lane, Offerton, Stockport, Cheshire, SK2 5TJ Tel: 0161-477 4805 Fax: 0161-477 4805

Buckleys Brushes, Lowland Works, Hurst Lane, Mirfield, West Yorkshire, WF14 8LY Tel: (01924) 498214 Fax: (01924) 480632 E-mail: bit.bung@telincon.co.uk

▶ Charles Bentley & Son, 1 Monarch Way, Loughborough, Leicestershire, LE11 5XG Tel: (01509) 232757 Fax: (01509) 233861 E-mail: sales@bentleybrushware.co.uk

Cooks Brushes Ltd, 52 The Street, Old Costessey, Norwich, NR8 5DD Tel: (01603) 748339 Fax: (01603) 748339 E-mail: sales@cooks-brushes.co.uk

Crown Artist Brush Ltd, Crown Street West, Lowestoft, Suffolk, NR32 1SG Tel: (01502) 573142 Fax: (01502) 562272

Danline International Ltd, Nebo Road, Llanrwst, Gwynedd, LL26 0SE Tel: (01492) 640651 Fax: (01492) 641601 E-mail: sales@danline.co.uk

Dawson & Son Ltd, Clayton Wood Rise, West Park Ring Road, Leeds, LS16 6RH Tel: 0113-275 9321 Fax: 0113-275 2761 E-mail: sales@dawsonbrush.co.uk

Farrar Bros, 49 Haugh Shaw Road, Halifax, West Yorkshire, HX1 3AR Tel: (01422) 352198 Fax: (01422) 349539 E-mail: farrarbros@aol.com

Formseal South Ltd, 23 Snowdrop Close, Narborough, Leicester, LE19 3YB Tel: 0116-275 0052 Fax: 0116-286 5808 E-mail: sales@brushstrip.co.uk

P. Gerratt Ltd, Baring Road, Northampton, NN5 7BA Tel: (01604) 758545 Fax: (01604) 588755 E-mail: sales@gerratt.com

L G Harris & Co. Ltd, Hanbury Road, Stoke Prior, Bromsgrove, Worcestershire, B60 4AE Tel: (01527) 575441 Fax: (01527) 575366 E-mail: enquiries@lgharris.co.uk

Samuel Latham Ltd, 475 Evesham Rd, Crabbs Cross, Redditch, Worcs, B97 5JQ Tel: (01527) 543238 Fax: (01527) 550824

Chris Naylor (SOMA) Ltd, The Bungalow, 6 West Shevin Road, Merston, Ilkley, West Yorkshire, LS29 6BG Tel: (01943) 876513 Fax: (01943) 878814 E-mail: chrisnaylor@chrisnaylorsoma.demon.co.uk

John Palmer Brushes Ltd, Unit 5, Oakley Industrial Estate, Norwich Road, Besthorpe, Attleborough, Norfolk, NR17 2LB Tel: (01953) 455003 Fax: (01953) 455905 E-mail: johnpalmerbrushes@line1.net

R Russell, 45 Townsend Road, Chesham, Buckinghamshire, HP5 2AA Tel: (01494) 782837 Fax: (01494) 791598 E-mail: info@r-russellbrush.co.uk

S & M Products Ltd, Compstall Mills Estate, Andrew Street, Compstall, Stockport, Cheshire, SK6 5HN Tel: 0161-427 3864 Fax: 0161-426 0019 E-mail: info@brushclosures.com

▶ Sovereign Brush Co Ltd, 29-43 Sydney Road, Watford, WD18 7PZ Tel: (01923) 227301 Fax: (01923) 817121 E-mail: sales@sovereignbrush.com

Stoddard Manufacturing Co. Ltd, Denturax Works, Icknield Way, Letchworth Garden City, Hertfordshire, SG6 4AH Tel: (01462) 686221 Fax: (01462) 480711 E-mail: admin@stoddard.co.uk

Weston, Shipley & Weston Ltd, Premier Works, Samson Road, Hermitage Industrial Estate, Coalville, Leicestershire, LE67 3FP Tel: (01530) 814062 Fax: (01530) 814064 E-mail: eberryson@aol.com

GENERAL CANNED GOODS

B K Whalley Ltd, 41 Chiswick Staithe, Hartington Road, London, W4 3TP Tel: (020) 8742 7371 Fax: (020) 8742 8371

Del Monte Europe Ltd, Del Monte House, London Road, Staines, Middlesex, TW18 4JD Tel: (01784) 447400 Fax: (01784) 465301

Donatantonio plc, Lupa House, York Way, Borehamwood, Hertfordshire, WD6 1PX Tel: (020) 8236 2222 Fax: (020) 8236 2288 E-mail: lupa@donatantonio.com

Heinz Foodservice, South Building, Hayes Park, Hayes, Middlesex, UB4 8AL Tel: (0800) 575755 E-mail: foodservice.enquiry@uk.hjheinz.com

Martin Mathew & Co. Ltd, Riverdene House, 140 High Street, Cheshunt, Waltham Cross, Hertfordshire, EN8 0AW Tel: (01992) 641641 Fax: (01992) 641888 E-mail: sales@martinmathew.co.uk

Princes Foods International Trading Group, Royal Liver Building, Pier Head, Liverpool, L3 1NX Tel: 0151-236 9282 Fax: 0151-236 1057

S & B Herba Foods Ltd, Berwick House, 8 - 10 Knoll Rise, Orpington, Kent, BR6 0EL Tel: (0870) 7243722 Fax: (0870) 7243622 E-mail: retail@sbhf.com

Silver Spring Mineral Water Co. Ltd, Park Farm Road, Park Farm Industrial Estate, Folkestone, Kent, CT19 5EA Tel: (01303) 856500 Fax: (01303) 256524 E-mail: eddie@silverspring.co.uk

Thomas & Jones Ltd, 101c Palm Grove, Prenton, Merseyside, CH43 1TQ Tel: 0151-653 6070 Fax: 0151-653 5040

Tulip Ltd, Beveridge Way, Hardwick Narrows Estate, King's Lynn, Norfolk, PE30 4NB Tel: (01553) 771937 Fax: (01553) 777139

John West Foods Ltd, Lancaster House Mercury Court, Tithebarn Street, Liverpool, L2 2GA Tel: 0151-243 6200 Fax: 0151-236 5465

Westler Foods Ltd, Amotherby, Malton, North Yorkshire, YO17 6TQ Tel: (0800) 0276336 Fax: (01653) 600187 E-mail: custserv@westler.com

GENERAL ENGINEERING

A Bush Engineering Services Ltd, 16-18 Manor Road, Leeds, LS11 9AH Tel: 0113-246 0581 Fax: 0113-246 0043E-mail: info@abush.co.uk

A C Moxom Ltd, Chalk Pit Lane, Litton Cheney, Dorchester, Dorset, DT2 9AN Tel: (01308) 482242 Fax: (01308) 482584 E-mail: alan@acmoxom.com

A C V Engineers, Units A-B, Camp Street, Bury, Lancashire, BL8 1FE Tel: 0161-764 0644 Fax: 0161-761 7202

A Form Tooling Ltd, 542 Aylestone Road, Leicester, LE2 8JB Tel: 0116-283 5936 Fax: 0116-244 0277 E-mail: aform.tooling@ntlworld.com

A G Block Ltd, 87 Church Road, Kessingland, Lowestoft, Suffolk, NR33 7SJ Tel: (01502) 741894 Fax: (01502) 742003

A Howe Light Engineering, 1 Priory Works, Priory Cresent, Southend-on-Sea, SS2 6LD Tel: (01702) 611451 Fax: (01702) 469078 E-mail: david.knight@steelfabricators1.co.uk

A J Adams Engineering, Hassall Road, Skegness, Lincolnshire, PE25 3TB Tel: (01754) 765421 Fax: (01754) 765435 E-mail: dave@adamsengineering.ffsnet.co.uk

A N Pecision Ltd, Salisbury Road, Hoddesdon, Hertfordshire, EN11 0HU Tel: (01992) 463666 Fax: (01992) 441730 E-mail: derek.heard@lineone.net

A S Allman Ltd, Newmarket Drive, Ascot Drive Indust Estate, Derby, DE24 8HT Tel: (01332) 753167 Fax: (01332) 296250

A S Mechanical Engineering Ltd, Unit 16, Depot Road, Middlesbrough, Cleveland, TS2 1LE Tel: (01642) 250180 Fax: (01642) 250180

A T Juniper Liverpool Ltd, Marshalls Works, 5-17 Bleasdale Road, Liverpool, L18 5JB Tel: 0151-733 1553 Fax: 0151-734 3166 E-mail: sales@juniper-liverpool.com

A V Birch Ltd, Aldenham Mill, Muckley Cross, Acton Round, Bridgnorth, Shropshire, WV16 4RR Tel: (01746) 714418 Fax: (01746) 714419 E-mail: enquiries@avbirch.co.uk

Abercorn Engineering Ltd, 49 New Sneddon Street, Paisley, Renfrewshire, PA3 2AZ Tel: 0141-840 1606 Fax: 0141-840 1607

William Abernethy Ltd, 10-14 Erskine Square, Glasgow, G52 4PE Tel: 0141-882 2289 Fax: 0141-883 7582 E-mail: enquiries@abernethy-eng.co.uk

Abtec Engineering Ltd, Rowhurst Close, Rowhurst Indust Estate, Newcstle Stfs, Newcastle, Staffordshire, ST5 6BD Tel: (01782) 565658 Fax: (01782) 565688

▶ Acumen Ltd, Unit 2, Harrison & Macklin Road, Foley Trading Estate, Hereford, HR1 2SF Tel: (01432) 344466 Fax: (01432) 379168 E-mail: high-care@btconnect.com

Adnor Ltd, Mill Place, Kingston upon Thames, Surrey, KT1 2RL Tel: (020) 8549 4728 Fax: (020) 8549 8989 E-mail: sales@adnor.co.uk

Agp, Mussons Path, Luton, LU2 7RQ Tel: (01582) 735446 Fax: (01582) 400875 E-mail: alanwithy@hotmail.com

Airedale Stainless Fabrications Ltd, Unit 2a, Crosshills Enterprise Centre, Keighley, West Yorkshire, BD20 7BX Tel: (01535) 636831 Fax: (01535) 636831

Aireworth Ltd, Parson Street, Keighley, West Yorkshire, BD21 3HD Tel: (01535) 662545 Fax: (01535) 611149 E-mail: aireworth@appelbe.com

Airport Engineering Co., 1 Harold Court Road, Romford, RM3 0YU Tel: (01708) 342358 Fax: (01708) 304598 E-mail: sales@propshafts.sagehost.co.uk

▶ Aitchee Engineering, Orchard Cottage Farm, Red Lane, Oxted, Surrey, RH8 0RT Tel: (01883) 723334 Fax: (01883) 723334 E-mail: aitchee@hotmail.co.uk

Akd Engineering, Horn Hill, Lowestoft, Suffolk, NR33 0PX Tel: (01502) 527800 Fax: (01502) 527848 E-mail: info@akd-engineering.co.uk

Alan Yorke Ltd, 4 Midland Business Centre, Bury Close, Higham Ferrers, Rushden, Northamptonshire, NN10 8BE Tel: (01933) 358219 Fax: (01933) 410546 E-mail: sales@alanyorke.co.uk

Alco Engineering (Sheet Metal) Co.Ltd, High Bullen, St. Giles, Torrington, Devon, EX38 7JA Tel: (01805) 622461 Fax: (01805) 624011 E-mail: sales@alcoeng.co.uk

Alexander Higgins & Sons 1987 Ltd, The Hayes, Stourbridge, West Midlands, DY9 8NH Tel: (01384) 422304

Alfa Precision & General Engineering Co. Ltd, Solway Trading Estate, Maryport, Cumbria, CA15 8NF Tel: (01900) 815678 Fax: (01900) 814191 E-mail: alfaprecision@btclick.com

Gordon Alison Ltd, 16 Jordan Street, Liverpool, L1 0BP Tel: 0151-709 4687 Fax: 0151-709 4723 E-mail: edwards@gordon-alison.fsnet.co.uk

Aljon Engineering, Lancaster House, 234-236 Fields New Road, Chadderton, Oldham, OL9 8NZ Tel: 0161-628 7800 Fax: 0161-628 7072 E-mail: atjoneng@zen.co.uk

Allen Engineering Rotherham Ltd, North Street, Rotherham, South Yorkshire, S60 1LG Tel: (01709) 836800 Fax: (01709) 830300 E-mail: sales@alleneng.co.uk

Allen Production Services, Unit 6b Tractor Spares Industrial Estate, Strawberry Lane, Willenhall, West Midlands, WV13 3RN Tel: (01902) 366035 Fax: (01902) 601221

Allendale Components, 28 Allendale Tee, New Marske, Redcar, Cleveland, TS11 8HN Tel: (01642) 478738 Fax: (01642) 272683 E-mail: p.wall@ntlworld.com

▶ Allmec Engineering Ltd, 8 Guardian Street Industrial Estate, Guardian Street, Warrington, WA5 1SJ Tel: (01925) 575820 Fax: (01925) 637796 E-mail: allmec@aol.com

Almal Engineering Ltd, Derrington Lane, Derrington, Stafford, ST18 9NH Tel: (01785) 255108 Fax: (01785) 248108 E-mail: almalengineering@supanet.com

Almik Engineering, Unit 22 Pershore Trading Estate, Pershore, Worcestershire, WR10 2DD Tel: (01386) 553550 Fax: (01386) 556048 E-mail: steve.almik@btconnect.com

Alpenbury Ltd, 11 Gateway Industrial Estate, Parkgate, Rotherham, South Yorkshire, S62 6JL Tel: (01709) 528186 Fax: (01709) 528287 E-mail: enquiries@alpenbury.co.uk

Alpha Precision Engineering (Poole) Ltd, Units 7-8 Alpha Centre, Upton Road, Poole, Dorset, BH17 7AG Tel: (01202) 683819 Fax: (01202) 665030 E-mail: sales@alphaprecision.net

Ambrose Wood & Son, Ovenhouse Farm Depot, Henshall Road, Bollington, Macclesfield, Cheshire, SK10 5DN Tel: (01625) 573291

Andawest Engineering Ltd, Unit 2a Boardman Industrial Estate, Boardman Road, Swadlincote, Derbyshire, DE11 9DL Tel: (01283) 214182 Fax: (01283) 550909 E-mail: andawest@aol.com

Apb Precision Engineers, Lakeside Business Park, Swan Lane, Sandhurst, Berkshire, GU47 9DN Tel: (01252) 890061 Fax: (01252) 890062

J.F. Appelbe & Co. Ltd, Littlefair Road, Hedon Road, Hull, HU9 5LN Tel: (01482) 781191 Fax: (01482) 781235 E-mail: enquiries@applebes.com

Arch Engineering Ltd, East Side North Dock, Alexandra Docks, Newport, Gwent, NP20 2NP Tel: (01633) 264154 Fax: (01633) 264154

Archibald Young Brassfounders Ltd, Motherwell Business Centre, Albert Street, Motherwell, Lanarkshire, ML1 1PR Tel: (01698) 263165 Fax: (01698) 263211 E-mail: enquiries@archibaldyoung.co.uk

Argee Instrument Co. Ltd, 14 Albert Road, Romford, RM1 2PL Tel: (01708) 747878 Fax: (01708) 733216

Arromax Structures Ltd, Langwith Road, Langwith Junction, Mansfield, Nottinghamshire, NG20 9RN Tel: (01623) 747466 Fax: (01623) 748197 E-mail: sales@aromax.co.uk

Arrow Engineers, 6 Izons Lane Industrial Estate, West Bromwich, West Midlands, B70 9BY Tel: 0121-553 6559 Fax: 0121-553 5872

Arte Engineering Co., Unit 8 Great Bridge Industrial Estate, Tipton, West Midlands, DY4 0HR Tel: 0121-520 8953 Fax: 0121-520 8953

Arthur Stephenson Engineers Ltd, Gibfield Works, Bag Lane, Atherton, Manchester, M46 0RD Tel: (01942) 883046 Fax: (01942) 896025 E-mail: ormerod@enterprise.net

Artisan Precision Engineering Co., Snatchwood Road, Abersychan, Pontypool, Gwent, NP4 7BT Tel: (01495) 772644 Fax: (01495) 773844 E-mail: artisan04@supernet.com

Artoray Engineering Ltd, 58 Thorney La North, Iver, Buckinghamshire, SL0 9LR Tel: (01753) 655987 Fax: (01753) 651540

Ashby Precision Engineering Drayton Ltd, Marcham Road, Drayton, Abingdon, Oxfordshire, OX14 4JH Tel: (01235) 531279 Fax: (01235) 535801 E-mail: sales@ashbyeng.com

Atc Engineering Services Ltd, C1 Oak Park Estate, Northarbour Road, Portsmouth, PO6 3TJ Tel: (023) 9232 6635 Fax: (023) 9221 0907 E-mail: info@atcengineering.co.uk

Atwell Engineering Holdings Ltd, Unit 1, Dinnington Business Park, Outgang Lane, Sheffield, S25 3QU Tel: (01909) 551133 Fax: (01909) 551123 E-mail: admin@ens-precision.com

Auto Components Ltd, 11 Coulman Road, Industrial Estate, Thorne, Doncaster, South Yorkshire, DN8 5JS Tel: (01405) 812424 Fax: (01405) 740072 E-mail: info@auto-components.co.uk

Automatic Forming, 7 Kinwarton Farm Road, Kinwarton, Alcester, Warwickshire, B49 6EH Tel: (01789) 400567 Fax: (01789) 765213

Aveco Teesside Ltd, The Slipways, Dockside Road, Middlesbrough, Cleveland, TS3 8AT Tel: (01642) 224994 Fax: (01642) 248138 E-mail: aveco.teeside@ntl.com

Awon Engineering, 26 Dunlop Road, Redditch, Worcestershire, B97 5XP Tel: (01527) 404699 Fax: (01527) 524868

Ayneson Engineering Co. Ltd, Commercial Road, Wolverhampton, WV1 3RD Tel: (01902) 452862 Fax: (01902) 455383

Aztec Precision Engineering, Pixmore Avenue, Letchworth Garden City, Hertfordshire, SG6 1JG Tel: (01462) 677888 Fax: (01462) 677888

B H T Engineering Ltd, Unit 8, Hayes Lane Factory Estate, Lye, Stourbridge, West Midlands, DY9 8RH Tel: (01384) 422294 Fax: (01384) 422562 E-mail: bhteng@compuserve.com

B I Engineering Ltd, Crane Close, Denington Industrial Estate, Wellingborough, Northamptonshire, NN8 2QG Tel: (01933) 228012 Fax: (01933) 441935 E-mail: biengineering@btconnect.com

B & I Fabrications, Farrington Place, Rossendale Road Industrial Estate, Burnley, Lancashire, BB11 5TY Tel: (01282) 411434 Fax: (01282) 838963

B & J Engineering Co., 7 Brampton Sidings Industrial Estate, Hempstalls Lane, Newcastle, Staffordshire, ST5 0SR Tel: (01782) 632132 Fax: (01782) 628591 E-mail: bjengltd@aol.com

B R E Ltd, Fowler Road, West Pitkerro Industrial Estate, Broughty Ferry, Dundee, DD5 3RU Tel: (01382) 739848 Fax: (01382) 739849 E-mail: info@breuk.com

B S B Engineering Co. Ltd, Phoenix Street, Bolton, BL1 2SY Tel: (01204) 535343 Fax: (01204) 389287 E-mail: enquiries@bsbengineering.com

B V Senior Engineering Co. Ltd, Hall Road, Maltby, Rotherham, South Yorkshire, S66 8ET Tel: (01709) 818511 Fax: (01709) 812557

B&T, Ironmould Lane, Bristol, BS4 5SA Tel: 0117-971 5295 Fax: 0117-971 5295

Baldwin & Wiser Ltd, Urban Road, Kirkby-in-Ashfield, Nottingham, NG17 8AP Tel: (01623) 754982 Fax: (01623) 754983

Balls Grinding Ltd, Unit K, Chosenview Road, Cheltenham, Gloucestershire, GL51 9LT Tel: (01242) 576621 Fax: (01242) 584298 E-mail: ballsgrinding@btconnect.com

R. Bance & Co. Ltd, Coc Crow Hill House, St. Marys Road, Surbiton, Surrey, KT6 5HE Tel: (020) 8398 7141 Fax: (020) 8398 4765 E-mail: admin@bance.com

Barnby Engineering, 2 Lakeside Park, Neptune Close, Medway City Estate, Rochester, Kent, ME2 4LT Tel: (01634) 711801 Fax: (01634) 711766

Barnes & Thomas Ltd, Cheetham Mill, Park Street, Stalybridge, Cheshire, SK15 2BT Tel: 0161-338 3630 Fax: 0161-304 8055 E-mail: brian_richard@barnesandthomas.com

Bartek Engineering Ltd, 24 Industrial Estate, Cornwall Road, Smethwick, West Midlands, B66 2JS Tel: 0121-555 8885 Fax: 0121-555 8885

Bawa Engineering Ltd, Units 4 & 5 Fenlake Industrial Estate, Fenlake Road, Bedford, MK42 0ET Tel: (01234) 215906 Fax: (01234) 327858

Beattie Flanigan & Partners, 174 Castlereagh Road, Belfast, BT5 5GX Tel: (028) 9073 2121 Fax: (028) 9073 2630 E-mail: info@beattieflanigan.com

T.G. Beddoe & Sons Ltd, Pontygwindy Industrial Estate, Caerphilly, Mid Glamorgan, CF83 2WF Tel: (029) 2088 3040 Fax: (029) 2088 3040

Beecroft Engineering Co., South Parade, Pudsey, West Yorkshire, LS28 8NZ Tel: 0113-256 5131 Fax: 0113-239 3126

Berkeley Car Company Scotland Ltd, Berryfauld, Forfar Road, Arbroath, Angus, DD11 3RA Tel: (01241) 875013 Fax: (01241) 875013 E-mail: berkeleycarco@btconnect.com

George Bethell Ltd, Unit 9 Rugby Park, Bletchley Road, Heaton Mersey, Stockport, Cheshire, SK4 3EJ Tel: 0161-442 8805 Fax: 0161-442 8818 E-mail: sales@bethell.com

Billcar Engineering Ltd, Unit 1a March Way, Battlefield Enterprise Park, Shrewsbury, SY1 3JE Tel: (01743) 469398 Fax: (01743) 450084 E-mail: billcarengine@hotmail.com

Billingham Machine Co. Ltd, Alvis Close, Billingham, Cleveland, TS23 4JB Tel: (01642) 560981 Fax: (01642) 565523 E-mail: bmc@billinghammachinecompany.fsnet.co.uk

Bingham Engineering Ltd, Wentdale, Doncaster Road, East Hardwick, Pontefract, West Yorkshire, WF8 3EQ Tel: (01977) 620517 Fax: (01977) 620863 E-mail: sales@universalbingham.co.uk

Black Gold Oil Tools Ltd, Souter Head Road, Altens Industrial Estate, Aberdeen, AB12 3LF Tel: (01224) 894019 Fax: (01224) 879731 E-mail: info@blackgoldoiltools.co.uk

BMP, 6 The Half Croft, Syston, Leicester, LE7 1LD Tel: 0116-260 2916 Fax: 0116-260 7296 E-mail: bnpengineers@btconnect.com

Boar Engineering Ltd, 39a Barking Industrial Park, Alfreds Way, Barking, Essex, IG11 0TJ Tel: (020) 8594 0526 Fax: (020) 8507 8050 E-mail: boareng@aol.com

Bobak Precision Engineers, 11 Berkeley Place, London, SW19 4NN Tel: (020) 8947 6323 Fax: (020) 8947 6323 E-mail: bobak_eng@lineone.net

Bonlea Engineering, 4 Ajax Works, Hertford Road, Barking, Essex, IG11 8DY Tel: (020) 8591 2183 Fax: (020) 8594 3605

GENERAL ENGINEERING – *continued*

Bootham Engineers Mechanical Services, Amy Johnson Way, Clifton Moor, York, YO30 4WT Tel: (01904) 477670 Fax: (01904) 691826 E-mail: engineering.location@dowdingandmills.com

Bowater Cordell Ltd, Dukesway, Teesside Industrial Estate, Thornaby, Stockton-On-Tees, Cleveland, TS17 9LT Tel: (01642) 750303 Fax: (01642) 750164 E-mail: bowater@cordellgroup.com

Bowers & Jones Ltd, Patrick Gregory Road, Wolverhampton, WV11 3DU Tel: (01902) 732110 Fax: (01902) 864654 E-mail: jim.willmott@bowers.jones.freeserve.co.uk

Branston Engineering Ltd, Grange Farm Cottages, Grange Lane, Nocton Hth, Lincoln, LN4 2AQ Tel: (01522) 791101 Fax: (01522) 793242 E-mail: branston@globalnet.co.uk

Brent Engineering Co. Ltd, The Barn, 13 Wycombe Gdns, Golders Green, London, NW11 8AN Tel: (020) 8455 4701

Bressingham Engineers Ltd, High Road, Bressingham, Diss, Norfolk, IP22 2AT Tel: (01379) 688163 Fax: (01379) 687437 E-mail: bresseng@enterprise.net

Brineton Engineering Co., Alma Street, Walsall, WS2 8JQ Tel: (01922) 620070 Fax: (01922) 722875 E-mail: sales@brineton-eng.co.uk

British Metallic Packings Co 1933 Ltd, 15 Invicta Road, Dartford, DA2 6AY Tel: (01322) 224514

Britten Engineering Ltd, 12 Morris Road, Leicester, LE2 6BR Tel: 0116-270 0448 Fax: 0116-270 4998

Britton Engineering, Carlyon Road, Atherstone, Warwickshire, CV9 1LQ Tel: (01827) 712578 Fax: (01827) 713561 E-mail: malcolm.crane@btconnect.com

Broad Oak Gears Ltd, Old Warburton Bakery, Jacob Street, Accrington, Lancashire, BB5 1HU Tel: (01254) 397489 Fax: (01254) 390550 E-mail: bogears@aol.com

Brookfield Engineering Co., James Street, Littleborough, Lancashire, OL15 8LT Tel: (01706) 378042 Fax: (01706) 378042

Brooks Engineering Services, Unit 3 Park La Industrial Estate, Stourport Road, Kidderminster, Worcestershire, DY11 6TJ Tel: (01562) 740661 Fax: (01562) 740661

Brooks Precision Engineering Ltd, 6 Chamberlain Road, Aylesbury, Buckinghamshire, HP19 8DY Tel: (01296) 393862 Fax: (01296) 421014

Robert Brown Engineering Ltd, Douglas Close, Preston Farm Industrial Estate, Stockton-on-Tees, Cleveland, TS18 3SB Tel: (01642) 675201 Fax: (01642) 615902

Building Design Patnership, 7 Hill Street, Bristol, BS1 5RW Tel: 0117-929 9861 Fax: 0117-922 5280 E-mail: bristol@bdp.co.uk

Burgess Marine Services, Channel View Road, Dover, Kent, CT17 9TJ Tel: (01304) 207707 Fax: (01304) 207727 E-mail: info@burgessengineering.co.uk

C F Booth Engineering Ltd, Northfield Road, Rotherham, South Yorkshire, S60 1RR Tel: (01709) 829523 Fax: (01709) 829710 E-mail: p.a.hardey@btconnect.com

C H Jones & Son, 1 The Square, North Tawton, Devon, EX20 2EW Tel: (01837) 82237 Fax: (01837) 82526 E-mail: chjengineers@aol.com

C O B Engineering, Midland Road, Luton, LU2 0BL Tel: (01582) 736721 Fax: (01582) 402497 E-mail: info@cobengineering.co.uk

C O'Connor Engineers Ltd, Halberton Street, Smethwick, West Midlands, B66 2QP Tel: 0121-555 5992 Fax: 0121-555 6007

C P H Thurmaston Ltd, 2 Upperton Road, Leicester, LE3 0BG Tel: 0116-254 1322 E-mail: martyngoode@cphthurmaston.co.uk

C S Milne Engineering, Unit 2 Peckleton Lane Business Park, Peckleton Common, Elmesthorpe, Leicester, LE9 7SH Tel: (01455) 822569 Fax: (01455) 824012 E-mail: sales@cs-milne.co.uk

C & W Production Engineering Ltd, Unit 9 Vaughan St Industrial Estate, Manchester, M12 5BT Tel: 0161-223 9993 Fax: 0161-231 3113 E-mail: info@candwengineering.com

Calder Engineering Ltd, Unit 15 Ormlie Industrial Estate, Thurso, Caithness, KW14 7QU Tel: (01847) 892122 Fax: (01847) 892345 E-mail: admin@calderengineering.co.uk

Caldwell Consulting Engineers, 8 Lorne Street, Belfast, BT9 7DU Tel: (028) 9066 9456 Fax: (028) 9066 2219 E-mail: admin@caldwellconsulting.net

Cambrian Foundry Ltd, Unit 34 Vastre Indust Estate, Kerry Road, Newtown, Powys, SY16 1DZ Tel: (01686) 626209 Fax: (01686) 629500 E-mail: camfound@hotmail.com

James Camden Engineering Ltd, Scar Bank, Warwick, CV34 5DB Tel: (01926) 491347 Fax: (01926) 411362 E-mail: jamescamden@btinternet.com

Camtool Engineering, 6b Purdy Road, Bilston, West Midlands, WV14 8UB Tel: (01902) 403562 Fax: (01902) 403562 E-mail: camtool.eng@btconnect.com

Candair Engineering Co. Ltd, Newton Moor Industrial Estate, Mill Street, Hyde, Cheshire, SK14 4LF Tel: 0161-368 7111

Canlin Castings Ltd, Star Foundry, North Street, Langley Mill, Nottingham, NG16 4BS Tel: (01773) 715412 Fax: (01773) 530434 E-mail: sales@canlincastings.co.uk

Caparo Industries P.L.C., Caparo House, Popes Lane, Oldbury, West Midlands, B69 4PJ Tel: 0121-202 4400 Fax: 0121-202 4401

G. Carter & Son (Thornton) Ltd, Brookside, Thornton-Cleveleys, Lancashire, FY5 4EZ Tel: (01253) 821068 Fax: (01253) 862072 E-mail: steve@gcarter.co.uk

Castle Engineering Lancaster Ltd, River Street, St Georges Quay, Lancaster, LA1 1TA Tel: (01524) 67604 Fax: (01524) 67604

Centralised Services, Piccadilly, Nottingham, NG6 9FN Tel: 0115-913 5000 Fax: 0115-977 0744 E-mail: centser@btconnect.com

Chad Engineering (UK) Ltd, Unit 2, Business Village, Wexham Road, Slough, SL2 5HF Tel: (01753) 537980 Fax: (01753) 553472 E-mail: enquiries@chad-engineering.co.uk

Charter P.L.C., 52 Grovenor Gardens, London, SW1W 0AU Tel: (020) 7881 7800 Fax: (020) 7259 9338 E-mail: investor-relations@charterplc.com

Cheltape Engineering Company Ltd, Stoneville Street, Cheltenham, Gloucestershire, GL51 8PH Tel: (01242) 245121 Fax: (01242) 224345 E-mail: sales@cheltape.co.uk

Chenalord Ltd, Unit 3 Turnoaks Lane, Chesterfield, Derbyshire, S40 2HA Tel: (01246) 211296 Fax: (01246) 277227 E-mail: chenalord@btconnect.com

Chesser Engineering Ltd, 6-8 West Gorgie Parks, Edinburgh, EH14 1UT Tel: 0131-443 4943 Fax: 0131-443 4943 E-mail: enquiries@chesserengineering.ltd.uk

Claas UK Ltd, Saxham, Bury St. Edmunds, Suffolk, IP28 6QZ Tel: (01284) 763100 Fax: (01284) 769839 E-mail: info-uk@claas.com

M. Clarke Engineering, 566 Attercliffe Road, Sheffield, S9 3QP Tel: 0114-244 7234 Fax: 0114-244 7234

Clayton (Twickenham) Precision Engineering Co. Ltd, Clock Tower Road, Isleworth, Middlesex, TW7 6DT Tel: (020) 8568 9527 Fax: (020) 8569 9526 E-mail: claytonprecision@aol.com

Clwyd Tool & Die, 35 Greenfield Business Park, Bagillt Road, Greenfield, Holywell, Clwyd, CH8 7HJ Tel: (01352) 715515 Fax: (01352) 715515

CNC Precision, Unit 15 Enfield Industrial Estate, Redditch, Worcestershire, B97 6BG Tel: (01527) 596727 Fax: (01527) 585049 E-mail: sales@c-n-c.co.uk

Coles, Steam Mill Lane, Great Yarmouth, Norfolk, NR31 0HP Tel: (01493) 602100 Fax: (01493) 602100

Colson Engineering, 8 Headlands Trading Estate, Swindon, SN2 7JQ Tel: (01793) 526660 Fax: (01793) 513294 E-mail: sales@colsonengineering.com

The Colston Manufacturing Engineering Company Ltd, Brunel Park, Vincients Road, Bumpers Farm, Chippenham, Wiltshire, SN14 6NQ Tel: (01249) 652652 Fax: (01249) 444684 E-mail: sales@colstonltd.co.uk

Combi Vent Engineering Ltd, Northumberland House, Emerald Street, Denton, Manchester, M34 3GQ Tel: 0161-336 5065 Fax: 0161-320 4218 E-mail: enquiries@combigroup.co.uk

Compton Engineering Ltd, Cheapside, Bridgend Industrial Estate, Bridgend, Mid Glamorgan, CF31 3UN Tel: (01656) 654341 Fax: (01656) 669936 E-mail: comptoneng@aol.com

Contract Engineering Ltd, Meadow Mill, Water Street, Stockport, Cheshire, SK1 2BY Tel: 0161-480 5673 Fax: 0161-477 2687

Conveyor Engineering Co., Walsall Street, Wolverhampton, WV1 3LN Tel: (01902) 871254 Fax: (01902) 871254 E-mail: ce.goodall@btopenworld.com

Ron Cook Engineers, 48-50 Oxford Street, Hull, HU2 0QP Tel: (01482) 327187 Fax: (01482) 213658

Coote & Hall Engineers Ltd, Spen Vale Street, Heckmondwike, West Yorkshire, WF16 0NQ Tel: (01924) 402854 Fax: (01924) 402854 E-mail: sales@coote-hall.co.uk

Cope Engineering (Radcliffe) Ltd, Sion St Works, Sion Street, Radcliffe, Manchester, M26 3SF Tel: 0161-723 6500 Fax: 0161-723 6501 E-mail: sales@cope-engineering.co.uk

Peter Copsey Engineering Ltd, 2 Wheaton Road, Witham, Essex, CM8 3UJ Tel: (01376) 518378 Fax: (01376) 515294 E-mail: sales@pcopseyuk.freeserve.co.uk

Cover Press Ltd, Unit 119 J C Albyn Complex, Burton Road, Sheffield, S3 8BZ Tel: 0114-276 5867 Fax: 0114-276 5867

Craft Engineering, Unit 21 Huffwood Trading Estate, Billingshurst, West Sussex, RH14 9UR Tel: (01403) 784603 Fax: (01403) 784603

Robert Craig & Sons Ltd, Unit 10, Knock Moore Hill, Industrial Estate, Fergusion Drive, Lisburn, County Antrim, BT28 2OX Tel: (028) 9266 8500 Fax: (028) 9266 8550 E-mail: sales@craigs-products.co.uk

Crescent Engineering & Technical Services Ltd, Unit 5, Lee Smith Street, Hull, HU9 1SD Tel: (01482) 329625 Fax: (01482) 581130

Croft Engineering, Green Croft, Oughterby, Carlisle, CA5 6JH Tel: (01228) 576336 Fax: (01228) 576155

Cromwell Industrial Supplies Ltd, Unit 11 Manton Centre, Manton Lane, Manton Industrial Estate, Bedford, MK41 7PX Tel: (01234) 716470 Fax: (01234) 211214 E-mail: bedford@cromwell-tools.co.uk

Cross Machine Components Ltd, 5 Mandervell Road, Oadby, Leicester, LE2 5LQ Tel: 0116-271 3315 Fax: 0116-272 0068 E-mail: kingsley.cross@tiscali.co.uk

Crosshall Engineering Ltd, 1 Wellington Street, Liverpool, L3 6JH Tel: 0151-207 4292 Fax: 0151-298 1447 E-mail: sales@crosshall.com

Crowther Engineering Ltd, 52 Hutton Close, Crowther, Washington, Tyne & Wear, NE38 0AH Tel: 0191-417 9916 Fax: 0191-415 5136 E-mail: nick@crowthereng.co.uk

CTR Engineering Ltd, Whitley Street, Bingley, West Yorkshire, BD16 4JH Tel: (01274) 562550 Fax: (01274) 551218 E-mail: ctrengltd@hotmail.com

Custance & Thomson Blackheath Ltd, Meadowcourt Road, London, SE3 9DX Tel: (020) 8852 1545 Fax: (020) 8852 4352

Cutler & Maclean Ltd, Daimler Drive, Cowpen Industrial Estate, Billingham, Cleveland, TS23 4JD Tel: (01642) 564585 Fax: (01642) 371142

CV Precision Engineering, Unit 2 Rea Court, 40 Trent Street, Birmingham, B5 5NL Tel: 0121-643 7144 Fax: 0121-633 3680 E-mail: tomcross@cvprecision.co.uk

CVH Fabrications, Unit 2a Crown Works, Little Poutney Street, Wolverhampton, WV2 4JH Tel: (01902) 426020 Fax: (01902) 425726

D D Fabrications, Blackdyke Road, Kingstown Industrial Estate, Kingstown, Carlisle, CA3 0PJ Tel: (01228) 536595 Fax: (01228) 536595 E-mail: enquiries@ddfabrications.co.uk

D E Fabrications, Unit 7e E Plan Estate, New Road, Newhaven, East Sussex, BN9 0EX Tel: (01273) 515876 Fax: (01273) 517963 E-mail: sales@defabrications.freeserve.co.uk

D & H Allied Engineering Ltd, Purdy Road, Bilston, West Midlands, WV14 8UB Tel: (01902) 493331 Fax: (01902) 493241

D J B Precision Engineering, 24 Chantry Road, Woburn Road Industrial Estate, Kempston, Bedford, MK42 7JF Tel: (01234) 840174 Fax: (01234) 855566 E-mail: djbeng@btconnect.com

D & J Fabrications Atherton Ltd, 160 Elizabeth Street, Atherton, Manchester, M46 9JL Tel: (01942) 873393 Fax: (01942) 897967 E-mail: sales@dandjfabrications.co.uk

Dale Engineering Services, 20 Manor Road, Scunthorpe, South Humberside, DN16 3PA Tel: (01724) 858748 Fax: (01724) 858748

Darren Sbo, Canklow Meadows Industrial Estate, Rotherham, South Yorkshire, S60 2XL Tel: (01709) 722600 Fax: (01709) 722657 E-mail: info@darron-sbo.com

Dartmouth Associates Ltd, 43 Baltimore Road, Great Barr, Birmingham, B42 1DD Tel: 0121-358 0422 Fax: 0121-358 1334 E-mail: dartmouth@dartmouth-associates.co.uk

Dar-Val Engineering Ltd, Ground Floor Unit B, 443-449 Holloway Road, London, N7 6LJ Tel: (020) 7263 7017 Fax: (020) 7263 7003

Data Tooling & Enginering Services Ltd, Unit 1-2 Paddock Farm, Bethersden Road, Hothfield, Ashford, Kent, TN26 1EP Tel: (01233) 620805 Fax: (01233) 620889 E-mail: info@datatooling.co.uk

Datum Engineering, Nedham St, Leicester, LE2 0HE Tel: 0116-251 9102 Fax: 0116-253 7538 E-mail: datum@2211.com

DCS, 2-4 Watt Road, Hillington Industrial Estate, Glasgow, G52 4RR Tel: 0141-883 8629 Fax: 0141-883 6436 E-mail: info@dcsuk.com

Deeley Precision Engineering Ltd, Unit 1 Aston Fields Industrial Estate, Aston Road, Bromsgrove, Worcestershire, B60 3EX Tel: (01527) 870001 Fax: (01527) 579101

Defontaine Ltd, Hinnegar Lodge, Didmarton, Badminton, Avon, GL9 1DN Tel: (01454) 238831 E-mail: janice@ukdefontaine.com

Denall Engineering Co. Ltd, 55 Bridgewater Street, Little Hulton, Manchester, M38 9ND Tel: 0161-799 2600 Fax: 0161-703 8342

Denholm Rees & O'Donnell Ltd, 116 Albany Road, Walton, Liverpool, L9 0HB Tel: 0151-525 1663 Fax: 0151-525 1618 E-mail: sales@denholms.co.uk

Denny Engineering, Titley Bawk Avenue, Earls Barton, Northampton, NN6 0LA Tel: (01604) 811403 Fax: (01604) 812514

Derwentside Precision Gears Ltd, Morrison Industrial Estate, Stanley, County Durham, DH9 7XW Tel: (01207) 231274 Fax: (01207) 231274

Diamant Precision Engineering Ltd, Unit 1 Marcus Close, Tilehurst, Reading, RG30 4EA Tel: 0118-945 1222 Fax: 0118-945 1077 E-mail: quality@damantltd.co.uk

Dicol Co. Ltd, Colchester Road, Tendring, Clacton-on-Sea, Essex, CO16 9AA Tel: (01255) 830119 Fax: (01255) 831362 E-mail: sales@dicol.com

Dimension Engineering, Unit 21 The Business Village, Wexham Road, Slough, SL2 5HF Tel: (01753) 538166 Fax: (01753) 518966

Direct Engineering, Regent Road, Countesthorpe, Leicester, LE8 5RF Tel: 0116-278 0416 Fax: 0116-247 7731

Dirk European Holdings Ltd, Dirk House, 29-31 Woodchurch Lane, Prenton, Birkenhead, Merseyside, CH42 9PJ Tel: 0151-608 8552 Fax: 0151-608 7579 E-mail: gdirk@dirkgroup.com

Dix & Sons Ltd, Havelock Street, Kettering, Northamptonshire, NN16 9QA Tel: (01536) 512827 Fax: (01536) 512827

Dowling & Fransen (Engineers) Ltd, North End Road, Wembley, Middlesex, HA9 0AN Tel: (020) 8903 2155 Fax: (020) 8903 2158 E-mail: dowling@fransen.fsbusiness.co.uk

Downhurst Engineering, 15 Aintree Road, Keytec 7 Business Park, Pershore, Worcestershire, WR10 2JN Tel: (01386) 554195 Fax: (01386) 561195 E-mail: downhurst@lineone.net

Dun Fab Engineering Company Ltd, Coulman Street, Thorne, Doncaster, South Yorkshire, DN8 5JS Tel: (01405) 812165 Fax: (01405) 740333 E-mail: dunfabengineering@aol.com

Dyke Engineering, Unit 4, Vastre Industrial Estate, Newtown, Powys, SY16 1DZ Tel: (01686) 624412 Fax: (01686) 623236 E-mail: dykeengineering@mid-wales.net

Dynamic Die & Steel (Sheffield) Ltd, 136 Savile Street East, Sheffield, S4 7UQ Tel: 0114-276 1100 Fax: 0114-275 0752

E Bacon & Co. Ltd, Hutton Road, Grimsby, South Humberside, DN31 3PS Tel: (01472) 350267 Fax: (01472) 250987 E-mail: info@baconengineering.com

E Binns & Sons Ltd, Stainland Road, Greetland, Halifax, West Yorkshire, HX4 8BD Tel: (01422) 372347 Fax: (01422) 377938

E G L Vaughan Ltd, Brook St, Glossop, Derbyshire, SK13 8BG Tel: (01457) 866614 Fax: (01457) 869364 E-mail: egl.vaughan@virgin.net

E L B Engineering 91, Meekings Road, Sudbury, Suffolk, CO10 2XE Tel: (01787) 373055

E M S Euroweld Ltd, 203 Strathmartine Road, Dundee, DD3 8PH Tel: (01382) 858947 Fax: (01382) 832359

E P Oakes & Son, 113 Middlemore Road, Middlemore Industrial Estate, Smethwick, West Midlands, B66 2EP Tel: 0121-558 4145 Fax: 0121-555 5623

E P S Page Ltd, Riverside House Unit, 1 New Mill Road, Orpington, Kent, BR5 3QA Tel: (020) 7407 6701 Fax: (0845) 6080354 E-mail: epspage@epsplc.com

E R P Engineering Ltd, Barton Forge, Alexandra Road, Enfield, Middlesex, EN3 7EH Tel: (020) 8805 7289 Fax: (020) 8443 5786

East Durham Manufacturing & Engineering Co. Ltd, Moreland Street, Hartlepool, Cleveland, TS24 7NL Tel: (01429) 869688 Fax: (01429) 222082 E-mail: derek.wheatley@btconnect.com

East Yorkshire Engineering, Unit B 133 Marfleet Avenue, Hull, HU9 5SA Tel: (01482) 788008 Fax: (01482) 788008

Ebbs & Dale Ltd, Unit 27 Austin Fields, King's Lynn, Norfolk, PE30 1PH Tel: (01553) 765554 Fax: (01553) 769140 E-mail: sales@ebbsanddale.com

Ece Engineering Dundee Ltd, Unit 12 Faraday Street, Dryburgh Industrial Estate, Dundee, DD2 3QQ Tel: (01382) 811978 Fax: (01382) 812058 E-mail: ece.engineering@btinternet.com

Edwards Engineering (Liverpool) Ltd, Lipton Close, St. Johns Road, Brasenose Industrial Estate, Bootle, Merseyside, L20 8PU Tel: 0151-933 5242 Fax: 0151-922 3383 E-mail: edseng@edwardsenglpoolltd.freeserve.co.uk

Edwards Engineering (Perth) Ltd, Glenearn Road, Perth, PH2 0NJ Tel: (01738) 627101 Fax: (01738) 630769 E-mail: mail@edwardsengineering.co.uk

Electrical Cabinets (Bradford) Ltd, 2 Essex Street, Wakefield Road, Bradford, West Yorkshire, BD4 7PG Tel: (01274) 729076 Fax: (01274) 732297

Engine Services (Croydon) Ltd, 173 Handcroft Road, Croydon, CR0 3LF Tel: (020) 8665 1952 Fax: (020) 8665 1952

Engineering & Electrical Products Ltd, Bayton Road, Exhall, Coventry, CV7 9EL Tel: (024) 7636 3565 Fax: (024) 7664 4414

Engineering Tech Pgp Ltd, Unit 5 Harbour Road Industrial Estate, Lowestoft, Suffolk, NR32 3LZ Tel: (01502) 515768 Fax: (01502) 563211 E-mail: pete@eng-tech.co.uk

Engineering UK Ltd, Dale View Works, Martin Lane, Blacker Hill, Barnsley, South Yorkshire, S74 0RX Tel: (01226) 742738 Fax: (01226) 350806 E-mail: enquiries@engineeringukltd.co.uk

Enterpriseforce Metal Pressing, Unit 3c-Unit 3d Canal Estate, Station Road, Langley, Slough, SL3 6EG Tel: (01753) 585018 Fax: (01753) 542685 E-mail: david@dmpgroup.co.uk

Epic Engineering, 7 Crest Industrial Estate, Pattenden Lane, Marden, Tonbridge, Kent, TN12 9QJ Tel: (01622) 831327 Fax: (01622) 833085

Equinox Precision Engineering, Station Road, Great Harwood, Blackburn, BB6 7BB Tel: (01254) 888009 Fax: (01254) 885550

Evak Ltd, Brentwood Grove, Wallsend, Tyne & Wear, NE28 6PT Tel: 0191-263 5843 Fax: 0191-234 1065

F C Curran Ltd, Duke Street, Nottingham, NG7 7JN Tel: 0115-970 6801 Fax: 0115-942 2221 E-mail: enquiries@fccurran.co.uk

F J R Engineering Ltd, 65b Blackpole Trading Estate West, Worcester, WR3 8TJ Tel: (01905) 454143 Fax: (01905) 454143

F & R Belbin Ltd, 165-169 Whitley Road, Whitley Bay, Tyne & Wear, NE26 2DN Tel: 0191-252 4703 Fax: 0191-297 0812 E-mail: sales@frbelbin.co.uk

F T V Proclad (UK) Ltd, Viewfield Industrial Estate, Glenrothes, Fife, KY6 2RD Tel: (01592) 772568 Fax: (01592) 775310 E-mail: sales@forthtool.co.uk

Fabrication & Installation Ltd, Units 6-9 Enterprise Way, Ladysmith Road, Grimsby, South Humberside, DN32 9TW Tel: (01472) 240409 Fax: (01472) 240408

Falcon Engineering Ltd, 28 Wash Road, Hutton, Brentwood, Essex, CM13 1TB Tel: (01277) 226861 Fax: (01277) 230091 E-mail: neil@faleng.demon.co.uk

Farnworth & Langan Blackburn Ltd, Unit 6 Stancliffe Street Industrial Estate, Blackburn, BB2 2QR Tel: (01254) 676935 Fax: (01254) 680113 E-mail: farnworth-langan@btconnect.com

GENERAL ENGINEERING – *continued*

Featherstone Ltd, Kelleythorpe Industrial Estate, Kellythorpe, Driffield, North Humberside, YO25 9DJ Tel: (01377) 255016 Fax: (01377) 241299 E-mail: office@fetherston.co.uk
Fen Manufacturing Engineers Ltd, Blenheim Way, Northfields Industrial Estate, Market Deeping, Peterborough, PE6 8LD Tel: (01778) 344994 Fax: (01778) 344040
Fielde Engineering Ltd, Unit 6-7 The Warren, East Goscote, Leicester, LE7 3XA Tel: 0116-260 8217 Fax: 0116-260 7921 E-mail: field@btconnect.com
Fieldgrove Engineering Services Ltd, Doynton Mill, Mill Lane, Doynton, Bristol, BS30 5TQ Tel: 0117-937 4139 Fax: 0117-937 3560 E-mail: dhyde@fieldgrove.co.uk
Filtronic Comtek Ltd, 11 Standalane, Stewarton, Kilmarnock, Ayrshire, KA3 5BG Tel: (01560) 482207 Fax: (01560) 485027 E-mail: enquiries@filtroniccomtek.co.uk
Firth Rixson P.L.C, PO Box 644, Sheffield, S9 1JD Tel: 0114-219 3000 Fax: 0114-219 1111 E-mail: info@firthrixson.com
Folsana Pressed Sections Ltd, Sidney Street, Bolton, BL3 6BF Tel: (01204) 393355 Fax: (01204) 393377 E-mail: dm@folsana.co.uk
Ford & Slater Of Peterborough, America House, Newark Road, Peterborough, PE1 5YD Tel: (01733) 295000 Fax: (01733) 295010 E-mail: enquiries@fordandslater.co.uk
Forest Heath Ltd, 195 Bexhill Road, St. Leonards-on-Sea, East Sussex, TN38 8BG Tel: (01424) 714888 Fax: (01424) 714888 E-mail: forestheath@hotmail.co.uk
Forgeway Engineering Co. Ltd, 2-3 Forgehammer Industrial Estate, Cwmbran, Gwent, NP44 3AA Tel: (01633) 485468 Fax: (01633) 875439
Forth & Foyle Euro Ltd, 3 Carrakeel Industrial Park, Maytown, Londonderry, BT47 6SZ Tel: (028) 7186 0661 Fax: (028) 7186 0699 E-mail: s_hegarty@btinternet.com
Fpe, 21 Blatchford Close, Horsham, West Sussex, RH13 5RG Tel: (01403) 269069 Fax: (01403) 211391
FSC (Halifax) Ltd, Grantham House, Grantham Road, Halifax, West Yorkshire, HX3 6PL Tel: (01422) 347872 Fax: (01422) 321758 E-mail: kw@fscooper.com
G B M Engineering, Unit 4 Inngae Park, Holly Lane Industrial Estate, Atherstone, Warwickshire, CV9 2NA Tel: (01827) 712213 Fax: (01827) 718503
G E M Engineering Services, Unit B9 Tweedale Industrial Estate, Madeley, Telford, Shropshire, TF7 4JR Tel: (01952) 588525 Fax: (01952) 588525
G E M S, 31 Hatchett Street, Birmingham, B19 3NX Tel: 0121-333 4151 Fax: 0121-359 4934 E-mail: gems2@btconnet.com
G Leddington Electrical Ltd, 15 Church Parade, Telford, Shropshire, TF2 6EX Tel: (01952) 615958 Fax: (01952) 620473 E-mail: info@leddingtons.co.uk
G R F Engineering Ltd, 18 Bilton Way, Luton, LU1 1UU Tel: (01582) 411717 Fax: (01582) 728700 E-mail: sales@grfeng.co.uk
G R Pook Engineering Ltd, Howden Industrial Estate, Tiverton, Devon, EX16 5HW Tel: (01884) 254331 Fax: (01884) 258834
Galm Ltd, 129a London Road, Bexhill-on-Sea, East Sussex, TN39 4AB Tel: (01424) 223290 Fax: (01424) 223290
V. Garcia & Son, Malakoff Works, Malakoff Street, Stalybridge, Cheshire, SK15 1TD Tel: 0161-303 7383 Fax: 0161-338 2151 E-mail: bill-garcia@btconnect.com
Gardiners, The Batts, Frosterley, Bishop Auckland, County Durham, DL13 2SE Tel: (07711) 356444 Fax: (01388) 527295
Gardner Services Ltd, 7 Camphill Industrial Estate, Camphill Road, West Byfleet, Surrey, KT14 6EW Tel: (01932) 346190 Fax: (01932) 353861 E-mail: sales@gardnerservices.co.uk
Garrick Engineering Co. Ltd, Crowland Street Industrial Estate, Crowland Street, Southport, Merseyside, PR9 7RQ Tel: (01704) 534906 Fax: (01704) 537952 E-mail: info@garrickeng.co.uk
James Garside & Son Ltd, Grantham Works, Grantham Road, Halifax, West Yorkshire, HX3 6PL Tel: (01422) 340559 Fax: (01422) 349465
GB Engineering Ltd, Croespenmaen Industrial Estate, Crumlin, Newport, Gwent, NP11 3AG Tel: (01495) 248080 Fax: (01495) 246470 E-mail: bordergroup@tiscali.co.uk
Gem Engineering, Gemini House, Bolton Road Industrial Estate, Westhoughton, Bolton, BL5 3JQ Tel: (01942) 814464 Fax: (01942) 842414 E-mail: gem.engineering@ic24.net
Gemweld Fabrications & Engineering Co. Ltd, Lancaster Way, Market Deeping, Peterborough, PE6 8LA Tel: (01778) 344733 Fax: (01778) 343988 E-mail: cam@gemweld.co.uk
George Bros Engineers Ltd, Dyffryn Close, Swansea Enterprise Park, Swansea, SA6 8QG Tel: (01792) 790550 Fax: (01792) 701608
George Lister & Sons Ltd, 505 Coldhams Lane, Cambridge, CB1 3JS Tel: (01223) 518888 Fax: (01223) 504700 E-mail: martin@georgelister.co.uk
Gifthorn & Co. Ltd, Unit 14, West Point Trading Park, Liverpool Street, Hull, HU3 4UU Tel: (01482) 323844 Fax: (01482) 213198 E-mail: egon@giffhornengkaroo.co.uk
Gissing & Lonsdale Ltd, Wellhouse Road, Barnoldswick, Lancashire, BB18 6DD Tel: (01282) 812821 Fax: (01282) 816135 E-mail: enquiries@gissingandlonsdale.co.uk
Glenaber Engineers Ltd, Denfield House, 5 Smeaton Road, Kirkcaldy, Fife, KY1 2EY Tel: (01592) 651940 Fax: (01592) 651963 E-mail: admin-glenaberengineers@ecosse.net
Global Engineering, Eagle Iron Works, Crawford Street, Rochdale, Lancashire, OL16 5NU Tel: (01706) 715757 Fax: (01706) 649969 E-mail: sales@golbaleng.co.uk
Goddard & Co 1992 Ltd, Copley Mill, Demesne Drive, St. Pauls Trading Estate, Stalybridge, Cheshire, SK15 2QF Tel: 0161-304 9690 Fax: 0161-304 9694 E-mail: goddardco1992@btinternet.com
Goldcrest Engineering Ltd, 1 Glebe Close, Swinton, Mexborough, South Yorkshire, S64 8LN Tel: (01709) 577144 Fax: (01709) 577144
Goldwell Services Ltd, Cherry Tree Road, Milford, Godalming, Surrey, GU8 5AX Tel: (01483) 422083 Fax: (01483) 421198
Goodland Engineering Ltd, Cannon Lane, Tonbridge, Kent, TN9 1PP Tel: (01732) 771010 Fax: (01732) 356472 E-mail: goodlandengineering@yahoo.co.uk
Goodrow Engineering Ltd, Unit 5, Ebbsfleet Industrial Estate, Northfleet, Gravesend, Kent, DA11 9DZ Tel: (01474) 359990 Fax: (01474) 359994
Gosport Engineering Co. Ltd, Lordship Lane, London, N17 8NS Tel: (020) 8808 2326 Fax: (020) 8885 2867 E-mail: gosporteng@btconnect.com
Grange Industries, Unit 2 Bessemer Close, Cardiff, CF11 8DL Tel: (02920) 345366 Fax: (02920) 399111 E-mail: ryan@grangeindustries.co.uk
Grangestone Engineering Co., Grangestone Industrial Estate, Ladywell Avenue, Girvan, Ayrshire, KA26 9PL Tel: (01465) 712505 Fax: (01465) 712505
Grantham Fabrications & Profile Services Ltd, Venture Way, Grantham, Lincolnshire, NG31 7XS Tel: (01476) 577037 Fax: (01476) 576967E-mail: reception@g-fabs.demon.co.uk
Gravesend Engineering Co. Ltd, East Crescent Road, Gravesend, Kent, DA12 2AR Tel: (01474) 365475 Fax: (01474) 365475
Green Engineering, Cheethams Mill, Park Street, Stalybridge, Cheshire, SK15 2BT Tel: 0161-303 7129 Fax: 0161-303 7129
Green Goose Tooling Co., Unit 1-2 Falcons Gate, Dean Road, Yate, Bristol, BS37 5NH Tel: (01454) 312948 Fax: (01454) 313704
Greenberry Bros Engineers Ltd, Brunel Drive, Newark, Nottinghamshire, NG24 2EG Tel: (01636) 676694 Fax: (01636) 675830 E-mail: sales@greenberrybros.co.uk
Griffiths Devereaux, 334 Bristol Road, Gloucester, GL2 5DN Tel: (01452) 520418 Fax: (01452) 307877
H B D Engineering 2000, Unit F4 The Seedbed Centre, Harlow, Essex, CM19 5AF Tel: (01279) 436894 Fax: (01279) 436894 E-mail: sales@hbd2000.co.uk
H Beesley Ltd, Commercial Square, Freemans Common, Leicester, LE2 7SR Tel: 0116-255 4233 Fax: 0116-255 4366 E-mail: enquiries@hbeesley.co.uk
H M B Machinists & Engineers Ltd, 7 Meadow Lane, Alfreton, Derbyshire, DE55 7EZ Tel: (01773) 835868 Fax: (01773) 520359
H W Whiteley Engineering, Holmfield Industrial Estate, Holmfield, Halifax, West Yorkshire, HX2 9TN Tel: (01422) 244870 Fax: (01422) 248666 E-mail: gordonwhitaker@hwwhiteley.co.uk
Hadee Engineering Co. Ltd, New Street, Holbrook Industrial Estate, Holbrook, Sheffield, S20 3GH Tel: 0114-248 3711 Fax: 0114-247 7858 E-mail: peterlowe@hadee.co.uk
Haden Building Management Ltd, 10a Fore Street, St. Marychurch, Torquay, TQ1 4NE Tel: (01803) 329435 Fax: (01803) 324982
Haggart Commercial Marine, 98-100 Vauxhall Street, Plymouth, PL4 0DD Tel: (01752) 660117 Fax: (01752) 660117
Haith Industrial, Cowhouse Lane, Armthorpe, Doncaster, South Yorkshire, DN3 3EE Tel: (01302) 831911 Fax: (01302) 300173 E-mail: sales@haith.co.uk
Halan Machine Tools & Engineering, Unit D1 Sketchley Meadows, Hinckley, Leicestershire, LE10 3EN Tel: (01455) 617226 Fax: (01455) 617226
Harbrook Engineering, Limefield House, Wrexham Road, Burland, Nantwich, Cheshire, CW5 8ND Tel: (01270) 524263 Fax: (01270) 524343 E-mail: sales@steelfabrication.co.uk
Hargreaves Hamilton Gears Ltd, Nelson Mill Gaskell Street, Bolton, BL1 2QE Tel: (01204) 456190 Fax: (01204) 371355
Harnden Plastics, Manchester Road, Hyde, Cheshire, SK14 2BP Tel: 0161-368 1817 Fax: 0161-368 1140 E-mail: harnden@a-m.co.uk
Harris & Garrod Ltd, Humber Bank South, Grimsby, South Humberside, DN31 3SD Tel: (01472) 343965 Fax: (01472) 240878 E-mail: hggrimsby@aol.com
J.A. Harris Ltd, Malinslee, Telford, Shropshire, TF4 2BN Tel: (01952) 505537 Fax: (01952) 504456 E-mail: accounts.harris@virgin.net
Hawk Fabrications & Engineering Ltd, Unit 10 Wanstead Industrial Park, Wanstead Road, Leicester, LE3 1TR Tel: 0116-287 3749 Fax: 0116-287 4692
Allan Hayes Engineering Ltd, Charlwoods Road, East Grinstead, West Sussex, RH19 2HR Tel: (01342) 324536 Fax: (01342) 312556
Henderson Engineering (N E) Ltd, Vickers Close, Preston Farm Industrial Estate, Stockton-on-Tees, Cleveland, TS18 3TD Tel: (01642) 608008 Fax: (01642) 612636 E-mail: enquiries@hendersonengineering.com
Hewaswater Ltd, Hewas Water Ltd, Hewas Water, St. Austell, Cornwall, PL26 7JF Tel: (01726) 885200 Fax: (01726) 885212 E-mail: info@heltd.demon.co.uk
Higgins Engineering Ltd, 816A Oxford Road, Reading, RG30 1EL Tel: 0118-957 1058 Fax: 0118-957 1058 E-mail: higginsengineering@ntlworld.com
High Lee Engineering Co. Ltd, Unti 1 Princess Street, Rochdale, Lancashire, OL12 0HA Tel: (01706) 644269 Fax: (01706) 524810
High Speed Engineering (West Bromwich) Ltd, Unit 22 Spartan Industrial Centre, Brickhouse Lane, West Bromwich, West Midlands, B70 0DH Tel: 0121-520 9655 Fax: 0121-520 9588 E-mail: sales@highspeedeng.co.uk
Hill & Webster Ltd, Ashbourne Indust Estate, Ashbourne, Derbyshire, DE6 1HD Tel: (01335) 343119 Fax: (01335) 346400 E-mail: hillwebster@compuserve.com
Hillsmen Engineering Ltd, 2 Bergen Way, Hull, HU7 0YQ Tel: (01482) 877111 Fax: (01482) 877112 E-mail: sales@hillsmen2000.freeserve.co.uk
Hindles Ltd, 22 Moorland Way, Lincoln, LN6 7JP Tel: (01522) 683000 Fax: (01522) 500127 E-mail: sales@psm-sportswear.co.uk
Holdens Pattern & Tooling Ltd, Unit 3 Hargreaves Street, Haslingden, Rossendale, Lancashire, BB4 5RQ Tel: (01706) 213711 Fax: (01706) 213007 E-mail: holdenspatterns@aol.com
Holland & Holland, 906 Harrow Road, London, NW10 5JT Tel: (020) 8960 4358 Fax: (020) 8969 3523
Hollinwood Sheet Metal Co., Under Lane, Chadderton, Oldham, OL9 7PP Tel: 0161-683 5277 Fax: 0161-684 8608
Bernard Holmes Precision Ltd, The Old Pony Field, Grosvenor Road, Billingborough, Sleaford, Lincolnshire, NG34 0QN Tel: (01529) 240241 Fax: (01529) 240802
Holmes Engineering, Unit 2 Furtho Court, Towcester Road, Old Stratford, Milton Keynes, MK19 6AN Tel: (01908) 563169 Fax: (01908) 563169
Horley Metal Productions Ltd, 30 Balcombe Road, Horley, Surrey, RH6 9AA Tel: (01293) 820234 Fax: (01293) 820235
A. & D. Hughes Ltd, Pope's Lane, Nelson Street, Oldbury, West Midlands, B69 4PA Tel: 0121-552 4500 Fax: 0121-511 1072
Ben Hughes Engineering Ltd, Gwydr Place, Loughor, Swansea, SA4 6TW Tel: (01792) 892794 Fax: (01792) 898299 E-mail: bheng@btconnect.com
Hunprenco Precision Engineering Ltd, Bridlington Road, Hunmanby Industrial Estate, Filey, North Yorkshire, YO14 0PH Tel: (01723) 890105 Fax: (01723) 890018
► Hunslet Engine Co., 2 Maple Park, Lowfields Avenue, Leeds, LS12 6HH Tel: 0113-277 4007 Fax: 0113-277 3005 E-mail: info@hunsletenginw.com
Hutchinson Engineering Ltd, Hutchinson Street, Widnes, Cheshire, WA8 0PZ Tel: 0151-423 5850 Fax: 0151-495 1688 E-mail: enquiries@hutchinsonengineering.co.uk
Hydram Engineering Ltd, Avenue Two, Chilton Industrial Estate, Chilton, Ferryhill, County Durham, DL17 0SG Tel: (01388) 720222 Fax: (01388) 721025 E-mail: hydram@hydram.co.uk
Idec Ltd, Concorde House, Concorde Way, Preston Farm Industrial Estate, Stockton-on-Tees, Cleveland, TS18 3RB Tel: (01642) 677333 Fax: (01642) 603641 E-mail: sales@idec.ltd.uk
IDEO London, White Bear Yard, 144A Clerkenwell Road, London, EC1R 5DF Tel: (020) 7713 2600 Fax: (020) 7713 2601 E-mail: mhoenle@ideo.com
Index Machining, James Scott Road, Halesowen, West Midlands, B63 2QT Tel: (01384) 410925 Fax: (01384) 410925
Industrial Systems & Controls Ltd, 50 George Street, Glasgow, G1 1QE Tel: 0141-553 1111 Fax: 0141-553 1232 E-mail: iscmail@isc-ltd.com
Instrument & Control Services Ltd, Unit 2, Westlake Trading Estate, Canal Lane, Stoke-on-Trent, ST6 4NZ Tel: (01782) 819900 Fax: (01782) 575190 E-mail: admin@icsluk.com
Integrated Media Installations Ltd, Unit K, Manaway Business Park, Holder Road, Aldershot, Hampshire, GU12 4RH Tel: (01252) 350280 Fax: (01252) 350682 E-mail: intermediainstalls@imi-ltd.co.uk
International Business Networks, Brigade House, Brigade Close, Harrow, Middlesex, HA2 0LQ Tel: (020) 8515 9000 Fax: (020) 8515 9001 E-mail: info@ibnetworks.com
Iron By Design, Unit 31 Steeton Grove, Steeton, Keighley, West Yorkshire, BD20 6TT Tel: (01535) 654146 Fax: (01535) 654146 E-mail: enquiries@iron-by-design.co.uk
J A Clark & Co Engineers Ltd, Charrold Works, Stephenson Way, Thetford, Norfolk, IP24 3RJ Tel: (01842) 752348 Fax: (01842) 755194 E-mail: sales@jaclark.co.uk
J A Martin, 2 Beechvale Road, Killinchy, Newtownards, County Down, BT23 6PH Tel: (028) 9754 1062
J Browne Construction Co. Ltd, Beacon House, North Circular Road, London, NW10 0HF Tel: (020) 8451 4111 Fax: (020) 8459 6879 E-mail: info@jbconstruction.co.uk
J C Components Ltd, Unit 7 Paper Mill End Industrial Estate, Birmingham, B44 8NH Tel: 0121-356 3663 Fax: 0121-356 3663 E-mail: jccomponents@mail2worlds.com
J & C R Wood, 66 Clough Road, Hull, HU5 1SR Tel: (01482) 345067 Fax: (01482) 441141 E-mail: info@jandcrwood.co.uk
J Colburn, Aldrington Basin South, Basin Road South, Portslade, Brighton, BN41 1WF Tel: (01273) 413190 Fax: (01273) 423684
J D Engineering, Unit 5a, Ramsden Road, Rotherwas Industrial Estate, Hereford, HR2 6LR Tel: (01432) 344030 Fax: (01432) 352905
J D Engineering, York House, Sleaford Road, Wellingore, Lincoln, LN5 0HR Tel: (01522) 810215 Fax: (01522) 810525 E-mail: jim.dixon@eliteuk.net
J H Hardy & Son, Dunkirk Street, Halifax, West Yorkshire, HX1 3TD Tel: (01422) 361437 Fax: (01422) 349066
J Marklew Engineering Ltd, Chapel Street, Dudley, West Midlands, DY2 9PN Tel: (01384) 252118 Fax: (01384) 456078
J & P Contracts Angus Ltd, 73 Dundee Street, Carnoustie, Angus, DD7 7PN Tel: (01241) 854911 Fax: (01241) 855860 E-mail: sales@jp-coatech.com
J P Forrest & Son Ltd, Claylands Avenue, Worksop, Nottinghamshire, S81 7DJ Tel: (01909) 472031 Fax: (01909) 530124 E-mail: sales@jpforrest.com
J R J Engineering, Ty Isaf, Llangennech, Llanelli, Dyfed, SA14 8UU Tel: (01554) 820464 Fax: (01554) 820070 E-mail: jrjengineering@btconnect.com
J S M Deeside Ltd, Station Road, Sandycroft, Deeside, Flintshire, CH5 2PT Tel: (01244) 535827 Fax: (01244) 535635
J T Grout Ltd, Albert Road, Braintree, Essex, CM7 3JQ Tel: (01376) 320702 Fax: (01376) 349912 E-mail: jtgrout@btclick.com
J W Stamp & Son LLP, Holydyke, Barton On Humber, Barton-upon-Humber, South Humberside, DN18 5PS Tel: (01652) 632421 Fax: (01652) 635878
Jade Engineering (Coventry) Ltd, 70 Bayton Road Industrial Estate, Exhall, Coventry, CV7 9EJ Tel: (024) 7636 5336 Fax: (024) 7664 4308 E-mail: sales@jade-eng.co.uk
Jamestan Engineering Ltd, Kynochs, Nuttaberry, Bideford, Devon, EX39 4DT Tel: (01237) 471878 Fax: (01237) 471370
Jan Engineering Ltd, Cheethams Mill, Park Street, Stalybridge, Cheshire, SK15 2BT Tel: 0161-338 6024 Fax: 0161-338 6024
► Jay Cee Lichfield Engineering Ltd, Coppice Side Industrial Estate, Brownhills, Walsall, WS8 7EX Tel: (01543) 377633 Fax: (01543) 374100 E-mail: jc@jaycee-eng.co.uk
John Crossley, Tan Yard Road, Catterall, Preston, PR3 0HP Tel: (01995) 606058 Fax: (01995) 606058 E-mail: sharonhenriques@btconnect.com
John D Hotchkiss Ltd, Main Road, West Kingsdown, Sevenoaks, Kent, TN15 6ER Tel: (01474) 853131 Fax: (01474) 853288 E-mail: sales@hotchkiss-engineers.co.uk
Johnson Porter Industrial Services, Attwood Street, Stourbridge, West Midlands, DY9 8RY Tel: (01384) 897080 Fax: (01384) 897170
Johnson's Engineering & Electrical Co., 61 High Street, Standlake, Witney, Oxfordshire, OX29 7RH Tel: (01865) 300270 Fax: (01865) 300911
George Jones Engineering Services Ltd, Lionel Works, 89-91 Rolfe Street, Smethwick, West Midlands, B66 2AY Tel: 0121-558 1884 Fax: 0121-558 0017 E-mail: sales.georgejonesengservices@zyworld.com
Joy Mining Machinery Ltd, Kirkby La, Pinxton, Nottingham, NG16 6HX Tel: (01773) 515200 Fax: (01773) 515300E-mail: rbailey@joy.co.uk
Judge & Dalton, 6 College Road, Northfleet, Gravesend, Kent, DA11 9AU Tel: (01474) 564504 Fax: (01474) 535809 E-mail: knjudg@aol.com
Justell Precision Engineers, Unit 2 & 17 Manor Park, 35 Willis Way, Poole, Dorset, BH15 3SZ Tel: (01202) 680500 Fax: (01202) 680510 E-mail: enquires@justellengineering.co.uk
K Murray & Co. Ltd, 29 Windsor Street, Cheltenham, Gloucestershire, GL52 2DG Tel: (01242) 521774 Fax: (01242) 227137
K R M Engineering, Marshlands Road, Farlington Industrial Estate, Farlington, Portsmouth, PO6 1SS Tel: (023) 9237 2141 Fax: (023) 9264 2288
K S W Engineering Ltd, 7 Stirling Road, Glenrothes, Fife, KY6 2ST Tel: (01592) 774822 Fax: (01592) 772891 E-mail: stewart@kswengineering.com
K&S, 1 Hardess Street, London, SE24 0HN Tel: (020) 7274 2215 Fax: (020) 7738 4531
Kaby Engineers Ltd, 14-16 Upper Charnwood Street, Leicester, LE2 0AU Tel: 0116-253 6353 Fax: 0116-251 5237 E-mail: kaby@kaby.co.uk
Karson 2002 Engineering Ltd, Tram Way, Oldbury Road, Smethwick, West Midlands, B66 1NR Tel: 0121-558 4852 Fax: 0121-558 4852 E-mail: sales@karson.co.uk
Kaygee Engineering, 55 Great Union Street, Hull, HU9 1AG Tel: (01482) 326281 Fax: (01482) 219240 E-mail: info@kaygee.co.uk
Kaytu Systems Ltd, 6A & 6B Throckley Way, Middlefields Industrial Estate, South Shields, Tyne & Wear, NE34 0NU Tel: 0191-456 2046 Fax: 0191-456 1971 E-mail: kaytusystems@kaytu-systems.co.uk
Kerndale Ltd, Pontygwindy Industrial Estate, Caerphilly, Mid Glamorgan, CF83 3HU Tel: (029) 2086 5152 Fax: (029) 2088 7742 E-mail: tonydoel@kerndale.demon.co.uk
Ketlon Ltd, Paddock Wood Distribution Centre, Paddock Wood, Tonbridge, Kent, TN12 6UU Tel: (01892) 835555 Fax: (01892) 832389 E-mail: sales@ketlon.co.uk

► indicates data change since last edition

GENERAL ENGINEERING - *continued*

Knightsridge Engineering Services Ltd, 10 Nettlehill Road, Houstoun Industrial Estate, Livingston, West Lothian, EH54 5DL Tel: (01506) 430605 Fax: (01506) 440380 E-mail: kesl@btconnect.com

L & D Precision Engineers Ltd, Peace Mills, Perry Road, Nottingham, NG5 3AL Tel: 0115-962 4116 Fax: 0115-969 1354 E-mail: sales@ldprecision.co.uk

L H Wilson Ltd, Unit 1 Sandbeck Trading Estate, Sandbeck Lane, Wetherby, West Yorkshire, LS22 7TW Tel: (01937) 583563 Fax: (01937) 584500 E-mail: pw@lubeoilsystems.com

L J Bearing & Engineering Services, Unit A5 Imex Business Park, Kings Rd, Tyseley, Birmingham, B11 2AL Tel: 0121-604 7131 Fax: 0121-604 7122 E-mail: enquiries@bearings-uk.com

L L P, Office 1, Arkwright Suite Coppull Enterprise Centre, Mill La, Coppull, Chorley, Lancs, PR7 5BW Tel: (01257) 470111 Fax: (01257) 470111 E-mail: diagseervol@aol.com

L & R Engineering Ltd, 53 Colvilles Place, Kelvin Industrial Estate, East Kilbride, Glasgow, G75 0PZ Tel: (01355) 241744 Fax: (01355) 241744

L & S Engineers Ltd, Unit 5 West Coppice Road, Walsall, WS8 7HB Tel: (01543) 378189 Fax: (01543) 370006

L V Tomlinson & Son Ltd, Catwick Lane, Brandesburton, Driffield, North Humberside, YO25 8RY Tel: (01964) 542969 Fax: (01964) 543431

Lace Mechanics Ltd, Atlas Mills, Birchwood Avenue, Long Eaton, Nottingham, NG10 3ND Tel: 0115-973 2852 Fax: 0115-946 5917 E-mail: lacemechanics@btconnect.com

Lake & Nicholls Engineering, 4 Cornish Way, North Walsham, Norfolk, NR28 0AW Tel: (01692) 404602 Fax: (01692) 406723 E-mail: enquiries@lakeandnicholls.co.uk

Laranca Engineering Ltd, Earlswood Trading Estate, Poolhead Lane, Earlswood, Solihull, West Midlands, B94 5EW Tel: (01564) 702651 Fax: (01564) 702341 E-mail: sales@laranca.com

Larssen Engineering Ltd, Globe Industrial Estate, Rectory Road, Grays, Essex, RM17 6ST Tel: (01375) 371909 Fax: (01375) 390582 E-mail: sales@larssen.com

Laycast Ltd, Sheffield Road, Woodhouse Mill, Sheffield, S13 9ZD Tel: 0114-288 9995 Fax: 0114-288 9500 E-mail: info@laycast.com

E.G. Laycock & Sons Ltd, Layco Works, Smithfield, Sheffield, S3 7AR Tel: 0114-272 0880 Fax: 0114-276 8519 E-mail: chefcutler@aol.com

Lazgill Ltd, 1 Vicarage Road, Hampton Wick, Kingston Upon Thames, Surrey, KT1 4EB Tel: (020) 8977 2125 Fax: (020) 8943 3248 E-mail: sales@lazgill.co.uk

Lecol Engineering Ltd, 123 Barr Street, Birmingham, B19 3DE Tel: 0121-523 0404 Fax: 0121-523 2372

Leonard Bowes Engineering Co. Ltd, 31 Mill Street, Brierley Hill, West Midlands, DY5 2RG Tel: (01384) 573000 Fax: (01384) 573000

Lewis & Raby (Engineers) Ltd, Birchill Road, Knowsley Industrial Park, Liverpool, L33 7TG Tel: 0151-546 2882 Fax: 0151-549 1585

Lexden Engineering Co. Ltd, 277 Crescent Drive, Petts Wood, Orpington, Kent, BR5 1AY Tel: (01689) 833366 Fax: (01689) 833366 E-mail: lexdenengineering@ntlworld.com

Leytoner De Montfort Ltd, 8 Layton Road, Leicester, LE5 0PU Tel: 0116-276 7272 E-mail: leytoner@aol.com

Lincoln Castings Ltd, Station Road, North Hykeham, Lincoln, LN6 9XB Tel: (01522) 681515 Fax: (01522) 692021 E-mail: info@licolncasting.com

Linkester Chemical & Supply Co. Ltd, Gaw End Lane, Macclesfield, Cheshire, SK11 0LB Tel: (01260) 252116

Lion Engineering Services Ltd, Gapton Hall Road, Great Yarmouth, Norfolk, NR31 0NL Tel: (01493) 653642 Fax: (01493) 653353 E-mail: sales@lion-oil-tools.demon.co.uk

Lipco Engineering Ltd, Hightown Industrial Estate, Crow Arch Lane, Ringwood, Hampshire, BH24 1ND Tel: (01425) 476036 Fax: (01425) 475527

Littler Co. Ltd, 2 Greaves Way Industrial Estate, Stanbridge Road, Leighton Buzzard, Bedfordshire, LU7 4UB Tel: (01525) 373310 Fax: (01525) 381371

Locke Engineering Egham, Unit 19, Eversley Way, Thorpe Industrial Estate, Egham, Surrey, TW20 8RG Tel: (01784) 438120 Fax: (01784) 438120

Long Engineering Ltd, Wood Road, Kingswood, Bristol, BS15 8DX Tel: 0117-960 0193 Fax: 0117-935 3203 E-mail: admin@longengineering.co.uk

Longden Engineering, The Farriers, Annscroft, Shrewsbury, SY5 8AN Tel: (01743) 860131 Fax: (01743) 860315

Lothian Engineering Co Whitburn Ltd, 1 Burnhouse Industrial Estate, Whitburn, Bathgate, West Lothian, EH47 0LQ Tel: (01501) 740624 Fax: (01501) 741831 E-mail: lothian.eng@btinternet.com

Lothian Projects 2000 Ltd, Methilhaven Road, Methil, Leven, Fife, KY8 3LA Tel: (01333) 429134 Fax: (01333) 423582 E-mail: info@stegroup.com

Lund Engineering Co. Ltd, Clayton Street, Nelson, Lancashire, BB9 7ES Tel: (01282) 695641 Fax: (01282) 602496

M A P Systems, Unit 51, Bergen Way, North Lynn Industrial Estate, King's Lynn, Norfolk, PE30 2JG Tel: (01553) 764314 Fax: (01553) 769388 E-mail: eng@mapsystems.co.uk

M G C Engineering Ltd, Bradfords Quay, Wadebridge, Cornwall, PL27 6DB Tel: (01208) 812585 Fax: (01208) 814066 E-mail: mgceng@tiscali.co.uk

M & G Engineering, 1 James Chalmers Road, Kirkton Industrial Estate, Arbroath, Angus, DD11 3LR Tel: (01241) 870874 Fax: (01241) 870874

M J B Engineering Ltd, 133 Barkers Lane, Bedford, MK41 9RX Tel: (01234) 358454 Fax: (01234) 273423 E-mail: sales@mjbengineering.co.uk

M J B Engineering Services, Greg Street, Stockport, Cheshire, SK5 7BU Tel: 0161-476 5811 Fax: 0161-476 5844 E-mail: sales@mjb-engineering-services.com

M J Raven & Son Ltd, Unit 22 Patricia Way, Pysons Road Industrial Estate, Broadstairs, Kent, CT10 2LF Tel: (01843) 866676 Fax: (01843) 866070 E-mail: sales@mjraven.co.uk

M K W Engineering Ltd, Stargate Industrial Estate, Ryton, Tyne & Wear, NE40 3EX Tel: 0191-413 0000 Fax: 0191-413 2736 E-mail: sales@mkw.co.uk

M & M Technical Services Ltd, Ebberns Road, Hemel Hempstead, Hertfordshire, HP3 9RD Tel: (01442) 213602 Fax: (01442) 242152 E-mail: glfoord@tiscali.co.uk

M P Engineering, 7 Locke Place, Birmingham, B7 4HH Tel: 0121-359 5854 Fax: 0121-359 5854

Macleod Engineering, North Street Industrial Estate, Droitwich, Worcestershire, WR9 8JB Tel: (01905) 794578 Fax: (01905) 794965

Madeira Engineering, Queens Road, Southall, Middlesex, UB2 5BA Tel: (020) 8571 4627 Fax: (020) 8843 0292

Malin Bridge Engineering Ltd, 40 Worthing Road, Sheffield, S9 3JJ Tel: 0114-275 0860 Fax: 0114-275 0405

Man Ltd, 4-5 Grosvenor Place, London, SW1X 7DG Tel: (020) 7201 3366 Fax: (020) 7235 9450 E-mail: manfred.stelz@man-ltd.co.uk

Manuel Engineering Co. Ltd, Unit 33 Barking Industrial Park, Alfreds Way, Barking, Essex, IG11 0TJ Tel: (020) 8594 9264 Fax: (020) 8594 5507

Marine & General Engineers Ltd, PO Box 470, Guernsey, GY1 6AT Tel: (01481) 245808 Fax: (01481) 248765

D.R. Markey & Sons, Adcroft Street, Higher Hillgate, Stockport, Cheshire, SK1 3HZ Tel: 0161-480 1440 Fax: 0161-480 6164

Markwell Ltd, 24-25 Littlewood Lane, Hoveton, Norwich, NR12 8DZ Tel: (01603) 783053 Fax: (01603) 783053

N.& G. Marsh, Unit 12, Meadow Industrial Estate, Reach Road, Burwell, Cambridge, CB25 0GH Tel: (01638) 741354 Fax: (01638) 743424

Marske Fabrication & Engineering Ltd, Longbeck Estate, Marske-by-the-Sea, Redcar, Cleveland, TS11 6HB Tel: (01642) 482123 Fax: (01642) 470463

Marske Site Services Ltd, Suite 311, The Innovation Centre, Vienna Court, Kirkleatham Business Park, Redcar, Cleveland, TS10 5SH Tel: (01642) 777993 Fax: (01642) 777994 E-mail: tim.mccullagh@marske.com

Martec Engineering, Grange Road, Tipree, Colchester, CO5 0QQ Tel: (01621) 819673 Fax: (01621) 817297 E-mail: marteng@aol.com

Martin Aerospace Ltd, 2 Block 6, Caldwellside Industrial Estate, Lanark, ML11 7SR Tel: (01555) 664751 Fax: (01555) 665860 E-mail: sales@martinaerospace.com

Martin Jenkins Engineering Co. Ltd, Nicholls Road, Tipton, West Midlands, DY4 9LG Tel: 0121-557 3663 Fax: 0121-557 9517 E-mail: a7vos@aol.com

Marvic Textiles Ltd, Chelsea Harbour Design Centre, London, SW10 0XE Tel: (020) 7352 3119 Fax: (020) 8879 3448

Max Stone, Unit 3 Jubilee Trade Centre, Pershore Street, Birmingham, B5 6ND Tel: 0121-666 6704 Fax: 0121-622 2247 E-mail: sales@maxstone.co.uk

Mayflower Engineering Ltd, Coleridge Road, Sheffield, S9 5DA Tel: 0114-244 1353 Fax: 0114-244 5977 E-mail: sales@mayflower-engineering.co.uk

Maysmith Engineering Co Ltd, Unit 9, Woodlands Business Park, Woodlands Park Avenue, Maidenhead, Berkshire, SL6 3UA Tel: (01628) 828494 Fax: (01628) 829779

A.H. Mead & Son (Engineering) Ltd, Martel Works, High Easter Road, Dunmow, Essex, CM6 1NB Tel: (01371) 873907 Fax: (01371) 876703

Colin Mealing Ironworks, Mealings Yard, 55 High Street, Westbury-on-Trym, Bristol, BS9 3ED Tel: 0117-950 6262

Mecca Engineering, 13 Farrington Court, Burnley, Lancashire, BB11 5SS Tel: (01282) 452290 Fax: (01282) 452290

Mechanical Installations International Ltd, Richmond House, 66 Chepstow Road, Newport, Gwent, NP19 8JF Tel: (01633) 282115 Fax: (01633) 290159

Merlin Motor Co. Ltd, 3 Lodge Estate, Withybush Road, Haverfordwest, Dyfed, SA62 4BW Tel: (01437) 764928 Fax: (01437) 769628

Metal Fabrication Co (Cardiff) Ltd, East Moors Road, Cardiff, CF24 5EE Tel: (029) 2048 9767 Fax: (029) 2048 0407 E-mail: sales@metal-fab.co.uk

Metal Technology, 9 Viking Way, Bar Hill, Cambridge, CB23 8EL Tel: (01954) 781729 Fax: (01954) 789901

Metmachex Engineering Ltd, 9 Monk Road, Alfreton, Derbyshire, DE55 7RL Tel: (01773) 836241 Fax: (01773) 520109 E-mail: sales@metmachex.com

Metro Engineering Co., Unit 12 Chillington Fields, Wolverhampton, WV1 2BY Tel: (01902) 455254 Fax: (01902) 455254

Metsol Engineering, Ridgacre Enterprise Park, Ridgacre Road, West Bromwich, West Midlands, B71 1BW Tel: 0121-553 2189 Fax: 0121-525 3375 E-mail: metsolcnc@aol.com

Michill Engineering, Westcroft, Orton, Kettering, Northamptonshire, NN14 1LJ Tel: (01536) 710463 Fax: (01536) 710463

Micron Engineering Co., Dominion Works, Freshwater Road, Dagenham, Essex, RM8 1RX Tel: (020) 8983 8800 Fax: (020) 8983 8866 E-mail: micronengineering@unit5.freeserve.co.uk

Midd Engineering Coventry Ltd, Blackhorse Road, Exhall, Coventry, CV7 9FW Tel: (024) 7636 3033 Fax: (024) 7636 3044 E-mail: sales@midd-engineering.co.uk

Milbor Engineering Co. Ltd, Belswains Lane, Hemel Hempstead, Hertfordshire, HP3 9XE Tel: (01442) 242945 Fax: (01442) 257308 E-mail: enquiries@nashmills.herts.sch.uk

Mil-Tu-Fit, 246 Broomhill Road, Bristol, BS4 5RG Tel: 0117-971 7234 Fax: 0117-971 4789 E-mail: miltofit@hotmail.com

Mitchell Engineering Ltd, 10 Bridge Street, Cambuslang, Glasgow, G72 7ED Tel: 0141-641 2177 Fax: 0141-641 5185

Mitie Engineering Services Bristol Ltd, Novers House, Novers Hill, Bedminster, Bristol, BS3 5QY Tel: 0117-963 7361 Fax: 0117-966 9100 E-mail: helen.young@mitie.co.uk

Mogul Engineers Ltd, Chesterton Road, Eastwood Trading Estate, Rotherham, South Yorkshire, S65 1SU Tel: (01709) 379293 Fax: (01709) 378869 E-mail: enquires@mogul-engineers.co.uk

Morrison & Murray Engineering Ltd, Roxburgh Street, Galashiels, Selkirkshire, TD1 1PB Tel: (01896) 753226 Fax: (01896) 752570

Morse Systems Engineering, Unit 3, Wotton Road, Ashford, Kent, TN23 6LL Tel: (01233) 633800 Fax: (01233) 635500 E-mail: enquiries@morsesystems.co.uk

Mti Ltd, 8 Paramount Industrial Estate, Sandown Road, Watford, WD24 7XA Tel: (01923) 249844 Fax: (01923) 228951 E-mail: mti@dial.pipex.com

Mulco Engineering Ltd, 9-10 St Machar Road, Aberdeen, AB24 2UU Tel: (01224) 481215 Fax: (01224) 486041 E-mail: info@mulco.co.uk

Mycol Engineering, 75 Tenter Road, Moulton Park Industrial Estate, Northampton, NN3 6AX Tel: (01604) 790389 Fax: (01604) 790389

N S J Engineering, 231 Handsworth Road, Handsworth, Sheffield, S13 9BL Tel: 0114-243 1769 Fax: 0114-243 1408 E-mail: neil@nsjengineering.co.uk

Napier Bros Engineers Ltd, 67 King Street, Rutherglen, Glasgow, G73 1JS Tel: 0141-647 6282 Fax: 0141-613 1611

Neil Engineering, 28 Main Street, Glengarnock, Beith, Ayrshire, KA14 3AT Tel: (01505) 683608 Fax: (01505) 683608

Nelsons Birstall Ltd, Perseverance Works, Gelderd Road, Batley, West Yorkshire, WF17 9PX Tel: (01924) 474981 Fax: (01924) 440871 E-mail: sales@nelsonseng.co.uk

Newfold Ltd, Bridgewater Close, Reading, RG30 1NS Tel: 0118-957 3074 E-mail: sales@newfold.com

Newman Stallard Precision Engineers Ltd, 2 Westwood Court, Brunel Road, Totton, Southampton, SO40 3WX Tel: (023) 8086 4291 Fax: (023) 8042 8146

Nicolson Engineering Services Ltd, The Smiddy, Bowermadden, Wick, Caithness, KW1 4TT Tel: (01955) 641309 Fax: (01955) 641409

Nordic Marine Ltd, Unit 15 Prince Consort Industrial Estate, Hebburn, Tyne & Wear, NE31 1EH Tel: 0191-483 8370 Fax: 0191-483 2330

Norman Bailey Engineers Ltd, Britannia Works, Britannia Street, Bingley, West Yorkshire, BD16 2NS Tel: (01274) 562194 Fax: (01274) 562121 E-mail: norman-bailey@lycos.co.uk

NS Engineering Solutions, Units 23/24, Snibston Drive, Coalville, Leicestershire, LE67 3NQ Tel: (01530) 835400 Fax: (01530) 510947 E-mail: sales@nsengineering.co.uk

Nusell Engineering Co, 484 Penistone Road, Sheffield, S6 2FU Tel: 0114-233 0244 Fax: 0114-232 6998

Offa Industries Ltd, Offa House Unit 3 Knighton Enterprise Park, Ludlow Road, Knighton, Powys, LD7 1HJ Tel: (01547) 529401 Fax: (01547) 529398

Old Oak Engineering, Unit 11, Gilchrist Thomas Industrial Estate, Blaenavon, Pontypool, Gwent, NP4 9RL Tel: (01495) 791615 Fax: (01495) 790866

Onward Fabrications Ltd, Unit 65 Owen Road, Willenhall, West Midlands, WV13 2PZ Tel: 0121-526 5263 Fax: 0121-568 6138 E-mail: sales@onwardfabs.co.uk

Optima Products Ltd, Mill Road, Radstock, BA3 5TX Tel: (01761) 433461 Fax: (01761) 433919

Edward Owen Engineering, Unit 2, The Mazes, East Street, Braintree, Essex, CM7 3JJ Tel: (01376) 345631 Fax: (01376) 345631

P & A Leat Engineering Ltd, First Avenue, Midsomer Norton, Radstock, BA3 4BS Tel: (01761) 416964 Fax: (01761) 417134

P B H Precision Engineering Co. Ltd, 112 Windmill Road, Sunbury-on-Thames, Middlesex, TW16 7HB Tel: (01932) 785211 Fax: (01932) 781180 E-mail: sales@pbhprecision.com

P D O'Rourke Ltd, 30 Grafton Street, Liverpool, L8 5SF Tel: 0151-709 1694 Fax: 0151-709 3293 E-mail: admin@pdorourke.co.uk

P J Douglas Engineering Ltd, 2-4 Short Street, Uttoxeter, Staffordshire, ST14 7LH Tel: (01889) 568800 Fax: (01889) 568801 E-mail: peterdouglas@pjdltd.co.uk

P R Hollowayltd, 34 West Barnes Lane, Raynes Park, London, SW20 0BP Tel: (020) 8946 8872 Fax: (020) 8946 8872

P R Kyte, Unit 2 Hamilton Road, Sutton-in-Ashfield, Nottinghamshire, NG17 5LD Tel: (01623) 556636 Fax: (01623) 556636

Paramatta Tool & Gauge Co. Ltd, Worrall St, Salford, M5 4TH Tel: 0161-873 7655

Park Engineering, 20 Surrey Close, Granby Industrial Estate, Weymouth, Dorset, DT4 9TY Tel: (01305) 778420 Fax: (01305) 771401 E-mail: parkengin@aol.com

Parland Engineering Ltd, Unit 7, Cobblestone Court, Hoults Estate, Newcastle upon Tyne, NE6 1AB Tel: 0191-276 6660

John Parry-Jones Engineering, Unit 8A, Garth Works, Taffs Well, Cardiff, CF15 7YG Tel: (029) 2081 0089 Fax: (029) 2081 0089

Partex Engineering, 7a Hicks Road, Markyate, St. Albans, Hertfordshire, AL3 8LJ Tel: (01582) 840188 Fax: (01582) 840188

Pattison Eurotech Engineering Ltd, Western Industrial Estate, Caerleon, Newport, NP18 3NN Tel: (01633) 420133 Fax: (01633) 430181 E-mail: office@patteuro.com

Peers Jackson Engineering Company Ltd, Timmis Road, Stourbridge, West Midlands, DY9 7BQ Tel: (01384) 422503 Fax: (01384) 422568

Pel Engineering Ltd, Ashforth Street, Nottingham, NG3 4BG Tel: 0115-958 3022 Fax: 0115-958 3022

Penarth Industrial Services Ltd, 8 Gripoly Mills, Sloper Road, Cardiff, CF11 8AA Tel: (029) 2064 1555 Fax: (029) 2064 1899 E-mail: info@pisltd.com

Jack Pennington Ltd, 3 Hird Street, Shipley, West Yorkshire, BD17 7ED Tel: (01274) 534444 Fax: (01274) 534433 E-mail: sales@pennington.co.uk

Pepperl & Fuchs, 77 Ripponden Road, Oldham, OL1 4EL Tel: 0161-633 6431 Fax: 0161-624 6537 E-mail: sales@pepperl-fuchs.com

Percival Engineering Ltd, Spring Valley Lane, Ardleigh, Colchester, CO7 7SB Tel: (01206) 230064 Fax: (01206) 231655 E-mail: sales@percivalengineering.co.uk

▶ Peter Grant Associates Ltd, 18 Bakewell Road, Loughborough, Leicestershire, LE11 5QY Tel: (01509) 610580 Fax: (01509) 217346

Peterson Engineering Cleveland Ltd, Limerick Road, Redcar, Cleveland, TS10 5JU Tel: (01642) 472361 Fax: (01642) 488816 E-mail: info@peterson-engineering.co.uk

Philip Lodge Ltd, Machine Works, New Mill Road, Brockholes, Holmfirth, HD9 7AE Tel: (01484) 661143 Fax: (01484) 661164

Phillips Engineering, Bulmer Road Industrial Estate, Bulmer Road, Sudbury, Suffolk, CO10 7HJ Tel: (01787) 373549 Fax: (01787) 880276

Pipaway Engineering Ltd, Milton Road, Drayton, Abingdon, Oxfordshire, OX14 4EZ Tel: (01235) 531272 Fax: (01235) 523833

Plasian Products, Alkincote Street, Unit 5, Keighley, West Yorkshire, BD21 5JT Tel: (01535) 681975 Fax: (01535) 611471

Playle Engineering Co., Home Farm Works, Birch Park, Birch, Colchester, CO2 0LS Tel: (01206) 330315 Fax: (01206) 330138 E-mail: sales@playleengineering.com

Predominant Engs Ltd, Park Mill Industrial Estate, Manchester Road, Mossley, Ashton-under-Lyne, Lancashire, OL5 9BQ Tel: (01457) 832050 Fax: (01457) 835263

Premier Engineering Co. Ltd, 59a Virginia Street, Southport, Merseyside, PR8 6SJ Tel: (01704) 535955 Fax: (01704) 535955

Premier Plant Engineering, Hud Hey Road, Haslingden, Rossendale, Lancashire, BB4 5JH Tel: (01706) 222181 Fax: (01706) 222133 E-mail: info@premierplantengineering.co.uk

Priory Engineering Co Christchurch Ltd, 60 Purewell, Christchurch, Dorset, BH23 1ES Tel: (01202) 486538 Fax: (01202) 473740 E-mail: enquire@prioryengineering.co.uk

Projexe Engineering, 7 Merriott House, Hennock Road, Marsh Barton Trading Estate, Exeter, EX2 8NJ Tel: (01392) 258441 Fax: (01392) 498441

Qualicut Engineering Ltd, Wharf Street, Chadderton, Oldham, OL9 7PF Tel: 0161-633 1633 Fax: 0161-633 1660 E-mail: info@qualicut.co.uk

Quartic Engineering Ltd, Priory Road, Rochester, Kent, ME2 2EG Tel: (01634) 722522 Fax: (01634) 714150 E-mail: stewart@quarticeng.co.uk

Queensway Engineering Scunthorpe Ltd, 3a Banbury Road, Scunthorpe, South Humberside, DN16 1UL Tel: (01724) 851219 Fax: (01724) 849814

R G G Malmos, 52 Hainge Road, Tividale, Oldbury, West Midlands, B69 2PD Tel: 0121-522 2140 Fax: 0121-520 1773

R H Loveys, Lower Hare Farm, Whitestone, Exeter, EX4 2HW Tel: (01392) 811368

GENERAL ENGINEERING – *continued*

R J H Engineering, Eagle Road, Quarry Hill Industrial Estate, Ilkeston, Derbyshire, DE7 4RB Tel: 0115-944 5202 Fax: 0115-944 5202
R & J Hill Engineering Ltd, Parker Drive Business Centre, 47 Parker Drive, Leicester, LE4 0JP Tel: 0116-236 6888 Fax: 0116-236 8777 E-mail: sales@hillsport.com
R & J Turner Engineering, Purfleet Industrial Park, London Road, Aveley, South Ockendon, Essex, RM15 4YA Tel: (01708) 865043 Fax: (01708) 869403 E-mail: roger@rjturner.com
R M Mallen C N C Machinery Ltd, 15 Hainge Road, Tividale, Oldbury, West Midlands, B69 2NR Tel: 0121-557 3141 Fax: 0121-557 3814
R S Tools Ltd, Unit 8, Brunswick Road, Birmingham, B12 8NP Tel: 0121-440 4484 Fax: 0121-440 4484 E-mail: r.s.tools@btconnect.com
R Tindall Fabricators Ltd, Ward Street, Chadderton, Oldham, OL9 9EX Tel: 0161-624 3961 Fax: 0161-627 2978 E-mail: john@tindall-fabricators.co.uk
R Yates, 231 Scotia Road, Stoke-on-Trent, ST6 4EZ Tel: (01782) 837579 Fax: (01782) 835646
Radcot Armoured Components Ltd, Park Road, Faringdon, Oxfordshire, SN7 7BP Tel: (01367) 240970 Fax: (01367) 242641
Raffray Ltd, La Rue Sinnatt, La Rue Des Pres Trading Estate, St. Saviour, Jersey, JE2 7QT Tel: (07797) 721087 Fax: (01534) 769489 E-mail: michael@raffray.co.uk
Rainham Welding Works Ltd, 152 New Road, Rainham, Essex, RM13 8RS Tel: (01708) 554107 Fax: (01708) 554107
Ramic Engineering Co. Ltd, 96 Upper Wickham Lane, Welling, Kent, DA16 3HQ Tel: (020) 8855 7122 Fax: (020) 8854 8801 E-mail: ramengco@btconnect.com
Rank Engineering, Unit 4b Barton Hill Trading Estate, Herapath Street, Bristol, BS5 9RD Tel: 0117-955 1298 Fax: 0117-955 6528
Raywill Engineering Ltd, 87b Whitby Road, Slough, SL1 3DR Tel: (01753) 533552 Fax: (01753) 534464 E-mail: r_welch@btconnect.com
Reardon Engineering Co., Unit 6 9, 35 River Road, Barking, Essex, IG11 0DA Tel: (01708) 748253 Fax: (020) 8594 7398
Reboc Engineering Corp Ltd, 66 Sunbeam Road, Park Royal, London, NW10 6JQ Tel: (020) 8453 0284 Fax: (020) 8453 0288
Redco Ltd, Airedale House Sapphire Way, Rhombus Business Park, Norwich, NR6 6NN Tel: (01603) 400920 Fax: (01603) 418716 E-mail: rhredco@aol.com
Reliance Engineering, Unit 5 Knowle Industrial Estate, Knowle, Braunton, Devon, EX33 2NA Tel: (01271) 817642 Fax: (01271) 816594 E-mail: ggre240208@aol.com
Renco Engineering Machine Services, Unit 14 Deeleys Trading Estate, Leamore Lane, Walsall, WS2 7BY Tel: (01922) 476868 Fax: (01922) 476878
Renegade Engineering Co. Ltd, Unit F Penfold Works, Imperial Way, Watford, WD24 4YY Tel: (01923) 230788 Fax: (01923) 219496
Renown Engineering Ltd, South Cramlington Industrial Estate, Cramlington, Northumberland, NE23 7RH Tel: 0191-250 0113 Fax: 0191-250 1980 E-mail: sales@renown-engineering.co.uk
Resurgem Engineering Co. Ltd, Bury Manor, High Street, Wick, Bristol, BS30 5SH Tel: 0117-937 2987 Fax: 0117-937 3516 E-mail: sales@resurgem.co.uk
Ripling Engineering Ltd, Globe Mills, Lower Globe Street, Bradford, West Yorkshire, BD8 8JW Tel: (01274) 726727 Fax: (01274) 307772 E-mail: ripling@riplingeng.com
Robert Flannigan Engineering, 1 Flemington Industrial Park, Craigneuk Street, Motherwell, Lanarkshire, ML1 2NT Tel: (01698) 309307 Fax: (01698) 309312 E-mail: rfeconveyors@aol.com
Robson & Moss Ltd, Ings Road, Batley, West Yorkshire, WF17 8LT Tel: (01924) 477745 Fax: (01924) 470053
Rod Rite Engeering Ltd, Unit 15 Horsehay Works, Horsehay Estate, Telford, Shropshire, TF4 3PY Tel: (01952) 630055 Fax: (01952) 505289
Rollo Engineering Ltd, St Andrews Works, Bonnybridge, Stirlingshire, FK4 2EJ Tel: (01324) 812469 Fax: (01324) 814040 E-mail: mail@rolloeng.co.uk
Rollo UK Ltd, Womersley Road, Grimsby, South Humberside, DN31 3SH Tel: (01472) 358989 Fax: (01472) 241141 E-mail: b.merrison@rollouk.com
Rylandes Engineering Ltd, Broomfield Barn, Coolham Road, Shipley, Horsham, West Sussex, RH13 8PF Tel: (01403) 741268 Fax: (01403) 741605 E-mail: sales@rylandesengineering.co.uk
S A S Engineering Ltd, Fengate, Peterborough, PE1 5XB Tel: (01733) 312522 Fax: (01733) 314221 E-mail: sasfengate@aol.com
S G D Engineers, Unit 14c Whitebridge Industrial Estate, Whitebridge Lane, Stone, Staffordshire, ST15 8LQ Tel: (01785) 811104 Fax: (01785) 811104 E-mail: andrew.ward6@btconnect.com
S J Clifford & Co. Ltd, B 19 Bayton Road Industrial Estate, Bayton Road, Exhall, Coventry, CV7 9EL Tel: (024) 7636 3961 Fax: (024) 7664 4097 E-mail: sales@sjclifford.co.uk
S J H Sparkes & Sons Ltd, 20 Devonshire Road, Cambridge, CB1 2BH Tel: (01223) 356172 Fax: (01223) 356172
S.J.S. Engineering, 114-116 Newhall Street, Willenhall, West Midlands, WV13 1LQ Tel: (01902) 606602 Fax: (01902) 606011
S L W Engineering, Dereham Road, New Costessey, Norwich, NR5 0SB Tel: (01603) 749346
S & P Blair & Son, Bayswell Park, Dunbar, East Lothian, EH42 1AE Tel: (01368) 862371 Fax: (01368) 862051 E-mail: sales@spblair.com
S Z Gears Ltd, Pontymister Industrial Estate, Risca, Newport, Gwent, NP11 6NP Tel: (01633) 612071 Fax: (01633) 612626
S2 Engineering, 4 Derwenthaugh Marina, Blaydon-on-Tyne, Tyne & Wear, NE21 5LL Tel: 0191-414 2300 Fax: 0191-414 2287 E-mail: info@s2eng.co.uk
Sampson Engineering Co., Stanley Road, Bradford, West Yorkshire, BD2 1AS Tel: (01274) 723299
Seafab Consultants Ltd, Wellheads Terrace, Wellheads Industrial Estate, Aberdeen, AB21 7GF Tel: (01224) 770287 Fax: (01224) 723400 E-mail: info@seafab.co.uk
Select Engineering, Broad Ground Road, Redditch, Worcestershire, B98 8YP Tel: (01527) 517157 Fax: (01527) 517145 E-mail: info@select-engineering.co.uk
Selva Engineering Ltd, Checketts Lane, Worcester, WR3 7JP Tel: (01905) 452877 Fax: (01905) 452699
Seychell Engineering & Fabrication Ltd, 8 Arkwright Road, Bicester, Oxfordshire, OX26 4SU Tel: (01869) 322035 Fax: (01869) 321174 E-mail: seychellgroup@btconnect.com
Shepcote Engineering Ltd, Davy Indust Park, Prince of Wales Road, Sheffield, S9 4EX Tel: 0114-256 2505 Fax: 0114-261 1910 E-mail: enquiries@shepcote-eng.com
Sheridan Engineering, Unit 7, Hunters Lane Industrial Estate, Rugby, Warwickshire, CV21 1EA Tel: (01788) 579483 Fax: (01788) 579483
Sheridan Engineering Hereford, 4 Parkwood Court, Rotherwas Industrial Estate, Hereford, HR2 6NU Tel: (01432) 269683 Fax: (01432) 354410 E-mail: sales@sheridanengineering.co.uk
Shilldown Ltd, 16g Chalwyn Industrial Estate, Old Wareham Road, Poole, Dorset, BH12 4PE Tel: (01202) 722711 Fax: (01202) 722711
Silverthorne Engineering Co., Attwood Street, Stourbridge, West Midlands, DY9 8RU Tel: (01384) 897639 Fax: (01384) 423980 E-mail: t.hoskins@virgin.net
Silvester Engineering Ltd, Kingsmead, Marringdean Rd, Billingshurst, West Sussex, RH14 9HE Tel: (01403) 782255 Fax: (01403) 782703 E-mail: sales@silvesterengineering.co.uk
Skerritt Electrical Ltd, 1087 Kingsbury Road, Castle Vale, Birmingham, B35 6AJ Tel: 0121-776 5710 Fax: 0121-322 2216 E-mail: admin@skerrittelectrical.co.uk
Slater & Green, Bath Mill, Byron Street, Royton, Oldham, OL2 6QZ Tel: 0161-624 7160 Fax: 0161-628 7552
Smart Manufacturing Ltd, Clovelly Road Ind Estate, Bideford, Devon, EX39 3HN Tel: 01237 471977
Smillie & Cuthbertson Ltd, 17 James Little St, Kilmarnock, Ayrshire, KA1 4AU Tel: 01563 521819
Smith Engineering GB Ltd, Solway Trading Estate, Maryport, Cumbria, CA15 8NF Tel: (01900) 815831 Fax: (01900) 815553 E-mail: r.smith@moonbuggy.com
Smiths Engineering Works N I Ltd, Larne Road, Ballymena, County Antrim, BT42 3HA Tel: (028) 2564 1621 Fax: (028) 2564 3724
Specialised Assemblies (Wellingborough) Ltd, Engineering Works, Higham Road, Burton Latimer, Kettering, Northamptonshire, NN15 5PU Tel: (01536) 420102 Fax: (01536) 420097 E-mail: markv@specassy.com
Specialist Heavy Engineers plc, Alexandra Docks, Newport, Gwent, NP20 2NP Tel: (01633) 262961 Fax: (01633) 246342 E-mail: she.industrial@btinternet.com
Spectroform Engineering Services Ltd, 1a Saxby Road Industrial Estate, Hudson Road, Melton Mowbray, Leicestershire, LE13 1BS Tel: (01664) 500728 Fax: (01664) 410509 E-mail: sales@spectroform.co.uk
Speed Bird Engineering, 21 Cunliffe Drive Industrial Estate, Cunliffe Drive, Kettering, Northamptonshire, NN16 8LD Tel: (01536) 524240 Fax: (01536) 520689 E-mail: nitulpanchal@speedbird-engineering.com
Sprague Equipment Ltd, 2 Roberts Street, Liverpool, L3 7AS Tel: 0151-236 0317 Fax: 0151-236 0260
Spur Engineering Services Ltd, River Gardens Business Centre, Spur Road, Feltham, Middlesex, TW14 0SN Tel: (020) 8844 0887 Fax: (020) 8844 0887 E-mail: sales@spurengineering.co.uk
Spyder Engineering Ltd, Fenland District Industrial Estate, Station Road, Whittlesey, Peterborough, PE7 2EY Tel: (01733) 203986 Fax: (01733) 350662
Stable Engineering Ltd, Dinas Road, Tonypandy, Mid Glamorgan, CF40 1JQ Tel: (01443) 682364 Fax: (01443) 686109
▶ Stable Precision, 7 Silver Business Park, Airfield Way, Christchurch, Dorset, BH23 3TA Tel: (01202) 487755 Fax: (01202) 485522 E-mail: sales@stableprecision.co.uk
Standish Engineering Co. Ltd, Mayflower Works, Bradley Lane, Standish, Wigan, Lancashire, WN6 0XF Tel: (01257) 422838 Fax: (01257) 422381 E-mail: enquiries@cnc-machining.co.uk
Steadman Engineering Ltd, Steadman House, Dockfield Road, Shipley, West Yorkshire, BD17 7AZ Tel: (01274) 531531 Fax: (01274) 531044
Steelock Engineering Ltd, Unit 42 Pioneer Mills, Milltown Street, Radcliffe, Manchester, M26 1WN Tel: 0161-724 4066 Fax: 0161-724 4066
Stoneway Engineering, Unit 2 The Warehouse, Benson Lane, Normanton, West Yorkshire, WF6 2HX Tel: (01924) 895959 Fax: (01924) 890721
Stroma Engineering Ltd, 21 Bickford Road, Birmingham, B6 7EE Tel: 0121-327 5550 Fax: 0121-327 2314
Sunbury Engineering Co. Ltd, Town Mill Works, Hanbury Street, Droitwich, Worcestershire, WR9 8PL Tel: (01905) 773341 Fax: (01905) 779072
Swefco Ltd, 188 Corporation Road, Newport, Gwent, NP19 0DQ Tel: (01633) 250170 Fax: (01633) 250171E-mail: swefco@aol.com
T Crossling & Co. Ltd, Portrack Grange Road, Stockton-on-Tees, Cleveland, TS18 2PF Tel: (01642) 616996 Fax: (01642) 616231 E-mail: sales@crossling.co.uk
T H G Engineering Services (Chepstow) Ltd, Rivendell, Rockwood Road, Chepstow, Gwent, NP16 5DT Tel: (01291) 624134
T & P Tooling Co., Mardyke Works, St Marys Lane, North Ockendon, Upminster, Essex, RM14 3PA Tel: (01708) 224220 Fax: (01708) 224220
T R A Engineering New Mills Ltd, Hague Bar, High Peak, Derbyshire, SK22 3AT Tel: (01663) 743541 Fax: (01663) 743541
Tate Engineering, Tate Estate, Kingsdown Road, Swindon, SN25 6SF Tel: (01793) 820503 Fax: (01793) 820504 E-mail: tate.engineering@virgin.net
Taylor Made Fabrication, 6 Pipers Industrial Estate, Pipers Lane, Thatcham, Berkshire, RG19 4NA Tel: (01635) 873737 Fax: (01635) 874747 E-mail: info.request@taylormadefabrication.co.uk
Taylor & Sons Ltd, Briton Ferry, Neath, West Glamorgan, SA11 2JA Tel: (01639) 813251 Fax: (01639) 812342
Taylors Engineering, Nether Works, Nethergate Street, Bungay, Suffolk, NR35 1HE Tel: (01986) 892422 Fax: (01986) 892422
Team Rewinds Ltd, Don Street, Princes Way North, Team Valley Trading Estate, Gateshead, Tyne & Wear, NE11 0TU Tel: 0191-482 3374 Fax: 0191-482 6222 E-mail: sales@teamrewindsltd.co.uk
Techman Engineering Ltd, Techman House, Broombank Park, Chesterfield Trading Estate, Sheepbridge, Chesterfield, Derbyshire, S41 9RT Tel: (01246) 261385 Fax: (01246) 453734 E-mail: enquiries@techman-engineering.co.uk
Tews Engineering Ltd, 34 Lavant Street, Petersfield, Hampshire, GU32 3EF Tel: (01730) 268531 Fax: (01730) 262141 E-mail: admin@tews.uk.com
Thing Ama Jigs Ltd, 136 Oyster Lane, Byfleet, West Byfleet, Surrey, KT14 7JQ Tel: (01932) 340764 Fax: (01932) 351280
Thomas Hamlin & Co., 64 Monmouth Street, Bridgwater, Somerset, TA6 5EJ Tel: (01278) 422452 Fax: (01278) 424036
Thomson Pettie, Canal Bank Estate, Seabegs Road, Bonnybridge, Stirlingshire, FK4 2BP Tel: (01324) 815747 Fax: (01324) 819072
Thorne Engineers Ltd, Millfield Industrial Estate, York, YO19 6NA Tel: 01904 448890
Thurston Engineering Ltd, Hallsford Bridge Industrial Estate, Stondon Road, Ongar, Essex, CM5 9RB Tel: (01277) 362135 Fax: (01277) 365076 E-mail: sales@thurstonengineering.co.uk
Timac, Unit 8 Stratton Business Park, Edworth, Biggleswade, Bedfordshire, SG18 8QB Tel: (01767) 312849 Fax: (01767) 601388 E-mail: timac.engineering@freenet.co.uk
Times of Wigan Ltd, Bridge St, Wigan, Lancashire, WN3 4EY Tel: 01942 234852
Timmick Precision Engineering, 17 Arkwright Court, Astmoor, Runcorn, Cheshire, WA7 1NX Tel: (01928) 563009 Fax: (01928) 563009
Tow Path Ltd, Unit 150 Medway Enterprise Centre, Enterprise Close, Medway City Estate, Rochester, Kent, ME2 4SY Tel: (01634) 296644 Fax: (01634) 724152
Towler Engineering Ltd, 34 Oxford Road, Clacton-on-Sea, Essex, CO15 3TB Tel: (01255) 423723 Fax: (01255) 434484
Trafalgar Engineering Co., Station Road, Station Mills, Cottingham, North Humberside, HU16 4LL Tel: (01482) 843558
Trafalgar Textile Co. Ltd, Greenbrook Works, Lowerhouse Lane, Burnley, Lancashire, BB12 6ND Tel: (01282) 772923 Fax: (01282) 772923
Trelawney Engineering, Old Yard Workshop, Vansittart, Windsor, Berkshire, SL4 1SE Tel: (01753) 850300 E-mail: info@trelawneyengineering.co.uk
Trevus Tools, Park View Works, Park Street, Stalybridge, Cheshire, SK15 2BT Tel: 0161-338 8398 Fax: 0161-338 8398
Triad Phoenix Engineering Ltd, Wigwam Lane, Hucknall, Nottingham, NG15 7TA Tel: 0115-963 4020 Fax: 0115-963 4020
Tritan Engineering Ltd, Bondgate, Green Lane, Ripon, North Yorkshire, HG4 1QQ Tel: (01765) 601608 Fax: (01765) 606800
Tryst Engineering Ltd, Fairfield Works, West Wycombe Road, High Wycombe, Buckinghamshire, HP11 2LR Tel: (01494) 442497 Fax: (01494) 465829 E-mail: tryst@ndirect.co.uk
Tubros Engineering Ltd, Stanley Street, Workington, Cumbria, CA14 2JD Tel: (01900) 64444 Fax: (01900) 603292
Tunnicliff Engineering Co. Ltd, 30 Derby Road, Hinckley, Leicestershire, LE10 1QF Tel: (01455) 637220 Fax: (01455) 637220
Turnwell Engineering, 4 Heritage Way, Corby, Northamptonshire, NN17 5XW Tel: (01536) 260043 Fax: (01536) 260043
Twinbridge Engineering Co., Langley Place, Burscough Industrial Estate, Ormskirk, Lancashire, L40 8JS Tel: (01704) 892959 Fax: (01704) 894892 E-mail: sales@twinbridge.co.uk
Ufone Precision Engineers Ltd, Unit 21 Thornleigh Trading Estate, Dudley, West Midlands, DY2 8UB Tel: (01384) 233288 Fax: (01384) 252931 E-mail: enquiries@ufone-eng.com
Victoria Production Engineering Ltd, Oldham Street, Denton, Manchester, M34 3SA Tel: 0161-320 1800 Fax: 0161-320 1810 E-mail: sales@victoriaproduction.co.uk
Volkobind Engineering Company Ltd, Unit 1 Tansey Green Trading Estate, Tansey Green Road, Brierley Hill, West Midlands, DY5 4TA Tel: (01384) 79746 Fax: (01384) 75737 E-mail: sales@volkobind.co.uk
W A Carr Engineering Ltd, 60 Broad Oaks, Sheffield, S9 3HJ Tel: 0114-256 2222 Fax: 0114-256 2474
W D M Engineers Ltd, Units 4-6, Pontygwindy Industrial Estate, Caerphilly, Mid Glamorgan, CF83 3HU Tel: (029) 2086 7750 Fax: (029) 2086 9938
W Stone & Sons, 20 Lodge Causeway, Bristol, BS16 3JB Tel: 0117-965 3125 Fax: 0117-965 3125
William Waddell Ltd, 30 Russell Street, Wishaw, Lanarkshire, ML2 7AN Tel: (01698) 355034 Fax: (01698) 374970
David Walker Engineering Services, St Lawrence Industrial Estate, Manston Road, Ramsgate, Kent, CT11 0QZ Tel: (01843) 589954 Fax: (01843) 589954
J. Walsh Spinnings, Unit 2, 58 Caroline Street, Hockley, Birmingham, B3 1UF Tel: 0121-233 3258 Fax: 0121-233 3258
Wantage Engineering Co. Ltd, 6 W & G Industrial Estate, Faringdon Road, East Challow, Wantage, Oxfordshire, OX12 9TF Tel: (01235) 764161 Fax: (01235) 764163 E-mail: sales@wantageengineer.f9.co.uk
Warbeck Engineering Services, 12 Regent Road, Liverpool, L3 7DS Tel: 0151-236 9494 Fax: 0151-236 9988 E-mail: warbreckengineering.servicesltd@virgin.net
Washford Engineering Ltd, Unit 41, Crossgate Road, Park Farm Industrial Estate, Redditch, Worcestershire, B98 7SN Tel: (01527) 525390 Fax: (01527) 510241 E-mail: enquiries@washfordengineering.co.uk
Washington Components Ltd, Prestex House, Hertburn Industrial Estate, Hertburn, Washington, Tyne & Wear, NE37 2SF Tel: 0191-416 9676 Fax: 0191-417 7087 E-mail: sales@washingtoncomponents.co.uk
Watmoor Engineering Co. Ltd, Dawley Road, Hayes, Middlesex, UB3 1EE Tel: (020) 8573 6877 Fax: (020) 8573 1880 E-mail: barry.robins@btclick.com
Waveney Engineering Co. Ltd, 12a Crankill Road, Ballymena, County Antrim, BT43 5JF Tel: (028) 2564 4700 Fax: (028) 2565 9533 E-mail: sales@waveneyengltd.co.uk
Welburn Precision Engineering Ltd, Barrys Lane, Scarborough, North Yorkshire, YO12 4HA Tel: (01723) 366453 Fax: (01723) 500729
Weltool Engineering Co. Ltd, 25 Aston Court, Kingsland Grange, Woolston, Warrington, WA1 4SG Tel: (01925) 813449
West Surrey Engineering Ltd, Enterprise House, Ashford Road, Ashford, Middlesex, TW15 1XG Tel: (01784) 254085 Fax: (01784) 247785 E-mail: sales@wse.co.uk
Westcombe Industries Ltd, Royce Road, Peterborough, PE1 5YB Tel: (01733) 746300 Fax: (01733) 746310
Wetherby Engineering Co. Ltd, Britannia Mills, Portland St, Bradford, West Yorkshire, BD5 0DW Tel: (01274) 827216 Fax: (01274) 390527 E-mail: sales@wetherby-engineering.co.uk
Whiddon Valley Engineering Ltd, Units 4 & 5, Castle Park Road, Whiddon Valley Industrial Estate, Barnstaple, Devon, EX32 8PA Tel: (01271) 376288 Fax: (01271) 323474 E-mail: wve@btconnect.com
Whipple Engineering Co. Ltd, Manor Farm, Caldecott, Wellingborough, Northamptonshire, NN9 6AR Tel: (01933) 461711
Whittlesey Engineering Co. Ltd, Fenland District Industrial Estate, Station Road, Whittlesey, Peterborough, PE7 2EY Tel: (01733) 203766 Fax: (01733) 350808
William Hinsley Engineers Ltd, 1 Croft Street, Sowerby Bridge, West Yorkshire, HX6 2AJ Tel: (01422) 839968
Wilson Tool & Engineering Co Essex Ltd, 2-4 Parsons Road, Manor Trading Estate, Benfleet, Essex, SS7 4PY Tel: (01268) 752836 Fax: (01268) 565323 E-mail: sales@wilson-tool.co.uk
Winstanley & Co. Ltd, Racecourse Road, Pershore, Worcestershire, WR10 2DG Tel: (01386) 552278 Fax: (01386) 556531 E-mail: winstanleyco@compuserve.com

GENERAL ENGINEERING – *continued*

Wood Group Pressure Control Ltd, Blackhouse Circle, Blackhouse Industrial Estate, Peterhead, Aberdeenshire, AB42 1BN Tel: (01779) 474293 Fax: (01779) 474298

R.J. Woods Engineering & Materials Consultancy, 86 Stanley Green Road, Poole, Dorset, BH15 3AG Tel: (01202) 671169 Fax: (01202) 671169

Woolf Engineering, Pennybridge Industrial Estate, Ballymena, County Antrim, BT42 3HB Tel: (028) 2564 7938 Fax: (028) 2564 5102 E-mail: info@woolfengineering.com

Wragg Bros Engineering Ltd, Keys Road, Nixs Hill Industrial Estate, Alfreton, Derbyshire, DE55 7FQ Tel: (01773) 832288 Fax: (01773) 520776

Wright Engineering Rainham Ltd, Imperial Trading Estate, Lambs La North, Rainham, Essex, RM13 9XL Tel: (01708) 554618 Fax: (01708) 553395 E-mail: wright0458@aol.com

Xavier Engineering Ltd, Fleetwood Road, Lune Street, Padiham, Burnley, Lancashire, BB12 8DG Tel: (01282) 680000 Fax: (01282) 680888 E-mail: sales@xavier-eng.co.uk

Zendstate Invicta Ltd, Chegworth Court, Chegworth Road, Harrietsham, Maidstone, Kent, ME17 1DG Tel: (01622) 859941 Fax: (01622) 859941

GENERAL ENGINEERING ULTRASONIC CLEANING EQUIPMENT

▶ Alphasonics Ultrasonic Equipment Mnfrs, Caddick Road, Knowsley Business Park, Prescot, Merseyside, L34 9HP Tel: 0151-547 3777 Fax: 0151-547 1333 E-mail: alphasonics@alphasonics.co.uk

GENERAL ENGRAVERS

A D Signs & Engraving Ltd, Unit 3 Webner Industrial Estate, Alltingshaw Road, Wolverhampton, WV2 2LD Tel: (01902) 353535 Fax: (01902) 496775 E-mail: sales@ad-signs.co.uk

A E S Engraving Co. Ltd, Unit 19, Boulton Industrial Centre, Hockley, Birmingham, B18 5AU Tel: 0121-551 9525 Fax: 0121-551 9535 E-mail: enquiries@aes-signs.com

A & H Brass, 209 Edgware Road, London, W2 1ES Tel: (020) 7706 2262 Fax: (020) 7402 0110 E-mail: sales@aandhbrass.co.uk

A W Engraving, 11 Lifford Way, Binley Industrial Estate, Coventry, CV3 2RN Tel: (024) 7663 5453 Fax: (024) 7663 5486

Abbey Engraving, Unit 15 New Horizon Business Centre, Barrows Road, Harlow, Essex, CM19 5FN Tel: (01279) 626277 Fax: (01279) 626277 E-mail: info@abbeyengraving.co.uk

Ace Engraving Ltd, 12 Vulcan House, Vulcan Road North, Norwich, NR6 6AQ Tel: (01603) 485667 Fax: (01603) 485667 E-mail: sales@aceengraving.co.uk

Acorn Engraving Co., 4 Pump Lane, Regent Business Centre, Hayes, Middlesex, UB3 3NP Tel: (020) 8848 7367 Fax: (020) 8756 1028

Allen Signs Ltd, Waddington House, Whisby Way, Lincoln, LN6 3LQ Tel: (01522) 501500 Fax: (01522) 501600 E-mail: enquiries@allensigns.co.uk

Almonds Engravers, 12 Duke Street, Darlington, County Durham, DL3 7AA Tel: (01325) 464808 Fax: (01325) 464808

W.R. Anderton Group, Maltings Lane, Castleton, Rochdale, Lancs, OL11 2UY Tel: (01706) 631277 Fax: (01706) 358201 E-mail: info@andertongroup.com

B.H.R. Precision Engraving, Units 215 Victory Business Centre, Somers Road North, Portsmouth, PO1 1PJ Tel: (023) 9281 6613 Fax: (023) 9281 6613

▶ Bay Area Sign Solutions, Unit 1, Farfield Business Park, Main Road, Wykeham, Scarborough, North Yorkshire, YO13 9QB Tel: (01723) 866680 Fax: (01723) 865509 E-mail: info@bay-area.co.uk

Beta Engravers (Northampton) Ltd, Clarence Avenue, Northampton, NN2 6NY Tel: (01604) 715152 Fax: (01604) 717131

Bon Accord Trophies, 121 Crown Street, Aberdeen, AB11 6HN Tel: (01224) 576226 Fax: (01224) 585089 E-mail: info@soccerworldscotland.co.uk

Briggs Priestley Ltd, 1-3 Lord Street, Halifax, West Yorkshire, HX1 5AE Tel: (01422) 354565 Fax: (01422) 356687 E-mail: dan@briggspriestley.ndo.co.uk

Bromsgrove & Redditch Trophies Ltd, 485 Evesham Road, Redditch, Worcestershire, B97 5JJ Tel: (01527) 550556 Fax: (01527) 550866 E-mail: admin@brchc.u-net.com

Roger Brown Trophies, 372 Carden Avenue, Brighton, BN1 8LJ Tel: (01273) 559110 Fax: (01273) 500298

C & M Trophies & Engraving, 5 Arundel Road, Littlehampton, West Sussex, BN17 7BY Tel: (01903) 717766 Fax: (01903) 731377 E-mail: enquires@candmtrophies.co.uk

C & R Walne, 74 Burnley Road, Accrington, Lancashire, BB5 1AF Tel: (01254) 231384 Fax: (01254) 390737 E-mail: info@walne-engravers.co.uk

Chandlers Engraver & Sign Co., 42 Market Row, Great Yarmouth, Norfolk, NR30 1PB Tel: (01493) 844126 Fax: (01493) 844126

Classic Miniatures Ltd, 8 Heathlands Close, Twickenham, TW1 4BP Tel: (020) 8892 3686 Fax: (020) 8744 1142 E-mail: sales@classicminiatures.co.uk

Classic Trophies UK, 27 Roman Road, Middlesbrough, Cleveland, TS5 6EA Tel: (01642) 881040 Fax: (01642) 881035

Clifton Services, 18 Donegall Street, Belfast, BT1 2GP Tel: (028) 9024 2396

Computerised Engraving, 10 Waterloo Road, Widnes, Cheshire, WA8 0PY Tel: 0151-420 4590 Fax: 0151-495 1132 E-mail: info@computerisedengraving.com

Contelec Engravings Ltd, Spring Lane, Willenhall, West Midlands, WV12 4JG Tel: (01902) 369307 Fax: (01902) 369309 E-mail: engrave@contelec.co.uk

County Engravers, 1 Newcombe Road, Northampton, NN5 7AZ Tel: (01604) 585565 Fax: (01604) 585565 E-mail: countyengrevers@supanet.com

Crescent Signs & Engraving, Unit 5q, Faraday Road, Newbury, Berkshire, RG14 2AD Tel: (01635) 528037 Fax: (01635) 49549 E-mail: enquiries@crescentsigns.co.uk

Crescent Silver Repairs & Restoration, 85 Spencer Street, Birmingham, B18 6DE Tel: 0121-236 9006 Fax: 0121-212 1466 E-mail: mail@cresent-silver.co.uk

Crystal Class, Unit 2b Mill Park Industrial Estate, Woodbury Salterton, Exeter, EX5 1EL Tel: (01395) 233362 Fax: (01395) 233362

D J Morgan Engravers Ltd, 53 Warwick Street, Coventry, CV5 6ET Tel: (024) 7671 1232 Fax: (024) 7671 1232 E-mail: djmorgan@btconnect.com

Dartford Engraving Ltd, 4 Power Works Estate, Slade Green Road, Erith, Kent, DA8 2HY Tel: (01322) 340194 Fax: (01322) 347819 E-mail: mail@desp.co.uk

Direct Auto Electrics, 126 Myton Drive, Shirley, Solihull, West Midlands, B90 1HH Tel: (07966) 398848 Fax: 0121-436 6235 E-mail: sales@directautoelectrics.co.uk

Dry Transfers Ltd, 1 Jubilee Street, Melton Mowbray, Leicestershire, LE13 1ND Tel: (01664) 565785 Fax: (01664) 410344 E-mail: sales@dry-transfers.co.uk

▶ Peter Dudley Exhibitions & Displays, Uttoxer Road, Blithbury, Rugeley, Staffordshire, WS15 3JG Tel: (01889) 504284 Fax: (01889) 504284

East Herts Signs & Engraving, 3 Old Cross, Hertford, SG14 1HX Tel: (01992) 553004 Fax: (01992) 501165

Elite Engraving, 6 Park Road, Kingswood, Bristol, BS15 1QU Tel: 0117-967 0034 Fax: 0117-967 0043 E-mail: eliteengraving@btconnect.com

Ellis Signs, Dunstan Road Railway Street, Gateshead, Tyne & Wear, NE11 9EE Tel: 0191-477 1600 Fax: 0191-460 4460 E-mail: bernerd@ellisssigns.fsnet.co.uk

Emslie Industrial Engraving Co., 62 West Harbour Road, Edinburgh, EH5 1PW Tel: 0131-552 9944 Fax: 0131-552 1093

England Signs, The Malthouse, Main St, Offenham, Evesham, Worcs, WR11 8QD Tel: (01386) 442712 Fax: (01386) 442977

Engraving Services, 102 Chester Road, Talke, Stoke-on-Trent, ST7 1SD Tel: (01782) 782270 Fax: (01782) 787020 E-mail: engravingservices@tinyworld.co.uk

Entech Precision Engraving, 4 Old Forge Cottage, Pearson Road, Sonning, Reading, RG4 6UH Tel: 0118-927 2499 Fax: 0118-927 2499 E-mail: ejak@btclick.com

▶ Eyre & Baxter (Stampcraft) Ltd, 229 Derbyshire Lane, Sheffield, S8 8SD Tel: 0114-250 0153 Fax: 0114-258 0856 E-mail: sales@eyreandbaxter.co.uk

Fairway Engineering (Bristol) Ltd, Station Road Workshops, Station Road, Kingswood, Bristol, BS15 4PJ Tel: 0117-940 9030 Fax: 0117-940 9030E-mail: tony@fairwayeng.freeserve.co.uk

▶ Fine Cut Graphic Imaging Ltd, Marlborough Road, Lancing Business Park, Lancing, West Sussex, BN15 8UF Tel: (01903) 751666 Fax: (01903) 750462 E-mail: info@finecut.co.uk

Fitt Signs Ltd, 60-62 Pitt Street, Norwich, NR3 1DF Tel: (01603) 619128 Fax: (01603) 760524 E-mail: info@fitt-signs.co.uk

Flo-Code (UK) Ltd, Gable End, Holmbury St. Mary, Dorking, Surrey, RH5 6LQ Tel: 01306 731863 Fax: 01306 731864 E-mail: info@flo-code.co.uk

Fortune UK Ltd, Wyvenhoe, Farnham Road, Farnham Royal, Slough, SL2 3AE Tel: (01753) 669471 Fax: (01753) 669472 E-mail: info@fortuneuk.com

G R C Engraving Ltd, 14 Darley Road, Ferndown, Dorset, BH22 8QX Tel: (01202) 861297 Fax: (01202) 861297

G R S Sign Co. Ltd, Tateshall Way, Fairfield Industrial Estate, Louth, Lincolnshire, LN11 0YZ Tel: (01507) 609485 Fax: (01507) 609489 E-mail: sales@grssigns.co.uk

Gilchrist & Co., 90 Donegall Passage, Belfast, BT7 1BX Tel: (028) 9023 2453 Fax: (028) 9032 6790

Global Signs & Engraving Ltd, Admiralty Road, Great Yarmouth, Norfolk, NR30 3PU Tel: (01493) 843300 Fax: (01493) 843340 E-mail: globalsigns@ukonline.co.uk

Good Acre Engraving, 120 Main Street, Sutton Bonington, Loughborough, Leicestershire, LE12 5PF Tel: (01509) 673082 Fax: (01509) 673082 E-mail: goodacre@ndirect.co.uk

Grabern Engraving, Oyster Place, 28 Montrose Rd, Chelmsford, CM2 6TX Tel: (01245) 468223 Fax: (01245) 469121 E-mail: sales@grabernengraving.com

Gravutex Eschmann International Ltd, Unit 10 Peakdale Road, Brookfield Industrial Estate, Glossop, Derbyshire, SK13 6LQ Tel: (01457) 867627 Fax: (01457) 855536 E-mail: aharrison@gravutexeshman.co.uk

Greengate Engraving Ltd, 292 High Street, Stoke-on-Trent, ST6 5TY Tel: (01782) 822884 Fax: (01782) 815345

Hallmark Engraving, 116-118 Selsdon Road, South Croydon, Surrey, CR2 6PG Tel: (020) 8686 6649 Fax: (020) 8760 0899 E-mail: sales@hallmarksigns.co.uk

Hi Tech Hardware, 219 Station Road, Harrow, Middlesex, HA1 2TH Tel: (020) 8863 9462 Fax: (020) 8863 9462

Horsham Engraving Ltd, Foundry Lane, Horsham, West Sussex, RH13 5PX Tel: (01403) 260729 Fax: (01403) 210057 E-mail: horshamengraving@aol.com

Howard 2000 Ltd, Howard Centre, Paper Mill End, Great Barr, Unit 4, Birmingham, B44 8NH Tel: 0121-356 9833 Fax: 0121-356 0280

Howdens Signs Ltd, 94 Burley Road, Leeds, LS3 1JP Tel: 0113-245 7752 Fax: 0113-242 6993 E-mail: sales@howdenssigns.com

I D C Signs & Engraving, 26 Harwood Street, Blackburn, BB1 3BS Tel: (01254) 263679 Fax: (01254) 263699 E-mail: sales@idcsigns.co.uk

Ica Solutions Ltd, 1 115 Loverock Road, Reading, RG30 1DZ Tel: 0118-939 3663 Fax: 0118-939 3653 E-mail: info@icasolutions.co.uk

Intersign Signs & Nameplates, 92 Bowesfield Lane, Stockton-on-Tees, Cleveland, TS18 3EU Tel: (01642) 674242 Fax: (01642) 617203 E-mail: intersign@lineone.net

Inverkeithing Trophy & Engraving Centre, 29 Church Street, Inverkeithing, Fife, KY11 1LG Tel: (01383) 411348 Fax: (01383) 411348

J S Drew, 856 Plymouth Road, Slough, SL1 4LP Tel: (01753) 568181 Fax: (01753) 568121 E-mail: jsdrewengravers@aol.com

James Langford, 81-83 Adelaide Street, Belfast, BT2 8FE Tel: (028) 9032 0610 Fax: (028) 9032 0610

Just Engraving, 138 St. Neots Road, Eaton Ford, St. Neots, Cambridgeshire, PE19 7AL Tel: (01480) 472715 Fax: (01480) 386716 E-mail: engraving@endersby.com

KD Engraving, 37 Boston Road, Leicester, LE4 1AW Tel: 0116-234 0131 Fax: 0116-234 0131

Kedon Industrial Supplies, Oaklands Farm Industrial Estate, Goatsmoor Lane, Stock, Ingatestone, Essex, CM4 9RS Tel: (01277) 636346 Fax: (01277) 636356 E-mail: enquiries@kedonengravers.com

Alexander Kirkwood & Son, 13 Albany Street, Edinburgh, EH1 3PY Tel: 0131-556 7843 Fax: 0131-556 4779

Laser Techniques Ltd, Unit 11 Shaw Crescent, Hutton, Brentwood, Essex, CM13 1JD Tel: (01277) 228194 Fax: (01277) 232840 E-mail: sales@laser-techniques.com

Links Engraving, 150 Duke Street, Edinburgh, EH6 8HR Tel: 0131-554 5156 Fax: 0131-553 6827 E-mail: sales@linksengraving.co.uk

Litho Supplies, Flagship Square, Shaw Cross Business Park, Dewsbury, West Yorkshire, WF12 7TH Tel: (01924) 486130 Fax: (01924) 460502 E-mail: dewsbury@litho.co.uk

Lymm Engraving, 199 Liverpool Road, Cadishead, Manchester, M44 5XH Tel: 0161-775 7625 Fax: 0161-775 7247 E-mail: enquires@lymmengraving.co.uk

M G Engraving, 135 Somerset Road, Coventry, CV1 4EF Tel: (024) 7622 5110 Fax: (024) 7663 2894 E-mail: mg@mgengineering.fsnet.co.uk

M & L Engravers, 14 Ravenswood Industrial Estate, Shernhall Street, London, E17 9HQ Tel: (020) 8520 5144 Fax: (020) 8509 3803

M T M Products Ltd, Dunston Trading Estate, Foxwood Road, Sheepbridge, Chesterfield, Derbyshire, S41 9RF Tel: (01246) 450228 Fax: (01246) 455635 E-mail: sales@mtmlabels.co.uk

Mcbride Signs & Engraving Services, 2 Henderson Drive, Inverness, IV1 1TR Tel: (01463) 237303 Fax: (01463) 713373 E-mail: mcbsigns@aol.com

The Manchester Rubber Stamp Company Ltd, 63 Red Bank, Manchester, M8 8RD Tel: 0161-834 1988 Fax: 0161-835 1529 E-mail: geoff@mrsengravers.co.uk

Mandale Engraving Co. Ltd, 11-12 Bissell Street, Birmingham, B5 7HQ Tel: 0121-622 3906 Fax: 0121-622 1817 E-mail: email@mandaleengraving.co.uk

▶ Manx Workshop For The Disabled, Victoria Avenue, Douglas, Isle of Man, IM2 4AW Tel: (01624) 620149 Fax: (01624) 662516

Matform Ltd, Matform Business Centre, Terminus Road, Chichester, West Sussex, PO19 8UL Tel: (01243) 780157 Fax: (01243) 789029 E-mail: pdown@matform.net

Medway Engraving Products, 62 High Street, Newington, Sittingbourne, Kent, ME9 7JL Tel: (01795) 842617 Fax: (01795) 843782

Metanet Engravers, Unit 10 Threeways Farm, Melton Road, Queniborough, Leicester, LE7 3FN Tel: 0116-264 0567 Fax: 0116-264 0567

Millington's Angling Equipment, 32 Steeley Lane, Chorley, Lancashire, PR6 0RD Tel: (01257) 272392

Modern Engraving Ltd, Leese Street, Stoke-on-Trent, ST4 1AL Tel: (01782) 849055 Fax: (01782) 744565 E-mail: sales@modernengraving.co.uk

Montgomery Engravers Ltd, Red Doles Road, Huddersfield, HD2 1AT Tel: (01484) 429520 Fax: (01484) 435022

N T N Signs, Donegall Street, Belfast, BT1 2FJ Tel: (028) 9023 0703 Fax: (028) 9023 0703

Nash & Co., 14 Bridge Street, Caversham, Reading, RG4 8AA Tel: 0118-947 2295 Fax: 0118-947 7010 E-mail: paulthejewel@aol.com

Northern Engraving & Sign Co Ltd, John Spence Sands, Courtney St, Hull, HU8 7QF Tel: (01482) 328110 Fax: (01482) 323077 E-mail: enquiries@northernengraving.co.uk

Oaklands Signs, 70 Draycott, Cam, Dursley, Gloucestershire, GL11 5DH Tel: (01453) 542312 Fax: (01453) 543353 E-mail: jilldavis.oaklands@btinternet.com

P C Engravers World Of Trophies, 29 Lower Addiscombe Road, Croydon, CR0 6PQ Tel: (020) 8680 1354 Fax: (020) 8686 8706 E-mail: pcengravers@btconnect.com

P J Drew Engravers Ltd, Lower Vicarage Road, Southampton, SO19 7RJ Tel: (023) 8044 6062 Fax: (023) 8042 2981 E-mail: sales@pjdrew.co.uk

Paragon Signs & Labels Ltd, Paragon House, Homefield Road, Haverhill, Suffolk, CB9 8QP Tel: (01440) 761405 Fax: (01440) 712147 E-mail: sales@paragon-signs.co.uk

Paul Spencer Ltd, Consulate House, Sheffield Street, Stockport, Cheshire, SK4 1RU Tel: 0161-477 1688 Fax: 0161-480 4950 E-mail: sales@paulspencersigns.com

Pearson Bros (Engravers) Ltd, Chapel Lane, Halifax, West Yorkshire, HX3 0QN Tel: (01422) 360674 Fax: (01422) 348678 E-mail: sales@pearsonbrothers.co.uk

Peter Devine, 94 Matilda Street, Sheffield, S1 4QF Tel: 0114-275 0479 Fax: 0114-275 0479

Phoenix Engraving Ltd, 108 Alcester Road, Birmingham, B13 8EF Tel: 0121-449 3711 Fax: 0121-449 3712 E-mail: info@phoenixengraving.com

Plastics W Graham Ltd, 114 Cowgate, Dundee, DD1 2JU Tel: (01382) 223734 Fax: (01382) 201799 E-mail: sales@pwgsigns.com

Plastisigns, Oak Tre Farm, Escrick Road, Wheldrake, York, YO19 6BQ Tel: (01904) 449970 Fax: (01904) 449970 E-mail: plastisigns@supanet.com

Alexander Pollock Ltd, Hospital Road, Haddington, East Lothian, EH41 3PD Tel: (01620) 823344 Fax: (01620) 824252 E-mail: jstewart@alexander-pollock.co.uk

Precision General Engravers, Unit 10 Mowat Industrial Estate, Sandown Road, Watford, WD24 7UY Tel: (01923) 233826 Fax: (01923) 817124 E-mail: pngengravers@yahoo.co.uk

Precision Units Dorset Ltd, 2a Gloucester Road, Poole, Dorset, BH12 2AP Tel: (01202) 741664 Fax: (01202) 716473 E-mail: enquiries@precisionunits.co.uk

Print One Ltd, Mayfield House, Tockholes Road, Darwen, Lancashire, BB3 1LL Tel: (01254) 776735 Fax: (01254) 775802 E-mail: mail@print1uk.com

Prysm Electrics Ltd, Daniels Way, Watnall Road, Hucknall, Nottingham, NG15 7LL Tel: 0115-968 1111 Fax: 0115-968 1110 E-mail: sales@prysm.co.uk

Quicksign Signs & Nameplates, 7 Hightown Industrial Estate, Crow Arch Lane, Ringwood, Hampshire, BH24 1ND Tel: (01425) 470445 Fax: (01425) 476289 E-mail: steve@quicksign.co.uk

R E Bowers & Freeman Ltd, 15 Saffron Road, Wigston, Leicestershire, LE18 4TG Tel: 0116-278 5311 Fax: 0116-277 9544 E-mail: info@bowersfreeman.co.uk

R H Wilkins Ltd, 31-35 Kirby Street, London, EC1N 8TE Tel: (020) 7405 5187 Fax: (020) 7831 2805 E-mail: sales@rhwilkins.co.uk

R & T Industrial Engravers, 26 The Tanneries, Brockhampton Lane, Havant, Hampshire, PO9 1JB Tel: (023) 9245 4751 Fax: (023) 9247 2709 E-mail: rt.engraving@tinyworld.co.uk

Read T, 30 Elmtree Road, Basildon, Essex, SS16 4TN Tel: (01268) 456160

Alan Roberts (Engravers) Ltd, 39A-43A Knight Street, Liverpool, L1 9DT Tel: 0151-709 3404 Fax: 0151-707 8081 E-mail: mail@alanrobertsengravers.co.uk

F.J. Rogers Engravers, 10 Tacket Street, Ipswich, IP4 1AY Tel: (01473) 251836

B. Ross, 1B Windermere Avenue, London, SW19 3EP Tel: (020) 8540 9333 Fax: (020) 8543 3869

Rossendale Plastics, Station Road, Haslingden, Rossendale, Lancashire, BB4 5HX Tel: (01706) 214652 Fax: (01706) 830829 E-mail: info@rossendaleplastics.co.uk

Ryder & Chaddock, 6 162 Armley Road, Leeds, LS12 2QN Tel: 0113-231 1116 Fax: 0113-231 1118 E-mail: anything@ryderandchaddock.co.uk

S B Services, 86 Chelwood Avenue, Hatfield, Hertfordshire, AL10 0RE Tel: (01707) 256644 Fax: (01707) 262599 E-mail: s.brayshaw@btopenworld.com

S K Signs & Labels Ltd, The Brookside Centre, Sumpters Way, Southend-on-Sea, SS2 5RR Tel: (01702) 462401 Fax: (01702) 662404 E-mail: info@sksigns.co.uk

Shaftesbury Engraving/Printing Unit 7, 7 Plaza Business Centre, Stockingswater Lane, Enfield, Middlesex, EN3 7XT Tel: (020) 8443 3970 Fax: (020) 8443 3972 E-mail: sales@shaftesburyengraving.co.uk

Shawcross Ltd, Priory Street, Priory Industrial Estate, Birkenhead, Merseyside, CH41 5JH Tel: 0151-647 6692 Fax: 0151-666 1569 E-mail: info@shawcrosssigns.co.uk

GENERAL ENGRAVERS – *continued*

The Sign Factory, Burnbank Road, Bainsford, Falkirk, FK2 7PE Tel: (01324) 501950 Fax: (01324) 501951 E-mail: info@falkirk.gov.uk

Signgrave Signs & Nameplates, Tudor Court, Harold Court Road, Romford, RM3 0AE Tel: (01708) 373827 Fax: (01708) 381069 E-mail: sign.grave@virgin.net

Signpost Engraving, 5 Dalton Court, Astmoor Industrial Estate, Runcorn, Cheshire, WA7 1PU Tel: (01928) 574777 Fax: (01928) 567314 E-mail: signpost.eng@btconnect.com

Signs Of The Times, Unit 6, 3 Campsie Rosd, Kirkintilloch, Glasgow, G66 1SL Tel: 0141-775 0456 Fax: 0141-776 3322 E-mail: signsofthetimes@aol.com

Simpsons Of Aberdeen, 30 Anderson Drive, Aberdeen, AB15 4TY Tel: (01224) 316260 Fax: (01224) 316260

SJH Engraving, 74 Cecil Street, Birmingham, B19 3SU Tel: 0121-359 1321 Fax: 0121-333 4668

Stalite Signs Ltd, 7 Apple Lane, Exeter, EX2 5GL Tel: (01392) 447001 Fax: (01392) 447002 E-mail: sales@stalite.co.uk

Stanmark Engraving, Unit 8, Catherington Business Park, Catherington, Waterlooville, Hampshire, PO8 0AQ Tel: (023) 9259 8414 Fax: (023) 9259 4791 E-mail: stanmark@crossmanm.freeserve.co.uk

Swinnertons Of Walsall, 1 Holtshill Lane, Walsall, WS1 2JA Tel: (01922) 626081 Fax: (01922) 626082

TCE Ltd, Newstead Industrial Estate, Trentham, Stoke-On-Trent, ST4 8HX Tel: (01782) 643278 Fax: (01782) 657766 E-mail: tce@tcelabels.co.uk

Tealwood Company, 1 Seagull Lane, Emsworth, Hampshire, PO10 7QH Tel: (01243) 371524 Fax: (01243) 378123 E-mail: sales@tealwood.co.uk

Teamwork Trophey Centre, St. Marks Road, St. James Industrial Estate, Corby, Northamptonshire, NN18 8AN Tel: (01536) 263487 Fax: (01536) 263487

Thermograve Ltd, 171 Scudamore Road, Leicester, LE3 1UQ Tel: 0116-291 9000 Fax: 0116-291 9001 E-mail: info@thermograve.co.uk

Town & Country Signs Ltd, 125 Poplar High Street, London, E14 0AE Tel: (020) 7515 8383 Fax: (020) 7538 8657 E-mail: info@tcsigns.co.uk

Trafalgar House Engraving, 4 Trafalgar Street, Brighton, BN1 4EQ Tel: (01273) 603498 Fax: (01273) 680181

Trapex Hardware Ltd, Pindar Road, Hoddesdon, Hertfordshire, EN11 0DE Tel: (01992) 462150 Fax: (01992) 446736 E-mail: info@trapex.com

Trident (Hull) Ltd, Unit H 330-338 Wincolmlee, Kingston Upon Hull, Hull, HU2 0QE Tel: (01482) 213134 Fax: (01482) 213722 E-mail: john@tridentltd.Karoo.co.uk

Trophies & Engraving, 43 Valley Mount, Harrogate, North Yorkshire, HG2 0JG Tel: (01423) 507319 Fax: (01423) 507319 E-mail: sales@trophies-and-engraving.co.uk

Trophies & Engraving Services, 651 Stockport Road, Manchester, M12 4QA Tel: 0161-224 7879

Twenty Twenty Displays Ltd, Unit 25, Tregoniggie Industrial Estate, Falmouth, Cornwall, TR11 4SN Tel: (01326) 372520 Fax: (01326) 377243 E-mail: info@twentytwentydisplays.com

V & P Fox Engravers, 23 Cecil Court, London, WC2N 4EZ Tel: (020) 7836 2902 Fax: (020) 7379 8676 E-mail: foxloxs@aol.com

Valley Engraving Ltd, 91-92 High Street, Clydach, Swansea, SA6 5LN Tel: (01792) 842374 Fax: (01792) 846130

W E Services Ltd, 1 Shillingford Close, Appleton, Warrington, WA4 5QB Tel: (01925) 263490 Fax: (07092) 304593 E-mail: wayne@weservices.wanado.com

W & K Rossiter, 79 Aldwick Road, Bognor Regis, West Sussex, PO21 2NW Tel: (01243) 828017 Fax: (01243) 828017 E-mail: trophieswk@yahoo.co.uk

W L Jones Engravers Ltd, North Lonsdale Road, Ulverston, Cumbria, LA12 9DJ Tel: (01229) 583856 Fax: (01229) 580847

W.R Engraving Name Plate Manufacturers, 12a Green Lane Industrial Estate, Green Lane, Letchworth Garden City, Hertfordshire, SG6 1HP Tel: (01462) 686845 Fax: (01462) 686845

West Riding Engravers Ltd, 60 Wellington Street, Leeds, LS1 2EE Tel: 0113-243 9156 Fax: 0113-246 0787 E-mail: sales@wre-ltd.com

William Jones Clifton Ltd, 32 Lower Essex Street, Birmingham, B5 6SN Tel: 0121-622 8900 Fax: 0121-622 8909 E-mail: sales@jonesclifton.com

Wimborne Engraving Co., Wimborne Industrial Estate, Mill Lane, Wimborne, Dorset, BH21 1LN Tel: (01202) 886373 Fax: (01202) 886373

Wright Sign Service, 1 Greenside, Pudsey, West Yorkshire, LS28 8PU Tel: 0113-255 7259 Fax: 0113-255 7259 E-mail: jon808@btclick.com

GENERAL FLOORING CONTRACTORS, *See also headings for particular types & Material under Flooring*

A W R Ceilings & Partitions, Jack O Watton Industrial Estate, Lichfield Road, Water Orton, Birmingham, B46 1NU Tel: 0121-748 2608 Fax: 0121-776 7561 E-mail: triciaharris@eidosnet.co.uk

Abs Brymar Floor's Ltd, Dane Road Industrial Estate, Sale, Cheshire, M33 7BH Tel: 0161-972 5000 Fax: 0161-972 5001 E-mail: sales@absbrymarfloors.co.uk

▶ Ace Flooring UK Ltd, 6 Warden Mill Close, Wateringbury, Maidstone, Kent, ME18 5DJ Tel: (01622) 815544 E-mail: aceflooring@btinternet.com

Acrylicon UK, Unit 11/12, Brook Road, Bicton Industrial Park, Kimbolton, Huntingdon, Cambridgeshire, PE28 0LR Tel: (01480) 861034

▶ Advanced Ergonomic Technologies Ltd, 201-203 London Road, East Grinstead, West Sussex, RH19 1HA Tel: (01342) 310400 Fax: (01342) 310401 E-mail: aet@flexiblespace.com

Ammonite Flooring, 22 Hayes Street, Bromley, BR2 7LD Tel: (020) 8462 4671 Fax: (020) 8462 1013

Arvin Roofing Ltd, Prestage Works, 1 Prestage Way, London, E14 9QE Tel: (020) 7987 4711 Fax: (020) 7538 3177 E-mail: contract@arvin.sons.co.uk

D. & J. Bailey (Flooring) Ltd, Churchill House, Farncote Drive, Four Oaks, Sutton Coldfield, West Midlands, B74 4QS Tel: 0121-308 0402 Fax: 0121-308 7327 E-mail: lisab@bailey-flooring.co.uk

Beckett Construction Solutions Ltd, 99 Kingsway, Dunmurry, Belfast, BT17 9NU Tel: (028) 9066 3631 Fax: (028) 9055 1309 E-mail: mail@whbeckett.com

Bilton Flooring Contractors, 11 Firside Grove, Sidcup, Kent, DA15 8WB Tel: (020) 8300 3250

Building Tecnics, Regents Trade Park, Barwell Lane, Gosport, Hampshire, PO13 0EQ Tel: (01329) 282900 Fax: (0870) 200517 E-mail: info@buildingtecnics.com

C A T Industrial Flooring Ltd, 34 Laburnum Avenue, Garden Village, Hull, HU8 8PH Tel: (01482) 783259 Fax: (01482) 783259 E-mail: sales@catindustrialflooring.co.uk

▶ Carrara-Tiling, 17 Lytham Close, Doncaster, South Yorkshire, DN4 6UT Tel: (01302) 370352 Fax: (01302) 370352 E-mail: carrara-tiling@tiscali.co.uk

Castlepar, 37 Lodlow Avenue, Luton, LU1 3RW Tel: (01582) 726976 Fax: (01582) 459200

City Mastic Asphalt Ltd, 315a Weston Road, Stoke-on-Trent, ST3 6HA Tel: (01782) 311249 Fax: (01782) 311249

City Roofing & Asphalt Services Ltd, 3a Pennyburn Industrial Estate, Londonderry, BT48 0LU Tel: (028) 7126 9648 Fax: (028) 7136 7016

Clarke Contracts, 89 Bann Road, Rasharkin, Ballymena, County Antrim, BT44 8SZ Tel: (028) 2954 0191 Fax: (028) 2954 0401 E-mail: sales@clarkecontracts.com

Cottage Flooring, 5 Oakhurst Close, Barkingside, Ilford, Essex, IG6 2LT Tel: (020) 8551 8875 Fax: (020) 8551 8875 E-mail: cottageflooring@aol.com

D & D Flooring, 42 Colinward Street, Belfast, BT12 7EP Tel: (028) 9024 6060 Fax: (028) 9024 6047 E-mail: danddflooring@aol.com

D Kelleher Flooring Ltd, Unit 1 B Alexandria Park 1, Penner Road, Havant, Hampshire, PO9 1QY Tel: (023) 9247 1029 Fax: (023) 9245 3288E-mail: mail@kelleherflooring.co.uk

Dave Hunt Flooring NW Ltd, 1 Laskey Lane Farm, Laskey Lane, Thelwall, Warrington, WA4 2TF Tel: (01925) 757505 Fax: (01925) 754467

De Witt Floors, The Green, Boughton Monchelsea, Maidstone, Kent, ME17 4LT Tel: (01622) 744886 Fax: (01622) 747461

Dorgrove Floors Ltd, 9 Causeway Green Road, Oldbury, West Midlands, B68 8LA Tel: 0121-544 7877 Fax: 0121-511 1386 E-mail: dorgrove@aol.com

Durastic, 47 Cuthbert Court, Bede Trading Estate, Jarrow, Tyne & Wear, NE32 3EG Tel: 0191-483 2299 Fax: 0191-483 2295

Excel Plastering Ilford Ltd, 1 Natal Road, Ilford, Essex, IG1 2HA Tel: (020) 8553 2244 Fax: (020) 8553 4489 E-mail: excelplastering1@btopenworld.com

Fenton Flooring & Ceramics, 157 Queens Road, Buckhurst Hill, Essex, IG9 5AZ Tel: (020) 8504 0529 Fax: (020) 8504 1296

▶ First Flooring, 9 Rosedale Gardens, Sutton-in-Ashfield, Nottinghamshire, NG17 1ND Tel: (01623) 476988 Fax: (01623) 477326 E-mail: firstflooring@ntlworld.com

Floor Maintenance Services Ltd, 215 Melton Road, Edwalton, Nottingham, NG12 4AF Tel: 0115-945 2186 Fax: 0115-974 7656 E-mail: sonia.mabbott@ntlworld.com

Floorcraft Contractors Ltd, 17a Station Road, London, E17 8AA Tel: (020) 8521 4446 Fax: (020) 8521 9165 E-mail: mailbox@floorcraft.co.uk

Floorings Of Frome, Textile House, Manor Furlong, Frome, Somerset, BA11 4RJ Tel: (01373) 462666 Fax: (01373) 466651 E-mail: fromecarpetsandflooring@btconnect.com

G & M Floorlayers Derby Ltd, Sandown Road, Derby, DE24 8SR Tel: (01332) 344282 Fax: (01332) 298491

Geo Brady Flooring Ltd, Brunswick Industrial Estate, Brunswick Village, Newcastle upon Tyne, NE13 7BA Tel: 0191-217 0202 Fax: 0191-217 0202

Grange Flooring (S.G. Lersch) Ltd, Unit H6, Park Avenue Estate, Sundon Park, Luton, LU3 3BP Tel: (01582) 596999 Fax: (01582) 599638

Granwood Flooring Ltd, Greenhill Lane, Riddings, Alfreton, Derbyshire, DE55 4AT Tel: (01773) 602341 Fax: (01773) 540043

H B D Floors Ltd, 6 Falcon Units, Bradley Lane, Newton Abbot, Devon, TQ12 1NB Tel: (01626) 366333 Fax: (01626) 366444

Hollywood Plasterers, Woodhouse, Packhorse Lane, Kings Norton, Birmingham, B38 0DN Tel: (01564) 824100 Fax: (01564) 823447

Industrial Flooring Services Ltd, Sankey Valley Industrial Estate, Newton-le-Willows, Merseyside, WA12 8DN Tel: (01925) 220000 Fax: (01925) 220011 E-mail: info@industrial-flooring.co.uk

▶ Iona Flooring Services Ltd, 109 Langside Drive, Glasgow, G43 2SX Tel: 0141-637 7444 Fax: 0141 6375026 E-mail: ionaflooring@aol.com

Ironbridge Construction Ltd, Unit B6 Hortonwood 10, Telford, Shropshire, TF1 7ES Tel: (01952) 676555 Fax: (01952) 676567 E-mail: sales@ironbridgeconstruction.co.uk

J T Shakespeare & Co. Ltd, Hot Lane, Hot Lane Industrial Estate, Stoke-on-Trent, ST6 2BN Tel: (01782) 839311 Fax: (01782) 835783 E-mail: floors@jtshakespeare.com

Jennor Electrical, 57-59 Brynn Street, St. Helens, Merseyside, WA10 1JB Tel: (01744) 730717 Fax: (01744) 759657 E-mail: general@jennor.co.uk

John Abbott Flooring Contractors Ltd, Wallshaw House, Wallshaw Street, Oldham, OL1 3XD Tel: 0161-624 8246 Fax: 0161-627 1779 E-mail: sales@johnabbottflooring.co.uk

K A P Blinds, 6 Lower Grange, Peterhead, Aberdeenshire, AB42 2AT Tel: (01779) 474949 Fax: (01779) 474949

▶ Keystone, 204 Duggins Lane, Coventry, CV4 9GP Tel: (024) 7642 2580

L & S Carpet Co. Ltd, 48 Central Road, Morden, Surrey, SM4 5RU Tel: (020) 8648 6131 Fax: (020) 8648 6193

Alfred McAlpine Slate Ltd, Penrhyn Quarry, Bethesda, Bangor, Gwynedd, LL57 4YG Tel: (01248) 600656 Fax: (01248) 601171 E-mail: slate@mcalpineplc.co.uk

Mercia Flooring Ltd, 59 The Square, Dunchurch, Rugby, Warwickshire, CV22 6NU Tel: (01788) 522168 Fax: (01788) 811847 E-mail: sales@merciaflooring.co.uk

Midas Floors Ltd, 20 Dollman Street, Birmingham, B7 4RP Tel: 0121-333 5846 Fax: 0121-333 6476 E-mail: midas.floors@dial.pipex.com

Newton Abbot Flooring, 129 Winner Street, Paignton, Devon, TQ3 3BP Tel: (01803) 525177 Fax: (01803) 520359 E-mail: classic.floors@virgin.net

North Wales Floorings Ltd, 117-119 Conway Road, Colwyn Bay, Clwyd, LL29 7LT Tel: (01492) 530448 Fax: (01492) 532800

O&W, 5 Grange Court Road, Bristol, BS9 4DP Tel: 0117-962 1777 Fax: 0117-962 1166

▶ PCS, Unit 60-62 Stephenson Way, Formby Business Park, Formby, Liverpool, L37 8EG Tel: (01704) 879204 Fax: (01704) 879204 E-mail: webdevelopment@pcsflooring.com

Pelican Flooring, 178 Stoke Newington Road, London, N16 7UY Tel: (020) 7254 7955 Fax: (020) 7254 7955

Price Bros (Ascot) Ltd, Unit 1 Peter James Business Centre, Pump Lane, Hayes, Middlesex, UB3 3NT Tel: (020) 8569 2251 Fax: (020) 8569 2458 E-mail: info@pricebrothersascot.co.uk

Progressive Floor Surfaces Ltd, Unit 10 Westward House, Glebeland Road, Camberley, Surrey, GU15 3DB Tel: (01276) 681111 Fax: (01276) 66166

Purdie Floors Ltd, 351 Stratford Road, Shirley, Solihull, West Midlands, B90 3BW Tel: 0121-744 4471 Fax: 0121-744 4471 E-mail: info@purdiefloors.co.uk

Quickset Chemical Flooring Ltd, 30 Runcorn Road, Birmingham, B12 8RQ Tel: 0121-440 0737 Fax: 0121-440 2255 E-mail: sales@uk-quickset.com

R P S Industrial Flooring Contractors Ltd, Woodhouse, Packhorse Lane, Headley Heath, Birmingham, B38 0DN Tel: (01564) 824900 Fax: (01564) 823447

Rembrand Timber Ltd, Bonnington Road Lane, Edinburgh, EH6 5BJ Tel: 0131-553 5351 Fax: 0131-554 2332 E-mail: leith@rembrand-timber.co.uk

Renovate Contracts Ltd, 91 Park Road, Earl Shilton, Leicester, LE9 7ZY Tel: 01455 851900 Fax: 01455 851900 E-mail: duncan@renovatecontracts.wanadoo.co.uk

Resilient Tile & Flooring Co. (Ealing) Ltd, 2 Replingham Rd, London, SW18 5LS Tel: (020) 8874 6655 Fax: (020) 8874 6656

Rowbotham Decorative Flooring Ltd, 35 Bakewell Road, Loughborough, Leicestershire, LE11 5QY Tel: (01509) 263330 Fax: (01509) 237424 E-mail: enquiries@rdflooring.demon.co.uk

▶ S D Flooring, 30 Guildford Road, Worthing, West Sussex, BN14 7LL Tel: (01903) 538201 E-mail: sales@sdflooring.co.uk

Shepherd Interiors, Unit 4, 10 First Avenue, Bletchley, Milton Keynes, MK1 1DN Tel: (01908) 644688 Fax: (01908) 646606 E-mail: info@rgnsltd.co.uk

Specialist Environmental Flooring Ltd, 38 Fowler Avenue, Spondon, Derby, DE21 7GR Tel: (01332) 669353 Fax: (01332) 669011

Stanford Design & Construct Ltd, 5 Richmond St South, West Bromwich, West Midlands, B70 0DG Tel: 0121-522 2220 Fax: 0121-522 2020 E-mail: sales@stanford-flooring.co.uk

Stanmor Floors Ltd, Holly Park Industrial Estate Unit 6, Spitfire Road, Birmingham, B24 9PB Tel: 0121-384 8868 Fax: 0121-384 6424 E-mail: bmorton@stanmorfloors.co.uk

Stebro Flooring Co. Ltd, Station Road Industrial Estate, Station Road, Rowley Regis, West Midlands, B65 0JY Tel: 0121-559 0544 Fax: 0121-559 0705 E-mail: sales@stebro-flooring.co.uk

Tiling Co., Unit 1, Hampson Mill Lane, Bury, Lancashire, BL9 9TZ Tel: 0161-766 4710 Fax: 0161-796 3190 E-mail: ttc.northwest@thetilingcompany.co.uk

Trade Flooring Ltd, 8 St. James Mill Road, Northampton, NN5 5JW Tel: (01604) 751721 Fax: (01604) 755506 E-mail: sales@tflcarpets.co.uk

Tudor Bros (Flooring) Ltd, Unit 5 Warrior Business Centre, Fitzherbert Road, Farlington, Portsmouth, PO6 1TX Tel: (023) 9232 1244 Fax: (023) 9221 9267 E-mail: tudorbros@aol.com

Universal Flooring Contractors, 7a George Road, Erdington, Birmingham, B23 7QE Tel: 0121-377 8808 Fax: 0121-377 8184 E-mail: sales@universal-flooring.co.uk

Veitchi (Scotland) Ltd, Unit 7, Hareness Circle, Altens Industrial Estate, Aberdeen, AB12 3LY Tel: (01224) 896333 Fax: (01224) 890354 E-mail: aberdeen@veitchi.com

Watson Brook, 119a High Street, Tewkesbury, Gloucestershire, GL20 5JY Tel: (01684) 291155 Fax: (01684) 291166 E-mail: sales@watsonbrook.co.uk

Wecando Flooring Specialists Lincoln Ltd, Lincoln Road, Nettleham, Lincoln, LN2 2NE Tel: (01522) 595770 Fax: (01522) 595887 E-mail: wecandofg@aol.com

Welland Flooring Co Corby Ltd, Weldon Road, Corby, Northamptonshire, NN17 1UZ Tel: (01536) 265195 Fax: (01536) 261323 E-mail: sales@wellandflooring.co.uk

Wrights Flooring Contractors, 78a Sabine Road, London, SW11 5LW Tel: (020) 7223 5970 Fax: (020) 7228 4616

GENERAL HYDRAULIC VALVES

Hydraulic Components & Systems Ltd, Unit 14 Sovereign Park, Cleveland Way, Hemel Hempstead, Hertfordshire, HP2 7DA Tel: (01442) 240202 Fax: (01442) 243133 E-mail: hydcompdrf@hotmail.com

GENERAL LAMINATING

Archbond Ltd, Mill Hill Factory, Desford Road, Enderby, Leicester, LE19 4AD Tel: 0116-284 1222 Fax: 0116-284 9954 E-mail: lizhayes@archbond.co.uk

C L S Fabrication Ltd, 1 Caswell Road, Leamington Spa, Warwickshire, CV31 1QD Tel: (01926) 336126 Fax: (01926) 312022 E-mail: sales@clsfab.co.uk

Celloglass Ltd, Headley Road East, Woodley, Reading, RG5 4UA Tel: 0118-944 1441 Fax: 0118-944 1913 E-mail: yvonne.parks@celloglas.co.uk

Copyworld Duplicating Services, 6 Merville Garden Village, Newtownabbey, County Antrim, BT37 9TF Tel: (028) 9080 0500 Fax: (028) 9087 9087 E-mail: info@copyworld.co.uk

Decorshades LLP, 5 Brewery Mews Business Centre, St Johns Road, Isleworth, Middlesex, TW7 6PH Tel: (020) 8847 1939 Fax: (020) 8847 1939 E-mail: martin@decshade.demon.co.uk

Duraseal, 7 27 Black Moor Road, Ebblake Industrial Estate, Verwood, Dorset, BH31 6BE Tel: (01202) 826911 Fax: (01202) 813811

Elmstok, 4-6 Algores Way, Wisbech, Cambridgeshire, PE13 2TQ Tel: (01945) 463434 Fax: (01945) 582598 E-mail: sales@elmstok.co.uk

Libran Laminations Ltd, Coles Green Road, London, NW2 7HW Tel: (020) 8452 2006 Fax: (020) 8452 4456 E-mail: info@libranlaminations.co.uk

Plastic Art Company, Unit 7 Glover Way, Leeds, LS11 5JP Tel: 0113-271 7744 Fax: 0113-271 9590

Plastic Art Co., Unit 6f Hewlett House, 5 Havelock Terrace, London, SW8 4AS Tel: (020) 7627 1976 Fax: (020) 7498 2369 E-mail: london@plastic-art.co.uk

Technical Convertors Ltd, Unit 5 Third Way, Avonmouth, Bristol, BS11 9HL Tel: 0117-982 8808 Fax: 0117-938 4868 E-mail: sales@technicalconverters.co.uk

Total Laminate Systems Ltd, 11 Nimrod Way, East Dorset Trade Park, Wimborne, Dorset, BH21 7SH Tel: (01202) 877600 Fax: (01202) 861638 E-mail: sales@total-laminate.co.uk

Xcard Printers, 8 Cowley Mill Trading Estate, Longbridge Way, Cowley, Uxbridge, Middlesex, UB8 2YG Tel: (01895) 256332 Fax: (01895) 230902 E-mail: info@xcardtechnology.com

GENERAL LASERS, *See also headings for particular types*

▶ Pro-Lite Technology LLP, The Cranfield Innovation Centre, University Way, Cranfield, Bedford, MK43 0BT Tel: (01234) 436110 Fax: (01234) 436111 E-mail: sales@pro-lite.uk.com

Topcon GB Ltd, 25 Breakfield, Coulsdon, Surrey, CR5 2HS Tel: (020) 8668 2233 Fax: (020) 8668 8322 E-mail: sales@topcon.co.uk

GENERAL LOCKS

A Lewis & Sons Willenhall Ltd, 47 Church Street, Willenhall, West Midlands, WV13 1QW Tel: (01902) 605428 Fax: (01902) 601181 E-mail: lewislocksltd@aol.com

▶ Access 24, 3 Stadhampton Road, Drayton St. Leonard, Wallingford, Oxfordshire, OX10 7AR Tel: (01865) 400928 E-mail: admin@access24.co.uk

B & G Lock & Tool Co. Ltd, Chapel Green, Willenhall, West Midlands, WV13 1RD Tel: (01902) 630290 Fax: (01902) 633794 E-mail: sales@bgpadlocks.co.uk

J. Banks & Co. Ltd, Excelsior Works, Wood Street, Willenhall, West Midlands, WV13 1JY Tel: (01902) 605084 Fax: (01902) 603248 E-mail: contact@jbanks.co.uk

Baton Lock Ltd, Baton House, 4TH Avenue The Village, Trafford Park, Manchester, M17 1DB Tel: 0161-877 4444 Fax: 0161-877 4545 E-mail: kevin.bratt@batonlockuk.com

Benton Security Locks Ltd, 16 Victoria Street, Willenhall, West Midlands, WV13 1DR Tel: (01902) 602102 Fax: (01902) 366512 E-mail: info@bentonsecuritylocks.co.uk

D Lycett & Sons Ltd, Long Street, Premier Business Park, Walsall, WS2 9DY Tel: (01922) 625393 Fax: (01922) 616761 E-mail: donshir@tiscali.co.uk

Guardian Lock & Engineering Co. Ltd, Imperial Works, Wednesfield Road, Willenhall, West Midlands, WV13 1AL Tel: (01902) 633396 Fax: (01902) 630675

Henry Squire & Sons Ltd, Unit 2 Hilton Cross Business Park, Cannock Road, Wolverhampton, WV10 7QZ Tel: (01902) 308050 E-mail: info@henry-squire.co.uk

Regent Lock Co. Ltd, Bath Road Industrial Estate, Chippenham, Wiltshire, SN14 0AB Tel: (01249) 650416 Fax: (01249) 443014

Securefast plc, Meadow Dale Works, Dimminsdale, Willenhall, West Midlands, WV13 2BE Tel: (01902) 607503 Fax: (01902) 609327 E-mail: sales@securefast.co.uk

Special Security Products, 37 Warren Hill Road, Birmingham, B44 8HA Tel: 0121-344 4593 Fax: 0121-356 0867 E-mail: enquiries@special-locks.com

Surelock Mcgill Ltd, 26 The Business Centre, Molly Millars Lane, Wokingham, Berkshire, RG41 2QY Tel: 0118-977 2525 Fax: 0118-977 1913 E-mail: info@surelock.co.uk

Telco Security Locks Ltd, Connaught Road, Bournemouth, BH7 6NA Tel: (01202) 420444 Fax: (01202) 432073 E-mail: sales@telcolocks.fsnet.co.uk

Van Locks Ltd, 76 Portland Street, Manchester, M1 4GU Tel: 0161-236 1231 Fax: 0161-236 2885 E-mail: vanlock@talk21.com

Willenhall Locks Ltd, Stringes Lane, Willenhall, West Midlands, WV13 1LF Tel: (01902) 636041 Fax: (01902) 636733 E-mail: sales@willenhall-locks.co.uk

GENERAL MERCHANTS, INTERNATIONAL IMPORT/ EXPORT

▶ A E Kenwell & Sons, 44 Main Street, Dromore, Omagh, County Tyrone, BT78 3AB Tel: (028) 8289 8205 Fax: (028) 8289 8209 E-mail: kenwelld@hotmail.com

Abbott & Co Wessex Ltd, Abberley House, Park Street, Cirencester, Gloucestershire, GL7 2BX Tel: (01285) 653738 Fax: (01285) 885134 E-mail: sales@air-receivers.co.uk

Adnan UK Ltd, 25 Friar Mews, West Norwood, London, SE27 0PU Tel: (020) 8766 0262 Fax: (020) 8766 6260

Alphachem Ltd, 55 Nutfield Rd, Merstham, Redhill, RH1 3ER Tel: (01737) 644836 Fax: (01737) 644500

Autorise Ltd, Maspro House, Chadwick Road, Astmoor Industrial Estate, Runcorn, Cheshire, WA7 1PW Tel: (01928) 561552 Fax: (01928) 591531

Biddle Sawyer Silks, 22 Rook Street, St Mary''s Courtyard, Manchester, M15 5PS Tel: 0161-227 9428 Fax: 0161-227 8023 E-mail: info@biddlesawyersilks.com

Brooks McRobbie Ltd, 43 St. John Street, London, EC1M 4LX Tel: (020) 7490 0304 Fax: (020) 7490 0307 E-mail: john.brooks2@ukonline.co.uk

BT International Ltd, Regatta House, 67-71 High Street, Marlow, Buckinghamshire, SL7 1AB Tel: (01628) 470040 Fax: (01628) 470041 E-mail: info@bt-international.com

Elbee Traders, 839 Harrow Road, London, NW10 5NH Tel: (020) 8969 9423 Fax: (020) 8969 2611 E-mail: sales@elbee-traders.co.uk

F P S International, Flat 45, Sandringham Court Maida Vale, London, W9 1UA Tel: (020) 7289 5158 Fax: (020) 7286 5137 E-mail: bev.colson@fpsinternational.com

F S M Enterprises Ltd, 2 Adams Close, London, NW9 8PT Tel: (020) 8200 7736 Fax: (020) 8200 6112 E-mail: fmalik1541@aol.com

Faisal's Enterprises Ltd, 98 Mitcham Road, London, SW17 9NG Tel: (020) 8767 5577 Fax: (020) 8767 8269 E-mail: erick@faisals.co.uk

Fieldyork International Ltd, The Manor, 306 -308 Leicester Road, Wigston, Leicestershire, LE18 1JX Tel: 0116-257 1572 Fax: 0116-257 8969

Hilton of London, Flat 11, Leamington House, 11 Stonegrove, Edgware, Middlesex, HA8 7TN Tel: (020) 8958 9372 Fax: (020) 8905 4954 E-mail: brian@hiltonoflondon.co.uk

Imperial Merchants Ltd, 199a Munster Rd, London, SW6 6BX Tel: 0207 385 0333

Inprojex International UK Ltd, 58 Uxbridge Road, London, W5 2ST Tel: (020) 8567 9680 Fax: (020) 8579 5241 E-mail: inprojex@inprojex.co.uk

Kalimex Ltd, Unit 3, Plumpton Green Studios, St. Helena Lane, Plumpton Green, Lewes, East Sussex, BN7 3DQ Tel: (01273) 891162 Fax: (01273) 890704 E-mail: enquiries@kalimex.co.uk

Leventis Overseas Ltd, West Africa House, Ashbourne Road, London, W5 3QP Tel: (020) 8997 6651 Fax: (020) 8997 2621 E-mail: leventis@overseas.com

M E I Unitech Ltd, PO Box 457, Sheffield, S9 3UU Tel: 0114-243 7296 Fax: 0114-242 5958

Mathesons & Co. Ltd, 3 Lombard Street, 1 Undershaft, London, EC3V 9AQ Tel: (020) 7816 8100 Fax: (020) 7816 8182

Media Market Ltd, 24 Gordon Avenue, Stanmore, Middlesex, HA7 3QD Tel: (020) 8954 5994 Fax: (020) 8954 1624

Newport Fish Co. Ltd, 200 Battery Road, Cookstown, County Tyrone, BT80 0HY Tel: (028) 8673 7326 Fax: (028) 8673 6132

Norfolk Lavender Ltd, Caley Mill, Lynn Road, Heacham, King's Lynn, Norfolk, PE31 7JE Tel: (01485) 570384 Fax: (01485) 571176 E-mail: admin@norfolk-lavender.co.uk

P H D Import & Export Ltd, 1st Floor, 44-45 Great Hampston Street, Hockley, Birmingham, B18 6EL Tel: 0121-554 3722 Fax: 0121-554 8978 E-mail: sjhutti2000@yahoo.co.uk

Phoenix International Freight Services, Trent Lane Indust Estate Unit 2, Sycamore Road, Castle Donnington, Derby, DE74 2LL Tel: (01332) 817350 Fax: (01332) 850530

Rajan Trading International Ltd, Rajan House, 61 Great Ducie Street, Manchester, M3 1RR Tel: 0161-834 2147 Fax: 0161-835 2435 E-mail: sales@rajan-group.co.uk

T C D Ltd, 31 Sinclair Road, London, W14 0NS Tel: (020) 7603 1325 Fax: (020) 7603 1536

T R S Cash & Carry Ltd, 2 Southbridge Way, Southall, Middlesex, UB2 4BY Tel: (020) 8843 5400 Fax: (020) 8574 5254

Tecapet Ltd, Unitec House, Albert Place, London, N3 1QB Tel: (020) 8349 4299 Fax: (020) 8349 0252 E-mail: tecapet@aol.com

UK Steel Export Ltd, Blackvein Industrial Estate, Cross Keys, Newport, Gwent, NP11 7PX Tel: (01495) 270033 Fax: (01495) 273190 E-mail: ukstlexp@aol.com

Robert Vanderpump & Co. Ltd, Clarks Farm Road, Danbury, Chelmsford, CM3 4PH Tel: (01245) 225966 Fax: (01245) 225866 E-mail: vanderpump@btconnect.com

West Point Engineering & Commercial Ltd, 3 St James's Square, London, SW1Y 4JU Tel: (020) 7930 0042 Fax: (020) 7839 2875

GENERAL OR BUILDING BRICKS

Acheson & Glover Ltd, 60 Creagh Road, Toomebridge, Antrim, BT41 3SE Tel: (028) 7965 0631 Fax: (028) 7965 0751 E-mail: info@acheson-glover.co.uk

Baggeridge Brick plc, Fir Street, Sedgley, Dudley, West Midlands, DY3 4AA Tel: (01902) 880555 Fax: (01902) 880432

Baggeridge Brick plc, Lynwick Street, Rudgwick, Horsham, West Sussex, RH12 3DH Tel: (01403) 822212 Fax: (01403) 823357 E-mail: info@baggeridge.co.uk

Baggeridge Brick plc, Gresham House, 24 Holborn Viaduct, London, EC1A 2BN Tel: (020) 7236 6222 Fax: (020) 7248 6363

Blockleys Brick Ltd, Sommerfeld Road, Trench Lock, Telford, Shropshire, TF1 5RY Tel: (01952) 251933 Fax: (01952) 265377 E-mail: info@blockleys.com

Bolt Ltd, Bluebridge Industrial Estate, Colchester Road, Halstead, Essex, CO9 2EX Tel: (01787) 477261 Fax: (01787) 475680 E-mail: enquiries@boltbuildingsupplies.co.uk

Bovingdon Brickworks Ltd, Pudds Cross, Bovingdon, Hemel Hempstead, Hertfordshire, HP3 0NW Tel: (01442) 833176 Fax: (01442) 834539 E-mail: info@bovingdonbrickworks.co.uk

Brick Bond Northern, 7 Healey New Mills, Healey Road, Ossett, West Yorkshire, WF5 8NF Tel: (01924) 266194 Fax: (01924) 266195 E-mail: admin@brickmanufacturers.com

Brick Business, Steer Point Factory, Brixton, Plymouth, PL8 2DG Tel: (01752) 880659 Fax: (01752) 881734 E-mail: info@thebrickbusiness.com

Brick Specialists (Midlands) Ltd, 2 Cottage Terrace, The Rope Walk, Nottingham, NG1 5DX Tel: 0115-985 9100 Fax: 0115-947 8960 E-mail: rgb@bricks99.freserve.co.uk

Broadmoor Brickworks Ltd, Whimsey Industrial Estate, Steam Mills, Whimsey, Cinderford, Gloucestershire, GL14 3JA Tel: (01594) 822255 Fax: (01594) 826782 E-mail: sales@broadmoor-brickworks.co.uk

Builders Supplies (West Coast) Ltd, Kilbane Street, Fleetwood, Lancashire, FY7 7PF Tel: (01253) 776600 Fax: (01253) 776800 E-mail: sales@bswc.biz

Builders Supply Co Leabrooks, 33 Greenhill Lane, Leabrooks, Alfreton, Derbyshire, DE55 4AS Tel: (01773) 602727 Fax: (01773) 540324

James Burrell Ltd, Lockheed Close, Preston Farm Industrial Estate, Stockton-on-Tees, Cleveland, TS18 3SE Tel: (01642) 660820 Fax: (01642) 678616 E-mail: jamesburrell@compuserve.com

Burton Bell & Co. Ltd, 3 Kildonan Road, Liverpool, L17 0BU Tel: 0151-727 2231 Fax: 0151-727 2231

Cambrian Concrete Products, Old Sand Gravel Quarry, Rhosesmor Road, Rhosesmor, Mold, Clwyd, CH7 6PE Tel: (01352) 741412 Fax: (01352) 741531

Charnwood Forest Brick Ltd, Old Station Close, Shepshed, Loughborough, Leicestershire, LE12 9NJ Tel: (01509) 503203 Fax: (01509) 507566 E-mail: sales@charnwoodforest.com

Chelwood Brick Ltd, Eurolink Industrial Estate, Castle Road, Sittingbourne, Kent, ME10 3TN Tel: (01795) 421651 Fax: (01795) 426489

Chelwood Group, Adswood Road, Cheadle Hulme, Cheadle, Cheshire, SK8 5QY Tel: 0161-485 8211 Fax: 0161-486 1968 E-mail: marketing@chelwood.co.uk

Consolidated Brick, Brindley Road, Cardiff, CF11 8TL Tel: (029) 2034 0168 Fax: (029) 2034 2466

Days Buildbase, Burrfields Road, Portsmouth, PO3 5NA Tel: (023) 9266 2261 Fax: (023) 9266 6497 E-mail: portsmouth@buildbase.co.uk

Dunton Bros Ltd, Blackwell Hall Lane, Chesham, Buckinghamshire, HP5 1TN Tel: (01494) 783730 Fax: (01494) 791255 E-mail: sales@duntons.com

Furness Brick & Tile Co. Ltd, Dalton Road, Askam-in-Furness, Cumbria, LA16 7HF Tel: (01229) 462411 Fax: (01229) 462363 E-mail: furnessbrick@mac.com

Hanson Brick Ltd, Heather Brick Works, Mill Lane, Heather, Coalville, Leicestershire, LE67 2QE Tel: (01530) 260209 Fax: (01530) 263258

▶ Hanson Brick Ltd, Station Road, Kirton, Newark, Nottinghamshire, NG22 9LG Tel: (01623) 860481 Fax: (01623) 862064

Hanson Building Products, Stewartby, Bedford, MK43 9LZ Tel: (0870) 5258258 Fax: (01234) 762040 E-mail: info@hanson.biz

Hanson Building Products, Unicorn House, Wellington Street, Ripley, Derbyshire, DE5 3DZ Tel: (0870) 5258258 Fax: (01773) 514040 E-mail: info@hanson.biz

Hinton, Perry & Davenhill Ltd, Pensnett, Brierley Hill, West Midlands, DY5 4TH Tel: (01384) 77405 Fax: (01384) 74553 E-mail: office@drednort.tiles.co.uk

Ibstock Brick Ltd, Over Lane, Almondsbury, Bristol, BS32 4BX Tel: (01454) 456800 Fax: (0870) 9040696

Ibstock Brick Ltd, Hamsey Road, Sharpthorne, East Grinstead, West Sussex, RH19 4PB Tel: (01342) 810678 Fax: (01342) 810453

Ibstock Brick Ltd, Leicester Road, Ibstock, Leicestershire, LE67 6HF Tel: (01530) 261999 Fax: (01530) 257457 E-mail: marketing@ibstock.co.uk

Ibstock Brick Ltd, Atlas Factory, Stubbers Green Road, Walsall, WS9 8BL Tel: (01922) 459194 Fax: (01922) 741761

Ibstock Bricks Ltd, Turkey Road, Bexhill-on-Sea, East Sussex, TN39 5HY Tel: (01424) 846273 Fax: (01424) 846415

Ibstock Building Products Ltd, Union Brickworks, Station Lane, Birtley, Chester le Street, County Durham, DH2 1AJ Tel: 0191-410 2555 Fax: 0191-492 0601

Ibstock Building Products Ltd, Throckley Works, Throckley, Newcastle upon Tyne, NE15 9EQ Tel: (0870) 9034004 Fax: 0191-229 0502

Ibstock Building Products Ltd, Funton Factory, Sheerness Road, Lower Halstow, Sittingbourne, Kent, ME9 7EG Tel: (01795) 842551 Fax: (01795) 845387

Ibstock Building Products Ltd, Brickyard Road, Aldridge, Walsall, WS9 8TB Tel: (01922) 741400 Fax: (01922) 743086

Ibstock Scottish Brick Ltd, Tannochside Factory, Old Edinburgh Road, Uddingston, Glasgow, G71 6HL Tel: (01698) 810686 Fax: (01698) 812364

Jay's Refractory Specialists Ltd, Callywhite Lane, Dronfield, Derbyshire, S18 2XR Tel: (01246) 410241 Fax: (01246) 290221 E-mail: info@jrsuk.com

Keyline Brick & Builders Merchant, Beaufort Road, Plasmarl, Swansea, SA6 8HR Tel: (01792) 792264 Fax: (01792) 796279 E-mail: swanseavea@keyline.co.uk

W.T Lamb & Sons Ltd, Pitsham Brickyard, Midhurst, West Sussex, GU29 9QJ Tel: (01403) 785141 Fax: (01730) 816836

Tom Langton & Son, Knowsthorpe Lane, Leeds, LS9 0AT Tel: 0113-249 9440 Fax: 0113-240 2287 E-mail: chris@tomlangtons.com

Manchester Brick Services, Haigh Avenue, Whitehill Indust Estate, Reddish, Stockport, Cheshire, SK4 1NU Tel: 0161-480 2621 Fax: 0161-480 0108

Mansfield Brick Co. Ltd, Sandhurst Avenue, Mansfield, Nottinghamshire, NG18 4BE Tel: (01623) 622441 Fax: (01623) 420904

Marshalls Clay Products, 4 Park Terrace, Glasgow, G3 6BY Tel: 0141-333 0985 Fax: 0141-332 6877

Maxit Ltd, A46 The Heath Business & Technical Park, Runcorn, Cheshire, WA7 4QX Tel: (01928) 515656 Fax: (01928) 576792 E-mail: sales@maxit.co.uk

Michelmersh Brick & Tile Co. Ltd, Hill View Road, Michelmersh, Romsey, Hampshire, SO51 0NN Tel: (01794) 368506 Fax: (01794) 368845 E-mail: sales@michelmersh.co.uk

Millenium Brick Ltd, Unit B Levenshulme Trading Estate, Printworks Lane, Manchester, M19 3JP Tel: 0161-248 0882 Fax: 0161-248 5445 E-mail: sales@millenniumbrick.plus.com

▶ Northern Brick Fabrications, Unit 7 Ascot Drive, Stockton-on-Tees, Cleveland, TS18 2QQ Tel: (01642) 602010 Fax: (01642) 672096 E-mail: brick-special@surffree.co.uk

P D Brick Ltd, Smalldale, Buxton, Derbyshire, SK17 8EA Tel: (01298) 25396

P D Bricks, Somerset Works, Merehead Quarry, East Cranmore, Shepton Mallet, Somerset, BA4 4SQ Tel: (01749) 881100 Fax: (01749) 880707

Pagets Builders Merchants Ltd, 94 Broadfield Road, Sheffield, S8 0XL Tel: 0114-292 3000 Fax: 0114-250 9350 E-mail: info@c-paget.co.uk

R M C Concrete Products Ltd, Dale Road, Dove Holes, Buxton, Derbyshire, SK17 8BG Tel: (01298) 22324 Fax: (01298) 815221

Raeburn Brick Ltd, East Avenue, Blantyre, Glasgow, G72 0JB Tel: (01698) 828888 Fax: (01698) 824039

Readyblock, 45 Craighulliar Road, Portrush, County Antrim, BT56 8NN Tel: (028) 7082 3374 Fax: (028) 7082 2682

Sussex Hand Made Bricks, Fourteen Acre Lane, Three Oaks, Hastings, East Sussex, TN35 4NB Tel: (01424) 814344 Fax: (01226) 700350

Travis Perkins plc, The Quay, Fen Lane, Beccles, Suffolk, NR34 9BH Tel: (01502) 712421 Fax: (01502) 711110

W Fayers & Sons, 15 Margaret Road, Barnet, Hertfordshire, EN4 9NR Tel: (020) 8370 6400 Fax: (020) 8370 6415

Websters Hemming & Sons Ltd, 274 Stoney Stanton Road, Coventry, CV6 5DJ Tel: (024) 7668 8300 Fax: (024) 7663 7671

Wienerberger Ltd, Smoke Jack Brickworks, Horsham Lane, Wallis Wood, Dorking, Surrey, RH5 5QH Tel: (01306) 627481 Fax: (01306) 627561

York Handmade Brick Co. Ltd, Winchester House, Forest Lane, Alne, York, YO61 1TU Tel: (01347) 838881 Fax: (01347) 838885 E-mail: sales@yorkhandmade.co.uk

GENERAL OR ROAD SURFACING ASPHALT CONTRACTORS

Ayton Asphalte, Browick Works, Ayton Road, Wymondham, Norfolk, NR18 0RJ Tel: (01953) 602002 Fax: (01953) 604965 E-mail: sales@ayton.co.uk

BDP Surfacing Ltd, Raynesway, Derby, DE24 0DW Tel: (01332) 571806 Fax: (01332) 574278

Bestco Surfacing Ltd, Hope Yard, Monroe Industrial Estate, Waltham Cross, Hertfordshire, EN8 7LX Tel: (01992) 652477 Fax: (01992) 652479

Brennans Of Wiltshire Ltd, Harepath Farm, Burbage, Marlborough, Wiltshire, SN8 3BT Tel: (01672) 810380 Fax: (01672) 811157 E-mail: bofwilts@aol.com

F T Gearing Landscape Services Ltd, Crompton Road Depot, Stevenage, Hertfordshire, SG1 2EE Tel: (01438) 369321 Fax: (01438) 353039 E-mail: fred@ft-gearing.co.uk

Granville Steel Contracting plc, Steel Close, Eaton Socon, St. Neots, Cambridgeshire, PE19 8TT Tel: (01480) 213513 Fax: (01480) 405994 E-mail: jane.taylor@aggregate.co.uk

H C Lewis & Co. Ltd, 47 Hogshill Street, Beaminster, Dorset, DT8 3AG Tel: (01308) 862421 Fax: (01308) 863782 E-mail: hclewisandson@hotmail.com

Huyton Asphalt Ltd, Merton Bank Road, St. Helens, Merseyside, WA9 1HZ Tel: (01744) 755291 Fax: (01744) 451696

John Williams & Co Crwbin Quarries Ltd, Pantyrathro Manor, Llangain, Carmarthen, Dyfed, SA33 5AJ Tel: (01267) 241226 Fax: (01267) 241630

Kennedy Asphalt, Downs Road, Willenhall, West Midlands, WV13 2PF Tel: 0121-568 7903 Fax: 0121-526 7265

O'Hara Property Investment Holding Co. Ltd, 101 Rowlands Avenue, Hatch End, Pinner, Middlesex, HA5 4AW Tel: (020) 8900 0694 Fax: (020) 8900 1540

W Pollard & Son Ltd, 19 Kirk Road, Nottingham, NG3 6GX Tel: 0115-950 4791 Fax: 0115-950 4791

GENERAL OR STANDARD BOLTS AND NUTS

Asco Fixings Ltd, Colliery Road, West Bromwich, West Midlands, B71 4JT Tel: 0121-553 1177 Fax: 0121-553 1199 E-mail: info@ascofixings.co.uk

B & C Fixings Ltd, Archimedes House, 20 Cleveland Trading Estate, Darlington, County Durham, DL1 2PB Tel: (01325) 286842 Fax: (01325) 352563

Boka Bolt Supplies, 10 Cormorant Drive, Picow Farm Road, Runcorn, Cheshire, WA7 4UD Tel: (01928) 590440 Fax: (01928) 590400

Bonner-Regis Manufacturing Ltd, High Street, Princes End, Tipton, West Midlands, DY4 9HR Tel: 0121-522 2616 Fax: 0121-557 6864 E-mail: sales@regis-bolt.co.uk

C H Morgan & Co. Ltd, 1 Clifton Business Park, Chamberlain Road, Aylesbury, Buckinghamshire, HP19 8DY Tel: (01296) 434878 Fax: (01296) 338520

Clark Fixings Ltd, Unit 1, Crescent Works Industrial Estate, Willenhall Road, Darlaston, Wednesbury, West Midlands, WS10 8JJ Tel: 0121-568 6968 Fax: 0121-568 8719 E-mail: clarkfixings@btconnect.com

Commando Fasteners Co. Ltd, 3 Canal Street, Stourbridge, West Midlands, DY8 4LU Tel: (01384) 393949 Fax: (01384) 393933 E-mail: info@comfast.co.uk

Cooper & Turner Ltd, Sheffield Road, Sheffield, S9 1RS Tel: 0114-256 0057 Fax: 0114-244 5529 E-mail: sales@cooperandturner.co.uk

Elite Engineering, 9 Neptune Works, Upper Trinity Street, Birmingham, B9 4EG Tel: 0121-772 8070 Fax: 0121-772 2230

Eurofast Petrochemical Supplies Ltd, Unit 30 Planetary Industrial Estate, Planetary Road, Willenhall, West Midlands, WV13 3TA Tel: (01902) 307788 Fax: (01902) 307744 E-mail: eps-sales@eurofast.co.uk

Griffin Fastener Supplies Ltd, PO Box 7098, Solihull, West Midlands, B93 9LD Tel: (01564) 772161 Fax: (01564) 772162

Group Components Ltd, The Potteries, Woodgreen Road, Waltham Abbey, Essex, EN9 3TN Tel: (01992) 715900 Fax: (01992) 711993E-mail: sales@groupcomponents.co.uk

Hawk Fasteners Ltd, Brunel Road, Middlesbrough, Cleveland, TS6 6JA Tel: (01642) 468581 Fax: (01642) 440880 E-mail: sales@hawkfast.com

Holtbolt Ltd, Victoria Road, Halesowen, West Midlands, B62 8HZ Tel: 0121-561 3114 Fax: 0121-561 4566 E-mail: sales@holtbolt.co.uk

I E Bolt & Nut Ltd, Unit 14 Alma Works, Alma Street, Cutler Heights, Bradford, West Yorkshire, BD4 9JE Tel: (01274) 686805 Fax: (01274) 680361 E-mail: sales@iebolt.co.uk

J Cooke Engineering Ltd, Ashwell Street, Baldock, Hertfordshire, SG7 5QT Tel: (01462) 742236 Fax: (01462) 742188 E-mail: sales@jcooke.co.uk

John Sylvester Fasteners & Plastics Ltd, Vulcan Street, Bradford, West Yorkshire, BD4 9QU Tel: (01274) 684040 Fax: (01274) 684240 E-mail: sales.fp@btconnect.com

Kwik Turn Engineering, Unit 4 The Hayes Trading Estate, Folkes Road, Stourbridge, West Midlands, DY9 8RN Tel: (01384) 898011 Fax: (01384) 896869

London Screw Co. Ltd, Park Lane, Halesowen, West Midlands, B63 2QY Tel: (01384) 569832 Fax: (01384) 410296 E-mail: sales@londonscrew.com

Midland Fixings (Manchester), 3 Rufford Parade, Rufford Drive, Whitefield, Manchester, M45 8PL Tel: 0161-766 2491 Fax: 0161-767 9023

P R D Fasteners Ltd, Unit 10 Monmer Close Industrial Estate, Willenhall, West Midlands, WV13 1JR Tel: (01902) 636246 Fax: (01902) 605759 E-mail: sales@prdfasteners.co.uk

P R D Holdings Ltd, Unit 13, Monmer Close, Willenhall, West Midlands, WV13 1JR Tel: (01902) 639360 Fax: (01902) 639365 E-mail: info@prdholdings.com

Peers Jackson Engineering Company Ltd, Timmis Road, Stourbridge, West Midlands, DY9 7BQ Tel: (01384) 422503 Fax: (01384) 422568

Precise Fastenings & Supplies Ltd, Ivanhoe Road, Finchampstead, Wokingham, Berkshire, RG40 4QQ Tel: 0118-932 8832 Fax: 0118-932 8519 E-mail: precisefastenings@fixings.fsworld.co.uk

R C F Bolt & Nut Co. Ltd, Park Lane East, Tipton, West Midlands, DY4 8RF Tel: 0121-522 2353 Fax: 0121-522 2304 E-mail: rcf@dial.pipex.com

Slotted Nut Service Ltd, Woden Road South, Wednesbury, West Midlands, WS10 0AH Tel: 0121-556 0865

Socket & Allied Screws Ltd, 121 Camden Street, Birmingham, B1 3DJ Tel: 0121-200 2880 Fax: 0121-236 8991 E-mail: sales@socket-allied.com

Stainless & Alloy (Aberdeen) Ltd, 1 Crombie Road, Aberdeen, AB11 9QQ Tel: (01224) 874666 Fax: (01224) 874699 E-mail: sales@stainlessandalloy.co.uk

Tigges UK Ltd, Unit 13, Road 32, Telford, Shropshire, TF1 7EU Tel: (01952) 670173 Fax: (01952) 670190 E-mail: tigges@icom-web.com

TLW Fasteners Ltd, 115 Lodgefield Road, Halesowen, West Midlands, B62 8AX Tel: 0121-602 4040 Fax: 0121-602 4040

Triplefast International Ltd, Unit 13 Monmer Close Industrial Estate, Willenhall, West Midlands, WV13 1JR Tel: (01902) 636399 Fax: (01902) 609880 E-mail: sales@triplefast.co.uk

Universal Boltforgers, Unit 28 Dudley Road West, Tividale, Oldbury, West Midlands, B69 2PJ Tel: 0121-522 5950 Fax: 0121-520 5333 E-mail: office@universal-boltforgers.co.uk

GENERAL PRESSWORK PRESSINGS

A E Harris & Co Birmingham Ltd, 109-138 Northwood Street, Birmingham, B3 1SZ Tel: 0121-233 2386 Fax: 0121-200 3702 E-mail: sales@aeharris.co.uk

A E Oscroft & Sons, 49d Pipers Road, Park Farm Industrial Estate, Redditch, Worcestershire, B98 0HU Tel: (01527) 502203 Fax: (01527) 510378 E-mail: info@aeoscroft.co.uk

A H Hanson Ltd, Marley Street, Keighley, West Yorkshire, BD21 5JX Tel: (01535) 604112 Fax: (01535) 610085 E-mail: sales@wheel-clamp.com

A J Pressings Ltd, 95 Reddings Lane, Tyseley, Birmingham, B11 3EY Tel: 0121-706 9886 Fax: 0121-706 9887 E-mail: tony@ajwilliams.co.uk

A P Smith & Son Metal Pressing Ltd, 8 Kings St, Birmingham, B19 3AR Tel: 0121-523 0011 Fax: 0121-554 7244 E-mail: sales@apsmith.co.uk

Able Production, 77 Arthur Street, Redditch, Worcestershire, B98 8JY Tel: (01527) 510899 Fax: (01527) 514234

Acme Spinning Co. Ltd, Garratts Lane, Cradley Heath, West Midlands, B64 5RE Tel: 0121-559 1648 Fax: 0121-559 1299 E-mail: info@acmespinning.com

Ambery Metalform Components, Unit F6 Newton Business Park, Talbot Road, Hyde, Cheshire, SK14 4UQ Tel: 0161-367 9616 Fax: 0161-368 0689 E-mail: sales@ambery-metalform.co.uk

Arba Engineering, 32g Heming Road, Redditch, Worcestershire, B98 0DH Tel: (01527) 520629 Fax: (01527) 520629 E-mail: arba32g@hotmail.com

B B R Engineering (Shropshire) Ltd, King Street, Broseley, Shropshire, TF12 5LT Tel: (01952) 882597 Fax: (01952) 883955 E-mail: sales@bbrengineering.co.uk

B B S Gloucester Ltd, Unit 1 Ross Site, Alton Road Industrial Estate, Ross-on-Wye, Herefordshire, HR9 5NB Tel: (01989) 564404 Fax: (01989) 566635

Bacol Industries Ltd, Middlemore Road, Middlemore Industrial Estate, Smethwick, West Midlands, B66 2EQ Tel: 0121-558 3911 Fax: 0121-555 5720 E-mail: eng@bacol.co.uk

Fred Baker Ltd, 30 Park Street, Birmingham, B5 5JH Tel: 0121-643 5409 Fax: 0121-643 0914

Batey Metallic Packing Co. Ltd, Back Ellison Road, Gateshead, Tyne & Wear, NE11 9TR Tel: 0191-460 4167 Fax: 0191-493 2148

Baylis Automotive, Unit 49g, Pipers Road, Park Farm Industrial Estate, Redditch, Worcestershire, B98 0HU Tel: (01527) 517220 Fax: (01527) 517114 E-mail: tclews@baylisautomotive.com

Better Badges, C 9 Garman Road, London, N17 0UR Tel: (020) 8365 1035 Fax: (020) 8365 1905 E-mail: john@abetterbadge.com

Bevans Holdings Leicester Ltd, Gloucester Cresent, Wigston, Leicestershire, LE18 4YR Tel: 0116-278 2331 Fax: 0116-277 8307 E-mail: sales@bevanscomponents.co.uk

Binns Security Fencing Ltd, Pressmetal House St. Augustines Business Park, Estuary Close, Whitstable, Kent, CT5 2QJ Tel: (01227) 794490 Fax: (01227) 794488

Bird Stevens & Co. Ltd, Sun Street, Brierley Hill, West Midlands, DY5 2JE Tel: (01384) 567381 Fax: (01384) 637357 E-mail: sales@birdstevens.co.uk

Birmingham Stopper, 235 Icknield Street, Hockley, Birmingham, B18 6QU Tel: 0121-551 7781 Fax: 0121-554 4567 E-mail: robertp@birminghamstopper.co.uk

BMR Presswork, Market Street, Draycott, Derby, DE72 3NB Tel: (01332) 875384 Fax: (01332) 874022

Bolivar Ltd, Unit 9B Devonshire Works, Riparian Way, Cross Hills, Keighley, West Yorkshire, BD20 7BW Tel: (01535) 631222 Fax: (01535) 637555 E-mail: sales@bolivar-limited.com

Border Precision Ltd, Pinnaclehill Industrial Estate, Kelso, Roxburghshire, TD5 8DW Tel: (01573) 224941 Fax: (01573) 225220 E-mail: sales@borderprecision.com

Bowman & Sanderson Ltd, Icknield Way, Baldock, Hertfordshire, SG7 5BD Tel: (01462) 892292 Fax: (01462) 490457 E-mail: bowsand@tiscali.co.uk

John Bradley & Son Ltd, Spring Works, Russell Street, Heywood, Lancashire, OL10 1NU Tel: (01706) 360353 Fax: (01706) 366154 E-mail: jbs@johnbradleygroup.co.uk

Brayman Springs & Production Engineering, 7 28 Heming Road, Redditch, Worcestershire, B98 0DH Tel: (01527) 510004 Fax: (01527) 510004

Bridgford Pressings Ltd, Building No. 3 Gotham Business Complex, Leake Road, Gotham, Nottingham, NG11 0LB Tel: 0115-983 0884 Fax: 0115-983 0155 E-mail: enquiries@bridgfordpressings.co.uk

Broadway Stamping Ltd, Denbigh Road, Bletchley, Milton Keynes, MK1 1DT Tel: (01908) 647703 Fax: (01908) 649279 E-mail: broadways@broadwaysstampings.co.uk

Brookvale Manufacturing Co. Ltd, 15 Reddicap Trading Estate, Sutton Coldfield, West Midlands, B75 7DQ Tel: 0121-378 0833 Fax: 0121-311 1794 E-mail: enquiries@brookvale-manufacturing.co.uk

Burrafirm Ltd, Croxstalls Road, Walsall, WS3 2XY Tel: (01922) 476836 Fax: (01922) 479442 E-mail: user@albert-jagger.co.uk

C Brandauer & Co. Ltd, 235 Bridge Street West, Birmingham, B19 2YU Tel: 0121-359 2822 Fax: 0121-359 2836 E-mail: aedwards@brandauer.co.uk

C J Armstrong Manufacturing Co. Ltd, Unit 7-8 River Brent Business Park, Trumpers Way, London, W7 2QA Tel: (020) 8574 4602 Fax: (020) 8574 1078 E-mail: cjarmstrong@lycos.co.uk

Ceandess Ltd, Ashford Industrial Estate, Dixon Street, Wolverhampton, WV2 2BX Tel: (01902) 872000 Fax: (01902) 872019 E-mail: sales@ceandess.co.uk

Central Tools & Pressings, Unit D1, Bill House, Birmingham, B19 1AP Tel: 0121-523 7522 Fax: 0121-523 9922

Cheshire Pressings, Road Five, Winsford, Cheshire, CW7 3QX Tel: (01606) 863557 Fax: (01606) 869483

Chidlow & Cheshire Ltd, Steward Street, Birmingham, B18 7AE Tel: 0121-454 1003 Fax: 0121-456 3935

Clamason Industries Ltd, Gibbons Industrial Park, Dudley Road, Kingswinford, West Midlands, DY6 8XG Tel: (01384) 400000 Fax: (01384) 400588 E-mail: sales@clamason.co.uk

Coronet Rail Ltd, Castor Road, Sheffield, S9 2TL Tel: 0114-256 2225 Fax: 0114-261 7826 E-mail: sales@coronetrail.co.uk

Cullen Engineering Ltd, 51 Naysmith Rd, Southfield Industrial Estate, Glenrothes, Fife, KY6 2SD Tel: (01592) 771132 Fax: (01383) 771182 E-mail: sales@cullen-bp.co.uk

D B Springs Ltd, 1 Double Century Works, High Street, Astwood Bank, Redditch, Worcestershire, B96 6AR Tel: (01527) 893220 Fax: (01527) 893220

D G C Engineering UK Ltd, Unit 7 Building 6, Stanmore Industrial Estate, Bridgnorth, Shropshire, WV15 5HP Tel: (01746) 767133 Fax: (01746) 767133

Damax Electrical Laminations Ltd, Unit C Amyco Works, Doris Road, Bordesley Green, Birmingham, B9 4SJ Tel: 0121-771 3857 Fax: 0121-771 1913 E-mail: info@damaxlams.co.uk

David Bowler & Sons Ltd, Hardley Industrial Estate, Hardley, Hythe, Southampton, SO45 3YQ Tel: (023) 8084 3109 Fax: (023) 8084 0034 E-mail: bowler.group@virgin.net

Mark Davis Engineering Co. Ltd, Hayes Lane, Lye, Stourbridge, West Midlands, DY9 8RA Tel: (01384) 424404 Fax: (01384) 424707 E-mail: enquiries@markdavis.co.uk

Diametric Metal Fabrications Ltd, The Brookland, Blithbury Road, Rugeley, Staffordshire, WS15 3HQ Tel: (01889) 577243 Fax: (01889) 584672 E-mail: sales@diametricmetalfabrications.co.uk

Diaploy Ltd, Manners Avenue, Manners Industrial Estate, Ilkeston, Derbyshire, DE7 8EF Tel: 0115-944 2272 Fax: 0115-944 2272

DMP Group, Unit 5F Canal Estate, Station Road, Langley, Slough, SL3 6EG Tel: (01753) 580101 Fax: (01753) 542685 E-mail: sales@dmpgroup.co.uk

Frank Dudley Ltd, Unit 2 Wiggin Street, Hockley, Birmingham, B16 0AH Tel: 0121-523 0742 Fax: 0121-452 8159 E-mail: sales@frankdudley.com

Dudley Tool & Engineering Co. Ltd, Mill Street, Wordsley, Stourbridge, West Midlands, DY8 5SX Tel: (01384) 571181 Fax: (01384) 265435 E-mail: info@dudley-tool.co.uk

Dyson Presswork Ltd, Moor St Industrial Estate, Brierley Hill, West Midlands, DY5 3TS Tel: (01384) 77252 Fax: (01384) 480429 E-mail: gbh26@dial.pipex.com

Ecam Engineering Ltd, Tower Crane Drive, Stoke-on-Trent, ST10 4DB Tel: (01538) 757166 Fax: (01538) 755857 E-mail: nick@ecam.co.uk

Enterpriseforce Metal Pressing, Unit 3c-Unit 3d Canal Estate, Station Road, Langley, Slough, SL3 6EG Tel: (01753) 585018 Fax: (01753) 542685 E-mail: david@dmpgroup.co.uk

European Springs & Pressings Ltd, Chaffinch Business Park, Croydon Road, Beckenham, Kent, BR3 4DW Tel: (020) 8663 1800 Fax: (020) 8663 1900 E-mail: sales@europeansprings.com

F I S Loveday Ltd, 16-18 Princip Street, Birmingham, B4 6LE Tel: 0121-359 3176 Fax: 0121-359 1098 E-mail: fisloveday@aol.com

F & L Smout & Sons Ltd, Woods Lane, Cradley Heath, West Midlands, B64 7AH Tel: (01384) 569508 Fax: (01384) 412155 E-mail: lgreen@smout.sagehost.co.uk

FGH Products, 68 Hunters Vale, Birmingham, B19 2XH Tel: 0121-554 4329 Fax: 0121-554 1857 E-mail: fghsilver@btconnect.com

Fiamma Ltd, Siddon Factory Estate, Howard Street, West Bromwich, West Midlands, B70 0TE Tel: 0121-556 1618 Fax: 0121-556 2132 E-mail: fiamma@talktalk.business.net

Fourjay Ltd Presswork, Royal Works, Coleshill Street, Sutton Coldfield, West Midlands, B72 1SJ Tel: 0121-354 1115 Fax: 0121-354 1205 E-mail: enquiries@fourjay.co.uk

Fowkes & Danks Ltd, Howard Road, Park Farm Industrial Estate, Redditch, Worcestershire, B98 7SE Tel: (01527) 830800 Fax: (01527) 830801 E-mail: enquiries@fowkes&danks.co.uk

Friary Metal Products Ltd, 106-110 Bishop Street, Birmingham, B5 6JP Tel: 0121-622 2088 Fax: 0121-666 7277 E-mail: info@thefriarygroup.co.uk

G B Metal Spinnings Ltd, 68a Glover Street, Birmingham, B9 4EL Tel: 0121-773 5444 Fax: 0121-773 5666 E-mail: lee@gb-metalspinnings.com

G & D Engineering Vickers Ltd, Poplars Industrial Estate, Moor Lane, Birmingham, B6 7AD Tel: 0121-356 3378

G E Starr Ltd, Dixon Street, Wolverhampton, WV2 2BS Tel: (01902) 576675 Fax: (01902) 350099 E-mail: info@gestarr.co.uk

Ghyllside Manufacturing, Unit 11 Ivyhouse Lane, Hastings, East Sussex, TN35 4NN Tel: (01424) 465547

A.J. Gilbert (Birmingham) Ltd, 66-77 Buckingham Street, Birmingham, B19 3HU Tel: 0121-236 7774 Fax: 0121-236 6024 E-mail: lucysox@aol.com

Goss Components Ltd, 43 Fulbourne Road, London, E17 4AF Tel: (020) 8527 5599 Fax: (020) 8527 1142 E-mail: enquiries@gosscomponent.com

A. & J. Green Engineering Ltd, Units 12-13, Enfield Industrial Estate, Redditch, Worcestershire, B97 6BG Tel: (01527) 62666 Fax: (01527) 584298 E-mail: ddptools@aol.com

Grorud Engineering Ltd, Castleside Industrial Estate, Spruce Way, Consett, County Durham, DH8 8JA Tel: (01207) 590471 Fax: (01207) 599810 E-mail: mail@grorud.com

GWR Engineering Ltd, 36 Derby Road, Liverpool, L20 1AB Tel: 0151-933 3150 Fax: 0151-944 2410 E-mail: gwrengineering@aol.com

H Case & Son Cradley Heath Ltd, Mount Works, Foxoak Street, Cradley Heath, West Midlands, B64 5DQ Tel: (01384) 566358 Fax: (01384) 634601 E-mail: sales@h-caseandson.co.uk

H Hipkiss & Co. Ltd, Park House, Clapgate Lane, Birmingham, B32 3BL Tel: 0121-421 5777 Fax: 0121-421 5333 E-mail: info@hipkiss.co.uk

H L Tool Co Ltd, Gardenvale Mill, Greenfield Road, Colne, Lancashire, BB8 9PD Tel: (01282) 864850 Fax: (01282) 870244 E-mail: sales@hltool.co.uk

H T Brigham & Co. Ltd, Station Road, Coleshill, Birmingham, B46 1JQ Tel: (01675) 463882 Fax: (01675) 467441 E-mail: admin@htbrigham.co.uk

H T Fabrications Ltd, 420 Thurmaston Boulevard, Leicester, LE4 9LE Tel: 0116-276 1814 Fax: 0116-246 0576 E-mail: ht@fabs.freeserve.co.uk

Hampton Works Ltd, Twyning Road, Stirchley, Birmingham, B30 2XZ Tel: 0121-458 2901 Fax: 0121-433 3819 E-mail: sales@hampton-works.co.uk

Harlech Tool & Engineering Co., 5 Ynyscedwyn Industrial Estate, Trawsffordd Road, Ystradgynlais, Swansea, SA9 1DT Tel: (01639) 849044 Fax: (01639) 849045 E-mail: info@harlech-tools.co.uk

Harlow Pressings Ltd, 57-60 Llantarnam Industrial Park, Cwmbran, Gwent, NP44 3AW Tel: (01633) 487400 Fax: (01633) 863010

Hawkes Metalmex, Holbrook Trading Estate, Old Lane, Halfway, Sheffield, S20 3GZ Tel: 0114-251 0251 Fax: 0114-251 0151 E-mail: sales@pct-automotive.co.uk

Henshaw Manufacturing Co. Ltd, Stratford St North, Birmingham, B11 1BP Tel: 0121-772 2232 Fax: 0121-771 1788 E-mail: weekshenshaw@aol.com

Holywell Engineering Ltd, Station Road, Backworth, Newcastle Upon Tyne, NE27 0AE Tel: 0191-268 4365 Fax: 0191-268 9506 E-mail: eng@holywell.com

Indenco Co., Unit 35, St. Richards Road, Four Pools Industrial Estate, Evesham, Worcestershire, WR11 1XJ Tel: (01386) 443946 Fax: (01386) 45279 E-mail: enquiries@indenco.co.uk

J G Ross & Co Components Ltd, 19b Pershore Trading Estate, Station Road, Pershore, Worcestershire, WR10 2DD Tel: (01386) 552140 Fax: (01386) 555628 E-mail: info@jgross.co.uk

J T Pearce Springs Ltd, Arrow Road North, Redditch, Worcestershire, B98 8NT Tel: (01527) 61123 Fax: (01527) 61124

Jenks & Cattell Engineering Ltd, Neachells Lane, Wolverhampton, WV11 3PU Tel: (01902) 305530 Fax: (01902) 305529 E-mail: sales@jenks-cattell.co.uk

JJ Engineering (Birmingham) Ltd, Granby Avenue, Garretts Green, Birmingham, B33 0TJ Tel: 0121-784 9990 Fax: 0121-784 8588 E-mail: enquiries@jjeng.co.uk

Just Fittings Ltd, 122 Sydenham Road, Sparkbrook, Birmingham, B11 1DQ Tel: 0121-773 8730 Fax: 0121-766 7012

Kaybee Engineering, Station Street, Bromsgrove, Worcestershire, B60 2BS Tel: (01527) 870845 Fax: (01527) 870845 E-mail: andy.knight@kpe.demon.co.uk

Kerri Engineering, South March, Long March Industrial Estate, Daventry, Northamptonshire, NN11 4PH Tel: (01327) 876944 Fax: (01327) 300713

Kimber Allen Ltd, Broomfield Works, London Road, Swanley, Kent, BR8 8DF Tel: (01322) 663234 Fax: (01322) 668318 E-mail: ka@kimberallen.freeserve.co.uk

GENERAL PRESSWORK PRESSINGS - *continued*

King & Rawlings, 278-284 High Street, Waltham Cross, Hertfordshire, EN8 7EA Tel: (01992) 623575 Fax: (01992) 640570

Leaco Ltd, Lamberhead Industrial Estate, Leopold Street, Wigan, Lancashire, WN5 8DH Tel: (01942) 221188 Fax: (01942) 226682 E-mail: sales@leaco.ltd.uk

Leigh & Letcher, Chequers Lane, Dagenham, Essex, RM9 6QD Tel: (020) 8984 1015 Fax: (020) 8984 1735 E-mail: sales@leighandletcher.co.uk

London Taxis (International) Plc, Holyhead Road, Coventry, CV5 8JJ Tel: (024) 7657 2000 Fax: (024) 7657 2001 E-mail: exports@lti.co.uk

Longcroft Engineering Ltd, Rochdale Road Industrial Estate, Walsden, Todmorden, Lancashire, OL14 6UD Tel: (01706) 819955 Fax: (01706) 819966 E-mail: paul@longcroftengineering.co.uk

Ludlow, 6 Prospect View, Rock Lane, Ludlow, Shropshire, SY8 1ST Tel: (01584) 875096

Mamod Ltd, Unit 1a Summit Crescent, Smethwick, West Midlands, B66 1BT Tel: 0121-500 6433 Fax: 0121-500 6309 E-mail: accommodation@mamod.co.uk

Meath Engineering Tools Ltd, Black Bourton Road, Carterton, Oxfordshire, OX18 3EZ Tel: (01993) 841041

Metal Pressings Group Ltd, Howard Road, Redditch, Worcestershire, B98 7SE Tel: (01527) 526933 Fax: (01527) 510009 E-mail: cmp@metal-pressings.com

Metallifacture Ltd, Mansfield Road, Redhill, Nottingham, NG5 8PY Tel: 0115-966 0200 Fax: 0115-967 0133 E-mail: mail@metallifacture.co.uk

Middleton Metal Spinning, Clough Road, Manchester, M9 4FP Tel: 0161 2058687

Mortimer Springs Ltd, Coleman Works, Villiers Road, London, NW2 5PU Tel: (020) 8459 1420 Fax: (020) 8451 7614 E-mail: sales@mortimersprings.com

N D Jig & Gauge Co.Ltd, Bush Works, Leabrook Road, Wednesbury, West Midlands, WS10 7NB Tel: 0121-556 0824 Fax: 0121-556 8177 E-mail: sqplatewashers@aol.com

North Engineering Works, Block 24 Kilspindie Road, Dunsinane Industrial Estate, Dundee, DD2 3QH Tel: (01382) 889693 Fax: (01382) 889808 E-mail: sales@northeng.co.uk

North West Fabrications Ltd, Station Works, Berry Street, Bootle, Merseyside, L20 8AT Tel: 0151-922 9518 Fax: 0151-933 6395

Oakham Sheet Metal Co. Ltd, Brickhouse Lane, Great Bridge, West Bromwich, West Midlands, B70 0DS Tel: 0121-557 9656 Fax: 0121-522 2186

▶ Oswald Springs, 76 Arthur Street, Redditch, Worcestershire, B98 8LJ Tel: (01527) 527777 Fax: (01527) 527785 E-mail: oswald@oswaldsprings.co.uk

P F C Industries, 1 Livingstone Road, Sheffield, S9 3XX Tel: 0114-256 1508 Fax: 0114-256 1485

Patterson Pressings Ltd, Reliance Works, Newpound Common, Wisborough Green, Billingshurst, West Sussex, RH14 0AZ Tel: (01403) 700088 Fax: (01403) 700001 E-mail: r.patterson@patterson.uk.com

Pegrex, Unit 1e Pearsall Drive, Oldbury, West Midlands, B69 2RA Tel: 0121-511 1475 Fax: 0121-511 1474 E-mail: nstruman@aol.com

Phoenix Pressings Ltd, Wakefield Road, Brighouse, West Yorkshire, HD6 1PE Tel: (01484) 712422 Fax: (01484) 716471 E-mail: sales@phoenixpressings.co.uk

Portland Pressings Ltd, Moor Lane, Birmingham, B6 7HH Tel: 0121-356 8187 Fax: 0121-344 3039

Prescient Engineering Ltd, 25 Mereside, Soham, Ely, Cambridgeshire, CB7 5EE Tel: (01353) 720787 Fax: (01353) 723356 E-mail: contact@prescientengineeringltd.co.uk

Prescott Powell Ltd, 466 Moseley Road, Birmingham, B12 9AN Tel: 0121-446 4411 Fax: 0121-446 4681 E-mail: liam.duggan@prescottpowell.co.uk

Press Metal Products Ltd, 5 Abberley Industrial Centre, Abberley Street, Smethwick, West Midlands, B66 2QL Tel: 0121-555 6061 Fax: 0121-555 6058 E-mail: sales@pressed-metal.com

Presscraft Components Ltd, 3 Woodburn Road, Smethwick, West Midlands, B66 2PU Tel: 0121-558 1888 Fax: 0121-555 5498 E-mail: info@presscraft-limited.co.uk

Pressfab Products Pressworkers, 9 Lion Industrial Estate, Clinton Road, Leominster, Herefordshire, HR6 0RJ Tel: (01568) 613693 Fax: (01568) 613501

Pressrite Engineering Ltd, 24 Ogmore Crescent, Bridgend Industrial Estate, Bridgend, Mid Glamorgan, CF31 3TE Tel: (01656) 657067 Fax: (01656) 645857

Prestige Engineering, 27 Thornleigh Trading Estate, Dudley, West Midlands, DY2 8UB Tel: (01384) 234488 Fax: (01384) 238884 E-mail: prestigeengineering@btconnect.com

Prestision Engineers, 15-16 St Andrews Industrial Estate, Sydney Road, Birmingham, B9 4QB Tel: 0121-772 4414 Fax: 0121-771 0472 E-mail: geoff@prestision.co.uk

Pugh Engineering Co., Unit 20 Poplar Drive, Witton, Birmingham, B6 7AD Tel: 0121-344 3240 Fax: 0121-344 3240

Quality Tool & Engineering Ltd, Maesyllan, Llanidloes, Powys, SY18 6DF Tel: (01686) 412679 Fax: (01686) 413554 E-mail: qualitytools@btconnect.com

R C Beresford Ltd, 48 St. Georges Street, Birmingham, B19 3QU Tel: 0121-236 8455 Fax: 0121-236 8493

R G G Malmos, 52 Hainge Road, Tividale, Oldbury, West Midlands, B69 2PD Tel: 0121-522 2140 Fax: 0121-520 1773

R J Vickers & Son Ltd, 152 Soho Hill, Birmingham, B19 1AF Tel: 0121-523 6235 Fax: 0121-523 9397 E-mail: vickers.metform@virgin.net

R S M Industries Ltd, School Lane, Exhall, Coventry, CV7 9NN Tel: (024) 7636 2082 Fax: (024) 7655 3715 E-mail: admin@rsmindustries.co.uk

Redbourn Engineering Ltd, Chiswick Avenue, Mildenhall, Bury St. Edmunds, Suffolk, IP28 7AY Tel: (01638) 713484 Fax: (01638) 713809 E-mail: sales@redbourn.com

▶ Responsive Engineering Group, Kingsway South, Team Valley, Gateshead, Tyne & Wear, NE11 0SH Tel: 0191-497 3400 Fax: 0191-497 3401 E-mail: sales@responsive-engineering.com

Ricor Ltd, Arrow Works, Birmingham Road, Studley, Warwickshire, B80 7AS Tel: (01527) 857757 Fax: (01527) 857224 E-mail: ricorjrobinson@aol.com

Frank Rigg Ltd, 489 Edenfield Road, Rochdale, Lancashire, OL11 5XR Tel: (01706) 644509 Fax: (01706) 643910

Rushall Tool & Engineering, Darlaston Central Trading Estate, Wednesbury, West Midlands, WS10 8XB Tel: 0121-526 3617 Fax: 0121-568 6015

S B Engineering (Precision) Ltd, 1 Dyke Road Mews, Brighton, BN1 3JD Tel: 01273 821397

S G Springs Ltd, 43 Crossgate Road, Park Farm Industrial Estate, Redditch, Worcestershire, B98 7SN Tel: (01527) 500955 Fax: (01527) 510278

S P Engineering, M Hawthorns Industrial Estate, Middlemore Road, Handsworth, Birmingham, B21 0BH Tel: 0121-554 1404 Fax: 0121-523 5834

Saren Engineering Ltd, Unit 10 Premier Trading Estate, 118 Dartmouth Middleway, Birmingham, B7 4AT Tel: 0121-359 4890 Fax: 0121-359 6951 E-mail: info@saren.co.uk

Scanway Engineering Ltd, 123 Vincent Street, Birmingham, B12 9SG Tel: 0121-440 3759 Fax: 0121-440 3759 E-mail: scanway.engineering@virgin.net

▶ Selcraft Ltd, Leigh Sinton, Malvern, Worcestershire, WR13 5XS Tel: (01886) 834850 Fax: (01886) 834851 E-mail: info@selcraft.com

Senior Press & Tool Co. Ltd, Unit 34b Marlborough Road, Churchill Industrial Estate, Lancing, West Sussex, BN15 8TR Tel: (01903) 762835 Fax: (01903) 762835

Sertec Birmingham Ltd, Gorsey Lane, Coleshill, Birmingham, B46 1JU Tel: (01675) 463361 Fax: (01675) 465539 E-mail: sertecgroup@sertec.co.uk

Shelley (Halesowen) Ltd, 39 The Old Woodyard, Hagley Hall Hagley, Hagley, Stourbridge, West Midlands, DY9 9LQ Tel: (01562) 885905 Fax: (01562) 884941

Shermaynes Welders Engineers Ltd, Units 2d 3a/3b Southgate Industrial Centre, Southgate, Lancaster, Morecambe, LA3 3PB Tel: (01524) 69333

Shire Pressings Ltd, Doubak Works, Barton Industrial Estate, Bilston, West Midlands, WV14 7LH Tel: (01902) 490155 Fax: (01902) 490155

Skelding's Ltd, 126 Oldbury Road, Smethwick, West Midlands, B66 1JE Tel: 0121-558 0622 Fax: 0121-558 6115

Spring Developments Ltd, Lyng Lane, West Bromwich, West Midlands, B70 7RP Tel: 0121-553 6543 Fax: 0121-553 7552

Spring & Press Developments Ltd, Unit 49 Enfield Industrial Estate, Redditch, Worcestershire, B97 6DE Tel: (01527) 67602 Fax: (01527) 60183 E-mail: sales@kn-products.co.uk

▶ Stadco Ltd, Harlescott Lane, Shrewsbury, SY1 3AS Tel: (01743) 462227 Fax: (01743) 447709 E-mail: info@stadco.co.uk

Steel Stamping Products Ltd, 15-17 Highmeres Road, Troon Industrial Estate, Leicester, LE4 9LZ Tel: 0116-276 6572 Fax: 0116-276 1624 E-mail: info@steelstampings.co.uk

Stowfledge Ltd, Mill Works, Mountsorrel Lane, Sileby, Loughborough, Leicestershire, LE12 7NF Tel: (01509) 812915 Fax: (01509) 816648

Structural Accessories Ltd, Unit 2a Bilston Key Industrial Estate, Oxford Street, Bilston, West Midlands, WV14 7DW Tel: (01902) 492298 Fax: (01902) 354055

Supaclad Ltd, Timmis Road, Stourbridge, West Midlands, DY9 7BQ Tel: (01384) 896647 Fax: (01384) 892457

Swindon Pressings, Bridge End Road, Swindon, SN3 4PE Tel: (01793) 536281 Fax: (01793) 551888 E-mail: info@swindon-pressings.co.uk

T K A Body Stampings Ltd, Wolverhampton Road, Cannock, Staffordshire, WS11 1LY Tel: (01543) 466664 Fax: (01543) 466665 E-mail: info@tkbs.thyssenkrupp.com

Texecom Ltd, Slackcote Lane, Delph, Oldham, OL3 5TW Tel: (01457) 821100 Fax: (01457) 871058

Town Bent Products Ltd, Unit 10-11 Daisyhill Industrial Estate, Ashworth Street, Rishton, Blackburn, BB1 4JW Tel: (01254) 876644 Fax: (01254) 876646 E-mail: townbent.products@virgin.net

Townend Precision Presswork, Unit 12 Ladbroke Park Industrial Estate, Millers Road, Warwick, CV34 5AN Tel: (01926) 490023 Fax: (01926) 402052

Triad Fabrications, Globe Works, Queensway, Rochdale, Lancashire, OL11 2QY Tel: (01706) 655099 Fax: (01706) 658712 E-mail: admin@triadfabs.com

Trimetals Ltd, Sunrise Business Park, Higher Shaftesbury Road, Blandford Forum, Dorset, DT11 8ST Tel: (01258) 459441 Fax: (01258) 480408 E-mail: trimetals@btconnect.com

Tritools, 15 Albert Road, Aldershot, Hampshire, GU11 1SZ Tel: (01252) 310429 Fax: (01252) 324428

Troy Components Ltd, Troy Industrial Estate, Jill Lane, Sambourne, Redditch, Worcestershire, B96 6ES Tel: (01527) 892941 Fax: (01527) 893310

Tulgrove Ltd, Jameson Road, Aston, Birmingham, B6 7SJ Tel: 0121-327 2296 Fax: 0121-328 5612 E-mail: tulgrove@tulgrove.co.uk

V.C.W. Engineering Ltd, Unit 8 Ailwin Road, Morton Hall industrial Estate, Bury St. Edmunds, Suffolk, IP32 7DS Tel: (01284) 768371 Fax: (01284) 768371 E-mail: brucewhiteman@aol.com

Vere Engineering Ltd, 17 Jameson Road, Birmingham, B6 7SJ Tel: 0121-327 3630 Fax: 0121-327 3050

Victor Engineering Co., 6d Arndale Road, Wick, Littlehampton, West Sussex, BN17 7HD Tel: 01903 716650

W R R Pedley & Co. Ltd, Ann Street, Willenhall, West Midlands, WV13 1EW Tel: (01902) 366060 Fax: (01902) 603411

Wagon Automotive, Tysley Plant, Saville House, Redfern Park Way, Birmingham, B11 2BF Tel: 0121-706 0330 Fax: 0121-706 1929

G W Waite Ltd, North Lonsdale Road, Ulverston, Cumbria, LA12 9DN Tel: (01229) 582046 Fax: (01229) 583893 E-mail: sales@gwwaite.com

▶ Walker Bros (Elland) Ltd, Ainleys Industrial Estate, Huddersfield Road, Elland, West Yorkshire, HX5 9JP Tel: (01422) 310767 Fax: (01422) 377837 E-mail: sales@wbelland.com

Wardtec Ltd, Unit 92, Heming Road, Washford, Redditch, Worcestershire, B98 0DH Tel: (01527) 520594 Fax: (01527) 502235 E-mail: ward-tec@btconnect.com

Waterhouse Pressings Ltd, Unit 4f Snaygill Industrial Estate, Keighley Road, Skipton, North Yorkshire, BD23 2QR Tel: (01756) 794577 Fax: (01756) 701481

Waterton Engineering Co. Ltd, 2 Raymond Avenue, Chadderton, Oldham, OL9 7HW Tel: 0161-624 0004 Fax: 0161-624 8276

E.J. Watts Engineering Group, Faldo Road, Barton-le-Clay, Bedford, MK45 4RJ Tel: (01582) 881601 Fax: (01582) 881075 E-mail: info@ejwatts.co.uk

Webbro Ltd, Whinfield Drive, Aycliffe Industrial Estate, Aycliffe Industrial Park, Newton Aycliffe, County Durham, DL5 6AU Tel: (01325) 313781 Fax: (01325) 300762

Werneth Manufacturing Co., Unit 2 Dawson Street, Redfern Industrial Estate, Hyde, Cheshire, SK14 1RD Tel: 0161-368 3079 Fax: 0161-368 3079

West Bromwich Pressings Ltd, Pleasant Street, Lyng, West Bromwich, West Midlands, B70 7DT Tel: 0121-525 5540 Fax: 0121-525 0581

Westpark Fabrications Ltd, Unit 4 Waterfield Mill, 4 Balmoral Road, Darwen, Lancashire, BB3 2EW Tel: (01254) 760136 Fax: (01254) 762116

Wild Manufacturing Group Ltd, PO Box 103, Birmingham, B5 5SJ Tel: 0121-643 9611 Fax: 0121-766 5278 E-mail: csd@wild.uk.com

Winston & Allan Ltd, Unit 5-6 Nutwood Trading Estate, Limestone Cottage Lane, Sheffield, S6 1NJ Tel: 0114-231 4744 Fax: 0114-232 3967 E-mail: sales@winstonandallan.co.uk

Witan Pressings Ltd, Unit 3, Alexander Mill, Gibb Street, Long Eaton, Nottingham, NG10 1EE Tel: 0115-946 1545 Fax: 0115-946 0874 E-mail: witan-pressings@btconnect.com

Wolverhampton Pressings Co. Ltd, Whetstone House, Fordhouse Road, Wolverhampton, WV10 9EA Tel: (01902) 307799 Fax: (01902) 721026 E-mail: sales@ralphmartindale.com

Woodseats Engineering, 3 Canal Works, Cadman Street, Sheffield, S4 7ZG Tel: 0114-279 6143 Fax: 0114-279 6143 E-mail: sales@woodseatsengineering.com

GENERAL PUBLICATION PRINTING

Allinson's, Allinson House, Lincoln Way, Fairfield Industrial Estate, Louth, Lincolnshire, LN11 0LS Tel: (01507) 600911 Fax: (01507) 600434 E-mail: admin@allinsonwilcox.co.uk

Apollo Press, 8 Decoy Road, Worthing, West Sussex, BN14 8ND Tel: (01903) 232444 Fax: (01903) 230354 E-mail: dyerpress72@aol.com

Badger Print, 1 Blatchford Close, Horsham, West Sussex, RH13 5RG Tel: (01403) 257722 Fax: (01403) 263276 E-mail: info@mrprinters.com

Copy Centre, 70 Park Lane, London, N17 0JR Tel: (020) 8808 7275 Fax: (020) 8365 1430

Cottesmore Press, Baxters Yard, Stuart Street, Grantham, Lincolnshire, NG31 9AF Tel: (01476) 405959 Fax: (01476) 405959 E-mail: fastrack@cottersmorepressfsbusiness.co.uk

F W Cupit Printers Ltd, The Rope Walk, 23 Louth Road, Horncastle, Lincolnshire, LN9 5ED Tel: (01507) 522339 Fax: (01507) 525438 E-mail: cupits@btinternet.com

Goodman Baylis Ltd, The Trinity Press, London Road, Worcester, WR5 2JH Tel: (01905) 357979 Fax: (01905) 354919 E-mail: theworks@goodmanbaylis.co.uk

Hackney Press Ltd, Unit 1 Phoenix Business Centre, 2-4 Bow Common Lane, London, E3 4AX Tel: (020) 7537 7579 Fax: (020) 7538 5691 E-mail: sales@hackneypress.co.uk

Holbrooks Printers Ltd, Norway Road, Portsmouth, PO3 5HX Tel: (023) 9266 1485 Fax: (023) 9267 1119 E-mail: sales@holbrooks.com

John E Wright & Co. Ltd, 3 Oxford Business Centre, Osney Lane, Oxford, OX1 1TB Tel: (01865) 244455 Fax: (01865) 793921

Lister & Durling Printers, 69 Station Road, Flitwick, Bedford, MK45 1JU Tel: (01525) 713770

M M Palmer Ltd, 3-5 Capital Place, Harlow, Essex, CM19 5AS Tel: (01279) 439023 Fax: (01279) 635940 E-mail: sales@palmersprint.co.uk

▶ McGrath Regional Publications Ltd, 23 Bolton Road, Farnworth, Bolton, BL4 7JN Tel: (01204) 796494 Fax: (01204) 791494 E-mail: mcgrathartwork@aol.com

Masterange Business Services Ltd, 9 East Road, Harlow, Essex, CM20 2BJ Tel: (01279) 300600 Fax: (01279) 306911 E-mail: services@masterange.co.uk

F. Newman Ltd, 33 Linford St, London, SW8 4UP Tel: (020) 7720 1981 Fax: (020) 7622 0016 E-mail: fnewmans@aol.com

Newsquest Printing Colchester, A Caxton Court, Newcomen Way, Severalls Industrial Park, Colchester, CO4 9TG Tel: (01206) 224600 Fax: (01206) 844335 E-mail: martyn_reed@essex-news.co.uk

Quantum Print Services Ltd, 1b Bardsley Road, Earlstrees Industrial Estate, Corby, Northamptonshire, NN17 4AR Tel: (01536) 408392 Fax: (01536) 408492 E-mail: sales@quantum-print.co.uk

Red Devil, Unit 2e Beehive Lane Works, Beehive Lane, Chelmsford, CM2 9TE Tel: (01255) 553555 Fax: (01255) 553555 E-mail: sales@reddevilmachines.co.uk

Rotaflow Ltd, Unit 16 Peterley Business Centre, 472 Hackney Road, London, E2 9EQ Tel: (020) 7739 7072 Fax: (020) 7729 9179 E-mail: rotaflow@mwfree.co.uk

Scotforms Computer Stationery Ltd, 3 Hatton Square, Livingston, West Lothian, EH54 9BJ Tel: (01506) 410871 Fax: (01506) 416805 E-mail: info@scotforms.co.uk

▶ Sign Update, 1 Allens Orchard, Chipping Warden, Banbury, Oxfordshire, OX17 1LX Tel: (01295) 660666 Fax: (0560) 1162164 E-mail: sb@freerbutler-gds.co.uk

T S O Ltd, Publications Centre, 51 Nine Elms Lane, London, SW8 5DR Tel: (020) 7873 8787 Fax: (0870) 600 5533 E-mail: customer.services@tso.co.uk

The Universities Press (Belfast) Ltd, Alanbrooke Road, Belfast, BT6 9HF Tel: (028) 9070 4464 Fax: (028) 9079 3295

Weald Print Solutions Ltd, Unit 3, Daux Rd, Billingshurst, W. Sussex, RH14 9SJ Tel: (01403) 783176 Fax: (01403) 785461 E-mail: info@wealdprintsolutions.co.uk

Zing Design & Print, Loughanhill Industrial Estate, Gateside Road, Coleraine, County Londonderry, BT52 2NR Tel: (028) 7035 7049 Fax: (028) 7034 4152 E-mail: info@zingdp.com

GENERAL PURPOSE ASPHALT

Midland Quarry Products Ltd, Leicester Road, Whitwick, Coalville, Leicestershire, LE67 5GR Tel: (01530) 832244 Fax: (01530) 832299 E-mail: sales@mqp.co.uk

Premier Coatings Ltd, Marley Farm, Headcorn Road, Smarden, Ashford, Kent, TN27 8PJ Tel: (01233) 770663 Fax: (01233) 770633 E-mail: premiercoating@aol.com

Rock Asphalte, Latymer House, 2 Ravenscourt Road, London, W6 0UX Tel: (020) 8748 7881 Fax: (020) 8748 7225 E-mail: enquiries@rockasphalte.com

Tarmac Southern, Durnford Quarry, Long Ashton, Bristol, BS41 9DW Tel: (01275) 392510 Fax: (01275) 392205

GENERAL PURPOSE CAMERAS

Arri GB Ltd, 2 Highbridge Industrial Estate, Oxford Road, Uxbridge, Middlesex, UB8 1LX Tel: (01895) 457000 Fax: (01895) 457001 E-mail: sales@arri-gb.com

Ikegami Electronics, Unit E1 Cologne Court, Brooklands Close, Sunbury-on-Thames, Middlesex, TW16 7EB Tel: (01932) 769700 Fax: (01932) 769710 E-mail: info@ikegami.co.uk

Polaroid UK Ltd, Vale of Leven Industrial Estate, Dumbarton, G82 3PW Tel: (01389) 712000 Fax: (01389) 755101

GENERAL PURPOSE CANDLES

Hayes & Finch Ltd, Hanson Road, Liverpool, L9 7BP Tel: 0151-523 6303 Fax: 0151-523 4537 E-mail: sales@hflitd.com

▶ indicates data change since last edition

GENERAL PURPOSE CASTORS

Blickle Castors & Wheels Ltd, 30 Vincent Avenue, Crownhill, Milton Keynes, MK8 0AB Tel: (01908) 560904 Fax: (01908) 260510 E-mail: sales@blickle.co.uk

Brauer Limited, Dawson Road, Mount Farm, Milton Keynes, MK1 1JP Tel: (01908) 374022 Fax: (01908) 641628 E-mail: sales@brauer.co.uk

CMS Industries, Downsview Road, Wantage, Oxfordshire, OX12 9FF Tel: (01235) 773370 Fax: (01235) 773371 E-mail: sales@cmsindustries.com

Colson Castors Ltd, Golds Green Works, Bagnall Street, Hill Top, West Bromwich, West Midlands, B70 0TZ Tel: 0121-556 7221 Fax: 0121-502 2658

Colson Castors Ltd, Golds Green Works, Bagnall Street, West Bromwich, West Midlands, B70 0TS Tel: 0121-556 7221 Fax: 0121-502 6258 E-mail: info@colson-castors.co.uk

Eurocastors Ltd, Dalton Road, Southfield Industrial Estate, Glenrothes, Fife, KY6 2SS Tel: (01592) 774770 Fax: (01592) 772736 E-mail: sales@eurocastors.co.uk

Flexello Ltd, Bagnall Street, Hill Top, Golds Hill, West Bromwich, West Midlands, B70 0TS Tel: 0121-506 1770 Fax: 0121-502 2658 E-mail: sales@flexello.co.uk

Guitel Ltd, Unit 1, Lisle Road, High Wycombe, Buckinghamshire, HP13 5SH Tel: (01494) 473030 Fax: (01494) 473031 E-mail: guiteluk@msn.com

Guy Raymond Engineering Company Ltd, Rollesby Road, King's Lynn, Norfolk, PE30 4LX Tel: (01553) 761401 Fax: (01553) 767459 E-mail: info@guy-raymond.co.uk

H Varley Ltd, Unit 5, Century Park, Unit 5, Pacific Road, Altrincham, Cheshire, WA14 5BJ Tel: 0161-928 9617 Fax: 0161-928 7824 E-mail: sales@varley.co.uk

M S A Wheels & Casters Ltd, 10 Maclure Road, Rochdale, Lancashire, OL11 1DN Tel: (01706) 516640 Fax: (0870) 7590160 E-mail: sales@msawhhelsandcasters.co.uk

Manner UK Ltd, 13 Station Road, Cam, Dursley, Gloucestershire, GL11 5NS Tel: (01453) 546333 Fax: (01453) 549222 E-mail: sales@manner.co.uk

Rollrite Manufacturing (Sales) Ltd, 20 Regent Parade, Birmingham, B1 3NS Tel: (0121) 236 1643 Fax: (0121) 212 1550

▶ Tellure Rota, PO Box 29, Ashton-under-Lyne, Lancashire, OL5 9NB Tel: (01457) 832556 Fax: (01457) 838406 E-mail: sales@aut.co.uk

GENERAL PURPOSE CEMENT

The Appley Group, Teesport Works, Middlesbrough, Cleveland, TS6 6UF Tel: (01642) 446100 Fax: (01642) 467176 E-mail: orders@theappleygroup.co.uk

Ash Resources Ltd, Lynemouth, Ashington, Northumberland, NE63 9YH Tel: (01670) 811166 Fax: (01670) 856847

Blue Circle Cement, 84 Eccleston Sq, London, SW1V 1PX Tel: (020) 7828 3456 Fax: (020) 7245 8400

Cem-Spec Ltd, Harby Mill, Colston Lane, Harby, Melton Mowbray, Leicestershire, LE14 4BE Tel: (01949) 860193 Fax: (01949) 860324 E-mail: office@cemspec.co.uk

Civil & Marine Slag Cement Ltd, 7 Sinclair Road, Belfast, BT3 9LY Tel: (028) 9074 1690 Fax: (028) 9035 7127

Civil & Marine Slag Cement Ltd, London Road, Grays, Essex, RM20 3NL Tel: (01708) 864813 Fax: (01708) 865907 E-mail: enquiries@civilmarine.co.uk

Hanson Cement Ltd, 3160 Solihull Parkway, Birmingham Business Park, Birmingham, B37 7YN Tel: (0845) 6001616 Fax: 0121-606 1436 E-mail: customer.services@castlecement.co.uk

Hanson Cement Ltd, Ribblesdale Works, West Bradford Road, Clitheroe, Lancashire, BB7 4QF Tel: (01200) 422401 Fax: (01200) 414139

Hanson Cement Ltd, Cefn Mawr Quarry, Pantybuarth, Mold, Flintshire, CH7 5EA Tel: (01244) 550330 Fax: (01352) 742009

Instarmac Group plc, Kingsbury Link, Trinity Road, Piccadilly, Tamworth, Staffordshire, B78 2EX Tel: (01827) 872244 Fax: (01827) 874466 E-mail: enquiries@instarmac.co.uk

Lafarge Aluminates Ltd, Dolphin Way, Purfleet, Essex, RM19 1NZ Tel: (01708) 863333 Fax: (01708) 861033

Lafarge Cement UK, At Watling Street, Bean, Dartford, DA2 8AH Tel: (01474) 833551 Fax: (01474) 834325

Modern Mix Concrete Supplies Ltd, Unit 1 Empson Street, London, E3 3LT Tel: (020) 7538 2266 Fax: (020) 7537 3256

N I C Ltd, Mariners Street, Goole, North Humberside, DN14 5BW Tel: (01405) 782600 Fax: (01405) 782612 E-mail: nic@damacgroup.co.uk

Seament UK Ltd, Imperial Dock, Leith Docks, Edinburgh, EH6 7DR Tel: 0131-554 1555 Fax: 0131-553 2700

GENERAL PURPOSE COMPUTERS

A B Computers, 12 Union Street, Andover, Hampshire, SP10 1PA Tel: (01264) 406406 Fax: (01264) 395880 E-mail: support@andover.co.uk

A B M Computer Services, 356 York Road, Leeds, LS9 9DN Tel: 0113-240 5543 Fax: 0113-235 0541

A I Systems, 548 Scott Hall Road, Leeds, LS7 3RA Tel: 0113-237 0626

A P G Technology, Units 13-14 Raleigh Court, Priestley Way, Crawley, West Sussex, RH10 9PD Tel: (01293) 428565 Fax: (01293) 428566 E-mail: andrew.bause@apgtechnology.co.uk

A P Systems, 16 Grant Street, Cullen, Buckie, Banffshire, AB56 4RS Tel: (01542) 841121 Fax: (01542) 841334

A T M Ltd, Knaves Beech Industrial Estate, Knaves Beech Way, Loudwater, High Wycombe, Buckinghamshire, HP10 9QY Tel: (01628) 642200 Fax: (01628) 642226

Ace Computer Co. Ltd, 13 Queens Road, London, N11 2QJ Tel: (020) 8889 3622 Fax: (020) 8889 9566

Adscom UK, Thurston Lodge, Thedwastre Rd, Thurston, Bury St. Edmunds, Suffolk, IP31 3SD Tel: (01359) 232661 Fax: (01359) 232549

Alpha Computer Products, 6 Portershill Drive, Shirley, Solihull, West Midlands, B90 4DS Tel: 0121-744 0377 Fax: 0121-744 2392 E-mail: info@alphacomputers.co.uk

Armagh Computer World, 43 Scotch Street, Armagh, BT61 7DF Tel: (028) 3751 0002 Fax: (028) 3751 0009 E-mail: sales@computerworlds.co.uk

Atech Computer Systems, 122 Broadway, Didcot, Oxfordshire, OX11 8AB Tel: (01235) 812900 Fax: (01235) 812900

Autonomy Systems Ltd, Cambridge Business Park, Cowley Road, Cambridge, CB4 0WZ Tel: (01223) 448000 Fax: (01223) 448001

Avatea Ltd, Bulldog House, 267-269 Reading Road, Winnersh, Wokingham, Berkshire, RG41 5AB Tel: 0118-977 0270 Fax: 0118-977 0278 E-mail: peter@avatea.co.uk

Baydel Ltd, Brook Way, Leatherhead, Surrey, KT22 7NA Tel: (01372) 378811 Fax: (01372) 386960 E-mail: enquiry@baydel.com

Beyond 2000 PC Systems Software, 97-103 Upper Parliament Street, Nottingham, NG1 6LA Tel: 0115-924 3000 Fax: (0870) 3304300

Bridgewater Computers, 42 Green End, Whitchurch, Shropshire, SY13 1AA Tel: (01948) 666630 Fax: (01948) 666630 E-mail: bridgewatermcg@aol.com

C C S Computers Ltd, 13 Clarkes La, Pocklington, York, YO42 2AW Tel: 01759 302251 Fax: 01759 302251

C Pac, 33a Morland Way, Nelson Park, Cramlington, Northumberland, NE23 1WE Tel: 0191-491 0405 Fax: 0191-491 0465 E-mail: sales@c-pac.co.uk

C S D Technology, 1 Mclachlan Street, Stenhousemuir, Larbert, Stirlingshire, FK5 3HJ Tel: (01324) 882515 Fax: (01324) 882516 E-mail: sales@csdtechnology.co.uk

Cablink UK Ltd, 74 Tenter Road, Moulton Park Industrial Estate, Northampton, NN3 6AX Tel: (01604) 670005 Fax: (01604) 670011

Central Computer Technology, 11 Greskine Clo, Bedford, MK41 0NW Tel: (01234) 357932

Coastline Business Computers Northern Ltd, 10-11 Avenue Cresent, Seaton Delaval, Whitley Bay, Tyne & Wear, NE25 0DN Tel: 0191-237 4000 Fax: 0191-237 7788 E-mail: sales@cbcnorthern.com

Computer Builders, 42 Janson Cl, London, E15 1TF Tel: 020 82212424

Computer Care 2000, 14 St. Bryde Street, East Kilbride, Glasgow, G74 4HQ Tel: (01355) 241628 Fax: (01355) 573073 E-mail: sales@cc2000.co.uk

Computer Scene, 5 Kings Street, Mildenhall, Bury St. Edmunds, Suffolk, IP28 7EZ Tel: (01638) 717726 Fax: (01638) 510079 E-mail: sales@computerscene.co.uk

The Computer Shop, 1 Brewery Street, Grimsby, South Humberside, DN31 1EJ Tel: (01472) 268777

Computers North Ltd, Unit 1 Derwentside Business Centre, Consett Business Park, Villa Real, Consett, County Durham, DH8 6BP Tel: (01207) 583978 Fax: (01207) 508206 E-mail: info@durhamofficesystems.ltd.uk

Crane Computers, Unit 4 Exter Road Industrial State, Okehampton, Devon, EX20 1UA Tel: 01837 55664

Creative Edge, P O Box 13492, Edinburgh, EH6 6YH Tel: 0131-226 3339

Csea Services Ltd, 114 High Street, Gorleston, Great Yarmouth, Norfolk, NR31 6RE Tel: (01493) 444666 Fax: (01493) 444646 E-mail: martyn@csea.co.uk

D Tech Computers, 31 Fore Bondgate, Bishop Auckland, County Durham, DL14 7PE Tel: (01388) 662891 Fax: (01388) 665702 E-mail: dtech@nildram.co.uk

Dexdyne Ltd, Oakley House, Tetbury Road, Cirencester, Gloucestershire, GL7 1US Tel: (01285) 658122 Fax: (01285) 655644 E-mail: sales@dexdyne.com

Digital Systems, Solutions House Derby Road, Sandiacre, Nottingham, NG10 5HU Tel: 0115-849 9984 Fax: 0115-849 9993

Dot Hill Systems Europe Ltd, Network House, Basing View, Basingstoke, Hampshire, RG21 4HG Tel: (01256) 840600 Fax: (01256) 814462 E-mail: uk@dothill.com

Dtec Computers, White Ox Building, Inglewood Road, Penrith, Cumbria, CA11 8QN Tel: (01768) 895600 Fax: (01768) 895700

Elite Group Computer Systems (UK) Ltd, Units 1-3, Newmarket Court, Kingston, Milton Keynes, MK10 0AG Tel: (01908) 481830 Fax: (01908) 481831

Emc Computer Systems, E M C Tower, Great West Road, Brentford, Middlesex, TW8 9AN Tel: (0870) 6087777 Fax: (0870) 6087788 E-mail: sales@uk.emc.com

Enlight Uk Ltd, 53 Church Rd, London, NW4 4DU Tel: (020) 8830 6479 Fax: (020) 8830 6480

Epic Computers Ltd, 4 Sybron Way, Crowborough, East Sussex, TN6 3DZ Tel: (01892) 667770 Fax: (01892) 665777 E-mail: sales@epicpc.co.uk

Fellcroft Computing, 1 Hill Street, Corbridge, Northumberland, NE45 5AA Tel: (01434) 633300 Fax: (01434) 633440

Friendly Computers, 274 Harehills Lane, Leeds, LS9 7BD Tel: 0113-216 1999 Fax: 0113-216 1400

Fujitsu U K Ltd, Hayes Park Central Building, Hayes End Road, Hayes, Middlesex, UB4 8FE Tel: (020) 8573 4444 Fax: (020) 8573 2643 E-mail: sales@uk.fujitsu.com

G Systems, PO Box 100, Bury St. Edmunds, Suffolk, IP28 7HD Tel: (01638) 717500 E-mail: john@gsystems.co.uk

Game Stores Ltd, 43 Friargate, Freshney Place, Grimsby, South Humberside, DN31 1EL Tel: (01472) 345466

Game Stores Ltd, 4-6 Pydar Street, Truro, Cornwall, TR1 2AR Tel: (01872) 272861

Geddes Business Systems Ltd, 18 London Road, Peterborough, PE2 8AR Tel: (01733) 560291 Fax: (01733) 558526

Hexel Developments Ltd, Wash Lane, Warrington, WA4 1HS Tel: (01925) 444439 Fax: (01925) 655899E-mail: admin@hexel.net

Hi-Grade Computers plc, Hi-Grade House, 43 Thames Road, Barking, Essex, IG11 0HQ Tel: (020) 8532 6111 Fax: (020) 8532 6101 E-mail: sales@higrade.com

I B M (UK) Ltd, Rosanne House, Bridge Road, Welwyn Garden City, Hertfordshire, AL8 6UB Tel: (01707) 363000 Fax: (01707) 338732 E-mail: info@ibm.com

I D Computer Services, 9 Bolton Road West, Ramsbottom, Bury, Lancashire, BL0 9NA Tel: (01706) 824080 Fax: (01706) 829930 E-mail: mail@idcomputerservices.co.uk

KVJ Computers, 5 Ashley Road, Gillingham, Kent, ME8 6TT Tel: (01634) 263786 Fax: (01634) 263787 E-mail: sales@kvjcomputers.co.uk

L A Computers, 12 Magister Road, Bowerhill, Melksham, Wiltshire, SN12 6FE Tel: (01225) 793337 Fax: (01225) 793335

▶ Langsett Computers, 334 Langsett Road, Sheffield, S6 2UF Tel: 0114-234 4422

Lazer Printing, 65 Coniston Road, Peterborough, PE4 7UL Tel: (01733) 324404 Fax: (01733) 324404

Leading Computer Ltd, 27 Vesta Avenue, St. Albans, Hertfordshire, AL1 2PG Tel: (01727) 867705 Fax: (01727) 867705

M Computer Technologies, Stirling House, 226 St. Vincent Street, Glasgow, G2 5RQ Tel: (0845) 4753695 Fax: (0845) 4753694 E-mail: info@mcomputer.com

M D Distribution Ltd, 167 London Road, Stoke-on-Trent, ST4 7QE Tel: (01782) 746693 Fax: (01782) 746695

M, M & M Ltd, 102 Seymour Place, London, W1H 1NF Tel: (020) 7724 5117 Fax: (020) 7724 5087 E-mail: mmm@mmmltd.com

Maple Systems, 5 Mercia Business Village, Torwood Close, Westwood Business Park, Coventry, CV4 8HX Tel: (024) 7669 4489 Fax: (024) 7669 4474 E-mail: sales@maplesys.com

Maxtor (Europe) Ltd, Langwood House, 63-81 High Street, Rickmansworth, Hertfordshire, WD3 1EQ Tel: (01923) 712448 Fax: (01923) 712888

Memory House Ltd, Technology House Glaisher Drive, Wolverhampton Science Park, Wolverhampton, WV10 9RU Tel: (01902) 824190 Fax: (01902) 824191 E-mail: enquiries@memoryhouse.co.uk

Micro Computer Solutions, 10 Carn Industrial Area, Portadown, Craigavon, County Armagh, BT63 5YY Tel: (028) 3839 3839 Fax: (028) 3839 3838 E-mail: sales@mcsgroup.co.uk

Microtech Business Systems, Units 1-3, 139A Moorland Road, Weston-Super-Mare, Avon, BS23 4HU Tel: (01934) 633875 Fax: (01934) 612011

Mitec Computer Solutions, 2 Lesley Smith Drive, Faversham, Kent, ME13 7LE Tel: (01795) 533393 Fax: (01795) 533318

Modern Business Technology Ltd, Tregurtha Downs, Goldsithney, Penzance, Cornwall, TR20 9LD Tel: (01736) 711756

N C R UK Group Ltd, 206 Marylebone Road, London, NW1 6LY Tel: (020) 7723 7070 Fax: (020) 7725 8224

N S Enterprise Training, 22a Church Street, Dungannon, County Tyrone, BT71 6AB Tel: (028) 8772 9773 Fax: (028) 8772 4775 E-mail: sales@nsenterprise.co.uk

N S Optimum Ltd, 7a Jenton Road, Leamington Spa, Warwickshire, CV31 1XS Tel: (01926) 880300 Fax: (01926) 886983 E-mail: sales@nsoptimum.co.uk

Netcom Systems, 4 Beach Station Road, Felixstowe, Suffolk, IP11 2DR Tel: (01394) 271600 Fax: (01394) 271680

Northants Computer Service, 67-69 Morley Street, Kettering, Northamptonshire, NN16 9LJ Tel: (01536) 522800 Fax: (01536) 414838

P A Computers, Highcross Road, Southfleet, Gravesend, Kent, DA13 9PH Tel: (01474) 833933 Fax: (01474) 834446 E-mail: mail@pacomputers.co.uk

P C 2000, 1339 Dumbarton Road, Glasgow, G14 9UZ Tel: 0141-959 4877 Fax: 0141-576 0156

P C Express, 13 Whitchurch Lane, Edgware, Middlesex, HA8 6JZ Tel: (020) 8951 3304 Fax: (020) 8951 3305 E-mail: support@pcexpress.co.uk

P C S, 143 East Reach, Taunton, Somerset, TA1 3HN Tel: (01823) 354000

PC Healthcare Ltd, 767 Wimborne Road, Bournemouth, BH9 2BA Tel: (01202) 525952 Fax: (01202) 526843 E-mail: sales@pchealthcare.co.uk

Pickering Computer Exchange, Old Drill Hall Coopers Building, Southgate, Pickering, North Yorkshire, YO18 8BL Tel: (01751) 474777 Fax: (01751) 474777 E-mail: sales@pickeringcomputerexchange.com

Pucella U K, Unit 4a St. Theodores Way, Brynmenyn Industrial Estate, Brynmenyn, Bridgend, CF32 9TZ Tel: (01656) 724848 Fax: (01656) 724838 E-mail: anielp@aol.com

Pulsar Systems Ltd, Brynmeurig, Penrhyncoch, Aberystwyth, Dyfed, SY23 3EY Tel: (01970) 820520 Fax: (01970) 820529

Quantum Data Solutions Ltd, 3-5 Marischal Street, Peterhead, Aberdeenshire, AB42 1BS Tel: (01779) 490426 Fax: (01779) 480074 E-mail: purchasing@qds.uk.net

Ranmor Computing Ltd, Lake Meadows Office Village, 14 Woodbrook Cresent, Billericay, Essex, CM12 0EQ Tel: (01277) 635500 Fax: (01277) 631777E-mail: info@ranmor.com

Retellin Ltd, 78 Rainham Road, Rainham, Essex, RM13 7RL Tel: (01708) 553310

Rivendale Systems Ltd, The Old Bakery, North End, Newbury, Berkshire, RG20 0AY Tel: (01635) 254464 Fax: (01635) 255359 E-mail: enquiries@rivendale.co.uk

Sapient Systems, 106 Queens Road, Carterton, Oxfordshire, OX18 3YF Tel: (01993) 845291 Fax: (01993) 845291

Scott Office & Computer Services, Unit 11 Nortonthorpe Mills Nortonthorpe Industrial Estate, Wakefield Road, Scissett, Huddersfield, HD8 9LA Tel: (01484) 864205 Fax: (01484) 865684

Serin Computers Ltd, 4 Fairfax Court, Yarm, Cleveland, TS15 9QZ Tel: (01642) 650466 E-mail: serincomputers@aol.com

Harry Shaw Business Computers Ltd, 29-31 Leicester Street, Bedworth, Warwickshire, CV12 8GG Tel: (024) 7631 6666 Fax: (024) 7631 6187 E-mail: info@harryshaw.net

Shift F7 Ltd, 142 South Street, Dorking, Surrey, RH5 5EN Tel: (01306) 873900 Fax: (01306) 873910

Skyetime Computer Maintenance, Clock House, Wadhurst Road, Frant, Tunbridge Wells, Kent, TN3 9EJ Tel: (01892) 750800 Fax: (01892) 750076 E-mail: info@skyetime.co.uk

Spruce Technology, 40 High Street, Langholm, Dumfriesshire, DG13 0JH Tel: (01387) 381529 Fax: (01387) 381779 E-mail: office@sprucetechnology.com

Star Computer Group plc, 2 Spar Centre Boulevard, Blackmoor Lane, Watford, WD18 8UX Tel: (01923) 246414 Fax: (01923) 254301 E-mail: sales@starplc.com

Stour Computer Services, Croft Road, Sudbury, Suffolk, CO10 1HJ Tel: (01787) 374959

Straker Systems Ltd, 9 Mollins Court, Cumbernauld, Glasgow, G68 9HP Tel: (01236) 456666 Fax: (01236) 722912 E-mail: sales@straker.com

Swan C D Computers, 36 Carnglas Road, Sketty, Swansea, SA2 9BW Tel: (01792) 521158 Fax: (01792) 522957 E-mail: swancd@swancd.co.uk

System One Ltd, Lavant House, 39 Lavant Street, Petersfield, Hampshire, GU32 3EL Tel: (01730) 267000 Fax: (01730) 266676 E-mail: sales@systemone.co.uk

Time Computer Systems Ltd, School Brow, Warrington, WA1 2TA Tel: 01925 419797

Transtec Computers Ltd, 39 North Bar Street, Banbury, Oxfordshire, OX16 0TH Tel: (01295) 756100 Fax: (01295) 276133

Triarom Ltd, Triarom House, Birch Street, Windermere, Cumbria, LA23 1EG Tel: (01539) 444639 Fax: (01539) 448701 E-mail: sales@triarom.co.uk

U S I Ltd, Unit 1 Steadman Place, Riverside Business Park, Irvine, Ayrshire, KA11 5DN Tel: (01294) 222444 Fax: (01294) 222456

Vector Microsystems Ltd, Unit 41, Claydon Industrial Park, Ipswich, IP6 0NL Tel: (01473) 833999 Fax: (01473) 833222

W P B Computer Supplies Ltd, Longacres House, Lower Stock Road, West Hanningfield, Chelmsford, CM2 8UY Tel: (01277) 841343 Fax: (01277) 840372 E-mail: s.flint@wpbnet.com

W3 Dot Wigtown, 16 Albert St, Newton Stewart, Wigtownshire, DG8 6EJ Tel: (01671) 404492 Fax: (01671) 402139

Westek Holdings Ltd, Unit 1 Lancaster Park Industrial Estate, Bowerhill, Melksham, Wiltshire, SN12 6TT Tel: (01225) 790600 Fax: (01225) 702968 E-mail: sales@westekuk.com

Wyvern Business Systems, Wyvern House, Netherwood Road, Rotherwas Industrial Estate, Hereford, HR2 6JJ Tel: (01432) 271233 Fax: (01432) 263550 E-mail: buyer@wbs.uk.com

GENERAL PURPOSE ENCLOSURES

C N C Loughborough Ltd, 35 Bakewell Road, Loughborough, Leicestershire, LE11 5QY Tel: (01509) 215302 Fax: (01509) 215302 E-mail: cncloughborough@btconnect.com
Sure Punch Precision Ltd, Tameside Mills, Park Road, Dukinfield, Cheshire, SK16 5PU Tel: 0161-343 7999 Fax: 0161-343 8999 E-mail: surepunch@surepunch.co.uk

GENERAL PURPOSE HOSES

A S D Fire Protection, Fisher Street, Newcastle upon Tyne, NE6 4LT Tel: (01698) 356444 Fax: (01698) 356678 E-mail: asdfire@btconnect.com
Arcflex, Old Bank Mill, Ball Haye Road, Leek, Staffordshire, ST13 6AT Tel: (01538) 386000 Fax: (01538) 398999 E-mail: sales@arcflex.com
Leigh Baxter Associates Ltd, 15-17 Robert Leonard Industrial Site, Stock Road, Southend-on-Sea, SS2 5QD Tel: (01702) 460970 Fax: (01702) 600544 E-mail: sales@leighbaxter.co.uk
Dunlop Hiflex Fluid Power Ltd, Unit 31-32 Church Road Business Centre, Church Road, Sittingbourne, Kent, ME10 3RS Tel: (01795) 429807 Fax: (01795) 420423 E-mail: sales@dunlophiflex.xom

GENERAL PURPOSE LUBRICANTS, *See also headings under Lubricants*

Acheson Industries Europe Ltd, Cattewater Road, Plymouth, PL4 0SP Tel: (01752) 218788 Fax: (01752) 207133 E-mail: acheson.plymouth@nstarch.com
Acheson Industries Europe Ltd, Sun Life House, 85 Queens Road, Reading, RG1 4LP Tel: 0118-958 8844 Fax: 0118-957 4897
B P Plc, Witan Gate House, 500-600 Witan Gate, Milton Keynes, MK9 1ES Tel: (01908) 853000 Fax: (01908) 852020 E-mail: clarkez@bp.com
Batoyle Freedom Group, 1 Charles Wood Road, Dereham, Norfolk, NR19 1SX Tel: (01362) 698728 Fax: (01362) 690254
Batoyle Freedom Group, Colne Vale Road, Milnsbridge, Huddersfield, HD3 4NT Tel: (01484) 653015 Fax: (01484) 460078 E-mail: bfgsales@aol.com
Bretts Oils, Pipewellgate, Gateshead, Tyne & Wear, NE8 2BN Tel: 0191-477 0856 Fax: 0191-490 0360 E-mail: uksales@ovoline.co.uk
Calder Oils Ltd, Netherfield Road, Dewsbury, West Yorkshire, WF13 3JX Tel: (01924) 461058 Fax: (01924) 459773 E-mail: sales@calder-oils.co.uk
Caldo Oils Ltd, Worsley Brow, St. Helens, Merseyside, WA9 3EZ Tel: (01744) 813535 Fax: (01744) 816031E-mail: info@caldo.co.uk
Castrol (U K) Ltd, 65 Stanlow Works South, Wirrel, Ellesmere Port, CH65 4ES Tel: 0151-355 3737 Fax: 0151-357 1130 E-mail:
Claymore Lubricants (Midlands) Ltd, 48 Heming Road, Washford, Redditch, Worcestershire, B98 0EA Tel: (01527) 502252 Fax: (01527) 502253 E-mail: sales@claymore-lubricants.co.uk
Electrolube, Midland Road, Swadlincote, Derbyshire, DE11 0AN Tel: (01283) 222111 Fax: (01283) 550177 E-mail: el_sales@hkw.co.uk
Ferguson & Menzies Ltd, 312 Broomloan Road, Glasgow, G51 2JW Tel: 0141-445 3555 Fax: 0141-425 1079 E-mail: sales@fergusonmenzies.co.uk
Fuchs Lubricants (UK) Plc, P O Box 20, Stoke-on-Trent, ST1 5HU Tel: (0870) 1200400 Fax: (01782) 202072 E-mail: contact-uk@fuchs-oil.com
Granville Oil & Chemicals Ltd, Unit 29 Goldthorpe Industrial Estate, Commercial Road, Goldthorpe, Rotherham, South Yorkshire, S63 9BL Tel: (01709) 890099 Fax: (01709) 891121 E-mail: info@granvilleoilchem.co.uk
Henry Morris 1958 Ltd, Old Town Dock, Newport, Gwent, NP20 2BW Tel: (01633) 265603 Fax: (01633) 253186
Hydralube Ltd, 72A Parker Road, Hastings, East Sussex, TN34 3TT Tel: (01424) 465527 Fax: (01424) 201363 E-mail: sales@hydralube.co.uk
Ironsides Lubricants Ltd, Shield Street, Stockport, Cheshire, SK3 0DS Tel: 0161-477 5858 Fax: 0161-480 6203 E-mail: sales@ironsideslubricants.co.uk
Jet Lube UK Ltd, Reform Road, Maidenhead, Berkshire, SL6 8BY Tel: (01628) 631913 Fax: (01628) 773138 E-mail: uksales@jetlube.com
Kernow Oils, Hayle Industrial Park, Hayle, Cornwall, TR27 5JR Tel: (01736) 757002 Fax: (01736) 757979 E-mail: sales@kernowoils.co.uk
Kluber Lubrication, Bradford Road, Halifax, West Yorkshire, HX3 7BN Tel: (01422) 319149 Fax: (01422) 206073 E-mail: info@uk.klueber.com
Kuwait Petroleum International Lubricants UK Ltd, Knowsthorpe Gate, Cross Green Industrial Estate, Leeds, LS9 0NP Tel: 0113-235 0555 Fax: 0113-248 5026 E-mail: marketing@q8oils.com
Lubrication Engineers UK Ltd, Latton Bush Business Ctr, Southern Way, Harlow, Essex, CM18 7BH Tel: (01763) 274253 Fax: (01763) 274253 E-mail: sales@le-lubricants.co.uk
Midland Oil Refinery Ltd, Shelah Road, Halesowen, West Midlands, B63 3PN Tel: 0121-585 6006 Fax: 0121-585 5405
Mobil Oil Co. Ltd, ExxonMobil House, Ermyn Way, Leatherhead, Surrey, KT22 8UX Tel: (01372) 222000 Fax: (01372) 222556
▶ Morris Lubricants, Castle Foregate, Shrewsbury, SY1 2EL Tel: (01743) 232200 Fax: (01743) 353584 E-mail: info@morris-lubricants.co.uk
Oel Held UK Ltd, 16 Colomendy Industrial Estate, Rhyl Road, Denbigh, Clwyd, LL16 5TA Tel: (01745) 814777 Fax: (01745) 813222 E-mail: info@oelheldgroup.co.uk
Oiline Ltd, Whitehall Road, Tipton, West Midlands, DY4 7JZ Tel: 0121-557 1475 Fax: 0121-522 2311
Olenol Ltd, Olenol House, Plot 7 Greenfield Farm Industrial Estate, Congleton, Cheshire, CW12 4TR Tel: (01260) 298276 Fax: (01260) 298267
Pennine Lubricants, Unit 35 Limestone Cottage Lane, Sheffield, S6 1NJ Tel: 0114-285 2987 Fax: 0114-285 2988 E-mail: sales@penninelubricants.co.uk
Polartech Ltd, Nash Road, Trafford Park, Manchester, M17 1SX Tel: 0161-876 5673 Fax: 0161-872 1922 E-mail: marketing@polartech.co.uk
S F R East Anglia, 22 Clements Way, Beck Row, Bury St. Edmunds, Suffolk, IP28 8AB Tel: (01638) 713758 Fax: (01638) 715541 E-mail: gary@sfrea.co.uk
Solar Petroleum Ltd, Ditton Road, Widnes, Cheshire, WA8 0NN Tel: 0151-424 2488 Fax: 0151-495 1007 E-mail: sales@solar-lubricants.com
Sovereign Lubricants UK Ltd, Sovereign House, Crowtrees Lane, Brighouse, West Yorkshire, HD6 3LZ Tel: (01484) 718674 Fax: (01484) 400164 E-mail: schesters@btconnect.com
Spanjaard UK Ltd, PO Box 21, Huntingdon, Cambridgeshire, PE29 2EQ Tel: (01480) 457022 Fax: (01480) 457022
Spectrum Industrial Ltd, Unit 19-24 Bedesway, Bede Trading Estate, Jarrow, Tyne & Wear, NE32 3EG Tel: 0191-430 1111 Fax: 0191-483 7422 E-mail: sales@spectrum-ind.co.uk
Thames Hose & Couplings Ltd, Units 1-2 Canal Industrial Park, Canal Road, Gravesend, Kent, DA12 2PA Tel: (01474) 356485 Fax: (01474) 320392 E-mail: thc.sales@btconnect.com
Thomas Proctor & Son Ltd, Dukesway, Team Valley Trading Estate, Gateshead, Tyne & Wear, NE11 0NW Tel: 0191-491 3027 Fax: 0191-491 3028 E-mail: sales@thomasproctor.co.uk
Total Butler Ltd, Fengate, Peterborough, PE1 5XB Tel: (01733) 568223 Fax: (01733) 564733
United Oil Products Ltd, Unit 2 Wonastow Road Industrial Estate East, Monmouth, Gwent, NP25 5JB Tel: (01600) 772110 Fax: (01600) 772660 E-mail: unitedoil@hotmail.com

GENERAL PURPOSE METAL HINGES

Ames Stokes Stevens & Son, Hanley Works, Hanley Street, Birmingham, B19 3SP Tel: 0121-359 5561 Fax: 0121-359 2336 E-mail: sales@amesstokes.com
Daro Factors Ltd, 80-84 Wallis Road, London, E9 5LW Tel: (020) 8510 4000 Fax: (020) 8510 4001 E-mail: sales@daro.com
Era Products Ltd, Straight Road, Willenhall, West Midlands, WV12 5RA Tel: (01922) 490049 Fax: (01922) 494420 E-mail: bevans@era-security.com
Oak Engineering Ltd, Oak Street, Cradley Heath, West Midlands, B64 5JZ Tel: (01384) 569859 Fax: (01384) 410954 E-mail: oakhinges@woden.com
Perry & Co Hinges Ltd, Doulton Road, Cradley Heath, West Midlands, B64 5QW Tel: (01384) 414000 Fax: (01384) 411100 E-mail: aperry@hinges.co.uk
Pianoforte Supplies Ltd, Simplex Works, Ashton Road, Roade, Northampton, NN7 2LG Tel: (01604) 862441 Fax: (01604) 862427 E-mail: sales@psluk.co.uk
Royde & Tucker Ltd, Unit 15-16 The High Cross Centre, Fountayne Road, London, N15 4QN Tel: (020) 8801 7717 Fax: (020) 8801 5747 E-mail: sales@ratman.co.uk
Surelock Mcgill Ltd, 26 The Business Centre, Molly Millars Lane, Wokingham, Berkshire, RG41 2QY Tel: 0118-977 2525 Fax: 0118-977 1913 E-mail: info@surelock.co.uk

GENERAL PURPOSE PAINTS

3p Paint Co Stockport Ltd, Hallam Mill, Hallam Street, Stockport, Cheshire, SK2 6PT Tel: 0161-477 4202 Fax: 0161-477 4202 E-mail: 3ppaintcompany@tiscali.co.uk
Andrews, Littles Lane, Wolverhampton, WV1 1JY Tel: (01902) 429190 Fax: (01902) 426574 E-mail: info@andrewscoatings.co.uk
Andura Coatings Ltd, 20 Murdock Road, Bicester, Oxfordshire, OX26 4PP Tel: (01869) 240374 Fax: (01869) 240375 E-mail: admin@andura.com
Becker Industrial Coatings Ltd, Goodlass Road, Liverpool, L24 9HJ Tel: 0151-448 1010 Fax: 0151-448 2589 E-mail: info-uk@beckers-bic.com
Bradite Ltd, Ogwen Valley Works, Bethesda, Bangor, Gwynedd, LL57 4YP Tel: (01248) 600315 Fax: (01248) 602782 E-mail: sales@bradite.co.uk
C. Brewer & Sons Ltd, 81 Alston Drive, Bradwell Abbey, Milton Keynes, MK13 9HF Tel: (01908) 316719 Fax: (01908) 311423
Coo Var, Ellenshaw Works, Lockwood St, Hull, HU2 0HN Tel: (01482) 328053 Fax: (01482) 219266 E-mail: sales@coo-var.co.uk
Crosbie Casco Ltd, Wood Lane, Partington, Manchester, M31 4BT Tel: 0161-775 3025 Fax: 0161-777 9076 E-mail: sales@crosbie-casco.co.uk
Crosbie Coatings Ltd, Walsall Street, Wolverhampton, WV1 3LP Tel: (01902) 352020 Fax: (01902) 456392 E-mail: ccsales@crosbie-casco.co.uk
Dexter Paints Ltd, Albert Works, Trafalgar Street, Burnley, Lancashire, BB11 1RE Tel: (01282) 423361 Fax: (01282) 414573
▶ Durable Coatings Ltd, 21-29 Napier Court, Wardpark North, Cumbernauld, Glasgow, G68 0LG Tel: (01236) 860450 Fax: (01236) 781356
E H Jones Ltd, Irlam Road, Bootle, Merseyside, L20 4TU Tel: 0151-922 6454 Fax: 0151-922 5425
E J Rawlins & Co. Ltd, Unit 6 Croydon Street, Leeds, LS11 9RT Tel: 0113-245 5450 Fax: 0113-245 2649 E-mail: sales@rawlinspaints.com
Hicks & Weatherburn Ltd, Lawnswood Works, Otley Road, Leeds, LS16 8AA Tel: 0113-267 1057 Fax: 0113-267 1057
HMG Coatings South Ltd, Faraday Park, Andover, Hampshire, SP10 3SA Tel: (01264) 337824 Fax: (01264) 338123 E-mail: mail@hmgcoatings.co.uk
Intercoat Industrial Paints & Lacquers Ltd, Bridgeman Street, Walsall, WS2 9NW Tel: (01922) 638821 Fax: (01922) 722952
J & L Industrial Paint Services Ltd, Unit 21, Knightcott Industrial Estate, Banwell, Avon, BS29 6JN Tel: (01934) 820780 Fax: (01934) 820323 E-mail: jl.paints@virgin.net
Jotun Paints Europe Ltd, 1 Altens Trade Centre, Hareness Circle, Altens Industrial Estate, Aberdeen, AB12 3LY Tel: (01224) 895238 Fax: (01224) 879174 E-mail: sales@jotun.co.uk
Kingstonian Paints Ltd, Sculcoates Lane, Hull, HU5 1DR Tel: (01482) 342216 Fax: (01482) 493096 E-mail: info@kpaints.co.uk
Mason Coatings P.L.C., Nottingham Rd, Derby, DE21 6AR Tel: (01332) 295959 Fax: (01332) 295252 E-mail: mason@masoncoatings.com
Meynell Paints Ltd, 400 Roding Lane South, Woodford Green, Essex, IG8 8EZ Tel: (020) 8550 9999 Fax: (020) 8551 8555 E-mail: gaye.brown@talk21.com
Myland's Paints & Woodfinishes, 80 Norwood High Street, London, SE27 9NW Tel: (020) 8761 5197 Fax: (020) 8761 5700 E-mail: sales@mylands.co.uk
Newmarket Paint Company Ltd, Unit 5 Studlands Business Centre, Newmarket, Suffolk, CB8 7EA Tel: (01638) 660262 Fax: (01638) 660262
Palatine Paints, Smallbrook Lane, Leigh, Lancashire, WN7 5PZ Tel: (01942) 884122 Fax: (01942) 887085
Plaspertex Paint Co. Ltd, 71 Mereside, Soham, Ely, Cambridgeshire, CB7 5EE Tel: (01353) 720796 Fax: (01353) 624327 E-mail: mail@plaspertex.co.uk
Protega Coatings Ltd, Kelvin Way, West Bromwich, West Midlands, B70 7JZ Tel: 0121-525 5665 Fax: 0121-553 2787 E-mail: info@tikkurila.co.uk
▶ R J Stokes & Co. Ltd, Little London Road, Heeley, Sheffield, S8 0UH Tel: 0114-258 9595 Fax: 0114-250 9836 E-mail: sales@rjstokes.co.uk
Serene Paint, Serene Works, 67 Victoria Road, Burgess Hill, West Sussex, RH15 9YL Tel: (01273) 495393 Fax: (01273) 492853
Stelmax Ltd, 21-23 Gloster Road, Martlesham Heath, Ipswich, IP5 3RD Tel: (01473) 626651 Fax: (01473) 610651 E-mail: stelmaxltd@aol.com
T & R Williamson Ltd, 36 Stonebridgegate, Ripon, North Yorkshire, HG4 1TP Tel: (01765) 607711 Fax: (01765) 607908 E-mail: sales@trwilliamson.co.uk
Teal & Mackrill Ltd, Lockwood Street, Hull, HU2 0HN Tel: (01482) 328053 Fax: (01482) 219266
Trimite Ltd, 38 Welbeck Road, Glasgow, G53 7RG Tel: 0141-881 9595 Fax: 0141-881 9333 E-mail: glasgow.sales@trimite.com
Upoxy Research Ltd, Newbattle Industrial Estate, Dalkeith, Midlothian, EH22 4AD Tel: 0131-663 1111 Fax: 0131-663 7220 E-mail: mail@upoxy.co.uk
Witham Oil & Paint (Lowestoft) Ltd, Stanley Road, Oulton Broad, Lowestoft, Suffolk, NR33 9ND Tel: (01502) 563434 Fax: (01502) 500010 E-mail: kathy.rowlands@withamoil-lowestoft.co.uk

GENERAL PURPOSE POLYPROPYLENE (PP) OR NYLON NETS

Henry Cowls & Sons, Gilly Gabben Industrial Estate, Mawgan, Helston, Cornwall, TR12 6BB Tel: (01326) 221514 Fax: (01326) 221382

GENERAL PURPOSE PRESSURE COOKERS

Kuhn Rikon (UK) Ltd, Landport Road, Wolverhampton, WV2 2QJ Tel: (01902) 458410 Fax: (01902) 458160 E-mail: gourmets@kuhnrikon.demon.co.uk

GENERAL PURPOSE SCREWDRIVERS

Snap On Tools, Telford Way, Telford Way Industrial Estate, Kettering, Northamptonshire, NN16 8SN Tel: (01536) 413800 Fax: (01536) 413900 E-mail: max.christmas@snapon.com
Stanley Acmetrack, Drake House, Beighton Rd. East, Sheffield, S19 6GJ Tel: 0114-251 0570 Fax: (08701) 654654

GENERAL PURPOSE SOLDERS

M B O (U K) Ltd, Mill End, Standon, Ware, Hertfordshire, SG11 1LR Tel: (01920) 823999 Fax: (01920) 823631 E-mail: sales@mbouk.co.uk
Summit Solder Products, Rail Works, Railway Sidings, Biggleswade, Bedfordshire, SG18 8BD Tel: (01767) 318999 Fax: (01767) 318912 E-mail: summit@mountstar.com

GENERAL PURPOSE TABLES

Gopak Ltd, Range Road, Hythe, Kent, CT21 6HG Tel: (01303) 265751 Fax: (01303) 268282 E-mail: sales@gopak.co.uk

GENERAL ROOFING CONTRACTORS, *See also headings for particular types*

A & E Elkins Ltd, 6 Insulcrete Works, Yeoman Street, London, SE8 5DT Tel: (020) 7231 8808 Fax: (020) 7252 3758 E-mail: sales@roofingspecialistuk.com
A E Hughes & Sons Contracts Ltd, Plough Industrial Estate, Kingston Road, Leatherhead, Surrey, KT22 7LF Tel: (01372) 373851 Fax: (01372) 373557
A M G Roofing Services, 1 Trent Rise, Spondon, Derby, DE21 7PE Tel: (01332) 677163
▶ K. Addams Industrial Roofing Contractors Limited, ARC House, Sundon Road, Chalton, Luton, LU4 9UA Tel: (01525) 877740 Fax: (01525) 877118 E-mail: k.addams@btinternet.com
Alpha Roofing Ltd, Unit 9 Crompton Mrne Industria, Est Victoria Rd, Oulton Broad, Lowestoft, Suffolk, NR33 9NQ Tel: (01502) 569847 Fax: (01502) 567573 E-mail: info@alpharoof.co.uk
▶ Amber Construction Services Ltd, Unit 62 Uplands Business Park, Blackhorse Lane, London, E17 5QJ Tel: (020) 8531 4553 Fax: (020) 8531 7553
Anglia Industrial Roofing Co. Ltd, Bunyan Close, Gamlingay, Sandy, Bedfordshire, SG19 3JD Tel: (01767) 651550 Fax: (01767) 651566 E-mail: sales@angliaindustrialroofing.co.uk
Apex Asphalt & Paving Co. Ltd, 60 Cato Street, Nechells, Birmingham, B7 4TS Tel: 0121-359 8447 Fax: 0121-359 5418 E-mail: apex@apex-asphalt.co.uk
Apex Roofing Services, Apex Lodge, Great Tey Road, Little Tey, Colchester, CO6 1HZ Tel: (01206) 210762 Fax: (01206) 211622
Arvin Roofing Ltd, Prestage Works, 1 Prestage Way, London, E14 9QE Tel: (020) 7987 4711 Fax: (020) 7538 3177 E-mail: contract@arvin.co.uk
Ascon Industrial Roofing Ltd, Hope Street, Dudley, West Midlands, DY2 8RS Tel: (01384) 233171 Fax: (01384) 456162
Asphalt Roofing Ltd, 78b Warwick Road, London, N18 1RT Tel: (020) 8807 9806 Fax: (020) 8807 9806
Baker & Sons Danbury Ltd, Eves Corner, Danbury, Chelmsford, CM3 4QB Tel: (01245) 225876 Fax: (01245) 226821 E-mail: enq@bakersofdanbury.co.uk
BJN Roofing Contractors Ltd, Gladstone House, Gladstone Road, Horsham, West Sussex, RH12 2NN Tel: (01403) 255155 Fax: (01403) 211794
Bowller Roofing Supplies, Station Road, Harston, Cambridge, CB22 7QP Tel: (01223) 872260 Fax: (01223) 871143 E-mail: admin@bowller.co.uk
Bridgwaters Ltd, Unit 19 Excelsior Works, Rollins Street, London, SE15 1EP Tel: (020) 7639 2003 Fax: (020) 7252 9627

GENERAL ROOFING CONTRACTORS – *continued*

L. Brown & Sons Ltd, St. Anns House, St. Anns Parade, Alderley Road, Wilmslow, Cheshire, SK9 1HG Tel: (01625) 522251 Fax: (01625) 533653 E-mail: mikemason@lbrowns.co.uk

C W Property Services Ltd, 126 Ashleigh Road, London, SW14 8PX Tel: (020) 8876 9941 Fax: (020) 8878 3942 E-mail: cwps126@hotmail.com

Capricorn Roofing Ltd, 96a Dundonald Road, London, SW19 3PN Tel: (020) 8542 5393 Fax: (020) 8542 3593

Central Cladding Systems Ltd, Unit C4 Staverton Technology Park, Gloucester Road, Staverton Technology Park, Cheltenham, Gloucestershire, GL51 6TQ Tel: (01452) 856252 Fax: (01452) 856136 E-mail: ccs@centralcladding.co.uk

Matthew Charlton & Sons (Slaters) Ltd, Chareway Lane, Hexham, Northumberland, NE46 3HW Tel: (01434) 606177 Fax: (01434) 601679 E-mail: slaters@matthewcharlton.com

City Mastic Asphalt Ltd, 315a Weston Road, Stoke-on-Trent, ST3 6HA Tel: (01782) 311249 Fax: (01782) 311249

City Plumbing Supplies Ltd, George Cayley Drive, York, YO30 4XE Tel: (01904) 690088 Fax: (01904) 692990

City Roofing & Asphalt Services Ltd, 3a Pennyburn Industrial Estate, Londonderry, BT48 0LU Tel: (028) 7126 9648 Fax: (028) 7136 7016

Clifton Partners Co. Ltd, 18a Shaw Road, Newhey, Rochdale, Lancashire, OL16 4LT Tel: (01706) 848224 Fax: (01706) 881441 E-mail: clifton.partners@jtemail.co.uk

Cobsen-Davies Roofing Leicester Ltd, 20 Sompting Road, Worthing, West Sussex, BN14 9EP Tel: (01903) 821616 Fax: (01903) 208044 E-mail: info@cobsen-davies.co.uk

Barry Collen Ltd, 31 Northampton Road, Scunthorpe, North Lincolnshire, DN16 1UJ Tel: (01724) 867817 Fax: (01724) 877111 E-mail: info@barrycollen.co.uk

Composite Cladding Systems Ltd, Eckington Business Park, Rotherside Road, Eckington, Sheffield, S21 4HL Tel: (01246) 434275 Fax: (01246) 434452 E-mail: mick.herbert@compclad.co.uk

Cubby Construction Ltd, Unit H, Knights Drive, Kingmoor Park Central, Carlisle, CA6 4SG Tel: (01228) 521284 Fax: (01228) 591952 E-mail: info@cubby.co.uk

D H Keys & Sons Ltd, 45 Belvedere Road, Ipswich, IP4 4AB Tel: (01473) 728117 Fax: (01473) 729729

▶ Steve Davis, 25 Camross Drive, Shrewsbury, SY1 3XH Tel: (01743) 242116

Delomac Ltd, 1b Orchard Street, Kempston, Bedford, MK42 7JA Tel: (01234) 851222 Fax: (01234) 840864 E-mail: delomac@aol.com

Durable Contracts Ltd, Durable House, Crabtree Manorway, Belvedere, Kent, DA17 6AB Tel: (020) 8311 1211 Fax: (020) 8310 7893 E-mail: sales@durable-online.com

E H Smith Builders Merchants Ltd, Mill Hill, Enderby, Leicester, LE19 4AJ Tel: 0116-275 0999 Fax: 0116-275 0135 E-mail: leicester@ehsmith.co.uk

Ehs Roofing, Delta View 2309, 2311 Coventry Road, Sheldon, Birmingham, B26 3PG Tel: 0121-742 5799 Fax: (0845) 6343130

Finlaysons, Botany Mill, Roxburgh Street, Galashiels, Selkirkshire, TD1 1PB Tel: (01896) 752673 Fax: (01896) 751239

Firenzi Asphalte Drayton Park Ltd, Triumph Trading Estate, Tariff Road, London, N17 0EB Tel: (020) 8801 8016 Fax: (020) 8801 8015

Gable (UK) Ltd, 17-19 Station Road, Hayling Island, Hampshire, PO11 0EA Tel: (023) 9246 6416 Fax: (023) 9246 7142 E-mail: gable@gable.co.uk

Gale Construction Co. Ltd, Ayton Road, Wymondham, Norfolk, NR18 0QQ Tel: (01953) 604537 Fax: (01953) 602680 E-mail: info@gale-construction.co.uk

Garnet Roofing Ltd, Airport Industrial Estate, Newcastle upon Tyne, NE3 2EF Tel: 0191-286 3215 Fax: 0191-214 2650 E-mail: garnett@dorin.co.uk

▶ getabuilder.co.uk, Offices 343, 14 Clifton Down Road, Clifton Village, Clifton, Bristol, BS8 4BF Tel: 0117 9390418 E-mail: theteam@getabuilder.co.uk

Gillman Group Ltd, Chipstead Road, Erdington, Birmingham, B23 5HD Tel: 0121-244 4141 Fax: 0121-244 4142 E-mail: info@gillman-group.com

Grantham Roofing Services, Withambrook Park Industrial Estate, Grantham, Lincolnshire, NG31 9ST Tel: (01476) 570771 Fax: (01476) 570746 E-mail: granroof@btinternet.com

Joseph Hardgrave Ltd, 42-44 Church Lane, Bishopthorpe, York, YO23 2QG Tel: (01904) 704161 Fax: (01904) 703711

Hewitson North East, Unit 24E North Tyne Industrial Estate, Whitley Road, Longbenton, Newcastle Upon Tyne, NE12 9SZ Tel: 0191-266 6194 Fax: 0191-266 6194

▶ Hi Spek Roofing Ltd, Hi-Spek House, Pitsford Road, Moulton, Northampton, NN3 7RS Tel: (01604) 492999 Fax: (01604) 492666 E-mail: info@hispekroofing.co.uk

Highgate Felt Roofing, 18a Moat Road, Walsall, WS2 9PJ Tel: (01922) 648791 Fax: (01922) 625183 E-mail: enquiries@highgateroofing.fsbusiness.co.uk

Hill Bros Ltd, 14 Stone Street, Brighton, BN1 2HB Tel: (01273) 326200 Fax: (01273) 326200 E-mail: info@hill-bros.co.uk

Hyflex Roofing, Halfords Lane, Smethwick, West Midlands, B66 1BJ Tel: 0121-555 6464 Fax: 0121-555 5862 E-mail: smethwick@hyflex.co.uk

Independent Roofing Systems Ltd, 118 Eastbourne Road, Darlington, County Durham, DL1 4ER Tel: (01325) 466423 Fax: (01325) 466493 E-mail: irsltd@globalnet.co.uk

Instafoam & Fibre Ltd, Insta House, Ivanhoe Road, Hogwood Business Park, Wokingham, Berkshire, RG40 4PZ Tel: 0118-932 8811 Fax: 0118-932 8314 E-mail: info@instagroup.co.uk

Ironbridge Construction Ltd, Unit B6 Hortonwood 10, Telford, Shropshire, TF1 7ES Tel: (01952) 676555 Fax: (01952) 676567 E-mail: sales@ironbridgeconstruction.co.uk

J R Roofing Co. Ltd, 5 Swinburne Avenue, Hitchin, Hertfordshire, SG5 2RG Tel: (01462) 422300 Fax: (01462) 421342 E-mail: services@jr-roofing.co.uk

James M Green & Co. Ltd, 186b Drews Lane, Birmingham, B8 2SL Tel: 0121-327 8777 Fax: 0121-328 7076 E-mail: jamesmgreen@btconnect.com

John Williams & Co. Ltd, Stone Street, Lympne, Hythe, Kent, CT21 4LD Tel: (01303) 265198 Fax: (01303) 261513 E-mail: sales@johnwilliamsroofing.co.uk

K A D Roofing Ltd, 14 Dongan Road, Warwick, CV34 4JW Tel: (01926) 400044 Fax: (01926) 494775 E-mail: nick@kadroofing.co.uk

Kinder Roofing Ltd, Conservation House, 116 Darwen Road, Bromley Cross, Bolton, BL7 9BQ Tel: (01204) 592200 Fax: (01204) 597700 E-mail: roofing@kinders.co.uk

L A Hall (Hull) Ltd, 19-27 Lime Street, Hull, HU8 7AB Tel: (01482) 320367 Fax: (01482) 320367

▶ Lane Roofing, Walsall House, 167 Walsall Road, Perry Barr, Birmingham, B42 1TX Tel: 0121-331 4407 Fax: 0121-344 3782 E-mail: info@laneroofing.co.uk

Letchworth Roofing Co. Ltd, Roof Centre, Works Road, Letchworth Garden City, Hertfordshire, SG6 1JY Tel: (01462) 755766 Fax: (01462) 755750 E-mail: sales@letchworthroofing.co.uk

Levy Associates Ltd, Pilgrims Lodge Holywell Hill, St. Albans, Hertfordshire, AL1 1ER Tel: (01727) 792200 Fax: (01727) 868890 E-mail: mail@levynet.co.uk

▶ Lingfield Roofing, 52 Saxbys Lane, Lingfield, Surrey, RH7 6DR Tel: (01342) 833018

LPC Contracts Ltd, 370 Coventry Road, Hinckley, Leicestershire, LE10 0NH Tel: (01455) 635816 Fax: (01455) 615329

M & C Roofing Contractors, Brunswick Industrial Estate, Brunswick Village, Newcastle upon Tyne, NE13 7BA Tel: 0191-236 7901 Fax: 0191-236 2086

M Camilleri & Sons Roofing Ltd, Sully Moors Road, Sully, Penarth, South Glamorgan, CF64 5RP Tel: (01446) 721450 Fax: (01446) 749710 E-mail: general@camilleri.co.uk

▶ M D G Property Services, 60 Sandholme Drive, Bradford, West Yorkshire, BD10 8EY Tel: (01274) 200078 E-mail: mikegreasley@blueyonder.co.uk

M & J Flat Roofing Ltd, Triumph Way, Kempston, Bedford, MK42 7QB Tel: (01234) 854890 Fax: (01234) 840776 E-mail: mj@mjroofing.com

▶ Melling Roofing, 2 Fowler Street, Fulwood,, Preston, PR2 2LT Tel: 01772 461878 E-mail: mellingmark@blueyonder.co.uk

Met Spec Roofing Services Ltd, 252 Peel Green Road, Eccles, Manchester, M30 7BU Tel: 0161-787 8821 Fax: 0161-707 0070

▶ Millers Roofing & Roofline, Bourne House, Milbourne Street, Carlisle, CA2 5XF Tel: (0800) 0837641 E-mail: millers@roofing111.wanadoo.co.uk

▶ Mountain Roofing, 4 Micklemoss Drive, Mountain, Queensbury, Bradford, West Yorkshire, BD13 1NF Tel: 07941 693963 E-mail: David158@btinternet.com

National Federation of Roofing Contractors, 24 Weymouth Street, London, W1G 7LX Tel: (020) 7436 0387 Fax: (020) 7637 5215 E-mail: info@nfrc.co.uk

▶ Norfolk Scaffolding Service, Woodside, Fakenham Road, Morton on the Hill, Norwich, NR9 5SP Tel: (01603) 872183 Fax: (01603) 872293

North Eastern Slating & Building Co., 6 Balmoral Terrace, Aberdeen, AB10 6HH Tel: (01224) 211179 Fax: (01224) 211180

North Sea Roofing Co., 32 Arbroath Road, Dundee, DD4 6EP Tel: (01382) 453334 Fax: (01382) 458310

Northern Industrial Roofing, Howley Lane, Warrington, WA1 2DN Tel: (01925) 244442 Fax: (01925) 244299 E-mail: david.gillam@northernindustrialroofing.co.uk

Northwich Industrial Roofing Ltd, 4 Bridge Street, Northwich, Cheshire, CW9 7NR Tel: (01606) 43884 Fax: (01606) 43884

Nu-Style Products Ltd, 25 Silverburn Crescent, Bridge Of Don Industrial Estate, Aberdeen, AB23 8EW Tel: (01224) 823000 Fax: (01224) 823111 E-mail: info@nu-styles.co.uk

▶ P & S Construction (Swindon) Ltd, Unit 5, Kendrick Trading Estate, Galton Way, Swindon, SN2 2DU Tel: (01793) 534921

Palgrave Brown, Unit C2-C5 16-17 Boston Industrial Centre, Norfolk Street, Boston, Lincolnshire, PE21 9HG Tel: (01205) 362468 Fax: (01205) 350892 E-mail: sales@palgravebrown.co.uk

Pallard Contracts Ltd, 84 Court Lane, Cosham, Portsmouth, PO6 2LR Tel: (023) 9221 0075 Fax: (023) 9232 5716 E-mail: enquiries@pallard.co.uk

Pattinson Roofing Co. Ltd, Oak Park East Road Industrial Estate, East Road, Sleaford, Lincolnshire, NG34 7EQ Tel: (01529) 302586 Fax: (01529) 305069 E-mail: brian@pattinsonroofing.co.uk

Permaseal Roofing, PO Box 2, Wellington, Somerset, TA21 0AW Tel: (01823) 662262 Fax: (01823) 662262

Peters Roofing Contractors, 564 Davidson Road, Croydon, CR0 6DG Tel: (020) 8655 3598 Fax: (020) 8655 3598 E-mail: pete@petersroofing.co.uk

Pickles Bros Slaters Ltd, 2 323 Burley Road, Leeds, LS4 2HY Tel: 0113-275 2620 Fax: 0113-275 2620 E-mail: sales@picklesbros.co.uk

▶ Prentice Roofing, 2 Front Road, Lisburn, County Antrim, BT27 5JZ Tel: (028) 9082 7187 Fax: (028) 9082 7167 E-mail: info@prenticeroofing.co.uk

Ridgewood Roofing Contracts Ltd, Oakfield House, 31 Main Street, Glasgow, G74 4JU Tel: (01355) 236336 Fax: (01355) 573150

Robseal Roofing Ltd, Unit 3 Nimrod Way, Elgar Road South, Reading, RG2 0EB Tel: 0118-975 4800 Fax: 0118-975 4854 E-mail: mail@robseal.co.uk

Roofdec Ltd, Braithwell Way, Hellaby, Rotherham, South Yorkshire, S66 8QY Tel: (01709) 546421 Fax: (01709) 701409

Roofing Construction Services Ltd, 122 High Street, Lye, Stourbridge, West Midlands, DY9 8NF Tel: (01384) 423586 Fax: (01384) 894079

Roofproof Ltd, The Reach, Remenham, Henley-on-Thames, Oxfordshire, RG9 3DD Tel: (01491) 572966 Fax: (01491) 572967 E-mail: sales@roofproof.co.uk

Roofrite (East Anglia) Ltd, The Street, Sheering, Bishop's Stortford, Hertfordshire, CM22 7LY Tel: (01279) 734515 Fax: (01279) 734568

Rooftech, RoofTech House, Four Seasons Crescent, Kimpton Road, Sutton, Surrey, SM3 9QR Tel: (020) 8641 7077 Fax: (020) 8641 7006 E-mail: mail@rooftech.info

Rooksby Roofing Ltd, Rooksby House, Lindway Lane, Brackenfield, Alfreton, Derbyshire, DE55 6DA Tel: (0844) 5762529 Fax: (0844) 5760149 E-mail: reception@rooksbyroofing.co.uk

S M A Roofing, 22 Thornhill Way, Plymouth, PL3 5NP Tel: (01752) 665918 Fax: (01752) 600123 E-mail: sales@hotmail.com

Shenley Roofing Ltd, Shenley House, Cherrycourt Way, Stanbridge Road, Leighton Buzzard, Bedfordshire, LU7 4AB Tel: (01525) 374723 Fax: (01525) 851493 E-mail: dcook@shenley.co.uk

Solihull Roofing & Building Co. Ltd, 236 Wharfdale Road, Tyseley, Birmingham, B11 2EG Tel: 0121-707 8600 Fax: 0121-706 4693 E-mail: sales@solihullroofing.co.uk

Spanclad Construction Ltd, 337 Heath Street, Smethwick, West Midlands, B66 2QY Tel: 0121-558 2131 Fax: 0121-555 5604 E-mail: spanclad@compuserve.com

Straits Construction, Bloomfield Road, Tipton, West Midlands, DY4 9ET Tel: 0121-557 8758 Fax: 0121-520 0435

Sussex Asphalte, Clarendon Place, Portslade, Brighton, BN41 1DJ Tel: (01273) 417315 Fax: (01273) 422304 E-mail: info@sussexasphalte.co.uk

Swift Roofing Contracts Ltd, Kent House, Ware Street, Bearsted, Maidstone, Kent, ME14 4PA Tel: (01622) 632420 Fax: (01622) 632510

T R C International Ltd, 36 Acorn Industrial Park, Crayford Road, Dartford, DA1 4AL Tel: (01322) 521784 Fax: (01322) 524804 E-mail: contracts@trcgroup.co.uk

T R C Midlands Ltd, Mount Pleasant Street, West Bromwich, West Midlands, B70 7DL Tel: 0121-500 6181 Fax: 0121-500 5075 E-mail: info@totalroofcontrol.co.uk

Teams Roofing Ltd, Wylam Close, Stephenson Industrial Estate East, Washington, Tyne & Wear, NE37 3BE Tel: 0191-419 2233 Fax: 0191-416 2210 E-mail: enquiries@teamsroofing.com

▶ Tradecall, 4 Bracknell Road, Camberley, Surrey, GU15 4BG Tel: (01276) 501755 Fax: (01276) 501755 E-mail: dave@the-roofer.co.uk

Valent Ltd, 49 Longford Road, Chorlton-Cum-Hardy, Manchester, M21 9WP Tel: 0161-881 3503 Fax: 0161-860 5519

W H Hillerby & Sons Ltd, Ballast Hill, Blyth, Northumberland, NE24 2AU Tel: (01670) 352423 Fax: (01670) 356795

▶ Wiltshire Roofing & Building, 157 Bath Road, Longwell Green, Bristol, BS30 9DD Tel: 0117-377 5315 E-mail: katyryan@blueyonder.co.uk

Woodhull Roofing Ltd, Unit S3 Olton Wharf, Richmond Road, Solihull, West Midlands, B92 7RN Tel: 0121-707 3111 Fax: 0121-708 1222 E-mail: woodhull.roofing@ic24.net

Yorkshire Sheeting & Insulation Services Ltd, Green Lane Trading Estate, Clifton, York, YO30 5PY Tel: (01904) 695800 Fax: (01904) 695815

GENERAL SALVAGE CONTRACTORS

Mark James Ltd, 9 Churchill Close, Streatley, Luton, LU3 3PJ Tel: (01582) 881534 Fax: (01582) 883486

GENERAL THREAD PROTECTORS

Pioneer Oil Tools Ltd, Sir William Smith Road, Kirkton Industrial Estate, Arbroath, Angus, DD11 3RD Tel: (01241) 877776 Fax: (01241) 871037 E-mail: sales@pioneeroiltools.com

GENERAL WOODWORK

Ace Wood Turners & Machinists Ltd, Hazel La, Great Wyrley, Walsall, WS6 6AA Tel: (01922) 416645

▶ Ashfield Wood Carvings, Unit 6, Stanmore Industrial Estate, Bridgnorth, Shropshire, WV15 5HR Tel: (01746) 769691

B G W Woodcraft Ltd, 1 Retreat Pl, London, E9 6RH Tel: (020) 8533 9885

Bloxwich Co., Park Road, Bloxwich, Walsall, WS3 3SS Tel: (01922) 710588 Fax: (01922) 710588

Briggs Trading Co Southern Ltd, Ebblake Industrial Estate, 21 Blackmoor Road, Verwood, Dorset, BH31 6AX Tel: (01202) 825555 Fax: (01202) 823980 E-mail: enquiries@briggsproducts.com

Broom Joinery Ltd, 14 Arden Business Centre, Arden Road, Alcester, Warwickshire, B49 6HW Tel: (01789) 764156 Fax: (01789) 764156

Brown & Wakelin Sales Ltd, The Croft, Marsh Gibbon, Bicester, Oxfordshire, OX27 0EU Tel: (01869) 277337 Fax: (01869) 278844 E-mail: sales@brownandwakling.co.uk

▶ Carroll Bros, Units 51 & 52 Mackley Industrial Estate, Henfield Road, Small Dole, Henfield, West Sussex, BN5 9XR Tel: (01273) 494911 Fax: (01273) 494912 E-mail: brothers@carolmanufacturing.co.uk

County Enterprises Sheltered Workshop, St Pauls Street, Worcester, WR1 2BA Tel: (01905) 23819 Fax: (01905) 27832 E-mail: countyenteprises@worcestershire.gov.uk

D W General Wood Machinists Ltd, 855 High Road, Tottenham, London, N17 8EY Tel: (020) 8801 1127 Fax: (020) 8808 1215 E-mail: sales@dw-group.co.uk

Dawson's Pattern Works Ltd, Westland Square, Leeds, LS11 5SS Tel: 0113-270 5142 Fax: 0113-276 1335

Endeavor Woodcrafts Ltd, 71 Darlington Road, Ferryhill, County Durham, DL17 8EX Tel: (01740) 657676 Fax: (01740) 657676

F G Parker & Co. Ltd, The Factory, 20 East Road, Bridport, Dorset, DT6 4AA Tel: (01308) 422987 Fax: (01308) 458257

F W Mason & Sons Ltd, Private Road, Number 8, Colwick Industrial Estate, Nottingham, NG4 2EQ Tel: 0115-911 3500 Fax: 0115-911 3555 E-mail: mail@masons-timber.co.uk

Feasibility Ltd, Weston Green, Hampton Court Way, Thames Ditton, Surrey, KT7 0JP Tel: (020) 8398 8088 Fax: (020) 8398 1547 E-mail: feasibility@btconnsct.com

▶ Fine Finish, 58 Randolph Street, Buckhaven, Leven, Fife, KY8 1AT Tel: (01592) 719039

Grantham Woodmill Ltd, Ruston Road, Grantham, Lincolnshire, NG31 9SW Tel: (01476) 568175 Fax: (01476) 591427

H & K Joinery Ltd, Moravian Road, Bristol, BS15 8ND Tel: 0117-960 2849 Fax: 0117-961 8250

House & Patten, 1 Kennard Road, Kingswood, Bristol, BS15 8AA Tel: 0117-967 3347 Fax: 0117-967 3347

Hughes & Allen Ltd, Canalside Industrial Estate, Oil Sites Road, Ellesmere Port, CH65 4EN Tel: 0151-355 3170 Fax: 0151-355 5074

▶ Kingswood Cabinets, HCS Workshops, Binders Industrial Estate, Cryers Hill, High Wycombe, Buckinghamshire, HP15 6LJ Tel: 07966 263491 E-mail: Mat@KingswoodCabinets.com

Kirolite Products, 34-35 Dawkins Road, Poole, Dorset, BH15 4JW Tel: (01202) 676500 Fax: (01202) 681922E-mail: info@kirolite.com

Leitz Tooling UK Ltd, Flex Meadow, Harlow, Essex, CM19 5TN Tel: (01279) 454530 Fax: (01279) 454509 E-mail: sales@har.leitz.org

M A P Woodcraft (Caerphilly) Ltd, The Rhos, Bedwas Road, Caerphilly, Mid Glamorgan, CF83 3AU Tel: (029) 2088 2339 Fax: (029) 2086 8315

Tony Murray Interiors Ltd, Rowden Works, Chaffinch Road, Beckenham, Kent, BR3 4NA Tel: (020) 8650 9331 Fax: (020) 8663 6576

Norman Joinery Coventry Ltd, 207 Torrington Avenue, Coventry, CV4 9AP Tel: (024) 7647 4116 Fax: (024) 7646 0494

Ruralcraft Furniture Ltd, Kimberley Road, Clevedon, Avon, BS21 6QJ Tel: (01275) 873869 Fax: (01275) 340969

Somerlap Forest Products, Wells Road, Mark, Highbridge, Somerset, TA9 4NR Tel: (01278) 641671 Fax: (01278) 641629 E-mail: admin@somerlap.net

▶ Stephen Anthony, 4 Ridge Farm, Horsham Road, Rowhook, Horsham, West Sussex, RH12 3QB Tel: (01306) 627502 Fax: (01306) 627502

Philip Straughton, 8 High Sand Lane, Cockermouth, Cumbria, CA13 9NA Tel: (01900) 825444

Tecton Timber Products, Abbey Road, Hempsted, Gloucester, GL2 5HU Tel: (01452) 381146 Fax: (01452) 381147 E-mail: paul@tecton.freeserve.co.uk

GENERAL WOODWORK – *continued*

▶ VM UK Ltd, Unit 7 Rough Farm Industrial Estate, Atherstone on Stour, Stratford-upon-Avon, Warwickshire, CV37 8DX Tel: (01789) 459262 Fax: (01789) 459262

K.J. Wood Beveller, 34 Slades Road, Golcar, Huddersfield, HD7 4NE Tel: (01484) 653283 Fax: (01484) 653283

GENERATING SETS, MOTOR, ELECTRIC MOTOR DRIVEN

BEVI Group UK, 62 Alleyn Park, London, SE21 8SF Tel: (020) 8670 0806 Fax: (0870) 4601131 E-mail: sales@bevi.co.uk

Wartsila UK Ltd, Peterseat Drive, Altens Industrial Estate, Aberdeen, AB12 3HT Tel: (01224) 871166 Fax: (01224) 871188 E-mail: enquiries@wartsila.com

GENERATING SETS, PETROL ELECTRIC

Clarke International Ltd, Hemnall Street, Epping, Essex, CM16 4LG Tel: (01992) 565300 Fax: (01992) 561562 E-mail: sales@clarkeinternational.com

Harrington Generators International Ltd, Ravenstor Road, Wirksworth, Matlock, Derbyshire, DE4 4FY Tel: (01629) 824284 Fax: (01629) 824613 E-mail: sales@harringtongen.co.uk

GENERATOR CONTROL SYSTEMS

C N Controls Ltd, Thorpe Way Indust Estate, Thorpe Way, Banbury, Oxfordshire, OX16 4SP Tel: (01295) 266704 Fax: (01295) 266704 E-mail: sales@cncontrols.co.uk

Computer Aid, 4 Hothfield Road, Rainham, Gillingham, Kent, ME8 8BJ Tel: (01634) 262534 Fax: (01634) 267215 E-mail: denise@computer-aid.co.uk

Direct Generation, Newstead Industrial Trading Estate, Stoke-on-Trent, ST4 8HX Tel: (01782) 646767 Fax: (01782) 646868 E-mail: sales@directgeneration.co.uk

Genpart UK Ltd, 5 Threxton Road Industrial Estate, Watton, Thetford, Norfolk, IP25 6NG Tel: (01953) 882436 Fax: (01953) 885597 E-mail: sales@genpart.co.uk

Megacon Controls Ltd, 21 Oldends Industrial Estate, Oldends, Stonehouse, Gloucestershire, GL10 3RQ Tel: (01453) 824471 Fax: (01453) 825234 E-mail: sales@megacon.co.uk

N J Froment & Co. Ltd, Cliffe Road, Easton on the Hill, Stamford, Lincolnshire, PE9 3NP Tel: (01780) 480033 Fax: (01780) 480044 E-mail: sales@froment.co.uk

Roper Electronic Engineering Ltd, Unit 22 Industrial Estate, Station Road, Ditton Priors, Bridgnorth, Shropshire, WV16 6SS Tel: (01746) 712670 Fax: (01746) 712746 E-mail: sales@roperelectronics.co.uk

GENERATOR LOAD FRAMES, MAINTENANCE/TESTING

Elmatic (Cardiff) Ltd, Wentloog Road, Rumney, Cardiff, CF3 1XH Tel: (029) 2077 8727 Fax: (029) 2079 2297 E-mail: sales@elmatic.co.uk

GENERATOR OR STANDBY POWER SUPPLY BATTERIES

▶ Mid Lincs Generators, Spridlington Road, Faldingworth, Market Rasen, Lincolnshire, LN8 3SQ Tel: 01673 885296 Fax: 01673 885296 E-mail: gennyman.2@virgin.net

Nersys, Stephenson Street, Newport, Gwent, NP19 4XJ Tel: (01633) 277673 Fax: (01633) 281787 E-mail: forename.surname@uk.nss.com

Westman Systems Ltd, Unit 5-6 Thistle Park, Crossways Road, Bridgwater, Somerset, TA6 6LS Tel: (01278) 424717 Fax: (01278) 424718E-mail: westman.systems@lineone.net

GENERATOR REGULATORS

Roper Electronic Engineering Ltd, Unit 22 Industrial Estate, Station Road, Ditton Priors, Bridgnorth, Shropshire, WV16 6SS Tel: (01746) 712670 Fax: (01746) 712746 E-mail: sales@roperelectronics.co.uk

GENERATOR SET HIRE

Abird Ltd, Ramsgate Road, Sandwich, Kent, CT13 9ND Tel: (01304) 613221 Fax: (01304) 614833 E-mail: info@abird.co.uk

Aggreko UK Ltd, Exchange House, Watling Street, Bridgtown, Cannock, Staffordshire, WS11 0BN Tel: (01543) 437777 Fax: (01543) 437788 E-mail: doncaster@aggreko.co.uk

Ashstead Group plc, Kings Court, 41-51 Kingston Road, Leatherhead, Surrey, KT22 7AP Tel: (01372) 362300 Fax: (01372) 376610

Beta Plant Ltd, Alpha Works, Ashton Road, Bredbury, Stockport, Cheshire, SK6 2QF Tel: 0161-430 7549 Fax: 0161-494 2758

▶ Event Energy, Russet Knowle, Wild Duck Lane, Cleasby, Darlington, County Durham, DL2 2RB Tel: (01325) 467684

FLD Pumps And Power, 2 Ness Road, Erith, Kent, DA8 2LD Tel: (01322) 350088 Fax: (01322) 350066 E-mail: erith@fldpumpspowerpowerent.co.uk

Fox & Cooper Ltd, Lancaster Approach, North Killingholme, Immingham, South Humberside, DN40 3JZ Tel: (01469) 540461 Fax: (01469) 541028 E-mail: power4@foxandcooper.co.uk

Generated Power Services Ltd, Argosons Hunsdon Stud, Eastwick Road, Hunsdon, Ware, Hertfordshire, SG12 8PP Tel: (01920) 877171 Fax: (01920) 877128

Golden Triangle Power Generation, Units 1-2 Weaver Park Industrial Estate, Mill Lane, Frodsham, WA6 7JB Tel: (01928) 722137 Fax: (01928) 722240E-mail: hire@gtgen.co.uk

Graggo Ltd, Littlebrook Industrial Park, Dartford, DA1 5PZ Tel: (0845) 6013350 Fax: (01322) 293138 E-mail: geer.sales@ge.com

Harman Plant Hire Ltd, The Hyde, Brighton, BN2 4JE Tel: (01273) 603021 Fax: (01273) 690647 E-mail: info@harmanhire.co.uk

J P L Services, 15 High Street, Rampton, Cambridge, CB24 8QE Tel: (01954) 250851 Fax: (01954) 250543

K & W Services, Unit 15, Waterloo Park Industrial Estate, Bidford-on-Avon, Alcester, Warwickshire, B50 4JG Tel: (01789) 491492 Fax: (01789) 491493 E-mail: sales@kwservice.co.uk

▶ L C H Generators, 3 Telford Road, Bayton Road Industrial Estate, Exhall, Coventry, CV7 9ES Tel: (024) 7636 1333 Fax: (024) 7636 3633

Longville, 119 Burcott Road, Bristol, BS11 8AD Tel: 0117-982 7657 Fax: 0117-938 4109 E-mail: bristol@sldpumps.com

Mems Power Generation, Beechings Way, Gillingham, Kent, ME8 6PS Tel: (01634) 264666 Fax: (01634) 263666 E-mail: sales@memsgen.co.uk

P T E Plant Co., Kelham St, Doncaster, South Yorkshire, DN1 3TA Tel: (01302) 321221

Phase Hire, 140a Kents Hill Road, Benfleet, Essex, SS7 5PH Tel: (01268) 792648 Fax: (01268) 792641

Woodlands Generators, Crab Apple Way, Vale Park, Evesham, Worcestershire, WR11 1GP Tel: (01386) 760256 Fax: (01386) 442740 E-mail: sales@woodlands-generators.com

GENERATOR SET INSTALLATION

Advanced Diesel Engineering, Unit 14, Langthwaite Road, Langthwaite Business Park, South Kirkby, Pontefract, West Yorkshire, WF9 3AP Tel: (01977) 658100 Fax: (01977) 608111 E-mail: r.brown@adeltd.co.uk

Chloride UK, George Curl Way, Southampton, SO18 2RY Tel: (023) 8061 0311 Fax: (023) 8061 2039

Electromech Engineering Services, 174 Manchester Road, Astley, Tyldesley, Manchester, M29 7FB Tel: (01942) 888181 Fax: (01942) 888802 E-mail: sales@electromech.org

Ingram Installations Ltd, Unit 13, Newby Road Industrial Estate, Hazel Grove, Stockport, Cheshire, SK7 5DA Tel: 0161-456 8288 Fax: 0161-456 8089 E-mail: sales@ingraminstallations.co.uk

Mems Power Generation, Beechings Way, Gillingham, Kent, ME8 6PS Tel: (01634) 264666 Fax: (01634) 263666 E-mail: sales@memsgen.co.uk

J. Parrish & Son, Stanford Bury, Stanford Road, Shefford, Bedfordshire, SG17 5NS Tel: (01462) 814870 Fax: (01462) 814644 E-mail: info@jparrish.co.uk

Phase Hire, 140a Kents Hill Road, Benfleet, Essex, SS7 5PH Tel: (01268) 792648 Fax: (01268) 792641

Rollo UK Ltd, 2 Rochester Airport Industrial Estate, Laker Road, Rochester, Kent, ME1 3QX Tel: (01634) 669100 Fax: (01634) 669101

UK Power Systems Ltd, Hunmanby Industrial Estate, Hunmanby, Filey, North Yorkshire, YO14 0PH Tel: (01723) 892999 Fax: (01723) 892674 E-mail: sales@ukpowersystems.com

GENERATOR SET MAINTENANCE OR REPAIR

Advanced Diesel Engineering, Unit 14, Langthwaite Road, Langthwaite Business Park, South Kirkby, Pontefract, West Yorkshire, WF9 3AP Tel: (01977) 658100 Fax: (01977) 608111 E-mail: r.brown@adeltd.co.uk

Chloride UK, George Curl Way, Southampton, SO18 2RY Tel: (023) 8061 0311 Fax: (023) 8061 2039

Electromech Engineering Services, 174 Manchester Road, Astley, Tyldesley, Manchester, M29 7FB Tel: (01942) 888181 Fax: (01942) 888802 E-mail: sales@electromech.org

▶ Gentech Electrical (UK) Ltd, Unit 8, Breightmet Industrial Estate, Bury Road, Bolton, BL2 6PX Tel: 0161-761 0484 Fax: 0161-761 0485 E-mail: sales@gentech-electrical.co.uk

J Robinson Engineering Ltd, 12 Clarence Road, Fleet, Hampshire, GU51 3RZ Tel: (01252) 621312 Fax: (01252) 819100 E-mail: jim@jrobinsoneng.fsnet.co.uk

K & W Services, Unit 15, Waterloo Park Industrial Estate, Bidford-on-Avon, Alcester, Warwickshire, B50 4JG Tel: (01789) 491492 Fax: (01789) 491493 E-mail: sales@kwservice.co.uk

▶ L C H Generators, 3 Telford Road, Bayton Road Industrial Estate, Exhall, Coventry, CV7 9ES Tel: (024) 7636 1333 Fax: (024) 7636 3633

Limel Engines & Generators, Unit 54 The Bluebird Centre, Park Lane, Wolverhampton, WV10 9QQ Tel: (01902) 739903 Fax: (01902) 739903

Mems Power Generation, Beechings Way, Gillingham, Kent, ME8 6PS Tel: (01634) 264666 Fax: (01634) 263666 E-mail: sales@memsgen.co.uk

Multequip Power Tools, 61 Willow Road, Bedford, MK42 0QU Tel: (01234) 340461 Fax: (01234) 340461

Powerplant Stamford Ltd, Wackerley Works, Bourne Road, Essendine, Stamford, Lincolnshire, PE9 4LT Tel: (01780) 766017 Fax: (01780) 750910 E-mail: sales@powerplantstamford.co.uk

Rollo UK Ltd, 2 Balm Road Industrial Estate, Beza Street, Leeds, LS10 2BG Tel: 0113-272 0444 Fax: 0113-272 0499 E-mail: info@rollouk.com

Rolls Wood Group Repair & Overhauls Ltd, Wellheads CR, Wellheads Industrial Estate, Aberdeen, AB21 7GA Tel: (01224) 797000 Fax: (01224) 771552 E-mail: reception@rwgroup.co.uk

Thistle Generators Ltd, Faraday House Coalburn Road, Fallside, Bothwell, Glasgow, G71 8DA Tel: (01698) 814888 Fax: (01698) 802592 E-mail: mailroom@thistlegenerators.com

UK Power Systems Ltd, Hunmanby Industrial Estate, Hunmanby, Filey, North Yorkshire, YO14 0PH Tel: (01723) 892999 Fax: (01723) 892674 E-mail: sales@ukpowersystems.com

Wagenaar Generators Ltd, Gilfach-Y-Rhiw, Abergwili, Carmarthen, SA32 7ER Tel: (01267) 237078 Fax: (01267) 234113 E-mail: johndenver@amgenerators.com

GENERATOR SET SPARE PARTS

Amc Diesel Engineering Ltd, Beverley House, Hall Lane, Longton, Preston, PR4 5ZD Tel: (01772) 613003 Fax: (01772) 616364 E-mail: sales@amcdiesel.co.uk

Daf Trucks Ltd, Eastern By Passage, Thame, Oxfordshire, OX9 3FB Tel: (01844) 261111 Fax: (01844) 217111 E-mail: info@daftrucks.com

Dale Power Solutions Ltd, Salter Road, Eastfield, Scarborough, North Yorkshire, YO11 3DU Tel: (01723) 583511 Fax: (01723) 581231 E-mail: sales@dalepowersolutions.com

Eagle Power, Johnson Bridge Road, Off Church Lane, West Bromwich, West Midlands, B71 1DG Tel: 0121-580 3222 Fax: 0121-525 4796 E-mail: eagle@kw1.com

Roper Electronic Engineering Ltd, Unit 22 Industrial Estate, Station Road, Ditton Priors, Bridgnorth, Shropshire, WV16 6SS Tel: (01746) 712670 Fax: (01746) 712746 E-mail: sales@roperelectronics.co.uk

Watpower International Ltd, PO Box 1389, London, W5 1JJ Tel: (020) 8810 9148 Fax: (020) 8810 5509 E-mail: info@watpower.co.uk

Welland Engineering Ltd, 31a Cranmore Lane, Holbeach, Spalding, Lincolnshire, PE12 7HT Tel: (01406) 490660 Fax: (01406) 490444 E-mail: sales@generating-sets.com

GENERATOR SETS TO SPECIFICATION

Euro-Diesel (U K) Ltd, Stato House, Somerford Road, Cirencester, Gloucestershire, GL7 1TW Tel: (01285) 640879 Fax: (01285) 652509 E-mail: info@euro-diesel.co.uk

GENERATORS

E Rand & Sons Ltd, Chapel Lane, Great Blakenham, Ipswich, IP6 0JY Tel: (01473) 832833 Fax: (01473) 832834 E-mail: sales@rand.uk.com

▶ Northern Power Plant Ltd, 1 Burdon Main Row, North Shields, Tyne & Wear, NE29 6SU Tel: 0191-257 2670 Fax: 0191-296 1434 E-mail: powerplant@btconnect.com

▶ Techknol Developments Ltd, Station Approach Industrial Estate, Station Approach, Oakham, Leicestershire, LE15 6QW Tel: (01572) 724445 Fax: (01572) 723484 E-mail: info@techknolpower.co.uk

▶ W B Power Services Ltd, Manners Avenue, Manners Industrial Estate, Ilkeston, Derbyshire, DE7 8EF Tel: 0115-930 0359 Fax: 0115-944 4433 E-mail: sales@wbpsltd.co.uk

GENERATORS OR GENERATING SETS

▶ Addicott Electrics Ltd, Quay Road, Teignmouth, Devon, TQ14 8EL Tel: (01626) 774087 Fax: (01626) 778463 E-mail: addicott@netcomuk.co.uk

B R Sippy & Co., 118 Pepys Road, London, SW20 8NY Tel: (020) 8946 5964 Fax: (020) 8944 6083

Beta Plant Ltd, Alpha Works, Ashton Road, Bredbury, Stockport, Cheshire, SK6 2QF Tel: 0161-430 7549 Fax: 0161-494 2758

Brimotor Ltd, 10-12 Culverden Down, Tunbridge Wells, Kent, TN4 9SA Tel: (01892) 537588 Fax: (01892) 527724 E-mail: info@brimotor.co.uk

Brush Electrical Machines Ltd, PO Box 18, Loughborough, Leicestershire, LE11 1HJ Tel: (01509) 611511 Fax: (01509) 610440 E-mail: sales@bem.fki-et.com

Burtonwood Generator & Switchgear Services Ltd, St Michaels Road, St. Helens, Merseyside, WA9 4WZ Tel: (01744) 814444 Fax: (01744) 814455 E-mail: sales@burtonwoodgroup.com

Compressors & Washers Ltd, James David Building, 134 Widemarsh Street, Hereford, HR4 9HN Tel: (01432) 268799 Fax: (01432) 279922 E-mail: sales@compressorsandwashers.co.uk

G T & G Ltd, 1 Miltons Yard, Petworth Road, Witley, Godalming, Surrey, GU8 5LT Tel: (01428) 683088 Fax: (01428) 680902

Graggo Ltd, Littlebrook Industrial Park, Dartford, DA1 5PZ Tel: (0845) 6013350 Fax: (01322) 293138 E-mail: geer.sales@ge.com

Grimes Industrial Machinery & Equipment Solutions Ltd, 199 Hyde End Rd, Spencers Wood, Reading, RG7 1BU Tel: 0118-988 4825 Fax: 0118-988 4825 E-mail: grimesindmach@aol.com

▶ L C H Generators, 3 Telford Road, Bayton Road Industrial Estate, Exhall, Coventry, CV7 9ES Tel: (024) 7636 1333 Fax: (024) 7636 3633

Marathon Electric, 6 Thistleton Road, Market Overton, Oakham, Leicestershire, LE15 7PP Tel: (01572) 768206 Fax: (01572) 768217 E-mail: meuk@btinternet.com

Pickhill Engineers Hipperholme Ltd, Broad Lea, Pickhill, Thirsk, North Yorkshire, YO7 4JU Tel: (01845) 567234 Fax: (01845) 567690 E-mail: sales@pickhill-engineers.co.uk

Redbreast Industrial Equipment Ltd, 1 Stavely Way, Brixworth, Northampton, NN6 9EU Tel: (01604) 882088 Fax: (01604) 882015 E-mail: sales@redbreastrobin.co.uk

Leroy Somer Ltd, Heathrow Interchange, Bullsbrook Road, Hayes, Middlesex, UB4 0JR Tel: (020) 8756 7000 Fax: (020) 8756 7028 E-mail: leroy-somer@leroy.somer.co.uk

Thistle Generators Ltd, Faraday House Coalburn Road, Fallside, Bothwell, Glasgow, G71 8DA Tel: (01698) 814888 Fax: (01698) 802592 E-mail: mailroom@thistlegenerators.com

Watermota Ltd, Cavalier Road, Heathfield Industrial Estate, Newton Abbot, Devon, TQ12 6TQ Tel: (01626) 830910 Fax: (01626) 830911 E-mail: mike@watermota.co.uk

Westac Power Ltd, Powerpac House, Eastern Road, Aldershot, Hampshire, GU12 4TD Tel: (01252) 341134 Fax: (01252) 345353 E-mail: sales@westac.co.uk

GENERATORS, DIESEL, MARINE

Advance Yacht Systems Ltd, Unit 3, Saxon Wharf, Lower York Street, Southampton, SO14 5QF Tel: (023) 8033 7722 Fax: (023) 8033 7622 E-mail: info@advanceyacht.co.uk

GENERIC PHARMACEUTICALS

Ardern Healthcare Ltd, Pipers Brook Farm, Eastham, Tenbury Wells, Worcestershire, WR15 8NP Tel: (01584) 781777 Fax: (01584) 781788 E-mail: info@ardernhealthcare.com

K B Supplies Astral Ltd, 126 Weeland Road, Knottingley, West Yorkshire, WF11 8DB Tel: 01977 671345 Fax: 01977 636004

Kent Pharmaceuticals Ltd, Wotton Road, Ashford, Kent, TN23 6LL Tel: (01233) 638614 Fax: (01233) 646899 E-mail: sales@kentpharm.co.uk

Merc Serono, Bedfont Cross, Bedfont, Feltham, Middlesex, TW14 8NX Tel: (01895) 452200 Fax: (01895) 420605 E-mail: info@merckpharma.co.uk

Norgine Ltd, New Road, Tiryberth, Hengoed, Mid Glamorgan, CF82 8SJ Tel: (01443) 812183

Shah-British Enterprises Ltd, 38 Upper Town Road, Greenford, Middlesex, UB6 9JF Tel: (020) 8575 0104 Fax: (020) 8575 6066

Teva UK, Unit 3 Leeds Business Park, 18 Bruntcliffe Way, Morley, Leeds, LS27 0JG Tel: 0113-238 0099 Fax: 0113-201 3936 E-mail: morleyreception@tevauk.co.uk

▶ Tillomed Laboratories Ltd, 3 Howard Road Industrial Estate, Eaton Socon, St. Neots, Cambridgeshire, PE19 8ET Tel: (01480) 402400 Fax: (01480) 402402

U C B Celltech Ltd, 208 Bath Road, Slough, SL1 3WE Tel: (01753) 534655 Fax: (01753) 536632

GEOENVIRONMENTAL CONSULTANCY

Southern Testing Laboratories Ltd, Keeble House, Stuart Way, East Grinstead, West Sussex, RH19 4QA Tel: (01342) 333100 Fax: (01342) 410321 E-mail: enquiries@southerntesting.co.uk

GEOGRAPHICAL INFORMATION SYSTEMS (GIS) SERVICES

Martin Clark Consultants, Trendle Cottage, Trendal Street, Sherborne, Dorset, DT9 3NT Tel: (01935) 815777 Fax: (0870) 1360933 E-mail: victor@cahor.plus.com

▶ D S M Geodata Ltd, 3 Hope Street, Bo'Ness, West Lothian, EH51 0AA Tel: (01506) 518000 Fax: (01506) 517777 E-mail: info@dsmgeodata.com

G E Netwrok Solutions, Elizabeth House, 1 High Street, Chesterton, Cambridge, CB4 1WR Tel: (01223) 301144 Fax: (01223) 311145

▶ Gmap Consulting, 1 Park Lane, Leeds, LS3 1EP Tel: 0113-242 4334 Fax: 0113-242 4554 E-mail: info@gmap.com

▶ Landscope Engineering Ltd, Wrentnall Stables, Wrentnall Farm, Pulverbatch, Shrewsbury, SY5 8ED Tel: (01743) 719204 Fax: (01743) 719215 E-mail: enquiries@land-scope.com

Lovell Johns Ltd, 10 Hanborough Business Park, Lodge Road, Long Hanborough, Witney, Oxfordshire, OX29 8RU Tel: (01993) 883161 Fax: (01993) 883096 E-mail: enquiries@lovelljohns.com

Plowman Craven & Associates, 141 Lower Luton Road, Harpenden, Hertfordshire, AL5 5EQ Tel: (01582) 765566 Fax: (01582) 765370 E-mail: sbarnes@plowmancraven.co.uk

GEOLOGICAL CONSULTANCY OR CONSULTING ENGINEERS

Blackbourn Geological Services, Carriden House, Bo'Ness, West Lothian, EH51 9SN Tel: (01506) 826777 Fax: (01506) 826888 E-mail: carriden_house@compuserve.com

Corex (UK) Ltd, Units B1-B3 Airport Industrial Park, Howe Moss Drive, Dyce, Aberdeen, AB21 0GL Tel: (01224) 770434 Fax: (01224) 771716 E-mail: mail@corex.co.uk

Geoscience Ltd, Falmouth Business Park, Bickland Water Road, Falmouth, Cornwall, TR11 4SZ Tel: (01326) 211070 Fax: (01326) 212754 E-mail: batchelor@geoscience.co.uk

Halliburton Manufacturing & Services Ltd, Kirkhill Industrial Estate, Howemoss Cresent, Aberdeen, AB21 0GN Tel: (01224) 795000 Fax: (01224) 771438

▶ M G Associates Construction Consultancy Ltd, 11 The Quadrant, Manor Park CR, Edgware, Middlesex, HA8 7LU Tel: (020) 8381 1429 Fax: (020) 8381 1425 E-mail: info@mg-assoc.co.uk

R P S Consultants Ltd, Executive Freight Building, Kirkhill Drive, Kirkhill Industrial Estate, Aberdeen, AB21 0EU Tel: (01224) 773734 Fax: (01224) 724220 E-mail: rpsad@rpsplc.co.uk

Sugro Robertson Ltd, Tynycoed, Llanrhos, Llandudno, Gwynedd, LL30 1SA Tel: (01492) 581811 Fax: (01492) 583416 E-mail: info@fugro-robertson.com

GEOLOGICAL SURVEYORS

Corex (UK) Ltd, Units B1-B3 Airport Industrial Park, Howe Moss Drive, Dyce, Aberdeen, AB21 0GL Tel: (01224) 770434 Fax: (01224) 771716 E-mail: mail@corex.co.uk

Halliburton Manufacturing & Services Ltd, Kirkhill Industrial Estate, Howemoss Cresent, Aberdeen, AB21 0GN Tel: (01224) 795000 Fax: (01224) 771438

Southern Testing Laboratories Ltd, Keeble House, Stuart Way, East Grinstead, West Sussex, RH19 4QA Tel: (01342) 333100 Fax: (01342) 410321 E-mail: enquiries@southerntesting.co.uk

GEOPHYSICAL CONSULTANCY OR CONSULTING ENGINEERS

Can Geotechnical Ltd, Smeckley Wood Close, Chesterfield Trading Estate, Chesterfield, Derbyshire, S41 9PZ Tel: (01246) 261111 Fax: (01246) 261626 E-mail: info@can.ltd.uk

Maritech Consultants Ltd, 10 South Quay, Great Yarmouth, Norfolk, NR30 2QH Tel: (01493) 331822 Fax: (01493) 331687 E-mail: sales@maritech.co.uk

Scott Pickford Ltd, 4th Floor, Leon House, 233 High Street, Croydon, CR0 9XT Tel: (020) 8253 4000 Fax: (020) 8253 4001

▶ Resolution (UK) Ltd, 2 Rose Hill Arch Mews, Rose Hill, Dorking, Surrey, RH4 2ER Tel: (01306) 640004 Fax: (01306) 640004 E-mail: director@resolutionuk.com

RPS Energy Ltd, Goldsworth House, Denton Way, Woking, Surrey, GU21 3LG Tel: (01483) 746500 Fax: (01483) 746505 E-mail: info@rpsgroup.com

Sugro Robertson Ltd, Tynycoed, Llanrhos, Llandudno, Gwynedd, LL30 1SA Tel: (01492) 581811 Fax: (01492) 583416 E-mail: info@fugro-robertson.com

Survey Systems Ltd, Willow Bank House, Old Road, Handforth, Wilmslow, Cheshire, SK9 3AZ Tel: (01625) 533444 Fax: (01625) 526815 E-mail: sales@survsys.co.uk

Veritas DGC Ltd, Crompton Way, Crawley, West Sussex, RH10 9QN Tel: (01293) 443000 Fax: (01293) 443010 E-mail: info@veritasdgc.com

Westerngeco, Schlumberger House, Buckingham Gate, London Gatwick Airport, Gatwick, West Sussex, RH6 0NZ Tel: (01293) 556000 Fax: (01293) 556080 E-mail: sales@westerngeco.com

GEOPHYSICAL EQUIPMENT

G S E Rentals Ltd, Unit 32, Wellheads Industrial Estate, Aberdeen, AB21 7GA Tel: (01224) 771247 Fax: (01224) 723116 E-mail: info@gserentals.co.uk

M K Services Ltd, Unit 24 Pages Industrial Park, Eden Way, Leighton Buzzard, Bedfordshire, LU7 4TZ Tel: (01525) 382333 Fax: (01525) 850073 E-mail: sales@mkservices.co.uk

▶ Resolution (UK) Ltd, 2 Rose Hill Arch Mews, Rose Hill, Dorking, Surrey, RH4 2ER Tel: (01306) 640004 Fax: (01306) 640004 E-mail: director@resolutionuk.com

Syntron Europe Ltd, Birchwood Way, Cotes Park Industrial Estate, Somercotes, Alfreton, Derbyshire, DE55 4QQ Tel: (01773) 605078 Fax: (01773) 605078 E-mail: chris.toner@sercelengland.com

GEOPHYSICAL EQUIPMENT HIRE

Allied Associates Geophysical Ltd, Concept House, Townsend Centre, Blackburn Road, Houghton Regis, Dunstable, Bedfordshire, LU5 5BQ Tel: (01582) 606999 Fax: (01582) 606991 E-mail: info@allied-associates.co.uk

GEOPHYSICAL SURVEYORS

E G S (International) Ltd, 27 Woolmore Way, Bordon, Hampshire, GU35 9QE Tel: (01420) 489329 Fax: (01420) 489434 E-mail: info@egssurvey.co.uk

G E O Services Int UK Ltd, Holdan House, 26 Bridge Street, Witney, Oxfordshire, OX28 1HY Tel: (01993) 706767 Fax: (01993) 773040

Maritech Consultants Ltd, 10 South Quay, Great Yarmouth, Norfolk, NR30 2QH Tel: (01493) 331822 Fax: (01493) 331687 E-mail: sales@maritech.co.uk

Stratascan, Vinyard House, Upper Hook Road, Upton-Upon-Severn, Worcester, WR8 0SA Tel: (01684) 592266 Fax: (01684) 594142 E-mail: info@stratascan.co.uk

Survey Systems Ltd, Willow Bank House, Old Road, Handforth, Wilmslow, Cheshire, SK9 3AZ Tel: (01625) 533444 Fax: (01625) 526815 E-mail: sales@survsys.co.uk

▶ TerraDat Geophysics Ltd, Unit 2, Ocean Ho, Hunter St, Cardiff, CF10 5FR Tel: (0870) 7303050 Fax: (0870) 7303051 E-mail: info@terradat.co.uk

GEOTECHNICAL CONSULTANCY OR CONSULTING ENGINEERS

Black & Veatch Group Ltd, Grosvenor House 69 London Road, Redhill, RH1 1LQ Tel: (01737) 789918 Fax: (01737) 772767 E-mail: bvcs@bv.com

Bureau Veritas, The Oast, Newnham Court, Bearsted Road, Maidstone, Kent, ME14 5LH Tel: (01622) 632100 Fax: (01622) 739620 E-mail: oasts@uk.bureauveritas.com

D T S Raeburn Ltd, Moor Lane, Witton, Birmingham, B6 7HG Tel: 0121-344 3826 Fax: 0121-344 4754 E-mail: enquiries@dts-raeburn.co.uk

Dolphin Drilling Ltd, Howe Moss Drive, Kirkhill Industrial Estate, Dyce, Aberdeen, AB21 0GL Tel: (01224) 411411 Fax: (01224) 723627

Fugro Ltd, Hithercroft Road, Wallingford, Oxfordshire, OX10 9RB Tel: (0870) 4021300 Fax: (0870) 4021399 E-mail: info@fugro.co.uk

Geoscience Ltd, Falmouth Business Park, Bickland Water Road, Falmouth, Cornwall, TR11 4SZ Tel: (01326) 211070 Fax: (01326) 212754 E-mail: batchelor@geoscience.co.uk

Geosynthetic Technology Ltd, Little Bulmer Farm, Wiston Road, Nayland, Colchester, CO6 4LT Tel: (01206) 262676 Fax: (01206) 262998 E-mail: sales@geosynthetic.co.uk

Geotechnical Engineering Ltd, Centurion House, Olympus Park, Quedgeley, Gloucester, GL2 4NF Tel: (01452) 527743 Fax: (01452) 507435 E-mail: sales@geoeng.co.uk

Golder Associates (UK) Ltd, Clyde House, Reform Road, Maidenhead, Berkshire, SL6 8BY Tel: (01628) 771731 Fax: (01628) 770699 E-mail: golder_uk@golder.com

High Point Rendel, Suite 3 Bowling Hill Business Park, Quarry Road, Chipping Sodbury, Bristol, BS37 6JL Tel: (01454) 312266 Fax: (01454) 312266 E-mail: bris-hpr@netcomuk.co.uk

High Point Rendel Ltd, 61 Southwark Street, London, SE1 1SA Tel: (020) 7654 0400 Fax: (020) 7654 0401 E-mail: london@highpointrendel.com

Integral Geotechnique (Wales) Ltd, 50 Cathedral Road, Cardiff, CF11 9LL Tel: (029) 2022 0462 Fax: (029) 2034 0789 E-mail: mail@integralgeotec.com

Landline Ltd, 1 First Avenue, Halstead, Essex, CO9 2EX Tel: (01787) 476699 Fax: (01787) 472507 E-mail: sales@landline.co.uk

▶ Lusted Consulting Ltd, 5 Alliance Way, Paddock Wood, Tonbridge, Kent, TN12 6TY Tel: (01892) 835937 E-mail: info@lustedconsulting.ltd.uk

RPS Energy Ltd, Goldsworth House, Denton Way, Woking, Surrey, GU21 3LG Tel: (01483) 746500 Fax: (01483) 746505 E-mail: info@rpsgroup.com

Scientifics, 4-6 Wharfside, Oldbury, West Midlands, B69 2BU Tel: 0121-552 1565 Fax: 0121-544 8581 E-mail: admin@scientifics.com

Soil Mechanics, Glossop House, Hogwood Lane, Finchampstead, Wokingham, Berkshire, RG40 4QW Tel: 0118-932 8888 Fax: 0118-932 8383 E-mail: sm@wokingham.mesgl.co.uk

Southern Testing Laboratories Ltd, Keeble House, Stuart Way, East Grinstead, West Sussex, RH19 4QA Tel: (01342) 333100 Fax: (01342) 410321 E-mail: enquiries@southerntesting.co.uk

Sub Soil Consultancy Services Ltd, Kennedy Road, Off Chaddocks Lane, Manchester, M29 7LD Tel: (01942) 883565 Fax: (01942) 883566 E-mail: richard@subsoil.co.uk

▶ Van Elle Ltd, Windsor Terrace, Springwell, Gateshead, Tyne & Wear, NE9 7QN Tel: 0191-417 8332 Fax: 0191-417 8334 E-mail: info@van-elle.co.uk

W A Fairhurst & Partners, 1 Arngrove Court, Newcastle upon Tyne, NE4 6DB Tel: 0191-221 0505 Fax: 0191-221 0949 E-mail: newcastle@fairhurst.co.uk

GEOTECHNICAL EQUIPMENT

▶ Dando Drilling International Ltd, Old Customs House, Wharf Road, Littlehampton, West Sussex, BN17 5DD Tel: (01903) 731312 Fax: (01903) 730305 E-mail: info@dando.co.uk

GEOTEXTILE FABRICS

A & E Russell Ltd, 5 Brown Street, Coatbridge, Lanarkshire, ML5 4AS Tel: (01236) 433511 Fax: (01236) 440070 E-mail: sales@aerussell.co.uk

A & E Russell Ltd, Baird Avenue, Dryburgh Industrial Estate, Dundee, DD2 3TN Tel: (01382) 811566 Fax: (01382) 833455 E-mail: enquiries@aerussell.com

A & E Russell Ltd, 33 Tennant Street, Edinburgh, EH6 5NA Tel: 0131-555 0577 Fax: 0131-553 4722 E-mail: enquiries@aerussell.co.uk

A & E Russell Ltd, Unit 18 Crystal Drive, Smethwick, West Midlands, B66 1QG Tel: 0121-543 4850 Fax: 0121-543 4855 E-mail: birmingham@aerussell.co.uk

A & E Russell Ltd, 7-9 Chetham Court, Winwick Quay, Warrington, WA2 8RF Tel: (01925) 643700 Fax: (01925) 643707 E-mail: warrington@aerussell.co.uk

Environmental Lining Systems Ltd, Westland Square, Leeds, LS11 5SS Tel: 0113-277 5635 Fax: 0113-277 5454 E-mail: sales@environmentallinings.co.uk

Parker Merchanting Ltd, John O Gaunts Trading Estate, Leeds Road, Rothwell, Leeds, LS26 0DU Tel: 0113-282 2933 Fax: 0113-282 2620 E-mail: info.parker@hagemeyer.co.uk

▶ Pipeclear Ltd, Cliff Mount, Whins Lane, Simonstone, Burnley, Lancashire, BB12 7QU Tel: (01282) 776454 Fax: (01282) 779829 E-mail: stephenatpipeclear@btinternet.com

▶ Technical Textiles Executive, Batchworth Lock House, 99 Church Street, Rickmansworth, Hertfordshire, WD3 1JJ Tel: 01923 498001 E-mail: info@technicaltextiles.co.uk

GEOTEXTILE NON WOVEN FABRIC, ROAD CONSTRUCTION

Monomet Ltd, 14 Eton Grove, Dacre Park, London, SE13 5BY Tel: (020) 8463 9300 Fax: (020) 8318 3594

Pyricon Membrane Systems, PO Box 4641, London, SE11 Tel: (020) 7735 8777 Fax: (020) 7735 8778

Peter Savage Ltd, Liberty House, Liberty Way, Attleborough Fields Ind Estate, Nuneaton, Warwickshire, CV11 6RZ Tel: (024) 7664 1777 Fax: (024) 7637 5250 E-mail: sales@peter-savage.co.uk

Terram Ltd, Mamhilad, Pontypool, Gwent, NP4 0YR Tel: (01495) 757722 Fax: (01495) 762383 E-mail: info@terram.com

Tex Steel Tubes Ltd, Claydon Business Park, Gipping Road, Great Blakenham, Ipswich, IP6 0NL Tel: (01473) 830030 Fax: (01473) 831664 E-mail: wsctst@texholdings.demon.co.uk

GEOTEXTILE WOVEN FABRIC, ROAD CONSTRUCTION

Pyricon Membrane Systems, PO Box 4641, London, SE11 Tel: (020) 7735 8777 Fax: (020) 7735 8778

GIFT BASKETS

▶ Feathers Favours, 16 Burnpark, Catrine, Mauchline, Ayrshire, KA5 6ER Tel: (01290) 553105 E-mail: enquires@feathersfavours.co.uk

▶ Flower Shop, 29 Foxhall Road, Ipswich, IP3 8JU Tel: (01473) 255970 Fax: (01473) 255970 E-mail: sheila.bloom@intamail.com

▶ Gifts 2 Have, 7 Hunton Bridge Hill, Hunton Bridge, Kings Langley, Hertfordshire, WD4 8PX Tel: (07901) 671349 E-mail: gifts2have@lycos.co.uk

▶ The Gourmet House, Market Place, Durham, DH1 3NJ Tel: 0191-375 7511 E-mail: info@thegourmethouse.co.uk

GIFT BOXES

▶ Baby B Gifts, 33A Wilberforce Road, London, N4 2SN Tel: 020 76908992

Ideal Packaging Co, Unit 49, Queens Court Trading Estate Greets Green Road, West Bromwich, West Midlands, B70 9EL Tel: 0121-557 3624 Fax: 0121-520 5316 E-mail: sales@idealpackaging.co.uk

Pink Wedding Days, The Business Centre, Edward Street, Redditch, Worcestershire, B97 6HA Tel: (01527) 596913 Fax: (01527) 66332 E-mail: info@pinkweddingdays.co.uk

▶ PresentstoGo Christening & Birthday Gifts Co., Sunnywood Drive, Haywards Heath, West Sussex, RH16 4PE Tel: 01444 415096 E-mail: jw@presentstogo.co.uk

▶ Q R 8 Design, Arundel Street, Sheffield, S1 2NS Tel: 0114-221 1818 Fax: (0870) 1338957 E-mail: jerry@lampson.co.uk

▶ Wild Wood & Rose, 110 Johnson Road, Emersons Green, Bristol, BS16 7JG Tel: 0117-957 1420 Fax: 0117-970 2285 E-mail: shop@wildwoodrose.com

GIFT BOXES, CORRUGATED

BoxMart Ltd, Unit 1C, Ringway Industrial Estate, Eastern Avenue, Lichfield, Staffordshire, WS13 7SF Tel: (01543) 411574 Fax: (01543) 258952 E-mail: enquiries@boxmart.co.uk

GIFT BOXES, PAPER

▶ Dreamcrafts Ltd, 107 Thistledene, Thames Ditton, Surrey, KT7 0YW Tel: (020) 8873 2893 Fax: (020) 8873 2893 E-mail: sales@dreamcraftstore.co.uk

GIFT CERTIFICATES

Dining 4 You, 8 Saunders Street, Gillingham, Kent, ME7 1ET Tel: 07804 325697 E-mail: info@dining4you.co.uk

▶ Sharemymemory.com, P.O. Box 3756, Sheffield, S6 9AB Tel: 08707 202 686 Fax: 08707 202 687 E-mail: mail@sharemymemory.com

GIFT SET SOAPS

▶ GotchaSomething, 44 Penrhyn Road, Far Cotton, Northampton, NN4 8ED Tel: 0845 1565470 E-mail: general@gotchasomething.co.uk

▶ Wild Wood & Rose, 110 Johnson Road, Emersons Green, Bristol, BS16 7JG Tel: 0117-957 1420 Fax: 0117-970 2285 E-mail: shop@wildwoodrose.com

World Of Fragrance, Units 1-3 Mile End, Brandon, Suffolk, IP27 0NG Tel: (01842) 815551 Fax: (01842) 814481 E-mail: wofs@prince4828.fsworld.co.uk

GIFT VOUCHERS, BUSINESS, CHAMPAGNE

▶ Fantastic Days Out Ltd, The Coach House, 4 Main Street, Humberstone, Leicester, LE5 1AE Tel: 0116-276 6061 Fax: 0116-276 5960 E-mail: enquiries@fantasticdaysout.com

GIFT WRAPPINGS OR ACCESSORIES

Belgrave Graphics Ltd, Belgrave House, Hatfield Business Park, Frobisher Way, Hatfield, Hertfordshire, AL10 9TQ Tel: (01707) 274549 Fax: (01707) 630660 E-mail: mail@intg.co.uk

Carlton Cards Ltd, Mill St East, Dewsbury, West Yorkshire, WF12 9AW Tel: (01924) 465200 Fax: (01924) 453908

GIFT WRAPPINGS OR ACCESSORIES – *continued*

▶ EZ Wrap Ltd, Team House, 27 Nine Mile Ride, Finchampstead, Wokingham, Berkshire, RG40 4QD Tel: 0118-973 5000 Fax: 0118-973 7878 E-mail: enquires@ezwrap.co.uk
Frith's Flexible Packaging Ltd, 1 The Forum Coopers Way, Temple Farm Industrial Estate, Southend-on-Sea, SS2 5TE Tel: (01702) 462605 Fax: (01702) 616954 E-mail: sales@friths.co.uk
Hallons Display Fixtures, Riverside Works, Forde Road, Newton Abbot, Devon, TQ12 4AD Tel: (01626) 358700 Fax: (01626) 358701 E-mail: sales@hallons.co.uk
Sharon Jervis Illustrations, Farndon Grange, East Farndon, Market Harborough, Leics, LE16 9SL Tel: (01858) 434344 Fax: (01858) 434181
Maxdean, PO Box 19, Manchester, M25 9JP Tel: 0161-796 6696 Fax: 0161-796 6400 E-mail: maxdean@uk2.net

GIFTS, ADVERTISING/BUSINESS INCENTIVES, *See Advertising Gift etc*

GIFTS, BUSINESS, CHAMPAGNE

▶ Archway Promotions, 7 Kempston Court, Kempston Hardwick, Bedford, MK43 9PQ Tel: (01234) 853500 Fax: (01234) 852826 E-mail: sales@archwaypromotions.co.uk

GIFTWARE, *See also headings for particular types such as Silver Plated; also those for Fancy Goods*

A W Raybould Ltd, Barons Court, Newhouse Lane, Upton Warren, Bromsgrove, Worcestershire, B61 9ET Tel: (01527) 861006 Fax: (01527) 861292 E-mail: info@academypewter.co.uk
▶ Anastasia Flowers, 131 Easterly Road, Leeds, LS8 2TP Tel: 0113-235 1010 Fax: 0113-235 1010 E-mail: lana@anastasiaflowers.co.uk
Ansteys Of Worcester Traditional Cheese Makers, Broomhall Lane, Broomhall, Worcester, WR5 2NT Tel: (01905) 820232 Fax: (01905) 828032 E-mail: gifts@ansteys.com
Apex Print & Promotion, Sapphire Way, Rhombus Business Park, Norwich, NR6 6NN Tel: (01603) 410035 Fax: (01603) 410049 E-mail: admin@promotion.co.uk
Bowbrook Studios Ltd, Unit 7, Highgrove Farm, Seaford, Pinvin, Pershore, Worcestershire, WR10 2LF Tel: (01905) 840694 Fax: (01905) 840695 E-mail: sales@bowbrookstudios.co.uk
▶ Brandart Giftware, Studio House, Heckworth Close, Severalls Industrial Park, Colchester, CO4 9TB Tel: (01206) 224466 Fax: (01206) 224460
Broomecupboard.com, Knole Ho, Otham La, Bearsted, Maidstone, Kent, ME15 8SJ Tel: (01622) 738006 E-mail: info@broomecupboard.com
▶ Broughton Minerals, 2 Station Yard, Kirkby Stephen, Cumbria, CA17 4LA Tel: (01768) 371155 Fax: (01768) 371166
▶ Business Baubles, North Oast, Reed Court Farm, Hunton Road, Tonbridge, Kent, TN12 9SX Tel: (01622) 820005 Fax: (01622) 820006 E-mail: sales@businessbaubles.com
BusinessGift.UK.Com, 92 Langdale Road, Leyland, PR25 3AS Tel: (01772) 435010 Fax: (01772) 457280 E-mail: steve@ad-options.co.uk
C Robathon & Sons Ltd, 63 Hunters Vale, Birmingham, B19 2XH Tel: 0121-554 6990 Fax: 0121-554 4389 E-mail: sales@c-robathan.com
Coppercraft Of Malton, Delamere House, Main Street, Scagglethorpe, Malton, North Yorkshire, YO17 8DT Tel: (01944) 758638 Fax: (01944) 758638 E-mail: coppercraft@btconnect.com
Country Secrets, The Annex Downside House, Wells Road, Chilcompton, Radstock, BA3 4EU Tel: (01761) 233880 Fax: (01761) 233990 E-mail: countrysecrets@care4free.net
Customworks Giftware Mnfrs, Unit 1-3 Bo'Mains Industrial Estate, Linlithgow Road, Bo'Ness, West Lothian, EH51 0QG Tel: (01506) 821910 Fax: (01506) 821911 E-mail: sales@customworks.co.uk
Daub & Wattle Ceramics Ltd, 50 High Street, Bromsgrove, Worcestershire, B61 8EX Tel: (01527) 574004
Delmore, Chiswick Avenue, Mildenhall, Bury St. Edmunds, Suffolk, IP28 7AY Tel: (01638) 714805 Fax: (01638) 713043
Design Clinic, Unit 5-7 Wheal Vor, Breage, Helston, Cornwall, TR13 9NW Tel: (01736) 762813 Fax: (01736) 762813
DJH Engineering Ltd, Consett Business Park, Consett, County Durham, DH8 6BP Tel: (01207) 500050 Fax: (01207) 599757 E-mail: sales@djhpewterworks.co.uk
▶ Dora Mouse, 8 Thorley Crescent, Peterborough, PE2 9RF Tel: (01733) 892026
Flights Of Fancy, 15 New Street, Leamington Spa, Warwickshire, CV31 1HP Tel: (01926) 423436 Fax: (01926) 311925 E-mail: mail@flightsoffancy.co.uk
G E R International Ltd, PO Box 7, Colwyn Bay, Clwyd, LL28 4HP Tel: (01492) 544288 Fax: (01492) 547799
▶ The Gift Box Co., 7, Zille Estate, East Street, Ryde, Isle Of Wight, PO33 1JS Tel: (01983) 568844 Fax: (01983) 568844
Green Stone Arts, Watcarrick, Eskdalemuir, Langholm, Dumfriesshire, DG13 0PL Tel: (01387) 373230 Fax: 013873 73230
Halligan & Raby, 55 The Avenue, Rubery, Rednal, Birmingham, B45 9AL Tel: 0121-453 1741 Fax: 0121-453 7657 E-mail: sales@halliganraby.co.uk
Happy Mats Ltd, 23 Mill Road, Glasson, Wigton, Cumbria, CA7 5EE Tel: (01697) 351152 Fax: (01697) 351000
The Hardwicke Collection, Castee Works, 21 Sandy Lane, Aston, Birmingham, B62 1TP Tel: 0121-326 7013 Fax: 0121-327 9964
Harkison Petermill Crafts, 2 Block 3 Lochshore South Industrial Estate, Caledonia Place, Glengarnock, Beith, Ayrshire, KA14 3AZ Tel: (01505) 683353 Fax: (01505) 683353
Horwood Homewares Ltd, Avonmouth Way, Bristol, BS11 9HX Tel: 0117-940 0000 Fax: 0117-940 1100 E-mail: sales@horwood.co.uk
Hudson & Middleton, Sutherland Works, Normacot Road, Stoke-on-Trent, ST3 1PP Tel: (01782) 319256 Fax: (01782) 343300 E-mail: enquiries@hudsonandmiddleton.co.uk
▶ I F Cardboard Creation Ltd, 40B, Burgate, Pickering, North Yorkshire, YO18 7AU Tel: (01751) 475757 E-mail: info@thatcompanycalled.com
▶ If Cardboard Creation (UK) Ltd, If House, Thornton Road, Pickering, North Yorkshire, YO18 7JB Tel: (01751) 475757 Fax: (01751) 472555 E-mail: info@thatcompanycalledif.com
Instant Gift International, 1 Leigh Green Industrial Estate, Appledore Road, Tenterden, Kent, TN30 7DF Tel: (01580) 765040 Fax: (01580) 765056
Into Design, 8 Dyke Road Avenue, Brighton, BN1 5LB Tel: (01273) 330070 E-mail: intodesi@btconnect.com
Emma Jefferson, 16 Cross Bank, Great Easton, Market Harborough, Leicestershire, LE16 8SR Tel: (01536) 772074 Fax: (01536) 772134
Joe Davies Ltd, 149 Broadstone Road, Stockport, Cheshire, SK5 7GA Tel: 0161-975 6300 Fax: 0161-975 6301
John Hinde UK Ltd, Unit 12b-D, Cardrew Industrial Estate, Redruth, Cornwall, TR15 1SS Tel: (01209) 211111 Fax: (01209) 210088 E-mail: sales@johnhinde.co.uk
Julius A Meller Holdings plc, Meller House, 42-43 Chagford Street, London, NW1 6EB Tel: (020) 7724 5222 Fax: (020) 7724 3898
Karrylite, PO Box 3, Markfield, Leicestershire, LE67 9ZR Tel: (01530) 817555 Fax: (01530) 244471 E-mail: karrylite@aol.com
▶ Lancaster & Gibbings, H The Scope Complex, Wills Road, Totnes, Devon, TQ9 5XN Tel: (01803) 868181
Lance Leathers, 14 Bedford Road, Stagsden, Bedford, MK43 8TP Tel: (01234) 823200 Fax: (01234) 826110 E-mail: david@lanceleathers.co.uk
▶ Landreflections, Running Waters, Dorstone, Hereford, HR3 6AD Tel: (01981) 550465 E-mail: landreflections@hotmail.co.uk
Lansdale Engineering Ltd, Norfolk House, Drake Avenue, Staines, Middlesex, TW18 2AP Tel: (01784) 460793 Fax: (01784) 440628 E-mail: jason@lansdaledirect.fsnet.co.uk
Margot Steel, Johnstonebridge, Lockerbie, Dumfriesshire, DG11 1HD Tel: (01576) 470258 Fax: (01576) 470640 E-mail: sales@margotsteel.com
Marshall Group Ltd, Cader House, Cader Avenue, Kinmel Bay, Rhyl, Clwyd, LL18 5HU Tel: (01745) 343131 Fax: (01745) 345223 E-mail: mmar@dialstart.net
Nauticalia Ltd, Ferry Lane, Shepperton, Middlesex, TW17 9LQ Tel: (01932) 244396 Fax: (01932) 241679 E-mail: sales@nauticalia.com
Nimbus Laboratories Ltd, Lower Farm Road, Moulton Park Industrial Estate, Northampton, NN3 6XF Tel: (01604) 646411 Fax: (01604) 647375 E-mail: keith@nimbus-labs.co.uk
Old Toll House, 1 Droitwich Road, Worcester, WR3 7LG Tel: (01905) 20608 Fax: (01905) 20608 E-mail: merylaskew@aol.com
P O S Packaging Ltd, Cressex Business Park, 30A Wellington Road, High Wycombe, Buckinghamshire, HP12 3PR Tel: (01494) 473701 Fax: (01494) 473801 E-mail: unique.pkg@online.rednet.co.uk
Park Rose Ltd, Covert Court Lane, Bridlington, North Humberside, YO15 3QF Tel: (01262) 602823 Fax: (01262) 400202 E-mail: sales@parkrose.fsbusiness.co.uk
▶ Pendelfin Studios Ltd, PO Box 431, Burnley, Lancashire, BB10 2HG Tel: (01282) 432301 Fax: (01282) 459464
▶ Postpots Ltd, 108 Titan House, Cardiff Bay Business Centre, Cardiff, CF24 5BS Tel: (02920) 472002 Fax: (02920) 472003
▶ Potato Academy Ltd, The Old Barn, Ferringham Lane, Ferring, Worthing, West Sussex, BN12 5LL Tel: (01903) 500368 E-mail: contact@potatoacademy.co.uk
Pumpkin Balloon Company, 12 Swadford Street, Skipton, North Yorkshire, BD23 1RD Tel: (01756) 701505 Fax: (01756) 701522 E-mail: info@pumpkinballoons.co.uk
Purbeck Pottery Ltd, 11 Allens Lane, Poole, Dorset, BH16 5DA Tel: (01202) 621162 Fax: (01202) 625129 E-mail: sales@purbeckpottery.com
Regal House International Ltd, 1102 High Road, London, N20 0QX Tel: (020) 8446 7448 Fax: (020) 8446 7448 E-mail: regalds@btinternet.com
▶ Rockoco Contemparary Slate Design, Middle Hill, Freystrop, Haverfordwest, Dyfed, SA62 4LD Tel: (01437) 764034 Fax: (01437) 764034
▶ S F Oakley Ltd, Bussavean Farm House, Kenwyn, Truro, Cornwall, TR4 9BY Tel: (01872) 240919 Fax: (01872) 240919
Sifcon International plc, New Ford Road, Waltham Cross, Hertfordshire, EN8 7PG Tel: (01992) 718033 Fax: (01992) 718033 E-mail: sales@sil.demon.co.uk
▶ Simply Doughlightful, Unit 30 Barleylands Farm, Barleylands Road, Billericay, Essex, CM11 2UD Tel: (01268) 272766
Frank Smythson Ltd, 40 New Bond Street, London, W1S 2DE Tel: (020) 7629 8558 Fax: (020) 7495 6111 E-mail: 101451.2265@compuserve.com
Spence Bryson Ltd, Unit 14a Seagoe Industrial Area, Portadown, Craigavon, County Armagh, BT63 5QD Tel: (028) 3833 2521 Fax: (028) 3835 1043E-mail: sales@spencebryson.co.uk
Squink, West Winds, Gong Hill Dr, Lower Bourne, Farnham, Surrey, GU10 3HQ Tel: 01252 792900 Fax: 01252 792022
▶ Sterling Collection, Unit 401 Via Gellia Mill, Via Gellia Road, Bonsall, Matlock, Derbyshire, DE4 2AJ Tel: (01629) 824994 Fax: (01629) 824994
Taylor Agencies, Narrow Gates Stable Cottage, Main Street, St. Boswells, Melrose, Roxburghshire, TD6 0AX Tel: (01835) 823555
Towell & Scott Ltd, Homefield Farm, Sherford, Kingsbridge, Devon, TQ7 2AT Tel: (01548) 531325 Fax: (01548) 531777 E-mail: mail@towell-scott.co.uk
Tregawne, PO Box 48, Pershore, Worcestershire, WR10 3YE Tel: (01386) 861800 Fax: (01386) 861900 E-mail: sales@tregawne.freeserve.co.uk
Typhoon Ltd, K Colindale Business Park, Carlisle Road, London, NW9 0HN Tel: (020) 8200 5688 Fax: (020) 8205 5088
▶ Victoria Cartridge Creations, 67 Lower Parliament Street, Nottingham, NG1 3BB Tel: 0115-911 5100 Fax: 0115-911 5100 E-mail: sales@victoriagartlidge.co.uk
W J Nigh & Sons, 1 Station Approach, Shanklin, Isle of Wight, PO37 7AS Tel: (01983) 863291 Fax: (01983) 866283 E-mail: sales@wjnigh.co.uk
Watersmeet, Metal & Ores Industrial Estate, 138 Hanbury Road, Stoke Prior, Bromsgrove, Worcestershire, B60 4JZ Tel: (01527) 832292 Fax: (01527) 832949 E-mail: sales@watersmeetltd.co.uk
Widdop Bingham & Co. Ltd, Broadgate, Broadway Business Park, Chadderton, Oldham, OL9 9XE Tel: 0161-688 1200 Fax: 0161-682 6808 E-mail: sales@widdop.co.uk
Wild Things, 12 Denmark Road, Exeter, EX1 1SL Tel: (01392) 493775 Fax: (01392) 413538 E-mail: info@wildthingsgifts.com
▶ Yeldray Agencies, Langley Drive, Birmingham, B35 7AD Tel: 0121-730 2000

GIFTWARE PACKING SERVICES

Graham Lloyd Bedford Ltd, Ampthill Road, Bedford, MK42 9JN Tel: (01234) 267810 Fax: (01234) 212942 E-mail: graham@grahamlloyd.co.uk

GIFTWARE, CHRISTMAS

▶ Big Al's, The Old Vicarage, 24 Zetland Street, Wakefield, West Yorkshire, WF1 1QT Tel: 07971 635051 E-mail: big_als_comics@hotmail.co.uk

GILDING SERVICES TO THE TRADE

Modern Metal Finishes Ltd, Burstwick Industrial Estate, Ellifoot Lane, Burstwick, Hull, HU12 9EF Tel: (01964) 671040 Fax: (01964) 671040 E-mail: sales@mmfgold.co.uk

GLAND PACKINGS

Tom-Pac (G.B.) Ltd, PO Box 8450, Prestwick, Ayrshire, KA9 1RG Tel: (01292) 471196 Fax: (01292) 471196 E-mail: tompacgb@btconnect.com

GLANDLESS PUMPS

Klaus Union (UK) Ltd, Charles Industrial Estate, Stowmarket, Suffolk, IP14 5AH Tel: (01449) 677645 Fax: (01449) 678136 E-mail: peter@klausunionltd.demon.co.uk

GLASS ACID ETCHING

▶ Rainbow Glass Studios, 172 Stoke Newington Church Street, London, N16 0JL Tel: (020) 7249 0276 Fax: E-mail: richard@rainbowglassstudios.co.uk
Signline, Wayside House, Chapel Road, Meppershall, Shefford, Bedfordshire, SG17 5NQ Tel: (01462) 850718 Fax: (01462) 851212 E-mail: sales@signline.co.uk

GLASS AMPOULES

Antigen Pharmaceuticals UK, NLA Tower, 12-16 Adiscombe Road, Croydon, CR0 0XT Tel: (020) 8649 8500 Fax: (020) 8686 0807 E-mail: info@gshieldplc.com
F B G Trident, Unit 1, Humber Road, Cricklewood, London, NW2 6DN Tel: (020) 8830 8000 Fax: (020) 8830 5347

GLASS BEAD BLASTING CONTRACTORS

Surface Technik (Old Hill) Ltd, Sovereign Works, Deepdale Lane, Lower Gornal, Dudley, West Midlands, DY3 2AF Tel: (01384) 457610 Fax: (01384) 238563

GLASS BEADS

▶ Bead Envy, 4 Killerby Lane, Cayton, Scarborough, North Yorkshire, YO11 3TP Tel: 01262 470229 E-mail: emma@beadenvy.co.uk
▶ Beads By Design, 4, Nunnery Walk, South Cave, Brough, East Yorkshire, HU15 2JA Tel: (01430) 471007 E-mail: info@beadsbydesign.co.uk
▶ Judith Johnston Lampwork Beads, 21 Kendal Road, Hove, East Sussex, BN3 5HZ Tel: (01273) 776985
Potters Ballotini Ne Ltd, Darlington Road, West Auckland, Bishop Auckland, County Durham, DL14 9PR Tel: (01388) 830800 Fax: (01388) 830819
▶ Q A Equipment Ltd, Hutton Place, Grasslot, Maryport, Cumbria, CA15 8ED Tel: (01900) 812777 Fax: (0870) 7598333 E-mail: sales@qaequipment.co.uk
Tillerman Beads, Baltimore Marina, Stackhills Road, Todmorden, LANCS, OL14 5QW Tel: (01706) 810158 Fax: (01706) 810158 E-mail: sales@tillmerman.co.uk
Tuffnell Glass, Unit 2b, 35 Eastgate North, Driffield, North Humberside, YO25 6DG Tel: (01377) 240745 Fax: (01377) 240746 E-mail: sales@tuffnellglass.co.uk

GLASS BEADS, COATED

▶ Bead Solutions, 13 Seaway Road, Paignton, Devon, TQ3 2NX Tel: (01803) 552072 Fax: 01803 552072 E-mail: beads@beadsolutions.co.uk

GLASS BENDING

B & S Glass Industries Ltd, 47 Sutherland Road, London, E17 6BH Tel: (020) 8527 7575 Fax: (020) 8531 4875 E-mail: colin.tucker4@btopenworld.com
Curved Glass (UK) Ltd, 10 Marshgate Lane, London, E15 2NH Tel: (020) 8555 9660 Fax: (020) 8519 5934 E-mail: info@curvedglassuk.co.uk
Skan Processing, The Howard John Glass Centre, Bodmin Road, Coventry, CV2 5DB Tel: (024) 7660 4999 Fax: (024) 7660 4888
Technical Glass Ltd, Kelvin Way, West Bromwich, West Midlands, B70 7LB Tel: 0121-553 3334 Fax: 0121-553 3336 E-mail: sales@technicalglass.net

GLASS BEVELLING

Cameo Glass, Old Saw Mills Road, Faringdon, Oxfordshire, SN7 7DS Tel: (01367) 242421 Fax: (01367) 242978 E-mail: sales@camio-glass.com
JP Glass & Decor Ltd, 3 Eastcote Industrial Estate, Field End Road, Ruislip, Middlesex, HA4 9XG Tel: (020) 8429 2999 Fax: (020) 8868 4314 E-mail: sales@jpglass.com
McCollins, Boynton Hall, Boynton St, Hull, HU3 3BZ Tel: (01482) 329634 Fax: (01482) 329634
Southport Glass, 19 St James Street, Southport, Merseyside, PR8 5AE Tel: (01704) 537474 Fax: (01704) 534418
Witham Glass Works, 1 Wilton Street, Hull, HU8 7LG Tel: (01482) 329183 Fax: (01482) 211959

GLASS BLOCKS OR BRICKS

▶ Glass Block Shop The Ltd, 146 Stamford Street Central, Ashton-under-Lyne, Lancashire, OL6 6AD Tel: (0870) 7601112 Fax: 0161- 343 8834 E-mail: sales@glassblocksuk.com
Glassblock Warehouse Ltd, Suite 111, 79 Friar Street, Worcester, WR1 2NT Tel: (01886) 833891 Fax: (01886) 832534 E-mail: 1glassblocks@tiscali.co.uk
John Morris Developments Ltd, Stanton House, 6 Eastham Village Road, Eastham, Wirral, Merseyside, CH62 0DE Tel: 0151-326 2275 Fax: 0151-326 2276E-mail: i.lee@tiscali.co.uk
K2 Glass Ltd, Sett End Road, Shadsworth Business Park, Blackburn, BB1 2PT Tel: (01254) 260040 Fax: (01254) 692389 E-mail: enquiry@k2glassltd.com

GLASS BLOCKS OR BRICKS – *continued*

Luxcrete Ltd, Premier House, Disraeli Road, London, NW10 7BT Tel: (020) 8965 7292 Fax: (020) 8961 6337 E-mail: sales@luxcrete.co.uk

GLASS BLOWERS OR BLOWN GLASSWARE

Anthony Stern Glass Ltd, Unit 205 Avro House, Havelock Terrace, London, SW8 4AL Tel: (020) 7622 9463 Fax: (020) 7738 8100 E-mail: anthony@anthonysternglass.com

Artfull, 12 Victoria Terrace, London, N4 4DA Tel: (020) 7272 9341 Fax: (020) 7281 9252 E-mail: nnewglass@aol.com

▶ Bristol Blue Glass Ltd, 7 Whitby Road, Bristol, BS4 3QF Tel: 0117-972 0888 Fax: 0117-972 1050 E-mail: bristolblueglass@bristol-glass.co.uk

E & M Glass Ltd, Sarn Glass Studio, Sarn, Malpas, Cheshire, SY14 7LN Tel: (01948) 770464 Fax: (01948) 770592 E-mail: info@emglass.co.uk

Facets Glass Restoration, 107 Boundary Road, London, E17 8NQ Tel: (020) 8520 3392 Fax: (020) 8520 3392

Isle Of Wight Studio Glass Ltd, Old Park Road, Ventnor, Isle of Wight, PO38 1XR Tel: (01983) 853526 Fax: (01983) 854054 E-mail: sales@isleofwightstudioglass.co.uk

J A Winward & Sons, Rear of, 120 High St South, London, E6 3RW Tel: (020) 8472 5986 Fax: (020) 8503 4743 E-mail: winward@btconnect.com

Moores Evic Glassworks Ltd, Evic Works, 143 Hersham Road, Walton-on-Thames, Surrey, KT12 1RR Tel: (01932) 222314 Fax: (01932) 243330 E-mail: sales@moores-glass.co.uk

Nazeing Glassworks Ltd, Nazeing New Road, Broxbourne, Hertfordshire, EN10 6SU Tel: (01992) 464485 Fax: (01992) 450966 E-mail: admin@nazeing-glass.com

Plowden & Thompson Ltd, Dial Glass Work, Stourbridge, West Midlands, DY8 4YN Tel: (01384) 393398 Fax: (01384) 376638 E-mail: sales@plowden-thompson.com

Tuffnell Glass, Unit 2b, 35 Eastgate North, Driffield, North Humberside, YO25 6DG Tel: (01377) 240745 Fax: (01377) 240746 E-mail: sales@tuffnellglass.co.uk

GLASS BOTTLE MAKING MACHINES

▶ Tekpak (UK), Unit 203, 57 Great George Street, Leeds, LS1 3AJ Tel: (0845) 0537622 Fax: 0113-242 9176 E-mail: andrew.jackson@tekpak.co.uk

GLASS BOTTLE PRINTING

A E Chapman & Son Ltd, Timbermill Way, Gauden Road, London, SW4 6LY Tel: (020) 7622 4414 Fax: (020) 7720 0189 E-mail: aecsonltd@aol.com

GLASS BOTTLES

Allied Glass Containers, Fernley Green Road, Knottingley, West Yorkshire, WF11 8DH Tel: (01977) 672661 Fax: (01977) 607116 E-mail: admin@allied-glass.com

Allied Glass Containers Ltd, South Accommodation Road, Leeds, LS10 1NQ Tel: 0113-245 1568 Fax: 0113-244 9349 E-mail: sales@allied-glass.com

Beatson Clark P.L.C., The Glass Works, Greasbrough Road, Rotherham, South Yorkshire, S60 1TZ Tel: (01709) 828141 Fax: (01709) 828476 E-mail: sales@beatsonclark.co.uk

Cap It All Closures Ltd, 149d Pack Lane, Basingstoke, Hampshire, RG22 5HN Tel: (01256) 466178 Fax: (01256) 816333

EWS Railways, Channel Gate Rd, London, NW10 6TY Tel: 020 89636587 Fax: 020 89636582

Falgard Ltd, 235 Bickenhall Mansions, Bickenhall Street, London, W1U 6BW Tel: (020) 7487 5161 Fax: (020) 7486 0939 E-mail: falgard@falgard.com

Johnsen & Jorgensen Group Ltd, Newtons Court, Crossways Business Park, Dartford, DA2 6QL Tel: (01332) 291111 Fax: (01322) 293501 E-mail: info@jjpack.com

O I Manufacturing Ltd, PO Box 6068, Harlow, Essex, CM20 2UG Tel: (01279) 422222 Fax: (01279) 773165

Radagh Glass Ltd, Monk Bretton, Barnsley, South Yorkshire, S71 2QG Tel: (01226) 710211 Fax: (01226) 716808 E-mail:

Roma International P.L.C., Lady Lane Industrial Estate, Hadleigh, Ipswich, IP7 6BQ Tel: (01473) 823279 Fax: (01473) 827773 E-mail: sales@roma.co.uk

GLASS CLEANING SOLUTIONS

C K Chemicals, Unit 16 Lady La Industrial Estate, Hadleigh, Ipswich, IP7 6BQ Tel: (01473) 822836 Fax: (01473) 824044 E-mail: sales@ckchemicals.co.uk

GLASS COATINGS

▶ Nemacom Computer Mnfrs, 6 Morgans Business Park, Bettys Lane, Norton Canes, Cannock, Staffordshire, WS11 9UU Tel: (01543) 495020 Fax: (01543) 495021 E-mail: sales@nemacom.co.uk

Ritec International Ltd, 15 Royal London Estate, West Road, London, N17 0XL Tel: (020) 8885 5155 Fax: (020) 8885 5072 E-mail: admin@ritec.co.uk

GLASS COLOURED RODS OR TUBING

Plowden & Thompson Ltd, Dial Glass Work, Stourbridge, West Midlands, DY8 4YN Tel: (01384) 393398 Fax: (01384) 376638 E-mail: sales@plowden-thompson.com

GLASS COLOURING CONTRACTORS OR SERVICES

Colorlites, Unit 23 Lordswood Industrial Estate, Revenge Road, Chatham, Kent, ME5 8UD Tel: (01634) 862839 Fax: (01634) 865285 E-mail: salesdesk@colorlites.com

GLASS COMPONENTS

Dyson Precision Ceramics, Low Road, Earlsheaton, Dewsbury, West Yorkshire, WF12 8BU Tel: (01924) 468201 Fax: (01924) 459429

▶ Hour Glass, Abernant Enterprise Workshop, Pontardawe Road, Rhydyfro, Pontardawe, Swansea, SA8 4SX Tel: (01269) 825999 Fax: (01269) 825999

J T Nex Ltd, Griffin Industrial Estate, Rowley Regis, West Midlands, B65 0SN Tel: 0121-559 1777 Fax: 0121-561 5945 E-mail: alan@jtnex.co.uk

Lethenian Enterprises, Barnsurges, Mincombe Post, Sidbury, Sidmouth, Devon, EX10 0QP Tel: (01395) 597666 Fax: (01395) 222894

▶ Novaglaze, Queens Mill Road, Huddersfield, HD1 3PG Tel: (01484) 517010 Fax: (01484) 517050 E-mail: sales@novaglaze.co.uk

▶ Olympic Glass Products, 3 Queenborough Business Park, Main Road, Queenborough, Kent, ME11 5DY Tel: (01795) 668333 Fax: (01795) 668777

Pilkington UK Ltd, 2-6 Mallard Road, Victoria Business Park, Netherfield, Nottingham, NG4 2PE Tel: 0115-940 0980 Fax: 0115-961 7993

Pilkington UK Ltd, 10-12 Alder Hills, Poole, Dorset, BH12 4AL Tel: (01202) 742700 Fax: (01202) 736155

Solaglas Ltd, Unit 1 Binley Way, Binley, Coventry, CV3 2ZG Tel: (024) 7654 7400 Fax: 024 7654 7793 E-mail: solaglas.gpd@saint-gobain-glass.com

Zytronic Displays Ltd, Patterson Street, Blaydon-on-Tyne, Tyne & Wear, NE21 5SG Tel: 0191-414 5511 Fax: 0191-414 0545 E-mail: info@zytronic.co.uk

GLASS CONTAINER PRODUCTION MACHINERY

Maul Technology, 13 Bridge House, Bridge Street, Sunderland, SR1 1TE Tel: 0191-514 0611 Fax: 0191-565 5309 E-mail: sales@maultechnology.co.uk

GLASS CONTAINER PRODUCTION VARIABLE EQUIPMENT

Stolzle Flaconnage Ltd, Weeland Road, Knottingley, West Yorkshire, WF11 8AP Tel: (01977) 607124 Fax: (01977) 672879

GLASS CONTAINERS

Allied Glass Containers, Fernley Green Road, Knottingley, West Yorkshire, WF11 8DH Tel: (01977) 672661 Fax: (01977) 607116 E-mail: admin@allied-glass.com

Allied Glass Containers Ltd, South Accommodation Road, Leeds, LS10 1NQ Tel: 0113-245 1568 Fax: 0113-244 9349 E-mail: sales@allied-glass.com

Beatson Clark P.L.C., The Glass Works, Greasbrough Road, Rotherham, South Yorkshire, S60 1TZ Tel: (01709) 828141 Fax: (01709) 828476 E-mail: sales@beatsonclark.co.uk

▶ Broxburn Bottlers Ltd, 3 Dunnet Way, East Mains Industrial Estate, Broxburn, West Lothian, EH52 5NN Tel: (01506) 854373 Fax: (01506) 854611

F B G Trident, Unit 1, Humber Road, Cricklewood, London, NW2 6DN Tel: (020) 8830 8000 Fax: (020) 8830 5347

▶ Gleneagles Of Edinburgh Ltd, 9 Simpson Road, East Mains Industrial Estate, Broxburn, West Lothian, EH52 5NP Tel: (01506) 852566 Fax: (01506) 855735 E-mail: enquiries@gleneaglescrystal.com

▶ Krysteline Group, One Thorne Way, Three Legged Cross, Wimborne, Dorset, BH21 6FB Tel: (0870) 6000033 Fax: (0870) 6003014 E-mail: enq@krysteline.net

O I Manufacturing Ltd, PO Box 6068, Harlow, Essex, CM20 2UG Tel: (01279) 422222 Fax: (01279) 773165

GLASS CULLET OR WASTE RECYCLING CONTRACTORS OR PROCESSORS

▶ James D Philbin Ltd, Chapel Lane, Wigan, Lancashire, WN3 5DH Tel: (01942) 246690 Fax: 01942 825920 E-mail: sales@philbin-glassrecycling.co.uk

Northern Cullet Ltd, Pontefract Road, Barnsley, South Yorkshire, S71 1HJ Tel: (01226) 246541 Fax: (01226) 704529 E-mail: sales@northerncullet.co.uk

Reuse Collections Ltd, 49 Lidgate CR, South Kirkby, Pontefract, West Yorkshire, WF9 3NR Tel: (01977) 608020 Fax: (01977) 644021 E-mail: info@berrymans-uk.co.uk

GLASS CUTTING DIAMOND DRILL BITS

▶ Access Diamond Drilling Ltd, Elm View, 2 Longley Road, Croydon, CR0 3LH Tel: (020) 8239 1486 Fax: (020) 8239 1486 E-mail: davidhann@blueyonder.co.uk

GLASS CUTTING MACHINES

Exceldee Ltd, Unit 120 Culham No1 Site, Station Road, Culham, Oxford, OX14 3DA Tel: (01865) 407003 Fax: (01865) 407390 E-mail: martingibson@exceldee.co.uk

GLASS DECORATING SERVICES

B & S Glass Industries Ltd, 47 Sutherland Road, London, E17 6BH Tel: (020) 8527 7575 Fax: (020) 8531 4875 E-mail: colin.tucker4@btopenworld.com

Barritt Associates Ltd, 6 Firwood Close, Longridge, Preston, PR3 3HB Tel: (01772) 780555 Fax: (01772) 780777 E-mail: sales@barrittglassprint.co.uk

Barron Glass, Unit 11 Lansdown Industrial Estate, Gloucester Road, Cheltenham, Gloucestershire, GL51 8PL Tel: (01242) 228000 Fax: (01242) 226555 E-mail: admin@barronglass.co.uk

Glass Design & Decorating, 7a Queens Road, Sunninghill, Ascot, Berkshire, SL5 9AF Tel: (01344) 623017 Fax: (01344) 623017 E-mail: info@gdd-glassdesign.co.uk

Harling & Watson Ltd, 416 Ashton Old Road, Manchester, M11 2DT Tel: 0161-231 4978 Fax: 0161-220 9193 E-mail: sales@harlingandwatson.sagehost.co.uk

IMPAMARK, 1Dammerwick Farm, Marsh Road, Burnham-On-Crouch, Essex, CM0 8AG Tel: (01621) 783550 Fax: (01621) 784548 E-mail: info@impamark.co.uk

Livermead Art Glass Ltd, Greenwich Industrial Estate, Greenwich High Rd, London, SE10 8JF Tel: (020) 8858 6441 Fax: (020) 8858 7119

McNeill-McManus Ltd, Hydepark Industrial Estate, Mallusk, Newtownabbey, County Antrim, BT36 4PX Tel: (028) 9084 2611 Fax: (028) 9034 2317 E-mail: mailbox@mcneill-mcmanus.com

Nazeing Glassworks Ltd, Nazeing New Road, Broxbourne, Hertfordshire, EN10 6SU Tel: (01992) 464485 Fax: (01992) 450966 E-mail: admin@nazeing-glass.com

Nero Signs Glass/Designs Ltd, 332-334 Brixton Road, London, SW9 7AA Tel: (020) 7737 8021 Fax: (020) 7733 8589 E-mail: sales@nerodesigns.co.uk

Parker & Osborn Ltd, 342 Summer Lane, Birmingham, B19 3QL Tel: 0121-359 8222 Fax: 0121-359 8555E-mail: parkosb@aol.com

R Foster Screenprint Ltd, 184 Uxbridge Road, London, W7 3TB Tel: (020) 8567 2272 Fax: (020) 8567 2485 E-mail: sales@rfoster.co.uk

GLASS DOORS

▶ JOHN MONAGHAN (southern) Ltd, Units 24/25, Mount Pleasant Industrial Estate, Northam, Southampton, SO14 0SP Tel: (023) 8023 2238 Fax: (023) 8021 1218 E-mail: info@monaghansouthern.co.uk

▶ John Plank Ltd, 17-18 Haywards Place, Clerkenwell Green, London, EC1R 0EQ Tel: (020) 7608 0074 Fax: (020) 7608 0075 E-mail: sales@johnplanck.co.uk

GLASS EMBOSSING

Glass Design & Decorating, 7a Queens Road, Sunninghill, Ascot, Berkshire, SL5 9AF Tel: (01344) 623017 Fax: (01344) 623017 E-mail: info@gdd-glassdesign.co.uk

Nero Signs Glass/Designs Ltd, 332-334 Brixton Road, London, SW9 7AA Tel: (020) 7737 8021 Fax: (020) 7733 8589 E-mail: sales@nerodesigns.co.uk

GLASS ENGRAVING

Aldas Trophies & Glass Engraving, 72 High Street, Ringwood, Hampshire, BH24 1AQ Tel: (01425) 479822 Fax: (01425) 479822 E-mail: mail@aldaglassengraving.com

Aliblast Services, 5a Greenpark, Edinburgh Road, Linlithgow, West Lothian, EH49 6AA Tel: (01506) 671844 Fax: (01506) 671844

▶ Andover Rubber Stamp Service, Unit 1, Balksbury Estate, Upper Clatford, Andover, Hampshire, SP11 7LW Tel: (01264) 362925 Fax: (01264) 333079 E-mail: service@andover-rubberstamp.com

Barritt Associates Ltd, 6 Firwood Close, Longridge, Preston, PR3 3HB Tel: (01772) 780555 Fax: (01772) 780777 E-mail: sales@barrittglassprint.co.uk

Bromsgrove & Redditch Trophies Ltd, 485 Evesham Road, Redditch, Worcestershire, B97 5JJ Tel: (01527) 550556 Fax: (01527) 550866 E-mail: admin@brchc.u-net.com

Roger Brown Trophies, 372 Carden Avenue, Brighton, BN1 8LJ Tel: (01273) 559110 Fax: (01273) 500298

Colborne Ltd, Park Road, Trowbridge, Wiltshire, BA14 8AP Tel: (01225) 764101 Fax: (01225) 762009 E-mail: sales@awards.uk.com

Crystal Clear Glass Engravers, 37A Lisburn Road, Belfast, BT9 7AA Tel: (028) 9032 9655 Fax: (028) 9032 9655 E-mail: info@crystal_engravers.com

Direct Auto Electrics, 126 Myton Drive, Shirley, Solihull, West Midlands, B90 1HH Tel: (07966) 398848 Fax: 0121-436 6235 E-mail: sales@directautoelectrics.co.uk

F W Aldridge Ltd, Unit 3 St Johns Industrial Estate, Dunmow Road, Takeley, Bishop's Stortford, Hertfordshire, CM22 6SP Tel: (01279) 874000 Fax: (01279) 874002 E-mail: fwaldridge@fwaldridge.abel.co.uk

▶ Glass Scribe International Ltd, Spencer House, Caberfeidh Avenue, Dingwall, Ross-Shire, IV15 9TD Tel: (01349) 867088 Fax: (01349) 867089 E-mail: admin@glassscribe.com

H W Mclean, 1-5 George Place, Paisley, Renfrewshire, PA1 2HZ Tel: 0141-889 9268 Fax: 0141-889 9268

Links Engraving, 150 Duke Street, Edinburgh, EH6 8HR Tel: 0131-554 5156 Fax: 0131-553 6827 E-mail: sales@linksengraving.co.uk

Majestic Crystal Ltd, The Old Chapel, High Street, Martin, Lincoln, LN4 3QY Tel: (01526) 378676 Fax: (01526) 378633 E-mail: sales@majesticcrystal.co.uk

Mega Creations Ltd, Mega House, The Grip, Linton, Cambridge, CB21 4XN Tel: (01223) 897057 Fax: (01223) 893 94 E-mail: info@megacreations.co.uk

Michael Virden Ltd, Folgate Road, North Walsham, Norfolk, NR28 0AJ Tel: (01692) 404417 Fax: (01692) 406698 E-mail: sales@mvirden.com

P & M Dabner Ltd, Unit C2 Springhead Enterprise Park, Springhead Road, Northfleet, Gravesend, Kent, DA11 8HD Tel: (01474) 335678 Fax: (01474) 334678 E-mail: enquiries@etchedglass.co.uk

▶ Peter Warr, 6 Newing Close, Littlebourne, Canterbury, Kent, CT3 1UX Tel: (07736) 060302 E-mail: peter.warr@btinternet.com

Plymouth Trophyman, 75 Hyde Park Road, Plymouth, PL3 4JN Tel: (01752) 226787

R Foster Screenprint Ltd, 184 Uxbridge Road, London, W7 3TB Tel: (020) 8567 2272 Fax: (020) 8567 2485 E-mail: sales@rfoster.co.uk

The Rowton Group, Unit 14B, Hartlebury Trading Estate, Hartlebury, Kidderminster, Worcestershire, DY10 4JB Tel: (01299) 250107 Fax: (01299) 251141 E-mail: sales@rowtongroup.com

Wessex Crystal, Unit 4 Silver End Industrial Estate, Brierley Hill, West Midlands, DY5 3LA Tel: (01384) 481390 Fax: (01384) 481600

GLASS ENGRAVING SERVICES, AWARDS

▶ Crisp Design, 5 Market Square, Winslow, Buckingham, MK18 3AB Tel: (01296) 712387 Fax: (01296) 715281 E-mail: sales@crispdesign.com

▶ Peter Warr, 6 Newing Close, Littlebourne, Canterbury, Kent, CT3 1UX Tel: (07736) 060302 E-mail: peter.warr@btinternet.com

GLASS ENGRAVING SERVICES, MIRRORS

▶ Peter Warr, 6 Newing Close, Littlebourne, Canterbury, Kent, CT3 1UX Tel: (07736) 060302 E-mail: peter.warr@btinternet.com

GLASS FIBRE OR FIBREGLASS,

See also headings for particular products

A K Plastics, Unit 8 Reindeer Close, Horncastle, Lincolnshire, LN9 5AA Tel: (01507) 523883 Fax: (01507) 523883
Aberdeen Glass Fibre Ltd, Lethenty, Inverurie, Aberdeenshire, AB51 0HQ Tel: (01467) 623564 Fax: (01467) 623564 E-mail: ab.glassfibre@btopenworld.com
Advanced Mouldings, The Broyle, Ringmer, Lewes, East Sussex, BN8 5NP Tel: (01273) 813456 Fax: (01273) 813456
▶ Ambrose Versak Group, Knarr Mill, Oldham Road, Delph, Oldham, OL3 5RQ Tel: (01457) 875901 Fax: (01457) 810687
Anglia Composite, Runway Farm, Parham Airfield, Parham, Woodbridge, Suffolk, IP13 9AF Tel: (01728) 664194 Fax: (01728) 664195
Aristocast Originals Ltd, 2 Wardsend Road, Sheffield, S6 1RQ Tel: 0114-269 0900 Fax: 0114-234 4885 E-mail: sales@troikaam.co.uk
▶ Auto Design, Workshop, Lincoln Road, Horncastle, Lincolnshire, LN9 5AW Tel: (01507) 525300 Fax: (01507) 525300 E-mail: sales@autodesignkent.com
Burman Laminates, 30 Broomfield Green, Canvey Island, Essex, SS8 9TY Tel: (01268) 690820 Fax: (01268) 690820 E-mail: andre@burmanlaminates.co.uk
▶ Channel Line Sewer Systems Ltd, Invicta House, Sandpit Road, Dartford, DA1 5BU Tel: (01322) 281112 Fax: (01322) 281113
Corporate Engineering Ltd, Culham Mill, Little London Road, Silchester, Reading, RG7 2PP Tel: 0118-970 1366 Fax: 0118-970 1566 E-mail: sales@corporateengineering.co.uk
D K Fibreglass Works, Montana Place, Rotterdam Road, Lowestoft, Suffolk, NR32 2EX Tel: (01502) 572562 Fax: (01502) 589119
Euroresins UK Ltd, 2 First Avenue, Halstead, Essex, CO9 2EX Tel: (01787) 472300 Fax: (01787) 473686
Fibre Technics, Unit 7a Mulberry Road, Canvey Island, Essex, SS8 0PR Tel: (01268) 511171 Fax: (01268) 511170
▶ Frerrie, Holly Close, Holly Road, Thornton-Cleveleys, Lancashire, FY5 4LR Tel: (01253) 851088
G F P Engineering Ltd, Europa Way, Britannia Enterprise Park, Lichfield, Staffordshire, WS14 9TZ Tel: (01543) 263121 Fax: (01543) 418873 E-mail: gfpeng@btconnect.com
G R P Ltd, Robin Hood Industrial Estate, Alfred St South, Nottingham, NG3 1GE Tel: 0115-924 3244 Fax: 0115-924 3236
G R P Consultants, 12 The Park Pale, Tutbury, Burton-on-Trent, Staffordshire, DE13 9LB Tel: (01283) 814733 Fax: (01283) 814733 E-mail: sales@grpconsultants.co.uk
▶ G R P Laminates, Prospect Road, Cowes, Isle of Wight, PO31 7AD Tel: (01983) 200988 Fax: (01983) 200995 E-mail: enquiries@grplaminates.com
▶ G R P Mouldings, Unit 5 Kingswood Trading Estate, Pembroke Dock, Dyfed, SA72 4RS Tel: (01646) 682264 Fax: (01646) 687732
G R P Specialist, Unit 17 Enterprise Park, Piddlehinton, Dorchester, Dorset, DT2 7UA Tel: (01305) 848548 Fax: (01305) 848548
Glasplies Ltd, 2 Crowland Street, Southport, Merseyside, PR9 7RZ Tel: (01704) 540626 Fax: (01704) 537322 E-mail: office@glasplies.co.uk
GLP Glass Fibre Mnfrs, 66 Arundel Road, Worthing, West Sussex, BN13 3EL Tel: (01903) 267249 Fax: (01903) 267249
Holmes, 1 Kilnhurst Business Park, Glasshouse Road, Kilnhurst, Mexborough, South Yorkshire, S64 5TH Tel: (01709) 583338 Fax: (01709) 583338
Kidderminster Mirror, 86-88 Blackwell Street, Kidderminster, Worcestershire, DY10 2DZ Tel: (01562) 823117 Fax: (01562) 743592
Latches Ltd, 24 Hebden Road, Scunthorpe, South Humberside, DN15 8DT Tel: (01724) 270660 Fax: (01724) 271750
▶ Magnel Ltd, Unit 11 Mercury Units, Tir Llwyd Enterprise Park, Kinmel Bay, Rhyl, Clwyd, LL18 5JZ Tel: (01745) 338000 Fax: (01745) 338000 E-mail: sales@magnel.com
N & M Fibreglass (Holdings) Ltd, The Barns Unit 4, Hewell Lane Tardebigge, Tardebigge, Bromsgrove, Worcestershire, B60 1LP Tel: (01527) 870282 Fax: (01527) 576269 E-mail: nmfibreglass@aol.com
Panache Fibreglass Ltd, Unit 1c The Foundry, Market Street, Shipdham, Thetford, Norfolk, IP25 7LZ Tel: (01362) 821515 Fax: (01362) 821505 E-mail: sales@panache-fibreglass.freeserve.co.uk
Polybeam Ltd, Polybeam House, Isleport Business Park, Highbridge, Somerset, TA9 4JU Tel: (01278) 780807 Fax: (01278) 780907
Resinbond Ltd, 2A Bugle Industrial Estate, Rosevear Road, Bugle, St. Austell, Cornwall, PL26 8PJ Tel: (01726) 851497
Specialist Laminates Ltd, Station Road, Gordon, Berwickshire, TD3 6LR Tel: (01573) 410243 Fax: (01573) 410243 E-mail: sales@speclams.co.uk
▶ Thames Group, Green Lane, Burghfield Bridge, Burghfield, Reading, RG30 3XN Tel: 0118-958 4499 Fax: 0118-959 6442 E-mail: sales@thamesgrp.com

GLASS FIBRE OR FIBREGLASS BOXES/CASES/CONTAINERS

Latches Ltd, 24 Hebden Road, Scunthorpe, South Humberside, DN15 8DT Tel: (01724) 270660 Fax: (01724) 271750
Nicholson Plastics Ltd, 20b Lansdowne Road, Croydon, CR0 2BX Tel: (020) 8760 0930 Fax: (020) 8688 1811

GLASS FIBRE OR FIBREGLASS FABRIC MANUFRS

▶ Ahlstrom Chirnside Ltd, Chirnside, Duns, Berwickshire, TD11 3JW Tel: (01890) 818303 Fax: (01890) 818256 E-mail: karen.renton@ahlstrom.com
Carr Reinforcements, Carr House, Brighton Road, Stockport, Cheshire, SK4 2BE Tel: 0161-443 3377 Fax: 0161-443 3388 E-mail: erictaylor@btconnect.com
Euroresins UK Ltd, 2 First Avenue, Halstead, Essex, CO9 2EX Tel: (01787) 472300 Fax: (01787) 473686
Fleming's Textiles Ltd, Belford Mills, Lawson Street, Kilmarnock, Ayrshire, KA1 3HZ Tel: (01563) 525203 Fax: (01563) 522022
Glasplies Ltd, 2 Crowland Street, Southport, Merseyside, PR9 7RZ Tel: (01704) 540626 Fax: (01704) 537322 E-mail: office@glasplies.co.uk
Holmes, 1 Kilnhurst Business Park, Glasshouse Road, Kilnhurst, Mexborough, South Yorkshire, S64 5TH Tel: (01709) 583338 Fax: (01709) 583338
Saint Gobain Technical Fabrics UK Ltd, 15-19 Pit Hey Place, Skelmersdale, Lancashire, WN8 9PS Tel: (01695) 723946 Fax: (01695) 723947
Vetrotex UK Ltd, Units 1-2 Thames Park, Lester Way, Wallingford, Oxfordshire, OX10 9TA Tel: (01491) 833280 Fax: (01491) 833280

GLASS FIBRE OR FIBREGLASS FABRICATORS

B B Beresford, Goods Road, Belper, Derbyshire, DE56 1UU Tel: (01773) 825959 Fax: (01773) 821213 E-mail: beresford@btconnect.com
B P Marine, 11 Durham Road, Basildon, Essex, SS15 6PH Tel: (01268) 541737 Fax: (01268) 541737 E-mail: bpmarine@blueyonder.co.uk
Burman Laminates, 30 Broomfield Green, Canvey Island, Essex, SS8 9TY Tel: (01268) 690820 Fax: (01268) 690820 E-mail: andre@burmanlaminates.co.uk
Castle Mouldings, 1 Dew Farm, Church Lane, Peasmarsh, Rye, East Sussex, TN31 6XD Tel: (01797) 230734 E-mail: castlemouldings@hotmail.com
W.L. Cunliffe (Southport) Ltd, Gratton Place, Skelmersdale, Lancashire, WN8 9UE Tel: (01695) 711800 Fax: (01695) 711811 E-mail: sales@wlcunliffe.com
Dail Design Products, St Mary Church, Cowbridge, South Glamorgan, CF71 7LT Tel: (01446) 773123 Fax: (01446) 773123
Delta Styling.co.uk, Unit 12, Carlton Industrial Estate, Albion Road, Carlton, Barnsley, South Yorkshire, S71 3HW Tel: (01226) 722761
Derby Laminates, 1 The Old Boatyard, Church Broughton Lane, Foston, Derby, DE65 5PW Tel: (01283) 521183 Fax: (01283) 521183
E & F Composites Ltd, Graythorp Industrial Estate, Hartlepool, Cleveland, TS25 2DF Tel: (01429) 272356 Fax: (01429) 861571 E-mail: sales@eandf-composites.co.uk
E M J Plastics Ltd, Clarence Drive, Filey, North Yorkshire, YO14 0AA Tel: (01723) 512224 Fax: (01723) 515512 E-mail: support@emjplastics.com
Fibre Technics, Unit 7a Mulberry Road, Canvey Island, Essex, SS8 0PR Tel: (01268) 511171 Fax: (01268) 511170
Fibresports Glass Fibre, 34 Bowlers Croft, Basildon, Essex, SS14 3ED Tel: (01268) 282723 Fax: (01268) 282273 E-mail: fibresports@aol.com
Fibretex Mouldings, Waterloo Road, Pudsey, West Yorkshire, LS28 8DQ Tel: 0113-236 1094 Fax: 0113-255 5345
Fi-Glass Developments Ltd, Station Road, Edenbridge, Kent, TN8 6EB Tel: (01732) 863465 Fax: (01732) 867287 E-mail: sales@fi-glass.co.uk
G & A Plastics Ltd, Springhill Works, Exchange St, Accrington, Lancashire, BB5 0LE Tel: (01254) 871919 Fax: (01254) 390967 E-mail: david@gaplastics.co.uk
G R P Fabrications, Unit 12 Jubilee Industrial Estate, Ashington, Northumberland, NE63 8UB Tel: (01670) 811800 Fax: (01670) 811800 E-mail: info@grpfabrications.com
▶ Hygrade Industrial Plastics Ltd, Hunters Lane, Rugby, Warwickshire, CV21 1EA Tel: (01788) 571316 Fax: (01788) 541184 E-mail: techsales@hygradeplastics.com
Kerton Plastics Ltd, Unit 2 Phoenix Way, Gorseinon, Swansea, SA4 9WF Tel: (01792) 897779 Fax: (01792) 896668 E-mail: enquiries@kerton.co.uk
Owens Corning Veil UK Ltd, PO Box 30, Liversedge, West Yorkshire, WF15 8AA Tel: (01274) 863336 Fax: (01274) 862597
Plasticon, 7 Dunlop Way, Queensway Industrial Estate, Scunthorpe, South Humberside, DN16 3RN Tel: (01724) 855036 Fax: (01724) 872526 E-mail: sales@plasticon.co.uk
Quadplas Ltd, Mulberry Trading Estate, Foundry Lane, Horsham, West Sussex, RH13 5PX Tel: (01403) 241533 Fax: (01403) 268234 E-mail: steve.botting@quadplas.co.uk
Slipstream Ltd, Pooley Hall Farm, Pooley Lane, Polesworth, Tamworth, Staffordshire, B78 1JA Tel: (01827) 330027 Fax: (01827) 330027
Smith & Deakin Plastics, 75 Blackpole Trading Estate West, Worcester, WR3 8TJ Tel: (01905) 458886 Fax: (01905) 458889 E-mail: sales@smithanddeakin.co.uk
Sycamore Mouldings Ltd, Sycamore Industrial Estate, Sycamore Road, Handsworth, Birmingham, B21 0QW Tel: 0121-523 0732 Fax: 0121-523 5918 E-mail: ralph@sycamore76.freeserve.co.uk
W A Simpson Marine Ltd, 1 Logie Avenue, Dundee, DD2 2AS Tel: (01382) 566670 Fax: (01382) 668661 E-mail: admin@wasimpsonmarine.com
Westway Composites, Unit H The Factory, Dippenhall, Farnham, Surrey, GU10 5DW Tel: (01252) 820200 Fax: (01252) 820217 E-mail: enquiries@westway.co.uk

GLASS FIBRE OR FIBREGLASS KIOSKS

Fi-Glass Developments Ltd, Station Road, Edenbridge, Kent, TN8 6EB Tel: (01732) 863465 Fax: (01732) 867287 E-mail: sales@fi-glass.co.uk

GLASS FIBRE OR FIBREGLASS LAMINATED PRODUCTS

Wards Welding & Fabrications, Cranfield Road, Woburn Sands, Milton Keynes, MK17 8UR Tel: (01908) 586505 Fax: (01908) 587505 E-mail: steve@wardsweldingandfsnet.co.uk

GLASS FIBRE OR FIBREGLASS LAMINATES

1st Choice Superseal Ltd, 688 Aldridge Road, Great Barr, Birmingham, B44 8NJ Tel: 0121-366 6782 Fax: 0121-366 6624
Bastion Glassfibre Rod & Sections Ltd, 12 Harvey Close, Crowther Industrial Estate, District 3, Washington, Tyne & Wear, NE38 0AB Tel: 0191-416 6394 Fax: 0191-415 4961 E-mail: gf-admin@bastion-ltd.co.uk
W.L. Cunliffe (Southport) Ltd, Gratton Place, Skelmersdale, Lancashire, WN8 9UE Tel: (01695) 711800 Fax: (01695) 711811 E-mail: sales@wlcunliffe.com
Exallot Ltd, Patent Drive, Moorcroft Business Park, Wednesbury, West Midlands, WS10 7XD Tel: 0121-506 7330 Fax: 0121-506 7333
Octaveward Ltd, Balle Street Mill, Balle Street, Darwen, Lancashire, BB3 2AZ Tel: (01254) 773300 Fax: (01254) 773950 E-mail: info@octaveward.com
Pro Laminates, The Billet, Parsonage Lane, Sawbridgeworth, Hertfordshire, CM21 0ND Tel: (01279) 721035 Fax: (01279) 721048 E-mail: sales@pro-laminates.com
Sycamore Mouldings Ltd, Sycamore Industrial Estate, Sycamore Road, Handsworth, Birmingham, B21 0QW Tel: 0121-523 0732 Fax: 0121-523 5918 E-mail: ralph@sycamore76.freeserve.co.uk

GLASS FIBRE OR FIBREGLASS MACHINISTS

Plancraft Marine Ltd, 4 Little Shellwood Farm, Clayhill Road, Leigh, Reigate, Surrey, RH2 8PA Tel: (01306) 611100 Fax: (01306) 611101 E-mail: sales@plancraft.co.uk

GLASS FIBRE OR FIBREGLASS MOULDING MACHINES

Magnum Venus Platech Ltd, MTC, Chilsworthy Beam, Gunnislake, Cornwall, PL18 9AT Tel: (01822) 832621 Fax: (01822) 833999 E-mail: rtm@plastech.co.uk

GLASS FIBRE OR FIBREGLASS MOULDING MATERIALS

A Docker, The Windmill, Edlesborough, Dunstable, Bedfordshire, LU6 1RU Tel: (01525) 229321
▶ A M Mouldings, Lower Copy, Allerton Road, Allerton, Bradford, West Yorkshire, BD15 7QQ Tel: (01274) 547844 Fax: (01274) 483350 E-mail: j.barraclough@btinternet.com
Bondaglass Voss Ltd, 158 Ravenscroft Road, Beckenham, Kent, BR3 4TW Tel: (020) 8778 0071 Fax: (020) 8659 5297 E-mail: bondaglass@btconnect.com
Capvond Plastics Ltd, 32 Welbeck Road, Glasgow, G53 7SD Tel: 0141-876 9000 Fax: 0141-876 4123 E-mail: office@capvond.co.uk
Cheltenham Laminating Company Ltd, Unit 10, Bamfurlong Indust Park, Staverton, Cheltenham, Gloucestershire, GL51 6SX Tel: (01452) 713098 Fax: 01452 715114 E-mail: murray.derek@sky.com
Fibrecraft Glass Fibre, Main Hall Farm, Conington, Cambridge, CB23 4LR Tel: (01954) 267622 Fax: (01954) 267622
Marplas Ltd, Martineau Lane, Norwich, NR1 2HU Tel: (01603) 667303 Fax: (01603) 764089
Menzolit, Perseverance Works, Halifax Road, Todmorden, Lancashire, OL14 6EG Tel: (01706) 814714 Fax: (01706) 814717 E-mail: sales@menzolit-uk.co.uk
Phillips (1969) Ltd, Unit 3, Stambermill Industrial Estate, Lye, Stourbridge, West Midlands, DY9 7BJ Tel: (01384) 897324 Fax: (01384) 895435 E-mail: phillips@bradleeboilers.com
Polyfibre UK, 18 Wainwright St, Aston, Birmingham, B6 5TJ Tel: 0121-327 2360 Fax: 0121-327 3089 E-mail: polyfibre@allcomm.co.uk

GLASS FIBRE OR FIBREGLASS MOULDING PATTERN OR MOULD TOOLMAKERS

Articole Ltd, 9 Alexander Road, Stotfold, Hitchin, Hertfordshire, SG5 4NA Tel: (01462) 835640 Fax: (01462) 834896 E-mail: steve@articolestudios.co.uk
Conbury Consultants Ltd, Bowcombe Business Park, Bowcombe Road, Newport, Isle Of Wight, PO30 3HZ Tel: (01983) 532727 Fax: (01983) 532727
▶ Creative Patternmaking by T J B Design, 5 Pinfold Close, Wheaton Aston, Stafford, ST19 9PF Tel: (01785) 840067 Fax: (01785) 840067
D R B Precision Ltd, Unit H, Bowen Industrial Estate, Aberbargoed, Bargoed, Mid Glamorgan, CF81 9EP Tel: (01443) 828940 Fax: (01443) 879133 E-mail: sales@drbprecision.com
Dial Patterns Ltd, 5 Bridge Road Business Centre, Bridge Road, Ashford, Kent, TN23 1BB Tel: (01233) 663073 Fax: (01233) 643775 E-mail: sales@dialpatterns.co.uk
Elkington Bros Ltd, 53-69 Baltimore Road, Birmingham, B42 1DD Tel: 0121-358 2431 Fax: 0121-358 7527 E-mail: lawrence.kelly@elkingtonbrothers.net
Exallot Ltd, Patent Drive, Moorcroft Business Park, Wednesbury, West Midlands, WS10 7XD Tel: 0121-506 7330 Fax: 0121-506 7333
Jetmarine Ltd, 1 National Trading Estate, Bramhall Moor Lane, Hazel Grove, Stockport, Cheshire, SK7 5AA Tel: 0161-487 1648 Fax: 0161-483 7820 E-mail: sales@jetmarine.co.uk
Protechnol Precision Engineers, Unit 4, Christie Place, Bognor Regis, West Sussex, PO22 9RT Tel: (01243) 842233 Fax: (01243) 842233
S P Fibreglass, Station Road, Northiam, Rye, East Sussex, TN31 6QA Tel: (01797) 252476 Fax: (01797) 253093
Shape Design, Unit 1 Bankhall Lane, Liverpool, L20 8EW Tel: 0151-933 4438 Fax: 0151-933 4438 E-mail: dave@shapedesign.co.uk

GLASS FIBRE OR FIBREGLASS MOULDING RAW MATERIALS

G.R.P Mouldings, Oak Tree Farm, Stembridge, Martock, Somerset, TA12 6BP Tel: (01460) 240069 Fax: (01460) 240069
Phillips (1969) Ltd, Unit 3, Stambermill Industrial Estate, Lye, Stourbridge, West Midlands, DY9 7BJ Tel: (01384) 897324 Fax: (01384) 895435 E-mail: phillips@bradleeboilers.com

GLASS FIBRE OR FIBREGLASS MOULDINGS, RESIN TRANSFER

Bill Dibden G R P, 8 Littletowns Estate, Blandford Heights, Blandford Forum, Dorset, DT11 7UR Tel: (01258) 459703 Fax: (01258) 459714

GLASS FIBRE OR FIBREGLASS PULTRUSIONS

Bastion Glassfibre Rod & Sections Ltd, 12 Harvey Close, Crowther Industrial Estate, District 3, Washington, Tyne & Wear, NE38 0AB Tel: 0191-416 6394 Fax: 0191-415 4961 E-mail: gf-admin@bastion-ltd.co.uk
Engineered Composites Ltd, 41 Hope St., Chester, CH4 8BU Tel: (01244) 676000 Fax: (01244) 677267 E-mail: info@engineered-composites.co.uk

GLASS FIBRE OR FIBREGLASS PULTRUSIONS – *continued*

Exel P.L.C., 23 Hall Rd, Hebburn, Tyne & Wear, NE31 2UG Tel: 0191-483 2671 Fax: 0191-489 0422 E-mail: jim.edmunds@btinternet.com

Exel Ltd, Fairoak Lane, Whitehouse, Runcorn, Cheshire, WA7 3DU Tel: (01928) 701515 Fax: (01928) 713572 E-mail: sales@exel.net

Fibrerod Pultrusions, Wemco House 477, Whippendell Road, Watford, WD18 7PS Tel: (01923) 221255 Fax: (01923) 221255 E-mail: sales@fibrerodpultrusions.co.uk

GLASS FIBRE OR FIBREGLASS RODS

Bastion Glassfibre Rod & Sections Ltd, 12 Harvey Close, Crowther Industrial Estate, District 3, Washington, Tyne & Wear, NE38 0AB Tel: 0191-416 6394 Fax: 0191-415 4961 E-mail: gf-admin@bastion-ltd.co.uk

Exel Ltd, Fairoak Lane, Whitehouse, Runcorn, Cheshire, WA7 3DU Tel: (01928) 701515 Fax: (01928) 713572 E-mail: sales@exel.net

Fibrerod Pultrusions, Wemco House 477, Whippendell Road, Watford, WD18 7PS Tel: (01923) 221255 Fax: (01923) 221255 E-mail: sales@fibrerodpultrusions.co.uk

GLASS FIBRE OR FIBREGLASS TAPES

Cheshire Ribbon Manufacturing Co., Kingston Mills, Manchester Road, Hyde, Cheshire, SK14 2BZ Tel: 0161-368 2048 Fax: 0161-367 8193 E-mail: sales@cheshirerib.co.uk

Saint Gobain Technical Fabrics UK Ltd, 15-19 Pit Hey Place, Skelmersdale, Lancashire, WN8 9PS Tel: (01695) 723946 Fax: (01695) 723947

GLASS FIBRE OR FIBREGLASS WEBBING

Hattersley Aladdin UK, Greengate, Keighley, West Yorkshire, BD21 5JL Tel: (01639) 730997 Fax: (01535) 610195 E-mail: info@hattersley.co.uk

GLASS FIBRE OR FIBREGLASS YARNS

NGF Europe Ltd, Lea Green Road, St. Helens, Merseyside, WA9 4PR Tel: (01744) 853065 Fax: (01744) 816147 E-mail: sales@ngfeurope.com

GLASS FIBRE OR FIBREGLASS, PHENOLIC LAMINATES

Goodman Glass Fibre Ltd, Ryehill Farm, Long Buckby Wharf, Long Buckby, Northampton, NN6 7PW Tel: (01327) 843585 Fax: (01327) 842639

GLASS FIBRE OR FIBREGLASS, RUBBER COATED

NGF Europe Ltd, Lea Green Road, St. Helens, Merseyside, WA9 4PR Tel: (01744) 853065 Fax: (01744) 816147 E-mail: sales@ngfeurope.com

GLASS FIBRE REINFORCED (GFR) CONCRETE PRODUCTION EQUIPMENT

K & C Mouldings (England) Ltd, Spa House, Shelfanger, Diss, Norfolk, IP22 2DF Tel: (01379) 642660 Fax: (01379) 650304 E-mail: kcmouldings@kcmouldings.co.uk

GLASS FIBRE REINFORCED (GFR) PLASTIC OR ACRYLIC BATHS

Adamsez Ltd, 766 Upper Newtownards Road, Dundonald, Belfast, BT16 1TQ Tel: (028) 9048 0465 Fax: (028) 9048 0485 E-mail: mail@adamsez.com

Armitage Shanks Group Pension Trustees Ltd, Old Road, Armitage, Rugeley, Staffordshire, WS15 4BT Tel: (01543) 490253 Fax: (01543) 491677 E-mail: merrickj1@aseur.com

Carron Bathrooms Ltd, PO Box 32, Falkirk, FK2 8UW Tel: (01324) 638407 Fax: (01324) 611490 E-mail: mailroom@carronbathrooms.com

Magnet Ltd, 12 St Machar Road, Aberdeen, AB24 2UU Tel: (01224) 492894 Fax: (01224) 488276

Harold Moore & Son Ltd, 16 Rawson Spring Road, Sheffield, S6 1PD Tel: 0114-233 6161 Fax: 0114-232 6375 E-mail: admin@haroldmoorebaths.co.uk

Renaissance Sales & Distribution Ltd, Pennywell Industrial Estate, Sunderland, SR4 9EN Tel: 0191-534 6061 Fax: 0191-534 3626 E-mail: info@armour-plastics.com

Showerlux UK Ltd, Stonebridge Trading Estate, Sibree Road, Coventry, CV3 4FD Tel: (024) 7663 9400 Fax: (024) 7630 5457 E-mail: sales@showerlux.co.uk

Trojan Plastics Ltd, Ramsden Mills, Britannia Road, Huddersfield, HD3 4QG Tel: (01484) 648181 Fax: (01484) 657098 E-mail: sales@trojanplastics.co.uk

GLASS FIBRE REINFORCED (GFR) PLASTIC OR ACRYLIC SHOWER TRAYS

Harold Moore & Son Ltd, 16 Rawson Spring Road, Sheffield, S6 1PD Tel: 0114-233 6161 Fax: 0114-232 6375 E-mail: admin@haroldmoorebaths.co.uk

Trojan Plastics Ltd, Ramsden Mills, Britannia Road, Huddersfield, HD3 4QG Tel: (01484) 648181 Fax: (01484) 657098 E-mail: sales@trojanplastics.co.uk

GLASS FIBRE REINFORCED (GFR) WALL CLADDING

Chevron Lifts Ltd, The I O Centre, Barn Way, Lodge Farm Industrial Estate, Northampton, NN5 7UW Tel: (01604) 750080 Fax: (01604) 750081 E-mail: email@chevron-lift.com

GLASS FINISHING WASHING MACHINES

Air Conditioning Refrigeration and Environmental, 56 Moathouse Lane East, Wednesfield, Wolverhampton, WV11 3DD Tel: (01902) 733503 Fax: (01902) 307899

GLASS FITTINGS

Spiral Hardware Ltd, Unit 36, Wimbledon Avenue, Brandon, Suffolk, IP27 0NZ Tel: (01842) 816086 Fax: (01842) 813867 E-mail: info@spiralhardware.co.uk

GLASS FOLDING DOORS

Door Centre, Eastfield Industrial Estate, Penicuik, Midlothian, EH26 8HA Tel: (01968) 671680 Fax: (01968) 671684 E-mail: sales@thedoorcentre.co.uk

▶ Origin Frames, Unit 9 Lincolns Park Business Centre, Lincoln Road, Cressex Business Park, High Wycombe, Buckinghamshire, HP12 3RD Tel: (0845) 4506662 Fax: (0845) 4506663 E-mail: info@originframes.co.uk

GLASS FURNACE, *See Furnaces, Glass etc*

GLASS FURNITURE DESIGN

▶ Artistry In Iron Ltd, Unit D2 Commercial Avenue, Cheadle Hulme, Cheadle, Cheshire, SK8 6QH Tel: 0161-482 8022 Fax: 0161-482 8023 E-mail: sales@artistryuk.com

GLASS GRINDING

Shanoc Precision Engineering, Unit 11 Bondor Business Centre, London Road, Baldock, Hertfordshire, SG7 6HP Tel: (01462) 895936 Fax: (01462) 895936

GLASS GRINDING WHEELS

▶ Kilncare Ltd, The Kiln Works, 907 Leek New Road Baddeley Green, Stoke-on-Trent, ST2 7HQ Tel: (01782) 535915 Fax: (01782) 535338 E-mail: sales@kilncare.co.uk

GLASS HANDLING EQUIPMENT

Harrier Engineering Ltd, 20a Kendale Road, Scunthorpe, South Humberside, DN16 1DT Tel: (01724) 872935 Fax: (01724) 271218

▶ mh design, 6 Willand Court, Retford, Retford, Nottinghamshire, DN22 7GD Tel: 01777 704967 Fax: 01777 719517 E-mail: sales@mhdesign.co.uk

▶ S R Burke Engineering Ltd, Derwent Way, Wath-upon-Dearne, Rotherham, South Yorkshire, S63 6EX Tel: (01709) 877888 Fax: (01709) 877888 E-mail: info@srburke.co.uk

GLASS IMPORT/EXPORT (PLATE/SHEET/FLOAT) MERCHANTS OR AGENTS

Glassex Holdings Ltd, Ailsa Street, London, E14 0LE Tel: (020) 7987 4191 Fax: (020) 7987 4194 E-mail: glassexltd@virgin.net

Mawby & King Ltd, Upperton Road, Leicester, LE2 7AY Tel: 0116-204 6000 Fax: 0116-204 6001 E-mail: sales@mawbyandking.co.uk

Profile Ltd, Sir Frank Whittle Road, Derby, DE21 4XE Tel: 01332 366900 Fax: (01332) 369613 E-mail: mail@profileuk.com

Wilson Glass & Mirror, Weston Road, Norwich, NR3 3WG Tel: (01603) 415400 Fax: (01603) 415401 E-mail: wilsonglass@btconnect.com

GLASS INSTALLATION

Cab Glazing Services, Unit D3, Button End Industrial Estate, Harston, Cambridge, CB2 5NX Tel: (01223) 872400 Fax: (01223) 872866 E-mail: sales@cabglazing.co.uk

E.N.L Audio Visual, Alfreton Road, Nottingham, NG7 3NR Tel: 0115-924 8305 Fax: 0115-924 8329 E-mail: sales@hotkit.co.uk

Glass & Glazing Federation, 44-48 Borough High Street, London, SE1 1XB Tel: (020) 7403 7177 Fax: (020) 7357 7458 E-mail: info@ggf.org.uk

Laws Glass, 22 Marston Lane, Bedworth, Warwickshire, CV12 8DH Tel: (024) 7664 0030 Fax: (024) 7664 0777 E-mail: info@shopfronts-midlands.com

Surrey Glasshouse, 288b Woodham Lane, New Haw, Addlestone, Surrey, KT15 3NT Tel: (01932) 336086 Fax: (01932) 336086 E-mail: enquiries@surreyglasshouse.co.uk

▶ Wiltshire Glass & Windows, Unit 6 Parkers Close, Downton Industrial Estate, Salisbury, SP5 3RB Tel: (01725) 513030 Fax: (01725) 510145

GLASS LEVEL GAUGES

A J D Instruments, 9 Lindfield Enterprise Park, Lewes Road, Lindfield, Haywards Heath, West Sussex, RH16 2LX Tel: (01444) 484055 Fax: (01444) 484042 E-mail: sales@ajdinstruments.co.uk

GLASS LIGHTING COMPONENTS

Piper Toughened Glass Ltd, 29-43 Sydney Road, Watford, WD18 7PZ Tel: (01923) 224047 Fax: (01923) 222741 E-mail: sales@piperglass.co.uk

GLASS LINED TANKS

Pfaudler Balfour, Riverside Road, Leven, Fife, KY8 4RW Tel: (01333) 423020 Fax: (01333) 427432 E-mail: sales@pfaudlerbalfour.co.uk

GLASS MILLING

Shanoc Precision Engineering, Unit 11 Bondor Business Centre, London Road, Baldock, Hertfordshire, SG7 6HP Tel: (01462) 895936 Fax: (01462) 895936

GLASS MOSAIC TILES

▶ Azurra Mosaics, PO Box 2801, Purley, Surrey, CR8 1WX Tel: (0845) 0908110 Fax: (0870) 1313319 E-mail: info@mosaics.co.uk

▶ Mosaic Co., Mosaic House, Phoenix Park, Eaton Socon, St. Neots, Cambridgeshire, PE19 8EP Tel: (01480) 474714 Fax: (01480) 474715 E-mail: sales@mosaiccompany.co.uk

GLASS MOULDS

Walker Engineering (Essex) Ltd, Unit 2A North Hill Business Park, North Hill, Horndon-On-The-Hill, Stanford-Le-Hope, Essex, SS17 8QA Tel: (01375) 361428 Fax: (01375) 361428 E-mail: walkereng@btconnect.com

GLASS PIPEWORK ERECTION OR INSTALLATION CONTRACTORS

Stanfield Building Services Ltd, Imex Technology Park, Unit 7 Bellringer Road, Trentham, Stoke-on-Trent, ST4 8LJ Tel: (01782) 658877 Fax: (01782) 658899 E-mail: info@stanfieldbs.co.uk

GLASS POWDERS

Plowden & Thompson Ltd, Dial Glass Work, Stourbridge, West Midlands, DY8 4YN Tel: (01384) 393398 Fax: (01384) 376638 E-mail: sales@plowden-thompson.com

GLASS PRINTING

Barritt Associates Ltd, 6 Firwood Close, Longridge, Preston, PR3 3HB Tel: (01772) 780555 Fax: (01772) 780777 E-mail: sales@barrittglassprint.co.uk

▶ Glass Scribe International Ltd, Spencer House, Caberfeidh Avenue, Dingwall, Ross-Shire, IV15 9TD Tel: (01349) 867088 Fax: (01349) 867089 E-mail: admin@glassscribe.com

GLASS PROCESSING/ SILVERING SERVICES

Basildon Glassworks Ltd, 12 Winstanley Way, Basildon, Essex, SS14 3BP Tel: (01268) 282424 Fax: (01268) 532348 E-mail: basildonglass@aol.com

Bromsgrove Glass & Windows Ltd, Sherwood Road, Aston Fields Industrial Estate, Bromsgrove, Worcestershire, B60 3DR Tel: (01527) 836777 Fax: (01527) 579148 E-mail: enquiries@bromsgroveglass.co.uk

Curved Glass (UK) Ltd, 10 Marshgate Lane, London, E15 2NH Tel: (020) 8555 9660 Fax: (020) 8519 5934 E-mail: info@curvedglassuk.co.uk

D C Carter Ltd, Meadow Farm, Packards Lane, Wormingford, Colchester, CO6 3AH Tel: (01206) 243309 Fax: (01206) 242161 E-mail: dccarter@onetel.com

Darby Glass Ltd, Darby House, Sunningdale Road, Scunthorpe, South Humberside, DN17 2SS Tel: (01724) 280044 Fax: (01724) 868295

F W Aldridge Ltd, Unit 3 St Johns Industrial Estate, Dunmow Road, Takeley, Bishop's Stortford, Hertfordshire, CM22 6SP Tel: (01279) 874000 Fax: (01279) 874002 E-mail: fwaldridge@fwaldridge.abel.co.uk

Glass Bending & Decorating Ltd, 47 Sutherland Road, London, E17 6BH Tel: (020) 8531 7626 Fax: (020) 8531 4875 E-mail: collintucker4.@btopenworld.com

Glassex Holdings Ltd, Ailsa Street, London, E14 0LE Tel: (020) 7987 4191 Fax: (020) 7987 4194 E-mail: glassexltd@virgin.net

Nicholls & Clarke Glass Ltd, Units 27 Gemini Business Park, Hornet Way, Beckton, London, E6 7FF Tel: (020) 7473 0999 Fax: (020) 7476 1017

Parker & Osborn Ltd, 342 Summer Lane, Birmingham, B19 3QL Tel: 0121-359 8222 Fax: 0121-359 8555E-mail: parkosb@aol.com

Peterlee Glass Co. Ltd, 28 Lister Road, North West Industrial Estate, Peterlee, County Durham, SR8 2RB Tel: 0191-586 4626 Fax: 0191-518 0459 E-mail: sales@peterleeglass.com

Pilkington Plyglass, Cotes Park, Somercotes, Alfreton, Derbyshire, DE55 4PL Tel: (01773) 520000 Fax: (01773) 520052

Rugby Glass Centre, 17 Somers Road, Rugby, Warwickshire, CV22 7DG Tel: (01788) 543756 Fax: (01788) 540078

Saint-Gobain Solaglas, 11 Bridle Way, Bootle, Merseyside, L30 4UA Tel: (0151) 525 7241 Fax: (0151) 523 8212

Shaws Glass Ltd, 66 North Street, Horsham, West Sussex, RH12 1RD Tel: (01403) 211133 Fax: (01293) 852340

Skan Processing, The Howard John Glass Centre, Bodmin Road, Coventry, CV2 5DB Tel: (024) 7660 4999 Fax: (024) 7660 4888

Solaglas Ltd, Guild House, Cradley Road, Dudley, West Midlands, DY2 9TH Tel: (01384) 411511 Fax: (01384) 411234 E-mail: midlandsales@solaglass.co.uk

Toughglaze UK Ltd, 12 Chandos Road, London, NW10 6NF Tel: (020) 8838 4400 Fax: (020) 8838 3322 E-mail: info@toughglaze.com

Tower Glass Ltd, Yeomans Industrial Park, Yeomans Way, Bournemouth, BH8 0BJ Tel: (01202) 518555 Fax: (01202) 539015 E-mail: sales@towerglass.co.uk

Universal Glass Co, 8-16 Camelon Street, Glasgow, G32 6AF Tel: 0141-764 0444 Fax: 0141-764 0044 E-mail: universalglass@btinternet.com

Warner Glass Croydon Ltd, 431 Brighton Road, South Croydon, Surrey, CR2 6YG Tel: (020) 8660 9271 Fax: (020) 8668 0374

GLASS PRODUCT MOULDS

Mettallicut, Deepdale Lane, Lower Gornal, Dudley, West Midlands, DY3 2AF Tel: (01384) 455115 Fax: (01384) 455015

Pudsey Mould Company Ltd, Albert Mills St Vincent Road, Pudsey, West Yorkshire, LS28 9EW Tel: 0113-257 4742

GLASS PRODUCTION PLANT

B H F Engineering Ltd, 4a Churchward, Southmead Industrial Park, Didcot, Oxfordshire, OX11 7HB Tel: (01235) 811111 Fax: (01235) 817676 E-mail: peter_vilk@bh-fing.com
Cameo Mirror & Glass, Anglian Road, Walsall, WS9 8EP Tel: (0845) 1709881 Fax: (0845) 1709882 E-mail: enquiries@cameoglass.co.uk
De Dietrich Process Systems Ltd, Tollgate Drive, Tollgate Industrial Estate, Stafford, ST16 3HS Tel: (01785) 609900 Fax: (01785) 609899 E-mail: reception@qvf.co.uk

GLASS PRODUCTION PLANT CONTRACTORS OR DESIGNERS

Elumatec UK Ltd, 2 Europa Business Park, Maidstone Road, Kingston, Milton Keynes, MK10 0BD Tel: (01908) 580800 Fax: (01908) 580825 E-mail: sales@elumatec.co.uk

GLASS RAW MATERIALS

Calumite Ltd, Brigg Road, Scunthorpe, North Lincolnshire, DN16 1AW Tel: (01724) 282211 Fax: (01724) 270435 E-mail: info@applebygroup.co.uk
▶ Darby Express, Ocean House, Dundas Lane, Portsmouth, PO3 5ND Tel: (023) 9269 9752 Fax: (023) 9267 7235

GLASS REINFORCED GYPSUM GRG)

Gillespie (UK) Ltd, Alma House, 38 Crimea Road, Aldershot, Hampshire, GU11 1UD Tel: (01252) 323311 Fax: (01252) 336836 E-mail: info@gillespieuk.co.uk
Hodkin & Jones (Sheffield) Ltd, Callywhite Lane, Dronfield, Derbyshire, S18 2XP Tel: (01246) 290890 Fax: (01246) 290292 E-mail: info@hodkin-jones.co.uk
Millfield F R P Ltd, Newburn Industrial Estate, Shelley Road, Newcastle upon Tyne, NE15 9RT Tel: 0191-264 8541 Fax: 0191-264 6962 E-mail: mail@millfield-group.co.uk

GLASS REPLACEMENT

Davian Designs, 81 Main Road, Waterside, Kilmarnock, Ayrshire, KA3 6JU Tel: (01563) 550091 Fax: (01563) 550091 E-mail: mark@davian79.fsnet.co.uk
▶ Glass Studio, 180 John Wilson Business Park, Chestfield, Whitstable, Kent, CT5 3RB Tel: (01227) 770613 Fax: (01227) 770613 E-mail: sales@theglassstudio.co.uk

GLASS SAFETY DOORS

Door Centre, Eastfield Industrial Estate, Penicuik, Midlothian, EH26 8HA Tel: (01968) 671680 Fax: (01968) 671684 E-mail: sales@thedoorcentre.co.uk
▶ Essex Safety Glass Ltd, Moss Road, Witham, Essex, CM8 3UQ Tel: (01376) 520061 Fax: (01376) 521176 E-mail: graeme.brouder@essexsafetyglass.co.uk
▶ Glass Studio, 180 John Wilson Business Park, Chestfield, Whitstable, Kent, CT5 3RB Tel: (01227) 770613 Fax: (01227) 770613 E-mail: sales@theglassstudio.co.uk

GLASS SCRATCH REMOVAL

▶ Glass Technics, Church Lane, Hartley Wespall, Basingstoke, Hampshire, RG27 0BB Tel: (01256) 882339 E-mail: tony@glasstechnics.co.uk

GLASS SURFACE PROTECTION SYSTEMS

Ritec International Ltd, 15 Royal London Estate, West Road, London, N17 0XL Tel: (020) 8885 5155 Fax: (020) 8885 5072 E-mail: admin@ritec.co.uk

GLASS TABLE TOPS

Nelder & Southam, Mulberry Street, Stratford-upon-Avon, Warwickshire, CV37 6RS Tel: (01789) 267974 Fax: (01789) 267974

GLASS TEMPERING FURNACES

Efco Group Ltd, 29 Avro Way, Brooklands Business Park, Weybridge, Surrey, KT13 0YZ Tel: (01932) 350534 Fax: (01932) 350543

GLASS TEMPERING SYSTEMS

Glasstech Ltd, PO Box 62, Worcester, WR4 9RQ Tel: (01905) 723663 Fax: (01905) 20400 E-mail: sales@glasstech.com

GLASS TEXTILES

Johns Manville, Unit 4 Roundwood Drive, Sherdley Road Industrial Estate, St. Helens, Merseyside, WA9 5JD Tel: (01744) 762500 Fax: (01744) 451076 E-mail: jeff.nash@jm.com

GLASS TO METAL SEALS

Micrometics Ltd, 26 Hollands Rd, Haverhill, Suffolk, CB9 8PR Tel: (01440) 707010 Fax: (01440) 762116 E-mail: info@micrometics.co.uk

GLASS TUBE PROCESSORS OR CONVERTERS

J T Nex Ltd, Griffin Industrial Estate, Rowley Regis, West Midlands, B65 0SN Tel: 0121-559 1777 Fax: 0121-561 5945 E-mail: alan@jtnex.co.uk

GLASS TUBES

Chance Glass Ltd, Pickersleigh Avenue, Malvern, Worcestershire, WR14 2LP Tel: (01684) 892353 Fax: (01684) 892647 E-mail: sales@chanceglass.co.uk

GLASS WINDOWS

▶ Christie's Emergency Glazing, 2 Trafalgar Road, Dartford, DA1 1NS Tel: (01322) 229874 Fax: (0845) 4309391 E-mail: john@glassforhome.com

GLASS WORKING EQUIPMENT OR TOOLS

Jepson Bolton & Co. Ltd, Suite 1, 186 St Albans Road, Watford, WD24 4AS Tel: (020) 8386 6853 Fax: (020) 8386 5130 E-mail: sales@jepbol.com

GLASS WORKING MACHINES

Ashton Industrial Sales Ltd, 4 Anderson Road, Woodford Green, Essex, IG8 8ET Tel: (020) 8551 4046 Fax: (020) 8551 1433 E-mail: ashton@ashton-industrial.com
Peter Hawkins Ltd, Castle Lane, Castle Street, Melbourne, Derby, DE73 8DY Tel: (01332) 864747 Fax: (01332) 864748 E-mail: sales@phawkins.co.uk
Jepson Bolton & Co. Ltd, Suite 1, 186 St Albans Road, Watford, WD24 4AS Tel: (020) 8386 6853 Fax: (020) 8386 5130 E-mail: sales@jepbol.com
Seco Engineering Co. Ltd, 32 Reading Road South, Fleet, Hampshire, GU52 7QL Tel: (01252) 622333 Fax: (01252) 623888 E-mail: sales@secoeng.co.uk

GLASS, PLATE, SHEET OR FLOAT

A & B Glassworks, 124 Stoke Newington High Street, London, N16 7NY Tel: (020) 7254 4541 Fax: (020) 7254 4541
A M Glazing (Contractors) Ltd, 440a Hornsey Road, London, N19 4EB Tel: (020) 7263 7796 Fax: (020) 7281 7112 E-mail: sales@amglazing.com
Art Glass Processing Ltd, Ripley Road, Bradford, West Yorkshire, BD4 7TP Tel: (01274) 393161 Fax: (01274) 393895
Artfull, 12 Victoria Terrace, London, N4 4DA Tel: (020) 7272 9341 Fax: (020) 7281 9252 E-mail: nnewglass@aol.com
B B Glass Ltd, 7a Buddle Road, Clay Flatts Industrial Estate, Workington, Cumbria, CA14 3YD Tel: (01900) 65445 Fax: (01900) 64789
Baldwin Glass Ltd, Spyvee St/Durban Street, Hull, HU8 7JU Tel: (01482) 223128 Fax: (01482) 586583
Balham Glass & Joinery, 260-262 Cavendish Road, London, SW12 0BT Tel: (020) 8675 1640 Fax: (020) 8657 6784 E-mail: balhamglass@btclick.com
Bell Glass, 2 Bloors Lane, Rainham, Gillingham, Kent, ME8 7EG Tel: (01634) 377776 Fax: (01634) 265813
Billenness Keith Ltd, 22 Birch Road, Eastbourne, East Sussex, BN23 6PD Tel: (01323) 411028 Fax: (01323) 411704 E-mail: keith@kbglass.fsnet.co.uk
Browns Glass & Glazing, 6 Silver Street, Bridgwater, Somerset, TA6 3EG Tel: (01278) 423157 Fax: (01278) 423157
Cameo Glass, Old Saw Mills Road, Faringdon, Oxfordshire, SN7 7DS Tel: (01367) 242421 Fax: (01367) 242978 E-mail: sales@camio-glass.com
Caplin Glass, Unit 9a Queens Yard, White Post Lane, London, E9 5EN Tel: (020) 8986 0047 Fax: (020) 8986 0455
Carters Glass Company Ltd, 14-16 Crouch End Hill, London, N8 8AA Tel: (020) 8340 2297
Cheadle Glass Co. Ltd, Adswood Road, Cheadle Hulme, Cheadle, Cheshire, SK8 5QA Tel: 0161-486 9333 Fax: 0161-486 9335
Chelsea Glass Ltd, 650 Portslade Road, London, SW8 3DH Tel: (020) 7720 6905 Fax: (020) 7978 2827
Chesham Glass Co., 1 Broad Street, Chesham, Buckinghamshire, HP5 3EA Tel: (01494) 792266 Fax: (01494) 782377
Chiswick Lane Glass Ltd, 44 Chiswick Lane, London, W4 2JQ Tel: (020) 8994 5779 Fax: (020) 8742 1467 E-mail: sales@chiswickglass.co.uk
County Glass Ltd, Easton Lane, Winchester, Hampshire, SO23 7RU Tel: (01962) 869447 Fax: (01962) 841532
Crawford Bros (Walthamstow) Ltd, 1A-3A Hoe St, London, E17 4SD Tel: (020) 8520 3981 Fax: (020) 8509 3158 E-mail: crawfordj@btconnect.com
Daylight Insulation Ltd, Brandleside, Dunlop, Kilmarnock, Ayrshire, KA3 4BJ Tel: (01560) 486688 Fax: (01560) 486699
Diamond Glass Works, Brown Street, Bolton, BL1 1TY Tel: (01204) 527853 Fax: (01204) 527853
Dorset Glass Co. Ltd, 51 Nuffield Road, Nuffield Industrial Estate, Poole, Dorset, BH17 0RJ Tel: (01202) 673926 Fax: (01202) 684394 E-mail: duncan@dorsetglass.co.uk
F E Moss Glass Ltd, 678 Green Lane, Ilford, Essex, IG3 9RX Tel: (020) 8590 5180 Fax: (020) 8599 1008
Flat Glass Ltd, 186 Wigan Road, Westhoughton, Bolton, BL5 2AG Tel: (01942) 813037 Fax: (01942) 812203 E-mail: info@flatglass.co.uk
▶ Flat Glass Merchants, Unit C, Cronin Road Weldon South Indust Estate, Weldon South Industrial Estate, Corby, Northamptonshire, NN18 8AG Tel: (01536) 268419 Fax: (01536) 268469E-mail: sales@flatglassmerchants.com
Glass Design Ltd, 51-63 Sangley Road, London, SE6 2DT Tel: (020) 8698 8811 Fax: (020) 8695 5181
Glass Express Ltd, Unit 1-2 Cobbswood Industrial Estate, Brunswick Road, Ashford, Kent, TN23 1EL Tel: (01233) 642220 Fax: (01233) 641475 E-mail: info@glassexpress.co.uk
Glass & Glazing Federation, 44-48 Borough High Street, London, SE1 1XB Tel: (020) 7403 7177 Fax: (020) 7357 7458 E-mail: info@ggf.org.uk
Glassex Holdings Ltd, Ailsa Street, London, E14 0LE Tel: (020) 7987 4191 Fax: (020) 7987 4194 E-mail: glassexltd@virgin.net
Great Yarmouth Glass, 113 Nelson Road Central, Great Yarmouth, Norfolk, NR30 2NJ Tel: (01493) 842323 Fax: (01493) 850913 E-mail: info@gyglass.co.uk
Greenberg Glass Ltd, Beddington Lane, Croydon, CR0 4TD Tel: (020) 8684 9207 Fax: (020) 8689 8189 E-mail: croydon@greenbergglass.co.uk
Harris Glass Ltd, St Albans Works, Commercial Road, Wolverhampton, WV1 3RD Tel: (01902) 452709 Fax: (01902) 455722 E-mail: anthony@harrisglass.fsnet.co.uk
Huddersfield Plate Glass Co. Ltd, 43 Spring Street, Huddersfield, HD1 4BA Tel: (01484) 535106 Fax: (01484) 535106 E-mail: sales@hpglass.com
Jack's Glass, 41-43 Princes Road, Hull, HU5 2QS Tel: (01482) 491989 Fax: (01482) 444581
Juno Glass Ltd, 50 Lydden Road, London, SW18 4LR Tel: (020) 8874 8949 Fax: (020) 8877 1353 E-mail: chris@junoglass.co.uk
K C Glass Ltd, Unit 23 Central Trading Estate, Cable Street, Wolverhampton, WV2 2RJ Tel: (01902) 457765 Fax: (01902) 456417 E-mail: sales@kcglass.co.uk
Kent Blaxill & Co. Ltd, 129-139 Layer Road, Colchester, CO2 9JY Tel: (01206) 216000 Fax: (01206) 762981 E-mail: sales@kentblaxill.co.uk
Leicester Glass Co. Ltd, 119-125 Bridge Road, Leicester, LE5 3QP Tel: 0116-276 8316 Fax: 0116-246 0462 E-mail: enquiries@leicesterglass.co.uk
Lombards Of Cheshunt Ltd, 25 High Street, Cheshunt, Waltham Cross, Hertfordshire, EN8 0BS Tel: (01992) 623160 Fax: (01992) 622422
McNeill-McManus Ltd, Hydepark Industrial Estate, Mallusk, Newtownabbey, County Antrim, BT36 4PX Tel: (028) 9084 2611 Fax: (028) 9034 2317 E-mail: mailbox@mcneill-mcmanus.com
Matthieson Bros, 177 Yardley Road, Acocks Green, Birmingham, B27 6LZ Tel: 0121-706 4915 Fax: 0121-764 5202
Merrick & Heath, Rolfe Street, Smethwick, West Midlands, B66 2AW Tel: 0121-558 1291 Fax: 0121-558 1291
Mirrors & Glass Stockport Ltd, 84 Wellington Road North, Stockport, Cheshire, SK4 1HW Tel: 0161-480 1875 Fax: 0161-480 7008 E-mail: sales@mirrorsandglass.co.uk
Nero Signs Glass/Designs Ltd, 332-334 Brixton Road, London, SW9 7AA Tel: (020) 7737 8021 Fax: (020) 7733 8589 E-mail: sales@nerodesigns.co.uk
Nicholls & Clarke Glass Ltd, Units 27 Gemini Business Park, Hornet Way, Beckton, London, E6 7FF Tel: (020) 7473 0999 Fax: (020) 7476 1017
Norman & Underwood Group Ltd, The Freeschool Building, 170 Scudamore Road, Leicester, LE3 1HP Tel: 0116-231 8000 Fax: 0116-231 8005E-mail: info@nandu.co.uk
Oddyssey Glass Ltd, High Level Way, Halifax, W. Yorkshire, HX1 4PR Tel: (01422) 359028 Fax: (01422) 347888 E-mail: info@oddysseyglass.co.uk
Padiham Glass Ltd, Glasstec Centre, Unit 10A Shuttleworth Mead Business Park, Padiham, Burnley, Lancashire, BB12 7NG Tel: (01282) 774124 Fax: (01282) 774951 E-mail: sales@padihamglass.co.uk
Parker & Osborn Ltd, 342 Summer Lane, Birmingham, B19 3QL Tel: 0121-359 8222 Fax: 0121-359 8555E-mail: parkosb@aol.com
Paxton Home Improvements, Goddards Yard, Thaxted Road, Saffron Walden, Essex, CB11 3AG Tel: (01799) 527542 Fax: (01799) 527541 E-mail: sales@paxtonsonline.com
Pearsons Glass Ltd, 9-11 Maddrell Street, Liverpool, L3 7EH Tel: 0151-207 2874 Fax: 0151-207 2110 E-mail: info@pearsonsglass.co.uk
Pilkington Automotives, Triplex House, Eckersall Road, Birmingham, B38 8SR Tel: 0121-254 3000 Fax: 0121-254 3188
Pilkington Birmingham, Nechells Park Road, Birmingham, B7 5NQ Tel: 0121-326 5300 Fax: 0121-328 4277 E-mail: john.hawkins@pilkington.com
Pilkington Glass, Unit 10 12, Sherrington Way, Basingstoke, Hampshire, RG22 4DQ Tel: (01256) 469651 Fax: (01256) 464047
Pilkington Plymouth, Plymbridge Road, Plymouth, PL6 7JS Tel: (01752) 761500 Fax: (01752) 761506 E-mail: sales@pilkington.com
Pilkington UK Ltd, Unit 26 Bermondsey Trading Estate, Rotherhithe New Road, London, SE16 3LE Tel: (020) 7252 0004 Fax: (020) 7237 1428 E-mail: glazing@pilkington.com
Pilkington UK Ltd, 2-6 Mallard Road, Victoria Business Park, Netherfield, Nottingham, NG4 2PE Tel: 0115-940 0980 Fax: 0115-961 7993
Pilkington UK Ltd, Orgreave Drive, Sheffield, S13 9NR Tel: 0114-254 0444 Fax: 0114-254 0861 E-mail: joanne.marlow@pilkington.com
Pope & Parr, 118-120 Talbot Street, Nottingham, NG1 5HH Tel: 0115-947 3015 Fax: 0115-950 3194
Profile Ltd, Sir Frank Whittle Road, Derby, DE21 4XE Tel: 01332 366900 Fax: (01332) 369613 E-mail: mail@profileuk.com
Putney Glass & Glazing, Arch 5 Deodar Road, London, SW15 2NP Tel: (020) 8870 0380 Fax: (020) 8874 6668
St. Ann's Building Supplies, Bentalls Close, Sutton Road, Southend-On-Sea, SS2 5PT Tel: (01702) 463363 Fax: (01702) 469043
▶ Schott UK Ltd, Drummond Road, Stafford, ST16 3EL Tel: (01785) 223166 Fax: (01785) 223522 E-mail: info.uk@schott.com
Solaglas Ltd, Guild House, Cradley Road, Dudley, West Midlands, DY2 9TH Tel: (01384) 411511 Fax: (01384) 411234 E-mail: midlandsales@solaglass.co.uk
Solaglas Ltd, Horton Road, West Drayton, Middlesex, UB7 8JL Tel: (01895) 424900 Fax: (01895) 421937 E-mail: solaglas.gpd@saint-gobain-glass.com
Therm Tempered Ltd, Unit E1 E2 Coedcae Lane Industrial Estate, Coedcae Lane, Pontyclun, Mid Glamorgan, CF72 9HG Tel: (01443) 228122 Fax: (01443) 233500 E-mail: sale@therm.co.uk
Vencel Resil Ltd, Infinity House, Anderson Way, Belvedere, Kent, DA17 6BG Tel: (020) 8320 9100 Fax: (020) 8320 9110 E-mail: sales@vencel.co.uk
W H Constable & Co. Ltd, 16 Barnwell Business Park, Barnwell Drive, Cambridge, CB5 8UZ Tel: (01223) 211888 Fax: (01223) 416888
W H Halmshaw Ltd, Pioneer Works, Goulton St, Hull, HU3 4AS Tel: (01482) 589689 Fax: (01482) 325084 E-mail: info@halmshaws.co.uk
Wilsons Glass Ltd, 6 St Marys Lane, Upminster, Essex, RM14 2QT Tel: (01708) 224215 Fax: (01708) 224215
Window Craft (Nuneaton) Ltd, Whitacre Road, Nuneaton, Warwickshire, CV11 6BY Tel: (024) 7638 4896 Fax: (024) 7638 4896
Wyvale Associates Ltd, Wilson Street, Southampton, SO14 5AY Tel: (023) 8063 8066 Fax: (023) 8033 3138

GLASSWARE, *See also headings for particular types*

Bradford Bar Supplies, Unit 2 Napoleon Business Park, Wakefield Road, Bradford, West Yorkshire, BD4 7NL Tel: (01274) 741739 Fax: (01274) 741739
▶ Bristol Blue Glass Ltd, 7 Whitby Road, Bristol, BS4 3QF Tel: 0117-972 0888 Fax: 0117-972 1050 E-mail: bristolblueglass@bristol-glass.co.uk
Centre Glass & Hygiene, Worrall Street, Salford, M5 4TH Tel: 0161-873 3000 Fax: 0161-877 2717 E-mail: zentreglassmail@aol.com
Dalton & Ditcham Agencies Ltd, Brent House, 3rd Floor Kenton Road, Harrow, Middlesex, HA3 8BT Tel: (020) 8909 3996 Fax: (020) 8909 2686 E-mail: dalton.ditcham@btinternet.com

GLASSWARE – *continued*

F. Eardley (Potteries) Ltd, Foley Works, Brocksford Street, Fenton, Stoke-on-Trent, ST4 3HF Tel: (01782) 313871 Fax: (01782) 325057

▶ Glass Scribe International Ltd, Spencer House, Caberfeidh Avenue, Dingwall, Ross-Shire, IV15 9TD Tel: (01349) 867088 Fax: (01349) 867089 E-mail: admin@glassscribe.com

Glassart, Cross Bank Farm, Burnt Fen, Freckenham, Bury St. Edmunds, Suffolk, IP28 8EA Tel: (01353) 675285 Fax: (01353) 675285 E-mail: sales@glassartuk.com

Thomas Goode & Co. Ltd, 19 South Audley Street, London, W1K 2BN Tel: (020) 7499 2823 Fax: (020) 7629 4230 E-mail: info@thomasgoode.com

Habasco International Ltd, Stafford Mills, George Street, Milnsbridge, Huddersfield, HD3 4JD Tel: (01484) 642115 Fax: (01484) 640058 E-mail: sales@habasco.net

Hargreaves & Son Ltd, 16-18 Spring Gardens, Buxton, Derbyshire, SK17 6DE Tel: (01298) 23083 Fax: (01298) 25323 E-mail: hargreaves.son@freeuk.com

Harry Hancock Bar & Catering Equipment, 12c Scott Lidgett Industrial Estate, Scott Lidgett Road, Stoke-on-Trent, ST6 4NQ Tel: (01782) 837303 Fax: (01782) 838612 E-mail: sales@hancocks-catering.co.uk

Harvey Reed Top Table Ltd, Sterling Way, Borehamwood, Hertfordshire, WD6 2BT Tel: (020) 8207 2666 Fax: (020) 8207 6173

J. Reuben Hobson & Co. Ltd, Albany House, 6 Wicker Lane, Sheffield, S3 8HQ Tel: 0114-272 1604 Fax: 0114-275 5567

Jacksons, Victory House, Cox Lane, Chessington, Surrey, KT9 1SG Tel: (020) 8391 5555 Fax: (020) 8391 5333 E-mail: info@jacksonscg.co.uk

Lesser & Pavey Ltd, Leonardo House Fawkes Avenue, Dartford Trade Park, Dartford, DA1 1JQ Tel: (01322) 279225 Fax: (01322) 279586 E-mail: sales@leonardo.co.uk

Lubkowski Saunders & Associates Designs & Exports Ltd, E Dolphin Estate, Windmill Road West, Sunbury-on-Thames, Middlesex, TW16 7HE Tel: (01932) 789721 Fax: (01932) 789793 E-mail: sales@lsa-international.co.uk

▶ Manor Direct Ltd, 27-31 Francis Street, Hull, HU2 8DT Tel: (01482) 586312 Fax: (01482) 585310 E-mail: sales@manorglass.co.uk

Payne Bros UK Ltd, 20 Beatrice Street, Warrington, WA4 1DR Tel: (01925) 418180 Fax: (01925) 411717 E-mail: warrington.sales@paynebros.com

R B Wholesale Ltd, The Broadway, Mansfield, Nottinghamshire, NG18 2RL Tel: (01623) 623247 Fax: (01623) 629311 E-mail: sales@rbwholesale.co.uk

Reject Pot Shop, 56 Chalk Farm Road, London, NW1 8AN Tel: (020) 7485 2326 Fax: (020) 7485 2326 E-mail: sales@rejectpotshop.co.uk

Solmedia Laboratory Supplies, 6 The Parade, Colchester Road, Romford, RM3 0AQ Tel: (01708) 343334 Fax: (01708) 372785 E-mail: labsupplies@solmedialtd.com

Trauffler, Unit 1, 307 Merton Road, London, SW18 5JS Tel: (020) 7251 0240 Fax: (020) 8874 8627 E-mail: sales@trauffler.com

W Watson & Sons, 165 High Street, Perth, PH1 5UP Tel: (01738) 639861 Fax: (01738) 634662 E-mail: watsonsofperth@aol.com

GLASSWARE IMPORT MERCHANTS OR AGENTS

Bohemia Crystal (UK) Ltd, Hammond Road, Elms Industrial Estate, Bedford, MK41 0UD Tel: (01234) 347069 Fax: (01234) 271553

C. Quitman Ltd, Ullswater Crescent, Coulsdon, Surrey, CR5 2HR Tel: (020) 8668 5295 Fax: (020) 8660 2589 E-mail: sales@cquitman.co.uk

Selco Crystal Ltd, The Bond Street Silver Galleries, 111-112 New Bond Street, London, W1S 1DP Tel: (0870) 3307215 Fax: (0870) 3301003 E-mail: info@selcocrystal.com

GLASSWARE TO SPECIFICATION

CPS Supply Co. Ltd, 5 Riverside Road, London, SW17 0BA Tel: (020) 8944 9016 Fax: (020) 8944 9018

J A Winward & Sons, Rear of, 120 High St South, London, E6 3RW Tel: (020) 8472 5986 Fax: (020) 8503 4743 E-mail: winward@btconnect.com

Teign Valley Glass, The Old Pottery, Pottery Road, Bovey Tracey, Newton Abbot, Devon, TQ13 9DS Tel: (01626) 835285 Fax: (01626) 835315 E-mail: info@houseofmarbles.com

GLAZED CANOPIES

▶ SFG Structural Facade Glazing, Cedar House, Cedar Lane, Frimley, Surrey, GU16 7HZ Tel: 01276 671815 Fax: 01276 678743 E-mail: info@sfgltd.com

GLAZED TRANSPARENT PAPER PRODUCTS, BAG/POCKET/TUBE ETC

Stonehouse Paper & Bag Mills Ltd, Lower Mills, Stonehouse, Gloucestershire, GL10 2BD Tel: (01453) 822173 Fax: (01453) 822174 E-mail: stonehousepaper@aol.com

GLAZING ACCESSORIES OR MATERIALS SUPPLIES TO THE TRADE

Carlton Building Plastics Ltd, 6 Beddington Trading Estate, Bath House Road, Croydon, CR0 4TT Tel: (020) 8665 1221 Fax: (020) 8665 1444

M C Building Chemicals, Stechford Trading Estate Lyndon Road, Unit 17, Stechford, Birmingham, B33 8BU Tel: 0121-789 8333 Fax: 0121-789 8595 E-mail: sales@mc-bauchemie.de

Robert Horne Group plc, Huntsman House, B2 Evelyn Street, London, SE8 5DL Tel: (020) 7231 9634 Fax: (020) 7231 5641

Robert Horne Group Plc, Huntsman House, Mansion Close, Moulton Park, Northampton, NN3 6LA Tel: (01604) 495333 Fax: (01604) 673495 E-mail: terry.cattle@roberthorne.co.uk

▶ Union Glass Centres Ltd, 1 Armada Street, Plymouth, PL4 8LS Tel: (01752) 664418 Fax: (01752) 225195 E-mail: info@unionglass.co.uk

GLAZING CONTRACTORS

A & B Glassworks, 124 Stoke Newington High Street, London, N16 7NY Tel: (020) 7254 4541 Fax: (020) 7254 4541

A C Yule & Son Ltd, Craigshaw Road, West Tullos Industrial Estate, Aberdeen, AB12 3ZG Tel: (01224) 230000 Fax: (01224) 230011 E-mail: admin@acyule.com

A M Glazing (Contractors) Ltd, 440a Hornsey Road, London, N19 4EB Tel: (020) 7263 7796 Fax: (020) 7281 7112 E-mail: sales@amglazing.com

A T Free & Co. Ltd, Jackson Street, St. Helens, Merseyside, WA9 1AH Tel: (01744) 22252 Fax: (01744) 453036

Addison Glass Works Ltd, 175 Walnut Tree Close, Guildford, Surrey, GU1 4TX Tel: (01483) 538480 Fax: (01483) 531273 E-mail: addisons@cix.compulink.co.uk

Advanced Woodford Glazing, Maybank Industrial Estate, Unit 10 Maybank Road, London, E18 1EJ Tel: (020) 8559 0900 Fax: (020) 8559 0933

All Regions, B 2 Miller Road, Bedford, MK42 9NY Tel: (01234) 355388 Fax: (01234) 355504 E-mail: all.regions@ntlworld.com

Andrew Wright, 4 Boundary Road, Heathfield Industrial Estate, Ayr, KA8 9DJ Tel: (01292) 611999 Fax: (01292) 610298

Ansoroy Ltd, 237 Railton Road, London, SE24 0LX Tel: (020) 7738 6030 Fax: (020) 7738 6030 E-mail: sales@ansoroy.co.uk

Art Glass Ltd, Ellis Ashton Street, Liverpool, L36 6BN Tel: 0151-489 2214 Fax: 0151-489 2214 E-mail: sales@artglass.co.uk

B & M Glazing Ltd, 330 Eastcote Lane, Harrow, Middlesex, HA2 9AJ Tel: (020) 8423 6031 Fax: (020) 8423 6171

Barretts Glass & Window Centre Ltd, 24a Edward Road, Dorchester, Dorset, DT1 2HL Tel: (01305) 264299 Fax: (01305) 260083 E-mail: sales@barrettsglass.com

Bell Glass, 2 Bloors Lane, Rainham, Gillingham, Kent, ME8 7EG Tel: (01634) 377776 Fax: (01634) 265813

Billenness Keith Ltd, 22 Birch Road, Eastbourne, East Sussex, BN23 6PD Tel: (01323) 411028 Fax: (01323) 411704 E-mail: keith@kbglass.fsnet.co.uk

Birmingham Glass Studios Ltd, Units 5 & 6 The Stained Glass Centre, 100-102 Edward Road, Balsall Heath, Birmingham, B12 9LS Tel: 0121-706 3131 Fax: 0121706 3130 E-mail: bhamglass@aol.com

Bishops Glass, 164-166 Main Road, Romford, RM2 5HT Tel: (01708) 744870 Fax: (01708) 733643

Bridgewater Glass, 44-52 Vicarage Road, Watford, WD18 0EN Tel: (01923) 237533 Fax: (01923) 817118 E-mail: bridgewaterglass@aol.com

C & W Summers, 131 Sydney Street, Glasgow, G31 1JF Tel: 0141-554 7997 Fax: 0141-556 2882

Cab Glazing Services, Unit D3, Button End Industrial Estate, Harston, Cambridge, CB2 5NX Tel: (01223) 872400 Fax: (01223) 872866 E-mail: sales@cabglazing.co.uk

Camberley Glass Ltd, 453 London Road, Camberley, Surrey, GU15 3JA Tel: (01276) 684444 Fax: (01276) 28277 E-mail: sales@camberleyglass.co.uk

Chiswick Lane Glass Ltd, 44 Chiswick Lane, London, W4 2JQ Tel: (020) 8994 5779 Fax: (020) 8742 1467 E-mail: sales@chiswickglass.co.uk

Cornpool Ltd, 174 Station Road, March, Cambs, PE15 8NG Tel: (01354) 655200 Fax: (01354) 656421

County Glass Ltd, Easton Lane, Winchester, Hampshire, SO23 7RU Tel: (01962) 869447 Fax: (01962) 841532

Cyril Isaacs & Co. Ltd, 1 Apex Way, Leeds, LS11 5LN Tel: 0113-245 4143 Fax: 0113-245 0486

D Glass, 9 Artillery Road, Lufton Trading Estate, Lufton, Yeovil, Somerset, BA22 8RP Tel: (01935) 471359 Fax: (01935) 420464

Dailly Glazing & Interiors, 15 Mains Road, Dundee, DD3 7RH Tel: (01382) 825400 Fax: (01382) 832978 E-mail: dailly.glazing@btconnect.com

▶ DMC Glass & Glazing, 36 Marbles Way, Tadworth, Surrey, KT20 5LG Tel: (01737) 212687 Fax: (01737) 212687 E-mail: dmcglazingservices@hotmail.co.uk

Dorset Glass Co. Ltd, 51 Nuffield Road, Nuffield Industrial Estate, Poole, Dorset, BH17 0RJ Tel: (01202) 673926 Fax: (01202) 684394 E-mail: duncan@dorsetglass.co.uk

E.N.L Audio Visual, Alfreton Road, Nottingham, NG7 3NR Tel: 0115-924 8305 Fax: 0115-924 8329 E-mail: sales@hotkit.co.uk

E R Wright & Son, 53 Millbrook Road East, Southampton, SO15 1HN Tel: (023) 8022 3334 Fax: (023) 8063 1956 E-mail: erwrightandson@tiscali.co.uk

L.R. Easton & Co. Ltd, 5 & 7 Hollytree Parade, Sidcup Hill, Footscray, Sidcup, Kent, DA14 6JR Tel: (020) 8300 3955 Fax: (020) 8302 2562

▶ Elders Walker Glass Ltd, Glasscraft House, Mcnay Street, Darlington, County Durham, DL3 6SP Tel: (01325) 463354 Fax: (01325) 489232 E-mail: peterkelly5@netscape.net

Empire Glass Co. Ltd, Unit 17, Saville Rd, Peterborough, PE3 7PR Tel: (01733) 260880 Fax: (01733) 262458

Excalibur Glass & Windows Ltd, 137 Ringwood Road, Poole, Dorset, BH14 0RH Tel: (01202) 743144 Fax: (01202) 716449 E-mail: sales@glassandwindows.co.uk

Forsyth Glazing Ltd, 30 London Road, Glasgow, G1 5NB Tel: 0141-552 5343 Fax: 0141-552 5133

John Frackelton & Son Ltd, 30c Sydney Street West, Belfast, BT13 1RP Tel: (028) 9035 1049 Fax: (028) 9074 5312

▶ Glass Doctor, 56 Little Glen Road, Glen Parva, Leicester, LE2 9TS Tel: (0800) 6346494 Fax: 0116-299 1898 E-mail: info@glassandlock.co.uk

Glass Express Ltd, Unit 1-2 Cobbswood Industrial Estate, Brunswick Road, Ashford, Kent, TN23 1EL Tel: (01233) 642220 Fax: (01233) 641475 E-mail: info@glassexpress.co.uk

Great Yarmouth Glass, 113 Nelson Road Central, Great Yarmouth, Norfolk, NR30 2NJ Tel: (01493) 842323 Fax: (01493) 850913 E-mail: info@gyglass.co.uk

Greenberg Glass Ltd, 10 Bard St, Birmingham, B11 4SA Tel: 0121-753 1900 Fax: 0121-772 3683 E-mail: website@greenbergglass.co.uk

Greenberg Glass Ltd, Beddington Lane, Croydon, CR0 4TD Tel: (020) 8684 9207 Fax: (020) 8689 8189 E-mail: croydon@greenbergglass.co.uk

Greenberg Glass Contract Ltd, unit 33 Dunes Way, Liverpool, L5 9RJ Tel: 0151-207 2574 Fax: 0151-298 1050

H Dobson Ltd, 26-28 West Row, Stockton-on-Tees, Cleveland, TS18 1BN Tel: (01642) 676480 Fax: (01642) 670698 E-mail: sales@dobsonglass.co.uk

Hanwell Glass Co. Ltd, 183 Uxbridge Road, London, W7 3TH Tel: (020) 8567 2186 Fax: (020) 8840 0042

Harris Glass Ltd, St Albans Works, Commercial Road, Wolverhampton, WV1 3RD Tel: (01902) 452709 Fax: (01902) 455722 E-mail: anthony@harrisglass.fsnet.co.uk

Howells Glazing, Clock House, Forge Lane, Cradley Heath, West Midlands, B64 5AL Tel: (01384) 820060 Fax: (01384) 820061 E-mail: enquiries@howellsglazing.co.uk

J Preedy & Sons Ltd, Lamb Works, North Road, London, N7 9DP Tel: (020) 7700 0377 Fax: (020) 7700 7579 E-mail: sales@preedyglass.com

▶ Jackson Glass, 25 Robinson Road, High Wycombe, Bucks, HP13 7BL Tel: 01494 812207 Fax: 0870 1367557 E-mail: enquiries@jacksonglass.co.uk

James Pearson & Co West Bromwich Ltd, Mount Pleasant Street, West Bromwich, West Midlands, B70 7DL Tel: 0121-553 3580 Fax: 0121-553 7903

Juno Glass Ltd, 50 Lydden Road, London, SW18 4LR Tel: (020) 8874 8949 Fax: (020) 8877 1353 E-mail: chris@junoglass.co.uk

L F Moon Ltd, Unit 12 Brickfields, Liverpool, L36 6HY Tel: 0151-480 5848 Fax: 0151-480 8339

Ledlite Glass Ltd, 168 London Road, Southend-on-Sea, SS1 1PH Tel: (01702) 345893 Fax: (01702) 435099 E-mail: sales@ledlite-glass.co.uk

Leicester Glass Co. Ltd, 119-125 Bridge Road, Leicester, LE5 3QP Tel: 0116-276 8316 Fax: 0116-246 0462 E-mail: enquiries@leicesterglass.co.uk

Luton Glass, 2b Miller Road, Bedford, MK42 9NY Tel: (01582) 726000 Fax: (01582) 480980 E-mail: info@allregionsglazing.co.uk

Mackenzie Glass, Grace Road, Marsh Barton Trading Estate, Exeter, EX2 8QE Tel: (01392) 258538 Fax: (01392) 420096 E-mail: mackenzieglass@btinternet.com

Matthieson Bros, 177 Yardley Road, Acocks Green, Birmingham, B27 6LZ Tel: 0121-706 4915 Fax: 0121-764 5202

Merseyside Multi Glazing Ltd, St Michaels Industrial Estate, Widnes, Cheshire, WA8 8TL Tel: 0151-424 7070 Fax: 0151-420 6944 E-mail: contact@multiglazing.co.uk

Milton Keynes City Glaziers Ltd, Vicarage Road, Stony Stratford, Milton Keynes, MK11 1BN Tel: (01908) 563866 Fax: (01908) 560102 E-mail: jackie@mkcg.freeserve.co.uk

Norman & Underwood Group Ltd, The Freeschool Building, 170 Scudamore Road, Leicester, LE3 1HP Tel: 0116-231 8000 Fax: 0116-231 8005E-mail: info@nandu.co.uk

Northolt Glass Co. Ltd, 151-159 Church Road, Northolt, Middlesex, UB5 5AG Tel: (020) 8841 6989 Fax: (020) 8842 1944 E-mail: n.glass@talk21.com

Paignton Glassworks Ltd, 16 Marldon Road, Paignton, Devon, TQ3 3QZ Tel: (01803) 558096 Fax: (01803) 522044 E-mail: enquiries@paigntonglass.co.uk

Panoramic Window & Door Centre, 2 Richmond Road, Mangotsfield, Bristol, BS16 9HB Tel: 0117-956 0321 Fax: 0117-956 0456 E-mail: info@panoramicwindows.co.uk

Park Glass Supplies Ltd, 139 Kings Road, Kingston upon Thames, Surrey, KT2 5JE Tel: (020) 8546 8737 Fax: (020) 8546 4001

Pilkington UK Ltd, Orgreave Drive, Sheffield, S13 9NR Tel: 0114-254 0444 Fax: 0114-254 0861 E-mail: joanne.marlow@pilkington.com

Priory Glass Centre, Dormston Trading Estate, Burton Road, Dudley, West Midlands, DY1 2UF Tel: (01902) 665999 Fax: (01902) 663300

R H W Spooner Glass Merchants Ltd, 203 Gillingham Road, Gillingham, Kent, ME7 4EX Tel: (01634) 851848 Fax: (01634) 575105 E-mail: sales@spooners.sagehost.co.uk

▶ R S Sykes & Co. Ltd, 2 Warlingham Court Farm, Tithepit Shaw Lane, Warlingham, Surrey, CR6 9AT Tel: (01883) 626757 Fax: (01883) 622618 E-mail: sales@rssykes.co.uk

Douglas Rae, 55 Regent Street, Greenock, Renfrewshire, PA15 4NP Tel: (01475) 723469 Fax: (01475) 723469

Rankins Glass Company Ltd, 24-34 Pearson Street, London, E2 8JD Tel: (020) 7729 4200 Fax: (020) 7729 7135 E-mail: sales@rankinsglass.co.uk

Regency Glass, Hope Carr Industrial Estate, Butt St, Leigh, Lancashire, WN7 3XA Tel: (01942) 262162 Fax: (01942) 261555 E-mail: dean@regencyglass.co.uk

Ringwood Glass, 14 Lions Wood, St. Leonards, Ringwood, Hampshire, BH24 2LU Tel: (01425) 478445 Fax: (01425) 478484

River Street Glassworks, Bridgeman Street, Bolton, BL3 6BS Tel: (01204) 454444 Fax: (01204) 454445

Robsons Glass, 101 Church Road, Formby, Liverpool, L37 3ND Tel: (01704) 875855 Fax: (01704) 875855

Roman Glass Hereford Ltd, 6 Berrington Street, Hereford, HR4 0BJ Tel: (01432) 272764 Fax: (01432) 358511 E-mail: hereford@romanglass.co.uk

S Clarke & Son, 1 Kennel Lane, Newtownards, County Down, BT23 7HR Tel: (028) 9182 0333 Fax: (028) 9182 0333

S J H Sparkes & Sons Ltd, 20 Devonshire Road, Cambridge, CB1 2BH Tel: (01223) 356172 Fax: (01223) 356172

Safety Glass Replacements Ltd, Garden Street, Newcastle, Staffordshire, ST5 1BW Tel: (01782) 614693 Fax: (01782) 614633

St. Albans Glass, 19A Elstow Road, Bedford, MK42 9NU Tel: (01727) 830325 Fax: (01582) 480980

Saper Glass Industries Ltd, Thames House, Longreach Road, Barking, Essex, IG11 0JR Tel: (020) 8594 5757 Fax: (020) 8594 5252 E-mail: info@saperglass.co.uk

Shaws Glass Ltd, 66 North Street, Horsham, West Sussex, RH12 1RD Tel: (01403) 211133 Fax: (01293) 852340

Sheerwater Glass Centre, 23-27 Dartmouth Avenue, Woking, Surrey, GU21 5PE Tel: (01932) 349247 Fax: (01932) 346580

Southern Counties Glass, Unit I Foundry Close, Horsham, West Sussex, RH13 5TX Tel: (01403) 264723 Fax: (01403) 268153 E-mail: derek@southerncountiesglass.co.uk

Space Decks Holdings Ltd, Leach Road, Chard Business Park, Chard, Somerset, TA20 1FA Tel: (01460) 260800 Fax: (01460) 66123 E-mail: skysystems@spacedecks.co.uk

Tankersley Properties, 6 Henshall Street, Barnsley, South Yorkshire, S70 1XX Tel: (01226) 286361 Fax: (01226) 286361

Harry Thow & Co., 11 Crown Street, Ayr, KA8 8AG Tel: (01292) 264115 Fax: (01292) 282531 E-mail: h.thow@connectfree.co.uk

Tolland Glass & Windows, 11 Tudor Parade, Well Hall Road, London, SE9 6SX Tel: (020) 8850 9236 Fax: (020) 8294 0036

Treforest Glass, Units 9 & 10, Upper Boat Industrial Park, Pontypridd, Mid Glamorgan, CF37 5BP Tel: (01443) 841313 Fax: (01443) 841221E-mail: enquiries@treforestglass.co.uk

Universal Glass Co, 8-16 Camelon Street, Glasgow, G32 6AF Tel: 0141-764 0444 Fax: 0141-764 0044 E-mail: universalglass@btinternet.com

W G Spink & Sons, 1 Harrow Road, Hereford, HR4 0EH Tel: (01432) 272575 Fax: (01432) 342361

W J Richardson Glazing Ltd, 46 Glebe Way, West Wickham, Kent, BR4 0RL Tel: (020) 8777 6330 Fax: (020) 8777 4453

Warner Glass Croydon Ltd, 431 Brighton Road, South Croydon, Surrey, CR2 6YG Tel: (020) 8660 9271 Fax: (020) 8668 0374

GLAZING CONTRACTORS – *continued*

Wessex Glass Co. Ltd, 42 Stanley Hill, Bristol, BS4 3BA Tel: 0117-977 4012 Fax: 0117-977 2526

Wilson Glass & Mirror, Weston Road, Norwich, NR3 3WG Tel: (01603) 415400 Fax: (01603) 415401 E-mail: wilsonglass@btconnect.com

Windglass Windows Ltd, 536 Kingston Road, London, SW20 8DT Tel: (020) 8540 8848 Fax: (020) 8540 8065 E-mail: windows.windglass@virgin.net

▶ Winkhaus UK Ltd, 2950 Kettering Parkway, Kettering Venture Park, Kettering, Northamptonshire, NN15 6XZ Tel: (01536) 316000 Fax: (01536) 416516

GLAZING CONTRACTORS, LARGE APPLICATIONS

▶ DMC Glass & Glazing, 36 Marbles Way, Tadworth, Surrey, KT20 5LG Tel: (01737) 212687 Fax: (01737) 212687 E-mail: dmcglazingservices@hotmail.co.uk

GLAZING GASKETS

Collins Extrusions Ltd, Bidavon Industrial Estate, Waterloo Road, Bidford-on-Avon, Alcester, Warwickshire, B50 4JW Tel: (01789) 773536 Fax: (01789) 490225 E-mail: coltec1@yahoo.com

Polyplas Extrusions Ltd, Unit 1 Wilden Industrial Estate, Wilden Lane, Stourport-on-Severn, Worcestershire, DY13 9JY Tel: (0845) 5314086 Fax: (01299) 827016 E-mail: info@polyplas.co.uk

Slottseal Extrusions Ltd, Tyne Road, Weadon Road Industrial Estate, Northampton, NN5 5AF Tel: (01604) 759535 Fax: (01604) 752780 E-mail: tecplastics@btinternet

Tag Plastic Extrusions Ltd, 21 Marsh Green Road North, Marsh Barton Trading Estate, Exeter, EX2 8NY Tel: (01392) 479036 Fax: (01392) 432835

GLAZING MAINTENANCE CONTRACTORS

▶ Jackson Glass, 25 Robinson Road, High Wycombe, Bucks, HP13 7BL Tel: 01494 812207 Fax: 0870 1367557 E-mail: enquiries@jacksonglass.co.uk

GLAZING SYSTEMS OR UNITS FABRICATORS

Astrofade Ltd, Kyle Road, Gateshead, Tyne & Wear, NE8 2YE Tel: 0191-420 0515 Fax: 0191-460 4185 E-mail: sales@astrofade.co.uk

County Glass Ltd, Easton Lane, Winchester, Hampshire, SO23 7RU Tel: (01962) 869447 Fax: (01962) 841532

Daylight Insulation Ltd, Brandleside, Dunlop, Kilmarnock, Ayrshire, KA3 4BJ Tel: (01560) 486688 Fax: (01560) 486699

Duplus Architectural Systems Ltd, 370 Melton Road, Leicester, LE4 7SL Tel: 0116-261 0710 Fax: 0116-261 0539 E-mail: sales@duplus.co.uk

Charles Henshaw & Sons Ltd, Russell Road, Edinburgh, EH11 2LS Tel: 0131-337 4204 Fax: 0131-346 2441 E-mail: admin@charles-henshaw.co.uk

Lonsdale Metal Industries, Unit 40 Milmead Industrial Centre, Mill Mead Road, London, N17 9QU Tel: (020) 8801 4221 Fax: (020) 8801 1287 E-mail: info@lonsdalemetal.co.uk

New Image Windows, Unit 1 Wood Street, Warsop, Mansfield, Nottinghamshire, NG20 0AX Tel: (01623) 842727 Fax: (01623) 842727

▶ Scott James Glass Ltd, 12A-14 Armstrong Close, St. Leonards-On-Sea, East Sussex, TN38 9ST Tel: (01424) 854161 Fax: (01424) 853418

GLAZING TAPES

▶ Industrial Tape Solutions Ltd, 2-6 Station Road, Shipley, West Yorkshire, BD18 2JL Tel: (01274) 592244 Fax: (01274) 591144 E-mail: sales@tapesolutions.co.uk

Tremco Illbruck Production Ltd, 393 Edinburgh Avenue, Slough, SL1 4UF Tel: (01753) 691696 Fax: (01753) 822640

Vitec, Oldham Road, Middleton, Manchester, M24 2DB Tel: 0161-653 8231 Fax: 0161-654 8942 E-mail: vitec@kay-metzeler.co.uk

GLAZING WINDOWS

▶ Custom Glass Ltd, Unit 2, Custom Complex, Yardley Road, Liverpool, L33 7SS Tel: 0151-549 1264 E-mail: sales@customglass.co.uk

GLITTER POWDER

Ronald Britton & Co., Lower Eccleshill Road, Darwen, Lancashire, BB3 0RP Tel: (01254) 874750 Fax: (01254) 873009 E-mail: lara.thornhill@r-britton.com

Brian Clegg Educational Products Ltd, Regent Mill, Regent Street, Rochdale, Lancashire, OL12 0HQ Tel: (01706) 666620 Fax: (01706) 666621 E-mail: office@brianclegg.co.uk

Colourmaster, Stock Lane, Peel St, Chadderton, Oldham, OL9 9EY Tel: 0161-624 9479 Fax: 0161-678 8877 E-mail: sales@colour-master.co.uk

GLOBAL POSITIONING SYSTEMS (GPS)

▶ DogEgg Ltd, Network House, Bolton Road, Pendlebury, Swinton, Manchester, M27 8BB Tel: 0161-728 4666 Fax: (07869) 078013 E-mail: sales@dogegg.net

▶ Souterrain Archaeological Services Ltd, 50 Rectory Drive, Exhall, Coventry, CV7 9PD Tel: (024) 7631 1567 Fax: (01794) 523528 E-mail: gps@souterrain.biz

Terrafix Ltd, Unit 23c Newfields Industrial Estate, High Street, Stoke-on-Trent, ST6 5PD Tel: (01782) 577015 Fax: (01782) 835667 E-mail: sales@terrafix.co.uk

Toad plc, National Control Centre, Drake Road, Mitcham, Surrey, CR4 4HQ Tel: (020) 8710 7770 Fax: (020) 8710 7708 E-mail: info@toad.co.uk

GLOBAL POSITIONING SYSTEMS (GPS) VEHICLE STATUS MONITORING

▶ Digicore, Sage House, 319 Pinner Road, Harrow, Middlesex, HA1 4HF Tel: (020) 8515 2900 Fax: (020) 8861 3888 E-mail: mark.naldrett@digicore.co.uk

▶ GPS4Less, The Chimneys, Dauntsey Lock, Chippenham, Wiltshire, SN15 4HD Tel: (0845) 4309207 Fax: (0845) 4309208 E-mail: sales@gps4less.co.uk

▶ Mobile Tracking Systems, 1-2 Kingdom Close, Fareham, Hampshire, PO15 5TJ Tel: (01489) 571600 E-mail: admin@mtsgroup.co.uk

Siemens V D O Trading Ltd, Wiltshire House County Park, Shrivenham Road, Swindon, SN1 2NR Tel: (01793) 500100 Fax: (01793) 500101E-mail: sales@siemens-datatrack.com

Talk Telecom Ltd, Unit 35 City Industrial Park, Southern Road, Southampton, SO15 1HG Tel: (023) 8071 8730 Fax: (023) 8071 8738

GLOBAL POSITIONING SYSTEMS (GPS), PORTABLE

▶ Adventure Electronics, 46 Back Lane, Baxenden, Accrington, Lancashire, BB5 2RE Tel: 01254 399731 Fax: 01254 399731 E-mail: info@adventureelectronics.co.uk

Gadget & Gizmos, North Gate Business Centre, North Gate, Newark, Nottinghamshire, NG24 1EZ Tel: 01636 642855 Fax: 01636 862400E-mail: info@gadget-and-gizmos.co.uk

▶ Marcle Leisure .Co.Uk, Huntleys Farm Lane, Much Marcle, Ledbury, Herefordshire, HR8 2NB Tel: (01531) 660797 Fax: (01531) 660462 E-mail: mail@marcleleisure.co.uk

▶ Smarttalk Communications, 23 Burlington Lane, London, W4 2RN Tel: (020) 8742 0321 Fax: 0870 2854888 E-mail: solutions@smarttalkuk.com

▶ SuperEtrader, PO Box 4788, Walsall, WS1 9DZ Tel: (0870) 4438446 Fax: (0870) 4438445 E-mail: sales@superetrader.co.uk

▶ Watchkeeper Security, Guggleton Farm, Station Road, Stalbridge, Sturminster Newton, Dorset, DT10 2RQ Tel: 01258 817743 Fax: 01747 841556 E-mail: info@watchkeepersecurity.co.uk

GLOBAL SYSTEM FOR MOBILE COMMUNICATION (GSM) MODEMS

SeNd Technology Ltd, Hunters End, Cox Green Lane, Maidenhead, Berkshire, SL6 3EU Tel: (0870) 4587363 Fax: (07092) 383861 E-mail: sales@sendtech.co.uk

GLOBAL SYSTEM FOR MOBILE COMMUNICATION (GSM) SURVEILLANCE UNITS

▶ G A P, 88 Castle Street, Portchester, Fareham, Hampshire, PO16 9QG Tel: (023) 9238 6602 Fax: (023) 9261 7230 E-mail: gerry@mobilarm.co.uk

GLOBE CONTROL VALVES

▶ Schuf UK Ltd, 157 Park Road, Teddington, Middlesex, TW11 0BP Tel: (020) 8977 2992 Fax: (020) 8943 3898 E-mail: sales@schuf.co.uk

▶ Wealden Engineering Services Ltd, The Coach House, Harts Green, Sedlescombe, Battle, East Sussex, TN33 0RS Tel: (01424) 870500 Fax: (0870) 4604089 E-mail: patrick@wealden-services.com

GLOBE VALVE DESIGN

▶ TC Fluid Control Ltd, Broadgate, Broadway Business Park, Oldham, OL9 9XA Tel: 0161-684 7488 Fax: 0161-684 7487 E-mail: info@tc-fluidcontrol.com

GLOBE VALVES

Hattersley Newman Hender Ltd, 2 Burscough Road, Ormskirk, Lancashire, L39 2XG Tel: (01695) 577199 Fax: (01695) 578775 E-mail: uksales@hattersley.com

Peter Smith Valve Co. Ltd, Occupation Road, Nottingham, NG6 8RX Tel: 0115-927 2831 Fax: 0115-977 0233 E-mail: sales@petersmithvalve.co.uk

Taylor Shaw, Albert St, Lockwood, Huddersfield, HD1 3QG Tel: (01484) 532425 Fax: (01484) 512426 E-mail: sales@taylor-shaw.co.uk

Transmark FCX Ltd, Heaton House, Riverside Drive, Hunsworth Lane, Bradford, West Yorkshire, BD19 4DH Tel: (01274) 700000 Fax: (01274) 700152 E-mail: jhill@heaton-valves.co.uk

W T Armatur UK Ltd, Singleton Court Business Centre, Wonastow Road Industrial Estate (West), Monmouth, Gwent, NP25 5JA Tel: (01600) 712178 Fax: (01600) 712179

GLOVE BOX ACCESSORIES

Marine & Industrial Plastics Ltd, Unit D/1, Segensworth Business Centre, Segensworth Road, Fareham, Hampshire, PO15 5RQ Tel: (01329) 847443 Fax: (01329) 847451 E-mail: sales@mipltd.co.uk

GLOVE BOX SYSTEMS

Applied Containment Engineering Ltd, Unit 4, Shaw Cross Business Park, Dewsbury, West Yorkshire, WF12 7RF Tel: (01924) 455339 Fax: (01924) 452295 E-mail: applied.containment@ace-ltd.com

Bassaire Ltd, Duncan Road, Park Gate, Southampton, SO31 1ZS Tel: (01489) 885111 Fax: (01489) 885211 E-mail: sales@bassaire.co.uk

Marine & Industrial Plastics Ltd, Unit D/1, Segensworth Business Centre, Segensworth Road, Fareham, Hampshire, PO15 5RQ Tel: (01329) 847443 Fax: (01329) 847451 E-mail: sales@mipltd.co.uk

▶ Saffron Scientific Equipment Ltd, GSPK Technology Park, Manse Lane, Knaresborough, North Yorkshire, HG5 8LF Tel: (01423) 796138 Fax: (01423) 798268 E-mail: sales@saffron-uk.com

GLOVE FABRICS

Southcombe Bros Ltd, Cole Lane, Stoke-sub-Hamdon, Somerset, TA14 6QD Tel: (01935) 823567 Fax: (01935) 822918 E-mail: sales@southcombe.com

GLOVE MANUFACTURING SUPPLIES WHOLESALERS

▶ Briers Horticultural Equipment, 1 St. Martins Courtyard, Chapel Lane, Zeals, Warminster, Wiltshire, BA12 6NZ Tel: (0870) 8015650 Fax: (0870) 8015651 E-mail: sales@briersuk.com

Capemist Gloves Ltd, 158 Fenaghy Road, Cullybackey, Ballymena, County Antrim, BT42 1DZ Tel: (028) 2588 1190 Fax: (028) 2588 1682E-mail: capemist.gloves@virgin.net

Denholm Glove Co., Eastgate, Denholm, Hawick, Roxburghshire, TD9 8NQ Tel: (01450) 870597 Fax: (01450) 870597

Handfield Accessories Ltd, 2 Industrial Centre, Gower Street, Ipswich, IP2 8EX Tel: (01473) 686846 Fax: (01473) 686846

Stanley Roberts Ltd, Townsend, Montacute, Somerset, TA15 6XH Tel: (01935) 822645 Fax: (01935) 822645

GLOVES, *See also headings for particular types*

▶ A V Trading Co., 22 St Lukes Terrace, Sunderland, SR4 6NQ Tel: 0191-565 6136 Fax: 0191-565 6136 E-mail: avtrad@yahoo.co.uk

Boardman Bros Ltd, 50 Red Bank, Manchester, M4 4HF Tel: 0161-832 2381 Fax: 0161-833 2456 E-mail: reception@boardmanbros.co.uk

Dents, Fairfield Road, Warminster, Wiltshire, BA12 9DL Tel: (01985) 212291 Fax: (01985) 216435 E-mail: dents@dents.co.uk

▶ Eastman (UK) Ltd, Suite 1, Wesley House, Unit 2 Chapel Lane, Birstall, Batley, West Yorkshire, WF17 9EJ Tel: (0870) 7503003 Fax: (0870) 7503004 E-mail: sales@eastmanuk.copm

Reynolds & Kent Ltd, Unit 5 Wessex Business Centre, Meadow Lane, Westbury, Wiltshire, BA13 3EG Tel: (01373) 864767 Fax: (01373) 858697 E-mail: rnkglobes@aol.com

GLOVES, LEATHER WORKING

▶ Awanstars Leather Fashion, 42 Foxton Road, Birmingham, B8 3HP Tel: (0781) 2817248 E-mail: awanstars@yahoo.co.uk

GLOVES, MEDICAL/SURGICAL

C.G.R. Polythene Company Ltd, Unit 72 Powder Mill Lane, Questor Trade Park, Dartford, DA1 1JA Tel: (01322) 292681 Fax: (0845) 6800084 E-mail: gary@cgrpolythene.co.uk

Depuy International Holdings Ltd, St Anthonys Road, Beeston, Leeds, LS11 8DT Tel: 0113-270 0461 Fax: 0113-272 4101 E-mail: depuy@dpygb.jnj.com

Medisavers Ltd, Southgate Way, Orton, Peterborough, PE2 6YQ Tel: (01733) 361414 Fax: (01733) 230030 E-mail: sales@medisavers.co.uk

Phoenix Dental Castings Ltd, Unit 1 The Alpha Centre, Osprey Road, Sowton Industrial Estate, Exeter, EX2 7LH Tel: (01392) 444456 Fax: (01392) 445725 E-mail: phoenix.dental@btinternet.com

Semperit Industrial Products Ltd, Cottesbrooke Park, Heartlands Business Park, Daventry, Northamptonshire, NN11 8YL Tel: (01327) 313140 Fax: (01327) 313149 E-mail: paul.phillips@semperit.co.uk

GLOVES, MOTORCYCLE

▶ Beck Powersports, Suite 2, 27 Colmore Row, Birmingham, B3 2EW Tel: 0121 557 8837 Fax: 08701 257572 E-mail: info@beckpowersports.co.uk

▶ Gaz Bikes, Beckfield Arabians, Midville Lane, Stickney, Boston, Lincolnshire, PE22 8DN Tel: 08456 434310 Fax: 08456 434310 E-mail: sales@gazbikes.co.uk

GLUCOSE REFINERS

Cargill P.L.C., Cargill, Guiness Road, Trafford Park, Manchester, M17 1PA Tel: 0161-872 5959 Fax: 0161-848 9034 E-mail: graham_fletcher@cargill.com

GLUE DOTS

Fantas Tak Ltd, 2-6 Station Road, Shipley, West Yorkshire, BD18 2JL Tel: (01274) 466666 Fax: (01274) 466664 E-mail: sales@fantastak.com

Viking Industrial Products Ltd, 1 Coronation Business Centre, Hard Ings Road, Keighley, West Yorkshire, BD21 3ND Tel: (01535) 610373 Fax: (01535) 616231 E-mail: sales@vikingtapes.co.uk

GO KART COMPONENT CASTINGS

▶ Pacer Leisure Vehicles Ltd, Unit 10 Bates Industrial Estate, Wycombe Road, Stokenchurch, High Wycombe, Buckinghamshire, HP14 3RQ Tel: (01494) 484664 Fax: (01494) 484424 E-mail: sales@pacerleisure.co.uk

GOLD BLOCKING/STAMPING/PRINTING SERVICES

▶ Abacus Presentation Services, Unit 5 Hermitage Road, London, N4 1LZ Tel: (020) 8211 1600 Fax: (020) 8211 1600 E-mail: info@abacuspresentationservices.co.uk

Chapman & Mellor, 20 Hockley Hill, Birmingham, B18 5AQ Tel: 0121-554 3778 Fax: 0121-554 7931 E-mail: sales@foilprinters.co.uk

Crown Gold Blocking Co. Ltd, 63 Camden Street, Birmingham, B1 3DD Tel: 0121-233 1670 Fax: 0121-233 1670

Foil Ribbon & Impact Printing Scotland Ltd, 4 Rutherford Court, 15 North Avenue, Clydebank Business Park, Clydebank, Dunbartonshire, G81 2QP Tel: 0141-952 5525 Fax: 0141-952 5524 E-mail: scotland@foilribbon.com

Hedleys Gold Embossers, Unit 8-9 Poland Industrial Estate, Manchester, M4 6AZ Tel: 0161-205 4496 Fax: 0161-205 4496 E-mail: sales@goldblocking.co.uk

GOLD BLOCKING/STAMPING/ PRINTING SERVICES – *continued*

K R Snoxell & Sons Ltd, 24-26 Clarendon Road, Luton, LU2 7PQ Tel: (01582) 724704 Fax: (01582) 452928 E-mail: snoxell-headwear@lineone.net

Kimco Hot Foil Printers, 1 Waterside Court, Bone Lane, Newbury, Berkshire, RG14 5SH Tel: (01635) 30154 Fax: (01635) 32245 E-mail: petekimco@aol.com

Kingfob, 4 John Street, Walsall, WS2 8AF Tel: (01922) 722561 Fax: (01922) 722442 E-mail: artwork@keyfob.co.uk

S Q L Ltd, Unit 1a, Stock Road, Southend-on-Sea, SS2 5QF Tel: (01702) 464978 Fax: (01702) 612929 E-mail: paul@sqlsouthend.co.uk

Selfstyle, 54-57 Acorn Centre, Barry Street, Oldham, OL1 3NE Tel: 0161-626 7926 Fax: 0161-627 4732 E-mail: sales@selfstyle.co.uk

▶ Stubbs Tickets, Streethay Farm, Burton Road, Streethay, Lichfield, Staffordshire, WS13 8RJ Tel: 01543 410107 Fax: 01543 410180 E-mail: sales@stubbstickets.com

▶ Studio Tone Ltd, 6-8 Crown Close Business Centre, Crown Close, London, E3 2JQ Tel: (020) 8980 4242

Walsall Gold Blocking Service, John Street, Walsall, WS2 8AF Tel: (01922) 630031 Fax: (01922) 722855

GOLD BLOCKING/STAMPING/ PRINTING SYSTEMS, *See Hot Foil etc*

GOLD JEWELLERY

Aetee Ltd, Unit 11 Spring Mill Industrial Estate, Avening Road, Nailsworth, Stroud, Gloucestershire, GL6 0BS Tel: (01453) 835857 Fax: (01453) 836009 E-mail: admin@aetee.com

▶ C Howe, 100 High Street, Deal, Kent, CT14 6EE Tel: (01304) 368897 E-mail: cjuk@xln.co.uk

▶ Daniel Prince Of London, 24 Hatton Garden, London, EC1N 8BQ Tel: (0845) 1083684 Fax: (020) 8944 8418 E-mail: sales@danielprince.co.uk

▶ Georgina Ettridge, 12 St. Johns Glebe, Rownhams, Southampton, SO16 8AX Tel: (023) 8073 6704 E-mail: designer@georginaettridge.co.uk

Hotstorm Jewellery, Sheepy Parva, Atherstone, Warwickshire, CV9 3RL Tel: 07929 726821 E-mail: info@hotstorm-jewellery.co.uk

▶ Iceni Amber, 53 Waveney Road, Bungay, Suffolk, NR35 1LJ Tel: (01986) 895542 Fax: (01986) 895542 E-mail: sales@iceni-amber.co.uk

▶ Jewellery TV, Leeds, LS17 6WY Tel: (0870) 7447371 Fax: (0870) 1342096 E-mail: sales@jewellery.tv

▶ Jill Paton Contemporary Jewellery, 24 Aubery Crescent, 'Glenogle', Largs, Ayrshire, KA30 8AP Tel: (01475) 672914 E-mail: jill@jillpaton.co.uk

▶ Rayment & Hull, Bedlam Court Lane, Minster, Ramsgate, Kent, CT12 4HQ Tel: (01843) 822619 Fax: (01843) 821635 E-mail: r.h2004@btinternet.com

▶ Sandy Menzies Designer Jewellers Ltd, The Academy, Belmont Street, Aberdeen, AB10 1LB Tel: (01224) 641031 Fax: (01224) 641031 E-mail: shop@sandymenzies.co.uk

▶ Wholesale Italian Charms UK Ltd, 2 Waverly Court, Rowlands Road, Worthing, West Sussex, BN11 3JD Tel: (0799) 0553775 Fax: (01903) 217119 E-mail: info@carla-mar.co.uk

GOLD LEAF

W. Habberley Meadows Ltd, 5 Saxon Way, Chelmsley Wood, Birmingham, B37 5AY Tel: 0121-770 0103 Fax: 0121-770 6512 E-mail: gold@habberleymeadows.co.uk

James Laird Gold Leaf Ltd, 18 Craig Road, Glasgow, G44 3DR Tel: 0141-637 8288 Fax: 0141-637 8288 E-mail: goldleaf@jameslaird.com

Services Supply Co., 26 Penybont Road, Pencoed, Bridgend, Mid Glamorgan, CF35 5RA Tel: (01656) 860344 Fax: (01656) 862555 E-mail: sales@goldleafsupplies.com

GOLD PLATING

▶ E L Chaplain & Co., 33 Frederick Street, Birmingham, B1 3HH Tel: 0121-236 3065

GOLD PLATING SERVICES TO THE TRADE

Antique Renovating Co., 43 Bent Street, Manchester, M8 8NW Tel: 0161-834 8000

B J S Co. Ltd, 65 Bideford Avenue, Greenford, Middlesex, UB6 7PP Tel: (020) 8810 5779 Fax: (020) 8810 5883 E-mail: enquiries@bjsco.com

C S M Plating Ltd, Progress Works, Heath Mill La, Birmingham, B9 4AP Tel: 0121-772 2084 Fax: 0121-772 5190

F H Lambert Ltd, Rembrandt House, King Georges Avenue, Watford, WD18 7PW Tel: (01923) 229444 Fax: (01923) 255717 E-mail: info@fhlambert.co.uk

Goldrite Ltd, 322 Coleford Road, Darnall, Sheffield, S9 5PH Tel: 0114-243 3011 Fax: 0114-242 1902

Heer Platers Ltd, 9 Auster Industrial Estate, Silverdale Drive, Thurmaston, Leicester, LE4 8NG Tel: 0116-264 0931 Fax: 0116-264 0931

Ingram & Glass Ltd, Catteshall Lane, Godalming, Surrey, GU7 1LB Tel: (01483) 415262 Fax: (01483) 426951 E-mail: patrick@ingram-glass.co.uk

Raycell Ltd, Unit 2 Sherwood Works, Brighton Road, Handcross, Haywards Heath, West Sussex, RH17 6BZ Tel: (01444) 400999 Fax: (01444) 400883 E-mail: raycell@mistral.co.uk

Silchrome Plating Ltd, Barras Garth Road, Leeds, LS12 4JW Tel: 0113-263 7808 Fax: 0113-263 2682 E-mail: sales@silchrome.co.uk

Tecan Ltd, Tecan Way, Granby Industrial Estate, Weymouth, Dorset, DT4 9TU Tel: (01305) 765432 Fax: (01305) 780194 E-mail: info@tecan.co.uk

Tintplush Ltd, 16 The Crunnis, Bradley Stoke, Bristol, BS32 8AD Tel: 0117-987 2482 Fax: 0117-987 2482

Y & B Plating Ltd, 6 Priestley Way, Crawley, West Sussex, RH10 9NT Tel: (01293) 528974 Fax: (01293) 552877

GOLD REFINERS

Mayhan & Co. Ltd, 24 Tenby Street, Birmingham, B1 3EE Tel: 0121-236 3284 Fax: 0121-236 1981 E-mail: andrew.mayor@btclick.com

GOLD THREAD/WIRE

Benton & Johnson Ltd, Regalia House, Newtown Road, Bedworth, Warwickshire, CV12 8QR Tel: (024) 7684 8800 Fax: (024) 7664 3018 E-mail: bentonandjohnson@toye.com

GOLDWARE, MANUFACTURING GOLDSMITHS

Clarke, 25-26 Kenyon Street, Birmingham, B18 6AR Tel: 0121-236 4642 Fax: 0121-455 6430 E-mail: efc@jeweler.co.uk

▶ David Baggaley, 79 West Bar, Sheffield, S3 8PS Tel: (07877) 162431 E-mail: david.baggaley1@btinternet.com

Dragon Workshop, 47 Princess Victoria Street, Bristol, BS8 4BX Tel: 0117-973 2656

Richard Fox & Associates, 8-28 Luton Avenue, Croydon, CR0 2BP Tel: (020) 8683 3331 Fax: (020) 8683 2223 E-mail: richard@foxsilver.net

Charles Green & Son Ltd, 37-42 Tenby Street, Birmingham, B1 3EF Tel: 0121-236 1874 Fax: 0121-236 6617 E-mail: info@charles-green.co.uk

William Griffith & Sons (Birmingham) Ltd, 55-57 Vittoria St, Birmingham, B1 3NY Tel: 0121-236 1772

Jane Chantler Ltd, Clifford House, Market Street, Brough, Kirkby Stephen, Cumbria, CA17 4AX Tel: (01768) 341296 E-mail: jane@touchstone2000.freeserve.co.uk

▶ Jill Paton Contemporary Jewellery, 24 Aubery Crescent, 'Glenogle', Largs, Ayrshire, KA30 8AP Tel: (01475) 672914 E-mail: jill@jillpaton.co.uk

K Weiss Ltd, PO Box 78, Radlett, Hertfordshire, WD7 9ZT Tel: (01923) 855237 Fax: (020) 7504 8100 E-mail: handmade@weiss.co.uk

Martyn Pugh Ltd, Unit 8 Winyates Centre, Redditch, Worcestershire, B98 0NR Tel: (01527) 502513 Fax: (01527) 502513

Padgett & Braham Ltd, 10 Shacklewell Road, London, N16 7TA Tel: (020) 7254 6362 Fax: (020) 7254 7175 E-mail: p&b@tinyworld.co.uk

V. & F. Parker Ltd, 51 Vyse Street, Hockley, Birmingham, B18 6HS Tel: 0121-554 3587 Fax: 0121-523 2232

Remane Bros Ltd, 63-66 Hatton Garden, London, EC1N 8RF Tel: (020) 7405 6794 Fax: (020) 7831 6289 E-mail: remanegems@aol.com

Smith & Harris, 31 Hatton Garden, London, EC1N 8DH Tel: (020) 7405 1056 Fax: (020) 7405 1056

W H Wilmot Ltd, 62 Albion Street, Birmingham, B1 3EA Tel: 0121-236 1729 Fax: 0121-233 4957 E-mail: sales@whwilmot.com

GOLF BAGS

▶ GlenGolf (Clubmaker), 16 Witchford Road, Lincoln, LN6 0ST Tel: 01522 879830 E-mail: muirfield60@ntlworld.com

GOLF BALLS

▶ TFG Subs, Saturn Centre, Wolverhampton, WV4 6JX Tel: 0845 125 9520

GOLF BALLS, PROMOTIONAL

▶ Connect 2, 49 Meads Street, Eastbourne, East Sussex, BN20 7RN Tel: (01323) 641644 Fax: (01323) 643904 E-mail: info@connect2sussex.com

▶ Promotional Identity, 35 Muscovy Road, Kennington, Ashford, Kent, TN25 4QN Tel: (01233) 651651 Fax: (01233) 650707 E-mail: info@promotionalid.co.uk

GOLF BUGGIES, ELECTRIC

▶ SIRRIS Golf Tpa Ltd, 44 Heightington Place, Stourport-On-Severn, Worcestershire, DY13 0BE Tel: (07813) 117649 E-mail: info@SIRRISgolf.com

GOLF CART ACCESSORIES

▶ SIRRIS Golf Tpa Ltd, 44 Heightington Place, Stourport-On-Severn, Worcestershire, DY13 0BE Tel: (07813) 117649 E-mail: info@SIRRISgolf.com

GOLF CLOTHING

Talking T's, 1 149b Histon Road, Cambridge, CB4 3JD Tel: (01223) 304104 Fax: (01223) 304110 E-mail: sales@t-shirts.co.uk

GOLF CLOTHING, CARDIGANS, LADIES'

▶ Sevenwood, PO Box 1147, Luton, LU2 8WZ Tel: (01582) 420480 E-mail: enquiries@sevenwood.co.uk

GOLF CLUBS, LADIES

▶ SIRRIS Golf Tpa Ltd, 44 Heightington Place, Stourport-On-Severn, Worcestershire, DY13 0BE Tel: (07813) 117649 E-mail: info@SIRRISgolf.com

GOLF GOODS, *See also headings for particular items*

Flyght Golf Ltd, 21 Biglands Drive, Huyton, Liverpool, L36 0XS Tel: 0151-480 3645 Fax: 0151-480 1785 E-mail: johnfarrell7200@tiscali.co.uk

Hymec Backspin Ltd, Omega, Gipsy Lane, Wokingham, Berkshire, RG40 2HP Tel: 0118-978 0557 Fax: 0118-978 0558 E-mail: tt@hymec.co.uk

New Angle Promotions, Temuka House, School Road, Foulden, Thetford, Norfolk, IP26 5AJ Tel: (01366) 328282 Fax: (01366) 328283 E-mail: mediagolf@aol.com

Taylor Made Golf Ltd, Spectrum House, Jays Close, Basingstoke, Hampshire, RG22 4BS Tel: (01256) 408600 Fax: (01256) 465562

GOLF POLO SHIRTS

▶ Sevenwood, PO Box 1147, Luton, LU2 8WZ Tel: (01582) 420480 E-mail: enquiries@sevenwood.co.uk

GOLF SHIRTS

Talking T's, 1 149b Histon Road, Cambridge, CB4 3JD Tel: (01223) 304104 Fax: (01223) 304110 E-mail: sales@t-shirts.co.uk

GOLF SHOE FIXINGS

Trisport Ltd, 38 Amber Close, Tamworth Business Park, Amington, Tamworth, Staffordshire, B77 4RP Tel: (01827) 56544 Fax: (01827) 53181 E-mail: salesinfo@trisportgolf.com

GOLF SPORTS CLOTHING

▶ Sevenwood, PO Box 1147, Luton, LU2 8WZ Tel: (01582) 420480 E-mail: enquiries@sevenwood.co.uk

GOLF TEES

Flyght Golf Ltd, 21 Biglands Drive, Huyton, Liverpool, L36 0XS Tel: 0151-480 3645 Fax: 0151-480 1785 E-mail: johnfarrell7200@tiscali.co.uk

Pegasus Plastics UK Ltd, Unit 24 Eldon Way, Paddock Wood, Tonbridge, Kent, TN12 6BE Tel: (01892) 832326 Fax: (01892) 832328 E-mail: sales@pegasusplastics.co.uk

GOLF TROLLEYS

Electra Caddie, 99 Main Road, Bolton le Sands, Carnforth, Lancashire, LA5 8EQ Tel: (01902) 823300 Fax: (01524) 822382 E-mail: enquiries@kaddy.co.uk

Flyght Golf Ltd, 21 Biglands Drive, Huyton, Liverpool, L36 0XS Tel: 0151-480 3645 Fax: 0151-480 1785 E-mail: johnfarrell7200@tiscali.co.uk

Greenhill Leisure Products, Harmby Road, Leyburn, North Yorkshire, DL8 5QA Tel: (01969) 624324 Fax: (01969) 624324 E-mail: mail@green2hill.co.uk

▶ Standel Dawman Ltd, Pasture Lane Works, Factory La, Barrowford, Nelson, Lancs, BB9 6ES Tel: (01282) 613175 Fax: (01282) 615429E-mail: sales@standeldawman.uk.com

GOLF UMBRELLAS

Harrod Business Promotions Ltd, 3 Goodwood Rise, Marlow BTM, Marlow, Buckinghamshire, SL7 3QE Tel: (01628) 891133 Fax: (01628) 891134 E-mail: sales@harrodpromotions.com

▶ Simply Umbrellas, 17 Hampstead Gardens, Chadwell Heath, RM6 4FE Tel: (020) 8598 2811E-mail: enquiries@simplyumbrellas.co.uk

Stephens Umbrellas, Sandall Stones Road, Kirk Sandall Industrial Estate, Kirk Sandall, Doncaster, South Yorkshire, DN3 1QR Tel: (01302) 790790 Fax: (01302) 790088 E-mail: sue@oasisleisure.ltd.uk

GOLIATH CRANES

Matterson King Cranes, PO Box 31, Glasgow, G15 8TE Tel: 0141-944 4000 Fax: 0141-944 0111 E-mail: pct@pctgroup.co.uk

GOODS LIFTS

Foster & Cross (Lifts) Ltd, Black Country House, Rounds Green Road, Oldbury, West Midlands, B69 2DG Tel: (0845) 004 8027 Fax: (0870) 068 1354 E-mail: info@phosters.co.uk

Husbands Group Ltd, Shelah Road, Halesowen, West Midlands, B63 3PP Tel: 0121-550 1560 Fax: 0121-585 5285 E-mail: sales@servicelifts.co.uk

Kone plc, Global House Station Place, Fox La North, Chertsey, Surrey, KT16 9HW Tel: (0870) 7701122 Fax: (0870) 7701122 E-mail: salesandmarketing.uk@kone.com

Kone plc, 86 Broad Street, Glasgow, G40 2PX Tel: 0141-554 7604 Fax: 0141-554 6762

KONE PLC, Blisworth Hill Farm, Stoke Road, Blisworth, Northampton, NN7 3DB Tel: 08451 999 999 Fax: 0870 7701144 E-mail: sales.marketinguk@kone.com

London Hoist Ltd, Rifle Street, London, E14 6PB Tel: (020) 7538 4833 Fax: (020) 7515 3593 E-mail: info@londonhoist.co.uk

Power-Lifts Ltd, Marlborough House, 18 Marlborough Road, Woodthorpe, Nottingham, NG5 4FG Tel: 0115-926 9996 Fax: 0115-966 1173 E-mail: info@powerlift.co.uk

Schindler, Benwell House, Green Street, Sunbury-on-Thames, Middlesex, TW16 6QT Tel: (01932) 785281 Fax: (020) 8818 7999 E-mail: marketing@schindler.com

GOURMET SNACKS

▶ ScottishJerky.Com, Unit 11A4, Balmakeith Industrial Estate, Nairn, IV12 5QW Tel: (07798) 934 920 E-mail: brian@scottishjerky.com

GOVERNMENT SURPLUS BULK CONTRACTORS/DEALERS

Hoopers Surplus, 20 Pottergate, Norwich, NR2 1DX Tel: (01603) 764375 Fax: (01603) 665585

Katz & Co. (Folkestone) Ltd, 331-333 Cheriton Road, Folkestone, Kent, CT19 4BQ Tel: (01303) 271001 Fax: (01303) 279959 E-mail: sales@katzltd.com

GOVERNMENT SURPLUS CLOTHING

Heswall Army & Navy Stores, 7 The Mount, Heswall, Wirral, Merseyside, CH60 4RE Tel: 0151-342 4538 Fax: 0151-342 8626

Plaskett Protective Equipment, 10 Robert Street, Scunthorpe, South Humberside, DN15 6LU Tel: (01724) 871750 Fax: (01724) 874941

Yeomans Outdoors, 3 Victoria Square, Ashbourne, Derbyshire, DE6 1GG Tel: (01335) 342468

Yeomans Outdoors, 84-86 St. Peters Street, Derby, DE1 1SR Tel: (01332) 384684 E-mail: enquiries@yeomansoutdoors.co.uk

GOVERNMENT SURPLUS VEHICLES AND ACCESSORIES CONTRACTORS/DEALERS

Border Holdings UK Ltd, The Grove, Craven Arms, Shropshire, SY7 8DA Tel: (01588) 672711 Fax: (01588) 672660 E-mail: info@britparc.co.uk

GRABS, *See also headings for particular types*

I J C (International) Ltd, 9 Lisburne Square, Torquay, TQ1 2PT Tel: (01803) 211350 Fax: (01803) 211351 E-mail: sales@ijcinternational.com
NRC Plant Ltd, Neagron House, Stanford Road, Orsett, Grays, Essex, RM16 3BX Tel: (01375) 361616 Fax: (01375) 361818 E-mail: sales@nrcplant.co.uk
Plant Equipment Ltd, Clover Nook Road, Cotes Park Industrial Estate, Somercotes, Alfreton, Derbyshire, DE55 4RF Tel: (01773) 836060 Fax: (01773) 520630 E-mail: info@plantequip.co.uk

GRAFFITI REMOVAL OR PROTECTION PRODUCTS

▶ Branova Cleaning Services, Meadow Mills, Carlton Road, Dewsbury, West Yorkshire, WF13 2BA Tel: (01924) 486000 Fax: (01924) 486010 E-mail: sales@branova.com
▶ S D I Ltd, Trinity Buoy Wharf, Orchard Place, London, E14 0JU Tel: (020) 8924 7722 E-mail: keith@safetydirectglobal.co.uk
Tensid UK plc, 70a Wheatash Road, Addlestone, Surrey, KT15 2ES Tel: (01932) 564133 Fax: (01932) 562046 E-mail: info@tensid.com

GRAFFITI REMOVAL SERVICES

A1 Sandblasting, Reeds Farm, Cow Watering Lane, Writtle, Chelmsford, CM1 3SB Tel: (01245) 422188
▶ Coleman F M Ltd, PO Box 2088, Rayleigh, Essex, SS6 8WB Tel: (0845) 2261756 Fax: (0845) 2261757
Masonry Cleaning Services, 1a Allpits Road, Calow, Chesterfield, Derbyshire, S44 5AU Tel: (01246) 209926 Fax: (01246) 211620 E-mail: mike@masonrycleaningservices.com
Proclean Tectonics Ltd, 19 Bourton Road, Solihull, West Midlands, B92 8AY Tel: 0121-707 8090 Fax: 0121-707 2896
▶ S D I Ltd, Trinity Buoy Wharf, Orchard Place, London, E14 0JU Tel: (020) 8924 7722 E-mail: keith@safetydirectglobal.co.uk
Wesco Access Ltd, 1 Struan Place, Douglas Water, Lanark, ML11 9LW Tel: (01555) 880808 Fax: (01555) 880901 E-mail: neil@wescoaccess.com

GRAIN

▶ Lakefield Trading, Flat 6 Bearstead House, Abbey Park, Beckenham, Kent, BR3 1PP Tel: (020) 8650 2341 Fax: (0870) 8912953

GRAIN AERATION EQUIPMENT

Isle Of Wight Grain Storage Ltd, Medina Wharf, Arctic Road, Cowes, Isle of Wight, PO31 7PG Tel: (01983) 282022
West Engineering Ltd, Olympus Close, Ipswich, IP1 5LN Tel: (01473) 467930 Fax: (01473) 467931 E-mail: west@engineering40.fsbusiness.co.uk

GRAIN CONVEYORS/ ELEVATORS

A B & S Taysom, The Parks, Canon Pyon, Hereford, HR4 8NP Tel: (01432) 830282 Fax: (01432) 830282

GRAIN DRYING EQUIPMENT

A B & S Taysom, The Parks, Canon Pyon, Hereford, HR4 8NP Tel: (01432) 830282 Fax: (01432) 830282
Danagri - 3 S Ltd, Wenlock Road, Bridgnorth, Shropshire, WV16 4QR Tel: (01746) 762777 Fax: (01746) 764777 E-mail: info@danagri-3s.com
Farmway Machinery Ltd, Cock Lane, Piercebridge, Darlington, County Durham, DL2 3TJ Tel: (01325) 374000 Fax: (01325) 374094 E-mail: csd@farmway.co.uk
Harvest Installations, Unit H1 North Yard, The Brents, Faversham, Kent, ME13 7DZ Tel: (01795) 533903 Fax: (01795) 538524 E-mail: mike@harvestinstallations.co.uk
F.J. Pirie & Co. Ltd, Unit 2 Palmermount Works, Bypass Road, Dundonald, Kilmarnock, Ayrshire, KA2 9BL Tel: (01563) 850325 Fax: (01563) 851081

GRAIN DRYING OR STORAGE CONTRACTORS

A B & S Taysom, The Parks, Canon Pyon, Hereford, HR4 8NP Tel: (01432) 830282 Fax: (01432) 830282

GRAIN HANDLING PLANT AND EQUIPMENT

Highland Grain Group Ltd, Glackmore, North Kessock, Inverness, IV1 3UD Tel: (01463) 811435 Fax: (01463) 811618
Robert Bellairs Ltd, The Old Saddlery, Main Street, Woodnewton, Peterborough, PE8 5EB Tel: (01780) 470450 Fax: (01780) 470130

GRAIN PROCESSING/ TREATMENT PLANT

Alvan Blanch Development Co. Ltd, Chelworth, Malmesbury, Wiltshire, SN16 9SG Tel: (01666) 577333 Fax: (01666) 577339 E-mail: info@alvanblanch.co.uk
Berwyn Engineering Ltd, Euridge Works, Thickwood, Colerne, Chippenham, Wiltshire, SN14 8BG Tel: (01225) 742301 Fax: (01225) 743457 E-mail: info@jetway.co.uk
Blair Engineering Ltd, Balmoral Road, Rattray, Blairgowrie, Perthshire, PH10 7AH Tel: (01250) 872244 Fax: (01250) 872244 E-mail: sales@blairengineering.co.uk
Law-Denis Engineering Ltd, Fengate, Peterborough, PE1 5PE Tel: (01733) 563000 Fax: (01733) 563300 E-mail: info@lawdenis.com
M R M Engineering Ltd, Units 15-16, Enterprise Drive, Westhill Industrial Estate, Westhill, Aberdeenshire, AB32 6TQ Tel: (01224) 742383 Fax: (01224) 742326 E-mail: sales@mrmengineering.co.uk
Philip Wilson Ltd, 9 Blair Street, Edinburgh, EH1 1QR Tel: 0131-225 3040 Fax: 0131-225 3009
Satake Corporation (U K) Division, Horsefield Way, Bredbury Industrial Park, Stockport, Cheshire, SK6 2FG Tel: 0161-406 3800 Fax: 0161-406 3801 E-mail: sales@satake.co.uk

GRANITE

A Robinson & Son, 14 Main Street, Annalong, Newry, County Down, BT34 4TR Tel: (028) 4376 8213 Fax: (028) 4376 8872 E-mail: enquiries@arobinson.co.uk
▶ Callisto Trading Ltd, 2 Duckett Mews, London, N4 1BP Tel: (07092) 008537 Fax: (07092) 020256 E-mail: info@callistotrading.co.uk
▶ Francis N Lowe Ltd, New Road, Middleton, Matlock, Derbyshire, DE4 4NA Tel: (01629) 822216 Fax: (01629) 824348
Galloway Granite Works, Sorbie, Newton Stewart, Wigtownshire, DG8 8EW Tel: (01988) 850350 Fax: (01988) 850340 E-mail: galloway-granite@btconect.com
Granite Granite Ltd, Russell Gardens, Wickford, Essex, SS11 8QG Tel: (01268) 761214 Fax: (01268) 560088
Harris & Bailey Ltd, 50 Hastings Road, Croydon, CR9 6BR Tel: (020) 8654 3181 Fax: (020) 8656 9369 E-mail: mail@harris-bailey.co.uk
J & R Marble Company Ltd, Unit 9, Period Works, London, E10 7QT Tel: (020) 8539 6471 Fax: (020) 8539 9264 E-mail: sales@jrmarble.co.uk
▶ Landford Stone Ltd, Giles Lane, Landford, Salisbury, SP5 2BG Tel: (01794) 324232 Fax: (01794) 324242 E-mail: sales@landfordstone.co.uk
Marbonyx Ltd, Welton Way, Purdeys Indust Estate, Purdeys Industrial Estate, Rochford, Essex, SS4 1LA Tel: (01702) 543235 Fax: (01702) 543266 E-mail: sales@marbonyx.com
▶ Medusa Creations, Unit 2b Carnaby Industrial Estate, Lancaster Road, Carnaby, Bridlington, North Humberside, YO15 3QY Tel: (01262) 605222 Fax: (01262) 605654
Pauls Malt Ltd, Sidlaw, Burrelton, Blairgowrie, Perthshire, PH13 9PX Tel: 01821 650466
Pisani plc, Unit 12 Transport Avenue, Brentford, Middlesex, TW8 9HF Tel: (020) 8568 5001 Fax: (020) 8847 3406 E-mail: sales@pisani.co.uk
Prestige Marble Co., Armoury Works, Armoury Way, London, SW18 1EZ Tel: (020) 8874 7100 Fax: (020) 8870 0025 E-mail: prestigemarble@aol.com
Riskend Quarry Ltd, 6 Garrell Road, Kilsyth, Glasgow, G65 9JY Tel: (01236) 821486 Fax: (01236) 823256 E-mail: riskendquarry@supanet.com
Rocktops Ltd, Matts Hill Farm, Matts Hill Road, Hartlip, Sittingbourne, Kent, ME9 7UY Tel: (01634) 264606 Fax: (01322) 349251
Scottish Natural Stones Ltd, Westwood Estate, West Calder, West Lothian, EH55 8PN Tel: (01506) 874222 Fax: (01506) 874285
Shackerley (Holdings) Group Ltd, 139 Wigan Road, Euxton, Chorley, Lancashire, PR7 6JH Tel: (01257) 273114 Fax: (01257) 262386 E-mail: sales@shackerley.co.uk
Sussex Marble Co. Ltd, 16 Wainwright Close, St. Leonards-on-Sea, East Sussex, TN38 9PP Tel: (01424) 852575 Fax: (01424) 852798 E-mail: sales@sussexmarble.co.uk
Tramar Trading Ltd, Trinity Buoy Wharf, 64 Orchard Place, London, E14 0JW Tel: (020) 7093 1155 Fax: (020) 7093 1133 E-mail: info@tramartrading.co.uk
UK Marble Ltd, 21 Burcott Road, Hereford, HR4 9LW Tel: (01432) 352178 Fax: (01432) 352112 E-mail: sales@ukmarble.co.uk

GRANITE BALL WATER FEATURES

▶ Kinsman Water Features & Fountains, 56a Priory Road, Reigate, Surrey, RH2 8JB Tel: (01737) 222040 Fax: (01737) 222040 E-mail: mark@moesmoulds.co.uk

GRANITE CONTRACTORS AND WORKERS

A Andrews & Sons Ltd, 324-330 Meanwood Road, Leeds, LS7 2JE Tel: 0113-262 4751 Fax: 0113-262 3337 E-mail: contracts@andrews-tiles.co.uk
▶ DG Stone, 33 Farm Crescent, Wexham, Slough, SL2 5TQ Tel: 01753 524316 Fax: 01753 524316 E-mail: dgstone@hotmail.co.uk
F W Poole (Marble Mason) Ltd, 12 Larkhall Lane, London, SW4 6SP Tel: (020) 7622 5154 Fax: (020) 7622 4232 E-mail: poole.marble@virgin.net
Gormley (Marble Specialists) Ltd, Gormley House, Waxlow Road, Park Royal, London, NW10 7NU Tel: (020) 8961 5651 Fax: (020) 8961 5658 E-mail: info@gormley.co.uk
Premier Marble Ltd, 3 Dewing Road, Rackheath Industrial Estate, Rackheath, Norwich, NR13 6PS Tel: (01603) 721995 Fax: (01603) 721948 E-mail: premarble@aol.com
R C Coppin Ltd, Unit 2 Park Drive, Braintree, Essex, CM7 1AP Tel: (01376) 550009 Fax: (01376) 551436 E-mail: sales@rccoppinltd.co.uk

GRANITE FIREPLACE FRONTS

▶ MBS, 4 Bush Industrial Estate, Standard Road, London, NW10 6DF Tel: (020) 8453 1166 Fax: (020) 8963 0128 E-mail: marketing@mbsgroupcompanies.com

GRANITE KERBS OR SETTS

C E D Ltd, 728 London Road, Grays, Essex, RM20 3LU Tel: (01708) 867237 Fax: (01708) 867230 E-mail: sales@ced.ltd.uk
Harris & Bailey Ltd, 50 Hastings Road, Croydon, CR9 6BR Tel: (020) 8654 3181 Fax: (020) 8656 9369 E-mail: mail@harris-bailey.co.uk

GRANITE OR QUARTZITE OR MARBLE FLOORING

▶ Affordable Cranite & Marble Ltd, Stoney Ley Sawmills, Main Road, Stanton-in-the-Peak, Matlock, Derbyshire, DE4 2LW Tel: (01629) 630022 Fax: (01629) 630041 E-mail: info@ukaffordablegranite.com
Carew, Shutterton Bridge, Exeter Road, Dawlish, Devon, EX7 0LX Tel: (01626) 864856 Fax: (01626) 867168
▶ Hard Rock UK, 2a Lowercroft Business Park, Lowercroft Road, Bury, Lancashire, BL8 3PA Tel: 0161-762 4106 Fax: (01706) 220795 E-mail: sales@hardrockuk.co.uk
Jersey Monumental Co, 82 New Street, St. Helier, Jersey, JE2 3TE Tel: (01534) 730252 Fax: (01534) 731374 E-mail: jmco@jerseymail.co.uk
▶ Keystone, 204 Duggins Lane, Coventry, CV4 9GP Tel: (024) 7642 2580
▶ Lawrence & Co., 17 Cook Street, Leigh, Lancashire, WN7 4BT Tel: (01942) 674785 Fax: (01942) 674785 E-mail: enquires@lawcoflooring.co.uk
Rock Revelations Ltd, 19A High Street, Broughton, Kettering, Northamptonshire, NN14 1NF Tel: (0845) 3510415 Fax: (0845) 3510419 E-mail: info@rock-revelations.co.uk
Rocktops Ltd, Matts Hill Farm, Matts Hill Road, Hartlip, Sittingbourne, Kent, ME9 7UY Tel: (01634) 264606 Fax: (01322) 349251
▶ Studio Stone, The Stone Yard, Alton Lane, Four Marks, Alton, Hampshire, GU34 5AJ Tel: (01420) 562500 Fax: (01420) 563192 E-mail: info@studiostone.co.uk
▶ Tabounchik Trading, 1a Maxim Cottages, Hophurst Lane, Crawley Down, Crawley, West Sussex, RH10 4LJ Tel: (01342) 717188 E-mail: tabounchik@fsmail.net
Tramar Trading Ltd, Trinity Buoy Wharf, 64 Orchard Place, London, E14 0JW Tel: (020) 7093 1155 Fax: (020) 7093 1133 E-mail: info@tramartrading.co.uk

GRANITE PRODUCTS

▶ Kirk Natural Stone Ltd, Bridgend, Fyvie, Turriff, Aberdeenshire, AB53 8LL Tel: (01651) 891891 Fax: (01651) 891891 E-mail: info@kirknaturalstone.com

GRANITE WORKTOPS

▶ Bespoke Granite Worktops, Goosey Lodge Farm, Wymington Lane (off A6), Rushden, Northamptonshire, NN10 9LU Tel: (07905) 401697 Fax: (01933) 387059 E-mail: neil@stoneinstallations.co.uk

GRANT ADVISORY SERVICE, INSULATION

▶ Insuheat Ltd, Bay 2 Tractor Spares Industrial Estate, Strawberry Lane, Willenhall, West Midlands, WV13 3RN Tel: (01902) 603334 Fax: (01902) 604442 E-mail: admin@insuheat.co.uk

GRANULATING MACHINE BLADES

A F Whiteley & Co. Ltd, Bingswood Road, Whaley Bridge, High Peak, Derbyshire, SK23 7NB Tel: (01663) 732288 Fax: (01663) 734180 E-mail: sales@whiteley-knives.com
Mastercut Cutting Systems Ltd, 8 Bridge St Industrial Estate, Bridge Street, Clay Cross, Chesterfield, Derbyshire, S45 9NU Tel: (01246) 860811 Fax: (01246) 866928 E-mail: info@mastercut.co.uk

GRANULATING MACHINES

Blackfriars Ltd, Roman Way, Market Harborough, Leicestershire, LE16 7PQ Tel: (01858) 462249 Fax: (01858) 464755 E-mail: sales@blackfriars.com
Cumberland Europe Ltd, Daniels Industrial Estate, 104 Bath Road, Stroud, Gloucestershire, GL5 3TJ Tel: (01453) 768980 Fax: (01453) 768990 E-mail: europeansales@cumberland-plastics.com
Orthos (Engineering) Ltd, No 2, 2 The Point, Market Harborough, Leicestershire, LE16 7QU Tel: (01858) 464246 Fax: (01858) 434480 E-mail: sales@orthos.uk.com

GRANULATION PROCESSING

Custom Powders Ltd, Gateway, Crewe, CW1 6YT Tel: (01270) 530000 Fax: (01270) 500250 E-mail: powders@custompowders.co.uk

GRAPHIC ACCELERATORS, COMPUTER MULTIPLE SCREEN

Quad Vision Ltd, Unit C17, Arena Business Systems, 9 Nimrod Way, Ferndown, Dorset, BH21 7SH Tel: (01202) 862325 Fax: (01202) 862326 E-mail: sales@quadvision.co.uk

GRAPHIC AND PRINT INDUSTRY PUMPS

Rap, Clowes Street, Hollinwood, Oldham, OL9 7LY Tel: 0161-947 3700 Fax: 0161-947 3729 E-mail: enquiries@rapspiderweb.com

GRAPHIC ART FILM/DRAFTING FILM

A & R Printing, The Gables, 160A London Road, Brandon, Suffolk, IP27 0LP Tel: (01842) 811331 Fax: (01842) 811375 E-mail: ray.boreham@btinternet.com
Artstore (Scotland) Ltd, 94 Queen Street, Glasgow, G1 3AQ Tel: 0141-221 1101 Fax: 0141-204 2902 E-mail: artstore@artstore.co.uk
Cotech Ltd, Unit 13-16, Tafarnaubach Industrial Estate, Tafarnaubach, Tredegar, Gwent, NP22 3AA Tel: (01495) 711970 Fax: (01495) 725765 E-mail: sales@cotech-uk.com

GRAPHIC DESIGN CONSULTANTS

▶ Aloof Design, 5 Fisher Street, Lewes, East Sussex, BN7 2DG Tel: (01273) 470887 E-mail: michellekostyrka@aloofdesign.com
▶ Arris, The Granary, Hunsingore, Wetherby, West Yorkshire, LS22 5HY Tel: (01423) 358881 Fax: (01423) 359490 E-mail: enquires@arris.co.uk

GRAPHIC DESIGN CONSULTANTS – *continued*

Axyswebs Ltd, Host Media Centre, Saville Mount, Leeds, LS7 3HZ Tel: 0113-200 7070 Fax: 0113-200 7071 E-mail: info@axyswebs.com

▶ Blinding Web Site Design, 8 Dalkeith Street, Barrow-in-Furness, Cumbria, LA14 1SP Tel: (01229) 828028 E-mail: info@blindingwebdesign.co.uk

Bright Spark Ltd, 178-180 Hotwell Road, Bristol, BS8 4RP Tel: 0117-925 9300 Fax: 0117-925 9301 E-mail: sales@bsmg.co.uk

▶ Clear Design Services, 44 Seaford Road, Wokingham, Berkshire, RG40 2EL Tel: 0118 9894455 E-mail: info@cleardesignservices.co.uk

▶ CreaCom Design, 181 High Street, Invergordon, Ross-Shire, IV18 0AL Tel: (01349) 853003 E-mail: info@creacomdesign.com

▶ D C Group, Corsley, Corsley, Warminster, Wiltshire, BA12 7QH Tel: (01373) 832288 Fax: (01373) 832589 E-mail: stefen@dcgroup.uk.net

▶ Decipher Design, 107, Boundary Rd, London, NW8 0RG Tel: (020) 7328 2545 E-mail: info@decipherdesign.co.uk

▶ Definitive Consulting, Parkfield Business Centre, Park Street, Stafford, ST17 4AL Tel: (01785) 226430 Fax: (01785) 222217 E-mail: info@definitiveuk.com

▶ Design Distillery Ltd, 12 Northgate, Chichester, West Sussex, PO19 1BA Tel: (01243) 537837 Fax: (01243) 839448 E-mail: leslie@design-distillery.co.uk

▶ Design Ontap, 200 Brook Drive, GreenPark, Reading, RG2 6UB Tel: 0845 644 7782 Fax: 0845 644 7783 E-mail: glen.richardson@design-ontap.co.uk

▶ Evolve, 35 Townfield Road, Mobberley, Knutsford, Cheshire, WA16 7HG Tel: (01565) 872683 Fax: (01565) 872534

Exposed Design, PO Box 35575, London, NW4 4UH Tel: 020 8202 5964 Fax: 0870 125 9115 E-mail: kellys@exposed.co.uk

▶ Fli Backward Ltd, 557 Wilmslow Road, Manchester, M20 4GJ Tel: 0161-445 0273

Giant, 36 Queen Square, Bristol, BS1 4QS Tel: 0117 9086666 Fax: 0117 9085566 E-mail: info@gianteffect.co.uk

▶ Greensplash Ltd, 308 Chester Road, Hartford, Northwich, Cheshire, CW8 2AB Tel: (01606) 884123 Fax: (01606) 884212 E-mail: enquiries@greensplash.com

▶ Grove Creative Ltd, 15 Wentworth Grove, Winsford, Cheshire, CW7 2LJ Tel: (01606) 553793 E-mail: info@grovecreative.co.uk

▶ Harmony Internet Ltd, 3 The Granary Buildings, Millow, Biggleswade, Bedfordshire, SG18 8RH Tel: (01767) 317614 Fax: (01767) 317647 E-mail: info@harmony.co.uk

▶ Kreative Juice, 24 Martholme Close, Blackburn, BB6 7TZ Tel: (01254) 884917 E-mail: info@kreativejuice.co.uk

▶ Magic Pencil, 16 Upper Meadow Road, Birmingham, B32 1NX Tel: (0870) 2863881 Fax: (0870) 2863882 E-mail: creative@magicpencil.co.uk

▶ Merge Design Consultancy, 37 Dinorben Avenue, Fleet, Hampshire, GU52 7SQ Tel: (07980) 626443 E-mail: nick.green@mergedc.co.uk

▶ Mill Design & Marketing, Hilliard House, Lester Way, Wallingford, Oxfordshire, OX10 9TA Tel: (01491) 833822 Fax: (01491) 833002 E-mail: steve@millmarketing.co.uk

▶ Nightingale Austen Designs, The Lodge, Guildford Road, Effingham, Leatherhead, Surrey, KT24 5PE Tel: (01372) 457815 Fax: (01372) 456804 E-mail: richard@naduk.com

Oppo Consulting Ltd, 38 Stoke Fields, Guildford, Surrey, GU1 4LS Tel: (01483) 563502 Fax: (01483) 453773 E-mail: sales@oppo-consulting.co.uk

Origin One UK Ltd, Dukes Yard Shakespeare Industrial Estate, Acme Road, Watford, WD24 5AL Tel: (01923) 246116 Fax: (01923) 246113 E-mail: info@origin-1.co.uk

Paul Cartwright Branding, 53 Park Road, Ramsgate, Kent, CT11 9TL Tel: (0560) 2960506 Fax: 01843 591510 E-mail: info@paulcartwrightbranding.co.uk

▶ Pentacor plc, Capital House 4 Parkhouse Business Centre, Desborough Park Road, High Wycombe, Buckinghamshire, HP12 3DJ Tel: (01494) 898300 Fax: (01494) 898301 E-mail: info@pentacor.co.uk

▶ Profile Design, 10 West Pallant, Chichester, West Sussex, PO19 1TF Tel: (01243) 537444 Fax: (01243) 537440 E-mail: sales@profiledesign.net

QD Ltd, 93 Great Titchfield Street, London, W1W 6RP Tel: (020) 7462 1700 Fax: (020) 7636 0652

▶ RT Media Ltd, Allen House, 2a East Borough, Wimborne, Dorset, BH21 1PF Tel: (01202) 888192 Fax: (01202) 888192 E-mail: info@rtmedia.com

Shaw Marketing & Design Ltd, 18 Albany Street, Edinburgh, EH1 3QB Tel: 0131-557 5663 Fax: 0131-556 7379 E-mail: enquiries@shawltd.demon.co.uk

▶ Sheldon-Mann, 16 B Nuxley Road, Belvedere, Kent, DA17 5JF Tel: 01322 412157 Fax: 01322 412157 E-mail: sheldonmann@gmail.com

▶ Studiohope, 2 Oolite Grove, Bath, BA2 2UF Tel: (01225) 830634 Fax: (01225) 830634 E-mail: mcmaster@studiohope.co.uk

Toucan Graphic Design Ltd, 25 Southernhay East, Exeter, EX1 1NS Tel: (01392) 438463 Fax: (01392) 495415 E-mail: designers@toucandesign.co.uk

▶ Travisbead, 611 South Eighth Street, Milton Keynes, MK9 3DE Tel: (01908) 231401 E-mail: info@travisbead.com

▶ Unity Art, 18 Nelson Road, Hastings, East Sussex, TN34 3RZ Tel: (01424) 201158 Fax: (01424) 201158 E-mail: enquiries@unitydesignandprint.com

▶ Westgate Design, 37 The Drive, Sevenoaks, Kent, TN13 3AD Tel: (01732) 454588 Fax: (01732) 779087 E-mail: shaun@westgatedesign.co.uk

Wida Group, 2 Brookside Road, Ruddington, Nottingham, NG11 6AT Tel: 0115-921 4797 Fax: 0115-984 5097 E-mail: info@widagroup.com

▶ Benjamin H.W. Wills, Argoed Uchaf Farm, Sunnyview, Argoed, Blackwood, Gwent, NP12 0AJ Tel: (07980) 019849 E-mail: theartist@bhww.co.uk

▶ Woods Design & Print, Bumpers Way, Bumpers Farm, Chippenham, Wiltshire, SN14 6NG Tel: (01249) 460630 Fax: (01249) 460631

GRAPHIC DESIGN RECRUITMENT AGENCIES

▶ 999print, 251 Kingsway, Manchester, M19 1AL Tel: 0161-610 8032 Fax: 0161-610 6015 E-mail: sales@999print.com

▶ And Design, 39 Derment Drive, Maidenhead, Berkshire, SL6 6LE Tel: (07747) 782816 E-mail: ant@and-design.co.uk

▶ Car Design Jobs, PO Box 8208, Colchester, CO3 3WU Tel: 0845 838 1598

Creative Communications Recruitment, Leaf House, Bluebell Lane, Sharpthorne, East Grinstead, West Sussex, RH19 4PF Tel: (01342) 811572 Fax: (01342) 811572 E-mail: mick@ccrecruit.co.uk

▶ The CV People, 46 Woodhead Grove, Armadale, Bathgate, West Lothian, EH48 3HU Tel: (07981) 347380

▶ E Design House, 20 Elm Street, Blackburn, BB1 5NL Tel: (0871) 2221406 Fax: (0871) 2221407 E-mail: info@e-designhouse.co.uk

▶ Brian Ford Powell Executive Recruitment, Claybrooke House, Claybrooke Parva, Lutterworth, Leicestershire, LE17 5AE Tel: (01455) 209968 Fax: (01455) 202788 E-mail: contact@bfpexecutiverecruitment.co.uk

▶ Friendly People Ltd, The Old Post Office, 2, Church Street, Brigstock, Kettering, Northamptonshire, NN14 3EX Tel: (01536) 373648 E-mail: info@friendly-people.co.uk

▶ Fuel Recruitment, Clarendon Place, Leamington Spa, Warwickshire, CV32 5QL Tel: (01926) 833000 Fax: (01926) 833001 E-mail: info@bigfishrecruitment.com

▶ Ingenius One, Express Courtyard, Luke Lane, Brailsford, Ashbourne, DE6 3BY Tel: (01335) 361199 Fax: (01335) 361188 E-mail: enquiries@ingeniusone.com

▶ Looseleaf Design, The Coach House, Balkerne Close, Colchester, CO1 1NZ Tel: (01206) 545495 Fax: (01206) 545495 E-mail: paul@looseleafdesign.co.uk

▶ Management Consultancy 4 Limited, 7-111 Fleet Street, London, EC4A 2AB Tel: 0 870 770 9116 Fax: 0 870 770 9117 E-mail: info@mc4.co.uk

▶ Misura Recruitment Services Ltd, PO BOX 625, Rotherham, South Yorkshire, S60 9BB Tel: (01709) 739278 Fax: (01709) 739278 E-mail: info@misurajobs.co.uk

▶ Stafforce Recruitment, 39A Minerva Road, London, NW10 6HJ Tel: (020) 8537 9070 Fax: (020) 8537 9071 E-mail: parkroyal@stafforce.co.uk

GRAPHIC DESIGNERS OR ARTISTS

▶ 3dtp Ltd, Cardrew Industrial Estate, Redruth, Cornwall, TR15 1SS Tel: (01209) 314458

Beaver Graphic Services, Graphic House, Wiggenhall Road, Watford, WD18 0FG Tel: (01923) 229387 Fax: (01923) 223957 E-mail: sales@beaver.co.uk

▶ Angela Berry, Hag Hill Rise, Taplow, Maidenhead, Berkshire, SL6 0LS Tel: (01628) 661073 Fax: (01628) 661073 E-mail: design@angelaberry.co.uk

Simon Birtall, West Kirby, Wirral, Merseyside, CH48 2HL Tel: (0779) 0471098 E-mail: simon@birtall.co.uk

▶ Bluesky Designers, College Road, Bromley, BR1 3PU Tel: (020) 8313 9881 Fax: (020) 8290 5932 E-mail: bluesky@easynet.co.uk

▶ Breeze Design Ltd, Studio 4, Weston Farm, The Street, Albury, Guildford, Surrey, GU5 9BZ Tel: (0845) 0943701 E-mail: info@breezedesign.co.uk

Bright Spark Ltd, 178-180 Hotwell Road, Bristol, BS8 4RP Tel: 0117-925 9300 Fax: 0117-925 9301 E-mail: sales@bsmg.co.uk

▶ Caricature/Cartoon Portrait Wedding Invitations, 5 Hillview Cottages (Off Plough Hill), Basted, Borough Green, Sevenoaks, Kent, TN15 8PS Tel: (01732) 883555 E-mail: weddings@christmanncreative.co.uk

▶ Cathartic Designs, 20 Albert Mews, Lockside, London, E14 8EH Tel: (07976) 718081 E-mail: info@cathartic.co.uk

▶ Designbern, 31 Yorkland Avenue, Welling, Kent, DA16 2LE Tel: (07855) 856529 E-mail: bern@designbern.com

▶ Digital Progression, 123 Old Christchurch Road, Bournemouth, BH1 1EP Tel: (01202) 316660 Fax: (01202) 311185 E-mail: mail@digitalprogression.co.uk

E D S, 57 Castle Street, Aberdeen, AB11 5BB Tel: (01224) 595705 Fax: (01224) 595705 E-mail: finnieseds@dsl.pipex.com

East Coast Design, 23 Sidmouth Street, Hull, HU5 2LB Tel: (07811) 437205 E-mail: dave@eastcoastdesign.co.uk

▶ Give Me Graphics, 93 Burnside, Cambridge, CB1 3PA Tel: (07949) 548772 E-mail: sales@givemegraphics.net

▶ Graphic Evidence Ltd, Wood Farm, Moreton Road, Ongar, Essex, CM5 0EY Tel: (01277) 890900 Fax: (01277) 890473 E-mail: info@graphic-evidence.co.uk

▶ Greensplash Ltd, 308 Chester Road, Hartford, Northwich, Cheshire, CW8 2AB Tel: (01606) 884123 Fax: (01606) 884212 E-mail: enquiries@greensplash.com

Greenwich Design Associates, 11a Greenwich South Street, London, SE10 8NJ Tel: (020) 8853 3028 Fax: (020) 8858 2128 E-mail: simon@greenwich-design.co.uk

HTDL, 6 Ardent Court, William James Way, Henley-in-Arden, West Midlands, B95 5GF Tel: 01564 797420 Fax: 01564 795247 E-mail: post@htdl.co.uk

▶ Ice Age Media, The Cottage, Old Mold Road, Gwersyllt, Wrexham, LL11 4SB Tel: (01978) 758071 E-mail: andy@theiceage.co.uk

▶ Ident Design Ltd, Ground Floor Suite, 7 Woodlands Grove, Isleworth, Middlesex, TW7 6NS Tel: (07941) 007175 E-mail: info@identdesign.co.uk

▶ Indrum Website & Graphic Design, 2c Bennett Road, Brighton, BN2 5JL Tel: (01273) 530275 E-mail: indrum@indrum.com

▶ Irphoto, Burn Cottage, Southwick, Dumfries, DG2 8AN Tel: (01387) 780635 E-mail: mackay@irphoto.co.uk

▶ Merge Design Consultancy, 37 Dinorben Avenue, Fleet, Hampshire, GU52 7SQ Tel: (07980) 626443 E-mail: nick.green@mergedc.co.uk

▶ Mill Design & Marketing, Hilliard House, Lester Way, Wallingford, Oxfordshire, OX10 9TA Tel: (01491) 833822 Fax: (01491) 833002 E-mail: steve@millmarketing.co.uk

Mystic East Cushions, PO BOX 51568, London, LONDON, SE1 2JT Tel: 0845 612 1551 E-mail: mysticeastcushions@miscobjects.com

▶ Node Design, 43 Blaker Street, Brighton, BN2 0JJ Tel: (01273) 299119 Fax: (01273) 603162 E-mail: info@node.uk.com

▶ Pha Multimedia, The Studio, 6 Foxley Grove, Welwyn, Hertfordshire, AL6 0DW Tel: (01438) 840084 E-mail: peter.holt@pha.uk

▶ Pixel Perfect, The White House, Copse Road, Haslemere, Surrey, GU27 3QQ Tel: (01428) 643500 E-mail: sales@pixelperfect.co.uk

▶ Psychological Media 3-D, Milward Road, Hastings, East Sussex, TN34 3RT Tel: (01424) 715445 E-mail: marie@psymedia3d.com

▶ Punctum, Unit 57, Enterprise Way, Newport, Gwent, NP20 2AQ Tel: (01633) 843237 E-mail: enquiries@punctumphotographic.co.uk

▶ Sign & Digital Print Solutions, The Sign Workshop, Rear of 78 Ham Lane, Longham, Ferndown, Dorset, BH22 9DP Tel: (01202) 572625

Slave to Design, Suite 5, Unit 9, Oldham Street Business Centre, Hanley, Stoke-on-Trent, ST1 3EY Tel: (01782) 207884 Fax: (01782) 207884 E-mail: info@slavetodesign.com

▶ Studiohope, 2 Oolite Grove, Bath, BA2 2UF Tel: (01225) 830634 Fax: (01225) 830634 E-mail: mcmaster@studiohope.co.uk

▶ Thumbprint Design, 37 St. Leonards Street, Stamford, Lincolnshire, PE9 2HL Tel: (07949) 330316 E-mail: enquiry@thumb-print.co.uk

Toucan Graphic Design Ltd, 25 Southernhay East, Exeter, EX1 1NS Tel: (01392) 438463 Fax: (01392) 495415 E-mail: designers@toucandesign.co.uk

▶ Unity Art, 18 Nelson Road, Hastings, East Sussex, TN34 3RZ Tel: (01424) 201158 Fax: (01424) 201158 E-mail: enquiries@unitydesignandprint.com

▶ Vivid Image Ltd, Unit 4, Bamfords Yard, Bamford Lane, Turvey, Bedford, MK43 8DL Tel: (01234) 881515 E-mail: sales@viplimited.co.uk

▶ Benjamin H.W. Wills, Argoed Uchaf Farm, Sunnyview, Argoed, Blackwood, Gwent, NP12 0AJ Tel: (07980) 019849 E-mail: theartist@bhww.co.uk

GRAPHIC DESIGNERS, PRINTING INDUSTRY

1066 Design T O Print, 7 St James Road, Bexhill-On-Sea, East Sussex, TN40 2DE Tel: (01424) 810033

Advance, 18 Overbury Cres, Croydon, CR0 0LL Tel: 020 8123 0389 E-mail: info@advancestudio.co.uk

Avatar, 5 Elizabeth Close, Attleborough, Norfolk, NR17 1QJ Tel: 07747 610805 E-mail: info@avatargraphics.co.uk

▶ Angela Berry, Hag Hill Rise, Taplow, Maidenhead, Berkshire, SL6 0LS Tel: (01628) 661073 Fax: (01628) 661073 E-mail: design@angelaberry.co.uk

John Blanks, 17 Presburg Road, New Malden, Surrey, KT3 5AH Tel: (020) 8942 2100 Fax: (020) 8336 2337

▶ Bluprint Design & Copy, 79 Wellgate, Rotherham, South Yorkshire, S60 2LZ Tel: (01709) 838965 Fax: (01709) 365449 E-mail: info@bluprintdesign.co.uk

▶ City Of Stirling Media Ltd, Suite 1, Castle House, 1 Baker Street, Stirling, FK8 1AL Tel: 0845 226 1896 E-mail: hello@cos-media.co.uk

▶ CreaCom Design, 181 High Street, Invergordon, Ross-Shire, IV18 0AL Tel: (01349) 853003 E-mail: info@creacomdesign.com

Darby Design & Print, 6 Kerry Close, Ancells Park, Fleet, Hampshire, GU51 2UF Tel: 01252 669948 E-mail: designandprint@ntlworld.com

▶ design indeed, Top flat, 80 Cavendish Road, London, N4 1RS Tel: 0794 4231340 E-mail: info@design-indeed.co.uk

East Coast Design, 23 Sidmouth Street, Hull, HU5 2LB Tel: (07811) 437205 E-mail: dave@eastcoastdesign.co.uk

Fir Tree Design Co., 2 Turpyn Court, Woughton on the Green, Milton Keynes, MK6 3BW Tel: (01908) 661100 Fax: (01908) 670055 E-mail: info@firtreedesign.com

▶ Fresh Biz Marketing, 1 Oban Close, Wakefield, West Yorkshire, WF3 1JU Tel: 0870 284 6180 Fax: 0870 284 6181 E-mail: info@freshbizmarketing.com

▶ Gem Stone Graphics Ltd, 4 Highdown Court, Forestfield, Crawley, West Sussex, RH10 6PR Tel: (01293) 524546E-mail: info@gsg-ltd.co.uk

Gilmour Print, Irvinehill Farm, Stewarton, Kilmarnock, Ayrshire, KA3 3EL Tel: (01294) 850217 Fax: (01294) 850444 E-mail: sales@gilmourprint.co.uk

▶ Graphic Evidence Ltd, Wood Farm, Moreton Road, Ongar, Essex, CM5 0EY Tel: (01277) 890900 Fax: (01277) 890473 E-mail: info@graphic-evidence.co.uk

▶ Hughes Design Ltd, Tai Tywyn Business Centre, Sandy Lane, Prestatyn, Clwyd, LL19 7SF Tel: (01745) 888828 Fax: (01745) 859020 E-mail: sion@hughesdesign.ltd.uk

▶ Ice Age Media, The Cottage, Old Mold Road, Gwersyllt, Wrexham, LL11 4SB Tel: (01978) 758071 E-mail: andy@theiceage.co.uk

▶ Ident Design Ltd, Ground Floor Suite, 7 Woodlands Grove, Isleworth, Middlesex, TW7 6NS Tel: (07941) 007175 E-mail: info@identdesign.co.uk

▶ Kobu Ltd, 3 Manor Farm Offices, Northend Road, Fenny Compton, Southam, Warwickshire, CV47 2YY Tel: (01295) 771182 Fax: (01295) 771185 E-mail: info@kobu.co.uk

MMV Design, 30 Rosewood Court, Rothwell, LEEDS, LS26 0XG Tel: 0113 2825831 E-mail: enquiries@mmvdesign.co.uk

▶ Pha Multimedia, The Studio, 6 Foxley Grove, Welwyn, Hertfordshire, AL6 0DW Tel: (01438) 840084 E-mail: peter.holt@pha.uk

Printing Com (Orpington), 98 High Street, Farnborough, Orpington, Kent, BR6 7BA Tel: (01689) 870380 Fax: 01689 823590 E-mail: orpington@printing.com

▶ S H O Design, 57 Farringdon Road, London, EC1M 3JB Tel: (020) 7993 5472 E-mail: adam@sho-mail.com

Sale Print & Design, 5 Georges Road, Sale, Cheshire, M33 3NJ Tel: 0161-962 3365

▶ Sign & Digital Print Solutions, The Sign Workshop, Rear of 78 Ham Lane, Longham, Ferndown, Dorset, BH22 9DP Tel: (01202) 572625

Slave to Design, Suite 5, Unit 9, Oldham Street Business Centre, Hanley, Stoke-on-Trent, ST1 3EY Tel: (01782) 207884 Fax: (01782) 207884 E-mail: info@slavetodesign.com

▶ Snafu Design, 8 South Street, Torrington, Devon, EX38 8HE Tel: (01805) 623387 E-mail: rob@snafudesign.co.uk

Studio, Gill Lane, Mersham, Ashford, Kent, TN25 7HZ Tel: (01233) 721511 Fax: (01303) 721662 E-mail: jan@studio2uk.com

▶ Subcircle Creative, 5 Luther Mews, Brighton, BN2 9YR Tel: 01273 675428

Tandem Design, The Cottage, Eastgate Street, Southampton, SO14 3HB Tel: (023) 8063 2159 Fax: (023) 8033 2352 E-mail: studio@tandem-design.co.uk

▶ Westgate Design, 37 The Drive, Sevenoaks, Kent, TN13 3AD Tel: (01732) 454588 Fax: (01732) 779087 E-mail: shaun@westgatedesign.co.uk

GRAPHIC DISPLAY SYSTEMS

E S L Displays & Graphics, Units 3-5 Hillside Mews, Riding Barn Hill, Wick, Bristol, BS30 5PA Tel: 0117-937 4777 Fax: 0117-937 4550 E-mail: info@eslgroupuk.co.uk

George Gidden Graphics Ltd, 14 Park Street, Guildford, Surrey, GU1 4XB Tel: (01483) 303040 Fax: (01483) 303222 E-mail: paul@giddenplace.com

M R G Systems Ltd, Willow Court, Beeches Green, Stroud, Gloucestershire, GL5 4BJ Tel: (01453) 751871 Fax: (01453) 753125 E-mail: sales@mrgsystems.co.uk

Marlowe Graphic Services Ltd, Marlowe House, 346 High Street, Berkhamsted, Hertfordshire, HP4 1HT Tel: (01442) 878785 Fax: (01442) 878828 E-mail: sales@marlowe.co.uk

Merit Display, 8-10 Maudslay Road, Coventry, CV5 8EL Tel: (024) 7667 6700

Re-Graphics, Unit 10 Freshways House, 16 Eastman Road, London, W3 7YG Tel: (020) 8743 3529 Fax: (020) 8743 3629

GRAPHIC EDITING EQUIPMENT

Quantel Ltd, 31 Turnpike Road, Newbury, Berkshire, RG14 2NX Tel: (01635) 48222 Fax: (01635) 815815 E-mail: quantel@quantel.com

GRAPHIC EFFECTS EQUIPMENT

Quantel Ltd, 31 Turnpike Road, Newbury, Berkshire, RG14 2NX Tel: (01635) 48222 Fax: (01635) 815815 E-mail: quantel@quantel.com

GRAPHIC INLAY FLOORING

Designer Logo Matting, 56 Southbury Road, Enfield, Middlesex, EN1 1YB Tel: (020) 8342 2020 Fax: (020) 8342 2021

GRAPHIC OVERLAYS, FASCIA PANEL ETC

Electro Serigraphic Products Ltd, Unit 8 Collers Way, Reepham, Norwich, NR10 4SW Tel: (01603) 871227 Fax: (01603) 871237 E-mail: esp@membrane-switches.co.uk

Instrument Component Labels Ltd, Unit L1, Beversbrook Centre, Redman Road, Calne, Wiltshire, SN11 9PR Tel: (01249) 822010 Fax: (01249) 821330 E-mail: robertbromley@ic-labels.com

GRAPHIC PANEL DESIGN AND MANUFACTURING

G S M Primographic, Unit 2b Ffrwdgrech Industrial Estate, Ffrwdgrech Road, Brecon, Powys, LD3 8LA Tel: (01874) 624433 Fax: (01874) 624575 E-mail: info@gsmprimographic.co.uk

GRAPHICS PACKAGE COMPUTER SOFTWARE TRAINING

▶ Agile Training Limited, 8 Grafton Court, Canning Circus, Nottingham, NG7 3GH Tel: 07932 696228 E-mail: enquiries@agile-training.co.uk

GRAPHITE

Agrimark Europe Agricultural Merchants, Folly Lane, Bell Royd Farm, Thurlstone, Sheffield, S36 7QF Tel: (01226) 370013 Fax: (01226) 370178

Branwell Graphite Ltd, 58-62 High St, Epping, Essex, CM16 4AE Tel: (01992) 577334 Fax: (01992) 561138 E-mail: sales@branwell.com

Tokai Carbon UK Ltd, Roway Lane, Oldbury, West Midlands, B69 3EJ Tel: 0121-552 5577 Fax: 0121-552 6748 E-mail: john@tokaicarboneurope.com

GRAPHITE COMPONENTS

BS&B Safety Systems (UK) Ltd, Adamson House, Tower Business Pk, Wilmslow Rd, Didsbury, Manchester, M20 2YY Tel: 0161-955 4202 Fax: 0161-955 4282 E-mail: sales@bsb-systems.co.uk

Marlowe Graphic Services Ltd, Marlowe House, 346 High Street, Berkhamsted, Hertfordshire, HP4 1HT Tel: (01442) 878785 Fax: (01442) 878828 E-mail: sales@marlowe.co.uk

Ralph Coidan Ltd, 2 Boltby Way, Eaglescliffe, Stockton-on-Tees, Cleveland, TS16 0RH Tel: (01642) 790100 Fax: (01642) 790488 E-mail: sales@coidan.co.uk

SGL Carbon, 4 Arden Court, Arden Road, Alcester, Warwickshire, B49 6HN Tel: (01789) 400221 Fax: (01789) 400822 E-mail: enquiries@sglcarbon.co.uk

Tokai Carbon UK Ltd, Roway Lane, Oldbury, West Midlands, B69 3EJ Tel: 0121-552 5577 Fax: 0121-552 6748 E-mail: john@tokaicarboneurope.com

GRAPHITE ELECTRODES

Erodex (UK) Ltd, Tipper Industrial Estate, Park Road, Halesowen, West Midlands, B63 2RH Tel: (01384) 892011 Fax: (01384) 897162 E-mail: sales@erodex.com

Erodex UK Ltd, 42 Station Street, Wednesbury, West Midlands, WS10 8BW Tel: 0121-526 7368 Fax: 0121-526 6582 E-mail: sales@afshaw.com

SGL Technic Ltd, Muir of Ord Industrial Estate, Great North Road, Muir of Ord, Ross-Shire, IV6 7UA Tel: (01463) 870000 Fax: (01463) 871402

GRAPHITE ENGINE OIL ADDITIVES

Intro Marketing Ltd, Old Freight Depot, Roberts Road, Doncaster, South Yorkshire, DN4 0JW Tel: (01302) 320269 Fax: (01302) 340678 E-mail: sales@intro.co.uk

GRAPHITE GASKETS

Avon Group Manufacturing Ltd, 30 Vale Lane, Bristol, BS3 5RU Tel: 0117-904 3355 Fax: 0117-904 3366 E-mail: admin@avon-group.co.uk

GRAPHITE LUBRICANTS

Acheson Industries Europe Ltd, Cattewater Road, Plymouth, PL4 0SP Tel: (01752) 218788 Fax: (01752) 207133 E-mail: acheson.plymouth@nstarch.com

Fenco-Aldridge (Barton) Ltd, Lovat Court, Caldecote St, Newport Pagnell, Buckinghamshire, MK16 0YZ Tel: (01908) 614646 Fax: (01908) 214482 E-mail: fab@fenco.co.uk

Revol Ltd, Samson Close, Newcastle upon Tyne, NE12 6DZ Tel: 0191-268 4555 Fax: 0191-216 0004 E-mail: sales@revol.co.uk

GRAPHITE MACHINING

Erodex (UK) Ltd, Tipper Industrial Estate, Park Road, Halesowen, West Midlands, B63 2RH Tel: (01384) 892011 Fax: (01384) 897162 E-mail: sales@erodex.com

Ralph Coidan Ltd, 2 Boltby Way, Eaglescliffe, Stockton-on-Tees, Cleveland, TS16 0RH Tel: (01642) 790100 Fax: (01642) 790488 E-mail: sales@coidan.co.uk

Tokai Carbon UK Ltd, Roway Lane, Oldbury, West Midlands, B69 3EJ Tel: 0121-552 5577 Fax: 0121-552 6748 E-mail: john@tokaicarboneurope.com

GRAPHITE SEMICONDUCTOR TOOLING

Erodex (UK) Ltd, Tipper Industrial Estate, Park Road, Halesowen, West Midlands, B63 2RH Tel: (01384) 892011 Fax: (01384) 897162 E-mail: sales@erodex.com

GRAPHITE SHAFT GOLF CLUBS

▶ GlenGolf (Clubmaker), 16 Witchford Road, Lincoln, LN6 0ST Tel: 01522 879830 E-mail: muirfield60@ntlworld.com

GRASS CARPETS

▶ Money For Old Rope, PO Box 332, Bushey, WD23 3XZ Tel: 07050 686012 Fax: 07050 686013 E-mail: john@solditonline.net

GRATING, GRP

The Grating Co. Ltd, 1 Warner Way, Chilton Business Park, Sudbury, Suffolk, CO10 2GG Tel: (01787) 319922 Fax: (01787) 319963 E-mail: info@gratingco.co.uk

GRAVEL

Allen Newport Ltd, 31 New Path, Walton House, Fordham, Ely, Cambridgeshire, CB7 5JZ Tel: (01638) 720228 Fax: (01638) 721332 E-mail: info@allen-newport.co.uk

Bardon Concrete Ltd, Lichfield Road, Barton under Needwood, Burton-on-Trent, Staffordshire, DE13 8EF Tel: (01283) 712677 Fax: (01283) 716598 E-mail: general@aggregate.com

Joseph Barrett & Sons Ltd, 128 Eglish Road, Dungannon, County Tyrone, BT70 1LB Tel: (028) 3754 8646 Fax: (028) 3754 8863 E-mail: info@barrettconcrete.com

Bathgate Silica Sand Ltd, Arclid Quarry, Congleton Road, Arclid, Sandbach, Cheshire, CW11 4SN Tel: (01270) 762492 Fax: (01270) 759449 E-mail: info@bathgatesilica.co.uk

Boswell Bros (Salisbury) Ltd, Ford, Salisbury, SP4 6DJ Tel: (01722) 333781 Fax: (01722) 327858 E-mail: boswell.broth@virgin.net

Brett Aggregates Ltd, Brett House, Bysing Wood Road, Faversham, Kent, ME13 7UD Tel: (01795) 594051 Fax: (01795) 594027

Brett Aggregates, Waldringfield Road, Brightwell, Ipswich, IP10 0BL Tel: (01473) 621007 Fax: (01473) 736721

Brett Aggregates, North Sea Terminal, Cliffe, Rochester, Kent, ME3 7SX Tel: (01634) 220631 Fax: (01634) 220067

▶ Bridgemary Library, 74 Brewers Lane, Gosport, Hampshire, PO13 0LA Tel: (0845) 6035631 Fax: (01329) 511390 E-mail: bridgemaryaquatics@ntlworld.com

Buckingham Aggregates Ltd, Unit 6 Ballmoor, Buckingham Industrial Estate, Buckingham, MK18 1RT Tel: (01280) 817611 Fax: (01280) 817749

Builders Supply (Wakefield) Ltd, 2 Thornes Lane, Wakefield, West Yorkshire, WF1 5QH Tel: (01924) 376821 Fax: (01924) 362018

Cemex (NI) Ltd, 30 Creagh Road, Toomebridge, Antrim, BT41 3SE Tel: (028) 7965 0626 Fax: (028) 7965 0204

Cemex (NI) Ltd, 41 Manse Road, Carrowdore, Newtownards, County Down, BT22 2EZ Tel: (028) 9186 1450 Fax: (028) 9186 1555

Moreton C. Cullimore Gravels Ltd, 47 London Road, Stroud, Gloucestershire, GL5 2AU Tel: (01453) 765381 Fax: (01453) 766491

Cwmna Gro Ltd, Penybryn Farm, Sarnau, Bala, Gwynedd, LL23 7LH Tel: (01678) 530297 Fax: (01678) 530389

D P Passmore Ltd, Hunts Lane, London, E15 2QE Tel: (020) 8555 7676 Fax: (020) 8534 4470

M. Dickerson Ltd, Ely Road, Waterbeach, Cambridge, CB5 9PG Tel: (01223) 860000 Fax: (01223) 440378 E-mail: reception@m-dickerson.co.uk

Stanley Evans Ltd, Sandy Lane, Wildmoor, Bromsgrove, Worcestershire, B61 0QT Tel: 0121-366 7300 Fax: 0121-460 1397

Gibson Bros, Magherally, Banbridge, County Down, BT32 4YN Tel: (028) 4066 2771 Fax: (028) 4062 6704 E-mail: liam@gibbros.freeserve.co.uk

Norman Good & Sons Ltd, Station Road, West Bay, Bridport, Dorset, DT6 4EW Tel: (01308) 422007 Fax: (01308) 421171

J. Handford & Son Ltd, Milford House, 431 Buxton Road, Stockport, Cheshire, SK2 7HE Tel: 0161-487 3888 Fax: 0161-487 4555

Harleyford Aggregates, Harleyford, Henley Road, Marlow, Buckinghamshire, SL7 2DY Tel: (01628) 475976 Fax: (01628) 481640 E-mail: info@harleyford.co.uk

Holderness Aggregates Ltd, Mill Hill Quarry, Hull Road, Keyingham, Hull, HU12 9ST Tel: (01964) 622347

Humberside Aggregates & Excavations Ltd, The Quarry, Newport Road, North Cave, Brough, North Humberside, HU15 2NU Tel: (01430) 421503 Fax: (01430) 421116 E-mail: enquiries@hag.com

J Clubb Ltd, Church Hill, Wilmington, Dartford, DA2 7DZ Tel: (01322) 225431 Fax: (01322) 289932 E-mail: sales@jclubb.co.uk

J Curtis & Sons Ltd, Thrupp Lane, Radley, Abingdon, Oxfordshire, OX14 3NG Tel: (01235) 524545 Fax: (01235) 524545

Lafarge Aggregates Ltd, Whisby Quarry, Thorpe Road, Whisby, Lincoln, LN6 9BT Tel: (01522) 694342 Fax: (01522) 694226

Longwater Gravel, Longwater Industrial Estate, Dereham Road, New Costessey, Norwich, NR5 0TX Tel: (01603) 743767 Fax: (01603) 747302

Mid-Essex Gravel Ltd, Essex Regiment Way, Broomfield, Chelmsford, CM3 3PZ Tel: (01245) 440621 Fax: (01245) 442212 E-mail: info@midessexgravel.co.uk

Norman Emerson, 118 Ardmore Road, Derryadd, Craigavon, County Armagh, BT66 6QP Tel: (028) 3834 0700 Fax: (028) 3834 0011 E-mail: sales@normanemerson.com

Progenitive Filtration Ltd, Hampson Street, Horwich, Bolton, BL6 7JH Tel: (01204) 478210 Fax: (01204) 478211 E-mail: sales@pflfiltermedia.com

Rotherham Sand & Gravel Co. Ltd, Scrooby Top Quarry, Scrooby Top, Doncaster, South Yorkshire, DN10 6AY Tel: (01777) 818203 Fax: (01777) 816040

Smith & Sons (Bletchington) Ltd, Enslow, Kidlington, Oxfordshire, OX5 3AY Tel: (01869) 331281 Fax: (01869) 331734

The Summerleaze Waste Company Ltd, Lakeside, Summerleaze Road, Maidenhead, Berkshire, SL6 8HZ Tel: (01628) 630444 Fax: (01628) 773160 E-mail: info@summerleaze.co.uk

Supermix Concrete, 76 Strabane Road, Newtownstewart, Omagh, County Tyrone, BT78 4JZ Tel: (028) 8166 1391 Fax: (028) 8166 1391

W. Clifford Watts Ltd, 118-122 Scarborough Road, Bridlington, East Yorkshire, YO16 7NU Tel: (01262) 675383 Fax: (01262) 604629 E-mail: wcliffordwatts@aol.com

William Boyer & Sons Transport Ltd, Trout Road, West Drayton, Middlesex, UB7 7SN Tel: (01895) 445141 Fax: (01895) 442027

Thomas Williams (Euxton) Ltd, Springfield, Wigan Road, Euxton, Chorley, Lancashire, PR7 6LB Tel: (01257) 262642

GRAVITY DIE CASTINGS

A D & C Ltd, 80 Wrentham Street, Birmingham, B5 6QL Tel: 0121-666 6070 Fax: 0121-666 7585 E-mail: davidaustin@btconnect.com

Alucast Ltd, Western Way, Wednesbury, West Midlands, WS10 7BW Tel: 0121-556 6111 Fax: 0121-505 1302 E-mail: sales@alucast.co.uk

Apex Patterns, Unit 10 Redland Indust Estate, Station Hill St.Georges, Madeley, Telford, Shropshire, TF7 5EF Tel: (01952) 614337 Fax: (01952) 614337 E-mail: apexpatterns1@btclick.com

Astral Pattern Co. Ltd, Roway La, Oldbury, W. Midlands, B69 3EJ Tel: 0121-552 3507 Fax: 0121-544 2471

Bridgnorth Castings Ltd, Alveley Industrial Estate, Alveley, Bridgnorth, Shropshire, WV15 6HG Tel: (01746) 781177 Fax: (01746) 781188 E-mail: vp32@dial.pipex.com

Caddy Castings Ltd, Springfield Road, Grantham, Lincolnshire, NG31 7BQ Tel: (01476) 566667 Fax: (01476) 570220 E-mail: caddycastings@btinternet.com

Charter Castings Ltd, Bagnall Street, Great Bridge, Tipton, West Midlands, DY4 7BS Tel: 0121-557 9831 Fax: 0121-520 4761 E-mail: mail@chartercastings.co.uk

David Hunt Castings, Romsey Industrial Estate, Budds La, Romsey, Hants, SO51 0HA Tel: (01794) 511259 Fax: (01794) 518325 E-mail: davidhunt.castings@btopenworld.com

Davis & Hill, 56 Pritchett Street, Birmingham, B6 4EY Tel: 0121-359 4091 Fax: 0121-333 3163 E-mail: sales@davisandhill.co.uk

Essex Replica Castings (Basildon) Ltd, 108-112 Westmoor Street, Charlton, London, SE7 8NQ Tel: (020) 8858 6110 Fax: (020) 8305 0907 E-mail: nicktownsend@jardineinternational.com

Ferndowne, Reform Industrial Estate, Maidenhead, Berkshire, SL6 8BY Tel: (01628) 630211 Fax: (01628) 623459

Gravitech Ltd, 136 Kentish Road, Middlemore Industrial Estate, Birmingham, B21 0AY Tel: 0121-558 0847 Fax: 0121-555 8171

Hemphill Castings Ltd, 273 Bromford Lane, Washwood Heath, Birmingham, B8 2SG Tel: 0121-327 5459 Fax: 0121-322 2040

Hyde Die Casting & Manufactring Ltd, 1 Providence Mill, Alexandra Street, Hyde, Cheshire, SK14 1DX Tel: 0161-368 0996 Fax: 0161-368 6022 E-mail: hydediecasting@aol.com

Lenton Brook, Unit D Hawthorns Industrial Estate, Middlemore Road, Middlemore Road, Birmingham, B21 0BH Tel: 0121-523 9390 Fax: 0121-523 9390 E-mail: graham@lentonbrook.freeserve.co.uk

Melloy Ltd, Main Avenue, Unit C10, Treforest Industrial Estate, Pontypridd, Mid Glamorgan, CF37 5UD Tel: (01443) 824880 Fax: (01443) 844797 E-mail: enquiries@melloy.co.uk

Perry Castings, Bank Street, Wolverhampton, WV10 9DU Tel: (01902) 732910 Fax: (01902) 721046

Surecast Devizes Ltd, Roundway Mill, London Road, Devizes, Wiltshire, SN10 2EA Tel: (01380) 723402 Fax: (01380) 729063 E-mail: sales@surecast.co.uk

Thomas Bros Leeds Ltd, Stanningley Field Close, Leeds, LS13 4QG Tel: 0113-256 7210 Fax: 0113-256 9199E-mail: info@tbleeds.com

Turner Aluminium Castings Ltd, 1 Robinson Close, Telford Way Industrial Estate, Kettering, Northamptonshire, NN16 8PU Tel: (01536) 525270 Fax: (01536) 412367

W H Rowe & Son Ltd, Quayside Road, Southampton, SO18 1DH Tel: (023) 8022 5636 Fax: (023) 8022 5146 E-mail: sales@whrowe.com

GRAVITY DIES

M K Tool & Die Ltd, 19 Spackmans Way, Slough, SL1 2SA Tel: 01753 539159

GRAVITY ROLLER CONVEYOR SYSTEMS

▶ 4 Conveyor Solutions Ltd, PO Box 87, Batley, West Yorkshire, WF17 9YB Tel: (01924) 422110 Fax: (01924) 422009 E-mail: enquiries@nuwavesystems.plus.com

Amberlan Ltd, Building No 2, Brick Kiln Street, Brierley Hill, West Midlands, DY5 1JG Tel: (01384) 74332 Fax: (01384) 74334 E-mail: amberlan@blueyonder.co.uk

Clark Handling Ltd, Hobson Industrial Estate, Hobson, Newcastle upon Tyne, NE16 6EA Tel: (01207) 270825 Fax: (01207) 271393 E-mail: sales@clarkhandling.co.uk

Handling Technology, 11 Cavendish Road, Halesowen, West Midlands, B62 0DB Tel: 0121-421 6153 Fax: 0121-423 1709

Haven Equipment Co., Duncote Mill, Walcot, Telford, Shropshire, TF6 5ER Tel: (01952) 740484 Fax: (01952) 740464 E-mail: sales@havenequipment.co.uk

Kimbermatics Ltd, Cheethams Mill, Park Street, Stalybridge, Cheshire, SK15 2BT Tel: 0161-368 4891 Fax: 0161-304 8152 E-mail: kimbermatics@aol.com

Logan Teleflex UK Ltd, Sutton Road, Kingston Upon Hull, Hull, HU7 0DR Tel: (01482) 785600 Fax: (01482) 785699 E-mail: marketing@loganteleflex.co.uk

The Nicholson Group of Companies, Meridian Centre, King Street, Oldham, OL8 1EZ Tel: (08450) 540526 Fax: (08450) 540527 E-mail: enquiries@nicholson-group.co.uk

Wolverhampton Handling Ltd, Unit 10 Planetary Industrial Estate, Planetary Road, Willenhall, West Midlands, WV13 3XQ Tel: (01902) 726481 Fax: (01902) 864744 E-mail: sales@wolverhamptonhandling.co.uk

GRAVURE PRINTING SERVICES, PACKAGING, REEL TO REEL

Mipa (UK) Ltd, 25 Robin Ride, Brackley, Northamptonshire, NN13 6PU Tel: (01280) 841190 Fax: (01280) 841191 E-mail: mipauk@aol.com

GREASE, *See also headings for particular types*

Browns Of Burwell Ltd, 7 North Street, Burwell, Whittlesford, Cambridge, CB4 3QW Tel: (01638) 741306 Fax: (01638) 743497 E-mail: sales@brownsofburwell.co.uk
Forte Lubricants Ltd, Unit 4 Parbrook Close, Coventry, CV4 9XY Tel: (024) 7647 4069 Fax: (024) 7647 1213
Total Butler, County House, Bayshill Road, Cheltenham, Gloucestershire, GL50 3BA Tel: (0845) 6027283 Fax: (01242) 229498 E-mail: rm.gb-mb-cssteam@totalbutler.co.uk

GREASE CONVERTERS

Aluline (Greasetraps) Ltd, Harbour House, 1 Aldborough Street, Blyth, Northumberland, NE24 2EU Tel: (01670) 544322 Fax: (01670) 544340 E-mail: design@aluline.co.uk

GREASE FITTINGS

Kingfisher (Lubrication) Ltd, 136 Meanwood Road, Leeds, LS7 2BT Tel: 0113-209 8989 Fax: 0113-237 4027 E-mail: enquiries@kingfisherlub.co.uk

GREASE GUNS, *See also headings for particular types*

A E Westwood Ltd, Tything Road, Kinwarton, Alcester, Warwickshire, B49 6ES Tel: (01789) 765777 Fax: (01789) 765727 E-mail: aewestwood@thesjgroup.com
Lumatic Ga Ltd, Theaklen Drive, St. Leonards-on-Sea, East Sussex, TN38 9AZ Tel: (01424) 436343 Fax: (01424) 429926 E-mail: sales@lumatic.co.uk
Samoa Ltd, Asturias House Barrs Fold Road, Wingates Industrial Estate, Westhoughton, Bolton, BL5 3XP Tel: (01942) 850600 Fax: (01204) 812160 E-mail: sales@samoa.ltd.uk
Stephens (Midlands) Ltd, Greets Green Industrial Estate, West Bromwich, West Midlands, B70 9EW Tel: 0121-522 2221 Fax: 0121-557 6861 E-mail: info@stephenslube.co.uk

GREASE NIPPLE MANUFRS

Kingfisher (Lubrication) Ltd, 136 Meanwood Road, Leeds, LS7 2BT Tel: 0113-209 8989 Fax: 0113-237 4027 E-mail: enquiries@kingfisherlub.co.uk
Stephens (Midlands) Ltd, Greets Green Industrial Estate, West Bromwich, West Midlands, B70 9EW Tel: 0121-522 2221 Fax: 0121-557 6861 E-mail: info@stephenslube.co.uk

GREASE TRAP/INTERCEPTOR MAINTENANCE/REPAIR SERVICES

Aluline (Greasetraps) Ltd, Harbour House, 1 Aldborough Street, Blyth, Northumberland, NE24 2EU Tel: (01670) 544322 Fax: (01670) 544340 E-mail: design@aluline.co.uk
Bioclear Environmental Ltd, Unit 10, Carver Road, Astonfields Industrial Estate, Stafford, ST16 3HR Tel: (01785) 254410 Fax: (01785) 254553 E-mail: sales@bioclear.fsnet.co.uk
▶ Blockstopper Greasetraps, Unit 6, Priestfield Industria Estate, Blantyre, Glasgow, G72 OJA Tel: (01698) 828131 E-mail: cyoker@hotmail.com

GREASE TRAPS OR INTERCEPTORS

Aluline (Greasetraps) Ltd, Harbour House, 1 Aldborough Street, Blyth, Northumberland, NE24 2EU Tel: (01670) 544322 Fax: (01670) 544340 E-mail: design@aluline.co.uk
▶ Blockstopper Greasetraps, Unit 6, Priestfield Industria Estate, Blantyre, Glasgow, G72 OJA Tel: (01698) 828131 E-mail: cyoker@hotmail.com
Hunter Plastics Ltd, Nathan Way, London, SE28 0AE Tel: (020) 8317 1551 Fax: (020) 8317 7764 E-mail: info@hunterplastics.co.uk
Swan Enviro Freshmesh Systems, 10 Engine Road, Loanhead, Midlothian, EH20 9RF Tel: 0131-440 3812 Fax: 0131-448 2119 E-mail: sales@swanenviro.com

GREENHOUSE BOILERS

▶ Cambridge Glass House Co. Ltd, 236 Main Road, Newport, Brough, North Humberside, HU15 2RH Tel: (01430) 449440 Fax: (01430) 449331 E-mail: info@cambridgeglasshouse.co.uk
Metallic Construction Co. Ltd, Alfreton Road, Derby, DE21 4AQ Tel: (01332) 831296 Fax: (01332) 833712

GREENHOUSE VENTILATION CONTROLS

Electroflora Ltd, The Old Transmitter House, The Baulk, Clapham, Bedford, MK41 6AA Tel: (01234) 262745 Fax: (01234) 262753
Thermoforce Ltd, Wakefield Road, Cockermouth, Cumbria, CA13 0HS Tel: (01900) 823231 Fax: (01900) 825965 E-mail: sales@thermoforce.co.uk

GREENHOUSES

Bridge Greenhouses Ltd, Keynor Farm, Keynor Lane, Sidlesham, Chichester, West Sussex, PO20 7NQ Tel: (01243) 641789 Fax: (01243) 641788 E-mail: south@bridgegreenhouses.co.uk
C H Whitehouse Ltd, Buckhurst Works, Bells Yew Green, Tunbridge Wells, Kent, TN3 9BN Tel: (01892) 750247 Fax: (01892) 750247
Cambridge Glass House Co. Ltd, 236 Main Road, Newport, Brough, North Humberside, HU15 2RH Tel: (01430) 449440 Fax: (01430) 449331 E-mail: info@cambridgeglasshouse.co.uk
E C Walton & Co. Ltd, Old North Road, Sutton-on-Trent, Newark, Nottinghamshire, NG23 6QN Tel: (01636) 821215 Fax: (01636) 822027 E-mail: waltons@waltons.co.uk
Elite Greenhouses Ltd, Bent Spur Road, Kearsley, Bolton, BL4 8PD Tel: (01204) 791488 Fax: (01204) 862412 E-mail: enquiries@elite-greenhouses.co.uk
Halls Garden Products, PO Box 947, Maidstone, Kent, ME20 6SQ Tel: (01622) 791234 Fax: (01622) 791060 E-mail: enquiries@halls.uk.com
Hartley Botanic Ltd, Wellington Road, Greenfield, Oldham, OL3 7AG Tel: (0870) 7770320 Fax: (0870) 7770323 E-mail: info@hartleybotanic.co.uk
Morris Polythene Greenhouses, 53a Lenagh Road, Omagh, County Tyrone, BT79 7RG Tel: (028) 8164 8205 E-mail: sales@morrispolytunnels.co.uk
Norfolk Greenhouses Ltd, Chiswick Avenue, Mildenhall, Bury St. Edmunds, Suffolk, IP28 7AZ Tel: (01638) 713418 Fax: (01638) 714715 E-mail: sales@norfolk-greenhouses.co.uk
Northern Polytunnels Ltd, Mill Green, Waterside Road, Colne, Lancashire, BB8 0TA Tel: (01282) 873120 Fax: (01282) 871733 E-mail: info@npstructures.co.uk
Edward Owen Engineering, Unit 2, The Mazes, East Street, Braintree, Essex, CM7 3JJ Tel: (01376) 345631 Fax: (01376) 345631
Peritys Greenhouses, Bona Lane, Leverington, Wisbech, Cambridgeshire, PE13 5JQ Tel: (01945) 410471 Fax: (01945) 410471 E-mail: sales@peritys.co.uk
Solardome Industries, Unit 3 Hammerley Enterprise Park, Burnetts Lane, Horton Heath, Eastleigh, Hampshire, SO50 7DJ Tel: (023) 8069 7128 Fax: (023) 8069 7129 E-mail: sales@solardome.co.uk
▶ T C Munro, The Hall, George Street, Falkirk, FK2 7EY Tel: (01324) 623729 Fax: (01324) 620693 E-mail: info@tcmunro.co.uk
▶ Timber-Cabins.Co.Uk, Red Mayes Farm, Limewalk, Long Sutton, Spalding, Spalding, Lincolnshire, PE12 9HG Tel: (01406) 363978 Fax: (01406) 365689 E-mail: enquires@timber-cabins.co.uk
Unique Dutch Light Co. Ltd, Bent Spur Road, Kearsley, Bolton, BL4 8PD Tel: (01204) 571800 Fax: (01204) 862412 E-mail: enquiries@elite-greenhouses.co.uk
▶ Veerman's Shed Centre, 130 High Street, Tranent, East Lothian, EH33 1HJ Tel: (01875) 613090 Fax: (01875) 617492 E-mail: email@veermans.co.uk

GREETING CARD ACCESSORIES

▶ Craft Fairy, 8 Park View, Coychurch, Bridgend, Mid Glamorgan, CF35 5HS Tel: (01656) 653796 E-mail: yvonne@craftfairy.co.uk

GREETING CARD BLANKS

Arcraft Products 2005 Ltd, 1 Mousell Street, Cheetham, Manchester, M8 8HY Tel: 0161-833 2269 Fax: 0161-833 2269 E-mail: greetings16@hotmail.com

GREETING CARD DESIGN

▶ Bag a Card, 2 Falmouth Way, London, E17 7NZ Tel: (0845) 6445787 E-mail: sales@bag-a-card.com
▶ Cardtoon Creations, 7 Kiln Crescent, Bishop Middleham, Ferryhill, County Durham, DL17 9AP Tel: (07747) 746123 E-mail: sales@cardsgifts.co.uk
▶ Little Gems Handmade Cards, 63 Wentworth Road, Southend-on-Sea, SS2 5LF Tel: (01702) 613945
▶ Minty Designs, 1 New Buildings, Harbertonford, Totnes, Devon, TQ9 7SZ Tel: 01803 731077 Fax: (01803) 864649 E-mail: sales@mintydesigns.com
▶ Minuteman Press, 3/5 Highfield Road, Hall Green, Birmingham, B28 0EL Tel: 0121-777 0018 Fax: 0121-777 5810 E-mail: karl.mccabe@minutemanpress.com
▶ SilverTripod.com, PO Box 553, Redhill, RH1 6XU Tel: 07793 155569 E-mail: info@silvertripod.com
▶ The Strawberry Card Co., 8 Clarence Road, Exmouth, Devon, EX8 1LE Tel: (01395) 274923 Fax: (01395) 274923 E-mail: sian@thestrawberrycardcompany.co.uk

GREETING CARDS

▶ Aileen's Cards, 5 Finlay Avenue, East Calder, Livingston, West Lothian, EH53 0RP Tel: (01506) 881760 E-mail: info@aileens-cards.co.uk
Atmosphere, 3 Manners Corner, Manners Way, Southend-on-Sea, SS2 6QR Tel: (01702) 335186 Fax: (01702) 337218
Carlton Cards Ltd, Mill St East, Dewsbury, West Yorkshire, WF12 9AW Tel: (01924) 465200 Fax: (01924) 453908
▶ Celebrity Voices Ltd, 23 Springfeilds, Waltham Abbey, Essex, EN9 1UD Tel: (01992) 611097 E-mail: stuart@celebrityvoices.co.uk
▶ Compass Business Promotions Ltd, 16 Crosslee Gardens, Crosslee, Johnstone, Renfrewshire, PA6 7AF Tel: (01505) 613569 Fax: (01505) 612603
▶ Craft Fairy, 8 Park View, Coychurch, Bridgend, Mid Glamorgan, CF35 5HS Tel: (01656) 653796 E-mail: yvonne@craftfairy.co.uk
▶ Creative Detail, 32 Thorncliffe Drive, Darwen, Lancashire, BB3 3QA Tel: 01254 773391 E-mail: val@creative-detail.co.uk
▶ D & P Shop, 76 Huddersfield Road, Elland, West Yorkshire, HX5 9AA Tel: (01422) 310552 Fax: (01422) 310552 E-mail: sales@dandpshop.co.uk
Eason & Son Ni Ltd, 21-25 Boucher Road, Belfast, BT12 6QU Tel: (028) 9038 1200 Fax: (028) 9068 2544 E-mail: accountsreceivable@eason.co.uk
Flights Of Fancy, 15 New Street, Leamington Spa, Warwickshire, CV31 1HP Tel: (01926) 423436 Fax: (01926) 311925 E-mail: mail@flightsoffancy.co.uk
▶ greetings2u.co.uk, 7 Coldstream Terrace, Riverside, Cardiff, CF11 6LJ Tel: 07855 282576 E-mail: anthony.thomas120@ntlworld.com
Hallmark Cards, Dawson Lane, Dudley Hill, Bradford, West Yorkshire, BD4 6HW Tel: (01274) 784200 Fax: (01274) 784002 E-mail: name@hallmark.com
▶ Handmade Wedding Invitations & Stationery By Datz Creationz, 5 Alwin Road, Rowley Regis, West Midlands, B65 8BN Tel: (07759) 820406 E-mail: datzcreationz@blueyonder.co.uk
▶ Hertfordshire Graphics Ltd, 6 St Andrew Street, Hertford, SG14 1JE Tel: (01992) 503636 Fax: (01992) 503244 E-mail: sales@hertfordshiregraphics.co.uk
Hughes & Coleman Ltd, Delta Close, Norwich, NR6 6BG Tel: (01603) 426159 Fax: (01603) 486853 E-mail: sales@hughesandcoleman.co.uk
Limavady Printing Co. Ltd, 26C Catherine Street, Limavady, County Londonderry, BT49 9DB Tel: (028) 7776 2051 Fax: (028) 7776 2132 E-mail: print@limprint.com
▶ Rachel Ellen Design, 313 Hucknall Road, Nottingham, NG5 1FJ Tel: 0115-962 2862 Fax: 0115-969 2724 E-mail: rachel@rachelellen.fsworld.co.uk
Siop Y Bont, 69-70a, The Market Market Street, Pontypridd, Mid Glamorgan, CF37 2SP Tel: (01443) 402584 E-mail: siopybont@yahoo.com
▶ Specialcards4you, 65 Oakfield Road, Benfleet, Essex, SS7 5NS Tel: (01268) 752104 Fax: (01268) 752104 E-mail: specialcards4you@googlemail.com
▶ Susieart, 38 Hill Close, Lightpill, Stroud, Gloucestershire, GL5 3PG Tel: (01453) 762013 E-mail: sue-halliday@tiscali.co.uk
Paul White Ltd, 69 Upper Accomodation Road, Leeds, LS9 8LS Tel: 0113-248 9898 Fax: 0113-248 4863 E-mail: leeds@paulwhiteltd.co.uk
▶ www.greetingcards-online.co.uk, Barley Sheaf School House, Holland Fen, Lincoln, LN4 4QH Tel: (01205) 280469 Fax: (01205) 280469 E-mail: enquiries@greetingcards-online.co.uk

GREETINGS CARDS, BLANK

▶ Aileen's Cards, 5 Finlay Avenue, East Calder, Livingston, West Lothian, EH53 0RP Tel: (01506) 881760 E-mail: info@aileens-cards.co.uk
▶ Bag a Card, 2 Falmouth Way, London, E17 7NZ Tel: (0845) 6445787 E-mail: sales@bag-a-card.com
▶ Minty Designs, 1 New Buildings, Harbertonford, Totnes, Devon, TQ9 7SZ Tel: 01803 731077 Fax: (01803) 864649 E-mail: sales@mintydesigns.com
Seaton Hobby Shop, Goulden Lion House, 23 Fore Street, Seaton, Devon, EX12 2LE Tel: (01297) 22025 Fax: (01297) 22025 E-mail: email@seatonhobbyshop.com
SendaCard, 19, Business Science Park, Nuns Corner, Grimsby, North East Lincolnshire, DN34 5FQ Tel: 01472 822554 E-mail: sales@sendacard.co.uk
▶ SilverTripod.com, PO Box 553, Redhill, RH1 6XU Tel: 07793 155569 E-mail: info@silvertripod.com

GREETINGS CARDS, CORPORATE

▶ Little Gems Handmade Cards, 63 Wentworth Road, Southend-on-Sea, SS2 5LF Tel: (01702) 613945
▶ SilverTripod.com, PO Box 553, Redhill, RH1 6XU Tel: 07793 155569 E-mail: info@silvertripod.com

GREY CLOTH/LOOM STATE FABRICS

Broome & Wellington Aviation Ltd, 86 Princess Street, Manchester, M1 6NG Tel: 0161-236 2317 Fax: 0161-228 1326 E-mail: broom@broomwell.com
G C Newbury & Co. Ltd, Walmar House, 296 Regent Street, London, W1B 3HR Tel: (020) 7255 2303 Fax: (020) 7255 1453 E-mail: general@gcnewbury.co.uk
Ernest Griffith & Sons Ltd, Praed Rd, Trafford Park, Manchester, M17 1PQ Tel: 0161-877 1655 Fax: 0161-877 6577 E-mail: pdbrearley@aol.com
Indo African Exports Ltd, Failsworth Mill, Ashton Road West, Failsworth, Manchester, M35 0FR Tel: 0161-934 4004 Fax: 0161-683 4280 E-mail: indo@fabric.co.uk
M & N Textiles Ltd, Wrengate House, 221 Palatine Road, Didsbury, Manchester, M20 2EE Tel: 0161-438 1050 Fax: 0161-438 1021 E-mail: mandn@wrengate.co.uk
Premier Textiles Ltd, 61 Bloom Street, Manchester, M1 3LY Tel: 0161-236 2212 Fax: 0161-236 9786 E-mail: info@premier-textiles.com
Swiscot Textiles Ltd, Canada House, 3 Chepstow Street, Manchester, M1 5FW Tel: 0161-236 1025 Fax: 0161-236 6635 E-mail: info@swiscot.com

GREY IRON CASTINGS

▶ B A S Castings Ltd, Wharf Road Industrial Estate, Pinxton, Nottingham, NG16 6LE Tel: (01773) 812028 Fax: (01773) 861948 E-mail: sales@bascastings.com
Blackwood Engineering Ltd, Glandwr Industrial Estate, Aberbeeg, Abertillery, Gwent, NP13 2LN Tel: (01495) 214331 Fax: (01495) 217309
Cannop Foundry 1981 Ltd, Forest Vale Indust Estate, Crabtree Road, Forest Vale Industrial Estate, Cinderford, Gloucestershire, GL14 2YQ Tel: (01594) 822143 Fax: (01594) 824200 E-mail: sales@cannop.co.uk
Chamberlin & Hill plc, Chuckery Foundary, Chuckery Road, Walsall, WS1 2DU Tel: (01922) 492000 Fax: (01922) 638370 E-mail: plc@chamberlin.co.uk
Crane Foundry Ltd, PO Box 43, Wolverhampton, WV1 2QX Tel: (01902) 452731 Fax: (01902) 454895
Crowncast Ltd, Rushenden Road, Queenborough, Kent, ME11 5HD Tel: (01795) 662722 Fax: (01795) 666552 E-mail: crowncast@whsmithnet.co.uk
Deeleys Castings Ltd, Leamore Lane, Walsall, WS2 7BY Tel: (01922) 476898 Fax: (01922) 493507 E-mail: deeleys@fsmail.net
Feldaroll Foundry Ltd, Units 14-21A, Bailie Gate Industrial Estate, Sturminster Marshall, Wimborne, Dorset, BH21 4DB Tel: (01258) 857754 Fax: (01258) 857353
Graydon Castings Ltd, Canal Side Indust Estate, Brettell Lane, Brockmoor, Brierley Hill, West Midlands, DY5 3JU Tel: (01384) 571559 Fax: (01384) 571559
H Downs & Sons Huddersfield Ltd, Peacock Works, Leeds Road, Huddersfield, HD2 1XR Tel: (01484) 428203 Fax: (01484) 546993 E-mail: sales@hdowns.co.uk
H & H Iron Foundries Ltd, St. Annes Road, Willenhall, West Midlands, WV13 1EB Tel: (01902) 607988 Fax: (01902) 609987 E-mail: chris@hhironfoundries.com
Hillsyde Foundry (Staffordshire) Ltd, Apedale Works, Rowhurst Industrial Estate, Chesterton, Newcastle, Staffordshire, ST5 6BD Tel: (01782) 564411 Fax: (01782) 562546 E-mail: sales@hillsyde.com
Jennings Winch & Foundry Co. Ltd, Tatham Street, Sunderland, SR1 2AG Tel: 0191-567 4408 Fax: 0191-510 1549 E-mail: jwf.co.ltd@aol.com
John Rhodes & Son Ltd, Hightown Foundry, Rhodes Street, Castleford, West Yorkshire, WF10 5LN Tel: (01977) 552324 Fax: (01977) 668011E-mail: richardshaw@johnrhodes.co.uk
Joseph & Jesse Siddons Ltd, Howard Street, Hill Top, West Bromwich, West Midlands, B70 0TB Tel: 0121-556 0218 Fax: 0121-556 3843 E-mail: info@jjsiddons.co.uk
Laycast Ltd, Sheffield Road, Woodhouse Mill, Sheffield, S13 9ZD Tel: 0114-288 9995 Fax: 0114-288 9500 E-mail: info@laycast.com
Majorfax Ltd, Charles Street, Walsall, WS2 9LZ Tel: (01922) 645815 Fax: (01922) 620500 E-mail: castings@majorfax.co.uk
Newby & Son Ironfounders Ltd, Smiths Road, Wednesbury, West Midlands, WS10 0PB Tel: 0121-556 4451 Fax: 0121-505 3626 E-mail: sales@newbyfoundries.co.uk

GREY IRON CASTINGS – *continued*

Ouzledale Foundry Co. Ltd, PO Box 4, Barnoldswick, Lancashire, BB18 6BN Tel: (01282) 813235 Fax: (01282) 816876

Treforest Foundry Ltd, 16 Windsor Road, Pontypridd, Mid Glamorgan, CF37 1BY Tel: (01443) 402075 Fax: (01443) 486182 E-mail: enquiries@treforest-foundry.com

Vald Birn (UK) Ltd, Cambois, Blyth, Northumberland, NE24 1SW Tel: (01670) 818111 Fax: (01670) 855511 E-mail: sales@valdbirn.co.uk

GRILLES

▶ Renson Fabrications, Fairfax House, Bircholt Road, Maidstone, Kent, ME15 9SF Tel: (01622) 685658 Fax: (01622) 688762 E-mail: info@rensonuk.net

GRINDING DISCS

Arkwell Fasteners Ltd, Unit 1, Chapel Street, Long Eaton, Nottingham, NG10 1EQ Tel: 0115-973 1181 Fax: 0115-946 1123 E-mail: sales@arkwell.co.uk

Tyrolit Ltd, Eldon Close, Crick, Northampton, NN6 7UD Tel: (01788) 823738 Fax: (01788) 823089

GRINDING LUBRICANTS

Oel Held UK Ltd, 16 Colomendy Industrial Estate, Rhyl Road, Denbigh, Clwyd, LL16 5TA Tel: (01745) 814777 Fax: (01745) 813222 E-mail: info@oelheldgroup.co.uk

GRINDING MACHINES, *See also headings under Grinding Machines*

Abwood Machine Tools, 615 Princes Road, Dartford, DA2 6EF Tel: (01322) 225271 Fax: (01322) 291862 E-mail: sales@abwoodcnc.co.uk

▶ All Saints, 18 Syston Mill, Mill Lane, Syston, Leicester, LE7 1NS Tel: 0116-269 2909

A.J. Baker (Grinding) Ltd, Middlemore Lane West, Redhouse Industrial Estate, Aldridge, Walsall, WS9 8BG Tel: (01922) 745075 Fax: 0121-378 3291 E-mail: enquiries@ajbaker.com

Churchill Tool Co. Ltd, Empress Street, Old Trafford, Manchester, M16 9EN Tel: 0161-848 9539 Fax: 0161-872 9234 E-mail: info@churchill-grinders.co.uk

▶ Created, Newhouses Road, Broxburn, West Lothian, EH52 5MZ Tel: (01506) 853587 Fax: (01506) 856106

Equip (Midlands) Ltd, Byron Street, Buxton, Derbyshire, SK17 6NT Tel: (01298) 22233 Fax: (01298) 72097

Ingersoll International UK Ltd, 7 Sopwith Way, Drayton Fields, Daventry, Northamptonshire, NN11 5PB Tel: (01327) 313500 Fax: (01327) 313509 E-mail: inggmbh@ingersoll-uk.co.uk

Jubilee Machine Tools, Nuns Street, Derby, DE1 3LS Tel: (01332) 348749 Fax: (01332) 342416 E-mail: sales@jubileemactools.com

Lambert Machine Tool Co. Ltd, Luton Street, Keighley, West Yorkshire, BD21 2LE Tel: (01535) 611996 Fax: (01535) 610771 E-mail: ray@lambertmt.co.uk

Machinery Products UK Ltd, Four Trees, Main Road, South Elkington, Louth, Lincolnshire, LN11 0RU Tel: (01507) 610108 Fax: (01507) 610044 E-mail: johnny.walker@btconnect.com

RJH Morrisflex Holdings Ltd, Artillery Street, Heckmondwike, West Yorkshire, WF16 0NR Tel: (01924) 402490 Fax: (01924) 404635 E-mail: sales@rjheng.co.uk

▶ Supreme Grinding Machines, Church Gates, Church Street, Mexborough, South Yorkshire, S64 0ER Tel: (07710) 945439 Fax: (01709) 570475 E-mail: supremegrindingmachines@hotmail.co.uk

▶ T H S Tools Group, Salisbury House Unit 4, Centurion Business Park, Bessemer Way, Rotherham, South Yorkshire, S60 1FB Tel: (01709) 724000 Fax: (01709) 724014 E-mail: guy.farmer@thstools.co.uk

▶ Techni Grind Preston Machining Ltd, Unit 62 Red Scar Industrial Estate, Longridge Road, Ribbleton, Preston, PR2 5ND Tel: (01772) 797589 Fax: (01772) 797682 E-mail: sales@tgmeng.co.uk

Toyoda Mitsui Europe, Matrix House, Loughborough Motorway Trading Estate, Gelders Hall Road, Shepshed, Loughborough, Leicestershire, LE12 9NH Tel: (01509) 501730 Fax: (01509) 501730 E-mail: sales@toyoda-mitsui.com

Wendt Boart (UK) Ltd, Station Road, Staplehurst, Tonbridge, Kent, TN12 0QD Tel: (01580) 890800 Fax: (01580) 890888 E-mail: sales@wbuk.wendtgroup.com

GRINDING MACHINES TO SPECIFICATION

▶ Kemutec Powder Technologies Ltd, Springwood Way, Macclesfield, Cheshire, SK10 2ND Tel: (01625) 412000 Fax: (01625) 412001 E-mail: sales@kemutec.com

GRINDING MEDIA, *See also headings for particular types*

Britcast Plant & Machinery Dealer, Green Acres, Shere Road, West Clandon, Guildford, Surrey, GU4 8SG Tel: (01483) 223696 Fax: (01483) 223696 E-mail: britcast@lineone.net

C 4 Carbides (International) Ltd, 9 Nuffield Road, Cambridge, CB4 1TF Tel: (01223) 506406 Fax: (01223) 225405 E-mail: janice@c4carbides.com

Helipebs Controls Ltd, Premier Works, Sisson Road, Gloucester, GL2 0RE Tel: (01452) 423201 Fax: (01452) 307665 E-mail: sales@helipebs.co.uk

P E Hines & Sons Ltd, Whitebridge Lane, Stone, Staffordshire, ST15 8LU Tel: (01785) 814921 Fax: (01785) 818808 E-mail: p.e.hines@iclwebkit.co.uk

Potters Ballotini Ne Ltd, Darlington Road, West Auckland, Bishop Auckland, County Durham, DL14 9PR Tel: (01388) 830800 Fax: (01388) 830819

Royal Steel Ball Products, 6 Egerton Square, Knutsford, Cheshire, WA16 6EY Tel: (01565) 653881 Fax: (01565) 653870 E-mail: pmather@onetel.net.uk

Sivil & Marine Ltd, Gibson Lane, Melton, North Ferriby, East Yorkshire, HU14 3HN Tel: (01482) 633305 Fax: (01482) 634835 E-mail: info@sivilandmarine.co.uk

GRINDING MILLS

Blacklake Systems Ltd, Unit 6a Whitebridge Estate, Stone, Staffordshire, ST15 8LQ Tel: (01785) 817170 Fax: (01785) 812406 E-mail: charles@whitebridge.co.uk

Bradley Pulverizer Co., 15 Kennet Road, Crayford, Crayford, Dartford, DA1 4QN Tel: (01322) 559106 Fax: (01322) 528690 E-mail: bradley.pulverizer@btinternet.com

British Rema Manufacturing Co. Ltd, Image Works, Foxwood Close, Chesterfield, Derbyshire, S41 9RN Tel: (01246) 269955 Fax: (01246) 269944 E-mail: sales@britishrema.co.uk

Capco Test Ltd, Riverside View, Wickham Market, Suffolk, IP13 0TA Tel: (01728) 747407 Fax: (01728) 747599 E-mail: sales@capco.co.uk

Midland Precision Equipment Co. Ltd, Haslucks Green Road, Shirley, Solihull, West Midlands, B90 2LY Tel: 0121-744 2719 Fax: 0121-733 1296 E-mail: sales@midland-precision.co.uk

Sardon International Ltd, 28 Wylde Green Road, Sutton Coldfield, West Midlands, B72 1HD Tel: 0121-354 2165 Fax: 0121-354 2165

GRINDING SERVICES, *See also headings for particular types*

A Maffei & Sons, Pollard Street East, Manchester, M40 7FS Tel: 0161-273 4029

Abbey Precision Ltd, 72 Alston Drive, Bradwell Abbey, Milton Keynes, MK13 9HG Tel: (01908) 225858 Fax: (01908) 225848 E-mail: sales@abbeyprecision.com

Accurate Grinding, Unit 6 Dawsons Lane, Barwell, Leicester, LE9 8BE Tel: (01455) 840888 Fax: (01455) 840888

Alpha Tool Grinding, Unit 6 Stafford Park 4, Telford, Shropshire, TF3 3BA Tel: (01952) 292988 Fax: (01952) 292988

Ambit Precision Grinding, 38a Kenilworth Drive, Oadby, Leicester, LE2 5LG Tel: 0116-271 1011 Fax: 0161-627 1101 E-mail: adam@ambit.fsnet.co.uk

Automatic Engineers (Hinckley) Ltd, Burbage Road, Burbage, Hinckley, Leicestershire, LE10 2TP Tel: (01455) 238033 Fax: (01455) 615101 E-mail: roger@automaticengineers.com

Bedestone Ltd, Boulton Ho, 41 Icknield St, Hockley, Birmingham, B18 5AY Tel: 0121-554 3283 Fax: 0121-507 0140 E-mail: bedestone@aol.com

Bosworth Tools (Cutters) Ltd, Unit 19 20, Sketchley Meadows Industrial Estate, Hinckley, Leicestershire, LE10 3ES Tel: (01455) 250066 Fax: (01455) 250077

Bramco Steel Services Ltd, Thorncliffe Park Estate, Chapeltown, Sheffield, S35 2PH Tel: 0114-246 3033 Fax: 0114-245 5901

Crusherform Grinding Co., 30 Kennington Road, Nuffield Industrial Estate, Poole, Dorset, BH17 0GF Tel: (01202) 679363 Fax: (01202) 682970

Davies Precision Grinding Ltd, 282 Upper Balsall Heath Road, Birmingham, B12 9DR Tel: 0121-440 4400 Fax: 0121-440 1414

Drurys Engineering Ltd, 21 Knowl Piece, Wilbury Way, Hitchin, Hertfordshire, SG4 0TY Tel: (01462) 420123 Fax: (01462) 420124 E-mail: info@drurys.co.uk

Enterprise Grinding Ltd, 58 Sapcote Trading Centre, Powke Lane, Cradley Heath, West Midlands, B64 5QX Tel: (01384) 413598 Fax: (01384) 413599

Ewen Engineering, Roscoe Road, Sheffield, S3 7DZ Tel: 0114-273 0327 Fax: 0114-275 1955 E-mail: sales@ewenengineering.co.uk

G B Precision Engineering Co., 1 Port Hope Road, Birmingham, B11 1JS Tel: 0121-766 7008 Fax: 0121-773 2824 E-mail: info@gbprecision.co.uk

G & W Grinding Services Ltd, Unit A Thomas Street, Walsall, WS2 8NE Tel: (01922) 723481 Fax: (01922) 724968

Kenval Precision Grinding, 204 St Andrews Road, Northampton, NN2 6DA Tel: (01604) 622960 Fax: (01604) 630435

Kepston Holdings Ltd, Unit 2 Coppice Lane, Walsall, WS9 9AA Tel: (01922) 743133 Fax: (01922) 743130 E-mail: sales@kepston.co.uk

Magchucks (UK), 16-22 Lodge Road, Hockley, Birmingham, B18 5PN Tel: 0121-551 1566 Fax: 0121-523 9188

▶ Microplus Engineering Ltd, Unit 12 Gainsborough Trad Estate, Rufford Road, Stourbridge, West Midlands, DY9 7ND Tel: (01384) 442991 Fax: (01384) 441164

Moorgate Precision Engineering, Polymer House, Admin Road, Knowsley Industrial Park, Liverpool, L33 7TZ Tel: 0151-548 7766 Fax: 0151-548 7788 E-mail: ian@moorgate-precison.com

Neville Roe Industries Ltd, Euro Works, Liverpool Street, Sheffield, S9 2PU Tel: 0114-243 0395 Fax: 0114-243 3310 E-mail: enquiries@nevroeind.com

Promac Precision Engineering Ltd, 49 Ivatt Way, Peterborough, PE3 7PN Tel: (01733) 333000 Fax: (01733) 333001 E-mail: management@promac.fsnet.co.uk

R V J Engineering, Cannock Chase Enterprise Centre, Hednesford, Cannock, Staffordshire, WS12 0QU Tel: (01543) 425264 Fax: (01543) 512451 E-mail: rvj.com@virgin.net

T & G Engineering Co. Ltd, Unit 14 Camphill Industrial Estate, Camphill Road, West Byfleet, Surrey, KT14 6EW Tel: (01932) 353228 Fax: (01932) 349692 E-mail: sales@tgengineering.co.uk

GRINDING SERVICES, CRYOGENIC, *See Cryogenic Grinding*

GRINDING WHEEL BALANCERS

Schmitt Europe Ltd, Sir William Lyons Road, University of Warwick Science Park, Coventry, CV4 7EZ Tel: (024) 7669 7192 Fax: (024) 7641 2697 E-mail: enquiries@schmitt.co.uk

GRINDING WHEELS

▶ AbTec Industries Ltd, Unit 4, Venture Court, Boleness Road, Wisbech, Cambridgeshire, PE13 2XQ Tel: (01945) 585500 Fax: (01945) 585052 E-mail: sales@abrasivetechnology.net

Consort Abrasives Products Ltd, Swallowfields, Welwyn Garden City, Hertfordshire, AL7 1JD Tel: (01707) 330319 Fax: (01707) 376697 E-mail: consortabrasives@btconnect.com

D G S Grinding Wheels & Machines Ltd, 90-92 Dovedale Road, Wolverhampton, WV4 6RA Tel: (01902) 661111 Fax: (01902) 880311 E-mail: sales@dgsabrasives.co.uk

Drake Tooling & Abrasives Ltd, Unit 12 Chantry Park, Cowley Road, Nuffield Industrial Park, Poole, Dorset, BH17 0UJ Tel: (01202) 666467 Fax: (01202) 666468 E-mail: drake@poolebranch.co.uk

Grinding Centre, 62 Berkeley Street, Glasgow, G3 7DS Tel: 0141-564 8888 Fax: 0141-564 1084 E-mail: sales@thegrindingcentre.co.uk

Jewel Abrasives, Stanley Street, Worksop, Nottinghamshire, S81 7HX Tel: (01909) 472650 Fax: (01909) 532186

P V R Direct Ltd, 8 St. Stephens Business Centre, Poplar Road, Warmley, Bristol, BS30 5HT Tel: 0117-967 5115 Fax: 0117-935 2399 E-mail: vivrooker@aol.com

Phoenix Abrasive Wheel Co. Ltd, 71 Shepley Industrial Estate South, Audenshaw, Manchester, M34 5DW Tel: 0161-320 9580 Fax: 0161-335 9074 E-mail: phoenixabr@aol.com

Saint-Gobain Abrasives, Doxey Road, Stafford, ST16 1EA Tel: (01785) 223281 Fax: (01785) 213487 E-mail: sales.gloucester.uk@saint-gobain.com

GRINDING WHEELS, ALLOY

▶ Ayce Systems Ltd, C Snaygill Industrial Estate, Keighley Road, Skipton, North Yorkshire, BD23 2QR Tel: (01756) 709709 Fax: (01756) 709409 E-mail: info@aycesystems.co.uk

GRIT BLASTING ABRASIVE MATERIALS

Kuhmichel U K, Friars Mill, Friars Terrace, Stafford, ST17 4AU Tel: (01785) 252200 Fax: (01785) 252100 E-mail: andrew.shepphaerd@kuhmichel.com

Metalltechnik UK Ltd, 8 Mere Close, Shifnal, Shropshire, TF11 9QA Tel: (01952) 461242 Fax: (01952) 417489 E-mail: metuk@dialstart.net

Washington Mills Electro Minerals Ltd, Mosley Road, Trafford Park, Manchester, M17 1NR Tel: 0161-848 0271 Fax: 0161-872 2974 E-mail: sales@washingtonmills.co.uk

GRIT BLASTING CONTRACTORS

Aberdeen Blast Cleaning Services Ltd, Hillview Road, East Tullos Industrial Estate, Aberdeen, AB12 3HB Tel: (01224) 896565 Fax: (01224) 894989

Aliblast Services, 5a Greenpark, Edinburgh Road, Linlithgow, West Lothian, EH49 6AA Tel: (01506) 671844 Fax: (01506) 671844

Aquablast Blast Cleaning, Crutched Friars, Little Whelnetham, Bury St. Edmunds, Suffolk, IP30 0UH Tel: (01284) 388700 Fax: (01284) 388701 E-mail: sales@aquablast.uk.com

Bernie Richardson, Unit 2 Abbey Manor Industrial Estate, Yeovil, Somerset, BA21 3AR Tel: (01935) 413317

Ferrous Protection Ltd, Hanson House, Grains Road, Delph, Oldham, OL3 5RN Tel: (01457) 873419 Fax: (01457) 871091 E-mail: ferrous_protection@yahoo.com

Gardwell Coatings Ltd, Ellough Airfield, Ellough, Beccles, Suffolk, NR34 7TE Tel: (01502) 712793 Fax: (01502) 711636 E-mail: sales@gardwellcoatings.co.uk

Halls Specialised Services, Brooklyn Farm, North Hill, Horndon-on-the-Hill, Stanford-le-Hope, Essex, SS17 8QA Tel: (01375) 361408 Fax: (01375) 361448 E-mail: enquiries@hallsspecialisedservices.co.uk

Hastie & Co, Morfa Road, Swansea, SA1 2EP Tel: (01792) 651541 Fax: (01792) 468119 E-mail: steven.miller@hastiegroup.co.uk

Hereford Abrasives Co. Ltd, Unit 702, Fordshill Road, Rotherwas Industrial Estate, Hereford, HR2 6NS Tel: (01432) 270289 Fax: (01432) 274278E-mail: sales@blasting.freeserve.co.uk

J J Williams Painting Services Ltd, 75 Village Farm Road, Pyle, Bridgend, Mid Glamorgan, CF33 6BN Tel: (01656) 744311 Fax: (01656) 744617 E-mail: enquiries@jjwilliamsltd.com

Jack Tighe Decorating Ltd, Redbourne Mere, Kirton Lindsey, Gainsborough, Lincolnshire, DN21 4NW Tel: (01652) 649215 Fax: (01652) 648159

JMS Coatings Ltd, Units 8-9, Harlaw Business Centre, Inverurie, Aberdeenshire, AB51 4FR Tel: (01467) 622385 Fax: (01467) 624431

▶ K & N Finishers Southern Ltd, Castle Trading Estate, Fareham, Hampshire, PO16 9SF Tel: (023) 9237 0591 Fax: (023) 9238 0130 E-mail: kandnfinishers@bt.com

Palace Perma Signs Ltd, Lowmoor Industrial Estate, Prospect Close, Kirkby-in-Ashfield, Nottingham, NG17 7LF Tel: (01623) 754899 Fax: (01623) 752341

Penfold Metalising Co. Ltd, Barnham Road, Barnham, Bognor Regis, West Sussex, PO22 0ES Tel: (01243) 552178 Fax: (01243) 554472 E-mail: info@penmet.co.uk

Spa Engineering, Eastfield Fcty, Frank Perkins Way, Peterborough, PE1 2TD Tel: (01733) 345798 Fax: (01733) 345798 E-mail: spaengineering@btinternet.com

Washington Mills Electro Minerals Ltd, Mosley Road, Trafford Park, Manchester, M17 1NR Tel: 0161-848 0271 Fax: 0161-872 2974 E-mail: sales@washingtonmills.co.uk

GROOVE AND SNAP RING BEARINGS

DCN Bearings & Engineering, The Old Foundary, Wood Street, Lye, Stourbridge, West Midlands, DY9 8RX Tel: (01384) 896528 Fax: (01384) 896534 E-mail: sales@dcnbearings.com

GROOVED ROLLERS

Bowers & Jones Ltd, Patrick Gregory Road, Wolverhampton, WV11 3DU Tel: (01902) 732110 Fax: (01902) 864654 E-mail: jim.willmott@bowers.jones.freeserve.co.uk

Roll Ezy, Warrington Lane, Agden, Lymm, Cheshire, WA13 0SW Tel: (01925) 759554 Fax: (01925) 759588 E-mail: sales@rollezy.com

GROUND FLAT STOCK STEEL

Corus Ltd, PO Box 4, Wolverhampton, WV5 8AT Tel: (01902) 324444 Fax: (01902) 324204 E-mail: enquiries@corus.com

▶ Saxon Steels Ltd, Callywhite Lane, Dronfield, Derbyshire, S18 2XR Tel: (01246) 418363 Fax: (01246) 290309 E-mail: enquiries@saxonsteels.com

GROUND FLAT STOCK/ PRECISION GROUND TOOL STEEL

Allgrind, Unit 8 Century Street, Sheffield, S9 5DX Tel: 0114-244 4491 Fax: 0114-244 4491 E-mail: murbeck@aol.com

Hopkins & Bryant Small Tools Ltd, Phillips Street Industrial Estate, 103 Phillips Street, Birmingham, B6 4PT Tel: 0121-359 2195 Fax: 0121-359 1843

Intersteel, European Business Pk, Taylors Lane, Oldbury, West Midlands, B69 2BN Tel: 0121-627 9279 Fax: 0121-627 9270 E-mail: sales@intersteel.co.uk

GROUND FLAT STOCK/PRECISION GROUND TOOL STEEL – *continued*

▶ Saxon Steels Ltd, Callywhite Lane, Dronfield, Derbyshire, S18 2XR Tel: (01246) 418363 Fax: (01246) 290309 E-mail: enquiries@saxonsteels.com
▶ Sheffield Gauge Plate Ltd, Bastock Road, Sheffield, S6 2AE Tel: 0114-233 5291

GROUND GEARS

Ground Form Gears Ltd, Unit 4-5 Abeles Way, Holly Lane Industrial Estate, Atherstone, Warwickshire, CV9 2QZ Tel: (01827) 718555 Fax: (01827) 718789 E-mail: gearsground@yahoo.co.uk
Hindle Gears, Caledonia Street, Bradford, West Yorkshire, BD5 0EL Tel: (01274) 727234 Fax: (01274) 737343 E-mail: gears@hindle.co.uk
Northern Tool & Gear Co. Ltd, John St West, Arbroath, Angus, DD11 1RT Tel: (01241) 872626 Fax: (01241) 870040 E-mail: general@ntgear.co.uk
Renold Gears, Station Road, Milnrow, Rochdale, Lancashire, OL16 3LS Tel: (01706) 751000 Fax: (01706) 751001 E-mail: gears.sales@renold.com

GROUND IMPROVEMENT OR STABILISATION

▶ Groundforce Gardening, 94 Church Road, Emneth, Wisbech, Cambridgeshire, PE14 8AF Tel: (01945) 466555 Fax: (01945) 466192 E-mail: graham.brindley@groundforcegardening.net

GROUND PENETRATING RADAR SURVEY SERVICES

▶ Geotec, PO Box 99, Godalming, Surrey, GU7 2XT Tel: (01483) 271171

GROUNDWATER REMEDIATION PUMPS

W J Groundwater Ltd, 9 Park Road, Bushey, WD23 3EE Tel: (020) 8950 7256 Fax: (020) 8950 5207 E-mail: info@wjgl.com

GROUT

Factory Improvements Supplies Ltd, 24-26 Imperial Ave, Shirley, Southampton, SO15 8QH Tel: (023) 8078 6759 Fax: (023) 8070 2989
Sika Armorex, Riverside House, Bury Road, Lavenham, Sudbury, Suffolk, CO10 9QD Tel: (01787) 248005 Fax: (01787) 248315

GROUT PUMPS

Power-Sprays Ltd, Avonmouth Way, Bristol, BS11 9YA Tel: 0117-982 0067 Fax: 0117-982 0060

GROUTING CONTRACTORS

Concrete Repair & Grouting Ltd, 163 Sutton Road, Kidderminster, Worcestershire, DY11 6QN Tel: (01562) 748101 Fax: (01562) 829007 E-mail: enquiries@crg-ltd.co.uk
Core Cut Ltd, Bankhead, Winchburgh, Broxburn, West Lothian, EH52 6PP Tel: (01506) 854710 Fax: (01506) 853068 E-mail: info@corecut.co.uk
Keller Ground Engineering, Thorp Arch Trading Estate, Thorp Arch, Wetherby, West Yorkshire, LS23 7BJ Tel: (01937) 541118 Fax: (01937) 541371 E-mail: info@keller-ge.co.uk
Kent Grouting Services Ltd, 10 Gun Lane, Rochester, Kent, ME2 4UB Tel: (01634) 717554 Fax: (01634) 711396 E-mail: martinstromsoy@freenetname.co.uk

GRP ANTENNA SHROUDING

Custom Composites Ltd, Hugo Street, Rochdale, Lancashire, OL11 2PH Tel: (01706) 526255 Fax: (01706) 350187 E-mail: mail@customcom.co.uk

GRP ARCHITECTURAL MOULDINGS

▶ Arbory Group Ltd, Holker Business Centre, Burnley Road, Colne, Lancashire, BB8 8EG Tel: (0870) 0802322 Fax: (0870) 0802325 E-mail: sales@arborygroup.co.uk
Eiger (UK) Ltd, Unit 12, Landsdown Industrial Estate, Cheltenham, Gloucestershire, GL51 8PL Tel: (01242) 245678 Fax: (01242) 224643 E-mail: valform@aol.com
▶ Fibre World, 7 West Caplaw, Neilston, Glasgow, G78 3AW Tel: (01505) 812884 Fax: (01505) 814910 E-mail: enquires@fibreworlduk.com
▶ G R P Structures Ltd, Fitzherbert Road, Portsmouth, PO6 1RU Tel: (023) 9238 4921 Fax: (023) 9221 0716 E-mail: sales@grpstructures.com
Hilton Docker Mouldings Ltd, Freedo Mill, Foxcroft Street, Littleborough, Lancashire, OL15 8LB Tel: (01706) 379358 Fax: (01706) 378546 E-mail: sales@hiltondoc.co.uk

GRP BUILDING CUPOLAS

Good Directions Ltd, 8 Bottings Industrial Estate, Hillsons Road, Botley, Southampton, SO30 2DY Tel: 01489 797773 Fax: 01489 796700 E-mail: sales@good-directions.co.uk

GRP DISPLAYS

▶ Leeson Designs Ltd, Brook St, Nelson, Lancs, BB9 9PU Tel: (01282) 696009 Fax: (01282) 411728 E-mail: sales@leesondesigns.co.uk

GRP DOORS

▶ Garage Door Solutions, 11 Lotland Street, Inverness, IV1 1ST Tel: (01463) 714123 Fax: (01463) 714123
GBW Panels Ltd, 2 Berkeley Business Park, Wainwright Road, Worcester, WR4 9FA Tel: (01905) 340095 Fax: (01905) 340188 E-mail: mark_cuthbert@gbwuk.com
Minster Composite Products, Minster House, Private Road 2, Colwick Industrial Estate, Nottingham, NG4 2JR Tel: 0115-940 0644 Fax: 0115-940 0655 E-mail: minster@btclick.com
Price Glass Ltd, 414-414a Bath Road, Slough, SL1 6JA Tel: (01628) 664466 Fax: (01753) 733121 E-mail: sales@priceglass.co.uk

GRP ENCLOSURES

▶ Arbory Group Ltd, Holker Business Centre, Burnley Road, Colne, Lancashire, BB8 8EG Tel: (0870) 0802322 Fax: (0870) 0802325 E-mail: sales@arborygroup.co.uk

GRP ENGINEERING INCLUDING ON SITE

Broadwater Mouldings Ltd, Denham Site, Horham Road, Denham, Eye, Suffolk, IP21 5DQ Tel: (01379) 384145 Fax: (01379) 384150 E-mail: info@broadwater.co.uk
Sharp Site Services Ltd, 49 Mountain Road, Brynaman, Upper Brynamman, Ammanford, Dyfed, SA18 1AE Tel: (01269) 825932 Fax: (01269) 825932 E-mail: margaret@sharpsiteservices.com

GRP FABRICATORS

Accuvac Prototypes Ltd, Unit F2 Watlington Industrial Estate, Cuxham Road, Watlington, Oxfordshire, OX49 5LU Tel: (01491) 613161 Fax: (01491) 613161 E-mail: enquiries@accuvac.co.uk
Aqua Signal & Telegraphic Systems Ltd, Belmont House, Garnett Place, Skelmersdale, Lancashire, WN8 9UB Tel: (01695) 51933 Fax: (01695) 51891
Architectural Contract Services Ltd, Stable Cottage Industries, Wheatsheaf Road, Woodmancote, Henfield, West Sussex, BN5 9AU Tel: (01273) 495188 Fax: (01273) 495199 E-mail: archconserv@onetel.com
A. E. & N. Ashton & Co. Ltd, Sedgeway Farm, Common Road, Wichford, Ely, Cambridgeshire, CB6 2HY Tel: (01353) 662473 Fax: (01353) 667726
Beck Engineering Co (Bridlington) Ltd, Camlock Works, 13 & 15 Bridlington Road, Hunmanby, Filey, North Yorkshire, YO14 0LR Tel: (01723) 890631 Fax: (01723) 891554 E-mail: shane@becktransglobal.co.uk
C C P Gransden Bi-Chem, 17 Moss Road, Ballygowan, Newtownards, County Down, BT23 6JQ Tel: (028) 9752 8501 Fax: (028) 9752 1024 E-mail: info@ccp-gransden.com
Country Leisure Ltd, Cholderton, Salisbury, SP4 0EQ Tel: (01980) 629555 Fax: (01980) 629501 E-mail: sales@countryleisure.co.uk
▶ Filon Products, Unit 3 Ring Road Zone 2, Burntwood Business Park, Burntwood, Staffordshire, WS7 3JQ Tel: (01543) 687300 Fax: (01543) 687303 E-mail: admin@filon.co.uk
M P M (Moulds Patterns & Models) Ltd, 1 Centre St, Bradford, West Yorkshire, BD5 9DB Tel: (01274) 572515 Fax: (01274) 571880
Merrill Brown Ltd, Trent Lane, Nottingham, NG2 4DS Tel: 0115-950 6669 Fax: 0115-950 3486 E-mail: sales@merrillbrown.co.uk
Millfield F R P Ltd, Newburn Industrial Estate, Shelley Road, Newcastle upon Tyne, NE15 9RT Tel: 0191-264 8541 Fax: 0191-264 6962 E-mail: mail@millfield-group.co.uk
Northshore Composites Ltd, Brockhampton Road, Havant, Hampshire, PO9 1JU Tel: (023) 9247 1428 Fax: (023) 9245 2228 E-mail: info@northshore-composites.co.uk
P P S Glassfibre Ltd, Harlaw Way, Harlaw Road Industrial Estate, Inverurie, Aberdeenshire, AB51 4SG Tel: (01467) 621907 Fax: (01467) 620265 E-mail: ppsglassfibre@btconnect.com
Panelkraft Ltd, Unit 18a-20c Hixon Airfield Estate, New Road, Hixon, Stafford, ST18 0PF Tel: (01889) 270018 Fax: (01889) 270977
Plasticon (U K) Ltd, Grovehill Industrial Estate, Beverley, North Humberside, HU17 0JT Tel: (01482) 862194 Fax: (01482) 871398 E-mail: sales@plasticon.co.uk
Quantum Mouldings Ltd, Emville Street, Stourbridge, West Midlands, DY8 3TD Tel: (01384) 834422 Fax: (01384) 443743 E-mail: sales@quantummouldings.co.uk

GRP FLOOR GRATINGS

▶ Nonslip Safety Products, 5-8 Chilford Court, Rayne Road, Braintree, Essex, CM7 2QS Tel: (01376) 333315 Fax: (01376) 551849 E-mail: info@nonslipsp.co.uk

GRP HOUSINGS

Danetech Glass Fibre Mnfrs, 2b The CR, Witney, Oxfordshire, OX28 2EL Tel: (01327) 311011 Fax: (01327) 300216 E-mail: sales@danetech.co.uk
Image Composites Ltd, Govan Road, Fenton Industrial Estate, Fenton, Stoke-on-Trent, ST4 2RS Tel: (01782) 411611 Fax: (01782) 411888 E-mail: info@imageplastics.co.uk
Prima Plastics & Associates Ltd, London Road, Bagshot, Surrey, GU19 5HZ Tel: (01276) 453849 Fax: (01276) 453849 E-mail: sales@primaplastics.co.uk

GRP KIOSKS

Pow Ltd, Conitor House, Denbury Road, Newton Abbot, Devon, TQ12 6AD Tel: (01626) 361490 Fax: (01626) 333359 E-mail: sales@powplastics.co.uk

GRP LADDERS

A Bratt & Son Ltd, Abbeyfield Road, Nottingham, NG7 2SZ Tel: 0115-986 6851 Fax: 0115-986 1991 E-mail: sales@brattsladders.com

GRP MOULDING EQUIPMENT

▶ Composite Integration, Unit 21f Saltash Industrial Estate, Saltash, Cornwall, PL12 6LF Tel: (01752) 849998 Fax: (01752) 849808 E-mail: info@composite-integration.co.uk
Magnum Venus Platech Ltd, MTC, Chilsworthy Beam, Gunnislake, Cornwall, PL18 9AT Tel: (01822) 832621 Fax: (01822) 833999 E-mail: rtm@plastech.co.uk
Matrix Moulds & Models Ltd, Glover Street, St. Helens, Merseyside, WA10 3LF Tel: (01744) 24333 Fax: (01744) 27999 E-mail: mmm@rapid.co.uk

GRP MOULDINGS

Abrichem Composite Ltd, Unit 20 Heath Farm Estate, Iron Mould Lane Brislington, Bristol, BS4 4FZ Tel: 0117-977 1213 Fax: 0117-971 7623
Architectural & Industrial Group, 29 High Street, Hampton Wick, Kingston upon Thames, Surrey, KT1 4DA Tel: (020) 8977 8203 Fax: (01932) 829706 E-mail: sales@boschkitchens.com
Armfibre Ltd, Unit 7, Wilstead Industrial Park, Kenneth Way, Wilstead, Bedford, MK45 3PD Tel: (01234) 741444 Fax: (01767) 651901 E-mail: sales@armfibre.com
A. E. & N. Ashton & Co. Ltd, Sedgeway Farm, Common Road, Wichford, Ely, Cambridgeshire, CB6 2HY Tel: (01353) 662473 Fax: (01353) 667726
Bainbridge GRP Ltd, Unit 3D, Peel Mill, Chamberhall Street, Bury, Lancashire, BL9 0JU Tel: 0161-764 5034 Fax: 0161-764 5020
Bridgland Moulders Ltd, Rectory Road, Ashmanhaugh, Norwich, NR12 8YP Tel: (01603) 783130 Fax: (01603) 783701
Broadwater Mouldings Ltd, Denham Site, Horham Road, Denham, Eye, Suffolk, IP21 5DQ Tel: (01379) 384145 Fax: (01379) 384150 E-mail: info@broadwater.co.uk
Group Four Glass Fibre Co. Ltd, Unit 42 Church Road Business Centre, Church Road, Sittingbourne, Kent, ME10 3RS Tel: (01795) 429424 Fax: (01795) 476248 E-mail: info@groupfourglassfibre.co.uk
Harrison Thompson & Co. Ltd, Yeoman House Whitehall Industrial Estate, Whitehall Road, Leeds, LS12 5JB Tel: 0113-279 5854 Fax: 0113-231 0406 E-mail: info@yeomanshield.com
Hepworth Composites, Pollard Moor, Padiham, Burnley, Lancashire, BB12 7JR Tel: (01282) 683444 Fax: (01282) 683445 E-mail: ann.booth@hepworth.co.uk
Hippo Marine Ltd, 1 Gilston Road, Saltash, Cornwall, PL12 6TW Tel: (01752) 843333 Fax: (01752) 843333
J R Technology Ltd, 81 North End, Meldreth, Royston, Hertfordshire, SG8 6NU Tel: (01763) 260721 Fax: (01763) 260809 E-mail: enquiries@jrtech.co.uk
Menzolit, Perseverance Works, Halifax Road, Todmorden, Lancashire, OL14 6EG Tel: (01706) 814714 Fax: (01706) 814717 E-mail: sales@menzolit-uk.co.uk
Patterns & Moulds Ltd, Unit D2 Wymeswold Industrial Park, Wymeswold Road, Burton-on-the-Wolds, Loughborough, Leicestershire, LE12 5TY Tel: (01509) 881581 Fax: (01509) 881681 E-mail: info@patternsandmoulds.com
Prima Plastics & Associates Ltd, London Road, Bagshot, Surrey, GU19 5HZ Tel: (01276) 453849 Fax: (01276) 453849 E-mail: sales@primaplastics.co.uk
Regency Swimming Pools, Regency House, 88A Great Brickkiln Street, Graisley, Wolverhampton, WV3 0PU Tel: (01902) 427709 Fax: (01902) 422632 E-mail: info@jwgswimming.co.uk
Sycamore Mouldings Ltd, Sycamore Industrial Estate, Sycamore Road, Handsworth, Birmingham, B21 0QW Tel: 0121-523 0732 Fax: 0121-523 5918 E-mail: ralph@sycamore76.freeserve.co.uk
Vulcan Plastics Ltd, Hosey Hill, Westerham, Kent, TN16 1TZ Tel: (01959) 562304
Westward Mouldings Ltd, The New Factory, Delaware Road, Gunnislake, Cornwall, PL18 9AS Tel: (01822) 832120 Fax: (01822) 833938 E-mail: enquiry@fleetscale.co.uk
Westway Composites, Unit H The Factory, Dippenhall, Farnham, Surrey, GU10 5DW Tel: (01252) 820200 Fax: (01252) 820217 E-mail: enquiries@westway.co.uk

GRP PREFABRICATED BUILDINGS

Sharp Site Services Ltd, 49 Mountain Road, Brynaman, Upper Brynamman, Ammanford, Dyfed, SA18 1AE Tel: (01269) 825932 Fax: (01269) 825932 E-mail: margaret@sharpsiteservices.com

GRP ROOFING MATERIALS

▶ Filon Products, Unit 3 Ring Road Zone 2, Burntwood Business Park, Burntwood, Staffordshire, WS7 3JQ Tel: (01543) 687300 Fax: (01543) 687303 E-mail: admin@filon.co.uk

GRP SIGNS

Danetech Glass Fibre Mnfrs, 2b The CR, Witney, Oxfordshire, OX28 2EL Tel: (01327) 311011 Fax: (01327) 300216 E-mail: sales@danetech.co.uk
▶ Leeson Designs Ltd, Brook St, Nelson, Lancs, BB9 9PU Tel: (01282) 696009 Fax: (01282) 411728 E-mail: sales@leesondesigns.co.uk
Merrill Brown Ltd, Trent Lane, Nottingham, NG2 4DS Tel: 0115-950 6669 Fax: 0115-950 3486 E-mail: sales@merrillbrown.co.uk
Roys Signs, 15 Hoobrook Industrial Estate, Worcester Road, Kidderminster, Worcestershire, DY10 1HY Tel: (01562) 829299 Fax: (01562) 829299

GRP SMOKING SHELTERS

C B Fabrications, Units 4-4a The Old Co-Op Bakery, Kellet Road, Carnforth, Lancashire, LA5 9LR Tel: (01524) 736577 Fax: (01524) 736577 E-mail: sales@cbfabrications.co.uk

GRP TANK COVERS

Polypipe Civils Ltd, Bishop Meadow Road, Loughborough, Leicestershire, LE11 5RE Tel: (01509) 615100 Fax: (01609) 610215 E-mail: sales@polypipecivils.co.uk

GRP WATER TANKS

Braithwaite Engineers Ltd, Neptune Works Cork Wharf, Mill Parade, Newport, Gwent, NP20 2UY Tel: (01633) 262141 Fax: (01633) 250631 E-mail: tanks@braithwaite.co.uk
Brimar Plastic Ltd, North Road, Yate, Bristol, BS37 7PR Tel: (01454) 322111 Fax: (01454) 316955 E-mail: brimar@brimarplastics.co.uk
Caravan Accessories Kenilworth Ltd, Unit 10 Princes Drive Industrial Estate, Coventry Road, Kenilworth, Warwickshire, CV8 2FD Tel: (01926) 854271 Fax: (01926) 853954 E-mail: sales@caktanks.co.uk
Group Four Glass Fibre Co. Ltd, Unit 42 Church Road Business Centre, Church Road, Sittingbourne, Kent, ME10 3RS Tel: (01795) 429424 Fax: (01795) 476248 E-mail: info@groupfourglassfibre.co.uk
H Cooper & Sons Bristol, Westerleigh Road, Yate, Bristol, BS37 8QA Tel: (01454) 312081 Fax: (01454) 318880E-mail: info@hcooper.net

GRP WATER TANKS – *continued*

Hydroserve Sewage Disposal, Kingsley House, Ganders Park, Kingsley, Bordon, Hampshire, GU35 9LU Tel: (01420) 470800 Fax: (01420) 470820
E-mail: enquiries@conderproducts.com
Nicholson Plastics Ltd, 20b Lansdowne Road, Croydon, CR0 2BX Tel: (020) 8760 0930 Fax: (020) 8688 1811

GUAR GUM

Essential Ingredients Ltd, 25 Church Road, East Huntspill, Highbridge, Somerset, TA9 3PQ Tel: (01278) 783231 Fax: (01278) 783231

GUARDRAILS

Nu Weld Engineering Services Ltd, 36 Oxford Street, Birmingham, B5 5NR Tel: 0121-633 0909 Fax: 0121-633 3124
E-mail: enquiries@nu-weld.co.uk

GUDGEON PINS

▶ ADEPT Precision Ltd, Unit 7 Deacon Trading Estate, 203 Vale Road, Tonbridge, Kent, TN9 1SU Tel: 01732 773777 Fax: 01732 771115 E-mail: sales@adeptprecision.com

GUIDED AUGER BORING

Avoidatrench Ltd, Brooks Lane, Middlewich, Cheshire, CW10 0JQ Tel: (01606) 831600 Fax: (01606) 831620
E-mail: admin@avoidatrench.co.uk

GUILLOTINE KNIFE GRINDING MACHINES

Kennedy Grinding Ltd, Commerce Park, Commerce Way, Colchester, CO2 8HX Tel: (01206) 790407 Fax: (01206) 793113

GUILLOTINES

▶ Albion Machinery Ltd, Unit 57a The Washford Industrial Estate, Heming Road, Redditch, Worcestershire, B98 0DH Tel: (01527) 517928 Fax: (01527) 517912
E-mail: info@albionmac.co.uk

GUILLOTINES, PAPER/BOARD CUTTING

Babs UK Ltd, Plot 1 Oakwood Hill Industrial Estate, Oakwood Hill, Loughton, Essex, IG10 3TZ Tel: (020) 8965 9821 Fax: (020) 8502 4187 E-mail: info@babs.co.uk
Norman Haynes Ltd, 900 Thornton Road, Bradford, West Yorkshire, BD8 0JG Tel: (01274) 545115 Fax: (01274) 545113
Mastercut Cutting Systems Ltd, 8 Bridge St Industrial Estate, Bridge Street, Clay Cross, Chesterfield, Derbyshire, S45 9NU Tel: (01246) 860811 Fax: (01246) 866928
E-mail: info@mastercut.co.uk
Rotatrim, 8 Caxton Park, Caxton Road, Elm Farm Industrial Estate, Bedford, MK41 0TY Tel: (01234) 224545 Fax: (01234) 224540
E-mail: sales@rotatrim.co.uk
Stanley Press Equipment Ltd, Sutton Mill, Byrons Lane, Macclesfield, Cheshire, SK11 7JL Tel: (01625) 619094 Fax: (01625) 619094
E-mail: sales@s-p-e.co.uk

GUITAR AMPLIFIERS, CUSTOM BUILT

Crockett Guitars, Nethersole Farm, The Street, Womenswold, Canterbury, Kent, CT4 6HE Tel: (01227) 832832
E-mail: info@crockettguitars.com

GUITARS

▶ Blake-Robson Northumbria Tuning Machines, Low Lambton Farm, Penshaw, Houghton le Spring, Tyne & Wear, DH4 7NQ Tel: 0191-246 2007 Fax: 0191-385 8013
E-mail: tuningmachines@aol.com
Crockett Guitars, Nethersole Farm, The Street, Womenswold, Canterbury, Kent, CT4 6HE Tel: (01227) 832832
E-mail: info@crockettguitars.com
Freebird Guitars, 40 Marrowbrook Lane, Farnborough, Hampshire, GU14 0AE Tel: (01252) 541417
E-mail: enquiries@freebirdguitars.com
▶ G B Guitars, 41 Prestonville Road, Brighton, BN1 3TJ Tel: (01273) 220055 Fax: (01273) 775780
▶ George Lowden, Down Business Park, 46 Belfast Road, Downpatrick, County Down, BT30 9UP Tel: (028) 4461 9161 Fax: (028) 4461 7043 E-mail: sales@georgelowden.com
▶ Henry Nurdin Instrument Repairs, 51 Garth Owen, Newtown, Powys, SY16 1JL Tel: (07779) 755814
E-mail: info@guitar-repairs.co.uk
▶ Sounds in Scale, Trefaes Bellaf, Sarn, Pwllheli, Gwynedd, LL53 8RL Tel: 01758 730529 E-mail: enquiries@soundsinscale.com

GULLY EMPTYING CONTRACTORS OR SERVICES

Goplant, 88 Hawkcliffe Road, Mount Sorrel, Mount Sorrel, Loughborough, Leicestershire, LE12 7AH Tel: (01509) 414677 Fax: (01509) 416853

GUM, ARABIC

Agri Products, Finchley Road, London, NW3 6JG Tel: (020) 7483 2737 Fax: (020) 7586 7338
E-mail: gtitchener@agriproducts.com
Arthur Bramwell & Co. Ltd, Bronte House, 58-62 High Street, Epping, Essex, CM16 4AE Tel: (01992) 577333 Fax: (01992) 561138
E-mail: arthurbranwell@branwell.com
▶ Koenig & Wiegand, 45 Sarisbury Close, Tadley, Hampshire, RG26 3SZ Tel: 0118-981 9481 Fax: (020) 7117 3273
E-mail: s.hewett@koenig-wiegand.de

GUMMED LABELS

Eurohill Traders Ltd, 195 Vale Road, Tonbridge, Kent, TN9 1SU Tel: (01732) 770777 Fax: (01732) 770757
E-mail: sales@apac.co.uk

GUMMED PAPER/TAPE

Makkipak Ltd, Mallard Close, Earls Barton, Northampton, NN6 0JF Tel: (01604) 812755 Fax: (01604) 812413
E-mail: sales@makkipak.com
Scannedstick UK Ltd, Butterfly House, St. Neots, Cambridgeshire, PE19 6EE Tel: (01480) 362000 Fax: (01480) 217722
E-mail: sales@scannedstick.co.uk
Tapekraft Ltd, Unit C Castlehills Court, Howard Road, Eaton Socon, St. Neots, Cambridgeshire, PE19 8ET Tel: (01480) 216161 Fax: (01480) 216162
E-mail: enquiries@tapekraft.co.uk
Windmill Tapes & Labels, 6 Mackenzie Industrial Estate, Bird Hall Lane, Stockport, Cheshire, SK3 0SB Tel: 0161-495 3959 Fax: 0161-428 1603 E-mail: sales@windmilltapes.co.uk

GUMMING MACHINES, *See Adhesive Application etc*

GUN BLACKING SERVICES

Fieldsports Equipe, 20a Elwy Street, Rhyl, Clwyd, LL18 1BP Tel: (01745) 353476 Fax: (01745) 353476 E-mail: enquiries@fieldsports.co.uk
Peter Gardner, Water Lane Farm, 9 Water Lane, Sherington, Newport Pagnell, Buckinghamshire, MK16 9NP Tel: (01908) 610333 E-mail: clayshoting@lineone.net
Jason Abbot Gunmakers Ltd, The Swan, 5 High Street, Tetsworth, Thame, Oxfordshire, OX9 7AB Tel: (01844) 281765 Fax: (01844) 281815 E-mail: jasonabbott@bicksnet.co.uk

GUN DRILL BITS

Hammond & Co. Ltd, Finway Road, Hemel Hempstead Industrial Estate, Hemel Hempstead, Hertfordshire, HP2 7PT Tel: (01442) 212211 Fax: (01442) 252003
E-mail: sales@hammco.com

GUN DRILLING

Ims UK, International House, Saltley Trading Estate, Saltley, Birmingham, B8 1BB Tel: 0121-326 3100 Fax: 0121-326 3105

GUN DRILLING MACHINES

Mollart Engineering Ltd, Roebuck Road, Chessington, Surrey, KT9 1EU Tel: (020) 8391 2282 Fax: (020) 8391 6626
E-mail: info@mollart.co.uk

GUN SAFES

Winterfield Safes, The Hall, Newton Le Willows, Bedale, North Yorkshire, DL8 1SW Tel: (01677) 450774 Fax: (01677) 450774
E-mail: helen@winterfieldsafes.co.uk

GUNITE APPLICATION EQUIPMENT

Windrush Guns Ltd, PO Box 127, Witney, Oxfordshire, OX28 6FX Tel: (01993) 703035 Fax: (01993) 771014

GUNITE CONTRACTORS

Concrete Repairs Ltd, Cathite House, 23a Willow Lane, Mitcham, Surrey, CR4 4TU Tel: (020) 8288 4848 Fax: (020) 8288 4847
E-mail: sales@concrete-repairs.co.uk
Ferro Monk Systems Ltd, 16 Astley Way, Astley Lane Industrial Estate, Swillington, Leeds, LS26 8XT Tel: 0113-287 7577 Fax: 0113 287 7778 E-mail: info@ferromonk.co.uk
SHL Refractories UK Limited, Celcius House, Lawn Road, Carlton-In-Lindrick, Worksop, Nottinghamshire, S81 9LB Tel: (01909) 731959 Fax: (01909) 731579
E-mail: sales@shl-refractories.co.uk

GUNMETAL CASTINGS

David Hunt Castings, Romsey Industrial Estate, Budds La, Romsey, Hants, SO51 0HA Tel: (01794) 511259 Fax: (01794) 518325
E-mail: davidhunt.castings@btopenworld.com
Peter Dyson & Son Ltd, 3 Cuckoo Lane, Honley, Holmfirth, HD9 6AS Tel: (01484) 661062 Fax: (01484) 663709

GUNS AND GUNSMITHS

A A Brown & Sons, 1 Snake Lane, Alvechurch, Birmingham, B48 7NT Tel: 0121-445 5395 Fax: 0121-445 2113
E-mail: sales@aabrownandsons.com
Airgun Centre, 107 London Road, Rayleigh, Essex, SS6 9AX Tel: (01268) 780730 Fax: (01268) 783102
E-mail: sales@theairguncentre.co.uk
Alfred J Parker Ltd, Armoury Works, 348 Moseley Road, Birmingham, B12 9AZ Tel: 0121-440 1480 Fax: 0121-446 4194
E-mail: alfredjparker@yahoo.co.uk
Armalon Ltd, 44 Harrowby Street, London, W1H 5HY Tel: (020) 7262 1881 Fax: (020) 7402 0959 E-mail: info@armalon.com
Arnold Heal Ltd, 86b St. James Street, Newport, Isle of Wight, PO30 1LB Tel: (01983) 523352
B K Webster, Main Street, West Tanfield, Ripon, North Yorkshire, HG4 5JH Tel: (01677) 470505
E-mail: info@gunfitting.co.uk
Bagnall & Kirkwood Ltd, 28 Grey Street, Newcastle upon Tyne, NE1 6AE Tel: 0191-232 5873 Fax: 0191-230 5656
Banbury Gunsmiths, 47a Broad Street, Banbury, Oxfordshire, OX16 5BT Tel: (01295) 265819 Fax: (01295) 265810
E-mail: sales@banburygunsmiths.com
Bannvalley Guns & Tackle, 20 Finlayston, Portglenone, Ballymena, County Antrim, BT44 8EA Tel: (028) 2582 1383 Fax: (028) 2582 1383
Bloomfield Guns & Tackle, 157 Bloomfield Avenue, Belfast, BT5 5AB Tel: (028) 9020 9730 Fax: (028) 9058 0222
Brampton Gun Room, 47-49 Old Hall Road, Chesterfield, Derbyshire, S40 1HD Tel: (01246) 211294
▶ Brown's Lock Stock & Barrel, 224 Holme Lane, Sheffield, S6 4JZ Tel: 0114-234 6222 Fax: 0114-234 6222
Bywell Shooting Ground, Bywell Farm, Felton, Morpeth, Northumberland, NE65 9QQ Tel: (01670) 787827 Fax: (01670) 787093
C & H Weston Ltd, 12 East Street, Brighton, BN1 1HP Tel: (01273) 326338 Fax: (01273) 720107 E-mail: info@chweston.co.uk
C M R International (UK) Military Firearms & Antiquities, 53 High Street, Ashford, Kent, TN24 8SG Tel: (0871) 2301318 Fax: (0871) 2301318 E-mail: cmrinternational@aol.com
C Potter, 2-6 Grover Street, Tunbridge Wells, Kent, TN1 2QB Tel: (01892) 522208 Fax: (01892) 543515
Chambers Gunmakers, Ideal Gunworks, River Close South, Alness, Ross-Shire, IV17 0XS Tel: (01349) 883310 Fax: (01349) 883310
Chichester Armoury, 43 West Street, Chichester, West Sussex, PO19 1RP Tel: (01243) 774687 Fax: (01243) 778865
Colchester Shooting Centre, 27a North Station Road, Colchester, CO1 1RE Tel: (01206) 763336
Coley Ian Gunsmith, 444 High Street, Cheltenham, Gloucestershire, GL50 3JA Tel: (01242) 522443 Fax: (01242) 226703
Arthur Conyers, 3 West Street, Blandford Forum, Dorset, DT11 7AW Tel: (01258) 452307 Fax: (01258) 452307 E-mail: jay@conyers.biz
Jas Crockart & Son, 26 Allan Street, Blairgowrie, Perthshire, PH10 6AD Tel: (01250) 872056 Fax: (01250) 872168
E-mail: info@jamescrockartandson.co.uk
Ronnie Crowe Ltd, 63 Maldon Road, Great Baddow, Chelmsford, CM2 7DN Tel: (01245) 471246
Custom Stock, 1 Rotherham Close, Norwood Industrial Estate, Killamarsh, Sheffield, S21 2JU Tel: 0114-247 6965 Fax: 0114-247 2947
▶ Daves, 215 Freeman Street, Grimsby, South Humberside, DN32 9DW Tel: (01472) 267325
David Mckay Brown (Gunmakers) Ltd, 32 Hamilton Road, Bothwell, Glasgow, G71 8NA Tel: (01698) 853727 Fax: (01698) 854207
E-mail: info@mckaybrown.com
Drapers Air Gun Centre, 122-128 Hartley Road, Nottingham, NG7 3AJ Tel: 0115-970 2525 Fax: 0115-970 2525
Peter Dyson & Son Ltd, 3 Cuckoo Lane, Honley, Holmfirth, HD9 6AS Tel: (01484) 661062 Fax: (01484) 663709
E J Churchill Shooting Ground, Park Lane, Lane End, High Wycombe, Buckinghamshire, HP14 3NS Tel: (01494) 883227 Fax: (01494) 883215 E-mail: sales@ejchurchill.com
Edgar Bros, Heather Close, Lyme Green Business Park, Macclesfield, Cheshire, SK11 0LR Tel: (01625) 613177 Fax: (01625) 615276 E-mail: admin@edgar-brothers.co.uk
Elderkin & Son Gunmakers Ltd, 17 Broad Street, Spalding, Lincolnshire, PE11 1TG Tel: (01775) 722919 Fax: (01775) 760556
E-mail: william@elderkin.co.uk
Euroguns Gunsmiths, School House, Main Street, Mattersey, Doncaster, South Yorkshire, DN10 5DZ Tel: (01777) 817809 Fax: (01777) 817809 E-mail: sales@euroguns.co.uk
William Evans Ltd, 67a St James's Street, London, SW1A 1PH Tel: (020) 7493 0415 Fax: (020) 7499 1912
E-mail: salew@willa.com
F J Wiseman & Co. Ltd, 262 Walsall Road, Cannock, Staffordshire, WS11 0JL Tel: (01543) 504088 Fax: (01543) 574806
▶ Feather & Financial, Church Street, Shifnal, Shropshire, TF11 9AA Tel: (01952) 462979
Fieldsports Wigglesworth Gunsmiths, 45 Market Place, South Cave, Brough, North Humberside, HU15 2BS Tel: (01430) 424666 Fax: (01430) 471203
E-mail: info@wigglesworthgunsmiths.co.uk
John Foster, Thorpe Road, Carlton, Stockton-on-Tees, Cleveland, TS21 3LB Tel: (01740) 631110 Fax: (01740) 631112
E-mail: enquiries@johnfostergunmaker.co.uk
G E Fulton & Son, Bisley Camp, Brookwood, Woking, Surrey, GU24 0NY Tel: (01483) 473204 Fax: (01483) 475011
G W Hutchinson & Co., 31 Anlaby Road, Hull, HU1 2PG Tel: (01482) 223869
Gallyon & Sons Ltd, 4 Dereham Road, Garvestone, Norwich, NR9 4AD Tel: (01953) 850215 Fax: (01953) 851800
E-mail: rgallyon@freenetname.co.uk
Godiva Guns (Coventry), 191 Canley Road, Coventry, CV5 6AS Tel: (024) 7667 6077 Fax: (024) 7667 6077
E-mail: edward.braso@btopenworld.com
Jack Hallam & Sons, 33 Buxton Road, Whaley Bridge, High Peak, Derbyshire, SK23 7HT Tel: (01663) 733900 Fax: (01663) 733900
Hendry Ramsay & Waters, 55-57 North Methven Street, Perth, PH1 5PX Tel: (01738) 623679 Fax: (01738) 443327
E-mail: sales@scothunt.co.uk
Henry Krank & Co. Ltd, 100-104 Lowtown, Pudsey, West Yorkshire, LS28 9AY Tel: 0113-256 9163 Fax: 0113-257 4962
Henry Monk Gunmaker Ltd, 8 Queen Street, Chester, CH1 3LG Tel: (01244) 320988 Fax: (01244) 320988
Jesse Hill, 1a Ash Tree Road, Birmingham, B30 2BJ Tel: 0121-458 3625
Holland & Holland Holdings Ltd, 31-33 Bruton Street, London, W1J 6HH Tel: (020) 7499 4411 Fax: (020) 7499 4544
Ian Wilson Gunmakers, 53 Wide Bargate, Boston, Lincolnshire, PE21 6SH Tel: (01205) 365668
J Graham & Co., 37-39 Castle Street, Inverness, IV2 3DU Tel: (01463) 233178 Fax: (01463) 710287
E-mail: william@johngrahamandco.co.uk
J Roberts & Son Ltd, 22 Wyvil Road, London, SW8 2TG Tel: (020) 7622 1131 Fax: (020) 7627 4442
E-mail: shop@jroberts-gunmakers.co.uk
J S Ramsbottom, Park Lane, Keighley, West Yorkshire, BD21 4QQ Tel: (01535) 605445 Fax: (01535) 602218
E-mail: sales@jsramsbottom.com
John Knibbs, Hillside, Shawbury Lane, Coleshill, Birmingham, B46 2RR Tel: (01675) 481006 Fax: (01675) 481984
E-mail: enquiries@airgunspares.com
John R Gow Ltd, 12 Union Street, Dundee, DD1 4BH Tel: (01382) 225427 Fax: (01382) 225427 E-mail: sales@scotland-fishing.co.uk
Joseph Braddell & Sons, 11 North Street, Belfast, BT1 1NA Tel: (028) 9032 0525 Fax: (028) 9032 2657
E-mail: fishing@braddells.fsnet.co.uk
Ladbrook & Langton, Hill Farm, Watling Street, Radlett, Hertfordshire, WD7 7HP Tel: (01923) 854639 Fax: (01923) 856530
E-mail: cal303@aol.com
Leech & Son, 4a Church Road, Boreham, Chelmsford, CM3 3EF Tel: (01245) 465249 Fax: (01245) 261130
Clive C. Lemon, The Gun Room, Park Cottage, Upper Bentley, Redditch, Worcestershire, B97 5TD Tel: (01527) 550080 Fax: (01527) 550080
Linsley Bros Established 1780 Ltd, 55 Tower Street, Harrogate, North Yorkshire, HG1 1HS Tel: (01423) 505677 Fax: (01423) 563673
Norfolk Gun Trading Co., 14 Greevegate, Hunstanton, Norfolk, PE36 6AA Tel: (01485) 533600
Park Street Test Centre, Paynes Yard, Park Street Lane, Park Street, St. Albans, Hertfordshire, AL2 2NE Tel: (01727) 873814 Fax: (01727) 875449
E-mail: parkstreetguns@talk21.com

GUNS AND GUNSMITHS – *continued*

Phase Ii Firearms, 57 The Chase, Rayleigh, Essex, SS6 8QW Tel: (01268) 774606 Fax: (01702) 300201 E-mail: sales@stalkingscotland.com
Portsmouth Gun Centre, 295 London Road, Portsmouth, PO2 9HF Tel: (023) 9266 0574 Fax: (023) 9264 4666
James Purdey & Sons Ltd, 57 South Audley Street, London, W1K 2ED Tel: (020) 7499 1801 Fax: (020) 7355 3297 E-mail: sales@james-purdey.co.uk
R Martin, School House, Darlton Road, Dunham-on-Trent, Newark, Nottinghamshire, NG22 0UJ Tel: (01777) 228259 Fax: (01777) 228259
R P A International Ltd, P.O. Box 441, Tonbridge, Kent, TN9 9DZ Tel: (0845) 8803222 E-mail: info@rpainternational.co.uk
R Welsh & Son, 28 Castle Street, Duns, Berwickshire, TD11 3DP Tel: (01361) 883466 Fax: (01361) 883466
Ray Ward Gunsmith (London) Ltd, 12 Cadogan Place, Knightsbridge, London, SW1X 9PU Tel: (020) 7235 2550 Fax: (020) 7259 6359 E-mail: john@raywardgunsmith.co.uk
S S M International, Tedstone Wafre, Bromyard, Herefordshire, HR7 4PY Tel: (01886) 853646 Fax: (01886) 853539
Southern Counties Shooting Ltd, Wardon Hill, Evershot, Dorchester, Dorset, DT2 9PW Tel: (01935) 83625 Fax: (01935) 83756 E-mail: scshooting@aol.com
Stephen J Fawcett, 7 Great John Street, Lancaster, LA1 1NQ Tel: (01524) 32033 Fax: (01524) 843470 E-mail: sales@fawcettonline.com
T A L Shooting & Scuba Diving, 8 St. Catherines Parade, Fairmile Road, Christchurch, Dorset, BH23 2LQ Tel: (01202) 473030 Fax: (01202) 479600 E-mail: sales@go-diving.co.uk
T Stensby & Co. Ltd, 1 Shudehill, Manchester, M4 2AF Tel: 0161-834 6589 Fax: 0161-834 6589 E-mail: sales@stensby.co.uk
Tackle & Gun, 3 East Well, High Street, Tenterden, Kent, TN30 6AH Tel: (01580) 764851
Michael Tawn & Sons, The Barn, Hannath Rd, Tydd Gote, Wisbech, Cambs, PE13 5ND Tel: 01945 420770
Thompson & Campbell Ltd, Unit 2 Whitedykes Industrial Estate, Cromarty, Ross-Shire, IV11 8YB Tel: (01381) 600536 Fax: (01381) 600767
Valley Arms Co., Bolero Camp, Park Road, Ruthin, Clwyd, LL15 1NB Tel: (01824) 704438 Fax: (01824) 704438
Viking Arms Ltd, New York Mill, New York Industrial Estate, Harrogate, North Yorkshire, HG3 4BW Tel: (01423) 780810 Fax: (01423) 781500 E-mail: info@vikingarms.com
W Powell & Son Ltd, 35-37 Carrs Lane, Birmingham, B4 7SX Tel: 0121-643 0689 Fax: 0121-631 3504 E-mail: sales@william-powell.co.uk
W R Hardy, 153 East High Street, Forfar, Angus, DD8 2EQ Tel: (01307) 466635 Fax: (01307) 468820
Webley & Scott Ltd, Frankly Industrial Park, Tay Road, Rednal Rubery, Birmingham, B45 0PA Tel: (0121) 453 1864 Fax: (0121) 457 7846 E-mail: guns@webley.co.uk
Westley Engineering Ltd, 120 Pritchett Street, Birmingham, B6 4EH Tel: 0121-333 1925 Fax: 0121-333 1926 E-mail: engineering@westleyrichards.co.uk
Benjamin Wild & Son, 55 Price Street, Birmingham, B4 6JZ Tel: 0121-359 2303 Fax: 0121-359 2303
▶ Woodland Park C T S G, Lower Road, Bookham, Leatherhead, Surrey, KT23 4EF Tel: (01372) 451040 Fax: (01372) 451040
York & Wallin Ltd, 3 Pendeford Mill Lane, Codsall, Wolverhampton, WV8 1JB Tel: (01902) 845547 Fax: (01902) 846349 E-mail: sales@yorkandwallin.co.uk
Yorkshire Gun Room, Bishop Thornton, Harrogate, North Yorkshire, HG3 3JN Tel: (01765) 620602 Fax: (01765) 620656

GUNS, PAINTBALL

▶ Campaign Paintball Park, Old Lane, Cobham, Surrey, KT11 1NH Tel: (01932) 865999 Fax: (01932) 865744 E-mail: sales@campaignpaintball.com
▶ Group Sales Limited, GSL House, 21 Kitchener Close, Daventry, Northamptonshire, NN11 9AJ Tel: 0870 6094591 Fax: 0870 1709874 E-mail: enquiries@groupsales.co.uk
▶ Holmbush Paintball, C/O Holmbush Farm, Crawley Road, Faygate, Horsham, West Sussex, RH12 4SE Tel: (01293) 852261 E-mail: euenquiries@holmbushpaintballshop.com
▶ Sas Paintball, Codsall Wood Road, Codsall Wood, Wolverhampton, WV8 1QR Tel: (01902) 844467 Fax: (01902) 713117 E-mail: info@saspaintball.co.uk

GUT CLEANING EQUIPMENT

E.A. Bitterling Ltd, Poulton Drive, Daleside Road Industrial Estate, Nottingham, NG2 4BN Tel: 0115-986 2934 Fax: 0115-986 3027 E-mail: info@bitterling.co.uk

GUTTER CLEANING

▶ Amanassas, 2 Briarfield Gardens, Shipley, West Yorkshire, BD18 2BE Tel: (07890) 194132 E-mail: panther1966uk@yahoo.co.uk
Central Window Cleaners Ltd, 21 Sussex Close, Nuneaton, Warwickshire, CV10 8JZ Tel: (024) 7675 7615 Fax: E-mail: enquires@centralwindowcleaners.co.uk
▶ NoMoreBlockedGutters, 11 Victoria Ave, Scotforth, Lancaster, LA1 4SY Tel: 01524 849156 E-mail: nomoreblockedgutters@gmail.com

GUTTER INSTALLATION CONTRACTORS

▶ A & D Joinery Ltd, Unit 14, Bolton Road Mill, Bolton Road, Bolton, BL5 3JG Tel: (01942) 814501 Fax: (01942) 810468 E-mail: john@aanddjoinery
Roweaver Developments, Prospect House, Ainsdale Drive, Shrewsbury, SY1 3TL Tel: (01743) 445880 Fax: (01743) 441697 E-mail: sales@roweaver.co.uk

GUTTERING ACCESSORIES

▶ Associated Agency Co., Factory 1, Pottery Close, Winterstoke Road, Weston-Super-Mare, Avon, BS23 3YH Tel: (01934) 622960 Fax: (01934) 621456
▶ Bedford Building Plastics, 11 Grisedale Court, Woburn Road Industrial Estate, Kempston, Bedford, MK42 7EE Tel: (01234) 855388 Fax: (01234) 855399
▶ NoMoreBlockedGutters, 11 Victoria Ave, Scotforth, Lancaster, LA1 4SY Tel: 01524 849156 E-mail: nomoreblockedgutters@gmail.com

GUTTERS

▶ Bedford Building Plastics, 11 Grisedale Court, Woburn Road Industrial Estate, Kempston, Bedford, MK42 7EE Tel: (01234) 855388 Fax: (01234) 855399
▶ Hylton Stormaster Ltd, 7 Harvey Close, Crowther, Washington, Tyne & Wear, NE38 0AB Tel: 0191-417 0055

GYMNASTIC EQUIPMENT

▶ Auction Fitness, Unit 10 Bakers Park, Cater Road, Bishopsworth, Bristol, BS13 7TW Tel: (0870) 8519419 Fax: 0117-964 9679 E-mail: info@auctionfitness.com
Carr Of Nottingham Ltd, Ronald Street, Radford, Nottingham, NG7 3GY Tel: 0115-942 2252 Fax: 0115-942 2276 E-mail: carrofnottm@btconnect.com
▶ Custom Fitness LLP, 15 The New Poplars, Ash Street Ash, Aldershot, Hampshire, GU12 6LH Tel: (01252) 328837 E-mail:
I W F Ltd, Ilderton Station, West Lilburn, Alnwick, Northumberland, NE66 4PH Tel: (01668) 217900 Fax: (01668) 217909 E-mail: neil@iwf.co.uk
Olympic Gymnasium Services, Greatworth Park, Welsh Lane, Greatworth, Banbury, Oxfordshire, OX17 2HB Tel: (01295) 760192 Fax: (01295) 768092 E-mail: sales@olympicgymnasium.com

GYPSUM WALLBOARDS

▶ Ash Plastering, 8 Benson Road, Kings Heath, Birmingham, B14 4PH Tel: 0121- 430 5058 E-mail: quote@ashplastering.co.uk

GYROSCOPIC COMPASSES

Seatronics Ltd, 4 Denmore Industrial Estate, Denmore Road, Bridge Of Don, Aberdeen, AB23 8JW Tel: (01224) 853100 Fax: (01224) 853101 E-mail: david.currie@seatronics-group.com

HABERDASHERY MANUFRS, *See also headings for particular types*

Arcraft Products 2005 Ltd, 1 Mousell Street, Cheetham, Manchester, M8 8HY Tel: 0161-833 2269 Fax: 0161-833 2269 E-mail: greetings16@hotmail.com
Ashcott Equestuim Ltd, Reme Drive, Heath Park Industrial Estate, Honiton, Devon, EX14 1SE Tel: (01404) 44680 Fax: (01404) 46688
Bray Group Ltd, Olive House, Regal Way, Faringdon, Oxfordshire, SN7 7BX Tel: (01367) 240736 Fax: (01367) 242625 E-mail: info@bray.co.uk
G K & Sons Ltd, 235-243 Sussex Way, London, N19 4JD Tel: (020) 7281 3282 Fax: (020) 7272 8992
Groves & Banks, Drakes Drive Industrial Estate, Long Crendon, Aylesbury, Buckinghamshire, HP18 9BA Tel: (01844) 258100 Fax: (01844) 258058 E-mail: sales@groves-banks.com
J T Morgan, 128 Railway Arches, Behind Macfarlane Road, London, W12 7LA Tel: (020) 8222 6711 Fax: (020) 8969 2260 E-mail: jtmorgan@amserve.net
John Downs Hull Ltd, 13 Unit Factory Estate, Boulevard, Hull, HU3 4AY Tel: (01482) 329099 Fax: (01482) 329099
Leicester Thread & Trimming Manufacturers Ltd, 105 Barkby Road, Leicester, LE4 9LG Tel: 0116-276 5858 Fax: 0116-246 0451
M Courts Ltd, 31 Commercial Road, London, N18 1TP Tel: (020) 8884 0999 Fax: (020) 8884 4666 E-mail: mcourtsltd@btconnect.com
Macculloch & Wallis Ltd, 25-26 Dering Street, London, W1S 1AT Tel: (020) 7629 0311 Fax: (020) 7629 8097 E-mail: macculloch@psilink.co.uk
Nova Trimmings Ltd, 15 Abbey Gate, Leicester, LE4 0AA Tel: 0116-253 1144 Fax: 0116-251 5631 E-mail: nova.trimmings@virgin.net
Orxiom Fabrics, 43 Nicholsons Centre, Maidenhead, Berkshire, SL6 1LL Tel: (01628) 620703 Fax: (01628) 773677
M.& J. Shapero Ltd, 70 Thomas Street, Aston, Birmingham, B6 4TN Tel: 0121-359 7731 Fax: 0121-353 4557 E-mail: shapero@netcomuk.co.uk
Spentex B C A Ltd, Thorp Arch Trading Estate, Thorp Arch, Wetherby, West Yorkshire, LS23 7BJ Tel: (01937) 845848 Fax: (01937) 541237 E-mail: sales@spentex.co.uk
Welling Sewing Centre, 104-106 Welling High Street, Welling, Kent, DA16 1TJ Tel: (020) 8304 0470 Fax: (020) 8298 1582
W. Williams & Son (Bread Street) Ltd, Unit 15-16, High Cross Center, Fountayne Road, London, N15 4QN Tel: (020) 8885 8440 Fax: (020) 8880 9294 E-mail: sales@williamsltd.co.uk
Wool 'N' Things, Broadway, Totland Bay, Isle of Wight, PO39 0AS Tel: (01983) 752434 Fax: (01983) 752434

HACKSAW BLADES

Carroll Tools Ltd, 16-18 Factory Lane, Croydon, CR0 3RL Tel: (020) 8781 1268 Fax: (020) 8781 1278 E-mail: info@carrolltools.com
Irwin Industial Tool Co. Ltd, Parkway Works, Kettlebridge Road, Sheffield, S9 3BL Tel: 0114-244 9066 Fax: 0114-256 1788 E-mail: sales@record.co.uk

HACKSAWING MACHINES

Benchmaster Machine Tool Co., Holmfield Industrial Estate, Holmfield, Halifax, West Yorkshire, HX2 9TN Tel: (01422) 247185 Fax: (01422) 247234

HACKSAWS

Simonds Industries Ltd, 3 Motorway Industrial Estate, Tyler Street, Sheffield, S9 1DH Tel: 0114-243 3701 Fax: 0114-243 3879

HAIR CARE PRODUCTS

▶ Alpha 7, 3 Tipping Brow, Mobberley, Knutsford, Cheshire, WA16 7JE Tel: (01565) 880012 E-mail: contactus@alpha7haircare.co.uk
▶ HAZ Afro Cosmetics, Unit 2, Alpine House, Honeypot Lane, London, NW9 9RX Tel: (020) 8732 2929 Fax: (020) 8204 9955 E-mail: hussain@hazafro.co.uk
▶ Liannes Mobile Hairdresser, 7 New Rectory Lane, Kingsnorth, Ashford, Kent, TN23 3LY Tel: (01233) 503226 E-mail: hair@liannes.co.uk
▶ T3 Magic, Unit 2 Lochside Court, Irongray Road, Dumfries, DG2 0HS Tel: (01387) 721170 E-mail: info@t3magic.com

HAIR COLOURS

▶ Academy Hair & Beauty UK Ltd, 4 Kent Street Industrial Estate, 26 Kent Street, Leicester, LE5 3BD Tel: 0116-262 4946 Fax: 0116-251 6489 E-mail: mail@academy-beauty.com

HAIR DRYERS

Alco Electric Hairdryer Repairs, Fernhill Road, Solihull, West Midlands, B92 7RU Tel: 0121-706 1404 Fax: 0121-706 1404
▶ Capital Hair & Beauty Ltd, 3 Burton Road, Norwich, NR6 6AX Tel: (01603) 788778 Fax: (01603) 788856 E-mail: norwich@capitalhairandbeauty.co.uk
Conair Group Ltd, Prospect Court, 3 Waterfront Business Park, Fleet, Hampshire, GU51 3TW Tel: (01252) 813000 Fax: (01252) 813028
▶ Cotswold Hygiene, 29 Davenport Road, Witney, Oxfordshire, OX28 6EL Tel: (01993) 704406 Fax: (01993) 700224
Deltagroom Beauty Products, 13 Dodnor Park, Newport, Isle of Wight, PO30 5XE Tel: (01983) 522004 Fax: (01983) 522004
Saloneasy.Com, 3 Pye Road, Wirral, Merseyside, CH60 0DB Tel: 0151-342 6271 Fax: 0151-342 1130 E-mail: sales@saloneasy.com
Salton Europe Ltd, Sisson Street, Failsworth, Manchester, M35 0HS Tel: 0161-947 3000 Fax: 0161-682 1708

HAIR DRYERS, COIN/PUSH BUTTON OPERATED

▶ Cotswold Hygiene, 29 Davenport Road, Witney, Oxfordshire, OX28 6EL Tel: (01993) 704406 Fax: (01993) 700224
Leisure Control Systems, Clump Farm Industrial Estate, Shaftesbury Lane, Blandford Forum, Dorset, DT11 7TD Tel: (01258) 489075 Fax: (01258) 488526 E-mail: sales@wyvern-innleisure.co.uk

HAIR EXTENSION GLUE STICKS

Dome Cosmetics, 30 West Hill, Epsom, Surrey, KT19 8JD Tel: (01372) 745577 Fax: (01372) 747274 E-mail: press@domeltd.freeserve.co.uk
▶ Hair Braid, 3 Mossley Hall, Congleton, Cheshire, CW1 2LZ Tel: 07092 847194 Fax: (07092) 306109 E-mail: sandrawalkden@googlemail.com
▶ Ismag Ltd, 483 Green Lanes, London, N13 4BS Tel: (0870) 7773174 Fax: (0870) 7773176 E-mail: sales@ismag.co.uk
▶ Just Bonds, 1546 Stratford Road, Hall Green, Birmingham, B28 9HA Tel: 0121-682 1401 E-mail: justbonds@blueyonder.co.uk
▶ Rapunzel's Hair Shop Ltd, 429 Smithdown Road, Wavertree, Liverpool, L15 3JJ Tel: 0151-733 4333 Fax: 0151-733 4303

HAIR EXTENSION TRAINING

▶ Hair Braid, 3 Mossley Hall, Congleton, Cheshire, CW1 2LZ Tel: 07092 847194 Fax: (07092) 306109 E-mail: sandrawalkden@googlemail.com
▶ Just Bonds, 1546 Stratford Road, Hall Green, Birmingham, B28 9HA Tel: 0121-682 1401 E-mail: justbonds@blueyonder.co.uk

HAIR EXTENSIONS

▶ Amazing Lengths, 7 Gladstone Close, Newport Pagnell, Bucks, MK16 0EU Tel: 01908 612489 E-mail: info@amazinglengths.co.uk
▶ Amazing Lengths Hair Extensions, 16 Guernsey Close, Aylesbury, Buckinghamshire, HP19 9GU Tel: (01296) 397046 E-mail: info@amazinglengths.co.uk
Dome Cosmetics, 30 West Hill, Epsom, Surrey, KT19 8JD Tel: (01372) 745577 Fax: (01372) 747274 E-mail: press@domeltd.freeserve.co.uk
▶ Hair Braid, 3 Mossley Hall, Congleton, Cheshire, CW1 2LZ Tel: 07092 847194 Fax: (07092) 306109 E-mail: sandrawalkden@googlemail.com
▶ Hair Extensions By Beautiful Manes, 20 Oakpits Way, Rushden, Northants, NN10 0PP Tel: 07901 948830
▶ Ismag Ltd, 483 Green Lanes, London, N13 4BS Tel: (0870) 7773174 Fax: (0870) 7773176 E-mail: sales@ismag.co.uk
▶ Just Bonds, 1546 Stratford Road, Hall Green, Birmingham, B28 9HA Tel: 0121-682 1401 E-mail: justbonds@blueyonder.co.uk
▶ Rapunzel's Hair Shop Ltd, 429 Smithdown Road, Wavertree, Liverpool, L15 3JJ Tel: 0151-733 4333 Fax: 0151-733 4303
▶ Soewitos Hair And Beauty Salon, Brunel Centre, Bletchley, Milton Keynes, MK2 2ES Tel: 01908 642985

HAIR PREPARATIONS

Alberto-Culver Co. (UK) Ltd, Lime Tree Way, Hampshire International Business Park, Chineham, Basingstoke, Hampshire, RG24 8ER Tel: (01256) 705000 Fax: (01256) 705001
Applejacks, Unit 28 The Mall, The Stratford Centre, London, E15 1XD Tel: (020) 8519 5809 Fax: (020) 8519 1099 E-mail: robert@applejacks.co.uk
Creightons P.L.C., Lincoln Road, Peterborough, PE4 6ND Tel: (01733) 281000 Fax: (01733) 281028 E-mail: sales@creightons.com
La Riche, PO Box 2093, Southend-on-Sea, SS3 9QP Tel: (01702) 297532 Fax: (01702) 297533 E-mail: laricheltd@aol.com
Morgans Pomade Co. Ltd, Tyler Way, Swalecliffe, Whitstable, Kent, CT5 2RT Tel: (01227) 792761 Fax: (01227) 794463 E-mail: sales@morganspomade.co.uk
Stantondown Ltd, Shafton Lane, Leeds, LS11 9QY Tel: 0113-243 5746 Fax: 0113-242 1706 E-mail: stantondown@btclick.com
Topaz Hair Cosmetics Ltd, The House Of Topaz, Guilden Sutton Lane, Guilden Sutton, Chester, CH3 7EX Tel: (01244) 312606 Fax: (01244) 317482 E-mail: glenn@topazhaircosmetics.co.uk
Weleda U K Ltd, Heanor Road, Ilkeston, Derbyshire, DE7 8DR Tel: 0115-944 8200 Fax: 0115-944 8210 E-mail: weledauk@compuserve.com

HAIR STRAIGHTENERS

▶ T3 Magic, Unit 2 Lochside Court, Irongray Road, Dumfries, DG2 0HS Tel: (01387) 721170 E-mail: info@t3magic.com

HAIR STYLING PRODUCTS

▶ Alpha 7, 3 Tipping Brow, Mobberley, Knutsford, Cheshire, WA16 7JE Tel: (01565) 880012 E-mail: contactus@alpha7haircare.co.uk
▶ Liannes Mobile Hairdresser, 7 New Rectory Lane, Kingsnorth, Ashford, Kent, TN23 3LY Tel: (01233) 503226 E-mail: hair@liannes.co.uk

HAIRCLOTH INTERLININGS

Mitchell Interflex Ltd, County Brook Mill, County Brook Lane, Foulridge, Colne, Lancashire, BB8 7LT Tel: (01282) 813221 Fax: (01282) 813633 E-mail: sales@mitchell-interflex.co.uk

HAIRDRESSING ACCESSORIES AND REQUISITES, *See also headings for particular types*

▶ 1 Stop Ltd, Boardman Industrial Estate, Boardman Road, Swadlincote, Derbyshire, DE11 9DL Tel: (01283) 819933 Fax: (01283) 819947 E-mail: martin@rosehouse.co.uk
A K S Hairdressing Supplies, 3 H C M Industrial Estate, Wetmore Road, Burton-on-Trent, Staffordshire, DE14 1QR Tel: (01283) 535408 Fax: (01283) 535409
Aks Hair & Beauty Ltd, 8 Peter Baines Industrial Estate, Woods Lane, Derby, DE22 3UD Tel: (01332) 380028 Fax: (01332) 380073
Alan Howard, Unit 6 Healey Wood Road Industrial Estate, Burnley, Lancashire, BB11 2LZ Tel: (01282) 433444 Fax: (01282) 433444 E-mail: info@salonlink.co.uk
Allen Howard Stockport, Thornley Avenue, Blackburn, BB1 3HJ Tel: (01254) 664113 Fax: (01254) 664113
Allens Hairdressers Wholesalers, 31 Somerset Avenue, Leicester, LE4 0JX Tel: 0116-235 6855 Fax: 0116-234 1996
Aston & Fincher Ltd, Unit 2 Pavillion Drive, Off Holford Drive, Perry Barr, Birmingham, B6 7BB Tel: 0121-331 2000 Fax: 0121-331 2001
Aston & Fincher Ltd, 213a Mill Road, Cambridge, CB1 3BE Tel: (01223) 249555 Fax: (01223) 249038
Aston & Fincher Ltd, 60 Cyprus Road, Leicester, LE2 8QS Tel: 0116-283 3451
▶ Aston & Fincher Ltd, 3 Trafalgar Way, Erskine Industrial Estate, Liverpool, L6 1NA Tel: 0151-263 8811 Fax: 0151-263 8855
Aston & Fincher Ltd, 9-10 Embankment Lane, Plymouth, PL4 9LQ Tel: (01752) 221213 Fax: (01752) 260275
Athertons, 593 Ormskirk Road, Wigan, Lancashire, WN5 8AG Tel: (01942) 214579
▶ Beauty Styles Ltd, The Agora Centre, Church Street, Wolverton, Milton Keynes, MK12 5LG Tel: (07946) 599661
Belmont Hair & Beauty, 2 Plot 46 Colville Road, London, W3 8BL Tel: (020) 8992 7708 Fax: (020) 8992 7709
Callinan Hair & Beauty Products, Glebe Farm, Dennis Street, Hugglescote, Coalville, Leicestershire, LE67 2FP Tel: (01530) 814074
Capital Hair & Beauty Ltd, 6 Sackville Trading Estate, Sackville Road, Hove, East Sussex, BN3 7AN Tel: (01273) 327215 Fax: (01273) 735305 E-mail: hove@capitalhairandbeauty.co.uk
▶ Capital Hair & Beauty Ltd, Unit 18, Chiltonian Industrial Estate, Manor Lane, Lee, London, SE12 0TX Tel: (020) 8852 9959 E-mail: lee@capitalhairandbeauty.co.uk
Catford Agencies, 23a Harberson Road, London, SW12 9QX Tel: (020) 8675 7492 Fax: (020) 8675 7469
Cetuem Cosmetics Ltd, 115 Brunswick Park Road, London, N11 1EA Tel: (020) 8368 0008 Fax: (020) 8368 9579 E-mail: info@centuem.com
Coldhams Of East Anglia Ltd, 23 Kingsway, Norwich, NR2 4UE Tel: (01603) 629531 Fax: (01603) 632686
Colomer Professional International, 22-24 Claremont Road, Claremont House, Surbiton, Surrey, KT6 4QU Tel: (020) 8339 9080 Fax: (020) 8390 9853
Conair Group Ltd, Prospect Court, 3 Waterfront Business Park, Fleet, Hampshire, GU51 3TW Tel: (01252) 813000 Fax: (01252) 813028
Darley Couches, Unit 5 Restormel Industrial Estate, Lostwithiel, Cornwall, PL22 0HG Tel: (01208) 873200 Fax: (01208) 872772
Deltagroom Beauty Products, 13 Dodnor Park, Newport, Isle of Wight, PO30 5XE Tel: (01983) 522004 Fax: (01983) 522004
Diamond Edge Ltd, 126 Gloucester Road, Brighton, BN1 4BU Tel: (01273) 605922 Fax: (01273) 625074 E-mail: diamondedge@btclick.com
E A Ellison & Co. Ltd, Crondal Road, Bayton Industrial Estate, Exhall, Coventry, CV7 9NH Tel: (024) 7636 1619 Fax: (024) 7637 9183 E-mail: sales@ellisons.co.uk
E W D Hair & Beauty Supplies Ltd, Units 1-3, Rainbow Street, Crewe, CW1 2AU Tel: (01270) 581307 Fax: (01270) 581307
▶ Euro Hair Fashion UK Ltd, 4 North Cresent Business Park, Diplocks Way, Hailsham, East Sussex, BN27 3JF Tel: (01323) 842288 Fax: (01323) 449211 E-mail: info@eurohair.co.uk
Exclusive Salon Products Ltd, 64 High Street, Gravesend, Kent, DA11 0BB Tel: (01474) 320555 Fax: (01474) 320555
▶ Foila Ltd, Valley House Hornbeam Park, Hookstone Road, Harrogate, North Yorkshire, HG2 8QT Tel: (01423) 810480 Fax: (01423) 810490 E-mail: info@foila.co.uk
▶ Gala Distribution Ltd, 209 Uxbridge Road, London, W13 9AA Tel: (020) 8840 1222
Giltsharp Europe Ltd, PO Box 121, Shipley, West Yorkshire, BD17 5YQ Tel: (01274) 533345 Fax: (0870) 7061721 E-mail: sales@giltsharp.com
▶ Giltsharp Wezblade (UK), 1 Collingwood Road, Witham, Essex, CM8 2DY Tel: 07979 307831
H.E.R.S., 15 Bills St, Darlaston, W. Midlands, WS10 8BB Tel: 0121 526 3608 Fax: 0121 568 6487
Hair & Beauty Direct Trading Co., Unit D.5 Seedbed Centre, Davidson Way, Romford, RM7 0AZ Tel: (01708) 714251 Fax: (01708) 714222
Hair Cosmetics Ltd, 11 Queens Court Business Centre, Carrmere Road, Leechmere Industrial Estate, Sunderland, SR2 9TW Tel: 0191-521 4000 Fax: 0191-521 4040
The Hair Factory, 4 North Square, London, N9 0HW Tel: (020) 8660 5520
Hairdressers Electrical Equipment, 38-42 Sussex St, Leeds, LS9 8SE Tel: 0113-235 0502 Fax: 0113-235 0502
Alan Howard, Unit6 Park Road, Timperley, Altrincham, Cheshire, WA14 5AB Tel: 0161-973 5457 Fax: 0161-973 5424
▶ Alan Howard, 2 41 Clifford Road, Blackpool, FY1 2PU Tel: (01253) 628008 Fax: (01253) 628008
Alan Howard (Stockport) Ltd, Hulley Road, Macclesfield, Cheshire, SK10 2LX Tel: (01625) 422424 Fax: (01625) 425147
▶ Inca Jewellery Ltd, Unit 2, Gelders Hall Ind Est, Shepshed, Loughborough, Leics, LE12 9NH Tel: 01509 501000 Fax: 01509 501010 E-mail: sales@IncaUK.com
Jack Kaye Ltd, 1143 London Road, Leigh-on-Sea, Essex, SS9 3JE Tel: (01702) 476268 Fax: (01702) 476268
Jaffa International Marketing Ltd, Mullany Business Park, Deanland Road, Golden Cross, Hailsham, East Sussex, BN27 3RP Tel: (01825) 872875 Fax: (01825) 872877 E-mail: jim@jaffa-international.co.uk
Jamels Hairdressers' Equipment, 140 Queensway, Agora Shopping Centre, Bletchley, Milton Keynes, MK2 2RS Tel: (01908) 366636 Fax: (01908) 366636
John Dobson Milnthorpe Ltd, Bela Mill, Milnthorpe, Cumbria, LA7 7QP Tel: (01539) 563528 Fax: (01539) 562481 E-mail: enquiries@combs.co.uk
Kayjay Hairdressers' Equipment, 6 Old Hall Industrial Estate, Revival Street, Walsall, WS3 3HJ Tel: (01922) 400001 Fax: (01922) 400001
Lacey's Hair & Beauty Supplies, Unit 5 The Markham Centre, Station Road, Theale, Reading, RG7 4PE Tel: 0118-930 2338
M Criscuolo & Co. Ltd, Crisco House, 169 Godstone Road, Kenley, Surrey, CR8 5BL Tel: (020) 8660 7949 Fax: (020) 8668 5334 E-mail: sales@crisco.co.uk
▶ M & S Hairdressing Supplies, Unit 5 United Business Park, Lowfields Road, Leeds, LS12 6UB Tel: 0113-244 5581 Fax: 0113-247 1082
M & S Supplies Liverpool Ltd, Haigh Avenue, Stockport, Cheshire, SK4 1NU Tel: 0161-477 5479 Fax: 0161-480 5505
▶ Medusa, 95 Albion Road, Broadstairs, Kent, CT10 2UT Tel: (01843) 602500
Ore An Ltd, Unit 15-21 Branxholme Industrial Estate, Bradford Road, Brighouse, West Yorkshire, HD6 4EA Tel: (01484) 400818 Fax: (01484) 711115
Personalised Coiffeur Products, 1 Kincath Avenue, Rutherglen, Glasgow, G73 4RP Tel: 0141-634 3935 Fax: 0141-570 3453
Pompadour Ltd, Chequers Road, West Meadows Industrial Estate, Derby, DE21 6EN Tel: (01332) 342228 Fax: (01332) 342228
Pompadour Laboratories Ltd, Mount Street, New Basford, Nottingham, NG7 7HF Tel: 0115-978 1383 Fax: 0115-978 4598
Power Promotions, Prospect House, West Craven Drive, Earby, Barnoldswick, Lancashire, BB18 6JZ Tel: (01282) 841000 Fax: (01282) 841010 E-mail: powerpromotions@compuserve.com
Premier Hair & Beauty Supplies, 28 Martello Drive, Hythe, Kent, CT21 6PH Tel: (01303) 238383 Fax: (01303) 238950
Pro Hair Supplies, 320 Lymington Road, Highcliffe, Christchurch, Dorset, BH23 5EY Tel: (01425) 276074 Fax: (01425) 276074
Professional Choice, 3 Wood Street, Corby, Northamptonshire, NN17 1PT Tel: (01536) 407300 Fax: (01536) 407353
Professional Hairdressing Agencies Ltd, 76 Botley Road, Park Gate, Southampton, SO31 1BA Tel: (01489) 589553 Fax: (01489) 581441 E-mail: phaltd@fsbdial.co.uk
Professional Hairdressing Distributors, 4 Haithwaite, Two Mile Ash, Milton Keynes, MK8 8LJ Tel: 01908 265168 Fax: 01908 265168
Ray & Company Hairdressers Sundries Men Ltd, Green Street, Darlington, County Durham, DL1 1HL Tel: (01325) 288840 Fax: (01325) 284620
Ready Heat UK Ltd, Unit B5 Bulwell Business Centre, Sellers Wood Drive, Bulwell, Nottingham, NG6 8GN Tel: 0115-975 4500 Fax: 0115-975 4500
Regency Hair Supplies, Common BNK Indust Estate, Ackhurst Road, Chorley, Lancashire, PR7 1NH Tel: (01257) 263943 Fax: (01257) 263943
▶ Rendezvous (Lincoln) Ltd, Unit 4 Lydon Business Park, Farrier Road, Lincoln, LN6 3RU Tel: (01522) 500000 Fax: (01522) 500000
Rollin Stock Hair & Beauty Supplies Ltd, 139 London Road, Benfleet, Essex, SS7 5UH Tel: (01268) 793300 Fax: (01268) 795689 E-mail: rollinstock@btopenworld.com
▶ Sally, Harbour Deck, Princes Quay, Hull, HU1 2PQ Tel: (01482) 620044
Sally, 7 Clifton Street, Lincoln, LN5 8LQ Tel: (01522) 542656 Fax: 01522 568918
▶ Sally, 138 Peascod Street, Windsor, Berkshire, SL4 1DS Tel: (01753) 832414
▶ Sally Hair & Beauty Supplies Ltd, 1b Broadway, Accrington, Lancashire, BB5 1JZ Tel: (01254) 391002 E-mail: admin@sallybeauty.co.uk
▶ Sally Hair & Beauty Supplies Ltd, 57 Grosvenor Shopping Centre, Northfield, Northfield, Birmingham, B31 2JU Tel: 0121-476 5110
Sally Hair & Beauty Supplies, 17 Canal Road, Bradford, West Yorkshire, BD1 4AT Tel: (01274) 739261
▶ Sally Hair & Beauty Supplies Ltd, Sherbourne Arcade, Lower Precinct, Coventry, CV1 1DN Tel: (024) 7622 7077
Sally Hair & Beauty Supplies, 90- 92 Kilmarnock Road, Glasgow, G41 3NN Tel: 0141-636 5096
Sally Hair & Beauty Supplies Ltd, 79 High Street, Hounslow, TW3 1RB Tel: (020) 8572 2476
Sally Hair & Beauty Supplies, 537 Cranbrook Road, Ilford, Essex, IG2 6HA Tel: (020) 8554 1210
Sally Hair & Beauty Supplies Ltd, Unit 5 Bellsland Grove, Kilmarnock, Ayrshire, KA1 4BD Tel: (01563) 543211
▶ Sally Hair & Beauty Supplies Ltd, 28 Nicholsons Walk, Maidenhead, Berkshire, SL6 1LB Tel: (01628) 777456
Sally Hair & Beauty Supplies Ltd, 86 Stockwell Gate, Mansfield, Nottinghamshire, NG18 5QD Tel: (01623) 624300
Sally Hair & Beauty Supplies Ltd, Unit 11 The Gateway Industrial Estate, Parkgate, Rotherham, South Yorkshire, S62 6JL Tel: (01709) 528848
▶ Sally Hair & Beauty Supplies Ltd, Lord Street, Southport, Merseyside, PR8 1NH Tel: (01704) 538679
Sally Hair & Beauty Supplies Ltd, 675 Eskdale Road, Winnersh, Wokingham, Berkshire, RG41 5TS Tel: 0118-944 3600 Fax: 0118-944 3601
Sallys, Harwood Street, Blackburn, BB1 3BD Tel: (01254) 680138
Sally's, 5 The Brickyard Excelsior Road, Excelsior Industrial Estate, Cardiff, CF14 3AT Tel: (029) 2052 0259
Sally's, 1-2 Hope Street, Crewe, CW2 7DR Tel: (01270) 589206
Sally's, 7 Margram Business Centre, Horne Street, Halifax, West Yorkshire, HX1 5UA Tel: (01422) 323077
Sallys, 2 Abacus Park, Forth Avenue Industrial Estate, Kirkcaldy, Fife, KY2 5NZ Tel: (01592) 260438 Fax: (01592) 260438
Sally's, Royds Lane, Leeds, LS12 6AD Tel: 0113-279 8441
Sallys Hair & Beauty, 18 Derby Street, Manchester, M8 8RY Tel: 0161-832 5199
▶ Salon Beauty Supplies, Equipment House, Marshfield Bank, Crewe, CW2 8UY Tel: (01270) 848535 Fax: (01270) 848613
Salon Centre, Unit 5-6 Riverside, Bolton, BL1 8TU Tel: (01204) 386004 Fax: (01204) 361750
▶ Salon Connect, The Rear of, 157 High Street, Barkingside, Ilford, Essex, IG6 2AJ Tel: (020) 8418 2490 Fax: (020) 8551 5719 E-mail: salon@salonconnect.co.uk
▶ Salon Focus Ltd, 33 Gibbfield Park Avenue, Gibbfield Park, Atherton, Manchester, M46 0SY Tel: (01942) 886000 Fax: (01942) 888588
▶ Salon Revolution, Stilebrook Road, Olney, Buckinghamshire, MK46 5EA Tel: (01234) 714010 Fax: (0845) 0714568 E-mail: info@salonrevolution.com
Salon Services Ltd, Units P Pitreavie Business Park, Queensferry Road, Dunfermline, Fife, KY11 8PU Tel: (01383) 622205 Fax: (01383) 620598
Salon Services Ltd, 8 Darland Avenue, Gillingham, Kent, ME7 3AL Tel: (01634) 854003 Fax: (01634) 854003
Salon Services Ltd, 54-62 Broomielaw, Glasgow, G1 4QN Tel: 0141-248 5522 Fax: 0141-248 1785
Salon Services Ltd, Unit 2 Brunel Avenue, Salford, M5 4BE Tel: 0161-737 7100 Fax: 0161-737 1362
Salon Success, Kiln Pit Hill, Consett, County Durham, DH8 9SL Tel: (01207) 255333 Fax: (01207) 255366
Salon Supplies, Unit 7, Tuffley Park, Lower Tuffley Lane, Gloucester, GL2 5DP Tel: (01452) 383383 Fax: (01452) 413228
Saloneasy.Com, 3 Pye Road, Wirral, Merseyside, CH60 0DB Tel: 0151-342 6271 Fax: 0151-342 1130 E-mail: sales@saloneasy.com
Schwarzkopf, Oxford House, Oxford Road, Aylesbury, Buckinghamshire, HP21 8SZ Tel: (01296) 314000 Fax: (01296) 398012
Scorpio, 206a Watford Road, Croxley Green, Rickmansworth, Hertfordshire, WD3 3DD Tel: (01923) 212552 Fax: (01923) 468590
Scott & Storey, 19 Norfolk Street, Sunderland, SR1 1EA Tel: 0191-565 8745 Fax: 0191-565 8745
Soft Sheen Carson Europe, 11a Hagley Road, Stourbridge, West Midlands, DY8 1QH Tel: (01384) 372466 Fax: (01384) 440513
State Of The Art Hair Products Ltd, Unit 2, Nelson Park Network Centre, Cramlington, Northumberland, NE23 1WD Tel: (01670) 716234 Fax: (01670) 716234
Synergy, 57 Cotton Street, Aberdeen, AB11 5EG Tel: (01224) 211841 Fax: (01224) 211841
▶ Tash Jacks, Oakland, The Street, Shorne, Gravesend, Kent, DA12 3EA Tel: (01474) 823666 Fax: (01474) 823777 E-mail: info@tashjacks.com
Turvey & Co., 14 Glasgow Road, Edinburgh, EH12 8HZ Tel: 0131-334 0707 Fax: (0870) 0555651 E-mail: pam@turfys.com
Ultimate Hair Co., 104 Eastgate Centre, Basildon, Essex, SS14 1AG Tel: (01268) 282008
Ultimate Hair Co., 15-17 Queens Road, Southend-On-Sea, SS1 1LT Tel: (01702) 433334
Ultimate Hairdressing & Beauty Supplies, 10 George Road, Guildford, Surrey, GU1 4NP Tel: (01483) 566255 Fax: (01483) 574333
▶ Urban Icon, 1 Drill Hall Business Centre, East Parade, Ilkley, West Yorkshire, LS29 8EZ Tel: (01943) 605861 Fax: (01943) 605862
W J Sait (Bristol) Ltd, 87-89 Church Road, Redfield, Bristol, BS5 9JR Tel: 0117-955 5898 Fax: 0117-955 5898
Weston Hair & Beauty Supplies, 8 Orchard House, Station Road, Worle, Weston-super-Mare, Avon, BS22 6AU Tel: (01934) 520252 Fax: (01934) 520252
Williams Dennis Ltd, Unit C 6 Wharncliffe Street, Barnsley, South Yorkshire, S70 6BP Tel: (01226) 207600 Fax: (01226) 207600
Dennis Williams Ltd, Off Abb Scott Lane, Huddesfield Road, Bradford, West Yorkshire, BD12 0TU Tel: (01274) 675636 Fax: (01274) 694043
Dennis Williams Ltd, Unit 2 Fotherby Street, Grimsby, South Humberside, DN31 3AH Tel: (01472) 240810 Fax: (01472) 240810

HAIRDRESSING BRUSHES

Deltagroom Beauty Products, 13 Dodnor Park, Newport, Isle of Wight, PO30 5XE Tel: (01983) 522004 Fax: (01983) 522004
Denman International Ltd, Clandeboye Road, Bangor, County Down, BT20 3JH Tel: (028) 9146 2141 Fax: (028) 9145 1654
G B Kent & Sons plc, London Road, Hemel Hempstead, Hertfordshire, HP3 9SA Tel: (01442) 251531 Fax: (01442) 231672 E-mail: info@kentbrushes.com
Mason Pearson Bros Ltd, 37 Old Bond Street, London, W1S 4AB Tel: (020) 7491 2613 Fax: (020) 7499 2635 E-mail: sales@masonpearson.com
Shaws Pet Products Ltd, Unit 13 Bordesley Trading Estate, Bordesley Green Road, Birmingham, B8 1BZ Tel: 0121-326 7667 Fax: 0121-328 1734 E-mail: info@shawspet.co.uk

HAIRDRESSING CLIPPER LUBRICATING OIL

Regency Hair Supplies, Common BNK Indust Estate, Ackhurst Road, Chorley, Lancashire, PR7 1NH Tel: (01257) 263943 Fax: (01257) 263943

HAIRDRESSING NECK WOOL

▶ Capital Hair & Beauty Ltd, 3 Burton Road, Norwich, NR6 6AX Tel: (01603) 788778 Fax: (01603) 788856 E-mail: norwich@capitalhairandbeauty.co.uk

HAIRDRESSING SALON FURNITURE, USED

▶ Alphatask Salon Solutions, 12B Gaisford Street, London, NW5 2ED Tel: 0870 1417370 E-mail: info@alphatask.net

HAIRDRESSING SALON SCISSORS

▶ Alphatask Salon Solutions, 12B Gaisford Street, London, NW5 2ED Tel: 0870 1417370 E-mail: info@alphatask.net
▶ D B Hair, 161 Brownroyd Hill Road, Bradford, West Yorkshire, BD6 1RU Tel: (01274) 690909 E-mail: info@dbhair.co.uk
Regency Hair Supplies, Common BNK Indust Estate, Ackhurst Road, Chorley, Lancashire, PR7 1NH Tel: (01257) 263943 Fax: (01257) 263943

HAIRDRESSING SALON WASH BASINS

▶ Alphatask Salon Solutions, 12B Gaisford Street, London, NW5 2ED Tel: 0870 1417370 E-mail: info@alphatask.net

HAIRNETS, BEAUTY

▶ Madison Avenue, 5 Stanford House, Princess Margaret Road, East Tilbury, Tilbury, Essex, RM18 8YP Tel: (01375) 840022 E-mail: enquires@madavesalon.co.uk

HAIRPIECE/WIG EXPORT/ IMPORT MERCHANTS OR AGENTS

Freestyle Hair Co. Ltd, Unit 22 Haigh Park, Haigh Avenue, Stockport, Cheshire, SK4 1QR Tel: 0161-476 1115 Fax: 0161-429 0730 E-mail: info@freestylehair.co.uk

HAIRPIECES/WIGS

Burlington Bertie's, 329 Haydons Road, London, SW19 8LA Tel: (020) 8543 9700 E-mail: bertie@burlingtonberties.co.uk

▶ Continental Wigs, 39 Granada Road, Southsea, Hampshire, PO4 0RD Tel: (01455) 559679 Fax: (01455) 559541 E-mail: continental.wigs@ntlworld.com

I.F.E Ltd, 8 Well Street, London, E9 7PX Tel: (020) 8985 6501 Fax: (020) 8985 6501 E-mail: sales@ife-co.com

Smiffy's, Heapham Road South, Caldicott Drive, Heapham Road Industrial Estate, Gainsborough, Lincolnshire, DN21 1FJ Tel: (01427) 616831 Fax: (01427) 617190 E-mail: info@smiffys.com

▶ Tash Jacks, Oakland, The Street, Shorne, Gravesend, Kent, DA12 3EA Tel: (01474) 823666 Fax: (01474) 823777 E-mail: info@tashjacks.com

▶ Wig Advice.co.uk, Trentham, Stoke-on-Trent, ST4 8TU Tel: (01782) 644287 E-mail: sallywigshelp@tiscali.co.uk

▶ Wigtopia, Unit 106, 9 St Johns Street, Colchester, CO2 7NN Tel: (01206) 570976 E-mail: sales@wigtopia.co.uk

HAIRPINS

ALBRI FASHION ACCESSORIES, 69 Thornham Street, Greenwich, London, SE10 9SB Tel: (07957) 254825 Fax: (0870) 242 0473 E-mail: info@albrifashion.com

HAIRSPRINGS

Tormo Ltd, 7 Devonshire Business Park, Chester Road, Borehamwood, Hertfordshire, WD6 1NA Tel: (020) 8207 5777 Fax: (020) 8207 5888 E-mail: sales@tormo.co.uk

HALOGEN FREE FIRE RETARDANT (FR) THERMOPLASTIC CABLE COMPOUNDS

▶ Eclipse Presentations Ltd, 5 Chaffinch Business Park, Croydon Road, Beckenham, Kent, BR3 4AA Tel: (020) 8662 6444 Fax: (020) 8650 4635 E-mail: info@eclipse-presentations.co.uk

HALOGEN FREE FIRE RETARDANT (FR) THERMOSETTING CABLE COMPOUNDS

▶ Eclipse Presentations Ltd, 5 Chaffinch Business Park, Croydon Road, Beckenham, Kent, BR3 4AA Tel: (020) 8662 6444 Fax: (020) 8650 4635 E-mail: info@eclipse-presentations.co.uk

HALOGEN LAMPS

▶ Ebulbshop Lighting Retailers, 42 44 High Street, Hythe, Kent, CT21 5AT Tel: (01303) 264400 Fax: (01303) 264664 E-mail: andrew@ebulbshop.com

HAMBURGERS

R A Robinson & Son, Unit 7 Turnpike Industrial Estate, Newbury, Berkshire, RG14 2LR Tel: (01635) 41045 Fax: (01635) 41045

HAMMER DRIVE SCREWS

John Reynolds & Sons Ltd, Units 5-6 Church Lane Industrial Estate, West Bromwich, West Midlands, B71 1AR Tel: 0121-553 2754 Fax: 0121-500 5460 E-mail: sales@johnreynolds.co.uk

HAMMER FINISH PAINTS

▶ Howses Paint & Powder Ltd, Cakemore Road, Rowley Regis, West Midlands, B65 0RD Tel: 0121-559 1451 Fax: 0121-559 2722 E-mail: sales@howsepaints.co.uk

HAMMER MILLS

▶ Christie Turner Ltd, Knightsdale Road, Ipswich, IP1 4LE Tel: (01473) 742325 Fax: (01473) 462 773 E-mail: info@christyhunt.co.uk

Lanway Ltd, PO Box 3568, Bewdley, Worcestershire, DY12 1ZU Tel: (01299) 861733 Fax: (0871) 7333899 E-mail: sales@lanway.ltd.uk

Miracle Mills Ltd, Knightsdale Road, Ipswich, IP1 4LE Tel: (01473) 742325 Fax: (01473) 462773 E-mail: info@cristy-turner.com

HAND ACTUATED PRESSES

Hunton Ltd, Hilton Rd, Cobbs Wood Industrial Estate, Ashford, Kent, TN23 1EW Tel: (01233) 628976 Fax: (01233) 664909 E-mail: sales@mjallen.co.uk

Matten Ltd, Market Street, Whitworth, Rochdale, Lancashire, OL12 8PW Tel: (01706) 341197 Fax: (01706) 342580 E-mail: john@mattenltd.co.uk

HAND AND ARM VIBRATION TESTING

▶ Nationwide Healthcare Connections Ltd, Connections House, 105 Bellingdon Road, Chesham, Buckinghamshire, HP5 2HQ Tel: (01494) 773007 Fax: (01494) 773008 E-mail: sales@healthcare-connections.com

HAND CLEANSER SUPPLY SERVICES

Ashdown Brookworth, 5 Parkway House, Worth Way, Keighley, West Yorkshire, BD21 5LD Tel: (01535) 663336 Fax: (01535) 610338

HAND DRYER (ELECTRIC) SUPPLY SERVICES

▶ Cotswold Hygiene, 29 Davenport Road, Witney, Oxfordshire, OX28 6EL Tel: (01993) 704406 Fax: (01993) 700224

Leisure Control Systems, Clump Farm Industrial Estate, Shaftesbury Lane, Blandford Forum, Dorset, DT11 7TD Tel: (01258) 489075 Fax: (01258) 488526 E-mail: sales@wyvern-innleisure.co.uk

Lovair, The Old Stables, Brook Street, Macclesfield, Cheshire, SK11 7AA Tel: (0845) 1302907 Fax: (0845) 1302908 E-mail: sales@lovair.co.uk

HAND ENGRAVERS

A W Engraving, 11 Lifford Way, Binley Industrial Estate, Coventry, CV3 2RN Tel: (024) 7663 5453 Fax: (024) 7663 5486

Almonds Engravers Ltd, 12 Duke Street, Darlington, County Durham, DL3 7AA Tel: (01325) 464808 Fax: (01325) 464808

Deco Bishop Auckland Ltd, Roman Way Industrial Estate, Bishop Auckland, County Durham, DL14 9AW Tel: (01388) 604590 Fax: (01388) 604590

Downey & Co. Ltd, Unit 1 Peterley Business Centre, 472 Hackney Road, London, E2 9EG Tel: (020) 7739 8696 Fax: (020) 7739 9877 E-mail: orders@downey.co.uk

F & G Lancaster, 16 Hockley Street, Birmingham, B18 6BL Tel: 0121-554 1454 Fax: 0121-554 1454

Flint & Son, 43 Nursery Road, Hockley, Birmingham, B19 2XN Tel: 0121-523 2875

J S Drew, 856 Plymouth Road, Slough, SL1 4LP Tel: (01753) 568181 Fax: (01753) 568121 E-mail: jsdrewengravers@aol.com

North Wales Trophies & Engravers, 34 Tan-Y-Bryn Road, Llandudno, Gwynedd, LL30 1UU Tel: (01492) 860363

Peter Devine, 94 Matilda Street, Sheffield, S1 4QF Tel: 0114-275 0479 Fax: 0114-275 0479

R H Wilkins Ltd, 31-35 Kirby Street, London, EC1N 8TE Tel: (020) 7405 5187 Fax: (020) 7831 2805 E-mail: sales@rhwilkins.co.uk

S B Services, 86 Chelwood Avenue, Hatfield, Hertfordshire, AL10 0RE Tel: (01707) 256644 Fax: (01707) 262599 E-mail: s.brayshaw@btopenworld.com

Michael Smith Engraving Services Ltd, Unit 3, Leicester, LE2 8AA Tel: 0116-283 0712 Fax: 0116-244 0198 E-mail: sales@michaelsmithswitchgear.co.uk

Trafalgar House Engraving, 4 Trafalgar Street, Brighton, BN1 4EQ Tel: (01273) 603498 Fax: (01273) 680181

C.J. Watson, Hilton Chambers, Roushill, Shrewsbury, SY1 1PN Tel: (01743) 362898 Fax: (01743) 362898

HAND FORGINGS

Dixons Forge, Unit 47 Salthouse Mills Industrial Estate, Barrow-in-Furness, Cumbria, LA13 0DH Tel: (01229) 431618 Fax: (01229) 431618

Graythorpe Forge & Engineering Ltd, 99 Graythorp Industrial Estate, Hartlepool, Cleveland, TS25 2DP Tel: (01429) 273268 Fax: (01429) 236553

HAND GARDEN TOOLS

Bosch Lawn & Garden Limited, Suffolk Works, Stowmarket, Suffolk, IP14 1EY Tel: (01449) 742000 Fax: (01449) 675444

Hand Tools Ltd, Stubley Works, Wreakes Lane, Dronfield, Derbyshire, S18 1PN Tel: (01246) 413139 Fax: (01246) 415208 E-mail: handtools@tiscali.co.uk

J. Newsome (Tools) Ltd, Unit 1, Harleston Street, Sheffield, S4 7QB Tel: 0114-275 7002 Fax: 0114-279 7070 E-mail: newsome@syol.com

Two Wests & Elliott Ltd, Carrwood Road, Chesterfield, Derbyshire, S41 9RH Tel: (01246) 451077 Fax: (01246) 260115 E-mail: sales@twowests.co.uk

HAND HAMMERS

Buck & Hickman Ltd, Unit 5 Waterside, Trafford Park, Manchester, M17 1WD Tel: 0161-877 7888 Fax: 0161-877 7111 E-mail: manchester@buckhickmaninone.com

Bullock Bros Edge Tools Ltd, Landywood Lane, Cheslyn Hay, Walsall, WS6 7AL Tel: (01922) 414360 Fax: (01922) 410359 E-mail: sales@bullocktools.co.uk

Thor Hammer Co. Ltd, Highlands Road, Shirley, Solihull, West Midlands, B90 4NJ Tel: 0121-705 4695 Fax: 0121-705 4727 E-mail: info@thorhammer.com

Visa Hand Tools Ltd, Gibson House, Barrowby Lane, Garforth, Leeds, LS25 1NG Tel: 0113-286 9245 Fax: 0113-286 6859 E-mail: enq@visatools.co.uk

HAND KNITTING YARN

Coats Crafts U.K, Lingfield, McMullen Road, Darlington, County Durham, DL1 1YQ Tel: (01325) 394394 Fax: (01325) 394200 E-mail: consumer.services@coats.com

James C Brett, 30-34 Clyde Street, Bingley, West Yorkshire, BD16 2NT Tel: (01274) 569381 Fax: (01274) 566851

HAND LAMPS

Furneaux Riddall & Co. Ltd, Alchorne Place, Portsmouth, PO3 5PA Tel: (023) 9266 8621 Fax: (023) 9269 0521 E-mail: info@furneauxriddall.com

HAND LAWN MOWERS

Countrywide Stores P.L.C., Station Road, Stockton, Southam, Warwickshire, CV47 8HA Tel: (01926) 812513 Fax: (01926) 815105

Ernest Doe & Sons Ltd, Whempstead Road, Benington, Stevenage, Hertfordshire, SG2 7BZ Tel: (01438) 869251 Fax: (01438) 869302 E-mail: ernestdoe@benington.com

Honda UK Ltd, 470 London Road, Slough, SL3 8QY Tel: (01753) 590500 Fax: (01753) 590000

HAND LOOMS

Harris Looms, Kingsnorth Industrial Estate, Wotton Road, Ashford, Kent, TN23 6JY Tel: (01233) 622686 Fax: (01233) 645801 E-mail: sales@emir.co.uk

HAND MIRRORS

Lethenian Enterprises, Barnsurges, Mincombe Post, Sidbury, Sidmouth, Devon, EX10 0QP Tel: (01395) 597666 Fax: (01395) 222894

HAND OPERATED COMMERCIAL VEHICLE UNIT MOVING EQUIPMENT

Powrwheel Ltd, 8 Queensway, New Milton, Hampshire, BH25 5NN Tel: (01425) 623123 Fax: (01425) 623111 E-mail: info@powrwheel.com

HAND OPERATED SHEET METAL BENDING MACHINES

Castlerigg Engineering Co. Ltd, Browfoot Works, Penrith Road, Keswick, Cumbria, CA12 4LH Tel: (01768) 772876 Fax: (01768) 772885 E-mail: info@castlerigg-eng.co.uk

HAND OR MANUALLY OPERATED HOISTS

Didsbury Engineering, Unit 1b Lower Meadow Road, Brooke Park, Handforth, Wilmslow, Cheshire, SK9 3LP Tel: 0161-486 2200 Fax: 0161-486 2211 E-mail: sales@didsbury.com

HAND OR MANUALLY OPERATED LIFTS

Equilift Ltd, 8 Barrington Park, Leycroft Road, Leicester, LE4 1ET Tel: 0116-234 4310 Fax: 0116-234 4360 E-mail: info@equilift.com

▶ Transdek UK Ltd, PO Box 76, Retford, Nottinghamshire, DN22 8ST Tel: (01777) 705958 Fax: (01777) 706756 E-mail: info@transdek.com

HAND OR MECHANICAL JACKS

Dorvic Engineering Co. Ltd, New Street, Holbrook Industrial Estate, Holbrook, Sheffield, S20 3GH Tel: 0114-248 5633 Fax: 0114-251 0654 E-mail: sales@dorvic.com

Metallifacture Ltd, Mansfield Road, Redhill, Nottingham, NG5 8PY Tel: 0115-966 0200 Fax: 0115-967 0133 E-mail: mail@metallifacture.co.uk

P A R Communications (Leeds) Ltd, Mile End Road, Colwick Industrial Estate, Colwick, Nottingham, NG4 2BU Tel: 0115-961 4744 Fax: 0115-940 0714 E-mail: parcom@btconnect.com

HAND PAPER TOWELS

Peter Grant Papers Ltd, Stafford Park 12, Telford, Shropshire, TF3 3BJ Tel: (01952) 292200 Fax: (01952) 291108 E-mail: sales@pgpapers.com

Hygiene Warehouse, Unit 6, Ashmead Park, Ashmead Road, Keynsham, Bristol, BS31 1SU Tel: 0117-946 1978 Fax: 0117-946 1959 E-mail: sales@hygienewarehouse.co.uk

K P P Converters Ltd, Site 72, Units 1-4, Manners Industrial Estate, Ilkeston, Derbyshire, DE7 8EF Tel: 0115-930 5777 Fax: 0115-932 9184 E-mail: enquiries@kpptissue.co.uk

Unicorn Containers Ltd, 5 Ferguson Drive, Lisburn, County Antrim, BT28 2EX Tel: (028) 9266 7264 Fax: (028) 9262 5616 E-mail: sales@unicorn-containers.com

HAND PUMPS

Micom Engineering Ltd, 7 Industrial Estate, The St, Heybridge, Maldon, Essex, CM9 4XB Tel: (01621) 856324 Fax: (01621) 858778 E-mail: sales@micomltd.co.uk

Pump International Ltd, Trevool, Praze, Camborne, Cornwall, TR14 0PJ Tel: (01209) 831937 Fax: (01209) 831939 E-mail: sales@pumpinternational.com

Roach Pumps Ltd, Rotten Row Farm, Hambleden, Henley-on-Thames, Oxfordshire, RG9 6NB Tel: (01491) 410716 Fax: (01491) 410718 E-mail: roachpumps@aol.com

Sigma Engineering Ltd, 26 Church Street, Altrincham, Cheshire, WA14 4DW Tel: 0161-928 9988 Fax: 0161-926 8726 E-mail: sigmapumps@aol.com

HAND SAWS

Saw & Tooling Services, 50a Sighthill CR, Edinburgh, EH11 4QB Tel: 0131-458 3886 Fax: 0131-458 3887

SNA Europe Ltd, Bahco Thorne, Moorhead Way, Bramley, Rotherham, South Yorkshire, S66 1YY Tel: (01709) 731731 Fax: (01709) 731741 E-mail: uksales@bahco.com

HAND SEWING NEEDLES

Entaco Ltd, Royal Victoria Works, Birmingham Road, Studley, Warwickshire, B80 7AP Tel: (01527) 852306 Fax: (01527) 857447 E-mail: sales@entaco.com

H Webber & Sons Ltd, Bridge House, Station Road Gomshall, Guildford, Surrey, GU5 9NP Tel: (01483) 202963 Fax: (01306) 740811 E-mail: info@hwebber.co.uk

The Needle Co. Ltd, 27a Lubenham Hill, Market Harborough, Leicestershire, LE16 9DG Tel: (01858) 555500 Fax: (01858) 555588 E-mail: needles@btconnect.com

HAND TACHOMETERS

Compact Instruments Ltd, 61-65 Lever Street, Bolton, BL3 2AB Tel: (01204) 532544 Fax: (01204) 522285 E-mail: info@compactinstruments.co.uk

HAND TOOL RECONDITIONING

Lawrence & Hayward, 148 Abercromby Avenue, High Wycombe, Buckinghamshire, HP12 3BJ Tel: (01494) 520329 Fax: (01494) 520329

Limbrick Jig & Tool Co., Unit 14 Wilden Industrial Estate, Stourport-on-Severn, Worcestershire, DY13 9JY Tel: (01299) 823139 Fax: (01299) 823139

HAND TOOLS, *See also headings for particular types under Tools*

A & E Russell Ltd, Unit 18 Crystal Drive, Smethwick, West Midlands, B66 1QG Tel: 0121-543 4850 Fax: 0121-543 4855 E-mail: birmingham@aerussell.co.uk

A J Middleton & Co. Ltd, 45 York Road, Ilford, Essex, IG1 3AD Tel: (020) 8514 1123 Fax: (020) 8478 1501

A M Designs Powergrip, 45 Tyler Hill Road, Blean, Canterbury, Kent, CT2 9HU Tel: (01227) 472203 Fax: (01227) 454749 E-mail: am@powergrip.co.uk

A P T, 27 Pant-Y-Fid Road, Aberbargoed, Bargoed, Mid Glamorgan, CF81 9DT Tel: (01443) 835086 Fax: (01443) 835086 E-mail: apt@handtools.org.uk

A Pollard & Sons Ltd, 51 Aylesbury St, Bletchley, Milton Keynes, MK2 2BQ Tel: (01908) 375221 Fax: (01908) 271552 E-mail: sales@pollards.co.uk

A W Phillips Awp Ltd, 47-51 Plashet Grove, London, E6 1AD Tel: (020) 8472 6656 Fax: (020) 8471 8317

Abingdon King Dick, Unit 11 Roman Way, Coleshill, Birmingham, B46 1HG Tel: (01675) 467776 Fax: (01675) 464277 E-mail: sales@kingdicktools.co.uk

Aeroparts International Ltd, 2 George House, Beam Heath Way, Nantwich, Cheshire, CW5 6GD Tel: (01270) 620260 Fax: (01270) 620261 E-mail: sales@aeroparts-international.com

Annasbrook Supply Co. Ltd, Gapton Hall Road, Great Yarmouth, Norfolk, NR31 0HX Tel: (01493) 668721 Fax: (01493) 440250 E-mail: sales@annasbrook.com

Ansell Handtools Sheffield Ltd, 72 Catley Road, Sheffield, S9 5JF Tel: 0114-244 8098 Fax: 0114-261 0252 E-mail: enquiries@ansell-handtools.com

▶ Anti Contamination Equipement Supplies, Carr Mills, Bradford Road, Batley, West Yorkshire, WF17 9JY Tel: (01924) 420750 Fax: (01924) 420530 E-mail: sales@aces.uk.com

Apex Industrial Ltd, 26c Orgreave CR, Sheffield, S13 9NQ Tel: 0114-254 0011 Fax: 0114-254 8002 E-mail: sheffield@apexindustrial.co.uk

Artisan Tools Ltd, Edison Courtyard, Brunel Road, Earlstrees Industrial Estate, Corby, Northamptonshire, NN17 4LS Tel: (01536) 201000 Fax: (01536) 201389 E-mail: sales@artisan-tools.co.uk

Atkinson Walker Saws Ltd, Bower Street, Sheffield, S3 8RU Tel: 0114-272 4748 Fax: 0114-272 5065 E-mail: sales@atkinson-walker-saws.co.uk

Austin Mcgillivray & Co., 124 Scotland Street, Sheffield, S3 7DE Tel: 0114-273 8041 Fax: 0114-275 0290 E-mail: enquiries@sheffieldknives.co.uk

Avenue Tools Ltd, 3 David Road, Colnbrook, Slough, SL3 0TW Tel: (01753) 685921 Fax: (01753) 685922 E-mail: avenue@avenue-group.co.uk

Avon Fastenings & Industrial Supplies Ltd, Unit 10, Western Road Industrial Estate, Stratford-Upon-Avon, Warwickshire, CV37 0AH Tel: (01789) 269661 Fax: (01789) 267051 E-mail: avonfastenings@aol.com

Azgard Engineering Products, 10 Compton Road, Kinver, Stourbridge, West Midlands, DY7 6DN Tel: (01384) 872286 Fax: (01384) 878203

B & H Precision Tooling Ltd, Unit 14 Glover Estate, Egmont Street, Mossley, Ashton-Under-Lyne, Lancashire, OL5 9PY Tel: (01457) 833434 Fax: (01457) 835685 E-mail: sales@bh-precision.co.uk

Bedingfield Hirebase Ltd, Faraday Road, Harfreys Industrial Estate, Great Yarmouth, Norfolk, NR31 0NH Tel: (01493) 440522 Fax: (01493) 442555

Ben Ford Paul Ltd, 41 West Princes Street, Glasgow, G4 9BU Tel: 0141-332 0585 Fax: 0141-333 1607 E-mail: benfordpaul@aol.com

Bennetts & Son Ltd, 2 Centre Point, Knights Way, Battlefield Enterprise Park, Shrewsbury, SY1 3AB Tel: (01743) 467226 Fax: (01743) 467238 E-mail: shewsbury@bennetts.com

Benson Industries Ltd, 5 Norcroft Industrial Estate, Norcroft Street, Bradford, West Yorkshire, BD7 1JA Tel: (01274) 722204 Fax: (01274) 306319 E-mail: enquiries@bensonindustries.co.uk

Robert Bernard & Son Ltd, 26 Oxton Road, Birkenhead, Merseyside, CH41 2QJ Tel: 0151-652 3136 Fax: 0151-652 7552 E-mail: sales@bernards.co.uk

▶ Bitrex, 10 Wheatfield Road, Edinburgh, EH11 2QA Tel: 0131-337 2434 Fax: 0131-337 9813

Blundell Files & Tools Ltd, Pottery Fields, Prescot, Merseyside, L34 5RL Tel: 0151-426 6745 Fax: 0151-493 1576 E-mail: enquiries@blundell-files.com

▶ BND UK Limited, Suite 501,, International House,, 223 Regent Street,, London, W1R 8QD Tel: 0870 2863725 Fax: 0870 7064636 E-mail: ht-sales@bndhardware.co.uk

Brabbin & Rudd Ltd, Walker Street, Bolton, BL1 4TB Tel: (01204) 521171 Fax: (01204) 364972E-mail: sales@brabbin-and-rudd.co.uk

Brandon Pipe Hire, Unit 1 Claremont Centre, Cornwall Street South, Kinning Park, Glasgow, G41 1AA Tel: 0141-427 9000 Fax: 0141-427 9009 E-mail: glagow.k65@wilsley.co.uk

Bristol Design (Tools) Ltd, 14 Perry Road, Bristol, BS1 5BG Tel: 0117-929 1740

Britool Ltd, Churchbridge Works, Walsall Road, Cannock, Staffordshire, WS11 3JR Tel: (01922) 702100 Fax: (01922) 702101 E-mail: uk_sales@britool.co.uk

Brooke Ltd, 324a Holderness Road, Hull, HU9 3DE Tel: (01482) 320592 Fax: (01482) 213193

Buck & Hickman Ltd, 4 Block A Hareness Park, Hareness Circle, Altens Industrial Estate, Aberdeen, AB12 3QY Tel: (01224) 895272 Fax: (01224) 895248 E-mail: aberdeen@buckhickmaninone.com

Buck & Hickman Ltd, 5 Mod Department, Spitfire Road, Birmingham, B24 9PR Tel: 0121-386 8000 Fax: 0121-386 8011 E-mail: manchester@buckhickman.co.uk

Buck & Hickman Ltd, 203 Longmead Road, Emersons Green, Bristol, BS16 7FG Tel: 0117-957 9797 Fax: 0117-957 9799 E-mail: bristol@buckhickmaninone.com

Buck & Hickman Ltd, R Kingsville Road, Kingsditch Trading Estate, Cheltenham, Gloucestershire, GL51 9NZ Tel: (01242) 519665 Fax: (01242) 224097 E-mail: cheltenham@buckhickmaninone.co.uk

Buck & Hickman Ltd, Unit 16 Gatwick Int Distribution Centre, Cobham Way, Crawley, West Sussex, RH10 9RX Tel: (01293) 561651 Fax: (01293) 561637 E-mail: crawley@buckhickmaninone.com

Buck & Hickman Ltd, Rosswood Road, Rossmore Industrial Estate, Ellesmere Port, CH65 3BU Tel: 0151-356 2160 Fax: 0151-357 2019 E-mail: ellesmere@buckhickmaninone.com

Buck & Hickman Ltd, Unit 19 Ringway Industrial Estate, Beck Road, Huddersfield, HD1 5DG Tel: (01484) 426611 Fax: (01484) 435368 E-mail: huddersfield@buckhickman.co.uk

Buck & Hickman Ltd, Unit 9a, Finway, Dallow Road, Luton, LU1 1TR Tel: (01582) 419887 Fax: (01582) 425824 E-mail: luton@buckhickmaninone.co.uk

Buck & Hickman Ltd, 7 Cannon Park Way, Cannon Park Industrial Estate, Middlesbrough, Cleveland, TS1 5JU Tel: (01642) 240116 Fax: (01642) 245299 E-mail: middlesbrough@buckhickmaninone. com

Buck & Hickman Ltd, A Hambridge Road, Newbury, Berkshire, RG14 5SS Tel: (01635) 521747 Fax: (01635) 32605 E-mail: newbury@buckhickmaninone.com

Buck & Hickman Ltd, Hamar Close, Tyne Tunnel Trading Estate, North Shields, Tyne & Wear, NE29 7UY Tel: 0191-296 0333 Fax: 0191-296 0335 E-mail: newcastle@buckhickman.co.uk

Buck & Hickman Ltd, Unit 2 Longwall Avenue, Queens Drive Industrial Estate, Nottingham, NG2 1NA Tel: 0115-986 8282 Fax: 0115-986 8486 E-mail: nottingham@buckhickmaninone.com

Buck & Hickman Ltd, Unit 2a Treelyn Park, Welbeck Way Woodston, Peterborough, PE2 7WH Tel: (01733) 371737 Fax: (01733) 232245 E-mail: peterborough@buckhickmaninone.co. uk

Buck & Hickman Ltd, 4 Phoenix Business Park, Estover Road, Plymouth, PL6 7PY Tel: (01752) 692700 Fax: (01752) 692701 E-mail: plymouth@buckhickmaninone.com

Buck & Hickman Ltd, Unit 12, Riverside Court, Don Road, Sheffield, S9 2TJ Tel: 0114-244 1012 Fax: 0114-244 5372 E-mail: sheffield@buckhickman.co.uk

Buck & Hickman Ltd, Building 110 Nursling Industrial Estate, Mauretania Road, Nursling, Southampton, SO16 0YS Tel: (023) 8074 2300 Fax: (023) 8074 2301 E-mail: southampton@buckhickmaninone.com

Buck & Hickman Ltd, Lyme Vale Court, Parklands Business Park, Parklands, Stoke-on-Trent, ST4 6NW Tel: (01782) 279927 Fax: (01782) 286355 E-mail: stoke@buckhickman.co.uk

Buck & Hickman Ltd, Unit 12 Ferryboat Close, Enterprise Park, Swansea Enterprise Park, Swansea, SA6 8QN Tel: (01792) 799998 Fax: (01792) 700678 E-mail: swansea@buckhickman.co.uk

Buck & Hickman Ltd, 103-109 Waldegrave Road, Teddington, Middlesex, TW11 8LL Tel: (020) 8977 8844 Fax: (020) 8943 2826 E-mail: teddington@buckhickman.co.uk

Buck Hickman In One Ltd, 70 Lancefield Street, Glasgow, G3 8JD Tel: 0141-221 7174 Fax: 0141-221 8877 E-mail: glasgow@buckhickman.co.uk

Buck In Hickman, Neptune Point, Vanguard Way, Ocean Park, Cardiff, CF24 5PG Tel: (029) 2030 6000 Fax: (029) 2030 6030 E-mail: cardiff@buckhickmaninone.co.uk

Buckhickman Ltd, Castleton Road, Armley, Leeds, LS12 2EN Tel: 0113-246 0911 Fax: 0113-244 6888 E-mail: sales@buckhickmaninone.com

BuckHickman InOne, Unit 2, Chartergate, Moulton Park, Northampton, NN3 6QF Tel: (01604) 797400 Fax: (01604) 797401 E-mail: northampton@buckhickmaninone.co.uk

C A Clemson & Sons Ltd, Shenstone Trading Estate, Bromsgrove Road, Halesowen, West Midlands, B63 3XB Tel: 0121-550 8833 Fax: 0121-550 7617 E-mail: halesowen.sales@toolbank.com

Central Fasteners (Staffs) Ltd, Airfield Trading Estate, Hixon, Stafford, ST18 0PY Tel: (01889) 270163 Fax: (01889) 271270 E-mail: centralfasteners@aol.com

Clico Sheffield Tooling Ltd, 7 Fell Road, Sheffield, S9 2AL Tel: 0114-243 3007 Fax: 0114-243 4158 E-mail: info@clico.co.uk

Columbia Saw Works Ltd, 120 Hackney Road, London, E2 7QL Tel: (01708) 550601 Fax: (020) 8281 1260 E-mail: kevin@columbia37.freeserve.co.uk

Compass Components, Greta Lodge, Southey Hill, Keswick, Cumbria, CA12 5ND Tel: (01768) 772118 Fax: (01768) 772118

Cooper Tools, Pennine House, Washington, Tyne & Wear, NE37 1LY Tel: 0191-419 7700 Fax: 0191-417 9421 E-mail: sales@coopertools.com

Coronhurst Ltd, Unit 16 Martindale Trading Estate, Martindale, Cannock, Staffordshire, WS11 7XL Tel: (01543) 577101 Fax: (01543) 571876 E-mail: info@coronhurst.co.uk

Crown Hand Tools Ltd, Excelsior Works, Burnt Tree Lane, Hoyle Street, Sheffield, S3 7EX Tel: 0114-272 3366 Fax: 0114-272 5252 E-mail: info@crowntools.com

Curtis Holt Southampton Ltd, Westwood Business Park, Nutwood Way, Totton, Southampton, SO40 3WW Tel: (023) 8086 1991 Fax: (023) 8066 4505 E-mail: sales@tallbank.com

Curtis Holt Southampton Ltd, Westwood Business Park, Nutwood Way, Totton, Southampton, SO40 3WW Tel: (023) 8086 1991 Fax: (023) 8066 4555 E-mail: sales@tallbank.com

Curtis Holt (St. Albans), Unit 10B Brick Knoll Park, Ashley Road, St. Albans, Hertfordshire, AL1 5UG Tel: (01727) 845095 Fax: (01727) 845082 E-mail: stalbons.sales@torbank.com

D F Wishart & Co. Ltd, St Clair St, Edinburgh, EH6 8LJ Tel: 0131-554 4393 Fax: 0131-553 7242 E-mail: sales@wishart.co.uk

Damar Industrial Machinery Ltd, Clipper Road, Troon Industrial Estate, Leicester, LE4 9JE Tel: 0116-276 4144 Fax: 0116-246 0663 E-mail: sales@damar.biz

Desoutter Ltd, Eton Road, Hemel Hempstead, Hertfordshire, HP2 7DR Tel: (01442) 344300 Fax: (01442) 344600 E-mail: desoutter.sales@cp.com

Diytools Com Ltd, 20 Market Street, Watford, WD18 0PD Tel: (01923) 250295 Fax: (01923) 818219 E-mail: mur@diytools.com

Draper Tools Ltd, Hursley Road, Chandler's Ford, Eastleigh, Hampshire, SO53 1YF Tel: (023) 8026 6355 Fax: (023) 8026 0784 E-mail: sales@draper.co.uk

E R Varney (Tools) Ltd, Botsford Street, Sheffield, S3 9PF Tel: 0114-272 7650 Fax: 0114-272 7030

E T & Lee Roberts, 1b Graeme Road, Enfield, Middlesex, EN1 3UU Tel: (020) 8363 6452 Fax: (020) 8804 1102

Emmerich (Berlon) Ltd, Kingsnorth Industrial Estate, Wotton Road, Ashford, Kent, TN23 6JY Tel: (01233) 622684 Fax: (01233) 645801 E-mail: emmerick@emir.co.uk

Engineering & Factory Supplies Ltd, Algores Way, Wisbech, Cambridgeshire, PE13 2TQ Tel: (01945) 466644 Fax: (01945) 466232

ERIKS UK, Industrial Distribution Service Centre, Greenwell Place, East Tullos, Aberdeen, AB12 3AY Tel: (01224) 877523 Fax: (01224) 879645 E-mail: mcw.aberdeen@wyko.co.uk

Express Welding Suppliers Ltd, Express House, Wilmington Commercial Park, Bedford St, Hull, HU8 8AR Tel: (01482) 223745 Fax: (01482) 210350 E-mail: paul.woodgate@brc.com

F M Instruments, 66A High Street, Oakington, Cambridge, CB4 5AG Tel: (01223) 234141 Fax: (01223) 234141

Fast Tools Holdings Ltd, Llanthony Road, Hempsted, Gloucester, GL2 5HL Tel: (01452) 529671 Fax: (01452) 307992 E-mail: sales@fasttoolsltd.co.uk

Firth Powerfix, 71 Gelderd Road, Leeds, LS12 6HF Tel: 0113-245 1626 Fax: 0113-242 3887 E-mail: sales@powerfixonline.co.uk

Footprint Tools Ltd, PO Box 19, Sheffield, S1 3HY Tel: 0114-275 3200 Fax: 0114-275 9613 E-mail: sales@footprint-tools.co.uk

F.F. Franklin & Co. Ltd, Platt Street, Sheffield, S3 8BQ Tel: 0114-272 1429 Fax: 0114-272 7030 E-mail: sales@franklin-tools.co.uk

Fyfe & Mcgrouther, 218-254 Kennedy Street, Glasgow, G4 0BS Tel: 0141-552 4966 Fax: 0141-552 7917

G W Metals & Tools, Unit O & Q Newtown Road Trading Estate, Newtown Road, Worcester, WR5 1HA Tel: (01905) 612342 Fax: (01905) 25544

Greenwoods (Coleshill) Ltd, Unit 28, Roman Way, Coleshill, Birmingham, B46 1HQ Tel: (01675) 464280 Fax: (01675) 467160 E-mail: sales@greenwoodtools.demon.co.uk

Guildford Tool Supplies Ltd, A Victoria Farm, Brunswick Road, Brookwood, Woking, Surrey, GU24 0AQ Tel: (01483) 480000 Fax: (01483) 486886 E-mail: sales@guildfordtools.co.uk

H M Hampson Ltd, 29-31 Shaw Street, St. Helens, Merseyside, WA10 1DG Tel: (01744) 23881 Fax: (01744) 453485

Halfords Ltd, Icknield St Drive, Redditch, Worcestershire, B98 0DE Tel: (01527) 517601 Fax: (01527) 513201

Hampshire Bolt & Tool Supplies Ltd, Armstrong Road, Daneshill East, Basingstoke, Hampshire, RG24 8NU Tel: (01256) 329781 Fax: (01256) 817150 E-mail: jillcorreale@aol.com

Hand Tools Ltd, Stubley Works, Wreakes Lane, Dronfield, Derbyshire, S18 1PN Tel: (01246) 413139 Fax: (01246) 415208 E-mail: handtools@tiscali.co.uk

Harrison & Clough Ltd, PO Box 9, Keighley, West Yorkshire, BD21 4EG Tel: (0870) 8892222 Fax: (0870) 8892233

Hayway Tool & Hardware Co. Ltd, Cunliffe Drive, Kettering, Northamptonshire, NN16 8LD Tel: (01536) 481114 Fax: (01536) 483514 E-mail: sales@haywaytools.com

Henri Picard & Frere, 8 Pixham Court, Pixham Lane, Dorking, Surrey, RH4 1PG Tel: (020) 8949 3142 Fax: (020) 8949 3142 E-mail: sales@picard.co.uk

Herting & Son plc, Frederick House, 25 Armstrong Way, Southall, Middlesex, UB2 4SD Tel: (020) 8606 7000 Fax: (020) 8606 7010 E-mail: sales@fpherting.co.uk

Heward & Dean Ltd, Spurling Works, Pindar Road, Hoddesdon, Hertfordshire, EN11 0DB Tel: (01992) 467557 Fax: (01992) 467477 E-mail: sales@hewardanddean.com

Hewden Hire Centres Ltd, 39-40 New Summer Street, Birmingham, B19 3QN Tel: 0121-359 4282 Fax: 0121-333 6866

Highland Industrial Supplies Ltd, 36 Seafield Road, Inverness, IV1 1SG Tel: (01463) 239160 Fax: (01463) 233424 E-mail: sales@hisltd.co.uk

Hilka Tools (UK) Ltd, 1 Roebuck Place, Roebuck Road, Chessington, Surrey, KT9 1EU Tel: (020) 8391 7570 Fax: (020) 8391 7575 E-mail: hilka@bix.co.uk

Curtis Holt Ltd, Longreach, Gallion Boulevard, Crossways Business Park, Dartford, DA2 6QE Tel: (01322) 321300 Fax: (01322) 383641 E-mail: sales@toolbank.com

Curtis Holt (North West), Toolbank House, Appleton Thorn Trading Estate, Lyncastle Way, Appleton, Warrington, WA4 4ST Tel: (01925) 261333 Fax: (01925) 604478

House Of Hastings Ltd, 181-182 Queens Road, Hastings, East Sussex, TN34 1RQ Tel: (01424) 423072 Fax: (01424) 431501 E-mail: enquiries@houseofhastings.com

Brian Hyde Ltd, Stirling Road, Shirley, Solihull, West Midlands, B90 4LZ Tel: 0121-705 7987 Fax: 0121-711 2465 E-mail: sales@brianhyde.co.uk

I T S Tools Ltd, Daish Way, Dodnor Lane Industrial Estate, Newport, Isle of Wight, PO30 5XB Tel: (01983) 526344 Fax: (01983) 821547 E-mail: itstools@tiscali.co.uk

Imtech Services, 33 The Warren, Worcester Park, Surrey, KT4 7DH Tel: (020) 8337 6254 Fax: (020) 8337 6254 E-mail: ian.male@btopenworld.com

Industrial Tools Supplies (London) Ltd, 607-617 High Road, Leyton, London, E10 6RF Tel: (020) 8539 2231 Fax: (020) 8558 0247 E-mail: sales@itslondon.co.uk

Insulated Tools Ltd, Charlwoods Road, East Grinstead, West Sussex, RH19 2HR Tel: (01342) 324255 Fax: (01342) 327115 E-mail: enquiries@insulatedtools.co.uk

Irwin Industrial Tool Co. Ltd, Parkway Works, Kettlebridge Road, Sheffield, S9 3BL Tel: 0114-244 9066 Fax: 0114-256 1788 E-mail: nroshier@recordtools.co.uk

J.B.G. (Marketing) Ltd, Jay Bee House, 226a Whitehorse Road, Croydon, CR0 2LB Tel: (020) 8683 2610 Fax: (020) 8684 2523 E-mail: enquiries@jbgroves.freeserve.co.uk

Jafco Tools Ltd, Access House, Great Western Street, Wednesbury, West Midlands, WS10 7LE Tel: 0121-556 7700 Fax: 0121-556 7788 E-mail: sales@jafco-tools.com

James Lister, 2 Miller Street, Birmingham, B6 4NF Tel: 0121-359 3774 Fax: 0121-333 3021 E-mail: birmingham@lister.co.uk

Jones & Clark (Burton-on-Trent) Ltd, 77-80 Waterloo Street, Burton-On-Trent, Staffordshire, DE14 2NE Tel: (01283) 541771 Fax: (01283) 542466 E-mail: sales@jonesandclark.co.uk

The Kennedy Group Ltd, Wigston Works, Victoria St, Wigston, Leicestershire, LE18 1AJ Tel: 0116-288 8777 Fax: 0116-288 8222 E-mail: overseas@cromwell-kennedy-group.co. uk

Kestrel Engineering, School Works, School Lane, Coleorton, Coalville, Leicestershire, LE67 8HT Tel: (01530) 223100 Fax: (01530) 223100 E-mail: kestrelengineering@btinternet.com

▶ indicates data change since last edition

HAND TOOLS – *continued*

Kew Technik Ltd, Rankine Road, Basingstoke, Hampshire, RG24 8PP Tel: (01256) 864100 Fax: (01256) 864164 E-mail: sales@kewt.co.uk

L J Hydleman & Co. Ltd, Marton Street, Skipton, North Yorkshire, BD23 1TF Tel: (01756) 706700 Fax: (01756) 798083 E-mail: sales@hydleman.co.uk

L S Starrett Co. Ltd, Oxnam Road, Jedburgh, Roxburghshire, TD8 6LR Tel: (01835) 863501 Fax: (01835) 863018 E-mail: sales@starrett.co.uk

H.I.S. Lawson Ltd, 84-88 Millbrook Road East, Southampton, SO15 1BG Tel: (023) 8063 2927 Fax: (023) 8033 9878 E-mail: enquiries@lawson-his.co.uk

Laxton Tool Supplies Ltd, Royal Leamington Spa, Leamington Spa, Warwickshire, CV32 5GN Tel: (01239) 820212 Fax: (01239) 820763 E-mail: laxtontool@aol.com

M & F Components, Marlbrough Road, Accrington, Lancashire, BB5 5BE Tel: (01254) 301121 Fax: (01254) 391416 E-mail: ucount@mafcobell.co.uk

M T S Power Tools, 97 St James Mill Road, Northampton, NN5 5JP Tel: (01604) 751688 Fax: (01604) 759041E-mail: sales@mts.co.uk

John Macnamara & Co. Ltd, 19a Bush Road, London, SE8 5AR Tel: (020) 7237 1591 Fax: (020) 7231 5173

Marshall & Parsons Ltd, 1111 London Road, Leigh-on-Sea, Essex, SS9 3JL Tel: (01702) 470100 Fax: (01702) 471160 E-mail: marshallandparsons@ancatown.co.uk

Maun Industries Ltd, Moor Lane, Mansfield, Nottinghamshire, NG18 5SE Tel: (01623) 624525 Fax: (01623) 659969 E-mail: maun.industries@btinternet.com

Thomas Meldrum Ltd, Freedom Works, John Street, Sheffield, S2 4QT Tel: 0114-272 5156 Fax: 0114-272 6409 E-mail: sales@thomasmeldrumltd.co.uk

Merton Timber Ltd, 102 Rose Hill, Sutton, Surrey, SM1 3HB Tel: (020) 8644 7884 Fax: (020) 8641 0943 E-mail: sales@merton-timber.co.uk

Merton Timber & Builders Merchants, Unit E 2 Endeavour Way, London, SW19 8UH Tel: (020) 8879 0626 Fax: (020) 8947 6061 E-mail: sales@mertontimber.com

Metal Work Supplies, Unit 15 Grandstand Business Centre, Westfields Trading Estate, Hereford, HR4 9NS Tel: (01432) 266621 Fax: (01432) 270323

Monument Tools, Restmor Way, Hackbridge Road, Hackbridge, Wallington, Surrey, SM6 7AH Tel: (020) 8288 1100 Fax: (020) 8288 1108 E-mail: info@monument-tools.com

Northern Tools & Accessories Ltd, PO Box 5, Newcastle upon Tyne, NE6 5XB Tel: 0191-265 2821 Fax: 0191-276 2668 E-mail: marketing@crossling.co.uk

Graham Oxley Tool Steels Ltd, 55-57 Bridge Street, Sheffield, S3 8NS Tel: 0114-272 0403 Fax: 0114-275 2489

P B Baumann Hand Tools, Wharf Street, Warwick, CV34 5LB Tel: (01926) 403483 Fax: (01926) 403777 E-mail: sales@warwicksupplies.com

P.E.T. Hire Centre Ltd, 68-70 Earle Street, Crewe, CW1 2AT Tel: (01270) 582222 Fax: (01270) 505938

Paget Ltd, 115 Penarth Road, Cardiff, CF11 6JU Tel: (029) 2022 2552 Fax: (029) 2037 8439

Paramo Tools Group Ltd, Bailey St, Sheffield, S1 3BS Tel: 0114-249 0880 Fax: 0114-249 0881

Paramount Tools & Fasteners Ltd, Unit 7 Paramount Business Park, Nile Street, Burslem, Stoke-on-Trent, ST6 2BG Tel: (01782) 821444 Fax: (01782) 821777 E-mail: paramtoolandfast@aol.com

Parkins Industrial Supplies, Blundells Road, Tiverton, Devon, EX16 4DA Tel: (01884) 254444 Fax: (01884) 258142

Pinnacle Tooling Ltd, Aston Hill, Lewknor, Watlington, Oxfordshire, OX49 5SG Tel: (01844) 354999 Fax: (01844) 354888 E-mail: sales@pin-tooling.co.uk

Proops Brothers Ltd, Victoria Works, Saddington Road, Leicester, LE8 8AW Tel: 0116-240 3400 Fax: 0116-240 3300

Q-Max (Electronics) Ltd, Bilton Road, Bletchley, Milton Keynes, MK1 1HW Tel: (01908) 368006 Fax: (01908) 270483

R E Thorns & Co., 22 Exchange Street, Norwich, NR2 1AT Tel: (01603) 622891 Fax: (01603) 622952 E-mail: mail@thornsdiy.com

R J Pryce & Co. Ltd, Trinity Road, Lowestoft, Suffolk, NR32 1XJ Tel: (01502) 574141 Fax: (01502) 501213 E-mail: sales@rjpryce.co.uk

Rail Order, Unit 2, Anglia Way, Mansfield, Nottinghamshire, NG18 4LP Tel: 01623 627208 Fax: 01623 633914 E-mail: sales@rail-order.co.uk

Readyfix, Lodge Street, Preston, PR1 8XE Tel: (01772) 250060 Fax: (01772) 250075

Howard Richard Sales Ltd, 10 Holkham Road, Orton Southgate, Peterborough, PE2 6TE Tel: (01733) 237779 Fax: (01733) 230027 E-mail: sales@hrsales.co.uk

Bob Richardson Tools & Fasteners Ltd, Pedmore Road, Dudley, West Midlands, DY2 0RL Tel: (01384) 482789 Fax: (01384) 481888 E-mail: sales@toolstoday.co.uk

Robert Samuel & Co. Ltd, 7 Court Parade, Wembley, Middlesex, HA0 3JA Tel: (020) 8904 1144 Fax: (020) 8904 6349

Rollins, 1 Parkway, Harlow Business Park, Harlow, Essex, CM19 5QF Tel: (01279) 401570 Fax: (01279) 401581 E-mail: sales@rollins.co.uk

Rosskerr Plant & Tools Ltd, Coombe Works, Coombe Road, London, NW10 0EB Tel: (020) 8450 6606 Fax: (020) 8450 7372

S A F Power Tools Ltd, 5 Anjou Cresent, Fareham, Hampshire, PO15 5DA Tel: (01329) 844205 Fax: (01329) 844142 E-mail: netsales@safpt.co.uk

S K S Plant & Equipment Ltd, 11 Redehall Road, Smallfield, Horley, Surrey, RH6 9PY Tel: (01342) 843688 Fax: (01342) 842236 E-mail: jpeters@sks-group.co.uk

S K S Plant & Equipment Ltd, 11 Redehall Road, Smallfield, Horley, Surrey, RH6 9PY Tel: (01342) 843688 Fax: (01342) 842140 E-mail: sks@sks-group.co.uk

Sallco Tools Ltd, 3-4 Baddesley Park Industrial Estate, Botley Road, North Baddesley, Southampton, SO52 9NW Tel: (023) 8073 7355 Fax: (023) 8073 8647 E-mail: sales@sallcotools.co.uk

Saxon Industries, Everland Road, Hungerford, Berkshire, RG17 0DX Tel: (01488) 684545 Fax: (01488) 684317 E-mail: sales@saxonind.co.uk

Selectequip Ltd, Unit 7, Brittannia Way, Brittania Enterprise Park, Lichfield, Staffordshire, WS14 9UY Tel: (01543) 416641 Fax: (01543) 416083 E-mail: sales@selectequip.co.uk

Simbles Ltd, 76 Queens Road, Watford, WD17 2LD Tel: (01923) 226052 Fax: (01923) 817526 E-mail: sales@simbles.com

James Sime & Co. Ltd, 29 Cow Wynd, Falkirk, FK1 1PT Tel: (01324) 622592 Fax: (01324) 612522

SNA Europe Ltd, Bahco Thorne, Moorhead Way, Bramley, Rotherham, South Yorkshire, S66 1YY Tel: (01709) 731731 Fax: (01709) 731741 E-mail: uksales@bahco.com

Snap On Tools, Telford Way, Telford Way Industrial Estate, Kettering, Northamptonshire, NN16 8SN Tel: (01536) 413800 Fax: (01536) 413900 E-mail: max.christmas@snapon.com

Spec Tools Europe, Petersfield Road, Greatham, Liss, Hampshire, GU33 6AA Tel: (01420) 538539 Fax: (01420) 538111 E-mail: nsb@eurotec-intl.co.uk

Stahlwille Tools Ltd, Albany Park, Camberley, Surrey, GU16 7PD Tel: (01276) 24080 Fax: (01276) 24696 E-mail: sales@stahlwille.co.uk

Stanley Acmetrack, Drake House, Beighton Rd. East, Sheffield, S19 6GJ Tel: 0114-251 0570 Fax: (08701) 654654

Stanley Tools, The Stanley Works, Woodside, Sheffield, S3 9PD Tel: (0870) 1650650 Fax: (0870) 1654654

Stevenage Machine Tools Ltd, Unit 12, Ironcraft Industrial Estate, Stotfold, Hitchin, Hertfordshire, SG5 4NZ Tel: (01462) 731691 Fax: (01462) 835214

Swansea Fastners, Unit 8, Horizon Park, Swansea Enterprise Park, Swansea, SA6 8RG Tel: (01792) 310284 Fax: (01792) 310291 E-mail: sales@swanseafasteners.com

Tailored Panels, Unit 4 Minster Park, Grundymore Estate West Moors, Wimborne, Dorset, BH21 6QW Tel: (01202) 871998 Fax: (01202) 861215 E-mail: tailored-panels@hotmail.com

Teamvise Ltd, Unit 5 & 6, Flitwick Industrial Estate, Flitwick, Bedford, MK45 1UF Tel: (01525) 718080 Fax: (01525) 718882 E-mail: daniel.king@toolstars.co.uk

Tilgear Tool Merchants, 69 Station Road, Cuffley, Potters Bar, Hertfordshire, EN6 4HY Tel: (01707) 873434 Fax: (01707) 870383 E-mail: orders@tilgear.co.uk

Till & Whitehead, 65 Brindley Road, Astmoor Industrial Estate, Runcorn, Cheshire, WA7 1PF Tel: (01928) 581200 Fax: (01928) 580859 E-mail: info@tillwite.com

Tool Connection Ltd, Unit 2, Kineton Road, Southam, Warwickshire, CV47 0DR Tel: (01926) 815999 Fax: (01926) 815888 E-mail: lesleyscott@lasertools.co.uk

▶ The Tool & Gauge Co., Flat E, 200 Iverson Road, London, NW6 2HL Tel: (020) 7372 1973 Fax: (020) 7813 3345 E-mail: thetoolngaugeco@aol.com

Toolmaster (Oxford) Ltd, 148 Oxford Road, Cowley, Oxford, OX4 2EA Tel: (01865) 712152 Fax: (01865) 747380 E-mail: sales@toolmaster.co.uk

Tooltek Supplies Ltd, Spyvee Street, Hull, HU8 7JJ Tel: (01482) 229628 Fax: (01482) 229630 E-mail: info@tooltek.co.uk

Unimaster Components, 9 Arnhem Road, Newbury, Berkshire, RG14 5RU Tel: (01635) 528692 E-mail: sales@unimaster.co.uk

Universal Engineering, Unit 10 Mid Wynd, Dundee, DD1 4JG Tel: (01382) 223592 Fax: (01382) 202506 E-mail: sales@universalengtool.co.uk

Visa Hand Tools Ltd, Gibson House, Barrowby Lane, Garforth, Leeds, LS25 1NG Tel: 0113-286 9245 Fax: 0113-286 6859 E-mail: enq@visatools.co.uk

VPM Ltd, Birch House, Fraser Road, Erith, Kent, DA8 1QX Tel: (01322) 430043 Fax: (01322) 430044 E-mail: comptonshaun@aol.com

Alan Wasden Ltd, Niloc Works, Penistone Road, Sheffield, S6 2FW Tel: 0114-234 8824 Fax: 0114-232 1246

Waverly Cutting Tools, 55 Abbotswell Road, Aberdeen, AB12 3AD Tel: (01224) 879714 Fax: (01224) 872385

Welland Supplies, Blenheim Way, Northfields Industrial Estate, Market Deeping, Peterborough, PE6 8LD Tel: (01778) 380371 Fax: (01778) 346916 E-mail: sales@welland-supplies.co.uk

Wera Tools, Unit 2 McGregors Way, Turnoaks Business Park, Off Storforth Lane, Chesterfield, Derbyshire, S40 2WB Tel: (01246) 277756 Fax: (01246) 273335

Westward Building Services Ltd, Burraton Road, Saltash, Cornwall, PL12 6LU Tel: (01752) 844600 Fax: (01752) 854254 E-mail: sales@westwoodbuildingservices.com

John Wilkinson (Machinery & Tools) Ltd, 27 Arthur Street, Edinburgh, EH6 5DA Tel: 0131-554 1641 Fax: 0131-553 7961 E-mail: sales@wilkinsonmachinery.com

Williams Distributors, 108-110 Burghley Road, Peterborough, PE1 2QE Tel: (01733) 564252 Fax: (01733) 555275

Williams Technical Services Ltd, 36 Station Road, North Harrow, Harrow, Middlesex, HA2 7SE Tel: (020) 8863 2492 Fax: (020) 8863 1524

Wilson Tool International Ltd, Stirling Road, South Marston Industrial Estat, Swindon, SN3 4TQ Tel: (01793) 831818 Fax: (0800) 373758 E-mail: sales@wilsontool.eu

Worcester Tools & Fixings Ltd, Unit 10A Shrub Hill Industrial Estate, Shrub Hill Road, Worcester, WR4 9EL Tel: (01905) 723421 Fax: (01905) 25116 E-mail: sales@worcestertool.co.uk

Wurth (UK) Ltd, 1 Centurion Way, Erith, Kent, DA18 4AE Tel: (0870) 5987841 Fax: (0870) 5987842 E-mail: info@wurth.co.uk

HAND TOWELS, COTTON

▶ Pelican Trading UK Ltd, Galloway Lane, Pudsey, West Yorkshire, LS28 7UG Tel: 0113-257 2468 Fax: 0113-229 5834

HAND VICES

Build Centre Ltd, Unit 8 Etna Court, Falkirk, FK2 9ED Tel: (01324) 611787 Fax: (01324) 621375 E-mail: sales@buildcentre.co.uk

Swindens Revolving Head Vices Ltd, Suite 401 Langham Ho, 302 Regent St, London, W1B 3AT Tel: (020) 7580 6491 Fax: (020) 7580 4729 E-mail: am@swindens-vices.co.uk

HANDBAGS

Acompany P.L.C., Elsley House, 24-30 Great Titchfield Street, London, W1W 8BF Tel: (020) 8443 1236 Fax: (020) 7631 1163 E-mail: info@acompany.co.uk

Albany Belt Co., 31-33 Beler Way, Leicester Road Industrial Estate, Melton Mowbray, Leicestershire, LE13 0DG Tel: (01664) 566055 Fax: (01664) 410205 E-mail: albany.belt@btinternet.com

▶ Alpa UK Ltd, 497 Saffron Lane, Leicester, LE2 6UG Tel: 0116-244 0880 Fax: 0116-283 4854

▶ Aru's 4 Accessories, 4 Courtlands Avenue, Langley, Slough, SL3 7LE Tel: (01753) 549388 Fax: (01753) 549388 E-mail: arus4accessories@yahoo.co.uk

Ashlie Craft, 10 Wheatley Grove, Beeston, Nottingham, NG9 5AG Tel: 0115-922 9735 Fax: 0115-922 9735 E-mail: baglady@ashliecraft.com

▶ W.B. Ashworth & Sons Ltd, Tudor Industrial Estate, Ashton Street, Dukinfield, Cheshire, SK16 4RN Tel: 0161-330 3555 Fax: 0161-330 6777 E-mail: wba@btinternet.com

▶ Bay Ridge, Design House, 20-22 Beulah Road, London, SW19 3SB Tel: (020) 8543 8598 Fax: (020) 8542 6831 E-mail: office@bayridge-uk.com

Brenton Handbags Ltd, Darren Mill, Wash Lane, Bury, Lancashire, BL9 7DU Tel: 0161-764 8528 Fax: 0161-763 1503 E-mail: info@brentonbags.com

▶ Casson & Co Handbags Ltd, Market Hall, The Mall, Bury, Lancashire, BL9 0BD Tel: 0161-761 6479 E-mail: info@handbag.uk.net

▶ Chantesse, 25 Orchard Estate, Twyford, Reading, RG10 9JY Tel: 0118-970 6846 Fax: (0870) 1383878 E-mail: sally@chantesse.com

Dressy Styles Ltd, 35 Hall Street, Birmingham, B18 6BS Tel: 0121-212 3499 Fax: 0121-212 3499 E-mail: dressystyles1@activemail.co.uk

Heritage Leathergoods Co. Ltd, 24-32 Princip Street, Birmingham, B4 6LE Tel: 0121-333 3339 Fax: 0121-359 3487 E-mail: inquiries@heritageleathergoods.co.uk

Hillmar Products, New Victoria Mills, Wellington Street, Bury, Lancashire, BL8 2AL Tel: 0161-763 5598 Fax: 0161-764 1368 E-mail: hilmarproducts@btopenworld.com

I B W Ltd, 64 Seven Kings Road, Ilford, Essex, IG3 8DG Tel: (020) 8220 1177 Fax: (020) 8220 1166

J B Hats & Things, 18 Ellesmere Road, Sheffield, S4 7JB Tel: 0114-278 6660 E-mail: jbahatsnthing@aol.com

J&R Designs Ltd, 5-7 Shepherds Lane, London, E9 6JJ Tel: (020) 8985 0717 Fax: (020) 8985 7987

Japinda Products Ltd, Constellation Works, Fernhurst Street, Chadderton, Oldham, OL1 2RN Tel: 0161-620 4231 Fax: 0161-627 0914 E-mail: sales@japinda.co.uk

Lance Leathers, 14 Bedford Road, Stagsden, Bedford, MK43 8TP Tel: (01234) 823200 Fax: (01234) 826110 E-mail: david@lanceleathers.co.uk

Launer London Ltd, 86 Clarendon Road, Croydon, CR0 3SG Tel: (020) 8681 3573 Fax: (020) 8681 3530 E-mail: sales@launer.com

▶ Mobarak, 1 Harrogate Road, Rawdon, Leeds, LS19 6HW Tel: 0113-250 0880 E-mail: info@mobarak.co.uk

Noble Furs Regent Street Ltd, 3 New Burlington Place, London, W1S 2HR Tel: (020) 8734 6394 Fax: (020) 7734 6396 E-mail: enquiries@noblefurs.com

One Accessories, Pasture Lane, Gaddesby, Leicester, LE7 4XD Tel: (01664) 840846 Fax: (01664) 840946 E-mail: sales@wileysdesign.co.uk

Regent Belt Co. Ltd, Leo House The Business Centre, Ross Road, Weedon Road Industrial Estate, Northampton, NN5 5AX Tel: (01604) 684700 Fax: (01604) 684719 E-mail: sales@regentbelt.co.uk

S Perviz & Co. Ltd, Solmar House, 7-9 Blackfriars Road, Salford, M3 7AG Tel: 0161-833 9910 Fax: 0161-839 0543 E-mail: mp@perviz.co.uk

▶ Scootles Bags, 19 High Street, Castle Donington, Derby, DE74 2PP Tel: 01332 811740 Fax: 01332 811740 E-mail: info@scootles.co.uk

Seipel Ltd, Crescent Road, Dukinfield, Cheshire, SK16 4HQ Tel: 0161-330 9321 Fax: 0161-343 1287 E-mail: sales@seipel.co.uk

Shilton plc, 90 Peterborough Road, London, SW6 3HH Tel: (020) 7736 7771 Fax: (020) 7731 7683 E-mail: info@janeshilton.co.uk

▶ Swaggers, 51 St. Martins Street, Wallingford, Oxfordshire, OX10 0AJ Tel: (01491) 824022 Fax: (01491) 613039 E-mail: sales@swaggers.co.uk

HANDBAGS, LEATHER

▶ W.B. Ashworth & Sons Ltd, Tudor Industrial Estate, Ashton Street, Dukinfield, Cheshire, SK16 4RN Tel: 0161-330 3555 Fax: 0161-330 6777 E-mail: wba@btinternet.com

Casson & Co. Ltd, 117 Huddersfield Road, Oldham, OL1 3NY Tel: 0161-624 2227 Fax: 0161-627 5231

▶ Casson & Co Handbags Ltd, Market Hall, The Mall, Bury, Lancashire, BL9 0BD Tel: 0161-761 6479 E-mail: info@handbag.uk.net

Chi-Chi Style, The Old Schoolhouse, Church Street, Netherseal, Swadlincote, Derbyshire, DE12 8DF Tel: (01283) 763604 E-mail: sales@chi-chi-style.com

▶ David Frank Hair & Beauty, 18 Dalton Square, Lancaster, LA1 1PL Tel: (01524) 843434 Fax:

▶ P O Ltd, 311 Spitfire Studios, 63-71 Colier Street, London, N1 9BE Tel: (020) 7837 2322 Fax: (020) 7837 2321 E-mail: paula@poltd.co.uk

▶ Vivid Trading, Mere Farm Bell, Bell Lane, Saham Toney, Thetford, Norfolk, IP25 7HD Tel: (01953) 883264 E-mail: vividmail@hotmail.com

HANDBELLS

Whitechapel Bell Foundry Ltd, 34 Whitechapel Road, London, E1 1DY Tel: (020) 7247 2599 Fax: (020) 7375 1979 E-mail: sales@whitechapelbellfoundry.co.uk

HANDCRAFTED WOODEN GARDEN FURNITURE

▶ D'arcy Diggers, Hitcham Road, Walthamstow, London, E17 8HL Tel: (020) 8923 6062

▶ Event Prop Hire, Unit 1, Green Park Business Centre, Eastmoor, Sutton on the Forrest, York, YO61 1ET Tel: (01347) 811713 Fax: (0845) 0940817E-mail: enquiries@eventprophire.com

▶ Gibbs Bros, Kitesbridge Farm, Asthall, Burford, Oxfordshire, OX18 4HL Tel: (01993) 878600 E-mail: info@gibbsbrothers.co.uk

▶ Odd Ltd, Oxford, OX7 6WZ Tel: (01993) 830674 Fax: (01993) 832474 E-mail: mail@oddlimited.com

▶ P J Milligan, 54 Wilson Place, East Kilbride, Glasgow, G74 4QD Tel: (01355) 260990 E-mail: craig.hamilton@pjmilligan.com

▶ treehousebuilders.co.uk, 60 Court Leet, Coventry, CV3 2JR Tel: (07879) 224260 E-mail: chris@treehousebuilders.co.uk

HANDHELD COMPUTERS

Blueleaf Ltd, 73 Steventon Road, Drayton, Abingdon, Oxfordshire, OX14 4LA Tel: (01235) 554677 Fax: (01235) 554977

Fujitsu Siemens Computers Ltd, The Boulevard, Cain Road, Bracknell, Berkshire, RG12 1HH Tel: (01344) 475000 Fax: (01344) 475666 E-mail: sales@fujitsu-siemens.com

Microscribe, PO Box 738, Cambridge, CB2 5WY Tel: 0845 064 5555 E-mail: info@microscribe.co.uk

S B Electronic Systems Ltd, Arden Grove, Harpenden, Hertfordshire, AL5 4SL Tel: (01582) 769991 Fax: (01582) 461705 E-mail: sales@telepen.co.uk

Symbol Technologies Ltd, Symbol Place, Wharfedale Road, Winnersh, Wokingham, Berkshire, RG41 5TP Tel: 0118-945 7000 Fax: 0118-945 7500

Your PC, 23-25 Station Road, Holmfirth, HD9 1AB Tel: (01484) 687814 Fax: (01484) 687685

HANDICRAFT EMBELLISHMENT CHARMS

▶ Pewter Charms, 12 Ponsford Road, Bristol, BS4 2UP Tel: 0117-300 5635 Fax: 0117 971 9927
E-mail: customer-service@pewtercharms.co.uk

HANDICRAFT/HOBBY MATERIALS

A & J Hobby Ceramics, 876 Wimborne Road, Bournemouth, BH9 2DR Tel: (01202) 516160 Fax: (01202) 523971
E-mail: sales@ajhobbyceramics.co.uk
Fred Aldous Ltd, Handicraft Centre, 37 Lever Street, Manchester, M1 1LW Tel: 0161-236 2477 Fax: 0161-236 6075
E-mail: aldous@btinternet.com
Calder Colours Ashby Ltd, Dents Road, Nottingham Road Indust Estate, Ashby DeLa Zouch, Ashby-de-la-Zouch, Leicestershire, LE65 1JS Tel: (01530) 412885 Fax: (01530) 417315 E-mail: office@caldercolours.co.uk
▶ The Design Station Ltd, 9 Turnstone Drive, Featherstone, Wolverhampton, WV10 7TA Tel: (01902) 722192
E-mail: jackie@thedesignstation.co.uk
DMC Creative World, 62 Pullman Road, Wigston, Leicestershire, LE18 2DY Tel: 0116-281 1040 Fax: 0116-281 3592
E-mail: salesandmarketing@dmc.com
Frame Craft Minitures Ltd, Lichfield Road, Brownhills, Walsall, WS8 6LH Tel: (01543) 373076 Fax: (01543) 453154
E-mail: sales@framecraft.com
Arthur Heath & Co. Ltd, Hall Road, Aylesford, Kent, ME20 7QZ Tel: (01622) 717507 Fax: (01622) 710551
E-mail: admin@arthurheath.com
Impress Cards, Slough Farm, Westhall, Halesworth, Suffolk, IP19 8RN Tel: (01986) 781422 Fax: (01986) 781677
E-mail: sales@impresscards.com
J Burhouse, Inver Sawmill, Inver, Dunkeld, Perthshire, PH8 0JR Tel: (01350) 727723 Fax: (01350) 727261
Oasis Art & Craft Products Ltd, Goldthorn Road, Kidderminster, Worcestershire, DY11 7JD Tel: (01562) 744522 Fax: (01562) 823181
E-mail: sales@oasisart.co.uk
S G Magnets Ltd, Tesla House, 85 Ferry Lane, Rainham, Essex, RM13 9YH Tel: (01708) 558411 Fax: (01708) 554021
E-mail: sales@sgmagnets.com

HANDKERCHIEFS

Spence Bryson Ltd, Unit 14a Seagoe Industrial Area, Portadown, Craigavon, County Armagh, BT63 5QD Tel: (028) 3833 2521 Fax: (028) 3835 1043E-mail: sales@spencebryson.co.uk
Stockbridge Mill Co. Ltd, Green Lane, Padiham, Burnley, Lancashire, BB12 7AE Tel: (01282) 772231 Fax: (01282) 771084
E-mail: sales@stockbridgemill.com

HANDLE GRIPS

Gripworks, Units 11-13 Spectrum West, 20-20 Maidstone Business Estate, St. Laurence Avenue, Allington, Maidstone, Kent, ME16 0LL Tel: (0800) 7311150 Fax: (01622) 693201
E-mail: sales@sinclair-rush.co.uk

HANDLES, GLASS FIBRE OR FIBREGLASS

Jafco Tools Ltd, Access House, Great Western Street, Wednesbury, West Midlands, WS10 7LE Tel: 0121-556 7700 Fax: 0121-556 7788 E-mail: sales@jafco-tools.com

HANDMADE BATHROOM FITTINGS OR ACCESSORIES

▶ D J B Ceramics Ltd, Beaufort Mill, Beaufort Road, Stoke-on-Trent, ST3 1RH Tel: (01782) 312121 Fax: (01782) 312121
E-mail: djb.ceramics@btinternet.com

HANDMADE BISCUITS

Sharp & Nickless Ltd, 77 College Street, Long Eaton, Nottingham, NG10 4NN Tel: 0115-973 2169 Fax: 0115-973 2169
E-mail: sharp@brandysnap.co.uk

HANDMADE GREETING CARDS

▶ Aileen's Cards, 5 Finlay Avenue, East Calder, Livingston, West Lothian, EH53 0RP Tel: (01506) 881760
E-mail: info@aileens-cards.co.uk
▶ Bespoke Cards, 9B Higham Road, Woodford Green, Essex, IG8 9JN Tel: (0845) 270 1410 Fax: (0845) 270 1411
E-mail: theteam@bespokecards.net
▶ Craft Fairy, 8 Park View, Coychurch, Bridgend, Mid Glamorgan, CF35 5HS Tel: (01656) 653796 E-mail: yvonne@craftfairy.co.uk
▶ Handmade Wedding Invitations & Stationery By Datz Creationz, 5 Alwin Road, Rowley Regis, West Midlands, B65 8BN Tel: (07759) 820406
E-mail: datzcreationz@blueyonder.co.uk
▶ Porosol Ltd, Tennis House, 249-251 Belper Road, Stanley Common, Ilkeston, Derbyshire, DE7 6FY Tel: 0115-930 7977 Fax: 0115-944 2147 E-mail: t.shaw@porosol.fsnet.co.uk
▶ Susieart, 38 Hill Close, Lightpill, Stroud, Gloucestershire, GL5 3PG Tel: (01453) 762013 E-mail: sue-halliday@tiscali.co.uk
▶ Thread-bare, 72 Berecroft, Harlow, Essex, CM18 7SB Tel: (07736) 833632
E-mail: clare@thread-bare.co.uk
▶ YCARTwedding Stationary, 1B Union Street, Greenock, Renfrewshire, PA16 8JH Tel: (07951) 145871E-mail: tracy@ycart.co.uk

HANDMADE SCRAPBOOKS

▶ The Mulberry Bush, Limberlost Farm, Swife Lane, nr. Broad Oak, Heathfield, East Sussex, TN21 8YA Tel: (01435) 882014

HANDMADE SOAPS

Caurnie Soap Co., The Soaperie, Canal Street, Kirkintilloch, Glasgow, G66 1QZ Tel: 0141-776 1218 Fax: 0141-776 1218
E-mail: office@caurnie.com
▶ Shelley's Wood, 41 Kirtley, Tamworth, Staffordshire, B77 2HF Tel: (01827) 739050 Fax: E-mail: shelleyswood@yahoo.co.uk
▶ The Soap-Hut, Wayside, The Slough, Redditch, Worcestershire, B97 5JT Tel: 07835 555775 E-mail: thesoaphut@hotmail.com

HANDRAIL CUTTERS

▶ Delta Balustrades, Millbuck Way, Sandbach, Cheshire, CW11 3JA Tel: (01270) 753383

HANDRAILS, *See also headings for particular types*

Boyco Co., Europa Way, Stockport, Cheshire, SK3 0XE Tel: 0161-428 7077
Castle Fabrication & Installation Ltd, 3a Cold Hesledon Industrial Estate, Cold Hesledon, Seaham, County Durham, SR7 8ST Tel: 0191-581 5177 Fax: 0191-581 4792
E-mail: sales@castlefab.com
D C Plastic Handrails Ltd, Unit 6, Cowen Road, Cowen Road Industrial Estate, Blaydon-On-Tyne, Tyne & Wear, NE21 5TW Tel: 0191-414 0034 Fax: 0191-414 0034
E-mail: davey@dchandrails.freeserve.co.uk
D J Engineering, 4 Camp Industrial Estate, Rycote Lane, Milton Common, Thame, Oxfordshire, OX9 2NP Tel: (01844) 278749 Fax: (01844) 278749 E-mail: djjeff@aol.com
Nailsworth Services Ltd, Unit 5 Strensham Business Park, Strensham, Worcester, WR8 9JZ Tel: (01684) 274758 Fax: (01684) 274758
E-mail: helen@nailsworth.eclipse.co.uk

HANDWHEELS, *See also headings for particular types*

Knobs, Leone Works, John Street, New Basford, Nottingham, NG7 7HL Tel: 0115-942 0006 Fax: 0115-970 2106
E-mail: sales@knobs.uk.com

HARD ANODISING PROCESSORS OR SERVICES

A & R Metal Finishers, Streetbridge Works, Royton, Oldham, OL2 5ZY Tel: 0161-627 0177 Fax: 0161-627 0177
Alpha, Westbury, Sherborne, Dorset, DT9 3RB Tel: (01935) 813722 Fax: (01935) 811822
C B F Aluminium Treatments Ltd, Claybank Road, Portsmouth, PO3 5NH Tel: (023) 9266 5253 Fax: (023) 9266 7710
Colne Anodising Co. Ltd, Calder Mill, Green Road, Colne, Lancashire, BB8 8AL Tel: (01282) 867300 Fax: (01282) 867407
E-mail: sales@colneanodising.co.uk
Hard Anodising Ltd, Firs Industrial Estate, Kidderminster, Worcestershire, DY11 7QN Tel: (01562) 865158 Fax: (01562) 66118
E-mail: sales@hard-anodising.co.uk
Standard & Pochin Ltd, 94 Lyde Road, Yeovil, Somerset, BA21 5DS Tel: (01935) 421481 Fax: (01935) 428030
E-mail: info@ijmcgilltransport.com
Dave Walch Ltd, 121 Percival Lane, Runcorn, Cheshire, WA7 4UY Tel: (01928) 574681 Fax: (01928) 577790
E-mail: dave@anodisersruncorn.com

HARD CHROME PLATED STEEL BARS

E H M Ltd, Unit 10 Eagle Industrial Estate, Bagnall Street, Great Bridge, Tipton, West Midlands, DY4 7BS Tel: 0121-557 0626 Fax: 0121-557 0646
H Reis Ltd, Powke Lane, Cradley Heath, West Midlands, B64 5QF Tel: (01384) 567727 Fax: (01384) 410317
E-mail: terry.reis@chromebar.co.uk

HARD COVER BINDERS

▶ Chivers Period Book Binders, Aintree Avenue, White Horse Business Park, Trowbridge, Wiltshire, BA14 0XB Tel: (01225) 752888 Fax: (01225) 752666
E-mail: info@chivers-period.co.uk
Goodman Baylis Ltd, The Trinity Press, London Road, Worcester, WR5 2JH Tel: (01905) 357979 Fax: (01905) 354919
E-mail: theworks@goodmanbaylis.co.uk
Nolene Ltd, Brunel Road, Newton Abbot, Devon, TQ12 4PB Tel: (01626) 333800 Fax: (01626) 368168 E-mail: info@nolene.co.uk
R G Scales, 92 Southwark Bridge Road, London, SE1 0EX Tel: (020) 7928 9738 Fax: (0845) 3459182 E-mail: info@document-centre.co.uk

HARD DISK DRIVES (HDD)

3d Computer Systems Ltd, Albany House, 11 New Road, Chippenham, Wiltshire, SN15 1HJ Tel: (01249) 460766 Fax: (01249) 460583
E-mail: sales@3d-computers.co.uk
Akhter Group Holdings P.L.C., Akhter House, Perry Road, Harlow, Essex, CM18 7PN Tel: (01279) 443521 Fax: (01279) 821300
▶ Apex Technology Ltd, PO Box 2364, Stafford, ST16 3DA Tel: (01785) 227989
E-mail: enquiry@apextechnology.co.uk
Camlab Computer Systems, 27 Faringdon Road, Swindon, SN1 5AR Tel: (01793) 534917 Fax: (01793) 513120
E-mail: sales@camlab.net
Chaplin Computer Consultants, 331 Walsall Road, Great Wyrley, Walsall, WS6 6DR Tel: (01922) 411117 Fax: (01922) 411001
E-mail: chris@ccc1.demon.co.uk
D & P Data Systems Ltd, 15 Carnarvon Street, Manchester, M3 1HJ Tel: 0161-832 6969 Fax: 0161-832 6970
E-mail: sales@dpdata.co.uk
Discount Computer Supplies, 58 Copley Road, Doncaster, South Yorkshire, DN1 2QW Tel: (01302) 364155 Fax: (01302) 366062
E-mail: sales@dcs.uk.com
Sion Elliott Ltd, 124A High Street, Nailsea, Bristol, BS48 1AH Tel: (01275) 851460
E-mail: info@sioncomputers.co.uk
Eurotek HSM, Manor Drive, Aylesbury, Buckinghamshire, HP20 1EW Tel: (01296) 435036 Fax: (01296) 431967
E-mail: james@eurotekhsm.co.uk
Evolution Computers, 135 Bradford Road, Shipley, West Yorkshire, BD18 3TB Tel: (01274) 773394 Fax: (01274) 778788
E-mail: info@evolutiondirect.com
F M K Ltd, 3a Crown Buildings, The Green, London, E4 7EX Tel: (020) 8524 3595 Fax: (020) 8524 3566
E-mail: sales@fmk.co.uk
Highridge Computers Ltd, 275 Tutbury Road, Burton-on-Trent, Staffordshire, DE13 0NZ Tel: (01283) 500530 Fax: (01283) 500540
E-mail: karl@highridge.net
I B M (UK) Ltd, 1 New Square, Feltham, Middlesex, TW14 8HB Tel: (020) 8818 6060 Fax: (020) 8818 5499
I B M (UK) Ltd, Po Box 41, Portsmouth, PO6 3AU Tel: (023) 9256 1000 Fax: (023) 9238 8914 E-mail: uk_crc@uk.ibm.com
Level 7 Computers Ltd, 39 Eastover, Bridgwater, Somerset, TA6 5AW Tel: (01278) 444770
E-mail: mail@level7.co.uk
Micro Plus Computers, 33 Bailey Street, Oswestry, Shropshire, SY11 1PX Tel: (01691) 656875 Fax: (01691) 671285
E-mail: chris@micro-plus.co.uk
Modern Computers Ltd, 181 Old Kent Road, London, SE1 5NA Tel: (020) 7231 1313 Fax: (020) 7231 3225
E-mail: sales@moderncomputers.com
P C Ideals, 89 Albert Road, Southsea, Hampshire, PO5 2SG Tel: (023) 9282 9239 Fax: (023) 9286 2111
E-mail: sales@pcideals.com
PC Tech Ltd, 33 Cleveland Street, Normanby, Middlesbrough, Cleveland, TS6 0LT Tel: (01642) 460704 Fax: (01642) 461002
E-mail: sales@pctechcomputers.com
▶ Three Counties Computers, 14 Woodsage Drive, Gillingham, Dorset, SP8 4UF Tel: (01747) 823994
E-mail: sales@threecountiescomputers.co.uk
Worldwide PC UK Ltd, 88-90 Manningham Lane, Bradford, West Yorkshire, BD1 3ES Tel: (01274) 745515E-mail: gary@wwpc.co.uk

HARD TOOLING PRESSES

Kirkby Precision Engineering Ltd, Ashcroft Road, Liverpool, L33 7TW Tel: 0151-549 1007 Fax: 0151-549 2400
E-mail: kirkbyprecision@btclick.com

HARD WATER SCALE PREVENTION TREATMENT PLANT AND EQUIPMENT

Hydropath UK Ltd, Acorn Park, Lenton Lane Industrial Estate, Nottingham, NG7 2TR Tel: 0115-986 9966 Fax: 0115-986 9944
E-mail: sales@hydroflow.com
Silkstream Water Treatment Equipment, 36 Spencer Close, Potton, Sandy, Bedfordshire, SG19 2QY Tel: (01767) 261942
E-mail: sales@silkstream.co.uk

HARDBOARD

▶ L F P (UK) Ltd, LFP House, 1 Grange Meadows, Elmswell, Bury St. Edmunds, Suffolk, IP30 9GE Tel: (01359) 242900 Fax: (01359) 242121 E-mail: info@lfpuk.co.uk

HARDCOAT CLEAR COATINGS

Charvo Finishing Ltd, Snaygill Industrial Estate, Keighley Road, Skipton, North Yorkshire, BD23 2QR Tel: (01756) 795028 Fax: (01756) 798473 E-mail: sales@charvo.co.uk

HARDCORE

Aaron White Ltd, 20 Bland Street, Sheffield, S4 8DG Tel: 0114-261 9519 Fax: 0114-261 9348
▶ Recyclo, Prince William Avenue, Sandycroft, Deeside, Clwyd, CH5 2QZ Tel: (01244) 521800 Fax: (0845) 4515332
E-mail: enquiries@recyclowastemanagement.co.uk
S B H (SW) Ltd, 61D Ivy Court, High Street, Nailsea, Bristol, BS48 1AW Tel: (01275) 851739 Fax: (01275) 540211
E-mail: barbara@sbhcrushing.co.uk
Simpson Environmental Services Ltd, Simpsons Way, Stoke Poges Lane, Slough, SL1 3GD Tel: (01753) 533311 Fax: (01753) 533311
E-mail: jeff@simpsonrecycling.com
W A Banham & Sons Ltd, The Pipeworks, Eye Road, Hoxne, Eye, Suffolk, IP21 5BA Tel: (01379) 668268 Fax: (01379) 668268

HARDENED AND TEMPERED STEEL STRIPS

George Ibbotson Steels Ltd, 16 Atlas Way, Sheffield, S4 7QQ Tel: 0114-244 7400 Fax: 0114-244 7412
E-mail: sales@ibbotsonsteels.co.uk
K T S Wire Industries Ltd, Park Mills, South Street, Morley, Leeds, LS27 8AT Tel: 0113-253 2421 Fax: 0113-307 6868
E-mail: mail@ktswire.com

HARDFACING MATERIALS/ ALLOYS

Cutting & Wear Resistant Development Ltd, Greasbrough Road, Rotherham, South Yorkshire, S60 1RW Tel: (01709) 361041 Fax: (01709) 374211E-mail: sales@cwuk.com
Sulzer Metco (UK) Ltd, Suflex Estate, Newport Road, Risca, Newport, Gwent, NP11 6YD Tel: (01633) 600970 Fax: (01633) 601717
E-mail: simon.hiiemal@sulzer.com
Triten International Ltd, Shawfield Road, Barnsley, South Yorkshire, S71 3HS Tel: (01226) 702300 Fax: (01226) 702311
E-mail: triten@triten.co.uk

HARDFACING SERVICES

Allstyle Engineering Ltd, Unit 5 60 Arthur Street, Redditch, Worcestershire, B98 8JY Tel: (01527) 527687 Fax: (01527) 500467
E-mail: allstyle@tesco.net
Croboride Engineering Ltd, Little Burton West, Burton-on-Trent, Staffordshire, DE14 1PP Tel: (01283) 511188 Fax: (01283) 530845
E-mail: info@croboride.co.uk
Cutting & Wear Resistant Development Ltd, Greasbrough Road, Rotherham, South Yorkshire, S60 1RW Tel: (01709) 361041 Fax: (01709) 374211E-mail: sales@cwuk.com
Greville Hardfacing & Engineering Co. Ltd, 4 Palmers Road, Redditch, Worcestershire, B98 0RF Tel: (01527) 525395 Fax: (01527) 510949 E-mail: ghf@btconnect.com
Monitor Coatings Ltd, Monitor House 2 Elm Road, West Chirton Industrial Estate, North Shields, Tyne & Wear, NE29 8SE Tel: 0191-293 7040 Fax: 0191-293 7041
E-mail: info@monitorcoatings.co.uk
Penistone Hard Metals Ltd, Roman Ridge Road, Sheffield, S9 1FH Tel: 0114-243 2471 Fax: 0114-242 6570
E-mail: info@penistonehardmetals.co.uk
Technical Welding Services, Corporation Road, Rochdale, Lancashire, OL11 4HJ Tel: (01706) 655402 Fax: (01706) 657735
E-mail: sales@technicalwelding.co.uk

▶ indicates data change since last edition

HARDFACING SERVICES – *continued*

Techniques Surfaces (UK) Ltd, Wood Lane, Erdington, Birmingham, B24 9QL Tel: 0121-382 8060 Fax: 0121-377 8928 E-mail: info@ts-uk.com

Triten International Ltd, Shawfield Road, Barnsley, South Yorkshire, S71 3HS Tel: (01226) 702300 Fax: (01226) 702311 E-mail: triten@triten.co.uk

HARDNESS TEST EQUIPMENT, *See also headings for particular types*

C V Instruments, 32 Leeds Old Road, Bradford, West Yorkshire, BD3 8HU Tel: (01274) 223456 Fax: (01274) 223444 E-mail: sales@bowersmetrology.com

Hampden Test Equipment Ltd, Satra House, Rockingham Road, Kettering, Northamptonshire, NN16 9JH Tel: (01536) 518563 Fax: (01536) 519256 E-mail: hampden-test@satra.co.uk

▶ Hartest Precision Instruments Ltd, 4 St Georges Industrial Estate, Richmond Road, Kingston upon Thames, Surrey, KT2 5BQ Tel: (020) 8541 4333 Fax: (020) 8549 3374 E-mail: sales@sheeninstruments.com

Indentec Hardness Testing Machines Ltd, Lye Valley Industrial Estate, Bromley Street, Lye, Stourbridge, West Midlands, DY9 8HX Tel: (01384) 896949 Fax: (01384) 424470 E-mail: mail@indentec.demon.co.uk

Leica Microsystems UK Ltd, Davy Avenue, Knowlhill, Milton Keynes, MK5 8LB Tel: (0800) 437 0492 Fax: (01908) 609992 E-mail: sales@leica-geosystems.com

Q C Plus Ltd, PO Box 229, Romsey, Hampshire, SO51 0GJ Tel: (01794) 341218 Fax:

HARDSURFACING, *See Hardfacing etc*

HARDWARE, SECURITY

Fred Duncombe Ltd, Progress Drive, Cannock, Staffordshire, WS11 0JE Tel: (01543) 578661 Fax: (01543) 570050 E-mail: sales@fredduncombe.co.uk

Help4IT Ltd, 61 Queen Street, London, EC4R 1AE Tel: (0845) 2574448 Fax: (0845) 2574449 E-mail: sanjay.patel@help4it.co.uk

Softek Computer Security, La Rue Du Pont Marquet, St. Brelade, Jersey, JE3 8DS Tel: (01534) 811182 Fax: (01534) 811183 E-mail: sales@softek.co.uk

Specialty Fasteners & Components Ltd, Seymour Wharf, Steamer Quay Road, Totnes, Devon, TQ9 5AL Tel: (01803) 868677 Fax: (01803) 868678 E-mail: sales@specialty-fasteners.co.uk

HARDWOOD FLOORING

▶ Antique Oak Flooring Co., 94 High Street, London, N8 7NT Tel: (020) 8347 8222 Fax: (020) 8347 8333 E-mail: info@antiqueoakflooring.com

Boen UK Ltd, Elgar House, Green Street, Kidderminster, Worcestershire, DY10 1JF Tel: (0800) 6525280 Fax: (0870) 7704340 E-mail: sales@boen.co.uk

C Blumsom Ltd, Maple Wharf, 36-38 River Road, Barking, Essex, IG11 0DN Tel: (020) 8594 5175 Fax: (020) 8594 1089 E-mail: sales@blumson.co.uk

Coraff Ltd, 51 Market Place, London, NW11 6JT Tel: (020) 8731 7766 Fax: (020) 8209 0098 E-mail: sales@coraffcarpets.co.uk

Finnforest UK Ltd, 46 Berth Tilbury Docks, Tilbury, Essex, RM18 7HS Tel: (01375) 856855 Fax: (01375) 851555 E-mail: email@finnforest.com

GPG Sales Ltd, Unit 6, Luton Street, Liverpool, L5 9XR Tel: 0151-298 1509 Fax: 0151-298 2276 E-mail: sales@gpg-sales.com

▶ Greentimber Forest Products, 3 Victoria Road, Harpenden, Hertfordshire, AL5 4EA Tel: (01582) 799050 Fax: (01582) 799040 E-mail: green@greentimber.com

Livingwood Floorcoverings, The Mount, Flimwell, Wadhurst, East Sussex, TN5 7QP Tel: (01580) 879888 Fax: (01580) 879444 E-mail: sales@livingwood.net

▶ Majestic Floors, Corner Glades, 16 Elmton Close, Leeds, LS10 3UD Tel: 0113-270 9921 E-mail: majesticfloors@hotmail.com

Mercia Flooring Ltd, 59 The Square, Dunchurch, Rugby, Warwickshire, CV22 6NU Tel: (01788) 522168 Fax: (01788) 811847 E-mail: sales@merciaflooring.co.uk

Merton Timber & Builders Merchants, Unit E 2 Endeavour Way, London, SW19 8UH Tel: (020) 8879 0626 Fax: (020) 8947 6061 E-mail: sales@mertontimber.com

P M N Aviation Ltd, Unit B, Crawford Street, Rochdale, Lancashire, OL16 5NU Tel: (01706) 655134 Fax: (01706) 631561 E-mail: info@pegasusaviation.co.uk

Renovate Contracts Ltd, 91 Park Road, Earl Shilton, Leicester, LE9 7ZY Tel: 01455 851900 Fax: 01455 851900 E-mail: duncan@renovatecontracts.wanadoo.co.uk

Timbmet Rochdale Ltd, The Klondike, Chichester Street, Rochdale, Lancashire, OL16 2AU Tel: (01706) 863800 Fax: (01706) 750484 E-mail: sales@timbmet.com

Watson Brook, 119a High Street, Tewkesbury, Gloucestershire, GL20 5JY Tel: (01684) 291155 Fax: (01684) 291166 E-mail: sales@watsonbrook.co.uk

HARDWOOD FLOORING BLOCKS

▶ Eden Floor Store,The, 64 Wyle Cop, Shrewsbury, SY1 1UX Tel: 01743 340077 E-mail: sales@theedenfloorstore.com

▶ Isle of Wight Hardwoods, 45 Central way, Sandown, Isle of Wight, PO36 9DW Tel: (01983) 408322 Fax: (01983) 408322 E-mail: info@isleofwighthardwoods.co.uk

▶ Lewis, Unit 92 Dolphin House Stephenson Way, Formby Business Park, Formby, Liverpool, L37 8EG Tel: (01704) 831142 Fax: (01704) 879767 E-mail: enquiries@ablewis.co.uk

▶ Majestic Floors, Corner Glades, 16 Elmton Close, Leeds, LS10 3UD Tel: 0113-270 9921 E-mail: majesticfloors@hotmail.com

▶ Scandinavian Hardwood Flooring, 18 Blackford Road, Watford, WD19 6YN Tel: (020) 8428 9168 Fax: (020) 8421 6505 E-mail: gudnason.jorgen@btconnect.com

HARDWOOD IMPORT

C Blumsom Ltd, Maple Wharf, 36-38 River Road, Barking, Essex, IG11 0DN Tel: (020) 8594 5175 Fax: (020) 8594 1089 E-mail: sales@blumson.co.uk

▶ Greentimber Forest Products, 3 Victoria Road, Harpenden, Hertfordshire, AL5 4EA Tel: (01582) 799050 Fax: (01582) 799040 E-mail: green@greentimber.com

James Latham Sales plc, Unit 2 Swallow Park, Finway Road, Hemel Hempstead Industrial Estate, Hemel Hempstead, Hertfordshire, HP2 7QU Tel: (01442) 849000 Fax: (01442) 239287 E-mail: marketing@lathams.co.uk

James Latham, Badminton Road Trading Estate, Badminton Road, Yate, Bristol, BS37 5JX Tel: (01454) 315421 Fax: (01454) 323488 E-mail: panals.yate@lathams.co.uk

O C M Business Systems Ltd, O C M House, St. Peters Road, Droitwich, Worcestershire, WR9 7BJ Tel: (01905) 795001 Fax: (01905) 794567

P K Hardwood, Wotton Road, Brill, Aylesbury, Buckinghamshire, HP18 9UB Tel: (01844) 238282 Fax: (01844) 238016

Thorogood Timber plc, Colchester Road, Ardleigh, Colchester, CO7 7PQ Tel: (01206) 233100 Fax: (01206) 233115 E-mail: sales@thorogood.co.uk

HARDWOOD INTERLOCKING PLANK FLOORING

▶ Eden Floor Store,The, 64 Wyle Cop, Shrewsbury, SY1 1UX Tel: 01743 340077 E-mail: sales@theedenfloorstore.com

▶ Floorboy, 9 Malpas drive, Northampton, NN5 6XL Tel: (01604) 461142 E-mail: floorboy@hotmail.com

▶ Isle of Wight Hardwoods, 45 Central way, Sandown, Isle of Wight, PO36 9DW Tel: (01983) 408322 Fax: (01983) 408322 E-mail: info@isleofwighthardwoods.co.uk

▶ The Laminator Flooring Company Ltd, 53 Warwick Road, Cliftonville, Margate, Kent, CT9 2JU Tel: 0800 1955196 E-mail: a1jonathanweston@hotmail.com

▶ Lewis, Unit 92 Dolphin House Stephenson Way, Formby Business Park, Formby, Liverpool, L37 8EG Tel: (01704) 831142 Fax: (01704) 879767 E-mail: enquiries@ablewis.co.uk

▶ Scandinavian Hardwood Flooring, 18 Blackford Road, Watford, WD19 6YN Tel: (020) 8428 9168 Fax: (020) 8421 6505 E-mail: gudnason.jorgen@btconnect.com

HARDWOOD STRIP FLOORING

▶ Eden Floor Store,The, 64 Wyle Cop, Shrewsbury, SY1 1UX Tel: 01743 340077 E-mail: sales@theedenfloorstore.com

▶ Floorboy, 9 Malpas drive, Northampton, NN5 6XL Tel: (01604) 461142 E-mail: floorboy@hotmail.com

▶ Scandinavian Hardwood Flooring, 18 Blackford Road, Watford, WD19 6YN Tel: (020) 8428 9168 Fax: (020) 8421 6505 E-mail: gudnason.jorgen@btconnect.com

HARDWOODS

C Blumsom Ltd, Maple Wharf, 36-38 River Road, Barking, Essex, IG11 0DN Tel: (020) 8594 5175 Fax: (020) 8594 1089 E-mail: sales@blumson.co.uk

C Blumsom Ltd, Maple Wharf, 36-38 River Road, Barking, Essex, IG11 0DN Tel: (020) 8594 5175 Fax: (020) 8507 1334 E-mail: sales@blumson.co.uk

John Chapman, 77 Hilliard Road, Northwood, Middlesex, HA6 1SL Tel: (01923) 824201

Dartmoor Hardwoods, Duchy Yard, Station Road, Princetown, Yelverton, Devon, PL20 6QX Tel: (01822) 890559 Fax: (01822) 890559

Dawson Bros Timber Ltd, Blowers Green Cresent, Dudley, West Midlands, DY2 8XQ Tel: (01384) 253816 Fax: (01384) 457248 E-mail: sales@dawsontimber.co.uk

E O Burton, Thorndon Sawmills, The Avenue, Brentwood, Essex, CM13 3RZ Tel: (01277) 260810 Fax: (01277) 262823 E-mail: timber@eoburton.com

▶ Greentimber Forest Products, 3 Victoria Road, Harpenden, Hertfordshire, AL5 4EA Tel: (01582) 799050 Fax: (01582) 799040 E-mail: green@greentimber.com

J S Wright & Sons Ltd, Boreham Road, Great Leighs, Chelmsford, CM3 1PR Tel: (01245) 361639 Fax: (01245) 361882 E-mail: jsw@cricketbatwillow.com

James Latham, 13 Chartwell Drive, Wigston, Leicestershire, LE18 2FN Tel: 0116-288 9161 Fax: 0116-281 3806 E-mail: panels.wigston@lathams.co.uk

James Mcgregor & Sons Ltd, 49 Sydenham Road, Belfast, BT3 9DR Tel: (028) 9045 1244 Fax: (028) 9045 6433 E-mail: sales@hardwoodni.com

Knotbox, 47A High Street, Witney, Oxfordshire, OX28 6JA Tel: (01993) 778772 Fax: (01993) 701184

Palmer Timber Ltd, 104 Station Road, Cradley Heath, West Midlands, B64 6PW Tel: 0121-559 5511 Fax: 0121-561 4562 E-mail: sales@palmertimber.com

Priday Sydney & Snewin Ltd, Oak Wharf, Timberwharf Road, London, N16 6DB Tel: (020) 8800 5661 Fax: (020) 8809 5521 E-mail: sales@pridays.sagehost.co.uk

Robert Duncan Ltd, Green Lane, Gateshead, Tyne & Wear, NE10 0JS Tel: 0191-469 8743 Fax: 0191-469 8903 E-mail: enquiries@robertduncan.co.uk

Saint Gobain Building Distribution Ltd, Merchant House, Binley Business Park, Harry Weston Road, Coventry, CV3 2TT Tel: (024) 7643 8400 Fax: (024) 7643 8505 E-mail: shelley.knowles@jewson.co.uk

Sykes Timber, Carlyon Road, Atherstone, Warwickshire, CV9 1JD Tel: (01827) 718951 Fax: (01827) 714257 E-mail: wood@sykestimber.co.uk

Timbmet Ltd, PO Box 39, Oxford, OX2 9PP Tel: (01865) 862223 Fax: (01865) 860342 E-mail: marketing@timbmet.com

Whitmores Timber Co. Ltd, Main Road, Claybrooke Magna, Lutterworth, Leicestershire, LE17 5AQ Tel: (01455) 209121 Fax: (01455) 209041 E-mail: info@whitmores.co.uk

G.R. Wiltshire & Co., Smoke Hall Lane, Winsford, Cheshire, CW7 3BE Tel: (01455) 202666 Fax: (01606) 555511 E-mail: sales@smeetimber.com

HARMONIC FILTER DESIGN/ FABRICATION/ENGINEERING SERVICES

▶ Enspec Power Ltd, Stanfield Business Centre, Addison Street, Sunderland, SR2 8BL Tel: 0191-514 2090 Fax: 0191-514 2151 E-mail: info@enspecpower.com

HARRIS TWEED

Harris Tweed Trading Co. Ltd, Sandwick Road, Stornoway, Isle of Lewis, HS1 2SJ Tel: (01851) 702772 Fax: (01851) 705271

Kenneth Mackenzie Holdings Ltd, Sandwick Road, Stornoway, Isle of Lewis, HS1 2SJ Tel: (01851) 702772 Fax: (01851) 705271 E-mail: sales.kennethmckenzie@fsmail.net

HARSH ENVIRONMENT IMAGING EQUIPMENT

Kongsberg Simrad, Campus 1 Balgownie Road, Aberdeen Science & Technology Park, Bridge of Don, Aberdeen, AB22 8GT Tel: (01224) 226500 Fax: (01224) 226501

HARVESTERS

Blair Engineering Ltd, Balmoral Road, Rattray, Blairgowrie, Perthshire, PH10 7AH Tel: (01250) 872244 Fax: (01250) 872244 E-mail: sales@blairengineering.co.uk

Hallmark Tractors Ltd, Smisby Road, Ashby-de-la-Zouch, Leicestershire, LE65 2UE Tel: (01530) 412811 Fax: (01530) 412512 E-mail: sales@tractors.co.uk

Mbe Fabrications Ltd, 1 Town Drove, Quadring, Spalding, Lincolnshire, PE11 4PU Tel: (01775) 821222 Fax: (01775) 820914 E-mail: sales@mbefabs.com

R W Marsh, London Road, Sleaford, Lincolnshire, NG34 8NX Tel: (01529) 303093 Fax: (01529) 413363 E-mail: sales@rwmarsh.com

Shelbourne Reynolds Engineering Ltd, Shepherds Grove Industrial Estate, Stanton, Bury St. Edmunds, Suffolk, IP31 2AR Tel: (01359) 250415 Fax: (01359) 250464 E-mail: info@shelbourne.com

HAT BLOCKS

Boone & Lane Ltd, 7-11 Taylor Street, Luton, LU2 0EY Tel: (01582) 723224 Fax: (01582) 402298

Guy Morse Brown, Mill Lane Farmhouse, Mill Lane, Wombourne, Wolverhampton, WV5 0LE Tel: (01902) 893683 Fax: (01902) 893683 E-mail: mail@hatblocks.co.uk

HAT BOXES

Printhouse Group, 8 Albert Drive, Burgess Hill, West Sussex, RH15 9TN Tel: (01444) 871776 Fax: (01444) 871731 E-mail: info@printhousegroup.com

HAT TRIMMINGS/ACCESSORIES MANUFRS

Barford Bros Ltd, 111 North Street, Luton, LU2 7QG Tel: (01582) 720371 Fax: (01582) 611098

C W Headdress Ltd, Unit 7, Witan Park, Avenue Two, Station Lane, Witney, Oxfordshire, OX28 4FH Tel: (01993) 703515 Fax: (01993) 775904 E-mail: sales@christy.techex.co.uk

▶ Drayfords Of Chesterfield, 4 Shap Close, Chesterfield, Derbyshire, S40 4NB Tel: (01246) 205914

▶ Kinkajou Accessories, 58 Allaston Road, Lydney, Gloucestershire, GL15 5ST Tel: 01594 840312

Randall Ribbons, 12 Frederick Street, Luton, LU2 7QS Tel: (01582) 721301 Fax: (01582) 720060 E-mail: sales@randallribbons.com

T W Bracher & Co. Ltd, Royal George Street, Stockport, Cheshire, SK3 8AS Tel: 0161-480 2005 Fax: 0161-477 1673 E-mail: sales@tw-bracher.co.uk

HATS, *See also headings for particular types*

Burgess Hats Ltd, 21 Parkside Centre, Potters Way, Temple Farm Industrial Estate, Southend-on-Sea, SS2 5SJ Tel: (01702) 617231 Fax: (01702) 460613 E-mail: admin@burgesshats.co.uk

C W Headdress Ltd, Unit 7, Witan Park, Avenue Two, Station Lane, Witney, Oxfordshire, OX28 4FH Tel: (01993) 703515 Fax: (01993) 775904 E-mail: sales@christy.techex.co.uk

Capemist Gloves Ltd, 158 Fenaghy Road, Cullybackey, Ballymena, County Antrim, BT42 1DZ Tel: (028) 2588 1190 Fax: (028) 2588 1682E-mail: capemist.gloves@virgin.net

Christy Group, Wood Street, Barnsley, South Yorkshire, S70 1NB Tel: (01226) 730226 Fax: (01226) 771234

Hat Box, 1 The Courtyard, George Street, Pontypool, Gwent, NP4 6LR Tel: (01495) 761901 E-mail: david@davidhead.wanadoo.co.uk

J B Hats & Things, 18 Ellesmere Road, Sheffield, S4 7JB Tel: 0114-278 6660 E-mail: jbahatsnthing@aol.com

James Lock & Co. Ltd, 6 Saint James's Street, London, SW1A 1EF Tel: (020) 7930 2421 Fax: (020) 7930 6616 E-mail: sales@lockhatters.co.uk

▶ Kinkajou Accessories, 58 Allaston Road, Lydney, Gloucestershire, GL15 5ST Tel: 01594 840312

Macculloch & Wallis Ltd, 25-26 Dering Street, London, W1S 1AT Tel: (020) 7629 0311 Fax: (020) 7629 8097 E-mail: macculloch@psilink.co.uk

S D L Imports Ltd, 2-18 Windham Road, Bournemouth, BH1 4RW Tel: (01202) 291122 Fax: (01202) 293322 E-mail: sales@sdlimports.co.uk

W. Shaw (Millinery), 58 Howard Street, Belfast, BT1 6PL Tel: (028) 9032 0135 Fax: (028) 9032 9026

▶ Talulah & Fox, 27 Barnham Road, Barnham, Bognor Regis, West Sussex, PO22 0ER Tel: (01243) 551733 E-mail: info@talulahandfox.co.uk

W Fischer & Sons Luton Ltd, 4a William Street, Luton, LU2 7RE Tel: (01582) 404022 Fax: (01582) 400455

▶ Woolyhats.com, 30 Westonfields, Totnes, Devon, TQ9 5QU Tel: 07077 400681 E-mail: admin@woolyhats.com

HATS, FOOD/CATERING INDUSTRY

Aburnet Ltd, Walter Street, Draycott, Derby, DE72 3NU Tel: (01332) 874797 Fax: (01332) 875284 E-mail: info@aburnet.co.uk

Olney Headwear Ltd, 106 Old Bedford Road, Luton, LU2 7PD Tel: (01582) 731512 Fax: (01582) 729066 E-mail: info@olney-headwear.co.uk

Turton Manufacturing Ltd, Unit 3 The Furlong, Berry Hill Industrial Estate, Droitwich, Worcestershire, WR9 9AH Tel: (01905) 796166 Fax: (01905) 796199 E-mail: sales@turtonslimited.com

HATS, LADIES'

Bollman Headwear Europe Ltd, Cleator Mills, Cleator, Cumbria, CA23 3DJ Tel: (01946) 810312 Fax: (01946) 811087 E-mail: enquireies@kangolheadweareurope.com

Carryon Clothing Mnfrs, Ravenscroft, Stoney Lane, Urpeth, Stanley, County Durham, DH9 0SJ Tel: 0191-370 0250 Fax: 0191-370 1226 E-mail: sales@carryonclothing.co.uk

Failsworth Hats Ltd, Crown Street, Crown Street, Failsworth, Manchester, M35 9BD Tel: 0161-681 3131 Fax: 0161-683 4754 E-mail: sales@failsworth-hats.co.uk

Walter Gurney & Son Ltd, 64 Bute Street, Luton, LU1 2EY Tel: (01582) 729471 Fax: (01582) 721060

Hat Box, 1 The Courtyard, George Street, Pontypool, Gwent, NP4 6LR Tel: (01495) 761901 E-mail: david@davidhead.wanadoo.co.uk

K R Snoxell & Sons Ltd, 24-26 Clarendon Road, Luton, LU2 7PQ Tel: (01582) 724704 Fax: (01582) 452928 E-mail: snoxell-headwear@lineone.net

▶ Kinkajou Accessories, 58 Allaston Road, Lydney, Gloucestershire, GL15 5ST Tel: 01594 840312

N Balfour & Sons, 12 Bilton Way, Luton, LU1 1UU Tel: (01582) 729621 Fax: (01582) 723334 E-mail: info@balfourhats.co.uk

Olney Headwear Ltd, 106 Old Bedford Road, Luton, LU2 7PD Tel: (01582) 731512 Fax: (01582) 729066 E-mail: info@olney-headwear.co.uk

Owen Barry, 32 Orchard Road, Street, Somerset, BA16 0BT Tel: (01458) 442858 Fax: (01458) 447319 E-mail: info@owenbarry.com

Princess Hats Ltd, 28 Reginald Street, Luton, LU2 7QZ Tel: (01582) 400488

Quill and Caplin Ltd, 12 Ogle Street, London, W1W 6HU Tel: (020) 7637 7213 Fax: (01582) 483462 E-mail: sales@quillcaplin.co.uk

Rees Productions Ltd, Unit 14 Cygnus Business Centre, Dalmeyer Road, London, NW10 2XA Tel: (020) 8459 1886 Fax: (020) 8459 8126 E-mail: info@reesproductions.co.uk

Robert Mackie & Co. Ltd, Holm Mill, Stewarton, Kilmarnock, Ayrshire, KA3 5HT Tel: (01560) 482124 Fax: (01560) 485213 E-mail: mackies@dial.pipex.com

Philip Somerville Ltd, 38 Chiltern Street, London, W1U 7QL Tel: (020) 7224 1517 Fax: (020) 7486 5885 E-mail: info@philipsomerville.com

▶ Talulah & Fox, 27 Barnham Road, Barnham, Bognor Regis, West Sussex, PO22 0ER Tel: (01243) 551733 E-mail: info@talulahandfox.co.uk

Walter Wright, 29 Albion Road, Luton, LU2 0DS Tel: (01582) 721616 Fax: (01582) 725055 E-mail: enquiries@walterwright.com

▶ The Whiteley H A T Co. Ltd, Unitb 1, Bramingham Business Park, Enterprise Way, Luton, LU3 4BU Tel: (01582) 493393 Fax: (01582) 491838 E-mail: sales@whiteley-hat.co.uk

▶ Woolyhats.com, 30 Westonfields, Totnes, Devon, TQ9 5QU Tel: 07077 400681 E-mail: admin@woolyhats.com

HATS, MEN'S

Bollman Headwear Europe Ltd, Cleator Mills, Cleator, Cumbria, CA23 3DJ Tel: (01946) 810312 Fax: (01946) 811087 E-mail: enquireies@kangolheadweareurope.com

Carryon Clothing Mnfrs, Ravenscroft, Stoney Lane, Urpeth, Stanley, County Durham, DH9 0SJ Tel: 0191-370 0250 Fax: 0191-370 1226 E-mail: sales@carryonclothing.co.uk

Failsworth Hats Ltd, Crown Street, Crown Street, Failsworth, Manchester, M35 9BD Tel: 0161-681 3131 Fax: 0161-683 4754 E-mail: sales@failsworth-hats.co.uk

J B Hats & Things, 18 Ellesmere Road, Sheffield, S4 7JB Tel: 0114-278 6660 E-mail: jbahatsnthing@aol.com

M S Michael & Co. Ltd, 4 Batchelor Street, Chatham, Kent, ME4 4BJ Tel: (01634) 844994 Fax: (01634) 844995

Olney Headwear Ltd, 106 Old Bedford Road, Luton, LU2 7PD Tel: (01582) 731512 Fax: (01582) 729066 E-mail: info@olney-headwear.co.uk

▶ Woolyhats.com, 30 Westonfields, Totnes, Devon, TQ9 5QU Tel: 07077 400681 E-mail: admin@woolyhats.com

HATS, MILITARY/UNIFORM

C M R International (UK) Military Firearms & Antiquities, 53 High Street, Ashford, Kent, TN24 8SG Tel: (0871) 2301318 Fax: (0871) 2301318 E-mail: cmrinternational@aol.com

C W Headdress Ltd, Unit 7, Witan Park, Avenue Two, Station Lane, Witney, Oxfordshire, OX28 4FH Tel: (01993) 703515 Fax: (01993) 775904 E-mail: sales@christy.techex.co.uk

HAUL OFF BELTING

Beltech Belting Mnfrs, 7 Acacia Close Business Estate, Off Cherrycourt Way, Leighton Buzzard, Bedfordshire, LU7 4QE Tel: (01525) 851155 Fax: (01525) 851156 E-mail: beltech@globalnet.co.uk

HAULAGE CLIPS

Crosby Europe (U K) Ltd, Unit 10, Fallbank Industrial Estate, Dodworth, Barnsley, South Yorkshire, S75 3LS Tel: (01226) 290516 Fax: (01226) 240118 E-mail: sales@crosbyeurope.co.uk

HAY

L R & Sons, Laindon Common Road, Little Burstead, Billericay, Essex, CM12 9SY Tel: (01277) 652381 Fax: (01277) 652381 E-mail: lrandsons@aol.com

HAZARDOUS AREA ALARM SYSTEMS

J C E (Europe) Ltd, East Way, Lee Mill Industrial Estate, Ivybridge, Devon, PL21 9LL Tel: (01752) 690530 Fax: (01752) 690531 E-mail: info.euro@jcegroup.com

LGM Products Ltd, 18 Riverside Park Industrial Estate, Dogflud Way, Farnham, Surrey, GU9 7UG Tel: (01252) 725257 Fax: (01252) 727627 E-mail: sales@lgmproducts.com

HAZARDOUS AREA BAR CODE SCANNERS

Bartec (UK) Ltd, Arundel House, Hollins Brook Park, Pilsworth Road, Bury, Lancashire, BL9 8RN Tel: (0844) 4992710 Fax: (0844) 4992715 E-mail: info@bartec.co.uk

HAZARDOUS AREA COMMUNICATION SYSTEMS

Dytecna Ltd, Spring Lane, Malvern, Worcestershire, WR14 1AL Tel: (01684) 892320 Fax: (01684) 892320 E-mail: info@dytecna.co.uk

HAZARDOUS AREA CONTROL GEAR

P F P Electrical Products Ltd, 22 Fortnum Close, Mackadown Lane, Kitts Green, Birmingham, B33 0LB Tel: 0121-783 7161 Fax: 0121-783 5717 E-mail: sales@pfp-elec.co.uk

HAZARDOUS AREA CONTROL STATIONS

Bartec (UK) Ltd, Arundel House, Hollins Brook Park, Pilsworth Road, Bury, Lancashire, BL9 8RN Tel: (0844) 4992710 Fax: (0844) 4992715 E-mail: info@bartec.co.uk

J B Systems Ltd, 8 Bridgegate Business Park, Gatehouse Way, Gatehouse Industrial Area, Aylesbury, Buckinghamshire, HP19 8XN Tel: (01296) 489967 Fax: (01296) 393515 E-mail: info@jbsystems.co.uk

HAZARDOUS AREA CRANES

J Barnsley Cranes Ltd, Unit 16 Pedmore Road Industrial Estate, Pedmore Road, Brierley Hill, West Midlands, DY5 1TJ Tel: (01384) 484811 Fax: (01384) 484333 E-mail: jsatch@jbarnsleycranes.com

Wellman Booth, 2 Kirkfields Industrial Centre, Kirk Lane, Yeadon, Leeds, LS19 7LX Tel: 0113-387 9730 Fax: 0113-250 6180 E-mail: sales@wellmanbooth.co.uk

HAZARDOUS AREA DISPLAY TERMINALS

Bartec (UK) Ltd, Arundel House, Hollins Brook Park, Pilsworth Road, Bury, Lancashire, BL9 8RN Tel: (0844) 4992710 Fax: (0844) 4992715 E-mail: info@bartec.co.uk

HAZARDOUS AREA ELECTRIC HEATERS

Intertec, Unit 5, Verwood Industrial Estate, Black Hill, Verwood, Dorset, BH31 6HA Tel: (01202) 822277 Fax: (01202) 821188 E-mail: sales@intertec-inst.co.uk

HAZARDOUS AREA ELECTRIC MOTORS

Premium Power Units Ltd, Block 10, Unit 4, Beardmore Way, Clydebank, Dunbartonshire, G81 4HT Tel: 0141-952 4344 Fax: 0141-952 6350 E-mail: sales@premiumpowerunits.co.uk

HAZARDOUS AREA ELECTRICAL EQUIPMENT

A C Electrical Wholesale Ltd, 2 Parkway Industrial Estate, Heneage Street, Birmingham, B7 4LY Tel: 0121-333 4959 Fax: 0121-333 4403 E-mail: birmingham@ac-electrical.co.uk

Aberdeen Control Ltd, Unit 1 Union Glen, Aberdeen, AB11 6ER Tel: (01224) 211133 Fax: (01224) 211177E-mail: gcraig@rsc.co.uk

Moflash Signalling, 18 Klaxon Tysley Industrial Estate, 751 Warwick Road, Tyseley, Birmingham, B11 2HA Tel: 0121-707 6681 Fax: 0121-707 8305 E-mail: uksales@moflash.co.uk

Ross Electrical, Cloverhill Road, Bridge of Don, Aberdeen, AB23 8FE Tel: (01224) 222700 Fax: (01224) 823008

RS Components (Watford), Unit 2A, Colonial Way, Watford, WD24 4WP Tel: (01923) 219696 Fax: (01923) 211177 E-mail: watford.tradecounter@rs-components.com

W F Electrical plc, 50-51 Burnt Mill, Elizabeth Way, Harlow, Essex, CM20 2HU Tel: (01279) 417171 Fax: (01279) 450902

HAZARDOUS AREA ENCLOSURES

Flameproof Electrical Enclosures Ltd, Units 1-1a St Martins Industrial Estate, Tat Bank Road, Oldbury, West Midlands, B69 4NP Tel: 0121-541 1315 Fax: 0121-552 0592 E-mail: flameproof@btinternet.com

John Hemy (Systems) Ltd, Dukesway, Teeside Industrial Estate, Stockton-On-Tees, Cleveland, TS17 9LT Tel: (01642) 769440 Fax: (01642) 763440 E-mail: info@johnhemysystems.co.uk

HAZARDOUS AREA FLASHING BEACONS

Delta Design, 1 Kings Park Industrial Estate, Primrose Hill, Kings Langley, Hertfordshire, WD4 8ST Tel: (01923) 269522 Fax: (01923) 260167 E-mail: sales@deltadesign.co.uk

HAZARDOUS AREA GLOBE VALVES

Taylor Shaw, Albert St, Lockwood, Huddersfield, HD1 3QG Tel: (01484) 532425 Fax: (01484) 512426 E-mail: sales@taylor-shaw.co.uk

HAZARDOUS AREA JUNCTION BOXES

▶ Hawke Cable Glands Ltd, Oxford St West, Ashton-under-Lyne, Lancashire, OL7 0NA Tel: 0161-308 3611 Fax: 0161-830 6648 E-mail: sales@ehawke.com

John Hemy (Systems) Ltd, Dukesway, Teeside Industrial Estate, Stockton-On-Tees, Cleveland, TS17 9LT Tel: (01642) 769440 Fax: (01642) 763440 E-mail: info@johnhemysystems.co.uk

Wellhead Electrical Supplies Ltd, Unit 4d Wellheads CR, Wellheads Industrial Estate, Aberdeen, AB21 7GA Tel: (01224) 723606 Fax: (01224) 723606 E-mail: sales@wellheads.co.uk

HAZARDOUS AREA LEAK DETECTORS

Ion Science Ltd, The Way, Fowlmere, Royston, Herts, SG8 7UJ Tel: (01763) 208503 Fax: (01763) 208814 E-mail: info@ionscience.com

Jola Ltd, Sprinfield Works, Lloyd St, Hopwood, Heywood, Lancs, OL10 2BP Tel: (01706) 366339 Fax: (01706) 366382 E-mail: bernie.mjola@tinyworld.co.uk

HAZARDOUS AREA OPTICAL ENCODERS

Hohner Automation Ltd, Unit 15 Whitegate Industrial Estate, Whitegate Road, Wrexham, Clwyd, LL13 8UG Tel: (01978) 363888 Fax: (01978) 364586 E-mail: uksales@hohner.com

Hubner Elektromaschinen A.G., PO Box 4022, Reading, RG8 8UD Tel: 0118-984 5351 Fax: 0118-984 3979 E-mail: sales@powertronic.co.uk

HAZARDOUS AREA SAFETY EQUIPMENT

Diktron Developments Ltd, Griptight House Unit 19, Spitfire Road, Castle Bromwich, Birmingham, B24 9PR Tel: 0121-382 4938 Fax: 0121-747 3009 E-mail: diktron@btconnect.com

Extronics Ltd, Meridian House, Roe Street, Congleton, Cheshire, CW12 1PG Tel: (01260) 297274 Fax: (01260) 297280 E-mail: sales@extronics.com

Fire Trade, Mayflower House, Bodmin Road, Coventry, CV2 5DB Tel: (024) 7661 6600 Fax: (024) 7662 1990

M F Fire & Safety Equipment, The Safety Centre, 198 Cator Lane, Beeston, Nottingham, NG9 4BE Tel: 0115-925 2261

McCabe Safety Air Services Ltd, 7 Centre Way, Claverings Industrial Estate, London, N9 0AP Tel: (020) 8884 0222 Fax: (020) 8884 0333

PH Industrial Ltd, 8 Wheldon Road, Widnes, Cheshire, WA8 8FW Tel: 0151-257 9696 Fax: 0151-257 8585

Playsafe, 7 Churchfields Rd, Folkingham, Sleaford, Lincs, NG34 0TR Tel: 01529 497513 Fax: 01529 497513

Safe Wear, Unit 13 Faraday Mill Business Park, Faraday Road, Plymouth, PL4 0ST Tel: (01752) 484045 Fax: (01752) 484045 E-mail: safewear@talk.to

HAZARDOUS AREA TELEPHONES

Arnesys Telecommunications Equipment, Queens Bridge Road, Nottingham, NG2 1NB Tel: 0115-985 2525 Fax: 0115-985 2526 E-mail: admin@arnesys.com

HAZARDOUS CHEMICAL CONTAINERS

Denios Ltd, Unit 1 - 3, Audley Avenue Enterprise Park, Newport, Shropshire, TF10 7DW Tel: (01952) 811991 Fax: (01952) 825687 E-mail: sales@denios.co.uk

HAZARDOUS FLUID FILTERS

Microelectronics, Europa House, Havant Street, Portsmouth, PO1 3PD Tel: (023) 9230 3303 Fax: (023) 9230 2506 E-mail: processuk@pall.com

HAZARDOUS LOAD TRANSPORTATION CONTRACTORS

Dews, Yew Green Road, Huddersfield, HD4 5EN Tel: (01484) 304060 Fax: (01484) 304477 E-mail: traffic@dews-haulage.co.uk

Geodis Overseas (U K) Ltd, PO Box 92, High Wycombe, Buckinghamshire, HP12 3TW Tel: (01494) 446541 Fax: (01494) 446329 E-mail: hwcustomerservies@geodisuk.com

Huktra Road Haulage Services, Westpoint Enterprise Park, Clarence Avenue, Trafford Park, Manchester, M17 1QS Tel: 0161-877 8488 Fax: 0161-877 8522 E-mail: info@huktra.com

▶ W. Walker Transport, Granitehill Road, Aberdeen, AB16 7AX Tel: (01224) 698844 Fax: (01224) 685967 E-mail: steve@williamwalkertransport.co.uk

HAZARDOUS PRODUCT PACKAGING

▶ Boxes And Packaging (Cambridge)Ltd, Edison Road, St. Ives Industrial Estate, St. Ives, Cambridgeshire, PE27 3LF Tel: (01480) 467633 Fax: (01480) 309100 E-mail: cambridge@boxesandpackaging.com

HEAD HUNTING EXECUTIVE RECRUITMENT

▶ Alexander James Executive Search Ltd, Winslow House, 16 Rumford Court, Rumford Place, Liverpool, L3 9DG Tel: 0151 236 1875 Fax: 0151 258 2018 E-mail: info@alexanderjamesltd.co.uk

▶ Excelsior Professional Search Ltd, 34 South Molton Street, London, W1K 5RG Tel: 020 7495 3088 Fax: 020 7495 3089 E-mail: general@excelsiorsearch.com

▶ Skills UK, 17 Britannia Road, Burbage, Hinckley, Leics, LE10 2HE Tel: 01455 617776 E-mail: ted@skills.uk.com

HEADLAMP TORCHES

Tiger Tools Ltd, PO Box 11, Wokingham, Berkshire, RG40 4RG Tel: 0118-973 4284 Fax: 0118-973 0597 E-mail: info@headtorches.com

HEADLINER MATERIALS

▶ David Nightingale, 20 Gastard Lane, Gastard, Corsham, Wiltshire, SN13 9QN Tel: (01249) 701271 Fax: (01249) 701271 E-mail: david.nightingale@coachtrimming.co.uk

HEALTH AND BEAUTY MAGAZINES

▶ Attractive Partners, The Old Coach House, Upper Grove Street, Leamington Spa, Warwickshire, CV32 5AN Tel: 0870 2424212 Fax: 0870 2407227 E-mail: liz@attractivepartners.co.uk

▶ The Beauty Studio, 33 Greystone Avenue, Worthing, West Sussex, BN13 1LR Tel: (01903) 262447 E-mail: wendy.greaves2@ntlworld.com

▶ Find A Reflexologist Ltd, 35 Coventry Road Flushing, Flushing, Falmouth, Cornwall, TR11 5TX Tel: (0870) 2432320 E-mail: info@findareflexologist.com

The Retreat, 61 Coronation Road, Crosby, Liverpool, L23 5RE Tel: 0151-931 1991 Fax: 0151-931 1991

▶ SPA MOMENTS UK (Pure Fiji Retailers), c/o The Perfect Balance, Dunston Hole Farm, Dunston Road, Chesterfield, Derbyshire, S41 9RL Tel: 01246 269819 E-mail: products@spamoments.co.uk

HEALTH AND SAFETY APPROVED FLOORING

▶ National Health & Safety Company Ltd, Suite 14 - 15 Axwel House, East Mains Industrial Estate, Broxburn, West Lothian, EH52 5AU Tel: 08700 611725 Fax: 0707 5023614 E-mail: admin@nhasco.com

HEALTH AND SAFETY AWARENESS TRAINING

▶ A T & F Solutions Ltd, The Great Barn, Dunstall, Earls Croome, Worcester, WR8 9DF Tel: (0870) 1657321 Fax: (0870) 1657421 E-mail: sales@atfsolutions.com

▶ Amtri Veritas Ltd, Hulley Road, Macclesfield, Cheshire, SK10 2LU Tel: (01625) 425421 Fax: (01625) 427038 E-mail: info@amtri.co.uk

▶ Barracuda Safety & Training Services, 19 Kingsmead, Nailsea, North Somerset, BS48 2XH Tel: (01275) 859285 Fax: (01275) 859285 E-mail: info@barracudatraining.co.uk

▶ Basegold Rail Ltd, 51 William Hunter Way, Brentwood, Essex, CM14 4WQ Tel: (01277) 228788 Fax: (01277) 228122 E-mail: info@basegoldrail.co.uk

▶ Commercial Training, Training & Development Centre, Longfield, Hitchin Road, Stevenage, Herts, SG1 4AE Tel: 01438 847321 Fax: 01438 314031 E-mail: commercial.training@hertscc.gov.uk

Construction Site Safety Training (CSST), 29a Market Square, Biggleswade, Beds, SG18 8AQ Tel: 07815 154157 E-mail: paul@csst-ltd.org

▶ Drug & Alcohol Training, 15 Eilean Rise, Ellon, Aberdeenshire, AB41 9NF Tel: (01358) 729547 Fax: (01358) 729547 E-mail: les@datacservices.co.uk

▶ First Aid Nursing Enterprises, Unit 6, Consett Business Park, Consett, County Durham, DH8 6BP Tel: (01207) 693828 E-mail: mike.green@fane.org.uk

▶ Fremantle Training & Transport LLP Ltd, 90 Barewell Road, Torquay, TQ1 4PA Tel: (01404) 43433 Fax: 01803 293555

▶ Global Training Ltd, 15 Ripley Crescent, Urmston, Manchester, M41 8PH Tel: (0800) 0730818 E-mail: infoman@globaltrainingltd.com

▶ Global Training Ltd, 6 Hillside Avenue, Queenborough, Kent, ME11 5LE Tel: (0800) 0730818 E-mail: info@globaltrainingltd.com

HACCP Solutions Ltd, 18 Knoll Drive, Woodloes Park, Warwick, CV34 5YQ Tel: 01926 408 375 Fax: 01926 409 635 E-mail: info@haccpsolutionsltd.com

▶ HartfordPharma, 4 Kingsley Close, Hartford, Northwich, Cheshire, CW8 1SD Tel: (01606) 79230 Fax: (07092) 150518 E-mail: admin@hartfordpharma.com

HSE Group, PO Box 9, Ripon, North Yorkshire, HG4 1WT Tel: (01765) 698107 E-mail: phild@pdenvironmental.co.uk

▶ Lansdale Health and Safety Services, 1 Pennine Way, Kettering, Northants, NN16 9AX Tel: 01536 500840 Fax: 01536 500840 E-mail: lansdalehs@ntlworld.com

▶ Leading Health & Safety Consultants Ltd, 26 Chaplin Walk, Great Cornard, Sudbury, Suffolk, CO10 0YT Tel: (01787) 377265 Fax: (01787) 883190 E-mail: info@leadinghealthandsafety.co.uk

Myton Systems Ltd, 3 West End, Lund, Driffield, North Humberside, YO25 9TN Tel: (01377) 217364 Fax: (01377) 217364 E-mail: sales@mytonsystems.co.uk

▶ Optimum Training Flintshire Ltd, 14 Bryn Awelon, Buckley, Clwyd, CH7 2QA Tel: (01244) 545745 Fax: (01244) 545745 E-mail: optimumflintshire@btinternet.com

▶ Slade Edwards & Co Insurance Brokers Ltd, 10 East Street, Horsham, West Sussex, RH12 1HL Tel: (01403) 250606 Fax: (01403) 210539 E-mail: anthony.birch@sladeedwards.co.uk

WotWot.com, Armstrong House, 4-6 First Avenue, Doncaster Finningley Airport, Hayfield Lane, Doncaster, South Yorkshire, DN9 3GA Tel: (0870) 1657305 Fax: (0870) 1657319 E-mail: enquiries@envico-online.com

HEALTH AND SAFETY CONSULTANCY

▶ A F Consulting, 19 Waylands, Cricklade, Swindon, SN6 6BT Tel: (01793) 751398 Fax: (01793) 751398 E-mail: info@afcons.co.uk

▶ Abbey Safety Solutions Ltd, 17 Honeypot Road, Brompton on Swale, Richmond, North Yorkshire, DL10 7HT Tel: (01748) 810813 E-mail: info@assluk.com

Aberdeen Quality Associates Ltd, 8 Rubislaw Den North, Aberdeen, AB15 4AN Tel: (01224) 315406 E-mail: bill@aqa.co.uk

Aims, Unit 15C Compton Place Business Centre, Surrey Avenue, Camberley, Surrey, GU15 3DX Tel: (01276) 691366 Fax: (01276) 61488

Astrocare Ltd, Bolton Enterprise Centre, Washington Street, Bolton, BL3 5EY Tel: (01204) 370861 Fax: (01204) 548742 E-mail: astrocare@aol.com

BHSF, 2 Darnley Road, Birmingham, B16 8TE Tel: 0121-454 3601 Fax: 0121-454 7725 E-mail: sales@bhsff.co.uk

BK Safety, 20 Pembroke Rise, Cusworth, Doncaster, South Yorkshire, DN5 8PP Tel: (01302) 785063 Fax: (01302) 785063 E-mail: info@bksafety.co.uk

British Safety Council Services, 70 Chancellors Road, London, W6 9RS Tel: (020) 8741 1231 Fax: (020) 8741 4555 E-mail: mail@britsafe.org

Complete Projects CDM Ltd, 25 Cadman Street, Mosborough, Sheffield, S20 5BU Tel: 0114-251 4106 Fax: 0114-251 4106 E-mail: info@completeprojectscdm.co.uk

Corporate Health Ltd, 30 Bradford Road, Slough, SL1 4PG Tel: (01753) 781600 Fax: (01753) 517889 E-mail: enquiries@corporatehealth.co.uk

Croner Consulting, Croner House, Wheatfield Way, Hinckley, Leicestershire, LE10 1YG Tel: (01455) 897000 Fax: (01455) 897400 E-mail: info@cronerconsulting.co.uk

▶ D C W Training Services, 63 Barnwell Street, Kettering, Northamptonshire, NN16 0JD Tel: (07947) 641457 Fax: (01536) 392137 E-mail: sedcwe17@ntlworld.com

D S C Associates, Chester Court Chester Park, Alfreton Road, Derby, DE21 4AB Tel: (01332) 204144 Fax: (01332) 200344 E-mail: info@derwentsafetycentre.co.uk

▶ Derek C Miles Fire & Safety Consultants, 502 Fulwood Road, Sheffield, S10 3QD Tel: 0114-230 2200 Fax: 0114-230 7700 E-mail: info@dcmfiresafe.co.uk

Dr Burns, Craigton Frant Road, Grantown-on-Spey, Morayshire, PH26 3LB Tel: (01479) 872297

E R M Risks, 8 Cavendish Square, London, W1G OER Tel: (020) 7465 7349 Fax: (020) 7465 7270 E-mail: tawg@ermuk.com

▶ East Services Ltd, 69 Scarletts Road, Colchester, CO1 2HA Tel: 01206 792103 Fax: 01206 792157 E-mail: a.stoddart@eastservices.net

Employee Management, Stone Cross Place, Stone Cross La North, Lowton, Warrington, WA3 2SH Tel: (01942) 727200 Fax: (01942) 727225 E-mail: sales@employeemanagement.co.uk

▶ Ensafe Consultants Ltd, 9 Ladys Lane, Northampton, NN1 3AH Tel: (01604) 636436 Fax: (01604) 745339

Health & Safety Technology & Management Ltd, The Old Bakehouse, Fullbridge, Maldon, Essex, CM9 4LE Tel: (01621) 854111 Fax: (01621) 851756 E-mail: hastam@hastam.co.uk

In House, The Old Church, 31 Rochester Road, Aylesford, Kent, ME20 7PR Tel: (0845) 8732390 Fax: (0800) 6190212 E-mail: info@inhouse-hygiene.co.uk

Institution Of Occupational Safety & Health, The Grange, Highfield Drive, Wigston, Leicestershire, LE18 1NN Tel: 0116-257 3100 Fax: 0116-257 3101

Invicta Analytical Services, Alexandra House, 5 Blyth Road, Bromley, BR1 3RS Tel: (020) 8290 5629 Fax: (020) 8290 4443 E-mail: admin@invictaas.co.uk

▶ Liability Risk Services Ltd, 33 Burndale Drive, Sunnybank, Bury, Lancs, BL9 8EN Tel: 0161 2809269 E-mail: info@liability-risk.com

▶ Lloyd Management Systems Ltd, 73 Arethusa Road, Rochester, Kent, ME1 2UR Tel: (01634) 846519 Fax: 01634 846519 E-mail: lloydmanagementsystems@blueyonder.co.uk

Macgregor Associates Consulting, Sherwood House, 7 Gregory, Nottingham, NG7 6LB Tel: 0115-962 0222 Fax: 0115-962 2144 E-mail: info@macgregorassociates.co.uk

Brian Milligan Associates, 57 Wensley Road, Salford, M7 3GJ Tel: 0845 5314073 Fax: 0161-792 2269 E-mail: brian@brian-milligan.co.uk

Moonlight Environmental Ltd, 48 Rommany Road, London, SE27 9PX Tel: (020) 8766 7587 Fax: (020) 8766 7587 E-mail: office@me-ltd.biz

National Brittania Ltd, Caerphilly Business Park, Caerphilly Business Park, Caerphilly, Mid Glamorgan, CF83 3GG Tel: (029) 2085 2852 Fax: (029) 2086 7738 E-mail: enquiries@natbrit.com

▶ National Brittania Group, 17 Brenkley Way, Blezard Business Park, Seaton Burn, Newcastle upon Tyne, NE13 6DS Tel: 0191-236 6061 Fax: 0191-236 6061

▶ National Health & Safety Company Ltd, Suite 14 - 15 Axwel House, East Mains Industrial Estate, Broxburn, West Lothian, EH52 5AU Tel: 08700 611725 Fax: 0707 5023614 E-mail: admin@nhasco.com

O H S Ltd, 11-17 Campus Road, Listerhills Science Park, Bradford, West Yorkshire, BD7 1HR Tel: (01274) 735848 Fax: (01274) 392280 E-mail: info@ohs.co.uk

▶ One Stop Safety Services Ltd, Po Box 124, Bolton, BL3 1LX Tel: 01204 597454 Fax: 01204 604364 E-mail: sales@onestopsafetyservices.co.uk

▶ OneSafety Ltd, 33 Wadham Road, Woodthorpe, Nottingham, NG5 4JB Tel: 0115-920 8007 E-mail: info@onesafety.co.uk

P A R Harris, Cloneen, Hindon Lane, Tisbury, Salisbury, SP3 6PU Tel: (01747) 871991 Fax: (01747) 871991

Parsons Brinckerhoff, Quadrant Court, 45 Calthorpe Road, Edgbaston, Birmingham, B15 1TH Tel: 0121-452 7400 Fax: 0121-452 1799

Parsons Brinckerhoff, Crown House, River Way, Harlow, Essex, CM20 2DL Tel: (01279) 450900 Fax: (01279) 450898

▶ Parsons Brinckerhoff, Calyx House, South Road, Taunton, Somerset, TA1 3DU Tel: (01823) 424400 Fax: (01823) 424401 E-mail: slocomben@pbworld.com

Paul Temple Associates Ltd, Laurel Cottage, 15a Hillside Road, Haslemere, Surrey, GU27 3RL Tel: (01428) 656150 Fax: (01428) 642676 E-mail: paul@paultempleassociates.com

Doug Payne Kinetics Ltd, 35 Billesley Lane, Moseley, Birmingham, B13 9QT Tel: 0121-449 1513 Fax: 0121-449 2613

▶ Positive Health & Safety Ltd, 218 Gazette Buildings, 168 Corporation Street, Birmingham, B4 6TF Tel: 0121-212 2020 E-mail: info@positivehands.co.uk

Quality Assurance Advisors Ltd, 68 Ferryhill Road, Aberdeen, AB11 6RR Tel: (01224) 588885 Fax: (01224) 588885 E-mail: qaa@dial.pipex.com

R G Wilbrey Consultants Ltd, Aspen House, Great Brickkiln Street, Wolverhampton, WV3 0PT Tel: (01902) 420920 Fax: (01902) 426981 E-mail: wilbrey@compuserve.com

R L S Associates, 68 Crabtree Lane, Bromsgrove, Worcestershire, B61 8NZ Tel: (01527) 875144 Fax: (01527) 575912

R P S Engineering & Safety, Dalton House, 105 Dalton Avenue, Birchwood, Warrington, WA3 6YF Tel: (01925) 831000 Fax: (01925) 831231 E-mail: rpswa@rpsgroup.com

Royal Society For The Prevention Of Accidents Ltd, 353 Bristol Road, Edgbaston, Birmingham, B5 7ST Tel: 0121-248 2000 Fax: 0121-248 2001 E-mail: help@rospa.com

▶ Safety Simply, 23 Cock Close Road, Yaxley, Peterborough, PE7 3HJ Tel: (0845) 2600710 Fax: (0845) 2600711 E-mail: info@safetysimplifield.co.uk

Schwops Ltd, 34 Ashton Road, Luton, LU1 3QE Tel: (01582) 412622 Fax: (01582) 412095 E-mail: mo@schwops.co.uk

▶ Slade Edwards & Co Insurance Brokers Ltd, 10 East Street, Horsham, West Sussex, RH12 1HL Tel: (01403) 250606 Fax: (01403) 210539 E-mail: anthony.birch@sladeedwards.co.uk

Spanset Ltd, Telford Way, Middlewich Bus Industrial, Park, Middlewich, Cheshire, CW10 0HX Tel: (01606) 737494 Fax: (01606) 737502 E-mail: sales@spanset.com

Sypol Ltd, Elsinore House, Buckingham Street, Aylesbury, Buckinghamshire, HP20 2NQ Tel: (01296) 415715 Fax: (01296) 397106 E-mail: helpme@sypol.com

Systems Audits Inspections Ltd, 51 Delph New Road, Delph, Oldham, OL3 5BY Tel: (01457) 870946 Fax: (01457) 870946 E-mail: philiptaylor@sai-online.co.uk

T P S Consultants, Centre Tower, Whitgift Centre, Croydon, CR9 0AU Tel: (020) 8256 4000 Fax: (020) 8256 4116 E-mail: sales@tpsconsult.ltd.uk

▶ TCH Safety, Jasmine Cottage, Middle Street, East Harptree, Bristol, BS40 6AZ Tel: 01761 221874 E-mail: info@tchsafety.co.uk

▶ TLC Safety, 198 Bellmead Lane, Newport, Isle of Wight, PO30 2JN Tel: (07841) 236269 E-mail: forwardto@tlcsafety.co.uk

Vectra Group Ltd, Europa House, 310 Europa Boulevard, Westbrook, Warrington, WA5 7YQ Tel: (01925) 444648 Fax: (01925) 444701 E-mail: info@vectragroup.co.uk

Virkonnen Ltd, 17a High Street, Reigate, Surrey, RH2 9AA Tel: (01737) 223233 Fax: (01737) 243061 E-mail: sales@virkonnen.co.uk

W A Fairhurst & Partners, 1 Arngrove Court, Newcastle upon Tyne, NE4 6DB Tel: 0191-221 0505 Fax: 0191-221 0949 E-mail: newcastle@fairhurst.co.uk

HEALTH AND SAFETY EQUIPMENT

▶ Buck & Hickman Ltd, C2 Waterside Road, Hamilton, Leicester, LE5 1TL Tel: 0116-299 2990 Fax: 0116-299 3301 E-mail: leicester@buckhickmaninone.com

General Nutrition Centre, 7 Chequers Square, Uxbridge, Middlesex, UB8 1LN Tel: (01895) 254538

Hayes UK Ltd, 7 Eagle Estate, Brookers Road, Billingshurst, West Sussex, RH14 9RZ Tel: (0870) 0711700 Fax: (0870) 0711701 E-mail: sales@hayes-uk.com

Morsafe Supplies, 192 Monkmoor Road, Shrewsbury, SY2 5BH Tel: (01743) 356319 Fax: (01743) 350875

Nikken UK Ltd, 1 Deltic Avenue, Rooksley, Milton Keynes, MK13 8LD Tel: (01908) 202400 Fax: (0870) 4445445 E-mail: info@nikkenuk.com

▶ One Stop Safety Services Ltd, Po Box 124, Bolton, BL3 1LX Tel: 01204 597454 Fax: 01204 604364 E-mail: sales@onestopsafetyservices.co.uk

Pascal Scientific Ltd, 10 Chesterfield Way, Hayes, Middlesex, UB3 3NW Tel: (020) 8848 1849 Fax: (020) 8848 8595 E-mail: admin@pascalscientific.co.uk

Specialist Equipment, 18 Derwent Road, Honley, Holmfirth, HD9 6HS Tel: (01484) 661962 Fax: (01484) 329468 E-mail: sales@specialistequipment.com

Therapy Equipment Ltd, 1 Cranborne Industrial Estate, Cranborne Road, Potters Bar, Hertfordshire, EN6 3JN Tel: (01707) 652270 Fax: (01707) 652622 E-mail: sales@therapyequipment.co.uk

HEALTH AND SAFETY MANAGEMENT TRAINING

Aaa Training Co., East Anglian Training Centre, 9 Churchfield Road, Sudbury, Suffolk, CO10 2YA Tel: (0800) 5878063 Fax: (01787) 313113 E-mail: sales@aaa-training.com

▶ Active Safety Associates, 39 Tindale Close, Sanderstead, South Croydon, Surrey, CR2 0RT Tel: 020 8651 6601 Fax: 020 8651 6601 E-mail: rmeech@activesafetyassociates.co.uk

▶ Adamson Laboratory Services, 49 Lampits Hill, Corringham, Stanford-le-Hope, Essex, SS17 9AA Tel: (01375) 673279 Fax: (01375) 678059 E-mail: sales@alsltd.com

AF Associates, Chantry House, Askrigg, Leyburn, North Yorkshire, DL8 3BW Tel: 01592 882550 Fax: 0871 6613347 E-mail: office@foodsafety-training.co.uk

▶ Cavendish Management Training, Kings Court, 17 School Road, Hall Green, Birmingham, B28 8JG Tel: (0870) 3219451 Fax: 0121-733 2902 E-mail: sales@mgt-services.com

▶ Employee Development Forum, Unit 11a Lyons Farm Estate, Lyons Road, Slinfold, Horsham, West Sussex, RH13 0QP Tel: (01403) 791292 Fax: (01403) 791293 E-mail: sales@theedf.com

▶ Imsys Ltd, 15 Dawlish Close, Blackburn, BB2 4NS Tel: (01254) 692077 Fax: (01254) 671539 E-mail: abw@imsys.biz

▶ Lansdale Health and Safety Services, 1 Pennine Way, Kettering, Northants, NN16 9AX Tel: 01536 500840 Fax: 01536 500840 E-mail: lansdalehs@ntlworld.com

▶ Learning 4 Business, Fromehall Mill, Lodgemore Lane, Stroud, Gloucestershire, GL5 3EH Tel: (01453) 756000 Fax: (01453) 751148

Mabbett & Associates Ltd, Mabbett House, 11 Sandyford Place, Glasgow, G3 7NB Tel: 0141-227 2300 Fax: 0141 227 2301 E-mail: bradley@mabbett.com

▶ Safety Train, 25 Raines Avenue, Worksop, Nottinghamshire, S81 7PA Tel: (01909) 532589 Fax: (01909) 532589 E-mail: thesafetyman@tiscali.co.uk

▶ Safety Training Unit Ltd, 1062 Cornforth Drive, Sittingbourne Research Centre, Sittingbourne, Kent, ME9 8HL Tel: (01795) 438841 Fax: (0870) 131920 E-mail: enquiries@stunit.co.uk

▶ Christopher Swann, 408-410 Corn Exchange Building, Fenwick Street, Liverpool, L2 7QS Tel: (0845) 1259010 Fax: (0845) 1259014 E-mail: sales@christopherswann.com

WotWot.com, Armstrong House, 4-6 First Avenue, Doncaster Finningley Airport, Hayfield Lane, Doncaster, South Yorkshire, DN9 3GA Tel: (0870) 1657305 Fax: (0870) 1657319 E-mail: enquiries@envico-online.com

HEALTH AND SAFETY POLICY DOCUMENT CONSULTANCY

▶ AEGIS Risk and Safety Solutions Ltd, Unit, 15 Tenlands, Middleton Cheney, Banbury, Oxfordshire, OX17 2NL Tel: 01295 713532 E-mail: info@aegisrss.co.uk

▶ Chandoz Ltd, Krattigen, Toynton St. Peter, Spilsby, Lincolnshire, PE23 5AT Tel: (01754) 830279 Fax: (01754) 830279 E-mail: ray@pidgley7229.fslife.co.uk

HEALTH AND SAFETY TRAINING

▶ A F Consulting, 19 Waylands, Cricklade, Swindon, SN6 6BT Tel: (01793) 751398 Fax: (01793) 751398 E-mail: info@afcons.co.uk
▶ Aberdeen Skills & Enterprise Training Ltd, Units 3-9 Minto Operations Training Centre, Minto Avenue, Altens Industrial Estate, Aberdeen, AB12 3JZ Tel: (01224) 859624 Fax: (01224) 859640 E-mail: aset-enquiry@abcol.ac.uk
Ace Safety Services, The Court, Holywell Business Park, Kineton Road Industrial Estate, Southam, Warwickshire, CV47 0FS Tel: (01926) 813356 Fax: (01926) 817311
▶ E-mail: enquiries@theacegroup.co.uk
▶ Achor Limited, 82 Northgate, Beccles, Suffolk, NR34 9AY Tel: (01502) 716870 Fax: (01502) 716587 E-mail: info@achor.co.uk
Amega Training (Wigan), Hewitt House, Hewitt Business Park, Winstanley Road, Orrell, WIGAN, LANCASHIRE, WN5 7XA Tel: 01695 682057 Fax: 01695 682058 E-mail: info@amegatraining.co.uk
Athena Training U K, Suite 3, 13 Sheppey Gardens, Dagenham, Essex, RM9 4LD Tel: (07973) 869163 Fax: (020) 8517 0007 E-mail: enquiries@athenatraininguk.net
▶ Bead Training, Development House, 24 Heaton Close, Poulton-Le-Fylde, Lancashire, FY6 7TY Tel: 01253 890790 Fax: 01253 890790 E-mail: enquiries@beadtraining.com
Blackpool & The Fylde College Fleetwood Office Shore Survival Cen, Fleetwood Road, Nautical Campus, Fleetwood, Lancashire, FY7 8JZ Tel: (01253) 779123 Fax: (01253) 773014 E-mail: jbo@blackpool.ac.uk
▶ Complete Health & Safety, 15-19 Norway Street, Portslade, Brighton, BN41 1GN Tel: (01273) 833919 Fax: (01273) 414199 E-mail: info@complete-hs.co.uk
▶ Crossroad Health & Safety Systems, Barn 6 Watsome Farm Development Wotton Road, Kingswood, Wotton-under-Edge, Gloucestershire, GL12 8SP Tel: (01453) 845108 Fax: (08700) 941122 E-mail: info@safetycrossroad.com
▶ Denby Training, Sadler Road, Lincoln, LN6 3JR Tel: 01522 503902 Fax: 01522 686372 E-mail: terry.rose@denbytransport.co.uk
▶ Derek C Miles Fire & Safety Consultants, 502 Fulwood Road, Sheffield, S10 3QD Tel: 0114-230 2200 Fax: 0114-230 7700 E-mail: info@dcmfiresafe.co.uk
▶ First Aid Focus, Atrium Business Centrenorth Caldeen Road, Coatbridge, Lanarkshire, ML5 4EF Tel: (01236) 702011 Fax: (01236) 702021
First For Aid Training, 30 Cennon Group, Ingleby Barwick, Stockton-On-Tees, Cleveland, TS17 5DB Tel: (01642) 769014 E-mail: firstforaid@talk21.com
Generation Software, 59 Victoria Road, Tilehurst, Reading, RG31 5AB Tel: 0118-948 2468 Fax: 0118-948 2470 E-mail: office@generationsoftware.com
Huddersfield & District Textile Training Co. Ltd, Textile House, Red Doles Lane, Huddersfield, HD2 1YF Tel: (01484) 346500 Fax: (01484) 346501 E-mail: hdtt@textile-training.com
I T S (UK) Ltd, PO Box 335, Cardiff, CF23 7YQ Tel: (029) 2073 6080 Fax: (029) 2073 6080
▶ E-mail: training@itsukltd.com
▶ IDP Safety Services Ltd, 289 Kings Drive, Eastbourne, East Sussex, BN21 2YA Tel: (01323) 507017 Fax: (01323) 507017 E-mail: info@idpsafety.co.uk
Instant Training Ltd, Audley Avenue Enterprise Park, Newport, Shropshire, TF10 7DW Tel: (01952) 585555 Fax: (01952) 815758 E-mail: sales@instant-training.com
▶ L R B Consulting Ltd, 2 Fairmeadows Way, Loughborough, Leicestershire, LE11 2QT Tel: (01509) 550023 Fax: (01509) 550023 E-mail: enquiries@lrbconsulting.co.uk
▶ Lagta Group Training Ltd, 3 Dryden Place, Loanhead, Midlothian, EH20 9HP Tel: 0131-440 2922 Fax: 0131-440 3933 E-mail: sales@lagta.co.uk
▶ M Spiller, 43 Linmere Walk, Houghton Regis, Dunstable, Bedfordshire, LU5 5PS Tel: (01582) 866363 Fax: 01582 656046 E-mail: mike@michaelspiller.co.uk
▶ McPhedran Co. UK, 23 Carriage Drive, Kettering, Northamptonshire, NN16 9EN Tel: (07778) 211855
MBG Management Consultants Ltd, 50 Greenhill Road, Moseley, Birmingham, B13 9SS Tel: 0121-449 5434 Fax: 0121-449 5844 E-mail: mbgmb@globalnet.co.uk
Mid & North Wales Training Group Ltd, Myrick House, Hen-Domen, Montgomery, Powys, SY15 6EZ Tel: (01686) 668670 Fax: (01686) 668771 E-mail: myrick@btinternet.com
▶ Onsite Training Services, 3 Burnside Industrial Centre Wellheads Road, Farburn Industrial Estate, Dyce, Aberdeen, AB21 7HG Tel: (01224) 729500 Fax: (01224) 729300
▶ Risktec Solutions, Riverside House, Riverside Drive, Aberdeen, AB11 7LH Tel: (01224) 224454 Fax: (01224) 224455 E-mail: mark.taylor@risktec.co.uk
▶ Safety Training Unit Ltd, 1062 Cornforth Drive, Sittingbourne Research Centre, Sittingbourne, Kent, ME9 8HL Tel: (01795) 438841 Fax: (0870) 131920 E-mail: enquiries@stunit.co.uk
▶ Scottish Training Consultants, 28 Oldmill Crescent, Belmedie, Aberdeen, AB23 8WA Tel: (01358) 742470 Fax: (01358) 742775
Technique Training, Midland Court, Barlborough Links, Chesterfield, Derbyshire, S43 4UL Tel: (01246) 813703 Fax: (01246) 571090 E-mail: mark@techniquetraining.co.uk
Training World, 22 Larchwood Close, Romford, RM5 3QX Tel: (01708) 746948 Fax: (01708) 739041 E-mail: info@trainingworld.co.uk
▶ What No Safety Services Ltd, Thornaby, Cecil Avenue, Salisbury, SP2 8EE Tel: 01722 326390 Fax: 01722 326390 E-mail: abarrett@whatnosafety.co.uk

HEALTH CARE CONSULTANTS

Aloevera Co UK, PO Box 15, Towcester, Northamptonshire, NN12 8DJ Tel: (01327) 830855 Fax: (01327) 831000
Amazon Herbal Products UK, PO Box 12958, Birmingham, B11 9BG Tel: (0870) 8113611 E-mail: webmaster@amazonherbalproducts.co.uk
Applejacks, Unit 28 The Mall, The Stratford Centre, London, E15 1XD Tel: (020) 8519 5809 Fax: (020) 8519 1099 E-mail: robert@applejacks.co.uk
I B A Associates, Dorford House, Perks Lane, Prestwood, Great Missenden, Buckinghamshire, HP16 0JD Tel: (01494) 865393 Fax: (01494) 865395 E-mail: miranda@ibaassociates.co.uk
B Healthy Solutions Ltd, Brookside, Pinmill Road, Chelmondiston, Ipswich, IP9 1JF Tel: (01473) 780155 Fax: (01473) 780155
Body Fitnesse, Unit 15B National Trading Estate, Hazel Grove, Stockport, Cheshire, SK7 5AA Tel: 0161-456 8556
Bullen Healthcare Group, 479a Alfreton Road, Nottingham, NG7 5NH Tel: 0115-970 4072 Fax: 0115-970 8993 E-mail: info@bullens.com
Care UK, Unit 15C, Ground Floor, Imex Business Park, Shobnall Road, Burton-On-Trent, Staffordshire, DE14 2AU Tel: (01283) 568254 Fax: (01283) 512010
▶ Clinical Hypnotherapy, St Mark's Clinic, 47 St Mark's Road, Teddington, Middlesex, TW11 9DE Tel: 01483 825649 E-mail: info@hypno-clinic.com
▶ CliniServ, Harley Street, London, UK, W1G 9PF Tel: 0845 6100670 Fax: 0845 6100671 E-mail: customerservice@cliniserv.com
Community Training Services NHS Trust, Oaklands Road, Salford, M7 3QQ Tel: 0161-792 9545 Fax: 0161-792 9708
▶ Continental Medical, Ashby House, 64 High Street, Walton-on-Thames, Surrey, KT12 1BW Tel: (01932) 231733
Drop In The Ocean, 17 City Arcade, Coventry, CV1 3HX Tel: (024) 7622 5273 Fax: (024) 7622 5273
▶ Feel Good Clinic, 6 Shaw Road, London, SE22 8DP Tel: 0208 693 1503 E-mail: info@feelgoodclinic.co.uk
Feltham Associates Ltd, Carlton House, Carlton Road, Kibworth Harcourt, Leicester, LE8 0PE Tel: 0116-279 3232 Fax: 0116-279 2473 E-mail: fal@btinternet.com
Gareth James Pharmacy Ltd, 59 Herbert Street, Pontardawe, Swansea, SA8 4ED Tel: (01792) 863217 Fax: (01792) 863217
Haelan Centre, 41 The Broadway, London, N8 8DT Tel: (020) 8340 4258 Fax: (020) 8292 2232
Health Intelligence Ltd, Bradwall Road, Sandbach, Cheshire, CW11 1GE Tel: (01270) 765124 Fax: (01270) 765078 E-mail: info@health-intelligence.com
Health Matters, 8 Widmore Road, Bromley, BR1 1RY Tel: (020) 8460 3894 Fax: (020) 8313 3443
Health Of The Nation, P O Box 4833, Reading, RG10 8XY Tel: 0118-940 1794 Fax: 0118 9404143
Health Options Ltd, 27-28 The Water Front, Soverign Harbour, Eastbourne, East Sussex, BN23 5UZ Tel: (01323) 470090 Fax: (01323) 470851
▶ Health & Well-Being, 4 Crathorne Avenue, Wolverhampton, WV10 6BT Tel: (01902) 786785 E-mail: battlingtheweight@btinternet.com
Healthquest Ltd, Unit 7 Waverley Industrial Business Park, Hailsham Drive, Harrow, Middlesex, HA1 4TR Tel: (020) 8424 8844
Healthy Life, 4 Little Brittox, Devizes, Wiltshire, SN10 1AR Tel: (01380) 725558 Fax: (01380) 727772
Herbalife, 5b Third Avenue, Hove, East Sussex, BN3 2PB Tel: (01273) 723884 Fax: (01273) 723884
Holland & Barrett Ltd, 55 St Johns Wood High Street, London, NW8 7NL Tel: (020) 7586 5494
Institute of Public Care, 8 Palace Yard Mews, Bath, BA1 2NH Tel: (01225) 484088 Fax: (01225) 330313 E-mail: ipc@brookes.ac.uk
International Hospitals Group Ltd, Manor House, Park Road, Stoke Poges, Slough, SL2 4PG Tel: (01753) 784777 Fax: (01753) 784784 E-mail: info@ihg.co.uk
▶ Lifestyle Assessment Ltd, 39 Watery Lane, Keresley, Coventry, CV6 2GF Tel: (0800) 2985521 Fax: 02476 722053
Nicholson House Coffee Shop, 14 St Georges Terrace, Millom, Cumbria, LA18 4DB Tel: (01229) 774534
Nicola & Mark Chadbourne, 69 Crowberry Drive, Harrogate, North Yorkshire, HG3 2UF Tel: (01423) 564237
Nuffield Hospitals Ltd, Nuffield House, 1-4 The Crescent, Surbiton, Surrey, KT6 4BN Tel: (020) 8390 1200 Fax: (020) 8399 6726
Omex Medical Ltd, Unit T6, Rudford Industrial Estate, Ford Road, Ford, Arundel, West Sussex, BN18 0BF Tel: (01903) 783744 Fax: (01903) 734368
▶ Physio In The City, Seymour Leisure Centre, Seymour Place, London, W1H 5TJ Tel: (020) 7724 8008 Fax: (020) 7724 7150 E-mail: info@physiointhecity.co.uk
▶ Plabeasy, PO Box 4160, Cardiff, CF14 3ZY Tel: (0777) 9850236 Fax: E-mail: info@plabeasy.com
Potters Bar Health Foods, 21 The Broadway, Darkes Lane, Potters Bar, Hertfordshire, EN6 2HX Tel: (01707) 652255 Fax: (01707) 652255
▶ SlimSeekers, 11 Huntleys Park, Tunbridge Wells, Kent, TN4 9TD Tel: (01892) 535300 Fax: (01892) 535311 E-mail: suehay@slimseekers.co.uk
▶ Therapy Resources, 16 Canal Warf, Chesterfield, Derbyshire, S41 7RY Tel: 01246 551421

HEALTH CARE PREPARATIONS/ PRODUCTS

▶ Aloe Vera, Haydon House, Church Street, Chipping Campden, Gloucestershire, GL55 6JG Tel: (01386) 841521
Amazon Herbal Products UK, PO Box 12958, Birmingham, B11 9BG Tel: (0870) 8113611 E-mail: webmaster@amazonherbalproducts.co.uk
▶ Bio Vite, Unit 9A Albany Park, Cabot Lane, Poole, Dorset, BH17 7BX Tel: (01202) 606660 Fax: (01202) 694321
Dansac Ltd, Victory House, Vision Park, Histon, Cambridge, CB4 9ZR Tel: (01223) 235100 Fax: (01223) 235145 E-mail: dansac.ltd@dansac.com
▶ Elite Body Supplements, Sharma Park Industrial Estate, Grant Avenue, Leeds, LS7 1QB Tel: 0113-244 4959 Fax: 0113-244 4962
▶ The Feel Good Factory, 3 Boroughgate, Appleby-in-Westmorland, Cumbria, CA16 6XF Tel: (01768) 354129 Fax: (01768) 354129
▶ Forever Living Products, 35 St. James Road, Hastings, East Sussex, TN34 3LH Tel: (01424) 444851
▶ Forever Living Products, 19 Boyn Hill Avenue, Maidenhead, Berkshire, SL6 4EY Tel: (01628) 776708
Forever Living Products UK Ltd, Longbridge Manor, Longbridge, Warwick, CV34 6RB Tel: (01926) 626600 Fax: (01926) 626636
▶ E-mail: customerservices@flpuk.net
▶ Good Health, Shop F Church Road, Port Erin, Isle of Man, IM9 6AH Tel: (01624) 832865 E-mail: thegoodhealthstore@manx.net
▶ Julian Graves Ltd, 21 Toll Gavel, Beverley, North Humberside, HU17 9AR Tel: (01482) 880866 Fax: (01482) 880866
▶ Julien Graves, Isaac Newton Centre, Grantham, Lincolnshire, NG31 6EE Tel: (01476) 594529 Fax: (01476) 594529
▶ Health Haven, 173 Findon Road, Worthing, West Sussex, BN14 0BQ Tel: (01903) 877717 E-mail: info@health-haven.com
▶ Healthspan Health Foods, 47 King Street, St. Helier, Jersey, JE2 4WE Tel: (01534) 758391 E-mail: sales@healthspan.com
▶ Healthy Living, 31 Newland Street, Witham, Essex, CM8 2AF Tel: (01376) 520374 Fax: (01376) 520374
▶ Healthy Living Shop, 282-284 St. Pauls Road, London, N1 2LH Tel: (020) 7704 8123 Fax: (020) 7704 6050
▶ Healthy Spirit, 37 Barlow Moor Road, Manchester, M20 6TW Tel: 0161-434 6784 Fax: 0161-434 6784
▶ Heathy Options, 83 Argyll Street, Dunoon, Argyll, PA23 7DH Tel: (01369) 703892
Herbalife UK Ltd, Units 6-7 Perth Trading Estate, Perth Avenue, Slough, SL1 4XX Tel: (01895) 819000 Fax: (01753) 898627
▶ I Cy Group, Hurst House, Crown Heights, Guildford, Surrey, GU1 3TX Tel: (01483) 539090
▶ Juice Master, 22 Moseley Gate, Birmingham, B13 8JJ Tel: (0845) 1302829 Fax: 0121-449 5392 E-mail: sales@thejuicemaster.com
▶ Julian Graves Ltd, 57-58 High Street, Taunton, Somerset, TA1 3PT Tel: (01823) 288197 Fax: (01384) 297707
▶ Kerry D Ltd, 12 North Street, Pinxton, Nottingham, NG16 6LP Tel: (07971) 439487
Marigold Health Foods Ltd, 102 Camley Street, London, NW1 0PF Tel: (020) 7388 4515 Fax: (020) 7388 4516 E-mail: info@marigoldhealth.co.uk
▶ Migra-Cap (UK) Ltd, Venture Wales, Merthyr Industrial Park, Pentrebach, Merthyr Tydfil, Mid Glamorgan, CF48 4DR Tel: (01443) 693464 Fax: (01443) 693511 E-mail: info@migracap.com
▶ Natrahealth Health Foods, Unit 3-4 Jupiter Business Park, Airfield Industrial Estate, Hixon, Stafford, ST18 0PA Tel: (01889) 271333 Fax: (01889) 271355
▶ Nature Nook, 14 Church Street, Ballymoney, County Antrim, BT53 6DL Tel: (028) 2766 4178 Fax: (028) 2766 4178
▶ New Life Health, Rose Cottage, Ting Tang, Carharrack, Redruth, Cornwall, TR16 5SF Tel: (01209) 822207 Fax: (01209) 822207 E-mail: info@newlifehealth.co.uk
Nikken UK Ltd, 1 Deltic Avenue, Rooksley, Milton Keynes, MK13 8LD Tel: (01908) 202400 Fax: (0870) 4445445 E-mail: info@nikkenuk.com
Novartis Consumer Health UK Ltd, Novartis Horsham Research Centre, Wimblehurst Road, Horsham, West Sussex, RH12 5AB Tel: (01403) 210211 Fax: (01403) 323919
▶ Open Sesame, 32 Botanic Avenue, Belfast, BT7 1JQ Tel: (028) 9032 4343
Optima Health Ltd, 47-48 St. Mary Street, Cardiff, CF10 1AD Tel: (029) 2038 8422 Fax: (029) 2023 3010 E-mail: admin@optimah.com
▶ Personal Comfort Ltd, 9 Woodside, Wimbledon, Woodside, London, SW19 7AR Tel: (020) 8404 1319
▶ R U 21, 1b Mallard Court, Mallard Way, Crewe, CW1 6ZQ Tel: (01270) 254445 E-mail: info@ru21sales.co.uk
▶ Ralphs Health Foods, 73 St. James Street, Newport, Isle of Wight, PO30 1LQ Tel: (01983) 522353 Fax: (01983) 522353
Robinson Healthcare Ltd, Lawn Road, Carlton In Lindrick, Carlton-in-Lindrick, Worksop, Nottinghamshire, S81 9LB Tel: (01909) 735001 Fax: (01909) 731103 E-mail: enquiry@robinsoncare.com
▶ Salute Health Foods, 2 Cheam Common Road, Worcester Park, Surrey, KT4 8RW Tel: (020) 8337 5959 Fax: (020) 8337 5959
▶ Therapy Resources, 16 Canal Warf, Chesterfield, Derbyshire, S41 7RY Tel: 01246 551421
Wheelton Health Care, 11 Dalton Court, Commercial Road, Darwen, Lancashire, BB3 0DG Tel: (01254) 777977 Fax: (01254) 777978 E-mail: info@wheeltonhealthcare.net
Wholistic Research Co., Five House Farm, Sandon Road, Therfield, Royston, Hertfordshire, SG8 9RE Tel: (0845) 4303100 Fax: (01763) 287467 E-mail: info@wholisticresearch.com
▶ Wright Healthy, Ashburner Street, Bolton, BL1 1TQ Tel: (01204) 386700 E-mail: wrighthealthy@aol.com
▶ Wyedean Wholefoods, 28 High Street, Chepstow, Gwent, NP16 5LJ Tel: (01291) 630002 Fax: (01291) 630002

HEALTH CARE/SCREENING SERVICES

Bay Tree, 15 Pennys Walk, Ferndown, Dorset, BH22 9TH Tel: (01202) 896096 Fax: (01202) 895296
▶ Chemist On Call Ltd, 11 Queensway, Hemel Hempstead, Hertfordshire, HP1 1LS Tel: (0871) 2240740 Fax: (020) 8287 8007 E-mail: sales@chemist-on-call.com
▶ Clinical Hypnotherapy, St Mark's Clinic, 47 St Mark's Road, Teddington, Middlesex, TW11 9DE Tel: 01483 825649 E-mail: info@hypno-clinic.com
▶ CliniServ, Harley Street, London, UK, W1G 9PF Tel: 0845 6100670 Fax: 0845 6100671 E-mail: customerservice@cliniserv.com
Health Screening UK Ltd, 1 Church Square, Taunton, Somerset, TA1 1SA Tel: (01823) 325022 Fax: (01823) 325024 E-mail: info@screen4health.com
Hearing & Healthcare, 376 Buxton Road, Macclesfield, Cheshire, SK11 7ES Tel: (01625) 433108 Fax: (01625) 502323 E-mail: hearinghc@aol.com
▶ Lifestyle Assessment Ltd, 39 Watery Lane, Keresley, Coventry, CV6 2GF Tel: (0800) 2985521 Fax: 02476 722053
▶ N. H. S. Edinburgh, Nine Mile Burn, Penicuik, Midlothian, EH26 9LT Tel: (01968) 679333 Fax: (01968) 679222
▶ Nationwide Healthcare Connections Ltd, Connections House, 105 Bellingdon Road, Chesham, Buckinghamshire, HP5 2HQ Tel: (01494) 773007 Fax: (01494) 773008 E-mail: sales@healthcare-connections.com
▶ Plabeasy, PO Box 4160, Cardiff, CF14 3ZY Tel: (0777) 9850236 Fax: E-mail: info@plabeasy.com
▶ South West Adult Placement Scheme, Zeally House, Greenhill Way, Kingsteignton, Newton Abbot, Devon, TQ12 3SB Tel: (01626) 360170 Fax: (01626) 368252 E-mail: enquiries@swaps.org.uk

HEALTH FOOD PRODUCTS

▶ Ableworld, 39 Beam Street, Nantwich, Cheshire, CW5 5NF Tel: (01270) 626971 Fax: (01270) 626971
▶ Acg Nutri Snacks, Unit 10 Elmfield Business Park, Lotherton Way, Garforth, Leeds, LS25 2JY Tel: 0113-287 7819 Fax: 0113-287 7434 E-mail: acgnutri@hotmail.com
Airdrie Grain & Health Foods, 37 Hallcraig Street, Airdrie, Lanarkshire, ML6 6AH Tel: (01236) 754291
Alara Health Foods, 58-60 Marchmont Street, London, WC1N 1AB Tel: (020) 7837 1172 Fax: (020) 7833 8089
Aloe Vera Health Products & Information Service, 55 Amity Grove, London, SW20 0LQ Tel: (020) 8947 6528 Fax: (020) 8947 1463
Aquasource (UK) Ltd, 12 Oaktree Place, Marsh Barton Trading Estate, Matford Business Park, Exeter, EX2 8WA Tel: (01392) 822155 Fax: (01392) 822151 E-mail: info@aquasource.co.uk

HEALTH FOOD PRODUCTS – *continued*

B Healthy Solutions Ltd, Brookside, Pinmill Road, Chelmondiston, Ipswich, IP9 1JF Tel: (01473) 780155 Fax: (01473) 780155

Balance, 59 High St, Fochabers, Morayshire, IV32 7DU Tel: 01343 820780

Beanfreaks, 5 Chartist Tower, Upper Dock Street, Newport, Gwent, NP20 1DX Tel: (01633) 251823 Fax: (01633) 666150

Bio-Synergy Licensing Ltd, 10a Nutford Place, London, W1H 5YL Tel: (020) 7569 2528 Fax: (020) 7487 2581 E-mail: natalie@bio-synergy.co.uk

Bran Tub Ltd, 20 Lavant Street, Petersfield, Hampshire, GU32 3EW Tel: (01730) 267043 Fax: (01730) 267043

Ceres Health Food, 29 Goring Road, Goring-by-Sea, Worthing, West Sussex, BN12 4AR Tel: (01903) 242023

Chelsea Health Store, 402 Kings Road, London, SW10 0LJ Tel: (020) 7352 4663 Fax: (020) 7532 4663 E-mail: enquiries@chelseahealthstore.com

Cobbs Health Foods, Unit 7 Brunel Shopping Centre, Somerton, Somerset, TA11 7PY Tel: (01458) 274066 Fax: (01458) 274190

Cornflower Wholefoods, 49 High Street, Brightlingsea, Colchester, CO7 0AQ Tel: (01206) 306679 Fax: (01206) 308515 E-mail: cornflowerbsea@aol.com

D & A Health & Pet Foods, 94 Connaught Avenue, Frinton-on-Sea, Essex, CO13 9PT Tel: (01255) 679603

Dandelion Natural Foods, 120 Northcote Road, London, SW11 6QU Tel: (020) 7350 0902 Fax: (020) 7350 0902

Dietary Foods Ltd, Cumberland House, Brook Street, Soham, Ely, Cambridgeshire, CB7 5BA Tel: (01353) 720791 Fax: (01353) 721705 E-mail: info@dietaryfoods.co.uk

Down To Earth, 406 Sharrow Vale Road, Sheffield, S11 8ZP Tel: 0114-268 5220

▶ Earth Force Ltd, Park Chambers, 10 Hereford Road, Abergavenny, Monmouthshire, NP7 5PR Tel: (01873) 851953 Fax: (01873) 851951 E-mail: info@earthforce.com

▶ FeelAmazing, Marvell Rise, Harrogate, North Yorkshire, HG1 3LT Tel: 07976 533827 E-mail: feelamazing@earnyourdream.co.uk

Finbarr's Whole Foods & Organic Wines, 57 George St, Hastings, E. Sussex, TN34 3EE Tel: (01424) 443025 Fax: (01424) 443025

FOCUS Organic Ltd, 14 Thoroughfare, Halesworth, Suffolk, IP19 8AH Tel: (01986) 872899 Fax: (01986) 872995

Fodder The Health Store, 26-27 Church Street, Hereford, HR1 2LR Tel: (01432) 358171 Fax: (01432) 277861

Fresh & Wild, 208-210 Westbourne Grove, London, W11 2RH Tel: (020) 7229 1063 Fax: (020) 7792 1341 E-mail: guini.short@wholefoods.com

Fruits Of The Earth, 2a Victoria Grove, Bridport, Dorset, DT6 3AA Tel: (01308) 425827

G & N, 14 East Street, Southampton, SO14 3HG Tel: (023) 8063 4680

G N C Livewell, 79 Nicholsons Walk, Maidenhead, Berkshire, SL6 1LJ Tel: (01628) 783594

G R Lane Health Products Ltd, Sisson Road, Gloucester, GL2 0GR Tel: (01452) 524012 Fax: (01452) 300105 E-mail: export@laneshealth.com

Garnell Corporation, 13a London Road, St. Albans, Hertfordshire, AL1 1LA Tel: (01727) 842222 Fax: (01727) 844446 E-mail: sales@garnell.co.uk

Glossop Whole Food, 8 Henry Street, Glossop, Derbyshire, SK13 8BW Tel: (01457) 865678

Golden Hamper Ltd, 19 Queen Street, Seaton, Devon, EX12 2NY Tel: (01297) 21076 Fax: (01297) 21076 E-mail: seatonhealthshop@aol.com

For Goodness Sake, 28 Westgate, Guisborough, Cleveland, TS14 6BA Tel: (01287) 637074 Fax: (01287) 637074

For Goodness Sake, 13 Newport Road, Middlesbrough, Cleveland, TS1 1LE Tel: (01642) 219249 Fax: (01642) 231080

Julian Graves Ltd, Tudor Arcade, South Street, Dorchester, Dorset, DT1 1BN Tel: (01305) 257934 Fax: (01384) 297707

Julian Graves Ltd, 9 The Sovereign Centre, High Street, Weston-super-Mare, Avon, BS23 1HL Tel: (01934) 643144 Fax: (01934) 643144

The Green House, Unit 60-61 Markethall, High Rd, Wood Green Shopping City, London, N22 6YE Tel: 020 88811471

Haldane Foods Ltd, Howard Way, Newport Pagnell, Buckinghamshire, MK16 9PY Tel: (01908) 211311 Fax: (01908) 210514

The Health Corner, 41b High St, Grantown-on-Spey, Morayshire, PH26 3EG Tel: (01479) 870400 Fax: (01479) 851293

Health & Diet Centres Ltd, 65 Princess Square, Bracknell, Berkshire, RG12 1LA Tel: (01344) 411870

Health & Diet Centres Ltd, 201 Centre Court Shopping Centre, 4 Queens Road, London, SW19 8YE Tel: (020) 8947 3583

Health Food Centre, 91 High Street, Gorleston, Great Yarmouth, Norfolk, NR31 6RQ Tel: (01493) 662162

The Health Haven, 63 Murray Street, Montrose, Angus, DD10 8JZ Tel: (01674) 676854

Health Matters, 34 Chatsworth Parade, Orpington, Kent, BR5 1DE Tel: (01689) 824953 Fax: (01689) 823253

Health Perception (U K) Ltd, Unit 12 Lakeside Business Park, Swan Lane, Sandhurst, Berkshire, GU47 9DN Tel: (01252) 861454 Fax: (01252) 861455

Health Warehouse, 15 Post House Wynd, Darlington, County Durham, DL3 7LU Tel: (01325) 468570

Healthright Health Foods, 48c Friars Square, Aylesbury, Buckinghamshire, HP20 2SP Tel: (01296) 397022

Healthy Way, 30 High Street, Ilfracombe, Devon, EX34 9DA Tel: (01271) 865883

Helanbeck Provisions, 6A High Street, Hythe, Southampton, SO45 6AH Tel: (023) 8084 7987

▶ Herbalife - Top Nutrition 99, 3 Talbot Avenue, Edgerton, Huddersfield, HD3 3BQ Tel: 01484 531426 E-mail: mikestephenson50@hotmail.com

Herbies Health Food, 72 High Street, Biddulph, Stoke-on-Trent, ST8 6AS Tel: (01782) 522133

▶ Herbs Gardens & Health, 27 Northdown Road, Broadstairs, Kent, CT10 2UW Tel: (01843) 600201 Fax: (01843) 863134 E-mail: juliet@herbsgardenshealth.com

Highland Health Store, 7 St John Street, Perth, PH1 5SP Tel: (01738) 628102 Fax: (01738) 447541

Margaret Hills, 7 Millar Court, 43 Station Road, Kenilworth, Warwickshire, CV8 1JD Tel: (01926) 850019

Holbeach Wholefoods, 32 High Street, Holbeach, Spalding, Lincolnshire, PE12 7DY Tel: (01406) 422149 Fax: (01406) 362939

Holland & Barrett Ltd, 12a South Street, Bishop's Stortford, Hertfordshire, CM23 3AT Tel: (01279) 651637

Holland & Barrett Ltd, 14 St Marys Way, Thornbury, Bristol, BS35 2BH Tel: (01454) 417201

Holland & Barrett Ltd, 14 Carlton Lanes Shopping Centre, Castleford, West Yorkshire, WF10 1AD Tel: (01977) 603858

Holland & Barrett Ltd, 25 London Road, East Grinstead, West Sussex, RH19 1AL Tel: (01342) 325089

Holland & Barrett Ltd, 64 Towngate, Keighley, West Yorkshire, BD21 3QE Tel: (01535) 663338

Holland & Barrett Ltd, 55 St Johns Wood High Street, London, NW8 7NL Tel: (020) 7586 5494

Holland & Barrett Ltd, 42 Kilburn High Road, London, NW6 4HJ Tel: (020) 7624 9297

Holland & Barrett Ltd, 31 Tranquil Vale, London, SE3 0BU Tel: (020) 8318 0448

Holland & Barrett Ltd, 81 Golders Green Road, London, NW11 8EN Tel: (020) 8455 5811

Holland & Barrett Ltd, 3 Selborne Walk, London, E17 7JR Tel: (020) 8520 5459

Holland & Barrett Ltd, 105a Northbrook Street, Newbury, Berkshire, RG14 1AA Tel: (01635) 552218

Holland & Barrett Ltd, 13 The Broadwalk, The Broad Marsh Centre, Nottingham, NG1 7LE Tel: 0115-979 9409

Holland & Barrett Ltd, 55a High Street, Rayleigh, Essex, SS6 7EW Tel: (01268) 779249

Holland & Barrett Ltd, 77 Town Square, Halton Lea, Runcorn, Cheshire, WA7 2EU Tel: (01928) 791188

Holland & Barrett Ltd, 59 Silver Street, Salisbury, SP1 2NG Tel: (01722) 324064

Holland & Barrett Ltd, 1 Gaolgate Street, Stafford, ST16 2BG Tel: (01785) 252758

Holland & Barrett Ltd, 28 Union Street, Torquay, TQ2 5PW Tel: (01803) 212215

Holland & Barrett Ltd, 52 The Mall, Warrington, WA1 1QE Tel: (01925) 418424

Honeypot Health Foods, 96 Lumley Road, Skegness, Lincolnshire, PE25 3ND Tel: (01754) 767387 Fax: (01754) 767387

Honeysuckle Health Foods, 4 Hawthorn Lane, Wilmslow, Cheshire, SK9 1AA Tel: (01625) 526144 Fax: (01625) 526144

Hungate Health Store, 4 Hungate, Beccles, Suffolk, NR34 9TL Tel: (01502) 715009

In A Nutshell, 31 Chesterfield Road, Sheffield, S8 0RL Tel: 0114-250 8555

▶ Independant Herbalife Distributor Network International, 258, Kingsland Road, London, E8 4DG Tel: (020) 7923 7827 Fax: (020) 7923 7827

▶ Intelligent Health & Nutrition Consultancy, 4 Woodleys Yard, West Street, Aldbourne, Marlborough, Wiltshire, SN8 2BL Tel: (0800) 6526608

J Dodd & Co. Ltd, 6 Byram Street, Huddersfield, HD1 1BX Tel: (01484) 420028

Kershaw's Health Foods, 127 Queen Street, Whitehaven, Cumbria, CA28 7QF Tel: (01946) 66627 Fax: (01946) 599237

Lawncourt Harvest Ltd, Unit 6a Eastlands Industrial Estate, Leiston, Suffolk, IP16 4LL Tel: (01728) 833003 Fax: (01728) 833005 E-mail: sales@munchyseeds.co.uk

Lonsdale Health Products Ltd, Unit 4 Ingleton Industrial Estate, Ingleton, Carnforth, Lancashire, LA6 3NU Tel: (01524) 241007 Fax: (01524) 241971 E-mail: info@lonsdalehealth.com

Man Shuen Hong London, 4 Tring Close, Ilford, Essex, IG2 7LQ Tel: (020) 8554 3838 Fax: (020) 8554 3883

The Market Shop, 48 Bridge Street, Berwick-upon-Tweed, TD15 1AQ Tel: (01289) 307749 Fax: (01289) 307749

Medex Scientific (UK) Ltd, 4 Denne Road, Horsham, West Sussex, RH12 1JE Tel: (01403) 218999

Meridian Foods, The Estate Office, Stockbridge Road, Sutton Scotney, Winchester, Hampshire, SO21 3JW Tel: (01962) 761935 Fax: (01962) 761860 E-mail: info@meridianfoods.co.uk

Mustard Seed, Boscawen Road, Perranporth, Cornwall, TR6 0EW Tel: (01872) 571421

Natural Choice, 13 Bridge Street, Darwen, Lancashire, BB3 2AA Tel: (01254) 773311 Fax: (01254) 773311

Natural Choice, 72 Westbourne Road, Huddersfield, HD1 4LE Tel: (01484) 513162 Fax: (01484) 687466

Natural Choice, 4 Market Place, Knaresborough, North Yorkshire, HG5 8AG Tel: (01423) 867705

Natural Food Co., 37a Mansfield Road, Nottingham, NG1 3FB Tel: (01949) 876483 Fax: 0115-955 9914 E-mail: info@naturalfoodcompany.net

Natural Remedy Warehouse, 7 The Flaxmill Lane, Pinchbeck, Spalding, Lincolnshire, PE11 3YP Tel: (01775) 724994 Fax: (01775) 761104 E-mail: info@enzymepro.com

Naturally Health Foods, 5 Waterloo Court, Andover, Hampshire, SP10 1QJ Tel: (01264) 332375 Fax: (01264) 364084 E-mail: sales@naturallyhealthfoods.co.uk

Nature Fare, 5 Towngate, Leyland, PR25 2EN Tel: (01772) 434693

Natures Aid Ltd, St. Georges Park, Kirkham, Preston, PR4 2DQ Tel: (01772) 686231 Fax: (01772) 671688 E-mail: sales@naturesaid.co.uk

Nature's Own Ltd, Unit 8, Hanley Workshops, Hanley Road, Hanley Swan, Worcester, WR8 0DX Tel: (01684) 310022 Fax: (01684) 312022 E-mail: peter@well-being.co.uk

Natures Remedies, Bank Street, Warrington, WA1 2AR Tel: (01925) 444885 Fax: (01925) 654821

Natures Way, 305 Upper Newtownards Road, Belfast, BT4 3JH Tel: (028) 9047 1333 Fax: (028) 9065 6694

Natures Way, 1 North Road, Holsworthy, Devon, EX22 6EJ Tel: (01409) 254305

Nutrica Ltd, Newmarket Avenue, White Horse Business Park, Trowbridge, Wiltshire, BA14 0XQ Tel: (01225) 768381 Fax: (01225) 768847

Orangeburst, 5 Hollingbury Terrace, Brighton, BN1 7JE Tel: (01273) 558112 Fax: (01273) 561249 E-mail: info@lemonburst.net

Oxted Health Foods, 75 Station Road East, Oxted, Surrey, RH8 0AX Tel: (01883) 730060 Fax: (01883) 730060

Planet Organic Ltd, 42 Westbourne Grove, London, W2 5SH Tel: (020) 7221 7171 Fax: (020) 7221 1923

Potters, 1 Botanic Court, Martland Park, Orrell, Wigan, Lancashire, WN5 0JZ Tel: (01942) 219960 Fax: (01942) 219966 E-mail: info@pottersherbals.co.uk

Potters Herbal Supplies Ltd, Leyland Mill Lane, Wigan, Lancashire, WN1 2SB Tel: (01942) 405100 Fax: (01942) 820255 E-mail: info@pottersherbals.co.uk

Power Health Products Ltd, Air Field Estate, Pocklington, York, YO42 1NR Tel: (01759) 302734 Fax: (01759) 304286 E-mail: jenny.baillie@power-health.co.uk

The Pulse, Mafeking Pl, Burnbank St, Campbeltown, Argyll, PA28 6JD Tel: 01586 552411 Fax: 01586 552411

Pumpernickel, 7 The Arcade, Bedford, MK40 1NS Tel: (01234) 348179 Fax: (01234) 219982

Purbeck Wholefoods, 37 North Street, Wareham, Dorset, BH20 4AD Tel: (01929) 552332

Quality Foods, 3 Ferry Court, Broadway, Bath, BA2 4JA Tel: (01225) 336800

The Quarry Shop, 27 Maengwyn, Machynlleth, Powys, SY20 8EB Tel: (01654) 702339 Fax: (01654) 702624 E-mail: amanda.green@cat.org.uk

Reflex Nutrition Ltd, 77A Rutland Road, Hove, East Sussex, BN3 5FE Tel: (01273) 297295 Fax: (01273) 297357

▶ Dennis Regan, Suites 2 & 4, Beauford House, Serpentine Road, Cleckheaton, West Yorkshire, BD19 3HU Tel: (01274) 850940 Fax: (01274) 850940 E-mail: sales@therapyexpressltd.co.uk

▶ RIS Products Ltd, Prospect Place, Welwyn, Hertfordshire, AL6 9EW Tel: (01438) 840135 Fax: (01438) 716067 E-mail: sales@risproducts.co.uk

▶ Safe Remedies Ltd, 11 North Road Industrial Estate, Berwick-upon-Tweed, TD15 1UN Tel: (01289) 332888 Fax: (01289) 331888 E-mail: sales@saferemedies.net

St Andrews Health Foods, 123 Market Street, St. Andrews, Fife, KY16 9PE Tel: (01334) 478887 Fax: (01334) 478887

Savant Distribution, Clayton Wood Close, Leeds, LS16 6QE Tel: 0113-388 5230 Fax: 0113-274 5777 E-mail: info@savant-health.com

Seaford Laboratories Ltd, Cradle Hill Industrial Estate, Seaford, East Sussex, BN25 3JE Tel: (01323) 896779 Fax: (01323) 490452

Seven Seas Ltd, Hedon Road, Hull, HU9 5NJ Tel: (01482) 375234 Fax: (01482) 374345 E-mail: terry.simpson@sseas.com

Sherwood Wholefoods, 1 Wilkinson Walk, Market Drayton, Shropshire, TF9 1PW Tel: (01630) 655155

Siop Newydd, 50 High Street, Criccieth, Gwynedd, LL52 0EY Tel: (01766) 522737

Solgar Vitamins & Herbs, Aldbury, Tring, Hertfordshire, HP23 5PT Tel: (01442) 890355 Fax: (01442) 890366

Stirling Health Food Store, 29 Dumbarton Road, Stirling, FK8 2LQ Tel: (01786) 464903 Fax: (01786) 464903

Swisshealth Health Foods, 11 St Mary Abbots Terrace, London, W14 8NX Tel: (020) 7602 5344 Fax: 020 7602 5344

T3 Therapy To Takeaway, 7/Nunhold Business Centre, Dark Lane, Hatton, Warwick, CV35 8XB Tel: (01926) 843714 Fax: (01926) 843739 E-mail: info@t3therapy.co.uk

Temple Health Foods, 17 Temple Fortune Parade, London, NW11 0QS Tel: (020) 8458 6087 Fax: (020) 8209 0059

Topfit Ltd, 156 Old Church Road, Clevedon, Avon, BS21 7TU Tel: (01275) 340042 Fax: (01275) 872733 E-mail: sales@topfithealth.co.uk

Tropicana Health & Fitness, Unit 38 Forge Lane, Minworth, Sutton Coldfield, West Midlands, B76 1AH Tel: 0121-351 3110 Fax: (0845) 3450917 E-mail: sales@tropicanahealthandfitness.com

Vega Nutritionals Ltd, 41 Central Avenue, West Molesey, Surrey, KT8 2QZ Tel: (020) 8939 3480 Fax: (0845) 2267400 E-mail: sales@vegavitamins.co.uk

Vita Health Foods, 565 Lea Bridge Road, London, E10 7EQ Tel: (020) 8539 3245

Vitalabs Europe Ltd, 18 Old Saintfield Road, Carryduff, Belfast, BT8 8EY Tel: (028) 9081 2323 Fax: (028) 9081 2454 E-mail: info@vitalabseurope.com

Wassen International Ltd, Unit 14 Mole Business Park, Randalls Road, Leatherhead, Surrey, KT22 7BA Tel: (01372) 379828 Fax: (01372) 376599 E-mail: info@wassen.com

Wholefoods Bedford, 1 Thurlow Street, Bedford, MK40 1LR Tel: (01234) 219618 Fax: (01234) 213929

Withington Health Foods, 486 Wilmslow Road, Manchester, M20 3BG Tel: 0161-445 6696

Wyedean Wholefoods, 18 Newerne Street, Lydney, Gloucestershire, GL15 5RF Tel: (01594) 841907 Fax: (01594) 841907

Zinaxin Health Foods, Palladium House, 1-4 Argyll Street, London, W1F 7LD Tel: (020) 7328 9797 Fax: (020) 7328 8555 E-mail: enquiries@zinaxin.com

HEALTH SUPPLEMENTS

▶ Gymking, 67 Belvedere Avenue, Ilford, Essex, IG5 0UH Tel: 0208 5512285 E-mail: gymking1@hotmail.co.uk

▶ myNaturalife.com, 3 Horncastle Cottages, Plawhatch Lane, Sharpthorne, East Grinstead, West Sussex, RH19 4JH Tel: (020) 7990 7744 Fax: (020) 7990 7744

HEALTHCARE COUNSELLING

▶ CliniServ, Harley Street, London, UK, W1G 9PF Tel: 0845 6100670 Fax: 0845 6100671 E-mail: customerservice@cliniserv.com

▶ Essex Counselling Practice, 442 Ipswich Road, Colchester, CO4 0EY Tel: 01206 842459 E-mail: brenda@essex-counselling-practice.co.uk

▶ Feel Good Clinic, 6 Shaw Road, London, SE22 8DP Tel: 0208 693 1503 E-mail: info@feelgoodclinic.co.uk

▶ Health & Well-Being, 4 Crathorne Avenue, Wolverhampton, WV10 6BT Tel: (01902) 786785 E-mail: battlingtheweight@btinternet.com

▶ Val Williams, Winnington Hall, Winnington, Northwich, Cheshire, CW8 4DU Tel: (01606) 48715 E-mail: val.williams@nissimo.co.uk

HEALTHCARE DEVICES

▶ Ranier Technology Ltd, Greenhouse Farm, Newmarket Road, Teversham, Cambridge, CB5 8AA Tel: (01223) 505045 Fax: (01223) 505046E-mail: ranier.technology@ranier.co.uk

HEALTHCARE PREPARATIONS, COMPLEMENTARY

▶ Awareness Centre Of Natural Health, 41 Abbeville Road, London, SW4 9JX Tel: (020) 8673 8844 Fax: (020) 8673 8844 E-mail: sales@awarness.com

▶ Clinical Hypnotherapy, St Mark's Clinic, 47 St Mark's Road, Teddington, Middlesex, TW11 9DE Tel: 01483 825649 E-mail: info@hypno-clinic.com

▶ Health & Well-Being, 4 Crathorne Avenue, Wolverhampton, WV10 6BT Tel: (01902) 786785 E-mail: battlingtheweight@btinternet.com

▶ Herbal Wellbeing, 37 Marlowe Road, Herringthorpe, Rotherham, South Yorkshire, S65 2JQ Tel: (01709) 305627 Fax: (0709) 2865304E-mail: herbalwellbeing@yahoo.co.uk

▶ Jan De Vries Health Care Ltd, Auchenkyle, South Wood Road, Troon, Ayrshire, KA10 7EL Tel: (01292) 317485

▶ Rae Marion Chandler, 3 Sudbourne Avenue, Clacton-on-Sea, Essex, CO16 7EN Tel: (01255) 426448 E-mail: sunnyside1946@onetel.com

▶ Rotherham Reiki, 6 Rowan Rise, Maltby, Rotherham, South Yorkshire, S66 8BZ Tel: (01709) 817008 E-mail: rotherhamreiki@tiscali.co.uk

▶ Ruth Lewis Complementary Therapy, 100 Manor Park Drive, Yateley, Hampshire, GU46 6JH Tel: 07879 465702 E-mail: ruth_lewis01@yahoo.co.uk

Safeandsound, Alma House, Perranporth, Cornwall, TR6 2QT Tel: (07854) 825599 E-mail: allysafeandsound@hotmail.co.uk

HEALTHCARE PREPARATIONS, COMPLEMENTARY – *continued*

▶ Seasplash Herbalists, 1045 Manchester Road, Linthwaite, Huddersfield, HD7 5LS Tel: (01484) 846252 E-mail: seasplash@btconnect.com
▶ Utopia Valley - Natural Healthcare Intelligent Selfcare, Concorde House, Grenville Place, London, NW7 3SA Tel: (0870) 6091280
▶ Vitamin UK, PO Box 98, Manchester, M20 6PZ Tel: (0800) 0568148 Fax: 0161-445 4939 E-mail: info@vitaminuk.com
Yankel Importers, Wirral, Merseyside, CH44 Tel: (0870) 7433396

HEARING AID BATTERIES

Duracell Wrexham, Unit 11 Ash Road North, Wrexham Industrial Estate, Wrexham, Clwyd, LL13 9JT Tel: (01978) 221000 Fax: (01978) 221001

HEARING AID INDUCTION LOOPS

Ampetronic Ltd, Northern Road, Newark, Nottinghamshire, NG24 2ET Tel: (01636) 610062 Fax: (01636) 610063 E-mail: sales@ampetronic.com
Audio Design Services Ltd, St Davids House, Adcroft St, Higher Hillgate, Stockport, Cheshire, SK1 3HW Tel: 0161-476 1010 Fax: 0161-666 6366 E-mail: sales@ads-worldwide.net
▶ Communications & Sound Systems Ltd, Unit 1, Sandhurst Barn, Sandhurst Lane, Bexhill-On-Sea, East Sussex, TN39 4RH Tel: (01424) 848400 Fax: (01424) 848300 E-mail: sales@commsandsound.com
Puretone plc, Unit 9-10 Henley Business Park, Trident Close, Medway City Estate, Rochester, Kent, ME2 4FR Tel: (01634) 719427 Fax: (01634) 719450 E-mail: sales@puretone.net
Signet A C Ltd, 5 Tower Road, Washington, Tyne & Wear, NE37 2SH Tel: 0191-417 4551 Fax: 0191-417 0634 E-mail: sales@signet-ac.co.uk

HEARING AIDS AND EQUIPMENT

B & J Stevenson, 19 Peverel Road, Cambridge, CB5 8RN Tel: (01223) 241901 Fax: (01223) 241901E-mail: bansjstevenson@freenet.co.uk
Connevans Ltd Equipment For The Deaf, 54 Albert Road North, Reigate, Surrey, RH2 9YR Tel: (01737) 247571 Fax: (01737) 223475 E-mail: mail@connevans.com
D S P G Ltd, 253a Kilburn Lane, London, W10 4BQ Tel: (020) 8964 0774 Fax: (020) 8964 0720 E-mail: info@dspg.co.uk
▶ Hidden Hearing Ltd, 51 New Row, Coleraine, County Londonderry, BT52 1EJ Tel: (028) 7032 0301 Fax: (028) 7035 8210
Oticon Ltd, PO Box 20, Hamilton, Lanarkshire, ML3 7QE Tel: (01698) 283363 Fax: (01698) 284308 E-mail: info@oticon.co.uk
PC Werth, 45 Nightingale Lane, London, SW12 8SP Tel: (020) 8675 5151 Fax: (020) 8772 2701 E-mail: pcwerth@pcwerth.co.uk
Puretone plc, Unit 9-10 Henley Business Park, Trident Close, Medway City Estate, Rochester, Kent, ME2 4FR Tel: (01634) 719427 Fax: (01634) 719450 E-mail: sales@puretone.net
Starkey Laboratories Ltd, William F Austin House, Pepper Road, Hazel Grove, Stockport, Cheshire, SK7 5BX Tel: 0161-483 2200 Fax: 0161-483 9833 E-mail: sales@starkey.co.uk

HEARING ASSESSMENT HEALTH AND SAFETY CONSULTANCY

Auricle Screening, 27 High Street, Petersfield, Hampshire, GU32 3JR Tel: (0800) 1804097 Fax: (01252) 720820 E-mail: iatkinson@noiseatwork.org

HEAT APPLIED TRANSFERS

Britannia Transprint, 38 Boundary Road, Saffron Works, Leicester, LE2 8QL Tel: 0116-283 8485 E-mail: info@tranfereprint.co.uk
P C I, Duke Street, New Basford, Nottingham, NG7 7JN Tel: 0115-970 3451 Fax: 0115-978 1547 E-mail: info@pacificconcept.com
Target Transfers Ltd, Anglia Way, Braintree, Essex, CM7 3RG Tel: (01376) 326351 Fax: (01376) 345876 E-mail: info@targettransfers.com
Technographics UK, Polymark House, Abbeydale Road, Wembley, Middlesex, HA0 1LQ Tel: (020) 8991 0011 Fax: (020) 8998 8080 E-mail: sales@technographics.co.uk
Transfra Graphics Ltd, Stadium Place, Leicester, LE4 0JS Tel: 0116-234 0440 Fax: 0116-235 1881 E-mail: sales@transfragraphics.com

Wellan Studios Printers)Ltd, Unit 1, Grange Valley Road, Batley, West Yorkshire, WF17 6GG Tel: (01924) 473481 Fax: (01924) 477353 E-mail: sales@wellanstudios.com

HEAT CONVERSION PUMPS, *See Heat Pump etc*

HEAT DETECTORS

Halma P.L.C., Misbourne Court, Rectory Way, Amersham, Buckinghamshire, HP7 0DE Tel: (01494) 721111 Fax: (01494) 728032 E-mail: halma@halma.com

HEAT DISSIPATOR/SINK MACHINISTS

Semikron UK Ltd, Martin House, 7 Fountain Drive, Hertford, SG13 7UB Tel: (01992) 584677 Fax: (01992) 554942 E-mail: sales.skuk@semikron.com

HEAT DISSIPATOR/SINK MANUFRS

Aavid Thermalloy Ltd, Cheney Manor, Swindon, SN2 2QN Tel: (01793) 401400 Fax: (01793) 615396 E-mail: sales@uk.aavid.com
Columbia Staver Ltd, Russell Gardens Industrial Estate, Wickford, Essex, SS11 8QR Tel: (01268) 733346 Fax: (01268) 735893 E-mail: info@columbia-staver.co.uk
Robotica Ltd, 17-19 Park Terrace Lane, Glasgow, G3 6BQ Tel: 0141-353 2261 Fax: 0141-353 2614
Staub Precision, 4 Vincients Road, Bumpers Farm, Chippenham, Wiltshire, SN14 6NQ Tel: (01249) 658197 Fax: (01249) 443408 E-mail: sales@staub.co.uk

HEAT EXCHANGER CLEANING SERVICES

Hedley (Engineering Services) Ltd, West Havelock Street, South Shields, Tyne & Wear, NE33 5DZ Tel: 0191-456 0250 Fax: 0191-455 6040 E-mail: info@hedley.co.uk
Tube Tech (International) Ltd, Rawreth Industrial Estate, Rawreth Lane, Rayleigh, Essex, SS6 9RL Tel: (0870) 2414999 Fax: (01268) 786998 E-mail: info@tubetech.com

HEAT EXCHANGER COILS

Beehive Coils Ltd, Studlands Park Industrial Estate, Newmarket, Suffolk, CB8 7AU Tel: (01638) 664134 Fax: (01638) 661623 E-mail: info@beehivecoils.co.uk
▶ Tranter Ltd, Unit 50, Moncton Road Industrial Estate, Wakefield, West Yorkshire, WF2 7AL Tel: (01924) 298393 Fax: (01924) 291596 E-mail: sales@tranterphe.com

HEAT EXCHANGER CONSULTANCY OR DESIGN

WBR Design Ltd, 126 High Street West, Glossop, Derbyshire, SK13 8HJ Tel: (01457) 857664 Fax: (01457) 851580 E-mail: wbr@wbrdesign.com

HEAT EXCHANGER DEBOTTLENECKING

Cal Gavin Ltd, 1 Station Road, Alcester, Warwickshire, B49 5ET Tel: (01789) 400401 Fax: (01789) 400411 E-mail: info@calgavin.co.uk

HEAT EXCHANGER INSTALLATION OR SERVICING

Eemech Ltd, Unit 1 Kenn Court Business Park, Roman Farm Road, Bristol, BS4 1UL Tel: 0117-964 4497 Fax: 0117-964 4487 E-mail: eemech@hotmail.com

HEAT EXCHANGER MAINTENANCE OR REPAIR EQUIPMENT

▶ Brittania Heatex Ltd, Unit 36-38 Coleshill Industrial Estate, Station Road, Coleshill, Birmingham, B46 1JP Tel: (01675) 466060 Fax: (01675) 467675 E-mail: info@britheat.co.uk
Buck & Hickman Ltd, Unit 5 Waterside, Trafford Park, Manchester, M17 1WD Tel: 0161-877 7888 Fax: 0161-877 7111 E-mail: manchester@buckhickmaninone.com

HEAT EXCHANGER PRODUCTION EQUIPMENT

Surface Engineering Process Equipment Ltd, Bennetts Field Trading Estate, Bennetts Field, Wincanton, Somerset, BA9 9DT Tel: (01963) 31274 Fax: (01963) 31288

HEAT EXCHANGER PROTECTIVE INSERTS

Ensign Plastics Ltd, PO Box 55, Leatherhead, Surrey, KT22 7TD Tel: (01372) 377827 Fax: (01372) 377828 E-mail: sales@ensign-uk.com

HEAT EXCHANGER REPAIR OR RETUBING

Abbey Heat Transfer Ltd, Unit 6 Parham Drive, Eastleigh, Hampshire, SO50 4NU Tel: (023) 8065 3331 Fax: (023) 8065 3332 E-mail: hugh@abbeyheat.co.uk
Alfa Laval 2000, 7 Doman Road, Camberley, Surrey, GU15 3DN Tel: (01276) 663383 Fax: (01276) 413603 E-mail:
Bells Heat Transfer Ltd, Factory Road, Blaydon-on-Tyne, Tyne & Wear, NE21 5SA Tel: 0191-414 6789 Fax: 0191-414 5890 E-mail: bells.heat.transfer@talk21.com
Broadland Radiators & Heat Exchangers Ltd, Burton Road, Norwich, NR6 6AU Tel: (01603) 413050 Fax: (01603) 413066 E-mail: sales@broadlandradiators.co.uk
County Engineering Southern Ltd, Unit 9, Annington Commercial Centre, Annington Road, Bramber, Steyning, West Sussex, BN44 3WA Tel: (01903) 879428 Fax: (01903) 815077 E-mail: ces@countyeng.demon.co.uk
J.L. Harrison & Son (Air Conditioning) Ltd, Unit 17, Olympic Business Centre, Paycocke Road, Basildon, Essex, SS14 3EX Tel: (01268) 532414 Fax: (01268) 532415 E-mail: info@chillerservices.co.uk
J M Heat Exchangers Ltd, 3 Albion Place, Doncaster, South Yorkshire, DN1 2EG Tel: (01302) 325179 Fax: (01302) 760353 E-mail: bryan@jmheatexchanges.com
Ross Heat Exchangers Ltd, Units 6 & 7, Dryden Glen, Loanhead, Midlothian, EH20 9NA Tel: 0131-440 0066 Fax: 0131-440 4188 E-mail: sales@ross-heatexchangers.co.uk
Serck Aviation, Oscar House, Wharfdale Road, Tyseley, Birmingham, B11 2DG Tel: 0121-623 6000 Fax: 0121-623 6100 E-mail: john.felton@dunlop-aerospace.com
SVR, Unit 1 35 Little London, Spalding, Lincolnshire, PE11 2UE Tel: (01775) 760999 Fax: (01775) 724547
Thermo Logistics, 3 21-23 Emery Road, Bristol, BS4 5PF Tel: 0117-971 7001 Fax: 0117-971 7113 E-mail: thermologistics@btconnect.com
Thornhill Service UK Ltd, Springvale Indust Estate, Park Springs Road, Grimethorpe, Barnsley, South Yorkshire, S72 7PT Tel: (01226) 710000 Fax: (01226) 717172 E-mail: sales@thornhill-ltd.co.uk

HEAT EXCHANGER TUBE CLEANING EQUIPMENT

Multilink Resources Ltd, Suite 18, Vermont House, Bradley Lane, Standish, Wigan, Lancashire, WN6 0XF Tel: (01257) 427053 Fax: (01257) 427053 E-mail: enquire@multilink.co.uk
Taprogge U K Ltd, Unit 6, Hurlbutt Road, Heathcote Industrial Estate, Warwick, CV34 6TD Tel: (01926) 336614 Fax: (01926) 336617 E-mail: taprogge@taprogge.co.uk

HEAT EXCHANGER TUBE ENHANCEMENT INSERTS

Cal Gavin Ltd, 1 Station Road, Alcester, Warwickshire, B49 5ET Tel: (01789) 400401 Fax: (01789) 400411 E-mail: info@calgavin.co.uk

HEAT EXCHANGER TUBE EXTRACTING OR PULLING EQUIPMENT

Wicksteed Engineering Ltd, Hove Road, Rushden, Northamptonshire, NN10 0JB Tel: (01933) 318555 Fax: (01933) 410103 E-mail: mail@wicksteed.com

HEAT EXCHANGER TUBE MANUFRS

Blackheath Tube Co Ltd, Castle Mill Works, Birmingham New Road, Dudley, West Midlands, DY1 4DA Tel: (01384) 255300 Fax: (01384) 255400 E-mail: sales@blackheathtube.co.uk
Metal Sections Ltd, Broadwell Road, Oldbury, West Midlands, B69 4HE Tel: 0121-601 6000 Fax: 0121-601 6121 E-mail: metsecplc@metsec.com
Profins Ltd, Burdon Drive, North West Industrial Estate, Peterlee, County Durham, SR8 2JH Tel: 0191-586 7669 Fax: 0191-586 0777 E-mail: info@profins.com
Salem Tube International Ltd, Unit 8, Regents Drive, Low Prudhoe Industrial Estate, Prudhoe, Northumberland, NE42 6PX Tel: (01661) 839240 Fax: (01661) 839248 E-mail: salem@btinternet.com
Tube Fins Ltd, N Riverside Industrial Estate, Atherstone Street, Fazeley, Tamworth, Staffordshire, B78 3SD Tel: (01827) 251234 Fax: (01827) 286612 E-mail: bob@tubefins.co.uk

HEAT EXCHANGER TUBE TURBULATORS

Midland Wire Cordage Co. Ltd, 2a Eagle Road, Moons Moat North Industrial Estate, Redditch, Worcestershire, B98 9HF Tel: (01527) 594150 Fax: (01527) 64322 E-mail: info@mid-cord.co.uk

HEAT EXCHANGER TUBEPLATES

Courtney Bell Ltd, Lawson Road, Dartford, DA1 5BP Tel: (01322) 221833 Fax: (01322) 228581

HEAT EXCHANGER/TRANSFER EQUIPMENT MANUFRS

Aberdeen Radiators Ltd, 53 Wellington Street, Aberdeen, AB11 5BX Tel: (01224) 575692 Fax: (01224) 211023 E-mail: len.hubert@aberdeen-radiators.co.uk
B I Engineering Ltd, Crane Close, Denington Industrial Estate, Wellingborough, Northamptonshire, NN8 2QG Tel: (01933) 228012 Fax: (01933) 441935 E-mail: biengineering@btconnect.com
Boiler Management Systems (International) Ltd, 189-191 Rutland Road, Sheffield, S3 9PT Tel: 0114-275 5500 Fax: 0114-275 5533 E-mail: isd@bmsint.com
▶ Brittania Heatex Ltd, Unit 36-38 Coleshill Industrial Estate, Station Road, Coleshill, Birmingham, B46 1JP Tel: (01675) 466060 Fax: (01675) 467675 E-mail: info@britheat.co.uk
Chemtec UK Ltd, PO Box 3, Beith, Ayrshire, KA15 1JQ Tel: (01505) 502206 Fax: (01505) 502545 E-mail: sales@chemtecuklimted.co.uk
Coil Products Ltd, Evington Valley Road, Leicester, LE5 5LU Tel: 0116-249 0044 Fax: 0116-249 0033
Custom Coils, Newgate Lane, Fareham, Hampshire, PO14 1AR Tel: (01329) 822222 Fax: (01329) 821238 E-mail: sales@custom-coils.co.uk
DMS Flow Measurement & Control Ltd, The Lodge, 9 Mansfield Rd, Eastwood, Nottingham, NG16 3AQ Tel: (01773) 534555 Fax: (01773) 534666 E-mail: sales@dmsltd.com
Engineering & Maintenance Services Ltd, Unit 12 St. Davids Industrial Estate, St. Davids Road, Swansea Enterprise Park, Swansea, SA6 8RX Tel: (01792) 797579 Fax: (01792) 772490 E-mail: ems@swanseauk.fsworld.co.uk
Eurocoils Ltd, Unit D3, Bonham Drive, Eurolink Commercial Park, Sittingbourne, Kent, ME10 3RX Tel: (01795) 475275 Fax: (01795) 422210 E-mail: ecoils@globalnet.co.uk
Eventemp (Midlands) Ltd, Carrwood Road, Chesterfield Trading Estate, Sheepbridge, Chesterfield, Derbyshire, S41 9QB Tel: (01246) 453685 Fax: (01246) 260359 E-mail: enquiries@eventempmidland.ltd.uk
Exchange Engineering Ltd, Ruston Road, Grantham, Lincolnshire, NG31 9SW Tel: (01476) 578505 Fax: (01476) 590908 E-mail: admin@exchange-engineering.co.uk
G D M Heat Transfer Ltd, Boston Industrial Estate, Power Station Road, Rugeley, Staffordshire, WS15 2HS Tel: (01889) 574880 Fax: (01889) 575074 E-mail: sales@gdmcoolers.co.uk
Gallay Ltd, Paterson Road, Finedon Road Industrial Estate, Wellingborough, Northamptonshire, NN8 4BZ Tel: (01933) 224801 Fax: (01933) 279902 E-mail: sales@gallay.co.uk
H R S Heat Exchangers Ltd, 10-12 Caxton Way, Watford Business Park, Watford, WD18 8TX Tel: (01923) 232335 Fax: (01923) 230266 E-mail: mail@hrs.co.uk
Heat Exchange Industries Ltd, Willow Road, Trent Lane, Castle Donnington, Castle Donington, Derby, DE74 2NP Tel: (01332) 853862 Fax: (01332) 3850590
Occo Coolers Telford Ltd, St. Georges Road Industrial Estate, Donnington, Telford, Shropshire, TF2 7QZ Tel: (01952) 616381 Fax: (05600) 753354 E-mail: sales@occocoolers.co.uk
Ormandy Rycroft, Duncombe Road, Bradford, West Yorkshire, BD8 9TB Tel: (01274) 490911 Fax: (01274) 498580 E-mail: sales@rycroft.com

HEAT EXCHANGER/TRANSFER EQUIPMENT MANUFRS – *continued*

Poole Process Equipment Ltd, 43-49 Nuffield Road, Nuffield Industrial Estate, Poole, Dorset, BH17 0RA Tel: (01202) 674683 Fax: (01202) 665265
E-mail: postmaster@poole-process.co.uk

Portobello Fabrications Ltd, Coleford Road, Sheffield, S9 5PE Tel: (0870) 4284406
Fax: 0114-244 2261
E-mail: sales@portobello-fab.co.uk

S P P Pumps Ltd, Greg St, Reddish, Stockport, Cheshire, SK5 7BU Tel: 0161-480 4955
Fax: 0161-476 2193

S S T Process Engineering Ltd, Unit 22 Autumn Park, Dysart Road, Grantham, Lincolnshire, NG31 7DD Tel: (01476) 590112 Fax: (01476) 590113 E-mail: sales@sstpe.co.uk

Serck Aviation, Oscar House, Wharfdale Road, Tyseley, Birmingham, B11 2DG Tel: 0121-623 6000 Fax: 0121-623 6100
E-mail: john.felton@dunlop-aerospace.com

Specialist Heat Exchangers Ltd, Freeman Road, North Hykeham, Lincoln, LN6 9AP
Tel: (01522) 881100 Fax: (01522) 684900
E-mail: info@specheat.co.uk

Therm Tech Ltd, Unit 4a Kayley Industrial Estate, Richmond Street, Ashton-under-Lyne, Lancashire, OL7 0AU Tel: 0161 339 3049
Fax: 0161 343 3305
E-mail: thermtech@msn.com

Thermex Ltd, Merse Road, North Moons Moat Industrial Estate, Moons Moat North Industrial Estate, Redditch, Worcestershire, B98 9HL
Tel: (01527) 62210 Fax: (01527) 60138
E-mail: enquiry@thermex.co.uk

Thermo Logistics, 3 21-23 Emery Road, Bristol, BS4 5PF Tel: 0117-971 7001 Fax: 0117-971 7113 E-mail: thermologistics@btconnect.com

UK Exchangers Ltd, Unit 13 StileBrook Road, Olney, Buckinghamshire, MK46 5EA
Tel: (01234) 244320 Fax: (01234) 714978
E-mail: sales@uk-exchangers.com

Wellman Hunt Graham Ltd, Astley Street, Dukinfield, Cheshire, SK16 4QT Tel: 0161-331 4400 Fax: 0161-331 4434

HEAT EXCHANGERS, *See also headings for particular types*

A S A Hydraulik, 22 Brewers Lane, Badsey, Evesham, Worcestershire, WR11 7EU
Tel: 01386 833400 Fax: 01386 833555
E-mail: support@asahydraulik.com

Alfalaval Ltd, Salvesen Tower, Blaikies Quay, Aberdeen, AB11 5PW Tel: (01224) 424300
Fax: (01224) 424315

▶ Aquafirm Heat Transfer Ltd, Racecourse Road, Pershore, Worcestershire, WR10 2EY
Tel: (01386) 552251 Fax: (01386) 561948

Bells Heat Transfer Ltd, Factory Road, Blaydon-on-Tyne, Tyne & Wear, NE21 5SA
Tel: 0191-414 6789 Fax: 0191-414 5890
E-mail: bells.heat.transfer@talk21.com

Broadland Radiators & Heat Exchangers Ltd, Burton Road, Norwich, NR6 6AU Tel: (01603) 413050 Fax: (01603) 413066
E-mail: sales@broadlandradiators.co.uk

Central Aircoil Service Ltd, 5 Icknield Street, Bidford On Avon, Alcester, Warwickshire, B50 4BX Tel: (01789) 774558 Fax: (01789) 774559 E-mail: sales@central-aircoil.co.uk

DMS Flow Measurement & Control Ltd, The Lodge, 9 Mansfield Rd, Eastwood, Nottingham, NG16 3AQ Tel: (01773) 534555
Fax: (01773) 534666
E-mail: sales@dmsltd.com

▶ GMS Thermal Products, Glover Centre, Egmont Street, Mossley, Ashton-under-Lyne, Lancashire, OL5 9PY Tel: (01457) 835700
Fax: (01457) 832700
E-mail: sales@gmsthermol.co.uk

▶ Greenbox Heat Exchangers, 11 Wassage Way, Hampton Lovett, Droitwich, Worcestershire, WR9 0NX Tel: (01905) 777050 Fax: (01905) 777051 E-mail: sales@greenbox.uk.com

Ipc Industrial Power Cooling Ltd, 14 Hillmorton Road, Knowle, Solihull, West Midlands, B93 9JL Tel: (01564) 776456 Fax: (01564) 777625 E-mail: nh@ipcltd.freeserve.co.uk

Jadealto Ltd, Sagana Lodge, Scotton Road, Scotter, Gainsborough, Lincolnshire, DN21 3SB Tel: (01724) 764747 Fax: (01724) 764352

Mueller Cooling Systems Ltd, Unit B Manor Farm, Main Street, Pinvin, Pershore, Worcestershire, WR10 2ES Tel: (01386) 561757 Fax: (01386) 561750
E-mail: phil.valentine@mueller-cooling.co.uk

Portobello Fabrications Ltd, Coleford Road, Sheffield, S9 5PE Tel: (0870) 4284406
Fax: 0114-244 2261
E-mail: sales@portobello-fab.co.uk

▶ Ross Off Shore, Unit 12b, Peterseat Drive, Altens Industrial Estate, Aberdeen, AB12 3HT
Tel: (01224) 877774 Fax: (01224) 876066

Thermal Solutions, 3 Orchard Avenue, Poole, Dorset, BH14 8AH Tel: (01202) 715792
Fax: (01202) 718134
E-mail: sales@thermalsolutions.co.uk

▶ Transcool Ltd, Gilmans Industrial Estate, Billingshurst, West Sussex, RH14 9EZ
Tel: 01403 786326

HEAT EXCHANGERS, AIR COOLED/AIR BLAST

A M I Exchanges Ltd, Apex Workshops, Graythorp Industrial Estate, Hartlepool, Cleveland, TS25 2DF Tel: (01429) 860187
Fax: (01429) 860673
E-mail: sales@ami-exchangers.co.uk

Baltairco West Ltd, Ivy House Farm, Wolvershill, Banwell, Avon, BS29 6LB Tel: (01934) 824411
Fax: (01934) 824477

Cov Rad Heat Transfer, Canley Works, Sir Henry Parkes Road, Coventry, CV5 6BN Tel: (024) 7671 3316 Fax: (024) 7671 3316
E-mail: glen.hurst@covrad.co.uk

Custom Coils, Newgate Lane, Fareham, Hampshire, PO14 1AR Tel: (01329) 822222
Fax: (01329) 821238
E-mail: sales@custom-coils.co.uk

Flowcool Systems, Wimsey Way, Somercotes, Alfreton, Derbyshire, DE55 4LS Tel: (01773) 608888 Fax: (01773) 609001
E-mail: sales@flowcool.com

Heap Dawson Ltd, Oldham Road, Rochdale, Lancashire, OL11 1BU Tel: (01706) 656222
Fax: (01706) 641852
E-mail: enquiries@heapdawson.co.uk

J M Heat Exchangers Ltd, 3 Albion Place, Doncaster, South Yorkshire, DN1 2EG
Tel: (01302) 325179 Fax: (01302) 760353
E-mail: bryan@jmheatexchanges.com

Manchester Calorifiers Ltd, Lund Street, Manchester, M16 9EJ Tel: 0161-872 3613
Fax: 0161-872 3027

Russell Ltd, 125 Business Park, Llanthony Road, Gloucester, GL2 5JQ Tel: (01452) 312851
Fax: (01452) 306388
E-mail: info@russell.co.uk

Specialist Heat Exchangers Ltd, Freeman Road, North Hykeham, Lincoln, LN6 9AP
Tel: (01522) 881100 Fax: (01522) 684900
E-mail: info@specheat.co.uk

Stadco Ltd, Harlescott Lane, Shrewsbury, SY1 3AS Tel: (01743) 462227 Fax: (01743) 447709 E-mail: cooling@stadco.co.uk

Thermal Exchange Ltd, 15 Chiswick Road, Leicester, LE2 7SX Tel: 0116-254 6652
Fax: 0116-255 9176
E-mail: sales@thermalexchange.co.uk

Thermex Ltd, Merse Road, North Moons Moat Industrial Estate, Moons Moat North Industrial Estate, Redditch, Worcestershire, B98 9HL
Tel: (01527) 62210 Fax: (01527) 60138
E-mail: enquiry@thermex.co.uk

HEAT INSERTION MACHINES

Spirol Industries Ltd, 17 Princewood Road, Earlstrees Industrial Estate, Corby, Northamptonshire, NN17 4ET Tel: (01536) 444800 Fax: (01536) 203415
E-mail: info@spirol.co.uk

HEAT LAMINATING FOAM

▶ Copex UK, 30 Princes Avenue, Walsall, WS1 2DG Tel: (01922) 649990 Fax: (01922) 649750 E-mail: copex@tiscali.co.uk

HEAT METERS

Powerminster Ltd, 20 Don Road, Sheffield, S9 2UB Tel: 0114-282 0220 Fax: 0114-282 0221 E-mail: info@powerminster.co.uk

Ranger Instrument Co. Ltd, Rutherford Road, Basingstoke, Hampshire, RG24 8PG
Tel: (01256) 464911 Fax: (01256) 464366
E-mail: ranger@bayham.demon.co.uk

HEAT PIPES

Pipcar Ltd, Unit 4b Valley Industries, Hadlow Road, Hadlow, Tonbridge, Kent, TN11 0AH
Tel: (01732) 851807 Fax: (01732) 850255
E-mail: admin@pipcar.co.uk

HEAT PUMP INSTALLATION OR SERVICING

A C R C Ltd, The Courtyard, North Street, Wigston, Leicestershire, LE18 1PS
Tel: 0116-257 0066 Fax: 0116-257 0099
E-mail: info@acrcltd.co.uk

Air Improve Ltd, Unit 4 City Business Centre, Hyde Street, Winchester, Hampshire, SO23 7TA Tel: (01962) 841366 Fax: (01962) 840185 E-mail: enquiries@airimprove.ltd.uk

Central Heat Pumps Ltd, 1 Mill Street, Islip, Kidlington, Oxfordshire, OX5 2SZ Tel: (01865) 370998 Fax: (01865) 370902

Edenaire Ltd, Station Road, Edenbridge, Kent, TN8 6EG Tel: (01732) 866066 Fax: (01732) 866653

Miracle Astec Ltd, PO Box 119, Horsham, West Sussex, RH12 4YZ Tel: (01403) 255140
Fax: (01403) 260855

HEAT PUMPS

▶ 3D Air Sales Ltd Scotland, McGregor House, South Bank Business Park, Kirkintilloch, Glasgow, G66 1XF Tel: 0141-777 5007
Fax: 0141-777 5009

Chillaire-Isis, 4b Black Bourton Road, Carterton, Oxfordshire, OX18 3EZ Tel: (01993) 841527
Fax: (01993) 841846
E-mail: sales@chillaire-isis.co.uk

Ciat Ozonair Ltd, 5 Byfleet Technical Centre, Canada Road, Byfleet, Surrey, KT14 7JX
Tel: (01932) 354955 Fax: (01932) 342998
E-mail: sales@ciat.co.uk

Hushon UK Ltd, A6 Railway Triangle, Walton Road, Drayton, Portsmouth, PO6 1TN
Tel: (023) 9232 4335 Fax: (023) 9232 4348
E-mail: sales@hushonuk.co.uk

HEAT RECOVERY DESIGN OR INSTALLATION OR COMMISSIONING OR SERVICING

Proto Associates, 26 Fox Lane, Hilltop, Bromsgrove, Worcestershire, B61 7NL
Tel: (01527) 831567 Fax: (01527) 831567
E-mail: aturchyn@globalnet.co.uk

HEAT RECOVERY PLANT/ SYSTEMS MANUFRS

Air Handlers Northern Ltd, Bute Street, Salford, M50 1DU Tel: 0161-745 8888 Fax: 0161-745 9900 E-mail: sales@airhandlers.com

Brook Design Hardware Ltd, Brook House, Dunmurry Industrial Estate, Dunmurry, Belfast, BT17 9HU Tel: (028) 9061 6505 Fax: (028) 9061 6518 E-mail: sales@brookvent.co.uk

Calorex Heat Pumps Ltd, Unit 2, The Causeway, Heybridge, Maldon, Essex, CM9 4XL
Tel: (01621) 856611 Fax: (01621) 850871
E-mail: sales@calorex.com

Coil Products Ltd, Evington Valley Road, Leicester, LE5 5LU Tel: 0116-249 0044
Fax: 0116-249 0033

E C E Environmental Control Equipment Ltd, Harvel Works, Harvel, Meopham, Gravesend, Kent, DA13 0BT Tel: (01474) 814432
Fax: (01474) 812488
E-mail: richardbarnes@ece.uk.com

Heatstar Ltd, 22 Daish Way, Newport, Isle of Wight, PO30 5XB Tel: (01983) 521465
Fax: (01983) 822016
E-mail: info@heatstar.co.uk

Recuperator Ltd, 1437 Pershore Road, Stirchley, Birmingham, B30 2JL Tel: 0121-433 3677
Fax: 0121-433 3601
E-mail: sales@recuperator.co.uk

Therm Tech Engineering Ltd, PO Box 30, Stockport, Cheshire, SK12 1BD Tel: (01625) 878831 Fax: (01625) 878832
E-mail: economisers@thermtech.fsnet.co.uk

U E S Ltd, Newark Road South, Glenrothes, Fife, KY7 4NS Tel: (01592) 773275 Fax: (01952) 773753

Villavent Ltd, Avenue Two, Station Lane, Witney, Oxfordshire, OX28 4YL Tel: (01993) 778481
Fax: (01993) 779962
E-mail: sales@villavent.co.uk

HEAT RESISTANT ADHESIVES

Fortafix Ltd, First Drove, Fengate, Peterborough, PE1 5BJ Tel: (01733) 566136 Fax: (01733) 315393 E-mail: sales@fortafix.com

Microbus Designs Ltd, Treadaway Hill, Loudwater, High Wycombe, Buckinghamshire, HP10 9QL Tel: (01628) 537300 Fax: (01628) 537301 E-mail: microbus@microbus.co.uk

HEAT RESISTANT ALLOY CASTINGS

Blantyre Castings Ltd, Block 9a West Avenue, Blantyre, Glasgow, G72 0UZ Tel: (01698) 829572 Fax: (01698) 824093
E-mail: blantyrecastings@btconnect.com

Darwins Holdings Ltd, Fitzwilliam Works, Sheffield Road, Sheffield, S9 1RL
Tel: 0114-244 8421 Fax: 0114-256 1775

Doncasters F B C Ltd, PO Box 160, Sheffield, S4 7QY Tel: 0114-243 1041 Fax: 0114-243 1358

Wearparts UK Ltd, Oaks Industrial Estate, Gilmorton Road, Lutterworth, Leicestershire, LE17 4HA Tel: (01455) 553551 Fax: (01455) 550907 E-mail: sales@wearparts.com

Westland Casting Co. Ltd, 4-5 Vaux Road, Finedon Road Industrial Estate, Wellingborough, Northamptonshire, NN8 4TG
Tel: (01933) 276718 Fax: (01933) 442185
E-mail: info@westlandcastings.co.uk

HEAT RESISTANT ALLOYS

Non Ferrous Stockholders Ltd, Dock Meadow Drive, Wolverhampton, WV4 6LE Tel: (01902) 353747 Fax: (01902) 491030
E-mail: info@non-ferrous.co.uk

Resistalloy International Ltd, 36 Wheatacre Road, Stocksbridge, Sheffield, S36 2GB
Tel: 0114-288 3872

HEAT RESISTANT CABLES

C & T Harnesses Ltd, Unit 2 Lanwades Business Park, Kennett, Newmarket, Suffolk, CB8 7PN
Tel: (01638) 751511 Fax: (01638) 751965
E-mail: info@ctharnesses.com

H T Cables, 40 Lancaster Gardens, Penn, Wolverhampton, WV4 4DN Tel: (01902) 339926 Fax: (01902) 659426
E-mail: seona_macrae@lineone.net

Heatsense Cables Ltd, 3 Astra Centre, Royle Barn Road, Rochdale, Lancashire, OL11 3DT
Tel: (01706) 355330 Fax: (01706) 657691
E-mail: sales@heatsensecables.co.uk

HEAT RESISTANT GLASS

H V Skan Ltd, 425-433 Stratford Road, Shirley, Solihull, West Midlands, B90 4AE
Tel: 0121-733 3003 Fax: 0121-733 1030
E-mail: info@skan.co.uk

Pilkington UK Ltd, 10-12 Alder Hills, Poole, Dorset, BH12 4AL Tel: (01202) 742700
Fax: (01202) 736155

Price Glass Ltd, 414-414a Bath Road, Slough, SL1 6JA Tel: (01628) 664466 Fax: (01753) 733121 E-mail: sales@priceglass.co.uk

W H Constable & Co. Ltd, 16 Barnwell Business Park, Barnwell Drive, Cambridge, CB5 8UZ
Tel: (01223) 211888 Fax: (01223) 416888

HEAT RESISTANT PAINTS

Fortafix Ltd, First Drove, Fengate, Peterborough, PE1 5BJ Tel: (01733) 566136 Fax: (01733) 315393 E-mail: sales@fortafix.com

Indestructible Paint Ltd, 23-25 Pentos Drive, Sparkhill, Birmingham, B11 3TA Tel: 0121-702 2485 Fax: 0121-778 4338
E-mail: sales@indestructible.co.uk

HEAT SEAL ADHESIVE APPLICATORS, *See Adhesive etc*

HEAT SEALERS

▶ B P I Packaging Services, 3-4 Manor Industrial Estate, Flint, Clwyd, CH6 5UY Tel: (01352) 735122 Fax: (01352) 734032
E-mail: packagingsales@bpipoly.com

▶ B P I Packaging Services, 96 Port Glasgow Road, Greenock, Renfrewshire, PA15 2UL
Tel: (01475) 501100 Fax: (01475) 744868

HEAT SEALING HAND TOOLS

Astrapac Midlands Ltd, Mount Road, Burntwood, Staffordshire, WS7 0AJ Tel: (01543) 677262
Fax: (01543) 672718
E-mail: sales@astrapac.co.uk

Lyteze Products Ltd, 8 Colne Road, Brightlingsea, Colchester, CO7 0DL
Tel: (01206) 302699 Fax: (01206) 302699
E-mail: annecook@lyteze.com

HEAT SEALING MACHINE MANUFRS, *See also headings for particular types*

Astrapac Midlands Ltd, Mount Road, Burntwood, Staffordshire, WS7 0AJ Tel: (01543) 677262
Fax: (01543) 672718
E-mail: sales@astrapac.co.uk

Coote Vibratory Co. Ltd, 10 The Apex Centre, Speedfields Park, Newgate Lane, Fareham, Hampshire, PO14 1TP Tel: (01329) 287841
Fax: (01329) 827451
E-mail: info@coote-vibratory.co.uk

Davies Machinery, 21 Harris Road, Lostock Gralam, Northwich, Cheshire, CW9 7PE
Tel: (01606) 48683 Fax: (01606) 48683

Enercon Industries Ltd, 64 Edison Road, Rabans Lane Industrial Area, Aylesbury, Buckinghamshire, HP19 8UX Tel: (01296) 330542 Fax: (01296) 432098
E-mail: info@enerconind.co.uk

Fischbein-Saxon, 274 Alma Road, Enfield, Middlesex, EN3 7RS Tel: (020) 8805 6111
Fax: (020) 8344 6625
E-mail: sales@fischbein-saxon.co.uk

Future Technology Heat Sealers Ltd, Yew Tree Farm, Main Street, Barton In The Beans, Nuneaton, Warwickshire, CV13 0DJ
Tel: (01455) 299000
E-mail: sales@futuresealers.co.uk

Johnston Lightning Filler Ltd, K Prescot Trade Centre, Oliver Lyme Road, Prescot, Merseyside, L34 2SH Tel: 0151-430 0900
Fax: 0151-430 7350
E-mail: sales@jlf-packaging.co.uk

Machine Technology Ltd, 22-23 Arcadia Avenue, London, N3 2JU Tel: (020) 8349 4814
Fax: (020) 8346 6251
E-mail: machinetech@btconnect.com

▶ indicates data change since last edition

HEAT SEALING MACHINE MANUFRS

– continued

Packaging Automation Ltd, 1 Montgomery Close, Parkgate Industrial Estate, Knutsford, Cheshire, WA16 8XW Tel: (01565) 755000 Fax: (01565) 751015 E-mail: sales@pal.co.uk
Proseal UK Ltd, Adlington Road Business Park, Bollington, Macclesfield, Cheshire, SK10 5HG Tel: (01625) 856600 Fax: (01625) 856611 E-mail: info@prosealuk.com
Sontex Machinery Ltd, 61 Westgate, Cleckheaton, West Yorkshire, BD19 5JZ Tel: (01274) 872299 Fax: (01274) 862829 E-mail: info@sontex.co.uk
Star Universal Gosport Ltd, 2 Clarence Wharf, Mumby Road, Gosport, Hampshire, PO12 1AJ Tel: (023) 9258 2857 Fax: (023) 9251 1731 E-mail: sales@staruniversal.com
Surrey Wholesale, Fleming Way, Crawley, West Sussex, RH10 9JY Tel: (01293) 611111 Fax: (01293) 550555
Swissvac (G B) Ltd, Marish Wharf, St Marys Road, Middlegreen, Slough, SL3 6DA Tel: (01753) 546777 Fax: (01753) 585564 E-mail: mail@swissvac.co.uk

HEAT SEALING MATERIALS, *See Adhesives, Hot Melt etc*

HEAT SEALING STAINLESS STEEL BANDS

East Anglian Fine Weld Ltd, Unit 1, St. Margarets Way, Stukeley Meadows Industrial Estate, Huntingdon, Cambridgeshire, PE29 6EB Tel: (01480) 453412 Fax: (01480) 434952 E-mail: sales@eafw.co.uk
Global Enterprises, The Old Stores, Penny Royal Road, Danbury, Chelmsford, CM3 4ED Tel: (01245) 226004 Fax: (01245) 225995 E-mail: enquiries@globalheatseal.com

HEAT SHIELDS, AUTOMOTIVE, STAINLESS STEEL

▶ John Shaw Engineering Ltd, Kilbane Street, Fleetwood, Lancashire, FY7 7PF Tel: (01253) 875732 Fax: (01253) 771163 E-mail: office@jshaweng.co.uk

HEAT SHRINK CABLE SYSTEMS

Sicane Electrical Distribution Ltd, Amington Industrial Estate, Tamworth, Staffordshire, B77 4DS Tel: (01827) 68333 Fax: (01827) 65700 E-mail: barbara.shewan@sicame.co.uk

HEAT SHRINK PRODUCTS DISTRIBUTORS OR AGENTS

Canusa Systems Ltd, 3 Sterling Park, Gatwick Road, Crawley, West Sussex, RH10 9QT Tel: (01293) 541254 Fax: (01293) 541777 E-mail: sales@canusa-cps.co.uk
Channel Ltd, Fairway, Orpington, Kent, BR5 1EG Tel: (01689) 871522 Fax: (01689) 833428
Express Electrical & Engineering Supplies, 37 Cable Depot Road, Clydebank, Dunbartonshire, G81 1UY Tel: 0141-941 3689 Fax: 0141-952 8155 E-mail: sales@expresselectrical.co.uk

HEAT SHRINK SLEEVING OR TUBING

Birch Valley Plastics Ltd, Darklake View, Estover, Plymouth, PL6 7TL Tel: (01752) 696515 Fax: (01752) 696724 E-mail: admin@birchvalley.co.uk
D S G Canusa GmbH & Co., Sales Bergstrand House, Parkwood Close, Roborough, Plymouth, PL6 7SG Tel: (01752) 209880 Fax: (01752) 209850 E-mail: info@dsgcanusa.com
Hayward Holdings Ltd, 5 Howard Industrial Estate, Chilton Road, Chesham, Buckinghamshire, HP5 2AS Tel: (01494) 775075 Fax: (01494) 784861 E-mail: enquiries@hayward-holdings.demon.co.uk
Majortek Components Ltd, Netley Firs, Kanes Hill, Southampton, SO19 6AJ Tel: (023) 8040 5276 Fax: (023) 8040 2873 E-mail: sales@majortek.co.uk
Thermal Memory, The Deanery, 6 Dodd Croft, Rochdale, Lancashire, OL16 4QX Tel: (01706) 522611 E-mail: enquiries@shrinkfit.co.uk

HEAT TRANSFER CONSULTANCY

Flowsolve Ltd, 130 Arthur Road, London, SW19 8AA Tel: (020) 8944 0940 Fax: (020) 8944 1218 E-mail: cfd@flowsolve.com

HEAT TRANSFER FLUIDS

Brain Power International Ltd, 3 Prospect Way, Butlers Leap, Rugby, Warwickshire, CV21 3UU Tel: (01788) 568686 Fax: (01788) 568686 E-mail: paul@callbpi.com

HEAT TRANSFER LIQUID

▶ Multisol Ltd, Sorby Road, Irlam, Manchester, M44 5BA Tel: 0161-775 1622 Fax: 0161-777 9783 E-mail: sales@multisol.co.uk

HEAT TRANSFER PRESSES

Pressmech Sewing Machines, 3 Walton New Road, Bruntingthorpe, Lutterworth, Leicestershire, LE17 5RD Tel: 0116-247 8071 Fax: (01455) 251320 E-mail: pressmech@aol.com

HEAT TREATMENT FURNACES

Can-Eng Furnaces UK Ltd, Unit 8, Ninian Park, Ninian Way, Wilnecote, Tamworth, Staffordshire, B77 5ES Tel: (01827) 262601 Fax: (01827) 262602 E-mail: can-enguk@mcmail.com
Cromartie Kilns Ltd, Park Hall Road, Longton, Stoke-On-Trent, ST3 5AY Tel: (01782) 313947 Fax: (01782) 599723 E-mail: enquiries@cromartie.co.uk
Excel Heat, Oak St Trading Estate, Oak Street, Quarry Bank, Brierley Hill, West Midlands, DY5 2JQ Tel: (01384) 560713 Fax: (01384) 411742 E-mail: excelheat@freeuk.com
Inductotherm Heating & Welding Technologies Ltd, Thermatool House, Crockford Lane, Chineham, Basingstoke, Hampshire, RG24 8NA Tel: (01256) 337722 Fax: (01256) 467224 E-mail: sales@inductoheat.co.uk
Isoheat, Unit 5, Aurilac Court, Hallcroft Industrial Estate, Aurilac Way, Retford, Nottinghamshire, DN22 7PX Tel: (01777) 708811 Fax: (01777) 708866 E-mail: isoheat@fsbdial.co.uk
J L S Redditch, Holberrow Green, Holberrow Green, Redditch, Worcestershire, B96 6JY Tel: (01386) 791513 Fax: 01386 791518 E-mail: sales@jlsovens.com
Kilns & Furnaces Ltd, 1 Cinderhill Industrial Estate, Weston Coyney Road, Stoke-on-Trent, ST3 5JU Tel: (01782) 344620 Fax: (01782) 344621 E-mail: sales@kilns.co.uk
Leerco Engineering Ltd, Full Sutton Industrial Estate, Stamford Bridge, York, YO41 1HS Tel: (01759) 371128 Fax: (01759) 371034 E-mail: leercoeng@aol.com
Tynok Ltd, Midland Ho, Vicarage Road West, Woodsetton, Dudley, W. Midlands, DY1 4NP Tel: (01902) 887270 Fax: (01902) 880428
Vecstar Furnaces, Unit 11-12 Dunston Trading Estate, Foxwood Road, Chesterfield, Derbyshire, S41 9RF Tel: (01246) 260094 Fax: (01246) 450213 E-mail: enquiries@vecstar.co.uk

HEAT TREATMENT (METAL) EQUIPMENT

Control & Power Engineering Ltd, Fox Covert Lane, Misterton, Doncaster, South Yorkshire, DN10 4ER Tel: (01427) 891256 Fax: (01427) 891307 E-mail: capeuk@aol.com
Globe Heat Treatment Services Ltd, Unit 4 & 5 Venture Works, Charleywood Road, Knowsley Industrial Park, Liverpool, L33 7SG Tel: 0151-548 5281 Fax: 0151-548 3530 E-mail: sales@globeheat.com
Monometer Holdings Ltd, Monometer House, Rectory Grove, Leigh-on-Sea, Essex, SS9 2HN Tel: (01702) 472201 Fax: (01702) 715112 E-mail: sales@monometer.co.uk
Multijet Hardening Ltd, 8 West Don Street, Sheffield, S6 3BH Tel: 0114-234 5592 Fax: 0114-231 4772
T T I Group Ltd, Bamfurlong Industrial Park, Staverton, Cheltenham, Gloucestershire, GL51 6SX Tel: (01452) 712023 Fax: (01452) 714418

HEAT TREATMENT (METAL) EQUIPMENT REFURBISHMENT SERVICES

T T I Group Ltd, Bamfurlong Industrial Park, Staverton, Cheltenham, Gloucestershire, GL51 6SX Tel: (01452) 712023 Fax: (01452) 714418

HEAT TREATMENT (METAL) MATERIALS

Metaltech Ltd, Hownsgill Drive, Consett, County Durham, DH8 9HU Tel: (01207) 501085 Fax: (01207) 580743 E-mail: gf@metaltech.co.uk
P P Profiles Ltd, Neills Road, Bold, St. Helens, Merseyside, WA9 4SY Tel: (01744) 818992 Fax: (01744) 820179 E-mail: sales@ppprofilesltd.co.uk

HEAT TREATMENT PANELS/ BASKETS, WIRE MESH

▶ Eurowire Containers Ltd, Maypole Fields, Cradley, Halesowen, West Midlands, B63 2QB Tel: (01384) 561786 Fax: (01384) 564044 E-mail: support@eurowirecontainers.com

HEAT TREATMENT SERVICES

Alpha Rowen Treatments Ltd, 3-4 & 7 Brymill Industrial Units, Brown Lion Street, Tipton, West Midlands, DY4 9EG Tel: 0121-557 2376 Fax: 0121-557 2580 E-mail: kevin.p.rowen@btinternet.com
Alpha Rowen Treatments Ltd, 3-4 & 7 Brymill Industrial Units, Brown Lion Street, Tipton, West Midlands, DY4 9EG Tel: 0121-557 2376 Fax: 0121-557 2580
Bluelimit Surveys Ltd, 6 Riverside Road, Gorleston, Great Yarmouth, Norfolk, NR31 6PU Tel: (01493) 653900 Fax: (01493) 442774 E-mail: bluelimit@paston.co.uk
Bodycote Birmingham, Britannia House, Austin Way, Hampstead Industrial Estate, Birmingham, B42 1DU Tel: 0121-358 7266 Fax: 0121-358 0478 E-mail: info@bodycote.co.uk
Bodycote Birmingham, Britannia House, Austin Way, Hampstead Industrial Estate, Birmingham, B42 1DU Tel: 0121-358 7266 Fax: 0121-358 0478 E-mail: sales@bodycote.com
Bodycote Heat Treatment Ltd, Field Way, Rotherham, South Yorkshire, S60 1QG Tel: (01709) 361047 Fax: (01709) 828529 E-mail: sales@bodycote.co.uk
Bodycote Heat Treatment Ltd, 437 Chester Road, Woodford, Stockport, Cheshire, SK7 1QP Tel: 0161-440 0288 Fax: 0161-440 8017 E-mail: sales@bodycote.co.uk
Bodycote Heat Treatments Ltd, Springwood Court, Springwood Close, Tytherington Business Park, Macclesfield, Cheshire, SK10 2XF Tel: (01625) 505300 Fax: (01625) 505320 E-mail: info@bodycote.co.uk
Bodycote (Somerset) Ltd, Leach Road, Chard Business Park, Chard, Somerset, TA20 1FA Tel: (01460) 67957 Fax: (01460) 67962 E-mail: sales@bodycote.co.uk
Coventry Heat Treatment Ltd, Unit A-B, Brindley Road, Bayton Road Industrial Estate, Coventry, CV7 9EP Tel: (024) 7636 0099 Fax: (024) 7636 6222 E-mail: covheat@aol.com
Darchem Engineering Ltd, Iron Masters Way, Stillington, Stockton-on-Tees, Cleveland, TS21 1LB Tel: (01740) 630461 Fax: (01740) 630529 E-mail: sales@darchem.co.uk
Harbex Profiling & Grinding Ltd, Blackberry Farm, High Oak Hill, Bobbing, Sittingbourne, Kent, ME9 8QD Tel: (01795) 842925 Fax: (01795) 843868 E-mail: sales@harbex.co.uk
T T I Nitriding Services Ltd, Hortonwood 40, Telford, Shropshire, TF1 7YU Tel: (01952) 677372 Fax: (01952) 677370 E-mail: info@nitriding.co.uk
Tamworth Heat Treatment Ltd, 7 Darwell Park, Mica Close, Tamworth, Staffordshire, B77 4DR Tel: (01827) 318030 Fax: (01827) 318039

HEAT TREATMENT TO SPECIFICATION

Alpha Rowen Treatments Ltd, 3-4 & 7 Brymill Industrial Units, Brown Lion Street, Tipton, West Midlands, DY4 9EG Tel: 0121-557 2376 Fax: 0121-557 2580
Coventry Heat Treatment Ltd, Unit A-B, Brindley Road, Bayton Road Industrial Estate, Coventry, CV7 9EP Tel: (024) 7636 0099 Fax: (024) 7636 6222 E-mail: covheat@aol.com
Globe Heat Treatment Services Ltd, Unit 4 & 5 Venture Works, Charleywood Road, Knowsley Industrial Park, Liverpool, L33 7SG Tel: 0151-548 5281 Fax: 0151-548 3530 E-mail: sales@globeheat.com
Induction Heat Treatment Ltd, Station Works, Station Road, New Mills, High Peak, Derbyshire, SK22 3JB Tel: (01663) 742483 Fax: (01663) 746223 E-mail: sales@inductionheat.co.uk

HEAT TREATMENT, AUSTEMPERING

Alpha Rowen Treatments Ltd, 3-4 & 7 Brymill Industrial Units, Brown Lion Street, Tipton, West Midlands, DY4 9EG Tel: 0121-557 2376 Fax: 0121-557 2580 E-mail: kevin.p.rowen@btinternet.com

HEAT TREATMENT, CARBONITRIDING

T T I Nitriding Services Ltd, Hortonwood 40, Telford, Shropshire, TF1 7YU Tel: (01952) 677372 Fax: (01952) 677370 E-mail: info@nitriding.co.uk

HEAT TREATMENT, NITROCARBURISING

Bodycote Birmingham, Britannia House, Austin Way, Hampstead Industrial Estate, Birmingham, B42 1DU Tel: 0121-358 7266 Fax: 0121-358 0478 E-mail: info@bodycote.co.uk
Bodycote Birmingham, Britannia House, Austin Way, Hampstead Industrial Estate, Birmingham, B42 1DU Tel: 0121-358 7266 Fax: 0121-358 0478 E-mail: sales@bodycote.com
Bodycote Heat Treatment Ltd, Field Way, Rotherham, South Yorkshire, S60 1QG Tel: (01709) 361047 Fax: (01709) 828529 E-mail: sales@bodycote.co.uk
Bodycote Heat Treatment Ltd, 437 Chester Road, Woodford, Stockport, Cheshire, SK7 1QP Tel: 0161-440 0288 Fax: 0161-440 8017 E-mail: sales@bodycote.co.uk
Bodycote (Somerset) Ltd, Leach Road, Chard Business Park, Chard, Somerset, TA20 1FA Tel: (01460) 67957 Fax: (01460) 67962 E-mail: sales@bodycote.co.uk

HEAT TREATMENT, NORMALISING

Body Coating Treatments Ltd, Cranbourne Road, Gosport, Hampshire, PO12 1RW Tel: (023) 9258 0946 Fax: (023) 9251 0292 E-mail: markdavies@bodycoat.com
Expert Heat Treatments Kent, 12 Tribune Drive, Trinity Trading Estate, Sittingbourne, Kent, ME10 2PT Tel: (01795) 426545 Fax: (01795) 424449 E-mail: southsales@eht.co.uk
HHT Midlands Ltd, Heath Road, Darlaston, West Midlands, WS10 8LU Tel: 0121-526 4771 Fax: 0121-526 4153 E-mail: sales@hht.co.uk
Lyndhurst Precision Engineering Ltd, Weir Mill, Crosse Hall Street, Chorley, Lancashire, PR6 0UH Tel: (01257) 267876 Fax: (01257) 260724 E-mail: sales@lyndhurst-precision.co.uk
Metaltech Ltd, Hownsgill Drive, Consett, County Durham, DH8 9HU Tel: (01207) 501085 Fax: (01207) 580743 E-mail: gf@metaltech.co.uk

HEAT TREATMENT, PRECIPITATION

Alloy Heat Treatment, Block 6 Grazebrook Industrial Park, Peartree Lane, Dudley, West Midlands, DY2 0XW Tel: (01384) 456777 Fax: (01384) 453900 E-mail: sales@alloyheat.co.uk
Servis Heat Treatment Co. Ltd, 258b Ipswich Road, Trading Estate, Slough, SL1 4EP Tel: (01753) 521823 Fax: (01753) 531094 E-mail: sales@servisheattreatment.com

HEAT TREATMENT, TUFFTRIDING

Body Coat Heat Treatment, Stillington, Stockton-on-Tees, Cleveland, TS21 1LD Tel: (01740) 630353 Fax: (01740) 630075

HEAT WASTE RECOVERY SYSTEMS

Boustead International Heaters Ltd, Southwick Square, Southwick, Brighton, BN42 4UA Tel: (01273) 596868 Fax: (01273) 596860 E-mail: sales@bihl.com

HEATED DISPLAY CABINETS OR CASES

Bailey & Smith Ltd, Hammerstone Road, Gorton, Manchester, M18 8EF Tel: 0161-223 5000 Fax: 0161-223 2989 E-mail: info@baileysmith.co.uk
Fri-Jado UK, Ashley House, Ashley Road, Uxbridge, Middlesex, UB8 2GA Tel: (01895) 272227 Fax: (01895) 256360 E-mail: sales@frijado.co.uk

HEATED PLATENS

Thompson & Son (Millwall) Ltd, Cuba Street, Isle of Dogs, London, E14 8LF Tel: (020) 7987 1844 Fax: (020) 7987 4416

HEATED TOWEL RAILS

▶ Pyramide UK Trading Ltd, Suite 306, Parkway House, Sheen Lane, East Sheen, London, SW14 8LS Tel: (020) 8392 1123 Fax: (0870) 7628545 E-mail: sales@towelradiator.co.uk

▶ indicates data change since last edition

HEATER CABLES

Thermon Electrical Heating Equipment, Seventh Avenue, Team Valley Trading Estate, Gateshead, Tyne & Wear, NE11 0JW Tel: 0191-499 4900 Fax: 0191-499 4901 E-mail: sales@thermon.com

HEATER HIRE

Airflo Envirorental, Kelham Street, Doncaster, South Yorkshire, DN1 3TA Tel: (01302) 730000 Fax: (01302) 321222

Andrews Sykes Hire Ltd, Unit F17 Ashmount Business Park, Upper Fforest Way, Swansea Enterprise Park, Swansea, SA6 8QR Tel: (01792) 701701 Fax: (01792) 701700

Ashtead Plant Hire Co. Ltd, Vale Industrial Estate, Tolpits Lane, Watford, WD18 9QP Tel: (01923) 771577 Fax: (01923) 771090 E-mail: watford@aplant.com

Heat Hire Ltd, 109-111 Beverley Road, Hull, HU3 1TS Tel: (01482) 218288 Fax: (01482) 227897

Hirepro Ltd, Unit 6 Atlas Business Centre, Oxgate La, Staples Corner, London, NW2 7HJ Tel: (020) 8438 0200 Fax: (020) 8438 0300

▶ Oldham Plant Hire & Sales Ltd, 50 Oldham Road, Royton, Oldham, OL2 5PF Tel: 0161-627 0427 Fax: 0161-633 6590 E-mail: sales@oldhamhirecentre.co.uk

Winterwarm UK Ltd, Unit H3, Taylor Industrial Estate, Risley, Warrington, WA3 6BL Tel: (01925) 765799 Fax: (01925) 762996 E-mail: enquiries@winterwarm.com

HEATERS OR FITTINGS, *See also headings for particular types under Heaters*

A B Plumbing Supplies Ltd, Savoy Works, Pershore Road, Kingsnorton, Birmingham, B30 3DR Tel: 0121-433 3099 Fax: 0121-458 5698 E-mail: sales@abplumbing.co.uk

A R Ellis Ltd, The Green, Horton Road, Horton, Slough, SL3 9NU Tel: (01753) 685333 Fax: (01753) 680749E-mail: tony@arellis.com

Abercorn Heating Ltd, 105 Abercorn Street, Paisley, Renfrewshire, PA3 4AT Tel: 0141-887 0308 Fax: 0141-887 6823 E-mail: markbrooks@abercorn-heating.co.uk

Acrelane Builders Merchants Ltd, 53 Acre Lane, London, SW2 5TN Tel: (020) 7738 3777 Fax: (020) 7738 6842 E-mail: info@diamond-merchants.co.uk

The Albion, Station Road, Caythorpe, Grantham, Lincolnshire, NG32 3EW Tel: (01400) 272726 Fax: (01400) 273508 E-mail: caythorpe@albionwaterheaters.com

Alpha Therm Ltd, Nepicar House, London Road, Wrotham Heath, Sevenoaks, Kent, TN15 7RS Tel: (01732) 783000 Fax: (01732) 783080 E-mail: info@alphatherm.co.uk

Andrews Sykes Hire Ltd, Premier House, Darlington Street, Wolverhampton, WV1 4JJ Tel: (01902) 328700 Fax: (01902) 422466 E-mail: info@andrews-sykes.com

Anglo Nordic Burner Products Ltd, Units 12-14, Island Farm Avenue, West Molesey, Surrey, KT8 2UZ Tel: (020) 8979 0988 Fax: (020) 8979 6961 E-mail: sales@anglonordic.co.uk

Aqua Heat Ltd, Unit 33 Three Elms Trading Estate, Hereford, HR4 9PU Tel: (01432) 340111 Fax: (01432) 271888

B & B Supplies, 641 Garratt Lane, London, SW18 4SX Tel: (020) 8946 2957 Fax: (020) 8946 2435

B Danby & Co, Albermarle Back Road, Scarborough, North Yorkshire, YO11 1YA Tel: (01723) 360580 Fax: (01723) 352010

B G Perimeter Systems Ltd, Tomo Industrial Estate, Packet Boat Lane, Uxbridge, Middlesex, UB8 2JP Tel: (01895) 441794 Fax: (01895) 448597 E-mail: sales@bgperimeter.co.uk

B.K. Gas Supplies, 35 Kings Road, West Drayton, Middlesex, UB7 9EF Tel: (01895) 446115 Fax: (01895) 446115

Ballcock & Bits Ltd, Broad Lane, Bracknell, Berkshire, RG12 9BJ Tel: (01344) 481212 Fax: (01344) 302512

Basingstoke Control Systems, 12 Mallard Close, Basingstoke, Hampshire, RG22 5JP Tel: (01256) 466639 Fax: (01256) 842876 E-mail: basingstokecobtrolsystems@ukonline.co.uk

Bergstrom Inc., Hengoed, Mid Glamorgan, CF82 7YH Tel: (01443) 865100 Fax: (01443) 865157

Bilbeck Ltd, Yorke Street, Mansfield Woodhouse, Mansfield, Nottinghamshire, NG19 9NU Tel: (01623) 651101 Fax: (01623) 653387 E-mail: sales@bilbeck.com

C A Baldwin & Co. Ltd, 146-154 Wells Way, London, SE5 7SY Tel: (020) 7703 2138 Fax: (020) 7701 8436 E-mail: info@baldwin.co.uk

Cascade Systems (UK) Ltd, Unit 10, West Place, West Road, Harlow, Essex, CM20 2GY Tel: (01279) 626695 Fax: (01279) 626799 E-mail: infocascade@aol.com

City Plumbing Supplies Ltd, 1 Faraday Street, Dryburgh Industrial Estate, Dundee, DD2 3QQ Tel: (01382) 825625 Fax: (01382) 826926

City Plumbing Supplies plc, 27 Aston Road, Waterlooville, Hampshire, PO7 7XJ Tel: (023) 9226 7341 Fax: (023) 9225 5698 E-mail: ian@city-plumbingsupplies.co.uk

City Pluming Supplies, 65-67 Kelvin Avenue, Hillington Industrial Estate, Glasgow, G52 4LP Tel: 0141-882 7700 Fax: 0141-882 9390

Clipvalve Ltd, 88 Stonefield Road, Hastings, East Sussex, TN34 1QA Tel: (01424) 425682 Fax: (01424) 438789 E-mail: enquiries@clipvalve.co.uk

Colbear Ltd, 45 Lady Lane Industrial Estate, Hadleigh, Ipswich, IP7 6BQ Tel: (01473) 823722 Fax: (01473) 827466 E-mail: info@colbearuk.com

Colman Moducel, Oldfields Business Park, Birrell Street, Stoke-on-Trent, ST4 3ES Tel: (01782) 599995 Fax: (01782) 599220 E-mail: sales@eaton-williams.com

Crossling Ltd, Coast Road, Heaton, Newcastle upon Tyne, NE6 5TP Tel: 0191-265 4166 Fax: 0191-276 4839 E-mail: marketing@crossling.co.uk

Don Heating, Osprey Road, Sowton Industrial Estate, Exeter, EX2 7JG Tel: (01392) 444070 Fax: (01392) 444804 E-mail: donsales@gazco.com

Dunsley Heat Ltd, Bridge Mills, Holmfirth, HD9 3TW Tel: (01484) 682635 Fax: (01484) 688428 E-mail: sales@dunsleyheat.co.uk

▶ Ecoflam UK Ltd, 12 Goodwood Road, Pershore, Worcestershire, WR10 2JL Tel: (01386) 556092 Fax: (01386) 553789 E-mail: sales@ecoflam.co.uk

Elan Dragonair Ltd, 162 Southampton Road, Portsmouth, PO6 4RY Tel: (023) 9237 6451 Fax: (023) 9237 0411

Et Environmental Ltd, 47 Central Avenue, West Molesey, Surrey, KT8 2QZ Tel: (020) 8783 0033 Fax: (020) 8783 0140 E-mail: diffusion@etenv.co.uk

Euroheat Distributors (HBS) Ltd, Unit 2, Court Farm Business Park, Bishops Frome, Worcester, WR6 5AY Tel: (01885) 491100 Fax: (01885) 491101 E-mail: info@euroheat.co.uk

Express Radiators & Bathrooms Ltd, Abbey Mills, Charfield Road, Kingswood, Wotton-under-Edge, Gloucestershire, GL12 8RL Tel: (01453) 521166 Fax: (01453) 521799

F & P Wholesale, Chantry Road, Woburn Road Industrial Estate, Kempston, Bedford, MK42 7SU Tel: (01234) 845600 Fax: (01234) 840379

F & P Wholesale, 30 Engate Street, London, SE13 7HA Tel: (020) 8463 1000 Fax: (020) 8297 2661

Flamco Ltd, 4 St. Michaels Road, St. Helens, Merseyside, WA9 4WZ Tel: (01744) 818100 Fax: (01744) 830400 E-mail: info@flamco.co.uk

Grahams Group plc, 96 Temple Park Cresent, Edinburgh, EH11 1JR Tel: 0131-228 2345 Fax: 0131-228 5405 E-mail: mikedick@graham-group.co.uk

Grove Plumbing & Heating Supplies Ltd, Unit 11a National Trading Estate, Bramhall Moor Lane, Hazel Grove, Stockport, Cheshire, SK7 5AA Tel: 0161-456 4495 Fax: 0161-456 2678 E-mail: sales@groveplg.co.uk

Halstead Boilers Ltd, 16-22 First Avenue, Halstead, Essex, CO9 2EX Tel: (01787) 475557 Fax: (01787) 474588 E-mail: sales@halsteadboilers.co.uk

Harry Taylor Ltd, Kitsons Works, Aylesbury Road, Bromley, BR2 0QZ Tel: (020) 8464 0915 Fax: (020) 8464 0916 E-mail: heaters@harrytaylor.co.uk

Heating & Process Engineering Services Ltd, Crompton Road Industrial Estate, Ilkeston, Derbyshire, DE7 4BG Tel: 0115-930 5838 Fax: 0115-930 8899 E-mail: sales@heatpro.co.uk

Hotfrost, 72-76 Brighton Road, Surbiton, Surrey, KT6 5PP Tel: (020) 8399 7151 Fax: (020) 8399 9549

Johnson & Starley Ltd, Brackmills Indust Estate, Brackmills Industrial Estate, Northampton, NN4 7HR Tel: (01604) 762881 Fax: (01604) 767408 E-mail: sales@johnsonandstarley.co.uk

▶ Kongskilde UK Ltd, Hempstead Road, Holt, Norfolk, NR25 6EE Tel: (01263) 713291 Fax: (01263) 712922 E-mail: mail@kuk.kongskilde.com

Link Southern Heating Supplies, Bridge House, 283 Kingsland Road, London, E2 8AS Tel: (020) 7729 9328 Fax: (020) 7739 4336

Lochinvar Ltd, 7 Lombard Way, Banbury, Oxfordshire, OX16 4TJ Tel: (01295) 269981 Fax: (01295) 271640 E-mail: sales@lochinvar.ltd.uk

M H S Ltd, 35 Nobel Square, Burnt Mills Industrial Estate, Basildon, Essex, SS13 1LT Tel: (01268) 591010 Fax: (01268) 728202 E-mail: sales@modular-heating-group.co.uk

Metallic Construction Co. Ltd, Alfreton Road, Derby, DE21 4AQ Tel: (01332) 831296 Fax: (01332) 833712

Midland Brass Fittings Ltd, Wynford Industrial Trading Estate, Wynford Road, Birmingham, B27 6JT Tel: 0121-707 6666 Fax: 0121-708 1270 E-mail: sales@midbras.co.uk

Mikrofill Systems Ltd, West Court, Buntsford Park Road, Bromsgrove, Worcestershire, B60 3DX Tel: (01527) 574574 Fax: (01527) 575565 E-mail: info@mikrofill.com

Mikuni Heating UK Ltd, Unit 6 Second Avenue, Southampton, SO15 0LP Tel: (023) 8052 8777 Fax: (023) 8052 8800 E-mail: sales@mikuniheating.com

Nomoco Ltd, 77 Shaftesbury Avenue, Roundhay, Leeds, LS8 1DR Tel: (0870) 7001925 Fax: (0870) 7002024 E-mail: contactus@warmco.co.uk

Parts Centre, PO Box 48, Ripon, North Yorkshire, HG4 5NB Tel: (01765) 690690

T. Patton Ltd, 588 Lea Bridge Road, Leyton, London, E10 7DN Tel: (020) 8539 1599 Fax: (020) 8558 3578 E-mail: sales@tpatton.co.uk

Peco Services Ltd, Unit 13 Stonefield Park Industrial Estate, Martins Lane, Chilbolton, Stockbridge, Hampshire, SO20 6BL Tel: (01264) 860888 Fax: (01264) 860564 E-mail: pecoservices@btopenworld.com

Pipeline Centre, 17 Mowlem Trading Estate, Leeside Road, London, N17 0QJ Tel: (020) 8808 6633 Fax: (020) 8801 0632

Plumb Center, Station Approach, Coulsdon, Surrey, CR5 2YB Tel: (020) 8668 4121 Fax: (020) 8660 8795 E-mail: bk.colcon@woloseley.co.uk

Plumbase Ltd, 123-129 Portland Road, Hove, East Sussex, BN3 5QW Tel: (01273) 746161 Fax: (01273) 737677 E-mail: admin.marketing@plumbase.com

Plumbing & Heating Services, 194 Winchester Road, London, E4 9JP Tel: (020) 8523 2222 Fax: (020) 8527 6776 E-mail: phs@chris14.fsnet.co.uk

Propex Heating UK Ltd, Unit 5 Second Avenue, Millbrook, Southampton, SO15 0LP Tel: (023) 8052 8555 Fax: (023) 8052 8800

PTS Plumbing Trade Supplies Ltd, 2 Sabre Close, Quedgeley, Gloucester, GL2 4NZ Tel: (01452) 726100 Fax: (01452) 724474 E-mail: sales@bssgroup.com

Reznor UK Ltd, Park Farm Road, Park Farm Industrial Estate, Folkestone, Kent, CT19 5DR Tel: (01303) 259141 Fax: (01303) 850002 E-mail: marketing@reznor.co.uk

Roberts-Gordon, Oxford Street, Bilston, West Midlands, WV14 7EG Tel: (01902) 494425 Fax: (01902) 403200 E-mail: uksales@rg-inc.com

Rowland Tysoe Ltd, 80 High Street, Cranleigh, Surrey, GU6 8AH Tel: (01483) 272060 Fax: (01483) 278076

S W Heating Equipment Ltd, Environmental Centre, 98 Holmesdale Street, Cardiff, CF11 7BU Tel: (029) 2023 7654 Fax: (029) 2023 7685 E-mail: mail@swgroup.org.uk

Seagoe Technology Ltd, Church Road, Portadown, Craigavon, County Armagh, BT63 5HU Tel: (028) 3833 3131 Fax: (028) 3835 1390 E-mail: info@jltgroup.com

Shoreheat Ltd, Unit 5 226 Purley Way, Croydon, CR0 4XG Tel: (020) 8688 7438 Fax: (020) 8680 0663

Sloan Agencies Ltd, Unit 3 Duncrue Industrial Park, Duncrue Road, Belfast, BT3 9BP Tel: (028) 9037 0377 Fax: (028) 9037 0344

Space-Ray UK, 4-6 Chapel Lane, Claydon, Ipswich, IP6 0JL Tel: (01473) 830551 Fax: (01473) 832055 E-mail: info@spaceray.co.uk

T G Lynes Ltd, 115 Brancroft Way, Enfield, Middlesex, EN3 7QE Tel: (0845) 0716071 Fax: (020) 7278 1560 E-mail: sales@tglynes.co.uk

Tansun Ltd, 1 Ridgacre Road, West Bromwich, West Midlands, B71 1BW Tel: 0121-580 6200 Fax: 0121-580 6222 E-mail: quartzinfo@tansun.co.uk

Tayside Plumbing & Building Supplies Ltd, 1 Dens Road, Dundee, DD3 7SR Tel: (01382) 229401 Fax: (01382) 202447 E-mail: office@tayside-plumbing.co.uk

Thermobile UK Ltd, 12 Buckingham Close, Bermuda Industrial Estate, Nuneaton, Warwickshire, CV10 7JT Tel: (024) 7635 7960 Fax: (024) 7635 7969 E-mail: sales@thermobile.co.uk

Thompson Plumbase, 10 Chapel Street, Redruth, Cornwall, TR15 2DE Tel: (01209) 215676 Fax: (01209) 213222

Travis Perkins plc, Fairfield Street, Bradford, West Yorkshire, BD4 9QP Tel: (01274) 681065 Fax: (01274) 688843

Travis Perkins plc, Thurman Street, Ilkeston, Derbyshire, DE7 4BY Tel: 0115-932 4278 Fax: 0115-944 1338

Travis Perkins Trading Co. Ltd, Rowlandson Street, Grimsby, North East Lincolnshire, DN31 3LL Tel: (01472) 345471 Fax: (01472) 242760

Ultimate Discount Heating, 28 Rushgrove Avenue, London, NW9 6QS Tel: (020) 8205 6688 Fax: (020) 8205 8899

Unit F, F Liver Industrial Estate, Long Lane, Walton, Liverpool, L9 7ES Tel: 0151-525 3344 Fax: 0151-525 3113 E-mail: liverpool@williamwilson.co.uk

Vulcana Gas Appliances Ltd, 30 Bridge Road, Haywards Heath, West Sussex, RH16 1TX Tel: (01444) 415871 Fax: (01444) 441433 E-mail: vulcanagas@pavilion.co.uk

Warmac Ltd, Bear House, 7 Tootal Grove, Salford, Manchester, M6 8DN Tel: (0870) 0500739 Fax: (0870) 0552670 E-mail: info@warmac.co.uk

G.B. Willbond Ltd, Deakins Placed, Radford, Nottingham, NG7 3FT Tel: 0115-841 8888 Fax: 0115-841 8876 E-mail: thogg@willbond.co.uk

Winterwarm UK Ltd, Unit H3, Taylor Industrial Estate, Risley, Warrington, WA3 6BL Tel: (01925) 765799 Fax: (01925) 762996 E-mail: enquiries@winterwarm.com

Wolseley Centers Ltd, Boroughbridge Road, Ripon, North Yorkshire, HG4 1SL Tel: (01765) 690690 Fax: (01765) 694516

HEATERS, SURFACE, ELECTRIC

Surface Heating Systems Ltd, 1 Heath Mill Enterprise Park, Heath Mill Road, Wombourne, Wolverhampton, WV5 8AP Tel: (01902) 326062 Fax: (01902) 892866 E-mail: surfheat@aol.com

HEATING AND VENTILATING EQUIPMENT POWER REGULATORS

Dale Heating Services (U.K.) Ltd, Unit 2, Rookery Lane, Thurmaston, Leicester, LE4 8AU Tel: 0116-264 0055 Fax: 0116-269 7007

HEATING AND VENTILATING SYSTEMS

▶ Biocraft Ltd, 25b Chapel Hill, Tilehurst, Reading, RG31 5BT Tel: 0118-945 1144 E-mail: sales@biocraft.co.uk

Energy Technique plc, 47 Central Avenue, West Molesey, Surrey, KT8 2QZ Tel: (020) 8941 2199 Fax: (020) 8783 0140 E-mail: sales@energytechniqueplc.co.uk

Industrial Metal Forms Ltd, Units 15 Wynford Industrial Trading Estate, Wynford Road, Birmingham, B27 6JP Tel: 0121-765 4800 Fax: 0121-765 4810

Strathclyde Fans Ltd, Unit B4 Somervell Trading Estate, Somervell Street, Cambuslang, Glasgow, G72 7EB Tel: 0141-641 0224 Fax: 0141-641 7796

HEATING AND VENTILATION CONSULTANCY

Force Heating & Cooling Services, 80 Rawmarsh Hill, Parkgate, Rotherham, South Yorkshire, S62 6EX Tel: (01709) 527920 Fax: (01709) 526290 E-mail: force.heating@virgin.net

J K Enterprises Ltd, Unit 2 Hewell Lane, Barnt Green, Birmingham, B45 8NZ Tel: 0121-447 7678 Fax: 0121-447 8333

Lagerstedt & Krantz (UK) Ltd, Unit 3, Metana House, Priestley Way, Crawley, West Sussex, RH10 9NT Tel: (0870) 2424873 Fax: (0870) 2424874 E-mail: info@lagerstedt-krantz.co.uk

▶ NRM Partnership Ltd, Brunell House, Swanwick Lane, Broughton, Milton Keynes, MK10 9LB Tel: (01908) 663307 Fax: (01908) 663260 E-mail: kat@cdpartner.co.uk

Siemans Building Technologies Ltd, Hawthorne Road, Staines, Middlesex, TW18 3AY Tel: (01784) 461616 Fax: (01784) 464646

HEATING AND VENTILATION DAMPERS

▶ Blocker Products Ltd, Pals Haven, Hook Lane, Aldingbourne, Chichester, West Sussex, PO20 3TE Tel: (01243) 545465 Fax: (01243) 545475 E-mail: millerbrian@btconnect.com

HEATING AND VENTILATION INSTALLATION OR SERVICING, *See also headings under Central Heating*

A A Duncan Biggar Ltd, 16a Broughton Road, Biggar, Lanarkshire, ML12 6HA Tel: (01899) 220170 Fax: (01899) 220170

A B S Ltd, New House, Christchurch Road, Ringwood, Hampshire, BH24 3AP Tel: (01425) 477777 Fax: (01425) 474400 E-mail: first@absme.co.uk

A & K Services Co., 807 Lea Bridge Road, London, E17 9DS Tel: (020) 8509 2600 Fax: (020) 8520 9678 E-mail: a.kservices@btconnect.com

Abercorn Heating Ltd, 105 Abercorn Street, Paisley, Renfrewshire, PA3 4AT Tel: 0141-887 0308 Fax: 0141-887 6823 E-mail: markbrooks@abercorn-heating.co.uk

Advanced Maintenance Services Ltd, Alchorne Place, The Airport, Portsmouth, PO3 5QL Tel: (023) 9267 3333 Fax: (023) 9269 3319 E-mail: ams@zoom.co.uk

Air Care Mechanical Services Ltd, 297 Avenue Road Extension, Clarendon Park, Leicester, LE2 3ER Tel: 0116-270 9707 Fax: 0116-270 5737 E-mail: sales@aircaremechanical.co.uk

Airconstruct Midlands Ltd, Littleton Drive, Cannock, Staffordshire, WS12 4TS Tel: (01543) 572300 Fax: (01543) 574090 E-mail: sales@airconstruct.co.uk

Airflow Engineering Services Heating Ventilation Air Conditioning, Drift Road, Kymba House, Whitehill, Bordon, Hampshire, GU35 9DZ Tel: (01420) 473401 Fax: (01420) 489955

Air-O-Ducts Contracts Ltd, Unit 10, 865 Ringwood Road, Bournemouth, BH11 8LL Tel: (01202) 576511 Fax: (01202) 570511

Aqua Mechanical Services Ltd, Aqua House, Rose & Crown Road, Swavesey, Cambridge, CB4 5RB Tel: (01954) 230948 Fax: (01954) 230593 E-mail: group@aqua.co.uk

HEATING AND VENTILATION INSTALLATION OR SERVICING – *continued*

Arnold Building Services Ltd, Rudgeway, Bristol, BS35 3ZQ Tel: (01453) 547730 Fax: (01453) 547766 E-mail: info@abs-radiantheating.co.uk

Arnold James St Albans Ltd, 1 Metro Centre, Ronsons Way, Sandridge, St. Albans, Hertfordshire, AL4 9QT Tel: (01727) 851477 Fax: (01727) 842912

Associated Contract Energy Ltd, 73-75 Church Road, Redfield, Bristol, BS5 9JR Tel: 0117-939 4495 Fax: 0117-939 4496 E-mail: vivre21@hotmail.com

J. Atha & Son, 9 Norton Church Glebe, Sheffield, S8 8JX Tel: 0114-274 6407

Automated Systems, 1-3 Mossley Road, Grasscroft, Oldham, OL4 4HH Tel: (0870) 2402771 Fax: (0870) 2402773 E-mail: stevepage@automatedsystem.org

Avonside Plumbing & Heating Yorkshire Ltd, Dunswell Road, Cottingham, North Humberside, HU16 4JU Tel: (01482) 841146 Fax: (01482) 875137

B M S Ltd, 1 Dalzells Lane, Burwell, Cambridge, CB5 0GA Tel: (01638) 741275 Fax: (01638) 742236 E-mail: reception@burmech.co.uk

B T U (Heating) Ltd, 38 Weyside Road, Guildford, Surrey, GU1 1JB Tel: (01483) 590600 Fax: (01483) 590601 E-mail: enquiries@btu-heating.com

William Bailey Ltd, Merlin Court, Ripley Road, Ambergate, Belper, Derbyshire, DE56 2EP Tel: (01773) 853703 Fax: (01773) 856930 E-mail: enquiries@williambailey.co.uk

Beaver Co. Ltd, 968 North Circular Road, London, NW2 7JR Tel: (020) 8208 1839 Fax: (020) 8452 4610 E-mail: bopco@aol.com

F. Bentley & Co. (Heating & Plumbing) Ltd, 312 Ware Road, Hertford, SG13 7ER Tel: (01992) 500009 Fax: (01992) 505005

Benz Industrial Heating Ltd, 15 Dover Road, Northfleet, Gravesend, Kent, DA11 9PH Tel: (01474) 332522 Fax: (01474) 564267

Bering Heating Supplies Ltd, Unit 9 Station Industrial Estate, Oxford Road, Wokingham, Berkshire, RG41 2YQ Tel: 0118-978 9886 Fax: 0118-978 7460

James Boardman Ltd, Weir Street, Blackburn, BB2 2BB Tel: (01254) 59755 Fax: (01254) 682482 E-mail: eng@jboardman.co.uk

▶ Boiler Diagnostics Ltd, 127 Simpson Road, Snodland, Kent, ME6 5QH Tel: (01634) 244120 Fax: (01634) 245305 E-mail: matt@boilerdiagnostics.co.uk

Bostel Brothers Ltd, 1-3 The Compound, Northease Close, Hove, East Sussex, BN3 8LJ Tel: (01273) 430264 Fax: (01273) 422605

Bradshaw Boiler & Heating Services Ltd, 624 Tonge Moor Road, Bolton, BL2 3BJ Tel: (01204) 307484 Fax: (01204) 593835 E-mail: bradshawboilers@fsbdial.co.uk

Brian Cooper, 1 Market Street, Hollingworth, Hyde, Cheshire, SK14 8NE Tel: (01457) 763861 Fax: (01457) 855712

Brittain Adams (Holdings) Ltd, 40 The Boulevard, Stoke-on-Trent, ST6 6DP Tel: (01782) 834175 Fax: (01782) 834176

Colin Bullot & Sons Ltd, 7 Glendale Walk, Cheshunt, Waltham Cross, Hertfordshire, EN8 9RJ Tel: (01992) 627407 Fax: (01992) 633198 E-mail: colin@bullot.co.uk

C H Lindsey & Son Ltd, Brunel Way, Severalls Industrial Park, Colchester, CO4 9QW Tel: (01206) 844567 Fax: (01206) 844483 E-mail: info@lindsey-aircon.com

▶ C & S Erections Ltd, 31 Cuddington Avenue, Worcester Park, Surrey, KT4 7DB Tel: (020) 8330 3307

Camrose Air Conditioning Ltd, Unit D4 Brunswick Place, Cranbourne Lane, Basingstoke, Hampshire, RG21 3NN Tel: 0845 4941703 Fax: (01256) 322801 E-mail: peter@camroseair.co.uk

Claverbury Ltd, 11 Tindale Cl, South Croydon, Surrey, CR2 0RT Tel: (020) 8651 5265 Fax: (020) 8651 6037

Clean Heat & Engineering Co. Ltd, Southbank House, Black Prince Road, London, SE1 7SJ Tel: (020) 7793 4002 Fax: (020) 7735 7253 E-mail: email@cleanheat.co.uk

Combi Services Heating Ltd, 196 Whittington Road, London, N22 8YL Tel: (020) 8881 1941 Fax: (020) 8881 3740

Complete Air Systems, Unit H & I Maybrook Industrial Estate, Maybrook Road, Walsall, WS8 7DG Tel: (01543) 361301 Fax: (01543) 372530

Consent Services Ltd, 168 Repps Rd, Martham, Great Yarmouth, Norfolk, NR29 4QZ Tel: (01493) 748647 Fax: (01493) 748647

Constant Air Systems Ltd, Hillbottom Road, Sands Industrial Estate, High Wycombe, Buckinghamshire, HP12 4HJ Tel: (01494) 469529 Fax: (01494) 469549 E-mail: admin@constantair.co.uk

Cordell Engineering, 26-28 Elmtree Road, Teddington, Middlesex, TW11 8ST Tel: (020) 8943 8884 Fax: (020) 8943 8852

Craig Wyllie Plumbing & Heating, 20 Scott Court, Alva, Clackmannanshire, FK12 5LZ Tel: (07917) 033271 Fax: (01259) 769027 E-mail: craigwyllie@hotmail.co.uk

D H Bryant Ltd, 33 Station Road, Shalford, Guildford, Surrey, GU4 8HF Tel: (01483) 577721 Fax: (01483) 579888 E-mail: dhbryant.ltd@btconnect.com

D Train, 43-45 Fisher Street, Stranraer, Wigtownshire, DG9 7LH Tel: (01776) 702357 Fax: (01776) 702357

Dale Heating Services (U.K.) Ltd, Unit 2, Rookery Lane, Thurmaston, Leicester, LE4 8AU Tel: 0116-264 0055 Fax: 0116-269 7007

Darnells Ltd, Oakfield Industrial Estate, Eynsham, Witney, Oxfordshire, OX29 4TH Tel: (01865) 883996 Fax: (01865) 883986 E-mail: mail@darnells.ltd.uk

Delsol Air Systems Ltd, Bankfield Mills, Huddersfield Road, Mirfield, West Yorkshire, WF14 9DD Tel: (01924) 498971 Fax: (01924) 499554 E-mail: enquiries@delsolairsystems.co.uk

B.P. Dempsey Ltd, Units 6 & 8, March Street, Sheffield, S9 5DQ Tel: 0114-242 1900 Fax: 0114-243 2232

Design Installation Service Electrical Ltd, P O Box 137, Cheltenham, Gloucestershire, GL53 7ZF Tel: (01242) 533100 Fax: (01242) 221187

Dix & Sons Ltd, Havelock Street, Kettering, Northamptonshire, NN16 9QA Tel: (01536) 512827 Fax: (01536) 512827

Dove Heating Ltd, 227 Kingston Road, New Malden, Surrey, KT3 3SZ Tel: (020) 8241 0141 Fax: (020) 8942 9992

Ducatt Heating Co. Ltd, Platts Road, Stourbridge, West Midlands, DY8 4YT Tel: (01384) 394641 Fax: (01384) 440455 E-mail: info@ducattheating.co.uk

Duct Com Ltd, 94 Shrewsbury Lane, London, Greater London, SE18 3JL Tel: 0208 3172563 Fax: 0208 3174554E-mail: info@ductcom.com

Duct Engineering Luton Ltd, Cradock Industrial Estate, Cradock Road, Luton, LU4 0JF Tel: (01582) 562626 Fax: (01582) 583046 E-mail: ductengineering@aol.com

E M S Ltd, 15-29 Eyre Street Hill, London, EC1R 5LB Tel: (020) 7837 4707 Fax: (020) 7833 8299 E-mail: enquiries@ems-maintenance.co.uk

Edward Foster & Son Bradford Ltd, Benton House, Nelson Street, Bradford, West Yorkshire, BD5 0DP Tel: (01274) 733511 Fax: (01274) 730227

Elyo UK Ltd, Walker Office Park, Walker Road, Guide, Blackburn, BB1 2QE Tel: (01254) 662323 Fax: (01254) 664084

▶ Emo Oil Ltd, Derwent Valley Industrial Estate, Dunnington, York, YO19 5PD Tel: (0800) 685685 E-mail: info@emooil.co.uk

Engineering Installation Teesside Ltd, Owens Road, Middlesbrough, Cleveland, TS6 6HX Tel: (01642) 452471 Fax: (01642) 462005 E-mail: sales@enginst.co.uk

Engineering Services (Paisley) Ltd (ESL), 65 Espedair Street, Paisley, Renfrewshire, PA2 6RL Tel: 0141-889 1316 Fax: 0141-887 5344 E-mail: info@eslpaisley.co.uk

Enright Engineering Services, Unit 8 Team Valley Business Centre, Earlsway, Team Valley Trading Estate, Gateshead, Tyne & Wear, NE11 0QH Tel: 0191-482 0002 Fax: 0191-482 0027 E-mail: info@enrightengineering.co.uk

Eric C Flower Ltd, 413 Petre Street, Sheffield, S4 8LL Tel: 0114-243 1221 Fax: 0114-243 7196 E-mail: johnwilliams@ericcflowers.co.uk

Erskine Environmental Engineering Ltd., 16 Lady Lane, Paisley, Renfrewshire, PA1 2LJ Tel: 0141-887 7784 Fax: 0141-889 4338

▶ Essex Mechanical Services, 3 Peartree Business Centre, Peartree Road, Stanway, Colchester, CO3 0JN Tel: (01206) 368821 Fax: (01206) 368826

E-Tech Group (HVAC Div), The E-Tech Centre, Boundary Road, Great Yarmouth, Norfolk, NR31 0LY Tel: 01493 419800 Fax: 01493 419805 E-mail: etech-hvac@etechcentre.com

Evans Mechanical Services Ltd, Derby House, 29 Castle Street, Caergwrle, Wrexham, Clwyd, LL12 9AD Tel: (01978) 760000 Fax: (01978) 761082 E-mail: enquiries@evans-mech.co.uk

F P Hurley & Sons Ltd, Queens Road, Bridgend Industrial Estate, Bridgend, Mid Glamorgan, CF31 3UR Tel: (01656) 661151 Fax: (01656) 645477 E-mail: bridgend@fphurley.co.uk

F R Scott Ltd, Canning Street, Hull, HU2 8QS Tel: (01482) 324731 Fax: (01482) 214290 E-mail: sales@frscott.co.uk

Fabricair Systems Ltd, 5 Burbidge Road, Birmingham, B9 4US Tel: 0121-766 7707 Fax: 0121-766 8356 E-mail: sales@fabricairsystems.co.uk

Fairley Brown & Co. Ltd, 77a Wilson Road, Reading, RG30 2RT Tel: 0118-958 1641 Fax: 0118-950 3233 E-mail: office@fairleybrown.fsnet.co.uk

Fairs & Green (MS) Ltd, 15-17 Vale Road, Tunbridge Wells, Kent, TN1 1BS Tel: (01892) 615678 Fax: (01892) 515788

Farrelly Facilities & Engineering Ltd, Facilities House, 386-388 Boldmere Road, Sutton Coldfield, West Midlands, B73 5EZ Tel: 0121-382 9988 Fax: 0121-382 4155 E-mail: sales@farrellyfacilities.com

Fenweld Engineering Services, Unit 8 Addington Works, Knutsford Way Sealand Indust Estate, Chester, CH1 4LT Tel: (01244) 380880 Fax: (01244) 380294 E-mail: fenweld@compuserve.com

First In Service Ltd, Windsor Industrial Estate, Rupert Street, Birmingham, B7 4PR Tel: 0121-333 3301 Fax: 0121-333 3302 E-mail: sellis@firstinservice.co.uk

Fisher & Sons Fakenham Ltd, 7 Dereham Road, Hempton, Fakenham, Norfolk, NR21 7LD Tel: (01328) 862781 Fax: (01328) 856229 E-mail: mail@fishers-fakenham.co.uk

Fletcher, Jubilee Lodge, Jubilee Way, Chessington, Surrey, KT9 1TR Tel: (020) 8391 1876 Fax: (020) 8391 1876

Fred G Alden Ltd, Langford Locks, Kidlington, Oxfordshire, OX5 1LJ Tel: (01865) 855000 Fax: (01865) 855008

Frise M S & Sons Ltd, 7 Trowbridge Road, Westbury, Wiltshire, BA13 3AY Tel: (01373) 826333 Fax: (01373) 826444 E-mail: sales@frise.co.uk

G F Cross & Sons, Unit 10 Kings Meadow, Ferry Hinksey Road, Oxford, OX2 0DP Tel: (01865) 242358 Fax: (01865) 241648 E-mail: info@gfcrossandsons.co.uk

G H Marshall Ltd, 10 Carey St, Reading, RG1 7JT Tel: 0118-959 5522 Fax: 0118-958 5582 E-mail: info@ghmarshall.co.uk

G O C Engineering Services, Buckingham Cottage, Crow Road, Fintry, Glasgow, G63 0XJ Tel: (01360) 860478 Fax: (01360) 860478 E-mail: jchesney@goceng.co.uk

Gas Service Agents Ltd, 39-43 Harrison Road, Southampton, SO17 3TL Tel: (023) 8051 6611 Fax: (023) 8067 1968 E-mail: info@gascare.com

Gas Technical Services, Unit 1, Richmond Road, West Llanion Business Centre, Pembroke Dock, Dyfed, SA72 6TZ Tel: (01646) 683845 Fax: (01646) 686542 E-mail: gastechnicalservices@hotmail.co.uk

Gazelle Ventures Ltd, 276B New Road, Croxley Green, Rickmansworth, Hertfordshire, WD3 3HH Tel: (01923) 720466 Fax: (01923) 720411 E-mail: sales@gazelleventures.co.uk

Gibson Wight Ltd, 14-18 East Shaw Street, Kilmarnock, Ayrshire, KA1 4AN Tel: (01563) 523633 Fax: (01563) 536472 E-mail: charles.gibson@gibsonwight.co.uk

GK Maintenance, Leamore Industrial Estate, 8 Wall End Close, Walsall, WS2 7PH Tel: (01922) 479462 Fax: (01922) 404842 E-mail: staff@gkmaintenance.co.uk

Glenfield Plumbers Ltd, Southfield Industrial Estate, 62 Nasmyth Road, Glenrothes, Fife, KY6 2SD Tel: (01592) 774818 Fax: (01592) 630552

Goldace Industries, Unit 17 Harmill Industrial Estate, Grovebury Road, Leighton Buzzard, Bedfordshire, LU7 4FF Tel: (01525) 851815 Fax: (01525) 852484 E-mail: info@goldaceindustries.com

Gradwood Ltd, Lansdown House, 85 Buxton Road, Stockport, Cheshire, SK2 6LR Tel: 0161-480 9629 Fax: 0161-474 7433 E-mail: sales@gradwood.co.uk

Griffiths & Son, 34 Clwyd Close Manor Lane, Hawarden Industrial Park, Hawarden, Deeside, Clwyd, CH5 3PZ Tel: (01244) 537800 Fax: (01244) 537757 E-mail: griffiths-son@btinternet.com

GSH Ltd, GSH House, Forge Lane, Stoke-on-Trent, ST1 5PZ Tel: (01782) 200400 Fax: (01782) 285552 E-mail: vacancies@gshgroup.com

▶ Guardian Environmental, 117 Clophill Road, Maulden, Bedford, MK45 2AE Tel: (01525) 862528 Fax: (01525) 862163 E-mail: val.barnes@guardian.uk.com

H.E.S. Maintenance Co. Ltd, 141-143 Worcester Road, Bromsgrove, Worcestershire, B61 7HN Tel: (01527) 878707 Fax: (01527) 575264

H Mitton Ltd, 451 Cleckheaton Road, Low Moor, Bradford, West Yorkshire, BD12 0HS Tel: (01274) 691177 Fax: (01274) 691188 E-mail: projects@mittonmechanical.com

Harpers Weybridge, 135 Stubbington Lane, Fareham, Hampshire, PO14 2NF Tel: (01329) 662293 Fax: (01329) 665518

Harry Taylor Ltd, Kitsons Works, Aylesbury Road, Bromley, BR2 0QZ Tel: (020) 8464 0915 Fax: (020) 8464 0916 E-mail: heaters@harrytaylor.co.uk

Heat Works Ltd, Unit 2 Moorend Indust Estate, Bradford Road, Cleckheaton, West Yorkshire, BD19 3TT Tel: (01274) 852900 Fax: (01274) 852911 E-mail: info@heatworks.co.uk

Heatfast Mechanical Services Ltd, 55 Halesowen Road, Netherton, Dudley, West Midlands, DY2 9PY Tel: (01384) 235054 Fax: (01384) 455343

Heating & Industrial Pipework Ltd, 19-35 Warwick Street, Coventry, CV5 6ET Tel: (024) 7667 2224 Fax: (024) 7671 3391 E-mail: hipcov@aol.com

Heating & Pipework Installations Leeds Ltd, 353 Tong Road, Leeds, LS12 4QG Tel: 0113-263 0318 Fax: 0113-231 0687 E-mail: drawings@hpileeds.co.uk

Heating & Ventilating Services Ltd, 50 Park Lane, Basford, Nottingham, NG6 0DT Tel: 0115-978 1445 Fax: 0115-978 1596

Hesflo Installations Ltd, 6 Dial Lane, Bristol, BS16 5UH Tel: 0117-970 1930 Fax: 0117-970 1931 E-mail: design@hesflo.co.uk

Heventech Mechanical Service Ltd, 3 Redbridge Enterprise Centre, Thompson Close, Ilford, Essex, IG1 1TY Tel: (0845) 1298565 E-mail: sales@heventech.co.uk

Hills Electrical & Mechanical plc, Green Lane, Walsall, WS2 8HB Tel: (01922) 721105 Fax: (01922) 721151 E-mail: admin@hillelec.plc.uk

Howard & Buckner Ltd, Unit E1, The Seedbed Centre, Harlow, Essex, CM19 5AF Tel: (01279) 422955 Fax: (01279) 422955

Hutcheon Services Ltd, Bowtree House, Minto Drive, Altens Industrial Estate, Aberdeen, AB12 3LW Tel: (01224) 874875 Fax: (01224) 895975 E-mail: info@hutcheon-services.ltd.uk

Indtherm Ltd, 120 Wellington Road, Dudley, West Midlands, DY1 1UB Tel: (01384) 456666 Fax: (01384) 456666 E-mail: action@indtherm.co.uk

▶ Industrial & Commercial Environment Ltd, Bowdens, Broad Oak, Sturminster Newton, Dorset, DT10 2HG Tel: (01258) 471954 Fax: (01258) 471904 E-mail: office@ice-uk.eu.com

Inviron Ltd, 17 Portman Road, Ipswich, IP1 2BP Tel: (01473) 219921 Fax: (01473) 231317

J F Heppelthwaite Ltd, Sherwood House 6 Marlborough Parade, Uxbridge Road, Uxbridge, Middlesex, UB10 0LR Tel: (01895) 460002 Fax: (01895) 460004

J S A Mechanical Services Ltd, Unit 28 Croft Road Industrial Estate, Croft Road, Newcastle, Staffordshire, ST5 0TW Tel: (01782) 635517 Fax: (01782) 630485

James Ramsey Glasgow Ltd, 85 Dykehead Street, Queenslie Industrial Estate, Glasgow, G33 4AQ Tel: 0141-774 2602 Fax: 0141-774 4321 E-mail: jamesramseyltd@btconnect.com

Jarvis Heating Ltd, Jarvis House, 212 Station Road, Harpenden, Hertfordshire, AL5 4EH Tel: (01582) 761211 Fax: (01582) 764100 E-mail: info@jarvisheating.co.uk

Jaydee Heating Ltd, Nobel Road, Wester Gourdie Industrial Estate, West Gourdie Industrial Estate, Dundee, DD2 4XE Tel: (01382) 611118 Fax: (01382) 400540

Jennersons Ltd, 17a Highfield Road, Dartford, DA1 2JS Tel: (01322) 275255 Fax: (01322) 225710

John Carter Salt Lane Ltd, 6-10 Salt Lane, Salisbury, SP1 1EE Tel: (01722) 322407 Fax: (01722) 412146 E-mail: enquiry@john-carters.co.uk

Richard Johnson Ltd, Northacre House, 80B High Street, Northwood, Middlesex, HA6 1BJ Tel: (01923) 835930 Fax: (01923) 836045 E-mail: info@relianceplumbing.co.uk

K Binks Heating Ltd, Environment House, Witty Street, Hull, HU3 4BH Tel: (01482) 328979 Fax: (01482) 213897 E-mail: enquiries@binksheating.co.uk

K M Services Ltd, 16 Bourne Industrial Estate, Wrotham Road, Borough Green, Sevenoaks, Kent, TN15 8DG Tel: (01732) 882280 Fax: (01732) 886011

K & P Heating & Plumbing, Saxon House, Edward Street, Cambridge, CB1 2LS Tel: (01223) 364129 Fax: (01223) 313886 E-mail: sales@kpheatingplumbing.co.uk

Kembery Group Ltd, 67-69 Sutherland Road, London, E17 6BH Tel: (020) 8527 1520 Fax: (020) 8527 1524

▶ Kershaw Mechanical Services Ltd, Beadle Trading Estate, Ditton Walk, Cambridge, CB5 8PD Tel: (01223) 715800 Fax: (01223) 411061 E-mail: enquiries@kershaw-grp.co.uk

Lee Air Conditioning Services Ltd, Lee House, Lower Road, Kenley, Surrey, CR8 5NH Tel: (020) 8660 5022 Fax: (020) 8668 0296 E-mail: nick.taylor@leeac.co.uk

Lightfoot Bros Ltd, 32 Castle Street, Aylesbury, Buckinghamshire, HP20 2RA Tel: (01296) 482855 Fax: (01296) 482855

Lindon Environmental Air Services Ltd, Stoke Heath Terminal, Warrant Road, Market Drayton, Shropshire, TF9 2JH Tel: (01630) 655100 Fax: (01630) 654675

A. Longworth & Sons Ltd, 55 Waverley Road, Sale, Cheshire, M33 7AY Tel: 0161-973 8398 Fax: 0161-905 1095

Lorne Stewart plc, Barley House, Duncan Road, Park Gate, Southampton, SO31 1ZT Tel: (01489) 885444 Fax: (01489) 885606 E-mail: soton@lornestewart.co.uk

M Bielby Ltd, 4 Cave Street, Hull, HU5 2TZ Tel: (01482) 342653 Fax: (01482) 447366 E-mail: info@mbielby.com

M & J Lossos Co. Ltd, 31 Beethoven St, London, W10 4LJ Tel: (020) 8969 1367 Fax: (020) 8968 8913 E-mail: admin@kaloricheater.co.uk

M J N Ltd, Davis House, 69-73 High Street, Croydon, CR9 1PY Tel: (020) 8686 5577 Fax: (020) 8681 3114 E-mail: jhipwell@mjncolston.co.uk

MacFarlane Environmental Ltd, Unit 20, East Belfast Enterprise Park, Belfast, BT5 4GX Tel: (028) 9045 7961 Fax: (028) 9045 9275 E-mail: macfarlane@btinternet.com

Mckiernan Group Ltd, Crown St Works, Crown Street, Accrington, Lancashire, BB5 0RW Tel: (01254) 398532 Fax: (01254) 392157 E-mail: design@themckiernangroup.co.uk

Macwhirter Ltd, 5 Stoke View Business Park, Stoke View Road, Bristol, BS16 3AE Tel: 0117-939 6661 Fax: 0117-939 6662 E-mail: sales@macwhirter.co.uk

Mantells, A, 2 Holland Road, London, SE25 5RF Tel: (020) 8654 3163 Fax: (020) 8654 3163

Maval Ltd, Skippers Lane, Skippers Lane Industrial Estat, Middlesbrough, Cleveland, TS6 6HA Tel: (01642) 455101 Fax: (01642) 458507 E-mail: maval@talk21.com

Mechelec Building Services Ltd, Poulton Close, Dover, Kent, CT17 0HL Tel: (01304) 205559 Fax: (01304) 242068

Mellor Bromley, 141 Barkby Road, Leicester, LE4 9LW Tel: 0116-276 6636 Fax: 0116-246 0426 E-mail: dbloxam@mellorbromley.co.uk

Metal Fabrication Co (Cardiff) Ltd, East Moors Road, Cardiff, CF24 5EE Tel: (029) 2048 9767 Fax: (029) 2048 0407 E-mail: sales@metal-fab.co.uk

Midland Air Conditioning Ltd, 253 Walsall Road, Perry Barr, Birmingham, B42 1TY Tel: 0121-356 1809 Fax: 0121-356 9478 E-mail: midlandaircon@btclick.com

Miracle Astec Ltd, PO Box 119, Horsham, West Sussex, RH12 4YZ Tel: (01403) 255140 Fax: (01403) 260855

C.A. Mulkern, 8 Springfield Road, Chesham, Buckinghamshire, HP5 1PW Tel: (01494) 783802

Mytchett Engineering Services, Sunnyhaven, Salisbury Terrace, Mytchett, Camberley, Surrey, GU16 6DB Tel: (01252) 511397 Fax: (01252) 377460

N J R Installations Ltd, Chapel Street, Dudley, West Midlands, DY2 9PN Tel: (01384) 455555 Fax: (01384) 456177

HEATING AND VENTILATION INSTALLATION OR SERVICING – *continued*

Neville Tucker, Rotterdam Road, Hull, HU7 0XD Tel: (01482) 834900 Fax: (01482) 879852 E-mail: info@nevilletucker.co.uk

New Burn Services, Bird House, Bishopswood Lane, Crossway Green, Stourport-on-Severn, Worcestershire, DY13 9SE Tel: (01299) 251200 Fax: (01299) 822831

Newbury Heating, 1 Stainforth Road, Ilford, Essex, IG2 7EH Tel: (020) 8550 8175

John Nicholls Trading Ltd, Overthorpe Road, Banbury, Oxfordshire, OX16 4TB Tel: (01295) 262294 Fax: (01295) 270895

Nomoco Ltd, 77 Shaftesbury Avenue, Roundhay, Leeds, LS8 1DR Tel: (0870) 7001925 Fax: (0870) 7002024 E-mail: contactus@warmco.co.uk

Norfolk Heating Ltd, Prestige House, Salhouse Road, Norwich, NR7 9AR Tel: (01603) 429426 Fax: (01603) 424380 E-mail: nhlmech@aol.com

Oco Ltd, 15 Essex Road, Dartford, DA1 2AU Tel: (01322) 276614 Fax: (01322) 227790 E-mail: headoffice@ocoltd.co.uk

Omega Mechanical Services Ltd, 14 Sringtown Road, Springtown Industrial Estate, Londonderry, BT48 0LY Tel: (028) 7137 0219 Fax: (028) 7137 2102 E-mail: omegamechanical@btinternet.com

P S I (Resources) Ltd, Unit 3, Barlow Street, Walkden, Manchester, M28 3BQ Tel: 0161-703 8911 Fax: 0161-703 8995 E-mail: sales@p-s-i.co.uk

Paine Manwaring Ltd, 7-11 Ardsheal Road, Worthing, West Sussex, BN14 7RW Tel: (01903) 237522 Fax: (01903) 236511 E-mail: enquires@painemanwearing.co.uk

Paterson J Son Plumbers Ltd, 28 East London Street, Edinburgh, EH7 4BQ Tel: 0131-556 7563 Fax: 0131-557 9080 E-mail: sales@ppservices.co.uk

Pickup H Mechanical Electrical Services Ltd, Durham House, Lower Clark Street, Scarborough, North Yorkshire, YO12 7PW Tel: (01723) 369191 Fax: (01723) 362044 E-mail: pickup@hpickup.co.uk

Pidra Environments Ltd, 23 Avebury Avenue, Sherbourne Park Estate, Choppington, Northumberland, NE62 5HE Tel: 0191-267 7111 Fax: 0191-267 7222 E-mail: david@pidra.ltd.uk

▶ Portway Plumbing Ltd, Castlegate Business Park, Salisbury, SP4 6QX Tel: (01722) 329268 Fax: (01722) 328257

▶ Pruce Newman Pipework, 5 Riverside House, Lower Southend Road, Wickford, Essex, SS11 8BB Tel: (01268) 739470 Fax: (01268) 764183 E-mail: mail@prucenewman.co.uk

▶ Pruce Newman Pipework Ltd, Ayton Road, Wymondham, Norfolk, NR18 0QJ Tel: (01953) 605123 Fax: (01953) 601115 E-mail: info@prucenewman.co.uk

R Kirkland Blyth Ltd, 62-66 Bridge Street, Blyth, Northumberland, NE24 2AP Tel: (01670) 352196 Fax: (01670) 360238

R T S Engineering (Somerset) Ltd, Unit 6, Sedgemount Industrial Park, Bristol Road, Bridgwater, Somerset, TA6 4AR Tel: (01278) 457294 Fax: (01278) 453772

Rally Industrial Services Ltd, Beacon Works, Bilston Street, Dudley, West Midlands, DY3 1JE Tel: (01902) 884341 Fax: (01902) 880333

Refrigeration Yorkshire Ltd, Woodhouse Street, Hull, HU9 1RJ Tel: (01482) 587333 Fax: (01482) 589593E-mail: ryorks1@aol.com

Relyon Heating Engineering Ltd, Bridge Works, Midland Road, Luton, LU2 0BL Tel: (01582) 730806 Fax: (01582) 481499 E-mail: admin@relyonheating.co.uk

Reznor UK Ltd, Park Farm Road, Park Farm Industrial Estate, Folkestone, Kent, CT19 5DR Tel: (01303) 259141 Fax: (01303) 850002 E-mail: marketing@reznor.co.uk

Robbins & Chapman, 24 Hill Road, Middleton, King's Lynn, Norfolk, PE32 1RN Tel: (01553) 774619 Fax: (01553) 774619

Robell Control Systems Ltd, 56 Cato Street, Nechells, Birmingham, B7 4TS Tel: 0121-333 4306 Fax: 0121-333 4811

Robert Prettie Co., Colwick Business Park, Private Road 2, Colwick Industrial Estate, Nottingham, NG4 2JR Tel: 0115-940 2222 Fax: 0115-940 2232 E-mail: r.prettie@robert-prettie.co.uk

Robinson Geoffrey Ltd, Macklin Avenue, Cowpen Lane Industrial Estate, Billingham, Cleveland, TS23 4ET Tel: (01642) 370500 Fax: (01642) 370600 E-mail: enquiry@geoffreyrobinson.ltd.uk

Rogan Heating Services, 4 Reach Road Industrial Estate, Reach Road, Burwell, Cambridge, CB5 0AH Tel: (01638) 743500 Fax: (01638) 743843 E-mail: roganhs@globalnet.co.uk

Rosser & Russell Building Services Ltd, Orbit House, 1-6 Ritz Parade, London, W5 3RD Tel: (020) 8982 2222 Fax: (020) 8982 2331

RP Metal Ltd, The Coach House, 32 The Crescent, Belmont, Sutton, Surrey, SM2 6BS Tel: (020) 8642 8899 Fax: (020) 8661 9993 E-mail: info@rpmetal.co.uk

Ryton Heating & Ventilating Co. Ltd, Sovereign House, 14 Warwick Street, Earlsdon, Coventry, CV5 6ET Tel: (024) 7667 7382 Fax: (024) 7667 7382

S I A S Building Services Ltd, Unit 4 Knowle Spring Industrial Estate, South Street, Keighley, West Yorkshire, BD21 1AQ Tel: (01535) 611336 Fax: (01535) 611361 E-mail: consultants@siasbuildingservices.co.uk

S & S Burner Services Ltd, Unit 14 193 The Garth Road Industrial Centre, Garth Road, Morden, Surrey, SM4 4LZ Tel: (020) 8330 7992 Fax: (020) 8330 7993

J.F. Sale Ltd, Newhouse Farm, Tompkin Lane, Stanley, Stoke-On-Trent, ST9 9LY Tel: (01782) 503206 Fax: (01782) 503206

Sansom Heating, Limber Road, Lufton Trading Estate, Yeovil, Somerset, BA22 8RR Tel: (01935) 444660 Fax: (01935) 433523

Saunders & Taylor Ltd, 9 Boston Court, Kansas Avenue, Salford, M50 2GN Tel: 0161-848 9393 Fax: 0161-848 9696 E-mail: enquiries@saunders-taylor.co.uk

Sayes & Co. Ltd, Richardshaw Road, Grangefield Industrial Estate, Stanningley, Pudsey, West Yorkshire, LS28 6BR Tel: 0113-257 8411 Fax: 0113-256 9275 E-mail: contact@sayesandcoltd.co.uk

Scanlock Overseas Property Agents, 208 Pensby Road, Heswall, Wirral, Merseyside, CH60 7RJ Tel: 0151-342 6530 Fax: 0151-342 6530 E-mail: sales@scanlock.com

Scomo (Heating & Ventilating) Ltd, Escon House, 8 Fieldings Road, Cheshunt, Waltham Cross, Hertfordshire, EN8 9TL Tel: (01992) 635515 Fax: (01992) 635168 E-mail: esl@8escon.fsnet.co.uk

Scorahs Ltd, 699 Huddersfield Road, Ravensthorpe, Dewsbury, West Yorkshire, WF13 3LQ Tel: (01924) 493222 Fax: (01924) 493222

Ses Mechanical Services Ltd, Telford Way, Severalls Industrial Park, Colchester, CO4 9QP Tel: (01206) 845333 Fax: (01206) 844601 E-mail: sales@sesmechanical.co.uk

Shelbourne Letheby & Co. Ltd, 154 New Kings Road, London, SW6 4LZ Tel: (020) 7736 4211 Fax: (020) 7371 0634

Sidney Cubbage Heating & Ventilating Ltd, 37-43 Green Street, High Wycombe, Buckinghamshire, HP11 2RF Tel: (01494) 523661 Fax: (01494) 462707 E-mail: scl@sidneycubbage.com

Sinclair Decorators, Roscoe Street, Scarborough, North Yorkshire, YO12 7BY Tel: (01723) 367361 Fax: (01723) 370848 E-mail: admin@sinclair.co.uk

J.E. Smith (Higham Ferrers) Ltd., 24 Saffron Road, Higham Ferrers, Rushden, Northamptonshire, NN10 8ED Tel: (01933) 312495 Fax: (01933) 410424 E-mail: aircon@jesmith.sagehost.co.uk

Sonning Heating Co. Ltd, Mayflower Close, Chandler's Ford, Eastleigh, Hampshire, SO53 4AR Tel: (023) 8026 2826 Fax: (023) 8027 3869 E-mail: sonnaire@sonning-heating.demon.co.uk

Southern Heating Co., 272 South Coast Road, Peacehaven, East Sussex, BN10 7PD Tel: (01273) 588123 Fax: (01273) 588121 E-mail: southtg@fastnet.co.uk

Sprague & Ouseley, 1 Knowle Business Units, Silverton Road, Exeter, EX2 8HD Tel: (01392) 825930 Fax: (01392) 825629 E-mail: info@spragueandouseley.co.uk

Sterling Environmental Engineering Ltd, Sterling House, 12 Gate Lane, Sutton Coldfield, West Midlands, B73 5TT Tel: 0121-321 2244 Fax: 0121-321 3151 E-mail: enquiries@sterling.uk.com

Fred Stoddart Ltd, 28 Wilson Street North, Sunderland, SR5 1BB Tel: 0191-567 3960 Fax: 0191-564 1624 E-mail: enquiries@fredstoddartltd.co.uk

▶ T Jolly Services Ltd, Unit G Central Industrial Estate, St. Marks Street, Bolton, BL3 6NR Tel: (07738) 486426 Fax: (01204) 365361 E-mail: john.taylor@tjolly.co.uk

T W Steam & Heating Services Ltd, Unit 7-8 Rennys Lane, Durham, DH1 2RS Tel: 0191-384 1400 Fax: 0191-386 4251

Team National Ltd, Triumph House, Birmingham Road, Millisons Wood, Coventry, CV5 9AZ Tel: (01676) 526000 Fax: (01676) 522966 E-mail: sales@teamnational.co.uk

Thermal Transfer (U K) Ltd, Scottish Enterprise Technology Park, Rankine Avenue, East Kilbride, Glasgow, G75 0QF Tel: (01355) 234567 Fax: (01355) 266466

Thermatic Maintenance Ltd, 3 Sovereign Enterprise Park, King William Street, Salford, M50 3UP Tel: 0161-872 3724 Fax: 0161-848 0516 E-mail: dave.oakley@thermatic.co.uk

Thermodiffusion Ltd, Hill Place, London Road, Southborough, Tunbridge Wells, Kent, TN4 0PY Tel: (01892) 511533 Fax: (01892) 515140 E-mail: thermodiffusion@btconnect.com

Tolman & Co. Ltd, 30 Hogshill Street, Beaminster, Dorset, DT8 3AD Tel: (01308) 862351

Townley Hughes & Co. Ltd, Unit 7 Meadow La Industrial Park, Ellesmere Port, CH65 4TY Tel: 0151-357 1800 Fax: 0151-357 2117 E-mail: townleyhughes@aol.com

Ventek Ltd, Unit 5, Starcrest Industrial Estate, Talbots Lane, Brierley Hill, West Midlands, DY5 2YT Tel: (01384) 79414 Fax: (01384) 79434 E-mail: sales@ventek.co.uk

Ventitherm Ltd, 121 Park Road, London, W4 3EX Tel: (020) 8994 5583 Fax: (020) 8994 8221

Verwin Plumbing & Heating Ltd, Maisonette, 223b London Road, Reading, RG1 3NY Tel: 0118-966 6049 Fax: 0118-935 2686

W T Rowley & Sons, 37 Canon Street, Shrewsbury, SY2 5HQ Tel: (01743) 356020

Walker & Holmes Ltd, Linton Street, Bradford, West Yorkshire, BD4 7EZ Tel: (01274) 728655 Fax: (01274) 723678 E-mail: walkerholmesltd@aol.com

Willey & Dalley, Palace Gate, Exeter, EX1 1JA Tel: (01392) 272694 Fax: (01392) 271220 E-mail: willeyanddalley@exe52.wanadoo.co.uk

▶ J.P. Woollacott Ltd, 10 Ash Hill Road, Torquay, TQ1 3HZ Tel: (01803) 213235 Fax: (01803) 213247 E-mail: jpw@email.com

Wright Bros Partnership Ltd, Waverley Road, Sheffield, S9 4PL Tel: 0114-244 1807 Fax: 0114-243 9277

HEATING AND VENTILATION PLANT

Wright Air Systems Ltd, 11 Regent Street, Rochdale, Lancashire, OL12 0HQ Tel: (01706) 343980 Fax: (01706) 525771 E-mail: was@ame-services.co.uk

HEATING CONSULTANCY OR DESIGN

Arnold James St Albans Ltd, 1 Metro Centre, Ronsons Way, Sandridge, St. Albans, Hertfordshire, AL4 9QT Tel: (01727) 851477 Fax: (01727) 842912

▶ Charttape Ltd, 14 Witt Road, Fair Oak, Eastleigh, Hampshire, SO50 7FR Tel: (07836) 671676 Fax: (023) 8069 6743 E-mail: charttape@btinternet.com

Driscoll & Crowley Ltd, 496a Barking Road, London, E13 8QB Tel: (020) 7511 9287 Fax: (020) 7473 3019 E-mail: info@driscoll-crowley.co.uk

Ellesmere Engineering Co. Ltd, Pennington Street, Worsley, Manchester, M28 3LR Tel: 0161-799 7626 Fax: 0161-703 8254 E-mail: marion@ellesmereeng.com

Emberheat, 295 Aylestone Road, Leicester, LE2 7PB Tel: 0116-287 8300

Fenweld Engineering Services, Unit 8 Addington Works, Knutsford Way Sealand Indust Estate, Chester, CH1 4LT Tel: (01244) 380880 Fax: (01244) 380294 E-mail: fenweld@compuserve.com

▶ Heat Force, 135 Maindy Road, Cardiff, CF24 4HN Tel: (029) 2037 8887 Fax: (029) 2037 8889 E-mail: enquiries@heatforce.co.uk

Industrial Air Control Ltd, Bath Lodge, Park Street, Royton, Oldham, OL2 6QN Tel: 0161-626 0242 Fax: 0161-627 0231 E-mail: sales@iacontrol.co.uk

Jones, PO Box 141, Wallingford, Oxfordshire, OX10 6AF Tel: (01491) 835032 Fax: (01491) 834765

PWB Industrial Heating Services Ltd, Unit 14 Dawkins Road, Poole, Dorset, BH15 4JY Tel: (01202) 682500 Fax: (01202) 682565 E-mail: enquiries@pwbltd.co.uk

Thermatic Maintenance Ltd, 3 Sovereign Enterprise Park, King William Street, Salford, M50 3UP Tel: 0161-872 3724 Fax: 0161-848 0516 E-mail: dave.oakley@thermatic.co.uk

Uxbridge Engineering Co. Ltd, Robinswood, Dukes Kiln Drive, Gerrards Cross, Buckinghamshire, SL9 7HD Tel: (01753) 889511 Fax: (01753) 880118 E-mail: enquiries@uxbridge-eng.demon.co.uk

HEATING CONTRACTORS

▶ A Pank & Son Ltd, 29 St Giles Street, Norwich, NR2 1JW Tel: (01603) 621501

▶ Asm Services, The Wharf Offices, Glynde, Lewes, East Sussex, BN8 6SS Tel: (01273) 858839 Fax: (01273) 858840 E-mail: maintanence@asmpromptcle.com

▶ Boiler Healthcare, 16 Kent Road, Folkestone, Kent, CT19 4NT Tel: (01303) 275729 Fax: (01303) 279081 E-mail: sales@boilerhealthcare.co.uk

Booker & Best, Windmill House, Windmill Road, St. Leonards-on-Sea, East Sussex, TN38 9BY Tel: (01424) 434391 Fax: (01424) 446833 E-mail: adrianstallworthy@bookerbest.co.uk

▶ Brenden Fern Heating & Plumbing, 27 Paradise Street, Stoke-on-Trent, ST6 5AG Tel: (01782) 818577 Fax: (01782) 818578 E-mail: info@bfplum.co.uk

▶ Chris Hatcher & Son Ltd, 33 High Street, Seaford, East Sussex, BN25 1PL Tel: (01323) 890100 Fax: (01323) 891400

▶ Evans & Graham Heating Co. Ltd, 108 Westmead Road, Sutton, Surrey, SM1 4JD Tel: (020) 8661 1712 Fax: (020) 8642 3755

▶ G W Sparrow & Co. Ltd, 5 Cobham Centre, Westmead Industrial Estate, Westlea, Swindon, SN5 7UJ Tel: (01793) 541701 Fax: (01793) 541702

▶ L H Plumbing & Heating Services Ltd, 132 Vaughan Road, Harrow, Middlesex, HA1 4ED Tel: (020) 8864 2311 Fax: (020) 8423 2020

▶ Morgan & Fone Ltd, Unit 1, Royston Road, Baldock, Hertfordshire, SG7 6PA Tel: (01462) 894455

▶ P & G Contractors Ltd, 1 Birch Street, Ashton-under-Lyne, Lancashire, OL7 0NX Tel: 0161-339 0831 Fax: 0161-285 3393

▶ P R S Plumbing & Heating Services Ltd, Premier House, Popham, Micheldever, Winchester, Hampshire, SO21 3BJ Tel: (01256) 398881 Fax: (01256) 398889

▶ Pro-Tec BS Ltd, 67-69, George Street, London, W1U 8LT Tel: 020 8830 5545 Fax: 020 8830 5545 E-mail: enquiries@pro-tecbsltd.co.uk

▶ R & M Wheildon Ltd, 10 Stonegate, Burton Road, Lower Bentham, Lancaster, LA2 7DY Tel: (01524) 262330 Fax: (01524) 262330

▶ Seaforth Services, Unit 6 Slader Business Park, Witney Road, Nuffield Industrial Estate, Poole, Dorset, BH17 0GP Tel: (01202) 330630 Fax: (01202) 679100

▶ W H Dunn & Co., 10 William Street, South Shields, Tyne & Wear, NE33 1PQ Tel: 0191-456 7503 Fax: 0191-454 5520

HEATING CONTROL INSTALLATION

Brunswick Engineering, 27 Sterling Road, Enfield, Middlesex, EN2 0LN Tel: (020) 8882 1877 Fax: (020) 8886 7933 E-mail: brunswick@wwmail.co.uk

Control Design, Unit Z Paddock Wood Distribution Centre, Paddock Wood, Tonbridge, Kent, TN12 6UU Tel: (01892) 836350 Fax: (01892) 837292 E-mail: controldesign@btconnect.com

Force Heating & Cooling Services, 80 Rawmarsh Hill, Parkgate, Rotherham, South Yorkshire, S62 6EX Tel: (01709) 527920 Fax: (01709) 526290 E-mail: force.heating@virgin.net

G A Gas Services 2000 Ltd, 676 Pershore Road, Selly Park, Birmingham, B29 7NX Tel: 0121-472 7293 Fax: 0121-472 7294

The Grant Group Ltd, 47A Linfield Industrial Estate, Belfast, BT12 5LA Tel: (028) 9032 3329 Fax: (028) 9032 3218 E-mail: info@thegrantgroup.com

Hydro Mechanical Services Ltd, Unit 1-2 17 Reddicap Trading Estate, Sutton Coldfield, West Midlands, B75 7BU Tel: 0121-378 4000 Fax: 0121-311 1523 E-mail: mailbox@hydrogroup.co.uk

Invensys Building Systems, Unit 3 Earls Court, Fifth Avenue, Team Valley Trading Estate, Gateshead, Tyne & Wear, NE11 0HF Tel: 0191-499 4500 Fax: 0191-499 4501 E-mail: andrew.kingston@invensys.com

J H Shouksmith & Sons Ltd, Murton Way, Osbaldwick, York, YO19 5GS Tel: (01904) 411261 Fax: (01904) 412038 E-mail: rps@shouksmiths.co.uk

Kingsford Services Ltd, Bromley Road, Elmstead, Colchester, CO7 7BY Tel: (01206) 827653 Fax: (01206) 827654 E-mail: enquiries@kingsfordservices.co.uk

M T Buxton Industrial Services Ltd, 237 Station Road, Langley Mill, Nottingham, NG16 4AD Tel: (01773) 714339 Fax: (01773) 535251 E-mail: enquiries@mtbuxton.com

Multibasics Gas Service Engineers, 12 Thornton Road, Morecambe, Lancashire, LA4 5PE Tel: (01524) 415346 Fax: (01524) 412509 E-mail: sales@multibasics.com

Nairb Controls, PO Box 1610, Salisbury, SP1 3XH Tel: (01722) 322922 Fax: (01722) 322922

R H Adams Forest Hill Ltd, Hindsleys Place, London, SE23 2NQ Tel: (020) 8699 4803 Fax: (020) 8699 8493

Service Systems Ltd, 178 Oxford Road, Basford, Newcastle, Staffordshire, ST5 0QB Tel: (01782) 711077 Fax: (01782) 638538 E-mail: enquiries@servicesystemsltd.co.uk

HEATING CONTROLS

▶ Abtap, 326B St Albans Road, Watford, WD24 6PQ Tel: (01923) 630022 Fax: (01923) 630011 E-mail: abtap@btconnect.com

▶ Adlink UK Ltd, Nagi House, Alperton Lane, Wembley, Middlesex, HA0 1DX Tel: (020) 8991 5017 Fax: (020) 8991 9496 E-mail: sales@adlinkuk.com

▶ Allison Heating Plumbing & Electrical Ltd, Old Station Way, Holt, Norfolk, NR25 6DH Tel: (01263) 713260 Fax: (01263) 713174

Anglo Nordic Burner Products Ltd, Units 12-14, Island Farm Avenue, West Molesey, Surrey, KT8 2UZ Tel: (020) 8979 0988 Fax: (020) 8979 6961 E-mail: sales@anglonordic.co.uk

Apsley Controls Ltd, Unit 14 Kents Avenue, Hemel Hempstead, Hertfordshire, HP3 9XH Tel: (01442) 235464 Fax: (01442) 249479 E-mail: martinturnbull@virgin.net

Automotive Cable Products Ltd, Copperworks Road, Llanelli, Dyfed, SA15 2NE Tel: (01554) 752207 Fax: (01554) 749600 E-mail: info@automotivecableproducts.co.uk

▶ Banico Ltd, Tilson Road, Roundthorn Industrial Estate, Manchester, M23 9GF Tel: (0845) 1700740 Fax: (0845) 1700750 E-mail: sales@banico.co.uk

Coster Environmental Controls Ltd, Unit 5 Sir Francis Ley Indust Park, Derby, DE23 8XA Tel: (01332) 200555 Fax: (01332) 204181

Danfoss Randall Ltd, Ampthill Road, Bedford, MK42 9ER Tel: (0845) 1217400 Fax: (0845) 1217515 E-mail: danfossrandall@randall.com

Furness Heating Components Ltd, 19 Abbey Road, Barrow-in-Furness, Cumbria, LA14 5UD Tel: (01229) 430575 Fax: (01229) 433080

Gilman Control Systems Ltd, 15 Bridge Gate Business Park, Gatehouse Way, Aylesbury, Buckinghamshire, HP19 8XN Tel: (01296) 434810 Fax: (01296) 434847 E-mail: sales@gilman-controls.co.uk

HEATING CONTROLS – *continued*

The Grant Group Ltd, 47A Linfield Industrial Estate, Belfast, BT12 5LA Tel: (028) 9032 3329 Fax: (028) 9032 3218 E-mail: info@thegrantgroup.com

▶ Heatmiser UK Ltd, Primrose House, Primrose Street, Darwen, Lancashire, BB3 2DE Tel: (01254) 776343 Fax: (01254) 704143 E-mail: info@heatmiser.co.uk

Herz Valves (UK) Ltd, Progress House, Moorfield Point, Moorfield Road, Guildford, Surrey, GU1 1RU Tel: 01483 502211 Fax: 01483 502025 E-mail: sales@herzvalves.com

Horstmann Group Ltd, Roman Farm Road, Bristol, BS4 1UP Tel: 0117-978 8700 Fax: 0117-987 8701 E-mail: reception@horstmann.co.uk

▶ I M E L, Unit 6, Pages Industrial Park, Eden Way, Leighton Buzzard, Bedfordshire, LU7 4TZ Tel: (01525) 383555 Fax: (01525) 383700 E-mail: info@imel.biz

Invensys Building Systems, Unit 3 Earls Court, Fifth Avenue, Team Valley Trading Estate, Gateshead, Tyne & Wear, NE11 0HF Tel: 0191-499 4500 Fax: 0191-499 4501 E-mail: andrew.kingston@invensys.com

▶ Kingswood Building Services Ltd, Rainbow Industrial Park, Station Approach, London, SW20 0JY Tel: (020) 8946 1556 Fax: (020) 8946 1585

M G Building Services Engineers Ltd, 31a High Street, Alcester, Warwickshire, B49 5AF Tel: (01789) 400270 Fax: (01789) 400396 E-mail: mgbse@globalnet.co.uk

M J T Controls Ltd, Unit 10, Novers Hill Trading Estate, Novers Hill, Bedminster, Bristol, BS3 5QY Tel: 0117-963 7142 Fax: 0117-963 2332 E-mail: mjtcontrols@btinternet.com

Mercury Control Ltd, The Cottage, Back Dawson Terrace, Harrogate, North Yorkshire, HG1 2AJ Tel: (01423) 566613 Fax: (01423) 566614

Metron Energy Management Ltd, PO Box 190, Winsford, Cheshire, CW7 9AH Tel: (01606) 882722 Fax: (01606) 889440 E-mail: enquiries@demmetron.co.uk

▶ O E M Group Ltd, London Business Innovation Centre, Innova Science Park, Mollison Avenue, Enfield, Middlesex, EN3 7XH Tel: (020) 8344 8777 Fax: (020) 8344 8778 E-mail: steve@secureseal.com

Parts Center Commercial, Unit 14, Harp Road, Off Guinness Road, Trafford Park, Manchester, M17 1SR Tel: 0161-848 0546 Fax: 0161-872 0265

Peglar, Belmont Works, St. Catherines Avenue, Doncaster, South Yorkshire, DN4 8DF Tel: (0870) 1200285 Fax: (01302) 367661 E-mail: export@pegler.com

Pipeline & Electrical Supplies, 75 Reddal Hill Road, Cradley Heath, West Midlands, B64 5JT Tel: (01384) 566381 Fax: (01384) 410781 E-mail: paulacton@btconnect.com

Powrmatic Ltd, Hort Bridge, Ilminster, Somerset, TA19 9PS Tel: (01460) 53535 Fax: (01460) 52341 E-mail: info@powrmatic.co.uk

Sutronics, 62 Park Road, Swanage, Dorset, BH19 2AE Tel: (01929) 426400 E-mail: sales@sutronics.com

Tour & Andersson, Unit 3 Nimbus Park Porz Avenue, Houghton Hall Park, Houghton Regis, Dunstable, Bedfordshire, LU5 5XR Tel: (01582) 866377 Fax: (01582) 865655 E-mail: samuel.coe@tourandersson.co.uk

HEATING ELEMENT FORMERS

Industrial Composites Ltd, Churchill Way, Nelson, Lancashire, BB9 6RT Tel: (01282) 619336 Fax: (01282) 619337 E-mail: info@indcomps.co.uk

HEATING ELEMENT MANUFRS, *See also headings under Heating Elements*

▶ Backer Electric Co. Ltd, Fitzwilliam Road, Eastwood Trading Estate, Rotherham, South Yorkshire, S65 1TF Tel: (01709) 828292 Fax: (01709) 828388 E-mail: sales@backer.co.uk

▶ Bomac Electric Ltd, Randles Road, Knowsley Business Park, Prescot, Merseyside, L34 9HX Tel: 0151-546 4401 Fax: 0151-549 1661 E-mail: sales@bomac-elec.co.uk

Buckley Elements Ltd, Galveston Grove, Fenton, Stoke-on-Trent, ST3 2JT Tel: (01782) 333071 Fax: (01782) 593485 E-mail: sales@buckleyelements.co.uk

Carlingwood Ltd, 1 Bridge Green, Prestbury, Macclesfield, Cheshire, SK10 4HR Tel: (01625) 828342 Fax: (01625) 827471

Chromalox (U K) Ltd, Eltron House, 20-28 Whitehorse Road, Croydon, CR0 2JA Tel: (020) 8665 8900 Fax: (020) 8689 0571 E-mail: uksales@chromalox.com

Cozier's Ltd, Littlebrook, Llangolman, Clynderwen, Dyfed, SA66 7XL Tel: (01437) 532660 Fax: (01437) 532670 E-mail: sales@coziers-ltd.co.uk

DBK Technitherm Ltd, 11 Llantrisant Business Park, Llantrisant, Pontyclun, Mid Glamorgan, CF72 8LF Tel: (01443) 237927 Fax: (01443) 237867 E-mail: info@dbktechnitherm.ltd.uk

De Icers M H G Ltd, 11 Hamilton Street, Charlton Kings, Cheltenham, Gloucestershire, GL53 8HN Tel: (01242) 573321 Fax: (01242) 573543

E X Heat Ltd, Threxton Road Industrial Estate, Watton, Thetford, Norfolk, IP25 6NG Tel: (01953) 886200 Fax: (01953) 886222 E-mail: sales@exheat.com

Electrical Elements Hinckley Ltd, 1 Willow Park Industrial Estate, Upton Lane, Stoke Golding, Nuneaton, Warwickshire, CV13 6EU Tel: (01455) 213171 Fax: (01455) 213614 E-mail: enquiries@electricalelements.co.uk

Elmatic (Cardiff) Ltd, Wentloog Road, Rumney, Cardiff, CF3 1XH Tel: (029) 2077 8727 Fax: (029) 2079 2297 E-mail: sales@elmatic.co.uk

Esh Trace Heating, A Station Road, Guiseley, Leeds, LS20 8BX Tel: (01943) 884044 Fax: (01943) 884041 E-mail: enquiries@eshltd.com

Foil Engineering Ltd, 12c Gorst Road, London, NW10 6LE Tel: (020) 8961 3466 Fax: (020) 8961 3466

Heater Bands Ltd, Bott Lane, Walsall, WS1 2JQ Tel: (01922) 636888 Fax: (01922) 722360 E-mail: brian@heaterbands.freeserve.co.uk

Heatrae Sadia Ltd, Brooks House, Coventry Road, Warwick, CV34 4LL Tel: (0870) 0603262 Fax: (0870) 0600403 E-mail: sales@heatraesadia.com

Holroyd Components Ltd, Shire Hill Industrial Estate, Saffron Walden, Essex, CB11 3AQ Tel: (01799) 523177 Fax: (01799) 513714 E-mail: sales@holroydcomponents.com

Hotset UK Ltd, Unit M, Bowen Industrial Estate, Aberbargoed, Bargoed, Mid Glamorgan, CF81 9EP Tel: (01443) 875581 Fax: (01443) 831422 E-mail: sales@hotset.u-net.com

LPC Holdings Ltd, Coundon Industrial Estate, Coundon, Bishop Auckland, County Durham, DL14 8NR Tel: (01388) 608270 Fax: (01388) 450048 E-mail: enquiries@lpcholdings.co.uk

Midland Elements Ltd, 58 Sutherland Road, Stoke-on-Trent, ST3 1HU Tel: (01782) 333377 Fax: (01782) 599940

San Electroheat, PO Box 259, Hereford, HR1 9AU Tel: (01432) 851999 Fax: (01432) 851299 E-mail: h_comerford@btconnect.com

Sheathed Heating Elements Holdings Ltd, Wardley Industrial Estate North, Worsley, Manchester, M28 2DP Tel: 0161-794 6122 Fax: 0161-794 8601 E-mail: sales@shealuk.free.com

Soloheat Electrical Heating Equipment, Units 1 & 2 Lightpill Trading Estate, Bath Road, Stroud, Gloucestershire, GL5 3LL Tel: (01453) 752459 Fax: (01453) 752458 E-mail: heatit@aol.com

▶ Surface Heating Systems Ltd, 129-130 Whitehill Road, Whitehill Industrial Estate, Glenrothes, Fife, KY6 2RP Tel: (01592) 770003 Fax: (01592) 773339

T P Fay (Kirkby) Ltd, 1 Spinney Close, Kirkby, Liverpool, L33 7XZ Tel: 0151-546 6232 Fax: 0151-549 1477E-mail: sales@tpfay.co.uk

Thermaglow Ltd, North Market Road, Winterton-On-Sea, Great Yarmouth, Norfolk, NR29 4BH Tel: (01493) 393555 Fax: (01493) 393860 E-mail: sales@thermaglow.co.uk

Thermocable (Flexible Elements) Ltd, Pasture Lane, Clayton, Bradford, West Yorkshire, BD14 6LU Tel: (01274) 882359 Fax: (01274) 882229 E-mail: info@thermocable.com

ThermTec Ltd, Rectory Farm, Martham, Great Yarmouth, Norfolk, NR29 4RE Tel: 01493 748666

TP Fay Ltd, 57 Admin Road, Knowsley Industrial Park, Liverpool, L33 7TX Tel: (0870) 3505058 Fax: (0870) 3505059 E-mail: sales@tpfay.co.uk

Vulcan Refractories Ltd, Brookhouse Industrial Estate, Cheadle, Stoke-on-Trent, ST10 1PN Tel: (01538) 752238 Fax: (01538) 753349 E-mail: sales@vulcan-refractories.co.uk

Welbeck Catering Spares, 20 Bushey Hall Road, Bushey, WD23 2ED Tel: (01923) 801555

HEATING ELEMENTS TO SPECIFICATION

Dankfern Ltd, 11 Tait Road, Croydon, CR0 2DP Tel: (020) 8683 2748 Fax: (020) 8665 6627

HEATING ELEMENTS, COOKER (ELECTRIC)

Ceramaspeed Ltd, Zortech Avenue, Kidderminster, Worcestershire, DY11 7DY Tel: (01562) 756000 Fax: (01562) 756030

Kaloric Heater Co. Ltd, 31 33 Beethoven Street, London, W10 4LJ Tel: (020) 8969 1367 Fax: (020) 8968 8913 E-mail: admin@kaloricheater.co.uk

HEATING ELEMENTS, DOMESTIC APPLIANCE

▶ Backer Electric Co. Ltd, Fitzwilliam Road, Eastwood Trading Estate, Rotherham, South Yorkshire, S65 1TF Tel: (01709) 828292 Fax: (01709) 828388 E-mail: sales@backer.co.uk

▶ Bomac Electric Ltd, Randles Road, Knowsley Business Park, Prescot, Merseyside, L34 9HX Tel: 0151-546 4401 Fax: 0151-549 1661 E-mail: sales@bomac-elec.co.uk

Dankfern Ltd, 11 Tait Road, Croydon, CR0 2DP Tel: (020) 8683 2748 Fax: (020) 8665 6627

DBK Technitherm Ltd, 11 Llantrisant Business Park, Llantrisant, Pontyclun, Mid Glamorgan, CF72 8LF Tel: (01443) 237927 Fax: (01443) 237867 E-mail: info@dbktechnitherm.ltd.uk

▶ I M E L, Unit 6, Pages Industrial Park, Eden Way, Leighton Buzzard, Bedfordshire, LU7 4TZ Tel: (01525) 383555 Fax: (01525) 383700 E-mail: info@imel.biz

Sheathed Heating Elements Holdings Ltd, Wardley Industrial Estate North, Worsley, Manchester, M28 2DP Tel: 0161-794 6122 Fax: 0161-794 8601 E-mail: sales@shealuk.free.com

Thermaglow Ltd, North Market Road, Winterton-On-Sea, Great Yarmouth, Norfolk, NR29 4BH Tel: (01493) 393555 Fax: (01493) 393860 E-mail: sales@thermaglow.co.uk

HEATING ENGINEERS, *See Heating & Ventilating Engineers etc*

HEATING OR VENTILATING GRILLES

Diepress Refresherator Ltd, 27-31 Cato St North, Birmingham, B7 5AP Tel: 0121-333 3139 Fax: 0121-359 1729 E-mail: diepress@birmingham.co.uk

Environmental Supply Co. Ltd, Unit 1, 10 Prince Regent Road, Belfast, BT5 6QR Tel: (028) 9040 2100 Fax: (028) 9040 2123 E-mail: environmental@btconnect.com

F N W (Engineering Developments) Ltd, New Street, Skelmanthorpe, Huddersfield, HD8 9BL Tel: (01484) 861233 Fax: (01484) 864928

G D L Air Systems Ltd, Air Diffusion Works, Woolley Bridge Road, Hadfield, Glossop, Derbyshire, SK13 1AB Tel: (01457) 861538 Fax: (01457) 866010 E-mail: sales@grille.co.uk

Halton Products Ltd, 5 Waterside Business Park, Eastways, Witham, Essex, CM8 3YQ Tel: (01376) 503040 Fax: (01376) 503060 E-mail: enquiries@haltongroup.com

J A Glover Ltd, 23 Lordswood Industrial Estate, Revenge Road, Chatham, Kent, ME5 8UD Tel: (01634) 684419 Fax: (01634) 200423 E-mail: chatham@jagglover.demon.co.uk

J C Vents Ltd, J.C. House, Hurricane Way, Wickford Business Park, Wickford, Essex, SS11 8YB Tel: (01268) 561122 Fax: (01268) 560606 E-mail: sales@jcvents.co.uk

Polyaire Ltd, 17 Enterprise Court, Newton Close, Park Farm Industrial Estate, Wellingborough, Northamptonshire, NN8 6UW Tel: (01933) 402666 Fax: (01933) 402777 E-mail: sales@polyaireuk.demon.co.uk

R C M Products, 19 Burners Lane, Kiln Farm, Milton Keynes, MK11 3HA Tel: (01908) 263131 Fax: (01908) 265454 E-mail: sales@rcmproducts.co.uk

Tek Ltd, Unit 14, Tyseley Industrial Estate, Seeleys Road, Birmingham, B11 2LQ Tel: 0121-766 5005 Fax: 0121-766 5010 E-mail: sales@tek.ltd.uk

HEATING RADIATORS

Aestus Ltd, Unit 5, Strawberry Lane, Willenhall, West Midlands, WV13 3RF Tel: (01902) 632256 Fax: (01902) 635800 E-mail: sales@aestus-radiators.com

Boston Radiator Services Ltd, Maud Street, Boston, Lincolnshire, PE21 6TP Tel: (01205) 369555 Fax: (01205) 364829

Quinn Radiators, Spinning Jenny Way, Leigh, Lancashire, WN7 4PE Tel: (01942) 261291 Fax: (01942) 261801

Sensotherm Europanel Ltd, Stafford Park 16, Telford, Shropshire, TF3 3BS Tel: (01952) 292219 Fax: (01952) 292128 E-mail: sales@sensotherm.co.uk

Strebel Ltd, Unit 1f Albany Park, Camberley, Surrey, GU16 7PB Tel: (01276) 685422 Fax: (01276) 685405 E-mail: andy.parker@strebel.co.uk

Vogue Management Services Ltd, Unit 8-10 Strawberry La Industrial Estate, Strawberry Lane, Willenhall, West Midlands, WV13 3RS Tel: (0870) 4030107 Fax: (0870) 4030108 E-mail: info@vogue-uk.co.uk

HEATING STOVES

Dingley Dell Enterprises, Kidderminster, Worcestershire, DY14 9ZE Tel: (01905) 621636 Fax: (01905) 620311

Euroheat Distributors (HBS) Ltd, Unit 2, Court Farm Business Park, Bishops Frome, Worcester, WR6 5AY Tel: (01885) 491100 Fax: (01885) 491101 E-mail: info@euroheat.co.uk

Dean Forge, Dean Prior, Lower Dean, Buckfastleigh, Devon, TQ11 0LS Tel: (01364) 643574 Fax: (01364) 643982 E-mail: stoves@dean-forge.co.uk

Stovax Ltd, Falcon Road, Sowton Industrial Estate, Exeter, EX2 7LF Tel: (01392) 474011 Fax: (01392) 219932E-mail: info@stovax.com

HEATING SYSTEMS

Allheat & Plumbing Services Ltd, Thames House Charfleets Road, Charfleets Industrial Estate, Canvey Island, Essex, SS8 0PQ Tel: (01268) 684414 E-mail: andy@allheat.com

▶ Aveat Heating Ltd, Lambert House, 7 Driberg Way, Braintree, Essex, CM7 1NB Tel: (01376) 325670 Fax: (01376) 551210 E-mail: aveat@btconnect.com

▶ County Plumbimg and Heating, R/O, 33 High Street, Aveley, South Ockendon, Essex, RM15 4BE Tel: (01708) 861878

Fairhaven H & V Services, 3 Glenavy Road, Moira, Craigavon, County Armagh, BT67 0LT Tel: (028) 9261 1648 Fax: (028) 9261 1997 E-mail: sales@fairhavenltd.co.uk

Falcon Plumbing & Heating Engineers, 3 Lingfield Close, Enfield, Middlesex, EN1 2JL Tel: (020) 8360 0115 Fax: (020) 8360 0115

▶ G B Services, Blackberry Lane, Lingfield, Surrey, RH7 6NG Tel: (01342) 837691 Fax: (01342) 835655

▶ Industrial & Commercial Environment Ltd, Bowdens, Broad Oak, Sturminster Newton, Dorset, DT10 2HG Tel: (01258) 471954 Fax: (01258) 471904 E-mail: office@ice-uk.eu.com

Roberts-Gordon, Oxford Street, Bilston, West Midlands, WV14 7EG Tel: (01902) 494425 Fax: (01902) 403200 E-mail: uksales@rg-inc.com

▶ Scotia Energy Saving Systems Ltd, 49 Nasmyth Road, Glenrothes, Fife, KY6 2SD Tel: (01592) 773623 Fax: (01592) 773562 E-mail: contracts@scotia-aircon.co.uk

▶ Surface Heating Systems Ltd, 129-130 Whitehill Road, Whitehill Industrial Estate, Glenrothes, Fife, KY6 2RP Tel: (01592) 770003 Fax: (01592) 773339

▶ Taunton Plumbing & Heating, Unit 6, Venture 11, Priorswood Industrial Estate, Taunton, Somerset, TA2 8DG Tel: (01823) 278887

▶ Thermalfloor Underfloor Heating Systems Ltd, School Road, Tnepher Friartor, Perth, PH2 8DF Tel: (08450) 620400 Fax: (01828) 628130

HEATING TAPES/STRIPS, ELECTRIC ELEMENT

Esh Trace Heating, A Station Road, Guiseley, Leeds, LS20 8BX Tel: (01943) 884044 Fax: (01943) 884041 E-mail: enquiries@eshltd.com

HEATING VENTILATION AND AIR CONDITIONING (HVAC) AIR DISTRIBUTION SYSTEMS

▶ Air Conditioning Solutions UK Ltd, Concept Park, Watling Street, Towcester, Northamptonshire, NN12 7YD Tel: (01327) 810510 Fax: (01327) 811529 E-mail: info@airconsolutions.co.uk

▶ E & A Site Services, 34 Kingsman Road, Stanford-le-Hope, Essex, SS17 0JW Tel: (01375) 644400 Fax: (01375) 644400 E-mail: eass@approvedtrading.com

▶ Global Heating Services, 15 Wheeler Gate, Nottingham, NG1 2NA Tel: (0800) 2980692 Fax: (0871) 6616082 E-mail: globalheating@bulldoghome.com

HEATING VENTILATION AND AIR CONDITIONING (HVAC) CONSULTANCY

R A Green (Mechanical Servises) Ltd, Southdown, Western Road, Crowborough, East Sussex, TN6 3EW Tel: (01892) 652177 Fax: (01892) 667225 E-mail: ragreen@btinternet.com

HEATING VENTILATION AND AIR CONDITIONING (HVAC) CONTRACTORS

▶ 1 A Emergency Services, Ashley House, 1f Ashley Terrace, Edinburgh, EH11 1RF Tel: 0131-477 7901 Fax: 0131-477 7902

▶ 24 Hour Plumbing Services, Brand Street, Glasgow, G51 1DG Tel: 0141-427 3320 Fax: 0141-427 5639

▶ 2as Ltd, Logic House, Marsh Lane, Easton-in-Gordano, Bristol, BS20 0NH Tel: (01275) 374524 Fax: (01275) 373820

▶ A A Glanville Ltd, 53 Ashford Road, Plymouth, PL4 7BL Tel: (01752) 660906

▶ A B Humbercraft Ltd, Unit 6b Kingston Way, Stockholm Road, Hull, HU7 0XW Tel: (01482) 370223 Fax: (01482) 823673

▶ A B Prattis & Sons, 15 Main Street, Hillend, Dunfermline, Fife, KY11 9ND Tel: (01383) 414793

▶ A C Air Systems, Newburgh Building, Selby Place, Stanley Industrial Estate, Skelmersdale, Lancashire, WN8 8EF Tel: (01695) 722066 Fax: (01695) 722933

HEATING VENTILATION AND AIR CONDITIONING (HVAC) CONTRACTORS – *continued*

▶ A D Broughton Ltd, 17 Harefield Road, Bognor Regis, West Sussex, PO22 6EE Tel: (01243) 584114 Fax: (01243) 583657 E-mail: enquiries@adbroughton.co.uk

▶ A E M Ltd, 31 Risborough Lane, Folkestone, Kent, CT19 4JH Tel: (01303) 275862 Fax: (01303) 270766

▶ A H Hales Ltd, 35 Northampton Road, Scunthorpe, South Humberside, DN16 1UJ Tel: (01724) 843703 Fax: (01724) 271863

▶ A & J Gough Ltd, 370 Portland Road, Hove, East Sussex, BN3 5SD Tel: (01273) 417638 Fax: (01273) 418488

▶ A M Norris Ltd, Brunel Way, Stephenson Industrial Estate, Coalville, Leicestershire, LE67 3HF Tel: (01530) 831451 Fax: (01530) 813767

▶ A M Reid Plumbing & Heating Ltd, 16 Christie Street, Dunfermline, Fife, KY12 0AQ Tel: (01383) 730293 Fax: (01383) 730293

▶ A M W Ltd, 18-20 Lindsay Street, Kilmarnock, Ayrshire, KA1 2BB Tel: (01563) 533086

▶ A P Chant Ltd, Gore Cross Business Park, Corbin Way, Bridport, Dorset, DT6 3UX Tel: (01308) 420170

▶ A R B Mechanical Ltd, Winchester Road, Waltham Chase, Southampton, SO32 2LL Tel: (01489) 896611

▶ A & T Engineering Ltd, 9 Carr Lane Industrial Estate, Carr Lane, Hoylake, Wirral, Merseyside, CH47 4AX Tel: 0151-632 1308 Fax: 0151-632 6383

▶ Aberdeen Mechanical Services Ltd, 39 Fraser Place, Aberdeen, AB25 3TY Tel: (01224) 620330 Fax: (01224) 620331

▶ Able Services, Ayton Smiddy House, Newburgh, Cupar, Fife, KY14 6JQ Tel: (0800) 9178539

▶ Able Services (Scotland) Ltd, The Conifers, Station Road, Springfield, Cupar, Fife, KY15 5RU Tel: (01334) 652538

▶ Accurate Mechanical Services, Unit 18 Pegasus Court, North Lane, Aldershot, Hampshire, GU12 4QP Tel: (01252) 315000 Fax: (01252) 315252

▶ Ace Heating Ltd, 24 Camaultmuir, Camault Muir, Kiltarlity, Beauly, Inverness-Shire, IV4 7JH Tel: (01463) 741300 Fax: (01463) 741224

▶ Ace Home Heating, 14 Seafield Road, Inverness, IV1 1SG Tel: (01463) 718300 Fax: (01463) 718800

▶ Ace Maintenance, Unit 4 & 5, Coatbank Business Centre, Coatbridge, Lanarkshire, ML5 3AG Tel: (01236) 440858

▶ Ace Plumbing, 78 Spring Road, Bournemouth, BH1 4PT Tel: (01202) 669171 Fax: (01202) 399751

▶ Acorn Mechanical Pipework Services Ltd, Suite F Lancaster House Grange Business Park, Enderby Road, Whetstone, Leicester, LE8 6EP Tel: 0116-277 8687 Fax: 0116-277 8106

▶ The Air Conditioning Showroom, 28 Brookley Road, Brockenhurst, Hampshire, SO42 7RR Tel: (01590) 623244 Fax: (01590) 623756

▶ Air Environmental Technology Ltd, 52 Springvale Industrial Estate, Cwmbran, Gwent, NP44 5BB Tel: (01633) 875520 Fax: (01633) 875540

▶ Airco Air Conditioning, 120 Stoneferry Road, Hull, HU8 8DA Tel: (01482) 587038 Fax: (01482) 229997

▶ Airtech Environmental Services, 3 Hampton Court Road, East Molesey, Surrey, KT8 9BN Tel: (020) 8979 2158 Fax: (020) 8941 9623 E-mail: airtechlondon@mcmail.com

▶ Alba Engineering, 2 Camlachie Street, Glasgow, G31 4JH Tel: 0141-554 5831 Fax: 0141-556 4947

▶ Alert 24 Hour Plumbing Services Ltd, 11 Dumgoyne Drive, Bearsden, Glasgow, G61 3AP Tel: 0141-942 0103

▶ Alexander Anderson Ltd, 30-32 Byron Street, Glasgow, G11 6LS Tel: 0141-334 9354 Fax: 0141-357 4542

▶ Alexander Duthie & Sons Ltd, 103 Berryden Road, Aberdeen, AB25 3SJ Tel: (01224) 639983 Fax: (01224) 639983

▶ Alexander Duthie & Sons Ltd, 2 St. Andrew Street, Peterhead, Aberdeenshire, AB42 1DS Tel: (01779) 472628 Fax: (01779) 492628

Allheat & Plumbing Services Ltd, Thames House Charfleets Road, Charfleets Industrial Estate, Canvey Island, Essex, SS8 0PQ Tel: (01268) 684414 E-mail: andy@allheat.com

▶ The Angus Plumbing Co. Ltd, 38-40 Glengate, Kirriemuir, Forfar, Angus, DD8 4HD Tel: (01575) 573777

▶ Annandale, 773 Spring Bank West, Hull, HU5 5BA Tel: (01482) 354908 Fax: (01482) 506544

▶ Applied Cooling Systems Ltd, M2 Cody Court, Kansas Avenue, Salford, M50 2GE Tel: 0161-877 7262 Fax: 0161-877 7378

▶ Aqua Gas, Unit 300, 405 Kings Road, London, SW10 0BB Tel: (020) 7351 0000

▶ Aqualine Services Ltd, 59 Wassand Street, Kingston Upon Hull, Hull, HU3 4AL Tel: (01482) 657709 Fax: (01482) 655777

▶ Armstrong, 6 James Carter Road, Mildenhall, Bury St. Edmunds, Suffolk, IP28 7DE Tel: (01638) 715713 Fax: (01638) 713007

▶ Avonside Plumbing & Heating Ltd, Unit 19, Colvilles Park, Glasgow, G75 0GZ Tel: (01355) 237021

▶ B & K Boiler Services Ltd, 2-4 Vicarage Road, Blackwater, Camberley, Surrey, GU17 9AX Tel: (01276) 705000 Fax: (01276) 705009

▶ B S J Mechanical & Plumbing Services Ltd, 87 Princess Street, Sheffield, S4 7UU Tel: 0114-276 6004

▶ Banlaw Europe Ltd, Unit 1-3 Rosendale Way, Blantyre, Glasgow, G72 0NJ Tel: (01698) 824431 Fax: (01698) 826725 E-mail: andymcateer@banlawsystems.com

▶ Barnsley Refrigeration Services Ltd, D Beevor Industrial Estate, Beevor Street, Barnsley, South Yorkshire, S71 1HN Tel: (01226) 732068 Fax: (01226) 732068

▶ Bedford Engineering Services, Blanche House, Cross Blanche Street, Dowlais, Merthyr Tydfil, CF48 3PD Tel: (01685) 350798 Fax: (01685) 350798

▶ Bentley Mechanical Services Ltd, 140 Barton Road, Comberton, Cambridge, CB23 7BT Tel: (01223) 264240 Fax: (01223) 264240 E-mail: office@bentleymechanicalservices.co.uk

▶ Berkshire Heating & Plumbing, 299 Basingstoke Road, Reading, RG2 0JA Tel: 0118-942 8300

▶ Bestaire Conditioning, Unit 2 Wessex Business Centre, Cheddar, Somerset, BS27 3EJ Tel: (01934) 741174 Fax: (01934) 741141

▶ Billings & Hathaway Ltd, Unit 3, Centenary Industrial Estate, Hughes Road, Brighton, BN2 4AW Tel: (01273) 570680

▶ Boatman Air Conditioning Ltd, Unit 1a Abbey Trading Estate, Bell Green Lane, London, SE26 5TW Tel: (0500) 300971 Fax: (020) 8778 9500

▶ Bofa Electrical Ltd, 22 Broadleys Road, Stirling, FK7 7ST Tel: (01786) 450260 Fax: (01786) 451763

▶ Boiler & Burner Maintenance, Unit 317 Woodside Way, Springvale Industrial Estate, Cwmbran, Gwent, NP44 5BR Tel: (01633) 871377 Fax: (01633) 838670

▶ Boiler Scot Ltd, Victoria Buildings Business Ce, Violet Street, Paisley, Renfrewshire, PA1 1PA Tel: 0141-889 5447

▶ Boland Jarrett (Edinburgh) Ltd, 49 Northumberland St, Edinburgh, EH3 6JJ Tel: 0131-557 8155 E-mail: mail@johnstonfinancial.co.uk

Booker & Best, Windmill House, Windmill Road, St. Leonards-on-Sea, East Sussex, TN38 9BY Tel: (01424) 434391 Fax: (01424) 446833 E-mail: adrianstallworthy@bookerbest.co.uk

▶ Bournville Heating Service, 50 Camp Hill Industrial Estate, John Kempe Way, Birmingham, B12 0HU Tel: 0121-753 3456 Fax: 0121-753 3698

▶ British Gas Services Ltd, 30 The Causeway, Staines, Middlesex, TW18 3BY Tel: (01784) 874000

▶ Brookside Southern Ltd, 2 The Shops, Wonersh Common, Wonersh, Guildford, Surrey, GU5 0PJ Tel: (01483) 893182 Fax: (01483) 894331

▶ Brooktherm Refrigeration Ltd, 3 Kelvin Park, Dock Road, Birkenhead, Merseyside, CH41 1LT Tel: 0151-650 1070 Fax: 0151-649 9001 E-mail: sales@brooktherm.co.uk

▶ Bryers & Heaton Ltd, Richmond Hill, Wigan, Lancashire, WN5 8AA Tel: (01942) 211726 Fax: (01942) 214171

▶ BSW Building Services TD, Rock Lodge Vineyard, Lewes Road, Scaynes Hill, Haywards Heath, West Sussex, RH17 7NG Tel: (01444) 831138 Fax: (01444) 831183

BSW Heating Ltd, 3 Old Barn Lane, Kenley, Surrey, CR8 5AT Tel: (020) 8763 5300 Fax: (020) 8763 5353 E-mail: enquiries@bsw-heating.com

▶ Bumford Heating Ltd, Millhouses Street, Hoyland, Barnsley, South Yorkshire, S74 9LU Tel: (01226) 749300 Fax: (01226) 747952 E-mail: sales@bhl.co.uk

▶ Burnertech Heating Contractors, Unit 2a Osman House, Prince Street, Bolton, BL1 2NP Tel: (01204) 393222 Fax: (01204) 394222

▶ C & D Heating Services Ltd, 3 Balgray Road, Glengarnock, Beith, Ayrshire, KA14 3AG Tel: (01505) 683131

▶ C N C Heating Ltd, Fawkham Road, Longfield, Kent, DA3 7BE Tel: (01474) 700111 Fax: (01474) 700123

▶ C Raymond Heating Co. Ltd, 93-97 Pall Mall, Leigh-on-Sea, Essex, SS9 1RF Tel: (01702) 714959

▶ C & V Plumbing & Heating Ltd, Hanrhys House, Main Road, New Brighton, Mold, Clwyd, CH7 6QW Tel: (01352) 751800 Fax: (01352) 751802 E-mail: info@cvplumbing.co.uk

▶ Calder Building Services, 4 Keighley Road, Halifax, West Yorkshire, HX3 6QP Tel: (01422) 383113 Fax: (01422) 383117 E-mail: info@calderbuild.com

▶ Cam Water Ltd, Cam House, 5 York Street, Aberdeen, AB11 5DL Tel: (01224) 596777 Fax: (01224) 594477

▶ Cameronaire Environmental Ltd, Willow House, Kestrel View, Strathclyde Business Park, Bellshill, Lanarkshire, ML4 3PB Tel: (01698) 464321

▶ Capital Plumbing, 138 Comiston Road, Edinburgh, EH10 5QN Tel: 0131-447 7555 Fax: 0131-447 7556

▶ Carrier Air Conditioning, 133 Barfillan Drive, Glasgow, G52 1BE Tel: 0141-810 2300 Fax: 0141-810 2313

▶ Carrier Services, Europa Boulevard, Westbrook, Warrington, WA5 7TN Tel: (01925) 656464 Fax: (01925) 656404

▶ Carters Heating & Plumbing Ltd, Unit 45a Enterprise House, 44-46 Terrace Road, Walton-on-Thames, Surrey, KT12 2SD Tel: (01932) 262521 Fax: (01932) 262521

▶ Central Heating Advisory Service, 120 A-B, Eastwoodmains Road, Clarkston, Glasgow, G76 7HH Tel: 0141-571 7711

▶ Central Heating Services, 46 Camp Road, Farnborough, Hampshire, GU14 6EP Tel: (01252) 524649 Fax: (01252) 376765 E-mail: service@chsltd.co.uk

▶ Cer, 7 Monaco Works, Station Road, Kings Langley, Hertfordshire, WD4 8LQ Tel: (01923) 266866 Fax: (01923) 261784

▶ CFM Building Services Ltd, Units 1-2 Crathie Court, Castlehill Industrial Estate, Carluke, Lanarkshire, ML8 5UF Tel: (01555) 771178 Fax: (01555) 771226

▶ Chard Construction Ltd, Unit 9, Block 2 Blantyre Industrial Es, Glasgow, G72 0UD Tel: (01698) 820333

▶ City Centre Maintenance Services, 13 Duke Street, Glasgow, G4 0UL Tel: 0141-552 2419 Fax: 0141-552 4010

▶ Climate Services Ltd, Haigh Park, Haigh Avenue, Stockport, Cheshire, SK4 1QR Tel: 0161-480 4625 Fax: 0161-476 5423

▶ Climate Services Ltd, 4 Swan Wharf Business Centre, Waterloo Road, Uxbridge, Middlesex, UB8 2RA Tel: (01895) 812280 Fax: (01895) 234136

▶ Colin Laver, Riverside Buildings, Nile Road, Pontypridd, Mid Glamorgan, CF37 1BW Tel: (01443) 404516 Fax: (01443) 486048

▶ Commercial Property Maintenance Services, Victoria House, Mary Street, Johnstone, Renfrewshire, PA5 8BT Tel: (01505) 382333 Fax: (01505) 382338

▶ Complete Gas Maintenance, St James Business Centre, 10A Linwood Road, Linwood, Paisley, Renfrewshire, PA3 3AT Tel: 0141-887 3798

▶ Complete Temperature Solutions Ltd, Unit 1, Gardners Business Park, Brent Road, Cossington, Bridgwater, Somerset, TA7 8LF Tel: (01278) 723744

▶ Corrie Plumbing & Heating Ltd, 12-14 Seafield Road, Inverness, IV1 1SG Tel: (01463) 250883

Crawford Ltd, Zetland Road, Hillington Industrial Estate, Glasgow, G52 4BW Tel: 0141-810 9900 Fax: 0141-810 9901

▶ Crest Bathrooms Ltd, 9 Colquhoun Avenue, Hillington Industrial Estate, Glasgow, G52 4BN Tel: 0141-882 7799 Fax: 0141-882 2777

▶ Crestbrook Heating Ltd, 9-11 Whitby Street, Hartlepool, Cleveland, TS24 7AD Tel: (01429) 263191 Fax: (01429) 861965

▶ Crowthorne Heating Co. Ltd, Devonshire House, 4 Dukes Ride, Crowthorne, Berkshire, RG45 6LT Tel: (01344) 772397

▶ Cussen & Sons Mechanical Services Contractors, 3 Bowman Trading Estate, Bessemer Drive, Stevenage, Hertfordshire, SG1 2DL Tel: (01438) 728525

▶ D Astin & Son, 16 Waddington Road, Clitheroe, Lancashire, BB7 2HJ Tel: (01200) 422315 Fax: (01200) 422315

▶ D Clarke, 2 Southfield Road, Hinckley, Leicestershire, LE10 1UB Tel: (01455) 618187 Fax: (01455) 233600

▶ D E S Heating & Plumbing, 253 Fenwick Road, Giffnock, Glasgow, G46 6JQ Tel: 0141-638 9589

▶ D J Hewer & Co., 39-41 Haverly Street, Gloucester, GL1 4PN Tel: (01452) 525854

▶ D J R Services 2000 Ltd, Buntsford Park Road, Bromsgrove, Worcestershire, B60 3DX Tel: (01527) 833222

▶ Dalkia Energy & Technical Services Ltd, 506-510 Old Kent Road, London, SE1 5BA Tel: (020) 7231 1338

▶ Daly Engineering Services Ltd, 19 Falkland House, Falkland Close, Coventry, CV4 8AG Tel: (024) 7646 5281 Fax: (024) 7669 4156

▶ David C Osborne Ltd, 2-4 Park Avenue, Deal, Kent, CT14 9AL Tel: (01304) 381999

▶ David M Blyth, 153 Commercial Street, Kirkcaldy, Fife, KY1 2NS Tel: (01592) 263378 Fax: (01592) 263378

▶ Design Heat Winchester Ltd, 5 Bar End Road, Winchester, Hampshire, SO23 9NT Tel: 01962 867564

▶ Domestic Plumbing & Heating, 7 Fairfield Street, Dundee, DD3 8HX Tel: (01382) 880030

▶ Donald C Mcrobert & Son, Millbank, Lochfoot, Dumfries, DG2 8NN Tel: (01387) 730250 Fax: (01387) 730500

▶ Donald Mackenzie, Park House, Dunvegan, Isle of Skye, IV55 8GU Tel: (01470) 521434

▶ Drain Doctor Plumbing, 1 East School Road, Dundee, DD3 8NU Tel: (01382) 811899

▶ Duncan Bathroom Centre, 22-24 Auchmill Road, Bucksburn, Aberdeen, AB21 9LD Tel: (01224) 713330 Fax: (01224) 713310 E-mail: sales@dbc.demon.co.uk

▶ E & B Engineering Services Special Works Ltd, 71-77 Brighton Road, Horley, Surrey, RH6 7HL Tel: (01293) 783344

▶ E Wilkinson Plumbing & Heating Contractors Ltd, 120d Milton Park, Milton, Abingdon, Oxfordshire, OX14 4SA Tel: (01235) 835070 Fax: (01235) 832033

▶ East Goscote Plumbers Ltd, East Goscote Industrial Estate, East Goscote, Leicester, LE7 3SL Tel: 0116-260 7766

▶ East Kirkby Engineering Co Lincs Ltd, International House, Lealand Way, Boston, Lincolnshire, PE21 7SW Tel: (01205) 366833 Fax: (01205) 353811

▶ East Lancashire Refrigeration Ltd, Clarendon Road, Blackburn, BB1 9SS Tel: (01254) 262787 Fax: (01254) 661576

▶ Edinburgh Plumbing & Drainage Co. Ltd, Unit 4, Fisherrow Industrial Estate, Newhailes Road, Musselburgh, Midlothian, EH21 6RU Tel: 0131-665 9090

▶ Embleton Services Ltd, 5 Freeland Way, Erith, Kent, DA8 2LQ Tel: (01322) 335373 Fax: (01322) 333510

▶ Encon Special Contracts Ltd, Encon House Astin Court, Tenter Road Moulton Park, Moulton Park Industrial Estate, Northampton, NN3 6PZ Tel: (01604) 648200

▶ Engineering Pipework Services Ltd, Unit 4 Derwent Howe Industrial Estate, Adams Road, Workington, Cumbria, CA14 3YS Tel: (01900) 603376 Fax: (01900) 65514

▶ Enginite Ltd, 25 & 26 College Street, Kempston, Bedford, MK42 8LU Tel: (01234) 344710

▶ Environmental Control Services Ltd, Liberty Centre, Mount Pleasant, Wembley, Middlesex, HA0 1TX Tel: (020) 8902 1901

▶ Eps Maintenance Ltd, Unit A The Homesdale Centre, 216 - 218 Homesdale Road, Bromley, BR1 2QZ Tel: (020) 8460 0960 Fax: (020) 8313 3550

▶ Essex Mechanical Services, 3 Peartree Business Centre, Peartree Road, Stanway, Colchester, CO3 0JN Tel: (01206) 368821 Fax: (01206) 368826

▶ Eurojet Scotland Ltd, 22 Taxi Way, Hillend, Dunfermline, Fife, KY11 9JT Tel: (01383) 825324

▶ Eva-Pro Heating Services, Unit 7A, Pant Industrial Estate, Dowlais, Merthyr Tydfil, Mid Glamorgan, CF48 2SR Tel: (01685) 722467

▶ Eva-Pro Heating Services, Unit 1, Old Rediffusion Buildings, Merthyr Tydfil, Mid Glamorgan, CF47 0AX Tel: (01685) 379969

▶ Express Heating Co. Ltd, Broughton Market, Edinburgh, EH3 6NU Tel: 0131-556 8242 Fax: 0131-557 2989 E-mail: sales@express-heating.co.uk

▶ F G Fennell & Co. Ltd, Service House, Wildes Street, Lowestoft, Suffolk, NR32 1XH Tel: (01502) 572065 Fax: (01502) 588933

▶ F Humphrey Heating Sussex Ltd, 62 Bates Road, Brighton, BN1 6PG Tel: (01273) 558571 Fax: (01273) 550160

▶ F J Jones Holdings Ltd, 9-10 Yates Lane, Cakemore, Rowley Regis, West Midlands, B65 0RA Tel: 0121-561 4494 Fax: 0121-561 5402

▶ Ford, 2 Alexandria Trading Estate, Alexandria Road, Sidmouth, Devon, EX10 9HA Tel: (01395) 571020 Fax: (01395) 571005

▶ Ford Mainwaring Ltd, 2a Eagle Street, Stoke-on-Trent, ST1 3PE Tel: (01782) 271772 Fax: (01782) 204969

▶ Fre Flo Plumbing & Heating Services Ltd, Unit 29 800 Brightside Lane, Sheffield, S9 2RX Tel: 0114-242 0004 Fax: 0114-244 5948

▶ Fred Margarson Ltd, R/O 12 Southfield Road, Grimsby, South Humberside, DN33 2PL Tel: (01472) 822226 Fax: (01472) 827709

▶ Frederick Thomas (Building Services) Ltd, Units 11 & 19, Attenburys Park Estate, Attenburys Lane, Timperley, Altrincham, Cheshire, WA14 5QE Tel: 0161-905 2302

▶ Freemans Maintenance & Building Services Ltd, Unit 62, Mill Lane, Fazeley, Tamworth, Staffordshire, B78 3QD Tel: (01827) 260085

▶ James Frew Ltd, 83 New Street, Stevenston, Ayrshire, KA20 3HD Tel: (01294) 468113 Fax: (01294) 469371 E-mail: admin@jamesfrew.co.uk

▶ G & A Plumbing & Heating Ltd, 1 Primrose Lane, Arlesey, Bedfordshire, SG15 6RD Tel: (01462) 731896 Fax: (01462) 835588 E-mail: carole@gaplumbing.co.uk

▶ G K D Building Services Ltd, 305 Town St, Bramley, Leeds, LS13 3JT Tel: 0113-255 6550

▶ G McHardy & Son, 26 High Street, Oban, Argyll, PA34 4BG Tel: (01631) 565307

▶ G S Brown Gas & Heating Services, 27 Woodbine Terrace, Edinburgh, EH6 8DA Tel: 0131-467 5907

▶ G S Whyte & Co. Ltd, 13 Princes Street, Monifieth, Dundee, DD5 4AW Tel: (01382) 532172

▶ G W Sparrow & Co. Ltd, 5 Cobham Centre, Westmead Industrial Estate, Westlea, Swindon, SN5 7UJ Tel: (01793) 541701 Fax: (01793) 541702

▶ Gasplan Ltd, 3 East Lane, Paisley, Renfrewshire, PA1 1QA Tel: 0141-889 2425 Fax: 0141-849 1466

GBS Building Services Ltd, 4 Thornybank, Dalkeith, Midlothian, EH22 2NQ Tel: 0131-663 7899 Fax: 0131-660 4074

▶ George Brown & Sons, Millett House, Millett Street, Bury, Lancashire, BL9 0JA Tel: 0161-764 9000 Fax: 0161-705 1082

▶ George S Hall Ltd, Building 75, Valley, Holyhead, Gwynedd, LL65 3NY Tel: (01407) 742408 Fax: (01407) 740308

▶ Glen Farrow UK Ltd, Spalding Road, Pinchbeck, Spalding, Lincolnshire, PE11 3UE Tel: (01775) 725444

▶ Grange Buildig Services, Granary Cottage, Vogrie, Gorebridge, Midlothian, EH23 4NT Tel: 0131-665 0101

▶ Greystone Plumbing Ltd, 23 Townhead Street, Strathaven, Lanarkshire, ML10 6AB Tel: (01357) 522037 Fax: (01357) 520214

▶ J.M. Guild, Market Street, Forfar, Angus, DD8 3EW Tel: (01307) 464794

▶ Guilfram Heating Co. Ltd, 1 Wonersh Common, Wonersh, Guildford, Surrey, GU5 0PJ Tel: (01483) 894248 Fax: (01483) 894219 E-mail: ianwarner@guilfram.co.uk

▶ H F Brown & Son Ltd, Portland Works, Main Street, Hemingbrough, Selby, North Yorkshire, YO8 6QF Tel: (01757) 638262

HEATING VENTILATION AND AIR CONDITIONING (HVAC) CONTRACTORS – *continued*

▶ H G Bruce & Partners Ltd, Nelson Road, Winchester, Hampshire, SO23 0QG Tel: (01962) 853968 Fax: (01962) 862141

▶ H M L Group Ltd, Unit 76 Riverside Estate, Sir Thomas Longley Road, Medway City Estate, Rochester, Kent, ME2 4BH Tel: (01634) 715120 Fax: (01634) 715001

H & R Boilercare, 58a Amwell Street, Hoddesdon, Hertfordshire, EN11 8UA Tel: (01992) 463919 Fax: (01992) 451326 E-mail: shaun.raynor@ntlworld.com

▶ H2o Plumbing Services Ltd, 158 Beeches Road, Birmingham, B42 2HN Tel: 0121-357 9400 Fax: 0121-357 9400

▶ Haden Young Ltd, 93-105 Blenheim Street, Newcastle upon Tyne, NE1 4BW Tel: 0191-222 9200 Fax: 0191-232 3334

▶ Hannah & Howie Services Ltd, 26 Tollpark Road, Cumbernauld, Glasgow, G68 0LW Tel: (01236) 737414 Fax: (01236) 457607

▶ Haydon Mechanical & Electrical, The Isis Building Thames Quay, 193 Marsh Wall, London, E14 9SG Tel: (020) 7987 3555

▶ Heatcare, 112 Maxwell Avenue, Bearsden, Glasgow, G61 1HU Tel: 0141-943 2200

▶ Heatcare Services Scotland Ltd, 1 16 Wellington Road, Bishopbriggs, Glasgow, G64 2SA Tel: 0141-772 1515 Fax: 0141-772 1616

▶ Heath & Arnold Ltd, St Day Road, Redruth, Cornwall, TR15 2EH Tel: (01209) 213886 Fax: (01209) 313047

▶ Heating & Boiler Services Ltd, Sayce Street, Widnes, Cheshire, WA8 6EE Tel: 0151-420 4030 Fax: 0151-420 4071 E-mail: sales@heatingandboilerservices.co.uk

▶ Hellabys Ltd, 8 Hallsford Bridge Industrial Estate, Stondon Road, Ongar, Essex, CM5 9RB Tel: (01277) 363993 Fax: (01277) 366997

▶ Hert's Cooling Ltd, Bridgeman House, Pindar Road, Hoddesdon, Hertfordshire, EN11 0DA Tel: (01992) 470740 Fax: (01992) 470220

▶ Hickman Brothers Ltd, Unit 5, Eagle Industrial Estate, Church Green, Witney, Oxfordshire, OX28 4YR Tel: (01993) 772774 Fax: (01993) 703057

▶ Holland Heating UK Ltd, United Technologies House, Guildford Road, Fetcham, Leatherhead, Surrey, KT22 9UT Tel: (01372) 220230 Fax: (01372) 220221

▶ Holt Heat, 23 Dukehaugh, Peebles, EH45 9DN Tel: (01721) 720366

▶ Hopol Central Heating, 4a Rhiw Road, Colwyn Bay, Clwyd, LL29 7TE Tel: (01492) 536676 Fax: (01492) 535193 E-mail: sales@hopol.com

▶ Ho'Ton Heating Ltd, Chilton Moor School, Chilton Moor, Houghton le Spring, Tyne & Wear, DH4 6LU Tel: 0191-385 4556 Fax: 0191-385 5472

▶ Hoveair Building Services Ltd, 24-26 Hermitage Lane, London, SE25 5HH Tel: (020) 8656 7744

▶ HRP Ltd, Unit 18 Britannia Industrial Estate, Poyle Road, Colnbrook, Slough, SL3 0BH Tel: (01753) 688100 Fax: (01753) 688101

▶ Hugh Stirling Ltd, 87 Middlesex Street, Glasgow, G41 1EE Tel: 0141-420 1666 Fax: 0141-429 2615

▶ Hurlstone & Champ Ltd, 95 High Street, Silverdale, Newcastle, Staffordshire, ST5 6LY Tel: (01782) 626575 Fax: (01782) 710950

▶ Hutchesons Of Portsoy, 27 Seafield Terrace, Portsoy, Banff, AB45 2FB Tel: (01261) 842396 Fax: (01261) 843981

I Marvin, Unit 10a Clintons Yard, Rigs Road, Stornoway, Isle of Lewis, HS1 2RF Tel: (01851) 702178 Fax: (01851) 704233

▶ Image Ltd, Murhall Street, Stoke-on-Trent, ST6 4BL Tel: (01782) 825006 Fax: (01782) 825474

▶ Incontrol Gas Services, 130 Queens Road, Nuneaton, Warwickshire, CV11 5LG Tel: (024) 7635 0060 Fax: (024) 7635 0056

▶ Industrial & Commercial Heating Ltd, Unit 42 Stirling Enterprise Park, Stirling, FK7 7RP Tel: (01786) 445525 Fax: (01786) 445525

▶ Industrial Pipe Services, North Road, Widmer End, High Wycombe, Buckinghamshire, HP15 6NE Tel: (01494) 711150 Fax: (01494) 711180

▶ J & B Hopkins Ltd, 96 Botley Road, Richmond Court, Park Gate, Southampton, SO31 1BA Tel: (01489) 584706

▶ J E Dean Hazel Grove Ltd, 15 Napier Street, Hazel Grove, Stockport, Cheshire, SK7 4EW Tel: 0161-483 5110 Fax: 0161-456 5118

▶ J.& F.May Ltd, Trinity Works, 1a Hermit Road, London, E16 4HP Tel: (020) 7476 3786 E-mail: sales@jfmay.demon.co.uk

▶ J Frood & Sons, 47 Wellgate, Lanark, ML11 9DS Tel: (01555) 663927 Fax: (01555) 666158

▶ J H Horn, 522 Crow Road, Glasgow, G13 1NU Tel: 0141-954 5911 Fax: 0141-959 9821 E-mail: enquiries@hunterbs.co.uk

▶ J H Horn Plumbers Ltd, 101-103 Holmlea Road, Glasgow, G44 4AQ Tel: 0141-632 0085 Fax: 0141-649 8374

▶ J Higgs Lowdham Ltd, 10 Kirk Hill, East Bridgford, Nottingham, NG13 8PE Tel: (01949) 20671 Fax: (01949) 21150

▶ J Mitchell & Son (Laurencekirk) Ltd, Aberdeen Road, Laurencekirk, Kincardineshire, AB30 1AJ Tel: (01561) 377357

▶ J N B Boliers, Boiler House, Calderhead Road, Shotts, Lanarkshire, ML7 4EQ Tel: (01501) 822177

▶ J N Weatherby Ltd, 133 Frankwell, Shrewsbury, SY3 8JX Tel: (01743) 235392 Fax: (01743) 368619

▶ J P Price (Plumbers), Paragon House, 8 Milltown Street, Radcliffe, Manchester, M26 1WD Tel: 0161-723 2830 Fax: 0161-724 1020

▶ J R Smith, 2 Cambuslea Road, Ayr, KA8 9HT Tel: (01292) 269499 Fax: (01292) 284631 E-mail: sales@johnrsmith.co.uk

▶ J T Dove Ltd, Northumberland Road, Tweedmouth, Berwick-upon-Tweed, TD15 2AS Tel: (01289) 304211 Fax: (01289) 306497

▶ J W Bennie & Son, 6 Dundas Street, Grangemouth, Stirlingshire, FK3 8BX Tel: (01324) 482815 Fax: (01324) 665805

▶ J W Housden Ltd, 1 Margetts Road, Kempston, Bedford, MK42 8DS Tel: (01234) 852033 Fax: (01234) 841226

▶ James Frew Ltd, 4 Lawmoor Avenue, Dixons Blazes Industrial Estat, Glasgow, G5 0XN Tel: 0141-429 4000

▶ James Mackie Ltd, 1 Tams Brig, Ayr, KA8 8DF Tel: (01292) 269053

▶ James Paterson Plumbing & Heating Ltd, 23 Winchester Avenue Industrial, Denny, Stirlingshire, FK6 6QE Tel: (01324) 823613 Fax: (01324) 822342

▶ Jaydee Heating Ltd, 78 Jane Street, Edinburgh, EH6 5HG Tel: 0131-555 0388 Fax: 0131-555 2826

▶ Jimmy Jackson Heating & Plumbing Engineers, 44 Rainford Road, Billinge, Wigan, Lancashire, WN5 7PF Tel: (01744) 892629 Fax: (01744) 892626

▶ John L McLellan, 59 Main Street, Prestwick, Ayrshire, KA9 1JN Tel: (01292) 478630

▶ John N Dunn Scotland Ltd, 6b Dunnet Way, East Mains Industrial Estate, Broxburn, West Lothian, EH52 5NN Tel: (01506) 854831 Fax: (01506) 852565E-mail: info@laxcon.com

▶ John Taylor Plumbers Ltd, Mitchell Industrial Estate, Orebridge, Thornton, Kirkcaldy, Fife, KY1 4DT Tel: (01592) 771264 Fax: (01592) 630626

▶ F. Johnson & Co. Heating (1983) Ltd, Chapel Street, Halstead, Essex, CO9 2LS Tel: (01787) 472382 Fax: (01787) 477563 E-mail: info@johnsonheating.co.uk

▶ Jones, Ryehill Court, Lodge Farm Industrial Estate, Northampton, NN5 7EU Tel: (01604) 588811

▶ JSB Plumbing & Sons, 6 Carron Place, Edinburgh, EH6 7RE Tel: 0131-555 1230 Fax: 0131-467 2555

▶ K G Wagstaff & Sons, 136-138 Upminster Road, Hornchurch, Essex, RM12 6PL Tel: (01708) 442666 Fax: (01708) 437334 E-mail: info@wagstaffheating.co.uk

▶ Kestrel Mechanical Services Ltd, Betsom Farm, 2 Pilgrims Way, Westerham, Kent, TN16 2DS Tel: (01959) 564269 Fax: (01959) 564387

▶ Kielder Plumbing & Heating Contracts Ltd, Unit 6a Colliery Lane, Hetton-le-Hole, Houghton le Spring, Tyne & Wear, DH5 0BG Tel: 0191-526 2222 Fax: 0191-526 6622

▶ Kirklees Plumbing & Heating Wigan Ltd, Unit H2 Belle Green Industrial Estate, Belle Green Lane, Ince, Wigan, Lancashire, WN2 2EP Tel: (01942) 324058 Fax: (01942) 491273

▶ KSN Northage & Co. Ltd, Vulcan House, Goliath Road, Coalville, Leicestershire, LE67 3FT Tel: (01530) 513599 Fax: (01530) 513594

▶ L K F Ltd, Unit 4 Technology Centre, White Oak Square, London Road, Swanley, Kent, BR8 7AG Tel: (01322) 614621

▶ T. Laird Plumbers & Electrical Contractors, Unit 1, Woodilee Industrial Estate, Kirkintilloch, Glasgow, G66 3TY Tel: 0141-776 2843

▶ James Lammond Ltd, 32 Market Street, Brechin, Angus, DD9 6BB Tel: (01356) 622072 Fax: (01356) 622350 E-mail: sales@jameslammondltd.com

▶ Livingston Mechanical Services, Nettlehill Road, Houstoun Industrial Estate, Livingston, West Lothian, EH54 5DL Tel: (01506) 442669 Fax: (01506) 442671

▶ Lothian Heating Services Ltd, Edgefield Road Industrial Estate, Edgefield Road, Loanhead, Midlothian, EH20 9TB Tel: 0131-440 2958 Fax: 0131-440 4244

▶ Lowlands Gas Ltd, Wellwood Service Centre, Ettrick Terrace, Selkirk, TD7 4JS Tel: (01750) 23054 Fax: (01750) 22160

▶ M B Heating Ltd, Unit 1 Darby Lane, Hindley, Wigan, Lancashire, WN2 3DW Tel: (01942) 520100 Fax: (01942) 523173

▶ M B Plumbing, 18 Westend Court, Law, Carluke, Lanarkshire, ML8 5SL Tel: (01698) 375968

▶ M & C Environmental Services, Teresa Gavin House, Southend Road, Woodford Green, Essex, IG8 8FA Tel: (020) 8550 3838 Fax: (020) 8551 7995

▶ M C Freeze Refrigeration & Air Conditioning, Barrs Court Road, Hereford, HR1 1EG Tel: (01432) 355164 Fax: (01432) 273612

▶ M C Plumbing, Unit 7, Ermine Point Business Park, Westmill Road, Ware, Hertfordshire, SG12 0EF Tel: (01920) 465111

▶ M D & B W Buxton, 80 Derby Road, Heanor, Derbyshire, DE75 7QJ Tel: (01773) 714804 Fax: (01773) 531113

▶ M H Cragg & Sons Ltd, Ingleside, 11 Lee Lane, Horwich, Bolton, BL6 7BP Tel: (01204) 697157 Fax: (01204) 699113

▶ M M P S Plumbing Services Ltd, 9 McLennan Street, Glasgow, G42 9DH Tel: 0141-632 6622

▶ M & M Services Ltd, 662 Holburn Street, Aberdeen, AB10 7JQ Tel: (01224) 589222

▶ M & R Heating Services, 9 St John Street, Stranraer, Wigtownshire, DG9 7HS Tel: (01776) 706655 Fax: (01776) 706655

▶ M Y Boiler Services, Thieves Lane, Attleborough, Norfolk, NR17 2AP Tel: (01953) 497177 Fax: (01953) 456531 E-mail: sales@myboilerservices.co.uk

▶ Mcausland & Co, 112 Mid Wharf Street, Glasgow, G4 0LD Tel: 0141-333 0700 Fax: 0141-332 7817

▶ McKerron & Milne Ltd, Fisherton Yard, Aberlour, Banffshire, AB38 9LB Tel: (01340) 871410

▶ Mckerron & Milne, 35 New Street, Rothes, Aberlour, Banffshire, AB38 7BQ Tel: (01340) 831523 Fax: (01340) 831804

▶ Malvern Cooling Services Ltd, Unit 21B, Oak Road, West Chirton North Industrial, North Shields, Tyne & Wear, NE29 8SF Tel: 0191-296 1766

▶ Maq Air Conditioning, Hillhouse Community Workshop, Argyle CR, Hillhouse Industrial Estate, Hamilton, Lanarkshire, ML3 9BQ Tel: (01698) 286721 Fax: (01698) 200426

▶ Maxitherm Heating Ltd, Unit 6 Ford La Business Park, Ford, Arundel, West Sussex, BN18 0UZ Tel: (01243) 558885 Fax: (01243) 558886

▶ Meadow Line Services Ltd, Cameron Court, Cameron Street, Hillington Industrial Estate, Glasgow, G52 4JX Tel: 0141-883 7722

▶ Meads Ltd, 3 90a Tideswell Road, Eastbourne, East Sussex, BN21 3RT Tel: (01323) 726425 Fax: (01323) 726425

▶ Measham Heating Air Conditioning Ltd, 142 Birmingham Road, Aldridge, Walsall, WS9 0AH Tel: (01922) 456567 Fax: (01922) 456446 E-mail: reception@measham.co.uk

▶ Melville & Whitson, 22a Edinburgh Road, Dalkeith, Midlothian, EH22 1JR Tel: 0131-660 1480 Fax: 0131-654 2687

▶ Mercia Gas Ltd, Mercia House, 63 Holyhead Road, Coventry, CV1 3AA Tel: (024) 7652 5150 Fax: (024) 7652 5800 E-mail: service@merciagas.co.uk

▶ Midland Counties Heating Services Ltd, Bridge House, Upper St. John Street, Lichfield, Staffordshire, WS14 9DT Tel: (01543) 251152 Fax: (01543) 414256

▶ Miller Freeman & Sons Nottingham Ltd, Adco Business Centre, Bobbers Mill, Nottingham, NG8 5AH Tel: 0115-978 9895 Fax: 0115-978 9896

▶ Mitie Engineering Services Scotland Ltd, Seafield House, Seafield Road, Inverness, IV1 1SG Tel: (01463) 715233

▶ Mitie Engineering Services (South East) Ltd, London Road, Hook, Hampshire, RG27 9BY Tel: (01256) 768768

▶ Morgram Services Ltd, Staffordshire House, 28 New Road, Dudley, West Midlands, DY2 8TA Tel: (01384) 458880

▶ Muir Morrison Ltd, 322 Broomloan Road, Glasgow, G51 2JQ Tel: 0141-440 1655 Fax: 0141-445 3911

▶ Multiheat Ltd, 4 Cardinal House, 629 Stanningley Road, Leeds, LS13 4EP Tel: 0113-204 7555 Fax: 0113-204 7666

▶ Multiserve Ltd, Bowden Hall, Bowden Lane, Marple, Stockport, Cheshire, SK6 6ND Tel: 0161-427 4270 Fax: 0161-427 8800 E-mail: sales@multiserveltd.com

▶ James Munro & Son Ltd, 8 Stanley Road, Edinburgh, EH6 4SJ Tel: 0131-552 2538 Fax: 0131-552 5767

▶ N J Evans & Son, Jehu Road, Welshpool, Powys, SY21 7PE Tel: (01938) 552976 Fax: (01938) 552976

▶ Nicolsons, Terregles Street, Dumfries, DG2 9AT Tel: (01387) 269700 Fax: (01387) 257677

▶ North Channel Energy Services, 5 Lambhill Quadrant, Kinning Park, Glasgow, G41 1SB Tel: 0141-429 4557

▶ Oco Ltd, Unit 3-4 Sherwood Court, Thurston Road, London, SE13 7SD Tel: (01322) 276614 Fax: (01322) 227790 E-mail: john-moore@ocoltd.co.uk

▶ OCS Denver, Dairy Courtyard, 152-154 Ewell Road, Surbiton, Surrey, KT6 6HE Tel: (020) 8399 4253 Fax: (020) 8390 6044 E-mail: contact@denver.co.uk

▶ Opus Airconditioning Ltd, Unit 52 Victoria Industrial Park, Victoria Road, Dartford, DA1 5AJ Tel: (01322) 225111 Fax: (01322) 291389

▶ P Chester & Sons Bedford Ltd, 31 Howard Avenue, Bedford, MK40 4EE Tel: (0800) 0520535 Fax: (01234) 404088

▶ P G Bones & Sons Ltd, Unit 25 Riverside Industrial Park, Rapier Street, Ipswich, IP2 8JX Tel: (01473) 602555 Fax: (01473) 602580

▶ P & G Contractors Ltd, 1 Birch Street, Ashton-under-Lyne, Lancashire, OL7 0NX Tel: 0161-339 0831 Fax: 0161-285 3393

▶ P H Jones, Unit 18 The Bell Centre, Newton Road, Crawley, West Sussex, RH10 9FZ Tel: (01293) 518829 Fax: (01293) 534924

▶ P H Jones Ltd, Aqua House, Hampton Heath Industrial Estate, Hampton, Malpas, Cheshire, SY14 8LY Tel: (01948) 820244 Fax: (01948) 820484

▶ P & H Services, 24b Northbrook Industrial Estate, Newmills Road, Coleraine, County Londonderry, BT52 2JB Tel: (028) 7035 2579 Fax: (028) 7035 1182

▶ P J D Heating, 623 Manchester Road, Wardley, Swinton, Manchester, M27 9QH Tel: 0161-793 9471 Fax: 0161-728 4300

▶ P & R Installations Co. Ltd, 35-37 Waite Davies Road, London, SE12 0NE Tel: (020) 8851 2211 Fax: (020) 8851 6611

▶ Pan Heat, 126 Allerton Road, Mossley Hill, Liverpool, L18 2DG Tel: 0151-733 2121 Fax: 0151-733 3131

▶ Paul Brant Plumbing & Heating, 4 The Beaver Centre, Putney Road West, Leicester, LE2 7TD Tel: 0116-255 3520 Fax: 0116-255 6755

▶ Pepi Plumbers, 7 Wellburn Street, Dundee, DD2 2RR Tel: (01382) 623222

▶ Peter Reid, 23-27 High Street, Buckie, Banffshire, AB56 1AL Tel: (01542) 832158 Fax: (01542) 835551

▶ Phil Rogerson Ltd, Tarnwater, A6 Road, Yealand Conyers, Carnforth, Lancashire, LA5 9RJ Tel: (01524) 736432 Fax: (01524) 734236

▶ Pinnacle Heating Services Ltd, 1 Trinity Place Park Street, Aston, Birmingham, B6 5SH Tel: 0121-328 7800 Fax: 0121-773 3004

▶ Pipemaster Mechanical Services Ltd, 489 Hartshill Road, Stoke-On-Trent, ST4 6AA Tel: (01782) 710881

▶ Pirie & Hunter, 12 College Bounds, Aberdeen, AB24 3DU Tel: (01224) 483137 Fax: (01224) 277321

▶ Portway Plumbing Ltd, Castlegate Business Park, Salisbury, SP4 6QX Tel: (01722) 329268 Fax: (01722) 328257

Power Rod & Crann Ltd, 237 Clarkston Road, Glasgow, G44 3DS Tel: 0141-637 4452

▶ Prima Air Conditioning & Refrigeration Ltd, 44 London Road, Cowplain, Waterlooville, Hampshire, PO8 8EN Tel: (023) 9226 8882

▶ Principal Cooling, Old Eglish Road, Dungannon, County Tyrone, BT71 7PG Tel: (028) 8775 0111 Fax: (028) 8775 0222

▶ Project Heating Co. Ltd, 4 Norman Court, Budlake Road, Marsh Barton Trading Estate, Exeter, EX2 8PY Tel: (01392) 215790 Fax: (01392) 431528 E-mail: sales@projectheating.co.uk

▶ Pro-Tec BS Ltd, 67-69, George Street, London, W1U 8LT Tel: 020 8830 5545 Fax: 020 8830 5545 E-mail: enquiries@pro-tecbsltd.co.uk

▶ Quality Gas Services Ltd, 10-12 Eldon Street, Greenock, Renfrewshire, PA16 7UE Tel: (01475) 720865 Fax: (01475) 784681

▶ R A C E (Engineering) Services Ltd, 4 Mulberry Court, Bourne Industrial Park, Crayford, Dartford, DA1 4BF Tel: (01322) 429140 Fax: (01322) 429144

▶ R C H Group, 93-95 Pall Mall, Leigh-on-Sea, Essex, SS9 1RF Tel: (01702) 714959 Fax: (01702) 710005

▶ R & F Mechanical Services Ltd, 13 Seymour Street, Ballymoney, County Antrim, BT53 6JR Tel: (028) 2766 2627 Fax: (028) 2766 4056

▶ R H F Boiler Service Ltd, 71 73 Enville Street, Stourbridge, West Midlands, DY8 1XW Tel: (01384) 393694 Fax: (01384) 393744

▶ R I Building Services, 30 Tyock Industrial Estate, Elgin, Morayshire, IV31 1XY Tel: (01343) 548062

▶ R J S Heating Plumbing & Mechanical Services Ltd, 26 Chipstead Station Parade, Chipstead, Coulsdon, Surrey, CR5 3TF Tel: (01737) 550110 Fax: (01737) 556770

▶ R M C Mechanical Services, 3 Landport Road, Wolverhampton, WV2 2QJ Tel: (01902) 451541 Fax: (01902) 871534

▶ R M J Engineering Ltd, Lion Works, Station Road, Whittlesford, Cambridge, CB2 4NL Tel: (01223) 839900

▶ R Park & Sons Ltd, Unit 1 Aldwych Court, 586A Blackpool Road, Ashton-On-Ribble, Preston, PR2 1JA Tel: (01772) 720007

R S Plumbing & Heating Engineers, Oaklands, Smithwood Lodge, Cranleigh, Surrey, GU6 8QY Tel: (01483) 276494 Fax: (01483) 548949

▶ Reflections Bathroom & Tile Centres, Old Laundry Trading Estate, Bridport, Dorset, DT6 3BD Tel: (01308) 428555

▶ Roger Bullivant Ltd, Unit 160 Hayward Drive, Dartford Trade Park, Dartford, DA1 1JH Tel: (01322) 286565 Fax: (01322) 286566

▶ Roselands Heating Ltd, 340 Seaside, Eastbourne, East Sussex, BN22 7RJ Tel: (01323) 639455 Fax: (01323) 649912

▶ Rotary Scotland Ltd, 72 Kirk Road, Bathgate, West Lothian, EH48 1EH Tel: (01506) 633877 Fax: (01506) 634740

▶ Russell C Soper, 57 Farringdon Road, Plymouth, PL4 9ER Tel: (01752) 268666

Ryan Jayberg Ltd, Delta House, Riverside Road, London, SW17 0BA Tel: (020) 8944 6288 Fax: (020) 8944 6295

▶ S M Plumbing & Heating Ltd, St Leonards House, St Leonards Place, Kinghorn, Burntisland, Fife, KY3 9UL Tel: (01592) 890000 Fax: (01592) 890023

▶ S M S Maintenance Ltd, Faircross Offices, Stratfield Saye, Reading, RG7 2BT Tel: (01256) 880188 Fax: (01256) 880177 E-mail: sales@smsmaintenance.com

▶ S T Plumbing & Heating, 11 Hill Top, Knottingley, West Yorkshire, WF11 8EB Tel: (01977) 671859 Fax: (01977) 677699

▶ Sainsbury Heating Ltd, Unit 11 Cambrian Court Ferryboat Close, Morriston Enterprise Park, Swansea Enterprise Park, Swansea, SA6 8PZ Tel: (01792) 793400 Fax: (01792) 793600

▶ Saltire Facilities Management Ltd, Unit 3, Arbroath Business Centre, 31 Dens Road, Arbroath, Angus, DD11 1RS Tel: (01241) 430987

HEATING VENTILATION AND AIR CONDITIONING (HVAC) CONTRACTORS – *continued*

▶ Sandy Macgregor, 5 Saltoun Street, Wick, Caithness, KW1 5ET Tel: (01955) 602265 Fax: (01955) 606028

▶ Scan Building Services Ltd, 35 Byron Street, Dundee, DD3 6QT Tel: (01382) 889700 Fax: (01382) 814980

▶ Scotia Thermal Engineering Ltd, 1 Newark Road South, Glenrothes, Fife, KY7 4NS Tel: (01592) 770094 Fax: (01592) 770095

▶ Scotiathermel, 2B Craiglockhart Drive South, Edinburgh, EH14 1HZ Tel: 0131-455 7805 Fax: 0131-443 6190

▶ Scott & Rafferty, 66-68 Mains Street, Lockerbie, Dumfriesshire, DG11 2DQ Tel: (01576) 202613 Fax: (01576) 204720

▶ Seaforth Services, Unit 6 Slader Business Park, Witney Road, Nuffield Industrial Estate, Poole, Dorset, BH17 0GP Tel: (01202) 330630 Fax: (01202) 679100

▶ Skene Blair & Son Forfar Ltd, Unit 1 Station Place, Forfar, Angus, DD8 3TB Tel: (01307) 463431 Fax: (01307) 468595

▶ Snell & Mackay, 2A Sivell Place, Heavitree, Exeter, EX2 5ER Tel: (01392) 211882

▶ Somerset Gas Co. Ltd, 17 Knights Road, Chelston Business Park, Wellington, Somerset, TA21 9JH Tel: (01823) 661144 Fax: (01823) 661155 E-mail: info@somersetgas.eclipse.co.uk

▶ Spark's Mechanical Services Ltd, Unit 12 Tyock Industrial Estate, Elgin, Morayshire, IV30 1XY Tel: (01343) 547840 Fax: (01343) 549525

▶ Star Refrigeration Ltd, Wincanton Close, Derby, DE24 8NB Tel: (01332) 756041 Fax: (01332) 757289

▶ Status Heating Ltd, 178 Sladepool Farm Road, Birmingham, B14 5EE Tel: 0121-430 3668 Fax: 0121-436 6765 E-mail: info@statusheating.co.uk

▶ Status Mechanical Services, Lightning Works Birmingham Road, Hopwood, Alvechurch, Birmingham, B48 7AL Tel: 0121-447 7677 Fax: 0121-447 7432

▶ Steve Wall Plumbing & Heating Ltd, Furlong Road, Stoke-on-Trent, ST6 5UN Tel: (01782) 821730 Fax: (01782) 812155

▶ Steven R Paterson Ltd, 10 Crowness Road, Hatston, Kirkwall, Orkney, KW15 1RG Tel: (01856) 870888 Fax: (01856) 870066

▶ Stretton Bros Leicester, 27 Lunsford Road, Leicester, LE5 0HW Tel: 0116-274 1166 Fax: 0116-246 0299

▶ Strowger & Smith, 5 Seaview Road, Sandend, Banff, AB45 2UE Tel: (01261) 842226 Fax: (01261) 842226

▶ Strysen Heating & Plumbing, 4 St James Rd, Sutton Coldfield, West Midlands, B75 5EH Tel: 0121-308 0962 Fax: 0121-323 2838

▶ Stuart Kennedy Heating Services, 14 Hillview Place, Dumfries, DG1 4DU Tel: (01387) 268852

▶ Superior Plumbing Installations Ltd, 7 High Street, Chasetown, Burntwood, Staffordshire, WS7 3XE Tel: (01543) 677161 Fax: (01543) 685730

▶ Superior Plumbing Installations Ltd, Unit1 Wheeler Road, Binley Industrial Estate, Whitley, Coventry, CV3 4LA Tel: (024) 7621 7980 Fax: (024) 7663 9766

▶ Sutton Service International Ltd, 48 Darnley Street, Glasgow, G41 2SE Tel: 0141-420 3277

▶ T Brown Group Ltd, 24 High Street, Ewell, Epsom, Surrey, KT17 1SJ Tel: (020) 8394 1166 Fax: (020) 8393 9947

▶ T D Heating & Pipework Ltd, Sneyd Street, Stoke-on-Trent, ST6 2NZ Tel: (01782) 264279 Fax: (01782) 204692

▶ T D R Mechanical Services Ltd, Tansey Green Road, Brierley Hill, West Midlands, DY5 4TL Tel: (01384) 263463 Fax: (01384) 76245

▶ T Findlay Ltd, 1 Mansion Street, Cambuslang, Glasgow, G72 7JN Tel: 0141-641 6412

▶ T T F (Scotland) Ltd, 4 Block 3 12 King's Haugh, Peffermill Road, Edinburgh, EH16 5UY Tel: 0131-652 0030 Fax: 0131-661 0550 E-mail: admin@ttf-aircon.com

▶ Taunton Plumbing & Heating, Unit 6, Venture 11, Priorswood Industrial Estate, Taunton, Somerset, TA2 8DG Tel: (01823) 278887

▶ Taylor Mechanical Services, Unit 6, Marybank Lane, Dundee, DD2 3DY Tel: (01382) 612863 Fax: (01382) 623134

▶ Taylor Robinson Ltd, Fire Protection House, Woolley Colliery Road, Darton, Barnsley, South Yorkshire, S75 5JA Tel: 0161-764 8674 Fax: (01226) 388206

▶ Team Services, Unit 8 Caen View, Swindon, SN5 8WQ Tel: (01793) 878989 Fax: (01793) 878989

▶ Teams Southern Ltd, 30 The Half Croft, Syston, Leicester, LE7 1LD Tel: 0116-269 1940 Fax: 0116-269 8901

▶ Tej Heating Plymouth Ltd, 247 Victoria Road, Plymouth, PL5 2DQ Tel: (01752) 351411 Fax: (01752) 351808

▶ Thermocool Ltd, 14 Millcroft Road, Rutherglen, Glasgow, G73 1EN Tel: 0141-647 9871 Fax: 0141-643 0850

▶ Thermoserve Ltd, 359 Bright Road, South Croydon, Surrey, CR2 6ER Tel: (020) 8681 7330

▶ Thomas Laird, Woodilee Industrial Estate, Woodilee Road Lenzie, Lenzie, Glasgow, G66 3UU Tel: 0141-776 2843

▶ Thorne Air Conditioning, 35 Mere View Industrial Estate, Yaxley, Peterborough, PE7 3HS Tel: (01733) 240200 Fax: (01733) 244554

▶ Toomeys, 3 Mill Court, Mill Lane, Newbury, Berkshire, RG14 5RE Tel: (01635) 33206

▶ Total Trade Services, Unit 1, Cefndy Road Employment Park, Cefndy Road, Rhyl, Clwyd, LL18 2HJ Tel: (01745) 360336

▶ Turner & Pritchard, 9 Block C Tuffley Park, Lower Tuffley Lane, Gloucester, GL2 5DP Tel: (01452) 522488 Fax: (01452) 303653

▶ Twin Services Ltd, 70-72 Skinner Street, Stockton-on-Tees, Cleveland, TS18 1EG Tel: (01642) 606067 Fax: (01642) 618551 E-mail: mail@twinservices.co.uk

▶ Uniheat Oxford Ltd, 33-37 Stockmore Street, Oxford, OX4 1JT Tel: (01865) 242708 Fax: (01865) 798347

▶ Urquhart & Co, Rhevackin, Kiltarlity, Beauly, Inverness-Shire, IV4 7HT Tel: (01463) 741564

▶ Urquhart & Co, 9 Lotland Street, Inverness, IV1 1ST Tel: (01463) 223500 Fax: (01463) 226060

▶ Vaillant Ltd, Unit D1, Lowfields Business Park, Elland, West Yorkshire, HX5 9DG Tel: (01422) 376070 Fax: (01422) 311986

▶ Ventilation & Hygiene Specialists, Unit 2 Wilson Street, Thornaby, Stockton-on-Tees, Cleveland, TS17 7AR Tel: (01642) 675755 Fax: (01642) 675760

▶ W D Smurthwaite & Sons, Sotherby Road, South Bank, Middlesbrough, Cleveland, TS6 6LP Tel: (01642) 462222 Fax: (01642) 463333

▶ W G Mackenzie, 4 Pinefield Parade, Elgin, Morayshire, IV30 6AG Tel: (01343) 541665 Fax: (01343) 540016

▶ W H Dunn & Co., 10 William Street, South Shields, Tyne & Wear, NE33 1PQ Tel: 0191-456 7503 Fax: 0191-454 5520

▶ W M Donnelly & Co. Ltd, Myre House, 15 Law Place, Nerston, Glasgow, G74 4QL Tel: (01355) 221718 Fax: (01355) 909001

▶ W R Refrigeration Ltd, Austin Fields, King's Lynn, Norfolk, PE30 1PH Tel: (01553) 773259 Fax: (01553) 767756

W R Refrigeration Ltd, 96 Nepshaw La South, Gildersome, Morley, Leeds, LS27 7JQ Tel: 0113-238 0038 Fax: 0113-238 0708

▶ Watret & Co. Ltd, 65-67 Park Street, St. Albans, Hertfordshire, AL2 2PE Tel: (01727) 873765

▶ Westward Energy Services, Energy House, Alloy Industrial Estate, Pontardawe, Swansea, SA8 4EN Tel: (01792) 862424 Fax: (01792) 830354

▶ Wilden Services Ltd, 131 Belswains Lane, Hemel Hempstead, Hertfordshire, HP3 9UZ Tel: (01442) 212941 Fax: (01442) 251164

▶ William Austin Engineering Services Ltd, Arden House, 341-343 Kenilworth Road, Balsall Common, Coventry, CV7 7DL Tel: (01676) 533666 Fax: (01676) 535536

▶ William Marjoribanks, Rose Bank, Main Street, St. Boswells, Melrose, Roxburghshire, TD6 0AU Tel: (01835) 822787 Fax: (01835) 822809

▶ William Wilson Ltd, Caxton Place, Mitchelston Industrial Estate, Kirkcaldy, Fife, KY1 3LT Tel: (01592) 653295 Fax: (01592) 655179

▶ Woodside Group Ltd, Unit 10 Imperial Park, Rawreth Lane, Rayleigh, Essex, SS6 9RS Tel: (01268) 785111 Fax: (01268) 785666 E-mail: sales@woodsidegroup.co.uk

▶ WT Flockhart Ltd, 17c, Water-Ma-Trout, Helston, Cornwall, TR13 0LW Tel: (01326) 561971 E-mail: sales@flockhart-heating.co.uk

▶ Wyre Heating Ltd, Unit 3 Lisle Avenue, Kidderminster, Worcestershire, DY11 7DE Tel: (01562) 751832 Fax: (01562) 748383

▶ York International, 37 Deerdykes View, Cumbernauld, Glasgow, G68 9HN Tel: (01236) 786000

▶ York International Ltd, 4 Zealley Estate, Greenhill Way, Kingsteignton, Newton Abbot, Devon, TQ12 3TD Tel: (01626) 333734 Fax: (01626) 335220

▶ York International Ltd, Arden House, Marsh Lane, Hampton-in-Arden, Solihull, West Midlands, B92 0AJ Tel: (01675) 443341 Fax: (01675) 442402

HEATING VENTILATION AND AIR CONDITIONING (HVAC) SYSTEMS

▶ Cammach Group Oilfield Services, Greenbank Business Centre, Greenbank Road, East Tullos, Aberdeen, AB12 3BN Tel: (01224) 249977 Fax: (01224) 248977

▶ Star Building Services Ltd, Thermal House, 89 Wellington Street, Leicester, LE1 6HJ Tel: 0116-254 2013 Fax: 0116-254 4866 E-mail: sales@starbuildingservs.co.uk

HEAVY DUTY AGGREGATE SACKS

British Polythene Industries, 96 Port Glasgow Road, Greenock, Renfrewshire, PA15 2UL Tel: (01475) 501000 Fax: (01475) 743143 E-mail: carolanderson@bpipoly.com

HEAVY DUTY CARRYING BAGS

John Lee Sacks Ltd, Old Wharf Road, Grantham, Lincolnshire, NG31 7AA Tel: (01476) 565501 Fax: (01476) 590580 E-mail:

HEAVY DUTY CLAMPS

Staveley Tools, Bailey Drive, Norwood Industrial Estate, Killamarsh, Sheffield, S21 2JF Tel: 0114-247 3367

HEAVY DUTY CORRUGATED FIBREBOARD CASES

Catesby Packing Case Co Ltd, 647 Melton Road, Thurmaston, Leicester, LE4 8EB Tel: 0116-269 3503 Fax: 0116-269 3503

HEAVY DUTY CRANES

▶ Ainscough Crane Hire Ltd, Rugby Road, Princethorpe, Rugby, Warwickshire, CV23 9PN Tel: (01926) 634786 Fax: (01926) 634763 E-mail: coventry@ainscough.co.uk

Wellman Booth, 2 Kirkfields Industrial Centre, Kirk Lane, Yeadon, Leeds, LS19 7LX Tel: 0113-387 9730 Fax: 0113-250 6180 E-mail: sales@wellmanbooth.co.uk

HEAVY DUTY FLOOR CLEANERS

▶ An Other Cleaning Company, 11 Pembrook Road, Holbrook, Coventry, CV6 4FD Tel: (024) 7666 5921 Fax: (024) 7666 5921 E-mail: rob@aocc.co.uk

▶ Kleanstone Floor Maintenance Equipment, 204 Duggins Lane, Coventry, CV4 9GP Tel: (024) 7642 2609 Fax: (024) 7669 5794

HEAVY DUTY HOSE CLIP AND CLAMPS

Flowtech Ltd, Pimbo Road, Skelmersdale, Lancashire, WN8 9RB Tel: (01695) 52770 Fax: (0800) 2987230 E-mail: sales@flowtech.co.uk

Holdtite Ltd, 1 Oughton Road, Birmingham, B12 0DF Tel: 0121-440 2617 Fax: 0121-440 2716 E-mail: holdtite@globalnet.co.uk

L. Robinson & Co., London Chambers, Mill Road, Gillingham, Kent, ME7 1HJ Tel: (01634) 851182 Fax: (01634) 280101 E-mail: sales@jubileeclips.co.uk

HEAVY DUTY SACKS

▶ B P I Packaging Services, 3-4 Manor Industrial Estate, Flint, Clwyd, CH6 5UY Tel: (01352) 735122 Fax: (01352) 734032 E-mail: packagingsales@bpipoly.com

▶ B P I Packaging Services, 96 Port Glasgow Road, Greenock, Renfrewshire, PA15 2UL Tel: (01475) 501100 Fax: (01475) 744868

▶ Expert Marketing UK Ltd, 3 Simpkin Close Eaton Socon, St. Neots, Cambridgeshire, PE19 8PD Tel: (0778) 8131611 Fax: 01480 471221 E-mail: info@emlbigbags.com

HEAVY DUTY TRAILERS

Appleton Commercial Engineering, Unit 3c Lyncastle Way, Barleycastle Lane, Appleton, Warrington, WA4 4ST Tel: (01925) 601855 Fax: (01925) 860478 E-mail: email@ace-commercials.com

Collease Ltd, Choats Road, Chequers Lane, Dagenham, Essex, RM9 6RJ Tel: (020) 8517 1171 Fax: (020) 8593 0300

Marston Agricultural Services Ltd, Toll Bar Road, Marston, Grantham, Lincolnshire, NG32 2HT Tel: (01400) 250226 Fax: (01400) 250540 E-mail: sales@mas-trailers-group.co.uk

Rolling Transport Systems Ltd, Unit 21 Old Yarn Mills, Westbury, Sherborne, Dorset, DT9 3RQ Tel: (01935) 814390 Fax: (01935) 815720

HEAVY DUTY WHEELBARROWS

Maingate Ltd, PO Box 330, Woking, Surrey, GU22 9XS Tel: (0845) 2306585 Fax: (0845) 2307585

HEAVY GOODS VEHICLE (HGV) SECURITY EQUIPMENT

▶ A F S Security Ltd, 582-584 Barking Road, London, E13 9JU Tel: (020) 8471 9000 Fax: (020) 8475 0877 E-mail: afssecurity@btconnect.com

HEAVY GOODS VEHICLES (HGV)

▶ Big Rigs LGV Driver Training, Hereford, Hereford, HR4 7SG Tel: 01432 761004 Fax: 01432 769305 E-mail: info@bigrigstraining.com

▶ Sussex Horseboxes, 1 Woollett Street, Maidstone, Kent, ME14 1UX Tel: (01622) 206006 E-mail: sussex_horseboxes@hotmail.com

HEAVY INDUSTRIAL CHAINS

Zinco Midlands, Midland House, 52 Lower Forster Street, Walsall, WS1 1XB Tel: (01922) 625586 Fax: (0800) 0286370 E-mail: info@zincomids.co.uk

HEAVY IRON CASTINGS

Crane Foundry Ltd, PO Box 43, Wolverhampton, WV1 2QX Tel: (01902) 452731 Fax: (01902) 454895

Hargreaves Foundry Drainage Ltd, Carr House, Water Lane, Halifax, West Yorkshire, HX3 9HG Tel: (01422) 330607 Fax: (01422) 320349 E-mail: sales@hargreavesfoundry.co.uk

Incanite Foundries Ltd, Solar Works, Cornwall Road, Smethwick, West Midlands, B66 2JR Tel: 0121-565 2882 Fax: 0121-555 5190 E-mail: sales@incanite.co.uk

HEAVY LIFTING AND MOVING ENGINEERING

Bidlift Ltd, 1-3 Dudley Street, Grimsby, South Humberside, DN31 2AW Tel: (01472) 341932 Fax: (01472) 341919 E-mail: jacking@bidlift.co.uk

▶ Cic Omec Ltd, Moor Lane Trading Estate, Sherburn In Elmet, Leeds, LS25 6ES Tel: (01977) 682966

Doorman Long Tech, The Charles Parker Building, Midland Road, Higham Ferrers, Rushden, Northamptonshire, NN10 8DN Tel: (01933) 319133 Fax: (01933) 319135 E-mail: dlt@dormanlong.com

Fagioli PSC Ltd, The Ridgeway, Iver, Buckinghamshire, SL0 9JE Tel: (01753) 659000 Fax: (01753) 655998 E-mail: info@fagiolipsc.co.uk

▶ John Gibson Projects Ltd, Sotherby Road, Middlesbrough, Cleveland, TS3 8BS Tel: (01642) 292299 Fax: (01642) 242004 E-mail: enqiries@johngibsonprojects.com

Lowther Rolton International Ltd, The Charles Parker Building, Midland Road, Higham Ferrers, Rushden, Northamptonshire, NN10 8DN Tel: (01933) 411837 Fax: (01933) 411887

Rotech Systems, Unit 53 Canal Bridge Enterprise Centre, Meadow Lane, Ellesmere Port, CH65 4EH Tel: 0151-356 2322 Fax: 0151-356 2437

Safelift Offshore Ltd, Forties Business Centre, School Road, Kintore, Inverurie, Aberdeenshire, AB51 0UX Tel: (01224) 775774 Fax: (01224) 775779 E-mail: sales@safelift.co.uk

Watkinson Lifting & Transportation Ltd, Invincible Works, Marriner Road, Keighley, West Yorkshire, BD21 5LW Tel: (01535) 600151 Fax: (01535) 692249 E-mail: sales@watkinsons.com

HEAVY LOAD ROAD HAULAGE

B R Saunders Ltd, Molesey Road, Walton-on-Thames, Surrey, KT12 3PW Tel: (01932) 245161 Fax: (01932) 254764 E-mail: info@brsaunders.co.uk

▶ International Heavy Haulage (GB) Limited, Wesley Street, Langley Mill, NG16 4AL Tel: 01773 768833 Fax: 01773 768844 E-mail: tim.ihhgb@btconnect.com

▶ Leiths (Scotland) Ltd, Rigifa, Cove, Aberdeen, AB12 3LR Tel: (01224) 876333

P J Butler & Son Ltd, Parsonage St, Oldbury, West Midlands, B69 4PH Tel: 0121-552 1052 Fax: 0121-544 8618

▶ Teahan Abnormal Load Escort Services, 49 Cobbett Close, Enfield, Middlesex, EN3 6QT Tel: (07944) 136886 Fax: (01992) 851590 E-mail: info@abnormalloadescort.com

▶ Thomas Fox & Co. Ltd, 3 Rhodes Way, Watford, WD24 4YA Tel: (01923) 811700 Fax: (01923) 811710 E-mail: helpdesk@thomasfox.co.uk

HEAVY STEEL PRESSINGS

B C Barton & Son Ltd, Granville Iron Works, Oldbury, West Midlands, B69 2NJ Tel: 0121-557 2272 Fax: 0121-557 2276 E-mail: pressworkers@b-c-b.co.uk

HEAVY WALL STEEL TUBES

M K Wheeler Ltd, Nine Lock Works, Mill Street, Brierley Hill, West Midlands, DY5 2SX Tel: (01384) 487600 Fax: (01384) 487619 E-mail: sales@vanleeuwenwheeler.co.uk
Pipe & Tube Group Ltd, Armstrong Road, Basingstoke, Hampshire, RG24 8NU Tel: (01256) 811121 Fax: (01256) 842310 E-mail: info@pipeandtubegroup.co.uk
Stevenson & Cheyne, Unit 7 Butlerfield Industrial Estate, Bonnyrigg, Midlothian, EH19 3JQ Tel: (01875) 822822 Fax: (01875) 823723 E-mail: sales@platerolling.co.uk
Wyman Gordon Ltd, Houstoun Road, Houstoun Industrial Estate, Livingston, West Lothian, EH54 5BZ Tel: (01506) 446200 Fax: (01506) 446300

HEDGE CUTTING MACHINES

Bosch Lawn & Garden Limited, Suffolk Works, Stowmarket, Suffolk, IP14 1EY Tel: (01449) 742000 Fax: (01449) 675444
Hydrocut Ltd, PO Box 2926, Colchester, CO6 2QP Tel: (01787) 222266 Fax: (01787) 222210 E-mail: sales@hydrocut.co.uk
Meadhams Lawnmowers Sales & Service, 12 Bankside, Kidlington, Oxfordshire, OX5 1JE Tel: (01865) 378010 Fax: (01865) 378010 E-mail: meadhams@btinternet.com

HEIGHT ADJUSTABLE TABLES

Panilet Tables, 17 Dragon Court, Crofts End Road, Bristol, BS5 7XX Tel: 0117-951 1858 Fax: 0117-951 1858 E-mail: info@panilettables.co.uk

HEIGHT GAUGES

C & D Precision, Bluebird House, Povey Cross Road, Horley, Surrey, RH6 0AG Tel: (01293) 820092 Fax: (01293) 820093 E-mail: dedman@cdprecision.freeserve.co.uk

HEIGHT SAFETY TRAINING

Access Training Services Ltd, Unit 4, 45 Mowbray Street, Sheffield, S3 8EN Tel: 0114-273 1333 Fax: 0114-280 2010 E-mail: info@the-access-group.com
Key Consultancy Ltd, 277 Birmingham Road, Bromsgrove, Worcestershire, B61 0EP Tel: (01527) 575182 Fax: (01527) 576288 E-mail: sales@thekeyconsultancy.co.uk

HELICAL GEARS

Comma Tech Ltd, Carlyon Road, Atherstone, Warwickshire, CV9 1LW Tel: (01827) 714741 Fax: (01827) 718943 E-mail: sales@commatech.co.uk
Cornish Engineering Ltd, Popham Street, Nottingham, NG1 7JD Tel: 0115-950 4944 Fax: 0115-950 4215
Greenwood Gears Ltd, Digital House, Royd Way, Keighley, West Yorkshire, BD21 3LG Tel: (01535) 604393 Fax: (01535) 680587 E-mail: sales@hewitt-topham.co.uk
Hindle Gears, Caledonia Street, Bradford, West Yorkshire, BD5 0EL Tel: (01274) 727234 Fax: (01274) 737343 E-mail: gears@hindle.co.uk
R A Howarth Engineering Ltd, Earl Road, Rackheath Industrial Estate, Rackheath, Norwich, NR13 6NT Tel: (01603) 721155 Fax: (01603) 721648
The Reid Gear Co., Napier Street, Linwood, Paisley, Renfrewshire, PA3 3AN Tel: (01505) 321591 Fax: (01505) 321645 E-mail: info@reidgear.com
Renold Gears, Station Road, Milnrow, Rochdale, Lancashire, OL16 3LS Tel: (01706) 751000 Fax: (01706) 751001 E-mail: gears.sales@renold.com
T B Engineering Ltd, Network House, Perry Road, Harlow, Essex, CM18 7NS Tel: (01279) 418300 Fax: (01279) 418100
T K Engineering & Gear Cutting Ltd, Forest Mills, Denman Street East, Nottingham, NG7 3PZ Tel: 0115-970 0978 Fax: 0115-942 2928
Woollacott Gears Ltd, Llay Hall Industrial Estate, Cefn-Y-Bedd, Wrexham, Clwyd, LL12 9YG Tel: (01978) 761848 Fax: (01978) 762340

HELICAL STAIRCASES

Cambridge Structures Ltd, 2 Huntingdon Street, St. Neots, Cambridgeshire, PE19 1BG Tel: (01480) 477700 Fax: (01480) 477766 E-mail: contact@cambridgestructures.com
Lewes Design Contracts Ltd, The Mill, Glynde, Lewes, East Sussex, BN8 6SS Tel: (01273) 858341 Fax: (01273) 858200 E-mail: info@spiralstairs.co.uk

HELICOPTER BUILDERS

Agustawestland Aircraft Services, Lysander Road, Yeovil, Somerset, BA20 2YB Tel: (01935) 475222 Fax: (01935) 702131 E-mail: info@gkn-whl.co.uk
Northern Helicopter Products Ltd, Woodfield House, Woodfield Road, Broadheath, Altrincham, Cheshire, WA14 4ED Tel: 0161-928 5984 Fax: 0161-929 5984

HELICOPTER CHARTERING

▶ Nicki Thomas, Studridge Lane, Hedgerow, Booker, Speen, Princes Risborough, Buckinghamshire, HP27 0SA Tel: (01494) 488665 Fax: (0870) 1623908 E-mail: nicki.thomas@storecompact.co.uk

HELICOPTER FUEL SERVICES

Swire Oil Field Services, Swire House, Souter Head Road, Altens Industrial Estate, Aberdeen, AB12 3LF Tel: (01224) 872707 Fax: (01224) 874516 E-mail: jlucas@swireos.com

HELICOPTER MAINTENANCE/ REPAIR SPECIALIST SERVICES

Aeromaritime UK Ltd, Thruxton Airport, Andover, Hampshire, SP11 8PN Tel: (01264) 771700 Fax: (01264) 774630 E-mail: info@aeromaritime.co.uk
The Cabair Group Ltd, Elstree Aerodrome, Elstree, Borehamwood, Hertfordshire, WD6 3AW Tel: (020) 8236 2400 Fax: (020) 8207 0995 E-mail: group@cabair.com
Composite Technology Ltd, Thruxton Airport, Thruxton, Andover, Hampshire, SP11 8PW Tel: (01264) 773361 Fax: (01264) 773980 E-mail: repairs@composite-technology.co.uk
Mann Aviation Group Engineering Ltd, Fairoaks Airport, Chobham, Woking, Surrey, GU24 8HX Tel: (01276) 857888 Fax: (01276) 857510 E-mail: engineering@alanmann.co.uk
Rotorspan Ltd, The Heliport, Hampton Lovett, Droitwich, Worcestershire, WR9 0LW Tel: (01905) 774831 Fax: (01905) 794657 E-mail: rotorspan@tesco.net
Signature Aircraft Engineering, Hangar Road, Denham Airfield, Uxbridge, Middlesex, UB9 5DF Tel: (01895) 834777 Fax: (01252) 864399

HELICOPTER PILOT TRAINING

▶ Flight Academy Scotland.com, Building 25, Inverness Airport, Inverness, IV2 7JB Tel: 01667 461181 Fax: 01667 462202

HELICOPTER SUPPLIERS OR BROKERS

R C R Aviation Ltd, Andover, Hampshire, SP10 5XZ Tel: (01264) 359352 Fax: (01264) 359351 E-mail: sales@rcr-aviation.com

HELIDECK FABRICATORS

N C M P Ltd, 4 Falcon Way, Feltham, Middlesex, TW14 0XJ Tel: (020) 8751 0986 Fax: (020) 8751 5793 E-mail: ncmp-feltham@ncmp.co.uk

HELIDECK LIGHTING EQUIPMENT

Orga, A1 Kingsway Business Park, Oldfield Road, Hampton, Middlesex, TW12 2HD Tel: (0870) 6092452 Fax: (020) 8941 6683 E-mail: sales@orga.nl

HELIUM BALLOONS

▶ Balloonprint Balloons, Trevordale House, Pius Drove, Upwell, Wisbech, Cambridgeshire, PE14 9AL Tel: (01945) 773559 Fax: (0845) 0090903 E-mail: peter@balloonprint.co.uk
▶ Balloons For All Occasions, 52 King Street, Ramsgate, Kent, CT11 8NT Tel: (01843) 851087 Fax: (01843) 851087
▶ Bur Boing, 8 Beacon Court, Northampton, NN4 8JU Tel: (01604) 674733 E-mail: bur-boing@tesco.net
▶ Celebration-Balloons, 859 Whittingham Lane, Goosnargh, Preston, PR3 2AU Tel: (01772) 861190 Fax: (01772) 861190 E-mail: info@celebration-balloons.co.uk
▶ Delta Balloons, OAKLEIGH, BROADWAY, Sandown, Isle of Wight, PO36 9BY Tel: (01983) 400321 E-mail: info@deltaballoons.demon.co.uk
▶ Rainbow Florist Supplies, Unit 2e Herald Industrial Estate, Hedge End, Southampton, SO30 2JW Tel: (01489) 787955 Fax: (01489) 790322 E-mail: sales@rainbowfloristsupplies.co.uk
▶ Send Me a Balloon, 23 Woodthorpe Road, Ashford, Middlesex, TW15 2RP Tel: (0870) 0117550 Fax: (0870) 0117660 E-mail: sales@staggerin.com

HEMP FIBRE

Landauer Ltd, 25 Beaufort Court, Admirals Way, London, E14 9XL Tel: (020) 7538 5383 Fax: (020) 7538 2007 E-mail: trading@landauerseafood.com
James Sharp & Co., 80 Bell Street, Dundee, DD1 1HW Tel: (01382) 226321 Fax: (01382) 202052
H.L. Wilkinson & Co. Ltd, 49-51 Central Street, London, EC1V 8AB Tel: (020) 7253 5241 Fax: (020) 7250 1562 E-mail: info@hlwilkinson.co.uk

HERALDIC ENGRAVERS

Bolsons Ltd, The Gatehouse, Cooks Road, London, E15 2PW Tel: (020) 8555 7137 Fax: (020) 8519 6641 E-mail: info@bolsons.co.uk

HERALDIC SHIELDS

G K Beaulah & Co. Ltd, 23 Park Street, Hull, HU2 8RU Tel: (01482) 223521 Fax: (01482) 216328 E-mail: info@beaulah.co.uk
Munday C H Ltd, 8 St. Johns Road, Woking, Surrey, GU21 7SE Tel: (01483) 771588 Fax: (01483) 756627 E-mail: enquiries@chmunday.co.uk
Salopia Heraldic Plaques Ltd, Severn House Business Centre, 66 Spring Gardens, Shrewsbury, SY1 2TE Tel: (01743) 232700 Fax: (01743) 271275

HERB MIXES

▶ Freshwashed Herbs Ltd, Chestnuts Farm, Langton Green, Eye, Suffolk, IP23 7HL Tel: (01379) 871410 Fax: (01379) 873322 E-mail: info@freshwashedherbs.co.uk

HERBAL PRODUCTS

Amazon Herbal Products UK, PO Box 12958, Birmingham, B11 9BG Tel: (0870) 8113611 E-mail: webmaster@amazonherbalproducts.co.uk
Aphrodite, 1a Priory Lane, Penwortham, Preston, PR1 0AR Tel: (01772) 746555
Balham Wholefoods & Health Store, 8 Bedford Hill, London, SW12 9RG Tel: (020) 8673 4842
Big Apple, Unit 1 Queen Street, Morley, Leeds, LS27 8EG Tel: 0113-253 4525
Caurnie Soap Co., The Soaperie, Canal Street, Kirkintilloch, Glasgow, G66 1QZ Tel: 0141-776 1218 Fax: 0141-776 1218 E-mail: office@caurnie.com
Culpeper Ltd, Pall Mall Deposit, Unit 47, 124-128 Barlby Road, London, W10 6BL Tel: (020) 8962 3010 Fax: (020) 8969 9247 E-mail: info@culpeper.co.uk
▶ Denis Brinicombe Ltd, Fordton Trading Estate, Crediton, Devon, EX17 3BZ Tel: (01363) 775115 Fax: (01363) 776761 E-mail: info@brinicombe-equine.co.uk
Firefly Tonics Ltd, 1 Petersham Mews, London, SW7 5NR Tel: (020) 7052 9720 Fax: (020) 7052 9729 E-mail: info@fireflytonics.com
▶ Global Nutrition, 1 Furness Close, South Wootton, King's Lynn, Norfolk, PE30 3TR Tel: (01553) 671467 E-mail: kath@wellness4all.org.uk
Godshaer Herbalist, The Old Stables, Ducking Stool Lane, Christchurch, Dorset, BH23 1DS Tel: (01202) 488122 Fax: (01202) 488122 E-mail: alanhopking@goshaer.co.uk
▶ Healthfarm, 23 Cumpsty Road, Liverpool, L21 9HX Tel: 0151 9206654 E-mail: stephmc.uk@hotmail.co.uk
Holland & Barrett Ltd, 42 Kilburn High Road, London, NW6 4HJ Tel: (020) 7624 9297
▶ Life Healthcare, Freepost JE723, St. Helier, Jersey, JE1 1AF Tel: (0845) 1667070 E-mail: help@elixireurope.com
Mawsons, 57 George Street, Oldham, OL1 1LT Tel: 0161-624 8182 Fax: 0161-624 8182
Perfecta Ltd, Ashmead Business Centre, Ashmead Road, Keynsham, Bristol, BS31 1SX Tel: 0117-986 8800 Fax: 0117-986 1687 E-mail: info@perfecta.ltd.uk
Phyto Products Ltd, Park Works, Park Road, Mansfield Woodhouse, Mansfield, Nottinghamshire, NG19 8EF Tel: (01623) 644334 Fax: (01623) 657232 E-mail: info@phyto.co.uk
Portobello Wholefoods, 266 Portobello Road, London, W10 5TY Tel: (020) 8968 9133 Fax: (020) 8560 1840
Potters Herbal Supplies Ltd, Leyland Mill Lane, Wigan, Lancashire, WN1 2SB Tel: (01942) 405100 Fax: (01942) 820255 E-mail: info@pottersherbals.co.uk
Power Health Products Ltd, Air Field Estate, Pocklington, York, YO42 1NR Tel: (01759) 302734 Fax: (01759) 304286 E-mail: jenny.baillie@power-health.co.uk
Sherwood Wholefoods, 1 Wilkinson Walk, Market Drayton, Shropshire, TF9 1PW Tel: (01630) 655155

HERBAL TEA

▶ Global Nutrition, 1 Furness Close, South Wootton, King's Lynn, Norfolk, PE30 3TR Tel: (01553) 671467 E-mail: kath@wellness4all.org.uk
▶ Healthfarm, 23 Cumpsty Road, Liverpool, L21 9HX Tel: 0151 9206654 E-mail: stephmc.uk@hotmail.co.uk
Sherwood Wholefoods, 1 Wilkinson Walk, Market Drayton, Shropshire, TF9 1PW Tel: (01630) 655155

HERMETIC CONNECTORS

Micrometics Ltd, 26 Hollands Rd, Haverhill, Suffolk, CB9 8PR Tel: (01440) 707010 Fax: (01440) 762116 E-mail: info@micrometics.co.uk

HERMETIC SEALING

Handmark Engineering, Unit 3c Park Road Industrial Estate, Park Road, Barrow-in-Furness, Cumbria, LA14 4EQ Tel: (01229) 835922 Fax: (01229) 877461 E-mail: enquiries@handmark-engineering.co.uk

HESSIAN CLOTH

Fibrous Ltd, Unit E2, Newton Business Park, Talbot Road, Newton, Hyde, Cheshire, SK14 4UQ Tel: (0845) 4508935 Fax: (0845) 4508936 E-mail: info@fibrous.com
Hessian Co., 27 Palace Avenue, Paignton, Devon, TQ3 3EQ Tel: (01803) 556782 Fax: (01803) 664656

HESSIAN SACKS

Allan Austin Ltd, Crystal Drive, Smethwick, West Midlands, B66 1QG Tel: 0121-552 8513 Fax: 0121-552 1480 E-mail: allan@austinltd.freeserve.co.uk
J W Martin Ltd, Prince Regent Road, Belfast, BT5 6QR Tel: (028) 9070 2021 Fax: (028) 9070 5566 E-mail: mail@jwmartin.co.uk
John Lee Sacks Ltd, Old Wharf Road, Grantham, Lincolnshire, NG31 7AA Tel: (01476) 565501 Fax: (01476) 590580 E-mail:
Mason & Jones Packaging, Unit 7, Aston Road, Aston Fields Industrial Estate, Bromsgrove, Worcestershire, B60 3EX Tel: (01527) 577123 Fax: (01527) 577248 E-mail: sales@masonandjones.com
S G Baker Ltd, Union St, Friockheim, Arbroath, Angus, DD11 4TD Tel: (01241) 828681 Fax: (01241) 828349 E-mail: sales@sgbaker.co.uk
▶ Zenick Group Ltd, 184 Stanley Green Road, Poole, Dorset, BH15 3AH Tel: (01202) 673744 Fax: (01202) 678798 E-mail: jane@zenickgroup.fsnet.co.uk

HIDES AND SKINS

A. Henry & Co., Langford Arch, London Road, Sawston, CB2 4EE Tel: (01223) 833132 Fax: (01223) 833400
Hollander Hyams Ltd, 9 Berners Place, London, W1T 3HH Tel: (020) 7636 1562 Fax: (020) 7636 1564 E-mail: sales@hollanderhyams.com
L H Nichols Ltd, Nautilus Works, Reckleford, Yeovil, Somerset, BA21 4EL Tel: (01935) 476288 Fax: (01935) 431474 E-mail: office@lhnichols.com
Mcconomy & Co. Ltd, 1f Columbus Quay, Riverside Drive, Liverpool, L3 4DB Tel: 0151-726 1942 Fax: 0151-728 9935 E-mail: mccon@mcconomy.com

HIGH ACCESS WINDOW CLEANING CONTRACTORS OR SERVICES

▶ AQC, 9 Hartfield Road, Eastbourne, East Sussex, BN21 2AP Tel: 01323 720659 E-mail: info@a-q-c.co.uk
▶ GECS Cleaning, 3 Church View, Wyverstone, Stowmarket, Suffolk, IP14 4SQ Tel: 01449 781603 E-mail: glenn@gecomputerservices.co.uk
H2o Window Cleaning, 47 Muirfield, Blunsdon, Swindon, SN25 2DD Tel: (07833) 681329 E-mail: info@h2owindowcleaning.co.uk
Hugh Evans HDR Window Cleaning Services, 25 Trent Valley Rd, Lichfield, Staffs, WS13 6EZ Tel: 01543 258339 E-mail: Randa@tadelevenone.fsnet.co.uk
▶ Jay, 59 Grove Gardens, Southampton, SO19 9QZ Tel: (07840) 183969 E-mail: graftersinfo@hotmail.co.uk
▶ Jellyfish, 33 Buckland Road, Newton Abbot, Devon, TQ12 4DQ Tel: (01626) 205134 E-mail: jellyfish.uk@virgin.net
▶ Majestic Window Cleaning Services, 36 Darbishire Road, Fleetwood, Lancashire, FY7 6QA Tel: (01253) 777584 E-mail: thegarnetts2003@yahoo.co.uk

▶ indicates data change since last edition

HIGH ACCESS WINDOW CLEANING CONTRACTORS OR SERVICES – *continued*

▶ Pristine Cleaning, 4 Woodside Grove, Bristol, BS10 7RF Tel: 0117-950 1772 E-mail: pristine@marketable.co.uk
▶ Stephen Kinsella, 200 Garston Old Road, Garston, Liverpool, L19 1QL Tel: 0151-427 4698 E-mail: ste.kinsella@ntlworld.com
▶ Superior Cleaning Services, 111 George Street, Edinburgh, EH2 4JN Tel: 0131-624 7169 Fax: 0131-624 7168 E-mail: info@superiorcs.co.uk
▶ The UPVC Cleaning Company Ltd, PO BOX 559, Edgware, Middlesex, HA8 4BM Tel: 0800 1973033 E-mail: enquiries@upvc-cleaning.co.uk

HIGH CHAIRS

Minui HandySitt (Cheeky Rascals Ltd), Stone Barn, 1 The Brows, Farnham Road, Liss, Hampshire, GU33 6JG Tel: (01730) 895761 Fax: (01730) 897549 E-mail: sales@cheekyrascals.co.uk

HIGH CURRENT CONNECTORS

Elcon Products International, 7 Merlin Court, Gatehouse Close, Gatehouse Industrial Area, Aylesbury, Buckinghamshire, HP19 8DP Tel: (01296) 331855 Fax: (01296) 331856 E-mail: elcon.sales@tycoelectronics.com

HIGH CURRENT POWER SUPPLIES, DIRECT CURRENT (DC)

General High Voltage, New Road, Highley, Bridgnorth, Shropshire, WV16 6NN Tel: (01746) 862555 Fax: (01746) 862666 E-mail: info@genvolt.co.uk

HIGH DENSITY PALLET RACKING

Dugard Logistics Ltd, 2 Sherwood Road, Bromsgrove, Worcestershire, B60 3DU Tel: (01527) 575947 Fax: (01527) 576100 E-mail: richardshowell@msn.com

HIGH DENSITY POLYETHYLENE (HDPE) CARRIER BAGS

Lesta Packaging plc, 21 Nedham Street, Leicester, LE2 0HD Tel: (0116) 2624448 Fax: (0116) 2624449 E-mail: enquiries@lestapackaging.co.uk
Wessex Polybags, Unit 1 Ashville Trading Estate, Royston Road, Baldock, Hertfordshire, SG7 6NN Tel: (01462) 490600 Fax: (01462) 490800 E-mail: sales@wessexpolybags.co.uk

HIGH DENSITY POLYETHYLENE (HDPE) FILM AND SHEET

Samuel Grant Ltd, 146-148 Garnet Road, Leeds, LS11 5LA Tel: 0113-270 7221 Fax: 0113-277 9867 E-mail: sales@samuelgrant.co.uk

HIGH DENSITY POLYETHYLENE (HDPE) ULTRAHIGH MOLECULAR WEIGHT POLYETHYLENE (UHMWPE) SEMI FINISHED COMPONENTS

Drain Center Ltd, Lincoln Road, Cressex Business Park, High Wycombe, Buckinghamshire, HP12 3RB Tel: (01494) 462351 Fax: (01494) 444923
Drain Center, Unit 20, West Churton Industrial Estate, Alder Road, North Shields, Tyne & Wear, NE29 8SD Tel: 0191-257 8125 Fax: 0191-257 8819
Drain Center Civils, 248 Gosport Road, Fareham, Hampshire, PO16 0SS Tel: (01329) 232129 Fax: (01329) 822368 E-mail: p16.fareham@wolseley.co.uk
Drain Centre, Stenplas Works, Grecian Crescent, Bolton, BL3 6QS Tel: (01204) 388388 Fax: (01204) 389411
Drain Centre, 19 Bank Head Drive, St. Hillndustrial Estate, St.Hill, Edinburgh, EH11 4DW Tel: 0131-552 8181 Fax: 0131-453 2008 E-mail: edinbr@capperplastics.com
Drain Centre, Cinderhill Industrial Estate, Weston Coyney Road, Longton, Stoke-On-Trent, ST3 5JT Tel: (01782) 311311 Fax: (01782) 343400 E-mail: p23.stoke@wolseley.co.uk
Drains Centre, Unit 2B, St. Georges Trading Estate, Avonmouth, Bristol, BS11 9HS Tel: 0117-916 2700 Fax: 0117-982 6820 E-mail: bristol.p11@wolseley.co.uk

I A C Plastics, Oak Mill, Manchester Road, Dunnockshaw, Burnley, Lancashire, BB11 5PW Tel: (01706) 212225 Fax: (01706) 229926 E-mail: sales@iacplastics.com
Johnstech Interconnect Ltd, 1-2 Usk Street, Newport, Gwent, NP19 7BE Tel: (01633) 674452 Fax: (01633) 674453 E-mail: info@johnstech.com
K C Tooling Ltd, Unit 22, Hayhill Industrial Estate, Sileby Road, Barrow Upon Soar, Loughborough, Leicestershire, LE12 8LD Tel: (01509) 814724 Fax: (01509) 816076
Pipe Centre Plus, Unit 8, Spring Road Industrial Estate, Ettingshall, Wolverhampton, WV4 6JZ Tel: (01902) 409341 Fax: (01902) 353817 E-mail: p15.wolverhampton@wolseley.co.uk
Poly Hi Solidur (U K) Ltd, Halifax Road, Todmorden, Lancashire, OL14 5QQ Tel: (01706) 811000 Fax: (01706) 817571 E-mail: sales@polyhisolidur.co.uk

HIGH EFFICIENCY FUEL GAS PRODUCTION SCRUBBERS

Fluid Technologies Environmental Ltd, 50 Old London Road, Kingston upon Thames, Surrey, KT2 6QF Tel: (020) 8549 7722 Fax: (020) 8549 7733E-mail: info@fluidtechnologies.com

HIGH FREQUENCY ALTERNATING CURRENT (AC) GENERATORS

Newton Derby Ltd, Belgrave Works, Town Street, Stanningley, Pudsey, West Yorkshire, LS28 6ES Tel: 0113-218 0717 Fax: 0113-257 2206 E-mail: sales@newtonderby.co.uk

HIGH FREQUENCY ELECTRIC MOTORS

Elektro Magnetix Ltd, Sussex Innovation Centre, Science Park Square, Falmer, Brighton, BN1 9SB Tel: (01273) 704471 Fax: (01273) 704472 E-mail: elektro@elektro.co.uk
G B Electrical Engineering Co, Springvale Street, Willenhall, West Midlands, WV13 1EJ Tel: (01902) 605934 Fax: (01902) 632198 E-mail: sales@gbelectrical.co.uk

HIGH FREQUENCY EQUIPMENT, *See headings for particular application*

HIGH FREQUENCY LIGHTING

Adv Lighting Ltd, 22 Electric Avenue, Harrogate, North Yorkshire, HG1 2BB Tel: (01423) 545493 Fax: (0845) 2801640 E-mail: advlighting@advlighting.co.uk

HIGH FRICTION ROAD SURFACING

Conren Ltd, Astwith Close, Holmewood, Chesterfield, Derbyshire, S42 5UR Tel: (01246) 853900 Fax: (01246) 856348 E-mail: info@conren.com

HIGH LEVEL PERSONNEL RESCUE SERVICES

Ropesafe, P.O. Box 115, West Wickham, Kent, BR4 9YZ Tel: 07730 677936 E-mail: ropesafe@totalise.co.uk

HIGH LEVEL PERSONNEL RESCUE TRAINING

Ropesafe, P.O. Box 115, West Wickham, Kent, BR4 9YZ Tel: 07730 677936 E-mail: ropesafe@totalise.co.uk

HIGH LIFT FORKLIFT TRUCKS

Crown Lift Trucks Ltd, Tollbridge House, 135 Windmill Road, Sunbury-on-Thames, Middlesex, TW16 7EF Tel: (01932) 777500 Fax: (0845) 8509277 E-mail: info@crown.com

HIGH PERFORMANCE AIR COMPRESSORS

Compair UK Ltd, Reavell House, 53-56 White House Road, Ipswich, IP1 5PB Tel: (01473) 242000 Fax: (01473) 745451 E-mail: sales.ipswich@compair.com

HIGH PERFORMANCE ELECTRIC WIRE

Nexsan Technologies, 33-35 Parker Industrial Estate, Mansfield Road, Derby, DE21 4SZ Tel: (01332) 291600 Fax: (01332) 291616 E-mail: info@nexsan.com

HIGH PERFORMANCE EXHAUST SYSTEMS

BTB Exhausts Ltd, 3-5 The Beaver Centre, Great Central Way, Woodford Halse, Daventry, Northamptonshire, NN11 3DP Tel: (01327) 261797 Fax: (01327) 263577
Primary Designs Ltd, Unit 4 International House, Station Yard, Thame, Oxfordshire, OX9 3UH Tel: (01844) 216057 Fax: (01844) 216058 E-mail: patbarrett@primarydesigns.co.uk
▶ Wyatt Engineering, Darrow Wood Farm, Shelfanger Road, Diss, Norfolk, IP22 4XY Tel: (01379) 640200 Fax: (01379) 640200

HIGH PERFORMANCE LUBRICANTS

Jet Lube UK Ltd, Reform Road, Maidenhead, Berkshire, SL6 8BY Tel: (01628) 631913 Fax: (01628) 773138 E-mail: uksales@jetlube.com
Lubysil UK Ltd, Suite 401 Langham House, 302 Regent Street, London, W1B 3AT Tel: (020) 7580 6491 Fax: (020) 7580 4729 E-mail: info@swindens-vices.co.uk

HIGH PERFORMANCE PLASTIC MATERIALS

▶ Barkston Plastics Ltd, D5-D7 Unit, Drypool Way, Hull, HU9 1LG Tel: (01482) 323886 Fax: (01482) 214193 E-mail: mailbox@barkstonltd.co.uk
Chesterfield Plastics, 61 Foljambe Avenue, Chesterfield, Derbyshire, S40 3EY Tel: (01246) 540670 Fax: (01246) 540106 E-mail: clive.cooper1@virgin.net

HIGH PERFORMANCE PLASTIC PUMP COMPONENTS

Jtekt Automotive UK Ltd, New Factory, Neath Vale Supplier Park, Resolven, Neath, West Glamorgan, SA11 4SP Tel: (01639) 713100 Fax: (01639) 713128

HIGH POWER CAPACITORS

Industrial Capacitors Wrexham Ltd, Miners Road, Llay Industrial Estate, Llay, Wrexham, Clwyd, LL12 0PJ Tel: (01978) 853805 Fax: (01978) 853785 E-mail: sales@icwltd.co.uk
Phasetech Ltd, Industry Park, Cricketts Lane, Chippenham, Wiltshire, SN15 3EQ Tel: (01249) 651436 Fax: (01249) 462356 E-mail: sales@phasetech.co.uk

HIGH POWER CONNECTORS

Elcon Products International, 7 Merlin Court, Gatehouse Close, Gatehouse Industrial Area, Aylesbury, Buckinghamshire, HP19 8DP Tel: (01296) 331855 Fax: (01296) 331856 E-mail: elcon.sales@tycoelectronics.com

HIGH POWER ELECTRICAL EQUIPMENT TESTING

▶ G J ELECTRICAL, 65 FAWNBRAKE AVENUE, HERNE HILL, LONDON, SE24 0BE Tel: 020 73264668E-mail: GJONAS4@HOTMAIL.COM

HIGH PRECISION BEARINGS

Snfa Bearings Ltd, Wotton Road, Charfield, Wotton-under-Edge, Gloucestershire, GL12 8SP Tel: (01453) 843501 Fax: (01453) 842577 E-mail: sales@snfa-bearings.co.uk
Timken Aerospace Uk Ltd, PO Box 667, Wolverhampton, WV2 4UH Tel: (01902) 719300 Fax: (01902) 719301 E-mail: talkbox@timken.com

HIGH PRESSURE CLEANING, *See Steam etc; or Water etc*

HIGH PRESSURE CLEANING EQUIPMENT

▶ Cleanwright Ltd, Ings farm, West Torrington, Market Rasen, Lincolnshire, LN8 5SQ Tel: (01673) 857454 Fax: (01673) 857456 E-mail: sales@cleanwrightltd.co.uk

HIGH PRESSURE DIE CASTINGS

A M E Pressure Die Casting Ltd, Unit 59c Siddons Factory Estate, Howard Street, West Bromwich, West Midlands, B70 0SU Tel: 0121-505 5222 Fax: 0121-505 5444 E-mail: amediecasting@aol.com
Avon P D C, 40 Holford Way, Witton, Birmingham, B6 7AX Tel: 0121-681 1160 Fax: 0121-344 3902 E-mail: enquiries@avonpdc.co.uk
▶ G T Group Ltd, 8 Faraday Road, Peterlee, County Durham, SR8 5AP Tel: 0191-586 2366 Fax: 0191-587 2111 E-mail: info@gtgroup.co.uk

HIGH PRESSURE EQUIPMENT TO SPECIFICATION

Kaye Presteigne, Harper Lane, Presteigne, Powys, LD8 2AH Tel: (01544) 267551 Fax: (01544) 267032 E-mail: reception@kayepresteigne.co.uk

HIGH PRESSURE EQUIPMENT/ FITTINGS, *See headings for particular types*

HIGH PRESSURE GAUGES

Gauge Developments Ltd, Langham Street, Ashton-under-Lyne, Lancashire, OL7 9AX Tel: 0161-343 3020 Fax: 0161-343 2969 E-mail: gdev@btconnect.com

HIGH PRESSURE HOSE COUPLINGS

Alltype Hose & Couplings Ltd, Units 14 & 15 Palace Industrial Estate, Bircholt Road, Parkwood, Maidstone, Kent, ME15 9XU Tel: (01622) 757512 Fax: (01622) 757663 E-mail: sales@alltypehose.co.uk
▶ Phoenix Beattie Ltd, Jubilee Industrial Estate, Ashington, Northumberland, NE63 8UB Tel: (01670) 520565 Fax: (01670) 520535 E-mail: sales@phoenixbeattie.co.uk

HIGH PRESSURE HOSES

Abdex Hose & Couplings Ltd, Unit 3 Commerce Way, Leighton Buzzard, Bedfordshire, LU7 4RW Tel: (01525) 377770 Fax: (01525) 851990 E-mail: enquiries@abdexhose.com
Ferschl Hose & Hydraulics Ltd, Dukesway, Team Valley Trading Estate, Gateshead, Tyne & Wear, NE11 0PZ Tel: 0191-482 2511 Fax: 0191-491 0604 E-mail: info@jferschl.co.uk
Manuli-hydraulics UK Ltd, Unit C Nasmyth Business Centre, Green Lane, Patricroft, Eccles, Manchester, M30 0SN Tel: 0161-787 8085 Fax: 0161-787 8086
▶ Phoenix Beattie Ltd, Jubilee Industrial Estate, Ashington, Northumberland, NE63 8UB Tel: (01670) 520565 Fax: (01670) 520535 E-mail: sales@phoenixbeattie.co.uk
Pressure Flex, 111 Great Barr Street, Birmingham, B9 4BB Tel: 0121-766 8228 Fax: 0121-766 7818 E-mail: sales@wakefind.co.uk
Trist Draper Hydraulics, Unit 6f Redbrook Business Park, Wilthorpe Road, Barnsley, South Yorkshire, S75 1JN Tel: (01226) 281140 Fax: (01226) 243223 E-mail: sales@tristdraper.co.uk

HIGH PRESSURE HYDRAULIC BALL VALVES

Dutch Engineering Services Ltd, Dutch House, Pentney Lane, West Bilney, Pentney, King's Lynn, Norfolk, PE32 1JE Tel: (01760) 339111 Fax: (01760) 339112 E-mail: enquiries@dutchengineering.co.uk
San Precision Engineering Co. Ltd, Units 9-10 Harnall Industrial Estate, Harnall Lane East, Coventry, CV1 5AE Tel: (024) 7622 0613 Fax: (024) 7652 0004 E-mail: sales@sanprecision.com

HIGH PRESSURE HYDRAULIC TEST EQUIPMENT

Curtis Machine Tools Ltd, Martells Industrial Estate, Ardleigh, Colchester, CO7 7RU Tel: (01206) 230032 Fax: (01206) 231426 E-mail: cnt@douglascurtis.co.uk

HIGH PRESSURE INDUSTRIAL GAS CYLINDER MANIFOLD SYSTEMS

Daniel Pipework Services, Unit 44 Owen Road Industrial Estate, Willenhall, West Midlands, WV13 2PX Tel: 0121-526 5311 Fax: 0121-526 6900 E-mail: enquiries@danielpipework.co.uk

HIGH PRESSURE LIQUID PUMPS

Hi-Pro Pressure Products Ltd, Unit 9, Beffemer Crescent, Rabans Lane Industrial Area, Aylesbury, Buckinghamshire, HP19 8TF Tel: (01296) 431804 Fax: (01296) 431845 E-mail: sales@hi-pro.co.uk

HIGH PRESSURE PIPEWORK FABRICATORS

High Pressure Welding Ltd, Sundon Business Park, Dencora Way, Luton, LU3 3HP Tel: (01582) 565400 Fax: (01582) 565500 E-mail: hpweldingltd@aol.com

Malcolm Robertson and Sons Ltd, Unit 2 Church Street, Caldewgate, Carlisle, CA2 5TJ Tel: (01228) 521018 Fax: (01228) 542458

HIGH PRESSURE PUMPS

Haskel Energy Systems Ltd, North Hylton Road, Sunderland, SR5 3JD Tel: 0191-549 1212 Fax: 0191-549 0911 E-mail: sales@haskel.co.uk

Longville, 119 Burcott Road, Bristol, BS11 8AD Tel: 0117-982 7657 Fax: 0117-938 4109 E-mail: bristol@sldpumps.com

HIGH PRESSURE SODIUM LIGHTING

▶ Wallace Whittle & Partners, 166 Great Western Road, Aberdeen, AB10 6QE Tel: (01224) 285300 Fax: (01224) 285301 E-mail: aberdeen@wallacewhittle.com

HIGH PRESSURE STEAM/ WATER CLEANING/WASHING,

See Steam etc; also Water etc

HIGH PRESSURE THERMOPLASTIC HOSES

Exitflex (UK) Ltd, 5 Airfield Road, Airfield Industrial Estate, Christchurch, Dorset, BH23 3TG Tel: (01202) 478334 Fax: (01202) 488110 E-mail: sales@exitflex.co.uk

HIGH PRESSURE VALVES

Hi-Pro Pressure Products Ltd, Unit 9, Beffemer Crescent, Rabans Lane Industrial Area, Aylesbury, Buckinghamshire, HP19 8TF Tel: (01296) 431804 Fax: (01296) 431845 E-mail: sales@hi-pro.co.uk

▶ Schrader S A Ltd, Unit 3 Castle Place, Adelaide Street, Coventry, CV1 5TS Tel: (024) 7655 0880 Fax: (024) 7655 1118 E-mail: jcarter@schrader-valves.co.uk

HIGH PRESSURE WATER JETTING SERVICES

▶ Clear Drains UK Ltd, Beaconsfield House, Fieldhouse Lane, Marlow, Buckinghamshire, SL7 1LW Tel: (01628) 484995 Fax: (01628) 890434 E-mail: helpdesk@cleardrainsnet-revenue.com

Fast Clean Group Drains R Us, 156 Neachells Lane, Wolverhampton, WV11 3RF Tel: (01902) 736424 Fax: (01902) 865665

London & Essex Power Washers Ltd, 2 North Drive, Chelmsford, CM2 7EU Tel: (01245) 472227 Fax: (01245) 477498 E-mail: bramigk@aol.com

HIGH RUPTURING CAPACITY FUSE CARTRIDGES

Cooper UK Ltd, Melton Road, Burton-on-the-Wolds, Loughborough, Leicestershire, LE12 5TH Tel: (01509) 882600 Fax: (01509) 882786 E-mail: eurosales@bussmann.co.uk

Lawson Fuses Ltd, Meadowfield, Ponteland, Newcastle upon Tyne, NE20 9SW Tel: (01661) 823232 Fax: (01661) 824213 E-mail: sales@lawson-fuses.co.uk

HIGH SECURITY ACCESS COVERS OR FRAMES

Centralised Services, Piccadilly, Nottingham, NG6 9FN Tel: 0115-913 5000 Fax: 0115-977 0744 E-mail: centser@btconnect.com

▶ Garrison Vehicle Locks, 3 Rolleston Close, Market Harborough, Leicestershire, LE16 8BZ Tel: (07891) 340168 E-mail: info@garrisonlocks.co.uk

▶ Harrisons Electrical Mechanical & Property Services Ltd, Harrison House, Sheep Walk, Langford Road, Biggleswade, Bedfordshire, SG18 9RB Tel: (01767) 600259 Fax: (01767) 600269 E-mail: info@harrisonselec.co.uk

Midas Technologies, Unit A Roundhouse Close, Fengate, Peterborough, PE1 5TA Tel: (01733) 342600 Fax: (01733) 346672 E-mail: sales@midastech.co.uk

Rhodes Engineering Group Ltd, High Street Mills, High Street, Heckmondwike, West Yorkshire, WF16 0DL Tel: (01924) 410740 Fax: (01924) 410164 E-mail: tranter@rhodesengineering.co.uk

▶ Salmor Industries, 4 Silverwood Industrial Area, Silverwood Road, Lurgan, Craigavon, County Armagh, BT66 6LN Tel: (028) 3831 3100 Fax: (028) 3831 7770 E-mail: sales@salmor.co.uk

HIGH SECURITY LABELS

Applied Holographics plc, 40 Phoenix Road, Washington, Tyne & Wear, NE38 0AD Tel: 0191-417 5434 Fax: 0191-417 6591 E-mail: sales@applied-holographics.com

L G L Protectaseal Ltd, Unit 8 & 9, Hitchin Road Industrial Estate, Oxen Road, Luton, LU2 0DZ Tel: (01582) 422976 Fax: (01582) 404082 E-mail: contact@protectaseal.com

Langley Labels Ltd, Harthall Lane, Kings Langley, Hertfordshire, WD4 8JJ Tel: (01923) 263777 Fax: (01923) 270392 E-mail: info@langleylabels.com

HIGH SPEED BIPARTING DOORS

Wellgate Door Systems, Ladyship Centre, Old Lane, Halifax, West Yorkshire, HX3 5QN Tel: (01422) 320520 Fax: (01422) 320499 E-mail: sales@wellgate-doors.co.uk

HIGH SPEED BROADBAND INTERNET ACCESS

▶ NatWeb, 345 Addiscombe Road, Croydon, CR0 7LG Tel: (020) 8407 0771 Fax: (020) 8407 0772 E-mail: robert.macleod@natweb.net

▶ WizzLink Ltd, 23 Avondale Avenue, Esher, Surrey, KT10 0DB Tel: (020) 8339 0508 Fax: (020) 8398 0206 E-mail: simon.kim@wizzlink.com

HIGH SPEED CAMERAS

Polaroid UK Ltd, Vale of Leven Industrial Estate, Dumbarton, G82 3PW Tel: (01389) 712000 Fax: (01389) 755101

HIGH SPEED CENTRIFUGES

Alfalaval Ltd, Salvesen Tower, Blaikies Quay, Aberdeen, AB11 5PW Tel: (01224) 424300 Fax: (01224) 424315

Centri-Force Engineering Co. Ltd, 1-7 Montrose Avenue, Hillington Industrial Estate, Glasgow, G52 4DX Tel: 0141-882 3351 Fax: 0141-882 9965 E-mail: enquiries@centri-force.co.uk

HIGH SPEED CRASH DOORS

Amber Doors Ltd, Mason Way, Platts Common Industrial Estate Hoyland, Barnsley, South Yorkshire, S74 9TG Tel: (01226) 351135 Fax: (01226) 350176 E-mail: sales@amberdoors.co.uk

Guardian Industrial Doors Ltd, 45 Progress Road, Leigh-On-Sea, Essex, SS9 5PR Tel: (0800) 7836602 Fax: (01702) 510015 E-mail: ross@guardiandoors.com

HIGH SPEED DRILLING SPARK EROSION MACHINES

Layton-Fine Machine Technologies Ltd, Units E8-E9, Park La, Castle Vale, Birmingham, B35 6LJ Tel: 0121-776 8883 Fax: 0121-776 8884 E-mail: enquiries@layton-fine.co.uk

HIGH SPEED DYNAMIC RANDOM ACCESS MEMORY (DRAM)

▶ Ware247 Ltd, 16 Castle Grove Drive, Leeds, LS6 4BR Tel: (0845) 3457859 E-mail: sales@ware247.co.uk

HIGH SPEED POWER PRESSES

Sweeney & Blocksidge (Power Presses) Ltd, 126 Parkfield Road, Saltley, Birmingham, B8 3AZ Tel: 0121-327 3231 Fax: 0121-327 4329 E-mail: enquires@sweeneyandblocksidge.co.uk

HIGH SPEED STEEL (HSS) CUTTERS

Impact Carbides Ltd, 36 East Bank Road, Sheffield, S2 3PS Tel: 0114-272 7216 Fax: 0114-272 4854 E-mail: sales@impactcarbides.co.uk

HIGH SPEED STEEL (HSS) TOOL BITS

Fairway Form Tools, Unit B1-B5 Canklow Meadows Industrial Estate, West Bawtry Road, Rotherham, South Yorkshire, S60 2XL Tel: (01709) 820055 Fax: (01709) 820066 E-mail: sales@fairwayformtools.co.uk

Harry Fisher & Co., London Works, Bridge St, Sheffield, S3 8NT Tel: 0114-272 1998 Fax: 0114-275 2489

Rennie Tool Co. Ltd, 227 Upper Brook Street, Manchester, M13 0HB Tel: 0161-273 3901 Fax: 0161-273 3348 E-mail: rennietool@btconnect.com

HIGH SPEED STEEL (HSS) TOOLS

Clico Sheffield Tooling Ltd, 7 Fell Road, Sheffield, S9 2AL Tel: 0114-243 3007 Fax: 0114-243 4158 E-mail: info@clico.co.uk

G & J Hall Ltd, Burgess Road, Sheffield, S9 3WD Tel: 0114-244 0562 Fax: 0114-244 9256 E-mail: sales@gjhall.co.uk

Samwell Tooling Ltd, 29 Benson Road, Nuffield Industrial Estate, Poole, Dorset, BH17 0GB Tel: 01202 687258 Fax: 01202 665698 E-mail: sales@samwell.co.uk

Sorby (UK) Ltd, 7 Orgreave Close, Handsworth, Sheffield, S13 9NP Tel: 0114-269 3803 Fax: 0114-254 0523 E-mail: sales@sorbyuk.co.uk

HIGH STRENGTH FRICTION GRIP BOLTS AND NUTS

Cooper & Turner Ltd, Sheffield Road, Sheffield, S9 1RS Tel: 0114-256 0057 Fax: 0114-244 5529 E-mail: sales@cooperandturner.co.uk

Dinstock Ltd, Unit C1, Hortonwood row 10, Telford, Shropshire, TF1 7ES Tel: (01952) 676700 Fax: (01952) 676800

TLW Fasteners Ltd, 115 Lodgefield Road, Halesowen, West Midlands, B62 8AX Tel: 0121-602 4040 Fax: 0121-602 4040

HIGH STRENGTH REINFORCING BARS

BRC Ltd, 79-81 Station Road, Sutton-in-Ashfield, Nottinghamshire, NG17 5FR Tel: (01623) 440932 Fax: (01623) 440932 E-mail: sales@eastmidlands.brc.ltd.uk

BRC, 11 Mulberry Business Park, Fishponds Road, Wokingham, Berkshire, RG41 2FH Tel: 0118-977 3822 Fax: 0118-977 3913 E-mail: sales@brc-uk.co.uk

Enterprise Metals, Kemys Way, Swansea Enterprise Park, Swansea Enterprise Park, Swansea, SA6 8QF Tel: (01792) 796774 Fax: (01792) 792974 E-mail: sales@ellissteelgroup.co.uk

Express Reinforcements Ltd, High Street, Newburn, Newcastle upon Tyne, NE15 8LN Tel: 0191-264 3311 Fax: 0191-264 7842

Roe Bros & Co. Ltd, 1 Fenlake Bus Centre, Fengate, Peterborough, PE1 5BQ Tel: (01733) 558321 Fax: (01733) 555260 E-mail: roegroup@btconnect.com

HIGH STRENGTH STEEL PLATE

A S D Metal Services Cardiff, East Moors Road, Cardiff, CF24 5SP Tel: (029) 2046 0622 Fax: (029) 2049 0105 E-mail: cardiff@asdmetalservices.co.uk

Armstrong Glen Metals, 14 Palacecraig Street, Coatbridge, Lanarkshire, ML5 4RY Tel: (01236) 424396 Fax: (01236) 433330 E-mail: glenmetals@asdmetalservices.co.uk

Asd Metal Services, Thames Wharf, Dock Road, London, E16 1AF Tel: (020) 7476 0444 Fax: (020) 7476 0239 E-mail: customer.care@asdmetalservices.co.uk

James Bridge Steel Services Ltd, B S A Business Park, Armoury Road, Birmingham, B11 2RQ Tel: 0121-753 4444 Fax: 0121-753 4446 E-mail: sales@steelplates.co.uk

Corus Construction & Industrial UK Ltd, Brigg Road, Scunthorpe, South Humberside, DN16 1BP Tel: (01724) 404040 Fax: (01724) 402191E-mail: andrew.page@corusgroup.com

Swedish Steel, De Salis Court, De Salis Drive, Hampton Lovett, Droitwich, Worcestershire, WR9 0QE Tel: (01905) 795794 Fax: (01905) 794736 E-mail: ssabuk@ssab.com

HIGH TECHNOLOGY CERAMIC PRODUCTS

Advanced Ceramics Ltd, Castle Works, Stafford, ST16 2ET Tel: (01785) 241000 Fax: (01785) 214073 E-mail: mail@aclstafford.co.uk

Ceramic Seals Ltd, Westwood Industrial Estate, Arkwright Street, Oldham, OL9 9LZ Tel: 0161-627 2353 Fax: 0161-627 2356 E-mail: admin@ceramicseals.co.uk

Coorstek, 64-66 Cavendish Way, Glenrothes, Fife, KY6 2SB Tel: (01592) 773743 Fax: (01592) 774925 E-mail: sales@coorstek.co.uk

Custom Grind Ltd, Unit 1c Brown Lees Road Industrial Estate, Forge Way, Knypersley, Stoke-on-Trent, ST8 7DN Tel: (01782) 518503 Fax: (01782) 522110 E-mail: sales@customgrind.com

Powerwave (UK) Ltd, Enterprise Drive, Station Road, Four Ashes, Wolverhampton, WV10 7DF Tel: (01902) 798204 Fax: (01902) 798205

VZS Seagoe Advanced Ceramics, 35-38 Cavendish Way, Glenrothes, Fife, KY6 2SB Tel: (01592) 630505 Fax: (01592) 773192 E-mail: sales@vzs-seagoe.com

Wade Ceramics Ltd, Royal Victoria Pottery, Westport Road, Burslem, Stoke-On-Trent, ST6 4AG Tel: (01782) 577321 Fax: (01782) 575195 E-mail: alan.keenan@wade.co.uk

HIGH TEMPERATURE CABLES

H T Cables, 40 Lancaster Gardens, Penn, Wolverhampton, WV4 4DN Tel: (01902) 339926 Fax: (01902) 659426 E-mail: seona_macrae@lineone.net

S E I Interconnect Products Ltd, 10 Axis Court, Mallard Way, Riverside Business Park, Swansea, SA7 0AJ Tel: (01639) 822806 Fax: (01792) 794357 E-mail: nperkins@sumi-electric.com

Soloheat Electrical Heating Equipment, Units 1 & 2 Lightpill Trading Estate, Bath Road, Stroud, Gloucestershire, GL5 3LL Tel: (01453) 752459 Fax: (01453) 752458 E-mail: heatit@aol.com

HIGH TEMPERATURE EPOXY ADHESIVES

Pi-Kem Ltd, Yew Tree House, Tilley Wem, Wem, Shrewsbury, SY4 5HE Tel: (01939) 234801 Fax: (01939) 235394 E-mail: pikem.rouse@virgin.net

HIGH TEMPERATURE FANS

Alfa Fans Ltd, Unit 7, Green Lane, Bridgtown, Cannock, Staffordshire, WS11 0JJ Tel: (01543) 466420 Fax: (01543) 462393 E-mail: sales@alfafans.co.uk

Daniels Fans Ltd, Heol Gors, Dafen Indust Estate, Felinfoel, Llanelli, Dyfed, SA14 8QR Tel: (01554) 752148 Fax: (01554) 741109 E-mail: sales@danielsfans.ltd.uk

London Fan Co. Ltd, 75-81 Stirling Road, London, W3 8DJ Tel: (020) 8992 6923 Fax: (020) 8992 6928 E-mail: sales@londonfan.co.uk

HIGH TEMPERATURE FIBRE CONVERTERS

Fireprotect Chester Ltd, Factory Road, Sandycroft, Deeside, Clwyd, CH5 2QJ Tel: (01244) 536595 Fax: (01244) 533592 E-mail: sales@fireprotect.co.uk

HIGH TEMPERATURE FILTERS

Filters For Industry, 12c Queensway, New Milton, Hampshire, BH25 5NN Tel: (01425) 628533 Fax: (01425) 621767 E-mail: sales@porvairfiltration.com

HIGH TEMPERATURE GASKETS

Chemical Reactor Services, Unit 5 Lyon Road Industrial Estate, Kearsley, Bolton, BL4 8TG Tel: (01204) 862777 Fax: (01204) 577484

HIGH TEMPERATURE GASKETS – continued

Premier Gaskets, Unit 16 Bell Farm Industrial Park, Nuthampstead, Royston, Hertfordshire, SG8 8ND Tel: (01763) 848849 Fax: (01763) 848848

HIGH TEMPERATURE HEAT EXCHANGERS

Thermex Ltd, Merse Road, North Moons Moat Industrial Estate, Moons Moat North Industrial Estate, Redditch, Worcestershire, B98 9HL Tel: (01527) 62210 Fax: (01527) 60138 E-mail: enquiry@thermex.co.uk

HIGH TEMPERATURE INSULATING MATERIALS

Edward Keirby & Co. Ltd, Vine Works, Chichester Street, Rochdale, Lancashire, OL16 2BG Tel: (01706) 645330 Fax: (01706) 352882 E-mail: info@edwardkeirby.co.uk

HIGH TEMPERATURE REFRACTORY INSULATION MATERIALS

D S F Refractories & Minerals Ltd, Friden, Newhaven, Buxton, Derbyshire, SK17 0DX Tel: (01629) 636271 Fax: (01629) 636892 E-mail: dsf@dsf.co.uk

F K Fiber Products Ltd, The Croft, Long Lane, Waverton, Chester, CH3 7RB Tel: (01244) 335912 Fax: (01244) 332499 E-mail: mike@fkfiber.freeserve.co.uk

Monocon International Refractories Ltd, Denaby Lane, Old Denaby, Doncaster, South Yorkshire, DN12 4LQ Tel: (01709) 864848 Fax: (01709) 860481 E-mail: sales@monocon.com

HIGH TEMPERATURE SEALS

Advanced Products (Seals & Gaskets) Ltd, Unit 25C, Number One Industrial Estate, Consett, Co. Durham, DH8 6SR Tel: (01207) 500317 Fax: (01207) 501210 E-mail: gc@advancedproducts.co.uk

John Crane UK Ltd, Buckingham House, 361-366 Buckingham Avenue, Slough, SL1 4LU Tel: (01753) 224000 Fax: (01753) 224224

Ramsay Services Ltd, Unit C Bamburgh Court, Team Valley Trading Estate, Gateshead, Tyne & Wear, NE11 0TX Tel: 0191-422 4200 Fax: 0191-422 4222

Vulcan Engineering Ltd, Troutbeck Road, Sheffield, S7 2QA Tel: 0114-249 3333 Fax: 0114-249 3322 E-mail: service@vulcan-eng.com

HIGH TEMPERATURE VALVES

L G Ball Valves Ltd, Units 5-6, Westgate Trading Estate, Aldridge, Walsall, WS9 8EX Tel: (01922) 459999 Fax: (01922) 458688 E-mail: sales@lgball-valves.co.uk

HIGH TENSILE BOLTS AND NUTS

Escafeld Alloys Ltd, Bacon Lane, Sheffield, S9 3NH Tel: 0114-276 1091 Fax: 0114-273 9433

Ratae Engineers Ltd, Green Lane Works, George Street, Manchester, M30 0RG Tel: 0116-253 1721 Fax: 0161-787 7508 E-mail: sales@rataeengineers.com

HIGH TENSILE STEEL (HTS) STRAPPING

Bandapac Packaging Materials, 9 Fieldings Road, Cheshunt, Waltham Cross, Hertfordshire, EN8 9TL Tel: (01992) 622799 Fax: (01992) 628873

Band-Tite Co. Ltd, 9 Aizlewood Road, Sheffield, S8 0YX Tel: 0114-250 0393 Fax: 0114-250 0394 E-mail: sales@band-tite.co.uk

Flip Lock Ltd, 177 Ashby Road, Scunthorpe, South Humberside, DN16 2AQ Tel: (01724) 865692 E-mail: mgdeans@btconnect.com

Strapex, Unit 50 Empire Industrial Park, Aldridge, Walsall, WS9 8UQ Tel: (01922) 742500 Fax: (01922) 742501 E-mail: info@strapex.co.uk

HIGH VACUUM COATING EQUIPMENT

▶ Oxford Vacuum Science Ltd, 39 South Street, Middle Barton, Chipping Norton, Oxfordshire, OX7 7BU Tel: (01869) 349161 Fax: (01869) 349157 E-mail: ovs@oxford-vacuum.com

HIGH VACUUM EQUIPMENT/ COMPONENT MANUFRS

B O C Edwards, Manor Royal, Crawley, West Sussex, RH10 9LW Tel: (01293) 528844 Fax: (01293) 533453 E-mail: admin@edwards.boc.com

Ceramic Seals Ltd, Westwood Industrial Estate, Arkwright Street, Oldham, OL9 9LZ Tel: 0161-627 2353 Fax: 0161-627 2356 E-mail: admin@ceramicseals.co.uk

Instrument Technology Ltd, Menzies Road, Ponswood Industrial Estate, St. Leonards-On-Sea, East Sussex, TN38 9BB Tel: (01424) 442121 Fax: (01424) 719696 E-mail: sales@itl-vacuum.com

Middleburn Ltd, 6 Bentley Park, Blacknest Road, Blacknest, Alton, Hampshire, GU34 4PX Tel: (01420) 520227 Fax: (01420) 23796 E-mail: bob@middleburn.co.uk

Rideout Engineering Ltd, 197 South Liberty Lane, Bristol, BS3 2TN Tel: 0117-953 8900 Fax: 0117-953 8800

V G Scinta Ltd, Maunsell Road, St. Leonards-On-Sea, East Sussex, TN38 9NN Tel: (01424) 851291 Fax: (01424) 851489 E-mail: sales@vgscinta.com

HIGH VACUUM FURNACES

Consarc Engineering Ltd, 12 North Road, Bellshill, Lanarkshire, ML4 1EN Tel: (01698) 748845 Fax: (01698) 747925 E-mail: sales@consarceng.com

Vacua Therm Sales Ltd, 5 Parkburn Court, Parkburn Industrial Estate, Hamilton, Lanarkshire, ML3 0QQ Tel: (01698) 825169 Fax: (01698) 824265

HIGH VACUUM METALLISING,

See Metallising etc

HIGH VACUUM PUMP MANUFRS

B O C Edwards, Manor Royal, Crawley, West Sussex, RH10 9LW Tel: (01293) 528844 Fax: (01293) 533453 E-mail: admin@edwards.boc.com

Girovac Ltd, Units 1 & 2, Douglas Bader Close, North Walsham, Norfolk, NR28 0TZ Tel: (01692) 403008 Fax: (01692) 404611 E-mail: enquiries@girovac.com

Tuthill Vacuum Systems, Pennine Business Park, Pilsworth Road, Heywood, Lancashire, OL10 2TL Tel: (01706) 362400 Fax: (01706) 362444 E-mail: uksales@tuthill.com

HIGH VACUUM PUMPING OIL

Apiezon Products, Hibernia Way, Trafford Park, Manchester, M32 0ZD Tel: 0161-864 5419 Fax: 0161-864 5444 E-mail: sales@apiezon.com

Duravac Products Ltd, 170 John Wilson Business Park, Chestfield, Whitstable, Kent, CT5 3RA Tel: (01227) 770828 Fax: (01227) 770878 E-mail: sales@duravac.co.uk

HIGH VELOCITY OXYGEN FUEL SPRAYING SERVICES

Ceramet Plasma Coatings Ltd, Ryeford Industrial Estate, Ryeford, Stonehouse, Gloucestershire, GL10 2LA Tel: (01453) 828416 Fax: (01453) 823068 E-mail: sales@ceramet.co.uk

Monitor Coatings Ltd, Monitor House 2 Elm Road, West Chirton Industrial Estate, North Shields, Tyne & Wear, NE29 8SE Tel: 0191-293 7040 Fax: 0191-293 7041 E-mail: info@monitorcoatings.co.uk

Plasma & Thermal Coating Ltd, Unit 20 Maesglas Industrial Estate, Newport, Gwent, NP20 2NN Tel: (01633) 245600 Fax: (01633) 245601 E-mail: sales@plasmacoat.co.uk

Rolls Wood Group Repair & Overhauls Ltd, Wellheads CR, Wellheads Industrial Estate, Aberdeen, AB21 7GA Tel: (01224) 797000 Fax: (01224) 771552 E-mail: reception@rwgroup.co.uk

HIGH VISIBILITY HAZARD OR WARNING ROAD SAFETY OR DANGER TAPES

U K Tapes Ltd, 5 Cooper Drive, Springwood Industrial Estate, Braintree, Essex, CM7 2RF Tel: (01376) 349090 Fax: (01376) 348989 E-mail: sales@uktapes.com

HIGH VISIBILITY PLASTIC FENCING

A Fax Ltd, Drakes Industrial Estate, Shay Lane, Ovenden, Halifax, West Yorkshire, HX3 6RL Tel: (01422) 331133 Fax: (01422) 323533 E-mail: sales@a-fax.com

Polypipe Civils Ltd, Boston Road Industrial Estate, Holmes Way, Horncastle, Lincolnshire, LN9 6JW Tel: (01507) 527373 Fax: (01507) 525099

HIGH VISIBILITY REFLECTIVE SAFETY PRODUCTS

Halo Reflective Wear Ltd, Pump Station House, Daleside Road, Nottingham, NG2 4DH Tel: 0115-911 8183 Fax: 0115-911 8074 E-mail: sales@haloreflectivewear.co.uk

Highway Safety Systems Ltd, Units 4A-B, Manor Lane Business Park, Manor Lane, Holmes Chapel, Crewe, CW4 8AF Tel: (01477) 536000 Fax: (01477) 536006

HIGH VISIBILITY SAFETY CLOTHING

Armor Products, Cranfield Road, Lostock Industrial Estate, Lostock, Bolton, BL6 4SB Tel: (01204) 664000 Fax: (01204) 664001

Cardno Ltd, 128a New Town Street, Luton, LU1 3ED Tel: (01582) 405080 Fax: (01582) 412054 E-mail: sales@cardno.co.uk

Century Clothing, Swinburne Street, Nottingham, NG3 2GD Tel: 0115-950 4744 Fax: 0115-924 1896 E-mail: paul@centuryclothing.co.uk

Dickies Workwear, Second Avenue, Westfield Trading Estate, Midsomer Norton, Radstock, BA3 4BH Tel: (01761) 410041 Fax: (01761) 414825 E-mail: uksales@dickies.com

Halo Reflective Wear Ltd, Pump Station House, Daleside Road, Nottingham, NG2 4DH Tel: 0115-911 8183 Fax: 0115-911 8074 E-mail: sales@haloreflectivewear.co.uk

Manchester Safety Services Ltd, Fir Street, Heywood, Lancashire, OL10 1NW Tel: (01706) 364943 Fax: (01706) 360026 E-mail: sales@manchestersafety.co.uk

Matek Business Media Ltd, 4 Field Place Estate, Field Place, Broadbridge Heath, Horsham, West Sussex, RH12 3PB Tel: (01403) 276300 Fax: (01403) 276311E-mail: sales@matek.net

Naturellr Consumer Products Ltd, 21 Mountjoy Road, Omagh, County Tyrone, BT79 7EQ Tel: (028) 8224 9396 Fax: (028) 8224 7793 E-mail: info@naturelle.ie

Phoenix-Saxton Ltd, Pomeroy Works, Clarence Road, Cardiff Bay, Cardiff, CF10 5FA Tel: (029) 2048 7848 Fax: (029) 2049 3493 E-mail: sales@phoenix-saxton.com

Southern Safety Centres Ltd, 3 South Parade, Stafford Road, Wallington, Surrey, SM6 9AJ Tel: (020) 8395 8913 Fax: (020) 8773 2937 E-mail: safety@sscltd.fsnet.co.uk

Turton Manufacturing Ltd, Unit 3 The Furlong, Berry Hill Industrial Estate, Droitwich, Worcestershire, WR9 9AH Tel: (01905) 796166 Fax: (01905) 796199 E-mail: sales@turtonslimited.com

Wearwell Group Ltd, Gargarin, Lichfield Road, Tamworth, Staffordshire, B79 7TR Tel: (01827) 310553 Fax: (01827) 66139 E-mail: sales@wearwell.co.uk

HIGH VOLTAGE CABLE GLANDS

▶ Cable Jointing Scotland, Tandle Hill Road, Kilbarchan, Johnstone, Renfrewshire, PA10 2AL Tel: (01505) 703445 E-mail: chaddow1111@fsmail.net

HIGH VOLTAGE CABLE JOINTING KITS

▶ Cable Jointing Scotland, Tandle Hill Road, Kilbarchan, Johnstone, Renfrewshire, PA10 2AL Tel: (01505) 703445 E-mail: chaddow1111@fsmail.net

HIGH VOLTAGE CABLES

High Voltage Technology Ltd, Flitch Industrial Estate, Chelmsford Road, Dunmow, Essex, CM6 1XJ Tel: (01371) 875668 Fax: (01371) 875665 E-mail: sales@essex-x-ray.com

Teledyne Reynolds Industries Ltd, Navigation House, Canal View Road, Newbury, Berkshire, RG14 5UR Tel: (01635) 262200 Fax: (01635) 30920 E-mail: trlsales@teledyne.com

HIGH VOLTAGE CAPACITORS

Eton M E M Low Voltage Products Ltd, Grimshaw Lane, Middleton Farm, Manchester, M24 1GQ Tel: 0161-655 8900 Fax: (0870) 0507525 E-mail: ukresiorders@eton.com

Europtronic Group, 5 Kerry Avenue, Stanmore, Middlesex, HA7 4NJ Tel: (020) 8954 9798 Fax: (020) 8954 8918 E-mail: evelina.huang@europtronic.com

High Voltage Technology Ltd, Flitch Industrial Estate, Chelmsford Road, Dunmow, Essex, CM6 1XJ Tel: (01371) 875668 Fax: (01371) 875665 E-mail: sales@essex-x-ray.com

Hivolt Capacitors Ltd, Maydown, Londonderry, BT47 6UQ Tel: (028) 7186 0265 Fax: (028) 7186 0479 E-mail: hivoltcapacitors@easynet.co.uk

L C R Capacitors Eu Ltd, Unit 18 Rassau Industrial Estate, Rassau, Ebbw Vale, Gwent, NP23 5SD Tel: (01495) 307070 Fax: (01495) 306965 E-mail: sales@lcrcapacitors.co.uk

Phasetech Ltd, Industry Park, Cricketts Lane, Chippenham, Wiltshire, SN15 3EQ Tel: (01249) 651436 Fax: (01249) 462356 E-mail: sales@phasetech.co.uk

HIGH VOLTAGE CONNECTORS

Colton Electrical Equipment Co. Ltd, 329 Front Lane, Upminster, Essex, RM14 1LW Tel: (01708) 224454 Fax: (01708) 221191 E-mail: sales@coltonelectricalequipment.co.uk

Connectors & Switchgear Ltd, 25 Chacombe Road, Middleton Cheney, Banbury, Oxfordshire, OX17 2QS Tel: (01295) 710505 Fax: (01295) 712667 E-mail: sales@connectorandswitchgear.co.uk

HIGH VOLTAGE DIODES

High Voltage Technology Ltd, Flitch Industrial Estate, Chelmsford Road, Dunmow, Essex, CM6 1XJ Tel: (01371) 875668 Fax: (01371) 875665 E-mail: sales@essex-x-ray.com

HIGH VOLTAGE DIRECT CURRENT (DC) ELECTRIC MOTORS

Euromotor Ltd, 5 Bolney Grange Business Park, Stairbridge Lane, Bolney, Haywards Heath, West Sussex, RH17 5PB Tel: (07000) 226276 Fax: (07002) 668677 E-mail: sales@euromotor.net

HIGH VOLTAGE DIRECT CURRENT (DC) POWER SUPPLIES

A C Components Ltd, A1 Springmeadow Road, Springmeadow Business Park, Rumney, Cardiff, CF3 2GA Tel: (029) 2077 6200 Fax: (029) 2077 6111

General High Voltage, New Road, Highley, Bridgnorth, Shropshire, WV16 6NN Tel: (01746) 862555 Fax: (01746) 862666 E-mail: info@genvolt.co.uk

HIGH VOLTAGE ELECTRICAL CONTRACTORS

▶ Countrywide Electrical Service Ltd, 76 Summer Lane, Birmingham, B19 3NG Tel: 0121-248 1400 Fax: 0121-248 1401 E-mail: admin@ceslimited.uk.com

G S Adams Ltd, Station House, 98 Station Road, Studley, Warwickshire, B80 7JS Tel: (01527) 857718 Fax: (01527) 857716 E-mail: admin@gsaelec.co.uk

▶ Grant Smith Electrical, 16 Hutcheson Drive, Largs, Ayrshire, KA30 8EE Tel: (07717) 734880 E-mail: enquiry@gselectrical.com

▶ JDR Reactive Ltd, 31 Harcote Street, London, W1H 4HU Tel: (020) 7724 9361 Fax: (020) 7723 9034 E-mail: jdreactive@aol.com

▶ R E Field Services Ltd, Unit 3, Fieldhouse Way, Industrial Estate, Petre Street, Sheffield, S4 7SF Tel: 0114-256 0425 Fax: 0114-242 5545 E-mail: sales@refieldservices.com

HIGH VOLTAGE ELECTRICAL EQUIPMENT TESTING

▶ G J ELECTRICAL, 65 FAWNBRAKE AVENUE, HERNE HILL, LONDON, SE24 0BE Tel: 020 73264668E-mail: GJONAS4@HOTMAIL.COM

HIGH VOLTAGE ELECTRICAL INSULATION BUSHINGS

Siemens Protection Devices Ltd, PO Box 7, Hebburn, Tyne & Wear, NE31 1TZ Tel: 0191-401 5555 Fax: 0191-401 5575

▶ Spares-Direct-2-U, 20 Allerton Grange Gardens, Moortown, Leeds, LS17 6LL Tel: 0113 2263384 Fax: 0113 2955753 E-mail: info@sparesdirect2u.com

Trench UK Ltd, South Drive, Hebburn, Tyne & Wear, NE31 1UW Tel: 0191-483 4711 Fax: 0191-430 0633 E-mail: sales@trench-uk.com

HIGH VOLTAGE ELECTRONIC COMPONENTS

Bournlea Instruments Ltd, The Old Rectory, 34 Pauls Lane, Overstrand, Cromer, Norfolk, NR27 0PF Tel: (01263) 578186 Fax: (01263) 579186 E-mail: enquiries@bournlea.com

▶ Mateleco UK Ltd, Northgate Close, Mansell Way, Middlebrook, Bolton, BL6 6PQ Tel: (01204) 673040 Fax: (01204) 693209 E-mail: sales@mateleco.co.uk

HIGH VOLTAGE ELECTRONIC COMPONENTS – *continued*

St Micro Electronics Ltd, Planer House, Parkway, Marlow, Buckinghamshire, SL7 1YL Tel: (01628) 890800 Fax: (01628) 890391

HIGH VOLTAGE INSULATORS

Mathew C Blythe & Son Ltd, The Green, Tredington, Shipston-on-Stour, Warwickshire, CV36 4NJ Tel: (01608) 662295 Fax: (01608) 662006 E-mail: sales@matthewcblythe.co.uk

HIGH VOLTAGE SWITCHGEARS

Engineered Systems (Electrical) Ltd, Systems House, Unit 1, Waterside Industrial Park, Waterside Road, Leeds, LS10 1RW Tel: 0113-272 1222 Fax: 0113-272 1333 E-mail: mick@eselimited.co.uk
I C W Power Ltd, Joule House, 108-110 Primrose Hill, Kings Langley, Hertfordshire, WD4 8HR Tel: (01923) 266869 Fax: (01923) 264472 E-mail: sales@icwpower.com
Mathew C Blythe & Son Ltd, The Green, Tredington, Shipston-on-Stour, Warwickshire, CV36 4NJ Tel: (01608) 662295 Fax: (01608) 662006 E-mail: sales@matthewcblythe.co.uk

HIGH VOLTAGE TEST EQUIPMENT

E H P Technical Services Ltd, 6 Lincoln Road, Northborough, Peterborough, PE6 9BL Tel: (01733) 252428 Fax: (01733) 252674 E-mail: rayevans@ehpltd.freeserve.co.uk

HIGH VOLTAGE TRANSFORMERS

Zeta Windings Ltd, 416-418 London Road, Isleworth, Middlesex, TW7 5XB Tel: (020) 8568 6875 Fax: (020) 8568 7194 E-mail: chris@zetacool.com

HIGHER NICKEL ALLOY FLANGES OR FITTINGS

Multi Process, Unit 8 Stroud Enterprise Centre, Lightpill, Stroud, Gloucestershire, GL5 3NL Tel: (01453) 750002 Fax: (01453) 758271

HIGHWAY ACOUSTIC BARRIERS

▶ Sound Control Services, White Lodge Farm, Nottingham Road, Ab Kettleby, Melton Mowbray, Leicestershire, LE14 3JB Tel: (01664) 823704 Fax: (01664) 823663 E-mail: sales@soundcontrolservices.co.uk

HIGHWAY MAINTENANCE CONTRACTORS

▶ The Civils, 500 Pavilion Drive, Northampton, NN4 7YJ Tel: (01604) 664200 Fax: (01604) 708373 E-mail: glyn.holt@birse.co.uk
▶ West Hampshire Tarmacadam Ltd, Unit 14, Liberty Close, Woolsbridge Industrial Park, Three Legged Cross, Wimborne, Dorset, BH21 6SY Tel: 01202 813508 Fax: 01202 813508 E-mail: office@w-h-t.co.uk

HILL AND MOUNTAIN CLIMBING EQUIPMENT

▶ Kings Road Sporting Club Ltd, 40-42 Kings Road, London, SW3 4UD Tel: (020) 7589 5418
Rock City, Hawthorne Avenue, Hull, HU3 5JX Tel: (01482) 223030 Fax: (01482) 223030 E-mail: info@rockcity.co.uk
▶ Snow + Rock - Romford, Unit 1A, Davidson Way, Rom Valley Way, Romford, RM7 0AZ Tel: (01708) 436400 E-mail: direct@snowandrock.com
▶ Snow + Rock - Wirral Ltd, Unit 1, Eastham Point, 1062 New Chester Road, Wirral, Merseyside, CH62 8HJ Tel: 0151-328 5500 Fax: 0151-328 5501 E-mail: manager.liverpool@snowandrock.com
▶ Snow & Rock, 188 Kensington High Street, London, W8 7RG Tel: (020) 7937 0872 Fax: (020) 7938 2758 E-mail: manager.kensington@snowandrock.com
▶ Snow & Rock, 150 Holborn, London, EC1N 2LR Tel: (020) 7831 6900 Fax: (020) 7831 8545 E-mail: phil@mackechnie.co.nz
▶ Snow & Rock, 4 Mercer Street, London, WC2H 9QA Tel: (020) 7420 1444 Fax: (020) 7420 1445 E-mail: manager.coventgarden@snowandrock.com
▶ Snow & Rock Sports Ltd, 14-16 The Priory Queensway, Birmingham, B4 6BS Tel: 0121-236 8280 Fax: 0121-212 2177
▶ Snow & Rock Sports Ltd, Units 1-3, Gloucester Road North, Filton, Bristol, BS34 7BQ Tel: 0117-914 3000 Fax: 0117-907 4278
▶ Snow & Rock Sports Ltd, 97 Fordwater Road, Chertsey, Surrey, KT16 8HH Tel: (01932) 566886 Fax: (01932) 561553
▶ Snow & Rock Sports Ltd, 31 The Boardwalk, Port Solent, Portsmouth, PO6 4TP Tel: (023) 9220 5388 Fax: (023) 9220 5399
▶ Snow & Rock Sports Ltd, Sheffield Ski Village, Vale Road, Sheffield, S3 9SJ Tel: 0114-275 1700 Fax: 0114-273 0003
▶ Spike Outdoors Ltd, 20 Castle Gates, Shrewsbury, SY1 2AD Tel: (01743) 364455 Fax: (01743) 350550 E-mail: info@spikeoutdoors.co.uk

HILL AND TREKKING BOOTS

▶ Spike Outdoors Ltd, 20 Castle Gates, Shrewsbury, SY1 2AD Tel: (01743) 364455 Fax: (01743) 350550 E-mail: info@spikeoutdoors.co.uk

HINGED AUTOMATIC FIRE DOOR CLOSERS

Modern Door Closures, Lloyds Bank Chambers, High Street, Littlehampton, West Sussex, BN17 5AG Tel: (01903) 724003 Fax: (01903) 739806 E-mail: tradersnetwork@btconnect.com

HINGES, *See also headings for particular types*

Bonlea Ltd, Q Net House, Malleable Way, Stockton-on-Tees, Cleveland, TS18 2SZ Tel: (01642) 617611 Fax: (01642) 674490 E-mail: enquiries@bonlea.co.uk
Kirkpatrick Ltd, PO Box 17, Walsall, WS2 9NF Tel: (01922) 620026 Fax: (01922) 722525 E-mail: sales@kirkpatrick.co.uk
Salice UK Ltd, Kingfisher Way, Hinchingbrooke Business Park, Huntingdon, Cambridgeshire, PE29 6FN Tel: (01480) 413831 Fax: (01480) 451489 E-mail: info.salice@saliceuk.co.uk
Eliza Tinsley & Co. Ltd, Unit 12, Cinder Road, Chasetown Industrial Estate, Burntwood, Staffordshire, WS7 8XD Tel: (01543) 683595 Fax: (01543) 674620
W P Notcutt Ltd, Homewood Farm, Newark Lane, Ripley, Woking, Surrey, GU23 6DJ Tel: (01483) 223311 Fax: (01483) 479594 E-mail: sales@notcutt.com
Woodfit Ltd, Kem Mill, Kem Mill Lane, Whittle-le-Woods, Chorley, Lancashire, PR6 7EA Tel: (01257) 266421 Fax: (01257) 264271 E-mail: sales@woodfit.com

HINGES, CONTINUOUS/PIANO

▶ Bedhampton Piano Shop Ltd, 90 Bedhampton Road, Havant, Hampshire, PO9 3EZ Tel: (023) 9248 4802 Fax: (0800) 2985087 E-mail: graham@bpspianos.com
Gold & Wassall (Hinges) Ltd, Castle Works, Lichfield Road Industrial Estate, Tamworth, Staffordshire, B79 7TH Tel: (01827) 63391 Fax: (01827) 310819 E-mail: enquiries@goldwassallhinges.co.uk

HINGES, DOOR, KITCHEN CABINET

▶ Bespoke Kitchens, 1 Hillcrest, Stoodleigh, Tiverton, Devon, EX16 9PJ Tel: (01398) 351467
▶ Brighton & Hove Removals, 190 Portland Road, Hove, East Sussex, BN3 5QN Tel: (01273) 735111 E-mail: sales@brightonandhovekitchens.com
▶ Canty Designs Ltd, 17 Westbourne Avenue, Hull, HU5 3HN Tel: (01480) 491654 Fax: (0870) 7627278 E-mail: info@cantydesigns.com
▶ Essex Specialised Joinery, Essexquay House, Quayside Industrial Estate, Maldon, Essex, CM9 5FA Tel: (01621) 843384 Fax: (01621) 843411
▶ Gates D I Y, 6 Vesey Path, London, E14 6BT Tel: (020) 7987 4045 Fax: (020) 7987 4015 E-mail: info@gatesdiy.com
▶ Kitchen Heaven, 26 Nibley Lane, Iron Acton, Bristol, BS37 9UP Tel: (01454) 228100 E-mail: sales@kitchenheaven.co.uk
Niche Kitchens, 28 Kay Street, Rossendale, Lancashire, BB4 7LS Tel: (01706) 217121 Fax: (01706) 212893 E-mail: info@nichekitchens.co.uk
Rubber Duck Home Improvements, 361 Holburn Street, Aberdeen, AB10 7FQ Tel: (01224) 212397
▶ Verona Kitchens Ltd, 24 Grasgarth Close, London, W3 9HS Tel: (020) 8993 1540 Fax: (020) 8993 1540 E-mail: sales@veronakitchens.co.uk
WOODLAND LINE, INGLENOOK COTTAGE, MILL LANE, HORSEMANS GREEN, WHITCHURCH, SHROPSHIRE, SY13 3DT Tel: 01948 830334 Fax: 01948 830334 E-mail: ingrid.geoff@tesco.net

HIRE PURCHASE FINANCE

Barclays Mercantile Business Finance Ltd, Churchill Plaza, Churchill Way, Basingstoke, Hampshire, RG21 7GP Tel: (01256) 314108 Fax: (01256) 791850 E-mail: bassf@barclays.co.uk
Guardian Finance Ltd, 207 Barkby Road, Leicester, LE4 9HZ Tel: 0116-276 6631 Fax: 0116-246 0447 E-mail: sales@guardian-finance.co.uk
HSBC Equipment Finance (UK) Ltd, 12 Calthorpe Road, Edge Baston, Birmingham, B15 1HT Tel: 0121-450 1515 Fax: (0845) 6076067
Humberclyde Farm Finance, Northern Cross, Basing View, Basingstoke, Hampshire, RG21 4HL Tel: (0845) 2267378 Fax: (0845) 2267379 E-mail: enquiries@humberclyde.co.uk
Lloyds T S B, St. William House, Tresillian Terrace, Cardiff, CF10 5BH Tel: (029) 2029 6000 Fax: (0870) 8503105
▶ New Car Discount.com Ltd, Unit 7A, Kayley Industrial Estate, Richmond Street, Ashton-under-Lyne, Lancashire, OL7 0AU Tel: (08703) 500144 Fax: (08703) 500244 E-mail: sales@new-car-discount.com

HISTOLOGY LABORATORY EQUIPMENT

Cellpath plc, Unit 66 Mochdre Industrial Estate, Mochdre, Newtown, Powys, SY16 4LE Tel: (01686) 611333 Fax: (01686) 622946 E-mail: sales@cellpath.co.uk

HITCHES

▶ Hill Engineering Ltd, 1 Sandy Road, Newry, County Down, BT34 2LB Tel: (028) 3025 2555 Fax: (028) 3026 4020 E-mail: sales@hillengineeringltd.com

HOBBY REQUISITES, *See Handicraft/Hobby etc*

HOCKEY REQUISITES

Kookaburra Reader Ltd, Unit 25, The Alders, Seven Mile Lane, Mereworth, Maidstone, Kent, ME18 5JG Tel: (01622) 812230 Fax: (01622) 814224 E-mail: sales@alfredreader.co.uk

HOCKEY STICKS

RJM Sports Ltd, 54 Cow Wynd, Falkirk, FK1 1PU Tel: (01324) 873804 Fax: (01324) 873804 E-mail: sales@rjmsports.co.uk

HOG ROASTERS

▶ Bowser Bros, Stainton by Langworth, Lincoln, LN3 5BL Tel: (01673) 862423 Fax: (01673) 862423

HOIST HIRE

Compact Fork Trucks Ltd, Unit 8B Blackbrook Business Park, Narrowboat Way, Dudley, West Midlands, DY2 0XQ Tel: (01384) 238000 Fax: (01384) 240300 E-mail: sales@thecompactgroup.co.uk
Evans Gwyn Plant Ltd, Brackla Industrial Estate, Bridgend, Mid Glamorgan, CF31 2AN Tel: (01656) 655393 Fax: (01656) 655393
Fenton Plant Hire, A Culverlands Industrial Estate, Winchester Road, Shedfield, Southampton, SO32 2JF Tel: (01329) 830011 Fax: (01329) 833683 E-mail: sales@fentonplant.co.uk
HSS Lift & Shift, Crafton St East, Leicester, LE1 2DG Tel: 0116-262 7179 Fax: 0116-262 7179
HSS Lift & Shift, 288 Hartshill Road, Stoke-on-Trent, ST4 7NA Tel: (01782) 412266 Fax: (01782) 846643
Jacksons Fork Trucks, Rosenheath, Norwich Road, Barham, Ipswich, IP6 0PA Tel: (01473) 830691 Fax: (01473) 831492
Lifting Gear Hire Ltd, Avon Trading Estate, 20A Albert Road, Bristol, BS2 0XA Tel: 0117-977 9514 Fax: 0117-972 3076
Speedy LGH Ltd, Unit A, Castleblair Works, Inglis Lane, Dunfermline, Fife, KY12 9DP Tel: (01383) 721079 Fax: (01383) 732781
Yorkshire Hoist Ltd, Woodlands, Dale Street, Longwood, Huddersfield, HD3 4TG Tel: (01484) 655300 Fax: (01484) 655301 E-mail: yorkshirehoist@btconnect.com

HOISTS, *See also headings for particular types under Hoists*

▶ Abco Lifting Equipment Ltd, Unit 11, Mundells Industrial Centre, Welwyn Garden City, Hertfordshire, AL7 1EW Tel: (01707) 328847 E-mail: liambullough@hotmail.com
Calder Lifting Services Ltd, Warehouse 1, Cromwell House, Elland Road, Brighouse, West Yorkshire, HD6 2RG Tel: (01422) 376589 Fax: (01422) 374686 E-mail: sales@calderlifting.com
Compact Fork Trucks Ltd, Unit 8B Blackbrook Business Park, Narrowboat Way, Dudley, West Midlands, DY2 0XQ Tel: (01384) 238000 Fax: (01384) 240300 E-mail: sales@thecompactgroup.co.uk
Dale Lifting and Handling, 2 Kelbrook Road, Manchester, M11 2QA Tel: 0161-223 1990 Fax: 0161-223 6767 E-mail: ingfo@dale_lifiting.com
Ensor Lifting Services, 3 Park Road, Thurnscoe, Rotherham, South Yorkshire, S63 0TG Tel: (01709) 881908 Fax: (01709) 881908 E-mail: grahamensor-els@hotmail.com
G B Access Ltd, 10 Nene Valley Business Park, Oundle, Peterborough, PE8 4HN Tel: (01832) 272408 Fax: (01832) 272484 E-mail: hire@gbaccess.co.uk
G Taylor Midlands Ltd, 9 Haddow Street, Hamilton, Lanarkshire, ML3 7HX Tel: (01698) 283561 Fax: (01698) 457914 E-mail: enquiries@gtlifting.co.uk
I & P Lifting Gear Ltd, 237 Scotia Road, Stoke-on-Trent, ST6 4PS Tel: (01782) 814411 Fax: (01782) 575510 E-mail: info@iandplifting.co.uk
Lifting Gear Hire plc, Hockley Way, Nixs Hill Industrial Estate, Alfreton, Derbyshire, DE55 7FA Tel: (01773) 608325 Fax: (01773) 540566 E-mail: sales@lgh.co.uk
Lifting Gear Hire Ltd, Avon Trading Estate, 20A Albert Road, Bristol, BS2 0XA Tel: 0117-977 9514 Fax: 0117-972 3076
Lifting Gear Hire Ltd, Brunel Industrial Estate, Blyth Road, Harworth, Doncaster, South Yorkshire, DN11 8QA Tel: (01302) 743600 Fax: (01302) 750697
Lifting Gear Hire plc, 17 Rosscliffe Road, Ellesmere Port, CH65 3AS Tel: 0151-357 2906 Fax: 0151-357 2380 E-mail: info@lgh.co.uk
Lifting Gear Hire plc, Unit D4 South Orbital Trading Park, Hedon Road, Hull, HU9 1NJ Tel: (01482) 223737 Fax: (01482) 219491 E-mail: hull-lifting@speedydepots.co.uk
Lifting Gear Hire Ltd, Unit 27 Boston Road, Gorse Hill Industrial Estate, Beaumont Leys, Leicester, LE4 1AW Tel: 0116-234 0255 Fax: 0116-234 0254 E-mail: leicester@lgh.co.uk
Lifting Gear Hire plc, 74 Roding Road, London, E6 6LS Tel: (020) 7511 0233 Fax: (020) 7511 1784
Lifting Gear Hire plc, 120 Bolton Road, Atherton, Manchester, M46 9YZ Tel: (01942) 878081 Fax: (01942) 895018 E-mail: info@lgh.co.uk
Lifting Gear Hire Ltd, High Yard, Wincomblee Road, Newcastle upon Tyne, NE6 3PL Tel: 0191-295 5301 Fax: 0191-295 4311 E-mail: tyneside@lgh.co.uk
Lifting Gear Hire Ltd, Unit 1, Kings Parade, Newport, Gwent, NP20 2DU Tel: (01633) 243244 Fax: (01633) 243236 E-mail: newport@lgh.co.uk
Lifting Gear Supplies Ltd, 23 Anstey Lane, Leicester, LE4 0FF Tel: 0116-262 8023 Fax: 0116-251 4862 E-mail: sales@liftinggearsuppliesltd.co.uk
London Hoist Ltd, Rifle Street, London, E14 6PB Tel: (020) 7538 4833 Fax: (020) 7515 3593 E-mail: info@londonhoist.co.uk
Midway Material Handling, 7 Pinewood Drive, Little Haywood, Stafford, ST18 0NX Tel: (01889) 882014 Fax: (01889) 882014
Speedy L G H, Unit 13, Royce Road, Fleming Way, Crawley, West Sussex, RH10 2NX Tel: (01293) 615898 Fax: (01293) 615818 E-mail: crawley@lgh.co.uk
Speedy L G H, Unit 2, Crescent Industrial Park, Peartree Lane, Dudley, West Midlands, DY2 0QQ Tel: (01384) 239966 Fax: (01384) 455782 E-mail: rob.langford@lgh.co.uk
Speedy LGH, Bentley Avenue, Cowpen Bewley Industrial Estate, Billingham, Cleveland, TS23 4BU Tel: (01642) 561611 Fax: (01642) 566032 E-mail: teeside@lgh.co.uk
Speedy LGH, Units 36-37, Millers Bridge Industrial Estate, Bootle, Merseyside, L20 1EE Tel: 0151-922 5596 Fax: 0151-922 0361 E-mail: liverpool@lgh.co.uk
Speedy LGH, Long Island Park, Carlisle, CA2 5AS Tel: (01228) 599766 Fax: (01228) 599788 E-mail: info@lgh.co.uk
Speedy LGH Ltd, Unit A, Castleblair Works, Inglis Lane, Dunfermline, Fife, KY12 9DP Tel: (01383) 721079 Fax: (01383) 732781
Speedy LGH, 100 Brook Street, Glasgow, G40 3AP Tel: 0141-554 6477 Fax: 0141-554 6162
Speedy LGH, Unit 2, 40 Adam Smith Street, Grimsby, South Humberside, DN31 1SJ Tel: (01472) 362685 Fax: (01472) 342612 E-mail: grimsby@lgh.co.uk
Speedy LGH Ltd, Unit 5, Farthing Road, Ipswich, IP1 5AP Tel: (01473) 461083 Fax: (01473) 240532 E-mail: ipswich@lgh.co.uk
Speedy LGH, West Thamesmead Business Park, 7 Kellner Road, London, SE28 0AX Tel: (020) 8854 6248 Fax: (020) 8316 0501 E-mail: south-thames@lgh.co.uk
Speedy Lifting Ltd, Cronin Road, Weldon South Industrial Estate, Corby, Northamptonshire, NN18 8AQ Tel: (01536) 206306 Fax: (01536) 264513 E-mail: corby-lifting@speedydepots.co.uk
Speedy Lifting, 3 Vulcan House, Vulcan Road North, Norwich, NR6 6AQ Tel: (01603) 764642 Fax: (01603) 620839 E-mail: norwich@lgh.co.uk

HOISTS - *continued*

Speedy Lifting, Unit 1, Llewellyns Quay, The Docks, Port Talbot, West Glamorgan, SA13 1RF Tel: (01639) 890875 Fax: (01639) 895009 E-mail: port-talbot@lgh.co.uk
Speedy Lifting, Unit 4 Meridian Park, Neptune Close, Rochester, Kent, ME2 4LE Tel: (01634) 297373 Fax: (01634) 296638 E-mail: medway@lgh.co.uk
Speedy Lifting, Unit 10, Central Trading Estate, Marine Parade, Southampton, SO14 5JP Tel: (023) 9223 8236 Fax: (023) 8063 1712 E-mail: southampton-lifting@speedydepos.co.uk
Speedy/LGH, Unit 1C, Walney Road Industrial Estate, Barrow-In-Furness, Cumbria, LA14 5UG Tel: (01229) 835407 Fax: (01229) 811236 E-mail: cumbria@lgh.co.uk

HOLDING COMPANIES OR GROUPS

Abacus, Unit 29, Ardent Way, Mountheath Industrial Park, Prestwich, Manchester, M25 9WE Tel: 0161-773 7594 Fax: 0161-773 0093 E-mail: info@abacusweighing.com
Abbott Mead Vickers Bbdo Ltd, 151 Marylebone Road, London, NW1 5QE Tel: (020) 7616 3500 Fax: (020) 7616 3600 E-mail: malona.a@amvbbdo.com
ADM Pura Foods Ltd, Erith Oil Works, Church Manorway, Erith, Kent, DA8 1DL Tel: (01322) 443000 Fax: (01322) 443027
Adroit Group Ltd, Trow Way, Worcester, WR5 3BX Tel: (01905) 356443 Fax: (01905) 351868 E-mail: sales@adroitgroup.co.uk
Aggregate Industries Ltd, Bardon Hill, Coalville, Leicestershire, LE67 1TL Tel: (01530) 510066 Fax: (01530) 510123 E-mail: ukenquiries@ukaggregate.com
Agri Products, Finchley Road, London, NW3 6JG Tel: (020) 7483 2737 Fax: (020) 7586 7338
Agustawestland Aircraft Services, Lysander Road, Yeovil, Somerset, BA20 2YB Tel: (01935) 475222 Fax: (01935) 702131 E-mail: info@gkn-whl.co.uk
Alba plc, Bush House The Waterfront, Elstree Road, Elstree, Borehamwood, Hertfordshire, WD6 3BS Tel: (020) 8238 7660 Fax: (020) 8953 8465 E-mail: albaplc@netcomuk.co.uk
Antofagasta, 5 Princes Gate, London, SW7 1QJ Tel: (020) 7808 0988 Fax: (020) 7808 0986
Aon Trust Corporation Ltd, 8 Devonshire Square, London, EC2M 4PL Tel: (020) 7623 5500 Fax: (020) 7621 1511 E-mail: nicola.fairley@aon.co.uk
Associated British Engineering P.L.C., 63 Church Street, Harston, Cambridge, CB2 5NP Tel: (01223) 873600 Fax: (01223) 872652 E-mail: peter.morton@abeplc.co.uk
Automobile Association, Fanum House, Basing View, Basingstoke, Hampshire, RG21 4EA Tel: (0870) 5448866 Fax: (01256) 493389
B O C Group P.L.C., Chertsey Road, Windlesham, Surrey, GU20 6HJ Tel: (01276) 477222 Fax: (01276) 471333
Bae Systems Defence Systems Ltd, Warwick House, P O Box 87, Farnborough, Hampshire, GU14 6YU Tel: (01252) 373232 Fax: (01252) 383000
Barnfield Hughes Ltd, Barnfield, Leek, Staffordshire, ST13 5QG Tel: (01538) 385626 Fax: (01538) 386302
Bohler-Uddeholm, Taylors Lane, Oldbury, West Midlands, B69 2BN Tel: 0121-511 1121 Fax: 0121-544 2911 E-mail: info@bohler-uddeholm.co.uk
Booth Industries Group P.L.C, 1-4 The Courtyard, Gaulby Lane, Stoughton, Leicester, LE2 2FL Tel: 0116-271 2713 Fax: 0116-271 6786
Brammer plc, Claverton Court, Claverton Road, Roundthorn Industrial Estate, Manchester, M23 9NE Tel: 0161-902 5599 Fax: 0161-902 5595 E-mail: sales@brammer.plc.uk
Brent Group Ltd, Brent House, Travellers Lane, North Mymms, Hatfield, Hertfordshire, AL9 7HF Tel: (01707) 282300 Fax: (01707) 282333 E-mail: hq@brentgroup.com
Britax International Holdings Ltd, Seton House, Warwick Technology Park, Warwick, CV34 6DE Tel: (01926) 400040 Fax: (01926) 406350 E-mail: info@britax.com
British American Tobacco plc, Globe House, 4 Temple Place, London, WC2R 2PG Tel: (020) 7845 1000 Fax: (020) 7240 0555
Brown Butlin Group Ltd, Brook House, Ruskington, Sleaford, Lincolnshire, NG34 9EP Tel: (01526) 831000 Fax: (01526) 832967 E-mail: ken.matthews@bbgdirect.co.uk
Buchanan Communications Ltd, 107 Cheapside, London, EC2V 6DN Tel: (020) 7466 5000 Fax: (020) 7466 5001 E-mail: contact@buchanan.uk.com
Bunzl plc, 110 Park Street, London, W1K 6NX Tel: (020) 7495 4950 Fax: (020) 7495 4953 E-mail: enquiries@bunzl.com
Cable and Wireless P.L.C., Redlion Square, London, WC1R 4HQ Tel: (020) 7315 4000 Fax: (020) 7315 5182
Camelia P.L.C., Linton Park, Maidstone, Kent, ME17 4AB Tel: (01622) 746655 Fax: (01622) 747422 E-mail: camelia@lintonpark.plc.uk
Caparo Group Ltd, 101-103 Baker Street, London, W1U 6LN Tel: (020) 7486 1417 Fax: (020) 7224 4109 E-mail: sales@caparo.co.uk
Capitb Trust Ltd, 80 Richardshaw Lane, Stanningley, Pudsey, West Yorkshire, LS28 6BN Tel: 0113-227 3345 Fax: 0113-227 3322 E-mail: sales@capitb.co.uk
Cattles plc, Kingston House Centre 27 Business Park, Woodhead Road, Birstall, Batley, West Yorkshire, WF17 9TD Tel: (01924) 444466 Fax: (01924) 442255
Century Life P.L.C., Century House, 5 Old Bailey, London, EC4M 7BA Tel: (01708) 758196
Chloride Group plc, Third Floor, 23 Lower Belgrave Street, London, SW1W 0NR Tel: (020) 7881 1440 Fax: (020) 7730 5085 E-mail: info@chloridegroup.com
Cleckheaton Holdings Ltd, P O Box 24, Cleckheaton, West Yorkshire, BD19 3LN Tel: (01274) 863704 Fax: (01274) 863705 E-mail: cleckhol@globalnet.co.uk
Clifford Thames Ltd, Springfield Lyons House, Chelmsford Business Park, Chelmsford, CM2 5TH Tel: (01245) 236600 Fax: (01245) 236611 E-mail: sales@clifford-thames.com
Clugston Estates Ltd, St Vincent House, Normanby Road, Scunthorpe, South Humberside, DN15 8QT Tel: (01724) 843491 Fax: (01724) 281714 E-mail: group@clugston.co.uk
Compass Group plc, Compass House, Guilford Street, Chertsey, Surrey, KT16 9BQ Tel: 0121-457 5555 Fax: (01932) 569956
Cosalt International Ltd, Fish Dock Road, Grimsby, South Humberside, DN31 3NW Tel: (01472) 504300 Fax: (01472) 504200 E-mail: sales@cosaltlighting.co.uk
CP Holdings Ltd, C P House, Otterspool Way, Watford, WD25 8HG Tel: (01923) 250500 Fax: (01923) 221628 E-mail: someone@cpholdingsltd.com
Crest Nicholson P.L.C., Crest House, Thurcroft Road, Chertsey, Surrey, KT16 9GN Tel: (01932) 580555 Fax: (0870) 3363990 E-mail: info@crestnicholson.com
Daejan Holdings P.L.C., 158-162 Shaftesbury Avenue, London, WC2H 8HR Tel: (020) 7836 1555 Fax: (020) 7379 6365
Diversified Agency Services Ltd, 239 Old Marylebone Road, London, NW1 5QT Tel: (020) 7298 7000 Fax: (020) 7724 8292 E-mail: sales@dasglobal.com
DP World, 16 Palace Street, London, SW1E 5JQ Tel: (020) 7930 4343 Fax: (020) 7901 4015
Enodis plc, Washington House, 40-41 Conduit Street, London, W1S 2YQ Tel: (020) 7312 2500 Fax: (020) 7304 6001 E-mail: contact@enodis.com
Envirohold Ltd, Viking Close, Willerby, Hull, HU10 6BS Tel: (01482) 651090 Fax: (01482) 651002 E-mail: sales@envirodoor.com
Exel, Ocean House, The Ring, Bracknell, Berkshire, RG12 1AN Tel: (01344) 302000 Fax: (01344) 710037
Eyre & Elliston Holdings Ltd, 191 Chatsworth Road, Chesterfield, Derbyshire, S40 2BD Tel: (01246) 274358 Fax: (01246) 220512
F Bamford & Co. Ltd, Ajax Works, Whitehill Industrial Estate, Stockport, Cheshire, SK4 1NT Tel: 0161-480 6507 Fax: 0161-477 7990 E-mail: sales@bamfordajax.com
G C A S Designs Ltd, Russell Court, Lisburn Road, Belfast, BT9 6AA Tel: (028) 9055 7700 Fax: (028) 9024 5741 E-mail: advertising@gcasgroup.com
G K N AutoStructures Ltd, Hadley, Castleworks, Telford, Shropshire, TF1 6TE Tel: (01952) 244321
Geo Kingsbury Holdings Ltd, 45 Portsmouth Road, Cobham, Surrey, KT11 1JQ Tel: (01932) 863836 Fax: (01932) 865596
George Williamson & Co. Ltd, 5 West Mills, Newbury, Berkshire, RG14 5HG Tel: (01635) 522088 Fax: (01635) 551992 E-mail: plantations@williamsontea.com
Goodacre Carpets Of Kendal Ltd, Castle Mill, Aynam Road, Kendal, Cumbria, LA9 7DF Tel: (01539) 792916 Fax: (01539) 732442 E-mail: admin@goodacrecarpets.com
Goodall Bates & Todd Ltd, Albany Road, Gateshead, Tyne & Wear, NE8 3BP Tel: 0191-477 4221 Fax: 0191-477 9544 E-mail: cbaker@gb-lubricants-fuels.co.uk
Granwood Flooring Group Ltd, Stubben Edge Hall, Ashover, Chesterfield, Derbyshire, S45 0EU Tel: (01246) 590543 Fax: (01246) 590449
Harland & Wolff Ltd, Queens Island, Belfast, BT3 9DU Tel: (028) 9045 8456 Fax: (028) 9045 8515 E-mail: webmaster@harland-wolff.com
Harris & Sheldon Group Ltd, North Court, Packington Park, Meriden, Coventry, CV7 7HF Tel: (01676) 522990 Fax: (01676) 523609 E-mail: group@harris-sheldon.co.uk
Hill & Smith Holdings plc, Unit 2 Highlands Court, Cranmore Avenue, Shirley, Solihull, West Midlands, B90 4LE Tel: 0121-704 7430 Fax: 0121-704 7439 E-mail: enquiries@hsholdings.co.uk
L.F. Hoare Ltd, Unit 18, Shrivenham Hundred Business Park, Majors Road, Watchfield, Swindon, SN6 8TZ Tel: (01793) 783880 Fax: (01793) 782977 E-mail: info@welding.fsnet.co.uk
Samuel Hodge Ltd, 2 Bluecoats Avenue, Hertford, SG14 1PB Tel: (01992) 558675 Fax: (01992) 581881
Holderness Energy Group Ltd, 9-11 Godmans Lane, Kirk Ella, Hull, HU10 7NX Tel: (01482) 652632 Fax: (01482) 651295 E-mail: bernet@ukgateway.net
Hunt & Co. (Bournemouth) Ltd, PO Box 3470, Sherborne, Dorset, DT9 4YZ Tel: (01935) 814848 Fax: (01935) 814333
Imi, Lakeside, Birmingham Business Park, Birmingham, B37 7UX Tel: 0121-717 3700 Fax: 0121-717 3701
Inchcape Ford, 245 Finchampstead Road, Wokingham, Berkshire, RG40 3JS Tel: 0118-936 1100 Fax: 0118-979 7135
Inchcape Motors International P.L.C., 22A St. James Square, London, SW1Y 5LP Tel: (020) 7546 0011 Fax: (020) 7546 0010 E-mail: contact@inchcape.com
Intelek Properties Ltd, South Marston Park, South Marston Park, Swindon, SN3 4TR Tel: (01793) 827000 Fax: (01793) 827578 E-mail: sales@intelek.plc.uk
Intellect Computers, 12 Scarsdale Place, Buxton, Derbyshire, SK17 6EF Tel: (01298) 70055 Fax: (01298) 70066 E-mail: enquiries@oxin.net
Intereurope Ltd, 21-23 East Street, Fareham, Hampshire, PO16 0BZ Tel: (01329) 823047 Fax: (01329) 822058
Invensys P.L.C., Portland House, Bressend Place, London, SW1E 5BF Tel: (020) 7834 3848 Fax: (020) 7834 3879 E-mail: sales@invensys.com
J W Holdings, 4th Floor, Regant Centre, Regant Road, Aberdeen, AB11 5NS Tel: (01224) 890022 Fax: (01224) 582734
James Drewitt & Son Ltd, 865 Ringwood Road, West Howe, Bournemouth, BH11 8IW Tel: (01202) 575757 Fax: (01202) 582500
Jardine Lloyds Underwriting Agents Ltd, Jardine House, 6 Crutched Friars, London, EC3N 2HT Tel: (020) 7528 4444 Fax: (020) 7528 4488
▶ Jotun Paints Ltd, Stather Road, Flixborough, Scunthorpe, South Humberside, DN15 8RR Tel: (01724) 400000 Fax: (01724) 400100 E-mail: enquiries@jotun.co.uk
Jourdan plc, Elm House, Elmer St North, Grantham, Lincolnshire, NG31 6RE Tel: (01476) 403456 Fax: (01476) 403458 E-mail: jda@jourdanplc.fsnet.co.uk
K B Benfield Group Holdings Ltd, 88 Paynes Lane, Coventry, CV1 5LJ Tel: (024) 7622 7557 Fax: (024) 7622 1217 E-mail: mail@benfieldgroup.co.uk
Kall Kwik UK Ltd, Kall Kwik House, 106 Pembroke Road, Ruislip, Middlesex, HA4 8NW Tel: (0500) 872060 Fax: (01895) 872111 E-mail: info@kallkwik.co.uk
Killby & Gayford Group Ltd, Osborne House, 9 - 11 Macauley Road, London, SW4 0QP Tel: (020) 7498 9898 Fax: (020) 7498 0838 E-mail: info@killbygayford.co.uk
Kingfisher P.L.C, 3 Sheldon Square, London, W2 6PX Tel: (020) 7372 8008 Fax: (020) 7644 1001
Kvaerner P.L.C., Kvaerner House, 68 Hammersmith Road, London, W14 8YW Tel: (020) 7339 1082 Fax: (020) 7339 1100
Lafarge Cement Ltd, Manor Court, Chilton, Didcot, Oxfordshire, OX11 0RN Tel: (01235) 448400 Fax: (01235) 448600
Laird Group Ltd, 3 St. James's Square, London, SW1Y 4JU Tel: (020) 7468 4040 Fax: (020) 7839 2921 E-mail: info@laird-plc.co.uk
Lakeland Investments Ltd, Estate Office, Lowtheriu Trust, Penrith, Cumbria, CA10 2HG Tel: (01931) 712577 Fax: (01931) 712679 E-mail: john.r@lowther.co.uk
Lithgow Factoring Ltd, Langbank, Port Glasgow, Renfrewshire, PA14 6YG Tel: (01475) 540692 Fax: (01475) 540558 E-mail: admin@lithgows.co.uk
London Transport Ltd, 55 Broadway, London, SW1H 0BD Tel: (020) 7222 5600 Fax: (020) 7918 4093
Lookers plc, 776 Chester Road, Stretford, Manchester, M32 0QH Tel: 0161-291 0043 Fax: 0161-864 2363 E-mail: administrator@lookers.co.uk
The Lord Group Ltd, Oak Mill Mellor Street, Rochdale, Lancashire, OL12 6UY Tel: (01706) 341311 Fax: (01706) 861810 E-mail: info@thelordgroup.co.uk
Lumley Letsure Ltd, Hargrave House, Belmont Road, Maidenhead, Berkshire, SL6 6TB Tel: (01628) 581500 Fax: (01628) 581401
M K Services, 199 Middlewood Road, Sheffield, S6 4HD Tel: 0114-232 6394 Fax: 0114-285 2189
Macfarlane Group plc, 21 Newton Place, Glasgow, G3 7PY Tel: 0141-333 9666 Fax: 0141-333 1988
Marbaix Holdings Ltd, Marbaix House, Wella Road, Basingstoke, Hampshire, RG22 4AG Tel: (01256) 473141 Fax: (01256) 462352
Marsh Mclennan & Companies, 1 Tower Place West, London, EC3R 5BU Tel: (020) 7357 1000 Fax: (020) 7929 2705
Mayborn Group P.L.C., Dylon House, Worsley Bridge Road, London, SE26 5HD Tel: (020) 8663 4801 E-mail: dylonimp@dylon.co.uk
Metalrax Group plc, Ardath Road, Birmingham, B38 9PN Tel: 0121-433 3444 Fax: 0121-433 3325 E-mail: info@toolspec.co.uk
Monopol Holdings Ltd, Oakley House, Dennis Road, Widnes, Cheshire, WA8 0YQ Tel: 0151-424 4121 Fax: 0151-423 3417 E-mail: mail@monopol.co.uk
The Morgan Crucible Co. P.L.C., Quadrant, 55-57 High Street, Windsor, Berkshire, SL4 1LP Tel: (01753) 837000 Fax: (01753) 850872
James Neill Holdings Ltd, Atlas Way, Atlas North, Sheffield, S4 7QQ Tel: 0114-281 4242 Fax: 0114-281 4201 E-mail: sales@neill-tools.co.uk
Nestor Healthcare Group P.L.C., The Colonnades, Beaconsfield Court, Beaconsfield Road, Hatfield, Hertfordshire, AL10 8HU Tel: (01707) 255635 Fax: (0845) 8501435 E-mail: info@nestorplc.co.uk
North Gate P.L.C., Norflex House, Allington Way, Darlington, County Durham, DL1 4DY Tel: (01325) 467558 Fax: (01325) 381009 E-mail: info@northgateplc.com
P & O Steam Navigation Co, Peninsular House, 79 Pall Mall, London, SW1Y 5EJ Tel: (020) 7930 4343 Fax: (020) 7930 8572 E-mail: groupinformation@pogroup.com
P&O Property Accounts Ltd, 247 Tottenham Court Road, London, W1T 7HH Tel: (020) 7637 1400 Fax: (020) 7631 4280
Paice Ventilation Ltd, 5 Vinegar Hill, Alconbury Weston, Huntingdon, Cambridgeshire, PE28 4JA Tel: (01480) 890778
Palmer & Harvey Mclane Holdings Ltd, 106 112 Davigdor Road, Hove, East Sussex, BN3 1RE Tel: (01273) 222100 Fax: (01273) 222101
Perrott Engineering Group Ltd, Woodroyd, Lightcliffe, Halifax, West Yorkshire, HX3 8PS Tel: (01422) 202575 Fax: (01422) 202959
Pertemps Group, Main Road, Meriden, Coventry, CV7 7LA Tel: (01676) 525598 Fax: (01676) 525259
Peter Black Europe Ltd, Lawkholme Lane, Keighley, West Yorkshire, BD21 3BB Tel: (01535) 661131 Fax: (01535) 609973 E-mail: pbh@peterblack.co.uk
PGI Group P.L.C., 81 Carter Lane, London, EC4V 5EP Tel: (020) 7236 6135 Fax: (020) 7248 1081
Polymark International P.L.C., Polymark House, Abbeydale Road, Wembley, Middlesex, HA0 1LQ Tel: (020) 8991 0011 Fax: (020) 8998 8080 E-mail: sales@technographics.co.uk
Pressac Communications Ltd, Glaisdale Dr West, Nottingham, NG8 4GY Tel: 0115-936 5200 Fax: 0115-936 5252 E-mail: sales@presscom.co.uk
Purico Ltd, Environment House, 6 Union Road, Nottingham, NG3 1FH Tel: 0115-901 3000 Fax: 0115-901 3100 E-mail: sales@purico.co.uk
Quibell & Son Holdings Ltd, Stepney Lane, Hull, HU5 1LJ Tel: (01482) 342177 Fax: (01482) 440296 E-mail: info@quibell.co.uk
Rank.Com, 6 Connaught Place, London, W2 2ET Tel: (020) 7766 1111 Fax: (020) 7262 9886 E-mail: enquiries@rank.com
Reed Elsevier Group plc, Second Floor, Grand Buildings, London, WC2N 5JR Tel: (020) 7930 7077 Fax: (020) 7166 5799 E-mail: strand.reception@reedelsevier.com
Reekie Engineering Ltd, Baden Powell Road, Kirkton Industrial Estate, Arbroath, Angus, DD11 3LS Tel: (01241) 871997 Fax: (01241) 877419
Rio Tinto P.L.C., 6 St. Jamess Square, London, SW1Y 4LD Tel: (020) 7930 2399 Fax: (020) 7930 3249 E-mail: sales@riotinto.co.uk
Roadcare Ltd, Roadcare House, New Works Road, Low Moor, Bradford, West Yorkshire, BD12 0RU Tel: (01274) 606770 Fax: (01274) 602802
Roetan Holdings Ltd, Roetan House, Thorns Road, Brierley Hill, West Midlands, DY5 2PF Tel: (01384) 424227 Fax: (01384) 424906
▶ Rowe Group of Companies, Cardrew Industrial Estate, Cardrew Business Park, Redruth, Cornwall, TR15 1SP Tel: (01209) 310800 Fax: (01209) 210140 E-mail: enquiries@rowegroup.co.uk
Royal & Sun Alliance Insurance Group P.L.C., 1 Bartholomew La, London, EC2N 2AB Tel: (0845) 0772772 Fax: (01403) 232111
Ryland Group Services Ltd, School House, St Philip's Court, Birmingham, B46 3AD Tel: (01675) 466566 Fax: (01675) 466568
Andrew Scott Ltd, The Grange, Margam, Port Talbot, West Glamorgan, SA13 2SP Tel: (01639) 889800 Fax: (01639) 889829 E-mail: asl@andrewscott.co.uk
Scottish Tanning Industries Ltd, 1 Seedhill, Paisley, Renfrewshire, PA1 1JL Tel: 0141-847 4520 Fax: 0141-848 7246 E-mail: enquiries@scottishleathergroup.com
Seabourne Group P.L.C., Unit 13, Saxon Way Trading Centre, Saxon Way, Harmondsworth, West Drayton, Middlesex, UB7 0LW Tel: (020) 7536 6360 Fax: (020) 7987 9889
Senior Engineering Investments Ltd, 59-61 High Street, Rickmansworth, Hertfordshire, WD3 1RH Tel: (01923) 775547 Fax: (01923) 896027 E-mail: info@seniorplc.com
Shaftsbury P.L.C., Pegasus House, 37-43 Sackville Street, London, W1S 3DL Tel: (020) 7333 8118 Fax: (020) 7333 0660 E-mail: shaftesbury@shaftesbury.co.uk
Sheldon Industrial Cleaners Ltd, 117-122 High Street, Bordesley, Birmingham, B12 0JU Tel: 0121-772 6001 Fax: 0121-771 0075 E-mail: mail@sheldon.uk.com
Shepherd Building Group Ltd, Huntington House, Jockey Lane, Huntington, York, YO32 9XW Tel: (01904) 650700 Fax: (01904) 650889 E-mail: information@shepherd-buildinggroup.com
Morgan Sindall P.L.C., 77 Newman Street, London, W1T 3EW Tel: (020) 7307 9200 Fax: (020) 7307 9201
F.P. Smith (Holdings) Ltd, Garton House, 179A Newark Avenue, Peterborough, PE1 4NL Tel: (01733) 344800 Fax: (01733) 560392
Stirling Group P.L.C., Union Bank, King Street, Knutsford, Cheshire, WA16 6EF Tel: (01565) 633111 Fax: (01565) 633555 E-mail: adrian.pettiford@stirlinggroup.com
John Swire & Sons Ltd, Swire House, 59 Buckingham Gate, London, SW1E 6AJ Tel: (020) 7834 7717 Fax: (020) 7630 0353
T & R Group Ltd, 15-16 Woodbridge Meadows, Guildford, Surrey, GU1 1BJ Tel: (01483) 568281 Fax: (01483) 504961 E-mail: sales@transformers.co.uk
Tex Holdings plc, Claydon Industrial Park, Great Blakenham, Ipswich, IP6 0NL Tel: (01473) 830144 Fax: (01473) 832545 E-mail: cap@tex-holdings.co.uk
Thama Holdings Ltd, Sharrocks Street, Wolverhampton, WV1 3RP Tel: (01902) 457575 Fax: (01902) 457797

HOLDING COMPANIES OR GROUPS

– *continued*

The Thomson Corporation P.L.C., 1st Floor, 180 Wardour Street, London, W1A 4YG Tel: (020) 7437 9787 Fax: (020) 7734 0561
G.F. Tomlinson Group Ltd, 16 City Road, Derby, DE1 3RQ Tel: (01332) 296565 Fax: (01322) 381510 E-mail: office@gftomlinson.co.uk
Toshiba of Europe Ltd, Audrey House, Ely Place, London, EC1N 6SN Tel: (020) 7242 7295 Fax: (020) 7421 7626
Toye & Co. P.L.C., 19-21 Great Queen Street, London, WC2B 5BE Tel: (020) 7242 0471 Fax: (020) 7831 8692 E-mail: gqf@toye.demon.co.uk
Turnbull Scott & Co. Ltd, 5 Spring Lakes, Deadbrook Lane, Aldershot, Hampshire, GU12 4UH Tel: (01252) 343949 Fax: (01252) 343939 E-mail: enquiries@turnbullscott.co.uk
Tyco Fire and Intergrated Solutions Ltd, Tyco Park, Grimshaw Lane, Newton Heath, Manchester, M40 2WL Tel: 0161-205 2321 Fax: 0161-455 4459
Umeco plc, Concorde House, 24 Warwick New Road, Leamington Spa, Warwickshire, CV32 5JG Tel: (01926) 331800 Fax: (01926) 312680
Unilever Overseas Holdings Ltd, PO Box 68, London, EC4P 4BQ Tel: (020) 7822 5252 Fax: (020) 7822 5898 E-mail: press-office.london@unilever.com
Viacom Networks Italia Ltd, 2nd Floor UK House, London, W1D 1DS Tel: (020) 7478 5240 Fax: (020) 7478 5250 E-mail: info@viacom.com
Vitec Group plc, 1 Wheatfield Way, Kingston upon Thames, Surrey, KT1 2TU Tel: (020) 8939 4650 Fax: (020) 8939 4680 E-mail: info@vitecgroup.com
Volex Group plc, Dornoch House, Kelvin Close, Birchwood, Warrington, WA3 7JX Tel: (01925) 830101 Fax: (01925) 830141
Ward Holdings Ltd, 2 Ash Tree Lane, Chatham, Kent, ME5 7BZ Tel: (01634) 855111 Fax: (01634) 577172 E-mail: inbox@ward-homes.co.uk
Watts Clift Holdings Ltd, Westgate, Aldridge, Walsall, WS9 8DJ Tel: (01922) 743360 Fax: (01922) 743362
Weir Group P.L.C., 20 Waterloo Street, Glasgow, G2 6DB Tel: 0141-637 7111 Fax: 0141-221 9789 E-mail: investor-relations@wg.weir.co.uk
Wellman P.L.C., Newfield Road, Oldbury, West Midlands, B69 3ET Tel: 0121-601 3000 Fax: 0121-543 0010
West Hartlepool Steam Navigation Co. Ltd, Kepwick Mill, Kepwick, Thirsk, North Yorkshire, YO7 4BH Tel: (01845) 537888 Fax: (01845) 537793 E-mail: mail@whsn.co.uk
Whatman International Ltd, Springfield Mill, Sandling Road, Maidstone, Kent, ME14 2LE Tel: (01622) 676670 Fax: (01622) 677011 E-mail: info@whatman.com
Whitworth Holdings Ltd, Victoria Mills, London Road, Wellingborough, Northamptonshire, NN8 2DT Tel: (01933) 443444 Fax: (01933) 222523E-mail: enquiries@whitworthbros.ltd.uk
William Hill plc, Greenside House, 50 Station Road, London, N22 7TP Tel: (020) 8918 3600 Fax: (020) 8918 3726 E-mail: name.@williamhill.co.uk
William Sinclair Holdings Public Ltd Company, Firth Road, Lincoln, LN6 7AH Tel: (01522) 537561 Fax: (01522) 560648 E-mail: info@william-sinclair.co.uk
Wolseley P.L.C., Park View 1220, Arlington Business Park, Theale, Reading, RG7 4GA Tel: 0118-929 8700 Fax: 0118-929 8701
Worcestershire Metal Holdings Ltd, Trentham House, 40 Red Lion Street, Alvechurch, Birmingham, B48 7LF Tel: 0121-445 3316 Fax: 0121-447 7053
T. Wright & Son (Holdings) Ltd, Main Street, Fountain Road, Hull, HU2 0LA Tel: (01482) 326845 Fax: (01482) 323636 E-mail: enquiry@wrightgroup.co.uk
Yule Catto & Co plc, Central Road, Harlow, Essex, CM20 2BH Tel: (01279) 442791 Fax: (01279) 641360 E-mail: info@yulecatto.com

HOLE CUTTERS

Jancy Engineering Inc, New Hall Hey Road, Rossendale, Lancashire, BB4 6HR Tel: (01706) 229490 Fax: (01706) 830496 E-mail: sales@jancy.com
Q-Max (Electronics) Ltd, Bilton Road, Bletchley, Milton Keynes, MK1 1HW Tel: (01908) 368006 Fax: (01908) 270483
Rotabroach, Imperial Works, Sheffield Road, Tinsley, Sheffield, S9 2YL Tel: 0114-221 2510 Fax: 0114-221 2563 E-mail: info@rotabroach.co.uk
S M L, 3 Little Common, Stanmore, Middlesex, HA7 3BZ Tel: (020) 8954 7302 Fax: (020) 8954 1703 E-mail: punches@sml.co.uk
Tedbar Tinker Hire, 53 Carlisle Street, Sheffield, S4 7LJ Tel: 0114-275 3666 Fax: 0114-275 4183 E-mail: sales@tedbartinkerhire.co.uk

HOLE MAKING TOOLS

Formbend Ltd, Unit 4-5 Charles St Industrial Estate, Charles Street, West Bromwich, West Midlands, B70 0AZ Tel: 0121-557 0555 Fax: 0121-557 0888 E-mail: sales@formbend.com

HOLIDAY CHALETS

▶ Hoe Grange Holidays, Brassington, Matlock, Derbyshire, DE4 4HP Tel: 01629 540261

HOLIDAY HOME CLOSED CIRCUIT TELEVISION (CCTV) SYSTEMS

▶ Home Entertainment & Management Systems, 124 Harborough Road, Rushden, Northamptonshire, NN10 0LP Tel: (09065) 840201 Fax: (08701) 638572 E-mail: info@heams.co.uk

HOLIDAY HOME LETTING AGENTS

▶ Beach Huts.com, 23 Richmond Park Avenue, Bournemouth, BH8 9DL Tel: (01202) 315437 E-mail: beach-huts@jxwd.co.uk
▶ Brennan Lettings & Property Management, Weddington Road, Nuneaton, Warwickshire, CV10 0EG Tel: (024) 7635 2537
▶ Coastal Cottage, 26 North Road, Kingsdown, Deal, Kent, CT14 8HP Tel: 01304 367585
▶ French Property, PO Box 46, Wirral, Merseyside, CH60 9LR Tel: (07747) 888181 E-mail: frenchproperty@ic24.net
▶ Hoe Grange Holidays, Brassington, Matlock, Derbyshire, DE4 4HP Tel: 01629 540261
▶ Holhomes, The Pavilion, Torpenhow, Montgomery Hill, Wirral, Merseyside, CH48 1NF Tel: 0151-625 1104
▶ Homes Go Fast, Floor 6, 456-458 Strand, London, WC2R 0DZ Tel: (0845) 4581413 E-mail: sales@homesgofast.com
▶ Klosters Chalet, 19 Blakesley Avenue, LONDON, W5 2DN Tel: 020 8810 5657 E-mail: chalet@klosterschalet.com
▶ Last Minute Cottages, Pondmead, Seldon Farm, Monkokehampton, Winkleigh, Devon, EX19 8RY Tel: (01837) 811150 E-mail: enquiries@lastminute-cottages.co.uk
mrs c bowen, 80 Quarrysprings, Harlow, Essex, CM20 3HS Tel: 07916 226171 Fax: 01279 869605 E-mail: hotelbooked@yahoo.co.uk
▶ NP Residential Management, 85 Granville Avenue, Northborough, Peterborough, PE6 9DE Tel: (0870) 7574461
▶ Pipe Flow (Worthing) Ltd, 14 Third Avenue, Worthing, West Sussex, BN14 9NZ Tel: 01903 236714 E-mail: pipeflow@aol.com
▶ RS Villas, Caxton House, Caxton Avenue, Blackpool, FY2 9AP Tel: (01253) 591169 E-mail: info@rsvillas.com
Skiathos Villa Rentals, 1 Tower View, Uckfield, East Sussex, TN22 1TP Tel: (01825) 763328 E-mail: webmaster@skiathosvillarentals.com
▶ Spain Property, PO Box 46, Wirral, Merseyside, CH60 9LR Tel: 0774 788 8181
▶ Tregrehan Garden, Tregrehan House, Par, Cornwall, PL24 2SJ Tel: (01726) 814389

HOLIDAY MAGAZINES

▶ Ecosse Unique, Lilliesleaf, Melrose, Roxburghshire, TD6 9JD Tel: (01835) 870779 Fax: (01835) 870417 E-mail: mark@uniquescotland.com

HOLLOW BORE BARS/SHAFTS

Bored Bar Engineering Ltd, New Street, Halfway, Sheffield, S20 3GH Tel: 0114-248 3631 Fax: 0114-247 7133 E-mail: sales@bored-bar.co.uk
Darren Sbo, Canklow Meadows Industrial Estate, Rotherham, South Yorkshire, S60 2XL Tel: (01709) 722600 Fax: (01709) 722657 E-mail: pspeechley@darron.co.uk
Keeton,Sons & Co.,Limited, Keetona House, Acres Hill Lane, Sheffield, S9 4LR Tel: 0114-242 0328 Fax: 0114-261 8860 E-mail: keetons@keetons.com

HOLLOW BORED STEEL BARS

Darren Sbo, Canklow Meadows Industrial Estate, Rotherham, South Yorkshire, S60 2XL Tel: (01709) 722600 Fax: (01709) 722657 E-mail: pspeechley@darron.co.uk
Energy Alloys, Chesterfield Trading Estate, Carrwood Road, Sheepbridge, Chesterfield, Derbyshire, S41 9QB Tel: (01246) 264500 Fax: (01246) 264550 E-mail: imsuk.energy@ims-group.com
Wyko Tubes, Vauxhall Street, Queens Cross, Dudley, W. Midlands, DY1 1TA Tel: (01384) 237816 Fax: (01384) 457463 E-mail: sales@wyko-tubes.co.uk

HOLLOW CATHODE LAMPS

Chandos Intercontinental, 6 St Anns Close, Chapel-en-le-Frith, High Peak, Derbyshire, SK23 9SG Tel: (01298) 814949 Fax: (01298) 814949 E-mail: chandos6@highpeak14.freeserve.co.uk

HOLLOW GLASS BLOCKS OR BRICKS

Glass Block Outlet, PO Box 272, Liverpool, L13 7DA Tel: (07940) 895369 Fax: (0845) 2262683 E-mail: info@glassblockoutlet.co.uk
Glassblock Warehouse Ltd, Suite 111, 79 Friar Street, Worcester, WR1 2NT Tel: (01886) 833891 Fax: (01886) 832534 E-mail: 1glassblocks@tiscali.co.uk

HOLLOW STEEL SECTIONS

Barnes Morris Steels, Bay 3 5 Grazebrook Industrial Park, Peartree Lane, Dudley, West Midlands, DY2 0XW Tel: (01384) 233393 Fax: (01384) 253111 E-mail: info@barnesmorris.co.uk

HOLLOW-WARE MANUFACTURE OR DISTRIBUTION, *See headings for particular types*

HOLLOW-WARE SEMIFINISHED PRODUCT, *See Metal Spinners/Spinnings etc; also other headings for particular types*

HOLOGRAMS

A P I Foils Ltd, Loughborough University, Ashby Road, Loughborough, Leicester, LE11 3TU Tel: (01509) 265232 Fax: (01509) 232772
A P I Foils Ltd, Astor Road, Salford, M50 1BB Tel: 0161-789 8131 Fax: 0161-707 5315 E-mail: marketing@apigroup.com
Applied Holographics plc, 40 Phoenix Road, Washington, Tyne & Wear, NE38 0AD Tel: 0191-417 5434 Fax: 0191-417 6591 E-mail: sales@applied-holographics.com
▶ Assistpoint Limited, 40 Allendale Road, Barnsley, South Yorkshire, S75 1BJ Tel: 0114 2387569 E-mail: sales@assistpoint.co.uk
Hi Tec Interface Ltd, Unit 15 The Wenta Business Centre, Colne Way, Watford, WD24 7ND Tel: (020) 8958 4735 Fax: (020) 8958 9770 E-mail: hitec@himet.com

HOLOGRAPHIC LABELS

L G L Protectaseal Ltd, Unit 8 & 9, Hitchin Road Industrial Estate, Oxen Road, Luton, LU2 0DZ Tel: (01582) 422976 Fax: (01582) 404082 E-mail: contact@protectaseal.com
Opsec Security Group P.L.C., Braxted House, 2 Penman Way, Enderby, Leicester, LE19 1ST Tel: 0116-282 2000 Fax: 0116-282 2100

HOLOGRAPHIC PACKAGING

▶ Momentum Packaging Ltd, Enterprise Way, Lowton, Warrington, WA3 2BP Tel: (01942) 267211 Fax: (01942) 267200 E-mail: info@foilco.co.uk

HOLOGRAPHIC PAPER OR BOARD

▶ A P I Group plc, Second Avenue, Poynton, Stockport, Cheshire, SK12 1ND Tel: (01625) 858700 Fax: (01625) 858701 E-mail: enquiries@apilaminates.com
Foilco Ltd, Enterprise Way, Lowton, Warrington, WA3 2BP Tel: (01942) 262622 Fax: (01942) 267200 E-mail: sales@foilco.co.uk

HOME AUTOMATION SYSTEMS

▶ East Technology Integrators, Lyndhurst, Seer Mead, Seer Green, Beaconsfield, Buckinghamshire, HP9 2QL Tel: 0845 0560245 E-mail: sales@east-ti.co.uk
▶ ISEC Solutions, Meadowcroft, Nottingham Road, Ravenshead, Nottingham, NG15 9HP Tel: 01623 792200 Fax: 01623 792293 E-mail: mark@isec-solutions.co.uk
▶ Reality Logic Ltd, 28 Harsfold Road, Rustington, Littlehampton, West Sussex, BN16 2QE Tel: (01903) 775352 Fax: (0870) 4589021 E-mail: jeremy.aston@realitylogic.com

HOME CINEMA EQUIPMENT

▶ Ovation Audio Visual Systems, Belgrave Business Centre, 45 Frederick Street, Edinburgh, EH2 1EP Tel: (0845) 6448851 Fax: 0131-666 2556 E-mail: sales@ovationaudiovisual.com
P J Hifi, 3 Bridge Street, Guildford, Surrey, GU1 4RY Tel: (01483) 504801 Fax: (01483) 504801 E-mail: info@pjhifi.co.uk

HOME CINEMA INSTALLATION

▶ Ovation Audio Visual Systems, Belgrave Business Centre, 45 Frederick Street, Edinburgh, EH2 1EP Tel: (0845) 6448851 Fax: 0131-666 2556 E-mail: sales@ovationaudiovisual.com
P J Hifi, 3 Bridge Street, Guildford, Surrey, GU1 4RY Tel: (01483) 504801 Fax: (01483) 504801 E-mail: info@pjhifi.co.uk
▶ Visual Sounds Ltd, 891 Old Lode Lane, Solihull, West Midlands, B92 8JF Tel: 0121-242 3279 E-mail: enquiries@visualsounds.co.uk

HOME DIAGNOSTIC HEALTH TEST KITS

SelfDiagnosis Limited, P O Box 162, Stockport, Cheshire, SK7 3WJ Tel: 07699 392121
▶ Simplicity Health, PO Box 4087, Kingswinford, West Midlands, DY6 9WY Tel: (0871) 2500120 Fax: (0871) 2500121 E-mail: info@simplicityhealth.co.uk

HOME ENTERTAINMENT SYSTEMS

Bose Ltd, 138-139 Cheshire Oaks Outlet Village, Kinsey Road, Ellesmere Port, CH65 9JJ Tel: 0151-357 8300 Fax: (08707) 415546 E-mail: cheshire_oaks@bose.com

HOME EQUITY LOAN FINANCIAL SERVICES

▶ Sophiee Parker, 12 Jupiter House, Calleva Park, Aldermaston, Reading, RG7 8NN Tel: (0800) 0015446 E-mail: sophiee.parker@gmail.com
▶ Shakespeare finance ltd, 501 International House, 223 Regent Street, London, W1B 2EB Tel: (0808) 1602576 E-mail: webmaster@go4ukloans.co.uk
▶ Shakespeare Finance Ltd, 11 Parade House, 135 The Parade, High Street, Watford, WD17 1NA Tel: (020) 7097 3654 E-mail: m.wali@shakespearefinance.co.uk

HOME MADE BEER INGREDIENTS

Inbev Ireland Ltd, Ulster Brewery, Glen Road, Belfast, BT11 8BY Tel: (028) 9030 1301 Fax: (028) 9062 4884
Muntons Agricultural Merchants, Needham Road, Stowmarket, Suffolk, IP14 2AG Tel: (01449) 618300 Fax: (01449) 677800 E-mail: grain@muntons.com

HOME MAGAZINES

Hamerville Magazines Ltd, Regal House, Regal Way, Watford, WD24 4YF Tel: (01923) 237799 Fax: (01923) 246901 E-mail: office@hamerville.co.uk

HOME OFFICE FURNITURE

▶ Your Home Furniture, 145 West Street, Banbury, Oxfordshire, OX16 3HE Tel: (0871) 2006251 Fax: (0871) 2006251 E-mail: enquiries@yourhomefurniture.co.uk

HOME TEXTILES

▶ Custom Images Ltd, 12 Mill Brow, Armathwaite, Carlisle, CA4 9PJ Tel: (01697) 472522 E-mail: julie@customimages.co.uk
▶ TD Textiles Direct, Wilson Road, Huyton, Liverpool, L36 6JG Tel: 0151-489 2121

HOMEOPATHIC MEDICINES

▶ Touch Alternative Health, PO Box 4462, London, W1A 7NX Tel: 020 7935 2205 Fax: 020 7935 2008 E-mail: getintouch@londontouch.com

HOMEOPATHIC VETERINARY MEDICINES

Wellington Pharmacy, 39 Knightsbridge, London, SW1X 7NL Tel: (020) 7235 2653 Fax: (020) 7235 0158E-mail: wellington1@btconnect.com

HOMOGENISERS

G C Hurrell & Co. Ltd, Knight Road, Rochester, Kent, ME2 2AH Tel: (01634) 718330 Fax: (01634) 710601 E-mail:

▶ indicates data change since last edition

HOMOGENISERS – *continued*

Silverson Machines Ltd, Waterside, Chesham, Buckinghamshire, HP5 1PQ Tel: (01494) 786331 Fax: (01494) 791452 E-mail: sales@silverson.co.uk

HONEYCOMB CORE BOARD OR PANELS

Plascore (UK), PO Box 2, Cheltenham, Gloucestershire, GL54 5YR Tel: (0871) 918 1525 Fax: (0871) 918 1525 E-mail: info@coretexgroup.co.uk
QK Honeycomb Products Ltd, Creeting Road, Stowmarket, Suffolk, IP14 5AS Tel: (01449) 612145 Fax: (01449) 677604 E-mail: sales@qkhoneycomb.co.uk
Speirs Robertson Ltd, 42 Bedford Road, London, N2 9DA Tel: (01234) 823410 Fax: (0870) 7624234 E-mail: sales@robertson.co.uk
Technical Resin Bonders Ltd, 12 Clifton Road, Huntingdon, Cambridgeshire, PE29 7EN Tel: 0845 5314225 Fax: (01480) 414992 E-mail: sales@trbonders.co.uk

HONEYCOMB CORE LAMINATED SANDWICH PANELS

Bonded Components Ltd, Brookside, Glatton Road, Sawtry, Huntingdon, Cambridgeshire, PE28 5SB Tel: (01487) 831278 Fax: (01487) 832274
Speirs Robertson Ltd, 42 Bedford Road, London, N2 9DA Tel: (01234) 823410 Fax: (0870) 7624234 E-mail: sales@robertson.co.uk

HONING MACHINES

Apperley Honing Ltd, Alpha Works, Alstone La, Cheltenham, Glos, GL51 8ES Tel: (01242) 525868 Fax: (01242) 224738 E-mail: sales@apperleyhoning.co.uk
Equipment For You, PO Box 6, Cheltenham, Gloucestershire, GL51 9NJ Tel: (01242) 241822 Fax: (01242) 222994 E-mail: sales@3dsports.co.uk
Permat Machines Ltd, Station Road, Coleshill, Birmingham, B46 1JG Tel: (01675) 463351 Fax: (01675) 465816 E-mail: sales@permat.com
Sunnen Products Ltd, Enterprise House, Maxted Road Hemel Hempstead Industrial Estate, Hemel Hempstead, Hertfordshire, HP2 7BT Tel: (01442) 393939 Fax: (01442) 391212 E-mail: sales@sunnen.com

HONING SERVICES

Abrahone Engineering, Unit 4 Thornes Trading Estate, Wakefield, West Yorkshire, WF1 5QN Tel: (01924) 378733 Fax: (01924) 200014 E-mail: abrahone@btconnect.com
Apperley Honing Ltd, Alpha Works, Alstone La, Cheltenham, Glos, GL51 8ES Tel: (01242) 525868 Fax: (01242) 224738 E-mail: sales@apperleyhoning.co.uk
C A Honemaster Ltd, Unit 14 Malmesbury Road, Kingsditch Trading Estate, Cheltenham, Gloucestershire, GL51 9PL Tel: (01242) 584326 Fax: (01242) 226158 E-mail: kieran.reel@btconnect.com
C F Smith Precision Grinding, The Station, Station Hill, Overton, Basingstoke, Hampshire, RG25 3JH Tel: (01256) 770457 Fax: (01256) 771701 E-mail: cfsmith@btconnect.com
Enterprise Engineering Gloucester Ltd, Units D5-D6 Innsworth Technology Park, Innsworth Lane, Gloucester, GL3 1DL Tel: (01452) 731881 Fax: (01452) 731887 E-mail: dave@honing.co.uk
Holemoor Engineering Ltd, Shaw Road, Dudley, West Midlands, DY2 8TP Tel: (01384) 237574 Fax: (01384) 230013
Permat Machines Ltd, Station Road, Coleshill, Birmingham, B46 1JG Tel: (01675) 463351 Fax: (01675) 465816 E-mail: sales@permat.com
Titan Holdings Ltd, 334 Meanwood Road, Leeds, LS7 2JF Tel: 0113-262 4612 Fax: 0113-262 6557 E-mail: sales@titanhc.co.uk
Toolmasters Technical Ltd, Instanta Work, Charles Street, West Bromwich, West Midlands, B70 0AZ Tel: 0121-520 1889 Fax: 0121-520 1890 E-mail: sales@toolmasters.co.uk
V I Precision Grinders Ltd, Pingemead Farm, Pingewood, Reading, RG30 3UR Tel: 0118 9866546
W E C S Precision Ltd, Blenheim Road, Longmead Industrial Estate, Epsom, Surrey, KT19 9BE Tel: (01372) 741633 Fax: (01372) 740539 E-mail: npooles@wecsprecision.com

HONING STONE SEGMENTS

Abrahone Engineering, Unit 4 Thornes Trading Estate, Wakefield, West Yorkshire, WF1 5QN Tel: (01924) 378733 Fax: (01924) 200014 E-mail: abrahone@btconnect.com
Kayson Green Ltd, 9 Commerce Park, Commerce Way, Colchester, CO2 8HX Tel: (01206) 751500 Fax: (01206) 791916 E-mail: abrasives@kaysongreen.co.uk

HONING STONES OR OILSTONES OR WHETSTONES

Water Of Ayr, Dalmore, Stair, Mauchline, Ayrshire, KA5 5PA Tel: (01292) 591204

HONING TOOLS, *See also headings for particular types*

Bonnell Engineering Ltd, 28-33 Stewart Street, Wolverhampton, WV2 4JW Tel: (01902) 712855 Fax: (01902) 712855
Sunnen Products Ltd, Enterprise House, Maxted Road Hemel Hempstead Industrial Estate, Hemel Hempstead, Hertfordshire, HP2 7BT Tel: (01442) 393939 Fax: (01442) 391212 E-mail: sales@sunnen.com

HOOKS, SPRING

John Anslow Ltd, Stafford Street, Wednesbury, West Midlands, WS10 7JX Tel: 0121-556 1125 Fax: 0121-556 5414
Juraise (Springs) Ltd, Sugarbrook Mill, Buntsford Hill, Stoke Pound, Bromsgrove, Worcestershire, B60 3AR Tel: (01527) 878811 Fax: (01527) 877537 E-mail: adrian@juraise.com

HOPPER FEEDERS

Colormax Ltd, Unit 3, Stafford Park 12, Telford, Shropshire, TF3 3BJ Tel: (01952) 292101 Fax: (01952) 292761 E-mail: info@colormax.co.uk

HOPPERS

Colormax Ltd, Unit 3, Stafford Park 12, Telford, Shropshire, TF3 3BJ Tel: (01952) 292101 Fax: (01952) 292761 E-mail: info@colormax.co.uk
G M P (Banbury) Ltd, Unit 2, Power Park, Station Approach, Banbury, Oxfordshire, OX16 5AB Tel: (01295) 275300 Fax: (01295) 275400 E-mail: gmpb@globalnet.co.uk
Peter Cox Marketing Ltd, High Street, Wrestlingworth, Sandy, Bedfordshire, SG19 2EN Tel: (01767) 631733 Fax: (01767) 631722 E-mail: info@petercoxmarketing.co.uk

HORIZONTAL BLINDS

▶ Natural Blinds, PO Box 2082, Gloucester, GL3 3WX Tel: 0845 056 4415 Fax: 0845 056 4415 E-mail: info@naturalblinds.co.uk
▶ Windowcharm, Kent Road, Sheffield, S8 9RN Tel: (01709) 379092 Fax: 0114-255 8142

HORIZONTAL BORING

Advance Engineering HX Ltd, Park Road Buildings, Park Road, Elland, West Yorkshire, HX5 9HP Tel: (01422) 375228 Fax: (01422) 310433 E-mail: phillgibson@advanceengineering.fsbusiness.co.uk
Ajax Minerva Ltd, Edderthorpe Street, Bradford, West Yorkshire, BD3 9JX Tel: (01274) 735910 Fax: (01274) 307706 E-mail: ajax_minerva@hotmail.com
Bridgeforth Engineering, Unit 13-14, Belleknowes Industrial Estate, Inverkeithing, Fife, KY11 1HZ Tel: (01383) 413441 Fax: (01383) 418391 E-mail: sales@bridgeforthl.co.uk
Brookes Specialist Engineers Ltd, Gospel End Street, Sedgley, Dudley, West Midlands, DY3 3LS Tel: (01902) 882233 Fax: (01902) 885284 E-mail: mike@brookes-engineering.co.uk
Crowther Engineering Ltd, 52 Hutton Close, Crowther, Washington, Tyne & Wear, NE38 0AH Tel: 0191-417 9916 Fax: 0191-415 5136 E-mail: nick@crowthereng.co.uk
Dawton Engineers Ltd, Unit 11-12, Waleswood Road, Wales Bar, Sheffield, S26 5PY Tel: (01909) 515313 Fax: (01909) 515499 E-mail: enquiries@dawton.co.uk
Dixi & Associates, Unit 3 Riverstone Middlemarch Business Park, Coventry Tradin, Middlemarch Business Park, Coventry, CV3 4FJ Tel: (024) 7688 2108 Fax: (024) 7688 2115
Evans & White Manufacturing Ltd, Canal Street, Stourbridge, West Midlands, DY8 4LU Tel: (01384) 394731 Fax: (01384) 442603 E-mail: sandra@evansandwhite.co.uk
George Bros Engineers Ltd, Dyffryn Close, Swansea Enterprise Park, Swansea, SA6 8QG Tel: (01792) 790550 Fax: (01792) 701608
Moorgate Precision Engineering, Polymer House, Admin Road, Knowsley Industrial Park, Liverpool, L33 7TZ Tel: 0151-548 7766 Fax: 0151-548 7788 E-mail: ian@moorgate-precison.com
R & S Whiting, Oak Lodge, North Walsham Road, Norwich, NR6 7JG Tel: (01603) 425832 Fax: (01603) 787900
▶ S W S Machining Ltd, Progress Drive, Cannock, Staffordshire, WS11 0JE Tel: (01543) 504181 Fax: (01543) 573834 E-mail: sales@swsmachining.co.uk

HORIZONTAL BORING MACHINES

Alpenbury Ltd, 11 Gateway Industrial Estate, Parkgate, Rotherham, South Yorkshire, S62 6JL Tel: (01709) 528186 Fax: (01709) 528287 E-mail: enquiries@alpenbury.co.uk

HORIZONTAL CNC MACHINING CENTRES

▶ Saro Engineering Ltd, Unit 2, 64-66 Tregwilym Road, Rogerstone, Newport, Gwent, NP10 9EJ Tel: (01633) 892466

HORIZONTAL DRILLING

Avoidatrench Ltd, Brooks Lane, Middlewich, Cheshire, CW10 0JQ Tel: (01606) 831600 Fax: (01606) 831620 E-mail: admin@avoidatrench.co.uk
Stockton Drilling Ltd, Unit 15 Navigation Court, Calder Park, Wakefield, West Yorkshire, WF2 7BJ Tel: (01924) 242128 Fax: (01924) 253177 E-mail: info@stocktondrilling.com

HORIZONTAL FORM FILL AND SEAL PACKAGING EQUIPMENT

Adpak Machinery Systems Ltd, 3 Pendleside, Lomeshaye Industrial Estate, Nelson, Lancashire, BB9 6RY Tel: (01282) 601444 Fax: (01282) 612201 E-mail: info@adpak.co.uk

HORIZONTAL FORM FILLING/ SEALING MACHINERY

Gainsborough Engineering Co., Corringham Road Industrial Estate, Corringham Road, Gainsborough, Lincolnshire, DN21 1QB Tel: (01427) 617677 Fax: (01427) 810443 E-mail: info@gains-eng.co.uk

HORIZONTAL HONING MACHINES

Engis UK Ltd, Unit 9 Centenary Business Park, Station Road, Henley-on-Thames, Oxfordshire, RG9 1DS Tel: (01491) 411117 Fax: (01491) 412252 E-mail: sales@engis.uk.com
Equipment For You, PO Box 6, Cheltenham, Gloucestershire, GL51 9NJ Tel: (01242) 241822 Fax: (01242) 222994 E-mail: sales@3dsports.co.uk

HORIZONTAL MACHINING CENTRE MACHINE TOOLS

▶ Machine Tool Technologies Ltd. (MTT), 307 Ecroyd Suite, Turner Road, Lomeshaye Business Village, Nelson, Lancashire, BB9 7DR Tel: (01282) 607854 Fax: (01282) 607894 E-mail: info@mtt.uk.com

HORIZONTAL MACHINING CENTRES

▶ D S Technology Ltd, 43-45 Phoenix Park, Avenue Close, Nechells, Birmingham, B7 4NU Tel: 0121-359 3637 Fax: 0121-359 1135 E-mail: info@ds-technology.co.uk

HORIZONTAL MILLING MACHINES

▶ One Off Engineering Ltd, Simpson Street, Hyde, Cheshire, SK14 1BJ Tel: 0161-366 7276 Fax: 0161-366 7276 E-mail: oneoffeng@fsmail.net
Toyoda Mitsui Europe, Matrix House, Loughborough Motorway Trading Estate, Gelders Hall Road, Shepshed, Loughborough, Leicestershire, LE12 9NH Tel: (01509) 501700 Fax: (01509) 501730 E-mail: sales@toyoda-mitsui.com

HORN BUTTONS

James Grove & Sons Ltd, PO Box 5, Halesowen, West Midlands, B63 3UW Tel: 0121-550 4015 Fax: 0121-501 3905 E-mail: sales@jamesgroveandsons.co.uk

HORSE BOXES/TRAILERS

A Walter, Stones Tenement, Croford, Wiveliscombe, Taunton, Somerset, TA4 2TS Tel: (01984) 623624 Fax: (01984) 624768
Airlec Truck & Bus Parts, Unit 24 Tomlinson Business Park, Tomlinson Road, Leyland, PR25 2DY Tel: (01772) 433564 Fax: (01772) 433568 E-mail: sales@airlec.co.uk
Atacanter Horsebox Hire, Kimpton House Farm, Oldhurst Road, Woodhurst, Huntingdon, Cambridgeshire, PE28 3BY Tel: (01487) 840448 Fax: (01487) 840448 E-mail: claire@atacanterhorseboxhire.co.uk
Batley Body Builders Ltd, Thomas St, Bradford Road, Batley, West Yorkshire, WF17 8PR Tel: (01924) 473602 Fax: (01924) 471161
Beacon Horseboxes, The Haulage Yard, Wyck Beacon, Upper Rissington, Cheltenham, Gloucestershire, GL54 2NE Tel: (01451) 821289 Fax: (01451) 810423
Browns Coachworks Ltd, 282 Moira Road, Lisburn, County Antrim, BT28 2TU Tel: (028) 9262 1711 Fax: (028) 9262 1962 E-mail: info@brownscoachworks.com
▶ Commercial Window Supplies, Unit 4 Little Fountain Street, Morley, Leeds, LS27 9EN Tel: 0113-252 5544 Fax: 0113-252 5544
Country Vehicles Horse Box Manufacturer, Mount Pleasant Farm, Main St, Pymoor, Ely, Cambs, CB6 2DY Tel: 01353 698075
Gerald Dinnis Ltd, Tedburn Road, Whitestone, Exeter, EX4 2HF Tel: (01392) 811581 Fax: (01392) 811722 E-mail: info@whitehorsemotors.co.uk
▶ Equus Enterprises, Speddyd, Llandyrnog, Denbigh, Clwyd, LL16 4LE Tel: (01824) 790687 Fax: (01824) 790338 E-mail: equusenterprises@i12.com
Front Runner Race Horse Transport, Jennet Tree Lane, Madresfield, Malvern, Worcestershire, WR13 5BE Tel: (01905) 831161 Fax: (01905) 831161
H F B Trailers (Leek), Horton Head Farm, Horton, Leek, Staffordshire, ST13 8PQ Tel: (01538) 306212 Fax: (01538) 306396 E-mail: nathan@hfbtrailers.com
Hedgers Racehorse Transport, Nigel Hardy Transport, Melcroft, Eastergate Lane, Eastergate, Chichester, West Sussex, PO20 3SJ Tel: (01243) 543863 Fax: (01243) 543913
Hoof Aloof, 29 Oakwood Drive, Ravenshead, Nottingham, NG15 9DP Tel: (01623) 795628 Fax: (01623) 795628 E-mail: sales@hoofaloof.co.uk
Horseproud Containers, Main Road, Ryton, Tyne & Wear, NE40 3AG Tel: 0191-413 4936 Fax: 0191-413 1700
Huish Horseboxes, East Huish Farm, Tedburn St. Mary, Exeter, EX6 6AF Tel: (01647) 61716 Fax: (01647) 61716 E-mail: sales@huishengineering.co.uk
J H Commercials, West Park, Arlington, Barnstaple, Devon, EX31 4SN Tel: (01271) 850860
▶ J M & J M Ratcliffe, Manor Farm Stud, High Street, Chippenham, Ely, Cambridgeshire, CB7 5PR Tel: (01638) 720888 Fax: (01638) 721310
J Prescott, Lesser Marsh Farm, Station Road, Little Hoole, Preston, PR4 5LH Tel: (01772) 613688 Fax: (01772) 619561
M G Trevett Ltd, Winterborne Stickland, Blandford Forum, Dorset, DT11 0NT Tel: (01258) 880490 Fax: (01258) 880470
M K M Agriculture, Sun Valley Works, Woodend, Marston Moretaine, Bedford, MK43 0NJ Tel: (01234) 768889 Fax: (01234) 767935 E-mail: info@mkmagri.com
▶ Maneline Coachworks, Basil Road, West Dereham, King's Lynn, Norfolk, PE33 9RP Tel: (01366) 502254 Fax: (01366) 502254
David Murray Horseboxes Ltd, 5 Hartford Industrial Estate, Suthers Street, Oldham, OL9 7TQ Tel: 0161-628 2649 Fax: 0161-628 2649
Newmarket Racehorse Transport, Cricket Field Road, Newmarket, Suffolk, CB8 8BT Tel: (01638) 663155 Fax: (01638) 560894
Oakland Coachbuilders Ltd, Unit 3, KDO Business Centre, Little Witley, Worcester, WR6 6LR Tel: (01299) 896754 Fax: (01299) 896885 E-mail: oakland.horsebox@btconnect.com
Oakley Coachbuilders, High Cross, Ware, Hertfordshire, SG11 1AD Tel: (01920) 466781 Fax: (01920) 467895 E-mail: sales@oakleyhorseboxes.co.uk
Organisation Of Horse Box & Trailer Owners, Whitehill Farm, Hamstead Marshall, Newbury, Berkshire, RG20 0HP Tel: (01488) 657651 Fax: (01488) 657652 E-mail: sales@horsebox-rescue.co.uk
Shamrock Horseboxes Ltd, 5 Soham Rd, Fordham, Ely, Cambs, CB7 5LB Tel: 01638 723050 Fax: 01638 723051
Thorpe Horse Boxes, Tendring Road, Thorpe-le-Soken, Clacton-on-Sea, Essex, CO16 0AA Tel: (01255) 862411 Fax: (01255) 862340 E-mail: sales@thorpehorseboxes.com
Tills Horse Transport, Meadowside, Chartway Street, Kingswood, Maidstone, Kent, ME17 3QA Tel: (01622) 843675 Fax: (01622) 843675
Vehicle Window Centre, Unit 2-3 Ashley Estate, Carr Wood Road, Castleford, West Yorkshire, WF10 4SR Tel: (01977) 604977 Fax: (01977) 603466 E-mail: sales@horsebox.co.uk
W E Collier & Sons Ltd, 12 Soham Road, Fordham, Ely, Cambridgeshire, CB7 5LD Tel: (01638) 720045 Fax: (01638) 721442
Ifor Williams Trailers Ltd, The Smithy, Cynwyd, Corwen, Clwyd, LL21 0LB Tel: (01490) 412527 Fax: (01490) 412770 E-mail: sales@iwt.co.uk

HORSE FEED

Equimix Feeds & Saddlery, Sandy Lane, Titton, Stourport-on-Severn, Worcestershire, DY13 9QA Tel: (01299) 827744 Fax: (01299) 879470 E-mail: info@equimix.co.uk

HORSE FEED SUPPLEMENTS

▶ Chestnut Horse Feeds, Newnham Fields Farm, Willey, Rugby, Warwickshire, CV23 0SL Tel: (01455) 558808 Fax: (01455) 559401 E-mail: sales@anifeed.co.uk

▶ Denis Brinicombe Ltd, Fordton Trading Estate, Crediton, Devon, EX17 3BZ Tel: (01363) 775115 Fax: (01363) 776761 E-mail: info@brinicombe-equine.co.uk

Horse Power Self Drive Equine Transport, 7 Riverside, Storrington, Pulborough, West Sussex, RH20 4NN Tel: (01903) 746800 Fax: (0845) 1275210 E-mail: sales@horsebox-selfdrive.com

HORSE HEALTHCARE PRODUCTS

▶ Cherry Tree Pet Crematorium, Cherry Tree Farm, Pot Kiln Road, High Halden, Ashford, Kent, TN26 3HJ Tel: (01233) 850929 Fax: (01233) 850316 E-mail: cherrytree@petcrem.fsnet.co.uk

Horse Power Self Drive Equine Transport, 7 Riverside, Storrington, Pulborough, West Sussex, RH20 4NN Tel: (01903) 746800 Fax: (0845) 1275210 E-mail: sales@horsebox-selfdrive.com

▶ Horseswap.co.uk, East Lodge, Potterhanworth, Longhills, Branston, Lincoln, LN4 1HR Tel: (01522) 797131 Fax: (01522) 797131 E-mail: gaynor@horseswap.co.uk

HORSE LIVERY

Tudor Stud Farm Equestrian Centre, Tudor Stud Farm, Chinnor road, Bledlow Ridge, High Wycombe, Buckinghamshire, HP14 4AA Tel: 01494 481056 Fax: 01494 481056 E-mail: tracey-tudorstudfarm@hotmail.co.uk

HORSE MINERAL SALT BLOCKS OR LICKS

▶ Horseswap.co.uk, East Lodge, Potterhanworth, Longhills, Branston, Lincoln, LN4 1HR Tel: (01522) 797131 Fax: (01522) 797131 E-mail: gaynor@horseswap.co.uk

HORSE PAPER BEDDING

▶ Paul Garner, 4 Poplar Grove, Ravenfield, Rotherham, South Yorkshire, S65 4LJ Tel: (07737) 036085 E-mail: pj1racing@hotmail.com

HORSE RIDING EQUIPMENT

▶ Discount Equestrian Ltd, 197/199 Barnsley Road, Wombwell, Barnsley, South Yorkshire, S73 8DR Tel: 01226 270555 E-mail: sales@discountequestrian.co.uk

HORSE RUGS

▶ Equestrian Originals, 57 Severn Way, Bletchley, Milton Keynes, MK3 7QG Tel: (01908) 647555 E-mail: info@equestrian-originals.co.uk

HORSE STABLE ACCESSORIES

▶ Ashley Davies Livery & Competition Yard, Ysgubor Fach Farm, Crwbin, Kidwelly, Carmarthenshire, SA17 5EB Tel: (01269) 870831

▶ New Forest Horse Boxes Ltd, Peartree Cottage, Arnewood Bridge Road, Sway, Lymington, Hampshire, SO41 6ER Tel: (01590) 682633 Fax: (01590) 683497 E-mail: sales@newforesthorseboxes.co.uk

HORSE STABLES

▶ Bowser Bros, Stainton by Langworth, Lincoln, LN3 5BL Tel: (01673) 862423 Fax: (01673) 862423

▶ Ashley Davies Livery & Competition Yard, Ysgubor Fach Farm, Crwbin, Kidwelly, Carmarthenshire, SA17 5EB Tel: (01269) 870831

Tudor Stud Farm Equestrian Centre, Tudor Stud Farm, Chinnor road, Bledlow Ridge, High Wycombe, Buckinghamshire, HP14 4AA Tel: 01494 481056 Fax: 01494 481056 E-mail: tracey-tudorstudfarm@hotmail.co.uk

HORSE STUD SERVICES

▶ Cherry Tree Pet Crematorium, Cherry Tree Farm, Pot Kiln Road, High Halden, Ashford, Kent, TN26 3HJ Tel: (01233) 850929 Fax: (01233) 850316 E-mail: cherrytree@petcrem.fsnet.co.uk

▶ Ashley Davies Livery & Competition Yard, Ysgubor Fach Farm, Crwbin, Kidwelly, Carmarthenshire, SA17 5EB Tel: (01269) 870831

HORSE WEIGHING SYSTEMS

Marsden Weighing Machine Group, 47 Market Place, Henley-on-Thames, Oxfordshire, RG9 2AD Tel: (0845) 1307330 Fax: (0845) 1307440 E-mail: sales@marsdengroup.demon.co.uk

HORSEBOX FINANCE

▶ Business Jungle Ltd, Hammerain House, Hookstone Avenue, Harrogate, North Yorkshire, HG2 8ER Tel: 0845-838 2240 Fax: 0845-838 2260 E-mail: david@businessjungle.co.uk

▶ Liberte' Horsebox Hire, Unit 7, Greetby Place, East Gillibrands, Skelmersdale, Lancashire, WN8 9UL Tel: (01928) 740020 E-mail: info@libertehorseboxes.co.uk

▶ Wentworth Equine Travel - Self Drive Horseboxes, Elm Villas, Crazies Hill, Wargrave, RG10 8LU Tel: 07946 451629 E-mail: sales@wentworthequinetravel.co.uk

HORSEBOX MATS

▶ New Forest Horse Boxes Ltd, Peartree Cottage, Arnewood Bridge Road, Sway, Lymington, Hampshire, SO41 6ER Tel: (01590) 682633 Fax: (01590) 683497 E-mail: sales@newforesthorseboxes.co.uk

HORSEBOX REFURBISHMENT

Atacanter Horsebox Hire, Kimpton House Farm, Oldhurst Road, Woodhurst, Huntingdon, Cambridgeshire, PE28 3BY Tel: (01487) 840448 Fax: (01487) 840448 E-mail: claire@atacanterhorseboxhire.co.uk

▶ Commercial Bodies East Anglia, 9 Hurricane Way, Norwich, NR6 6EZ Tel: (01603) 484047 Fax: (01603) 417834 E-mail: mwcbea@freenet.co.uk

▶ Wentworth Equine Travel - Self Drive Horseboxes, Elm Villas, Crazies Hill, Wargrave, RG10 8LU Tel: 07946 451629 E-mail: sales@wentworthequinetravel.co.uk

HORSES

T R Clark, Crawl Farm, Crawl Lane, Clandown, Radstock, BA3 2XH Tel: (01761) 413120 Fax: (01761) 413120

Timbertops Equestrian Supplies, Jackson Lane, Wentbridge, Pontefract, West Yorkshire, WF8 3HZ Tel: (01977) 620374 Fax: (01977) 621039 E-mail: sue@sue-clark.co.uk

HORSESHOES

Chapel Forge Farriers Ltd, Upper Lambourn, Hungerford, Berkshire, RG17 8QP Tel: (01488) 72613 Fax: (01488) 73835 E-mail: gary@chappelforge.co.uk

Arthur Cottam & Co., Carrwood Road, Chesterfield, Derbyshire, S41 9QB Tel: (01246) 453672 Fax: (01246) 260274 E-mail: sales@cottamhorseshoes.com

Handmade Shoes UK Ltd, Lever Hall, Steelworks Road, Ebbw Vale, Gwent, NP23 6AA Tel: (01495) 309040 Fax: (01495) 301404

J. Todd (A F C L) Ltd, The Forge, Great Warley Street, Great Warley, Brentwood, Essex, CM13 3JF Tel: (01277) 222645 Fax: (01277) 224522

Ian Wilson, 2 Edinborough Road, Lanark, ML11 7RS Tel: (01555) 660666 Fax: (01555) 663901 E-mail: info@smiddywroughtiron.com

HORTICULTURAL CHEMICAL PRODUCTS

Bio Natura Ltd, PO Box 2, Ilkley, West Yorkshire, LS29 8AS Tel: (01943) 816816 Fax: (01943) 816818 E-mail: sales@bionutura.co.uk

Humax Horticulture Ltd, Richardson House, Mill Hill, Gretna, Dumfriesshire, DG16 5HU Tel: (01461) 339260 Fax: (01461) 339269 E-mail: sales@humax.co.uk

J.F.C. Monro, Guildford Road Industrial Estate, Hayle, Cornwall, TR27 4QZ Tel: (01736) 755766 Fax: (01736) 755767 E-mail: sales@jfcmonro.co.uk

Vitax Ltd, Owen Street, Coalville, Leicestershire, LE67 3DE Tel: (01530) 510060 Fax: (01530) 510299 E-mail: info@vitax.co.uk

HORTICULTURAL ENGINEERING

Bradmore Garden Centres, Pendock Lane, Bradmore, Nottingham, NG11 6PQ Tel: 0115-984 7990 Fax: 0115-940 6175

Burgess, Europa Way, Martineau Lane, Norwich, NR1 2EN Tel: (01603) 628251 Fax: (01603) 762194 E-mail: enquiries@benburgess.co.uk

C & O Tractors Ltd, West Street, Wilton, Salisbury, SP2 0DG Tel: (01722) 742141 Fax: (01722) 744497 E-mail: admin@candotractors.co.uk

F G Adamson & Son, Adamsons, Occupation Lane, Swanland, North Ferriby, North Humberside, HU14 3QZ Tel: (01482) 636200 Fax: (01482) 631672 E-mail: enquiry@buyamower.co.uk

G Bryan Jones Ltd, Love La Industrial Estate, Bishops Castle, Shropshire, SY9 5DW Tel: (01588) 638638 Fax: (01588) 638741 E-mail: sales@gbj1.freeserve.co.uk

Lincolnshire Motors Ltd, Windsor Road, Fairfield Industrial Estate, Louth, Lincolnshire, LN11 0LF Tel: (01507) 604061 Fax: (01507) 605609 E-mail: sales@lincsmotors.co.uk

Meadhams Lawnmowers Sales & Service, 12 Bankside, Kidlington, Oxfordshire, OX5 1JE Tel: (01865) 378010 Fax: (01865) 378010 E-mail: meadhams@btinternet.com

Mitchell Industries Ltd, Unit 18H, Hilton Business Park, The Mease, Hilton, Derby, DE65 5JD Tel: (01283) 731100 Fax: (01283) 734309 E-mail: danny.hall@mitchell-industries.co.uk

Oakes Brothers, Cowdown Farm, Micheldever, Winchester, Hampshire, SO21 3DN Tel: (01962) 794100 Fax: (01962) 794118

Ratcliffe & Son, Westport Iron Works, Foundry Road, Malmesbury, Wiltshire, SN16 0AW Tel: (01666) 823222 Fax: (01666) 823222

Stubbings Bros., Chale Green, Ventnor, Isle Of Wight, PO38 2JN Tel: (01983) 551443 Fax: (01983) 551400 E-mail: sales@stubbings-bros.co.uk

HORTICULTURAL ESTATE AGENTS

▶ Angel Property Services, Silton Road, Bourton, Gillingham, Dorset, SP8 5DD Tel: (08712) 715128 E-mail: rennie@angelpropertyservices.net

▶ Sands Home Search, PO Box 5561, Ringwood, Hampshire, BH24 1EN Tel: (01425) 462549 Fax: (0871) 6612892 E-mail: info@sandshomesearch.com

HORTICULTURAL FERTILISER

Goundrey Horticultural Equipment, Unit 18 Enstone Airfield, Enstone, Chipping Norton, Oxfordshire, OX7 4NP Tel: (01608) 678724 Fax: (0870) 2421091 E-mail: sales@goundreys.co.uk

W L Dingley & Co, Buckle Street, Honeybourne, Evesham, Worcestershire, WR11 7QE Tel: (01386) 830242 Fax: (01386) 833541

HORTICULTURAL HEATING SYSTEMS

▶ Parwin Heaters UK Ltd, 21 High Haden Road, Glatton, Huntingdon, Cambridgeshire, PE28 5RU Tel: (01487) 834630 Fax: (01487) 830407 E-mail: paul@metalspec.freeserve.co.uk

Thermoforce Ltd, Wakefield Road, Cockermouth, Cumbria, CA13 0HS Tel: (01900) 823231 Fax: (01900) 825965 E-mail: sales@thermoforce.co.uk

HORTICULTURAL MACHINERY OR EQUIPMENT TO SPECIFICATION

Richard Pearson Ltd, Priory Road, Freiston, Boston, Lincolnshire, PE22 0JZ Tel: (01205) 760383 Fax: (01205) 761064 E-mail: info@richardpearson.com

HORTICULTURAL MACHINERY/ EQUIPMENT/IMPLEMENT MAINTENANCE/REPAIR SERVICES

A T Oliver & Sons Ltd, Home Park Works, Station Road, Kings Langley, Hertfordshire, WD4 8LW Tel: (01923) 265211 Fax: (01923) 261759

Bartons Of Bawtry Ltd, Market Place, Bawtry, Doncaster, South Yorkshire, DN10 6JL Tel: (01302) 710212 Fax: (01302) 710212

Central Spares Ltd, Units 3-7, Brook Road, Wimborne, Dorset, BH21 2BH Tel: (01202) 882000 Fax: (01202) 881783 E-mail: sales@the-trolley-shop.co.uk

▶ Ecotechnics (UK) Ltd, 11 Storey Street, Leicester, LE3 5GR Tel: 0116-262 0200 Fax: 0116-251 0800 E-mail: daniel@dpelectronics.co.uk

Fletcher-Stewart Ltd, Unit 1, Newby Road Industrial Estate, Hazel Grove, Stockport, Cheshire, SK7 5DA Tel: 0161-456 8450 Fax: 0161-483 5569 E-mail: info@fletcherstewart.co.uk

Leach's Lawnmower Centre, Unit 2 Ford Street, Stockport, Cheshire, SK3 0BT Tel: 0161-477 5688 Fax: 0161-477 5688 E-mail: leachs.lawnmowers@virgin.net

Marshall Farm Machinery, Rugby Road, Leicester, LE9 7TB Tel: (01788) 832300 Fax: (01455) 888179 E-mail: sales@marshallfarmmachinery.co.uk

Mower Services, Croft Road, Crowborough, East Sussex, TN6 1HA Tel: (01892) 662960 Fax: (01892) 664987 E-mail: mowerservices@btconnect.com

▶ Oakley's Ltd, Unit1 Leasowes Business Park, Cressage, Shrewsbury, SY5 6AF Tel: (01952) 511000 Fax: (01952) 511005 E-mail: sales@oakleysgroundcare.co.uk

Sandwich Mowers Ltd, Homestead Farm, Woodnesborough Road, Sandwich, Kent, CT13 0AE Tel: (01304) 611000 Fax: (01304) 611000 E-mail: sandwichmowersltd@btinternet.com

Tullibaridine, Castleton Road, Auchterarder, Perthshire, PH3 1JS Tel: (01764) 662696 Fax: (01764) 662011

Yorkshire Turf Machinery Ltd, Unit 3 Brent Road, Stockport, Cheshire, SK4 2LD Tel: 0161-429 8750 Fax: 0161-429 8882 E-mail: ctm@ctmpro.com

HORTICULTURAL MACHINERY/ EQUIPMENT/IMPLEMENT MANUFRS

Bradmore Garden Centres, Pendock Lane, Bradmore, Nottingham, NG11 6PQ Tel: 0115-984 7990 Fax: 0115-940 6175

Burrows GM Ltd, Wigan Road, Leyland, PR25 5UE Tel: (01772) 421778 Fax: (01772) 622530

C T Hayton Ltd, Sandylands Road, Kendal, Cumbria, LA9 6EX Tel: (01539) 721518 Fax: (01539) 722977 E-mail: sales@cthayton.co.uk

The Caledonian Tree Company Ltd, Cowbraehill, Tynehead, Pathhead, Midlothian, EH37 5XT Tel: (01875) 835360 Fax: (01875) 835636 E-mail: single@superoots.co.uk

Crewkerne Horticultural Engineers, North Street Trading Estate, North Street, Crewkerne, Somerset, TA18 7AW Tel: (01460) 72428 Fax: (01460) 75644

Cullum Plant Hire & Sales Ltd, 11 Boleness Road, Wisbech, Cambridgeshire, PE13 2RB Tel: (01945) 463356 Fax: (01945) 463248 E-mail: cullumsales@btinternet.com

Decco, Crabtree Manor Way North, Belvedere, Kent, DA17 6LJ Tel: (0870) 9506565 Fax: (020) 8310 4665

Desch Plantpak Ltd, Varey Road, Eaton Bank Trading Estate, Congleton, Cheshire, CW12 1HD Tel: (01260) 279432 Fax: (01260) 280856 E-mail: sales@desch-plantpak.co.uk

Downpatrick Farm & Garden Supplies Ltd, Ballydugan Industrial Estate, Ballydugan Road, Downpatrick, County Down, BT30 6TE Tel: (028) 4461 3719 Fax: (028) 4461 3719

E Bowden & Sons, Little Woodland, Old Newton Road, Bovey Tracey, Newton Abbot, Devon, TQ13 9DT Tel: (01626) 833374 Fax: (01626) 832144 E-mail: ebowden@btconnect.com

E H Penny, Fowl Ing Works, Fowl Ing Lane, Kendal, Cumbria, LA9 6PH Tel: (01539) 721605 Fax: (01539) 721605

Ernest Doe & Sons Ltd, Ulting, Maldon, Essex, CM9 6QH Tel: (01245) 380311 Fax: (01245) 381194 E-mail: info@ernestdoe.com

Eurogreen Machinery, The Tythe Barn, North Barn Farm, Titnore Lane, Worthing, West Sussex, BN12 6NZ Tel: (01903) 700678 Fax: (01903) 247585 E-mail: admin@eurogreenuk.com

Farm Supplies Dorking Ltd, Ansell Road, Dorking, Surrey, RH4 1QW Tel: (01306) 880456 Fax: (01306) 876869

Globe Organic Services, Unit S2 Olton Wharf, Richmond Road, Solihull, West Midlands, B92 7RN Tel: 0121-707 4120 Fax: 0121-707 4934 E-mail: globeorganic@btinternet.com

▶ Gloucestershire Hydroponics, Unit 4 Hope Mill Busines Centre, Hope Mill Lane, Brimscombe, Stroud, Gloucestershire, GL5 2SE Tel: (01453) 887481 Fax: (01453) 887481 E-mail: sales@gloucestershirehydroponics.com

Grahams Garden Machinery Ltd, Brighton Cross Grampound Road, Grampound Road, Truro, Cornwall, TR2 4HD Tel: (01726) 884001 Fax: (01726) 883991 E-mail: parkinsgm@bt.connect.com

Gunn J C B Ltd, Atlantic Street, Broadheath, Altrincham, Cheshire, WA14 5DN Tel: 0161-941 2631 Fax: 0161-942 3399 E-mail: enguireis@gunn-jcb.co.uk

Hayter Ltd, Spellbrook La West, Spellbrook, Bishop's Stortford, Hertfordshire, CM23 4BU Tel: (01279) 723444 Fax: (01279) 723821 E-mail: sales@hayter.co.uk

▶ Henderson Grass Machinery Ltd, Tweedbank Industrial Estate, Tweedbank, Galashiels, Selkirkshire, TD1 3RS Tel: (01896) 753870 Fax: (01896) 752598

Henton & Chattell Ltd, London Road, Nottingham, NG2 3HW Tel: 0115-986 6646 Fax: 0115-986 6169 E-mail: info@hentonandchattell.co.uk

HORTICULTURAL MACHINERY/ EQUIPMENT/IMPLEMENT MANUFRS

– *continued*

▶ Hi-Tech Horticulture, Setters Farm, Mount Pleasant Lane, Lymington, Hants, SO41 8LS Tel: (01590) 672835 Fax: (01590) 688932

Huddersfield Saw & Tool Co., Vine Street, Huddersfield, HD1 6NT Tel: (01484) 424055 Fax: (01484) 421244

Interior Landscaping Products, The Sussex Barn, New Lodge Farm, Hooe, Battle, East Sussex, TN33 9HJ Tel: (01424) 844444 Fax: (01424) 843666 E-mail: sales@interiorlandscaping.co.uk

Ironcraft, 92 High Street, Earl Shilton, Leicester, LE9 7DG Tel: (01455) 847548 Fax: (01455) 842422 E-mail: office@ironcraft.co.uk

John K Cathcart Ltd, Trory, Ballinamallard, Enniskillen, County Fermanagh, BT94 2FH Tel: (028) 6632 4325 Fax: (028) 6632 5939 E-mail: general@cathcart.co.uk

Kilworth Agricultural Machinery, Annwell Lane, Smisby, Ashby-de-la-Zouch, Leicestershire, LE65 2TA Tel: (01530) 412690 Fax: (01530) 560002E-mail: sales@kilworthmachinery.co.uk

Lely (UK) Ltd, 1 Station Road, St. Neots, Cambridgeshire, PE19 1QH Tel: (01480) 226810 Fax: (01480) 226811 E-mail: ag.sales.uk@lely.com

M P S Garden Machinery, 288 Frome Road, Trowbridge, Wiltshire, BA14 0DT Tel: (01225) 776667 Fax: (01225) 776667

Mark Hellier Tractors Se Ltd, Thousand Acre Farm, Biddenden, Ashford, Kent, TN27 8BF Tel: (01580) 291271 Fax: (01580) 292432 E-mail: mail@markhellier.co.uk

Montrose Garden Supply Co., Paradise Avenue, Ballymena, County Antrim, BT42 3AE Tel: (028) 2565 3796 Fax: (028) 2564 8642

▶ Parwin Heaters UK Ltd, 21 High Haden Road, Glatton, Huntingdon, Cambridgeshire, PE28 5RU Tel: (01487) 834630 Fax: (01487) 830407 E-mail: paul@metalspec.freeserve.co.uk

Power Equipment Services Ltd, Oldington Trading Estate, Kidderminster, Worcestershire, DY11 7QP Tel: (01562) 742400 Fax: (01562) 865826

Randell NFM Ltd, 3 Maurice Gaymer Road, Attleborough, Norfolk, NR17 2QZ Tel: (01953) 452468 Fax: (01953) 453229 E-mail: enquiries@randallnfm.co.uk

Redbreast Industrial Equipment Ltd, 1 Stavely Way, Brixworth, Northampton, NN6 9EU Tel: (01604) 882088 Fax: (01604) 882015 E-mail: sales@redbreastrobin.co.uk

S C H (Supplies) Ltd, S C H Supplies, Holbrook, Ipswich, IP9 2PT Tel: (01473) 328272 E-mail: enquiries@schsupplies.co.uk

Sandwich Mowers Ltd, Homestead Farm, Woodnesborough Road, Sandwich, Kent, CT13 0AE Tel: (01304) 611000 Fax: (01304) 611000 E-mail: sandwichmowersltd@btinternet.com

Saxon Industries, Everland Road, Hungerford, Berkshire, RG17 0DX Tel: (01488) 684545 Fax: (01488) 684317 E-mail: sales@saxonind.co.uk

Sims Garden Machinery Ltd, 2 Western Road, Stratford-upon-Avon, Warwickshire, CV37 0AH Tel: (01789) 205671 Fax: (01789) 299006

Tuthill Temperley, Wardington House, Wardington, Banbury, Oxfordshire, OX17 1SD Tel: (01295) 750513 Fax: (01295) 750036 E-mail: george.tuthill@wardington.com

Westwood Automation Ltd, Bell Close, Newnham Industrial Estate, Plympton, Plymouth, PL7 4JH Tel: (01752) 202113 Fax: (01752) 202117

William Sinclair Horticulture Ltd, Malvern Road, Knottingley, West Yorkshire, WF11 8EG Tel: (01977) 677676 Fax: (01977) 607138 E-mail: fyba@william-sinclair.co.uk

J. Wood & Son Ltd, Kirkby Mills Industrial Estate, Kirby Mills, Kirkbymoorside, York, YO62 6NL Tel: (01751) 433434 Fax: (01751) 433094 E-mail: sales@johnwoods.co.uk

Yorkshire Turf Machinery Ltd, Unit 3 Brent Road, Stockport, Cheshire, SK4 2LD Tel: 0161-429 8750 Fax: 0161-429 8882 E-mail: ctm@ctmpro.com

HORTICULTURAL PACKAGING PRODUCTS MANUFRS

John Dowty Ltd, Kidderminster Road, Ombersley, Droitwich, Worcestershire, WR9 0JH Tel: (01905) 620404 Fax: (01905) 621016 E-mail: n.dowty@ombersleygolfclub.co.uk

Jardin Corrugated Cases Ltd, Elean Business Park, Sutton, Ely, Cambridgeshire, CB6 2QE Tel: (01353) 778522 Fax: (01353) 777708 E-mail: jcc.enquiries@jccltd.com

Keith & A M Singleton, Nethertown, Egremont, Cumbria, CA22 2UQ Tel: (01946) 820412 Fax: (01946) 824091

Saklok, Roughway Mill, Dunks Green, Tonbridge, Kent, TN11 9SG Tel: (01732) 810813 Fax: (01732) 810838 E-mail: roughway@btconnect.com

Wentus Ltd, 2 Business Centre, Osbournby, Sleaford, Lincolnshire, NG34 0DH Tel: 01529 455695

HORTICULTURAL PLANT DISPLAY STANDS

Claude Fenton (Plant Hire) Ltd, Unit 1 Kennet Weir Business Park, Arrowhead Road, Theale, Reading, RG7 4AE Tel: 0118-930 3066 Fax: 0118-930 3411

Greengrace Floral & Plant Displays, 129 Elmbridge Avenue, Surbiton, Surrey, KT5 9HE Tel: (020) 8399 8174 Fax: (020) 8390 1871

HORTICULTURAL PLANT GROWTH CHAMBERS

Mobile Seeds Ltd, Village Farm Buildings, Sheriffhales, Shifnal, Shropshire, TF11 8RD Tel: (01952) 463097 Fax: (01952) 463097

HORTICULTURAL PLANTS

▶ Flora Design, 106 Cromwell Road, St. Andrews, Bristol, BS6 5EZ Tel: 0117-944 1494 Fax: 0117-944 1494 E-mail: sales@floradesign.co.uk

HORTICULTURAL PLASTIC PRODUCTS/SUNDRIES

▶ binbagloader.co.uk, 1 Stone Cottages, Green End, Goathland, Whitby, North Yorkshire, YO22 5LQ Tel: (01947) 896398 Fax: (01947) 896398 E-mail: info@binbagloader.co.uk

Desch Plantpak Ltd, Burnham Road, Mundon, Maldon, Essex, CM9 6NT Tel: (01621) 745500 Fax: (01621) 745525 E-mail: sales@desch-plantpak.co.uk

Fordingbridge plc, Arundel Road, Fontwell, Arundel, West Sussex, BN18 0SD Tel: (01243) 554455 Fax: (01243) 554433 E-mail: sales@nurserybitz.co.uk

Fourfold Mouldings, New Close Mills, Howden Road, Silsden, Keighley, West Yorkshire, BD20 0HA Tel: (01535) 654604 Fax: (01535) 654829 E-mail: sales@fourfold.co.uk

Murray Duguid Ltd, Mill of Cromlet, Oldmeldrum, Inverurie, Aberdeenshire, AB51 0BD Tel: (01651) 872535 Fax: (01651) 872933

Par-Fox Products Ltd, High Street, Golborne, Warrington, WA3 3AN Tel: (01942) 726862 Fax: (01942) 722080

Richard Sankey & Son Ltd, Bennerley Road, Bulwell, Nottingham, NG6 8PE Tel: 0115-927 7335 Fax: 0115-977 0197 E-mail: info@rsankey.co.uk

H. Smith Plastics Ltd, Mayphil Industrial Area, Battlesbridge, Wickford, Essex, SS11 7RJ Tel: (01268) 733088 Fax: (01268) 560561 E-mail: hsp@plantcell.co.uk

HORTICULTURAL SHREDDING MACHINES

Globe Organic Services, Unit S2 Olton Wharf, Richmond Road, Solihull, West Midlands, B92 7RN Tel: 0121-707 4120 Fax: 0121-707 4934 E-mail: globeorganic@btinternet.com

HORTICULTURAL SPRAY EQUIPMENT

Claxton Engineering Co., 1 Buckminster Lane, Skillington, Grantham, Lincolnshire, NG33 5EY Tel: (01476) 860870 Fax: (01476) 861681 E-mail: claxtonsprayers@lineone.net

Decco, Crabtree Manor Way North, Belvedere, Kent, DA17 6LJ Tel: (0870) 9506565 Fax: (020) 8310 4665

Hozelock Ltd, Midpoint Park, Kingsbury Road, Minworth, Sutton Coldfield, West Midlands, B76 1AB Tel: 0121-313 4242 Fax: 0121-313 4243

Solo Sprayers Ltd, 4 Brunel Road, Leigh-on-Sea, Essex, SS9 5JN Tel: (01702) 525740 Fax: (01702) 522752 E-mail: solo.sprayers@fsbdial.co.uk

HORTICULTURAL STAFF RECRUITMENT

▶ Blooming Good Jobs, BGJ House, Ashford, Kent, TN21 0LT Tel: (0871) 24225232 E-mail: info@bloominggoodjobs.com

HORTICULTURAL SUNDRIESMEN/TRADE DISTRIBUTORS OR AGENTS

Anglo Aquarium Plant Co. Ltd, Strayfield Road, Enfield, Middlesex, EN2 9JE Tel: (020) 8363 8548 Fax: (020) 8363 8547 E-mail: sales@anglo-aquarium.co.uk

Bartram Mowers, Bluebell Road, Norwich, NR4 7LG Tel: (01603) 458916 Fax: (01603) 250643 E-mail: sales@bartrammowers.co.uk

Blount UK, Unit 3 Arianda Warwhouses, Steinhoff Business Park, Tewkesbury, Gloucestershire, GL20 8GY Tel: (01684) 297600 Fax: (01684) 855497 E-mail: sales@blount.co.uk

Cadbury Garden & Leisure, Smallway, Congresbury, Bristol, BS49 5AA Tel: (01934) 876464 Fax: (01934) 875701 E-mail: info@cadbury.g-l.co.uk

▶ Capatex Ltd, 127 North Gate, Nottingham, NG7 7FZ Tel: 0115-978 6111 Fax: 0115-978 6222 E-mail: info@capatex.com

Clapro Ltd, 2 Sussex Road, New Malden, Surrey, KT3 3PY Tel: (020) 8949 4963 Fax: (020) 8949 7517

Decco, Crabtree Manor Way North, Belvedere, Kent, DA17 6LJ Tel: (0870) 9506565 Fax: (020) 8310 4665

Deroma UK Ltd, Quedgeley Trading Estate East, Haresfield, Stonehouse, Gloucestershire, GL10 3EX Tel: (01452) 725520 Fax: (01452) 725521

John Dowty Ltd, Kidderminster Road, Ombersley, Droitwich, Worcestershire, WR9 0JH Tel: (01905) 620404 Fax: (01905) 621016 E-mail: n.dowty@ombersleygolfclub.co.uk

Eifionydd Farmers Association Ltd, Station Road, Tywyn, Gwynedd, LL36 9BG Tel: (01654) 710233 Fax: (01654) 712009

Eynsham Park Sawmill, Cuckoo Lane, North Leigh, Witney, Oxfordshire, OX29 6PS Tel: (01993) 881391 Fax: (01993) 881391 E-mail: sales@eynshamparksawmill.co.uk

Fargro Ltd, Toddington Lane, Wick, Littlehampton, West Sussex, BN17 7QR Tel: (01903) 721591 Fax: (01903) 730737 E-mail: sales@fargro.co.uk

Forizo Co., Walker Street, Higher Tranmere, Birkenhead, Merseyside, CH42 0LY Tel: 0151-652 2275

Garden Products, 1 River Side Industrial Estate, Dodsworth Street, Darlington, County Durham, DL1 2UH Tel: (01325) 488341 Fax: (01325) 488341

Hugh Page Sussex Ltd, Station Road, Heathfield, East Sussex, TN21 8DH Tel: (01435) 862235 Fax: (01435) 865653

Humax Horticulture Ltd, Richardson House, Mill Hill, Gretna, Dumfriesshire, DG16 5HU Tel: (01461) 339260 Fax: (01461) 339269 E-mail: sales@humax.co.uk

Interior Landscaping Products, The Sussex Barn, New Lodge Farm, Hooe, Battle, East Sussex, TN33 9HJ Tel: (01424) 844444 Fax: (01424) 843666 E-mail: sales@interiorlandscaping.co.uk

John Bourne & Co. Ltd, Rye Road, Newenden, Cranbrook, Kent, TN18 5QG Tel: (01797) 252298 Fax: (01797) 253115 E-mail: enquiries@bourne.uk.com

K9 Pet Foods, 44 Station Road, Framlingham, Woodbridge, Suffolk, IP13 9EE Tel: (01728) 621054 Fax: (01728) 621122

Le Marquand Bros, 5-6 Peirson Road, St. Helier, Jersey, JE2 3PD Tel: (01534) 723261 Fax: (01534) 768971

M W Partridge & Co. Ltd, 60 High Street, Hadleigh, Ipswich, IP7 5EE Tel: (01473) 822333 Fax: (01473) 828009 E-mail: sales@partridgemw.co.uk

William Main, 9 West Port, Dunbar, East Lothian, EH42 1BT Tel: (01368) 863258 Fax: (01368) 865336

Monro South, Unit 1, Quarrywood Industrial Estate, Burntash Road, Maidstone, Kent, ME20 7XB Tel: (01622) 717373 Fax: (01622) 716339 E-mail: sales@monrosouth.co.uk

Montrose Garden Supply Co., Paradise Avenue, Ballymena, County Antrim, BT42 3AE Tel: (028) 2565 3796 Fax: (028) 2564 8642

Newmans Cheltenham Ltd, 180 Bath Road, Cheltenham, Gloucestershire, GL53 7NF Tel: (01242) 512361 Fax: (01242) 521666

Nutscene Ltd, Forfar, Angus, DD8 2NS Tel: (01307) 468589 Fax: (01307) 467051 E-mail: sales@nutscene.com

Patio Garden Centres, 100 Tooting Bec Road, London, SW17 8BG Tel: (020) 8672 2251 Fax: (020) 8682 2105

James Pollock & Son, 53-61 Castle Street, Ballymoney, County Antrim, BT53 6JZ Tel: (028) 2766 3333 Fax: (028) 2766 5951

The Potted Plant Co., 72 Austrey Road, Warton, Tamworth, Staffordshire, B79 0HQ Tel: (01827) 330032

▶ Promoseeds UK, White Hart Hill, Guestling, Hastings, East Sussex, TN35 4LP Tel: (01424) 813572 Fax: (01424) 814631 E-mail: tony@promoseeds.co.uk

Spread Garden Supplies Ltd, Edward Street, St. Helens, Merseyside, WA9 3DS Tel: (01744) 753431 Fax: (01744) 24513 E-mail: kenb@spread.co.uk

Thurlow Nunn Standen Ltd, 61 The Street, Melton, Woodbridge, Suffolk, IP12 1PN Tel: (01394) 382801 Fax: (01394) 384330 E-mail: adrianbrown@tnsgroup.co.uk

Trenchex Garden Machinery, Dove Fields Industrial Estate, Uttoxeter, Staffordshire, ST14 8ER Tel: (01889) 565155 Fax: (01889) 563140 E-mail: enquiries@trenchax.com

Sam Turner & Sons Ltd, Darlington Road, Northallerton, North Yorkshire, DL6 2XB Tel: (01609) 772422 Fax: (01609) 770653 E-mail: clothing@sam-turner.co.uk

▶ Veerman's Shed Centre, 130 High Street, Tranent, East Lothian, EH33 1HJ Tel: (01875) 613090 Fax: (01875) 617492 E-mail: email@veermans.co.uk

Wiggly Wigglers Ltd, Lower Blakemere Farm, Blakemere, Hereford, HR2 9PX Tel: (01981) 500391 Fax: (01981) 500108 E-mail: wiggly@wigglywigglers.co.uk

William Lillico & Sons Ltd, The Forstal, Beddow Way, Aylesford, Kent, ME20 7BT Tel: (01622) 718487 Fax: (01622) 882475 E-mail: post@lillico.co.uk

William Sinclair Holdings Public Ltd Company, Firth Road, Lincoln, LN6 7AH Tel: (01522) 537561 Fax: (01522) 560648 E-mail: info@william-sinclair.co.uk

Woodland Improvement & Conservation Ltd, Newent Lane, Huntley, Gloucester, GL19 3HG Tel: (01452) 832100 Fax: (01452) 831039 E-mail: sales@woodimp.co.uk

Wyevale Garden Centres Ltd, Dunstable Road, Caddington, Luton, LU1 4AN Tel: (01582) 457313 Fax: (01582) 480716

HORTICULTURAL TWINE

Nutscene Ltd, Forfar, Angus, DD8 2NS Tel: (01307) 468589 Fax: (01307) 467051 E-mail: sales@nutscene.com

HORTICULTURE RESEARCH AND DEVELOPMENT SERVICES

Chiltern Seeds, Bortree Stile, Ulverston, Cumbria, LA12 7PB Tel: (01229) 581137 Fax: (01229) 584549 E-mail: info@chilternseeds.co.uk

Plant Zone Ltd, Silver House Ireland Industrial Estate, Adelphi Way, Staveley, Chesterfield, Derbyshire, S43 3LJ Tel: (01246) 472727 Fax: (01246) 472727 E-mail: michael@plantzone.co.uk

Tytherley Nurseries, Dean Road, West Tytherley, Salisbury, SP5 1NR Tel: (01794) 341213

HOSE ACCESSORIES

A R P Co. Ltd, Unit 2 Jubilee Way, Avonmouth, Bristol, BS11 9HU Tel: 0117-982 6301 Fax: 0117-923 5487 E-mail: sales@avonmouth-rubber.co.uk

▶ Lamp-Light, 49 Catley Road, Sheffield, S9 5JF Tel: (01142) 430406 Fax: (01142) 430602 E-mail: sales@lamp-light.co.uk

HOSE ASSEMBLY MANUFRS

Alfa Gomma UK Ltd, 3 Cranford Court, Hardwick Grange, Woolston, Warrington, WA1 4RX Tel: (01925) 820800 Fax: (01925) 810926

Amnitec Ltd, Abercanaid, Merthyr Tydfil, Mid Glamorgan, CF48 1UX Tel: (01685) 385641 Fax: (01685) 389683 E-mail: sales@amnitec.co.uk

Arnold Hose Ltd, 2 Rothersthorpe Avenue, Rothersthorpe Avenue Industrial Estate, Northampton, NN4 8JH Tel: (01604) 706570 Fax: (01604) 661170 E-mail: ahl@arnoldhose.demon.co.uk

Comet Fluid Power, Horace Waller V C Parade, Shaw Cross Business Park, Dewsbury, West Yorkshire, WF12 7RF Tel: (01924) 455667 Fax: (01924) 456292 E-mail: comet@challenger-group.co.uk

Covflex Hydraulic & Engineering Co. Ltd, Rowleys Green Industrial Estate, Rowleys Green Lane, Coventry, CV6 6AN Tel: (024) 7668 8714 Fax: (024) 7668 8720 E-mail: sales@covflex.freeserve.co.uk

The Crane Centre Ltd, Norton Way, Moss Lane Industrial Estate, Sandbach, Cheshire, CW11 3YT Tel: (01270) 753435 Fax: (01270) 759389 E-mail: info@cranecentre.co.uk

Dunlop Hi Flex Fluidpower Ltd, Unit 59 Holly Court, St. Modwen Road, Plymouth, PL6 8LG Tel: (01752) 262268 Fax: (01752) 664722 E-mail: dunlophiflex@shelmerdined.freeserve.co.uk

Dunlop Hiflex Fluid Power Ltd, Howley Park Road, Morley, Leeds, LS27 0BN Tel: 0113-238 1547 Fax: 0113-238 3391 E-mail: leeds@dunlophiflex.com

Dura Hose & Fittings Ltd, Unit 8, Mountheath Industrial Park, Prestwich, Manchester, M25 9WB Tel: 0161-798 8665 Fax: 0161-773 3048 E-mail: sales@dura-hose.com

First Hose Ltd, 21 Denmore Industrial Estate, Denmore Road, Bridge of Don, Aberdeen, AB23 8JW Tel: (01224) 823413 Fax: (01224) 823113 E-mail: sales@1st-hose.co.uk

Hiflex Fluid Power, Units 8-9 Sun Valley Business Park, Winnall Close, Winchester, Hampshire, SO23 0LB Tel: (01962) 860311 Fax: (01962) 860673 E-mail: winchester@dunlophiflex.com

Ideal Hose & Safety Ltd, Spring Lane, Northampton, NN1 2JW Tel: (01604) 621964 Fax: (01604) 232936 E-mail: sales@idealhose.co.uk

J.W Hydraulics, Springvale Industrial Park, Unit 33, Bilston, West Midlands, WV14 0QL Tel: (01902) 408771 Fax: (01902) 354448

Kutting UK Ltd, 16 Tanners Drive, Blakelands, Milton Keynes, MK14 5BN Tel: (01908) 218100 Fax: (01908) 218666 E-mail: info@kuttinguk.co.uk

Metalflex Industrial Supplies Ltd, Unit 9 Adlington Court, Birchwood, Warrington, WA3 6PL Tel: (01925) 814999 Fax: (01925) 838999 E-mail: john.milsom@metalflex.co.uk

Nelson Stokes Ltd, Highfield Industrial Estate, Camelford, Cornwall, PL32 9RA Tel: (01840) 213711 Fax: (01840) 213338 E-mail: enquiries@nelsonstokes.com

O M C Fluidpower Ltd, Unit N, Harlow House, Corby, Northamptonshire, NN17 5XH Tel: (01536) 260372 Fax: (01536) 264422

HOSE ASSEMBLY MANUFRS –
continued

Oakbray Ltd, Whieldon Industrial Estate, Whieldon Road, Stoke-on-Trent, ST4 4JP Tel: (01782) 744555 Fax: (01782) 414244 E-mail: sales@oakbray.co.uk

Parkland Engineering Ltd, 72 Dykehead Street, Glasgow, G33 4AQ Tel: 0141-774 6200 Fax: 0141-774 0034 E-mail: glasgowsales@parkland-eng.co.uk

Pearson Hydraulics Ltd, 11 Cardinal Close, Lincoln, LN2 4SY Tel: (01522) 510777 Fax: (01522) 510508 E-mail: sales@pearson-hyds.co.uk

Pirtek, 2 Oxford Court, Oxford Street, Birmingham, B5 5NF Tel: 0121-633 0101 Fax: 0121-633 0043 E-mail: info@pirtekbirmingham.co.uk

Shire Fluid Power Ltd, 6 Racecourse Road, Pershore, Worcestershire, WR10 2EY Tel: (01386) 554744 Fax: (01386) 553743

Silflex Ltd, Coedcae Lane, Pontyclun, Mid Glamorgan, CF72 9HJ Tel: (01443) 238464 Fax: 01443 238464 E-mail: silflex@silflex.com

South Scotland Valve & Fitting Co Ltd, 9-11 Macadam Place, Irvine, Ayrshire, KA11 4HP Tel: (01294) 213341 Fax: (01294) 213484 E-mail: enquiries@ssvf.co.uk

W E Couplings Ltd, 2 Grimeford Industrial Estate, Grimeford Lane, Anderton, Chorley, Lancashire, PR6 9HL Tel: (01257) 475101 Fax: (01257) 482424 E-mail: info@we-couplings.com

HOSE ASSEMBLY SERVICES

Hydrasun Ltd, Hydrasun House, 392 King Street, Aberdeen, AB24 3BU Tel: (01224) 618618 Fax: (01224) 618701 E-mail: info@hydrasun.com

HOSE CLIP AND CLAMP DISTRIBUTORS OR AGENTS

Pirtek, 2 Oxford Court, Oxford Street, Birmingham, B5 5NF Tel: 0121-633 0101 Fax: 0121-633 0043 E-mail: info@pirtekbirmingham.co.uk

Pirtek, Unit 35 Seymour Street, Millers Bridge Industrial Estate, Bootle, Merseyside, L20 1EE Tel: 0151-933 9000 Fax: 0151-933 5333 E-mail: info@pirtekuk.com

Pirtek, St. Andrews Road, Avonmouth, Bristol, BS11 9HQ Tel: 0117-982 0056 Fax: 0117-982 4361 E-mail: info@pirtekbristol.co.uk

Pirtek, Unit 35, Acton Park Industrial Estate, The Vale, Acton, London, W3 7QE Tel: (020) 8749 8444 Fax: (020) 8749 8333 E-mail: info@pirtek.co.uk

Pirtek, 6 Westbrook Trading Estate, Westbrook Road, Trafford Park, Manchester, M17 1AY Tel: 0161-877 0000 Fax: 0161-877 8899 E-mail: pirtek-manchester@supanet.com

Pirtek, Unit 11 Liongate Enterprise Park, Morden Road, Mitcham, Surrey, CR4 4NY Tel: (020) 8640 6565 Fax: (020) 8640 2252 E-mail: pirtek.mitcham@zen.co.uk

Pirtek, 337 Ranglet Road, Walton Summit Centre, Bamber Bridge, Preston, PR5 8AR Tel: (01772) 620111 Fax: (01772) 629996 E-mail: preston@pirtekcentre.co.uk

Pirtek, 5 Bergland Park, Maritime Close, Medway City Estate, Rochester, Kent, ME2 4AD Tel: (01634) 297080 Fax: (01634) 297087 E-mail: zen24815@zen.co.uk

Pirtek, 3 Alert House, Dannemora Drive, Sheffield, S9 5DF Tel: 0114-249 3666 Fax: 0114-249 3667 E-mail: sheffield@pirtekcentre.co.uk

Pirtek, Unit 8 Westmill Street, Stoke-on-Trent, ST1 3EL Tel: (01782) 206206 Fax: (01782) 206306 E-mail: stoke@pirtekcentre.co.uk

Pirtek (Nottingham) Ltd, Unit 4 Trentview Court, Moreland Street, Nottingham, NG2 3FX Tel: 0115-985 0081 Fax: 0115-985 0132 E-mail: info@pirteknottingham.co.uk

Trecarn Engineering, 1 Ivanhoe Industrial Estate, Tournament Way, Ashby-de-la-Zouch, Leicestershire, LE65 2UU Tel: (01530) 412802 Fax: (01530) 417515

HOSE CLIP AND CLAMPS

A B A Clamping & Connecting Products Ltd, 48 Hemming Road, Washford, Redditch, Worcestershire, B98 0EA Tel: (01527) 517100 Fax: (01527) 517300 E-mail: office@abagroup.com

Ernest H Hill Ltd, Unit 10-12, Meadowbrook Park, Halfway, Sheffield, S20 3PJ Tel: 0114-248 4882 Fax: 0114-248 9142 E-mail: sales@hillpumps.com

General Hoseclips Ltd, Royston Road, Byfleet, West Byfleet, Surrey, KT14 7NY Tel: (01932) 343224 Fax: (01932) 351285 E-mail: info@generalhoseclips.com

H & D Worm Drive Clips, 197-199 Mare Street, London, E8 3QF Tel: (020) 8985 0752 Fax: (020) 8985 3123 E-mail: nautilus@talk21.com

Holdtite Ltd, 1 Oughton Road, Birmingham, B12 0DF Tel: 0121-440 2617 Fax: 0121-440 2716 E-mail: holdtite@globalnet.co.uk

Morris Gordon Engineering, Unit 1 New Mill End Farm, Chiltern Green Rd, Luton, LU1 3TS Tel: (01582) 460002 Fax: (01582) 460038 E-mail: sales@morrisgordon.co.uk

Peterborough Hose & Couplings Ltd, Cranesgate South, Whaplode St. Catherines, Spalding, Lincolnshire, PE12 6SN Tel: (01406) 540592 Fax: (01406) 540561 E-mail: sales@phccouplings.co.uk

Pinstructure Ltd, Unit 50, Enfield Industrial Estate, Redditch, Worcestershire, B97 6DE Tel: (01527) 67999 Fax: (01527) 66557 E-mail: sales@pinstructure.com

L. Robinson & Co., London Chambers, Mill Road, Gillingham, Kent, ME7 1HJ Tel: (01634) 851182 Fax: (01634) 280101 E-mail: sales@jubileeclips.co.uk

Springmasters Ltd, Arthur Street, Redditch, Worcestershire, B98 8LF Tel: (01527) 521000 Fax: (01527) 528866 E-mail: sales@springmasters.com

Uniclip Ltd, Royston Road, Byfleet, Surrey, KT14 7NY Tel: (01932) 355277 Fax: (01932) 351285 E-mail: info@uniclipengland.com

HOSE CONNECTORS OR ADAPTERS

▶ Calder Ltd, Gregory's Bank, Worcester, WR3 8AB Tel: (01905) 723255 Fax: (01905) 723904 E-mail: pumps@calder.co.uk

Oracstar, Weddell Way, Brackmills, Northampton, NN4 7HS Tel: (01604) 702181 Fax: (01604) 701743 E-mail: orac@oracstar.co.uk

Peterborough Hose & Couplings Ltd, Cranesgate South, Whaplode St. Catherines, Spalding, Lincolnshire, PE12 6SN Tel: (01406) 540592 Fax: (01406) 540561 E-mail: sales@phccouplings.co.uk

HOSE COUPLINGS, *See also Hose Fittings etc*

Aflex Hose Ltd, Spring Bank Industrial Estate, Watson Mill Lane, Sowerby Bridge, West Yorkshire, HX6 3BW Tel: (01422) 317200 Fax: (01422) 836000 E-mail: sales@aflex-hose.co.uk

Bristols & Round Ltd, Longford Road, Cannock, Staffordshire, WS11 0LF Tel: (01543) 503027 Fax: (01543) 505693 E-mail: sales@bristolround.co.uk

Connectomatic Ltd, 31 Bretton Street, Dewsbury, West Yorkshire, WF12 9BJ Tel: (01924) 452444 Fax: (01924) 430607 E-mail: sales@connectomatic.co.uk

Covflex Hydraulic & Engineering Co. Ltd, Rowleys Green Industrial Estate, Rowleys Green Lane, Coventry, CV6 6AN Tel: (024) 7668 8714 Fax: (024) 7668 8720 E-mail: sales@covflex.freeserve.co.uk

CPP-LM Ltd, 38 Swaisland Drive, Crayford, Dartford, DA1 4HS Tel: (01322) 551940 Fax: (01322) 550212E-mail: info@cpp-lm.com

Eaton Fluid Power Group, Thorns Road, Brierley Hill, West Midlands, DY5 2BQ Tel: (01384) 426320 Fax: (01384) 891506 E-mail: mark.ward@aeroquip.com

Flowtech Ltd, Pimbo Road, Skelmersdale, Lancashire, WN8 9RB Tel: (01695) 52770 Fax: (0800) 2987230 E-mail: sales@flowtech.co.uk

Hiflex Fluidpower Ltd, Unit 6, Monklands Industrial Estate, Kirkshaws Road, Coatbridge, Lanarkshire, ML5 4RP Tel: 01236 702680 Fax: 01236 702685 E-mail: sales@hiflex-fluidpower.com

Hydrafit Ltd, Walsall Street, Wolverhampton, WV1 3LN Tel: (01902) 451172 Fax: (01902) 450804 E-mail: hydrafit@btinternet.com

Norton Hydraulics Ltd, Factory 2, Kenninghall Road, London, N18 2PD Tel: (020) 8807 4295 Fax: (020) 8807 9990 E-mail: info@norton-hydraulics.co.uk

Peterborough Hose & Couplings Ltd, Cranesgate South, Whaplode St. Catherines, Spalding, Lincolnshire, PE12 6SN Tel: (01406) 540592 Fax: (01406) 540561 E-mail: sales@phccouplings.co.uk

Shand Engineering Ltd, Kiln Lane, Stallingborough, Grimsby, South Humberside, DN41 8DL Tel: (01469) 571586 Fax: (01469) 571073

Tech Hose, Unit 14 Tarsmill Court, Rotherwas Industrial Estate, Hereford, HR2 6JZ Tel: (01432) 270466 Fax: (01432) 351548 E-mail: sales@tech-hose.co.uk

Wright Engineering Co. Ltd, Masons Road, Stratford-upon-Avon, Warwickshire, CV37 9JA Tel: (01789) 292939 Fax: (01789) 297458 E-mail: sales@wright-eng.co.uk

HOSE DISTRIBUTORS OR AGENTS

A B Hoses & Fittings Ltd, Units 6-7 Warwick Street Industrial Estate, Storforth Lane, Chesterfield, Derbyshire, S40 2TT Tel: (01246) 208831 Fax: (01246) 209302 E-mail: sales@ab-hoses.org.uk

Airedale Tubes & Fittings Ltd, Royds Farm Road, Leeds, LS12 6DX Tel: 0113-231 1227 Fax: 0113-231 1866 E-mail: airedaleinfo@btconnect.com

Alba Hydraflow Ltd, Unit 7, Block 4, Woodend Industrial Estate, Cowdenbeath, Fife, KY4 8HW Tel: (01383) 514543 Fax: (01383) 510324 E-mail: sales@albahydraflow.co.uk

Albion Hose Ltd, Albion Works, Alma Street, Smethwick, West Midlands, B66 2RL Tel: 0121-565 4103 Fax: 0121-558 7220 E-mail: sales@albionhose.co.uk

All Hose & Hydraulics Norwich Ltd, 2 Javelin Road, Norwich, NR6 6HX Tel: (01603) 788686 Fax: (01603) 483081 E-mail: allhosesales@btinternet.com

Alltype Hose & Couplings Ltd, Units 14 & 15 Palace Industrial Estate, Bircholt Road, Parkwood, Maidstone, Kent, ME15 9XU Tel: (01622) 757512 Fax: (01622) 757663 E-mail: sales@alltypehose.co.uk

Aquatic Discount Centre, 1a Haydock Street, Newton-le-Willows, Merseyside, WA12 9AB Tel: (01925) 291439 Fax: (01925) 291439

Ashford Flexible Hose & Couplings Supplies Ltd, 110 Ellingham Way, Ashford, Kent, TN23 6LZ Tel: (01233) 629528 Fax: (01233) 625420

Blackwell Hydraulics Ltd, Unit 13 Industrial Estate, Llandudno Junction, Gwynedd, LL31 9SX Tel: (01492) 583821 Fax: (01492) 593591 E-mail: sales@blackwellhydrolics.co.uk

Burton Hydraulics & Pneumatics, Paget Street, Burton-on-Trent, Staffordshire, DE14 3TQ Tel: (01283) 532745 Fax: (01283) 530637 E-mail: sales@burtonhydraulics.co.uk

C M T Flexibles, Unit 14D Two Locks, Hurst Business Park, Brierley Hill, West Midlands, DY5 1UU Tel: (01384) 480197 Fax: (01384) 74840 E-mail: sales@cmtflexibles.com

Charvo Finishing Ltd, Snaygill Industrial Estate, Keighley Road, Skipton, North Yorkshire, BD23 2QR Tel: (01756) 795028 Fax: (01756) 798473 E-mail: sales@charvo.co.uk

Corby Hose & Hydraulics Ltd, Geddington Road, Corby, Northamptonshire, NN18 8AA Tel: (01536) 201534 Fax: (01536) 400986

Custom Hose & Fitting, 194 Queens Road, Watford, WD17 2NT Tel: (01923) 225534 Fax: (01923) 818714 E-mail: sales@customhose.co.uk

D Cave Hydraulics Ltd, Rainford Road, Bickerstaffe, Ormskirk, Lancashire, L39 0HG Tel: (01695) 735888 Fax: (01695) 725511

D I K Bearings & Transmissions Ltd, J Hawkhill Court, Mid Wynd, Dundee, DD1 4JG Tel: (01382) 228711 Fax: (01382) 202559 E-mail: sales@dik.sol.co.uk

Dapp Hydraulics, Bentley Mill Close, Walsall, WS2 0BN Tel: (01922) 632885 Fax: (01922) 721980 E-mail: sales@dapp.co.uk

Derbyshire Hose & Fittings Ltd, Calow Lane, Hasland, Chesterfield, Derbyshire, S41 0AL Tel: (01246) 477707 Fax: (01246) 222251 E-mail: dhfhyds@aol.com

Designation Ltd, Newark Road, Peterborough, PE1 5YD Tel: (01733) 893333 Fax: (01733) 314889 E-mail: sales@desihose.com

Drain Center Civils, 386 Coleridge Road, Sheffield, S9 5DD Tel: 0114-244 0926 Fax: 0114-243 5990 E-mail: sheffield.p24@wolsley.co.uk

Euro Hydraulics Ltd, Unit 4 Park Parade Industrial Estate, Welbeck St South, Ashton-under-Lyne, Lancashire, OL6 7PP Tel: 0161-308 2624 Fax: 0161-343 1926 E-mail: info@eurohydraulics.com

Flotec Industrial Ltd, Royal Way, Loughborough, Leicestershire, LE11 5XR Tel: (01509) 230100 Fax: (01509) 264100

Forest Hydraulics Ltd, 19-20 Greenshield Industrial Estate, Bradfield Road, London, E16 2AU Tel: (020) 7474 5738 Fax: (020) 7474 5181E-mail: forest.hydraulics@virgin.net

Friction & Hydraulic Services, Gower Street Industrial Estate, St. Georges, Telford, Shropshire, TF2 9HW Tel: (01952) 615793 Fax: (01952) 620408 E-mail: sales@friction-hydraulics.co.uk

Hi Flex Fluids, 2 Cowan Road, Blaydon-on-Tyne, Tyne & Wear, NE21 5TW Tel: 0191-414 7771 Fax: 0191-414 0625 E-mail: sales@hiflex-fluidpower.com

Hiflex Fluidpower Ltd, Unit 6, Monklands Industrial Estate, Kirkshaws Road, Coatbridge, Lanarkshire, ML5 4RP Tel: 01236 702680 Fax: 01236 702685 E-mail: sales@hiflex-fluidpower.com

Hose Depot Direct Ltd, Units 8 Brunel Park, Blyth Road, Harworth, Doncaster, South Yorkshire, DN11 8NE Tel: (01302) 746969 Fax: (01302) 746974

Hose & General Supplies Ltd, Daux Road, Billingshurst, West Sussex, RH14 9SJ Tel: (01403) 783221 Fax: (01403) 783221

Hoselines & Industrial Supplies (North West) Ltd, Units 8 & 9 Knoll Street Industrial Estate, Bury New Rd, Salford, M7 2BL Tel: 0161-792 0481 Fax: 0161-792 5328 E-mail: sales@hoselines.com

Hydraflow Hydraulics (UK) Ltd, Unit 1, Price Street, Bristol Road, Gloucester, GL1 5SZ Tel: (01452) 387061 Fax: (01452) 381332

Hydraulic Equipment Supply Co. Ltd, 419 New Kings Road, London, SW6 4RN Tel: (020) 7736 7391 Fax: (020) 7736 7019

Hydraulic Pipework Services, 4 Smallbridge Industrial Park, Riverside Drive, Rochdale, Lancashire, OL16 2SH Tel: (01706) 345670 Fax: (01706) 641112

Hydroelectic (UK) Ltd, 3 High Road, Byfleet, West Byfleet, Surrey, KT14 7QE Tel: (01932) 334210 Fax: (01932) 334211 E-mail: sales@qualflex.demon.co.uk

Hyphose Ltd, 2 Witney Road, Nuffield Industrial Estate, Poole, Dorset, BH17 0GH Tel: (01202) 673333 Fax: (01202) 687788 E-mail: sales@hyphose.com

J.W Hydraulics, Springvale Industrial Park, Unit 33, Bilston, West Midlands, WV14 0QL Tel: (01902) 408771 Fax: (01902) 354448

K & J Brakes & Hoses Ltd, Alamein Road, Morfa Industrial Estate, Landore, Swansea, SA1 2HY Tel: (01792) 460582 Fax: (01792) 642675

King Industrial Products Ltd, Unit 12, Techno Trading Estate, Brambell Road, Swindon, SN2 8HB Tel: (01793) 491606 Fax: (01793) 530461 E-mail: sales@kingindustrial.co.uk

Kingsley Commercial Components Ltd, Oak Hill Works, Broad Street, Guildford, Surrey, GU3 3BJ Tel: (01483) 303092 Fax: (01483) 572242

M F Hydraulics Ltd, Unit 2, Pony Rd, Horspath Industrial Estate, Oxford, OX4 2RD Tel: (01865) 714126 Fax: (01865) 748140 E-mail: sales@mfhydraulics.co.uk

Machineair Engineering Ltd, 70 Colliers Water Lane, Thornton Heath, Surrey, CR7 7LB Tel: (020) 8684 4849 Fax: (020) 8683 4635

Nelson Hydraulics Ltd, Unit H1, Knockmore Industrial Estate, Lisburn, County Antrim, BT28 2AR Tel: (028) 9266 2781 Fax: (028) 9260 2952E-mail: info@nelsonhydraulics.com

Norton Hydraulics Midland Ltd, 43-45 Meriden Street, Birmingham, B5 5LS Tel: 0121-643 0184 Fax: 0121-631 3617 E-mail: sales@nortonhydraulics.com

O M C Fluidpower Ltd, Unit N, Harlow House, Corby, Northamptonshire, NN17 5XH Tel: (01536) 260372 Fax: (01536) 264422

P P S Hydraulics & Pneumatics Ltd, Foxwood Close, Foxwood Industrial Park, Sheepbridge, Chesterfield, Derbyshire, S41 9RN Tel: (01246) 451509 Fax: (01246) 450831 E-mail: ppshydraulics@btconnect.com

Parkland Engineering Ltd, 72 Dykehead Street, Glasgow, G33 4AQ Tel: 0141-774 6200 Fax: 0141-774 0034 E-mail: glasgowsales@parkland-eng.co.uk

Paul Stuart & Co., 9 Forge Industrial Estate, Greenacres Road, Oldham, OL4 1LE Tel: 0161-620 4129 Fax: 0161-628 4413

Pearson Hydraulics Ltd, 11 Cardinal Close, Lincoln, LN2 4SY Tel: (01522) 510777 Fax: (01522) 510508 E-mail: sales@pearson-hyds.co.uk

▶ Phoenix Beattie Ltd, Jubilee Industrial Estate, Ashington, Northumberland, NE63 8UB Tel: (01670) 520565 Fax: (01670) 520535 E-mail: sales@phoenixbeattie.co.uk

Pirtek, 5 Stockwell Centre, Stephenson Way, Crawley, West Sussex, RH10 1TN Tel: (01293) 571707 Fax: (01293) 571711 E-mail: pirtekcrawley@fsbdial.co.uk

Power Pipes Pendle, Maud Street Works, Maud Street, Barrowford, Nelson, Lancashire, BB9 8NX Tel: (01282) 601896 Fax: (01282) 697034 E-mail: sales@powerpipes.co.uk

Powertran Hydraulic Equipment, 13 Comber Road, Newtownards, County Down, BT23 4QP Tel: (028) 9181 3427 Fax: (028) 9182 6516

Premier Hydraulics & Pneumatics, Unit 4, Cliffton Business Park, Preston New Road, Clifton, Preston, PR4 0XQ Tel: (01772) 253455 Fax: (01772) 204155

Regent Hose & Hydraulics Ltd, Unit 16-18, Rabans Close, Rabans Lane Industrial Area, Aylesbury, Buckinghamshire, HP19 8RS Tel: (01296) 420171 Fax: (01296) 392306 E-mail: info@regenthose.co.uk

S H Service Hydraulics Ltd, 56 Pinfold Street, Wednesbury, West Midlands, WS10 8TQ Tel: 0121-526 6431 Fax: 0121-568 6683

Stauff UK Southampton, Unit 1-2 Millbrook Trading Estate, Third Avenue, Southampton, SO15 0LD Tel: (023) 8079 9518 Fax: (023) 8079 9519 E-mail: sales@stauffsouthampton.co.uk

Test Valley Engineers Ltd, Stoneymarsh, Michelmersh, Romsey, Hampshire, SO51 0LB Tel: (01794) 368308 Fax: (01794) 368693 E-mail: sales@test-valley.co.uk

Thames Hose & Couplings Ltd, Units 1-2 Canal Industrial Park, Canal Road, Gravesend, Kent, DA12 2PA Tel: (01474) 356485 Fax: (01474) 320392 E-mail: thc.sales@btconnect.com

Trist Draper Hydraulics, Unit 16, Merdock Road, Manton Lane Industrial Estate, Bedford, MK41 7PD Tel: (01234) 212661 Fax: (01234) 270421 E-mail: sales.bedford@trysisdraper.com

Tubes Fittings Valves Ltd, Bath Lane, Mansfield, Nottinghamshire, NG18 2BZ Tel: (01623) 643235 Fax: (01623) 420920 E-mail: sales@tubefiitingsvalves.co.uk

UK Industrial Supplies Ltd, Unit G Motorway Distribution Centre, Avonmouth Way West, Avonmouth, Bristol, BS11 9YT Tel: 0117-923 5653 Fax: 0117-982 0505 E-mail: admin@ukindsup.co.uk

Universal Hydraulic Power, Unit 6 Arden Business Park, Enterprise Close, Medway City Estate, Rochester, Kent, ME2 4LY Tel: (01322) 555452 Fax: (01634) 290871 E-mail: unihose@fastnet.co.uk

Usk Valley Fluid Power, Unit 16 Mill Street Industrial Estate, Mill Street, Abergavenny, Gwent, NP7 5HE Tel: (01873) 857225 Fax: (01873) 858790 E-mail: sales@uskvalleyfp.co.uk

HOSE FITTINGS

A B Trade Supplies, South Denes Road, Great Yarmouth, Norfolk, NR30 3PF Tel: (01493) 859475 Fax: (01493) 330544 E-mail: sales@abtradesupplies.co.uk

Alfa Gomma UK Ltd, 3 Cranford Court, Hardwick Grange, Woolston, Warrington, WA1 4RX Tel: (01925) 820800 Fax: (01925) 810926

▶ Anchor Hydraulics Ltd, Unit 6 Leeds Street, Wigan, Lancashire, WN3 4BW Tel: (01942) 820615 Fax: (01942) 820615 E-mail: anchorhydraulics@btclick.com

NGS – *continued*

...oft & Co. Ltd, 56 Broadbent ..., OL1 4HY Tel: 0161-624 5236 ... 8413 ...ooks20944@aol.com

...Co. (Manchester) Ltd, Newby Road Industrial Estate, Hazel Grove, Stockport, Cheshire, SK7 5DD Tel: 0161-483 9311 Fax: 0161-483 1080 E-mail: sales@bowbros.co.uk

Burnett & Hillman Engineers, Havyatt Road, Coxs Green, Wrington, Bristol, BS40 5NL Tel: (01934) 862980 Fax: (01934) 862616 E-mail: sales@burnettandhillman.co.uk

Carlton Hydraulics Ltd, Chesterton Road, Eastwood Trading Estate, Rotherham, South Yorkshire, S65 1SU Tel: (01709) 378999 Fax: (01709) 820292 E-mail: sales@carlton-hydraulics.co.uk

Comet Fluid Power, Horace Waller V C Parade, Shaw Cross Business Park, Dewsbury, West Yorkshire, WF12 7RF Tel: (01924) 455667 Fax: (01924) 456292 E-mail: comet@challenger-group.co.uk

Custom Fittings Ltd, Pavilion, Cleckheaton, West Yorkshire, BD19 3UD Tel: (01274) 852066 Fax: (01274) 852029 E-mail: sales@customfittings.co.uk

James Dawson & Son Ltd, Unit 7, 2ND Avenue, Poynton Industrial Estate, Poynton, Cheshire, SK12 1ND Tel: (01625) 879494 Fax: (01625) 879555 E-mail: indico@indico-europe.co.uk

Derbyshire Hose & Fittings Ltd, Calow Lane, Hasland, Chesterfield, Derbyshire, S41 0AL Tel: (01246) 477707 Fax: (01246) 222251 E-mail: dhfhyds@aol.com

Elaflex Ltd, Riverside House, Plumpton Road, Hoddesdon, Hertfordshire, EN11 0PA Tel: (01992) 452950 Fax: (01992) 452911 E-mail: info@elaflex.co.uk

Exact Engineering Ltd, 1-4 Burke Road, Totnes, Devon, TQ9 5XL Tel: (01803) 866464 Fax: (01803) 866385 E-mail: sales@exact-eng.co.uk

Flotec Industrial Ltd, Royal Way, Loughborough, Leicestershire, LE11 5XR Tel: (01509) 230100 Fax: (01509) 264100

Forest Hydraulics Ltd, 19-20 Greenshield Industrial Estate, Bradfield Road, London, E16 2AU Tel: (020) 7474 5738 Fax: (020) 7474 5181E-mail: forest.hydraulics@virgin.net

Hiflex Fluidpower Ltd, Unit 6, Monklands Industrial Estate, Kirkshaws Road, Coatbridge, Lanarkshire, ML5 4RP Tel: 01236 702680 Fax: 01236 702685 E-mail: sales@hiflex-fluidpower.com

Hozelock Ltd, Midpoint Park, Kingsbury Road, Minworth, Sutton Coldfield, West Midlands, B76 1AB Tel: 0121-313 4242 Fax: 0121-313 4243

Hydraulic Equipment Supply Co. Ltd, 419 New Kings Road, London, SW6 4RN Tel: (020) 7736 7391 Fax: (020) 7736 7019

Hydraulic Pneumatic Services, Unit 23-24 The Old Mill, School Lane, Bamber Bridge, Preston, PR5 6SY Tel: (01772) 629993 Fax: (01772) 629995 E-mail: info@hps-group.co.uk

Hydroelectic (UK) Ltd, 3 High Road, Byfleet, West Byfleet, Surrey, KT14 7QE Tel: (01932) 334210 Fax: (01932) 334211 E-mail: sales@qualflex.demon.co.uk

Industrial Supply Specialists Ltd, Unit 2, Nelson Way, Nelson Park West, Cramlington, Northumberland, NE23 1WG Tel: (01670) 734422 Fax: (01670) 738877 E-mail: iss@ukf.net

Kingsley Commercial Components Ltd, Oak Hill Works, Broad Street, Guildford, Surrey, GU3 3BJ Tel: (01483) 303092 Fax: (01483) 572242

Kutting UK Ltd, 16 Tanners Drive, Blakelands, Milton Keynes, MK14 5BN Tel: (01908) 218100 Fax: (01908) 218666 E-mail: info@kuttinguk.co.uk

M.A.C.-Rk Precision Engineering Ltd, Unit A1, Bridge Road Industrial Estate, Southall, Middlesex, UB2 4AB Tel: (020) 8843 1999 Fax: (020) 8843 1666 E-mail: office@macfittings.co.uk

Merseyflex Ltd, 46 Mason Street, Edge Hill, Liverpool, L7 3EW Tel: 0151-707 1652 Fax: 0151-708 0128 E-mail: sales@merseyflex.co.uk

Norton Hydraulics Midland Ltd, 43-45 Meriden Street, Birmingham, B5 5LS Tel: 0121-643 0184 Fax: 0121-631 3617 E-mail: sales@nortonhydraulics.com

Parker Dayco, Belfont Trading Estate, Mucklow Hill, Halesowen, West Midlands, B62 8DR Tel: 0121-504 3400 Fax: 0121-550 4274 E-mail: sales@parker.com

Pearson Hydraulics Ltd, 11 Cardinal Close, Lincoln, LN2 4SY Tel: (01522) 510777 Fax: (01522) 510508 E-mail: sales@pearson-hyds.co.uk

H. Potter Engineering Ltd, Fisher Street, Low Walker, Newcastle Upon Tyne, NE6 4LT Tel: 0191-295 4420 Fax: 0191-295 4482

Powertran Hydraulic Equipment, 13 Comber Road, Newtownards, County Down, BT23 4QP Tel: (028) 9181 3427 Fax: (028) 9182 6516

Read Precision Engineering Ltd, 10 William Street, Northampton, NN1 3EW Tel: (01604) 601372 Fax: (01604) 601373 E-mail: sales@readengineering.co.uk

S H Service Hydraulics Ltd, 56 Pinfold Street, Wednesbury, West Midlands, WS10 8TQ Tel: 0121-526 6431 Fax: 0121-568 6683

Shand Engineering Ltd, Kiln Lane, Stallingborough, Grimsby, South Humberside, DN41 8DL Tel: (01469) 571586 Fax: (01469) 571073

Stauff UK Southampton, Unit 1-2 Millbrook Trading Estate, Third Avenue, Southampton, SO15 0LD Tel: (023) 8079 9518 Fax: (023) 8079 9519 E-mail: sales@stauffsouthampton.co.uk

Trist Draper Hydraulics, Unit 16, Merdock Road, Manton Lane Industrial Estate, Bedford, MK41 7PD Tel: (01234) 212661 Fax: (01234) 270421 E-mail: sales.bedford@trysisdraper.com

Truflow Hydraulic Components Ltd, Unit F5 Lockside, Anchor Brook Industrial Park, Aldridge, Walsall, WS9 8BZ Tel: (01922) 745488 Fax: (01922) 745399 E-mail: truflow@bt.co.uk

Universal Hydraulic Power, Unit 6 Arden Business Park, Enterprise Close, Medway City Estate, Rochester, Kent, ME2 4LY Tel: (01322) 555452 Fax: (01634) 290871 E-mail: unihose@fastnet.co.uk

W G Bingham & Co. Ltd, New Warehouse, Manby Road, Immingham, South Humberside, DN40 2LH Tel: (01469) 573945 Fax: (01469) 576057 E-mail: imminghamsales@sorsky.com

HOSE FITTINGS ASSEMBLY SERVICES

J P Miles, Sophurst Wood Lane, Matfield, Tonbridge, Kent, TN12 7LH Tel: (01892) 724315 Fax: (01892) 724319 E-mail: jpmiles@seedersti.co.uk

Tech Hose, Unit 14 Tarsmill Court, Rotherwas Industrial Estate, Hereford, HR2 6JZ Tel: (01432) 270466 Fax: (01432) 351548 E-mail: sales@tech-hose.co.uk

HOSE REELS

Airtec Filtration Ltd, Manor Street, St. Helens, Merseyside, WA9 3AX Tel: (01744) 733211 Fax: (01744) 730917 E-mail: sales@airtecfiltration.com

▶ Fire Break Fire Securities, Tweedside Trading Estate, Tweedmouth, Berwick-upon-Tweed, TD15 2XF Tel: (01289) 307691

Pirtek, 5 Stockwell Centre, Stephenson Way, Crawley, West Sussex, RH10 1TN Tel: (01293) 571707 Fax: (01293) 571711 E-mail: pirtekcrawley@fsbdial.co.uk

Redashe Ltd, Unit 8 The Brook Trading Estate, Deadbrook Lane, Aldershot, Hampshire, GU12 4XB Tel: (01252) 785010 Fax: (01252) 329328 E-mail: info@redashe.co.uk

HOSES, *See also other headings for particular types under Hose*

Captivair Pneumatics Ltd, Unit B2 Imperial Business Estate, Gravesend, Kent, DA11 0DL Tel: (01474) 334537 Fax: (01474) 333657 E-mail: sales@captivair.co.uk

Cebo UK Ltd, Badentoy Road, Portlethen, Aberdeen, AB12 4YA Tel: (01224) 782020 Fax: (01224) 782340 E-mail: info@cebo-uk.com

Emplas Ltd, Saddington Road, Fleckney, Leicester, LE8 8AW Tel: 0116-240 3407

Esen Group, Heywood House, High Street, Bolton, BL3 6SR Tel: (01204) 386363 Fax: (01204) 386365 E-mail: industrialhose@esengroup.co.uk

Gwent Hydraulics, 8 Skillion Business Centre, Corporation Road, Newport, Gwent, NP19 4RF Tel: (01633) 280005 Fax: (01633) 273140

Hydraquip Hose, Head Office, 2 Raleigh Court, Crawley, West Sussex, RH10 9PD Tel: (01293) 615166 Fax: (01293) 614965 E-mail: sales@hydraquip.co.uk

Kutting UK Ltd, 16 Tanners Drive, Blakelands, Milton Keynes, MK14 5BN Tel: (01908) 218100 Fax: (01908) 218666 E-mail: info@kuttinguk.co.uk

Merlett Plastics (UK) Ltd, Unit 2, Waverley Road, Beeches Industrial Estate, Yate, Bristol, BS37 5QT Tel: (01454) 329888 Fax: (01454) 324499

Tech Hose, Unit 14 Tarsmill Court, Rotherwas Industrial Estate, Hereford, HR2 6JZ Tel: (01432) 270466 Fax: (01432) 351548 E-mail: sales@tech-hose.co.uk

HOSES, COOLANT, SILICONE

▶ Viper Performance, Registered Office: 21 Kiniths Way, Birmingham, B62 9HJ Tel: 0121 6028359 E-mail: pitstoptuning@blueyonder.co.uk

HOSES, FOOD/BEVERAGE INDUSTRY

A R P Co. Ltd, Unit 2 Jubilee Way, Avonmouth, Bristol, BS11 9HU Tel: 0117-982 6301 Fax: 0117-923 5487 E-mail: sales@avonmouth-rubber.co.uk

Abdex Hose & Couplings Ltd, Unit 3 Commerce Way, Leighton Buzzard, Bedfordshire, LU7 4RW Tel: (01525) 377770 Fax: (01525) 851990 E-mail: enquiries@abdexhose.com

Flexible Hose Supplies Ltd, 12 Osyth Close, Brackmills Industrial Estate, Northampton, NN4 7DY Tel: (01604) 762175 Fax: (01604) 769915 E-mail: sales@fhsn.co.uk

Hose Tech Ltd, 3 Wheatlea Industrial Estate, Wheatlea Road, Wigan, Lancashire, WN3 6XP Tel: (01942) 233036 Fax: (01942) 322915 E-mail: sales@hose-tech.co.uk

Saint Gobain Performance Plastics, 13 Earlstrees Road, Earlstrees Industrial Estate, Corby, Northamptonshire, NN17 4AZ Tel: (01536) 276000 Fax: (01536) 203427 E-mail: pplcorbyuk@aol.com

HOSES, GARDEN, *See headings according to material used*

HOSES, HYDRAULIC, SPRING ARMOURING

Bywell Springs & Pressings Ltd, Unit 4, Millsborough House, Ipsley St, Redditch, Worcestershire, B98 7AL Tel: (01527) 66551 Fax: (01527) 66024 E-mail: sales@bywell.co.uk

HOSIERY

A Bennett Hosiery Ltd, North End Mills, North End, Wirksworth, Matlock, Derbyshire, DE4 4FG Tel: (01629) 822677 Fax: (01629) 824731

Albert Harrison Company Ltd, Queens Road, Accrington, Lancashire, BB5 6DS Tel: (01254) 306840 Fax: (01254) 872174 E-mail: sales@albert-harrison.co.uk

Andrea Hosiery Manufacturing Co. Ltd, 107-115 Humberstone Road, Leicester, LE5 3AN Tel: 0116-262 5543 Fax: 0116-262 8732

Angell Hosiery Ltd, Ashford Road, Leicester, LE2 6AA Tel: 0116-270 0698 Fax: 0116-270 1040

Bedewear Manufacturing Co. Ltd, Bede Street, Leicester, LE3 5LD Tel: 0116-254 9031

Burt Bros Hosiery Ltd, A-C Willow Road, Nottingham, NG7 2TA Tel: 0115-970 6133 Fax: 0115-942 0576 E-mail: burtbros@premier.co.uk

Cautaulds UK, West Mill, Bridge Foot, Belper, Derbyshire, DE56 1BH Tel: (01773) 525525 Fax: (01773) 525545 E-mail:

▶ Cheeky Legs Wholesale Tights and Hosiery, Unit 10 Coombe Park, Ashprington, Totnes, Devon, TQ9 7DY Tel: (0845) 2576847 E-mail: admin@cheekylegs.co.uk

Corgi Hosiery Ltd, New Road, Ammanford, Dyfed, SA18 3DS Tel: (01269) 592104 Fax: (01269) 593220 E-mail: sales@corgihosiery.co.uk

Daner Ltd, 36 Walsall Road, Willenhall, West Midlands, WV13 2EG Tel: (01902) 368788 Fax: (01902) 637584E-mail: info@daner.co.uk

Drew Brady & Co. Ltd, Dove Mill, Dove Road, Bolton, BL3 4ET Tel: (01204) 854800 Fax: (01204) 854854 E-mail: drewbrady@ruia.co.uk

Samuel Eden & Son Ltd, Station Road, Sutton-in-Ashfield, Nottinghamshire, NG17 5FQ Tel: (01623) 553521 Fax: (01623) 552115 E-mail: sales@samueleden.co.uk

Elegant Textile, 93 Commerce Street, Glasgow, G5 8EP Tel: 0141-420 1533 Fax: 0141-420 1533 E-mail: eleganttextiles@hotmail.com

Eleganti Ltd, 3 Derby Road, Eastwood, Nottingham, NG16 3PA Tel: (01773) 534700 Fax: (01773) 534700

F & B Hosiery Manufacturing Co. Ltd, 10 Nether Street, Manchester, M12 6HY Tel: 0161-273 5689 Fax: 0161-273 5691

F J Bamkin & Son Ltd, Unit 3 Washdyke Lane Workshops, Washdyke Lane, Hucknall, Nottingham, NG15 6NH Tel: 0115-963 2020 Fax: 0115-968 0013 E-mail: info@penninebamkin.co.uk

Flude Hosiery, Rugby Road, Hinckley, Leicestershire, LE10 0QQ Tel: (01455) 615543 Fax: (01455) 615543 E-mail: sales@flude.co.uk

M. Holt (M/C) Ltd, 159 Cheetham Hill Road, Manchester, M8 8LG Tel: 0161-832 2210 Fax: 0161-839 5217

Jade Hosiery Ltd, 598 Atlas Road, Wembley, Middlesex, HA9 0JH Tel: (020) 8902 1292 Fax: (020) 8902 7942 E-mail: sales@jade.co.uk

Instra Textiles, 37 Equity Road, Leicester, LE3 0AS Tel: 0116-255 1588 Fax: 0116-255 1589 E-mail: instra@amserve.net

J Alex Swift Ltd, Cross Street, Hathern, Loughborough, Leicestershire, LE12 5LB Tel: (01509) 842284 Fax: (01509) 646106 E-mail: socks@jalexswift.co.uk

Ladkin Hosiery Ltd, Seagrave Road, Sileby, Loughborough, Leicestershire, LE12 7TT Tel: (01509) 813344 Fax: (01509) 816663

Madison Hosiery, Mill Green, Leeds, LS12 6HE Tel: 0113-244 3434 Fax: 0113-242 5634

Nylon Hosiery, 44 Upper Bond Street, Hinckley, Leicestershire, LE10 1RJ Tel: (01455) 631413 Fax: (01455) 636345 E-mail: rob@nylonhosiery.co.uk

Pak Nylon Hosiery Co, 31 Broughton Street, Cheetham Hill, Manchester, M8 8LZ Tel: 0161 832 7371 Fax: 0161 839 5134 E-mail: C_M_Afzal_Khan@hotmail.co.uk

Gregory Pollard Ltd, Regent Road, Countesthorpe, Leicester, LE8 5RF Tel: 0116-277 9789 Fax: 0116-278 4395 E-mail: info@magicfit.co.uk

Reeling Systems Ltd, Unit A3 Pegasus Court, Ardglen Road, Whitchurch, Hampshire, RG28 7BP Tel: (01256) 896517 Fax: (01256) 895624

▶ Seductive Lingerie, 14 Enderby Road, Scunthorpe, South Humberside, DN17 2HD Tel: (01724) 332874 E-mail: seller.seller@ntlworld.com

Swift Ltd, Mistral House, Parsons Lane, Hinckley, Leicestershire, LE10 1XT Tel: (01455) 238398 Fax: (01455) 238866

Tartan Hose, 44 Newry Road, Kilkeel, Newry, County Down, BT34 4DU Tel: (028) 4176 5717 Fax: (028) 4176 3241 E-mail: tartanhose@btconnect.com

Tots & Teens Ltd, Unit B Cumberland Business Park, 17 Cumberland Avenue, London, NW10 7RT Tel: (020) 8965 8158 Fax: (020) 8961 6184 E-mail: contex@babybright.co.uk

W Brewin & Co Ltd, Eastern Boulevard, Leicester, LE2 7BE Tel: 0116-254 6372 Fax: 0116-254 2856

HOSIERY PRODUCTION MACHINERY, *See Knitting Machinery etc*

HOSPITAL BEDS/BEDSTEADS

Hill-Rom UK Ltd, Clinitron House, Ashby Park, Ashby-de-la-Zouch, Leicestershire, LE65 1JG Tel: (01530) 411000 Fax: (01530) 411555 E-mail: name@hill-rom.co.uk

Hoskins Medical Equipment, Woodsbank Trading Estate, Woden Road West, Wednesbury, West Midlands, WS10 7BL Tel: 0121-707 6600 Fax: 0121-502 2092 E-mail: sales@hoskinsme.co.uk

Huntleigh Healthcare Ltd, 310-312 Dallow Road, Luton, LU1 1TD Tel: (01582) 413104 Fax: (01582) 459100 E-mail: sales.admin@huntleigh-healthcare.com

Huntleigh Nesbit Evans Ltd, Woodsbank Trading Estate, Woden Road West, Wednesbury, West Midlands, WS10 7BL Tel: 0121-556 1511 Fax: 0121-502 2092 E-mail: sales@huntcare.co.uk

Pennine Systems Ltd, Crossley Works, Stockfield Mount, Off Peel Street, Chadderton, Oldham, OL9 9LR Tel: 0161 678 2998 Fax: 0161 678 2997 E-mail: sales@penninesystems.co.uk

Turnwright Ltd, 12 & 19 Barking Industrial Park, Alfreds Way, Barking, Essex, IG11 0TJ Tel: (020) 8591 2862 Fax: (020) 8594 6999 E-mail: sales@turnwright.freeserve.co.uk

HOSPITAL CATERING EQUIPMENT

Promart Manufacturing Ltd, Caddick Road, Knowsley Industrial Park South, Knowsley Business Park, Prescot, Merseyside, L34 9HP Tel: 0151-547 4666 Fax: 0151-546 6152 E-mail: sales@promart.co.uk

HOSPITAL CLEANING CONTRACTORS OR SERVICES

I S S Support Services, Strathdon Drive, London, SW17 0PS Tel: (020) 8947 9045 Fax: (020) 8947 9732

T C M S Ltd, St. Shads Industrial Estate, Brearley Street, Hockley, Birmingham, B19 3NP Tel: 0121-333 5824 Fax: 0121-333 5829 E-mail: tcmsmidland@ukonline.co.uk

HOSPITAL CUBICLE TRACKS

Manor Supplies Incorporating Manor Blinds, The Old Forge, Hall Lane, Upminster, Essex, RM14 1TT Tel: (01708) 377518 Fax: (01708) 343003

Ritetrack, Harrowby Business Centre, Harrowby Place, Cardiff, CF10 5GB Tel: (029) 2049 9877 Fax: (029) 2046 2462

Silent Gliss Ltd, Pyramid Business Park, Poorhole Lane, Broadstairs, Kent, CT10 2PT Tel: (01843) 863571 Fax: (01843) 864503 E-mail: info@silentgliss.co.uk

HOSPITAL DISPOSABLE PAPER PRODUCTS

I P S Hospital Services, Unit 5 Featherstall Road South, Oldham, OL9 6HS Tel: 0161-626 1844 Fax: 0161-627 5202 E-mail: ips@ipshospitalservices.co.uk

Kimberly Clark Ltd, 1 Tower View, Kings Hill, West Malling, Kent, ME19 4HA Tel: (01732) 594000 Fax: (01732) 594001

HOSPITAL DISPOSABLE PRODUCTS

Asher Andell Ltd, Midway House, Main Road, Upper Broughton, Melton Mowbray, Leicestershire, LE14 3BG Tel: (01664) 822131 Fax: (01664) 823332 E-mail: medical@asher-andell.co.uk

HOSPITAL DISPOSABLE PRODUCTS

– continued

Associated Hospital Supply Ltd, Sherwood Road, Aston Fields, Bromsgrove, Worcestershire, B60 3DR Tel: (01527) 876776 Fax: (01527) 872022 E-mail: info@associatedhospitalsupply.com
Flexicare Medical Ltd, CWM Cynon Business Park, Mountain Ash, Mid Glamorgan, CF45 4ER Tel: (01443) 474647 Fax: (01443) 474222 E-mail: sales@flexicare.com
Fourstones Paper Mill Co. Ltd, South Tyne Mill, Hexham, Northumberland, NE46 3SD Tel: (01434) 602444 Fax: (01434) 607046 E-mail: team@fourstonespapermill.co.uk
Haddenham Healthcare Ltd, Crendon House, Drakes Drive, Long Crendon, Aylesbury, Buckinghamshire, HP18 9BB Tel: (01844) 208842 Fax: (01844) 208843 E-mail: sales@hadhealth.com
I P S Hospital Services, Unit 5 Featherstall Road South, Oldham, OL9 6HS Tel: 0161-626 1844 Fax: 0161-627 5202 E-mail: ips@ipshospitalservices.co.uk
Kimal plc, Sherwood Road, Bromsgrove, Worcestershire, B60 3DR Tel: (01527) 572300 Fax: (01527) 579936 E-mail: sales@kimal.co.uk
Kimal P.L.C., Arundel Road, Uxbridge Industrial Estate, Uxbridge, Middlesex, UB8 2SA Tel: (01895) 270951 Fax: (01895) 274035
Lantor (UK) Ltd, 73 St. Helens Road, Bolton, BL3 3PP Tel: (01204) 855000 Fax: (01204) 61722 E-mail: sales@lantor.co.uk
▶ Lifecare Hospital Supplies Ltd, Shenstone Drive, Aldridge, Walsall, WS9 8TP Tel: (01922) 455405 Fax: (01922) 749943 E-mail: rhall@hs-lifecare.com
Omni-Pac UK Ltd, South Denes, Great Yarmouth, Norfolk, NR30 3QH Tel: (01493) 855381 Fax: (01493) 858464
Orvec International Ltd, Malmo Road, Hull, HU7 0YF Tel: (01482) 879146 Fax: (01482) 625325 E-mail: service@orvec.com
Rocialle Medical Ltd, Dales Manor Business Park, Grove Road, Sawston, Cambridge, CB22 3TJ Tel: (01223) 495700 Fax: (01223) 495701 E-mail: info@rocialle.com
Ross Lab plc, Ross Lab House, Fence Avenue Industrial Estate, Macclesfield, Cheshire, SK10 1LT Tel: (01625) 610077 Fax: (01625) 619877 E-mail: sales@rosslab.com
Ivor Shaw Ltd, 300 City Gate Business Park, City Gate, Derby, DE24 8WY Tel: (01332) 794880 Fax: (01332) 794891 E-mail: ivorshawltd@penninehealthcare.co.uk
Smiths Medical International, The Belfry, Colonial Way, Watford, WD24 4LG Tel: (01706) 233821 Fax: (01706) 218834 E-mail: ukcs@smiths-medical.com
Synergie Healthcare Ltd, Lyon Mill, Fitton Street, Royton, Oldham, OL2 5JX Tel: 0161-624 5641 Fax: 0161-627 0902
Vygon UK Ltd, Bridge Road, Cirencester, Gloucestershire, GL7 1PT Tel: (01285) 657051 Fax: (01285) 650293 E-mail: vygon@vygon.co.uk

HOSPITAL ENGINEERING SERVICES OR CONTRACTORS

▶ Fulbourn Medical, 5 Station Yard, Wilbraham Road, Fulbourn, Cambridge, CB21 5ET Tel: (01223) 880909 Fax: (01223) 880078 E-mail: info@fulbournmedical.com
Henderson Biomedical Ltd, 97 Avenue Road, Beckenham, Kent, BR3 4RX Tel: (020) 8402 4426 Fax: (020) 8778 4571 E-mail: info@henderson-biomedical.co.uk

HOSPITAL EQUIPMENT CASTORS

Colson Castors Ltd, Golds Green Works, Bagnall Street, Hill Top, West Bromwich, West Midlands, B70 0TZ Tel: 0121-556 7221 Fax: 0121-502 2658
Colson Castors Ltd, Golds Green Works, Bagnall Street, West Bromwich, West Midlands, B70 0TS Tel: 0121-556 7221 Fax: 0121-502 6258 E-mail: info@colson-castors.co.uk
Guitel Ltd, Unit 1, Lisle Road, High Wycombe, Buckinghamshire, HP13 5SH Tel: (01494) 473030 Fax: (01494) 473031 E-mail: guiteluk@msn.com
Manner UK Ltd, 13 Station Road, Cam, Dursley, Gloucestershire, GL11 5NS Tel: (01453) 546333 Fax: (01453) 549222 E-mail: sales@manner.co.uk
Turnwright Ltd, 12 & 19 Barking Industrial Park, Alfreds Way, Barking, Essex, IG11 0TJ Tel: (020) 8591 2862 Fax: (020) 8594 6999 E-mail: sales@turnwright.freeserve.co.uk

HOSPITAL FITTERS AND FURNISHERS

Domino Equipping Solutions, Ashmead Close, Newcastle Upon Tyne, NE12 6GB Tel: 0191-268 1171 Fax: 0191-268 1171

HOSPITAL GARMENTS

Harveys & Co. Clothing Ltd, Glodwick Road, Oldham, OL4 1YU Tel: 0161-624 9535 Fax: 0161-627 2028 E-mail: info@harveys.co.uk
John Maden & Sons Ltd, Market Street, Bacup, Lancashire, OL13 0AU Tel: (01706) 873544 Fax: (01706) 879130 E-mail: info@johnmaden.com
Work In Style Ltd, Keighley Business Centre, South Street, Keighley, West Yorkshire, BD21 1AG Tel: (01535) 667625 Fax: (01535) 610488 E-mail: sales@workinstyle.com

HOSPITAL INFECTION CONTROL PRODUCTS

Daniels Healthcare, Unit 14 Station Field Industrial Estate, Kidlington, Oxfordshire, OX5 1JD Tel: (01865) 371841 Fax: (01865) 841869 E-mail: info@daniels.co.uk

HOSPITAL LAUNDRY SERVICES

Blackpool Laundry Co. Ltd, Unit 6e Moor Park Industrial Estate, Kincraig Road, Blackpool, FY2 0JY Tel: (01253) 500014 Fax: (01253) 500014 E-mail: sales@blackpoollaundry.com

HOSPITAL LIGHTING

▶ Anglepoise Ltd, 6 Stratfield Park, Elettra Avenue, Waterlooville, Hampshire, PO7 7XN Tel: (023) 9225 0934 Fax: (023) 9225 0696 E-mail: sales@anglepoise.co.uk
Brandon Medical Co. Ltd, Holme Well Road, Leeds, LS10 4TQ Tel: 0113 2777393 Fax: 0113 2728844 E-mail: enquiries@brandon-medical.com
Daray Lighting Ltd, Unit 6A, Commerce Way, Stanbridge Road, Leighton Buzzard, Bedfordshire, LU7 4RW Tel: (01525) 376766 Fax: (01525) 216519 E-mail: info@daray.com

HOSPITAL MATTRESSES

Spenco Healthcare International, Brian Royd Mills, Saddleworth Road, Greetland, Halifax, West Yorkshire, HX4 8NF Tel: (01422) 378569 Fax: (01422) 376064 E-mail: sales@spenco-healthcare.co.uk
S. Teasdale (Hospital Equipment) Ltd, Unit 1 & 2, Brighton Road, Stockport, Cheshire, SK4 2BE Tel: 0161-219 0080 Fax: 0161-219 0081

HOSPITAL NURSE CALL EQUIPMENT

Care Com Ltd, Unit 24 Kenfig Industrial Estate, Margam, Port Talbot, West Glamorgan, SA13 2PE Tel: (01656) 749500 Fax: (01656) 749200 E-mail: sales@carecom.co.uk
Dove Technology UK Ltd, 8 London Road, Worcester, WR5 2DL Tel: (01905) 353153 Fax: (01905) 352863 E-mail: sales@dovetech.co.uk
Initial Attendo Ltd, Shadsworth Business Park, Blackburn, BB1 2PR Tel: (01254) 688688 Fax: (01254) 696460 E-mail: info@attendo.co.uk
Live-Link Communications Ltd, 6 Milrig Cottage, Kirknewton, Midlothian, EH27 8DE Tel: (01506) 884404 Fax: (01506) 884406 E-mail: nursecallalarms@aol.com
Medical & Industrial Manufacturing Co. Ltd, Broadway, Dukinfield, Cheshire, SK16 4UU Tel: 0161-339 6028 Fax: 0161-330 0944 E-mail: mimcoltd@compuserve.com
Overseas Medical Supplies UK Ltd, 14 Cumberland Avenue, London, NW10 7QL Tel: (020) 8965 9711 Fax: (020) 8965 6894 E-mail: oms@overseasmedical.com
The Wandsworth Group Ltd, Albert Drive, Sheerwater, Woking, Surrey, GU21 5SE Tel: (01483) 713400 Fax: (01483) 740384 E-mail: info@wandsworthgroup.com

HOSPITAL OCCUPATIONAL THERAPY EQUIPMENT OR MATERIALS

Nomeq Ltd, Unit 25-26 North St Industrial Estate, Droitwich, Worcestershire, WR9 8JB Tel: (01905) 795005 Fax: (01905) 796655 E-mail: info@nomeq.co.uk
Therapy Equipment Ltd, 1 Cranborne Industrial Estate, Cranborne Road, Potters Bar, Hertfordshire, EN6 3JN Tel: (01707) 652270 Fax: (01707) 652622 E-mail: sales@therapyequipment.co.uk

HOSPITAL PLASTIC EQUIPMENT/PRODUCTS, *See also Medical or Surgical Goods, Plastic*

B C I Stretchers Ltd, 386-388 South Eldon Street, South Shields, Tyne & Wear, NE33 5SY Tel: 0191-455 3984 Fax: 0191-456 9653 E-mail: info@bci-stretchers.co.uk
Cape Warwick Ltd, 47 Britannia Way, Britannia Enterprise Park, Lichfield, Staffordshire, WS14 9UY Tel: (01543) 414544 Fax: (01543) 414599E-mail: enquiries@cape-warwick.co.uk

HOSPITAL SECURITY SERVICES

▶ Censor Security, Unit 342 Camberwell Business Centre, 99-103 Lomond Grove, London, SE5 7HN Tel: (0845) 2309816 Fax: (020) 7703 7243 E-mail: admin@censorgroup.co.uk

HOSPITAL STAINLESS STEEL EQUIPMENT/PRODUCTS

Philip Chapper & Co. Ltd, Unit 1, Orbital 25 Business Park, Dwight Road, Watford, WD18 9DA Tel: (01923) 235179 Fax: (01923) 242278
Ensign Associates, 75 Bourn Lea, Houghton le Spring, Tyne & Wear, DH4 4PF Tel: 0191-385 5188 Fax: 0191-385 5188
Gulfex Medical Supplies Ltd, 7 Burgess Wood Road South, Beaconsfield, Buckinghamshire, HP9 1EU Tel: (01494) 675353 Fax: (01494) 675399
Sanitary Appliances Ltd, 3 Sandiford Road, Sutton, Surrey, SM3 9RN Tel: (020) 8641 0310 Fax: (020) 8641 6426 E-mail: info@sanitaryappliances.co.uk
Stainless Design Services Ltd, C The Old Bakery, Kiln Lane, Swindon, SN2 2NP Tel: (01793) 692666 Fax: (01793) 487242 E-mail: sds@stainlessdesign.co.uk
William G. Fuller & Co. Ltd, 43 Earl Street, Hastings, East Sussex, TN34 1SG Tel: (01424) 426094 Fax: (01424) 444763 E-mail: sales@fullermedical.co.uk

HOSPITALITY PROFIT CONSULTANCY

Trinity Expert Systems, 1 The Oaks, Westwood Way, Westwood Business Park, Coventry, CV4 8JB Tel: (024) 7642 0100 Fax: (024) 7642 0111 E-mail: info@tesl.com

HOT AIR BALLOON FABRICS

▶ Classic Hot Air Ballooning, Home Farm Cottage, Lenham Heath Road, Sandway, Maidstone, Kent, ME17 2HX Tel: (01622) 858956 Fax: (01622) 853817 E-mail: glen@ballooning.fsnet.co.uk
▶ Hot Air Balloons, 1 Home Farm Cottage, Lenham Heath Road, Sandway, Maidstone, Kent, ME17 2HX Tel: (01622) 858956 Fax: (01622) 853817 E-mail: lizmeek@ballooning.fsnet.co.uk

HOT AIR SOLDER LEVELLING EQUIPMENT

Circuit Engineering Marketing Co. Ltd, 1 Silverthorne Way, Waterlooville, Hampshire, PO7 7XB Tel: (023) 9226 2120 Fax: (023) 9226 2089 E-mail: sales@cemco.com

HOT BRASS PRESSINGS

Cerro Ems Ltd, Liverpool Street, Birmingham, B9 4DS Tel: 0121-772 6515 Fax: 0121-772 6126
John Buckley Dudley Ltd, Alma Place, Dudley, West Midlands, DY2 8QH Tel: (01384) 252554 Fax: (01384) 456172 E-mail: sales@buckleybrass.co.uk

HOT BRASS STAMPINGS

John Buckley Dudley Ltd, Alma Place, Dudley, West Midlands, DY2 8QH Tel: (01384) 252554 Fax: (01384) 456172 E-mail: sales@buckleybrass.co.uk
Leslie Group Ltd, 198-202 Waterloo Road, Yardley, Birmingham, B25 8LD Tel: 0121-708 1123 Fax: 0121-707 7793 E-mail: sales@leslie.co.uk
M Wellings Engineering, Unit 38 Premier Partnership Estate, Leys Road, Brierley Hill, West Midlands, DY5 3UP Tel: (01384) 74927 Fax: (01384) 74927 E-mail: mick@mwellings.fsnet.co.uk
Midcast Stampings Ltd, Enterprise Drive, Four Ashes, Wolverhampton, WV10 7DF Tel: (01902) 791971 Fax: (01902) 791030
R J Clark, Unit 7 Enterprise Trading Est, Pedmore Road, Brierley Hill, West Midlands, DY5 1TX Tel: (01384) 480290 Fax: (01384) 481961
Rainsford & Lynes Ltd, Diadem Works, Kings Road, Tyseley, Birmingham, B11 2AJ Tel: 0121-706 6301 Fax: 0121-707 0995 E-mail: sales@rainsford-lynes.co.uk

HOT COLD PACKS

▶ C S & S Ltd, 5 Tavistock Road, West Bridgford, Nottingham, NG2 6FH Tel: 0115-974 5146 Fax: 0870 762 0539 E-mail: info@chinasourceandsupply.com

HOT FIRE TRAINING EQUIPMENT

Baron Fire, Lubbards Lodge, Hullbridge Road, Rayleigh, Essex, SS6 9QG Tel: (01702) 230082 Fax: (01702) 230082 E-mail: info@baronfire.co.uk
Concept Engineering Ltd, 7 Woodlands Business Park, Woodlands Park Avenue, Maidenhead, Berkshire, SL6 3UA Tel: (01628) 825555 Fax: (01628) 826261 E-mail: info@concept-smoke.co.uk
Kidde Fire Protection Services Ltd, Unit 12 Llwyn' Y' Graig, Garngoth Industrial Estate, Gorsenion, Swansea, SA4 9WG Tel: (01792) 898884 Fax: (01792) 891808 E-mail: kfpfswansea@kiddefps.com
Kidde Fire Training Ltd, M1 Markham Lane, Duckmanton, Chesterfield, Derbyshire, S44 5HS Tel: (01246) 242700 Fax: (01246) 242701

HOT FOIL, *See Hot Foil etc*

HOT FOIL PRESSES, *See Hot Foil etc*

HOT FOIL (STAMPING/ BLOCKING) MANUFRS

A P I Foils Ltd, Astor Road, Salford, M50 1BB Tel: 0161-789 8131 Fax: 0161-707 5315 E-mail: marketing@apigroup.com
▶ Abacus Presentation Services, Unit 5 Hermitage Road, London, N4 1LZ Tel: (020) 8211 1600 Fax: (020) 8211 1600 E-mail: info@abacuspresentationservices.co.uk
Applied Holographics plc, 40 Phoenix Road, Washington, Tyne & Wear, NE38 0AD Tel: 0191-417 5434 Fax: 0191-417 6591 E-mail: sales@applied-holographics.com
H.M. Avison & Co. Ltd, 305 Feltham Hill Road, Ashford, Middlesex, TW15 1LT Tel: (01784) 253130 Fax: (01784) 253130
Chiltern Foil Printing Co., 6 Acorn Business Centre, Cublington Road, Wing, Leighton Buzzard, Bedfordshire, LU7 0LB Tel: (01296) 682299 Fax: (01296) 682299 E-mail: plucas@fsbdial.co.uk
▶ Empress Foil Blocking, The Old Ebenezer Chapel, Sweetshouse, Bodmin, Cornwall, PL30 5AL Tel: (01208) 871487 Fax: (01208) 871487 E-mail: sales@empressfoilblocking.co.uk
Foil & Tool Services Ltd, Tudor Business Centre, Marsden Road, Redditch, Worcestershire, B98 7AY Tel: (01527) 65352 Fax: (01527) 591790 E-mail: foilandtoolservices@onetel.net.com
Foilco Ltd, Enterprise Way, Lowton, Warrington, WA3 2BP Tel: (01942) 262622 Fax: (01942) 267200 E-mail: sales@foilco.co.uk
G K Marketing Services Ltd, Unit 22 Crossfield Industrial Estate, Crossfield Road, Lichfield, Staffordshire, WS13 6RJ Tel: (01543) 414130 Fax: (01543) 250660 E-mail: sales@gkmktg.com
Hot Metal Press, Museum Works Elscar Workshops, Wath Road, Elsecar, Barnsley, South Yorkshire, S74 8HJ Tel: (01226) 740498 Fax: (01226) 350201 E-mail: info@hotmetalpress.co.uk
I T W Foils, Kays & Kears Industrial Estate, Blaenavon, Pontypool, Gwent, NP4 9AZ Tel: (01495) 796500 Fax: (01495) 790797 E-mail: info@itwfoils.co.uk
Oak Die Stamping & Engraving Co. Ltd, Tyburn Industrial Estate, Ashold Farm Road, Birmingham, B24 9QG Tel: 0121-382 4585 Fax: 0121-377 6359 E-mail: ordes-oak@btconnect.com

HOT FOIL STAMPING/ BLOCKING/PRINTING MACHINE MANUFRS

Foil & Tool Services Ltd, Tudor Business Centre, Marsden Road, Redditch, Worcestershire, B98 7AY Tel: (01527) 65352 Fax: (01527) 591790 E-mail: foilandtoolservices@onetel.net.com

HOT FOIL STAMPING/BLOCKING/ PRINTING MACHINE MANUFRS –

continued

Newfoil Ltd, Bradford Street, Farnworth, Bolton, BL4 9LS Tel: (01204) 861110 Fax: (01204) 862201 E-mail: info@newfoil.co.uk
Overprint Packaging Ltd, 12 Canal Way, Harefield, Uxbridge, Middlesex, UB9 6TH Tel: (01895) 824090 Fax: (01428) 654769 E-mail: enquiries@prestonprinters.com
Sas Machine, Watton Road, Ware, Hertfordshire, SG12 0AE Tel: (01920) 465281 Fax: (01920) 465285 E-mail: sales@sasmachines.co.uk
Team Decorating Co., Unit 4 Beggarlee Park, Engine Lane, Newthorpe, Nottingham, NG16 3RN Tel: (01773) 760060 Fax: (01773) 760081 E-mail: teamdecorating@tiscali.co.uk

HOT FOIL STAMPING/ BLOCKING/PRINTING SERVICES

A P I Foils Ltd, Loughborough University, Ashby Road, Loughborough, Leicester, LE11 3TU Tel: (01509) 265232 Fax: (01509) 232772
▶ Abacus Presentation Services, Unit 5 Hermitage Road, London, N4 1LZ Tel: (020) 8211 1600 Fax: (020) 8211 1600 E-mail: info@abacuspresentationservices.co.uk
Abm Labels & Print, Blaenant Industrial Estate, Blaenavon Road, Brynmawr, Ebbw Vale, Gwent, NP23 4BX Tel: (01495) 312835 Fax: (01495) 312819 E-mail: info@abmlabels.co.uk
Benwell Cebard Ltd, 24 Crimscott Street, London, SE1 5TE Tel: (020) 7237 5111 Fax: (020) 7252 0683 E-mail: info@benwellsebard.co.uk
Boxpak Ltd, 65 Church Road, Newtownabbey, County Antrim, BT36 7LR Tel: (028) 9036 5421 Fax: (028) 9086 6731 E-mail: sales@boxpak.co.uk
Chapman & Mellor, 20 Hockley Hill, Birmingham, B18 5AQ Tel: 0121-554 3778 Fax: 0121-554 7931 E-mail: sales@foilprinters.co.uk
Crown Gold Blocking Co. Ltd, 63 Camden Street, Birmingham, B1 3DD Tel: 0121-233 1670 Fax: 0121-233 1670
Crown Manufactory Rotherham Ltd, Chapel Walk, Masborough Street, Rotherham, South Yorkshire, S60 1EP Tel: (01709) 562957 Fax: (01709) 554728
▶ Fine Cut Graphic Imaging Ltd, Marlborough Road, Lancing Business Park, Lancing, West Sussex, BN15 8UF Tel: (01903) 751666 Fax: (01903) 750462 E-mail: info@finecut.co.uk
Foil & Bookcraft, Unit 27 Baldock Industrial Estate, London Road, Baldock, Hertfordshire, SG7 6NG Tel: (01462) 490074 Fax: (01462) 490074
Foilco Ltd, Enterprise Way, Lowton, Warrington, WA3 2BP Tel: (01942) 262622 Fax: (01942) 267200 E-mail: sales@foilco.co.uk
G K Marketing Services Ltd, Unit 22 Crossfield Industrial Estate, Crossfield Road, Lichfield, Staffordshire, WS13 6RJ Tel: (01543) 414130 Fax: (01543) 250660 E-mail: sales@gkmktg.com
Gilt Edge Plastics, The Elms, Church Road, Harold Wood, Romford, RM3 0JU Tel: (01708) 379005 Fax: (01708) 379045 E-mail: sales@giltedgeplastics.co.uk
Grabern Engraving, Oyster Place, 28 Montrose Rd, Chelmsford, CM2 6TX Tel: (01245) 468223 Fax: (01245) 469121 E-mail: sales@grabernengraving.com
H M T Plastics Ltd, 31a Framfield Road, Uckfield, East Sussex, TN22 5AH Tel: (01825) 769393 Fax: (01825) 769494 E-mail: hmtp@aol.com
Hedleys Gold Embossers, Unit 8-9 Poland Industrial Estate, Manchester, M4 6AZ Tel: 0161-205 4496 Fax: 0161-205 4496 E-mail: sales@goldblocking.co.uk
Holloid Plastics Ltd, Stephenson Road, Basingstoke, Hampshire, RG21 6XR Tel: (01256) 334700 Fax: (01256) 473735 E-mail: mail@holloid-plastics.co.uk
Kimco Hot Foil Printers, 1 Waterside Court, Bone Lane, Newbury, Berkshire, RG14 5SH Tel: (01635) 30154 Fax: (01635) 32245 E-mail: petekimco@aol.com
▶ Millennium Printing Services, 12 Barnsbury Close, New Malden, Surrey, KT3 5BP Tel: 020 89425488 Fax: 070 92300436 E-mail: barryrnps@blueyonder.co.uk
Nicol & Moon Ltd, 7 Wimbledon Stadium Business Centre, Riverside Road, London, SW17 0BA Tel: (020) 8879 6000 Fax: (020) 8879 6111 E-mail: info@nicolandmoon.ltd.uk
Nicro Print Services, Unit 13 Faraday Close, Washington, Tyne & Wear, NE38 8QJ Tel: 0191-417 8905 Fax: 0191-417 3496 E-mail: ray_foster@btconnect.co.uk
Printafoil Ltd, 5 Mitcham Industrial Estate, Streatham Road, Mitcham, Surrey, CR4 2AP Tel: (020) 8640 3074 Fax: (020) 8640 2136 E-mail: info@blockfoil.com
R W Plastics (UK) Ltd, 16 Manor Park, 35 Willis Way, Fleet Industrial Estate, Poole, Dorset, BH15 3SZ Tel: (01202) 673373 Fax: (01202) 632018
S Q L Ltd, Unit 1a, Stock Road, Southend-on-Sea, SS2 5QF Tel: (01702) 464978 Fax: (01702) 612929 E-mail: paul@sqlsouthend.co.uk
Selfstyle, 54-57 Acorn Centre, Barry Street, Oldham, OL1 3NE Tel: 0161-626 7926 Fax: 0161-627 4732 E-mail: sales@selfstyle.co.uk
▶ Stubbs Tickets, Streethay Farm, Burton Road, Streethay, Lichfield, Staffordshire, WS13 8RJ Tel: 01543 410107 Fax: 01543 410180 E-mail: sales@stubbstickets.com
Unicorn Print & Design, 143 North Street, Romford, RM1 1ED Tel: (01708) 765017 Fax: (01708) 733491 E-mail: unicorndie@aol.com
Wright Plastics Ltd, Fernie Road, Market Harborough, Leicestershire, LE16 7PH Tel: (01858) 465661 Fax: (01858) 431831 E-mail: sales@wplastic.co.uk

HOT FORGED BOLTS

Doran Engineering Co Holdings Ltd, Planetary Industrial Estate, Planetary Road, Willenhall, West Midlands, WV13 3XW Tel: (01902) 866000 Fax: (01902) 866222

HOT FORMING PRESSES

Aeroform H L M Ltd, Southway, Walworth Industrial Estate, Andover, Hants, SP10 5AF Tel: (01264) 337788 Fax: (01264) 337755 E-mail: hlm@andover.co.uk

HOT GLASS HANDLING EQUIPMENT

▶ S R Burke Engineering Ltd, Derwent Way, Wath-upon-Dearne, Rotherham, South Yorkshire, S63 6EX Tel: (01709) 877788 Fax: (01709) 877888 E-mail: info@srburke.co.uk

HOT INJECTION MOULDING SERVICES

Manuplastics Ltd, Lombard Road, London, SW19 3TZ Tel: (020) 8542 3421 Fax: (020) 8540 0594 E-mail: sales@manuplastics.co.uk

HOT ISOSTATIC PRESSING SERVICES

Bodycote, Carlisle Close, Sheffield Road, Sheepbridge, Chesterfield, Derbyshire, S41 9ED Tel: (01246) 260888 Fax: (01246) 260889
Tti Group Ltd, 39-43 Bilton Way, Luton, LU1 1UU Tel: (01582) 486644 Fax: (01582) 481148 E-mail: sales@ttigroup.co.uk

HOT MELT ADHESIVES (HMA)

Adhesives International Ltd, Northleigh Business Park, Woodstock Road, North Leigh, Witney, Oxfordshire, OX29 6RN Tel: (01993) 882749 Fax: (01993) 883887 E-mail: info@adhesivesintnl.com
▶ Aldcroft Adhesives Ltd, Unit 13A Horwich Loco Industrial Estate, Chorley New Road, Horwich, Bolton, BL6 5UE Tel: (01204) 668282 Fax: (01204) 668780 E-mail: info@aldcroftadhesives.com
Arrow Fastener (U K) Ltd, Unit 5 ZK Park, 23 Commerce Way, Croydon, CR0 4ZS Tel: 0845 5314109 Fax: (020) 8686 9197 E-mail: arrowfast@aol.com
▶ Bostik Findley Ltd, Common Road, Stafford, ST16 3EH Tel: (01785) 272727 Fax: (01785) 257236 E-mail: jackie.scarfe@bostikfindley.com
C B Adhesives, Adlington Industrial Estate, Adlington, Macclesfield, Cheshire, SK10 4NL Tel: (01625) 850180 Fax: (01625) 875932
EMS-CHEMIE (UK) Ltd, Darfin House, Priestly Court, Stafford Technology Park, Stafford, ST18 0AR Tel: (01785) 283739 Fax: (01785) 283722 E-mail: welcome@uk.emsgrivory.com
Fantas Tak Ltd, 2-6 Station Road, Shipley, West Yorkshire, BD18 2JL Tel: (01274) 466666 Fax: (01274) 466664 E-mail: sales@fantastak.com
Flexible Heating Hoses Ltd, Unit Z Sapcote Trading Centre, 68 Wyrley Road, Aston, Birmingham, B6 7BN Tel: 0121-250 2525 Fax: 0121-250 2526 E-mail: sales@flexible-heated-hoses.co.uk
Forbo Swift Adhesives Ltd, Bridge Street, Chatteris, Cambridgeshire, PE16 6RD Tel: (01354) 692345 Fax: (01354) 696661
H B Fuller UK Ltd, Outram Road, Globe Lane Industrial Estate, Dukinfield, Cheshire, SK16 4XE Tel: (01773) 601315 Fax: (0161) 666 0667
H & R ESP, Witan Gate House, 500-600 Witan Gate, Milton Keynes, MK9 1ES Tel: (01908) 853596 Fax: (01908) 853896 E-mail: wethers@bp.com
Power Adhesives Ltd, 1 Lords Way, Basildon, Essex, SS13 1TN Tel: (01268) 885800 Fax: (01268) 885810 E-mail: sales@poweradhesives.com
Stapling Centre P.L.C., Rapesco House, One Connections Business Place, Otford Road, Sevenoaks, Kent, TN14 5DF Tel: (01732) 464800 Fax: (01732) 464888
▶ UK HAIR SUPPLIES, 11 Denholme Avenue, Stockton-on-Tees, Cleveland, TS18 3QE Tel: (01642) 871716 E-mail: deborahmd@ntlworld.com

HOT MELT MATERIAL MIXERS

G C Hurrell & Co. Ltd, Knight Road, Rochester, Kent, ME2 2AH Tel: (01634) 718330 Fax: (01634) 710601 E-mail:

HOT MELT SEALING, *See Heat Sealing etc*

HOT NON FERROUS STAMPINGS

Cerro Ems Ltd, Liverpool Street, Birmingham, B9 4DS Tel: 0121-772 6515 Fax: 0121-772 6126
John Buckley Dudley Ltd, Alma Place, Dudley, West Midlands, DY2 8QH Tel: (01384) 252554 Fax: (01384) 456172 E-mail: sales@buckleybrass.co.uk
Leslie Group Ltd, 198-202 Waterloo Road, Yardley, Birmingham, B25 8LD Tel: 0121-708 1123 Fax: 0121-707 7793 E-mail: sales@leslie.co.uk
Rainsford & Lynes Ltd, Diadem Works, Kings Road, Tyseley, Birmingham, B11 2AJ Tel: 0121-706 6301 Fax: 0121-707 0995 E-mail: sales@rainsford-lynes.co.uk
T W Stamping Ltd, 112-117 Charles Henry Street, Birmingham, B12 0SJ Tel: 0121-622 2600 Fax: 0121-622 2700 E-mail: sales@gueststamping.co.uk

HOT ROLLED METAL, *See Rolled etc*

HOT ROLLED STAINLESS STEEL ANGLES

Caparo Industries P.L.C., Caparo House, Popes Lane, Oldbury, West Midlands, B69 4PJ Tel: 0121-202 4400 Fax: 0121-202 4401

HOT ROLLED STAINLESS STEEL FLATS

J B Stainless Ltd, 61 Washford Road, Sheffield, S9 3XW Tel: 0114-242 0042 Fax: 0114-243 0043 E-mail: michael@jbstainless.co.uk

HOT ROLLED STEEL, *See Steel Sections, Sheet etc*

HOT ROLLED STEEL SECTIONS

Asd Metal Services, Thames Wharf, Dock Road, London, E16 1AF Tel: (020) 7476 0444 Fax: (020) 7476 0239 E-mail: customer.care@asdmetalservices.co.uk
Bromford Iron & Steel Co. Ltd, Bromford Lane, West Bromwich, West Midlands, B70 7JJ Tel: 0121-553 6121 Fax: 0121-525 0913 E-mail: enquiries@bromfordsteels.co.uk
Hickman Steels International Ltd, PO Box 6, Bridgnorth, Shropshire, WV16 5JJ Tel: (01746) 761733 Fax: (01746) 767299 E-mail: mikemansfield@hickmansteels.com
Legg Brothers Holdings Ltd, Spring Road, Ettingshall, Wolverhampton, WV4 6JT Tel: (01902) 408188 Fax: (01902) 408228 E-mail: mail@leggbrothers.co.uk

HOT ROLLED STEEL SHEET

Argent Independant Steel (UK) Ltd, Lake Road, Leeway Industrial Estate, Newport, Gwent, NP19 4WN Tel: (01633) 290260 Fax: (01633) 290911 E-mail: info@argentindependantsteel.ltd.uk
Metal Enterprises & Co. Ltd, 150 Buckingham Palace Road, London, SW1W 9TR Tel: (020) 7730 6134 Fax: (020) 7730 0740

HOT ROLLED STEEL STRIPS

BSS Steelstrip Ltd, 42 Gatcombe Way, Priorslee, Telford, Shropshire, TF2 9GZ Tel: (01952) 290313 E-mail: bss@steelstrip.co.uk
Corus Ltd, PO Box 69, Rotherham, South Yorkshire, S60 1BN Tel: (01709) 377113 Fax: (01709) 375250 E-mail: info@corusgroup.com
Corus UK Ltd, Glamorgan Works, Pontarddulais, Swansea, SA4 8SB Tel: (01792) 882548 Fax: (01792) 885196
Pinnstrip Steel Services Ltd, Portway Road, Wednesbury, West Midlands, WS10 7DZ Tel: 0121-556 4493 Fax: 0121-556 6526 E-mail: sales@pinnstrip.co.uk

HOT RUNNER COMPONENTS

▶ Invotec Solutions, 18 High Greeve, Wootton, Northampton, NN4 6BA Tel: (01604) 876831 Fax: (0845) 8381520 E-mail: info@invotecsolutions.co.uk

HOT RUNNER SYSTEM TEMPERATURE CONTROL SYSTEMS

▶ E F I Ltd, 46 Melbourne Road, Lowestoft, Suffolk, NR32 1ST Tel: (01502) 518397 Fax: (01502) 566692 E-mail: sales@efisystems.co.uk

HOT TOWEL CABINETS

▶ P Telling, Lower Broad Oak, Elstead Road, Seale, Farnham, Surrey, GU10 1JA Tel: (01252) 781709 Fax: (01252) 783617 E-mail: sales@paultelling.co.uk

HOT TUB ACCESSORIES

▶ Arctic Spas Hot Tub Centre, 19b Alston Road, Hellesdon Park Road, Norwich, NR6 5DS Tel: (01603) 416016 Fax: (01603) 416016 E-mail: info@arctichottubcentre.co.uk
▶ Budget Marquees, 18 Cliff Hill, Gorleston, Great Yarmouth, Norfolk, NR31 6DQ Tel: (01493) 300721 E-mail: info@BudgetMarquees.co.uk
Crystal Waters Spas UK Ltd, Island Road, Hersden, Canterbury, Kent, CT3 4JD Tel: (01227) 361163 Fax: (01227) 361163 E-mail: mike@crystalwatersspas.co.uk
MARINA SPA, 40 Portsmouth Road, Camberley, Surrey, GU15 1JU Tel: 01276 686682 Fax: 01276 686682 E-mail: info@marinaspa.co.uk
▶ MR HOT TUBS LIMITED, UNIT 4 SHAW WOOD, BUSINESS PARK, LEGER WAY, Doncaster, South Yorkshire, DN2 5TB Tel: 01302 343988 E-mail: sales@mrhottubs.co.uk
▶ Spa City, Beechwood Nurseries, Broxburn, West Lothian, EH52 6PA Tel: (01506) 811170 E-mail: info@spaconnection.co.uk
▶ Sundance Spas, Unit 23 Waterhouse Business Centre, Cromar Way, Chelmsford, CM1 2QE Tel: (01245) 392288

HOT TUB OR SPA WATER FILTERS

▶ Arctic Spas Hot Tub Centre, 19b Alston Road, Hellesdon Park Road, Norwich, NR6 5DS Tel: (01603) 416016 Fax: (01603) 416016 E-mail: info@arctichottubcentre.co.uk
▶ Cheshire Spas & Pools, Buildwas Road, Clayhill Light Industrial Park, Neston, CH64 3RU Tel: 0151-336 3417 Fax: 0151-336 8671
▶ Mid Cornwall Plumbing & Electrical Services, 24 Chyverton Close, Newquay, Cornwall, TR7 2AR Tel: (01637) 872727 Fax: (0870) 1350579 E-mail: mcpe@btconnect.com

HOT TUBS

▶ Aqua Warehouse, Unit 2, Rignals Lane, Chelmsford, CM2 8RE Tel: (0845) 4024303 Fax: (0845) 4024304 E-mail: richard@aquawarehouse.co.uk
▶ Arctic Spas Hot Tub Centre, 19b Alston Road, Hellesdon Park Road, Norwich, NR6 5DS Tel: (01603) 416016 Fax: (01603) 416016 E-mail: info@arctichottubcentre.co.uk
Crystal Waters Spas UK Ltd, Island Road, Hersden, Canterbury, Kent, CT3 4JD Tel: (01227) 361163 Fax: (01227) 361163 E-mail: mike@crystalwatersspas.co.uk
▶ HGM Landscapes Ltd, 90 Harrowby Road, Grantham, Lincolnshire, NG31 9DS Tel: (01476) 573345 Fax: (01476) 573345 E-mail: enquiries@hgmlandscapes.co.uk
▶ Mid Cornwall Plumbing & Electrical Services, 24 Chyverton Close, Newquay, Cornwall, TR7 2AR Tel: (01637) 872727 Fax: (0870) 1350579 E-mail: mcpe@btconnect.com
Oyster Pools & Leisure Ltd, Raglan Garden Centre, Abergavenny Road, Raglan, Usk, Gwent, NP15 2BH Tel: (01291) 690614 Fax: (01291) 690951 E-mail: info@oysterpools.co.uk
▶ Sundance Spas, Unit 23 Waterhouse Business Centre, Cromar Way, Chelmsford, CM1 2QE Tel: (01245) 392288

HOT WATER DISPENSERS

▶ Aquator Water Coolers, Unit 8, Packhorse Place, Watling Street, Kensworth, Dunstable, Bedfordshire, LU6 3QL Tel: (01582) 842828 Fax: (01582) 842727

HOT WATER HEATING SYSTEM PRESSURISING EQUIPMENT

Brooks Ltd, Causeway Park Manchester Road, Audenshaw, Manchester, M34 5UU Tel: 0161-666 5000 Fax: 0161-666 5050 E-mail: sales@brooks.ltd.uk

Mikrofill Systems Ltd, West Court, Buntsford Park Road, Bromsgrove, Worcestershire, B60 3DX Tel: (01527) 574574 Fax: (01527) 575565 E-mail: info@mikrofill.com

Pressmain (Pressurisation) Co. Ltd, Opal Works, Denhill Road Industrial Estate, Moss Side, Manchester, M15 5NR Tel: 0161-226 4727 Fax: 0161-226 5848 E-mail: sales@pressmain.com

Warmac Ltd, Bear House, 7 Tootal Grove, Salford, Manchester, M6 8DN Tel: (0870) 0500739 Fax: (0870) 0552670 E-mail: info@warmac.co.uk

HOTEL BEDROOM FURNITURE

▶ Anthony Warwick, 73 London Road, Copford, Colchester, CO6 1LG Tel: (01206) 211227 Fax: (01206) 211216 E-mail: sales@anthonywarwick.co.uk

▶ Northcroft Ltd, Argall Works, Argall Avenue, London, E10 7QE Tel: (020) 8558 6919 Fax: (020) 8556 1097 E-mail: info@northcroft.uk.com

▶ Shimu Oriental Furniture Ltd, 3C-3D Harrogate Road, Rawdon, Leeds, LS19 6HW Tel: (0870) 2071433 Fax: 0113-250 8284 E-mail: info@shimu.co.uk

HOTEL BROCHURES

▶ The Beeches, Boston Road, Heckington, Sleaford, Lincolnshire, NG34 9JQ Tel: (01529) 462059 E-mail: thebeeches@lycos.co.uk

▶ Bull Hotel, Bulkley Square, Llangefni, Gwynedd, LL77 7LR Tel: (01248) 722119 Fax: (01248) 750488 E-mail: bull@welsh-historic-inns.com

▶ South Lodge, 19 The Vale, Broadstairs, Kent, CT10 1RB Tel: (01843) 600478 E-mail: Info@VisitSouthLodge.co.uk

HOTEL BROKERS

▶ Keytel International, 402 Edgware Road, London, W2 1ED Tel: (020) 7616 0300 Fax: (020) 7616 0317 E-mail: enquiries@keytel.co.uk

HOTEL CHINAWARE/ EARTHENWARE

Churchill Fine Bone China (Holdings) Ltd, Marlborough Works, High Street, Stoke-on-Trent, ST6 5NZ Tel: (01782) 577566 Fax: (01782) 810318 E-mail: churchill@churchillchina.plc.uk

Dudson Ltd, 200 Scotia Road, Stoke-on-Trent, ST6 4JD Tel: (01782) 819337 Fax: (01782) 813230 E-mail: info@dudson-group.co.uk

Ulster Ceramics, 29 Garvagh Road, Swatragh, Maghera, County Londonderry, BT46 5QE Tel: (028) 7940 1260 Fax: (028) 7940 1739 E-mail: ulsterceramics@btinternet.com

HOTEL CLEARANCE

▶ Party Supplies, North Kelsey Road, Caistor, Market Rasen, Lincolnshire, LN7 6SF Tel: (01472) 851430 E-mail: info@partysupplies-for-u.co.uk

HOTEL CONTRACT FURNITURE

Bramwell Furniture Ltd, Unit 50 Crayford Industrial Estate, Swaisland Drive, Crayford, Dartford, DA1 4HS Tel: (01322) 556223 Fax: (01322) 550900 E-mail: sales@bramwellfurniture.co.uk

Dovetail Enterprises Ltd, Dunsinane Avenue, Dunsinane Industrial Estate, Dundee, DD2 3QN Tel: (01382) 810099 Fax: (01382) 814816 E-mail: enquiries@dovetailenterprises.co.uk

Hatherway Office Furniture Ltd, The Farmhouse On The Green, Upper Quinton, Stratford-Upon-Avon, Warwickshire, CV37 8SX Tel: (01789) 721113 Fax: (01789) 721220 E-mail: fbs@freeola.com

Modus Furniture Ltd, Unit 12-14, Rose Mills Industrial Estate, Hort Bridge, Ilminster, Somerset, TA19 9PS Tel: (01460) 57465 Fax: (01460) 57004 E-mail: sales@modusfurniture.co.uk

K.A. Owen, 3 St. John Street, Low Town, Bridgnorth, Shropshire, WV15 6AG Tel: (01746) 765476 Fax: (01746) 767344

Ritchie Stoke, 315 Hartshill Road, Stoke-on-Trent, ST4 7NR Tel: (01782) 633733 Fax: (01782) 714864 E-mail: sales@ritchies-ltd.com

Roberts & Chick (Timber Lines) Ltd, 95 St James Mill Road, St James Business Park, Northampton, NN5 5JP Tel: (01604) 753223 Fax: (01604) 586100 E-mail: sales@roberts-chick.co.uk

Scaramanga Ltd, Etsome Barn, Etsome Road, Somerton, Somerset, TA11 6LU Tel: (01458) 273999 Fax: (01458) 272220 E-mail: scaramanga@mcmail.com

HOTEL CUTLERY/PLATED TABLEWARE

Arthur Price, Britannia Way, Lichfield, Staffordshire, WS14 9UY Tel: (01543) 267324 Fax: (01543) 414488 E-mail: catering@arthur-price.com

Jones Bros & Warriss Ltd, 104 Mary St, Sheffield, S1 4RU Tel: 0114-272 0820 Fax: 0114-272 9011 E-mail: warriss@gxn.co.uk

HOTEL FURNISHING OR REFURBISHMENT OR FITTING SERVICES

Art Forma (Furniture) Ltd, Station Road, Castle Donington, Derby, DE74 2NU Tel: (01332) 810474 Fax: (01332) 810277 E-mail: sales@artforma.co.uk

Cheshire Contracts Shopfitting Ltd, Imperial Works, 151 Bennett Street, Manchester, M12 5BH Tel: 0161-273 6253 Fax: 0161-274 3454 E-mail: enquiries@cheshire-contracts.co.uk

F K Electrical Services Ltd, Hyde Park Corner, Leeds, LS6 1AE Tel: 0113-275 9044 Fax: 0113-230 4631 E-mail: fkelectrical@fsmail.net

H & J Forbes Middlesbrough Ltd, 147 Stockton Street, Middlesbrough, Cleveland, TS2 1BU Tel: (01642) 222611 Fax: (01642) 232419 E-mail: frances@forbes-group.demon.co.uk

Lynn & Jones Storefitters Ltd, Falcon House, Kenneth Street Off Ingram Road, Holbeck, Leeds, LS11 9RF Tel: 0113-234 0737 Fax: 0113-245 6130 E-mail: enquiries@lynnandjones.co.uk

▶ Newman Scott Ltd, 1 Sadler Foster Way, Teesside Industrial Estate, Stockton-on-Tees, Cleveland, TS17 9JY Tel: (01642) 769696 Fax: (01642) 769669 E-mail: columbr@newmanscott.co.uk

Space Craft Projects Ltd, Sandbeck Way, Wetherby, West Yorkshire, LS22 7DN Tel: (01937) 584554 Fax: (01937) 580012 E-mail: info@space-craft.co.uk

HOTEL GUEST SERVICE TRAINING

▶ Farren Training, 25A Fullarton Street, Kilmarnock, Ayrshire, KA1 2QX Tel: (0787) 1551700 E-mail: neil@nfconsultants.com

HOTEL INTERIOR DESIGN

▶ Cheshire Interiors, 75 Shepperton Close, Appleton, Warrington, WA4 5JZ Tel: 01925 213339 E-mail: tamara@cheshireinteriors.com

▶ Emma Pettifer Richardson, Cavenagh House, The Square, Sheriff Hutton, York, YO60 6QX Tel: (01347) 878173 Fax: (01347) 878176 E-mail: info@abouthouse.co.uk

▶ in2style Ltd, 143 Richmond Road, London, E8 3NJ Tel: (020) 7249 4286 E-mail: info@in2style.org

▶ Interior Love, 15 Bridle Lane, Streetly, Sutton Coldfield, Birmingham, B74 3PT Tel: (0797) 1425195 E-mail: design@interiorlove.co.uk

▶ Ladesigns.Co.Uk, 20 Hartfield Road, Eastbourne, East Sussex, BN21 2AR Tel: (07801) 421368 E-mail: info@ladesigns.co.uk

Photography & Philosophy Ltd, 20 Camden Crescent, Bath, BA1 5HY Tel: (01225) 484446 Fax: (01225) 484446 E-mail: jacquimustard@photographyphilosophy.com

▶ Smith & Brown, 21 Regent Park Square, Glasgow, G41 2AF Tel: 0141-424 3107 Fax: 0141-424 0610 E-mail: fiona@smithandbrown.co.uk

▶ WonderFalls, Manderley, Auldgirth, Dumfries, DG2 0SA Tel: 01387 740685 Fax: 01387 740697 E-mail: ian@wonderfalls.co.uk

HOTEL ROOM ACCESS SECURITY LOCKS OR SYSTEMS

Greenlight Locksmith, 42 Preston Parade, Whitstable, Kent, CT5 4AJ Tel: (01227) 274738 E-mail: greenlightlocks@btinternet.com

▶ Locksmiths I/C Supplies Division, Unit B6, Rudford Industrial Estate, Ford, Arundel, West Sussex, BN18 0BF Tel: (01903) 735321 Fax: (01903) 732777 E-mail: sales@icsupplies.co.uk

HOTEL ROOM FURNISHINGS

▶ Black Boy Inn, Northgate Street, Caernarfon, Gwynedd, LL55 1RW Tel: (01286) 673604 Fax: (01286) 674130 E-mail: black@welsh-historic-inns.com

HOTEL WARDROBES

▶ Cozyslide, 208 Bruce Road, London, E3 3EU Tel: (07795) 967321 Fax: (020) 8981 3807

HOTPLATES

Johnsons Catering Equipment Ltd, G/3, Unit, Cowlairs, Bulwell, Nottingham, NG5 9RA Tel: 0115-976 1621 Fax: 0115-979 4639 E-mail: paul@johnsonsce.co.uk

HOTPLATES, SINGLE

Johnsons Catering Equipment Ltd, G/3, Unit, Cowlairs, Bulwell, Nottingham, NG5 9RA Tel: 0115-976 1621 Fax: 0115-979 4639 E-mail: paul@johnsonsce.co.uk

HOUR COUNTERS

Albroco Ltd, Unit C28 Ashmount Enterprise Park, Aber Road, Flint, Clwyd, CH6 5YL Tel: (01352) 734182 Fax: (01352) 734159 E-mail: sales@albrocos.co.uk

Autoswitch Electronics Ltd, 46 Lammas Way, Letchworth Garden City, Hertfordshire, SG6 4LW Tel: (01462) 677778 Fax: (01462) 480449

HOUSE BUILDING CONTRACTORS, *See also Building Contractors*

▶ A Purkiss Ltd, 2A Limberline Road, Portsmouth, PO3 5JS Tel: (023) 9269 8668

A S Russell, Craigowmill Farm Cottage, Kinross, KY13 0RR Tel: (01577) 865111 Fax: (01577) 865111

Abbey Developments Ltd, Abbey House, 2 Southgate Road, Potters Bar, Hertfordshire, EN6 5DU Tel: (01707) 651266 Fax: (01707) 646836

Arnold B Johnston, Dean Road, Yate, Bristol, BS37 5NR Tel: (01454) 316175 Fax: (01454) 884455 E-mail: mail@erh.co.uk

▶ Arthur Simms New Homes, The Old Barn, Harpenden Road, Wheathampstead, St. Albans, Hertfordshire, AL4 8EE Tel: (01582) 834200 Fax: (01582) 832981

Barratt Newcastle Ltd, Barratt House, City West Business Park, Newcastle upon Tyne, NE4 7DF Tel: 0191-298 6100

Barratt (West Scotland) P.L.C., Mayfield House, 7 Maggie Woods Loan, Falkirk, FK1 5SJ Tel: (01324) 620011 Fax: (01324) 625916

C D C 2020, 1 Forest Gate Tilgate Forest Business Centre, Brighton Road, Crawley, West Sussex, RH11 9PT Tel: (0845) 8502020 Fax: (01403) 756341

Charles Church Western, Churchward House, Churchward Road, Yate, Bristol, BS37 5NN Tel: (01454) 333800 Fax: (01454) 327123

CM Yuill, Cecil House, Loyalty Road, Hartlepool, Cleveland, TS25 5BD Tel: (01429) 266620

Crest Nicholson P.L.C., Crest House, Thurcroft Road, Chertsey, Surrey, KT16 9GN Tel: (01932) 580555 Fax: (0870) 3363990 E-mail: info@crestnicholson.com

Croudace Services Ltd, Croudace House, 97 Godstone Road, Caterham, Surrey, CR3 6XQ Tel: (01883) 346464 Fax: (01883) 349927 E-mail: info@croudacehomes.co.uk

William Davis Ltd, Forest Field, Forest Road, Loughborough, Leicestershire, LE11 3NS Tel: (01509) 231181 Fax: (01509) 239773 E-mail: post@williamdavis.co.uk

F A Would Ltd, Ladysmith Road, Grimsby, South Humberside, DN32 9SH Tel: (01472) 241303 Fax: (01472) 360262 E-mail: enquries@wouldgroup.com

Fairgrove Homes Ltd, 1 Heron Court Merlin Way, Quarry Hill Industrial Estate, Ilkeston, Derbyshire, DE7 4RA Tel: 0115-932 6531 Fax: 0115-944 6701 E-mail: sales@fairgrove.co.uk

Friargreen Construction, Woodlands, Skeet Hill Lane, Orpington, Kent, BR5 4HB Tel: (01689) 823749 Fax: (01689) 832047

▶ George Wimpey, 1 Harbour Exchange Square, London, E14 9GE Tel: (020) 7987 0500 Fax: (020) 7531 8383

George Wimpey NW Ltd, Lichfield House, Gadbrook Park, Rudheath, Northwich, Cheshire, CW9 7RF Tel: (01606) 815300 Fax: (01606 40276

Hayes Control Systems, The Boathouse, Station Road, Henley-on-Thames, Oxfordshire, RG9 1AZ Tel: (01491) 410539 Fax: (01491) 577267 E-mail: sales@hayescontrol.co.uk

Hogarth Estates, 16b Hogarth Place, London, SW5 0QT Tel: (020) 7373 5222 Fax: (020) 7370 7960 E-mail: hogarthestates@btinternet.com

Humberts, Mansfield House, Silver Street, Taunton, Somerset, TA1 3DN Tel: (01823) 331234 Fax: (01823) 332034 E-mail: taunton.ag@humberts.co.uk

Leck Construction Ltd, Leck House, Ironworks Road, Barrow-in-Furness, Cumbria, LA14 2PQ Tel: (01229) 820394 Fax: (01229) 811414 E-mail: leckcon.bar@btinternet.com

Lovell Partnerships Ltd, Marston Park, Tamworth, Staffordshire, B78 3HN Tel: (01827) 305600 Fax: (01827) 305601 E-mail: enquiries@lovell.co.uk

Mccarthy & Stone Quest Trustees Ltd, 26-32 Oxford Road, Bournemouth, BH8 8EZ Tel: (01202) 292480 Fax: (01202) 557261 E-mail: info@mccarthyandstone.co.uk

▶ Persimmon Homes South West Ltd, Mallard Road, Sowton Trading Estate, Sowton Industrial Estate, Exeter, EX2 7LD Tel: (01392) 252541 Fax: (01392) 430195

▶ Rippon Homes Ltd, Leeming Lane South, Mansfield Woodhouse, Mansfield, Nottinghamshire, NG19 9AQ Tel: (01623) 659000 Fax: (01623) 420807 E-mail: info@ripponhomes.co.uk

Scruton & Co Builders Ltd, Redcliff House, Waterside Park, Hessle, North Humberside, HU13 0EG Tel: (01482) 644200 Fax: (01482) 647338 E-mail: annwelbourne@scruton.co.uk

▶ Southdale Homes Ltd, Westholme Road, Halifax, West Yorkshire, HX1 4JF Tel: (01422) 380090 Fax: (01422) 321636

Stamford Homes, Ashurst Southgate Park, Bakewell Road, Orton Southgate, Peterborough, PE2 6YS Tel: (01733) 396600 Fax: (01733) 396669 E-mail: sales@stamford-homes.co.uk

▶ Turnberg Homes Ltd, 18 Allerdyce Drive, Great Weston Retail Park, Glasgow, G15 6RY Tel: 0141-944 6544 Fax: 0141-944 9494

Waterhouse Building Refurbishment & Interiors, 98 Bradford Road, East Ardsley, Wakefield, West Yorkshire, WF3 2JL Tel: (01924) 822274 Fax: (01924) 823951 E-mail: info@waterhouse-ideas.co.uk

Wilson Connolly Lancashire, Bradley Lane, Standish, Wigan, Lancashire, WN6 0XN Tel: (01257) 425511 Fax: (01257) 426674

George Wimpy West Yorkshire Ltd, Sandpiper House, Peel Avenue, Calder Park, Wakefield, West Yorkshire, WF2 7UA Tel: (01924) 241500 Fax: (01924) 241580

▶ Woodstock Homes, 14 Redland Park, Bristol, BS6 6SB Tel: 0117-974 1021 Fax: 0117-974 4113 E-mail: sales@woodstockhomes.co.uk

Younger Homes Ltd, 1 Hall Street, Maghera, County Londonderry, BT46 5DA Tel: (028) 7964 3725 Fax: (028) 7964 4249

HOUSE CLEARANCE

▶ Any Junk, Unit A06 Riverside Business Centre, Haldane Place, London, SW18 4UQ Tel: (020) 8877 1155 Fax: (020) 8875 0055 E-mail: enquiries@anyjunk.co.uk

▶ Easiclear, Atlas Transport Estate, Lombard Road, London, SW11 3RE Tel: (02077) 389555 E-mail: info@easiclear.co.uk

▶ Man With A Van!!, 27 Banners walk, Kingstanding, Birmingham, B44 0TB Tel: 0121 3508269

▶ Party Supplies, North Kelsey Road, Caistor, Market Rasen, Lincolnshire, LN7 6SF Tel: (01472) 851430 E-mail: info@partysupplies-for-u.co.uk

▶ Richmond House Clearance, 5 Grena Gardens, Richmond, Surrey, TW9 1XP Tel: 0208 9407920 E-mail: info@bluekatzhosting.co.uk

▶ Smart Move, 23 Nash Gardens, Dawlish, Devon, EX7 9RR Tel: (01626) 889171 Fax: E-mail: enquiries@smartmoveremovals.com

▶ Stephen Roberts, Watton Salerooms Breckland House, Norwich Road, Watton, Thetford, Norfolk, IP25 6JT Tel: (01953) 885676 Fax: (01953) 885676 E-mail: watton.salerooms@eidosnet.co.uk

HOUSEHOLD CHAIRS

Alstons Upholstery Ltd, Albro Works, Gosbecks Road, Colchester, CO2 9JU Tel: (01206) 765343 Fax: (01206) 763401 E-mail: enquiries@alstons.co.uk

William Bartlett & Son Ltd, Grafton Street, High Wycombe, Buckinghamshire, HP12 3AJ Tel: (01494) 526491 Fax: (01494) 451021 E-mail: sales@williambartlett.co.uk

Cintique Ltd, 43 Andrews Road, London, E8 4RN Tel: (020) 7254 1262 Fax: (020) 7254 6774 E-mail: sales@cintique.co.uk

Cove Workshop, 61 Gobbins Road, Islandmagee, Larne, County Antrim, BT40 3TY Tel: (028) 9335 3403 Fax: (028) 9335 3404 E-mail: sales@thechairmaker.com

Glencraft, 132 Wellington Road, Aberdeen, AB12 3LQ Tel: (01224) 873366 Fax: (01224) 894659 E-mail: sales@glencraft.co.uk

▶ Lawrence Neal, 22 High Street, Stockton, Southam, Warwickshire, CV47 8JZ Tel: (01926) 811998 E-mail: sales@lawrencenealchairs.co.uk

HOUSEHOLD FURNITURE

Abbey Upholsterers Ltd, 8 Abbeyville Place, Newtownabbey, County Antrim, BT37 0AQ Tel: (028) 9086 9345 Fax: (028) 9036 5034 E-mail: info@abbeyupholsterers.com

HOUSEHOLD FURNITURE – *continued*

▶ Akita, 16 Dalrymple Street, Girvan, Ayrshire, KA26 9AE Tel: (01465) 712930

Alstons Upholstery Ltd, Albro Works, Gosbecks Road, Colchester, CO2 9JU Tel: (01206) 765343 Fax: (01206) 763401 E-mail: enquiries@alstons.co.uk

Anbercraft Furniture, 315 Princes Road, Stoke-on-Trent, ST4 7JS Tel: (01782) 413719 Fax: (01782) 749156

▶ Ancholme Discount Furniture, Unit 7 Island Carr Industrial Estate, Island Carr Road, Brigg, South Humberside, DN20 8PD Tel: (01652) 653644 Fax: (01652) 653644 E-mail: chizel@btopenworld.com

Art Forma (Furniture) Ltd, Station Road, Castle Donington, Derby, DE74 2NU Tel: (01332) 810474 Fax: (01332) 810277 E-mail: sales@artforma.co.uk

Artistic Upholstery Ltd, Bridge Street, Long Eaton, Nottingham, NG10 4QQ Tel: 0115-973 4481 Fax: 0115-946 1018 E-mail: sales@artisticupholstery.co.uk

Ashcraft Furniture Ltd, Unit 1, Orchard Industrial Estate, Toddington, Cheltenham, Gloucestershire, GL54 5EB Tel: (01242) 620731 Fax: (01242) 621939

Bannons Ltd, 75 North Street, Belfast, BT1 1NL Tel: (028) 9032 9335 Fax: (028) 9023 5152

William Bartlett & Son Ltd, Grafton Street, High Wycombe, Buckinghamshire, HP12 3AJ Tel: (01494) 526491 Fax: (01494) 451021 E-mail: sales@williambartlett.co.uk

Alfred Briggs (Alwood) Ltd, PO Box 6, Lurgan, County Armagh, BT66 8DD Tel: (028) 3832 3296 Fax: (028) 3832 4256 E-mail: mail@alwood.co.uk

Celebrity Motion Furniture Ltd, Unit 1 Wimsey Way, Somercotes, Alfreton, Derbyshire, DE55 4LS Tel: (01773) 604607 Fax: (01773) 541408 E-mail: reception@celebrity-furniture.co.uk

Christie-Tyler Ltd, Abergaroo Road, Brynmenyn, Bridgend, Mid Glamorgan, CF32 9LN Tel: (01656) 726200 Fax: (01656) 726233

Cintique Ltd, 43 Andrews Road, London, E8 4RN Tel: (020) 7254 1262 Fax: (020) 7254 6774 E-mail: sales@cintique.co.uk

Clairtex Gwent, Merthyr Road, Tredegar, Gwent, NP22 3AY Tel: (01495) 711226 Fax: (01495) 718124

Classic Windsors, Coventry Street, Coventry, CV2 4LZ Tel: (024) 7665 0907 Fax: (024) 7665 0907

Collins & Hayes Ltd, Menzies Road, Ponswood, St. Leonards-On-Sea, East Sussex, TN38 9XF Tel: (01424) 720027 Fax: (01424) 720270 E-mail: sales@collinsandhayes.com

Country Furniture Makers, Victoria Road, Yeovil, Somerset, BA21 5AZ Tel: (01935) 428404 Fax: (01935) 424261

▶ Davis Haworth Jacob, A 449 Holloway Road, London, N7 6LJ Tel: (020) 7263 7744 Fax: (020) 7263 6644 E-mail: clive@davishowarthjacob.com

Stephen Down Furniture, Unit 5 Whitehouse Centre, Stannington, Morpeth, Northumberland, NE61 6AW Tel: (01670) 789727 Fax: (01670) 789418

Furniture Direct, Southfield Street, Nelson, Lancashire, BB9 9QA Tel: (01282) 690921 Fax: (01282) 690921

Gainsborough Ltd, Canal Road, Trowbridge, Wiltshire, BA14 8RQ Tel: (01225) 766341 Fax: (01225) 779129 E-mail: sales@gainsborough.ltd.uk

Greensmith Upholstery Ltd, New Tythe Street, Long Eaton, Nottingham, NG10 2DL Tel: 0115-973 3446 Fax: 0115-946 0743

Joynson Holland Ltd, Abercromby Avenue, High Wycombe, Buckinghamshire, HP12 3AZ Tel: (01494) 530274 Fax: (01494) 473387 E-mail: sales@joynsonholland.co.uk

Kandu Table Care, Sudden Mill, Manchester Road, Rochdale, Lancashire, OL11 4QR Tel: (01706) 868983 Fax: (01706) 868797

Lawson Wood Ltd, 4 Heliport Estate, Lombard Road, London, SW11 3RE Tel: (020) 7228 9812 Fax: (020) 7738 2499

Mccollin Furniture, 39 Urlwin Street, London, SE5 0NF Tel: (020) 7703 2262 Fax: (020) 7703 2262 E-mail: mccollinbryan@aol.com

Mfi Furniture Centre Ltd, Astmoor Road, Astmoor Industrial Estate, Runcorn, Cheshire, WA7 1PQ Tel: (01928) 581111 Fax: (01928) 573997

H. Morris & Co. Ltd, 24 Rosyth Road, Glasgow, G5 0YD Tel: 0141-300 7200 Fax: 0141-300 7240

New Concept Upholsterer, 70 Thomas Street, Tamworth, Staffordshire, B77 3PR Tel: (01827) 51414

Olympia Furniture Ltd, Whitelands Road, Ashton-under-Lyne, Lancashire, OL6 6UX Tel: 0161-331 4000 Fax: 0161-331 4029 E-mail: sales@olympia-furniture.co.uk

P E C Furniture Ltd, Amble Industrial Estate, Amble, Morpeth, Northumberland, NE65 0PE Tel: (01665) 710593 Fax: (01665) 712735 E-mail: pecfurn@aol.com

Parker Knoll Cabinets Ltd, London Road, Chipping Norton, Oxfordshire, OX7 5AX Tel: (0870) 7429904 Fax: (0870) 7429906 E-mail: retailsales@parkerknoll.co.uk

Poetstyle Ltd, 1 Bayford Street Industrial Units, Bayford Street, London, E8 3SE Tel: (020) 8533 0915 Fax: (020) 8985 2953 E-mail: sofachairs@aol.com

Richwood Furniture, Unit 3 Mill Lane, Billinghay, Lincoln, LN4 4ES Tel: (01526) 861440 Fax: (01526) 861440

Scaramanga Ltd, Etsome Barn, Etsome Road, Somerton, Somerset, TA11 6LU Tel: (01458) 273999 Fax: (01458) 272220 E-mail: scaramanga@mcmail.com

Sherborne Upholstery Ltd, Pasture Lane, Clayton, Bradford, West Yorkshire, BD14 6LT Tel: (01274) 882633 Fax: (01274) 815129 E-mail: mail@sherbourne-uph.co.uk

Sofa Workshop Ltd, Llantrisant Business Park, Llantrisant, Pontyclun, Mid Glamorgan, CF72 8LF Tel: (01798) 345345 Fax: (01443) 237752 E-mail: sales@sofaworkshop.co.uk

Southernwood Furnishings, The Rocks, Ashwicke, Chippenham, Wiltshire, SN14 8AP Tel: (01225) 852213 Fax: (01225) 859699

Stonebridge Cabinet Works (Rowntrees) Ltd, 118 Battlehill Rd, Richhill, Armagh, BT61 8QL Tel: (028) 3887 1229 Fax: (028) 3887 0402

Teemo Designs Ltd, Roman Bank, Cherry Holt Road, Bourne, Lincolnshire, PE10 9LQ Tel: (01778) 421421 Fax: (01778) 393135 E-mail: teemo@globalnet.co.uk

Tetrad plc, Hartford Mill, Swan Street, Preston, PR1 5PQ Tel: (01772) 792936 Fax: (01772) 798319 E-mail: sales@tetrad.co.uk

Topknot Furniture & Kitchen Co. Ltd, 290 Leverington Common, Leverington, Wisbech, Cambridgeshire, PE13 5JG Tel: (01945) 410117 Fax: (01945) 410979 E-mail: sales@topknot-furniture.co.uk

Unit Design, 9d Portaferry Road, Newtownards, County Down, BT23 8NN Tel: (028) 9181 7160 Fax: (028) 9181 3172 E-mail: info@unitdesign-ni.co.uk

Village World Ltd, Manor Orchard, Staplegrove, Taunton, Somerset, TA2 6EQ Tel: (01823) 326767 Fax: (01823) 326917 E-mail: info@villageworld.co.uk

W Oliver Exorna Ltd, Hillmans Way, Coleraine, County Londonderry, BT52 2EB Tel: (028) 7035 6501 Fax: (028) 7035 3674

W T Parkes Upholstery, Regency Works, 1a Shakleton Road, Coventry, CV5 6HT Tel: (024) 7669 1199

Gerald Weir Enterprises Woodcraft Ltd, 7 Vermont Road, Ipswich, IP4 2SR Tel: (01473) 252606 Fax: (01473) 214621

Wood Bros Furniture Ltd, London Road, Ware, Hertfordshire, SG12 9QH Tel: (0845) 1303303 Fax: (01920) 464388 E-mail: sales@oldcharm.co.uk

Woodberry Bros & Haines Ltd, Commerce Way, Walrow, Highbridge, Somerset, TA9 4AJ Tel: (0870) 0600555 Fax: (01278) 781337 E-mail: info@wbhltd.com

Yeoman Upholstery plc, Enterprise Way, Flitwick, Bedford, MK45 5BS Tel: (01525) 713771 Fax: (01525) 717877 E-mail: peter@yeomanupholstery.co.uk

HOUSEHOLD GOODS, *See headings for particular types such as Hardware; Plastic; Textile*

HOUSEHOLD INSURANCE

▶ Alan Boswell Insurance Brokers, Harbour House, 126 Thorpe Road, Norwich, NR1 1UL Tel: (01603) 218000 Fax: (01603) 762862 E-mail: info@alanboswell.com

▶ Clear Cut Mortgages, St. James House, St. James Square, Cheltenham, Gloucestershire, GL50 3WD Tel: (0845) 0698000 E-mail: info@clearcutmortgages.com

▶ Giles Financial Services, 12 Beresford Terrace, Ayr, KA7 2EG Tel: (01292) 619900 Fax: (01292) 610037

▶ Haydock Finance Ltd, 2 The Cottage, Main Street, Kinnesswood, Kinross, KY13 9HN Tel: (01592) 840480 Fax: (01592) 840480

▶ Utopia Mortgage Solutions, The Bearings, Bowbridge Road, Newark, Nottinghamshire, NG24 4BZ Tel: (01636) 593990 Fax: (08700) 501222E-mail: craig@utopia4mortgages.co.uk

HOVERCRAFT CONSULTANTS OR DESIGNERS

A B S Hovercraft Ltd, Coopers House, The Horsefair, Romsey, Hampshire, SO51 8JZ Tel: (01794) 526300 Fax: (01794) 526301 E-mail: info@abs-hovercraft.com

Air Vehicles Design & Engineering Ltd, Unit 4 Three Gates Road, Cowes, Isle of Wight, PO31 7UT Tel: (01983) 293194 Fax: (01983) 291987 E-mail: info@airvehicles.co.uk

G K N Aerospace Services, Ferry Road, East Cowes, Isle of Wight, PO32 6RA Tel: (01983) 294101 Fax: (01983) 291006 E-mail: info@gknwae.com

Hovercraft Consultants, Unit 43 South Hampshire Industrial Park, Totton, Southampton, SO40 3SA Tel: (023) 8087 1188 Fax: (023) 8087 1799 E-mail: enquiries@duratank.com

HOVERCRAFTS

A B S Hovercraft Ltd, Coopers House, The Horsefair, Romsey, Hampshire, SO51 8JZ Tel: (01794) 526300 Fax: (01794) 526301 E-mail: info@abs-hovercraft.com

Griffon Hoverwork Ltd, Quay Road, Ryde, Isle Of Wight, PO33 2HB Tel: (01983) 565181 Fax: (01983) 812859 E-mail: info@hoverwork.co.uk

Slingsby Aviation Ltd, Ings Lane, Kirkbymoorside, York, YO62 6EZ Tel: (01751) 432474 Fax: (01751) 431173 E-mail: sal1@slingsby.co.uk

HUMAN RESOURCES (HR) CONSULTANCY

Altus Recruitment Services Ltd, Moseley, Birmingham, B13 9ZQ Tel: 0121-442 4030 Fax: 0121-442 4030

Aon Consulting Ltd, Briarcliffe House, Kingsmead, Farnborough, Hampshire, GU14 7TE Tel: (01252) 544484 Fax: (01252) 522206 E-mail: enquiries@aon.com

▶ Aspecthr Business Consultants, 6 Abbotsford Crescent, Wishaw, Lanarkshire, ML2 7DH Tel: (01698) 385075 E-mail: enquiries@aspectHR.co.uk

▶ Baldock Advanced Motorcycle Training, 31 Bush Spring, Baldock, Hertfordshire, SG7 6QT Tel: (01462) 641775 Fax: (0871) 4335485 E-mail: tclarke@evprecruit.com

▶ BCHR Ltd, 14 Marlborough Crescent, Sevenoaks, Kent, TN13 2HP Tel: (01732) 459743 Fax: 01732 779271 E-mail: barry@bchr.com

▶ Clearwater Business Consulting Ltd, 28 Clearwater, Londonderry, BT47 6BE Tel: (028) 7131 3660 E-mail: peter@clearwaterconsulting.org

Collinson Grant, Ryecroft, Aviary Road, Worsley, Manchester, M28 2WF Tel: 0161-703 5600 Fax: 0161-790 9177 E-mail: postmaster@collinsongrant.com

▶ Jo Dale Consulting Ltd, 90 Stourvale Road Southbourne, Bournemouth, BH6 5JB Tel: (01202) 248731 E-mail: mail@jodaleconsulting.com

Development Dimensions International Ltd, B Sefton Park, Bells Hill, Stokes Poges, Slough, SL2 4JS Tel: (01753) 616000 Fax: (01753) 616099 E-mail: info@ddi-europe.com

▶ Donna Chapman & Co., Daisy Hill, Knarr Barn Lane, Dobcross, Oldham, OL3 5RF Tel: (01457) 871533 Fax: (01457) 871533 E-mail: sales@donnachapman.com

Employee Management, Stone Cross Place, Stone Cross La North, Lowton, Warrington, WA3 2SH Tel: (01942) 727200 Fax: (01942) 727225 E-mail: sales@employeemanagement.co.uk

Gipping Occupational Health Ltd, Mill Lodge, Mendlesham Green, Stowmarket, Suffolk, IP14 5RB Tel: (01449) 766913 Fax: (01449) 766891 E-mail: advice@gipping.co.uk

HR Insight Ltd, Reeves Way, South Woodham Ferrers, Chelmsford, CM3 5XF Tel: (01245) 324824 Fax: (01245) 324103 E-mail: support@hrinsight.co.uk

▶ HR2HR Solutions Ltd, Ravensbourne, Westerham Road, Keston, Kent, BR2 6HE Tel: (01689) 868068 Fax: (01689) 868069 E-mail: info@hr2hrsolutions.co.uk

▶ I H R Ltd, 17 Eleanor Grove, Ickenham, Uxbridge, Middlesex, UB10 8BH Tel: (07005) 964088 Fax: (07005) 964099 E-mail: lynn.claydon@tiscali.co.uk

Ics Computing Ltd, Wessex House, Oxford Road, Newbury, Berkshire, RG14 1PA Tel: (01635) 580802 Fax: (01635) 580803 E-mail: enquiries@icscomputing.co.uk

Link H R Systems, Normant House, 121-123 Long Lane, Upton, Chester, CH2 1JF Tel: (01244) 399555 Fax: (01244) 399666 E-mail: general@link-hrsystems.com

Manpower UK Ltd, Capital Court, 30 Windsor Street, Uxbridge, Middlesex, UB8 1AB Tel: (01895) 205200 Fax: (01895) 205201

MBG Management Consultants Ltd, 50 Greenhill Road, Moseley, Birmingham, B13 9SS Tel: 0121-449 5434 Fax: 0121-449 5844 E-mail: mbgmb@globalnet.co.uk

▶ Medics Recruitment Agency, Banchory Business Centre, Burn O' Bennie Road, Banchory, Kincardineshire, AB31 5ZU Tel: (01330) 826700 Fax: (01330) 820670 E-mail: sam@triowise.com

▶ Payne Associates Ltd, R B R House, Hawksworth Road, Central Park, Telford, Shropshire, TF2 9TU Tel: (01952) 210300 Fax: (01952) 210301 E-mail: ian.payne@payne-associates.co.uk

▶ Positivexperience Ltd, The Old Vicarage, Market Place, Castle Donington, Derby, DE74 2JB Tel: (01332) 856393 Fax: (01332) 810769 E-mail: gordon.beck@positivexperience.co.uk

▶ Purple Plum HR, Denewood, Pitt Court, North Nibley, Dursley, Gloucestershire, GL11 6EB Tel: (0845) 4666123 Fax: (0870) 7628212 E-mail: info@purpleplumHR.co.uk

Rab Personnel Management Services, 18 Dolphin Close, London, SE28 8PY Tel: (020) 8311 1261 Fax: (020) 8311 1261 E-mail: sales@rabpms.co.uk

▶ Selection & Development Ltd, Bronzeoak House, Stafford Road, Caterham, Surrey, CR3 6JG Tel: (01883) 332651 Fax: (01883) 332652 E-mail: info@selectionanddevelopment.com

▶ Skills UK, 17 Britannia Road, Burbage, Hinckley, Leics, LE10 2HE Tel: 01455 617776 E-mail: ted@skills.uk.com

▶ UP Consulting Ltd, 186 Allesley old Road, Coventry, CV5 8GJ Tel: (0870) 0678803 Fax: (0870) 0671850 E-mail: mail@upconsulting.co.uk

HUMAN RESOURCES (HR) CONSULTANCY, 360 DEGREE REVIEW

▶ Affinity Consultancy Services Ltd, Innovation House, Turnhams Green Park, Pincents Lane, Tilehurst, RG31 4UH Tel: 0845 601 4565 Fax: 0118 972 8459 E-mail: sriches@arcsuk.com

HUMAN RESOURCES (HR) CONSULTANCY, COMPETENCY FRAMEWORKING

▶ Affinity Consultancy Services Ltd, Innovation House, Turnhams Green Park, Pincents Lane, Tilehurst, RG31 4UH Tel: 0845 601 4565 Fax: 0118 972 8459 E-mail: sriches@arcsuk.com

▶ NiceHR, 42 C Southcote Road, Bournemouth, BH1 3SR Tel: 01202 315437 E-mail: stephanie@nicehr.co.uk

HUMAN RESOURCES (HR) CONSULTANCY, CULTURAL AUDITING

▶ Jo Dale Consulting Ltd, 90 Stourvale Road Southbourne, Bournemouth, BH6 5JB Tel: (01202) 248731 E-mail: mail@jodaleconsulting.com

▶ NiceHR, 42 C Southcote Road, Bournemouth, BH1 3SR Tel: 01202 315437 E-mail: stephanie@nicehr.co.uk

HUMAN RESOURCES (HR) CONSULTANCY, EMPLOYMENT ASSESSMENT REPORT

▶ Affinity Consultancy Services Ltd, Innovation House, Turnhams Green Park, Pincents Lane, Tilehurst, RG31 4UH Tel: 0845 601 4565 Fax: 0118 972 8459 E-mail: sriches@arcsuk.com

▶ Leap Coaching Associates, 7 Hopewell Way, Crigglestone, Wakefield, West Yorkshire, WF4 3PU Tel: (01924) 254173

▶ NiceHR, 42 C Southcote Road, Bournemouth, BH1 3SR Tel: 01202 315437 E-mail: stephanie@nicehr.co.uk

▶ Outsourced Personnel Services Ltd, PO Box 251, Sunbury-on-Thames, Middlesex, TW16 5SH Tel: (01932) 786066 Fax: (01932) 772032 E-mail: sean@personnelmanagement.co.uk

▶ Protocol 4 Business, 3 Bishops Road, Whitchurch, Cardiff, CF14 1LT Tel: (029) 2069 1111 Fax: (029) 2069 1001 E-mail: info@protocol4business.co.uk

HUMAN RESOURCES (HR) CONSULTANCY, JOB ANALYSIS

▶ BCHR Ltd, 14 Marlborough Crescent, Sevenoaks, Kent, TN13 2HP Tel: (01732) 459743 Fax: 01732 779271 E-mail: barry@bchr.com

▶ Jo Dale Consulting Ltd, 90 Stourvale Road Southbourne, Bournemouth, BH6 5JB Tel: (01202) 248731 E-mail: mail@jodaleconsulting.com

▶ HR2HR Solutions Ltd, Ravensbourne, Westerham Road, Keston, Kent, BR2 6HE Tel: (01689) 868068 Fax: (01689) 868069 E-mail: info@hr2hrsolutions.co.uk

HUMAN RESOURCES (HR) CONSULTANCY, PSYCHOMETRIC PROFILING

▶ Anova Communications Group, 41 Market Place, Henley-on-Thames, Oxfordshire, RG9 2AA Tel: (01491) 636300 Fax: (0870) 1336271 E-mail: info@futureincoms.com

HUMAN RESOURCES (HR) CONSULTANCY, SALARY BENCHMARKING

▶ BCHR Ltd, 14 Marlborough Crescent, Sevenoaks, Kent, TN13 2HP Tel: (01732) 459743 Fax: 01732 779271 E-mail: barry@bchr.com

HUMAN RESOURCES (HR) CONSULTANCY, STRESS AUDITING

Keenan Research Ltd, Victoria House, 15 Gay Street, Bath, BA1 2PH Tel: (01225) 336569 Fax: (01225) 442685 E-mail: kmkeenan@keenan-research.com

HUMAN RESOURCES (HR) OUTSOURCING CONSULTANCY

Gates B 2 B Ltd, Electric Wharf, Coventry, CV1 4JF Tel: (024) 7652 5558 Fax: (0870) 6001092 E-mail: steve.williams@gatesb2b.com
▶ HR2HR Solutions Ltd, Ravensbourne, Westerham Road, Keston, Kent, BR2 6HE Tel: (01689) 868068 Fax: (01689) 868069 E-mail: info@hr2hrsolutions.co.uk
▶ I H R Ltd, 17 Eleanor Grove, Ickenham, Uxbridge, Middlesex, UB10 8BH Tel: (07005) 964088 Fax: (07005) 964099 E-mail: lynn.claydon@tiscali.co.uk

HUMAN RESOURCES (HR) PERFORMANCE MANAGEMENT CONSULTANCY

A S K Europe plc, Trent House University Way, Cranfield Technology Park, Cranfield, Bedford, MK43 0AN Tel: (01234) 757575 Fax: (01234) 757576 E-mail: mail@askeurope.com
▶ Clearwater Business Consulting Ltd, 28 Clearwater, Londonderry, BT47 6BE Tel: (028) 7131 3660 E-mail: peter@clearwaterconsulting.org
H D A International, 4 Park Place, 12 Lawn Lane, Vauxhall, London, SW8 1UD Tel: (020) 7820 9199 Fax: (020) 7735 8175 E-mail: admin@hda.co.uk
▶ Lifescales, Spectrum House, Dunstable Road, Redbourn, St. Albans, Hertfordshire, AL3 7PR Tel: (0845) 6381330 E-mail: info@workscales.co.uk
▶ Selection & Development Ltd, Bronzeoak House, Stafford Road, Caterham, Surrey, CR3 6JG Tel: (01883) 332651 Fax: (01883) 332652 E-mail: info@selectionanddevelopment.com

HUMAN RESOURCES (HR) SOFTWARE

Bond International, Unit 10 Coped Hall Business Park, Wootton Bassett, Swindon, SN4 8DP Tel: (01793) 856300 Fax: (01793) 856301 E-mail: helpdesk@infosupport.co.uk
Computers In Personnel Ltd, Abbey House, 28-30 Chapel Street, Marlow, Buckinghamshire, SL7 1DD Tel: (01628) 814000 Fax: (0870) 3662346 E-mail: sales@ciphr.com
K C S Management Systems Ltd, Royal Oak Centre, Brighton Road, Purley, Surrey, CR8 2PG Tel: (020) 8660 2444 Fax: (020) 8668 8196 E-mail: sales@kcsconnect.com
Link H R Systems, Normant House, 121-123 Long Lane, Upton, Chester, CH2 1JF Tel: (01244) 399555 Fax: (01244) 399666 E-mail: general@link-hrsystems.com
Northgate Information Solutions, Prolog House, Littlemoor, Eckington, Sheffield, S21 4EF Tel: (01246) 439400 Fax: (01246) 439401 E-mail: enquiries@northgate-is.com
Safe Computing Ltd, 20 Freeschool Lane, Leicester, LE1 4FY Tel: 0116-262 9321 Fax: 0116-251 5535 E-mail: sales@safecomputing.co.uk
Team Spirit Software Ltd, Warwick House, 48 Collingwood Road, Witham, Essex, CM8 2DZ Tel: (01376) 519413 Fax: (01376) 520471 E-mail: sales@teamspiritsoftware.co.uk

HUMAN RESOURCES (HR) TRAINING

Active Training, 2 Fair Oaks, Slitting Mill, Rugeley, Staffs, WS15 2UU Tel: (07973) 482002 Fax: (01889) 574939 E-mail: yvonneclarke@activetraining.fsnet.co.uk
▶ Aspecthr Business Consultants, 6 Abbotsford Crescent, Wishaw, Lanarkshire, ML2 7DH Tel: (01698) 385075 E-mail: enquiries@aspectHR.co.uk
Cert Consultancy & Training, Dairy Farm, Little Gringley, Retford, Nottinghamshire, DN22 0DU Tel: (01777) 860835 Fax: (01777) 702353 E-mail: cert@certuk.com
D C Gardner Training, Nestor House, Playhouse Yard, London, EC4V 5EX Tel: (020) 7779 8917 Fax: (020) 7779 8786
Government Office For London, Riverwalk House, 157-161 Millbank, London, SW1P 4RR Tel: (020) 7217 3222 Fax: (020) 7217 3473
Interactive Training Management, Church House, 90 Deansgate, Manchester, M3 2GP Tel: 0161-834 3334 Fax: 0161-834 8696 E-mail: debbiesmithitm@btconnect.com
JRK Consultants, Silverdale, Leatherhead Road, Bookham, Leatherhead, Surrey, KT23 4RR Tel: (01372) 457134 Fax: (01372) 381499 E-mail: sales@jrkconsultants.co.uk
Leapwade International Training Ltd, Jordangate House, Jordangate, Macclesfield, Cheshire, SK10 1EQ Tel: (01625) 500694 Fax: (01625) 500696
Leeds Training Trust, Mitchell House, 139 Richardshaw Lane, Stanningley, Pudsey, West Yorkshire, LS28 6AA Tel: 0113-255 2417 Fax: 0113-236 1004 E-mail: admin@ltt.co.uk
MBG Management Consultants Ltd, 50 Greenhill Road, Moseley, Birmingham, B13 9SS Tel: 0121-449 5434 Fax: 0121-449 5844 E-mail: mbgmb@globalnet.co.uk
Mid & North Wales Training Group Ltd, Myrick House, Hen-Domen, Montgomery, Powys, SY15 6EZ Tel: (01686) 668670 Fax: (01686) 668771 E-mail: myrick@btinternet.com
Newry & Mourne Enterprise Agency, Win Business Park, Canal Quay, Newry, County Down, BT35 6PH Tel: (028) 3026 7011 Fax: (028) 3026 1316 E-mail: info@nmea.net
▶ Positivexperience Ltd, The Old Vicarage, Market Place, Castle Donington, Derby, DE74 2JB Tel: (01332) 856393 Fax: (01332) 810769 E-mail: gordon.beck@positivexperience.co.uk

HUMAN RESOURCES INFORMATION SYSTEM (HRIS) SOFTWARE

▶ Human Concepts, Suite 10 The White House, 42 The Terrace, Torquay, TQ1 1DE Tel: (01803) 390490 Fax: (01803) 203304 E-mail: sales@orgplus.co.uk
▶ Logical Innovations, 24 Castle View, Airth, Falkirk, FK2 8GE Tel: (01324) 832333 E-mail: enquiries@logicalinnovations.co.uk

HUMAN RESOURCES MANAGEMENT (HRM)

▶ Outsourced Personnel Services Ltd, PO Box 251, Sunbury-on-Thames, Middlesex, TW16 5SH Tel: (01932) 786066 Fax: (01932) 772032 E-mail: sean@personnelmanagement.co.uk

HUMAN RESOURCES MANAGEMENT SYSTEM (HRMS) SOFTWARE

▶ Human Concepts, Suite 10 The White House, 42 The Terrace, Torquay, TQ1 1DE Tel: (01803) 390490 Fax: (01803) 203304 E-mail: sales@orgplus.co.uk
▶ Logical Innovations, 24 Castle View, Airth, Falkirk, FK2 8GE Tel: (01324) 832333 E-mail: enquiries@logicalinnovations.co.uk

HUMIDIFICATION CONSULTANCY OR DESIGN

C S Environmental Services, 270 Manchester Road, Audenshaw, Manchester, M34 5GJ Tel: 0161-371 1638 Fax: 0161-371 7081

HUMIDIFICATION SYSTEM SPRAY NOZZLES

Delavan Ltd, Gorsey Lane, Widnes, Cheshire, WA8 0RJ Tel: 0151-424 6821 Fax: 0151-495 1043 E-mail: sales@delavan.co.uk
P N R UK Ltd, 13 16 Sugarbrook Road, Bromsgrove, Worcestershire, B60 3DW Tel: (01527) 579066 Fax: (01527) 579067 E-mail: sales@pnr.co.uk

HUMIDIFIERS

Air And Water Centre.Com, Artex Avenue, Rustington, Littlehampton, West Sussex, BN16 3LN Tel: (01903) 858657 Fax: (01903) 850345 E-mail: sales@airandwatercentre.com
C S Environmental Services, 270 Manchester Road, Audenshaw, Manchester, M34 5GJ Tel: 0161-371 1638 Fax: 0161-371 7081
Taprex, 2-6 Victor Road, Harrow, Middlesex, HA2 6PU Tel: (020) 8863 4698
Vapac Humidity Control Ltd, Station Road, Edenbridge, Kent, TN8 6EG Tel: (01732) 863447 E-mail: peter.dewdney@eton_williams.com

HUMIDITY CONTROLLER OR CONTROL SYSTEMS

Brownell Ltd, Commercial Way, Abbey Road, London, NW10 7XF Tel: (020) 8965 9281 Fax: (020) 8965 3239 E-mail: sales@brownell.co.uk
John Godrich, Pellow House, Old Street, Ludlow, Shropshire, SY8 1NU Tel: (01584) 873153 Fax: (01584) 872424 E-mail: johngodrich@johngodrich.co.uk
Munters Ltd, Blackstone Road, Stukeley Meadows Industrial Estate, Huntingdon, Cambridgeshire, PE29 6EE Tel: (01480) 442327 Fax: (01480) 458333 E-mail: info@munters.co.uk
Robydome Ltd, Woodhall Business Park, Sudbury, Suffolk, CO10 1WH Tel: (01787) 310163 Fax: (01787) 880631 E-mail: peter@robydome.co.uk
Vapac Humidity Control Ltd, Station Road, Edenbridge, Kent, TN8 6EG Tel: (01732) 863447 E-mail: peter.dewdney@eton_williams.com

HUMIDITY INDICATING/ RECORDING INSTRUMENTS

IMA Ltd, Parkwell House, Otley Rd, Guiseley, Leeds, LS20 8BH Tel: 0845 4941692 Fax: (01943) 879988E-mail: sales@ima.co.uk

HUMIDITY INSTRUMENTS

Comark Ltd, Comark House Gunnels Wood Park, Gunnels Wood Road, Stevenage, Hertfordshire, SG1 2TA Tel: (01438) 367367 Fax: (01438) 367400 E-mail: salesuk@comarkltd.com
S Brannan & Sons Ltd, Leconfield Industrial Estate, Cleator Moor, Cumbria, CA25 5QE Tel: (01946) 816624 Fax: (01946) 816625 E-mail: sales@brannan.co.uk

HUMIDITY SENSORS

Data Harvest Group Ltd, 1 Eden Court, Eden Way, Leighton Buzzard, Bedfordshire, LU7 4FY Tel: (01525) 373666 Fax: (01525) 851638 E-mail: sales@data-harvest.co.uk

HUNTING AND SHOOTING LUGGAGE

▶ The Sporting Experience, 4 Meadow La, Lapworth, Solihull, W. Midlands, B94 6LS Tel: (01564) 782234 Fax: (01564) 782234 E-mail: info@thesportingexperience.co.uk

HYBRID INTEGRATED CIRCUITS (IC)

▶ C Mac Microcircuits Ltd, South Denes, Great Yarmouth, Norfolk, NR30 3PX Tel: (01493) 856122 Fax: (01493) 858536 E-mail: KenTurrell@cmac.com
▶ Sanyo Component Europe GmbH, Unit 1, Walton Lodge, Bridge Street, Walton-on-Thames, Surrey, KT12 1BT Tel: (01932) 233600 Fax: (01932) 230104

HYDRANTS

Armstrong Priestley, 77 Holbeck Lane, Leeds, LS11 9UL Tel: 0113-244 3138 Fax: 0113-394 4041 E-mail: sales@armstrongpriestley.co.uk

HYDRAULIC ACTUATORS

A T U K Ltd, Unit A4 Sovereign Park Industrial Estate, Market Harborough, Leicestershire, LE16 9EG Tel: (01858) 468199 Fax: (01858) 468187 E-mail: sales@airtorque.co.uk
Claverham Ltd, Bishops Road, Claverham, Bristol, BS49 4NF Tel: (01934) 835224 Fax: (01934) 835337 E-mail: reception@claverham.com
Eland Engineering Company, 29 Lyon Road, Walton-on-Thames, Surrey, KT12 3PU Tel: (01932) 252666 Fax: (01932) 252583 E-mail: info@elandeng.co.uk
Emmerson Process Management Bettis UK Division, 3 Furz Court, Wickham Road, Fareham, Hampshire, PO16 7SH Tel: (01329) 848900 Fax: (01329) 848901 E-mail: bettisuk_sales@msn.com
Ernest Fairbairn Ltd, PO Box 1410, Gerrards Cross, Buckinghamshire, SL9 8UB Tel: (01753) 882542 Fax: (01753) 882546 E-mail: ernestfairbairn@aol.com
Hydrassist Ltd, Unit 15 Fordhouse Road Industrial Estate, Steel Drive, Wolverhampton, WV10 9XB Tel: (01902) 787000 Fax: (01902) 397963
Koso Kent Introl Ltd, Armytage Road, Brighouse, West Yorkshire, HD6 1QF Tel: (01484) 710311 Fax: (01484) 407407 E-mail: control.valve@kentintrol.com
Paladon Systems Ltd, Ferro Fields, Brixworth Industrial Estate, Brixworth, Northampton, NN6 9UA Tel: (01604) 880700 Fax: (01604) 882424 E-mail: enquiries@paladon.co.uk
Titan Holdings Ltd, 334 Meanwood Road, Leeds, LS7 2JF Tel: 0113-262 4612 Fax: 0113-262 6557 E-mail: sales@titanhc.co.uk

HYDRAULIC BOLT TENSIONERS

Hydraclamp, Unit 2, Burnsall Road Industrial Estate, Burnsall Road, Coventry, CV5 6BU Tel: (024) 7667 4646 Fax: (024) 7671 2742 E-mail: steadkm@aol.com
Torque Tension Systems Ltd, 5 Stephenson Court, Barrington Industrial Estate, Bedlington, Northumberland, NE22 7DQ Tel: (01670) 530411 Fax: (01670) 531991 E-mail: enquiries@tts-ltd.com

HYDRAULIC BOLTS AND NUTS

Hydraclamp, Unit 2, Burnsall Road Industrial Estate, Burnsall Road, Coventry, CV5 6BU Tel: (024) 7667 4646 Fax: (024) 7671 2742 E-mail: steadkm@aol.com
Pilgrim International Ltd, Southlink Business Park Unit 10, Oldham, OL4 1DE Tel: 0161-785 7700 E-mail: info@pilgrim-international.co.uk

HYDRAULIC BRAKES

Ortlinghaus (UK) Ltd, 19 Sugarbrook Rd, Aston Fields Industrial Estate, Bromsgrove, Worcestershire, B60 3DN Tel: (01527) 579123 Fax: (01527) 579077 E-mail: sales@ortlinghaus.co.uk
Wichita Co. Ltd, Ampthill Road, Bedford, MK42 9RD Tel: (01234) 350311 Fax: (01234) 350317 E-mail: clutch@wichita.co.uk

HYDRAULIC BUFFERS

Oleo International Ltd, Longford Road, Longford Road, Coventry, CV7 9ND Tel: (024) 7664 5555 Fax: (024) 7664 5777 E-mail: roy@oleo.co.uk

HYDRAULIC CARTRIDGE VALVES

Bucher Hydraulics Ltd, 9 Hemdale Business Park, Hemdale, Nuneaton, Warwickshire, CV11 6GY Tel: (024) 7635 3561 Fax: (024) 7635 3572 E-mail: info.uk@bucherhydraulics.com
▶ Hydraulic Actuators & Controls, Minekeep House, Bridge Road, Camberley, Surrey, GU15 2QZ Tel: (01276) 24914 Fax: (01276) 683332 E-mail: sales@hacltd.co.uk

HYDRAULIC CLAMP NUTS

Hydraclamp, Unit 2, Burnsall Road Industrial Estate, Burnsall Road, Coventry, CV5 6BU Tel: (024) 7667 4646 Fax: (024) 7671 2742 E-mail: steadkm@aol.com

HYDRAULIC CLAMPS

Pharos Redco Ltd, 228 Lythalls Lane, Foleshill, Coventry, CV6 6GF Tel: (024) 7668 7235 Fax: (024) 7666 6355 E-mail: mwinstone@pharosengineering.co.uk

HYDRAULIC COMPONENTS/ FITTINGS DISTRIBUTORS OR AGENTS

Blackwell Hydraulics Ltd, Unit 13 Industrial Estate, Llandudno Junction, Gwynedd, LL31 9SX Tel: (01492) 583821 Fax: (01492) 593591 E-mail: sales@blackwellhydrolics.co.uk
Bonding & Reline Services Co. Ltd, Unit 4, Carls Way, Thurmaston, Leicester, LE4 8DL Tel: 0116-260 1717 Fax: 0116-260 1958
Circuit Hydraulics Ltd, Unit 16 Kensington Industrial Park, Kensington Road, Southport, Merseyside, PR9 0RY Tel: (01704) 546288 Fax: (01704) 546313 E-mail: circuit.hyd@btinternet.com
Cylinder Service Centre, W3/1 BENTALL BUSINESS PARK, WASHINGTON, TYNE & WEAR, NE37 3JD Tel: 0191 4166288 Fax: 0191 4160644 E-mail: gary@cylinder.co.uk
D Cave Hydraulics Ltd, Rainford Road, Bickerstaffe, Ormskirk, Lancashire, L39 0HG Tel: (01695) 725511 Fax: (01695) 725511
Dapp Hydraulics, Bentley Mill Close, Walsall, WS2 0BN Tel: (01922) 632885 Fax: (01922) 721980 E-mail: sales@dapp.co.uk
Eaton Hydralics Ltd, 46 New Lane, Havant, Hampshire, PO9 2NB Tel: (023) 9248 6451 Fax: (023) 9248 7110 E-mail: barryking@eaton.com
Euro Hydraulics Ltd, Unit 4 Park Parade Industrial Estate, Welbeck St South, Ashton-under-Lyne, Lancashire, OL6 7PP Tel: 0161-308 2624 Fax: 0161-343 1926 E-mail: info@eurohydraulics.com
Eurotec Hydraulics Ltd, 173 Ashby Road, Moira, Swadlincote, Derbyshire, DE12 6DW Tel: (01283) 225224 Fax: (01283) 819921 E-mail: eurotecleics@aol.com

HYDRAULIC COMPONENTS/ FITTINGS DISTRIBUTORS OR AGENTS – *continued*

Fluid Power Components, 14 The Oakwood Centre, Downley Road, Havant, Hampshire, PO9 2NP Tel: (023) 9245 4981 Fax: (023) 9245 4981
E-mail: sales@fluidpowercomponents.com

Friction & Hydraulic Services, Gower Street Industrial Estate, St. Georges, Telford, Shropshire, TF2 9HW Tel: (01952) 615793 Fax: (01952) 620408
E-mail: sales@friction-hydraulics.co.uk

Hydrafit Ltd, 40 Brighton Street, Coventry, CV2 4JH Tel: (024) 7645 6621 Fax: (024) 7644 5256

Hydrafit Ltd, Walsall Street, Wolverhampton, WV1 3LN Tel: (01902) 451172 Fax: (01902) 450804 E-mail: hydrafit@btinternet.com

Hydrafit Hydraulic Equipment, 4 Sanderson Street, Sheffield, S9 2TW Tel: 0114-244 6721 Fax: 0114-243 5969

Hydrainer Pumps Ltd, Bedgrave Close, Norwood Industrial Estate, Killamarsh, Sheffield, S21 2HB Tel: 0114-248 4868 Fax: 0114-251 0136 E-mail: info@hydrainer-pumps-ltd.co.uk

Hydraulic Components & Systems Ltd, Unit 14 Sovereign Park, Cleveland Way, Hemel Hempstead, Hertfordshire, HP2 7DA Tel: (01442) 240202 Fax: (01442) 243133
E-mail: hydcompdrf@hotmail.com

Hymid Hydraulics Ltd, 9 Glenbarr Avenue, Leicester, LE4 0AE Tel: 0116-251 8888 Fax: 0116-251 8800E-mail: sales@hymid.com

Hyphose Ltd, 2 Witney Road, Nuffield Industrial Estate, Poole, Dorset, BH17 0GH Tel: (01202) 673333 Fax: (01202) 687788
E-mail: sales@hyphose.com

M F Hydraulics Ltd, Unit 2, Pony Rd, Horspath Industrial Estate, Oxford, OX4 2RD Tel: (01865) 714126 Fax: (01865) 748140
E-mail: sales@mfhydraulics.co.uk

M & R Hydraulics Ltd, Unit 13, Thornton Industrial Estate, Ellesmere Port, CH65 5EU Tel: 0151 3571901

Miric Engineering Ltd, Wigwam Lane, Hucknall, Nottingham, NG15 7SZ Tel: 0115-968 1163 Fax: 0115-968 1483
E-mail: janeyates@mirícengineering.com

Mounts Bay Engineering Ltd, North Pier, Newlyn, Penzance, Cornwall, TR18 5JB Tel: (01736) 363095 Fax: (01736) 332010

Nelson Hydraulics Ltd, Unit H1, Knockmore Industrial Estate, Lisburn, County Antrim, BT28 2AR Tel: (028) 9266 2781 Fax: (028) 9260 2952E-mail: info@nelsonhydraulics.com

Newtown Pneumatic Services Ltd, Newtown Road, Worcester, WR5 1HA Tel: (01905) 29068 Fax: (01905) 24118

Paul Stuart & Co., 9 Forge Industrial Estate, Greenacres Road, Oldham, OL4 1LE Tel: 0161-620 4129 Fax: 0161-628 4413

R A M Ltd, Unit B3 Guy Motors Industrial Park, Park Lane, Wolverhampton, WV10 9QF Tel: (01902) 863506 Fax: (01902) 728402
E-mail: r.a.m.ltd@eur-is.co.uk

Robertson & Armitage Ltd, 10 Limekiln Road, Ayr, KA8 8DG Tel: (01292) 282733 Fax: (01292) 287932

South Eastern Hydraulics Ltd, 40b Holmethorpe Avenue, Redhill, RH1 2NL Tel: (01737) 768011 Fax: (01737) 773469
E-mail: mail@seh-ltd.co.uk

Southern Fluid Power, E Altbarn Industrial Estate, Revenge Road, Chatham, Kent, ME5 8UD Tel: (01634) 686060 Fax: (01634) 683332
E-mail: info@s-f-p.co.uk

Specialised Management Services, Harfreys Road, Great Yarmouth, Norfolk, NR31 0LS Tel: (01493) 655515 Fax: (01224) 657408

Stauff, Unit 30-31, Point Pleasant Industrial Estate, Wallsend, Tyne & Wear, NE28 6HA Tel: 0191-262 6390 Fax: 0191-262 8825
E-mail: enquiries@stauff.com

Stauff Scotland, Unit 3-4 Altens Trade Centre, Hareness Circle, Altens Industrial Estate, Aberdeen, AB12 3LY Tel: (01224) 238518 Fax: (01224) 238500
E-mail: sales@stauffscotland.co.uk

Stauff UK, 3 Rennie Place, East Kilbride, Glasgow, G74 5HD Tel: (01355) 244445 Fax: (01355) 243399
E-mail: sales@stauffuk.co.uk

Titan Advanced Ltd, Titan Works, Claremount Road, Halifax, West Yorkshire, HX3 6NT Tel: (01422) 330265 Fax: (01422) 343295
E-mail: sales@titangroup.co.uk

Titan Fluid Power Ltd, Titan Works, Claremount Road, Halifax, West Yorkshire, HX3 6NT Tel: (01422) 398288 Fax: (01422) 398287
E-mail: sales@titangroup.co.uk

Trecarn Engineering, 1 Ivanhoe Industrial Estate, Tournament Way, Ashby-de-la-Zouch, Leicestershire, LE65 2UU Tel: (01530) 412802 Fax: (01530) 417515

Truflow Hydraulic Components Ltd, Unit F5 Lockside, Anchor Brook Industrial Park, Aldridge, Walsall, WS9 8BZ Tel: (01922) 745488 Fax: (01922) 745399
E-mail: truflow@bt.co.uk

Western Automation, Western House, Ipswich Road, Cardiff, CF23 9AQ Tel: (029) 2048 8446 Fax: (029) 2047 1843
E-mail: sales@appliedautomation.co.uk

HYDRAULIC COMPONENTS/ FITTINGS MANUFRS

Acsl Precision Engineering, 3 Cartwright Road, Stevenage, Hertfordshire, SG1 4QJ Tel: (01438) 359123 Fax: (01438) 741819
E-mail: acsl@btinternet.com

Atom Hydraulics, 1 Wicks Close, Springwood Industrial Estate, Braintree, Essex, CM7 2GE Tel: (01376) 348889 Fax: (01376) 348311

Beaumanor Engineering Ltd, 47 Highmeres Road, Leicester, LE4 9LZ Tel: 0116-276 4728 Fax: 0116-246 0133
E-mail: info@beaumanor.com

Blagden Hydraulic Ltd, 110 Tuddenham Road, Ipswich, IP4 2SZ Tel: (01473) 252623 Fax: (01473) 233732
E-mail: brianblagden@lineone.net

Burnett & Hillman Engineers, Havyatt Road, Coxs Green, Wrington, Bristol, BS40 5NL Tel: (01934) 862980 Fax: (01934) 862616
E-mail: sales@burnettandhillman.co.uk

Dunlop Hiflex Fluid Power Ltd, Unit 31-32 Church Road Business Centre, Church Road, Sittingbourne, Kent, ME10 3RS Tel: (01795) 429807 Fax: (01795) 420423
E-mail: sales@dunlophiflex.xom

Eftee Metal Bodies Ltd, Glencraig Street, Airdrie, Lanarkshire, ML6 9AS Tel: (01236) 765975 Fax: (01236) 747415
E-mail: mail@efteetmetals.co.uk

Erlson Engineering Ltd, 4 Priorswood Place, Skelmersdale, Lancashire, WN8 9QB Tel: (01695) 720149 Fax: (01695) 556426
E-mail: sales@erlson.co.uk

Express Hoses, Unit 1 18 West Bank Road, Belfast, BT3 9JL Tel: (028) 9037 0274 Fax: (028) 9037 0256
E-mail: expresshoses@btopenworld.com

Flexal Springs UK, 179 Park Avenue, London, NW10 7XH Tel: (020) 8453 0867 Fax: (020) 8961 9181
E-mail: flexalspringsuk@btconnect.com

Forest Hydraulics Ltd, 19-20 Greenshield Industrial Estate, Bradfield Road, London, E16 2AU Tel: (020) 7474 5738 Fax: (020) 7474 5181E-mail: forest.hydraulics@virgin.net

GS Hydro Ltd, Unit C Endeavour Court, Hall Dene Way, Seaham Grange Industrial Estat, Seaham, County Durham, SR7 0HB Tel: 0191-523 9643 Fax: 0191-521 8001
E-mail: sales@gshydro.com

Hoselines Ltd, 25 Longfields Road, Carlton, Barnsley, South Yorkshire, S71 3HT Tel: (01226) 240838 Fax: (01226) 204315

Hycon Ltd, F Bridge Farm, Reading Road, Arborfield, Reading, RG2 9HT Tel: 0118-976 1616 Fax: 0118-976 1626
E-mail: hydroliccontrol@aol.com

Hydac Technology Ltd, Woodstock Road, Charlbury, Charlbury, Chipping Norton, Oxfordshire, OX7 3ES Tel: (01608) 811211 Fax: (01608) 811259E-mail: info@hydac.co.uk

Hydrafit Ltd, 40 Brighton Street, Coventry, CV2 4JH Tel: (024) 7645 6621 Fax: (024) 7644 5256

Hydrafit Ltd, Walsall Street, Wolverhampton, WV1 3LN Tel: (01902) 451172 Fax: (01902) 450804 E-mail: hydrafit@btinternet.com

Hydrafit Hydraulic Equipment, 4 Sanderson Street, Sheffield, S9 2TW Tel: 0114-244 6721 Fax: 0114-243 5969

▶ Hydraulic Alliance Ltd, 80 Allaston Road, Lydney, Gloucestershire, GL15 4EZ Tel: (01594) 843322 Fax: (01594) 843322
E-mail: sales@hydraulicalliance.com

▶ Hydraulic Power Services Ltd, 84 Bridgeman Street, Bolton, BL3 6AT Tel: (01204) 363660 Fax: (01204) 363670
E-mail: info@hydraulicpower.co.uk

Hydraulic System Products Ltd, Monckton Road, Wakefield, West Yorkshire, WF2 7AL Tel: (01924) 364748 Fax: (01924) 290450
E-mail: sales@h-s-p.co.uk

M F Hydraulics Ltd, Unit 2, Pony Rd, Horspath Industrial Estate, Oxford, OX4 2RD Tel: (01865) 714126 Fax: (01865) 748140
E-mail: sales@mfhydraulics.co.uk

Melnei Engineering, Unit F4 Heath Place, Bognor Regis, West Sussex, PO22 9SL Tel: (01243) 829103 Fax: (01243) 829103
E-mail: melnei@melneiengineering.co.uk

Miric Engineering Ltd, Wigwam Lane, Hucknall, Nottingham, NG15 7SZ Tel: 0115-968 1163 Fax: 0115-968 1483
E-mail: janeyates@miricengineering.com

Mykro Hydraulics Distributors Ltd, Nortonthorpe Industrial Estate, Wakefield Road, Scissett, Huddersfield, HD8 9LA Tel: (01484) 865977 Fax: (01484) 865809
E-mail: mykrohydraulics@aol.co.uk

Newbow Hydraulic Equipment, Benacre Drive, Fazeley Street, Birmingham, B5 5RE Tel: 0121-772 6861 Fax: 0121-643 2637
E-mail: sales@newbow.co.uk

P K Engineering West Bromwich Ltd, Unit 3 Kelvin Way, West Bromwich, West Midlands, B70 7TN Tel: 0121-500 5847 Fax: 0121-553 1622 E-mail: sales@pk-engineering.co.uk

Tom Parker Ltd, PO Box 36, Preston, PR1 1HY Tel: (01772) 251405 Fax: (01772) 827088
E-mail: sales@tom-parker.co.uk

Pneumatic & Hydraulic Couplings Ltd, Atlas Way, Sheffield, S4 7QQ Tel: 0114-244 2704 Fax: 0114-244 2705 E-mail: sales@phcltd.net

R & J Industrial Supplies, Clay Flatts Trading Estate, Workington, Cumbria, CA14 2TQ Tel: (01900) 605411 Fax: (01900) 605415

Ranger Caradoc Hydraulics Ltd, The Gables, Worcester Road, Great Witley, Worcester, WR6 6HR Tel: (01299) 896953 Fax: (01299) 896963 E-mail: sales@rangercaradoc.com

▶ Ringwood Hydraulics Ltd, 78 Cobham Road, Ferndown Industrial Estate, Wimborne, Dorset, BH21 7RW Tel: (01202) 890401 Fax: (01202) 897713

San Precision Engineering Co. Ltd, Units 9-10 Harnall Industrial Estate, Harnall Lane East, Coventry, CV1 5AE Tel: (024) 7622 0613 Fax: (024) 7652 0004
E-mail: sales@sanprecision.com

Steerforth Sales Ltd, Unit 7, Holder Road, Aldershot, Hampshire, GU12 4RH Tel: (01252) 333633 Fax: (01252) 343080
E-mail: sales@steerforth.co.uk

Titan Fluid Power Ltd, Titan Works, Claremount Road, Halifax, West Yorkshire, HX3 6NT Tel: (01422) 398288 Fax: (01422) 398287
E-mail: sales@titangroup.co.uk

Tritech International Ltd, Peregrine Road, Westhill Business Park, Westhill, Aberdeenshire, AB32 6JL Tel: (01224) 744111 Fax: (01224) 741771 E-mail: sales@tritech.co.uk

▶ Universal Supplies Clydesdale Ltd, Hozier Street, Carluke, Lanarkshire, ML8 5DW Tel: (01555) 772474 Fax: (01555) 772426
E-mail: sales@uscltd.co.uk

Wide Range Engineering Services Ltd, Coventry Road, Acan Way, Narborough, Leicester, LE19 2FT Tel: 0116-275 0100 Fax: 0116-275 0086 E-mail: sales@wres.co.uk

Wilbar Components Ltd, Martindale Industrial Estate, Hawks Green, Cannock, Staffordshire, WS11 7XN Tel: (01543) 578873 Fax: (01543) 570450 E-mail: enquiries@wilbar.co.uk

HYDRAULIC COMPONENTS/ FITTINGS, AUTOMOTIVE INDUSTRY

Kingsdown, Brook Street, Snodland, Kent, ME6 5BB Tel: (01634) 249555 Fax: (01634) 249550 E-mail: sales@kingsdownuk.com

Pressure Flex, 111 Great Barr Street, Birmingham, B9 4BB Tel: 0121-766 8228 Fax: 0121-766 7818
E-mail: sales@wakefind.co.uk

Titan Fluid Power Ltd, Titan Works, Claremount Road, Halifax, West Yorkshire, HX3 6NT Tel: (01422) 398288 Fax: (01422) 398287
E-mail: sales@titangroup.co.uk

HYDRAULIC CONTROL SYSTEMS

Airfluid Hydraulics & Pneumatics Ltd, Tong Road, Bishops Wood, Stafford, ST19 9AB Tel: (01952) 850246 Fax: (01952) 850246
E-mail: hydraulicbjr@aol.com

Armstrong Lyon Hydraulics Ltd, 13 Faraday Road, Knowsley Industrial Park, Liverpool, L33 7UT Tel: 0151-545 2180 Fax: 0151-547 1309
E-mail: sales@armstronglyon.freeserve.co.uk

Atos Spa (UK), 17A Longwood Avenue, Cowplain, Waterlooville, Hampshire, PO8 8HX Tel: (023) 9226 5880 Fax: (023) 9226 5881
E-mail: atos-uk@fsmail.net

Bell Hydraulic Services Ltd, Chapel Lane, Cwmbran, Gwent, NP44 2PP Tel: (01633) 861423 Fax: (01633) 864472
E-mail: dave.bell@bellhydraulics.co.uk

Bewick Engineering Ltd, 4 Walker Riverside, Wincomblee Road, Newcastle upon Tyne, NE6 3PF Tel: 0191-295 1975 Fax: 0191-295 1973 E-mail: robq@bewick.clara.co.uk

Blagden Hydraulic Ltd, 110 Tuddenham Road, Ipswich, IP4 2SZ Tel: (01473) 252623 Fax: (01473) 233732
E-mail: brianblagden@lineone.net

Branch Hydraulic Systems Ltd, Unit H, Innsworth Technology Park, Innsworth Lane, Gloucester, GL3 1DL Tel: (01452) 730562 Fax: (01452) 731579 E-mail: branch@dowco.co.uk

Bucher Hydraulics Ltd, 9 Hemdale Business Park, Hemdale, Nuneaton, Warwickshire, CV11 6GY Tel: (024) 7635 3561 Fax: (024) 7635 3572
E-mail: info.uk@bucherhydraulics.com

Denley Hydraulics Ltd, Spen Vale Street, Heckmondwike, West Yorkshire, WF16 0NQ Tel: (01924) 413400 Fax: (01924) 410109
E-mail: sales@denleyhydraulics.co.uk

Grampian Plant & Machinery, Moss-Side of Arthrath, Ellon, Aberdeenshire, AB41 8EF Tel: (01358) 711393 Fax: (01358) 711398

Hydar Fluid Power Ltd, Unit 20-21, Midsomer Enterprise Park, Radstock Road, Midsomer Norton, Radstock, BA3 2BB Tel: (01249) 651666 Fax: (01761) 414050
E-mail: carol@hydar.co.uk

Macscott Bond Ltd, PO Box 1, Loanhead, Midlothian, EH20 9SW Tel: 0131-448 2950 Fax: 0131-448 2941

Ovalway Hydraulics, 11 Cannon Park Way, Middlesbrough, Cleveland, TS1 5JU Tel: (01642) 247106 Fax: (01642) 241874
E-mail: ohe@ovalway.co.uk

Parker Hannifin plc, 66 Wakefield Road, Ossett, West Yorkshire, WF5 9JS Tel: (01924) 282200 Fax: (01924) 282299 E-mail:

Parker Hannifin Dennison, Unit F1 Sheddingdean Business Centre, Marchants Way, Burgess Hill, West Sussex, RH15 8QY Tel: (01444) 238300 Fax: (01444) 246121

Ram Power Ltd, 16 Greenhill Crescent, Watford, WD18 8SE Tel: (01923) 231661 Fax: (01923) 246856 E-mail: rmpwr@aol.com

Skytec Aviation Ltd, Unit 23 Langlands Avenue, Kelvin South Business Park, East Kilbride, Glasgow, G75 0YG Tel: (01355) 279633 Fax: (01355) 279634
E-mail: skytecaviation@btconnect.com

Summit Equipment Supplies Ltd, Clover Nook Road, Clover Nook Industrial Estate, Alfreton, Derbyshire, DE55 4RF Tel: (01773) 520488 Fax: (01773) 831004
E-mail: sumhyd@lineone.net

System 910 Hydraulics Ltd, 7 The Old Granary, The Street, Boxgrove, Chichester, West Sussex, PO18 0ES Tel: (01243) 539789 Fax: (01243) 530307
E-mail: system910@mistral.co.uk

Voith Turbo Ltd, Meir Road, Park Farm North, Redditch, Worcestershire, B98 7SY Tel: (01527) 516666 Fax: (01527) 516777
E-mail: info@hlhydraulic.demon.co.uk

Yeovil Hydraulics, 14 Gazelle Road, Lynx Trading Estate, Yeovil, Somerset, BA20 2PJ Tel: (01935) 472233 Fax: (01935) 431211
E-mail: enquiries@yeovilhydraulics.co.uk

HYDRAULIC CONTROL VALVES

Bucher Hydraulics Ltd, 9 Hemdale Business Park, Hemdale, Nuneaton, Warwickshire, CV11 6GY Tel: (024) 7635 3561 Fax: (024) 7635 3572
E-mail: info.uk@bucherhydraulics.com

▶ Hydraulic Actuators & Controls, Minekeep House, Bridge Road, Camberley, Surrey, GU15 2QZ Tel: (01276) 24914 Fax: (01276) 683332 E-mail: sales@hacltd.co.uk

Hydraulic & Pneumatic Supplies Ltd, Unit 39, Second Drove Industrial Estate, Fengate, Peterborough, PE1 5XA Tel: (01733) 894500 Fax: (01733) 894892
E-mail: sales@hps-ltd.co.uk

S A M Hydraulic UK Ltd, Planet House 910 Lakeside Drive, Centre Park, Warrington, WA1 1QX Tel: (01925) 624800 Fax: (01925) 624801 E-mail: sales@samhydraulik.co.uk

Valtec Controls Ltd, Halifax Works, St. Marys Lane, Tewkesbury, Gloucestershire, GL20 5SF Tel: (01684) 292383 Fax: (01684) 294498
E-mail: valtec.controls@btinternet.com

Voith Turbo Ltd, Meir Road, Park Farm North, Redditch, Worcestershire, B98 7SY Tel: (01527) 516666 Fax: (01527) 516777
E-mail: info@hlhydraulic.demon.co.uk

HYDRAULIC CRANES

Fassi UK Ltd, 26 Blick Road, Heathcote Industrial Estate, Warwick, CV34 6TA Tel: (01926) 889779 Fax: (01926) 885777
E-mail: mail@fassi.co.uk

Lawson Engineers Ltd, Barras Lane, Dalston, Carlisle, CA5 7ND Tel: (01228) 711470 Fax: (01228) 711255
E-mail: sales@lawson-engineers.com

Manitowoc Europe Holdings Ltd, 1 Azure Court, Doxford International Business Park, Sunderland, SR3 3BE Tel: 0191-522 2000 Fax: 0191-522 2053
E-mail: info@manitowoc.com

Plant Equipment Ltd, Clover Nook Road, Cotes Park Industrial Estate, Somercotes, Alfreton, Derbyshire, DE55 4RF Tel: (01773) 836060 Fax: (01773) 520630
E-mail: info@plantequip.co.uk

Herbert Pool Ltd, 95 Fleet Road, Fleet, Hampshire, GU51 3PJ Tel: (01252) 620444 Fax: (01252) 622292

Walker Crane Services Ltd, Trading Estate, Motherwell Way, Grays, Essex, RM20 3XD Tel: (01708) 867251 Fax: (01708) 863636
E-mail: info@walkercranes.co.uk

HYDRAULIC CUTTERS

Allspeeds Ltd, Royal Works, Atlas Street, Clayton le Moors, Accrington, Lancashire, BB5 5LP Tel: (01254) 615100 Fax: (01254) 615199
E-mail: sales@allspeeds.co.uk

Enerpac Ltd, PO Box 33, Darlaston, West Midlands, WS10 8LQ Tel: (01527) 598900 Fax: 0121-505 0799
E-mail: info@enerpac.com

HYDRAULIC CYLINDER OR RAM MAINTENANCE OR REPAIR

▶ C & G Hydraulic Services, 4 Newark Storage Industrial Estate, Bowbridge Road, Newark, Nottinghamshire, NG24 4EQ Tel: (01636) 613113 Fax: (01636) 613113
E-mail: cghydraulic@btconnect.com

Hydraulic Technical Services Ltd, 10-12 Galleymead Road, Colnbrook, Slough, SL3 0EN Tel: (01753) 689689 Fax: (01753) 689700 E-mail: info@hydraulictechnical.co.uk

Ray Larrington Hydraulics Brothertoft Ltd, North Forty Foot Bank, Brothertoft, Boston, Lincolnshire, PE20 3SU Tel: (01205) 280304 Fax: (01205) 280230

Silvester Engineering Ltd, Kingsmead, Marringdean Rd, Billingshurst, West Sussex, RH14 9HE Tel: (01403) 782255 Fax: (01403) 782703
E-mail: sales@silvesterengineering.co.uk

HYDRAULIC CYLINDER/RAM MANUFRS

A E S Industries Ltd, Unit 3 Appleby Glade Industrial Estate, Ryder Close, Swadlincote, Derbyshire, DE11 9EU Tel: (01283) 210033 Fax: (01283) 229330

A H Garner Ltd, Harrimans Lane, Lenton Lane Industrial Estate, Nottingham, NG7 2SD Tel: 0115-978 5161 Fax: 0115-924 4704 E-mail: sales@ahgarner.co.uk

A M Hydraulics, Unit 4 Hockley Brook Trading Estate, South Road Avenue, Birmingham, B18 5JR Tel: 0121-554 7576 Fax: 0121-554 4640 E-mail: info@amhydraulics.com

A5 Hydraulics Ltd, 46a Alliance Industrial Estate, Dodsworth Street, Darlington, County Durham, DL1 2NG Tel: (01325) 464354 Fax: (01325) 464356 E-mail: sales@a5hydraulics.co.uk

Abco Engineering Hydraulics, Mill Park, Station Road, Southwell, Nottinghamshire, NG25 0Et Tel: (01636) 812674 Fax: 01636 815448 E-mail: sales@abcohydraulics.com

Air Power & Hydraulics Ltd, 15 Watt Rd, Hillington Park, Glasgow, G52 4PQ Tel: 0141-810 4511 Fax: 0141-883 3825 E-mail: hydraulics@aph.co.uk

Armstrong Lyon Hydraulics Ltd, 13 Faraday Road, Knowsley Industrial Park, Liverpool, L33 7UT Tel: 0151-545 2180 Fax: 0151-547 1309 E-mail: sales@armstronglyon.freeserve.co.uk

Atos Spa (UK), 17A Longwood Avenue, Cowplain, Waterlooville, Hampshire, PO8 8HX Tel: (023) 9226 5880 Fax: (023) 9226 5881 E-mail: atos-uk@fsmail.net

Avon Hydraulics Ltd, Waterloo Road, Bidford-on-Avon, Alcester, Warwickshire, B50 4JN Tel: (01789) 772613 Fax: (01789) 490051

Blagden Hydraulic Ltd, 110 Tuddenham Road, Ipswich, IP4 2SZ Tel: (01473) 252623 Fax: (01473) 233732 E-mail: brianblagden@lineone.net

Bosch Rexroth Ltd, Viewfield Industrial Estate, Glenrothes, Fife, KY6 2RD Tel: (01592) 631515 Fax: (01592) 631888

Boxrite Hydraulics, 1A May Avenue, Northfleet, Gravesend, Kent, DA11 8RH Tel: (01474) 327722 Fax: (01322) 327722

C A Honemaster Ltd, Unit 14 Malmesbury Road, Kingsditch Trading Estate, Cheltenham, Gloucestershire, GL51 9PL Tel: (01242) 584326 Fax: (01242) 226158 E-mail: kieran.reel@btconnect.com

Centech Hydraulics, 62 Arnold Road, Nottingham, NG6 0DZ Tel: 0115-924 4822 Fax: 0115-924 4818

Challenger Hydraulics Ltd, Shaw Cross Business Pk, Owl La, Dewsbury, West Yorkshire, WF12 7RF Tel: (01924) 464433 Fax: (01924) 456292 E-mail: sales@challenger-group.co.uk

Cityown Ltd, Unit M Charlwoods Business Centre, East Grinstead, West Sussex, RH19 2HH Tel: (01342) 327787 Fax: (01342) 324289

Cylinder Service Centre, W3/1 BENTALL BUSINESS PARK, WASHINGTON, TYNE & WEAR, NE37 3JD Tel: 0191 4166288 Fax: 0191 4160644 E-mail: gary@cylinder.co.uk

Dale Mansfield Ltd, Rotherham Road, New Houghton, Mansfield, Nottinghamshire, NG19 8TF Tel: (01623) 810659 Fax: (01623) 811660 E-mail: enquiry@dale-mansfield.co.uk

Denley Hydraulics Ltd, Spen Vale Street, Heckmondwike, West Yorkshire, WF16 0NQ Tel: (01924) 413400 Fax: (01924) 410109 E-mail: sales@denleyhydraulics.co.uk

Dicol Co. Ltd, Colchester Road, Tendring, Clacton-on-Sea, Essex, CO16 9AA Tel: (01255) 830119 Fax: (01255) 831362 E-mail: sales@dicol.com

Double M Nottingham Ltd, Nunn Brook Road, County Estate, Huthwaite, Sutton-in-Ashfield, Nottinghamshire, NG17 2HU Tel: (01623) 515904 Fax: (01623) 515929

Eland Engineering Company, 29 Lyon Road, Walton-on-Thames, Surrey, KT12 3PU Tel: (01932) 252666 Fax: (01932) 252583 E-mail: info@elandeng.co.uk

Ellgee Hydraulics Ltd, 103 Perry Road, Nottingham, NG5 3AL Tel: 0115-962 4126 Fax: 0115-969 2890 E-mail: ellgee@btconnect.com

Enerpac Ltd, PO Box 33, Darlaston, West Midlands, WS10 8LQ Tel: (01527) 598900 Fax: 0121-505 0799 E-mail: info@enerpac.com

Force Hydraulics, 14a Saxon Business Park, Hanbury Road, Stoke Prior, Bromsgrove, Worcestershire, B60 4AD Tel: (01527) 575704 Fax: (01527) 576668

Forest Press Hydraulics Ltd, 6 Hollywood Works, Valley Road, Cinderford, Gloucestershire, GL14 2PD Tel: (01594) 826009 Fax: (01594) 822377 E-mail: sales@forestpresshyd.com

Garfield Hydrol Ltd, Fengate, Peterborough, PE1 5XG Tel: (01733) 568444 Fax: (01733) 893516 E-mail: sales@rsg.co.uk

General Hydraulics, Banbury Road, Thrupp, Kidlington, Oxfordshire, OX5 1JF Tel: (01865) 377559

Harsh Ltd, The Industrial Estate, Full Sutton, York, YO41 1HS Tel: (01759) 372100 Fax: (01759) 371414 E-mail: sales@harshuk.com

Hebble Hydraulic Services Ltd, Spring Grove Mills, Linthwaite, Huddersfield, HD7 5QG Tel: (01484) 846688 Fax: (01484) 847701 E-mail: hebble@btconnect.com

Hydraflow Hydraulics (UK) Ltd, Unit 1, Price Street, Bristol Road, Gloucester, GL1 5SZ Tel: (01452) 387061 Fax: (01452) 381332

▶ Hydraulic & Engineering Services Ltd, Unit 5-6 Victory Park, Trident Close, Medway City Estate, Rochester, Kent, ME2 4ER Tel: (01634) 295650 Fax: (01634) 295670 E-mail: info@hydraulicengineering.co.uk

Hydraulic & Pneumatic Power Services, Methilhaven Road, Methil, Leven, Fife, KY8 3LA Tel: (01333) 429690 Fax: (01333) 422952 E-mail: info@fcegroup.com

Hydraulic Supplies Ltd, Unit 5-6 Block 2, Wednesbury Trading Estate, Wednesbury, West Midlands, WS10 7JN Tel: 0121-505 3663 Fax: 0121-505 3375 E-mail: sales@hydraulicsupplies.co.uk

Hydrax Ltd, Wylds Road, Bridgwater, Somerset, TA6 4BH Tel: (01278) 727600 Fax: (01278) 727601 E-mail: info@hydrax.co.uk

Jason Hydraulics Ltd, Burford Road, Minster Lovell, Witney, Oxfordshire, OX29 0RD Tel: (01993) 705565 Fax: (01993) 776856 E-mail: sales@jasonhydraulics.co.uk

JC Fluid Power, 5 Readmans Industrial Estate, Station Road, East Tilbury, Tilbury, Essex, RM18 8QR Tel: (01375) 843995 Fax: (01375) 859010 E-mail: info@jcfluidpower.co.uk

Jespro 2000 Ltd, Central Mills, Raymond Street, Bradford, West Yorkshire, BD5 8DT Tel: (01274) 735446 Fax: (01274) 394909 E-mail: sales@jespro.com

Jonic Engineering Ltd, Speedwell Road, Yardley, Birmingham, B25 8EU Tel: 0121-707 8222 Fax: 0121-706 7303 E-mail: sales@jonicengineering.co.uk

K P Engineering Components, Barlow Road, Aldermans Green Industrial Estate, Coventry, CV2 2LD Tel: (024) 7660 3333 Fax: (024) 7660 4444 E-mail: sales@kpecltd.com

M & P Hydraulic Ltd, Unit 3c Bergen Way, Hull, HU7 0YQ Tel: (01482) 820701 Fax: (01482) 823101

Max Stone, Unit 3 Jubilee Trade Centre, Pershore Street, Birmingham, B5 6ND Tel: 0121-666 6704 Fax: 0121-622 2247 E-mail: sales@maxstone.co.uk

Miller Fluid Power, 3 Bailey Drive, Norwood Industrial Estate, Killamarsh, Sheffield, S21 2JF Tel: 0114-247 2936 Fax: 0114-247 8371

Neilson Hydraulics & Engineering Ltd, 22 Atlas Way, Sheffield, S4 7QQ Tel: (01709) 821002 Fax: 0114-244 0111 E-mail: sales@neilson-hydraulics.co.uk

Nicol & Andrew plc, 2 Mossland Road, Hillington Industrial Estate, Glasgow, G52 4XZ Tel: 0141-882 4724 Fax: 0141-883 3350 E-mail: info@nicolandandrew.com

Northern Hydraulics, 51 Gortgonis Road, Coalisland, Dungannon, County Tyrone, BT71 4QG Tel: (028) 8774 7444 Fax: (028) 8774 7544 E-mail: info@northernhydraulics.com

Northfield Engineering, 41 Hedon Road, Hull, HU9 1LH Tel: (01482) 320888 Fax: (01482) 587271 E-mail: sales@northfieldeng.co.uk

P H C (UK) Ltd, Bassington Industrial Estate, Cramlington, Northumberland, NE23 8AE Tel: (01670) 707203 Fax: (01670) 707204

Ram Power Ltd, 16 Greenhill Crescent, Watford, WD18 8SE Tel: (01923) 231661 Fax: (01923) 246856 E-mail: rmpwr@aol.com

Ram Reman Ltd, Gundrymoor Trading Estate, Collingwood Road, West Moors, Wimborne, Dorset, BH21 6QJ Tel: (01202) 861888 Fax: (01202) 861668

Ranger Caradoc Hydraulics Ltd, The Gables, Worcester Road, Great Witley, Worcester, WR6 6HR Tel: (01299) 896953 Fax: (01299) 896963 E-mail: sales@rangercaradoc.com

Schoolhill Hydraulic Engineering Co. Ltd, 3 Greenbank Place, East Tullos Industrial Estate, Aberdeen, AB12 3RJ Tel: (01224) 871086 Fax: (01224) 897135 E-mail: hydraulics@scheng.demon.co.uk

Shepcote Engineering Ltd, Davy Indust Park, Prince of Wales Road, Sheffield, S9 4EX Tel: 0114-256 2505 Fax: 0114-261 1910 E-mail: enquiries@shepcote-eng.com

Steerforth Sales Ltd, Unit 7, Holder Road, Aldershot, Hampshire, GU12 4RH Tel: (01252) 333633 Fax: (01252) 343080 E-mail: sales@steerforth.co.uk

T & P Productions, Unit 5 Parkwood Court, Rotherwas Industrial Estate, Hereford, HR2 6NU Tel: (01432) 270554 Fax: (01432) 341172

Tangye Ltd, Royal Works, Atlas Street, Clayton Le Moors, Accrington, Lancashire, BB5 5LW Tel: (01254) 615100 Fax: (01254) 615199 E-mail: sales@allspeeds.co.uk

Taskers UK Ltd, 4 Roman Ridge Road, Sheffield, S9 1GB Tel: 0114-243 0927 Fax: 0114-242 5507 E-mail: sales@taskersuk.com

Thorne Hydraulics Ltd, Unit 24 Frontier Works, 12 King Edward Road, Thorne, Doncaster, South Yorkshire, DN8 4HU Tel: (01405) 816067 Fax: (01405) 741060

Titan Fluid Power Ltd, Titan Works, Claremount Road, Halifax, West Yorkshire, HX3 6NT Tel: (01422) 398288 Fax: (01422) 398287

Titan Holdings Ltd, 334 Meanwood Road, Leeds, LS7 2JF Tel: 0113-262 4612 Fax: 0113-262 6557 E-mail: sales@titanhc.co.uk

Tomlin Hydraulics Ltd, Vicarage Farm Road, Peterborough, PE1 5TP Tel: (01733) 558833 Fax: (01733) 897801 E-mail: tomlinhydraulics@btconnect.com

Toolmasters Technical Ltd, Instanta Work, Charles Street, West Bromwich, West Midlands, B70 0AZ Tel: 0121-520 1889 Fax: 0121-520 1890 E-mail: sales@toolmasters.co.uk

Tox Pressotechnik Ltd, Unit 35, Stafford Business Village, Dyson Way, Staffordshire Technology Park, Stafford, ST18 0TW Tel: (01785) 887903 Fax: (01785) 887027 E-mail: sales@tox-uk.com

Universal Hydraulics Ltd, Carrwood Road, Chesterfield, Derbyshire, S41 9QB Tel: (01246) 451711 Fax: (01246) 450399 E-mail: sales@universalhydraulics.co.uk

WB Hydraulic Services, 45 Boston Road, Leicester, LE4 1AW Tel: 0116-235 2606 E-mail: bill@wbhydserv.freeserve.co.uk

Wrayram Engineers Ltd, 403 Netherwood Road, Rotherwas Industrial Estate, Hereford, HR2 6JU Tel: (01432) 355454 Fax: (01432) 358727 E-mail: enquiries@wrayram.com

Wycis Engineering Co. Ltd, 1 Wheatear, Perry Road, Witham, Essex, CM8 3YY Tel: (01376) 516247 Fax: (01376) 514721 E-mail: wycis@btinternet.com

Yeadon Hydraulics Ltd, Sizers Court, Off Henshaw Lane, Yeadon, Leeds, LS19 7DP Tel: 0113-250 3296 Fax: 0113-250 5624 E-mail: johnhall@dynamicshydraulics.com

HYDRAULIC CYLINDER/RAM REFURBISHMENT SERVICES

Abco Engineering Hydraulics, Mill Park, Station Road, Southwell, Nottinghamshire, NG25 0Et Tel: (01636) 812674 Fax: 01636 815448 E-mail: sales@abcohydraulics.com

HYDRAULIC CYLINDERS/RAMS, MULTISTAGE

Jonic Engineering Ltd, Speedwell Road, Yardley, Birmingham, B25 8EU Tel: 0121-707 8222 Fax: 0121-706 7303 E-mail: sales@jonicengineering.co.uk

HYDRAULIC CYLINDERS/RAMS, RECONDITIONED

A M Hydraulics, Unit 4 Hockley Brook Trading Estate, South Road Avenue, Birmingham, B18 5JR Tel: 0121-554 7576 Fax: 0121-554 4640 E-mail: info@amhydraulics.com

A5 Hydraulics Ltd, 46a Alliance Industrial Estate, Dodsworth Street, Darlington, County Durham, DL1 2NG Tel: (01325) 464354 Fax: (01325) 464356 E-mail: sales@a5hydraulics.co.uk

Boxrite Hydraulics, 1A May Avenue, Northfleet, Gravesend, Kent, DA11 8RH Tel: (01474) 327722 Fax: (01322) 327722

Central Engineering & Hydraulic Services Ltd, Brook Works, 174 Bromyard Road, St. Johns, Worcester, WR2 5EE Tel: (01905) 748569 Fax: (01905) 420700 E-mail: chs0999@aol.com

Central Hydraulic Systems Ltd, Walker Street, Rochdale, Lancashire, OL16 2AB Tel: (01706) 343007 Fax: (01706) 645354

Cylinder Repair Services, 168 Rede Court Road, Rochester, Kent, ME2 3TU Tel: (01634) 723366 Fax: (01634) 723388 E-mail: crs.hydraulics@ukonline.co.uk

Cylinder Service Centre, W3/1 BENTALL BUSINESS PARK, WASHINGTON, TYNE & WEAR, NE37 3JD Tel: 0191 4166288 Fax: 0191 4160644 E-mail: gary@cylinder.co.uk

Ellgee Hydraulics Ltd, 103 Perry Road, Nottingham, NG5 3AL Tel: 0115-962 4126 Fax: 0115-969 2890 E-mail: ellgee@btconnect.com

Force Hydraulics, 14a Saxon Business Park, Hanbury Road, Stoke Prior, Bromsgrove, Worcestershire, B60 4AD Tel: (01527) 575704 Fax: (01527) 576668

Garfield Hydrol Ltd, Fengate, Peterborough, PE1 5XG Tel: (01733) 568444 Fax: (01733) 893516 E-mail: sales@rsg.co.uk

General Hydraulics, Banbury Road, Thrupp, Kidlington, Oxfordshire, OX5 1JF Tel: (01865) 377559

Gildon Components, 5 Trafalgar Court, Widnes, Cheshire, WA8 0SZ Tel: 0151-420 2499 Fax: 0151-420 2499

Gilson Engineering Newbury Ltd, 3 Sandleford Farm, Sandleford, Newtown, Newbury, Berkshire, RG20 9BB Tel: (01635) 41924 Fax: (01635) 42286 E-mail: info@gilsoneng.co.uk

▶ Hydraulic & Engineering Services Ltd, Unit 5-6 Victory Park, Trident Close, Medway City Estate, Rochester, Kent, ME2 4ER Tel: (01634) 295650 Fax: (01634) 295670 E-mail: info@hydraulicengineering.co.uk

Hydraulic & Pneumatic Cylinders Ltd, 4 Birmingham New Enterprise Workshops, All Saints Road, Birmingham, B18 7RL Tel: 0121-523 8400 Fax: 0121-523 8400 E-mail: sales@hydraulic-pneumatic-cylinders.co.uk

Hydraulic & Pneumatic Power Services, Methilhaven Road, Methil, Leven, Fife, KY8 3LA Tel: (01333) 429690 Fax: (01333) 422952 E-mail: info@fcegroup.com

Hydrax Ltd, Wylds Road, Bridgwater, Somerset, TA6 4BH Tel: (01278) 727600 Fax: (01278) 727601 E-mail: info@hydrax.co.uk

J G Engineering Ltd, Alanbrooke Industrial Park, Station Road, Topcliffe, Thirsk, North Yorkshire, YO7 3SE Tel: (01845) 578097 Fax: (01845) 578097

JC Fluid Power, 5 Readmans Industrial Estate, Station Road, East Tilbury, Tilbury, Essex, RM18 8QR Tel: (01375) 843995 Fax: (01375) 859010 E-mail: info@jcfluidpower.co.uk

M & R Hydraulics Ltd, Unit 13, Thornton Industrial Estate, Ellesmere Port, CH65 5EU Tel: 0151 3571901

Miller Fluid Power, 3 Bailey Drive, Norwood Industrial Estate, Killamarsh, Sheffield, S21 2JF Tel: 0114-247 2936 Fax: 0114-247 8371

Nicol & Andrew plc, 2 Mossland Road, Hillington Industrial Estate, Glasgow, G52 4XZ Tel: 0141-882 4724 Fax: 0141-883 3350 E-mail: info@nicolandandrew.com

Ram Reman Ltd, Gundrymoor Trading Estate, Collingwood Road, West Moors, Wimborne, Dorset, BH21 6QJ Tel: (01202) 861888 Fax: (01202) 861668

Redgold Hydraulic & Engineering Services, 5 Bradley Hall Trading Estate, Bradley Lane, Standish, Wigan, Lancashire, WN6 0XQ Tel: (01257) 425917 Fax: (01257) 425927 E-mail: francistaylor@redgoldhydraulics.co.uk

REP-RAM Hydraulic Services, Unit 6 Prospect Court, Nunn Close, County Estate, Sutton-In-Ashfield, Nottinghamshire, NG17 2HW Tel: (01623) 557471

Shepcote Engineering Ltd, Davy Indust Park, Prince of Wales Road, Sheffield, S9 4EX Tel: 0114-256 2505 Fax: 0114-261 1910 E-mail: enquiries@shepcote-eng.com

Thorne Hydraulics Ltd, Unit 24 Frontier Works, 12 King Edward Road, Thorne, Doncaster, South Yorkshire, DN8 4HU Tel: (01405) 816067 Fax: (01405) 741060

Werecon Engineering Ltd, 403 Netherwood Road, Rotherwas Industrial Estate, Hereford, HR2 6JU Tel: (01432) 355454 Fax: (01432) 358727

West Of Scotland Engineering Co. Ltd, 200 Old Dumbarton Road, Glasgow, G3 8QB Tel: 0141-339 6746 Fax: 0141-357 2325 E-mail: enquiries@wose.co.uk

Worlifts Ltd, 90 Roebuck Lane, West Bromwich, West Midlands, B70 6QX Tel: 0121-460 1113 Fax: 0121-525 1022 E-mail: sales@worlifts.co.uk

Wycis Engineering Co. Ltd, 1 Wheatear, Perry Road, Witham, Essex, CM8 3YY Tel: (01376) 516247 Fax: (01376) 514721 E-mail: wycis@btinternet.com

HYDRAULIC CYLINDERS/RAMS, STAINLESS STEEL

Delstar Engineering Ltd, Homefield Road, Haverhill, Suffolk, CB9 8QP Tel: (01440) 762518 Fax: (01440) 703820 E-mail: general@delstar.co.uk

HYDRAULIC CYLINDERS/RAMS, TELESCOPIC

Camera One Ltd, 1275 Stratford Road, Hall Green, Birmingham, B28 9AJ Tel: 0121-733 1999

Jonic Engineering Ltd, Speedwell Road, Yardley, Birmingham, B25 8EU Tel: 0121-707 8222 Fax: 0121-706 7303 E-mail: sales@jonicengineering.co.uk

HYDRAULIC DAMPERS

Stabilus, Unit 4 Canada Close, Banbury, Oxfordshire, OX16 2RT Tel: (01295) 700100 Fax: (01295) 700106 E-mail: info@uk.stabilus.com

HYDRAULIC DRIVE SYSTEMS

Hagglund Drives, Foxbridge Way, Normanton Industrial Estate, Normanton, West Yorkshire, WF6 1TN Tel: (01924) 220100 Fax: (01924) 890111 E-mail: sales@hagglund.com

HYDRAULIC ENGINEERING CONSULTANTS

Double M Nottingham Ltd, Nunn Brook Road, County Estate, Huthwaite, Sutton-in-Ashfield, Nottinghamshire, NG17 2HU Tel: (01623) 515904 Fax: (01623) 515929

Hydraulic Analysis Ltd, Mill House, Hawksworth Road, Horsforth, Leeds, LS18 4JP Tel: 0113-258 1622 Fax: 0113-259 0863 E-mail: sales@hydraulic-analysis.com

HYDRAULIC EQUIPMENT OR SYSTEM MAINTENANCE OR REPAIR

Amba Hydraulics Ltd, 25 Schneider Close, Felixstowe, Suffolk, IP11 3SS Tel: (01394) 673830 Fax: (01394) 673380 E-mail: ambahydraulics@hotmail.com

Anross Ltd, Leadgate Industrial Estate, Lope Hill Road, Consett, County Durham, DH8 7RN Tel: (01207) 509448 Fax: (01207) 592158 E-mail: sales@anross.co.uk

HYDRAULIC EQUIPMENT OR SYSTEM MAINTENANCE OR REPAIR – *continued*

Approved Hydraulics Ltd, Brook Business Complex, Bennett Street, Manchester, M12 5AU Tel: 0161-273 1999 Fax: 0161-273 7979 E-mail: approvedhyd@aol.com

Boxrite Hydraulics, 1A May Avenue, Northfleet, Gravesend, Kent, DA11 8RH Tel: (01474) 327722 Fax: (01322) 327722

Cam Hydraulics, Unit 8 Hillfoot Industrial Estate, 17 Hoyland Road, Sheffield, S3 8AB Tel: 0114-231 4833 Fax: 0114-285 5810 E-mail: info@camhydraulics.co.uk

Challenger Hydraulics Ltd, Shaw Cross Business Pk, Owl La, Dewsbury, West Yorkshire, WF12 7RF Tel: (01924) 464433 Fax: (01924) 456292 E-mail: sales@challenger-group.co.uk

Cullimore Hydraulic Engineering, C 14 Copt Elm Close, Charlton Kings, Cheltenham, Gloucestershire, GL53 8AD Tel: (01242) 241112 Fax: (01242) 241112

Cylinder Repair Services, 168 Rede Court Road, Rochester, Kent, ME2 3TU Tel: (01634) 723366 Fax: (01634) 723388 E-mail: crs.hydraulics@ukonline.co.uk

Doreth Engineering Co. Ltd, 1514 Pershore Road, Stirchley, Birmingham, B30 2NW Tel: 0121-458 3178 Fax: 0121-458 3178

G. Elliot Engineering Services Ltd, Bircotes, Doncaster, East Yorkshire, DN11 8WR Tel: (0844) 8002989 Fax: (01302) 745071 E-mail: sales@elliotteng.co.uk

Fluid Lift Systems Ltd, 4b Loxley Road, Wellesbourne, Warwick, CV35 9JY Tel: (01789) 470264 Fax: (01789) 470266 E-mail: info@fluidliftsystems.co.uk

Fraser Hydraulic Power, Unit BT 96/4 Fisher Industrial Estate, Fisher St, Walker, Newcastle upon Tyne, NE6 4LT Tel: 0191-263 7272 Fax: 0191-263 4016 E-mail: joanner@fhpltd.co.uk

Garfield Hydrol Ltd, Fengate, Peterborough, PE1 5XG Tel: (01733) 568444 Fax: (01733) 893516 E-mail: sales@rsg.co.uk

Gilson Engineering Newbury Ltd, 3 Sandleford Farm, Sandleford, Newtown, Newbury, Berkshire, RG20 9BB Tel: (01635) 41924 Fax: (01635) 42286 E-mail: info@gilsoneng.co.uk

Hydraflow Systems, Strathfield House, Smithymoor, Stretton, Alfreton, Derbyshire, DE55 6FE Tel: 01246 250958 Fax: 05600 492268E-mail: sales@hydraflowsystems.co.uk

Hydraulic Crane Services, Uplands Farm, Highstreet Road, Hernhill, Faversham, Kent, ME13 9EJ Tel: (01227) 751588 Fax: (01227) 751458 E-mail: hydecraneserv@aol.com

Hydraulic Spares Centre Ltd, Unit 18 Pilot Industrial Estate, Manchester Road, Bolton, BL3 2ND Tel: (01204) 388233 Fax: (01204) 383037 E-mail: hydsc.ltd@tiscali.co.uk

Industrial & Marine Hydraulics Ltd, 2 Snowdon Rd, Middlesbrough, Cleveland, TS2 1LP Tel: (01642) 802700 Fax: (01642) 802701 E-mail: info@imh-uk.com

Linden Group Ltd, 1 Leaside North, Aycliffe Industrial Estate, Aycliffe Industrial Park, Newton Aycliffe, County Durham, DL5 6DU Tel: (01325) 311331 Fax: (01325) 300128 E-mail: sales@lindengroup.co.uk

Maselec Ltd, Unit A2 The Courtyard, Lonesome Lane, Reigate, Surrey, RH2 7QT Tel: (01737) 225335 Fax: (01737) 225559 E-mail: sales@maselec.co.uk

Massey Engineering Ltd, Ludlow Business Park, Orleton Road, Ludlow Business Park, Ludlow, Shropshire, SY8 1XF Tel: (01584) 875210 Fax: (01584) 874089

P M W Precision Engineering Ltd, 47-55 Alcester Street, Deritend, Birmingham, B12 0PY Tel: 0121-773 9105 Fax: 0121-773 9141

▶ Petrology Ltd, Robert Clyde House, Erskine Ferry Road, Old Kilpatrick, Glasgow, G60 5EU Tel: (01389) 801700 Fax: (01389) 801702 E-mail: rose.pollock@petrology.com

Poclain Hydraulics Ltd, Nene Valley Business Park, Oundle, Peterborough, PE8 4HN Tel: (01832) 273773 Fax: (01832) 274990 E-mail: info@poclain-hydraulics.com

Quick Hydraulics Ltd, North Tyne Industrial Estate, Benton, Newcastle upon Tyne, NE12 9SZ Tel: 0191-270 1160 Fax: 0191-270 1143 E-mail: quick@quick-hydraulics.com

D. Waterhouse & Co., Lambert Works, Luton St, Keighley, W. Yorkshire, BD21 2LE Tel: (01535) 642539 Fax: (01535) 642539

WB Hydraulic Services, 45 Boston Road, Leicester, LE4 1AW Tel: 0116-235 2606 E-mail: bill@wbhydserv.freeserve.co.uk

West Mercia Hydraulics, 9 Horton Court, Hortonwood 50, Telford, Shropshire, TF1 7GY Tel: (01952) 606696 Fax: (01952) 670333 E-mail: wm.telford@wyko.co.uk

Yarl Hydracentre Ltd, Scarth Road, Sowerby Wood Industrial Estate, Barrow-In-Furness, Cumbria, LA14 4RF Tel: (01229) 845560 Fax: (01229) 845561 E-mail: yarl@hydracentre.com

HYDRAULIC EQUIPMENT/ SYSTEMS CONSULTANTS OR DESIGNERS

Carling Hydraulics (Mfg) Ltd, Hawkins Drive, Cannock, Staffordshire, WS11 0XT Tel: (01922) 701600 Fax: (01922) 701606 E-mail: sales@carlinghydraulics.com

Eagle Hydraulic Systems Ltd, 14 Chartwell Road, Lancing, West Sussex, BN15 8TU Tel: (01903) 751494 Fax: (01903) 751522

Mayflower Hydraulics Ltd, Castlefields Trading Estate, Symons Way, Bridgwater, Somerset, TA6 4DR Tel: (01278) 450226 Fax: (01278) 446678

Primary Fluid Power, Caddick Road, Knowsley Business Park, Prescot, Merseyside, L34 9HP Tel: 0151-632 9500 Fax: 0151-548 9896 E-mail:

HYDRAULIC EQUIPMENT/ SYSTEMS DISTRIBUTORS OR AGENTS

A G Hydraulics Ltd, Unit 40 Plume Street Industrial Estate, Plume Street, Birmingham, B6 7RT Tel: 0121-326 6395 Fax: 0121-328 2923 E-mail: sales@aghydraulics.com

Airedale Tubes & Fittings Ltd, Royds Farm Road, Leeds, LS12 6DX Tel: 0113-231 1227 Fax: 0113-231 1866 E-mail: airedaleinfo@btconnect.com

Alba Hydraflow Ltd, Unit 7, Block 4, Woodend Industrial Estate, Cowdenbeath, Fife, KY4 8HW Tel: (01383) 514543 Fax: (01383) 510324 E-mail: sales@albahydraflow.co.uk

All Hose & Hydraulics Norwich Ltd, 2 Javelin Road, Norwich, NR6 6HX Tel: (01603) 788686 Fax: (01603) 483081 E-mail: allhosesales@btinternet.com

Ash UK Ltd, 63 James Watt Place, East Kilbride, Glasgow, G74 5HG Tel: (01355) 224445 Fax: (01355) 223055 E-mail: ashukltd@btopenworld.com

B S H Ltd, 15 Powdrake Road, Grangemouth, Stirlingshire, FK3 9UT Tel: (01324) 474242 Fax: (01324) 665456 E-mail: sales@bshltd.co.uk

Bewick Engineering Ltd, 4 Walker Riverside, Wincomblee Road, Newcastle upon Tyne, NE6 3PF Tel: 0191-295 1975 Fax: 0191-295 1973 E-mail: robq@bewick.clara.co.uk

Border Hydraulics & Pneumatics Ltd, 9 Currock Road Trade Centre, Currock Road, Carlisle, CA2 5AD Tel: (01228) 530010 Fax: (01228) 818087

Brammer Ltd, Claverton Court, Claverton Road, Roundthorn Industrial Estate, Manchester, M23 9NE Tel: 0161-953 8600 Fax: 0161-953 8680 E-mail: enquiries@bslbrammer.co.uk

Burton Hydraulics & Pneumatics, Paget Street, Burton-on-Trent, Staffordshire, DE14 3TQ Tel: (01283) 532745 Fax: (01283) 530637 E-mail: sales@burtonhydraulics.co.uk

Castle Hydraulics & Pneumatics Ltd, 3 Amherst Business Centre, Budbrooke Road Industrial Estate, Budbrooke Industrial Estate, Warwick, CV34 5WE Tel: (01926) 419926 Fax: (01926) 497196

Central Hydraulic Systems Ltd, Walker Street, Rochdale, Lancashire, OL16 2AB Tel: (01706) 343007 Fax: (01706) 645354

D C A & Co. Ltd, The Old Chapel, Chapel Street, Taylor Hill, Huddersfield, HD4 6HL Tel: (01484) 510066 Fax: (01484) 467800 E-mail: sales@dca-ltd.com

Doreth Engineering Co. Ltd, 1514 Pershore Road, Stirchley, Birmingham, B30 2NW Tel: 0121-458 3178 Fax: 0121-458 3178

Eastern Fluid Power Ltd, Gapton Hall Road, Great Yarmouth, Norfolk, NR31 0NL Tel: (01493) 441353 Fax: (01493) 440757 E-mail: sales@efphyd.co.uk

Eaton Hydralics Ltd, 46 New Lane, Havant, Hampshire, PO9 2NB Tel: (023) 9248 6451 Fax: (023) 9248 7110 E-mail: barryking@eaton.com

Fluid Lift Systems Ltd, 4b Loxley Road, Wellesbourne, Warwick, CV35 9JY Tel: (01789) 470264 Fax: (01789) 470266 E-mail: info@fluidliftsystems.co.uk

Fluid Power Services Ltd, 1 Aston Court, Kingsland Grange, Woolston, Warrington, WA1 4SG Tel: (01925) 828590 Fax: (01925) 828590 E-mail: sales@fluidpowerservices.co.uk

Gardi Industrial Services Ltd, 9 Kennel Terrace, Brixworth, Northampton, NN6 9DL Tel: (01604) 882442 Fax: (01604) 882880 E-mail: enquiries@gardi.co.uk

HCS Control Systems Ltd, Unit V2, Viewfield Industrial Estate, Glenrothes, Fife, KY6 2RG Tel: (01592) 770786 Fax: (01592) 775737 E-mail: sales@hcscsl.com

Hi Flex Fluids, 2 Cowan Road, Blaydon-on-Tyne, Tyne & Wear, NE21 5TW Tel: 0191-414 7771 Fax: 0191-414 0625 E-mail: sales@hiflex-fluidpower.com

Hi-Force Ltd, Royal Oak Industrial Estate, Bentley Way, Daventry, Northamptonshire, NN11 8QH Tel: (01327) 301000 Fax: (01327) 706555 E-mail: sales@hi-force.com

Hi-Press Hydraulics Ltd, Riverside Works, Forge Road, Whaley Bridge, High Peak, Derbyshire, SK23 7HY Tel: (01663) 735089 Fax: (01663) 735090 E-mail: sales@hi-press.co.uk

Hydrafit Ltd, 40 Brighton Street, Coventry, CV2 4JH Tel: (024) 7645 6621 Fax: (024) 7644 5256

Hydrafit Hydraulic Equipment, 4 Sanderson Street, Sheffield, S9 2TW Tel: 0114-244 6721 Fax: 0114-243 5969

Hydramatics Ltd, Unit 2b The Quantum, Marshfield Bank Industrial Estate, Crewe, CW2 8UY Tel: (01270) 584348 Fax: (01270) 584348 E-mail: hydramatics@aol.com

Hydraulic Equipment Supermarkets Ltd, 424 Bromford Lane, Washwood Heath, Birmingham, B8 2RX Tel: 0121-327 2664 Fax: 0121-322 2488 E-mail: birmingham@dowco.co.uk

Hydraulic Equipment Supermarkets Ltd, 7a Drum Industrial Estate, Drum Industrial Estate, Chester le Street, County Durham, DH2 1AG Tel: 0191-410 6619 Fax: 0191-411 1055 E-mail: durham@dowco.co.uk

Hydraulic Equipment Supermarkets Ltd, 7 Glover Way, Leeds, LS11 5JP Tel: 0113-270 3213 Fax: 0113-270 3213 E-mail: leeds@grouphes.com

Hydraulic Pneumatic Services, Unit 23-24 The Old Mill, School Lane, Bamber Bridge, Preston, PR5 6SY Tel: (01772) 629993 Fax: (01772) 629995 E-mail: info@hps-group.co.uk

Hydraulic Pressure Services Ltd, 289 Elland Road, Leeds, LS11 8AX Tel: 0113-271 1310 Fax: 0113-270 0254 E-mail: hps.leedsonline@absonline.net

Hymec Backspin Ltd, Omega, Gipsy Lane, Wokingham, Berkshire, RG40 2HP Tel: 0118-978 0557 Fax: 0118-978 0558 E-mail: tt@hymec.co.uk

Hymid Hydraulics Ltd, 9 Glenbarr Avenue, Leicester, LE4 0AE Tel: 0116-251 8888 Fax: 0116-251 8800E-mail: sales@hymid.com

Kaybee Pneumatics, 6 Shaw Drive, Burntwood, Staffordshire, WS7 2JE Tel: (01543) 675309 Fax: (01543) 677743

Kingsley Commercial Components Ltd, Oak Hill Works, Broad Street, Guildford, Surrey, GU3 3BJ Tel: (01483) 303092 Fax: (01483) 572242

Koppen & Lethem Ltd, 6 Glenholm Park, Brunel Drive, Newark, Nottinghamshire, NG24 2EG Tel: (01636) 676794 Fax: (01636) 671055 E-mail: sales@koppen-lethem.co.uk

M E C-Air (Pneumatics & Hydraulics) Ltd, Unit 5c, Enterprise Way, Five Lane Ends, Bradford, West Yorkshire, BD10 8EW Tel: (01274) 621037 Fax: (01274) 621230

Maselec Ltd, Unit A2 The Courtyard, Lonesome Lane, Reigate, Surrey, RH2 7QT Tel: (01737) 225335 Fax: (01737) 225559 E-mail: sales@maselec.co.uk

Merseyside Hydraulics & Pneumatics, Unit C5 Kingfisher Business Park, Hawthorne Road, Bootle, Merseyside, L20 6PF Tel: 0151-944 2668 Fax: 0151-944 2669

Mykro Hydraulics Distributors Ltd, Nortonthorpe Industrial Estate, Wakefield Road, Scissett, Huddersfield, HD8 9LA Tel: (01484) 865977 Fax: (01484) 865809 E-mail: mykrohydraulics@aol.co.uk

Nelson Hydraulics Ltd, Unit H1, Knockmore Industrial Estate, Lisburn, County Antrim, BT28 2AR Tel: (028) 9266 2781 Fax: (028) 9260 2952E-mail: info@nelsonhydraulics.com

Oddy Hydraulics Ltd, Tristran Centre, Brown Lane West, Leeds, LS12 6BF Tel: 0113-244 8787 Fax: 0113-244 9786 E-mail: sales@oddy-hyds.com

P D Supplies Ltd, Walker Road, Bardon Hill, Coalville, Leicestershire, LE67 1TU Tel: (01530) 813996 Fax: (01530) 839111

Poclain Hydraulics Ltd, Nene Valley Business Park, Oundle, Peterborough, PE8 4HN Tel: (01832) 273773 Fax: (01832) 274990 E-mail: info@poclain-hydraulics.com

Quick Hydraulics Ltd, North Tyne Industrial Estate, Benton, Newcastle upon Tyne, NE12 9SZ Tel: 0191-270 1160 Fax: 0191-270 1143 E-mail: quick@quick-hydraulics.com

R C S Hose & Hydraulics Ltd, Crucible Road, Corby, Northamptonshire, NN17 5TS Tel: 0800 3893132

Regent Hose & Hydraulics Ltd, 128-130 Tanners Drive, Blakelands, Milton Keynes, MK14 5BP Tel: (01908) 612602 Fax: (01908) 211009 E-mail: info.mk@regenthose.co.uk

▶ Ringwood Hydraulics Ltd, 78 Cobham Road, Ferndown Industrial Estate, Wimborne, Dorset, BH21 7RW Tel: (01202) 890401 Fax: (01202) 897713

S H Service Hydraulics Ltd, 56 Pinfold Street, Wednesbury, West Midlands, WS10 8TQ Tel: 0121-526 6431 Fax: 0121-568 6683

Sermec Engineering Ltd, 2X South Nelson Road, Cramlington, Northumberland, NE23 1WF Tel: 01670 731000

Solent Fluid Power, 9 Enterprise Industrial Estate, Enterprise Road, Waterlooville, Hampshire, PO8 0BB Tel: (023) 9259 7437 Fax: (023) 9259 9899 E-mail: sales@solentfluidpower.co.uk

South Eastern Hydraulics Ltd, 40b Holmethorpe Avenue, Redhill, RH1 2NL Tel: (01737) 768011 Fax: (01737) 773469 E-mail: mail@seh-ltd.co.uk

Southern Fluid Power, E Altbarn Industrial Estate, Revenge Road, Chatham, Kent, ME5 8UD Tel: (01634) 686060 Fax: (01634) 683332 E-mail: info@s-f-p.co.uk

▶ Spear Engineering (Scotland) Ltd, Christianhall, Cuminestown, Turriff, Aberdeenshire, AB53 5UE Tel: (01888) 544398 Fax: (01888) 544012

T T C Lifting Gear Ltd, Newlyn Road, Cradley Heath, West Midlands, B64 6BE Tel: (01384) 564059 Fax: (01384) 410587

Target Fluid Services, Millhouse Centre, 118 Commercial Road, Totton, Southampton, SO40 3ZW Tel: (023) 8087 2142 Fax: (023) 8066 6882 E-mail: target.fluid@btinternet.com

Taskers UK Ltd, 4 Roman Ridge Road, Sheffield, S9 1GB Tel: 0114-243 0927 Fax: 0114-242 5507 E-mail: sales@taskersuk.com

Thread & Pipe Services Ltd, 26 Elliott Road, Bournemouth, BH11 8JZ Tel: (01202) 576789 Fax: (01202) 579816 E-mail: sales@threadandpipe.com

Turner Hydraulics, Old Station Yard, Magor, Caldicot, Gwent, NP26 3HT Tel: (01633) 881966 Fax: (01633) 881991 E-mail: ian@turnerhydraulics.co.uk

Usk Valley Fluid Power, Unit 16 Mill Street Industrial Estate, Mill Street, Abergavenny, Gwent, NP7 5HE Tel: (01873) 857225 Fax: (01873) 858790 E-mail: sales@uskvalleyfp.co.uk

Voith Turbo Ltd, 6 Beddington Farm Road, Croydon, CR0 4XB Tel: (020) 8667 0333 Fax: (020) 8667 0403 E-mail: turbo.uk@voith.com

W H Fluidpower Ltd, Unit 9, Rossbank Road, Rossmoor Industrial Estate, Ellesmere Port, CH65 3AN Tel: (0151) 355 2211 Fax: (0151) 355 2277 E-mail: whfluidpower@ukonline.co.uk

West Mercia Hydraulics, 9 Horton Court, Hortonwood 50, Telford, Shropshire, TF1 7GY Tel: (01952) 606696 Fax: (01952) 670333 E-mail: wm.telford@wyko.co.uk

Wrekin Pneumatics Telford Ltd, Park Road, Dawley Bank, Telford, Shropshire, TF4 2BE Tel: (01952) 505566 Fax: (01952) 504703 E-mail: wrekin@interramp.co.uk

Yuken (UK) Ltd, 51 Spindus Road, Speke Hall Industrial Estate, Liverpool, L24 1YA Tel: 0151-486 4696 Fax: 0151-486 3537 E-mail: office@yuken.co.uk

HYDRAULIC EQUIPMENT/ SYSTEMS MAINTENANCE/ REPAIR TOOLS/EQUIPMENT

Cylinder Repair Services, 168 Rede Court Road, Rochester, Kent, ME2 3TU Tel: (01634) 723366 Fax: (01634) 723388 E-mail: crs.hydraulics@ukonline.co.uk

Fluid Lift Systems Ltd, 4b Loxley Road, Wellesbourne, Warwick, CV35 9JY Tel: (01789) 470264 Fax: (01789) 470266 E-mail: info@fluidliftsystems.co.uk

▶ Petrology Ltd, Robert Clyde House, Erskine Ferry Road, Old Kilpatrick, Glasgow, G60 5EU Tel: (01389) 801700 Fax: (01389) 801702 E-mail: rose.pollock@petrology.com

Woodsome Tool & Electric Co. Ltd, Tape Lane, Hurst, Reading, RG10 0DN Tel: 0118-934 1142 Fax: (01488) 71820

HYDRAULIC EQUIPMENT/ SYSTEMS MANUFRS

Airfluid Hydraulics & Pneumatics Ltd, Tong Road, Bishops Wood, Stafford, ST19 9AB Tel: (01952) 850246 Fax: (01952) 850246 E-mail: hydraulicbjr@aol.com

Allison Hydraulics Ltd, Unit 2, Factory Lane, Rooley Lane, Bradford, West Yorkshire, BD4 9NW Tel: (01274) 687327 Fax: (01274) 688869 E-mail: sales@allisonhydraulics.com

Amba Hydraulics Ltd, 25 Schneider Close, Felixstowe, Suffolk, IP11 3SS Tel: (01394) 673830 Fax: (01394) 673380 E-mail: ambahydraulics@hotmail.com

Andrews Hydraulics Ltd, Unit 27-28, Craftsmans Way, East Goscote, Leicester, LE7 3SL Tel: 0116-260 1001 Fax: 0116-264 0186 E-mail: design@andrewshydraulics.co.uk

Antech Hydraulics, Cocker Avenue, Poulton Industrial Estate, Poulton-le-Fylde, Lancashire, FY6 8JU Tel: (01253) 890037 Fax: (01253) 890073 E-mail: enquiries@antech-hyd.co.uk

Atos Spa (UK), 17A Longwood Avenue, Cowplain, Waterlooville, Hampshire, PO8 8HX Tel: (023) 9226 5880 Fax: (023) 9226 5881 E-mail: atos-uk@fsmail.net

Barricade Roller Shutters, 7 St. Thomas's Place, Manchester, M8 8TP Tel: 0161-833 0007 Fax: 0161-835 1546 E-mail: shutters@barricade.fsnet.co.uk

Bell Hydraulic Services Ltd, Chapel Lane, Cwmbran, Gwent, NP44 2PP Tel: (01633) 861423 Fax: (01633) 864472 E-mail: dave.bell@bellhydraulics.co.uk

Bewick Engineering Ltd, 4 Walker Riverside, Wincomblee Road, Newcastle upon Tyne, NE6 3PF Tel: 0191-295 1975 Fax: 0191-295 1973 E-mail: robq@bewick.clara.co.uk

Branch Hydraulic Systems Ltd, Unit H, Innsworth Technology Park, Innsworth Lane, Gloucester, GL3 1DL Tel: (01452) 730562 Fax: (01452) 731579 E-mail: branch@dowco.co.uk

British Engineering Productions Ltd, 19 Arnside Road, Waterlooville, Hampshire, PO7 7UP Tel: (023) 9226 8733 Fax: (023) 9225 1104 E-mail: sales@bep-manifolds.com

Cam Hydraulics, Unit 8 Hillfoot Industrial Estate, 17 Hoyland Road, Sheffield, S3 8AB Tel: 0114-231 4833 Fax: 0114-285 5810 E-mail: info@camhydraulics.co.uk

Central Hydraulic Systems Ltd, Walker Street, Rochdale, Lancashire, OL16 2AB Tel: (01706) 343007 Fax: (01706) 645354

Cityown Ltd, Unit M Charlwoods Business Centre, East Grinstead, West Sussex, RH19 2HH Tel: (01342) 327787 Fax: (01342) 324289

David Brown Hydraulics Ltd, 32 Factory Road, Poole, Dorset, BH16 5SL Tel: (01202) 627500 Fax: (01202) 627555 E-mail: info@dbh.textron.com

▶ indicates data change since last edition

HYDRAULIC EQUIPMENT/SYSTEMS MANUFRS – *continued*

Dawson Bowman Ltd, 16 Flakefield, College Milton, East Kilbride, Glasgow, G74 1PF Tel: (01355) 229445 Fax: (01355) 264744 E-mail: sales@dawsonbowman.co.uk

Dli Seals Ltd, Unit A-D Trimdon Court, Trimdon Grange Industrial Estate, Trimdon Grange, Trimdon Station, County Durham, TS29 6PE Tel: (01429) 881660 Fax: (01429) 882299 E-mail: sales@dliseals.co.uk

Dunlop Hiflex Fluid Power Ltd, Howley Park Road, Morley, Leeds, LS27 0BN Tel: 0113-238 1547 Fax: 0113-238 3391 E-mail: leeds@dunlophiflex.com

E P P Magnus Ltd, Ashbourne Estate, 174 Mile Cross Lane, Norwich, NR6 6RY Tel: (01603) 400861 Fax: (01603) 788496 E-mail: welcome@magnus-int.co.uk

Eagle Hydraulic Systems Ltd, 14 Chartwell Road, Lancing, West Sussex, BN15 8TU Tel: (01903) 751494 Fax: (01903) 751522

Eaton Hydralics Ltd, 46 New Lane, Havant, Hampshire, PO9 2NB Tel: (023) 9248 6451 Fax: (023) 9248 7110 E-mail: barryking@eaton.com

Enerpac Ltd, PO Box 33, Darlaston, West Midlands, WS10 8LQ Tel: (01527) 598900 Fax: 0121-505 0799 E-mail: info@enerpac.com

Exeter Hose & Hydraulics Ltd, Unit 1 Kenton Place, Marsh Green Road, Exeter, EX2 8NY Tel: (01392) 218604 Fax: (01392) 412687

Fairway Hydraulic & Engineering Co., Unit 96 Blackpole Trading Estate West, Worcester, WR3 8TJ Tel: (01905) 457519 Fax: (01905) 456054 E-mail: fairway.hydraulic@ic24.net

Flexiquip Hydraulics Ltd, Altona Road, Lisburn, County Antrim, BT27 5QB Tel: (028) 9267 7131 Fax: (028) 9260 7231 E-mail: flexequip.sales@flexequip.com

Force Hydraulics, 14a Saxon Business Park, Hanbury Road, Stoke Prior, Bromsgrove, Worcestershire, B60 4AD Tel: (01527) 575704 Fax: (01527) 576668

G C Ogle & Sons Ltd, Victoria Road, Ripley, Derbyshire, DE5 3FX Tel: (01773) 742381 Fax: (0870) 4601807

G D Hydraulics & Pneumatics, 13 Broadhurst Street, Stockport, Cheshire, SK3 8JH Tel: 0161-480 5151

H P C Engineering Plc, Victoria Gardens, Victoria Gardens Industrial Estate, Burgess Hill, West Sussex, RH15 9RQ Tel: (01444) 241671 Fax: (01444) 247587 E-mail: peterhowell@hpcplc.co.uk

Hendry Hydraulics Ltd, Pinefield Industrial Estate, 2 Perimeter Road, Elgin, Morayshire, IV30 6DF Tel: (01343) 545207 Fax: (01343) 545200 E-mail: enquiries@hendry-hydraulic-cylinders.co.uk

Hopespare Ltd, 3 Plaza Business Centre, Stockingswater Lane, Enfield, Middlesex, EN3 7XT Tel: (020) 8804 9001 Fax: (020) 8805 3359 E-mail: sales@hopespare.com

Husco International Ltd, 6 Rivington Road, Whitehouse Industrial Estate, Runcorn, Cheshire, WA7 3DT Tel: (01928) 701888 Fax: (01928) 710813 E-mail: uksales@huscointl.com

Hydar Fluid Power Ltd, Unit 20-21, Midsomer Enterprise Park, Radstock Road, Midsomer Norton, Radstock, BA3 2BB Tel: (01249) 651666 Fax: (01761) 414050 E-mail: carol@hydar.co.uk

Hydrassist Ltd, Unit 15 Fordhouse Road Industrial Estate, Steel Drive, Wolverhampton, WV10 9XB Tel: (01902) 787000 Fax: (01902) 397963

Hydraulic Equipment Supermarkets Ltd, 424 Bromford Lane, Washwood Heath, Birmingham, B8 2RX Tel: 0121-327 2664 Fax: 0121-322 2488 E-mail: birmingham@dowco.co.uk

Hydraulic Equipment Supermarkets Ltd, 7a Drum Industrial Estate, Drum Industrial Estate, Chester le Street, County Durham, DH2 1AG Tel: 0191-410 6619 Fax: 0191-411 1055 E-mail: durham@dowco.co.uk

Hydraulic Equipment Supermarkets Ltd, J Innsworth Technology Park, Innsworth Lane, Gloucester, GL3 1DL Tel: (01452) 730774 Fax: (01452) 731637 E-mail: sales@dowco.co.uk

Hydraulic Equipment Supermarkets Ltd, 7 Glover Way, Leeds, LS11 5JP Tel: 0113-270 3213 Fax: 0113-270 3213 E-mail: leeds@grouphes.com

Hydraulic Project Ltd, Shutterton Industrial Estate, Dawlish, Devon, EX7 0NH Tel: (01626) 863634 Fax: (01626) 866283 E-mail: sales@hypro.co.uk

Hypec, Royal Works, Atlas Street, Clayton-Le-Moors, Accrington, Lancashire, BB5 5LP Tel: (01254) 615100 Fax: (01254) 615199 E-mail: sales@allspeeds.co.uk

Industrial & Marine Hydraulics Ltd, 2 Snowdon Rd, Middlesbrough, Cleveland, TS2 1LP Tel: (01642) 802700 Fax: (01642) 802701 E-mail: info@imh-uk.com

Jordan Cylinders, Little Folley, Eardisland, Leominster, Herefordshire, HR6 9BS Tel: (01544) 388227

K T R Couplings Ltd, Robert House Unit 7, Acorn Business Park, Woodseats Close, Sheffield, S8 0TB Tel: 0114-258 7757 Fax: 0114-258 7740 E-mail: ktr-uk@ktr.com

Link Hydraulic Services Ltd, 38 Sherwood Road, Bromsgrove, Worcestershire, B60 3DR Tel: (01527) 579145 Fax: (01527) 576555 E-mail: link.hydraulics@btconnect.com

Macscott Bond Ltd, PO Box 1, Loanhead, Midlothian, EH20 9SW Tel: 0131-448 2950 Fax: 0131-448 2941

Modular Hydraulic Systems Ltd, 9 Redan Hill Estate, Redan Road, Aldershot, Hampshire, GU12 4SJ Tel: (01252) 333883 Fax: (01252) 343615 E-mail: sales@mhs.co.uk

Mykro Hydraulics Distributors Ltd, Nortonthorpe Industrial Estate, Wakefield Road, Scissett, Huddersfield, HD8 9LA Tel: (01484) 865977 Fax: (01484) 865809 E-mail: mykrohydraulics@aol.co.uk

Norson Services Ltd, Greenwell Place, East Tullos Industrial Estate, Aberdeen, AB12 3AY Tel: (01224) 895524 Fax: (01224) 879010

▶ NPK UK Ltd, PO Box 375, Fleet, Hampshire, GU51 5ZQ Tel: (01276) 20011

O S L Group Ltd, Imperial Works, Sheffield Road, Tinsley, Sheffield, S9 2YL Tel: 0114-221 2500 Fax: 0114-221 2560 E-mail: sales@oslgroup.com

Oddy Hydraulics Ltd, Tristran Centre, Brown Lane West, Leeds, LS12 6BF Tel: 0113-244 8787 Fax: 0113-244 9786 E-mail: sales@oddy-hyds.com

▶ Oilgear European Holdings, 37 Burley Road, Leeds, LS3 1JT Tel: 0113-394 7300 Fax: 0113-394 7301 E-mail: enquiries@oilgear-towler.co.uk

Ovalway Hydraulics, 11 Cannon Park Way, Middlesbrough, Cleveland, TS1 5JU Tel: (01642) 247106 Fax: (01642) 241874 E-mail: ohe@ovalway.co.uk

Parker Dayco, Belfont Trading Estate, Mucklow Hill, Halesowen, West Midlands, B62 8DR Tel: 0121-504 3400 Fax: 0121-550 4274 E-mail: sales@parker.com

Parker Hannifin plc, 66 Wakefield Road, Ossett, West Yorkshire, WF5 9JS Tel: (01924) 282200 Fax: (01924) 282299 E-mail:

Parker Hannifin plc, Tachbrook Park Drive, Warwick, CV34 6TU Tel: (01926) 833700 Fax: (01926) 889172E-mail: epic@parker.com

▶ Parker-Hannifin plc, Sheddingdean Business Centre, Marchants Way, Burgess Hill, West Sussex, RH15 8QY Tel: (01444) 238300 Fax: (01444) 246121

Pressure Design Hydraulics Ltd, Goldthorpe Industrial Estate, Goldthorpe, Rotherham, S. Yorkshire, S63 9BL Tel: (01709) 897121 Fax: (01709) 895305 E-mail: sales@pressuredesign.co.uk

Ram Power Ltd, 16 Greenhill Crescent, Watford, WD18 8SE Tel: (01923) 231661 Fax: (01923) 246856 E-mail: rmpwr@aol.com

Ranger Caradoc Hydraulics Ltd, The Gables, Worcester Road, Great Witley, Worcester, WR6 6HR Tel: (01299) 896953 Fax: (01299) 896963 E-mail: sales@rangercaradoc.com

Rodmatic Precision Engineering Co. Ltd, Battle Farm Trading Estate, 30 Portman Road, Reading, RG30 1PD Tel: 0118-959 6969 Fax: 0118-939 3060 E-mail: sales@rodmatic.co.uk

South Eastern Hydraulics Ltd, 40b Holmethorpe Avenue, Redhill, RH1 2NL Tel: (01737) 768011 Fax: (01737) 773469 E-mail: mail@seh-ltd.co.uk

Stallion Hydraulic Services Ltd, Wharf Road, Gravesend, Kent, DA12 2RU Tel: (01474) 564707 Fax: (01474) 564752 E-mail: sales@stallion-group.com

▶ Sterling Hydraulics Ltd, Sterling House, Blacknell Lane, Crewkerne, Somerset, TA18 8LL Tel: (01460) 271800 Fax: (01460) 271801 E-mail: mktng@sterling-hydraulics.co.uk

Summit Equipment Supplies Ltd, Clover Nook Road, Clover Nook Industrial Estate, Alfreton, Derbyshire, DE55 4RF Tel: (01773) 520488 Fax: (01773) 831004 E-mail: sumhyd@lineone.net

System 910 Hydraulics Ltd, 7 The Old Granary, The Street, Boxgrove, Chichester, West Sussex, PO18 0ES Tel: (01243) 539789 Fax: (01243) 530307 E-mail: system910@mistral.co.uk

T A Savery & Co. Ltd, Bracebridge Street, Birmingham, B6 4PF Tel: 0121-380 4514 Fax: 0121-380 4507 E-mail: sales@savery.co.uk

Titan Advanced Ltd, Titan Works, Claremount Road, Halifax, West Yorkshire, HX3 6NT Tel: (01422) 330265 Fax: (01422) 343295 E-mail: sales@titangroup.co.uk

Tomlin Hydraulics Ltd, Vicarage Farm Road, Peterborough, PE1 5TP Tel: (01733) 558833 Fax: (01733) 897801 E-mail: tomlinhydraulics@btconnect.com

Trist Draper Hydraulics, Unit 16, Merdock Road, Manton Lane Industrial Estate, Bedford, MK41 7PD Tel: (01234) 212661 Fax: (01234) 270421 E-mail: sales.bedford@trysisdraper.com

Universal Hydraulics Ltd, Carrwood Road, Chesterfield, Derbyshire, S41 9QB Tel: (01246) 451711 Fax: (01246) 450399 E-mail: sales@universalhydraulics.co.uk

Venus Services, The Old Rectory, Church Street, Southwell, Nottinghamshire, NG25 0HG Tel: (01636) 814633 Fax: (01636) 815403 E-mail: audley@btopenworld.com

Voith Turbo Ltd, Meir Road, Park Farm North, Redditch, Worcestershire, B98 7SY Tel: (01527) 516666 Fax: (01527) 516777 E-mail: info@hlhydraulic.demon.co.uk

Yarl Hydracentre Ltd, Scarth Road, Sowerby Wood Industrial Estate, Barrow-In-Furness, Cumbria, LA14 4RF Tel: (01229) 845560 Fax: (01229) 845561 E-mail: yarl@hydracentre.com

Yeovil Hydraulics, 14 Gazelle Road, Lynx Trading Estate, Yeovil, Somerset, BA20 2PJ Tel: (01935) 472233 Fax: (01935) 431211 E-mail: enquiries@yeovilhydraulics.co.uk

HYDRAULIC EQUIPMENT/ SYSTEMS, MARINE

▶ Caudle Contracts & Design Ltd, Everglades, Maiden St, Weston, Hitchin, Hertfordshire, SG4 7AA Tel: (01462) 790580 Fax: (01462) 790398 E-mail: sales@caudle.co.uk

HYDRAULIC EQUIPMENT/ SYSTEMS, TO SPECIFICATION

Dreelside Engineering Ltd, Station Road, Anstruther, Fife, KY10 3JA Tel: (01333) 311060 Fax: (01333) 312197

HYDRAULIC FILTERS

D G Howell (Hydraulic Engineers) Ltd, 78-84 Commercial St, Risca, Newport, Gwent, NP11 6BA Tel: (01633) 614326 Fax: (01633) 601581 E-mail: dghowell@aol.com

Filtakleen (Manufacturing) Ltd, Forelle Centre, 30 Black Moor Road, Ebblake Industrial Estate, Verwood, Dorset, BH31 6BB Tel: (01202) 826280 Fax: (01202) 813207 E-mail: sales@filtakleen.com

Filtech 2000 Ltd, East Market Street, Newport, Gwent, NP20 2AY Tel: (01633) 253878 Fax: (01633) 267914 E-mail: bc.hydraulics@btinternet.com

Filter Services (UK) Ltd, Units 6/7/8, Broombank Park, Sheepbridge, Chesterfield, Derbyshire, S41 9RT Tel: (01246) 455481 Fax: (01246) 455346 E-mail: sales@filter-services.co.uk

▶ Harrier Fluid Power Ltd, Parys Road, Ludlow Business Park, Ludlow, Shropshire, SY8 1XY Tel: (01584) 876033 Fax: (01584) 876044 E-mail: sales@harrieronline.co.uk

Hydraulic Equipment Supermarkets Ltd, J Innsworth Technology Park, Innsworth Lane, Gloucester, GL3 1DL Tel: (01452) 730774 Fax: (01452) 731637 E-mail: sales@dowco.co.uk

Pressure Tech Ltd, Unit 6, Graphite Way, Hadfield, Glossop, Derbyshire, SK13 1QG Tel: (01457) 899307 Fax: (01457) 899308 E-mail: steve@pressure-tech.com

HYDRAULIC FITTING ASSEMBLY MACHINES

Fencol Hydraulic Fittings Ltd, Unit 5 Europa Way, Britannia Enterprise Park, Lichfield, Staffordshire, WS14 9TZ Tel: (01543) 416343 Fax: (01543) 416343E-mail: nick@fencol.com

HYDRAULIC FLUIDS

Aztec Oils Ltd, 31 Intake Road, Bolsover Business Park, Bolsover, Chesterfield, Derbyshire, S44 6BB Tel: (01246) 823007 Fax: (01246) 823014 E-mail: sales@aztecoils.co.uk

Houghton plc, Beacon Road, Trafford Park, Manchester, M17 1AF Tel: 0161-874 5000 Fax: 0161-877 9764 E-mail: info@houghtonintl.com

Miswa Chemicals Ltd, Caswell Road, Brackmills Industrial Estate, Northampton, NN4 7PW Tel: (01604) 701111 Fax: (01604) 701120 E-mail: sales@miswa.com

Mobil Oil Co. Ltd, ExxonMobil House, Ermyn Way, Leatherhead, Surrey, KT22 8UX Tel: (01372) 222000 Fax: (01372) 222556

HYDRAULIC GEAR PUMPS

Camera One Ltd, 1275 Stratford Road, Hall Green, Birmingham, B28 9AJ Tel: 0121-733 1999

HYDRAULIC GEARED MOTORS

S A M Hydraulic UK Ltd, Planet House 910 Lakeside Drive, Centre Park, Warrington, WA1 1QX Tel: (01925) 624800 Fax: (01925) 624801 E-mail: sales@samhydraulik.co.uk

HYDRAULIC HAMMERS

▶ Sandhurst Equipment Rental, Thames House, College Road, Northfleet, Gravesend, Kent, DA11 9AU Tel: (0845) 120 6622 Fax: (01474) 567611 E-mail: info@sandhurst-rent.co.uk

HYDRAULIC HIGH PRESSURE VALVES

Aqua-Gas Manufacturing Ltd, Arnsley Road, Weldon North Industrial Estate, Corby, Northamptonshire, NN17 5QW Tel: (01536) 275910 Fax: (01536) 204256 E-mail: fran.brody@agmc.co.uk

B I S Valves Ltd, Unit 17 Kingfisher Park, Three Cross Road, West Moors, Wimborne, Dorset, BH21 6US Tel: (01202) 896322 Fax: (01202) 896718 E-mail: info@bisvalves.co.uk

Hale Hamilton Ltd, Cowley Road, Uxbridge, Middlesex, UB8 2AF Tel: (01895) 236525 Fax: (01895) 231407 E-mail: enquiries@halehamilton.com

HYDRAULIC HOSE ADAPTERS

D & P Services, 2 Ceres Street, Liverpool, L20 8PZ Tel: 0151-922 2071 Fax: 0151-922 2425

Gwent Hydraulics, 8 Skillion Business Centre, Corporation Road, Newport, Gwent, NP19 4RF Tel: (01633) 280005 Fax: (01633) 273140

▶ Universal Supplies Clydesdale Ltd, Hozier Street, Carluke, Lanarkshire, ML8 5DW Tel: (01555) 772474 Fax: (01555) 772426 E-mail: sales@uscltd.co.uk

HYDRAULIC HOSE ASSEMBLY SERVICES

Alltype Hose & Couplings Ltd, Units 14 & 15 Palace Industrial Estate, Bircholt Road, Parkwood, Maidstone, Kent, ME15 9XU Tel: (01622) 757512 Fax: (01622) 757663 E-mail: sales@alltypehose.co.uk

C F E Hydraulics Ltd, Unit 3, Milton Industrial Estate, Milton, Cambridge, CB24 6AZ Tel: (01223) 420466 Fax: (01223) 423233 E-mail: cfehydraulics@tiscali.co.uk

▶ C & G Hydraulic Services, 4 Newark Storage Industrial Estate, Bowbridge Road, Newark, Nottinghamshire, NG24 4EQ Tel: (01636) 613113 Fax: (01636) 613113 E-mail: cghydraulic@btconnect.com

Cougar Flex, 59 Rixon Road, Wellingborough, Northamptonshire, NN8 4BA Tel: (01933) 223354 Fax: (01933) 224522 E-mail: salescougarflex@btconnect.com

D & P Services, 2 Ceres Street, Liverpool, L20 8PZ Tel: 0151-922 2071 Fax: 0151-922 2425

Gwent Hydraulics, 8 Skillion Business Centre, Corporation Road, Newport, Gwent, NP19 4RF Tel: (01633) 280005 Fax: (01633) 273140

H.A.S. Supplies Ltd, Unit 2, Chamberlayne Road, Moreton Hall Industrial Estate, Bury St. Edmunds, Suffolk, IP32 7EY Tel: (01284) 767547 Fax: (01284) 769057 E-mail: info@has-supplies.co.uk

Hose & General Supplies Ltd, Daux Road, Billingshurst, West Sussex, RH14 9SJ Tel: (01403) 783221 Fax: (01403) 783221

Hoselines Ltd, 25 Longfields Road, Carlton, Barnsley, South Yorkshire, S71 3HT Tel: (01226) 240838 Fax: (01226) 204315

Hoselines & Industrial Supplies (North West) Ltd, Units 8 & 9 Knoll Street Industrial Estate, Bury New Rd, Salford, M7 2BL Tel: 0161-792 0481 Fax: 0161-792 5328 E-mail: sales@hoselines.com

J G Engineering Ltd, Alanbrooke Industrial Park, Station Road, Topcliffe, Thirsk, North Yorkshire, YO7 3SE Tel: (01845) 578097 Fax: (01845) 578097

J P Miles, Sophurst Wood Lane, Matfield, Tonbridge, Kent, TN12 7LH Tel: (01892) 724315 Fax: (01892) 724319 E-mail: jpmiles@seedersti.co.uk

▶ Kelly Hydraulics Ltd, 67 Amhurst Gardens, Isleworth, Middlesex, TW7 6AN Tel: (020) 8847 3414 Fax: (020) 8847 3414 E-mail: raymondkelly50@hotmail.com

Manuli-hydraulics UK Ltd, Unit C Nasmyth Business Centre, Green Lane, Patricroft, Eccles, Manchester, M30 0SN Tel: 0161-787 8085 Fax: 0161-787 8086

P C Hydraulics (Northern) Ltd, 6-8 Hillkirk Street, Beswick, Manchester, M11 3EZ Tel: 0161-273 1660 Fax: 0161-273 5002 E-mail: enquiries@pc-hydraulics.co.uk

Pirtek, 10 Tuffley Trading Estate, Pearce Way, Gloucester, GL2 5YD Tel: (01452) 308010 Fax: (01452) 307447 E-mail: gloucester@pirtekcentre.co.uk

Pirtek, 5 Bergland Park, Maritime Close, Medway City Estate, Rochester, Kent, ME2 4AD Tel: (01634) 297080 Fax: (01634) 297087 E-mail: zen24815@zen.co.uk

Pirtek (Nottingham) Ltd, Unit 4 Trentview Court, Moreland Street, Nottingham, NG2 3FX Tel: 0115-985 0081 Fax: 0115-985 0132 E-mail: info@pirteknottingham.co.uk

S O S Hose Services, 30 Drome Road, Deeside Industrial Park, Deeside, Clwyd, CH5 2NY Tel: (01244) 280505 Fax: (01244) 281505

Specialised Management Services, Harfreys Road, Great Yarmouth, Norfolk, NR31 0LS Tel: (01493) 655515 Fax: (01224) 657408

Stauff, Unit 30-31, Point Pleasant Industrial Estate, Wallsend, Tyne & Wear, NE28 6HA Tel: 0191-262 6390 Fax: 0191-262 8825 E-mail: enquiries@stauff.com

HYDRAULIC HOSE ASSEMBLY SERVICES – *continued*

Trax Hydraulics North West Ltd, Unit 3, Langley Road, Burscough Industrial Estate, Burscough, Ormskirk, Lancashire, L40 8JR Tel: (01704) 892411 Fax: (01704) 896593

Turner Hydraulics, Old Station Yard, Magor, Caldicot, Gwent, NP26 3HT Tel: (01633) 881966 Fax: (01633) 881991 E-mail: ian@turnerhydraulics.co.uk

Unimaster Components, 9 Arnhem Road, Newbury, Berkshire, RG14 5RU Tel: (01635) 528692 E-mail: sales@unimaster.co.uk

HYDRAULIC HOSE MAINTENANCE OR REPAIR

▶ Kelly Hydraulics Ltd, 67 Amhurst Gardens, Isleworth, Middlesex, TW7 6AN Tel: (020) 8847 3414 Fax: (020) 8847 3414 E-mail: raymondkelly50@hotmail.com

RM Hydraulics, Station Street, Leek, Staffordshire, ST13 8BP Tel: (01538) 399980 Fax: (01538) 388869

S O S Hose Services, 30 Drome Road, Deeside Industrial Park, Deeside, Clwyd, CH5 2NY Tel: (01244) 280505 Fax: (01244) 281505

HYDRAULIC HOSES, *See also headings for particular types*

A B Hoses & Fittings Ltd, Units 6-7 Warwick Street Industrial Estate, Storforth Lane, Chesterfield, Derbyshire, S40 2TT Tel: (01246) 208831 Fax: (01246) 209302 E-mail: sales@ab-hoses.org.uk

A B Trade Supplies, South Denes Road, Great Yarmouth, Norfolk, NR30 3PF Tel: (01493) 859475 Fax: (01493) 330544 E-mail: sales@abtradesupplies.co.uk

Abdex Hose & Couplings Ltd, Unit 3 Commerce Way, Leighton Buzzard, Bedfordshire, LU7 4RW Tel: (01525) 377770 Fax: (01525) 851990 E-mail: enquiries@abdexhose.com

Alfa Gomma UK Ltd, 3 Cranford Court, Hardwick Grange, Woolston, Warrington, WA1 4RX Tel: (01925) 820800 Fax: (01925) 810926

Approved Hydraulics Ltd, Brook Business Complex, Bennett Street, Manchester, M12 5AU Tel: 0161-273 1999 Fax: 0161-273 7979 E-mail: approvedhyd@aol.com

Border Hydraulics & Pneumatics Ltd, 9 Currock Road Trade Centre, Currock Road, Carlisle, CA2 5AD Tel: (01228) 530010 Fax: (01228) 818087

Burley Hydraulics Cambridgeshire Ltd, 27 Stephenson Road, St. Ives, Cambridgeshire, PE27 3WJ Tel: (01480) 497725 Fax: (01480) 497778E-mail: burley-hydraulics@tiscali.co.uk

Comet Fluid Power, Horace Waller V C Parade, Shaw Cross Business Park, Dewsbury, West Yorkshire, WF12 7RF Tel: (01924) 455667 Fax: (01924) 456292 E-mail: comet@challenger-group.co.uk

Corby Hose & Hydraulics Ltd, Geddington Road, Corby, Northamptonshire, NN18 8AA Tel: (01536) 201534 Fax: (01536) 400986

Dunlop Hi Flex Fluidpower Ltd, Unit 59 Holly Court, St. Modwen Road, Plymouth, PL6 8LG Tel: (01752) 262268 Fax: (01752) 664722 E-mail: dunlophiflex@shelmerdined.freeserve.co.uk

Dunlop Hiflex Fluid Power Ltd, Howley Park Road, Morley, Leeds, LS27 0BN Tel: 0113-238 1547 Fax: 0113-238 3391 E-mail: leeds@dunlophiflex.com

Equipment Supply Co.Ltd, Unit 21, Kirkhill Place, Kirkhill Industrial Estate, Dyce, Aberdeen, AB21 0GU Tel: (01224) 772555 Fax: (01224) 723681

ERIKS UK, Industrial Distribution Service Centre, Unit 2-1 Festival Court, Govan, Glasgow, G51 1AR Tel: 0141-419 0112 Fax: 0141-419 0444 E-mail: glasgow@eriks.co.uk

Eurotec Hydraulics Ltd, 173 Ashby Road, Moira, Swadlincote, Derbyshire, DE12 6DW Tel: (01283) 225224 Fax: (01283) 819921 E-mail: euroteclelcs@aol.com

Hiflex Fluid Power, Units 8-9 Sun Valley Business Park, Winnall Close, Winchester, Hampshire, SO23 0LB Tel: (01962) 860311 Fax: (01962) 860673 E-mail: winchester@dunlophiflex.com

Hoses Direct, Brighton, BN2 5AW Tel: (0800) 6526038 Fax: (0800) 6526039 E-mail: sales@hoses.co.uk

Hydraulic Equipment Supermarkets Ltd, J Innsworth Technology Park, Innsworth Lane, Gloucester, GL3 1DL Tel: (01452) 730774 Fax: (01452) 731637 E-mail: sales@dowco.co.uk

Hydraulic Equipment Supply Co. Ltd, 67 Victoria Road, Worthing, West Sussex, BN11 1UN Tel: (01903) 203154 Fax: (01903) 236147

Hydraulic Pipework Services, 4 Smallbridge Industrial Park, Riverside Drive, Rochdale, Lancashire, OL16 2SH Tel: (01706) 345670 Fax: (01706) 641112

Hydraulic Pneumatic Services, Unit 23-24 The Old Mill, School Lane, Bamber Bridge, Preston, PR5 6SY Tel: (01772) 629993 Fax: (01772) 629995 E-mail: info@hps-group.co.uk

▶ Hydraulic Power Services Ltd, 84 Bridgeman Street, Bolton, BL3 6AT Tel: (01204) 363660 Fax: (01204) 363670 E-mail: info@hydraulicpower.co.uk

Interlube Systems Ltd, 85 St. Modwen Road, Plymouth, PL6 8LH Tel: (01752) 676000 Fax: (01752) 676001 E-mail: info@interlubesystems.co.uk

J.W Hydraulics, Springvale Industrial Park, Unit 33, Bilston, West Midlands, WV14 0QL Tel: (01902) 408771 Fax: (01902) 354448

King Industrial Products Ltd, Unit 12, Techno Trading Estate, Brambell Road, Swindon, SN2 8HB Tel: (01793) 491606 Fax: (01793) 530461 E-mail: sales@kingindustrial.co.uk

M & P Hydraulic Ltd, Unit 3c Bergen Way, Hull, HU7 0YQ Tel: (01482) 820701 Fax: (01482) 823101

Manuli-hydraulics UK Ltd, Unit C Nasmyth Business Centre, Green Lane, Patricroft, Eccles, Manchester, M30 0SN Tel: 0161-787 8085 Fax: 0161-787 8086

Nelson Stokes Ltd, Highfield Industrial Estate, Camelford, Cornwall, PL32 9RA Tel: (01840) 213711 Fax: (01840) 213338 E-mail: enquiries@nelsonstokes.com

North Devon Hose & Hydraulics Ltd, Unit 20 Castle Park Road, Whiddon Valley Industrial Estate, Barnstaple, Devon, EX32 8PA Tel: (01271) 324443 Fax: (01271) 324568 E-mail: northdevon@hosehyd.fsnet.co.uk

North Kent Hydraulics, Unit 24 Castle View Business Centre, Gas House Road, Rochester, Kent, ME1 1PB Tel: (01634) 832211 Fax: (01634) 831981

Pirtek, Unit 35 Seymour Street, Millers Bridge Industrial Estate, Bootle, Merseyside, L20 1EE Tel: 0151-933 9000 Fax: 0151-933 5333 E-mail: info@pirtekuk.com

Pirtek, Unit 35, Acton Park Industrial Estate, The Vale, Acton, London, W3 7QE Tel: (020) 8749 8444 Fax: (020) 8749 8333 E-mail: info@pirtek.co.uk

Pirtek, 6 Westbrook Trading Estate, Westbrook Road, Trafford Park, Manchester, M17 1AY Tel: 0161-877 0000 Fax: 0161-877 8899 E-mail: pirtek-manchester@supanet.com

Pirtek, Unit 11 Liongate Enterprise Park, Morden Road, Mitcham, Surrey, CR4 4NY Tel: (020) 8640 6565 Fax: (020) 8640 2252 E-mail: pirtek.mitcham@zen.co.uk

Pirtek, 337 Ranglet Road, Walton Summit Centre, Bamber Bridge, Preston, PR5 8AR Tel: (01772) 620111 Fax: (01772) 629996 E-mail: preston@pirtekcentre.co.uk

Pirtek, 3 Alert House, Dannemora Drive, Sheffield, S9 5DF Tel: 0114-249 3666 Fax: 0114-249 3667 E-mail: sheffield@pirtekcentre.co.uk

Pirtek, Unit 8 Westmill Street, Stoke-on-Trent, ST1 3EL Tel: (01782) 206206 Fax: (01782) 206306 E-mail: stoke@pirtekcentre.co.uk

Premier Hydraulics & Pneumatics, Unit 4, Cliffton Business Park, Preston New Road, Clifton, Preston, PR4 0XQ Tel: (01772) 253455 Fax: (01772) 204155

Pressure Flex, 111 Great Barr Street, Birmingham, B9 4BB Tel: 0121-766 8228 Fax: 0121-766 7818 E-mail: sales@wakefind.co.uk

Regent Hose & Hydraulics Ltd, Unit 16-18, Rabans Close, Rabans Lane Industrial Area, Aylesbury, Buckinghamshire, HP19 8RS Tel: (01296) 420171 Fax: (01296) 392306 E-mail: info@regenthose.co.uk

Robertson & Armitage Ltd, 10 Limekiln Road, Ayr, KA8 8DG Tel: (01292) 282733 Fax: (01292) 287932

Rogers Duncan Engineering Ltd, 396 Hillington Road, Hillington Industrial Estate, Glasgow, G52 4BL Tel: 0141-882 6211 Fax: 0141-882 5818 E-mail: info@duncanrogers.com

Savilles Motor Factors Ltd, 15 Elders Street, Scarborough, North Yorkshire, YO11 1DZ Tel: (01723) 375010 Fax: (01723) 353798

Seagull Fittings Ltd, 90 Roebuck Lane, West Bromwich, West Midlands, B70 6QX Tel: 0121-525 0020 Fax: 0121-525 1116 E-mail: sales@seagullfittings.co.uk

▶ Spear Engineering (Scotland) Ltd, Christianhall, Cuminestown, Turriff, Aberdeenshire, AB53 5UE Tel: (01888) 544398 Fax: (01888) 544012

Specialised Management Services, Harfreys Road, Great Yarmouth, Norfolk, NR31 0LS Tel: (01493) 655515 Fax: (01493) 657408

Thorne Hydraulics Ltd, Unit 24 Frontier Works, 12 King Edward Road, Thorne, Doncaster, South Yorkshire, DN8 4HU Tel: (01405) 816067 Fax: (01405) 741060

Trist Draper Hydraulics, Unit 6f Redbrook Business Park, Wilthorpe Road, Barnsley, South Yorkshire, S75 1JN Tel: (01226) 281140 Fax: (01226) 243223 E-mail: sales@tristdraper.co.uk

Wath Rubber & Plastics Ltd, Pump House, Station Road, Wath-upon-Dearne, Rotherham, South Yorkshire, S63 7DQ Tel: (01709) 876900 Fax: (01709) 877998 E-mail: info@wath.co.uk

HYDRAULIC JACKS

Allspeeds Ltd, Royal Works, Atlas Street, Clayton le Moors, Accrington, Lancashire, BB5 5LP Tel: (01254) 615100 Fax: (01254) 615199 E-mail: sales@allspeeds.co.uk

Dorvic Engineering Co. Ltd, New Street, Holbrook Industrial Estate, Holbrook, Sheffield, S20 3GH Tel: 0114-248 5633 Fax: 0114-251 0654 E-mail: sales@dorvic.com

E P P Magnus Ltd, Ashbourne Estate, 174 Mile Cross Lane, Norwich, NR6 6RY Tel: (01603) 400861 Fax: (01603) 788496 E-mail: welcome@magnus-int.co.uk

Era Hydraulics & Pneumatics Ltd, Unit 5 Loaland Business Centre, Maritime Close Medway City, Estate Rochester, Rochester, Kent, ME2 4AZ Tel: (01634) 717499 Fax: (0845) 2412446 E-mail: erahydraulice@btconnect.com

Hypec, Royal Works, Atlas Street, Clayton-Le-Moors, Accrington, Lancashire, BB5 5LP Tel: (01254) 615100 Fax: (01254) 615199 E-mail: sales@allspeeds.co.uk

Skate Systems Ltd, 55 London Road, Hurst Green, Etchingham, East Sussex, TN19 7QP Tel: (01580) 860020 Fax: (01580) 860021 E-mail: sales@skatesystems.co.uk

Tangye Ltd, Royal Works, Atlas Street, Clayton Le Moors, Accrington, Lancashire, BB5 5LW Tel: (01254) 615100 Fax: (01254) 615199 E-mail: sales@allspeeds.co.uk

HYDRAULIC LIFT COMPONENTS OR EQUIPMENT

Hydrax Ltd, Wylds Road, Bridgwater, Somerset, TA6 4BH Tel: (01278) 727600 Fax: (01278) 727601 E-mail: info@hydrax.co.uk

HYDRAULIC LIFTING GEAR

Fagioli PSC Ltd, The Ridgeway, Iver, Buckinghamshire, SL0 9JE Tel: (01753) 659000 Fax: (01753) 655998 E-mail: info@fagiolipsc.co.uk

George Jones Engineering Services Ltd, Lionel Works, 89-91 Rolfe Street, Smethwick, West Midlands, B66 2AY Tel: 0121-558 1884 Fax: 0121-558 0017 E-mail: sales.georgejonesengservices@zyworld.com

Lifting Equipment & Services Ltd, B6 Foundry Way, Eaton Socon, St. Neots, Cambridgeshire, PE19 8TR Tel: (01480) 217605 Fax: (01480) 407108 E-mail: info@liftingequipmenthire.com

▶ Skyscrapers UK Ltd, 81 Cheam Road, Epsom, Surrey, KT17 3EG Tel: (020) 8786 7456 Fax: (020) 8786 7456 E-mail: info@skyscrapersuk.com

HYDRAULIC LIFTING PLATFORMS

Power-Lifts Ltd, Marlborough House, 18 Marlborough Road, Woodthorpe, Nottingham, NG5 4FG Tel: 0115-926 9996 Fax: 0115-966 1173 E-mail: info@powerlift.co.uk

Wessex Medical Equipment Co. Ltd, Budds Lane, Romsey, Hampshire, SO51 0HA Tel: (01794) 830303 Fax: (01794) 512621 E-mail: info@wessexmedical.co.uk

HYDRAULIC LIFTS

Accord Lift Services Ltd, Unit 5A Beechcroft Farm Industries, Chapel Wood Road, Ash, Sevenoaks, Kent, TN15 7HX Tel: (01474) 879858 Fax: (01474) 874143 E-mail: info@accordlifts.co.uk

Ace Elevators Ltd, Galven House, Bakewell Road, Loughborough, Leicestershire, LE11 5QY Tel: (01509) 265383 Fax: (01509) 269275E-mail: midlands@ace-elevators.co.uk

The Britannic Lift Company plc, Riverview Buildings, Bradford Road, Riddlesden, Keighley, West Yorkshire, BD20 5JH Tel: (01535) 600066 Fax: (01535) 600077 E-mail: sales@lifts.co.uk

Britton Price Ltd, Unit 14 Hove Business Centre, Fonthill Road, Hove, East Sussex, BN3 6HA Tel: (01273) 235035 Fax: (01273) 235036 E-mail: sales@brittonprice.co.uk

Edbro plc, Nelson Street, Bolton, BL3 2JJ Tel: (01204) 528888 Fax: (01204) 531957 E-mail: sales@edbro.co.uk

▶ Gartec Ltd, 6 Midshires Business Park, Smeaton Close, Aylesbury, Buckinghamshire, HP19 8HL Tel: (01296) 397100 Fax: (01296) 397600 E-mail: sales@gartec.com

H. Breakell & Co. (Blackburn) Ltd, P1/15 Parklands, Heywood Distribution Park, Heywood, Lancashire, OL10 2TT Tel: (01706) 369272 Fax: (01706) 629448 E-mail: enquirires@breakell-lifts.co.uk

Kone plc, Global House Station Place, Fox La North, Chertsey, Surrey, KT16 9HW Tel: (0870) 7701122 Fax: (0870) 7701122 E-mail: salesandmarketing.uk@kone.com

KONE PLC, Blisworth Hill Farm, Stoke Road, Blisworth, Northampton, NN7 3DB Tel: 08451 999 999 Fax: 0870 7701144 E-mail: sales.marketinguk@kone.com

Lift & Engineering Services Ltd, 16 Portersfield Road, Cradley Heath, West Midlands, B64 7BN Tel: (01384) 633115 Fax: (01384) 633119 E-mail: mailbox@lift-engineering.co.uk

Logitrans UK Ltd, Unit 5 Ascot Industrial Estate, Icknield Way, Letchworth Garden City, Hertfordshire, SG6 1TD Tel: (01462) 678444 Fax: (01462) 678555

Oakland Elevators Ltd, 6 Mandervell Road, Oadby, Leicester, LE2 5LL Tel: 0116-272 0800 Fax: 0116-272 0904 E-mail: sales@oakland-elevators.co.uk

Omega City Lifts Ltd, 8 Bridge Gate Centre, Martinfield, Welwyn Garden City, Hertfordshire, AL7 1JG Tel: (01707) 334962 Fax: (01707) 376594 E-mail: sanjay@omegacitylifts.co.uk

Pickerings Europe Ltd, PO Box 19, Stockton-on-Tees, Cleveland, TS20 2AD Tel: (01642) 607161 Fax: (01642) 677638 E-mail: sales@pickerings.com

Ritchie Hart, 18 Cyprus Avenue, Belfast, BT5 5NT Tel: (028) 9065 4594 Fax: (028) 9065 6196 E-mail: ritchie.hart@charity.vfree.com

HYDRAULIC LOADERS

C C T Ltd, Park Road, Holmewood, Chesterfield, Derbyshire, S42 5UY Tel: (01246) 855995 Fax: (01246) 854028 E-mail: cctltd@breathemail.net

Lewis Equipment Ltd, Waterloo Road, Bidford-on-Avon, Alcester, Warwickshire, B50 4JH Tel: (01789) 773044 Fax: (01789) 490379 E-mail: sales@lewis-equipment.co.uk

HYDRAULIC MACHINE VICES

Pharos Redco Ltd, 228 Lythalls Lane, Foleshill, Coventry, CV6 6GF Tel: (024) 7668 7235 Fax: (024) 7666 6355 E-mail: mwinstone@pharosengineering.co.uk

HYDRAULIC MANIFOLDS

B P Hydraulics Ltd, Douglas Drive, Godalming, Surrey, GU7 1JX Tel: (01483) 423321 Fax: (01483) 426581 E-mail: enquiry@bp-hydraulics.fsnet.co.uk

British Engineering Productions Ltd, 19 Arnside Road, Waterlooville, Hampshire, PO7 7UP Tel: (023) 9226 8733 Fax: (023) 9225 1104 E-mail: sales@bep-manifolds.com

C D Engineering, 1 Bartleet Road, Redditch, Worcestershire, B98 0DQ Tel: (01527) 524661 Fax: (01527) 510889 E-mail: cdeng100@yahoo.co.uk

Cityown Ltd, Unit M Charlwoods Business Centre, East Grinstead, West Sussex, RH19 2HH Tel: (01342) 327787 Fax: (01342) 324289

Cullimore Hydraulic Engineering, C 14 Copt Elm Close, Charlton Kings, Cheltenham, Gloucestershire, GL53 8AD Tel: (01242) 241112 Fax: (01242) 241112

Denley Hydraulics Ltd, Spen Vale Street, Heckmondwike, West Yorkshire, WF16 0NQ Tel: (01924) 413400 Fax: (01924) 410109 E-mail: sales@denleyhydraulics.co.uk

Moog Controls Ltd, Ashchurch, Tewkesbury, Gloucestershire, GL20 8NA Tel: (01684) 296600 Fax: (01684) 296760 E-mail: sales@moog.co.uk

Parker Hannifin plc, 66 Wakefield Road, Ossett, West Yorkshire, WF5 9JS Tel: (01924) 282200 Fax: (01924) 282299 E-mail:

▶ Sterling Hydraulics Ltd, Sterling House, Blacknell Lane, Crewkerne, Somerset, TA18 8LL Tel: (01460) 271800 Fax: (01460) 271801 E-mail: mktng@sterling-hydraulics.co.uk

System 910 Hydraulics Ltd, 7 The Old Granary, The Street, Boxgrove, Chichester, West Sussex, PO18 0ES Tel: (01243) 539789 Fax: (01243) 530307 E-mail: system910@mistral.co.uk

HYDRAULIC MOTOR MANUFRS

A N Hydraulics, Sandlow Green Farm, Marsh Lane, Holmes Chapel, Crewe, CW4 8AS Tel: (01477) 533522 Fax: (01477) 533522

Adan Ltd, Nursery Road Industrial Estate, Boston, Lincolnshire, PE21 7TN Tel: (01205) 311500 Fax: (01205) 358013 E-mail: sales@adanltd.co.uk

Albroco Ltd, Unit C28 Ashmount Enterprise Park, Aber Road, Flint, Clwyd, CH6 5YL Tel: (01352) 734182 Fax: (01352) 734159 E-mail: sales@albrocos.co.uk

▶ Anchor Hydraulics Ltd, Unit 6 Leeds Street, Wigan, Lancashire, WN3 4BW Tel: (01942) 820615 Fax: (01942) 820615 E-mail: anchorhydraulics@btclick.com

Bosch Rexroth Ltd, Viewfield Industrial Estate, Glenrothes, Fife, KY6 2RD Tel: (01592) 631515 Fax: (01592) 631888

Eagle Hydraulic Systems Ltd, 14 Chartwell Road, Lancing, West Sussex, BN15 8TU Tel: (01903) 751494 Fax: (01903) 751522

Kawasaki Precision Machinery UK Ltd, Ernesettle Lane, Plymouth, PL5 2SA Tel: (01752) 364394 Fax: (01752) 364816 E-mail: sales@kpm-uk.co.uk

Rotary Power Ltd, St. Peters, Newcastle upon Tyne, NE6 1BS Tel: 0191-276 4444 Fax: 0191-276 4462 E-mail: rotary.power@bel.co.uk

Sauer-Danfoss Ltd, Cheney Manor, Swindon, SN2 2PZ Tel: (01793) 530101 Fax: (01793) 481925

HYDRAULIC NUT CUTTERS

Torque Tension Systems Ltd, 5 Stephenson Court, Barrington Industrial Estate, Bedlington, Northumberland, NE22 7DQ Tel: (01670) 530411 Fax: (01670) 531991 E-mail: enquiries@tts-ltd.com

HYDRAULIC OFFSHORE OR SUBMERSIBLE OR UNDERWATER EQUIPMENT

Air Power & Hydraulics Ltd, 15 Watt Rd, Hillington Park, Glasgow, G52 4PQ Tel: 0141-810 4511 Fax: 0141-883 3825 E-mail: hydraulics@aph.co.uk

Searchwise Ltd, 6 Broomiesburn Road, Ellon, Aberdeenshire, AB41 9RD Tel: (01358) 722990 Fax: (01358) 722933 E-mail: sales@searchwise.co.uk

HYDRAULIC OIL FILTRATION EQUIPMENT

Donaldson Filter Components Ltd, Oslo Road, Hull, HU7 0YN Tel: (01482) 835213 Fax: (01482) 835411 E-mail: info@donaldson.com

HYDRAULIC PACKINGS AND JOINTINGS MANUFRS

Arefco Special Products Ltd, Jubilee Industrial Estate, Ashington, Northumberland, NE63 8UA Tel: (01670) 819513 Fax: (01670) 816132 E-mail: sales@arefco.co.uk

Beldam Lascar Seals Ltd, Lascar Works, Staines Road, Hounslow, TW3 3JL Tel: (020) 8570 7722 Fax: (020) 8570 4438 E-mail: enquiries@beldamlascargroup.com

Claron Hydraulic Seals Ltd, Station Road, Cradley Heath, West Midlands, B64 6PN Tel: 0121-559 9711 Fax: 0121-559 1036 E-mail: sales@claron-seals.co.uk

Dli Seals Ltd, Unit A-D Trimdon Court, Trimdon Grange Industrial Estate, Trimdon Grange, Trimdon Station, County Durham, TS29 6PE Tel: (01429) 881660 Fax: (01429) 882299 E-mail: sales@dliseals.co.uk

Polyurethane Progress Ltd, Church Street, Wakefield, West Yorkshire, WF1 5QY Tel: (01924) 387310 Fax: (01924) 382951 E-mail: enquiries@polyurethane-progress.co.uk

HYDRAULIC PASSENGER LIFTS

▶ Sector Lifts, 37 The Arcade, North Street, Keighley, West Yorkshire, BD21 3SL Tel: (01535) 606099 Fax: (01535) 606049 E-mail: info@sectorlifts.co.uk

HYDRAULIC PIPELINE EQUIPMENT

Metallink Fluid Power Systems, Prospect Road, Crook, County Durham, DL15 8JG Tel: 01388 761200

HYDRAULIC PIPELINE FLUSHING CONTRACTORS

GS Hydro Ltd, Unit C Endeavour Court, Hall Dene Way, Seaham Grange Industrial Estat, Seaham, County Durham, SR7 0HB Tel: 0191-523 9643 Fax: 0191-521 8001 E-mail: sales@gshydro.com

HYDRAULIC PISTON PUMPS

C-Tronix UK Ltd, 185a Lower Blandford Road, Broadstone, Dorset, BH18 8DH Tel: (01202) 695500 E-mail: ap9000mart@aol.com

S A M Hydraulic UK Ltd, Planet House 910 Lakeside Drive, Centre Park, Warrington, WA1 1QX Tel: (01925) 624800 Fax: (01925) 624801 E-mail: sales@samhydraulik.co.uk

White House Products Ltd, Kelburn Business Pk, Port Glasgow, Renfrewshire, PA14 6TD Tel: (01475) 742500 Fax: (01475) 742888 E-mail: info@whp.co.uk

HYDRAULIC POWER PACK MANUFRS

A G Hydraulics Ltd, Unit 40 Plume Street Industrial Estate, Plume Street, Birmingham, B6 7RT Tel: 0121-326 6395 Fax: 0121-328 2923 E-mail: sales@aghydraulics.com

A M C Engineering Ltd, Unit 3, Blackhill Industrial Estate, Findon, Aberdeen, AB12 4RL Tel: (01224) 782232 Fax: (01224) 782480 E-mail: sales@amc-engineering.co.uk

Andrews Hydraulics Ltd, Unit 27-28, Craftsmans Way, East Goscote, Leicester, LE7 3SL Tel: 0116-260 1001 Fax: 0116-264 0186 E-mail: design@andrewshydraulics.co.uk

Ash UK Ltd, 63 James Watt Place, East Kilbride, Glasgow, G74 5HG Tel: (01355) 224445 Fax: (01355) 223055 E-mail: ashukltd@btopenworld.com

Bell Hydraulic Services Ltd, Chapel Lane, Cwmbran, Gwent, NP44 2PP Tel: (01633) 861423 Fax: (01633) 864472 E-mail: dave.bell@bellhydraulics.co.uk

Branch Hydraulic Systems Ltd, Unit H, Innsworth Technology Park, Innsworth Lane, Gloucester, GL3 1DL Tel: (01452) 730562 Fax: (01452) 731579 E-mail: branch@dowco.co.uk

Centech Hydraulics, 62 Arnold Road, Nottingham, NG6 0DZ Tel: 0115-924 4822 Fax: 0115-924 4818

Central Engineering & Hydraulic Services Ltd, Brook Works, 174 Bromyard Road, St. Johns, Worcester, WR2 5EE Tel: (01905) 748569 Fax: (01905) 420700 E-mail: chs0999@aol.com

D G Howell (Hydraulic Engineers) Ltd, 78-84 Commercial St, Risca, Newport, Gwent, NP11 6BA Tel: (01633) 614326 Fax: (01633) 601581 E-mail: dghowell@aol.com

Dapp Hydraulics, Bentley Mill Close, Walsall, WS2 0BN Tel: (01922) 632885 Fax: (01922) 721980 E-mail: sales@dapp.co.uk

Fairway Hydraulic & Engineering Co., Unit 96 Blackpole Trading Estate West, Worcester, WR3 8TJ Tel: (01905) 457519 Fax: (01905) 456054 E-mail: fairway.hydraulic@ic24.net

Hedley Hydraulics Ltd, High Street, Crigglestone, Wakefield, West Yorkshire, WF4 3HT Tel: (01924) 259999 Fax: (01924) 252211 E-mail: hedley@hedley-hyd.com

Hydar Fluid Power Ltd, Unit 20-21, Midsomer Enterprise Park, Radstock Road, Midsomer Norton, Radstock, BA3 2BB Tel: (01249) 651666 Fax: (01761) 414050 E-mail: carol@hydar.co.uk

Hydraflow Systems, Strathfield House, Smithymoor, Stretton, Alfreton, Derbyshire, DE55 6FE Tel: 01246 250958 Fax: 05600 492268E-mail: sales@hydraflowsystems.co.uk

Hymid Hydraulics Ltd, 9 Glenbarr Avenue, Leicester, LE4 0AE Tel: 0116-251 8888 Fax: 0116-251 8800E-mail: sales@hymid.com

J C B Cab Systems Ltd, Riverside, Rugeley, Staffordshire, WS15 2WA Tel: (01889) 572700 Fax: (01889) 585999 E-mail: enquiries@jcb.com

Jespro 2000 Ltd, Central Mills, Raymond Street, Bradford, West Yorkshire, BD5 8DT Tel: (01274) 735446 Fax: (01274) 394909 E-mail: sales@jespro.com

Link Hydraulic Services Ltd, 38 Sherwood Road, Bromsgrove, Worcestershire, B60 3DR Tel: (01527) 579145 Fax: (01527) 576555 E-mail: link.hydraulics@btconnect.com

Macscott Bond Ltd, PO Box 1, Loanhead, Midlothian, EH20 9SW Tel: 0131-448 2950 Fax: 0131-448 2941

Modular Hydraulic Systems Ltd, 9 Redan Hill Estate, Redan Road, Aldershot, Hampshire, GU12 4SJ Tel: (01252) 333883 Fax: (01252) 343615 E-mail: sales@mhs.co.uk

Neilson Hydraulics & Engineering Ltd, 22 Atlas Way, Sheffield, S4 7QQ Tel: (01709) 821002 Fax: 0114-244 0111 E-mail: sales@neilson-hydraulics.co.uk

Oddy Hydraulics Ltd, Tristran Centre, Brown Lane West, Leeds, LS12 6BF Tel: 0113-244 8787 Fax: 0113-244 9786 E-mail: sales@oddy-hyds.com

Portsmouth Water P.L.C., 8 West Street, Havant, Hampshire, PO9 1LG Tel: (023) 9249 9888 Fax: (023) 9245 3632

Quick Hydraulics Ltd, North Tyne Industrial Estate, Benton, Newcastle upon Tyne, NE12 9SZ Tel: 0191-270 1160 Fax: 0191-270 1143 E-mail: quick@quick-hydraulics.com

Rotherham Presition Engineering, Unit 2, Gateway Place, Parkgate, Rotherham, South Yorkshire, S62 6LL Tel: (01709) 526177 Fax: (01709) 710717

System Hydraulics Ltd, Unit 5 Long Island Park, Carlisle, CA2 5AS Tel: (01228) 511444 Fax: (01228) 514206

T A Savery & Co. Ltd, Bracebridge Street, Birmingham, B6 4PF Tel: 0121-380 4514 Fax: 0121-380 4507 E-mail: sales@savery.co.uk

Taskers UK Ltd, 4 Roman Ridge Road, Sheffield, S9 1GB Tel: 0114-243 0927 Fax: 0114-242 5507 E-mail: sales@taskersuk.com

Tendring Hundred Water Services Ltd, Mill Hill, Manningtree, Essex, CO11 2AZ Tel: (01206) 399200 Fax: (01206) 399212 E-mail: info@thws.co.uk

V H S Hydraulic Components, Unit 1, Block A, Waleswood Road, Wales Bar, Sheffield, S26 5PY Tel: (01909) 772666 Fax: (01909) 773226 E-mail: sales@hydraulic-components.net

Wescombe Maurice B, Silverdale Road, Hayes, Middlesex, UB3 3BN Tel: (020) 8561 0862 Fax: (020) 8561 7007

Wills Ridley, Kernick Industrial Estate, Unit One, Annear Road, Penryn, Cornwall, TR10 9EW Tel: (01326) 376015 Fax: (01326) 376212 E-mail: info@wills-ridley.com

Wycis Engineering Co. Ltd, 1 Wheatear, Perry Road, Witham, Essex, CM8 3YY Tel: (01376) 516247 Fax: (01376) 514721 E-mail: wycis@btinternet.com

Yeovil Hydraulics, 14 Gazelle Road, Lynx Trading Estate, Yeovil, Somerset, BA20 2PJ Tel: (01935) 472233 Fax: (01935) 431211 E-mail: enquiries@yeovilhydraulics.co.uk

HYDRAULIC POWER TRANSMISSION EQUIPMENT

A R S Anglian Diesels Ltd, Unit 9c Headway Business Park, Denby Dale Road, Wakefield, West Yorkshire, WF2 7AZ Tel: (01924) 332492 Fax: (01924) 332493 E-mail: enquiries@arsangliandiesels.co.uk

Comer Industries (UK) Ltd, Units 2-3, Heath Road, Merrylees Industrial Estate, Desford, Leicester, LE9 9FE Tel: (01530) 231504 Fax: (01530) 231503 E-mail: sales@comer.co.uk

Poclain Hydraulics Ltd, Nene Valley Business Park, Oundle, Peterborough, PE8 4HN Tel: (01832) 273773 Fax: (01832) 274990 E-mail: info@poclain-hydraulics.com

Rotary Power Ltd, St. Peters, Newcastle upon Tyne, NE6 1BS Tel: 0191-276 4444 Fax: 0191-276 4462 E-mail: rotary.power@bel.co.uk

HYDRAULIC PRESS INSTALLATION

J R D Bipel Ltd, Unit 4 Merryhills House, Middlemore Lane West, Aldridge, Walsall, WS9 8BG Tel: (01922) 451245 Fax: (01922) 743040 E-mail: sales@jrdbipel.com

HYDRAULIC PRESS REPAIR OR RECONDITIONING

J R D Bipel Ltd, Unit 4 Merryhills House, Middlemore Lane West, Aldridge, Walsall, WS9 8BG Tel: (01922) 451245 Fax: (01922) 743040 E-mail: sales@jrdbipel.com

Pressure Design Hydraulics Ltd, Goldthorpe Industrial Estate, Goldthorpe, Rotherham, S. Yorkshire, S63 9BL Tel: (01709) 897121 Fax: (01709) 895305 E-mail: sales@pressuredesign.co.uk

HYDRAULIC PRESSES

H M Machinery UK Ltd, 41 Scholey Close, Halling, Rochester, Kent, ME2 1JZ Tel: (01634) 244600 Fax: (01634) 244599

Hawkes Technical Ltd, Spencer Parade, Stanwick, Wellingborough, Northamptonshire, NN9 6QJ Tel: (01933) 622492 Fax: (01933) 624092 E-mail: info@hawkestechnical.com

J R D Bipel Ltd, Unit 4 Merryhills House, Middlemore Lane West, Aldridge, Walsall, WS9 8BG Tel: (01922) 451245 Fax: (01922) 743040 E-mail: sales@jrdbipel.com

George Jones Engineering Services Ltd, Lionel Works, 89-91 Rolfe Street, Smethwick, West Midlands, B66 2AY Tel: 0121-558 1884 Fax: 0121-558 0017 E-mail: sales.georgejonesengservices@zyworld.com

Palamine Ltd, Homefield Road, Haverhill, Suffolk, CB9 8QP Tel: (01440) 762616 Fax: (01440) 762573 E-mail: sales@palamine.co.uk

Pearson Panke Equipment Ltd, 1 3 Halegrove Gardens, Mill Hill, London, NW7 3LR Tel: (020) 8959 3232 Fax: (020) 8959 5613 E-mail: sales@pearsonpanke.co.uk

Pearson Production Systems Ltd, Stargate Industrial Estate, Ryton, Tyne & Wear, NE40 3EX Tel: 0191-413 8080 Fax: 0191-413 8822

Pressure Design Hydraulics Ltd, Goldthorpe Industrial Estate, Goldthorpe, Rotherham, S. Yorkshire, S63 9BL Tel: (01709) 897121 Fax: (01709) 895305 E-mail: sales@pressuredesign.co.uk

Joseph Rhodes Ltd, Bell Vue, Elm Tree Street, Wakefield, West Yorkshire, WF1 5EQ Tel: (01924) 371161 Fax: (01924) 370928 E-mail: sales@joseph-rhodes.co.uk

Specac Ltd, River House, 97 Cray Avenue, Orpington, Kent, BR5 4HE Tel: (01689) 873134 Fax: (01689) 878527 E-mail: sales@specac.co.uk

Thompson & Son (Millwall) Ltd, Cuba Street, Isle of Dogs, London, E14 8LF Tel: (020) 7987 1844 Fax: (020) 7987 4416

HYDRAULIC PRESSES TO SPECIFICATION

Palamine Ltd, Homefield Road, Haverhill, Suffolk, CB9 8QP Tel: (01440) 762616 Fax: (01440) 762573 E-mail: sales@palamine.co.uk

HYDRAULIC PUMP MAINTENANCE OR REPAIR

J S G Hydraulics, Unit E2 Enterprise Way, Bradford Road, Idle, Bradford, West Yorkshire, BD10 8EW Tel: (01274) 615800 Fax: (01274) 615552

HYDRAULIC PUMPS

A N Hydraulics, Sandlow Green Farm, Marsh Lane, Holmes Chapel, Crewe, CW4 8AS Tel: (01477) 533522 Fax: (01477) 533522

▶ Anchor Hydraulics Ltd, Unit 6 Leeds Street, Wigan, Lancashire, WN3 4BW Tel: (01942) 820615 Fax: (01942) 820615 E-mail: anchorhydraulics@btclick.com

Antech Hydraulics, Cocker Avenue, Poulton Industrial Estate, Poulton-le-Fylde, Lancashire, FY6 8JU Tel: (01253) 890037 Fax: (01253) 890073 E-mail: enquiries@antech-hyd.co.uk

Armstrong Holden Brooke Pullen, Ormside House, 21 Ormside Way, Redhill, RH1 2JG Tel: (01737) 378100 Fax: (01737) 378140 E-mail: sales@holdenbrookpullen.com

David Brown Hydraulics Ltd, 32 Factory Road, Poole, Dorset, BH16 5SL Tel: (01202) 627500 Fax: (01202) 627555 E-mail: info@dbh.textron.com

Dynamic Pump Services Ltd, Unit 11 Loomer Road Industrial Estate, Loomer Road, Newcastle, Staffordshire, ST5 7LB Tel: (01782) 566116 Fax: (01782) 566556 E-mail: sales@dynamicpumps.co.uk

Dynex-Rivett Inc, Unit C5, Steel Close, Eaton Socon, St. Neots, Cambridgeshire, PE19 8TT Tel: (01480) 213980 Fax: (01480) 405662 E-mail: sales@dynexhydraulics.co.uk

Eastern Hydraulic Systems Ltd, Unit 10 Brookhouse Business Park, Brunel Road, Hadleigh Road Industrial Estate, Ipswich, IP2 0EF Tel: (01473) 289529 Fax: (01473) 289529 E-mail: ehs@ukf.net

G C Ogle & Sons Ltd, Victoria Road, Ripley, Derbyshire, DE5 3FX Tel: (01773) 742381 Fax: (0870) 4601807

Hauhinco Water Hydraulics Ltd, PO Box 51, Heckmondwike, West Yorkshire, WF16 9DP Tel: (01924) 510600 Fax: (01924) 511539 E-mail: info@hauhinco.co.uk

Hydraulic Equipment Supermarkets Ltd, 424 Bromford Lane, Washwood Heath, Birmingham, B8 2RX Tel: 0121-327 2664 Fax: 0121-322 2488 E-mail: birmingham@dowco.co.uk

Hydraulic Equipment Supermarkets Ltd, 7a Drum Industrial Estate, Drum Industrial Estate, Chester le Street, County Durham, DH2 1AG Tel: 0191-410 6619 Fax: 0191-411 1055 E-mail: durham@dowco.co.uk

Hydraulic Equipment Supermarkets Ltd, 7 Glover Way, Leeds, LS11 5JP Tel: 0113-270 3213 Fax: 0113-270 3213 E-mail: leeds@grouphes.com

J S G Hydraulics, Unit E2 Enterprise Way, Bradford Road, Idle, Bradford, West Yorkshire, BD10 8EW Tel: (01274) 615800 Fax: (01274) 615552

Kawasaki Precision Machinery UK Ltd, Ernesettle Lane, Plymouth, PL5 2SA Tel: (01752) 364394 Fax: (01752) 364816 E-mail: sales@kpm-uk.co.uk

▶ Oilgear European Holdings, 37 Burley Road, Leeds, LS3 1JT Tel: 0113-394 7300 Fax: 0113-394 7301 E-mail: enquiries@oilgear-towler.co.uk

Sauer-Danfoss Ltd, Cheney Manor, Swindon, SN2 2PZ Tel: (01793) 530101 Fax: (01793) 481925

Scotech International Services, Craigshaw Road, West Tullos Industrial Estate, Aberdeen, AB12 3AR Tel: (01224) 248450 Fax: (01224) 248023 E-mail: sales@scotech.co.uk

Stallion Hydraulic Services Ltd, Wharf Road, Gravesend, Kent, DA12 2RU Tel: (01474) 564707 Fax: (01474) 564752 E-mail: sales@stallion-group.com

T A Savery & Co. Ltd, Bracebridge Street, Birmingham, B6 4PF Tel: 0121-380 4514 Fax: 0121-380 4507 E-mail: sales@savery.co.uk

Webster Drives Ltd, Folds Road, Bolton, BL1 2SE Tel: (01204) 382121 Fax: (01204) 386100

Webtec Products Ltd, Nuffield Road, St. Ives, Cambridgeshire, PE27 3LZ Tel: (01480) 397444 Fax: (01480) 466555 E-mail: sales@webtec.co.uk

White House Products Ltd, Kelburn Business Pk, Port Glasgow, Renfrewshire, PA14 6TD Tel: (01475) 742500 Fax: (01475) 742888 E-mail: info@whp.co.uk

HYDRAULIC RESCUE EQUIPMENT

▶ Specialist Training Consultants Ltd, The Sycamores, 7 Rugby Close, Seaford, East Sussex, BN25 3PQ Tel: (01323) 873043 Fax: (01323) 872308 E-mail: pgwilliam@aol.com

HYDRAULIC ROCK OR CONCRETE BREAKERS

Indeco UK Ltd, 11 Oasis Business Park Road One, Winsford, Cheshire, CW7 3RY Tel: (01606) 553918 Fax: (01606) 597561 E-mail: enquiries@indeco.uk.com

HYDRAULIC SEALS

Seals & Components Ltd, Village Road, Norton, Shifnal, Shropshire, TF11 9ED Tel: (01952) 730685 Fax: (01952) 730665

HYDRAULIC TEST EQUIPMENT

Hydraulic System Products Ltd, Monckton Road, Wakefield, West Yorkshire, WF2 7AL Tel: (01924) 364748 Fax: (01924) 290450 E-mail: sales@h-s-p.co.uk

Webtec Products Ltd, Nuffield Road, St. Ives, Cambridgeshire, PE27 3LZ Tel: (01480) 397444 Fax: (01480) 466555 E-mail: sales@webtec.co.uk

HYDRAULIC TOOL HIRE

▶ HSS Hire, Unit 20 Basingstoke Business Centre, Winchester Road, Basingstoke, Hampshire, RG21 8UE Tel: (01256) 461959 Fax: (01256) 331449

HYDRAULIC TOOLS

W Christie (Industrial) Ltd, Christie House, Meadow Bank Road, Rotherham, South Yorkshire, S61 2NF Tel: (01709) 550088 Fax: (01709) 550030 E-mail: sales@wchristie.com

HYDRAULIC TUBE OR TUBING COUPLINGS OR FITTINGS

Airedale Tubes & Fittings Ltd, Royds Farm Road, Leeds, LS12 6DX Tel: 0113-231 1227 Fax: 0113-231 1866 E-mail: airedaleinfo@btconnect.com

Cougar Flex, 59 Rixon Road, Wellingborough, Northamptonshire, NN8 4BA Tel: (01933) 223354 Fax: (01933) 224522 E-mail: salescougarflex@btconnect.com

Ferschl Hose & Hydraulics Ltd, Dukesway, Team Valley Trading Estate, Gateshead, Tyne & Wear, NE11 0PZ Tel: 0191-482 2511 Fax: 0191-491 0604 E-mail: info@jferschl.co.uk

Hyphose Ltd, 2 Witney Road, Nuffield Industrial Estate, Poole, Dorset, BH17 0GH Tel: (01202) 673333 Fax: (01202) 687788 E-mail: sales@hyphose.com

Miric Engineering Ltd, Wigwam Lane, Hucknall, Nottingham, NG15 7SZ Tel: 0115-968 1163 Fax: 0115-968 1483 E-mail: janeyates@mlricengineering.com

Pneumatic & Hydraulic Couplings Ltd, Atlas Way, Sheffield, S4 7QQ Tel: 0114-244 2704 Fax: 0114-244 2705 E-mail: sales@phcltd.net

Stauff UK Southampton, Unit 1-2 Millbrook Trading Estate, Third Avenue, Southampton, SO15 0LD Tel: (023) 8079 9518 Fax: (023) 8079 9519 E-mail: sales@stauffsouthampton.co.uk

Universal Hydraulic Power, Unit 6 Arden Business Park, Enterprise Close, Medway City Estate, Rochester, Kent, ME2 4LY Tel: (01322) 555452 Fax: (01634) 290871 E-mail: unihose@fastnet.co.uk

HYDRAULIC TUBE/TUBING (RIGID) COUPLING/FITTINGS

Metallink Fluid Power Systems, Prospect Road, Crook, County Durham, DL15 8JG Tel: 01388 761200

Rubbernek Fittings Ltd, Hall Lane, Walsall Wood, Walsall, WS9 9AP Tel: (01543) 453533 Fax: (01543) 453531 E-mail: mjones@rubbernek.co.uk

HYDRAULIC TUBE/TUBING, FLEXIBLE, *See Hose, Hydraulic etc*

HYDRAULIC TUBE/TUBING, RIGID

▶ Ferschl Tube Form, 2 Doxford Drive, South West Industrial Estate, Peterlee, County Durham, SR8 2RL Tel: 0191-518 0878 Fax: 0191-518 0938

Hopespare Ltd, Units 2, East Burrowfields, Welwyn Garden City, Hertfordshire, AL7 4TB Tel: (01707) 321212 Fax: (01707) 371717 E-mail: darrene@hopespare.com

Metallink Fluid Power Systems, Prospect Road, Crook, County Durham, DL15 8JG Tel: 01388 761200

HYDRAULIC VALVE ACTUATORS

Score Europe, Unit 8 Alpha Business Park, 20 White House Road, Ipswich, IP1 5LT Tel: (01473) 242460 Fax: (01473) 747644 E-mail: customersupport@score-group.com

HYDRAULIC VALVES

Atom Hydraulics, 1 Wicks Close, Springwood Industrial Estate, Braintree, Essex, CM7 2GE Tel: (01376) 348889 Fax: (01376) 348311

David Brown Hydraulics Ltd, 32 Factory Road, Poole, Dorset, BH16 5SL Tel: (01202) 627500 Fax: (01202) 627555 E-mail: info@dbh.textron.com

Dynex-Rivett Inc, Unit C5, Steel Close, Eaton Socon, St. Neots, Cambridgeshire, PE19 8TT Tel: (01480) 213980 Fax: (01480) 405662 E-mail: sales@dynexhydraulics.co.uk

ERIKS UK, Industrial Distribution Service Centre, Unit 2-1 Festival Court, Govan, Glasgow, G51 1AR Tel: 0141-419 0112 Fax: 0141-419 0444 E-mail: glasgow@eriks.co.uk

G C Ogle & Sons Ltd, Victoria Road, Ripley, Derbyshire, DE5 3FX Tel: (01773) 742381 Fax: (0870) 4601807

Gilson Engineering Newbury Ltd, 3 Sandleford Farm, Sandleford, Newtown, Newbury, Berkshire, RG20 9BB Tel: (01635) 41924 Fax: (01635) 42286 E-mail: info@gilsoneng.co.uk

Husco International Ltd, 6 Rivington Road, Whitehouse Industrial Estate, Runcorn, Cheshire, WA7 3DT Tel: (01928) 701888 Fax: (01928) 710813 E-mail: uksales@huscointl.com

Hycon Ltd, F Bridge Farm, Reading Road, Arborfield, Reading, RG2 9HT Tel: 0118-976 1616 Fax: 0118-976 1626 E-mail: hydroliccontrol@aol.com

Hydraulic Components & Systems Ltd, Unit 14 Sovereign Park, Cleveland Way, Hemel Hempstead, Hertfordshire, HP2 7DA Tel: (01442) 240202 Fax: (01442) 243133 E-mail: hydcompdrf@hotmail.com

Hydraulic Project Ltd, Shutterton Industrial Estate, Dawlish, Devon, EX7 0NH Tel: (01626) 863634 Fax: (01626) 866283 E-mail: sales@hypro.co.uk

Kawasaki Precision Machinery UK Ltd, Ernesettle Lane, Plymouth, PL5 2SA Tel: (01752) 364394 Fax: (01752) 364816 E-mail: sales@kpm-uk.co.uk

Modular Hydraulic Systems Ltd, 9 Redan Hill Estate, Redan Road, Aldershot, Hampshire, GU12 4SJ Tel: (01252) 333883 Fax: (01252) 343615 E-mail: sales@mhs.co.uk

Nord Hydraulic Ltd, Unit Lkr3 L & M Business Park, Norman Road, Altrincham, Cheshire, WA14 4ES Tel: 0161-928 1199 Fax: 0161-941 5667 E-mail: david@nordhydraulic.co.uk

Oil Control Ltd, Unit 7 Herald Business Park, Golden Acres Lane, Binley Industrial Estate, Coventry, CV3 2SY Tel: (024) 7663 5711 Fax: (024) 7663 5041 E-mail: sales@oilcontrol.co.uk

▶ Sterling Hydraulics Ltd, Sterling House, Blacknell Lane, Crewkerne, Somerset, TA18 8LL Tel: (01460) 271800 Fax: (01460) 271801 E-mail: mktng@sterling-hydraulics.co.uk

Subsea Components, 59 Clivemont Road, Maidenhead, Berkshire, SL6 7BZ Tel: (01628) 506560 Fax: (01628) 506501 E-mail: sales@subsea-components.co.uk

Turner Hydraulics, Old Station Yard, Magor, Caldicot, Gwent, NP26 3HT Tel: (01633) 881966 Fax: (01633) 881991 E-mail: ian@turnerhydraulics.co.uk

Versatile Controls Ltd, Unit R1 Innsworth Technology Park, Innsworth Lane, Gloucester, GL3 1DL Tel: (01452) 731447 Fax: (01452) 731621 E-mail: sales@versatilecontrols.co.uk

HYDRAULIC VANE PUMPS

▶ Hydraulic Alliance Ltd, 80 Allaston Road, Lydney, Gloucestershire, GL15 4EZ Tel: (01594) 843322 Fax: (01594) 843322 E-mail: sales@hydraulicalliance.com

White House Products Ltd, Kelburn Business Pk, Port Glasgow, Renfrewshire, PA14 6TD Tel: (01475) 742500 Fax: (01475) 742888 E-mail: info@whp.co.uk

HYDRAULIC WATER PUMPS

Alan Dale Pumps Ltd, 75 Clockhouse Lane, Ashford, Middlesex, TW15 2HA Tel: (01784) 421114 Fax: (01784) 421092 E-mail: info@alandalepumps.wanadoo.co.uk

HYDRAULIC WHEEL MOTORS

Rotary Power Ltd, St. Peters, Newcastle upon Tyne, NE6 1BS Tel: 0191-276 4444 Fax: 0191-276 4462 E-mail: rotary.power@bel.co.uk

HYDRAULIC WINCHES

Able Engineering, Dunslow Road, Eastfield, Scarborough, North Yorkshire, YO11 3UT Tel: (01723) 585639 Fax: (01723) 581605 E-mail: admin@nswinches.co.uk

Fisher Offshore, North Meadows, Oldmeldrum, Inverurie, Aberdeenshire, AB51 0GQ Tel: (01651) 873932 Fax: (01651) 873939 E-mail: info@fisheroffshore.com

Hardy Engineering, Unit D Foundry Lane, Burnham-on-Crouch, Essex, CM0 8SH Tel: (01621) 782726 Fax: (01621) 785645 E-mail: email@hardyengineering.com

North Sea Winches Ltd, Dunslow Road, Eastfield, Scarborough, North Yorkshire, YO11 3UT Tel: (01723) 584080 Fax: (01723) 581605 E-mail: sales@nswinches.co.uk

V H S Hydraulic Components, Unit 1, Block A, Waleswood Road, Wales Bar, Sheffield, S26 5PY Tel: (01909) 772666 Fax: (01909) 773226 E-mail: sales@hydraulic-components.net

HYDRAULICS AND PNEUMATICS

▶ Advantiv Ltd, 46-47 Centerprise House, New Greenham Park, Greenham, Newbury, Berkshire, RG19 6HP Tel: (01635) 817371 Fax: (01635) 817471 E-mail: sales@advantiv.co.uk

▶ AS Bearings and Drives Services, 5 Oadby Drive, Hasland, Chesterfield, Derbyshire, S41 0YF Tel: 07813 717741 Fax: 01246 224995 E-mail: alastair.stewart@astewart.fsnet.co.uk

Era Hydraulics & Pneumatics Ltd, Unit 5 Loaland Business Centre, Maritime Close Medway City, Estate Rochester, Rochester, Kent, ME2 4AZ Tel: (01634) 717499 Fax: (0845) 2412446 E-mail: erahydraulice@btconnect.com

Fencol Hydraulic Fittings Ltd, Unit 5 Europa Way, Britannia Enterprise Park, Lichfield, Staffordshire, WS14 9TZ Tel: (01543) 416343 Fax: (01543) 416343E-mail: nick@fencol.com

▶ Hydramatic Source & Supply Ltd, Unit 4 Oakes Green Court, Oakes Green, Sheffield, S9 3WR Tel: 0114-261 0667 Fax: 0114-261 9671 E-mail: chris@hsslimited.co.uk

Hydramatic Source & Supply Ltd, Unit 4 Oakes Green Court, Oakes Green, Sheffield, S9 3WR Tel: 0114-261 0667 Fax: 0114-261 9671 E-mail: sales@hsslimited.co.uk

Leach Lewis Ltd, Victoria House, Britannia Road, Waltham Cross, Hertfordshire, EN8 7NU Tel: (01992) 704100 Fax: (01992) 704170 E-mail: enquiries@leachlewis.co.uk

HYDRAULICS INSTALLATION OR SERVICING

A G Hydraulics Ltd, Unit 40 Plume Street Industrial Estate, Plume Street, Birmingham, B6 7RT Tel: 0121-326 6395 Fax: 0121-328 2923 E-mail: sales@aghydraulics.com

A5 Hydraulics Ltd, 46a Alliance Industrial Estate, Dodsworth Street, Darlington, County Durham, DL1 2NG Tel: (01325) 464354 Fax: (01325) 464356 E-mail: sales@a5hydraulics.co.uk

Aghabridge Ltd, Unit 1-4 Sheldon Business Centre, Maritime Close, Medway City Estate, Rochester, Kent, ME2 4AF Tel: (01634) 294944 Fax: (01634) 294577 E-mail: ahgabridge@aol.com

Airfluid Hydraulics & Pneumatics Ltd, Tong Road, Bishops Wood, Stafford, ST19 9AB Tel: (01952) 850246 Fax: (01952) 850246 E-mail: hydraulicbjr@aol.com

Approved Hydraulics Ltd, Brook Business Complex, Bennett Street, Manchester, M12 5AU Tel: 0161-273 1999 Fax: 0161-273 7979 E-mail: approvedhyd@aol.com

Armstrong Hydraulic Services (Hull) Ltd, Unit 8 Tom Thumb Industrial Estate, English Street, Hull, HU3 2BT Tel: (01482) 210680 Fax: (01482) 211947 E-mail: info@arma-hydraulic.co.uk

Armstrong Hydraulic Services Hull Ltd, 8 Tom Thumb Industrial Estate, English Street, Hull, HU3 2BT Tel: (01482) 210680 Fax: (01482) 211947 E-mail: info@arma-hydraulic.co.uk

Armstrong Lyon Hydraulics Ltd, 13 Faraday Road, Knowsley Industrial Park, Liverpool, L33 7UT Tel: 0151-545 2180 Fax: 0151-547 1309 E-mail: sales@armstronglyon.freeserve.co.uk

C C T Ltd, Park Road, Holmewood, Chesterfield, Derbyshire, S42 5UY Tel: (01246) 855995 Fax: (01246) 854028 E-mail: cctltd@breathemail.net

Cam Hydraulics, Unit 8 Hillfoot Industrial Estate, 17 Hoyland Road, Sheffield, S3 8AB Tel: 0114-231 4833 Fax: 0114-285 5810 E-mail: info@camhydraulics.co.uk

Central Engineering & Hydraulic Services Ltd, Brook Works, 174 Bromyard Road, St. Johns, Worcester, WR2 5EE Tel: (01905) 748569 Fax: (01905) 420700 E-mail: chs0999@aol.com

Challenger Hydraulics Ltd, Shaw Cross Business Pk, Owl La, Dewsbury, West Yorkshire, WF12 7RF Tel: (01924) 464433 Fax: (01924) 456292 E-mail: sales@challenger-group.co.uk

▶ Complete Hydraulic Services Ltd, Unit 46 Weaver Industrial Estate, Blackburne Street, Liverpool, L19 8JA Tel: 0151-494 3887 Fax: 0151-494 2388

Cullimore Hydraulic Engineering, C 14 Copt Elm Close, Charlton Kings, Cheltenham, Gloucestershire, GL53 8AD Tel: (01242) 241112 Fax: (01242) 241112

D & P Services, 2 Ceres Street, Liverpool, L20 8PZ Tel: 0151-922 2071 Fax: 0151-922 2425

Doreth Engineering Co. Ltd, 1514 Pershore Road, Stirchley, Birmingham, B30 2NW Tel: 0121-458 3178 Fax: 0121-458 3178

Dynamic Pump Services Ltd, Unit 11 Loomer Road Industrial Estate, Loomer Road, Newcastle, Staffordshire, ST5 7LB Tel: (01782) 566116 Fax: (01782) 566556 E-mail: sales@dynamicpumps.co.uk

G. Elliot Engineering Services Ltd, Bircotes, Doncaster, East Yorkshire, DN11 8WR Tel: (0844) 8002989 Fax: (01302) 745071 E-mail: sales@elliotteng.co.uk

Estuary Engineering Co Ltd, Hamlin Way, King's Lynn, Norfolk, PE30 4NG Tel: (01553) 773678 Fax: (01553) 769121 E-mail: tony@estuary.demon.co.uk

Forest Press Hydraulics Ltd, 6 Hollywood Works, Valley Road, Cinderford, Gloucestershire, GL14 2PD Tel: (01594) 826009 Fax: (01594) 822377 E-mail: sales@forestpresshyd.com

Fraser Hydraulic Power, Unit BT 96/4 Fisher Industrial Estate, Fisher St, Walker, Newcastle upon Tyne, NE6 4LT Tel: 0191-263 7272 Fax: 0191-263 4016 E-mail: joanner@fhpltd.co.uk

G C E Fluid Power Ltd, Unit 17 Atlas Estate, Brookvale Road, Witton, Birmingham, B6 7EX Tel: 0121-356 5727 Fax: 0121-344 3629 E-mail: gcefluidpower@btinternet.com

G E Plant Services Ltd, 10a Dawkins Road, Poole, Dorset, BH15 4JD Tel: (01202) 676463 Fax: (01202) 665725 E-mail: geplant@btinternet.com

General Hydraulics, Banbury Road, Thrupp, Kidlington, Oxfordshire, OX5 1JF Tel: (01865) 377559

Gildon Components, 5 Trafalgar Court, Widnes, Cheshire, WA8 0SZ Tel: 0151-420 2499 Fax: 0151-420 2499

GS Hydro Ltd, Unit C Endeavour Court, Hall Dene Way, Seaham Grange Industrial Estat, Seaham, County Durham, SR7 0HB Tel: 0191-523 9643 Fax: 0191-521 8001 E-mail: sales@gshydro.com

Hall Seals & Components, Oak Avenue, Hindley, Wigan, Lancashire, WN2 4LZ Tel: (01942) 522140 Fax: (01942) 522141

HCS Control Systems Ltd, Unit V2, Viewfield Industrial Estate, Glenrothes, Fife, KY6 2RG Tel: (01592) 770786 Fax: (01592) 775737 E-mail: sales@hcscsl.com

Hiflex Fluid Power, Units 8-9 Sun Valley Business Park, Winnall Close, Winchester, Hampshire, SO23 0LB Tel: (01962) 860311 Fax: (01962) 860673 E-mail: winchester@dunlophiflex.com

Hydraflow Systems, Strathfield House, Smithymoor, Stretton, Alfreton, Derbyshire, DE55 6FE Tel: 01246 250958 Fax: 05600 492268E-mail: sales@hydraflowsystems.co.uk

Hydrastore Ltd, Sandtoft Industrial Estate, Belton, Doncaster, South Yorkshire, DN9 1PN Tel: (01427) 874445 Fax: (01427) 874436 E-mail: sales@hydrastore.co.uk

Hydraulic Crane Services, Uplands Farm, Highstreet Road, Hernhill, Faversham, Kent, ME13 9EJ Tel: (01227) 751588 Fax: (01227) 751458 E-mail: hydecraneserv@aol.com

Hydraulic Engineering Services, 5 Station Yard, Swaffham, Norfolk, PE37 7JE Tel: (01760) 722296 Fax: (01760) 722296

Hydraulic & Pneumatic Cylinders Ltd, 4 Birmingham New Enterprise Workshops, All Saints Road, Birmingham, B18 7RL Tel: 0121-523 8400 Fax: 0121-523 8400 E-mail: sales@hydraulic-pneumatic-cylinders.co.uk

Hydraulic & Pneumatic Supplies Ltd, Unit 39, Second Drove Industrial Estate, Fengate, Peterborough, PE1 5XA Tel: (01733) 894500 Fax: (01733) 894892 E-mail: sales@hps-ltd.co.uk

▶ Hydraulic Power Services Ltd, 84 Bridgeman Street, Bolton, BL3 6AT Tel: (01204) 363660 Fax: (01204) 363670 E-mail: info@hydraulicpower.co.uk

Hydraulic Technical Services Ltd, 10-12 Galleymead Road, Colnbrook, Slough, SL3 0EN Tel: (01753) 689689 Fax: (01753) 689700 E-mail: info@hydraulictechnical.co.uk

Industrial & Marine Hydraulics Ltd, 2 Snowdon Rd, Middlesbrough, Cleveland, TS2 1LP Tel: (01642) 802700 Fax: (01642) 802701 E-mail: info@imh-uk.com

Ipswich Hydraulics Ltd, 37 Boss Hall Road, Ipswich, IP1 5BN Tel: (01473) 241271 Fax: (01473) 241293 E-mail: sales@ipswich-hydraulics.co.uk

J T Sawyer, 9 Pennine Industrial Estate, Modder Place, Armley, Leeds, LS12 3ES Tel: 0113-231 1255 Fax: 0113-231 1238

K B Pearson Servicing, 100 Ashkirk, Dudley, Cramlington, Northumberland, NE23 7DG Tel: 0191-250 0623 Fax: 0191-250 0623

Lamberton Ltd, Block G, West Way, Porterfield Road, Renfrew, PA4 8DJ Tel: 0141-889 1660 Fax: 0141-887 4829

Lenwade Hydraulic Service, 6 Emmerson Industrial Estate, Norwich Road, Lenwade, Norwich, NR9 5SA Tel: (01603) 872403 Fax: (01603) 872372 E-mail: lenhydser@aol.com

Link Hydraulic Services Ltd, 38 Sherwood Road, Bromsgrove, Worcestershire, B60 3DR Tel: (01527) 579145 Fax: (01527) 576555 E-mail: link.hydraulics@btconnect.com

M & P Hydraulic Ltd, Unit 3c Bergen Way, Hull, HU7 0YQ Tel: (01482) 820701 Fax: (01482) 823101

M & R Hydraulics Ltd, Unit 13, Thornton Industrial Estate, Ellesmere Port, CH65 5EU Tel: 0151 3571901

MacGREGOR (GBR) Ltd, Grampian House, 59 Palmerston Road, Aberdeen, AB11 5QJ Tel: (01224) 583300 Fax: (01224) 583450 E-mail: sales@macgregor-group.com

HYDRAULICS INSTALLATION OR SERVICING – *continued*

Mcnair Engineering Ltd, 11-12 Lovat Place, Glasgow, G52 4XE Tel: 0141-883 0496 Fax: 0141-882 7823 E-mail: enquiries@mcnair-engineering.co.uk
Mactaggart Scott (Holdings) Ltd, PO Box 1, Loanhead, Midlothian, EH20 9SP Tel: 0131-440 0311 Fax: 0131-440 4493
Maselec Ltd, Unit A2 The Courtyard, Lonesome Lane, Reigate, Surrey, RH2 7QT Tel: (01737) 225335 Fax: (01737) 225559 E-mail: sales@maselec.co.uk
Midland Hydraulic Services, Unit 4 Ariane, Tamworth, Staffordshire, B79 7XF Tel: (01827) 59012 Fax: (01827) 60615
Mill Lane Engineering, 24 Mill Lane, Briston, Melton Constable, Norfolk, NR24 2JG Tel: (01263) 860711 Fax: (01263) 860711
▶ Moidart Engineering, Mingarry, Acharacle, Argyll, PH36 4JX Tel: (07880) 706439 Fax: (01967) 431515 E-mail: jaz.maclellan@tiscali.co.uk
Mulco Engineering Ltd, 9-10 St Machar Road, Aberdeen, AB24 2UU Tel: (01224) 481215 Fax: (01224) 486041 E-mail: info@mulco.co.uk
Northern Jacks & Equipment Ltd, 4 Beverley Business Centre, St Nicholas Road, Beverley, North Humberside, HU17 0QT Tel: (01482) 882590 Fax: (01482) 867309 E-mail: info@scopeuk.fsnet.co.uk
Northfield Engineering, 41 Hedon Road, Hull, HU9 1LH Tel: (01482) 320888 Fax: (01482) 587271 E-mail: sales@northfieldeng.co.uk
O S L Group Ltd, Imperial Works, Sheffield Road, Tinsley, Sheffield, S9 2YL Tel: 0114-221 2500 Fax: 0114-221 2560 E-mail: sales@oslgroup.com
Olive & Padgett Ltd, Station Lane, Heckmondwike, West Yorkshire, WF16 0NF Tel: (01924) 405661
Ovalway Hydraulics, 11 Cannon Park Way, Middlesbrough, Cleveland, TS1 5JU Tel: (01642) 247106 Fax: (01642) 241874 E-mail: ohe@ovalway.co.uk
P C Hydraulics (Northern) Ltd, 6-8 Hillkirk Street, Beswick, Manchester, M11 3EZ Tel: 0161-273 1660 Fax: 0161-273 5002 E-mail: enquiries@pc-hydraulics.co.uk
Phoenix Hose & Couplings Ltd, Unit 1 Kencot Close, Waldrist Way, Yarnton Way, Thamesmead, Erith, Kent, DA18 4AB Tel: (020) 8311 7204 Fax: (020) 8310 0406 E-mail: phoenix999@btclick.com
Pirtek, St. Andrews Road, Avonmouth, Bristol, BS11 9HQ Tel: 0117-982 0056 Fax: 0117-982 4361 E-mail: info@pirtekbristol.co.uk
Pirtek, 10 Tuffley Trading Estate, Pearce Way, Gloucester, GL2 5YD Tel: (01452) 308010 Fax: (01452) 307447 E-mail: gloucester@pirtekcentre.co.uk
Rapp Ecosse UK Ltd, Station Brae, Ellon, Aberdeenshire, AB41 9DY Tel: (01358) 720717 Fax: (01358) 720173 E-mail: info@rappecosse.co.uk
▶ Spire Hydraulics Ltd, Brimington Road North, Chesterfield, Derbyshire, S41 9BE Tel: (01246) 208400 Fax: (01246) 559428
Strathclyde Hydraulics Ltd, 3 Bonnyton Industrial Estate, Munro Place, Kilmarnock, Ayrshire, KA1 2NP Tel: (01563) 543349 Fax: (01563) 533226
Sutton Hydraulics, Unit 4a Alton Road Industrial Estate, Ross-on-Wye, Herefordshire, HR9 5NB Tel: (01989) 768545 Fax: (01989) 762202
Target Fluid Services, Millhouse Centre, 118 Commercial Road, Totton, Southampton, SO40 3ZW Tel: (023) 8087 2142 Fax: (023) 8066 6882 E-mail: target.fluid@btinternet.com
Taylor Hydraulics & Mechanical Services, 36 Long Ridge, Brighouse, West Yorkshire, HD6 3RZ Tel: (01484) 717552 Fax: (01484) 717552
Thompson & Son (Millwall) Ltd, Cuba Street, Isle of Dogs, London, E14 8LF Tel: (020) 7987 1844 Fax: (020) 7987 4416
Trax Hydraulics North West Ltd, Unit 3, Langley Road, Burscough Industrial Estate, Burscough, Ormskirk, Lancashire, L40 8JR Tel: (01704) 892411 Fax: (01704) 896593
D. Waterhouse & Co., Lambert Works, Luton St, Keighley, W. Yorkshire, BD21 2LE Tel: (01535) 642539 Fax: (01535) 642539
WB Hydraulic Services, 45 Boston Road, Leicester, LE4 1AW Tel: 0116-235 2606 E-mail: bill@wbhydserv.freeserve.co.uk
Webb Hydraulic Equipment, Acton Place Industrial Estate, Acton, Sudbury, Suffolk, CO10 0BB Tel: (01787) 312563 Fax: (01787) 880618 E-mail: info@extrareach.co.uk
West Mercia Hydraulics, 9 Horton Court, Hortonwood 50, Telford, Shropshire, TF1 7GY Tel: (01952) 606696 Fax: (01952) 670333 E-mail: wm.telford@wyko.co.uk
Yardbury Kinetics Ltd, Castle Way, Castlepark Industrial Estate, Ellon, Aberdeenshire, AB41 9RG Tel: (01358) 722255 Fax: (01358) 725205 E-mail: a.huntley@yardburykinetics.com
Yeadon Hydraulics Ltd, Sizers Court, Off Henshaw Lane, Yeadon, Leeds, LS19 7DP Tel: 0113-250 3296 Fax: 0113-250 5624 E-mail: johnhall@dynamicshydraulics.com

HYDRODYNAMIC BEARINGS

K C Engineering Ltd, Hownsgill Drive, Consett, County Durham, DH8 9HU Tel: (01207) 583100 Fax: (01207) 581900 E-mail: sales@kceng.com

HYDROELECTRIC SYSTEMS

G E Energy UK Ltd, Kvaerner House, Ten Pound Walk, Doncaster, South Yorkshire, DN4 5HW Tel: (01302) 761761 Fax: (01302) 760230
G P Electronics, Pottery Road, Bovey Tracey, Newton Abbot, Devon, TQ13 9DS Tel: (01626) 832670 Fax: (01626) 832670

HYDROGEN GENERATORS

Wellman Defence, Airport Service Road, Portsmouth, PO3 5PG Tel: (023) 9266 4911 Fax: (023) 9269 7864 E-mail: enquiries@wellmandefence.co.uk

HYDROGEN PURIFICATION EQUIPMENT

Wellman Defence, Airport Service Road, Portsmouth, PO3 5PG Tel: (023) 9266 4911 Fax: (023) 9269 7864 E-mail: enquiries@wellmandefence.co.uk

HYDROGRAPHIC INSTRUMENTS

Valeport Ltd, St. Peters Quay, Totnes, Devon, TQ9 5EW Tel: (01803) 869292 Fax: (01803) 869293 E-mail: sales@valeport.co.uk

HYDROGRAPHIC POSITION FIXING SYSTEMS

▶ Del Norte Technology Ltd, Unit 20 Hunts Rise, South Marston Industrial Estat, Swindon, SN3 4TG Tel: (01793) 827982 Fax: (01793) 827984 E-mail: lsmith@del-norte.co.uk
Sam Electronics UK Ltd, 18 Dales Industrial Estate, Peterhead, Aberdeenshire, AB42 3JF Tel: (01779) 478233 Fax: (01779) 475060

HYDROGRAPHIC SURVEYORS

Andrews Survey, Salmon Road, Great Yarmouth, Norfolk, NR30 3QS Tel: (01493) 332111 Fax: (01493) 332265
▶ G O S S Consultants Ltd, Square Sail House, Charlestown Road, St. Austell, Cornwall, PL25 3NJ Tel: (01726) 71128 Fax: (01726) 71129 E-mail: info@goss-ltd.co.uk
G S E Rentals Ltd, Unit 32, Wellheads Industrial Estate, Aberdeen, AB21 7GA Tel: (01224) 771247 Fax: (01224) 723116 E-mail: info@gserentals.co.uk
Gardline Shipping Ltd, Admiralty Road, Great Yarmouth, Norfolk, NR30 3NG Tel: (01493) 850723 Fax: (01493) 852106 E-mail: sys@gardline.co.uk
▶ Landscope Engineering Ltd, Wrentnall Stables, Wrentnall Farm, Pulverbatch, Shrewsbury, SY5 8ED Tel: (01743) 719204 Fax: (01743) 719215 E-mail: enquiries@land-scope.com
M K Services Ltd, Unit 24 Pages Industrial Park, Eden Way, Leighton Buzzard, Bedfordshire, LU7 4TZ Tel: (01525) 382333 Fax: (01525) 850073 E-mail: sales@mkservices.co.uk
▶ Mag Surveys, Europa Business Park, 46 Bird Hall Lane Unit F-10, Stockport, Cheshire, SK3 0XA Tel: 0161-718 8213 Fax: 0161-718 8213 E-mail: greg@magsurveys.co.uk
Ocean Fix International Ltd, Waterton Grange, Stoneywood, Bucksburn, Aberdeen, AB21 9HX Tel: (01224) 714100 Fax: (01224) 714170 E-mail: pps@oceanfix-international.co.uk
Port of London Authority, Barkers Hall, 7 Harp Lane, London, EC3R 6LB Tel: (020) 7743 7900 Fax: (020) 7743 7998 E-mail: marketing@portoflondon.co.uk
RPS Energy Ltd, Goldsworth House, Denton Way, Woking, Surrey, GU21 3LG Tel: (01483) 746500 Fax: (01483) 746505 E-mail: info@rpsgroup.com
South West Surveys Projects Ltd, 43 Lower Fore Street, Saltash, Cornwall, PL12 6JQ Tel: (01752) 849190 Fax: (01752) 849229 E-mail: office@swsurveys.co.uk
Survey Systems Ltd, Willow Bank House, Old Road, Handforth, Wilmslow, Cheshire, SK9 3AZ Tel: (01625) 533444 Fax: (01625) 526815 E-mail: sales@survsys.co.uk

HYDROLOGICAL INSTRUMENTS

Planned Access Maintenance, 11 Hague Park Coppice, South Kirkby, Pontefract, West Yorkshire, WF9 3SU Tel: (01977) 649719 Fax: (01977) 649719 E-mail: plannedam@aol.com
Valeport Ltd, St. Peters Quay, Totnes, Devon, TQ9 5EW Tel: (01803) 869292 Fax: (01803) 869293 E-mail: sales@valeport.co.uk

HYDROMETER MANUFRS

S Brannan & Sons Ltd, Leconfield Industrial Estate, Cleator Moor, Cumbria, CA25 5QE Tel: (01946) 816624 Fax: (01946) 816625 E-mail: sales@brannan.co.uk

Stevenson Reeves Ltd, 40 Oxgangs Bank, Edinburgh, EH13 9LH Tel: 0131-445 7151 Fax: 0131-445 7323 E-mail: sales@stevenson-reeves.co.uk

HYDROPONIC FAN SPEED CONTROLLERS

▶ UK Hydroponic Suppliers Association, The Tower, Daltongate Business Centre, Daltongate, Ulverston, Cumbria, LA12 7AJ Tel: (07785) 788020

HYDROPONIC SYSTEM POLYETHYLENE TEREPHTHALATE (PET) FILM

▶ UK Hydroponic Suppliers Association, The Tower, Daltongate Business Centre, Daltongate, Ulverston, Cumbria, LA12 7AJ Tel: (07785) 788020

HYDROPONIC SYSTEMS

The Online Electrical Wholesaler Com Ltd, 36 Imex Business Centre, Balme Road, Cleckheaton, West Yorkshire, BD19 4EZ Tel: (01274) 865985 Fax: (01274) 865963 E-mail: onlineelec@tiscali.co.uk

HYDROPONIC SYSTEMS DESIGN/INSTALLATION SERVICES

▶ UK Hydroponic Suppliers Association, The Tower, Daltongate Business Centre, Daltongate, Ulverston, Cumbria, LA12 7AJ Tel: (07785) 788020

HYDROSTATIC TEST EQUIPMENT

Birchley Products, 7 Bush Hay, Church Down, Gloucester, GL3 2QR Tel: (01452) 855312 Fax: (01452) 859245 E-mail: ab@birchleyproducts.co.uk

HYGIENE CHEMICALS

C M R Chemical Services Ltd, Moorhey Street, Oldham, OL4 1JE Tel: 0161-626 4143 Fax: 0161-628 5081
Chem Products Ltd, 5 Poplar Place, Hayes, Middlesex, UB3 2DS Tel: (020) 8797 0567 Fax: (020) 8797 0567 E-mail: chemproducts@myisp.co.uk
Firkser Chemicals Ltd, 24 Willow Court, Abbey Road, Macclesfield, Cheshire, SK10 3PD Tel: (01625) 612900 Fax: (01625) 503763

HYGIENE SUPPORT SERVICES

Galgorm Group, 7 Corbally Road, Galgorm, Ballymena, County Antrim, BT42 1JQ Tel: (028) 2564 8521 Fax: (028) 2564 7614

HYGIENIC COATING PAINTS

▶ Nemacom Computer Mnfrs, 6 Morgans Business Park, Bettys Lane, Norton Canes, Cannock, Staffordshire, WS11 9UU Tel: (01543) 495020 Fax: (01543) 495021 E-mail: sales@nemacom.co.uk
Stewart Wales Somerville Ltd, 28 Glenburn Road, East Kilbride, Glasgow, G74 5BA Tel: (01355) 222101 Fax: (01355) 233847 E-mail: sales@sws-ltd.com

HYGIENIC HOSES

Hose Tech Ltd, 3 Wheatlea Industrial Estate, Wheatlea Road, Wigan, Lancashire, WN3 6XP Tel: (01942) 233036 Fax: (01942) 322915 E-mail: sales@hose-tech.co.uk
▶ Teleflex Fluids Systems Europe, Euroflex Centre, Foxbridge Way, Normanton Industrial Estate, Normanton, West Yorkshire, WF6 1TN Tel: (01924) 898188 Fax: (01924) 898008 E-mail: enquiry@teleflex.com

HYGIENIC PRODUCT DISPENSERS

Appor Ltd, Duffield Road Industrial Estate, Little Eaton, Derby, DE21 5EG Tel: (01332) 832455 Fax: (01332) 834427 E-mail: info@appor.com
Dudley Industries, Preston Road, Lytham St. Annes, Lancashire, FY8 5AT Tel: (01253) 738311 Fax: (01253) 794393 E-mail: dudley@cyberscape.net

HYGIENIC PUMPS

Alfa Laval Ltd, Castle Vale Industrial Estate, Maybrook Road, Minworth, Sutton Coldfield, West Midlands, B76 1AL Tel: 0121-351 3131 Fax: 0121-351 7888 E-mail: admin@alfalaval.com
Euro Industrial Engineering, 161 Fog Lane, Manchester, M20 6FJ Tel: 0161-438 0438 Fax: 0161-438 2538 E-mail: info@eieuk.com
Hydrair Ltd, Berry Hill, Berry Hill Industrial Estate, Droitwich, Worcestershire, WR9 9AB Tel: (01905) 772302 Fax: (01905) 770309 E-mail: name@hydrair.demom.co.uk

HYGIENIC VALVES

Alfa Laval Ltd, Castle Vale Industrial Estate, Maybrook Road, Minworth, Sutton Coldfield, West Midlands, B76 1AL Tel: 0121-351 3131 Fax: 0121-351 7888 E-mail: admin@alfalaval.com
Clifton Enterprises Ltd, Clifton House, 32 Cavendish Road, Sheffield, S11 9BH Tel: 0114-258 7229 Fax: 0114-250 0239 E-mail: vanasyl@aol.com
Defontaine Ltd, Hinnegar Lodge, Didmarton, Badminton, Avon, GL9 1DN Tel: (01454) 238831 E-mail: janice@ukdefontaine.com
Ebtrade Ltd, Albion Dockside Works, Bristol, BS1 6UT Tel: 0117-927 9204 Fax: 0117-929 8193 E-mail: enquiries@seetru.com
Inoxta-Realm Ltd, 29-35 Gladstone Road, Croydon, CR0 2BQ Tel: (020) 8689 5521 Fax: (020) 8689 0245 E-mail: inoxta@realm.co.uk

HYGIENIC WALLING OR DOORS

Campbell-lee Contracts, 84 Greasby Road, Greasby, Wirral, Merseyside, CH49 3NG Tel: 0151-606 8779 Fax: 0151-678 1640 E-mail: sales@campbelllee.co.uk
M.G. Duff International Ltd, Unit 1 Timberlane Industrial Estate, Gravel Lane, Chichester, West Sussex, PO19 8PP Tel: (01243) 533336 Fax: (01243) 533422 E-mail: sales@mgduff.co.uk

HYGROMETERS

Amber Instruments Ltd, Dunston House Sheepbridge Works, Dunston Road, Chesterfield, Derbyshire, S41 9QD Tel: (01246) 260250 Fax: (01246) 260955 E-mail: sales@amberinstruments.com
Protimeter plc, Meter House, Fieldhouse Lane, Marlow, Buckinghamshire, SL7 1LW Tel: (01628) 472722 Fax: (01628) 474312 E-mail: sales@protometer.com
Shaw Moisture Meters (UK) Ltd, Rawson Road, Westgate, Bradford, West Yorkshire, BD1 3SQ Tel: (01274) 733582 Fax: (01274) 370151 E-mail: mail@shawmeters.com

HYPODERMIC NEEDLES

Coopers Needleworks Ltd, 261-265 Aston Lane, Handsworth, Birmingham, B20 3HS Tel: 0121-356 4719 Fax: 0121-356 3050 E-mail: sales@coopernw.com
Sterimatic Ltd, Griffin Mill, London Road, Stroud, Gloucestershire, GL5 2AZ Tel: (01453) 884944 Fax: (01453) 886481 E-mail: sterimatic@sterimatic.com

HYPODERMIC SYRINGES

Kaycee Veterinary Products, Unit 14 Lindfield Enterprise Park, Lewes Road, Lindfield, Haywards Heath, West Sussex, RH16 2LH Tel: (01444) 482888 Fax: (01444) 483383 E-mail: tds@kaycee.co.uk
Sterimatic Ltd, Griffin Mill, London Road, Stroud, Gloucestershire, GL5 2AZ Tel: (01453) 884944 Fax: (01453) 886481 E-mail: sterimatic@sterimatic.com

ICE

▶ The Ice Co (Polarcube) Ltd, Jessop Way, Northern Road Industrial Estate, Newark, Nottinghamshire, NG24 2ER Tel: (01636) 704232 Fax: (01636) 611943 E-mail: ice@iceco.co.uk

ICE CONSERVATORS

Granite City Ice Ltd, Unit 3A, Albert Quay, Aberdeen, AB11 5PX Tel: (01224) 581888 Fax: (01224) 582666
Ice Sculptures Ltd, 33 St. James Road, Little Paxton, St. Neots, Cambridgeshire, PE19 6QW Tel: (01480) 213245 Fax: (01480) 476928

▶ indicates data change since last edition

ICE CREAM

A E Dennett & Son Ltd, 28 Boston Road, Spilsby, Lincolnshire, PE23 5HG Tel: (01790) 752573 Fax: (01790) 752598 E-mail: dennetts@mod-comp.co.uk
Criterion Ices, The Manor Farm Creamery, Bird Green, Thurston, Bury St. Edmunds, Suffolk, IP31 3QJ Tel: 01359 230208 Fax: 01359 232838 E-mail: enquiries@criterion-ices.co.uk
Crolla Ice Cream Co. Ltd, 48 Jessie Street, Glasgow, G42 0PG Tel: 0141-423 1161 Fax: 0141-423 2596 E-mail: sales@crollaicecream.co.uk
Dairyland Ices (East Anglia) Ltd, Little Plumstead, Norwich, NR13 5BY Tel: (01603) 720317
▶ Easons Ice Cream, Freckleton Road, Kirkham, Preston, PR4 3RB Tel: (01772) 684446 Fax: (01772) 683535
Hunts Frozen Foods Bristol Ltd, Unit 3 Pucklechurch Trading Estate, Pucklechurch, Bristol, BS16 9QH Tel: 0117-937 2341 Fax: 0117-937 4160 E-mail: sales@hunts-food-service.co.uk
▶ Just Rachel, The Old Dairy, Churches Farm, Bromsberrow, Ledbury, Herefordshire, HR8 1SA Tel: (01531) 650639 Fax: (01531) 650639 E-mail: info@justrachel.com
Kendall's Ices, Denholme Gate Road, Hipperholme, Halifax, West Yorkshire, HX3 8JQ Tel: (01422) 202246 Fax: (01422) 202246
Kingstonian Quality Ice Cream Co., 2 Glenville Road, Kingston upon Thames, Surrey, KT2 6DD Tel: (020) 8541 0585 Fax: (020) 8541 0585 E-mail: mail@kingstonianicecream.com
Leo's Ice Cream, 1 Thomas Street, Wolverhampton, WV2 4JS Tel: (01902) 424363 Fax: (01902) 712436
▶ Maypole Frozen Foods Ltd, Sandleas Way, Crossgates, Leeds, LS15 8AW Tel: 0113-260 4455 Fax: 0113-260 4455 E-mail: sales@maypolefrozenfoods.com
▶ Mediterranean Ices, 1a Riverside Road, London, SW17 0BA Tel: (020) 8879 6122 Fax: (020) 8879 6122
▶ Merit Ice Cream Ltd, Postford Mill, Mill Lane, Chilworth, Guildford, Surrey, GU4 8RT Tel: (01483) 209700 Fax: (01483) 209777
▶ Paolo's Ice Creams, Walls Ice Cream Depot, Unit 6A Cemetery Road Industrial Estate, Dawley Bank, Telford, Shropshire, TF4 2BS Tel: (01952) 505855 Fax: (01952) 505855
Penny Corporations Ltd, Unit 15, Brookvale Trading Estate, Moor Lane, Witton, Birmingham, B6 7AE Tel: 0121-356 5523 Fax: 0121-356 3511 E-mail: info@euro-icecream.co.uk
Rossi Southend On Sea Ltd, 31 Lucy Road, Southend-on-Sea, SS1 2AU Tel: (01702) 467532 Fax: (01702) 391432
▶ Solley's Farms Ltd, The Dairy, Ripple, Deal, Kent, CT14 8JL Tel: (01304) 374100 Fax: (01304) 379611 E-mail: sc.solley@solleysicecream.co.uk
▶ Tarrs Icecream Ltd, 2 Sandown Road, Brislington, Bristol, BS4 3PN Tel: 0117-977 7290 Fax: 0117-977 7290
Unilever UK Walls's Ltd, Station Avenue, Walton-On-Thames, Surrey, KT12 1NT Tel: (01932) 263000 Fax: (01932) 263152

ICE CREAM CONES

▶ Maypole Frozen Foods Ltd, Sandleas Way, Crossgates, Leeds, LS15 8AW Tel: 0113-260 4455 Fax: 0113-260 4455 E-mail: sales@maypolefrozenfoods.com

ICE CREAM CONTAINERS/ PACKAGING

A R Wilson Packaging, 151 Nottingham Road, Nottingham, NG6 0FU Tel: 0115-978 1047 Fax: 0115-942 2302 E-mail: arwilson@proweb.co.uk
Catering Equipment Ltd, Unit 7, Speedwell Trading Estate, 106 Kings Road, Tyseley, Birmingham, B11 2AT Tel: 0121-773 2228 Fax: 0121-772 4731 E-mail: sales@celonline.co.uk

ICE CREAM HOLDOVER CONSERVATORS

Geist Manufacturing Co. Ltd, Askern Industrial Estate, Moss Road, Askern, Doncaster, South Yorkshire, DN6 0DD Tel: (0845) 4941681 Fax: (01302) 709988 E-mail: geistmanltd@aol.com

ICE CREAM MIXES, LIQUID/ POWDER

Pritchitt Foods Ltd, Kingfisher House, 21-23 Elmfield Road, Bromley, BR1 1LT Tel: (020) 8290 7020 Fax: (020) 8290 7030 E-mail: sales@pritchitts.com
▶ R. Rossa & Son Ltd, 53 Stonebridge Street, Leicester, LE5 3PB Tel: 0116-276 7778 Fax: 0116-276 1424

ICE CREAM PRODUCTION EQUIPMENT

Alasdair W Woods Ltd, Largs, Ayrshire, KA30 8WA Tel: (01475) 673300 Fax: (01475) 673355
Carpigiani U.K. Ltd, Faculty House, 214 Holme Lacy Road, Hereford, HR2 6BQ Tel: (01432) 346010 Fax: (01432) 346019
Edoni Refrigeration Ltd, 100 Strathmore Road, Glasgow, G22 7TS Tel: 0141-336 7641 Fax: 0141-336 5302
Gram (UK) Ltd, 2 The Technology Centre, London Road, Swanley, Kent, BR8 7AG Tel: (01322) 616900 Fax: (01322) 616901 E-mail: info@gramuk.co.uk
I C Gears, 50 Bracken Road, Ferndown, Dorset, BH22 9PF Tel: (01202) 891324 E-mail: sales@icgears.co.uk
Servequip Ltd, 214 Purley Way, Croydon, CR0 4XG Tel: (020) 8686 8855 Fax: (020) 8681 7509 E-mail: info@servequip.co.uk

ICE CUBES

Blue Keld Springs Ltd, Fossil Nest Cranswick, Cranswick, Driffield, North Humberside, YO25 9RE Tel: (01377) 275302 Fax: (01377) 271360 E-mail: sales@bluekeld.co.uk

ICE DETECTION EQUIPMENT, ROAD SURFACE/RUNWAY

Findlay Irvine Ltd, 42-44 Bog Road, Penicuik, Midlothian, EH26 9BU Tel: (01968) 671200 Fax: (01968) 671237 E-mail: sales@findlayirvine.com

ICE TEA MAKERS

▶ American Drinks Ltd, Maple House, High Street, Potters Bar, Hertfordshire, EN6 5BS Tel: (0870) 3511718 Fax: (0870) 3511719 E-mail: info@arizona.uk.com

IDENTIFICATION RING OR TAG, ANIMAL/BIRD

Avid Ltd, Holroyd Suite, Oak Hall, Sheffield Park, Uckfield, East Sussex, TN22 3QY Tel: (01825) 791069 Fax: (01825) 791006
Dalton ID Systems Ltd, Dalton House, Newtown Road, Henley-on-Thames, Oxfordshire, RG9 1HG Tel: (0800) 838882 Fax: (0800) 7311957 E-mail: sales@dalton.co.uk
Denimex, Northdown Business Park, Ashford Road, Lenham, Maidstone, Kent, ME17 2DL Tel: (01622) 850057 Fax: (01622) 850097 E-mail: sales@denimex.co.uk
▶ Globalbagtag.Com, Everon Centre, 58 John Street, Filey, North Yorkshire, YO14 9NT Tel: (0870) 7657280 Fax: (0870) 7657281 E-mail: sales@globalbagtag.com
A.C. Hughes Ltd, 1 High Street, Hampton Hill, Hampton, Middlesex, TW12 1NA Tel: (020) 8979 1366
Press Metal Products Ltd, 5 Abberley Industrial Centre, Abberley Street, Smethwick, West Midlands, B66 2QL Tel: 0121-555 6061 Fax: 0121-555 6058 E-mail: sales@pressed-metal.com
Raytheon Systems Ltd, Fullerton Road, Queensway Industrial Estate, Glenrothes, Fife, KY7 5PY Tel: (01592) 754311 Fax: (01592) 759775 E-mail: carol.fleming@raytheon.co.uk

IDENTIFICATION TAGS

▶ GB Nametapes, 53 Honeyborough Industrial Estate, Neyland, Milford Haven, Dyfed, SA73 1SE Tel: (01646) 600664 Fax: (01646) 600664 E-mail: enqiury@gbnametapes.co.uk

IDENTITY (ID) BADGES

Cardex Facilities, Essex Technology & Innovation Centre, The Gables, Ongar, Essex, CM5 0GA Tel: (01277) 364455 Fax: (01277) 366330 E-mail: lillian.hill@cardex.co.uk
DED Ltd, Mill Road, Lydd, Romney Marsh, Kent, TN29 9EJ Tel: (01797) 320636 Fax: (01797) 320273 E-mail: sales@ded.co.uk
Hunter Nicholas Ltd, Unit 17 Chiltern Business Centre, Garsington Road, Oxford, OX4 6NG Tel: (01865) 777365 Fax: (01865) 773856 E-mail: office@nicholashunter.com

IDENTITY (ID) CARD DESIGN

▶ PCS Printing, PO Box 317, Cheltenham, Gloucestershire, GL51 9SN Tel: (0845) 0569463 E-mail: sales@pcsprinting.co.uk

IDENTITY (ID) CARD PRINTING

▶ PCS Printing, PO Box 317, Cheltenham, Gloucestershire, GL51 9SN Tel: (0845) 0569463 E-mail: sales@pcsprinting.co.uk

IDENTITY (ID) CARD SYSTEMS

Datum Automation Ltd, 18 Aston Road, Waterlooville, Hampshire, PO7 7XG Tel: (023) 9224 1154 Fax: (023) 9224 1156 E-mail: sales@datum-automation.com
Identifile Systems Ltd, Unit 2 Bridge Gate Centre, Martinfield, Welwyn Garden City, Hertfordshire, AL7 1JG Tel: (01707) 395396 Fax: (01707) 394083 E-mail: sales@identifile.co.uk
Identilam plc, Faygate Business Centre, Faygate Lane, Faygate, Horsham, West Sussex, RH12 4DN Tel: (01293) 851711 Fax: (01293) 851742 E-mail: sales@indentilam.co.uk
NBS Technologies Ltd, 7 Byfleet Technical Centre, Canada Road, West Byfleet, Surrey, KT14 7NB Tel: (01932) 351531 Fax: (01932) 351382 E-mail: sales@nbs.com
Novacroft Ltd, Harvest Barn Spring Hill, Harborough Road, Pitsford, Northampton, NN6 9AA Tel: (01604) 889500 Fax: (01604) 889508 E-mail: clivenotley@novacroft.com
Plastic Card Design Services Ltd, 15 Bramshill Ave, Kettering, Northamptonshire, NN16 9FL Tel: (01536) 410557 Fax: (01536) 510509 E-mail: info@plasticcardsuk.com
Plastic Card Imaging Ltd, 2 Rose Villa, Bressingham Road, Roydon, Diss, Norfolk, IP22 5XW Tel: (01379) 688344

IDENTITY (ID) CARDS

I D & C Ltd, 15 Colebrook Industrial Estate, Longfield Road, Tunbridge Wells, Kent, TN2 3DG Tel: (01892) 548364 Fax: (01892) 519048 E-mail: sales@idcband.co.uk
I D Management Systems, Temple Court, Cathedral Road, Cardiff, CF11 9HA Tel: (0870) 7413000 Fax: (0870) 7413001 E-mail: info@idmanagement.com
Identifile Systems Ltd, Unit 2 Bridge Gate Centre, Martinfield, Welwyn Garden City, Hertfordshire, AL7 1JG Tel: (01707) 395396 Fax: (01707) 394083 E-mail: sales@identifile.co.uk
Plastic Card Design Services Ltd, 15 Bramshill Ave, Kettering, Northamptonshire, NN16 9FL Tel: (01536) 410557 Fax: (01536) 510509 E-mail: info@plasticcardsuk.com
Securi Card, 2 Ings Croft, Low Fold, Ossett, West Yorkshire, WF5 9HZ Tel: (01924) 274007 Fax: (01924) 280868
Sevarg Engineering Ltd, 14 The High Cross Centre, Fountayne Road, London, N15 4QN Tel: (020) 8801 0082 Fax: (020) 8801 9907 E-mail: sales@sevarg.com
Sure Enterprises (UK) Ltd, 2 Chilton Corner, Chilton, Sudbury, Suffolk, CO10 0RL Tel: (01787) 881321 Fax: (01787) 881332 E-mail: amanda@sureenterprises.co.uk

IGNITION LEADS

Autospark UK Ltd, 284b Water Road, Wembley, Middlesex, HA0 1HX Tel: (020) 8998 9642 Fax: (020) 8810 9349
Carol Cable Ltd, 61 Stewarts Road, Finedon Road Industrial Estate, Wellingborough, Northamptonshire, NN8 4RJ Tel: (01933) 277700 Fax: (01933) 273696
Madison Wire (Europe) Ltd, Madison House, Davyfield Road, Roman Road Industrial Estate, Blackburn, BB1 2LU Tel: (01254) 663555 Fax: (01254) 663222 E-mail: info@madison-wire.co.uk
Standard Motor Product Europe, Occupation Road, Hucknall, Nottingham, NG15 6DZ Tel: 0115-952 8000 Fax: 0115-952 0050 E-mail: sales@intermotor.co.uk

IGNITION SYSTEMS COMPONENTS

Rex Caunt, 6 Kings Court, Kingsfield Road, Barwell, Leicester, LE9 8NZ Tel: (01455) 846963 Fax: (01455) 846963 E-mail: rex@rexcauntracing.com
Standard Motor Product Europe, Occupation Road, Hucknall, Nottingham, NG15 6DZ Tel: 0115-952 8000 Fax: 0115-952 0050 E-mail: sales@intermotor.co.uk

ILLUMINATED BOX SIGNS

Gee Tee Signs Ltd, Bestwood Road, Nottingham, NG6 8SS Tel: 0115-976 1188 Fax: 0115-976 1213 E-mail: sales@geeteesigns.com
J G Markland & Sons, Park Works, Borron Road, Newton-le-Willows, Merseyside, WA12 0EJ Tel: (01925) 220718 Fax: (01925) 220718
Northallerton Sign Co., The Units, Morton On Swale, Northallerton, N. Yorkshire, DL7 9RJ Tel: (01609) 777687 Fax: (01609) 777687 E-mail: sales@allertonsingns.co.uk

ILLUMINATED CEILING CONSTRUCTORS OR MANUFACTURERS OR CONTRACTORS

Byford Interiors Ltd, Canterbury Court, Camberwell New Road, London, SE5 0TG Tel: (020) 7793 0777 Fax: (020) 7793 0377 E-mail: reception@cealings-uk.com
Metfix Ceilings Ltd, 40b Humber Avenue, Coventry, CV3 1AY Tel: (024) 7645 7343 Fax: (024) 7663 5915

ILLUMINATED SIGNS

A Finch & Co., 1-21 Bedminster Down Road, Bristol, BS13 7AB Tel: 0117-963 2763 Fax: 0117-963 2826
Abbott Signs, 29 Victoria Road, Northampton, NN1 5ED Tel: (01604) 636793 Fax: (01604) 632302 E-mail: info@abbottsigns.co.uk
Admiral Signs Ltd, 121 Oak Street, Norwich, NR3 3BP Tel: (01603) 627573 Fax: (01603) 619954 E-mail: info@admiral-signs.co.uk
Alpha Signs (Northampton) Ltd, Clarence Avenue, Northampton, NN2 6NY Tel: (01604) 712233 Fax: (01604) 717131
AST Signs, Unit 2, Gilwilly Road, East Lakes Business Park, Penrith, Cumbria, CA11 9BF Tel: (01768) 892292 Fax: (01768) 892294 E-mail: mark@astsigns.com
Barry's Signs, 2 High Street, Wavertree, Liverpool, L15 8HG Tel: 0151-733 9741 Fax: 0151-734 0800
Blaze Neon Ltd, Patricia Way, Pysons Road Industrial Estate, Broadstairs, Kent, CT10 2XZ Tel: (01843) 601075 Fax: (01843) 867924 E-mail: chrisa@blazeneon.com
Brilliant Signs & Fabrications, Unit 2 Forty Green, Bledlow, Princes Risborough, Buckinghamshire, HP27 9PN Tel: (01844) 273602 Fax: (0871) 4330112 E-mail: peter.snellgrove@brilliant-signs.com
Brisbay Plastics Ltd, Adamsez Industrial Estate, Scotswood Road, Newcastle upon Tyne, NE15 6XA Tel: 0191-274 4774 Fax: 0191-228 0146 E-mail: steve@brisbay.co.uk
Broadway Signs, Unit 18 Elmbourne Industrial Estate, Crabtree Manorway, Belvedere, Kent, DA17 6AW Tel: (020) 8310 8100 Fax: (020) 8310 1950E-mail: curwood1954@hotmail.com
Bull Signs, Bayhorne Lane, Horley, Surrey, RH6 9ES Tel: (01293) 821313 Fax: (01293) 821414 E-mail: sales@bullsigns.com
Central Signs & Graphics, 6 Saltley Industrial Centre, Adderley Road, Birmingham, B8 1AW Tel: 0121-326 7744 Fax: 0121-326 8123 E-mail: reginold1@aol.com
Clarks Signs Ltd, Alchorn Place, Portsmouth, PO3 5QL Tel: (023) 9282 6411 Fax: (023) 9266 9991 E-mail: sales@clarks-signs.co.uk
Creative Signs, 10 Worcester Road Industrial Estate, Chipping Norton, Oxfordshire, OX7 5XW Tel: (01608) 643557 Fax: (01608) 643557 E-mail: sales@creativepubsigns.co.uk
D B Sign Associates Ltd, Dukeries Industrial Estate, Claylands Avenue, Worksop, Nottinghamshire, S81 7BQ Tel: (01909) 472922 Fax: (01909) 478698 E-mail: office@dbsigns.com
Dan Display & Imaging Ltd, Harlequin House, Coedcad Lane, Pontyclun, Mid Glamorgan, CF72 9EW Tel: (01443) 225656 Fax: (01443) 226544 E-mail: info@dandisplay.co.uk
Deltaband Ltd, 2280 Coventry Road, Sheldon, Birmingham, B26 3JR Tel: 0121-742 9922 Fax: 0121-742 9933 E-mail: enquiries@deltaband.co.uk
Design of Walton, 3 Lyln Road, Hersham Trading Estate, Walton-on-Thames, Surrey, KT12 3PU Tel: (01932) 240376 Fax: (01932) 241110 E-mail: signs@designofwalton.co.uk
▶ Eberhardt Signs Ltd, Victory Trading Estate, Kiln Road, Portsmouth, PO3 5LP Tel: (023) 9266 5466 Fax: (023) 9266 5681 E-mail: sales@eberhardtsigns.com
Ellis Signs, Dunstan Road Railway Street, Gateshead, Tyne & Wear, NE11 9EE Tel: 0191-477 1600 Fax: 0191-460 4460 E-mail: bernerd@ellissigns.fsnet.co.uk
Embassy Signs Ltd, 83 Bellenden Road, London, SE15 4QJ Tel: (020) 7732 1055 Fax: (020) 7732 4163E-mail: sales@embassysigns.co.uk
Graffiti Design International, Design House, Bell Lane Industrial Estate, Uckfield, East Sussex, TN22 1QL Tel: (01825) 763690 Fax: (01825) 763815 E-mail: sales@graffitidesign.co.uk
Hendon Sign Co., 25-27 The Burroughs, London, NW4 4AR Tel: (020) 8202 8900 Fax: (020) 8202 4071
J G Neon Signs, 639 Walsall Road, Great Barr, Birmingham, B42 1EH Tel: 0121-357 4033 Fax: 0121-357 4033
Lamb's Signs, Unit B3 Sapphire Way, Rhombus Business Park, Norwich, NR6 6NN Tel: (01603) 410400 Fax: (01603) 410700 E-mail: lambsigns@talk21.com
Lyons, 206 Lylehill Road, Belfast, BT14 8SN Tel: (028) 9082 5688 Fax: (028) 9082 5688
▶ Mersey Signs, Unit 24, Junction 8 Business Park, Ross Cliffe Road, Ellesmere Port, CH65 3AS Tel: 0151-355 0478 Fax: 0151-356 5352 E-mail: info@merseysigns.co.uk
Newsigns Sign Writers, Unit 6a The Arches, Loveridge Road, London, NW6 2DS Tel: (020) 7328 9251 Fax: (020) 7624 7465

ILLUMINATED SIGNS – *continued*

Northampton Signs Ltd, Unit 5,, Stour Road,, Weedon Road Industrial Estate,, Northampton, NN5 5AA Tel: (01604) 758198 E-mail: sales@northamptonsigns.co.uk
Northern Plastics 84 Ltd, Mount Street, Hyde, Cheshire, SK14 1NT Tel: 0161-368 2968 Fax: 0161-368 2183 E-mail: np84ltd@btconnect.com
Nuneaton Signs, 3 Kelsey Close, Attleborough Fields Industrial Estate, Nuneaton, Warwickshire, CV11 6RS Tel: (024) 7634 1922 Fax: (024) 7664 1305 E-mail: sales@nuneatonsigns.co.uk
Peco Signs, Unit 5, Arrow Road North, Lakeside, Redditch, Worcestershire, B98 8NT Tel: (01527) 595364 Fax: (01527) 595366 E-mail: info@pecostudios.com
Ram Signs, 4 Brighton Road, Lower Kingswood, Tadworth, Surrey, KT20 6SY Tel: (01737) 833444 Fax: (01737) 833432 E-mail: rsgsales@aol.com
Raysigns Ltd, 11-13 Tower Hamlets Road, Dover, Kent, CT17 0BJ Tel: (01304) 214506 Fax: (01304) 202915 E-mail: andrew@raysigns.fsnet.co.uk
Royal Signs, 167 Culford Road, London, N1 4DT Tel: (020) 7254 6969 Fax: (020) 7249 0880
Rye Signs Ltd, 4 11 Fieldings Road, Cheshunt, Waltham Cross, Hertfordshire, EN8 9TL Tel: (01992) 636348 Fax: (01992) 621579 E-mail: dave@ryesigns.demon.co.uk
Saltwell Signs (North East) Ltd, Princesway North, Team Valley Trading Estate, Gateshead, Tyne & Wear, NE11 0TU Tel: 0191-482 5555 Fax: 0191-491 0246 E-mail: sales@saltwellsigns.co.uk
Sign 2000 Ltd, Maidstone Road, Paddock Wood, Tonbridge, Kent, TN12 6QJ Tel: (01892) 834383 Fax: (01892) 838349 E-mail: info@sign2000.co.uk
Sign A Rama, 1 Parker Street, Warrington, WA1 1LT Tel: (01925) 445577 Fax: (01925) 244555 E-mail: signarama.warrington@talk21.com
The Sign & Blind Centre Ltd, 24 Cavendish Road, New Malden, Surrey, KT3 6DE Tel: (020) 8337 1538 E-mail: signblindcoltd@aol.com
Sign Factory, 1333 London Road, Leigh-on-Sea, Essex, SS9 2AD Tel: (01702) 716161 Fax: (01702) 716141 E-mail: sales@signfactory.ws
Sign Trading, 294grays Inn Road, London, WC1X 8DX Tel: (020) 7837 0703 Fax: (020) 7278 4717 E-mail: terrysigncentre@hotmail.com
Signs By Morrell Ltd, Tarran Way South, Tarran Industrial Estate, Wirral, Merseyside, CH46 4TP Tel: 0151-678 8989 Fax: 0151-678 8816 E-mail: sales@signs-by-morrell.com
Spa Display Ltd, 23 North Street Industrial Estate, Droitwich, Worcestershire, WR9 8JB Tel: (01905) 775428 Fax: (01905) 795417 E-mail: signs@spa-display.sagehost.co.uk
Sprint Signs Ltd, Holmes Way, Horncastle, Lincolnshire, LN9 6JW Tel: (01507) 522247 Fax: (01507) 522017 E-mail: sales@sprintsigns.co.uk
Studio 127, 127 East Parade, Keighley, West Yorkshire, BD21 5HX Tel: (01535) 605148 Fax: (01535) 691521 E-mail: enquiries@studio127.co.uk
Tara Signs Ltd, St. Peters Place, Western Road, Lancing, West Sussex, BN15 8SB Tel: (01903) 750710 Fax: (01903) 754008 E-mail: admin@tarasigns.com
Taylor Electronics Manchester Ltd, 287 Chester Road, Manchester, M15 4EY Tel: 0161-834 5050 Fax: 0161-834 5051
Wolverhampton Plastics Holdings Ltd, Sharrocks Street, Wolverhampton, WV1 3RP Tel: (01902) 455116 Fax: (01902) 455200 E-mail: wton.plastics@virgin.net

ILLUMINATED SWITCHES

Hi Tec Interface Ltd, Unit 15 The Wenta Business Centre, Colne Way, Watford, WD24 7ND Tel: (020) 8958 4735 Fax: (020) 8958 9770 E-mail: hitec@himet.com
Knitter Switch UK Ltd, Grove House, Lutyens Close, Lychpit, Basingstoke, Hampshire, RG24 8AG Tel: (01256) 338670 Fax: (01256) 338671 E-mail: ksuk@knitter-switch.com

ILLUSTRATION SERVICES

▶ Sue Hagerty Illustration, Unit 16, 100 Trostre Road Workshops, Llanelli, Dyfed, SA15 2EA Tel: (01554) 746504 E-mail: sue@suehagertyillustration.co.uk
T Christien, 46 Strawberry Vale, Twickenham, TW1 4SE Tel: (020) 8892 3621 Fax: (020) 8891 5946 E-mail: terry@cartoonology.com

IMAGE ANALYSIS EQUIPMENT MANUFRS

Hook & Tucker Zenyx Ltd, Vulcan Way, New Addington, Croydon, CR0 9UG Tel: (01689) 843345 Fax: (01689) 841792 E-mail: sales@htz.biz
Imagic UK P.L.C., Potterne, Devizes, Wiltshire, SN10 5XG Tel: (01380) 729099 Fax: (01380) 729092 E-mail: info@imageaccess.co.uk
Mast Group Ltd, Mast House, Derby Road, Bootle, Merseyside, L20 1EA Tel: 0151-933 7277 Fax: 0151-944 1332 E-mail: sales@mastgrp.com

IMAGE ARCHIVING SYSTEMS

Adem Ltd, Unit 15 Metro Business Centre, Kangley Bridge Road, London, SE26 5BW Tel: (020) 8676 8092 Fax: (020) 8659 0354 E-mail: mail@adem.co.uk

IMAGE CAPTURE SYSTEMS

M C B Imaging Services Ltd, 14 Fraser Road, Erith, Kent, DA8 1QJ Tel: (01322) 333062 Fax: (01322) 441654 E-mail: info@mcbimaging.co.uk
Multipix Imaging Ltd, 1 Tilmore Road, Petersfield, Hampshire, GU32 2HG Tel: (01730) 233332 Fax: (01730) 231062 E-mail: sales@multipix.com

IMAGE INTENSIFIERS

Thales Optics, Glascoed Road, St. Asaph, Clwyd, LL17 0LL Tel: (01745) 588000 Fax: (01745) 584258 E-mail: alan.jenson@thales.co.uk

IMAGE PROCESSING

Avoncolour Professional Imaging, 131-133 Duckmoor Road, Bristol, BS3 2BJ Tel: 0117-963 3456 Fax: 0117-966 3456 E-mail: sales@avoncolour.co.uk
D X Imaging, Units 19 & 20, Watford Enterprise Centre, Watford, WD18 8EA Tel: (01923) 227644 Fax: (01923) 816896 E-mail: dximaging@dximaging.co.uk
Kane Computing Ltd, 7 Theatre Court, London Road, Northwich, Cheshire, CW9 5HB Tel: (01606) 351006 Fax: (01606) 351007 E-mail: kane@kanecomputing.com
L T Printing, Alfred Road, Wallasey, Merseyside, CH44 7HY Tel: 0151-647 8006 Fax: 0151-666 1704 E-mail: post@ltprintgroup.co.uk
NPS Media, Ayrton Buildings, Forty Foot Road, Middlesbrough, Cleveland, TS2 1HG Tel: (01642) 231231 Fax: (01642) 256565 E-mail: sales@npsmedia.com
Square Group Ltd, 78 New Oxford Street, London, WC1A 1HB Tel: (020) 7692 9990 Fax: (020) 7692 6636 E-mail: sales@squaregroup.co.uk
Synoptics Ltd, Beacon House, Nuffield Road, Cambridge, CB4 1TF Tel: (01223) 727100 Fax: (01223) 727101 E-mail: sales@synoptics.co.uk

IMAGE PROCESSING EQUIPMENT MANUFRS

Alrad Instruments Ltd, Alder House, Turnpike Road Industrial Estate, Newbury, Berkshire, RG14 2NS Tel: (01635) 30345 Fax: (01635) 32630 E-mail: sales@alrad.co.uk
Applied Imaging International Ltd, International Centre For Life Times Square, Scotswood Road, Newcastle upon Tyne, NE1 4EP Tel: 0191-202 3100 Fax: 0191-202 3101 E-mail: sales@aii.co.uk
Castle Document Management, The Foundry, London Road, Kings Worthy, Winchester, Hampshire, SO23 7QN Tel: (01962) 882281 Fax: (01962) 882204 E-mail: scanning@castledoc.freeserve.co.uk
Cortex Controllers Ltd, 50 St. Stephens Place, Cambridge, CB3 0JE Tel: (01223) 368000 Fax: (01223) 462800 E-mail: info@cortexcontrollers.com
Multipix Imaging Ltd, 1 Tilmore Road, Petersfield, Hampshire, GU32 2HG Tel: (01730) 233332 Fax: (01730) 231062 E-mail: sales@multipix.com
Panasonic Electric Works UK Ltd, Sunrise Parkway, Linford Wood, Milton Keynes, MK14 6LF Tel: (01908) 231555 Fax: (01908) 231599 E-mail: info-uk@eu.pewg.panasonic.com
Brian Reece Scientific Ltd, 12 West Mills, Newbury, Berkshire, RG14 5HG Tel: (01635) 32827 Fax: (01635) 34542 E-mail: brian@brsl.co.uk
Storwave Ltd, 1 Flowers Hill Close, Flowers Hill Trading Estate, Bristol, BS4 5LF Tel: 0117-972 8855 Fax: 0117-916 9234 E-mail: sales@theedmgroup.co.uk
Synoptics Ltd, Beacon House, Nuffield Road, Cambridge, CB4 1TF Tel: (01223) 727100 Fax: (01223) 727101 E-mail: sales@synoptics.co.uk
Vision Assurance Systems, Basepoint Business & Innovation Centre, Caxton Close, Andover, Hampshire, SP10 3FG Tel: (01264) 326309 E-mail: sales@visionassurancesystems.com

IMAGE TRANSFER TECHNOLOGY SERVICES

Day International Ltd, Balgray Street, Dundee, DD3 8HN Tel: (01382) 422200 Fax: (01382) 832310 E-mail: bill_crowe@day-intel.com

IMAGING PRODUCT SUPPLY SERVICES

Itesoft Ltd, Headway House, Crosby Way, Farnham, Surrey, GU9 7XG Tel: (01252) 741500 Fax: (01252) 741515 E-mail: marketing@itesoft-uk.co.uk
A.J. Purdy & Co. Ltd, 30 Stort Mill, River Way, Harlow, Essex, CM20 2SN Tel: (01279) 414556 Fax: (01279) 450931 E-mail: info@ajpurdy.co.uk

IMAGING SYSTEMS

Oxford Positron Systems Ltd, 5 Landscape Close, Weston-on-the-Green, Bicester, Oxfordshire, OX25 3SX Tel: (01869) 343618 Fax: (01865) 343619

IMITATION JEWELLERY/ COSTUME JEWELLERY/ FASHION JEWELLERY

Agatha, 4 South Molton Street, London, W1K 5QD Tel: (020) 7495 2779 Fax: (020) 7495 3699
Art Pewter Silver Ltd, 3B Colvilles Road, Kelvin Industrial Estate, East Kilbride, Glasgow, G75 0RS Tel: (01355) 229446 Fax: (01355) 264762 E-mail: service@artpewter.co.uk
▶ Beads & Sparkly Things, 24 Larchwood Avenue, Romford, RM5 2QJ Tel: (07976) 035539 E-mail: carol.norman@ntlworld.com
Bijou, Unit 60a Castle Court, Royal Avenue, Belfast, BT1 1DD Tel: (028) 9023 5595 Fax: (028) 9023 5595 E-mail: sales@bijou.ltd.com
▶ Blingy Things, 45 Briston Road, Melton Constable, Norfolk, NR24 2AP Tel: 01263 861124
▶ Chic Costume Jewellery, 27 Lawrence Avenue, Letchworth Garden City, Hertfordshire, SG6 2EY Tel: (01462) 678288 E-mail: sales@chic-costume-jewellery.co.uk
Chi-Chi Style, The Old Schoolhouse, Church Street, Netherseal, Swadlincote, Derbyshire, DE12 8DF Tel: (01283) 763604 E-mail: sales@chi-chi-style.com
Ciro Pearls Ltd, C/o, 26-36 Silver St, Bedford, MK40 1SX Tel: 01234 327363 Fax: 01234 269703
Ciro Pearls Ltd, Welsh Designer Outlet Village, Bridgend, Mid Glamorgan, CF32 9SU Tel: (01656) 655916
Cotswold Perfumery Ltd, Victoria Street, Bourton-on-the-Water, Cheltenham, Gloucestershire, GL54 2BU Tel: (01451) 820698 Fax: (01451) 821717 E-mail: sales@cotswold-perfumery.co.uk
▶ Creative Angels, 3 New Buildings, Gandy Street, Exeter, EX4 3LS Tel: (01392) 422720 E-mail: creative1angels@aol.com
Creative Beadcraft Ltd, 20 Beak Street, London, W1F 9RE Tel: (01494) 778818 Fax: (01494) 718510 E-mail: sales@cb.co.uk
▶ Creative Max Imports, 5 Fourth Avenue, Bluebridge Industrial Estate, Halstead, Essex, CO9 2SY Tel: (01787) 473249 Fax: (01787) 474118 E-mail: sales@creativemax.com
▶ Farfallina, The Lodge, Gog Magog Hills Estate, Babraham, Cambridge, CB2 4AE Tel: (01223) 413321
Forever Jewellery Ltd, Hall Fabrications, Site F, Lamby Way, Rumney, Cardiff, CF3 2EQ Tel: (029) 2077 9210 Fax: (029) 2077 8838 E-mail: sales@foreverjewellery.co.uk
Fusion Metal Smiths, Flat 1 Wixenford Farm, Colesdown Hill, Plymouth, PL9 8AA Tel: (01752) 481778 E-mail: steve@fusionmetalsmiths.com
▶ Georgina Ettridge, 12 St. Johns Glebe, Rownhams, Southampton, SO16 8AX Tel: (023) 8073 6704 E-mail: designer@georginaettridge.co.uk
Grooms House Turnery, Grooms House, Stanshawes Court, Yate, Bristol, BS37 4DZ Tel: (01454) 325525 Fax: (01454) 325525 E-mail: info@grooms-house-turnery.co.uk
Lamez Ltd, 56C Minerva Road, London, NW10 6HJ Tel: (020) 8357 1300 Fax: (020) 8357 1600 E-mail: lamezltd@aol.com
▶ Le Rule Originals, 2 Selsey Close, Hayling Island, Hampshire, PO11 9SX Tel: 02392 463845 Fax: 02392 463845 E-mail: louise@leruleoriginals.co.uk
Long Island Products (Fashion) Ltd, Unit 3 Westmoreland House, Cumberland Park, Scrubs Lane, London, NW10 6RE Tel: (020) 8962 8688 Fax: (020) 8960 4481
Miracle Jewellery Ltd, 29 Shadwell Street, Birmingham, B4 6HB Tel: 0121-236 7456 Fax: 0121-233 1781 E-mail: miraclejewel@aol.com
▶ N Y C Jewellery, 333 Kilburn High Road, London, NW6 7QB Tel: (020) 7624 2900
Nemesis Accessories Ltd, 16 Simmons Road, Henley On Thames, Henley-on-Thames, Oxfordshire, RG9 2ER Tel: (01491) 575550 Fax: (01491) 575550 E-mail: nemesis@cmcgowan.freeserve.co.uk
▶ Oliver Goldsmiths Sunglasses, 15 All Saints Road, London, W11 1HA Tel: (0845) 0533440 Fax: (0870) 7541899 E-mail: info@olivergoldsmith.com
▶ Partytime Jewellery, 8 Magnet Road, East Lane Business Park, Wembley, Middlesex, HA9 7RG Tel: 0116-286 6632 Fax: (020) 8904 8802
Remane Bros Ltd, 63-66 Hatton Garden, London, EC1N 8RF Tel: (020) 7405 6794 Fax: (020) 7831 6289 E-mail: remanegems@aol.com
F. Simons Imports Ltd, Unit 10, The Parkwood Centre, Aston Road, Waterlooville, Hampshire, PO7 7HT Tel: (023) 9225 5339 Fax: (023) 9225 6800
▶ Vetas UK Ltd, Unit 16 Robinsons Industrial Estate, Shaftesbury Street, Derby, DE23 8NL Tel: (01332) 365300 Fax: (01332) 602455 E-mail: vetas100@hotmail.com
W B Muddeman & Son Ltd, The Scope Complex, Wills Road, Totnes, Devon, TQ9 5XN Tel: (01803) 862058 Fax: (01803) 866273 E-mail: su4555@eclipse.co.uk
West Products (Jewellery) Ltd, Hanworth Trading Estate, Hampton Road West, Feltham, Middlesex, TW13 6DH Tel: (020) 8755 2638 Fax: (020) 8755 2166 E-mail: jeff@westproducts.co.uk
Wild Things, 12 Denmark Road, Exeter, EX1 1SL Tel: (01392) 493775 Fax: (01392) 413538 E-mail: info@wildthingsgifts.com

IMMERSION HEATERS

▶ Backer Electric Co. Ltd, Fitzwilliam Road, Eastwood Trading Estate, Rotherham, South Yorkshire, S65 1TF Tel: (01709) 828292 Fax: (01709) 828388 E-mail: sales@backer.co.uk
Electric Water Heating Co., 2 Horsecroft Place, Harlow, Essex, CM19 5BT Tel: (0845) 0553811 Fax: (0845) 0553822E-mail: sales@ewh.co.uk
Telford Copper Cylinders, Haybridge Road, Wellington, Telford, Shropshire, TF1 2NW Tel: (01952) 262300 Fax: (01952) 253452 E-mail: sales@telford-group.com

IMMIGRATION SERVICES

▶ MediVisas UK, 1 Harley Street, London, W1G 9QD Tel: (020) 7307 8761 Fax: (020) 7307 8762 E-mail: chris.fysh@medivisas.com
▶ Work Permit Consultants, Mount Ephraim, Tunbridge Wells, Kent, TN4 8AS Tel: 01892 543939 Fax: 01892 527653 E-mail: enquiry@workpermitconsultants.com

IMPACT EXTRUSIONS

A W H Consultants, Chadburn House, Weighbridge Road, Mansfield, Nottinghamshire, NG18 1AH Tel: (01623) 465207 Fax: (01623) 400196 E-mail: enquiries@ynotwine.co.uk
Ashfield Extrusion Ltd, B Field Industrial Estate, Clover Street, Kirkby-in-Ashfield, Nottingham, NG17 7LH Tel: (01623) 757333 Fax: (01623) 751771 E-mail: ashfield.sales@btconnect.com
Gilmour Extrusion Ltd, 6 Greenhill Industrial Estate, Coatbridge, Lanarkshire, ML5 2AG Tel: (01236) 426165 Fax: (01236) 423263 E-mail: sales@monklandsextrusion.com
Radiotronic, Advance Park Rhonymedre, Wrexham, Clwyd, LL14 3YR Tel: (01978) 823900 Fax: (01978) 822913 E-mail: sales@aslgroup.uk.com

IMPACT SOCKETS

Abingdon King Dick, Unit 11 Roman Way, Coleshill, Birmingham, B46 1HG Tel: (01675) 467776 Fax: (01675) 464277 E-mail: sales@kingdicktools.co.uk
Impact Socket Supplies Ltd, Park Mills, Deighton Road, Chorley, Lancashire, PR7 2BL Tel: (01257) 277205 Fax: (01257) 270540 E-mail: sales@impactsockets.co.uk
Lantern Engineering Ltd, Hamilton Road, Maltby, Rotherham, South Yorkshire, S66 7NE Tel: (01709) 813636 Fax: (01709) 817130 E-mail: sales@lantern.co.uk
Yokota UK, Low Common Road, Dinnington, Sheffield, S25 2RJ Tel: (01909) 552471 Fax: (01909) 552472 E-mail: info@yokota.co.uk

IMPORT AND EXPORT AGENTS

Adeptstar Shipping Ltd, Estate House, Marsh Way, Fairview Industrial Park, Rainham, Essex, RM13 8UH Tel: (01708) 550909 Fax: (01708) 551945 E-mail: adeptstar@shipping-ltd.fsnet.co.uk
▶ Albion Robotics Ltd, 6 Castletown, Portland, Dorset, DT5 1BD Tel: (01305) 826384 Fax: (01305) 826056 E-mail: shipping@albiongroup.org
Archfield (Shipping) Ltd, Factory Road, London, E16 2HD Tel: (020) 7476 4386 Fax: (020) 7511 2238 E-mail: sales@archfield.co.uk
▶ Blenheim & Moorcroft, Unit 123 Lee Valley Technopark, Ashley Road, London, N17 9LN Tel: (020) 8880 4091 Fax: (020) 8880 4113 E-mail: info@blenheimandmoorcroft.com
▶ Business Management Services, 58 South Road, Sully, Penarth, South Glamorgan, CF64 5SJ Tel: (029) 2053 1691 Fax: (029) 2053 1691 E-mail: beads@btinternet.com

IMPORT AND EXPORT AGENTS – *continued*

Cohen & Wilks International Ltd, Aquatite House, Mabgate, Leeds, LS9 7DR Tel: 0113-245 0804 Fax: 0113-391 7858 E-mail: reception@cwil.co.uk

Davies Turner & Co. Ltd, Dartford Freight Terminal, Edison's Park, Dartford, DA2 6QJ Tel: (01322) 277558 Fax: (01322) 289063 E-mail: webmaster@daviesturner.co.uk

Davis Shipping Ltd, Enterprise Industrial Estate, Bolina Road, London, SE16 3LF Tel: (020) 7231 9340 Fax: (020) 7231 1120 E-mail: bevan@davis-se1.freeserve.co.uk

Denholm Shipping Company Ltd, Liner House, Test Road, Eastern Docks, Southampton, SO14 3GE Tel: (023) 8071 3100 Fax: (023) 8071 3129 E-mail: finadmin@denshipsouth.co.uk

▶ Dimensionize Ltd, 145-157 St. John Street, London, EC1V 4PY Tel: (0870) 7538485 Fax: (0870) 7538483 E-mail: contact@dimensionize.com

Exportential, 13 Beccelm Drive, Crowland, Peterborough, PE6 0AG Tel: (01733) 211873 E-mail: info@exportential.co.uk

Fairtrade International Co. Ltd, 12 Cockfosters Parade, Cockfosters Road, Barnet, Hertfordshire, EN4 0BX Tel: (020) 8447 0220 Fax: (020) 8447 0330 E-mail: info@fairtradeint.co.uk

Martintrux Dover, Lord Warden Square, Dover, Kent, CT17 9EQ Tel: (01304) 213122 Fax: (01304) 213247 E-mail: clearance@martintrux.co.uk

Mis Shipping Ltd, 34 The Mall, London, W5 3TJ Tel: (020) 8567 4456 Fax: (020) 8567 5890 E-mail: misshipping@msn.com

Orbit Import Export, Ferry Terminal, Ramsgate, Kent, CT11 9FT Tel: (01843) 588899 Fax: (01843) 850278

▶ Prestige Imports & Logistics Ltd, Porterfield House 157 Harton Lane, South Shields, Tyne & Wear, NE34 0PW Tel: 0191 4200585 Fax: 0191 4200585 E-mail: enquries@pil-ltd.com

Stonegalleon plc, The SPS Building, Burnaby Road, Coventry, CV6 4AE Tel: (024) 7658 4584 Fax: (024) 7657 4585 E-mail: stonegalleon@plc.com

World Transport Agency Ltd, Room 215-217, Building 308, World Freight Terminal, Manchester Airport, Manchester, M90 5PZ Tel: 0161-436 5656 Fax: 0161-499 1145

IMPORT MERCHANTS OR AGENTS

A Cohen, 10 Palace Gate, London, W8 5NF Tel: (020) 7225 0022 Fax: (020) 7584 9520

A W H Consultants, Chadburn House, Weighbridge Road, Mansfield, Nottinghamshire, NG18 1AH Tel: (01623) 465207 Fax: (01623) 400196 E-mail: enquiries@ynotwine.co.uk

Alma Steels Ltd, Steetley Industrial Estate, Bean Road, Bilston, West Midlands, WV14 9EE Tel: (01902) 880726 Fax: (01902) 880726

Andover Natural Products, Unit 7b Apollo House, Calleva Park, Aldermaston, Reading, RG7 8TN Tel: 0118-981 6111 Fax: 0118-981 7778

Babylon Health Ltd, 57 Uxbridge Road, Shepherds Bush, London, W12 8NR Tel: (020) 8749 0037 Fax: (020) 8749 5628 E-mail: merrell@globalnet.co.uk

Bargate International Ltd, 6 Premier Court, Boarden Close, Moulton Park Industrial Estate, Northampton, NN3 6LF Tel: (01604) 679500 Fax: (01604) 495919 E-mail: sales@bargateinternational.com

Benross Marketing Ltd, Benross House, Speke Hall Road, Liverpool, L24 9WD Tel: 0151-448 1200 Fax: 0151-448 1221 E-mail: sales@benross.com

ChaliT Richards & Co. Ltd, The Sovereign Distillery, Wilson Road, Liverpool, L36 6AD Tel: (01403) 250500 Fax: (0870) 6000866 E-mail: admin@chailt-richards.co.uk

▶ China Bandwagon, Invest House, Bruce Road, Fforestfach Industrial Estate, Swansea, SA5 4HS Tel: (01792) 412882 Fax: (01792) 587046 E-mail: import@chinabandwagon.com

Cohen & Wilks International Ltd, Aquatite House, Mabgate, Leeds, LS9 7DR Tel: 0113-245 0804 Fax: 0113-391 7858 E-mail: reception@cwil.co.uk

D Ramply, High Street, Great Paxton, St. Neots, Cambridgeshire, PE19 6RG Tel: (01480) 475979 Fax: (01480) 403555

Daltrade P.L.C., 16 Devonshire Street, London, W1G 7AF Tel: (020) 7436 5454 Fax: (020) 7436 1445 E-mail: info@daltrade.co.uk

Damartex UK Ltd, Bowling Green Mills, Bingley, West Yorkshire, BD97 1AD Tel: (0870) 8330000 Fax: (01274) 551024 E-mail: infouk@damart.com

Elbee Traders, 839 Harrow Road, London, NW10 5NH Tel: (020) 8969 9423 Fax: (020) 8969 2611 E-mail: sales@elbee-traders.co.uk

Ess Tee United Traders London Ltd, Northumberland House 11 The Pavement, Popes Lane, London, W5 4NG Tel: (020) 8566 3636 Fax: (020) 8566 1831

Estrade Ltd, 38-40 Eastcastle Street, London, W1W 8DT Tel: (020) 7580 4237 Fax: (020) 7436 5327

Eurolink Corporation Ltd, The Annexe Feildings, 11 Rosken Grove, Farnham Royal, Slough, SL2 3DZ Tel: (01753) 642500 Fax: (01753) 642999 E-mail: info@eurolinkcorp.com

Expotec Ltd, 10 Harles Arces, Hickling, Melton Mowbray, Leicestershire, LE14 3AF Tel: (01664) 822725 Fax: (01664) 822725 E-mail: tony.fox2@ntlworld.com

Foy Steels, Unit 4 Chevin Mill, Leeds Road, Otley, West Yorkshire, LS21 1BT Tel: (01943) 850183 Fax: (01943) 461034 E-mail: sales@foysteel.co.uk

Fraser Ross Finance Ltd, 185-187 High Road, Romford, RM6 6NA Tel: (020) 8597 8781 Fax: (020) 8597 8673 E-mail: sales@alex-fraser.co.uk

Gathercrest Ltd, Lynton House, 304 Bensham Lane, Thornton Heath, Surrey, CR7 7EQ Tel: (020) 8683 0494 Fax: (020) 8689 8155

General Dietary Ltd, PO Box 38, Kingston upon Thames, Surrey, KT2 7YP Tel: (020) 8336 2323 Fax: (020) 8942 8274 E-mail: greareal.dietary@vigin.net

Genesis Trading (UK) Corp, 32 Woodhall Drive, Pinner, Middlesex, HA5 4TQ Tel: (020) 8420 1177 Fax: (020) 8420 1155 E-mail: gentauk@hotmail.com

Hesley Trading London Ltd, 37 Emperors Gate, London, SW7 4HJ Tel: (020) 7370 5933 Fax: (020) 7244 8214 E-mail: kenhes@tiscali.co.uk

Hira Company Ltd The, Elizabeth House, Elizabeth Street, Manchester, M8 8JJ Tel: 0161-834 2868 Fax: 0161-832 4566 E-mail: info@texet.com

Immediate Transportation Co. Ltd, Mckay Trading Estate, Blackthorne Road, Colnbrook, Slough, SL3 0AH Tel: (01753) 684644 Fax: (01753) 683338 E-mail: itcolhr@itcolhr.co.uk

Inlines Furniture Ltd, PO Box 160, Amersham, Buckinghamshire, HP6 6UH Tel: (01494) 434030

Itl Impex Ltd, Commercial House, 19 Station Road, Bognor Regis, West Sussex, PO21 1QD Tel: (01243) 841734 Fax: (01243) 841734 E-mail: itl@hopcbroadband.com

▶ J W S Import Ltd, Unit 1 Haven Business Park, Slippery Gowt Lane, Wyberton, Boston, Lincolnshire, PE21 7AA Tel: (01205) 363999 Fax: (01205) 358713 E-mail: sales@doorsandmore.biz

Joe Davies Ltd, 149 Broadstone Road, Stockport, Cheshire, SK5 7GA Tel: 0161-975 6300 Fax: 0161-975 6301

Kanematsu Europe plc, Dashwood House, 69 Old Broad Street, London, EC2M 1NS Tel: (020) 7456 6300 Fax: (020) 7256 2850

Karimjee Jivanjee & Co UK Ltd, Hanging Sword House, 21 Whitefriars Street, London, EC4Y 8JJ Tel: (020) 7583 3768 Fax: (020) 7583 3916 E-mail: carol@karimjee.com

Kolon Imperial Graphics plc, Erico House, 93/99 Upper Richmond Road, London, SW15 2TG Tel: (020) 8780 1585 Fax: (020) 8785 7004 E-mail: junelee21@kolonuk.net

Kumho Tyre (U.K.) Ltd, 6th Floor 9 Sutton Court Road, Sutton, Surrey, SM1 4SZ Tel: (020) 8661 6112 Fax: (020) 8661 2771 E-mail: sales@kumho-euro.com

L G International (U K) Ltd, Profile West, 950 Great West Road, Brentford, Middlesex, TW8 9ES Tel: (020) 8326 1400 Fax: (020) 8560 5601 E-mail: bmsuh@lgi.co.kr

L & M Food Group Ltd, Trelawney House, 454-456 Larkshall Road, Highams Park, London, E4 9HH Tel: (020) 8531 7631 Fax: (020) 8531 8607

L & M Phoenix Luggage UK Ltd, Middlesex House, 29-45 High Street, Edgware, Middlesex, HA8 7UU Tel: (020) 8905 6678 Fax: (020) 8905 6644 E-mail: sales@phoenixint.net

Laxbrin Ltd, York House, Empire Way, Wembley, Middlesex, HA9 0QL Tel: (020) 8900 0243 Fax: (020) 8900 1804E-mail: laxbrin@aol.com

Martintrux Dover, Lord Warden Square, Dover, Kent, CT17 9EQ Tel: (01304) 213122 Fax: (01304) 213247 E-mail: clearance@martintrux.co.uk

Mayan Experience Latin American Crafts, 7 Castle Sq, Swansea, SA1 1DW Tel: 01792 472874

Mitsubishi Corporation (UK) P.L.C., Mid City Place, 71 High Holborn, London, WC1V 6BA Tel: (020) 7025 3000 Fax: (020) 7025 3499

Omicways Ltd, Bude Straton Business Park, Bude, Cornwall, EX23 8LY Tel: (01288) 353838 Fax: (01288) 354978 E-mail: office@containergroup.co.uk

Pintorex Ltd, Unit 16 The Royal London Estate, 33 West Road, London, N17 0XL Tel: (020) 8808 0882 Fax: (020) 8801 9846 E-mail: pintorex@pintorex.co.uk

Premier Decorations, Braintree Road, Ruislip, Middlesex, HA4 0EJ Tel: (020) 8624 5555 Fax: (020) 8624 5678 E-mail: sales@premierdec.com

R & C Imports Ltd, Orient House, 15 Newton St, Hyde, Cheshire, SK14 4RY Tel: 0161-366 8888 Fax: 0161-366 0000 E-mail: info@randcliving.co.uk

Raupack Ltd, 131 High Street, Old Woking, Woking, Surrey, GU22 9LD Tel: (01483) 736800 Fax: (01483) 736810

San & Sons Ltd, Argonaut House, 369 Burnt Oak, Broadway, Edgware, Middlesex, HA8 5XZ Tel: (020) 8951 6070 Fax: (020) 8951 6050 E-mail: pault@argonaut.com

The Sandbar, 120-122 Grosvenor Street, Manchester, M1 7HL Tel: 0161-273 1552 Fax: 0161 273 2814 E-mail: sales@sandbar-online.com

Sherbrook International Ltd, Unit 3, Upper Keys Business Park, Keys Park Road, Hednesford, Cannock, Staffordshire, WS12 2GE Tel: (01543) 495555 E-mail: export@sherbrook.co.uk

Smeaton Hanscomb & Co. Ltd, Lisle Road, Hughenden Avenue, High Wycombe, Buckinghamshire, HP13 5SQ Tel: (01494) 521051 Fax: (01494) 461176 E-mail: sales@smeathans.plus.com

Sojitz P.L.C., Old Change House, 128 Queen Victoria Street, London, EC4V 4HR Tel: (020) 7886 7000 Fax: (020) 7634 0490

Ivor Spry & Co. Ltd, The Granary, Cornwells Farm, Sheephurst Lane, Marden, Tonbridge, Kent, TN12 9NS Tel: (01622) 833414 E-mail: sales@spry.co.uk

Sumitomo Corporation Europe Holding Ltd, Vintners Place, 68 Upper Thames Street, London, EC4V 3BJ Tel: (020) 7246 3600 Fax: (020) 7246 3925 E-mail: info@sumitomocorp.co.uk

Tata Ltd, 18 Grosvenor Place, London, SW1X 7HS Tel: (020) 7235 8281 Fax: (020) 7235 8727 E-mail: tata@tata.co.uk

Team Overseas Ltd, Meridian House, Nazeing Glass Works Estate, Nazeing New Road, Broxbourne, Hertfordshire, EN10 6SX Tel: +44 (01992) 788233 Fax: +44 (01992) 788695 E-mail: sales@teamoverseas.com

Tecapet Ltd, Unitec House, Albert Place, London, N3 1QB Tel: (020) 8349 4299 Fax: (020) 8349 0252 E-mail: tecapet@aol.com

Teknion Distribution Services, 22-24 Southgate Industrial Estate, Cross Street, Heywood, Lancashire, OL10 1PW Tel: (01706) 669988 Fax: (01706) 669989 E-mail: info@teknion.co.uk

Teknoserv (U.K.) Ltd, Culford House Unit 7, 1/7 Orsman Road, London, N1 5RA Tel: (020) 7729 3676 Fax: (020) 7729 5184 E-mail: sorab@teknoserv.freeserve.co.uk

TLC International Ltd, 180 Okehampton Cresent, Welling, Kent, DA16 1DB Tel: (020) 8304 7545 Fax: (020) 8303 4561

Travelon International Ltd, Unit 7 The Oxgate Centre, Oxgate Lane, London, NW2 7JA Tel: (020) 8450 2345 Fax: (020) 8450 4224 E-mail: office@travelon-international.co.uk

Typhoon Ltd, K Colindale Business Park, Carlisle Road, London, NW9 0HN Tel: (020) 8200 5688 Fax: (020) 8205 5088

Vicomte Bernard De Romanet Ltd, 212 Fordham Road, Newmarket, Suffolk, CB8 7LG Tel: (01638) 721145 Fax: (01638) 720330

Worldwide Tropicals, 75 Commerce Street, Glasgow, G5 8EP Tel: 0141-427 1066 Fax: 0141-429 4448

York Wines, Wellington House, The Square, Sheriff Hutton, York, YO60 6QY Tel: (01347) 878716 Fax: (01347) 878546 E-mail: info@yorkwines.co.uk

IMPREGNATED WIPES

▶ Branova Cleaning Services, Meadow Mills, Carlton Road, Dewsbury, West Yorkshire, WF13 2BA Tel: (01924) 486000 Fax: (01924) 486010 E-mail: sales@branova.com

Guardpack Ltd, 12 & 14 Grafton Place, Dukes Park Industrial Estate, Chelmsford, CM2 6TG Tel: (01245) 451770 Fax: (01245) 451710 E-mail: jeremy@guardpack.co.uk

IMPREGNATION AND SEALING ENGINEERING SERVICES

Norman Hay plc, Godiva Place, Coventry, CV1 5PN Tel: (024) 7622 9373 Fax: (024) 7622 4420 E-mail: info@normanhay.com

Surface Technology plc, Godiva Place, Coventry, CV1 5PN Tel: (024) 7625 8444 Fax: (024) 7655 1402 E-mail: sales@ultraseal.co.uk

Surface Technology P.L.C. (Ultraseal), Godiva Place, Coventry, CV1 5PN Tel: (024) 7655 1401 Fax: (024) 7663 3411 E-mail: surfacetech@ultraseal.co.uk

IMPREGNATION SERVICES, CASTING/METAL ETC

Surface Technology P.L.C. (Ultraseal), Godiva Place, Coventry, CV1 5PN Tel: (024) 7655 1401 Fax: (024) 7663 3411 E-mail: surfacetech@ultraseal.co.uk

IN FLIGHT CATERING

Glennans Ltd, Dovefields, Dovefields Industrial Estate, Uttoxeter, Staffordshire, ST14 8HU Tel: (01889) 567338 Fax: (01889) 562701 E-mail: richard.thompson@glennans.co.uk

IN LINE MIXERS

Plenty Filters, Plenty House, Hambridge Road, Newbury, Berkshire, RG14 5TR Tel: +44 (0) 1635 42363 Fax: +44 (0) 1635 49758 E-mail: filters@plenty.co.uk

IN MOULD PAINTS

ECL Chemicals Ltd, Impex House, Leestone Road, Sharston, Manchester, M22 4RN Tel: 0161-491 6744 Fax: 0161-491 6774 E-mail: info@eclchem.com

IN-CAR-ENTERTAINMENT, *See Radio, Motor Car/Vehicle etc*

INACTIVATED FLOUR

British Diamalt, Maltkiln Lane, Newark, Nottinghamshire, NG24 1HN Tel: (01636) 614730 Fax: (01636) 614740 E-mail: sales@diamalt.co.uk

INCENSE BURNERS OR HOLDERS

▶ 9SKY, 135 High Street, Parade House, Watford, WD17 1NS Tel: 01923 630877 E-mail: admin@9sky.org.uk

▶ Exscentrix, 8 Fox Covert, River View Park, Nottingham, NG4 2DD Tel: 0115-847 8146 E-mail: sales@exscentrix.co.uk

INCINERATOR INSTALLATION OR SERVICING

Combustion Lining Ltd, Jacaidam Works, Walley Street, Stoke-on-Trent, ST6 2AH Tel: (01782) 822712 Fax: (01782) 823920 E-mail: info@combustionlinings.com

Giles D & B Ltd Service Engineers, 13 Ludgate Close, Waltham, Grimsby, South Humberside, DN37 0LX Tel: (01472) 822662 E-mail: manager@dbgilesltd.f9.co.uk

▶ Inciner8, Shakespeare House, 37-39 Shakespeare Street, Southport, Merseyside, PR8 5AB Tel: (01704) 548508 Fax: (01704) 542461 E-mail: info@inciner8.com

INCINERATORS, HOSPITAL/ CLINICAL WASTE

Facultatieve Technologies Ltd, Moor Road, Leeds, LS10 2DD Tel: 0113-276 8888 Fax: 0113-271 8188 E-mail: sales@facultatieve.com

INCLINOMETERS, *See also headings for particular types*

Clino Ltd, 54 Britten Drive, Malvern, Worcestershire, WR14 3LG Tel: (01684) 561525 Fax: (01684) 561721 E-mail: sales@clino.co.uk

INCONTINENCE APPLIANCES

Bodys Surgical Care Centre, 631 London Road, Westcliff-on-Sea, Essex, SS0 9PE Tel: (01702) 346204 Fax: (01702) 338631

Ontex UK Ltd, 97 Macadam Road, Earlstrees Industrial Estate, Corby, Northamptonshire, NN17 4JN Tel: (01536) 269744 Fax: (01536) 400134 E-mail: ontex@ontex.co.uk

INCONTINENCE PADS

Green of Lincoln, Pyke Road, Lincoln, LN6 3QS Tel: (01522) 500006

Ontex UK Ltd, 97 Macadam Road, Earlstrees Industrial Estate, Corby, Northamptonshire, NN17 4JN Tel: (01536) 269744 Fax: (01536) 400134 E-mail: ontex@ontex.co.uk

Synergie Healthcare Ltd, Lyon Mill, Fitton Street, Royton, Oldham, OL2 5JX Tel: 0161-624 5641 Fax: 0161-627 0902

▶ Tanner Business Centre, Waterside Mill, Chew Valley Road, Greenfield, Oldham, OL3 7NH Tel: (01457) 872273 Fax: (01457) 870133 E-mail: info@tannerbrothers.co.uk

INCREMENTAL OPTICAL ENCODERS

British Encoder Products Co., Unit 33, Whitegate Industrial Estate, Wrexham, Clwyd, LL13 8UG Tel: (01978) 262100 Fax: (01978) 262101 E-mail: sales@brit-encoder.com

Computer Optical Products, 45 Leaver Road, Henley-On-Thames, Oxfordshire, RG9 1UW Tel: (01491) 412055 Fax: (01491) 413006 E-mail: sales@sensortronic.co.uk

INCUBATOR MANUFRS

Chick Master UK Ltd, Unit 2 Express Park, Bristol Road, Bridgwater, Somerset, TA6 4RN Tel: (01278) 411000 Fax: (01278) 451213 E-mail: sales@chickmaster.com
Interhatch, Whittington Way, Old Whittington, Chesterfield, Derbyshire, S41 9AG Tel: (01246) 264646 Fax: (01246) 269634 E-mail: sales@interhatch.com
L T E Scientific Ltd, Greenbridge Lane, Greenfield, Oldham, OL3 7EN Tel: (01457) 876221 Fax: (01457) 870131 E-mail: info@lte-scientific.co.uk
N J Meagor, Trelawder, St. Minver, Wadebridge, Cornwall, PL27 6RF Tel: (01208) 813235 Fax: (01208) 816392 E-mail: nickpoultry@aol.com

INDEPENDENT FINANCIAL ADVISERS (IFA)

A W D Chase De Vere Ltd, 10 Paternoster Square, London, EC4M 7DY Tel: (020) 7618 0207 Fax: (020) 7248 7741
Ashley Law Rickmansworth, 11 Shepherds Way, Rickmansworth, Herts, WD3 7NH Tel: (01923) 710392 Fax: (01923) 710392 E-mail: rickmansworth@ashleylaw.co.uk
▶ Bevington Evans & Associates, 53 Harrowby Street, Cardiff, CF10 5GA Tel: (029) 2048 5221 Fax: (029) 2048 5231 E-mail: cbevev@ntlbusiness.com
Calkin Pattinson & Co. Ltd, 40 Piccadilly, London, W1J 0HR Tel: (020) 7734 2176 Fax: (020) 7437 0604 E-mail: info@calkin.org
Capita Hartshead, Castle House, Park Road, Banstead, Surrey, SM7 3BX Tel: (01737) 357272 Fax: (01737) 363106 E-mail: enquires@captia.co.uk
▶ Chamberlain Corporate Advisors, Gatsby Court, 1 Holliday Street, Birmingham, B1 1TJ Tel: 0121-248 5400 Fax: 0121-551 9606 E-mail: james@thechamberlaingroup.com
City Assurance Services Ltd, First Floor Gatton Place, St Matthews, Redhill, RH1 1TA Tel: (01737) 854440 Fax: (01737) 854445 E-mail: inquires@cityassurance.com
Croucher, Reoch & Partners Ltd, 3rd Floor Babmaes Ho, 2 Babmaes St, London, SW1Y 6HD Tel: (020) 7839 5735 Fax: (020) 7930 4281 E-mail: fiztwilliamfinancial@compuserve.com
▶ Financial Consultancy, 244a Broadway, Bexleyheath, Kent, DA6 8AS Tel: (0845) 4668866 Fax: (0845) 4668877 E-mail: sales@thefinancialconsultancy.com
Hawkins Russell Jones, 7-8 Portmill Lane, Hitchin, Hertfordshire, SG5 1AS Tel: (01462) 628888 Fax: (01462) 631233 E-mail: hitchin@hrjlaw.co.uk
Helm Godfrey Ltd, Warnford Court, 29 Throgmorton Street, London, EC2N 2AT Tel: (020) 7614 1000 Fax: (020) 7614 1001 E-mail: info@helmgodfrey.com
David Jameson Ltd, 116a High Street, Epping, Essex, CM16 4AF Tel: (01992) 560660 Fax: (01992) 577945 E-mail: russell@davidjameson.co.uk
La Bourse Ltd, 15 Harley House, 28-32 Marylebone Road, London, NW1 5HE Tel: (020) 7487 4745 Fax: (020) 7486 0055
Manhattan Properties, 1147 Greenford Road, Greenford, Middlesex, UB6 0DP Tel: (020) 8423 8161 Fax: (020) 8423 8165
Mason & Ball & Associates Ltd, Bourn House, Park Street, Bagshot, Surrey, GU19 5AQ Tel: (01276) 472774 Fax: (01276) 451520 E-mail: mail@mba-uk.co.uk
▶ Mortgage Port Ltd, 6 St John's Hill, Shrewsbury, SY1 1JD Tel: (0870) 9509600 E-mail: oneport@shawsolutions.co.uk
Origin, 32-33 Watling Street, Canterbury, Kent, CT1 2AN Tel: (01227) 762380 Fax: (01227) 760726
Riverside Financial Management, Cutter House, Woodrolfe Road, Tollesbury, Maldon, Essex, CM9 8SE Tel: (01621) 860700 Fax: (01621) 860400 E-mail: info@riverside-financial.co.uk
Rixon Matthews Appleyard Ltd, Exchange Court, Lowgate, Hull, HU1 1XW Tel: (01482) 327605 Fax: (01482) 217184 E-mail: sales@rixon-insurance.co.uk
▶ Russell Young Ifa Ltd, 18 Front Street, Low Pittington, Durham, DH6 1BQ Tel: 0191-372 3319 Fax: 0191-372 3319 E-mail: info@russellyoung-ifa.com
▶ Strata Financial, 11 Reynolds Wharf, Coalport, Telford, Shropshire, TF8 7HU Tel: (0845) 2260125 E-mail: info@strataifa.co.uk
▶ Surrex Financial Management, 2 Paddock Road, Ashford, Kent, TN23 5WH Tel: (01233) 665812 Fax: (01903) 261550 E-mail: walterb@surrexfm.com
West London Brokers, Hale Edge North, Crabhill Lane, South Nutfield, Redhill, RH1 5NR Tel: (01737) 823286 Fax: (01737) 822656 E-mail: w.l.b@btconnect.com

INDEX CARD CABINETS

Railex Systems Ltd, Station Road, Lawford, Manningtree, Essex, CO11 1DZ Tel: (08706) 006664 Fax: (01206) 391465 E-mail: info@railex.co.uk

INDEX CARDS

Rotadex Systems Ltd, Sytems House, Central Business Park, Mackadown Lane, Birmingham, B33 0JL Tel: 0121-783 7411 Fax: 0121-783 1876 E-mail: cathi.croton@rotadex.co.uk

INDEXABLE CARBIDE INSERT THREAD TURNING TOOLS

Vargus Tooling UK Ltd, Halesfield 4, Telford, Shropshire, TF7 4AP Tel: (01952) 583222 Fax: (01952) 583383 E-mail: sales@vargustooling.co.uk

INDEXABLE MILLING CUTTERS

Maydown International Tours Ltd, Mercury Park, Amber Close, Tamworth, Staffordshire, B77 4RP Tel: (01827) 309700 Fax: (01827) 309719
Tekron Hard Metals Ltd, 6 Marsh Green Close, Biddulph, Stoke-on-Trent, ST8 6TA Tel: (01782) 522563 Fax: (01782) 516452 E-mail: tekrontool@madasafish.com
Vargus Tooling UK Ltd, Halesfield 4, Telford, Shropshire, TF7 4AP Tel: (01952) 583222 Fax: (01952) 583383 E-mail: sales@vargustooling.co.uk

INDEXING DRIVE MECHANISM/ INDEX BOXES

Camco UK Ltd, 432 Perth Avenue, Slough, SL1 4TS Tel: (01753) 786100 Fax: (01753) 786101 E-mail: sales@camcoindex.com

INDEXING EQUIPMENT

Weiss UK Ltd, 27 Manchester Drive, Leegomery, Telford, Shropshire, TF1 6XY Tel: (01952) 240953 Fax: (01952) 244442 E-mail: info@weiss.uk.com

INDIAN SNACKS

▶ Butt Foods Ltd, The Midway, Nottingham, NG7 2TS Tel: 0115-985 0009 Fax: 0115-985 1460 E-mail: robert@buttfoods.co.uk

INDIAN SPECIALIST FOOD

▶ Bristol Sweet Mart, 71 St Marks Road, Bristol, BS5 6HX Tel: 0117-951 2257 Fax: 0117-952 5456 E-mail: sales@sweetmart.co.uk
▶ Butt Foods Ltd, The Midway, Nottingham, NG7 2TS Tel: 0115-985 0009 Fax: 0115-985 1460 E-mail: robert@buttfoods.co.uk
▶ The London Tiffin Co, Unit Cu533 St Martins Square Middle Mall, Bullring, Birmingham, B5 4BE Tel: 0121-616 2407 Fax: 0121-616 1448 E-mail: bullring@tiffinbite.com

INDICATING ELECTRICAL INSTRUMENTATION

Acksen Ltd, 42 University Road, Belfast, BT7 1NJ Tel: (028) 9020 1050 Fax: (028) 9020 1060 E-mail: sales@acksen.com
Amtek Instrumentation Engineers, 8 Mexico Lane, Phillack, Hayle, Cornwall, TR27 5AG Tel: (01736) 754015 Fax: (01736) 759389
Colwick Instruments Ltd, PO Box 8268, Nottingham, NG3 6AJ Tel: 0115-962 2999 Fax: 0115-961 4582 E-mail: enquires@colwickinstruments.co.uk
Instrument Solutions, The Laurels, The Square, Angmering, Littlehampton, West Sussex, BN16 4EA Tel: (01903) 856846 Fax: (01903) 856516 E-mail: info@instrumentsolutions.com
Kaiku Ltd, Greenheys Business Centre, Pencroft Way, Manchester, M15 6JJ Tel: 0161-227 8900 Fax: 0161-227 8902 E-mail: sales@kaiku.co.uk
Support Instrumentation Ltd, 52 Westhall Rd, Warlingham, Surrey, CR6 9BH Tel: 01883 623399 Fax: 01883 624499
▶ Techniquip Ltd, The Old Brewery Estate, Norton Fitzwarren, Taunton, Somerset, TA2 6RN Tel: (01823) 351255 Fax: (01823) 324824 E-mail: sales@techniquip.co.uk
Wirac Automation Ltd, 5 Parker Court, Dunston, Gateshead, Tyne & Wear, NE11 9EW Tel: 0191-460 1177 Fax: 0191-460 1079 E-mail: wirac@aol.com

INDICATOR LAMPS

Interactive Components, 2A Patrick Way, Aylesbury, Buckinghamshire, HP21 9XH Tel: (01296) 425656 Fax: (01296) 395332 E-mail: interactive@bucksnet.co.uk
Marl International Ltd, Morcambe Road, Ulverston, Cumbria, LA12 7RY Tel: (01229) 582430 Fax: (01229) 585155 E-mail: sales@marl.co.uk

Tranilamp Ltd, 69-70 Eastern Way, Bury St. Edmunds, Suffolk, IP32 7AB Tel: (01284) 767055 Fax: (01284) 701921 E-mail: sales@tranilamp.co.uk

INDICATORS, LEVEL, OIL TANK

▶ Payne's Heating & Plumbing Services, Oak Tree Barn, Lewes Road, Blackboys, Uckfield, East Sussex, TN22 5JL Tel: (01825) 891720 Fax: (01825) 891721 E-mail: keith@paynes-heating.co.uk

INDIRECT FIRED HEATERS

Elan Dragonair Ltd, 162 Southampton Road, Portsmouth, PO6 4RY Tel: (023) 9237 6451 Fax: (023) 9237 0411
Flaretec Alloys & Equipment Ltd, Hardwick View Road, Holmewood, Chesterfield, Derbyshire, S42 5SA Tel: (01246) 853522 Fax: (01246) 852415 E-mail: contact@flaretec.com

INDOOR AIR QUALITY MONITORING AND MANAGEMENT CONSULTANCY OR SERVICES

Air Quality Assurance, 1 Dunnings Lane, Rochester, Kent, ME1 1YB Tel: (01634) 832895 Fax: (01634) 832882
▶ Aquacair Ltd, 40 Parklands Road, Chichester, West Sussex, PO19 3DT Tel: (01243) 790808 Fax: (01243) 790809 E-mail: sales@aquacair.co.uk
Enstec Services, 141 Queen Ediths Way, Cambridge, CB1 8PT Tel: (01223) 566471 Fax: (01223) 413800 E-mail: ss_ens@netcomuk.co.uk
Marsh Environmental, Unit 8, 69 St. Marks Road, London, W10 6JG Tel: (020) 8962 0111 Fax: (020) 8962 0486 E-mail: enquiries@marshltd.co.uk
Towerite Environmental Consultants, Old Road, Lamport, Northampton, NN6 9HF Tel: (01604) 686772 Fax: (01604) 686773 E-mail: info@towerite.co.uk
Westfield Caledonian Ltd, 4 Mollins Court, Cumbernauld, Glasgow, G68 9HP Tel: (01236) 786300 Fax: (01236) 786301 E-mail: info@west-cal.co.uk

INDOOR GAMES

▶ Cardinal Sports Ltd, Newbridge Industrial Estate, Newbridge, Midlothian, EH28 8PJ Tel: 0131-335 3145 Fax: 0131-333 2133
▶ Chiltern Games & Puzzles, PO Box 5, Llanfyllin, Powys, SY22 5WD Tel: (01691) 648864

INDOOR PLAY EQUIPMENT

Eibe Play Ltd, Eibe House, Home Farm, A3 By-Pass Road, Hurtmore, Godalming, Surrey, GU8 6AD Tel: (01483) 813834 Fax: (01483) 813851 E-mail: eibe@eibe.co.uk

INDUCED DRAUGHT FANS

Flamgard Engineering Ltd, Unit 2-3 Pontnewynydd Industrial Estate, Pontnewynydd, Pontypool, Gwent, NP4 6YW Tel: (01495) 757347 Fax: (01495) 755443 E-mail: sales@flamgard.co.uk

INDUCTION BILLET HEATERS, FORGING

Newelco (Ukside) Ltd, Church Street, Newport, Gwent, NP20 2TW Tel: (01633) 263021 Fax: (01633) 264413 E-mail: sales@newelco.co.uk

INDUCTION COOKING EQUIPMENT

Gilberts Food Equipment Ltd, Gilbert House, 1 Warwick Place, Borehamwood, Hertfordshire, WD6 1UA Tel: (0845) 2300681 Fax: (0845) 2300682 E-mail: info@topgourmet.co.uk
M C S Technical Products Ltd, Factory 1, Cheney Manor Industrial Estate, Swindon, SN2 2PN Tel: (01793) 538308 Fax: (01793) 522324 E-mail: sales@mcstechproducts.co.uk

INDUCTION FURNACES

Inductotherm Europe Ltd, The Furlong, Berry Hill Industrial Estate, Droitwich, Worcestershire, WR9 9AH Tel: (01905) 795100 Fax: (01905) 795138 E-mail: sales@inductotherm.co.uk

Inductotherm Heating & Welding Technologies Ltd, Thermatool House, Crockford Lane, Chineham, Basingstoke, Hampshire, RG24 8NA Tel: (01256) 337722 Fax: (01256) 467224 E-mail: sales@inductoheat.co.uk
Otto Junker (U K) Ltd, Kingsbury Road, Curdworth, Sutton Coldfield, West Midlands, B76 9EE Tel: (01675) 470551 Fax: (01675) 470645 E-mail: sales@otto-junker.co.uk
RADYNE, Molly Millars Lane, Wokingham, Berks, RG41 2PX Tel: 0118-978 3333 Fax: 0118-977 1729 E-mail: sales@radyne.co.uk

INDUCTION HEAT APPLICATION EQUIPMENT/HEATERS

Cheltenham Induction Heating Ltd, Saxon Way, Cheltenham, Gloucestershire, GL52 6RU Tel: (01242) 222204 Fax: (01242) 224146 E-mail: sales@cihinduction.com
Cheltenham Induction Heating Ltd, Saxon Way, Cheltenham, Gloucestershire, GL52 6RU Tel: (01242) 222204 Fax: (01242) 224146 E-mail: sales@cihinduction.com
Force Engineering Ltd, Old Station Close, Shepshed, Loughborough, Leicestershire, LE12 9NJ Tel: (01509) 506025 Fax: (01509) 505433 E-mail: enquiries@force.co.uk
Inductelec Ltd, 137 Carlisle Street, Sheffield, S4 7LJ Tel: 0114-272 3369 Fax: 0114-276 1499 E-mail: sales@inductelec.co.uk

INDUCTION HEAT TREATMENT, *See also Heat Treatment Services, Metal*

Cheltenham Induction Heating Ltd, Saxon Way, Cheltenham, Gloucestershire, GL52 6RU Tel: (01242) 222204 Fax: (01242) 224146 E-mail: sales@cihinduction.com
Expert Heat Treatments Kent, 12 Tribune Drive, Trinity Trading Estate, Sittingbourne, Kent, ME10 2PT Tel: (01795) 426545 Fax: (01795) 424449 E-mail: southsales@eht.co.uk
Hartek Engineers Ltd, Hadrian Works, Wellington Road, Dunston, Gateshead, Tyne & Wear, NE11 9JL Tel: 0191-460 0672 Fax: 0191-460 1555 E-mail: techservices.ne@btinternet.com
HHT Midlands Ltd, Heath Road, Darlaston, West Midlands, WS10 8LU Tel: 0121-526 4771 Fax: 0121-526 4153 E-mail: sales@hht.co.uk
Induction Heat Treatment Ltd, Station Works, Station Road, New Mills, High Peak, Derbyshire, SK22 3JB Tel: (01663) 742483 Fax: (01663) 746223 E-mail: sales@inductionheat.co.uk
Induction Heating Service Ltd, Unit 28, Watery Lane Industrial Estate, Willenhall, West Midlands, WV13 3SU Tel: (01902) 605578 Fax: (01902) 605652 E-mail: sales@david-finch.fsnet.co.uk
Midland Heat Treatments Ltd, Chillington Works, Hickman Avenue, Wolverhampton, WV1 2BU Tel: (01902) 450757 Fax: (01902) 459093 E-mail: induction@midland-heat.co.uk
Paul Engineering Co. Ltd, Victoria Works, North Street, Coventry, CV2 3FW Tel: (024) 7645 8040 Fax: (024) 7644 9494
Pipeline Induction Heat Ltd, Farrington Road, Burnley, Lancashire, BB11 5SW Tel: (01282) 415323 Fax: (01282) 415326 E-mail: sales@pih.co.uk
Quantum Heat Treatment & Brazing Ltd, 43 Barton Road, Bletchley, Milton Keynes, MK2 3DE Tel: (01908) 642242 Fax: (01908) 368629 E-mail: quantumheat@hotmail.com

INDUCTION HEAT TREATMENT EQUIPMENT, *See also Heat Treatment etc*

RADYNE, Molly Millars Lane, Wokingham, Berks, RG41 2PX Tel: 0118-978 3333 Fax: 0118-977 1729 E-mail: sales@radyne.co.uk

INDUCTION HEATING EQUIPMENT MANUFRS

Cheltenham Induction Heating Ltd, Saxon Way, Cheltenham, Gloucestershire, GL52 6RU Tel: (01242) 222204 Fax: (01242) 224146 E-mail: sales@cihinduction.com
Cheltenham Induction Heating Ltd, Saxon Way, Cheltenham, Gloucestershire, GL52 6RU Tel: (01242) 222204 Fax: (01242) 224146 E-mail: sales@cihinduction.com
Inductelec Ltd, 137 Carlisle Street, Sheffield, S4 7LJ Tel: 0114-272 3369 Fax: 0114-276 1499 E-mail: sales@inductelec.co.uk
Inductotherm Heating & Welding Technologies Ltd, Thermatool House, Crockford Lane, Chineham, Basingstoke, Hampshire, RG24 8NA Tel: (01256) 337722 Fax: (01256) 467224 E-mail: sales@inductoheat.co.uk
M F Induction Heating, Martindale Trading Estate, Martindale, Cannock, Staffordshire, WS11 7XL Tel: (01543) 570642 Fax: (01543) 574460 E-mail: sales@mfinduction.com
Newelco (Ukside) Ltd, Church Street, Newport, Gwent, NP20 2TW Tel: (01633) 263021 Fax: (01633) 264413 E-mail: sales@newelco.co.uk

INDUCTION HEATING POWER SUPPLIES

▶ Universal Heating Supplies, 97 Heaton Park Road, Newcastle Upon Tyne, NE6 5NR Tel: 0191-209 9399 E-mail: enquires@universalheating.co.uk

INDUCTIVELY COUPLED PLASMA (ICP) SPECTROMETERS

Spectro Analytical UK Ltd, Fountain House, Great Cornbow, Halesowen, West Midlands, B63 3BL Tel: 0121-550 8997 Fax: 0121-550 5165 E-mail: sales@spectro.co.uk

INDUCTORS, ELECTRICAL/ GENERAL PURPOSE

B E C Distribution Ltd, Unit 5, Coronation Grove, Harrogate, North Yorkshire, HG2 8BU Tel: (0845) 4900405 Fax: (0845) 4900406 E-mail: sales@bec.co.uk

Delta Components, The Courtyard, Sevenacres, Smallfield Road, Horne, Horley, Surrey, RH6 9JP Tel: (01342) 844555 Fax: (01342) 844552 E-mail: sales@deltacomponents.com

Electro Inductors, 19-25 Neville Road, Croydon, CR0 2DS Tel: (020) 8684 6100 Fax: (020) 8684 6109 E-mail: sales@aluminium-inductors.co.uk

Pontiac Coil Europe Ltd, PO Box 246, Nottingham, NG2 1NQ Tel: 0115-986 1126 Fax: 0115-986 0563 E-mail: info@pontiaccoil.co.uk

INDUSTRIAL ADHESIVE TAPES,

See also Self-Adhesive Tapes

3M Tapes & Adhesives Group, 3M Centre, Cain Road, Bracknell, Berkshire, RG12 8HT Tel: (01344) 858000 Fax: (01344) 858278

Abaco Industrial Tapes, Marnic House, 37 Shooters Hill Road, Blackheath, London, SE3 7HS Tel: (020) 8858 8100 Fax: (020) 8305 1401 E-mail: tapes@marnic.com

Apollo Chemicals Holdings Ltd, Sandy Way, Amington Industrial Estate, Tamworth, Staffordshire, B77 4DS Tel: (01827) 54281 Fax: (01827) 53030 E-mail: sales@apolloadhesives.com

Biscor Ltd, Kingsmark Freeway, Bradford, West Yorkshire, BD12 7HW Tel: (01274) 694684 Fax: (01274) 694685 E-mail: info@biscor.com

Bruce Douglas Ultratape Ltd, Kilspindie Road, Dunsinane Industrial Estate, Dundee, DD2 3JP Tel: (01382) 832999 Fax: (01382) 833422 E-mail: sales@ultratape.com

FineCal (Cymru) Ltd, 3 Rhymney River Bridge Road, Rumney, Cardiff, CF23 9AF Tel: (029) 2046 2644 Fax: (029) 2048 4522 E-mail: sales@finecal.co.uk

Hadleigh Enterprises Ltd, Unit 11, Buckingham Square, Wickford, Essex, SS11 8YQ Tel: (01268) 572255 Fax: (01268) 572121 E-mail: info@hadleigh.u-net.com

Hi Bond Tapes Ltd, 1 Crucible Road, Corby, Northamptonshire, NN17 5TS Tel: (01536) 260022 Fax: (01536) 260044 E-mail: sales@hi-bondtapes.co.uk

J I T Industrial Products Ltd, 16 Melford Road, Righead Industrial Estate, Bellshill, Lanarkshire, ML4 3LR Tel: (01698) 748290 Fax: (01698) 749141 E-mail: sales@jitwebsite.com

Jeaton Tapes & Abrasives Ltd, Unit 1, Manchester Mill Industrial Estate, Geoffrey St, Preston, PR1 5NR Tel: (01772) 703636 Fax: (01772) 701271 E-mail: sales@jeaton.co.uk

Le Mark Self Adhesives Ltd, Houghton Hill Industries, Houghton Hill Farm, Houghton, Huntingdon, Cambridgeshire, PE28 2DH Tel: (01480) 494540 Fax: (01480) 494206 E-mail: info@lemark.co.uk

Marnic P.L.C., Armstrong Road, London, SE18 6RS Tel: (020) 8312 7200 Fax: (020) 8312 7250 E-mail: tapes@marnic.com

Nitto UK Ltd, Unit2 Berkshire Business Centre, Berkshire Drive, Thatcham, Berkshire, RG19 4EW Tel: (01635) 872172 Fax: (01635) 872332 E-mail: nitto_uk@nittoeur.com

P A L Adhesive Products Ltd, Old Park Industrial Estate, Old Park Road, Wednesbury, West Midlands, WS10 9LR Tel: 0121-556 6686 Fax: 0121-505 1487 E-mail: sales@paladhesives.co.uk

Prima Tapes & Labels Ltd, Prima House, Faraday Way, Orpington, Kent, BR5 3QW Tel: (01689) 816111 Fax: (01689) 816010 E-mail: sales@prima-tapes.com

Saint Gobain Performance Plastics, 13 Earlstrees Road, Earlstrees Industrial Estate, Corby, Northamptonshire, NN17 4AZ Tel: (01536) 276000 Fax: (01536) 203427 E-mail: pplcorbyuk@aol.com

Saint Gobain Technical Fabrics UK Ltd, 15-19 Pit Hey Place, Skelmersdale, Lancashire, WN8 9PS Tel: (01695) 723946 Fax: (01695) 723947

▶ Steratape Ltd, Carnaby Industrial Estate, Lancaster Road, Carnaby, Bridlington, East Yorkshire, YO15 3QY Tel: (01262) 603721 Fax: (01262) 400028 E-mail: carl@steratape.com

tesa UK Ltd, Yeomans Drive, Blakelands, Milton Keynes, MK14 5LS Tel: 0845 4941752 Fax: (01908) 211555 E-mail: ukenquiry@tesa.com

Tritel Ltd, Unit 1 Bolney Grange Business Park, Hickstead, Haywards Heath, West Sussex, RH17 5PB Tel: (01444) 871188 Fax: (01444) 871199 E-mail: sales@tritel.co.uk

R.A. Wood Adhesive Tapes Ltd, Unit 2 Waterside Business Centre, Wolverhampton Road, Cannock, Staffordshire, WS11 1SN Tel: (01543) 578331 Fax: (01543) 572301

INDUSTRIAL ADHESIVES

▶ 5 Star Adhesives, P O Box 96, Liverpool, L17 3BY Tel: 0151-733 7182 Fax: 0151-733 7182 E-mail: info@glue-shop.com

Ace Adhesives Ltd, Shenstone Drive, Walsall, WS9 8TP Tel: (01922) 459393 Fax: (01922) 743417 E-mail: sales@aceadhesives.com

Adhesive & Coating Supplies, Sherborne St West, Salford, M3 7LF Tel: 0161-835 1420 Fax: 0161-839 3543 E-mail: sales@chemipat.co.uk

Adhesive Developments Ltd, John Lee Fold, Middleton, Manchester, M24 2LR Tel: 0161-643 3965 Fax: 0161-643 7889 E-mail: gluee@supanet.com

Adhesives International Ltd, Northleigh Business Park, Woodstock Road, North Leigh, Witney, Oxfordshire, OX29 6RN Tel: (01993) 882749 Fax: (01993) 883887 E-mail: info@adhesivesintnl.com

Anglo American Adhesives, Cg10 Warrington Business Park, Long Lane, Warrington, WA2 8TX Tel: (01925) 419111 Fax: (01925) 419222 E-mail: colin.fitz@virgin.net

Anixter Adhesives, 3 Edmond Road, Sheffield, S2 4EB Tel: 0114-275 1496 Fax: 0114-269 7171 E-mail: sheffield.adesco@infast.com

Bin UK Ltd, Prince Street, Bolton, BL1 2NP Tel: (01204) 366997 Fax: (01204) 366998 E-mail: uk_sales@binkemi.com

Bondloc UK Ltd, Alton Works, Long Bank, Bewdley, Worcestershire, DY12 2UJ Tel: (01299) 269269 Fax: (01299) 269210 E-mail: sales@bondloc.co.uk

▶ Bostik Findley Ltd, Common Road, Stafford, ST16 3EH Tel: (01785) 272727 Fax: (01785) 257236 E-mail: jackie.scarfe@bostikfindley.com

Britannia Adhesives Ltd, 4b Horndon Industrial Park, Station Road, West Horndon, Brentwood, Essex, CM13 3XL Tel: (01277) 810480 Fax: (01277) 812028 E-mail: john.lown@britannia-adhesives.co.uk

Building Adhesives Ltd, Longton Road, Stoke-on-Trent, ST4 8JB Tel: (01782) 591100 Fax: (01782) 591101 E-mail: info@building-adhesives.com

C B Adhesives, Adlington Industrial Estate, Adlington, Macclesfield, Cheshire, SK10 4NL Tel: (01625) 850180 Fax: (01625) 875932

Caswell & Co Ltd, 6 Princewood Road, Earlstrees Industrial Estate, Corby, Northamptonshire, NN17 4AP Tel: (01536) 464800 Fax: (01536) 464801 E-mail: sales@caswell-adhesives.co.uk

Cedesa Ltd, Chater Lea Building, Icknield Way, Letchworth Garden City, Hertfordshire, SG6 1WT Tel: (01462) 480764 Fax: (01462) 480765 E-mail: neil.wildon@cedesa.co.uk

Coastline Adhesive Tapes Ltd, 8 Skye Road, Shaw Farm Industrial Estate, Shawfarm Industrial Estate, Prestwick, Ayrshire, KA9 2TA Tel: (01292) 470289 Fax: (01292) 671287 E-mail: sales@coastlinetapes.co.uk

Components Direct, Nunn Brook Road, County Estate, Huthwaite, Sutton-In-Ashfield, Nottinghamshire, NG17 2HU Tel: (01623) 788400 Fax: (01623) 788488 E-mail: sales@comdirect.co.uk

Couldridge Industrial Supplies, Crucible Close, Mushet Industrial Park, Coleford, Gloucestershire, GL16 8RE Tel: (01594) 833177 Fax: (01594) 837423

F Ball & Co. Ltd, Churnetside Business Park, Station Road, Cheddleton, Leek, Staffordshire, ST13 7RS Tel: (01538) 361633 Fax: (01538) 361622 E-mail: webmaster@f-ball.co.uk

Forbo Swift Adhesives Ltd, Bridge Street, Chatteris, Cambridgeshire, PE16 6RD Tel: (01354) 692345 Fax: (01354) 696661

Formulated Resins Ltd, Greg Street, Stockport, Cheshire, SK5 7LY Tel: 0161-480 2121 Fax: 0161-480 4445 E-mail: info@formulatedresins.com

Gurit, St. Cross Business Park, Newport, Isle of Wight, PO30 5WU Tel: (01983) 828000 Fax: (01983) 828100 E-mail: info@gurit.com

H B Fuller UK Ltd, Outram Road, Globe Lane Industrial Estate, Dukinfield, Cheshire, SK16 4XE Tel: (01773) 601315 Fax: (0161) 666 0667

Henkel Ltd, Apollo Court, Bishops Square Business Park, Hatfield, Hertfordshire, AL10 9EY Tel: (01707) 635000 Fax: (01707) 635099 E-mail: ukcorp.communications@henkel.co.uk

Howarine, Calvert Ltd, Howarine House, 5-6 Empire Way, Wembley, Middlesex, HA9 0XA Tel: (0870) 4420077 Fax: (0870) 4420078 E-mail: graham@howarine.co.uk

L J F UK Ltd, Centurion Way, Meridian Business Park, Leicester, LE19 1WH Tel: 0116-289 1888 Fax: 0116-289 2283 E-mail: sales@ljf-uk.com

Leeson Polyurethanes Ltd, Hermes Close, Tachbrook Park, Warwick, CV34 6NW Tel: (01926) 833367 Fax: (01926) 881469 E-mail: sales@lpultd.com

Microbus Designs Ltd, Treadaway Hill, Loudwater, High Wycombe, Buckinghamshire, HP10 9QL Tel: (01628) 537300 Fax: (01628) 537301 E-mail: microbus@microbus.co.uk

Neutra Rust International Ltd, 24-31 London Road, Newbury, Berkshire, RG14 1JX Tel: (01784) 455454 Fax: (01784) 450752

Orapi Ltd, 1 Rosse Street, Bradford, West Yorkshire, BD8 9AS Tel: (01274) 822000 Fax: (01274) 822002 E-mail: jo.greenwood@orapi.com

Polybond Ltd, Unit 6 William Street, Northam, Southampton, SO14 5QH Tel: (023) 8022 3266 Fax: (0870) 0527587 E-mail: tom@polybond.co.uk

Powerbond Adhesives Ltd, 253 Scotia Road, Stoke-on-Trent, ST6 6AB Tel: (01782) 823874 Fax: (01782) 837038 E-mail: info@preo.co.uk

Premier Bearing Co. Ltd, Chaucer Street, Northampton, NN2 7HB Tel: (01604) 718107 Fax: (01604) 720654 E-mail: sales@premierbearing.co.uk

Protak GB Ltd, Protak House, E1 Telford Road, Bicester, Oxfordshire, OX26 4LD Tel: (01869) 369997 Fax: (01869) 369994 E-mail: sales@protak.co.uk

R W Greeff, Tame Park, Vanguard, Wilnecote, Tamworth, Staffordshire, B77 5DY Tel: (01827) 255200 Fax: (01827) 255255 E-mail: rwgreeff@univareurope.com

Sealock Ltd, Scott Close, Walworth Industrial Estate, Andover, Hampshire, SP10 5NU Tel: (01264) 358185 Fax: (01264) 332203 E-mail: sales@sealock.co.uk

Sovereign Chemical Ltd, Park Road, Barrow-In-Furness, Cumbria, LA14 4EQ Tel: (01229) 870800 Fax: (01229) 870850 E-mail: sales@sovchem.co.uk

Sovereign Specialty Chemicals Ltd, Winthorpe Road, Newark, Nottinghamshire, NG24 2AL Tel: (01636) 646711 Fax: (01636) 605187

Stelmax Ltd, 21-23 Gloster Road, Martlesham Heath, Ipswich, IP5 3RD Tel: (01473) 626651 Fax: (01473) 610651 E-mail: stelmaxltd@aol.com

Strongbond Adhesives Ltd, Beehive Works, Hollins Lane, Bury, Lancashire, BL9 8AA Tel: 0161-766 2618 Fax: 0161-767 9024 E-mail: sales@strongbond.co.uk

Tetrosyl Ltd, Bevis Green Works, Mill Road, Walmersley, Bury, Lancashire, BL9 6RE Tel: 0161-764 5981 Fax: 0161-797 5899 E-mail: info@tetrosyl.com

ThreeBond Europe SAS, 5 Newmarket Court, Kingston, Milton Keynes, MK10 0AS Tel: (01908) 285000 Fax: (01908) 285001 E-mail: mark.beeson@threebond.co.uk

Walker Rubber & Plastics Ltd, Last House, 21-23 Burnet Road, Sweetbriar Industrial Estate, Norwich, NR3 2BS Tel: (01603) 487371 Fax: (01603) 406502 E-mail: sales@walker-rubber.co.uk

INDUSTRIAL AEROSOLS

Baroney Universal Products plc, Barony Industrial Estate, Auchinleck, Cumnock, Ayrshire, KA18 2BL Tel: (01290) 426400 Fax: (01290) 426399

Hydrokem Aerosols Ltd, Hickmans Road, Birkenhead, Merseyside, CH41 1JH Tel: 0151-630 4414 Fax: 0151-638 2353 E-mail: sales@hydrokem.co.uk

▶ Intercontinental Chemical Products Ltd, 56-62 Lincoln Road, Tuxford, Newark, Nottinghamshire, NG22 0HP Tel: (01777) 870756 Fax: (01777) 871766 E-mail: sales@intchems.com

New Guard Coatings Ltd, Sandbeck Way, Wetherby, West Yorkshire, LS22 7DN Tel: (01937) 586311 Fax: (01937) 580041 E-mail: sales@newguard.co.uk

Old Park Engineering Services Ltd, Woods Lane, Cradley Heath, West Midlands, B64 7AN Tel: (01384) 412550 Fax: (01384) 410784 E-mail: oldpark@blueyonder.co.uk

Specialised Chemicals Ltd, Spittlegate Level, Grantham, Lincolnshire, NG31 7UH Tel: (01476) 567615 Fax: (01476) 560837 E-mail: sales@specialisedchemicals.com

INDUSTRIAL AGITATORS

Mixing Solutions Ltd, Unit G Venture House, Bone Lane, Newbury, Berkshire, RG14 5SH Tel: (01635) 275300 Fax: (01635) 275375 E-mail: sales@mixingsolutions.com

Premier Colloid Mills, Building A302 Vickers Drive, Brooklands Industrial Park, Weybridge, Surrey, KT13 0YU Tel: (01932) 355366 Fax: (01932) 352660 E-mail: sales@bptskerman.com

INDUSTRIAL AIR CLEANING EQUIPMENT OR SYSTEMS

Aircare Europe Ltd, Unit 27 Tatton Court, Kingsland Grange, Woolston, Warrington, WA1 4RR Tel: (08707) 445588 Fax: (01925) 850325 E-mail: info@aircareeurope.com

C E-Air UK Ltd, Newton Moor Industrial Estate, Newton, Hyde, Cheshire, SK14 4LG Tel: 0161-368 1476 Fax: 0161-367 8145 E-mail: sales@ceair.co.uk

Freshtec Ltd, PO Box 18, Dawlish, Devon, EX7 9YL Tel: (01626) 867090 Fax: (01626) 867199 E-mail: sales@freshtec.co.uk

▶ LTL, Pear Mill Industrial Estate, Stockport Road West, Bredbury, Stockport, Cheshire, SK6 2BP Tel: 0161-406 8601 Fax: 0161-406 8073 E-mail: info@fresh-air.co.uk

P H S Group Kleenair, Western Industrial Estate, Lon-Y-Llyn, Caerphilly, Mid Glamorgan, CF83 1XH Tel: (029) 2080 9111 Fax: (029) 2086 3288 E-mail: sales@phs.co.uk

R G K (UK) Ltd, Champfleurie House, Linlithgow, West Lothian, EH49 6NB Tel: (01506) 847999 Fax: (01506) 847174 E-mail: sales@rgk.co.uk

Tecomak Co Ltd, Valley Industries, Tonbridge Road, Hadlow, Tonbridge, Kent, TN11 0AH Tel: (01732) 852250 Fax: (01732) 852251 E-mail: sales@tecomak.co.uk

W H K (Walton) Ltd, Walton Business Centre, 44-46 Terrace Road, Walton-on-Thames, Surrey, KT12 2SD Tel: (01932) 247979 Fax: (01932) 245948 E-mail: colin@whk.co.uk

INDUSTRIAL AIR COMPRESSORS

A J Metal Products Ltd, Cookley Wharf Industrial Estate, Bay 11, Leys Rd, Brierley Hill, West Midlands, DY5 3UP Tel: (01384) 74301 Fax: (01384) 485772 E-mail: sales@ajmetals.co.uk

Adams Ricardo Ltd, Millbrook Road, Yate, Bristol, BS37 5PB Tel: (01454) 311646 Fax: (01454) 324114 E-mail: sales@adamsricardo.com

Air Methods Ltd, Frederick House, Anchor Lane, Bilston, West Midlands, WV14 9NE Tel: (01902) 884466 Fax: (01902) 884632 E-mail: sales@airmethods.co.uk

Airmark, 6 Becket Road, London, N18 3PN Tel: (020) 8807 7891 Fax: (020) 8884 3898 E-mail: airmarkcom@aol.com

Bambi Air Compressors Ltd, 152 Thimble Mill Lane, Birmingham, B7 5HT Tel: 0121-322 2299 Fax: 0121-322 2297 E-mail: sales@bambi-air.co.uk

W. Bateman & Co., Garstang Rd, Barton, Preston, PR3 5AA Tel: (01772) 862948 Fax: (01772) 861639 E-mail: sales@bateman-sellarc.co.uk

Becker U K Ltd, Unit C, Brighton Street Trading Park, Hull, HU3 4XS Tel: (01482) 835280 Fax: (01482) 831275 E-mail: sales@becker.co.uk

Belliss & Morcom Ltd, Chequers Bridge, Gloucester, GL1 4LL Tel: (01452) 338338 Fax: (01452) 338307 E-mail: indsales@gardnerdenver.co.uk

Central Air International Ltd, 47-59 Green Lane, Small Heath, Birmingham, B9 5BU Tel: 0121-773 5630 Fax: 0121-773 1378 E-mail: info@centralaircompressors.com

Clarke International Ltd, Hemnall Street, Epping, Essex, CM16 4LG Tel: (01992) 565300 Fax: (01992) 561562 E-mail: sales@clarkeinternational.com

CompAir UK Ltd, Claybrook Drive, Washford Industrial Estate, Redditch, Worcestershire, B98 0DS Tel: (01527) 525522 Fax: (01527) 521140 E-mail: sales@compair.com

Compressor Valve Engineering Ltd, 4 Burnell Road, Ellesmere Port, CH65 5EX Tel: 0151-355 5937 Fax: 0151-357 1098 E-mail: sales@compvalve.co.uk

Cooper Freer Ltd, Kenilworth Drive, Oadby, Leicester, LE2 5LG Tel: 0116-271 0401 E-mail: sales@cooperfreer.co.uk

Durr Technik (UK) Ltd, Unit 5, Ashmead Business Centre, Ashmead Road, Keynsham, Bristol, BS31 1SX Tel: 0117-986 0414 Fax: 0117-986 0416 E-mail: info@durrtechnik.co.uk

H P C Engineering Plc, Victoria Gardens, Victoria Gardens Industrial Estate, Burgess Hill, West Sussex, RH15 9RQ Tel: (01444) 241671 Fax: (01444) 247304 E-mail: info@hpcplc.co.uk

Ingersoll Rand Co. Ltd, Swan Lane, Hindley Green, Wigan, Lancashire, WN2 4EZ Tel: (01942) 257171 Fax: (01942) 522747

Machine Mart Ltd, Machine Mart House, Derwent Street, Derby, DE1 2ED Tel: (01332) 290931 Fax: (01332) 366531 E-mail: sales@machinemart.co.uk

Midland Diving Equipment Ltd, 57 Sparkenhoe Street, Leicester, LE2 0TD Tel: 0116-212 4262 Fax: 0116-212 4263 E-mail: info@midlanddiving.com

P G Reeves & Sons, 129-133 Dogsthorpe Road, Peterborough, PE1 3AH Tel: (01733) 563887 Fax: (01733) 555582

Rep Air Services, Unit 23 Monarch Way, Loughborough, Leicestershire, LE11 5XG Tel: (01509) 213452 Fax: (01509) 212102 E-mail: sales@rep-air.co.uk

▶ S D I Equipment Ltd, Unit 13, Sovereign Enterprise Park, Salford Quays, Salford, M50 3UP Tel: 0161-873 8597 Fax: 0161-873 7261 E-mail: sdiequip@aol.com

S I P Industrial Products Ltd, Gelders Hall Road, Shepshed, Loughborough, Leicestershire, LE12 9NH Tel: (01509) 500300 Fax: (01509) 503154 E-mail: sales@sip-group.com

Standardair Ltd, Harleyford Estate, Henley Road, Marlow, Buckinghamshire, SL7 2DZ Tel: (01628) 472055 Fax: (01628) 473900 E-mail: sales@standardair.co.uk

Tailored Panels, Unit 4 Minster Park, Grundymore Estate West Moors, Wimborne, Dorset, BH21 6QW Tel: (01202) 871998 Fax: (01202) 861215 E-mail: tailored-panel@hotmail.com

Thorite Ltd, 55 Lowfields Road, Leeds, LS12 6BS Tel: 0113-244 4554 Fax: 0113-242 4700 E-mail: leeds@thorite.co.uk

▶ indicates data change since last edition

INDUSTRIAL AIR CONDITIONING (AC) EQUIPMENT

A C 2000, North Bridge Place, Frog Island, Leicester, LE3 5BG Tel: 0116-262 0411 Fax: 0116-251 8967 E-mail: aircon@ac2000.co.uk

Accord Air Systems, Lawmans Centre, 28-32 Beddington Lane, Croydon, CR0 4TB Tel: (020) 8401 2058 Fax: (020) 8401 2059 E-mail: accordair@lineone.net

Advanced Environmental Ltd, 31 Ermine St, Thundridge, Ware, Hertfordshire, SG12 0SY Tel: (01920) 487450

Air Handling Systems Ltd, Unit 3-5 Furnace Industrial Estate, Shildon, County Durham, DL4 1QB Tel: (01388) 776287 Fax: (01388) 775494 E-mail: general@ahs.uk.com

Anchor Ventilation Co Britain Ltd, Malt Lane, Stoke-on-Trent, ST3 1RR Tel: (01782) 312809 Fax: (01782) 311138

Atlantic Refrigeration Ltd, Peel Street, Northam, Southampton, SO14 5QT Tel: (023) 8033 9141 Fax: (023) 8022 9840 E-mail: grantwest@atlantic-refrig.co.uk

B B J Engineering Ltd, Apex Way, Diplocks Industrial Estate, Hailsham, East Sussex, BN27 3WA Tel: (01323) 848842 Fax: (01323) 848846 E-mail: sandy@aspenpumps.com

Basingstoke Control Systems, 12 Mallard Close, Basingstoke, Hampshire, RG22 5JP Tel: (01256) 466639 Fax: (01256) 842876 E-mail: basingstokecobtrolsystems@ukonline.co.uk

Beehive Coils Ltd, Studlands Park Industrial Estate, Newmarket, Suffolk, CB8 7AU Tel: (01638) 664134 Fax: (01638) 661623 E-mail: info@beehivecoils.co.uk

Bostel Brothers Ltd, 1-3 The Compound, Northease Close, Hove, East Sussex, BN3 8LJ Tel: (01273) 430264 Fax: (01273) 422605

Broughton Electroair Products, Clive Works, Edward Street, Redditch, Worcestershire, B97 6HA Tel: (01527) 597567 Fax: (01527) 67603 E-mail: sales@broughtoneap.com

Calserv Surveying Instruments, 5 Prospect Way, Rugby, Warwickshire, CV21 3UU Tel: (01788) 553666 Fax: (01788) 551666 E-mail: calserv@calserv.freeserve.co.uk

Carrier Service, Kettles Wood Drive, Birmingham, B32 3DB Tel: 0121-421 9610 Fax: 0121-421 8147 E-mail: tosibha.carrier@utc.com

Ciat Ozonair Ltd, 5 Byfleet Technical Centre, Canada Road, Byfleet, Surrey, KT14 7JX Tel: (01932) 354955 Fax: (01932) 342998 E-mail: sales@ciat.co.uk

City Engineering Ltd, 9 Cygnus Business Centre, Dalmeyer Road, London, NW10 2XA Tel: (020) 8451 4930 Fax: (020) 8459 1120 E-mail: roul@cityengineering.fsnet.uk

Cleen Flo Manchester Ltd, 5 Lower Chatham Street, Manchester, M1 5QL Tel: 0161-237 3880 Fax: 0161-236 9388

Clivet UK, Unit 4 Kingdom Close, Segenworth East, Fareham, Hampshire, PO15 5TJ Tel: (01489) 550621 Fax: (01489) 573033 E-mail: info@clivet-uk.co.uk

Clyde Air Conditioning Ltd, 72 North Vennel, Lanark, ML11 7PT Tel: (01555) 661366 Fax: (01555) 661367

Colman Moducel, Oldfields Business Park, Birrell Street, Stoke-on-Trent, ST4 3ES Tel: (01782) 599995 Fax: (01782) 599220 E-mail: sales@eaton-williams.com

▶ Dalair Ltd, Southern Way, Wednesbury, West Midlands, WS10 7BU Tel: 0121-556 9944 Fax: 0121-502 3124 E-mail: sales@dalair.co.uk

Denco Air Conditioning, Dolphin House, Morton On Legg, Hereford, HR4 8DS Tel: (01432) 277277 Fax: (01432) 268005

E C E Environmental Control Equipment Ltd, Harvel Works, Harvel, Meopham, Gravesend, Kent, DA13 0BT Tel: (01474) 814432 Fax: (01474) 812488 E-mail: richardbarnes@ece.uk.com

Elyo UK Ltd, 1 Sampson Road North, Birmingham, B11 1BL Tel: 0121-773 8421 Fax: 0121-773 2082

Envirotec Ltd, Desborough Park Road, High Wycombe, Buckinghamshire, HP12 3BX Tel: (01494) 525342 Fax: (01494) 440889 E-mail: sales@envirotec.co.uk

Et Environmental Ltd, 47 Central Avenue, West Molesey, Surrey, KT8 2QZ Tel: (020) 8783 0033 Fax: (020) 8783 0140 E-mail: diffusion@etenv.co.uk

Exact Air Ltd, 39 Horton Drive, Middleton Cheney, Banbury, Oxfordshire, OX17 2LN Tel: (01295) 710831 Fax: (01295) 711892 E-mail: sales@exactair.co.uk

GDK Air Conditioning & Refrigeration, Builders Yard, Barton Road, Bramley, Guildford, Surrey, GU5 0EB Tel: (01483) 894160 Fax: (01483) 894162 E-mail: info@gdkltd.co.uk

Hanover Maloney (U K) Ltd, Westgate, Aldridge, Walsall, WS9 8EX Tel: (01922) 450200 Fax: (01922) 450210 E-mail: info@hanover-maloney.co.uk

Interlock Flexible Products Ltd, 1 Burbidge Road, Birmingham, B9 4US Tel: 0121-766 7766 Fax: 0121-766 7799 E-mail: sales@interlockflex.com

Inviron Ltd, Deben House, 1 Selsdon Way, City Harbour, London, E14 9GL Tel: (020) 7515 5511 Fax: (020) 7515 5551 E-mail: admin@inviron.co.uk

Lee Air Conditioning Services Ltd, Lee House, Lower Road, Kenley, Surrey, CR8 5NH Tel: (020) 8660 5022 Fax: (020) 8668 0296 E-mail: nick.taylor@leeac.co.uk

Lightfoot Refrigeration Co. Ltd, Unit D2, Premier Business Centre, Newgate Lane, Fareham, Hampshire, PO14 1TY Tel: (01329) 237272 Fax: (01329) 237276 E-mail: office@lightfootrefrigeration.com

Luwa UK Ltd, Wrigley Street, Oldham, OL4 1HN Tel: 0161-624 8185 Fax: 0161-626 4609 E-mail: service@luwa.co.uk

Mcdowall Air Conditioning, Middlemore La West, Walsall, WS9 8EJ Tel: (01922) 454955 Fax: (01922) 454815 E-mail: sales@mcdowalls.co.uk

NGF, Unit 11, Allerton Bywater, Castleford, West Yorkshire, WF10 2DB Tel: (0845) 6444566 Fax: (0845) 6445123 E-mail: sales@ngfindustrialdoors.co.uk

Panasonic Air Conditioning, Panasonic House, Willoughby Road, Bracknell, Berkshire, RG12 8FP Tel: (01344) 853186 Fax: (01344) 853217 E-mail: nicky.dopson@panasonic.co.uk

▶ Polar Bear, 5 Faygate Business Centre, Faygate Lane, Faygate, Horsham, West Sussex, RH12 4DN Tel: (01293) 852258 Fax: (01293) 852244

Puma Products Ltd, Unit 6 Viscount Court, Andover, Hampshire, SP10 5NW Tel: (01264) 333305 Fax: (01264) 333310 E-mail: sales@pumaproducts.co.uk

Reycol S V C Ltd, Unit 6 Lagley Wharfe, Kings Langley, Watford, WD18 9EQ Tel: (01923) 262522 E-mail: reycolsvc@aol.com

Seagoe Technology Ltd, Church Road, Portadown, Craigavon, County Armagh, BT63 5HU Tel: (028) 3833 3131 Fax: (028) 3835 1390 E-mail: info@jltgroup.com

Temperature Control Ltd, 2a Chorlton Street, Manchester, M16 9HN Tel: 0161-872 5722 Fax: 0161-872 8306 E-mail: jeff@temperature-control.co.uk

Thermofrost Cryo plc, Ernest Avenue, London, SE27 0DA Tel: (020) 8670 3663 Fax: (020) 8761 8081E-mail: info@thermofrostcryo.co.uk

▶ Toshiba Carrier UK Ltd, United Technologies House, Guildford Road, Fetcham, Leatherhead, Surrey, KT22 9UT Tel: (01372) 220220 Fax: (01372) 220221

Uniflo Systems Ltd, 9 Neptune Industrial Estate, Neptune Close, Medway City Estate, Rochester, Kent, ME2 4LT Tel: (01634) 716117 Fax: (01634) 290235 E-mail: sales@uniflo.co.uk

York International Ltd, Gardiners La South, Basildon, Essex, SS14 3HE Tel: (01268) 246000 Fax: (01268) 246001 E-mail: sales@york.co.uk

INDUSTRIAL AIR PURIFIERS AND CLEANERS

Healthy Products, 3 Gordon Cres, Broadmeadows, South Normanton, Alfreton, Derbyshire, DE55 3AJ Tel: 01773 863034 Fax: 01773 863034

▶ LTL, Pear Mill Industrial Estate, Stockport Road West, Bredbury, Stockport, Cheshire, SK6 2BP Tel: 0161-406 8601 Fax: 0161-406 8073 E-mail: info@fresh-air.co.uk

North & South Industries, Sidings Court, Doncaster, South Yorkshire, DN4 5NU Tel: (01302) 730037 Fax: (01302) 730073

Oasis Environmental Products, 4 Nova Croft, Coventry, CV5 7FJ Tel: (024) 7646 6540 Fax: (024) 7646 4764

INDUSTRIAL ALTERNATING CURRENT (AC) POWER AMPLIFIERS

Mango Electronics, Mango House, 1 Buckhurst Road, Bexhill-On-Sea, East Sussex, TN40 1QF Tel: (01424) 731500 Fax: (01424) 731502E-mail: colin@mango-electronics.co.uk

INDUSTRIAL ANALYSERS

C S B Design Consultants Ltd, 10 Marathon Paddock, Gillingham, Kent, ME7 4HE Tel: (01634) 571749 Fax: (01634) 322206 E-mail: chrisb@cka1.fsnet.co.uk

Emmerson Process Management Ltd, Heath Place, Bognor Regis, West Sussex, PO22 9SH Tel: (01243) 867554 Fax: (01243) 867554

Kratos Analytical Ltd, Trafford Wharf Road, Trafford Park, Manchester, M17 1GP Tel: 0161-888 4400 Fax: 0161-888 4401 E-mail: sales@kratos.co.uk

L T H Electronics Ltd, Eltelec Works, Chaul End Lane, Luton, LU4 8EZ Tel: (01582) 593693 Fax: (01582) 598036 E-mail: sales@lth.co.uk

Oilab Lubrication Ltd, 31 Sutherland Road, Wolverhampton, WV4 5AR Tel: (01902) 334106 Fax: (01902) 333010 E-mail: sales@oilab.co.uk

INDUSTRIAL APRONS

E & E Workwear, Church Lane, Marple, Stockport, Cheshire, SK6 7AR Tel: 0161-427 6522 Fax: 0161-426 0906 E-mail: eeworkwear@hotmail.com

M G Rubber Co. Ltd, Moorbridge Road, Bingham Industrial Estate, Nottingham, NG13 8GG Tel: (01949) 839112 Fax: (01949) 831357 E-mail: sales@mgrubber.com

M T Developments Lancashire Ltd, Cornfield Cliffe, Industry Street, Darwen, Lancashire, BB3 0HA Tel: (01254) 873837 Fax: (01254) 775268 E-mail: info@aprons.co.uk

INDUSTRIAL ASPHALT CRUSHING PLANT

Phoenix Transworld Ltd, Wharf Way, Glen Parva, Leicester, LE2 9TF Tel: (0870) 7505022 Fax: (0870) 7505033 E-mail: sales@phoenixtransworld.com

INDUSTRIAL ASSEMBLY MACHINES

A B Precision Poole Ltd, 1 Fleets Lane, Poole, Dorset, BH15 3BZ Tel: (01202) 665000 Fax: (01202) 675965 E-mail: automation@abprecision.co.uk

Dynamic Access, Dairy Bungalow, Sodom Lane, Dauntsey, Chippenham, Wiltshire, SN15 4JA Tel: (01249) 891878 Fax: (01249) 891878 E-mail: storm@pgen.net

Precision 2000 Ltd, Princesway, Team Valley Trading Estate, Gateshead, Tyne & Wear, NE11 0TU Tel: 0191-420 0057 Fax: 0191-423 0100 E-mail: sales@precision2000.co.uk

INDUSTRIAL AUTOMATED SYSTEMS

Microtech Ltd, Leicester Grange, Wolvey, Hinckley, Leicestershire, LE10 3JB Tel: (01455) 603016 Fax: (01455) 251588 E-mail: microtech@btconnect.com

INDUSTRIAL AUTOMATIC CONTROL SYSTEMS

Industrial System Solutions Ltd, 21 Summerhill, East Herrington, Sunderland, SR3 3NJ Tel: (07949) 566186 Fax: 0191-511 0732 E-mail: enquiries@industrialsystemsolutions.co.uk

▶ Quasar Electronics Ltd, PO Box 6935, Bishop's Stortford, Hertfordshire, CM23 4WP Tel: (0870) 2461826 Fax: (0870) 4601045 E-mail: sales@quasarelectronics.com

INDUSTRIAL AUTOMATION BAR CODE EQUIPMENT

Datascan Systems Ltd, Harris Business Park, Hanbury Road, Stoke Prior, Bromsgrove, Worcestershire, B60 4BD Tel: (01527) 839010 Fax: (01527) 839011 E-mail: sales@datascansystems.com

▶ EG Coding, 9 Lochans Mill Avenue, Lochans, Stranraer, Wigtownshire, DG9 9BZ Tel: (07979) 692580 Fax: (07092) 870019 E-mail: ellisgaston@hotmail.com

INDUSTRIAL AUTOMATION COMPUTER SYSTEMS

Amplicon Liveline Ltd, Unit 11 Centenary Industrial Estate, Hughes Road, Brighton, BN2 4AW Tel: (01273) 570220 Fax: (01273) 570215 E-mail: sales@amplicon.co.uk

Batching & Blending Systems Ltd, 48 Marlow Road, Stokenchurch, High Wycombe, Buckinghamshire, HP14 3QJ Tel: (01494) 484952 Fax: (01494) 485696 E-mail: sales@bbsys.uk.com

Deep Blue Systems Ltd, Unit 1, Lawrence Parade, Lower Square, Isleworth, Middlesex, TW7 6RG Tel: (020) 8541 4131 Fax: (020) 8569 9691 E-mail: sales@deepbluesystems.com

Gower Consultants Ltd, 20 Davigdor Road, Hove, East Sussex, BN3 1TT Tel: (01273) 204646 Fax: (01273) 733043 E-mail: gowerconsultants@compuserve.com

Jaytec Systems, 1 Woodside View, Daisy Hill, Sacriston, Durham, DH7 6BP Tel: 0191-371 0867 Fax: 0191-371 9969 E-mail: info@jaytecsystems.com

INDUSTRIAL AUTOMATION SUPERVISORY COMPUTERS

3y2k Computer Maintenance, The Coach House, Trewyn, Pandy, Abergavenny, Gwent, NP7 7PG Tel: (01873) 890002 E-mail: threey2k@hotmail.com

INDUSTRIAL AUTOMATION SUPERVISORY CONTROL SYSTEMS

Adaptive Control Solutions Ltd, 1 Ashfield Road, Greetland, Halifax, West Yorkshire, HX4 8HY Tel: (01422) 313456 Fax: (01422) 313567 E-mail: richardarmitage@adaptivecontrol.com

Automation Control & Technology Ltd, 149 Tavistock Road, Fleet, Hampshire, GU51 4EE Tel: (01252) 623316 Fax: (01252) 623316 E-mail: sales@automationcontrol.co.uk

E D G S B Ltd, The Mews, 70 London Road, Burgess Hill, West Sussex, RH15 8NB Tel: (01444) 248691 Fax: (01444) 248721 E-mail: sales@edg.co.uk

Sercon Controls Ltd, Clay Lane, Spar Fields, Slarthwate, Huddersfield, HD7 5BG Tel: (01484) 845548 Fax: (01484) 847846 E-mail: gln@serconcontrols.com

Yokogawa Marex Ltd, 34 Medina Road, Cowes, Isle Of Wight, PO31 7DA Tel: (01983) 296011 Fax: (01983) 291776 E-mail: sales@ymx.yokogawa.com

INDUSTRIAL BALERS

K.K. Balers Ltd, Victory House, Victory Park Road, Addlestone, Surrey, KT15 2AX Tel: (01932) 852423 Fax: (01932) 847170 E-mail: sales@kkbalers.com

Dicom Ltd, Lydford Road, Alfreton, Derbyshire, DE55 7RQ Tel: (01773) 520565 Fax: (01773) 520881 E-mail: sales@dicom.ltd.uk

Lloyds International Ltd, Station Road, Reddish, Stockport, Cheshire, SK5 6ND Tel: 0161-219 0909 Fax: 0161-431 5780 E-mail: vicky@thos-storey.co.uk

Miltek, Rectory Farm, Brandon Road, Stubton, Newark, Nottinghamshire, NG23 5BY Tel: (01636) 626796 Fax: (01636) 626905 E-mail: sales@miltekbalers.com

Mil-tek (GB) Ltd, Saville Court, Saville Place, Clifton, Bristol, BS8 4EJ Tel: (0800) 0835713 Fax: 0117-973 6797 E-mail: info@miltek-uk.co.uk

INDUSTRIAL BALLS

Atlas Ball & Bearing Co. Ltd, Leamore Lane, Walsall, WS2 7DE Tel: (01922) 710515 Fax: (01922) 710575 E-mail: sales@atlasball.co.uk

Custom Grind Ltd, Unit 1c Brown Lees Road Industrial Estate, Forge Way, Knypersley, Stoke-on-Trent, ST8 7DN Tel: (01782) 518503 Fax: (01782) 522110 E-mail: sales@customgrind.com

Euro Matic Ltd, Clauson House Perryvale Industrial Park, Horsenden Road South, Greenford, Middlesex, UB6 7QE Tel: (020) 8991 2211 Fax: (020) 8997 5074 E-mail: sales@euro-matic.com

Flotronic Pumps Ltd, Ricebridge Works, Brighton Road, Bolney, Haywards Heath, West Sussex, RH17 5NA Tel: (01444) 881871 Fax: (01444) 881860 E-mail: salesdept@flotronicpumps.co.uk

INDUSTRIAL BELLOWS

Barlow Blinds Ltd, 54 Uppingham Road, Leicester, LE5 0QE Tel: 0116-276 9771 Fax: 0116-246 0490 E-mail: brian@barlow-bellows.co.uk

Beakbane Ltd, Stourport Road, Kidderminster, Worcestershire, DY11 7QT Tel: (01562) 820561 Fax: (01562) 820560 E-mail: sales@beakbane.co.uk

Camera Bellows, Units 3-5, St. Pauls Road, Birmingham, B12 8NG Tel: 0121-440 1695 Fax: 0121-440 0972 E-mail: sales@camerabellows.com

The Flexicon Company, 1 Larch Lea Trading Estate, Whitefield Road, Liverpool, L6 5BN Tel: 0151-260 6141 Fax: 0151-260 4477 E-mail: info@flexicon.org.uk

Senior Aerospace Bird Bellows, Radnor Park Industrial Estate, Congleton, Cheshire, CW12 4UQ Tel: (01260) 271411 Fax: (01260) 270910 E-mail: info@bird-bellows.co.uk

Thermosel Solutions Ltd, Calico Lane, Furness Vale, High Peak, Derbyshire, SK23 7SW Tel: (01663) 748220 Fax: (01663) 741685

INDUSTRIAL BLADES

A F Whiteley & Co. Ltd, Bingswood Road, Whaley Bridge, High Peak, Derbyshire, SK23 7NB Tel: (01663) 732288 Fax: (01663) 734180 E-mail: sales@whiteley-knives.com

Allgrind, Unit 8 Century Street, Sheffield, S9 5DX Tel: 0114-244 4491 Fax: 0114-244 4491 E-mail: murbeck@aol.com

William Pinder & Sons Ltd, 4 Harling Road, Sharston Industrial Estate, Manchester, M22 4UZ Tel: 0161-998 1729 Fax: 0161-946 0734 E-mail: info@pinderblades.com

Swemko (UK) Ltd, 29 Bonville Road, Brislington, Bristol, BS4 5QH Tel: (0845) 0760960 Fax: 0117-972 0470 E-mail: sales@swemkoknifes.com

INDUSTRIAL BOOT WASH UNITS

Shooshyne, 481 Meanwood Road, Leeds, LS6 2BH Tel: 0113-275 2283 Fax: 0113-275 2362 E-mail: shoeshine@compuserve.com

INDUSTRIAL BRAKES

W R P Construction, Southway House, Southway Drive, Bristol, BS30 5LW Tel: 0117-961 9111 Fax: 0117-961 9222 E-mail: sales@frictionservices.co.uk

INDUSTRIAL BRUSHES

Bee Gee Brushes Ltd, Unit 3c Saxon Business Park, Hanbury Road, Stoke Prior, Bromsgrove, Worcestershire, B60 4AD Tel: (01527) 837001 Fax: (01527) 837001 E-mail: mar_r_goddard@hotmail.com
The Brush Co., 36 North Lane, Aldershot, Hampshire, GU12 4QG Tel: (01252) 341300 Fax: (01252) 332993 E-mail: sales@lincolnfloor.co.uk
Brush Technology Ltd, 3 Throckley Industrial Estate, Ponteland Road, Throckley, Newcastle upon Tyne, NE15 9EW Tel: 0191-229 1666 Fax: 0191-229 1777 E-mail: info@brushtec.com
Cooks Brushes Ltd, 52 The Street, Old Costessey, Norwich, NR8 5DD Tel: (01603) 748339 Fax: (01603) 748339 E-mail: sales@cooks-brushes.co.uk
Danline International Ltd, Nebo Road, Llanrwst, Gwynedd, LL26 0SE Tel: (01492) 640651 Fax: (01492) 641601 E-mail: sales@danline.co.uk
Dawson & Son Ltd, Clayton Wood Rise, West Park Ring Road, Leeds, LS16 6RH Tel: 0113-275 9321 Fax: 0113-275 2761 E-mail: sales@dawsonbrush.co.uk
Farrar James Brushes Ltd, 103 Northgate, Halifax, West Yorkshire, HX1 1XF Tel: (01422) 361072 Fax: (01422) 361072 E-mail: philip.reid5@btinternet.com
Formseal South Ltd, 23 Snowdrop Close, Narborough, Leicester, LE19 3YB Tel: 0116-275 0052 Fax: 0116-286 5808 E-mail: sales@brushstrip.co.uk
Munitech Ltd, Hoo Marina Industrial Estate, Vicarage Lane, Hoo, Rochester, Kent, ME3 9LB Tel: (01634) 250771 Fax: (01634) 250388 E-mail: info@munitech.co.uk
Chris Naylor (SOMA) Ltd, The Bungalow, 6 West Shevin Road, Merston, Ilkley, West Yorkshire, LS29 6BG Tel: (01943) 876513 Fax: (01943) 878814 E-mail: chrisnaylor@chrisnaylorsoma.demon.co.uk
Osborn International Ltd, Dendix House, Lower Church Street, Chepstow, Gwent, NP16 5XT Tel: (01291) 634000 Fax: (01291) 634098 E-mail: uksales@osborn.co.uk
P M R Industrial Services, 13-21 Liverpool Road, Kidsgrove, Stoke-on-Trent, ST7 1EA Tel: (01782) 776325 Fax: (01782) 771912
R Russell, 45 Townsend Road, Chesham, Buckinghamshire, HP5 2AA Tel: (01494) 782837 Fax: (01494) 791598 E-mail: info@r-russellbrush.co.uk
▶ R S D Supplies & Services Ltd, 2 Norton Centre, Poynernook Road, Aberdeen, AB11 5RW Tel: (01224) 213213
South Wales Brush Co Ltd, 1 Ely Distribution Centre, Argyle Way, Cardiff, CF5 5NJ Tel: (029) 2059 9199 Fax: (029) 2059 9299 E-mail: sales@brush.co.uk
A.E. Southgate Ltd, Station Road, Coleshill, Birmingham, B46 1HT Tel: (01675) 463096 Fax: (01675) 467455
▶ Sovereign Brush Co Ltd, 29-43 Sydney Road, Watford, WD18 7PZ Tel: (01923) 227301 Fax: (01923) 817121 E-mail: sales@sovereignbrush.com
W T Clark & Co (Brushes) Ltd, P O Box 2, Birmingham, B46 1HX Tel: (01675) 463085 Fax: (01675) 467455
Weston, Shipley & Weston Ltd, Premier Works, Samson Road, Hermitage Industrial Estate, Coalville, Leicestershire, LE67 3FP Tel: (01530) 814062 Fax: (01530) 814064 E-mail: eberryson@aol.com
Whitaker & Sawyer Ltd, Unit 17 Midas Business Centre, Wantz Road, Dagenham, Essex, RM10 8PS Tel: (020) 8593 7204 Fax: (020) 8595 7353 E-mail: info@wsbrushes.co.uk

INDUSTRIAL BUILDING CONSTRUCTORS

Algo Business Centre, Glenearn Road, Perth, PH2 0NJ Tel: 01738) 450450 Fax: (01738) 450460 E-mail: pa@algo.co.uk
Allworks Ltd, Unit 4 Dene Valley Business Centre, Brookhampton Lane, Kineton, Warwick, CV3 0JD Tel: (01926) 642544 Fax: (01926) 642512 E-mail: allworksltd@warwicks.fsnet.co.uk
B & K Building Services Ltd, Peveril House, Alfreton Road, Derby, DE21 4AG Tel: (01332) 331444 Fax: (01332) 291067 E-mail: bkbs@rwkhouse.co.uk
Balfour Beatty Construction Ltd, Balfour House, Churchfield Road, Walton-on-Thames, Surrey, KT12 2TD Tel: (020) 7922 0000 Fax: (01932) 229032
Bowmer & Kirkland Ltd, High Edge Court, Church Street, Heage, Belper, Derbyshire, DE56 2BW Tel: (01773) 853131 Fax: (01773) 856710 E-mail: sales@bandk.co.uk
Browns of Wem Ltd, Four Lane Ends, Wem, SY4 5UQ Tel: (01939) 232382 Fax: (01939) 234032 E-mail: mail@brownsofwem.com
C J Ellmore & Co. Ltd, Henshaw Lane, Yeadon, Leeds, LS19 7RZ Tel: 0113-250 2881 Fax: 0113-239 1227 E-mail: mail@ellmore.co.uk
Costain Ltd, Costain House, 111 Westminster Bridge Road, London, SE1 7UE Tel: (020) 7705 8444 Fax: (020) 7705 8599
Cowlin Construction Ltd, Stratton House, 39 Cater Road, Bristol, BS13 7UH Tel: 0117-983 2000 Fax: 0117-987 7758 E-mail: bristol@cowlin.co.uk
Cowlin Construction, 5 Armtech Row, Houndstone Business Park, Yeovil, Somerset, BA22 8RW Tel: (01935) 423131 Fax: (01935) 847680
Cubitt Theobald & Sons Ltd, St Catherines Road, Long Melford, Sudbury, Suffolk, CO10 9JU Tel: (01787) 371002 Fax: (01787) 880625 E-mail: cubitt-theobald@cubitt.co.uk
D C P M Manuals, Rock Drive, Gelli, Pentre, Rhondda Cynon Taff, CF41 7NX Tel: (01443) 442029 Fax: (01443) 442199 E-mail: info@dcpmmanuals.com
D J Contracts South Ltd, 7 Kent Close, Granby Industrial Estate, Weymouth, Dorset, DT4 9TF Tel: (01305) 780111 Fax: (01305) 761409 E-mail: mail@darrenholland.co.uk
Danaher & Rolls Ltd, Rufus Centre, Steppingley Road, Flitwick, Bedford, MK45 1AH Tel: (01525) 721900 Fax: (01525) 721800 E-mail: office@danaherandrolls.co.uk
Duraframe Structures Ltd, 4 Springhead Way, Crowborough, East Sussex, TN6 1LR Tel: (01892) 610534 Fax: (01892) 611643
Eastwood Construction, Burns Lane, Warsop, Mansfield, Nottinghamshire, NG20 0QG Tel: (01623) 842581 Fax: (01623) 847955 E-mail: enquiries@adameastwood.co.uk
Edwards S M Building Contractors, 77 Old Coach Road, Kelsall, Tarporley, Cheshire, CW6 0RA Tel: (01829) 752028 Fax: (01829) 751559
G D L Air Systems Ltd, Air Diffusion Works, Woolley Bridge Road, Hadfield, Glossop, Derbyshire, SK13 1AB Tel: (01457) 861538 Fax: (01457) 866010 E-mail: sales@grille.co.uk
G M I Construction Group plc, Middleton House, Westland Road, Leeds, LS11 5UH Tel: 0113-276 0505 Fax: 0113-276 0180 E-mail: build@gmicon.co.uk
Goods Protection Ltd, 11/12 Shuttleworth Road, Elm Farm Industrial Estate, Bedford, MK41 0EP Tel: (01234) 327522 Fax: (01234) 270885 E-mail: info@goods-protection.co.uk
Harlow & Milner Ltd, Milner Way, Ossett, West Yorkshire, WF5 9JN Tel: (01924) 277771 Fax: (01924) 280102 E-mail: info@harlow-milner.co.uk
Holroyd Construction Ltd, Park Hill, Walton Road, Wetherby, West Yorkshire, LS22 5DZ Tel: (01937) 583131 Fax: (01937) 580034
Interserve Site Services, Woodhouse Drive, Wigan, Lancashire, WN6 7NT Tel: (01942) 236434 Fax: (01942) 824159 E-mail: wigan.office@interserveprojects.com
J Pullan & Sons Ltd, Sunnyview Gardens, Leeds, LS11 8QT Tel: 0113-271 7221 Fax: 0113-271 9238 E-mail: general@pullans.com
Brian Jones Engineering (Fabrications), Heulwen, Penrhyndeudraeth, Gwynedd, LL48 6AH Tel: (01766) 770731 Fax: (01766) 770731
Kitpac Buildings Ltd, Shares Hill, Great Saredon, Wolverhampton, WV10 7LN Tel: (01922) 415425 Fax: (01922) 414246 E-mail: lisa@kitpac.freeserve.co.uk
John Laing P.L.C., Allington House, 150 Victoria Street, London, SW1E 5LB Tel: (020) 7901 3200 Fax: (020) 7901 3520 E-mail: enquiries@equion.ltd.uk
Leominster Construction Co. Ltd, Leominster Industrial Estate, Southern Avenue, Leominster, Herefordshire, HR6 0QF Tel: (01568) 612943 Fax: (01568) 612910
Losberger Walter UK, 27 High Street, Collingham, Collingham, Newark, Nottinghamshire, NG23 7LA Tel: (01636) 893776 Fax: (01636) 893774 E-mail: losbergeruk@losberger.com
Lynxcourt Ltd, Unit 9 Victoria Way, Newmarket, Suffolk, CB8 7SH Tel: (01638) 669214 Fax: (01638) 660209 E-mail: kiteley@lynxcourt.freeserve.co.uk
Moss Joinery, 96 Leckhampton Road, Cheltenham, Gloucestershire, GL53 0BP Tel: (01242) 222622 Fax: (01242) 260265 E-mail: moss.cheltenham@kier.co.uk
Norman Cull, 10 Morville Road, Dudley, West Midlands, DY2 9HR Tel: (01384) 255339
Northern Structures Ltd, Amble Industrial Estate, Amble, Morpeth, Northumberland, NE65 0PE Tel: (01665) 710746 Fax: (01665) 712738 E-mail: sales@northernstructures.co.uk
Pitchmastic P M B Ltd, Royds Works, Attercliffe Road, Sheffield, S4 7WZ Tel: 0114-270 0100 Fax: 0114-276 8782 E-mail: info@pitchmasticpmb.co.uk
R J Cannon Ltd, Maldon Road, Tiptree, Colchester, CO5 0PH Tel: (01621) 815396 Fax: (01621) 817939 E-mail: rjcannon@btclick.com
Ridge Interiors Ltd, Contract House, 19a Watford Heath, Watford, WD19 4EU Tel: (01923) 240976 Fax: (01923) 212654
T C Dolman Construction Ltd, Broad Street, Bilston, West Midlands, WV14 0BZ Tel: (01902) 492792 Fax: (01902) 403618
Totty, Park House, Bradford Road, Chain Bar, Cleckheaton, West Yorkshire, BD19 6BW Tel: (01274) 866600 Fax: (01274) 866737
W Walters, Rope Walk, Ilkeston, Derbyshire, DE7 5HX Tel: 0115-932 4982
Westframe Investments Ltd, 162-164 Teignmouth Road, Torquay, TQ1 4RY Tel: (01803) 313861 Fax: (01803) 312063 E-mail: westframe@construction-ltd.fsnet.co.uk
Wilson Bowden Group Services Ltd, Wilson Bowden House, Leicester Road, Ibstock, Leicestershire, LE67 6WB Tel: (01530) 260777 Fax: (01532) 262805

INDUSTRIAL BUILDING SURVEY SERVICES

A K S Ward Ltd, 1 West Midfield, London, EC1A 9JU Tel: (020) 7236 0161 Fax: (020) 7236 3239 E-mail: consult@aksward.com
▶ ArchiTech Surveys Ltd, 86 Easton street, High Wycombe, Bucks, HP11 1LT Tel: (01494) 522455 Fax: (01494) 535667 E-mail: technical@architechsurveys.co.uk
▶ Building Surveying Solutions, 376 City Road, London, EC1V 2QA Tel: (020) 7278 4060 Fax: (020) 7287 4717
Callworth Ltd, 294 High Street, Rochester, Kent, ME1 1HS Tel: (01634) 402381 Fax: (01634) 201770 E-mail: pj.crook@btinternet.com
Checkley & Co., Broad St House, 212 Broad Street, Birmingham, B15 1AY Tel: 0121-643 8538 Fax: 0121-643 7416 E-mail: mailbox@checkleys.co.uk
Consoil Geotechnical Instruments UK, Clark House, 3 Brassey Drive, Aylesford, Kent, ME20 7QL Tel: (01622) 882093 Fax: (0870) 0543915 E-mail: info@consoil.co.uk
Dunster & Morton, 92 London Street, Reading, RG1 4SJ Tel: 0118-955 1700 Fax: 0118-955 1725 E-mail: info@dunsterandmorton.co.uk
Scadin, 304 Upper Newtownards Road, Belfast, BT4 3EU Tel: (028) 9065 5105 Fax: (028) 9067 3370 E-mail: cadd@scadin.com

INDUSTRIAL CABLE GLANDS

C M P Products, 36 Nelson Way, Nelson Park East, Cramlington, Northumberland, NE23 1WH Tel: 0191 2657411 Fax: 0191 2650581 E-mail: cmp@cmp-products.com
Hylec Components Ltd, 6 Stanton Close, Finedon Road Industrial Estate, Wellingborough, Northamptonshire, NN8 4HN Tel: (01933) 234400 Fax: (01933) 234411 E-mail: sales@hylec.co.uk

INDUSTRIAL CABLES

C & M Corporation, Dunfermline, Fife, KY12 9YX Tel: (01383) 621225 Fax: (01383) 623455 E-mail: sales@cmcorporation.co.uk

INDUSTRIAL CANS

D K S Packaging Ltd, 62-70 Litherland Road, Bootle, Merseyside, L20 3HZ Tel: 0151-922 2656 Fax: 0151-933 0547 E-mail: reception@dkspackaging.co.uk
Sure-Can Ltd, Unit 6, 8 & 9 Adam Business Centre, Henson Way, Telford Way Industrial Estate, Kettering, Northamptonshire, NN16 8PX Tel: (01536) 411882 Fax: (01536) 518086 E-mail: sales@sure-can.co.uk

INDUSTRIAL CARBON DIOXIDE (CO2) LASERS

▶ Prima Lasers, 121 Boundary Road, Wooburn Green, Buckinghamshire, HP10 0DJ Tel: (07841) 414839 E-mail: mail@primalasers.co.uk
Rofin Baasel UK Ltd, 3 Brunel Close, Drayton Fields Industrial Estate, Daventry, Northamptonshire, NN11 8RB Tel: (0870) 9901020 Fax: (0870) 9901030 E-mail: sales@rofin-baasel.co.uk

INDUSTRIAL CARBON PRODUCTS

Amber Composites Ltd, 94 Station Road, Langley Mill, Nottingham, NG16 4BP Tel: (01773) 530899 Fax: (01773) 768687 E-mail: sales@ambercomposites.co.uk
▶ Atlas Composites Ltd, Chelton House, Merlin Way, Quarry Hill Industrial Estate, Ilkeston, Derbyshire, DE7 4RA Tel: 0115-930 4058 Fax: 0115-930 4558
James Durrans & Sons Ltd, Phoenix Works, Thurlstone, Sheffield, S36 9QU Tel: (01226) 370000 Fax: (01226) 370336 E-mail: enquiries@durrans.co.uk
Graphite Electrodes Ltd, Coke Lane, Rotherham, South Yorkshire, S60 2JS Tel: (01709) 838522 Fax: (01709) 835340
Morganite Electrical Carbon Ltd, Upper Fforest Way, Swansea Enterprise Park, Swansea, SA6 8PP Tel: (01792) 763000 Fax: (01792) 763191 E-mail: sales@mecl.co.uk

INDUSTRIAL CARDBOARD TUBES

Kennet Plastics, Unit A, Aerial Business Park, Lambourn Woodlands, Hungerford, Berkshire, RG17 7RZ Tel: (01488) 72055 Fax: (01488) 71122 E-mail: sales@kennet-pack.co.uk

INDUSTRIAL CATALOGUES

▶ Oilcats, Clydesdale Bank Buildings, Little Square, Oldmeldrum, Aberdeen, AB51 0AY Tel: (01651) 873171 Fax: (01651) 873214 E-mail: sales@oilcats.co.uk

INDUSTRIAL CENTRIFUGES

Andritz Ltd, R & B Technology Centre, Speedwell Road, Parkhouse East Industrial Estate, Newcastle, Staffordshire, ST5 7RG Tel: (01782) 565656 Fax: (01782) 566130 E-mail: welcome@andritzltd.com
Ashbrook Simon-Hartley Ltd, Derby Road, Clay Cross, Chesterfield, Derbyshire, S45 9AG Tel: (01246) 252600 Fax: (01246) 252601 E-mail: enquiries@as-h.com
Rousselet Robatel UK Ltd, Parkside House, 17 East Parade, Harrogate, North Yorkshire, HG1 5LF Tel: (01423) 530093 Fax: (01423) 530120 E-mail: sales@rousselet.robatel.co.uk

INDUSTRIAL CERAMIC FIBRE INSULATION MATERIALS

Clwyd Refractory Fibres Ltd, Spencer Industrial Estate, Liverpool Road, Buckley, Clwyd, CH7 3LY Tel: (01244) 548308 Fax: (01244) 541121 E-mail: info@gasglo.co.uk
F K Fiber Products Ltd, The Croft, Long Lane, Waverton, Chester, CH3 7RB Tel: (01244) 335912 Fax: (01244) 332499 E-mail: mike@fkfiber.freeserve.co.uk

INDUSTRIAL CHAINS

A P Lifting Gear, Northfield Road, Dudley, West Midlands, DY2 9JQ Tel: (01384) 250552 Fax: (01384) 250282 E-mail: apliftingsales@btconnect.com
B & G Williams Ltd, Garratts Lane, Cradley Heath, West Midlands, B64 5RH Tel: 0121-559 2811 Fax: 0121-559 9412
B & S Chains (Midlands) Ltd, 29 Toys Lane, Halesowen, West Midlands, B63 2JX Tel: (01384) 413088 Fax: (01384) 413066 E-mail: enquiries@bandschains.co.uk
Chain Products Ltd, 49 Ward Street, Birmingham, B19 3TD Tel: 0121-359 0697 Fax: 0121-359 3672 E-mail: chainproducts@aol.com
Deacon Products Ltd, Unit 1, Penn Industrial Estate, Providence Street, Cradley Heath, West Midlands, B64 5DJ Tel: (01384) 416931 Fax: (01384) 635172 E-mail: info@chain-fittings.co.uk
F Martin & Son Ltd, Bridgeman Street, Walsall, WS2 9NR Tel: (01922) 624666 Fax: (01922) 724198 E-mail: info@fmartinandsonltd.co.uk
Griff Chains Ltd, Quarry Road, Dudley Wood, Dudley, West Midlands, DY2 0ED Tel: (01384) 569415 Fax: (01384) 410580 E-mail: sales@griffchains.co.uk
Harris Walton Lifting Gear Ltd, Two Woods Lane, Brierley Hill, West Midlands, DY5 1TR Tel: (01384) 74071 Fax: (01384) 74070 E-mail: sales@harriswaltonliftinggear.co.uk
Howth Chains & Chain Assemblies, Unit 6 Brierley Trading Estate, North St, Brierley Hill, W. Midlands, DY5 3SL Tel: (01384) 79458 Fax: (01384) 79458
I W I S Chain Ltd, Bridge House, Seven Bridge, Bewdley, Worcestershire, DY12 1AB Tel: (01299) 400080 Fax: (01299) 404588 E-mail: sales@iwischain.co.uk
Kobo (UK) Ltd, Ketten House, Leestone Road, Sharston Industrial Area, Manchester, M22 4RH Tel: 0161-491 9840 Fax: 0161-428 1999 E-mail: info@kobo.co.uk
Parsons Chain Co., Worcester Road, Stourport-On-Severn, Worcestershire, DY13 9AT Tel: (01299) 827700 Fax: (01299) 872659 E-mail: sales@parsonschain.co.uk
Precision Chains Ltd, Clee Road, Dudley, West Midlands, DY2 0YG Tel: (01384) 455455 Fax: (01384) 230751 E-mail: mark.kyte@precision-chains.co.uk
Sedis Co. Ltd, PO Box 6529, Wellingborough, Northamptonshire, NN8 4YS Tel: (0870) 1607840 Fax: (01604) 764162 E-mail: sedisco@sedis.com
Silcoms Ltd, Victoria Mill, Piggott Street, Farnworth, Bolton, BL4 9QN Tel: (01204) 571305 Fax: (01204) 861723 E-mail: pep@silcoms.co.uk
Eliza Tinsley & Co. Ltd, Unit 12, Cinder Road, Chasetown Industrial Estate, Burntwood, Staffordshire, WS7 8XD Tel: (01543) 683595 Fax: (01543) 674620
Tsubakimoto UK Ltd, Osier Drive, Annesley, Nottingham, NG15 0DX Tel: (01623) 688700 Fax: (01623) 688729 E-mail: sales@tsubaki.co.uk

INDUSTRIAL CHAINS – *continued*

Zinco Midlands, Midland House, 52 Lower Forster Street, Walsall, WS1 1XB Tel: (01922) 625586 Fax: (0800) 0286370 E-mail: info@zincomids.co.uk

INDUSTRIAL CHEMICAL PROCESSING CLEANING SERVICES

Ashland UK, Wimsey Way, Somercotes, Alfreton, Derbyshire, DE55 4LR Tel: (01773) 604321 Fax: (01773) 606901

Direct Water Services UK Ltd, 2 Woodford Road, Barnby Dun, Doncaster, South Yorkshire, DN3 1BN Tel: (01302) 883838 Fax: (01302) 883838

R B G, Norfolk House, Pitmedden Road, Dyce, Aberdeen, AB21 0DP Tel: (01224) 215100 Fax: (01224) 723406 E-mail: john.walker@rigblast.com

INDUSTRIAL CHEMICALS

Access Chemicals Ltd, Hedging Lane, Wilnecote, Tamworth, Staffordshire, B77 5EX Tel: (01827) 289000 Fax: (01827) 289080 E-mail: sales@accesschemicals.co.uk

R.P. Adam Ltd, Arpal Works, Riverside Road, Selkirk, TD7 5DU Tel: (01750) 21586 Fax: (01750) 21506 E-mail: salesinfo@rpadam.co.uk

Albion Chemicals Ltd, 46-50 Sydney Street West, Belfast, BT13 3GX Tel: (028) 9078 7450 Fax: (028) 9075 2500 E-mail: sales@albionchemicals.co.uk

Allchem (International) Ltd, Broadway House, 21 Broadway, Maidenhead, Berkshire, SL6 1NJ Tel: (01753) 443331 Fax: (01753) 443323 E-mail: info@allchem.co.uk

Allchem Midlands Ltd, Wingate Close, Nottingham, NG8 4LP Tel: 0115-929 5258 Fax: 0115-929 2379

Aqua Marine Chemicals Ltd, Unit 6 Strensham Business Park, Strensham, Worcester, WR8 9JZ Tel: (01684) 290077 Fax: (01684) 290608 E-mail: aquamarine@btconnect.com

B P Plc, Witan Gate House, 500-600 Witan Gate, Milton Keynes, MK9 1ES Tel: (01908) 853000 Fax: (01908) 852020 E-mail: clarkez@bp.com

Baker Petrolite, Howe Moss Avenue, Kirkhill Industrial Estate, Dyce, Aberdeen, AB21 0GP Tel: (01224) 405700 Fax: (01224) 405705

Banner Chemicals Ltd, Unit B, Hampton Court, Manor Park, Runcorn, Cheshire, WA7 1TU Tel: (01928) 597000 Fax: (01928) 597001 E-mail: reception@bannerchemicals.co.uk

Biachem Ltd, Boundary House, 91-93 Charterhouse Street, London, EC1M 6HR Tel: (020) 7250 1905 Fax: (020) 7250 1913 E-mail: info@biachem.com

Booth & Openshaw Blackburn Ltd, 17-19 St. Peter Street, Blackburn, BB2 2HH Tel: (01254) 52828

Cal Chem Ltd, Unit A3 Hortonwood 10, Telford, Shropshire, TF1 7ES Tel: (01952) 606220 Fax: (01952) 676278

Chem Products Ltd, 5 Poplar Place, Hayes, Middlesex, UB3 2DS Tel: (020) 8797 0567 Fax: (020) 8797 0567 E-mail: chemproducts@myisp.co.uk

Chemtura Manufacturing UK Ltd, Tenax Road, Trafford Park, Manchester, M17 1WT Tel: (01407) 830451 Fax: (01407) 830001 E-mail:

Collinda Investments Ltd, 25 Ottways Lane, Ashtead, Surrey, KT21 2PL Tel: (01372) 278416 Fax: (01372) 278559 E-mail: info@collinda.co.uk

Cornelius Group plc, Woodside, Dunmow Road, Birchanger, Bishop's Stortford, Hertfordshire, CM23 5RG Tel: (01279) 714300 Fax: (01279) 714320 E-mail: sales.dept@cornelius.co.uk

D R Chemicals Ltd, Viking Way, Winch Wen Industrial Estate, Winch Wen, Swansea, SA1 7DA Tel: (01792) 701135 Fax: (01792) 771797 E-mail: chemics@btconnect.com

Don Construction Products, Station Road, Churnetside Business Park, Cheddleton, Leek, Staffordshire, ST13 7RS Tel: (01538) 361799 Fax: (01538) 361899 E-mail: info@donconstruction.co.uk

Dow Chemical, 2 Heathrow Boulevard, 284 Bath Road, West Drayton, Middlesex, UB7 0DQ Tel: (020) 8917 5000 Fax: (020) 8917 5400

Ecokem Ltd, 4 Trafalgar Court, Widnes, Cheshire, WA8 0SZ Tel: 0151-420 0172 Fax: 0151-510 5455 E-mail: dclarkson@ecokem.co.uk

Elastomerics Ltd, Summit House, 48a Bramhall Lane South, Bramhall, Stockport, Cheshire, SK7 1AH Tel: 0161-439 9116 Fax: 0161-440 8035 E-mail: info@elastomerics.com

Ellis & Everard (Chemicals) P.L.C, 75 Bugsbys Way, Greenwich, London, SE10 0QD Tel: (020) 8858 5806 Fax: (020) 8858 1499

Grace Construction Products Ltd, 851-852 Birchwood Boulevard, Birchwood, Warrington, WA3 7QZ Tel: (01925) 824824 Fax: (01925) 824033 E-mail: enquiries@gcp-grace.com

Kronos Ltd, Barons Court, Manchester Road, Wilmslow, Cheshire, SK9 1BQ Tel: (01625) 547200 Fax: (01625) 533123 E-mail: kronos.sales.uk@nli-usa.com

Microchem Ltd, Unit 1 Belmont Industrial Estate, Durham, DH1 1TN Tel: 0191-386 9988 Fax: 0191-386 2722 E-mail: sales@microchem.co.uk

Micromix Solutions Ltd, Coachgap Lane, Langar, Nottingham, NG13 9HP Tel: (01949) 861087 Fax: (01949) 861061 E-mail: info@micromixsolutions.com

Omnichem Ltd, Mill Street East, Dewsbury, West Yorkshire, WF12 9BQ Tel: (01924) 461341 Fax: (01924) 458995 E-mail: info@nickersons.co.uk

Peter Whiting Chemicals Ltd, 8 Barb Mews, London, W6 7PA Tel: (020) 8741 4025 Fax: (020) 8741 1737 E-mail: sales@whiting-cemicals.co.uk

Rapideze Ltd, 2 Barnsdale, Great Easton, Market Harborough, Leicestershire, LE16 8SG Tel: (01536) 770282 Fax: (01327) 830725

Solvent Resource Management Ltd, Rye Harbour Road, Rye, East Sussex, TN31 7TE Tel: (01797) 223936 Fax: (01797) 223017 E-mail: sales@srm-ltd.com

Sparkford Chemicals Ltd, Sparkfrod House, 58 The Avenue, Southampton, SO17 1XS Tel: (023) 8022 8747 Fax: (023) 8021 0240 E-mail: info@sparkford.co.uk

Specialised Industrial Chemicals Ltd, 44 Henver Road, Newquay, Cornwall, TR7 3BN Tel: (01637) 850643 Fax: (01637) 880040 E-mail: sales@sic-uk.com

Stephenson Group Ltd, PO Box 305, Bradford, West Yorkshire, BD7 1HY Tel: (01274) 723811 Fax: (01274) 370108 E-mail: group@stephensongroup.co.uk

Thomson & Joseph Ltd, 119 Plumstead Road, Norwich, NR1 4JT Tel: (01603) 439511 Fax: (01603) 700243 E-mail: enquiries@tandj.co.uk

Toray Europe Ltd, 7 Old Park Lane, London, W1K 1AD Tel: (020) 7663 7700 Fax: (020) 7872 8071

Ulster Electro Finishes Ltd, 78 Ballyrashane Road, Coleraine, County Londonderry, BT52 2LJ Tel: (028) 7034 3022 Fax: (028) 7035 5985 E-mail: uefltd@aol.com

INDUSTRIAL CHIMNEY SWEEPING

▶ Aston Chimneys, 6 Bishops Field, Aston Clinton, Aylesbury, Buckinghamshire, HP22 5BB Tel: (0800) 5874098 E-mail: mick@astonchimneys.co.uk

Brabiner Maintenance, 3 Brabiner Lane, Whittingham, Preston, PR3 2AP Tel: 01772 865182 Fax: 01772 865182 E-mail: thegavaghanhouse@msn.com

▶ Dusty Sweeps, 3 Bridge End Road, Swindon, SN3 4PD Tel: 01793 326188 E-mail: dustysweeps@hotmail.co.uk

▶ Kaill & Co Chimney Sweeping, 57 Oakhampton Road, Mill Hill, London, NW7 1NG Tel: (07910) 412751 E-mail: austen@akaill.wanadoo.co.uk

INDUSTRIAL CLADDING, *See also headings for particular types*

▶ K. Addams Industrial Roofing Contractors Limited, ARC House, Sundon Road, Chalton, Luton, LU4 9UA Tel: (01525) 877740 Fax: (01525) 877118 E-mail: k.addams@btinternet.com

Colorgroup Ltd, Whitehead Estate, Docks Way, Newport, Gwent, NP20 2NW Tel: (01633) 223854 Fax: (01633) 253992 E-mail: dave.burston@colorgroup.co.uk

Coulter Claddings, 17 Lurgan Road, Banbridge, County Down, BT32 4LY Tel: (028) 4062 8855 Fax: (028) 4062 8866 E-mail: sales@coultercladdings.co.uk

Detrra Fabrications Ltd, Unit 12 Droicon Industrial Estate, Portway Road, Rowley Regis, West Midlands, B65 9BY Tel: 0121-559 1152 Fax: 0121-559 6909 E-mail: derekk@btconnect.com

M S P (Scotland) Ltd, 1 Telford Road, Cumbernauld, Glasgow, G67 2AX Tel: (01236) 729591 Fax: (01236) 721859 E-mail: helenshaw@mspscot.co.uk

Rigidal Systems Ltd, Unit 62 Blackpole Trading Estate West, Worcester, WR3 8ZJ Tel: (01905) 750500 Fax: (01905) 750555 E-mail: info@rigidal.co.uk

▶ Simanda Industrial Roofing & Cladding Ltd, Acreman Street, Little Hadham, Ware, Hertfordshire, SG11 2HD Tel: (01279) 461746 Fax: (01279) 461644 E-mail: sales@simanda.com

▶ Vetter UK Ltd, Barford Road, Little Barford, St. Neots, Cambridgeshire, PE19 6WB Tel: (01480) 402900 Fax: (01480) 402572 E-mail: vetteruk@laingorourke.com

INDUSTRIAL CLADDING CONTRACTORS

A M E, 5 Glebe Road, Skelmersdale, Lancashire, WN8 9JP Tel: (01695) 50658 Fax: (01695) 50652 E-mail: info@amefacades.com

Adstone Construction, Wassage Way, Hampton Lovett, Droitwich, Worcestershire, WR9 0NX Tel: (01905) 794561 Fax: (01905) 794040 E-mail: mail@adstone.org.uk

Ansoroy Ltd, 237 Railton Road, London, SE24 0LX Tel: (020) 7738 6030 Fax: (020) 7738 6030 E-mail: sales@ansoroy.co.uk

Ascon Industrial Roofing Ltd, Hope Street, Dudley, West Midlands, DY2 8RS Tel: (01384) 233171 Fax: (01384) 456162

Capricorn Roofing Ltd, 96a Dundonald Road, London, SW19 3PN Tel: (020) 8542 5393 Fax: (020) 8542 3593

Central Cladding Systems Ltd, Unit C4 Staverton Technology Park, Gloucester Road, Staverton Technology Park, Cheltenham, Gloucestershire, GL51 6TQ Tel: (01452) 856252 Fax: (01452) 856136 E-mail: ccs@centralcladding.co.uk

Barry Collen Ltd, 31 Northampton Road, Scunthorpe, North Lincolnshire, DN16 1UJ Tel: (01724) 867817 Fax: (01724) 877111 E-mail: info@barrycollen.co.uk

Construction Profiles Ltd, Carriage House, Little Broom Street, Birmingham, B12 0EU Tel: 0121-766 6633 Fax: 0121-766 7792 E-mail: accounts@construction-profiles.co.uk

D A Green & Sons Ltd, High Road, Whaplode, Spalding, Lincolnshire, PE12 6TL Tel: (01406) 370585 Fax: (01406) 370766 E-mail: sales@dagreen.co.uk

Factorycover Ltd, Eamont Park, Toft Farm West Industrial Estate, Hartlepool, Cleveland, TS25 2BQ Tel: (01429) 863366 Fax: (01429) 263188

Gale Construction Co. Ltd, Ayton Road, Wymondham, Norfolk, NR18 0QQ Tel: (01953) 604537 Fax: (01953) 602680 E-mail: info@gale-construction.co.uk

Hallford Refurbishments, A Silver End Business Park, Brettell Lane, Brierley Hill, West Midlands, DY5 3LG Tel: (01384) 573845 Fax: (01384) 573848

Hathaway Roofing Ltd, Tindale Cresent, Tindale Crescent, Bishop Auckland, County Durham, DL14 9TL Tel: (01388) 605636 Fax: (01388) 608841

Ivan J Cooper Moorside Ltd, Moorside Works, Ellastone Road, Cauldon Low, Stoke-on-Trent, ST10 3ET Tel: (01538) 702738 Fax: (01538) 702662E-mail: brenda-prince@btconnect.com

Jackson Steel Structures Ltd, Densfield Works, Tannadice Street, Dundee, DD3 7QP Tel: (01382) 858439 Fax: (01382) 833964 E-mail: sales@jacksonsteel.co.uk

James Brothers (Hamworthy) Ltd, 19 Blandford Road, Hamworthy, Poole, Dorset, BH15 4AW Tel: (01202) 673815 Fax: (01202) 684033 E-mail: inquiries@james-bros.co.uk

Levy Associates Ltd, Pilgrims Lodge Holywell Hill, St. Albans, Hertfordshire, AL1 1ER Tel: (01727) 792200 Fax: (01727) 868890 E-mail: mail@levynet.co.uk

Midland Erection Ltd, Roetan House, Thorns Road, Brierley Hill, West Midlands, DY5 2PF Tel: (01384) 424227 Fax: (01384) 424906 E-mail: miderect1@btconnect.com

Ocean Refit Ltd, The Barnyard, Stennack, St. Ives, Cornwall, TR26 1QR Tel: (01736) 799440 Fax: (01736) 799440 E-mail: oceanrefit@btopenworld.com

Reads Construction Ltd, 6 Speedwell Way, Harleston Industrial Estate, Harleston, Norfolk, IP20 9EH Tel: (01379) 853063 Fax: (01379) 853676 E-mail: readsconstruction@harleston.fsbusiness.co.uk

▶ Roofing Contracts & Building Ltd, A 121a Shirley Road, Southampton, SO15 3FF Tel: (023) 8063 3030 Fax: (023) 8063 3998 E-mail: sales@roofingcladdingbuilding.com

▶ Simanda Industrial Roofing & Cladding Ltd, Acreman Street, Little Hadham, Ware, Hertfordshire, SG11 2HD Tel: (01279) 461746 Fax: (01279) 461644 E-mail: sales@simanda.com

Neville Tong, Tudor Lodge, Scotter, Gainsborough, Lincolnshire, DN21 3UR Tel: (01724) 762650 E-mail: jone.tong@btopenworld.com

Valent Ltd, 49 Longford Road, Chorlton-Cum-Hardy, Manchester, M21 9WP Tel: 0161-881 3503 Fax: 0161-860 5519

▶ Vetter UK Ltd, Barford Road, Little Barford, St. Neots, Cambridgeshire, PE19 6WB Tel: (01480) 402900 Fax: (01480) 402572 E-mail: vetteruk@laingorourke.com

Wall Engineering Co. Ltd, Cromer Road, North Walsham, Norfolk, NR28 0NB Tel: (01692) 403701 Fax: (01692) 406610 E-mail: info@wallengineering.co.uk

INDUSTRIAL CLEANING

A1 Blasting Cleaning & Painting, Riverside House Wallerscote Island, Winnington Lane, Northwich, Cheshire, CW8 4YF Tel: (01606) 783203 Fax: (01606) 781581

Aadvark, 242 Gosport Road, Fareham, Hampshire, PO16 0SS Tel: (01329) 822515 Fax: (01329) 823630

Abbey Janitorial, Abbey House, Derry Street, Wolverhampton, WV2 1EY Tel: (01902) 838700 Fax: (01902) 835202

Abcas Cleaning Services, 8 Coningham Gardens, Aberdeen, AB24 2TS Tel: (01224) 485592

Ace Cleaning Services Ltd, 72-74 High Street, Dawlish, Devon, EX7 9HF Tel: (01626) 889500 Fax: (01626) 889500 E-mail: david@acecleaning.co.uk

Ace Specialist Hire Ltd, PO Box 498, Folkestone, Kent, CT18 7GG Tel: (01797) 369222 Fax: (01797) 369333 E-mail: sales@ashclean.co.uk

Albatross Commercial & Industrial Cleaning Co. Ltd, Marlborough Business Centre, Marlborough Road, London, E18 1AH Tel: (020) 8530 5888 Fax: (020) 8530 4747 E-mail: alb@btconnect.com

Andron Contract Services, 3 Greenwood Court, Risley, Warrington, WA3 6DD Tel: (01925) 767389 Fax: (01925) 766011 E-mail: warrington@andron.co.uk

Anglian Cleaning Services Ltd, 8 Magdalen St, Colchester, CO1 2JT Tel: (01206) 763501 Fax: (01206) 571794 E-mail: info@angliancleaning.com

Arrow Cleaning Services, 17 The Hudson, Wyke, Bradford, West Yorkshire, BD12 8HZ Tel: (01274) 690805 Fax: (01274) 690805 E-mail: sales@cleaningservicesleeds.co.uk

Arrow Environmental Services Ltd, Exchange Works, Kelvin Way, West Bromwich, West Midlands, B70 7JW Tel: 0121-525 0757 Fax: 0121-525 1179 E-mail: arrow.environmental@virgin.net

Atlas Industrial Services Ltd, Tofts Farm Industrial Estate East, Brenda Road, Hartlepool, Cleveland, TS25 2BS Tel: (01429) 233018 Fax: (01429) 863316 E-mail: m.gcoop@tiscali.co.uk

Autosmart, Huncote Road, Stoney Stanton, Leicester, LE9 4DJ Tel: (01455) 271166 Fax: (01455) 271166

Aztec Plant Displays, 18 Eden Way, Pages Industrial Estate, Leighton Buzzard, Bedfordshire, LU7 4TZ Tel: (01525) 372322 Fax: (01525) 379426E-mail: info@aztec.co.uk

Ken Beardall Ltd, 67 Howards Wood Drive, Gerrards Cross, Buckinghamshire, SL9 7HS Tel: (01753) 884974 Fax: (01753) 880553

Bizley Cleaning Services Ltd, Unit 1, Kings Cliffe Industrial Estate, Kings Cliffe Road, Wansford, Peterborough, PE8 6PB Tel: (0870) 9033323 Fax: (0870) 9033324 E-mail: info@bizley.com

Branchand Ltd, Ashwellthorpe Industrial Estate, Ashwellthorpe, Norwich, NR16 1ER Tel: (01508) 488450 Fax: (01508) 488451 E-mail: info@branchand.co.uk

Britannia Services UK Ltd, Lysways House, 45 Britannia Way, Lichfield, Staffordshire, WS14 9UY Tel: (01543) 418855 Fax: (01543) 418699 E-mail: sales@britanniagroup.co.uk

Business Premises Cleaning Services Ltd, Long Acre, Pewitt Hill, Bursledon, Southampton, SO31 8BL Tel: (023) 8040 5060 Fax: (023) 8040 7549 E-mail: enquiries@businesspremisescleaning.com

Cameron Industrial Services Ltd, 351 Hale Road, Widnes, Cheshire, WA8 8TS Tel: 0151-423 3892 Fax: 0151-423 3892 E-mail: enquiries@cameronltd.co.uk

Care Group Ltd, Unit 7 Hartham Lane, Hertford, SG14 1QN Tel: (01992) 505100 Fax: (01992) 509599 E-mail: caregroup@btconnect.com

▶ CHR Commercial Cleaning Services Ltd, Unit 12 Union Bridge Mills, Roker Lane, Pudsey, West Yorkshire, LS28 9LE Tel: 0113-257 7893 Fax: 0113-236 0916 E-mail: brendan@chrservices.co.uk

Churchills Cleaning Contractors, Unit 45, Woolsbridge Industrial Park, Three Legged Cross, Wimborne, Dorset, BH21 6SZ Tel: (01202) 825284 Fax: (01202) 828229

City Clean, 67-69 Richardson Street, Wallsend, Tyne & Wear, NE28 7PS Tel: 0191-263 6218 Fax: 0191-262 1172 E-mail: Richard@cityclean77freeservce.uk

Clean & Tidy (UK), 351 Cambridge Heath Road, London, E2 9RA Tel: (020) 7739 4194 Fax: (020) 7739 2072 E-mail: cleanandtidyuk@yahoo.co.uk

Cleanforce Contracting Ltd, Force Group House, 31-33 Albion Street, Stoke-on-Trent, ST1 1QF Tel: (01782) 213333 Fax: (01782) 284555 E-mail: info@clean-force.biz

Commando Security Services Ltd, Black Friars House, West Street, Warwick, CV34 6AN Tel: (01926) 499495 Fax: (01926) 499802

Complete Cleaning Services Scotland, 6 Muriel Street, Barrhead, Glasgow, G78 1QB Tel: 0141-880 8118 Fax: 0141-880 6673 E-mail: info@completecleaningservices.com

Courtesy Cleaning Services Ltd, Courtesy House 35 Redburn Industrial Estate, Woodall Road, Enfield, Middlesex, EN3 4LQ Tel: (020) 8805 8586 Fax: (020) 8805 5868

Crofton House Associates, Crofton House, The Moor, Hawkhurst, Cranbrook, Kent, TN18 4NN Tel: (01580) 752919 Fax: (01580) 754173 E-mail: info@crofton-house.co.uk

Crown Cleaning Equipment & Hygiene Supplies, 494 Calder Street, Glasgow, G42 0QD Tel: 0141-423 1022 Fax: 0141-423 0306

D B I Ailsa, 33-35 McFarlane Street, Paisley, Renfrewshire, PA3 1FE Tel: 0141-887 0666 Fax: 0141-889 8765 E-mail: info@dbigroup.co.uk

▶ Dan Lee Cleaning & Hygiene Supplies Ltd, Elliott Road, Plymouth, PL4 0SG Tel: (01752) 665838 Fax: (01752) 226361

Design & Care Cleaning Services Ltd, 89 Walcot Square, London, SE11 4UB Tel: (020) 7261 1502 Fax: (020) 7820 0032 E-mail: design.care@virgin.net

Donau Express Services, 52 Factory Lane, Croydon, CR0 3RL Tel: (020) 8256 5000 Fax: (020) 8256 5001 E-mail: donau@donau.co.uk

Dougland Holdings Ltd, Little Park Farm, Segensworth West Industrial Estate, Fareham, Hampshire, PO15 5SN Tel: (01489) 574234 Fax: (01489) 576104 E-mail: margaret@dougland.co.uk

▶ Drain Brain Offshore, Unit 5 Dales Industrial Estate, Peterhead, Aberdeenshire, AB42 3JF Tel: (01779) 471536 Fax: (01779) 473694 E-mail: enquiries@dbigroup.co.uk

Dynamic Access, Dairy Bungalow, Sodom Lane, Dauntsey, Chippenham, Wiltshire, SN15 4JA Tel: (01249) 891878 Fax: (01249) 891878 E-mail: storm@pgen.net

Enba NI Ltd, The Old Mill, Drumaness, Ballynahinch, County Down, BT24 8LS Tel: (028) 9756 1574 Fax: (028) 9756 1576 E-mail: sales@enbani.com

INDUSTRIAL CLEANING – *continued*

Excel Kids' Club & Chilcare Services Ltd, 9 Holliday Square, Battersea, London, SW11 2HR Tel: (020) 8672 3800 Fax: (020) 8767 5139E-mail: admin@excelservices.co.uk

F & G Cleaners Ltd, 31 Engleheart Road, London, SE6 2HN Tel: (020) 8698 1337 Fax: (020) 8697 0391 E-mail: mainoffice@fandgcleaners.co.uk

F & G Services, Charfield Road, Kingswood, Wotton-Under-Edge, Gloucestershire, GL12 8RL Tel: (01453) 842307 Fax: (01453) 844303

Fernley Airport Services Ltd, Concorde House, Colndale Road, Colnbrook, Slough, SL3 0HQ Tel: (0870) 8400611 Fax: (0870) 8400622

Fleming Technical Ltd, Brunel Road, Croft Business Park, Wirral, Merseyside, CH62 3NY Tel: 0151-343 1800 Fax: 0151-343 1801 E-mail: gil@fleming-tech.co.uk

General & Industrial Window Cleaning Co. Ltd, 203-209 Gateford Road, Worksop, Nottinghamshire, S81 7BB Tel: (01909) 472967 Fax: (01909) 472967

H A Z Environmental, Bullock Street, West Bromwich, West Midlands, B70 7HE Tel: 0121-580 3055 Fax: 0121-580 3056 E-mail: mail@haz-enviro.co.uk

Hako Machines Ltd, Eldon Close, Crick, Northampton, NN6 7SL Tel: (01788) 823535 Fax: (01788) 823969 E-mail: sales@hako.co.uk

Hanson Support Services, Scotter Road South, Bottesford, Scunthorpe, South Humberside, DN17 2BU Tel: (01724) 842637 Fax: (01724) 282411 E-mail: enquiries@hanserve.com

Hygiene Group Ltd, 409-412 Montrose Avenue, Slough, SL1 4TJ Tel: (01753) 820991 Fax: (01753) 578189 E-mail: sales@hygiene.co.uk

Imperial Cleaning, Unit 7 Springwood, Cheshunt, Waltham Cross, Hertfordshire, EN7 6AZ Tel: (01992) 628342 Fax: (01992) 628342 E-mail: imperialenquiries@btinternet.com

Interclean Support Services Ltd, Unit 4C Sterling Industrial Estate, Kings Road, Newbury, Berkshire, RG14 5RQ Tel: (01635) 550199 Fax: (01635) 550037E-mail: sales@icss.co.uk

ISS Facility Services Ltd, 15A Huntingdon Street, St. Neots, Cambridgeshire, PE19 1BL Tel: (01480) 403404 Fax: (01480) 408579

J J Williams Painting Services Ltd, 75 Village Farm Road, Pyle, Bridgend, Mid Glamorgan, CF33 6BN Tel: (01656) 744311 Fax: (01656) 744617 E-mail: enquiries@jjwilliamsltd.com

Jefco Services Ltd, Queens Road, Immingham, South Humberside, DN40 1QR Tel: (01469) 574888 Fax: (01469) 574224

Kitchen Deep Cleaning, 9 High Street, Orpington, Kent, BR6 0JE Tel: (01689) 828233 Fax: (01689) 828233

M O S Cold Cutting Systems Ltd, Acorn Park Industrial Estate, Charlestown, Shipley, W. Yorkshire, BD17 7SW Tel: (01274) 588066 Fax: (01274) 588077 E-mail: stm@constructionplus.net

Marmon Contracts Ltd, 8 Boundary Street, Liverpool, L5 9UF Tel: 0151-207 2491

Marylebone Cleaning Co. Ltd, Sherlock Mews, Baker St, London, W1U 6DW Tel: (020) 7581 9847 Fax: (020) 7581 9847

Mechanical Cleansing Services Ltd, Unit G, Salford Street Industrial Estate, Aston, Birmingham, B6 7SH Tel: (0845) 5314243 Fax: 0121-327 3105 E-mail: droemcsltd@aol.com

Metrovac Co., 1016 Harrow Road, Kensal Green, London, NW10 5NS Tel: (020) 8969 4522

Mike O'Leary Cleaning Services, 181 Scribers Lane, Birmingham, B28 0PN Tel: 0121-745 4662 Fax: 0121-745 4662

Morris, Maes Y Clawdd Industrial Estate, Maesbury Road, Oswestry, Shropshire, SY10 8NN Tel: (01691) 670666 Fax: (01691) 670760 E-mail: info@morriscontractcleaning.co.uk

▶ Nevron Eurotherm Insulation Services Ltd, Unit 16, Valley Road Business Park, Birkenhead, Merseyside, CH41 7EL Tel: 0151-652 6213 Fax: 0151-652 6213 E-mail: info@nevroninsulation.co.uk

Nottingham Industrial Cleaners Ltd, Elizabeth House, Wigman Road, Bilborough, Nottingham, NG8 3HY Tel: 0115-900 7300 Fax: 0115-900 7310

O C S Group, Servia Road, Leeds, LS7 1NJ Tel: 0113-246 1281 Fax: 0113-234 1682 E-mail: ecleaning@ocs.co.uk

O'Neill Cleaning Ltd, Unit 5 Mitchelston Drive, Mitchelston Industrial Estate, Kirkcaldy, Fife, KY1 3NF Tel: (01592) 655777 Fax: (01592) 655777 E-mail: sales@oneillcleaning.com

Optim Contract Services Ltd, The Hop Exchange, 24 Southwark Street, London, SE1 1TY Tel: (020) 7940 2727 Fax: (020) 7378 0580 E-mail: info@optimgroup.co.uk

Ottimo Supplies Ltd, 7 Livingstone Mills, Howard Street, Batley, West Yorkshire, WF17 6JH Tel: (01924) 469665 Fax: (01924) 463328 E-mail: sales@ottimo-supplies.com

Progress Cleaning Services White Plume Ltd, 19 Middle Street, Southampton, SO14 6GH Tel: (023) 8022 5181 Fax: (023) 8063 0622 E-mail: sales@progresscleaningservices.co.uk

▶ Quick Response, 101 Commercial Road, London, E1 1RD Tel: (020) 7247 5555 Fax: (020) 7247 9477 E-mail: cs@quickcleaning.co.uk

R E L Contracts, Springfield, Brumstead Road, Stalham, Norwich, NR12 9DE Tel: (01692) 582238

Ray Bros, 9-13 Pleasant Hill Street, Liverpool, L8 5SY Tel: 0151-709 2271 Fax: 0151-709 7763

Remchem Ltd, Unit K Harlow House, Shelton Road, Willowbrook East Industrial Estate, Corby, Northamptonshire, NN17 5XH Tel: (01536) 205562 Fax: (01536) 401608 E-mail: sales@remchem.co.uk

Safeway Office Services Ltd, 7 Leathermarket Street, London, SE1 3HN Tel: (020) 7403 2944

Shadow Sales & Service, 6 Lyttleton Court, Droitwich, Worcestershire, WR9 7BG Tel: (01905) 797898 Fax: (01905) 798399 E-mail: mike.ssslimited@btconnect.com

South Central Cleaning Services, 7 Acorn Workshops, Empress Road, Southampton, SO14 0JY Tel: (023) 8032 2752 Fax: (023) 8032 2752E-mail: russellbowley@hotmail.com

South Midlands Group plc, 48 Oakley Road, Luton, LU4 9PU Tel: (01582) 490606 Fax: (01582) 581305 E-mail: info@smgplc.co.uk

Spic 'N' Span, 20 Edith Avenue, Plymouth, PL4 8TH Tel: (01752) 666707 Fax: (01752) 666707

Spick & Span, 375 Tunstall Road, Knypersley, Stoke-on-Trent, ST8 7PT Tel: (01782) 815800 Fax: (01782) 822881

Spurgeons Clean-Plan Ltd, 3 Royce Road, Crawley, West Sussex, RH10 9NX Tel: (01293) 437511 Fax: (01293) 437517

Square 1 Cleaning Services, Botany Bay Ii, Playhatch, Reading, RG4 9QU Tel: 0118-946 1503 E-mail: square1@botanybayii.freeserve.co.uk

Sunlight Services Group Ltd, 226 Whitehorse Road, Croydon, CR9 2NE Tel: (020) 8684 2255 Fax: (020) 8683 4050 E-mail: croydon@sunlight.co.uk

T C & D Technical Services Ltd, Kirkcroft Farm, Thorpe Hesley, Rotherham, South Yorkshire, S61 2RP Tel: 0114-246 9410 Fax: 0114-257 7935

T C M S Ltd, St. Shads Industrial Estate, Brearley Street, Hockley, Birmingham, B19 3NP Tel: 0121-333 5824 Fax: 0121-333 5829 E-mail: tcmsmidland@ukonline.co.uk

Taylors Industrial Services Ltd, Hareness Circle, Altens Industrial Estate, Aberdeen, AB12 3LY Tel: (01224) 872972 Fax: (01224) 872697 E-mail: taylors_industrial_services@btinternet.com

▶ Yorkshire Cottage Services, Heathfield, Ugthorpe, Whitby, North Yorkshire, YO21 2BG Tel: (01947) 841114 Fax: (01947) 841189 E-mail: ugthorpe@btinternet.com

INDUSTRIAL CLEANING EQUIPMENT

Ace Specialist Hire Ltd, PO Box 498, Folkestone, Kent, CT18 7GG Tel: (01797) 369222 Fax: (01797) 369333 E-mail: sales@ashclean.co.uk

Addis, Zone 3 Waterton Point, Brocastle Avenue, Waterton Industrial Estate, Bridgend, Mid Glamorgan, CF31 3US Tel: (01656) 664455 Fax: (01656) 664456 E-mail: e.marketing@addis.co.uk

Admor Services, Foxes Retreat, Worlds End, Beedon, Newbury, Berkshire, RG20 8SE Tel: (01635) 248088 Fax: (01635) 247877 E-mail: terry@admorservices.co.uk

Allbrite Cleaning Services Ltd, Darleydale Road, Corby, Northamptonshire, NN17 2DF Tel: (01536) 202295 Fax: (01536) 266246

Apex General Supplies Ltd, Unit 14 Apex House, Radford Crescent, Radford Way, Billericay, Essex, CM12 0DG Tel: (01277) 623269 Fax: (01277) 630739

Appor Ltd, Duffield Road Industrial Estate, Little Eaton, Derby, DE21 5EG Tel: (01332) 832455 Fax: (01332) 834427 E-mail: info@appor.com

B & G Cleaning Systems Ltd, Abeles Way, Holly Lane Industrial Estate, Atherstone, Warwickshire, CV9 2QZ Tel: (01827) 717028 Fax: (01827) 714041 E-mail: sales@bgclean.co.uk

Barton Electrical Ltd, Leondore House, 142 Molesdey Avenue, West Molesey, Surrey, KT8 2RY Tel: (020) 8979 4444 Fax: (020) 8979 6555

Bio-Clean Equipment Sales Ltd, Waterhouse, Greenfields Road, Horley, Surrey, RH6 8HW Tel: (01293) 424200 Fax: (01293) 424444 E-mail: sales@bioclean.co.uk

Central Hygiene Ltd, Unit 4e Brymau Three Trading Estate, River Lane, Saltney, Chester, CH4 8RQ Tel: (01244) 675066 Fax: (01244) 680129 E-mail: sales@central-hygiene.co.uk

Check Equipment, 2 Spencer Drive, Melbourn, Royston, Hertfordshire, SG8 6HP Tel: (01763) 261971 Fax: (01763) 262995 E-mail:

Clean Tech, Corporate House, Carmarthen Road, Kilgetty, Dyfed, SA68 0UG Tel: (01834) 813827 Fax: (01834) 811962

▶ Cleaning Equipment Supplies Ltd, Unit 5 Caldicot Way, Avondale Industrial Estate, Cwmbran, Gwent, NP44 1UF Tel: (01633) 868866 Fax: (01633) 862286 E-mail: admin@ces-ltd.uk.com

Cleanwell High Pressure Washers Ltd, Unit 12a Apsley Industrial Estate, Kents Avenue, Hemel Hempstead, Hertfordshire, HP3 9XH Tel: (01442) 263552 Fax: (01442) 266871 E-mail: sales@cleanwell.co.uk

▶ Hugh Crane Cleaning Equipment Ltd, Fishley Lane, South Walsham Road, Acle, Norwich, NR13 3ES Tel: (01493) 750072 Fax: (01493) 751854 E-mail: sales@hughcrane.co.uk

Freddy Products Ltd, Units 6-7, Goodwood Rd, Pershore, Worcestershire, WR10 2JL Tel: (01386) 561113 Fax: (01386) 556401 E-mail: sales@freddy-products.co.uk

▶ Freudenberg Household Products, 2 Chichester Street, Rochdale, Lancashire, OL16 2AX Tel: (01706) 759597 Fax: (01706) 350143 E-mail: steve.barber@fhp.com

G D M S UK Ltd, 14 The Meadway, Syston, Leicester, LE7 2BD Tel: 0116-264 0381 Fax: 0116-264 0381 E-mail: sales@gdms.org.uk

Hako Machines Ltd, Eldon Close, Crick, Northampton, NN6 7SL Tel: (01788) 823535 Fax: (01788) 823969 E-mail: sales@hako.co.uk

Haskel Energy Systems Ltd, North Hylton Road, Sunderland, SR5 3JD Tel: 0191-549 1212 Fax: 0191-549 0911 E-mail: sales@haskel.co.uk

Industrial Cleaning Machines, Icm House, Showell Road, Wolverhampton, WV10 9LN Tel: (01902) 306039 Fax: (01902) 304774 E-mail: sales@industrialcleaningmachines.co.uk

Industrial Cleaning Supplies Liverpool Ltd, 7-29 Brasenose Road, Liverpool, L20 8HL Tel: 0151-922 2000 Fax: 0151-922 3733 E-mail: sales@theicsgroup.co.uk

JTT Equipment Services Ltd, 6 Factory Units, Belton Lane, Grantham, Lincolnshire, NG31 9HN Tel: (01476) 576704 Fax: (01476) 576217 E-mail: sales@jttltd.co.uk

Karcher UK, Lion court, Staunton Harold Hall, Melbourne Road, Staunton Harold, Ashby-de-la-Zouch, Leicestershire, LE65 1RT Tel: (01332) 695035 Fax: (01332) 695036 E-mail: enquiries@karcheruk.co.uk

Kleen Tex Industries Ltd, Causeway Mill Express Trading Estate, Stone Hill Road, Farnworth, Bolton, BL4 9TP Tel: (01204) 863000 Fax: (01204) 863001 E-mail: sales@kleentexuk.com

Metklean Products Ltd, 23 Hailey Road, Erith, Kent, DA18 4AA Tel: (020) 8310 9882 Fax: (020) 8312 1336

Millwood Marketing, Fivefield House, Bennetts Road, Keresley End, Coventry, CV7 8HX Tel: (024) 7633 1433 Fax: (024) 7633 5663

Nilfisk-ALTO, Bowerbank Way, Penrith, Cumbria, CA11 9BQ Tel: (01768) 868995 Fax: (01768) 864713 E-mail: sales.uk@nilfisk-alto.com

Premiere Products, Bouncers Lane, Cheltenham, Gloucestershire, GL52 5JD Tel: (01242) 537150 Fax: (01242) 528445 E-mail: premiere@premiereproducts.co.uk

Projectworld Ltd, Morvern Works, Church Street, Briton Ferry, Neath, West Glamorgan, SA11 2JP Tel: (01639) 812332 Fax: (01639) 812496 E-mail: info@projectworld.co.uk

Ray Bros, 9-13 Pleasant Hill Street, Liverpool, L8 5SY Tel: 0151-709 2271 Fax: 0151-709 7763

Raynor Industrial, The Poplars, Foxwood Lane, Woodborough, Nottingham, NG14 6ED Tel: 0115-965 5424 Fax: 0115-965 6481

Riley Industries Ltd, 152 Wellhead Lane, Birmingham, B42 2SY Tel: 0121-356 2020 Fax: 0121-356 1117 E-mail: sales@rileyindustries.co.uk

▶ Russell Mainstream Supply Ltd, 8 Crown Square, Kingskettle, Cupar, Fife, KY15 7PW Tel: (01337) 831192 Fax: (01337) 371192 E-mail: wrussell@rmsupply.co.uk

Spray Systems, Merlin Centre, Gatehouse Close, Gatehouse Industrial Area, Aylesbury, Buckinghamshire, HP19 8DP Tel: (01296) 393822 Fax: (01296) 399757 E-mail: spraysys@btconnect.com

Spraychem Ltd, Cardrew Industrial Estate, Redruth, Cornwall, TR15 1ST Tel: (01209) 315222 Fax: (01209) 314333 E-mail: sales@contico.co.uk

▶ Standard Industrial Systems Ltd, Stanton House, Eastham Village Rd, Eastham, Wirral, Merseyside, CH62 0DE Tel: (0845) 2571985 Fax: (0845) 2571986 E-mail: sales@standardindustrial.co.uk

Vapormatt Ltd, Monarch Centre, Venture Way, Priorswood Industrial Est, Taunton, Somerset, TA2 8DE Tel: (01823) 257976 Fax: (01823) 336446 E-mail: sales@vapormatt.com

INDUSTRIAL CLEANING EQUIPMENT HIRE

▶ B & M Industrial Floor Cleaning Machinery, 6 Town Lane, Denton, Manchester, M34 6LE Tel: 0161-320 4291 Fax: 0161-320 4291

P S Engineering, 2 London Road, West Kingsdown, Sevenoaks, Kent, TN15 6ET Tel: (01474) 853586 Fax: (01474) 853586

INDUSTRIAL CLEANING EQUIPMENT OR MATERIALS DISTRIBUTORS OR AGENTS OR SUPPLIERS

A I S Countdown, 8 Carronshore Road, Carron, Falkirk, FK2 8DZ Tel: (01324) 570627 Fax: (01324) 562535 E-mail: admin@aisltd.co.uk

Adlib Cleaning Materials, Willesley Road, Willesley, Ashby-de-la-Zouch, Leicestershire, LE65 2UN Tel: (01530) 274444 Fax: (01530) 274999

Admiral Cleaning Supplies Ltd, Admiral House Whitwick Business Park, Stenson Road, Coalville, Leicestershire, LE67 4JP Tel: (01530) 278920 Fax: (01530) 278930 E-mail: info@admiral-cleaning-supplies.co.uk

Albatross Commercial & Industrial Cleaning Co. Ltd, Marlborough Business Centre, Marlborough Road, London, E18 1AH Tel: (020) 8530 5888 Fax: (020) 8530 4747 E-mail: alb@btconnect.com

Alkal Leisure, Unit 24, Lyon Road, Walton-on-Thames, Surrey, KT12 3PU Tel: (0845) 2305656 Fax: (0845) 2305676 E-mail: info@akc-uk.com

▶ Amandas Direct (UK) Washroom Supplies, Amandas Direct Ltd, Po Box 572, Worcester, WR5 3XW Tel: 0800 3898701 E-mail: customercare@amandasdirect.com

Anderson Electrical Ltd, PO Box 91, Derby, DE24 8HY Tel: (01332) 343121 Fax: (01332) 294736

Anglian Chemicals Ltd, Fakenham Industrial Estae, Millers Close, Fakenham, Norfolk, NR21 8NW Tel: (01328) 851407 Fax: (01328) 855701 E-mail: sales@anglianchemicals.com

Apex General Supplies Ltd, Unit 14 Apex House, Radford Crescent, Radford Way, Billericay, Essex, CM12 0DG Tel: (01277) 623269 Fax: (01277) 630739

Ashcroft Agencies Ltd, 14a Airfield Road, Christchurch, Dorset, BH23 3TG Tel: (01202) 499945 Fax: (01202) 499207

B & D Clays & Chemicals Ltd, 10 Wandle Way, Willow Lane Trading Estate, Mitcham, Surrey, CR4 4NB Tel: (020) 8640 9221 Fax: (020) 8648 5033 E-mail: sales@bdclays.co.uk

B M S Janitorial, 351 Nuthall Road, Nottingham, NG8 5BX Tel: 0115-913 2200 Fax: 0115-913 2222

Baker Engineering, 15 Bishops Orchard, East Hagbourne, Didcot, Oxfordshire, OX11 9JS Tel: (01235) 512447 Fax: (01235) 512447 E-mail: georgebakerengineering@freeserve.co.uk

Bell Brush Co., 286 Alma Road, Enfield, Middlesex, EN3 7BB Tel: (020) 8804 4144 Fax: (020) 8804 4235 E-mail: sales@bellbrush.com

Besglos Polish Co Ltd, George Street, Burnley, Lancashire, BB11 1ND Tel: (01282) 432351 Fax: (01282) 421558 E-mail: sales@besglos.co.uk

Blue Diamond Hygiene Supplies, 104 Havest Lane, Sheffield, S3 8EG Tel: 0114-278 7777

Bonnett Maintenance Chemicals, Unit 44 Corringham Industrial Estate, Corringham Road, Gainsborough, Lincolnshire, DN21 1QB Tel: (01427) 613240 Fax: (01427) 617308 E-mail: enquiries@bonnetts.f9.co.uk

Bunzl Ltd, 5 Bonnington Road Lane, Edinburgh, EH6 5BJ Tel: 0131-553 5555 Fax: 0131-554 6068 E-mail: service@bunzlcleaningsupplies.co.uk

C S A, Broad Lane, Cottenham, Cambridge, CB24 8SW Tel: (01954) 251573 Fax: (01954) 206506 E-mail: csaeagle@fsbdial.co.uk

Cambridge IT Solutions Ltd, May Ho, 4 Sheepcoat Clo, Shenley Church End, Milton Keynes, MK5 6JL Tel: (01908) 506888 Fax: (01908) 507088

Chemi Supply Cleaning & Hygiene Ltd, Ewell House, Brunel Road, Earlstrees Industrial Estate, Corby, Northamptonshire, NN17 4JW Tel: (01536) 402522 Fax: (01536) 401341

Clean Solutions, Unit 1 Kenwood Road, Stockport, Cheshire, SK5 6PH Tel: 0161-947 9947 Fax: 0161-947 9940 E-mail: enquiries@cleansolutions.co.uk

▶ Cleenol Group Ltd, Neville House, Beaumont Road, Banbury, Oxfordshire, OX16 1RB Tel: (01295) 251721 Fax: (01295) 269561 E-mail: sales@cleanol.co.uk

CPS Supply Co. Ltd, 5 Riverside Road, London, SW17 0BA Tel: (020) 8944 9016 Fax: (020) 8944 9018

Crofton House Associates, Crofton House, The Moor, Hawkhurst, Cranbrook, Kent, TN18 4NN Tel: (01580) 752919 Fax: (01580) 754173 E-mail: info@crofton-house.co.uk

Crystal Cleaning Supplies, 82 St James Way, Sidcup, Kent, DA14 5HF Tel: (020) 8309 0237 Fax: (020) 8308 0825 E-mail: sales@crystalcleaningsupplies.co.uk

Dry Cleaning & Laundry Services, 34 Mayfield Industrial Estate, Dalkeith, Midlothian, EH22 4AD Tel: 0131-663 5956 Fax: 0131-654 2102 E-mail: info@dlsdls.co.uk

Duplex Cleaning Machines UK Ltd, Unit 27 Joseph Wilson Industrial Estate, Millstrood Road, Whitstable, Kent, CT5 3PS Tel: (01227) 771276 Fax: (01227) 770220 E-mail: info@duplex-cleaning.com

F & G Services, Charfield Road, Kingswood, Wotton-Under-Edge, Gloucestershire, GL12 8RL Tel: (01453) 842307 Fax: (01453) 844303

Fleetfield Chemical Co. Ltd, Norfolk Barocks, 76-136 Edmund Road(Clough Road Entrance), Sheffield, S2 4EE Tel: 0114-273 8999 Fax: 0114-243 3739

Forestdale Business Services Ltd, Unit 3, Wandle Way, Mitcham, Surrey, CR4 4NB Tel: (020) 8640 3340 Fax: (020) 8640 3374 E-mail: sales@forestdalebs.co.uk

Maurice Fox Ltd, Warehouse Unit, Foel, Welshpool, Powys, SY21 0NS Tel: (01938) 820664 Fax: (01938) 820642

Global Cleaning Supplies, Unit 86-87, John Wilson Business Park, Chestfield, Whitstable, Kent, CT5 3QT Tel: (01227) 266426 Fax: (01227) 770545 E-mail: gcs@global-cleaning-supplies.co.uk

INDUSTRIAL CLEANING EQUIPMENT OR MATERIALS DISTRIBUTORS OR AGENTS OR SUPPLIERS – *continued*

Green & White Ltd, 112 Fortune Green Road, London, NW6 1DH Tel: (020) 7794 7783 Fax: (020) 7433 1143 E-mail: green.white.ltd@lineone.net

H G S Cleaning Supplies, Unit F, 61 Albert Road North, Reigate, Surrey, RH2 9EL Tel: (01737) 240162 Fax: (01737) 223384 E-mail: sales@hgscleaningsupplies.co.uk

Halls Northern Ltd, Unit 9 Stadium Industrial Estate, Gateshead, Tyne & Wear, NE10 0XF Tel: 0191-378 4500 Fax: 0191-378 9796 E-mail: enquiries@hallsnorthern.co.uk

Hartford Russel Supply Co. Ltd, 5 Trafalgar Trading Estate, Jeffreys Road, Enfield, Middlesex, EN3 7TY Tel: (020) 8804 2425 Fax: (020) 8804 8203 E-mail: hrsupplycode@aol.com

HPSC Moxons Ltd, Courtney Street, Hull, HU8 7QF Tel: (01482) 229016 Fax: (01482) 589562 E-mail: info@hpcsltd.co.uk

Roger Hyde Ltd, 4 St. James Street, Castle Hedingham, Halstead, Essex, CO9 3EJ Tel: (01787) 463348 Fax: (01787) 461868 E-mail: info@rogerhyde.co.uk

Hygenitec Disposables, Unit G7/9, Blackpole Trading Estate East, Worcester, WR3 8SG Tel: (01905) 755535 Fax: (01905) 755705

I & K Supplies, 8 Barrasgate Road, Fraserburgh, Aberdeenshire, AB43 9HH Tel: (01346) 510424 Fax: (01346) 510424

Ideal Cleaning Services Ltd, 2581 Coventry Road, Sheldon, Birmingham, B26 3PX Tel: 0121-743 5802 Fax: 0121-742 5040

Industrial Chemicals & Equipment Ltd, 59 Cranes Park, Surbiton, Surrey, KT5 8AS Tel: (020) 8399 9333 Fax: (020) 8399 9555 E-mail: ice.ltd@virgin.net

Industrial Supplies Peterborough Ltd, Waterworks Lane, Glinton, Peterborough, PE6 7LP Tel: (01733) 252771 Fax: (01733) 252362 E-mail: ispeterborough@aol.com

Invicta Cleaning Supplies Ltd, 46 Dale Wood Road, Orpington, Kent, BR6 0BZ Tel: (01689) 898785 Fax: (01689) 898785

J & J Services, 29 Dunville Road, Bedford, MK40 4DY Tel: (01234) 378289 Fax: (01234) 325479 E-mail: lindopjj@aol.com

J S Cleaning Supplies, 12 Charles Berrington Road, Liverpool, L15 9HQ Tel: 0151-722 3966

Jacksons, Victory House, Cox Lane, Chessington, Surrey, KT9 1SG Tel: (020) 8391 5555 Fax: (020) 8391 5333 E-mail: info@jacksonscg.co.uk

JTT Equipment Services Ltd, 6 Factory Units, Belton Lane, Grantham, Lincolnshire, NG31 9HN Tel: (01476) 576704 Fax: (01476) 576217 E-mail: sales@jttltd.co.uk

Kenmac (U K) Ltd, Unit D Wigan Hall Road, Good Yard, Wigan Hall Road, Watford, WD18 0EZ Tel: (01923) 218998 Fax: (01923) 818454 E-mail: enquiries@kenmacuk.com

Kleaning Equipment Western Ltd, Park Road, Dawley Bank, Telford, Shropshire, TF4 2BE Tel: (01952) 502600 Fax: (01952) 504703 E-mail: enquiries@cleaning-equipment.co.uk

London Cleaning Supplies, 180-182 Brownhill Road, London, SE6 2DJ Tel: (020) 8697 3444 Fax: (020) 8461 5713

M & A Environmental Ltd, Unit 3 Gidleys Meadow, Christow, Exeter, EX6 7QB Tel: (01647) 252855 Fax: (01647) 252882 E-mail: sales@ma-enviro.co.uk

M & D Cleaning Supplies Ltd, Grove Road, Upholland, Skelmersdale, Lancashire, WN8 0LH Tel: (01695) 632765 Fax: (01695) 632760 E-mail: sales@mandd.co.uk

Midland Vacum Cleaner Services, 1477-1479 Pershore Road, Stirchley, Birmingham, B30 2JL Tel: 0121-458 7185 Fax: 0121-458 4226 E-mail: enquries@midlandvac.co.uk

Minatol Ltd, Mandarin House, 4 Manorgate Road, Kingston upon Thames, Surrey, KT2 7UB Tel: (020) 8549 9222 Fax: (020) 8547 1635 E-mail: sales@minatol.co.uk

Mountview Services Ltd, 41 Killyleagh Road, Saintfield, Ballynahinch, County Down, BT24 7EH Tel: (028) 9751 1111 Fax: (028) 9751 1700

Multi Clean Services Ltd, Lion Works, Paternoster Lane, Bradford, West Yorkshire, BD7 3LP Tel: (01274) 501666 Fax: (01274) 501777 E-mail: info@multiclean-services.com

James Mutch Ltd, 105 King Street, Aberdeen, AB24 5SN Tel: (01224) 643452 Fax: (01224) 630763 E-mail: sales@jamesmutch.co.uk

Myona Ltd, Watery La Middleway, Bordesley, Birmingham, B9 4HE Tel: 0121-773 4333 Fax: 0121-773 4970 E-mail: sales@myona.co.uk

Nor Chem Supplies, Loch Flemington, Inverness, IV2 7QR Tel: (01667) 462500 Fax: (01667) 462173

Pollards Woodworking Machines Of Switzerland Ltd, 49 Aylesbury Street, Bletchley, Milton Keynes, MK2 2BQ Tel: (01908) 644877 Fax: (01908) 271552 E-mail: sales@pollards.co.uk

Power Clean Services, 3 Regent Business Centre, Pump Lane, Hayes, Middlesex, UB3 3NP Tel: (020) 8573 9893 Fax: (020) 8573 7765

Real Kleen, Units 12-13 Harmill Industrial Estate, Grovebury Road, Leighton Buzzard, Bedfordshire, LU7 4FF Tel: (01525) 370795 Fax: (01525) 852267

S W F Sales & Service, Office 6 Mill House Offices, Lichfield Street, Fazeley, Tamworth, Staffordshire, B78 3QA Tel: (01827) 61601 Fax: (01827) 312177

Smith & Moore, 82-86 New Street, West Bromwich, West Midlands, B70 7PT Tel: 0121-553 0337 Fax: 0121-500 5463 E-mail: smithmoore@supernet.com

Southern Chemical Services Ltd, 16 Williams Industrial Park, Gore Road, New Milton, Hampshire, BH25 6SH Tel: (01425) 617197 Fax: (01425) 617197 E-mail: scsltd@scsltd.fsnet.co.uk

Surrey Hants & Cleaning Supplies, Hygiene House, 14 St. Josephs Road, Aldershot, Hampshire, GU12 4LG Tel: (01252) 313131 Fax: (01252) 334433 E-mail: sales@tiagroup.co.uk

System Hygiene Ltd, Altham Business Park, Altham, Accrington, Lancashire, BB5 5YT Tel: (01282) 777999 Fax: (01282) 777900 E-mail: sales@systemhygiene.co.uk

T D C Services, T D C House, Ferry Hill, Ewloe, Deeside, Clwyd, CH5 3AW Tel: (01244) 534521 Fax: (01244) 533562 E-mail: sales@tdcservices.co.uk

T G B Cleaning Supplies Ltd, 370 Northolt Road, Harrow, Middlesex, HA2 8ES Tel: (020) 8423 2155 Fax: (020) 8423 6409 E-mail: tgb@tgb.co.uk

Technijet, Old Station Yard, Kirkby Lonsdale, Carnforth, Lancashire, LA6 2HP Tel: (01524) 273000 Fax: (01524) 272161

Tooltec Industrial & Cleaning Supplies, Unit C2 Forge Meadow, Canterbury Road, Hawkinge, Folkestone, Kent, CT18 7JA Tel: (01303) 894799 Fax: (01303) 894799

Total Cleaning Equipment Ltd, 223-225 Ilderton Road, London, SE15 1NS Tel: (020) 7732 0191 Fax: (020) 7732 0194 E-mail: tcelimited@aol.com

Triple Crown CHS, 43 High Street, Middleton Cheney, Banbury, Oxfordshire, OX17 2NX Tel: (01295) 712269 Fax: (01295) 713191

Unico Ltd, North Main Street, Carronshore, Falkirk, FK2 8HT Tel: (01324) 573410 Fax: (01324) 573401 E-mail: sales@unicodirect.com

Van Zelm Chem, 82 Williams St, Grays, Essex, RM17 6DZ Tel: (01375) 374612 Fax: (01375) 404007 E-mail: sales@vanzelm.co.uk

Venture Chemicals, Unit 2 Spring Lane Industrial Estate, Ashmore Lake, Willenhall, West Midlands, WV12 4HW Tel: (01902) 368585 Fax: (01902) 366356

Victory Workwear Ltd, 5 Holder Road, Aldershot, Hampshire, GU12 4RH Tel: (01252) 352800 Fax: (01252) 352805

Wacs Trade Centre, Bond House, Goodwood Road, London, SE14 6BL Tel: (020) 8692 5864 Fax: (020) 8692 1322 E-mail: sales@wacstradecentre.com

Wessex Cleaning Equipment & Janitorial Supplies Ltd, Unit 1 Mount Pleasant Industrial Estate, Mount Pleasant Road, Southampton, SO14 0SP Tel: (023) 8023 4304 Fax: (023) 8023 7226 E-mail: sales@wessexcleaning.com

Wightman & Parrish Ltd, Station Road Industrial Estate, Hailsham, East Sussex, BN27 2QA Tel: (01323) 440444 Fax: (01323) 846027 E-mail: sales@w-p.co.uk

INDUSTRIAL CLEANING MATERIALS

Abco Janitorial Supplies, 78-90 Cheshire Street, London, E2 6EH Tel: (020) 7729 6465 Fax: (020) 7739 9400

▶ Advance Products Ltd, Meadow Mills, Carlton Road, Dewsbury, West Yorkshire, WF13 2BA Tel: (01924) 486000 Fax: (01924) 486001 E-mail: sales@advance-products.co.uk

▶ Allclean & Safety, Garston Industrial Estate, Blackburne Street, Liverpool, L19 8JB Tel: 0151-494 2929 Fax: 0151-494 2206 E-mail: sales@allclean.net

Ashland Chemical & Hygiene Supplies Ltd, Unit 17-18 Aghanloo Industrial Estate, Aghanloo Road, Limavady, County Londonderry, BT49 0HE Tel: (028) 7776 7007 Fax: (028) 7776 7008 E-mail: ian.ashfield@ashlandchemicals.co.uk

C C L Supplies, 153 High Street, Chesterton, Cambridge, CB4 1NL Tel: (01223) 520575 Fax: (01223) 520175 E-mail: sales@cclsupplies.co.uk

Carpet Guard, 9-11 Holborn Square, Birkenhead, Merseyside, CH41 9HQ Tel: 0151-649 8800 Fax: 0151-649 8800 E-mail: mail@carpetgard.co.uk

Ceetek Chemicals Ltd, Firs Industrial Estate, Kidderminster, Worcestershire, DY11 7QN Tel: (01562) 755337 Fax: (01562) 865660 E-mail: ceetek@aol.com

Chempact (Yorkshire) Ltd, Wayside Units, Darley, Harrogate, North Yorkshire, HG3 2QQ Tel: 01423 780848

Clean Approach Ltd, 86 Sydney Road, Watford, WD18 7QX Tel: (01923) 210009 Fax: (01923) 210065

▶ Hugh Crane Cleaning Equipment Ltd, Fishley Lane, South Walsham Road, Acle, Norwich, NR13 3ES Tel: (01493) 750072 Fax: (01493) 751854 E-mail: sales@hughcrane.co.uk

Dispo Products Ltd, 2 Carrakeel Drive, Maydown Industrial Estate, Maydown, Londonderry, BT47 6UQ Tel: (028) 7186 1086 Fax: (028) 7186 0170 E-mail: dispo-products@91.net

E S B Environmental, 126 Hillcroft Crescent, Watford, WD19 4NZ Tel: (01923) 800852 Fax: (01923) 229003 E-mail: jbird@moose.co.uk

High Technology Solvents UK Ltd, Millfield, Ashwells Road, Brentwood, Essex, CM15 9SF Tel: (01277) 375222 Fax: (01277) 373115 E-mail: htsukltd@aol.com

Industrial Cleaning Supplies Liverpool Ltd, 7-29 Brasenose Road, Liverpool, L20 8HL Tel: 0151-922 2000 Fax: 0151-922 3733 E-mail: sales@theicsgroup.co.uk

L A Brook Ltd, Royds Mill, Leeds Road, Ossett, West Yorkshire, WF5 9YA Tel: (01924) 277026 Fax: (01924) 262074 E-mail: sales@labrook.com

Multy Abrasives Ltd, First Avenue, Deeside Industrial Park, Deeside, Clwyd, CH5 2NU Tel: (01244) 288261 Fax: (01244) 280305 E-mail: clare@multyabrasives.co.uk

▶ Needfull Things, 3 Woodlands Drive, Grantham, Lincolnshire, NG31 9DJ Tel: (01476) 569571 Fax: (01529) 455405

▶ Nursing & General Supplies, Ivyhouse Industrial Estate, Haywood Way, Hastings, East Sussex, TN35 4PL Tel: (01424) 444411 Fax: (01424) 435009

Omnipole UK Ltd, 281 Addiscombe Road, Croydon, CR0 7HZ Tel: (020) 8654 4188 Fax: (020) 8407 0439

Quality Services, Unit 35 Mountney Bridge Business Park, Westham, Pevensey, East Sussex, BN24 5NJ Tel: (01323) 767344 Fax: (01323) 460440 E-mail: qualityservices@jangro.net

Ray Bros, 9-13 Pleasant Hill Street, Liverpool, L8 5SY Tel: 0151-709 2271 Fax: 0151-709 7763

Robert Mcbride Group Ltd, Park Road, Barrow-in-Furness, Cumbria, LA14 4BN Tel: (01229) 814000 Fax: (01229) 836518

Solvitol Ltd, Shadon Way, Birtley, Chester Le Street, County Durham, DH3 2RE Tel: 0191-410 9131 Fax: 0191-492 0503

Specialised Aerosols Co. Ltd, Carr Green Lane, Mapplewell, Barnsley, South Yorkshire, S75 6DY Tel: (01226) 387101 Fax: (01226) 387100 E-mail: sales@specialised-aerosols.co.uk

Summit Hygiene, Cameron Road, Chesham, Buckinghamshire, HP5 3BX Tel: (01494) 793414 Fax: (0870) 3001143

Tayside Pressure Washers, 89 Airlie Street, Alyth, Blairgowrie, Perthshire, PH11 8EE Tel: (01828) 632329 Fax: (01828) 632314

Trafalgar Equipment, Commercial Street, Ystrad Mynach, Hengoed, Mid Glamorgan, CF82 7DY Tel: (01443) 812491 Fax: (01443) 816501 E-mail: trafalgarclean@aol.com

Venture Chemicals, Unit 2 Spring Lane Industrial Estate, Ashmore Lake, Willenhall, West Midlands, WV12 4HW Tel: (01902) 368585 Fax: (01902) 366356

Yorkshire Cleaning Fabrics Ltd, Drakes Industrial Estate, Shay Lane, Ovenden, Halifax, West Yorkshire, HX3 6RL Tel: (01422) 358286 Fax: (01422) 346891 E-mail: sales@ycfcleaning.co.uk

INDUSTRIAL COMPRESSORS

Belliss & Morcom Ltd, Chequers Bridge, Gloucester, GL1 4LL Tel: (01452) 338338 Fax: (01452) 338307 E-mail: indsales@gardnerdenver.co.uk

Drum International Ltd, Springmill Street, Bradford, West Yorkshire, BD5 7YH Tel: (01274) 718100 Fax: (01274) 718101 E-mail: sales@eu.gardnerdenver.com

▶ Gardner Denver Alton Ltd, Larkfield Trading Estate, New Hythe Lane, Larkfield, Aylesford, Kent, ME20 6SW Tel: (01622) 716816 Fax: (01622) 715115 E-mail: ukinfo@eu.gardnerdenver.com

KKK Limited, 7 Regent Park, Park Farm Industrial Estate, Off Booth Drive, Wellingborough, Northants, NN8 6GR Tel: (01933) 671480 Fax: (01933) 671470 E-mail: kkk.limited@agkkk.de

INDUSTRIAL COMPUTER LABELS

Berkshire Labels Ltd, Swangate, Hungerford, Berkshire, RG17 0YX Tel: (01488) 683628 Fax: (01488) 684186 E-mail: sales@berkshirelabels.co.uk

Ennis Labels & Print, Tower Studios, Market Street, Darwen, Lancashire, BB3 1AZ Tel: (01254) 826138 Fax: (01254) 702135 E-mail: sales@ennislabels.co.uk

Labels Plus Ltd, Unit 3, River Side Industrial Estate, Bordercot Lane, Wickham Market, Woodbridge, Suffolk, IP13 0TA Tel: (0870) 7705161 Fax: (01728) 745385

M B F Business Forms Ltd, 20 Rectory Road, West Bridgford, Nottingham, NG2 6BG Tel: 0115-981 3786 Fax: 0115-945 5249 E-mail: info@mbf-business-forms.co.uk

Nu Tac Trade Labels Ltd, Bradford Street, Farnworth, Bolton, BL4 9LS Tel: (01204) 861436 Fax: (01204) 862923 E-mail: info@newfoil.co.uk

Stampiton Group Of Companies Ltd, Bingswood Industrial Estate, Whaley Bridge, High Peak, Derbyshire, SK23 7SP Tel: (01663) 733535 Fax: (01663) 734253 E-mail: enq@stampiton.co.uk

▶ Thermaltran, Label House, 14 Summerfield Road, Kettering, Northamptonshire, NN15 6EN Tel: (01536) 392900 E-mail: Sales@thermaltran.co.uk

Worldmark, 4 Redwood CR, East Kilbride, Glasgow, G74 5PA Tel: (01355) 249191 Fax: (01355) 230875 E-mail: info@donprint.com

Worldmark, 4 Redwood CR, East Kilbride, Glasgow, G74 5PA Tel: (01355) 249191 Fax: (01355) 230875 E-mail: info@donprint.com

INDUSTRIAL COMPUTERS

C K S Holdings Ltd, Swallow End, Swallowfields, Welwyn Garden City, Hertfordshire, AL7 1JA Tel: (01707) 322528 Fax: (01707) 372851 E-mail: info@cksholdings.com

Fairchild Ltd, Fairchild House, Southampton Street, Southampton, SO15 2ED Tel: (023) 8021 1789 Fax: (023) 8021 1678 E-mail: sales@fairchild.co.uk

I F C C O Systems Ltd, Unit 3, Basingstoke Business Centre, Winchester Road, Basingstoke, Hampshire, RG22 4AU Tel: (01256) 357351 Fax: (01256) 357354

Kontron UK Ltd, 9 Ben Turner Industrial Estate, Oving Road, Chichester, West Sussex, PO19 7ET Tel: (01243) 523500 Fax: (01243) 532949 E-mail: uksales@kontron.com

Pro Face UK Ltd, Orchard Court Binley Business Park, Harry Weston Road, Coventry, CV3 2TQ Tel: (024) 7644 0088 Fax: (024) 7644 0099 E-mail: sales@profaceuk.com

▶ QSI Europe, Unit 4, Commerce Way, Leighton Buzzard, Bedfordshire, LU7 4RW Tel: 01525 373800 Fax: 01525 374468 E-mail: gp@cirris.co.uk

Real Time Systems Ltd, 78 Cannon St, London, EC4P 4LN Tel: (020) 7861 0700 Fax: (020) 7861 0899 E-mail: sales@rtsgroup.net

Trident Microsystems Ltd, Perrywood Business Park, Honeycrock Lane, Redhill, RH1 5JQ Tel: (01737) 780790 Fax: (01737) 771908 E-mail: sales@trident-uk.co.uk

INDUSTRIAL CONNECTORS

Ceep Ltd, Unit 7 Weydown Industrial Estate, Haslemere, Surrey, GU27 1DW Tel: (01428) 661515 Fax: (01428) 644147 E-mail: sales@ceep.co.uk

Grundfos Pumps Ltd, Orford Court, Green Fold Way, Leigh, Lancashire, WN7 3XJ Tel: (0870) 7503888 Fax: (01942) 605970

INDUSTRIAL CONSULTANTS

B F P Instruments Ltd, Unit 9b Alstone Trading Estate, Alstone Lane, Cheltenham, Gloucestershire, GL51 8HF Tel: (01242) 251281 Fax: (01242) 251468

Challinor & Sons, Malverne, Church Bank, Goostrey, Crewe, CW4 8PG Tel: (01477) 533282 Fax: (01260) 276924

Dunlop Design Engineering, 1 Sackville Street, Lisburn, County Antrim, BT27 4AB Tel: (028) 9267 2333 Fax: (028) 9267 2383 E-mail: info@dnet.co.uk

H M Sitec Ltd, St. Georges Lodge, 33 Oldfield Road, Bath, BA2 3NE Tel: (01225) 428221 Fax: (01225) 444697 E-mail: info@hmbath.com

I T S Ltd, PO Box 331, Slough, SL2 3DQ Tel: (01753) 642144 Fax: (01753) 646461 E-mail: dir@its.ltd.uk

John Young Foam Consultants Ltd, 97 Cote Green Road, Marple Bridge, Stockport, Cheshire, SK6 5EN Tel: 0161-427 3734 Fax: 0161-449 0982 E-mail: jyfc@btconnect.com

Maxwell Stamp Group plc, Abbots Court, 34 Farringdon Lane, London, EC1R 3AX Tel: (020) 7251 0147 Fax: (020) 7251 0140 E-mail: london@maxwellstamp.com

Modular Mouldings Ltd, Lower Quay, Gweek, Helston, Cornwall, TR12 6UD Tel: (01326) 221722 Fax: (01326) 221800 E-mail: mml@clara.net

Operational UK Ltd, 7 Berkeley Court, Manor Park, Runcorn, Cheshire, WA7 1TQ Tel: (01928) 579473 Fax: (01928) 579517 E-mail: sales@operational.co.uk

Pera, Pera Innovation Park, Melton Mowbray, Leicestershire, LE13 0PB Tel: (01664) 501501 Fax: (01664) 501264 E-mail: sales@pera.com

R G P Design Innovation, 62 Cause End Road, Wootton, Bedford, MK43 9DE Tel: (01234) 767143 Fax: (01234) 767143 E-mail: rgpdesign@talk21.com

T W I Ltd, Granta Park, Great Abington, Cambridge, CB1 6AL Tel: (01223) 899000 Fax: (01223) 892794 E-mail: twi@twi.co.uk

INDUSTRIAL CONTROL COMPUTERS

Arcom Control Systems Ltd, 8 Clifton Road, Cambridge, CB1 7EA Tel: (01223) 411200 Fax: (01223) 403400 E-mail: sales@arcom.co.uk

Blue Chip Technology Ltd, Chowley Oak, Chowley Oak Lane, Tattenhall, Chester, CH3 9EX Tel: (01829) 772000 Fax: (01829) 772001 E-mail: sales@bluechiptechnology.co.uk

▶ indicates data change since last edition

INDUSTRIAL CONTROL COMPUTERS – *continued*

Brodersen Control Systems, Unit 11 Canbury Business Park, Elm Cresent, Kingston upon Thames, Surrey, KT2 6HJ Tel: (020) 8546 4283 Fax: (020) 8547 3628 E-mail: bcs@brodersen.co.uk

C P Engineering, Sandys Road, Malvern, Worcestershire, WR14 1JJ Tel: (01684) 584850 Fax: (01684) 573088 E-mail: sales@cpengineering.com

Cambridge Microprocessor Systems Ltd, 17-18 Zone D, Chelmsford Road Industrial Estate, Great Dunmow, Dunmow, Essex, CM6 1XG Tel: (01371) 875644 Fax: (01371) 876077 E-mail: info@cms.uk.com

Densitron Technologies P.L.C., 145 Cannon Street, London, EC4N 5BP Tel: (020) 7648 4200 Fax: (020) 7648 4201 E-mail: sales@densitron.com

Ego Computers Ltd, Salisbury Hall, London Colney, St. Albans, Hertfordshire, AL2 1BU Tel: (01727) 828400 Fax: (01727) 824141 E-mail: rdrinkwater@ego-computers.ltd.uk

Geedev Ltd, 21 Barndale Drive, Arne, Wareham, Dorset, BH20 5BX Tel: (01929) 551122 Fax: (01929) 552936 E-mail: design@geedev.co.uk

H M Computing Ltd, Harmac House, Enigma Park, Malvern, Worcestershire, WR14 1GP Tel: (01684) 581850 Fax: (01684) 581851 E-mail: sales@hmcomputing.net

Mitac Synnex UK Ltd, Synnex House, Nedge Hill, Telford, Shropshire, TF3 3AH Tel: (01952) 207200 Fax: (01952) 201216

Pro Face UK Ltd, Orchard Court Binley Business Park, Harry Weston Road, Coventry, CV3 2TQ Tel: (024) 7644 0088 Fax: (024) 7644 0099 E-mail: sales@profaceuk.com

▶ QSI Europe, Unit 4, Commerce Way, Leighton Buzzard, Bedfordshire, LU7 4RW Tel: 01525 373800 Fax: 01525 374468 E-mail: gp@cirris.co.uk

INDUSTRIAL CONTROL GEAR

DBM Electrical Supplies Ltd, Unit B6 Halesfield 8, Telford, Shropshire, TF7 4QN Tel: (01952) 588800 Fax: (01952) 588822 E-mail: DMASON@DBMELECTRICAL.CO.UK

INDUSTRIAL CONTROL KEYBOARDS

Tipro Keyboards UK Ltd, Unit 19/20, Kingston Farm Industrial Units, Down Hall Road, Matching Green, Harlow, Essex, CM17 0RB Tel: (01279) 732360 Fax: (01279) 732369 E-mail: sales@tiprokeyboards.co.uk

INDUSTRIAL CONTROL SOFTWARE

Agency Sector Management UK Ltd, Ashford House, 41-45 Church Road, Ashford, Middlesex, TW15 2TQ Tel: (01784) 242200 Fax: (01784) 242012 E-mail: info@asm.org.uk

Alpha Co Consulting Engineers Ltd, 30 Stowell Cresent, Wareham, Dorset, BH20 4PZ Tel: (01929) 551207 Fax: (07802) 431378 E-mail: info@alpha-comp.co.uk

B L Computer Services, McPhail Ho, 1 Alexandra Rd, Clevedon, Avon, BS21 7QE Tel: (01275) 340500 Fax: (01275) 340470 E-mail: admin@blcomp.co.uk

Datalink Software UK Ltd, Unit 61 Old Market Court, George Street, Glastonbury, Somerset, BA6 9LT Tel: (01458) 830134 Fax: (01458) 830135 E-mail: info@datalinklpg.co.uk

Future Software Systems, Woodville, Hatton, Market Rasen, Lincs, LN8 5QG Tel: 01673 857118 Fax: 01673 857176

S C M Software, Ty Gwyn Pen Y Garnedd, Llanrhaeadr Ym, Oswestry, Shropshire, SY10 0AN Tel: (01691) 860583 Fax: (01691) 860456

Tascomp Ltd, Newburgh Court, Belasis Hall Technology Park, Billingham, Cleveland, TS23 4EE Tel: (01642) 370666 Fax: (01642) 370012 E-mail: sales@tascomp.com

INDUSTRIAL CONTROL SYSTEMS TO SPECIFICATION

C C S Technology Ltd, School Street, Wolston, Coventry, CV8 3HG Tel: (024) 7654 5711 Fax: (024) 7654 5722 E-mail: markf@ccstech.co.uk

Tellima Technology Ltd, Unit 1g Denby Dale Industrial Park, Wakefield Road, Denby Dale, Huddersfield, HD8 8QH Tel: (01484) 866806 Fax: (01484) 866816 E-mail: sales@tellima.co.uk

INDUSTRIAL CONVEYOR SYSTEMS

Crown Conveyors Ltd, 8 Clamp Road, Wishaw, Lanarkshire, ML2 7XQ Tel: (01698) 254621 Fax: (01698) 261027 E-mail: sales@crownconveyors.co.uk

▶ G L W Engineering & Construction, Unit 3 Wisbech Business Centre, Oldfield Lane, Friday Bridge, Wisbech, Cambridgeshire, PE14 0NX Tel: (01945) 464637 Fax: (07000) 785497 E-mail: geoff@glwengineering.co.uk

G P M Engineering Systems Ltd, 1585 Bristol Road South, Rednal, Birmingham, B45 9UA Tel: 0121-457 7132 Fax: 0121-457 9035 E-mail: scrow@gpmengineering.com

Hallanshire Engineering Holdings Ltd, Unit 14, North Anston Trading Estate, Dinnington, Sheffield, S25 4JJ Tel: (01909) 562091 Fax: (01909) 550206E-mail: sales@heh.co.uk

Stewart Gill Conveyor Ltd, 2 Christy Estate, Ivy Road, Aldershot, Hampshire, GU12 4TX Tel: (01252) 332221 Fax: (01252) 334387 E-mail: info@stewart-gill.co.uk

INDUSTRIAL COOLERS

Aberdeen Radiators Ltd, 53 Wellington Street, Aberdeen, AB11 5BX Tel: (01224) 575692 Fax: (01224) 211023 E-mail: len.hubert@aberdeen-radiators.co.uk

Acrokool Ltd, 1 Veerman Park, Thaxted Road, Saffron Walden, Essex, CB10 2UP Tel: (01799) 513631 Fax: (01799) 513635 E-mail: sales@acrokool.co.uk

Aquafan Cooling Towers Ltd, 47 Down St, West Molesey, Surrey, KT8 2SY Tel: (020) 8941 4378

Balticare Ltd, Princewood Road, Earlstrees Industrial Estate, Corby, Northamptonshire, NN17 4AP Tel: (01536) 200312 Fax: (01536) 408623 E-mail: info@baltaircoil.be

Becool Radiators Ltd, Paterson Road, Wellingborough, Northamptonshire, NN8 4BZ Tel: (01933) 230420 Fax: (01933) 279902 E-mail: sales@gallay.co.uk

Central Cooling Services Ltd, Garrison House, Garrison Street, Bordesley, Birmingham, B9 4BN Tel: 0121-766 7227 Fax: 0121-766 6156 E-mail: centralcoolingservices@btinternet.com

Cold Box Ltd, 28 Benson Road, Nuffield Industrial Estate, Poole, Dorset, BH17 0GB Tel: (01202) 667667 Fax: (01202) 667666 E-mail: ian@coldbox.co.uk

Faudler Balfour, P O Box 15, Leven, Fife, KY8 4RW Tel: (01333) 423020 Fax: (01333) 427432 E-mail: mailus@pfaudlerbalfour.co.uk

Flowcool Systems, Wimsey Way, Somercotes, Alfreton, Derbyshire, DE55 4LS Tel: (01773) 608888 Fax: (01773) 609001 E-mail: sales@flowcool.com

Heat Exchange Industries Ltd, Willow Road, Trent Lane, Castle Donnington, Castle Donington, Derby, DE74 2NP Tel: (01332) 853862 Fax: (01332) 3850590

I C S Group, Gore Road Industrial Estate, New Milton, Hampshire, BH25 6SA Tel: (01425) 625900 Fax: (01425) 639041 E-mail: info@industrialcooling.co.uk

I M I Cornelius UK Ltd, 1-3 Tything Road East, Kinwarton, Alcester, Warwickshire, B49 6EU Tel: (01789) 763101 Fax: (01789) 763644 E-mail: sales@cornelius.com

Ipc Industrial Power Cooling Ltd, 14 Hillmorton Road, Knowle, Solihull, West Midlands, B93 9JL Tel: (01564) 776456 Fax: (01564) 777625 E-mail: nh@ipcltd.freeserve.co.uk

Occo Coolers Telford Ltd, St. Georges Road Industrial Estate, Donnington, Telford, Shropshire, TF2 7QZ Tel: (01952) 616381 Fax: (05600) 753354 E-mail: sales@occocoolers.co.uk

Process Cooling Solutions, 916 Castle La East, Bournemouth, BH7 6SN Tel: (01202) 434328 Fax: (01202) 434329 E-mail: office@ptcltd.co.uk

Refrigeration On The Wolds, Albion Street, Driffield, North Humberside, YO25 6PZ Tel: (01377) 252518

Stadco Ltd, Harlescott Lane, Shrewsbury, SY1 3AS Tel: (01743) 462227 Fax: (01743) 447709 E-mail: cooling@stadco.co.uk

Thermal Exchange Ltd, 15 Chiswick Road, Leicester, LE2 7SX Tel: 0116-254 6652 Fax: 0116-255 9176 E-mail: sales@thermalexchange.co.uk

Watermiser Ltd, Tower Works, 4-8 Stoneygate Road, Newmilns, Ayrshire, KA16 9AJ Tel: (01560) 320762 Fax: (01560) 323093 E-mail: info@watermiser.co.uk

INDUSTRIAL CRUSHING PLANT

B J D Crushers Ltd, B B I Centre, Innovation Way, Wilthorpe, Barnsley, South Yorkshire, S75 1JL Tel: (01226) 241425 Fax: (01226) 296713 E-mail: sales@bjdcrushers.co.uk

Lanway Ltd, PO Box 3568, Bewdley, Worcestershire, DY12 1ZU Tel: (01299) 861733 Fax: (0871) 7333899 E-mail: sales@lanway.ltd.uk

Miracle Mills Ltd, Knightsdale Road, Ipswich, IP1 4LE Tel: (01473) 742325 Fax: (01473) 462773 E-mail: info@cristy-turner.com

Terex Pegson Ltd, Mammoth Street, Coalville, Leicestershire, LE67 3GN Tel: (01530) 518600 Fax: (01530) 518618 E-mail: sales@bl-pegson.com

INDUSTRIAL CUBICLES

▶ Bushboard Ltd, Rixon Road, Wellingborough, Northamptonshire, NN8 4BA Tel: (01933) 232200 Fax: (01933) 232280 E-mail: washrooms@bushboard.co.uk

Cubical Systems Ltd, Units 1-4 Nova Business Unit, Gore Road Industrial Estate, New Milton, Hampshire, BH25 6RP Tel: (01425) 615585 Fax: (01425) 628144 E-mail: sales@cubicalsystems.co.uk

Mermaid Panels Ltd, DBC House, Grimsby Road, Laceby, Grimsby, South Humberside, DN37 7DP Tel: (01472) 279940 Fax: (01472) 752575 E-mail: sales@mermaidpanels.com

INDUSTRIAL CUTTING BOARDS

ABG Rubber & Plastics Ltd, Galowhill Rd, Brackmills Industrial Estate, Northampton, NN4 7EE Tel: (01604) 700880 Fax: (01604) 766113 E-mail: sales@abgrp.co.uk

Alpress Hydraulic Engineers, 65 Back Sneddon Street, Paisley, Renfrewshire, PA3 2DD Tel: 0141-848 7175 Fax: 0141-889 5280 E-mail: alpresshs@tiscali.co.uk

INDUSTRIAL DEFROSTING EQUIPMENT

Petrie Technologies Ltd, Common Bank Industrial Estate, Ackhurst Road, Chorley, Lancashire, PR7 1NH Tel: (01257) 241206 Fax: (01257) 267562 E-mail: sales@petrieltd.com

INDUSTRIAL DEODORANTS

Fragrance Oils International Ltd, Eton Hill Road, Radcliffe, Manchester, M26 2FR Tel: 0161-724 9311 Fax: 0161-725 5225 E-mail: uk_sales@fragrance-oils.com

Odour Control Systems Ltd, Manor Lane, Hawarden, Deeside, Clwyd, CH5 3PP Tel: (01244) 536700 Fax: (01244) 535184 E-mail: mail@odourcontrolsystems.ltd.co.uk

INDUSTRIAL DESIGNERS/ DESIGN CONSULTANTS

3form Design, Unit 63 Basepoint Business & Innovation Centre, Caxton Close, Andover, Hampshire, SP10 3FG Tel: (01264) 326306 Fax: (01264) 326308 E-mail: info@3formdesign.com

Anthony Van Tulleken Associates, 88 Brook Green, London, W6 7BD Tel: (020) 7603 7649 Fax: (020) 7603 8762

Belton Technological Services Ltd, 2 Church Street, Henfield, West Sussex, BN5 9NR Tel: (01273) 492320 Fax: (01273) 494849 E-mail: bts.ltd@btopenworld.com

C L E Design Ltd, 69-71 Haydons Road, London, SW19 1HQ Tel: (020) 8540 5772 E-mail: admin@cle-design.com

Ltd Design Consultants, 54 Warwick Square, London, SW1V 2AJ Tel: (020) 7931 7607 Fax: (020) 7931 7608 E-mail: enquiries@ltddesign.co.uk

Donland Engineering Southern Ltd, Foundation House, Stoneylands Road, Egham, Surrey, TW20 9QR Tel: (01784) 436151 Fax: (01784) 436038 E-mail: e@donlandeng.co.uk

Fin Engineering Group Ltd, 541 Saintfield Road, Belfast, BT8 8ES Tel: (028) 9081 4074 Fax: (028) 9081 4957 E-mail: info@fin-engineering.com

Frazer Designers Ltd, 6 Hampstead West, 224 Iverson Road, London, NW6 2HL Tel: (020) 7624 6011 Fax: (020) 7328 6085 E-mail: info@frazerdesigners.com

Hothouse Product Development Partners, Unit 1 College Fields Business Centre, Prince Georges Road, Merton, London, SW19 2PT Tel: (020) 8687 2093 Fax: (020) 8646 1822 E-mail: studio@hothouse-design.com

JHP Design, 2 6 Erskine Road, London, NW3 3AJ Tel: (020) 7722 3932 Fax: (020) 7586 7048 E-mail: jhp@jhp-design.co.uk

John Ewans Design, Westbourne Street, High Wycombe, Buckinghamshire, HP11 2PZ Tel: (01494) 473441 Fax: (01494) 473442 E-mail: design@john-ewans-design.co.uk

Looking Glass Design Ltd, 95 High Street, Crowthorne, Berkshire, RG45 7AD Tel: (020) 7384 1322 E-mail: info@lookingglassdesign.com

▶ One To One Industrial Design, Middle Meadow, Middle Street, Ilmington, Shipston-on-Stour, Warwickshire, CV36 4LS Tel: (01608) 682101 Fax: (01608) 682099 E-mail: enquiry@121id.co.uk

P R Designs, 13 Davenport Park Road, Davenport Park, Stockport, Cheshire, SK2 6JU Tel: 0161-483 2655 Fax: 0161-483 2655 E-mail: info@prdesigns.co.uk

Paul Usher, 91 Luton Road, Harpenden, Hertfordshire, AL5 3BA Tel: (01582) 766449 Fax: (01582) 765619 E-mail: usherdesign@btinternet.com

Pearson Matthews Ltd, 9 Princess Mews, Horace Road, Kingston upon Thames, Surrey, KT1 2SZ Tel: (020) 8547 0470 Fax: (020) 8547 0123 E-mail: design@pearsonmatthews.com

▶ Platform44, Sparkhouse Studios, Rope Walk, Lincoln, LN6 7DQ Tel: (01522) 837241 Fax: (01522) 837201 E-mail: projects@platform44.com

Product Partners Ltd, Church Street, Biggleswade, Bedfordshire, SG18 0JS Tel: (01767) 600456 Fax: (01767) 600155 E-mail: sales@productpartners.co.uk

R G P Design Innovation, 62 Cause End Road, Wootton, Bedford, MK43 9DE Tel: (01234) 767143 Fax: (01234) 767143 E-mail: rgpdesign@talk21.com

Renfrew Group, 33 Rutland St, Leicester, LE1 1RE Tel: 0116-253 1961 Fax: 0116-253 9827 E-mail: info@renfrew.com

▶ Rodd Industrial Design, Chart House, Sandy Lane, Lyndhurst, Hampshire, SO43 7DN Tel: (023) 8028 2456 Fax: (023) 8028 3183 E-mail: sales@rodd.uk.com

Royle Design Associates, 12 Old Street, London, EC1V 9BE Tel: (020) 7253 7108 Fax: (020) 7608 2074 E-mail: rda@royle-design.co.uk

plc Solutions, Unit 3 Oakford Place, Tog Lane, Great Horkesley, Colchester, CO6 4BX Tel: (01206) 273644 Fax: 01206-273655

Richard Threadgill Associates, Tetra, 28a Grafton Square, London, SW4 0DB Tel: (020) 7207 1710 Fax: (020) 7622 2734 E-mail: richard@richardthreadgillassociates.co.uk

Warwick Design Consultants Ltd, Unit 12, Waterloo Park, Bidford-on-Avon, Alcester, Warwickshire, B50 4JG Tel: (01789) 490591 Fax: (01789) 490592 E-mail: wdc@warwickdesign.com

Robert Welch Designs Ltd, Lower High Street, Chipping Campden, Gloucestershire, GL55 6DY Tel: (01386) 840522 Fax: (01386) 841111

Westframe Investments Ltd, 162-164 Teignmouth Road, Torquay, TQ1 4RY Tel: (01803) 313861 Fax: (01803) 312063 E-mail: westframe@construction-ltd.fsnet.co.uk

Withnall Design Consultants, Trinity House, Church Lane, Croughton, Brackley, Northamptonshire, NN13 5LS Tel: (01869) 810590 Fax: (01869) 810590 E-mail: withnall@btopenworld.com

Works Design Ltd, The Co-Op Centre, 11 Mowll Street, London, SW9 6BG Tel: (020) 7820 8501 Fax: (020) 7820 8502 E-mail: sales@worksdesign.co.uk

INDUSTRIAL DEVELOPMENT HOLDING OR INVESTMENT AUTHORITIES OR COMPANIES

Ashford Borough Council, Civic Centre, Tannery Lane, Ashford, Kent, TN23 1PL Tel: (01233) 330310 Fax: (01233) 330682

Barton Kendal, 122 Yorkshire Street, Rochdale, Lancashire, OL16 1LA Tel: (01706) 653214 Fax: (01706) 341476 E-mail: sales@barton-kendal.co.uk

Bexley Council For Racial Equality, 1 Maran Way, Erith, Kent, DA18 4BP Tel: (020) 8310 0138 Fax: (020) 8312 0238 E-mail: EDUBBC@bexley.gov.uk

Blackburn With Darwen Borough Council, Town Hall, King William St, Blackburn, BB1 7DY Tel: (01254) 585585 E-mail: regeneration@blackburn.gov.uk

Calderdale Economic Development Services, North Gate House, North Gate, Halifax, West Yorkshire, HX1 1UN Tel: (01422) 392222 Fax: (01422) 392260 E-mail: john.hodgson@calderdale.gov.uk

Dalmec Ltd, Quebec Street, Elland, West Yorkshire, HX5 9BX Tel: (01422) 376899 Fax: (01422) 379802 E-mail: sales@dalmecltd.co.uk

Falcon Photographic Supplies Ltd, Falcon House, Kerne Bridge, Ross-on-Wye, Herefordshire, HR9 5QT Tel: (01600) 890720 Fax: (01600) 890858 E-mail: sales@falconphotographic.co.uk

Fife Council, Fife House, North Street, Glenrothes, Fife, KY7 5LT Tel: (01592) 414141 Fax: (01592) 414142 E-mail: fifecouncil@fife.gov.uk

Folkes Group Ltd, 7orge House, Dudley Road, Stourbridge, West Midlands, DY9 8EL Tel: (01384) 424242 Fax: (01384) 424425

Glasgow City Council, Development & Regeneration Services Business Services Unit, 229 George Street, Glasgow, G2 1DU Tel: 0141-287 0901 Fax: 0141-287 7237 E-mail: ian.nicholson@drs.glasgow.gov.uk

Hambridge Investments Newbury, 4 Vulcan Close, Sandhurst, Berkshire, GU47 9DD Tel: (01252) 860043 Fax: (01252) 890154

Samuel Harding & Sons Ltd, 57 Bath Lane, Leicester, LE3 5BA Tel: 0116-262 3000 Fax: 0116-262 9000

L C P Developments Ltd, L C P House, The Pensnett Estate, Kingswinford, West Midlands, DY6 7NA Tel: (01384) 400123 Fax: (01384) 400862

Lancaster City Council, 4-5 Dalton Square, Lancaster, LA1 1PJ Tel: (01524) 582000 Fax: (01524) 582161 E-mail: llogan@lancaster.gov.uk

Mashlin Friction Ltd, 404-408 Cricket Inn Road, Sheffield, S2 5AX Tel: 0114-272 5650 Fax: 0114-265 1665

Mountcity Investments Ltd, Wellington House, Bean Road, Bilston, West Midlands, WV14 9EE Tel: (01902) 887644 Fax: (01902) 887638 E-mail: mountcity@mountcity.com

Ross & Cromarty Enterprise, 69-71 High Street, Invergordon, Ross-Shire, IV18 0AA Tel: (01349) 853666 Fax: (01349) 853833 E-mail: sales@race.co.uk

St. James Property Development Ltd, 180 Brompton Road, London, SW3 1HQ Tel: (020) 7565 8000 Fax: (020) 7565 8008

INDUSTRIAL DEVELOPMENT HOLDING OR INVESTMENT AUTHORITIES OR COMPANIES – *continued*

Scottish Council For Development & Industry, 23 Chester Street, Edinburgh, EH3 7ET Tel: 0131-225 7911 Fax: 0131-220 2116 E-mail: enquiries@scdi.org.uk
Scottish Development International, Dover House, Whitehall, London, SW1A 2AU Tel: (020) 7270 6838 Fax: (020) 7270 6790
Scottish Enterprise, 3 Greenmarket, Dundee, DD1 4QB Tel: (01382) 223100 Fax: (01382) 305576 E-mail: set.reception@scotent.co.uk
Tendring District Council, Town Hall, Station Road, Clacton-on-Sea, Essex, CO15 1SE Tel: (01255) 425501 Fax: (01255) 253118 E-mail: edu@tendringdc.gov.uk
Walsall Metropolitan Borough Council All Enquiries Walsall Boroug, Civic Centre, Walsall, WS1 1DQ Tel: (01922) 654709 Fax: (01922) 615737
P. Whelan Ltd, 113 New Bridge Street, Newcastle Upon Tyne, NE1 2SW Tel: 0191-261 2677 Fax: 0191-261 1248 E-mail: info@whelanconstruction.co.uk

INDUSTRIAL DIESEL ENGINE RADIATORS

Bearward Ltd, Main Road, Far Cotton, Northampton, NN4 8HJ Tel: (01604) 762851 Fax: (01604) 766168 E-mail: bernard.harrison@bearward.com
Boston Radiator Services Ltd, Maud Street, Boston, Lincolnshire, PE21 6TP Tel: (01205) 369555 Fax: (01205) 364829
Broadland Radiators & Heat Exchangers Ltd, Burton Road, Norwich, NR6 6AU Tel: (01603) 413050 Fax: (01603) 413066 E-mail: sales@broadlandradiators.co.uk
Ipc Industrial Power Cooling Ltd, 14 Hillmorton Road, Knowle, Solihull, West Midlands, B93 9JL Tel: (01564) 776456 Fax: (01564) 777625 E-mail: nh@ipcltd.freeserve.co.uk

INDUSTRIAL DISTILLATION PLANT

Koch Glitsch (U K), Hobson Lane, Kirkby Stephen, Cumbria, CA17 4RN Tel: (01768) 374400 Fax: (01768) 374401
R G Abercrombie, Caledonian Road, Alloa, Clackmannanshire, FK10 1NB Tel: (01259) 222500 Fax: (01259) 222528 E-mail: info@diageo.com

INDUSTRIAL DOLLIES

Panelmate Handling Ltd, Staveley Grange, Kanaresborough, Staveley, Knaresborough, North Yorkshire, HG5 9LD Tel: (0845) 6653534 Fax: (0845) 6653533 E-mail: peter@panelmatehandling.com

INDUSTRIAL DOOR CONTRACTORS OR INSTALLATION OR SERVICE

▶ A S R Shutters, 2 Woodseats Road, Woodseats, Sheffield, S8 0PJ Tel: (0800) 9230016
▶ Advance Door Engineering Ltd, Malthouse Road, Tipton, West Midlands, DY4 9AE Tel: 0121-557 0611 Fax: 0121-520 1233 E-mail: sales@advancedooreng.com
B M Door Services, 34 Brookside, Totton, Southampton, SO40 9FL Tel: (023) 8086 1601 Fax: (023) 8086 9466
Behind Closed Doors Ltd, 20 Sands Road, South Moreton, Didcot, Oxfordshire, OX11 9AB Tel: (01235) 818278 Fax: (01235) 818278
Cambridge Door Services, 127 Mereside, Soham, Ely, Cambridgeshire, CB7 5EG Tel: (01353) 725000 Fax: (01353) 725001 E-mail: alan@camdoor.fsnet.co.uk
Central Doors, 3 Arleston Drive, Nottingham, NG8 2FR Tel: 0115-913 0071 Fax: 0115-928 2814
East Yorkshire Glazing Co. Ltd, Wiltshire Road, Hull, HU4 6QQ Tel: (01482) 561101 Fax: (01482) 565307 E-mail: eygsales@ukonline.co.uk
Faltec Doors Ltd, Statham Street, Stoke-on-Trent, ST1 4HB Tel: (01782) 205205
Brian Fuller & Co., 106 Brockhurst Rd, Gosport, Hants, PO12 3DG Tel: (023) 9258 3107 Fax: (023) 9258 3107 E-mail: brian.fuller3@btinternet.com
Marks Shutters, 189 Church End, Harlow, Essex, CM19 5PE Tel: (01279) 445282 E-mail: marksshutters@hotmail.co.uk
QRS Ltd, Malthouse Road, Tipton, West Midlands, DY4 9AE Tel: 0121-557 3601 Fax: 0121-520 1233
▶ S & B Roller Shutters, Unit 16 Mayfair House, Redburn Road, Newcastle upon Tyne, NE5 1NB Tel: 0191-271 3777 Fax: 0191-271 4322 E-mail: enquires@sbrollershutters.co.uk
T S Designs Ltd, PO Box 102, Macclesfield, Cheshire, SK11 9EP Tel: (01477) 571357 Fax: (01477) 571881

INDUSTRIAL DOOR MAINTENANCE

Ranford Doors, Unit 6 Sterling Industrial Estate, Rainham Road South, Dagenham, Essex, RM10 8TX Tel: (0800) 037 9133 Fax: (020) 8984 0378 E-mail: sales@lbsgroup.co.uk
Russell Shutters Ltd, Unit 6 Sterling Industrial Estate, Dagenham, Essex, RM10 8TX Tel: (020) 8592 4545 Fax: (020) 8984 0378 E-mail: sales@lbsgroup.co.uk

INDUSTRIAL DOOR UPGRADING

Industrial Door Co. Ltd, 23 Lord Byron Square, Salford, M50 2XH Tel: 0161-736 6484 Fax: 0161-736 6364 E-mail: enquires@industrialdoorco.net

INDUSTRIAL DOORS

A C Bacon Engineering Ltd, Norwich Road, Hingham, Norwich, NR9 4LS Tel: (01953) 850611 Fax: (01953) 851445 E-mail: steel@acbacon.co.uk
A M Doors Ltd, Unit 11 Borough Close, Paignton, Devon, TQ4 7EP Tel: (01803) 520344 Fax: (01803) 558510
Abbey Roller Shutters & Doors, Unit A-B Caxton St North, London, E16 1JL Tel: (020) 7476 4422 Fax: (020) 7476 4433
Access Door Services, Unit 6-7 Trent South Industrial Park, Nottingham, NG2 4EQ Tel: 0115-958 0768 Fax: 0115-985 9240
Access Industrial Door Co Midlands Ltd, 148a Crankhall Lane, Wednesbury, West Midlands, WS10 0ED Tel: 0121-505 1435 Fax: 0121-505 3318 E-mail: neelsangha@aol.com
Adcas 1997 Ltd, Unit 12a Parkview East Industrial Estate, Parkview Road East, Hartlepool, Cleveland, TS25 1PG Tel: (01429) 283212 Fax: (01429) 420900 E-mail: sales@adcas1997.co.uk
Alliance Industrial Doors Ltd, Unit 4a Sovereign Works, Deepdale Lane, Dudley, West Midlands, DY3 2AF Tel: (01384) 251951 Fax: (01384) 255888
Allswell Security Ltd, 3 Saville Road, Peterborough, PE3 7PR Tel: (01733) 333560 Fax: (01733) 332601 E-mail: martintaylor@ukdoor.co.uk
Amber Doors Ltd, Mason Way, Platts Common Industrial Estate Hoyland, Barnsley, South Yorkshire, S74 9TG Tel: (01226) 351135 Fax: (01226) 350176 E-mail: sales@amberdoors.co.uk
Amy Shutters, 8 Slader Business Park, Witney Roe, Nuffield Industrial Estate, Poole, Dorset, BH17 0GP Tel: (01202) 666702 Fax: (01202) 666705 E-mail: info@amyshutters.co.uk
Armour Blinds, Whitehouse Enterprise Centre, Whitehouse Road, Newcastle upon Tyne, NE15 6EP Tel: 0191-228 0912 Fax: 0191-228 0912 E-mail: armoursecurity@cwcom.net
Arrow Industrial Ltd, 930 Hedon Road, Hull, HU9 5QN Tel: (01482) 228202 Fax: (01482) 218697 E-mail: sales@arrow-industrial.co.uk
Attenborough Industrial Doors Ltd, Merlin Way, Quarry Hill Industrial Estate, Ilkeston, Derbyshire, DE7 4RA Tel: 0115-930 0815 Fax: 0115-944 8930 E-mail: information@attenboroughdoor.co.uk
Beacon Associates, The Pines, Templewood Lane, Farnham Common, Slough, SL2 3HQ Tel: (01753) 648234 Fax: (01753) 648234
BID Group Ltd, Elland Close, Wingates Industrial Estate, Westhoughton, Bolton, BL5 3XE Tel: 0870 607 5050 Fax: 0870 6081271 E-mail: sales@bidgroup.co.uk
Birmingham Garage & Industrial Doors Ltd, Griffin Industrial Estate, Rowley Regis, West Midlands, B65 0SN Tel: 0121-559 8666 Fax: 0121-561 5373 E-mail: sales@bgid.net
Britannia Security Group UK Ltd, Britannia House, Lake Street, Stockport, Cheshire, SK2 7NU Tel: 0161-456 2103 Fax: 0161-487 4174
Cabot Industrial Doors, 105 Garnet Street, Bristol, BS3 3JN Tel: 0117-940 1242 Fax: 0117-902 0567 E-mail: carbotdoors@msn.com
Central Shutters & Doors, Unit 39 Phoenix International Industrial Estate, Charles Street, West Bromwich, West Midlands, B70 0AY Tel: 0121-557 3434 Fax: 0121-557 3403
CNC Doors, Premier Partnership Estate, Leys Road, Brierley Hill, West Midlands, DY5 3UP Tel: (01384) 78833 Fax: (01384) 78867 E-mail: cncdoors@btconnect.com
Coletta Doors, Bulls Lane, North Mymms, Hatfield, Hertfordshire, AL9 7BB Tel: (01707) 665018 Fax: (01707) 665344 E-mail: office@colettadoors.com
County Installations, 15 Moore Road, Church Crookham, Fleet, Hampshire, GU52 6JB Tel: (01252) 616093 Fax: (01252) 627755 E-mail: patlowe@countyinstallations.co.uk
County Shutters & Grills Ltd, 8 Winstanley Way, Basildon, Essex, SS14 3BP Tel: (01268) 532048 Fax: (01268) 286161 E-mail: alison@countyshutters.com
Craig, Merton Bank Road, St. Helens, Merseyside, WA9 1HZ Tel: (01744) 25080 Fax: (01744) 26882 E-mail: enquiries@craigengineering.co.uk
Crawford Amber, Units 5 Dedridge East Industrial Estate, Abbotsford Rise, Livingston, West Lothian, EH54 6QD Tel: (01506) 417237 Fax: (01506) 412726 E-mail: sales@crawfordamber.co.uk
D C S Door Systems, Unit 5 Whitehall Industrial Park, Whitehall Road, Great Bridge, Tipton, West Midlands, DY4 7JU Tel: 0121-520 5151 Fax: 0121-520 0535 E-mail: sales@irsp.co.uk
D J Contracts South Ltd, 7 Kent Close, Granby Industrial Estate, Weymouth, Dorset, DT4 9TF Tel: (01305) 780111 Fax: (01305) 761409 E-mail: mail@darrenholland.co.uk
Defence Group Ltd, 411 Petre Street, Sheffield, S4 8LL Tel: 0114-244 1178 Fax: 0114-244 7710 E-mail: sales@defencegroup.co.uk
Diamond Seal Ltd, Bowling Back Lane, Bradford, West Yorkshire, BD4 8SX Tel: (01274) 303400 Fax: (01274) 303401
Dominion Shutters, 8 Argall Avenue, London, E10 7QD Tel: (020) 8558 6572 Fax: (020) 8556 6956 E-mail: dominionshutters@btconnect.com
Door Services, Severnside Trading Estate, St. Andrews Road, Avonmouth, Bristol, BS11 9YQ Tel: 0117-949 4919 Fax: 0117-938 1711 E-mail: doorservices@free-online.co.uk
Downham Door Services, 16 Woodward Close, Shouldham, King's Lynn, Norfolk, PE33 0DE Tel: (01366) 347669 Fax: (01366) 347669
Dudley Factory Doors Ltd, Unit G6, Grice Street, West Bromwich, West Midlands, B70 7EZ Tel: 0121-555 8989 Fax: 0121-558 4616
East Yorkshire Glazing Co. Ltd, Wiltshire Road, Hull, HU4 6QQ Tel: (01482) 561101 Fax: (01482) 565307 E-mail: eygsales@ukonline.co.uk
Elero UK Ltd, Foundry Lane, Halebank, Widnes, Cheshire, WA8 8TZ Tel: (0870) 2404219 Fax: (0870) 2404086 E-mail: sales@elerouk.co.uk
Ellard Ltd, Dallimore Road, Roundthorn Industrial Estate, Manchester, M23 9NX Tel: 0161-945 4561 Fax: 0161-945 4566 E-mail: sales@ellard.co.uk
Martin Elliott, The Laurels, Sling, Coleford, Gloucestershire, GL16 8JJ Tel: (01594) 836758
Emmerson Industrial Doors Ltd, Enterprise Way, Sherburn in Elmet, Leeds, LS25 6NA Tel: (01977) 685566 Fax: (01977) 681981 E-mail: sales@emmerson-doors.co.uk
Enfield Roller Shutter Co., Unit 10 Kimberley Road Works, Billet Road, London, E17 5DT Tel: (020) 8527 2406 Fax: (01708) 750900 E-mail: ersco@lineone.net
Envirodoor Ltd, Viking Close, Willerby, Hull, HU10 6BS Tel: (01482) 659375 Fax: (01482) 655131 E-mail: sales@envirodoor.com
Envirohold Ltd, Viking Close, Willerby, Hull, HU10 6BS Tel: (01482) 651090 Fax: (01482) 651002 E-mail: sales@envirodoor.com
Euro Shutter Engineers Ltd, Woodside, Thornwood, Epping, Essex, CM16 6LJ Tel: (01992) 570044 Fax: (01992) 561176 E-mail: office@euroshutters.co.uk
Factory Door Services, 14 Vernon Avenue, Rayleigh, Essex, SS6 9BS Tel: (01268) 786687 Fax: (01268) 780795 E-mail: factorydoors@aol.com
Faltec Doors Ltd, Statham Street, Stoke-on-Trent, ST1 4HB Tel: (01782) 205205
Fix A Door Ltd, 1 Library Road, Ferndown, Dorset, BH22 9JP Tel: (01202) 855999 Fax: (01202) 855888 E-mail: fixadoor@aol.com
G B R Industries Ltd, Galebreaker House, New Mills Industrial Estate, Ledbury, Herefordshire, HR8 2SS Tel: (01531) 637900 Fax: (01531) 637901 E-mail: jps@galebreaker.co.uk
The Garage Door Co., Unit 7 Russell Road Industrial Estate, Sauchiebank, Edinburgh, EH11 2NN Tel: 0131-337 3332 Fax: 0131-313 2778 E-mail: sales@garage-door.co.uk
Griffin Grilles & Shutters, Maryfields, Bangors Road North, Iver, Buckinghamshire, SL0 0BH Tel: (01753) 652129 Fax: (01753) 717686 E-mail: griffingp@tiscali.co.uk
Guthrie Douglas Ltd, Collins Rd, Heathcote Industrial Estate, Warwick, CV34 6TF Tel: (01926) 452452 Fax: (01926) 336417 E-mail: sales@guthrie-douglas.uk.com
H & C Fabrications Ltd, Corporation Road, Birkenhead, Merseyside, CH41 8FA Tel: 0151-653 7677 Fax: 0151-652 0626
H V P Security Shutters Ltd, 4 Grace Road West, Marsh Barton, Exeter, EX2 8PU Tel: (01392) 270218 Fax: (01392) 278548 E-mail: info@hvpshutters.co.uk
Harling Security Products, 237 Church Road, Hayes, Middlesex, UB3 2LG Tel: (020) 8561 3787 Fax: (020) 8848 0999 E-mail: harlingsec@aol.com
Hiflex Doors, Unit 16 Such Close, Letchworth Garden City, Hertfordshire, SG6 1JF Tel: (01462) 620250 Fax: (01462) 620330 E-mail: hiflex@ukonline.co.uk
Industrial Door Co. Ltd, 23 Lord Byron Square, Salford, M50 2XH Tel: 0161-736 6484 Fax: 0161-736 6364 E-mail: enquires@industrialdoorco.net
Industrial Door Parts Master, PO Box 291, Bolton, BL5 3XE Tel: (0870) 6084040 Fax: (0870) 6081271
Industrial Door Repair, Unit 4 Windmill La Industrial Estate, Denton, Manchester, M34 3RB Tel: 0161-336 2228 Fax: 0161-336 8742
Industrial Doors Ltd, 8 Alexandra Industrial Estate, Locarno Road, Tipton, West Midlands, DY4 9SJ Tel: 0121-557 8757 Fax: 0121-520 9011 E-mail: mac@mandsshutterservicesltd.co.uk
Industrial Doors Scotland Ltd, 199 Broughton Road, Edinburgh, EH7 4LN Tel: 0131-553 6685 Fax: 0131-555 0482 E-mail: industrialdoors@talk21.com
J B Industrial Doors Ltd, Straw Mill Hill, Maidstone, Kent, ME15 6FL Tel: (01622) 679501 Fax: (01622) 685456
J R S Roller Shutter Doors, Unit B8 Valleys Enterprise Centre, Merthyr Tydfil Industrial Park, Pentrebach, Merthyr Tydfil, Mid Glamorgan, CF48 4DR Tel: (01443) 692962 Fax: (01443) 692912
K B Door Sales, Chester Road, Gresford, Wrexham, Clwyd, LL12 8NT Tel: (01978) 855599 Fax: (01978) 855599
Kenfield Ltd, 23-25 Prince Road, Kings Norton Business Centre, Norton, Birmingham, B30 3HB Tel: 0121-451 3051 Fax: 0121-433 3247 E-mail: info@pvc-strip-doors.co.uk
Leyton Engineering Services Ltd, Unit 8 Horndon Industrial Park, Station Road, West Horndon, Brentwood, Essex, CM13 3XL Tel: (01277) 812404 Fax: (01277) 810853 E-mail: sales@leytongroup.com
Loading Bay Specialists Ltd, 4 Garnet Close, Watford, WD24 7JX Tel: (01923) 208888 Fax: (01923) 208899 E-mail: info@saralbs.co.uk
M & S Products Ltd, Unit 16 Riverside Industrial Estate, Thames Road, Barking, Essex, IG11 0ND Tel: (020) 8507 3940 Fax: (020) 8594 7033
M & S Shutter Services Ltd, 8 Alexandra Industrial Estate, Locarno Road, Tipton, West Midlands, DY4 9SJ Tel: 0121-520 6505 Fax: 0121-520 9011 E-mail: mandsshutters@hotmail.com
Mandor Engineering Ltd, Units 1 & 2 93 Oxford Street, West, Ashton-under-Lyne, Lancashire, OL7 0LZ Tel: 0161-330 6837 Fax: 0161-308 3336 E-mail: info@mandor.co.uk
Marian Engineering Ltd, First Avenue, Team Valley Trading Estate, Gateshead, Tyne & Wear, NE11 0NU Tel: 0191-482 2891 Fax: 0191-491 0891 E-mail: admin@mariandoors.co.uk
Meridian Doors Ltd, The Croft, High Street, Whetstone, Leicester, LE8 6LQ Tel: 0116-275 0666 Fax: 0116-275 0606 E-mail: meridiandoors@webleicester.co.uk
NGF, Unit 11, Allerton Bywater, Castleford, West Yorkshire, WF10 2DB Tel: (0845) 6444566 Fax: (0845) 6445123 E-mail: sales@ngfindustrialdoors.co.uk
Nightguard Security Systems Ltd, Unit 4, Handloom House, Rabone Lane, Smethwick, West Midlands, B66 5JH Tel: 0121-555 5523 Fax: 0121-555 6466
North East Security Shutters, Ness House, Knox Lane, Scarborough, North Yorkshire, YO11 2BD Tel: (01723) 361644 Fax: (01723) 361644 E-mail: nessdoors@aol.com
Northern Doors (UK) Ltd, Kingsforth Road, Thurcroft, Rotherham, South Yorkshire, S66 9HU Tel: (01709) 545999 Fax: (01709) 545341 E-mail: mail@northerndoors.co.uk
▶ Norton Industrial Doors Ltd, Unit 58 Birch Road East Industrial Estate, Birch Road East, Birmingham, B6 7DB Tel: 0121-327 7775 Fax: 0121-327 6512 E-mail: sales@nortonindustrialdoors.co.uk
Paramount 26 Ltd, Unit 5 B & 5 C, Thames Road, Barking, Essex, IG11 0JP Tel: 020 85327940
Portman Doors Ltd, Unit 3 Bradshaw Works, Printers Lane, Bolton, BL2 3DW Tel: (01204) 699521 Fax: (01204) 669094 E-mail: info@portmandoors.co.uk
R N B Industrial Door Service Ltd, 6 Davenport Centre, Renwick Road, Barking, Essex, IG11 0SH Tel: (020) 8595 1242 Fax: (020) 8595 3849
Ranford Doors, Unit 6 Sterling Industrial Estate, Rainham Road South, Dagenham, Essex, RM10 8TX Tel: (0800) 037 9133 Fax: (020) 8984 0378 E-mail: sales@lbsgroup.co.uk
Rubbarite Ltd, 23-27 Boundary Street, Liverpool, L5 9ZQ Tel: 0151-298 1038 Fax: 0151-298 1910 E-mail: rubbarite@btconnect.com
Runners, Signal Hill, Lenborough Road, Gawcott, Buckingham, MK18 4BU Tel: (01280) 822288
Russell Shutters Ltd, Unit 6 Sterling Industrial Estate, Dagenham, Essex, RM10 8TX Tel: (020) 8592 4545 Fax: (020) 8984 0378 E-mail: sales@lbsgroup.co.uk
Sampson Industrial Doors, 6-8 Ise Valley Industrial Estate, Meadow Close, Wellingborough, Northamptonshire, NN8 4BH Tel: (01933) 274276 Fax: (01933) 442676 E-mail: enquiries@dovegroup.co.uk
Secure Shutters, 105 Richmond Road, Grays, Essex, RM17 6DN Tel: (01375) 397100 Fax: (01375) 397101 E-mail: sales@secureshutters.co.uk
Shutter Door Services, Unit 15 Pant Industrial Estate, Dowlais, Merthyr Tydfil, CF48 2SR Tel: (01685) 375777 Fax: (01685) 373344
South West Doors, 112 Eden Vale Road, Westbury, Wiltshire, BA13 3QE Tel: (01373) 865067 Fax: (01373) 301811 E-mail: sales@southwestdoors.co.uk
Stanair Industrial Door Services Ltd, Unit 2 Henson Way, Telford Way Industrial Estate, Kettering, Northamptonshire, NN16 8PX Tel: (01536) 482187 Fax: (01536) 411799 E-mail: admin@shiresecurity.co.uk
Stanair Industrial Door Services Ltd, 5 Fairweather Court, Peterborough, PE1 5UN Tel: (01733) 314097 Fax: (01733) 314097 E-mail: info@stanair.co.uk

INDUSTRIAL DOORS – *continued*

Stanair Industrial Door Services Ltd, Unit A-D Great Central Indust Estate, Great Central Way, Rugby, Warwickshire, CV21 3XH Tel: (01788) 568888 Fax: (01788) 568999 E-mail: sales@stanair.co.uk
Stirling Industrial Doors, Stirling House, Eridge Road, Crowborough, East Sussex, TN6 2SY Tel: (01892) 665530 Fax: (01892) 665520
Stratford Wire Works, Rowse Close, London, E15 2HX Tel: (020) 8534 1950 Fax: (020) 8534 8280
Sunray Engineering Ltd, Wotton Road, Ashford, Kent, TN23 6LL Tel: (01233) 639039 Fax: (01233) 625137 E-mail: sales@sunraydoors.co.uk
▶ Swift Shutters, Unit 3-4 Harp Industrial Estate, Queensway, Rochdale, Lancashire, OL11 2QQ Tel: (01706) 653777 Fax: (01706) 653666
Syston Rolling Shutters Ltd, 33 Albert Street, Syston, Leicester, LE7 2JB Tel: 0116-260 8841 Fax: 0116-264 0846 E-mail: sales@syston.com
Tambour Doors Ltd, 21 Marston Lane, Marston, Northwich, Cheshire, CW9 6DL Tel: (01606) 42423 Fax: (01606) 48118
Tyco Fire & Integrated Solutions, Tyco Park, Grimshaw Lane, Manchester, M40 2WL Tel: 0161-455 4475 Fax: 0161-455 4532 E-mail: wfs.doors.uk@tycoint.com
Tyco Fire & Intergrated Solutions, Unit 4 Bradley Hall Trading Estate, Standish, Wigan, Lancashire, WN6 0XQ Tel: (01257) 427164 Fax: (01257) 427490 E-mail: wfs.wigan.uk@tycoint.com
Welding Engineers Ltd, 2a Orange Lane, Montrose, Angus, DD10 8ND Tel: (01674) 674825 Fax: (01674) 671314 E-mail: enquiries@weldingengineers.co.uk
Welding Engineers (Glasgow) Ltd, 38 Dalness Street, Glasgow, G32 7RF Tel: 0141-778 8461 Fax: 0141-763 0152 E-mail: sales@weldingengineers.co.uk
Welding Engineers (Mersey) Ltd, Units 2-4 Navigation Trading Estate, Bower Street, Newton Heath, Manchester, M40 2AR Tel: 0161-205 2797 Fax: 0161-205 4032 E-mail: enquiries@liftgates.co.uk
Wessex Industrial Doors (Yeovil) Ltd, Artillery Road, Lufton, Yeovil, Somerset, BA22 8RP Tel: (01935) 473708 Fax: (01935) 479413 E-mail: george@wessexindustrialdoors.com
Westrow Control Systems, 33 Westrow Gardens, Ilford, Essex, IG3 9NF Tel: (020) 8590 2798 Fax: (020) 8220 2442 E-mail: sales@westrowcontrolsystems.co.uk
Zenith Garage Doors Ltd, Pottery Road, Bovey Tracey, Newton Abbot, Devon, TQ13 9DS Tel: (01626) 833016 Fax: (01626) 833788 E-mail: sales@zenithdoors.co.uk

INDUSTRIAL DRIVE CHAINS

Diamond Chain Co., Unit 7-9 Blaydon Industrial Park, Chainbridge Road, Blaydon-on-Tyne, Tyne & Wear, NE21 5AB Tel: 0191-414 8822 Fax: 0191-414 8877 E-mail: sales@diamondchain.co.uk

INDUSTRIAL DRIVESHAFTS

▶ EURO Driveshafts & Hydraulics, Tannahill, Kilmaurs, Kilmarnock, Ayrshire, KA3 2LN Tel: (01563) 538011 Fax: (01563) 572389
Spicer Driveshaft UK Ltd, Rutherford Drive, Park Farm Industrial Estate, Wellingborough, Northamptonshire, NN8 6AQ Tel: (01933) 402000 Fax: (01933) 401322

INDUSTRIAL DRYING PLANT OR EQUIPMENT

Ambuco (2000) Ltd, 55 London Rd, Raunds, Northants, NN9 6EH Tel: (01933) 624424 Fax: (01933) 626400
Atritor Ltd, PO Box 101, Coventry, CV6 5RD Tel: (024) 7666 2266 Fax: (024) 7666 5751 E-mail: sales@atritor.com
British Rema Manufacturing Co. Ltd, Image Works, Foxwood Close, Chesterfield, Derbyshire, S41 9RN Tel: (01246) 269955 Fax: (01246) 269944 E-mail: sales@britishrema.co.uk
Brownell Ltd, Commercial Way, Abbey Road, London, NW10 7XF Tel: (020) 8965 9281 Fax: (020) 8965 3239 E-mail: sales@brownell.co.uk
C C Process Engineering Ltd, Unit 44 Carlisle Enterprise Centre, James Street, Carlisle, CA2 5BB Tel: (01228) 819550 Fax: (01228) 819551 E-mail: sales@ccprocessengineering.com
Caltherm UK Ltd, Rowhurst Industrial Estate, Newcastle, Staffordshire, ST5 6BD Tel: (01782) 563865 Fax: (01782) 561607 E-mail: info@caltherm.co.uk
Europrocessing Ltd, Euro Vent Ltd, Govan Road Fenton Industrial, Fenton Industrial Estate, Stoke-on-Trent, ST4 2RS Tel: (01782) 744242 Fax: (01782) 744475 E-mail: sales@eurovent.com
Greenbank Technology Ltd, Unit 420 Glenfield Park Two, Blakewater Road, Blackburn, BB1 5QH Tel: (01254) 690555 Fax: (01254) 690666 E-mail: info@greenbanktechnology.co.uk
Hanover Maloney (U K) Ltd, Westgate, Aldridge, Walsall, WS9 8EX Tel: (01922) 450200 Fax: (01922) 450210 E-mail: info@hanover-maloney.co.uk
J Rostron Engineering Ltd, Lindred Road, Brierfield, Nelson, Lancashire, BB9 5SR Tel: (01282) 611110 Fax: (01282) 619961 E-mail: sales@rostron.co.uk
Kenyon Group Ltd, Regent House, Regent Street, Oldham, OL1 3TZ Tel: 0161-633 6328 Fax: 0161-627 5072 E-mail: sales@gluegunsdirect.com
Kypol Ltd, Suven House, 55 Gosforth Close, Middlefield Industrial Estate, Sandy, Bedfordshire, SG19 1RB Tel: (01767) 682424 Fax: (01767) 681180 E-mail: info@kypol.co.uk
Mitchell Dryers Ltd, Denton Holme, Carlisle, CA2 5DU Tel: (01228) 534433 Fax: (01228) 633555 E-mail: sales@mitchell-dryers.co.uk
Mitchinson Engineering, Airfield, Kirkbride, Wigton, Cumbria, CA7 5LF Tel: (01697) 351925 Fax: (01697) 352060
Motan Ltd, Unit 10 Blacklands Way, Abingdon Business Park, Abingdon, Oxfordshire, OX14 1RD Tel: (01235) 550011 Fax: (01235) 550033 E-mail: sales.ltd@motan.com
Petrie Technologies Ltd, Common Bank Industrial Estate, Ackhurst Road, Chorley, Lancashire, PR7 1NH Tel: (01257) 241206 Fax: (01257) 267562 E-mail: sales@petrieltd.com
R Simon Dryers Ltd, Private Road No 3 Colwick Industrial Estate, Colwick Industrial Estate, Nottingham, NG4 2BD Tel: 0115-961 6276 Fax: 0115-961 6351 E-mail: sales@simon-dryers.co.uk
Robank Engineering Ltd, Meridian Centre, King Street, Oldham, OL8 1EZ Tel: 0161-633 9126 Fax: 0161-633 9136 E-mail: robank@globalnet.co.uk
Sardon International Ltd, 28 Wylde Green Road, Sutton Coldfield, West Midlands, B72 1HD Tel: 0121-354 2165 Fax: 0121-354 2165
▶ Wolverine Proctor & Schwartz, 3 Langlands Avenue, East Kilbride, Glasgow, G75 0YG Tel: (01355) 575350 Fax: (01355) 575351

INDUSTRIAL ELECTRIC CABLES

Eltham Export Ltd, Crown House, Home Gardens, Dartford, DA1 1DZ Tel: (01322) 424600 Fax: (01322) 424601 E-mail: sales@elthamexport.com

INDUSTRIAL ELECTRIC FAN HEATERS

BN Thermic Ltd, 34 Woodside Road, London, SE25 5DY Tel: (01293) 547361 Fax: (01293) 531432 E-mail: sales@bnthermic.co.uk
Ductair Electrics Ltd, Unit 10c Castle Vale Industrial Estate, Maybrook Road, Castle Vale Industrial Estate, Sutton Coldfield, West Midlands, B76 1AL Tel: 0121-351 5742 Fax: 0121-313 1018
Electrical Wholesale Specialists, Unit12a Marshfield Avenue Village Farm Indust Estate, Pyle, Bridgend, Mid Glamorgan, CF33 6BJ Tel: (01656) 741133 Fax: (01656) 749957 E-mail: ewssalesteam@btconnect.com
Kaloric Heater Co. Ltd, 31 33 Beethoven Street, London, W10 4LJ Tel: (020) 8969 1367 Fax: (020) 8968 8913 E-mail: admin@kaloricheater.co.uk

INDUSTRIAL ELECTRIC HEATERS

Consort 1996 Ltd, Thornton Industrial Estate, Milford Haven, Dyfed, SA73 2RT Tel: (01646) 692172 Fax: (01646) 695195 E-mail: enquiries@consortepl.com
Delta T Trace Heating Ltd, 7 Alston Works, Alston Road, Barnet, Hertfordshire, EN5 4EL Tel: (020) 8441 9499 Fax: (020) 8441 4459 E-mail: enquiries@deltat.co.uk
Ductair Electrics Ltd, Unit 10c Castle Vale Industrial Estate, Maybrook Road, Castle Vale Industrial Estate, Sutton Coldfield, West Midlands, B76 1AL Tel: 0121-351 5742 Fax: 0121-313 1018
Edwards & Edwards Ltd, 385 Holywood Road, Belfast, BT4 2LS Tel: (028) 9047 1727 Fax: (028) 9047 1153 E-mail: sales@edwardsandedwards.co.uk
Eyre & Elliston Ltd, New Henry Street, Leicester, LE3 5AL Tel: 0116-262 9951 Fax: 0116-251 5542 E-mail: leicester@eyreandelliston.co.uk
Fiamma Ltd, Siddon Factory Estate, Howard Street, West Bromwich, West Midlands, B70 0TE Tel: 0121-556 1618 Fax: 0121-556 2132 E-mail: fiamma@talktalk.business.net
H D Howden Ltd, 10 Belgowan Street, Bellshill Industrial Estate, Bellshill, Lanarkshire, ML4 3NS Tel: (01698) 573100 Fax: (01698) 573121 E-mail: sales@howden-electroheating.com
Heatrae Industrial, Duncombe Road, Bradford, West Yorkshire, BD8 9TB Tel: (01274) 362798 Fax: (01274) 493580 E-mail: sales@heatrae-industrial.com
Howden Electro Heating (Howden Electroheating), 10-12 Belgowan Street, Bellshill Industrial Estate, Bellshill, Lanarkshire, ML4 3NS Tel: (01698) 573111 Fax: (01698) 573121 E-mail: sales@howden-electroheating.com
Lectroheat Industrial Heating Ltd, Unit 16 Pantglas Industrial Estate, Bedwas, Caerphilly, Mid Glamorgan, CF83 8DR Tel: (029) 2088 9300 Fax: (029) 2086 1872 E-mail: info@lectroheat.com
Mercian Electric, 79-93 Ratcliffe Road, Sileby, Loughborough, Leicestershire, LE12 7PU Tel: (01509) 816181 Fax: (01509) 816060
Process Heating Services, 12 Noddington Avenue, Lichfield, Staffordshire, WS14 9NQ Tel: (01543) 432661 Fax: (01543) 432782 E-mail: sales@processheatingservices.com
Processheat Ltd, Chain Caul Road, Ashton On Ribble, Preston, PR2 2PD Tel: (01772) 722412 Fax: (01772) 722325
R & H Electric Ltd, Unit 2, Rose Green Road, Fishponds Trading Estate, Fishponds, Bristol, BS5 7XE Tel: 0117-952 1261 Fax: 0117-952 0590E-mail: dangerfield-moir@rhelectric.co.uk
San Electroheat, PO Box 259, Hereford, HR1 9AU Tel: (01432) 851999 Fax: (01432) 851299 E-mail: h_comerford@btconnect.com
Ron Sims, Gregorys Mill Street, Worcester, WR3 8BA Tel: (01905) 25214 Fax: (01905) 22284
Stabilag (E.S.H.) Ltd, 34 Mark Road, Hemel Hempstead, Hertfordshire, HP2 7DD Tel: (0870) 9906763 Fax: (0870) 9906762 E-mail: sales@stabilag.com
ThermTec Ltd, Rectory Farm, Martham, Great Yarmouth, Norfolk, NR29 4RE Tel: 01493 748666

INDUSTRIAL ELECTRICAL EQUIPMENT

Bender UK, Low Mill Business Park, Ulverston, Cumbria, LA12 9EE Tel: (01229) 480123 Fax: (01229) 480345 E-mail: info@bender-uk.com
Berwickshire Electronic Manufacturing Ltd, G Industrial Estate, Station Road, Duns, Berwickshire, TD11 3EJ Tel: (01361) 883888 Fax: (01361) 883888
Best Deals, 58 London Road, Dover, Kent, CT17 0SP Tel: (01304) 208255
Blakley Electrics Ltd, 1 Thomas Road, Crayford, Dartford, DA1 4GA Tel: (0845) 0740084 Fax: (0845) 0740085 E-mail: sales@blakley.co.uk
Bonus Accessories, Citadel Trading Park, Citadel Way, Hull, HU9 1TQ Tel: (01482) 580077 Fax: (01482) 588753 E-mail: bonusacc@aol.com
Brighton Electrical Assemblies Ltd, Cradle Hill Industrial Estate, Seaford, East Sussex, BN25 3JE Tel: (01323) 893295 Fax: (01323) 897429 E-mail: info@bealtd.co.uk
City Electrical Factors Ltd, 19 Bedford Business Centre, Mile Road, Bedford, MK42 9TW Tel: (01234) 212444 Fax: (01234) 268081 E-mail: sales.bedford@cef.co.uk
City Electrical Factors Ltd, Units 4-6, St Nicholas Road, Beverley, North Humberside, HU17 0QT Tel: (01482) 869861 Fax: (01482) 866297
City Electrical Factors Ltd, 2 Blackstone Road, Stukeley Meadows Industrial Estate, Huntingdon, Cambridgeshire, PE29 6EF Tel: (01480) 456456 Fax: (01480) 457457 E-mail: sales.huntingdon@cef.co.uk
City Electrical Factors Ltd, Tritton Road, Lincoln, LN6 7QY Tel: (01522) 682548 Fax: (01582) 694512 E-mail: info.lincoln@cef.co.uk
City Electrical Factors Ltd, Unit N6 Riverside Industrial Estate, Bridge Road, Littlehampton, West Sussex, BN17 5DF Tel: (01903) 723801 Fax: (01903) 730361
Edmundson Electrical Ltd, 2 Portland Road Industrial Estate, Portland Road, Hove, East Sussex, BN3 5NT Tel: (01273) 430789 Fax: (01273) 430650 E-mail: brighton.122@eel.co.uk
Edmundson Electrical Ltd, 2 Bilton Way, Luton, LU1 1UU Tel: (01582) 728811 Fax: (01582) 418508 E-mail: luton.015@eel.co.uk
Edwards & Edwards Ltd, 385 Holywood Road, Belfast, BT4 2LS Tel: (028) 9047 1727 Fax: (028) 9047 1153 E-mail: sales@edwardsandedwards.co.uk
Etsgap Electrical Wholesalers, Energy House, Falkland Close, Charter Avenue Industrial Estate, Coventry, CV4 8AU Tel: (024) 7646 8259 Fax: (024) 7669 4090 E-mail: ets.gap@btconnect.com
Eyre & Elliston Ltd, 1 Moseley Street, Birmingham, B12 0RT Tel: 0121-766 7273 Fax: 0121-766 7275
Eyre & Elliston Ltd, H Bolton Central Industrial Estate, St Marks Street, Bolton, BL3 6NR Tel: (01204) 366601 Fax: (01204) 366602 E-mail: bolton@eyreandelliston.co.uk
Eyre & Elliston Ltd, New Henry Street, Leicester, LE3 5AL Tel: 0116-262 9951 Fax: 0116-251 5542 E-mail: leicester@eyreandelliston.co.uk
Eyre & Elliston Ltd, 49-57 Bridgewater Street, Liverpool, L1 0AU Tel: 0151-709 3154 Fax: 0151-709 6775 E-mail: liverpool@eyreandellitson.co.uk
Eyre & Elliston Ltd, 68 Arthur Street, Redditch, Worcestershire, B98 8JY Tel: (01527) 510101 Fax: (01527) 510131
Eyre & Elliston Ltd, 40 Brownfields, Welwyn Garden City, Hertfordshire, AL7 1AX Tel: (01707) 326344 Fax: (01707) 372334
Fellows & Fullwood Ltd, Prospect Row, Dudley, West Midlands, DY2 8SG Tel: (01384) 213311 Fax: (01384) 214014
FKI Switchgear Ltd, Newport Road, Pontllanfraith, Blackwood, Gwent, NP12 2XH Tel: (01495) 223001 Fax: (01495) 225674
Harline Ltd, 1 Kelmore Villas, East Dulwich, London, SE22 9BJ Tel: (020) 8693 0990 Fax: (020) 8693 0991 E-mail: admin@harline.co.uk
▶ Hyco Manufacturing Ltd, Units 1 & 2, Calder Works, Methley Road, Castleford, West Yorkshire, WF10 1NX Tel: (01977) 517555 Fax: (01977) 517666 E-mail: sales@hycomanufacturing.co.uk
J & F Controls, 2 South Bank, Westerham, Kent, TN16 1EN Tel: (01959) 562490 Fax: (01959) 561110E-mail: jandfcontrolsltd@ukgateway.net
M K Electric Ltd, Glascoed Road, St. Asaph, Clwyd, LL17 0ER Tel: (01745) 532000 Fax: (01745) 532127
Machine Mart Ltd, Hay Mills, 1152 Coventry Road, Sheldon, Birmingham, B26 3EA Tel: 0121-771 3433 Fax: 0121-771 3262
Ormrod Electric Ltd, 173 Chiswick High Road, London, W4 2DR Tel: (020) 8994 0118 Fax: (020) 8994 6008
Pageantry Electronic Systems, Unit 7 55 Weir Road Industrial Estate, London, SW19 8UG Tel: (020) 8947 3100 Fax: (020) 8879 0068 E-mail: sales@pageantry.co.uk
Prestolite Electric Ltd, Larden Road, Acton, London, W3 7SX Tel: (020) 8735 4500 Fax: (020) 8735 4777
R Barker Tarring Ltd, 32 South Street, Tarring, Worthing, West Sussex, BN14 7LN Tel: (01903) 233680 Fax: (01903) 824690 E-mail: rbarkerltd@mail.com
R & H Electric Ltd, Unit 2, Rose Green Road, Fishponds Trading Estate, Fishponds, Bristol, BS5 7XE Tel: 0117-952 1261 Fax: 0117-952 0590E-mail: dangerfield-moir@rhelectric.co.uk
Sussex Electrical Supplies Ltd, Unit 34 Cradle Hill Industrial Estate, Seaford, East Sussex, BN25 3JE Tel: (01323) 873333 Fax: (01323) 873344 E-mail: sussex.elec@virgin.net

INDUSTRIAL ELECTRICAL EQUIPMENT HIRE

A F G Electronics, Fairfield House, Goose Hill, Headley, Thatcham, Berkshire, RG19 8AU Tel: (01635) 268496 Fax: (01635) 268020 E-mail: sales@afg.pins.co.uk
W F Electrical Wholesalers Plc, Snowdrop Lane, Haverfordwest, Dyfed, SA61 1JB Tel: (01437) 764141 Fax: (01437) 760479
W F Wades, 12 Falcon Business Centre, Falcon Close, Burton-on-Trent, Staffordshire, DE14 1SG Tel: (01283) 541621 Fax: (01283) 510382

INDUSTRIAL ELECTRONIC EQUIPMENT

▶ A C Panel Services Ltd, 7C-7D Weston Way Industrial Estate, Lower Road, Stoke Mandeville, Aylesbury, Buckinghamshire, HP22 5GT Tel: (01296) 614005 Fax: (01296) 614005
▶ A W Electronic, 2 Sandford Dairy, Shanklin Road, Sandford, Ventnor, Isle of Wight, PO38 3EX Tel: (01983) 840211 Fax: (01983) 840211
▶ Aditech Ltd, 3 Midshires Business Park, Smeaton Close, Aylesbury, Buckinghamshire, HP19 8HL Tel: (01296) 398085 Fax: (01296) 337755 E-mail: sales@aditech.co.uk
Alrian Industries Ltd, Unit 2D Lake Enterprise Park, Sandall Stones Road, Kirk Sandall, Doncaster, South Yorkshire, DN3 1QR Tel: (01302) 885851 Fax: (01302) 885851 E-mail: sales@alrian.idps.co.uk
▶ Amplicore Ltd, 163 Wensley Road, Reading, RG1 6DU Tel: 0118-377 3197
Arbarr Electronics Ltd, 2 Kilgavanagh Road, Antrim, BT41 2LJ Tel: (028) 9442 9334 Fax: (028) 9442 9178 E-mail: enquiries@arbarr.co.uk
▶ Asm GmbH, Tanyard House, 37 High Street, Measham, Swadlincote, Derbyshire, DE12 7HR Tel: (01530) 515342 Fax: (0845) 1222124 E-mail: sales@asm-sensor.co.uk
▶ Baytree Industries Ltd, Resource House, Brunel Road, St. Leonards-on-Sea, East Sussex, TN38 9RT Tel: (01424) 854460 Fax: (01424) 854461 E-mail: sales@bt-ind.com
Benning UK Ltd, Oakley House, Hogwood Lane, Finchampstead, Wokingham, Berkshire, RG40 4QW Tel: 0118-973 1506 Fax: 0118-973 1508 E-mail: info@benninguk.com
Bowens International Ltd, 355 Old Road, Clacton-on-Sea, Essex, CO15 3RH Tel: (01255) 422807 Fax: (01255) 475503 E-mail: sales@bowensinternational.co.uk
Brynleigh Technology, Unit 11 Heybridge House, Industrial Estate, Maldon, Essex, CM9 4XL Tel: (01621) 877920 Fax: (01621) 877921 E-mail: sales@brynleigh.co.uk
▶ C S M Electronics, 2 Century Road, High Carr Business Park, Newcastle, Staffordshire, ST5 7UG Tel: (01782) 563334 Fax: (01782) 563345 E-mail: sale@csmelectronics.co.uk
▶ Collingwood Consultancy, 20 Estcourt Road, Great Yarmouth, Norfolk, NR30 4JG Tel: (01493) 842022 Fax: (01493) 331955
Cooper Electronics, Tenlons Road, Nuneaton, Warwickshire, CV10 7HT Tel: (024) 7632 0585 Fax: (024) 7632 0564 E-mail: enquiries@cooper-electronics.com
Crawford Hansford & Kimber Ltd, 18 Farnborough Road, Farnborough, Hampshire, GU14 6AY Tel: (01252) 377077 Fax: (01252) 377228 E-mail: admin@crawfordhk.com

INDUSTRIAL ELECTRONIC EQUIPMENT – *continued*

▶ CST Automation, Unit B2 93-95 Turner Lane, Ashton-under-Lyne, Lancashire, OL6 8SS Tel: 0161-330 9287 Fax: 0161-330 9287 E-mail: sales@cstautomation.co.uk

Cuff Services Ltd, Unit 4 Elmham Enterprises, Billingford Road, North Elmham, Dereham, Norfolk, NR20 5HN Tel: (01362) 668684 Fax: (01362) 668684

Daewoo Electronics UK Ltd, Rathenraw Industrial Estate, 62-82 Greystone Road, Antrim, BT41 1NU Tel: (028) 9442 5117 Fax: (028) 9442 5100

Darpan Controls Ltd, Sandford Works, Cobden Street, Long Eaton, Nottingham, NG10 1BL Tel: 0115-973 2672 Fax: 0115-972 0682

Date Electronic Supplies Ltd, Lilleshall Street, Newport, Gwent, NP19 0FB Tel: (01633) 259666 Fax: (01633) 266939 E-mail: alwin.treharne@pavecost.com

Design International Ltd, Unit 8, Clwydfro Business Centre, Lon Parcwr Industrial Estate, Ruthin, Clwyd, LL15 1NJ Tel: (01824) 704327 Fax: (0871) 2215698 E-mail: sales@designinternational.ltd.uk

Deva Electronic Controls Ltd, Unit 52 Woodside Business Park, Birkenhead, Merseyside, CH41 1EL Tel: 0151-647 3222 Fax: 0151-647 4511 E-mail: sales@deva.co.uk

Digitel Technology Ltd, 7 Cross Street, Barnstaple, Devon, EX31 1BA Tel: (01271) 311913 E-mail: sales@digitel.uk.net

Double D Electronics Ltd, 6 Robins Wharf, Grove Road, Northfleet, Gravesend, Kent, DA11 9AX Tel: (01474) 333456 Fax: (01474) 333414 E-mail: sales@ddelec.co.uk

E I B M Electronics Ltd, Unit B2 Greengate Industrial Estate, Greenside Way, Middleton, Manchester, M24 1SW Tel: 0161-653 8181 Fax: 0161-653 8282 E-mail: jacki.eibm@boltblue.net

Eclipse Energy Controls Ltd, Unit 4, Wombourne Enterprise Park, Bridgnorth Road, Wombourne, Wolverhampton, WV5 0AL Tel: (01902) 897760 Fax: (01902) 897613 E-mail: sales@eclipse-energy.co.uk

Electronic Terminations Ltd, High Street, Wickham Market, Woodbridge, Suffolk, IP13 0RF Tel: (01728) 748111 Fax: (01728) 748222 E-mail: etl@grouproland.com

Ems Synthesizers, Trendeal Vean Barn, Trendeal, Ladock, Truro, Cornwall, TR2 4NW Tel: (01726) 883265 Fax: (01726) 883283 E-mail: enquiries@ems-synthi.demon.co.uk

Esr Electronic Components, Station Road, Cullercoats, North Shields, Tyne & Wear, NE30 4PQ Tel: 0191-251 4363 Fax: 0191-252 2296 E-mail: sales@esr.co.uk

▶ Fastpack 2000, 36 Manor Industrial Estate, Flint, Clwyd, CH6 5UY Tel: (01352) 734366 Fax: (01352) 734399 E-mail: rob@fastpack2000.co.uk

Findlay Irvine Ltd, 42-44 Bog Road, Penicuik, Midlothian, EH26 9BU Tel: (01968) 671200 Fax: (01968) 671237 E-mail: sales@findlayirvine.com

Fluke UK Ltd, 52 Hurricane Way, Norwich, NR6 6JB Tel: (01603) 256600 Fax: (01603) 483670 E-mail: sales@flukeprecision.co.uk

Fourway Electronics Ltd, 3 Bone Lane, Newbury, Berkshire, RG14 5SH Tel: (01635) 45955 Fax: (01635) 551140 E-mail: 4wayelectronic@btclick.com

▶ Green Electronics, 1 Kennet Enterprise Centre, Charnham Lane, Hungerford, Berkshire, RG17 0EY Tel: (01488) 686244

▶ I C E Installations, 246 Cannock Road, Heath Hayes, Cannock, Staffordshire, WS12 3HA Tel: (01543) 271630 Fax: (01543) 271630 E-mail: iceinstalations@tiscali.co.uk

▶ Impact Automotive Services Ltd, Unit 24 Parkside Industrial Estate, Edge La Street, Royton, Oldham, OL2 6DS Tel: 0161-620 2948 Fax: 0161-628 9572

J A M Ltd, 24 Farriers Way, Temple Farm Industrial Estate, Southend-on-Sea, SS2 5RY Tel: (01702) 602333 Fax: (01702) 602330 E-mail: sales@jam.uk.com

Kelsea Assembly, 55 Eastlea Avenue, Bishop Auckland, County Durham, DL14 6HD Tel: (01388) 450489 Fax: (01388) 450489

Kemo Ltd, 3 Brook Co, Blakeney Road, Beckenham, Kent, BR3 1HG Tel: (020) 8658 3838 Fax: (020) 8658 4084 E-mail: technical@kemo.com

▶ Liverpool Electronics Ltd, 6 Brunel Road, Bromborough, Wirral, Merseyside, CH62 3NY Tel: 0151-343 9980 Fax: 0151-343 9985

Mantracourt Electronics Ltd, The Drive, Farringdon, Exeter, EX5 2JB Tel: (01395) 232020 Fax: (01395) 233190 E-mail: info@mantracourt.co.uk

Micro Precision Instruments Ltd, The Welsh Mill, Park Hill Drive, Frome, Somerset, BA11 2LE Tel: (01373) 461057 Fax: (01373) 451835

▶ Microdrive (UK) Ltd, Passfield Business Centre, Lynchborough Road, Passfield, Liphook, Hants, GU30 7SB Tel: (01428) 751116 Fax: (01428) 751117

Nessco, Seymour House, The Street, Appledore, Ashford, Kent, TN26 2AF Tel: (01233) 758784

Newring Electronics Ltd, Unit 7-8 Justin Business Park, Sandford Lane, Wareham, Dorset, BH20 4DY Tel: (01929) 554790 Fax: (01929) 554789 E-mail: mail@newring.co.uk

O J Electronics Trustee Ltd, Crusader House, Roman Way Crusader Park, Warminster, Wiltshire, BA12 8SJ Tel: (01985) 213003 Fax: (01985) 213310

Parmley Graham Ltd, Unit 6 Pasadena Close Trading Estate, Hayes, Middlesex, UB3 3NQ Tel: (020) 8848 9667 Fax: (020) 8848 1968 E-mail: london@parmley-graham.co.uk

Primagraphics Ltd, New Cambridge House, Bassingbourn Road, Litlington, Royston, Hertfordshire, SG8 0SS Tel: (01763) 852222 Fax: (01763) 853324 E-mail: cambridge_support@curtisswright.co.uk

Profile Automation, Unit 6 Crayfields Industrial Park, Main Road, St. Pauls Cray, Orpington, Kent, BR5 3HP Tel: (01689) 878004 Fax: (01689) 821190 E-mail: info@profile-automation.com

▶ Q Motorsport Systems, 29 Stalham Road, Industrial Estate, Hoveton, Norwich, NR12 8DG Tel: (01603) 784408 Fax: (01603) 784409

R D S Technology Ltd, Cirencester Road, Minchinhampton, Stroud, Gloucestershire, GL6 9BH Tel: (01453) 733300 Fax: (01453) 733311 E-mail: info@rdstec.com

Raytheon UK Ltd, Harman House, George Street, London, Uxbridge, Middlesex, UB8 1QQ Tel: (020) 7569 5500 Fax: (020) 7569 5599 E-mail: corporatecommunications@raytheon.co.uk

Rem Electronic Equipment, Arkle House, Mill Lane, Birch, Colchester, CO2 0NG Tel: (01206) 331657 Fax: (01206) 331657

Robotas Ltd, Broadlands House, Foxendown Lane, Gravesend, Kent, DA13 0AE Tel: (01474) 815815 Fax: (0870) 0056914 E-mail: sales@robotas.co.uk

Romotex Ltd, 22 London Road, Hazel Grove, Stockport, Cheshire, SK7 4AH Tel: 0161-419 9999 Fax: 0161-483 0101

▶ S 1 Systems, Unit 15 Piccadilly Mill, Lower Street, Stroud, Gloucestershire, GL5 2HT Tel: (01453) 767006 E-mail: sales@s1systems.co.uk

S T S Signals Ltd, 2 Stone Lane Industrial Estate, Stone Lane, Wimborne, Dorset, BH21 1HB Tel: (01202) 888402 Fax: (01202) 841717 E-mail: wimborne@spacetechsys.co.uk

Sargrove Automation, The Chestnuts, 11 Eastern Road, Havant, Hampshire, PO9 2JE Tel: (023) 9247 1981 Fax: (023) 9247 1981 E-mail: sargrove@btinternet.com

▶ Sedo Systems Ltd, 19 Hertford Road, Stevenage, Hertfordshire, SG2 8RS Tel: (01438) 362033 Fax: (01438) 721888 E-mail: sales@sedosystems.com

Selex Communications Ltd, Marconi House, New Street, Chelmsford, CM1 1PL Tel: (01245) 353221 Fax: (01245) 287125 E-mail: alan.heritage@selex-comms.com

Silent Power Systems Ltd, Unit 9 Dain Street, Stoke-on-Trent, ST6 3LN Tel: (01782) 822402 Fax: (01782) 577262

Sinclair Voicenet Ltd, 2 Orbital Court, Peel Park, East Kilbride, Glasgow, G74 5PH Tel: (01355) 900000 Fax: (01355) 900001 E-mail: enquiries@voicerecording.co.uk

▶ Skyline International Electronics, Harbour House, Coldharbour Lane, Rainham, Essex, RM13 9YA Tel: (01708) 522211

Slencrest Ltd, Broad Oak House, Pheasant Lane, Maidstone, Kent, ME15 9QR Tel: (01622) 741122 Fax: (01622) 747722 E-mail: sales@slencrest.com

Socomec Sicon Ltd, 401-402 Love Lane, Cirencester, Gloucestershire, GL7 1YG Tel: (01285) 644444 Fax: (01285) 644414 E-mail: enquires@socomec.com

Sony UK Ltd, The Heights, Brooklands, Weybridge, Surrey, KT13 0XW Tel: (01932) 816000 Fax: (01932) 817000

Surface Technology Systems plc, Imperial Park, Newport, Gwent, NP10 8UJ Tel: (01633) 652400 Fax: (01633) 652405 E-mail: webenquiries@stsystems.com

Tech Ltd, The Granery, Leacon Farm, Leacon Lane, Charing, Ashford, Kent, TN27 0EN Tel: (01634) 290308 Fax: (01233) 714040 E-mail: johnbridges1@btconnect.com

Technical Systems Ltd, Long View, Simms Lane, Reading, RG7 2JP Tel: 0118-933 3700

Thurlaston Instrument Services, 5 Church Street, Thurlaston, Leicester, LE9 7TA Tel: (01455) 888484 E-mail: sales@thurlaston.com

▶ Total Electronic Systems Ltd, 36-38 Nuffield Road, Nuffield Industrial Estate, Poole, Dorset, BH17 0RT Tel: (01202) 686100 Fax: (01202) 686100

Ultrasound Technologies Ltd, Lodge Way, Severn Bridge Industrial Estate, Portskewett, Caldicot, Gwent, NP26 5PS Tel: (01291) 425425 Fax: (01291) 427093 E-mail: ultratech@doppler.co.uk

V A Electronic Design Ltd, Unit 16 Canongate Venture, 5 New Street, Edinburgh, EH8 8BH Tel: 0131-556 4668 Fax: 0131-556 4669

V P Equipment Ltd, Longford Business Centre Orchard Lea, Winkfield Lane, Windsor, Berkshire, SL4 4RU Tel: (01753) 623336 Fax: (01753) 623337 E-mail: graeme.crowder@vpe.co.uk

Valro Manufacturing Ltd, Units 2-4, The Grove, Parkgate Industrial Estate, Knutsford, Cheshire, WA16 8XP Tel: (01565) 650204 Fax: (01565) 650755 E-mail: enquiries@valro.co.uk

▶ Winchester Electro Optics, Unit 20a Home Farm Rural Industries, East Tytherley Road, Lockerley, Romsey, Hampshire, SO51 0JT Tel: (01794) 340005 Fax: (01794) 340005 E-mail: info@w-e-o.co.uk

▶ Wye Technology UK Ltd, 6 Mitcheldean Enterprise Workshops, Brook Street, Mitcheldean, Gloucestershire, GL17 0SL Tel: (01594) 544806 Fax: (01594) 544609 E-mail: wyetecukltd@aol.com

INDUSTRIAL ELECTRONIC EQUIPMENT TESTING

Advanced Control Electronics, 98 Ashby Road, Loughborough, Leicestershire, LE11 3AF Tel: (01509) 211333 Fax: (01509) 211333 E-mail: ac.electronics@lycos.co.uk

Eurotronix, 19, Telford, Shropshire, TF6 6HD Tel: (01952) 541873 Fax: (01952) 541874 E-mail: sales@eurotronixgb.co.uk

▶ Fluke (UK) Ltd, 52 Hurricane Way, Norwich, NR6 6JB Tel: (020) 7942 0700 Fax: (020) 7942 0701 E-mail: industrial@uk.fluke.nl

Item Ltd, 65 Bury Mead Road, Hitchin, Hertfordshire, SG5 1RT Tel: (01462) 453838 Fax: (01462) 453619 E-mail: item@co.com

Testlink Ltd, Poole, Dorset, BH16 5SJ Tel: (01202) 621100 Fax: (01202) 625577 E-mail: sales@testlink.co.uk

INDUSTRIAL ELECTRONIC TRAINING

Intek Europe, 24 Thomas Drive, Newport Pagnell, Buckinghamshire, MK16 8TH Tel: (01908) 610093 E-mail: sales@intek.co.uk

L J Technical Systems Ltd, 5-6 Francis Way, Bowthorpe Employment Area, Norwich, NR5 9JA Tel: (01603) 740421 Fax: (01603) 746340 E-mail: uksales@ljgroup.com

INDUSTRIAL ELEVATORS

Alimak Hek Ltd, Northampton Road, Rushden, Northamptonshire, NN10 6BW Tel: (01933) 354700 Fax: (01933) 410600 E-mail: ukinfo@alimakhek.com

Crescent-Webb Ltd, 14-15 Weller Street, London, SE1 1LQ Tel: (020) 7407 0085 Fax: (020) 7403 0889

Miracon Conveyors Ltd, Drayton Road, Shirley, Solihull, West Midlands, B90 4NG Tel: 0121-705 8468 Fax: 0121-711 2074 E-mail: sales@miracon.com

Otis Ltd, Unit 1e & H, Wavertree Technology Park, Wavertree Boulevard South, Liverpool, L7 9PF Tel: 0151-472 1500 Fax: 0151-472 1520

Pickerings Europe Ltd, 31 Stanley Road, Worsley, Manchester, M28 3DT Tel: 0161-703 8028 Fax: 0161-703 8035

INDUSTRIAL EMBOSSING MACHINES

P R O Marketing Co. Ltd, Unit 10 Jubilee Trade Centre, Jubilee Road, Letchworth Garden City, Hertfordshire, SG6 1SP Tel: (01462) 677188 Fax: (01462) 685275 E-mail: sales@proengraving.com

INDUSTRIAL ENGINEERING

Brandl Engineering Ltd, 1st Floor, 5 Nimrod Pass, London, N1 4BU Tel: 020 72492375 Fax: 020 72545525

Contract Maintenance Team, 10 Promenade Terrace, Edinburgh, EH15 1DT Tel: 0131-657 5246

E T Marine & Industrial Engineering Co Ltd, Manor Way, Grays, Essex, RM17 6BJ Tel: (01375) 378282 Fax: (01375) 385804 E-mail: works@etmarine.com

Electro Soft Development, 15 Sterndale Road, Long Eaton, Nottingham, NG10 3HQ Tel: 0115-973 2284 Fax: 0115-973 2284

H Mell & Son, Old Trent Road, Beckingham, Doncaster, South Yorkshire, DN10 4PY Tel: (01427) 848210 Fax: (01427) 848869

Industrial & Welding Systems Ltd, Fallons Road, Wardley Industrial Estate, Worsley, Manchester, M28 2NY Tel: 0161-728 3366 Fax: 0161-728 5878 E-mail: paul.rushton@boc.com

Line Performance Improvement Ltd, The Granary, Stoke Mills, Mill Road, Bedford, MK44 1NN Tel: (01234) 782333

M Squared Instrumentation, Copse Business Centre, Hounsdown Business Park, Bulls Copse Road, Totton, Southampton, SO40 9LR Tel: (023) 8086 8393 Fax: (023) 8066 7720 E-mail: sales@msquaredinst.co.uk

Perkins Engines Co. Ltd, Perkins Powerpart Distribution Centre, Frank Perkins Way, Irlam, Manchester, M44 5PP Tel: 0161-776 5000 Fax: 0161-776 5100

R & J Dickinson Brighouse Ltd, 11 Owlers Ings Road, Brighouse, West Yorkshire, HD6 1EJ Tel: (01484) 400049

Rademaker, Suite 105 Standish Centre, Cross Street, Standish, Wigan, Lancashire, WN6 0HQ Tel: (01257) 421120 Fax: (01257) 422339 E-mail: sales@rademaker.co.uk

INDUSTRIAL ENGINES

▶ Allards Staffs Ltd, Ephraim Street, Stoke-on-Trent, ST1 3SH Tel: (01782) 266441 Fax: (01782) 273856

▶ Dragon Engines Ltd, Henry Street, Chesterfield, Derbyshire, S41 9BT Tel: (01246) 456123 Fax: (01246) 453666

▶ Ecotrax, Plaitford, Romsey, Hampshire, SO51 6YZ Tel: (01794) 324772 Fax: (01794) 324420 E-mail: ns@m977.com

Ford Motor Co Ltd, Waterton Industrial Estate, Bridgend, Mid Glamorgan, CF31 3PJ Tel: (01656) 672300 Fax: (01656) 672201

▶ Jackson Engine Auto Spares, 36 Dundrod Road, Nutts Corner, Crumlin, County Antrim, BT29 4ST Tel: (028) 9082 5396

Marshalls Industrial Ltd, Hithercroft Road, Wallingford, Oxfordshire, OX10 9DG Tel: (01491) 834666 Fax: (01491) 839777 E-mail: sales@marshalls-industrial.co.uk

▶ Norwich Engine Centre Ltd, Vulcan Road South, Mile Cross Lane, Norwich, NR6 6AF Tel: (01603) 425701 Fax: (01603) 484046

Nova Controls Ltd, Cheshire House, Murhall Street, Stoke-On-Trent, ST6 4BL Tel: (01782) 824866 Fax: (01782) 825474

▶ Power Train Projects, Trinity House, Coventry Road, Hinckley, Leicestershire, LE10 0NB Tel: (01455) 622229 Fax: (01455) 622370 E-mail: sales@ptp-ltd.co.uk

INDUSTRIAL ENGRAVERS

Alliance Engraving & Lettering Co. Ltd, Unit 18 Barton Hill Trading Estate, Maze Street, Bristol, BS5 9TE Tel: 0117-955 5292 Fax: 0117-955 7518 E-mail: sales@alliance-signs.co.uk

D B Sign & Engraving Co., Unit 4, Windmill Lane Industrial Estate, Denton, Manchester, M34 3RB Tel: 0161-320 0068 Fax: 0161-320 6829

Falcontec Ltd, Falcon House, Mucklow Hill, Halesowen, West Midlands, B62 8DT Tel: 0121-550 1076 Fax: 0121-585 5126 E-mail: info@falcontec.co.uk

Gem Engraving, 33 Hayes Close, Wimborne, Dorset, BH21 2JJ Tel: (01202) 881907 Fax: (01202) 887691 E-mail: sales@gemengraving.co.uk

▶ Ils, 25-29 Brearton Street, Bradford, West Yorkshire, BD1 3ED Tel: (01274) 740494 Fax: (01274) 740504 E-mail: marketing@ilsonline.com

Newlove Ingravers & Signs Ltd, Unit 5 Hood Street, Hull, HU8 7AL Tel: (01482) 224670 Fax: (01482) 215610 E-mail: info@new-engravers.com

INDUSTRIAL ESTATE AGENTS

Embley Business Unit, 41 Warwick Road, Solihull, West Midlands, B92 7HS Tel: 0121-707 8666 Fax: 0121-708 2858

Gatehouse Trading Estate Ltd, The Gate House, Lichfield Road, Brownhills, Walsall, WS8 6JZ Tel: (01543) 370892

Edwin Hill, 18 Saville Row, London, W1S 3PW Tel: (020) 7287 2020 Fax: (020) 7734 1255 E-mail: ehlondon@edwinhill.co.uk

Hunt & Co Hinckley Ltd, 4 Turville Close, Burbage, Hinckley, Leicestershire, LE10 2GZ Tel: (01455) 637263 Fax: (01455) 637263

John Grout & Co. Ltd, Dallow Street, Burton-on-Trent, Staffordshire, DE14 2PQ Tel: (01283) 813454

Knight Frank Property Company, Knight Frank 20 Hanover Square, London, W1S 1HZ Tel: (020) 7408 1100 Fax: (020) 7493 4114 E-mail: farms.estates@knightfrank.com

Last & Mazin, 21 Welbeck Street, London, W1G 8EE Tel: (020) 7763 7763 Fax: (020) 7763 7764 E-mail: post@lastandmazin.com

Miller Property Consultants, 17 Hogarth Avenue, Brentwood, Essex, CM15 8BE Tel: (01277) 233100 Fax: (01277) 233300 E-mail: advice@millerproperty.co.uk

Mills & Wood, 18 Grosvenor Street, London, W1K 4QQ Tel: (020) 7499 0934 Fax: (020) 7408 0250 E-mail: sales@millsandwood.co.uk

Peter Taylor & Co., 8 Hanover Street, London, W1S 1PT Tel: (020) 7290 2662 Fax: (020) 7290 2686

Stonehill Estates Ltd, Stonehill Business Park, Harbet Road, Edmonton, London, N18 3LD Tel: (020) 8807 1020 Fax: (020) 8884 3528

Tallett Charter Surveyors, 18 Long Ashton Road, Long Ashton, Bristol, BS41 9LD Tel: (01275) 540200 Fax: (01275) 540203 E-mail: tallett@tallett.co.uk

W R Winton Ltd, Richmond House, Forsyth Road, Woking, Surrey, GU21 5SB Tel: (01483) 770121 Fax: (01483) 715630 E-mail: info@winton-antlia.com

Walsall Metropolitan Borough Council All Enquiries Walsall Boroug, Civic Centre, Walsall, WS1 1DQ Tel: (01922) 654709 Fax: (01922) 615737

John D. Wood International Ltd, 19 Berkeley Street, London, W1J 8ED Tel: (020) 7629 9050 Fax: (020) 7493 9815 E-mail: property@johndwood.com

INDUSTRIAL EXPLOSION PROTECTION EQUIPMENT

BS&B Safety Systems (UK) Ltd, Adamson House, Tower Business Pk, Wilmslow Rd, Didsbury, Manchester, M20 2YY Tel: 0161-955 4202 Fax: 0161-955 4282 E-mail: sales@bsb-systems.co.uk

Expo Technologies Ltd, Summer Road, Thames Ditton, Surrey, KT7 0RH Tel: (020) 8398 8011 Fax: (020) 8398 8014 E-mail: sales@expoworldwide.com

Schischek Ltd, 1 Saddlestones, New Road, Princes Risborough, Buckinghamshire, HP27 0JJ Tel: (01494) 794904 Fax: (01494) 794905 E-mail: schischek@msn.com

INDUSTRIAL FABRIC MANUFRS,

See also headings for particular types under application or type of fibre

BDS Industrial Fabrics, 44-46 Percy Road, Leicester, LE2 8FP Tel: 0116-283 9933 Fax: 0116-283 9966

J.H. Birtwistle Ltd, Grane Road Mill, Grane Road, Haslingden, Rossendale, Lancashire, BB4 5ES Tel: (01706) 215351 Fax: (01706) 831054 E-mail: birtwistle@johnlewis.co.uk

Calig Industrial Wipers, Saw Mill Lane, Great Yarmouth, Norfolk, NR31 0AE Tel: (01493) 603762 Fax: (01493) 442846 E-mail: denisecalig@lineone.net

Camtex Fabrics Ltd, Blackwood Road, Lillyhall Industrial Estate, Lillyhall, Workington, Cumbria, CA14 4JJ Tel: (01900) 602646 Fax: (01900) 66827 E-mail: info@cambrelle.com

Colletex Ltd, Whitebirk Road, Blackburn, BB1 3JA Tel: (01254) 261768 Fax: (01254) 665425 E-mail: sales@colletex.co.uk

James Dewhurst Ltd, Altham Lane, Altham, Accrington, Lancashire, BB5 5YA Tel: (01282) 775311 Fax: (01282) 774717 E-mail: sales@james-dewhurst.co.uk

Don & Low, Glamis Road, Forfar, Angus, DD8 1FR Tel: (01307) 452249 Fax: (01307) 452201 E-mail: sales@donlow.co.uk

J & D Wilkie Ltd, Gairie Works, Bellies Brae, Kirriemuir, Angus, DD8 4BL Tel: (01575) 572502 Fax: (01575) 574564 E-mail: sales@jdwilkie.co.uk

John Spencer Textiles Ltd, Ashfield Mill, Active Way, Burnley, Lancashire, BB11 1BS Tel: (01282) 423111 Fax: (01282) 416283 E-mail: sales@johnspencer.com

▶ Kindon Textiles Ltd, 31 Belmont Way, Rochdale, Lancashire, OL12 6HR Tel: (01706) 656951 Fax: (01706) 345496 E-mail: g-kindon@msn.com

Lantor (UK) Ltd, 73 St. Helens Road, Bolton, BL3 3PP Tel: (01204) 855000 Fax: (01204) 61722 E-mail: sales@lantor.co.uk

McAndrews Textiles Ltd, West Scholes Mill, West Scholes, Queensbury, Bradford, West Yorkshire, BD13 1NQ Tel: (01274) 881111 Fax: (01274) 883311 E-mail: info@mcandrewtextiles.co.uk

Milliken Industrials Ltd, Wellington Street, Bury, Lancashire, BL8 2AY Tel: 0161-764 2244 Fax: 0161-705 2148 E-mail: john.lancashire@milliken.com

Milliken Industrials Ltd, Wellington Street, Bury, Lancashire, BL8 2AY Tel: 0161-764 2244 Fax: 0161-705 2148 E-mail: peter_janczyk@milliken.com

Murmar-Phipps Ltd, PO Box 1, Northampton, NN4 8WN Tel: (01604) 763033 Fax: (01604) 23297

P & S Textiles Ltd, Hornby Street, Bury, Lancashire, BL9 5BL Tel: 0161-764 8617 Fax: 0161-763 7260 E-mail: info@pstextiles.co.uk

Palmhive Technical Textiles Ltd, NTG House, Willow Road, Nottingham, NG7 2TA Tel: 0115-970 7900 Fax: 0115-970 7999 E-mail: enquiries@palmhive.co.uk

Wirral Fospray Ltd, Old Tramway, Stoke-on-Trent, ST4 3PX Tel: (01782) 334077 Fax: (01782) 596608

Woodrow Universal Ltd, Junction Mills, Skipton Road, Cross Hills, Keighley, West Yorkshire, BD20 7SE Tel: (01535) 633364 Fax: (01535) 634439 E-mail: sales@woodrowuniversal.co.uk

INDUSTRIAL FAILURE INVESTIGATION

Quality Assessments (Sheffield) Ltd, 4 Rudyard Court, Rudyard Road, Sheffield, S6 2LD Tel: 0114-234 3343 Fax: 0114-234 3343

INDUSTRIAL FAN CONSULTANCY OR DESIGN

Elta Fans, 17 Barnes Wallis Road, Fareham, Hampshire, PO15 5TT Tel: (01489) 583044 Fax: (01489) 566555 E-mail: mailbox@eltafans.co.uk

INDUSTRIAL FAN HEATERS

▶ County Plumbing & Heating, Unit 5 Norris Way, Norris Way Industrial Estate, Rushden, Northamptonshire, NN10 6BP Tel: (01933) 413055 Fax: (01933) 413002 E-mail: info@countyplumbingandheating.com

▶ Heatshop, Unit 44, Westley Grange, West Avenue, Wigston, Leicestershire, LE18 2FB Tel: 0116-288 4333 Fax: 0116-288 1444

INDUSTRIAL FAN HIRE

Airflo Envirorental, Kelham Street, Doncaster, South Yorkshire, DN1 3TA Tel: (01302) 730000 Fax: (01302) 321222

INDUSTRIAL FAN MAINTENANCE OR REPAIR

▶ Howden Industrial, Braehead Industrial Estate, Old Govan Road, Renfrew, PA4 8XJ Tel: 0141-885 7500 Fax: 0141-886 1963 E-mail: marketing@howden.com

Royston Fan Co. Ltd, Lumen Road, Royston, Hertfordshire, SG8 7AF Tel: (01763) 241400 Fax: (01763) 245654 E-mail: alan@roystonfan.co.uk

INDUSTRIAL FANS

Airflow Ventilation Supplies, Shackleton Rd, Cressex Business Pk, High Wycombe, Bucks, HP12 3RH Tel: (01494) 463490 Fax: (01494) 471507 E-mail: info@avs.co.uk

Alldays Peacock & Co., First Floor, 7 Morston Court, Aise Combe, Weston-Super-Mare, Avon, BS22 8NA Tel: (01422) 313351 Fax: (01934) 623727 E-mail: apco@alldays-peacock-co.com

C E-Air UK Ltd, Newton Moor Industrial Estate, Newton, Hyde, Cheshire, SK14 4LG Tel: 0161-368 1476 Fax: 0161-367 8145 E-mail: sales@ceair.co.uk

C N Air Mach Ltd, 255 Monton Road, Eccles, Manchester, M30 9PS Tel: 0161-788 7465 Fax: 0161-787 7002 E-mail: airmachltd@aol.com

Fans & Blowers Ltd, Walrow Industrial Estate, Commerce Way, Highbridge, Somerset, TA9 4AG Tel: (01278) 784004 Fax: (01278) 792848 E-mail: fab-sales@btconnect.com

Finna Fans, Unit 2 Hill Street, Kidderminster, Worcestershire, DY11 6TD Tel: (01562) 60035 Fax: (01562) 753188

Imofa UK Ltd, New Coach House, 21 Grange Way, Colchester, CO2 8HF Tel: (01206) 505909 Fax: (01206) 794095 E-mail: sales@imofa.co.uk

M Y Fans Ltd, Westend Street, Oldham, OL9 6AJ Tel: 0161-628 3337 Fax: 0161-627 4153 E-mail: m.y.fans@mmp-ltd.co.uk

Stockbridge Airco Ltd, Blossom Street Works, Ancoats, Manchester, M4 6AE Tel: 0161-236 9314 Fax: 0161-228 0009 E-mail: mark@stockbridge-airco.com

Swan Enviro Freshmesh Systems, 10 Engine Road, Loanhead, Midlothian, EH20 9RF Tel: 0131-440 3812 Fax: 0131-448 2119 E-mail: sales@swanenviro.com

Victoria Fan & Engineering Supplies Ltd, Audley Street Works, Audley Street, Mossley, Ashton-under-Lyne, Lancashire, OL5 9HW Tel: (01457) 835391 Fax: (01457) 833378 E-mail: sales@victoriafans.co.uk

INDUSTRIAL FASTENERS

3d Machine Shop Engineering Ltd, 23 The Business Centre, 20 James Road, Tyseley, Birmingham, B11 2BA Tel: 0121-628 6628 Fax: 0121-628 2008 E-mail: cliffdavies1@btconnect.com

A C Fixings, 10 Montrose Road, Chelmsford, CM2 6TX Tel: (01245) 451234 Fax: (01245) 451701 E-mail: acfixingsltd@blueyonder.com

A C Supply Ltd, St. Christopher House, 126 Ridge Road, Letchworth Garden City, Hertfordshire, SG6 1PT Tel: (01462) 481808 Fax: (01462) 481806 E-mail: sales@acsupply.co.uk

A C T (Fasteners & Components) Ltd, Units 13 & 16, Four Ashes Industrial Estate, Station Road, Four Ashes, Wolverhampton, WV10 7DB Tel: (01902) 791880 Fax: (01902) 791884 E-mail: info@actfasteners.co.uk

▶ A D A Fastfix Ltd, 5 Parkhouse Business Centre, Desborough Park Road, Parkhouse Business Centre, High Wycombe, Buckinghamshire, HP12 3DJ Tel: (0870) 7207100 Fax: (0870) 7207120 E-mail: alan@adafastfix.co.uk

A H C Camberley Ltd, 415-417 London Road, Camberley, Surrey, GU15 3HZ Tel: (01252) 735176 Fax: (01276) 709068 E-mail: oliver@ahc-camberley.co.uk

A & J Fasteners, 19 Manor Trading Estate, Brunel Road, Benfleet, Essex, SS7 4PS Tel: (01268) 566422 Fax: (01268) 566422

A J S Fasteners Ltd, 9 Maple Business Park, Walter Street, Birmingham, B7 5ET Tel: 0121-327 0660 Fax: 0121-327 3553 E-mail: sales@ajsfasteners.co.uk

A M S Connections Ltd, 14 Highmeres Road, Leicester, LE4 9LZ Tel: 0116-224 0070 Fax: 0116-224 0073 E-mail: astrid@amsconnections.co.uk

A T Engineering Supplies Ltd, Garstang Road, Claughton-on-Brock, Preston, PR3 0RB Tel: (01995) 640058 Fax: (01995) 640031

A1 Fasteners Ltd, Unit 5/6, Brookwood Insutrial Estate, Eastleigh, Southampton, SO50 9EY Tel: (023) 8065 0666 Fax: (023) 8065 0601 E-mail: sales@a1-fasteners.co.uk

Abel Fasteners, 25 Albion Street, Rugeley, Staffordshire, WS15 2BY Tel: (01889) 586675 Fax: (01889) 586676

Abell Fasteners, Unit 337 Rushock Trading Estate, Rushock, Droitwich, Worcestershire, WR9 0NR Tel: (01299) 251533 Fax: (01299) 251533

Abrasives & Screw Products Ltd, Cropton House, Three Tuns Lane, Liverpool, L37 4AQ Tel: (01704) 879311 Fax: (01704) 870158 E-mail: sales@aspltd.co.uk

Acclaim Fasteners & Turned Parts, Unit 17 Premier Park Estate, Leys Road, Brierley Hill, West Midlands, DY5 3UP Tel: (01384) 76263 Fax: (01384) 76268

Aces Fans Ltd, 6 Ryefield Crescent, Northwood, Middlesex, HA6 1LR Tel: (01923) 827533 Fax: (01923) 835514 E-mail: sales@fixings-diy.co.uk

Acorn Fasteners Ltd, Unit W4 Lambs Business Park, Tilburstow Hill Road, South Godstone, Godstone, Surrey, RH9 8LJ Tel: (01342) 893500 Fax: (01342) 892820 E-mail: sales@acornfastenersltd.co.uk

Ajot UK Ltd, Hurricane Close, Sherburn in Elmet, Leeds, LS25 6PB Tel: (01977) 687040 Fax: (01977) 687041E-mail: sales@ejot.co.uk

Alcoa Fastening Systems Ltd, Stafford Park 7, Telford, Shropshire, TF3 3BQ Tel: (01952) 290011 Fax: (01952) 290459 E-mail: info@huck.co.uk

Alfast Engineering Supplies Ltd, 2 Gloucester Road, Luton, LU1 3HX Tel: (01582) 418498 Fax: (01582) 418833 E-mail: sales@alfast.co.uk

Allcap Ltd, Unit 24c Morelands Trading Estate, Bristol Road, Gloucester, GL1 5RZ Tel: (01452) 525800 Fax: (01452) 331125 E-mail: sales@allcap.co.uk

Allman Fasteners Ltd, PO Box 5, Wilmslow, Cheshire, SK9 2EF Tel: (01625) 537535 Fax: (01625) 537635

Alpha Fasteners, Unit 13 Ffrwdgrech Industrial Estate, Ffrwdgrech Road, Brecon, Powys, LD3 8LA Tel: (01874) 625631 Fax: (01874) 625326 E-mail: sales@alphafasteners.co.uk

Anglian Fasteners Ltd, 16 Millbrook Close, Northampton, NN5 5JF Tel: (01604) 758585 Fax: (01604) 758565 E-mail: anglianf@micromat.net

Annalex Bute Ltd, Unit B6 Blaby Industrial Park, Winchester Avenue, Blaby, Leicester, LE8 4GZ Tel: 0116-277 9537 Fax: 0116-277 8623 E-mail: sales@annalexbyute.co.uk

Antron Engineers Supplies, Unit 11 Broomers Hill Par, Broomers Hill Lane, Pulborough, West Sussex, RH20 2RY Tel: (01798) 872720 E-mail: sales@antroneng.co.uk

Archerdale Ltd, Hirstwood Works, Hirst Wood Road, Shipley, West Yorkshire, BD18 4BU Tel: (01274) 595783 Fax: (01274) 531263 E-mail: sales@archerdale.co.uk

Armstrong Fastenings Ltd, PO Box 6, Wednesbury, West Midlands, WS10 8UL Tel: 0121-224 2000 Fax: 0121-224 2007 E-mail: info@armfast.com

Astley Components, 623-625 High Road Leyton, London, E10 6RF Tel: (020) 8556 9711 Fax: (020) 8556 6641 E-mail: sales@astleycomp.co.uk

Avery Knight & Bowlers Engineering Ltd, 33-35 James St West, Bath, BA1 2BT Tel: (01225) 425894 Fax: (01225) 445753 E-mail: sales@averyknight.co.uk

Azgard Engineering Products, 10 Compton Road, Kinver, Stourbridge, West Midlands, DY7 6DN Tel: (01384) 872286 Fax: (01384) 878203

B & D Bolts Ltd, Central Warehouse, Bradford Road, Batley, West Yorkshire, WF17 5LW Tel: (01924) 470331 Fax: (01924) 473749

B G B Services & Supply Ltd, Unit 52, Sovereign Road, Kings Norton Business Centre, Birmingham, B30 3HN Tel: 0121-458 5424 Fax: 0121-459 4756 E-mail: ian@bgbservices.co.uk

B & S Threaded Products Ltd, 28 Newtown Street, Cradley Heath, West Midlands, B64 5LD Tel: (01384) 569899 Fax: (01384) 410392

Bapp Industrial Supplies Lancs Ltd, Trafalgar Centre, Belfield Road, Rochdale, Lancashire, OL16 2UX Tel: (01706) 359500 Fax: (01706) 640270

Bapp Industrial Supplies Preston Ltd, 57 Roman Way Industrial Estate, Ribbleton, Preston, PR2 5BE Tel: (01772) 704700 Fax: (01772) 704701

Barnket Ltd, 128 Milton Road, Gravesend, Kent, DA12 2PG Tel: (01474) 327576 Fax: (01474) 567318

BBN Industrial Fasteners Ltd, Locksley, London End, Beaconsfield, Buckinghamshire, HP9 2JB Tel: (01494) 680078 Fax: (01494) 680093

Beardshaw Bolts & Fixings, Stalham Road, Hoveton, Norwich, NR12 8DU Tel: (01603) 783811 Fax: (01603) 783859 E-mail: sales@beardshaw.co.uk

Bedford Fixings, 1a Dean Street, Bedford, MK40 3EQ Tel: (01234) 360747 Fax: (01234) 217414

Bescol Ltd, Unit 8a Number One Industrial Estate, Consett, County Durham, DH8 6SS Tel: (01207) 582555 Fax: (01207) 583951 E-mail: name@btconnect.com

▶ Bigtoolbox, Unit 12, Hampstead Avenue, Mildenhall, Bury St. Edmunds, Suffolk, IP28 7AS Tel: (01638) 716170 Fax: (01638) 510728 E-mail: john@bigtoolbox.co.uk

Birmtool Engineering Ltd, 74 Warwick Street, Birmingham, B12 0NH Tel: 0121-772 3534 Fax: 0121-766 7548

Blakeacre Ltd, Austin Way, Hampstead Industrial Estate, Birmingham, B42 1DU Tel: 0121-358 5066 Fax: 0121-358 1721 E-mail: sales@blakeacre.co.uk

Bold Transmission Parts Ltd, Webber Road, Knowsley Industrial Park North, Knowsley Industrial Park, Liverpool, L33 7SW Tel: 0151-548 2303 Fax: 0151-549 1117 E-mail: sales@engineerskeys.co.uk

Bolhoff Fastenings Ltd, Midacre, Willenhall, West Midlands, WV13 2JW Tel: (01902) 637161 Fax: (01902) 609495 E-mail: enquiries@bollhoff.co.uk

Boltworthy Ltd, Unit I1 Cowlairs, Nottingham, NG5 9RA Tel: 0115-977 0432 Fax: 0115-977 0424

Bon Accord Metal Supplies Ltd, 86 Sinclair Road, Aberdeen, AB11 9PP Tel: (01224) 878898 Fax: (01224) 879730 E-mail: info@bonaccordmetals.co.uk

Brabbin & Rudd Ltd, Walker Street, Bolton, BL1 4TB Tel: (01204) 521171 Fax: (01204) 364972E-mail: sales@brabbin-and-rudd.co.uk

Brandon Bolt Co., 4 Faraday Place, Thetford, Norfolk, IP24 3RG Tel: (01842) 766612 Fax: (01842) 755526 E-mail: sales@brandonbolt.fsnet.co.uk

Britannia Fasteners, 4/6 Auckland Street, Hot Lane Industrial Estate, Stoke-on-Trent, ST6 2AT Tel: (01782) 833233 Fax: (01782) 833255E-mail: sales@britanniafasteners.co.uk

Burntwood Fasteners Ltd, Hawks Green Business Park, Cannock, Staffordshire, WS11 7XN Tel: (01543) 572731 Fax: (01543) 572735 E-mail: sales@burntwoodfasteners.co.uk

C F E Fasteners Ltd, Unit 18, Central Trading Estate, Cable Street, Wolverhampton, WV2 2HX Tel: (01902) 871777 Fax: (01902) 351410 E-mail: sales@cfe.co.uk

C H Morgan & Co. Ltd, 1 Clifton Business Park, Chamberlain Road, Aylesbury, Buckinghamshire, HP19 8DY Tel: (01296) 434878 Fax: (01296) 338520

C W W Engineers Supply Co. Ltd, 7 Stanlake Mews, London, W12 7HA Tel: (020) 8743 0651 Fax: (020) 8740 7731 E-mail: sales@cww.uk

Capital Supplies Ltd, 87 Boston Road, Croydon, CR0 3EJ Tel: (020) 8665 5520 Fax: (020) 8665 5838 E-mail: info@capitalsupplies.co.uk

Capstan Screws & Fastenings Ltd, Unit 4 Evingar Trading Estate, Ardglen Road, Whitchurch, Hampshire, RG28 7BB Tel: (01256) 895245 Fax: (01256) 892440

Carona Reuter Industrial Ltd, Coppen Road, Selinas Lane, Dagenham, Essex, RM8 1HN Tel: (020) 8592 2576 Fax: (020) 8595 8024 E-mail: carona_reuter@hotmail.com

Charnwood Fasteners Ltd, F27-30 Trading Estate, Cumberland Road, Loughborough, Leicestershire, LE11 5DF Tel: (01509) 237280 Fax: (01509) 262428

Cirteq Ltd, Hayfield, Colne Road, Keighley, West Yorkshire, BD20 8QP Tel: (01535) 633333 Fax: (01535) 632966 E-mail: sales@cirteq.com

Clyde Fasteners Ltd, Hawbank Road, East Kilbride, Glasgow, G74 5ET Tel: (01355) 225451 Fax: (01355) 263191 E-mail: info@clydefasteners.com

Compass Industrial Manufacturing, Units 26-27 Izons Industrial Estate, Oldbury Road, West Bromwich, West Midlands, B70 9BS Tel: 0121-553 1298 Fax: 0121-500 6452

Cooper & Turner Ltd, Sheffield Road, Sheffield, S9 1RS Tel: 0114-256 0057 Fax: 0114-244 5529 E-mail: sales@cooperandturner.co.uk

Cotswold Autoflo Ltd, Unit 2, Willow Park, Hinton Road, Childswickham, Broadway, Worcestershire, WR12 7HY Tel: (01386) 853284 Fax: (01386) 854636 E-mail: sales@autoflo.co.uk

Cotswold Fasteners, Winterwell, Ampney Crucis, Cirencester, Gloucestershire, GL7 5EA Tel: (01285) 651711 Fax: (01285) 651096 E-mail: sales@cotsfast.com

Cutlass Fasteners Ltd, Dixon Close, Old Boston Trading Estate, Haydock, St. Helens, Merseyside, WA11 9SL Tel: (01942) 712387 Fax: (01942) 722306 E-mail: sales@cutlass-studwelding.com

D J T Engineering, Willenhall Lane, Bloxwich, Walsall, WS3 2XN Tel: (01922) 491919 Fax: (01922) 497332 E-mail: djtsales@btconnect.com

▶ D M R Engineering, Somerton Industrial Park, Newport Road, Cowes, Isle of Wight, PO31 8PB Tel: (01983) 209030 Fax: (01983) 209060

D.T.P. Supplies, 242 Whitworth Rd, Rochdale, Lancashire, OL12 0SA Tel: 0845 8550605 Fax: (01706) 648180 E-mail: jon@dtpsupplies.com

Dagar Tools Ltd, 6 Providence Industrial Estate, Providence Street, Stourbridge, West Midlands, DY9 8HQ Tel: (01384) 893344 Fax: (01384) 422996

Darvill Engineering, 2 Bilston Street, Willenhall, West Midlands, WV13 2AW Tel: (01902) 605872 Fax: (01902) 605872

INDUSTRIAL FASTENERS – *continued*

▶ Data Day Supplies, 8, Halesowen Drive, Elstow, Bedford, MK42 9GG Tel: (01234) 245923 Fax: (01293) 782277

Davart Fasteners, Unit 10 Honeybourne Airfield Trading Estate, Honeybourne, Evesham, Worcestershire, WR11 7QF Tel: (01386) 833784 Fax: (01386) 833002 E-mail: sales@davart.co.uk

Dave Vickers, Thame Station Industrial Estate, Thame, Oxon, OX9 3UH Tel: (01844) 260100 Fax: (01844) 260900

Disc-Lock Europe Ltd, PO Box 134, Sittingbourne, Kent, ME9 7TF Tel: (01795) 844332 Fax: (01795) 843986 E-mail: info@disc-lock.com

Diss Fasteners Ltd, A8 Gilray Road, Diss, Norfolk, IP22 4EU Tel: (01379) 643506 Fax: (01379) 651121 E-mail: sales@dissfasteners.co.uk

Dobson & Beaumont Ltd, Appleby Street, Blackburn, BB1 3BH Tel: (01254) 53297 Fax: (01254) 676121 E-mail: philip@dobsonandbeaumont.co.uk

East Midlands Fastener, 101 Sanders Road, Finedon Road Industrial Estate, Finedon Road Industrial Estate, Wellingborough, Northamptonshire, NN8 4NL Tel: (01933) 229110 Fax: (01933) 271600 E-mail: sales@emfast.co.uk

Elite Engineering, 9 Neptune Works, Upper Trinity Street, Birmingham, B9 4EG Tel: 0121-772 8070 Fax: 0121-772 2230

Emhart Fastening Technology Ltd, Walsall Road, Perry Barr, Birmingham, B42 1BP Tel: 0121-331 2408 Fax: 0121-356 1598 E-mail: uk.marketing@bdk.com

Emlux Holdings Ltd, The Industrial Estate, Black Bourton Road, Brize Norton, Carterton, Oxfordshire, OX18 3LY Tel: (01993) 841574 Fax: (01993) 843186 E-mail: info@walraven.com

Engineering & Factory Supplies Ltd, Algores Way, Wisbech, Cambridgeshire, PE13 2TQ Tel: (01945) 466644 Fax: (01945) 466232

European Rivet Supplies, Uynit 4b Sovereign Park Industrial Estate, Market Harborough, Leicestershire, LE16 9EG Tel: (01858) 469191 Fax: (01858) 469190 E-mail: sales@eurorivet.co.uk

F R Scott Ltd, Canning Street, Hull, HU2 8QS Tel: (01482) 324731 Fax: (01482) 214290 E-mail: sales@frscott.co.uk

F R Smith & Co Newton Heath Ltd, Daisy Bank Mill, Terence Street, Manchester, M40 1GD Tel: 0161-681 1313 Fax: 0161-683 4763

Fabory UK Ltd, Block D Bay 9 Bescot Industrial Estate, Woden Road West, Wednesbury, West Midlands, WS10 7SG Tel: 0121-556 3474 Fax: 0121-556 7337E-mail: sales@fabory.com

Fairclough & Wood Ltd, Unit 10b Carcroft Enterprise Park, Carcroft, Doncaster, South Yorkshire, DN6 8DD Tel: (01302) 726027 Fax: (01302) 330221 E-mail: sales@faircloughwood.co.uk

Fastener & Machining Supply Ltd, Unit 12 South Staffs Business Park, Hawkins Drive, Cannock, Staffordshire, WS11 0XU Tel: (01922) 419418 Fax: (01922) 411314 E-mail: enquiries@fmsltd.net

Fastener Warehouse Ltd, 5 Ambassador Industrial Estate, 9 Airfield Road, Christchurch, Dorset, BH23 3TG Tel: (01202) 479621 Fax: (01202) 477222 E-mail: sales@fastenerwarehouse.co.uk

Fasteners Midlands Ltd, 16-17 Longford Industrial Estate, Longford Road, Cannock, Staffordshire, WS11 0DG Tel: (01543) 462416 Fax: (01543) 574308

Fengate Fasteners Ltd, Putney Close, Brandon, Suffolk, IP27 0PA Tel: (01842) 810771 Fax: (01842) 814097 E-mail: sales@fengatefasteners.co.uk

Fewell Fasteners Ltd, Unit 47, Victoria Industrial Park, Victoria Road, Dartford, DA1 5AJ Tel: (01322) 291595 Fax: (01322) 289524

Firmafix Fastenings, Unit 3, Pioneer Park Clough Road, Hull, HU8 8BB Tel: (01482) 224334 Fax: (01482) 224341 E-mail: sales@firmafix.com

Fitlock, 6 Vaughan St Industrial Estate, Manchester, M12 5BT Tel: 0161-231 3724 Fax: 0161-231 7392 E-mail: sales@fitlocksystems.com

Fitlock Systems Ltd, Albert Street, Off Hanson Lane, Halifax, West Yorkshire, HX1 5NW Tel: (01422) 354286 Fax: (01422) 383413 E-mail: elaine.Whatley@fitlocksystems.com

Fixfast Fasteners & Fixing Devices Ltd, Forge Works, Horsham Road, Mid Holmwood, Dorking, Surrey, RH5 4EJ Tel: (01306) 880299 Fax: (01306) 880038 E-mail:

Fixing Point Ltd, Rowan Trade Park, Neville Road, Bradford, West Yorkshire, BD4 8TQ Tel: (01274) 370078 Fax: (01274) 738678 E-mail: enquiries@fixingpoint.com

Fixing Point Ltd, Runnings Road, Kingsditch Trading Estate, Cheltenham, Gloucestershire, GL51 9NQ Tel: (01242) 265100 Fax: (01242) 236155 E-mail: sales@fixing.point.co.uk

Fixings Delivery, Unit 6 Catford Road, Roundthorn Industrial Estate, Roundthorn Industrial Estate, Manchester, M23 9LR Tel: 0161-945 0444 Fax: 0161-947 2710

▶ Flat Roofing Supplies, Tinsley Lane North, Crawley, West Sussex, RH10 9FF Tel: (01293) 590970 Fax: (01293) 543562

Flintnine Fasteners Ltd, Highfield Road, Little Hulton, Manchester, M38 9ST Tel: 0161-790 7817 Fax: 0161-703 8314 E-mail: sales@flintnine.co.uk

Friulsider UK Ltd, Unit 16 Court Farm Business Park, Bishops Frome, Worcester, WR6 5AY Tel: (01885) 490445 Fax: (01885) 490452 E-mail: sales@friulsider.co.uk

G I Fasteners Ltd, 8 Windmill Road Industrial Estate, Windmill Road, Loughborough, Leicestershire, LE11 1RA Tel: (01509) 260747 Fax: (01509) 217945

G T C Fixings Ltd, 84 Witt Road, Fair Oak, Eastleigh, Hampshire, SO50 7FQ Tel: 0845 5261414 Fax: (0800) 1975000 E-mail: sales@gtc-direct.com

Galino Ltd, 2 South Caldeen Road, Coatbridge, Lanarkshire, ML5 4EG Tel: (01236) 449898 Fax: (01236) 449899 E-mail: galino.ltd@virgin.net

Galvanised Bolts & Nuts Ltd, 115 Lodgefield Road, Halesowen, West Midlands, B62 8AX Tel: 0121-602 3333 Fax: 0121-602 4040 E-mail: galvanised.boltsandnuts@btconnect.com

Garth T Wright Fasteners, Colwickwood Works, Colwick Road, Nottingham, NG2 4BG Tel: 0115-958 8360 Fax: 0115-948 4967 E-mail: wright@wright-engineers.co.uk

Gemini Supplies Scotland Ltd, Unit 3 St. Johns Sawmill, Etna Road, Falkirk, FK2 9EG Tel: (01324) 629425 Fax: (01324) 630323

Glenwood Bolts, 2 Lintech Court, The Grip, Linton, Cambridge, CB21 4XN Tel: (01223) 893931 Fax: (01223) 894122 E-mail: glenwoodbolts@talk21.com

▶ Grampian Fastners, Grampian House, Pitmedden Road, Dyce, Aberdeen, AB21 0DP Tel: (01224) 772777 Fax: (01224) 772778 E-mail: sales@grampianfasteners.com

H Schreiber, Stadium Industrial Estate, 8 Cradock Road, Luton, LU4 0JF Tel: (01582) 575727 Fax: (01582) 575733 E-mail: laraine@techscrew.com

Habko Tools & Fastenings Ltd, Unit 1, Joseph Wilson Industrial Estate, South St, Whitstable, Kent, CT5 3PS Tel: (01227) 265444 Fax: (01227) 263517

Henry Halstead Ltd, 492 Holly Place, Walton Summit, Bamber Bridge, Preston, PR5 8AX Tel: (01772) 339521 Fax: (01772) 332233 E-mail: sales@henry-halstead.co.uk

Henrob, Second Avenue, Deeside Industrial Park, Deeside, Clwyd, CH5 2NX Tel: (01244) 837220 Fax: (01244) 837222 E-mail: sales@henrob.co.uk

Hobby Homes, 3 Industrial Estate, Thomas Road, London, E14 7BN Tel: (020) 7987 0550 Fax: (020) 7537 6501 E-mail: sales@hobbyhomes.com

Icon, Unit 2-3 Beldray Park, Beldray Road, Bilston, West Midlands, WV14 7NH Tel: (01902) 491122 Fax: (01902) 404044 E-mail: icon@icon-fasteners.co.uk

J & H Rosenheim & Co. Ltd, Lancaster Fields, Crewe, CW1 6FF Tel: (01270) 585959 Fax: (01270) 586611 E-mail: enquiries@rosenheim.co.uk

J Hall & Son Fasteners Ltd, Bentley Mill Industrial Estate, Longmore Avenue, Walsall, WS2 0BW Tel: (01922) 626652 Fax: (01922) 649942 E-mail: jhallsales@btconnect.com

J P Aero-Com Engineering Company Ltd, Station Approach, Cherry Tree Rise, Buckhurst Hill, Essex, IG9 6EY Tel: (020) 8504 8833 Fax: (020) 8505 0697 E-mail: sales@jpaero-com-eng.co.uk

J R Webster, Unit 1 Prince William Avenue, Sandycroft, Deeside, Clwyd, CH5 2QZ Tel: (01244) 534747 Fax: (01244) 535866 E-mail: kwalker.jrw@cuk.com

J & T Group Ltd, Victoria Works, 153 Victoria Street, Hartshill, Stoke-on-Trent, ST4 6HA Tel: (01782) 349440 Fax: (01782) 349449 E-mail: sales@storagebins.co.uk

Jaton, Patriot Drive, Rooksley, Milton Keynes, MK13 8PB Tel: (01908) 690055 Fax: (01908) 690401 E-mail: milton.keynes@outlet-jaton.com

John Smith & Co., PO Box 8, Aberdeen, AB11 5EA Tel: (01224) 586868 Fax: (01224) 590768 E-mail: sales@johnsmithaberdeen.co.uk

John Walsh & Co Inserts Ltd, 183 High Street, Wealdstone, Harrow, Middlesex, HA3 5EA Tel: (020) 8863 9133 Fax: (020) 8427 3307 E-mail: thinsheetfastner@btinternet.com

Julius Cee, 65-69 County Street, London, SE1 4AD Tel: (020) 7407 7273 Fax: (020) 7923 1794 E-mail: juliuscee@btconnect.com

Just Fasteners, 4 Alpha Centre, 10 South Douglas Street, Clydebank, Dunbartonshire, G81 1PD Tel: (01236) 429444 Fax: 0141-941 0088 E-mail: sales@justfasteners.co.uk

K Engineering, Unit 29 Parkrose Industrial Estate, Middlemore Road, Smethwick, West Midlands, B66 2DZ Tel: 0121-558 4367 Fax: 0121-565 1129 E-mail: sales@k-engineering.co.uk

K I Fasteners Blackburn Ltd, Unit 8 Pearson Street, Blackburn, BB2 2ES Tel: (01254) 678017 Fax: (01254) 678018

K Supplies Ltd, Unit 14 Harwood Street, Blackburn, BB1 3BS Tel: (01254) 679025 Fax: (01254) 677010 E-mail: salesblackburn@ksupplies.co.uk

Kebrell Nuts & Bolts Ltd, Imperial Works, Lockfield Avenue, Enfield, Middlesex, EN3 7PY Tel: (020) 8805 8510 Fax: (020) 8805 1553 E-mail: kebrell@montal-internet.co.uk

Kerb Konus, Unit B5 Hortonwood 10, Telford, Shropshire, TF1 7ES Tel: (01952) 677388 Fax: (01952) 677488E-mail: kkuk@pipex.com

L A Sarb Engineering, Unit 6b, George Street, West Bromwich, West Midlands, B70 6NH Tel: 0121-525 2569 Fax: 0121-525 2459

Lawson Distributors Ltd, Scotshaw Brook House, Scotshaw Brook Estate, Lower Darwen, Darwen, Lancashire, BB3 0PR Tel: (01254) 677121 Fax: (01254) 665922 E-mail: sales@johnlawsondist.co.uk

Lawson Products Ltd, 300 Quadrant, Ash Ridge Road, Bradley Stoke, Bristol, BS32 4QA Tel: (01454) 202223 Fax: (01454) 618510

Lesmac Fasteners Ltd, 73 Dykehead Street, Glasgow, G33 4AQ Tel: 0141-774 0004 Fax: 0141-774 2229 E-mail: sales@lesmac.co.uk

Samuel Lewis Ltd, PO Box 65, Cradley Heath, West Midlands, B64 5PS Tel: 0121-561 2157 Fax: 0121-561 5273

Leyton Fasteners Ltd, 9-15 Cook Street, Ellesmere Port, CH65 4AU Tel: 0151-355 8045 Fax: 0151-356 1885 E-mail: sales@leytonfasteners.co.uk

Lime Grove Services, Edison Road, Elm Farm Industrial Estate, Bedford, MK41 0HU Tel: (01234) 348709 Fax: (01234) 271724

Lincolnshire Fastener Co., Hadley Road, Sleaford, Lincolnshire, NG34 7EG Tel: (01529) 306443 Fax: (01529) 306168

Lindapter International, Brackenbeck Road, Bradford, West Yorkshire, BD7 2NF Tel: (01274) 521444 Fax: (01274) 521130 E-mail: enquiries@lindapter.com

Linread Northbridge, Viking Road, Wigston, Leicestershire, LE18 2BL Tel: 0116-288 1192 Fax: 0116-257 2901

James Lister & Sons Ltd, Spon La South, Smethwick, West Midlands, B66 1QJ Tel: 0121-553 2949 Fax: 0121-525 6116 E-mail: tools@lister.co.uk

Logistic Fasteners (UK) Ltd, Unit 2A Odell House, Summerleys Road, Princes Risborough, Buckinghamshire, HP27 9DT Tel: (01844) 275816 Fax: (01844) 342880 E-mail: logfast@aol.com

Lokfast Special Fasteners Ltd, Audley Street, Mossley, Ashton-under-Lyne, Lancashire, OL5 9NH Tel: (01457) 837514 Fax: (01457) 832213 E-mail: lockfast@aol.com

M D Fasteners Ltd, 129 Smiths Lane, Windsor, Berkshire, SL4 5PF Tel: (01753) 855773 Fax: (05600) 759015 E-mail: mdkfateners@yahoo.co.uk

M J Wilson Ltd, Charlton Street, Grimsby, South Humberside, DN31 1SQ Tel: (01472) 345361 Fax: (01472) 340172 E-mail: sales@dcmarshinstruments.co.uk

Machineair Engineering Ltd, 70 Colliers Water Lane, Thornton Heath, Surrey, CR7 7LB Tel: (020) 8684 4849 Fax: (020) 8683 4635

Mclean Buchanan & Wilson Glasgow Ltd, 250 Helen Street, Glasgow, G51 3JG Tel: 0141-445 3045 Fax: 0141-440 1225 E-mail: sales@mbw.co.uk

Martin Fasteners Ltd, 5 Saddlers Court, Fryers Road, Walsall, WS2 7LZ Tel: (01922) 712169 Fax: (01922) 416452

Marwill Tools & Fasteners Ltd, Units 4 & 5 Thomas Street, Whalley Banks Trading Estate, Blackburn, BB2 2HZ Tel: (01254) 264879 Fax: (01254) 680636 E-mail: marwill.uk@btopenworld.com

Masons Fasteners Ltd, 3-4 Doris Road, Bordesley Green, Birmingham, B9 4SJ Tel: 0121-766 7500 Fax: 0121-766 8551

Mattersons Ltd, Kingfield Road, Coventry, CV6 5AS Tel: (024) 7670 3713 Fax: (024) 7666 8156 E-mail: sales@matterson.co.uk

C.J.D. Mayers & Co. Ltd, Unit 6, Speedwell Close Industrial Estate, Speedwell Road, Yardley, Birmingham, B25 8HT Tel: 0121-773 0101 Fax: 0121-773 0104 E-mail: mayers@madasafish.com

Merlin Accessories Ltd, Unit G, St. Martins Trade Park, Nickel Close, Winchester, Hampshire, SO23 7RJ Tel: (01962) 842002 Fax: (01962) 842420 E-mail: sales@merlinaccessories.com

Millwood Stainless Fasteners, Unit 20 Lea Hall Enterprise Park, Rugeley, Staffordshire, WS15 1LH Tel: 01889 577712

Minster Distribution Ltd, Unit 11 Oldington Trading Estate, Stourport Road, Kidderminster, Worcestershire, DY10 1HE Tel: (01562) 747422 Fax: (01562) 60715 E-mail: minsterdist@aol.com

MLM Fasteners Ltd, Building 81, The Pensnett Estate, Kingswinford, West Midlands, DY6 7FJ Tel: (01384) 276280 Fax: (01384) 276299 E-mail: sales@mlmfast.co.uk

Mod Fix Ltd, Zygology House, Seawall Road, Cardiff, CF24 5ZY Tel: (029) 2049 9999 Fax: (029) 2049 1188 E-mail: info@modfix.com

Modern Screws Ltd, 5 Dartford Road, Bexley, Kent, DA5 2BH Tel: (01322) 553224 Fax: (01322) 555093 E-mail: sales@modern-screws.co.uk

Mohling UK Ltd, Dudley Road, Halesowen, West Midlands, B63 3NR Tel: 0121-585 7222 Fax: 0121-501 6817 E-mail: info@mohling.co.uk

Monofix Ltd, 4 Premier Trading Estate, Dartmouth Middleway, Birmingham, B7 4AT Tel: 0121-359 2117 Fax: 0121-359 2187 E-mail: sales@monofix.co.uk

▶ Montravia Fasteners & Fixing Devices, Unit 10 St. Augustines Business Park, Estuary Close, Whitstable, Kent, CT5 2QJ Tel: (01227) 791790 Fax: (01227) 791789 E-mail: robknight@sky.com

Moorhouse Fasteners, 17 Malmesbury Road, Kingsditch Trading Estate, Cheltenham, Gloucestershire, GL51 9PL Tel: (01242) 690392 Fax: (01242) 690391 E-mail: peterhamer@hambury.fsnet.co.uk

Nalex Ltd, 4 Edgemead Close, Round Spinney Industrial Estate, Northampton, NN3 8RG Tel: (01604) 648133 Fax: (01604) 790435 E-mail: sales@nalex.co.uk

Namrick Ltd, 124 Portland Road, Hove, East Sussex, BN3 5QL Tel: (01273) 736963 Fax: (01273) 726708 E-mail: sales@namrick.co.uk

Nelson Stud Welding UK, Rabans Lane Industrial Area, 47-49 Edison Road, Aylesbury, Buckinghamshire, HP19 8TE Tel: (01296) 433500 Fax: (01296) 487930 E-mail: enquiries@nelson-europe.co.uk

Newform Distribution Ltd, Unit B4-5 Dudley Central Trading Estate, Shaw Road, Dudley, West Midlands, DY2 8QX Tel: (01384) 230666 Fax: (01384) 235666 E-mail: sales@newformdistribution.co.uk

Non Standard Socket Screw Ltd, Unit 2, Liddall Way, Horton Road, West Drayton, Middlesex, UB7 8PG Tel: (01895) 430003 Fax: (01895) 430004 E-mail: salestsa@aol.com

Non Standard Socket Screws Ltd, 358-364 Farm Street, Birmingham, B19 2TZ Tel: 0121-515 0121 Fax: 0121-523 4440 E-mail: sales@nssocketscrews.com

Norfolk Fasteners, Rash's Green, Dereham, Norfolk, NR19 1JG Tel: (01362) 696848 Fax: (01362) 695356

Nu Screw & Nut, 311 Neasden La North, London, NW10 0AG Tel: (020) 8452 8633 Fax: (020) 8452 2987 E-mail: sales@nu-screw.co.uk

Nufast Ltd, 17 Hayward Industrial Estate, Vigo Place Aldridge, Walsall, WS9 8UG Tel: (01922) 740360 Fax: (01922) 453610 E-mail: sales@nufast.co.uk

Nuts, Cowling Brow Industrial Estate, Cowling Brow, Chorley, Lancashire, PR6 0QG Tel: (01257) 264040 Fax: (01257) 273782 E-mail: sales@nutsofchorley.co.uk

Nuts & Bolts, Unit 10, Longton Industrial Estate, Weston-super-Mare, Avon, BS23 3YB Tel: (01934) 416765 Fax: (01934) 418704 E-mail: enquires@nut-and-bolts.co.uk

Nycholwood Ltd, 17 Brindley Road, Hinckley, Leicestershire, LE10 3BY Tel: 01455 610300

Olympia Triumph International Ltd, 5 Queens Road, Swanage, Dorset, BH19 2EQ Tel: (01929) 424326 Fax: (01929) 427403 E-mail: sales@olympia-triumph.co.uk

Oxford Bearings Ltd, 41 Wedgewood Road, Bicester, Oxfordshire, OX26 4UL Tel: (01869) 249292 Fax: (01869) 241443

P C Supplies, 4 The Metro Centre, Peterborough, PE2 7UH Tel: (01733) 370000 Fax: (01733) 235528

P & D Fasteners Ltd, Mapplewell BSNS Park, Blacker Road, Staincross, Barnsley, South Yorkshire, S75 6BP Tel: (01226) 388899

P & M Fixings, Franchise Street, Wednesbury, West Midlands, WS10 9RG Tel: 0121-526 5775 Fax: 0121-568 6108 E-mail: info@pmfixings.com

P M Tools & Fasteners Ltd, 7 Phoenix Road Industrial Estate, Phoenix Road, Wolverhampton, WV11 3PX Tel: (01902) 727959 Fax: (01902) 738558 E-mail: info@pmtools.co.uk

P S M International plc, Longacre, Willenhall, West Midlands, WV13 2JS Tel: (01902) 600000 Fax: (01902) 600073 E-mail: tlspsm@compuserve.com

Parkins Industrial Supplies, Blundells Road, Tiverton, Devon, EX16 4DA Tel: (01884) 254444 Fax: (01884) 258142

Pennant Automotive & Industrial Supplies, University Farm, Wasthill Lane, Kings Norton, Birmingham, B38 9EP Tel: 0121-459 4276 Fax: 0121-451 2488

Jack Pennington Ltd, 3 Hird Street, Shipley, West Yorkshire, BD17 7ED Tel: (01274) 534444 Fax: (01274) 534433 E-mail: sales@pennington.co.uk

Permafast Ltd, Derby Road, Clay Cross, Chesterfield, Derbyshire, S45 9AG Tel: (01246) 250150 Fax: (01246) 250085 E-mail: info@permafast.co.uk

Peter Abbott, Unit 10 Keyford Court, Marston Trading Estate, Frome, Somerset, BA11 4BD Tel: (01373) 461261 Fax: (01373) 451513 E-mail: sales@peterabbott.co.uk

Phoenix-Saxton Ltd, Pomeroy Works, Clarence Road, Cardiff Bay, Cardiff, CF10 5FA Tel: (029) 2048 7848 Fax: (029) 2049 3493 E-mail: sales@phoenix-saxton.com

Pneutek (International) Ltd, Unit 1, Sovereign Way, Trafalgar Industrial Estate, Downham Market, Norfolk, PE38 9SW Tel: (01366) 388866 E-mail: airfasteners@thesmallbusinessclinique.com

Precision Stainless Fasteners, Unit 5 Bilston Industrial Estate, Oxford Street, Bilston, West Midlands, WV14 7EG Tel: (01902) 408222 Fax: (01902) 409222 E-mail: apexbilston@btinternet.com

Priority Industrial Supplies, Unit 15, Prince Of Wales Industrial Estate, Abercarn, Newport, Gwent, NP11 5AR Tel: (01495) 244940 Fax: (01495) 243469 E-mail: sales@priorityind.co.uk

Prosper Engineering Ltd, 3 Arkwright Way, North Newmoor Industrial Estate, Irvine, Ayrshire, KA11 4JU Tel: (01294) 224422 Fax: (01294) 215003 E-mail: sales@prosper-engineering.com

Pugh & Sanders Ltd, Unit 1 Moseley Business Park, Moseley Street, Burton-on-Trent, Staffordshire, DE14 1DW Tel: (01283) 510824 Fax: (01283) 511403 E-mail: pughsanders@aol.com

Pugh & Sanders Ltd, Woods Lane, Derby, DE22 3UD Tel: (01332) 206770 Fax: (01332) 206771

INDUSTRIAL FASTENERS – *continued*

Q A Bolting Systems, 41 Harding Avenue, Rawmarsh, Rotherham, South Yorkshire, S62 7ED Tel: (01709) 524680 Fax: (01709) 527887

Quickfix, Arch 13 Bridgewater, Goswell Road, Windsor Castle, Windsor, Berkshire, SL4 1QY Tel: (01753) 840508 Fax: (01753) 831189 E-mail: fixings@quickfix.demon.co.uk

Quickfix Midlands, Unit B1, The Haysfield Business Centre, Malvern, Worcestershire, WR14 1GF Tel: (01684) 560700 Fax: (01684) 560020 E-mail: sales@quick-fix.demon.co.uk

R A K Fasteners Ltd, R A K Fasteners Ltd Unit 18 Pinfold Industrial Estate, Field Close, Bloxwich, Walsall, WS3 3JS Tel: (01922) 408508 Fax: (01922) 402037

R A Poole, 5 Kingston Business Centre, Fullers Way South, Chessington, Surrey, KT9 1DQ Tel: (020) 8391 9140 Fax: (020) 8391 9150 E-mail: sales@rapoole.com

R & D Fastenings Systems Ltd, 135 High St, Newton-le-Willows, Merseyside, WA12 9SQ Tel: (01925) 224442 Fax: (01925) 222711 E-mail: david.cunningham@f9.co.uk

R & M Distribution Ltd, 1 Mitchelson Drive, Mitchelston Indust Estate, Mitchelston Industrial Estate, Kirkcaldy, Fife, KY1 3NF Tel: (01592) 655565 Fax: (01592) 655542 E-mail: enquiries@rmdist.com

R S Paskin & Co. Ltd, Mount Pleasant, Brierley Hill, West Midlands, DY5 2YR Tel: (01384) 78081 Fax: (01384) 76480 E-mail: sales@rspaskin.co.uk

Ranger Fixings Ltd, 8 Central Business Park, Southcote Road, Bournemouth, BH1 3SJ Tel: (01202) 297125 Fax: (01202) 294087 E-mail: ranger.fixings@tiscali.co.uk

Rapid Industrial Fasteners Ltd, 9 Gun Barrel Industrial Centre, Hayseech, Cradley Heath, West Midlands, B64 7JZ Tel: 0121-501 3903 Fax: 0121-585 5163 E-mail: sales@rapidfast.co.uk

Readyfix, Lodge Street, Preston, PR1 8XE Tel: (01772) 250060 Fax: (01772) 250075

Reisser Ltd, Pepper Road, Hazel Grove, Stockport, Cheshire, SK7 5BW Tel: 0161-483 5557 Fax: 0161-483 4631 E-mail: reisser@dial.pipex.com

Righton Ltd, Unit 13b Anniesland Industrial Estate, Glasgow, G13 1EU Tel: 0141-954 8962 Fax: 0141-959 3467 E-mail: info@righton.co.uk

Rocfast, Unit 20, Worton Hall Industrial Estate, Worton Road, Isleworth, Middlesex, TW7 6ER Tel: (020) 8568 1616 Fax: (020) 8568 5656 E-mail: Info@rocfast.co.uk

M.D. Roe, Whitford Drive, Shirley, Solihull, West Midlands, B90 4YG Tel: 0121-246 3465 Fax: 0121-246 3466

Rollstud Ltd, 5 Denmore Industrial Estate, Denmore Road, Denmore Industrial Estate, Aberdeen, AB23 8JW Tel: (01224) 425300 Fax: (01224) 425333

Rose Auto Supplies, Merlin Centre, County Oak Way, Crawley, West Sussex, RH11 7XA Tel: (01293) 536769 Fax: (01293) 553666 E-mail: roseautos@gogglemail.com

Rotaloc Europe, 8 Wyvern Buildings, Grove Trading Estate, Dorchester, Dorset, DT1 1ST Tel: (01305) 257800 Fax: (01305) 259420 E-mail: sales@rotaloc.co.uk

S D Products, The Broadway, Mansfield, Nottinghamshire, NG18 2RL Tel: (01623) 655265 Fax: (01623) 420689 E-mail: sales@sdproducts.co.uk

S E A C, 46 Chesterfield Road, Leicester, LE5 5LP Tel: 0116-273 9501 Fax: 0116-273 8373 E-mail: enquiries@seac.uk.com

S G B Formwork, 609 London Road, Grays, Essex, RM20 3BJ Tel: (01708) 861666 Fax: (01708) 869560

S W G Ltd, Unit B6 Newbury Industrial Centre, Faraday Road, Newbury, Berkshire, RG14 2AD Tel: (01635) 30059 Fax: (01635) 521249 E-mail: sales@swgltd.co.uk

Samuel Fields & Co., Croft Street, Willenhall, West Midlands, WV13 2NU Tel: (01902) 607177 Fax: (01902) 606582

Sapphire Products Ltd, 4 Dunton Trading Estate, Mount Street, Birmingham, B7 5QL Tel: 0121-326 6000 Fax: 0121-328 5518 E-mail: sapphireproducts@boltblue.com

Screwplan Ltd, Hazelwood St Works, Hazelwood Street, Todmorden, Lancashire, OL14 5BW Tel: (01706) 812299 Fax: (01706) 816258 E-mail: sales@screwplan.com

Secure Bolts, Unit 18 Blenheim Way, Liverpool, L24 1YH Tel: 0151-486 3154 Fax: 0151-486 3154

Serco Ryan, Unit 45, Thornleigh Trading Estate, Dudley, West Midlands, DY2 8UB Tel: (01384) 459000 Fax: (01384) 456952 E-mail: dudley@sercoryan.co.uk

SFS Intec Ltd, 153 Kirkstall Road, Leeds, LS4 2AT Tel: 0113-208 5500 Fax: 0113-208 5519 E-mail: gb.leeds@sfsintec.biz

Sheffield Bolt & Nut Co. Ltd, Unit G Harrison Street, Rotherham, South Yorkshire, S61 1EE Tel: (01709) 550101 Fax: (01709) 550176 E-mail: sales.sbn@btconnect.com

Shellbourne Manufacturing Co. Ltd, Bolton Bus Centre, 44-49 Lower Bridgeman St, Bolton, BL2 1DG Tel: (01204) 546410 Fax: (01925) 740062 E-mail: sales@shellbourne.co.uk

▶ The Site Supply Co. Ltd, Unit 20, Haigh Park, Whitehill Industrial Estate, Stockport, Cheshire, SK4 1QR Tel: (0845) 0096750 Fax: (0845) 0096751 E-mail: info@sitesuppyco.com

SKM Products Ltd, Unit N3 Troon Way Business Centre, Humberstone Lane, Leicester, LE4 9HA Tel: 0116-246 1727 Fax: 0116-246 0313

Smart Screw Ltd, Portland House, Floodgate Street, Digbeth, Birmingham, B5 5SL Tel: 0121-772 2115 Fax: 0121-766 5828 E-mail: sales@smartscrew.co.uk

Snapfast Fasteners & Fixing Devices, Unit 1-2 Park Court, Ninth Avenue, Team Valley Trading Estate, Gateshead, Tyne & Wear, NE11 0EH Tel: 0191-482 4075 Fax: 0191-491 1799 E-mail: snapfast@natlineuk.net

Socket & Allied Screws Ltd, 121 Camden Street, Birmingham, B1 3DJ Tel: 0121-200 2880 Fax: 0121-236 8991 E-mail: sales@socket-allied.com

South West Fasteners, 1 Shepherd Road, Gloucester, GL2 5EL Tel: (01452) 424346 Fax: (01452) 309313

Southco Europe, Farnham Trading Estate, Farnham, Surrey, GU9 9PL Tel: (01252) 714422 Fax: (01252) 712738 E-mail: info@dzus.com

Southco Manufacturing Co., Shire Business Park, Wainwright Road, Worcester, WR4 9FA Tel: (01905) 751000 Fax: (01905) 751090 E-mail: info@southco.com

Southwest Fasteners Ltd, Unit 7-8 306 Industrial Estate, 242-244 Broomhill Road, Bristol, BS4 5RG Tel: 0117-972 3242 Fax: 0117-971 7555 E-mail: southwestfastners@dial.pipex.com

Spa Fasteners Ltd, 26 Hurlbutt Road, Heathcote Industrial Estate, Warwick, CV34 6TD Tel: (01926) 883671 Fax: (01926) 430953 E-mail: postmaster@spafasteners.co.uk

Specthread Ltd, Unit 20, Field Close, Bloxwich, Walsall, WS3 3JS Tel: (01922) 710180 Fax: (01922) 710181

Spiralock Europe, 11 Court Yard Workshops, Bath Street, Market Harborough, Leicestershire, LE16 9EW Tel: (01858) 468646 Fax: (01858) 466808 E-mail: sl-europe@spiralock.com

Ivor Spry & Co. Ltd, The Granary, Cornwells Farm, Sheephurst Lane, Marden, Tonbridge, Kent, TN12 9NS Tel: (01622) 833414 E-mail: sales@spry.co.uk

Stainless Steel Centre Ltd, Renown Close, Chandler's Ford, Eastleigh, Hampshire, SO53 4HZ Tel: (023) 8027 1155 Fax: (023) 8027 1110 E-mail: sales@stainlesssteelcentre.co.uk

Stainless Steel Fixings Ltd, 10 Charlwoods Road, East Grinstead, West Sussex, RH19 2HU Tel: (01342) 328608 Fax: (01342) 314861

Staytite Ltd, Unit B Coronation Road, Cressex BSNS Park, High Wycombe, Buckinghamshire, HP12 4PR Tel: (01494) 462322 Fax: (01494) 464747 E-mail: fasteners@staytite.com

Steadfast Fastenings, 167 Junction Road, Burgess Hill, West Sussex, RH15 0JW Tel: (01444) 247755 Fax: (01444) 248022

Steadfast Scotland Ltd, Units 7-8, Barratt Trading Estate, Denmore Road, Bridge Of Don, Aberdeen, AB23 8JW Tel: (01224) 823555 Fax: (01224) 823666 E-mail: brian.sherwood@steadscott.co.uk

Sterling Power Tools & Fixings, 103 Newland Road, Worthing, West Sussex, BN11 1LB Tel: (01903) 211543 Fax: (01903) 523066

Suffolk Fastener & Engineering Co. Ltd, Unit 17 Hummable Industrial Estate, Toppesfield Road, Great Yeldham, Halstead, Essex, CO9 4HD Tel: (01787) 237007 Fax: (01787) 238052

Surrey Fastners, Course Road, Ascot, Berkshire, SL5 7HQ Tel: (01344) 876104 Fax: (01344) 620185 E-mail: surreyfast@aol.com

Swansea Fastners, Unit 8, Horizon Park, Swansea Enterprise Park, Swansea, SA6 8RG Tel: (01792) 310284 Fax: (01792) 310291 E-mail: sales@swanseafasteners.com

Swift Fasteners Ltd, Unit 20 Oldends Industrial Estate, Oldends, Stonehouse, Gloucestershire, GL10 3RQ Tel: (01453) 825222 Fax: (01453) 827824E-mail: sales@swift-fasteners-ltd.co.uk

Swift Screw Products, Dunmore, Alexandra Park Avenue, Belfast, BT15 3GD Tel: (028) 9077 0721 Fax: (028) 9037 0914 E-mail: sales@swiftscrewproducts.co.uk

T E Stone Ltd, 82-84 West Street, St. Philips, Bristol, BS2 0BP Tel: 0117-955 5144 Fax: 0117-941 2233

T L M Construction Fasteners Ltd, 13 Davy Road, Astmoor Industrial Estate, Runcorn, Cheshire, WA7 1PZ Tel: (01928) 576193 Fax: (01928) 581308 E-mail: sales@tlmfasteners.co.uk

T Potter (1982) Ltd, 63 Whitehill Road, Glenrothes, Fife, KY6 2RP Tel: 0141-429 1500 Fax: (01592) 774666 E-mail: thos.potter@btinternet.com

T R Fastenings Ltd, Unit 1 TR Business Park, 8A Trench Road, Newtownabbey, County Antrim, BT36 4TY Tel: (028) 9084 2621 Fax: (028) 9083 7436

Teesside Industrial Fasteners Ltd, 6 Douglas Close, Preston Farm Industrial Estate, Stockton-on-Tees, Cleveland, TS18 3SB Tel: 01642 675630

Threaded Fastener Supplies Ltd, 72 & 73 Heming Rd, Washford, Redditch, Worcs, B98 0EA Tel: (01527) 518533 Fax: (01527) 518527 E-mail: threaded.fastener@virgin.net

Tolway East Ltd, 1 Nuffield Close, Cambridge, CB4 1SS Tel: (01223) 425425 Fax: (01223) 420200

Tolwood Ltd, Coatham Avenue, Aycliffe Industrial Park, Newton Aycliffe, County Durham, DL5 6DB Tel: (01325) 300777 Fax: (01325) 300399 E-mail: info@tolwood.co.uk

Toolcom Supplies Ltd, Pitreavie Business Park, Pitreavie Business Park, Dunfermline, Fife, KY11 8UQ Tel: (01383) 728970 Fax: (01383) 620079 E-mail: sales@toolcom.co.uk

Tox Pressotechnik Ltd, Unit 35, Stafford Business Village, Dyson Way, Staffordshire Technology Park, Stafford, ST18 0TW Tel: (01785) 887903 Fax: (01785) 887027 E-mail: sales@tox-uk.com

TR Fastenings Ltd, Trifast House, Bellbrook Industrial Estate, Uckfield, East Sussex, TN22 1QW Tel: (0800) 7315553 Fax: (0800) 525230 E-mail: sales@trfastenings.com

Trifast P.L.C., Trifast House, Bellbrook Park, Uckfield, East Sussex, TN22 1QW Tel: (01825) 769696 Fax: (01825) 767882

Trojan Special Fasteners Ltd, 18 Fortnum Close, Tile Cross, Birmingham, B33 0LG Tel: 0121-789 8586 Fax: 0121-789 8006 E-mail: sales@trojanspecialfastenersltd.co.uk

▶ Trutek Fasteners Ltd, Leigh Street, Sheffield, S9 2PR Tel: 0114-242 3333 Fax: 0114-242 3300

Turbo Engineering Ltd, Unit 14, Prince Consort Industrial Estate, Hebburn, Tyne & Wear, NE31 1EH Tel: (0845) 4941706 Fax: 0191-483 6745 E-mail: dominic.rutherford@btinternet.com

Tyne Tees Power Tool Co., 96 Heaton Road, Newcastle upon Tyne, NE6 5HL Tel: 0191-265 9054 Fax: 0191-276 5872

Unbrako, 12-14 Tower Street, BIRMINGHAM, B19 3RR Tel: 0121 333 4610 Fax: 0121 333 4525 E-mail: unbrako.uk@spstech.com

Universal Engineering, Unit 10 Mid Wynd, Dundee, DD1 4JG Tel: (01382) 223592 Fax: (01382) 202506 E-mail: sales@universalengtool.co.uk

Vulcan Industrial Fasteners Ltd, Unit 6, Emerald Way, Stone Business Park, Stone, Staffordshire, ST15 0SR Tel: (01785) 818494 Fax: (01785) 818399 E-mail: sales@vulcanfasteners.co.uk

W H Povoas Ltd, Radnor Street, Stretford, Manchester, M32 8LP Tel: 0161-865 1086 Fax: 0161-864 3584 E-mail: sales@whpovoas.co.uk

Bernard F. Wade Ltd, PO Box 1865, Sheffield, S36 8BY Tel: (01226) 370860 Fax: (01226) 370836 E-mail: berniebolt@talk21.com

Walker & Howell Ltd, Forge Road, Whaley Bridge, High Peak, Derbyshire, SK23 7HY Tel: (01663) 732471 Fax: (01663) 733927 E-mail: sales@walkerandhowell.co.uk

Steven Walker & Sons Ltd, Portersfield Road, Cradley Heath, West Midlands, B64 7BE Tel: (01384) 569087 Fax: (01384) 633727 E-mail: sales@swsltd.co.uk

Welfix Fasteners & Fixing Devices, 192 Monkmoor Road, Shrewsbury, SY2 5BH Tel: (01743) 344766 Fax: (01743) 350875

Welland Supplies, Blenheim Way, Northfields Industrial Estate, Market Deeping, Peterborough, PE6 8LD Tel: (01778) 380371 Fax: (01778) 346916 E-mail: sales@welland-supplies.co.uk

Wessex Fixings, Unit 60 South Way, Andover, Hampshire, SP10 5AF Tel: (01264) 332332 Fax: (01264) 332550

Westgate Fastenings, Gapton Hall Industrial Estate, Viking Road, Great Yarmouth, Norfolk, NR31 0NU Tel: (01493) 603207 Fax: (01493) 656284 E-mail: westgatefastenings@connectfree.co.uk

Westgate Fastenings, 5-6 Cumberland Place, Lowestoft, Suffolk, NR32 1UQ Tel: (01502) 560061 Fax: (01502) 517505

Westline Distributors Ltd, West Line Industrial Estate, Birtley, Chester le Street, County Durham, DH2 1AU Tel: 0191-410 2636 Fax: 0191-492 2108 E-mail: LINDA@bedegroup.net

Westwood Bolt & Nut Co. Ltd, Claypit Lane, West Bromwich, West Midlands, B70 9UP Tel: 0121 5532405

Willenhall Fasteners Holdings Ltd, Frederick William Street, Willenhall, West Midlands, WV13 1NE Tel: (01902) 630760 Fax: (01902) 636447 E-mail: sales@willenfast.co.uk

Williams Fasteners Ltd, 8 Tees Court, Wallis Road, Skippers Lane Industrial Estate, Middlesbrough, Cleveland, TS6 6DX Tel: (01642) 460261 Fax: (01642) 440966

Williams Fasteners, 3 Burton Close, Norwich, NR6 6AZ Tel: (01603) 483447 Fax: (01603) 482145 E-mail: darren.ray@williamsfasteners.com

Williams Fasteners, Unit 4a, Shepcote Way, Tinsley Industrial Estate, Sheffield, S9 1TH Tel: 0114-256 5200 Fax: 0114-256 5210 E-mail: sales@williamsfasteners.com

▶ Woods & Hughes (Bolts & Screws) Ltd, Unit 9, Hill Top Industrial Estate, Shaw Street, West Bromwich, West Midlands, B70 0TX Tel: 0121-505 7551 Fax: 0121-505 7652 E-mail: sales@socketscrews.co.uk

Wrights Hose Clips Ltd, Unit 15 Portway Close, Coventry, CV4 9UY Tel: (024) 7647 0377

X R Fasteners Ltd, Unit 85 86 Imperial Trading Estate, Lambs La North, Rainham, Essex, RM13 9XL Tel: (01708) 526274 Fax: (01708) 525981

Y K K Europe Ltd, 61 Central Street, London, EC1V 8AN Tel: (020) 7017 8555 Fax: (020) 7017 8585 E-mail: enquiries@ykkeurope.com

INDUSTRIAL FEED OR FEEDER SYSTEMS

A C Automation, Hartland Avenue, Tattenhoe, Milton Keynes, MK4 3DN Tel: (01908) 501796 Fax: (01908) 501796 E-mail: sales@ac-automation.co.uk

Alphamation Ltd, Bassett Road, Halesowen, West Midlands, B63 2RE Tel: (01384) 412255 Fax: (01384) 413191 E-mail: info@alphamation.co.uk

B. & W. Mechanical Handling Ltd, Gemini House Cambridgeshire, Business Park, Ely, Cambridgeshire, CB7 4EA Tel: (01353) 665001 Fax: (01353) 666734 E-mail: sales@bwmech.co.uk

Performance Feeders, Lavender House, Station Road, Hammerwich, Burntwood, Staffordshire, WS7 0JZ Tel: (01543) 454055 Fax: (01543) 454047 E-mail: enquiries@performancefeeders.co.uk

Rotex Europe Ltd, Whitehouse Vale, Aston La North, Runcorn, Cheshire, WA7 3FA Tel: (01928) 706100 Fax: (0870) 7529920

Tool Production & Design Co. Ltd, Borman, Apollo, Tamworth, Staffordshire, B79 7TA Tel: (01827) 67767 Fax: (01827) 53670

INDUSTRIAL FILTERS

K & N Filters Europe Ltd, John Street, Warrington, WA2 7UB Tel: (01925) 636950 Fax: (01925) 418948E-mail: kn@knfilters.com

M F & T, 22 Dawkins Road Industrial Estate, Hamworthy, Poole, Dorset, BH15 4JY Tel: (01202) 666456 Fax: (01202) 685545 E-mail: steve.hunt@porvairfilteration.com

▶ R S E Associates Ltd, Seascape, Main Road, Trevone, Padstow, Cornwall, PL28 8QX Tel: (01841) 520915 Fax: (01841) 520833

Rellumit Filters Ltd, PO Box 69, Princes Risborough, Buckinghamshire, HP27 9RW Tel: (01844) 273213 Fax: (01844) 273235

INDUSTRIAL FINISH PROTECTIVE COATINGS

Argosy Control Engineering Ltd, Murcar Industrial Estate, Denmore Road, Bridge of Don, Aberdeen, AB23 8JW Tel: (01224) 704788 Fax: (01224) 704831

Atherstone Industrial Coatings Ltd, Spring Hill Industrial Estate, Colliers Way, Arley, Coventry, CV7 8HN Tel: (01676) 541114 Fax: (01676) 541241

Classcoat, 21 High Street, Upper Heyford, Bicester, Oxfordshire, OX25 5LE Tel: (01869) 232793 Fax: (01869) 233625 E-mail: classcoat7921718@aol.com

Crosbie Casco Ltd, Wood Lane, Partington, Manchester, M31 4BT Tel: 0161-775 3025 Fax: 0161-777 9076 E-mail: sales@crosbie-casco.co.uk

Morrells Wood Finishers Ltd, 99 Mabgate Street, Leeds, LS9 7DR Tel: 0113-245 0371 Fax: (0845) 4501717 E-mail: leeds@morrells-woodfinishers.com

R F Shielding Ltd, Unit 16, Rising Sun Industrial Estate, Blaina, Abertillery, Gwent, NP13 3JW Tel: (01495) 292399 Fax: (01495) 292550 E-mail: info@rfshielding.co.uk

Teknos (UK) Ltd, Unit E1 Heath Farm, Banbury Road, Swerford, Chipping Norton, Oxfordshire, OX7 4BN Tel: (01608) 683494 Fax: (01608) 683487 E-mail: sales@teknos.co.uk

INDUSTRIAL FINISHES

Dacrylate Ltd, Lime Street, Kirkby-In-Ashfield, Nottingham, NG17 8AL Tel: (01623) 753845 Fax: (01623) 757151 E-mail: sales@dacrylate.co.uk

Dispec Anodizing Ltd, Unit 4 Sough Bridge Mill, Colne Road, Barnoldswick, Lancashire, BB18 6UH Tel: (01282) 841341 Fax: (01282) 841341 E-mail: dispec@ic24.net

E J Rawlins & Co. Ltd, Unit 6 Croydon Street, Leeds, LS11 9RT Tel: 0113-245 5450 Fax: 0113-245 2649 E-mail: sales@rawlinspaints.com

E Wood Ltd, Standard Way Industrial Estate, Northallerton, North Yorkshire, DL6 2XA Tel: (01609) 778907 Fax: (01609) 783762 E-mail: thortex@ewood.co.uk

Hicks & Weatherburn Ltd, Lawnswood Works, Otley Road, Leeds, LS16 8AA Tel: 0113-267 1057 Fax: 0113-267 1057

J & S Industrial Coatings Ltd, Unit 16 17 Old Mill Park, Kirkintilloch, Glasgow, G66 1SS Tel: 0141-775 2233 Fax: 0141-775 1999

Kingstonian Paints Ltd, Sculcoates Lane, Hull, HU5 1DR Tel: (01482) 342216 Fax: (01482) 493096 E-mail: info@kpaints.co.uk

North West Enamellers, Unit 14-15 Catheralls Industrial Estate, Brookhill Way, Buckley, Clwyd, CH7 3PS Tel: (01244) 549185 Fax: (01244) 544739

Opticron Plastics, Unit 3 Sabre Court, Gillingham Business Park, Gillingham, Kent, ME8 0RW Tel: (01634) 366385 Fax: (01634) 366397 E-mail: info@opticron.co.uk

Trimite Ltd, Arundel Road, Uxbridge, Middlesex, UB8 2SD Tel: (01895) 251234 Fax: (01895) 256489 E-mail: info@trimite.com

INDUSTRIAL FINISHING

Extrude Hone Ltd, 1 Sovereign Business Park, Joplin Court, Crownhill, Milton Keynes, MK8 0JP Tel: (01908) 263636 Fax: (01908) 262141 E-mail: miltonkeynes.sales@extrudehone.com

INDUSTRIAL FINISHING – *continued*

G F L Industrial Finishing, William Kelvin Building, Claylands Road, Bishops Waltham, Southampton, SO32 1BH Tel: (01489) 897480 Fax: (01489) 897489 E-mail: sales@gfl-uk.com

Hankoe Advanced Surface Treatments Ltd, 823 Yeovil Road, Slough Trading Estate, Slough, SL1 4JA Tel: (01753) 522779 Fax: (01753) 539320 E-mail: hankoe@btconnect.com

Sureline Finishing, 1-2 Quarry CR, Pennygillam Industrial Estate, Launceston, Cornwall, PL15 7PF Tel: (01566) 776630 Fax: (01566) 777773

INDUSTRIAL FINISHING ABRASIVE PRODUCTS

3M Abrasive Systems, 3 M Centre, Cain Road, Bracknell, Berkshire, RG12 8HT Tel: (01344) 858974 Fax: (01344) 858195 E-mail: abrasives.uk@mmm.com

▶ A T A Grinding Processes Ltd, 37 Dalsetter Avenue, Drumchapel, Glasgow, G15 8TE Tel: 0141-940 4720 Fax: 0141-940 4721 E-mail: ata@atagrinding.co.uk

B N D Abrasives & Tapes Ltd, Unit 3a Stephenson Close, Andover, Hampshire, SP10 3RU Tel: (01264) 354133 Fax: (01264) 323873 E-mail: info@bnd-abrasives.co.uk

Consort Abrasives Products Ltd, Swallowfields, Welwyn Garden City, Hertfordshire, AL7 1JD Tel: (01707) 330319 Fax: (01707) 376697 E-mail: consortabrasives@btconnect.com

Ervin Amasteel Ltd, George Henry Road, Tipton, West Midlands, DY4 7BZ Tel: 0121-522 2777 Fax: 0121-522 2927 E-mail: info@ervinamasteel.com

Finishing Aids & Tools, Unit 25 Woolfold Industrial Estate, Mitchell Street, Bury, Lancashire, BL8 1SF Tel: 0161-705 1300 Fax: 0161-763 1959

Finishing Components Co., 1-8 Silverdale, Meadow Road, Worthing, West Sussex, BN11 2RZ Tel: (01903) 205155 Fax: (01903) 205166 E-mail: finishingcomponents@supanet.com

Flextol Ltd, 20 Swannington Road, Cottage Lane Industrial Estate, Broughton Astley, Leicester, LE9 6TU Tel: (01455) 285333 Fax: (01455) 285238 E-mail: sales@flextol.co.uk

Hermes Abrasives Ltd, Wyncolls Road, Severalls Industrial Park, Colchester, CO4 9LW Tel: (01206) 754400 Fax: (01206) 754401 E-mail: huk@hermes-abrasives.com

Herzbi Ltd, Grosvenor Works, Mount Pleasant Hill, London, E5 9NE Tel: (020) 8806 3232 Fax: (020) 8806 3236

Industrial Abrasives & Tool Co. Ltd, Amberwood, Wantage Road, Harwell, Didcot, Oxfordshire, OX11 0LL Tel: (01235) 834850 Fax: (01235) 832857 E-mail: trudy@industrialabrasives.net

Klingspor Abrasives Ltd, Dukeries Close, Worksop, Nottinghamshire, S81 7DN Tel: (01909) 504400 Fax: (01909) 504405 E-mail: sales@klingspor.co.uk

Meister Abrasives UK Ltd, High March Industrial Estate, Daventry, Northamptonshire, NN11 4PG Tel: (01327) 703813 Fax: (01327) 871617E-mail: sales@master-abrasives.co.uk

Metalltechnik UK Ltd, 8 Mere Close, Shifnal, Shropshire, TF11 9QA Tel: (01952) 461242 Fax: (01952) 417489 E-mail: metuk@dialstart.net

F.A. Morris (Sheffield) Ltd, 83 Headford Street, Sheffield, S3 7WA Tel: 0114-276 7327 Fax: 0114-275 3862 E-mail: sales@famorris.co.uk

Norfinish Engineering Ltd, Sleekburn Business Centre, West Sleekburn, Bedlington, Northumberland, NE22 7DD Tel: (01670) 855087 Fax: (01670) 855079 E-mail: info@norfinish.co.uk

P B R (Abrasives) Ltd, The Quadrant, 99 Parkway Avenue, Sheffield, S9 4WG Tel: 0114-243 3700 Fax: 0114-243 3527 E-mail: sales@pbrabrasives.com

P B R Abrasives (Wolverhampton) Ltd, 8-10 Wolverhampton Street, Willenhall, West Midlands, WV13 2NF Tel: (01902) 368624 Fax: (01902) 634635 E-mail: sales@pbrabrasives.com

Saint-Gobain Abrasives, Doxey Road, Stafford, ST16 1EA Tel: (01785) 223281 Fax: (01785) 213487 E-mail: sales.gloucester.uk@saint-gobain.com

Scangrit, Eastfield Road, South Killingholme, Immingham, South Humberside, DN40 3NF Tel: (01469) 574715 Fax: (01469) 571644 E-mail: sales@scangrit.co.uk

Swift Abrasive Wheels, Toll End Road, Tipton, West Midlands, DY4 0HF Tel: 0121-557 8337 Fax: 0121-520 4770 E-mail: swiftandwhitmore@virgin.net

United Abrasives Ltd, Unit 1 Charles Street, Walsall, WS2 9LZ Tel: (01922) 625544 Fax: (01922) 626345 E-mail: unitedabrasives@btconnect.com

Vixen Surface Treatments Ltd, Jay Avenue, Teeside Industrial Estate, Stockton-on-Tees, Cleveland, TS17 9LZ Tel: (01642) 769333 Fax: (01642) 769441

Wolverhampton Abrasives, Orgreave Drive, Sheffield, S13 9NR Tel: (0800) 0853085 Fax: 0114-254 0913E-mail: gritsales@aol.com

INDUSTRIAL FINISHING PLANT

D J B Associates Ltd, 4-6 Roman Court, Watling Street, Bridgtown, Cannock, Staffordshire, WS11 0BN Tel: (01543) 574162 Fax: (01543) 574282

Harry Dalby Engineering Incoporating Dalby Sheetmetal, Gloucester Crescent, Wigston, Leicestershire, LE18 4YQ Tel: 0116-291 6000 Fax: 0116-291 6001 E-mail: enquiries@dalby.co.uk

Seco Engineering Co. Ltd, 32 Reading Road South, Fleet, Hampshire, GU52 7QL Tel: (01252) 622333 Fax: (01252) 623888 E-mail: sales@secoeng.co.uk

INDUSTRIAL FINISHING SPRAY EQUIPMENT

ITW Automotive Finishing UK, Lockside, Anchor Brook Industrial Estate, Aldridge, Walsall, WS9 8EG Tel: (01922) 423700 Fax: (01922) 423705 E-mail: info@itwautofin.co.uk

Kestrel Equipment Ltd, 21-23, Scott Road, Luton, LU3 3BF Tel: (01582) 563600 Fax: (01582) 563323 E-mail: info@kestrelequipment.co.uk

Lechler Ltd, 1 Fell Street, Sheffield, S9 2TP Tel: 0114-249 2020 Fax: 0114-249 3600 E-mail: info@lechler.com

Spray Systems, Merlin Centre, Gatehouse Close, Gatehouse Industrial Area, Aylesbury, Buckinghamshire, HP19 8DP Tel: (01296) 393822 Fax: (01296) 399757 E-mail: spraysys@btconnect.com

INDUSTRIAL FIRE ALARMS

B B C Fire Protection Ltd, St Florian House, Ayton Road, Wymondham, Norfolk, NR18 0RD Tel: (01953) 857700 Fax: (01953) 857750 E-mail: sales@bbcfire.co.uk

B S A Bath, 91 Mount Road, Southdown, Bath, BA2 1LL Tel: (01225) 313088 Fax: (01225) 303341 E-mail: bsa.lg@btinternet.com

▶ Clymac Ltd, Unit 1 Cloudway Court, Belton Road, Loughborough, Leicestershire, LE11 1LW Tel: (01509) 232651 Fax: (01509) 232665 E-mail: sales@clymac.co.uk

Detection Supplies, 14 Fordingbridge Business Park, Ashford Road, Fordingbridge, Hampshire, SP6 1BD Tel: (01425) 658239 Fax: (0870) 2430305 E-mail: sales@detectionsupplies.co.uk

Hallmark Fire Ltd, Systems House, Stoke Road, Hoo, Rochester, Kent, ME3 9NT Tel: (08700) 111150 Fax: (08700) 111160 E-mail: sales@hallmarkfire.co.uk

INDUSTRIAL FIRST AID SUPPLY SERVICES

▶ Bell Stretchers, Unit 1B, Boundary Bank, Underbarrow Road, Kendal, Cumbria, LA9 5RR Tel: (01539) 732281 E-mail: info@bellstretchers.co.uk

INDUSTRIAL FIXING SYSTEMS, *See also Fastener etc*

B & C Fixings Ltd, Archimedes House, 20 Cleveland Trading Estate, Darlington, County Durham, DL1 2PB Tel: (01325) 286842 Fax: (01325) 352563

Bluebird Fixings Ltd, Westminster Industrial Estate, Station Road, North Hykeham, Lincoln, LN6 3QY Tel: (01522) 697776 Fax: (01522) 697771 E-mail: info@bluebird-fixings.ltd.uk

Firmafix Fastenings, Unit 3, Pioneer Park Clough Road, Hull, HU8 8BB Tel: (01482) 224334 Fax: (01482) 224341 E-mail: sales@firmafix.com

Fischer Group Of Companies, Whiteley Road, Hithercroft Industrial Estate, Wallingford, Oxfordshire, OX10 9AT Tel: (01491) 827919 Fax: (01491) 827953 E-mail: sales@fischer.co.uk

▶ Flat Roofing Supplies, Tinsley Lane North, Crawley, West Sussex, RH10 9FF Tel: (01293) 590970 Fax: (01293) 543562

G T C Fixings Ltd, 84 Witt Road, Fair Oak, Eastleigh, Hampshire, SO50 7FQ Tel: 0845 5261414 Fax: (0800) 1975000 E-mail: sales@gtc-direct.com

Tornado Fixings Ltd, Donisthorpe Street, Leeds, LS10 1PL Tel: 0113-242 4342 Fax: 0113-246 0272 E-mail: sales@tornado-fixings.co.uk

INDUSTRIAL FLOATS

J L Float Ltd, Westgate, Aldridge, Walsall, WS9 8UF Tel: (01922) 455677 Fax: (01922) 743193 E-mail: info@jlfloat.com

INDUSTRIAL FLOOR MATS

FloorFit LLP, 60 Windsor Avenue, London, SW19 2RR Tel: 0800 8818124 Fax: 0870 1217073 E-mail: floorfitsales@floorfit.co.uk

P H S Group Kleenair, Western Industrial Estate, Lon-Y-Llyn, Caerphilly, Mid Glamorgan, CF83 1XH Tel: (029) 2080 9111 Fax: (029) 2080 9091 E-mail: sales@phs.co.uk

INDUSTRIAL FLOOR PAINTING OR COATING CONTRACTORS

▶ Acuityflooring, 32 Henry Street, Rhostyllen, Wrexham, Clwyd, LL14 4DA Tel: (01978) 266302 Fax: (01978) 266302 E-mail: dianeandacuity@tiscali.co.uk

Anglo Building Products Ltd, Branksome House, Filmer Grove, Godalming, Surrey, GU7 3AB Tel: (01483) 427777 Fax: (01483) 428888 E-mail: sales@anglobuild.co.uk

▶ painting@decorating, 35 Phoenix Road, Chatham, Kent, ME5 8SY Tel: (01634) 306379 E-mail: keithnegus@blueyonder.co.uk

INDUSTRIAL FLOOR TILES

▶ Tile Express, Unit 2 Fordview Estate, New Road, Rainham, Essex, RM13 8ET Tel: (01708) 555592 Fax: (01708) 551902

INDUSTRIAL FLOORING

4m Flooring UK Ltd, House The Wharf, Thomas Street, Crewe, CW1 2BD Tel: (01270) 251244 Fax: (01270) 251344 E-mail: sales@4m-flooring.co.uk

▶ Acuityflooring, 32 Henry Street, Rhostyllen, Wrexham, Clwyd, LL14 4DA Tel: (01978) 266302 Fax: (01978) 266302 E-mail: dianeandacuity@tiscali.co.uk

▶ Fraser Bruce, Millhall, Stirling, FK7 7LT Tel: (01786) 448822 Fax: (01786) 451192 E-mail: info@fraser-bruce.com

▶ Jet Resin Flooring Ltd, 1 Defender Drive, Aylesby Park, Grimsby, South Humberside, DN37 9PS Tel: (01472) 310203 Fax: (01472) 310203

▶ Ryebrook Resins Ltd, Unit 4, Kelvin Bus Centre, Kelvin Way, Crawley, West Sussex, RH10 9SF Tel: (01293) 565500 Fax: (01293) 565472 E-mail: sales@ryebrook.co.uk

▶ Veitchi Scotland Ltd, 15 Bouverie Street, Rutherglen, Glasgow, G73 2RY Tel: 0141-647 0661 Fax: 0141-613 1575

INDUSTRIAL FLUOROELASTOMER PRODUCTS

J-Flex Rubber Products Ltd, Unit 1, London Road Business Park, Retford, Nottinghamshire, DN22 6HG Tel: (01777) 712400 Fax: (01777) 712409 E-mail: john@j-flex.co.uk

INDUSTRIAL FURNACES

A E S Industries Ltd, Unit 3 Appleby Glade Industrial Estate, Ryder Close, Swadlincote, Derbyshire, DE11 9EU Tel: (01283) 210033 Fax: (01283) 229330

Comco Combustion & Equipment Ltd, Building 50 Third Avenue, Pensnett Trading Estate, Kingswinford, West Midlands, DY6 7XD Tel: (01384) 297788 Fax: (01384) 297789 E-mail: comcoice@globalnet.co.uk

Corby Kilns Ltd, Corby, Northamptonshire, NN17 5WA Tel: (01536) 269229 Fax: (01536) 269229 E-mail: info@corbykilns.co.uk

Furnace & Oven Technologies, PO Box 10114, Redditch, Worcestershire, B97 6WD Tel: (01527) 595971 Fax: (01527) 596043

Hendrick Industrial Equipment Ltd, Unit 32d The Washford Industrial Estate, Heming Road, Redditch, Worcestershire, B98 0DH Tel: (01527) 523712 Fax: (01527) 514545 E-mail: heat@hendrick.co.uk

L T M Furnaces Ltd, 21 Fenlow Avenue, Stoke-on-Trent, ST2 9NE Tel: (01782) 501441 Fax: (01782) 598676

Mechatherm International Ltd, Hampshire House, High Street, Kingswinford, West Midlands, DY6 8AW Tel: (01384) 279132 Fax: (01384) 291211 E-mail: milcom@mechatherm.co.uk

Midland Elements Ltd, 58 Sutherland Road, Stoke-on-Trent, ST3 1HU Tel: (01782) 333377 Fax: (01782) 599940

Protherm Engineering Shenstone Ltd, Unit 33 Birchbrook Industrial Estate, Lynn Lane, Lichfield, Staffordshire, WS14 0DJ Tel: (01543) 481143 Fax: (01543) 480330 E-mail: prothermeng@aol.com

INDUSTRIAL FUSEGEAR

ABB Limited, East Kingsway, Dundee, DD4 7RP Tel: (01382) 454500 Fax: (01382) 457305

INDUSTRIAL GAS CONTROLS

Caledonian Control Technology Ltd, 2 Kelsey Close, Attleborough Fields Industrial Estate, Nuneaton, Warwickshire, CV11 6RS Tel: (024) 7634 2071 Fax: (024) 7635 1443 E-mail: info@caledonian-control.co.uk

Kromschroder UK Ltd, Unit 15a Frederick Road, Hoo Farm Industrial Estate, Kidderminster, Worcestershire, DY11 7RA Tel: (01562) 747756 Fax: (01562) 744129

▶ Peerless Gas Controls Ltd, Unit 11 Maple Business Park, Walter Street, Aston, Birmingham, B7 5ET Tel: 0121-327 6777 Fax: 0121-327 4555 E-mail: info@peerlesscontrols.com

INDUSTRIAL GAS MIXTURES

Air Liquide Ltd, Johnsons Bridge Road, West Bromwich, West Midlands, B71 1LG Tel: 0121-500 1000 Fax: 0121-500 1111 E-mail: trevor.longley@uk.linde-gas.com

Daniel Pipework Services, Unit 44 Owen Road Industrial Estate, Willenhall, West Midlands, WV13 2PX Tel: 0121-526 5311 Fax: 0121-526 6900 E-mail: enquiries@danielpipework.co.uk

Linde Gas UK Ltd, Newfield Industrial Estate, High Street, Stoke-on-Trent, ST6 5PD Tel: (01782) 822058 Fax: (01782) 822350

▶ Scientific & Technical Gases Ltd, 1 Speedwell Road, Parkhouse Industrial Estate East, Newcastle, Staffordshire, ST5 7RG Tel: (01782) 564906 Fax: (01782) 564906 E-mail: info@stgas.eu

INDUSTRIAL GAS PIPEWORK INSTALLATION

▶ Process Installations Ltd, Riverside Industrial Estate, Bridge Road, Littlehampton, West Sussex, BN17 5DF Tel: (01903) 730900 Fax: (01903) 730234 E-mail: peterb@pumpeng.co.uk

INDUSTRIAL GASES

Air Liquide Ltd, Johnsons Bridge Road, West Bromwich, West Midlands, B71 1LG Tel: 0121-500 1000 Fax: 0121-500 1111 E-mail: trevor.longley@uk.linde-gas.com

Air Liquide UK Ltd, Cedar House, 39 London Road, Reigate, Surrey, RH2 9QE Tel: (01737) 241133 Fax: (01737) 241842 E-mail: genenq.aluk@airliquide.com

Air Products plc, Enterprise Drive, Westhill Industrial Estate, Westhill, Aberdeenshire, AB32 6TQ Tel: (0845) 6015163 Fax: (01224) 749065

▶ Air Products (B R) Ltd, Hersham Place, Molesey Road, Walton-on-Thames, Surrey, KT12 4RZ Tel: (0800) 3890202 Fax: (01932) 249565

B O C Group P.L.C., Chertsey Road, Windlesham, Surrey, GU20 6HJ Tel: (01276) 477222 Fax: (01276) 471333

▶ Boc Gases Ltd, Chapelknowe Road, Motherwell, Lanarkshire, ML1 5LF Tel: (01698) 860721 Fax: (01698) 861870

Comainwells Ltd, Harfreys Road, Great Yarmouth, Norfolk, NR31 0LS Tel: (01493) 656444 Fax: (01493) 656444 E-mail: comwell@hotmail.co.uk

Cotswold Industrial & Welding Supplies, B Staverton Connection, Gloucester Road, Staverton, Cheltenham, Gloucestershire, GL51 0TF Tel: (01452) 855507 Fax: (01452) 859006

Daniel Pipework Services, Unit 44 Owen Road Industrial Estate, Willenhall, West Midlands, WV13 2PX Tel: 0121-526 5311 Fax: 0121-526 6900 E-mail: enquiries@danielpipework.co.uk

Energas Ltd, Westmorland Street, Hull, HU2 0HX Tel: (01482) 329333 Fax: (01482) 212335 E-mail: sales@energas.co.uk

▶ Enviroquest U K Ltd, Derwent Business Centre, Clarke Street, Derby, DE1 2BU Tel: (01332) 362492 Fax: (01332) 345477

Foster Industrial, Church Street, Lenton, Lenton, Nottingham, NG7 2FH Tel: 0115-970 0598 Fax: 0115-942 3388 E-mail: richard@fosterindustrial.co.uk

Gaffney Gas Welding Supplies Ltd, 32-33 Brewsdale Road, Middlesbrough, Cleveland, TS3 6LJ Tel: (01642) 223466 Fax: (01642) 230224

▶ Microshield Solutions Ltd, 1-1a Greenhill Avenue, Giffnock, Glasgow, G46 6QX Tel: 0141-639 1734 Fax: 0141-616 0503

North West Gases Ltd, Alma Street, St. Helens, Merseyside, WA9 3AR Tel: (01744) 753634 Fax: (01744) 24264 E-mail: sales@northwestgases.com

Porthmadog Skip Hire, Penamser Industrial Estate, Porthmadog, Gwynedd, LL49 9NZ Tel: (07979) 506624 Fax: (01766) 515217 E-mail: welshskips@supanet.com

▶ Quality Welding Equipment Ltd, Unit C11 Rosehill Industrial Estate, Rosehill Road, Stoke Heath, Market Drayton, Shropshire, TF9 2JU Tel: (01630) 638905 Fax: (01630) 638605 E-mail: sales@qweltd.com

Rimco Services, 20 Orchard Road, Malton, North Yorkshire, YO17 7BH Tel: (01653) 600707 Fax: (01653) 600707 E-mail: sales@rimco.co.uk

Thomas Silvey Ltd, 111-119 Newfoundland Road, Bristol, BS2 9LU Tel: 0117-954 8900 Fax: 0117-955 1436 E-mail: sales@silvey.co.uk

SWALEC, Ty Meridian, Malthouse Avenue, Cardiff Gate Business Park, Cardiff, CF23 8AU Tel: (0800) 7834121 Fax: (01920) 249760 E-mail: ian.mason@scottish-7.co.uk

INDUSTRIAL GASES – *continued*

Widget World, Unit F9 Blackpole Trading Estate East, Blackpole Road, Worcester, WR3 8SG Tel: (01905) 754520 Fax: (01905) 759488 E-mail: gas@widgetworld.freeserve.co.uk

INDUSTRIAL GATES

A6 Gates, Unit 1, Causeway Mill Longcauseway, Farnworth, Bolton, BL4 9BQ Tel: 01204 701690 Fax: 01204 701690
B P T Automation Ltd, Unit 16 Sovereign Park, Cleveland Way, Hemel Hempstead, Hertfordshire, HP2 7DA Tel: (01442) 235355 Fax: (01442) 244729
E J Collins & Son, 57 Addington Village Road, Croydon, CR0 5AS Tel: (01689) 843059
Eagledale Gate Mnfrs, Unit H Cavans Way, Binley Industrial Estate, Coventry, CV3 2SF Tel: (024) 7663 6064 Fax: (024) 7645 5378
Easeserve Ltd, 3 The Mill, Durham Street, Droylsden, Manchester, M43 6DT Tel: 0161-370 9580 Fax: 0161-370 6746
L M P Market Supplies, 4 Marine Industrial Estate, Marine Street, Cwm, Ebbw Vale, Gwent, NP23 7TB Tel: (01495) 370052 Fax: (01495) 370052
Tarporley Gates, Moorcroft, Clotton, Tarporley, Cheshire, CW6 0EG Tel: (01829) 781444
Welding Engineers (Mersey) Ltd, Units 2-4 Navigation Trading Estate, Bower Street, Newton Heath, Manchester, M40 2AR Tel: 0161-205 2797 Fax: 0161-205 4032 E-mail: enquiries@liftgates.co.uk

INDUSTRIAL GEARS

Sumitomo Drive Technologies SM Cyclo (UK) Ltd, Unit 29, Bergen Way, Hull, HU7 0YQ Tel: (01482) 790340 Fax: (01482) 790321 E-mail: marketing@sumitomoeurope.com

INDUSTRIAL GENERAL PURPOSE SOAPS

Allens (Disinfectants) Ltd, 462 Cleveland St, Birkenhead, Merseyside, CH41 8EQ Tel: 0151-652 4877 Fax: 0151-652 3800
William Clements (Chemicals) Ltd, 38a Witham Street, Belfast, BT4 1HP Tel: (028) 9073 8395 Fax: (028) 9045 0532
Kays Ramsbottom Ltd, Britannia Works, Kenyon Street, Ramsbottom, Bury, Lancashire, BL0 0AE Tel: (01706) 824010 Fax: (01706) 828615 E-mail: sales@kays-soap.com
Lever Faberge, PO Box 69, Wirral, Merseyside, CH62 4ZD Tel: 0151-641 4000 Fax: 0151-641 4029
P Z Cussons International Ltd, Cussons House, Bird Hall Lane, Stockport, Cheshire, SK3 0XN Tel: 0161-491 8000 Fax: 0161-491 8191
Soapworks Ltd, Coltness Street, Glasgow, G33 4JD Tel: 0141-774 2282 Fax: 0141-774 9273

INDUSTRIAL GLASS BALLS

House Of Marbles Ltd, Pottery Road, Bovey Tracey, Newton Abbot, Devon, TQ13 9DS Tel: (01626) 835358 Fax: (01626) 835315 E-mail: sales@houseofmarbles.com

INDUSTRIAL GLASSWARE

Piper Toughened Glass Ltd, 29-43 Sydney Road, Watford, WD18 7PZ Tel: (01923) 224047 Fax: (01923) 222741 E-mail: sales@piperglass.co.uk
▶ Schott UK Ltd, Drummond Road, Stafford, ST16 3EL Tel: (01785) 223166 Fax: (01785) 223522 E-mail: info.uk@schott.com
Select Windows, Select House, Walsall Road, Walsall Wood, Walsall, WS9 9AQ Tel: (01543) 370666 Fax: (01543) 370270 E-mail: sales@selectwindows.co.uk

INDUSTRIAL GLOVES

C A C Industrial Products Ltd, Thornton Industrial Trading Estate, Milford Haven, Dyfed, SA73 2RU Tel: (01646) 692626 Fax: (01646) 690144 E-mail: sales@cac-industrial.co.uk
Collard Industrial Gloves Ltd, Portskewett Street, Newport, Gwent, NP19 0GJ Tel: (01633) 213471 Fax: (01633) 257696
F J Bamkin & Son Ltd, Unit 3 Washdyke Lane Workshops, Washdyke Lane, Hucknall, Nottingham, NG15 6NH Tel: 0115-963 2020 Fax: 0115-968 0013 E-mail: info@penninebamkin.co.uk
Jayco Welding Supplies, 10 Old Bridge Close, Bursledon, Southampton, SO31 8AX Tel: (023) 8040 2025 Fax: (023) 8040 5812 E-mail: gloves@jaycowelding.freeserve.co.uk
John Liscombe Ltd, Mariner Way, Felnex Industrial Estate, Newport, Gwent, NP19 4PQ Tel: (01633) 284100 Fax: (01633) 284125 E-mail: sales@liscombe.co.uk
Main Man Supplies, Station Approach, Adisham, Canterbury, Kent, CT3 3JE Tel: (01304) 842030 Fax: (01304) 841312 E-mail: mnshydra@hotmail.com
Marigold Industrial Ltd, B2 Vantage Park, Old Gloucester Road, Hambrook, Bristol, BS16 1GW Tel: (01454) 323633 Fax: (0845) 0753356 E-mail: sales@marigold-industrial.com
Medisavers Ltd, Southgate Way, Orton, Peterborough, PE2 6YQ Tel: (01733) 361414 Fax: (01733) 230030 E-mail: sales@medisavers.co.uk
North Safety Products, The Courtyard, Green Lane, Heywood, Lancashire, OL10 2EX Tel: (01706) 693800 Fax: (01706) 693801 E-mail: info@northsafety.co.uk
Protec Manchester Ltd, 2 Rainard Street, Hyde, Cheshire, SK14 2HW Tel: (0870) 3333081 Fax: (0870) 3333061 E-mail: sales@protecdirect.co.uk
R Glover Ascroft Ltd, Ace Works, 157 Ordnance Road, Enfield, Middlesex, EN3 6AW Tel: (01992) 717272 Fax: (01992) 714040 E-mail: enquiries@r-glover-ascroft.com
Semperit Industrial Products Ltd, Cottesbrooke Park, Heartlands Business Park, Daventry, Northamptonshire, NN11 8YL Tel: (01327) 313140 Fax: (01327) 313149 E-mail: paul.phillips@semperit.co.uk
Turton Safety Ltd, 1 Britannia Park, Trident Drive, Wednesbury, West Midlands, WS10 7XB Tel: 0121-567 4100 Fax: 0121-567 4141 E-mail: sales@turton.co.uk

INDUSTRIAL GREASE

Ironsides Lubricants Ltd, Shield Street, Stockport, Cheshire, SK3 0DS Tel: 0161-477 5858 Fax: 0161-480 6203 E-mail: sales@ironsideslubricants.co.uk
R S Clare & Co. Ltd, 8 Stanhope Street, Liverpool, L8 5RQ Tel: 0151-709 2902 Fax: 0151-709 0518 E-mail: sales@rsclare.com
Thames Lubricants Ltd, Garner Street, Stoke-on-Trent, ST4 7DE Tel: (01782) 844388 Fax: (01782) 848437 E-mail: sales@thameslubricants.co.uk

INDUSTRIAL HAND CLEANSERS

Delmex Cleaning Materials, Ghyll Industrial Estate, Heathfield, East Sussex, TN21 8AW Tel: (01435) 868520 Fax: (01435) 864838 E-mail: mikethompson@airvert.freeserve.co.uk
Go Jo Industries Europe Ltd, 15 Avant Business Centre, Bletchley, Milton Keynes, MK1 1DL Tel: (01908) 370757 Fax: (01908) 370797

INDUSTRIAL HAND KNIVES

Edward Turner & Son Ltd, The Limes, 14 Crowgate, South Anston, Sheffield, S25 5AL Tel: (01909) 550097 Fax: (01909) 560544
Martor Direct UK Ltd, Ahed House, Sandbeds Trading Estate, Ossett, West Yorkshire, WF5 9ND Tel: (01924) 281333 Fax: (01924) 281444 E-mail: dennis@martor-uk-demon.co.uk
Sheffield Shears Co. Ltd, 28 Trinity Street, Sheffield, S3 7AJ Tel: 0114-272 2644 Fax: 0114-272 2644
Stanley Acmetrack, Drake House, Beighton Rd. East, Sheffield, S19 6GJ Tel: 0114-251 0570 Fax: (08701) 654654

INDUSTRIAL HANDS FREE COMMUNICATION SYSTEMS

▶ Intak Ltd, Unit 41, Criftin Park, Oxton Road, Epperstone, Nottingham, NG14 6AT Tel: 0115-965 6598 Fax: 0115-956 6546 E-mail: info@intak.co.uk
Markham (Sheffield) Ltd, Marspal House, Lawn Road Industrial Estate, Carlton-In-Lindrick, Worksop, Nottinghamshire, S81 9LB Tel: (01909) 730861 Fax: (01909) 733584 E-mail: sales@markham-sheffield.co.uk
Plantronics Ltd, Interface Business Park, Binknoll Lane, Wootton Bassett, Swindon, SN4 8QQ Tel: (01793) 842200 Fax: (01793) 848853

INDUSTRIAL HEAT PUMPS

Scottish Electric (Services) Ltd, Locarno Works, Brown Street, Dundee, DD1 5EE Tel: (01382) 228071 Fax: (01382) 322898 E-mail: scot.elec.grp@btconnect.com
▶ Toshiba Carrier UK Ltd, United Technologies House, Guildford Road, Fetcham, Leatherhead, Surrey, KT22 9UT Tel: (01372) 220220 Fax: (01372) 220221
York International Ltd, Gardiners La South, Basildon, Essex, SS14 3HE Tel: (01268) 246000 Fax: (01268) 246001 E-mail: sales@york.co.uk

INDUSTRIAL HEATERS

GMF Equipment Ltd, 9A High Street, Kegworth, Derby, DE74 2DA Tel: (01509) 673656 Fax: (01509) 674729 E-mail: sales@gmfequipment.co.uk

INDUSTRIAL HEATING ELEMENTS

Buckley Elements Ltd, Galveston Grove, Fenton, Stoke-on-Trent, ST3 2JT Tel: (01782) 333071 Fax: (01782) 593485 E-mail: sales@buckleyelements.co.uk
Chromalox (U K) Ltd, Eltron House, 20-28 Whitehorse Road, Croydon, CR0 2JA Tel: (020) 8665 8900 Fax: (020) 8689 0571 E-mail: uksales@chromalox.com
Dankfern Ltd, 11 Tait Road, Croydon, CR0 2DP Tel: (020) 8683 2748 Fax: (020) 8665 6627
DBK Technitherm Ltd, 11 Llantrisant Business Park, Llantrisant, Pontyclun, Mid Glamorgan, CF72 8LF Tel: (01443) 237927 Fax: (01443) 237867 E-mail: info@dbktechnitherm.ltd.uk
Ductair Electrics Ltd, Unit 10c Castle Vale Industrial Estate, Maybrook Road, Castle Vale Industrial Estate, Sutton Coldfield, West Midlands, B76 1AL Tel: 0121-351 5742 Fax: 0121-313 1018
The Electric Elements Co., Tokenhouse Yard, Nottingham, NG1 2HH Tel: 0115-950 5253 Fax: 0115-958 8283
Electric Water Heating Co., 2 Horsecroft Place, Harlow, Essex, CM19 5BT Tel: (0845) 0553811 Fax: (0845) 0553822E-mail: sales@ewh.co.uk
Electrical Elements Hinckley Ltd, 1 Willow Park Industrial Estate, Upton Lane, Stoke Golding, Nuneaton, Warwickshire, CV13 6EU Tel: (01455) 213171 Fax: (01455) 213614 E-mail: enquiries@electricalelements.co.uk
Heater Bands Ltd, Bott Lane, Walsall, WS1 2JQ Tel: (01922) 636888 Fax: (01922) 722360 E-mail: brian@heaterbands.freeserve.co.uk
Holroyd Components Ltd, Shire Hill Industrial Estate, Saffron Walden, Essex, CB11 3AQ Tel: (01799) 523177 Fax: (01799) 513714 E-mail: sales@holroydcomponents.com
Kanthal Ltd, Ruthvenfield Road, Inveralmond Industrial Estate, Perth, PH1 3ED Tel: (01738) 493300 Fax: (01738) 493301 E-mail: info.ukperth@sandvik.com
LPC Holdings Ltd, Coundon Industrial Estate, Coundon, Bishop Auckland, County Durham, DL14 8NR Tel: (01388) 608270 Fax: (01388) 450048 E-mail: enquiries@lpcholdings.co.uk
M F Induction Heating, Martindale Trading Estate, Martindale, Cannock, Staffordshire, WS11 7XL Tel: (01543) 570642 Fax: (01543) 574460 E-mail: sales@mfinduction.com
Plas Heat, 33 Cramlington Road, Birmingham, B42 2EE Tel: 0121-357 5077 Fax: 0121-358 1377 E-mail: plasheat@yahoo.co.uk
Sheathed Heating Elements Holdings Ltd, Wardley Industrial Estate North, Worsley, Manchester, M28 2DP Tel: 0161-794 6122 Fax: 0161-794 8601 E-mail: sales@shealuk.free.com
T P Fay (Kirkby) Ltd, 1 Spinney Close, Kirkby, Liverpool, L33 7XZ Tel: 0151-546 6232 Fax: 0151-549 1477E-mail: sales@tpfay.co.uk
Thermaglow Ltd, North Market Road, Winterton-On-Sea, Great Yarmouth, Norfolk, NR29 4BH Tel: (01493) 393555 Fax: (01493) 393860 E-mail: sales@thermaglow.co.uk
ThermTec Ltd, Rectory Farm, Martham, Great Yarmouth, Norfolk, NR29 4RE Tel: 01493 748666

INDUSTRIAL HYGIENE SERVICES

▶ Casp Products Ltd, W.H.S. Building, Harcourt Road, Harrogate, North Yorkshire, HG1 5NL Tel: (01423) 525206 Fax: (01423) 536500 E-mail: sales@casp-products.com
Cleaning Supplies UK, Lovet House, Lovet Road, The Pinnacles, Harlow, Essex, CM19 5TB Tel: (01279) 459345 Fax: (01279) 772376 E-mail: websupport@cleaningsuppliesuk.com
Coleman Fumigation Services, Wester Glentore, Greengairs, Airdrie, Lanarkshire, ML6 7TU Tel: (01236) 830700 Fax: (01236) 830703
Metrovac Co., 1016 Harrow Road, Kensal Green, London, NW10 5NS Tel: (020) 8969 4522
P H S Group plc, Unit D Austin House, Austin Road, Ashford, Kent, TN23 6JR Tel: (01233) 623414 Fax: (01233) 645885 E-mail: wynnglenn@phs.co.uk
Rentokil, 4 Singer Road, East Kilbride, Glasgow, G75 0UL Tel: (01355) 239140 Fax: (01355) 264172
The Sunlight Service Group Ltd, Shap Road, Kendal, Cumbria, LA9 6DQ Tel: (01539) 723378 Fax: (01539) 740921 E-mail: kendal@sunlight.co.uk
Universal Towel Co. Ltd, 1 Spa Industrial Park, Longfield Road, Tunbridge Wells, Kent, TN2 3EN Tel: (01892) 518822 Fax: (01892) 518118 E-mail: info@u-t-c.co.uk

INDUSTRIAL ICE BANK COOLER SYSTEMS

Acorn Ice Cubes, 66A Waldeck Road, London, W4 3NU Tel: (020) 8994 9339

INDUSTRIAL ICE PRODUCTION MACHINES

Hutt Refrigeration, 11-13 Station Parade, Station Hill, Cookham, Maidenhead, Berkshire, SL6 9BR Tel: (01628) 530605 Fax: (01628) 530505
Ziegra Ice Machines UK Ltd, 2 Phoenix Court Hammond Avenue, Whitehill Industrial Estate, Stockport, Cheshire, SK4 1PQ Tel: 0161-429 0525 Fax: 0161-480 7927 E-mail: sales@ziegra.co.uk

INDUSTRIAL IGNITION SYSTEMS

Chamjtes Ltd, Mason Fold, Lea Lane, Lea Town, Preston, PR4 0RN Tel: (01772) 726975 Fax: (01772) 721277 E-mail: john@chamjets.com

INDUSTRIAL INCINERATORS

Facultatieve Technologies Ltd, Moor Road, Leeds, LS10 2DD Tel: 0113-276 8888 Fax: 0113-271 8188 E-mail: sales@facultatieve.com
Hirt Combustion Engineers Ltd, Woodford Green Works, Leslie Road, Woodford Park Industrial Estate, Winsford, Cheshire, CW7 2RB Tel: (01606) 861366 Fax: (01606) 861408 E-mail: sales@hirt.co.uk

INDUSTRIAL INFLATABLE PRODUCTS

Bee Tee Products, Cemetery Lane, Carlton, Wakefield, West Yorkshire, WF3 3QT Tel: 0113-282 4494 Fax: 0113-282 4706
C Y Inflatables Ltd, Units 3-3a Queniborough Industrial Estate, Melton Road, Queniborough, Leicester, LE7 3FP Tel: 0116-260 2506 E-mail: steve@inflatables.uk.com
Ferguson Polycom Ltd, Windsor Mill, Hollinwood, Oldham, OL8 3RA Tel: 0161-681 2206 Fax: 0161-947 1326 E-mail: info@fergusonpolycom.co.uk
Humber Fabrications (Hull) Ltd, 99 Wincolmlee, Hull, HU2 8AH Tel: (01482) 226100 Fax: (01482) 215884 E-mail: sales@rigid-inflatables.com

INDUSTRIAL INFORMATION SERVICES

Aberdeen City Libraries, Rosemount Viaduct, Aberdeen, AB25 1GW Tel: (01224) 634622 Fax: (01224) 636811 E-mail: bustech@-rec.aberdeen.net.uk
Barbour Index, Kingswood, Kings Ride, Ascot, Berkshire, SL5 8AD Tel: (01344) 884999 Fax: (01344) 899377 E-mail: reception@barbourindex.co.uk
Glass's Information Services Ltd, 1 Princes Road, Weybridge, Surrey, KT13 9TU Tel: (01932) 823823 Fax: (01932) 846564 E-mail: enquiries@glass.co.uk
Hawk Information, Glebe Farm House, Milton, Banbury, Oxfordshire, OX15 4HH Tel: (01295) 720251 Fax: (01295) 722207 E-mail: cjr@hawk-eye.demon.co.uk
I H S Global Insight, Wimbledon Bridge House, 1 Hartfield Road, London, SW19 3RU Tel: (020) 8544 7800 Fax: (020) 8544 7801 E-mail: receptionist.london@globalinsight.com
I H S Technical Indexes Ltd, Viewpoint One, Willoughby Road, Bracknell, Berkshire, RG12 8FB Tel: (01344) 426311 Fax: (01344) 328004 E-mail: info@ihs.com
Infield Systems Ltd, 15 London Fruit Exchange, Brushfield Street, London, E1 6HB Tel: (020) 7426 9660 Fax: (020) 7247 5035 E-mail: data@infield.com
The Institution Of Engineering & Technology Benevolent Fund, Michael Faraday House, Stevenage, Hertfordshire, SG1 2AY Tel: (01438) 313311 Fax: (01438) 313465 E-mail: postmaster@theiat.org
Jane's Information Group, 163 Brighton Road, Coulsdon, Surrey, CR5 2YH Tel: (020) 8700 3700 Fax: (020) 8763 1005 E-mail: info@janes.com
Reed Business Information, Windsor Court, East Grinstead Ho, Wood St, East Grinstead, West Sussex, RH19 1XA Tel: (01342) 326972 Fax: (01342) 335612 E-mail: information@reedinfo.co.uk
Reed Business Information Ltd, Quadrant House, The Quadrant, Sutton, Surrey, SM2 5AS Tel: (020) 8652 3500 E-mail: webmaster@rbi.co.uk

INDUSTRIAL INSPECTION SERVICES

Trac International Ltd, Unit 12 Kirkhill Industrial Estate, Howe Moss Drive, Dyce, Aberdeen, AB21 0GL Tel: (01224) 725800 Fax: (01224) 725801 E-mail: info@tracinternational.com

INDUSTRIAL INSTRUMENT HIRE

Acksen Ltd, 42 University Road, Belfast, BT7 1NJ Tel: (028) 9020 1050 Fax: (028) 9020 1060 E-mail: sales@acksen.com
Aughton Automation Ltd, 66 Brindley Road, Astmoor Industrial Estate, Runcorn, Cheshire, WA7 1PF Tel: (01928) 589606 Fax: (01928) 589601 E-mail: brian.duffy@aughtonuk.com

INDUSTRIAL INSTRUMENT INSTALLATION

Argee Instrument Co. Ltd, 14 Albert Road, Romford, RM1 2PL Tel: (01708) 747878 Fax: (01708) 733216
Bee Instruments Ltd, 46 Spindus Road, Speke Hall Industrial Estate, Liverpool, L24 1YA Tel: 0151-486 5775 Fax: 0151-448 1677
Engineering Service Co. Ltd, Albion Works, Bridgeman Street, Bolton, BL3 6BS Tel: (01204) 525647 Fax: (01204) 391705 E-mail: cad@eng-service.co.uk
Pitts Wilson Electrical Ltd, Cutler House, Wakefield Road, Bradford, West Yorkshire, BD4 7LU Tel: (01274) 771100 Fax: (01274) 771188 E-mail: enquiries@pwe-elec.com
Trevor James & Co., Worldwind House Ashmill Business Park, Ashford Road, Lenham, Maidstone, Kent, ME17 2GQ Tel: (01622) 859590 Fax: (01622) 859596 E-mail: sales@worldwind.co.uk
Whites Electronics Ltd, 35j Harbour Road, Inverness, IV1 1UA Tel: (01463) 223456 Fax: (01463) 224048 E-mail: sales@whelects.demon.co.uk

INDUSTRIAL INTERCOM SYSTEMS

▶ Intak Ltd, Unit 41, Criftin Park, Oxton Road, Epperstone, Nottingham, NG14 6AT Tel: 0115-965 6598 Fax: 0115-956 6546 E-mail: info@intak.co.uk
▶ No Cables Necessary, 3 Crown House, Andover Road, Ludgershall, Andover, Hants, SP11 9LZ Tel: (01264) 395426 Fax: (01264) 395426 E-mail: lee.patterson4@ntlworld.com
▶ Telecor UK, 21 Coopers Court, Newport Pagnell, Buckinghamshire, MK16 8JS Tel: (01908) 211782 Fax: (01908) 216946 E-mail: chris.jones@telecor.co.uk

INDUSTRIAL IRONING PRESSES

Danor Engineering Ltd, 465 Hornsey Road, London, N19 4DR Tel: (020) 7281 0182 Fax: (020) 7263 0154 E-mail: danor.uk@btinternet.com

INDUSTRIAL KILNS

Arterial Engineering Works Ltd, Morston Road, Blakeney, Holt, Norfolk, NR25 7BE Tel: (01263) 740444 Fax: (01263) 740444
Consultant Gas Engineers, Peel Road, West Pimbo, Skelmersdale, Lancashire, WN8 9PT Tel: (01695) 727441 Fax: (01695) 729466 E-mail: sales@cgekilns.co.uk
Kilns & Furnaces Ltd, 1 Cinderhill Industrial Estate, Weston Coyney Road, Stoke-on-Trent, ST3 5JU Tel: (01782) 344620 Fax: (01782) 344621 E-mail: sales@kilns.co.uk
Kilnstruct, Walley St, Stoke-on-Trent, ST6 2AH Tel: (01782) 833383 Fax: (01782) 833411
Stanton Kilns, Foley Works, King Street, Stoke-on-Trent, ST4 3DE Tel: (01782) 312316 Fax: (01782) 598978 E-mail: sales@stanton-kilns.co.uk

INDUSTRIAL LAMINATED PLASTIC PRODUCTS

G & D Joinery, 1 Chater Street, Belfast, BT4 1BL Tel: (028) 9045 1375 Fax: (028) 9073 8414
▶ Vulcascot Ltd, Gatwick Gate Industrial Estate, Lowfield Heath, Crawley, West Sussex, RH11 0TG Tel: (01293) 560130 Fax: (01293) 537743 E-mail: sales@vulcascot.co.uk

INDUSTRIAL LASER PRINTING EQUIPMENT

Rofin Sinar UK Ltd, York Way, Willerby, Hull, HU10 6HD Tel: (01482) 650088 Fax: (01482) 650022 E-mail: info@rofin-uk.com

INDUSTRIAL LAWN MOWERS

Bomford Turner Ltd, Station Road, Salford Priors, Evesham, Worcestershire, WR11 8SW Tel: (01789) 773383 Fax: (01789) 773238 E-mail: sales@bomford-turner.com
Honda UK Ltd, 470 London Road, Slough, SL3 8QY Tel: (01753) 590500 Fax: (01753) 590000
T H White Ltd, Sherston Works, Knockdown, Tetbury, Gloucestershire, GL8 8QY Tel: (01454) 238181 Fax: (01454) 238772

INDUSTRIAL LEATHER COMPONENTS

Aldersons (Northampton) Ltd, 4 William St, Northampton, NN1 3EW Tel: (01604) 639346 Fax: (01604) 638542 E-mail: aldersonsltd@aol.com
B C Whitmore Ltd, 146 Bridgeman Street, Walsall, WS2 9PG Tel: (01922) 646212 Fax: (01922) 627591
Checker Leather Ltd, The Station, Crosshouse Road, Kilmaurs, Kilmarnock, Ayrshire, KA3 2TU Tel: (01563) 541709 Fax: (01563) 537819 E-mail: sales@glenroyal.com
Cheshire Leathers UK Ltd, 3 Cobden Industrial Centre, Quakers Coppice, Crewe, CW1 6FA Tel: (01270) 251556 Fax: (01270) 251557 E-mail: cheshireleather@aol.com
Lichfield Side Saddle, Huckers Buildings, Long Acre Street, Walsall, WS2 8HP Tel: (01922) 646468 Fax: (01922) 628936
Oxford Leathercraft, Northfield Works Sharps Yard, Long Wittenham, Abingdon, Oxfordshire, OX14 4QW Tel: (01865) 407100 Fax: (01865) 417120
John Spurrier & Co. Ltd, 3 Turners Hill Road, Craven Arms Business Park, Craven Arms, Shropshire, SY7 8DZ Tel: (01588) 673332 Fax: (01588) 673333 E-mail: gspurrier@aol.com

INDUSTRIAL LIGHTWEIGHT GLOVES

Sudburys Gloves Ltd, Calvesford Road, Greenbank, Torrington, Devon, EX38 7DP Tel: (01805) 622006 Fax: (0870) 4100089 E-mail: sales@sudburys-gloves.co.uk

INDUSTRIAL LOAD CELLS

Davis Decade Ltd, 30 Spring Lane, Birmingham, B24 9BX Tel: 0121-377 6292 Fax: 0121-377 6645 E-mail: dmg@decade.co.uk
Direct Weigh, 14 Milldown Avenue, Goring, Reading, RG8 0AS Tel: (01491) 872042 Fax: (01491) 873782E-mail: sales@flintec.net
Electronic Weighing Services Ltd, Lytton Street, Stoke-On-Trent, ST4 2AG Tel: (01782) 416322 Fax: (01782) 413660 E-mail: sales@electronicweighing.co.uk

INDUSTRIAL LOCKS

▶ Access 24, 3 Stadhampton Road, Drayton St. Leonard, Wallingford, Oxfordshire, OX10 7AR Tel: (01865) 400928 E-mail: admin@access24.co.uk
Henry Squire & Sons Ltd, Unit 2 Hilton Cross Business Park, Cannock Road, Wolverhampton, WV10 7QZ Tel: (01902) 308050 E-mail: info@henry-squire.co.uk

INDUSTRIAL LUBRICANTS

Acrylube Technical Services, Clegg Street, Brierfield, Nelson, Lancashire, BB9 5JQ Tel: (01282) 698595 Fax: (01282) 611244 E-mail: sales@lubricantsuk.co.uk
Henry Morris 1958 Ltd, Old Town Dock, Newport, Gwent, NP20 2BW Tel: (01633) 265603 Fax: (01633) 253186
▶ J B Lubes & Tools, Hillborough Business Park, Sweechbridge Road, Herne Bay, Kent, CT6 6TE Tel: (0787) 6025560 Fax: (01227) 740475 E-mail: jblubes@yahoo.co.uk

INDUSTRIAL MACHINE GUARDS

Abaca Engineering, Unit 2, Jackson Road, Holbrooks, Coventry, CV6 4BT Tel: (024) 7666 7390 Fax: (024) 7668 2845 E-mail: sales@abacaengineering.co.uk
Boreflex Ltd, Unit 9 Gateway Court, Parkgate, Rotherham, South Yorkshire, S62 6LH Tel: (01709) 522333 Fax: (01709) 522663 E-mail: sales@boreflex.co.uk
Browse Engineering Services, 34b Cowleigh Road, Malvern, Worcestershire, WR14 1QD Tel: (01684) 567125 Fax: (01684) 568240 E-mail: sales@ibrowse2.com
C Aiano & Sons Ltd, 64-70 Chrisp Street, London, E14 6LR Tel: (020) 7987 1184 Fax: (020) 7538 2786 E-mail: caianoandson@aol.com
C H Barnett Ltd, 18 Tyseley Industrial Estate, Seeleys Road, Birmingham, B11 2LQ Tel: 0121-773 5222 Fax: 0121-773 7800 E-mail: sales@chbarnett.co.uk
Cambrake Ltd, Crescent Mill, Foundry Street, Todmorden, Lancashire, OL14 7NA Tel: (01706) 815711 Fax: (01706) 817967 E-mail: info@cambrake.co.uk
Centreline Machine Guards Ltd, 2 Old Forge Trading Estate, Dudley Road, Stourbridge, West Midlands, DY9 8EL Tel: (01384) 422751 Fax: (01384) 422824 E-mail: neil.centreline@btconnect.co.uk
Compliance Modules Ltd, Platts La Industrial Estate, Burscough, Ormskirk, Lancashire, L40 7TP Tel: (0791) 7407559 Fax: (01704) 891501 E-mail: sales@compliancemodules.co.uk
Crossfield Excalibur Ltd, Unit 21 Woolfold Trading Estate, Mitchell Street, Bury, Lancashire, BL8 1SF Tel: 0161-763 4377 Fax: 0161-763 4926 E-mail: enquiry@excalibur-rm.co.uk
Crossley Charles & Son Ltd, 9-11 Astley Street, Stockport, Cheshire, SK4 1AW Tel: 0161-480 2858 Fax: 0161-429 7353 E-mail: mail@charlescrossley.com
Don Valley Engineering Co. Ltd, Sandall Stones Road, Kirk Sandall Industrial Estate, Doncaster, South Yorkshire, DN3 1QR Tel: (01302) 881188 E-mail: info@donvalleyeng.com
East Anglian Wire Works, Wright Road, Ipswich, IP3 9RN Tel: (01473) 270820
Elstone Engineering Co., Earlsway, Teesside Industrial Estate, Stockton-on-Tees, Cleveland, TS17 9JU Tel: (01642) 769442 Fax: (01642) 763068
Essex Wirework Company Ltd, PO Box 1, Hockley, Essex, SS5 5LD Tel: (01702) 205022 Fax: (01702) 207678
Henton Guarding Ltd, Unit 14 Eversley Way, Thorpe Industrial Estate, Egham, Surrey, TW20 8RG Tel: (01784) 439255 Fax: (01784) 477860
Highwood Engineering Ltd, Parkfield Road, Birmingham, B8 3AZ Tel: 0121-327 9212 Fax: 0121-327 4329
Imagineering Plastic Fabrication, 21 Cater Road, Bristol, BS13 7TW Tel: 0117-978 4114 Fax: 0117-978 4114 E-mail: plasticfabrication@hotmail.com
Lall Engineering Ltd, 343 Bedworth Road, Longford, Coventry, CV6 6BN Tel: (024) 7636 4904 Fax: (024) 7636 2083
Leuze Mayser Electronic Ltd, Generation Business Park, Barford Road, St. Neots, Cambridgeshire, PE19 6YQ Tel: (01480) 408500 Fax: (01480) 403808 E-mail: mail@leuzemayser.co.uk
Marcol Fabrications Ltd, Unit 10 Southfield Road Trading Estate, Nailsea, Bristol, BS48 1JJ Tel: (01275) 810022 Fax: (01275) 810033 E-mail: sales@marcolplastics.co.uk
Mirlyn Ltd, 57 Coleridge Street, Hove, East Sussex, BN3 5AB Tel: (01273) 733404 Fax: (01273) 703330
Narvida Ltd, Taxi Way, Hillend Industrial Park, Hillend, Dunfermline, Fife, KY11 9JT Tel: (01383) 823417 Fax: (01383) 823148 E-mail: info@narvida.co.uk
Northern Machine Guard & Fabrications, Unit 14 Albert Mill, Albert Place, Lower Darwen, Darwen, Lancashire, BB3 0QE Tel: (01254) 662595 Fax: (01254) 662595
Oscar Engineering Ltd, Michaels Lane, West Yoke, Ash, Sevenoaks, Kent, TN15 7HT Tel: (01474) 873122 Fax: (01474) 879554 E-mail: mail@oscar-acoustics.co.uk
P C G Hydraulics Ltd, Dutton Road, Aldermans Green Industrial Estate, Coventry, CV2 2LE Tel: (024) 7661 8533 Fax: (024) 7661 5944 E-mail: sales@pcg-hydraulics.co.uk
Philton Fire & Security Ltd, 61 Lower Road, Harrow, Middlesex, HA2 0DE Tel: (020) 8864 7534 Fax: (020) 8864 8631
Plastic Fabrications Ltd, Unit 12 Newstead Industrial Park, Hazelford Way, Newstead Village, Nottingham, NG15 0DQ Tel: (01623) 720400 Fax: (01623) 720800 E-mail: fabrications@btconnect.com
Price Guarding Systems, Waterside Estate, Cradley Road, Dudley, West Midlands, DY2 9RG Tel: 0121-525 4973 Fax: (01384) 241039
Print Guard Ltd, Unit 2, Parsonage Street, Oldbury, West Midlands, B69 4PH Tel: 0121-552 5707 Fax: 0121-552 5506 E-mail: sales@printguard.co.uk
Reid Wire Ltd, 162 Glenpark Street, Glasgow, G31 1PG Tel: 0141-554 7081 Fax: 0141-556 4483 E-mail: sales@reidwire.com
Safety Engineers Ltd, 18 Dudley Wood Road, Dudley, West Midlands, DY2 0DB Tel: 01384 569024
Sheet Metal Services, Hill Street, Kidderminster, Worcestershire, DY11 6TD Tel: (01562) 824995 Fax: (01562) 743998 E-mail: sales@saferack-sheetmetalservices.com
Sheet Metals Sherwood Ltd, Dako House, Vernon Road, Nottingham, NG6 0AR Tel: 0115-978 4456 Fax: 0115-978 4456
Silvaflame Co. Ltd, Cannock, Staffordshire, WS11 0BX Tel: (01543) 431060 Fax: (01543) 509140 E-mail: silvaflame@cleervue.com
Tapeswitch Ltd, Unit 38 Drumhead Road, Chorley North Industrial Estate, Chorley, Lancashire, PR6 7BX Tel: (01257) 249777 Fax: (01257) 246600 E-mail: sales@tapeswitch.co.uk
Versaduct Sheet Metal Ltd, Edwin Avenue, Hoo Farm Industrial Estate, Kidderminster, Worcestershire, DY11 7RA Tel: (01562) 824913 Fax: (01562) 823809
Wireguard Ltd, Crabtree Manorway South, Belvedere, Kent, DA17 6AW Tel: (020) 8320 6181 Fax: (020) 8311 6435
Bernard J. Wood, 13-17 Hayes Lane, Stourbridge, West Midlands, DY9 8QJ Tel: (01384) 892775 Fax: (01384) 892662
Zedi Signs, Connaught House, 32 Connaught Street, Northampton, NN1 3BP Tel: (01604) 231525 Fax: (01604) 231527 E-mail: zedisigns@aol.com

INDUSTRIAL MAINTENANCE CHEMICALS

Apex Industrial Chemicals Ltd, Peterseat Drive, Altens Industrial Estate, Aberdeen, AB12 3HT Tel: (01224) 878420 Fax: (01224) 871195 E-mail: sales@apex-chemical.co.uk
Carona Reuter Industrial Ltd, Coppen Road, Selinas Lane, Dagenham, Essex, RM8 1HN Tel: (020) 8592 2576 Fax: (020) 8595 8024 E-mail: carona_reuter@hotmail.com
Chemical Corporation UK Ltd, Atlas House Unit 9, Bedwas House Business Centre, Bedwas, Caerphilly, Mid Glamorgan, CF83 8DU Tel: (029) 2088 0222 Fax: (029) 2088 0676 E-mail: sales@chemicalcorporation.co.uk
Chemsearch, Landchard House, Victoria Street, West Bromwich, West Midlands, B70 8ER Tel: 0121-525 1666 Fax: 0121-500 5386 E-mail: patrick.toye1@btinternet.com
F I S Chemicals Ltd, Chapel Croft, Bucksburn, Aberdeen, AB21 9TN Tel: (01224) 723796 Fax: (01224) 722807 E-mail: sales@fischem.co.uk
I M C C O Ltd, 1 Ashleigh Close, Barby, Rugby, Warwickshire, CV23 8UG Tel: (01788) 891866 Fax: (01788) 891953 E-mail: imcco_2000@yahoo.com
Lenrich Labs, 7 Shefton Rise, Northwood, Middlesex, HA6 3RE Tel: (01923) 826590 Fax: (01923) 841575 E-mail: bud@sheftonfreeserve.co.uk
Omnichem Ltd, Mill Street East, Dewsbury, West Yorkshire, WF12 9BQ Tel: (01924) 461341 Fax: (01924) 458995 E-mail: info@nickersons.co.uk
Saxton Manufacturing Ltd, Unit 1 Bruntingthorpe Industrial Estate, Upper Bruntingthorpe, Lutterworth, Leicestershire, LE17 5QZ Tel: 0116-247 8665
Specialised Chemicals Ltd, Spittlegate Level, Grantham, Lincolnshire, NG31 7UH Tel: (01476) 567615 Fax: (01476) 560837 E-mail: sales@specialisedchemicals.com

INDUSTRIAL MAINTENANCE OR REPAIR CONTRACTORS, *See also headings for particular types*

▶ Fletcher UK Ltd, PO Box 150, Houghton le Spring, Tyne & Wear, DH5 9DY Tel: 0191-526 9195 Fax: 0191-526 9195 E-mail: info@fletcheruklimited.com
▶ L K F Ltd, Unit 4 Technology Centre, White Oak Square, London Road, Swanley, Kent, BR8 7AG Tel: (01322) 614621
Vapour Safe Ltd, Rosscliffe Rd, Ellesmere Port, CH65 3AS Tel: 0151-356 3955

INDUSTRIAL MARKET RESEARCH

▶ B D S Marketing & Research Ltd, Lonsdale, Single Hill, Shoscombe, Bath, BA2 8LZ Tel: (01761) 433035 Fax: (01761) 434579 E-mail: julian.clapp@bdsmarketing.co.uk
▶ Marketwise Strategies Ltd, Adamson House, 65 Westgate Road, Newcastle upon Tyne, NE1 1SG Tel: 0191-261 4426 E-mail: info@marketwisestrategies.com

INDUSTRIAL MEDICAL CONTRACT SCREENING SERVICES

Aberdeen Medical Services, 6 Rubislaw Terrace, Aberdeen, AB10 1XE Tel: (01224) 625766 Fax: (01224) 646612

INDUSTRIAL MELTING EQUIPMENT

Controlled Equipment, 17 The Mead Business Centre, Mead Lane, Hertford, SG13 7BJ Tel: (01992) 584404 Fax: (01992) 500177 E-mail: sales@meltingtank.com

INDUSTRIAL METAL DETECTORS

Chudleigh Second Hand Shop, 30 Fore Street, Chudleigh, Newton Abbot, Devon, TQ13 0HX Tel: (01626) 853309
Constant Instruments, Unit 8 Minster Court, Courtwick Lane, Wick, Littlehampton, West Sussex, BN17 7RN Tel: (01903) 739333 Fax: (01903) 739222 E-mail: sales@constant-ceia.com
C-Scope International Ltd, Kingsnorth Technology Park, Wotton Road, Ashford, Kent, TN23 6LN Tel: (01233) 629181 Fax: (01233) 645897 E-mail: info@cscope.co.uk
DBM Electrical Supplies Ltd, Unit B6 Halesfield 8, Telford, Shropshire, TF7 4QN Tel: (01952) 588800 Fax: (01952) 588822 E-mail: DMASON@DBMELECTRICAL.CO.UK
Mettler Toledo Safeline Ltd, Montford Street, Salford, M50 2XD Tel: 0161-848 8636 Fax: 0161-848 8595

INDUSTRIAL METAL DETECTORS – *continued*

P C L Machinery, 5 Elan Court, Norris Way, Rushden, Northants, NN10 6BP Tel: (01933) 410707 Fax: (01933) 410807 E-mail: sales@pclmachinery.co.uk
Thermo Electron, 2a Swift Park, Old Leicester Road, Rugby, Warwickshire, CV21 1DZ Tel: (01788) 820300 Fax: (01788) 820419 E-mail: sales.wi.uk@dermofisher.com

INDUSTRIAL MONITORING AND CONTROL SOFTWARE

Ceres System Ltd, Unit 15 The Old Malthouse, Springfield Road, Grantham, Lincolnshire, NG31 7BG Tel: (01476) 563188 E-mail: sales@vertexplus.co.uk
Symdex Ltd, 3 Mill Lane, Broxbourne, Hertfordshire, EN10 7AZ Tel: 01992 451515 E-mail: info@symdex.co.uk

INDUSTRIAL NET FABRICS

Swisstulle UK plc, Pelham Road, Nottingham, NG5 1AP Tel: 0115-969 2500 Fax: 0115-969 3270 E-mail: sales@swisstulle.co.uk
William Arnold Tarpaulins Ltd, 30 Thames Road, Barking, Essex, IG11 0HZ Tel: (020) 8594 1500 Fax: (020) 8594 7773 E-mail: www.tarpaulins.co.uk

INDUSTRIAL NOISE CONTROL SERVICES, *See also Noise Control etc*

▶ Acousticabs Industrial Noise Control Ltd, Unit 52, Pocklington Industrial Estate, Pocklington, York, YO42 1NR Tel: (01759) 305266 Fax: (01759) 305268 E-mail: info@acousticabs.com
Keiss Contracts (UK) Ltd, 9-10 Cooper Drive, Braintree, Essex, CM7 2RF Tel: (01376) 326962 Fax: (01376) 322555 E-mail: keiss-contracts@btconnect.com

INDUSTRIAL NON SLIP FLOORING

▶ Hi-Tec Roofing, 4 Gallowhill Road, Paisley, Renfrewshire, PA3 4TF Tel: 0141-887 5775 Fax: 0141-887 5775 E-mail: sales@hi-tecroofing.co.uk

INDUSTRIAL OIL BURNERS

E O G B Energy Products Ltd, Howard Road, Eaton Socon, St. Neots, Cambridgeshire, PE19 8ET Tel: (01480) 477066 Fax: (01480) 477022 E-mail: sales@eogb.co.uk
Eurograde Plant Ltd, 3 Viscount Industrial Estate, Horton Road, Colnbrook, Slough, SL3 0DF Tel: (020) 8606 0420 Fax: (01753) 681452 E-mail: david@eurograde.com
▶ Kroll, 49 Azura Close, Woolsbridge Industrial Est/Three Legg, Three Legged Cross, Wimborne, Dorset, BH21 6SZ Tel: (01202) 822221 Fax: (01202) 822222 E-mail: sales@krolluk.com
Nu Way Ltd, PO Box 1, Droitwich, Worcestershire, WR9 8NA Tel: (01905) 794331 Fax: (01905) 794017 E-mail: info@nu-way.co.uk
Oil Equipment & Engineering Co. Ltd, Southgate Avenue, Mildenhall, Bury St. Edmunds, Suffolk, IP28 7AT Tel: (01638) 713586 Fax: (01638) 510762
Riello Ltd, Ermine Centre, Hurricane Close, Ermine Business Park, Huntingdon, Cambridgeshire, PE29 6WX Tel: (01480) 432144 Fax: (01480) 432191 E-mail: sales@rielloburners.co.uk
Viessmann Ltd, Hortonwood 30, Telford, Shropshire, TF1 7YP Tel: (01952) 675000 Fax: (01952) 675040 E-mail: info-uk@viessmann.com
Weishaupt UK Ltd, Stoke Gardens, Slough, SL1 3QD Tel: (01753) 512345 Fax: (01753) 512585 E-mail: sales@weishaupt.idps.co.uk
Whites Burners Ltd, 9 Ilfracombe Gardens, Whitley Bay, Tyne & Wear, NE26 3ND Tel: 0191-252 9933 Fax: 0191-252 9955

INDUSTRIAL OIL HEATING SYSTEMS, *See Oil Burner etc; also Oil Preheaters etc*

INDUSTRIAL OPTICAL LENSES

Image Optics Components, Harvey Road, Basildon, Essex, SS13 1ES Tel: (01268) 728477 Fax: (01268) 590445 E-mail: sales@image-optics.fsnet.co.uk

INDUSTRIAL OR COMMERCIAL BOILER SPARE PARTS

C M S Tools Ltd, Don Pedro Close, Normanton Industrial Estate, Normanton, West Yorkshire, WF6 1TD Tel: (01924) 895999 Fax: (01924) 896999 E-mail: info@cmstools.co.uk
Chanter Bio Med Ltd, 1 Hanworth Road, Low Moor, Bradford, West Yorkshire, BD12 0SG Tel: (01274) 414666 Fax: (01274) 414470 E-mail: info@chanterbiomed.co.uk
Parts Centre Ltd, Unit 1A, New Market Business Park, Newmarket, Suffolk, CB8 7ER Tel: (01638) 668341 Fax: (01638) 660014 E-mail: leighnarracott@wolseley.co.uk

INDUSTRIAL OR COMMERCIAL BOILERS

A E Griffin & Son, 10 North Street, Bere Regis, Wareham, Dorset, BH20 7LA Tel: (01929) 471253 Fax: (01929) 472208 E-mail: aegriffinandson@aol.com
Babcock Wanson UK Ltd, 7 Elstree Way, Borehamwood, Hertfordshire, WD6 1SA Tel: (020) 8953 7111 Fax: (020) 8207 5177 E-mail:
Boulter Boilers Ltd, Magnet House, Whitehouse Road, Ipswich, IP1 5JA Tel: (01473) 241555 Fax: (01473) 241321 E-mail: sales@boulter-buderus.com
Bradlee Boilers Ltd, 3 Stambermill Industrial Estate, Timmis Road, Stourbridge, West Midlands, DY9 7BJ Tel: (01384) 423859 Fax: (01384) 895435 E-mail: sales@bradleeboilers.com
Guillot-Ygnis Heating Ltd, 2 Fitzhamon Court, Featherstone Road, Wolverton Mill, Milton Keynes, MK12 6LB Tel: (01908) 227720 Fax: (01908) 227716 E-mail: smalcolm@groupe-atlantic.com
Hamworthy Heating Ltd, Fleets Corner, Poole, Dorset, BH17 0HH Tel: (01202) 662500 Fax: (01202) 662550 E-mail: sales@hamworthy-heating.com
Hartley & Sugden, Atlas Works, Gibbet Street, Halifax, West Yorkshire, HX1 4DB Tel: (01422) 355651 Fax: (01422) 359636
Hoval Ltd, North Gate, Newark, Nottinghamshire, NG24 1JN Tel: (01636) 672711 Fax: (01636) 673532 E-mail: boilersales@hoval.co.uk
Ideal Boilers Ltd, PO Box 103, Hull, HU5 4JN Tel: (01482) 492251 Fax: (01482) 448858 E-mail: enquires@idealboilers.com
J O B Export/Import Ltd, 15 Iberian Way, Camberley, Surrey, GU15 1LZ Tel: (01276) 21119 Fax: (01276) 62190
Lochinvar Ltd, 7 Lombard Way, Banbury, Oxfordshire, OX16 4TJ Tel: (01295) 269981 Fax: (01295) 271640 E-mail: sales@lochinvar.ltd.uk
Mikrofill Systems Ltd, West Court, Buntsford Park Road, Bromsgrove, Worcestershire, B60 3DX Tel: (01527) 574574 Fax: (01527) 575565 E-mail: info@mikrofill.com
Strebel Ltd, Unit 1f Albany Park, Camberley, Surrey, GU16 7PB Tel: (01276) 685422 Fax: (01276) 685405 E-mail: andy.parker@strebel.co.uk

INDUSTRIAL OR COMMERCIAL LIGHTING

A.L.D. Lighting, Unit 6E Southbourne Business Park, Courtlands Road, Eastbourne, East Sussex, BN22 8UY Tel: (01323) 729337 Fax: (01323) 732356 E-mail: sales@aldlighting.com
Accent Lighting Ltd, 3 Candidus Court, Werrington, Peterborough, PE4 5DB Tel: (01733) 574524 Fax: (01733) 574524 E-mail: sales@accent-lighting.co.uk
Advanced Lighting Technology Ltd, Admail 3614, Oxford, OX1 1XZ Tel: (01706) 713240 E-mail: sales@advancedlighting.co.uk
▶ Anglepoise Ltd, 6 Stratfield Park, Elettra Avenue, Waterlooville, Hampshire, PO7 7XN Tel: (023) 9225 0934 Fax: (023) 9225 0696 E-mail: sales@anglepoise.co.uk
Anglo American Electrical Co., 67 Bradley Lane, Bolton, BL2 6RA Tel: (01204) 527251 Fax: (01204) 527257 E-mail: angloamerican1@btconnect.com
Avon Lighting, Unit 23, Avondale Business Centre, Woodland Way, Bristol, BS15 1AW Tel: 0117-935 3678 Fax: 0117-935 3678 E-mail: sales@avonlighting.co.uk
B J B (UK) Ltd, 9 Ivory House, Plantation Wharf, York Road, London, SW11 3TN Tel: (020) 7924 1177 Fax: (020) 7924 5357 E-mail: bjbuk@bjb.com
Barrel Lighting Ltd, Southend Airport, Southend-on-Sea, SS2 6YF Tel: (01702) 530995 Fax: (01702) 531030 E-mail: sales@barrel-lighting.com
Bonus Accessories, Citadel Trading Park, Citadel Way, Hull, HU9 1TQ Tel: (01482) 580077 Fax: (01482) 588753 E-mail: bonusacc@aol.com
Bookham Technology Ltd, Brixham Road, Paignton, Devon, TQ4 7BE Tel: (01803) 662000 Fax: (01803) 559218
Bright Designs, Station Road, Mexborough, South Yorkshire, S64 9AQ Tel: (01709) 570838 Fax: (01709) 570838
Brilliant (UK) Ltd, Hanworth Trading Estate, Hampton Road West, Feltham, Middlesex, TW13 6DR Tel: (020) 8898 3131 Fax: (020) 8898 3232 E-mail: sales@brilliant-ag.com
C B Lighting Co., 56 Staplehill Road, Fishponds, Bristol, BS16 5BS Tel: 0117-907 4906 Fax: 0117-966 0311
C U Thosco Lighting Ltd, Charles House, Furlong, Ware, Hertfordshire, SG12 9TA Tel: (01920) 462272 Fax: (01920) 485915 E-mail: export@cuphosco.co.uk
Cascade Electrolite Ltd, Gorse Mill, Gorse Street, Chadderton, Oldham, OL9 9RJ Tel: 0161-628 6622 Fax: 0161-628 2831
Ceag Ltd, Zenith Park, Whaley Road, Barnsley, South Yorkshire, S75 1HT Tel: (01226) 206842 Fax: (01226) 731645 E-mail: sales@ceag.co.uk
Commercial Lighting Systems Ltd, Unit 16-17, Park Gate Business Centre, Chandlers Way, Park Gate, Southampton, SO31 1FQ Tel: (01489) 581002 Fax: (01489) 576262 E-mail: sales@commercial-lighting.co.uk
Concord Marlin Ltd, Avis Way, Newhaven, East Sussex, BN9 0ED Tel: (01273) 515811 Fax: (01273) 512688 E-mail: info@concordmarlin.com
Cooper Lighting & Security, Wheatley Hall Road, Doncaster, South Yorkshire, DN2 4NB Tel: (01302) 321541 Fax: (01302) 303220 E-mail: sales@cooper-ls.com
Covershield Lighting Consultants, 10 Heatons Bridge Road, Scarisbrick, Ormskirk, Lancashire, L40 8JG Tel: (01704) 841073 Fax: (01704) 841362 E-mail: sales@covershield.co.uk
Cryselco Lighting Ltd, 274 Ampthill Road, Bedford, MK42 9QJ Tel: (01234) 273355 Fax: (01234) 210867 E-mail: sales@cryselco.co.uk
Daray Lighting Ltd, Unit 6A, Commerce Way, Stanbridge Road, Leighton Buzzard, Bedfordshire, LU7 4RW Tel: (01525) 376766 Fax: (01525) 216519 E-mail: info@daray.com
Dextra Lighting Systems plc, 17 Brickfields Business Park, Gillingham, Dorset, SP8 4PX Tel: (01747) 826096 Fax: (01747) 858119 E-mail: sales@dextralighting.co.uk
Endon Group, Cross Green Industrial Park, Felnex Road, Leeds, LS9 0SS Tel: 0113-249 2755 Fax: 0113-248 4519 E-mail: sales@endon.co.uk
Fantastic Lighting Ltd, 4 Kennet Road, Dartford, DA1 4QN Tel: (01322) 558649 Fax: (01322) 521117 E-mail: sales@fantastic-lighting.co.uk
Fluorel Ltd, 312 Broadmead Road, Woodford Green, Essex, IG8 8PG Tel: (020) 8504 9691 Fax: (020) 8506 1792 E-mail: djones@fluorel.co.uk
Graylands Trading Co., 38 Sherwood Road, Winnersh, Wokingham, Berkshire, RG41 5NJ Tel: 0118-989 0002 Fax: 0118-989 0003 E-mail: graylands@supernet.com
H Tyson & Co. Ltd, Gibson House, Walpole St, Blackburn, BB1 1DB Tel: (01254) 266000 Fax: (01254) 266001 E-mail: info@tyson-lighting.co.uk
Hacel Lighting Ltd, Harcel House, Silverlink, Wallsend, Tyne & Wear, NE28 9ND Tel: 0191-280 9911 Fax: 0191-263 1144 E-mail: purchasing@hacel.co.uk
Hilclare Ltd, Unit 1 Bond Street Industrial Estate, Mancunian Way, Manchester, M12 6HW Tel: 0161-274 3626 Fax: 0161-274 3731 E-mail: sales@hilclare.com
Hodgson Lighting, 41 High Street, Hampton Hill, Hampton, Middlesex, TW12 1NB Tel: (020) 8941 3375 Fax: (020) 8979 5178 E-mail: johnatjhlight@tiscali.co.uk
Holophane (Europe) Ltd, Bond Avenue, Bletchley, Milton Keynes, MK1 1JG Tel: (01908) 649292 Fax: (01908) 367618 E-mail: info@holophane.co.uk
Horsell Electrics Ltd, 30 Hollingdean Road, Brighton, BN2 4AA Tel: (01273) 694124 Fax: (01273) 603361 E-mail: horsell@globalnet.co.uk
Hughes Light, Unit 11, Shell Corner Trading Estate, Long Lane, Halesowen, West Midlands, B62 9LD Tel: (0793) 9087548 E-mail: tim@hugheslight.co.uk
Illuma Lighting Ltd, 11a Sills Road, Castle Donington, Derby, DE74 2US Tel: (01332) 818200 Fax: (01332) 818222 E-mail: info@illuma.co.uk
J & G Coughtrie Ltd, Montrose Avenue, Hillington, Glasgow, G52 4LZ Tel: 0141-810 4516 Fax: 0141-882 0191 E-mail: sales@coughtree.com
John Trafford, Unit 16 Phoebe La Industrial Estate, Halifax, West Yorkshire, HX3 9EX Tel: (01422) 345575 Fax: (01422) 356300 E-mail: spintraff@aol.com
Just Lighting Ltd, 21 Kenyon Road, Brierfield, Nelson, Lancashire, BB9 5SP Tel: (01282) 698507 Fax: (01282) 695588
Kandela Lighting Ltd, 200 Nottingham Road, Spondon, Derby, DE21 7NP Tel: (01332) 662793 Fax: (01332) 663525 E-mail: barry.kandela@gmail.com
Keylighting Ltd, Northbrook Works, Alkincote Street, Keighley, West Yorkshire, BD21 5JT Tel: (01535) 616300 Fax: (01535) 616301 E-mail: sales@keylighting.co.uk
Kingfisher Lighting, Ratcher Way, Forest Town, Mansfield, Nottinghamshire, NG19 0FS Tel: (01623) 415900 Fax: (01623) 415910 E-mail: sales@kingfisher-lighting.co.uk
Knightsbridge Lighting Ltd, Unit 9 Station Road Industrial Estate, Attleborough, Norfolk, NR17 2NP Tel: (01953) 452323 Fax: (01953) 453037 E-mail: sales@lightingforall.com
L B Lighting Ltd, Unit 6E, Southbourne Business Park, Courtlands Road, Eastbourne, East Sussex, BN22 8UY Tel: (01323) 430047 Fax: (01323) 732356 E-mail: sales@lblighting.co.uk
Lamps & Lighting, Bridgewater Court, Network 65 Business Park, Hapton, Burnley, Lancashire, BB11 5ST Tel: (01282) 448666 Fax: (01282) 417705 E-mail: sales@lamps-lighting.co.uk
Lightique Ltd, 7 Bayton Way, Exhall, Coventry, CV7 9ER Tel: (024) 7636 5665 Fax: (024) 7636 5520 E-mail: lightique@btinternet.com
Littledown Products Ltd, 7a Wincombe Business Park, Shaftesbury, Dorset, SP7 9QJ Tel: (01747) 851177
Loblite International Ltd, 3rd Avenue, Team Valley Trading Estate, Gateshead, Tyne & Wear, NE11 0QQ Tel: 0191-487 8103 Fax: 0191-482 0270 E-mail: info@loblite.co.uk
Lumalite Ltd, Unit 2 Greenhill Industrial Estate, Mytholmroyd, Hebden Bridge, West Yorkshire, HX7 5QF Tel: (01422) 884879 Fax: (01422) 882366 E-mail: sales@lumalite.co.uk
Luminaire UK Ltd, 9-15 Henley Street, Birmingham, B11 1JB Tel: 0121-766 1490 Fax: 0121-766 1491 E-mail: sales@luminaireuk.com
Luminars Lighting Mnfrs, 68 Miskin Street, Cardiff, CF24 4AR Tel: (029) 2022 8878 Fax: (029) 2022 8878
Lumitron Ltd, Park House, 15-23 Greenhill Crescent, Watford Business Park, Watford, WD18 8PH Tel: (01923) 226222 Fax: (01923) 211300 E-mail: sales@lumitron.co.uk
Mccroft Lighting, 54a Woods Lane, Derby, DE22 3UD Tel: (01332) 299100 Fax: (01332) 200365
Metro Ltd, 13 Imperial Park, Rawreth Lane, Rayleigh, Essex, SS6 9RS Tel: (01268) 782084 Fax: (01268) 782653 E-mail: sales@metroltd.co.uk
O.E.M Louvres & Lighting, Browsholme Street, Keighley, West Yorkshire, BD21 5JZ Tel: (01535) 607025 Fax: 01535 663522
Parkersell Lighting & Electrical Services Ltd, Unit 24 Heads of The Valley Industrial Estate, Rhymney, Tredegar, Gwent, NP22 5RL Tel: (01685) 844678 Fax: (01685) 844504
Poselco Lighting, 1 Bristol Road, Greenford, Middlesex, UB6 8UW Tel: (020) 8813 0101 Fax: (020) 8813 0099 E-mail: sales@poselco.com
Profile Lighting Services Ltd, 7-8 Links Business Centre, Raynham Road, Bishop's Stortford, Hertfordshire, CM23 5NZ Tel: (01279) 757595 Fax: (01279) 755599 E-mail: mailbox@profile-lighting.co.uk
Projection Lighting Ltd, Fourth Aveune, The Village, Trafford Park, Manchester, M17 1DB Tel: 0161-872 6868 Fax: 0161-872 6869 E-mail: pll@projectionlighting.co.uk
Reggiani Ltd, 7-8 Warwick Road, Borehamwood, Hertfordshire, WD6 1US Tel: (020) 8953 0855 Fax: (020) 8236 3099 E-mail: reggiani@reggiani.net
Ring Group Ltd, Nina Works, Gelderd Road, Leeds, LS12 6NB Tel: 0113-276 7676 Fax: 0113-263 0475 E-mail: enquiries@ring.ltd.uk
Mike Smith Designs Ltd, Unit 10 Fordhouse Road Industrial Estate, Steel Drive, Wolverhampton, WV10 9XE Tel: (01902) 784400 Fax: (01902) 785980 E-mail: sales@mikesmithdesigns.com
Sondia Lighting Ltd, 45 Portland Place, Hull, HU2 8QP Tel: (01482) 223353 Fax: (01482) 225681 E-mail: sales@sondialighting.com
▶ K.J. Tait Engineers, 15 Woodside Terrace, Glasgow, G3 7XH Tel: 0141-332 9676 Fax: 0141-332 0995 E-mail: glasgow@kjtait.com
Tamlite Lighting, Pipers Road, Park Farm Industrial Estate, Redditch, Worcestershire, B98 0HU Tel: (01527) 517777 Fax: (01527) 517666 E-mail: jrallden@tamlite.co.uk
Telco Lighting Ltd, Unit C Paynetts Lane, Cranbrook Road, Goudhurst, Cranbrook, Kent, TN17 1DY Tel: (01580) 212229 Fax: (01580) 212038 E-mail: telcolight@aol.com
Thorlux Lighting P.L.C., Merse Road, North Moons Moat, Redditch, Worcestershire, B98 9HH Tel: (01527) 583200 Fax: (01527) 584177 E-mail: marketing@thorlux.co.uk
Thorn Lighting Ltd, Silver Screens, Elstree Way, Borehamwood, Hertfordshire, WD6 1FE Tel: (0870) 1610710 Fax: (020) 8732 9801
WRTL Exterior Lighting, 2 Waterside Park, Golds Hill Way, Tipton, West Midlands, DY4 0PU Tel: 0121-521 1234 Fax: 0121-521 1250 E-mail: sales@wrtl.co.uk
Zumtobel Staff Lighting Ltd, Unit 4, Argent Centre, Pump Lane, Hayes, Middlesex, UB3 3BL Tel: (020) 8589 1800 Fax: (020) 8756 4800 E-mail: enquiries@uk.zumtobelstaff.co.at

INDUSTRIAL OR COMMERCIAL LIGHTING CONTRACTORS

Buchanan & Curwen (Leatherhead) Ltd, Fairfield Works, Upper Fairfield Road, Leatherhead, Surrey, KT22 7HJ Tel: (01372) 373481 Fax: (01372) 377458 E-mail: buchanans@b-and-c.co.uk
Hocken Sound Contracts Ltd, 50 Sovereign Road, Kings Norton Business Centre, Birmingham, B30 3HN Tel: 0121-459 4242 Fax: 0121-433 5362 E-mail: sales@hockensound.co.uk

INDUSTRIAL OR COMMERCIAL LIGHTING CONTRACTORS – *continued*

Lamps & Tubes Illuminations Ltd, Unit 1, Springfield Road Industrial Estate, Chesham, Buckinghamshire, HP5 1PW Tel: (01494) 783541 Fax: (01494) 773972 E-mail: enquires@ltilluminations.co.uk
Parkersell Lighting, 4th Floor The Connect Centre, Kingstone Crescent, Portsmouth, PO2 8AD Tel: (023) 9262 3700 Fax: (023) 9262 3720 E-mail: enquiries@parkersell.com
Vary-Lite, 20-22 Fairway Drive, Greenford, Middlesex, UB6 8PW Tel: (020) 8575 6666 Fax: (020) 8575 0424 E-mail: info@vari-lite.eu.com
Whitecroft Lighting Ltd, Burlington Street, Ashton-under-Lyne, Lancashire, OL7 0AX Tel: (0870) 5087087 Fax: (0870) 5084210 E-mail: sales@lightshow.co.uk

INDUSTRIAL OR FIRE OR SECURITY FLASHING LAMP BEACONS

Delta Design, 1 Kings Park Industrial Estate, Primrose Hill, Kings Langley, Hertfordshire, WD4 8ST Tel: (01923) 269522 Fax: (01923) 260167 E-mail: sales@deltadesign.co.uk
Moflash Signalling, 18 Klaxon Tysley Industrial Estate, 751 Warwick Road, Tyseley, Birmingham, B11 2HA Tel: 0121-707 6681 Fax: 0121-707 8305 E-mail: uksales@moflash.co.uk

INDUSTRIAL OR MUNICIPAL SWEEPING MACHINES

Dulevo UK Ltd, Royds House Royds Mill, Leeds Road, Ossett, West Yorkshire, WF5 9YA Tel: (01924) 277026 Fax: (01924) 262074 E-mail: dulevo@dial.pipex.com
Grand Age Engineering Ltd, Elm Tree Farm, Kirby Misperton, Malton, North Yorkshire, YO17 6XT Tel: (01653) 668288 Fax: (01653) 668289 E-mail: sales@grandsweep.com
Gurney Reeve & Co. Ltd, Station Road, Spooner Row, Wymondham, Norfolk, NR18 9SR Tel: (01953) 603303 Fax: (01953) 601331 E-mail: sales@sweepersuton.co.uk
Industrial Cleaning Machines, Icm House, Showell Road, Wolverhampton, WV10 9LN Tel: (01902) 306039 Fax: (01902) 304774 E-mail: sales@industrialcleaningmachines.co.uk
Scarab Holdings Ltd, Pattenden Lane, Marden, Tonbridge, Kent, TN12 9QD Tel: (01622) 831006 Fax: (01622) 831417 E-mail: scarab@scarab-sales.com
Schmidt Holdings Ltd, Southgate Way, Orton Southgate, Peterborough, PE2 6GP Tel: (01733) 363300 Fax: (01733) 363333 E-mail: sales@schmidt.co.uk
Tennant UK Ltd, Gladstone Road, Northampton, NN5 7RX Tel: (01604) 583191 Fax: (01604) 751517 E-mail: europe@tennantco.com

INDUSTRIAL OR SAFETY RESPIRATORS

Alpha Solway Ltd, Queensberry Street, Annan, Dumfriesshire, DG12 5BL Tel: (01461) 202452 Fax: (01461) 205684 E-mail: sales@alphasolway.com
Arden Winch & Co. Ltd, 116 Station Road, Beeston, Nottingham, NG9 2AY Tel: 0115-925 8222 Fax: 0115-925 8444 E-mail: roger.graves@ardenwinch.co.uk
Chapman & Smith Ltd, Safir Works, South Street, East Hoathly, Lewes, East Sussex, BN8 6EW Tel: (01825) 840323 Fax: 01825 840827 E-mail: sales@chapman-smith.co.uk
M S A Britain Ltd, Shawhead Industrial Estate, Coatbridge, Lanarkshire, ML5 4TD Tel: (01236) 424966 Fax: (01236) 440881 E-mail: sales@msabritain.co.uk
Pari Medical Ltd, The Old Sorting Office, Rosemount Avenue, West Byfleet, Surrey, KT14 6LB Tel: (01932) 341122 Fax: (01932) 341134E-mail: parimedical@compuserve.com

INDUSTRIAL OVENS

Capital Design Services Ltd, Bridge Buildings, 11A Ladybridge Road, Cheadle Hulme, Cheadle, Cheshire, SK8 5LL Tel: 0161-486 9524 Fax: 0161-485 8605
Harry Dalby Engineering Incoporating Dalby Sheetmetal, Gloucester Crescent, Wigston, Leicestershire, LE18 4YQ Tel: 0116-291 6000 Fax: 0116-291 6001 E-mail: enquiries@dalby.co.uk
▶ I & T Projects & Installations Ltd, Unit 2, James W. Properties Business Park, Wood Street, Burton-On-Trent, Staffordshire, DE14 3AB Tel: (01283) 541702 Fax: (01283) 548954 E-mail: sales@iandtprojects.co.uk
J L S Redditch, Holberrow Green, Holberrow Green, Redditch, Worcestershire, B96 6JY Tel: (01386) 791513 Fax: 01386 791518 E-mail: sales@jlsovens.com
J Rostron Engineering Ltd, Lindred Road, Brierfield, Nelson, Lancashire, BB9 5SR Tel: (01282) 611110 Fax: (01282) 619961 E-mail: sales@rostron.co.uk
Leerco Engineering Ltd, Full Sutton Industrial Estate, Stamford Bridge, York, YO41 1HS Tel: (01759) 371128 Fax: (01759) 371034 E-mail: leercoeng@aol.com
LTG Mailaender (UK) Ltd, 55 Winter Hey Lane, Horwich, Bolton, BL6 7NT Tel: (01204) 668606 Fax: (01204) 668450 E-mail: sales@ltguk.co.uk
Maywick Ltd, Unit 7, Hawk Hill, Battlesbridge, Wickford, Essex, SS11 7RJ Tel: (01268) 573165 Fax: (01268) 573085 E-mail: sales.maywick@btconnect.com
Mechatherm International Ltd, Hampshire House, High Street, Kingswinford, West Midlands, DY6 8AW Tel: (01384) 279132 Fax: (01384) 291211 E-mail: milcom@mechatherm.co.uk

INDUSTRIAL OVERHEAD RADIANT GAS HEATING SYSTEMS

AmbiRad Ltd, Fens Pool Avenue, Brierley Hill, West Midlands, DY5 1QA Tel: (01384) 489700 Fax: (01384) 489707 E-mail: marketing@ambirad.co.uk
Dale Heating Services (U.K.) Ltd, Unit 2, Rookery Lane, Thurmaston, Leicester, LE4 8AU Tel: 0116-264 0055 Fax: 0116-269 7007

INDUSTRIAL PAINTS

3p Paint Co Stockport Ltd, Hallam Mill, Hallam Street, Stockport, Cheshire, SK2 6PT Tel: 0161-477 4202 Fax: 0161-477 4202 E-mail: 3ppaintcompany@tiscali.co.uk
▶ Aquatec Coatings Ltd, Rock Road, Rhosymedre, Wrexham, Clwyd, LL14 3YF Tel: (01978) 822881 Fax: (01978) 821169 E-mail: sales@aquatecpaint.co.uk
Bradite Ltd, Ogwen Valley Works, Bethesda, Bangor, Gwynedd, LL57 4YP Tel: (01248) 600315 Fax: (01248) 602782 E-mail: sales@bradite.co.uk
Breakwells Paints Ltd, 1 Harden Road, Walsall, WS3 1EL Tel: (01922) 400444 Fax: (01922) 400555 E-mail: sales@breakwellspaints.co.uk
Chemical Innovations Ltd, 217 Walton Summit Road, Walton Summit Centre, Bamber Bridge, Preston, PR5 8AQ Tel: (01772) 322888 Fax: (01772) 315853 E-mail: sales@polycil.co.uk
Dacrylate Ltd, Lime Street, Kirkby-In-Ashfield, Nottingham, NG17 8AL Tel: (01623) 753845 Fax: (01623) 757151 E-mail: sales@dacrylate.co.uk
E G Lewis & Co. Ltd, Tank Farm Road, Llandarcy, Neath, West Glamorgan, SA10 6EN Tel: (01792) 323288 Fax: (01792) 323255 E-mail: timl@eglewis.com
Elgood Industrial Flooring Ltd, Yeoman Street, London, SE8 5DU Tel: (020) 7237 1144 Fax: (020) 7237 1629 E-mail: nigel@elgood.com
Firwood Paints Ltd, Victoria Works, Oakenbottom Road, Bolton, BL2 6DP Tel: (01204) 525231 Fax: (01204) 362522 E-mail: sales@firwood.co.uk
Hempel UK Ltd, Ty Coch Way, Llantarnam Industrial Park, Cwmbran, Gwent, NP44 3XF Tel: (01633) 874024 Fax: (01633) 489089 E-mail: sales@hempel.com
▶ Howses Paint & Powder Ltd, Cakemore Road, Rowley Regis, West Midlands, B65 0RD Tel: 0121-559 1451 Fax: 0121-559 2722 E-mail: sales@howsepaints.co.uk
I S F Paints Ltd, Thurmaston BLVD, Leicester, LE4 9HS Tel: 0116-274 2222 Fax: 0116-274 3333
J & L Industrial Paint Services Ltd, Unit 21, Knightcott Industrial Estate, Banwell, Avon, BS29 6JN Tel: (01934) 820780 Fax: (01934) 820323 E-mail: jl.paints@virgin.net
Kromex Ltd, Shepherds Grove Industrial Estate, Stanton, Bury St. Edmunds, Suffolk, IP31 2AR Tel: (01359) 250565 Fax: (01359) 250561 E-mail: sales@kromex.co.uk
Lechler Coatings UK Ltd, Unit 42 Pochin Way, Middlewich, Cheshire, CW10 0GY Tel: (01606) 738600 Fax: (01606) 738517 E-mail: sales@lechler.it
Manor Coating Systems Ltd, Otley Road, Baildon, Shipley, West Yorkshire, BD17 7DP Tel: (01274) 587351 Fax: (01274) 531360 E-mail: info@manorcoatingsystems.co.uk
Meynell Paints Ltd, 400 Roding Lane South, Woodford Green, Essex, IG8 8EZ Tel: (020) 8550 9999 Fax: (020) 8551 8555 E-mail: gaye.brown@talk21.com
Neogene Paints Ltd, 14 Caxton Way, Watford, WD18 8UJ Tel: (01923) 213737 Fax: (01923) 213617 E-mail: sales@neogenepaints.co.uk
Polybond Ltd, Unit 6 William Street, Northam, Southampton, SO14 5QH Tel: (023) 8022 3266 Fax: (0870) 0527587 E-mail: tom@polybond.co.uk
PPG Aerospace, Darlington Road, Shildon, County Durham, DL4 2QP Tel: (01388) 772541 Fax: (01388) 774373
Practical Compounds Ltd, West Side, Tyne Dock, South Shields, Tyne & Wear, NE34 9PL Tel: 0191-456 9191 Fax: 0191-454 5523 E-mail: practical.comp@btinternet.com
Protega Coatings Ltd, Kelvin Way, West Bromwich, West Midlands, B70 7JZ Tel: 0121-525 5665 Fax: 0121-553 2787 E-mail: info@tikkurila.co.uk
R C Stiven & Co., Unit 31 Faraday Street, Dryburgh Industrial Estate, Dundee, DD2 3QQ Tel: (01382) 833322 Fax: (01382) 889133 E-mail: aws@rcstiven.sol.co.uk
Scarborough Laquers Co., Merry Lees, Staxton, Scarborough, North Yorkshire, YO12 4NN Tel: (01944) 710349 Fax: (01944) 710470 E-mail: sales@scarboroughlacquers.co.uk
Spencer Coatings Ltd, Froghall Terrace, Aberdeen, AB24 3JN Tel: (01224) 788400 Fax: (01224) 648116 E-mail: info@spencercoatings.co.uk
Talke Chemical Co. Ltd, Radnor Works, 1 Back Lane, Congleton, Cheshire, CW12 4PP Tel: (01260) 273357 Fax: (01260) 298175 E-mail: sales@talkechem.co.uk
Trimite Ltd, 38 Welbeck Road, Glasgow, G53 7RG Tel: 0141-881 9595 Fax: 0141-881 9333 E-mail: glasgow.sales@trimite.com
Weilburger Schramm Coatings UK Ltd, Stuart Road, Manor Park, Runcorn, Cheshire, WA7 1SF Tel: (01928) 570900 Fax: (01928) 579235
Witham Oil & Paint (Lowestoft) Ltd, Stanley Road, Oulton Broad, Lowestoft, Suffolk, NR33 9ND Tel: (01502) 563434 Fax: (01502) 500010 E-mail: kathy.rowlands@withamoil-lowestoft.co.uk

INDUSTRIAL PLASTIC BALLS

Atlas Ball & Bearing Co. Ltd, Leamore Lane, Walsall, WS2 7DE Tel: (01922) 710515 Fax: (01922) 710575 E-mail: sales@atlasball.co.uk
Euro Matic Ltd, Clauson House Perryvale Industrial Park, Horsenden Road South, Greenford, Middlesex, UB6 7QE Tel: (020) 8991 2211 Fax: (020) 8997 5074 E-mail: sales@euro-matic.com
Industrial Plastic Supplies Ltd, 3 Milestone Court, Stanningley, Pudsey, West Yorkshire, LS28 6HE Tel: 0113-257 2222 Fax: 0113-257 2222 E-mail: sales@industrialplastics.co.uk
Kookaburra Reader Ltd, Unit 25, The Alders, Seven Mile Lane, Mereworth, Maidstone, Kent, ME18 5JG Tel: (01622) 812230 Fax: (01622) 814224 E-mail: sales@alfredreader.co.uk

INDUSTRIAL PLUGS AND SOCKETS

A-Belco Property Ltd, Jubilee Industrial Estate, Ashington, Northumberland, NE63 8UG Tel: (01670) 813275 Fax: (01670) 851141 E-mail: sscullion@a-belco.co.uk
C E E Norm UK Ltd, Unit A1, Stafford Park 11, Telford, Shropshire, TF3 3AY Tel: (01952) 212700 Fax: (01952) 212711 E-mail: sales@ceenorm.co.uk
F Walther Electrics Ltd, Cromwell Road, Bredbury, Stockport, Cheshire, SK6 2RF Tel: 0161-494 1233 Fax: 0161-494 5055 E-mail: mail@walther.demon.co.uk
Lewden Electrical Industries, Argall Avenue, London, E10 7QD Tel: (020) 8539 0233 Fax: (020) 8558 2718 E-mail: alan.green@lewden.co.uk
Novar ED&S, The Arnold Centre, Paycocke Road, Basildon, Essex, SS14 3EA Tel: (01268) 563000 Fax: (01268) 563538 E-mail: mk_reception@nova.com

INDUSTRIAL PLUMBING CONTRACTORS

▶ Concept Environmental Services, Galton Court, Newton Road, Birmingham, B43 6BW Tel: (0800) 0192560 E-mail: draintester@hotmail.co.uk

INDUSTRIAL POLISH

Honey Well Comsumer Products Group, Oakhurst Drive, Cheadle Heath, Stockport, Cheshire, SK3 0RZ Tel: 0161-491 7391 Fax: 0161-491 7399 E-mail: info@holtsauto.com

INDUSTRIAL POLYURETHANE (PU) COMPONENTS

Abbey Products Norfolk Ltd, Ayton Road, Wymondham, Norfolk, NR18 0QH Tel: (01953) 602627 Fax: (01953) 601428 E-mail: info@abbey4pu.com
Cellular Mouldings Ltd, 2 Pytchley Lodge Industrial Estate, Pytchley Lodge Road, Kettering, Northamptonshire, NN15 6JQ Tel: (01536) 513452 Fax: (01536) 411206 E-mail: sales@cellularmouldings.co.uk
Chase Mouldings Ltd, 5 Swaffield Park, Hyssop Close, Cannock, Staffordshire, WS11 7FU Tel: (01543) 572425 Fax: (01543) 572451 E-mail: chase@chasemouldings.fsnet.co.uk
Clifton Rubber Co. Ltd, 5 Edison Road, St. Ives, Cambridgeshire, PE27 3FF Tel: (01480) 496161 Fax: (01480) 484700 E-mail: sales@cliftonrubber.co.uk
▶ Davies Bros, 5 Holborn Square, Birkenhead, Merseyside, CH41 9HQ Tel: 0151-647 3002 Fax: 0151-647 3002 E-mail: dvsbrn@aol.com
Hallam Polymer Engineering Ltd, Trasco House, Callywhite Lane, Dronfield, Derbyshire, S18 2XR Tel: (01246) 415511 Fax: (01246) 414818 E-mail: sales@hallampolymer.com
Kay Dee Engineering Plastics Ltd, 2 Jubilee Court, Thackley Old Road, Shipley, West Yorkshire, BD18 1QF Tel: (01274) 590824 Fax: (01274) 531409 E-mail: info@kaylan.co.uk
Rim Plastics Technology Ltd, 1 Wollaston Way, Burnt Mills Industrial Estate, Basildon, Essex, SS13 1DJ Tel: (01268) 729679 Fax: (01268) 729031 E-mail: sales@rimplas.co.uk
Rubberatkins Ltd, Hareness Road, Altens Industrial Estate, Aberdeen, AB12 3LE Tel: (01224) 248341 Fax: (01224) 248342 E-mail: sales@rubberatkins.com
Trelleborg Applied Technology, Halfpenny Lane, Knaresborough, North Yorkshire, HG5 0PP Tel: (01423) 862677 Fax: (01423) 868340 E-mail: sales@unitex.co.uk
Urethane Industrial Products Ltd, Evingar Industrial Estate, Ardglen Road, Whitchurch, Hampshire, RG28 7BB Tel: (01256) 892830 Fax: (01256) 896899 E-mail: urethaneindustrial@hotmail.com

INDUSTRIAL POTTERY

Brick House Ceramic Supplies Ltd, The Barn, Sheepcotes Lane, Silver End, Witham, Essex, CM8 3PJ Tel: (01376) 585655 Fax: (01376) 585656 E-mail: sales@brickhouseceramics.co.uk
Broadhurst Bros Burslem Ltd, Waterloo Road, Burslem, Stoke-on-Trent, ST6 2EL Tel: (01782) 834561 Fax: (01782) 832102
Denby Ltd, Denby, Ripley, Derbyshire, DE5 8NX Tel: (01773) 740700 Fax: (01773) 570211
Emma Bridgewater, 739 Fulham Road, London, SW6 5UL Tel: (020) 7371 5264 Fax: (020) 7384 2457
Errington Reay & Co. Ltd, Tyneside Pottery Works, Bardon Mill, Hexham, Northumberland, NE47 7HU Tel: (01434) 344245 Fax: (01434) 344041 E-mail: sales@erringtonreay.co.uk
Leach Pottery, Higher Stennack, St. Ives, Cornwall, TR26 2HE Tel: (01736) 799703
Portmeirion Enterprises Ltd, London Road, Stoke-on-Trent, ST4 7QQ Tel: (01782) 744721 Fax: (01782) 744061 E-mail: nhuxley@portmeirion.co.uk
Purbeck Pottery Ltd, 11 Allens Lane, Poole, Dorset, BH16 5DA Tel: (01202) 621162 Fax: (01202) 625129 E-mail: sales@purbeckpottery.com
R C Design Ceramics, Unit 3 Chelson Street, Stoke-on-Trent, ST3 1PT Tel: (01782) 334886 Fax: (01782) 334886

INDUSTRIAL POWER SUPPLIES

Arian Electronic Systems, 34A High St, Syston, Leicester, LE7 1GP Tel: 0116-260 7663 Fax: 0116-260 7663
B T L Powertec Ltd, 4 Station Yard, Old Furnace Road, Coniston, Cumbria, LA21 8HU Tel: (01539) 441904 Fax: (01539) 441907
D P Energy Services, Unit 5 & 6, Heron Avenue, Wickford, Essex, SS11 8DL Tel: (01268) 560040 Fax: (01268) 560261 E-mail: sales@drakepower.com
▶ Douglas Electronic Industries Ltd, 55 Eastfield Road, Louth, Lincolnshire, LN11 7AL Tel: (01507) 603643 Fax: (01507) 600502 E-mail: sales@douglas-transformers.co.uk
Graphic Controls, Southcombe House, Southcombe, Chipping Norton, Oxfordshire, OX7 5QH Tel: (01608) 646303 Fax: (01608) 646304 E-mail: rickfordham@btconnect.com
Lambda UK, Kingsley Avenue, Ilfracombe, Devon, EX34 8ES Tel: (01271) 856600 Fax: (01271) 864894 E-mail: powersolutions@lambda-europe.com
Poerlink Electronic Ltd, Powerlink House, Ivy Arch Road, Worthing, West Sussex, BN14 8BX Tel: (01903) 209550 Fax: (01903) 215526 E-mail: admin@powerlinkelectronics.co.uk
Stadium Power Ltd, 23-29 Owen Road, Vinces Road Industrial Estate, Diss, Norfolk, IP22 4YU Tel: (01379) 644233 Fax: (01379) 650118 E-mail: sales@stadiumpower.co.uk
Tamura Europe Ltd, Hopton Park, London Road, Devizes, Wiltshire, SN10 2EY Tel: (01380) 731700 Fax: (01380) 731703 E-mail: business@tamura-europe.co.uk

INDUSTRIAL POWER TOOL HIRE

Action Hire Centres, 90 Cotmandene Crescent, St Pauls Cray, Orpington, Kent, BR5 2RG Tel: (020) 8300 2359 Fax: (020) 8302 7422
Ashtead Plant Hire Co. Ltd, St Georges Road, Donnington, Telford, Shropshire, TF2 7RA Tel: (01952) 620320 Fax: (01952) 610708 E-mail: telford@aplant.com
Bells Tool Hire, Unit 337 Rushock Trading Estate, Rushock, Droitwich, Worcestershire, WR9 0NR Tel: (01299) 250578 Fax: (01299) 250578
▶ Blythewood Plant Hire Ltd, Fenland District Industrial Estate, Station Road, Whittlesey, Peterborough, PE7 2EY Tel: (01733) 203201 Fax: (01733) 350308 E-mail: enquiries@blythewood-plant.co.uk

▶ indicates data change since last edition

INDUSTRIAL POWER TOOL HIRE – *continued*

Chertsey Tool Hire Ltd, 149 Upper Weybourne Lane, Farnham, Surrey, GU9 9DD Tel: (01252) 333122 Fax: (01252) 333155 E-mail: farnhamsales@chertseytoolhire.co.uk

Croydon Tool Hire Ltd, 87a Whitehorse Road, Croydon, CR0 2JJ Tel: (020) 8684 1751 Fax: (020) 8684 1811

▶ G A P Group Ltd, 79 Salamander Street, Leith, Edinburgh, EH6 7JZ Tel: 0131-554 0503 Fax: 0131-554 0861 E-mail: leith@gap-group.co.uk

▶ H.S.S. Hire Shops P.L.C., Unit 5 Rippleside Commercial Estate, Ripple Road, Barking, Essex, IG11 0RJ Tel: (020) 8595 3666 Fax: (020) 8595 4666

▶ HSS Hire, 336 Battersea Park Road, London, SW11 3BY Tel: (020) 7223 0025 Fax: (020) 7223 0035

▶ HSS Hire, 865 Fulham Road, London, SW6 5HP Tel: (020) 7736 1769 Fax: (020) 7736 3127

KSS Hire Services, Russell Gardens, Wickford, Essex, SS11 8BH Tel: (01268) 769531 Fax: (01268) 561034

Lord Hire Centre, Shields Road, Newcastle upon Tyne, NE6 2UD Tel: 0191-224 0044 E-mail: lord@lordhire.co.uk

M F Hire Ltd, 2 Highmeres Road, Leicester, LE4 9LZ Tel: 0116-276 3807 Fax: 0116-246 0198 E-mail: enquiries@mfhgroup.co.uk

M T S Power Tools, 97 St James Mill Road, Northampton, NN5 5JP Tel: (01604) 751688 Fax: (01604) 759041E-mail: sales@mts.co.uk

Multequip Power Tools, 61 Willow Road, Bedford, MK42 0QU Tel: (01234) 340461 Fax: (01234) 340461

Newbury Tools Ltd, 1 Hambridge Road, Newbury, Berkshire, RG14 5SS Tel: (01635) 30804 Fax: (01635) 529068 E-mail: sales@newburytools.com

Nortool Services Ltd, 573 Stanningley Road, Leeds, LS13 4EL Tel: 0113-257 9333 Fax: 0113-257 9222 E-mail: sales@nortool.com

P.E.T. Hire Centre Ltd, 68-70 Earle Street, Crewe, CW1 2AT Tel: (01270) 582222 Fax: (01270) 505938

Power Tool Rentals Ltd, Halifax Road, Hipperholme, Halifax, West Yorkshire, HX3 8ER Tel: (01422) 205616 Fax: (01422) 206282 E-mail: enquiries@powertoolrentals.co.uk

Power X Hire Ltd, 113 Penarth Road, Cardiff, CF11 6JT Tel: (029) 2066 5454

Rochdale Power Tools & Equipment, Unit 1 Primrose Street, Rochdale, Lancashire, OL12 6AW Tel: (01706) 642466 Fax: (01706) 860022

Telford Group Ltd, Enterprise House, Stafford Park 1, Telford, Shropshire, TF3 3BD Tel: (01952) 290800 Fax: (01952) 291303 E-mail: info@telfordgroup.co.uk

Toga Plant Hire Ltd, 67-71 Kingsland Road, London, E2 8AG Tel: (020) 7729 1471 Fax: (020) 7729 1592

Universal Access & Power Plants Ltd, 14 Pony Road, Cowley, Oxford, OX4 2RD Tel: (01865) 450000 Fax: (01865) 451111 E-mail: sales@universalhire.co.uk

V H S Hire Store, 1180 Aldridge Road, Great Barr, Birmingham, B44 8PE Tel: 0121-360 8500 Fax: 0121-366 6875

Webbs Power Tools Ltd, 146 Boldmere Road, Sutton Coldfield, West Midlands, B73 5UD Tel: 0121-355 3939 Fax: 0121-355 4747 E-mail: sales@webbs-site.co.uk

INDUSTRIAL POWER TOOLS

A C D Plant, Unit 20 Slingsby Close, Attleborough Fields Ind Estate, Nuneaton, Warwickshire, CV11 6RP Tel: (024) 7638 1503 Fax: (024) 7635 4445

Antex (Electronics) Ltd, 2 Westbridge Industrial Estate, Tavistock, Devon, PL19 8DE Tel: (01822) 613565 Fax: (01822) 617598 E-mail: sales@antex.co.uk

C D F Supplies Ltd, Unit 16 Highfield Industrial Estate, North Street, Chorley, Lancashire, PR7 1QD Tel: (01257) 274775 Fax: (01257) 233262 E-mail: sales@cdfsupplies.co.uk

▶ C H Power Tools, Bentley Road, Doncaster, South Yorkshire, DN5 9QP Tel: (01302) 821821

Desoutter Ltd, Eton Road, Hemel Hempstead, Hertfordshire, HP2 7DR Tel: (01442) 344300 Fax: (01442) 344600

Desoutter Ltd, Eton Road, Hemel Hempstead, Hertfordshire, HP2 7DR Tel: (01442) 344300 Fax: (01442) 344600

Desoutter Ltd, Eton Road, Hemel Hempstead, Hertfordshire, HP2 7DR Tel: (01442) 344300 Fax: (01442) 344600 E-mail: desoutter.sales@cp.com

Dewalt, 210 Bath Road, Slough, SL1 3YD Tel: (01753) 567055 Fax: (01753) 521312 E-mail: sales@dewalt.co.uk

F G Lang Grays Ltd, 44 Clarence Road, Grays, Essex, RM17 6QL Tel: (01375) 374901 Fax: (01375) 374216E-mail: info@langs.co.uk

▶ HSS Hire, 45-49 Barking Road, London, E16 4HB Tel: (020) 7474 7040 Fax: (020) 7474 7080

K J N Automation Ltd, 5 Peckleton Lane Business Park, Peckleton Common, Peckleton, Leicester, LE9 7RN Tel: (01455) 823304 Fax: (01455) 828186 E-mail: sales@kjnltd.co.uk

Kes, 262 Ashley Road, Poole, Dorset, BH14 9BZ Tel: (01202) 742393 Fax: (01202) 722042

M A C Tools, Gowerton Road, BlackMills, Northampton, NN4 7BW Tel: (01604) 827351 Fax: (01604) 661654

M Power Tools Ltd, Manor Farm, Newton Tony, Salisbury, SP4 0HA Tel: (01980) 629526

Makita UK Ltd, Vermont Place, Michigan Drive, Tongwell, Milton Keynes, MK15 8JD Tel: (01908) 211678 Fax: (01908) 211400 E-mail: info@makituk.com

Parfix Equipment Company Ltd, Locksley House, Unit 4 Locksley Business Park, Belfast, BT6 9JD Tel: (028) 9070 6800 Fax: (028) 9070 6801 E-mail: dflood@parfixwholesaledirect.com

R P R Power Tools, 15 Charterfield Drive, Cannock, Staffordshire, WS12 3XH Tel: (01543) 275862 Fax: (01543) 275862

Bob Richardson Tools & Fasteners Ltd, Pedmore Road, Dudley, West Midlands, DY2 0RL Tel: (01384) 482789 Fax: (01384) 481888 E-mail: sales@toolstoday.co.uk

Rycon Power Tools Ltd, Unit 13 Ely Valley Industrial Estate, Pontyclun, Mid Glamorgan, CF72 9DZ Tel: (01443) 230785 Fax: (01443) 237415

Techno Trade, 167 West Street, Fareham, Hampshire, PO16 0EF Tel: (01329) 234199 Fax: (01329) 220232

Tool Centre, 104 King Street, Blackburn, BB2 2DT Tel: (01254) 57282 Fax: (01254) 678992

Toolbox Supplies Ltd, 13 Hams Road, Lydney, Gloucestershire, GL15 5PE Tel: (01594) 841104 Fax: (01594) 841105

Torbay Power Tools & Equipment, 2a Barton Hill Road, Torquay, TQ2 8JH Tel: (01803) 324095 Fax: (01803) 324095

INDUSTRIAL PRECIOUS METAL COMPONENTS

Johnson Matthey plc, Orchard Road, Royston, Hertfordshire, SG8 5HE Tel: (01763) 253000 Fax: (01763) 253492 E-mail: nobleuk@matthey.com

INDUSTRIAL PRESSINGS

G W Waite Ltd, North Lonsdale Road, Ulverston, Cumbria, LA12 9DN Tel: (01229) 582046 Fax: (01229) 583893 E-mail: sales@gwwaite.com

INDUSTRIAL PROCESS HIGH VACUUM EQUIPMENT

Consarc Engineering Ltd, 12 North Road, Bellshill, Lanarkshire, ML4 1EN Tel: (01698) 748845 Fax: (01698) 747925 E-mail: sales@consarceng.com

CVT Ltd, 4-6 Carters Lane, Kiln Farm, Milton Keynes, MK11 3ER Tel: (01908) 563267 Fax: (01908) 568354

K & A Furness Ltd, Trent Industrial Estate, Duchess Street, Shaw, Oldham, OL2 7UT Tel: (01706) 843411 Fax: (01706) 882289 E-mail: sales@jet-vac.co.uk

Nordiko Technical Services Ltd, Butterick Building, New Lane, Havant, Hampshire, PO9 2ND Tel: (023) 9248 8200 Fax: (023) 9248 8218 E-mail: enquiries@nordiko-tech.com

Saes Getters (GB) Ltd, Heritage House, Vicker Lane, Daventry, Northamptonshire, NN11 5AA Tel: (01327) 310777 Fax: (01327) 310555 E-mail: saes-gb@saes-group.com

INDUSTRIAL PROCESS MIXERS

Chemineer Ltd, 7 Cranmer Road, West Meadows Industrial Estate, Derby, DE21 6XT Tel: (01332) 363175 Fax: (01332) 290323 E-mail: sales@chemineer.com

▶ Christie Turner Ltd, Knightsdale Road, Ipswich, IP1 4LE Tel: (01473) 742325 Fax: (01473) 462 773 E-mail: info@christyhunt.co.uk

Clayton Thermal Processes Ltd, 2 Summerton Road, Oldbury, West Midlands, B69 2EL Tel: 0121-511 1203 Fax: 0121-511 1192 E-mail: claytonthermal@claytonholdings.com

Colormax Ltd, Unit 3, Stafford Park 12, Telford, Shropshire, TF3 3BJ Tel: (01952) 292101 Fax: (01952) 292761 E-mail: info@colormax.co.uk

Eiger Torrance Ltd, 253 Europa Boulevard Westbrook, Westbrook, Warrington, WA5 7TN Tel: (01925) 232455 Fax: (01925) 237767 E-mail: sales@eiger-torrance.com

John R Boone Ltd, 18 Silk Street, Congleton, Cheshire, CW12 4DH Tel: (01260) 272894 Fax: (01260) 281128 E-mail: sales@jrboone.com

Morton Machine Co. Ltd, Atlantic Works, Newhouse Industrial Estate, Motherwell, Lanarkshire, ML1 5SW Tel: (01698) 732021 Fax: (01698) 732546 E-mail: info@morton-machines.co.uk

Orthos Projects Ltd, Fernie Road, Market Harborough, Leicestershire, LE16 7PH Tel: (01858) 462806 Fax: (01858) 464403 E-mail: sales@orthos.uk.com

Premier Colloid Mills, Building A302 Vickers Drive, Brooklands Industrial Park, Weybridge, Surrey, KT13 0YU Tel: (01932) 355366 Fax: (01932) 352660 E-mail: sales@bptskerman.com

Silverson Machines Ltd, Waterside, Chesham, Buckinghamshire, HP5 1PQ Tel: (01494) 786331 Fax: (01494) 791452 E-mail: sales@silverson.co.uk

Statiflo International Ltd, Crown Centre, Bond Street, Macclesfield, Cheshire, SK11 6QS Tel: (01625) 433100 Fax: (01625) 511376 E-mail: sales@statiflo.co.uk

Warbrick International, Cranford Court, King Street, Knutsford, Cheshire, WA16 8BW Tel: (01565) 652616 Fax: (01565) 633159 E-mail: sales@warbrick.co.uk

INDUSTRIAL PROCESS PUMPS

Pump Partners, Unit 50 Coney Green Business Centre, Wingfield View, Clay Cross, Chesterfield, Derbyshire, S45 9JW Tel: (01246) 250197 Fax: (01246) 250241 E-mail: admin@thepumppartners.co.uk

INDUSTRIAL PROCESSING ROLLMAKERS

Dilworth & Morris Engineering Ltd, Hyde Bank Road, New Mills, High Peak, Derbyshire, SK22 4BP Tel: (01663) 746383 Fax: (01663) 744230 E-mail: dillworth.morris@btconnect.com

William Hardill Sons & Co. Ltd, Westbury Works, Sticker Lane, Bradford, West Yorkshire, BD4 8RU Tel: (01274) 664422 Fax: (01274) 664433 E-mail: info@hardill.demon.co.uk

Park Cross Engineering, 33 Moss Lane, Worsley, Manchester, M28 3WD Tel: 0161-799 0660 Fax: 0161-703 8006 E-mail: mail@park-cross.co.uk

INDUSTRIAL PROTECTIVE CLOTHING, *See also Safety Clothing etc*

Alpha Solway Ltd, Queensberry Street, Annan, Dumfriesshire, DG12 5BL Tel: (01461) 202452 Fax: (01461) 205684 E-mail: sales@alphasolway.com

Angel Net Ltd, 193 Granville Avenue, Long Eaton, Nottingham, NG10 4HE Tel: 0115-973 3013 Fax: 0115-973 3166 E-mail: angelnet@proweb.co.uk

Arco Ltd, Tenax Circle, Trafford Park, Manchester, M17 1EZ Tel: 0161-869 5800 Fax: 0161-869 5858 E-mail: traffordpark.branch@arco.co.uk

Arco, PO Box 78, Watford, WD24 4YT Tel: (01923) 202090 Fax: (01923) 202010 E-mail: arco@watford.co.uk

Arco Ellesmere Port Ltd, Hooton Road, Hooton, Ellesmere Port, CH66 7PA Tel: 0151-327 6666 Fax: 0151-327 7930

Arco Glasgow, 210 Edmiston Drive, Glasgow, G51 2YY Tel: 0141-419 3200 Fax: 0141-419 3232 E-mail: arco-glasgow@arco.com

Arco South East, Cray Avenue, Orpington, Kent, BR5 3QB Tel: (01689) 875411 Fax: (01689) 876538 E-mail: orpington.branch@arco.co.uk

Arco Southwest Ltd, Unit 8a & 8b Point 4, Second Way, Avonmouth, Bristol, BS11 8YA Tel: 0117-982 3751 Fax: 0117-923 5574 E-mail: avonmouth.branch@arco.co.uk

Arco Tyne & Wear Ltd, PO Box 8, Blaydon-on-Tyne, Tyne & Wear, NE21 5TP Tel: 0191-414 7721 Fax: 0191-414 0258 E-mail: arco.tynewear@arco.co.uk

Armor Products, Cranfield Road, Lostock Industrial Estate, Lostock, Bolton, BL6 4SB Tel: (01204) 664000 Fax: (01204) 664001

Bunzl Safety & Work Wear, Unit 2b, Adergellay Road, Swansea, SA5 4DY Tel: (01792) 355600 Fax: (01792) 355700 E-mail: sales@bunzlsws.com

Bunzl Workware Ltd, Unit 2B, Abergelly Road, Forest Fach, Swansea, SA5 4DY Tel: (01792) 355600 Fax: (01792) 355700 E-mail: sales@unzlsws.com

C A C Industrial Products Ltd, Thornton Industrial Trading Estate, Milford Haven, Dyfed, SA73 2RU Tel: (01646) 692626 Fax: (01646) 690144 E-mail: sales@cac-industrial.co.uk

C & M Smith Partnership, 4 Potters Lane, Kiln Farm, Milton Keynes, MK11 3HE Tel: (01908) 265577 Fax: (01908) 265567 E-mail: salescandm@aol.com

Central Safety Ltd, 30 North Street Industrial Estate, Droitwich, Worcestershire, WR9 8JB Tel: (01905) 774737 Fax: (01905) 796356

Collard Industrial Gloves Ltd, Portskewett Street, Newport, Gwent, NP19 0GJ Tel: (01633) 213471 Fax: (01633) 257696

Contamination Control Apparel Ltd, Northolt Drive, Bolton, BL3 6RE Tel: (01204) 528019 Fax: (01204) 361549E-mail: cca@mikar.co.uk

Cookson & Clegg, PO Box 11, Blackburn, BB1 2WX Tel: (01254) 844544 Fax: (01254) 844545 E-mail: sales@cooksonclegg.com

Corporate Clothing, 5-7 Linkfield Corner, Station Road, Redhill, RH1 1BD Tel: (01737) 767912 Fax: (01737) 780666 E-mail: info@armawear.co.uk

Corton Sinclair Ltd, 36 Glenburn Road, East Kilbride, Glasgow, G74 5BA Tel: (01355) 222273 Fax: (01355) 263682 E-mail: sales@corstonsinclair.com

Davern Work Wear Ltd, Elliott Road, March, Cambridgeshire, PE15 8QU Tel: (01354) 654001 Fax: (01354) 658274 E-mail: info@davern.co.uk

Delf Freezer Wear Ltd, Delf House, Pool Close, West Molesey, Surrey, KT8 2HW Tel: 020 89412802 Fax: (020) 89417201 E-mail: david.barker@delf.co.uk

Dickies Workwear, Second Avenue, Westfield Trading Estate, Midsomer Norton, Radstock, BA3 4BH Tel: (01761) 410041 Fax: (01761) 414825 E-mail: uksales@dickies.com

E & E Workwear, Church Lane, Marple, Stockport, Cheshire, SK6 7AR Tel: 0161-427 6522 Fax: 0161-426 0906 E-mail: eeworkwear@hotmail.com

Faithful Ltd, Northwick Road, Worcester, WR3 7DU Tel: (01905) 450000 Fax: (01905) 457690 E-mail: sales@faithful.co.uk

Joseph Firth, 10 Pepper Road, Leeds, LS10 2EU Tel: 0113-271 1148 Fax: 0113-270 3101 E-mail: sales@josephfirth.co.uk

Future Garments Ltd, Aqua House, Buttress Way, Smethwick, West Midlands, B66 3DL Tel: 0121-555 7167 Fax: 0121-555 7168 E-mail: sales@future-gmts.com

▶ Grantham Clothing Co., Unit 1a Partnership House, Withambrook Park Industrial Estate, Grantham, Lincolnshire, NG31 9ST Tel: (01476) 594330 Fax: (01476) 593863 E-mail: granthamclothing@btclick.com

Harveys & Co. Clothing Ltd, Glodwick Road, Oldham, OL4 1YU Tel: 0161-624 9535 Fax: 0161-627 2028 E-mail: info@harveys.co.uk

Hurricane Protective Clothing, Tame Valley Industrial Estate, Wilnecote, Tamworth, Staffordshire, B77 5DQ Tel: (01827) 250808 Fax: (01827) 250808 E-mail: hurricane@mgrubber.com

Ilasco Ltd, 52-53 Nasmyth Road, Southfield Industrial Estate, Glenrothes, Fife, KY6 2SD Tel: (01592) 771241 Fax: (01592) 771071 E-mail: sales@ardmel-group.co.uk

Industrial Catering Industries Ltd, Sterling Works, Clarence Road, Cardiff, CF10 5FA Tel: (029) 2049 8498 Fax: (029) 2048 8838 E-mail: sales@phoenix-saxton.com

Lion Safety Products, Jackson Avenue, Grangemouth, Stirlingshire, FK3 8JU Tel: (01324) 474744

Louise Products Antrim Ltd, 18 Ballycraigy Road, Antrim, BT41 1PW Tel: (028) 9446 4088 Fax: (028) 9442 8276

M G Rubber Co. Ltd, Moorbridge Road, Bingham Industrial Estate, Nottingham, NG13 8GG Tel: (01949) 839112 Fax: (01949) 831357 E-mail: sales@mgrubber.com

Manufacturers Supplies Acton Ltd, 2 Langley Wharf, Railway Terrace, Kings Langley, Hertfordshire, WD4 8JE Tel: (01923) 260845 Fax: (01923) 260847 E-mail: manusupplies@aol.com

Matric Services & Supplies Ltd, Unit 25-26 Essington Light Industrial Estate, Bognop Road, Essington, Wolverhampton, WV11 2BJ Tel: (01922) 479132 Fax: (01922) 494450 E-mail: matric@amserve.com

Joseph Miller & Sons Ltd, 1 Denver Close, Orpington, Kent, BR6 0SB Tel: (01689) 609901 Fax: (01689) 609901 E-mail: hsjmiller@aol.com

Milton Keynes Workwear & Safety Co. Ltd, 15-16 Darin Court, Crownhill, Milton Keynes, MK8 0AD Tel: (01908) 566640 Fax: (01908) 566540 E-mail: sales@mkworkwear.com

Monarch Textiles, Lowmoor Business Park, Kirkby-in-Ashfield, Nottingham, NG17 7LF Tel: (01623) 750777 Fax: (01623) 720779 E-mail: enquiry@monarch-textiles.co.uk

Nalestar Ltd, Melton House, Melton Place, Leyland, Preston, PR25 4XU Tel: (01772) 431226 Fax: (01772) 622497 E-mail: sales@nalestar.co.uk

North Safety Products, The Courtyard, Green Lane, Heywood, Lancashire, OL10 2EX Tel: (01706) 693800 Fax: (01706) 693801 E-mail: info@northsafety.co.uk

Charles Ockwell & Co. Ltd, Alkerton Works, Cricklade, Swindon, SN6 6AE Tel: (01793) 750216 Fax: (01793) 752239 E-mail: ockwellsas@hotmail.com

Orvec International Ltd, Malmo Road, Hull, HU7 0YF Tel: (01482) 879146 Fax: (01482) 625325 E-mail: service@orvec.com

Pioner Fristads (UK) Ltd, 7 Wensum Mount Business Centre, Low Road, Hellesdon, Norwich, NR6 5AQ Tel: (01603) 786160 Fax: (01603) 414540 E-mail: enquiries@fristads-co.com

Protec Manchester Ltd, 2 Rainard Street, Hyde, Cheshire, SK14 2HW Tel: (0870) 3333081 Fax: (0870) 3333061 E-mail: sales@protecdirect.co.uk

Protective Clothing Co. Ltd, 8-14 Orsman Road, London, N1 5QJ Tel: (020) 7729 0405 Fax: (020) 7729 0405

Redgold Fashions Ltd, 219-221 Bow Road, London, E3 2SJ Tel: (020) 8980 9745 Fax: (020) 8980 4979

▶ Remco Safety Ltd, Unit 1 Haxter Close, Belliver Industrial Estate, Roborough, Plymouth, PL6 7DD Tel: (01752) 786452 Fax: (01752) 767198 E-mail: remglo@aol.com

Respirex, F Kingsfield Business Centre, Philanthropic Road, Redhill, RH1 4DP Tel: (01737) 778600 Fax: (01737) 779441 E-mail: sales@respirex.co.uk

INDUSTRIAL PROTECTIVE CLOTHING - *continued*

Rhayader Farm Supplies, Commerce Ho, West St, Rhayader, Powys, LD6 5AF Tel: 01597 810336
Rubitex Protective Clothing, 52 Lord Street, Manchester, M3 1HN Tel: 0161-834 3340 Fax: 0161-834 3326 E-mail: info@rubitex.co.uk
Rushall Protective Clothing Co. Ltd, 501 Bloxwich Road, Walsall, WS3 2XA Tel: (01922) 710055 Fax: (01922) 407885
Safewear, Unit 1 Seaview Industrial Estate, Lewis Road, East Moors, Cardiff, CF24 5EB Tel: (029) 2049 6585 Fax: (029) 2049 4057
South Wales Suppliers, Unit 40 Penmaen Business Centre, Pontllanfraith, Blackwood, Gwent, NP12 2DZ Tel: (01495) 229919 Fax: (01495) 229919
Starchem Ltd, Strawberry Lane, Willenhall, West Midlands, WV13 3RS Tel: (01902) 838880 Fax: (01902) 838881 E-mail: sales@starchem.co.uk
Stockbridge Mill Co. Ltd, Green Lane, Padiham, Burnley, Lancashire, BB12 7AE Tel: (01282) 772231 Fax: (01282) 771084 E-mail: sales@stockbridgemill.com
Swift Industiral Suppliers, Anstey Mill Lane, The Mill House, Alton, Hampshire, GU34 2QQ Tel: (01420) 592500 Fax: (01420) 592501
Synergie Healthcare Ltd, Lyon Mill, Fitton Street, Royton, Oldham, OL2 5JX Tel: 0161-624 5641 Fax: 0161-627 0902
Taskwear Clothing, Albert School, Church Lane, Marple, Stockport, Cheshire, SK6 7AR Tel: 0161-449 9449 Fax: 0161-426 0906 E-mail: eeworkwear@hotmail.com
Teejay Workwear Ltd, Dy2 Dean Clough Office Park, Halifax, West Yorkshire, HX3 5AX Tel: (01422) 369754 Fax: (01422) 383223 E-mail: sales@teejayworkwear.co.uk
Trelleborg Beadle, Unit 30 Bergen Way, Hull, HU7 0YQ Tel: (01482) 839119 Fax: (01482) 879418 E-mail: lesley.kidd@trelleborg.com
Tuf Work & Safety Wear, 26 North Road, Yate, Bristol, BS37 7PA Tel: (01454) 335050 Fax: (01454) 335001 E-mail: sales@tuf.com
Tunika Safety Products, Tannery House, Nelson Street, Bolton, BL3 2JW Tel: (01204) 366713 Fax: (01204) 366714 E-mail: sales@tunikasafety.co.uk
Turton Manufacturing Ltd, Unit 3 The Furlong, Berry Hill Industrial Estate, Droitwich, Worcestershire, WR9 9AH Tel: (01905) 796166 Fax: (01905) 796199 E-mail: sales@turtonslimited.com
W J Nelson & Son Ltd, Fashoda Street, Belfast, BT5 5EX Tel: (028) 9045 6020 Fax: (028) 9073 8312 E-mail: wjnsafe@aol.com
Wenaas UK Ltd, Wenaas Buildings, Hareness Circle, Altens Industrial Estate, Aberdeen, AB12 3LY Tel: (01224) 894000 Fax: (01224) 878789 E-mail: sales@wenaas.co.uk
Workware Protective Equipment, Tannery House, Tannery Road, Harraby Green Business Park, Carlisle, CA1 2SS Tel: (01228) 591091 Fax: (01228) 590026 E-mail: sales@workware.co.uk
S. Yaffy Protective Clothing, 310 Main Street, Glasgow, G40 1LW Tel: 0141-554 2202 Fax: 0141-556 4347 E-mail: admin@yaffy.co.uk

INDUSTRIAL RACKING AND SHELVING

▶ Commercial & Industrial Interiors Ltd, 1e Princess Court, Princess Way, Prudhoe, Northumberland, NE42 6PL Tel: (01661) 836304 Fax: (0845) 3454229 E-mail: john@ciinteriors.com

INDUSTRIAL RACKING SYSTEMS

Bigdug.Co.Uk, Unit 41 Staunton Court Business Park, Ledbury Road, Staunton, Gloucester, GL19 3QS Tel: (0845) 0654000 E-mail: racking9@gmail.com
Link 51 Ltd, Link House, Halesfield 6, Telford, Shropshire, TF7 4LN Tel: (0800) 515600 Fax: (01952) 682452 E-mail: enquiries@link51.co.uk
M H Group, M H House, Madeley Street, Hull, HU3 2AH Tel: (01482) 328896 Fax: (01482) 225867 E-mail: sales@mhindustrial.co.uk
▶ Norfolk Storage Equipment Ltd, 15 Maurice Gaymer Road, Attleborough, Norfolk, NR17 2QZ Tel: (01953) 458800 Fax: (01953) 458819 E-mail: sales@nsel.biz
Stor Tech, Unit A Castle Park Industrial Estate, Bower Street, Oldham, OL1 3LN Tel: 0161-678 8597 Fax: 0161-665 0579 E-mail: info@stortech.ltd.uk

INDUSTRIAL RACKMOUNTED COMPUTERS

Fairchild Ltd, Fairchild House, Southampton Street, Southampton, SO15 2ED Tel: (023) 8021 1789 Fax: (023) 8021 1678 E-mail: sales@fairchild.co.uk

INDUSTRIAL REELS

Hearl Heaton Ltd, Halifax Road, Liversedge, West Yorkshire, WF15 6JJ Tel: (01924) 406721 Fax: (01924) 400803 E-mail: info@hearlheaton.co.uk

INDUSTRIAL REFRIGERATION MAINTENANCE

PeakCooling Solutions Ltd, 9 Kellerr Close, Martland Mill Business Park, Wigan, Lancashire, WN5 0LP Tel: (01942) 223300 Fax: (01942) 218718 E-mail: enquries@peakcoolingsolutions.co.uk
▶ Star Refrigeration Ltd, 15 Tower Road, Washington, Tyne & Wear, NE37 2SH Tel: 0191-415 7755 Fax: 0191-415 0446 E-mail: jwilson@ref.co.uk

INDUSTRIAL REFRIGERATION PLANT

Climate Services, Intersection House, 110-120 Birmingham Road, West Bromwich, West Midlands, B70 6RP Tel: 0121-524 8825 Fax: 0121-524 8823 E-mail: mail@climate-services.co.uk
Delrac Acs, Fairman Law House, 1-3 Park Terrace, Worcester Park, Surrey, KT4 7JZ Tel: (020) 8335 3141 Fax: (020) 8337 5539 E-mail: enquiries@delrac-acs.co.uk
▶ Star Refrigeration Ltd, A8 Imperial Business Estate, West Mill, Gravesend, Kent, DA11 0DL Tel: (01474) 568221 Fax: (01474) 363004

INDUSTRIAL REFRIGERATION UNITS

Carrier Refrigeration, United Technologies House, Guildford Road, Fetcham, Leatherhead, Surrey, KT22 9UT Tel: (01865) 337700 Fax: (01372) 230190
Climate Services, Intersection House, 110-120 Birmingham Road, West Bromwich, West Midlands, B70 6RP Tel: 0121-524 8825 Fax: 0121-524 8823 E-mail: mail@climate-services.co.uk
Star Refrigeration Ltd, 4 Murray Place, Righead Industrial Estate, Bellshill, Lanarkshire, ML4 3LP Tel: (01698) 841535 Fax: (01698) 842074
▶ Ian Strange (Tansley) Ltd, Holly Lane, Tansley, Matlock, Derbyshire, DE4 5FF Tel: (01629) 583835 Fax: (01629) 583835 E-mail: admin@fosterfridge.co.uk
Waeco UK Ltd, Unit D1 Roman Hill Trading Estate, Broadmayne, Dorchester, Dorset, DT2 8LY Tel: (01305) 854000 Fax: (01305) 854288 E-mail: enquiries@waeco.co.uk

INDUSTRIAL RELOCATABLE BUILDINGS

ACS Cabins, Midlands Farm, Mill Lane, Headley, Bordon, Hampshire, GU35 0PB Tel: (01428) 714900
▶ Chiltern Shed Co, Unit 9b Chiltern Trading Estate, Earl Howe Road, Holmer Green, High Wycombe, Buckinghamshire, HP15 6QT Tel: (01494) 712230 Fax: (01494) 712230
Churchtown Ltd, 18A London Street, Southport, Merseyside, PR9 0UE Tel: (01704) 227826 Fax: (01704) 220247 E-mail: cabins@churchtown.co.uk
G E Capital Modular Space, Langford Bridge, Cambridge Road, Langford, Biggleswade, Bedfordshire, SG18 9PL Tel: (01462) 701711 Fax: (01462) 701355
▶ Portable Offices Hire Ltd, Woodyard Lane, Foston, Derby, DE65 5DJ Tel: (01283) 585822 Fax: (01283) 585833 E-mail: derby@portableoffice.co.uk
▶ Shomera, 63 Milton Road, London, SW14 8JP Tel: (020) 8332 3022 Fax: (020) 8487 8224 E-mail: info@shomera.com
Wernick Group Holdings Ltd, Molineux House, Russell Gardens, Wickford, Essex, SS11 8BL Tel: (01268) 735544 E-mail: simon.doran@wernickwickford.co.uk

INDUSTRIAL REMOVAL CONTRACTORS

Keith Rhodes Machinery Installations Ltd, Ashmore House, Lower Tuffley Lane, Gloucester, GL2 5DP Tel: (01452) 303037 Fax: (01452) 311166 E-mail: keithrhodes@lineone.net

INDUSTRIAL RESISTANCES

Omegaslate UK Ltd, 2 Chirk Close, Kidderminster, Worcestershire, DY10 1YG Tel: (01562) 755824 Fax: (01562) 742979 E-mail: info@omegaslate.com

INDUSTRIAL RIGGING

Arthur Beale Ltd, 194 Shaftesbury Avenue, London, WC2H 8JP Tel: (020) 7836 9034 Fax: (020) 7836 5807
Hamble Ropes & Rigging Ltd, 65-69 Bernard Street, Southampton, SO14 3BA Tel: (023) 8033 8286 Fax: (023) 8033 8288 E-mail: info@hrrlcovercraft.fsnet.co.uk
Petersen Stainless Rigging Ltd, Blaydon Business Centre, Cowen Road, Blaydon-on-Tyne, Tyne & Wear, NE21 5TW Tel: 0191-414 0156 Fax: 0191-499 0041 E-mail: admin@petersen-stainless.co.uk
Solent Rigging Services Ltd, 21 Shamrock Quay, William Street, Southampton, SO14 5QL Tel: (023) 8055 0444 Fax: (023) 8023 0608
Solid Stampings Ltd, Porters Field Road, Cradley Heath, West Midlands, B64 7BL Tel: (01384) 636421 Fax: (01384) 639163 E-mail: info@solidswivel.co.uk
Spencer Rigging Ltd, Empire Buildings, St. Mary's Road, Cowes, Isle Of Wight, PO31 7SX Tel: (01983) 292022 Fax: (01983) 291589 E-mail: info@spencerrigging.co.uk

INDUSTRIAL ROBOT SYSTEMS

A T M Automation Ltd, Winchester Avenue, Blaby Industrial Park, Blaby, Leicester, LE8 4GZ Tel: 0116-277 3607 Fax: 0116-277 9800 E-mail: sales@atmautomation.com
Automation Dynamics Ltd, PO Box 6842, Nottingham, NG9 3SS Tel: 0115-849 9878 E-mail: server@automation-dynamics.com
Bauromat UK, Beauchamp Business Centre, Sparrowhawk Close, Malvern, Worcestershire, WR14 1GL Tel: (01684) 575757 Fax: (01684) 569887 E-mail: info@bauromat.co.uk
Geiger Handling, Raleigh Hall Industrial Estate, Eccleshall, Stafford, ST21 6JL Tel: (01785) 851111 Fax: (01785) 859090 E-mail: s.hulse@geigerhandling.com
Labman Automation Ltd, Stokesley Industrial Park, Middlesbrough, Cleveland, TS9 5JZ Tel: 0845 4941644 Fax: (01642) 710667 E-mail: mailroom@labman.co.uk
Machine Technology Ltd, 22-23 Arcadia Avenue, London, N3 2JU Tel: (020) 8349 4814 Fax: (020) 8346 6251 E-mail: machinetech@btconnect.com
Proven Engineering Products Ltd, Wardhead Park, Stewarton, Kilmarnock, Ayrshire, KA3 5LH Tel: (01560) 485570 E-mail: info@provenenergy.com
R T S, Northbank Industrial Park, Irlam, Manchester, M44 5AY Tel: 0161-777 2000 Fax: 0161-777 2095 E-mail: sales@rts-group.co.uk
Senior Design Associates Ltd, Unit 4 Dukes Street, Windsor, Berkshire, SL4 1SE Tel: (01753) 833382 Fax: (01753) 833709 E-mail: contactus@sda.uk.com
Sixaxis Ltd, 3 Hinton Way, Houghton Regis, Dunstable, Bedfordshire, LU5 5RB Tel: (07801) 719853 Fax: (07808) 769198 E-mail: sales@sixaxis.ltd.uk
TQC Ltd, Hooton Street, Nottingham, NG3 2NJ Tel: 0115-950 3561 Fax: 0115-948 4642 E-mail: sales@tqc.co.uk

INDUSTRIAL ROBOTS

Complete Industrial Services Ltd, 63 Cromwell Road, Bushbury Wolverhampton, Wolverhampton, WV10 8UT Tel: (01902) 651795 Fax: (01902) 651795 E-mail: sales@ciservices.worldonline.co.uk
Cybernetic Applications Ltd, West Portway Industrial Estate, Andover, Hampshire, SP10 3LF Tel: (01264) 350093 Fax: (01264) 333771
Evershed Robotics Ltd, Unit D1 Hortonwood 10, Telford, Shropshire, TF1 7ES Tel: (01952) 608020 Fax: (01952) 608388 E-mail: sales@evershedrobotics.com
Motoman Robotics UK Ltd, Unit 2 Johnson Park, Wildmere Road, Banbury, Oxfordshire, OX16 3JU Tel: (01295) 272755 Fax: (01295) 267127 E-mail: derekpasquire@motoman.co.uk

INDUSTRIAL ROLLMAKERS

A T Roberts Ltd, 9-13 Aldenham Road, Watford, WD19 4AB Tel: (01923) 223969 Fax: (01923) 244497 E-mail: info@atroberts.fsnet.co.uk
Rotadyne UK Ltd, Saxon House, Henson Way, Telford Way Industrial Estate, Kettering, Northamptonshire, NN16 8PX Tel: (01536) 414421 Fax: (01536) 411091 E-mail: pevans@rotadyne.com
Tomah Engineers Ltd, 104 Fitzwalter Rd., Sheffield, S2 2SP Tel: 0114-272 1199 Fax: 0114-276 8675 E-mail: tomaheng@aol.com

INDUSTRIAL ROOFING CONTRACTORS

A & E Elkins Ltd, 6 Insulcrete Works, Yeoman Street, London, SE8 5DT Tel: (020) 7231 8808 Fax: (020) 7252 3758 E-mail: sales@roofingspecialistuk.com
▶ K. Addams Industrial Roofing Contractors Limited, ARC House, Sundon Road, Chalton, Luton, LU4 9UA Tel: (01525) 877740 Fax: (01525) 877118 E-mail: k.addams@btinternet.com
Anglia Industrial Roofing Co. Ltd, Bunyan Close, Gamlingay, Sandy, Bedfordshire, SG19 3JD Tel: (01767) 651550 Fax: (01767) 651566 E-mail: sales@angliaindustrialroofing.co.uk
Blackwell Stanistreet, 64 Talbot Road, Old Trafford, Manchester, M16 0PP Tel: 0161-872 2821 Fax: 0161-848 7427
BRC Industrial Roofing (Midlands) Ltd, Unit 1, Merchants Way, Aldridge, Walsall, WS9 8SW Tel: (01922) 454044 Fax: (01922) 454254 E-mail: sales@brcroofing.co.uk
Coatings & Safe Access Ltd, PO Box 11, York, YO41 5YP Tel: (01759) 380804 Fax: (01759) 380329 E-mail: casalyork@aol.com
Dagenham Construction Ltd, 3 Ardmore Road, South Ockendon, Essex, RM15 5TH Tel: (01708) 851631 Fax: (01708) 852247 E-mail: dagenhamcon@btconnect.com
Factorycover Ltd, Eamont Park, Toft Farm West Industrial Estate, Hartlepool, Cleveland, TS25 2BQ Tel: (01429) 863366 Fax: (01429) 263188
▶ First Choice Joinery, 3 Drayton Road, Tonbridge, Kent, TN9 2BE Tel: (01622) 873348 Fax: (01732) 365696 E-mail: sales@shawleygroup.co.uk
Grainger Building Services Ltd, 163 Church Road, Holywood, County Down, BT18 9BZ Tel: (028) 9042 2555 Fax: (028) 9042 5428 E-mail: info@grainger-uk.com
Hathaway Roofing Ltd, Tindale Cresent, Tindale Crescent, Bishop Auckland, County Durham, DL14 9TL Tel: (01388) 605636 Fax: (01388) 608841
James Petre & Co. Ltd, Bentley Avenue, Cowpen Lane Industrial Estate, Billingham, Cleveland, TS23 4BU Tel: (01642) 563800 Fax: (01642) 564947
Kelsey Roofing Industries Ltd, Kelsey House, Paper Mill Drive, Church Hill South, Redditch, Worcestershire, B98 8QJ Tel: (01527) 594400 Fax: (01527) 594444
Letchworth Roofing Co. Ltd, Roof Centre, Works Road, Letchworth Garden City, Hertfordshire, SG6 1JY Tel: (01462) 755766 Fax: (01462) 755750 E-mail: sales@letchworthroofing.co.uk
LPC Contracts Ltd, 370 Coventry Road, Hinckley, Leicestershire, LE10 0NH Tel: (01455) 635816 Fax: (01455) 615329
Midland Properties, Reeves Street, Walsall, WS3 2DL Tel: (01922) 404148 Fax: (01922) 400212
Northern Industrial Roofing, Howley Lane, Warrington, WA1 2DN Tel: (01925) 244442 Fax: (01925) 244299 E-mail: david.gillam@northernindustrialroofing.co.uk
Pickles Bros Slaters Ltd, 2 323 Burley Road, Leeds, LS4 2HY Tel: 0113-275 2620 Fax: 0113-275 2620 E-mail: sales@picklesbros.co.uk
Robertson Roofing Ltd, 21d Station Road, Knowle, Solihull, West Midlands, B93 0HL Tel: (01564) 776278 Fax: (01564) 779607 E-mail: enquiries@robertsonroofing.com
Robseal Roofing Ltd, Unit 3 Nimrod Way, Elgar Road South, Reading, RG2 0EB Tel: 0118-975 4800 Fax: 0118-975 4854 E-mail: mail@robseal.co.uk
▶ Roofing Contracts & Building Ltd, A 121a Shirley Road, Southampton, SO15 3FF Tel: (023) 8063 3030 Fax: (023) 8063 3998 E-mail: sales@roofingcladdingbuilding.com
Teams Roofing Ltd, Wylam Close, Stephenson Industrial Estate East, Washington, Tyne & Wear, NE37 3BE Tel: 0191-419 2233 Fax: 0191-416 2210 E-mail: enquiries@teamsroofing.com
Valent Ltd, 49 Longford Road, Chorlton-Cum-Hardy, Manchester, M21 9WP Tel: 0161-881 3503 Fax: 0161-860 5519
Ward Roofing, Cleatham Road, Kirton Lindsey, Gainsborough, Lincolnshire, DN21 4JR Tel: (01652) 641950 Fax: (01652) 648161 E-mail: reception@wardroofing.co.uk

INDUSTRIAL RUBBER PRODUCTS

A E Taylor & Co. Ltd, 44 Borough Road, Sunderland, SR1 1PW Tel: 0191-567 5078 Fax: 0191-510 2268
Allied Rubber Products, 15 Cornwall Road Industrial Estate, Smethwick, West Midlands, B66 2JT Tel: 0121-565 0961 Fax: 0121-565 0976
Arco, PO Box 78, Watford, WD24 4YT Tel: (01923) 202090 Fax: (01923) 202010 E-mail: arco@watford.co.uk
ARCO West Bromwich, PO Box 2210, West Bromwich, West Midlands, B71 1DQ Tel: 0121-500 4444 Fax: 0121-553 7554 E-mail: westbromwich.branch@arco.co.uk
Arefco Special Products Ltd, Jubilee Industrial Estate, Ashington, Northumberland, NE63 8UA Tel: (01670) 819513 Fax: (01670) 816132 E-mail: sales@arefco.co.uk
Aspfase Ltd, 4 Stepbridge Road, Tufthorn Industrial Estate, Coleford, Gloucestershire, GL16 2PL Tel: (01594) 833939 Fax: (01594) 833939
Bonded Motor Spares Ltd, 95 Cooperative Street, Stafford, ST16 3DA Tel: (01785) 250850 Fax: (01785) 250852

▶ indicates data change since last edition

INDUSTRIAL RUBBER PRODUCTS – *continued*

Bridgestone Industrial Ltd, 2nd Floor West, CP House, 97 -107 Uxbridge Road, Ealing, London, W5 5TL Tel: (020) 8567 8080 Fax: (020) 8567 2066 E-mail: info@bsil.co.uk

Camberley Rubber Mouldings Ltd, Unit 10, Springlake Industrial Estate, Aldershot, Hampshire, GU12 4UH Tel: (01252) 330200 Fax: (01252) 330218 E-mail: sales@camberleyrubber.com

Capital Rubber & Plastics Ltd, Units 9-11 Deans Factory Estate, Lambs Lane, Rainham, Essex, RM13 9XL Tel: (01708) 552214 Fax: (01708) 524004 E-mail: sales@capitalrubber.co.uk

Clwyd Compounders Ltd, Gardden Industrial Estate, Ruabon, Wrexham, Clwyd, LL14 6RG Tel: (01978) 810551 Fax: (01978) 810740 E-mail: sales@clwydcompounders.com

Alexander Comrie & Sons Ltd, Unit 8, Second Avenue Business Park, Millbrook, Southampton, SO15 0LP Tel: (023) 8070 2911 Fax: (023) 8070 2617

Cynflex Ltd, Highfield Street, Long Eaton, Nottingham, NG10 4GY Tel: 0115-973 5689 Fax: 0115-972 2149 E-mail: sales@cynflex.com

James Dawson & Son Ltd, Unit 7, 2ND Avenue, Poynton Industrial Estate, Poynton, Cheshire, SK12 1ND Tel: (01625) 879494 Fax: (01625) 879555 E-mail: indico@indico-europe.co.uk

Denber Trading Co., Unit H3 Rudford Industrial Estate, Ford Road, Ford, Arundel, West Sussex, BN18 0BD Tel: (01903) 723155 Fax: (01903) 733160 E-mail: denberint.rubber@virgin.net

Essential Equipment Ltd, Unit 24 Planetary Industrial Estate, Planetary Road, Willenhall, West Midlands, WV13 3XA Tel: (01902) 725055 Fax: (01902) 862684 E-mail: enquiries@essentialequipment.co.uk

Flexible Connections Ltd, King Street Trading Estate, Middlewich, Cheshire, CW10 9LF Tel: (01606) 836024 Fax: (01606) 836241 E-mail: flexibles@talk21.com

Flowseal Ltd, 34h Aston Road, Waterlooville, Hampshire, PO7 7XQ Tel: (023) 9226 5031 Fax: (023) 9224 0382 E-mail: sales@flowseal.co.uk

Hampshire Mouldings Ltd, Jetpac Works, Gravel Lane, Chichester, West Sussex, PO19 8PG Tel: (01243) 782296 Fax: (01243) 781933 E-mail: sales@oringslimited.co.uk

The Harborough Rubber Co. Ltd, Riverside, Market Harborough, Leicestershire, LE16 7PT Tel: (01858) 410610 Fax: (01858) 410006 E-mail: admin@harboro.co.uk

Hill's Rubber Co. Ltd, 85 Bedford Road, Reading, RG1 7EZ Tel: 0845 4940717 Fax: 0118-950 3083 E-mail: hillsrubber@hotmail.com

Icon Polymer Group Ltd, Thrumpton Lane, Retford, Nottinghamshire, DN22 6HH Tel: (01777) 714300 Fax: (01777) 709739 E-mail: info@iconpolymer.com

Industrial & Rubber Supplies Ltd, 184 Smithdown Road, Liverpool, L15 3JR Tel: 0151-733 7859 Fax: 0151-733 4980 E-mail: indrub@talk21.com

Inglecliff Ltd, Unit 2 Barsbank Lane, Lymm, Cheshire, WA13 0ER Tel: (01925) 752471 Fax: (01925) 755784 E-mail: sales@inglecliff.co.uk

Installation & Manufacturing Contractors Ltd, Thrifts House, London Road, Ware, Hertfordshire, SG12 9QT Tel: (01920) 468011 Fax: (01920) 460869 E-mail: info@monaflex.com

J P Polymer Sheetings Ltd, Coneygre Industrial Estate, Tipton, West Midlands, DY4 8XP Tel: 0121-520 5020 Fax: 0121-522 4610 E-mail: sales@jppolymer.co.uk

Jay Rubber Linings Ltd, 132 Queen Street, Crewe, CW1 4AU Tel: (01270) 254655 Fax: (01270) 254526 E-mail: sales@jayrubberlinings.co.uk

L J A Miers & Co. Ltd, Hawkesden Road, St. Neots, Cambridgeshire, PE19 1QS Tel: (01480) 211177 Fax: (01480) 211190 E-mail: sales@ljamiers.co.uk

Landline Ltd, 1 First Avenue, Halstead, Essex, CO9 2EX Tel: (01787) 476699 Fax: (01787) 472507 E-mail: sales@landline.co.uk

Lee-Healey, Manchester, M24 2XH Tel: 0161-655 0303 Fax: 0161-655 0304 E-mail: info@lee-healey.com

Marple Polymer Processors Ltd, Primrose Mill, Mill Brow, Marple Bridge, Stockport, Cheshire, SK6 5AS Tel: 0161-427 2534 Fax: 0161-427 7872

Mowtec Elastomeric Components Ltd, Units 28 & 29, Sketchley Lane Industrial Estate, Burbage, Hinckley, Leicestershire, LE10 3EF Tel: (01455) 251324 Fax: (01455) 610760 E-mail: terry.eyre1@btinternet.com

Moyer Manufacturing Co. Ltd, Vansittart Estate, Duke Street, Windsor, Berkshire, SL4 1SG Tel: (01753) 830088 Fax: (01753) 818793 E-mail: moyer@tcom.co.uk

O M C Fluidpower Ltd, Unit N, Harlow House, Corby, Northamptonshire, NN17 5XH Tel: (01536) 260372 Fax: (01536) 264422

Oakbray Ltd, Whieldon Industrial Estate, Whieldon Road, Stoke-on-Trent, ST4 4JP Tel: (01782) 744555 Fax: (01782) 414244 E-mail: sales@oakbray.co.uk

Piltec Rubber & Plastic Ltd, Waterloo Park, Bidford-on-Avon, Alcester, Warwickshire, B50 4JG Tel: (01789) 778271 Fax: (01789) 772886 E-mail: sales@piltec.com

R G H Rubber & Plastics Ltd, Acorn House, Oak Industrial Park, Chelmsford Road, Great Dunmow, Dunmow, Essex, CM6 1XN Tel: (01371) 875941 Fax: (01371) 873804 E-mail: sales@rghrubber.co.uk

Rubbarite Ltd, 23-27 Boundary Street, Liverpool, L5 9ZQ Tel: 0151-298 1038 Fax: 0151-298 1910 E-mail: rubbarite@btconnect.com

Rubber & Plastic Profiles Co., Unit 1, 35 Boldmere Road, Sutton Coldfield, West Midlands, B73 5UY Tel: 0121-354 6356 Fax: 0121-355 7290 E-mail: info@rubberandplasticprofiles.co.uk

S M Goodchild Ltd, East Common Lane, Scunthorpe, South Humberside, DN16 1DE Tel: (01724) 848200 Fax: (01724) 280274

Sealing Solutions Ltd, 1 Wheatear, Perry Road, Witham, Essex, CM8 3YY Tel: (01376) 503633 Fax: (01376) 503733

Stockwell Mouldings, 4 Oughton Road, Birmingham, B12 0DF Tel: 0121-440 6555 Fax: 0121-440 6555 E-mail: info@stockwell-mouldings.co.uk

▶ Trafford Rubber Products Ltd, Greengate Works, Broadoak Business Park, Ashburton Road West, Trafford Park, Manchester, M17 1RW Tel: 0161-873 7172 Fax: 0161-848 9762 E-mail: traffordrubber@beeb.net

Trelleborg Woodville, Hearthcote Road, Swadlincote, Derbyshire, DE11 9DX Tel: (01283) 222145 Fax: (01283) 222911 E-mail: john.blackham@trelleborg.com

Veker Extrusions Ltd, Shaftmoor Lane, Hall Green, Birmingham, B28 8SP Tel: 0121-777 5000 Fax: 0121-777 5015 E-mail: enquiries@vekex.com

Vredestein (UK) Ltd, Unit D, Whittle Close, Park Farm Industrial Estate, Wellingborough, Northamptonshire, NN8 6TY Tel: (01933) 677770 Fax: (01933) 675329 E-mail: customer.uk@vredestein.com

Wrexham Rubber & Fabrications Ltd, Unit 226B Redwither Complex, Wrexham Industrial Estate, Wrexham, Clwyd, LL13 9UE Tel: (01978) 661869 Fax: (01978) 664566

INDUSTRIAL SAFETY CLOTHING

Arco, PO Box 78, Watford, WD24 4YT Tel: (01923) 202090 Fax: (01923) 202010 E-mail: arco@watford.co.uk

Birmingham Safety Wear, Unit 14 Mount Street Business Centre, Mount Street, Nechells, Birmingham, B7 5RD Tel: 0121-327 0873 Fax: 0121-327 0873 E-mail: sales@birminghamsafetywear.co.uk

Collard Industrial Gloves Ltd, Portskewett Street, Newport, Gwent, NP19 0GJ Tel: (01633) 213471 Fax: (01633) 257696

Contamination Control Apparel Ltd, Northolt Drive, Bolton, BL3 6RE Tel: (01204) 528019 Fax: (01204) 361549E-mail: cca@mikar.co.uk

Cookson & Clegg, PO Box 11, Blackburn, BB1 2WX Tel: (01254) 844544 Fax: (01254) 844545 E-mail: sales@cooksonclegg.com

Cosalt Workwear Ltd, Banner House, Greg Street, Stockport, Cheshire, SK5 7BT Tel: (0800) 0188110 Fax: (0870) 8502378 E-mail: info@cosalt-workwear.com

Guardsman Ltd, 24 Pasture Lane, Leicester, LE1 4EY Tel: 0116-253 8688 Fax: 0116-251 4202 E-mail: sales@guardsmanltd.co.uk

Jays Racewear, Throstle Nest Mill, Leeds Road, Nelson, Lancashire, BB9 7QZ Tel: (01282) 677907 Fax: (01282) 697319 E-mail: sales@jaysracewear.co.uk

Longworth Ltd, Leltex House, Longley Lane, Manchester, M22 4SY Tel: 0161-945 1333 Fax: 0161-946 0026 E-mail: sales@longworth.co.uk

Maco Manufacturing Co. Ltd, 6d The St Industrial Estate, Heybridge Street, Maldon, Essex, CM9 4XT Tel: (01621) 856789 Fax: (01621) 851358 E-mail: info@maco.uk.com

Seasafe Systems Ltd, Mar, Cowes, Isle of Wight, PO31 8PB Tel: (01983) 282388 Fax: (01983) 282399 E-mail: admin@seasafe.co.uk

Teejay Workwear Ltd, Dy2 Dean Clough Office Park, Halifax, West Yorkshire, HX3 5AX Tel: (01422) 369754 Fax: (01422) 383223 E-mail: sales@teejayworkwear.co.uk

Trelleborg Beadle, Unit 30 Bergen Way, Hull, HU7 0YQ Tel: (01482) 839119 Fax: (01482) 879418 E-mail: lesley.kidd@trelleborg.com

Tunika Safety Products, Tannery House, Nelson Street, Bolton, BL3 2JW Tel: (01204) 366713 Fax: (01204) 366714 E-mail: sales@tunikasafety.co.uk

Wearwell Group Ltd, Gargarin, Lichfield Road, Tamworth, Staffordshire, B79 7TR Tel: (01827) 310553 Fax: (01827) 66139 E-mail: sales@wearwell.co.uk

INDUSTRIAL SAFETY EQUIPMENT

A B Trade Supplies, South Denes Road, Great Yarmouth, Norfolk, NR30 3PF Tel: (01493) 859475 Fax: (01493) 330544 E-mail: sales@abtradesupplies.co.uk

Airchannel, 115 Burrell Road, Ipswich, IP2 8AE Tel: (01473) 690000 Fax: (01473) 685058 E-mail: enquiries@anglair.co.uk

Allcord Ltd, Ilford Road, Newcastle upon Tyne, NE2 3NX Tel: 0191-284 8444 Fax: 0191-284 1550 E-mail: enquiries@allcord.co.uk

ARCO West Bromwich, PO Box 2210, West Bromwich, West Midlands, B71 1DQ Tel: 0121-500 4444 Fax: 0121-553 7554 E-mail: westbromwich.branch@arco.co.uk

Bacou Dalloz Ltd, Osborn Way Industrial Estate, Osborn Way, Hook, Hampshire, RG27 9HX Tel: (01256) 693200 Fax: (01256) 693300 E-mail: info@dalloz.co.uk

Bristol Industrial Protection Ltd, Avonmouth Docks Estate, Chittening, Bristol, BS11 0YB Tel: 0117-982 7418 Fax: 0117-923 5961 E-mail: eip@netgates.co.uk

Centurion Safety Products Ltd, 21 Howlett Way, Thetford, Norfolk, IP24 1HZ Tel: (01842) 754266 Fax: (01842) 765590 E-mail: sales@centurionsafety.co.uk

Chadwicks Liverpool Ltd, 62-64 Kitchen Street, Liverpool, L1 0AN Tel: 0151-709 3081 Fax: 0151-709 9115

Chas E Prossor & Co. Ltd, 14 Dryden Street, Liverpool, L5 5HD Tel: 0151-207 1832 Fax: 0151-298 1101 E-mail: richard.prossor@prossor.com

Clad Safety Products, PO Box 123, Harrogate, North Yorkshire, HG1 4PT Tel: (01423) 881266

Cleaning & Packaging Supplies (Worcester), A Perrywood Trading Park, Wylds Lane, Worcester, WR5 1DZ Tel: (01905) 763500 Fax: (01905) 763363 E-mail: cps.worcs@btinternet.com

Corton Sinclair Ltd, 36 Glenburn Road, East Kilbride, Glasgow, G74 5BA Tel: (01355) 222273 Fax: (01355) 263682 E-mail: sales@corstonsinclair.com

Cosalt International Ltd, School Road, Lowestoft, Suffolk, NR33 9NB Tel: (01502) 516731 Fax: (01502) 500659 E-mail: lowestoft@cosalt.co.uk

D D Health & Safety Supplies Ltd, Unit 2, Kingsway, City Trading Estate, Norwich, NR2 4UE Tel: (01603) 628891 Fax: (01603) 764882 E-mail: bpuplett@dd-healthandsafetysupplies.co.uk

Deltawaite Ltd, Old Dairy, Roose Road, Barrow-in-Furness, Cumbria, LA13 0EP Tel: (01229) 821959 Fax: (01229) 820377 E-mail: sales@deltawaite.co.uk

Enfield Safety Supplies, 40 Queensway, Enfield, Middlesex, EN3 4SP Tel: (020) 8805 1015 Fax: (0870) 3800077

Flameskill Ltd, Unit 1 R & A Development, Great Yarmouth, Norfolk, NR31 0LT Tel: (01493) 440464 Fax: (01493) 440581 E-mail: admin@flameskill.co.uk

Hexagon Safety Products Sales Ltd, Unit 4A Elstree Film Studios, Shenley Road, Borehamwood, Hertfordshire, WD6 1JG Tel: (020) 8207 0003 Fax: (020) 8905 1036 E-mail: borehamwood.hiredesk@hireorbuy.co.uk

Hy Protec Health & Safety Ltd, Withambrook Park Industrial Estate, Grantham, Lincolnshire, NG31 9ST Tel: (01476) 573460 Fax: (01476) 563635 E-mail: paul@hy-protec.com

Kelly's Industrial Clothing Ltd, 22a Allport Lane, Wirral, Merseyside, CH62 7HP Tel: 0151-334 2318

Kingtools Power Tools, Norris Way, Rushden, Northamptonshire, NN10 6BP Tel: (01933) 410900 Fax: (01933) 350471 E-mail: sales@kingtools.co.uk

Kirklands Ltd, Kirkland House, Main Cross Road, Great Yarmouth, Norfolk, NR30 3NZ Tel: (01493) 843060 Fax: (01493) 853001 E-mail: sales@kirkgroup.co.uk

Langstone Safetywear Ltd, 1 St. Johns Court, Upper Forest Way, Swansea Enterprise Park, Swansea, SA6 8QR Tel: (01792) 535500 Fax: (01792) 535509 E-mail: info@langstone.co.uk

Lion Safety Products, Jackson Avenue, Grangemouth, Stirlingshire, FK3 8JU Tel: (01324) 474744

John Liscombe Ltd, Mariner Way, Felnex Industrial Estate, Newport, Gwent, NP19 4PQ Tel: (01633) 284100 Fax: (01633) 284125 E-mail: sales@liscombe.co.uk

M J P Ltd, 9 Alpha Business Park, Travellers Close, North Mymms, Hatfield, Hertfordshire, AL9 7NT Tel: (01707) 261179 Fax: (01707) 272470 E-mail: mike.player@virgin.net

Mcarthur Group Ltd, Economy House Copley Hill Trading Estate, Whitehall Road, Leeds, LS12 1HE Tel: 0113-245 7557 Fax: 0113-242 1150 E-mail: marketing@mcarthur-group.com

Main Man Supplies, Station Approach, Adisham, Canterbury, Kent, CT3 3JE Tel: (01304) 842030 Fax: (01304) 841312 E-mail: mnshydra@hotmail.com

Mersey Equipment Co. Ltd, Arcade Housed, 82-90 Taylor Street, Birkenhead, Merseyside, CH41 1BQ Tel: 0151-647 9751 Fax: 0151-647 3343 E-mail: admin@merseq.fssbusiness.co.uk

Olympia Triumph International Ltd, 5 Queens Road, Swanage, Dorset, BH19 2EQ Tel: (01929) 424326 Fax: (01929) 427403 E-mail: sales@olympia-triumph.co.uk

Parker Merchanting, Unit 1 Block E Larkfield Trading Estate, New Hythe Lane, Aylesford, Kent, ME20 6XQ Tel: (01622) 710863 Fax: (01622) 719222

Parker Merchanting Ltd, Chester Street, Aston, Birmingham, B6 4AE Tel: 0121-503 4500 Fax: 0121-503 4501 E-mail: info.parker@hagemeyer.co.uk

Parker Merchanting Ltd, Cofton Road, Marsh Barton Trading Estate, Exeter, EX2 8QW Tel: (01392) 288900 Fax: (01392) 288901 E-mail: info.parker@hagemeyer.co.uk

Parker Merchanting Ltd, 730 South Street, Glasgow, G14 0TR Tel: 0141-342 5600 Fax: 0141-342 5601 E-mail: info.parker@hagemeyer.co.uk

Parker Merchanting Ltd, Spitfire Close, Ermine Business Park, Huntingdon, Cambridgeshire, PE29 6YF Tel: (01480) 433335 Fax: (01480) 433409

Parker Merchanting Ltd, Benfield Road, Newcastle upon Tyne, NE6 5XA Tel: 0191-265 8312 Fax: 0191-276 2509 E-mail: info.parker@hagemeyer.co.uk

Parker Merchanting Ltd, Units 19-20 White Lodge Business Park, Hall Road, Norwich, NR4 6DG Tel: (01603) 763778 Fax: (01603) 763776 E-mail: info.parker@hagemeyer.co.uk

Parker Merchanting Ltd, 1-2 Longwall Avenue, Queens Drive Industrial Estate, Nottingham, NG2 1NA Tel: 0115-986 2121 Fax: 0115-986 2509 E-mail: info.parker@hagemeyer.co.uk

Parker Merchanting Ltd, 3 Cowley Business Centre, Watlington Road, Cowley, Oxford, OX4 6NH Tel: (01865) 785700 Fax: (01865) 785777 E-mail: info.parker@hagemeyer.co.uk

Parker Merchanting Ltd, Unit 8-9 Seaway Parade Industrial Estate, Port Talbot, West Glamorgan, SA12 7BR Tel: (01639) 813878 Fax: (01639) 823079 E-mail: info.parker@hagemeyer.co.uk

Parker Merchanting Ltd, J Guild Trading Estate, Ribbleton Lane, Preston, PR1 5DP Tel: (01772) 796939 Fax: (01772) 793138 E-mail: info.parker@hagemeyer.co.uk

Parker Merchanting Ltd, Unit 38 South Hampshire Industrial Park, Totton, Southampton, SO40 3SA Tel: (023) 8066 1414 Fax: (023) 8066 1415 E-mail: info.parker@hagemeyer.co.uk

Parker Merchanting, Unit 3, 1 Glen Tye Road, Broadleys Industrial Estate, Stirling, FK7 7LH Tel: (01786) 463921 Fax: (01786) 450089 E-mail: stirling.parker@hagemeyer.co.uk

Parker Merchanting Ltd, 4 Horton Industrial Park, Horton Road, West Drayton, Middlesex, UB7 8JD Tel: (01895) 444040 Fax: (01895) 420036 E-mail: info.parker@hagemeyer.co.uk

Parker Merchanting, 2 Page Lane, Widnes, Cheshire, WA8 0AF Tel: 0151-420 7787 Fax: 0151-495 1589 E-mail: info.parker@hagemeyer.co.uk

Parker Merchanting, Ward Street, Ettingshall, Wolverhampton, WV2 2PJ Tel: (01902) 385066 Fax: (01902) 385060 E-mail: info.parker@hagemeyer.co.uk

Parker Merchanting, Unit 2 3, Orbital Centre Southend Road, Woodford Green, Essex, IG8 8HH Tel: (020) 8709 7600 Fax: (020) 8709 7636 E-mail: info.parker@hagemeyer.co.uk

PH Industrial Ltd, 8 Wheldon Road, Widnes, Cheshire, WA8 8FW Tel: 0151-257 9696 Fax: 0151-257 8585

Phoenix Accessories Safety Ltd, Waterloo Mills, Waterloo Road, Pudsey, West Yorkshire, LS28 8DQ Tel: 0113-257 4475 Fax: 0113-255 0208 E-mail: phoenixsafety@lineone.com

Phoenix Saxton Ltd, Thornton Industrial Trading Estate, Milford Haven, Dyfed, SA73 2RR Tel: (01646) 690588 Fax: (01646) 690570

Progressive Safety Footwear & Clothing Ltd, 101 Worthing Road, Sheffield, S9 3JN Tel: 0114-273 8349 Fax: 0114-275 2452 E-mail: info@psf.co.uk

Provincial Safety Services Ltd, Portway Road, Oldbury, West Midlands, B69 2BP Tel: 0121-544 5208 Fax: 0121-552 9075 E-mail: provincialsafety@btconnect.com

Randalls, 304-312 Selbourne Road, Luton, LU4 8NX Tel: (01582) 496911 Fax: (01582) 494144 E-mail: sales@randallsluton.co.uk

Regency International Safety Group Ltd, Allenby Street, Scunthorpe, South Humberside, DN15 6EL Tel: (01724) 277933 Fax: (01724) 277933 E-mail: regencyintgrp@aol.com

Resmar Ltd, 39 Dean Street, Winsford, Cheshire, CW7 1HG Tel: (01606) 863399 Fax: (01606) 558200 E-mail: wyn@resmar.co.uk

Safety Equipment South West, Tinney Hall Cottage, Lewannick, Launceston, Cornwall, PL15 7QE Tel: (01566) 782393 Fax: (01566) 782401

Safpro Industrial Supply Co., Unit 4-5 Ashville Industrial Estate, Ashville Road, Gloucester, GL2 5EU Tel: (01452) 529050 Fax: (01452) 311221

South Staffs Supplies, Langley Heath Business Park, Eastern Avenue, Lichfield, Staffordshire, WS13 6RL Tel: (01543) 258883 Fax: (01543) 417444

Subtech Safety Ltd, Unit 16e Top Barn Business Centre, Worcester Road, Holt Heath, Worcester, WR6 6NH Tel: (01905) 621553 E-mail: info@subtech.co.uk

▶ Taf Tyre Products, Littleton House, Littleton Road, Ashford, Middlesex, TW15 1UU Tel: (01784) 420505 Fax: (01784) 259707 E-mail: tas@tas-tryreproducts.com

Teleshore UK Ltd, Unit 3 Llanhilleth Industrial Estate, Llanhilleth, Abertillery, Gwent, NP13 2RX Tel: (01495) 212232 Fax: (01495) 211109 E-mail: info@teleshore.com

Till & Whitehead, 65 Brindley Road, Astmoor Industrial Estate, Runcorn, Cheshire, WA7 1PF Tel: (01928) 581200 Fax: (01928) 580859 E-mail: info@tillwite.com

W J Nelson & Son Ltd, Fashoda Street, Belfast, BT5 5EX Tel: (028) 9045 6020 Fax: (028) 9073 8312 E-mail: wjnsafe@aol.com

INDUSTRIAL SAFETY EQUIPMENT HIRE

Rossendale Group, Roman Way, South Hykeham, Lincoln, LN6 9UH Tel: (01522) 693423 Fax: (01522) 693988

INDUSTRIAL SAFETY EQUIPMENT HIRE – *continued*

Subtech Safety Ltd, Unit 16e Top Barn Business Centre, Worcester Road, Holt Heath, Worcester, WR6 6NH Tel: (01905) 621553 E-mail: info@subtech.co.uk
Universal Supplies UK Ltd, South Street, Retford, Nottinghamshire, DN22 6JJ Tel: (01777) 706600 Fax: (01777) 706600

INDUSTRIAL SAFETY EQUIPMENT INSTALLATION

Castell Iso Lok, The Castell Building, 217 Kingsbury Road, London, NW9 9PQ Tel: (020) 8511 1858 Fax: (020) 8205 0055 E-mail: sales@castell.com
Castell Safety International Ltd, The Castell Building, 217 Kingsbury Road, London, NW9 9PQ Tel: (020) 8200 1200 Fax: (020) 8205 0055 E-mail: sales@castell.com
Gecko Safety Systems Ltd, Unit M5 Cherrycourt Way, Leighton Buzzard, Bedfordshire, LU7 4UH Tel: (01525) 382040 Fax: (01525) 378956 E-mail: info@geckosafety.co.uk
Pascal Scientific Ltd, 10 Chesterfield Way, Hayes, Middlesex, UB3 3NW Tel: (020) 8848 1849 Fax: (020) 8848 8595 E-mail: admin@pascalscientific.co.uk

INDUSTRIAL SAFETY HELMETS

Centurion Safety Products Ltd, 21 Howlett Way, Thetford, Norfolk, IP24 1HZ Tel: (01842) 754266 Fax: (01842) 765590 E-mail: sales@centurionsafety.co.uk
Helmet Integrated Systems, 3 Focus 4, Fourth Avenue, Letchworth Garden City, Hertfordshire, SG6 2TU Tel: (01462) 478000 Fax: (01462) 478010 E-mail: sales@helmets.co.uk

INDUSTRIAL SALT SPREADERS

Kuhn Farm Machinery (UK) Ltd, Stafford Park 7, Telford, Shropshire, TF3 3BQ Tel: (01952) 239300 Fax: (01952) 290091 E-mail: infouk@kuhn.co.uk

INDUSTRIAL SCALES

Avery Weigh-Tronix Ltd, Unit 8 Fieldhouse Way, Sheffield, S4 7SF Tel: (0870) 4420000 Fax: 0114-243 2235 E-mail: info@awtxglobal.com
Avery Weigh-Tronix, Foundry Lane, Smethwick, West Midlands, B66 2LP Tel: (01624) 675770 Fax: (0870) 9000366 E-mail: info@awtxglobal.com
Direct Weigh, 14 Milldown Avenue, Goring, Reading, RG8 0AS Tel: (01491) 872042 Fax: (01491) 873782E-mail: sales@flintec.net
MK Scales Ltd, Cherrycourt Way, Leighton Buzzard, Bedfordshire, LU7 4UH Tel: (01525) 375519 Fax: (01525) 377290 E-mail: sales@mkscales.co.uk
Newtec Odense UK Ltd, 1 Park View, Arrow, Alcester, Warwickshire, B49 5PN Tel: (01789) 764590 Fax: (01789) 763836 E-mail: p.crouch@newtecuk.com
Scale Services, 33 Business Village, Wexham Road, Slough, SL2 5HF Tel: (01753) 511801 Fax: (01753) 694447
Scanvaegt N I Ltd, Unit 10 Mckibbin House, Eastbank Road, Carryduff, Belfast, BT8 8BD Tel: (028) 9081 3735 Fax: (028) 90813809
Weigh Control Systems Ltd, 2 Felton Mill, Felton, Morpeth, Northumberland, NE65 9HL Tel: (01670) 787177 Fax: (01670) 787179

INDUSTRIAL SCREENS

Agri Web, Enterprise House, 2-4 Balloo Avenue, Bangor, County Down, BT19 7QT Tel: (028) 9127 5913 Fax: (028) 9127 5563
Mono Pumps Ltd, Martin St, Audenshaw, Manchester, M34 5JA Tel: 0161-339 9000 Fax: 0161-344 0727 E-mail: info@mono-pumps.com
Thanet Coatings Ltd, Unit 4 Patricia Way, Pysons Road Industrial Estate, Broadstairs, Kent, CT10 2LF Tel: (01843) 861861 Fax: (01843) 866366
▶ W B Chadbourn Scaffolding & Industrial Screens Ltd, Unit 9 Curriers Close, Charter Avenue Industrial Esta, Coventry, CV4 8AW Tel: (024) 7646 2742 Fax: (024) 7646 4652 E-mail: jackie@chadbourn.co.uk

INDUSTRIAL SEALANTS

Adshead Ratcliffe, Derby Road, Belper, Derbyshire, DE56 1WJ Tel: (01773) 596300 Fax: (01773) 821215 E-mail: admin@arbo.co.uk
▶ Flat Roofing Supplies, Tinsley Lane North, Crawley, West Sussex, RH10 9FF Tel: (01293) 590970 Fax: (01293) 543562
Geocel Ltd, Western Wood Way, Langage Business Park, Plympton, Plymouth, PL7 5BG Tel: (01752) 202060 Fax: (01752) 202065 E-mail: info@geocel.co.uk

Orapi Ltd, 1 Rosse Street, Bradford, West Yorkshire, BD8 9AS Tel: (01274) 822000 Fax: (01274) 822002 E-mail: jo.greenwood@orapi.com

INDUSTRIAL SERVICES CONTRACTORS

Instrucomm Ltd, 2a Crosier Court, Upchurch, Sittingbourne, Kent, ME9 7AR Tel: (01634) 376147 Fax: (01634) 376147

INDUSTRIAL SEWING MACHINES

Alan Godrich, 17-20 Charter Street, Leicester, LE1 3UD Tel: 0116-253 2322 Fax: 0116-262 9887 E-mail: sales@alan-godrich.com
▶ Eastman Staples Ltd, 131 Lockwood Road, Huddersfield, HD1 3QW Tel: (01484) 888888 Fax: (01484) 888800 E-mail: enquiries@eastman.co.uk
Jobson Sewing Machines Ltd, 337 St. Saviours Road, Leicester, LE5 4HH Tel: 0116-273 3338 Fax: 0116-273 3339
Pressmech Sewing Machines, 3 Walton New Road, Bruntingthorpe, Lutterworth, Leicestershire, LE17 5RD Tel: 0116-247 8071 Fax: (01455) 251320 E-mail: pressmech@aol.com
A M F Reece (UK), Clayton Wood Close, West Park Ring Road, Leeds, LS16 6QE Tel: 0113-275 9131 Fax: 0113-275 4116 E-mail: amfreece@amfreece.co.uk
M. Robinson Inc Ltd, 20 Victoria Terrace, Newbridge, Newport, Gwent, NP11 4ET Tel: (01495) 244593 Fax: (01495) 244593 E-mail: mrsewingmachines@aol.com
Sew Amazing Ltd, 80 St. Stephen's Road, London, E3 5JL Tel: (020) 8980 8898 Fax: (020) 8980 6989 E-mail: sewamazing@hotmail.co.uk
Sew Europe, 88 Rice Lane, Walton, Liverpool, L9 1DD Tel: 0151-525 0511 Fax: 0151-525 0522 E-mail: seweurope@btopenworld.com
Singer Sewing Centre, 14 Donegall Road, Belfast, BT12 5JN Tel: (028) 9032 6002 Fax: (028) 9032 6002

INDUSTRIAL SHELVING

Bigdug.Co.Uk, Unit 41 Staunton Court Business Park, Ledbury Road, Staunton, Gloucester, GL19 3QS Tel: (0845) 0654000 E-mail: racking9@gmail.com
Cupboards Direct Ltd, PO BOX 6788, Northampton, NN1 4WP Tel: (0870) 7661826 Fax: (0800) 1698127 E-mail: sales@cupboardsdirect.co.uk
Link 51 (Shelving Storage) Ltd, 16 Mill St, Brierley Hill, West Midlands, DY5 2TB Tel: (01384) 472500 Fax: (01384) 472599 E-mail: shelving@link51.co.uk
Romstor Ltd, Unit 22,, West Station Ind. Estate, Spital Road,, Maldon, Essex, CM9 6TS Tel: 01621 855600 Fax: 01621 875919 E-mail: sales@romstor.co.uk
Sarralle UK UK Ltd, 87 West Street, Oundle, Peterborough, PE8 4EJ Tel: (01832) 270371 Fax: (01430) 473027 E-mail: mail@sarralleuk.fsnet.co.uk
▶ Transformer Systems, 9 Easy Road, Leeds, LS9 8QS Tel: 0113-216 8392 Fax: 0113-216 9491 E-mail: info@transformersystems.co.uk

INDUSTRIAL SHOCK ABSORBERS

Lisega Ltd, Unit3, Washington Centre, Hales Owen Road, Netherton, West Midlands, DY2 9RE Tel: (01384) 458660 Fax: (01384) 213301 E-mail: sales@lisega.co.uk
Oleo International Ltd, Longford Road, Longford Road, Coventry, CV7 9ND Tel: (024) 7664 5555 Fax: (024) 7664 5777 E-mail: roy@oleo.co.uk
Specialty Fasteners & Components Ltd, Seymour Wharf, Steamer Quay Road, Totnes, Devon, TQ9 5AL Tel: (01803) 868677 Fax: (01803) 868678 E-mail: sales@specialty-fasteners.co.uk
Tapmatic Engineers' Merchants, 7d Millers Close, Fakenham, Norfolk, NR21 8NW Tel: (01328) 863676 Fax: (01328) 856118 E-mail: info@tapmatic.co.uk

INDUSTRIAL SHREDDING MACHINES

C L Shredders, Unit 1, Angeldown Farm, Manor Rd, Wantage, Oxon, OX12 8NQ Tel: (0800) 9757235 Fax: (01235) 765474 E-mail: cluton@clshredders.co.uk
FCE Engineering Ltd, Methilhaven Road, Methil, Leven, Fife, KY8 3LA Tel: (01333) 423557 Fax: (01333) 423582
Lennox House Holdings Ltd, Beeding Close, Southern Cross Trading Estate, Bognor Regis, West Sussex, PO22 9TS Tel: (01243) 866565 Fax: (01243) 868301 E-mail: enquiries@ggcompacters.co.uk

▶ Middleton Engineering Ltd, Ashcott Road, Meare, Glastonbury, Somerset, BA6 9SU Tel: (01458) 860264 Fax: (01458) 860311 E-mail: middletonadmin@btconnect.com
Ulster Engineering Ltd, Cogry Mill, Cogry Road, Doagh, Ballyclare, County Antrim, BT39 0PU Tel: (028) 9335 2526 Fax: (028) 9335 2302 E-mail: sales@ulster-engineering.co.uk
Richard Western Ltd, The Durbans, Apsey Green, Framlingham, Woodbridge, Suffolk, IP13 9RP Tel: (01728) 723224 Fax: (01728) 724291 E-mail: sales@richard-western.co.uk

INDUSTRIAL SILENCERS

A & I (Peco) Acoustics Ltd, 100 Sandford Street, Birkenhead, Merseyside, CH41 1AZ Tel: 0151-647 9015 Fax: 0151-666 1805 E-mail: sales@peco.co.uk
Plastic Tanks & Fabrications Ltd, Unit 5, Stone Lane Industrial Estate, Wimborne, Dorset, BH21 1HD Tel: (01202) 888133 Fax: (01202) 886288 E-mail: ptf@avnet.co.uk

INDUSTRIAL SITE SAFETY BARRIERS

Craig Collier, Linney Lane, Shaw, Oldham, OL2 8HD Tel: (01706) 845800 Fax: (01706) 880877 E-mail: sales@craigcollier.co.uk
Luxtrade Ltd, Unit C5 Hilton Trading Estate, Hilton Road, Lanesfield, Wolverhampton, WV4 6DW Tel: (01902) 353182 Fax: (01902) 404628 E-mail: sales@luxtrade.co.uk

INDUSTRIAL SOUND INSULATION, *See Noise etc*

INDUSTRIAL SPRAYING CONTRACTORS

A G Bracey Paint Division, P O Box 8, Bristol, BS30 5NE Tel: 0117-937 4376 Fax: 0117-937 4326
▶ Icom Spray Paint Systems, Penn Road, Hazlemere, High Wycombe, Buckinghamshire, HP15 7PB Tel: (01494) 812733 E-mail: mail@icomsps.freeserve.co.uk
M & B Spraying, 2b Radnor Road, Wigston, Leicestershire, LE18 4XY Tel: 0116-277 8740 Fax: 0116-277 8740
Peter S Toms & Co., Charlton Mead Lane, Hoddesdon, Hertfordshire, EN11 0DJ Tel: (01992) 464436 Fax: (01992) 448433

INDUSTRIAL STEAM CLEANING CONTRACTORS

Scotkleen Warwick Power Washers, 149a Glasgow Road, Wishaw, Lanarkshire, ML2 7QJ Tel: (0870) 8600600 Fax: (01698) 356697 E-mail: info@scotkleen.co.uk

INDUSTRIAL STERILISERS

Diskovery Business Services, 123 Bournemouth Road, Poole, Dorset, BH14 9HR Tel: (01202) 733620 Fax: (01202) 737184 E-mail: dbs@diskovery.co.uk
Getinge UK Ltd, Orchard Way, Sutton-in-Ashfield, Nottinghamshire, NG17 1JU Tel: (01623) 510033 Fax: (01623) 440456
Hyclone UK Ltd, 9 Atley Way, North Nelson Industrial Estate, Cramlington, Northumberland, NE23 1WA Tel: (01670) 734093 Fax: (01670) 732537
Sal Europe Ltd, Houghton Road, Grantham, Lincolnshire, NG31 6JE Tel: (01476) 515550 Fax: (01476) 515551 E-mail: general@sal-europe.com

INDUSTRIAL STORAGE EQUIPMENT

▶ Atlas Handling Ltd, Unit 15, Bondor Business Centre, London Road, Baldock, Hertfordshire, SG7 6HP Tel: (01462) 491700 Fax: (01462) 491666 E-mail: john.p.johnson@btconnect.com
Autoscan Ltd, 61 High Road, Beeston, Nottingham, NG9 4AJ Tel: 0115-922 4249 Fax: 0115-922 9142 E-mail: info@autoscanuk.co.uk

INDUSTRIAL STRAINERS

Barton Firtop Engineering, Stoke Heath Works, Hanbury Road, Stoke Heath, Bromsgrove, Worcestershire, B60 4LT Tel: (01527) 831664 Fax: (01527) 832638 E-mail: sales@bartonfirtop.co.uk
Hogg Engineering Ltd, Lawson Street, North Shields, Tyne & Wear, NE29 6TF Tel: 0191-259 5181 Fax: 0191-296 0641 E-mail: hogg-engineering@talk21.com

INDUSTRIAL STRUCTURAL OR ENGINEERING DESIGN

Leslie Wilks Associates, 1 Sunnyside, Claygate Road, Laddingford, Maidstone, Kent, ME18 6BQ Tel: (01892) 730863 Fax: (01892) 730864 E-mail: info@leslie-wilks.co.uk

INDUSTRIAL SUPPLY SERVICES

A Winston & Sons, 461 Paisley Road, Glasgow, G5 8RJ Tel: 0141-429 4278 Fax: 0141-429 0577 E-mail: bryanwinston@hotmail.co.uk
Adco Industrial Wear Ltd, 61 Court Road, Kingswood, Bristol, BS15 9QG Tel: 0117-967 7656 Fax: 0117-935 2546
Arrow Industrial Ltd, 930 Hedon Road, Hull, HU9 5QN Tel: (01482) 228202 Fax: (01482) 218697 E-mail: sales@arrow-industrial.co.uk
Buck & Hickman Ltd, Sterling Industrial Estate, Rainham Road South, Dagenham, Essex, RM10 8TA Tel: (020) 8593 8177 Fax: (020) 8984 1163 E-mail: exports@buckhickmaninone.com
Cresco Industrial Supplies Ltd, Brunel Close, Harworth, Doncaster, South Yorkshire, DN11 8QA Tel: (01302) 750057 Fax: (01302) 752922 E-mail: sales@cresco.co.uk
The Forklift Co., 4 Bank View, Froghall, Stoke-On-Trent, ST10 2HA Tel: (01538) 755500 Fax: (01538) 752821
Grand Engineering, Premier Works, Providence Street, Cradley Heath, West Midlands, B64 5DR Tel: (01384) 562551 Fax: (01384) 410144
H C Slingsby plc, 1303 Argyle Street, Glasgow, G3 8TL Tel: 0141-339 2256 Fax: 0141-339 4775
H T Industrial Supplies, Chapel Street, Goole, North Humberside, DN14 5RJ Tel: (01405) 766428 Fax: (01405) 768053 E-mail: htsupplies@ic24.net
Colin Hickey Fork Trucks Ltd, Unit 4 Ribble Industrial Estate, Newport Lane, Stoke-on-Trent, ST6 3BB Tel: (01782) 838888 Fax: (01782) 819000
Jacksons Tool & Plant Hire & Industrial Supplies, Dormagen, Laurencekirk, Kincardineshire, AB30 1UP Tel: (01561) 377060 Fax: (01561) 377016
Ken Taylor Ltd, Unit 1-2 Crown Business Centre, George Street, Failsworth, Manchester, M35 9BW Tel: 0161-682 9400 Fax: 0161-682 6833 E-mail: sales@kpsupplies.com
Mashlin Friction Ltd, 404-408 Cricket Inn Road, Sheffield, S2 5AX Tel: 0114-272 5650 Fax: 0114-265 1665
Plant-Mec Ireland, 39 Drumconwell Road, Armagh, BT60 2AT Tel: (028) 3751 1717 Fax: (028) 3751 8448 E-mail: info@plantmecireland.com
R & J Industrial Supplies, Clay Flatts Trading Estate, Workington, Cumbria, CA14 2TQ Tel: (01900) 605411 Fax: (01900) 605415
H. Rothwell, 1 Simmonds Way, Brierfield, Nelson, Lancashire, BB9 5SS Tel: (01282) 601861 Fax: (01282) 605345 E-mail: nelson@rothwells.co.uk
Shepherd & Miller, 94 Whyterose Terrace, Aberhill, Methil, Leven, Fife, KY8 3AS Tel: (01333) 426823 Fax: (01333) 423064
T D Distribution (UK) Ltd, 169 New Chester Road, Wirral, Merseyside, CH62 4RB Tel: 0151-643 1171 Fax: 0151-643 1483 E-mail: info@tddistribution.com

INDUSTRIAL SWITCHGEARS

A B B Ltd, Hanover Place, Sunderland, SR4 6BY Tel: 0191-514 4555 Fax: 0191-514 5505
A-Belco Property Ltd, Jubilee Industrial Estate, Ashington, Northumberland, NE63 8UG Tel: (01670) 813275 Fax: (01670) 851141 E-mail: sscullion@a-belco.co.uk
Acme Electrical Manufacturing Tottenham Ltd, Tariff Road, Tottenham, London, N17 0EP Tel: (020) 8808 2702 Fax: (020) 8801 9017
Actemium, Meteor Business Park, Cheltenham Road East, Gloucester, GL2 9QL Tel: (01452) 713222 Fax: (01452) 713444 E-mail: actemium@actemium.co.uk
Agut Control Gear Ltd, Mosley Street Works, Mosley Street, Blackburn, BB2 3SU Tel: (01254) 683714 Fax: (01254) 663630 E-mail: sales@agut.co.uk
Albright Engineers Ltd, 125 Red Lion Road, Surbiton, Surrey, KT6 7QS Tel: (020) 8390 5357 Fax: (020) 8390 1927 E-mail: sales@albright.co.uk
Allenwest Wallacetown Ltd, 66 Third Avenue, Heatherhouse Industrial Estate, Irvine, Ayrshire, KA12 8HN Tel: (01294) 273111 Fax: (01294) 274063 E-mail: sales@wallacetown.com
Baldwin & Francis, President Park, Sheffield, S4 7UQ Tel: 0114-286 6000 Fax: 0114-286 6059 E-mail: enquiries@baldwinandfrancis.com
Balfour Kilpatrick Ltd, Glasgow Road, Deanside, Renfrew, PA4 8XZ Tel: 0141-885 4321 Fax: 0141-885 4480 E-mail: enquiry@balfourkilpatrick.com
Boulting Group plc, Chapel Road, Penketh, Warrington, WA5 2PL Tel: (01925) 726661 Fax: (01925) 723508 E-mail: info@boulting.co.uk

INDUSTRIAL SWITCHGEARS – *continued*

C H S Switchgear Ltd, 3 Batford Mill Industrial Estate, Lower Luton Road, Harpenden, Hertfordshire, AL5 5BZ Tel: (01582) 766008 Fax: (01582) 461386 E-mail: mailbox@chsswitchgear.co.uk

Eaton MEM, Grimshaw Lane, Middleton, Manchester, M24 1GQ Tel: 0161-655 8900 Fax: 0161-626 1709 E-mail: ukcommorders@eaton.com

Elecsis Ltd, Yeo Road, Bridgwater, Somerset, TA6 5NA Tel: (01278) 453198 Fax: (01278) 453198 E-mail: chris.pratt@elecsis.com

Genpart UK Ltd, 5 Threxton Road Industrial Estate, Watton, Thetford, Norfolk, IP25 6NG Tel: (01953) 882436 Fax: (01953) 885597 E-mail: sales@genpart.co.uk

Merlin Gerin, 123 Jack Lane, Leeds, LS10 1BS Tel: 0113-290 3500 Fax: 0113-290 3710 E-mail:

Hawker Siddeley Switchgear Ltd, Newport Road, Pontllanfraith, Blackwood, Gwent, NP12 2XH Tel: (01495) 223001 Fax: (01495) 225674 E-mail: sales@hss-ltd.com

Howarth Switchgear Ltd, Finlas Street, Cowlairs Industrial Estate, Glasgow, G22 5DT Tel: 0141-557 3553 Fax: 0141-558 0614 E-mail: sales@howarthswitchgear.co.uk

I C W Power Ltd, Joule House, 108-110 Primrose Hill, Kings Langley, Hertfordshire, WD4 8HR Tel: (01923) 266869 Fax: (01923) 264472 E-mail: sales@icwpower.com

Industrial & Marine Switchgear Ltd, Amsterdam Road, Sutton Fields Industrial Estate, Hull, HU7 0XF Tel: (01482) 831222 Fax: (01482) 826696 E-mail: information@ims-swgr.karoo.co.uk

Kane Engineering Ltd, Glenford Road, Newtownards, County Down, BT23 4AU Tel: (028) 9181 4465 Fax: (028) 9181 8900 E-mail: info@kane-engineering.co.uk

L C Switchgear Ltd, Unit 2, Hove Technology Centre, St Josephs Close, Hove, East Sussex, BN3 7ES Tel: (01273) 770540 Fax: (01273) 770547

Leicester Switch & Control Co. Ltd, Ross Walk, Leicester, LE4 5HA Tel: 0116-299 9277 Fax: 0116-299 9278 E-mail: lsc@lsandc.co.uk

Lucy Switchgear, Howland Road, Thame, Oxfordshire, OX9 3UJ Tel: (01844) 267222 Fax: (01844) 267223 E-mail: sales.switchgear@wlucy.co.uk

Northern Switch Gear & Controls, 2 Lloyd Court, Dunston, Gateshead, Tyne & Wear, NE11 9EP Tel: 0191-461 1130 Fax: 0191-461 1140 E-mail: nthnswitch@aol.com

P & B Power Engineering, Belle Vue Works, Boundary St, Manchester, M12 5NG Tel: 0161-223 5151 Fax: 0161-230 6464 E-mail: sales@pbeng.co.uk

Park Electrical Services, Crown Trading Centre, Clayton Road, Hayes, Middlesex, UB3 1DU Tel: (020) 8813 5889 Fax: (020) 8813 5946 E-mail: info@pes-group.co.uk

Rappell Switchgear Ltd, Moston Road, Sandbach, Cheshire, CW11 3HL Tel: (01270) 761135 Fax: (01270) 762997 E-mail: sales@rappell.co.uk

Rees Switchgear Ltd, 157 Clarence Avenue, Northampton, NN2 6NY Tel: (01604) 597860 Fax: (01604) 597861 E-mail: janwimpress@rf-plc.com

Specialist Switchgear Systems Ltd, 9 Kay Street, Bury, Lancashire, BL9 6BU Tel: 0161-764 1297 Fax: 0161-762 9807

Stroud Switchgear Developments Ltd, Unit 3, Lightpill Trading Estate, Stroud, Gloucestershire, GL5 3LL Tel: (01453) 762709 Fax: (01453) 751977 E-mail: sales@stroud-switchgear.com

Switchgear Services Ltd, Reme Drive, Heathpark Industrial Estate, Honiton, Devon, EX14 1SE Tel: (01404) 44337 Fax: (01404) 45993 E-mail: hq@switchgear-services.co.uk

INDUSTRIAL TABLETS

Stonehouse Tablet Manufacturing Co. Ltd, Nottingham Road, Beeston, Nottingham, NG9 6DT Tel: 0115-925 4552 Fax: 0115-922 4226 E-mail: info@stonehousetablet.co.uk

Thompson & Capper Ltd, Hardwick Road, Astmoor Industrial Estate, Runcorn, Cheshire, WA7 1PH Tel: (01928) 573734 Fax: (01928) 580694 E-mail: info@tablets2buy.com

INDUSTRIAL TANK ULTRASONIC CLEANING EQUIPMENT

▶ Alphasonics Ultrasonic Equipment Mnfrs, Caddick Road, Knowsley Business Park, Prescot, Merseyside, L34 9HP Tel: 0151-547 3777 Fax: 0151-547 1333 E-mail: alphasonics@alphasonics.co.uk

INDUSTRIAL TASK LIGHTING

James Thomas Engineering Ltd, Navigation Complex, Navigation Road, Worcester, WR5 3DE Tel: (01905) 363600 Fax: (01905) 363601 E-mail: sales@jamesthomas.co.uk

INDUSTRIAL TELEPHONES

Arnesys Telecommunications Equipment, Queens Bridge Road, Nottingham, NG2 1NB Tel: 0115-985 2525 Fax: 0115-985 2526 E-mail: admin@arnesys.com

INDUSTRIAL THERMOMETERS

Instruments To Industry Ltd, Woodward Road, Knowsley Industrial Park North, Knowsley Industrial Park, Liverpool, L33 7UZ Tel: 0151-546 4943 Fax: 0151-548 6262 E-mail: sales@itiuk.com

James Scientific Instruments Ltd, PO Box 18134, London, EC1R 4WD Tel: (020) 7837 1154 Fax: (020) 7278 7293 E-mail: sales@jamessciinst.com

Star Instruments Ltd, Barkway, Royston, Hertfordshire, SG8 8EH Tel: (01763) 848886 Fax: (01763) 848881 E-mail: sales@star-instruments.co.uk

Stevenson Reeves Ltd, 40 Oxgangs Bank, Edinburgh, EH13 9LH Tel: 0131-445 7151 Fax: 0131-445 7323 E-mail: sales@stevenson-reeves.co.uk

Test Plugs Ltd, 12 Falklands Road, Haverhill, Suffolk, CB9 0EA Tel: (01440) 704201 Fax: (01440) 763121 E-mail: sales@test-plugs.com

West Meters Ltd, Phoenix House, London Road, Corwen, Clwyd, LL21 0DR Tel: (01490) 412004 Fax: (01490) 413336 E-mail: mail@westmeters.co.uk

INDUSTRIAL THERMOSTATS

Seagas Industries Ltd, 152 Abbey Lane, Leicester, LE4 0DA Tel: 0116-266 9988 Fax: 0116-268 2557E-mail: sales@seagas.net

Sunvic Controls Ltd, Bellshill Road, Uddingston, Glasgow, G71 6NP Tel: (01698) 812944 Fax: (01698) 813637 E-mail: sales@sunvic.co.uk

Thermodisc Thermostats, Castle House, Old Road, Leighton Buzzard, Bedfordshire, LU7 2RG Tel: (01525) 375655 Fax: (01525) 378075 E-mail: thermodiscuk@btconnect.com

INDUSTRIAL TINPLATE PACKAGING

▶ Bowler Group Ltd, Bowler House Harvey Road, Burnt Mills Industrial Estate, Basildon, Essex, SS13 1DD Tel: (01268) 470700 Fax: (01268) 477717 E-mail: info@hjbowlerandsons.com

Crown Speciality Packaging (UK), Heysham Road, Bootle, Merseyside, L30 6UR Tel: 0151-522 2222 Fax: 0151-522 2200

INDUSTRIAL TRAILERS

A H P Trailers Ltd, Heath Mill Road, Wombourne, Wolverhampton, WV5 8AP Tel: (01902) 895281 Fax: (01902) 894577

Adaptatruck, Elm Lodge, North Street, Winkfield, Windsor, Berkshire, SL4 4TE Tel: (01344) 891734 Fax: (01344) 891738 E-mail: derekwine@aol.com

Artic Trailers, Holton Road, Nettleton, Market Rasen, Lincolnshire, LN7 6AW Tel: (01472) 851314 Fax: (01472) 851314

Bailey Trailers Ltd, Main Street, Aunsby, Sleaford, Lincolnshire, NG34 8TA Tel: (01529) 455232 Fax: (01529) 455248 E-mail: sales@baileytrailers.co.uk

Bank Farm Trailers, The Garage, Llangunnor, Carmarthen, Dyfed, SA31 2PG Tel: (01267) 231565 Fax: (01267) 222154 E-mail: sales@bankfarm-trailers.co.uk

Bank Farm Trailers, Bank Farm, Spytty Road, Newport, Gwent, NP19 4QW Tel: (01633) 290291 Fax: (01633) 270400

Bank Farm Trailers Ltd, Unit 1 Mill Brook Yard, Landore, Swansea, SA1 2JG Tel: (01792) 795834 Fax: (01792) 799251 E-mail: sales@bankfarm-trailers.co.uk

Bateson Trailers Ltd, Doodfield Works, Windlehurst Road, Marple, Stockport, Cheshire, SK6 7EN Tel: 0161-426 0500 Fax: 0161-426 0245 E-mail: sales@bateson-trailers.co.uk

Brumfitt Factory Equipment Ltd, Foundry Works, Gibson Street, Laisterdyke, Bradford, West Yorkshire, BD3 9TF Tel: (01274) 666760 Fax: (01274) 666760

S. Cartwright & Sons, Atlantic Street, Broadheath, Altrincham, Cheshire, WA14 5DH Tel: 0161-928 0966 Fax: 0161-926 8410 E-mail: sales@cartwright-group.co.uk

East Cheshire Trailers, Sandy Lane Garage, Sandy Lane, Macclesfield, Cheshire, SK10 4RJ Tel: (01625) 611550 Fax: (01625) 611550

Handling Aids Ltd, Crowe Arch Lane, Ringwood, Hampshire, BH24 1PB Tel: (01425) 472263 Fax: (01425) 471248

Owen Holland Engineering Ltd, Holland Way, Blandford Forum, Dorset, DT11 7TA Tel: (01258) 452461 Fax: (01258) 480169 E-mail: sales@owenholland.com

Hunton Legg (Running Gear) Ltd, Bridge Works, Bruisyard, Saxmundham, Suffolk, IP17 2DT Tel: (01728) 663010 Fax: (01728) 664057 E-mail: sales@huntonlegg.co.uk

Indespension Ltd, 38a Nimmings Road, Halesowen, West Midlands, B62 9JE Tel: 0121-561 5467 Fax: 0121-561 2180 E-mail: westmids@indespention.com

Kay Trailers, 27 Stirling Road, Milnathort, Kinross, KY13 9XS Tel: (01577) 862493 Fax: (01577) 864864 E-mail: dropbox@kaytrailers.co.uk

Marston Agricultural Services Ltd, Toll Bar Road, Marston, Grantham, Lincolnshire, NG32 2HT Tel: (01400) 250226 Fax: (01400) 250540 E-mail: sales@mas-trailers-group.co.uk

Merrick Loggin Trailers, College Farm, Bicester Hill, Evenley, Brackley, Northamptonshire, NN13 5SD Tel: (01280) 702725 Fax: (01280) 702060 E-mail: loggin@freeuk.com

Oldbury UK Ltd, Bulliol Buisiness Park, Wobaston Road, Wolverhampton, WV9 5EU Tel: (01902) 397216 Fax: (01902) 878265 E-mail: sales@oldburyuk.co.uk

PRG Trailers & Towing Equipment, The Old Wood Yard, Lightwood Green Avenue, Audlem, Crewe, CW3 0EN Tel: (01270) 812402 Fax: (01270) 811293 E-mail: info@prgtrailers.co.uk

S P S Ltd, Unit 9, Buildwas Road, Clayhill Light Industrial Park, Neston, CH64 3TU Tel: 0151-353 1775 Fax: 0151-353 1775 E-mail: pyeinc@supanet.com

SDC Trailers Ltd, Bradder Way, Mansfield, Nottinghamshire, NG18 5DQ Tel: (01623) 625354 Fax: (01623) 626946 E-mail: admin@sdctrailers.com

Towrite Electric Vehicles (Harborough) Ltd, Albert Road, Market Harborough, Leicestershire, LE16 7LU Tel: (01858) 433548 Fax: (01858) 434209 E-mail: sales@towrite.co.uk

W H Davis Ltd, Langwith Road, Langwith Junction, Mansfield, Nottinghamshire, NG20 9SA Tel: (01623) 742621 Fax: (01623) 744474 E-mail: management@whdavis.co.uk

Wigan Trailer Centre Ltd, Cricket St Business Park, Cricket Street, Wigan, Lancashire, WN6 7TP Tel: (01942) 248373 Fax: (01942) 821317 E-mail: info@wtcltd.co.uk

INDUSTRIAL TRANSPORTERS

Dawson Bros, Gauntlet Road, Bicker, Boston, Lincolnshire, PE20 3AU Tel: (01775) 820273 Fax: (01775) 821691

Dobbs Logistics Ltd, 23 Hawthorn Road, Eastbourne, East Sussex, BN23 6QA Tel: (08708) 518770 Fax: (01323) 641539 E-mail: services@dobbslogistics.co.uk

Duggan Transport Ltd, Church Road, Shilton, Coventry, CV7 9HX Tel: (024) 7661 2871 Fax: (024) 7661 2871

F Dickson Transport Ltd, 51 Imperial Way, Croydon, CR0 4RR Tel: (020) 8686 6707 Fax: (020) 8686 9297 E-mail: higher@dicksons.co.uk

▶ Kenley Warehousing & Distribution, Darwen Mill, Hilton Street, Darwen, Lancashire, BB3 2AY Tel: (01254) 701633 Fax: (01254) 703378

R E Fielding Trucking Ltd, Iconfield Park, Freshfields Road, Parkeston, Harwich, Essex, CO12 4EN Tel: (01255) 504848 Fax: (01255) 508754

INDUSTRIAL TROLLEYS, *See headings under Trucks/Trolleys etc*

INDUSTRIAL TURBOCHARGERS

Colchester Fuel Injection Ltd, Haven Road, Colchester, CO2 8HT Tel: (01206) 862049 Fax: (01206) 861771 E-mail: info@colchesterfuelinjection.co.uk

Cummins Turbo Technologies Ltd, St. Andrews Road, Huddersfield, HD1 6RA Tel: (01484) 422244 Fax: (01484) 511680 E-mail: enquiries@cummins.co.uk

Turbo Force Ltd, Unit 21 Old Mill Industrial Estate, Bamber Bridge, Preston, PR5 6SY Tel: (01772) 697979 Fax: (01772) 697989 E-mail: sales@turboforce.co.uk

Watson Diesel Ltd, Elm Grove, London, SW19 4HE Tel: (020) 8879 3854 Fax: (0870) 4441386 E-mail: sales@watsondiesel.com

INDUSTRIAL TURNING

Amek Precision Engineers, The Hollies, Campton Road, Meppershall, Shefford, Bedfordshire, SG17 5PB Tel: (01462) 851171 Fax: (01462) 851171

INDUSTRIAL TURNTABLES

A & N Plant, St. James House, 46 High Street, Amersham, Buckinghamshire, HP7 0DJ Tel: (01494) 722820 Fax: (01494) 729240 E-mail: info@anplant.com

INDUSTRIAL TYRES

Amcast Ltd, Unit 7, Alliance Close, Attleborough Fields Industrial Estate, Nuneaton, Warwickshire, CV11 6SD Tel: (024) 7635 0575 Fax: (024) 7635 0761 E-mail: enquiries@amcast.co.uk

Anchor Tyres, Unit 6, Oakwood Industrial Park, Gatwick Road, Crawley, West Sussex, RH10 9AZ Tel: (01293) 544577 Fax: (01293) 527477

Aromet Group Ltd, 15 Ballinderry Road, Lisburn, County Antrim, BT28 2SA Tel: (028) 9266 5721 Fax: (028) 9260 1611

Bestway Tyres Ltd, Leopold Street, Pemberton, Wigan, Lancashire, WN5 8DH Tel: (01942) 214827 Fax: (01942) 226311 E-mail: jdc@lancasterhouse.fsnet.co.uk

Bridgestone UK Ltd, Athena Drive, Tachbrook Park, Warwick, CV34 6UX Tel: (01926) 488500 Fax: (01926) 488600 E-mail: bfuk.reception@bridgestone-eu.com

Eurotek Industrial Tyres Ltd, 313-315 Whapload Road, Lowestoft, Suffolk, NR32 1UL Tel: (01502) 532200 Fax: (01502) 508273 E-mail: colinlong@eurotektyres.com

▶ Goodyear Dunlop, Tyrefort, 88-98 Wingfoot Way, Erdington, Birmingham, B24 9HY Tel: 0121-306 6166

Kirkby (Tyres) Ltd, Speke Hall Avenue, Speke, Liverpool, L24 1UU Tel: (07734) 870892 Fax: 0151-486 5391 E-mail: sales@kirkbytyres.co.uk

Michelin Tyre Plc, Campbell Road, Stoke-on-Trent, ST4 4EY Tel: (01782) 402000 Fax: (01782) 402253 E-mail: agr@uk.michelin.com

Solideal UK Ltd, Vale Business Park, Llandow, Cowbridge, South Glamorgan, CF71 7PF Tel: (01446) 774914 Fax: (01446) 775410 E-mail: sales@solidealuk.com

Titan Distribution (UK) Ltd, North Florida Road, Haydock Industrial Estate, St. Helens, Merseyside, WA11 9UB Tel: (01942) 715333 Fax: (01942) 715111 E-mail: enquiries@titandistributionuk.com

Watt Industrial Tyres Ltd, Church Road, Lydney, Gloucestershire, GL15 5EN Tel: (01594) 847100 Fax: (01594) 847181 E-mail: cliverickards@watts-polymers.co.uk

Watts Group Of Companies, Althorpe House, High Street, Lydney, Gloucestershire, GL15 5DD Tel: (01594) 847400 Fax: (01594) 847401 E-mail: info@watts-group.co.uk

Watts Industrial Tyres plc, 9a Brindley Road, Bayton Road Industrial Estate, Coventry, CV7 9EP Tel: (024) 7664 5222 Fax: (024) 7636 7111

Watts Industrial Tyres plc, 9 Spencer Street, Grimsby, South Humberside, DN31 3AA Tel: (01472) 362589 Fax: (01472) 352772

Watts Industrial Tyres plc, Unit 7 Brickfields, Liverpool, L36 6HY Tel: 0151-481 4500 Fax: 0151-481 4501 E-mail: liverpool@watts_tyres.co.uk

Watts Industrial Tyres plc, Albion Road, West Bromwich, West Midlands, B70 8AX Tel: 0121-553 5451 Fax: 0121-500 5079 E-mail: westbrom@watts.co.uk

Watts Tyre & Auto Centres, Unit 301, Dean Road, Bristol, BS11 8AT Tel: 0117-982 4896 Fax: 0117-982 4896

INDUSTRIAL USAGE FELT

Albany International Ltd, Pilsworth Road, Bury, Lancashire, BL9 8QE Tel: 0161-767 7531 Fax: 0161-766 2993

Andrew Webron Ltd, Hareholme Mill, Bacup Road, Rawtenstall, Rossendale, Lancashire, BB4 7JL Tel: (01706) 214001 Fax: (01706) 830003 E-mail: info@andrewwebron.com

Anglo Felt Industries Ltd, Bridge End Mills, Tong Lane, Whitworth, Rochdale, Lancashire, OL12 8BG Tel: (01706) 853513 Fax: (01706) 853625 E-mail: enquiries@anglofelt.com

Calderbrook Jute Co., Stansfield Mill, Calderbrook Road, Littleborough, Lancashire, OL15 9NP Tel: (01706) 378711 Fax: (01706) 371345

Hardy & Hanson Ltd, Summit Works, Longlands Road, Staincliffe, Dewsbury, West Yorkshire, WF13 4AB Tel: (01924) 462353 Fax: (01924) 457883E-mail: enquiries@hardy-hanson.co.uk

INDUSTRIAL USAGE WEB GUIDING UNITS

J T R Controls Ltd, Bank Street, Walshaw, Bury, Lancashire, BL8 3AZ Tel: 0161-764 3829 Fax: 0161-764 3829

INDUSTRIAL VACUUM CLEANER HIRE

GWS Engineers Ltd, First Avenue, Flixborough Industrial Estate, Flixborough, Scunthorpe, South Humberside, DN15 8SE Tel: (01724) 856665 Fax: (01724) 280805 E-mail: mail@gws-engineers.co.uk

Starbrite Chemicals Ltd, X L House, Rutherford Way, Crawley, West Sussex, RH10 9PB Tel: (01293) 434250 Fax: (01293) 434252 E-mail: sales@starbrite.co.uk

INDUSTRIAL VACUUM CLEANERS

Allbrite Cleaning Services Ltd, Darleydale Road, Corby, Northamptonshire, NN17 2DF Tel: (01536) 202295 Fax: (01536) 266246
B & G Cleaning Systems Ltd, Abeles Way, Holly Lane Industrial Estate, Atherstone, Warwickshire, CV9 2QZ Tel: (01827) 717028 Fax: (01827) 714041 E-mail: sales@bgclean.co.uk
Barloworld Vacuum Technology P.L.C, Harbour Road, Gosport, Hampshire, PO12 1BG Tel: (0870) 0107666 Fax: (0870) 0106916 E-mail: marketing@barloworldvt.com
Clyde Process Solutions plc, Carolina Court, Lakeside, Doncaster, South Yorkshire, DN4 5RA Tel: (01302) 321313 Fax: (01302) 554400 E-mail: solutions@clydematerials.co.uk
Durnbury Ltd, 30 First Avenue, Halstead, Essex, CO9 2EX Tel: (01787) 475351 Fax: (01787) 477821 E-mail: durnburyltd@aol.com
Green & White Ltd, 112 Fortune Green Road, London, NW6 1DH Tel: (020) 7794 7783 Fax: (020) 7433 1143 E-mail: green.white.ltd@lineone.net
GWS Engineers Ltd, First Avenue, Flixborough Industrial Estate, Flixborough, Scunthorpe, South Humberside, DN15 8SE Tel: (01724) 856665 Fax: (01724) 280805 E-mail: mail@gws-engineers.co.uk
Hako Machines Ltd, Eldon Close, Crick, Northampton, NN6 7SL Tel: (01788) 823535 Fax: (01788) 823969 E-mail: sales@hako.co.uk
Industrial Vacuum Co., Poynton Water, Mill Lane, Totley Rise, Sheffield, S17 4HQ Tel: 0114-262 0111 Fax: 0114-262 0111
Kerstar Ltd, 10-16 St. Georges Street, Northampton, NN1 2TR Tel: (01604) 637531 Fax: (01604) 620796 E-mail: sales@kerstar.co.uk
▶ Michael Williams Ltd, Wilbraham Road, Fulbourn, Cambridge, CB21 5ET Tel: (01223) 882222 Fax: (01223) 882598 E-mail: sales@mikewills.co.uk
Midland Vacum Cleaner Services, 1477-1479 Pershore Road, Stirchley, Birmingham, B30 2JL Tel: 0121-458 7185 Fax: 0121-458 4226 E-mail: enquries@midlandvac.co.uk
North & South Industries, Sidings Court, Doncaster, South Yorkshire, DN4 5NU Tel: (01302) 730037 Fax: (01302) 730073
Phoenix Floor Maintenance Equipment Ltd, Unit 7, Padgets Lane, South Moons Moat, Redditch, Worcestershire, B98 0RA Tel: (01527) 517161 Fax: (01527) 520765 E-mail: sales@jangro.co.uk
Premiere Products, Bouncers Lane, Cheltenham, Gloucestershire, GL52 5JD Tel: (01242) 537150 Fax: (01242) 528445 E-mail: premiere@premiereproducts.co.uk
Spraychem Ltd, Cardrew Industrial Estate, Redruth, Cornwall, TR15 1ST Tel: (01209) 315222 Fax: (01209) 314333 E-mail: sales@contico.co.uk
Unicorn Mucksuckers, 41, High Street, Clophill, Bedford, MK45 4AA Tel: (01525) 860255 Fax: (01525) 861635 E-mail: info@uti.co.uk
Vak Systems T G A Ltd, Redmoor Lane, New Mills, High Peak, Derbyshire, SK22 3LL Tel: 01663 745575

INDUSTRIAL VENTILATING VALVES

Circor Instrumentation Ltd, Frays Mill Works, Cowley Road, Uxbridge, Middlesex, UB8 2AF Tel: (01895) 206780 Fax: (020) 8423 5933 E-mail: aratna@circor.co.uk
Invicta Valves Ltd, Units 10-11, Boxmend, Bircholt Road, Parkwood Industrial Estate, Maidstone, Kent, ME15 9XT Tel: (01622) 754613 Fax: (01622) 750436 E-mail: sales@invictavalves.co.uk
Poultry Air Ltd, Unit 11 The Stables, Stonham Aspal, Stowmarket, Suffolk, IP14 6AU Tel: (01473) 890040 Fax: (01473) 890040

INDUSTRIAL VENTILATORS

Airforce Ventilation Products, 3 Brunel Gate, West Portway Industrial Estate, Andover, Hampshire, SP10 3SL Tel: (01264) 358101 Fax: (01264) 358404 E-mail: enquiries@airforcevp.com
Flamgard Engineering Ltd, Unit 2-3 Pontnewynydd Industrial Estate, Pontnewynydd, Pontypool, Gwent, NP4 6YW Tel: (01495) 757347 Fax: (01495) 755443 E-mail: sales@flamgard.co.uk
Lucas & Steen Ltd, Castle Works, 88 Hill Street, Ardrossan, Ayrshire, KA22 8HE Tel: (01294) 468671 Fax: (01294) 604018
Mckenzie Martin Ltd, Eton Hill Works, Eton Hill Road, Radcliffe, Manchester, M26 2US Tel: 0161-723 2234 Fax: 0161-725 9531 E-mail: general@mckenziemartin.co.uk
Silavent Ventilation Systems, Lea Mills, Lea Road, Batley, West Yorkshire, WF17 8BB Tel: (01924) 441874 Fax: (01924) 441892
V E S Andover Ltd, Eagle Close, Chandler Ford Industrial Estate, Eastleigh, Hampshire, SO53 4NF Tel: (0870) 2404340 Fax: (0870) 2404550 E-mail: vesltd@ves.co.uk

INDUSTRIAL VIBRATORS

Pulse Power Process Equipment Ltd, 43 Bishops Walk, Forthampton, Gloucester, GL19 4QF Tel: (01684) 290029 Fax: (01684) 290222 E-mail: info@pulse-piv.co.uk
Ward Bekker Ltd, Three Winds, Madge Hill, Kinnersley, Severn Stoke, Worcester, WR8 9JN Tel: (01905) 371200 Fax: (01905) 371049

INDUSTRIAL VISORS

Harrold Manufacturing Co. Ltd, Hinstock House, 30 Station Road, Firsby, Spilsby, Lincolnshire, PE23 5PX Tel: (01754) 830679 Fax: (01754) 830477

INDUSTRIAL VISUAL AID PRODUCTION

Line Out, Fosse Art Centre, Mantle Road, Leicester, LE3 5HG Tel: 0116-262 1265
Red Machine, Black Barn, Cornwells Farm, Sheephurst Lane, Marden, Kent, TN12 9NS Tel: (01622) 832010 Fax: (01622) 832177 E-mail: contact@redmachine.co.uk

INDUSTRIAL WASHING MACHINES

Bringate Sheet Metals, Cross Green Industrial Estate, Cross Green, Leeds, LS9 0SG Tel: 0113-240 7711 Fax: 0113-240 7722 E-mail: sales@bringate.co.uk
Oliver Douglas Ltd, Amberley Works, Chelsea Close, Leeds, LS12 4HP Tel: 0113-279 7373 Fax: 0113-279 1014 E-mail: admin@oliverdouglas.com
Durr Ltd, Broxell Close, Warwick, CV34 5QF Tel: (01926) 418800 Fax: (01926) 400679 E-mail: sales@durr.com
Industrial Washing Machines Ltd, Unit 2, Facet Road, Kings Norton, Birmingham, B38 9PT Tel: 0121-459 9511 Fax: 0121-451 3241 E-mail: sales@indwash.co.uk
Lancer UK Ltd, 1 Pembroke Avenue, Waterbeach, Cambridge, CB25 9QP Tel: (01223) 861665 Fax: (01223) 861990 E-mail: info@lancer.co.uk
LRS, Unit 7 New Way Estate, Dunkeswell Industrial Estate, Honiton, Devon, EX14 4LD Tel: (01404) 891521 Fax: (01404) 891521 E-mail: lrsgroup@fsbdial.co.uk
Mecwash Systems Ltd, Unit A 64 Hundred, 7 Drive, Tewkesbury Business Park, Tewkesbury, Gloucestershire, GL20 8TB Tel: (01684) 271600 E-mail: paulyoung@mecwash.co.uk
Newsmith Stainless Ltd, Fountain Works, Child Lane, Liversedge, West Yorkshire, WF15 7PH Tel: (01924) 405988 Fax: (01924) 403304 E-mail: sales@newsmiths.co.uk

INDUSTRIAL WATER COOLERS

▶ Angel Springs Ltd, Unit 4 Spring Road Indust Estate, Wolverhampton, WV4 6UD Tel: (01902) 353598 Fax: (01902) 385604 E-mail: admin@purecoolers.co.uk
▶ Aquaid (Midlands & South Wales), 36 Bidavon Industrial Estate, Waterloo Road, Bidford-on-Avon, Alcester, Warwickshire, B50 4JW Tel: (01789) 778345 Fax: (01789) 772314
▶ Aqualeader Ltd, Sweet Five, 16 Wilbury Gardens, Hove, East Sussex, BN3 6HY Tel: (01273) 299685 Fax: (01273) 377903
Cold Box Ltd, 28 Benson Road, Nuffield Industrial Estate, Poole, Dorset, BH17 0GB Tel: (01202) 667667 Fax: (01202) 667666 E-mail: ian@coldbox.co.uk
▶ Countrywise Spring Water, Dairycoates Industrial Estate, Wiltshire Road, Hull, HU4 6PA Tel: (01482) 351003 Fax: (01482) 358928 E-mail: info@countrywise.net
▶ Eau Coolers Ltd, Unit 6 Woolmer Way, Bordon, Hampshire, GU35 9QF Tel: (01420) 488600 Fax: (01420) 488691 E-mail: eaucoolers@drinkingwater.co.uk
▶ Forest Edge Water, Mill Cottage, Beaulieu, Hampshire, SO42 7YG Tel: (01590) 611227 Fax: (01590) 611487
▶ Intervend, 31 Abbey Road, West Bridgford, Nottingham, NG2 5NG Tel: 0115-981 0100
▶ Nestle Waters Powwow, Units C-D, Guiness Circle, Guiness Road, Trafford Park, Manchester, M17 1EB Tel: 0161-772 8716 Fax: (01865) 405441 E-mail: contactus@uk.nestle-waters-powwow.com
Oasis M V, Unit F Drapers Yard, Warrenwood Industrial Estate, Stapleford, Hertford, SG14 3NU Tel: (01992) 554733
P L Plastics Machinery Ltd, Unit 6 Telmere Industrial Estate, Albert Road, Luton, LU1 3QF Tel: (01582) 429224 Fax: (01582) 459133 E-mail: info@pl-plasticsmachinery.co.uk
▶ Quickchill, 7 Church Street, Highbridge, Somerset, TA9 3AE Tel: (01278) 780948 Fax: (01278) 780948 E-mail: info@quickchill.co.uk
▶ The Refreshing Water Co. Ltd, 113A Leyland Trading Estate, Wellingborough, Northamptonshire, NN8 1RT Tel: (01933) 443820 Fax: (01933) 225559
▶ Simply Pure Water, 4 Common Road, Skelmanthorpe, Huddersfield, HD1 5EU Tel: (01484) 868226 Fax: (01484) 866677 E-mail: sales@simplypurewater.co.uk
Syncro Ltd, 6th Floor Furness House, Furness Quay, Salford, M50 3XZ Tel: 0161-786 4400 Fax: 0161-877 5233
▶ Water Warehouse Ltd, Unit 32 Nailsworth Mills Estate, Avening Road, Nailsworth, Stroud, Gloucestershire, GL6 0BS Tel: (01453) 837400 Fax: (01453) 837401
▶ Waterflo Ltd, Kenyon Business Park, Pilkington Street, Bolton, BL3 6HL Tel: (01204) 385252 Fax: (01204) 385253 E-mail: info@waterflo.co.uk
▶ The Waterpoint, 2 Argyle Street, Stonehouse, Larkhall, Lanarkshire, ML9 3LL Tel: (01698) 793933 Fax: (01698) 793933 E-mail: sales@thewaterpoint.com
Windsor House Natural Water Co Ltd, Park Road, Emsworth, Hampshire, PO10 8NY Tel: (01243) 376156 Fax: (01243) 379100

INDUSTRIAL WATER JET HIGH PRESSURE CLEANING OR WASHING CONTRACTORS

Advanced Main Drain, 109 High Street, Edenbridge, Kent, TN8 5AX Tel: (01732) 863607 Fax: (01732) 866931
Arbscapes, Rawreth Lodge, Church Road, Rawreth, Wickford, Essex, SS11 8SG Tel: (01268) 560006 Fax: (01268) 733251 E-mail: info@arbscapes.co.uk
Brian Plant, Wickham Road, Grimsby, South Humberside, DN31 3SL Tel: (01472) 241342 Fax: (01472) 354329
▶ Jetstream, 15 Somerset Road, East Preston, Littlehampton, West Sussex, BN16 1BZ Tel: 01903 772804 E-mail: jetstream@firstcheckpoint.com
Lanes Engineering & Construction, 189 New Road, Rainham, Essex, RM13 8SH Tel: (01708) 553555 Fax: (01708) 630523
Metro Rod P.L.C., East Barnet, Barnet, Hertfordshire, EN4 8WR Tel: (020) 8449 8477 Fax: (020) 8449 8466 E-mail: ascriven@sgaservices.co.uk
R B G, Norfolk House, Pitmedden Road, Dyce, Aberdeen, AB21 0DP Tel: (01224) 215100 Fax: (01224) 723406 E-mail: john.walker@rigblast.com
R H Buxton Ltd, Fell Bank, Birtley, Chester le Street, County Durham, DH3 2SP Tel: 0191-410 6111 Fax: 0191-410 6655 E-mail: buxtonsne@beeb.net
Systematic Servicing Equipment Ltd, Field Works, Broadway Road, Willersey, Broadway, Worcestershire, WR12 7PH Tel: (01386) 852342 Fax: (01386) 858556 E-mail: sales@systematic-servicing.co.uk
Taylors Industrial Services Ltd, Hareness Circle, Altens Industrial Estate, Aberdeen, AB12 3LY Tel: (01224) 872972 Fax: (01224) 872697 E-mail: taylors_industrial_services@btinternet.com

INDUSTRIAL WATER SOFTENING EQUIPMENT

Aqua Spring Ltd, 177 Kingston Road, Leatherhead, Surrey, KT22 7NX Tel: (01372) 373023 Fax: (01372) 360003 E-mail: sales@aquaspring.co.uk
Culligan International UK Ltd, Culligan House, Coronation Road, High Wycombe, Buckinghamshire, HP12 3SU Tel: (01494) 436484 Fax: (01494) 523833 E-mail: enquires@culligan.co.uk
Ensign UK Ltd, A5 Faraday Road, Newbury, Berkshire, RG14 2AD Tel: (0870) 0113436 Fax: (0845) 6431882 E-mail: info@ensign-water.co.uk
European WaterCare Systems, Regal House, South Road, Harlow, Essex, CM20 2BL Tel: (01279) 780250 Fax: (01279) 780268 E-mail: info@watercare.co.uk
Freeston Water Treatment Ltd, West Quay Road, Southampton, SO15 1GZ Tel: (023) 8022 0738 Fax: (023) 8063 9853 E-mail: info@freeston.co.uk
Kinetico UK Ltd, Bridge House, Park Gate Business Centre, Park Gate, Southampton, SO31 1FQ Tel: (01489) 566970 Fax: (01489) 566976 E-mail: info@kinetico.co.uk
Rodol Ltd, Richmond Row, Liverpool, L3 3BP Tel: 0151-207 3161 Fax: 0151-207 3727
Veoilawater Solutions & Technologys, Marlow International, Parkway, Marlow, Buckinghamshire, SL7 1YL Tel: (01494) 887700 Fax: (01628) 897001 E-mail: sales.uk@veoliawater.com
Water Technology Ltd, Powke Lane Industrial Estate, Blackheath, Rowley Regis, West Midlands, B65 0AH Tel: 0121-561 3144 Fax: 0121-561 3329 E-mail: water.tech@virgin.net
Waterchem Ltd, Unit 2c, Derwent Close, Worcester, WR4 9TY Tel: (01905) 23669 Fax: (01905) 729959 E-mail: info@waterchem.co.uk

INDUSTRIAL WEBBING

Amsafe Bridport, The Court, West Street, Bridport, Dorset, DT6 3QU Tel: (01308) 456666 Fax: (01308) 456605 E-mail: david.rumney@amsafe.com
Bowmer Bond Narrow Fabrics Ltd, Hanging Bridge Mills, Ashbourne, Derbyshire, DE6 2EA Tel: (01335) 342244 Fax: (01335) 300651 E-mail: sales@bowmerbond.co.uk
Linear Composites Ltd, Vale Mills, Oakworth, Keighley, West Yorkshire, BD22 0EB Tel: (01535) 643363 Fax: (01535) 643605 E-mail: mail@linearcomposites.com
Ollard Westcombe, Bridge Street, Downpatrick, County Down, BT30 6HD Tel: (028) 4461 7557 Fax: (028) 4461 3580 E-mail: office@dthomason.freeserve.com
Ribbons Ltd, Cae Mawr Industrial Estate, Treorchy, Mid Glamorgan, CF42 6EJ Tel: (01443) 432473 Fax: (01443) 437413
Spa Web Ltd, Metcalf Drive, Altham Industrial Estate, Accrington, Lancashire, BB5 5TU Tel: (01282) 688100 Fax: (01282) 688105 E-mail: sales@spaweb.co.uk

INDUSTRIAL WHEELS

Eurocastors Ltd, Dalton Road, Southfield Industrial Estate, Glenrothes, Fife, KY6 2SS Tel: (01592) 774770 Fax: (01592) 772736 E-mail: sales@eurocastors.co.uk
Express Wills, 1-3 Tonbridge Road, Barming, Maidstone, Kent, ME16 9HB Tel: (01622) 729333 Fax: 01622 729333
Guitel Ltd, Unit E, Flaxley Park Way, Stechford Retail Park, Birmingham, B33 9AN Tel: 0121-783 4747 Fax: 0121-783 5959 E-mail: sales@guitel-castors.com
Michelin Tyre Plc, Campbell Road, Stoke-on-Trent, ST4 4EY Tel: (01782) 402000 Fax: (01782) 402253 E-mail: agr@uk.michelin.com
North West Wheels Ltd, Forward Works, Woolston, Warrington, WA1 4BA Tel: (01925) 816207 Fax: (01925) 825633
Texane Ltd, Valley Way, Market Harborough, Leicestershire, LE16 7PS Tel: (01858) 462040 Fax: (01858) 410029 E-mail: sales@taxane.com
Wheel Masters, Tufthorn Industrial Estate, Stepbridge Road, Coleford, Gloucestershire, GL16 8PJ Tel: (01594) 835678 Fax: (01594) 835789 E-mail: sales@wheelsuk.co.uk

INDUSTRIAL WIRE TIES

Tripack, Beels Road, Stallingborough, Grimsby, South Humberside, DN41 8DN Tel: (01469) 577075 Fax: (01469) 577076

INDUSTRIAL WORKWEAR

Advanced Clothing Co., Vantel House, Parkway South, Wheatley, Doncaster, South Yorkshire, DN2 4JR Tel: (01302) 320200
Afay Ltd, 6 Stoddart Street, South Shields, Tyne & Wear, NE34 0JT Tel: 0191-456 1253 Fax: 0191-454 2808
Arivatex Ltd, 17 Chatley Street, Manchester, M3 1HX Tel: 0161-834 9191 Fax: 0161-834 9161 E-mail: info@arivatex.co.uk
B J Industrial Supplies Ltd, 6 Harwood Street, Blackburn, BB1 3BD Tel: (01254) 675244 Fax: (01254) 663061 E-mail: info@thetradeshop.co.uk
Birmingham Safety Wear, Unit 14 Mount Street Business Centre, Mount Street, Nechells, Birmingham, B7 5RD Tel: 0121-327 0873 Fax: 0121-327 0873 E-mail: sales@birminghamsafetywear.co.uk
Broadweave, Hayhill Industrial Estate, Barrow Upon Soar, Loughborough, Leicestershire, LE12 8LD Tel: (01509) 816123 Fax: (01509) 814867 E-mail: sales@broadweaveltd.co.uk
Carrington Career & Workwear Ltd, Market Street, Adlington, Chorley, Lancashire, PR7 4HE Tel: (01257) 476850 Fax: (01257) 476852 E-mail: info@carrington.uk.com
Cookson & Clegg, PO Box 11, Blackburn, BB1 2WX Tel: (01254) 844544 Fax: (01254) 844545 E-mail: sales@cooksonclegg.com
Corporate Clothing, 5-7 Linkfield Corner, Station Road, Redhill, RH1 1BD Tel: (01737) 767912 Fax: (01737) 780666 E-mail: info@armawear.co.uk
Corton Sinclair Ltd, 36 Glenburn Road, East Kilbride, Glasgow, G74 5BA Tel: (01355) 222273 Fax: (01355) 263682 E-mail: sales@corstonsinclair.com
Cosalt Sea-Dog Ltd, 4 Albert Road, Leith, Edinburgh, EH6 7DP Tel: 0131-554 8531 Fax: 0131-554 8061
Cosalt Workwear Ltd, Banner House, Greg Street, Stockport, Cheshire, SK5 7BT Tel: (0800) 0188110 Fax: (0870) 8502378 E-mail: info@cosalt-workwear.com
Davern Work Wear Ltd, Elliott Road, March, Cambridgeshire, PE15 8QU Tel: (01354) 654001 Fax: (01354) 658274 E-mail: info@davern.co.uk
E & E Workwear, Church Lane, Marple, Stockport, Cheshire, SK6 7AR Tel: 0161-427 6522 Fax: 0161-426 0906 E-mail: eeworkwear@hotmail.com

INDUSTRIAL WORKWEAR – *continued*

Faithful Ltd, Northwick Road, Worcester, WR3 7DU Tel: (01905) 450000 Fax: (01905) 457690 E-mail: sales@faithful.co.uk
Gee, 138 Richmond Road, Kingston upon Thames, Surrey, KT2 5EZ Tel: (020) 8546 4453 Fax: (020) 8546 2057 E-mail: drewgoater@hotmail.co.uk
▶ Grantham Clothing Co., Unit 1a Partnership House, Withambrook Park Industrial Estate, Grantham, Lincolnshire, NG31 9ST Tel: (01476) 594330 Fax: (01476) 593863 E-mail: granthamclothing@btclick.com
Greenham Ltd, Tinsley Lane North, Crawley, West Sussex, RH10 9TP Tel: (01293) 525955 Fax: (01293) 522971 E-mail: crawley.sales@greenham.co.uk
Harveys & Co. Clothing Ltd, Glodwick Road, Oldham, OL4 1YU Tel: 0161-624 9535 Fax: 0161-627 2028 E-mail: info@harveys.co.uk
Histon Overalls Ltd, Unit 7, Cambrian Court, Ferryboat Close, Swansea Enterprise Park, Swansea, SA6 8PZ Tel: (01792) 772870 Fax: (01792) 772870
Jaten Fashion Manufacturing Co, Monemore Green Site, Bilston Road, Wolverhampton, WV2 2HT Tel: (01902) 455009 Fax: (01902) 455004 E-mail: jatenfashion@aol.com
Manufacturers Supplies Acton Ltd, 2 Langley Wharf, Railway Terrace, Kings Langley, Hertfordshire, WD4 8JE Tel: (01923) 260845 Fax: (01923) 260847 E-mail: manusupplies@aol.com
Meiklejohn Chef & Work Wear, 198 Swanston Street, Glasgow, G40 4HH Tel: 0141-554 2709 Fax: 0141-554 4645 E-mail: sales@meilkejohns.co.uk
Merv Hutchings Workwear, 169 Pinhoe Road, Exeter, EX4 7HZ Tel: (01392) 412376
Michael's Workwear, 56 Cricklade Road, Swindon, SN2 8AF Tel: (01793) 614721 Fax: (01793) 614721 E-mail: michaelsworkwear@aol.com
Monarch Textiles, Lowmoor Business Park, Kirkby-in-Ashfield, Nottingham, NG17 7LF Tel: (01623) 750777 Fax: (01623) 720779 E-mail: enquiry@monarch-textiles.co.uk
Monsoon Ruggur Farm & Country Clothing Ltd, 63 Teignmouth Road, Clevedon, Avon, BS21 6DL Tel: (01275) 870220 Fax: (01275) 342272 E-mail: sales@monmark.co.uk
Neatawash Laundriy, Boothen Green, Stoke-on-Trent, ST4 4BJ Tel: (01782) 413502 Fax: (01782) 747130 E-mail: service@neatawash.co.uk
Pinnees Clothing Co., 85 Liscard Road, Wallasey, Merseyside, CH44 9AE Tel: 0151-638 1073 Fax: 0151-638 1073 E-mail: sales@pinnees.com
Protective Clothing Co. Ltd, 8-14 Orsman Road, London, N1 5QJ Tel: (020) 7729 0405 Fax: (020) 7729 0405
Queen Eleanor Ltd, Rutland Street, Kettering, Northamptonshire, NN16 8PW Tel: (01536) 522798 Fax: (01536) 410967 E-mail: info@queeneleanor.co.uk
R F M Workwear Ltd, 36 Glenburn Road, College Milton North, East Kilbride, Glasgow, G74 5BA Tel: (01355) 238161 Fax: (01355) 263682 E-mail: sales@corstonsinclair.com
R K Styles Ltd, Unit 2 Alma Street, Smethwick, West Midlands, B66 2RL Tel: 0121-565 3630 Fax: 0121-565 1004 E-mail: sales@rkstyles.co.uk
R W H Supplies, 15 The Rodings, Upminster, Essex, RM14 1RL Tel: (01708) 780629 Fax: (01708) 780629
Safe & Warm Ltd, The Woodman Centre, 270 Vicarage Lane, Blackpool, FY4 4ND Tel: (01253) 792094 Fax: (01253) 292966 E-mail: sales@workwear-safety.co.uk
Southern Overall Service, Unit D Foundry Close, Horsham, West Sussex, RH13 5TX Tel: (01403) 263108 Fax: (01403) 254539 E-mail: sales@horshamanddistrictlaundry.co.uk
Stephens Plastics Ltd, Old School House, Sinclair Street, Halkirk, Caithness, KW12 6XT Tel: (01847) 831216 Fax: (01847) 831305 E-mail: info@stephens-plastics.co.uk
Stockbridge Mill Co. Ltd, Green Lane, Padiham, Burnley, Lancashire, BB12 7AE Tel: (01282) 772231 Fax: (01282) 771084 E-mail: sales@stockbridgemill.com
Taskwear Clothing, Albert School, Church Lane, Marple, Stockport, Cheshire, SK6 7AR Tel: 0161-449 9449 Fax: 0161-426 0906 E-mail: eeworkwear@hotmail.com
Tunika Safety Products, Tannery House, Nelson Street, Bolton, BL3 2JW Tel: (01204) 366713 Fax: (01204) 366714 E-mail: sales@tunikasafety.co.uk
Turton Safety Ltd, 1 Britannia Park, Trident Drive, Wednesbury, West Midlands, WS10 7XB Tel: 0121-567 4100 Fax: 0121-567 4141 E-mail: sales@turton.co.uk
Wearwell Group Ltd, Gargarin, Lichfield Road, Tamworth, Staffordshire, B79 7TR Tel: (01827) 310553 Fax: (01827) 66139 E-mail: sales@wearwell.co.uk
Wessex Textiles Ltd, Blake Industrial Park, Colley Lane, Bridgwater, Somerset, TA6 5LT Tel: (01278) 450450 Fax: (01278) 450550 E-mail: sales@wessextextiles.co.uk
Wick's Ltd, Unit 18L Ring Road, Burntwood Business Park, Burntwood, Staffordshire, WS7 3JQ Tel: (01543) 672488 Fax: (01543) 685211
Work In Style Ltd, Keighley Business Centre, South Street, Keighley, West Yorkshire, BD21 1AG Tel: (01535) 667625 Fax: (01535) 610488 E-mail: sales@workinstyle.com
Workware & Business Casuals, Unit 26 Snedshill Industrial Estate, Snedshill, Telford, Shropshire, TF2 9NH Tel: (01952) 615976 Fax: (01952) 614440 E-mail: enquiries@myworkwear.co.uk

INDUSTRIAL, BUILDING AND FACTORY CLEANING SERVICES

▶ A L S Cleaning Services, 12 The Close, Great Holland, Frinton-on-Sea, Essex, CO13 0JR Tel: (01255) 852781 E-mail: info@als-cleaning.co.uk
Almor Ltd, Daleside Road, Nottingham, NG2 3GJ Tel: 0115-986 8773 Fax: 0115-986 6716 E-mail: sales@mpcl.uk.com
▶ Benchmark Cleaning Services Ltd, 59 Grantock Road, Walthamstow, London, E17 4DF Tel: (020) 8297 9136 Fax: (020) 8418 5866 E-mail: info@benchmarkcleaning.co.uk
▶ CHR Commercial Cleaning Services Ltd, Unit 12 Union Bridge Mills, Roker Lane, Pudsey, West Yorkshire, LS28 9LE Tel: 0113-257 7893 Fax: 0113-236 0916 E-mail: brendan@chrservices.co.uk
▶ Cleaninc., 88 Kilmaurs Road, Kilmarnock, Ayrshire, KA3 1QF Tel: 01563) 539556 E-mail: rthass@ukonline.co.uk
▶ CoolClean Solutions Europe LTD, 86 Tilston Road, Aintree, Liverpool, L9 6AL Tel: 0151 2805172 E-mail: info@coolclean.co.uk
▶ D B Services, 194 West Street, Fareham, Hampshire, PO16 0HF Tel: (01329) 288464 Fax: (01329) 825815 E-mail: southern@dbservices.co.uk
▶ D & J Enterprises, Croftlands, Southstoke Lane, Bath, BA2 5SH Tel: (01225) 837837 Fax: (01225) 837507 E-mail: sales@dandjenterprises.co.uk
▶ Ecoclean Environmental Services, 7 Lynn Road, Swaffham, Norfolk, PE37 7AY Tel: (01760) 336028 Fax: (01760) 725752 E-mail: info@ecocleanltd.co.uk
▶ Enterprise Cleaning Co, Enterprise House, 9 Martinfield, Welwyn Garden City, Hertfordshire, AL7 1HG Tel: (01707) 373111 Fax: (01707) 323842 E-mail: sales@entss.com
▶ Exceed Cleaning Ltd, PO Box 8781, Stansted, Essex, CM24 8AN Tel: 01279 814990 Fax: 01279 814551 E-mail: info@exceedcleaning.com
▶ Gum Away Co., Unit E 1, Kestrel Road, Trafford Park, Manchester, M17 1SF Tel: (0845) 6440901 Fax: (0845) 6440902 E-mail: info@gum-away.co.uk
▶ High Access Cleaning Co., Unit E1, The Courts, Kestrel Road, Trafford Park, Manchester, M17 1SF Tel: (0845) 6440901 Fax: (0845) 6440902 E-mail: info@highaccesscleaning.co.uk
▶ Jardak Services Ltd, PO Box 187, Welwyn Garden City, Hertfordshire, AL8 6AL Tel: (01707) 321225 Fax: (01438) 820004 E-mail: info@jardak.co.uk
▶ Midland Cleaning Services, 152 Falcon Lodge Crescent, Sutton Coldfield, West Midlands, B75 7NA Tel: (0845) 2260881 Fax: (0870) 0940775 E-mail: pwayt@midlandcleaningservice.co.uk
Nviro Cleaning Services, Mountbatten Business Park, Jackson Close, Portsmouth, PO6 1US Tel: (023) 9237 0044 Fax: (023) 9237 0047 E-mail: sales@nviro.co.uk
▶ Omega Cleaning Contractors, 79 Dundrennan Road, Glasgow, G42 9SL Tel: 0141-636 6801 Fax: 0141-636 6801 E-mail: info@omegacleaningltd.co.uk
▶ Pro-Cleanse North, 105 Dale Street, Milnrow, Rochdale, Lancashire, OL16 3NW Tel: (01706) 759696 Fax: (0870) 1304019 E-mail: mail@pro-cleanse.co.uk
▶ R & G Services Ltd, Hillhouse International Site, Fleetwood Road North, Thornton-Cleveleys, Lancashire, FY5 4QD Tel: (01253) 864033 Fax: (01253) 828603 E-mail: cleanup@ukonline.co.uk
Selclene, 7 Mandeville Courtyard, 142 Battersea Park Road, London, SW11 4NB Tel: (020) 7627 3874 Fax: (020) 7720 9800 E-mail: info@selclen.biz
Spic 'N' Span, 20 Edith Avenue, Plymouth, PL4 8TH Tel: (01752) 666707 Fax: (01752) 666707
Total Industrial Cleaning, 16 Morden Road, Stechford, Birmingham, B33 8SR Tel: 0121-243 4975 E-mail: contact@totalindustrialcleaning.co.uk
▶ Vader Cleaning Service, 49 Carrigard, Dundrum, Newcastle, County Down, BT33 0SG Tel: (07814) 977145 E-mail: gmurf2001@yahoo.com

INFECTION CONTROL PRODUCT, *See Hospital Infection Control etc*

INFLATABLE BOATS

A B E Specialist Products, Haymoor Hall, Wybunbury Lane, Wybunbury, Nantwich, Cheshire, CW5 7HD Tel: (01270) 841174 Fax: (01270) 841128 E-mail: enquiries@haymoorleisure.co.uk
Delta Power Services, Newby Road Industrial Estate, Newby Road, Hazel Grove, Stockport, Cheshire, SK7 5DR Tel: 0161-456 6588 Fax: 0161-456 6686 E-mail: cdyas@deltarib.u-net.com
Humber Fabrications (Hull) Ltd, 99 Wincolmlee, Hull, HU2 8AH Tel: (01482) 226100 Fax: (01482) 215884 E-mail: sales@rigid-inflatables.com
Scorpion Ribs Ltd, Haven Quay, Mill Lane, Lymington, Hampshire, SO41 9AZ Tel: (01590) 677080 Fax: (01590) 671911 E-mail: sales@scorpionribs.com
Tornado Boats International Ltd, Dairycoates Industrial Estate, Wiltshire Road, Hull, HU4 6PA Tel: (01482) 353972 Fax: (01482) 572475 E-mail: sales@tornado-boats.com

INFLATABLE BUILDINGS/ STRUCTURE, PORTABLE

Ace Inflatables, 23 Alexandra Road, Uckfield, East Sussex, TN22 5BB Tel: (01825) 769951
Bee Tee Products, Cemetery Lane, Carlton, Wakefield, West Yorkshire, WF3 3QT Tel: 0113-282 4494 Fax: 0113-282 4706
Bouncy Castle Kingdom, 43 Higher Road, Liverpool, L25 0QG Tel: 0151-486 2050
C Y Inflatables Ltd, Units 3-3a Queniborough Industrial Estate, Melton Road, Queniborough, Leicester, LE7 3FP Tel: 0116-260 2506 E-mail: steve@inflatables.uk.com
J S W Inflatables, Unit 8, Church Hill Road, Thurmaston, Leicester, LE4 8DH Tel: 0116-264 0162 Fax: 0116-269 6814 E-mail: inflatafun@aol.com

INFLATABLE LIFERAFTS

R D F Beaufort Ltd, Kingsway, Dunmurry, Belfast, BT17 9AF Tel: (028) 9030 1531 Fax: (028) 9062 1765 E-mail: sales@rfdbeaufort.com

INFLATABLE MILKING MACHINE LINERS

Green Oak Equipment Ltd, 11 Boleyn Court, Manor Park, Runcorn, Cheshire, WA7 1SR Tel: (01928) 579971 Fax: (01928) 579269 E-mail: greenoak.runcorn@fsbdial.co.uk

INFLATABLE PACKING EQUIPMENT

Tam International North Sea Ltd, 1 Abbotswell Road, Aberdeen, AB12 3AB Tel: (01224) 875105 Fax: (01224) 890038 E-mail: info@tam-northsea.com

INFLATABLE PIPELINE STOPPERS

Flowstop Ltd, 98 Wellington Street, Sheffield, S1 4HX Tel: 0114-275 0509 Fax: 0114-279 8158
Pipestoppers Ltd, Stukeley Meadow, Gwscwm Road, Burry Port, Dyfed, SA16 0BU Tel: (01554) 836836 Fax: (01554) 836837 E-mail: pipestoppers@huntingdonfusion.com

INFLATABLE PRODUCTS REPAIR SPECIALIST SERVICES

Allsorts Inflatables, 8 Kings Road, New Haw, Addlestone, Surrey, KT15 3BG Tel: (01932) 336306 E-mail: sales@inflatafun.co.uk
▶ Bouncy Castle Hire Ltd, 6 Des Roches Square, Witney, Oxfordshire, OX28 4BE Tel: (01993) 709851 E-mail: enquiries@bouncycastlehire.ltd.uk
Westend Leisure, 21 Briar Close, Newhall, Swadlincote, Derbyshire, DE11 0RX Tel: (01283) 214064 E-mail: garyandbev@tiscali.co.uk

INFLATABLE PRODUCTS, ADVERTISING/PROMOTIONAL

3S Balloon Printers, Unit 9, Hortonwood 33, Telford, Shropshire, TF1 7EX Tel: (01952) 677506 Fax: (01952) 677464 E-mail: sales@3sballons.com
Bounce Higher, 20 Harland Street, Glasgow, G14 0AT Tel: 0141-950 6009
▶ Newline Products, 23 Royal Exchange Square, Glasgow, G1 3AJ Tel: 0141-248 4086 Fax: 0141-847 0530 E-mail: info@newlineproducts.co.uk

INFLATABLE PRODUCTS, DOMESTIC/RECREATIONAL

Bee Tee Products, Cemetery Lane, Carlton, Wakefield, West Yorkshire, WF3 3QT Tel: 0113-282 4494 Fax: 0113-282 4706
Bounceabout, 5 Warner Road, Selsey, Chichester, West Sussex, PO20 9AL Tel: (01243) 607772
Bounceabouts Leisure Ltd, Asfare Business Park, Hinckley Road, Wolvey, Hinckley, Leicestershire, LE10 3HQ Tel: (01455) 220886 Fax: (01455) 220988 E-mail: sales@bounceabouts.co.uk
Bristol Bouncy Castles Ltd, 22 Green Dragon Road, Winterbourn, Bristol, BS36 5EH Tel: (07796) 775522 Fax: (01454) 778888
Busy Bees, 311 Broad Lane, Leeds, LS13 3BU Tel: 0113-257 7757
Cheltenham Bouncy Castles, Unit 8, Mead Park, Mead Road, Cheltenham, Gloucestershire, GL53 7EF Tel: (01242) 235273 Fax: (01242) 235273
Cotswold Bouncy Castles, 35 Albemarle Gate, Cheltenham, Gloucestershire, GL50 4PH Tel: (01242) 231899 Fax: (01242) 525950
Designer Bounce Ltd, St Asaph Avenue, C C I Business Park, Kinmel Bay, Rhyl, Clwyd, LL18 5HA Tel: (01745) 345462 Fax: (01745) 344196
DMK Leisure Ltd, 5 Alexander Drive, Unsworth, Bury, Lancashire, BL9 8PF Tel: 0161-705 2282 E-mail: sales@ukbouncers.co.uk
Fete & Fiesta, 72/73 Orion House, Riverside 3, Thomas Longley Road, Rochester, Kent, ME2 4DU Tel: (01634) 294600 Fax: (01634) 730415
Goodwills Leisure Hire, 39-41 High Street, Dunmow, Essex, CM6 1AE Tel: (01371) 876666 Fax: (01371) 875544 E-mail: roger@gogb.net
H S H Leisure, Llwyn Coed, Rhydyfelin, Aberystwyth, Dyfed, SY23 4QD Tel: (07767) 632913 Fax: (01970) 624080
J S W Inflatables, Unit 8, Church Hill Road, Thurmaston, Leicester, LE4 8DH Tel: 0116-264 0162 Fax: 0116-269 6814 E-mail: inflatafun@aol.com
Jumbo Inflatables Ltd, 1 Harrowbrook Road, Hinckley, Leicestershire, LE10 3DJ Tel: (01455) 636478 Fax: (01455) 251275 E-mail: sales@jumbo.co.uk
K B L Event Hire, Unit 4 Banters Lane Industrial Estate, Great Leighs, Chelmsford, CM3 1QX Tel: (01245) 360920 Fax: (01245) 360442
Kidds Stuff Ltd, 1 Danby Avenue, Old Whittington, Chesterfield, Derbyshire, S41 9NH Tel: (01246) 453055
Lollipop Bouncy Castles, Galley Lane, Great Brickhill, Milton Keynes, MK17 9AA Tel: (0800) 3892088
Momentum Ltd, Clarkson Place, Dudley Road, Stourbridge, West Midlands, DY9 8EL Tel: (01384) 896879 Fax: (01384) 424691 E-mail: sales@hangar51.co.uk
Skils Ltd, 8 Mead Park, Mead Road, Leckhampton, Cheltenham, Gloucestershire, GL53 7EF Tel: (01242) 231231 Fax: (01242) 251212
Solutions Play By Design, Ninelands La, Garforth, Leeds, LS25 1NX Tel: 0113-287 7565 Fax: 0113-287 7565 E-mail: nev@fsbusiness.co.uk

INFORMATION DISPLAYS

Display Containers Ltd, 19b Moor Road, Broadstone, Dorset, BH18 8AZ Tel: (01202) 658838 Fax: (01202) 698284 E-mail: sales@displaycontainers.co.uk
Ketech Systems, Glaisdale Dr East, Nottingham, NG8 4GR Tel: 0115-900 5600 Fax: 0115-900 5601 E-mail: enquiry@ketech.com
Nexus Alpha Ltd, Unit 8 Beaufort Ho, Beaufort Court, Sir Thomas Longley Rd, Rochester, Kent, ME2 4FB Tel: (01634) 304226 Fax: (01634) 301315
Scanlite Electronics, Data House, Mowbray Drive, Blackpool, FY3 7UZ Tel: (01253) 302723 Fax: (01253) 300484 E-mail: info@scanlite.co.uk

INFORMATION INTEGRATION SOFTWARE

▶ SNS It, 18 Mount Close, Mount Avenue, London, W5 2RQ Tel: (020) 8991 4200 E-mail: info@snsitltd.com

INFORMATION SERVICES, COMPANY/CORPORATE/ CORPORATION

Access Company Formations Ltd, 31 Church Rd, Hendon, London, NW4 4EB Tel: (020) 8202 2220 Fax: (020) 8202 2202 E-mail: graham@offshorecos.freeserve.com
Bna International, Millbank Tower, 21-24 Millbank, London, SW1P 4QP Tel: (020) 7559 4800 Fax: (020) 7559 4848E-mail: sales@bnai.com
Cumbria Chamber Of Commerce, Carlisle Enterprise Centre, James Street, Carlisle, CA2 5DA Tel: (01228) 534120 Fax: (01228) 515602 E-mail: sales@cumbriachamberofcommerce.co.uk
▶ Icc Information Ltd, Field House, 72 Old Field Road, Hampton, Middlesex, TW12 2HQ Tel: (020) 7426 8510 Fax: (020) 7426 8551 E-mail: sales@icc-credit.co.uk

INFORMATION SERVICES, COMPANY/CORPORATE/ CORPORATION – *continued*

I-DocumentSystems Ltd, Tontine House, 8 Gordon Street, Glasgow, G1 3PL Tel: 0141-574 1900 Fax: 0141-574 1901 E-mail: ruth.rintoul@idoxplc.com
Iron Mountain Ltd, Mill Way, Sittingbourne, Kent, ME10 2PT Tel: (01795) 479241 Fax: (01795) 427224 E-mail: info@ronmountain.co.uk
Jordan Publishing Ltd, 21 St Thomas Street, Bristol, BS1 6JS Tel: 0117-923 0600 Fax: 0117-925 0486 E-mail: customersupport@jordans.co.uk
Kemps Publishing Ltd, 11 Swan Courtyard, Charles Edward Road, Birmingham, B26 1BU Tel: 0121-765 4144 Fax: 0121-706 6210 E-mail: enquiries@kempspublishing.co.uk
Law & Accountancy Agency Services Ltd, 31 Corsham Street, London, N1 6DR Tel: (020) 7250 1410 Fax: (020) 7250 1973 E-mail: searches@landa.ltd.uk
M & N Group Ltd, 118 London Road, Kingston upon Thames, Surrey, KT2 6QJ Tel: (020) 8974 5252 Fax: (020) 8974 5588 E-mail: sales@mn-group.com
Market Focus Research Ltd, Holt Barns, The Kilns, Frith End, Bordon, Hampshire, GU35 0QW Tel: (01420) 488355 Fax: (0845) 1309220 E-mail: admin@marketfocus.com
Raymond Morris Group Ltd, Invision House, Wilbury Way, Hitchin, Hertfordshire, SG4 0TW Tel: (020) 7729 1234 Fax: (020) 7251 0965 E-mail: infodesk@rmonline.com
Reed Business Information, Windsor Court, East Grinstead Ho, Wood St, East Grinstead, West Sussex, RH19 1XA Tel: (01342) 326972 Fax: (01342) 335612 E-mail: information@reedinfo.co.uk
Reed Business Information Ltd, Quadrant House, The Quadrant, Sutton, Surrey, SM2 5AS Tel: (020) 8652 3500 E-mail: webmaster@rbi.co.uk
Waterlow Secretaries Ltd, 6-8 Underwood Street, London, N1 7JQ Tel: (020) 7250 3350 Fax: (020) 7608 0867 E-mail: companyservices@waterlow.com
Weather Call, Avalon House, 57-63 Scrutton Street, London, EC2A 4PJ Tel: (020) 7613 6000 Fax: (020) 7613 5005 E-mail: weathercall@itouch.co.uk
David Winrow Marketing, PO Box 9, Northwich, Cheshire, CW9 7TP Tel: (01606) 41241 Fax: (01606) 47847 E-mail: sales@winrow.co.uk

INFORMATION SERVICES, FINANCE/INVESTMENT

Close Invoice Finance Ltd, 25 Bartholomew Street, Newbury, Berkshire, RG14 5LL Tel: (01635) 31517 Fax: (01635) 521180 E-mail: sales@closeinvoice.co.uk
I G Index plc, Friars House, 157-168 Blackfriars Road, London, SE1 8EZ Tel: (020) 7896 0011 Fax: (020) 7896 0010 E-mail: igindex@igindex.co.uk
Interactive Data, Fitzroy House, 13/17 Epworth Street, London, EC2A 4DL Tel: (020) 7825 8000 Fax: (020) 7251 2725 E-mail: investorrelations@interactivedatercorp.com
Mega Company Services P.L.C., Business Information House, Farmoor Court, Cumnor Road, Oxford, OX2 9LU Tel: (01865) 865666 Fax: (01865) 865465E-mail: info@mega.co.uk
Prospect Swetenhams, Field House, 72 Oldfield Road, Hampton, Middlesex, TW12 2HQ Tel: (020) 8481 8730 Fax: (020) 8783 1940 E-mail: sales@prospectshop.co.uk
Quick Corp London Branch, 110 Middlesex Street, London, E1 7HY Tel: (020) 7377 2222 Fax: (020) 7377 2201
Telerate Ltd, 122 Leadenhall Street, London, EC3V 4QH Tel: (020) 7832 9000 Fax: (0870) 4451440 E-mail: infoeurope@telerate.com
Thomson Financial Ltd, Aldgate House, 33 Aldgate High Street, London, EC3N 1DL Tel: (020) 7369 7000 Fax: (020) 7369 7240
Transterra Ltd, 2 Copperfields Orchard, Kemsing, Sevenoaks, Kent, TN15 6QH Tel: (01732) 761687 Fax: (01732) 761687
World Markets Co. P.L.C., 525 Ferry Road, Edinburgh, EH5 2AW Tel: 0131-315 2000 Fax: 0131-315 2999

INFORMATION SERVICES, INTERNET BASED

▶ Cafenet UK, 63 Watergate Street, Chester, CH1 2LB Tel: (01244) 401116 E-mail: info@cafenetuk.com
Internet Consultancy & Management Ltd, 12 Sycamore Avenue, Glapwell, Chesterfield, Derbyshire, S44 5LH Tel: (0800) 0431057 Fax: (0870) 1270965 E-mail: support@icamltd.co.uk
▶ ISKIV Information Strategies Key Intangible Value Ltd, Middle Spoad Barn, Newcastle, Craven Arms, Shropshire, SY7 8PB Tel: 0207 7887762 E-mail: i-info@iskiv.com
▶ Loud-N-Clear Com Ltd, 29 Castle Crescent, Reading, RG1 6AQ Tel: 0118-967 7693 Fax: 0118-954 2756 E-mail: enquiries@loud-n-clear.com
▶ Stockfolder.com, 1 North Avenue, Ealing, London, London, W13 8AP Tel: 0208 998 3445 E-mail: info@stockfolder.com
▶ Tektonisk (UK) Ltd, Palmerston House, 814 Brighton Road, Purley, Surrey, CR8 2BR Tel: (08707) 606282 Fax: (020) 8655 8501 E-mail: pg@tektonisk.com

INFORMATION SERVICES, PROFESSIONAL/MEDICAL/ SCIENTIFIC

Arthritis Research Campaign, Copeman House St. Marys Court, St. Marys Gate, Chesterfield, Derbyshire, S41 7TD Tel: (01246) 558033 Fax: (01246) 558007 E-mail: enquiries@arc.org.uk
Barbour Index, Kingswood, Kings Ride, Ascot, Berkshire, SL5 8AD Tel: (01344) 884999 Fax: (01344) 899377 E-mail: reception@barbourindex.co.uk
C P L Scientific Information Services Ltd, Nosworthy Way, Mongewell, Wallingford, Oxfordshire, OX10 8DE Tel: (01491) 829346 Fax: (01491) 836232 E-mail: sis@cplsis.com
Dora Wirth Languages Ltd, 86-87 Campden Street, London, W8 7EN Tel: (020) 7229 4552 Fax: (020) 7727 0744 E-mail: sales@dwlanguages.com
Office Of Health Economics Ltd, 12 Whitehall, London, SW1A 2DY Tel: (020) 7930 9203 Fax: (020) 7747 1419 E-mail: enquiries@ohe.org

INFORMATION SYSTEMS

▶ ADP, Phoenix House, Phoenix Crescent, Strathclyde Business Park, Bellshill, Lanarkshire, ML4 3NJ Tel: (01488) 662662 Fax: (01698) 501061
Baxter Associates, 24 Ben Madigan Heights, Newtownabbey, County Antrim, BT36 7PY Tel: (028) 9037 0567 Fax: (028) 9028 3324 E-mail: sales@baxterworld.com
BJL Business Consultants, The Old Rectory, St Marys Lane, Claxby, Market Rasen, Lincolnshire, LN8 3YX Tel: (01673) 828345 Fax: (01673) 828345
▶ Catalan IS Services Ltd, Glenbervie Business Centre, Larbert, Stirlingshire, FK5 4RB Tel: (01324) 682150 Fax: 01324 682149
Lysis UK Ltd, 334 Chiswick High Road, London, W4 5TA Tel: (020) 8742 7719 Fax: (020) 8742 8397
Modulex Systems Ltd, 9a North Portway Close, Round Spinney Industrial Estate, Northampton, NN3 8RQ Tel: (01604) 672100 Fax: (01604) 672161 E-mail: mxuk@modulex.co.uk
▶ Quartile Management Consulting Ltd, 10 Melville Crescent, Edinburgh, EH3 7LU Tel: 0131-666 1237 Fax: (07092) 313096
W I T Systems, Unit1 7 Business Development Centre, Main Avenue, Treforest Industrial Estate, Pontypridd, Mid Glamorgan, CF37 5UR Tel: (01443) 844565 Fax: (01443) 842925 E-mail: info@wit-systems.net

INFORMATION TECHNOLOGY DESIGN (ITD)

▶ Tiger Consultants Ltd, Tiger House, 86 Lind Road, Sutton, Surrey, SM1 4PL Tel: (020) 8395 8922 Fax: (020) 8395 8923 E-mail: info@tigerconsultants.co.uk
▶ Travology Limited, Business and IT Consultants, High Bank, Old Forge Lane, Horney Common, Uckfield, East Sussex, TN22 3EL Tel: 0871 871 2662 E-mail: enquiries@travology.ltd.uk

INFORMATION TECHNOLOGY (IT) CONSULTANTS

3 Thinking, 34 Windermere, Swindon, SN3 6JZ Tel: (0870) 1283075 Fax: (01793) 474522 E-mail: sales@3thinking.com
3d Computer Systems Ltd, Albany House, 11 New Road, Chippenham, Wiltshire, SN15 1HJ Tel: (01249) 460766 Fax: (01249) 460583 E-mail: sales@3d-computers.co.uk
▶ A C L Advanced Consulting Ltd, 55 Dublin Street, Edinburgh, EH3 6NL Tel: 0131-478 0976
A I M Ltd, Victoria House, Derringham Street, Hull, HU3 1EL Tel: (01482) 326971 Fax: (01482) 228465 E-mail: aim@aim.co.uk
Abacus Dc Ltd, 1 Russell Rd, Lee-on-the-Solent, Hants, PO13 9HR Tel: (023) 9255 2159
▶ Abc Computer Services, Highview, 5a King Edward Road, Stanford-le-Hope, Essex, SS17 0EF Tel: (01375) 404495 E-mail: sales@mitefixit.com
Access It Ltd, The Old Grain Store, Brenley Lane, Boughton-under-Blean, Faversham, Kent, ME13 9LY Tel: (01227) 750555 Fax: (01227) 750070 E-mail: sales@accessit.co.uk
Active Information Systems, Unit 3 Brooks Green Road, Coolham, Horsham, West Sussex, RH13 8GR Tel: (01403) 740400 Fax: (01403) 741125 E-mail: active@activegrp.co.uk
Advanced Thinking Systems Ltd, 1 South Lane, Waterlooville, Hampshire, PO8 0RB Tel: (023) 9259 5000 Fax: (023) 9259 5656 E-mail: sales@advanced-thinking.co.uk
Advantage Business Group Ltd, East St, Farnham, Surrey, GU9 7TB Tel: (01252) 738500 Fax: (01252) 717065 E-mail: enquiries@advantage-business.co.uk
Advantage Business Systems, 97-101 Cleveland Street, London, W1T 6PW Tel: (020) 7663 1234 Fax: (020) 7663 1200 E-mail: info@advantage.co.uk
▶ AEYE, 1 Glencairn House, 70 Ridgway, London, London, SW19 4RA Tel: (020) 8879 9832 Fax: (020) 9212 9079 E-mail: info@aeye.biz
Altis Consulting Ltd, 11 Thatcham Business Village, Colthrop Way, Thatcham, Berkshire, RG19 4LW Tel: (01635) 867575 Fax: (01635) 867576 E-mail: sales@altisltd.com
AMJ (UK), Epps Buildings, Bridge Road, Ashford, Kent, TN23 1BB Tel: (01233) 663205 Fax: (01233) 664181E-mail: info@amj-uk.com
Amtec Consulting plc, Millennium Centre, 2 Crosby Way, Farnham, Surrey, GU9 7XX Tel: (01252) 737866 Fax: (01252) 737855 E-mail: post@amtec.co.uk
▶ Angove Associates, 5 Marsh Grove Road, Huddersfield, HD3 3AQ Tel: 01484 539229 Fax: 01484 539229 E-mail: info@angoveassociates.co.uk
Applications Design Ltd, 91 Melciss Road, Wickersley, Rotherham, South Yorkshire, S66 2BU Tel: (01709) 543025 Fax: (01709) 543025 E-mail: appsdesign@btinternet.com
Asap Solutions International Ltd, 233 Uxbridge Road, Mill End, Rickmansworth, Hertfordshire, WD3 8DP Tel: (07985) 378402 Fax: (020) 8566 3653
Ashgoal Ltd, Cqueens Road, Barnet, Hertfordshire, EN5 4DJ Tel: (020) 8275 5100 Fax: (020) 8441 7240 E-mail: info@ashgoal.co.uk
Ashtel Systems Ltd, Unit 12, Central Business Centre, Great Central Way, London, NW10 0UR Tel: (0870) 9221140 Fax: (0870) 9221141
Aspentech Ltd, Birkdale House, Kelvin Close, Warrington, WA3 7RB Tel: (01925) 844400 Fax: (01925) 844455
Astrun Computers, 78 High Street, Lee-on-the-Solent, Hampshire, PO13 9DA Tel: (023) 9255 6007 Fax: (023) 9255 3514 E-mail: sales@smsit.co.uk
W.S. Atkins Ltd, Unit 3 Langstone Business Village, Langstone Park, Langstone, Newport, Gwent, NP18 2LG Tel: (01633) 415500 Fax: (01633) 411211
Attributes Associates, 52 Harvey Rd, Guildford, Surrey, GU1 3LU Tel: (01483) 577771 Fax: (01483) 577555
Aztech Microcentres Ltd, 322 Hemdean Road, Caversham, Reading, RG4 7QS Tel: 0118-946 6600 Fax: 0118-946 1076 E-mail: sales@aztechmicros.com
Baillie Associates Ltd, 50 Main Street, Lowdham, Nottingham, NG14 7BE Tel: 0115-966 3929 Fax: 0115-966 4745 E-mail: binfo@baillies.com
Balanced Solutions Ltd, 20 Juniper Road, Southampton, SO18 4EJ Tel: (023) 8063 8393 Fax: (023) 8063 8393 E-mail: info@balancedsolutions.co.uk
▶ Bluefin Solutions Ltd, Utell House, 2 Kew Bridge Road, Brentford, Middlesex, TW8 0JF Tel: (0870) 2330404 Fax: (0870) 2330405 E-mail: enquiries@bluefinsolutions.com
Blueprint Management Systems, 1 Pemberton Row, London, EC4A 3BG Tel: (020) 7832 1800 Fax: (020) 7832 1801
Broadskill Ltd, Hinderton Grange, Quarry Road, Neston, CH64 7UD Tel: 0151-336 8899 Fax: 0151-336 7799 E-mail: admin@broadskill.com
Bull Information Systems Ltd, Maxted Road, Hemel Hempstead, Hertfordshire, HP2 7DZ Tel: (01442) 232222 Fax: (01442) 884361 E-mail: information@bull.co.uk
Business Insights Group Ltd, Brandiston House, 98 High Street, Ingatestone, Essex, CM4 0BA Tel: (01277) 355755 Fax: (01277) 355753 E-mail: info@digroup.co.uk
Business Management Promotions Ltd, Lower Weaven, Little Dewchurch, Hereford, HR2 6QB Tel: (01432) 840456 Fax: (01432) 840450 E-mail: bmpltd@ticali.co.uk
Bytes Technology, Matrix House, North Fourth Street, Milton Keynes, MK9 1NJ Tel: (08707) 774646 Fax: (08707) 771021
C C T Infotech Ltd, Unit 7C Priory Tech Park, Saxon Way, Hull, HU13 9PB Tel: (01482) 647044 Fax: (01482) 647046 E-mail: sales@cct-infotech.co.uk
C G P Associates Ltd, 2 Maple Road, Enigma Business Park, Malvern, Worcestershire, WR14 1GQ Tel: (01684) 584700 Fax: (0870) 0522410 E-mail: derekc@cgp.co.uk
C K S Entertainment Systems, Logistics Centre, Willoughby Road, Bracknell, Berkshire, RG12 8FD Tel: (01344) 307788 Fax: (01344) 456710 E-mail: sales@cksgroup.co.uk
C W Computer Services Ltd, 62 St Anns Road, Southend-on-Sea, SS2 5AU Tel: (01702) 466161 Fax: (01702) 466162 E-mail: charles.whitmore@cwcomputerservices.com
▶ Cambridge Online Systems Ltd, 163 Milton Road, Cambridge, CB4 0GP Tel: (01223) 422600 Fax: (01223) 422601 E-mail: enquiries@cosl.co.uk
Castlepoint Associates Ltd, Castle Point House 180 Kiln Road, Benfleet, Essex, SS7 1SU Tel: (01702) 558165 Fax: (01702) 552550 E-mail: sales@castle-point-computers.co.uk
Causeway Technologies Ltd, Bucknalls Lane, Watford, WD25 9XX Tel: (01923) 892600 Fax: (01923) 679288 E-mail: partners@ecl.uk.com
Cedar Systems Ltd, 2440 The Quadrant, Aztec West, Almondsbury, Bristol, BS32 4AQ Tel: (01454) 878708 Fax: (01454) 878608 E-mail: cedar@cedar.co.uk
Cemoc Ltd, Cemoc House, Rectory Drive, Wootton Bridge, Ryde, Isle of Wight, PO33 4QQ Tel: (01983) 884321 E-mail: sales@cemoc.co.uk
Chaucer Group, 67 Preston Street, Faversham, Kent, ME13 8PB Tel: (0845) 0724500 Fax: (0845) 0724510 E-mail: sales@chaucer-group.com
CHP Consulting Ltd, Augustine House, 6a Austin Friars, London, EC2N 2HA Tel: (020) 7588 1800 Fax: (020) 7588 1802 E-mail: info@chp.co.uk
Civica It Systems Ltd, Regent Court, Laporte Way, Luton, LU4 8SP Tel: (01582) 644444 Fax: (01582) 644446
Clive Leyland Music Ltd, 4 Newmeadow, Lostock, Bolton, BL6 4PB Tel: (01204) 845459 Fax: (01204) 496767 E-mail: clive.leyland@btinternet.com
Coleman Bennett International P.L.C., 30 St. Mary Axe, London, EC3A 8AD Tel: (020) 7623 2000 Fax: (020) 7623 2001 E-mail: info@cbi-plc.com
Comcen Computer Supplies Ltd, 1 York Place, Leeds, LS1 2DS Tel: 0113-234 5000 Fax: 0113-234 2757 E-mail: leeds@comcen.co.uk
Compex Development & Marketing Ltd, Century House, The Lake, Northampton, NN4 7HD Tel: (01604) 233333 Fax: (01604) 233334 E-mail: sales@compexdm.co.uk
Computaphile Software Soltuions Ltd, 13 Surrey Close, Rugeley, Staffordshire, WS15 1JZ Tel: (01889) 579572 Fax: (01889) 579572 E-mail: brian@computaphile.com
Computer Solutions & Networks, 315 Lichfield Road, Sutton Coldfield, West Midlands, B74 4BZ Tel: 0121-323 3450 Fax: 0121-323 3358 E-mail: tony.h@csnuk.net
Computers For Linguists, 45 Endwell Road, London, SE4 2PQ Tel: (020) 7732 1740 Fax: (020) 7358 9214 E-mail: sales@marguet-ball.net
Concepts I T Training & Consultancy Ltd, 28 Norman Drive, Eastwood, Nottingham, NG16 3FJ Tel: (01773) 788907 Fax: (01773) 788907 E-mail: dorme@concepts-it.com
▶ Consortium Systems, Lint House, Linthouse Lane, Wolverhampton, WV11 3EA Tel: (01902) 723327 Fax: (01902) 739886
Constellation I X Ltd, Post Office House, Main Street, Leicester, LE9 2AL Tel: 0116-239 2300 E-mail: sales@conix.co.uk
Co-Operative Systems, 18-20 Miles Street, London, SW8 1SD Tel: (020) 7793 0395 Fax: (020) 7735 6472 E-mail: team@coopsys.net
▶ Copycare Ltd, Unit 3, Chiltern Works, Chiltern Drive, Surbiton, Surrey, KT5 8LS Tel: (020) 8296 0202 Fax: (020) 8296 0596 E-mail: info@copycare.net
Core Technology Systems UK Ltd, Holland House, 1-4 Bury Street, London, EC3A 5AW Tel: (020) 7626 0516 Fax: (020) 7953 3600 E-mail: sales@core.gb.com
Cotech Software Consultants Ltd, 9 Drakefield Road, London, SW17 8RT Tel: (020) 8682 0123 Fax: (020) 8682 4550 E-mail: faisal@cotech.co.uk
Creative Database Projects Ltd, Queens Wharf, Queen Caroline Street, London, W6 9RJ Tel: (020) 8600 2605 Fax: (020) 8600 2603 E-mail: enquiry@cdproj.com
▶ Crox Tech, 48 Crompton Drive, Liverpool, L12 0JX Tel: 0151-222 4691 E-mail: sales@croxtech.com
Cruse Control Ltd, 6 Wolsey Mansions, Main Avenue, Moor Park, Northwood, Middlesex, HA6 2HL Tel: (01923) 842295 Fax: (01923) 842698 E-mail: mail@crusecontrol.com
Cutec Ltd, 19 Branson Court, Plymouth, PL7 2WU Tel: (0870) 3211801 Fax: (0870) 3211802 E-mail: sales@cutec.co.uk
Cym Consulting Ltd, 14 Well Hall Parade, London, SE9 6SP Tel: (020) 8294 1622 Fax: (020) 8859 4562E-mail: cym@cymc.com
D C S Associates, 50 High Street, Kingswood, Bristol, BS15 4AJ Tel: 0117-960 3242 Fax: 0117-960 3282 E-mail: sales@dcs-imago.com
D L A Computers, 47 Southend Road, Hockley, Essex, SS5 4PZ Tel: (01702) 202655 Fax: (01702) 202540 E-mail: sales@dlacomputers.co.uk
Datadean Ltd, 60 Tinney Drive, Truro, Cornwall, TR1 1AQ Tel: (01872) 264008 Fax: (01872) 263972 E-mail: david.dawkins@quivivre.com
Daystar, Daystar House, 102 Burnage Lane, Manchester, M19 2NG Tel: 0161-248 8088 Fax: 0161-224 2522
Decisions Express Ltd, 15 17 Hatherley House, Wood Street, Barnet, Hertfordshire, EN5 4AT Tel: (020) 8441 9800 Fax: (020) 8449 9597 E-mail: info@decisions.co.uk
Deloitte, Stonecutter Court, 1 Stonecutter Street, London, EC4A 4TR Tel: (020) 7936 3000 Fax: (020) 7583 1198
Digital Dispatch Ltd, 38-39 Bar Hill Business Park, Saxon Way, Bar Hill, Cambridge, CB23 8SL Tel: (01954) 780888 Fax: (01954) 781612 E-mail: sales@digitaldispatch.com
Double Dean Ltd, Fallowfields, Dummer, Basingstoke, Hants, RG25 2AG Tel: (01256) 398550

INFORMATION TECHNOLOGY (IT) CONSULTANTS – *continued*

DPR Services, 171 Ranworth Avenue, Hoddesdon, Hertfordshire, EN11 9NU Tel: (01992) 470654 Fax: (0871) 6613985 E-mail: info@dprservices.co.uk

▶ The E R P Group, Bliss House, 251 Dewsbury Road, Ossett, West Yorkshire, WF5 9QF Tel: (0870) 3339032 Fax: (01924) 280117 E-mail: sales@theerpgroup.co.uk

E S I T Computer Consultancy, Suite A, Loughborough Technology Centre, Epinal Way, Loughborough, Leicestershire, LE11 3GE Tel: (01509) 235544 Fax: (01509) 260661 E-mail: info@esit.co.uk

Eds, 4 Roundwood Avenue, Stockley, Uxbridge, Middlesex, UB11 1BQ Tel: (020) 8848 8989 Fax: (020) 8535 3484 E-mail: info@eds.com

▶ EDS Global Field Services, D I A N House, 2 Aegean Road, Atlantic Street, Altrincham, Cheshire, WA14 5UW Tel: 0161-929 7889 Fax: (0870) 6067491

Elyzium, 12 Queensbrook, Bolton, BL1 4AY Tel: (01204) 528628 Fax: (01204) 534678 E-mail: sales@elyzium.co.uk

Empresa Ltd, 160 Northumberland Street, Norwich, NR2 4EE Tel: (01603) 623030 Fax: (01603) 623525 E-mail: sales@empresa.co.uk

▶ Enterprise Technology Solutions Ltd, 19 Paxton Crescent, Shenley Lodge, Milton Keynes, MK5 7PX Tel: (01908) 395500 Fax: (01908) 395499 E-mail: info@etsl.net

▶ Esys Plc, 1 Occam Court, Occam Road, Surrey Research Park, Guildford, Surrey, GU2 7HJ Tel: (01483) 304545 Fax: (01483) 303878 E-mail: info@esys.co.uk

Exel, Ocean House, The Ring, Bracknell, Berkshire, RG12 1AN Tel: (01344) 302000 Fax: (01344) 710037

F A C T Delta Solutions Ltd, 10Th Floor, Alexandra House, 1 Alexandra Road, Swansea, SA1 5ED Tel: (01792) 465503 Fax: (01792) 465504 E-mail: mailbox@factdelta.com

F M S Ltd, 82 Queens Rd, Brighton, BN1 3XE Tel: 01273 721063 Fax: 01273 721406

Fast Micros, 87 Canterbury Road, Margate, Kent, CT9 5AX Tel: (01843) 227522 Fax: (01843) 225109

Fisher Technology Ltd, Acre House, 11-15 William Road, London, NW1 3ER Tel: (020) 7874 7888 Fax: (020) 7380 4900 E-mail: enquiries@fishtech.net

Foresite Systems Ltd, Foresite House, Willenhall Lane, Binley, Coventry, CV3 2UA Tel: (024) 7665 2111 Fax: (024) 7665 5219 E-mail: info@foresite.org

Forvus Computer Services, Forvus House, 53 Clapham Common South Side, London, SW4 9BX Tel: (020) 7819 1000 Fax: (020) 7498 1939 E-mail: sales@forvus.co.uk

Fujitsu Services Ltd, Wenlock Way, West Gorton, Manchester, M12 5DR Tel: (08702) 345555

Futura Consulting UK Ltd, 51 Downside Close, Blandford Forum, Dorset, DT11 7SD Tel: (01258) 451007 Fax: (01258) 451007 E-mail: mick.gordon@futuraconsulting.com

Gallery Partnership Ltd, 53-55 The Hop Exchange, 24 Southwark Street, London, SE1 1TY Tel: (020) 7096 2800 Fax: (020) 7096 2810 E-mail: mkemp@gallerypartnership.co.uk

▶ Gecko It Services Ltd, 89 Chessel Avenue, Southampton, SO19 4DY Tel: (023) 8023 1030 E-mail: sales@gecko-it.com

General Technology Ltd, Unit E5 Fairchild Place, London, EC2A 3EN Tel: (020) 7375 0000 Fax: (020) 7377 1429 E-mail: hitech@gentec.co.uk

Geotech Systems Ltd, 3000 Cathedral Hill Industrial Estate, Guildford, Surrey, GU2 7YB Tel: (01483) 243530 Fax: (01483) 245330

Getronics UK Ltd, Cygnus House, 1 The Southwood Crescent, Apollo Rise, Farnborough, Hampshire, GU14 0NL Tel: (0870) 9068000 Fax: (020) 8874 3014 E-mail: getronics.helpdesk@getronics.com

Green It Solutions Ltd, Unit 1 King George Court, High Street, Billericay, Essex, CM12 9BY Tel: (01277) 844940 Fax: (01277) 844941 E-mail: info@greenit.co.uk

▶ HA Solutions Limited, The Chimes, 260 London Road, Wokingham, Berkshire, RG40 1QY Tel: 0845 0943092 E-mail: info@hasolutions.co.uk

Hallam Consultants, 30 Main Rd, Twycross, Atherstone, Warwickshire, CV9 3PL Tel: (01827) 880158

Headway Consultancy Ltd, Unit 19 Church Farm Business Park, Corston, Bath, BA2 9AP Tel: (01225) 872333 Fax: (01225) 872266 E-mail: contact@headway-ltd.com

Hi Europe, Hattori House, Vanwall Road, Maidenhead, Berkshire, SL6 4UB Tel: (01628) 770077 Fax: (01628) 785433 E-mail: sales@hieurope.com

Hoge 100 Business Systems Ltd, I M S House, Prescott Drive, Worcester, WR4 9NE Tel: (01905) 455227 Fax: (01905) 455035 E-mail: sales@hoge100.co.uk

Hyperion Systems Ltd, 12 The Mount, Guildford, Surrey, GU2 4HN Tel: (01483) 301793 Fax: (01483) 561657 E-mail: glor.benson@chyp.com

I B S Consulting Services Ltd, 5 Parkshot House, Kew Road, Richmond, Surrey, TW9 2PR Tel: (020) 8334 8018 Fax: (020) 8334 8558 E-mail: press@ibs-uk.co.uk

I D Computer Services (Scotland) Ltd, Barncluith Bus Centre, Townhead St, Hamilton, Lanarkshire, ML3 7DP Tel: (01698) 458200 Fax: (01698) 421188 E-mail: info@idcsl.com

I T At Bicester, 15 Manorsfield Road, Bicester, Oxfordshire, OX26 6EH Tel: (01869) 353939 E-mail: apine@occ.ac.uk

▶ I T R M Ltd, Thames House, St. Johns Road, Sidcup, Kent, DA14 4HD Tel: (07000) 284876 Fax: (020) 8308 3301 E-mail: info@itrm.co.uk

I T Works Alba Ltd, Building 1020 Rosyth Dockyard, Rosyth, Dunfermline, Fife, KY11 2YD Tel: (01383) 411442 Fax: (01383) 411488 E-mail: enquiries@itworks-alba.co.uk

Impact Computer Consultants Ltd, 210 Church Road, Hove, East Sussex, BN3 2DJ Tel: (01273) 821820 Fax: (01273) 821010 E-mail: sales@impactcc.co.uk

Imperial Business Systems, 7 Hill Street, Bristol, BS1 5PU Tel: 0117-925 1700 Fax: 0117-925 2515 E-mail: ibs@imperial.co.uk

Imtex Computer Consultants, Stratford Arcade, 75 High Street, Stony Stratford, Milton Keynes, MK11 1AY Tel: (01908) 261216 Fax: (01908) 261216

Infogain Ltd, 18 Forlease Road, Maidenhead, Berkshire, SL6 1RU Tel: (01628) 580600 Fax: (01628) 580610 E-mail: info@infogain.com

Information Technology Systems, Cygnet Lodge, Worcester Road, Worcester, WR8 0EA Tel: (01684) 311463 Fax: (01684) 311402 E-mail: sales@itsystems.co.uk

Infosystems, Bridge Farm, Holt Lane, Ashby Magna, Lutterworth, Leicestershire, LE17 5NJ Tel: (01455) 201000 Fax: (01455) 201001 E-mail: sales@infosystems.co.uk

Integranet Networking Services Ltd, 71 High Street, Harrold, Bedford, MK43 7BJ Tel: (01234) 721755 E-mail: info@integranet.co.uk

Intellect Security Ltd, 10 The Hub Station Road, Henley-on-Thames, Oxfordshire, RG9 1AY Tel: (01491) 411698 Fax: (01491) 411415 E-mail: sales@intellect.co.uk

Intelligent Business Strategies Ltd, Springfield House, Water Lane, Wilmslow, Cheshire, SK9 5BG Tel: (01625) 520700 Fax: (01625) 520700

Intelligent Communications, Market Hall, Market Street, Colne, Lancashire, BB8 0HS Tel: (01282) 864677 Fax: (01282) 860092 E-mail: sales@intelligent-marketing.co.uk

IT Service Link Ltd, The Black Barn, The Folley, Layer De La Haye, Colchester, CO2 0HZ Tel: (01206) 235000 Fax: (01206) 235001 E-mail: danielle@hi-tech-sales.co.uk

Jumpstart Ltd, 3 Medway Road, Birkenhead, Merseyside, CH42 2BD Tel: 0151-645 9398 Fax: 0151-645 9999 E-mail: nigel.birchenough@jumpstart.co.uk

K & K Computers, 1 Baker Street, Weston-super-Mare, Avon, BS23 3AA Tel: (01934) 419324 Fax: (01934) 419469

Keene Printing Co. Ltd, 33-41 Dallington St, London, EC1V 0BB Tel: (020) 7251 2722 Fax: (020) 7490 8736 E-mail: info@keenes.co.uk

Keynote Business Services Ltd, Unit 46 Alpha Business Centre, 60 South Grove, London, E17 7NX Tel: (020) 8926 9216 Fax: (020) 8926 9216 E-mail: info@keynotes.co.uk

Kudos Solutions Ltd, The Manor, Main Street, Tur Langton, Leicester, LE8 0PJ Tel: (01858) 545976 Fax: (01858) 545977

Lanmark Technical Services Ltd, 30-32 Thames Street, Hampton, Middlesex, TW12 2DX Tel: (020) 8783 3260 Fax: (020) 8783 3270 E-mail: sales@lanmark.co.uk

LapSafe(R) Products, Unit 3, Wakes Hall Business Centre, Colchester Road, Wakes Colne, Colchester, CO6 2DY Tel: (0845) 2301010 Fax: (0845) 2301020 E-mail: sales@lapsafe.com

Library Information Technology Centre, South Bank University, 103 Borough Road, London, SE1 0AA Tel: (020) 7815 7872 Fax: (020) 7815 7050

Logica P.L.C., Hamilton House, Church Street, Altrincham, Cheshire, WA14 4DQ Tel: 0161-927 7888 Fax: 0161-927 7889

Logma Systems Design Ltd, 27 Victoria Street, Chorley, Lancashire, PR7 2TX Tel: (01257) 233123 Fax: (01257) 237215 E-mail: sales@logma.net

Logsys, Ebor Court, Westgate, Leeds, LS1 4ND Tel: 0113-384 0400 Fax: 0113-245 4798

Lorien Group plc, Leadenhall Street, London, EC3A 4AF Tel: (020) 7654 1000 Fax: (020) 7654 1010 E-mail: asqfor@lorien.co.uk

▶ M L I T C, 40 Roman Way, Felixstowe, Suffolk, IP11 9NP Tel: (01394) 671579 E-mail: mark@mlconsultancy.co.uk

M & S Systems Ltd, 21 Excelsior Grove, Pelsall, Walsall, WS3 4PX Tel: (01922) 685615 E-mail: simon@mandssys.demon.co.uk

Macrovision Europe Ltd, 14-18 Bell Street, Maidenhead, Berkshire, SL6 1BR Tel: (01628) 786100 Fax: (0870) 8711161 E-mail: info@macrovison.com

Manumit Computers Ltd, Scope House, Weston Road, Crewe, CW1 6DD Tel: (01270) 250022 Fax: (01270) 250033 E-mail: contact@manumit-computers.com

Microguide Corporate Computer Consultants Ltd, Wyndham House, 82 Shortlands Road, Kingston upon Thames, Surrey, KT2 6HE Tel: (020) 8549 7152 Fax: (020) 8549 8112 E-mail: enquiry@microguide.co.uk

Monostar Ltd, Peggs Barn, Drinkstone, Bury St. Edmunds, Suffolk, IP30 9TW Tel: (01449) 736081 Fax: (01449) 736083 E-mail: info@monostar.co.uk

Myriad, 10 Lawn Avenue, Peterborough, PE1 3RB Tel: (01733) 766617 Fax: (01733) 759727 E-mail: enquiries@myriadit.net

N B Group It Consultancy, 34 Bedford Road, Gregans House, Hitchin, Hertfordshire, SG5 1HF Tel: (01462) 452452 E-mail: info@online-it.com

N I I T Europe Ltd, Westfields, London Road, High Wycombe, Buckinghamshire, HP11 1HP Tel: (01494) 539333 Fax: (01494) 539444

NCC Group, Oxford Road, Manchester, M1 7EF Tel: 0161-209 5200 Fax: 0161-209 5400 E-mail: response@nccgroup.co.uk

Network Training, Mitre House, Tower Street, Taunton, Somerset, TA1 4BH Tel: (01823) 353354 Fax: (01823) 352202 E-mail: mail@network-training.ac.uk

Newarke Designs Ltd, 502 Uppingham Rd, Leicester, LE5 2GG Tel: 0116-241 0170 Fax: 0116-241 0173

Newman Business Solutions Ltd, Newman House, Farningham Road, Crowborough, East Sussex, TN6 2JR Tel: (01892) 664155 Fax: (01892) 669591 E-mail: enquiries@newmanbs.co.uk

Noblestar Systems Ltd, Liberty House, 222 Regent Street, London, W1B 5TR Tel: (020) 7297 2038 Fax: (020) 7297 2142 E-mail: info@noblestar.co.uk

Nukta Ltd, PO Box 31434, London, W4 4FQ Tel: (020) 8996 9043 Fax: (07092) 336473 E-mail: sales@nuktaltd.co.uk

▶ Nverge Technologies Ltd, 81 Southfleet Road, Orpington, Kent, BR6 9SN Tel: 0168 9869319 Fax: 0168 9869319 E-mail: sam@nvergetechnologies.com

P C Computer Services, 16 South Avenue, Bognor Regis, West Sussex, PO21 3QS Tel: (01243) 820840 Fax: (01243) 842961 E-mail: sales@pc-computers.co.uk

▶ Pactum Partium Ltd, 24 Nursery Gardens, Bedford, MK41 8DU Tel: (07890) 267779 E-mail: info@pactern-partium.com

Panacea Ltd, Winton House, Winton Square, Basingstoke, Hampshire, RG21 8EN Tel: (01256) 305050 Fax: (01256) 305030

Panacea Ltd, Unit 6 Murrell Green Business Pk, London Road, Hook, Hampshire, RG27 9GR Tel: (01256) 305050 Fax: (01256) 305006 E-mail: support@panacea.co.uk

Panacea Services Ltd, 20 St Mary at Hill, London, EC3R 8EE Tel: (020) 7375 3757 Fax: (020) 7375 1525 E-mail: info@panacea-services.co.uk

Patech Solutions Ltd, Tame House, Wellington Crescent, Fradley Park, Lichfield, Staffordshire, WS13 8RZ Tel: (01543) 444707 Fax: (01543) 444709

Pav I T Services plc, King Business Centre, Reeds Lane, Sayers Common, Hassocks, West Sussex, BN6 9LS Tel: (01273) 834000 Fax: (01273) 834631 E-mail: info@pav.co.uk

Planit Systems, 21B Coda Centre, Munster Road, London, SW6 6AW Tel: (020) 7381 8494 Fax: (020) 7381 8817 E-mail: info@planitsystems.co.uk

▶ Precision Productions Ltd, 14 Cow Lane, Wareham, Dorset, BH20 4RD Tel: (01929) 551062 Fax: (0870) 7058657 E-mail: enquiries@precisionproductions.net

▶ Pride Computer Solutions, 21 Lynmouth Drive, Ilkeston, Derbyshire, DE7 9HN Tel: 0115-944 2410 Fax: (0870) 7063172 E-mail: info@pridecs.co.uk

Prion Associates, Branscombe, Chart Road, Sutton Valence, Maidstone, Kent, ME17 3AW Tel: (01622) 844595 Fax: (01622) 844595 E-mail: aq02@dial.pipex.com

Prompt Technical Services, 12 Pool Road, West Molesey, Surrey, KT8 2HE Tel: (020) 8941 6896 Fax: (020) 8941 2799 E-mail: theopet@golbalnet.co.uk

QA, QA House, Delta Office Business Park, Welton Road, Swindon, SN5 7WZ Tel: (08709) 060090 Fax: (01793) 696007 E-mail: responsecentre@qa.com

▶ Quasar Electronics Ltd, PO Box 6935, Bishop's Stortford, Hertfordshire, CM23 4WP Tel: (0870) 2461826 Fax: (0870) 4601045 E-mail: sales@quasarelectronics.com

R Q Consultancy, The Gables, Pankridge Drive, Prestwood, Great Missenden, Buckinghamshire, HP16 9BZ Tel: (01494) 862406 Fax: (01494) 862382 E-mail: info@trqc.co.uk

R2 B2, Wyse Hill House, Finchampstead, Wokingham, Berkshire, RG40 4JR Tel: 0118-973 7171 Fax: 0118-973 7172 E-mail: r2b2@r2b2.co.uk

Ramesys E Business Services Ltd, Glaisdale Dr East, Nottingham, NG8 4GU Tel: 0115-971 2000 Fax: 0115-971 4600 E-mail: enq@ramesys.com

React Computer Partnership, 38 Manor Farm Road, St. Neots, Cambridgeshire, PE19 1PW Tel: (01480) 356145 Fax: (01473) 630707

Real Solutions Ltd, Alexander House, Atlantic Street, Altrincham, Cheshire, WA14 5EW Tel: 0161-926 2600 Fax: 0161-996 1778 E-mail: enquiries@realsolutionsuk.com

Reality Consulting Ltd, 4 Waverley Court, Brinsea Road, Congresbury, Bristol, BS49 5JG Tel: (0870) 6070116

Reason Technology Ltd, Elmbank Mill, The Charrier, Menstrie, Clackmannanshire, FK11 7BU Tel: (01259) 763444 Fax: (01259) 763388 E-mail: info@reason-technology.com

Red River Technologies Ltd, 16 Marshall Street, Nottingham, NG5 4AF Tel: 0115-969 1008 E-mail: info@red-river.co.uk

Reflex Computer Recruitment Ltd, Regent House 1-3 Queensway, Redhill, RH1 1QT Tel: (01737) 778282 Fax: (01737) 778950 E-mail: reflexgroup@reflexgroup.co.uk

Reviseopen Ltd, 65 Sunfield Lane, Diggle, Oldham, OL3 5PT Tel: (01457) 875525 Fax: (01457) 875525 E-mail: admin@reviseopen.com

Road Research, Research House Norwich Road, Eastgate, Cawston, Norwich, NR10 4HA Tel: (01603) 872331 Fax: (01603) 879010 E-mail: info@looking.co.uk

▶ Rothco Ltd, Brook House Church Road, Charsfield, Woodbridge, Suffolk, IP13 7QB Tel: (01473) 737759 Fax: 07050 664249 E-mail: rothco@msn.com

▶ Scalable Communications, Wycombe Lane, Wooburn Green, High Wycombe, Buckinghamshire, HP10 0HH Tel: (01628) 852500 E-mail: info@scalablenetworks.co.uk

Siemens Communication, Turnells Mill Lane, Wellingborough, Northamptonshire, NN8 2RB Tel: (01933) 225000 Fax: (01933) 222650

▶ Sigma Office Ltd, 20 West End, Ashwell, Baldock, Hertfordshire, SG7 5PJ Tel: (01462) 742783 Fax: (01462) 743321 E-mail: info@sigma-office.net

Sirsi, Unicorn House, Station Close, Potters Bar, Hertfordshire, EN6 3JW Tel: (01707) 646848 Fax: (01707) 858111 E-mail: sirsi@sirsi.co.uk

Solution House Ltd, 359 Nuthall Road, Nottingham, NG8 5BU Tel: 0115-910 1010 Fax: 0115-910 1012 E-mail: will.pickles@soloutionhouse.co.uk

Specialist Computer Centre, 16 Dargan Crescent, Belfast, BT3 9JP Tel: (028) 9037 0160 Fax: (028) 9037 0195 E-mail: belfast.sales@scc.com

Specialist Computer Centres Ltd, Applied House, Killingbeck Drive, York Road, Leeds, LS14 6UF Tel: 0113-240 5250 Fax: 0113-240 1093

Specialist Computer Holdings UK plc, James House, Warwick Road, Birmingham, B11 2LE Tel: 0121-766 7000 Fax: 0121-773 3986 E-mail: pete_read@scc.com

▶ Steelworks It, C23 Houghton Enterprise Centre, Lake Road, Houghton le Spring, Tyne & Wear, DH5 8BJ Tel: 0191-584 8811 Fax: 0191-584 7856 E-mail: sales@switcms.com

Strategy In Computing Ltd, Mooring Business Centre Willows End House, 9 Carolus Creek, Penn Island, Milton Keynes, MK15 8AZ Tel: (01908) 201202 Fax: (01908) 201170 E-mail: reply@strategy-in-computing.co.uk

Syan Data Centre Ltd, Orton Wood, Telford, Shropshire, TF1 7TT Tel: (01952) 602510 Fax: (01952) 404200 E-mail: info@nsoft.co.uk

Symology Ltd, Cotswold Farm Business Park, Millfield Lane, Caddington, Luton, LU1 4AJ Tel: (01582) 842626 Fax: (01582) 842600 E-mail: webmaster@symology.co.uk

T D C I, Sopwith Close, Drayton Fields Industrial Esta, Daventry, Northamptonshire, NN11 8EA Tel: (01327) 312570 Fax: (01327) 312721 E-mail: info@tdci.eu.com

T M A Data Management Ltd, Surrey House, 34 Eden Street, Kingston upon Thames, Surrey, KT1 1ER Tel: (020) 8481 3988 Fax: (020) 8546 9794 E-mail: info@tma.co.uk

Tech Op Ltd, 268 London Road, Cheltenham, Gloucestershire, GL52 6HS Tel: (01242) 570999 Fax: (01242) 588955 E-mail: sales@techop.co.uk

Technique Ltd, 8 Saturn House, Calleva Park, Aldermaston, Reading, RG7 8HA Tel: 0118-982 9244 Fax: 0118-982 9255 E-mail: info@technique-ltd.co.uk

Technologies Group Ltd, Hampstead Avenue, Mildenhall, Bury St. Edmunds, Suffolk, IP28 7AS Tel: (01638) 713631 Fax: (01638) 712271 E-mail: sales@tech-group.co.uk

▶ Teckchek Europe Ltd, 1a Church Road, Croydon, CR0 1SG Tel: (020) 8401 1188 Fax: (020) 8401 0808 E-mail: dbeer@ikmnet.com

Thompson Consultants Ltd, The Mow Barton, Northend, Clutton, Bristol, BS39 5QS Tel: (01761) 453673 Fax: (01761) 452707 E-mail: sales@thompson-consultants.co.uk

▶ Tiger Digital Ltd, 31 Merchants House, Collington Street, Greenwich, London, SE10 9LX Tel: (0870) 1909745 Fax: (0870) 1909745 E-mail: helpme@tigerdigital.net

Toltec Systems, Exchange Quay, Salford, M5 3EQ Tel: 0161-876 4447 Fax: 0161-876 4448 E-mail: sales-uk@etoltec.com

▶ TopHat IT Services, 80B St. James's Street, Brighton, BN2 1PA Tel: (01273) 311224 E-mail: enquiries@tophatit.com

Total Needs Network, 18 Briars Close, Farnborough, Hampshire, GU14 0PB Tel: (01252) 378286 Fax: (01252) 375227 E-mail: info@total-needs.com

Touch I.T Mobile, 27 Goldsmith Avenue, Romford, RM7 0EX Tel: (07071) 222856 E-mail: admin@touchit.co.uk

Trade Wind Technology Ltd, The Old Stores, 11 North Street, Tillingham, Southminster, Essex, CM0 7TR Tel: (01621) 779037 Fax: (01621) 779034 E-mail: sales@t-w-t.co.uk

Transtel Communications Ltd, Baileys House, Stoke Poges Lane, Slough, SL1 3PB Tel: (01753) 691869 Fax: (01753) 505639 E-mail: admin@transtel.com

Tri Systems Ltd, 59 Mansell Street, London, E1 8AN Tel: (020) 7264 0440 Fax: (020) 7264 0450 E-mail: info@trisystems.co.uk

Triad Group P.L.C., Weyside Park, Catteshall Lane, Godalming, Surrey, GU7 1XE Tel: (01483) 860222 Fax: (01483) 860198 E-mail: mail@triad.plc.uk

Triarom Ltd, Triarom House, Birch Street, Windermere, Cumbria, LA23 1EG Tel: (01539) 444639 Fax: (01539) 448701 E-mail: sales@triarom.co.uk

INFORMATION TECHNOLOGY (IT) CONSULTANTS – *continued*

Trisoft Ltd, Accent Park, Bakewell Road, Orton Southgate, Peterborough, PE2 6XS Tel: (01733) 372700 Fax: (01733) 372729

TSG Ltd, High Street, Broom, Alcester, Warwickshire, B50 4HN Tel: (01789) 778900 Fax: (01789) 772272

TSG Ltd, 1 Gosforth Park Way, Salters Lane, Newcastle upon Tyne, NE12 8ET Tel: 0191-256 1166 Fax: 0191-256 1167 E-mail: sales@tsg.com

Ulysses Ltd, Unit A Troon Way Business Centre, Humberstone Lane, Leicester, LE4 9HA Tel: 0116-276 9152 Fax: (0845) 1300259 E-mail: info@ulysses.uk.com

Unisys Group Services Ltd, Bakers Court, Bakers Road, Uxbridge, Middlesex, UB8 1RG Tel: (01895) 237137 Fax: (01895) 862092 E-mail: sales@unisys.com

Vantage Micro Systems Ltd, 2 Airfield Park, Cheddington Lane, Long Marston, Tring, Hertfordshire, HP23 4QR Tel: (01296) 668966 Fax: (01296) 662798 E-mail: sales@vantageit.co.uk

Vertex Systems Ltd, 47 Holmlea Road, Goring, Reading, RG8 9EX Tel: (01491) 872812

▶ Virtual Systems Solutions Ltd, 2 Sable Court, Southfields Business Park, Basildon, Essex, SS15 6SR Tel: (01268) 582950 Fax: (01268) 582951 E-mail: jcampbell@vssolutions.co.uk

▶ W Accountancy Ltd, 369 Hertford Road, Enfield, Middlesex, EN3 5JW Tel: (020) 8804 0478 Fax: (020) 8804 0221 E-mail: c.wheatley@waccountancy.co.uk

W Accountancy Ltd, Victoria Rdknaphill, Knaphill, Woking, Surrey, GU21 2AA Tel: (01483) 797901 Fax: (01483) 797899 E-mail: m.wood@waccountancy.co.uk

W P C Software Ltd, 9 Wellsway, Keynsham, Bristol, BS31 1HS Tel: 0117-908 1484 Fax: 0117-940 2060 E-mail: wpc@wpcsoft.com

▶ WaveZone Ltd, 834 Stockport Rd, Manchester, M19 3AW Tel: (0845) 1668443 Fax: 0161-257 3248 E-mail: info@wavezone.co.uk

Wheatley Associates, Technology Park, Broad Road, Bacton, Stowmarket, Suffolk, IP14 4HN Tel: (01449) 781001 E-mail: info@wheatley-associates.co.uk

Wizardsoft Ltd, 88a High Street, Billericay, Essex, CM12 9BT Tel: (01277) 634771 Fax: (01277) 634770 E-mail: enquiries@wizardit.co.uk

▶ Xperience, Xperience House, 25 Paterson Road, Finedon Road Industrial Estate, Wellingborough, Northamptonshire, NN8 4BZ Tel: (01933) 231100 Fax: (01933) 231111

Zentek Computers Ltd, Zentek House, St. Marks Street, Bolton, BL3 6NR Tel: (01204) 397878 Fax: (01204) 397880

INFORMATION TECHNOLOGY (IT) CONSULTANTS, BUSINESS, MANAGEMENT

A4 Computers, 2nd Floor, 32 B Church Road, Ashford, Middlesex, TW15 2UY Tel: (0870) 0634283 Fax: (0870) 0632106 E-mail: info@a4it.co.uk

▶ Bawden Quinn Associates Ltd, Manchester Business Park, 3000 Aviator Way, Manchester, M22 5TG Tel: 0161-266 1017 Fax: 0161-266 1001 E-mail: sales@bawden-quinn.co.uk

▶ Fineline Networks Ltd, 37 Southwood Road, London, SE9 3QE Tel: (020) 8294 2499 E-mail: info@fineline-net.co.uk

Itdynamics Ltd, Lion Court, Staunton Harold, Ashby-de-la-Zouch, Leicestershire, LE65 1RT Tel: (01332) 695090 Fax: (01332) 695009 E-mail: info@itdynamics.co.uk

▶ Mcqueen-Simon Consultancy, PO Box 50663, London, SW6 7QN Tel: (07957) 296196 Fax: (020) 7384 5415 E-mail: info@mcqueen-enterprises.com

▶ ReformIS, 18 Christchurch Hill, London, NW3 1LG Tel: (020) 7152 9638 Fax: (020) 7152 9639

▶ Rothco Ltd, Brook House Church Road, Charsfield, Woodbridge, Suffolk, IP13 7QB Tel: (01473) 737759 Fax: 07050 664249 E-mail: rothco@msn.com

▶ SAC Consultancy & Design, 55 Olympia Close, Northampton, NN4 0RU Tel: (07733) 177743 E-mail: sacharlton@sac-consult-design.com

INFORMATION TECHNOLOGY (IT) CONSULTANTS, CUSTOMER RELATIONSHIP

▶ Bawden Quinn Associates, Sanderum House, 38 Oakley Road, Chinnor, Oxfordshire, OX39 4TW Tel: (01844) 355622 Fax: (01844) 353553 E-mail: contact@bawden-quinn.co.uk

▶ Bawden Quinn Associates Ltd, Manchester Business Park, 3000 Aviator Way, Manchester, M22 5TG Tel: 0161-266 1017 Fax: 0161-266 1001 E-mail: sales@bawden-quinn.co.uk

▶ Chameleon - Global ITIL Experts, Bracken Lodge, Bay Horse Lane, Scarcroft, Leeds, LS14 3JQ Tel: 0113-289 3355 Fax: 0113-289 2335 E-mail: info@chameleon-itil.com

▶ Gecko It Services Ltd, 89 Chessel Avenue, Southampton, SO19 4DY Tel: (023) 8023 1030 E-mail: sales@gecko-it.com

INFORMATION TECHNOLOGY (IT) CONSULTANTS, ESTATE AGENTS OR AGENCIES

View Point Internet Ltd, Venture House Arlington Square, Downshire Way, Bracknell, Berkshire, RG12 1WA Tel: (01344) 300100 Fax: (01344) 742950 E-mail: sales@viewpoint.net.uk

INFORMATION TECHNOLOGY (IT) ENGINEERING

Elcom ITG Ltd, Elcom House, 203 Bedford Avenue, Slough, SL1 4RY Tel: (01753) 442500 Fax: (01753) 442501 E-mail: info@elcom.co.uk

▶ Institute Of Applied Technology, Mitchelston Industrial Estate, Kirkcaldy, Fife, KY1 3LT Tel: (01592) 568500 Fax: (01592) 223601

▶ The Networking Co, Riddell Road, West End, Lilliesleaf, Melrose, Roxburghshire, TD6 9JA Tel: (08456) 3 40844 Fax: (01835) 870380

▶ PC Southwest Ltd, Unit 6 Bishops Court, Bishops Court Lane, Clyst St. Mary, Exeter, EX5 1DH Tel: (01392) 876600 E-mail: sales@pcsouthwest.co.uk

▶ Sigma Office Ltd, 20 West End, Ashwell, Baldock, Hertfordshire, SG7 5PJ Tel: (01462) 742783 Fax: (01462) 743321 E-mail: info@sigma-office.net

INFORMATION TECHNOLOGY (IT) EQUIPMENT DISPOSAL

▶ Bites UK Ltd, PO Box 2294, Woodford Green, Essex, IG8 0YF Tel: (0845) 2211000 Fax: (0870) 1350684 E-mail: sales@bites-uk.com

INFORMATION TECHNOLOGY (IT) INTERIM MANAGEMENT

▶ Cream Interim, Hudson House, 8 Tavistock Street, London, WC2E 7PP Tel: (020) 7559 6767 Fax: (0870) 0941613 E-mail: info@creaminterim.co.uk

INFORMATION TECHNOLOGY (IT) OUTSOURCING CONSULTANTS OR SERVICES

▶ Bluefin Solutions Ltd, Utell House, 2 Kew Bridge Road, Brentford, Middlesex, TW8 0JF Tel: (0870) 2330404 Fax: (0870) 2330405 E-mail: enquiries@bluefinsolutions.com

CDM Solutions Ltd, 60 Carter Street, Uttoxeter, Staffordshire, ST14 8EU Tel: (01889) 563434 Fax: (01889) 562797 E-mail: info@cdmsolutions.co.uk

Cym Consulting Ltd, 14 Well Hall Parade, London, SE9 6SP Tel: (020) 8294 1622 Fax: (020) 8859 4562E-mail: cym@cymc.com

D P Connect, Garrard House, 2-6 Homesdale Road, Bromley, BR2 9LZ Tel: (020) 8466 5666 Fax: (020) 8313 1716 E-mail: info@dpconnect.co.uk

Dammit Ltd, 11 Glenthorne Road, London, N11 3HU Tel: (020) 8361 7769 Fax: (07070) 800473

▶ Enterprise Technology Solutions Ltd, 19 Paxton Crescent, Shenley Lodge, Milton Keynes, MK5 7PX Tel: (01908) 395500 Fax: (01908) 395499 E-mail: info@etsl.net

Fisher Technology Ltd, Acre House, 11-15 William Road, London, NW1 3ER Tel: (020) 7874 7888 Fax: (020) 7380 4900 E-mail: enquiries@fishtech.net

▶ Goldnet Ltd, 3 Shire Close, Whiteley, Fareham, Hampshire, PO15 7BQ Tel: (01489) 886843 Fax: (01489) 886828 E-mail: info@goldnetltd.co.uk

▶ Hexaware Technologies UK Ltd, Cornwall House, High Street, Slough, SL1 1BZ Tel: (01753) 217160 Fax: (01753) 217161 E-mail: sales@euhexaware.com

I T Professionals International, 306 Grantham Park, Fulham, London, SW6 1SE Tel: (020) 7381 4620 E-mail: mahmoodint@aol.com

▶ I T R M Ltd, Thames House, St. Johns Road, Sidcup, Kent, DA14 4HD Tel: (07000) 284876 Fax: (020) 8308 3301 E-mail: info@itrm.co.uk

Idea Computers, 26 Stuart Road, Warlingham, Surrey, CR6 9JH Tel: (01883) 623327 Fax: (01883) 626102

iDeveloperNetwork, Suite 7, Grove House, Kensal Road, London, W10 5BZ Tel: (020) 7900 2071 Fax: (020) 7900 2071 E-mail: uk_contact@idevelopernetwork.com

Isoscan UK Ltd, Unit 1 Portelant Barns, Cowdown Farm, Micheldever, Winchester, Hampshire, SO21 3DN Tel: (01962) 774411 Fax: (01962) 774477 E-mail: sales@isoscan.co.uk

J Wilson & Co., 96 David Street, Glasgow, G40 2UH Tel: 0141-551 0268 Fax: 0141-554 4620 E-mail: info@jwilsongroup.co.uk

Kanbay Europe Ltd, Regus House, 1010 Cambourne Business Park, Cambourne, Cambridge, CB3 6DP Tel: (01223) 597836 Fax: (01223) 598062

Meta Skill P.L.C., 7 Fortuna Court, Aldermaston, Reading, RG7 8UB Tel: 0118-981 9316 Fax: 0118-981 7958 E-mail: rsmith@metaskill.com

Organised Computer Systems Ltd, East House, Newpound, Wisborough Green, Billingshurst, West Sussex, RH14 0AZ Tel: (01403) 700959 Fax: (01403) 700969E-mail: sales@ocsl.co.uk

Oxygen 8, 10 Mount Ephraim, Tunbridge Wells, Kent, TN4 8AS Tel: (01825) 762444 Fax: (01892) 527652 E-mail: info@oxygenonline.co.uk

Planworld Computers Ltd, 1 Farnham Road, Guildford, Surrey, GU2 4RG Tel: (01483) 549888 Fax: (01483) 549100 E-mail: kellysearch@planworld.co.uk

Real Solutions Ltd, Alexander House, Atlantic Street, Altrincham, Cheshire, WA14 5EW Tel: 0161-926 2600 Fax: 0161-996 1778 E-mail: enquiries@realsolutionsuk.com

S N E T Technology, 119 Cholmley Gardens, London, NW6 1AA Tel: (020) 7435 5855

Saic (UK) Ltd, 120 New Cavendish Street, London, W1W 6XX Tel: (020) 7533 3000 Fax: (020) 7533 3001

Serco Solutions, P O Box 57 Laburnum House, Birmingham, B30 2BD Tel: 0121-459 1155 Fax: 0121-459 2199 E-mail: mediaanddesign@serco.com

Unigraphics Solutions, Knoll Road, Camberley, Surrey, GU15 3SY Tel: (01276) 702000 Fax: (01276) 702100

Unisys Group Services Ltd, Bakers Court, Bakers Road, Uxbridge, Middlesex, UB8 1RG Tel: (01895) 237137 Fax: (01895) 862092 E-mail: sales@unisys.com

Wirebird Ltd, 39 Aquatical House, Bell Lane, London, E1 7LU Tel: (020) 7650 2390 Fax: (020) 7377 2912

INFORMATION TECHNOLOGY (IT) SECURITY CONSULTANCY

▶ Commissum Computer Security, 142 Commercial Street, Edinburgh, EH6 6LB Tel: 0131-625 2730 Fax: 0131-476 6061 E-mail: sales@commisum.com

▶ Iconium Computer Systems, Exchange House, Worthing Road, Horsham, West Sussex, RH12 1UU Tel: (01403) 754300

▶ Third Eye Services, 104 Mount View Road, London, N4 4JX Tel: (020) 8341 4133 Fax: (020) 8341 4133 E-mail: sales@thirdeyeservices.co.uk

▶ WaveZone Ltd, 834 Stockport Rd, Manchester, M19 3AW Tel: (0845) 1668443 Fax: 0161-257 3248 E-mail: info@wavezone.co.uk

INFORMATION TECHNOLOGY (IT) SUPPORT SERVICES

▶ Broxden Ltd, 8 Algo Business Centre, Glenearn Road, Perth, PH2 0NJ Tel: (01738) 450422 Fax: (01738) 783685 E-mail: sales@broxden.co.uk

▶ Camnet, 11 Mill View, London Road, Great Chesterford, Saffron Walden, Essex, CB10 1PD Tel: (01799) 530831 E-mail: james@camnet-communications.co.uk

INFORMATION TECHNOLOGY (IT) SYSTEM SUPPORT SERVICES

▶ Assert I T Ltd, 10 Knowle Avenue, Blackpool, FY5 3PP Tel: (01253) 865467 Fax: (0871) 2216078 E-mail: info@assert-it.co.uk

▶ Consortium Systems, Lint House, Linthouse Lane, Wolverhampton, WV11 3EA Tel: (01902) 723327 Fax: (01902) 739886

Cotech Software Consultants Ltd, 9 Drakefield Road, London, SW17 8RT Tel: (020) 8682 0123 Fax: (020) 8682 4550 E-mail: faisal@cotech.co.uk

▶ Fixit Systems Support, The Diary House Roxby Place, Rickett Street, London, SW6 1RU Tel: (0845) 1303595 Fax: (0870) 1374300 E-mail: sales@fixit.co.uk

▶ It Services 4 You Ltd, 18 Wright Avenue, Stanground, Peterborough, PE2 8TR Tel: (01733) 563080 E-mail: info@itservices4you.co.uk

Keynote Business Services Ltd, Unit 46 Alpha Business Centre, 60 South Grove, London, E17 7NX Tel: (020) 8926 9216 Fax: (020) 8926 9216 E-mail: info@keynotes.co.uk

Monostar Ltd, Peggs Barn, Drinkstone, Bury St. Edmunds, Suffolk, IP30 9TW Tel: (01449) 736081 Fax: (01449) 736083 E-mail: info@monostar.co.uk

▶ PC Southwest Ltd, Unit 6 Bishops Court, Bishops Court Lane, Clyst St. Mary, Exeter, EX5 1DH Tel: (01392) 876600 E-mail: sales@pcsouthwest.co.uk

▶ RedKite IT Solutions Ltd, 127 Stonegate, Hunmanby, Filey, North Yorkshire, YO14 0PU Tel: (01723) 890890 Fax: (07812) 356040 E-mail: enquiries@redkiteit.com

Symology Ltd, Cotswold Farm Business Park, Millfield Lane, Caddington, Luton, LU1 4AJ Tel: (01582) 842626 Fax: (01582) 842600 E-mail: webmaster@symology.co.uk

UniTek Technologies, 6 Wadsworth Road, Perivale Industrial Estate, Greenford, Middlesex, UB6 7JJ Tel: (0870) 9005100 Fax: (0870) 9005300 E-mail: info@unitek.co.uk

▶ Websters Ltd, 40 Crossdene Road, Crosshouse, Kilmarnock, Ayrshire, KA2 0JU Tel: (01563) 534540 Fax: (0845) 1232561

▶ Xperience, Xperience House, 25 Paterson Road, Finedon Road Industrial Estate, Wellingborough, Northamptonshire, NN8 4BZ Tel: (01933) 231100 Fax: (01933) 231111

INFORMATION TECHNOLOGY (IT) SYSTEMS INTEGRATORS

A I M Ltd, Victoria House, Derringham Street, Hull, HU3 1EL Tel: (01482) 326971 Fax: (01482) 228465 E-mail: aim@aim.co.uk

Balanced Solutions Ltd, 20 Juniper Road, Southampton, SO18 4EJ Tel: (023) 8063 8393 Fax: (023) 8063 8393 E-mail: info@balancedsolutions.co.uk

Bytes Technology, Matrix House, North Fourth Street, Milton Keynes, MK9 1NJ Tel: (08707) 774646 Fax: (08707) 771021

▶ Cambridge Online Systems Ltd, 163 Milton Road, Cambridge, CB4 0GP Tel: (01223) 422600 Fax: (01223) 422601 E-mail: enquiries@cosl.co.uk

▶ Digitalarkitec Ltd, 121 Eastern Avenue, Lichfield, Staffordshire, WS13 6RL Tel: (01543) 251123 E-mail: enquiries@digitalarkitec.co.uk

▶ Enterprise Technology Solutions Ltd, 19 Paxton Crescent, Shenley Lodge, Milton Keynes, MK5 7PX Tel: (01908) 395500 Fax: (01908) 395499 E-mail: info@etsl.net

G E Netwrok Solutions, Elizabeth House, 1 High Street, Chesterton, Cambridge, CB4 1WR Tel: (01223) 301144 Fax: (01223) 311145

H G Systems Ltd, Dunston House Sheepbridge Works, Dunston Road, Chesterfield, Derbyshire, S41 9QD Tel: (01246) 260270 Fax: (01246) 450323 E-mail: sales@hgsystems.co.uk

Isatech Ltd, Watermeadow House, Watermeadow, Chesham, Buckinghamshire, HP5 1LF Tel: (01494) 794633 Fax: (01494) 794644 E-mail: info@accumen-technology.co.uk

Kutana Computer Systems, The Old Mill, Mill Street, Wantage, Oxfordshire, OX12 9AB Tel: (0870) 2202275E-mail: info@kutana.co.uk

Lanmark Technical Services Ltd, 30-32 Thames Street, Hampton, Middlesex, TW12 2DX Tel: (020) 8783 3260 Fax: (020) 8783 3270 E-mail: sales@lanmark.co.uk

Makin Rochard Ltd, 5 Union Court, Richmond, Surrey, TW9 1AA Tel: (020) 8948 7757 Fax: (020) 8948 5981 E-mail: solutions@makinrochard.co.uk

Organised Computer Systems Ltd, East House, Newpound, Wisborough Green, Billingshurst, West Sussex, RH14 0AZ Tel: (01403) 700959 Fax: (01403) 700969E-mail: sales@ocsl.co.uk

Panacea Services Ltd, 20 St Mary at Hill, London, EC3R 8EE Tel: (020) 7375 3757 Fax: (020) 7375 1525 E-mail: info@panacea-services.co.uk

Patech Solutions Ltd, Tame House, Wellington Crescent, Fradley Park, Lichfield, Staffordshire, WS13 8RZ Tel: (01543) 444707 Fax: (01543) 444709

Pav I T Services plc, King Business Centre, Reeds Lane, Sayers Common, Hassocks, West Sussex, BN6 9LS Tel: (01273) 834000 Fax: (01273) 834631 E-mail: info@pav.co.uk

Principal Corporation Ltd, Principal House, Parsonage Business Park, Horsham, West Sussex, RH12 4AL Tel: (01403) 258486 Fax: (01403) 210131 E-mail: solutions@principalcorp.co.uk

Ramesys E Business Services Ltd, Glaisdale Dr East, Nottingham, NG8 4GU Tel: 0115-971 2000 Fax: 0115-971 4600 E-mail: enq@ramesys.com

Siemens Communication, Turnells Mill Lane, Wellingborough, Northamptonshire, NN8 2RB Tel: (01933) 225000 Fax: (01933) 222650

Trisoft Ltd, Accent Park, Bakewell Road, Orton Southgate, Peterborough, PE2 6XS Tel: (01733) 372700 Fax: (01733) 372729

Wirebird Ltd, 39 Aquatical House, Bell Lane, London, E1 7LU Tel: (020) 7650 2390 Fax: (020) 7377 2912

INFORMATION TECHNOLOGY (IT) SYSTEMS, TO SPECIFICATION OR CUSTOM BUILT

▶ Assert I T Ltd, 10 Knowle Avenue, Blackpool, FY5 3PP Tel: (01253) 865467 Fax: (0871) 2216078 E-mail: info@assert-it.co.uk

Principal Corporation Ltd, Principal House, Parsonage Business Park, Horsham, West Sussex, RH12 4AL Tel: (01403) 258486 Fax: (01403) 210131 E-mail: solutions@principalcorp.co.uk

INFORMATIVE PLAQUES

Ellis Rees & Co., The Old Foundry, Grove Road, Northfleet, Gravesend, Kent, DA11 9AX Tel: (01474) 567861 Fax: (01474) 537056

INFORMATIVE PLAQUES – *continued*

Handsworth Crown Memorial Co., 283 Oxhill Road, Birmingham, B21 8EY Tel: 0121-554 3234 Fax: 0121-554 3234
Hockerill Engraving, 2d Willis Vean Industrial Estate, Mullion, Helston, Cornwall, TR12 7DF Tel: (01326) 240400 Fax: (01326) 240620 E-mail: hockerill@dial.pipex.com
Sign Industries Ltd, Mains of Gardyne, Forfar, Angus, DD8 2SQ Tel: (01241) 828694 Fax: (01241) 828331 E-mail: info@signindustries.com

INFRARED ANALYSERS

Thermo Electron, 2a Swift Park, Old Leicester Road, Rugby, Warwickshire, CV21 1DZ Tel: (01788) 820300 Fax: (01788) 820419 E-mail: tewi@thermo.com

INFRARED BEAM SMOKE DETECTORS

Fire Fighting Enterprises, 9 Hunting Gate, Hitchin, Hertfordshire, SG4 0TJ Tel: (01462) 444740 Fax: (0845) 4024201 E-mail: sales@ffeuk.com

INFRARED DETECTOR MANUFRS

I P L, Unit 16, Llys y Fedwen, Parc Menai, Poundbury, Bangor, Gwynedd, LL57 4BN Tel: (01248) 672122 E-mail: sales@ipl-int.com
Pyronix Security Equipment Ltd, Pyronix House, Braithwell Way, Hellaby, Rotherham, South Yorkshire, S66 8QY Tel: (01709) 700100 Fax: (01709) 701042 E-mail: sales@pyronix.co.uk
Talentum Development Ltd, Beal Lane, Shaw, Oldham, OL2 8PF Tel: (01706) 844714 Fax: (01706) 882612 E-mail: info@talentum.co.uk

INFRARED DRYING EQUIPMENT

Advanced Infra Red Systems, 3 Galliford Road, Heybridge, Maldon, Essex, CM9 4XD Tel: (01621) 855000 Fax: (01621) 853847 E-mail: info@h-v2000.co.uk
Heraeus Noblelight Ltd, Unit 1 Millenium Court, Clayhill Industrial Estate, Buildwas Lane, Neston, CH64 3UZ Tel: 0151-353 2710 Fax: 0151-353 2719 E-mail: ian.bartley@heraeus.com
P E D Technologies Ltd, Brunel Close, Park Farm Industrial Estate, Wellingborough, Northamptonshire, NN8 6QX Tel: (01933) 403777 Fax: (01933) 403888 E-mail: sales@pafsystem.com
Panther Dryers, Hillside House, Intwood Road, Norwich, NR4 6TG Tel: (01603) 505509 E-mail: charlie@pantherd.freeserve.co.uk
Schwank Ltd, 62 Sunningdale Road, Sutton, Surrey, SM1 2JS Tel: (020) 8641 3900 Fax: (020) 8641 2594 E-mail: sales@schwank.co.uk
Xericweb Drying Systems Ltd, 158 Church Lane, Bocking, Braintree, Essex, CM7 5SG Tel: (01376) 346426 E-mail: p_eagle@xericweb.com

INFRARED EMITTERS

Heraeus Noblelight Ltd, Unit 1 Millenium Court, Clayhill Industrial Estate, Buildwas Lane, Neston, CH64 3UZ Tel: 0151-353 2710 Fax: 0151-353 2719 E-mail: ian.bartley@heraeus.com

INFRARED FILTERS

Northumbria Optical Coatings Ltd, Unit 10 Burford Way, Boldon Business Park, Boldon Colliery, Tyne & Wear, NE35 9PZ Tel: 0191-537 4888 Fax: 0191-537 4777 E-mail: sales@noc-ltd.com

INFRARED HEATERS

N A Stordy Combustion Ltd, Heath Mill Road, Wombourne, Wolverhampton, WV5 8BD Tel: (01902) 891200 Fax: (01902) 895552 E-mail: sales@stordy.co.uk
Robinson Willey Ltd, Mill Lane, Old Swan, Liverpool, L13 4AJ Tel: 0151-228 9111 Fax: 0151-228 6661 E-mail: info@robinson-willey.com
Schwank Ltd, 62 Sunningdale Road, Sutton, Surrey, SM1 2JS Tel: (020) 8641 3900 Fax: (020) 8641 2594 E-mail: sales@schwank.co.uk

INFRARED HEATING ELEMENTS

Ceramaspeed Ltd, Zortech Avenue, Kidderminster, Worcestershire, DY11 7DY Tel: (01562) 756000 Fax: (01562) 756030
Hassett Industries plc, Larkhill Road, Durrington, Salisbury, SP4 8DS Tel: (01980) 654333 Fax: (01980) 654326 E-mail: hassett@globalnet.co.uk
Heraeus Noblelight Ltd, Unit 1 Millenium Court, Clayhill Industrial Estate, Buildwas Lane, Neston, CH64 3UZ Tel: 0151-353 2710 Fax: 0151-353 2719 E-mail: ian.bartley@heraeus.com
Vulcan Refractories Ltd, Brookhouse Industrial Estate, Cheadle, Stoke-on-Trent, ST10 1PN Tel: (01538) 752238 Fax: (01538) 753349 E-mail: sales@vulcan-refractories.co.uk

INFRARED INSTRUMENTS

Metax Ltd, 77 Capital Business Centre, Carlton Road, South Croydon, Surrey, CR2 0BS Tel: (020) 8916 2077 Fax: (01689) 889994 E-mail: sales@metax.co.uk

INFRARED NIGHT VISION EQUIPMENT

B A E Systems Avionics Ltd, Christopher Martin Road, Basildon, Essex, SS14 3EL Tel: (01268) 522822 Fax: (01268) 883140
Simrad Optronics Ltd, 3 Medowbrook Industrial Estate, Maxwell Way, Crawley, West Sussex, RH10 9SA Tel: (01293) 560413 Fax: (01293) 560418
Vistar Night Vision Ltd, 24 Doman Road, Camberley, Surrey, GU15 3DF Tel: (01276) 708800 Fax: (01276) 708807 E-mail: info@vistar.co.uk

INFRARED OPERATED THERMOSTATIC MIXING VALVES

Broen Valves Ltd, 7 Cleton Street Business Park, Cleton Street, Tipton, West Midlands, DY4 7TR Tel: 0121-522 4505 Fax: 0121-522 4535 E-mail: broenvalves@broen.com

INFRARED OR MICROWAVE SECURITY DETECTORS

Optex Europe Ltd, 32a Clivemont Road, Maidenhead, Berkshire, SL6 7BZ Tel: (01628) 631000 Fax: (01628) 636311 E-mail: sales@optex-europe.com

INFRARED OVENS

Advanced Infra Red Systems, 3 Galliford Road, Heybridge, Maldon, Essex, CM9 4XD Tel: (01621) 855000 Fax: (01621) 853847 E-mail: info@h-v2000.co.uk
Hedinair Ovens Ltd, 3 Pilot Close, Fulmar Way, Wickford, Essex, SS11 8YW Tel: (01268) 761777 Fax: (01268) 760210 E-mail: sales@hedinair.co.uk
J Rostron Engineering Ltd, Lindred Road, Brierfield, Nelson, Lancashire, BB9 5SR Tel: (01282) 611110 Fax: (01282) 619961 E-mail: sales@rostron.co.uk
Schwank Ltd, 62 Sunningdale Road, Sutton, Surrey, SM1 2JS Tel: (020) 8641 3900 Fax: (020) 8641 2594 E-mail: sales@schwank.co.uk

INFRARED PROCESS EQUIPMENT

Advanced Infra Red Systems, 3 Galliford Road, Heybridge, Maldon, Essex, CM9 4XD Tel: (01621) 855000 Fax: (01621) 853847 E-mail: info@h-v2000.co.uk

INFRARED REMOTE CONTROL HANDSETS

F S L Electronics Ltd, Sandholes Road, Cookstown, County Tyrone, BT80 9AR Tel: (028) 8676 6131 Fax: (028) 8676 2414 E-mail: info@fslelectronics.com

INFRARED REMOTE CONTROL SYSTEMS

F S L Electronics Ltd, Sandholes Road, Cookstown, County Tyrone, BT80 9AR Tel: (028) 8676 6131 Fax: (028) 8676 2414 E-mail: info@fslelectronics.com

INFRARED SECURITY PERIMETERS

Optex Europe Ltd, 32a Clivemont Road, Maidenhead, Berkshire, SL6 7BZ Tel: (01628) 631000 Fax: (01628) 636311 E-mail: sales@optex-europe.com

INFRARED SPECTROMETERS

Bentham Instruments Ltd, 2 Boulton Road, Reading, RG2 0NH Tel: 0118-975 1355 Fax: 0118-931 2971 E-mail: sales@bentham.co.uk
Bruker BioSpin Ltd, Banner Lane, Coventry, CV4 9GH Tel: (024) 7685 5200 Fax: (024) 7646 5317 E-mail: admin@bruker.co.uk

INFRARED THERMOMETERS

Asten Instruments Ltd, 3 Millfields, Caistor, Market Rasen, Lincolnshire, LN7 6PD Tel: (01472) 851831 Fax: (01472) 859927 E-mail: info@asten.co.uk

INGOT CASTING MACHINES

▶ Worswick Engineering Ltd, Philips Road, Blackburn, BB1 5SG Tel: (01254) 261351 Fax: (01254) 682208 E-mail: sales@worswick.com

INJECTED CAVITY WALL INSULATION

Absolute Insulations, 21 Wanstead Road, Leicester, LE3 1TR Tel: 0116-287 8958 Fax: 0116-231 4002

INJECTION BLOW MOULDING MACHINERY

Battenfeld UK Ltd, 6 Valley Business Centre, Gordon Road, High Wycombe, Buckinghamshire, HP13 6EQ Tel: (01494) 450911 Fax: (01494) 444546 E-mail: abek.r@vuk.battenfeld.com

INJECTION MOULD DESIGN/ PROTOTYPING/TURNKEY SERVICES

Alliance Design & Manufacturing, Westbrook Trading Estate, Westbrook Road, Trafford Park, Manchester, M17 1AY Tel: 0161-872 8881 Fax: 0161-872 8883 E-mail: jimkelly@adm.eu.com
Chandu Mouldings, Unit 10 Corton Trading Estate, Benfleet, Essex, SS7 4QN Tel: (01268) 566048 Fax: (01268) 757740 E-mail: chandu@easynet.co.uk
Hi Tec Plastics, 1 Sett End Road, Shadsworth Business Park, Blackburn, BB1 2PT Tel: (01254) 581405 Fax: (01254) 680285 E-mail: dennishi-tech@quista.net
Hillside Plastics Ltd, St. Johns Road, Meadowfield, Durham, DH7 8XQ Tel: 0191-378 0598 Fax: 0191-378 9346 E-mail: enquiries@hillside-plastics.co.uk
Mold Systems, Millennium Way, Heighington Lane Business Park, Newton Aycliffe, County Durham, DL5 6JW Tel: (01325) 328700 Fax: (01325) 328707 E-mail: sales@moldsystems.com
Newbar Engineers Ltd, 3 Pound Lane Industrial Estate, Maypole Fields, Halesowen, West Midlands, B63 2QB Tel: (01384) 639139 Fax: (01384) 411128
P B Designs, The Courtyard, Milton Road, Aylesbury, Buckinghamshire, HP21 7LZ Tel: (01296) 433393 Fax: (01296) 433393 E-mail: all@pbdesigns.demon.co.uk
Pro-Tec Mouldings Ltd, Unit 22 Chadkirk Industrial Estate, Vale Road, Romiley, Stockport, Cheshire, SK6 3LE Tel: 0161-427 4944 Fax: 0161-427 8373

INJECTION MOULD PROTOTYPE TOOLMAKERS

Algram Groups, Eastern Wood Road, Langage Business Park, Plympton, Plymouth, PL7 5ET Tel: (01752) 342388 Fax: (01752) 342482 E-mail: sales@algram.com
B E Ebdon, Leafdale, London Road, Addington, West Malling, Kent, ME19 5PL Tel: (01732) 843351 Fax: (01732) 843351
Crossen Engineering Ltd, Maryland Industrial Estate, Crossnacrevey, Newtownards, County Down, BT23 6BL Tel: (028) 9044 8569 Fax: (028) 9044 8221 E-mail: paul@crossenengineering.co.uk
D R B Precision Ltd, Unit H, Bowen Industrial Estate, Aberbargoed, Bargoed, Mid Glamorgan, CF81 9EP Tel: (01443) 828940 Fax: (01443) 879133 E-mail: sales@drbprecision.com
Newark Tools Ltd, Coppice Side Industrial Estate, Brownhills, Walsall, WS8 7EX Tel: (01543) 454600
Newbar Engineers Ltd, 3 Pound Lane Industrial Estate, Maypole Fields, Halesowen, West Midlands, B63 2QB Tel: (01384) 639139 Fax: (01384) 411128
Pantograph Precision Ltd, 15 Willow Road, Colnbrook, Slough, SL3 0BS Tel: (01753) 684343 Fax: (01753) 681363 E-mail: stuart@pantograph.demon.co.uk
Plasmold Precision, Knightsbridge Gardens, Romford, RM7 9AD Tel: (01371) 876445 Fax: (01708) 732691 E-mail: lee@plasmoldplastics.co.uk

INJECTION MOULD TOOL MANAGEMENT SERVICES

Tobias Solutions, Westways, Otterbourne Rd, Shawford, Winchester, Hants, SO21 2DG Tel: (01962) 715354 Fax: (01962) 715354 E-mail: colin@tobias-solutions.co.uk

INJECTION MOULD TOOLMAKERS

3D Mouding Ltd, Unit 55-59, Broton Drive, Halstead, Essex, CO9 1HB Tel: (01787) 476864 Fax: (01787) 475856 E-mail: asmith@3dmouding.co.uk
A R G Tools Ltd, Harrier Road, Humber Bridge Industrial Estate, Barton-upon-Humber, South Humberside, DN18 5RP Tel: (01652) 660382 Fax: (01652) 660382
Abbey Plastics & Tooling Ltd, Unit 8, 108 Nathan Way, London, SE28 0AQ Tel: (020) 8316 4333 Fax: (020) 8316 4333
Advanced Cooling Systems U.K Ltd, Highfield Industrial Estate, Warren Road, Folkestone, Kent, CT19 6DD Tel: (01303) 255465 Fax: (01303) 246186 E-mail: info@atsuk.com
Agema Ltd, G4-G6 Little Heath Industrial Estate, Old Church Road, Coventry, CV6 7ND Tel: (024) 7663 7699 Fax: (024) 7663 8014 E-mail: sales@agema-ind.com
Algram Groups, Eastern Wood Road, Langage Business Park, Plympton, Plymouth, PL7 5ET Tel: (01752) 342388 Fax: (01752) 342482 E-mail: sales@algram.com
Alliance Design & Manufacturing, Westbrook Trading Estate, Westbrook Road, Trafford Park, Manchester, M17 1AY Tel: 0161-872 8881 Fax: 0161-872 8883 E-mail: jimkelly@adm.eu.com
Alltech Moulds, Unit 2, Foxley Court Farm, Ascot Road, Holyport, Maidenhead, Berkshire, SL6 3LA Tel: (01628) 789993 Fax: (01628) 789994 E-mail: andy@alltechmoulds.co.uk
Amery Engineering, Mill Lane, Alton, Hampshire, GU34 2QG Tel: (01420) 80298 Fax: (01420) 549559 E-mail: geoff@ameryeng.swiftserve.net
Andel Plastics Ltd, 1 Klaxon Tysley Industrial Estate, 751 Warwick Road, Tyseley, Birmingham, B11 2HA Tel: 0121-765 4042 Fax: 0121-707 3335 E-mail: enquiries@andel-plastics.demon.co.uk
Anker & Renton Ltd, 1-2 Caxton Hill, Hertford, SG13 7NE Tel: (01992) 551991 Fax: (01992) 500375 E-mail: info.ankerrenton@btinternet.com
Api Precision Toolmakers, Unit 2 Quell Farm Industrial Estate, Greatham, Pulborough, West Sussex, RH20 2ES Tel: (01798) 875688 Fax: (01798) 872701 E-mail: api@apiprecision.co.uk
Applied Energy Products Ltd, PO Box 220, Peterborough, PE2 9JJ Tel: (01733) 456789 Fax: (01733) 310606 E-mail: joe.barrasso@applied-energy.com
Astra Precision Engineering Ltd, Mnercian Works, Holyhead Road, Ketley, Telford, Shropshire, TF1 5DY Tel: (01952) 616622 Fax: (01952) 616622
Atkinson Engineering, Unit 1 Lancaster Close, Sherburn in Elmet, Leeds, LS25 6NS Tel: (01977) 689665 Fax: (01977) 685624 E-mail: sales@atkinsonprecision.co.uk
B E C Global Ltd, Gore Road Industrial Estate, New Milton, Hampshire, BH25 6SA Tel: (01425) 613131 Fax: (01425) 616551 E-mail: info@becgroup.com
B E Ebdon, Leafdale, London Road, Addington, West Malling, Kent, ME19 5PL Tel: (01732) 843351 Fax: (01732) 843351
Beavin Engineering Ltd, 33 Haviland Road, Ferndown Industrial Estate, Wimborne, Dorset, BH21 7SA Tel: (01202) 894404 Fax: (01202) 894404 E-mail: beavineng@btconnect.com
Bevenden Moulds & Tools Ltd, Unit 5c Triumph Trading Estate, Tariff Road, London, N17 0EB Tel: (020) 8801 2488 Fax: (020) 8808 0982 E-mail: bevendenmandt@btconnect.com
Buckfield Plastic Mould Tool, Moor Lane, Witton, Birmingham, B6 7AE Tel: 0121-356 9044 Fax: 0121-344 3108 E-mail: plastic@aol.com
C G P Engineering Ltd, Cross Street, Oadby, Leicester, LE2 4DD Tel: 0116-271 7715 Fax: 0116-272 0701 E-mail: info@cgp-engineering.com
C & M Mould Tools Ltd, Unit 1-3 Brunel Close, Ebblake Industrial Estate, Verwood, Dorset, BH31 6BA Tel: (01202) 813019 Fax: (01202) 814219 E-mail: cmmoulds@aol.com
Canteen Smithy, Crow Carings Mill North, Stansfield Road, Todmorden, Lancashire, OL14 5DL Tel: (01706) 818375 Fax: (01706) 818375 E-mail: cse@ntlbusiness.com
Capri Mouldings Ltd, 45 Padgets Lane, Redditch, Worcestershire, B98 0RD Tel: (01527) 510008 Fax: (01527) 518288
Celect Tools, Ainsworth Street, Rochdale, Lancashire, OL16 5QX Tel: (07814) 349636 Fax: (01706) 648106 E-mail: sales@celect-tools.co.uk

INJECTION MOULD TOOLMAKERS – *continued*

Clean Plastic Mouldings Ltd, Unit 6, Kenfig Industrial Estate, Margam, Port Talbot, West Glamorgan, SA13 2PE Tel: (01656) 740102 Fax: (01656) 745354 E-mail: cpm@bryncae.fsbusiness.co.uk

CMJ Mould Tools, 22 Benfield Way, Braintree, Essex, CM7 3YS Tel: (01376) 347776 Fax: (01376) 347776 E-mail: sales@cmjmouldtools.co.uk

▶ Complexatools Precision Engineers, Railway Stables, Surrey Street, Glossop, Derbyshire, SK13 7AJ Tel: (01457) 864446 Fax: (01457) 861010 E-mail: enquiries@complexatools.co.uk

CPM Moulds Solutions Ltd, Pattison House, Addison Road, Chesham, Buckinghamshire, HP5 2BD Tel: (01494) 782131 Fax: (01494) 778542 E-mail: precision@chesham-moulds.co.uk

Custom Tooling Ltd, Unit 65, Station Road Industrial Estate, Hailsham, East Sussex, BN27 2ED Tel: (01323) 641811 E-mail: custo@btconnect.com

D & E Plastics Ltd, Ogilvie Road, High Wycombe, Buckinghamshire, HP12 3DS Tel: (01494) 463111 Fax: (01494) 461194 E-mail: enquiries@deplastics.co.uk

D & G Toolmakers (Frome), Unit 13, Court Farm Trading Estate, Bishops Frome, Worcester, WR6 5AY Tel: (01885) 490714 Fax: (01885) 490380

D W Precision Engineering, 9 Sopwith CR, Hurricane Way, Wickford, Essex, SS11 8YU Tel: (01268) 571616 Fax: (01268) 571626 E-mail: dwp@netcomuk.co.uk

Danly UK Ltd, 2 Aintree Road, Perivale, Greenford, Middlesex, UB6 7LA Tel: (020) 8998 5381 Fax: (020) 8991 2461 E-mail: sales@danleyuk.com

Dearing Plastics Ltd, Unit 12 National Avenue, Hull, HU5 4HT Tel: (01482) 348588 Fax: (01482) 470255 E-mail: sales@dearingplastics.com

Den Mark Tools, 4 Queensway Link Industrial Estate, Stafford Park, Telford, Shropshire, TF3 3DN Tel: (01952) 200633 Fax: (01952) 200133 E-mail: mrowlands@den-mark.freeserve.co.uk

Denny Engineering Ltd, 10 Morgan Way, Bowthorpe Employment Area, Norwich, NR5 9JJ Tel: (01603) 747066 Fax: (01603) 748421 E-mail: dennengltd@aol.com

Detailed Plastic Components Ltd, 8 Rutherford Way, Thetford, Norfolk, IP24 1HA Tel: (01842) 764414 Fax: (01842) 762715 E-mail: sales@dpc.uk.com

Dickinson Philips & Co., Snaygill Industrial Estate, Keighley Road, Skipton, North Yorkshire, BD23 2QR Tel: (01756) 700359 Fax: (01756) 700360 E-mail: sales@dickinsonphilips.com

Elbesee Products, Cotswold Works, London Road, Chalford, Stroud, Gloucestershire, GL6 8DT Tel: (01453) 883014 Fax: (01453) 882987

Elbmar Ltd, 5 Oppenheimer Centre, Greenbridge Road, Greenbridge Industrial Estate, Swindon, SN3 3JD Tel: (01793) 644155 Fax: (01793) 513170 E-mail: elbmar@aol.com

Euro Moulds Ltd, Units 5 & 10 Borers Yard, Borers Arms Road, Copthorne, Crawley, West Sussex, RH10 3LH Tel: (01342) 712113 Fax: (01342) 717571 E-mail: euromoulds@btinternet.com

Firma Nicand Plastic Products Ltd, Unit D Woodley Airfield, Headley Road East, Woodley, Reading, RG5 4SA Tel: 0118-969 6939 Fax: 0118-944 1625 E-mail: kiran@firmanicand.com

G M Mouldings, 175A Brigstock Road, Thornton Heath, Surrey, CR7 7JP Tel: (020) 8665 5045 Fax: (020) 8665 5045

G T S Moulds, 15 South Lane, New Malden, Surrey, KT3 5HU Tel: (020) 8336 0335 Fax: (020) 8336 0335 E-mail: gtsmoulds@blueyonder.co.uk

G T Tools Ltd, Coxmoor Road, Sutton-in-Ashfield, Nottinghamshire, NG17 4NE Tel: (01623) 551000 Fax: (01623) 550784 E-mail: sales@gttools.co.uk

A.F. Gaskin Ltd, Downley Road, Naphill, High Wycombe, Buckinghamshire, HP14 4QY Tel: (01494) 563831 Fax: (01494) 562933 E-mail: sales@afgaskin.co.uk

Genes Plastics, Unit 21b Stafford Mill, London Road, Thrupp, Stroud, Gloucestershire, GL5 2AZ Tel: (01453) 751000 Fax: (01453) 755556

Grainger Plastics Ltd, Unit 3 Joseph Wilson Industrial Estate, Millstrood Road, Whitstable, Kent, CT5 3PS Tel: (01227) 276806 Fax: (01227) 770731

H D M Plastics, Waldeck Road, Maidenhead, Berkshire, SL6 8BR Tel: (01628) 673832 Fax: (01628) 673832 E-mail: hdmplastics68@yahoo.co.uk

Hi Spec Precision Toolmakers Ltd, 36 Rumer Hill Bus Estate, Rumer Hill Road, Cannock, Staffordshire, WS11 0ET Tel: (01543) 505323 Fax: (01543) 505230 E-mail: neil@hispec.uk.com

Highline Precision Engineering, Old Mill La Industrial Estate, Mansfield Woodhouse, Mansfield, Nottinghamshire, NG19 9BG Tel: (01623) 654251 Fax: (01623) 621384

Hollycroft Engineering Ltd, 7 Teal Business Park, Dodwells Road, Hinckley, Leicestershire, LE10 3BZ Tel: (01455) 635845 Fax: (01455) 250273 E-mail: sales@hollycrofteng.freeserve.co.uk

Investment Tooling International Ltd, Sidings Road, Lowmoor Business Park, Kirkby-in-Ashfield, Nottingham, NG17 7JZ Tel: (01623) 754814 Fax: (01623) 754914 E-mail: sales@iti-kirkby.co.uk

Jaymark Mould & Tool Co. Ltd, Unit 1, Capital Place, Lovet Road, The Pinnacles, Harlow, Essex, CM19 5AS Tel: (01279) 427945 Fax: (01279) 641330 E-mail: jaymark@btinternet.com

JHR Moulders Witney Ltd, Avenue Four, Witney, Oxfordshire, OX28 4BN Tel: (01993) 705059 Fax: (01993) 775949

K L Precision Engineering Ltd, Athelney Way, Cheltenham, Gloucestershire, GL52 6RT Tel: (01242) 244847 Fax: (01242) 244847

Thomas Keating Ltd, Station Mills, Daux Road, Billingshurst, West Sussex, RH14 9SH Tel: (01403) 782045 Fax: (01403) 785464 E-mail: m.clack@terahertz.co.uk

Kentone Plastics Ltd, Town Farm, Campton Road, Gravenhurst, Bedford, MK45 4JB Tel: (01462) 711797 Fax: (01462) 711031 E-mail: kentoneplastics@hotmail.com

Langdale Bros, Weatherhill Works, Hathersham Close, Smallfield, Horley, Surrey, RH6 9JE Tel: (01342) 843164 Fax: (01342) 843164 E-mail: langdalebros@aol.com

Linton Plastic Moulders Ltd, Unit 3, The Grip, Linton, Cambridge, CB21 4XN Tel: (01223) 892143 Fax: (01223) 894618 E-mail: info@lintonplasticmoulders.co.uk

M C M Machine Sales Ltd, 22 Bancrofts Road, South Woodham Ferrers, Chelmsford, CM3 5UQ Tel: (01245) 322545 Fax: (01245) 329468 E-mail: mc.m@talk21.com

M J M Toolmaking Ltd Ltd, Farfield Park, Manvers, Rotherham, South Yorkshire, S63 5DB Tel: (01709) 873131 Fax: (01709) 873131

Mcausbyrne Tools Ltd, 10 Westbourne Place, Hove, East Sussex, BN3 4GN Tel: (01273) 776318 Fax: (01273) 776318 E-mail: david.austin@btconnect.com

Modern Moulds & Tools, Commerce Way, Lancing, West Sussex, BN15 8TA Tel: (01903) 851905 Fax: (01903) 851907 E-mail: mail@modernmoulds.co.uk

Mold Systems, Millennium Way, Heighington Lane Business Park, Newton Aycliffe, County Durham, DL5 6JW Tel: (01325) 328700 Fax: (01325) 328707 E-mail: sales@moldsystems.com

Moldmet Ltd, Sandall Stones Road, Kirk Sandall Industrial Estate, Doncaster, South Yorkshire, DN3 1QR Tel: (01302) 888810 Fax: (01302) 880333 E-mail: ken@moldmet.com

Newark Tools Ltd, Coppice Side Industrial Estate, Brownhills, Walsall, WS8 7EX Tel: (01543) 454600

Newbar Engineers Ltd, 3 Pound Lane Industrial Estate, Maypole Fields, Halesowen, West Midlands, B63 2QB Tel: (01384) 639139 Fax: (01384) 411128

OPPM Ltd, Eagle Road, Quarry Hill Industrial Estate, Ilkeston, Derbyshire, DE7 4RB Tel: 0115-944 1236 Fax: 0115-944 0660 E-mail: sales@oppm.co.uk

Optical Products Ltd, 74-75 Brunner Road, London, E17 7NW Tel: (020) 8520 4047 Fax: (020) 8520 6593 E-mail: sales@ultrasolar.com

Orion Precision, 18 Orion Court, Cranes Farm Road, Basildon, Essex, SS14 3DB Tel: (01268) 282445 Fax: (01268) 282445

Partridge Plastics Worthing Ltd, G H Northbrook Trading Estate, Northbrook Road, Worthing, West Sussex, BN14 8PN Tel: (01903) 213178 Fax: (01903) 204684 E-mail: sales@partridgeplastics.com

Patterson & Rothwell Ltd, Mount Pleasant Street, Oldham, OL4 1HH Tel: 0161-621 5000 Fax: 0161-621 5001 E-mail: sales@patterson-rothwell.co.uk

Perfectools Plastics, Coombend, Radstock, BA3 3AS Tel: (01761) 432299 Fax: (01761) 435575 E-mail: sales@perfecttools.co.uk

Plasmold Precision, Knightsbridge Gardens, Romford, RM7 9AD Tel: (01371) 876445 Fax: (01708) 732691 E-mail: lee@plasmoldplastics.co.uk

Plastech, 4 Ricebridge Works, Brighton Road, Bolney, Haywards Heath, West Sussex, RH17 5NA Tel: (01444) 881960 Fax: (01444) 881244

Pobs Precision Tools Mould Toolmkrs, 44 Bickford Road, Birmingham, B6 7EE Tel: 0121-327 5736 Fax: 0121-328 5261 E-mail: pobs.tools@btconnect.com

Powell & Harber, Brickfields Road, Worcester, WR4 9WN Tel: (01905) 731717 Fax: (01905) 724787 E-mail: info@powell-harber.co.uk

Protomould Ltd, Unit B2 Springhead Enterprise Park, Springhead Road, Northfleet, Gravesend, Kent, DA11 8HB Tel: (01474) 353525 Fax: (01474) 353526 E-mail: sales@protomould.co.uk

Punctual Precision Tooling, Unit 15 Blatchford Road, Horsham, West Sussex, RH13 5QR Tel: (01403) 269005 Fax: (01403) 252869 E-mail: sales@punctual-precision-tooling.co.uk

Pyramid Tool & Die Co., Unit A, Leopold Street, Pemberton, Wigan, Lancashire, WN5 8DH Tel: (01942) 227938 Fax: (01942) 211179 E-mail: enquiries@pyramid-tool.co.uk

Quantum Manufacturing Ltd, 1 Heathcote Way, Heathcote Industrial Estate, Warwick, CV34 6TE Tel: (01926) 885564 Fax: (01926) 450387 E-mail: info@quantumprecisiontoolmakers.co.uk

Queensfield Precision Engineering, Unit 4, Beeding Close, Southern Cross Trading Estate, Bognor Regis, West Sussex, PO22 9TS Tel: (01243) 868254 Fax: (01243) 829609 E-mail: post@queensfield.co.uk

R K J Precision Engineering Ltd, Park Hall Workshop, Tonypandy, Mid Glamorgan, CF40 2BQ Tel: (01443) 434967

Rim Plastics Technology Ltd, 1 Wollaston Way, Burnt Mills Industrial Estate, Basildon, Essex, SS13 1DJ Tel: (01268) 729679 Fax: (01268) 729031 E-mail: sales@rimplas.co.uk

Ryetools Ltd, Westgate Carr Road, Pickering, North Yorkshire, YO18 8LX Tel: (01751) 476020 Fax: (01751) 477220 E-mail: ryetools@btinternet.co.uk

S L Mould Tools, 41 Albert Street, Syston, Leicester, LE7 2JA Tel: 0116-269 7080 Fax: 0116-269 8711

S L S Precision Engineers Ltd, 1 Hermitage Way, Mansfield, Nottinghamshire, NG18 5ES Tel: (01623) 456601 Fax: (01623) 456602 E-mail: slsprec@aol.com

Skiller Engineering Ltd, Unit 1, Pig Lane, Bishop'S Stortford, Hertfordshire, CM23 3HG Tel: 01279 501631

Supreme Tools Ltd, Lincoln Ho, Lincoln Rd, High Wycombe, Bucks, HP12 3RA Tel: (01494) 465423 Fax: (01494) 447560

Tarlow Engineering Ltd, Unit 22 Acorn Industrial Park, Crayford Road, Dartford, DA1 4AL Tel: (01322) 550328 Fax: (01322) 522998 E-mail: tarlow@mistral.co.uk

Technical Moulding Projects, Unit 5d Watlington Industrial Estate, Cuxham Road, Watlington, Oxfordshire, OX49 5LU Tel: (01491) 613539 Fax: (01491) 612096 E-mail: tmp@techmouldproj.demon.co.uk

TMT Toolmakers, Units 1, 3 & 7 Bilton Industrial Estate, Stockmans Close, Birmingham, B38 9TS Tel: 0121-459 0292 Fax: 0121-459 2141

Toolcraft Plastics Swindon Ltd, 2 Argyle Commercial Centre, 1-5 Argyle Street, Swindon, SN2 8AR Tel: (01793) 641040 Fax: (01793) 615483 E-mail: help@toolcraft.co.uk

▶ Total Mould & Insert, Edison Road, St. Ives, Cambridgeshire, PE27 3LF Tel: (01480) 484711 Fax: (01480) 484710 E-mail: sales@totalmould.co.uk

Tricrest Precision Toolmakers Ltd, 7 Poplar Drive, Witton, Birmingham, B6 7AD Tel: 0121-331 4078 Fax: 0121-331 4073 E-mail: tricrest@wwwuk.net

Triform Moulds Ltd, Oakridge Road, High Wycombe, Buckinghamshire, HP11 2PF Tel: (01494) 445354 Fax: (01494) 448200

Verifyne Plastic Products Ltd, Lever Mill, Slater Street, Blackburn, BB2 4PA Tel: (01254) 675639 Fax: (01254) 673787 E-mail: enquiries@verifyne-plastics.co.uk

W G Plastics Ltd, 55 Knights Hill Square, London, SE27 0HP Tel: (020) 8761 2464 Fax: (020) 8761 2464

Wessex Tool Co.Ltd, Wessex House, Devizes, Wiltshire, SN10 1PS Tel: (01380) 723423 Fax: (01380) 720100

Whitehead Gardner Tooling Ltd, Unit 2, Spring Gardens Industrial Estate, Romford, RM7 9LD Tel: (01708) 756023 Fax: (01708) 733219 E-mail: enquiries@whiteheads.co.uk

Wimborne Engineering, 58 Cobham Road, Ferndown Industrial Estate, Wimborne, Dorset, BH21 7QH Tel: (01202) 893043 E-mail: knud@moldtecknik.co.uk

Zeta Plastic Components Ltd, Ravensthorpe Industrial Estate, Dewsbury, West Yorkshire, WF13 3LN Tel: (01924) 491900 Fax: (01924) 491917

Zeus Products, Unit E2 Seaden Court, Clacton-on-Sea, Essex, CO15 4XN Tel: (01255) 220996 Fax: (01255) 429991

INJECTION MOULD TOOLS/ TOOLING REFURBISHMENT SERVICES

Advanced Cooling Systems U.K Ltd, Highfield Industrial Estate, Warren Road, Folkestone, Kent, CT19 6DD Tel: (01303) 255465 Fax: (01303) 246186 E-mail: info@atsuk.com

C & M Mould Tools Ltd, Unit 1-3 Brunel Close, Ebblake Industrial Estate, Verwood, Dorset, BH31 6BA Tel: (01202) 813019 Fax: (01202) 814219 E-mail: cmmoulds@aol.com

G K Precision 96, 4 Sidings Road, Lowmoor Industrial Estate, Kirkby-in-Ashfield, Nottingham, NG17 7JZ Tel: (01623) 721919 Fax: (01623) 751616

Pyramid Tool & Die Co., Unit A, Leopold Street, Pemberton, Wigan, Lancashire, WN5 8DH Tel: (01942) 227938 Fax: (01942) 211179 E-mail: enquiries@pyramid-tool.co.uk

INJECTION MOULDED CONTAINERS

Kingswood Tools & Mouldings, Victoria Avenue Industrial Estate, Swanage, Dorset, BH19 1BJ Tel: (01929) 425330 Fax: (01929) 424279

Manuplastics Ltd, Lombard Road, London, SW19 3TZ Tel: (020) 8542 3421 Fax: (020) 8540 0594 E-mail: sales@manuplastics.co.uk

INJECTION MOULDED PLASTIC COMPONENT CONSULTANTS OR DESIGNERS

A A V Plastic Design, Gore Cross Business Park, Corbin Way, Bradpole, Bridport, Dorset, DT6 3UX Tel: (01308) 427000 Fax: (01308) 420088 E-mail: office@aavplastics.com

Boverton Precision, Unit 2 Oxbutts Industrial Etate, Woodmancote, Cheltenham, Gloucestershire, GL52 9HW Tel: (01242) 675405 Fax: (01242) 677411 E-mail: bovertonprecision@wwmail.co.uk

Dearing Plastics Ltd, Unit 12 National Avenue, Hull, HU5 4HT Tel: (01482) 348588 Fax: (01482) 470255 E-mail: sales@dearingplastics.com

▶ Lynco, 110a Fenlake Road, Bedford, MK42 0EU Tel: (01234) 272425 Fax: (01234) 213141 E-mail: johncuthbert@ntlworld.com

Robert P D Frost & Co. Ltd, 45 Burrowfield, Welwyn Garden City, Hertfordshire, AL7 4SS Tel: (01707) 331188 Fax: (01707) 393714 E-mail: sales@rpdfrost.co.uk

Vactec Derby Ltd, Eagle Road, Quarry Hill Industrial Estate, Ilkeston, Derbyshire, DE7 4RB Tel: 0115-930 4806 Fax: 0115-930 4806

INJECTION MOULDED PLASTIC COMPONENTS

A V Plastics, Unit 1 Chiddingstone Causeway, Tonbridge, Kent, TN11 8JU Tel: (01892) 870461 Fax: (01892) 871262 E-mail: sales@avplastics.co.uk

Flambeau Europlast Ltd, Manston Road, Ramsgate, Kent, CT12 6HW Tel: (01843) 854000 Fax: (01843) 854010 E-mail: sales@flambeaueuro.com

Forcewell Ltd, 3A/3B Denaby Lane Industrial Estate, Denaby, Doncaster, South Yorkshire, DN12 4JL Tel: (01709) 860019 Fax: (01709) 869617

▶ Lintarealm Plastic Moulding Co. Ltd, Garth Industrial Estate, Gwaelod-y-Garth, Cardiff, CF15 9JN Tel: (029) 2081 3157 Fax: (029) 2081 1988

Nifco UK Ltd, Yarm Road, Stockton-on-Tees, Cleveland, TS18 3RX Tel: (01642) 672299 Fax: (01642) 611004 E-mail: sales@nifcoeu.com

Plasmold Plastics Ltd, 8-11 Oak Industrial Park, Chelmsford Road, Dunmow, Essex, CM6 1XN Tel: (01371) 876445 Fax: (01371) 876874 E-mail: lee@plasmoldplastics.co.uk

▶ PMJ Consultants, 77, Melford Road, Stowmarket, Suffolk, IP14 2PR Tel: 01449 673883 E-mail: peterjones@pmjconsultants.com

▶ Tekcomp Ltd, 17-18 Shipyard Estate, Brightlingsea, Colchester, CO7 0AR Tel: (01206) 303555 Fax: (01206) 303595 E-mail: info@tekcomp.co.uk

INJECTION MOULDING HOT FOIL PRINTING

▶ SPOTLIGHT IMPRESSIONS, 1BARONS CLOSE, FAKENHAM, NORFOLK, NR21 8BE Tel: 01328 851468 E-mail: spotlightimps@btconnect.com

INJECTION MOULDING MACHINE ACCESSORIES/ CONSUMABLES

Hartford Engineering Ltd, Bradford Road, Winsford, Cheshire, CW7 2PE Tel: (01606) 860888 Fax: (01606) 860889 E-mail: he@hartford-eng.co.uk

INJECTION MOULDING MACHINE (PLASTIC) ANCILLARY EQUIPMENT

Eastern Plastics Machinery Ltd, Eastern House, Priors Way, Coggeshall, Colchester, CO6 1TW Tel: (01376) 562288 Fax: (01376) 561385 E-mail: info@easternplastics.co.uk

GeKu UK Ltd, 35B Pattens Lane, Chatham, Kent, ME4 6JR Tel: (01634) 830122 Fax: (01634) 813523 E-mail: gekujohn@btinternet.com

INJECTION MOULDING MACHINE REFURBISHMENT/ MAINTENANCE/REPAIR SERVICES

Dassett Process Engineering Ltd, Daimler Close, Royal Oak Industrial Estate, Woodford Halse, Daventry, Northants, NN11 8QJ Tel: (01327) 312914 Fax: (01327) 314162 E-mail: info@dassett.com

▶ indicates data change since last edition

INJECTION MOULDING MACHINE/TOOLING SPARE PARTS

B S A Mouldings Ltd, Larch Road, Saddlebow, King's Lynn, Norfolk, PE34 3HW Tel: (01553) 772555 Fax: (01553) 776294
E-mail: bsamouldings@compuserve.com

INJECTION MOULDING MACHINES, *See also headings for particular types*

A1 Moulders Ltd, Smeckley Wood Close, Chesterfield, Derbyshire, S41 9PZ Tel: (01246) 455705 Fax: (01246) 454895
E-mail: a1moulders@bt.com

Mitsui Fanuc Mitsui, 21 Brunel Close, Drayton Fields Industrial Esta, Daventry, Northamptonshire, NN11 8RB Tel: (01327) 706880 Fax: (01327) 706661
E-mail: uksales@mmte.de

INJECTION MOULDING SCREWS

Magog Industries Ltd, Swains Mill, Crane Mead, Ware, Hertfordshire, SG12 9PY Tel: (01920) 465201 Fax: (01920) 463345
E-mail: enquiries@magog.co.uk

INJECTION MOULDING SERVICES

A A C Cyroma Ltd, C P L House, Beaumont Road, Banbury, Oxfordshire, OX16 1RJ Tel: (01295) 759200 Fax: (01295) 270614

A V Plastics, Unit 1 Chiddingstone Causeway, Tonbridge, Kent, TN11 8JU Tel: (01892) 870461 Fax: (01892) 871262
E-mail: sales@avplastics.co.uk

Barr Mason Ltd, 10 Greycaine Road, Watford, WD24 7GG Tel: (01923) 222248 Fax: (01923) 817024 E-mail: sales@barrmason.co.uk

Borough Ltd, 65 Progress Road, Leigh-on-Sea, Essex, SS9 5JT Tel: (01702) 425425 Fax: (01702) 425400
E-mail: sales@borough.co.uk

C P I UK Ltd, 107 Boston Road, Gorse Hill, Leicester, LE4 1AW Tel: 0116-234 0600 Fax: 0116-235 2592
E-mail: uk.info@cpiglobal.com

Chess Plastics Ltd, 2 George Baylis Road, Berry Hill Industrial Estate, Droitwich, Worcestershire, WR9 9RB Tel: (01905) 794405 Fax: (01905) 794495
E-mail: genmail@chessplastics.co.uk

Coda Plastics Ltd, Folgate Road, North Walsham, Norfolk, NR28 0AJ Tel: (01692) 501020 Fax: (01692) 501030
E-mail: admin@coda-plastics.co.uk

Dorset Technical Mouldings, Unit C20-24, Holton Road, Holton Heath Trading Park, Poole, Dorset, BH16 6LT Tel: (01202) 624790 Fax: (01202) 623761
E-mail: sales@dtm-poole.fsnet.co.uk

Dynamic Cassette (International) Ltd, Marsh Lane, Boston, Lincolnshire, PE21 7TX Tel: (01205) 355555 Fax: (01205) 354823
E-mail: sales@dci.co.uk

Ensign Plastic Moulders Ltd, 8 Woodfield Road, Welwyn Garden City, Hertfordshire, AL7 1JQ Tel: (01707) 886795 Fax: (01707) 882566
E-mail: ensignplastic.moulders@ntlbusiness.com

Erodatools Ltd, Unit 4 Laurence Works, Sheffield Road, Penistone, Sheffield, S36 6HF Tel: (01226) 763725 Fax: (01226) 767139
E-mail: krolfe@aol.com

Fastplas Technical Moulding Ltd, 22 Brunel Road, St. Leonards-on-Sea, East Sussex, TN38 9RT Tel: (01424) 851443 Fax: (01424) 851443
E-mail: info@fastplas.co.uk

Fleming's Ropes & Twines Woolston Ltd, Bridge Road, Woolston, Warrington, WA1 4AT Tel: (01925) 499955 Fax: (01925) 492208

I V M Ltd, Unit 3-4, Willington, Crook, County Durham, DL15 0UT Tel: (01388) 746538 Fax: (01388) 746538
E-mail: contact.ivm@btconnect.com

JHR Moulders Witney Ltd, Avenue Four, Witney, Oxfordshire, OX28 4BN Tel: (01993) 705059 Fax: (01993) 775949

▶ K M S 1996, 100 Ross Walk, Leicester, LE4 5HH Tel: 0116-261 1311 Fax: 0116-261 1313

Lotus Water Garden Products Ltd, Stewart House, Purley Way, Croydon, CR9 4HS Tel: (020) 8686 2231 Fax: (020) 8688 3857

▶ Machine Resources Ltd, 77 Poplars Close, Mardy, Abergavenny, Monmouthshire, NP7 6LQ Tel: (01873) 857093 Fax: (01873) 857093
E-mail: machine-resources@tiscali.co.uk

▶ P C Plastics, Unit A1, Locking Farm Industrial Estate, Locking Moor Road, Weston-Super-Mare, Avon, BS24 8PJ Tel: (01934) 820678 Fax: (01934) 820678

Shep Plastics Ltd, The Old Pottery, Lower Dicker, Hailsham, East Sussex, BN27 4AT Tel: (01323) 440088 Fax: (01323) 841930
E-mail: sales@shep-plastics.co.uk

Stapleton Engineering, 13 Orwell Court, Hurricane Way, Wickford, Essex, SS11 8YJ Tel: (01268) 764985 Fax: (01268) 764985

Tex Industrial Plastics Ltd, Wetherby Road, Derby, DE24 8HL Tel: (01332) 363249 Fax: (01332) 292186
E-mail: sales@tex-plastics.co.uk

INJECTION MOULDING TRAINING SERVICES/ CONSULTANTS

G & A Moulding Technology Ltd, Unit 2, Stonehill, Huntingdon, Cambridgeshire, PE29 6ED Tel: (01480) 414933 Fax: (01480) 414899
E-mail: info@gandamoulding.co.uk

INJECTION MOULDING, PLASTIC COMPONENTS, ADVICE AND DESIGN

A A V Plastic Design, Gore Cross Business Park, Corbin Way, Bradpole, Bridport, Dorset, DT6 3UX Tel: (01308) 427000 Fax: (01308) 420088 E-mail: office@aavplastics.com

Plasmold Plastics Ltd, 8-11 Oak Industrial Park, Chelmsford Road, Dunmow, Essex, CM6 1XN Tel: (01371) 876445 Fax: (01371) 876874
E-mail: lee@plasmoldplastics.co.uk

▶ Tekcomp Ltd, 17-18 Shipyard Estate, Brightlingsea, Colchester, CO7 0AR Tel: (01206) 303555 Fax: (01206) 303595
E-mail: info@tekcomp.co.uk

INJECTION MOULDINGS

A G M Plastics, 3-4 The Drove, West Wilts Trading Estate, Bratton, Westbury, Wiltshire, BA13 4JE Tel: (01373) 827771 Fax: (01373) 827772 E-mail: alan@agmplastics.co.uk

Barr Mason Ltd, 10 Greycaine Road, Watford, WD24 7GG Tel: (01923) 222248 Fax: (01923) 817024 E-mail: sales@barrmason.co.uk

Branston Plastics Ltd, 60 Spencer Street, Birmingham, B18 6DS Tel: 0121-236 8253 Fax: 0121-236 8253

Brush Technology Ltd, 3 Throckley Industrial Estate, Ponteland Road, Throckley, Newcastle upon Tyne, NE15 9EW Tel: 0191-229 1666 Fax: 0191-229 1777
E-mail: info@brushtec.com

Clearex Plastics Ltd, Dubmire Trading Estate, Houghton le Spring, Tyne & Wear, DH4 5RF Tel: 0191-385 2880 Fax: 0191-385 2855

Cobb-Slater Ltd, Cosim Works, Church Road, Darley Dale, Matlock, Derbyshire, DE4 2GG Tel: (01629) 732344 Fax: (01629) 733446
E-mail: technical@cobb-slater.co.uk

Eden Plastics & Media Ltd, 6 Prince Georges Road, London, SW19 2PX Tel: (020) 8646 5556 Fax: (020) 8640 0475
E-mail: general@edenplastics.co.uk

Ensign Plastic Moulders Ltd, 8 Woodfield Road, Welwyn Garden City, Hertfordshire, AL7 1JQ Tel: (01707) 886795 Fax: (01707) 882566
E-mail: ensignplastic.moulders@ntlbusiness.com

Fairgrieve Mouldings Ltd, 15 Sedling Road, Wear Industrial Estate, Washington, Tyne & Wear, NE38 9BZ Tel: 0191-415 9292 Fax: 0191-415 9696
E-mail: lindabiggins@fairgrieve87.freeserve.co.uk

I M Plastech Ltd, 7 Levellers Lane, Eynesbury, St. Neots, Cambridgeshire, PE19 2JL Tel: (01480) 407214 Fax: (01480) 406737

Icarus Housewares, Unit 1 & 2 Newman Lane, Alton, Hampshire, GU34 2PJ Tel: (01420) 593479 Fax: (01420) 87389
E-mail: lunchboxes@icarus-housewares.com

Inflite Engineering Services Ltd, Unit A, Broadlink, Manchester, M24 1UB Tel: 0161-653 4222 Fax: 0161-655 3375
E-mail: enquiries@ultratools.co.uk

Kingswood Tools & Mouldings, Victoria Avenue Industrial Estate, Swanage, Dorset, BH19 1BJ Tel: (01929) 425330 Fax: (01929) 424279

Purley Plastics, 41 Haviland Road, Ferndown Industrial Estate, Wimborne, Dorset, BH21 7RY Tel: (01202) 892255 Fax: (01202) 892255

Tatra Plastics Manufacturing, Station Road, Norwood Green, Halifax, West Yorkshire, HX3 8QD Tel: 0845 5314245 Fax: (01274) 690283 E-mail: extrusions@tatra.co.uk

Universal Moulding Co., 500 Ipswich Rd, Slough, SL1 4EP Tel: (01753) 570023 Fax: (01753) 535005 E-mail: andy@alltechmoulds.co.uk

Vertex Moulding Ltd, 4 Shornecliffe Industrial Estate, North Close, Folkestone, Kent, CT20 3UH Tel: (01303) 251298 Fax: (01303) 253198 E-mail: vml01@vml01.fsnet.co.uk

INJECTION MOULDINGS, GLASS FIBRE OR FIBREGLASS

▶ Haven Mouldings, 17 White Road, Off Charfleets Road, Canvey Island, Essex, SS8 0PQ Tel: (01268) 698823 Fax: (01268) 697125 E-mail: haven@btconnect.com

INJECTION MOULDINGS, MULTI SHOT

Formula Plastics Ltd, Unit 12 I E S Centre, Horndale Avenue, Aycliffe Industrial Park, Newton Aycliffe, County Durham, DL5 6DS Tel: (01325) 304104 Fax: (01325) 304103
E-mail: john.suggate@formula-plastics.co.uk

INJECTION MOULDINGS, PLASTIC

A A C Spectrum Ltd, Brierley Park Close, Sutton-in-Ashfield, Nottinghamshire, NG17 3FW Tel: (01623) 440111 Fax: (01623) 444670 E-mail: nottingham@aacgroup.co.uk

A C C Plastics, Unit A Peacock View, Fenton Industrial Estate, Stoke-on-Trent, ST4 2XJ Tel: (01782) 201601 Fax: (01782) 201782
E-mail: sales@accplastics.co.uk

A G M Plastics, 3-4 The Drove, West Wilts Trading Estate, Bratton, Westbury, Wiltshire, BA13 4JE Tel: (01373) 827771 Fax: (01373) 827772 E-mail: alan@agmplastics.co.uk

A H Engineering North East Ltd, Unit 5 Wagonway Road Industrial Estate, Hebburn, Tyne & Wear, NE31 1SP Tel: 0191-483 9807 Fax: 0191-483 8700
E-mail: aheng@lineone.net

A K Industries Ltd, Foxwood Court, Rotherwas Industrial Estate, Rotherwas, Hereford, HR2 6JQ Tel: (01432) 375100 Fax: (01432) 263532 E-mail: sales@aki.co.uk

▶ A K Plastic Mouldings Ltd, Unit 32 Herons Gate Trading Estate, Paycocke Road, Basildon, Essex, SS14 3EU Tel: (01268) 272241 Fax: (01268) 272097

A M A Plastics, Unit 1 Moreton Park Industrial Estate, Moreton Road South, Luton, LU2 0TL Tel: (01582) 734630 Fax: (01582) 419260

A P I C Plastics Ltd, 28 Plantation Road, Amersham, Buckinghamshire, HP6 6HJ Tel: (01494) 431066 Fax: (01494) 726309
E-mail: apicplastics@lineone.net

A1 Moulders Ltd, Smeckley Wood Close, Chesterfield, Derbyshire, S41 9PZ Tel: (01246) 455705 Fax: (01246) 454895
E-mail: a1moulders@bt.com

A2B Plastics Ltd, Swan Road, Mochdre Business Park, Mochdre, Colwyn Bay, Clwyd, LL28 5HB Tel: (01492) 544332 Fax: (01492) 543794
E-mail: james@a2bplastics.co.uk

Abaloid Plastics Ltd, 165 Scudamore Road, Leicester, LE3 1UQ Tel: 0116-232 0212 Fax: 0116-232 0569
E-mail: enquiries@abaloidplastics.co.uk

Abbey Plastics & Tooling Ltd, Unit 8, 108 Nathan Way, London, SE28 0AQ Tel: (020) 8316 4333 Fax: (020) 8316 4333

Abishot Mouldings, 6 Rushton Road, Rothwell, Kettering, Northamptonshire, NN14 6HF Tel: (01536) 712380 Fax: (01536) 418110

Accuromm UK Ltd, 20 Welsh Road, Garden City, Deeside, Clwyd, CH5 2RA Tel: (01244) 836385 Fax: (01244) 241100
E-mail: info@accurommuk.com

Ad Plastics, 13 Willow Road, Poyle Trading Estate, Colnbrook, Slough, SL3 0BS Tel: (01753) 684777 Fax: (01753) 683139
E-mail: adplasticsltd@hotmail.com

Advanced Plastics & Composites Ltd, 31 Bergen Way, Sutton Fields Industrial Estate, Hull, HU7 0YQ Tel: (01482) 823038 Fax: (01482) 822945 E-mail: info@advanced-plastics.co.uk

Aeroplas UK Ltd, Great Western Park, Great Bridge, Tipton, West Midlands, DY4 7AB Tel: 0121-522 3000 Fax: 0121-522 3333
E-mail: mail@aeroplas.net

Agentdraw Ltd, 42 Great Central Street, Leicester, LE1 4JT Tel: 0116-251 9990 Fax: 0116-251 9997
E-mail: kevin@agentdraw.co.uk

Aldersgate Technical Mouldings, Ebblake Industrial Estate, Verwood, Dorset, BH31 6AU Tel: (01202) 825454 Fax: (01202) 827516
E-mail: paul@aldersgateplastics.com

Fred Allen Products Ltd, Number 16, Balena Close, Creekmoore Trading Estate, Poole, Dorset, BH17 7DB Tel: (01202) 657740 Fax: (01202) 667778
E-mail: sales@fredallenproducts.com

Almont Plastics Ltd, Lower Road, Ledbury, Herefordshire, HR8 2DH Tel: (01531) 633640 Fax: (01531) 635925

Amco Products, 5 Orchard Road, Royston, Hertfordshire, SG8 5HD Tel: (01763) 242040 Fax: (01763) 245505
E-mail: sales@Amco-products.co.uk

Andel Plastics Ltd, 1 Klaxon Tysley Industrial Estate, 751 Warwick Road, Tyseley, Birmingham, B11 2HA Tel: 0121-765 4042 Fax: 0121-707 3335
E-mail: enquiries@andel-plastics.demon.co.uk

Antplace Ltd, Ford Airfield Industrial Estate, Ford, Arundel, West Sussex, BN18 0HY Tel: (01903) 714402 Fax: (01903) 732065

Archfact Ltd, 10 Pipers Wood Industrial Park, Waterberry Drive, Waterlooville, Hampshire, PO7 7XU Tel: (023) 9224 0700 Fax: (023) 9223 0157 E-mail: info@archfact.com

A-Tec Plastics, 6 Queensway, New Milton, Hampshire, BH25 5NN Tel: (01425) 638433 Fax: (01425) 616374E-mail: sales@atec.co.uk

Audus Noble Ltd, Blyth Industrial Estate, Cowpen Road, Blyth, Northumberland, NE24 5TD Tel: (01670) 543100 Fax: (01670) 364800

Automotive Applied Technologies Ltd, PO Box 22, Accrington, Lancashire, BB5 0LA Tel: (01254) 357500 Fax: (01254) 357600
E-mail: info@automotive-tech.co.uk

Avalon Plastics Ltd, Imco Works, Beckery New Road, Glastonbury, Somerset, BA6 9NR Tel: (01458) 831563 Fax: (01458) 834384
E-mail: enquiries@avalonplastics.co.uk

▶ Aycliffe Engineering Ltd, Beaumont Way, Aycliffe Industrial Park, Newton Aycliffe, County Durham, DL5 6SN Tel: (01325) 300223 Fax: (01325) 300233
E-mail: altringham@aycliffe-engineering.onyxnet.co.uk

Aztec Tooling & Moulding Co. Ltd, Buckholt Drive, Worcester, WR4 9ND Tel: (01905) 754466 Fax: (01905) 754475
E-mail: aztectmltd@aol.com

B E C Global Ltd, Gore Road Industrial Estate, New Milton, Hampshire, BH25 6SA Tel: (01425) 613131 Fax: (01425) 616551
E-mail: info@becgroup.com

B F M Plastics Ltd, Unit 17c Orgreave Close, Sheffield, S13 9NP Tel: 0114-269 1688 Fax: 0114-269 3995
E-mail: sales@bfmplastics.com

B H M Plastics Ltd, The Station, High Street, Meldreth, Royston, Hertfordshire, SG8 6JR Tel: (01763) 260452 Fax: (01763) 261152
E-mail: bhm.plastics@virgin.net

B P F Plastics, 33 The Vintners, Temple Farm Industrial Estate, Southend-on-Sea, SS2 5RZ Tel: (01702) 616224 Fax: (01702) 616224
E-mail: brian@bpf6r.freeserve.co.uk

B P Y Plastics, J Lincoln Park, Borough Road, Buckingham Road Industrial Estate, Brackley, Northamptonshire, NN13 7BE Tel: (01280) 706335 Fax: (01280) 705675
E-mail: tony@bpy-plastics.com

B & S Injection Moulders Ltd, Units 14-15 Joseph Wilson Industrial Estate, Millstrood Road, Whitstable, Kent, CT5 3PS Tel: (01227) 262599 Fax: (01227) 770767
E-mail: sales@bandsinjection.co.uk

B S R Technical Mouldings Services Ltd, Unit 13/14/18 Lagrange, Lichfield Road Industrial Estate, Tamworth, Staffordshire, B79 7XD Tel: (01827) 63626 Fax: (01827) 63242

Banbury Plastic Fittings Ltd, Unit 13, Overfield, Thorpe Way Industrial Estate, Banbury, Oxfordshire, OX16 4XR Tel: (01295) 264800 Fax: (01295) 264901
E-mail: sales@bpfittings.co.uk

Barkley Plastics Ltd, 120 Highgate Street, Birmingham, B12 0XR Tel: 0121-440 1303 Fax: 0121-440 4902
E-mail: mharwood@barkley.co.uk

Barr Mason Ltd, 10 Greycaine Road, Watford, WD24 7GG Tel: (01923) 222248 Fax: (01923) 817024 E-mail: sales@barrmason.co.uk

BC Plastic Mouldings Ltd, Commercial Road, Walsall, WS2 7NQ Tel: (01922) 497888 Fax: (01922) 478600
E-mail: cjms@btconnect.com

Beavin Engineering Ltd, 33 Haviland Road, Ferndown Industrial Estate, Wimborne, Dorset, BH21 7SA Tel: (01202) 894404 Fax: (01202) 894404 E-mail: beavineng@btconnect.com

Belgrade Insulations Ltd, Belgrade Centre, Denington Road, Denington Industrial Estate, Wellingborough, Northamptonshire, NN8 2QH Tel: (01933) 222205 Fax: (01933) 441433
E-mail: sales@belgrade-polymer.com

Beswick Engineering Co. Ltd, 21 Cowley Road, Blackpool, FY4 4NE Tel: (01253) 761661 Fax: (01253) 761661

Bishopsworth Group Ltd, Unit 14A Fiveways Industrial Estate, Westwells Road, Hawthorn, Corsham, Wiltshire, SN13 9RG Tel: (01225) 812177 Fax: (01225) 812188
E-mail: sales@keiron.demon.co.uk

BKS Plastics Ltd, Unit 2 Station Road Industrial Estate, Great Harwood, Blackburn, BB6 7BB Tel: (01254) 889139 Fax: (01254) 889187
E-mail: bksplastics@btclick.com

Bonair Plastics Ltd, Old Forge Yard, Swanley Village Road, Swanley, Kent, BR8 7NF Tel: (01322) 664347 Fax: (01322) 664347
E-mail: dave@bonair.freeserve.co.uk

Bonnay Ltd, 4 Wood Lane, Isleworth, Middlesex, TW7 5ER Tel: (020) 8568 1567 Fax: (020) 8568 3660

Boverton Precision, Unit 2 Oxbutts Industrial Etate, Woodmancote, Cheltenham, Gloucestershire, GL52 9HW Tel: (01242) 675405 Fax: (01242) 677411
E-mail: bovertonprecision@wwmail.co.uk

Britestar Plastics Ltd, Unit 7, Broomfield Works, London Road, Swanley, Kent, BR8 8DF Tel: (01322) 669964 Fax: (01322) 660083
E-mail: info@britestar.gb

Buckfield Plastic Mould Tool, Moor Lane, Witton, Birmingham, B6 7AE Tel: 0121-356 9044 Fax: 0121-344 3108 E-mail: plastic@aol.com

Bva Tools & Plastics Ltd, Oaks Road, Batley, West Yorkshire, WF17 6LT Tel: (01924) 474455 Fax: (01924) 477566

Cable Access Solutions Ltd, 11 Stanley Street, Luton, LU1 5AL Tel: (01582) 411022 Fax: (01582) 727117
E-mail: sales@zyteкltd.demon.co.uk

Cadman Group, The Twitchell, Sutton-In-Ashfield, Nottinghamshire, NG17 5BT Tel: (01623) 553005 Fax: (01623) 440370
E-mail: bcadman@ypm.net

Cameron-Price Medical Division Ltd, Charlotte Road, Stirchley, Birmingham, B30 2BT Tel: 0121-459 2121 Fax: 0121-451 2303
E-mail: info@cameron-price.co.uk

Capricorn Mouldings Ltd, Unit 23, Trench Lock 3, Telford, Shropshire, TF1 5ST Tel: (01952) 201090 Fax: (01952) 222744

INJECTION MOULDINGS, PLASTIC – *continued*

Captive Closures, Burma Road, Blidworth, Mansfield, Nottinghamshire, NG21 0RT Tel: (01623) 491112 Fax: (01623) 491113 E-mail: captive.mick@btconnect.com

Carclo Engineering Group, PO Box 14, Ossett, West Yorkshire, WF5 9LR Tel: (01924) 268040 Fax: (01924) 283226 E-mail: investor.relations@carclo-plc.com

Cartwright Plastics, 1a Birdcroft Lane, Ilkeston, Derbyshire, DE7 4BE Tel: 0115-932 2744 Fax: 0115-932 9762

Central Mouldings Ltd, Reform Street Industrial Estate, Reform Street, Sutton-In-Ashfield, Nottinghamshire, NG17 5DB Tel: (01623) 553005 Fax: (01623) 440370 E-mail: bcadman@ypm.net

Certwood Ltd, Laporte Way, Luton, LU4 8EF Tel: (01582) 456955 Fax: (01582) 485855 E-mail: sales@certwood.com

Chandu Toolmakers, Church Road, Benfleet, Essex, SS7 4QN Tel: (01268) 565960 Fax: (01268) 757740 E-mail: chandutools@btconnect.com

Charlesworth & Son Ltd, Wishaw Lane, Curdworth, Sutton Coldfield, West Midlands, B76 9EL Tel: (01675) 470382 E-mail: sales@charlesworth-son.co.uk

Chess Plastics Ltd, 2 George Baylis Road, Berry Hill Industrial Estate, Droitwich, Worcestershire, WR9 9RB Tel: (01905) 794405 Fax: (01905) 794495 E-mail: genmail@chessplastics.co.uk

Chick Plastics Ltd, 42 Kenilworth Drive, Oadby, Leicester, LE2 5LG Tel: 0116-271 3377

Cinro Plastics Ltd, Garden Street, Stockport, Cheshire, SK2 7PP Tel: 0161-483 0696 Fax: 0161-483 0696

Clean Plastic Mouldings Ltd, Unit 6, Kenfig Industrial Estate, Margam, Port Talbot, West Glamorgan, SA13 2PE Tel: (01656) 740102 Fax: (01656) 745354 E-mail: cpm@bryncae.fsbusiness.co.uk

Cobb-Slater Ltd, Cosim Works, Church Road, Darley Dale, Matlock, Derbyshire, DE4 2GG Tel: (01629) 732344 Fax: (01629) 733446 E-mail: technical@cobb-slater.co.uk

Coles Electroacoustics Ltd, Pindar Road, Hoddesdon, Hertfordshire, EN11 0BZ Tel: (01992) 466685 Fax: (01992) 446583 E-mail: sales@coleselectroacoustics.com

Component Moulders, 4-5 Teville Industrials, Dominion Way, Worthing, West Sussex, BN14 8NW Tel: (01903) 235765 Fax: (01903) 212751 E-mail: sales@nordell.co.uk

Conisborough Furniture Components Ltd, Denaby Lane Industrial Estate, Denaby Main, Doncaster, South Yorkshire, DN12 4JS Tel: (01709) 863122 Fax: (01709) 865068 E-mail: components@conisborough.com

▶ Cox Plastics Technologies Ltd, Weedon Road Industrial Estae, Northampton, NN5 5AX Tel: (01604) 752200 Fax: (01604) 752266 E-mail: info@arkplastics.co.uk

CPP-LM Ltd, 38 Swaisland Drive, Crayford, Dartford, DA1 4HS Tel: (01322) 551940 Fax: (01322) 550212E-mail: info@cpp-lm.com

Crown Plastic Moulding Ltd, Broad Lanes, Bilston, West Midlands, WV14 0RY Tel: (01902) 496151 Fax: (01902) 493102 E-mail: sales@crown-plastic-mouldings.co.uk

Daneplast Ltd, 6 Gunby Road, Sewstern, Grantham, Lincolnshire, NG33 5RD Tel: (01476) 860081 Fax: (01476) 861401 E-mail: sales@daneplast.co.uk

Data Plastics, Avenue Three, Witney, Oxfordshire, OX28 4BP Tel: (01993) 700777 Fax: (01993) 700555 E-mail: sales@dataplastics.co.uk

C.T.P. Davall Ltd, Durham Lane Industrial Park, Eaglescliffe, Stockton-On-Tees, Cleveland, TS16 0RB Tel: (01554) 749000 Fax: (01642) 790779 E-mail: paul.caldwell@carclo-plc.com

Dearing Plastics Ltd, Unit 12 National Avenue, Hull, HU5 4HT Tel: (01482) 348588 Fax: (01482) 470255 E-mail: sales@dearingplastics.com

Denman International Ltd, Clandeboye Road, Bangor, County Down, BT20 3JH Tel: (028) 9146 2141 Fax: (028) 9145 1654

Denroyd Ltd, Lockhill Mills, Holmes Road, Sowerby Bridge, West Yorkshire, HX6 3LD Tel: (01422) 833147 Fax: (01422) 833615 E-mail: sales@denroyd.co.uk

Desch Plantpak Ltd, Burnham Road, Mundon, Maldon, Essex, CM9 6NT Tel: (01621) 745500 Fax: (01621) 745525 E-mail: sales@desch-plantpak.co.uk

Detailed Plastic Components Ltd, 8 Rutherford Way, Thetford, Norfolk, IP24 1HA Tel: (01842) 764414 Fax: (01842) 762715 E-mail: sales@dpc.uk.com

Deyn Plastics Ltd, Netherwood Road, Rotherwas Industrial Estate, Hereford, HR2 6JU Tel: (01432) 359763 Fax: (01432) 351928 E-mail: enquires@deynplastics.co.uk

Dickinson Philips & Co., Snaygill Industrial Estate, Keighley Road, Skipton, North Yorkshire, BD23 2QR Tel: (01756) 700359 Fax: (01756) 700360 E-mail: sales@dickinsonphilips.com

Diemould Service Co. Ltd, 11 Blenheim Road, Cressex Business Park, High Wycombe, Buckinghamshire, HP12 3RS Tel: (01494) 523811 Fax: (01494) 452898 E-mail: sales@dms-diemould.co.uk

DL Plastics Ltd, 9-11 Commerce Way, Lawford, Manningtree, Essex, CO11 1UT Tel: (01206) 396646 Fax: (01206) 396602 E-mail: enquiries@dlplastics.co.uk

Dremm Packaging Ltd, Erewash Court, Manners Avenue, Manners Industrial Estate, Ilkeston, Derbyshire, DE7 8EF Tel: 0115-930 7555 Fax: 0115-930 7618 E-mail: sales@dremm.co.uk

Droitwich Plastics Ltd, Wassage Way, Hampton Lovett, Droitwich, Worcestershire, WR9 0NX Tel: (01905) 796709 Fax: (01905) 796067

Dual Metallising Ltd, Units 12-14 The Business Centre, James Rd, Tyseley, Birmingham, B11 2BA Tel: 0121-708 2748 Fax: 0121-708 2256 E-mail: sales@dual-metallising.co.uk

Earl Plastics Ltd, Albert Works, St Huberts Street, Great Harwood, Blackburn, BB6 7BE Tel: (01254) 887494 Fax: (01254) 876355 E-mail: earlplastics@aol.com

Eaton Automotive Fluid Connectors Operations, P O Box 12, Brierley Hill, West Midlands, DY5 2LB Tel: (01384) 424911 Fax: (01384) 426300

Edgewest Plastics Ltd, Malvern View Business Park, Stella Way, Bishops Cleeve, Cheltenham, Gloucestershire, GL52 7DQ Tel: (01242) 679000 Fax: (01242) 679011 E-mail: info@edgewestplastics.co.uk

Elbesee Products, Cotswold Works, London Road, Chalford, Stroud, Gloucestershire, GL6 8DT Tel: (01453) 883014 Fax: (01453) 882987

Elbmar Ltd, 5 Oppenheimer Centre, Greenbridge Road, Greenbridge Industrial Estate, Swindon, SN3 3JD Tel: (01793) 644155 Fax: (01793) 513170 E-mail: elbmar@aol.com

Enalon Ltd, Vale Rise, Tonbridge, Kent, TN9 1RR Tel: (01732) 358500 Fax: (01732) 770463 E-mail: office@enalon.co.uk

Engineering Plastic Products Ltd, Unit 6, Shaw Road, Dudley, West Midlands, DY2 8TS Tel: (01384) 235881 Fax: (01384) 255260

Ensign Plastic Moulders Ltd, 8 Woodfield Road, Welwyn Garden City, Hertfordshire, AL7 1JQ Tel: (01707) 886795 Fax: (01707) 882566 E-mail: ensignplastic.moulders@ntlbusiness.com

Enterprise Tackle, 6 Darlington Close, Sandy, Bedfordshire, SG19 1RW Tel: (01767) 691231 Fax: (01767) 691231

Essex Injection Mouldings Ltd, 15 Temple Farm Industrial Estate, Craftsman Square, Temple Farm Industrial Estate, Southend-on-Sea, SS2 5RH Tel: (01702) 461160 Fax: (01702) 600805 E-mail: ed@essexinjectionmouldings.co.uk

Esspee Fabrications Ltd, 149 Merton Bank Road, St. Helens, Merseyside, WA9 1DZ Tel: (01744) 28304 Fax: (01744) 28826 E-mail: sales@esspee.co.uk

Eurobung Ltd, Roe Head Mill, Far Common Road, Mirfield, West Yorkshire, WF14 0DG Tel: (01924) 496671 Fax: (01924) 480257 E-mail: sales@eurobung.co.uk

Express Moulds Ltd, Jubilee Works, 40 Alma Crescent, Vauxhall, Birmingham, B7 4RH Tel: 0121-359 6378 Fax: 0121-359 3792 E-mail: paul.yeomans@expressmoulds.co.uk

Fastplas Technical Moulding Ltd, 22 Brunel Road, St. Leonards-on-Sea, East Sussex, TN38 9RT Tel: (01424) 851443 Fax: (01424) 851443 E-mail: info@fastplas.co.uk

Fellside Plastics Ltd, Wilson Way, Pool, Redruth, Cornwall, TR15 3RX Tel: (01209) 212917 Fax: (01209) 212919 E-mail: fellside@blowit.fsbusiness.co.uk

Fenton Engineering Ltd, Finedon Sidings, Station Road, Finedon, Wellingborough, Northamptonshire, NN9 5NY Tel: (01536) 723488 Fax: (01536) 726642 E-mail: sales@fentonprecision.co.uk

Firstpress Plastic Moulders Ltd, 10 Haden Street, Balsall Heath, Birmingham, B12 9BH Tel: 0121-446 6266 Fax: 0121-446 6269 E-mail: info@firstpress.co.uk

Flemings Seals Ltd, Atlas Mills, Atlas Mill Road, Brighouse, West Yorkshire, HD6 1ES Tel: (01484) 718391 Fax: (01484) 711585 E-mail: sales@flemings-seals.co.uk

Formula Plastics Ltd, Unit 12 I E S Centre, Horndale Avenue, Aycliffe Industrial Park, Newton Aycliffe, County Durham, DL5 6DS Tel: (01325) 304104 Fax: (01325) 304103 E-mail: john.suggate@formula-plastics.co.uk

Forteq UK Ltd, Tandem Industrial Estate, Wakefield Road, Tandem, Huddersfield, HD5 0QR Tel: (01484) 424384 Fax: (01484) 535053

Fourfold Mouldings, New Close Mills, Howden Road, Silsden, Keighley, West Yorkshire, BD20 0HA Tel: (01535) 654604 Fax: (01535) 654829 E-mail: sales@fourfold.co.uk

G M D Mouldings Ltd, Dec House, 143-145 Cardiff Road, Reading, RG1 8JF Tel: 0118-957 2188 Fax: 0118-957 1218 E-mail: martin@mclayton.fsbusiness.co.uk

Genes Plastics, Unit 21b Stafford Mill, London Road, Thrupp, Stroud, Gloucestershire, GL5 2AZ Tel: (01453) 751000 Fax: (01453) 755556

Gilt Edge Plastics, The Elms, Church Road, Harold Wood, Romford, RM3 0JU Tel: (01708) 379005 Fax: (01708) 379045 E-mail: sales@giltedgeplastics.co.uk

▶ Glazpart Ltd, Wildmere Road, Daventry Road Industrial Estate, Banbury, Oxfordshire, OX16 3JU Tel: (01295) 264533 Fax: (01295) 266699 E-mail: sales@glazpart.co.uk

Glebe Engineering Ltd, Edensor Works, Greendock Street, Stoke-on-Trent, ST3 2NA Tel: (01782) 599161 Fax: (01782) 324410 E-mail: nick.cresswell@glebe.co.uk

Glendenning Plastics Ltd, First Avenue, The Pensnett Estate, Kingswinford, West Midlands, DY6 7TZ Tel: (01384) 278256 Fax: (01384) 400091 E-mail: sales@garlandproducts.com

Goodbrand Plastics Ltd, Millbuck Way, Sandbach, Cheshire, CW11 3GQ Tel: (01270) 753006 Fax: (01270) 750329 E-mail: sales@ultrastorage.co.uk

Grainger Plastics Ltd, Unit 3 Joseph Wilson Industrial Estate, Millstrood Road, Whitstable, Kent, CT5 3PS Tel: (01227) 276806 Fax: (01227) 770731

Grange Industries, Unit 2 Bessemer Close, Cardiff, CF11 8DL Tel: (02920) 345366 Fax: (02920) 399111 E-mail: ryan@grangeindustries.co.uk

H M T Ltd, Unit 7, Bessemer Park, Bessemer Road, Basingstoke, Hampshire, RG21 3NB Tel: (01256) 819977 Fax: (01256) 819988 E-mail: hampshire@btconnect.com

Harrison Adams Ltd, Victoria Mills, Knowler Hill, Liversedge, West Yorkshire, WF15 6DP Tel: (01924) 402435 Fax: (01924) 404814 E-mail: travor@harrisonadamsmouldings.wannado.co.uk

Hawk Mouldings, Mill Rythe Lane, Hayling Island, Hampshire, PO11 0QG Tel: (023) 9246 3864 Fax: (023) 9246 7204 E-mail: sales@hawkmouldings.co.uk

Hayes (Plastic) Engineering, Unit 59, Station Road Industrial Estate, Hailsham, East Sussex, BN27 2ES Tel: (01323) 844455 Fax: (01323) 844488 E-mail: info@hayesplastics.com

Hi Spec Precision Toolmakers Ltd, 36 Rumer Hill Bus Estate, Rumer Hill Road, Cannock, Staffordshire, WS11 0ET Tel: (01543) 505323 Fax: (01543) 505230 E-mail: neil@hispec.uk.com

Hi Tec Plastics, 1 Sett End Road, Shadsworth Business Park, Blackburn, BB1 2PT Tel: (01254) 581405 Fax: (01254) 680285 E-mail: dennishi-tech@quista.net

Hide & Hides Ltd, Portishead Road, Leicester, LE5 0JN Tel: 0116-276 6514

Hilbar Plastics, Windley Works, Wolsey Street, Radcliffe, Manchester, M26 3BB Tel: 0161-724 4325 Fax: 0161-725 9158

Hilcrest Design Ltd, Lea Road, Waltham Abbey, Essex, EN9 1AJ Tel: (01992) 713005 Fax: (01992) 710268 E-mail: sales@hilcrest.co.uk

Hillside Plastics Ltd, St. Johns Road, Meadowfield, Durham, DH7 8XQ Tel: 0191-378 0598 Fax: 0191-378 9346 E-mail: enquiries@hillside-plastics.co.uk

Hi-Tech Moulding Ltd, Unit 34, Kettlestring Lane, York, YO30 4XF Tel: (01904) 479888 Fax: (01904) 479966 E-mail: enquiries@hi-techmoulding.com

Hi-Tech Mouldings Ltd, Tyak House, Silverthorne Way, Waterlooville, Hampshire, PO7 7XY Tel: (023) 9225 9259 Fax: (023) 9236 6663 E-mail: sales@hitechltd.com

Holford Engineering Ltd, 13 Cromwell Road, St. Neots, Cambridgeshire, PE19 2EU Tel: (01480) 217271 Fax: (01480) 219687

Holloid Plastics Ltd, Stephenson Road, Basingstoke, Hampshire, RG21 6XR Tel: (01256) 334700 Fax: (01256) 473735 E-mail: mail@holloid-plastics.co.uk

Horizon Windows (Wales) Ltd, CWM Cynon Business Park, Mountain Ash, Mid Glamorgan, CF45 4ER Tel: (01443) 479993 Fax: (01443) 475738 E-mail: info@venturewales.com

Horne & Banks Group Ltd, 3 Merchant Drive, Mead Lane Industrial Estate, Hertford, SG13 7BH Tel: (01992) 501289 Fax: (01992) 501318 E-mail: david@horneandbanks.co.uk

Hydrovern Ltd, Unit 21, Wilden Industrial Estate, Wilden Lane, Stourport-On-Severn, Worcestershire, DY13 9JY Tel: (0870) 7706222 Fax: (0870) 7706223 E-mail: info@hydrovern.co.uk

I C M (Plastic Moulding) Ltd, Enterprise Close, Medway City Estate, Rochester, Kent, ME2 4LY Tel: (01634) 298500 Fax: (01634) 714338 E-mail: info@icm-plasticmoulding.co.uk

Inabata UK, Oaktree Place Road 35, Hortonwood Industrial Estate, Telford, Shropshire, TF1 7FR Tel: (01952) 670192 Fax: (01952) 608548 E-mail: enq@ikp.co.uk

Industrial Moulded Products Ltd, Unit 7 Reaymer Close, Walsall, WS2 7QZ Tel: (01922) 497376 Fax: (01922) 491117 E-mail: general@inmodprod.demon.co.uk

Injection Moulding Co., Unit 1b Betton Way, Moretonhampstead, Newton Abbot, Devon, TQ13 8NA Tel: (01647) 440055 Fax: (01647) 441055 E-mail: timco@tiscali.co.uk

Injection Mouldings Ltd, Cotswold Court Park, Gloucester Road, Staverton, Cheltenham, Gloucestershire, GL51 0TF Tel: (01452) 854077 Fax: (01452) 855077 E-mail: info@injectionmouldingsltd.co.uk

Injection Plastics Ltd, Winston Avenue, Croft, Leicester, LE9 3GQ Tel: (01455) 283898 Fax: (01455) 285330 E-mail: injectplasleics@aol.com

Inmould Ltd, Unit 10 Harmill Industrial Estate, Grovebury Road, Leighton Buzzard, Bedfordshire, LU7 4FF Tel: (01525) 376261 Fax: (01525) 376261 E-mail: sales.inmouldltd@btconnect.com

Inpress Plastics Ltd, 1 Harwood Road, Littlehampton, West Sussex, BN17 7AU Tel: (01903) 724128 Fax: (01903) 730357 E-mail: sales@impressplastics.co.uk

Invicta Toys & Games Ltd, PO Box 9, Leicester, LE2 4LB Tel: 0116-272 0555 Fax: 0116-272 0626 E-mail: sales@invictagroup.co.uk

J Clark & Co. Ltd, Hazel Croft, Shipley, West Yorkshire, BD18 2DY Tel: (01274) 590078 Fax: (01274) 598660 E-mail: jclarkco@btinternet.com

J G Coates Burnley Ltd, Trafalgar Street, Burnley, Lancashire, BB11 1TH Tel: (01282) 424376 Fax: (01282) 456166 E-mail: sales@cotel.co.uk

J R Cooper Ltd, 39a Church Street, Gamlingay, Sandy, Bedfordshire, SG19 3JJ Tel: (01767) 650763 Fax: (01767) 651273 E-mail: sales@jrcooperltd.co.uk

Jarzon Plastics Ltd, Golden Cresent, Hayes, Middlesex, UB3 1AQ Tel: (020) 8573 1537 Fax: (020) 8756 0138 E-mail: sales@jarzonplastics.co.uk

Jaycare Ltd, New York Way, New York Industrial Park, Newcastle Upon Tyne, NE27 0QF Tel: 0191-296 0303 Fax: 0191-296 1842

JHR Moulders Witney Ltd, Avenue Four, Witney, Oxfordshire, OX28 4BN Tel: (01993) 705059 Fax: (01993) 775949

Joal Engineering, 13 Orchard Road, Melbourn, Royston, Hertfordshire, SG8 6HL Tel: (01763) 245490 Fax: (01763) 247582

John Jerram, Alfreton Road, Derby, DE21 4AL Tel: (01332) 205295 Fax: (01332) 205295

K J K Plastics Ltd, 51 Knowl Piece, Wilbury Way, Hitchin, Hertfordshire, SG4 0TY Tel: (01462) 420422 Fax: (01462) 420242 E-mail: sales@kjkplastics.co.uk

K J T Plastics Ltd, Unit 4-5 Happy Valley Industrial Estate, Primrose Hill, Kings Langley, Hertfordshire, WD4 8HD Tel: (01923) 267913 Fax: (01923) 261853

K P Plastics (Bletchley) Ltd, Ward Road, Bilton Industrial Estate, Bletchley, Milton Keynes, MK1 1JA Tel: (01908) 374811 Fax: (01908) 270238 E-mail: sales@kpplastics.co.uk

Kavia Mouldings Ltd, Unit 8, Balderstone Close, Heasandford Industrial Estate, Burnley, Lancashire, BB10 2BS Tel: (01282) 423935 Fax: (01282) 426105 E-mail: kavia.mouldingsltd@virgin.net

Thomas Keating Ltd, Station Mills, Daux Road, Billingshurst, West Sussex, RH14 9SH Tel: (01403) 782045 Fax: (01403) 785464 E-mail: m.clack@terahertz.co.uk

Archibald Kenrick & Sons Ltd, Union Street, Kenrick Way, West Bromwich, West Midlands, B70 6DB Tel: 0121-553 2741 Fax: 0121-500 6332 E-mail: enquiries@kenricks.co.uk

Kent Plastics UK Ltd, Derrychara Rd, Enniskillen, County Fermanagh, BT74 6JG Tel: (028) 6632 3131 Fax: (028) 6632 7410

Kenter Plastics, Finches Yard, Eastwick Road, Bookham, Leatherhead, Surrey, KT23 4BA Tel: (01372) 456487 Fax: (01372) 450475

Kentone Plastics Ltd, Town Farm, Campton Road, Gravenhurst, Bedford, MK45 4JB Tel: (01462) 711797 Fax: (01462) 711031 E-mail: kentoneplastics@hotmail.com

Keter U.K Ltd, 12-14 Kettles Wood Drive, Birmingham, B32 3DB Tel: 0121-422 6633 Fax: 0121-422 0808 E-mail: sales@outstanding-keter.com

Kimlyn Products Ltd, 28 Armstrong Road, Tamworth, Staffordshire, B79 7TA Tel: (01827) 66933 Fax: (01827) 66323

Kingswood Tools & Mouldings, Victoria Avenue Industrial Estate, Swanage, Dorset, BH19 1BJ Tel: (01929) 425330 Fax: (01929) 424279

Knight Plastics Ltd, 1 Clydesmuir Industrial Estate, Clydesmuir Road, Cardiff, CF24 2QS Tel: (029) 2048 8129 Fax: (029) 2048 9132 E-mail: knight@kplastics.fsnet.co.uk

L H Plastics Ltd, Allenby House, Rees Way, Bradford, West Yorkshire, BD3 0DZ Tel: (01274) 736330 Fax: (01274) 736332 E-mail: sales@lhplastics.co.uk

Leaco Ltd, Lamberhead Industrial Estate, Leopold Street, Wigan, Lancashire, WN5 8DH Tel: (01942) 221188 Fax: (01942) 226682 E-mail: sales@leaco.ltd.uk

Ledwell Plastics Ltd, 33 Cannock Street, Leicester, LE4 9HR Tel: 0116-276 6221 Fax: 0116-246 0134 E-mail: sales@ledplasticsgroup.co.uk

Lee Taylor, Unit A10 Barton Industrial Estate, Faldo Road, Barton-le-Clay, Bedford, MK45 4RP Tel: (01582) 882518 Fax: (01582) 882518 E-mail: leetayloorplastics@metronet.co.uk

▶ Leicester Moulding Ltd, 10-12 Russell Square, Leicester, LE1 2DS Tel: 0116-233 0111 Fax: 0116-222 1110

Lesney Industries Ltd, Norwood House, Temple Bank, River way, Harlow, Essex, CM20 2DY Tel: (01279) 260130 Fax: (01279) 413100 E-mail:

Lettergold Plastics Ltd, 4 Hammond Close, Newmarket, Suffolk, CB8 0AZ Tel: (01638) 666888 Fax: (01638) 666999 E-mail: info@lettergold.co.uk

▶ Lifecare Hospital Supplies Ltd, Shenstone Drive, Aldridge, Walsall, WS9 8TP Tel: (01922) 455405 Fax: (01922) 749943 E-mail: rhall@hs-lifecare.com

LINPAC Allibert, Road One Industrial Estate, Winsford, Cheshire, CW7 3RA Tel: (01606) 561900 Fax: (01606) 561998 E-mail:

Linpac Materials Handling, Newfield Close, Walsall, WS2 7PB Tel: (01922) 726060 Fax: (01922) 643422 E-mail: lmhsolutions@linpac.com

Lintarealm Plastic Moulding Co. Ltd, Garth Industrial Estate, Gwaelod-y-Garth, Cardiff, CF15 9JN Tel: (029) 2081 3157 Fax: (029) 2081 1988

Linton Plastic Moulders Ltd, Unit 3, The Grip, Linton, Cambridge, CB21 4XN Tel: (01223) 892143 Fax: (01223) 894618 E-mail: info@lintonplasticmoulders.co.uk

▶ Lynco, 110a Fenlake Road, Bedford, MK42 0EU Tel: (01234) 272425 Fax: (01234) 213141 E-mail: johncuthbert@ntlworld.com

▶ indicates data change since last edition

INJECTION MOULDINGS, PLASTIC – *continued*

M C M Machine Sales Ltd, 22 Bancrofts Road, South Woodham Ferrers, Chelmsford, CM3 5UQ Tel: (01245) 322545 Fax: (01245) 329468 E-mail: mc.m@talk21.com
M G Plastics Ltd, Progress Mill, Marsh House Lane, Darwen, Lancashire, BB3 3JB Tel: (01254) 703930 Fax: (01254) 774472 E-mail: sales@mgplastics.com
M H C Industrials Ltd, Wetmore Road, Burton-On-Trent, Staffordshire, DE14 1QN Tel: (01283) 564651 Fax: (01283) 511526 E-mail: sales@mhcind.co.uk
M H Group plc, Dickinson Place, Bognor Regis, West Sussex, PO22 9QU Tel: (01243) 822963 Fax: (01243) 830398 E-mail: mhg@mh-group.co.uk
M P C Plastics Ltd, Unit 61, Enfield Industrial Estate, Redditch, Worcestershire, B97 6DE Tel: (01527) 584949 Fax: (01527) 61351
Mac Cartridges, Unit 11 Pinfold Lane, Llay Industrial Estate, Llay, Wrexham, Clwyd, LL12 0PX Tel: (01978) 853669 Fax: (01978) 853500
Malton Plastics UK Ltd, Enterprise Way, Thornton Road Industrial Estate, Pickering, North Yorkshire, YO18 7NA Tel: (01751) 477760 Fax: (01751) 477760 E-mail: sales@maltonplastics.com
Manningtree Engineering Ltd, Riverside Avenue West, Manningtree, Essex, CO11 1UN Tel: (01206) 395636 Fax: (01206) 391209 E-mail: peter.spurgeon@btconnect.com
Marlin Products Ltd, Boundary Road, Buckingham Road Industrial Estate, Brackley, Northamptonshire, NN13 7ES Tel: (01280) 705484 Fax: (01280) 700242 E-mail: marlinproducts@btconnect.com
Mason Pinder Tool Makers Ltd, Coulman Street, Thorne, Doncaster, South Yorkshire, DN8 5JS Tel: (01405) 814778 Fax: (01405) 814977
Masplas Mouldings, 8 Williams Way Industrial Estate, Industrial Estate, Wollaston, Wellingborough, Northamptonshire, NN29 7RQ Tel: (01933) 665577 Fax: (01933) 665680 E-mail: jmitchinson@btclick.com
Massmould Ltd, Cosgrove Way, Luton, LU1 1XL Tel: (01582) 728285 Fax: (01582) 723166
Matchless Mouldings, Stonebridge Mill, Stonebridge Lane, Oswaldtwistle, Accrington, Lancashire, BB5 3HX Tel: 0845 5260333 Fax: (01254) 356151 E-mail: david.rowbottom@ashleyengineering.com
G.H. Maughan Ltd, Bella Street Industrial Estate, Bolton, BL3 4DU Tel: (01204) 653516 Fax: (01204) 657362 E-mail: ghmaughan@lineone.net
Medical & Cosmetic Mouldings Ltd, Gas Road, Sittingbourne, Kent, ME10 2QD Tel: (01795) 426452 Fax: (01795) 422790 E-mail: informationmcm@aol.com
Megaplas (Peterlee) Ltd, Fiennes Road, North West Industrial Estate, Peterlee, County Durham, SR8 2QH Tel: 0191-518 5900 Fax: 0191-518 5909
Merit Plastic Mouldings Ltd, Vinces Road, Diss, Norfolk, IP22 4YE Tel: (01379) 644321 Fax: (01379) 644236 E-mail: mpm@meritplastics.co.uk
Merriott, Tail Mill Lane, Merriott, Somerset, TA16 5PG Tel: (01460) 72457 Fax: (01460) 74481 E-mail: sales@merriott.com
Metal & Plastics Products Fabrication Ltd, 2 Astley Park Estate Chaddock Lane, Astley, Tyldesley, Manchester, M29 7JY Tel: (01942) 894657 Fax: (01942) 897483 E-mail: sales@metalandplastics.co.uk
Metromold Ltd, Oak Road, West Chirton North Industrial Estate, North Shields, Tyne & Wear, NE29 8SF Tel: 0191-296 3303 Fax: 0191-296 3303 E-mail: sales@metromold.co.uk
Micro Matic Ltd, Millington House, Stancliffe St Industrial Estate, Blackburn, BB2 2QR Tel: (01254) 671231 Fax: (01254) 682229 E-mail: mmltv@micro-matic.co.uk
Milford Mouldings Ltd, Unit 36 38, Station Road Industrial Estate, Hailsham, East Sussex, BN27 2EY Tel: (01323) 440561 Fax: (01323) 449349
Mitre Plastics, Moss Way, Preston Farm Industrial Estate, Stockton-on-Tees, Cleveland, TS18 3TF Tel: (01642) 633366 Fax: (01642) 633377
Model Productions Dover Ltd, Hollow Wood Road, Dover, Kent, CT17 0UB Tel: (01304) 206784 Fax: (01304) 215067 E-mail: enquiries@modelproductions.co.uk
Modern Moulds Associates Ltd, Lightsfield, Oakley, Basingstoke, Hampshire, RG23 7BY Tel: (01256) 782333 Fax: (01256) 782915
Moldwell Products Ltd, John Street, Walsall, WS2 8AF Tel: (01922) 631252 Fax: (01922) 631225 E-mail: moldwel@aol.com
Mollertech UK Ltd, 1 Nine Mile Point Industrial Estate, Cwmfelinfach, Ynysddu, Newport, Gwent, NP11 7HZ Tel: (01495) 200044 Fax: (01495) 200055
Moorland Plastics Barnsley, Moorland Avenue, Barnsley, South Yorkshire, S70 6PQ Tel: (01226) 242753 Fax: (01226) 293401 E-mail: moorlandplastics@barnsley.gov.uk
Morris Plastics Comallo Ltd, Unit B Spring Bank Industrial Estate, Watson Mill Lane, Sowerby Bridge, West Yorkshire, HX6 3BW Tel: (01422) 831821 Fax: (01422) 834182
Moss Products Plastics Ltd, Isle of Wight Lane, Kensworth, Dunstable, Bedfordshire, LU6 2PP Tel: (01582) 873366 Fax: (01582) 873399 E-mail: sales@mossproducts.co.uk
Mouldline Ltd, The Old Granary, Station Road, Eccles, Norwich, NR16 2JG Tel: (01953) 887544 Fax: (01953) 887072 E-mail: enquiries@mouldline.com
Multikwik Ltd, 37 High Street, Totton, Southampton, SO40 9HL Tel: (023) 8066 3777 Fax: (023) 8086 9996 E-mail: sales@multikwik.com
Naiad Plastics Ltd, 16 Thorgate Road, Wick, Littlehampton, West Sussex, BN17 7LU Tel: (01903) 724302 Fax: (01903) 730925 E-mail: naiad@naiadplastics.com
Nenplas, Airfield Industrial Estate, Ashbourne, Derbyshire, DE6 1HA Tel: (01335) 347300 Fax: (01335) 340271 E-mail: enquiries@nenplas.com
Y.M. Newmark, Duchess Street Industrial Estate, Duchess Street, Shaw, Oldham, OL2 7UT Tel: (01706) 291295 Fax: (01706) 291297 E-mail: info@newmarks.co.uk
Nifco UK Ltd, Yarm Road, Stockton-on-Tees, Cleveland, TS18 3RX Tel: (01642) 672299 Fax: (01642) 611004 E-mail: sales@nifcoeu.com
Norton Plastics, The Old Gasworks, Belfield Street, Ilkeston, Derbyshire, DE7 8DU Tel: 0115-944 1245 Fax: 0115-932 8975 E-mail: norton.plastics@vigin.net
Norton Precision Mouldings, Unit 11, Crow Arch Lane Industrial Estate, Crow Arch Lane, Ringwood, Hampshire, BH24 1PD Tel: (01425) 461866 Fax: (01425) 471965 E-mail: sales@nortonmouldings.com
Norwich Plastics Ltd, Mission Road, Rackheath, Norwich, NR13 6PL Tel: (01603) 720714 Fax: (01603) 721539
Nypro (UK) Ltd, 70 Clywedog Road East, Wrexham Industrial Estate, Wrexham, Clwyd, LL13 9XE Tel: (01978) 661180 Fax: (01978) 729215 E-mail: anne.day@nypro.com
O G M Ltd, Stanton Harcourt Road, Witney, Oxfordshire, OX29 4JB Tel: (01865) 880444 Fax: (01865) 883838 E-mail: sales@ogm.uk.com
Oak Tree Plastic & Engineering Ltd, Spon La South, West Bromwich, West Midlands, B70 6AZ Tel: 0121-500 5164 Fax: 0121-500 5164
OPPM Ltd, Eagle Road, Quarry Hill Industrial Estate, Ilkeston, Derbyshire, DE7 4RB Tel: 0115-944 1236 Fax: 0115-944 0660 E-mail: sales@oppm.co.uk
Optical Products Ltd, 74-75 Brunner Road, London, E17 7NW Tel: (020) 8520 4047 Fax: (020) 8520 6593 E-mail: sales@ultrasolar.com
Origin Precision Mouldings Ltd, 19 Colvilles Place, Kelvin Industrial Estate, East Kilbride, Glasgow, G75 0PZ Tel: (01355) 244554 Fax: (01355) 245054 E-mail: admin@originprecision.com
Orion Industries Ltd, Syma House, Halifax Road, Cressex Business Park, High Wycombe, Buckinghamshire, HP12 3SN Tel: (01494) 453800 Fax: (01494) 442762 E-mail: terry@aquila-innovations.co.uk
Osprey Ltd, Unit 6-7, Mynd Industrial Estate, Church Stretton, Shropshire, SY6 6EA Tel: (01694) 723478 Fax: (01694) 724096 E-mail: sales@bec-uk.com
Osprey Ltd, Dunslow Road, Scarborough, North Yorkshire, YO11 3GS Tel: (01723) 585333 Fax: (01723) 585226 E-mail: jeff@osprey-plastics.co.uk
Otto UK Ltd, Beacon House, Reg's Way, Bardon Hill, Coalville, Leicestershire, LE67 1GH Tel: (01530) 277900 Fax: (01530) 277911 E-mail: sales@otto.co.uk
Owen Mumford Holdings Ltd, Brook Hill, Woodstock, Woodstock, Oxfordshire, OX20 1TU Tel: (01993) 812021 Fax: (01993) 813466 E-mail: steve.miles@owenmumford.co.uk
P 15 Plastics Ltd, 161 Waterside Road, Hamilton, Leicester, LE5 1TL Tel: 0116-276 1495 Fax: 0116-246 0489 E-mail: info@p15plastics.co.uk
P & D Manufacturing Ltd, Unit A11 Fiveways Industrial Estate, Westwells Road, Hawthorn, Corsham, Wiltshire, SN13 9RG Tel: (01225) 812900 Fax: (01225) 812600 E-mail: sales@pdmanufacturing.co.uk
P H I Design Ltd, Miles Lane, High Street, Long Buckby, Northampton, NN6 7RJ Tel: (01327) 842323 Fax: (01327) 843554
P J Mouldings Ltd, 423-424 Montrose Avenue, Slough, SL1 4TP Tel: (01753) 521002
P J Tooling, Hassall Road Industrial Estate, Skegness, Lincolnshire, PE25 3TB Tel: (01754) 767818 Fax: (01754) 767818
P P Injection Moulds & Moulding Ltd, Beversbrook Industrial Estate, Redman Road, Calne, Wiltshire, SN11 9PL Tel: (01249) 823100 Fax: (01249) 823103 E-mail: sales@ppmoulds.co.uk
Parksville Plastics, Unit 27-29 Crown Trading Centre, Clayton Road, Hayes, Middlesex, UB3 1DU Tel: (020) 8848 4500 Fax: (020) 8573 9596
Partridge Plastics Worthing Ltd, G H Northbrook Trading Estate, Northbrook Road, Worthing, West Sussex, BN14 8PN Tel: (01903) 213178 Fax: (01903) 204684 E-mail: sales@partridgeplastics.com
Pascoe Engineering Ltd, 127 Nitshill Road, Glasgow, G53 7TD Tel: 0141-880 6444 Fax: 0141-881 4832 E-mail: info@pascoelimited.com
Patterson & Rothwell Ltd, Mount Pleasant Street, Oldham, OL4 1HH Tel: 0161-621 5000 Fax: 0161-621 5001 E-mail: sales@patterson-rothwell.co.uk
Peak Plastics Ltd, Derwent Business Park, Heage Road, Ripley, Derbyshire, DE5 3GH Tel: (01773) 743152 Fax: (01773) 513478 E-mail: sales@peakplastics.co.uk
Penatube Ltd, Boomes Trading Estate Dovers Corner, New Road, Rainham, Essex, RM13 8QT Tel: (01708) 555595 Fax: (01708) 526276 E-mail: SAQIB21@GMAIL.COM
Penspell Ltd, 1 Bradfield Road, Finedon Road Industrial Estate, Wellingborough, Northamptonshire, NN8 4HB Tel: (01933) 443605 Fax: (01933) 271489 E-mail: penspell@btclick.com
Pioneer Associates Ltd, Ibex Barn, Ferro Fields, Brixworth, Northampton, NN6 9UA Tel: (01604) 882362 Fax: (01604) 882362 E-mail: sales@pioneer-associates-ltd.co.uk
Piper Media Products, Unit G Bastre Enterprise Park, Newtown, Powys, SY16 1DZ Tel: (01686) 610640 Fax: (01686) 610660
Plasmotec, F Lincoln Park, Ward Road, Buckingham Road Industrial Estate, Brackley, Northamptonshire, NN13 7LE Tel: (01280) 701335 Fax: (01280) 701341 E-mail: sales@plasmotec.co.uk
Plastech, 4 Ricebridge Works, Brighton Road, Bolney, Haywards Heath, West Sussex, RH17 5NA Tel: (01444) 881960 Fax: (01444) 881244
Plastech Group Ltd, Flemington Road, Glenrothes, Fife, KY7 5PZ Tel: (01592) 752212 Fax: (01592) 610315 E-mail: sales@plastechgroup.com
Plastech Precision Moulders, 31 Ivatt Way, Peterborough, PE3 7PH Tel: (01733) 266116 Fax: (01733) 266134 E-mail: sales@plastech-mld.freeserve.co.uk
Plastic Associates Ltd, Unit 1 North Street Trading Estate, Brierley Hill, West Midlands, DY5 3QF Tel: (01384) 480470 Fax: (01384) 480470
Plastic Development Techniques Ltd, Lyon Way, St. Albans, Hertfordshire, AL4 0LB Tel: (01727) 866317 Fax: (01727) 847060
Plastic Development Techniques Ltd, Unit 4, Block 2 Wednesbury Trading Estate, Darlaston Road, Wednesbury, West Midlands, WS10 7JN Tel: 0121-556 9966 Fax: 0121-556 0208 E-mail: charles@pdt-ltd.freeserve.co.uk
Plastic Engineering Ltd, Juno Drive, Leamington Spa, Warwickshire, CV31 3TA Tel: (01926) 334248 Fax: (01926) 461720 E-mail: plastic@pels.co.uk
Plastic Moulds Designs Kingston Ltd, Drake Road, Mitcham, Surrey, CR4 4HQ Tel: (020) 8640 0064 Fax: (020) 8640 0371 E-mail: terry.behing@pmdltd.com
Plastic Parts Centre, Unit 4, Harelaw Industrial Estate, Annfield Plain, Stanley, County Durham, DH9 8HN Tel: (01207) 290599 Fax: (01207) 299718 E-mail: newcastlesales@plastic-parts.co.uk
Plastic Products International Ltd, 8-11 Capital Place, Harlow, Essex, CM19 5AS Tel: (01279) 445041 Fax: (08704) 601340 E-mail: sales@plastics-products.net
Plasticum UK Ltd, 2 Bramble Way, Clover Nook Industrial Park, Somercotes, Alfreton, Derbyshire, DE55 4RH Tel: (01773) 833866 Fax: (01773) 520085
Polmeric Mouldings Ltd, 1 Spon Lane Trading Estate, Varney Avenue, West Bromwich, West Midlands, B70 6AE Tel: 0121-525 7887 Fax: 0121-500 6495 E-mail: fred.green@polmeric.co.uk
Polytech Plastic Products, Bullock Street, West Bromwich, West Midlands, B70 7HE Tel: 0121-525 7777 Fax: 0121-525 6777 E-mail: riaarnumber2@aol.com
Powell & Harber, Brickfields Road, Worcester, WR4 9WN Tel: (01905) 731717 Fax: (01905) 724787 E-mail: info@powell-harber.co.uk
Precision Engineering Plastics Ltd, Unit 4b Triumph Trading Estate, Tariff Road, London, N17 0EB Tel: (020) 8801 4226 Fax: (020) 8808 7421 E-mail: sales@pep-ltd.co.uk
Precision Machining Engineers (Harrow) Ltd, Brember Road, Harrow, Middlesex, HA2 8UN Tel: (020) 8590 5959 Fax: (020) 8422 5077 E-mail: info@cakedecoration.co.uk
▶ Prime Plastic Mouldings Ltd, 8 Heron Industrial Estate, Basingstoke Road, Spencers Wood, Reading, RG7 1PJ Tel: 0118-988 7525 Fax: 0118-988 7526 E-mail: sales@primeplas.com
Pritchard Plastics Ltd, Kings Hill Industrial Estate, Kings Hill, Bude, Cornwall, EX23 8QN Tel: (01288) 353211 Fax: (01288) 355686 E-mail: sales@pritchard-plastics.co.uk
Process Plastics, Process House, Norwich Street, Rochdale, Lancashire, OL11 1LJ Tel: (01706) 753623 Fax: (01706) 753624 E-mail: sales@processplastics.co.uk
Pro-Tec Mouldings Ltd, Unit 22 Chadkirk Industrial Estate, Vale Road, Romiley, Stockport, Cheshire, SK6 3LE Tel: 0161-427 4944 Fax: 0161-427 8373
Protomould Ltd, Unit B2 Springhead Enterprise Park, Springhead Road, Northfleet, Gravesend, Kent, DA11 8HB Tel: (01474) 353525 Fax: (01474) 353526 E-mail: sales@protomould.co.uk
Purley Plastics, 41 Haviland Road, Ferndown Industrial Estate, Wimborne, Dorset, BH21 7RY Tel: (01202) 892255 Fax: (01202) 892255
Quality Precision Mouldings Ltd, 70 Whitecraigs Road, Glenrothes, Fife, KY6 2RX Tel: (01592) 772314 Fax: (01592) 773426 E-mail: gplqpm@aol.com
Quansboro Plastics Ltd, Melford Road, Acton, Sudbury, Suffolk, CO10 0BB Tel: (01787) 377207 Fax: (01787) 311515 E-mail: quansboro@supanet.com
Quantock Plastics Ltd, Unit 2 Roughmoor, Williton Industrial Estate, Taunton, Somerset, TA4 4RF Tel: (01984) 632090 Fax: (01984) 632129 E-mail: qp@quantockplastics.fsnet.co.uk
R & A Components, Thompson Street, Padiham, Burnley, Lancashire, BB12 7BG Tel: (01282) 774397
R B Mouldings Ltd, 3 Kings Haven, Kings Road, Charfleets Industrial Estate, Canvey Island, Essex, SS8 0QW Tel: (01268) 690626 Fax: (01268) 510106 E-mail: roger@rbmouldings.fsbuisness.co.uk
R E Knight Ltd, Fishers Way, Belvedere, Kent, DA17 6BS Tel: (020) 8310 8900 Fax: (020) 8311 4530 E-mail: enquiries@reknight.co.uk
R F T Tooling Ltd, 2 Brickfields Industrial Estate, Finway Road, Hemel Hempstead, Hertfordshire, HP2 7QA Tel: (01442) 252566 Fax: (01442) 252532 E-mail: enquires@rft-tooling.com
R G E Engineering Co. Ltd, Bridge Works, The Avenue, Godmanchester, Huntingdon, Cambridgeshire, PE29 2AF Tel: (01480) 450771 Fax: (01480) 411359 E-mail: sales@rgegroup.com
R G Engineering, 54 Dunster Street, Northampton, NN1 3JY Tel: (01604) 639673 Fax: (01604) 639673 E-mail: rgengineering@btopenworld.com
R K J Precision Engineering Ltd, Park Hall Workshop, Tonypandy, Mid Glamorgan, CF40 2BQ Tel: (01443) 434967
Ravensbourn Plastics, Unit 6 7 Studio Two Waterside Court, Third Avenue, Burton-on-Trent, Staffordshire, DE14 2WQ Tel: (01283) 500525 Fax: (01283) 500535 E-mail: sales@ravensbourn.co.uk
Regency Mouldings Worcester Ltd, Hylton Road, Worcester, WR2 5JS Tel: (01905) 424909 Fax: (01905) 748310 E-mail: timco@btclick.com
Robinson Plastic, Lowmoor Road, Kirkby-in-Ashfield, Nottingham, NG17 7JU Tel: (01623) 752869 Fax: (01623) 751726 E-mail: plas@r1pp.co.uk
Rocon Plastics Ltd, Unit 9e Dukesway, Prudhoe, Northumberland, NE42 6PQ Tel: (01661) 836938 Fax: (01661) 836939 E-mail: harry@rocon.demon.co.uk
Rosti Scotland Ltd, Baird Avenue, Strutherhill Industrial Estate, Larkhall, Lanarkshire, ML9 2PJ Tel: (01698) 888186 Fax: (01698) 888389
Rugby Plastics Ltd, 11 Lanchester Way, Royal Oak Industrial Estate, Daventry, Northamptonshire, NN11 8PH Tel: (01327) 702668 Fax: (01327) 300468 E-mail: sales@rugbyplastics.com
Russell Plastics, 8a High St, Harpenden, Herts, AL5 2TB Tel: (01582) 762868 Fax: (01582) 461086 E-mail: sales@russellplastics.co.uk
S B Weston Ltd, 5 Cypress Court, Harris Way, Sunbury-on-Thames, Middlesex, TW16 7EL Tel: (01932) 785544 Fax: (01932) 761294 E-mail: sales@sbweston.com
S G H Moulds Ltd, Hypatia Street, Bolton, BL2 6AA Tel: (01204) 529374 Fax: (01204) 363356 E-mail: sgh@sghmoulds.freeserve.co.uk
S L M Model Engineers Ltd, Chiltern Road, Prestbury, Cheltenham, Gloucestershire, GL52 5JQ Tel: (01242) 525488 Fax: (01242) 226288 E-mail: mail@slm.uk.com
Selsmore (Marketing) Ltd, Unit 23 The Tanneries, Brockhampton Lane, Havant, Hampshire, PO9 1JB Tel: (023) 9249 2907 Fax: (023) 9247 3714 E-mail: selsmore@tiscali.co.uk
Serco Plastic Injection Moulders Ltd, Woden Road, Wolverhampton, WV10 0AU Tel: (01902) 351233 Fax: (01902) 351485
Sherwood Plastic Products Ltd, 25 Seavy Road, Goole, North Humberside, DN14 6TA Tel: (01405) 767338 Fax: (01405) 762222 E-mail: sherwoodplastic@btconnect.com
Showpla Plastics Ltd, Landywood Lane, Cheslyn Hay, Walsall, WS6 7AL Tel: (01922) 419203 Fax: (01922) 419225 E-mail: info@showplaplastics.co.uk
Skar Precision Mouldings Ltd, Lady Lane Industrial Estate, Hadleigh, Ipswich, IP7 6AZ Tel: (01473) 828000 Fax: (01473) 828001 E-mail: sales@skar.co.uk
Skelox Productions Ltd, Platts Common Industrial Estate, Barrowfield Road, Hoyland, Barnsley, South Yorkshire, S74 9TH Tel: (01226) 743993 Fax: (01226) 748974 E-mail: enquiries@skelox.co.uk
Skiffy, 5 Wombourne Enterprise Park, Bridgnorth Road, Wombourne, Wolverhampton, WV5 0AL Tel: (01902) 894658 Fax: (01902) 894661 E-mail: skiffyuk@btconnect.com
Sky Plastics Ltd, Eastfield Side, Sutton-in-Ashfield, Nottinghamshire, NG17 4JR Tel: (01623) 553527 Fax: (01623) 556737 E-mail: sales@skyplastics.demon.co.uk
Slatebond Ltd, Unit 27 Leafield Industrial Estate, Leafield Way, Neston, Corsham, Wiltshire, SN13 9RS Tel: (01225) 810099 Fax: (01225) 811413 E-mail: sales@slatebond.com
Sovrin Plastics Ltd, Stirling Road, Slough, SL1 4ST Tel: (01753) 825155 Fax: (01753) 654923 E-mail: sales@sovrin.com
Spar Plastics, 7 Park Trading Estate, Park Road, Hockley, Birmingham, B18 5HB Tel: 0121-551 6220 Fax: 0121-551 6220
▶ Starco DML Ltd, Marshfield Bank Employment Park, Middlewich Road, Crewe, CW2 8UY Tel: (01270) 253589 Fax: (01270) 253589 E-mail: paul@dmluk.com
Stef Plastics Ltd, Unit 5, Lakes Road, Braintree, Essex, CM7 3QS Tel: (01376) 349315 Fax: (01376) 349315

INJECTION MOULDINGS, PLASTIC – *continued*

Steroma International Ltd, 16 Metelr Close, Airport Industrial Estate, Norwich, NR6 6HG Tel: (01603) 612655 Fax: (01603) 618530 E-mail: sales@steroma.com
Straight Line Products Ltd, Unit 39 Uxbridge Trading Estate, Arundel Road, Uxbridge, Middlesex, UB8 2RP Tel: (01895) 850577 Fax: (01895) 850766 E-mail: george@straightlineproducts.co.uk
Stuma Plastics Ltd, Atlas Works, Mornington Road, Bolton, BL1 4EZ Tel: (01204) 492862 Fax: (01204) 493090 E-mail: enquiries@stuma.co.uk
Swallow Bros (Plastics) Ltd, Clay La, Slaithwaite, Huddersfield, HD7 5BG Tel: (01484) 842817 Fax: (01484) 845350
Synthotec Ltd, Sandys Road, Malvern, Worcestershire, WR14 1JJ Tel: (01684) 571900 Fax: (01684) 571909 E-mail: sales@synthotec.com
T J Mouldings, Spring Lane South, Malvern, Worcestershire, WR14 1AT Tel: (01684) 562792 Fax: (01684) 560081
T. & J. Plastics Ltd, 23 Cedar Close, Iver Heath, Iver, Buckinghamshire, SL0 0QX Tel: (01753) 652610 Fax: (01753) 652610 E-mail: tandjplast@aol.com
T.S.G Plastics Caerphilly Ltd, Pontygwindy Industrial Estate, Douglas Works, Caerphilly, Mid Glamorgan, CF83 3HU Tel: (029) 2086 8513 Fax: (029) 2088 8815 E-mail: dave.hunter@tsgplatics.co.uk
T T Audio Plastics Ltd, Unit 17, St. Margarets Way, Stukeley Meadows Industrial Estate, Huntingdon, Cambridgeshire, PE29 6EB Tel: (01480) 412345 Fax: (01480) 412533 E-mail: admin@ttap.co.uk
Talana Plastics Ltd, 28 Standard Way, Fareham, Hampshire, PO16 8XG Tel: (01329) 822940 Fax: (01329) 231034 E-mail: enquiries@talanaplastics.com
TCB-Arrow Ltd, Watchmoor House, Watchmoor Road, Camberley, Surrey, GU15 3AQ Tel: (01276) 679394 Fax: (01276) 679055 E-mail: sales@tcbarrow.co.uk
Teal Engineering, Breckland Business Park, Norwich Road, Watton, Thetford, Norfolk, IP25 6UP Tel: (01953) 885312 Fax: (01953) 883666 E-mail: info@tealengineering.co.uk
Technical Moulding Projects, Unit 5d Watlington Industrial Estate, Cuxham Road, Watlington, Oxfordshire, OX49 5LU Tel: (01491) 613539 Fax: (01491) 612096 E-mail: tmp@techmouldproj.demon.co.uk
Texecom Ltd, Slackcote Lane, Delph, Oldham, OL3 5TW Tel: (01457) 821100 Fax: (01457) 871058
TG Engineering Plastics Ltd, Britannia Mills, Stoney Battery, Huddersfield, HD1 4TL Tel: (01484) 655221 Fax: (01484) 644779 E-mail: tom.tgeng@btconnect.com
Third Axis Ltd, Unit N Oldham Central Trading Park, Coulton Close, Oldham, OL1 4EB Tel: (0161) 628 4447 Fax: (0161) 633 0833 E-mail: axiseds@compuserve.com
Toolcraft Plastics Swindon Ltd, 2 Argyle Commercial Centre, 1-5 Argyle Street, Swindon, SN2 8AR Tel: (01793) 641040 Fax: (01793) 615483 E-mail: help@toolcraft.co.uk
Tor Plastics Ltd, Unit 5 - 7, Dyehouse Lane, Glastonbury, Somerset, BA6 9LZ Tel: (01458) 832826 Fax: (01458) 834597 E-mail: chris@cpcenginerring.fsnet.co.uk
Sylvester Torpey & Sons Ltd, Birchall Street, Liverpool, L20 8PD Tel: 0151-944 1044 Fax: 0151-944 1575 E-mail: sales@torpey.co.uk
Trimfix Mouldings Ltd, 11 Leigh Road, Ramsgate, Kent, CT12 5EU Tel: (01843) 585698 Fax: (01843) 594351
Tri-Plas Mouldings Ltd, Unit 1, 3 & 7 Bilton Industrial Estate, Stockmans Close, Birmingham, B38 9TS Tel: 0121-459 0292 Fax: 0121-459 2141
Tru Group Ltd, Broad Lane, Gilberdyke, Brough, North Humberside, HU15 2TB Tel: (01430) 441528 Fax: (01430) 441904 E-mail: sales@trugroup.co.uk
United Moulders Ltd, Farnham Trading Estate, Farnham, Surrey, GU9 9NY Tel: (01420) 86616 Fax: (01252) 721250 E-mail: sales@uml.co.uk
Universal Moulding Co., 500 Ipswich Rd, Slough, SL1 4EP Tel: (01753) 570023 Fax: (01753) 535005 E-mail: andy@alltechmoulds.co.uk
V R Plastics Ltd, 1 Brookhill Road, Brookhill Industrial Estate, Pinxton, Nottingham, NG16 6NT Tel: (01773) 580505 Fax: (01773) 580496 E-mail: vrpinxton@vrscottgroup.com
Vertex Moulding Ltd, 4 Shornecliffe Industrial Estate, North Close, Folkestone, Kent, CT20 3UH Tel: (01303) 253198 Fax: (01303) 253198 E-mail: vml01@vml01.fsnet.co.uk
W G Plastics Ltd, 55 Knights Hill Square, London, SE27 0HP Tel: (020) 8761 2464 Fax: (020) 8761 2464
W H Smith & Sons Tools Ltd, Water Orton Lane, Minworth, Sutton Coldfield, West Midlands, B76 9BG Tel: 0121-748 7777 Fax: 0121-749 6213 E-mail: info@whs-tools.com
Wessex Tool Co.Ltd, Wessex House, Devizes, Wiltshire, SN10 1PS Tel: (01380) 723423 Fax: (01380) 720100
West Midland Mouldings Ltd, Unit 2 West Coppice Road, Walsall, WS8 7HB Tel: (01543) 378100 Fax: (01543) 378100
Wheatley Plastics Ltd, Reynolds Mill, Newbridge Lane, Stockport, Cheshire, SK1 2NR Tel: 0161-477 2800 Fax: 0161-480 6611 E-mail: wheatley.plastics@btconnect.com
Witan Pressings Ltd, Unit 3, Alexander Mill, Gibb Street, Long Eaton, Nottingham, NG10 1EE Tel: 0115-946 1545 Fax: 0115-946 0874 E-mail: witan-pressings@btconnect.com
Wright Plastics Ltd, Fernie Road, Market Harborough, Leicestershire, LE16 7PH Tel: (01858) 465661 Fax: (01858) 431831 E-mail: sales@wplastic.co.uk
Wyke Plastics Plastic Moulders, Bradford Road, Brighouse, West Yorkshire, HD6 4BW Tel: (01484) 710414 Fax: (01484) 711649
Wyvern Mouldings Ltd, Unit 6 Britannia Business Park, Britannia Way Enigma Bus Park, Malvern, Worcestershire, WR14 1GZ Tel: (01684) 564563 Fax: (01684) 560862 E-mail: info@wyvernmouldings.co.uk

INJECTION/COMPRESSION MOULDERS, PLASTIC TRADE

Avalon Plastics Ltd, Imco Works, Beckery New Road, Glastonbury, Somerset, BA6 9NR Tel: (01458) 831563 Fax: (01458) 834384 E-mail: enquiries@avalonplastics.co.uk
Charlesworth & Son Ltd, Wishaw Lane, Curdworth, Sutton Coldfield, West Midlands, B76 9EL Tel: (01675) 470382 E-mail: sales@charlesworth-son.co.uk
Chess Plastics Ltd, 2 George Baylis Road, Berry Hill Industrial Estate, Droitwich, Worcestershire, WR9 9RB Tel: (01905) 794405 Fax: (01905) 794495 E-mail: genmail@chessplastics.co.uk
Fairgrieve Mouldings Ltd, 15 Sedling Road, Wear Industrial Estate, Washington, Tyne & Wear, NE38 9BZ Tel: 0191-415 9292 Fax: 0191-415 9696 E-mail: lindabiggins@fairgrieve87.freeserve.co.uk
Merit Plastic Mouldings Ltd, Vinces Road, Diss, Norfolk, IP22 4YE Tel: (01379) 644321 Fax: (01379) 644236 E-mail: mpm@meritplastics.co.uk
Millpac Ltd, Basepoint Business Centre, Marsh Way, Rainham, Essex, RM13 8EU Tel: (020) 8965 9204 Fax: (020) 8965 3826 E-mail: info@millpac.co.uk
Plasian Products, Alkincote Street, Unit 5, Keighley, West Yorkshire, BD21 5JT Tel: (01535) 681975 Fax: (01535) 611471
Target Plastics Ltd, 138-140 Nathan Way, London, SE28 0AU Tel: (020) 8312 9090 Fax: (020) 8312 9191 E-mail: admin@targetplastics.co.uk

INK FILTERS

Fullbrook Systems Ltd, Unit 4 Bourne End Mills, Hemel Hempstead, Hertfordshire, HP1 2UJ Tel: (01442) 876777 Fax: (01442) 877144 E-mail: sales@fullbrook.com

INK JET PRINTING MACHINE CARTRIDGES

A1 Paper P.L.C., Roebuck Street, West Bromwich, West Midlands, B70 6RB Tel: 0121-553 7131 Fax: 0121-553 5040 E-mail: sales@a1paper.co.uk
Cartridge Concept, 5 Grampian Road, Elgin, Morayshire, IV30 1XN Tel: (01343) 544828 Fax: (01343) 544313 E-mail: alan@cartcon.co.uk
Cartridges UK, Corunna House, 42-44 Ousegate, Selby, North Yorkshire, YO8 4NH Tel: (01757) 212747 Fax: (01757) 212321 E-mail: nikki@cartridgesuk.com
Chiltern Colour Services, Unit 23 Titan Court, Laporte Way, Luton, LU4 8EF Tel: (01525) 385184 Fax: (01582) 482888
Computer Chaos, 1 Brookfield Dirve, Cannock, Staffordshire, WS11 0JN Tel: (01543) 578579 Fax: (01543) 571218
Diskovery Systems, 123 Bournemouth Road, Poole, Dorset, BH14 9HR Tel: (01202) 746353 Fax: (01202) 737184 E-mail: sales@diskovery.co.uk
Ergo Computer Accessories Ltd, 5 Pipers Industrial Estate, Pipers Lane, Thatcham, Berkshire, RG19 4NA Tel: (01635) 877979 Fax: (01635) 877676 E-mail: sales@ergo-consumables.co.uk
▶ Fastek Graphic Services Ltd, 3a Sheepscar St South, Leeds, LS7 1AD Tel: 0113-243 9808 Fax: 0113-246 9406 E-mail: sales@fastek.co.uk
Ink 4 U Ltd, Unit 11, Sharp St, Dewsbury, West Yorkshire, WF13 1QZ Tel: (01924) 455556 Fax: (01924) 458060 E-mail: nancybell@ink4u.co.uk
Ink Cycle Ltd, Drinsey Nook, Gainsborough Road, Saxilby, Lincoln, LN1 2JJ Tel: (01522) 704555 Fax: (01522) 704128 E-mail: sales@inkcycle.co.uk
Inkjet Direct, Stow Mill, Stow, Galashiels, Selkirkshire, TD1 2RB Tel: (01578) 730477 Fax: (01578) 730387 E-mail: sales@proprint.co.uk
Laser Services Cartridge Master, 2 Woodview Business Centre, Lockwood Close, Nottingham, NG5 9JN Tel: 0115-967 3445 Fax: 0115-967 3899 E-mail: sales@laserservices.co.uk
M, M & M Ltd, 102 Seymour Place, London, W1H 1NF Tel: (020) 7724 5117 Fax: (020) 7724 5087 E-mail: mmm@mmmltd.com
Mikrojet (UK), Unit 1 Leflaive Business Centre, Church Lane, Naphill, High Wycombe, Buckinghamshire, HP14 4US Tel: (01494) 565610 Fax: (01494) 565612 E-mail: info@mikrojet.co.uk
Red Shark Technologies, Unit 12a, North Road Industrial Estate, Berwick-upon-Tweed, TD15 1UN Tel: (01289) 303303 Fax: (01289) 302333 E-mail: sales@bigredshark.net

INK JET PRINTING MACHINES

Applied Technology Development, Unit K1 Valley Way, Market Harborough, Leicestershire, LE16 7PS Tel: (01858) 461014 Fax: (01858) 461015 E-mail: mail@atduk.com
Coding & Handling, 52 Meeting Lane, Burton Latimer, Kettering, Northamptonshire, NN15 5LS Tel: (01536) 721026 Fax: (01536) 725056 E-mail: inkjets@codinghandling.co.uk
▶ Fastek Graphic Services Ltd, 3a Sheepscar St South, Leeds, LS7 1AD Tel: 0113-243 9808 Fax: 0113-246 9406 E-mail: sales@fastek.co.uk
▶ Lawtons Group Ltd, 60 Vauxhall Road, Liverpool, L3 6DL Tel: 0151-479 3000 Fax: 0151-479 3001 E-mail: info@lawtonsgroup.co.uk
Martek, Unit 12b, Ridings Park, Eastern Way, Cannock, Staffordshire, WS11 7FJ Tel: (01543) 502202 Fax: (01543) 467726 E-mail: info@martekonline.co.uk

INK JET PRINTING MACHINES, INDUSTRIAL

Atlantic Zeiser Ltd, 53 Central Way, Andover, Hampshire, SP10 5AN Tel: (01264) 324222 Fax: (01264) 324333 E-mail: sales@atlanticzeiseruk.com
Coding & Handling, 52 Meeting Lane, Burton Latimer, Kettering, Northamptonshire, NN15 5LS Tel: (01536) 721026 Fax: (01536) 725056 E-mail: inkjets@codinghandling.co.uk
Keymax International Ltd, West Road, Templefields, Harlow, Essex, CM20 2AL Tel: (01279) 454455 Fax: (01279) 445550 E-mail: ttrsales@keymax.co.uk

INK JET PRINTING MATERIALS, DIGITAL MEDIA

A P A UK Ltd, Unit 10 Capital Industrial Estate, Crabtree Manorway South, Belvedere, Kent, DA17 6BJ Tel: (020) 8311 4400 Fax: (020) 8312 4777 E-mail: apauk@apaspa.com
Macdermot Autotype Ltd, Grove Road, Wantage, Oxfordshire, OX12 7BZ Tel: (01235) 771111 Fax: (01235) 771196 E-mail: feedback@autotype.com
Ritrama UK Ltd, Lynwell Road, Lyntown Trading Estate, Eccles, Manchester, M30 9QG Tel: 0161-786 1700 Fax: 0161-786 1701 E-mail: info@ritrama.co.uk

INK JET PRINTING SERVICES

Coding & Handling, 52 Meeting Lane, Burton Latimer, Kettering, Northamptonshire, NN15 5LS Tel: (01536) 721026 Fax: (01536) 725056 E-mail: inkjets@codinghandling.co.uk
Laser Lifeline UK Ltd, 2 Cavendish Enterprise Centre, Brassey Street, Birkenhead, Merseyside, CH41 8BY Tel: 0151-651 2037 Fax: 0151-651 2037

INK JET PRINTING SYSTEMS, LARGE CHARACTERS, CARTON CODING

Alpha Dot Ltd, 6 Hollom Down Road, Lopcombe, Salisbury, SP5 1BP Tel: (01264) 781989 Fax: (01264) 782017 E-mail: info@alphadot.co.uk
Applied Technology Development, Unit K1 Valley Way, Market Harborough, Leicestershire, LE16 7PS Tel: (01858) 461014 Fax: (01858) 461015 E-mail: mail@atduk.com

INK PUMPS

Lincoln Industrial Ltd, Unit 2 Canada Close, Banbury, Oxfordshire, OX16 2RT Tel: (01295) 256611 Fax: (01295) 275771 E-mail: sales@lincolnindustrial.co.uk

INK TOLL

Dispersion Technology Ltd, Factory Lane, Brantham, Manningtree, Essex, CO11 1NJ Tel: (01206) 395000 Fax: (01206) 392872 E-mail: christine@dispersion-technology.co.uk

INKED RIBBONS

K M P Crusader Manufacturing Co. Ltd, Oldmedow Road, King's Lynn, Norfolk, PE30 4LD Tel: (01553) 817200 Fax: (01553) 691909 E-mail: sales@kmp-uk.co.uk
Typerite Ltd, Upper Dromore Road, Warrenpoint, Newry, County Down, BT34 3PN Tel: (028) 4177 2111 Fax: (028) 4175 2022 E-mail: info@typerite.com

INKJET CARTRIDGES, REFILLABLE

Laser Lifeline UK Ltd, 2 Cavendish Enterprise Centre, Brassey Street, Birkenhead, Merseyside, CH41 8BY Tel: 0151-651 2037 Fax: 0151-651 2037

INKJET PRINTING MACHINE ORIGINAL EQUIPMENT MANUFACTURERS (OEM) CARTRIDGES

▶ Disccity Ltd, Unit 12, Westbrook Road, Westbrook Trading Estate, Trafford Park, Manchester, M17 1AY Tel: 0870 166 0757 Fax: 0870 166 0759 E-mail: enqs@disccity.co.uk
▶ Inkinkink Net, The Gospel Hall, Amanwy, Llanelli, Dyfed, SA14 9AH Tel: (0845) 2261941 Fax: (07092) 031765 E-mail: admin@inkinkink.net
▶ Net One Media Ltd, Newton Cap House, Bishop Auckland, County Durham, DL14 7SB Tel: (0870) 7668585 Fax: (0870) 7668595 E-mail: sales@365ink.co.uk
Print Partnership, Unit 11 Pacific Business Park, Pacific Road, Cardiff, CF24 5HJ Tel: (029) 2047 4010 Fax: (029) 2047 4011 E-mail: repro@printpartnership.co.uk

INKJET PRINTING MACHINES, LARGE FORMAT

▶ G5 Graphics Ltd, St Luke's Place, Unit 6, Glasgow, G5 0TS Tel: 0141-429 4240 Fax: 0141-429 4241 E-mail: info@g5graphics.com
▶ Graphics Store, Clough Mill, Bradford Road, Gomersal, West Yorkshire, BD19 4AZ Tel: (01274) 862051 Fax: (01274) 851173 E-mail: info@graphics-store.co.uk
▶ Inkjec, Inkjec House, Deepdale Mill Street, Preston, PR1 5BY Tel: (01772) 794300 Fax: (01772) 252215 E-mail: info@inkjec.com
▶ London Graphic Centre, 16-18 Shelton Street, London, WC2H 9JL Tel: (020) 7759 4500 Fax: (020) 7759 4585 E-mail: matt@londongraphicsystems.co.uk

INKJET PRINTING SYSTEMS, CONTINUOUS

▶ Printcartridge Direct.Com Ltd, Heinzel Park, Aber Park Aber Road, Flint, Clwyd, CH6 5EX Tel: (01352) 735100 Fax: (01352) 735500 E-mail: office@printcartridgedirect.com

INKS, SOLID STENCIL/PACKAGE MARKING

Pyramid Engineering & Manufacturing Co. Ltd, 8 Palace Road, East Molesey, Surrey, KT8 9DL Tel: (020) 8979 4814 Fax: (020) 8979 4814
Rollers' Inks & Marking Ltd, PO Box 69, Hull, HU2 8HS Tel: (01482) 218172 Fax: (01482) 214999 E-mail: info@markcbrown.co.uk

INLAND REVENUE IR35 LEGISLATION CONSULTANCY

Alternet, 5 Cardiff Road, Luton, LU1 1PP Tel: (0870) 6009968 Fax: (0870) 6009969 E-mail: jimrudd@alternetuk.com
▶ Osborne Sheen LLP, 73 Celandine Avenue,, Locks Heath, Southampton, SO31 6WZ Tel: 07740 901848

INORGANIC PIGMENTS

Rakem Ltd, Wellington Street, Bury, Lancashire, BL8 2BD Tel: 0161-762 0044 Fax: 0161-762 0033 E-mail: info@rakem.co.uk

INSECT EXTERMINATION PEST CONTROL MATERIALS

▶ Pestcontrolpro .Co.Uk, 37 Lyndon Road, Bramham, Wetherby, West Yorkshire, LS23 6RH Tel: (07725) 317112

INSECT SCREENS

All Guard, 2 Glan Yr Afon, Berriew, Welshpool, Powys, SY21 8PN Tel: (01686) 640235 Fax: (01686) 640693 E-mail: creaven@freenet.co.uk
B D X Insect Screen Sales, The Onsite Building, Stephenson Way, Crawley, West Sussex, RH10 1TN Tel: (01293) 744426
London & Lancashire Rubber Company Ltd, Unit 15 Decimus Park, Kingstanding Way, Royal Tunbridge Wells, Tunbridge Wells, Kent, TN2 3GP Tel: (01892) 515919 Fax: (01892) 615353 E-mail: sales@londonandlancs.com
Manor Supplies Incorporating Manor Blinds, The Old Forge, Hall Lane, Upminster, Essex, RM14 1TT Tel: (01708) 377518 Fax: (01708) 343003
Oecos Agricultural Services, 11 High Street, Kimpton, Hitchin, Hertfordshire, SG4 8RA Tel: (01438) 832481 Fax: (01438) 832157 E-mail: sales@oecos.co.uk
Safety Screens Ltd, Unit 11a, 11b Greenfield Farm Industrial Estate, Congleton, Cheshire, CW12 4TR Tel: (01260) 295999 Fax: (01260) 295998 E-mail: sales@safetyscreens.co.uk
▶ Windowscreens UK, PO Box 181, Upminster, Essex, RM14 1GX Tel: (01708) 222273 Fax: (01708) 641898 E-mail: info@flyscreensuk.co.uk
Woodland Flyscreen & Bird Exclusion Products, 73a Kennel Ride, Ascot, Berkshire, SL5 7NU Tel: (01344) 886459 Fax: (01344) 886459

INSECTICIDAL FOG APPLICATORS

Barrettine (Industrial) Ltd, St. Ivel Way, Bristol, BS30 8TY Tel: 0117-960 0060 Fax: 0117-935 2437 E-mail: sales@barrettine.co.uk

INSECTICIDE SPRAYERS

Barrettine (Industrial) Ltd, St. Ivel Way, Bristol, BS30 8TY Tel: 0117-960 0060 Fax: 0117-935 2437 E-mail: sales@barrettine.co.uk
Micron Sprayers Ltd, Bromyard Industrial Estate, Bromyard, Herefordshire, HR7 4HS Tel: (01885) 482397 Fax: (01885) 483043 E-mail: micron@micron.co.uk

INSECTICIDES

A M I UK Ltd, Lexus House, Rosslyn Crescent, Harrow, Middlesex, HA1 2RZ Tel: (020) 8863 6868 Fax: (020) 8426 0872 E-mail: harshad@ukaerosols.com
Agropharm Ltd, Buckingham House, Church Road, Penn, High Wycombe, Buckinghamshire, HP10 8LN Tel: (01494) 816575 Fax: (01494) 816578 E-mail: sales@agropharm.co.uk
Barrettine (Industrial) Ltd, St. Ivel Way, Bristol, BS30 8TY Tel: 0117-960 0060 Fax: 0117-935 2437 E-mail: sales@barrettine.co.uk
Bayer, 230 Science Park, Milton Road, Cambridge, CB4 0WB Tel: (01223) 226500 Fax: (01223) 426240
Certis, The Crown Business Park, Old Dalby, Melton Mowbray, Leicestershire, LE14 3NQ Tel: (01664) 820052 Fax: (01664) 820216 E-mail: enquiry@luxan.co.uk
Dalgety Arable Ltd, Throws Farm, Stebbing, Dunmow, Essex, CM6 3AQ Tel: (01371) 856431 Fax: (01371) 856616 E-mail: throws.farm@dalgety.co.uk
Dow Agro Sciences Ltd, Latchmore Court, Brand Sreet, Hitchin, Hertfordshire, SG5 1NH Tel: (01462) 457272 Fax: (01462) 426605 E-mail: dowagrosciencesuk@dow.com
Dow Mirfield, Steanard Lane, Mirfield, West Yorkshire, WF14 8HZ Tel: (01924) 493861 Fax: (01924) 490972 E-mail: enquiries@dow.com
DuPont Animal Health Solutions, Windham Road, Chilton Industrial Estate, Sudbury, Suffolk, CO10 2XD Tel: (01787) 377305 Fax: (01787) 310846 E-mail: biosecurity@gbr.dupont.com
Johnsons Veterinary Products Ltd, 5 Reddicap Trading Estate, Sutton Coldfield, West Midlands, B75 7DF Tel: 0121-378 1684 Fax: 0121-311 1758 E-mail: info@johnsons-vet.com
Sorex Ltd, Oldgate, Widnes, Cheshire, WA8 8TJ Tel: 0151-424 4328 Fax: 0151-495 1163 E-mail: enquiries@sorex.com

INSERT NUTS

Poly Fasteners Ltd, 11-12 Rabans Close, Rabans Lane Industrial Area, Aylesbury, Buckinghamshire, HP19 8TP Tel: (01296) 333500 Fax: (01296) 333509 E-mail: sales@polyfasteners.co.uk

INSERTION MACHINES

Unique Design Systemation, Manor Farm, Pickstock, Shifnal, Shropshire, TF10 8AH Tel: (01952) 550037 Fax: (01952) 551183 E-mail: bob@unique-design.co.uk

INSERTION MACHINES FOR THREADED INSERTS

Kerb Konus, Unit B5 Hortonwood 10, Telford, Shropshire, TF1 7ES Tel: (01952) 677388 Fax: (01952) 677488E-mail: kkuk@pipex.com

INSERTS FOR PLASTIC

Davart Fasteners, Unit 10 Honeybourne Airfield Trading Estate, Honeybourne, Evesham, Worcestershire, WR11 7QF Tel: (01386) 833784 Fax: (01386) 833002 E-mail: sales@davart.co.uk

INSOLVENCY PRACTITIONERS

Brindley Twist Tafft & James, Lowick Gate Coventry Trading Estate, Siskin Drive, Middlemarch Business Park, Coventry, CV3 4FJ Tel: (024) 7653 1532 Fax: (024) 7630 1300 E-mail: admin@bttj.com
Carrick Read Ltd, Norwich House, Savile Street, Hull, HU1 3ES Tel: (01482) 585795 Fax: (01482) 585798 E-mail: thepartners@cri-hull.co.uk
Cornfield Law LLP, 47 Cornfield Road, Eastbourne, East Sussex, BN21 4QN Tel: (01323) 412512 Fax: (01323) 411611
Geoghegan & Co, 6 St Colme Street, Edinburgh, EH3 6AD Tel: 0131-225 4681 Fax: 0131-220 1132 E-mail: mail@geoghegans.co.uk
Hawkins Russell Jones, 7-8 Portmill Lane, Hitchin, Hertfordshire, SG5 1AS Tel: (01462) 628888 Fax: (01462) 631233 E-mail: hitchin@hrjlaw.co.uk
Kenneth Elliott & Rowe Solicitors, 162 South Street, Romford, RM1 1RA Tel: (01708) 757575 Fax: (01708) 766674 E-mail: sales@ker.co.uk
KPMG UK Ltd, Peat House, 1 Waterloo Way, Leicester, LE1 6LP Tel: 0116-256 6000 Fax: 0116-256 6050
L P L Commercial Investigations, 890-900 Eastern Avenue, Ilford, Essex, IG2 7HH Tel: (020) 8597 2229 Fax: (020) 8597 1180 E-mail: info@lplgroup.com
Marten Walsh Cherer Ltd, Midway House, 27-29 Cursitor Street, London, EC4A 1LT Tel: (020) 7405 5010 Fax: (020) 7405 5026 E-mail: martinwc@aol.com
Martineau Johnson, St.Philips House, St. Phillips Place, Birmingham, B3 2PP Tel: 0121-200 3300 Fax: 0121-200 3300 E-mail: marketing@martjohn.com
Milsted Langdon Ltd, Winchester House, Deane Gate Avenue, Taunton, Somerset, TA1 2UH Tel: (01823) 445566 Fax: (01823) 445555 E-mail: simonlmilsted@milsted-langdon.co.uk
Rushtons, Ashley Lane, Shipley, West Yorkshire, BD17 7DB Tel: (01282) 429977 Fax: (01274) 599474 E-mail: rushtonsinfo@btinternet.com
Tenon, Salisbury House, 31 Finsbury Circus, London, EC2M 5SQ Tel: (020) 7628 2040 Fax: (020) 7638 0217 E-mail: info@tenongroup.com
▶ Turnkey Computer Technology Ltd, Thornton Lodge, East Kilbride Road, Clarkston, Glasgow, G76 9HW Tel: 0141-644 5444 Fax: 0141-644 5446
Turpin Barker Armstrong, 1 Westmead Road, Sutton, Surrey, SM1 4LA Tel: (020) 8661 7878 Fax: (020) 8661 0598 E-mail: tba@turpinba.co.uk

INSPECTION CERTIFICATION ENGINEERS

British Inspecting Engineers Ltd, Chatsworth Technology Park, Dunston Road, Chesterfield, Derbyshire, S41 8XA Tel: (01246) 260260 Fax: (01246) 260919E-mail: info@bieltd.co.uk
▶ Cotecna International Ltd, Hounslow Centre, Lampton Road, Hounslow, TW3 1JB Tel: (020) 8277 7700 Fax: (020) 8277 7809 E-mail: info@cotecna.co.uk
▶ Guthrie & Craig, Prospect Business Park, Crookhall Lane, Leadgate, Consett, County Durham, DH8 7PW Tel: (01207) 580033 Fax: (01207) 581903 E-mail: guthriecraigrjc@msn.com
H S B Inspection Quality Ltd, Cairo Mill, Greenacres Road, Oldham, OL4 3JA Tel: (01928) 579595 Fax: 0161-621 5680 E-mail: sales@hsbiq.com
▶ Intertek Caleb Brett, Caleb Brett House, 734 London Road, West Thurrock, Grays, Essex, RM20 3NL Tel: (01708) 680200 Fax: (01708) 680264 E-mail: uklaboratory@intertek.com
Lloyds Register, 71 Fenchurch Street, London, EC3M 4BS Tel: (020) 7709 9166 Fax: (020) 7488 4796 E-mail: lloydsreg@lr.org
Olympia Testing Holdings Ltd, Oldbush Street, Off Level Street, Brierley Hill, West Midlands, DY5 1UB Tel: (01384) 573164 Fax: (01384) 265832
Quality Control Metrology Services Ltd, Unit 10 Holly Park Industrial Estate, Spitfire Road, Birmingham, B24 9PB Tel: 0121-377 8989 Fax: 0121-377 8976 E-mail: qcms@qcms.fsnet.co.uk
R & H Testing Services Ltd, Cannel Road, Burntwood Business Park, Burntwood, Staffordshire, WS7 3FU Tel: (01543) 677400 Fax: (01543) 677477 E-mail: sales@randhtesting.com
Sandberg LLP, 40 Grosvenor Gardens, London, SW1W 0EB Tel: (020) 7730 3461 Fax: (020) 7565 7100 E-mail: ho@sandberg.co.uk
Servtech Ltd, 2 Abbotswell Road, West Tullos, Aberdeen, AB12 3AB Tel: (01224) 878322 Fax: (01224) 895080 E-mail: info@servtech.co.uk
SGS UK Ltd, S G S House, Johns Lane, Tividale, Oldbury, West Midlands, B69 3HX Tel: 0121-520 6454 Fax: 0121-522 4116 E-mail: admin@sgsuk.com
Tuv UK Quality Assurance Ltd, Surrey House, Surrey Street, Croydon, CR9 1XZ Tel: (020) 8686 3400 Fax: (020) 8680 4035 E-mail: london@tuv-uk.com

INSPECTION CONSULTANTS

Oceaneering International Services Ltd, Sledgegate Farm, Sledgegate Lane, Lea, Matlock, Derbyshire, DE4 5GL Tel: (01629) 534164 Fax: (01629) 534172

INSPECTION EQUIPMENT, *See also headings for particular types*

A D I Supplies & Services, Block 2, Rosendale Way, Blantyre, Glasgow, G72 0NJ Tel: (01698) 829991 Fax: (01698) 829992 E-mail: sales@adi-supplies.co.uk
Chelmsford Precision Services, 29 The Westerings, Great Baddow, Chelmsford, CM3 3UY Tel: (01245) 474901
▶ Cotecna International Ltd, Hounslow Centre, Lampton Road, Hounslow, TW3 1JB Tel: (020) 8277 7700 Fax: (020) 8277 7809 E-mail: info@cotecna.co.uk
Heuft, Unit 24 26 Innage Park, Abeles Way, Holly Lane Industrial Estate, Atherstone, Warwickshire, CV9 2QX Tel: (01827) 717002 Fax: (01827) 716146 E-mail: dominic.metcalfe@heuft.com
M K Services Ltd, Unit 24 Pages Industrial Park, Eden Way, Leighton Buzzard, Bedfordshire, LU7 4TZ Tel: (01525) 382333 Fax: (01525) 850073 E-mail: sales@mkservices.co.uk
▶ NDT Eagle, Kirkhill Place, Kirkhill Industrial Estate, Dyce, Aberdeen, AB21 0GU Tel: (01224) 722966 Fax: (01224) 773657 E-mail: sales@ndteagle.co.uk
Panasonic Electric Works UK Ltd, Sunrise Parkway, Linford Wood, Milton Keynes, MK14 6LF Tel: (01908) 231555 Fax: (01908) 231599 E-mail: info-uk@eu.pewg.panasonic.com
Veeco Instruments Ltd, Nanotech House Buckingway Business Park, Anderson Road, Swavesey, Cambridge, CB24 4UQ Tel: (01954) 233900 Fax: (01954) 231300 E-mail: info@veeco.co.uk

INSPECTION EQUIPMENT, ALTERNATING CURRENT POTENTIAL DROP (ACPD)/ ALTERNATING CURRENT FIELD MEASUREMENT (ACFM)

Technical Software Consultants Ltd, 6 Mill Square, Featherstone Road, Wolverton Mill, Milton Keynes, MK12 5RB Tel: (01908) 317444 Fax: (01908) 220959 E-mail: info@tscinspectionsystems.com

INSPECTION EQUIPMENT, AUTOMATIC

▶ Alpha Gauging Ltd, 11 Hoo Road, Meppershall, Shefford, Bedfordshire, SG17 5LP Tel: (01462) 819435 Fax: (01462) 812849 E-mail: sales@alphagauging.com

INSPECTION EQUIPMENT, OPTICAL

▶ M V P UK, Castle Court, Carnegie Campus, Castle Drive, Dunfermline, Fife, KY11 8PB Tel: (01383) 629960 Fax: (01383) 629979

INSPECTION EQUIPMENT, SUBSEA/UNDERWATER

A S A M S Ltd, Marine Building Owen Road, Harfreys Industrial Estate, Great Yarmouth, Norfolk, NR31 0NA Tel: (01493) 653535 Fax: (01493) 653254 E-mail: sales@asams.co.uk
Kongsberg Simrad, Campus 1 Balgownie Road, Aberdeen Science & Technology Park, Bridge of Don, Aberdeen, AB22 8GT Tel: (01224) 226500 Fax: (01224) 226501
SMD Hydrovision Ltd, Davy Banks, Wallsend, Tyne & Wear, NE28 6UZ Tel: +44 (0) 1224 772150 Fax: +44 (0) 1224 772166 E-mail: smd@smdhydrovision.com

INSPECTION SERVICES, ELECTRICAL/MECHANICAL

D & W Electrics West Bromwich, 29 Colshaw Road, Stourbridge, West Midlands, DY8 3AS Tel: (01384) 378289 Fax: (01384) 378289 E-mail: dw-electrics@blueyonder.co.uk
Fielding Engineering UK Ltd, 2 Lancaster Way, Earls Colne Industrial Park, Earls Colne, Colchester, CO6 2NS Tel: (01787) 224844 Fax: (01787) 224344 E-mail: jfield@fieldingltd.co.uk
Instaspect Ltd, 18 Miller Road, Ayr, KA7 2AY Tel: (01292) 289146 Fax: (01292) 610554 E-mail: eng@instaspect.co.uk
Systems Audits Inspections Ltd, 51 Delph New Road, Delph, Oldham, OL3 5BY Tel: (01457) 870946 Fax: (01457) 870946 E-mail: philiptaylor@sai-online.co.uk

INSPECTION SERVICES, VISUAL, CLOSED CIRCUIT TELEVISION (CCTV), INACCESSIBLE INTERIOR

B H P Alarms, Unit B3, Balliniska Business Park, Springtime Industrial Estate, Londonderry, BT48 0LY Tel: (028) 7126 2757 Fax: (028) 7137 2225 E-mail: info@bhpalarms.com
▶ Essex Security Services Ltd, 154 Church Hill, Loughton, Essex, IG10 1LJ Tel: (020) 8502 1360 Fax: (020) 8502 2700 E-mail: all@essexsecurity.co.uk
Holman Security Systems, 1 Mill View, Hinckley, Leicestershire, LE10 0HE Tel: (01455) 251025 Fax: (01455) 890059
Standfast Security Systems Ltd, 120 Coldharbour Road, Redland, Bristol, BS6 7SL Tel: 0117-942 3366 Fax: 0117-944 6241 E-mail: sales@standfast.co.uk

INSPECTION (VISION SYSTEMS) EQUIPMENT MANUFRS

Astro Technologies Ltd, 26 Brunel Way, Segansworth East, Fareham, Hampshire, PO15 5SD Tel: (01489) 555300 Fax: (01489) 555302 E-mail: sales@astrotec.co.uk
Cognex UK, Sunningdale House, Caldecotte Lake Drive, Caldecotte, Milton Keynes, MK7 8LF Tel: (0800) 0180018 Fax: (01908) 392463 E-mail: sales@cognex.co.uk
Moritex Europe Ltd, 14 Signet Court, Swann Road, Cambridge, CB5 8LA Tel: (01223) 301148 Fax: (01223) 301149 E-mail: moritex.europe@dial.pipex.com

INSTANT RICE

Eden Valley Wholefoods, 34 The Market, Scotch Street, Carlisle, CA3 8QX Tel: (01228) 546853

INSTANTANEOUS WATER HEATERS

Acv UK Ltd, St. Davids Drive, St. Davids Business Park, Dalgety Bay, Dunfermline, Fife, KY11 9PF Tel: (01383) 820100 Fax: (01383) 820180 E-mail: information@acv-uk.com
Morco Products Ltd, Morco House, 59 Beverley Road, Hull, HU3 1XW Tel: (01482) 325456 Fax: (01482) 212869

INSTRUMENT AIR DRYERS

▶ Global Drying Systems Ltd, Parkhall Road, Longton, Stoke-on-Trent, ST3 5AT Tel: (01782) 370200 Fax: (01782) 370222 E-mail: neilbeckett@cobwebworld.co.uk

INSTRUMENT AND CONTROL MECHANISM GEARS

Reliance Precision Mechatronics LLP, Rowley Mills, Penistone Road, Lepton, Huddersfield, HD8 0LE Tel: (01484) 601000 Fax: (01484) 601001 E-mail: sales@reliance.co.uk

INSTRUMENT ASSEMBLY SERVICES

North Downs Instrument Co. Ltd, Ashleigh, Wrotham Road, Meopham, Gravesend, Kent, DA13 0QB Tel: (01474) 812406 Fax: (01474) 814265 E-mail: sales@mjwilsongroup.com
Valley Instruments, Churchfield Court, 14 Bewcastle Road, Nottingham, NG5 9PJ Tel: 0115-967 0025 Fax: 0115-967 0025 E-mail: valley.ins@fsbdial.co.uk

▶ indicates data change since last edition

INSTRUMENT CASES

Antler Ltd, Pilot Works, Alfred Street, Bury, Lancashire, BL9 9EF Tel: 0161-764 0721 Fax: 0161-764 0723 E-mail: custserv@antler.co.uk
Arbour Engineering Ltd, Unit 23, West Station Yard Industrial Estate, Spital Road, Maldon, Essex, CM9 6TS Tel: (01621) 857320 Fax: (01621) 874609
B G W Woodcraft Ltd, 1 Retreat Pl, London, E9 6RH Tel: (020) 8533 9885
Barrowfield Leather Co. Ltd, 47 Solway Street, Glasgow, G40 4JG Tel: 0141-554 7863 Fax: 0141-554 8053 E-mail: office@barrowfield.com
Beyond Engineering Ltd, Bidewell Close, Drayton High Road, Norwich, NR8 6AP Tel: (01603) 868423 Fax: (01603) 261712 E-mail: sales@claydale.co.uk
A.C. Buckoke & Sons Ltd, Factory 11-25 Chatfield Road, London, SW11 3SE Tel: (020) 7223 3746 Fax: (020) 7223 3746 E-mail: acbuckoke@yahoo.co.uk
Gothard Flight Cases, 322 Beverley Road, Hull, HU5 1BA Tel: (07831) 421751 Fax: (01977) 680271 E-mail: info@gothardflightcases.co.uk
Charles Kirkby & Sons Ltd, 84 Sidney Street, Sheffield, S1 4RH Tel: 0114-272 1327 Fax: 0114-275 6506
Mansells Ltd, 20 Vanguard Way, Shoeburyness, Southend-on-Sea, SS3 9RA Tel: (01702) 294222 Fax: (08708) 722750 E-mail: man@oppenheimers.co.uk
Nefab Packaging UK Ltd, 151 Silbury Boulevard, Milton Keynes, MK9 1LH Tel: (01908) 424300 Fax: (01908) 424301 E-mail: helen.coffin@nefab.se
P C D Products Ltd, Cleveland Road, Hemel Hempstead Industrial Estate, Hemel Hempstead, Hertfordshire, HP2 7EY Tel: (01442) 248565 Fax: (01442) 241033 E-mail: sales@pcdproducts.co.uk
Parkwood Arts Ltd, Staple Ash Lane, Froxfield Green, Petersfield, Hampshire, GU32 1DJ Tel: (01730) 266151 Fax: (01730) 265866 E-mail: sales@parkwood-arts.co.uk
Quentor Ltd, 10 Fitzmaurice Court, Rackheath, Norwich, NR13 6PY Tel: (01603) 721604 Fax: (01603) 721992 E-mail: sales@quentor.com
Schroff UK Ltd, Maylands Avenue, Hemel Hempstead Industrial Estate, Hemel Hempstead, Hertfordshire, HP2 7DE Tel: (01442) 240471 Fax: (01442) 213508 E-mail: sales_uk@schroff.co.uk
Trifibre Containers International, Mill Road, Newbourne, Woodbridge, Suffolk, IP12 4NP Tel: (01473) 811865 Fax: (01473) 811873 E-mail: mukesh@trifibre.co.uk
Valleys Woodcraft Ltd, Unit 1-2 Cwmdraw Industrial Estate, Newtown, Ebbw Vale, Gwent, NP23 5AE Tel: (01495) 350758 Fax: (01495) 307054 E-mail: sales@valleyswoodcraft.com

INSTRUMENT DIALS

Bedford Dials Ltd, Corn Exchange, Teme Street, Tenbury Wells, Worcestershire, WR15 8BB Tel: (01584) 810345 Fax: (01584) 810683 E-mail: info@bedforddials.co.uk
Custom Print, 2 Ashvale Road, Tooting, London, SW17 8PW Tel: (020) 8672 3511 Fax: (020) 8682 2904 E-mail: sales@customprint.com
John Mcgavigan Information Technology Ltd, 111 Westerhill Road, Bishopbriggs, Glasgow, G64 2QR Tel: 0141-302 0000 Fax: 0141-302 0290 E-mail: enquiries@mcgavigan.com

INSTRUMENT DISTRIBUTORS OR AGENTS, INDUSTRIAL

Amtek Instrumentation Engineers, 8 Mexico Lane, Phillack, Hayle, Cornwall, TR27 5AG Tel: (01736) 754015 Fax: (01736) 759389
Canongate Technology Ltd, 17 Edgefield Road Industrial Estate, Loanhead, Midlothian, EH20 9TB Tel: 0131-448 0786 Fax: 0131-440 1739 E-mail: sales@canongatetechnology.co.uk
E G S Technologies, 17 Lea Hall Enterprise Park, Wheelhouse Road, Rugeley, Staffordshire, WS15 1LH Tel: 01889 583220 Fax: 07092 012948 E-mail: p.evans@egstec.co.uk
Fluid Controls Ltd, 4 Minerva House, Calleva Park, Aldermaston, Reading, RG7 8NA Tel: 0118-981 1004 Fax: 0118-981 0775 E-mail: sales@fluidcontrols.co.uk
▶ Kolectric Research, 41 Couching Street, Watlington, Oxfordshire, OX49 5PX Tel: (01491) 613523 Fax: (01491) 613339 E-mail: enquiries@kolectric.com
Mecdine Instruments Ltd, 7 Sherborne Road, Burbage, Hinckley, Leicestershire, LE10 2BE Tel: (01455) 250220 Fax: (01455) 238541
P J D Instruments, Unit 15 Antrim Enterprise Centre, 50 Upper Greystone Road, Antrim, BT41 1JZ Tel: (028) 9442 5700 Fax: (028) 9446 5760 E-mail: pjdinstruments@aol.com
Status Graphite, Unit 6a, Commerce Way, Colchester, CO2 8HR Tel: (01206) 868150 Fax: (01206) 868160
M.J. Wilson Group, Wrotham Road, Meopham, Gravesend, Kent, DA13 0QB Tel: (01474) 812406 Fax: (01474) 814265 E-mail: northdinst@freeuk.com

INSTRUMENT ENGINEERING,
See also headings for particular types

A J Mare Instruments, 110 Church Road, Perry Barr, Birmingham, B42 2LF Tel: 0121-356 8511 Fax: 0121-344 3644 E-mail: pimmy-21@hotmail.com
Abbeville Instrument Control Ltd, Bridge Street, Derby, DE1 3LA Tel: (01332) 371138 Fax: (01332) 291668 E-mail: sales@aicderby.co.uk
▶ Airflow Instrumentation, 7 West Vale, Neston, CH64 9SE Tel: 0151-336 1899 Fax: 0151-336 8705 E-mail: airflowinstrumentation@hotmail.co.uk
Asm GmbH, Tanyard House, 37 High Street, Measham, Swadlincote, Derbyshire, DE12 7HR Tel: (01530) 515342 Fax: (0845) 1222124 E-mail: sales@asm-sensor.co.uk
Bowyer Engineering Ltd, South Way, Walworth Industrial Estate, Andover, Hampshire, SP10 5AF Tel: (01264) 365921 Fax: (01264) 356547 E-mail: sales@bowyerengineering.co.uk
C M W Controls Ltd, Bryn Lane, Wrexham Industrial Estate, Wrexham, Clwyd, LL13 9UT Tel: (01978) 661516 Fax: (01978) 661626 E-mail: geoff.roberts@cmwcontrols.com
Coley Instruments Ltd, Burnside Industrial Estate, Kilsyth, Glasgow, G65 9JX Tel: (01236) 821533 Fax: (01236) 824090 E-mail: sales@stewarts-group.com
Colwick Instruments Ltd, PO Box 8268, Nottingham, NG3 6AJ Tel: 0115-962 2999 Fax: 0115-961 4582 E-mail: enquires@colwickinstruments.co.uk
Controlled Repair Instruments Ltd, Controlled Repair Institute Ltd, 1-5 Dock Tavern Lane, Gorleston, Great Yarmouth, Norfolk, NR31 6PY Tel: (01493) 602060 Fax: (01493) 441782 E-mail: sales@controlvalverepairs.co.uk
D P Instrumentation Ltd, 2 Ainslie Street, West Pitkerro Industrial Estate, Broughty Ferry, Dundee, DD5 3RR Tel: (01382) 731200 Fax: (01382) 731201 E-mail: sales@dpil.co.uk
Ei WHS, Staveley House, Fort Street, Blackburn, BB1 5EG Tel: (01254) 670261 Fax: (01254) 680832 E-mail: blackburn@eiwhs.co.uk
Eiwhs, 1 London Road, Great Shelford, Cambridge, CB22 5DB Tel: (01223) 845776 Fax: (01223) 842910 E-mail: cambridge.eiwhs@staveley.co.uk
Eiwhs, 23 Dunlop Way, Queensway Industrial Estate, Scunthorpe, South Humberside, DN16 3RN Tel: (01724) 282328 Fax: (01724) 282321 E-mail: rchallis.eiwhs@staveley.co.uk
Eiwhs, Unit 10, President Buildings Savile St East, Sheffield, S4 7UQ Tel: 0114-275 0012 Fax: 0114-276 1402 E-mail: sheffield.eiwhs@staveley.co.uk
Eiwhs, 21 Allensway, Thornaby, Stockton-on-Tees, Cleveland, TS17 9HA Tel: (01642) 769085 Fax: (01642) 761137 E-mail: eiwhs.thornaby@staveley.co.uk
Electrical Installations North West Ltd, Lawsons Road, Thornton-Cleveleys, Lancashire, FY5 4PW Tel: (01253) 822626 Fax: (01253) 827846 E-mail: sales@einw.co.uk
▶ Fluidic Ltd, 4-8 Lochend Street, Motherwell, Lanarkshire, ML1 1RX Tel: (01698) 327372 Fax: (01698) 327281 E-mail: sales@fluidic-ltd.co.uk
Gage Technique International Ltd, PO Box 30, Trowbridge, Wiltshire, BA14 8YD Tel: (01761) 431777 Fax: (01761) 431888 E-mail: info@gage-technique.demon.co.uk
▶ Global Instrumentation Ltd, Unit 1080 Galley Drive, Sittingbourne Research Centre, Sittingbourne, Kent, ME9 8GA Tel: (0870) 3820001 Fax: (0870) 3820002
Hillcrest Engineering Instrumentation Ltd, Upper Hulme, Leek, Staffordshire, ST13 8TY Tel: (01538) 300259 Fax: (01538) 300421 E-mail: sales@hei-engine.co.uk
Humberside Instruments Ltd, 13-15 Barkhouse Lane, Cleethorpes, South Humberside, DN35 8RA Tel: (01472) 691157 Fax: (01472) 692585 E-mail: sales@humbrsideinstruments.co.uk
Hydraulic & Gas Services Ltd, Unit 4a Ford Street, Stockport, Cheshire, SK3 0BT Tel: 0161-480 9966 Fax: 0161-480 9922 E-mail: sales@hgservicesltd.co.uk
Icel Group, Ashmill Bus Park, Ashford Road, Lenham, Maidstone, Kent, ME17 2GQ Tel: (01622) 858200 Fax: (01622) 850065 E-mail: sales@icel-group.co.uk
Industrial Instrumentation Services, 124 Hinton Way, Great Shelford, Cambridge, CB22 5AL Tel: (01223) 842127 E-mail: iis.cooper@ntlworld.com
Inmar Automation Ltd, Test House, 118 Ringwood Road, Totton, Southampton, SO40 8DS Tel: (023) 8086 4179 Fax: (023) 8086 1613 E-mail: sales@inmar.co.uk
Instrument & Gauges Electronics Ltd, Gravel Lane, Banks, Southport, Merseyside, PR9 8DE Tel: (01704) 505333 Fax: (01704) 505334 E-mail: sales@instruments-gauges.co.uk
Irpco Ltd, 9 Glan Llwyd, Tyn Y Bonau Road, Pontarddulais, Swansea, SA4 8SF Tel: (01792) 881212 Fax: (01792) 881119
▶ Mcleish Sales & Services Ltd, Endeavour Drive, Arnhall Business Park, Westhill, Aberdeenshire, AB32 6UF Tel: (01224) 279955 Fax: (01224) 279966 E-mail: graeme@mcleishsales.co.uk
Midlands Instrumentation Maintenance, Woodwards Place, Coppice Side, Swadlincote, Derbyshire, DE11 9AA Tel: (01283) 229000 Fax: (01283) 229111 E-mail: mimspeak@aol.com
P & I Design Ltd, 2 Reed Street, Thornaby, Stockton-on-Tees, Cleveland, TS17 7AF Tel: (01642) 617444 Fax: (01642) 616447 E-mail: drr@pidesign.co.uk
P J D Instruments, Unit 15 Antrim Enterprise Centre, 50 Upper Greystone Road, Antrim, BT41 1JZ Tel: (028) 9442 5700 Fax: (028) 9446 5760 E-mail: pjdinstruments@aol.com
Powys Instrument & Engineering Services Ltd, 3 Subway Road, Barry, South Glamorgan, CF63 4QT Tel: (01446) 737785 Fax: (01446) 742616
QC Lighting Systems, 83 Mercia Avenue, Charlton, Andover, Hampshire, SP10 4EJ Tel: (01264) 332892 Fax: (01264) 332892 E-mail: sales@qclightingsystems.co.uk
Scotia Instrumentation Ltd, Aberdeen Science & Technology Park, Balgownie Road, Bridge of Don, Aberdeen, AB22 8GT Tel: (01224) 222888 Fax: (01224) 826299 E-mail: info@scotia-instrumentation.com
Structural Statics Ltd, Burntwood, Martyr Worthy, Winchester, Hampshire, SO21 1AD Tel: (01962) 886644 Fax: (01962) 886788 E-mail: info@structuralstatics.co.uk
T A Group Ltd, Blackhouse Industrial Estate, Peterhead, Aberdeenshire, AB42 1BW Tel: (01779) 478515 Fax: (01779) 479722
Tecker Ltd, Kernow House, Tregoniggie Industrial Estate, Falmouth, Cornwall, TR11 4SN Tel: (01326) 378774 Fax: (01326) 378775 E-mail: mail@tecker.co.uk
Wesurail Ltd, 21-22 Auster Road, Clifton Moor, York, YO30 4XA Tel: (01904) 692544 Fax: (01904) 692566 E-mail: admin@wesurail.com
M.J. Wilson Group, Wrotham Road, Meopham, Gravesend, Kent, DA13 0QB Tel: (01474) 812406 Fax: (01474) 814265 E-mail: northdinst@freeuk.com

INSTRUMENT INSTALLATION/ COMMISSIONING SERVICES, INDUSTRIAL

Mark Hutchinson Ltd, 105 Elliot Rise, Hedge End, Southampton, SO30 2RW Tel: (01489) 798723 E-mail: m.r.hutchinson@talk21.com
Meldan Fabrications Ltd, St Marys Works, Marsh Lane, Barton-upon-Humber, South Humberside, DN18 5HB Tel: (01652) 632075 Fax: (01652) 660389 E-mail: sales@meldan.co.uk
Randall & Daniels (Electrical) Ltd, Abbey Industrial Estate, Neath Abbey, Neath, West Glamorgan, SA10 7DR Tel: (01792) 813231 Fax: (01792) 321816 E-mail: sales@rd-electrical.com

INSTRUMENT MAINTENANCE/ REPAIR SERVICES, INDUSTRIAL

Envogen UK Ltd, Greetby Place, Skelmersdale, Lancashire, WN8 9UL Tel: (01695) 724414 Fax: (01695) 713279
Inmar Automation Ltd, Test House, 118 Ringwood Road, Totton, Southampton, SO40 8DS Tel: (023) 8086 4179 Fax: (023) 8086 1613 E-mail: sales@inmar.co.uk
M T I Instruments & Calibration, Littleburn Industrial Estate, Langley Moor, Durham, DH7 8HJ Tel: 0191-378 3990 Fax: 0191-378 3973
Mecdine Instruments Ltd, 7 Sherborne Road, Burbage, Hinckley, Leicestershire, LE10 2BE Tel: (01455) 250220 Fax: (01455) 238541
New Forest Instrument Control Ltd, 84 Cobham Road, Ferndown Industrial Estate, Wimborne, Dorset, BH21 7RW Tel: (01202) 875308 Fax: (01202) 893462 E-mail: info@newforestinstruments.co.uk
M.J. Wilson Group, Wrotham Road, Meopham, Gravesend, Kent, DA13 0QB Tel: (01474) 812406 Fax: (01474) 814265 E-mail: northdinst@freeuk.com

INSTRUMENT PANELS

Chequers UK Ltd, 78 Ponders End Industrial Estate, East Duck Lees Lane, Enfield, Middlesex, EN3 7SR Tel: (020) 8805 8855 Fax: (020) 8805 9318
Dobbie McInnes, 42 Methil Street, Glasgow, G14 0AN Tel: 0141-959 2247 Fax: 0141-954 1172 E-mail: dobbie@yandc.co.uk
K A B Systems Ltd, Lansdowne Road, Chadderton, Oldham, OL9 9EG Tel: 0161-678 6367 Fax: 0161-678 6979 E-mail: sales@kabsystems.co.uk
Ketech Systems, Glaisdale Dr East, Nottingham, NG8 4GR Tel: 0115-900 5600 Fax: 0115-900 5601 E-mail: enquiry@ketech.com
Ravenscroft Cameras, 61 Grimsby Road, Cleethorpes, South Humberside, DN35 7AF Tel: (01472) 342007 Fax: (01472) 250504 E-mail: ravenscroftcameras@btinternet.com
Ritherdon & Co. Ltd, Lorne Street, Darwen, Lancashire, BB3 1QW Tel: (01254) 819100 Fax: (01254) 819101 E-mail: info@ritherdon.co.uk

INSTRUMENT TRANSFORMERS

D K Moriarty Ltd, Eastgates Industrial Estate, Moorside, Colchester, CO1 2TJ Tel: (01206) 867141 Fax: (01206) 867613 E-mail: sales@dk-moriarty.ltd.uk
Dagnall Electronics Ltd, 3 Shuttleworth Road, Elm Farm Industrial Estate, Bedford, MK41 0EP Tel: (01234) 330077 Fax: (01234) 330088 E-mail: sales@dagnall.co.uk
Trench UK Ltd, South Drive, Hebburn, Tyne & Wear, NE31 1UW Tel: 0191-483 4711 Fax: 0191-430 0633 E-mail: sales@trench-uk.com
▶ Tva Transformers Ltd, Unit 20/29, Teesway, North Tees Industrial Estate, Stockton-on-Tees, Cleveland, TS18 2RS Tel: (01642) 612444 Fax: (01642) 633997 E-mail: info@tvatransformers.co.uk

INSTRUMENT VALVES

▶ Alco Valves Ltd, Mission Works, Birds Royd Lane, Brighouse, West Yorkshire, HD6 1LQ Tel: 01484 710511 Fax: 01484 713009 E-mail: uk@alco-valves.com
K Controls Ltd, Stone Close, West Drayton, Middlesex, UB7 8JU Tel: (01895) 449601 Fax: (01895) 448586 E-mail: sales@k-controls.co.uk

INSTRUMENT, NON-ELECTRONIC, *See headings for particular usage*

INSTRUMENTATION AMPLIFIERS

Analog Devices Ltd, Rothwell House, Pembroke Road, Newbury, Berkshire, RG14 1BX Tel: (01635) 555400 Fax: (01635) 555401 E-mail: hilary.abbott@analog.com

INSTRUMENTATION CABLES

Central Cables, Unit 15 Brindley Business Park, Chaseside Drive, Hednesford, Cannock, Staffordshire, WS11 7GD Tel: (01543) 422477 Fax: (01543) 422420 E-mail: sales@centralcables.co.uk
Electro Cables Ltd, Unit 2 Alliance Close, Attleborough Fields Industrial Estate, Nuneaton, Warwickshire, CV11 6SD Tel: (024) 7632 0066 Fax: (024) 7632 0122 E-mail: sales@electrocables.co.uk

INSTRUMENTATION CONSULTANTS

Amelec Instruments Ltd, 3-5 Cochran Close, Crownhill, Milton Keynes, MK8 0AJ Tel: (01908) 567003 Fax: (01908) 566735 E-mail: sales@amelec-uk.com
Arrow Technical Services Ltd, 58 Nursery Street, Sheffield, S3 8GG Tel: 0114-281 2018 Fax: 0114-281 5404 E-mail: info@arrowtechnical.com
D P Controls Ltd, Giles Farm Oast, Pluckley, Ashford, Kent, TN27 0SY Tel: (01233) 840900 Fax: (01233) 840900 E-mail: sales@dpcontrols.com
Hine Engineering Ltd, 149 Bolton Hall Road, Bolton Woods, Bradford, West Yorkshire, BD2 1BQ Tel: (01274) 401850 Fax: (01274) 401850 E-mail: rod@akili.demon.co.uk
International Purchasing Services Ltd, Unit 17 Golborne Enterprise Park, Golborne, Warrington, WA3 3DR Tel: (01942) 713777 Fax: (01942) 713888 E-mail: intl.purch.serv@virgin.net
▶ Met Engineering Ltd, Unit 3, Mode Wheel Road, Salford, M5 5DQ Tel: 0161-737 2627 Fax: 0161-737 2628 E-mail: info@metenguk.com
South West Instrumentation, Swi House, High Street, Market Lavington, Devizes, Wiltshire, SN10 4AF Tel: (01380) 816444 Fax: (01380) 816999 E-mail: sales@swi.org.uk

INSTRUMENTATION CONTRACTORS

Booth Welsh Automation Ltd, The A P L Centre, Stevenston Industrial Estate, Stevenston, Ayrshire, KA20 3LR Tel: (01294) 605123 Fax: (01294) 605555 E-mail: sales@boothwelsh.com
J C M Scotload Ltd, Greenbank Cresent, East Tullos Industrial Estate, Aberdeen, AB12 3BG Tel: (01224) 877007 Fax: (01224) 895200 E-mail: sales@jcmscotload.co.uk
Ott Hydrometry, Criftin Enterprise Centre, Oxton Road, Epperstone, Nottingham, NG14 6AT Tel: 0115-965 6549 Fax: 0115-965 4726 E-mail: sales@ott-hydrometry.co.uk

▶ indicates data change since last edition

INSTRUMENTATION EQUIPMENT, PNEUMATIC/ HYDRAULIC

Specialised Pipe & Services Ltd, F1 Folland Way, Hull, HU9 1NB Tel: (01482) 587060 Fax: (01482) 587099 E-mail: sales@spsworld.com

INSTRUMENTATION EQUIPMENT/SPARE PARTS PACKAGES

Euro Trading Ltd, Shepperton Marina, Felix Lane, Shepperton, Middlesex, TW17 8NS Tel: (01932) 246153 Fax: (01932) 226711 E-mail: eurotrading.co@virgin.net

Midlands Instrumentation Maintenance, Woodwards Place, Coppice Side, Swadlincote, Derbyshire, DE11 9AA Tel: (01283) 229000 Fax: (01283) 229111 E-mail: mimspeak@aol.com

Quantum Production, Unit 25 Wornal Park, Menmarsh Road, Worminghall, Aylesbury, Buckinghamshire, HP18 9PH Tel: (01844) 339993 Fax: (01844) 339996 E-mail: info@quantumproduction.co.uk

Sabtek International Ltd, Unit 9, 10 Badentoy Place, Portlethen, Aberdeen, AB12 4YF Tel: (01224) 782289 Fax: (01224) 781645 E-mail: info@sabtek.co.uk

Tierway Systems Ltd, 17 Grenville Meadows, Lostwithiel, Cornwall, PL22 0JS Tel: (01208) 871114 Fax: (01208) 871114

INSTRUMENTATION HIRE

Euremica Ltd, Instrument House, Morgan Drive, Guisborough, Cleveland, TS14 7DG Tel: (01287) 204020 Fax: (01287) 204021 E-mail: sales@euremica.com

INSTRUMENTATION PROTOTYPING

Cambridge Scientific Instruments Ltd, 12-15 Sedgway Business Park, Common Road, Witchford, Ely, Cambridgeshire, CB6 2HY Tel: (01353) 669916 Fax: (01353) 669917 E-mail: camsci@btconnect.com

New Vision Associates Ltd, Vision Worksventnor Street, Bradford, West Yorkshire, BD3 9JP Tel: (01274) 728831 Fax: (01274) 308702 E-mail: sales@new-vision.co.uk

Richmond Measurement Services, Po Box 44, Derby, DE24 8ZT Tel: (01332) 364354 Fax: (01332) 362737

INSTRUMENTATION SYSTEMS DESIGN ENGINEERS

Dimension Data Advanced Infrastructure, Thelwall Industrial Estate, Thelwall New Road, Warrington, WA4 2LY Tel: (01925) 602942 Fax: (01925) 267464 E-mail: sales@uk.didata.com

G E D Designs, 400 Aviation Park West, Bournemouth Int Airp, Hurn, Christchurch, Dorset, BH23 6NW Tel: (01202) 578537 Fax: (01202) 578537

▶ Process Automation, 17 South Lodge Court, Chesterfield, Derbyshire, S40 3QG Tel: (01246) 568868 E-mail: process.automation@fsmail.net

Support Instrumentation Ltd, 52 Westhall Rd, Warlingham, Surrey, CR6 9BH Tel: 01883 623399 Fax: 01883 624499

Tierway Systems Ltd, 17 Grenville Meadows, Lostwithiel, Cornwall, PL22 0JS Tel: (01208) 871114 Fax: (01208) 871114

INSTRUMENTATION TO SPECIFICATION

▶ Bernafon UK Ltd, Cadzow Industrial Estate, Hamilton, Lanarkshire, ML3 7QE Tel: (01883) 331730 Fax: (01883) 331739

Hydrasun Ltd, 61h Lord Avenue, Thornaby, Stockton-on-Tees, Cleveland, TS17 9JX Tel: (01642) 750405 Fax: (01642) 750704

▶ Process Automation, 17 South Lodge Court, Chesterfield, Derbyshire, S40 3QG Tel: (01246) 568868 E-mail: process.automation@fsmail.net

Tecnicon Precision, Unit 20 Euro Business Park, New Road, Newhaven, East Sussex, BN9 0DQ Tel: (01273) 510952 Fax: (01273) 513579

W E Instrumentation Ltd, Unit 15 Chamberlayne Road, Bury St. Edmunds, Suffolk, IP32 7EY Tel: (01284) 704805 Fax: (01284) 762932 E-mail: sales@we-instrumentation.co.uk

Wexham Developments 93, Unit 8 Youngs Industrial Estate, Paices Hill, Aldermaston, Reading, RG7 4PW Tel: 0118- 981 0411 Fax: 0118-981 0811 E-mail: wexdev@compserve.com

INSTRUMENTATION, ENGINEERING MAINTENANCE AND REPAIR SERVICES

Automation Experts Ltd, Appic Elliot Innovation Centre, Elliot Business Park, 4 Barling Way, Nuneaton, Warwickshire, CV10 7RH Tel: (024) 7679 6666 Fax: (024) 7679 6667 E-mail: info@automationexperts.co.uk

INSULATED CABLES

Allied Cables Ltd, Liverpool Road, Warrington, WA5 1AP Tel: (01925) 445764 Fax: (01925) 232880 E-mail: alliedcables@absonline.net

Madison Wire (Europe) Ltd, Madison House, Davyfield Road, Roman Road Industrial Estate, Blackburn, BB1 2LU Tel: (01254) 663555 Fax: (01254) 663222 E-mail: info@madison-wire.co.uk

Wessel Energy Cables, Aghafad, Longford, County Longford, Tel: 0161-763 7474 Fax: 0161-763 7373 E-mail: abbcablesales.ie@abb.com

INSULATED COMPOSITE PANELS

▶ Commercial Panels, Unit 28, Fort Industrial Park, Chester Road, Castle Vale, Birmingham, B35 7AR Tel: 0121-749 2877

INSULATED CONCRETE FORMWORK

▶ Polarwall, Unit 3 Old Mill Industrial Estate, Stoke Canon, Exeter, EX5 4RJ Tel: (01392) 841777 Fax: (01392) 841936 E-mail: info@polarwall.co.uk

INSULATED CORE LAMINATED SANDWICH PANELS

▶ Laminated Supplies Ltd, Valletta House, Valletta Street, Hedon Road, Hull, HU9 5NP Tel: (01482) 781111 Fax: (01482) 701185 E-mail: sales@laminatedsupplies.com

Laser Claddings Ltd, Lowndes Road, Stourbridge, West Midlands, DY8 3ST Tel: (01384) 376200 Fax: (01384) 372737 E-mail: laser.cladding@blueyonder.co.uk

Panelkraft Ltd, Unit 18a-20c Hixon Airfield Estate, New Road, Hixon, Stafford, ST18 0PF Tel: (01889) 270018 Fax: (01889) 270977

Supaclad Ltd, Timmis Road, Stourbridge, West Midlands, DY9 7BQ Tel: (01384) 896647 Fax: (01384) 892457

INSULATED GATE BIPOLAR (IGBT) POWER TRANSISTORS

Dynex Semi Conductor Ltd, Doddington Road, Lincoln, LN6 3LF Tel: (01522) 500500 Fax: (01522) 500550

INSULATED PRODUCTS, *See headings for particular types such as Wire*

INSULATED SANDWICH PANELS

▶ Commercial Panels, Unit 28, Fort Industrial Park, Chester Road, Castle Vale, Birmingham, B35 7AR Tel: 0121-749 2877

INSULATED TARPAULINS

Controlla Covers Ltd, Brunswick Industrial Park, Hannah Street, Darwen, Lancashire, BB3 3HL Tel: (01254) 772020 Fax: (01254) 773030 E-mail: controlla@aol.com

J Clemishaw & Company Ltd, Barnbrook Building, Barnbrook Street, Bury, Lancashire, BL9 7DT Tel: 0161-764 4614 Fax: 0161-764 4615

INSULATED TOOLS FOR ELECTRICAL WORK

Insulated Tools Ltd, Charlwoods Road, East Grinstead, West Sussex, RH19 2HR Tel: (01342) 324255 Fax: (01342) 327115 E-mail: enquiries@insulatedtools.co.uk

INSULATED WIRE

Heatsense Cables Ltd, 3 Astra Centre, Royle Barn Road, Rochdale, Lancashire, OL11 3DT Tel: (01706) 355330 Fax: (01706) 657691 E-mail: sales@heatsensecables.co.uk

Madison Wire (Europe) Ltd, Madison House, Davyfield Road, Roman Road Industrial Estate, Blackburn, BB1 2LU Tel: (01254) 663555 Fax: (01254) 663222 E-mail: info@madison-wire.co.uk

INSULATING FIBREGLASS PRODUCTS

Beldam Lascar Seals Ltd, Lascar Works, Staines Road, Hounslow, TW3 3JL Tel: (020) 8570 7722 Fax: (020) 8570 4438 E-mail: enquiries@beldamlascargroup.com

▶ Pittsburgh Corning UK Ltd, 63 Milford Road, Reading, RG1 8LG Tel: 0118-950 0655 Fax: 0118-950 9019 E-mail: sales@foamglass.co.uk

Pyro Glass Ltd, Unit 12 Roman Way, Longridge Road, Ribbleton, Preston, PR2 5BB Tel: (01772) 651265 Fax: (01772) 654912 E-mail: sales@pyroglass.com

Wilhams Insulation Export Division Ltd, 117 Bohemia Road, St. Leonards-on-Sea, East Sussex, TN37 6RL Tel: (01424) 201000 Fax: (01424) 201000 E-mail: sales@wilhams.-insulation.co.uk

INSULATING JACKETS

I S O Covers Ltd, Trent Valley Industrial Estate, Station Road, Rugeley, Staffordshire, WS15 2HQ Tel: (01889) 574333 Fax: (01889) 574111 E-mail: info@isocovers.com

J A Young & Sons, 19-21 Alpine Way, London, E6 6LA Tel: (020) 7473 9300 Fax: (020) 7473 9301

B. & R. Loughlin, 19 Meadowcourt Road, Oadby, Leicester, LE2 2PD Tel: 0116-271 2373 Fax: 0116-272 0239

INSULATING MATERIAL MACHINISTS/CONVERTERS, ELECTRICAL

Insulation & Machining Services Ltd, Russell Road, Southport, Merseyside, PR9 7SB Tel: (01704) 226878 Fax: (01704) 225857 E-mail: sales@ims-insulation.com

Langtec Ltd, 1 Calder Court, Altham, Accrington, Lancashire, BB5 5YB Tel: (01282) 772544 Fax: (01282) 772740 E-mail: info@langtec.co.uk

Macgregor Radio Control Ltd, Macgregor House, Cordwalls Street, Maidenhead, Berkshire, SL6 7GF Tel: (01628) 760341 Fax: (01628) 760435

INSULATING MATERIAL MACHINISTS/CONVERTERS, THERMAL

A B C Insulation Co. Ltd, Alexandra Docks, Newport, Gwent, NP20 2NP Tel: (01633) 211473 Fax: (01633) 843212

Central Convertors, Unit 3 Bandeath Industrial Estate, Throsk, Stirling, FK7 7NP Tel: (01786) 814033 Fax: (01786) 817477 E-mail: convertors@superglass.co.uk

INSULATING MATERIALS, *See also headings for particular types*

Allpoint Safety Ltd, Unit 49, Hull Micro Firm Centre, 266-290 Wincolmlee, Hull, HU2 0PZ Tel: (01482) 222796 Fax: (01482) 229969

Allseal Insulation Products Ltd, Phoenix Works Industrial Estate, Richards Street, Wednesbury, West Midlands, WS10 8BZ Tel: 0121-526 4241 Fax: 0121-568 8177

Avonside Insulation Supplies Ltd, Unit 6a Pucklechurch Trading Estate, Pucklechurch, Bristol, BS16 9QH Tel: 0117-937 2232 Fax: 0117-937 2387

Encon, 1 Rippleside Commercial Estate, Ripple Road, Barking, Essex, IG11 0RJ Tel: (020) 8595 2121 Fax: (020) 8595 9003 E-mail: info@encon.co.uk

Encon Ltd, Langage Science Park, Western Wood Way, Plympton, Plymouth, PL7 5BG Tel: (01752) 333720 Fax: (01752) 348938

Encon Insulation Ltd, Unit F1-F2, St. Michaels Close, Aylesford, Kent, ME20 7BU Tel: (01622) 713400 Fax: (01622) 713403 E-mail: maidstone@encon.co.uk

Encon Insulation Ltd, Unit 2 Elmbank, Channel Commercial Park, Queens Road, Belfast, BT3 9DT Tel: (028) 9045 4646 Fax: (028) 9045 4656 E-mail: t.patterson@encon.co.uk

Encon Insulation Ltd, 3-4 Tamebridge Industrial Estate, Aldridge Road, Perry Barr, Birmingham, B42 2TX Tel: 0121-356 0606 Fax: 0121-356 4828

Encon Insulation Ltd, 3-4 Tamebridge Industrial Estate, Aldridge Road, Perry Barr, Birmingham, B42 2TX Tel: 0121-356 0606 Fax: 0121-356 4828

Encon Insulation Ltd, Buchanans Warehouse, Chittening Industrial Estate, Chittening, Bristol, BS11 0YB Tel: 0117-980 2100 Fax: 0117-980 2101

Encon Insulation Ltd, 23 Nettlefold Road, Cardiff, CF24 5JQ Tel: (029) 2089 5040 Fax: (029) 2089 5044

Encon Insulation Ltd, Unit 500, Fareham Reach, 166 Fareham Road, Gosport, Hampshire, PO13 0FP Tel: (01329) 230555 Fax: (01329) 230615 E-mail: fareham@encon.co.uk

Encon Insulation Ltd, Unit 9-10, Gelderd Road, Morley, Leeds, LS27 7JN Tel: 0113-289 7666 Fax: 0113-289 7555 E-mail: leeds@encon.co.uk

Encon Insulation Ltd, Unit E2, High Flatworth, Tyne Tunnel Trading Estate, Northshields, Newcastle Upon Tyne, NE29 7UZ Tel: 0191-293 1090 Fax: 0191-293 1099

Encon Insulation Ltd, Brunswick House, Deaghton Close, Wetherby, West Yorkshire, LS22 7GZ Tel: (01937) 524200 Fax: (01937) 524222

Encon Insulation Ltd, Unit 3, Industrial Estate, Stanton Harcourt, Witney, Oxfordshire, OX29 5UX Tel: (01865) 734500 Fax: (01865) 734518

Encon Insulation Materials, Unit 17-19, Bloomsgrove Industrial Estate, Nottingham, NG7 3JB Tel: 0115-978 0040 Fax: 0115-942 0264

Encon Insulation Northampton, 21 Saddleback Road, Westgate Industrial Estate, Northampton, NN5 5HL Tel: (01604) 580580 Fax: (01604) 580585 E-mail: info@encon.co.uk

Encon Insulation Scotland, 80 Cambuslang Road, Cambuslang, Clydesmill Industrial Estate, Glasgow, G32 8NB Tel: 0141-641 0011 Fax: 0141-641 5170

Encon Insulations, Unit 13 Studlands Park Industrial Estate, Newmarket, Suffolk, CB8 7AU Tel: (01638) 667292 Fax: (01638) 664081 E-mail: northampton@encon.co.uk

Encon Manchester Ltd, Chaddock Lane, Worsley, Manchester, M28 1DR Tel: 0161-703 7400 Fax: 0161-703 7411 E-mail: manchester@encon.co.uk

▶ Epthorn Ltd, Units 19-20, Hayleys Manor, Epping Upland, Epping, Essex, CM16 6PQ Tel: (01992) 560956 Fax: (01992) 561956

Excel Industries, Maerdy Industrial Estate, Rhymney, Tredegar, Gwent, NP22 5PY Tel: (01685) 845200 Fax: (01685) 844106 E-mail: info@excelfibre.com

F G F Ltd, Fernhurst Road, Bristol, BS5 7XN Tel: 0117-951 7755 Fax: 0117-935 4231 E-mail: sales@fgfltd.co.uk

F G F Ltd, West Quay Road, Southampton, SO15 1GZ Tel: (023) 8021 2121 Fax: (023) 8022 3274 E-mail: southampton@fgflimited.co.uk

F G F Continental Ltd, Shadwell House, Shadwell Street, Birmingham, B4 6LJ Tel: 0121-233 1144 Fax: 0121-212 2539 E-mail: sales.fgf@ukonline.co.uk

Fabric Service Oxford Ltd, 55 West End, Witney, Oxfordshire, OX28 1NJ Tel: (01993) 772995 Fax: (0845) 363 7151 E-mail: sales@soundservice.co.uk

Hampshire Insulations Products, Hotel & Conference Centre, Owslebury, Winchester, Hampshire, SO21 1JY Tel: (01962) 777730 Fax: (01962) 777740 E-mail: hampshireinsulations@tiscali.co.uk

Instafoam & Fibre Ltd, Insta House, Ivanhoe Road, Hogwood Business Park, Wokingham, Berkshire, RG40 4PZ Tel: 0118-932 8811 Fax: 0118-932 8314 E-mail: info@instagroup.co.uk

Insulation & Machining Services Ltd, Russell Road, Southport, Merseyside, PR9 7SB Tel: (01704) 226878 Fax: (01704) 225857 E-mail: sales@ims-insulation.com

J A Young & Sons, 19-21 Alpine Way, London, E6 6LA Tel: (020) 7473 9300 Fax: (020) 7473 9301

Keyline Builders Merchants Ltd, Moulton Park Industrial Estate, Northampton, NN3 6TE Tel: (01604) 643622 Fax: (01604) 790353 E-mail: welcome@keylineco.uk

Kitsons, 139 Scudamore Road, Leicester, LE3 1UQ Tel: 0116-232 5000 Fax: 0116-232 5001

Langtec Ltd, 1 Calder Court, Altham, Accrington, Lancashire, BB5 5YB Tel: (01282) 772544 Fax: (01282) 772740 E-mail: info@langtec.co.uk

M C Insulation Supplies Ltd, Unit 3 Brandon Way, West Bromwich, West Midlands, B70 9PQ Tel: 0121-525 0444 Fax: 0121-525 0440 E-mail: marycarthy@aol.com

Malcolm Insulation Ltd, 59 Beardmore Way, Clydebank, Dunbartonshire, G81 4HT Tel: 0141-941 2204 Fax: 0141-951 1487

Marmorit UK Ltd, 1 Port View Road, Avonmouth, Bristol, BS11 9LF Tel: 0117-982 1042 Fax: 0117-982 3025 E-mail: enquires@marmorit.co.uk

Miller Pattison Ltd, 3 Eldon Way, Biggleswade, Bedfordshire, SG18 8NH Tel: (01767) 314444 Fax: (01767) 317601 E-mail: biggleswade@miller-patterson.co.uk

Raven Insulation Supply Co., 39 Church Street, Weybridge, Surrey, KT13 8DG Tel: (01932) 856731 Fax: (01932) 855685

S I Board Supplies, 4 Victoria Retail Park, Crown Road, Ruislip, Middlesex, HA4 0AF Tel: (020) 8839 4343 Fax: (020) 8839 4344 E-mail: ruislip@siboards.co.uk

Sheffield Insulations Ltd, Telford Way, Bedford, MK42 0PQ Tel: (01234) 761100 Fax: (01234) 272157 E-mail: bedford@sheffins.co.uk

Sheffield Insulations Ltd, Cadleigh Close, Lee Mill Industrial Estate, Ivybridge, Devon, PL21 9GB Tel: (01752) 690969 Fax: (01752) 690527

INSULATING MATERIALS – *continued*

Travis Perkins plc, 7 Seph Way, York Road Industrial Park, Malton, North Yorkshire, YO17 6YF Tel: (01653) 692444 Fax: (01653) 600453 E-mail: malton@travisperkins.co.uk
Warren Insulation plc, Unit 8c, Harding Way, St. Ives, Cambridgeshire, PE27 3WR Tel: (01480) 467972 Fax: (01480) 464993 E-mail: headoffice@warren.co.uk

INSULATING MOULDING MACHINE BARREL JACKETS

Ic International Ltd, Gower Street Trading Estate, St. Georges, Telford, Shropshire, TF2 9HW Tel: (01952) 620206 Fax: (01952) 620456 E-mail: sales@ic-international.com
Speyside Cooperage Ltd, Dufftown Road, Craigellachie, Aberlour, Banffshire, AB38 9RS Tel: (01340) 881264 Fax: (01340) 881303 E-mail: info@speyside-cooperage.demon.co.uk

INSULATING OR PROTECTIVE BUILDING PAPER PRODUCTS

B P B Paperboard Ltd, B P B UK Service Centre, East Leake, Loughborough, Leicestershire, LE12 6JU Tel: 0115-945 1000 Fax: 0115-945 1199

INSULATING SLEEVING/TUBING (ELECTRICAL) MANUFRS

CP Films Solutia UK Ltd, Chadwick Road, Astmoor Industrial Estate, Runcorn, Cheshire, WA7 1PW Tel: (01928) 580508 Fax: (01928) 580100 E-mail: sales.runcorn@cpfilms.co.uk
Industrial Composites Ltd, Churchill Way, Nelson, Lancashire, BB9 6RT Tel: (01282) 619336 Fax: (01282) 619337 E-mail: info@indcomps.co.uk
Lamina Dielectrics Ltd, Daux Road, Billingshurst, West Sussex, RH14 9SJ Tel: (01403) 783131 Fax: (01403) 782237 E-mail: sales@lamina.uk.com

INSULATION

▶ 1st Insulation Partners Ltd, Insulation House, Shaw Road, Eastwood Trading Estate, Rotherham, South Yorkshire, S65 1SG Tel: (01709) 365785 Fax: 01709 365786 E-mail: office@firstinsulation.com
▶ A J Framemaker, 3 Alrewas Road, Kings Bromley, Burton-on-Trent, Staffordshire, DE13 7HW Tel: (01543) 473791 Fax: (01543) 473932 E-mail: sales@ajframemaker.co.uk
Cordtape Energy Management Systems, Unit 13-15 Broxtowe Park Business Centre, Calverton Drive, Strelley, Nottingham, NG8 6QP Tel: 0115-975 6551 Fax: 0115-975 6559 E-mail: cems@cordtapeenviromental.co.uk
▶ Elliotts, Unit 8 Goodwood Road, Eastleigh, Hampshire, SO50 4NT Tel: (023) 8062 3960 Fax: (023) 8062 3965 E-mail: insulation@elliott-brothers.co.uk
Encon Insulation Ltd, Buchanans Warehouse, Chittening Industrial Estate, Chittening, Bristol, BS11 0YB Tel: 0117-980 2100 Fax: 0117-980 2101
▶ Orion Insulations, Unit 5 Kingsmark Freeway, Oakenshaw, Bradford, West Yorkshire, BD12 7HW Tel: (01274) 711470 Fax: (01274) 711471 E-mail: bradford@oriontrent.co.uk
▶ Palziv Insulation Materials, Unit 10 Droicon Industrial Estate, Portway Road, Rowley Regis, West Midlands, B65 9BY Tel: 0121-559 7676 Fax: 0121-559 9191 E-mail: palziv@btconnect.com
▶ Rembrand Timber Ltd, Shielhill Wood, Tealing, Dundee, DD4 0PW Tel: (01382) 323200 Fax: (01382) 382520
▶ Rilmac Insulation Ltd, Crofton Drive, Allenby Road Industruial Estate, Lincoln, LN3 4NJ Tel: (01522) 531711 Fax: (01522) 510291 E-mail: enquiries@rilmac.co.uk
▶ Roofing Insulation Services, Hilldale House, 9 Hilldale Avenue, Blackley, Manchester, M9 6PQ Tel: (0800) 7318314 E-mail: info@sprayfoaminsulation.co.uk
▶ TIMSA, Association House, 99 West Street, Farnham, Surrey, GU9 7EN Tel: (01252) 739154 Fax: (01252) 739140 E-mail: timsa@associationhouse.org.uk
▶ Tyne Insulation Supplies, Firwood Industrial Estate, Thicketford Road, Bolton, BL2 3TR Tel: (01204) 302220 Fax: (01204) 302230

INSULATION BOARD, WATERPROOF

▶ Just Insulation, 27 Massetts Road, Horley, Surrey, RH6 7DQ Tel: (0845) 2606232 Fax: (0845) 2606242 E-mail: purchases@just-insulation.com

INSULATION INSTALLERS

▶ 4 Dimensions, Tall Pines, London Road, Crowborough, East Sussex, TN6 1TA Tel: 01892 663534 E-mail: handy@4dimensions.co.uk
▶ French Bros, 60 Main Street, Kibworth Harcourt, Leicester, LE8 0NQ Tel: 0116-279 6767 Fax: 0116-279 6868 E-mail: helen@insulate.co.uk

INSULATION PANELS

▶ A J Framemaker, 3 Alrewas Road, Kings Bromley, Burton-on-Trent, Staffordshire, DE13 7HW Tel: (01543) 473791 Fax: (01543) 473932 E-mail: sales@ajframemaker.co.uk
Frimatec UK Ltd, 5 Townsend Centre Blackburn Road, Townsend Industrial Estate, Houghton Regis, Dunstable, Bedfordshire, LU5 5BQ Tel: (01582) 471600 Fax: (01582) 472050 E-mail: frimatec@nildram.co.uk
Hemsec Developments Ltd, Stoney Lane, Rainhill, Prescot, Merseyside, L35 9LL Tel: 0151-426 7171 Fax: 0151-493 1331 E-mail: sales@hemsec.com
Panelbond Ltd, 1 King Edward Street, Grimsby, South Humberside, DN31 3JU Tel: (01472) 250130 Fax: (01472) 250784 E-mail: roybarber@panelbond.com
Panelkraft Ltd, Unit 18a-20c Hixon Airfield Estate, New Road, Hixon, Stafford, ST18 0PF Tel: (01889) 270018 Fax: (01889) 270977
Paneltex Ltd, Kingston International Park, Somerden Road, Hull, HU9 5PE Tel: (01482) 787236 Fax: (01482) 787238 E-mail: sales@paneltex.co.uk
Quantum Profile Systems, Salmon Fields, Royton, Oldham, OL2 6JG Tel: 0161-627 4222 Fax: 0161-627 4333 E-mail: sales@quantum-ps.co.uk
Seconds & Co. Ltd, Europa House, 16a High Street, Tenterden, Kent, TN30 6AP Tel: (01580) 767700 Fax: (01580) 767709 E-mail: sales@seconds.co.uk
U R S A UK Ltd, Crest House, 102-104 Church Road, Teddington, Middlesex, TW11 8PY Tel: (020) 8977 9697 Fax: (020) 8977 9456 E-mail: ursauk@uralita.com

INSULATION TEST SETS

Eco Therm Insulation UK Ltd, Unit 3 Cabinet Way, Eastwood, Leigh-on-Sea, Essex, SS9 5LP Tel: (01702) 520166 Fax: (01702) 420636 E-mail: info@ecotherm.co.uk

INSURANCE ADVICE

A A Insurance Services, St. Patricks House, 17 Pennarth Road, Cardiff, CF10 5ZA Tel: (0870) 5332211 Fax: (029) 2072 5516
A W D Chase Devere P.L.C., 10 Paternoster Square, London, EC4M 7DY Tel: (020) 7828 9297 Fax: (020) 7248 7742 E-mail: enquiries@awdplc.com
Anglo Assessors Ltd, 23 Canterbury Park, Liverpool, L18 9XP Tel: (07710) 510234 Fax: 0151-475 7867 E-mail: mrb.angloassessors@tiscali.co.uk
Aon Ltd, 21 Golden Square, Aberdeen, AB10 1RE Tel: (01224) 647201 Fax: (01224) 639715
Aon Entertainment Risk Services Ltd, Pinewood Road, Iver, Buckinghamshire, SL0 0NH Tel: (01753) 658200 Fax: (01753) 653152 E-mail: film@aon.co.uk
Ashburnham Insurance Services Ltd, 80 London Road, Southend-on-Sea, SS1 1PG Tel: (01702) 347400 Fax: (01702) 333890 E-mail: insure@ashburnham-insurance.co.uk
Aspect Insurance Services Ltd, Evans Business Centre Sycamore Trading Estate, Squires Gate Lane, Blackpool, FY4 3RL Tel: (0870) 0465540 Fax: (01253) 340551 E-mail: sales@aspectinsurance.co.uk
▶ Asset Protection Administration, The Terminal Building, Union Wharf, Leicester Road, Market Harborough, Leicestershire, LE16 7UW Tel: (01858) 469955 Fax: (01858) 466460 E-mail: apa@apa-admin.co.uk
George Baker (Insurance Brokers) Ltd, Richmond House, 1 Richmond Parade, Brighton, BN2 9GB Tel: (01273) 603066 Fax: (01273) 670324
Beaumonts Robinson Risk Services, 1 Clifton Villas, Bradford, West Yorkshire, BD8 7BY Tel: (01274) 404050 Fax: (01274) 404060
▶ Bevington Evans & Associates, 53 Harrowby Street, Cardiff, CF10 5GA Tel: (029) 2048 5221 Fax: (029) 2048 5231 E-mail: cbevev@ntlbusiness.com
Bishops plc, Halden House, High Halden, Ashford, Kent, TN26 3BT Tel: (01233) 649000 Fax: (01233) 850052 E-mail: enquiry@bishopsltd.com
Blue Moon Insurance, Church Street, Wellingborough, Northamptonshire, NN8 4PD Tel: (01933) 303020 Fax: (01933) 303021 E-mail: sales@bluemooninsurance.co.uk
Bond Lovis Insurance Brokers Ltd, 522 Barking Road, London, E13 8QE Tel: (020) 8552 6900 Fax: (020) 8470 3051 E-mail: sales@bondlovis.co.uk
J.K. Buckenham Ltd, 1 America Square, 17 Crosswall, London, EC3N 2LB Tel: (020) 7377 0110 Fax: (020) 7680 4080 E-mail: jkb@jkb.co.uk
Byas, Mosley & Co. UK Ltd, William Byas Ho, 14-18 St. Clare St, London, EC3N 1JX Tel: (020) 7481 0101 Fax: (020) 7481 3442 E-mail: uk-div@bya-mosley.co.uk
C J Coleman Holdings Ltd, Portsoken House, 155 Minories, London, EC3N 1BT Tel: (020) 7488 2211 Fax: (020) 7488 4436 E-mail: sales@cj-coleman.co.uk
C P U Direct, 20 Westerham Avenue, London, N9 9BU Tel: (020) 8887 0044 Fax: (020) 8887 0099
Caithness & Co. Ltd, 47 Old London Road, Kingston upon Thames, Surrey, KT2 6NG Tel: (020) 8549 8011 Fax: (020) 8547 2238 E-mail: mail@caithnessandco.com
Campbell Fisk & Partners Ltd, Campbell Fisk House, Eridge Road, Crowborough, East Sussex, TN6 2SW Tel: (01892) 664141 Fax: (01892) 665556 E-mail: info@greeninsurance.co.uk
Cardale Assurance Facilities Ltd, Old Bank Chambers, Station Road, Horley, Surrey, RH6 9HW Tel: (01293) 786295 Fax: (01293) 820353
Chapman Stevens, 21 Wintersells Road, Byfleet, West Byfleet, Surrey, KT14 7LF Tel: (01932) 334140 Fax: (01932) 351238
Cheltenham Insurance Brokers Ltd, Herriot House, North Place, Cheltenham, Gloucestershire, GL50 4DS Tel: (01242) 517787
Brian Chubb Insurance, Salt Quay House, Sutton Harbour, Plymouth, PL4 0RA Tel: (01752) 312680 Fax: (01752) 226727 E-mail: brianchubb@virginbus.co.uk
City Assurance Services Ltd, First Floor Gatton Place, St Matthews, Redhill, RH1 1TA Tel: (01737) 854440 Fax: (01737) 854445 E-mail: inquires@cityassurance.com
Collier Insurance, 146 Bellegrove Road, Welling, Kent, DA16 3QR Tel: (020) 8303 4761 Fax: (020) 8301 6021 E-mail: info@collierinsurance.co.uk
Cooper Gay & Co. Ltd, International Ho, 26 Creechurch La, London, EC3A 5JE Tel: (020) 7480 7322 Fax: (020) 7481 4695
Cordon Insurance Ltd, Andil House, Court Street, Trowbridge, Wiltshire, BA14 8BR Tel: (01225) 775566 Fax: (01225) 775544 E-mail: info@cordoninsurance.co.uk
Cox Braithwaite, Park House, Greyfriars Road, Cardiff, CF10 3AF Tel: (029) 2023 2148 Fax: (029) 2037 3687 E-mail: coxbr@coxbraithwaite.co.uk
Crossroads Insurance Services, 261 Kingsland Road, London, E2 8AS Tel: (020) 7739 1189 Fax: (020) 7256 0403 E-mail: crossroadsinsurance@btconnect.com
Crownsway Insurance Brokers Ltd, 185 Holyhead Road, Birmingham, B21 0AS Tel: 0121-554 3566 Fax: 0121-523 2992 E-mail: crowns@btconnect.com
Cuthbert Service & Jackson Ltd, 111 Bell Street, Glasgow, G4 0UA Tel: 0141-566 9651 Fax: 0141-566 9022 E-mail: mail@csjltd.co.uk
E H Morgan & Son Ltd, 105 Cricklade Street, Cirencester, Gloucestershire, GL7 1JF Tel: (01285) 883100 Fax: (01285) 883111 E-mail: ehm@ehmorgan-insurance.co.uk
Edn Insurance Services Ltd, Standeven House, 27 Union Street, Oldham, OL1 1XS Tel: 0161-624 3801 Fax: 0161-627 4045 E-mail: enquiries@edaviesnorthern.freeserve.co.uk
Ember J D Insurance, Belhaven House, 67 Walton Road, East Molesey, Surrey, KT8 0DP Tel: (020) 8941 2204 Fax: (020) 8979 9796 E-mail: ember1970@hotmail.com
First City Insurance Brokers Ltd, 13-15 Folgate Street, London, E1 6BX Tel: (020) 7247 6595 Fax: (020) 7410 4818
Frank Corrigan & Co., Regent House, 26 Queens Road, Coventry, CV1 3DQ Tel: (024) 7655 5594 Fax: (024) 7655 1194 E-mail: frank@corrigan-group.demon.co.uk
G D Anderson & Co. Ltd, 68 Lombard Street, London, EC3V 9LJ Tel: (020) 7437 5122 Fax: (020) 7481 9100 E-mail: admin@anderson-insurance.co.uk
General Insurance Brokers UK plc, 90 Bishops Bridge Road, London, W2 5AA Tel: (020) 7792 0123 Fax: (020) 7727 5794
Griffiths & Armour Ltd, 110 Fenchurch Street, London, EC3M 5JT Tel: (020) 7204 0014 Fax: (020) 7204 0019 E-mail: info@gallimited.com
Griffiths Mcalister Insurance, The Old School House, 14 Mill Road, Burgess Hill, West Sussex, RH15 8DR Tel: (01444) 242666 Fax: (01444) 245777 E-mail: general@griffiths-mcalister.com
Heath Lambert, Cloister House, New Bailey Street, Salford, M3 5AG Tel: 0161-935 2935 Fax: 0161-839 2839
Heath Lambert Overseas Ltd, 133 Houndsditch, London, EC3A 7AH Tel: (020) 7560 3000 Fax: (020) 7560 3000 E-mail: info@heathgroup.com
Hendersons Insurance Brokers, 5 Acorn Business Park, Woodseats Close, Sheffield, S8 0TB Tel: 0114-262 9911 Fax: 0114-280 2831 E-mail: enquiries@ecsbrokers.com
Hill Taylor Dickinson, Dukes Place, London, EC3A 7LQ Tel: (020) 7283 9033 Fax: (020) 7283 1144 E-mail: sales@htd.co.uk
HSBC Insurance Brokers Ltd, Bishops Court, 27-33 Artillery Lane, London, E1 7LP Tel: (020) 7247 5433 Fax: (020) 7377 2139
▶ I Need That Mortgage.com, 129 High St, Watton at Stone, Hertford, SG14 3SB Tel: 0870 991 7255 Fax: 07005 931146 E-mail: salesinformation@ineedthatmortgage.com
Insure Shop, 2 Brook Square, Rugeley, Staffordshire, WS15 2DR Tel: (01889) 583339 Fax: (01889) 575817
John Reynolds Group Ltd, Stamford House, Northenden Road, Sale, Cheshire, M33 2DH Tel: 0161-905 5500 Fax: 0161-905 5510 E-mail: sales@john-reynolds.co.uk
Anthony Kidd Agencies Ltd, Halford House, 2 Colvall Lane, Chelmsford, CM1 1TZ Tel: (08702) 411271 Fax: (08702) 874285
L P Dawe, Meneer House, 22 Berkeley Vale, Falmouth, Cornwall, TR11 3PA Tel: (01326) 312405 Fax: (01326) 316233 E-mail: lpdawe@btconnect.com
Lagrove Ltd, 51-53 The Green, Southall, Middlesex, UB2 4AR Tel: (020) 8574 4656 Fax: (020) 8843 0605E-mail: lagrove@cs.com
Layton Blackham Insurance Brokers Ltd, Weston House, 246 High Holborn, London, WC1V 7EX Tel: (0870) 1600201 Fax: (020) 7415 3910
Lycetts Insurance Brokers, Milburn House, Dean Street, Newcastle upon Tyne, NE1 1PP Tel: 0191-232 1151 Fax: 0191-232 1873 E-mail: info@lycetts.co.uk
Lyon Cole Insurance Management Ltd, King Harold Court, Sun Street, Waltham Abbey, Essex, EN9 1ER Tel: (01992) 787477 Fax: (01992) 787479 E-mail: carol.deal@lyoncole.com
M J M Software Ltd, 217-219 Hamstel Road, Southend-On-Sea, SS2 4LB Tel: (01702) 300441 Fax: (01702) 300115 E-mail: sales@mjm-ltd.com
MacRobins P.L.C., 40 Great Portland Street, London, W1W 7ND Tel: 08456 300740 Fax: 08456 300750 E-mail: postmaster@macrobins.co.uk
Marcus Hearn & Co. Ltd, 65 Shoreditch High Street, London, E1 6JL Tel: (020) 7739 3444 Fax: (020) 7739 7888 E-mail: mail@marcushearn.co.uk
Marsh Ltd, 48 St. Vincent Street, Glasgow, G2 5TR Tel: 0141-304 4300 Fax: 0141-221 5409
Mason & Ball & Associates Ltd, Bourn House, Park Street, Bagshot, Surrey, GU19 5AQ Tel: (01276) 472774 Fax: (01276) 451520 E-mail: mail@mba-uk.co.uk
Miles Smith (Insurance Brokers), Birchin Court, 20 Birchin Lane, London, EC3V 9DU Tel: (020) 7283 0040 Fax: (020) 7220 0860 E-mail: mhartshorn@milessmith.co.uk
Miller Insurance Services Ltd, Dawson House, 5 Jewry Street, London, EC3N 2PJ Tel: (020) 7488 2345 Fax: (020) 7265 1423 E-mail: sales@millerinsurance.co.uk
Mitchell & Partners, 13-15 Archway Road, London, N19 3TX Tel: (020) 7272 7661 Fax: (020) 7272 6628 E-mail: sales@mitch.co.uk
Network Direct Ltd, PO Box 117, Guernsey, GY1 4ED Tel: (01481) 701400 Fax: (01481) 701456 E-mail: network@direct.guernsey.net
Norwich Union Ltd, 5 Donegall Square South, Belfast, BT1 5AN Tel: (028) 9032 2232 Fax: (028) 9023 8731
Opus, Adams House, 14 Market Street, Hertford, SG14 1BD Tel: (01992) 513000 Fax: (01992) 513046
Primo plc, Cumberland House, 24-28 Baxter Avenue, Southend-on-Sea, SS2 6HZ Tel: (01702) 225400 Fax: (01702) 225409 E-mail: enquiries@primoplc.com
R F I B Group Ltd, Staple Hall, Stone House Court, 87-90 Houndsditch, London, EC3A 7NP Tel: (020) 7621 1263 Fax: (020) 7623 6175
R K Shipman Ltd, 1 Barnfield Crescent, Exeter, EX1 1QY Tel: (01392) 278491 Fax: (01392) 425793 E-mail: sales@rkshipman.co.uk
R M Gillingham & Son Ltd, 44 East Street, Bridport, Dorset, DT6 3LJ Tel: (01308) 423777 Fax: (01308) 458791 E-mail: info@gillinghams-insurance.co.uk
R&C, Unit 16 Earlsdon Business Centre, Warwick Street, Coventry, CV5 6ET Tel: (024) 7671 3313 Fax: (024) 7667 8905
SBJ Ltd, 100 Whitechapel Road, London, E1 1JG Tel: (020) 7816 2000 Fax: (020) 7816 2255 E-mail: info@sbjgroup.co.uk
Seascope Insurance Services Ltd, 57 Mansell Street, London, E1 8AN Tel: (020) 7488 3288 Fax: (020) 7481 4499 E-mail: enquiries@seains.com
Shephard Herriot, 12 Poverest Road, Orpington, Kent, BR5 2TP Tel: (01689) 877800 Fax: (01689) 877789
Sterling Hamilton Wright Ltd, City Reach, 5 Greenwich View Place, Mill Harbour, London, E14 9NN Tel: (020) 7716 5000 Fax: (020) 7716 5001 E-mail: info@shwgroup.co.uk
Steveni Kessler Insurance Services Ltd, Steveni Kessler House Dominion Business Park, Goodwin Road, London, N9 0BG Tel: (020) 8345 5500 Fax: (020) 8482 2000 E-mail: sales@steveni-kessler.co.uk
Stirling Hamilton Wright, City Reach, 5 Greenwich View Place, Millharbour, London, E14 9NN Tel: (020) 7712 6000 Fax: (020) 7712 6001 E-mail: info@shwgroup.co.uk
S.J. Stoddart Insurance Ltd, St. Peter's House, 119 High Street, Berkhamsted, Hertfordshire, HP4 2DJ Tel: (01442) 872331 Fax: (01442) 871025
▶ Stride Ltd, The Briars, Waterberry Drive, Waterlooville, Hampshire, PO7 7YH Tel: (023) 9224 8790 Fax: (023) 9224 8799 E-mail: info@stride.co.uk

INSURANCE ADVICE – *continued*

Stuart Neal Chartered Loss Adjusters Ltd, 26 White Horse Lane, Maldon, Essex, CM9 5QP Tel: (01621) 857111 Fax: (01621) 858111 E-mail: claims@stuartneal.co.uk

T H March & Co. Ltd, 10-12 Ely Place, London, EC1N 6RY Tel: (020) 7405 0009 Fax: (020) 7404 4629 E-mail: insurance@thmarch.co.uk

T H Martin Ltd, 112 Walter Road, Swansea, SA1 5QQ Tel: (01792) 466410 Fax: (01792) 641887 E-mail: ianmartin@thmartin.com

▶ Totally Insured Group Ltd, Unit 4, Abbey Walk Church Street, Romsey, Hampshire, SO51 8JQ Tel: (0870) 2408891 E-mail: info@totallyinsuredgroup.co.uk

Tower Insurance Co. Ltd, Jubilee Building, 1 Victoria Street, Douglas, Isle Of Man, IM99 1BF Tel: (01624) 673446 Fax: (01624) 663864

Tyser & Co. Ltd, 12-20 Camomile Street, London, EC3A 7PJ Tel: (020) 7623 6262 Fax: (020) 7397 4852

Westinsure Webb Ltd, Alexandra House, 63 Killigrew Street, Falmouth, Cornwall, TR11 3PE Tel: (01326) 313737 Fax: (01326) 211387 E-mail: enquiries@westinsurewebb.co.uk

Willis Ltd, 78-86 Dublin Road, Belfast, BT2 7BY Tel: (028) 9024 2131 Fax: (028) 9032 1087

Willis Overseas Investments Ltd, 10 Trinity Square, London, EC3P 3AX Tel: (020) 7488 8111 Fax: (020) 7488 8223

Wilson Insurance Broking Group Ltd, Wilson House, 1-3 Waverley Street, Nottingham, NG7 4HG Tel: 0115-942 0111 Fax: 0115-942 0459 E-mail: info@wilorg.co.uk

Woodgate & Partners Ltd, Brishing Court Barn, Brishing Lane, Boughton Monchelsea, Maidstone, Kent, ME17 4NF Tel: (01622) 744666 Fax: (01622) 741747

INSURANCE BROKERS

▶ D N A Insurance Services Ltd, New Enterprise House, 149-151 High Road, Chadwell Heath, Romford, RM6 6PJ Tel: (020) 8548 7300 Fax: (0870) 7872365 E-mail: mail@dnainsurance.co.uk

▶ James Ryan Thornhill Ltd, 41 Wollaton Road, Beeston, Nottingham, NG9 2RN Tel: 0115-876 0298 Fax: 0115-922 4212 E-mail: chris@jrtltd.co.uk

Rixon Matthews Appleyard Ltd, Exchange Court, Lowgate, Hull, HU1 1XW Tel: (01482) 327605 Fax: (01482) 217184 E-mail: sales@rixon-insurance.co.uk

▶ Taxi insurance from WYN Group Insurance Services, WYN House, 4 Eve Road, Woking, Surrey, GU21 5JT Tel: 01483 722266 E-mail: info@wyngroup.co.uk

INSURANCE COMPANIES, *See also specialist services*

A I G Europe UK Ltd, The Aig Building, 58 Fenchurch Street, London, EC3M 4AB Tel: (020) 7954 7000 Fax: (020) 7954 7001

A L I C O, Alico House, 22 Addiscombe Road, Croydon, CR9 5AZ Tel: (020) 8680 6000 Fax: (020) 8680 7217

Abbey Life Assurance Co. Ltd, 80 Holdenhurst Road, Bournemouth, BH8 8ZQ Tel: (01202) 292373 Fax: (01202) 293159

Ace European Group, The Ace Building, 100 Leadenhall Street, London, EC3A 3BP Tel: (020) 7173 7000 Fax: (020) 7173 7800 E-mail: info@ace-ina.com

▶ Alan Boswell Insurance Brokers, Harbour House, 126 Thorpe Road, Norwich, NR1 1UL Tel: (01603) 218000 Fax: (01603) 762862 E-mail: info@alanboswell.com

Allianz Cornhill Insurance plc, 57 Ladymead, Guildford, Surrey, GU1 1DB Tel: (01483) 568161 Fax: (01483) 300952 E-mail: cornhill@gho.cornhill.co.uk

Allianz Cornhill Insurance plc, Allianz Cornhill House, 27 Leadenhall Street, London, EC3A 1AA Tel: (020) 7264 1530 Fax: (020) 7929 3562

Amber Insurance Services, 889 Stockport Road, Manchester, M19 3PG Tel: 0161-224 7268 Fax: 0161-256 4798

Ansvar Insurance Co. Ltd, 31 St Leonards Road, Eastbourne, East Sussex, BN21 3UR Tel: (01323) 737541 Fax: (01323) 430977 E-mail: ansvar.insurance@ansvar.co.uk

Aon Risk Services, 3RD Floor, St. Georges Court, Douglas, Isle Of Man, IM1 1EE Tel: (01624) 673325 Fax: (01624) 623664 E-mail: mike.henthorn@ars.aon.co.uk

Ashburnham Insurance Services Ltd, 80 London Road, Southend-on-Sea, SS1 1PG Tel: (01702) 347400 Fax: (01702) 333890 E-mail: insure@ashburnham-insurance.co.uk

▶ Asset Protection Administration, The Terminal Building, Union Wharf, Leicester Road, Market Harborough, Leicestershire, LE16 7UW Tel: (01858) 469955 Fax: (01858) 466460 E-mail: apa@apa-admin.co.uk

Assicurazioni Generali, 100 Leman Street, London, E1 8AJ Tel: (020) 7265 6200 Fax: (020) 7702 3745 E-mail: sales@generaliglobal.com

▶ ATE Insurance.com, Riverbank House, Brownhill, Ruyton X1 Towns, Shrewsbury, SY4 1LR Tel: 01939 261730 Fax: 01939 261583 E-mail: bob@ATEinsurance.com

Axa Insurance, Windsor House, 9-15 Bedford Street, Belfast, BT2 7FT Tel: (028) 9033 3222 Fax: (028) 9053 5010

Axa Insurance, 1 Aldgate, London, EC3N 1RE Tel: (020) 7702 3109 Fax: (020) 7369 3909

Axa Insurance, 1 Aldgate, London, EC3N 1RE Tel: (020) 7702 3109 Fax: (020) 7369 3909

Axa PPP Healthcare Group plc, P P P House, Vale Road, Tunbridge Wells, Kent, TN1 1BJ Tel: (01892) 512345 Fax: (01892) 515143 E-mail: enquiries@axappphealthcare.com

B U P A, BUPA House, 15-19 Bloomsbury Way, London, WC1A 2BA Tel: (020) 7656 2000 Fax: (020) 7656 2701

Bar Mutual Indemnity Fund Ltd, International Ho, 26 Creechurch La, London, EC3A 5BA Tel: (020) 7283 4646 Fax: (020) 7283 5988

BHSF, 2 Darnley Road, Birmingham, B16 8TE Tel: 0121-454 3601 Fax: 0121-454 7725 E-mail: sales@bhsff.co.uk

Blue Moon Insurance, Church Street, Wellingborough, Northamptonshire, NN8 4PD Tel: (01933) 303020 Fax: (01933) 303021 E-mail: sales@bluemooninsurance.co.uk

Britannic Assurance P.L.C., 1 Wythall Green Way, Wythall, Birmingham, B47 6WG Tel: (01564) 828888 Fax: (0870) 8870002 E-mail: info@britannic.co.uk

Car Care Plan, Mid Point, Thornbury, Bradford, West Yorkshire, BD3 7AG Tel: (0870) 7527000 Fax: (0870) 7527100

Century Life P.L.C., Century House, 5 Old Bailey, London, EC4M 7BA Tel: (01708) 758196

Chapman Stevens, 21 Wintersells Road, Byfleet, West Byfleet, Surrey, KT14 7LF Tel: (01932) 334140 Fax: (01932) 351238

Cigna Health Care & Group Life, Cigna House, 1 Knowe Road, Greenock, Renfrewshire, PA15 4RJ Tel: (01475) 492222 Fax: (01475) 492326 E-mail: sales@cigna.co.uk

Coin & Leisure, Unit 1, Station Enterprises, Station Road, Abergavenny, Gwent, NP7 5HY Tel: (01873) 853360

Co-operative Insurance Society Ltd, Miller Street, Manchester, M60 0AL Tel: 0161-832 8686 Fax: 0161-837 5954 E-mail: cis@cis.co.uk

Co-Operative Systems, 18-20 Miles Street, London, SW8 1SD Tel: (020) 7793 0395 Fax: (020) 7735 6472 E-mail: team@coopsys.net

Copenhagen Reinsurance Co. (UK) Ltd, The London Underwriting Centre, 3 Minster Court, Mincing Lane, London, EC3R 7DD Tel: (020) 7369 0010 Fax: (020) 7369 0018

Cornish Mutual, CMA House, Newham Road, Truro, Cornwall, TR1 2SU Tel: (01872) 277151 Fax: (01872) 223053 E-mail: enq@cornishmutual.co.uk

Das Legal Expenses Insurance Co. Ltd, D A S House Quay Side, Temple Back, Bristol, BS1 6NH Tel: 0117-934 2000 Fax: 0117-934 2109 E-mail: sales@das.co.uk

Direct Line Group Ltd, 3 Edridge Road, Croydon, CR9 1AG Tel: (020) 8686 3313 Fax: (020) 8681 0512

Ecclesiastical Insurance Group, Beaufort House, Brunswick Road, Gloucester, GL1 1JZ Tel: (01452) 528533 Fax: (01452) 423557 E-mail: marketing@eigmail.com

Ecclesiastical Insurance Group, 19-21 Billiter Street, London, EC3M 2RY Tel: (020) 7528 7364 Fax: (020) 7528 7365

Edn Insurance Services Ltd, Standeven House, 27 Union Street, Oldham, OL1 1XS Tel: 0161-624 3801 Fax: 0161-627 4045 E-mail: enquiries@edaviesnorthern.freeserve.co.uk

Empire Travel & Insurance Services Ltd, 349 King Street, London, W6 9NH Tel: (020) 8748 1033 Fax: (020) 8748 1034 E-mail: empireti@hotmail.com

Euler Hermes Guarantee plc, Surety House, Lyons Cresent, Tonbridge, Kent, TN9 1EN Tel: (01732) 770311 Fax: (01732) 770361

Export Credits Guarantee Department, PO Box 2200, London, E14 9GS Tel: (020) 7512 7000 Fax: (020) 7512 7649 E-mail: help@ecgd.gsi.gov.uk

▶ F R Ball Insurance Ltd, 56 Frogmore Street, Abergavenny, Gwent, NP7 5AR Tel: (01873) 857533 Fax: (01873) 856915 E-mail: sales@frball.co.uk

First Assist Group Ltd, Marshalls Court, Marshalls Road, Sutton, Surrey, SM1 4DU Tel: (020) 8652 1313 Fax: (020) 8661 7604 E-mail: corporate.info@firstassit.co.uk

Folgate Risk Solutions Ltd, 2 Cathedral Square, Groat Market, Newcastle Upon Tyne, NE1 1EH Tel: (0870) 9056202 Fax: (0870) 9056203 E-mail: neil.forrest@towergate.co.uk

Gerling UK Ltd, 50 Fenchurch Street, London, EC3M 3JY Tel: (020) 7696 8099 Fax: (020) 7696 8119 E-mail: receptiondesk@gerling.co.uk

▶ Haydock Finance Ltd, 2 The Cottage, Main Street, Kinnesswood, Kinross, KY13 9HN Tel: (01592) 840480 Fax: (01592) 840480

▶ HomeCall+, Pendle Innovation Centre, Brook Street, Nelson, Lancashire, BB9 9PS Tel: 01282 877160 Fax: 01282 877139 E-mail: info@homecallplus.co.uk

Hospital Plan Insurance Services, 44 Baker Street, London, W1A 4WJ Tel: (020) 7487 4411 Fax: (020) 7487 5747 E-mail: info@hpis.co.uk

HSBC Insurance Brokers Ltd, Bishops Court, 27-33 Artillery Lane, London, E1 7LP Tel: (020) 7247 5433 Fax: (020) 7377 2139

I T I C Ltd, International House, 26-28 Creechurch Lane, London, EC3A 5BA Tel: (020) 7338 0150 Fax: (020) 7338 0151

▶ i4insurance, Ipswich, IP1 Tel: (01473) 268210 E-mail: advertising@i4insurance.co.uk

Anthony Kidd Agencies Ltd, Halford House, 2 Colvall Lane, Chelmsford, CM1 1TZ Tel: (08702) 411271 Fax: (08702) 874285

Life Insurance Corporation of India, 13th Floor, York House, Empire Way, Wembley, Middlesex, HA9 0PX Tel: (020) 8902 5294 Fax: (020) 8902 5281 E-mail: enquiries@liciuk.com

Liverpool & London P & I Management Ltd, Royal Liver Building, Pier Head, Liverpool, L3 1QR Tel: 0151-236 3777 Fax: 0151-236 0053 E-mail: info@livlon.co.uk

Liverpool Victoria Financial Advice Services Ltd, County Gates, Bournemouth, BH1 2NF Tel: (0845) 6020690 Fax: (01202) 292253 E-mail: sales@liverpoolvictoria.co.uk

Lloyd's Of London, 1 Lime Street, London, EC3M 7HA Tel: (020) 7327 1000 Fax: (020) 7626 2389 E-mail: alison.burnett@lloyds.com

London General Holdings Ltd, Combined House, 15 Wheatfield Way, Kingston Upon Thames, Surrey, KT1 2PA Tel: (020) 8247 9888 Fax: (020) 8549 5584

London Life Ltd, Spectrum Building, Bond Street, Bristol, BS1 3AL Tel: 0117-984 7777 Fax: 0117-984 7700 E-mail: sales@amp-online.co.uk

Low Quote Limited, 2a Alton House Office Park, Gatehouse Way, Gatehouse Industrial Area, Aylesbury, Bucks, HP19 8YF Tel: (07834) 542976 E-mail: admin@low-quote.net

M M A Insurance plc, 2 Norman Place, Reading, RG1 8DA Tel: 0118-955 2222 Fax: 0118-955 2211 E-mail: info@mma-insurance.com

Marine & General Mutual Life Assurance Society, M G M House, Heene Road, Worthing, West Sussex, BN11 2DY Tel: (01903) 836000 Fax: (01903) 836001 E-mail: customer.centre@mgm-assurance.co.uk

Medical Sickness Pensions Administration Ltd, Colmore Circus Queensway, Birmingham, B4 6AR Tel: (08081) 001884 Fax: 0121-200 9140

Medisure Group, 100 Temple Street, Bristol, BS1 6EN Tel: (0870) 3331174 Fax: (0870) 3330077 E-mail: natalie.delphin@medisure.co.uk

Methodist Insurance plc, Brazennose House West, Brazennose Street, Manchester, M2 5AS Tel: 0161-833 9696 Fax: 0161-833 1287 E-mail: enquiries@micmail.com

N I G, Crown House, 145 City Road, London, EC1V 1LP Tel: (020) 7656 6000 Fax: (020) 7251 0345 E-mail: marion.chan@nig-uk.com

NFU Mutual Ltd, Tiddington Road, Stratford-upon-Avon, Warwickshire, CV37 7BJ Tel: (01789) 204211 Fax: (01789) 298992

Norwich Union Ltd, 5 Donegall Square South, Belfast, BT1 5AN Tel: (028) 9032 2232 Fax: (028) 9023 8731

Norwich Union P.L.C., St. Helen's, 1 Undershaft, London, EC3P 3DQ Tel: (020) 7283 7500

Norwich Union Travel Leisure, 69 Park Lane, Croydon, CR9 1BG Tel: (020) 7283 8611 Fax: (020) 7662 4088

Omni Whittington Insurance Services Ltd, Bridgeway House, 21 Whitfield Street, Gloucester, GL1 1NA Tel: (01452) 428000 Fax: (01452) 301387 E-mail: info@omniwhittington.co.uk

One Call Claim Centre, Unit 1A, Spa Road Industrial Estate, New Holder Street, Bolton, BL1 4SS Tel: (01204) 523772 Fax: (01204) 388498 E-mail: boltoncarpets@zenlen.co.uk

▶ Oxygen Insurance Brokers Ltd, 34 Lime Street, London, EC3M 7AJ Tel: (0870) 1142643 Fax: (08701) 142644

Palmar Avard & Galloway Ltd, 2 Romney Place, Maidstone, Kent, ME15 6LE Tel: (01622) 691651 Fax: (01622) 678112 E-mail: insurance@pagib.co.uk

Paycare, Paycare House, George Street, Wolverhampton, WV2 4DX Tel: (01902) 371000 Fax: (01902) 371030 E-mail: enquiries@paycare.org

Pearl Assurance plc, The Pearl Centre, Peterborough Business Park, Lynch Wood, Peterborough, PE2 6FY Tel: (0870) 8970028 Fax: (01733) 475141

Royal London Management Services Ltd, Refuge House, Alderley Road, Wilmslow, Cheshire, SK9 1PF Tel: (01625) 605040 Fax: (01625) 605401 E-mail: postmaster@royal-london.co.uk

Royal London Management Services Ltd, Refuge House, Alderley Road, Wilmslow, Cheshire, SK9 1PF Tel: (01625) 605040 Fax: (01625) 605401 E-mail: postmaster@royal-london.co.uk

Royal National Pension Fund for Nurses, Frizzell House, County Gate, Bournemouth, BH1 2NF Tel: (01202) 292333

Royal & Sun Alliance Insurance P.L.C., Leadenhall Court, 1 Leadenhall St, London, EC3V 1PP Tel: (020) 7283 9000 Fax: (020) 7337 5200 E-mail: piumail@uk.royalsun.com

Royal & Sun Alliance Insurance Group P.L.C., Level 1, City Exchange, New Hall Place, Old Hall Street, Liverpool, L69 3EN Tel: (01422) 357211 Fax: (01422) 325911

Saga Group Ltd, The Saga Building, Middelburg Sqaure, Folkestone, Kent, CT20 1AZ Tel: (0800) 0150751

St. Pauls Specialist Services, Suite 1 London Underwriting Centre, 3 Minster Court, Mincing Lane, London, EC3R 7YJ Tel: (020) 7617 5959 Fax: (020) 7617 5970 E-mail: info@unionamerica.co.uk

Scottish Equitable P.L.C., 1/3 Lockside Crescent, Edinburgh Park, Edinburgh, EH12 9SE Tel: 0131-339 9191 Fax: 0131-339 9567 E-mail: clientsolutions@scottishequitable.co.uk

Sirius, 3 Minster Court, London, EC3R 7DD Tel: (020) 7617 4900 Fax: (020) 7617 4919

Graham Sykes Insurance, 37 Rolle Street, Exmouth, Devon, EX8 2SN Tel: (01395) 266621 Fax: (01395) 268829 E-mail: info@graham-sykes.co.uk

▶ Totally Insured Group Ltd, Unit 4, Abbey Walk Church Street, Romsey, Hampshire, SO51 8JQ Tel: (0870) 2408891 E-mail: info@totallyinsuredgroup.co.uk

Tower Insurance Co. Ltd, Jubilee Building, 1 Victoria Street, Douglas, Isle Of Man, IM99 1BF Tel: (01624) 673446 Fax: (01624) 663864

Tryg-Baltica International, 69-70 Mark Lane, London, EC3R 7HJ Tel: (020) 7709 1000 Fax: (020) 7709 1001

V A G Finance Ltd, Finance House, Orchard Bray, Edinburgh, EH4 1PF Tel: 0131-332 2451 Fax: 0131-332 1301

Wessex Funding Ltd, Jewry House, Jewry Street, Winchester, Hampshire, SO23 8RZ Tel: (01962) 877818 Fax: (01962) 890049 E-mail: wessex@tcp.co.uk

West Of England Mutual War Risks Association Ltd, Tower Bridge Court, 224 Tower Bridge Road, London, SE1 2UP Tel: (020) 7716 6000 Fax: (020) 7716 6100 E-mail: mail@westpandi.com

Westminster Motor Insurance Association Ltd, 21 Buckingham Palace Road, London, SW1W 0PN Tel: (020) 7834 3976 Fax: (020) 7834 4898

Willis Overseas Investments Ltd, 10 Trinity Square, London, EC3P 3AX Tel: (020) 7488 8111 Fax: (020) 7488 8223

Zurich Financial Services, Zurich House, Stanhope Road, Portsmouth, PO1 1DU Tel: (023) 9282 2200 Fax: (023) 9282 3772

Zurich Financial Services Ltd, Uk Life Centre, Station Road, Swindon, SN1 1EL Tel: (01793) 514514

Zurich Global Corporate, 3 Minsters Court, Mincing Lane, London, EC3R 7DD Tel: (020) 7617 4242 Fax: (020) 7617 4299

INSURANCE COMPANY ASSOCIATIONS

Motex Systems Ltd, The Motex Centre, Winterstoke Road, Weston-super-Mare, Avon, BS23 3YW Tel: (01934) 421100 Fax: (01934) 421101

INSURANCE CONSULTANCY, *See also Life Assurance Consultants*

Amber Insurance Services, 889 Stockport Road, Manchester, M19 3PG Tel: 0161-224 7268 Fax: 0161-256 4798

Anglo Assessors Ltd, 23 Canterbury Park, Liverpool, L18 9XP Tel: (07710) 510234 Fax: 0151-475 7867 E-mail: mrb.angloassessors@tiscali.co.uk

Aon Consulting Ltd, 8 Devonshire Square, London, EC2M 4PL Tel: (020) 7086 8000 Fax: (020) 7767 2001 E-mail: enquiries@aonconsulting.co.uk

Aspect Insurance Services Ltd, Evans Business Centre Sycamore Trading Estate, Squires Gate Lane, Blackpool, FY4 3RL Tel: (0870) 0465540 Fax: (01253) 340551 E-mail: sales@aspectinsurance.co.uk

Cardale Assurance Facilities Ltd, Old Bank Chambers, Station Road, Horley, Surrey, RH6 9HW Tel: (01293) 786295 Fax: (01293) 820353

Cassidy Insurance Services, First Floor Anchor House, 24 Anchor Road, Walsall, WS9 8PW Tel: (0870) 0422200 Fax: (0870) 0422201

Chelsea Financial Services plc, St James Hall, Moore Park Road, London, SW6 2JS Tel: (020) 7384 7300 Fax: (020) 7384 7320 E-mail: info@chelseafs.co.uk

Cheltenham Insurance Brokers Ltd, Herriot House, North Place, Cheltenham, Gloucestershire, GL50 4DS Tel: (01242) 517787

Cigna Health Care & Group Life, Cigna House, 1 Knowe Road, Greenock, Renfrewshire, PA15 4RJ Tel: (01475) 492222 Fax: (01475) 492326 E-mail: sales@cigna.co.uk

City Assurance Services Ltd, First Floor Gatton Place, St Matthews, Redhill, RH1 1TA Tel: (01737) 854440 Fax: (01737) 854445 E-mail: inquires@cityassurance.com

Citymain Insurance, 18 Church Road, Fleet, Hampshire, GU51 3RH Tel: (01252) 819504 Fax: (01252) 626440 E-mail: citymain@citymain-insurance.co.uk

Coin & Leisure, Unit 1, Station Enterprises, Station Road, Abergavenny, Gwent, NP7 5HY Tel: (01873) 853360

Collier Insurance, 146 Bellegrove Road, Welling, Kent, DA16 3QR Tel: (020) 8303 4761 Fax: (020) 8301 6021 E-mail: info@collierinsurance.co.uk

Cordon Insurance Ltd, Andil House, Court Street, Trowbridge, Wiltshire, BA14 8BR Tel: (01225) 775566 Fax: (01225) 775544 E-mail: info@cordoninsurance.co.uk

Donald Cope & Co., 1 Cheadle Shopping Centre, Cheadle, Stoke-on-Trent, ST10 1UY Tel: (01538) 755646 Fax: (01538) 750717 E-mail: sales@donaldcopeandco.com

Folgate Risk Solutions Ltd, 2 Cathedral Square, Groat Market, Newcastle Upon Tyne, NE1 1EH Tel: (0870) 9056202 Fax: (0870) 9056203 E-mail: neil.forrest@towergate.co.uk

INSURANCE CONSULTANCY – *continued*

Friends Provident, UK House, Castle Street, Salisbury, SP1 3SH Tel: (0870) 6071352 Fax: (0870) 5314151

Hayes Parsons Services Ltd, St Lawrence House, Broad Street, Bristol, BS1 2HF Tel: 0117-929 9381 Fax: 0117-926 5644 E-mail: marine@hayesparsons.co.uk

Hendersons Insurance Brokers, 5 Acorn Business Park, Woodseats Close, Sheffield, S8 0TB Tel: 0114-262 9911 Fax: 0114-280 2831 E-mail: enquiries@ecsbrokers.com

▶ I Need That Mortgage.com, 129 High St, Watton at Stone, Hertford, SG14 3SB Tel: 0870 991 7255 Fax: 07005 931146 E-mail: salesinformation@ineedthatmortgage.com

Ingram Insurance Services Ltd, 55-57 Southbourne Grove, Bournemouth, BH6 3QU Tel: (01202) 431041 Fax: (01202) 431043 E-mail: admin@ingraminsurance.demon.co.uk

▶ Julie Bell, The Dog House, Nomansland Farm, Wheathampstead, Herts, AL4 8EY Tel: 01582 834400 Fax: 01582 834400 E-mail: julie.bell@can-do.co.uk

M F S Checkland, 29 Hartfield Road, London, SW19 3SG Tel: (020) 8543 9166 Fax: (020) 8540 8977

M J M Software Ltd, 217-219 Hamstel Road, Southend-On-Sea, SS2 4LB Tel: (01702) 300441 Fax: (01702) 300115 E-mail: sales@mjm-ltd.com

Mid Cornwall Brokers Insurance, 68 Fore Street, Bodmin, Cornwall, PL31 2HR Tel: (01208) 72506 Fax: (01208) 72506

Norwich Union P.L.C., St. Helen's, 1 Undershaft, London, EC3P 3DQ Tel: (020) 7283 7500

One Call Claim Centre, Unit 1A, Spa Road Industrial Estate, New Holder Street, Bolton, BL1 4SS Tel: (01204) 523772 Fax: (01204) 388498 E-mail: boltoncarpets@zenlen.co.uk

Primo plc, Cumberland House, 24-28 Baxter Avenue, Southend-on-Sea, SS2 6HZ Tel: (01702) 225400 Fax: (01702) 225409 E-mail: enquiries@primoplc.com

▶ Stride Ltd, The Briars, Waterberry Drive, Waterlooville, Hampshire, PO7 7YH Tel: (023) 9224 8790 Fax: (023) 9224 8799 E-mail: info@stride.co.uk

Strike Club Correspondents London Ltd, 108 Fenchurch Street, London, EC3M 5JR Tel: (020) 7428 7708 Fax: (020) 7709 9401 E-mail: scc.lon@dial.pipex.com

Tower Insurance Co. Ltd, Jubilee Building, 1 Victoria Street, Douglas, Isle Of Man, IM99 1BF Tel: (01624) 673446 Fax: (01624) 663864

Westinsure Webb Ltd, Alexandra House, 63 Killigrew Street, Falmouth, Cornwall, TR11 3PE Tel: (01326) 313737 Fax: (01326) 211387 E-mail: enquiries@westinsurewebb.co.uk

INSURANCE LITIGATION SERVICES

Axa Insurance, Windsor House, 9-15 Bedford Street, Belfast, BT2 7FT Tel: (028) 9033 3222 Fax: (028) 9053 5010

Berrymans Lace Mawer, Salisbury House, London Wall, London, EC2M 5QN Tel: (020) 7638 2811 Fax: (020) 7920 0361 E-mail: damian.greiff@blm-law.com

Charles Lucas & Marshall, Eastcott House, 4 High Street, Swindon, SN1 3EP Tel: (01793) 511055 Fax: (01635) 570275

Intrum Justitia Group, Warwick House, Birmingham Road, Stratford-Upon-Avon, Warwickshire, CV37 0BP Tel: (01789) 415181 Fax: (01789) 412072

INSURANCE, MORTGAGE INDEMNITY

▶ Clear Cut Mortgages, St. James House, St. James Square, Cheltenham, Gloucestershire, GL50 3WD Tel: (0845) 0698000 E-mail: info@clearcutmortgages.com

▶ Finance Direct, PO Box 127, Birmingham, B20 2XB Tel: (0800) 1973707

▶ J N Finance, Congress House, 14 Lyon Road, Harrow, Middlesex, HA1 2EN Tel: (020) 8861 4445 Fax: (020) 8861 4450 E-mail: info@jnfinance.com

▶ Mortgage Simplicity, Inglewood House, Inglewood, Alloa, Clackmannanshire, FK10 2HU Tel: (0845) 8381502 E-mail: info@mortgagesimplicity.co.uk

▶ Northern Counties Insurance Broker, NCi House, Lowreys Lane, Low Fell, Gateshead, Tyne & Wear, NE9 5JB Tel: 0191 482 1219 Fax: 0191 420 0097 E-mail: contactus@northerncounties.com

▶ Sandham Davies & Jones Ltd, 3 Park Square, Newport, Gwent, NP20 4EL Tel: (01633) 213063 Fax: (01633) 244316 E-mail: enquiries@sdandjones.co.uk

▶ Tudor Associates Ltd, Stallington Hall Farm, Stallington Road, Blythe Bridge, Stoke-On-Trent, ST11 9QJ Tel: (01782) 388439 Fax: (01782) 399737 E-mail: rosiepatterson@hotmail.com

▶ Wholesale Mortgages, Lluest Pentre, Pentre Lane, Rhuddlan, Rhyl, Clwyd, LL18 6HY Tel: (01745) 590006 Fax: (01745) 590016

INSURANCE, MOTORCYCLE

▶ Alan Boswell, High Street, Attleborough, Norfolk, NR17 2EH Tel: (01953) 455600 Fax: (01953) 456400 E-mail: insurance@alanboswell.co.uk

▶ Insurance for Car Hire, Trans-World House, 0 City Road, London, EC1Y 2BP Tel: (020) 7012 6300 Fax: (020) 7012 6315 E-mail: iskra@webfactory.bg

INSURANCE, MUSICAL INSTRUMENT

▶ 18records Ltd, 16 Folly Terrace, Pity Me, Durham, DH1 5DS Tel: 0191-384 3415

▶ Bonners Music Superstore, 56 Langney Road, Eastbourne, East Sussex, BN21 3JN Tel: (01323) 639335 Fax: (01323) 649100 E-mail: info@bonnersmusic.co.uk

▶ Mike Robertson Associates, 3 Old Ladies Court, High Street, Battle, East Sussex, TN33 0AH Tel: (01424) 777156 Fax: (01424) 775668 E-mail: mike.robertson@mraltd.com

▶ Northern Counties Insurance Broker, NCi House, Lowreys Lane, Low Fell, Gateshead, Tyne & Wear, NE9 5JB Tel: 0191 482 1219 Fax: 0191 420 0097 E-mail: contactus@northerncounties.com

▶ Sandham Davies & Jones Ltd, 3 Park Square, Newport, Gwent, NP20 4EL Tel: (01633) 213063 Fax: (01633) 244316 E-mail: enquiries@sdandjones.co.uk

INSURANCE, PRODUCT LIABILITY

▶ Goss & Co Insurance Brokers Ltd, Clarendon House, 59-75 Queen Road, Reading, RG1 4BN Tel: 0118-955 1800 Fax: 0118 955 1848 E-mail: insure@goss.co.uk

Moorhouse Group Limited, Barclay House, Pontygwindy Road, Caerphilly, Mid Glamorgan, CF83 2WJ Tel: (029) 2080 8949 E-mail: nmadhavan@moorhouseinsurance.co.uk

INTEGRATED CIRCUIT (IC) ASSEMBLIES

Martin Woolman Ltd, Unit 12 Martinfield Business Centre, Martinfield, Welwyn Garden City, Hertfordshire, AL7 1HG Tel: (01707) 373181 Fax: (01707) 373174 E-mail: sales@martinwoolman.co.uk

INTEGRATED CIRCUIT (IC) CONSULTANTS/DESIGNERS/ PRODUCTION SERVICES

Consumer Microcircuits Ltd, Ovel Park, Langford, Maldon, Essex, CM9 6WG Tel: (01621) 875500 Fax: (01621) 875600 E-mail: sales@cmlmicro.com

IDT Europe, Prime House, Barnet Wood Lane, Leatherhead, Surrey, KT22 7DE Tel: (01372) 363339 Fax: (01372) 363052

Integrated Micro Systems Ltd, 49 Riverside, Medway City Estate, Rochester, Kent, ME2 4DP Tel: (01634) 714285 Fax: (01634) 715298

Oxford Semiconductor Ltd, 25 Milton Park, Milton, Abingdon, Oxfordshire, OX14 4SH Tel: (01235) 824900 Fax: (01235) 821141 E-mail: sales@oxsemi.com

Semtech Ltd, 218 St. Vincent Street, Glasgow, G2 5SG Tel: 0141-229 5570 Fax: 0141-229 5571

Tality, St. Johns Innovation Centre, Cowley Rd, Cambridge, CB4 0WS Tel: (01223) 421025 Fax: (01223) 421031 E-mail: hr-uk@tality.com

INTEGRATED CIRCUIT (IC) DESIGN

Swindon Silicon Systems Ltd, Radnor Street, Swindon, SN1 3PR Tel: (01793) 649400 Fax: (01793) 616215 E-mail: info@sssl.co.uk

INTEGRATED CIRCUIT (IC) MANUFRS, *See also headings for Particular types*

Semefab (Scotland) Ltd, Newark Road North, Eastfield Industrial Estate, Glenrothes, Fife, KY7 4NS Tel: (01592) 630630 Fax: (01592) 775265 E-mail: sales@semefab.co.uk

Semelab plc, Coventry Road, Lutterworth, Leicestershire, LE17 4JB Tel: (01455) 556565 Fax: (01455) 558371 E-mail: sales@semelab.co.uk

Sequoia Technology Ltd, Basingstoke Road, Spencers Wood, Reading, RG7 1PW Tel: 0118-976 9000 Fax: 0118-976 9070 E-mail: sales@sequoia.co.uk

Wolfson Microelectronics plc, Westfield Road, Edinburgh, EH11 2QB Tel: 0131-272 7000 Fax: 0131-272 7001 E-mail: info@wolfsonmicro.com

Zilog, First Floor Berkshire House, Queen Street, Maidenhead, Berkshire, SL6 1NF Tel: (01628) 639200 Fax: (01628) 781227

INTEGRATED CIRCUIT (IC) SEMICONDUCTORS

Philips, Cross Oak Lane, Redhill, RH1 5HA Tel: (01293) 815000 Fax: (01293) 815511

▶ Zetex Semiconductors, Zetex Technology Park, Chadderton, Oldham, OL9 9LL Tel: 0161-622 4400 Fax: 0161-622 4446 E-mail: europe.sales@zetex.com

INTEGRATED CIRCUITS (IC), LINEAR/LINEAR POWER

▶ Zetex Semiconductors, Zetex Technology Park, Chadderton, Oldham, OL9 9LL Tel: 0161-622 4400 Fax: 0161-622 4446 E-mail: europe.sales@zetex.com

INTEGRATED CIRCUITS, APPLICATION SPECIFIC (ASIC)

Dialog Semiconductor UK Ltd, Windmill Hill Business Park, Whitehill Way, Swindon, SN5 6PJ Tel: (01793) 875327 Fax: (01793) 875328 E-mail: mixed_signal@diasemi.com

Integrated Micro Systems Ltd, 49 Riverside, Medway City Estate, Rochester, Kent, ME2 4DP Tel: (01634) 714285 Fax: (01634) 715298

INTEGRATED COMMUNICATION NETWORK MANAGEMENT SERVICES

Orange Business Services, 217 Bath Road, Slough, SL1 4AA Tel: (020) 8321 4300 Fax: (020) 8321 4040

INTEGRATED COMMUNICATION SYSTEMS SERVICING/ INSTALLATION/MAINTENANCE/ REPAIR SERVICES

Computerworld Western, Unit 1 Fernhill Court, Fernhill, Almondsbury, Bristol, BS32 4LX Tel: (01454) 275400 Fax: (01454) 619931 E-mail: enquiries@computerworld.co.uk

INTEGRATED COMMUNICATION TRAINING SERVICES

▶ J S B Training & Consulting, Dove House, Arcadia Avenue, London, N3 2JU Tel: (020) 8371 7000 Fax: (020) 8371 7001 E-mail: enquiries@jsbonline.com

INTEGRATED MANAGEMENT SYSTEM SOFTWARE

Construction Industry Solutions Ltd, Coins Buildings, The Grove, Slough, SL1 1QP Tel: (01753) 501000 Fax: (01753) 711010 E-mail: info@coins-global.com

INTEGRATED RECYCLING SYSTEMS

▶ JMC Recycling Systems, Harrimans Lane, Lenton Lane Industrial Estate, Nottingham, NG7 2SD Tel: 0115-940 9630 Fax: 0115-979 1478 E-mail: neil@jmcrecycling.com

INTEGRATED SOURCING AND SUPPLY SYSTEMS

I E S A Ltd, Dallon Lane, Warrington, WA2 7PZ Tel: (01925) 634301 Fax: (01925) 417762 E-mail: info@iesa.co.uk

INTEGRATED WAREHOUSE DESIGN STORAGE EQUIPMENT OR SYSTEMS

I A S Storage Systems, Newtonsyde, Charleston, Nigg, Aberdeen, AB12 3LL Tel: (01224) 897305 Fax: (01224) 897305 E-mail: ias@totalise.co.uk

INTELLIGENT ANALOGUE FIRE ALARM SYSTEMS

N K M Fire Protection Ltd, Broadford Oast, Goudhurst Road, Tonbridge, Kent, TN12 8ET Tel: (01892) 724242 Fax: (01892) 723242

INTELLIGENT HOME AUTOMATION SYSTEMS

▶ East Technology Integrators, Lyndhurst, Seer Mead, Seer Green, Beaconsfield, Buckinghamshire, HP9 2QL Tel: 0845 0560245 E-mail: sales@east-ti.co.uk

INTELLIGENT LIGHTING CONTROL SYSTEMS

▶ Procom Services Ltd, 29 Broadmead, Tunbridge Wells, Kent, TN2 5RN Tel: (01892) 525387 E-mail: procom29@aol.com

INTERACTIVE TELEVISION SERVICES AND DESIGNERS

Wild Strawberry Interactive Multimedia Ltd, 1 Cartland Avenue, Shrewsbury, SY2 5UW Tel: (01743) 354386 Fax: (01743) 354386

INTERACTIVE WEBSITE DESIGN

▶ Brown Ink, 6 Home Ground, Shirehampton, Bristol, BS11 0HN Tel: 0117-938 1413 E-mail: rachel@brown-ink.co.uk

C H Media, 20 Marigold Walk, Bristol, BS3 2PD Tel: 0117-939 4061 Fax: (08701) 328330 E-mail: enquiries@chmedia.co.uk

▶ DVH Design, 75 Bedells Avenue, Black Notley, Braintree, Essex, CM77 8NA Tel: 01376 322782 E-mail: request@dvhdesign.co.uk

▶ Genner (Web Site) Construction, PO Box 653, Telford, Shropshire, TF3 1ZN Tel: (01952) 411902 E-mail: kevin@genner.co.uk

Lawrence Creative Ltd, 1 Newton Place, Glasgow, G3 7PR Tel: 0141-333 9009 Fax: 0141-333 9495 E-mail: design@lawrencecreative.com

Lighthouse, 7 Belgrave Terrace, Aberdeen, AB25 2NR Tel: (01224) 627396 Fax: (01224) 621115

▶ Magic Pencil, 16 Upper Meadow Road, Birmingham, B32 1NX Tel: (0870) 2863881 Fax: (0870) 2863882 E-mail: creative@magicpencil.co.uk

▶ Northstar Marketing & Design, Northstar House, 5 Ferns Mead, Farnham, Surrey, GU9 7XP Tel: (01252) 734070 Fax: (01252) 734071 E-mail: info@northstarmarketing.co.uk

▶ The Palmer & Rose Partnership, Maree House, 149 New Road, Booker, High Wycombe, Buckinghamshire, HP12 4RH Tel: (01494) 637499 Fax: (01494) 452630 E-mail: info@palmer-rose.co.uk

Redweb Ltd, Quay House, 7 The Quay, Poole, Dorset, BH15 1HA Tel: (01202) 779944 Fax: (01202) 773643 E-mail: stuart@redweb.co.uk

Savannah Web Design, Gatcombe Court, Dexter Close, St. Albans, Hertfordshire, AL1 5WA Tel: (01727) 763737

INTERCHANGEABLE LETTERING

Info Sign Systems Ltd, 17 East Cromwell Street, Edinburgh, EH6 6HD Tel: 0131-553 6433 Fax: 0131-554 5259 E-mail: admin@ellinfo.co.uk

Silvercases, Daux Road, Billingshurst, West Sussex, RH14 9SR Tel: (01403) 784671 Fax: (01403) 785353 E-mail: info@woodcon.co.uk

INTERCOM CABLES

▶ No Cables Necessary, 3 Crown House, Andover Road, Ludgershall, Andover, Hants, SP11 9LZ Tel: (01264) 395426 Fax: (01264) 395426 E-mail: lee.patterson4@ntlworld.com

INTERCOM DOOR BELLS

▶ Empire, 4 Rose Cottages, Station Road, Claygate, Esher, Surrey, KT10 9DJ Tel: (07010) 714766 Fax: (01372) 466158

▶ London Intercom, 119-123 Sandycombe Road, Richmond, Surrey, TW9 2EP Tel: 07790 145376 E-mail: londonintercom@yahoo.co.uk

▶ No Cables Necessary, 3 Crown House, Andover Road, Ludgershall, Andover, Hants, SP11 9LZ Tel: (01264) 395426 Fax: (01264) 395426 E-mail: lee.patterson4@ntlworld.com

INTERCOMMUNICATION EQUIPMENT/SYSTEMS MANUFRS, *See also headings for particular types*

Anchor Sound & Security, 474 Hatfield Road, St. Albans, Hertfordshire, AL4 0XS Tel: (01727) 831402

Cable Systems, 61 Corbett Road, Waterlooville, Hampshire, PO7 5TA Tel: (023) 9226 9187 Fax: (023) 9226 9187

Comsec, Unit 6-7 Manor Complex, Kirkby Bank Road, Knowsley Industrial Park, Liverpool, L33 7SY Tel: 0151-549 2300 Fax: 0151-549 2300

Folknoll Ltd, 26 Old North Road, Royston, Hertfordshire, SG8 5DT Tel: (01763) 248834 Fax: (01763) 248014 E-mail: general@folknoll.co.uk

Key Communication Systems Ltd, Key House, 21 Bourne Road, Bexley, Kent, DA5 1LW Tel: (01322) 555522 Fax: (01322) 555227 E-mail: info@keycoms.co.uk

Sonic Communications International Ltd, Starley Way, Birmingham, B37 7HB Tel: 0121-781 4400 Fax: 0121-781 4404 E-mail: sales@sonic-comms.com

Stento (U K) Ltd, 3 Baird Close, Maxwell Way, Crawley, West Sussex, RH10 9XE Tel: (01293) 545911 Fax: (01293) 545914 E-mail: intercom@globalnet.co.uk

Trilogy Broadcast, 26 Focus Way, Walworth Industrial Estate, Andover, Hampshire, SP10 5NY Tel: (01264) 384000 Fax: (01264) 334806 E-mail: sales@trilogycomms.com

Windcrest (HSP Electronics) Ltd, Unit 8 Abbey Manufacturing Estate, Mount Pleasant, Wembley, Middlesex, HA0 1NR Tel: (020) 8795 0333 Fax: (020) 8795 0444 E-mail: windcrest@aol.com

INTERFACE ELECTRONIC EQUIPMENT DESIGN

RGB Associates, 20 Newling Way, Worthing, West Sussex, BN13 3DG Tel: (01903) 694904 Fax: (01903) 260899 E-mail: sales@rgb.uk.com

INTERFERENCE ANALYSERS

E M C Hire Ltd, Ivel Road, Shefford, Bedfordshire, SG17 5JU Tel: (01462) 817111 Fax: (01462) 817444 E-mail: sales@emchire.co.uk

INTERFERENCE FILTER CONNECTORS

Amphenol Ltd, Thanet Way, Whitstable, Kent, CT5 3JF Tel: (01227) 773200 Fax: (01227) 276571 E-mail: info@amphenol.co.uk

INTERFERENCE FILTER MANUFRS

Ampohm Wound Products, Unit 1d Treburley Industrial Estate, Treburley, Launceston, Cornwall, PL15 9PU Tel: (01579) 370025 Fax: (01579) 370051 E-mail: ampcaps15@btconnect.com

B C Electrical Techniques Ltd, Stocklake, Aylesbury, Buckinghamshire, HP20 1DA Tel: (01296) 481995 Fax: (01296) 394158 E-mail: info@bcet.co.uk

INTERFERENCE SUPPRESSORS

Ampohm Wound Products, Unit 1d Treburley Industrial Estate, Treburley, Launceston, Cornwall, PL15 9PU Tel: (01579) 370025 Fax: (01579) 370051 E-mail: ampcaps15@btconnect.com

Evox Rifa Uk, 20-21 Cumberland Drive, Granby Industrial Estate, Weymouth, Dorset, DT4 9TE Tel: (01305) 830737 Fax: (01305) 760670

M P E Ltd, Hammond Road, Knowsley Industrial Park, Liverpool, L33 7UL Tel: 0151-632 9100 Fax: 0151-632 9112 E-mail: sales@mpe.co.uk

INTERFEROMETERS

Arden Photonics Ltd, Business & Innovation Centre Aston Science Park, Love Lane, Birmingham, B7 4BJ Tel: 0121-250 3588 Fax: (01564) 205043 E-mail: david@ardenphotonics.com

INTERIM MANAGEMENT CONSULTANCY

Albemarle Interim Management P.L.C., 26-28 Great Portland Street, London, W1W 8QT Tel: (020) 7079 3737 Fax: (020) 7631 1881 E-mail: managers@albemarle.co.uk

▶ Business Development International, Business House, Higher Wych, Malpas, Cheshire, SY14 7JT Tel: (01948) 780515 E-mail: info@bdinternational.co.uk

▶ Cream Interim, Hudson House, 8 Tavistock Street, London, WC2E 7PP Tel: (020) 7559 6767 Fax: (0870) 0941613 E-mail: info@creaminterim.co.uk

D B I Associates Ltd, Stoneleigh Park Mews, Stonleigh Abbey, Kenilworth, Warwickshire, CV8 2DB Tel: (01926) 312481 Fax: (01926) 515616 E-mail: consultants@dbiconsulting.co.uk

Executives Online, Dolphin House, St. Peter Street, Winchester, Hampshire, SO23 8BW Tel: (01962) 829705 Fax: (01962) 866116 E-mail: info@executivesonline.co.uk

Global Executives Ltd, 18 Stoneleigh Court, Frimley, Camberley, Surrey, GU16 8XH Tel: (01276) 671535 Fax: (01276) 671536 E-mail: sales@globalexecutives.com

Indacom Group Ltd, 131 Hollywood Lane Wainscott, Rochester, Kent, ME3 8AS Tel: (01634) 716286 Fax: (01634) 724821 E-mail: adavis.indacom@btopenworld.com

▶ John Macdonald Consultancy Ltd, Forest View, 62 Loughborough Road, Coleorton, Coalville, Leicestershire, LE67 8HG Tel: (01530) 223456 Fax: 01530 223456 E-mail: john@johnmaccon.freeserve.co.uk

▶ Marchaven Consulting Ltd, 8 Daisy Lane, Overseal, Swadlincote, Derbyshire, DE12 6JH Tel: (01283) 761813 E-mail: jarvis.whitehead@marchaven.co.uk

▶ Merlin Consultancy, 2 Upper Cosmeston Farm, Penarth, South Glamorgan, CF64 5UB Tel: (029) 2070 0045 Fax: (029) 2070 0045 E-mail: sales@merlinconsultancy.com

Newburgh Management Services Ltd, 13 Cobbs Brow Lane, Newburgh, Wigan, Lancashire, WN8 7ND Tel: 0161-746 8582 Fax: (08700) 549489 E-mail: nmsl.ewj@btinternet.com

PHS Associates Ltd, 38 Ashworth Park, Knutsford, Cheshire, WA16 9DL Tel: (01565) 653330 E-mail: sales@p-h-s.co.uk

Pressure Systems International Ltd, 124 Victoria Road, Farnborough, Hampshire, GU14 7PW Tel: (01252) 510000 Fax: (01252) 510099 E-mail: sales@pressure-systems.com

Supply Control Ltd, Broomlea, Pacemuir Road, Kilmacolm, Renfrewshire, PA13 4JJ Tel: (01505) 873255 E-mail: neilm@supplycontrol.com

W B S Consulting, Grove Business Centre, Grove Technology Park, Wantage, Oxfordshire, OX12 9FF Tel: (01235) 227434 Fax: (01235) 227435 E-mail: enquiries@wwbsgroup.com

▶ Wilson Alexander, Queen Caroline House, 3 High, Windsor, Berkshire, SL4 1LD Tel: (01753) 850540 Fax: 01753 850490 E-mail: info@wilsonalexander.com

INTERIM MANAGEMENT RECRUITMENT

▶ Cream Interim, Hudson House, 8 Tavistock Street, London, WC2E 7PP Tel: (020) 7559 6767 Fax: (0870) 0941613 E-mail: info@creaminterim.co.uk

INTERIOR ARCHITECTURAL DESIGN

▶ Abode Interior Design, Oxbow Farm, Avon Dassett, Southam, Warwickshire, CV47 2AQ Tel: (01295) 690196 Fax: (01295) 690194 E-mail: info@uk-designer.com

▶ Amber Radiator Covers, 14 Freemans Way, Harrogate, North Yorkshire, HG3 1DH Tel: (01423) 883386 Fax: (01423) 883386 E-mail: sales@amberradiatorcovers.co.uk

▶ Freeman Associates, 92 Church Street, Swinton, Mexborough, South Yorkshire, S64 8DQ Tel: (01709) 578078 Fax: (01709) 578153 E-mail: designs@freemanassociates.co.uk

Knight Architechtural Design, 181 Kathleen Road, Southampton, SO19 8GX Tel: (023) 8042 0938 Fax: (023) 8042 0938 E-mail: ian.kad@lineone.net

▶ Scail, B Claylands Road, Bishops Waltham, Southampton, SO32 1BH Tel: (01489) 893453 Fax: (01489) 894730 E-mail: neil.stantiall@scail.co.uk

INTERIOR DESIGN COMPUTER AIDED DESIGN (CAD) COMPUTER SOFTWARE

Hollis Design LLP, 30 St Catherines Road, Winchester, Hampshire, SO23 0PS Tel: (0845) 8382034 E-mail: architect@hollisdesign.co.uk

▶ Nortech Design Ltd, 3 Alstonefield, Emerson Valley, Milton Keynes, MK4 2HA Tel: (01908) 330427 Fax: (0870) 7064019 E-mail: enquiries@nortechdesign.ltd.uk

▶ Visuals 3D, 26 School Brow, Romiley, Stockport, Cheshire, SK6 3AT Tel: 0161-430 2623 E-mail: info@visuals-3d.co.uk

INTERIOR DESIGN MATERIALS CONSULTANCY

Handmade Curtain Co., 49 Turner Rise, Oadby, Leicester, LE2 5SH Tel: 0116-271 6954 E-mail: info@handmade-curtains.co.uk

INTERIOR DESIGN SUPPLIES

C Alexander, Dumbleton Lane, Eardiston, Tenbury Wells, Worcestershire, WR15 8JR Tel: (01584) 881501 Fax: (01584) 881168

INTERIOR DESIGN, OFFICE

M K H Ltd, 5 Gloster Drive, Kenilworth, Warwickshire, CV8 2TU Tel: (01926) 850555 Fax: (01926) 850888 E-mail: mkh.ltd@virgin.net

INTERIOR DESIGNERS OR PLANNERS

C Alexander, Dumbleton Lane, Eardiston, Tenbury Wells, Worcestershire, WR15 8JR Tel: (01584) 881501 Fax: (01584) 881168

▶ C J Design, 47 St. Dunstans Road, Bristol, BS3 5NZ Tel: (07798) 808594 Fax: (0870) 8555366

▶ C R D Interiors Ltd, 245 High Street, Aldershot, Hampshire, GU12 4NG Tel: (01252) 319588 Fax: (01252) 310698 E-mail: crd-interiors@lycos.co.uk

Careers In Design Recruitment Ltd, 28 New Road, Ware, Hertfordshire, SG12 7BU Tel: (01920) 486125 Fax: (01920) 412599 E-mail: recruit@careersindesign.com

▶ Chameleon Interior Design, 253 Greystones Road, Greystones, Sheffield, S11 7BT Tel: 0114-266 6252 E-mail: louise@chameleoninteriors.wanadoo.co.uk

▶ Chameleon Products Ltd, 8 Grange Close, Bradley Stoke, Bristol, BS32 0AH Tel: (01425) 655952 Fax: (01425) 655607 E-mail: tsw@chameleonproducts.net

▶ CheekyTiki Ltd, Unit E, 2 Leswin Place, Stoke Newington, London, N16 7NJ Tel: (020) 7241 0742 Fax: (020) 7241 0742 E-mail: info@cheekytiki.com

▶ Christian Garnett Partners, 195 High Holborn, London, WC1V 7BD Tel: (020) 7404 7677 Fax: (020) 7404 6648 E-mail: sales@christiangarnett.com

▶ Contemporary Living, 25 Peaseland Road, Cleckheaton, West Yorkshire, BD19 3EZ Tel: (01274) 861855 Fax: (01274) 876529 E-mail: design@contemporaryliving.tv

▶ Cunningham McLean Partnership, 4 Canniesburn Square, Bearsden, Bearsden, Glasgow, G61 1QW Tel: 0141-942 2221 Fax: 0141-942 3113

▶ Design4business, Design 4 Business, Prestwick Hall Farm, Ponteland, Newcastle upon Tyne, NE20 9TU Tel: 01661 820769

▶ Falcon Interiors, Bluesky House, Western Way, Melksham, Wiltshire, SN12 8BZ Tel: (01225) 704084 Fax: (01225) 700843 E-mail: sales@falconinteriors.biz

▶ Fun Art Design, Suite 205, The Citadel Business Centre, Bath Road, Chippenham, Wiltshire, SN15 2AB Tel: (0794) 0716747 E-mail: info@funartdesign.co.uk

Peter Hall & Son, Danes Road, Staveley, Kendal, Cumbria, LA8 9PR Tel: (01539) 821633 Fax: (01539) 821905 E-mail: info@peter-hall.co.uk

▶ Interior Matters UK Ltd, 18 Cecil Avenue, Bournemouth, BH8 9EH Tel: (01202) 528152 E-mail: sue@interiormatters.co.uk

▶ Kelson Interiors, Topcliffe Lane, Morley, Leeds, LS27 0HW Tel: 0113-252 7900 Fax: 0113-252 7977 E-mail: info@kelson.co.uk

Wilson Mason & Partners, 3 Chandos Street, London, W1G 9JU Tel: (020) 7637 1501 Fax: (020) 7631 0325 E-mail: enquiries@wilsonmason.co.uk

Mystic East Cushions, PO BOX 51568, London, LONDON, SE1 2JT Tel: 0845 612 1551 E-mail: mysticeastcushions@miscobjects.com

▶ Nicholas Pryke, 25 Hayfield Road, Oxford, OX2 6TX Tel: 07990 975261 Fax: 01865 510620 E-mail: angela.kennedy@xko.co.uk

▶ Sally Treloar, Southview, Whiteoak Green, Hailey, Witney, Oxfordshire, OX29 9XP Tel: 01993 869119 E-mail: support@firstideas.co.uk

▶ Seasons Textiles Ltd, 15 Gorst Road, London, NW10 6LA Tel: (020) 8965 6161 Fax: (020) 8961 6433 E-mail: enquiries@seasonstextiles.net

Spencer & Co., The Green, Long Lawford, Rugby, Warwickshire, CV23 9BL Tel: (01788) 560782 Fax: (01788) 537917 E-mail: enquiries@spencerfurniture.co.uk

▶ Starry Night Ceilings, 37A Bolton Street, Ramsbottom, Bury, Lancashire, BL0 9HU Tel: (07904) 811480 E-mail: info@starrynightceilings.net

▶ Visual Communications, 209 Lynchford Road, Farnborough, Hampshire, GU14 6HF Tel: (01252) 540044 Fax: (01252) 516616 E-mail: tara@vis-com.net

▶ Zemira Designs, 26 Fairwood Park, Marton-in-Cleveland, Middlesbrough, Cleveland, TS8 9XP Tel: (01642) 271440 E-mail: zemiradesigns@hotmail.com

INTERIOR FURNISHERS, *See Furnishers, Contract*

INTERIOR REFURBISHMENT OR RESTORATION

A.Davies & Co.(Shopfitters)Limited, Chiswick Studios, Power Road, London, W4 5PY Tel: (020) 8987 4100 Fax: (020) 8987 2647 E-mail: info@daviesshopfitters.com

F. Brown P.L.C., 75 Moor Lane, Preston, PR1 1JQ Tel: (01772) 824141 Fax: (01772) 203383 E-mail: fbrownplc@btconnect.com

Curtis Steel Ltd, Mill Road, Radstock, BA3 5TX Tel: (01761) 432841 Fax: (01761) 433919 E-mail: sales@unilockproducts.com

Epr Architects Ltd, 30 Millbank, London, SW1P 4WY Tel: (020) 7630 9027 Fax: (020) 7630 9027 E-mail: architects@epr.co.uk

Europa Shop & Office Fitting, 3 Maxted Road, Hemel Hempstead Industrial Estate, Hemel Hempstead, Hertfordshire, HP2 7DX Tel: (01442) 213412 Fax: (01442) 267672 E-mail: postmaster@europa-shopfitting.co.uk

Firco Construction Ltd, 1 Denton Slipways Site, Wharf Road, Gravesend, Kent, DA12 2RU Tel: (01474) 351644 Fax: (01474) 358936 E-mail: firco@gravesend.demon.co.uk

Fleurtations Workshop, Unit 11, Whin Park Industrial Estate, Cockenzie, Prestonpans, East Lothian, EH32 0JL Tel: 01875 813171

Interior Contracts Group, Ethos House, 52 Tanners Drive, Blakelands, Milton Keynes, MK14 5BW Tel: (01908) 216766 Fax: (01908) 216744

M.J.M Marine Ltd, 10 Loughbrickland Road, Rathfriland, Newry, County Down, BT34 5AA Tel: (028) 4063 8396 Fax: (028) 4063 8973 E-mail: sales@mjmmarine.com

Material Matters, 2 Ninian Park, Ninian Way, Wilnecote, Tamworth, Staffordshire, B77 5ES Tel: (01827) 262527 Fax: (01827) 262530

Millbrook Furnishings Industries, Stephenson Road, Calmore Industrial Estate, Totton, Southampton, SO40 3RY Tel: (023) 8066 2221 Fax: (023) 8066 2264E-mail: sales@mfil.co.uk

Modular Environment, 31 Dalsholm Avenue, Glasgow, G20 0TS Tel: 0141-946 2222 Fax: 0141-946 2211

Nova Interior Contracts, Millennium House, Centenary Place, Congleton, Cheshire, CW12 1EZ Tel: (01260) 273759 Fax: (01260) 297397

O C Interiors Ltd, 8 Swanwick Business Park, Bridge Road, Swanwick, Southampton, SO31 7GB Tel: (01489) 565522 Fax: (01489) 565585 E-mail: mail@ocinteriors.ltd.uk

Pieri Interiors Ltd, New Road, Sheerness, Kent, ME12 1BW Tel: (01795) 580100 Fax: (01795) 580654

Pub Dressing Co., 57 Lisanally La, Armagh, BT61 7HE Tel: (028) 3752 8899 Fax: (028) 3752 6358

R B Emerson, 8a Temple Farm Industrial Estate, Coopers Way, Temple Farm Industrial Estate, Southend-on-Sea, SS2 5TE Tel: (01702) 461999 Fax: (01702) 462001 E-mail: sales@emersons.uk.com

Sherlock Interiors Contracting Ltd, 20-22 Vestry Street, London, N1 7RE Tel: (020) 7336 7337 Fax: (020) 7336 7180 E-mail: info@sherlock.demon.co.uk

Space Craft Projects Ltd, Sandbeck Way, Wetherby, West Yorkshire, LS22 7DN Tel: (01937) 584554 Fax: (01937) 580012 E-mail: info@space-craft.co.uk

Town House : Country House, 56 Byron St, Glasgow, G11 6LZ Tel: 0141-357 2250 Fax: 0141-339 9005

INTERLININGS, *See also headings for particular types*

A E Davidson & Son Ltd, 3 Alton Road Industrial Estate, Ross-on-Wye, Herefordshire, HR9 5NB Tel: (01989) 764850 Fax: (01989) 768291 E-mail: aedties@btinternet.com

Lainiere De Picardie UK Ltd, 5 Danbury Court, Sunrise Parkway, Linford Wood, Milton Keynes, MK14 6PL Tel: (0870) 1213160 Fax: (0870) 1213161 E-mail: lpuk@chargeurs-interlining.com

INTERLININGS, MAN-MADE/ SYNTHETIC FIBRE

Calder Weaving Co. Ltd, Scout Road, Hebden Bridge, West Yorkshire, HX7 5HZ Tel: (01422) 882382 Fax: (01422) 883381 E-mail: sales@calderweaving.co.uk

Jaftextil Ltd, Unit 18, Hillgate Business Centre, Swallow Street, Higher Hillgate, Stockport, Cheshire, SK1 3AU Tel: 0161-480 2342 Fax: 0161-480 2397 E-mail: info@jaftextil.co.uk

Vilene Interlinings, PO Box 3, Elland, West Yorkshire, HX5 9DX Tel: (01422) 327900 Fax: (01422) 327999 E-mail: vilenesales@freudenberg-nw.com

INTERLOCK MACHINE GUARDS

Fortress Interlocks Ltd, Birmingham New Road, Wolverhampton, WV4 6NT Tel: (01902) 499600 Fax: (01902) 499610 E-mail: sales@fortress-interlocks.co.uk
Highwood Engineering Ltd, Parkfield Road, Birmingham, B8 3AZ Tel: 0121-327 9212 Fax: 0121-327 4329
Mechan Controls Ltd, 14 Seddon Place, Stanley Industrial Estate, Skelmersdale, Lancashire, WN8 8EB Tel: (01695) 722264 Fax: (01695) 729664 E-mail: info@mechancontrols.co.uk
Price Guarding Systems, Waterside Estate, Cradley Road, Dudley, West Midlands, DY2 9RG Tel: 0121-525 4973 Fax: (01384) 241039
Unimax, Unit 2, Acan Business Park, Garrard Way, Telford Way Industrial Estate, Kettering, Northamptonshire, NN16 8TD Tel: (01536) 419200 Fax: (01536) 419222 E-mail: sales@unimaxswitch.com

INTERLOCKED CHANGEOVER CONTACTOR SPARE PARTS

Unimax, Unit 2, Acan Business Park, Garrard Way, Telford Way Industrial Estate, Kettering, Northamptonshire, NN16 8TD Tel: (01536) 419200 Fax: (01536) 419222 E-mail: sales@unimaxswitch.com

INTERLOCKING SAFETY DEVICE LOCKS

Fortress Interlocks Ltd, Birmingham New Road, Wolverhampton, WV4 6NT Tel: (01902) 499600 Fax: (01902) 499610 E-mail: sales@fortress-interlocks.co.uk
Smith Flow Control Ltd, 6 Waterside Business Park, Eastways, Witham, Essex, CM8 3YQ Tel: (01376) 517901 Fax: (01376) 518720 E-mail: sales@smithflowcontrol.com
Unimax, Unit 2, Acan Business Park, Garrard Way, Telford Way Industrial Estate, Kettering, Northamptonshire, NN16 8TD Tel: (01536) 419200 Fax: (01536) 419222 E-mail: sales@unimaxswitch.com

INTERMEDIATE BULK CONTAINER (IBC) FABRICS

Wessex Rope & Packaging, 6 20 Abingdon Road, Nuffield Industrial Estate, Poole, Dorset, BH17 0UG Tel: (01202) 661066 Fax: (01202) 661077 E-mail: sales@wrp-poole.co.uk

INTERNAL FITTING OUT BUILDING CONTRACTORS

▶ Tvedt Group Ltd, Alma House, 38 Crimea Road, Aldershot, Hampshire, GU11 1UD Tel: (01252) 318388 Fax: 01252 336894 E-mail: enquiries@tvedt.co.uk

INTERNAL FLOATING TANK ROOFS

Johnson Hall Services Ltd, 93 Gorof Road, Ystradgynlais, Lower Cwmtwrch, Swansea, SA9 1DS Tel: (01639) 849564 Fax: (01639) 845348

INTERNAL GLASS DOORS

▶ Woodcraft Supplies, 163-165 Deanston Drive, Glasgow, G41 3LP Tel: 0141-649 3838 Fax: 0141-649 9181 E-mail: info@woodcraftsupplies.co.uk

INTERNAL GRINDING

Accurate Grinding, Unit 6 Dawsons Lane, Barwell, Leicester, LE9 8BE Tel: (01455) 840888 Fax: (01455) 840888
Ambit Precision Grinding, 38a Kenilworth Drive, Oadby, Leicester, LE2 5LG Tel: 0116-271 1011 Fax: 0161-627 1101 E-mail: adam@ambit.fsnet.co.uk
Bosworth Tools (Cutters) Ltd, Unit 19 20, Sketchley Meadows Industrial Estate, Hinckley, Leicestershire, LE10 3ES Tel: (01455) 250066 Fax: (01455) 250077
C R I Grinding Ltd, 2a Goodridge Avenue, Gloucester, GL2 5EA Tel: (01452) 529475 Fax: (01452) 306362 E-mail: cri.grinding@virgin.net
Enterprise Engineering Gloucester Ltd, Units D5-D6 Innsworth Technology Park, Innsworth Lane, Gloucester, GL3 1DL Tel: (01452) 731881 Fax: (01452) 731887 E-mail: dave@honing.co.uk
FCJ, 10a Bushey Hall Road, Bushey, WD23 2EA Tel: (01923) 220137 Fax: (01923) 233027 E-mail: sales@fcjprecisiongrinding.co.uk
G & W Grinding Services Ltd, Unit A Thomas Street, Walsall, WS2 8NE Tel: (01922) 723481 Fax: (01922) 724968
Leigh Precision Grinding, 132 Blyth Road, Hayes, Middlesex, UB3 1TD Tel: (020) 8573 0451 Fax: (020) 8561 6399 E-mail: leighgrinding@btinternet.co.uk
M & D Precision Grinding, Unit 8 North Weylands Industrial Estate, Molesey Road, Walton-on-Thames, Surrey, KT12 3PL Tel: (01932) 246270 Fax: (01932) 246270
Charles Styles Ltd, New Bond Street, Birmingham, B9 4EJ Tel: 0121-772 2424 Fax: 0121-771 2597 E-mail: sales@hexasports.co.uk

INTERNAL GRINDING MACHINES

Emag (U.K.) Ltd, Chestnut House, Kingswood Business Park, Albrighton, Wolverhampton, WV7 3AU Tel: (01902) 373121 Fax: (01902) 376091 E-mail: sales@emag-vsc.co.uk

INTERNAL MICROMETERS

Sangha Metrology, Blanche Street, Bradford, West Yorkshire, BD4 8DA Tel: (01274) 667785 Fax: (01274) 662523

INTERNAL WALL INSULATION SYSTEMS

Absolute Insulations, 21 Wanstead Road, Leicester, LE3 1TR Tel: 0116-287 8958 Fax: 0116-231 4002
▶ Roofing Insulation Services, Hilldale House, 9 Hilldale Avenue, Blackley, Manchester, M9 6PQ Tel: (0800) 7318314 E-mail: info@sprayfoaminsulation.co.uk

INTERNATIONAL AIR EXPRESS CARRIER SERVICES

A Cars Express Despatch Ltd, Unit 14 Langley Terrace Industrial Park, Latimer Road, Luton, LU1 3XQ Tel: (01582) 731900 Fax: (0870) 2330612 E-mail: acars@acars.co.uk
DHL Express (UK) Ltd, Orbital Pk, 178-188 Great South West Rd, Hounslow, TW4 6JS Tel: (08701) 100300
Target Worldwide Express Ltd, 6 Woodlands Park, Ashton Road, Newton-le-Willows, Merseyside, WA12 0HF Tel: (01925) 247000 Fax: (01925) 575700 E-mail: enquiries@targetexpress.co.uk

INTERNATIONAL DEBT RECOVERY

▶ CCI Legal Services Ltd, Unit 5, Snowdonia Business Park, Minffordd, Penrhyndeudraeth, Gwynedd, LL48 6LD Tel: (01766) 771166 Fax: (01766) 771840 E-mail: sales@ccilegal.co.uk
▶ Credit Tel International, Network House, 45 Warwick Road, Thames Ditton, Surrey, KT7 0PR Tel: (020) 8398 9555 Fax: (020) 8398 7831 E-mail: info@credittel.com
▶ CRS Debt Recovery Solicitors, 12 Park Place, Leeds, LS1 2RU Tel: 0113 2467887 Fax: 0113 2439822 E-mail: info@carrickread.com
Debt Collect, Baltic Chambers, 50 Wellington Street, Glasgow, G2 6HJ Tel: (0845) 1202935 Fax: (0845) 1302936 E-mail: enquiries@debtcollectuk.com
▶ Renaissance, 1 Emperor Way, Exeter Business Park, Exeter Business Park, Exeter, EX1 3QS Tel: (01803) 404047 Fax: (01803) 404048 E-mail: enquiries@debt-recovery-services.com
Tigon Corporate Debt Recovery Services, The Old School House, Stanley, Crook, County Durham, DL15 9AN Tel: (01388) 767306 Fax: (01453) 823520 E-mail: gtomaszko@turnstoneuk.co.uk
▶ Zero Cost Debt Recovery, Europa House, Barcroft Street, Bury, Lancashire, BL9 5BT Tel: 0161-447 8816 Fax: (0870) 4582900 E-mail: info@zero-cost-debt-recovery.com

INTERNATIONAL EXHIBITION SHIPPING OR TRANSPORT

D J G Exhibition Freight Services Ltd, Unit 34 Grace Business Centre, Willow Lane, Mitcham, Surrey, CR4 4TQ Tel: (020) 8646 4200 Fax: (020) 8646 6090 E-mail: d.j.g.efsl@btinternet.com
▶ European International, Unit 5 6 Skitts Manor Farm, Moor Lane, Marsh Green, Edenbridge, Kent, TN8 5RA Tel: (01732) 860330 Fax: (01732) 860331 E-mail: info@european-intl.com
Geologistics Expo Services Ltd, Unit 18 National Exhibition Centre, Third Exhibition Avenue, Birmingham, B40 1PJ Tel: 0121-780 2627 Fax: 0121-780 2329
Worldwide Exhibition Specialists Ltd, 1 York House, Langston Road, Loughton, Essex, IG10 3TQ Tel: (020) 8508 2224 Fax: (020) 8502 4969 E-mail: info@worldwidexpo.co.uk
Yorkshire Exhibtion Services, Unit 17 Industrial Estate, National Exhibition Centre, Birmingham, B40 1PJ Tel: 0121-782 4626 Fax: 0121-782 4680 E-mail: horst@yes-exh.com

INTERNATIONAL FUNDING CONSULTANCY

▶ Business Angel Finance, 21 Dapps Hill, Keynsham, Bristol, BS31 1ES Tel: (0845) 8380936 E-mail: info@businessangelfinance.co.uk
Project Monitor Ltd, 30 Gritstone Road, Matlock, Derbyshire, DE4 3GB Tel: (01629) 581384 Fax: (01629) 584972 E-mail: pdsl@dile.pipex.com
▶ vision40 finance, 7 Whymark Avenue, Woodgreen, London, N22 6DJ Tel: (07958) 630576 Fax: (020) 8352 3472 E-mail: tanwa@vision40finance.com

INTERNATIONAL MAILING HOUSES

DHL Global Mail Ltd, Mills Road, Quarry Wood, Aylesford, Kent, ME20 7WZ Tel: (01622) 792111 Fax: (01622) 792333

INTERNATIONAL SYSTEM MODEM TELEPHONE ADAPTERS

Mult-I-Tel, 27 Woodland Road, Melling, Liverpool, L31 1EB Tel: 0151-548 8122 E-mail: com_links@compuserve.com

INTERNATIONAL TRADE DEVELOPMENT OR PROMOTION ORGANISATIONS

Jersey Chamber of Commerce & Industry Inc., Chamber House, 25 Pier Road, St. Helier, Jersey, JE1 4HF Tel: (01534) 724536 Fax: (01534) 734942 E-mail: admin@jerseychamber.com
▶ Unit 17 Ltd, BBIC, 17 Innovation Way, Barnsley, South Yorkshire, S75 1JL Tel: (07919) 424954 Fax: (01226) 249590 E-mail: studio@unit17.co.uk

INTERNET ACCESS SERVICES

▶ Cafenet UK, 63 Watergate Street, Chester, CH1 2LB Tel: (01244) 401116 E-mail: info@cafenetuk.com

INTERNET ACCESSIBILITY CONSULTANCY

▶ Amberlight Partners, 58 Bloomsbury Street, London, WC1B 3QT Tel: (020) 7307 7770 E-mail: info@amber-light.co.uk

INTERNET ADVERTISING SALES MANAGEMENT

▶ Guava Ltd, Hurst Grove, Sandford Lane, Hurst, Reading, RG10 0SQ Tel: 0118-932 1100 Fax: 0118-932 1222 E-mail: info@guava.co.uk
Stanton Media Sales, 10 Grazing Lane, Redditch, Worcestershire, B97 5PE Tel: (01527) 404295 Fax: (01527) 540503 E-mail: sales@stantonmedia.co.uk

INTERNET APPLICATION DEVELOPMENT

Apex Computer International Ltd, Apex House, The Mallards, South Cerney, Cirencester, Gloucestershire, GL7 5TQ Tel: (01285) 862100 Fax: (01285) 862111
▶ Ashridge New Media, 131-151 Great Titchfield Street, London, W1W 5BB Tel: (0845) 2305105
Birlasoft UK Ltd, Cromwell House, 142 High Street, Stevenage, Hertfordshire, SG1 3HN Tel: (01438) 350270 Fax: (01438) 749309 E-mail: corp@birlasoft.co.uk
▶ Brand Attention Ltd, 30A Bridge Street, Hitchin, Hertfordshire, SG5 2DF Tel: (01462) 435330 E-mail: info@brandattention.com
C S T Group Ltd, 94 Lewes Road, Brighton, BN2 3QA Tel: (01273) 621393 Fax: (01273) 621390 E-mail: info@cst-group.com
▶ Clearpeople Ltd, 17 Heathmans Road, London, SW6 4TJ Tel: (0870) 1999910 Fax: (0709) 2163189 E-mail: info@clearpeople.com
Frog Networking Solutions Ltd, 1 Lion Works, Cambridge, CB2 4NL Tel: (01223) 493500 Fax: (0870) 4446772 E-mail: system@frog.co.uk
Frontline Consultancy Business Services Ltd, Frontline House, Epsom Avenue, Handforth, Wilmslow, Cheshire, SK9 3PW Tel: (0870) 2410715 Fax: (0870) 6067300 E-mail: sales@frontline-consultancy.co.uk
Heartfield Technologies Ltd, Bromley, BR2 0WL Tel: (020) 8313 3088 Fax: (020) 8313 3002 E-mail: info@heartfield.co.uk
▶ Initiative2 Web Site Design, Rosewood, Hareburn Road, Bridge of Don, Aberdeen, AB23 8AR Tel: (01224) 820960 E-mail: sales@initiative2.com
Kanbay Europe Ltd, Regus House, 1010 Cambourne Business Park, Cambourne, Cambridge, CB3 6DP Tel: (01223) 597836 Fax: (01223) 598062
Kutana Computer Systems, The Old Mill, Mill Street, Wantage, Oxfordshire, OX12 9AB Tel: (0870) 2202275E-mail: info@kutana.co.uk
▶ Online Design Media Ltd, Caversham House, 4 Gosbrook Road, Caversham, Reading, RG4 8BS Tel: 0118-947 6644 Fax: 0118-947 6690 E-mail: sales@online-design.co.uk
S F K Information, Langdale House, Lothersdale, Keighley, West Yorkshire, BD20 8HB Tel: (01535) 637390E-mail: info@sfkinfo.co.uk
▶ Steven Burrows, 12 Henderson Road, Bangor, County Down, BT19 1NN Tel: (07931) 362847 Fax: (08715) 227115 E-mail: info@steveburrows.co.uk
Telecetera Computer Consultants, Carden Close, Worcester, WR1 2AR Tel: (01905) 612220 Fax: (01905) 612226 E-mail: info@telecetera.co.uk
True Systems Ltd, Systems House, 127 High Street, Teddington, Middlesex, TW11 8HH Tel: (020) 8977 5151 E-mail: sales@truesystems.co.uk
W P C Software Ltd, 9 Wellsway, Keynsham, Bristol, BS31 1HS Tel: 0117-908 1484 Fax: 0117-940 2060 E-mail: wpc@wpcsoft.com
W S I Expert Net Solutions, 54 Gleneagles Road, Bloxwich, Walsall, WS3 3UJ Tel: (07855) 413370 Fax: (07813) 964997 E-mail: jon@wsiexpertnetsolutions.com

INTERNET BASED APPLICATION DEVELOPMENT

▶ TravellingPhotos.com, 1 Station Road, Lewes, East Sussex, BN7 2YY Tel: (07880) 730096
▶ Yonder Mountain, Maunview, 2 Old Mill Close, Forest Town, Mansfield, Nottinghamshire, NG19 0EA Tel: (01623) 625545 E-mail: ron.koch@yonder-mountain.co.uk

INTERNET BASED CATALOGUE CREATION SERVICES

▶ Benson Cairns Communications, 30B/9 Chambers Street, Edinburgh, EH1 1HR Tel: 0131 220 3785 Fax: 0131 220 3786 E-mail: rachelle@bensoncairns.co.uk

INTERNET BASED CUSTOMER RELATIONSHIP MANAGEMENT (CRM) SOFTWARE

▶ Advanced Solutions International Europe, The Old Pump House, The Stables, Pettaugh Road, Stonham Aspal, Stowmarket, Suffolk, IP14 6AU Tel: 08705 887700 Fax: 01473 892032 E-mail: info-eu@advsol.com
▶ Black Sun plc, Fulham Palace, Fulham, London, SW6 6EA Tel: (020) 7736 0011 Fax: (020) 7736 1294 E-mail: jobs@blacksunplc.com
▶ Cobault Computer Systems, 29 Great George Street, Bristol, BS1 5QT Tel: 0117-920 0123 Fax: 0117-920 0124E-mail: info@cobault.com
▶ Just C R M, Garden Cottage, Elsfield, Oxford, OX3 9UH Tel: (01865) 351771 E-mail: jonbowen@personal-computer-services.co.uk

INTERNET BASED SALES FORCE PERSONNEL RECRUITMENT

BSC Sales Specialists, BSC House, 16 Blackfriars Street, Salford, M3 5BQ Tel: 0161-834 6234 Fax: 0161-835 3114

INTERNET BASED SOFTWARE

DocIndexer, St. Martins House, 16 St. Martins le Grand, London, EC1A 4EN Tel: (0870) 7668440 Fax: (0871) 2884087 E-mail: kellysearch@tickboxdb.com

INTERNET BASED VIRTUAL TOUR TECHNOLOGY

▶ Circulate, 11 Reverdy Road, London, SE1 5QE Tel: (020) 7237 6042 Fax: (020) 7237 6042 E-mail: info@circulateonline.com

INTERNET BUSINESS DIRECTORIES

▶ Adwebtiser, 300 Bradford Road, Batley, West Yorkshire, WF17 5PW Tel: (01924) 420712 E-mail: info@adwebtiser.com
▶ City Of Stirling Media Ltd, Suite 1, Castle House, 1 Baker Street, Stirling, FK8 1AL Tel: 0845 226 1896 E-mail: hello@cos-media.co.uk
▶ Ealing Life Magazine, P O Box 54909, London, W3 9WP Tel: (020) 8932 8302
▶ Emily May Productions Ltd, Slaney Place, Staplehurst, Kent, TN12 0DT Tel: (01580) 893209 Fax: (01580) 893209 E-mail: doug@emilymayproductions.com
G B Direct, The Design Exchange, 34 Peckover Street, Bradford, West Yorkshire, BD1 5BD Tel: (0870) 2007273 E-mail: info@gbdirect.co.uk
▶ Loud-N-Clear Com Ltd, 29 Castle Crescent, Reading, RG1 6AQ Tel: 0118-967 7693 Fax: 0118-954 2756 E-mail: enquiries@loud-n-clear.com
▶ Omagh Business Forum, 33 Market Street, Omagh, County Tyrone, BT78 1EE Tel: (028) 8225 9595 Fax: (028) 8225 9596 E-mail: info@omaghchamber.com
Savcom Ltd, Little Acre, Coopers Hill Road, Nutfield, Redhill, RH1 4HS Tel: (01737) 822343 E-mail: martin@savcom.co.uk

INTERNET CONTENT CREATION TOOLS

▶ inCharge.co.uk, 49 Kingston Street, Cambridge, CB1 2NU Tel: (01223) 579600

INTERNET ILLUSTRATION SERVICES

▶ Ant Creations, 7 Granville Street, Market Harborough, Leicestershire, LE16 9EU Tel: 08444 778910 E-mail: nathan@antcreations.co.uk
Leythorne Ltd, Hawthorns Business Centre, Halfords Lane, Smethwick, West Midlands, B66 1BB Tel: 0121-558 1181 Fax: 0121-555 4913 E-mail: sales@leythorne.co.uk
▶ Magic Pencil, 16 Upper Meadow Road, Birmingham, B32 1NX Tel: (0870) 2863881 Fax: (0870) 2863882 E-mail: creative@magicpencil.co.uk
▶ Morse Brown, 517 Hagley Road, Smethwick, West Midlands, B66 4AX Tel: 0121-429 7770 E-mail: mail@morsebrowndesign.co.uk
Moira Munro Illustrations and Cartoons, Glasgow, G76 Tel: 0141-638 9851 E-mail: moira@moiramunro.com
▶ Pinebank Design, 30 Pine Bank, Hindhead, Surrey, GU26 6SS Tel: 020 88168613 E-mail: contact@pinebankdesign.com
▶ Visualize Digital, The Studio, 8 Westgate Road, Faversham, Kent, ME13 8HF Tel: 01795 538128 E-mail: info@visualizecreative.co.uk

INTERNET MARKETING STRATEGY CONSULTANCY

2 Aim Productions, 17 Clare Court, 829 Hertford Road, Enfield, Middlesex, EN3 6UJ Tel: (07958) 678583 E-mail: info@2aimproductions.com
▶ Marketing Team, Sensor House, Wrexham Technology Park, Wrexham, LL13 7YP Tel: (0870) 3501539 E-mail: info@marketing-team.co.uk
Mike Nash, PO Box 43, Hayle, Cornwall, TR27 5BG Tel: (01736) 756277 E-mail: sales@mikenash.co.uk
▶ Pinpointworld, 24 Orton Enterprise Centre, Bakewell Road, Orton Southgate, Peterborough, PE2 6XU Tel: (01733) 233550 Fax: (01733) 233650 E-mail: contact@pinpointworld.com
▶ Rating Room Ltd, 5 Swanston Village, Edinburgh, EH10 7DT Tel: 0131-313 1884
▶ S E Marketing, 6 Hallas Grove, Manchester, M23 0GZ Tel: 0161-946 1116 E-mail: semarketing@postmaster.co.uk
▶ Search Laboratory Ltd, 3 Littleway, Moortown, Leeds, LS17 6JN Tel: 0113-212 1211 E-mail: ian.harris@searchlaboratory.com

INTERNET MARKETING/PUBLIC RELATIONS SERVICES

2 Aim Productions, 17 Clare Court, 829 Hertford Road, Enfield, Middlesex, EN3 6UJ Tel: (07958) 678583 E-mail: info@2aimproductions.com
▶ ACPR, 18 Spencer Mews, Lansdowne Way, London, SW8 1HF Tel: (020) 7820 7768 E-mail: antonia@acpr.co.uk
Arthouse P R, 7a Market Street, Crediton, Devon, EX17 2EE Tel: (01363) 777002 Fax: (01363) 779956 E-mail: sales@arthouse-pr.com
Blue Rocket Group Ltd, 115 Church Road, Hove, East Sussex, BN3 2AF Tel: (01273) 779196 E-mail: daniel@bluerocketgroup.com
▶ Bojangle Communications Ltd, 2 Virginia Close, Ashtead, Surrey, KT21 2NW Tel: (01372) 274975 E-mail: lindsey@bojangle.co.uk
▶ Chrome Consulting Ltd, 26 Fitzroy Square, London, W1T 6BT Tel: 020 7323 1610 E-mail: enquiries@chromeconsulting.com
City Mutual Ltd, PO Box 521, Taunton, Somerset, TA3 6YB Tel: (01460) 281775 Fax: (01460) 281853 E-mail: edu@citymutual.com
Communique Public Relations Ltd, Waterside, 2 Canal Street, Manchester, M1 3HE Tel: 0161-228 6677 Fax: 0161-228 7391 E-mail: info@communiquepr.co.uk
▶ Declaration Ltd, The Bearings, Bowbridge Road, Newark, Nottinghamshire, NG24 4BZ Tel: (01636) 708330 Fax: (01636) 708331 E-mail: rcihard@declaration.co.uk
Elateral Trustees Ltd, Elateral House Unit 4, Crosby Way, Farnham, Surrey, GU9 7XX Tel: (01252) 740740 Fax: (01252) 740741
Freshwater UK, Freshwater House, Cardiff Gate Business Park, Pontprennau, Cardiff, CF23 8RS Tel: (029) 2054 5370 Fax: (029) 2054 5380 E-mail: sales@freshwater-uk.com
▶ Goldnet Ltd, 3 Shire Close, Whiteley, Fareham, Hampshire, PO15 7BQ Tel: (01489) 886843 Fax: (01489) 886828 E-mail: info@goldnetltd.co.uk
Harrison Cowley, Regus House, George Curl Way, Southampton, SO18 2RZ Tel: (023) 8033 7237 Fax: (023) 8023 1665 E-mail: enquiries@harrisoncowley.com
Heron Marketing Services Ltd, First Floor, 61-65 High Street, Standish, Wigan, Lancashire, WN6 0HD Tel: (01257) 472148 Fax: (01257) 472148 E-mail: info@heronmarketing.co.uk
▶ Info-mercial Marketing Services Ltd, 57 Heathwood Road, Bournemouth, BH9 2JZ Tel: (0845) 4592103 E-mail: mike.e@info-mercial.biz
▶ Jigsaw public relations, Tower Court, Oakdale Road, Clifton Moor, York, YO30 4XL Tel: 01904 557673 E-mail: sarah@jigsawpr.co.uk
▶ Loyal E, 39 Stonewell Park Road, Congresbury, Bristol, BS49 5DP Tel: (01934) 832143 Fax: (01934) 832143 E-mail: enquiries@loyal-e.com
▶ Mango Media, 49 Carnaby Street, London, W1F 9PY Tel: (020) 7292 9000 Fax: (020) 7434 1077 E-mail: info@mangomedia.net
▶ Marketing Team, Sensor House, Wrexham Technology Park, Wrexham, LL13 7YP Tel: (0870) 3501539 E-mail: info@marketing-team.co.uk
▶ Market-IT Direct Ltd, The Meridian, 4 Copthall House, Station Square, Coventry, CV1 2FL Tel: (0870) 8502365 E-mail: info@marketitdirect.com
Mike Nash, PO Box 43, Hayle, Cornwall, TR27 5BG Tel: (01736) 756277 E-mail: sales@mikenash.co.uk
Montague Tate Ltd, PO Box 179, Cirencester, Gloucestershire, GL7 7YT Tel: (0870) 4030007 Fax: (0870) 4030008 E-mail: admin@montague-tate.co.uk
Netxtra Ltd, The Old Foundry, Hall Street, Long Melford, Sudbury, Suffolk, CO10 9JG Tel: (01787) 319393 Fax: (01787) 319394 E-mail: info@netxtra.net
▶ Opera Public Relations, 4 West End, Baslow, Bakewell, Derbyshire, DE45 1RG Tel: (0845) 0600650 Fax: 0870 0113457 E-mail: pr@operapr.com
▶ Pawprintz, Barnsley BIC, Innovation Way, Barnsley, South Yorkshire, S75 1JL Tel: (01226) 249590 Fax: (01226) 731867 E-mail: info@pawprintz.co.uk
▶ Press Contact, 15 Old Mill Close, Eynsford, Dartford, DA4 0BN Tel: 01322 866293 E-mail: info@presscontact.co.uk
▶ Q R 8 Design, Arundel Street, Sheffield, S1 2NS Tel: 0114-221 1818 Fax: (0870) 1338957 E-mail: enquiries@miswebdesign.com
▶ Search Laboratory Ltd, 3 Littleway, Moortown, Leeds, LS17 6JN Tel: 0113-212 1211 E-mail: ian.harris@searchlaboratory.com
Signature Industries Ltd, Unit 19 Atlas Industrial Estate, Foundry Street, Glasgow, G21 4PR Tel: 0141-558 7272 Fax: 0141-558 9696 E-mail: info@sigcom.co.uk
Studio Digital Media Ltd, Windsor Park, Trent Valley Road, Lichfield, Staffordshire, WS13 6EU Tel: (01543) 416912 Fax: (01543) 416914 E-mail: info@studiodm.co.uk
▶ TENFOUR writing, 65 The Beckers, Rectory Road, London, N16 7QU Tel: 07971 669206 E-mail: chris@tenfourwriting.co.uk
▶ Transform ebusiness Ltd, Fortissat House, Newmill-Canthill Road, Shotts, Lanarkshire, ML7 4NS Tel: (07793) 973873 E-mail: imacg@transform-ebusiness.com

INTERNET NAME REGISTRATION

1 Websearch Marketing, 104 Dyke Rd, Brighton, BN1 3JD Tel: (08703) 219679 Fax: (01273) 771785
▶ Ace Internet, Business & Arts Centre Houldsworth Mill, Houldsworth Street, Stockport, Cheshire, SK5 6DA Tel: (0870) 7407555 Fax: (0870) 7405335 E-mail: sales@ace-internet.co.uk
Demon Internet Ltd, Gateway House, 322 Regents Park Road, Finchley, London, N3 2QQ Tel: (020) 8371 1000 Fax: (020) 8371 1150 E-mail: sales@demon.net
Go Internet Ltd, 36 Gloucester Avenue, London, NW1 7BB Tel: (020) 7419 0001 E-mail: jerry@go.co.uk

INTERNET SEARCH ENGINE ADVERTISING

▶ Rating Room Ltd, 5 Swanston Village, Edinburgh, EH10 7DT Tel: 0131-313 1884

INTERNET SEARCH ENGINE MARKETING

▶ Leapfrogg Ltd, Tower Point, 44 North Road, Brighton, BN1 1YR Tel: 01273 669450 E-mail: jody.mason@leapfrogg.co.uk
▶ Marketing Team, Sensor House, Wrexham Technology Park, Wrexham, LL13 7YP Tel: (0870) 3501539 E-mail: info@marketing-team.co.uk
▶ Rating Room Ltd, 5 Swanston Village, Edinburgh, EH10 7DT Tel: 0131-313 1884

INTERNET SEARCH ENGINE OPTIMISATION

▶ Access Appraisals Ltd, White Cottage, Stourton, Shipston-on-Stour, Warwickshire, CV36 5HG Tel: (01608) 685039 E-mail: md@wheelchair-ramps.co.uk
▶ Captain Seo, 3 The Croft, Park Hill, London, W5 2NB Tel: (020) 8816 8877 Fax: (0870) 1258147 E-mail: info@captainseo.com
▶ DVH Design, 75 Bedells Avenue, Black Notley, Braintree, Essex, CM77 8NA Tel: 01376 322782 E-mail: request@dvhdesign.co.uk
▶ Evans Bliss, 5 St. James Terrace, Suffolk Parade, Cheltenham, Gloucestershire, GL50 2AA Tel: (01242) 704074 E-mail: jonathan@evansbliss.co.uk
▶ inCharge.co.uk, 49 Kingston Street, Cambridge, CB1 2NU Tel: (01223) 579600

INTERNET SEARCH ENGINES

Toymaster Ltd, 725 Ormskirk Road, Wigan, Lancashire, WN5 8AT Tel: (01942) 214864 Fax: (01942) 205463 E-mail: info@webtouchsolutions.co.uk

INTERNET SECURITY CONSULTANCY

▶ Isc Computer Consultants, 16 Holford Way, Luton, LU3 4EB Tel: (01582) 585807 E-mail: gian@gianmahil.com

INTERNET SECURITY PRODUCTS

Advision Advertising, Vision House, Main Cross Road, Great Yarmouth, Norfolk, NR30 3NZ Tel: (01493) 854000 Fax: (01493) 330016 E-mail: advision@btconnect.com
Datamirror UK Ltd, Elizabeth House, 39 York Road, London, SE1 7NQ Tel: (020) 7633 5200 Fax: (020) 7633 5210
Fujitsu Services Ltd, Wenlock Way, West Gorton, Manchester, M12 5DR Tel: (08702) 345555
GB It Services, PO Box 429, Sheffield, S13 8YZ Tel: 0114-248 6200 Fax: (0870) 0517730 E-mail: admin@gbits.com
Intalect Ltd, Office 7, Grange Farm Business Park, Newtown Unthank, Leicester, LE9 9FL Tel: (0845) 6448860 Fax: (0845) 6448861 E-mail: info@intalect.co.uk
Intama Ltd, The Courtyard, High Street, Chobham, Surrey, GU25 8AF Tel: (01252) 815666 Fax: (01252) 815666
QAIQ Ltd, 55-65 Uxbridge Road, Slough, SL1 1SG Tel: (01753) 534421 Fax: (01753) 898305 E-mail: info@qa-iq.com
Softek Computer Security, La Rue Du Pont Marquet, St. Brelade, Jersey, JE3 8DS Tel: (01534) 811182 Fax: (01534) 811183 E-mail: sales@softek.co.uk
Transam Microsystems Ltd, 2 Bakers Yard, Bakers Row, London, EC1R 3HT Tel: (020) 7837 4050 Fax: (020) 7837 3804 E-mail: transam@transam.co.uk

INTERNET SERVICE/SOLUTION PROVIDERS (ISP)

A B C Net Internet Services, 386 Kenton Road, Harrow, Middlesex, HA3 9DP Tel: (020) 8909 1933 Fax: (020) 8909 2918 E-mail: info@abcnet.co.uk
A B Computers, 12 Union Street, Andover, Hampshire, SP10 1PA Tel: (01264) 406406 Fax: (01264) 395880 E-mail: support@andover.co.uk
Abel Internet, Pentland View House Damhead, Lothianburn, Edinburgh, EH10 7DZ Tel: 0131-445 5555 Fax: (0871) 7173452
Akhter Group Holdings P.L.C., Akhter House, Perry Road, Harlow, Essex, CM18 7PN Tel: (01279) 443521 Fax: (01279) 821300
Alpha Business Support Ltd, Cavendish House, Cavendish Avenue, New Malden, Surrey, KT3 6QQ Tel: (0845) 1110060 Fax: (020) 8942 1100 E-mail: info@alphabusiness.net
▶ David Anderson Associates, Unit 3 Saffron Walden Business Centre, Elizabeth Cl, Saffron Walden, Essex, CB10 2BL Tel: (0797) 3227402 Fax: (0870) 0527516 E-mail: sales@anderson.ath.cx
Apex Computer International Ltd, Apex House, The Mallards, South Cerney, Cirencester, Gloucestershire, GL7 5TQ Tel: (01285) 862100 Fax: (01285) 862111
Attunity UK Ltd, 6 Beacontree Plaza, Gillette Way, Reading, RG2 0BS Tel: (01344) 742805 Fax: 0118-975 3005 E-mail: info-uk@attunity.com
Cad Capture Ltd, Greenbank Technology Park, Challenge Way, Blackburn, BB1 5RR Tel: (01254) 504400 Fax: (01254) 504401 E-mail: info@cadcap.co.uk
Constellation I X Ltd, Post Office House, Main Street, Leicester, LE9 2AL Tel: 0116-239 2300 E-mail: sales@conix.co.uk
D J Consultants, The Leas, Elsworth Road, Conington, Cambridge, CB3 8LW Tel: (01954) 267441 Fax: (01954) 267441 E-mail: enquiries@djinter.net
Demon Internet Ltd, Gateway House, 322 Regents Park Road, Finchley, London, N3 2QQ Tel: (020) 8371 1000 Fax: (020) 8371 1150 E-mail: sales@demon.net
Diafade Ltd, 4 Norfolk Road, Buntingford, Hertfordshire, SG9 9AN Tel: (01763) 273379 E-mail: mailroom@diafade.co.uk
E Media Ltd, Ember House, Pleasant Place, Walton-on-Thames, Surrey, KT12 4HR Tel: (01932) 254787 Fax: (01932) 254786 E-mail: info@e-media.co.uk
Fine-Focus, 55 Warren Terrace, Hertford, SG14 3JF Tel: (0845) 2261726 E-mail: info@fine-focus.co.uk
GB It Services, PO Box 429, Sheffield, S13 8YZ Tel: 0114-248 6200 Fax: (0870) 0517730 E-mail: admin@gbits.com
Go Internet Ltd, 36 Gloucester Avenue, London, NW1 7BB Tel: (020) 7419 0001 E-mail: jerry@go.co.uk
▶ High Speed Communications Ltd, 5 Nevin House, Bourne Avenue, Hayes, Middlesex, UB3 1QU Tel: (0845) 6868021 Fax: (0845) 6868024 E-mail: glen.freeman@hscgroup.co.uk
I P C Media Ltd, Blue Fin Building, 110 Southwark Street, London, SE1 0SU Tel: (020) 3148 5000 Fax: E-mail: press_office@ipc.media.com
Instant Business, 8-10 Colston Avenue, Bristol, BS1 4ST Tel: 0117-915 5175 Fax: 0117-915 5185 E-mail: info@ibltd.com
Internet Central Ltd, The Innovation Centre, University of Keele, Keele, Newcastle, Staffordshire, ST5 5NB Tel: (01782) 667788 Fax: (01782) 667799 E-mail: enquiries@netcentral.co.uk
▶ Inty Ltd, 1700 Aztec West, Almondsbury, Bristol, BS32 4UA Tel: (01454) 640500 Fax: (0870) 0104689 E-mail: neil.watson@inty.com
J J Network Services Ltd, Meridian House, 62 Station Road, London, E4 7BA Tel: (020) 8559 3211 Fax: (020) 8559 3223 E-mail: info@jjnet.co.uk
Lion Bridge, Copthall Terrace, Coventry, CV1 2FP Tel: (024) 7622 2844 Fax: (024) 7625 8892
Media Communications Ltd, Research House, Fraser Road, Greenford, Middlesex, UB6 7AQ Tel: (020) 8998 1517 Fax: (020) 8566 8290 E-mail: info@mclweb.co.uk
Merula Ltd, 25-31 Huntingdon Street, St. Neots, Cambridgeshire, PE19 1BG Tel: (01480) 222940 Fax: (01480) 222941 E-mail: info@merula.net
Metalsolv Software, A1 House, Kengington Village, Avonemoor Rd, London, W14 8TS Tel: (020) 7348 1500 Fax: (020) 7348 1501
Microgen P.L.C., Fleet House Fleetwood Park, 3 Barley Way, Fleet, Hampshire, GU51 2QJ Tel: (01252) 772300 Fax: (01252) 772301 E-mail: marketing@microgen.co.uk
Netxtra Ltd, The Old Foundry, Hall Street, Long Melford, Sudbury, Suffolk, CO10 9JG Tel: (01787) 319393 Fax: (01787) 319394 E-mail: info@netxtra.net
NTL, Cambridge Research Park, Ely Road, Waterbeach, Cambridge, CB25 9TF Tel: (01223) 724040 Fax: (01223) 567222
Ovid Technologies Ltd, 250 Waterloo Road, London, SE1 8RD Tel: (020) 7981 0600 Fax: (020) 7981 0601 E-mail: europe@ovid.com
Pav I T Services plc, King Business Centre, Reeds Lane, Sayers Common, Hassocks, West Sussex, BN6 9LS Tel: (01273) 834000 Fax: (01273) 834631 E-mail: info@pav.co.uk
Pipex Internet Ltd, Unit 1 Pipex House, Medway Technology Park, Rutherford Close, Stevenage, Hertfordshire, SG1 2EF Tel: (08706) 004454 Fax: (01438) 311100 E-mail: sales@dial.pipex.com
Pixel Fountain, Bowden Hall, Bowden Lane, Marple, Stockport, Cheshire, SK6 6NE Tel: 0161-427 8684 Fax: 0161-427 8691 E-mail: pfinfo@pixelfountain.co.uk

INTERNET SERVICE/SOLUTION PROVIDERS (ISP) – *continued*

Plymouth Chamber Of Commerce, 22 Lockyer Street, Plymouth, PL1 2QW Tel: (01752) 220471 Fax: (01752) 600333 E-mail: chamber@plymouth-chamber.co.uk
Qurius UK Ltd, Waterfall Business Park, Bury, Lancashire, BL9 7BR Tel: 0161-705 6000 Fax: 0161-705 6001 E-mail: mike.dickson@cedilla.co.uk
R I T C Cambridge Ltd, 23 Signet Court, Swann Road, Cambridge, CB5 8LA Tel: (01223) 503190 Fax: (01223) 506293
Recycling World Magazines, Hilltop, Church Rd, Webheath, Redditch, Worcs, B97 5PQ Tel: (01527) 404550 Fax: (01527) 404644 E-mail: recycling@tecweb.com
Regional Webs, & Lanb Plot, Chetnole, Sherborne, Dorset, DT9 6PQ Tel: (0870) 7461290 Fax: (0870) 7461291
S & S Systems Ltd, Bretton Court, Manor Road, Wales, Sheffield, S26 5PS Tel: (08456) 441670 E-mail: info@astraaccounts.co.uk
Senator Communications Ltd, 5 Newton Court, Wavertree Technology Park, Liverpool, L13 1EJ Tel: 0151-259 5959 Fax: 0151-259 0099 E-mail: sales@senatorinternational.uk
Smart Technologies, 94 Sandy Lane, Higher Kinnerton, Chester, CH4 9BS Tel: (0800) 0186511 Fax: (0870) 7708332 E-mail: sales@smartserve.net
Sos Internet Ltd, Sosi House, Hacche Mill, South Molton, Devon, EX36 3NA Tel: (0870) 7442961 Fax: (0870) 9911730 E-mail: sosi@sosi.net
Spitfire Technology Group, Unit 6-7 Southbank Business Centre, Ponton Road, London, SW8 5BL Tel: (020) 7501 3000 Fax: (020) 7501 3001 E-mail: sales@spitfire.co.uk
▶ Suffolk Webs, 8 Warwick Drive, Bury St. Edmunds, Suffolk, IP32 6TF Tel: (01284) 717162 Fax: (01284) 717162 E-mail: sales@suffolkwebs.co.uk
UKO2, 1 Lamerton Way, Wilmslow, Cheshire, SK9 3UN Tel: (020) 7726 7123 E-mail: severine@netbooster.co.uk
Vivid Views, Aberlan House, Blackburn Industrial Estate, Kinellar, Aberdeen, AB21 0RX Tel: (01224) 798307 Fax: (01224) 790986 E-mail: info@vividviews.co.uk
Warp Systems Ltd, Debmarc House, 193 London Road, Staines, Middlesex, TW18 4HR Tel: (01784) 492222 Fax: (01784) 460100
Your Site Here, 10 Erles Road, Liphook, Hampshire, GU30 7BW Tel: 0870-742 4455 Fax: 0870-742 4454 E-mail: sales@yoursitehere.co.uk
Zen Broadband, Moss Bridge Road, Rochdale, Lancashire, OL16 5EA Tel: 0845 0589000 Fax: 0845 0589005 E-mail: sales@zen.co.uk

INTERNET SHOPPING DIRECTORIES

▶ BootBay.co.uk Ltd, New Barn, Hawk Hill, Battlesbridge, Wickford, Essex, SS11 7RJ Tel: (0870) 4447338 E-mail: info@bootbay.co.uk
▶ Dee's Bridalwear, Melbourne Road, Grantham, Lincolnshire, NG31 9RH Tel: 0773 6469276 E-mail: info@deesbridalwear.co.uk
▶ Eat Out Cornwall, Chiverton Lodge, The Saltings, Lelant, St. Ives, Cornwall, TR26 3DL Tel: (01736) 755113 Fax: (01736) 759413 E-mail: admin@eatoutcornwall.com
▶ Everyday Essentials, 2 Cranford Crescent, Kilfennan, Londonderry, BT47 5QN Tel: (028) 7129 1478 E-mail: everyday_essentials@hotmail.com
▶ Favouritesweetshop.co.uk, 10 Castle Drive, Kemsing, Sevenoaks, Kent, TN15 6RL Tel: 01732 760480 E-mail: info@favouritesweetshop.co.uk
▶ Gluten Free Foods Direct, PO Box 156, Selby, North Yorkshire, YO8 6WA Tel: (01757) 630725 Fax: (01757) 630725 E-mail: admin@glutenfreefoodsdirect.co.uk

INTERNET SHORT MESSAGE SERVICES (SMS)

▶ Adestra, Hollywell House, Osney Mead, Oxford, OX2 0EN Tel: (01865) 242425 Fax: (01865) 255241 E-mail: Sales@adestra.com
Reach2Mobile Ltd, Keswick House, 26 Myrtle Avenue, Ruislip, Middlesex, HA4 8RZ Tel: 08707 665232 E-mail: infok@reach2mobile.co.uk
▶ Text-Messaging 4 Business, 6 Station Road, London, NW4 4PZ Tel: (0870) 7606836 Fax: (0870) 7606836 E-mail: fambizzari@yahoo.co.uk

INTERNET SHORT MESSAGE SERVICES (SMS) PROMOTIONS

▶ Adestra, Hollywell House, Osney Mead, Oxford, OX2 0EN Tel: (01865) 242425 Fax: (01865) 255241 E-mail: Sales@adestra.com
Reach2Mobile Ltd, Keswick House, 26 Myrtle Avenue, Ruislip, Middlesex, HA4 8RZ Tel: 08707 665232 E-mail: infok@reach2mobile.co.uk
▶ Text-Messaging 4 Business, 6 Station Road, London, NW4 4PZ Tel: (0870) 7606836 Fax: (0870) 7606836 E-mail: fambizzari@yahoo.co.uk

INTERNET TRANSLATION SERVICES

▶ All French Translators, 407-409 Oxford Street, London, W1C 2PB Tel: 020 79079400 Fax: 020 79079427 E-mail: info@allfrenchtranslators.com
Andiamo, Swan Yard, West Market Place, Cirencester, Gloucestershire, GL7 2NH Tel: (01285) 659100 Fax: (01285) 659369 E-mail: sales@andiamo.com
▶ Castle Languages, 27 Oakland Drive, Netherton, Wakefield, West Yorkshire, WF4 4LZ Tel: (01924) 262891 Fax: (01924) 262891 E-mail: lisacastillo@castlelanguages.co.uk
Computers For Linguists, 45 Endwell Road, London, SE4 2PQ Tel: (020) 7732 1740 Fax: (020) 7358 9214 E-mail: sales@marguet-ball.net
First Edition Translations, 22 Newmarket Rd, Cambridge, CB5 8DT Tel: (01223) 356733 Fax: (01223) 321488 E-mail: info@firstedit.co.uk
▶ Hayes Translations, 45 Northfield Road, Doncaster, South Yorkshire, DN5 8AY Tel: (01302) 781142 E-mail: monica@hayestranslations.co.uk
▶ Hermann & Associates, 18 St Werburghs Road, Manchester, M21 0TN Tel: 0161-881 3034 Fax: 0161-862 9585 E-mail: sales@nhatranslations.com
K International plc, Carina Building, Sunrise Parkway, Milton Keynes, MK14 6PW Tel: (01908) 670399 Fax: (01908) 670170 E-mail: info@k-international.com
T & I Services UK Ltd, 3 Furtho Manor Farm, Northampton Road, Old Stratford, Milton Keynes, MK19 6NR Tel: (0845) 6008150 Fax: (01908) 265461 E-mail: enquiries@tiservicesuk.com
▶ Denise Vogt, 9 Valley Rise, Leeds, LS13 1HA Tel: 0113-255 2034 E-mail: contact@urtranslated.com
White Drift Translations Ltd, 2 Stanley Street, Llanelli, Dyfed, SA15 2EU Tel: (01554) 757700 Fax: (01554) 757222 E-mail: info@whitedrift.com

INTERNET USABILITY CONSULTANCY

▶ Amberlight Partners, 58 Bloomsbury Street, London, WC1B 3QT Tel: (020) 7307 7770 E-mail: info@amber-light.co.uk
▶ Metro Research Ltd, 118 The Chandlery, 50 Westminster Bridge Road, London, SE1 7QY Tel: (0870) 9979777 Fax: (020) 7953 7450 E-mail: vinesh@metroresearch.com

INTERNET/ELECTRONIC COMMERCE (ECOMMERCE) SERVICES

4 Web UK Ltd, 12 Maycroft Avenue, Withington, Manchester, M20 4XX Tel: 0161-291 8082 E-mail: ross@4webuk.com
▶ 4VisMedia, 18 Alderwood, Chineham, Basingstoke, Hampshire, RG24 8TU Tel: (01256) 320733 E-mail: enquiries@4vismedia.co.uk
A W C, 97 Commercial Road, Bournemouth, BH2 5RT Tel: (01202) 789269 Fax: (01202) 789277 E-mail: sales@awc.co.uk
Aldebaran Systems Ltd, Unit 47 Cressex Enterprise Centre, Lincoln Road, High Wycombe, Buckinghamshire, HP12 3RL Tel: (01494) 614630 E-mail: info@aldebaran.co.uk
Ammnet Ltd, Wentworth House, 3 Lichfield Road, Burntwood, Staffordshire, WS7 0HQ Tel: (01543) 305133 Fax: (0870) 0547750 E-mail: sales@ammnet.com
Barron Mccann Technology Ltd, Fifth Avenue, Letchworth Garden City, Hertfordshire, SG6 2HF Tel: (01462) 482333 Fax: (01462) 482112 E-mail: info@bemac.com
Birlasoft UK Ltd, Cromwell House, 142 High Street, Stevenage, Hertfordshire, SG1 3HN Tel: (01438) 350270 Fax: (01438) 749309 E-mail: corp@birlasoft.co.uk
Cad Capture Ltd, Greenbank Technology Park, Challenge Way, Blackburn, BB1 5RR Tel: (01254) 504400 Fax: (01254) 504401 E-mail: info@cadcap.co.uk
Campbell Lee Computer Services Ltd, Unit G1 Exploration House, Exploration Drive, Bridge Of Don, Aberdeen, AB23 8GX Tel: (01224) 355435 Fax: (01224) 677201 E-mail: info@campbell-lee.co.uk
Campbell Lee Computer Services Ltd, 24 Finlas Street, Cowlairs Industrial Estate, Glasgow, G22 5DT Tel: 0141-557 6400 Fax: 0141-557 6451 E-mail: hugh.gillan@cl-is.co.uk
Ci-Net, Langford Locks, Kidlington, Oxfordshire, OX5 1GA Tel: (01865) 856000 Fax: (01865) 856001 E-mail: info@ci-net.com
D C S Automotive Ltd, Clarendon House, Clarendon Square, Leamington Spa, Warwickshire, CV32 5QJ Tel: (01926) 831401 Fax: (01926) 450183 E-mail: info@dcs-automotive.co.uk
Datasouth UK, 5 Chevron Business Park, Limekiln Lane, Holbury, Southampton, SO45 2QL Tel: (023) 8089 0800 Fax: (023) 8089 0875 E-mail: info@datasouth.co.uk
East Finchley Electrical, 115 High Road, London, N2 8AG Tel: (020) 8883 9098 Fax: (020) 8444 3458 E-mail: dloizou@yahoo.co.uk
Encyclopaedia Britannica UK Ltd, Unity Wharf, 13 Mill Street, London, SE1 2BH Tel: (020) 7500 7800 Fax: (020) 7500 7878 E-mail: enquiries@britannica.co.uk
Entee Global Services Ltd, 2morrow Court, Appleford Road, Sutton Courtenay, Abingdon, Oxfordshire, OX14 4FH Tel: (01235) 845100 Fax: (01235) 845108 E-mail: mail@entee.co.uk
Flare Imaging Ltd, 200 Brook Drive, Greenpark, Reading, RG2 6UB Tel: 0118-922 2999 Fax: 0118-986 7999 E-mail: nick@flareimaging.com
Freeway Commerce Ltd, Unit 12, Sceptre Court, Sceptre Way, Bamber Bridge, Preston, PR5 6AW Tel: (01772) 646000 Fax: (01772) 646001 E-mail: info@freewaycommece.co.uk
▶ Hareslade Webs, 32 Hareslade, Bishopston, Swansea, SA3 3DX Tel: (01792) 234782 E-mail: p.hailey@virgin.net
I T C, 114 East Street, Southampton, SO14 3HD Tel: (01747) 842230 Fax: (0870) 7443381 E-mail: itc@itcinternet.com
Ikon Office Solutions plc, 160 Edinburgh Avenue, Slough, SL1 4UE Tel: (01753) 771000 Fax: (01753) 696045
Intama Ltd, The Courtyard, High Street, Chobham, Surrey, GU25 8AF Tel: (01252) 815666 Fax: (01252) 815666
Internet Central Ltd, The Innovation Centre, University of Keele, Keele, Newcastle, Staffordshire, ST5 5NB Tel: (01782) 667788 Fax: (01782) 667799 E-mail: enquiries@netcentral.co.uk
Knowledge Ability, 48 St. Dennis Road, Malmesbury, Wiltshire, SN16 9BH Tel: (01666) 826654
Linear Blue Ltd, 400 Thames Valley Park Drive, Thames Valley Park, Reading, RG6 1PT Tel: (0870) 351 6594 E-mail: info@linearblue.com
Logma Systems Design Ltd, 27 Victoria Street, Chorley, Lancashire, PR7 2TX Tel: (01257) 233123 Fax: (01257) 237215 E-mail: sales@logma.net
▶ Marknine Networks, 19 Crabtree Walk, Broxbourne, Hertfordshire, EN10 7NH Tel: (07075) 055577 Fax: (07075) 055577 E-mail: tonym@marknine.net
N B S Solutions, Kelvin Way, Crawley, West Sussex, RH10 9WE Tel: (01293) 442797 Fax: (01293) 442798 E-mail: sales@nbs-solutions.co.uk
Netcraft Ltd, Rockfield House, Charlcombe, Bath, BA1 9BQ Tel: (01225) 447500 Fax: (01225) 448600 E-mail: sales@netcraft.com
Netwinner Ltd, 15 The Maltings, Longton, Preston, PR4 5ZS Tel: (01772) 616078 Fax: (01772) 616086 E-mail: sales@netwinner.co.uk
Newgate Systems, NTS House, Headley Road East, Woodley, Reading, RG5 4SZ Tel: 0118-927 7700 Fax: 0118-927 2143
Perwill P.L.C., 13A Market Square, Alton, Hampshire, GU34 1UR Tel: (01420) 545000 Fax: (01420) 545001 E-mail: info@kewill.com
Roberts Forge Lift Ltd, 1 C Park Road Industrial Estate, Consett, County Durham, DH8 5PY Tel: (01207) 590163 Fax: (01207) 591600 E-mail: david@robertsforge.co.uk
Rossendale Group, Roman Way, South Hykeham, Lincoln, LN6 9UH Tel: (01522) 693423 Fax: (01522) 693988
Saa Consultants Ltd, The Computer Complex, Somerset Place, Plymouth, PL3 4BB Tel: (01752) 606000 Fax: (01752) 606838 E-mail: sales@saaconsultants.com
Sanderson Retail Sytems Ltd, Lakeside House, Waltham Business Park Brickyard Road, Swanmore, Southampton, SO32 2SA Tel: (01489) 896266 Fax: (01489) 892045 E-mail: enquiries@megabyte.co.uk
Seeburger UK Ltd, Heathrow Boulevard 4, 280 Bath Road, West Drayton, Middlesex, UB7 0DQ Tel: (020) 8564 3914 E-mail: c.blomstedt@seeburger.co.uk
Smart 421, North Felaw Malting, 48 Felaw Street, Ipswich, IP2 8HE Tel: (01473) 421421 Fax: (01473) 421422 E-mail: info@smart421.com
Unitron Systems & Developments Ltd, 76A Jameson House, High Street, Broseley, Shropshire, TF12 5EX Tel: (01952) 883817 Fax: (01952) 883672
Wick Hill Ltd, Rivercourt, Albert Drive, Woking, Surrey, GU21 5RP Tel: (01483) 227600 Fax: (01483) 227700 E-mail: info@wickhill.co.uk
Wise Systems Ltd, 7a High Street, Corsham, Wiltshire, SN13 0ES Tel: (01249) 717000 Fax: (01249) 717002 E-mail: info@wisesystems.co.uk

INTERPRETING SERVICES

Andiamo, Swan Yard, West Market Place, Cirencester, Gloucestershire, GL7 2NH Tel: (01285) 659100 Fax: (01285) 659369 E-mail: sales@andiamo.com
▶ Asahi Alumni Associates Limited, 56 Swainstone Road, Reading, RG2 0DX Tel: 0118 9869963 Fax: 0118 9869963 E-mail: julie.bell@can-do.co.uk
Biznet Services, 63 Abingdon Villas, London, W8 6XA Tel: (020) 7565 0909 Fax: (020) 7565 0111 E-mail: translate@biznetserv.com
▶ Hayes Translations, 45 Northfield Road, Doncaster, South Yorkshire, DN5 8AY Tel: (01302) 781142 E-mail: monica@hayestranslations.co.uk
Spanish & Portuguese At Fultons, The Chase, Behoes Lane, Woodcote, Reading, RG8 0PP Tel: (01491) 680042 Fax: (01491) 680085 E-mail: mike@mikefulton.co.uk
White Drift Translations Ltd, 2 Stanley Street, Llanelli, Dyfed, SA15 2EU Tel: (01554) 757700 Fax: (01554) 757222 E-mail: info@whitedrift.com

INTERPRETING (SIMULTANEOUS) EQUIPMENT/ SYSTEMS

Auditel Ltd, 2 Devonport Vernon Trading Estate, Cock Lane, High Wycombe, Buckinghamshire, HP13 7DE Tel: (01494) 465335 Fax: (01494) 446013 E-mail: sales@auditel.ltd.uk
Thebigword, 4-12 Morton Street, Leamington Spa, Warwickshire, CV32 5SY Tel: (0870) 7488060 Fax: (0870) 7488061 E-mail: sales@thebigword.com
▶ Westminster Sonus, Westminster House, Herschel Centre, Church Street, Slough, SL1 1PJ Tel: (01753) 553325 Fax: (01753) 553867 E-mail: crn@westminstersonus.com

INTERPRETING (SIMULTANEOUS) EQUIPMENT/ SYSTEMS HIRE

Brahler Ics UK Ltd, Unit 2 The Business Centre, Church End, Cambridge, CB1 3LB Tel: (01223) 411601 Fax: (01223) 411602 E-mail: info@brahler-ics.co.uk
Eurosis Ltd, 35 Rothschild Street, London, SE27 0JN Tel: (020) 8670 9351 Fax: (020) 8761 7954 E-mail: eurosis@dial.pipex.com
M & R Communications Ltd, 7 Bell Industrial Estate, Cunnington Street, London, W4 5HB Tel: (020) 8995 4714 Fax: (020) 8995 5136 E-mail: office@m-rcom.com
▶ Westminster Sonus, Westminster House, Herschel Centre, Church Street, Slough, SL1 1PJ Tel: (01753) 553325 Fax: (01753) 553867 E-mail: crn@westminstersonus.com

INTRINSICALLY SAFE INSTRUMENTATION

BEKA Associates Ltd, Old Charlton Road, Hitchin, Hertfordshire, SG5 2DA Tel: (01462) 438301 Fax: (01462) 453971 E-mail: sales@beka.co.uk

INTRUDER ALARM MAINTENANCE

▶ 1st Step Security, 164 Malpas Road, Lewisham, London, SE4 1DH Tel: (0845) 0092879 E-mail: sales@firststepsecurity.co.uk
▶ A P S Security, 18 Jubilee Avenue, Crewe, CW2 7PR Tel: (01270) 663553 Fax: (01270) 650044 E-mail: contact@apssecurity.co.uk
▶ Active Alarms Ltd, 3 Fayland Avenue, London, SW16 1TB Tel: (020) 8769 5003 E-mail: sales@active-alarms.com
▶ Allied Electronic Security Ltd, 10 Town End, Caterham, Surrey, CR3 5UG Tel: (01883) 381382 Fax: (01883) 340267 E-mail: info@allied-security.co.uk
▶ Anglo American Security Ltd, 160 Bridport Way, Braintree, Essex, CM7 9FF Tel: 01376 333631 Fax: 01376 333640 E-mail: info@anglo-american-security.com
▶ Better Environment & Security Technologies B E S T Ltd, Glen Rose, The Hollow, West Hoathly, East Grinstead, West Sussex, RH19 4QE Tel: (01342) 811990 Fax: 01342 811990 E-mail: britsectec@aol.com
▶ DNS Security Alarms, 154 Sandy Road,, Seaforth,, Liverpool, L21 1AQ Tel: 0151 7225505
▶ I F S Electronic Security Division, 20 St. Johns Road, Bootle, Merseyside, L20 8NJ Tel: 0151-955 4200 Fax: 0151-955 4240 E-mail: phill.ashton@ifscontractors.com
▶ Intruder Protection Services Ltd, 2 Wenban Road, Worthing, West Sussex, BN11 1HY Tel: (01903) 204845
▶ Oakley Systems Ltd, 10 Vickers House, Priestley Road, Basingstoke, Hampshire, RG24 9NP Tel: 01256 840010 Fax: 01256 840021
▶ Secure Solutions, 37 New Road, Burton Lazars, Melton Mowbray, Leicestershire, LE14 2UU Tel: 01664 568155 Fax: 01664 561990
▶ Securetec Ltd, 9 Firethorne Road, Liverpool, L26 7XE Tel: 0151-498 4845 Fax: 0151-284 1033 E-mail: securetec1@yahoo.co.uk

INTRUDER ALARM SYSTEMS

A G S Security Systems Ltd, Field Way, Denbigh Road, Mold, Flintshire, CH7 1BP Tel: (01244) 812222 Fax: (01352) 707889
E-mail: info@ags-security.co.uk
A1 Security Systems, 4 Viceroy Court, Bedford Road, Petersfield, Hampshire, GU32 3LJ
Tel: (01730) 266811 Fax: (01730) 262652
E-mail: admin@a1securitysystems.co.uk
Asg Midlands, 2 Old Walsall Road, Birmingham, B42 1NN Tel: 0121-358 1524 Fax: 0121-358 1525
B D S Electrical, 10 Calverley Drive, Leeds, LS13 3LN Tel: 0113-255 2389
Berkeley Guard Ltd, The Pottery, Ham Lane, Baughurst, Tadley, Hampshire, RG26 5SD
Tel: 0118-981 1428 Fax: 0118-981 0487
E-mail: info@berkeleyguard.com
Centurion Security System, Centurion House, Park Road West, Huddersfield, HD4 5RX
Tel: (01484) 321321 Fax: (01484) 351888
E-mail: sales@centurion.net
Cirrus Communication Systems Ltd, Hampton Lovett Industrial Estate, Lovett Road, Hampton Lovett, Droitwich, Worcestershire, WR9 0QG
Tel: (01905) 827252 Fax: (01905) 827253
E-mail: info@coltronic.co.uk
Concept Smoke Screens, North End, Swineshead, Swineshead, Boston, Lincolnshire, PE20 3LR Tel: (01205) 821111 Fax: (01205) 820316
E-mail: info@smoke-screen.co.uk
Coopers Security Ltd, Security House, Xerox Business Park, Mitcheldean, Gloucestershire, GL17 0SZ Tel: (01594) 543343 Fax: (01594) 545401
E-mail: marketing@menviersecurity.co.uk
Drive Way Alarm, 15 West Street, Hothfield, Ashford, Kent, TN26 1ET Tel: (0870) 2240315 Fax: (0870) 7625903
E-mail: sales@drivewayalarm.co.uk
Expo Link Alarms Ltd, 35 Knowley Road, Beach Hill, Wigan, Lancashire, WN6 7PZ Tel: (01942) 494004 Fax: (01942) 825991
E-mail: sales@linkalarms.co.uk
G E Security Ltd, Unit 5, Ashton Gate, Ashton Road, Harold Hill, Romford, RM3 8UF
Tel: (01708) 381496 Fax: (0870) 7773049
Guardian Alarms Ltd, 20-22 Sydenham Road, Croydon, CR0 2EF Tel: (020) 8686 8777 Fax: (020) 8686 9777
E-mail: sales@guardianalarms.co.uk
Hansett Electronics, 38 Kimpton Road, Sutton, Surrey, SM3 9QP Tel: (020) 8644 1777
E-mail: hansett@aol.com
▶ Home Security Services UK Ltd, 3 Campbell Street, Roe Lee, Blackburn, BB1 9AF
Tel: (0800) 6520642 Fax: (01254) 698064
E-mail: sales@homesecurityservicesuk.co.uk
Initial Electronic Security, Maxwelltown Industrial Estate, Glasgow Road, Dumfries, DG2 0NW
Tel: (01387) 261060 Fax: (01387) 250708
E-mail: dumfries@ies.uk.com
Initial Electronic Security Systems Ltd, 1 Orbit Centre, Ashworth Road, Bridgemead, Swindon, SN5 7YG Tel: (01793) 531955 Fax: (01793) 488850
E-mail: swindon@ies.uk.com
M & E Alarms Ltd, Lower Charlecott, Tawstock, Barnstaple, Devon, EX31 3JY Tel: (01271) 858550 Fax: (01271) 858423
E-mail: sales@m-and-e.co.uk
M P E Alarms & Security Systems, 22 Fennfields Road, South Woodham Ferrers, Chelmsford, CM3 5RZ Tel: (0870) 8505862 Fax: (01245) 320350
Mainline Security Systems, 39 Wrawby Street, Brigg, South Humberside, DN20 9BS
Tel: (01652) 650567 Fax: (01652) 658818
Metro Security, 5 Ashton Road, Harold Hill, Romford, RM3 8UJ Tel: (0870) 6090095 Fax: (0870) 6090096
E-mail: info@metrosecurity.co.uk
Northern Protection, Unit 38 The Brampton Centre, Brampton Road, Wath-upon-Dearne, Rotherham, South Yorkshire, S63 6BB
Tel: (01709) 879333 Fax: (01709) 879443
E-mail: cm@nightforce.co.uk
Secom plc, Unit 1 The Bell Centre, Newton Road, Crawley, West Sussex, RH10 9FZ
Tel: (01293) 532249 Fax: (01293) 514416
E-mail: enquiries@secom.plc.uk
Securi Plex Ltd, Swordfish Way, Sherburn in Elmet, Leeds, LS25 6NG Tel: (01977) 680700 Fax: (01977) 680701
E-mail: business@securi-plex.co.uk
Shire Security Ltd, 2 Henson Park, Henson Way, Telford Way Industrial Estate, Kettering, Northamptonshire, NN16 8PX Tel: (01536) 410483 Fax: (01536) 412631
E-mail: info@shiresecurity.co.uk
Stanair Industrial Door Services Ltd, Unit 11, Blundells Road, Bradville, Milton Keynes, MK13 7HA Tel: (01908) 222070 Fax: (01908) 222621 E-mail: info@stanair.co.uk
Tritech Security & Electrical Services, 22 Muriel Street, Barrhead, Glasgow, G78 1QB
Tel: 0141-881 1100 Fax: 0141-881 4449
West Riding Home Securities, 13 Cross Street, Wakefield, West Yorkshire, WF1 3BW
Tel: (01924) 377158 Fax: (01924) 201448

INTRUDER ALARM SYSTEMS INSTALLATION

B A C Fire & Security, 591 Fishponds Road, Fishponds, Bristol, BS16 3AA Tel: 0117-958 3838 Fax: 0117-958 3848
E-mail: admin@bacsecurity.com
▶ Blaby Alarms Ltd, 12 Waterloo Crescent, Wigston, Leicestershire, LE18 3QH
Tel: 0116-288 3493 Fax: 0116-288 4138
E-mail: beba@btconnect.com
▶ Optyma Security Systems, 6 Harcourt Road, Bexleyheath, Kent, DA6 8AQ Tel: (020) 8304 8635 Fax: (020) 8304 4633

INTUMESCENT PROTECTIVE COATINGS

Fireguard Ltd, 24-26 Boulton Road, Stevenage, Hertfordshire, SG1 4QX Tel: (01438) 313276 Fax: (01438) 727681
Thermoguard Ltd, 275 Oldham Road, Manchester, M40 7PS Tel: 0161-202 2861 Fax: 0161-202 4484
E-mail: sales@thermoguard.co.uk

INTUMESCENT SMOKE OR FIRE DOOR SEALS

Lorient Holdings Ltd, Fairfax Road, Heathfield Industrial Estate, Newton Abbot, Devon, TQ12 6UD Tel: (01626) 834252 Fax: (01626) 833166 E-mail: admin@lorient.co.uk
Mann Mcgowan Fabrications Ltd, 4 The Brook Trading Estate, Deadbrook Lane, Aldershot, Hampshire, GU12 4XB Tel: (01252) 333601 Fax: (01252) 322724
E-mail: sales@mannmcgowan.co.uk

INVENTION DEVELOPMENT CONSULTANTS/ ORGANISATIONS/SERVICES

Brand Development Co., 50 Long Acre, London, WC2E 9JR Tel: (020) 7497 9727 Fax: (020) 7497 3581 E-mail: info@brandevo.com
Institute of Inventors, 19-23 Fosse Way, Ealing, London, W13 0BZ Tel: (020) 8998 3540
▶ Merryfield Associates, Newcott Cottage, Newcott Near Honiton, Honiton, Devon, EX14 9ND Tel: (01404) 861587
E-mail: barriebc@btopenworld.com
R W Oliver, 38 Alma Street, Eccles, Manchester, M30 0EX Tel: 0161-789 8474
Supertron Ltd, 19-21 Fosse Way, London, W13 0BZ Tel: (020) 8998 4372

INVENTORY MANAGEMENT SERVICES

▶ Bellwether Inventory Software, Bickerton House, Bickerton Road, Archway, London, N19 5JT Tel: 0871 309 8353
E-mail: enq@bellwethersoftware.com
Inventor-Net.Com Ltd, 27 President Buildings, President Way, Sheffield, S4 7UR
Tel: 0114-275 7494 Fax: 0114-263 4325
E-mail: district5775@rgis.com
Vivitech Ltd, Westgate Lodge, Low Street, North Wheatley, Retford, Nottinghamshire, DN22 9DS Tel: (01427) 881277 Fax: (01427) 883018 E-mail: info@vivitech.co.uk
▶ West Kent Inventory Services, Elm Tree House, Row Dow Lane, Otford, Sevenoaks, Kent, TN15 6XN Tel: (01959) 523233
E-mail: mail@westkentinventoryservices.co.uk

INVENTORY MANAGEMENT SYSTEMS

▶ Unipart Logistics, Unipart House, Garsington Road, Cowley, Oxford, OX4 2PG Tel: (01865) 383793 Fax: (01865) 383669
E-mail: lyn_mcdowell@unipart.co.uk

INVERTER DRIVE SYSTEMS

Dynex Semi Conductor Ltd, Doddington Road, Lincoln, LN6 3LF Tel: (01522) 500500 Fax: (01522) 500550

INVESTMENT BANKING

Ahli United Bank (UK) P.L.C., 7 Baker Street, London, W1U 8EG Tel: (020) 7487 6500 Fax: (020) 7487 6808
E-mail: helpdesk@ahliunitedbank.com
Anglo Irish Asset Finance plc, Town Centre House, Southam Road, Banbury, Oxfordshire, OX16 2EN Tel: (01295) 755500 Fax: (01295) 755100
Barclays Capital, 7th Floor, 5 North Colonnade, London, E14 4BB Tel: (020) 7623 2323 Fax: (020) 7621 5290
GML International Ltd, Knighton House, 56 Mortimer Street, London, W1W 7RT Tel: (020) 7580 8588 Fax: (020) 7580 8688
E-mail: info@gml.net
Goldman Sachs International Ltd, Peterborough Court, 133 Fleet Street, London, EC4A 2BB Tel: (020) 7774 1000
JP Morgan, Finsbury Dials, 20 Finsbury Street, London, EC2Y 9AQ Tel: (020) 7742 4000 Fax: (020) 7880 3486
Jpmorgan Cazenove, 20 Moorgate, London, EC2R 6DA Tel: (020) 7588 2828 Fax: (020) 7155 9000
Lehman Brothers (Indonesia) Ltd, 25 Bank Street, London, E14 5LE Tel: (020) 7102 1000 Fax: (020) 7102 2999
Mizuho International plc, Bracken House, 1 Friday Street, London, EC4M 9JA Tel: (020) 7236 1090
Morgan Stanley Bank International Ltd, 25 Cabot Square, Canary Wharf, London, E14 4QA
Tel: (020) 7425 8000 Fax: (020) 7425 8990
E-mail: info@morganstanley.com
Numis Security, Cheapside House, 138 Cheapside, London, EC2V 6LH Tel: (020) 7776 1500 Fax: (020) 7776 1550
Sarasin Chiswell, Juxon House, 100 St. Pauls Church Yard, London, EC4M 8BU Tel: (020) 7038 7000 Fax: (020) 7038 6850
E-mail: mail@sarasin.co.uk
Skandinaviska Enskilda Banken, Scandinavian House, 2-6 Cannon Street, London, EC4M 6XX Tel: (020) 7246 4000 Fax: (020) 7588 0929
U B S Investment Bank, 100 Liverpool Street, London, EC2M 2RH Tel: (020) 7567 8000 Fax: (020) 7568 4800
Westlb UK Ltd, 25 Basinghall Street, London, EC2V 5HA Tel: (020) 7020 7300 Fax: (020) 7020 2002 E-mail: sales@westlb.com

INVESTMENT CASTING EQUIPMENT

Rolls-Royce P.L.C., PO Box 31, Derby, DE24 8BJ Tel: (01332) 247018 Fax: (01332) 246970

INVESTMENT CASTINGS

▶ A M E Product Development Solutions, Momentun House, Carrera Court, Dinnington, Sheffield, S25 2RG Tel: (01909) 550999 Fax: (01909) 550888
E-mail: ian.johannessen@ame-solutions.com
Aeromet International plc, Eurolink Industrial Centre, Castle Road, Sittingbourne, Kent, ME10 3RN Tel: (01795) 415000 Fax: (01795) 415015 E-mail: andrew.king@aeromet.co.uk
Brafe Engineering Ltd, Grundisburgh Road, Woodbridge, Suffolk, IP13 6HX Tel: (01394) 380000 Fax: (01394) 380300
E-mail: sclarke@brafe.com
L E W Diecastings Ltd, Trows Lane, Rochdale, Lancashire, OL11 2UF Tel: (01706) 632218 Fax: (01706) 638473 E-mail: alan@lew.co.uk
Masstech, 9 Valley Road, Markfield, Leicestershire, LE67 9QS Tel: (01530) 244467 Fax: (01530) 244467
E-mail: masstech@bigfoot.com
Salisbury Investment Castings Ltd, Building D Dinton Business Park, Catherine Ford Road, Dinton, Salisbury, SP3 5HZ Tel: (01722) 716151 Fax: (01722) 716509
E-mail: mark@casting.uk.com
Symmetry Medical, Beulah Road, Sheffield, S6 2AN Tel: (0114) 285 5881 Fax: (0114) 233 6978 E-mail: info@tpcl.com

INVESTMENT COMPANIES/ INVESTMENT TRUSTS

Bradford & Bingley plc, PO Box 88, Bingley, West Yorkshire, BD16 2UA Tel: (01274) 555555 Fax: (01274) 554422
E-mail: enquiries@bbg.co.uk
Britannic Assurance P.L.C., 1 Wythall Green Way, Wythall, Birmingham, B47 6WG Tel: (01564) 828888 Fax: (0870) 8870002
E-mail: info@britannic.co.uk
Candover Investments Public Ltd Company, 20 Old Bailey, London, EC4M 7LN Tel: (020) 7489 9848 Fax: (020) 7248 5483
E-mail: info@candover.com
▶ Finesco Financial Services Ltd, 6 Woodside Cresent, Glasgow, G3 7UL Tel: 0141-332 3113 Fax: 0141-331 2039
E-mail: sales@finesco.co.uk
Fleming Enterprise Investment Trust P.L.C, 20 Finsbury Street, London, EC2Y 9AQ Tel: (020) 7638 5858 Fax: (020) 7880 3486
Gresham House plc, 36 Elder Street, London, E1 6BT Tel: (020) 7588 7352 Fax: (020) 7377 2946
Henderson Global Investors, 4 Broadgate, London, EC2M 2DA Tel: (020) 7818 1818 Fax: (020) 7818 1819
E-mail: sales@henderson.co.uk
Investec Trust (Jersey) Ltd, PO Box 344, Jersey, JE4 8UW Tel: (01534) 512512 Fax: (01534) 512513 E-mail: enquiries@investectrust.com
Law Debenture Corporation Plc, 100 Wood St, London, EC2V 7EX Tel: (020) 7606 5451 Fax: (020) 7606 0643
E-mail: finance@lawdeb.co.uk
Marine & General Mutual Life Assurance Society, M G M House, Heene Road, Worthing, West Sussex, BN11 2DY Tel: (01903) 836000 Fax: (01903) 836001
E-mail: customer.centre@mgm-assurance.co.uk
NatWest Stockbrokers Ltd, 55 Mansell Street, London, E1 8AN Tel: (0870) 6004080 Fax: (0870) 1288324
Spencer Commercial Property P.L.C., Spencer House, Millbrook Business Park, Rainford, St. Helens, Merseyside, WA11 8LZ Tel: (01744) 887980 Fax: (01744) 887981
E-mail: info@spencerholdingsplc.com

INVESTMENT CONSULTANCY OR BROKERS

Anthony Bryant & Co Property Services Ltd, 25 Eccleston Square, London, SW1V 1NS
Tel: (020) 7630 9696 Fax: (020) 7630 5761
E-mail: info@athonybryant.com
Chelsea Financial Services plc, St James Hall, Moore Park Road, London, SW6 2JS
Tel: (020) 7384 7300 Fax: (020) 7384 7320
E-mail: info@chelseafs.co.uk
Legg Mason Investments, 32 Harbour Exchange Square, London, E14 9JX Tel: (020) 7537 0000 Fax: (020) 7070 7505
Manhattan Properties, 1147 Greenford Road, Greenford, Middlesex, UB6 0DP Tel: (020) 8423 8161 Fax: (020) 8423 8165
Marmerstein Ltd, 10-14 Hewett Street, London, EC2A 3RL Tel: (020) 7247 1483 Fax: (020) 7539 1111 E-mail: fein@kimpton.co.uk
O C & C Strategy Consultants Ltd, 233 Shaftesbury Avenue, London, WC2H 8EE
Tel: (020) 7010 8000 Fax: (020) 7010 8100
Russell Investments Ltd, Wrexhar, Lower Regent Street, London, SW1Y 4PE Tel: (020) 7024 6000 Fax: (020) 7024 6001
E-mail: rwhittaker@russell.com
West London Brokers, Hale Edge North, Crabhill Lane, South Nutfield, Redhill, RH1 5NR
Tel: (01737) 823286 Fax: (01737) 822656
E-mail: w.l.b@btconnect.com

INVESTMENT FINANCE

3 I Plc, 3 The Embankment, Sovereign St, Leeds, LS1 4BJ Tel: 0113-243 0511 Fax: 0113-244 5800 E-mail: leeds@3i.com
Aberdeen Asset Management plc, 123 St. Vincent Street, Glasgow, G2 5EA
Tel: 0141-306 7400 Fax: 0141-306 7401
E-mail: customer.services@aberdeen-asset.com
Fidelity International Investment Advisors UK Ltd, Oakhill House, 130 Tonbridge Road, Hildenborough, Tonbridge, Kent, TN11 9DZ
Tel: (020) 7283 9911 Fax: (01732) 838886
HFC Bank Ltd, North Street, Winkfield, Windsor, Berkshire, SL4 4TD Tel: (01344) 890000 Fax: (01344) 890014
Medical Sickness Pensions Administration Ltd, Colmore Circus Queensway, Birmingham, B4 6AR Tel: (08081) 001884 Fax: 0121-200 9140
NAI Fuller Peiser, Whittington House, 19-30 Alfred Place, London, WC1E 7EA Tel: (0870) 7002233 Fax: (020) 7182 7388
Prelude Technology Investment Holdings Ltd, Sycamore Studios, New Road Over, Cambridge, CB24 5PJ Tel: (01954) 288090 Fax: (01954) 288099
E-mail: prelude@prelude-ventures.com
Russell Investments Ltd, Wrexhar, Lower Regent Street, London, SW1Y 4PE Tel: (020) 7024 6000 Fax: (020) 7024 6001
E-mail: rwhittaker@russell.com
S G, S G House, 41 Tower Hill, London, EC3N 4SG Tel: (020) 7676 6000 Fax: (020) 7762 4555
E-mail: firstname.second@sgcib.com
F.A. Simms & Partners P.L.C., Insol House, 39 Station Road, Lutterworth, Leicestershire, LE17 4AP Tel: (01455) 557111 Fax: (01455) 552572
Warwickshire Investment Partnership, Shire Hall, Warwick, CV34 4SX Tel: (01926) 412830 Fax: (01926) 410268
E-mail: wips@warwickshire.gov.uk

INVESTMENT MANAGEMENT SERVICES

Alliance Capital Ltd, Devonshire Ho, 1 Mayfair Pl, London, W1J 8JJ Tel: (020) 7470 0100
Axa Investment Managers Ltd, 7 Newgate Street, London, EC1A 7NX Tel: (020) 7645 1000 Fax: (020) 7575 8585
Baring Asset Management, 155 Bishopsgate, London, EC2M 3XY Tel: (020) 7628 6000 Fax: (020) 7638 7928
E-mail: enquiries@baring-asset.com
Butterfield Private Bank, 99 Gresham Street, London, EC2V 7NG Tel: (020) 7776 6700 Fax: (020) 7776 6701
E-mail: info@butterfieldprivatebank.co.uk
C Hoare & Co., 37 Fleet Street, London, EC4P 4DQ Tel: (020) 7353 4522 Fax: (020) 7353 4521 E-mail: e-mail@hoaresbank.co.uk
Carr Sheppards Crosthwaite, 25 Imperial Square, Cheltenham, Gloucestershire, GL50 1QZ
Tel: (01242) 514756 Fax: (01242) 533000
Carr Sheppards Crosthwaite Ltd, 2 Gresham Street, London, EC2V 7QN Tel: (020) 7597 1234 Fax: (020) 7597 1000
E-mail: clientservices@carr-sheppards.co.uk
Deutsche Asset Management Group Ltd, 1 Appold Street, London, EC2A 2HE Tel: (020) 7545 6000 Fax: (020) 7545 7700
E B C Asset Management Ltd, East India House, 109-117 Middlesex Street, London, E1 7JF
Tel: (020) 7621 0101 Fax: (020) 7626 7915
Framlington Unit Management Ltd, 8th Floor, 155 Bishopsgate, London, EC2M 3XJ Tel: (020) 7374 4100 Fax: (020) 7330 6644
E-mail: contact@framlington.co.uk
Gartmore Securities Ltd, Gartmore House, 16-18 Monument Street, London, EC3R 8QQ
Tel: (020) 7623 1212 Fax: (020) 7782 2689

INVESTMENT MANAGEMENT SERVICES – *continued*

Invesco Asset Management Ltd, 30 Finsbury Square, London, EC2A 1AG Tel: (020) 7065 4000 Fax: (020) 7638 0752 E-mail: enquiry@invescoperpetual.co.uk

J.P. Morgan Fleming Asset Management, 10 Aldermanbury, London, EC2V 7RF Tel: (020) 7742 6000 Fax: (020) 7742 8000

M & G Group Plc, Governors House, 5 Laurence Pountney Hill, London, EC4R 0HH Tel: (020) 7626 4588 Fax: (020) 7623 8615 E-mail: sales@mandg.co.uk

Royal Bank Of Scotland, 135 Bishopsgate, London, EC2M 3UR Tel: (020) 7085 0000 Fax: (020) 7375 5050 E-mail: enquiries@rbsmarkets.com

Scottish Widows Investment Partnership, 10 Fleet Place, London, EC4M 7RH Tel: (020) 7203 3000 Fax: (020) 7203 3000

Thornhill Holdings Ltd, 77 South Audley Street, London, W1K 1DX Tel: (020) 7629 0662 Fax: (020) 7629 7332 E-mail: thornhill@thornhill.co.uk

Threadneedle Asset Management Ltd, 60 St Mary Axe, London, EC3A 8JQ Tel: (020) 7621 9100 Fax: (020) 7626 1266

Tilney Holdings Ltd, Royal Liver Building, Pier Head, Liverpool, L3 1NY Tel: 0151-236 6000 Fax: 0151-236 1252 E-mail: enqruies@tilney.com

Williams De Broe plc, PO Box 515, London, EC2N 2HD Tel: (020) 7588 7511 Fax: (020) 7588 1702

Russell Wood Ltd, 30 Great Guildford St, London, SE1 0HS Tel: (020) 7928 0505 Fax: (020) 7928 8931 E-mail: russellwoodltd@btinternet.com

INVESTMENT TRUST MANAGEMENT SERVICES

C C L A Investment Management, 80 Cheapside, London, EC2V 6DZ Tel: (020) 7489 6000 Fax: (020) 7489 6126 E-mail: info@ccla.co.uk

Investec Trust (Jersey) Ltd, PO Box 344, Jersey, JE4 8UW Tel: (01534) 512512 Fax: (01534) 512513 E-mail: enquiries@investectrust.com

INVITATION CARDS

Norman Printing Service, 32 Church Road, Ashford, Middlesex, TW15 2UY Tel: (01784) 253494 Fax: (01784) 257080 E-mail: normanprinting@btconnect.com

INVOICE DISCOUNTING SERVICES

▶ Cattles Invoice Finance Ltd, St. James House, Charlotte Street, Manchester, M1 4DZ Tel: 0161-237 1483 Fax: (0870) 0438333 E-mail: hotline@cattlesif.co.uk

Close Invoice Finance Ltd, 25 Bartholomew Street, Newbury, Berkshire, RG14 5LL Tel: (01635) 31517 Fax: (01635) 521180 E-mail: sales@closeinvoice.co.uk

▶ Factoring Partners, The Cottage, Bearley Road, Snitterfield, Stratford-upon-Avon, Warwickshire, CV37 0JH Tel: (01789) 730137 Fax: (01789) 730137 E-mail: julian@factor-broker.co.uk

Factoring UK Ltd, Gildredge Road, Eastbourne, East Sussex, BN21 4SA Tel: (01323) 411770 Fax: (01323) 430014 E-mail: info@factoringuk.com

G E Commercial Finance Ltd, 24 Bennetts Hill, Birmingham, B2 5QP Tel: 0121-616 3400 Fax: 0121-616 3418

Gmac Commercial Finance Plc, Sovereign House, Church St, Brighton, BN1 3WX Tel: (01273) 864069 Fax: (01273) 771501 E-mail: info@gmaccf.co.uk

HSBC Bank plc, 21 Farncombe Road, Worthing, West Sussex, BN11 2BW Tel: (0800) 343435 Fax: (01903) 214101 E-mail: info@invoicefinance.hsbc.co.uk

ION EXCHANGE RESINS/ MEMBRANES

G E Water, Hydro House, Newcombe Way, Olrton Southgate, Peterborough, PE2 6SE Tel: (01733) 394555 Fax: (01733) 390179

ION IMPLANTATION PROCESSORS/SERVICES

Tech-Ni-Plant Ltd, Unit 4 Holt Court North Heneage, Street West Aston Science Park, Birmingham, B7 4AX Tel: 0121-359 8545 Fax: 0121-333 4950

IONIC HAIRDRYERS

▶ T3 Magic, Unit 2 Lochside Court, Irongray Road, Dumfries, DG2 0HS Tel: (01387) 721170 E-mail: info@t3magic.com

IP RATED TELECOMMUNICATION SYSTEMS

Samsung Telecom UK Ltd, Unit B2 Brookside Business Park, Greengate, Middleton, Manchester, M24 1GS Tel: 0161-655 1100 Fax: 0161-655 1166 E-mail: marketing@samsungbusiness.co.uk

IRIS DIAPHRAGMS

Wilkes Iris Ltd, Widco Works, 80a London Road, Bexhill-on-Sea, East Sussex, TN39 3LE Tel: (01424) 217630 Fax: (01424) 215406

IRISH LANGUAGE NEWSPAPERS

▶ Hullachan Pro, 6 Milrig Road, Rutherglen, Glasgow, G73 2NH Tel: 0141-647 0257 E-mail: craig.coussins@btinternet.com

IRON CASTINGS, *See also headings for particular types*

Ballantine Engineering Ltd, Links Road, Bo'Ness, West Lothian, EH51 9PW Tel: (01506) 822721 Fax: (01506) 827326 E-mail: sales@ballantineboness.co.uk

Bevan Simpson Foundry Ltd, Hainge Road, Tividale, Oldbury, West Midlands, B69 2PB Tel: 0121-557 3621 Fax: 0121-520 6622

Blackwood Engineering Ltd, Glandwr Industrial Estate, Aberbeeg, Abertillery, Gwent, NP13 2LN Tel: (01495) 214331 Fax: (01495) 217309

Chamberlin & Hill plc, Chuckery Foundary, Chuckery Road, Walsall, WS1 2DU Tel: (01922) 492000 Fax: (01922) 638370 E-mail: plc@chamberlin.co.uk

Coupe Foundry Ltd, The Foundry, Kittlingbourne Brow, Higher Walton, Preston, PR5 4DQ Tel: (01772) 338151 Fax: (01772) 627609 E-mail: reception@coupefoundry.co.uk

▶ Coventry Castings Ltd, Barlow Road, Aldermans Green Industrial Estate, Coventry, CV2 2LD Tel: (024) 7662 2092 Fax: (024) 7662 1917 E-mail: cast01@btconnect.com

Crane Foundry Ltd, PO Box 43, Wolverhampton, WV1 2QX Tel: (01902) 452731 Fax: (01902) 454895

Davison Tyne Metal Ltd, Davison Tyne Works, Bridge End, Hexham, Northumberland, NE46 4JL Tel: (01434) 604211 Fax: (01434) 602733E-mail: sales@davisontynemetal.co.uk

Derwent Castings Ltd, Derwent Foundry, Derby Road, Whatstandwell, Matlock, Derbyshire, DE4 5HG Tel: (01773) 852173 Fax: (01773) 856632 E-mail: info@derwent-foundry.co.uk

Ductile Castings Ltd, Trent Foundary, Dawes Lane, Scunthorpe, South Humberside, DN15 6UW Tel: (01724) 862152 Fax: (01724) 280461 E-mail: info@ductile.co.uk

Durham Foundry (Sheffield) Ltd, Durham Foundry, Harleston Street, Sheffield, S4 7QB Tel: 0114-249 4977 Fax: 0114-249 4910 E-mail: castings@durhamfoundry.com

East Coast Castings Co. Ltd, The Foundry, Norwich Road, Carbrooke, Thetford, Norfolk, IP25 6TL Tel: (01953) 881741 Fax: (01953) 884769 E-mail: ecc@fsbdial.co.uk

Essex Replica Castings (Basildon) Ltd, 108-112 Westmoor Street, Charlton, London, SE7 8NQ Tel: (020) 8858 6110 Fax: (020) 8305 0907 E-mail: nicktownsend@jardineinternational.com

Grainger & Worrall Ltd, Unit 1-4 Stanmore Industrial Estate, Bridgnorth, Shropshire, WV15 5HP Tel: (01746) 768250 Fax: (01746) 768251 E-mail: sales@gwcast.co.uk

Great Warley Forge, The Forge, Great Warley Street, Great Warley, Brentwood, Essex, CM13 3JF Tel: (01277) 226547

H Downs & Sons Huddersfield Ltd, Peacock Works, Leeds Road, Huddersfield, HD2 1XR Tel: (01484) 428203 Fax: (01484) 546993 E-mail: sales@hdowns.co.uk

H & H Iron Foundries Ltd, St. Annes Road, Willenhall, West Midlands, WV13 1EB Tel: (01902) 607988 Fax: (01902) 609987 E-mail: chris@hhironfoundries.com

Hargreaves Foundry Drainage Ltd, Carr House, Water Lane, Halifax, West Yorkshire, HX3 9HG Tel: (01422) 330607 Fax: (01422) 320349 E-mail: sales@hargreavesfoundry.co.uk

Hockley Pattern & Tool Company Ltd, Lodgefield Road, Halesowen, West Midlands, B62 8AR Tel: 0121-561 4665 Fax: 0121-525 0595 E-mail: sales@hockleypattern.co.uk

Incanite Foundries Ltd, Solar Works, Cornwall Road, Smethwick, West Midlands, B66 2JR Tel: 0121-565 2882 Fax: 0121-555 5190 E-mail: sales@incanite.co.uk

J I Blackburn Foundry Ltd, Grove Works, West Road, Bridport, Dorset, DT6 5JT Tel: (01308) 459040 Fax: (01308) 459040

J T & E Castings Ltd, Leyland Mill Lane, Wigan, Lancashire, WN1 2SA Tel: (01942) 241966 Fax: (01942) 492136 E-mail: enquiries@jte-castings.co.uk

James Hoyle & Son, 50 Andrews Road, London, E8 4RL Tel: (020) 7254 2335 Fax: (020) 7254 8811 E-mail: jameshoyle@btclick.com

John Nicol Fabrications Welding & Fabrications, 4 Laygate, South Shields, Tyne & Wear, NE33 1SH Tel: 0191-454 5803 Fax: 0191-454 5803

John Rhodes & Son Ltd, Hightown Foundry, Rhodes Street, Castleford, West Yorkshire, WF10 5LN Tel: (01977) 552324 Fax: (01977) 668011E-mail: richardshaw@johnrhodes.co.uk

Joseph & Jesse Siddons Ltd, Howard Street, Hill Top, West Bromwich, West Midlands, B70 0TB Tel: 0121-556 0218 Fax: 0121-556 3843 E-mail: info@jjsiddons.co.uk

Jack Kilner & Son Ltd, Slaithwaite Road, Meltham, Holmfirth, HD9 5NY Tel: (01484) 850784 Fax: (01484) 852655

Laycast Ltd, Sheffield Road, Woodhouse Mill, Sheffield, S13 9ZD Tel: 0114-288 9995 Fax: 0114-288 9500 E-mail: info@laycast.com

William Lee Ltd, Callywhite Lane, Dronfield, Derbyshire, S18 2XU Tel: (01246) 416155 Fax: (01246) 292194 E-mail: sales@wmlee.co.uk

Lincoln Castings Ltd, Station Road, North Hykeham, Lincoln, LN6 9XB Tel: (01522) 681515 Fax: (01522) 692021 E-mail: info@licolncasting.com

Masstech, 9 Valley Road, Markfield, Leicestershire, LE67 9QS Tel: (01530) 244467 Fax: (01530) 244467 E-mail: masstech@bigfoot.com

Minstrel Metalcraft Co., 300a Hillhead Road, Knockloughrim, Magherafelt, County Londonderry, BT45 8QT Tel: (028) 7964 4454 Fax: (028) 7964 4453

Newark Foundry Ltd, 142 Grange Road, Newark, Nottinghamshire, NG24 4PW Tel: (01636) 702909

Newby & Son Ironfounders Ltd, Smiths Road, Wednesbury, West Midlands, WS10 0PB Tel: 0121-556 4451 Fax: 0121-505 3626 E-mail: sales@newbyfoundries.co.uk

Ouzledale Foundry Co. Ltd, PO Box 4, Barnoldswick, Lancashire, BB18 6BN Tel: (01282) 813235 Fax: (01282) 816876

Precision Disc Castings Ltd, 16 Mannings Heath Road, Poole, Dorset, BH12 4NJ Tel: (01202) 715050 Fax: (01202) 715068 E-mail: shumps@pdcastings.co.uk

Premiere Castings Ltd, The Old Foundry, Green Street, Oldham, OL8 1TA Tel: 0161-620 6605 Fax: 0161-678 6552 E-mail: premier.castings@btconnect.com

Rhodes Nicholson Ltd, Emerald Ironworks, Emerald Street, Huddersfield, HD1 6BY Tel: (01484) 537383 Fax: (01484) 542931 E-mail: gerry@rhodes-nicholson.co.uk

Ross Tooling International, West Ings Lane, Knottingley, West Yorkshire, WF11 9BJ Tel: (01977) 672622 Fax: (01977) 670733

Sabine Bros Ltd, Heath Works, Hearthcote Road, Swadlincote, Derbyshire, DE11 9DU Tel: (01283) 217359 Fax: (01283) 550749

▶ Sandawana Castings Ltd, Unit 4 Bromag Industrial Estate, Minster Lovell, Witney, Oxfordshire, OX29 0SR Tel: (01993) 775862 Fax: (01993) 776692 E-mail: sandawana@wlucy.co.uk

Sigmacast Iron Ltd, Upper Church Lane, Tipton, West Midlands, DY4 9PA Tel: 0121-557 1293 Fax: 0121-522 2024

South Lincs Patterns, Ivanhoe, Spalding Common, Spalding, Lincolnshire, PE11 3AS Tel: (01775) 722988 Fax: (01775) 760386 E-mail: sales@southlincsfoundry.co.uk

Swan Castings & Engineering (Banbury) Ltd, Swan Close Road, Banbury, Oxfordshire, OX16 5AL Tel: (01295) 263134 Fax: (01295) 270461 E-mail: info@swangroup.co.uk

Swinford Engineering Ltd, 191 Hagley Road, Stourbridge, West Midlands, DY8 2JJ Tel: (01384) 397531 Fax: (01384) 440118

T H Dick & Co Ltd, Church Row, Cleveland St, Hull, HU8 7BD Tel: (01482) 329652 Fax: (01482) 589986E-mail: info@thdick.co.uk

Thomas Dudley Group Ltd, PO Box 28, Dudley, West Midlands, DY1 4SN Tel: 0121-557 5411 Fax: 0121-557 5345 E-mail: info@thomasdudley.co.uk

Trefoil Steel Co. Ltd, Rotherfield Works, Deadmans Hole Lane, Sheffield, S9 1QQ Tel: (01709) 830701 Fax: (01709) 830737 E-mail: sales@trefoilsteel.com

Treforest Foundry Ltd, 16 Windsor Road, Pontypridd, Mid Glamorgan, CF37 1BY Tel: (01443) 402075 Fax: (01443) 486182 E-mail: enquiries@treforest-foundary.com

U C B Starkeys Technicast Ltd, 45 Kingston Way, Stockholm Road, Hull, HU7 0XW Tel: (01482) 825203 Fax: (01482) 878094 E-mail: enquiries@bi-group.com

Wagstaff Foundries Ltd, Poyle Trading Estate, 7 David Road, Colnbrook, Slough, SL3 0DB Tel: (01753) 683356 Fax: (01753) 683358 E-mail: andrew@asp-wagstaff.co.uk

IRON CASTINGS, ABRASION/ WEAR RESISTING, *See Castings etc*

IRON CASTINGS, MEEHANITE (PROPRIETARY PROCESS)

International Meehanite Metal Co. Ltd, 38 Albert Road North, Reigate, Surrey, RH2 9EH Tel: (01737) 244786 Fax: (01737) 226644 E-mail: meehaniteltd@btconnect.com

IRON CEMENT

F. Legge Thompson & Co., 1 Norfolk Street, Liverpool, L1 0BE Tel: 0151-709 7494 Fax: 0151-709 3774

IRON CORED CHOKES

▶ Transformer Equipment Ltd, Unit 9 Crystal Business Centre, Sandwich Industrial Estate, Sandwich, Kent, CT13 9QX Tel: (01304) 612551 Fax: (01304) 613630 E-mail: luke@transformers.freeserve.co.uk

IRON DRIVEWAY GATES

Da Plating Jigs & Light Fabrications, 16 Cornwall Road Industrial Estate, Smethwick, West Midlands, B66 2JS Tel: 0121-555 8687 Fax: 0121-555 8688 E-mail: david@daplating.wannadoo.co.uk

▶ The Garden Gate Co UK Ltd, Pepperhill Works, Hungary Hill, Stourbridge, West Midlands, DY9 7NH Tel: (01384) 392300 Fax: (01384) 372948 E-mail: enquiries@thegardengate.biz

▶ S A S (Safe and Secure) Ltd, 1 Yale Close, Owlsmoor, Sandhurst, Berkshire, GU47 0UJ Tel: (01276) 31749 Fax: (01276) 31749 E-mail: sasshop@btinternet.com

IRON GARDEN GATES

▶ Bygones Reclaimation Canterbury, Merton Lane, Canterbury, Kent, CT4 7BA Tel: (01227) 767453 Fax: (01227) 762153 E-mail: bob@bygones.net

Da Plating Jigs & Light Fabrications, 16 Cornwall Road Industrial Estate, Smethwick, West Midlands, B66 2JS Tel: 0121-555 8687 Fax: 0121-555 8688 E-mail: david@daplating.wannadoo.co.uk

▶ The Garden Gate Co UK Ltd, Pepperhill Works, Hungary Hill, Stourbridge, West Midlands, DY9 7NH Tel: (01384) 392300 Fax: (01384) 372948 E-mail: enquiries@thegardengate.biz

▶ Scenic Blue, 13 Ferndene, Bradley Stoke, Bristol, BS32 9DG Tel: (0800) 7833428 Fax: E-mail: tracy_graham@scenicblue.co.uk

IRON INGOTS

A K Steel (Stainless Steel Stockholders), Lloyds Bank Chmbrs, 3 High St, Baldock, Hertfordshire, SG7 6BB Tel: (01462) 499400 Fax: (01462) 896763 E-mail: sales@aksteel.co.uk

North Eastern Iron Refining Co., Ironmasters Way, Stillington, Stockton-on-Tees, Cleveland, TS21 1LE Tel: (01740) 630212 Fax: (01740) 630555 E-mail: sales@metabrasive.com

IRON ON NAMETAPES

▶ GB Nametapes, 53 Honeyborough Industrial Estate, Neyland, Milford Haven, Dyfed, SA73 1SE Tel: (01646) 600664 Fax: (01646) 600664 E-mail: enqiury@gbnametapes.co.uk

IRON ORE MERCHANTS (INTERNATIONAL), IMPORTERS, EXPORTERS OR TRADERS

British & European Sales Ltd, Plummer, Tenterden, Kent, TN30 6TU Tel: (01580) 762415 Fax: (01580) 764466

IRON OXIDES

Orange Chemicals Ltd, 34 St.Thomas Street, Winchester, Hampshire, SO23 9HJ Tel: (01962) 842525 Fax: (01962) 841101 E-mail: brianorange@orangechem.co.uk

IRONING BOARDS

Aslotel Ltd, Aslotel House, Pebble Close, Pebble Coombe, Tadworth, Surrey, KT20 7PA Tel: (01372) 362533 Fax: (01372) 362284 E-mail: asl@aslotel.co.uk

Malroy Products Dudley Ltd, Shaw Road, Dudley, West Midlands, DY2 8TR Tel: (01384) 254178 Fax: (01384) 230126 E-mail: info@malroy.co.freeserve.co.uk

IRONING SERVICES

▶ Crease Release, 53 Virginia Avenue, Stafford, ST17 4YA Tel: (01785) 223296 E-mail: iron@crease-release.co.uk

▶ Felixstowe Ironing Services, Elizabeth Way, Felixstowe, Suffolk, IP11 2PQ Tel: (07946) 833767 E-mail: raddas76@yahoo.co.uk

IRONING SERVICES – *continued*

▶ Ironing Bored, Lloyds Bank House, 2 Station Approach, Tadworth, Surrey, KT20 5AD Tel: 07973 984279 E-mail: rosielally@fsmail.net

▶ The Ironing Lady, 24 Birdwood Grove, Fareham, Hants, PO16 8AF Tel: 01329 516899 E-mail: carol.durrant@ntlworld.com

▶ Maids for You, 120 Mow Lane, Gillow Heath, Stoke-on-Trent, ST8 6RJ Tel: (01782) 515541 E-mail: avrily@aol.com

▶ Perfect Example, Kendall, Roack Road, St. Minver, Wadebridge, Cornwall, PL27 6PN Tel: (01208) 869555 E-mail: info@perfectexample.co.uk

▶ Press & Go, 1 Stockgill Close, West Bridgford, Nottingham, NG2 6SA Tel: 0115-981 5153 Fax: 0115-981 5153 E-mail: t.summerson@ntlworld.com

▶ Sutton Domestic Ironing Services, 28, Ringstead Road, Sutton, Surrey, SM1 4SJ Tel: 07 709 216338 E-mail: sdis@blueyonder.co.uk

IRONMONGERY METALWORKING OR FABRICATION TO SPECIFICATION, *See also headings for particular products or usage*

Broadbent Engineering, The Forge, Pavement Lane, Mobberley, Knutsford, Cheshire, WA16 7ED Tel: (01565) 889000 Fax: (01565) 872067 E-mail: sales@broadbentsforge.com

Brooks Bros (London) Ltd, Kingsbridge Wharf, Kingsbridge Road, Barking, Essex, IG11 0BT Tel: (020) 8591 5300 Fax: (020) 8594 7133 E-mail: enquires@brooksbroslondon.com

Central Steel Fabrications North West, Unit 5 Brickfields, Wilson Road Huyton, Liverpool, L36 6HY Tel: 0151-480 7504 Fax: 0151-480 7504 E-mail: enquiries@centralsteel.co.uk

Clow Group Ltd, 90 Camlachie Street, Glasgow, G31 4AD Tel: 0141-556 6324 Fax: 0141-551 9087 E-mail: engineering@clowgroup.co.uk

Brian Curtis, 60 Park Avenue, Maidstone, Kent, ME14 5HL Tel: (01622) 757759

J E B Supplies Ltd, Wheal Rose, Scorrier, Redruth, Cornwall, TR16 5DE Tel: (01209) 890636 Fax: (01209) 891260

John Smith & Co., PO Box 8, Aberdeen, AB11 5EA Tel: (01224) 586868 Fax: (01224) 590768 E-mail: sales@johnsmithaberdeen.co.uk

Trapp Forge, Trapp Lane, Simonstone, Burnley, Lancashire, BB12 7QW Tel: (01282) 771025 Fax: (01282) 779500 E-mail: trapp_forge@btconnect.com

IRRIGATION CONSULTANCY

Masdar International Ltd, Masdar House, 1 Reading Road, Hook, Hampshire, RG27 0RP Tel: 0118-973 0750 Fax: 0118-973 0002 E-mail: masdar@masdar.com

IRRIGATION CONTRACTORS

A & P Hill Fruit Ltd, Oakleigh, Thorn Road, Marden, Tonbridge, Kent, TN12 9EJ Tel: (01622) 728404 Fax: (01622) 832492 E-mail: graham@aphillfruit.co.uk

Evergreen Irrigation Ltd, 50a High Street, Wing, Leighton Buzzard, Bedfordshire, LU7 0NR Tel: (01296) 688317 Fax: (01296) 688332 E-mail: sales@evergreen-irrigation.co.uk

Field Water Services, Church-Farm, Ulcombe Hill, Ulcombe, Maidstone, Kent, ME17 1DN Tel: (01622) 844044 Fax: (01622) 842959 E-mail: irrigation@fieldwater.co.uk

Flatman Irrigation, Stud Farm, The Street, Bradfield, Manningtree, Essex, CO11 2UU Tel: (01255) 870867 Fax: (01255) 870047

Fuller Water Systems, Cyder Works, High Street, Ixworth, Bury St. Edmunds, Suffolk, IP31 2HT Tel: (01359) 231481 Fax: (01359) 232345 E-mail: enq@fullerwatersys.co.uk

Fullpoint Probe Services, 170 Heath Road, Ipswich, IP4 5SR Tel: (01473) 717810 Fax: (01473) 717863 E-mail: sales@fullpoint.net

Garden Systems, 103 Burrell Road, Ipswich, IP2 8AD Tel: (0845) 1181253 Fax: (0845) 1181380 E-mail: sales@gardensystems.co.uk

Irrigation Control Ltd, Smithy Paddock, Darnhall Lane, Darnhall, Winsford, Cheshire, CW7 4DE Tel: (01606) 558927 Fax: (01606) 862882 E-mail: mail@irrigationcontrol.co.uk

Irrigation Systems & Service, 18 Downton Industrial Estate, Batten Road, Downton Industrial Estate, Salisbury, SP5 3HU Tel: (01725) 513880 Fax: (01725) 513003 E-mail: gholdenparker@aol.com

Javelin Irrigation Systems Ltd, The Pump House, Belvoir Way, Fairfield Industrial Estate, Louth, Lincolnshire, LN11 0YA Tel: (01507) 607175 Fax: (01507) 607521 E-mail: mail@javelinirrigation.co.uk

Lakes & Greens Ltd, Ketches Lane, Sheffield Park, Uckfield, East Sussex, TN22 3RY Tel: (01825) 790483 Fax: (01825) 790271

Maddison Water Technology, 39 Cley Hall Drive, Spalding, Lincolnshire, PE11 2EB Tel: (01775) 725131 Fax: (01775) 760730 E-mail: sales@maddisonwatertech.co.uk

Mattrix Ltd, 23 Trowlock Avenue, Teddington, Middlesex, TW11 9QT Tel: (020) 8977 5453 Fax: (020) 8977 8337 E-mail: mattrix@btconnect.com

Ocmis UK Ltd, Higher Burrow, Burrow Hill, Kingsbury Episcopi, Martock, Somerset, TA12 6BU Tel: (0870) 6005131 Fax: (0870) 6005132 E-mail: sales@ocmis.com

Stenic Trading, 6 Stareton, Kenilworth, Warwickshire, CV8 2LL Tel: (01926) 450221 Fax: (01926) 429992

T & G Irrigation, 175 Westgate Road, Belton, Doncaster, South Yorkshire, DN9 1QA Tel: (01427) 874200 Fax: (01427) 875333 E-mail: david@oakdale.uk.com

Wells Rain Ltd, The Wardens, Watling Street, Leintwardine, Craven Arms, Shropshire, SY7 0LL Tel: (01547) 540498 Fax: (01547) 540500

IRRIGATION EQUIPMENT

Aj Freezer Water Services Ltd, Lynn Road, Swaffham, Norfolk, PE37 7PY Tel: (01760) 723400 Fax: (01760) 336199 E-mail: info@ajfreezer.co.uk

Aquamatic Irrigation, Stanroyd Mill, Cotton Tree, Colne, Lancashire, BB8 7BW Tel: (01282) 873322 Fax: (01282) 870904 E-mail: irrigation@lbs-group.co.uk

Boil Irrigation Ltd, 46 Montford Road, Sunbury-on-Thames, Middlesex, TW16 6EJ Tel: (01932) 788301 Fax: (01932) 780437 E-mail: davidjones@boilirrigation.co.uk

Connectomatic Ltd, 31 Bretton Street, Dewsbury, West Yorkshire, WF12 9BJ Tel: (01924) 452444 Fax: (01924) 430607 E-mail: sales@connectomatic.co.uk

E J Woollard Ltd, Fieldings Road, Cheshunt, Waltham Cross, Hertfordshire, EN8 9TY Tel: (01992) 623232 Fax: (01992) 641278 E-mail: sales@ejwoollard.co.uk

Hortech Systems Ltd, Hallgate, Holbeach, Spalding, Lincolnshire, PE12 7LG Tel: (01406) 426513 Fax: (01406) 426515 E-mail: wayne@hortech.irrigation.co.uk

▶ I L S Irrigation Systems & Equipment, 1 High Street, Brington, Huntingdon, Cambridgeshire, PE28 5AD Tel: (01832) 710029 Fax: (01832) 710136

Irrigation Systems & Service, 18 Downton Industrial Estate, Batten Road, Downton Industrial Estate, Salisbury, SP5 3HU Tel: (01725) 513880 Fax: (01725) 513003 E-mail: gholdenparker@aol.com

Javelin Irrigation Systems Ltd, The Pump House, Belvoir Way, Fairfield Industrial Estate, Louth, Lincolnshire, LN11 0YA Tel: (01507) 607175 Fax: (01507) 607521 E-mail: mail@javelinirrigation.co.uk

Johnson & Johnson, Glenthorne, Uxbridge Road, Uxbridge, Middlesex, UB10 0LF Tel: (01895) 270411 Fax: (01895) 270411

Long Reach Irrigation Ltd, Unit 6, Furnham Close, Furnham Road, Chard, Somerset, TA20 1AX Tel: (01460) 261255 Fax: (01460) 261266 E-mail: sales@xlreach.com

M L Propagators, Fairview, Shucknall Hill, Hereford, HR1 3SW Tel: 01432 850213 Fax: 01432 850213

Philmac (U K) Ltd, Diplocks Way, Hailsham, East Sussex, BN27 3JF Tel: (01323) 847323 Fax: (01323) 844775 E-mail: philmacorders@philmac.co.uk

Rainmec Systems Ltd, Roxley, Moor Lane, Copmanthorpe, York, YO23 3TJ Tel: (01653) 628535 Fax: (01653) 628535 E-mail: info@rainmec.co.uk

Ripple Irrigation Ltd, Bow Cottage, Bow Lane, Ripple, Tewkesbury, Gloucestershire, GL20 6EW Tel: (01684) 299371 Fax: (01684) 299371

Trinkle Irrigation Watering Systems, Reeves Hall, Coombe Lane, Bovey Tracey, Newton Abbot, Devon, TQ13 9PH Tel: (01626) 832977 Fax: (01626) 835369

Wright Rain Irrigation, 4 Christchurch Road, Ringwood, Hampshire, BH24 3SB Tel: (01425) 472251 Fax: (01425) 472258 E-mail: sales@wrightrain.com

IRRIGATION EQUIPMENT HIRE

Ripple Irrigation Ltd, Bow Cottage, Bow Lane, Ripple, Tewkesbury, Gloucestershire, GL20 6EW Tel: (01684) 299371 Fax: (01684) 299371

ISO 14001 QUALITY ASSESSMENT

▶ Lloyd Management Systems Ltd, 73 Arethusa Road, Rochester, Kent, ME1 2UR Tel: (01634) 846519 Fax: 01634 846519 E-mail: lloydmanagementsystems@blueyonder.co.uk

ISOLATING DAMPERS

Ace Controls International, 1 Belvedere Road, Newton-le-Willows, Merseyside, WA12 0JJ Tel: (01925) 227171 Fax: (01925) 229323 E-mail: sales@ace-controls.co.uk

Duct Engineering Luton Ltd, Cradock Industrial Estate, Cradock Road, Luton, LU4 0JF Tel: (01582) 562626 Fax: (01582) 583046 E-mail: ductengineering@aol.com

Flowrite Industrial Dampers Ltd, The Glasshouse Kings Lane, Norwich, NR1 3PS Tel: (01603) 633163 Fax: (01603) 633763 E-mail: sales@industrialdampers.com

ISOLATING SWITCHES

Salzer UK Ltd, 44 Edison Road, Aylesbury, Buckinghamshire, HP19 8TE Tel: (01296) 399992 Fax: (01296) 392229 E-mail: info@salzeruk.co.uk

ISOLATING TRANSFORMERS

Forrest Transformers Ltd, 349 Haslucks Green Road, Shirley, Solihull, West Midlands, B90 2NQ Tel: 0121-744 2483 Fax: 0121-733 2178E-mail: sales@forrest-transformers.co.uk

Inphase Transformers Ltd, Kenyon Business Centre, 21 Kenyon Road, Brierfield, Nelson, Lancashire, BB9 5SP Tel: (01282) 614684 Fax: (01282) 695588 E-mail: inphase-tf-ltd@tiscali.co.uk

Louth Transformer Co. Ltd, Belvoir Way, Fairfield Industrial Estate, Louth, Lincolnshire, LN11 0LQ Tel: (01507) 606436 Fax: (01507) 600168 E-mail: info@louthtransformers.co.uk

S T L Transtech Ltd, 64-66 Percy Road, Leicester, LE2 8FN Tel: 0116-283 3321 Fax: 0116-283 0730 E-mail: transtechsales@stlgroup.org

Transformer Manufacturing Co. Ltd, Riverside Industrial Estate, Mill Lane, Maldon, Essex, CM9 4LD Tel: (01621) 843322 Fax: (01621) 843355 E-mail: sales@tmc.co.uk

ISOLATION PARTITIONING

W P Ceiling Co. Ltd, 85 Mansfield Avenue, Barnet, Hertfordshire, EN4 8QF Tel: (020) 8449 9603 Fax: (020) 8449 2754 E-mail: rpayne7812@aol.com

ISOLATION VALVES

▶ TC Fluid Control Ltd, Broadgate, Broadway Business Park, Oldham, OL9 9XA Tel: 0161-684 7488 Fax: 0161-684 7487 E-mail: info@tc-fluidcontrol.com

ISOSTATIC PRESSING FLEXIBLE TOOLING

Isoform Ltd, Maer Lane Industrial Estate, Llewellyn Roberts Way, Market Drayton, Shropshire, TF9 1QS Tel: (01630) 652772 Fax: (01630) 652518 E-mail: isoform@btinternet.com

ISOSTATIC PRESSING SERVICES, *See Hot Isostatic etc*

ISOTOPE RATIO MASS SPECTROMETERS

Mass Sectrometry International Ltd, Unit C, Tudor Road, Broadheath, Altrincham, Cheshire, WA14 5RZ Tel: 0161-929 7583 Fax: 0161-941 5540

ITALIAN FOODS

Teesdale Trenchman, The Lendings, Barnard Castle, County Durham, DL12 9AB Tel: (01833) 638370 Fax: (01833) 631439 E-mail: orders@trenchermen.co.uk

JACK HIRE

Worlifts Ltd, 90 Roebuck Lane, West Bromwich, West Midlands, B70 6QX Tel: 0121-460 1113 Fax: 0121-525 1022 E-mail: sales@worlifts.co.uk

JACK INSPECTION OR MAINTENANCE OR REPAIR

Chains & Lifting Tackle Midlands Ltd, Dewsbury Road, Fenton Industrial Estate, Stoke-on-Trent, ST4 2TD Tel: (01782) 747400 Fax: (01782) 744508 E-mail: info@chainsandlifting.co.uk

JACK NUTS

Torque Control Ltd, 60 Alstone Lane, Cheltenham, Gloucestershire, GL51 8HE Tel: (01242) 261233 Fax: (01242) 221115 E-mail: torquecontrolltd@btinternet.com

JACKETED PIPEWORK SYSTEMS

Pipework Utilities Ltd, Newcastle Road, Smallwood, Sandbach, Cheshire, CW11 2TZ Tel: (01477) 500344 Fax: (01477) 500755 E-mail: sales@pipeworkutilities.co.uk

JACKING EQUIPMENT HIRE

Barricade Roller Shutters, 7 St. Thomas's Place, Manchester, M8 8TP Tel: 0161-833 0007 Fax: 0161-835 1546 E-mail: shutters@barricade.fsnet.co.uk

Speedy LGH Ltd, Unit A, Castleblair Works, Inglis Lane, Dunfermline, Fife, KY12 9DP Tel: (01383) 721079 Fax: (01383) 732781

JACKS, *See also headings for particular types*

Cougar Developments Glanford Ltd, Sixth Avenue, Flixborough Industrial Estate, Flixborough, Scunthorpe, South Humberside, DN15 8SH Tel: (01724) 841111 Fax: (01724) 841144 E-mail: christine@cougardevelopments.co.uk

TMC, Crease Drove, Crowland, Peterborough, PE6 0BN Tel: (01733) 211339 Fax: (01733) 211444 E-mail: tmc@crowlandcranes.co.uk

Worlifts Ltd, 90 Roebuck Lane, West Bromwich, West Midlands, B70 6QX Tel: 0121-460 1113 Fax: 0121-525 1022 E-mail: sales@worlifts.co.uk

JACQUARD FABRICS, MAN-MADE/SYNTHETIC FIBRE

Alif UK Ltd, 33 Parker Drive, Leicester, LE4 0JP Tel: 0116-235 5050 Fax: 0116-235 5500 E-mail: sales@alifuk.co.uk

JACQUARD MACHINES

Dracup (UK) Ltd, Lane Close Mills, Bartle Lane, Bradford, West Yorkshire, BD7 4QQ Tel: (01274) 571071 Fax: (01274) 501209 E-mail: email@dracupuk.com

JAMS

▶ Bracken Hill Preserves, 7 Cranbrook Close, Wheldrake, York, YO19 6BY Tel: (01904) 448286 Fax: (01904) 607799 E-mail: info@brackenhillfinefoods.co.uk

Crabtree & Evelyn Trading Ltd, The Oracle Centre, Reading, RG1 2AG Tel: 0118-950 8843

F. Duerr & Sons Ltd, Float Road, Roundthorn Industrial Estate, Manchester, M23 9DR Tel: 0161-226 2251 Fax: 0161-945 0143 E-mail: admin@duerrs.co.uk

Elsenham Quality Foods Ltd, Elsenham, Bishop's Stortford, Hertfordshire, CM22 6DT Tel: (01279) 818307 Fax: (01279) 812715

▶ Gillies Fine Foods Ltd, Inchrory Drive, Dingwall, Ross-Shire, IV15 9XH Tel: (01349) 861100 Fax: (01349) 864400 E-mail: info@gilliesfinefoods.co.uk

Nichols plc, Laurel House 3 Woodlands Park, Ashton Road, Newton-le-Willows, Merseyside, WA12 0HH Tel: (01925) 222222 Fax: (01925) 222233

Renshaw Scott Ltd, Crown Street, Liverpool, L8 7RF Tel: 0151-706 8200 Fax: 0151-706 8201 E-mail: info@renshawscott.co.uk

Rosebud Preserves Ltd, Rosebud Farm, Healey, Ripon, North Yorkshire, HG4 4LH Tel: (01765) 689174 Fax: (01765) 689174 E-mail: elspath@rosebud.fsworld.co.uk

T S & M E Darlington & Daughters, 47a Lancaster Fields, Crewe, CW1 6FF Tel: (01270) 250710 Fax: (01270) 250710 E-mail: sales@mrsdarlingtons.com

W T Mather Ltd, Lockett Road South Lancashire Industrial Estate, South Lancashire Industrial Es, Ashton-in-Makerfield, Wigan, Lancashire, WN4 8DE Tel: (01942) 711615 Fax: (01942) 271290 E-mail: sales@wt-mather.co.uk

Wilkin & Sons Ltd, Tiptree, Colchester, CO5 0RF Tel: (01621) 815407 Fax: (01621) 814555 E-mail: tiptree@tiptree.com

JANITORIAL EQUIPMENT

Alpha Chemicals Ltd, 29 Winchester Avenue, Denny, Stirlingshire, FK6 6QE Tel: (01324) 824181 Fax: (01324) 822101 E-mail: alphachem@winning.sol.co.uk

JANITORIAL EQUIPMENT MAINTENANCE OR REPAIR

▶ Jangro Janitorial Equipment, James House Worsley Road Industrial Estate, Worsley Road, Farnworth, Bolton, BL4 9NL Tel: (01204) 795955 Fax: (01204) 576801

JANITORIAL EQUIPMENT MAINTENANCE OR REPAIR – *continued*

▶ S & S Traders, 117 Williamson Street, Stoke-on-Trent, ST6 6AS Tel: (01782) 815581 Fax: (01782) 822881

JANITORIAL POLISHING PRODUCTS

▶ Mops 'R' Us, 30 Princip Street, Birmingham, B4 6LE Tel: 0121-359 0629 Fax: 0121-359 3487 E-mail: sales@mopsrus.com

JANITORIAL SERVICES

▶ A B C Hygiene Ltd, 39 The Rise, Loudwater, Buckinghamshire, HP13 7BD Tel: (0800) 3286452 Fax: (01494) 816750 E-mail: sales@abchygiene.co.uk

▶ D & J Enterprises, Croftlands, Southstoke Lane, Bath, BA2 5SH Tel: (01225) 837837 Fax: (01225) 837507 E-mail: sales@dandjenterprises.co.uk

JANITORIAL SUPPLIES

A I C (Automotive & Industrial Consumables) Ltd, 1 Kingsfield Close, Northampton, NN5 7QS Tel: (01604) 586500 Fax: (01604) 586576

A K Supplies, 5 Regent Road, Handsworth, Birmingham, B21 8AB Tel: 0121-554 7107 Fax: 0121-682 3958

A & M Associates, Unit 2, Stuart Street, Off Fishwick Street, Rochdale, Lancashire, OL16 5NB Tel: (01706) 710747 Fax: (01706) 710746 E-mail: amasso@zen.co.uk

Abco Janitorial Supplies, 78-90 Cheshire Street, London, E2 6EH Tel: (020) 7729 6465 Fax: (020) 7739 9400

Addis, Zone 3 Waterton Point, Brocastle Avenue, Waterton Industrial Estate, Bridgend, Mid Glamorgan, CF31 3US Tel: (01656) 664455 Fax: (01656) 664456 E-mail: e.marketing@addis.co.uk

Admiral Cleaning Supplies Ltd, Admiral House Whitwick Business Park, Stenson Road, Coalville, Leicestershire, LE67 4JP Tel: (01530) 278920 Fax: (01530) 278930 E-mail: info@admiral-cleaning-supplies.co.uk

▶ Advance Products Ltd, Meadow Mills, Carlton Road, Dewsbury, West Yorkshire, WF13 2BA Tel: (01924) 486000 Fax: (01924) 486001 E-mail: sales@advance-products.co.uk

▶ Advanced Cleaning Services, Chapel Street, Exning, Newmarket, Suffolk, CB8 7HA Tel: (01638) 578444 Fax: (01638) 578542 E-mail: adrian@actltd.co.uk

Alkal Leisure, Unit 24, Lyon Road, Walton-on-Thames, Surrey, KT12 3PU Tel: (0845) 2305656 Fax: (0845) 2305676 E-mail: info@akc-uk.com

Allchem Midlands Ltd, Wingate Close, Nottingham, NG8 4LP Tel: 0115-929 5258 Fax: 0115-929 2379

Ambassador Cleaning Services Company, 18 Ashwin Street, London, E8 3DL Tel: (020) 7241 0937 Fax: (020) 7249 9583

Analan Supplies Ltd, 62 High Street, Beighton, Sheffield, S20 1ED Tel: 0114-269 7060 Fax: 0114-254 8445 E-mail: analan@talk21.com

Anglian Chemicals Ltd, Fakenham Industrial Estae, Millers Close, Fakenham, Norfolk, NR21 8NW Tel: (01328) 851407 Fax: (01328) 855701 E-mail: sales@anglianchemicals.com

Anglian Cleaning Services Ltd, 8 Magdalen St, Colchester, CO1 2JT Tel: (01206) 763501 Fax: (01206) 571794 E-mail: info@angliancleaning.com

Anker International plc, Howard House, Howard Way, Interchange Park, Newport Pagnell, Buckinghamshire, MK16 9PX Tel: (01908) 618811 Fax: (01908) 612612 E-mail: info@anker.co.uk

Ashley Cleaning Supplies, 1 Culcheth Road, Altrincham, Cheshire, WA14 2LU Tel: 0161-928 2436 Fax: 0161-928 2436

Astleys, Renown Avenue, Coventry Business Park, Coventry, CV5 6UF Tel: (024) 7685 4545 Fax: (024) 7685 4515 E-mail: reception@astleys.co.uk

Avac, 38 Comiston Road, Edinburgh, EH10 5QQ Tel: 0131-452 8455 Fax: 0131-664 9085 E-mail: avac@netscapeonline.co.uk

B J Industrial Supplies Ltd, 6 Harwood Street, Blackburn, BB1 3BD Tel: (01254) 675244 Fax: (01254) 663061 E-mail: info@thetradeshop.co.uk

B & M Supplies, 99 Church Road, Formby, Liverpool, L37 3ND Tel: (01704) 876665 Fax: (01704) 380046 E-mail: bandmsupplies@hotmail.com

B T S Industrial Supplies, Unit 6, 692 Stratford Road, Sparkhill, Birmingham, B11 4AT Tel: 0121-702 2404 Fax: 0121-778 6092 E-mail: sales@btssupplies.co.uk

Bell Brush Co., 286 Alma Road, Enfield, Middlesex, EN3 7BB Tel: (020) 8804 4144 Fax: (020) 8804 4235 E-mail: sales@bellbrush.com

Bell Brush Co., 286 Alma Road, Enfield, Middlesex, EN3 7BB Tel: (020) 8804 4144 Fax: (020) 8804 4235 E-mail: sales@bellbrush.com

Blue Diamond Hygiene Supplies, 104 Havest Lane, Sheffield, S3 8EG Tel: 0114-278 7777

Bradford Bar Supplies, Unit 2 Napoleon Business Park, Wakefield Road, Bradford, West Yorkshire, BD4 7NL Tel: (01274) 741739 Fax: (01274) 741739

Bromley Brush Co Kent Ltd, 1 Pembroke Road, Bromley, BR1 2TJ Tel: (020) 8464 1707 Fax: (020) 8313 3494

Buchan Chemicals & Janitorial Supplies, Unit 2 Maxwell Place Industrial Estate, Fraserburgh, Aberdeenshire, AB43 9SX Tel: (01346) 517758 Fax: (01346) 510473

Bunzl Cleaning & Hygiene Supplies, Stansted Distribution Centre, Start Hill, Great Hallingbury, Bishop's Stortford, Hertfordshire, CM22 7DG Tel: (01279) 655544 Fax: (01279) 757899

Bunzl Cleaning & Hygiene Supplies, Henson Road, Darlington, County Durham, DL1 4QD Tel: (01325) 353551 Fax: (01325) 465952 E-mail: darlington@bunzlchs.co.uk

Bunzl Cleaning & Hygiene Supplies, Unit 4c Swallowfield Way, Hayes, Middlesex, UB3 1DQ Tel: (020) 8581 2345 Fax: (020) 8581 3344 E-mail: admin@bunzlcleaningsupplies.co.uk

Buzi Cleaning & Hygiene Centre, Units 64-65 Livestock Market, Hall Road, Norwich, NR4 6EQ Tel: (01603) 416226 Fax: (01603) 454872

C D S Cleaning Supplies, 177A Ash Road, Aldershot, Hampshire, GU12 4DB Tel: (01252) 342922 Fax: (01252) 342924 E-mail: sales@cleaningrepairs.co.uk

C M S, Telford Mill, Telford Street, Horwich, Bolton, BL6 6DY Tel: (01204) 694832 Fax: (01204) 690286

C S B Supplies, Unit 10 Dale Mill, Burnley Road East, Rossendale, Lancashire, BB4 9HU Tel: (01706) 213333 Fax: (01706) 217733 E-mail: sales@csbsupplies.co.uk

Caldo Oils Ltd, Unit 4 Rapier Court Sabre Close, Heathfield Industrial Estate, Newton Abbot, Devon, TQ12 6TW Tel: (01626) 835046 Fax: (01626) 836833

Capital Cleaning Supplies, 105 Sedlescombe Road North, St. Leonards-on-Sea, East Sussex, TN37 7EJ Tel: (01424) 718666 Fax: (01424) 782798

Capital Hygiene, 2 Colne Road, Sible Hedingham, Halstead, Essex, CO9 3JP Tel: (01787) 460088

Cesar Janitorial Supplies, 35-39 Old Street, London, EC1V 9HX Tel: (020) 7253 4655 Fax: (020) 7250 1516 E-mail: brad@cesar.demon.co.uk

▶ Charles Bentley & Son, 1 Monarch Way, Loughborough, Leicestershire, LE11 5XG Tel: (01509) 232757 Fax: (01509) 233861 E-mail: sales@bentleybrushware.co.uk

Chartway Janitorial Supplies, Great Tong Farm, Great Tong, Headcorn, Ashford, Kent, TN27 9PP Tel: (01622) 890220 Fax: (01622) 890991

Chaucer Solutions Ltd, Leycourt Farm, Etisley Road, Great Gransden, Sandy, Bedfordshire, SG19 3AS Tel: (01480) 476202 Fax: (01480) 356162

Chello Chemicals, Homme Castle, Shelsley Walsh, Worcester, WR6 6RR Tel: (01886) 812877 Fax: (01886) 812899 E-mail: sales@chellochemicals.co.uk

Chemi Supply Cleaning & Hygiene Ltd, Ewell House, Brunel Road, Earlstrees Industrial Estate, Corby, Northamptonshire, NN17 4JW Tel: (01536) 402522 Fax: (01536) 401341

Cleaning & Packaging Supplies (Worcester), A Perrywood Trading Park, Wylds Lane, Worcester, WR5 1DZ Tel: (01905) 763500 Fax: (01905) 763363 E-mail: cps.worcs@btinternet.com

Cleaning Supplies Direct, 424 Portswood Road, Southampton, SO17 3SD Tel: (023) 8043 4139 Fax: (023) 8090 0556 E-mail: sales@cleaningsuppliesltd.co.uk

Cleaning & Wiping Supplies Ltd, 23 Colvilles Road, East Kilbride, Glasgow, G75 0RS Tel: (01355) 245065 Fax: (01355) 227421 E-mail: cleaningandwiping@lineone.net

Cotswold Industrial Products, Westmead Drive, Westmead Industrial Estate, Swindon, SN5 7YT Tel: (01793) 610880 Fax: (01793) 616941 E-mail: sales@cpkgg.com

Cromwell Industrial Supplies Ltd, Unit 11 Manton Centre, Manton Lane, Manton Industrial Estate, Bedford, MK41 7PX Tel: (01234) 716470 Fax: (01234) 211214 E-mail: bedford@cromwell-tools.co.uk

Crystal Cleaning Supplies, 82 St James Way, Sidcup, Kent, DA14 5HF Tel: (020) 8309 0237 Fax: (020) 8308 0825 E-mail: sales@crystalcleaningsupplies.co.uk

Dale, Herriot Way, Scunthorpe, South Humberside, DN15 8XU Tel: (01724) 855645 Fax: (01724) 278278 E-mail: sales@daleuk.co.uk

Denby Industrial Supplies Ltd, Chandos Pole Street, Derby, DE22 3BA Tel: (01332) 332831 Fax: (01332) 371206

Disposable Supplies, Movement House Soho Mills, London Road, Wallington, Surrey, SM6 7HN Tel: (020) 8773 2692 Fax: (020) 8669 1907 E-mail: sales@disposablesupplies.co.uk

Ferry Chem Ltd, Unit 3c Pentre Industrial Estate, Pentre Queensferry, Pentre, Deeside, Clwyd, CH5 2DQ Tel: (01244) 533033 Fax: (01244) 533033

Forestdale Business Services Ltd, Unit 3, Wandle Way, Mitcham, Surrey, CR4 4NB Tel: (020) 8640 3340 Fax: (020) 8640 3374 E-mail: sales@forestdalebs.co.uk

▶ Freudenberg Household Products, 2 Chichester Street, Rochdale, Lancashire, OL16 2AX Tel: (01706) 759597 Fax: (01706) 350143 E-mail: steve.barber@fhp.com

G T Supplies, Old Llynf Power Station, Aberkenfig, Bridgend, Mid Glamorgan, CF32 0EJ Tel: (01656) 724656 Fax: (01656) 729261

Galgorm Group, 7 Corbally Road, Galgorm, Ballymena, County Antrim, BT42 1JQ Tel: (028) 2564 8521 Fax: (028) 2564 7614

Global Cleaning Supplies, Unit 86-87, John Wilson Business Park, Chestfield, Whitstable, Kent, CT5 3QT Tel: (01227) 266426 Fax: (01227) 770545 E-mail: gcs@global-cleaning-supplies.co.uk

Global Hygiene Ltd, Unit 18, Ladford Fields Industrial Park, Seigford, Stafford, ST18 9QE Tel: (01785) 282900 Fax: (01785) 282222

Greenham Ltd, Tinsley Lane North, Crawley, West Sussex, RH10 9TP Tel: (01293) 525955 Fax: (01293) 522971 E-mail: crawley.sales@greenham.co.uk

Gwynedd Disposables, 14 Glanydon Industrial Estate, Pwllheli, Gwynedd, LL53 5YT Tel: (01758) 614747 Fax: (01758) 701009

H G S Cleaning Supplies, Unit F, 61 Albert Road North, Reigate, Surrey, RH2 9EL Tel: (01737) 240162 Fax: (01737) 223384 E-mail: sales@hgscleaningsupplies.co.uk

James Hargreaves (Bacup) Ltd, Irwell Mill, Lee Street, Bacup, Lancashire, OL13 0AG Tel: (01706) 874701 Fax: (01706) 877005 E-mail: info@jameshargreaves.co.uk

Hartford Russel Supply Co. Ltd, 5 Trafalgar Trading Estate, Jeffreys Road, Enfield, Middlesex, EN3 7TY Tel: (020) 8804 2425 Fax: (020) 8804 8203 E-mail: hrsupplycode@aol.com

Harwoods Cleaning Contractors Ltd, Unit 3 Block 13 Whiteside Industrial Estate, Bathgate, West Lothian, EH48 2RX Tel: (01506) 633584 Fax: (01506) 636868 E-mail: harcc@aol.com

Hertsmere Group Services, 2 Chartmoor Road, Leighton Buzzard, Bedfordshire, LU7 4WG Tel: (01525) 219227 Fax: (01525) 219220 E-mail: sales@hgs-uk.com

Hull Vac, Unit 8 South Orbital Trading Park, Hedon Road, Hull, HU9 1NJ Tel: (01482) 320633 Fax: (01482) 213671 E-mail: hullvac@aoil.com

Hygenitec Disposables Ltd, Units G7 & 9, Blackpole Trading Estate East, Worcester, WR3 8SG Tel: (01905) 755535 Fax: (01905) 755705

Hygiene Express Ltd, Brookfield House, Heald Lane, Bacup, Lancashire, OL13 8QZ Tel: (01706) 879442 Fax: (01706) 879251

Hygienique Cleaning Materials, Unit C1 Broadway Industrial Estate, King William Street, Salford, M50 3UQ Tel: 0161-872 3666 Fax: 0161-873 7474 E-mail: hygienique@btopenworld.com

Icp Hygiene, 14 Ronald Close, Woburn Road Industrial Estate, Kempston, Bedford, MK42 7SH Tel: (01234) 843666 Fax: (01234) 843636 E-mail: icpsales@jangro.net

Industrial Catering Industries Ltd, Sterling Works, Clarence Road, Cardiff, CF10 5FA Tel: (029) 2049 8498 Fax: (029) 2048 8838 E-mail: sales@phoenix-saxton.com

Industrial Maintenance Suppliers, 23-29 Pasture Lane, Leicester, LE1 4EY Tel: 0116-262 0729 E-mail: sales@imsleicester.co.uk

Industrial Supplies, Unit 4 Martin Court, Bleneim Industrial Estate, Nottingham, NG6 8US Tel: 0115-927 2681 Fax: 0115-975 1135 E-mail: industialsuppliesnottm@yahoo.co.uk

Industrial Supplies (Peterborough) Ltd, Unit B, Great Blakenham Trading Estate, Gipping Road, Ipswich, IP6 0NX Tel: (01473) 831360 Fax: (01473) 830243 E-mail: isipswich@aol.com

Industrial Supplies Peterborough Ltd, Waterworks Lane, Glinton, Peterborough, PE6 7LP Tel: (01733) 252771 Fax: (01733) 252362 E-mail: ispeterborough@aol.com

J K Cleaning Supplies, 1012 Chester Road, Erdington, Birmingham, B24 0LL Tel: 0121-373 6069 Fax: 0121-382 3462

J & M Hygiene Supplies, Unit 11 Stanley Green Industrial Estate, Stanley Green CR, Poole, Dorset, BH15 3TH Tel: (01202) 676090 Fax: (01202) 676090

J P Hygiene Supplies, Britannia Estate, Leagrave Road, Luton, LU3 1RJ Tel: (01582) 488851 Fax: (01582) 410005 E-mail: sales@jphygiene.co.uk

J P Products (Chemicals) Ltd, 1-3 Evanton Place, Thornliebank Industrial Estate, Glasgow, G46 8SN Tel: 0141-638 0149 Fax: 0141-638 9388

J W Oxby & Son, The Big Red Shed, Cherry Tree Road, Doncaster, South Yorkshire, DN4 0BJ Tel: (01302) 361666 Fax: (01302) 323023 E-mail: sales@oxby.demon.co.uk

Janilec : Cleaning & Janitorial Supplies, Kingswood House, 26a St. Dunstans Hill, Sutton, Surrey, SM1 2UE Tel: (020) 8641 9996 Fax: (020) 8641 9997 E-mail: sales@janilecsupplies.co.uk

Jaytrade Cleaning Materials, Store 1 Brocks Farm, Runsell Lane, Danbury, Chelmsford, CM3 4PG Tel: (01245) 224646 Fax: (01245) 225078

Key Health Care Ltd, Key Health Care, Ashpoole House, Sandy Lane, Lowton, Warrington, WA3 1BG Tel: (01942) 673315 Fax: (01942) 673315

L A Brook Ltd, Royds Mill, Leeds Road, Ossett, West Yorkshire, WF5 9YA Tel: (01924) 277026 Fax: (01924) 262074 E-mail: sales@labrook.com

L D Supplies, 166 Kylepark Drive, Uddingston, Glasgow, G71 7DB Tel: (01698) 810440 Fax: 01698 810440

James Law (Chemicals) Ltd, Crossley Street Works, Royal Street, Smallbridge, Rochdale, Lancashire, OL16 2QA Tel: (01706) 644940 Fax: (01706) 644037

Link Contract Supplies Ltd, Unit 1, 172-174 Mile Cross Lane, Norwich, NR6 6RY Tel: (01603) 415355 Fax: (01603) 401921

▶ M & A Environmental Ltd, PO Box 479, Harrogate, North Yorkshire, HG3 4WW Tel: (01423) 781330 Fax: (01423) 780709 E-mail: Simon@ma-enviro.co.uk

M & A Environmental Northern Ltd, 2 Royd Business Park, Dye House Lane, Brighouse, West Yorkshire, HD6 1LL Tel: (01484) 475100 Fax: (01484) 475103 E-mail: sales@brook-industrial.fsnet.co.uk

M & D Cleaning Supplies Ltd, Grove Road, Upholland, Skelmersdale, Lancashire, WN8 0LH Tel: (01695) 632765 Fax: (01695) 632760 E-mail: sales@mandd.co.uk

Mcarthur Group Ltd, Economy House Copley Hill Trading Estate, Whitehall Road, Leeds, LS12 1HE Tel: 0113-245 7557 Fax: 0113-242 1150 E-mail: marketing@mcarthur-group.com

The Mayfair Cleaning Company Ltd, 374 Wandsworth Road, London, SW8 4TD Tel: (020) 7720 6447 Fax: (020) 7498 8246 E-mail: info@mayfaircleaning.co.uk

Milmont Marketing, 110 Montrose Avenue, Luton, LU3 1HS Tel: (01582) 418392 Fax: (01582) 418392 E-mail: sales@milmont.co.uk

Minatol Ltd, Mandarin House, 4 Manorgate Road, Kingston upon Thames, Surrey, KT2 7UB Tel: (020) 8549 9222 Fax: (020) 8547 1635 E-mail: sales@minatol.co.uk

Mitchell Oil Co. Ltd, Unit 4 Thornleigh Trading Estate, Dudley, West Midlands, DY2 8UB Tel: (01384) 233803 Fax: (01384) 456279 E-mail: mitchelloilltd@tiscali.co.uk

Myona Ltd, Watery La Middleway, Bordesley, Birmingham, B9 4HE Tel: 0121-773 4333 Fax: 0121-773 4970 E-mail: sales@myona.co.uk

Nielson Chemicals Ltd, Rawdon Road, Moira, Swadlincote, Derbyshire, DE12 6DA Tel: (01283) 222277 Fax: (01283) 225731 E-mail: sales@arrowchem.com

Nottingham Industrial Cleaners Ltd, Elizabeth House, Wigman Road, Bilborough, Nottingham, NG8 3HY Tel: 0115-900 7300 Fax: 0115-900 7310

Obtain-Wise Ltd, Captiva House, 34 Heathfield, Stacey Bushes, Milton Keynes, MK12 6HR Tel: (01604) 758999 Fax: (01908) 310555 E-mail: info@obtainwise.com

Ottimo Supplies Ltd, 7 Livingstone Mills, Howard Street, Batley, West Yorkshire, WF17 6JH Tel: (01924) 469665 Fax: (01924) 463328 E-mail: sales@ottimo-supplies.com

Paperline Northwest, 38 Blundell Drive, Southport, Merseyside, PR8 4RE Tel: (01704) 567162 Fax: (01704) 567144

Paramount Supplies, 12 Twizel Close, Fingel Drive, Stelnbridge, Milton Keynes, MK13 0TX Tel: (01908) 221141 Fax: (01908) 223212 E-mail: sales@phcleaningsupplies.co.uk

Parker Merchanting, Unit 1 Block E Larkfield Trading Estate, New Hythe Lane, Aylesford, Kent, ME20 6XQ Tel: (01622) 710863 Fax: (01622) 719222

Parker Merchanting Ltd, Chester Street, Aston, Birmingham, B6 4AE Tel: 0121-503 4500 Fax: 0121-503 4501 E-mail: info.parker@hagemeyer.co.uk

Parker Merchanting Ltd, Spitfire Close, Ermine Business Park, Huntingdon, Cambridgeshire, PE29 6YF Tel: (01480) 433335 Fax: (01480) 433409

Parker Merchanting Ltd, Benfield Road, Newcastle upon Tyne, NE6 5XA Tel: 0191-265 8312 Fax: 0191-276 2509 E-mail: info.parker@hagemeyer.co.uk

Parker Merchanting Ltd, Units 19-20 White Lodge Business Park, Hall Road, Norwich, NR4 6DG Tel: (01603) 763778 Fax: (01603) 763776 E-mail: info.parker@hagemeyer.co.uk

Parker Merchanting Ltd, 3 Cowley Business Centre, Watlington Road, Cowley, Oxford, OX4 6NH Tel: (01865) 785700 Fax: (01865) 785777 E-mail: info.parker@hagemeyer.co.uk

Parker Merchanting Ltd, Unit 38 South Hampshire Industrial Park, Totton, Southampton, SO40 3SA Tel: (023) 8066 1414 Fax: (023) 8066 1415 E-mail: info.parker@hagemeyer.co.uk

Parker Merchanting, Unit 3, 1 Glen Tye Road, Broadleys Industrial Estate, Stirling, FK7 7LH Tel: (01786) 463921 Fax: (01786) 450089 E-mail: stirling.parker@hagemeyer.co.uk

Parker Merchanting Ltd, 4 Horton Industrial Park, Horton Road, West Drayton, Middlesex, UB7 8JD Tel: (01895) 444040 Fax: (01895) 420036 E-mail: info.parker@hagemeyer.co.uk

Parker Merchanting, 2 Page Lane, Widnes, Cheshire, WA8 0AF Tel: 0151-420 7787 Fax: 0151-495 1589 E-mail: info.parker@hagemeyer.co.uk

Phillips Payne Products Ltd, Crabtree Farm, Church Street, Newnham, Daventry, Northamptonshire, NN11 3ET Tel: (01327) 879100 Fax: (01327) 871633 E-mail: mh@icm-cambs.co.uk

Pollards Woodworking Machines Of Switzerland Ltd, 49 Aylesbury Street, Bletchley, Milton Keynes, MK2 2BQ Tel: (01908) 644877 Fax: (01908) 271552 E-mail: sales@pollards.co.uk

Portland Janitorial Products Ltd, 14 York Street, Ayr, KA8 8AN Tel: (01292) 288388 Fax: (01292) 288189 E-mail: sales@portland-janitorial.co.uk

JANITORIAL SUPPLIES – *continued*

The Proton Group Ltd, Ripley Drive, Normanton Industrial Estate, Normanton, West Yorkshire, WF6 1QT Tel: (01924) 892834 Fax: (01924) 220213 E-mail: mail@proton-group.co.uk
R B Wholesale Ltd, The Broadway, Mansfield, Nottinghamshire, NG18 2RL Tel: (01623) 623247 Fax: (01623) 629311 E-mail: sales@rbwholesale.co.uk
R J Supplies, Wellington House, 65 Wellington Street, Stapleford, Nottingham, NG9 7BE Tel: 0115-939 3933
R M K Supplies, 9 Carterweys, Dunstable, Bedfordshire, LU5 4RB Tel: (01582) 699137 Fax: (01582) 814055
Raine and Shine, Haywood Way, Ivyhouse Industrial Estate, Hastings, East Sussex, TN35 4PL Tel: (01424) 444411
Randstad Ltd, Unit 37 Crow Hall Road, Nelson Park East, Cramlington, Northumberland, NE23 1WH Tel: (01670) 735575 Fax: (01670) 590739 E-mail: enquiries@ranstadltd.co.uk
Regent Distributors Ltd, 3 Regent Road, Handsworth, Birmingham, B21 8AB Tel: 0121-554 7107 Fax: 0121-682 3958 E-mail: info@regent-uk.com
Ribchester Janitorial Supplies, Barnard Terrace, Bradford, West Yorkshire, BD4 7DU Tel: (01274) 305290 Fax: (01274) 395786 E-mail: ribchester@btinternet.com
RMM Distribution Ltd, 5 Greets Green Road Industrial Estate, Greets Green Road, West Bromwich, West Midlands, B70 9EW Tel: 0121-520 5938 Fax: 0121-557 3089 E-mail: sales@wb-fast.demon.co.uk
Safety Equipment Supplies Ltd, 1 Manchester Row, Newton-le-Willows, Merseyside, WA12 8SD Tel: (0870) 1608130 Fax: (0870) 1608131 E-mail: sales@safety-supplies.co.uk
Saul D Harrison & Sons plc, 4 Langley Close, Romford, RM3 8XB Tel: (01708) 377330 Fax: (01708) 377220 E-mail: info@sauldharrison.com
Scott Janitorial Supplies Ltd, Beecroft House, Dalton Lane, Keighley, West Yorkshire, BD21 4JH Tel: (01535) 607335 Fax: (01535) 690097 E-mail: info@scottjanitorial.co.uk
Service Systems UK Ltd, Chester Road, Sandycroft, Deeside, Clwyd, CH5 2QW Tel: (01244) 535095 Fax: (01244) 538987 E-mail: service@servicesystems.co.uk
Solutions, 29 James Carter Road, Mildenhall, Bury St. Edmunds, Suffolk, IP28 7DE Tel: (01638) 717798 Fax: (01638) 713603 E-mail: sales@solutions-c-s.co.uk
Somerton Paper Services, Unit 15 Samuel Whites Business Estate, Bridge Road, Cowes, Isle of Wight, PO31 7DU Tel: (01983) 294702 Fax: (01983) 294702
South Staffs Supplies, Langley Heath Business Park, Eastern Avenue, Lichfield, Staffordshire, WS13 6RL Tel: (01543) 258883 Fax: (01543) 417444
Southern Cleaning Supplies, 8 Lindbergh Road, Ferndown Industrial Estate, Wimborne, Dorset, BH21 7SP Tel: (01202) 861769 Fax: (01202) 870436
Spectrum Industrial Ltd, Unit 19-24 Bedesway, Bede Trading Estate, Jarrow, Tyne & Wear, NE32 3EG Tel: 0191-430 1111 Fax: 0191-483 7422 E-mail: sales@spectrum-ind.co.uk
Springfields Supplies, 11 Bangor Road, Overton, Wrexham, Clwyd, LL13 0HB Tel: (01978) 710291 Fax: (01978) 710292 E-mail: sales@springfieldsupplies.co.uk
Stadium Disposables Ltd, 161-162 Dukes Road, Acton, London, W3 0SL Tel: (020) 8993 7686 Fax: (0845) 450 0694
Suncleen Specialist Cleaning Centre, 119 Seamer Road, Scarborough, North Yorkshire, YO12 4EY Tel: (01723) 352211 Fax: (01723) 352211
Supplies House Ltd, Unit 21 Interchange East Business Park, Grosvenor Way, London, E5 9ND Tel: (020) 8806 8666 Fax: (020) 8806 8686 E-mail: sales@supplieshouse.com
Surrey Hants & Cleaning Supplies, Hygiene House, 14 St. Josephs Road, Aldershot, Hampshire, GU12 4LG Tel: (01252) 313131 Fax: (01252) 334433 E-mail: sales@tiagroup.co.uk
System Hygiene Ltd, Altham Business Park, Altham, Accrington, Lancashire, BB5 5YT Tel: (01282) 777999 Fax: (01282) 777900 E-mail: sales@systemhygiene.co.uk
T G B Cleaning Supplies Ltd, 370 Northolt Road, Harrow, Middlesex, HA2 8ES Tel: (020) 8423 2155 Fax: (020) 8423 6409 E-mail: tgb@tgb.co.uk
Tamar, Unit A, Long Acre, Saltash, Cornwall, PL12 6LZ Tel: (01752) 840036 Fax: (01752) 842326 E-mail: tamar.industrial@virgin.net
Tank Storage & Services Ltd, Unit 9 Spring Rise, Falconer Road, Haverhill, Suffolk, CB9 7XU Tel: (01440) 712614 Fax: (01440) 712615 E-mail: admin@tankstorage.co.uk
▶ Techniclean Supply Co., Gomm Road, High Wycombe, Buckinghamshire, HP13 7DJ Tel: (01494) 459233
Terry Chemicals Ltd, Beckside Road, Dalton-in-Furness, Cumbria, LA15 8DZ Tel: (01229) 466373 Fax: (01229) 466604
Textino Cleaning Materials, Hulme Hall Lane, Manchester, M40 8YD Tel: 0161-223 0647 Fax: 0161-205 8401 E-mail: manchester.090@depot.co.uk
Thamesmead Business Services Ltd, 29 Pomeroy Street, London, SE14 5BW Tel: (020) 7639 0348 Fax: (020) 7639 3646 E-mail: info@thamesmeadonline.co.uk
Trevor Iles Ltd, Valley Mills, Valley Road, Bradford, West Yorkshire, BD1 4RU Tel: (01274) 728837 Fax: (01274) 734351 E-mail: sales@trevoriles.co.uk
Vanitorials Ltd, 8 Armstrong Road, Manor Trading Estate, Benfleet, Essex, SS7 4PW Tel: (01268) 752224 Fax: (01268) 792444
Victory Workwear Ltd, 5 Holder Road, Aldershot, Hampshire, GU12 4RH Tel: (01252) 352800 Fax: (01252) 352805
Wacs Trade Centre, Bond House, Goodwood Road, London, SE14 6BL Tel: (020) 8692 5864 Fax: (020) 8692 1322 E-mail: sales@wacstradecentre.com
Wellfast Industrial Supplies Ltd, 157-159 New John Street, Halesowen, West Midlands, B62 8HT Tel: 0121-559 3805 Fax: 0121-559 9836E-mail: david@page6745.freeserve.co.uk
Wightman & Parrish Ltd, Station Road Industrial Estate, Hailsham, East Sussex, BN27 2QA Tel: (01323) 440444 Fax: (01323) 846027 E-mail: sales@w-p.co.uk
Winlaton Hygiene Supplies, 2 Banks Court, Transbritannia Enterprise Park, Blaydon-on-Tyne, Tyne & Wear, NE21 5NH Tel: 0191-414 0708 Fax: 0191-414 0708 E-mail: whssales@btconnect.com

JAPANESE GOODS IMPORT MERCHANTS OR AGENTS

Kanematsu Europe plc, Dashwood House, 69 Old Broad Street, London, EC2M 1NS Tel: (020) 7456 6300 Fax: (020) 7256 2850
Mitsubishi Corporation (UK) P.L.C., Mid City Place, 71 High Holborn, London, WC1V 6BA Tel: (020) 7025 3000 Fax: (020) 7025 3499
Sumitomo Corporation Europe Holding Ltd, Vintners Place, 68 Upper Thames Street, London, EC4V 3BJ Tel: (020) 7246 3600 Fax: (020) 7246 3925 E-mail: info@sumitomocorp.co.uk

JAPANESE KNOTWEED CONTROL SERVICES

▶ Environmental Projects UK Ltd, 1 Cottered Road, Throcking, Buntingford, Hertfordshire, SG9 9RR Tel: (01763) 281400 Fax: (01763) 281500 E-mail: dave@environmentalprojectsuk.com

JAW CRUSHERS

▶ Haulmark Equipment Ltd, Barleycastle Lane, Appleton, Warrington, WA4 4RB Tel: (01925) 269900 Fax: (01925) 269901 E-mail: sales@haulmarkltd.co.uk

JEANS

Baltex Clothing, 63 Hume Street, Smethwick, West Midlands, B66 3PN Tel: (07956) 365202
Blackburn Clothing Co., Unit 1, Willow Street, Blackburn, BB1 5NQ Tel: (01254) 264762 Fax: (01254) 279464
Falcon Jeanswear, Argyle Works, Alma Street, Smethwick, Warley, West Midlands, B66 2RL Tel: 0121-565 1533 Fax: 0121-565 1533 E-mail: falcon@euroshops.co.uk
Fashion Wear Manufacturers Ltd, 135 Gipsy Lane, Leicester, LE4 6RH Tel: 0116-261 1122 Fax: 0116-261 1133 E-mail: enquiries@jeanmaker.co.uk
▶ Frens, 1 Malabar Road, Truro, Cornwall, TR1 3QU Tel: (01872) 260196 E-mail: info@frensclothing.com
Fudge Jeans Ltd, Queens Mill, Queen Street, Ossett, West Yorkshire, WF5 8AW Tel: (01924) 263391 Fax: (01924) 278419
▶ lastseason.com, 12 Myton Crescent, Warwick, CV34 6QA Tel: (01926) 313175 E-mail: info@lastseason.com
Lee Cooper Group Ltd, Lee Cooper House, 17 Bath Road, Slough, SL1 3UF Tel: (01753) 771908 Fax: (01753) 779299 E-mail: lcuk@aol.com
Levi Strauss UK Ltd, Swan Valley, Northampton, NN4 9BA Tel: (01604) 581501 Fax: (01604) 599815
Pepe Jeans (London) Ltd, 99C Talbot Road, London, W11 2AT Tel: (020) 7313 3800 Fax: (020) 7313 3803
S L K Kentex Fashions Ltd, 90-104 Constitution Hill, Hockley, Birmingham, B19 3JT Tel: 0121-236 6653 Fax: 0121-212 3530 E-mail: kentex@btinternet.com
Soames Chris Ltd, Randall House, New Road, Whaley Bridge, High Peak, Derbyshire, SK23 7JG Tel: (01663) 733599 Fax: (01663) 735480 E-mail: mail@chrissoames.co.uk
Zabou Clothing Co., Zabou House, Shelley Road, Preston, PR2 2ZH Tel: (01772) 558924 Fax: (01772) 558926 E-mail: sales@zabou.co.uk

JEANS LABELS

Original Blues Clothing Co. Ltd, Enterprise House, 133 Blyth Road, Hayes, Middlesex, UB3 1DD Tel: (020) 8813 7766 Fax: (020) 8813 7811 E-mail: sales@original-blues.com

JERSEY KNITTED FABRICS

Adam & Co Textiles Ltd, 52 London Street, Leicester, LE5 3RU Tel: 0116-276 8693 Fax: 0116-246 0955 E-mail: adamandco@mribiz.net
Cloverbrook, Peel Mill, Gannow Lane, Burnley, Lancashire, BB12 6JJ Tel: (01282) 712000 Fax: (01282) 457723 E-mail: info@cloverbrook.co.uk
David Burns, 44-46 Riding House Street, London, W1W 7EX Tel: (020) 7580 1422 Fax: (020) 7436 3046 E-mail: david@davidburnsinttex.com
Eskimo Knitwear, Vinola Ho, Bruin St, Leicester, LE4 5AB Tel: 0116-266 3895 Fax: 0116-266 5280
Shahtex Leicester Ltd, Krishna Buildings, 7 Claymill Road, Leicester, LE4 9JJ Tel: 0116-274 1647

JET PUMPS

Euro Carb Ltd, 256 Kentwood Hill, Tilehurst, Reading, RG31 6DR Tel: 0118-943 1180 Fax: 0118-943 1190 E-mail: sales@dellorto.co.uk

JET WASHING OR CLEANING HIGH PRESSURE WATER JET PUMPS

▶ Calder Ltd, Gregory's Bank, Worcester, WR3 8AB Tel: (01905) 723255 Fax: (01905) 723904 E-mail: pumps@calder.co.uk
Alan Dale Pumps Ltd, 75 Clockhouse Lane, Ashford, Middlesex, TW15 2HA Tel: (01784) 421114 Fax: (01784) 421092 E-mail: info@alandalepumps.wanadoo.co.uk
Phillard Pump Co., Unit B, Holmes Court, Horncastle, Lincolnshire, LN9 6AS Tel: (01507) 523281 Fax: (01507) 527437

JEWEL BEARING/INDUSTRIAL JEWEL DISTRIBUTORS OR AGENTS

Gold Workshop, Printing Office Street, Doncaster, South Yorkshire, DN1 1TR Tel: (01302) 325929
Scruples, 40 Brook Street, Tavistock, Devon, PL19 0HE Tel: (01822) 618168 Fax: (01822) 613244
Tormo Ltd, 7 Devonshire Business Park, Chester Road, Borehamwood, Hertfordshire, WD6 1NA Tel: (020) 8207 5777 Fax: (020) 8207 5888 E-mail: sales@tormo.co.uk

JEWEL BEARING/INDUSTRIAL JEWEL MANUFRS/CUTTERS/ GRINDERS

A Blundell Jewel Bearings Ltd, 203 Torrington Avenue, Coventry, CV4 9UT Tel: (024) 7647 3625 Fax: (024) 7646 6399
Juliette Designs, 90 Yerbury Road, London, N19 4RS Tel: (020) 7263 7878 Fax: (020) 7281 7326 E-mail: juliettedesigns@hotmail.com

JEWELLERS' MATERIAL/ FINDINGS

H A Light Ltd, Tram Way, Oldbury Road, Smethwick, West Midlands, B66 1NY Tel: 0121-327 2009 Fax: 0121-558 7513 E-mail: angelajones@btconnect.com
Maylin Clasps, Century Buildings, 35-38 Summerhill Road, Birmingham, B1 3RB Tel: 0121-236 4641 Fax: 0121-455 6430 E-mail: abros@jeweller.co.uk
Priory Products, Townfoot Industrial Estate, Brampton, Cumbria, CA8 1TB Tel: (01697) 72944 Fax: (01697) 741017 E-mail: priory.products@btconnect.com
T H Findings Ltd, 42 Hylton Street, Birmingham, B18 6HN Tel: 0121-554 9889 Fax: 0121-551 7588

JEWELLERS' RESIDUAL METAL,

See Precious Metal etc

JEWELLERS' TOOLS

Frank Pike, 14 Hatton Wall, London, EC1N 8JH Tel: (020) 7405 2688 Fax: (020) 7831 9680
Shesto Ltd, 2 Sapcote Trading Centre, 374 High Road, London, NW10 2DH Tel: (020) 8451 6188 Fax: (020) 8451 5450 E-mail: sales@shesto.co.uk
Simbles Ltd, 76 Queens Road, Watford, WD17 2LD Tel: (01923) 226052 Fax: (01923) 817526 E-mail: sales@simbles.com

JEWELLERY CASES

Boxpads Ltd, 59-61 Camden Street, Birmingham, B1 3BT Tel: 0121-236 2337 Fax: 0121-212 0977
Potters (London) Ltd, Rollesby Road, Hardwick Industrial Estate, King's Lynn, Norfolk, PE30 4HP Tel: (01553) 774271 Fax: (01553) 692312 E-mail: sales@pottersuk.com
Talbots Birmingham Ltd, 56-60 Princip Street, Birmingham, B4 6LN Tel: 0121-333 3544 Fax: 0121-333 3520 E-mail: sales@talbotsbirm.co.uk
Vincent Rickards, Unit 22 Blackworth Industrial Estate, Highworth, Swindon, SN6 7NA Tel: (01793) 765251 Fax: (01793) 765251 E-mail: vincerickards@onetel.com

JEWELLERY CASTING EQUIPMENT

T M Taylor & Sons, 110 St James Street, Newport, Isle of Wight, PO30 5HB Tel: (01983) 522802

JEWELLERY CASTING PROCESSORS OR SERVICES

A Wardle & Co., 51 Albion Street, Birmingham, B1 3EA Tel: 0121-236 2733 Fax: 0121-200 3056 E-mail: info@awardle.co.uk
Aconia Jewellery Casters Ltd, 43 Northampton Street, Birmingham, B18 6DU Tel: 0121-236 9838 Fax: 0121-212 1840
M & I Tunk, 16 Heathland Road, London, N16 5NH Tel: (020) 8800 1949 Fax: (020) 8809 6783
Merrell Casting Ltd, 70-71 Warstone Lane, Birmingham, B18 6NG Tel: 0121-236 3767 Fax: 0121-236 8439
Morflin Precision Castings Ltd, 21 Northampton Street, Birmingham, B18 6DU Tel: 0121-233 9361 Fax: 0121-233 0713 E-mail: sales@morflin.com

JEWELLERY DISPLAY UNITS

Pearce Display Ltd, Appleton Works, Holmfirth Road, Shepley, Huddersfield, HD8 8BB Tel: (01484) 605458 Fax: (01484) 606031 E-mail: info@pearcedisplays.co.uk

JEWELLERY FINISHING/ POLISHING/ENAMELLING/ REPAIR SERVICES TO THE TRADE

Alexes Jewels, 214-215 Straitmile Road, Rotherwas, Hereford, HR2 6JP Tel: (01432) 354959 Fax: (01432) 352767
Ashworth & Tennant, 12 The Moors Shopping Centre, South Hawksworth Street, Ilkley, West Yorkshire, LS29 9LB Tel: (01943) 817614 Fax: (01943) 817614 E-mail: na@working-jewellers.co.uk
Birmingham Stone Cutting Co. Ltd, 59 Caroline Street, Birmingham, B3 1UF Tel: 0121-236 1418 Fax: 0121-248 1418
Blackwood Discount Jewellers, 168 High Street, Blackwood, Gwent, NP12 1AH Tel: (01495) 222709
P.H. Bunting & Son Ltd, 2A Grange Avenue, Burntwood, Staffordshire, WS7 0BD Tel: (01543) 686481
D J Eade, 93a Cavendish Place, Eastbourne, East Sussex, BN21 3TZ Tel: (01323) 731730 Fax: (01323) 731730
▶ Diatherm & Ancillary Equipment, Gresham Works, Mornington Road, London, E4 7DR Tel: (020) 8524 9546 Fax: (020) 8524 9546 E-mail: diatherm@talk21.com
English Art Works Ltd, 175-176 New Bond Street, London, W1S 4RN Tel: (020) 7493 0807 Fax: (020) 7409 7594
Eric B Milner Ltd, Unit 106f The Big Peg, Vyse Street, Hockley, Birmingham, B18 6NE Tel: 0121-236 6821 Fax: 0121-236 6821
F Sinclair, 23 Hatton Garden, London, EC1N 8BQ Tel: (020) 7404 9198 Fax: (020) 7404 3252
Ian Keat Jewellers Ltd, 28 The Straight, Lincoln, LN2 1JD Tel: (01522) 539800 Fax: (01522) 520213 E-mail: enquiries@keat.com
J Hebson, 8 South Parade, Weston-super-Mare, Avon, BS23 1JN Tel: (01934) 624734
Jewellery Trade Repairs, 9 Castle Lane, Lurgan, Craigavon, County Armagh, BT67 9BD Tel: (028) 3834 1005
Jeff Jones, 7 Hannah Street, Porth, Mid Glamorgan, CF39 9PU Tel: (01443) 681626
M Leach Jewellers, 98 Worcester Road, Malvern, Worcestershire, WR14 1NY Tel: (01684) 573673 Fax: (01684) 573673
Morgan & Power, 20 Hockley Street, Birmingham, B18 6BL Tel: 0121-693 5065 Fax: 0121-693 5065 E-mail: manddpower@btconnect.com
Raycell Ltd, Unit 2 Sherwood Works, Brighton Road, Handcross, Haywards Heath, West Sussex, RH17 6BZ Tel: (01444) 400999 Fax: (01444) 400883 E-mail: raycell@mistral.co.uk

▶ indicates data change since last edition

JEWELLERY FINISHING/POLISHING/ ENAMELLING/REPAIR SERVICES TO THE TRADE – *continued*

S G Scott, 46 Guycroft, Otley, West Yorkshire, LS21 3DS Tel: (01943) 461195
Smith & Healey, 7 Upper Northgate Street, Chester, CH1 4EE Tel: (01244) 372684
Suter Ltd, 38 Vyse Street, Hockley, Birmingham, B18 6JY Tel: 0121-523 5039 Fax: 0121-523 5039
Norman Taylor & Sons, 21 Market Place, Oldham, OL1 3AB Tel: 0161-624 7940
Taylor & Whitlock, 170 Dukes Ride, Crowthorne, Berkshire, RG45 6DS Tel: (01344) 780212 Fax: (01344) 780212 E-mail: sales@twj.co.uk

JEWELLERY IMPORT MERCHANTS OR AGENTS

Nina Breddal Ltd, Mermaid House, Chertsey Road, Byfleet, West Byfleet, Surrey, KT14 7AP Tel: (01932) 340433 Fax: (01932) 336578
E & W Hopkins Ltd, 32-33 Hatton Garden, London, EC1N 8BR Tel: (020) 7405 6354 Fax: (020) 7405 1170 E-mail: ew_hopkins@hotmail.com
Ellison Bros, 24 Donegall Street, Belfast, BT1 2GP Tel: (028) 9032 5320 Fax: (028) 9032 8143E-mail: sales@ellisonbrothers.co.uk
Gem Creations Ltd, DHG House, 152 Mount Pleasant, Wembley, Middlesex, HA0 1RN Tel: (020) 8903 6781 Fax: (020) 8903 6922 E-mail: gemcreationltd@aol.com
International Bullion & Metal Brokers Ltd, Kovics House, 57D Hatton Garden, London, EC1N 8JD Tel: (020) 7242 2074 Fax: (020) 7831 3005 E-mail: ibb@ibblondon.com
M P G Accessories Ltd, 3 278 Alma Road, Enfield, Middlesex, EN3 7RS Tel: (020) 8804 0123 Fax: (020) 8804 6821
Mark Milton, Baird House, 15-17 St. Cross Street, London, EC1N 8UW Tel: (020) 7405 5402 Fax: (020) 7406 6858
F. Simons Imports Ltd, Unit 10, The Parkwood Centre, Aston Road, Waterlooville, Hampshire, PO7 7HT Tel: (023) 9225 5339 Fax: (023) 9225 6800
Simon's Workshop, 30 Royal Star Arcade, Maidstone, Kent, ME14 1JL Tel: (01622) 677841 Fax: (01622) 677841
Stubbs & Co UK Ltd, Assay House, 28 Greville Street, London, EC1N 8PQ Tel: (020) 7404 4000 Fax: (020) 7421 6901 E-mail: sales@stubbs.co.uk
T M Taylor & Sons, 110 St James Street, Newport, Isle of Wight, PO30 5HB Tel: (01983) 522802
W B Muddeman & Son Ltd, The Scope Complex, Wills Road, Totnes, Devon, TQ9 5XN Tel: (01803) 862058 Fax: (01803) 866273 E-mail: su4555@eclipse.co.uk
▶ Wholesale Italian Charms UK, 2 Waverly Court, Rowlands Road, Worthing, West Sussex, BN11 3JD Tel: (0799) 0553775 Fax: (01903) 217119 E-mail: info@carla-mar.co.uk

JEWELLERY MANUFRS

Agars Ltd, Port Hall Mews, Dyke Road, Brighton, BN1 5PB Tel: (01273) 540330 Fax: (01273) 540330
Alexes Jewels, 214-215 Straitmile Road, Rotherwas, Hereford, HR2 6JP Tel: (01432) 354959 Fax: (01432) 352767
Allied Workshops Ltd, 45 Hatton Garden, London, EC1N 8EU Tel: (020) 7831 7373 Fax: (020) 7242 4644
Amber Christian Workshops, 3a Old Market Avenue, Chichester, West Sussex, PO19 1SP Tel: (01243) 781474
Amblergem Jewellers, Unit 79 Grainger Market, Newcastle upon Tyne, NE1 5QQ Tel: 0191-232 3555 E-mail: amblergem@fsmail.net
Andrew Waugh Jewellery Ltd, 34-35 Hatton Garden, London, EC1N 8DY Tel: (020) 7405 8173 Fax: (020) 7405 8174 E-mail: tgwhattongdn@aol.com
Anglia Jewellers, 270-272 Lincoln Road, Peterborough, PE1 2ND Tel: (01733) 314670 Fax: (01733) 896228
Art Pewter Silver Ltd, 3B Colvilles Road, Kelvin Industrial Estate, East Kilbride, Glasgow, G75 0RS Tel: (01355) 229446 Fax: (01355) 264762 E-mail: service@artpewter.co.uk
Ashworth & Tennant, 12 The Moors Shopping Centre, South Hawksworth Street, Ilkley, West Yorkshire, LS29 9LB Tel: (01943) 817614 Fax: (01943) 817614 E-mail: na@working-jewellers.co.uk
▶ Aspiration Jewellery, PO Box 052, Glasgow, G71 7WW Tel: (0870) 757 1512
Aurora Jewellery, St. Ola, Kirkwall, Orkney, KW15 1TR Tel: (01856) 871861 Fax: (01856) 871861 E-mail: info@aurora-jewellery.co.uk
Avon Cosmetics Ltd, Nunn Mills Road, Northampton, NN1 5PA Tel: (01604) 232425 Fax: (01604) 232444 E-mail: info@avon.com
E.J. Baldock, 1A Cambridge Road, Ellesmere Port, CH65 4AE Tel: 0151-355 5689 Fax: 0151-355 5689
▶ Bates & Sons Ltd, 18 Vyse Street, Hockley, Birmingham, B18 6LE Tel: 0121-515 2550 Fax: 0121-515 3383
Bead Exclusive, 119-121 Teignmouth Road, Torquay, TQ1 4HA Tel: (01803) 322000 Fax: (01803) 322250 E-mail: sales@beadexclusive.com
Bead Shop Retail Wholesale, 21a Tower Street, London, WC2H 9NS Tel: (020) 7240 0931 E-mail: sales@beadworks.com
▶ Beads & Sparkly Things, 24 Larchwood Avenue, Romford, RM5 2QJ Tel: (07976) 035539 E-mail: carol.norman@ntlworld.com
Michael Beaumont, PO Box 8, Nottingham, NG4 4QZ Tel: 0115-987 8361 Fax: 0115-987 8361 E-mail: michael.beaumont1@ntlworld.com
Beech & James, 8 Vyse Street, Hockley, Birmingham, B18 6LT Tel: 0121-236 6589 Fax: 0121-236 6589
Bickerton Jewellery, 23 Vyse Street, Hockley, Birmingham, B18 6LE Tel: 0121-551 0509 Fax: 0121-523 0366
Birthstone Jewellery, 20 Ashley Gardens, Harpenden, Herts, AL5 3EY Tel: (01582) 766254 Fax: (02582) 712270
▶ BM Bijoux, 174 New Bond Street, London, W1S 4RG Tel: (020) 7409 3539 Fax: (020) 7409 2425 E-mail: sales@bmbijoux.com
Bodenham & Shorthouse, 50 Albion Street, Birmingham, B1 3EA Tel: 0121-236 5464 Fax: 0121-236 5465 E-mail: jb@bodshort.fsnet.co.uk
▶ Bourne & Kemp Jewellers, 35 Station Road, Longfield, Kent, DA3 7QD Tel: (01474) 702121 Fax: (01474) 702121 E-mail: bourne.kemp1@ticali.co.uk
Bramblee Design, 4 Tilgate Park Craft Units, Tilgate Drive, Crawley, West Sussex, RH10 5PQ Tel: (01227) 792716 Fax: (01293) 528486
Nina Breddal Ltd, Mermaid House, Chertsey Road, Byfleet, West Byfleet, Surrey, KT14 7AP Tel: (01932) 340433 Fax: (01932) 336578
P.H. Bunting & Son Ltd, 2A Grange Avenue, Burntwood, Staffordshire, WS7 0BD Tel: (01543) 686481
▶ C Howe, 100 High Street, Deal, Kent, CT14 6EE Tel: (01304) 368897 E-mail: cjuk@xln.co.uk
C L Edwards & Sons Ltd, Amy Johnson Way, Blackpool, FY4 2RP Tel: (01253) 345311 Fax: (01253) 343610 E-mail: signet@cledwards.co.uk
C N Ross-Feld MJ Ltd, Premier House, 12-13 Hatton Garden, London, EC1N 8AN Tel: (020) 7242 5037 Fax: (020) 7404 5413
Celtic Art Ltd, 3 Hawbank Road, East Kilbride, Glasgow, G74 5EG Tel: (01355) 244493 Fax: (01355) 232541 E-mail: info@celtic-art.ltd.uk
Cha Cha Dum Dum, 16 Osram Road, East Lane Business Park, East Lane, Wembley, Middlesex, HA9 7NG Tel: (020) 8908 0743 Fax: (020) 8904 9117 E-mail: info@chachadumdum.co.uk
Chard, 521 Lytham Road, Blackpool, FY4 1RJ Tel: (01253) 343081 Fax: (01235) 408058 E-mail: enquiries@24carat.co.uk
Charles Lucas & Sons, 72-74 Camden Street, Birmingham, B1 3DR Tel: 0121-265 6410
▶ Chic Costume Jewellery, 27 Lawrence Avenue, Letchworth Garden City, Hertfordshire, SG6 2EY Tel: (01462) 678288 E-mail: sales@chic-costume-jewellery.co.uk
Circles, A Summer Place, Golf Course Road, Hunstanton, Norfolk, PE36 6JG Tel: (01485) 533132
Clarke, 25-26 Kenyon Street, Birmingham, B18 6AR Tel: 0121-236 4642 Fax: 0121-455 6430 E-mail: efc@jeweler.co.uk
▶ Ian Clews, B8 Parkside Commercial Centre, Terry Avenue, York, YO23 1JP Tel: (01904) 629182
Clogau Gold Of Wales Ltd, Unit 5 Kinmel Park, Abergele Road, Bodelwyddan, Rhyl, Clwyd, LL18 5TX Tel: (0845) 6068877 Fax: (01745) 536191 E-mail: sales@clogau.co.uk
Cornish Stone Co. Ltd, 10a Belle Vue, Bude, Cornwall, EX23 8JL Tel: (01288) 352356 Fax: (01288) 352356
Craftstones Europe, 52-54 Holmethorpe Avenue, Holmethorpe Industrial Estate, Redhill, RH1 2NL Tel: (01737) 767363 Fax: (01737) 768627 E-mail: craftstones@craftstones.co.uk
▶ Creative Angels, 3 New Buildings, Gandy Street, Exeter, EX4 3LS Tel: (01392) 422720 E-mail: creative1angels@aol.com
Cresta Gems, 12 Victoria Street, Derby, DE1 1EQ Tel: (01332) 296666 Fax: (01332) 298888
Crystalink Jewellery Manufacturers, 32-35 Hall Street, Birmingham, B18 6BS Tel: 0121-233 2547 Fax: 0121-236 3203 E-mail: sales@crystalink.co.uk
Cultured Pearl Co. Ltd, 27 Hatton Garden, London, EC1N 8BR Tel: (020) 7405 3339 Fax: (020) 7405 5936 E-mail: info@theculturedpearl.co.uk
D G Scroggie Ltd, 11 Camden Street, Liverpool, L3 8JR Tel: 0151-207 2379
▶ Designer Time, High Street, Bridgnorth, Shropshire, WV16 4DX Tel: (01746) 768444 Fax: (01746) 780870 E-mail: info@Designer-Time.Com
Diamond Mine Jewellery, Marr House, Copley Hill, Leeds, LS12 1HY Tel: 0113-243 4950 Fax: 0113-242 3478 E-mail: dgm@dmj.co.uk
Diamonds Andrew Ltd, 11 Hatton Garden, London, EC1N 8AH Tel: (020) 7405 4402 Fax: (020) 7831 4807 E-mail: info@arlington.co.com
E Bundock, 172 Parrock Street, Gravesend, Kent, DA12 1ER Tel: (01474) 327191
▶ Easyline Ltd, 46 Northampton Street, Birmingham, B18 6DX Tel: 0121-233 1279 Fax: 0121-233 0706
Eric B Milner Ltd, Unit 106f The Big Peg, Vyse Street, Hockley, Birmingham, B18 6NE Tel: 0121-236 6821 Fax: 0121-236 6821
Europa Ltd, Belvue Road, Northolt, Middlesex, UB5 5HX Tel: (020) 8841 0272
▶ Farfallina, The Lodge, Gog Magog Hills Estate, Babraham, Cambridge, CB2 4AE Tel: (01223) 413321
Firth's Jewellers, 4 Gage St, Lancaster, LA1 1UH Tel: (01524) 848442 Fax: (01524) 63819
Folmer Amtoft Ltd, 4 Hounslow Road, Twickenham, TW2 7EX Tel: (020) 8898 6031 Fax: (020) 8893 3502 E-mail: info@folmeramtoft.com
Frederick Allen Ltd, 24 Winchcombe Street, Cheltenham, Gloucestershire, GL52 2LX Tel: (01242) 514869 Fax: (01242) 514869
G D S Design, 15 Avon Business Park, Lodge Causeway, Fishponds, Bristol, BS16 3JP Tel: 0117-958 6606 Fax: 0117-958 6605 E-mail: info@gds-design.freeserve.co.uk
G H Tyler, 195 North Street, Romford, RM1 1DT Tel: (01708) 742767
G & M Jewellery, 123 High Street, Ryde, Isle of Wight, PO33 2SU Tel: (01983) 611232 Fax: (01983) 611232 E-mail: sales@gmjewellery.co.uk
G Music & Sons Ltd, 88-90 Hatton Garden, London, EC1N 8PN Tel: (020) 7404 4008 Fax: (020) 7831 8346 E-mail: g.m.s.ltd@btinternet.com
Galleon Jewellery Manufacturing Co. Ltd, 1 Northampton Street, Birmingham, B18 6DU Tel: 0121-236 4600 Fax: 0121-212 1688
Gardiner Bros Belfast Ltd, 44-46 Waring Street, Belfast, BT1 2ED Tel: (028) 9023 4271 Fax: (028) 9024 4122
Gem Creations Ltd, DHG House, 152 Mount Pleasant, Wembley, Middlesex, HA0 1RN Tel: (020) 8903 6781 Fax: (020) 8903 6922 E-mail: gemcreationltd@aol.com
The Gem & Jewellery Workshop, Boscaswell Downs, Pendeen, Penzance, Cornwall, TR19 7DW Tel: (01736) 788217
▶ Gemmedbellybars, 33 Westbury Close, Bransgore, Christchurch, Dorset, BH23 8AZ Tel: (01425) 672711 E-mail: hantsgirl2@hotmail.com
Gemstone Designs Ltd, Bath Street, Bakewell, Derbyshire, DE45 1BX Tel: (01629) 815085 Fax: (01629) 815085 E-mail: enquiries@gemstonedesigns.co.uk
Gold Alice Ltd, 467 Dudley Road, Wolverhampton, WV2 3AF Tel: (01902) 456152 Fax: (01902) 456522
Gold Connections Ltd, 15 Key Hill, Hockley, Birmingham, B18 5PB Tel: 0121-554 7222 Fax: 0121-554 8533
Gold Directors, 8 School Street, Wolverhampton, WV1 4LR Tel: (01902) 425777
Goldcraft Products, 117 Vyse Street, Hockley, Birmingham, B18 6LP Tel: 0121-236 8270 Fax: 0121-693 8353
Golden Eye, 150 Huish, Yeovil, Somerset, BA20 1BN Tel: (01935) 478290
Goldsmith & Co. Ltd, 221 High Street, Henley-in-Arden, West Midlands, B95 5BG Tel: (01564) 794616 Fax: (01564) 794451 E-mail: diagold@fgoldsmith.fsnet.co.uk
Good Design, 7 Frenchs Wells, Woking, Surrey, GU21 3AS Tel: (01483) 889533 Fax: (01483) 833983
Angie Gooderham Ltd, 2A Metropolitan Wharf, Wapping Wall, London, E1W 3SW Tel: (020) 7480 6938 Fax: (020) 7702 1968
Goulding & Bird Ltd, 31 Hatton Wall, London, EC1N 8JJ Tel: (020) 7242 7525
Graff Diamonds (Japan) Ltd, 29 Albemarle Street, London, W1S 4JA Tel: (020) 7290 6760 Fax: (020) 7581 3415 E-mail: graff@graffdiamonds.com
Charles Green & Son Ltd, 37-42 Tenby Street, Birmingham, B1 3EF Tel: 0121-236 1874 Fax: 0121-236 6617 E-mail: info@charles-green.co.uk
Greenfield Engineering Titanium Ltd, 44 Hockley Street, Hockley, Birmingham, B18 6BH Tel: 0121-507 0994 E-mail: getiuk@aol.com
William Griffith & Sons (Birmingham) Ltd, 55-57 Vittoria St, Birmingham, B1 3NY Tel: 0121-236 1772
H A Jordon & Co. Ltd, 139A New Bond St, London, W1S 2TN Tel: (020) 7495 4874 Fax: (020) 7495 4804 E-mail: hajordan@tiscele.co.uk
H A N Jewellery Ltd, 14 Hylton Court, 27 Hylton Street, Birmingham, B18 6HJ Tel: 0121-551 1134 Fax: 0121-554 5155 E-mail: hanjewellery@hotmail.com
H L Brown & Son Ltd, Leopold Street, Sheffield, S1 1LZ Tel: 0114-272 5440 Fax: 0114-272 4580 E-mail: info@hl-brown.co.uk
H M Temple & Co. Ltd, 111 Broughton Street, Edinburgh, EH1 3RZ Tel: 0131-556 4791 Fax: 0131-556 3609
H Pollock Ltd, 13 Shudehill, Manchester, M4 2AF Tel: 0161-834 3103 Fax: 0161-839 6397 E-mail: stephen@pollock79.freeserve.co.uk
R. Hancocks Watch And Clocks Ltd, 17 Warstone Mews, Warstone Lane, Birmingham, B18 6JB Tel: 0121-236 9368 Fax: 0121-233 1358
E.& H. Harrington, Cowdray Centre House, Cowdray Avenue, Colchester, CO1 1QB Tel: (01206) 543680
Hathaway & Muddiman Ltd, 35 Frederick Street, Birmingham, B1 3HH Tel: 0121-233 3069 Fax: 0121-233 3029
M.T. Henrick Ltd, 22 Tenby Street, Birmingham, B1 3EE Tel: 0121-236 1627 Fax: 0121-212 1742
Herbert Marx Ltd, New House, 67-68 Hatton Garden, London, EC1N 8JY Tel: (020) 7242 4135 Fax: (020) 7831 9327 E-mail: herbertmarx@dial.pipex.com
Hirschfelds Ltd, Suite 26, 88-90 Hatton Garden, London, EC1N 8PN Tel: (020) 7405 1536 Fax: (020) 7831 4762 E-mail: info@hirschfelds.co.uk
Hotstorm Jewellery, Sheepy Parva, Atherstone, Warwickshire, CV9 3RL Tel: 07929 726821 E-mail: info@hotstorm-jewellery.co.uk
▶ Iceni Amber, 53 Waveney Road, Bungay, Suffolk, NR35 1LJ Tel: (01986) 895542 Fax: (01986) 895542 E-mail: sales@iceni-amber.co.uk
Imperial Pearl, 24 Hatton Garden, London, EC1N 8BQ Tel: (020) 7242 0575 Fax: (020) 7405 7373 E-mail: valdorltd@waitrose.com
International Bullion & Metal Brokers Ltd, Kovics House, 57D Hatton Garden, London, EC1N 8JD Tel: (020) 7242 2074 Fax: (020) 7831 3005 E-mail: ibb@ibblondon.com
J Rosenfeld & Sons, 11 Hatton Garden, London, EC1N 8AH Tel: (020) 7831 3470 Fax: (020) 7430 1137
▶ Steven James Jewellery, 22 Barleylands Road, Billericay, Essex, CM11 2UD Tel: (01268) 280488 Fax: (01268) 280488
Jeffrey Walton Jewellery Ltd, 62 Albion Street, Leeds, LS1 6AD Tel: 0113-246 8010 Fax: 0113-242 3751
Jewellers Workshop, 164 Fleetwood Market, Adelaide Street, Fleetwood, Lancashire, FY7 6AB Tel: (01253) 776076
Jewellery Quarter Ltd, 91 Vyse Street, Hockley, Birmingham, B18 6JZ Tel: 0121-554 1965 Fax: 0121-515 4619
Jewellery Trade Repairs, 9 Castle Lane, Lurgan, Craigavon, County Armagh, BT67 9BD Tel: (028) 3834 1005
Jewellery Trade Workshops, 17 St Giles Street, Norwich, NR2 1JL Tel: (01603) 625905
Jewellery Work Shop, 38 High Street, Renfrew, PA4 8QP Tel: 0141-885 2560 Fax: (01505) 874277
Jewellery Workshop, 3 Windsor Street, Burbage, Hinckley, Leicestershire, LE10 2EE Tel: (01455) 611848 Fax: (01455) 632820
Jewellery Workshop, 5 Kirk Wynd, Kirkcaldy, Fife, KY1 1EH Tel: (01592) 642950
▶ Jewellerybuymail.com, PO Box 3236, Rustington, West Sussex, BN16 2YT Tel: (07971) 989332 E-mail: sales@jewellerybuymail.com
Jonathan Kaye Jewellery, James Binney House, 52 Cross Street, Manchester, M2 7AR Tel: 0161-839 6138 Fax: 0161-839 5895 E-mail: j.kaye01@ntlworld.com
Joseph & Pearce Ltd, 6th Floor 63-66 Hatton Garden, London, EC1N 8LE Tel: (020) 7405 4604 Fax: (020) 7242 1902 E-mail: info@josephpearce.co.uk
▶ JSM, 56 Boldmere Road, Sutton Coldfield, West Midlands, B73 5TJ Tel: 0121-250 1550 Fax: 0121-250 1552 E-mail: enquiries@jsmmodelmakers.co.uk
K Bassam, Chambers, Court Street, Stourbridge, West Midlands, DY8 1EF Tel: (01384) 444028 Fax: (01384) 835028 E-mail: sales@jeweller.com
K J Roberts, 4 Abington Square, Northampton, NN1 4AA Tel: (01604) 635099
K Weiss Ltd, PO Box 78, Radlett, Hertfordshire, WD7 9ZT Tel: (01923) 855237 Fax: (020) 7504 8100 E-mail: handmade@weiss.co.uk
Keith Martin Jewellery, 25 Chapel Ash, Wolverhampton, WV3 0TZ Tel: (01902) 424742 Fax: (01902) 424742
Keyford Silverware, Roundabout Cottage, Hanch, Lichfield, Staffordshire, WS13 8HQ Tel: (01543) 264275 Fax: (01543) 257076
Korporate Creations Ltd, 151 Utney Bridge Road Shire Place, Swaffield Road, London, SW15 2NZ Tel: (020) 8870 2070 Fax: (020) 8870 2012 E-mail: info@korporate-creations.com
L & S Design, 11-13 Hatton Garden, London, EC1N 8AN Tel: (020) 7404 2302 Fax: (020) 7404 2321
L S Rumble, 5 Hatton Place, London, EC1N 8RU Tel: (020) 7242 5845
La Jana Ltd, 34-35 Hatton Garden, London, EC1N 8DX Tel: (020) 7242 6668 Fax: (020) 7242 1991
Lawrence Group Ltd, 63-66 Hatton Garden, London, EC1N 8LE Tel: (020) 7242 6521 Fax: (020) 7404 0551
Lawson Ward & Gammage Ltd, 4 Berry Street, London, EC1V 0AE Tel: (020) 7253 4146 Fax: (020) 7253 4944 E-mail: info@lwandg.com
Leif Design, Lambton House, High Street, Rothbury, Morpeth, Northumberland, NE65 7UZ Tel: (01669) 621162 Fax: (01669) 621162 E-mail: jo@leif-design.com
▶ Lily Design, 23 Bracken Road, North Baddesley, Southampton, SO52 9FP Tel: 07855 869318 E-mail: enquiries@lilydesign.co.uk
Lotus Jewellery, Alexandra House, Chartwell Drive, Wigston, Leicestershire, LE18 2EZ Tel: (0870) 8508200 Fax: (0870) 8508201 E-mail: apollo.sales@timeproducts.co.uk
M B Spanier, 22 Hatton Garden, London, EC1N 8BA Tel: (020) 7242 2586 Fax: (020) 7405 1472
▶ Mackay & Pearson, 46a High Street, Horbury, Wakefield, West Yorkshire, WF4 5LE Tel: (01924) 273122 Fax: (01924) 273122 E-mail: info@mackayandpearson.co.uk
J.A. Main Ltd, 20 Portway Road, Oldbury, West Midlands, B69 2BY Tel: 0121-552 2941 Fax: 0121-511 1401E-mail: info@jamain.co.uk

JEWELLERY MANUFRS – *continued*

Mappin & Webb Ltd, 170 Regent Street, London, W1B 5BQ Tel: (020) 7734 3801 Fax: (020) 7494 3766

Marcus Wilkinson The Time House, Bluecourt, Guildhall Street, Grantham, Lincolnshire, NG31 6NJ Tel: (01476) 560400 Fax: (01476) 568791 E-mail: sales@thetimehouse.com

Mark Barlow, 4 Buxton Street, Gatley, Cheadle, Cheshire, SK8 4NW Tel: 0161-428 6389

▶ Middleton On The Walds Natural Therapies, 2a Front Street, Middleton on the Wolds, Driffield, North Humberside, YO25 9UA Tel: (01377) 217623 E-mail: sales@middlemists.co

Myron Hunka Manufacturing Jewellers, 8a North Parade, Bradford, West Yorkshire, BD1 3HT Tel: (01274) 307634 Fax: (01274) 307634

N Deal & Sons Ltd, 100 Hatton Garden, London, EC1N 8NX Tel: (020) 7430 1615 Fax: (020) 7404 4786 E-mail: info@nvogel.co.uk

Napier Co (UK Division) Ltd, 3 Courtlands Rd, Eastbourne, E. Sussex, BN22 8SW Tel: (01323) 730196 Fax: (01323) 634206

Natural Treasures Ltd, Unit 21a, Ben Nevis Industrial Estate, Fort William, Inverness-Shire, PH33 6PR Tel: (01397) 700770 Fax: (01397) 700770

O C Jewellery Manufacturers & Design, 5 Rufus Court Row, Chester, CH1 2JW Tel: (01244) 319244 Fax: (01244) 342723

▶ Ogham Jewellery, Abbey House, Princes Street, Edinburgh, EH2 2ER Tel: 0131-225 7275 Fax: 0131-225 7275 E-mail: info@oghamjewellery.com

P T Phelan Ltd, 11 Manchester Street, Luton, LU1 2QB Tel: (01582) 725651 Fax: (01582) 700099 E-mail: sphelan@freenetname.co.uk

George Panton & Son Ltd, 34 Argyll Arcade, Glasgow, G2 8BE Tel: 0141-221 8579 Fax: 0141-204 4920 E-mail: georgepanton@sol.co.uk

V. & F. Parker Ltd, 51 Vyse Street, Hockley, Birmingham, B18 6HS Tel: 0121-554 3587 Fax: 0121-523 2232

Pearlpex Sales Ltd, Davis House, 29 Hatton Gardens, London, EC1N 8DA Tel: (020) 7242 3025 Fax: (020) 7405 4933

W.J. Pellow Ltd, 17 Regent Place, Birmingham, B1 3NL Tel: 0121-236 9121 Fax: 0121-236 7779

Peter's, 41a The Mall, Burnley, Lancashire, BB11 1BA Tel: (01282) 839859

Phoenix International, 7 Hendford Grove, Yeovil, Somerset, BA20 1UT Tel: (01935) 420721 Fax: (01935) 432598 E-mail: sales@phoenix-intl-ltd.com

R G Chapman, 53 Gainsborough Street, Sudbury, Suffolk, CO10 2ET Tel: (01787) 312850 E-mail: info@rgchapman.co.uk

R H B, Unit 115B The Big Peg, 120 Vyse Street, Hockley, Birmingham, B18 6NB Tel: 0121-236 5310 Fax: 0121-236 5310

R & R Models, Unit 13, Radway Industrial Estate, Shirley, Solihull, West Midlands, B90 4NR Tel: 0121-709 0343

Renoir Jewels Ltd, Pegasus Works, Roebuck Road, Hainault Business Park, Ilford, Essex, IG6 3UF Tel: (020) 8500 2301 Fax: (020) 8501 2301 E-mail: enquiries@renoirjewels.co.uk

Ring Mounts Ltd, 88-90 Hatton Garden, London, EC1N 8PN Tel: (020) 7405 9366 Fax: (020) 7430 0139 E-mail: info@ringmounts.co.uk

▶ Rocks, Studio 701 702 The Big Peg 120 The Big Peg, Vyse Street, Hockley, Birmingham, B18 6NF Tel: 0121-245 0500 Fax: 0121-245 0400 E-mail: rocksgb@yahoo.co.uk

Rok's Manufacturing Jewelers Ltd, 103 Hatton Garden, London, EC1N 8LY Tel: (020) 7405 4599 Fax: (020) 7831 3708 E-mail: sales@roks.co.uk

Ralph Rowe Jeweller Ltd, Unit 4, 10 Eastcliffe Road, Par, Cornwall, PL24 2AH Tel: (01726) 813018

Ruffs, 62 Shore Road, Warsash, Southampton, SO31 9FT Tel: (01489) 578867 Fax: (01489) 581104 E-mail: mail@ruffs.co.uk

S C Mitchell, 20a Castle Arcade Balcony, Cardiff, CF10 1BY Tel: (029) 2037 4838

S D V Jewellers, 100 Lower Marsh, London, SE1 7AB Tel: (020) 7261 1718 Fax: (020) 7261 1718

S J Phillips Ltd, 139 New Bond Street, London, W1S 2TL Tel: (020) 7629 6261 Fax: (020) 7495 6180 E-mail: enquiries@sjphillips.com

▶ Sam's Brother Co., 18 Cannon Hill Road, Birmingham, B12 9NN Tel: (07786) 476273 Fax: 0121-078 0987 E-mail: sam888uk@yahoo.co.uk

Samuel Pitt, 61 Albion St, Birmingham, B1 3EA Tel: 0121-236 7737 Fax: 0121-236 7737

▶ Sandy Menzies Designer Jewellers Ltd, The Academy, Belmont Street, Aberdeen, AB10 1LB Tel: (01224) 641031 Fax: (01224) 641031 E-mail: shop@sandymenzies.co.uk

▶ Scott, Back Lane, Mawdesley, Ormskirk, Lancashire, L40 3SY Tel: (01704) 823355

Shiva Internet, 418 High Street, Smethwick, West Midlands, B66 3PJ Tel: 0121-565 4279 Fax: 0121-555 6149 E-mail: shiv@shivajewellers.co.uk

Showbox Jewellery Manufacturers, 22 Miller Arcade, Preston, PR1 2QA Tel: (01772) 201061 Fax: (01772) 201061 E-mail: sales@showbox.co.uk

Simon Lewis Workshop, New House, 67-68 Hatton Garden, London, EC1N 8JY Tel: (020) 7831 4838 Fax: (020) 7405 5532

Simon's Workshop, 30 Royal Star Arcade, Maidstone, Kent, ME14 1JL Tel: (01622) 677841 Fax: (01622) 677841

Slade & Kempton, 1 New Brent Street, Hendon, London, NW4 2DF Tel: (020) 8202 9000 Fax: (020) 8202 1500 E-mail: sales@slade-kempton.com

David L. Solomons Ltd, 5 Hatton Place, London, EC1N 8RU Tel: (020) 7242 7659 Fax: (020) 7831 6647 E-mail: dsolo34962@aol.com

Sovereign UK Ltd, 38 Smith Street, Birmingham, B19 3ER Tel: 0121-551 4124 Fax: 0121-445 8413

Star Diamond Co Ltd, 91-94 Saffron Hill, London, EC1N 8PT Tel: (020) 7404 2222 Fax: (020) 7404 2950 E-mail: info@stardiamond.com

Stear & Bright Silversmiths, Studio 1 Clevedon Craft Centre, Moor Lane, Clevedon, Avon, BS21 6TD Tel: (01275) 872149

Steven Stone Ltd, 142 Bury Old Road, Whitefield, Manchester, M45 6AT Tel: 0161-766 1700 Fax: 0161-766 1330 E-mail: info@steven-stone.com

Sutton's Jewellery Workshop, 1a Upper Brook Street, Rugeley, Staffordshire, WS15 2DP Tel: (01889) 585065 Fax: (01889) 585065

T A Durant Ltd, Bidford House, High St, Bidford On Avon, Alcester, Warwickshire, B50 4BH Tel: (01789) 772353 Fax: (01789) 490320

T C J Designs, 16 Stonegate, York, YO1 8AS Tel: (01904) 611366 Fax: (01904) 611399

T Holland Jewellery Ltd, 5 Warstone Mews, Birmingham, B18 6JB Tel: 0121-236 4658 Fax: 0121-236 4658

T M Taylor & Sons, 110 St James Street, Newport, Isle of Wight, PO30 5HB Tel: (01983) 522802

T O'Donaghue Ltd, 31-35 Kirby Street, London, EC1N 8TL Tel: (020) 7242 8001 Fax: (020) 7405 1076 E-mail: tod@todjewellers.com

John Taylor Poston & Co. Ltd, 19-21 Great Queens Street, London, WC2B 5BE Tel: (020) 7242 0471 Fax: (020) 7831 8692 E-mail: gqs@toye.demon.co.uk

Taylor & Whitlock, 170 Dukes Ride, Crowthorne, Berkshire, RG45 6DS Tel: (01344) 780212 Fax: (01344) 780212 E-mail: sales@twj.co.uk

Terecast Ltd, 25 Hylton Street, Birmingham, B18 6HJ Tel: 0121-554 1722 Fax: 0121-551 5301 E-mail: terecast@aol.com

▶ Thelma's, 47 Vyse Street, Hockley, Birmingham, B18 6HF Tel: 0121-523 9020

Tintplush Ltd, 16 The Crunnis, Bradley Stoke, Bristol, BS32 8AD Tel: 0117-987 2482 Fax: 0117-987 2482

Toghill Jewellers, 16 Hockley Street, Birmingham, B18 6BL Tel: 0121-554 2727

Toll House Jewellery, Crown Buildings, Halifax Road, Ripponden, Sowerby Bridge, West Yorkshire, HX6 4DA Tel: (01422) 823846 Fax: (01422) 823846

Town Street Jewellers, 69 Town Street, Armley, Leeds, LS12 3HD Tel: 0113-231 9991 Fax: 0113-231 9991

Twemlow & Co Manufacturing Ltd, 1-2 St. Peters Church Walk, Nottingham, NG1 2JR Tel: 0115-950 5997

Fred E. Ullmann, 20-24 Kirby Street, London, EC1N 8TS Tel: (020) 7242 7810 Fax: (020) 7242 0205

Urban Haylo, 77 Whyke Lane, Chichester, West Sussex, PO19 7PD Tel: (01243) 783755 Fax: (01243) 783653

V J G Jewlery, 6 Warwick Lane, Warwick Street, Worthing, West Sussex, BN11 3DP Tel: (01903) 239574 Fax: (01903) 239574 E-mail: inquries@vjg-jewlery.co.uk

Val D'Or Ltd, 24 Hatton Gardens, London, EC1N 8BQ Tel: (020) 7405 5102 Fax: (020) 7405 7373

▶ Vetas UK Ltd, Unit 16 Robinsons Industrial Estate, Shaftesbury Street, Derby, DE23 8NL Tel: (01332) 365300 Fax: (01332) 602455 E-mail: vetas100@hotmail.com

Vipa Designs, 26 Digby Drive, Melton Mowbray, Leicestershire, LE13 0RQ Tel: (01664) 567890 Fax: (01664) 565314 E-mail: enquiries@vipadesigns.co.uk

W Bryer & Sons Ltd, 25a Hatton Garden, London, EC1N 8BN Tel: (020) 7404 9090 Fax: (020) 7404 9191

Jeffrey Walton Jewellery, 62 Albion Street, Leeds, LS1 6AD Tel: 0113-244 3198 Fax: 0113-242 3751

Watermans, 50 Parsons Street, Banbury, Oxfordshire, OX16 5NB Tel: (01295) 269210 Fax: (01295) 269210

P.J. Watson Ltd, 63-66 Hatton Garden, London, EC1N 8LE Tel: (020) 7831 3333 Fax: (020) 7831 7100 E-mail: info@pjwatson.co.uk

▶ Wave Contemporary Jewellery, 18a Finkle Sti, Kendal, Cumbria, LA9 4AB Tel: (01539) 729805 Fax: (01539) 48067 E-mail: info@wavejewellery.co.uk

William Webster, 107 Buchanan Street, Glasgow, G1 3HF Tel: 0141-248 5469

▶ White, 5 Kirby Street, London, EC1N 8TS Tel: (020) 7242 7472

Whiting & Wilson, 540 Burnley Road, Rossendale, Lancashire, BB4 8NE Tel: (01706) 830974 Fax: (01706) 830974

▶ Wholesale Italian Charms UK, 2 Waverly Court, Rowlands Road, Worthing, West Sussex, BN11 3JD Tel: (0799) 0553775 Fax: (01903) 217119 E-mail: info@carla-mar.co.uk

Y Constantine, 12-13 Greville Street, London, EC1N 8SB Tel: (020) 7242 7171 Fax: (020) 7242 7172

Zacharia Fashion, 3 Hanger Green, London, W5 3EL Tel: (020) 8997 6378 Fax: (020) 8998 0717

JEWELLERY POUCHES

Presentation Cases (Birmingham) Ltd, 51 Vyse Street, Hockley, Birmingham, B18 6HS Tel: (01453) 842181 Fax: 0121-523 2232 E-mail: ardenvfp@yahoo.com

JEWELLERY PRESENTATION BOXES

Presentation Cases (Birmingham) Ltd, 51 Vyse Street, Hockley, Birmingham, B18 6HS Tel: (01453) 842181 Fax: 0121-523 2232 E-mail: ardenvfp@yahoo.com

JEWELLERY PRODUCTION SUPPLIES

▶ gembasket.co.uk, 39 Belmont Drive, Westwood, East Kilbride, Glasgow, G75 8HB Tel: (01355) 232441 E-mail: orders@gembasket.co.uk

JEWELLERY ROLLS

Presentation Cases (Birmingham) Ltd, 51 Vyse Street, Hockley, Birmingham, B18 6HS Tel: (01453) 842181 Fax: 0121-523 2232 E-mail: ardenvfp@yahoo.com

JEWELLERY SOLDER PASTE

Fusion Automation Inc, Barrows Rd, The Pinnacles, Harlow, Essex, CM19 5FD Tel: (01279) 443122 Fax: (01279) 424057 E-mail: salesuk@fai-uk.com

JEWELLERY SOLDERS, *See Jewellery Solder Pastes etc*

JEWELLERY, STERLING SILVER

Aetee Ltd, Unit 11 Spring Mill Industrial Estate, Avening Road, Nailsworth, Stroud, Gloucestershire, GL6 0BS Tel: (01453) 835857 Fax: (01453) 836009 E-mail: admin@aetee.com

▶ C Howe, 100 High Street, Deal, Kent, CT14 6EE Tel: (01304) 368897 E-mail: cjuk@xln.co.uk

▶ Cavern Crystals, 376 Wakefield Road, Denby Dale, Huddersfield, HD8 8RT Tel: 01484 865427 Fax: 01484 865427 E-mail: info@crystalcavern.com

▶ Georgina Ettridge, 12 St. Johns Glebe, Rownhams, Southampton, SO16 8AX Tel: (023) 8073 6704 E-mail: designer@georginaettridge.co.uk

Hotstorm Jewellery, Sheepy Parva, Atherstone, Warwickshire, CV9 3RL Tel: 07929 726821 E-mail: info@hotstorm-jewellery.co.uk

▶ Iceni Amber, 53 Waveney Road, Bungay, Suffolk, NR35 1LJ Tel: (01986) 895542 Fax: (01986) 895542 E-mail: sales@iceni-amber.co.uk

▶ Jewellery TV, Leeds, LS17 6WY Tel: (0870) 7447371 Fax: (0870) 1342096 E-mail: sales@jewellery.tv

▶ Jill Paton Contemporary Jewellery, 24 Aubery Crescent, 'Glenogle', Largs, Ayrshire, KA30 8AP Tel: (01475) 672914 E-mail: jill@jillpaton.co.uk

▶ Lily Design, 23 Bracken Road, North Baddesley, Southampton, SO52 9FP Tel: 07855 869318 E-mail: enquiries@lilydesign.co.uk

▶ Rayment & Hull, Bedlam Court Lane, Minster, Ramsgate, Kent, CT12 4HQ Tel: (01843) 822619 Fax: (01843) 821635 E-mail: r.h2004@btinternet.com

▶ Sandy Menzies Designer Jewellers Ltd, The Academy, Belmont Street, Aberdeen, AB10 1LB Tel: (01224) 641031 Fax: (01224) 641031 E-mail: shop@sandymenzies.co.uk

▶ The Silver Company, 25 Tabor Road, London, W6 0BN Tel: (020) 8748 7799 Fax: (020) 8834 7123 E-mail: info@silvercompany.co.uk

▶ Silver Heaven, 20 Westham Road, Weymouth, Dorset, DT4 8NU Tel: (01305) 784005 E-mail: silverheaven@tesco.net

▶ Smithsonia Designers, 14-16 Piccadilly Arcade, Birmingham, B2 4HD Tel: 0121-643 8405 Fax: 0121-643 8194

JEWELS, CLOCK/WATCH

▶ Millers, 9 Cleveland Street, Wolverhampton, WV1 3HH Tel: (01902) 421215

JIB CRANES

Cobal Cranes Ltd, Doctor Lane, Sheffield, S9 5AP Tel: 0114-261 8003 Fax: 0114-261 9003 E-mail: steven.hides@btconnect.com

▶ Pelloby Engineering Ltd, Halesfield 19, Telford, Shropshire, TF7 4QT Tel: (01952) 586626 Fax: (01952) 587871 E-mail: sales@pelloby.com

Stothert & Pitt, Lower Bristol Road, Bath, BA2 3DJ Tel: (01225) 314400 Fax: (01225) 332529

JIG BORING TOOLS

Bedestone Ltd, Boulton Ho, 41 Icknield St, Hockley, Birmingham, B18 5AY Tel: 0121-554 3283 Fax: 0121-507 0140 E-mail: bedestone@aol.com

JIG TOOLMAKERS

C S L Technical Engineering Services, Office 2 Rainbow Business Centre, Phoenix Way, Swansea Enterprise Park, Swansea, SA7 9EH Tel: 01792 702200 E-mail: sales@csl-ltd.co.uk

▶ Peak Toolmakers Ltd, Smeckley Wood Close, Chesterfield Trading Estate, Chesterfield, Derbyshire, S41 9PZ Tel: (01246) 268588 Fax: (01246) 268599 E-mail: info@raprecision.com

▶ Plasticom Ltd, Hilton Road, Cobbs Wood Industrial Estate, Ashford, Kent, TN23 1EW Tel: (01233) 621604 Fax: (01233) 622169 E-mail: enquiries@plasticomgroup.com

Riverdale Mahoney Ltd, Unit 3 Dicker Mill, Hertford, SG13 7AE Tel: (01992) 583988 Fax: (01992) 583988 E-mail: riverdalema@btinternet.com

JIG/FIXTURE CONSTRUCTION/ BORING/GRINDING ENGINEERS/ CUSTOM BUILDERS

A & W Jigboring Ltd, 46 Padgets Lane, Redditch, Worcestershire, B98 0RD Tel: (01527) 522196 Fax: (01527) 517389 E-mail: sales@awjigboring.co.uk

A & W Precision Tools Ltd, Unit 2 Brookside Industrial Pk, Crankhall La, Wednesbury, W. Midlands, WS10 0QZ Tel: 0121-505 1359 Fax: 0121-505 1359

Aquatools Ltd, 54 Chapel Street, Tipton, West Midlands, DY4 8JB Tel: 0121-520 7978 Fax: 0121-522 2051 E-mail: sales@aquatools.co.uk

Argee Instrument Co. Ltd, 14 Albert Road, Romford, RM1 2PL Tel: (01708) 747878 Fax: (01708) 733216

Argyle Engineering Ltd, 21-29 Regent Street, Liverpool, L3 7BW Tel: 0151-236 0777 Fax: 0151-236 8073

Awon Engineering, 26 Dunlop Road, Redditch, Worcestershire, B97 5XP Tel: (01527) 404699 Fax: (01527) 524868

Bedestone Ltd, 41 Icknield Street, Hockley, Birmingham, B18 5AY Tel: 0121-554 3283 Fax: 0121-507 0140 E-mail: bedestone@aol.com

Bevan, 53a Frederick Street, Birmingham, B1 3HS Tel: 0121-236 9263 Fax: 0121-236 9263

Brookes Specialist Engineers Ltd, Gospel End Street, Sedgley, Dudley, West Midlands, DY3 3LS Tel: (01902) 882233 Fax: (01902) 885284 E-mail: mike@brookes-engineering.co.uk

Brynmawr Tools & Engineering Co. Ltd, Heritage Court Road, Gilchrist Thomas Industrial Estate, Blaenavon, Pontypool, Gwent, NP4 9RL Tel: (01495) 790230 Fax: (01495) 792757 E-mail: wnquiries@gosengomeering.co.uk

Burman Tool Co Ltd, Rye Road, Hoddesdon, Hertfordshire, EN11 0DZ Tel: (01992) 466311 Fax: 01992 468900 E-mail: info@burman.co.uk

Burton & Smith Ltd, Unit 32p The Washford Industrial Estate, Heming Road, Redditch, Worcestershire, B98 0DH Tel: (01527) 516925 Fax: (01527) 514900 E-mail: burtonandsmith@lycos.co.uk

C B Powell Ltd, 10 St Josephs Close, Hove, East Sussex, BN3 7ES Tel: (01273) 771144 Fax: (01273) 726966 E-mail: cbpowel@btconnect.com

Camtool Engineering, 6b Purdy Road, Bilston, West Midlands, WV14 8UB Tel: (01902) 403562 Fax: (01902) 403562 E-mail: camtool.eng@btconnect.com

Central Tools & Pressings, Unit D1, Bill House, Birmingham, B19 1AP Tel: 0121-523 7522 Fax: 0121-523 9922

Chris Jack Toolmaking, Block 6, Upper Mills Trading Estate, Bristol Road, Stonehouse, Gloucestershire, GL10 2BJ Tel: (01453) 826852 Fax: (01453) 826852

Cma Tools Burnley Ltd, Belle Vue Mill, Westgate, Burnley, Lancashire, BB11 1SD Tel: (01282) 423619 Fax: (01282) 427944 E-mail: cmatools@airtime.co.uk

Coburg Engineering Ltd, Unit 22F, Wincombe Business Park, Shaftesbury, Dorset, SP7 9QJ Tel: (01747) 855022 Fax: (01747) 854744 E-mail: info@coburg.co.uk

Conway Precision Engineering Group Ltd, 106 Tame Road, Birmingham, B6 7EZ Tel: 0121-327 8037 Fax: 0121-328 4885 E-mail: design@gauges.co.uk

Crompton & Rathbone (Tools) Ltd, 111-117 Sydenham Road, Birmingham, B11 1DG Tel: 0121-773 7140 Fax: 0121-773 7140

JIG/FIXTURE CONSTRUCTION/ BORING/GRINDING ENGINEERS/ CUSTOM BUILDERS – *continued*

D J J Precision Engineering Ltd, Unit 14 Pontyfelin Avenue Industrial Estate, New Inn, Pontypool, Gwent, NP4 0DQ Tel: (01495) 760561 Fax: (01495) 756256 E-mail: sales@djjengineering.com

Donart Engineering Co., Station Street, Bromsgrove, Worcestershire, B60 2BS Tel: (01527) 879722 Fax: (01527) 879722

E K W Fabrications Ltd, Coppice Side Industrial Estate, West Coppice Road, Walsall, WS8 7HB Tel: (01543) 378181 Fax: (01543) 361012

P.M.J. Engineering Co. Ltd, 5 & 6 Brunswick Road, Birmingham, B12 8NP Tel: 0121 4406760

Fielding Engineering UK Ltd, 2 Lancaster Way, Earls Colne Industrial Park, Earls Colne, Colchester, CO6 2NS Tel: (01787) 224844 Fax: (01787) 224344 E-mail: jfield@fieldingltd.co.uk

G E M Engineering Services, Unit B9 Tweedale Industrial Estate, Madeley, Telford, Shropshire, TF7 4JR Tel: (01952) 588525 Fax: (01952) 588525

G W J Engineering Ltd, 7 Ruston Road, Alma Park Industrial Estate, Grantham, Lincolnshire, NG31 9SW Tel: (01476) 568703 Fax: (01476) 578639 E-mail: enquiries@gwjengineering.co.uk

Grosvenor Tooling Services, Unit 12, Ash Road, Wrexham Industrial Estate, Wrexham, Clwyd, LL13 9UF Tel: (01978) 664359 Fax: (01978) 664359

H & H Tool & Engineering Ltd, Unit 4, Harvey Industrial Estate, Shelah Road, Halesowen, West Midlands, B63 3PG Tel: 0121-550 2231 Fax: 0121-585 5789 E-mail: office@hhtools.com

Hayward Engineering, Unit 6 11-15 Francis Avenue, Bournemouth, BH11 8NX Tel: (01202) 573235 Fax: (01202) 581903 E-mail: sales@haywardeng.co.uk

Highbank Tools Ltd, Unit 7 Reliance Trading Estate, Manchester, M40 3AG Tel: 0161-681 2506 Fax: 0161-683 4937

Hillfax Ltd, Park Road, Willenhall, West Midlands, WV13 1AQ Tel: (01902) 606442 Fax: (01902) 634982 E-mail: sprint@btclick.com

Holloway Tool Co. Ltd, 71-75 New Summer Street, Newtown, Birmingham, B19 3TE Tel: 0121-359 3777 Fax: 0121-359 6065 E-mail: cad@hollowaytool.co.uk

Hollycroft Engineering Ltd, 7 Teal Business Park, Dodwells Road, Hinckley, Leicestershire, LE10 3BZ Tel: (01455) 635845 Fax: (01455) 250273 E-mail: sales@hollycrofteng.freeserve.co.uk

Hyde Group Ltd, Hadfield Street, Dukinfield, Cheshire, SK16 4QX Tel: 0161-308 2111 Fax: 0161-330 2680 E-mail: sales@hydetool.co.uk

J B S Poyser Mansfield Ltd, Pleasley Vale Works, Pleasley Vale, Mansfield, Nottinghamshire, NG19 8SD Tel: (01623) 810066 Fax: (01623) 812266

J S Tool & Gauge Co., Unit 4 Victoria Buildings, Newhall St, Willenhall, West Midlands, WV13 1LQ Tel: (01902) 636028 Fax: (01902) 608187 E-mail: jstool@live1.net

Jas Bolland Engineering Ltd, Blantyre Industrial Estate, Blantyre, Glasgow, G72 0TT Tel: (01698) 821009 Fax: (01698) 820011 E-mail: sales@bolland-eng.co.uk

John Bradley Engineering Ltd, 5 Broadfield Road, Seymour St, Heywood, Lancashire, OL10 3AJ Tel: (01706) 366794 Fax: (01706) 620270 E-mail: jbe@johnbradleygroup.co.uk

Jubilee Engineering Co., 5 Runnings Road Kingsditch Trading Estate, Cheltenham, Gloucestershire, GL51 9NQ Tel: (01242) 584883 Fax: (01242) 226855

K F C Engineering Ltd, Unit 6 Little Forge Road, Redditch, Worcestershire, B98 7SF Tel: (01527) 520371 Fax: (01527) 520346 E-mail: kevin@kfcengineering.co.uk

K Pilcher Engineering, Unit D1 Guy Motors Industrial Park, Park Lane, Wolverhampton, WV10 9QF Tel: (01902) 728820 Fax: (01902) 304769 E-mail: kpeng@waverider.co.uk

Kestmark Precision Engineering, 3 Winster Grove Industrial Estate, Winster Grove, Birmingham, B44 9EG Tel: 0121-360 8850 Fax: 0121-360 8850 E-mail: eng@kestmark.fsnet.co.uk

Kirkby Jig & Tool Co. Ltd, Bradman Road, Knowsley Industrial Park, Liverpool, L33 7UR Tel: 0151-546 2681 Fax: 0151-546 4937

Knights Design & Manufacturer, Trident Business Park, 6 Park Street, Nuneaton, Warwickshire, CV11 4NS Tel: (024) 7634 4822 Fax: (024) 7634 4822

Limbrick Jig & Tool Co., Unit 14 Wilden Industrial Estate, Stourport-on-Severn, Worcestershire, DY13 9JY Tel: (01299) 823139 Fax: (01299) 823139

Lobro Tools Ltd, Long Street, Premier Business Park, Walsall, WS2 9XP Tel: (01922) 623140 Fax: (01922) 648297 E-mail: sales@lobrotools.com

Longbridge Tool & Gauge Ltd, Unit 74, Heming Road, Washford Industrial Estate, Redditch, Worcestershire, B98 0EA Tel: (01527) 520706 Fax: (01527) 510170

Luton Jig & Tool Co. Ltd, Unit 3 Chase Street, Luton, LU1 3QZ Tel: (01582) 725591 Fax: (01582) 735211E-mail: david@ljtco.co.uk

M D G Crest Ltd, Malvern View Business Park, Stella Way, Bishops Cleeve, Cheltenham, Gloucestershire, GL52 7DQ Tel: (01242) 675778 Fax: (01242) 676999

M N B Precision Ltd, Falkland Close, Charter Avenue Industrial Estate, Coventry, CV4 8AU Tel: (024) 7669 5959 Fax: (024) 7669 5909 E-mail: sales@mnbprecision.com

Manser Precision Engineering, Unit 2, 216 Barnes Lane, Sarisbury Green, Southampton, SO31 7BG Tel: (01489) 564646 Fax: (01489) 564647 E-mail: jigboremanser@onetel.com

Mor Brock Tool & Gauge Co., Maldon Road, Romford, RM7 0JB Tel: (01708) 706606 Fax: (01708) 740906

Nixon Engineering Ltd, 7 Peterfield Road, Kingstown Industrial Estate, Carlisle, CA3 0EY Tel: (01228) 523956 Fax: (01228) 401919 E-mail: eddie@nixonengltd.freeserve.co.uk

Oak Tree Plastic & Engineering Ltd, Spon La South, West Bromwich, West Midlands, B70 6AZ Tel: 0121-500 5164 Fax: 0121-500 5164

P H B Industries Ltd, Fitzherbert Road, Farlington, Portsmouth, PO6 1SB Tel: (023) 9237 9696 Fax: (023) 9237 5822

Perry Pearson Engineering Co. Ltd, Unit 6 219 Torrington Avenue, Coventry, CV4 9HN Tel: 024 76460339

Polesworth Jig & Tool, 49 High Street, Polesworth, Tamworth, Staffordshire, B78 1DX Tel: (01827) 893812 Fax: (01827) 893812

Precision Toolmakers & Engineers Rugby Ltd, 19 Somers Road, Rugby, Warwickshire, CV22 7DG Tel: (01788) 543661 Fax: (01788) 565742 E-mail: precisiontmrugby@aol.com

Produsit Ltd, Precision Works, 69-70 Moland Street, Birmingham, B4 7EY Tel: 0121-359 5571 Fax: 0121-359 5572 E-mail: produsit@msn.com

Projax Tools (1989) Ltd, Arthur St, Redditch, Worcestershire, B98 8DZ Tel: 01527 523734

Promac Precision Engineering Ltd, 49 Ivatt Way, Peterborough, PE3 7PN Tel: (01733) 333000 Fax: (01733) 333001 E-mail: management@promac.fsnet.co.uk

Proto Precision Engineering, Unit 28 Heath Hill Industrial Estate, Dawley, Telford, Shropshire, TF4 2RH Tel: (01952) 506227 Fax: (01952) 506227

Pugh Engineering Co., Unit 20 Poplar Drive, Witton, Birmingham, B6 7AD Tel: 0121-344 3240 Fax: 0121-344 3240

Quest Engineering, Coates Yard, Nottingham Road, Loughborough, Leicestershire, LE11 1EU Tel: (01509) 610474 Fax: (01509) 610474

R G Engineering, 3 Stoney Court, Hotchkiss Way, Binley, Coventry, CV3 2RL Tel: (024) 7644 0508 Fax: (024) 7663 6680 E-mail: r.g.eng@dial.pipex.com

Rhoda Precision Tooling Ltd, Unit 2 Lansdown Industrial Estate, Cheltenham, Gloucestershire, GL51 8PL Tel: (01242) 233791 Fax: (01242) 226236 E-mail: rhodaprecision@btinternet.com

Rod Rite Engeering Ltd, Unit 15 Horsehay Works, Horsehay Estate, Telford, Shropshire, TF4 3PY Tel: (01952) 630055 Fax: (01952) 505289

S & H Jig Boring Specialists, Hotchkiss Way, Binley Industrial Estate, Binley Industrial Estate, Coventry, CV3 2RL Tel: (024) 7663 5312 Fax: (024) 7663 6538 E-mail: office@shjigboring.co.uk

Salt Engineering (Midlands) Ltd, Unit 4, Macefield Close, Aldermans Green, Coventry, CV2 2PJ Tel: (024) 7661 6595 Fax: (024) 7660 2165 E-mail: vaughan@saltengineering.co.uk

Saluki Ltd, 7 Lewisher Road, Leicester, LE4 9LR Tel: 0116-276 3509 Fax: 0116-246 0265 E-mail: saluki.leicester@virgin.net

Shopfittings & Equipment, Waterloo Industrial Estate, Waterloo Road, Bidford-on-Avon, Alcester, Warwickshire, B50 4JH Tel: (01789) 778497 Fax: (01789) 490132 E-mail: sales@shopfittingsandequipment.co.uk

South Western Tools Ltd, 26 New Station Road, Bristol, BS16 3RU Tel: 0117-965 9596 Fax: 0117-965 9566

Stour Precision Tools Ltd, George Baylis Road, Berry Hill Industrial Estate, Droitwich, Worcestershire, WR9 9RB Tel: (01905) 773932 Fax: (01905) 776434

Sykes & Dyson, Albert Street, Lockwood, Huddersfield, HD1 3QG Tel: (01484) 541131 Fax: (01484) 512426 E-mail: sykes_dyson@shawvalves.co.uk

T B P Tools Ltd, 106-108 Lombard Street, Birmingham, B12 0QR Tel: 0121-622 1762 Fax: 0121-622 1174 E-mail: tbp@btconnect.com

▶ T Mann Ltd, 343 Eastwood Road North, Leigh-on-Sea, Essex, SS9 4LT Tel: (01702) 528437 Fax: (01702) 421344

Trac Heaton Ltd, Mount Pleasant Street, West Bromwich, West Midlands, B70 7DL Tel: 0121-553 1510 Fax: 0121-500 5846 E-mail: info@tracheaton.com

Tryang Jig & Gauge Co., Unit 3-4 Wynford Industrial Estate, Wynford Road, Birmingham, B27 6JP Tel: 0121-706 8050 Fax: 0121-765 4294 E-mail: mikedavis@tryang.fsbusiness.co.uk

V & P Engineering, Wakefield Road, Brighouse, West Yorkshire, HD6 1PE Tel: (01484) 719360 Fax: (01484) 400093

Vere Engineering Ltd, 17 Jameson Road, Birmingham, B6 7SJ Tel: 0121-327 3630 Fax: 0121-327 3050

Wellvil Engineering Company Ltd, Spring Place, New Street, Luton, LU1 5DF Tel: (01582) 727171

Westley Engineering Ltd, 120 Pritchett Street, Birmingham, B6 4EH Tel: 0121-333 1925 Fax: 0121-333 1926 E-mail: engineering@westleyrichards.co.uk

Wheeler & Clinch Ltd, 75-99 Nathan Way, West Thamesmead Business Park, London, SE28 0BQ Tel: (020) 8854 4261 Fax: (020) 8854 6341 E-mail: whclinch@aol.com

Whittingham Design & Manufacturing Co. Ltd, Chapel Works, Chapel Green, Willenhall, West Midlands, WV13 1QY Tel: (01902) 607272 Fax: (01902) 637884

Woodside Engineers (Cwmbran) Ltd, Forgehammer, 22 Woodside Road, Cwmbran, Gwent, NP44 3AA Tel: (01633) 484448 Fax: (01633) 484448

Woolley GMC Engineering Co. Ltd, 18 Crondal Road, Exhall, Coventry, CV7 9NH Tel: (024) 7636 2371 Fax: (024) 7636 8171

Wyken Tools Ltd, Unit 3, Bodmin Road, Coventry, CV2 5DZ Tel: (024) 7662 1515 Fax: (024) 7662 1472 E-mail: jezwykentools@aol.com

JIG/FIXTURE DESIGN SERVICES

Midas, 4 Rectory Road, Newton, Sudbury, Suffolk, CO10 0QZ Tel: (01787) 373898 Fax: (01787) 374882 E-mail: billaldworth@midas-eastanglia.freeserve.co.uk

Paramount Engineering Ltd, Unit 15 Pontcynon Industrial Estate, Abercynon, Mountain Ash, Mid Glamorgan, CF45 4EP Tel: (01443) 741897 Fax: (01443) 741897 E-mail: paramount@dial.pipex.com

JIGS AND FIXTURES COMPONENT MILLING TO SPECIFICATION

Malt Mill Engineering Co. Ltd, 4 Kinwarton Workshops, Kinwarton Farm Road, Kinwarton, Alcester, Warwickshire, B49 6EH Tel: (01789) 764497 Fax: (01789) 400161 E-mail: maltmill@aol.com

Penta Precision Engineering Ltd, Aspen House, Airport Service Road, Portsmouth, PO3 5RA Tel: (023) 9266 8334 Fax: (023) 9266 8335 E-mail: sales@pentaprecision.co.uk

▶ W A Billing, 53 Catley Road, Sheffield, S9 5JF Tel: 0114-242 4233 Fax: 0114-242 4266 E-mail: sales@wabilling.co.uk

JIGS/FIXTURES, SPECIAL PURPOSE/TO SPECIFICATION

CK Industrial Engineers Ltd, Units 4-6 Enterprise Way, Wickford Business Park, Wickford, Essex, SS11 8DH Tel: (01268) 561471 Fax: (01268) 764891 E-mail: enquiries@ck-ind.com

Enterprise Engineering, Unit 23 Tweedale Court, Tweedale North, Madeley, Telford, Shropshire, TF7 4JR Tel: (01952) 583179

Fielding Engineering UK Ltd, 2 Lancaster Way, Earls Colne Industrial Park, Earls Colne, Colchester, CO6 2NS Tel: (01787) 224844 Fax: (01787) 224344 E-mail: jfield@fieldingltd.co.uk

G W J Engineering Ltd, 7 Ruston Road, Alma Park Industrial Estate, Grantham, Lincolnshire, NG31 9SW Tel: (01476) 568703 Fax: (01476) 578639 E-mail: enquiries@gwjengineering.co.uk

Griffiths Precision Engineering, 5 Hicks Road, Markyate, St. Albans, Hertfordshire, AL3 8LG Tel: (01582) 841192 Fax: (01582) 841395 E-mail: griff@griffithseng.co.uk

Luton Jig & Tool Co. Ltd, Unit 3 Chase Street, Luton, LU1 3QZ Tel: (01582) 725591 Fax: (01582) 735211E-mail: david@ljtco.co.uk

Moldsytems Plastics, 1 Edwardson Road, Meadowfield Industrial Estate, Durham, DH7 8RL Tel: 0191-378 0747 Fax: 0191-378 9255

Paramount Engineering Ltd, Unit 15 Pontcynon Industrial Estate, Abercynon, Mountain Ash, Mid Glamorgan, CF45 4EP Tel: (01443) 741897 Fax: (01443) 741897 E-mail: paramount@dial.pipex.com

WDS, Richardshaw Road, Grangefield Industrial Estate, Pudsey, West Yorkshire, LS28 6LE Tel: 0113-290 9852 Fax: (0845) 6011173

JIGS/FIXTURES, STANDARD COMPONENTS

Upton & Scott, Huntspill Road, Highbridge, Somerset, TA9 3DE Tel: (01278) 783279 Fax: (01278) 783279

JOB AND STOCK BUYERS, *See Surplus etc*

JOINERS' TOOLS

Agricultural Timber Supplies & Forestry Products, Side House, Burneside, Kendal, Cumbria, LA8 9AA Tel: (01539) 822089 Fax: (01539) 822089

Cusden's, 104 Arlington Road, London, NW1 7HP Tel: (020) 7424 0349 Fax: (020) 7324 0352 E-mail: cusdens@aol.com

Eastwood Park Joinery, 9 Eastwood Road, Penryn, Cornwall, TR10 8LA Tel: (01326) 376119

Flack & Tucker Joinery Services, Hunts Farm, Bardfield Road, Shalford, Braintree, Essex, CM7 5HX Tel: (01371) 850055 Fax: (01371) 850055

Glebe Joinery Ltd, Barrington Road, Orwell, Royston, Hertfordshire, SG8 5QP Tel: (01223) 207800 Fax: (01223) 208888

Leitz Tooling UK Ltd, Flex Meadow, Harlow, Essex, CM19 5TN Tel: (01279) 454530 Fax: (01279) 454509 E-mail: sales@har.leitz.org

Mitech Joinery, 234 Derby Road, Denby, Ripley, Derbyshire, DE5 8NN Tel: (01773) 570577 Fax: (01773) 570577 E-mail: roberts@mitechjoinery.co.uk

Thomson & Jardine Joiners, Lanefoot, Rotchell Gardens, Dumfries, DG2 7SL Tel: (01387) 265032 Fax: (01387) 264635

JOINERY

3 J's, 70 Llandaff Road, Cardiff, CF11 9NL Tel: (029) 2022 6262 Fax: (029) 2022 6268

A & A Building Maintenance Ltd, 22 Tannoch Drive, Cumbernauld, Glasgow, G67 2XX Tel: (01236) 456027 Fax: (01236) 456027

A & C R Patchitt, The Pencil Works, Lenton Street, Sandiacre, Nottingham, NG10 5DX Tel: 0115-939 0011 Fax: 0115-939 0044

A Cuthbertson, Unit F Burnfoot Industrial Estate, Hawick, Roxburghshire, TD9 8SL Tel: (01450) 378188 Fax: (01450) 378188

A D T Joinery, Joinery Works, Llynfi St, Bridgend, Mid Glamorgan, CF31 1SY Tel: (01656) 653644 Fax: (01656) 653644 E-mail: arby.richard@virgin.net

▶ A Dee Kay Joinery Ltd, Unit 25 Sapcote Trading Centre, Small Heath Highway, Birmingham, B10 0HR Tel: 0121-766 6036 Fax: 0121-771 1367

A E Cox & Sons, Caretakers Caravan, North Street, Winterton, Scunthorpe, South Humberside, DN15 9QN Tel: (01724) 732676 Fax: (01724) 732676

A E Hadley Ltd, Limberline Spur, Portsmouth, PO3 5JR Tel: (023) 9266 4341 Fax: (023) 9266 4940 E-mail: info@aehadley.com

A F Joinery, 75 Seacoast Road, Limavady, County Londonderry, BT49 9DW Tel: (028) 7772 2202 Fax: (028) 7772 2202

A G B Narib Ltd, Fen End, Stotfold, Hitchin, Hertfordshire, SG5 4BA Tel: (01462) 730488 Fax: (01462) 835282

A G Duck & Sons Ltd, Charlton Mead Lane, Hoddesdon, Hertfordshire, EN11 0DJ Tel: (01992) 462188 Fax: (01992) 450991

A & G Joinery, Wheal Chance, Radnor Road, Redruth, Cornwall, TR16 5EQ Tel: (01209) 820144 Fax: (01209) 820144

A J B Joinery, Little Merebrook, Hanley Swan, Worcester, WR8 0EH Tel: (01684) 310610 Fax: (01684) 311917

A J Buckle Joinery, Hawthorn Farm, Willis Lane, Four Marks, Alton, Hampshire, GU34 5AP Tel: (01420) 588689 Fax: (01420) 588689 E-mail: andybuckle@hotmail.co.uk

A R Cartwright Ltd, 4 Berrington Road, Nuneaton, Warwickshire, CV10 0LA Tel: (024) 7639 2901 Fax: (024) 7639 6471

A R Manley & Son Ltd, Rodington, Shrewsbury, SY4 4RF Tel: (01952) 770278 Fax: (01952) 770976 E-mail: sales@armanley.co.uk

A & S Joinery, Coldwell Street, Linthwaite, Huddersfield, HD7 5QN Tel: (01484) 842782

▶ A & S Joinery Manufacturers Ltd, Unit 1 Imperial Road, Bulwell, Nottingham, NG6 9GB Tel: 0115-927 9927 Fax: 0115-927 9947

A Stewart & Sons, 5 Redford Road, Padanaram, Forfar, Angus, DD8 1PZ Tel: (01307) 463135

A Sturrock & Son Ltd, Whigstreet, Kirkbuddo, Forfar, Angus, DD8 2NN Tel: (01307) 820209 Fax: (01307) 820289 E-mail: info@asturrock.co.uk

A W H Joinery, The Old Workshop, Hyde Home Farmllower Luton Road, The Hyde, Luton, LU2 9PS Tel: (01582) 713255 Fax: (01582) 713255

▶ Abacus Joinery, Finnimore Indust Estate, Alansways, Venn Ottery, Ottery St. Mary, Devon, EX11 1RE Tel: (01404) 811700 Fax: (01404) 811700

▶ Abbey Joinery, Swingbridge Yard, Wincolmlee, Hull, HU5 1RH Tel: (01482) 586008 Fax: (01482) 581606E-mail: rita@wrshull.com

Abrahams & Carlisle Ltd, Carlham Works, Newman Street, Bradford, West Yorkshire, BD4 9NT Tel: (01274) 651555 Fax: (01274) 686135 E-mail: sales@abrahams-and-carlisle.co.uk

Acacia Joinery Ltd, Old Carpenters Shop, Old Gee, Bridgend, Mid Glamorgan, CF31 3AP Tel: (01656) 649639 Fax: (01656) 649639

Acorn Joinery, Floodgates Farm, Castle Lane, West Grinstead, Horsham, West Sussex, RH13 8LH Tel: (01403) 711330 Fax: (01403) 711330 E-mail: acornjoinery@resource24.net

▶ Acp Woodwork, 37a Newington Road, Ramsgate, Kent, CT12 6EJ Tel: (01843) 590957

Acre Joinery Ltd, 2 The Waterings, St Martins Road, Norwich, NR3 3EU Tel: (01603) 628602 Fax: (01603) 762483

▶ Advance Joinery Ltd, Old Brickyard, Pontrilas, Hereford, HR2 0DJ Tel: (01981) 241071 Fax: (01981) 241072

Akeister & Faulkner, 65 Market Street, Hoyland, Barnsley, South Yorkshire, S74 0ET Tel: (01226) 746347 Fax: (01226) 740252

JOINERY – *continued*

Alan Cox & Son, 19 Craigweil Crescent, Stockton-on-Tees, Cleveland, TS19 0DU Tel: (01642) 611672 Fax: (01642) 651349 E-mail: andrewcoxdec@hotmail.com

Alan Walter (Timber), 7-23 Louisa St, Midland Road, Bristol, BS2 0LE Tel: 0117-926 8370 Fax: 0117-926 8370

Albion Joinery, Albion Works, 23 Rectory Gro, Croydon, CR0 4JA Tel: (020) 8667 0067 Fax: (020) 8667 1267

Aldwick Doors & Windows, 59 Sunnymead Drive, Selsey, Chichester, West Sussex, PO20 0DG Tel: (01243) 778557 Fax: (01243) 778557 E-mail: sales@aldwickdoorsandwindows.co.uk

Alfreton Joinery Co., Old Swanwick Colliery Road, Derby Road, Swanwick, Alfreton, Derbyshire, DE55 1BH Tel: (01773) 832022 Fax: (01773) 836014

Alken Construction Ltd, Redmoss Business Centre, Greenbank Road, East Tullos Industrial Estate, Aberdeen, AB12 3BQ Tel: (01224) 875265 Fax: (01224) 879023

Allen Mouldings Ltd, 5 Boscombe Mews, Boscombe Road, Southend-on-Sea, SS2 5JD Tel: (01702) 617461 Fax: (01702) 617461

Allwood Design, Unit 3 Creek Rd Ind Est, 96-124 Creek Rd, London, SE8 3BZ Tel: (020) 8692 1935 Fax: (020) 8692 1935

Ambass-A-Door Windows & Doors Ltd, 18 Bidwell Road, Rackheath Industrial Estate, Norwich, NR13 6PT Tel: (01603) 720332 Fax: (01603) 721245 E-mail: sales@ambassadoor.fsnet.co.uk

D.S. & J. Anderson, Unit 4, Tayview Industrial Estate, Friarton Road, Perth, PH2 8DF Tel: (01738) 444885 Fax: (01738) 444885

Andersons, Denton Holme Sawmills, Denton Street, Carlisle, CA2 5EQ Tel: (01228) 526242 Fax: (01228) 515647

Anglia Shopfitting Norwich Ltd, Diamond Road, Norwich, NR6 6AB Tel: (01603) 426297 Fax: (01603) 483644

Annick Manufacturing Ltd, 13 Kyle Road, Irvine Industrial Estate, Irvine, Ayrshire, KA12 8JN Tel: (01294) 312895 Fax: (01294) 312895

Anything in Wood Ltd, 44-46a Hamilton Street, Grimsby, North East Lincolnshire, DN32 7HL Tel: (01472) 344176 Fax: (01472) 344176

Arch Construction Joinery Ltd, King Edward Court, Gee Cross, Hyde, Cheshire, SK14 5JR Tel: 0161-368 0609 Fax: 0161-367 9052 E-mail: enquiries@archjoinery.co.uk

Arjay Joinery Co. Ltd, Unit 6, Craufurd Business Park, Silverdale Road, Hayes, Middlesex, UB3 3BN Tel: (020) 8573 3746 Fax: (020) 8569 1807

Arundel Street Joinery, 151 Arundel Street, Sheffield, S1 2NU Tel: 0114-275 6255 Fax: 0114-275 6255

Avon Joinery Manufacturers, 8 Minto Road Industrial Centre, Ashley Parade, Bristol, BS2 9YW Tel: 0117-955 8142

Avonbank Joinery, Unit 3 Stratford Agri Park, Clifford Chambers, Upper Quinton, Stratford-upon-Avon, Warwickshire, CV37 8LP Tel: (01789) 720444 Fax: (01789) 720444

Avoncroft Joinery, 1c Shaw Lane, Stoke Prior, Bromsgrove, Worcestershire, B60 4DY Tel: (01527) 579229 Fax: (01527) 579229

Awlwood Joinery, Unit 4 Bruce Grove, Wickford, Essex, SS11 8BP Tel: (01268) 735994 Fax: (01268) 730451 E-mail: joconnor@abalone-awlwood.co.uk

B G H Joinery Co. Ltd, Unicorn Business Centre, Ridgeway, Chiseldon, Swindon, SN4 0HT Tel: (01793) 741330 Fax: (01793) 741310 E-mail: sales@bghjoinery.wanadoo.co.uk

B & J Builders, 98 Lightwood Road, Buxton, Derbyshire, SK17 7AN Tel: (01298) 79832

▶ B J M Joinery Manufacturers, Battye Street, Bradford, West Yorkshire, BD4 8AG Tel: (01274) 665000 Fax: (01274) 667000

B M Prickett, Unit 1 Dodwell Trading Estate, Dodwell, Stratford-upon-Avon, Warwickshire, CV37 9ST Tel: (01789) 204930 Fax: (01789) 204930

B Murphy, 2 Avenue Mews, London, N10 3NP Tel: (020) 8883 4555 Fax: (020) 8883 3363 E-mail: hathersichroger@hotmail.com

B & P Joiners Ltd, Thomas Street, Crewe, CW1 2BD Tel: (01270) 250969 Fax: (01270) 250969

B & S Quality Joinery, 3 Aylesham Industrial Estate, Covert Road, Aylesham, Canterbury, Kent, CT3 3EQ Tel: (01304) 842336 Fax: (01304) 841104

B S Tickle, Unit 5, Waterside Trading Estate, Leigh, Lancashire, WN7 2BG Tel: (01942) 676914 Fax: (01942) 676914

B Snelling, 1 The Laurels, Netherfield, Battle, East Sussex, TN33 9QJ Tel: (01424) 838886 Fax: (01424) 838273

B W Dove & Son, The Old Dairy, Darrow Green Road, Denton, Harleston, Norfolk, IP20 0BA Tel: (01986) 788377

B Young, The Riverside Workshop, John Martin Street, Haydon Bridge, Hexham, Northumberland, NE47 6AB Tel: (01434) 688007 Fax: (01434) 601938

Badman & Badman Ltd, The Drill Hall, Langford Road, Weston-super-Mare, Avon, BS23 3PQ Tel: (01934) 644122 Fax: (01934) 628189 E-mail: sales@badman.co.uk

Balham Joinery Works, Rear 102 Upper Tooting Road, London, SW17 7EN Tel: (020) 8767 9902 Fax: (020) 8767 9718

Bardini Bros, 1a St Johns Avenue, London, NW10 4ED Tel: (07811) 105727 Fax: (020) 8961 2526

▶ Barmaid Joinery Manufacturers, 3 Wesley Street, Swinton, Manchester, M27 6AD Tel: 0161-728 1122 Fax: 0161-728 2233

George Barnsdale & Sons Ltd, 24 High Street, Donington, Spalding, Lincolnshire, PE11 4TA Tel: (01775) 823000 Fax: (01775) 823010 E-mail: lnewell@gbstp.com

V.O. Barrett Joinery, 4 Goodson Road, London, NW10 9LR Tel: (020) 8963 1198 Fax: (020) 8963 1231 E-mail: barretjoinery@hotmail.com

Bartholomew Joinery Ltd, The Workshop Great Hidden Farm, Wantage Road, Eddington, Hungerford, Berkshire, RG17 0PW Tel: (01488) 685407 Fax: (01488) 681624 E-mail: bart.joinery@amserve.net

S.G. Bartram, Edward Street, Burton-On-Trent, Staffordshire, DE14 2JF Tel: (01283) 517300 Fax: (01283) 517401 E-mail: sgbartram@tiscali.co.uk

Batty & Dixon, Raymond Road, Doncaster, South Yorkshire, DN5 9PP Tel: (01302) 783130 Fax: (01302) 390440

Batty Joinery Manufacturers, Bridge Works, 101 West Dock Street, Hull, HU3 4HH Tel: (01482) 326377 Fax: (01482) 585566 E-mail: colinsmith@battyjoinery.co.uk

Beard Evans Joinery, Shepherd Road, Gloucester, GL2 5EL Tel: (01452) 423123 Fax: (01452) 501055 E-mail: sales@beardevansjoinery.co.uk

Beehive Joinery, 3 Beehive Trading Estate, Crews Hole Road, Bristol, BS5 8AY Tel: 0117-955 8974 Fax: 0117-955 8974

Beeston Joinery & Upvc, Littleworth Road, Cannock, Staffordshire, WS12 1QQ Tel: (01543) 877342

Ben Bydawell, Noth Barn, Wayners, Ashton, Leominster, Herefordshire, HR6 0DN Tel: (01584) 711580 Fax: (01584) 711580

Benbow Interiors, Bradley Mill, Newton Abbot, Devon, TQ12 1NF Tel: (01626) 367861 Fax: (01626) 355591 E-mail: mail@benbow-interiors.co.uk

Bestwood Joinery, 141 Mansfield Street, Nottingham, NG5 4BD Tel: 0115-960 7955 Fax: 0115-969 2843

▶ Bevanwood Joinery Ltd, 6 Albany Trading Estate, Albany Street, Newport, Gwent, NP20 5NQ Tel: (01633) 858811 Fax: (01633) 858811 E-mail: bevanwood@btconnect.com

Bishopton Joinery, Burton Farm, Bishopton, Stratford-upon-Avon, Warwickshire, CV37 0RW Tel: (01789) 298448 Fax: (01789) 298448

Blackstone Developments South West Ltd, 8 Kingswood Trading Estate, Southey Avenue, Bristol, BS15 1QX Tel: 0117-961 1122 Fax: 0117-961 1122

Blake Joinery Co. Ltd, 17 St John Street, Bridgwater, Somerset, TA6 5HR Tel: (01278) 444333 Fax: (01278) 439298

Blow & Scrimshaw Ltd, 10 Dixon Way, Lincoln, LN6 7XN Tel: (01522) 521319 Fax: (01522) 545718 E-mail: contact@blowandscrimshaw.com

BLP UK Ltd, B L P House, Sandall Stones Road, Kirk Sandall Industrial Estate, Doncaster, South Yorkshire, DN3 1QR Tel: (01302) 890555 Fax: (01302) 886724 E-mail: mail@blpuk.com

Bonlea Ltd, Q Net House, Malleable Way, Stockton-on-Tees, Cleveland, TS18 2SZ Tel: (01642) 617611 Fax: (01642) 674490 E-mail: enquiries@bonlea.co.uk

William Booth & Sons, Spring Street, Ramsbottom, Bury, Lancashire, BL0 9JQ Tel: (01706) 823104 Fax: (01706) 821874

Bourne Joinery, 196 London Road, Bexhill-On-Sea, East Sussex, TN39 4AE Tel: (01424) 212066

Colin Bowler, Church Farm, Main Street, Great Casterton, Stamford, Lincolnshire, PE9 4AP Tel: (01780) 752895

Boyland Joinery Ltd, Stony Lane, Christchurch, Dorset, BH23 1EZ Tel: (01202) 499499 Fax: (01202) 499037 E-mail: enquires@boylandjoinery.co.uk

Boys & Boden Ltd, Mill Lane, Welshpool, Powys, SY21 7BL Tel: (01938) 556677 Fax: (01938) 555773

▶ Braeside Joinery, Unit 1-5 Moore Acre, Manor Furlong, Marston Trading Estate, Frome, Somerset, BA11 4RL Tel: (01373) 451213 Fax: (01373) 451860

Brank Brook, Bescot Crescent, Walsall, WS1 4ND Tel: (01922) 728600 Fax: (01922) 728644

Braywood Joinery, Home Farm, Middle Green, Langley, Slough, SL3 6BS Tel: (01753) 534542 Fax: (01753) 546460 E-mail: braywood@homechoice.co.uk

S.N. & C. Brennan, The Old Workshop, The Common, Cranleigh, Surrey, GU6 8RZ Fax: (01483) 274228

Brent Taunton Joinery, 3 Coopers Industrial Estate, Littlehampton Road, Ferring, Worthing, West Sussex, BN12 6PW Tel: (01903) 248169 Fax: (01903) 248169

Brian A Powles, Staunton-on-Wye, Hereford, HR4 7LY Tel: (01981) 500327 Fax: (01981) 500683

Brian Fawcett Joinery, Ellifoot Lane, Burstwick, Hull, HU12 9EF Tel: (01964) 670818 Fax: (01964) 671138 E-mail: enquiries@brianfawcett-joinery.com

Brian J Hetherington Joiner & Contractor, 2 Barras La Industrial Estate, Station Road, Dalston, Carlisle, CA5 7LX Tel: (01228) 710314 Fax: (01697) 476568

Bridge Joinery, Unit 1, Limberline Spur, Hilsea, Portsmouth, PO3 5HJ Tel: (023) 9266 6479 Fax: (023) 9266 6479

▶ Bridgend Joinery, Lake District Business Park, Mint Bridge Road, Kendal, Cumbria, LA9 6NH Tel: (01539) 738387 Fax: (01539) 738388

Bridgwater Joinery Ltd, Crofton Drive, Allenby Industrial Estate, Lincoln, LN3 4NR Tel: (01522) 546699 Fax: (01522) 546644 E-mail: joinery@bridgwater.fsbusiness.co.uk

▶ Brimak Joinery Manufacturers, Unit 5 Wood Lane, Rothwell, Leeds, LS26 0RS Tel: 0113-393 4392

Brinard Joinery Ltd, 257 Somercotes Hill, Somercotes, Alfreton, Derbyshire, DE55 4HX Tel: (01773) 608693 Fax: (01773) 540743

Bristol & West Joinery & Turnings, 56-58 Park Rd, Stapleton, Bristol, BS16 1AU Tel: 0117-965 8662 Fax: 0117-965 8662

Bristow Buildbase, Kensington Way, Oakengates, Telford, Shropshire, TF2 6ER Tel: (01952) 613561 Fax: (01952) 616555 E-mail: telford@buildbase.co.uk

Brixham Joinery, 8 Brixham Enterprise Estate, Rea Barn Road, Brixham, Devon, TQ5 9DF Tel: (01803) 853138 Fax: (01803) 853138

Brook Bank Joinery, 15 Lenton Street, Sheffield, S2 4BH Tel: 0114-273 9086

Brookes & Simms Joiners, Corfe, Waltham Road, Thorpe Arnold, Melton Mowbray, Leicestershire, LE14 4SD Tel: (01664) 566565 Fax: (01664) 566565

T.A. Brooks, 1 Staffa Drive, Tibshelf, Alfreton, Derbyshire, DE55 5PJ Tel: (01773) 872361 Fax: (01773) 872361

Brookthorpe Joinery, Stroud Road, Brookthorpe, Gloucester, GL4 0UQ Tel: (01452) 813007 Fax: (01452) 813007

Broom Joinery Ltd, 14 Arden Business Centre, Arden Road, Alcester, Warwickshire, B49 6HW Tel: (01789) 764156 Fax: (01789) 764156

Broomhall Joinery Co. Ltd, Sunley House, Olds Approach, Tolpits Lane, Watford, WD18 9TB Tel: (01923) 777714 Fax: (01923) 711077

L. Brown & Sons Ltd, St. Anns House, St. Anns Parade, Alderley Road, Wilmslow, Cheshire, SK9 1HG Tel: (01625) 522251 Fax: (01625) 533653 E-mail: mikemason@lbrowns.co.uk

Broxbarn Joineries, Millbrook House, Chertsey Road, Shepperton, Middlesex, TW17 9LA Tel: (01932) 877600 Fax: (01932) 269261

Bryan Gelder Joinery, 7 Jack Straws Lane, Headington, Oxford, OX3 0DL Tel: (01865) 247197 Fax: (01865) 247197

Brystewood Veneering Co., The Hatcheries, Brackner Lane, Bilsthorpe, Newark, Nottinghamshire, NG22 8TU Tel: (01623) 411415 Fax: (01623) 411416 E-mail: brystewood@aol.com

Brystewood Veneering Co., The Hatcheries, Brackner Lane, Bilsthorpe, Newark, Nottinghamshire, NG22 8TU Tel: (01623) 411415 Fax: (01623) 411416 E-mail: brystewood@aol.com

Burns & Churchill, Unit 10 Tudor Yard, Lawnside Road, Ledbury, Herefordshire, HR8 2BZ Tel: (01531) 636177 Fax: (01531) 636177

William Burrell & Son, Joinery Works, Main Street, Great Ouseburn, York, YO26 9RQ Tel: (01423) 330291 Fax: (01423) 331386

Burwood Joinery Ltd, 46 Ridgeway Road, Sheffield, S12 2SX Tel: 0114-281 4113 Fax: 0114-281 4115

Buxton Building Supplies Ltd, Charles Street, Buxton, Derbyshire, SK17 7BD Tel: (01298) 28800 Fax: (01298) 28808 E-mail: info@bbs.fsnet.co.uk

C A B Joinery Services Ltd, C A B Joinery Services Ltd, Unit 3, Block A, Bescot Industrial Estate, Woden Road West, Wednesbury, West Midlands, WS10 7SG Tel: 0121-556 5445 Fax: 0121-505 4352 E-mail: enquiries@cab-joinery.co.uk

C B H (Joinery) Ltd, Meadow Street, Walsall, WS1 3QP Tel: (01922) 646690 Fax: (01922) 615244

C Canavan, 5 Annaghmore Road, Coalisland, Dungannon, County Tyrone, BT71 4QZ Tel: (028) 8774 7015 Fax: (028) 8774 7427

C D L Co. Ltd, 29 Grafton Road, Croydon, CR0 3RP Tel: (020) 8680 3077 Fax: (020) 8686 9225 E-mail: annaaustin@cdlco.fsnet.co.uk

C D Smith, Strine Acres, Crudgington Green, Crudgington, Telford, Shropshire, TF6 6JY Tel: (01952) 541419 Fax: (01952) 541128

C & E Joinery, 10 Rear Carr Street, Hindley, Wigan, Lancashire, WN2 3LG Tel: (01942) 254285

C F & M Tatlow, 47 Sutherland Road, Derby, DE23 8RX Tel: (01332) 761405 Fax: (01332) 761405

C Fewster & Son Ltd, 2 Church Lane, Patrington, Hull, HU12 0RJ Tel: (01964) 630228 Fax: (01964) 631309 E-mail: enquiries@cfewster.co.uk

C J Dolton, Browning Road, Heathfield, East Sussex, TN21 8DB Tel: (01435) 866350 Fax: (01435) 866416 E-mail: info@cjdoltonjoinery.co.uk

C & L Joinery, 30 The Retreat, Frome, Somerset, BA11 5JU Tel: (01373) 466722 Fax: (01373) 466722

C M Fair Joinery, Rigby Court, Bolton, BL3 6QY Tel: (01204) 528540 Fax: (01204) 396100

C M Joinery, Coggeshall Road, Bradwell, Braintree, Essex, CM77 8EU Tel: (01376) 331666 Fax: (01376) 331444 E-mail: info@wood-work.demon.co.uk

▶ C M Joinery, 9, Drovers Road, East Mains Industrial Estate, Broxburn, West Lothian, EH52 5ND Tel: (01506) 859949 Fax: (01506) 859949

C M Railton & Son Ltd, Poplar, Sunk Island Road, Ottringham, Hull, HU12 0DX Tel: (01964) 626105 Fax: (01964) 626105

C M Whitby Ltd, King John Bank, Walpole St. Andrew, Wisbech, Cambridgeshire, PE14 7JT Tel: (01945) 780304 Fax: (01945) 780827

C Pawson & Son, Caister House, 19 Market Place, Caistor, Market Rasen, Lincolnshire, LN7 6TR Tel: (01472) 851434 E-mail: paul@houndogtp-net.co.uk

C R Robinson & Son, 247 Broad Street, Crewe, CW1 4JJ Tel: (01270) 584531 Fax: (01270) 588054

▶ C T Joinery, 29 Hillcot Close, Gloucester, GL2 4FU Tel: (01452) 387300 Fax: (01452) 387300 E-mail: ctjoineryglos@msn.com

▶ C&C Property solutions ltd, 72 / 74 Birkendale Road, Sheffield, S6 3NL Tel: 0114 2444008

Cadgrange Ltd, 38-40 Sandy Road, Liverpool, L21 3TW Tel: 0151-949 0216 Fax: 0151-949 0419 E-mail: mail@cadgrange.co.uk

Calanpoint Ltd, 52 Linford Street, London, SW8 4UN Tel: (020) 7627 4740 Fax: (020) 7627 5091 E-mail: enq@calanpoint.co.uk

Caldicot Joinery, Unit 5g Castle Way, Severn Bridge Industrial Estate, Portskewett, Caldicot, Gwent, NP26 5PR Tel: (01291) 430532 Fax: (01291) 430532

Callow Shopfitters Ltd, 2 Middlemore La West, Walsall, WS9 8DR Tel: (01922) 744888 Fax: (01922) 744555 E-mail: davidrcallow@netscapeonline.co.uk

▶ Camborne Joinery Ltd, Trevu Industrial Estate, Unit 2 Trevu Road, Camborne, Cornwall, TR14 8DX Tel: (01209) 716000

Cambridge Joinery Ltd, 23 Fen End, Over, Cambridge, CB4 5NE Tel: (01954) 231008 Fax: (01954) 232263 E-mail: jim@cambridgejoinery.co.uk

Camlough Joinery Works, 12 Carrivekeeney Road, Newry, County Down, BT35 7LU Tel: (028) 3026 4218 Fax: (028) 3026 0848

Canterbury Joinery Ltd, Faussett Hill, Street End, Canterbury, Kent, CT4 7AL Tel: (01227) 700011 Fax: (01227) 700022

Gary Capstick Ltd, Green La West, Garstang, Preston, PR3 1NJ Tel: (01995) 600844 Fax: (01995) 600841 E-mail: enquiries@capstick.co.uk

Carcroft Joinery & Glassglass, 29-31 Owston Road, Carcroft, Doncaster, South Yorkshire, DN6 8DA Tel: (01302) 728260 Fax: (01302) 728260E-mail: enquiries@carcroftjoinery.co.uk

▶ Carlton Shopfitting Ltd, Carlton House, Carlton Road, Dewsbury, West Yorkshire, WF13 2AT Tel: (01924) 454612 Fax: (01924) 460042

Carlton Smith Projects Ltd, Station Approach, Station Road, Pershore, Worcestershire, WR10 2DB Tel: (01386) 555770 Fax: (01386) 556432 E-mail: info@carlton-smith.co.uk

N. Carpenter Custom Made Joinery & Furniture, Unit 7, Parklands Farm, Parklands, Shere, Guildford, Surrey, GU5 9JQ Tel: (01483) 203759 Fax: (01483) 203759

Carr Arthur & Henry Ltd, Lakeside, Drake Road, Tavistock, Devon, PL19 0EJ Tel: (01822) 612868 Fax: (01822) 614508

Carrington Architectural Joiners Ltd, Unit 10 Stock Industrial Park, Stock Road, Southend-on-Sea, SS2 5QN Tel: (01702) 616894 Fax: (01702) 602894 E-mail: cajltd@supanet.com

Cartology Wheel Mnfrs, Unit 3 Llanhilleth Industrial Estate, Llanhilleth, Abertillery, Gwent, NP13 2RX Tel: (01495) 216612 Fax: (01495) 211108 E-mail: mfc@cartology.co.uk

Castles Shopfitters Limited, Bowland Street Works, Bowland Street, Bradford, West Yorkshire, BD1 3BW Tel: (01274) 724271 E-mail: mail@castle_shopfitters.co.uk

Cavendish Joinery, Cavendish House, Plumpton Road, Hoddesdon, Hertfordshire, EN11 0LB Tel: (01992) 464506 Fax: (01992) 469506 E-mail: sales@liftcars.net

▶ Cedar Building Services, 27 Sackville Road, Heaton, Newcastle upon Tyne, NE6 5SY Tel: 0191-265 3406 Fax: 0191-265 3406 E-mail: jon@cedarbs.wanadoo.co.uk

Ceiling Grids Ltd, Branson Street, Manchester, M40 7FJ Tel: 0161-273 4511 Fax: 0161-274 3914

Central Joinery Co., 2 Cross Street, Honley, Holmfirth, HD9 6AN Tel: (01484) 667459

▶ Central Joinery Services Ltd, 33 Bower Way, Slough, SL1 5HW Tel: (01628) 550900 Fax: (01628) 666991

Channel Fisheries, Unit 4 Metherell Avenue Industrial Estate, Brixham, Devon, TQ5 9QL Tel: (01803) 858126 Fax: (01803) 857941 E-mail: martin@channelfisheries.com

Channel Woodcraft Ltd, Bowles Well Gardens, Dover Road, Folkestone, Kent, CT19 6NP Tel: (01303) 850231 Fax: (01303) 850734 E-mail: enquiry@channelwoodcraft.co.uk

John Chapman, 77 Hilliard Road, Northwood, Middlesex, HA6 1SL Tel: (01923) 824201

Chardstock Joinery, Chubbs Yard, Chardstock, Axminster, Devon, EX13 7BT Tel: (01460) 221148 Fax: (01460) 221148

Charlestown Joinery Ltd, West Haul Park, Par Moor Road, St. Austell, Cornwall, PL25 3RF Tel: (01726) 812666 Fax: (01726) 812666

Charlotte Street Joinery, Unit A1 New Normanton Mills, Charlotte Street, Derby, DE23 6QG Tel: (01332) 367962 Fax: (01332) 748452 E-mail: charlottestreet@hotmail.com

Charnley Joinery, 2 Concorde House, Charnley Road, Blackpool, FY1 4PP Tel: (01253) 752820 Fax: (01253) 752820

Chelford Joinery Co. Ltd, Boundary Cottage, Chelford Road, Ollerton, Knutsford, Cheshire, WA16 8TA Tel: (01565) 751012 Fax: (01565) 652087

JOINERY – *continued*

Chichester Joinery Ltd, Unit 12 Quarry Lane Industrial Estate, Gravel Lane, Chichester, West Sussex, PO19 8PQ Tel: (01243) 784723 Fax: (01243) 533382 E-mail: michaelcarter3@btconnect.com

Chilfen Joinery Ltd, 1 Flint Road, Letchworth Garden City, Hertfordshire, SG6 1HJ Tel: (01462) 705390 Fax: (01462) 674327 E-mail: michelled@chilfen.co.uk

Chilton Joinery Ltd, 3 Chilton Industrial Estate, Martins Road, Sudbury, Suffolk, CO10 2FT Tel: (01787) 378667 Fax: (01787) 880632 E-mail: lee@chiltonjoinery.co.uk

Clark & Kemp Joinery Ltd, Units 8-10 Baddow Park, West Hanningfield Road, Great Baddow, Chelmsford, CM2 7SY Tel: (01245) 476667 Fax: (01245) 474857 E-mail: clark@clark-kemp.freeserve.co.uk

Clarke Joinery, Dairy Works, Normans Road, Sutton, St. Helens, Merseyside, WA9 4JQ Tel: (01744) 815399

▶ Alan Clarke Joinery Works Ltd, 18 8 Meadowbank Road, Carrickfergus, County Antrim, BT38 8YF Tel: (028) 9336 8129 Fax: (028) 9336 8129

Clark's Of Headingley, 14-16 Clifton Green, Leeds, LS9 6EW Tel: 0113-249 7793

Clarman Joinery, Ferry Road, Fiskerton, Lincoln, LN3 4HW Tel: (01522) 751988 Fax: (01522) 751988

Classic Holdings, 55 Cradley Road, Cradley Heath, West Midlands, B64 7BB Tel: (01384) 637825 Fax: (01384) 564079 E-mail: classicholdings@aol.com

Classic Images Ltd, Oakcroft Works, Oakcroft Road, Chessington, Surrey, KT9 1RH Tel: (020) 8391 1133 Fax: (020) 8397 5040 E-mail: classicimages@ukonline.co.uk

Classic Joinery, Castle Hotel, Jewel Street, Barry, South Glamorgan, CF63 3NQ Tel: (01446) 722335 Fax: (01446) 722335

Classic Joinery, 91 Ballylough Road, Castlewellan, County Down, BT31 9JG Tel: (028) 4377 0556 Fax: (028) 4377 0556

Classic Joinery, 324 Guildford Road, Bisley, Woking, Surrey, GU24 9AE Tel: (01932) 354333 Fax: (01483) 797713 E-mail: john@classicjoinery.co.uk

▶ Classic Joinery Northwest Ltd, Unit 3 Albert Street, Droylsden, Manchester, M43 7BA Tel: 0161-371 0031 Fax: 0161-371 9840

Classic Joinery Products, Unit G, 6 The Roundel, Falkirk, FK2 9HG Tel: (01324) 670066 Fax: (01324) 670065

Cleveland Joinery Ltd, Cleveland Place, Farncombe Street, Godalming, Surrey, GU7 3LP Tel: (01483) 415522 Fax: (01483) 861103

Cleveland Joinery East Anglia Ltd, Joinery Works, Lake View Road, Lowestoft, Suffolk, NR33 9NE Tel: (01502) 501917 Fax: (01502) 585044

Cliffside Joinery, Cliff Side, Wakebridge, Matlock, Derbyshire, DE4 5HD Tel: (01773) 853077 Fax: (01773) 853077

▶ CMC Joinery, 3 Radnor Close, Congleton, Cheshire, CW12 4PT Tel: (01260) 297348

D. & J. Cole (Joinery), Palmers Yard, London Road, Newbury, Berkshire, RG14 2BA Tel: (01635) 49748 Fax: (01635) 528413

Cole Joinery, Unit H, 8 Park Avenue Estate, Sundon Park Road, Luton, LU3 3BP Tel: (01582) 584740 Fax: (01582) 494605 E-mail: nigel.cole@btconnect.com

Collinswood Joinery, 2 Rutherglen Road, Corby, Northamptonshire, NN17 1ER Tel: (01536) 201885 Fax: (01536) 409474

▶ Complete Joinery Services, Freeman Road, North Hykeham, Lincoln, LN6 9AP Tel: (01522) 509675 Fax: (01522) 509673 E-mail: info@completejoineryservices.co.uk

▶ Contact Building Services, Albert Street, Droylsden, Manchester, M43 7BA Tel: 0161-370 1200 Fax: 0161-371 9840

P.C. Cook & Co., Unit D Woddeley Industrial Estate, Woddeley Road, Kirkinploch, Glasgow, G66 3UU Tel: 0141-776 0993 Fax: 0141-776 2442

Cottingham Joinery Co. Ltd, Beckside North, Beverley, North Humberside, HU17 0PR Tel: (01482) 868145 Fax: (01482) 870728 E-mail: info@cottjoinery.co.uk

County Joinery, The Workshop, 13 Felpham Road, Bognor Regis, West Sussex, PO22 7AS Tel: (01243) 842714 E-mail: info@countyjoinery.co.uk

Coutts & Findlater Ltd, 15-18 Hudson Road, Sunderland, SR1 2LL Tel: 0191-567 1291 Fax: 0191-564 0590 E-mail: john@jfwilsonshopfittersltd.fsnet.co.uk

Cramar Contracts Ltd, Unit 8 Clipstone Brook Industrial Park, Cherrycourt Way, Leighton Buzzard, Bedfordshire, LU7 4GP Tel: (01525) 850957 Fax: (01525) 851347

Crawford Joinery, 21 Creevery Road, Antrim, BT41 2JP Tel: (028) 9446 7711 Fax: (028) 9446 7710

▶ Creative Joinery, 3 Gibson Street, Stoke-on-Trent, ST6 6AQ Tel: (01782) 825220 Fax: (01782) 825227

Critchley & Curtis, 7 Clegg Street, Liverpool, L5 3SP Tel: 0151-207 2437 Fax: 0151-207 2437

Croft Joinery, Castle Garage Yard, Croft Road, Neath, West Glamorgan, SA11 1RW Tel: (01639) 633355

Crown Joinery, Unit 6 Farthing Road, Ipswich, IP1 5AP Tel: (01473) 740030 Fax: (01473) 744231 E-mail: crownjoinery@aol.com

Croxfords Joinery Manufacturers, Meltham Joinery Works, New Street, Meltham, Holmfirth, HD9 5NT Tel: (01484) 850892 Fax: (01484) 850969 E-mail: ralph@croxfords.demon.co.uk

Cullum & Clarke Joinery, Brackendale, Felthorpe Road, Attlebridge, Norwich, NR9 5TF Tel: (01603) 860564 Fax: (01603) 261084 E-mail: info@cullumclarke.co.uk

▶ Cumbria Joinery, 3 Chapel Street, Egremont, Cumbria, CA22 2DU Tel: (01946) 823300 Fax: (01946) 823300

Cuthbertson & Rapson, 35 Wall Road, Gwinear, Hayle, Cornwall, TR27 5HA Tel: (01736) 850625 Fax: (01736) 850625

D Beacock & Son, Colin Road, Scunthorpe, South Humberside, DN16 1TT Tel: (01724) 854370 Fax: (01724) 854370

D Davies & Sons, Cornerswell Road, Penarth, South Glamorgan, CF64 2UZ Tel: (029) 2070 8524 Fax: (029) 2051 3189

D Dunkerley & Son, High Street, Hogsthorpe, Skegness, Lincolnshire, PE24 5ND Tel: (01754) 872371 Fax: (01754) 872361 E-mail: gary@dunkerleyjoiners.freeserve.co.uk

D G M Cabinet Makers & Joiners, The Barns, Linden Road, Clenchwarton, King's Lynn, Norfolk, PE34 4EL Tel: (01553) 768335 Fax: (01553) 766172 E-mail: inquries@dgmjoinery.co.uk

D & H Display Ltd, Facet Road, Birmingham, B38 9PT Tel: 0121-451 3666 Fax: 0121-451 3666

D Hurrell Joinery, Unit 3-4 Garden Mill Industrial Estate, Derby Road, Kingsbridge, Devon, TQ7 1SA Tel: (01548) 853513 Fax: (01548) 856652

D Ibbotson & Son, 219a Wakefield Road, Barnsley, South Yorkshire, S71 3TP Tel: (01226) 206044 Fax: (01226) 244456 E-mail: sales@ibbotsonjoinery.ak.com

D J Gardner (Joinery) Ltd, Forest Vale Industrial Estate, Cinderford, Gloucestershire, GL14 2YA Tel: (01594) 823030 Fax: (01594) 823030

D J Martin Joinery, 210 Springvale Road, Sheffield, S6 3NU Tel: 0114-268 6718 Fax: 0114-268 6718

D Lavington, Park Road, Crowborough, East Sussex, TN6 2QX Tel: (01892) 654227 Fax: (01892) 654227

D & M Burgess, 2a City Walk, Pendlebury, Swinton, Manchester, M27 8SA Tel: 0161-794 6008 Fax: 0161-790 6153

D M Lloyd & Son, Workshop 43a, Castle Street, Oswestry, Shropshire, SY11 1JZ Tel: (01691) 670254

D & P Joinery Manufacturers, 32a George Road, Carlton, Nottingham, NG4 3AE Tel: 0115-987 0128 Fax: 0115-956 0095 E-mail: dpjoinery@ntlworld.com

D Stephens & Co. Ltd, The Woodlands, New Haden Road, Cheadle, Stoke-on-Trent, ST10 1UF Tel: (01538) 753399

D T Wright, Herald Way, Binley Industrial Estate, Binley Industrial Estate, Coventry, CV3 2RQ Tel: (024) 7643 1055 Fax: (024) 7663 5730 E-mail: info@wrightjoinery.sage-host.co.uk

D Urquhart, Glenglassaugh, Portsoy, Banff, AB45 2SQ Tel: (01261) 842594 Fax: (01261) 842860

Dale Joinery Lichfield Ltd, Europa Way, Britannia Enterprise Park, Lichfield, Staffordshire, WS14 9TY Tel: (01543) 414223 Fax: (01543) 255538

Dalton Joinery, Glendale Works, Dacre, Penrith, Cumbria, CA11 0HL Tel: (01768) 486684 Fax: (01768) 486684 E-mail: radjoinery@aol.com

Dalton Joinery Ltd, The Old Malt Kiln, Westfield Road, Tockwith, York, YO26 7PY Tel: (01423) 358005 Fax: (01423) 358019

Dandf Garden Products Ltd, Unit 6, Onward Business Park, Wakefield Road, Ackworth, Pontefract, West Yorkshire, WF7 7BE Tel: (01977) 624200 Fax: (01977) 624201 E-mail: sales@dandf.co.uk

Dask Timber Products Ltd, Meenan Mill, Dublin Road, Banbridge, County Down, BT32 3PB Tel: (028) 3831 8696 Fax: (028) 3831 8698 E-mail: info@dasktimber.co.uk

Datone Joiners, Cemetery Road, Pudsey, West Yorkshire, LS28 7LW Tel: 0113-255 5532 Fax: 0113-255 5532

David Cover & Son Ltd, Chatfields Yard, Cooksbridge, Lewes, East Sussex, BN8 4TJ Tel: (01273) 476133 Fax: (01273) 400164 E-mail: sales@covers-group.co.uk

David Huish, 1-2 Rectors Way, Weston-super-Mare, Avon, BS23 3NP Tel: (01934) 636584 Fax: (01934) 636584

David Davies & Sons, 1 Waylands Upper Church Street, Oswestry, Shropshire, SY11 2AA Tel: (01691) 653116 Fax: (01691) 650702 E-mail: hugh@daviddaviesandsons.co.uk

Robert Dawson Joinery, Back Square Workshop, The Square, Ingleton, Carnforth, Lancashire, LA6 3EG Tel: (01524) 242474 Fax: (01524) 241474

Deane & Amos Group Ltd, South Portway Close, Round Spinney, Northampton, NN3 8RH Tel: (01604) 790990 Fax: (01604) 644644 E-mail: mail@deane-amos.co.uk

Delta Joiners Ltd, Brewsters Corner, Pendicke Street, Southam, Warwickshire, CV47 1PN Tel: (01926) 815253 Fax: (01926) 811040 E-mail: mail@deltajoiners.co.uk

Derek De'Ath Ltd, New Line, Bacup, Lancashire, OL13 9RY Tel: (01706) 879456 Fax: (01706) 878080 E-mail: office@derekd.co.uk

Descant Ltd, Inchcross, Bathgate, West Lothian, EH48 2HT Tel: (01506) 653252 Fax: (01506) 631362 E-mail: sales@descantltd.co.uk

Design Woodworking, 7 Vernon Place, Northern Court, Nottingham, NG6 0DE Tel: 0115-977 0302

Devoran Metals, Devoran Joinery Works, Greenbank Road, Devoran, Truro, Cornwall, TR3 6PQ Tel: (01872) 863376 Fax: (01872) 862123 E-mail: sales@devoran-metals.co.uk

R. Dillon (Clacton) Ltd, Ford Road Industrial Estate, Clacton-On-Sea, Essex, CO15 3DT Tel: (01255) 423059 Fax: (01255) 222836

Dokic Joinery Ltd, Porte Marsh Road, Calne, Wiltshire, SN11 9BN Tel: (01249) 811133 Fax: (01249) 811144

Dove Tail Joinery, 7 Field Barn Lane Industrial Estate, Field Barn Lane, Cropthorne, Pershore, Worcestershire, WR10 3LY Tel: (01386) 861123 Fax: (01386) 860975

E J Harris & Sons Ltd, 18-25 Queen Victoria Street, Bristol, BS2 0QR Tel: 0117-955 7023

E & R Joinery Ltd, Old Laughton Sawmills, Park Lane, Laughton, Lewes, East Sussex, BN8 6BP Tel: (01323) 811190 Fax: (01323) 811191 E-mail: sales@er-joinery.com

E S Plummer & Son, 82 High Street, Markyate, St. Albans, Hertfordshire, AL3 8LE Tel: (01582) 840611 Fax: (01582) 840611 E-mail: djp1947@ukgateway.net

▶ Ease & Co Banquet Seating Ltd, 47a Hawks Road, Kingston upon Thames, Surrey, KT1 3DS Tel: (020) 8541 4471 E-mail: contact@easeco.co.uk

East Joinery, Unit 2 Willow Lane, Rugby, Warwickshire, CV22 5LX Tel: (01788) 568427 Fax: (01788) 574252 E-mail: r.ingram@ntlworld.com

Eastfield Joinery, Shavington House Farm, Crewe Road, Shavington, Crewe, CW2 5AH Tel: (01270) 664769 Fax: (01270) 665327 E-mail: sales@eastfieldjoinery.sagenet.co.uk

Eckersley Joinery Ltd, Dawson Street, Swinton, Manchester, M27 4FJ Tel: 0161-794 5812 Fax: 0161-794 8586

Eclipse Joinery, Castle View Works, High Street, Harriseahead, Stoke-On-Trent, ST7 4JS Tel: (01782) 510148 Fax: (01782) 510100

Edgley Joinery Ltd, River Lane, Fordham, Ely, Cambridgeshire, CB7 5PF Tel: (01638) 720245 Fax: (01638) 721582

Edmont Joinery Ltd, Hyde Road, Swindon, SN2 7RB Tel: (01793) 825765 Fax: (01793) 825725 E-mail: admin@edmont.co.uk

Ellacombe Joinery Manufacturers, 26 Berachah Road, Torquay, TQ1 3AX Tel: (01803) 293416 Fax:

Elmwood (Glasgow) Ltd, 25 Eagle Street, Craighall Business Park, Glasgow, G4 9XA Tel: 0141-332 3086 Fax: 0141-331 1590 E-mail: mail@elmswoods.com

Elmwood Joinery, Unit 9 Blackmore Park Road, Hanley Swan, Worcester, WR8 0EF Tel: (01684) 569097 Fax: (01684) 569097

Elvet Structures Ltd, Low Willington Industrial Estate, Willington, Crook, County Durham, DL15 0UH Tel: (01388) 747120 Fax: (01388) 745861 E-mail: gordan.pearson@elvetstructures.co.uk

Emanuel Whittaker Ltd, 400 Rochdale Road, Oldham, OL1 2LW Tel: 0161-624 6222 Fax: 0161-785 5510 E-mail: mail@emanuel-whittaker.co.uk

Emerson Joinery, 50a Durham Road, Blackhill, Consett, County Durham, DH8 8NP Tel: (01207) 507805 Fax: (01207) 507805

England Joinery, Holehouse Lane, Glue Hill, Sturminster Newton, Dorset, DT10 2AA Tel: (01258) 472846 Fax: (01258) 472846 E-mail: info@englandjoinery.co.uk

Essex Stairs & Joinery, Holmewood Farm, Brookhall Road, Fingringhoe, Colchester, CO5 7DG Tel: (01206) 728716 Fax: (01206) 729587

Essex Woodcraft, Commerce Way, Colchester, CO2 8HJ Tel: (01206) 795464 Fax: (01206) 796596 E-mail: sales@essexwoodcraft.co.uk

▶ Everglaze, Corner Farm, Ashbourne, Derbyshire, DE6 4LY Tel: (01332) 824367 Fax: (01332) 824483

Evergreen, Clare Park, Unit 2, Farnham, Surrey, GU10 5DT Tel: (01252) 851849 Fax: (01252) 851849

Exhall Timber Products, Bayton Road, Exhall, Coventry, CV7 9EL Tel: (024) 7636 6706

F A North Carlton Ltd, 179 Carlton Hill, Carlton, Nottingham, NG4 1GZ Tel: 0115-987 2339 Fax: 0115-987 7504

F B Jennings & Sons, Mount Farm, Milverton, Taunton, Somerset, TA4 1QZ Tel: (01823) 400226 Fax: (01823) 401201

F Chadwick, Woodview, Willington Road, Willington, Tarporley, Cheshire, CW6 0ND Tel: (01829) 752211 Fax: (01829) 759080

F Cuff & Sons, The Joinery Works, Alweston, Sherborne, Dorset, DT9 5HS Tel: (01963) 23219 Fax: (01963) 23053 E-mail: david@cuffandsons.freeserve.co.uk

F D Anderson & Son, 19 St. Sepulchre Street, Scarborough, North Yorkshire, YO11 1QG Tel: (01723) 360072 Fax: (01723) 360072

F E Bailey, Highgate Factory, High Gate, Helpringham, Sleaford, Lincolnshire, NG34 0RD Tel: (01529) 421219 Fax: (01529) 421580 E-mail: rosemary@rbaily22.freeserve.co.uk

F & E Joinery Ltd, 288 Croxted Road, London, SE24 9DA Tel: (020) 8671 1771 Fax: (020) 8674 3294 E-mail: fejoineryltd@gmail.com

F E Jones Builders Ltd, 303 Mount Road, Manchester, M19 3ET Tel: 0161-224 8001 Fax: 0161-224 8001 E-mail: fej.builders@emerson.co.uk

F J Purkis & Sons, 1-4 Lower Green West, Mitcham, Surrey, CR4 3AF Tel: (020) 8646 5914 Fax: (020) 8646 5914

F J Williams & Son Ltd, 56 London Road, Teynham, Sittingbourne, Kent, ME9 9QN Tel: (01795) 521650 Fax: (01795) 522963

F P Philpott Joinery Ltd, 7 Beehive Workshops Parkengue, Penryn, Cornwall, TR10 9LX Tel: (01326) 377596 Fax: (01326) 377596 E-mail: info@joinerscornwall.com

F W Hawker & Sons Ltd, North End Joinery Works, Bath, BA1 7HN Tel: (01225) 858233 Fax: (01225) 852530 E-mail: joinery@hawker-bath.co.uk

Ken Fairweather, Seaton Joinery, Seaton Road, Arbroath, Angus, DD11 5SE Tel: (01241) 875265 Fax: (01241) 875265

▶ Falcon Interiors, Bluesky House, Western Way, Melksham, Wiltshire, SN12 8BZ Tel: (01225) 704084 Fax: (01225) 700843 E-mail: sales@falconinteriors.biz

Falkus Joinery Ltd, 14 Anning Street, London, EC2A 3LQ Tel: (020) 7729 2424 Fax: (020) 7739 9108 E-mail: enquiries@jerramfalkus.co.uk

Farnell Shaw, Haleys Yard, Upper Town Street, Leeds, LS13 3LA Tel: 0113-239 4123

Feasibility Ltd, Weston Green, Hampton Court Way, Thames Ditton, Surrey, KT7 0JP Tel: (020) 8398 8088 Fax: (020) 8398 1547 E-mail: feasibility@btconnsct.com

Field Developments Hull Ltd, Staithes Road, Hull, HU12 8TJ Tel: (01482) 896240 Fax: (01482) 896510 E-mail: info@shopfituk.co.uk

Fineline Joinery, Littlemoor Road, Mark, Highbridge, Somerset, TA9 4NQ Tel: (01278) 641352 Fax: (01278) 641352

David Finlay Ltd, 9 Main Street, Kingskettle, Cupar, Fife, KY15 7PN Tel: (01337) 830549 Fax: (01337) 831646

Finlaysons, Botany Mill, Roxburgh Street, Galashiels, Selkirkshire, TD1 1PB Tel: (01896) 752673 Fax: (01896) 751239

Firco Construction Ltd, 1 Denton Slipways Site, Wharf Road, Gravesend, Kent, DA12 2RU Tel: (01474) 351644 Fax: (01474) 358936 E-mail: firco@gravesend.demon.co.uk

Firth Manufacturing Ltd, Hole House Lane, Stocksbridge, Sheffield, S36 1BS Tel: 0114-288 3298 Fax: 0114-288 4176 E-mail: info@firths.co.uk

Fitzroy Joinery, Garden Close, Langage Business Park, Plympton, Plymouth, PL7 5EU Tel: (01752) 334940 Fax: (01752) 334942 E-mail: sales@fitzroy.co.uk

Flacke Turner & James, Elm Street Lane, Cardiff, CF24 3QQ Tel: (029) 2049 2023 Fax: (029) 2049 2023

Flaxton Street Auto Spares, Fifield Indust Estate, Usworth Road, Longhill Industrial Estate, Hartlepool, Cleveland, TS25 1PD Tel: (01429) 260592 Fax: (01429) 273339

Fletcher Joinery, Wildmoor Mill Farm, Mill Lane, Wildmoor, Bromsgrove, Worcestershire, B61 0BX Tel: (01527) 835015 Fax: (01527) 835015

Fletcher Joinery, 261 Whessoe Road, Darlington, County Durham, DL3 0YL Tel: (01325) 357347 Fax: (01325) 357347 E-mail: enquiries@fletcherjoinery.co.uk

Forbes West Ltd, 128 Tutbury Road, Burton-on-Trent, Staffordshire, DE13 0NU Tel: (01283) 564351 Fax: (01283) 535707

Forest Joinery, 87 Larch Street, Leicester, LE5 0ES Tel: 0116-253 6721 Fax: 0116-253 6721

Forest Joinery Ltd, 47 Framfield Road, Uckfield, East Sussex, TN22 5AJ Tel: (01825) 766466 Fax: (01825) 766468 E-mail: info@forestjoineryltd.com

Forewood Timber, Rossway Drive, Bushey, WD23 3RX Tel: (020) 8421 8231 Fax: (01208) 421850

Forrest Contracts, Pleckgate Road, Blackburn, BB1 8QW Tel: (01254) 245122 Fax: (01254) 245259

D.E. Fox (Joinery) Ltd, Chapel Works, Bamforth St, Sheffield, S6 2HE Tel: 0114-234 8036 Fax: 0114-234 8036

▶ FR Joinery & Construction Services, New Road, Littleborough, Lancashire, OL15 8LX Tel: 01706 379200 Fax: 01706 379200

Fraser & Renwick, 2 Mansfield Cresent, Hawick, Roxburghshire, TD9 8AQ Tel: (01450) 372148 Fax: (01450) 372148

Frost Woodworking, 3 School Lane, Parkgate, Rotherham, South Yorkshire, S62 6FH Tel: (01709) 522251 Fax: (01709) 719510

Fryer's Ltd, Old Church Hall, Battle Green, Pelton Fell, Chester le Street, County Durham, DH2 2QW Tel: 0191-388 4914 Fax: 0191-388 4974 E-mail: fryersltd@aol.com

Fulton Joinery, 144 Fulton Road, Sheffield, S6 3JP Tel: 0114-234 7676

G B J Cabinet Makers, 40b Worcester Road, Titton, Stourport-on-Severn, Worcestershire, DY13 9PD Tel: (01299) 823740 Fax: (01299) 823740

G Empson & Sons Ltd, Station Road, Gunness, Scunthorpe, South Humberside, DN15 8TR Tel: (01724) 782459 Fax: (01724) 783077

▶ G Potter Joinery Services, 391 Ashby Road, Coalville, Leicestershire, LE67 3LJ Tel: 01530 832204 Fax: 01530 832204 E-mail: v.thornley@btopenworld.com

G R Hathaway Joinery, St Georges Close, Grays Lane, Moreton-in-Marsh, Gloucestershire, GL56 0LP Tel: (01608) 651978 Fax: (01608) 651978

G Riggott, Westminster House, Gibbons Road, Mansfield, Nottinghamshire, NG18 5DZ Tel: (01623) 627454 Fax: (01623) 620335 E-mail: graham.roggott@ntlworld.com

Gale Tower Ltd, 102-106 Harrow Road, London, E11 3QE Tel: (020) 8519 3531 Fax: (020) 8519 3531

JOINERY – *continued*

Gate Makers, Petford Lea, Buckland, Aylesbury, Buckinghamshire, HP22 5HU Tel: (01296) 630798 Fax: (01296) 631373 E-mail: admin@thegatemakers.co.uk

Alan Geoffrey, 1a Jerry Clay Lane, Wrenthorpe, Wakefield, West Yorkshire, WF2 0NS Tel: (01924) 362467 Fax: (01924) 362467

Georgian Medal Joinery Ltd, Unit 1, Meadow St, Treforest, Pontypridd, Mid Glamorgan, CF37 1UD Tel: (01443) 493288 Fax: (01443) 493288 E-mail: sales@hitec-cathodic.co.uk

GMS Joinery, 6a Denmark Terrace, Fortis Green, London, N2 9HG Tel: (020) 8883 7462 E-mail: graham.gms@virgin.net

Golborne Joinery, Queen Street Saw Mill, Golborne, Warrington, WA3 3AF Tel: (01942) 719170 Fax: (01942) 717982

Golding Joinery Ltd, 4 Fern Close, Pen-Y-Fan Industrial Estate, Crumlin, Newport, Gwent, NP11 3EH Tel: (01495) 248778 Fax: (01495) 245296 E-mail: wgoldingjoinery@tiscali.co.uk

Goodwood Fencing & Co., Spencer Courtyard, Rear of 266 Regents Park Road, London, N3 3HN Tel: (020) 8346 0827 Fax: (020) 8346 6430 E-mail: sales@jwc-gwf.com

Grantham Woodmill Ltd, Ruston Road, Grantham, Lincolnshire, NG31 9SW Tel: (01476) 568175 Fax: (01476) 591427

Greenbirches Joiners Ltd, Unit 1, Greenbirches Industrial Estate, Stoke-on-Trent, ST6 5US Tel: (01782) 834888

Greenwich Wood Works, 1-5 Lewisham Road, London, SE13 7QS Tel: (020) 8694 8449 Fax: (020) 8694 8616 E-mail: sales@greenwichwoodworks.co.uk

Griff Woodwork Co. Ltd, Unit 4A, The Ridgeway Trading Estate, Iver, Buckinghamshire, SL0 9HW Tel: (01753) 652616 Fax: (01753) 652616

Griffin & Stenning, 2 Workshop, Milton Ave, Bath, BA2 4QZ Tel: (01225) 331069

David Groom Joinery, 5-8 Eastfield Road, Wollaston, Wellingborough, Northamptonshire, NN29 7RU Tel: (01933) 664494 Fax: (01933) 663085

Francis Guest, Park Street, Teddington, Middlesex, TW11 0LT Tel: (020) 8255 1004 Fax: (020) 8977 9907 E-mail: fguest@globalnet.co.uk

H C White & Son, Pegswood Village, Pegswood, Morpeth, Northumberland, NE61 6UD Tel: (01670) 513660 Fax: (01670) 513660

H D Shopfitters Ltd, May Avenue, Northfleet, Gravesend, Kent, DA11 8RH Tel: (01474) 567788 Fax: (01474) 536403 E-mail: hdshopfit@aol.com

H G Hughes & Son, 10 Back Greenfield Road, Colwyn Bay, Clwyd, LL29 8EP Tel: (01492) 533409

H Hammond & Sons Ltd, D Little Moor Lane, Loughborough, Leicestershire, LE11 1SF Tel: (01509) 212095 Fax: (01509) 238849

▶ H K B Joinery Ltd, Mountney Bridge Industrial Estate, Eastbourne Road, Westham, Pevensey, East Sussex, BN24 5NH Tel: (01323) 762704 Fax: (01323) 740200

H & K Joinery Ltd, Moravian Road, Bristol, BS15 8ND Tel: 0117-960 2849 Fax: 0117-961 8250

H Lee & Son, The Woodyard, Belle Vue Road, Ashbourne, Derbyshire, DE6 1AT Tel: (01335) 342530

Hall Bros Of Colchester Ltd, Haye Lane, Fingringhoe, Colchester, CO5 7AE Tel: (01206) 735287 Fax: (01206) 735889 E-mail: craftsman@hall-brothers.co.uk

Hallams, Wolsey Drive, Kirkby-in-Ashfield, Nottingham, NG17 7JR Tel: (01623) 723777 Fax: (01623) 723888

Hammerstones Ltd, Dewsbury Road, Elland, West Yorkshire, HX5 9BG Tel: (01422) 310842 Fax: (01422) 376713

Hamwyn Joinery, Bodenham, Hereford, HR1 3HT Tel: (01568) 797650 Fax: (01568) 797650

▶ Hannaford, Unit 6, Handley Page Way, Colney Street, St. Albans, Hertfordshire, AL2 2DQ Tel: (01923) 851070 Fax: (01923) 839873 E-mail: email@krhannaford.co.uk

Harlequin Woodcraft, 7 Industrial Road, Cambridge Road Industrial Estate, Milton, Cambridge, CB4 6AZ Tel: (01223) 420885 Fax: (01223) 420885

Harlock Joinery Ltd, Brook Street, Redditch, Worcestershire, B98 8NG Tel: (01527) 68541 Fax: (01527) 68541 E-mail: harlockjoinery@btconnect.com

Harris Windows & Joinery Ltd, Brighton Road, Tadworth, Surrey, KT20 6UP Tel: (01737) 832328 Fax: (01737) 833964

Hart & Co. Ltd, 18-19 Greenhey Place, Skelmersdale, Lancashire, WN8 9SA Tel: (01695) 732525 Fax: (01695) 50951 E-mail: reception@hartandco.gb.com

Hay Joinery, Chapel Road, Lingwood, Norwich, NR13 4NY Tel: (01603) 712392 Fax: (01603) 714248 E-mail: build@jshay.co.uk

Hayburn Wood Products, 299 Galgorm Road, Ahoghill, Ballymena, County Antrim, BT42 1JU Tel: (028) 2587 1442 Fax: (028) 2587 1177 E-mail: info@hayburn.co.uk

Hazelwood Cardiff, Unit 46 Splott Indust Estate, Portmanmoor Road, Cardiff, CF24 5FF Tel: (029) 2049 5950 Fax: (029) 2049 5607

R. Hemsworth & Son (Gosport) Ltd, 8 Westfield Industrial Estate, Gosport, Hampshire, PO12 3RX Tel: (023) 9258 2731 Fax: (023) 9251 0436

Heritage Joinery London Ltd, Alphabess Works, Selinas Lane, Dagenham, Essex, RM8 1QH Tel: (020) 8517 5171 Fax: (020) 8517 5172

Hewitt & Maughan Ltd, 11 Albion Close, Worksop, Nottinghamshire, S80 1RA Tel: (01909) 473581 Fax: (01909) 477960 E-mail: office@hewittandmaughan.sagehost.co.uk

Hiddleston Joiners, The Old School, Terregles, Dumfries, DG2 9RY Tel: (01387) 720100 Fax: (01387) 720555

▶ High Peak Remedial Services, New Mill, Park Road, Dukinfield, Cheshire, SK16 5LX Tel: 0161-339 4655 Fax: 0161-339 8216

Highgate Joinery, 18 Wightman Road, London, N4 1SQ Tel: (020) 8341 4823 Fax: (020) 8341 5656

Highland Wood Windows Ltd, 46 Station Road, Worthing, West Sussex, BN11 1JP Tel: (01903) 237613 Fax: (01903) 820253 E-mail: sales@parker-joinery.com

Hills Of Shoeburyness Ltd, 17 Towerfield Road, Shoeburyness, Southend-on-Sea, SS3 9QL Tel: (01702) 296321 Fax: (01702) 297072 E-mail: sales@hillsofshoeburyness.com

Hinderwell Joinery, 6 Rose Hill, Hinderwell, Saltburn-by-the-Sea, Cleveland, TS13 5EU Tel: (01947) 840685 Fax: (01947) 840685

Holmes & Pearcey, Breach Farm, St Johns Road, Oakley, Basingstoke, Hampshire, RG23 7DU Tel: (01256) 782575 Fax: (01256) 782575

Hope Allan Joinery, Orphans Yard, Brixton Station Road, London, SW9 8QB Tel: (020) 7274 6418 Fax: (020) 7274 6418

Horsley Joinery, Manston Green Industrial Estate, Preston Road, Manston, Ramsgate, Kent, CT12 5BA Tel: (01843) 824002 Fax: (01843) 848354

Hoskins Joinery, Honey Hill Lane, Wimbotsham, King's Lynn, Norfolk, PE34 3QD Tel: (01366) 383103 Fax: (01366) 385957

Housley & Birks, 7 Weston Street, Heanor, Derbyshire, DE75 7NG Tel: (01773) 716892

Hout Tek, Lodge Farm Mill Lane, Colne Engaine, Colchester, CO6 2HX Tel: (01787) 223136 Fax: (01787) 224535 E-mail: info@hout-tek.co.uk

Howard J Bangert, 1 Pointer Grove, Halton, Lancaster, LA2 6QR Tel: (01524) 811455

▶ Howden Joinery Ltd, 5 Shenstone Trading Estate, Bromsgrove Road, Halesowen, West Midlands, B63 3XB Tel: 0121-501 1621 Fax: 0121-585 7580

▶ Howden's Joinery Ltd, Unit 8a Tweedside Trading Estate, Tweedmouth, Berwick-upon-Tweed, TD15 2XF Tel: (01289) 307830 Fax: (01289) 331619

▶ Howdens Joinery Ltd, Blackhouse Way, Blackhouse Industrial Estate, Peterhead, Aberdeenshire, AB42 1BQ Tel: (01779) 480579 Fax: (01779) 480641

▶ Howden's Joinery Ltd, Unit 428 Camp Hill Close, Ripon, North Yorkshire, HG4 1QY Tel: (01765) 698407 Fax: (01765) 698289

Hucknall Joinery, Lowmoor Road, Kirkby-in-Ashfield, Nottingham, NG17 7JE Tel: (01623) 721277 Fax: (01623) 722210 E-mail: info@hucknalljoinery.co.uk

Hughes & Allen Ltd, Canalside Industrial Estate, Oil Sites Road, Ellesmere Port, CH65 4EN Tel: 0151-355 3170 Fax: 0151-355 5074

Humber Joiners Ltd, Stepney Lane, Hull, HU5 1HX Tel: (01482) 341954 Fax: (01482) 449516

Hutton Timber Products Ltd, Birch Business Centre, Maldon Road, Birch, Colchester, CO2 0LT Tel: (01206) 331450 Fax: (01206) 331581 E-mail: htp@globalnet.co.uk

Hydestile Joinery, Hambledon Road, Hydestile, Godalming, Surrey, GU8 4DE Tel: (01483) 420006 Fax: (01483) 416869

I B S Specialist Joinery Ltd, Wyfield Manor, Boxford, Newbury, Berkshire, RG20 8DY Tel: (01488) 608895 Fax: (01488) 608895 E-mail: enquiries@ibs4doors.com

Icklesham Joinery Ltd, Main Road, Icklesham, Winchelsea, East Sussex, TN36 4BA Tel: (01424) 814303 Fax: (01424) 814744 E-mail: enquiries@ickleshamjoineryltd.com

▶ Input Joinery Ltd, The Fairground, Weyhill, Andover, Hampshire, SP11 0QN Tel: (01264) 771900 Fax: (01264) 771901 E-mail: info@inputjoinery.co.uk

▶ Intext Bespoke, Tameside Works, Dukinfield, Cheshire, SK16 5PT Tel: 0161-339 1285 Fax: 0161-344 2744 E-mail: sales@intextjoinery.co.uk

Irwins Ltd, Low Hall Road, Horsforth, Leeds, LS18 4EW Tel: 0113-250 6811 Fax: 0113-250 6933 E-mail: sales@irwins.co.uk

Ivor Newton & Son Fuel & Car Sales, Aston Road, Haddenham, Aylesbury, Buckinghamshire, HP17 8AF Tel: (01844) 291461

▶ J B Joinery, Unit 7 Skelmanthorpe Business Park, Elm Street, Skelmanthorpe, Huddersfield, HD8 9DZ Tel: (01484) 860601 Fax: (01484) 860601

J B Joinery, Aitken Street, Stoke-on-Trent, ST6 3RG Tel: (01782) 825455 Fax: (01782) 825951

J C K Joinery, 8 Heanor Street, Leicester, LE1 4DD Tel: 0116-291 2288 Fax: 0116-291 2300 E-mail: enquiries@jckjoinery.co.uk

J & D Joinery Ltd, 6 Brockhill Works, Windsor Road, Redditch, Worcestershire, B97 6DJ Tel: (01527) 69469 Fax: (01527) 69172

▶ J D Joinery, Harold Mews, 10 Mews Road, St. Leonards-on-Sea, East Sussex, TN38 0EA Tel: (01424) 425600

J D Joinery Bonnybridge Ltd, Lyndeen Cottage, 61 Broomhill Road, Bonnybridge, Stirlingshire, FK4 2AT Tel: (01324) 813760

J Diver, A 5 School Lane, Impington, Cambridge, CB24 9NS Tel: (01223) 232256

J E Hamer Manufacturing & Joinery, Upper Cockroft Farm, Rishworth, Sowerby Bridge, West Yorkshire, HX6 4RE Tel: (01422) 822873 Fax: (01422) 822873 E-mail: edwin@jehamer.co.uk

J & E Woodworks, Barley Mow, Lampeter, Dyfed, SA48 7BY Tel: (01570) 422141 Fax: (01570) 422144 E-mail: sales@je-woodworks.co.uk

J G Smith, Beatrice Road, Kettering, Northamptonshire, NN16 9QR Tel: (01536) 514743 Fax: (01536) 416068

J H Joinery, 33 South Street, Pennington, Lymington, Hampshire, SO41 8EA Tel: (01590) 671870 Fax: (01590) 671966

J J Higgins Ltd, 42 Garden St, Magherafelt, County Londonderry, BT45 5DD Tel: (028) 7963 2369 Fax: (028) 7963 1790 E-mail: info@jjhiggins.com

J J M Joinery, Forstal Farm Business Park, Goudhurst Road, Lamberhurst, Tunbridge Wells, Kent, TN3 8AG Tel: (01892) 891040 Fax: (01892) 891040

▶ J K R Services Ltd, Orchard Building, Hewitts Road, Chelsfield, Orpington, Kent, BR6 7QL Tel: (01959) 533778 Fax: (01959) 532544 E-mail: admin@soundcraft-doors.co.uk

J L Holmes & Sons, 86a Leyland Road, Penwortham, Preston, PR1 9XS Tel: (01772) 743640 Fax: (01772) 743640

J N Supplies Ltd, Unit 27, 27 Beler Way, Melton Mowbray, Leicestershire, LE13 0DG Tel: (01664) 564050 Fax: 01664 564050 E-mail: sales@jnsupplies.co.uk

J Newbold Joinery & Shopfitters, Sherwood Street, Kirkby-in-Ashfield, Nottingham, NG17 9HU Tel: (01623) 721002 Fax: (01623) 721002

J P Joinery, Portmanmoor Road Lane, Cardiff, CF24 5EQ Tel: (029) 2049 3661 Fax: (029) 2049 1592

J P Kelly, 34 Market Street, Chapel-en-le-Frith, High Peak, Derbyshire, SK23 0HY Tel: (01298) 813449 Fax: (01298) 813449 E-mail: kellyj45@btinternet.com

J & R Hateley Ltd, Lockside Tat Bank Road, Oldbury, West Midlands, B69 4NS Tel: 0121-544 6327 Fax: 0121-552 1150

J R Lowry, Little Windsor Road, Southport, Merseyside, PR9 0RZ Tel: (01704) 537225 Fax: (01704) 537225 E-mail: ampdude@fsnet.co.uk

J S M Joinery, 390 Sydenham Road, Croydon, CR0 2EA Tel: (0800) 7316345 Fax: (020) 8683 0404 E-mail: info@slhardwoods.co.uk

J Scott Thrapston Ltd, Bridge Street, Thrapston, Kettering, Northamptonshire, NN14 4LR Tel: (01832) 732366 Fax: (01832) 733703 E-mail: julia@scottsofthrapston.co.uk

J T Ward, 2 Station Street, Holbeach, Spalding, Lincolnshire, PE12 7LF Tel: (01406) 423517 Fax: (01406) 425805 E-mail: ltwardmd@aol.com

J W Cooper Joinery, 6 Sea Lane, Rustington, Littlehampton, West Sussex, BN16 2RB Tel: (01903) 776941 Fax: (01903) 776941 E-mail: sales@cooperjoinery.co.uk

Jackson Joinery Manufacturing Ltd, 619 Liverpool Street, Salford, M5 5HQ Tel: 0161-281 9770 Fax: 0161-745 9217

▶ John Jackson & Sons Joiners Ltd, Victoria Building, 82 Hammond Street, Preston, PR1 7NU Tel: (01772) 881696

Jacowe Joinery Ltd, Clyde Yard, Cambridge Street, Godmanchester, Huntingdon, Cambridgeshire, PE29 2AT Tel: (01480) 457682 Fax: (01480) 434212 E-mail: jacowejoineryltd.@btconnect.com

Jarrett & Lawson Ltd, 5 The Old Quarry, Nene Valley Business Park, Oundle, Peterborough, PE8 4HN Tel: (01832) 275551 Fax: (01832) 275553 E-mail: jarrettlawson@pgrconstructions.co.uk

Jarvis H Son Joinery Ltd, Longbeck Trading Estate, Redcar, Cleveland, TS11 6HH Tel: (01642) 482366 Fax: (01642) 484015 E-mail: admin@jarvis.co.uk

▶ JCC Property Care Ltd, 6 Mid Street, Rosehearty, Fraserburgh, Aberdeenshire, AB43 7JS Tel: 0800 4582372 Fax: 0704 3301765 E-mail: solutions@goJCC.net

Jeld Wen UK Ltd, Retford Road, Woodhouse Mill, Sheffield, S13 9WH Tel: 0114-254 2000 Fax: 0114-269 6696

▶ John Beavan, Kyre, Tenbury Wells, Worcestershire, WR15 8RW Tel: (01885) 410549 Fax: (01885) 410563 E-mail: info@johnbeavan.com

John C Lillywhite Ltd, Gravel Lane, Chichester, West Sussex, PO19 8PQ Tel: (01243) 781911 Fax: (01243) 780168 E-mail: jcl.builders@virgin.net

John Richardson & Son, Roper Street, Penrith, Cumbria, CA11 8HS Tel: (01768) 895000 Fax: (01768) 895007

▶ Joinery Crew, Unit 1, 70 Bell Lane, Uckfield, East Sussex, TN22 1QL Tel: 01825 766777 Fax: 01825 766755

Jones & Baker, 1 Spring Lane, Swannington, Coalville, Leicestershire, LE67 8QR Tel: (01530) 837803 Fax: (01530) 837803

D.J. Jones, Maes Y Gwrdy, Llanarth, Dyfed, SA47 0QL Tel: (01545) 580353 Fax: (01545) 580353

Jones Joinery, 144 Hornby Boulevard, Liverpool, L21 8HQ Tel: 0151-933 0442

Jones Tim Carpentry Joinery Shopfitting, Trevanson Street, The Workshop, Wadebridge, Cornwall, PL27 7AR Tel: (01208) 814755 Fax: (01208) 814755

Joseph Thompson, Hendon Lodge Sawmills, Moor Terrace, Sunderland, SR1 2PA Tel: 0191-514 4663 Fax: 0191-514 3251

Jubilee Joinery Hull Ltd, Eagle House, Cleveland Street, Hull, HU8 7AU Tel: (01482) 224275 Fax: (01482) 217672 E-mail: jubilee@sagehost.co.uk

K & D Joinery Ltd, Joinery House, 69 Chequers Lane, Dagenham, Essex, RM9 6QJ Tel: (020) 8526 7020 Fax: (020) 8526 7030 E-mail: info@kandd.org

K J Joinery, Regent House, 15-21 Adam Street, Cardiff, CF24 2FH Tel: (029) 2049 5395 Fax: (029) 2049 5395

K J Shepherd, Unit 27 Bancombe Trading Estate, Bancombe Road, Somerton, Somerset, TA11 6SB Tel: (01458) 273990 Fax: (01458) 273990

K.L Joinery, Little Trenance Farm, Trenance Road, St. Austell, Cornwall, PL25 5RF Tel: (01726) 64680 Fax: (01726) 70668

K T Joinery Ltd, 9 Auckland New Business Centre, St. Helen Auckland Industrial Estate, Bishop Auckland, County Durham, DL14 9TX Tel: (01388) 458660 Fax: (01388) 606494 E-mail: office@ktjoinery.co.uk

Nigel Kelly (Joinery Division) Ltd, The Old Chapel, Main Street, Garton-On-The-Wolds, Driffield, East Yorkshire, YO25 3ET Tel: (01377) 241113 Fax: (01377) 241113 E-mail: info@collectiondisplays.com

Key Joinery Ltd, Peveril House, Alfreton Road, Derby, DE21 4AG Tel: (01332) 331457 Fax: (01332) 206434 E-mail: sales@key-joinery.co.uk

▶ Keycraft Nottingham, 24 West Street, Hucknall, Nottingham, NG15 7BY Tel: 0115-963 0323 Fax: 0115-963 0323

Kidlington Joinery, The Old Builders Yard, High Street, Islip, Kidlington, Oxfordshire, OX5 2RX Tel: (01865) 374880 Fax: (01865) 379246

Kildress Joinery Works, 4 Dunnamore Road, Cookstown, County Tyrone, BT80 9NR Tel: (028) 8675 1292 Fax: (028) 8675 1007

Kilby & Gayford Ltd, 30 Radford Way, Billericay, Essex, CM12 0DA Tel: (020) 7498 9898 Fax: (01277) 630193 E-mail: sales@killbygayford.com

Kingfisher Windows & Joinery, 296 Bolton Road, Hawkshaw, Bury, Lancashire, BL8 4JN Tel: (01204) 888595 Fax: (01204) 888595 E-mail: geoffside@hotmail.com

▶ Kings Lynn Joinery Ltd, Austin Fields, King's Lynn, Norfolk, PE30 1QH Tel: (01553) 777747 Fax: (01553) 771170

▶ Kirkland Kitchens & Joinery Co. Ltd, The Old Cooperage, Gatebeck, Kendal, Cumbria, LA8 0HW Tel: (01539) 566999 Fax: (01539) 567733 E-mail: info@kirkland-kitchens.co.uk

Kiwi Craftsmen In Wood, 13 Rea Barn Close, Brixham, Devon, TQ5 9EA Tel: (01803) 858093 Fax: (01803) 858093

L & S Joinery, 98 Lower Bedfords Road, Romford, RM1 4DQ Tel: (01708) 755966 Fax: (01708) 730748

William Langshaw & Sons Ltd, Abbey Works, Back King Street, Whalley, Clitheroe, Lancashire, BB7 9SP Tel: (01254) 824518 Fax: (01254) 823830 E-mail: enquiries@wmlangshaw.co.uk

Lawrence Joinery Pine Specialists, Unit 15b Greenhill Mills, Grange Road, Batley, West Yorkshire, WF17 6LH Tel: (01924) 422088 Fax: (01924) 422088

Leach & Clegg, Lily Street, Milnrow, Rochdale, Lancashire, OL16 3NQ Tel: (01706) 642757 Fax: (01706) 658369

▶ Lee & Broughton Ltd, Homestead Workshop, Skitham Lane, Out Rawcliffe, Preston, PR3 6BE Tel: (01995) 672599 Fax: (01995) 672599

Lee Zak, The Workshop, Fair View, Blackwood, Gwent, NP12 3NS Tel: (01443) 835049

Leigh & G Joinery, Butlers Lands Farm, Mortimer, Reading, RG7 2AG Tel: 0118-933 2481 Fax: 0118-933 2455

Leigh Joinery Co. Ltd, Clifton Street, Leigh, Lancashire, WN7 5AD Tel: (01942) 608182 Fax: (01942) 608182

Lester & Lester Ltd, 1-9 Tennyson Road, London, SW19 8SH Tel: (020) 8540 8687 Fax: (020) 8543 4322 E-mail: darren@lesters.ssworld.co.uk

Linden Bauer Ltd, Mid Kent Business Park, Sortmill Road, Snodland, Kent, ME6 5UA Tel: (01634) 243137 Fax: (01634) 249306 E-mail: christian@lindenbauer.freeserve.co.uk

Linford-Bridgeman Ltd, Quonians, Lichfield, Staffordshire, WS13 7LB Tel: (01543) 414234 Fax: (01543) 258250 E-mail: clare.millington@linfordgroup.co.uk

▶ Littlewoods Successors Ltd, Paddock Foot, Huddersfield, HD1 4RY Tel: (01484) 423960 Fax: (01484) 450172

The LodgeTaylor's Shopfitters, 280 Birchanger Lane, Birchanger, Bishop's Stortford, Hertfordshire, CM23 5QP Tel: (01279) 817003

Lol Summers Joinery Ltd, Barlow Road, Aldermans Green Industrial Estate, Coventry, CV2 2LD Tel: (024) 7661 9644 Fax: (024) 7661 6012

Lombards Of Cheshunt Ltd, 25 High Street, Cheshunt, Waltham Cross, Hertfordshire, EN8 0BS Tel: (01992) 623160 Fax: (01992) 622422

Longden & Jones, Wharf Road, Whaley Bridge, High Peak, Derbyshire, SK23 7AD Tel: (01663) 734273 Fax: (01663) 719156

Longwood Joinery Ltd, 656 Thorp Arch Trading Estate, Thorp Arch, Wetherby, West Yorkshire, LS23 7BJ Tel: (01937) 843072 Fax: (01937) 541110 E-mail: sales@longwood-joinery.co.uk

Lytchett Minster Joinery, 14-16 Holton Road, Holton Heath Trading Park, Poole, Dorset, BH16 6LT Tel: (01202) 622441 Fax: (01202) 622441

JOINERY – *continued*

M A & C E Hathaway, 7 Blackmoor Road, Ebblake Industrial Estate, Verwood, Dorset, BH31 6AX Tel: (01202) 824067 Fax: (01202) 821301

M C F Services Ltd, Units 4-5, Camden Drive, Hockley, Birmingham, B1 3LR Tel: 0121-236 8956 Fax: 0121-236 8048

M & D Joinery Ltd, 56 Stanworth Street, London, SE1 3NY Tel: (020) 7231 2965 Fax: (020) 7231 2965

M F Tofield & Sons, 14 Barton Road, Bletchley, Milton Keynes, MK2 3JG Tel: (01908) 274527 Fax: (01908) 371395 E-mail: enquiries@tofield.com

M G Joinery, 375 Stoney Stanton Road, Coventry, CV6 5DT Tel: (024) 7661 2330 Fax: (024) 7663 7916

M J Bradshaw & Sons, Glaston Road, Uppingham, Oakham, Leicestershire, LE15 9EU Tel: (01572) 822727 Fax: (01572) 822727

M J Brown Joinery, Hewitt Street, Crewe, CW2 6DZ Tel: (01270) 211518 Fax: (01270) 211941

M J Dowson, Station House, Station Road, Tollerton, York, YO61 1RD Tel: (01347) 838272 Fax: (01347) 838957

M J Joinery, Swift Farm, Hensting Lane, Fishers Pond, Eastleigh, Hampshire, SO50 7HH Tel: (023) 8069 2184

▶ M J & K Speck, The Gables, Northside Road, Hollym, Withernsea, North Humberside, HU19 2RS Tel: (01964) 613356 Fax: (01964) 613354

M & J Nuttall, Unit 14 Pearlbrook Industrial Estate, Chorley New Road, Horwich, Bolton, BL6 5PX Tel: (01204) 691311

M Musgrove Ltd, 1 Gunnersbury Mews, London, W4 4AP Tel: (020) 8994 2941 Fax: (020) 8994 4484

M & P Joinery Joinery, 39a Shaftesbury Avenue, Bristol, BS6 5LT Tel: 0117-941 3210 Fax: 0117-941 3210

M S Services, 18 Esk Place, Aberdeen, AB16 6SQ Tel: (01224) 691742 Fax: (01224) 691742 E-mail: msservices@fsmai8l.net

Mablethorpe Joinery Services, Unit 2, Golf Road Indust Estate, Mablethorpe, Lincolnshire, LN12 1NB Tel: (01507) 478594 Fax: (01507) 478594

Mcbeth Joinery, Cardiff Bay Workshops, Brindley Road, Cardiff, CF11 8TX Tel: (029) 2038 7676 Fax: (029) 2038 7676

Macinnes Joiners, Unit 10 C Coal Wynd, Kirkcaldy, Fife, KY1 2RA Tel: (01592) 597085 Fax: (01592) 597085

▶ Mackay Bros The Joinery Specialists, Showroom, 127 Eastbank Street, Southport, Merseyside, PR8 1DQ Tel: (01704) 540772 E-mail: mackaybrothers@btinternet.com

▶ McManus Joinery, 343 Dowling Road, Clonliff, Enniskillen, County Fermanagh, BT92 3BP Tel: (028) 6634 8161 Fax: (028) 6634 8601 E-mail: mcmanus_joinery@hotmail.com

Magnet Ltd, 12 St Machar Road, Aberdeen, AB24 2UU Tel: (01224) 492894 Fax: (01224) 488276

Magnet Ltd, Units 6 & 7 Pines Way Industrial Estate, Ivo Peters Road, Bath, BA2 3QS Tel: (01225) 335659 Fax: (01225) 448684

Magnet Ltd, Spa Road, Bolton, BL1 4SL Tel: (01204) 521611 Fax: (01204) 364779

Magnet Ltd, 390 Newport Road, Cardiff, CF23 9AE Tel: (029) 2047 3366 Fax: (029) 2048 0170E-mail: sales@magnetexpress.com

Magnet Ltd, Allington Way, Darlington, County Durham, DL1 4XT Tel: (01325) 481177 Fax: (01325) 744379

Magnet Ltd, 60 Grieve Street, Dunfermline, Fife, KY12 8DW Tel: (01383) 720155 Fax: (01383) 620615

Magnet Ltd, 66 Twyford Road, Eastleigh, Hampshire, SO50 4HN Tel: (023) 8061 3581 Fax: (023) 8061 2791

Magnet Ltd, Ambley Road, Gillingham Business Park, Gillingham, Kent, ME8 0PU Tel: (01634) 377242 Fax: (01634) 379047

Magnet Ltd, 2a Hillbottom Road, Sands Industrial Estate, High Wycombe, Buckinghamshire, HP12 4HJ Tel: (01494) 445243 Fax: (01494) 538685 E-mail: highwycombe@magnettrade.co.uk

Magnet Ltd, Rotterdam Road, Hull, HU7 0XD Tel: (01482) 825451 Fax: (01482) 830241

Magnet Ltd, 593-613 Old Kent Road, London, SE15 1LA Tel: (020) 7639 2128 Fax: (020) 7252 8117

Magnet Ltd, 5 Leagrave Street, London, E5 9QX Tel: (020) 8985 6382 Fax: (020) 8986 0489

Magnet Ltd, 2 Salter Street, London, NW10 6UN Tel: (020) 8960 4333 Fax: (020) 8964 0271 E-mail: willesden.branch@magnet.co.uk

Magnet Ltd, Sutton Road, Mansfield, Nottinghamshire, NG18 5HT Tel: (01623) 622359 Fax: (01623) 421049 E-mail: mansfield.branch@magnet.co.uk

Magnet Ltd, 108h Market Street, Musselburgh, Midlothian, EH21 6QA Tel: 0131-665 2451 Fax: 0131-653 3302

Magnet Ltd, 171 Mile Cross Lane, Norwich, NR6 6RE Tel: (01603) 429428 Fax: (01603) 406658

Magnet Ltd, Dunkeld Road, Perth, PH1 3AA Tel: (01738) 634007 Fax: (01738) 643764

Magnet Ltd, Fengate, Peterborough, PE1 5PE Tel: (01733) 558211 Fax: (01733) 563664

Magnet Ltd, Transit Way, Plymouth, PL5 3TW Tel: (01752) 703755 Fax: (01752) 766804

Magnet Ltd, Newington Road, Ramsgate, Kent, CT12 6ED Tel: (01843) 583147 Fax: (01843) 596276

Magnet Ltd, Unit 3a Redhill Distribution Centre, Salbrook Road, Redhill, RH1 5DY Tel: (01293) 824277 Fax: (01293) 824287

Magnet Ltd, Polebarn Road, Trowbridge, Wiltshire, BA14 7EG Tel: (01225) 763058 Fax: (01225) 768254 E-mail: trowbridge.branch@magnet.co.uk

Magnet Ltd, Rosehill, Willenhall, West Midlands, WV13 2AR Tel: (01902) 366330 Fax: (01902) 602328

Magnet Ltd, 2 Tebay Road, Wirral, Merseyside, CH62 3QJ Tel: 0151-334 6169 Fax: 0151-334 6122

Magnet Ltd, Kettlestring Lane, York, YO30 4XF Tel: (01904) 691962 Fax: (01904) 693134

Magnet Kitchens, Longfield Road, Tunbridge Wells, Kent, TN2 3UR Tel: (01892) 514427 Fax: (01892) 539215

Makinson & Worsley, Era Street, Bolton, BL2 6JB Tel: (01204) 523606 Fax: (01204) 388058

Malek Joinery Ltd, 16 Belsham Street, London, E9 6NG Tel: (020) 8985 2222 Fax: (020) 8985 2223

▶ Maplecroft Joinery, Unit 26 Limestone Cottage Lane, Sheffield, S6 1NJ Tel: 0114-231 4490 Fax: 0114-231 4490

Marc Five Ltd, Maydown Industrial Estate, Carrakeel Drive, Maydown, Londonderry, BT47 6UQ Tel: (028) 7186 1288 Fax: (028) 7186 1285 E-mail: marc_fiveltd@hotmail.com

▶ Marchant Joinery, Unit 21 Park Farm, Hundred Acre Lane, Wivelsfield Green, Haywards Heath, West Sussex, RH17 7RU Tel: (07753) 821124 Fax: (01273) 891977

Marco Joinery Ltd, 17-19 Downing Street, Sutton-in-Ashfield, Nottinghamshire, NG17 4EF Tel: (01623) 556684 Fax: (01623) 556664

Marshall Specialist Joinery Ltd, The Old Railway Station, Sampford Courtenay, Okehampton, Devon, EX20 2SN Tel: (01837) 54189 Fax: (01837) 54808

Marvic Joinery Ltd, Millers Road, Warwick, CV34 5AN Tel: (01926) 491990 Fax: (01926) 400673

Masher Bros, 97-103 Florence Road, London, SE14 6QL Tel: (020) 8691 1632 Fax: (020) 8691 1496 E-mail: sales@masherbros.com

Maskame & Tait, 9-11 St. Peter Street, Peterhead, Aberdeenshire, AB42 1QB Tel: (01779) 473661 Fax: (01779) 481482 E-mail: info@maskameandtait.co.uk

Masson Joinery Ltd, The Joinery Works, The Green, Frant, Tunbridge Wells, Kent, TN3 9DE Tel: (01892) 750351 Fax: (01892) 750695

Mastercraft Joinery Works Ltd, 24 Honey Hill Road, Bristol, BS15 4HQ Tel: 0117-947 7171 Fax: 0117-947 7171

Mercia Interiors, 8 Victoria Buildings, Newhall Street, Willenhall, West Midlands, WV13 1LN Tel: (01902) 636685 Fax: (01902) 637086 E-mail: info@mimltd.freeserve.co.uk

Merryworth Joinery Ltd, 21-23 Girton Street, Cambridge Industrial Area, Salford, M7 1UR Tel: 0161-839 3321 Fax: 0161-839 3321

Michael Pepper Joinery, Ascot Drive, Derby, DE24 8GW Tel: (01332) 371133 Fax: (01332) 371132 E-mail: enquires@npeperjoinery.co.uk

▶ Micon Joinery, Charlotte Despard Avenue, London, SW11 5JE Tel: (020) 7627 8484 Fax: (020) 7720 8159

Midas Marine & Joinery Co., Eastlands Boatyard Eastlands, Coal Park Lane, Swanwick, Southampton, SO31 7GW Tel: (01489) 583310 Fax: (01489) 581869 E-mail: midasmaraine@fsbdial.co.uk

Mike Brown Joinery Contractor, 1 Rainnieshill Road, Newmachar, Aberdeen, AB21 0XG Tel: (01651) 863086 Fax: (01651) 862832

▶ Millbank Manufacturing Ltd, Yardley Works, Stourbridge Road, Stourbridge, West Midlands, DY9 7BD Tel: (01384) 896229

Millbrook Furnishings Industries, Stephenson Road, Calmore Industrial Estate, Totton, Southampton, SO40 3RY Tel: (023) 8066 2221 Fax: (023) 8066 2264E-mail: sales@mfil.co.uk

▶ Millroad Joinery, Unit 5a, Ryehill Close, Lodge Farm Industrial Estate, Northampton, NN5 7UA Tel: (01604) 582200 Fax: (01604) 582200

Milton Lee Joinery, Unit 4 Rink Drive, Swadlincote, Derbyshire, DE11 8JL Tel: (01283) 225657 Fax: (01283) 225657

Mitchell & Hargreaves, Hough Side Works, Hough Side Road, Pudsey, West Yorkshire, LS28 9DD Tel: 0113-255 2861 Fax: 0113-239 3979

Model Branch Ltd, William Street, Bedworth, Warwickshire, CV12 9DS Tel: (024) 7631 4393 Fax: (024) 7631 4393

Monarch Ipswich Ltd, 5 Scrivener Drive, Ipswich, IP2 0SD Tel: (01473) 604010 Fax: (01473) 604011 E-mail: ed@monarchjoinery.co.uk

Monk Woodworkings, Boundary Way, Lufton Trading Estate, Lufton, Yeovil, Somerset, BA22 8HZ Tel: (01935) 425232 Fax: (01935) 431233 E-mail: info@monkwoodworking.fsnet.co.uk

Moore Bros, Unit 19 Midland Oak Trading Estate, Marlissa Drive, Coventry, CV6 6HQ Tel: (024) 7668 2888 Fax: (024) 7668 0888

Mount Sion Joinery, 17 Avon Street, Tunbridge Wells, Kent, TN1 2JG Tel: (01892) 547316 Fax: (01892) 547316

Tony Murray Interiors Ltd, Rowden Works, Chaffinch Road, Beckenham, Kent, BR3 4NA Tel: (020) 8650 9331 Fax: (020) 8663 6576

Mustang, Midland Road, Rotherham, South Yorkshire, S61 1SZ Tel: (01709) 559547 Fax: (01709) 556758

N G Joinery, Unit 2 The Stable Block Brewer Street Farm, Brewer Street, Brewer Street Farm Brewer Street, Redhill, RH1 4QP Tel: (01883) 744842 Fax: (01883) 744842

N Palmer, 131 Main Street, Horsley Woodhouse, Ilkeston, Derbyshire, DE7 6AX Tel: (01332) 780110 Fax: (01332) 780110

N Stephenson & Son Kettering Ltd, 49 Grafton Street, Kettering, Northamptonshire, NN16 9DF Tel: (01536) 512625 Fax: (01536) 522869 E-mail: nstephenson@realemail.co.uk

N Taylor & Sons, 2 Hall Street, Cheadle, Cheshire, SK8 1PJ Tel: 0161-491 1824 Fax: 0161-491 1824

Nash Conversions Ltd, Unit 5, Shaftesbury Court, Shaftesbury Road, Leyton, London, E10 7DA Tel: (020) 8539 2276 Fax: (020) 8558 3891

Naylor & Walkden Ltd, Hatton Street, Adlington, Chorley, Lancashire, PR7 4HT Tel: (01257) 480222 Fax: (01257) 482696 E-mail: info@naylorwalkden.co.uk

Neil W Ingram, The Workshop, Church Street, Laurencekirk, Kincardineshire, AB30 1AP Tel: (01561) 378102 Fax: (01561) 378102

Neilson Fjord Ltd, 51 Little Queen Street, Dartford, DA1 1TL Tel: (01322) 277322 Fax: (01322) 220630

▶ Newman Joinery Ltd, 4 Sandy Lane North, Wallington, Surrey, SM6 8JX Tel: (020) 8647 7031 Fax: (020) 8669 9661

Roy Nicholson, 101 Burringham Road, Scunthorpe, South Humberside, DN17 2DF Tel: (01724) 867213 Fax: (01724) 867213

Roy Nicholson, 2 Henderson Avenue, Scunthorpe, South Humberside, DN15 7RL Tel: (01724) 856249

Nixon Knowles, Longwall Avenue, Nottingham, NG2 1LP Tel: 0115-986 5252 Fax: 0115-986 2198 E-mail: sales@nixonknowles.co.uk

Norcliffe & Young, F Mill, Dean Clough Industrial Park, Halifax, West Yorkshire, HX3 5AJ Tel: (01422) 355830

Norman Joinery Coventry Ltd, 207 Torrington Avenue, Coventry, CV4 9AP Tel: (024) 7647 4116 Fax: (024) 7646 0494

Norscot Joinery Ltd, 20 Carsegate Road, Inverness, IV3 8EX Tel: (01463) 224040 Fax: (01463) 715755 E-mail: info@norscot.co.uk

North Manchester Joinery, Hulme St, Bury, Lancashire, BL8 1AN Tel: 0161-705 2960 Fax: 0161-764 0552

North Norfolk Joinery Ltd, Home Farm Ent, Hall Road, Cromer, Norfolk, NR27 9JG Tel: (01263) 515696 Fax: (01263) 515196

North Quay Trading Ltd, Unit 47 Joseph Wilson Industrial, Estate Millstrood Road, Whitstable, Kent, CT5 3PS Tel: (01227) 771700 Fax: (01227) 773026

▶ North Wales Joinery Ltd, Builder St, Llandudno, Gwynedd, LL30 1DR Tel: (01492) 870418

Northorpe Joinery, Northorpe, Atwick Road, Hornsea, North Humberside, HU18 1EJ Tel: (01964) 534407 Fax: (01964) 534407

Norton Joinery Ltd, Derwent Road, York Road Business Park, Malton, North Yorkshire, YO17 6NW Tel: (01653) 692377 Fax: (01653) 696565 E-mail: mail@nortonjoinery.co.uk

▶ Oakland Interiors Ltd, Unit 1, Butterwaite Business Park, Green Lane, Ecclesfield, Sheffield, S35 9ZY Tel: 0114-245 6820 Fax: 0114-245 6342

▶ Oaklands Joinery, Unit 2c Langham Street, Liverpool, L4 4DA Tel: 0151-207 4217 Fax: 0151-207 4217

O'Kane Bros Woodworking Ltd, 13 Hass Road, Dungiven, Londonderry, BT47 4QH Tel: (028) 7774 1705 Fax: (028) 7774 2343 E-mail: okanebros@aol.com

Old Manse Joinery, 32 Boveedy Road, Kilrea, Coleraine, County Londonderry, BT51 5XU Tel: (028) 2954 1453 Fax: (028) 2954 1453

Old Oak Joinery, 5-11 Westway, London, W12 0PT Tel: (020) 8749 6258 Fax: (020) 8749 1762

Olympia Interiors Ltd, Canterbury Road, Chilham, Canterbury, Kent, CT4 8DZ Tel: (01227) 732100 Fax: (01227) 732199

Orchard Joinery, Brick Kiln Farm, Heathfield, Bletchingdon, Kidlington, Oxfordshire, OX5 3DT Tel: (01869) 350008 Fax: (01869) 351361

Owen Joinery, 1a Derwent Street, Llanelli, Dyfed, SA15 3ES Tel: (01554) 777700

Owen Joinery, 50 Stepney Place, Llanelli, Dyfed, SA15 1SE Tel: (01554) 771111 Fax: (01554) 771111

Oxman & Walker, 4 Old Taunton Road, Bridgwater, Somerset, TA6 3NY Tel: (01278) 451783 Fax: (01278) 451783

▶ Oxon Joinery & Interiors, Oxon Business Park, Bicton Heath, Shrewsbury, SY3 5DD Tel: (01743) 341902 Fax: (01743) 241400

P Best Timber Preservation & Joinery, 1 Cowpen Lane, Billingham, Cleveland, TS23 1LA Tel: (01642) 551182 Fax: (01642) 361641

P D Morgan, Wyndham Street, Ogmore Vale, Bridgend, Mid Glamorgan, CF32 7EU Tel: (01656) 849260 Fax: (01656) 849396

P G Joinery, Gas Works Yard, Oakenshaw, Bradford, West Yorkshire, BD12 7AR Tel: (01274) 672257 Fax: (01274) 602898

P J Busby & Sons, 3 Main Road, Tadley, Hampshire, RG26 3NJ Tel: 0118-981 4710 Fax: 0118-981 4710

P & M Joinery, P & M Joinery Workshop At Bottom Of Drive, Rear Of 63 Lord Haddon Road, Ilkeston, Derbyshire, DE7 8AU Tel: 0115-930 1071

P & P Joinery, Unit 19 Lord Nelson Industrial Estate, Commercial Road, Hanley, Stoke-On-Trent, ST1 3QE Tel: (01782) 273708 Fax: (01782) 273708

P S Construction Doncaster Ltd, Grange Farm, Mere Lane, Edenthorpe, Doncaster, South Yorkshire, DN3 2HS Tel: (01302) 300100 Fax: (01302) 300354 E-mail: sales@psconstruction.co.uk

Pacegrade Ltd, Unit 1 Providence Street, Stourbridge, West Midlands, DY9 8HL Tel: (01384) 892237 Fax: (01384) 895041

R.J. Palin & Co. (Strensall) Ltd, Strensall Camp, York, YO32 5SW Tel: (01904) 492000

Patcham Joinery, 19-20 Melbourne Street, Brighton, BN2 3LH Tel: (01273) 690138 Fax: (01273) 690138

Pattern Shop, 27 Offerton Industrial Estate, Hempshaw Lane, Stockport, Cheshire, SK2 5TH Tel: 0161-480 5670 Fax: 0161-480 4565

Paul Snape Joinery Manufacturers, Harrison Street, Widnes, Cheshire, WA8 8TN Tel: 0151-423 6692 Fax: 0151-423 0812

Pawson & Son, 10 Marton Gill, Saltburn-by-the-Sea, Cleveland, TS12 1QU Tel: (01287) 622375

Peacock Joinery, Ranswood Farm, 18 The Common, West Wratting, Cambridge, CB21 5LR Tel: (01223) 290275 Fax: (01223) 290370

Pearce Joinery, Alderford Common, Swannington, Norwich, NR9 5NG Tel: (01603) 860856 Fax: (01603) 860856

Pettitt Joinery Co. Ltd, Royce Road, Peterborough, PE1 5YB Tel: (01733) 567742 Fax: (01733) 567742

Pitchdesign Ltd, Zion Works, Zion Street, Colne, Lancashire, BB8 0SP Tel: (01282) 869998 Fax: (01282) 860131

Pitman Joinery Works, Limington, Yeovil, Somerset, BA22 8EG Tel: (01935) 840431 Fax: (01935) 841100

Platonoff & Harris, Suite 206 Mill Studio Business Centre, Crane Mead, Ware, Hertfordshire, SG12 9PY Tel: (01920) 444255 Fax: (01920) 487673 E-mail: tony.ph@shopfitters.net

Plymouth Joinery, Warlow Street, Merthyr Tydfil, Mid Glamorgan, CF47 0YW Tel: (01685) 371328

Pogson Joinery, Unit 19 Heath House Mill, Heath House Lane, Golcar, Huddersfield, HD7 4JW Tel: (01484) 654059 Fax: (01484) 654059

Polesworth Patterns, Mount Farm, Warton Lane, Grendon, Atherstone, Warwickshire, CV9 3DT Tel: (01827) 895198 Fax: (01827) 895198

Pott Shrigley Joinery Ltd, Moorside Engine House The Old Brickworks, Bakestonedale Road, Pott Shrigley, Macclesfield, Cheshire, SK10 5RX Tel: (01625) 575590 Fax: (01625) 572446

▶ Precision Joinery Ltd, 1l Kingswood Douglas Estate, Kingswood, Bristol, BS15 8HJ Tel: 0117-961 2010 Fax: 0117-961 2087

Premier Manufacturing Joiners, 4 Canal Yard, Shieldhill Road, Glen Village, Falkirk, FK1 2BE Tel: (01324) 638802 Fax: (01324) 638802

Premier Radiator Cabinets, 3 Aintree Road, Bootle, Merseyside, L20 9DL Tel: 0151-933 0070 Fax: 0151-284 3274 E-mail: sales@premiercabinets.fsnet.co.uk

▶ Keith Preston Joinery Co. Ltd, 20 Brest Road, Plymouth, PL6 5XP Tel: (01752) 781700 Fax: (01752) 777423 E-mail: sales@keithprestonjoinery.co.uk

Progressive Woodworking Co. Ltd, West End Saw Mills, Broadbottom, Hyde, Cheshire, SK14 6BG Tel: (01457) 762102 Fax: (01457) 766080

▶ Project 17, Unit 9 Rossett Business Park, Rodley Lane, Leeds, LS13 1BQ Tel: 0113-255 7070 Fax: 0113-255 7070 E-mail: admin@project17.net

Project Building & Joinery Services, Burlais Works, Approach Road, Manselton, Swansea, SA5 8NL Tel: (01792) 649875 Fax: (01792) 465124 E-mail: sales@projectjoinery.co.uk

Pronto Joinery Ltd, Dog Lane, Horsford, Norwich, NR10 3DH Tel: (01603) 890239 Fax: (01603) 891677

▶ Purpose Made Joinery, 1 Bear Court, Basingstoke, Hampshire, RG24 8QT Tel: (01256) 818888 Fax: (01256) 818888

Quainton Cottage Furniture, Brixton Buildings, Station Road, Quainton, Aylesbury, Buckinghamshire, HP22 4BX Tel: (01296) 655726 Fax: (0870) 516601 E-mail: jeff@qcf.uk.com

Quayside Joinery Ltd, 24 Ullswater Close, Kitty Brewster Industrial Estate, Blyth, Northumberland, NE24 4RG Tel: (01670) 540111 Fax: (01670) 360479

▶ Quinn Interiors Ltd, Number 4, Moorhey Street, Oldham, OL4 1JD Tel: 0161-785 3150 E-mail: sales@quinninteriors.co.uk

R B Woodworking, Gidding Road, Hamerton, Huntingdon, Cambridgeshire, PE28 5QU Tel: (01832) 293384 Fax: (01832) 293384

R Bishop, Hill Grove Farm, Crawley Dry Lane, Minster Lovell, Witney, Oxfordshire, OX29 0NA Tel: (01993) 779009 Fax: (01993) 779009

▶ R C M Joinery, Unit 15 Four Crosses Creamery, Four Crosses, Llanymynech, Powys, SY22 6RH Tel: (01691) 830851

R Durtnell & Sons Ltd, Rectory Lane, Brasted, Westerham, Kent, TN16 1JR Tel: (01959) 564105 Fax: (01959) 564756 E-mail: rds@durtnell.co.uk

R E Olds & Co., 9 Ashmead Business Centre, Ashmead Road, Keynsham, Bristol, BS31 1SX Tel: 0117-986 0268 Fax: 0117-986 9594 E-mail: info@reolds.co.uk

JOINERY – *continued*

R G B Products, Unit 2 Gilmans Industrial Estate, Billingshurst, West Sussex, RH14 9EZ Tel: (01403) 783670 Fax: (01403) 783670

R G Obern Ltd, Overdale, Wells Road, Chilcompton, Radstock, BA3 4EY Tel: (01761) 232723 Fax: (01761) 233287

R H Stone & Son, 30 College Hill Road, Harrow, Middlesex, HA3 7HE Tel: (020) 8954 1835 Fax: (020) 895 6739

R J Joinery, 67-69 Oxford Street, Rugby, Warwickshire, CV21 3NE Tel: (01788) 565634 Fax: (01788) 565634

R J Parry Ltd, The Owl Complex, Manor Road, Sealand, Deeside, Clwyd, CH5 2SB Tel: (01244) 821600 Fax: (01244) 823181 E-mail: sales@parryjoinery.co.uk

R Jardine, Watchhill, Carlisle Road, Annan, Dumfriesshire, DG12 6QR Tel: (01461) 205319 Fax: (01461) 201457 E-mail: rjardine.annan@btopenworld.com

R K M Joinery, Unit 6, Lochty Industrial Estate, Almondbank, Perth, PH1 3NP Tel: (01738) 582060 Fax: (01738) 582060

R N Shields Ltd, 109 Leicester Road, New Packington, Ashby-de-la-Zouch, Leicestershire, LE65 1TR Tel: (01530) 412786 Fax: (01530) 415465 E-mail: rnshieldsltd@aol.com

R P Joinery, Unit 3, 2 Beresford Road, Whitstable, Kent, CT5 1JP Tel: (01227) 281820 Fax: (01227) 281830

R & R Joiners, Sthe Workshops, Lades Road, St. Austell, Cornwall, PL25 4HA Tel: (01726) 61891 Fax: (01726) 61891

R S Castle Joinery, 1a Tower Street, Hertford, SG14 3HD Tel: (01992) 584410 Fax: (01992) 584410

R S Joinery, 7-8 Chieveley Parade, Mayplace Road East, Bexleyheath, Kent, DA7 6EB Tel: (01322) 555922 Fax: (01322) 521995

R T A Joinery Ltd, 5 Birling Road, Tunbridge Wells, Kent, TN2 5LX Tel: (01892) 543897 Fax: (01892) 545345 E-mail: rtajoinery@btconnect.com

R W Joinery Stockport Ltd, Unit 26 Vernon Mill, Mersey Street, Stockport, Cheshire, SK1 2HX Tel: 0161-480 8722 Fax: 0161-474 7646 E-mail: info@rwjoinery.co.uk

R W P Joinery, 1 Sandcliff Road, Erith, Kent, DA8 1NY Tel: (01322) 430537 Fax: (01322) 430537 E-mail: info@rwp-joinery.co.uk

R W Taylor Joinery, 9b Catton Road, Arnold, Nottingham, NG5 7JD Tel: 0115-920 1656 Fax: 0115-967 3063

R Walker & Sons Preston Ltd, 103 Market St West, Preston, PR1 2HB Tel: (01772) 254176 Fax: (01772) 202246

G.K. Raw & Co. Ltd, Claro Way, Claro Road, Harrogate, North Yorkshire, HG1 4DE Tel: (01423) 501241 Fax: (01423) 530865

Reading Carpentry Services Ltd, 1a Eaton Place, Reading, RG1 7LP Tel: 0118-950 0971 Fax: 0118-950 0971

Red Interior Solutions Ltd, St. Johns Industrial Estate, Lees, Oldham, OL4 3DZ Tel: 0161-633 4740 Fax: 0161-633 4740 E-mail: redint@aol.com

Redcliffe Joinery, 82 Ballymena Road, Cullybackey, Ballymena, County Antrim, BT43 5QS Tel: (028) 2588 0972 Fax: (028) 2588 1443

Redditch Joinery (Holdings) Ltd, 21a Weights Farm, Weights Lane, Redditch, Worcestershire, B97 6RG Tel: (01527) 66111 Fax: (01527) 68180

Redwood Joinery Ltd, 26a Vicarage Road, Woolavington, Bridgwater, Somerset, TA7 8DX Tel: (01278) 685010 Fax: (01278) 685011 E-mail: jimtrowbridge@btconnect.com

Regal Joinery, 5 Tudor House, Moseley Road, Bilston, West Midlands, WV14 6JD Tel: (01902) 631322 Fax: (01902) 631322

Regency Stairs & Joinery Contractors Ltd, 13 Delling Bond Street, Greenock, Renfrewshire, PA15 4RN Tel: (01475) 722900 Fax: (01475) 787931 E-mail: enq@regencyjoinery.fsnet.co.uk

Renwick Bros Ltd, 16 Brougham Street, Penrith, Cumbria, CA11 9DW Tel: (01768) 864913 Fax: (01768) 864913 E-mail: peter.renwick@btconnect.com

Rhone Joinery Ltd, Mold Road Industrial Estate, Gwersyllt, Wrexham, Clwyd, LL11 4SB Tel: (01978) 262488 Fax: (01978) 262488 E-mail: enquiries@rhonejoinery.co.uk

Rich Wood Joinery, Unit 40, Gaerwen Indust Estate, Gaerwen, Gwynedd, LL60 6HR Tel: (01248) 421596 Fax: (01248) 421596

Richard Cullinan Joinery Ltd, 8 Ferrier Industrial Estate, Ferrier Street, London, SW18 1SW Tel: (020) 8871 0029 Fax: (020) 8871 0020 E-mail: richard@rcjoinery.co.uk

Richard Thraves Joinery Ltd, Mill Lane Workshops, Mill Lane, Scarborough, North Yorkshire, YO12 4ED Tel: (01723) 375708

Richard Williams Joinery, The Elms, Bratton Road, Bratton, Telford, Shropshire, TF5 0BT Tel: (01952) 242514 Fax: (01952) 242514

Richmond & Brown Joinery Services, Florence Street, Middlesbrough, Cleveland, TS2 1DR Tel: (01642) 246959 Fax: (01642) 246959

Riverside Joinery Co. Ltd, Barker Street, Norwich, NR2 4TN Tel: (01603) 624858 Fax: (01603) 614924

Robert Bell, Derby House, 60 Derby Road, Kirkdale, Liverpool, L20 8EA Tel: 0151-922 5186 Fax: 0151-922 3468

Robert Brydon & Sons, 12 Drumlanrig Square, Hawick, Roxburghshire, TD9 0AS Tel: (01450) 370462 Fax: (01450) 372431

G. Rogers & Co., Springfield Road, London, N11 1RP Tel: (020) 8368 2426

Rolfe Joinery Co., Holme Road, Stow Bridge, King's Lynn, Norfolk, PE34 3PW Tel: (01366) 382403 Fax: (01366) 388061

Romiley Glass & Windows Ltd, Green Lane, Romiley, Stockport, Cheshire, SK6 3JN Tel: 0161-494 0864 Fax: 0161-406 6290

Rooksmoor Timber Co. Ltd, Vatch Lane, Eastcombe, Stroud, Gloucestershire, GL6 7DY Tel: (01453) 882240 Fax: (01453) 731112 E-mail: enquiries@rooksmoor.com

Rosenwheel Ltd, 181 Cambuslang Road, Rutherglen, Glasgow, G73 1PX Tel: 0141-643 1986 Fax: 0141-643 2177

Rosewood Joinery, Unit D The Paddocks, 347 Cherry Hinton Road, Cambridge, CB1 8DH Tel: (01223) 508777 Fax: (01223) 508777

Rosewood Joinery, Unit 4 Hope & Aldridge Business Centre, Weddington Rd, Nuneaton, Warwickshire, CV10 0HF Tel: (024) 7638 3555 Fax: (024) 7638 3555

Rotherham Joinery Ltd, Coke Lane, Rotherham, South Yorkshire, S60 2JS Tel: (01709) 369676 Fax: (01709) 369676

S.P. Rowe, Rosabil, Buller Road, Crediton, Devon, EX17 2AX Tel: (01363) 774380 Fax: (01363) 774380

▶ Roy C Smith Ltd, Manchester Road, Marsden, Huddersfield, HD7 6ND Tel: (01484) 844405 Fax: (01484) 845338

Rudd Joinery, Treowen Road, Pembroke Dock, Dyfed, SA72 6NY Tel: (01646) 685712 Fax: (0871) 7334946 E-mail: ray@ruddjoinery.com

Ruddy Joinery Ltd, Enterprise Way, Flitwick, Bedford, MK45 5BS Tel: (01525) 716603 Fax: (01525) 718595 E-mail: enquiries@ruddy.co.uk

Runcent Joinery, 50 North Cross Road, London, SE22 9EU Tel: (020) 8299 2421 Fax: (020) 8299 4119 E-mail: info@runcent.com

Ivan Russell Joiners Ltd, Moycoft, Elgin, Morayshire, IV30 1XZ Tel: (01343) 549759 Fax: (01343) 549826

The Rye Joinery Co. Ltd, Unit 3 Rother Iron Works, Fishmarket Road, Rye, East Sussex, TN31 7LR Tel: (01797) 229044

S A Parsons Building Contractors Ltd, Mansfield Road, Killamarsh, Sheffield, S21 2BW Tel: 0114-247 9100 Fax: 0114-247 9101 E-mail: parsonsgroup@parsonsgroup.co.uk

S B Joinery, The Forge, Nettlestone Hill, Seaview, Isle of Wight, PO34 5DU Tel: (01983) 562147 Fax: (01983) 812166 E-mail: sales@sb-joinery.co.uk

S J S Newport Ltd, Avenue Road, Newport, Shropshire, TF10 7EA Tel: (01952) 814163

S L Joinery, 24 Walbrook Road, Derby, DE23 8RY Tel: (01332) 773230 Fax: (01332) 773230

S & M Specialist Joiners, Elvington Industrial Estate, York Road, Elvington, York, YO41 4AR Tel: (01904) 608677

S P Stow Ltd, Portland Street, Kirkby-in-Ashfield, Nottingham, NG17 7AD Tel: (01623) 752258 Fax: (01623) 752258

S R S Joinery High Wycombe Ltd, Wycombe Lane, Wooburn Green, High Wycombe, Buckinghamshire, HP10 0HE Tel: (01628) 520893 Fax: (01628) 810526

S & S Joinery, Anglebury Business Park, Sandford Lane, Wareham, Dorset, BH20 4DY Tel: (01929) 553433 Fax: (01929) 550868

S & S Windows, Unit 19 Phoenix Industrial Estate, Cheetham Street, Failsworth, Manchester, M35 9DS Tel: 0161-684 7361 Fax: 0161-684 7361

Salisbury Joinery, 3 Brunel Rd, Salisbury, SP2 7PU Tel: (01722) 337040 Fax: (01722) 337077

Sandiford Son & Bannister Ltd, 153 Croydon Road, Caterham, Surrey, CR3 6PF Tel: (01883) 343545 Fax: (01883) 346808

▶ Sawtooth, Unit 5, Victoria Works, Balls Street, Nottingham, NG3 3AR Tel: 0115-947 5184

SB Draughtproofing, Kintyre House, New Pentland, Loanhead, Midlothian, EH20 9NY Tel: 0131-440 3500 Fax: 0131-440 3500

Henry Scott & Son, 62 Doagh Rd, Newtownabbey, Co. Antrim, BT37 9NX Tel: (028) 9085 1604

▶ J Seamer & Son Ltd, 35 Shaftesbury Street South, Derby, DE23 8YH Tel: (01332) 348303 Fax: (01332) 291617

Sherlock Interiors Contracting Ltd, 20-22 Vestry Street, London, N1 7RE Tel: (020) 7336 7337 Fax: (020) 7336 7180 E-mail: info@sherlock.demon.co.uk

Shield Joinery Services, 30 Iverson Road, London, NW6 2QT Tel: (020) 7624 7098 Fax: (020) 7328 6309

M.J. Shiers & Co., Rydene, Reigate Road, Dorking, Surrey, RH4 1SP Tel: (01306) 889464

Shillingbury Joinery & Restoration Ltd, Yarwood Works, Ledsam Street, Birmingham, B16 8DW Tel: 0121-455 6900 Fax: 0121-455 6900

Shopfit UK Ktd, West End Works, Staithes Road, Preston, Hull, HU12 8TJ Tel: (01482) 896240 Fax: (01482) 896510 E-mail: info@shopfituk.co.uk

Signet Joinery, Laing Close, Grangetown, Middlesbrough, Cleveland, TS6 7EA Tel: (01642) 456777 Fax: (01642) 452912

Simon Price, 10 Straight Road, Old Windsor, Windsor, Berkshire, SL4 2RL Tel: (01753) 832542 Fax: (01753) 832542

Skotland Joinery Ltd, Lochshore Indust Estate, Caledonian Place, Glengarnock, Beith, Ayrshire, KA14 3AZ Tel: (01505) 682829 Fax: (01505) 685331

Smallthorne Joinery Manufacturers, Unit A4 Fraylings Business Park, Davenport Street, Stoke-on-Trent, ST6 4LN Tel: (01782) 577225 Fax: (01782) 865855

Smith Bros. Joinery Ltd, Pope Iron Road, Worcester, WR1 3HB Tel: (01905) 619830 Fax: (01905) 617294 E-mail: raymondwillden@smithbrothersjoinery.com

Smith & Choyce Ltd, 280 Barton Street, Gloucester, GL1 4JJ Tel: (01452) 523531 Fax: (01452) 310032 E-mail: m.choyce@btconnect.com

Smith & Jones Joinery, 1 Furnham Road Trading Estate, Furnham Road, Chard, Somerset, TA20 1AX Tel: (01460) 62262 Fax: (01460) 66355 E-mail: smithjonesjoinery@lineone.net

Noel Smith, Stratford Road, Milford Haven, Dyfed, SA73 2JA Tel: (01646) 690097 Fax: (01646) 695599 E-mail: nsjoinery@aol.com

Walter Smith Joinery Ltd, Westerby Road, East Middlesbrough Industrial Estate, Middlesbrough, Cleveland, TS3 8BQ Tel: (01642) 221171 Fax: (01642) 231342 E-mail: sales@waltersmithjoineryltd.co.uk

Smiths Timber & Joinery Ltd, Misterton Way, Lutterworth, Leicestershire, LE17 4AB Tel: (01455) 550194 Fax: (01455) 553974

▶ Smithy Joinery, The Barn, Blackleach Lane, Bartle, Preston, PR4 0RY Tel: (01772) 690417 Fax: (01772) 691797

Soham Joinery, 119 Mereside, Soham, Ely, Cambridgeshire, CB7 5EG Tel: (01353) 720396 Fax: (01353) 624941

Sorokin Joinery & Glazing Ltd, Unit 3 Monastery Business Centre, Monastery Road, Neath Abbey, Neath, West Glamorgan, SA10 7DP Tel: (01792) 815661 Fax: (01792) 816636

South Western Joinery, The Barn, Pymore Road, Bridport, Dorset, DT6 3GR Tel: (01308) 425543

South Wirral Joinery, 1 Newton Road, Ellesmere Port, CH65 4AP Tel: 0151-355 2541

▶ Specialist Woodworks, Unit 12a, Brookfield Industrial Estate, Tansley, Matlock, Derbyshire, DE4 5ND Tel: (01629) 583769 Fax: (01629) 583769

Splinter Group, 3 Lombard Trading Estate, 51 Anchor & Hope Lane, London, SE7 7SN Tel: (020) 8305 2702 Fax: (020) 8858 1922 E-mail: enquiries@thesplintergroup.com

Harry Spurr Ltd, Harvest Lane, Sheffield, S3 8EF Tel: 0114-272 4581 Fax: 0114-276 6246 E-mail: info@spurrs.co.uk

Stadia Sports, 19-20 Lancaster Way Business Park, Ely, Cambridgeshire, CB6 3NW Tel: (01353) 668686 Fax: (01353) 669444 E-mail: sales@stadia-sports.co.uk

Stag Specialised Joinery, 47a High Street, Ongar, Essex, CM5 9AQ Tel: (01277) 365551 Fax: (01277) 365551

Staircase Co., Unit 4 Silver Royd Business Park, Silver Royd Hill, Leeds, LS12 4QQ Tel: 0113-279 9022 Fax: 0113-279 9095

Stanley Welch & Son Ltd, 9 Greenway, Barton-upon-Humber, South Humberside, DN18 5HY Tel: (01652) 632933 Fax: (01652) 632933

Stelling Joinery Ltd, Green Copse, Etherley, Bishop Auckland, County Durham, DL14 0LT Tel: (01388) 832792 Fax: (01388) 835954

Steve's Joinery, Morgan Street Works, Morgan Street, Llanbradach, Caerphilly, Mid Glamorgan, CF83 3QT Tel: (029) 2085 1566

▶ Stockport Joinery Co., 10-16 King St West, Stockport, Cheshire, SK3 0DY Tel: 0161-477 5480 Fax: 0161-474 7248 E-mail: info@stockportjoinery.co.uk

Stockport Window Co., 10-16 King St West, Stockport, Cheshire, SK3 0DY Tel: 0161-480 7011 Fax: 0161-474 7248 E-mail: info@stockportwindows.co.uk

▶ Stone, 24b Hamilton Street, Carluke, Lanarkshire, ML8 4HA Tel: (01555) 752068 Fax: (01555) 752266

Stopps Ltd, Lyon Road, Walton-on-Thames, Surrey, KT12 3RU Tel: (01932) 242086 Fax: (01932) 228893 E-mail: mail@stopps.co.uk

Philip Straughton, 8 High Sand Lane, Cockermouth, Cumbria, CA13 9NA Tel: (01900) 825444

▶ Stretton Bros Ltd, Hamilton Street, Oldham, OL4 1DA Tel: 0161-633 3990 Fax: 0161-627 4772

Stroud Green Joinery, 178 Stroud Green Road, London, N4 3RS Tel: (020) 7281 1800 Fax: (020) 7263 8388

Strouds Woodworks, Ashmansworthy, Woolsery, Bideford, Devon, EX39 5RE Tel: (01409) 241624

Sturdy Joinery & Display, Unit 6 The Barns, Hewell Lane, Tardebigge, Bromsgrove, Worcestershire, B60 1LP Tel: (01527) 579306 Fax: (01527) 574492

▶ Suffolk Heritage Joinery Ltd, Bay 3 Building 89, Anglia Int Airpark, Rendlesham, Woodbridge, Suffolk, IP12 2TW Tel: (01394) 460331 Fax: (01394) 460661 E-mail: dean@sh-joinery.com

Sunningdale Joineries Ltd, The Timber Yard, Lucas Green, West End, Woking, Surrey, GU24 9YB Tel: (01483) 476444 Fax: (01483) 799967

Sussex County, Bookers Yard, Bersted Street, Bognor Regis, West Sussex, PO22 9PS Tel: (01243) 827131 Fax: (01243) 827131

Suttons Buildings, 66 Blackgate Lane, Tarleton, Preston, PR4 6UT Tel: (01772) 814865 Fax: (01772) 815643

Swindon Woodworking Co. Ltd, 9 Regal Way, Faringdon, Oxfordshire, SN7 7BX Tel: (01367) 240272 Fax: (01367) 243290 E-mail: info@swindonwoodworking.co.uk

Sykes Purston Ltd, 37 Ackworth Road, Featherstone, Pontefract, West Yorkshire, WF7 5LN Tel: (01977) 791922

▶ Syon Lodge, Unit C, Riding Court Farm, Riding Court Road, Datchet, Slough, SL3 9JT Tel: (01753) 540722 Fax: (01753) 549649

T & A Joinery, Oakwood House, 36 Wood Lane, Partington, Manchester, M31 4ND Tel: 0161-777 6277 Fax: 0161-777 6277

T Bacon, Spink Hall Farm, Spink Hall Lane, Stocksbridge, Sheffield, S36 1FL Tel: 0114-288 2556 Fax: 0114-288 2556

▶ T Clarke & Sons Joinery Ltd, The Workshop, Slippery Gowt Lane, Wyberton, Boston, Lincolnshire, PE21 7AA Tel: (01205) 354629 Fax: (01205) 358214 E-mail: sales@tclarkejoinery.co.uk

T D Jenkinson, 119 Constitution Street, Edinburgh, EH6 7AE Tel: 0131-554 6079 Fax: 0131-554 6079

T D Joinery, Unit 65 Millmead Industrial Estate, Millmead Road, London, N17 9UU Tel: (020) 8808 8215

T Edson & Sons Ltd, Main Road, Plumtree, Nottingham, NG12 5NB Tel: 0115-937 2247 Fax: 0115-937 2486 E-mail: sales@edsons.co.uk

T H F Joinery, Express Way, Hambridge Lane, Newbury, Berkshire, RG14 5TU Tel: (01635) 42588 Fax: (01635) 46681

T J A S Joinery, 42 Parcel Terrace, Derby, DE1 1LY Tel: (01332) 293687 Fax: (01332) 372353

T & J Joinery, New Barnes Cottage, Stourport Road, Bewdley, Worcestershire, DY12 1QD Tel: (01299) 822743 Fax: (01299) 877502

T Knipe Ltd, Sawmills, Church Road, Allithwaite, Grange-over-Sands, Cumbria, LA11 7QH Tel: (01539) 532404 Fax: (01539) 535313

T P Broombys Ltd, Currock Road, Carlisle, CA2 4AX Tel: (01228) 538511 Fax: (01228) 531488

T W Holden & Son, Yew Tree Farm, Chipping Road, Chaigley, Clitheroe, Lancashire, BB7 3LX Tel: (01995) 61300 Fax: (01995) 61300

▶ T W Joinery South Wales Ltd, Heol Ffaldau, Brackla, Bridgend, Mid Glamorgan, CF31 2HQ Tel: (01656) 667745 Fax: (01656) 650887

T W Wiseman Joinery, 116b Albert Road, Southsea, Hampshire, PO4 0JS Tel: (023) 9282 8186

Taylor & Son (Joinery) Ltd, 42 A Vicarage Road, Halesowen, West Midlands, B62 8HU Tel: 0121-559 3955 Fax: 0121-559 5412

Ternex Ltd, Ayot Green Sawmill, 27 Ayot Green, Ayot St. Peter, Welwyn, Hertfordshire, AL6 9BA Tel: (01707) 324606 Fax: (01707) 334371 E-mail: sales@ternex.co.uk

Tetbury Joinery, Priory Industrial Estate, London Road, Tetbury, Gloucestershire, GL8 8HZ Tel: (01666) 504250 Fax: (01666) 504660 E-mail: tetbury.joinery@btconnect.com

▶ Thompson Joinery Ltd, Kettle Lane, Creeting St. Mary, Ipswich, IP6 8LL Tel: (01449) 722489 Fax: (01449) 722489

Richard Thompson Joinery Ltd, South Back Lane, Tollerton, York, YO61 1PU Tel: (01347) 838387 Fax: (01347) 838943

Thomson & Douglas Ltd, Kingston Place, Kingsmuir, Forfar, Angus, DD8 2RG Tel: (01307) 466952 Fax: (01307) 462270 E-mail: tdj@freenetname.co.uk

Tigna Portable Buildings, Unit 47-2, Gilwilly Road, Gilwilly Industrial Estate, Penrith, Cumbria, CA11 9BL Tel: (01768) 891595 Fax: (01768) 891512 E-mail: sales@tigna.co.uk

Timber Box Co., Main Road, Ketsby, Louth, Lincolnshire, LN11 8QW Tel: (01507) 466250 Fax: (01507) 466250

▶ Timber To Go, Newport Road, Coventry, CV6 4BQ Tel: (024) 7668 8886 Fax: (024) 7668 8869 E-mail: sales@timbertogo.com

Timbertec Joinery UK Ltd, Union Lane, Headley, Kings Clear, Newbury, Berkshire, RG20 4ST Tel: (01635) 268663 Fax: (01635) 268411

TJ Joinery, Rospeath Lane, Crowlas, Penzance, Cornwall, TR20 8DU Tel: (01736) 740000 Fax: (01736) 740000

Tollhurst, 1 North St, Bromley, BR1 1RB Tel: 020 84641179

Touchwood Joinery (London) Ltd, Railway Arch, 384-385 Denmark Road, London, SE5 9JR Tel: (020) 7733 3003 Fax: (020) 7737 5247

Town Joinery, Garth Road, Morden, Surrey, SM4 4NJ Tel: (020) 8330 7451 Fax: (020) 8330 7336 E-mail: sales@townjoinery.co.uk

Treasure & Son Ltd, Temeside, Ludlow, Shropshire, SY8 1JW Tel: (01584) 872161 Fax: (01584) 874876 E-mail: mail@treasure&son.co.uk

Trent Joinery Manufacturing, Grassthorpe Road, Sutton-on-Trent, Newark, Nottinghamshire, NG23 6QX Tel: (01636) 822524 Fax: (01636) 822524

Trent Shopfitters, Gateway House, Beechdale Road, Nottingham, NG8 3EZ Tel: 0115-942 5151 Fax: 0115-942 5656

▶ Trinity Joinery, La Rue De La Hougette, St. Clement, Jersey, JE2 6LD Tel: (01534) 853567 Fax: (01534) 857191

Tristian Ltd, 11 Hastings Rd, Croydon, CR0 6PH Tel: (020) 8655 3373 Fax: (020) 8655 3336

▶ Turland Joinery Tewkesbury Ltd, Unit 1 Northway Lane, Tewkesbury, Gloucestershire, GL20 8JG Tel: (01684) 293245 Fax: (01684) 299444

Turners Bar Fitters & Joiners Ltd, Martins Mill, Pellon Lane, Halifax, West Yorkshire, HX1 5QJ Tel: (01422) 354984 Fax: (01422) 342770

Two Bee's, Minkstone Works, Normacot Road, Stoke-on-Trent, ST3 1PR Tel: (01782) 313280 Fax: (01782) 313055

JOINERY – *continued*

UK Contracts Warwick Ltd, Thorn Way, Long Itchington, Southam, Warwickshire, CV47 9PF Tel: (01926) 813308 Fax: (01926) 813349 E-mail: ukcontracts@connectfree.co.uk

▶ UK Stairparts, 18 Bowlers Croft, Basildon, Essex, SS14 3EE Tel: (01268) 284000 Fax: (01268) 534800

Unit Line Ltd, 1 The Avenue, West End Road, High Wycombe, Buckinghamshire, HP11 2QQ Tel: (01494) 440045 Fax: (01494) 438898 E-mail: sales@unitline.com

Universal Joineries (Newcastle) Ltd, Fisher Street, Newcastle Upon Tyne, NE6 4NH Tel: 0191-262 8554 Fax: 0191-263 6018

▶ Valley Joinery, Unit 23 Baldock Industrial Estate, London Road, Baldock, Hertfordshire, SG7 6NG Tel: (01462) 490404 Fax: (01462) 490210

Verleywood Ltd, Unit 1 Plot 5 Warrenwood Industrial Estate, Stapleford, Hertford, SG14 3NU Tel: (01992) 501218

▶ Versatile Ltd, Units 1-11, Prince of Wales Industrial Estate, Abercarn, Newport, Gwent, NP11 5AR Tel: (01495) 247233

Village Joinery Works, 242a North Deeside Road, Peterculter, Aberdeenshire, AB14 0UQ Tel: (01224) 735706 Fax: 01224 735706

Vinnell & Son, 6 West Street, Great Gransden, Sandy, Bedfordshire, SG19 3AT Tel: (01767) 677267

W A Hare & Son Ltd, 94 Main Street, Kelfield, York, YO19 6RG Tel: (01757) 248188 Fax: (01757) 248999 E-mail: sales@wahare.com

W France Successors, Luck Lane, Huddersfield, HD1 4QU Tel: (01484) 426032 Fax: (01484) 426032

W Hogg Joinery, 1 Back Bowman Street, Darlington, County Durham, DL3 0HG Tel: (01325) 351838

W J Gresham & Son, Commonside, Old Leake, Boston, Lincolnshire, PE22 9PR Tel: (01205) 870279 Fax: (01205) 870954

▶ W.J O'Neill Interiors, 132 Hamilton Road, Glasgow, G32 9QR Tel: 0141-764 1591 Fax: 0141-764 2309

W P Lang Ltd, Railway Road, Airdrie, Lanarkshire, ML6 9AB Tel: (01236) 752515 Fax: (01236) 753888

W S Dunsire & Sons Ltd, 40 Birkhill Road, Stirling, FK7 9JS Tel: (01786) 462954 Fax: (01786) 450008 E-mail: sales@wsdunsire.com

Wakefield Joinery, Unit 8, Heacham, King's Lynn, Norfolk, PE31 7BT Tel: (01485) 571313 Fax: (01485) 571313

Walker & Hartle Ltd, Derby Road, Ripley, Derbyshire, DE5 3HS Tel: (01773) 743334 Fax: (01773) 743334

Wards Woodcraft Furnishings, Termon Business Park, Quarry Road, Sixmilecross, Omagh, County Tyrone, BT79 9AL Tel: (028) 8076 0952 Fax: (028) 8076 0986

C. Wark & Sons, 6 West Road, Irvine, Ayrshire, KA12 8RE Tel: (01294) 273999 Fax: (01294) 273222

Waterhouse E J & Sons Ltd, Kings Lane, Chipperfield, Kings Langley, Hertfordshire, WD4 9ER Tel: (01923) 267444 Fax: (01923) 261883

Peter Waterhouse Contractors, 26C Coronation Road, Crosby, Liverpool, L23 5RQ Tel: 0151-924 1964 Fax: 0151-924 1964

Watson John Joinery Ltd, Usworth Road Indust Estate, Hartlepool, Cleveland, TS25 1PD Tel: (01429) 222023 Fax: (01429) 222630 E-mail: sales@johnwatson-joinery.co.uk

Watson Joinery, 11 Station Road, Thurlby, Bourne, Lincolnshire, PE10 0HD Tel: (01778) 422537 Fax: (01778) 394079

▶ Wave Interiors, Unit 1, Baron Road, Blackpool, FY1 6JU Tel: (01253) 401601

Weardale Joinery, Queensbury, Sedling Plain, Wearhead, Bishop Auckland, County Durham, DL13 1PW Tel: 01388 537434

Websters Burn Ltd, Whitings Lane, Burn, Selby, North Yorkshire, YO8 8LG Tel: (01757) 270233 Fax: (01757) 270459

Welland Timber Products Ltd, Geddington Road, Corby, Northamptonshire, NN18 8ET Tel: (01536) 201992 Fax: (01536) 401178 E-mail: info@wellandtimber.co.uk

West End Cabinet Co., Addison Industrial Estate, Blaydon-on-Tyne, Tyne & Wear, NE21 4SJ Tel: 0191-414 4469 Fax: 0191-414 0463 E-mail: enquiries@west-end-cabinet.com

Westmill Joinery, Belgravia Street, Penzance, Cornwall, TR18 2AJ Tel: (01736) 362579

Westminster Joinery, Bowcombe Meadows Business Park, Bowcombe Road, Newport, Isle of Wight, PO30 3HZ Tel: (01983) 825355

Whitaker & Co Denholme Ltd, Denholme Gate, Bradford, West Yorkshire, BD13 4EW Tel: (01274) 833611 Fax: (01274) 833782

L. White & Sons, 34 Newbury Lane, Oldbury, West Midlands, B69 1HF Tel: 0121-511 1096 Fax: 0121-511 1096

Willey & Bunker Ltd, Park Avenue Industrial Estate, Sundon Park Road, Luton, LU3 3BP Tel: (01582) 574382 Fax: (01582) 490043 E-mail: willey&bunker@itnet.co.uk

William R Pinchin, Unit 22, Ravenswood Industrial Estate Shernhall Street, London, E17 9HQ Tel: (020) 8521 5590 Fax: (020) 8509 2070 E-mail: williamrpinchin@aol.com

William Tilston, 3a-3c The Borders Industrial Park, River Lane, Saltney, Chester, CH4 8RJ Tel: (01244) 678786 Fax: (01244) 683935

▶ Willow Joinery, 5 Low March Indust Estate, Low March, Daventry, Northamptonshire, NN11 4SD Tel: (01327) 878419 Fax: (01604) 661251

Wills & Reynolds, 20 Henry Street, Northampton, NN1 4JE Tel: (01604) 638868

Winch, Tony, Chapel Farm, Chapel Lane, Westhumble, Dorking, Surrey, RH5 6AY Tel: (01306) 742373

Windrush Valley Joinery Ltd, The Barn, Sawpit Lane, Little Rissington, Cheltenham, Gloucestershire, GL54 2NB Tel: (01451) 820100 Fax: (01451) 820100

Wiswell Bros, 96 Clipsley Lane, Haydock, St. Helens, Merseyside, WA11 0UB Tel: (01744) 602236 Fax: (01744) 602236

Withey Contracts Ltd, Waburn House, Adams Close, Kempston, Bedford, MK42 7JE Tel: (01234) 844600 Fax: (01234) 844601 E-mail: info@withey.co.uk

Wood Brothers Ltd, Unit 10 Fairways Business Centre, Airport Service Road, Portsmouth, PO3 5NU Tel: (023) 9266 4492 Fax: (023) 9267 9865 E-mail: sales@woodbrothers.co.uk

Wood Shop, 130 New Road, Skewen, Neath, West Glamorgan, SA10 6HL Tel: (01792) 812360 Fax: (01792) 321359 E-mail: woodshop@woodshopjoinery.co.uk

Woodcraft Industries & DIY, 191 London Road, Glasgow, G40 1PA Tel: 0141-552 1437 Fax: 0141-552 1437

Woodcraft Joinery Ltd, Units 28 & 29 Delph Road Trading Estate, Delph Road, Brierley Hill, West Midlands, DY5 2TW Tel: (01384) 265888 Fax: (01384) 481949 E-mail: info@woodcraftjoinery.co.uk

Woodcraft Joinery, Wheal Rose, Scorrier, Redruth, Cornwall, TR16 5DA Tel: (01209) 821883 Fax: (01209) 821883

Woodgrain Joinery, 3 Roan Close, Dungannon, County Tyrone, BT70 1NE Tel: (028) 3754 8070 Fax: (028) 3754 8070

Woodheart Joinery Manufacturers, 2a Catton Road, Arnold, Nottingham, NG5 7JD Tel: 0115-967 0195 Fax: 0115-967 4068

Woodlands Joinery, The Barn Weir Courtney Yard, Blackberry Lane, Lingfield, Surrey, RH7 6NG Tel: (01342) 835856 Fax: (01342) 835856 E-mail: woodlands.joinery@ntlword.co.uk

Woodlark Interiors, Moorhurst Lane, Copse Farm, Holmwood, Dorking, Surrey, RH5 4LJ Tel: (01306) 713009 Fax: (01737) 841098

Woodleys Joinery Ltd, Exeter Road, Newton Poppleford, Sidmouth, Devon, EX10 0BJ Tel: (01395) 568666 Fax: (01395) 568122

Woodside Joinery Ltd, 33 Crossways, London Road, Sunninghill, Ascot, Berkshire, SL5 0PL Tel: (01344) 876625 Fax: (01344) 876625 E-mail: sales@woodsidejoinery.co.uk

Woodstock Interiors 2000, Garth Works, Taffs Well, Cardiff, CF15 7YF Tel: (029) 2081 0363 Fax: (029) 2081 0363 E-mail: derick.kingston@ntlworld.com

Woodstock Joinery Ltd, 3 Romar Court, West Denbigh, Bletchley, Milton Keynes, MK1 1RH Tel: (01908) 647369 Fax: (01908) 646554

Woodworks, 41-43 North Valley Road, Colne, Lancashire, BB8 9AQ Tel: (01282) 721843 Fax: (01282) 860664 E-mail: sales@matkinson.co.uk

Wratten Joinery, Aylesford Cottage, Guildford Road, Normandy, Guildford, Surrey, GU3 2AS Tel: (01483) 235324 Fax: (01483) 232131

Yearnhome Joinery Ltd, 11 Orchid Court, Ty Canol, Cwmbran, Gwent, NP44 6JP Tel: (01633) 866703 Fax: (01633) 866703 E-mail: yearnhomejoinery@aol.com

Yeovil Woodworking, Buckland Road, Pen Mill Trading Estate, Yeovil, Somerset, BA21 5HA Tel: (01935) 474190 Fax: (01935) 474355

Yew Tree Joinery, Yew Tree House, Hill Road, Sandford, Winscombe, Avon, BS25 5RJ Tel: (01934) 820585 Fax: (01934) 820585

Young & Blackmore Joiner, Portsmouth Road, Surbiton, Surrey, KT6 4ES Tel: (020) 8390 7272

JOINERY OR WOODWORKING WORKBENCHES

Don Farmer & Sons, Rendel Street, Birkenhead, Merseyside, CH41 3NJ Tel: 0151-666 1450 Fax: 0151-666 2540 E-mail: sales@doubleglaze.co.uk

▶ Fine Finish, 58 Randolph Street, Buckhaven, Leven, Fife, KY8 1AT Tel: (01592) 719039

Tudor, 3 Ellesmere Business Park, Oswestry Road, Ellesmere, Shropshire, SY12 0EW Tel: (01691) 623424 Fax: (01691) 624479 E-mail: nevilletudor@virgin.net

JOINERY TO SPECIFICATION

▶ C & G Joinery Services Ltd, Unit 13 W & G Industrial Estate, Faringdon Road, East Challow, Wantage, Oxfordshire, OX12 9TF Tel: (01235) 763233 Fax: (01235) 760259 E-mail: info@cgjoinery.co.uk

▶ David Kinns Joinery, 23 San Remo Road, Aspley Guise, Milton Keynes, MK17 8JY Tel: (01908) 582678 Fax: (01908) 586898

Decorfix, Halstow Lane, Upchurch, Sittingbourne, Kent, ME9 7AB Tel: (01795) 843124 Fax: (01795) 842465

Evergreen, Clare Park, Unit 2, Farnham, Surrey, GU10 5DT Tel: (01252) 851849 Fax: (01252) 851849

F E Jones Builders Ltd, 303 Mount Road, Manchester, M19 3ET Tel: 0161-224 8001 Fax: 0161-224 8001 E-mail: fej.builders@emerson.co.uk

Frank W Marshall & Co. Ltd, 25 Wolsey Mews, London, NW5 2DX Tel: (020) 7485 1212

G Riggott, Westminster House, Gibbons Road, Mansfield, Nottinghamshire, NG18 5DZ Tel: (01623) 627454 Fax: (01623) 620335 E-mail: graham.roggott@ntlworld.com

Gate Makers, Petford Lea, Buckland, Aylesbury, Buckinghamshire, HP22 5HU Tel: (01296) 630798 Fax: (01296) 631373 E-mail: admin@thegatemakers.co.uk

▶ Hertford Joinery Ltd, Great Northern Works, Hartham Lane, Hertford, SG14 1QN Tel: (01992) 550587 Fax: (01992) 558992

▶ Ladymead Joinery Ltd, Denham, Quainton, Aylesbury, Buckinghamshire, HP22 4AN Tel: (01296) 655770 Fax: (01296) 655377 E-mail: info@ladymeadjoinery.co.uk

Litton Furniture, Bonslea House, White Lane Close, Sturminster Newton, Dorset, DT10 1EJ Tel: (01258) 472359 Fax: (01258) 473512

Magnet Ltd, Fengate, Peterborough, PE1 5PE Tel: (01733) 558211 Fax: (01733) 563664

Marco Joinery Ltd, 17-19 Downing Street, Sutton-in-Ashfield, Nottinghamshire, NG17 4EF Tel: (01623) 556684 Fax: (01623) 556664

Tony Murray Interiors Ltd, Rowden Works, Chaffinch Road, Beckenham, Kent, BR3 4NA Tel: (020) 8650 9331 Fax: (020) 8663 6576

Park Way Joinery Ltd, Nicholson Road, Ryde, Isle of Wight, PO33 1BE Tel: (01983) 567812 Fax: (01983) 611775 E-mail: parkwayjoinery@btconnect.com

R T A Joinery Ltd, 5 Birling Road, Tunbridge Wells, Kent, TN2 5LX Tel: (01892) 543897 Fax: (01892) 545345 E-mail: rtajoinery@btconnect.com

Regency Stairs & Joinery Contractors Ltd, 13 Delling Bond Street, Greenock, Renfrewshire, PA15 4RN Tel: (01475) 722900 Fax: (01475) 787931 E-mail: enq@regencyjoinery.fsnet.co.uk

Romiley Glass & Windows Ltd, Green Lane, Romiley, Stockport, Cheshire, SK6 3JN Tel: 0161-494 0864 Fax: 0161-406 6290

S.P. Rowe, Rosabil, Buller Road, Crediton, Devon, EX17 2AX Tel: (01363) 774380 Fax: (01363) 774380

Rudd Joinery, Treowen Road, Pembroke Dock, Dyfed, SA72 6NY Tel: (01646) 685712 Fax: (0871) 7334946 E-mail: ray@ruddjoinery.com

Philip Straughton, 8 High Sand Lane, Cockermouth, Cumbria, CA13 9NA Tel: (01900) 825444

▶ Taw Valley Crafts Ltd, 1 Baron Court, Baron Way, Roundswell Business Park, Barnstaple, Devon, EX31 3TB Tel: (01271) 378296 Fax: (01271) 374118 E-mail: sales@teatrays.com

▶ Thorn Joinery, 115 College Street, Irthlingborough, Wellingborough, Northamptonshire, NN9 5TU Tel: (01933) 653991 Fax: (01933) 653991 E-mail: thornjoinery@msm.com

UK Contracts Warwick Ltd, Thorn Way, Long Itchington, Southam, Warwickshire, CV47 9PF Tel: (01926) 813308 Fax: (01926) 813349 E-mail: ukcontracts@connectfree.co.uk

JOINT FILLERS, *See Metal Filler etc*

JOINT SEALING SERVICES, CONSTRUCTION INDUSTRY

D J Joinery, William Street, Cwm, Ebbw Vale, Gwent, NP23 7TH Tel: (01495) 370217

The Door Canopy Company Ltd, 65 Coronation Road, Motherwell, Lanarkshire, ML1 4JF Tel: (01698) 733465

JOINTLESS RESIN OR CEMENTITIOUS BASED FLOORING

Ancorite, Moston Road, Sandbach, Cheshire, CW11 3AB Tel: (01270) 761720 Fax: (01270) 761697

Elgood Industrial Flooring Ltd, Yeoman Street, London, SE8 5DU Tel: (020) 7237 1144 Fax: (020) 7237 1629 E-mail: nigel@elgood.com

I R L Group Ltd, C1 Swingbridge Road, Loughborough, Leicestershire, LE11 5JD Tel: (01509) 217101 Fax: (01509) 611004 E-mail: info@irlgroup.com

Lasercroft Ltd, 9 Hedon Road, Hull, HU9 1LL Tel: (01482) 229119 Fax: (01482) 223077 E-mail: info@lasercroft.com

Maresco Ltd, 2 The Alcorns, Cambridge Road, Stansted, Essex, CM24 8DF Tel: (01279) 817333 Fax: (01279) 817334

P R Epoxy Systems Ltd, Unit D2 The Court, Kestrel Road, Trafford Park, Manchester, M17 1SF Tel: 0161-872 7618 Fax: 0161-876 4597 E-mail: prepoxy@aol.com

Remmers UK Ltd, Remmers House, 14 Victoria Way, Burgess Hill, West Sussex, RH15 9NF Tel: (01444) 244144 Fax: (01444) 243500 E-mail: sales@remmers.co.uk

Resdev Ltd, Puma Floor House, Ainley Industrial Estate, Elland, West Yorkshire, HX5 9JP Tel: (01422) 379131 Fax: (01422) 370943 E-mail: info@resdev.co.uk

Sika Armorex, Riverside House, Bury Road, Lavenham, Sudbury, Suffolk, CO10 9QD Tel: (01787) 248005 Fax: (01787) 248315

Specialist Environmental Flooring Ltd, 38 Fowler Avenue, Spondon, Derby, DE21 7GR Tel: (01332) 669353 Fax: (01332) 669011

JOIST HANGERS

B P C Building Products Ltd, Flanshaw Way, Wakefield, West Yorkshire, WF2 9LP Tel: (01924) 364794 Fax: (01924) 373846 E-mail: sales@bpcfixings.com

Powerplace Ltd, The Firs, Newton-By-Frodsham, Frodsham, WA6 6TE Tel: (01928) 787127 Fax: (01928) 788448 E-mail: powerplace@fsbdial.co.uk

JOYSTICK MANUFRS

Penny & Giles Controls Ltd, 15 Airfield Rd, Christchurch, Dorset, BH23 3TG Tel: (01202) 409409 Fax: (01202) 409475 E-mail: sales@pennyandgiles.com

Penny & Giles Controls Ltd, Unit 36 Nine Mile Point Industrial Estate, Cwmfelinfach, Ynysddu, Newport, Gwent, NP11 7HZ Tel: (01495) 202000 Fax: (01495) 202006 E-mail: sales@pennyandgiles.com

JUKEBOX HIRE

Jukebox Parts, 42 Eastcote Lane, Northolt, Middlesex, UB5 5RG Tel: (07986) 074574 E-mail: sales@jukeboxparts.co.uk

JUNCTION BOXES

▶ G F I Enterprises Ltd, Ellon Business Centre, Broomiesburn Road, Ellon, Aberdeenshire, AB41 9RD Tel: (01358) 722799 Fax: (01358) 725220

Gardiner Technology Ltd, Queensway, Rochdale, Lancashire, OL11 1TQ Tel: (0845) 7328328 Fax: (01706) 510100 E-mail: sales@gardiner-technology.com

▶ Household Electrics, The Workshop, Terreglestown Farm, Terregles, Dumfries, DG2 9RW Tel: (01387) 268672

Maxhunt Ltd, Yelverton Road, Bristol, BS4 5HP Tel: 0117-977 9001 Fax: 0117-971 5971 E-mail: sales@maxhunt.co.uk

Medc Ltd, Colliery Road, Pinxton, Nottingham, NG16 6JF Tel: (01773) 864111 Fax: (01773) 582800 E-mail: sales@medc.com

JUTE FABRICS

James Dewhurst Ltd, Altham Lane, Altham, Accrington, Lancashire, BB5 5YA Tel: (01282) 775311 Fax: (01282) 774717 E-mail: sales@james-dewhurst.co.uk

JUTE GOODS, MADE-UP, *See also particular products*

Douglas Fraser & Sons (London) Ltd, 4 Clifton Hill, London, NW8 0QG Tel: (020) 7328 9393 Fax: (020) 7247 5379

Godfreys Technical Textiles, Arrol Road, Wester Gourdie Industrial Estate, Dundee, DD2 4TH Tel: (01382) 618499 Fax: (01382) 618484 E-mail: sales@godfreysofdundee.co.uk

JUTE HESSIAN FABRICS

▶ Super Slitters, 7-8 Lessarna Court, Bowling Back Lane, Bradford, West Yorkshire, BD4 8ST Tel: (01274) 735290 Fax: (01274) 740193 E-mail: superslitters@hotmail.com

H.L. Wilkinson & Co. Ltd, 49-51 Central Street, London, EC1V 8AB Tel: (020) 7253 5241 Fax: (020) 7250 1562 E-mail: info@hlwilikinson.co.uk

JUTE WASTE RECYCLING/ DISPOSAL/RECOVERY CONTRACTORS/MERCHANTS/ PROCESSORS OR SERVICES

H. Hurst & Sons Contractors Ltd, Bolton's Mill, Bridge End, Waterfoot, Rossendale, Lancashire, BB4 7BY Tel: (01706) 214136 Fax: (01706) 214136

JUTE YARN

Malcolm Ross & Sons Ltd, PO Box 4, Alderley Edge, Cheshire, SK9 7PR Tel: (01625) 583853 Fax: (01625) 586340 E-mail: sales@malcolmross.co.uk

KARAOKE EQUIPMENT

▶ Croaky Karaoke, 11 Perrylands, Charlwood, Horley, Surrey, RH6 0BL Tel: (01293) 863796 E-mail: taylormadeentertainment@btconnect.com

▶ D J Empire, 888 High Road, East London, Chadwell Heath, Romford, RM6 4HU Tel: (020) 8597 0119 Fax: (020) 8983 8852 E-mail: sales@djempire.co.uk

▶ Discovery Media Direct, 1 Brookhampton Lane, Kineton, CV35 0JA Tel: 0871 474 2724

▶ Kopy Kats Karaoke & Disco, PO Box 8486, Prestwick, Ayrshire, KA9 2JJ Tel: (01292) 476708 Fax: (01292) 471938 E-mail: kopykatskaraoke@tiscali.co.uk

▶ Mixerman, 28 Marshall Avenue, Bridlington, North Humberside, YO15 2DS Tel: (01262) 401058 E-mail: info@mixerman.freeserve.co.uk

▶ Platterpuss Karaoke, 107 Station Road, Hayes, Middlesex, UB3 4BX Tel: (020) 8569 1090 Fax: (020) 8569 1036 E-mail: sales@platterpuss.com

KARAOKE EQUIPMENT HIRE

▶ M & G's Disco, 7 Gregory Close, Bow, Crediton, Devon, EX17 6LR Tel: (0800) 0754082 E-mail: mark@djbesty.co.uk

▶ Mixerman, 28 Marshall Avenue, Bridlington, North Humberside, YO15 2DS Tel: (01262) 401058 E-mail: info@mixerman.freeserve.co.uk

▶ Platterpuss Karaoke, 107 Station Road, Hayes, Middlesex, UB3 4BX Tel: (020) 8569 1090 Fax: (020) 8569 1036 E-mail: sales@platterpuss.com

KARATE SUITS

Levenshulme Karate Club, Klondyke Club, Burnage Range, Levenshulme, Manchester, M19 2UG Tel: 0161-221 2676 E-mail: shukokaikarate2000@yahoo.co.uk

KEY BLANKS

Credit Card Keys Ltd, 37 Sovereign Road, Kings Norton Business Centre, Birmingham, B30 3HN Tel: 0121-451 3911 Fax: 0121-451 3133 E-mail: sales@cckeys.co.uk

Davenport Burgess, 47 Wednesfield Road, Willenhall, West Midlands, WV13 1AL Tel: (01902) 366448 Fax: (01902) 602472 E-mail: sales@davenport-burgess.com

KEY CUTTING MACHINE MANUFRS

Standard Engineering Ltd, Lawson Street, Kettering, Northamptonshire, NN16 8XU Tel: (01536) 517070 Fax: (01536) 410755

KEY CUTTING SERVICES

▶ A & J Locksmiths, 34 Iveagh Close, Northwood, Middlesex, HA6 2TE Tel: (0800) 6951771 E-mail: john@a-jlocksmiths.com

▶ Avon Security, 21 Salisbury Street, Amesbury, Salisbury, SP4 7AW Tel: (01980) 626000 Fax: (01980) 626464 E-mail: info@avonsecurity.net

▶ JB Locksmith, 33 Park Road, Conisbrough, Doncaster, South Yorkshire, DN12 2EQ Tel: (01709) 867361 Fax: (01709) 867361 E-mail: john@jblocksmithdoncaster.co.uk

Lincoln Security Ltd, 79-83 High Street, Lincoln, LN5 8AA Tel: (01522) 532038 Fax: (01522) 536060E-mail: enquiries@lincolnsecurity.co.uk

R & R Security Services, 171 South Ealing Road, London, W5 4QP Tel: (020) 8560 3413 Fax: (020) 8560 3413 E-mail: info@randrsecurity.com

▶ St Annes, 26 St. Annes Road West, Lytham St. Annes, Lancashire, FY8 1RF Tel: (01253) 727575 Fax: (01253) 727575 E-mail: keycutters@blueyonder.co.uk

KEY FOBS

▶ 3D Group, 3D Group, 165 Westdale Lane, Mapperley, Nottingham, NG3 6DH Tel: 0115-952 2772 E-mail: ddkeypro@hotmail.com

Agentdraw Ltd, 42 Great Central Street, Leicester, LE1 4JT Tel: 0116-251 9990 Fax: 0116-251 9997 E-mail: kevin@agentdraw.co.uk

Crown Products International Ltd, Innovation House, Cobnar Wood Close, Chesterfield, Derbyshire, S41 9RQ Tel: (01246) 451451 Fax: (01246) 260122 E-mail: sales@crownproducts.demon.co.uk

A.J. Gilbert (Birmingham) Ltd, 66-77 Buckingham Street, Birmingham, B19 3HU Tel: 0121-236 7774 Fax: 0121-236 6024 E-mail: lucysox@aol.com

H M T Plastics Ltd, 31a Framfield Road, Uckfield, East Sussex, TN22 5AH Tel: (01825) 769393 Fax: (01825) 769494 E-mail: hmtp@aol.com

Instyle Leather Goods Ltd, Publicity House, Tweedy Lane, Newport, Gwent, NP19 8DZ Tel: (01633) 282412 Fax: (01633) 282413 E-mail: sales@watchstraps-uk.com

Peter Lewis Ltd, Unit 14, Red Lion Business Centre, Surbiton, Surrey, KT6 7QD Tel: (020) 8391 5477 Fax: (020) 8974 1650 E-mail: sales@peter-lewis.co.uk

▶ Lighthouse Printing, 1 Anglesey Street, Cardiff, CF5 1QZ Tel: (029) 2034 4899 Fax: (029) 2034 4899 E-mail: lighthouseprint@ntlworld.com

Menu Shop, 38 High Street, Warminster, Wiltshire, BA12 9AF Tel: (01985) 217000 Fax: (01985) 218000 E-mail: sales@menushop.co.uk

Pennine Products, Marsh House, Market Place, Honley, Holmfirth, HD9 6NG Tel: (01484) 666303 Fax: (01484) 663260 E-mail: sales@pennineproducts.co.uk

Plastech Print Ltd, Debdale Lane, Keyworth, Nottingham, NG12 5HN Tel: 0115-937 4041 Fax: 0115-937 3426 E-mail: sales@plastechprint.co.uk

R E V Gomm Ltd, 31 Commercial St, Birmingham, B1 1RJ Tel: 0121-643 7427 Fax: 0121-633 3394 E-mail: gomms@shawmunstergroup.co.uk

Rebus Badges & Regalia Ltd, Clayfields, Bodenham, Hereford, HR1 3LG Tel: (01568) 797401 Fax: (01568) 797402 E-mail: sales@e-badges.co.uk

Westfield Advertising Specialities Ltd, 1 Helena Street, Birmingham, B1 2RJ Tel: 0121-233 1671 Fax: 0121-236 4121 E-mail: sales@westfieldltd.co.uk

KEY FOBS, PLASTIC

Rugby Locksmiths Ltd, 3 St. Matthews Street, Rugby, Warwickshire, CV21 3BY Tel: (01455) 554999 Fax: (01788) 544222 E-mail: info@thekeyshop.co.uk

KEY HOLDING SECURITY SERVICES

▶ Advanced Security, Chevron House, 346 Long Lane, Hillingdon, Uxbridge, Middlesex, UB10 9PF Tel: (01895) 201800 Fax: (01895) 201801 E-mail: info@securiplan.co.uk

▶ Anubis Protection (UK), 46 Yewlands Avenue, Higher Blackley, Manchester, M9 6QR Tel: 0845 456 8717 Fax: 08712 365 328 E-mail: enquiries@anubis-protection.co.uk

Chubb Emergency Response, 5 Repton Court, Repton Close, Basildon, Essex, SS13 1LN Tel: (01268) 522066 Fax: (01268) 273070 E-mail: andrew.vaccari@chubb.co.uk

Grenadier Guards Security Services, Grenadier House, Condover, Shrewsbury, SY5 7BG Tel: 08450 539198 E-mail: info@grenadiersecurity.co.uk

Grenadier Security Nationwide, Quarry House, Telford, Shropshire, TF6 6NP Tel: (0845) 0539198 E-mail: info@grenadiersecurity.co.uk

▶ Maximeyes Security Ltd, Unit 2, Dalewood Road, Lymedale Business Park, Newcastle, Staffordshire, ST5 9QH Tel: (01782) 566611 Fax: (01782) 566616 E-mail: maximeyes2003@yahoo.co.uk

▶ Maximum Security, 60 Skylark Rise, Plymouth, PL6 7SN Tel: (01752) 695569 Fax: (01752) 548020 E-mail: safeandsecure@maximum-security.co.uk

Orbis Property Protection, 106 Oxford Road, Uxbridge, Middlesex, UB8 1NA Tel: (01895) 465500 Fax: (01895) 465499 E-mail: pat.sullivan@ux.orbis-opp.com

▶ Scion Electronics, 161 Hospital Street, Birmingham, B19 3XA Tel: 0121-359 6366 Fax: 0121-359 6448 E-mail: lee.davis@scionelectronics.co.uk

KEY MASTER SYSTEMS

▶ Locksmiths I/C Supplies Division, Unit B6, Rudford Industrial Estate, Ford, Arundel, West Sussex, BN18 0BF Tel: (01903) 735321 Fax: (01903) 732777 E-mail: sales@icsupplies.co.uk

KEY STEELS

Bold Transmission Parts Ltd, Webber Road, Knowsley Industrial Park North, Knowsley Industrial Park, Liverpool, L33 7SW Tel: 0151-548 2303 Fax: 0151-549 1117 E-mail: sales@engineerskeys.co.uk

KEYBOARD REPAIR

▶ Prestige Computer Services, 3-4 Park Road, Malmesbury, Wiltshire, SN16 0BX Tel: (01666) 825620 Fax: (01666) 826686 E-mail: service@pcs-uk.net

KEYBOARDS

Absolute Computers Ltd, 19 Old High Street, Headington, Oxford, OX3 9HS Tel: (01865) 744115 Fax: (01865) 744155 E-mail: admin@absolute.co.uk

Camlab Computer Systems, 27 Faringdon Road, Swindon, SN1 5AR Tel: (01793) 534917 Fax: (01793) 513120 E-mail: sales@camlab.net

Compuchange, 14 Parson Street, London, NW4 1QB Tel: (020) 8203 3363 Fax: (020) 8202 0860

Contech Electronics Ltd, Unit C Mindenhall Court, High Street, Stevenage, Hertfordshire, SG1 3BG Tel: (01438) 315757 Fax: (01438) 313679 E-mail: sales@contech.co.uk

Evolution Computers, 135 Bradford Road, Shipley, West Yorkshire, BD18 3TB Tel: (01274) 773394 Fax: (01274) 778788 E-mail: info@evolutiondirect.com

G M S Technologies, Unit 22, Brambles Enterprise Centre, Waterberry Drive, Waterlooville, Hampshire, PO7 7TH Tel: (023) 9223 1880 Fax: (023) 9223 1990

Jennings Computer Engineering Ltd, 24-28 Gain Lane, Bradford, West Yorkshire, BD3 7LS Tel: (01274) 637867 Fax: (01274) 633197 E-mail: info@jencomp.co.uk

▶ Taskforce Software Ltd, 158 Sturminster Road, Bristol, BS14 8AT Tel: (01458) 835097 E-mail: info@taskforce-software.co.uk

Technol 2000 Ltd, 5-7 Chester Road, Northwich, Cheshire, CW8 1EZ Tel: (01606) 784044 Fax: (01606) 784055 E-mail: info@technol.co.uk

Tipro Keyboards UK Ltd, Unit 19/20, Kingston Farm Industrial Units, Down Hall Road, Matching Green, Harlow, Essex, CM17 0RB Tel: (01279) 732360 Fax: (01279) 732369 E-mail: sales@tiprokeyboards.co.uk

KEYBOARDS, COMPUTER/ WORD PROCESSOR ETC

Flex Computer Services, 62 Clifton Road, Shefford, Bedfordshire, SG17 5AN Tel: (01462) 638777

Office Overload, Peelers End, May Lane, Pilley, Lymington, Hampshire, SO41 5QR Tel: (01590) 688476 Fax: (01590) 675133 E-mail: sue@officeoverload.com

Read Cosine Ltd, Unit 1 Leanne Business Centre, Sandford Lane, Wareham, Dorset, BH20 4DY Tel: (01929) 550727 Fax: (01929) 550357 E-mail: sales@readcosine.com

KEYBOARDS, CUSTOM DESIGNED

Rafi (GB) Ltd, Unit 1 Perrywood Business Park, Honeycrock Lane, Salfords, Redhill, RH1 5DZ Tel: (01737) 778660 Fax: (01737) 778722 E-mail: sales@rafi.co.uk

Tipro Keyboards UK Ltd, Unit 19/20, Kingston Farm Industrial Units, Down Hall Road, Matching Green, Harlow, Essex, CM17 0RB Tel: (01279) 732360 Fax: (01279) 732369 E-mail: sales@tiprokeyboards.co.uk

KEYBOARDS, PIANO

▶ Bedhampton Piano Shop Ltd, 90 Bedhampton Road, Havant, Hampshire, PO9 3EZ Tel: (023) 9248 4802 Fax: (0800) 2985087 E-mail: graham@bpspianos.com

KEYPADS, *See also headings for particular types*

The Harborough Rubber Co. Ltd, Riverside, Market Harborough, Leicestershire, LE16 7PT Tel: (01858) 410610 Fax: (01858) 410006 E-mail: admin@harboro.co.uk

Hi Tec Interface Ltd, Unit 15 The Wenta Business Centre, Colne Way, Watford, WD24 7ND Tel: (020) 8958 4735 Fax: (020) 8958 9770 E-mail: hitec@himet.com

KEYRINGS

Aaa Badges Of Quality, Tumble Weed House, Hamsterley, Bishop Auckland, County Durham, DL13 3RA Tel: (01388) 488733 Fax: (01388) 488048 E-mail: sales@aaabadgesofquality.co.uk

Instyle Leather Goods Ltd, Publicity House, Tweedy Lane, Newport, Gwent, NP19 8DZ Tel: (01633) 282412 Fax: (01633) 282413 E-mail: sales@watchstraps-uk.com

S M T Associates Ltd, 17 Sandford Street, Lichfield, Staffordshire, WS13 6QA Tel: (01543) 250211 Fax: (01543) 257015 E-mail: sales@smtbadges.co.uk

▶ TAGit, 21 Mead Road, Willesborough, Ashford, Kent, TN24 0BS Tel: (07946) 333292

▶ Ukp Accessories, Bank House, Bott Lane, Walsall, WS1 2JQ Tel: (01922) 640598 Fax: (01922) 611885 E-mail: enquires@ukpaccessories.com

KEYRINGS, METAL

GadgetandGift.co.uk, 1 Milhouse Crescent, Glasgow, G20 0UD Tel: 0870 7455030 Fax: 0870 7406812 E-mail: sales@gadgetandgift.co.uk

KEYRINGS, STAINLESS STEEL

GadgetandGift.co.uk, 1 Milhouse Crescent, Glasgow, G20 0UD Tel: 0870 7455030 Fax: 0870 7406812 E-mail: sales@gadgetandgift.co.uk

KEYS

▶ Fast Key Services Ltd, 5c Russell Court, Russell Gardens, Wickford, Essex, SS11 8QU Tel: (01268) 562562 Fax: (01268) 570121 E-mail: marc@fastkeys.co.uk

▶ Morlands Lock Smiths, 581 Charminster Road, Bournemouth, BH8 9RQ Tel: (01202) 513787 Fax: (01202) 510500 E-mail: sales@morlands.demon.co.uk

KEYS, MACHINE/ENGINEERS'

Bold Transmission Parts Ltd, Webber Road, Knowsley Industrial Park North, Knowsley Industrial Park, Liverpool, L33 7SW Tel: 0151-548 2303 Fax: 0151-549 1117 E-mail: sales@engineerskeys.co.uk

KILN DESIGN OR CONSTRUCTION OR INSTALLATION

Kiln Refractory Services Ltd, 221 Birches Head Road, Stoke-on-Trent, ST1 6NB Tel: (01782) 851685 Fax: (01782) 768949 E-mail: krs@cwcom.net

KILN FURNITURE

Saint Gobain Industrial Ceramics Ltd, Mill Lane, Rainford, St. Helens, Merseyside, WA11 8LP Tel: (01744) 882941 Fax: (01744) 883514 E-mail: andrew.smith.rainford@saint-gobain.com

KILNS, *See also headings for particular types*

▶ Diatherm & Ancillary Equipment, Gresham Works, Mornington Road, London, E4 7DR Tel: (020) 8524 9546 Fax: (020) 8524 9546 E-mail: diatherm@talk21.com

Ulster Ceramics, 29 Garvagh Road, Swatragh, Maghera, County Londonderry, BT46 5QE Tel: (028) 7940 1260 Fax: (028) 7940 1739 E-mail: ulsterceramics@btinternet.com

KILNS, HIGH TEMPERATURE

▶ Kiln Maintenance Ltd, 4 Florida Close, Hot Lane Industrial Estate, Stoke-on-Trent, ST6 2DJ Tel: (01782) 816383 Fax: (01782) 575651 E-mail: sales@kilnmaintenance.co.uk

KILOWATT HOUR METERS

Eltime Ltd, 10-14 Hall Road, Heybridge, Maldon, Essex, CM9 4NF Tel: (01621) 859500 Fax: (01621) 855335 E-mail: sales@eltime.co.uk

KILTS

▶ Chuck Mccall Highland Wear, 36 South Street, Elgin, Morayshire, IV30 1JX Tel: (01343) 542743 Fax: (01343) 542743 E-mail: kilts@chuckmccall.com

▶ Glen Prince Of Great Britain, Unit 8-8a North Street Workshops, North Street, Stoke-sub-Hamdon, Somerset, TA14 6QR Tel: (01935) 825082 Fax: (01935) 826283 E-mail: sales@glenprince.com

Glenisla Kilts Ltd, Braidhurst Industrial Estate, Motherwell, Lanarkshire, ML1 3ST Tel: (01698) 254579 Fax: (01698) 275372

Thomas Gordon & Sons, 19 Queen Street, Glasgow, G1 3ED Tel: 0141-221 2234 Fax: 0141-221 2230

▶ Highland Dress Hire, 39, Scotland Way,, Horsforth, Leeds, LS18 5SQ Tel: 0113 2280146 Fax: 0113 3682650 E-mail: john@highlandhire.co.uk

▶ The Scotland Kilt Co., 93 -95 South Bridge, Edinburgh, EH1 1HN Tel: 0131-225 3555 E-mail: thescotlandkiltco@hotmail.com

Sharp & C0 Bagpipe Makers Ltd, 113 Barrack Street, Glasgow, G4 0UE Tel: 0141-553 0902 Fax: 0141-553 0903 E-mail: greig@kintail.co.uk

Strathmore Woollen Co. Ltd, Station Works, North Street, Forfar, Angus, DD8 3BN Tel: (01307) 462135 Fax: (01307) 468603 E-mail: info@tartanbystrathmore.co.uk

KIOSK COMPONENTS

Cartology Wheel Mnfrs, Unit 3 Llanhilleth Industrial Estate, Llanhilleth, Abertillery, Gwent, NP13 2RX Tel: (01495) 216612 Fax: (01495) 211108 E-mail: mfc@cartology.co.uk

KIOSK DESIGN

▶ Datasphere, 25 St. Mary Street, Chepstow, Gwent, NP16 5EU Tel: (01291) 621628 E-mail: sales@data-sphere.co.uk

KIT CAR PARTS

▶ A S Bairds, 15 Michelin Road, Newtownabbey, County Antrim, BT36 4PT Tel: (028) 9083 5333 Fax: (028) 9083 5015 E-mail: bairds@btconnect.com

▶ Cellustar Ltd, Unit 8C, Beta Close, Tewkesbury Business Centre, Tewkesbury, Gloucestershire, GL20 8SR Tel: (01684) 273080 Fax: (01684) 273081 E-mail: info@cellustar.co.uk

KITCHEN APPLIANCE MAINTENANCE/REPAIR SERVICES

Carford Group Ltd, Units 1-4, Mitchell Road, Ferndown Industrial Estate, Wimborne, Dorset, BH21 7SG Tel: (01202) 851900 Fax: (01202) 851921 E-mail: sales@carford.co.uk

M D Phillips Appliances, 44 Hackenden Close, East Grinstead, West Sussex, RH19 3DS Tel: (01342) 314670 Fax: (01342) 325445

M & S Kitchens, 352 Oxford Road, Cleckheaton, West Yorkshire, BD19 4JR Tel: (01274) 813005 E-mail: sales@mandsinteriors.com

▶ Manor Direct Ltd, 27-31 Francis Street, Hull, HU2 8DT Tel: (01482) 586312 Fax: (01482) 585310 E-mail: sales@manorglass.co.uk

▶ A.C. Talbot - Appliance Repairs, 3 Carisbrooke Crescent, Barrow-in-Furness, Cumbria, LA13 0HU Tel: (01229) 835263 Fax: (0871) 2110099 E-mail: andee.talbot@tiscali.co.uk

KITCHEN APPLIANCES

A M P Electrical Wholesalers, 28 Amhurst Road, London, E8 1JN Tel: (020) 8985 3013 Fax: (020) 8986 7971 E-mail: enquiries@ampelectrical.co.uk

Ace Kitchens, 47-57 Feeder Road, Bristol, BS2 0SE Tel: 0117-971 3682 Fax: 0117-977 7004

Acrelane Builders Merchants Ltd, 53 Acre Lane, London, SW2 5TN Tel: (020) 7738 3777 Fax: (020) 7738 6842 E-mail: info@diamond-merchants.co.uk

Burco Commercial Catering Equipment Ltd, Glen Dimplex Professional Appliances, Stoney Lane, Prescot, Merseyside, L35 2XW Tel: (0871) 2225118 Fax: (0871) 2229636 E-mail: info@gdpa.co.uk

Carford Group Ltd, Units 1-4, Mitchell Road, Ferndown Industrial Estate, Wimborne, Dorset, BH21 7SG Tel: (01202) 851900 Fax: (01202) 851921 E-mail: sales@carford.co.uk

Complete Kitchens, 56-58 Springbank Road, London, SE13 6SN Tel: (020) 8852 5926 Fax: (020) 8244 0907 E-mail: completekitchens@talk21.com

▶ Designer Appliances, Candidus Court, Peterborough, PE4 5DB Tel: (01733) 755510 Fax: (0871) 6613572 E-mail: info@peterboroughappliances.co.uk

▶ Discount Appliance Centre Ltd, Cook House, Brunel Drive, Newark, Nottinghamshire, NG24 3FB Tel: (0870) 0671420 Fax: (01636) 707737 E-mail: info@thedac.co.uk

Walter Dix & Co., 1 Stirling Court, Team Valley Trading Estate, Gateshead, Tyne & Wear, NE11 0JF Tel: 0191-482 0033 Fax: 0191-491 1488 E-mail: sales@wdix.co.uk

▶ Keith Dowling, 35 Harris Road, Bexleyheath, Kent, DA7 4QD Tel: (020) 8303 0162 Fax: (020) 8303 0162 E-mail: homeplan2001@yahoo.com

Edwards & Godding Reading Ltd, 9d Loverock Road, Reading, RG30 1DZ Tel: 0118-939 3046 Fax: 0118-959 0294 E-mail: aga@edgod.globalnet.co.uk

Electrolux, Merrington Lane Trading Estate, Spennymoor, County Durham, DL16 7UU Tel: (01388) 814141 Fax: (01388) 812753 E-mail: graham.metcalfe@electrolux.co.uk

F K Ellis & Sons Ltd, Unit 2 Lower Sydenham Industrial Estate, Kangley Bridge Road, London, SE26 5BA Tel: (020) 8676 9428 Fax: (020) 8676 9429 E-mail: sales@fkellis.com

Grays Transport, The Rearing Site, Oldbury Lane, Oldbury-On-Severn, Bristol, BS35 1RF Tel: (01454) 411773 Fax: (01454) 281373

Harmony Kitchens, 32 Torrington Rd, Wallasey, Merseyside, CH44 3BU Tel: 0151-638 8370

Hills Panels Products Ltd, Crown Works, Rotherham Road, Beighton, Sheffield, S20 1AH Tel: 0114-269 3009 Fax: 0114-269 8202

Hoover Candy Group, New Chester Road, Bromborough, Wirral, Merseyside, CH62 3PE Tel: 0151-334 2781 Fax: 0151-334 0185

Ikas Ltd, Kingsview House Kingsview Court, Hodgson Way, Wickford, Essex, SS11 8YF Tel: (01268) 562689 Fax: (01268) 575545 E-mail: sales@ikas.co.uk

J W Fidler & Sons, Nile Street, Bolton, BL3 6BW Tel: (01204) 529948 Fax: (01204) 365263

KDS Appliances Ltd, 33-35 Beehive Lane, Ilford, Essex, IG1 3RG Tel: (020) 8518 1988

Kitchen Tech, 123 The Vale, London, W3 7RQ Tel: (020) 8749 7606 Fax: (020) 8746 7616

L W Cole Distributors Ltd, Castle Vale Industrial Estate, Maybrook Road, Minworth, Sutton Coldfield, West Midlands, B76 1BE Tel: 0121-313 1199 Fax: 0121-313 1560

M K Electric Ltd, Glascoed Road, St. Asaph, Clwyd, LL17 0ER Tel: (01745) 532000 Fax: (01745) 532127

Magnet Ltd, King George Close, Romford, RM7 7PN Tel: (01708) 755388 Fax: (01708) 746349

Max Appliances Ltd, Kingfisher House, Wheel Park, Westfield, Hastings, East Sussex, TN35 4SE Tel: (01424) 751666 Fax: (01424) 751444 E-mail: sales@max-appliances.co.uk

Merloni Domestic Appliances Ltd, Merloni Ho, 3 Cowley Business Pk, High St, Cowley, Uxbridge, Middx, UB8 2AD Tel: (01895) 858200 Fax: (01895) 858270

Miele Co. Ltd, Fairacres, Marcham Road, Abingdon, Oxfordshire, OX14 1TW Tel: (0845) 3303618 Fax: (01235) 554477 E-mail: miele-professional@miele.co.uk

Millers Catering Equipment, Unit 2 College Fields Business Centre, Prince Georges Road, Merton, London, SW19 2PT Tel: (020) 8687 5390 Fax: (020) 8687 5399 E-mail: sales@millerscatering.co.uk

▶ Peterborough Appliances, 25 Candidus Court, Peterborough, PE4 5DB Tel: (01733) 755200 Fax: (0871) 6613572E-mail: sales@i-ac.co.uk

Pulse Home Products Ltd, Vine Mill, Middleton Road, Royton, Oldham, OL2 5LN Tel: 0161-652 1211 Fax: 0161-626 0391 E-mail: info@pulse-uk.co.uk

Rowenta (UK) Ltd, 1A Langley Business Centre, Station Road, Slough, SL3 8PH Tel: (01753) 796400 Fax: (01753) 796499

S & K Fitted Furniture Ltd, 86 New Cleveland Street, Hull, HU8 7HE Tel: (01482) 227691 Fax: (01482) 589551 E-mail: designteam@skjoiners.karoo.co.uk

Salton Europe Ltd, Sisson Street, Failsworth, Manchester, M35 0HS Tel: 0161-947 3000 Fax: 0161-682 1708

Servis (U K) Ltd, Darlaston Road, Darlaston Road, Wednesbury, West Midlands, WS10 7TJ Tel: 0121-568 8333 Fax: 0121-568 8500

▶ Sinks & Appliances (UK) Ltd, 9 Tudor Court, Church Lane, Ash Green, Coventry, CV7 9GX Tel: (024) 7636 1721 Fax: (024) 7636 5214 E-mail: sales@sinksandappliances.com

Slicer Maintenance Services, PO Box 152, Macclesfield, Cheshire, SK10 4LX Tel: (01625) 827827 Fax: 01625 820011 E-mail: enquiries@smsfoodequip.com

Teka Products Ltd, 177 Milton Park, Milton, Abingdon, Oxfordshire, OX14 4SE Tel: (01235) 861916 Fax: (01235) 832137 E-mail: sales@teka.co.uk

▶ Thomas Whitaker (Eastburn) Ltd, Unit 11 A Sandylands Business Centre, Carleton New Road, Skipton, North Yorkshire, BD23 2AA Tel: (01756) 797579 Fax: (01756) 797580 E-mail: contact@twelimited.plus.com

KITCHEN CLEANING CONTRACTORS

Avac, 38 Comiston Road, Edinburgh, EH10 5QQ Tel: 0131-452 8455 Fax: 0131-664 9085 E-mail: avac@netscapeonline.co.uk

Blue Sparkle Cleaning Contractors, 2 Clarenden Place, Dartford, DA2 7HL Tel: (01322) 669494

Metrovac Co., 1016 Harrow Road, Kensal Green, London, NW10 5NS Tel: (020) 8969 4522

KITCHEN DOOR HANDLES

▶ David Edgar Kitchen Designs, 228 Spearing Road, High Wycombe, Buckinghamshire, HP12 3LA Tel: (01494) 472247 E-mail: daveedgar@rock.com

KITCHEN FLOORING

R C Marble & Sons Ltd, 158a Ovenden Road, Halifax, West Yorkshire, HX3 5QG Tel: (01422) 345990 E-mail: sales@rcmarble.co.uk

KITCHEN FURNITURE

Adlam & Beadle, Unit 5, North Lane, Newhaven, East Sussex, BN9 9BF Tel: (01273) 611091 Fax: (01273) 612989 E-mail: info@adlambeadle.co.uk

Albion Extrusions Ltd, Penrose Works, Penrose Street, Bolton, BL2 6DX Tel: (01204) 385803 Fax: (01204) 385816 E-mail: info@albionextrusions.co.uk

▶ Antix Pine Furniture, 5 Blatchford Road, Horsham, West Sussex, RH13 5QR Tel: (01403) 265040 E-mail: info@antixfurniture.co.uk

▶ Avanti Fitted Kitchens Ltd, Avanti House, Hayes Lane, Stourbridge, West Midlands, DY9 8RD Tel: (01384) 893929 Fax: (01384) 896734 E-mail: avanti@callnetuk.com

B G I Direct Furniture Fittings, 8 Harpur Road, Omagh, County Tyrone, BT78 5BY Tel: (028) 8289 8089 Fax: (028) 8289 8033

Barlows Boards Ltd, 8 Rushey Lane, Birmingham, B11 2BL Tel: 0121-706 2067 Fax: 0121-707 9550 E-mail: bugbashbar@yahoo.co.uk

Beaumont Structural Consultants, Goose Green Marsh, La Rue Du Craslin, St. Peter, Jersey, JE3 7BU Tel: (01534) 822888 Fax: (01534) 822889

Bee Line Fitted Bedrooms, 71 Station Road, Flitwick, Bedford, MK45 1JU Tel: (01525) 712090 Fax: (01525) 712090

Benchmark, 5 Oxwich Court, Fendrod Business Park Valley Way, Morriston, Swansea, SA6 8RA Tel: (01792) 772292 Fax: (01792) 771458

▶ Bespoke Tables - Stainless steel, Wood & Glass., The Old School House, Traboe, St Martin, Helston, Cornwall, TR12 6EA Tel: 01326 231020 E-mail: Jules@bespoke-tables.co.uk

Blackheath Products Ltd, Fairfield Park, Halesowen, West Midlands, B62 9JL Tel: 0121-561 4245 Fax: 0121-561 5904 E-mail: sales@blackheathproducts.co.uk

Bodel Manufacturing Ltd, 9 Hulls Lane, Lisburn, County Antrim, BT28 2SR Tel: (028) 9266 5266 Fax: (028) 9267 1873 E-mail: sales@bodel.com

Brakes Catering Equipment, Unit 3 Gloucester Court, Gloucester Terrace, Armley Road, Leeds, LS12 2ER Tel: (0845) 9319494 Fax: 0113-231 9495

Burbidge & Son Ltd, Burnsall Road, Coventry, CV5 6BS Tel: (024) 7667 1600 Fax: (024) 7669 1010 E-mail: sales@burbidge.co.uk

Cameron Interiors Ltd, 458-462 Crow Road, Glasgow, G11 7DR Tel: 0141-334 9532 Fax: 0141-357 3869 E-mail: sales@cameroninteriors.co.uk

Chamois Furnishings Ltd, Units 1-4, Showell Road, Wolverhampton, WV10 9LN Tel: (01902) 864685 Fax: (01902) 865828 E-mail: sales@chamois.co.uk

Cita Furniture, 36 Seein Road, Sion Mills, Strabane, County Tyrone, BT82 9NJ Tel: (028) 8165 9744 Fax: (028) 8165 9744

Colemans Kitchens & Bedrooms Ltd, 178 Victoria Road, Kirkby-in-Ashfield, Nottingham, NG17 8AT Tel: (01623) 751239 Fax: (01623) 754649

Cooper Callas Ltd, PO Box 32, Oxford, OX1 1LH Tel: (01865) 249931 Fax: (01865) 790561

Country Furniture Makers, Victoria Road, Yeovil, Somerset, BA21 5AZ Tel: (01935) 428404 Fax: (01935) 424261

Craigie & Scott, 3 Riverside, Station Road, Bruton, Somerset, BA10 0EH Tel: (01749) 812867 Fax: (01749) 812867 E-mail: craigiewoodworks@waitrose.com

▶ Darlingtonantqiue Pine Warehouse, 12 Union Street, Darlington, County Durham, DL3 6JE Tel: (01325) 361575

Diamond Interior Design, Century Street, Stoke-on-Trent, ST1 5HT Tel: (01782) 212242 Fax: (01782) 202375 E-mail: sales@diamond-interior-design.co.uk

Discount Furniture Manufacturing, Wilford Road, Nottingham, NG2 1EB Tel: 0115-986 6868 Fax: 0115-986 6868 E-mail: dfm_ltd@yahoo.co.uk

Drew Forsyth & Co. Ltd, Beehive Mills, Hebble End, Hebden Bridge, West Yorkshire, HX7 6HJ Tel: (01422) 842206 Fax: (01422) 844828 E-mail: info@drewforsyth.co.uk

▶ Drummonds Kitchens & Bedrooms, 116 New Road Side, Horsforth, Leeds, LS18 4QB Tel: 0113-258 8588 Fax: 0113-258 8588 E-mail: eddie.drummond@btconnect.com

E C Hodge MF Ltd, Norton Road, Stevenage, Hertfordshire, SG1 2BB Tel: (01438) 357341 Fax: (01438) 361408 E-mail: echodgemflimited@aol.com

Edenbrook Furniture Ltd, Unit Merchant, Mitchelston Industrial Estate, Kirkcaldy, Fife, KY1 3NJ Tel: (01592) 655185 Fax: (01592) 655185

Edwards Product, 2 Birkbeck Road, Beckenham, Kent, BR3 4SN Tel: (020) 8778 0918 Fax: (020) 8778 0918

▶ Exclusiv Fitted Interiors, 16a Longfield Road, Eglinton, Londonderry, BT47 3PY Tel: (028) 7181 1114 Fax: (028) 7181 4916

▶ F & B's Pine Shop, 119 Falls Road, Belfast, BT12 6AA Tel: (028) 9023 0124

Fairline Sales & Marketing, 35 Legacorry Road, Richhill, Armagh, BT61 9LA Tel: (028) 3887 1779 Fax: (028) 3887 0642

Fitura Kitchens, 14 Newlands Road, Westoning, Bedford, MK45 5LD Tel: (01525) 717586 Fax: (01525) 717586 E-mail: sales@filurakitchens.co.uk

Fox & Pheasant Ltd, Fox & Pheasant Center, Colchester Road, White Colne, Colchester, CO6 2PS Tel: (01787) 223297 Fax: (01787) 224497 E-mail: sales@foxandpheasant.co.uk

Galiform Corporate Services Ltd, Thorpe Road, Howden, Goole, North Humberside, DN14 7PA Tel: (01430) 430905 Fax: (01430) 431540

Garven Antique Reproductions, Gorphwysfa, Defynnog, Brecon, Powys, LD3 8SB Tel: (01874) 638028 Fax: (01874) 638028

Gemini Kitchens Ltd, Unit 14-15 Worsley Business Park, Mosley Common Road, Worsley, Manchester, M28 1NL Tel: 0161-703 9903 Fax: 0161-703 9934 E-mail: sales@geminikitchens.com

Gilberdyke Dyke, Unit 2 Main Road, Gilberdyke, Brough, North Humberside, HU15 2SW Tel: (01430) 449997 Fax: (01430) 449997

Godfrey Syrett Ltd, Littleburn Industrial Estate, Langley Moor, Durham, DH7 8HE Tel: 0191-268 1010 Fax: 0191-378 1660 E-mail: sales@godfreysyrett.co.uk

Haagensen Wardrobes, F A Would, Ladysmith Road, Grimsby, South Humberside, DN32 9SH Tel: (01472) 343030 Fax: (01472) 341333 E-mail: adrian@haaggensonwardrobes.com

Hale & Murray Ltd, 3 Abingdon Road, Nuffield Industrial Estate, Poole, Dorset, BH17 0UG Tel: (01202) 678431 Fax: (01202) 687843 E-mail: admin@haleandmurray.co.uk

Hands Woodcraft, Northgate, Aldridge, Walsall, WS9 8TH Tel: (01922) 455331

Harmony Fitted Furniture, Main Street, Rear of 51, Willerby, Hull, HU10 6BY Tel: (01482) 650685 Fax: (01482) 650685 E-mail: info@harmony.co.uk

▶ Higham Furniture, Flint Barn, New Barns Farm, Drove Road, Southwick, Fareham, Hampshire, PO17 6EW Tel: (0845) 8684477 Fax: (0870) 0681067 E-mail: tim@higham.co.uk

Housepoints Pine Furniture, 13 The Borough, Canterbury, Kent, CT1 2DR Tel: (01227) 451350

Interior Designers Guild, 19 Bridge Street, Winchester, Hampshire, SO23 9BH Tel: (01962) 861777 Fax: (01962) 854333 E-mail: enquiries@interiordesignersguild.co.uk

Intoto Furniture, 46-48 Barbourne Road, Worcester, WR1 1HU Tel: (01905) 24760 Fax: (01905) 726003 E-mail: worcester@intoto.co.uk

Johnson & Johnson Furniture plc, Unit 12-19 Guinness Road Trading Estate, Guinness Road, Trafford Park, Manchester, M17 1SB Tel: 0161-872 7041 Fax: 0161-872 7351 E-mail: mail@jjff.co.uk

K A Welding & Fabrications, Deptford Trading Estate, Blackhorse Road, London, SE8 5HY Tel: (020) 8691 2771 Fax: (020) 8691 2771

▶ Kitchen Concepts, 2 Anson Close, Aylesbury, Buckinghamshire, HP21 8AT Tel: (01296) 395558 Fax: (01296) 395558 E-mail: quainton@fsbdial.co.uk

Kitchen Design Centre, 789 Lisburn Road, Belfast, BT9 7GX Tel: (028) 9038 1265 Fax: (028) 9068 2452 E-mail: info@kdckitchendesign.com

Kitchen Warehouse, Appleton Village, Widnes, Cheshire, WA8 6EQ Tel: 0151-424 5991 Fax: 0151-423 3357

Latter's Pine Furniture, 18 Crescent Road, London, N22 7RS Tel: (020) 8888 7477

Lazer Promotions, Unit 26 Midland Oak Trading Es, Marlissa Dr, Coventry, CV6 6HQ Tel: 024 76661213 Fax: 024 76661213

Leamington Pine Workshop, Unit 2 Court Street, Milverton House, Leamington Spa, Warwickshire, CV31 2BB Tel: (01926) 312229 Fax: (01926) 312229

M F I UK Ltd, Southon House, 333 The Hyde, Edgeware Road, London, NW9 6TD Tel: (020) 8200 8000 Fax: (020) 8200 8636

▶ M & K Pine Co, Fisher Street, Newcastle upon Tyne, NE6 4LT Tel: 0191-263 0274

▶ M & K Units, 4 Lisburn Street, Hillsborough, County Down, BT26 6AB Tel: (028) 9268 3085 Fax: (028) 9268 3739 E-mail: mk_units@hotmail.com

Maghera Joinery Works Ltd, 100 Glen Road, Maghera, County Londonderry, BT46 5JG Tel: (028) 7964 2501 Fax: (028) 7964 4181 E-mail: info@beavercabinets.co.uk

Magnet Ltd, Spa Road, Bolton, BL1 4SL Tel: (01204) 521611 Fax: (01204) 364779

Magnet Ltd, 390 Newport Road, Cardiff, CF23 9AE Tel: (029) 2047 3366 Fax: (029) 2048 0170E-mail: sales@magnetexpress.com

Magnet Ltd, 253-255 Old Heath Road, Colchester, CO2 8BN Tel: (01206) 794233 Fax: (01206) 798832

Magnet Ltd, Allington Way, Darlington, County Durham, DL1 4XT Tel: (01325) 481177 Fax: (01325) 744379

Magnet Ltd, 60 Grieve Street, Dunfermline, Fife, KY12 8DW Tel: (01383) 720155 Fax: (01383) 620615

Magnet Ltd, Rotterdam Road, Hull, HU7 0XD Tel: (01482) 825451 Fax: (01482) 830241

Magnet Ltd, 153 Hurlingham Road, London, SW6 3NN Tel: (020) 7731 7304 Fax: (020) 7384 2217

Magnet Ltd, 5 Leagrave Street, London, E5 9QX Tel: (020) 8985 6382 Fax: (020) 8986 0489

Magnet Retail, Phoenix House, 315-323 High Street, Sutton, Surrey, SM1 1NH Tel: (020) 8643 1234 Fax: (020) 8770 7115

The Manor Cabinet Company Public Ltd Company, Kelvin Road, Swindon, SN3 3JW Tel: (01793) 423314 Fax: (01793) 423312 E-mail: info@manorcabinets.co.uk

Manse Furniture, 7 Curran Business Park, Portland Road, Larne, County Antrim, BT40 1DH Tel: (028) 2827 7744 Fax: (028) 2827 9137

Maurice Lay Ltd, Fourth Way, Bristol, BS11 8DW Tel: 0117-938 1900 Fax: 0117-938 2446 E-mail: sales@mlay.co.uk

Miele Co. Ltd, Fairacres, Marcham Road, Abingdon, Oxfordshire, OX14 1TW Tel: (0845) 3303618 Fax: (01235) 554477 E-mail: miele-professional@miele.co.uk

Mona Units, 56 Monadore Road, Claudy, Londonderry, BT47 4DP Tel: (028) 7778 1600 Fax: (028) 7778 1500 E-mail: tony@monaunits.com

Moores Furniture Group Ltd, Thorp Arch Estate, Thorp Arch, Wetherby, West Yorkshire, LS23 7DD Tel: (01937) 842394 Fax: (01937) 845396

KITCHEN FURNITURE – *continued*

▶ Ms Furniture Ltd, 123 Kettlebrook Road, Tamworth, Staffordshire, B77 1AG Tel: (01827) 313231 Fax: (01827) 314929 E-mail: info@msfurnituresolutions.co.uk

▶ Not Just Pine, New Cut Lane, Woolston, Warrington, WA1 4AG Tel: (01925) 289079

▶ The Olive Branch, Unit 2, Sandbeck Lane, Wetherby, West Yorkshire, LS22 7TW Tel: (01937) 582797 Fax: (01937) 582797 E-mail: info@olive-branch.biz

Olympic Kitchens & Bedrooms, Unit 1 Tulketh Industrial Estate, Manchester, M40 9LY Tel: 0161-205 0055 Fax: 0161-205 0101

Panache Fitted Furniture, Birches Bridge, Wolverhampton Road, Codsall, Wolverhampton, WV8 1PE Tel: (01902) 847910 Fax: (01902) 847902

Parkside Cabinets & Interiors Ltd, The Old Goods Yard, West Wycombe Road, High Wycombe, Buckinghamshire, HP12 4AH Tel: (01494) 530301 Fax: (01494) 472440 E-mail: worktop@globalnet.co.uk

Paula Rosa, Robell Way, Storrington, Pulborough, West Sussex, RH20 3DS Tel: (01903) 743322 Fax: (01903) 742140 E-mail: info@paularosa.com

Pepper Kitchens, Station Road, Warboys, Huntingdon, Cambridgeshire, PE28 2TH Tel: (01487) 822882 Fax: (01487) 826001 E-mail: pepperkit@aol.com

▶ Pinetime, Rutland Village, Ashwell Road, Oakham, Leicestershire, LE15 7QN Tel: 01572 756285 Fax: 01572 756983

Princess Fitted Bedroom & Kitchen Furniture, 40 Whalebone Lane South, Dagenham, Essex, RM8 1BB Tel: (020) 8593 3884

▶ Print Services UK Ltd, Print House, 66 Hartlebury Trading Estate, Hartlebury, Kidderminster, Worcestershire, DY10 4JB Tel: (01299) 250001 E-mail: visiboard@hotmail.com

▶ Priory Furniture, The Old Red House Farm, Stratton-on-the-Fosse, Radstock, BA3 4QE Tel: (01761) 419849 Fax: (01761) 419849 E-mail: patlepper@tesco.net

Q B Furniture & Wooden Components, 85 Marlacoo Road, Richhill, Armagh, BT60 1JN Tel: (028) 3887 1788 Fax: (028) 3887 9939 E-mail: sales@qbfurniture.co.uk

R M Canopies, 5 3 Lower Balloo Road, Groomsport, Bangor, County Down, BT19 6LU Tel: (028) 9188 4463 Fax: (028) 9188 4463

Rixonway Kitchens Ltd, Churwell Vale, Shaw Cross Business Park, Dewsbury, West Yorkshire, WF12 7RD Tel: (01924) 431300 Fax: (01924) 431301 E-mail: sales@rixonway.co.uk

Rixonway Kitchens Ltd, Churwell Vale, Shaw Cross Business Park, Dewsbury, West Yorkshire, WF12 7RD Tel: (01924) 431300 Fax: (01924) 431301 E-mail: sales@rixonway.co.uk

▶ Sandywood Furniture, 8 Boundary Business Court, Church Road, Mitcham, Surrey, CR4 3TD Tel: (020) 8687 7070 Fax: (020) 8648 7020 E-mail: sandywoodfurnitureltd@gmill.com

Sharrow Industries, Parkway Close, Sheffield, S9 4WJ Tel: 0114-203 9446 Fax: 0114-203 9448

▶ Simple Kitchens, 4 Chruchill Crescent, Thame, Oxfordshire, OX9 3JN Tel: (01844) 217804 Fax: (01844) 217804 E-mail: thomas@simple-kitchens.co.uk

▶ Simply Wood Ltd, The Showroom, Kilkhampton, Bude, Cornwall, EX23 9QN Tel: (01288) 321772 Fax: (01288) 321782 E-mail: info@simplywoodltd.co.uk

Smallbone & Co Devizes Ltd, 10 Princes Street, Harrogate, North Yorkshire, HG1 1NH Tel: (01423) 529222 Fax: (01423) 524443 E-mail: harrogate.showroom@smallbone.co.uk

Spectrum, Unit 26 Small Heath Trading Estate, Armoury Road, Birmingham, B11 2RJ Tel: (0121) 772 3867

Stoneham plc, Powerscroft Road, Sidcup, Kent, DA14 5DZ Tel: (020) 8300 8181 Fax: (020) 8300 8183 E-mail: kitchens@stoneham.plc.uk

Tayside Plumbing & Building Supplies Ltd, 1 Dens Road, Dundee, DD3 7SR Tel: (01382) 229401 Fax: (01382) 202447 E-mail: office@tayside-plumbing.co.uk

R.J. Thompson, 50 Whalfedale Avenue, Dacre, Harrogate, North Yorkshire, HG2 0AU Tel: (07973) 522404 Fax: (01423) 780001

Town & Country Pine, 24 Hanover Buildings, Southampton, SO14 1JU Tel: (023) 8083 7353 Fax: (023) 8070 3385

Treyone Woodcraft, Horningtops, Liskeard, Cornwall, PL14 3PX Tel: (01503) 240922 Fax: (01503) 240933 E-mail: enquiries@treyone.co.uk

Upstairs Downstairs Chester Ltd, 23 Chester Street, Saltney, Chester, CH4 8BL Tel: (01244) 679566 Fax: (01244) 680857 E-mail: ud_stairs1984@yahoo.co.uk

▶ Valley Pine & Gifts, 135 Enbrook Valley, Folkestone, Kent, CT20 3NE Tel: (01303) 245552

Vivian & Holt Kitchen Design Centre, 52a Lymington Road, New Milton, Hampshire, BH25 6PY Tel: (01425) 619963 Fax: (01425) 611114 E-mail: admin@qualitydesignedkitchens.com

Waterline Ltd, Jenna House, 6 Mollins Court, Cumbernauld, Glasgow, G68 9HP Tel: (0870) 5561560 Fax: (01236) 453868 E-mail: sales@waterline.co.uk

William Ball, London Road, Grays, Essex, RM20 4WB Tel: (01375) 375151 Fax: (01375) 393355 E-mail: sales@wball.co.uk

▶ Williamson Kitchens, 60 Union Street, Keith, Banffshire, AB55 5DP Tel: (01542) 888088 Fax: (01542) 888088

▶ Woodcraft Designs, 121 The Pannier Market, South Street, Torrington, Devon, EX38 8HD Tel: (01805) 625444 E-mail: info@woodcraftdesigns.co.uk

▶ Woodstock Designs Ltd, Manor House, Ryehill, Hull, HU12 9NH Tel: (01964) 621100

KITCHEN FURNITURE TO SPECIFICATION

A K Carcasses, 4B Priory Street, Dover, Kent, CT17 9AA Tel: (01304) 216190 Fax: (01304) 216190

Belvedere Manufacturing Co. Ltd, The Old Printing Works, Waterloo Road, Radstock, BA3 3EP Tel: (01761) 437621 Fax: (01761) 436616 E-mail: belvederemfg@aol.com

C N G Foodservice Equipment Ltd, Unit 2, Parker Court, Dunston, Gateshead, Tyne & Wear, NE11 9EW Tel: 0191-460 9408 Fax: 0191-460 7070 E-mail: info@cngfoodserv.co.uk

Cater-Quip Ltd, 81 Dargan Road, Belfast, BT3 9JU Tel: (028) 9077 0195 Fax: (028) 9037 0238

Dennis & Robinson Ltd, Blenheim Road, Lancing, West Sussex, BN15 8UH Tel: (01903) 755321 Fax: (01903) 750679 E-mail: sales@manhattan.co.uk

▶ Dimension Furniture, Church Lane, OXTED, Surrey, RH8 9LH Tel: 07860 809104 E-mail: martin.parsons@dimensionfurniture.co.uk

▶ Dream Doors Glasgow Ltd, 25 New Endrick Road, Killearn, Glasgow, G63 9QT Tel: (0845) 6009232 Fax: (0845) 6009232

Eight By Four Ltd, Eight By Four, 6A Kings Yard, Carpenters Road, London, E15 2HD Tel: (020) 8985 6001 Fax: (020) 8533 5372 E-mail: sales@eightbyfour.co.uk

H R Nicholson, 19 Ballyardle Road, Kilkeel, Newry, County Down, BT34 4JX Tel: (028) 4176 3104 Fax: (028) 4176 9216 E-mail: harold@hillsideinteriors.freeserve.co.uk

Halgrove Ltd, Unit A2 Stafford Park 11, Telford, Shropshire, TF3 3AY Tel: (01952) 290548 Fax: (01952) 290549

Hands Woodcraft, Northgate, Aldridge, Walsall, WS9 8TH Tel: (01922) 455331

Harmony Fitted Furniture, Main Street, Rear of 51, Willerby, Hull, HU10 6BY Tel: (01482) 650685 Fax: (01482) 650685 E-mail: info@harmony.co.uk

Graham Johnston, 2 Baird Street, Stonehaven, Kincardineshire, AB39 2SP Tel: (01569) 762293 Fax: (01569) 767449 E-mail: graham.johnston4@btopenworld.com

▶ Kitchen Concepts, 2 Anson Close, Aylesbury, Buckinghamshire, HP21 8AT Tel: (01296) 395558 Fax: (01296) 395558 E-mail: quainton@fsbdial.co.uk

▶ M & K Units, 4 Lisburn Street, Hillsborough, County Down, BT26 6AB Tel: (028) 9268 3085 Fax: (028) 9268 3739 E-mail: mk_units@hotmail.com

Magnet Ltd, 1581 Pershore Road, Stirchley, Birmingham, B30 2JF Tel: 0121-451 3001 Fax: 0121-458 5750

Out Of The Woods, Mill Lane, Halton, Lancaster, LA2 6ND Tel: (01524) 811968

Parkside Cabinets & Interiors Ltd, The Old Goods Yard, West Wycombe Road, High Wycombe, Buckinghamshire, HP12 4AH Tel: (01494) 530301 Fax: (01494) 472440 E-mail: worktop@globalnet.co.uk

Pine Workshop, 1a Northmill, North Mill Road, Bledlow, Princes Risborough, Buckinghamshire, HP27 9PU Tel: (01844) 342400 Fax: (01844) 342400

▶ Priory Furniture, The Old Red House Farm, Stratton-on-the-Fosse, Radstock, BA3 4QE Tel: (01761) 419849 Fax: (01761) 419849 E-mail: patlepper@tesco.net

▶ Rogeroger, 24 Clonbrock Road, London, N16 8RR Tel: (020) 7254 7706 Fax: (020) 7254 7706 E-mail: info@rogeroger.co.uk

▶ Simple Kitchens, 4 Chruchill Crescent, Thame, Oxfordshire, OX9 3JN Tel: (01844) 217804 Fax: (01844) 217804 E-mail: thomas@simple-kitchens.co.uk

R.J. Thompson, 50 Whalfedale Avenue, Dacre, Harrogate, North Yorkshire, HG2 0AU Tel: (07973) 522404 Fax: (01423) 780001

Traigo Kitchens & Furniture, Pasture Lane, Gaddesby, Leicester, LE7 4XD Tel: (01664) 840423 Fax: (01664) 840833

UK FITTED KITCHENS, 10 Rosemary Road, Norwich, NR7 8ER Tel: (0800) 075 8100 E-mail: uk.fittedkitchens@fsmail.net

Warwickshire Pine, 263 Tile Hill Lane, Coventry, CV4 9DW Tel: (024) 7667 5328 Fax: (024) 7667 5328

▶ Woodcraft Designs, 121 The Pannier Market, South Street, Torrington, Devon, EX38 8HD Tel: (01805) 625444 E-mail: info@woodcraftdesigns.co.uk

KITCHEN KNIVES

▶ Functional Art, 127 Homesdale Road, Bromley, BR2 9LE Tel: (0796) 7077808 E-mail: rosanna@functional-art.co.uk

KITCHEN ODOUR CONTROL SYSTEMS

Pedrette Engineering Ltd, Unit 1, Ashville Trading Estate, Bristol Road, Gloucester, GL2 5EU Tel: (01452) 410447

Vianen Ventilation Systems, Coten House, 59-63 Coten End, Warwick, CV34 4NU Tel: (01926) 496644 Fax: (01926) 493977 E-mail: info@vianen.co.uk

KITCHEN PAPER TOWELS

Cherwell Packaging Ltd, Southfield Road, Kineton Road Industrial Estate, Southam, Warwickshire, CV47 0FB Tel: (01926) 817585 Fax: (01926) 817806 E-mail: sparkle@cleaningnet.co.uk

John Hulme Ltd, 2 Burnside Road, Bolton, BL1 6EP Tel: (01204) 846077

KITCHEN PLANNERS OR INSTALLATION

▶ A.D.Moore & Son Kitchen Installations, Bryn Hafod, Aberhafesp, Newtown, Powys, SY16 3JJ Tel: (01686) 688967 E-mail: adrianmoore0@lycos.com

Advanced Property Solutions, 38 Riverside Steps, St. Annes Park, Bristol, BS4 4RH Tel: (07775) 671339 E-mail: anything@advancedpropertysolutions.co.uk

▶ Aquarians, 40 Bushby Close, Lancing, West Sussex, BN15 9JW Tel: (01903) 755978

C Alexander, Dumbleton Lane, Eardiston, Tenbury Wells, Worcestershire, WR15 8JR Tel: (01584) 881501 Fax: (01584) 881168

▶ First Call Plumbing, The Old Farmhouse, 9 North Street, Ipplepen, Newton Abbot, Devon, TQ12 5RT Tel: (01803) 814514 Fax: (01803) 814069 E-mail: fcplumbing@btinternet.com

Fitura Kitchens, 14 Newlands Road, Westoning, Bedford, MK45 5LD Tel: (01525) 717586 Fax: (01525) 717586 E-mail: sales@biturakitchens.co.uk

H D Ebbutt & Son, 63 Jarvis Road, South Croydon, Surrey, CR2 6HW Tel: (020) 8688 1157

Halls Mica Hardware, 116 Market Street, Chapel-en-le-Frith, High Peak, Derbyshire, SK23 0HZ Tel: (01298) 812260 Fax: (01298) 816143

▶ International Kitchens & Bedrooms, 753 Holderness Road, Hull, HU8 9AR Tel: (01482) 375251 Fax: (01482) 711364 E-mail: enquiries@internationalkitchens.co.uk

J W S Wardrobes Ltd, 5 Eastgate, Worksop, Nottinghamshire, S80 1RH Tel: (01909) 486715 Fax: (01909) 486715

John Norton & Son Ltd, 169 Rutland Road, Sheffield, S3 9PT Tel: 0114-272 1294 Fax: 0114-276 6336 E-mail: sales@nortons.co.uk

▶ Roger Kemp Associates, River View, High Street, Loxwood, Billingshurst, West Sussex, RH14 0RE Tel: (01403) 752370 E-mail: mattkemp70@hotmail.com

▶ The Kitchen Workshop, Norwich, Tel: 01603 702344 E-mail: enquiries@the-kitchen-workshop.co.uk

Living In Style, Unit 1, 162 Coles Green Road, London, NW2 7HW Tel: (020) 8450 9555 Fax: (020) 8450 7565 E-mail: sales@livinginstyle.co.uk

Magnet Ltd, 66 Twyford Road, Eastleigh, Hampshire, SO50 4HN Tel: (023) 8061 3581 Fax: (023) 8061 2791

Magnet Ltd, 45-51 Barnet Road, Potters Bar, Hertfordshire, EN6 2QY Tel: (01707) 651213 Fax: (01707) 650159

Magnet Ltd, Polebarn Road, Trowbridge, Wiltshire, BA14 7EG Tel: (01225) 763058 Fax: (01225) 768254 E-mail: trowbridge.branch@magnet.co.uk

▶ Manor Direct Ltd, 27-31 Francis Street, Hull, HU2 8DT Tel: (01482) 586312 Fax: (01482) 585310 E-mail: sales@manorglass.co.uk

▶ R & S Property Services, Unit 2, 14 Barr's Road, Taplow, Maidenhead, Berkshire, SL6 0LE Tel: (01628) 661666 E-mail: rnsa1@hotmail.com

Sterland & Elgar, 46 Church Street, Shipston-on-Stour, Warwickshire, CV36 4AS Tel: (01608) 663341 Fax: (01608) 661212

▶ Surrey Kitchen Installation, 19 Breech Lane, Walton on the Hill, Tadworth, Surrey, KT20 7SJ Tel: (01737) 813425 Fax: (01737) 813425 E-mail: johnantill@hotmail.co.uk

Traditional Design, Unit 7 Waterside Mill, Waterside, Macclesfield, Cheshire, SK11 7HG Tel: (01625) 425292

▶ Windsor Kitchens, 39 Martley Gardens, Hedge End, Southampton, SO30 2XB Tel: 01489 795489 E-mail: sales@windsorkitchens.com

Wrights Property Services, Unit 317 Tedco Bus Centre, Viking Industrial Park, Jarrow, Tyne & Wear, NE32 3DT Tel: 0191-428 3362 Fax: 0191-428 3314 E-mail: homeshields@hotmail.co.uk

KITCHEN PLASTIC GOODS

George Wilkinson Burnley Ltd, Progress Works, Elm Street, Burnley, Lancashire, BB10 1PB Tel: (01282) 415511 Fax: (01282) 433112 E-mail: info@progresshousewares.com

R H Products & The Sleep Doctor, 87-89 Shaw Street, St. Helens, Merseyside, WA10 1EN Tel: (01744) 733622 Fax: (01744) 733623 E-mail: roger9000h@hotmail.com

KITCHEN TEXTILE GOODS

Probus Housewares, Unit 19 Empire Industrial Park, Aldridge, Walsall, WS9 8UQ Tel: (01922) 743586 Fax: (01922) 452484 E-mail: sales@probusmayfair.co.uk

KITCHEN UNIT DOOR HANDLES

▶ David Edgar Kitchen Designs, 228 Spearing Road, High Wycombe, Buckinghamshire, HP12 3LA Tel: (01494) 472247 E-mail: daveedgar@rock.com

▶ Gates D I Y, 6 Vesey Path, London, E14 6BT Tel: (020) 7987 4045 Fax: (020) 7987 4015 E-mail: info@gatesdiy.com

▶ Redwood Kitchens, 81 Tamar Way, Wokingham, Berkshire, RG41 3UB Tel: 0118-977 2233 Fax: (0845) 2265658 E-mail: sales@redwoodkitchens.co.uk

KITCHEN UNIT DOORS

Intoto Furniture, 46-48 Barbourne Road, Worcester, WR1 1HU Tel: (01905) 24760 Fax: (01905) 726003 E-mail: worcester@intoto.co.uk

KITCHEN UNITS

▶ Bespoke Kitchens, 1 Hillcrest, Stoodleigh, Tiverton, Devon, EX16 9PJ Tel: (01398) 351467

▶ Brighton & Hove Removals, 190 Portland Road, Hove, East Sussex, BN3 5QN Tel: (01273) 735111 E-mail: sales@brightonandhovekitchens.com

▶ Canty Designs Ltd, 17 Westbourne Avenue, Hull, HU5 3HN Tel: (01480) 491654 Fax: (0870) 7627278 E-mail: info@cantydesigns.com

▶ Dorset Kitchen & Bathroom Studio, Unit 14 Jubilee Enterprise Centre, 15 Jubilee Close, Weymouth, Dorset, DT4 7BS Tel: (01305) 766776 Fax: (01305) 766776

▶ Essex Specialised Joinery, Essexquay House, Quayside Industrial Estate, Maldon, Essex, CM9 5FA Tel: (01621) 843384 Fax: (01621) 843411

J A P Contracts, Unit K4 Bentalls Complex, Colchester Road, Heybridge, Maldon, Essex, CM9 4GE Tel: (01621) 855177 Fax: (01621) 855080 E-mail: info@japcontracts.com

▶ Kirkland Kitchens & Joinery Co. Ltd, The Old Cooperage, Gatebeck, Kendal, Cumbria, LA8 0HW Tel: (01539) 566999 Fax: (01539) 567733 E-mail: info@kirkland-kitchens.co.uk

▶ Kitchen Heaven, 26 Nibley Lane, Iron Acton, Bristol, BS37 9UP Tel: (01454) 228100 E-mail: sales@kitchenheaven.co.uk

Niche Kitchens, 28 Kay Street, Rossendale, Lancashire, BB4 7LS Tel: (01706) 217121 Fax: (01706) 212893 E-mail: info@nichekitchens.co.uk

▶ R Austin, 35 Searle Way, Eight Ash Green, Colchester, CO6 3QS Tel: (01206) 572217 Fax: (01206) 572217

▶ Redwood Kitchens, 81 Tamar Way, Wokingham, Berkshire, RG41 3UB Tel: 0118-977 2233 Fax: (0845) 2265658 E-mail: sales@redwoodkitchens.co.uk

Rubber Duck Home Improvements, 361 Holburn Street, Aberdeen, AB10 7FQ Tel: (01224) 212397

▶ Verona Kitchens Ltd, 24 Grasgarth Close, London, W3 9HS Tel: (020) 8993 1540 Fax: (020) 8993 1540 E-mail: sales@veronakitchens.co.uk

WOODLAND LINE, INGLENOOK COTTAGE, MILL LANE, HORSEMANS GREEN, WHITCHURCH, SHROPSHIRE, SY13 3DT Tel: 01948 830334 Fax: 01948 830334 E-mail: ingrid.geoff@tesco.net

KITCHEN UNITS OR WORKTOPS

Ace Kitchens, 47-57 Feeder Road, Bristol, BS2 0SE Tel: 0117-971 3682 Fax: 0117-977 7004

Allied Manufacturing, Sarena House Grove Park Industrial Estate, Grove Park, London, NW9 0EB Tel: (020) 8905 8046 Fax: (020) 8200 9510 E-mail: sandra.mcguire@kingswood-allied.co.uk

Ashbee & Wood, 50 Ormside Way, Redhill, RH1 2LW Tel: (01737) 765711 Fax: (01737) 778579 E-mail: asbeewood@hardtoforget.co.uk

KITCHEN UNITS OR WORKTOPS – *continued*

Athena Solid Surfaces, 14 Sedling Road, Wear Industrial Estate, Washington, Tyne & Wear, NE38 9BZ Tel: 0191-416 7275 Fax: 0191-417 7510
E-mail: admin@athenasolidsurfaces.co.uk
Chamois Furnishings Ltd, Units 1-4, Showell Road, Wolverhampton, WV10 9LN
Tel: (01902) 864685 Fax: (01902) 865828
E-mail: sales@chamois.co.uk
F.G. Collier Kitchens & Bathrooms Ltd, 29-35 Edward Street, Westbury, Wiltshire, BA13 3BL
Tel: (01373) 822227 Fax: (01373) 824704
E-mail: sales@fgcollier.com
Commodore Kitchens Ltd, Acorn House, Gumley Road, Grays, Essex, RM20 4XP Tel: (01375) 382323 Fax: (01375) 394955
E-mail: info@commodorekitchens.co.uk
Complete Kitchens, 56-58 Springbank Road, London, SE13 6SN Tel: (020) 8852 5926
Fax: (020) 8244 0907
E-mail: completekitchens@talk21.com
Dennis & Robinson Ltd, Blenheim Road, Lancing, West Sussex, BN15 8UH Tel: (01903) 755321
Fax: (01903) 750679
E-mail: sales@manhattan.co.uk
G S K Fabrications, 3 Capel Road, Clydach, Swansea, SA6 5PZ Tel: (01792) 849494
Fax: (01792) 849494
E-mail: stephen@gsk-fabrications.co.uk
▶ International Kitchens & Bedrooms, 753 Holderness Road, Hull, HU8 9AR Tel: (01482) 375251 Fax: (01482) 711364
E-mail: enquiries@internationalkitchens.co.uk
J C Kitchens, Unit A2 Lintown Trading Estate, Old Wellington Road, Eccles, Manchester, M30 9QG Tel: 0161-788 8371 Fax: 0161-707 4217
▶ The Kitchen Workshop, Norwich, Tel: 01603 702344
E-mail: enquiries@the-kitchen-workshop.co.uk
Leicester Bar Fitting Co. Ltd, West Avenue, Wigston, Leicestershire, LE18 2FB
Tel: 0116-288 4897 Fax: 0116-281 3122
E-mail: sales@leicesterbarfitting.co.uk
Maghera Joinery Works Ltd, 100 Glen Road, Maghera, County Londonderry, BT46 5JG
Tel: (028) 7964 2501 Fax: (028) 7964 4181
E-mail: info@beavercabinets.co.uk
Magnet Ltd, Woodbridge Road, Guildford, Surrey, GU1 1DP Tel: (01483) 565411 Fax: (01483) 536522
Magnet Ltd, 65-67 Holmes Road, London, NW5 3AN Tel: (020) 7267 1149 Fax: (020) 7267 1149
E-mail: kentish.branch@magnet.co.uk
Magnet Ltd, 2 Salter Street, London, NW10 6UN
Tel: (020) 8960 4333 Fax: (020) 8964 0271
E-mail: willesden.branch@magnet.co.uk
Magnet Ltd, Leeway Industrial Estate, Newport, Gwent, NP19 4SL Tel: (01633) 274795
Fax: (01633) 277276
Magnet Ltd, Newington Road, Ramsgate, Kent, CT12 6ED Tel: (01843) 583147 Fax: (01843) 596276
Magnet Ltd, Unit 3a Redhill Distribution Centre, Salbrook Road, Redhill, RH1 5DY Tel: (01293) 824277 Fax: (01293) 824287
Magnet Ltd, Midland Sawmills, Broughton Road, Skipton, North Yorkshire, BD23 1RT
Tel: (01756) 798011 Fax: (01756) 700408
Maurice Lay Ltd, Fourth Way, Bristol, BS11 8DW
Tel: 0117-938 1900 Fax: 0117-938 2446
E-mail: sales@mlay.co.uk
Modern Laminates, 179b Queens Road, Watford, WD17 2QJ Tel: (01923) 229029 Fax: (01923) 246308
Norlica Plastics Ltd, 26-29 Rutherford Close, Leigh-on-Sea, Essex, SS9 5LQ Tel: (01702) 522945 Fax: (01702) 520140
Oakland Kitchens & Bedrooms Ltd, 14 Tile Cross Trading Estate, Tile Cross Road, Birmingham, B33 0NW Tel: 0121-779 5732 Fax: 0121-779 5732
P Hooper Designs, 1 Buckholt Business Centre, Buckholt Drive, Worcester, WR4 9ND
Tel: (01905) 457858 Fax: (01905) 757477
E-mail: sales@phooperdesigns.co.uk
Panelkraft Kitchen Planners, Unit 16d Birkdale Close, Manners Industrial Estate, Ilkeston, Derbyshire, DE7 8YA Tel: 0115-944 0911
Fax: 0115-932 6119
Pfleiderer Industry, Oakfield House, Springwood Way, Tytherington Business Park, Macclesfield, Cheshire, SK10 2XA Tel: (01625) 660410 Fax: (01625) 617301
E-mail: info@pfleiderer.co.uk
Potter Cowan & Co Belfast Ltd, Phoenix House, 20 Duncrue Cresent, Belfast, BT3 9BW
Tel: (028) 9037 0050 Fax: (028) 9077 7333
E-mail: pottercowan@btconnect.com
Programme Products UK Ltd, Newcourt Farm, Huntington Lane, Huntington, Hereford, HR4 7RA Tel: (01432) 354133 Fax: (01432) 270111
E-mail: sales@programmeproducts.co.uk
Q A Ironbridge Ltd, Lightmoor, Telford, Shropshire, TF4 3QN Tel: (01952) 432071
Fax: (01952) 432322
R C Marble & Sons Ltd, 158a Ovenden Road, Halifax, West Yorkshire, HX3 5QG Tel: (01422) 345990 E-mail: sales@rcmarble.co.uk
Richardson Cardy, 44a-48 Railway Street, Lisburn, County Antrim, BT28 1XP Tel: (028) 9267 8884 Fax: (028) 9266 3509
Rixonway Kitchens Ltd, Churwell Vale, Shaw Cross Business Park, Dewsbury, West Yorkshire, WF12 7RD Tel: (01924) 431300
Fax: (01924) 431301
E-mail: sales@rixonway.co.uk
▶ Rocky Tops, Unit 12c4, Anniesland Business Park, Glasgow, G13 1EU Tel: 0141-954 2455
Fax: 0141-954 2455
E-mail: kkirchmann@rockytops.co.uk
Stoneham plc, Powerscroft Road, Sidcup, Kent, DA14 5DZ Tel: (020) 8300 8181 Fax: (020) 8300 8183 E-mail: kitchens@stoneham.plc.uk
Stratton Woodcraft, Foxcote House, Broad Lane, East Chinnock, Yeovil, Somerset, BA22 9ES
Tel: (01935) 862776 Fax: (01935) 862776
R.J. Thompson, 50 Whalfedale Avenue, Dacre, Harrogate, North Yorkshire, HG2 0AU
Tel: (07973) 522404 Fax: (01423) 780001
Thomson Bros, D2 Up A Ringway, Bounds Green Industrial Estate, London, N11 2UD Tel: (020) 8361 1222 Fax: (020) 8361 1666
E-mail: enquiries@thomsonbrothers.com
Tramar Trading Ltd, Trinity Buoy Wharf, 64 Orchard Place, London, E14 0JW Tel: (020) 7093 1155 Fax: (020) 7093 1133
E-mail: info@tramartrading.co.uk
W Marfitt Kitchens & Bedrooms, 108a Upper Aughton Road, Southport, Merseyside, PR8 5EX Tel: (01704) 563701 Fax: (01704) 562313

KITCHEN UNITS, FREE STANDING

▶ Canty Designs Ltd, 17 Westbourne Avenue, Hull, HU5 3HN Tel: (01480) 491654
Fax: (0870) 7627278
E-mail: info@cantydesigns.com
▶ R Austin, 35 Searle Way, Eight Ash Green, Colchester, CO6 3QS Tel: (01206) 572217
Fax: (01206) 572217

KITCHEN UTENSILS

Afe Online, Unit 20 Centurion Way, Meridian Business Park, Leicester, LE19 1WJ
Tel: (01827) 309190 Fax: (0800) 525829
E-mail: sales@afeonline.net
Caterquip Midlands, 4 Albion Parade, Kingswinford, West Midlands, DY6 0NP
Tel: (01384) 402345 Fax: (01384) 402345
Delfinware, Pennypot Industrial Estate, Pennypot, Hythe, Kent, CT21 6PE Tel: (01303) 266061
Fax: (01303) 261080
E-mail: sampsonwwp@aol.com
Fiskars (U K) Ltd, Newlands Avenue, Brackle Industrial Estate, Bridgend, Mid Glamorgan, CF31 2XA Tel: (01656) 655595 Fax: 01656 659582 E-mail: sales@fiskars.com
Kenwood Appliances plc, New Lane, Havant, Hampshire, PO9 2NH Tel: (023) 9247 6000
Fax: (023) 9239 2400
E-mail: enquiries@kenwood.co.uk
Kuhn Rikon (UK) Ltd, Landport Road, Wolverhampton, WV2 2QJ Tel: (01902) 458410 Fax: (01902) 458160
E-mail: gourmets@kuhnrikon.demon.co.uk
Le Creuset (UK) Ltd, 4 Stephenson Close, East Portway, Andover, Hampshire, SP10 3RU
Tel: (01264) 343900 Fax: (01264) 356396
Magnet Ltd, 2 Morley Street, Nottingham Road, Loughborough, Leicestershire, LE11 1EW
Tel: (01509) 610484 Fax: (01509) 235990
E-mail: loughbroug.branch@magnet.co.uk
Metaltex UK Ltd, Brunleys, Kiln Farm, Milton Keynes, MK11 3HR Tel: (01908) 262062
Fax: (01908) 262162
E-mail: info@metaltex.com
R G Bennett & Co. Ltd, 60 Colvey Road, Dartford, DA1 1UH Tel: (01322) 224258
Fax: (01322) 289660
E-mail: sales@rgbennett.co.uk
Radmore Agencies Ltd, Perry House, Torton, Kidderminster, Worcestershire, DY10 4HY
Tel: (01299) 250621 Fax: (01299) 251444
T & G Woodware Ltd, Old Mill Road, Portishead, Bristol, BS20 7BX Tel: (01275) 841841
Fax: (01275) 841800
E-mail: info@tg-woodware.com
Thomas Plant (Birmingham) Ltd, Plumbob House Valepits Road, Garretts Green Trading Estate, Birmingham, B33 0TD Tel: 0121-604 6000
Fax: 0121-604 2222
E-mail: info@kitchencraft.co.uk

KITCHEN VEGETABLE CUTTING MACHINES

▶ Sinks & Appliances (UK) Ltd, 9 Tudor Court, Church Lane, Ash Green, Coventry, CV7 9GX
Tel: (024) 7636 1721 Fax: (024) 7636 5214
E-mail: sales@sinksandappliances.com

KITCHENWARE, PINE/WOODEN

Avon Pine Ltd, 34 Old Broughton Road, Melksham, Wiltshire, SN12 8BX Tel: (01225) 700878 Fax: (01225) 793540
E-mail: sales@avonpine.co.uk
C T Finishings (Services) (Manufacturing), Unit 29 Enterprise House, Balloo Industrial Estate, Bangor, County Down, BT19 7QT Tel: (028) 9127 1525 Fax: (028) 9127 0080
Chanterlands Pine Centre, 157 Chanterlands Avenue, Hull, HU5 3TJ Tel: (01482) 492682
Fax: (01482) 492682
George Wilkinson Burnley Ltd, Progress Works, Elm Street, Burnley, Lancashire, BB10 1PB
Tel: (01282) 415511 Fax: (01282) 433112
E-mail: info@progresshousewares.com

KITCHENWARE, STAINLESS STEEL

▶ Cookmate South West, 15 High Street, Barnstaple, Devon, EX31 1BG Tel: (01271) 373341 Fax: (01271) 373341
E-mail: cookmate@btconnect.com
▶ Functional Art, 127 Homesdale Road, Bromley, BR2 9LE Tel: (0796) 7077808
E-mail: rosanna@functional-art.co.uk

KITE BUGGIES

▶ Air Assault Kiteboarding, Air Assault Ltd, Horley, Surrey, RH6 7JX Tel: 07739 733600
E-mail: info@air-assault.com
▶ Atmosphere Kites, 137 St. Georges Road, Bristol, BS1 5UW Tel: 0117-908 7153
E-mail: sales@atmospherekites.com

KITES

Brookite Ltd, Brightly Mill, Okehampton, Devon, EX20 1RR Tel: (01837) 53315 Fax: (01837) 53223 E-mail: enquiries@brookite.com
Coastguard Kites, Outwood, Redhill, RH1 5QB
Tel: (0870) 2401018
E-mail: info@coastguard-kites.com
▶ Western Isles Kite Co., West View, Aird Timsgarry, Isle of Lewis, HS2 9JA Tel: (01851) 672771 E-mail: info@wikc.co.uk

KNEE OPERATED THERMOSTATIC MIXING VALVES

Broen Valves Ltd, 7 Cleton Street Business Park, Cleton Street, Tipton, West Midlands, DY4 7TR Tel: 0121-522 4505 Fax: 0121-522 4535 E-mail: broenvalves@broen.com

KNIFE DISTRIBUTORS OR AGENTS

Bishop's Express, 8-9 Flexi Units, Budlake Road, Marsh Barton Trading Estate, Exeter, EX2 8PY
Tel: (01392) 271237 Fax: (01392) 272171
Martor Direct UK Ltd, Ahed House, Sandbeds Trading Estate, Ossett, West Yorkshire, WF5 9ND Tel: (01924) 281333 Fax: (01924) 281444
E-mail: dennis@martor-uk-demon.co.uk

KNIFE GATE VALVES

Erhard Valves Ltd, Unit 4, Buckingham Close, Bermuda Industrial Estate, Nuneaton, Warwickshire, CV10 7JT Tel: (024) 7635 4470
Fax: (024) 7635 0225
E-mail: sales@erhardvalves.co.uk
Kempster Engineering Ltd, 1 Astra Centre, Royle Barn Road, Rochdale, Lancashire, OL11 3DT
Tel: (01706) 345599 Fax: (01706) 657396
E-mail: sales@kempsteruk.com
S & P Spanarc Ltd, Berwick House, 32 Dartford Road, Sevenoaks, Kent, TN13 3TQ
Tel: (01732) 743456 Fax: (01732) 742922
E-mail: chris.guinane@spanarc.co.uk
▶ Swiss Valve Supply Ltd, 2 Rose Court Maytum Farm, Vanity Lane, Linton, Maidstone, Kent, ME17 4BP Tel: (01622) 746945 Fax: (01622) 749406
E-mail: swissvalvesupply@btconnect.com

KNITTED ELASTIC

H Seal & Co. Ltd, Church Lane, Whitwick, Coalville, Leicestershire, LE67 5DJ
Tel: (01530) 832351 Fax: (01530) 813382
E-mail: sales@hseal.co.uk

KNITTED FABRICS

A Rowe Ltd, Unit 24 Newhaven Business Park, Barton Lane, Eccles, Manchester, M30 0HH
Tel: 0161-787 8150 Fax: 0161-787 8140
E-mail: sales@arowe.co.uk
Arc Fabrics Ltd, 47 Morris Road, Leicester, LE2 6BR Tel: 0116-270 0702
E-mail: arcfabrics@aol.com
Ava Knit GB Ltd, Dodwells Bridge Industrial Estate, Jacknell Road, Hinckley, Leicestershire, LE10 3BS Tel: (01455) 636419
Fax: (01455) 619989
Cannon Street Jersey Fabrics Ltd, Ashley Works, Ashley Road, London, N17 9LJ Tel: (020) 8885 9400 Fax: (020) 8885 9410
E-mail: enquiries@csjf.co.uk
Clarkson Knitting Ltd, Western Industrial Estate, Lon-Y-Llyn, Caerphilly, Mid Glamorgan, CF83 1XJ Tel: (029) 2086 1411 Fax: (029) 2086 0127
E-mail: paulslevin@clarksonknitting.com
Connoisseur Cashmere Ltd, 59 Huddersfield Road, Mirfield, West Yorkshire, WF14 8AA
Tel: (01924) 490044 Fax: (01924) 492637
E-mail: sales@connoisseurcashmere.com
Dawson Fur Fabrics Ltd, Saville Road, Skelmanthorpe, Huddersfield, HD8 9EE
Tel: (01484) 863433 Fax: (01484) 865635
Fleming's Textiles Ltd, Belford Mills, Lawson Street, Kilmarnock, Ayrshire, KA1 3HZ
Tel: (01563) 525203 Fax: (01563) 522022
Flexistyle Ltd, 446 Gipsy Lane, Leicester, LE4 9DB Tel: 0116-276 8442 Fax: 0116-276 8443
H O Bowley, Hudson Street, Loughborough, Leicestershire, LE11 1EJ Tel: (01509) 212161
Fax: (01509) 212167
J.F. Hodgett & Co. Ltd, 66 Bedford Street South, Leicester, LE1 3JR Tel: 0116-251 0705
Fax: 0116-251 2877
E-mail: jfhodgett@hotmail.com
J & J Fabrics (Coventry) Ltd, 113-113A Eagle Street, Foleshill, Coventry, CV1 4GP Tel: (024) 7625 1261 Fax: (024) 7622 3589
E-mail: jagdishpopat@aol.com
J T Knitting Ltd, Dobroyd Mills, New Mill, Holmfirth, HD9 1AF Tel: (01484) 685415
Fax: (01484) 686119
Kintyre Of Scotland Ltd, Victoria Rd, Hawick, Roxburghshire, TD9 7AH Tel: (01450) 72788
Fax: (01450) 360207
E-mail: info@pringlescotland.com
Laxmi Investments Ltd, 123 Barkby Road, Leicester, LE4 9LG Tel: 0116-276 6625
Fax: 0116-246 0787
Maxknit Fabrics Ltd, 9 Bath Street, Leicester, LE4 7QE Tel: 0116-266 4793 Fax: 0116-266 1348
Maytex Fabrics Ltd, Curzon Works, Curzon Street, Leicester, LE1 2HH Tel: 0116-262 4422
Fax: 0116-262 4447
E-mail: maytexfab@aol.com
Pauls Knitwear Co. Ltd, Units 10-14 The Bridge Trading Estate, Bridge St North, Smethwick, West Midlands, B66 2BZ Tel: 0121-525 9595
Fax: 0121-558 7930
R Hardaker & Co. Ltd, Ashley House, Ashley Lane, Shipley, West Yorkshire, BD17 7DB
Tel: (01274) 589166 Fax: (01274) 531511
E-mail: mail@hardakers.com
Simplex Knitting Ltd, Bye Pass Road, Beeston, Nottingham, NG9 5HN Tel: 0115-925 4980
Fax: 0115-943 0772
E-mail: enquiries@simplexknittingcompany.ltd.uk
Slip A Way, Slip Away, Lansallos Street, Polperro, Looe, Cornwall, PL13 2QU Tel: (01503) 272958
W Ball & Son Holdings Ltd, Albion Works, Burr Lane, Ilkeston, Derbyshire, DE7 5JD
Tel: 0115-932 2403 Fax: 0115-944 0630
E-mail: sales@baltex.co.uk
Wings Knitwear Co., 32-35 Walsall Road, Willenhall, West Midlands, WV13 2EG
Tel: (01902) 606867 Fax: (01902) 633365

KNITTED MESH ELECTRONIC SHIELDING

P & P Technology Ltd, 1 Kestrel Park, Finch Drive, Springwood Industrial Estate, Braintree, Essex, CM7 2SF Tel: (01376) 550525
Fax: (01376) 552389 E-mail: info@p-p-t.co.uk
R F I Shielding Ltd, Warner Drive, Springwood Industrial Estate, Braintree, Essex, CM7 2YW
Tel: 01342 315044 Fax: (01376) 346442

KNITTED TRIMMINGS

▶ Knitted Trimmings, 3 Fosse Way, Syston, Leicester, LE7 1NF Tel: 0116-327 0336
Fax: 0116-327 0336
E-mail: info@uk-trims.co.uk
Manor Signs, 62 Knighton Lane, Leicester, LE2 8BE Tel: (0116) 283 5007 Fax: (0116) 283 8946
Pauls Knitwear Co. Ltd, Units 10-14 The Bridge Trading Estate, Bridge St North, Smethwick, West Midlands, B66 2BZ Tel: 0121-525 9595
Fax: 0121-558 7930

KNITTED WIRE MESH

Knitwire Products, Dalton Court, Chadwick Road, Runcorn, Cheshire, WA7 1PU Tel: (01928) 566996 Fax: (01928) 566996
E-mail: sales@knitwire.com
Multi Weldmesh Ltd, Heasandford Industrial Estate, Widow Hill Road, Burnley, Lancashire, BB10 2TJ Tel: (01282) 425300 Fax: (01282) 422204
Wirecloth Sales & Development Ltd, 11a East View, Grappenhall, Warrington, WA4 2QH
Tel: (01925) 268417 Fax: (01925) 604861
E-mail: wireclothsales@aol.com

KNITTING MACHINE STANDS

Ultramatrix Production Services Ltd, Farfield Works, Birds Green, Romsley, Bridgnorth, Shropshire, WV15 6HJ Tel: (01746) 780360
Fax: (01746) 780933

KNITTING MACHINERY

Craft Engineering International Ltd, Lower Granby Street, Ilkeston, Derbyshire, DE7 8DJ
Tel: 0115-932 2810 Fax: 0115-944 0048
E-mail: sales@craftex.co.uk

KNITTING MACHINERY – *continued*

John C Laurie Textile Engineers Ltd, Teviot CR, Hawick, Roxburghshire, TD9 9RE Tel: (01450) 373149 Fax: (01450) 373091 E-mail: kjohnson@johnclaurie.com

Stoll UK Ltd, Craven Street, Leicester, LE1 4BX Tel: 0116-253 8296 Fax: 0116-253 8219 E-mail: sales@stolluk.co.uk

KNITTING MACHINERY ACCESSORIES, ANCILLARY EQUIPMENT OR COMPONENTS

Craft Engineering International Ltd, Lower Granby Street, Ilkeston, Derbyshire, DE7 8DJ Tel: 0115-932 2810 Fax: 0115-944 0048 E-mail: sales@craftex.co.uk

Dukerswell Engineers Ltd, 52 Buckland Road, Maidstone, Kent, ME16 0SH Tel: (01622) 757710 Fax: (01622) 755516 E-mail: dukerswell@skynow.net

Inchlines Ltd, 11 Hilltop Road, Hamilton Industrial Park, Leicester, LE5 1TT Tel: 0116-276 5111 Fax: 0116-276 6596 E-mail: info@inchlines.com

Kern-Liebers Ltd, Corringham Road Industrial Estate, Gainsborough, Lincolnshire, DN21 1QB Tel: (01427) 612085 Fax: (01427) 610301 E-mail: kl-uk@kern-liebers.com

Karl Mayer Textile Machinery Ltd, Kings Road, Shepshed, Loughborough, Leicestershire, LE12 9HT Tel: (01509) 502056 Fax: (01509) 508065 E-mail: mhyeabsley@karlmayer.co.uk

Monarch Knitting Machinery UK Ltd, 74 Boston Road, Beaumont Leys, Leicester, LE4 1BG Tel: 0116-235 1502 Fax: 0116-236 7201 E-mail: general@monarchknitting.co.uk

KNITTING YARN

Ahmad Textiles, Ahmad House, Downham Street, Bradford, West Yorkshire, BD3 9QY Tel: (01274) 727069 Fax: (01274) 390407 E-mail: info@ahmadtextiles.co.uk

F W Bramwell & Co Ltd, Old Empress Mills, King Street, Colne, Lancashire, BB8 9HU Tel: (01282) 860388 Fax: (01282) 860389 E-mail: info@bramwellcrafts.co.uk

King Cole Ltd, Merrie Mills, Old Souls Way, Crossflatts, Bingley, West Yorkshire, BD16 2AX Tel: (01274) 561331 Fax: (01274) 551095 E-mail: enquiries@kingcole.co.uk

KNITWEAR IMPORT MERCHANTS OR AGENTS

By Design plc, Unit 6 Mountheath Industrial Park, Prestwich, Manchester, M25 9WB Tel: 0161-281 4400 Fax: 0161-281 4481 E-mail: worldwide@by-design.co.uk

Caledonian Quilting, Rigby Lane, Bolton, BL2 3EQ Tel: (01204) 304462 Fax: (01204) 309770

Country Concept, Old Church School, Church Hill, Halkyn, Holywell, Clwyd, CH8 8BU Tel: (01352) 780749 Fax: (01352) 780769 E-mail: sales@countryconcept.co.uk

D R Warehouse Ltd, 60-64 Great Hampton Street, Birmingham, B18 6EL Tel: 0121-551 4920 Fax: 0121-551 6504

Hawick Cashmere, 20 Montpellier Parade, Harrogate, North Yorkshire, HG1 2TG Tel: (01423) 502519 Fax: (01423) 502519

B.L. Joshi UK Ltd, 212-214 Ealing Road, Wembley, Middlesex, HA0 4QG Tel: (020) 8903 0653 Fax: (020) 8902 2702 E-mail: bljoshiuk@aol.com

Paul Matthews Ltd, 47 Arbrook Lane, Esher, Surrey, KT10 9EG Tel: (01372) 470234

T S E Ltd, 57 Pingle Drive, Bicester, Oxfordshire, OX26 6WD Tel: (01869) 244030 Fax: (01869) 244045

KNITWEAR/KNITTED OUTERWEAR

A K Knitwear Manufacturing Co., 2 Springmill Street, Bradford, West Yorkshire, BD5 7HF Tel: (01274) 742287

Arctic Knitwear, 2nd Floor 2 Rochdale Road, Manchester, M4 4JR Tel: 0161-839 8092 Fax: 0161-831 9009

Ashfaq Knitwear Ltd, Majid House, 37-49 Devonshire Street North, Manchester, M12 6JR Tel: 0161-272 6368 Fax: 0161-272 6368

B A S Knitwear, 8 Woolley Street, Manchester, M8 8WE Tel: 0161-833 9870 Fax: 0161-833 9870

▶ B S M Knitware, Majid House, 39 Devonshire St North, Manchester, M12 6JR Tel: 0161-273 6033 Fax: 0161-273 6033

▶ Ballantyne Cashmere, 303 Westbourne Grove, London, W11 2QA Tel: (020) 7792 2563 Fax: (020) 7243 5816

Ballantyne Cashmere UK Ltd, Caerlee Mills, Innerleithen, Peeblesshire, EH44 6HP Tel: (01896) 830222 Fax: (01896) 831128 E-mail: enquiries@ballantyne-cashmere.co.uk

Balmoral Knitwear (Scotland) Ltd, 16 Church Lane, Galston, Ayrshire, KA4 8HF Tel: (01563) 820213 Fax: (01563) 821740 E-mail: info@balmoralknitwear.co.uk

Barana P.L.C., 2-3 Charter Street, Leicester, LE1 3UD Tel: 0116-253 9380 Fax: 0116-262 7023 E-mail: enquiries@barana.co.uk

Barkat Knitwear Manufacturing Co. Ltd, 64-66 Dale Street, Manchester, M1 2HR Tel: 0161-832 3388 Fax: 0161-228 7465

Barrie Knitwear, Burnfoot Industrial Estate, Hawick, Roxburghshire, TD9 8RJ Tel: (01450) 365500 Fax: (01450) 365501 E-mail: saleas@barrie.co.uk

James Bennett Ltd, Benco Works, Rugby Road, Hinckley, Leicestershire, LE10 0QG Tel: (01455) 637841 Fax: (01455) 636314 E-mail: sales@james-bennett.co.uk

Best Knitwear Ltd, 24-28 George Leigh Street, Manchester, M4 5DQ Tel: 0161-228 2526 Fax: 0161-228 2522 E-mail: info@bestknitwear.com

BHM Knitwear Ltd, 31 Churchill Way, Fleckney, Leicester, LE8 8UD Tel: 0116-240 2909 Fax: 0116-240 2708 E-mail: info@bhmknitwear.co.uk

▶ Boho Chic, 35 Bridge Street, Dollar, Clackmannanshire, FK14 7DG Tel: (01259) 743311

By Design plc, Unit 6 Mountheath Industrial Park, Prestwich, Manchester, M25 9WB Tel: 0161-281 4400 Fax: 0161-281 4481 E-mail: worldwide@by-design.co.uk

C & H Textile Menders, Market Street, Milnsbridge, Huddersfield, HD3 4HT Tel: (01484) 640850 Fax: (01484) 640850

C P Knitwear, Victoria Centre, Waterloo Road, Blackpool, FY4 1AD Tel: (01253) 406011

Capers UK Ltd, 8 Raymond Road, Leicester, LE3 2AS Tel: 0116-282 5557

▶ Cardrona Cashmere, 50 High Street, Peebles, EH45 8SW Tel: (01721) 724323

Cathryn Grosvenor Ltd, 3 Elystan Street, London, SW3 3NT Tel: (020) 7584 2112 Fax: (020) 7591 0905 E-mail: sales@cathryngrosvenor.co.uk

Cawthra Bros Ltd, Milton Shed, Gibbet Street, Halifax, West Yorkshire, HX1 5BA Tel: (01422) 352464 Fax: (01422) 354215

Celtic Knitwear Ltd, 37 Victoria St, Kirkwall, Orkney, KW15 1DN Tel: 01856 873171

Champ Knitwear, 82 Gipsy Road, Leicester, LE4 6QH Tel: 0116-266 9332 Fax: 0116-266 9332

John Charles, Unit 1, Foundry La, Leicester, LE1 3WU Tel: 0116-251 8565 Fax: 0116-251 8565

Charles Kirk & Co. Ltd, Horton Buildings, Goring Street, Goring-by-Sea, Worthing, West Sussex, BN12 5AD Tel: (01903) 244863 Fax: (01903) 700577 E-mail: sales@charleskirk.co.uk

Cherry Lewis Ltd, Brindley Road, Hinckley, Leicestershire, LE10 3BY Tel: (01455) 610386 Fax: (01455) 631296 E-mail: cherry@cherrylewis.demon.co.uk

▶ Chunkichilli Knitwear, Unit 4, St Arvans Court, Evesham Road, Cheltenham, Gloucestershire, GL52 3AA Tel: (07724) 625469

Chunkies Knitwear & Textiles, Tabernacle Street, Aberaeron, Dyfed, SA46 0BN Tel: (01545) 570144 Fax: (01545) 570144 E-mail: sueholder@hotmail.com

Claire International Ltd, 29 The Bank, Barnard Castle, County Durham, DL12 8PL Tel: (01833) 637325 Fax: (01833) 690880

Commando Knitwear Ltd, Countesthorpe Road, Wigston, Leicestershire, LE18 4PJ Tel: 0116-278 5288 E-mail: info@commando-knitwear.co.uk

Corgi Hosiery Ltd, New Road, Ammanford, Dyfed, SA18 3DS Tel: (01269) 592104 Fax: (01269) 593220 E-mail: sales@corgihosiery.co.uk

Crown Knitwear Ltd, 10-20 Grosvenor Street, Manchester, M1 7JJ Tel: 0161-274 3855 Fax: 0161-274 3855

Dee Kay Knitwear, 227-229 Belgrave Gate, Leicester, LE1 3HT Tel: 0116-253 7560 Fax: 0116-253 7852

Dunnes Stores (Bangor) Ltd, Unit 31 The Concourse, Skelmersdale, Lancashire, WN8 6LN Tel: (01695) 50233 Fax: (01695) 50577

E T H Ltd, 17 Pilrig Street, Edinburgh, EH6 5AN Tel: 0131-553 2721

EilisOg Handknits, 11 Stewartstown Avenue, Belfast, BT11 9GE Tel: (028) 9062 3763 Fax: (028) 9062 3763 E-mail: john_savage@hotmail.com

Emreco International Ltd, 69 Springkell Avenue, Glasgow, G41 4NU Tel: 0141-424 1914 Fax: 0141-423 2997 E-mail: info@emreco.co.uk

Eskimo Knitwear, Vinola Ho, Bruin St, Leicester, LE4 5AB Tel: 0116-266 3895 Fax: 0116-266 5280

Flamborough Marine Ltd, Tower Street, Flamborough, Bridlington, North Humberside, YO15 1PD Tel: (01262) 850943 Fax: (01262) 850943E-mail: gm@flamboroughmarine.co.uk

▶ Funki Fresh, 13 Upper Ground, London, SE1 9PP Tel: (020) 7928 1100

Future Knitting Co. Ltd, 39 Upper Bond Street, Hinckley, Leicestershire, LE10 1RH Tel: (01455) 619053 Fax: (01455) 619053

G B Knitwear, Abbey Park Street, Leicester, LE4 5AF Tel: 0116-291 2994

Garsdale Knitwear Ltd, 64 Chapeltown Street, Manchester, M1 2WQ Tel: 0161-273 7869 Fax: 0161-273 8810

Sue Gee, 9 Arcade, Accrington, Lancashire, BB5 2EL Tel: (01254) 234086

Glenhowe Of Scotland Ltd, Buccleuch Mills, Green Lane, Hawick, Roxburghshire, TD9 0HR Tel: (01450) 373839 Fax: (01450) 370423

Glenmuir Ltd, Linnville Factory, 25-29 Delves Road, Lanark, ML11 9DX Tel: (01555) 662244 Fax: (01555) 665734 E-mail: admin@glenmuir.co.uk

Goldgem Belvoir Ltd, Belvoir House, Paddock Street, Wigston, Leicestershire, LE18 2AN Tel: 0116-288 1909 Fax: 0116-257 0184

Goodbrand Knitwear, New Building Easter Corriehoul, Corgarff, Strathdon, Aberdeenshire, AB36 8YL Tel: (01975) 651433 Fax: (01975) 651442 E-mail: sales@highlandtradingpost.com

Guardian Knitwear Ltd, Majid House, 37-49 Devonshire Street North, Manchester, M12 6JR Tel: 0161-272 8130 Fax: 0161-272 6078

Hardre Knitwear Ltd, 12 Briton Street, Leicester, LE3 0AA Tel: 0116-254 9784 Fax: 0116-285 4624 E-mail: s.harbot@hardreknitwear.co.uk

▶ Harlequin Knitwear, Maranatha, Nelson Road, Forres, Morayshire, IV36 1DR Tel: (01309) 676455

Harley & Co. (Peterhead)Ltd, 44-46 Queen Street, Peterhead, Aberdeenshire, AB42 1TR Tel: (01779) 472109 Fax: (01779) 475924 E-mail: info@harleyofscotland.com

Hilary Highet, Archway Studio, Market Square, Axminster, Devon, EX13 5NJ Tel: (01297) 34538 Fax: (01297) 35627

Eric Hope Knitwear, 58 High Street, Hawick, Roxburghshire, TD9 7EE Tel: (01450) 370549 Fax: (01450) 370549

Horizon Knitwear Manufacturers Ltd, Harkness Street, Manchester, M12 6BT Tel: 0161-273 6410 Fax: 0161-273 2133

House Of Scotland, 467 Oxford Street, London, W1C 2PX Tel: (020) 7499 2404 Fax: (020) 7499 2404

G.H. Hurt & Son Ltd, 65 High Road, Chilwell, Nottingham, NG9 4AJ Tel: 0115-925 4080 Fax: 0115-925 5904

Ice Channel Ltd, International Building, Middleton Business Park, Cleckheaton, West Yorkshire, BD19 5LY Tel: (01274) 870600 Fax: (01274) 870222 E-mail: info@alicecollins.com

▶ J B Textiles, Bluepits Mill, Queensway, Rochdale, Lancashire, OL11 2PG Tel: (01706) 527273

J C Fabrics Ltd, 10 Storey Street, Leicester, LE3 5GR Tel: 0116-262 6100 Fax: 0116-262 9610

J P Knitwear, 36-38 Nansen Road, Leicester, LE5 5FX Tel: 0116-249 0991 Fax: 0116-249 0991

Johnstons, Eastfield Mills, Mansfield Road, Hawick, Roxburghshire, TD9 8AA Tel: (01450) 360500 Fax: (01450) 378532

Johnstons, Eastfield Mills, Mansfield Road, Hawick, Roxburghshire, TD9 8AA Tel: (01450) 360500 Fax: (01450) 378532 E-mail: enquiries@johnstonscashmere.com

Johnstons Of Elgin Ltd, Newmill, Elgin, Morayshire, IV30 4AF Tel: (01343) 554000 Fax: (01343) 554055 E-mail: elgin@johnstoncashmere.com

Just Knitwear Ltd, Evington Business Centre, Chesterfield Road, Leicester, LE5 5LG Tel: 0116-273 4383 Fax: 0116-273 0554

Karim & Sons, 152 Bradford Road, Dewsbury, West Yorkshire, WF13 2HA Tel: (01924) 458131

Kenda Knitwear Ltd, 7 Water Row, Glasgow, G51 3UW Tel: 0141-445 2231 Fax: 0141-445 5114

Kler Knitwear, 46 Jellicoe Road, Leicester, LE5 4FN Tel: 0116-274 0199 Fax: 0116-276 0327 E-mail: info@kler.co.uk

Koshka Knitwear, 250 Canongate, Edinburgh, EH8 8AA Tel: 0131-557 4757 E-mail: koshka@btconnect.com

▶ Le Missey Ltd, 18-20 Grosvenor Street, Manchester, M1 7JJ Tel: 0161-273 1777 Fax: 0161-273 7778

Leicester Trading Co. Ltd, 77-79 Chesterfield Road, Leicester, LE5 5LH Tel: 0116-273 0239 Fax: 0116-273 0237

Lex Knitwear Ltd, 28 Knowsley Street, Manchester, M8 8HQ Tel: 0161-834 9005 Fax: 0161-834 9005

William Lockie & Co. Ltd, 27-28 Drumlanrig Square, Hawick, Roxburghshire, TD9 0AW Tel: (01450) 372645 Fax: (01450) 373846 E-mail: sales@williamlockie.com

Lucky Knitwear Ltd, 53 Marshall Street, Manchester, M4 5FU Tel: 0161-832 1715

Mccornack Country Knitwear, 55 Scotts Street, Annan, Dumfriesshire, DG12 6JH Tel: (01461) 204244 Fax: (01461) 204244

Mackinnon Of Scotland, Kirkshaws Road, Coatbridge, Lanarkshire, ML5 4SL Tel: (01236) 423231 Fax: (01236) 433482

Manchester Knitwear Manufacturing Ltd, 20 Stamford Road, Manchester, M13 0SN Tel: 0161-224 5313

Marco Trading Co. Ltd, Marco House, Tariff Street, Manchester, M1 2FF Tel: 0161-228 6765 Fax: 0161-236 3611 E-mail: info@marco-uk.com

Marshall Deacon Knitwear Ltd, 122 Fairfax Road, Leicester, LE4 9EL Tel: 0116-246 1260 Fax: 0116-274 3528 E-mail: info@marshalldeacon.com

Martin's International, Kirkby Road, Sutton In Ashfield, Nottingham, NG17 1GZ Tel: (01623) 441122 Fax: (01623) 492083 E-mail: post@cooperandroe.co.uk

Merricknits, 80 Queen St, Newton Stewart, Wigtownshire, DG8 6JL Tel: (01671) 403842

Miller's, Borogate, Helmsley, York, YO62 5BN Tel: (01439) 771252

Moorings Knitwear, 11 Main Street, Largs, Ayrshire, KA30 8AA Tel: (01475) 686808

Nafeeze Knitwear, 37 Devonshire St South, Manchester, M13 9DA Tel: 0161-273 3178 Fax: 0161-273 6819 E-mail: info@knitwearemporium.com

▶ Narrow Fabric Services Ltd, The Scotlands, London Road, Coalville, Leicestershire, LE67 3JJ Tel: (01530) 510141 Fax: (01530) 510137

Nornova Knitwear Manufacturers, Muness, Uyeasound, Unst, Shetland, ZE2 9DL Tel: (01957) 755373 Fax: (01957) 755353 E-mail: nornovaknitwear@tiscali.co.uk

Laurence Odie Knitwear Ltd, Hoswick Woollen Mill, Sandwick, Shetland, ZE2 9HR Tel: (01950) 431215 Fax: (01950) 431202

Jeffrey Ohrenstein Ltd, 35 Brunel Road, East Acton, London, W3 7XR Tel: (020) 8740 1100 Fax: (020) 8749 9889 E-mail: jeffrey@jogroup.co.uk

Phull Knitwear Manufacturing Co., 146 Soho Road, Birmingham, B21 9LN Tel: 0121-554 1559 Fax: 0121-554 1559

Pitlochry Of Scotland, 2a Bell Street, St. Andrews, Fife, KY16 9UX Tel: (01334) 472113

Pope Group of Companies, Vernon Place, Northern Court, Nottingham, NG6 0DE Tel: 0115-976 0732 Fax: 0115-927 5169 E-mail: pope-group@lineone.net

Price & Buckland Ltd, Benneworth Close, Hucknall, Nottingham, NG15 6EL Tel: 0115-964 0827 Fax: 0115-964 0769 E-mail: sales@price-buckland.co.uk

James Pringle, 130 Buchanan Street, Glasgow, G1 2JR Tel: 0141-221 3434

Pringle of Scotland Ltd, 141-142 Sloane Street, London, SW1X 9AY Tel: (020) 7259 1660

R S Leisurewear, House of Rs, 26 Smith Dorien Road, Leicester, LE5 4BF Tel: 0116-274 0234 Fax: 0116-246 1259 E-mail: rsgroup@webleicester.co.uk

Ragamuffin, Armadale, Ardvasar, Isle of Skye, IV45 8RS Tel: (01471) 844217 Fax: (01471) 844225

Rannoch Knitwear, 17 Avenue Street, Stewarton, Kilmarnock, Ayrshire, KA3 5AP Tel: (01560) 485454 Fax: 01560 485454

Readyplus Ltd, 2 Rochdale Road, Manchester, M4 4JR Tel: 0161-832 2240 Fax: 0161-832 7236

Reny Martan, Carley Drive, Westfield, Sheffield, S20 8NQ Tel: 0114-251 1598 Fax: 0114-251 1599 E-mail: admin@renymartan.co.uk

▶ Riaz Knitwear U.K. Ltd, 8 Dolphin Street, Ardwick Manchester, Manchester, M12 6BG Tel: 0161-273 2321 Fax: 0161-273 2358

Rose Marie Fashions Ltd, Unit 5 First Floor, Sangra Building, Leicester, LE4 5AF Tel: 0116-262 8844

Rowlinson Knitwear Ltd, Woodbank Mills, Turncroft Lane, Stockport, Cheshire, SK1 4AR Tel: 0161-477 7791 Fax: 0161-480 2083 E-mail: info@rowlinson-knitwear.com

Roxburghe Hand Knits, 4 Dakers Place, Hawick, Roxburghshire, TD9 9JE Tel: (01450) 376689 Fax: (01450) 379571 E-mail: roxhandknits@aol.com

Rutherford Knitted Cape Specialists, Eastfield Mills, Mansfield Rd, Hawick, Roxburghshire, TD9 8AA Tel: 01450 376667 Fax: 01450 378532

Sandon Underwear & Hosiery Co., 21a St James Place, Mangotsfield, Bristol, BS16 9JB Tel: 0117-956 0835 Fax: 0117-961 6242

Sasha Kagan Knitwear, The Studio, Y Fron, Llawr-y-Glyn, Caersws, Powys, SY17 5RJ Tel: (01686) 430436

Scenetex Knitting Co Ltd, 17 Stephenson St, Thornaby, Stockton On Tees, Cleveland, TS17 6AL Tel: 01642 671417 Fax: 01642 646622

Scott Officer Knitwear, West Mill, Mill Wynd, Haddington, East Lothian, EH41 4DB Tel: (01620) 826111 Fax: (01620) 826777

Peter Scott & Co. Ltd, 11 Buccleuch Street, Hawick, Roxburghshire, TD9 0HJ Tel: (01450) 372311 Fax: (01450) 374610 E-mail: sales@peterscott.co.uk

Shawn Knitwear, 16-18 Hyde Road, Manchester, M12 6BW Tel: 0161-273 2841 Fax: 0161-273 7841

Sheena Knitwear Ltd, 46 Hamilton Road, Manchester, M13 0PE Tel: 0161-224 1381 Fax: 0161-224 1674 E-mail: info@sheenaknitwear.com

John Smedley Ltd, Eldon Street, Clay Cross, Chesterfield, Derbyshire, S45 9PE Tel: (01246) 862599 Fax: (01246) 862963

John Smedley Ltd, Rands Lane, Armthorpe, Doncaster, South Yorkshire, DN3 3DY Tel: (01302) 832346 Fax: (01302) 300384

Stevenage Knitting Co. Ltd, 18 Sish Lane, Stevenage, Hertfordshire, SG1 3LS Tel: (01438) 353240 Fax: (01438) 748364

T S S Technology Ltd, 214 Moss Lane, Bramhall, Stockport, Cheshire, SK7 1BD Tel: 0161-439 0005 Fax: 0161-439 0006 E-mail: sales@colorconsultancy.com

John Tulloch Ltd, Rogers Road, Selkirk, TD7 5DT Tel: (01750) 20586 Fax: (01750) 22586 E-mail: office@johntulloch.co.uk

Turner & Jarvis Ltd, Dunton Road, Broughton Astley, Leicester, LE9 6NA Tel: (01455) 282028 Fax: (01455) 285347 E-mail: turnjarvis@aol.com

▶ Uneek Fashions, Unit C, 27 Burleys Way, Leicester, LE1 3BE Tel: 0116-262 6662

▶ Unlimited Knits, 1a Darlton Drive, Arnold, Nottingham, NG5 7JS Tel: 0115-926 3999 Fax: 0115-926 3888

Veejay Knitwear, 62-68 Highcross Street, Leicester, LE1 4NN Tel: 0116-253 7732 Fax: 0116-251 9618

KNITWEAR/KNITTED OUTERWEAR

– *continued*

Village Knitware, 115 Kildoag Rd, Londonderry, BT47 3TH Tel: (028) 7139 7845

Vinola Knitwear, 191 Ross Walk, Leicester, LE4 5HH Tel: 0116-268 1461 Fax: 0116-266 5280

Wings Knitwear Co., 32-35 Walsall Road, Willenhall, West Midlands, WV13 2EG Tel: (01902) 606867 Fax: (01902) 633365

Wolsey, Abbey Meadows, Leicester, LE4 5AD Tel: 0116-262 6755 Fax: 0116-253 0154 E-mail: sales@wolsey.com

Peter Wylie, 26 Noel Street, London, W1F 8GY Tel: (020) 7734 6140 Fax: (020) 7734 4904 E-mail: ptrwylie@aol.com

KNITWEAR/KNITTED OUTERWEAR DESIGNERS

Cathryn Grosvenor Ltd, 3 Elystan Street, London, SW3 3NT Tel: (020) 7584 2112 Fax: (020) 7591 0905 E-mail: sales@cathryngrosvenor.co.uk

▶ Chunkichilli Knitwear, Unit 4, St Arvans Court, Evesham Road, Cheltenham, Gloucestershire, GL52 3AA Tel: (07724) 625469

Envy Designs Ltd, 88 Eltham High Street, London, SE9 1BW Tel: (020) 8850 3444

Rachel Grimmer Ltd, 1 Cambridge Terr, Harrogate, N. Yorkshire, HG1 1PN Tel: (01423) 524236 Fax: (01423) 524236

Kiosk Knitwear & Textiles, 134-146 Curtain Road, London, EC2A 3WB Tel: (020) 7729 6101 Fax: (020) 7729 6101 E-mail: sales@kioskuk.com

KNOBS, BRASS, ANTIQUE

▶ P.R. Hanman (Tools), The Market, Burwash Road, Heathfield, East Sussex, TN21 8RA Tel: (01435) 860760 E-mail: tools@hanman.fsnet.co.uk

KNURLING TOOL MANUFRS

Advanced Technology Machines Ltd, 4 Molly Millars Bridge, Wokingham, Berkshire, RG41 2WY Tel: 0118-977 0099 Fax: 0118-989 2288 E-mail: sales@atmmt.com

Floyd Automatic Tooling Ltd, 17 Bondor Business Centre, London Road, Baldock, Hertfordshire, SG7 6HP Tel: (01462) 491919 Fax: (01462) 490835 E-mail: info@floydautomatic.co.uk

KOI CARP

Koi Water Garden, Lower Morden Lane, Morden, Surrey, SM4 4SJ Tel: (020) 8337 3337 Fax: (020) 8335 3979 E-mail: sales@koiwatergarden.com

KOSHER CATERING

▶ Snowcrest Ice Cream Manufacturers, 1-7 Garman Road, London, N17 0UR Tel: (020) 8365 0000 Fax: (020) 8808 9789

KRAFT PAPER

▶ Forest Companies Ltd, Unit 5, Northfield Farm, Wantage Road, Great Shefford, Hungerford, Berkshire, RG17 7DQ Tel: (01488) 649120 Fax: (01488) 649121 E-mail: sales@forestcompanies.com

Allen Glenold Ltd, Glenold House, Crosby Road, Market Harborough, Leicestershire, LE16 9EE Tel: (01858) 467789 Fax: (01858) 432932 E-mail: sales@glenold.co.uk

LABEL APPLICATION SERVICES

Harland Machine Systems, 2 Michigan Ave, Salford, Manchester, M50 2GY Tel: 0161-848 4800 Fax: 0161-848 4830 E-mail: enquiries@harland-hms.com

LABEL CLOTH/FABRIC

Clark & Terry, Unit 25-26-Newhaven Business Park, Barton Lane, Eccles, Manchester, M30 0HH Tel: 0161-787 7898 Fax: 0161-787 7728 E-mail: clarkandterry@talk21.com

Inkreadible Label Co., 11 Chatto Way, Torquay, TQ1 4UE Tel: (01803) 326818 Fax: (01803) 313102 E-mail: sales@inkreadible.com

North & South Labels Ltd, Unit 1, 56A Bensham Grove, Thornton Heath, Surrey, CR7 8DA Tel: (020) 8653 4477 Fax: (020) 8653 5666 E-mail: sales@nslabels.co.uk

Pennine Labels Ltd, Unit 26 Clayton Street, Nelson, Lancashire, BB9 7PH Tel: (01282) 601602 Fax: (01282) 611566 E-mail: sales@penninelabels.co.uk

LABEL CODING MACHINE/ SYSTEMS MANUFRS

▶ Episys Group Ltd, Newark Close, York Way, Royston, Hertfordshire, SG8 5HL Tel: (01763) 248866 Fax: (01763) 246000

LABEL CORES

Cores & Tubes Ltd, 42 Vulcan Way, New Addington, Croydon, CR0 9UG Tel: (01689) 848586 Fax: (01689) 841468 E-mail: info@coresandtubes.co.uk

J F B Cores Ltd, 7 Boleyn Court, Manor Park, Runcorn, Cheshire, WA7 1SR Tel: (01928) 571812 Fax: (01928) 571813 E-mail: sales@cores.co.uk

Just Paper, Foxlea House, Cliffe-Cum-Lund, Selby, North Yorkshire, YO8 6PE Tel: (01757) 630226 Fax: (01757) 630227 E-mail: sales@justpapertubes.co.uk

LABEL COUNT/INSPECT/VERIFY SYSTEMS

▶ Multi-Tech Systems (Europe) Inc, Alain Young, 11 Pilmuir Estate, Pilmuir Road, Newton Mearns, Glasgow, G77 6PS Tel: (07770) 574573 Fax: 0141-639 7164

LABEL CUTTERS

A & M Rotary, Wheatear, Perry Road, Witham, Essex, CM8 3YY Tel: (01376) 515600 Fax: (01376) 513502

City Press Knives, 101 Weymouth Street, Leicester, LE4 6FR Tel: 0116-266 0709 Fax: 0116-266 0711

Joseph Dixon Tool Company Ltd, Unit 2 Charles Street, Town Wharf Business Park, Walsall, WS2 9LZ Tel: (01922) 622051 Fax: (01922) 721168 E-mail: sales@josephdixon.co.uk

LABEL DISPENSING MACHINES

Newman Labelling Systems Ltd, Queens Road, Barnet, Hertfordshire, EN5 4DL Tel: (020) 8440 0044 Fax: (020) 8449 2890 E-mail: sales@newman.co.uk

Overprint Packaging Ltd, 12 Canal Way, Harefield, Uxbridge, Middlesex, UB9 6TH Tel: (01895) 824090 Fax: (01428) 654769 E-mail: enquiries@prestonprinters.com

LABEL MANUFRS, *See also headings for particular types under labels*

A P L Industrial Ltd, 14 Carlisle Road, London, NW9 0HL Tel: (020) 8205 2444 Fax: (020) 8200 8037 E-mail: info@apl-industrial.co.uk

▶ Aberdeen Label Centre, 78 Great Western Road, Aberdeen, AB10 6QF Tel: (01224) 213313 Fax: (01224) 213316

Acorn Print, 5 Vale Road, Spilsby, Lincolnshire, PE23 5HE Tel: (01790) 754575 Fax: (01790) 754575

Adare Label Converters Ltd, Falconer Road, Haverhill, Suffolk, CB9 7XU Tel: (01440) 714996 Fax: (01440) 766501 E-mail: sales@labelconverters.co.uk

Adcal Labels Ltd, Jayem Works, Gomm Road, High Wycombe, Buckinghamshire, HP13 7DJ Tel: (01494) 530761 Fax: (01494) 461651 E-mail: sales@adcal-labels.co.uk

Andrew Lusk & Co., Lower Addicroft, Liskeard, Cornwall, PL14 5AH Tel: (01579) 363104 Fax: (01579) 363162

Ashley Industrial, South Wraxall, Bradford-on-Avon, Wiltshire, BA15 2RL Tel: (01225) 868083 Fax: 01225 868089 E-mail: japapps@aol.com

Blue Code Labelling Technology, Great Central Way Industrial Estate, Great Central Way, Rugby, Warwickshire, CV21 3XH Tel: (01788) 576100 Fax: (01788) 578900 E-mail: sales@bluecode.co.uk

Business Equipment Distributors, 16 Swanlow Avenue, Winsford, Cheshire, CW7 1PB Tel: (01606) 551755 Fax: (01606) 551755 E-mail: info@business-labels.co.uk

Care Labels, 181 Green La Road, Leicester, LE5 4PD Tel: 0116-276 1511 Fax: 0116-276 1511

CCL Label, Pioneer Way, Castleford, West Yorkshire, WF10 5QU Tel: (01977) 711111 Fax: (01977) 711102

▶ Crown Labels Ltd, 2 The I O Centre, Nash Road, Redditch, Worcestershire, B98 7AS Tel: (01527) 527444 Fax: (01527) 527565

Discount Label Suppliers Ltd, 25-31 Hill Street, Brierfield, Nelson, Lancashire, BB9 5AT Tel: (01282) 696061 Fax: (01282) 696122

Douglas Storrie Labels Ltd, Tudor Works, Tudor Rd, Lytham St. Annes, Lancashire, FY8 2LA Tel: (01253) 643000 Fax: (01253) 643001 E-mail: sales@storrielabels.com

Embassy Labels, Church Road, Tonge, Sittingbourne, Kent, ME9 9AP Tel: (01795) 473988 Fax: (01795) 420249

Eurosoft (Leeds) Ltd, Howcroft House, 919 Bradford Road, Birstall, Batley, West Yorkshire, WF17 9JX Tel: (01924) 474732 Fax: (01924) 475729 E-mail: sales@eurosoft-leeds.co.uk

Evans Graphics Ltd, G Boyn Valley Industrial Estate, Boyn Valley Road, Maidenhead, Berkshire, SL6 4EJ Tel: (0870) 7773630 Fax: (0870) 7773632 E-mail: sales@evansgraphics.co.uk

Excel Labels Ltd, 9 Crown Road, Kings Norton Business Centre, Birmingham, B30 3HY Tel: 0121-486 3300 Fax: 0121-486 3330 E-mail: enquiries@excellabels.co.uk

▶ FJF Labels, 74 Deer Park Drive, Plymouth, PL3 6SR Tel: (01752) 292807 Fax: (01752) 249065

Frank-a-Label, Ellesmere Rd, Weybridge, Surrey, KT13 0HQ Tel: 01932 855526 Fax: 01932 820801

Graphic Arts Coventry, 69-71 Hearsall Lane, Coventry, CV5 6HF Tel: (024) 7667 3415

Harvey Strong Ltd, Unit 1 Oakway Place, Radlett, Hertfordshire, WD7 7NR Tel: (01923) 670088 Fax: (01923) 858004

Hills Labels, 2 Chiswell Green Lane, St. Albans, Hertfordshire, AL2 3AH Tel: (01727) 830429 Fax: (01727) 830429 E-mail: hillslabels@talk21.com

I D Labels Ltd, 1 Eagle Estate, Brookers Road, Billingshurst, West Sussex, RH14 9RZ Tel: (01403) 786800 Fax: (01403) 786700

Image Grafix, 6 Manse Parade, London Road, Swanley, Kent, BR8 8DA Tel: (01322) 614669 Fax: (01322) 614878 E-mail: imagegrafix@btconnect.com

▶ Inspiration, 37 Nelson Road, Caterham, Surrey, CR3 5PP Tel: (01883) 371444 Fax: (01883) 373737

▶ Interlabel Labels & Tags, 106 The Street, Felthorpe, Norwich, NR10 4DH Tel: (01603) 754944 Fax: (01603) 754955 E-mail: sales@interlabel.co.uk

Keystone Media, Units 4 & 5, The Old Creamery, Highbridge, Somerset, TA9 3DF Tel: (01278) 780438 Fax: (01278) 793858

▶ L A Label, 10 Penvale Close, Barripper, Camborne, Cornwall, TR14 0QP Tel: (01209) 718440 Fax: (01209) 718440 E-mail: artwork@lalabels.co.uk

L S Francis, Unit 12a Mayfair Industrial Area, Maldon Road, Latchingdon, Chelmsford, CM3 6LF Tel: (01621) 740924 Fax: (01621) 740924

Label Talk, 145a Gallery Chambers, Connaught Avenue, Frinton-on-Sea, Essex, CO13 9AH Tel: (01255) 850110 Fax: (01255) 850043 E-mail: labeltalk@teliaco.co.uk

Label-Form Ltd, Reform Road, Maidenhead, Berkshire, SL6 8BY Tel: (01628) 782082 Fax: (01628) 770879 E-mail: sales@label-form.co.uk

Labels & Data Systems (UK) Ltd, 9 Cresswell Close, Pinchbeck, Spalding, Lincolnshire, PE11 3TY Tel: 0161-929 8828 Fax: 0161-929 8518 E-mail: labelsdata@aol.com

Labelsco, 29 Moat Way, Barwell, Leicester, LE9 8EY Tel: (01455) 852400 Fax: (01455) 841444 E-mail: sales@labelsco.co.uk

Langley Labels Ltd, Harthall Lane, Kings Langley, Hertfordshire, WD4 8JJ Tel: (01923) 263777 Fax: (01923) 270392 E-mail: info@langleylabels.com

Lara Marketing, 1st Floor, 93 East Street, Chichester, West Sussex, PO19 1HA Tel: (01243) 788006 Fax: (01243) 701347 E-mail: sales@laramarketing.co.uk

Leicester Labels Ltd, 51-53 Baggrave Street, Leicester, LE5 3QW Tel: 0116-251 5625 Fax: 0116-251 5621

▶ Malby, Zylo Works, Sussex Street, Brighton, BN2 0HH Tel: (01273) 607028 Fax: (01273) 571214

Mercury Labels Ltd, Foxtam House, Watts Street, Oldham, OL9 9LQ Tel: 0161-633 2984 Fax: 0161-725 8376 E-mail: accounts@mercurylabels.com

Mervian Label Co., 27 Alexandra Road, Skegness, Lincolnshire, PE25 3QY Tel: (01754) 767178 Fax: (01754) 762219 E-mail: sales@mervian.co.uk

▶ Midco Print & Packaging Ltd, Chantry House Grange Business Park, Enderby Road, Whetstone, Leicester, LE8 6EP Tel: 0116-277 4244 Fax: 0116-277 0167 E-mail: sales@midco-pp.co.uk

Alan Northrop Ltd, Enterprise Way Airedale Business Centre, Keighley Road, Skipton, North Yorkshire, BD23 2TZ Tel: (01756) 700555 Fax: (01756) 795505 E-mail: info@alan-northrop.co.uk

Nuprint Trimmings Ltd, Unit 21 Springtown Industrial Estate, Springtown Road, Londonderry, BT48 0LY Tel: (028) 7128 2080 Fax: (028) 7126 0009

Ormerod Developments Rochdale Ltd, Ormerod House, Caldershaw Business Park, Rochdale, Lancashire, OL12 7LQ Tel: (01706) 646808 Fax: (01706) 640694 E-mail: sales@ormerods.com

▶ P & J Labels Ltd, 18 Wharfedale Road, Ipswich, IP1 4JP Tel: (01473) 747424 Fax: (01473) 747425 E-mail: pjlabels@btconnect.com

Press Labels, Main Road, Sibsey, Boston, Lincolnshire, PE22 0RR Tel: (01205) 750095 Fax: (01205) 750008

R A P Marketing, 24 The Business Village, Wexham Road, Slough, SL2 5HF Tel: (01753) 554160 Fax: (01753) 518532 E-mail: awrap@aol.com

R G S Labels, Units 7 & 8, Roman Way Small Business Park, London Road, Godmanchester, Huntingdon, Cambridgeshire, PE29 2LN Tel: (01480) 456556 Fax: (01480) 456578 E-mail: sales@rgslabels.co.uk

Sharp Labels Ltd, Woodhall Business Park, Sudbury, Suffolk, CO10 1WH Tel: (01787) 880291 Fax: (01787) 881841 E-mail: sales@sharplabels.co.uk

Soabar Marking Systems, 7 Ashville Way, Whetstone, Leicester, LE8 6NU Tel: 0116-284 7000 Fax: 0116-284 7001 E-mail: sales@soabar.co.uk

Speedstick Adhesive Labels Ltd, The Street, Ulcombe, Maidstone, Kent, ME17 1DX Tel: (01622) 843705 Fax: (01622) 843751 E-mail: speedstick@blueyonder.co.uk

▶ Sterling Labels, Lubbards Lodge, Hullbridge Road, Rayleigh, Essex, SS6 9QG Tel: (01268) 782783 Fax: (01268) 783444

Tapekraft Ltd, Unit C Castlehills Court, Howard Road, Eaton Socon, St. Neots, Cambridgeshire, PE19 8ET Tel: (01480) 216161 Fax: (01480) 216162 E-mail: enquiries@tapekraft.co.uk

TCE Ltd, Newstead Industrial Estate, Trentham, Stoke-On-Trent, ST4 8HX Tel: (01782) 643278 Fax: (01782) 657766 E-mail: tce@tcelabels.co.uk

Tutin Garment Labels, 3 Imperial Works, Imperial Road, Nottingham, NG6 9GB Tel: 0115-975 7722 Fax: 0115-975 7744 E-mail: roger@tutin-labels.co.uk

Verdigris Ltd, Unit A 44 Askew CR, London, W12 9DP Tel: (020) 8749 7881 Fax: (020) 8740 6310

▶ Vitesse Labelling Products Ltd, Unit 6 Countess Street, Ashton-under-Lyne, Lancashire, OL6 6UE Tel: 0161-343 3883 Fax: 0161-339 0229 E-mail: vitesselabellingproductsltd@ic24.net

Warren Labels, 6 Ullswater Road, Kettering, Northamptonshire, NN16 8UD Tel: (01536) 410842 Fax: (01536) 417070 E-mail: bunnyjsh@warrenlabels.fsnet.co.uk

The Water Mill Press Ltd, 33-35 Pitcliffe Way, Upper Castle Street, Bradford, West Yorkshire, BD5 7SG Tel: (01274) 738833 Fax: (01274) 738844 E-mail: sales@watermillpress.co.uk

Watershed Packaging Ltd, 30 Chapman Way, Tunbridge Wells, Kent, TN2 3EF Tel: (01892) 515777 Fax: (01892) 510852 E-mail: enquiries@kent.watershed-packaging.co.uk

Weavabel Labels & Tags, 3 Focus Business Park, Focus Way, Yeadon, Leeds, LS19 7DB Tel: 0113-239 1122 Fax: 0113-250 6848

▶ Xebec Labels, Halesfield 17, Telford, Shropshire, TF7 4PW Tel: (01952) 587777 Fax: (01952) 680111

LABEL OVERPRINTING MACHINES

Computalabel International Ltd, 2ND Floor, 53A London Road, Leicester, LE2 0PD Tel: 0116-255 7898 Fax: 0116-255 7899 E-mail: info@computalabel.com

Ixapack UK Ltd, Unit A, King Street, Walsall, WS1 4AF Tel: (01922) 721102 Fax: (01922) 721921 E-mail: enquiries@ixapack.com

Newfoil Machines, Moorhey Street, Oldham, OL4 1JE Tel: 0161-620 5688 Fax: 0161-627 0551 E-mail: sales@newfoilmachines.co.uk

Overprint Packaging Ltd, 12 Canal Way, Harefield, Uxbridge, Middlesex, UB9 6TH Tel: (01895) 824090 Fax: (01428) 654769 E-mail: enquiries@prestonprinters.com

▶ Weyfringe Labelling Systems, Longbeck Road, Marske-by-the-Sea, Redcar, Cleveland, TS11 6HQ Tel: (01642) 490121 Fax: (01642) 490385 E-mail: sales@weyfringe.co.uk

LABEL PRINTERS/ OVERPRINTING SERVICES

Adastra Label Marketing Co. Ltd, 42 Gloucester Way, London, EC1R 0BR Tel: (020) 7278 8020 Fax: (020) 7837 3770 E-mail: sales@adastralabels.com

Advance Bunzl Ltd, West Point, New Hive Lane, Larkfield, Kent, ME20 6XJ Tel: (01622) 764504 Fax: (01622) 208157 E-mail: sales@advancebunzl.com

Allstat Ltd, Bowmans Trading Estate, Bessemer Drive, Stevenage, Hertfordshire, SG1 2DL Tel: (01438) 759084 Fax: (01438) 740958 E-mail: info@allstat.co.uk

Alpha Print & Design, Unit 12, Sedgemount Industrial Park, Bristol Road, Bridgwater, Somerset, TA6 4AR Tel: (01278) 426958 Fax: (01278) 424001 E-mail: alphaprint@ukonline.co.uk

Alsager Printing Co. Ltd, Excalibur Industrial Estate, Fields Road, Alsager, Stoke-on-Trent, ST7 2LX Tel: (01270) 873897 Fax: (01270) 882804

Arkley Labels, Unit 8, Aslton Works, Alston Road, Barnet, Hertfordshire, EN5 4EL Tel: (020) 8441 2011 Fax: (020) 8441 5909

Aspect Print Services Ltd, Main Street, Aslockton, Nottingham, NG13 9AL Tel: (01949) 851611 Fax: (01949) 851609 E-mail: aspect-print@btconnect.com

Aydon Silver & Co. Ltd, Units 1-2 Stoney Lane Industrial Estate, Red Suns Road, Kidderminster, Worcestershire, DY10 2LG Tel: (01562) 820107 Fax: (01562) 822253 E-mail: enquiries@aydonsilver.co.uk

LABEL PRINTERS/OVERPRINTING SERVICES – *continued*

Berkshire Labels Ltd, Swangate, Hungerford, Berkshire, RG17 0YX Tel: (01488) 683628 Fax: (01488) 684186 E-mail: sales@berkshirelabels.co.uk
Blackdown Plant Ltd, The Cross, 2 Midhurst Road, Haslemere, Surrey, GU27 3EE Tel: (01428) 643309 Fax: (01428) 661630 E-mail: sales@blackdownpress.co.uk
Business Equipment Distributors, 16 Swanlow Avenue, Winsford, Cheshire, CW7 1PB Tel: (01606) 551755 Fax: (01606) 551755 E-mail: info@business-labels.co.uk
Caligraving Ltd, Brunel Way, Thetford, Norfolk, IP24 1HP Tel: (01842) 752116 Fax: (01842) 755512
M.S.O. Cleland Ltd, The Linenhall Press, 399 Castlereagh Road, Belfast, BT5 6QP Tel: (028) 9040 0200 Fax: (028) 9070 5446 E-mail: info@mso.com
Compass Printing Packaging Ltd, 49-51 Bridgeman Place, Bolton, BL2 1DE Tel: (01204) 527130 Fax: (01204) 381629 E-mail: mail@compasslabels2002.freeserve.co.uk
Daymark Ltd, Unit 70 Hartlebury Trading Estate, Hartlebury, Kidderminster, Worcestershire, DY10 4JB Tel: (01299) 251365 Fax: (01299) 251386 E-mail: sales@labelsandtags.com
Decorative Sleeves, Unit 6 Pioneer Way, Castleford, West Yorkshire, WF10 5QU Tel: (01977) 510030 Fax: (01977) 521240
Denny Brothers Ltd, Kempson Way, Bury St. Edmunds, Suffolk, IP32 7AR Tel: (01284) 701381 Fax: (01284) 705575 E-mail: denny.bros@dennybros.com
Douglas Storrie Labels Ltd, Tudor Works, Tudor Rd, Lytham St. Annes, Lancashire, FY8 2LA Tel: (01253) 643000 Fax: (01253) 643001 E-mail: sales@storrielabels.com
Easy2name Labels & Tags, 2 Malthouse Cottages, Ecchinswell, Newbury, Berkshire, RG20 4UA Tel: (01635) 298326 Fax: (01635) 298352
Elliott Marshall Signs, Morven Road, Morven Studio, St. Austell, Cornwall, PL25 4PP Tel: (01726) 72863 Fax: (01726) 72863 E-mail: sales@elliottmarshall.com
Eurohill Labels Ltd, 195 Vale Road, Tonbridge, Kent, TN9 1SU Tel: (01732) 770700 Fax: (01732) 770779 E-mail: sales@eurohill.com
Field Box More Labels, Roman Bank, Bourne, Lincolnshire, PE10 9LQ Tel: (01778) 426444 Fax: (01778) 421862
Harlands of Hull Ltd, Burma Drive, Hull, HU9 5SD Tel: (01482) 785300 Fax: (01482) 785329 E-mail: enquiries@harlands.co.uk
Hart Boulton & Co. Ltd, Hampton Street, Joiners Square Industrial Estate, Stoke-on-Trent, ST1 3EX Tel: (01782) 260723 Fax: (01782) 263466
I M B Systems, 298 Nantwich Road, Crewe, CW2 6NY Tel: (01270) 663306 Fax: (01270) 650010 E-mail: imbsystems@btconnect.com
Impact Boston Ltd, Victoria Road, Skegness, Lincolnshire, PE25 3SN Tel: (01754) 767275 Fax: (01754) 613100 E-mail: sales@impactboston.ltd.uk
Inkreadible Label Co., 11 Chatto Way, Torquay, TQ1 4UE Tel: (01803) 326818 Fax: (01803) 313102 E-mail: sales@inkreadible.com
Intereel Group Ltd, Unit 11, Mountbatten Road, Tiverton, Devon, EX16 6SW Tel: (01884) 256364 Fax: (01884) 257898 E-mail: sales@intereel.co.uk
Intereel Group Ltd, Unit 11, Mountbatten Road, Tiverton, Devon, EX16 6SW Tel: (01884) 256364 Fax: (01884) 257898 E-mail: sales@intereel.co.uk
Ixapack UK Ltd, Unit A, King Street, Walsall, WS1 4AF Tel: (01922) 721102 Fax: (01922) 721921 E-mail: enquiries@ixapack.com
Jordison Ltd, Tralee, Kirkleatham Business Park, Redcar, Cleveland, TS10 5SG Tel: (01642) 495270 Fax: (01642) 495271
Label-Form Ltd, Reform Road, Maidenhead, Berkshire, SL6 8BY Tel: (01628) 782082 Fax: (01628) 770879 E-mail: sales@label-form.co.uk
Lancer Labels, Riverview, Blackburn Road, Ribchester, Preston, PR3 3ZQ Tel: (01254) 878744 Fax: (01254) 878280 E-mail: admin@ancerlabelsuk.com
Leyprint Ltd, Leyland Lane, Leyland, PR25 1UT Tel: (01772) 425000 Fax: (01772) 425001 E-mail: info@leyprint.co.uk
Lithoprint Ltd, 4 Earl Haig Road, Hillington Park, Glasgow, G52 4RP Tel: 0141-891 8000 Fax: 0141-810 5496
London Labels Ltd, 20 Oval Road, London, NW1 7DJ Tel: (020) 7267 7105 Fax: (020) 7267 1165
Macfarlane Group Ukltd, 22 Bentinck Street, Kilmarnock, Ayrshire, KA1 4AS Tel: (01563) 525151 Fax: (01563) 539963 E-mail: kwoodhouse@macfarlanelabels.com
Martin Mulligan (UK) Ltd, Barcode House, Shaw Street, St. Helens, Merseyside, WA10 1EN Tel: (01744) 744200 Fax: (01744) 744216 E-mail: sales@martinmulligan.com
National Labels, Unit 70, Hartlebury Trading Estate, Hartlebury, Kidderminster, Worcestershire, DY10 4JB Tel: (01299) 250981 Fax: (01299) 251386 E-mail: enquiries@labelsandtags.com
Norprint Ltd, Horncastle Road, Boston, Lincolnshire, PE21 9HZ Tel: (01205) 365161 Fax: (01205) 364825 E-mail: norprint@norprint.co.uk
North & South Labels Ltd, Unit 1, 56A Bensham Grove, Thornton Heath, Surrey, CR7 8DA Tel: (020) 8653 4477 Fax: (020) 8653 5666 E-mail: sales@nslabels.co.uk
Ovalring Ltd, 60 Prince of Wales Lane, Birmingham, B14 4JY Tel: 0121-436 6060 Fax: 0121-436 6061
P B F Press Ltd, 12 Little Ridge, Welwyn Garden City, Hertfordshire, AL7 2BH Tel: (01707) 372185 Fax: (01707) 375580 E-mail: pbf-press@btconnect.com
P D Labels, Unit 3, Elmcross Business Park, Bradford-On-Avon, Wiltshire, BA15 2AY Tel: (01225) 863627 Fax: (01225) 868152
P F C Group Ltd, Roman Way Business Centre, Berry Hill Industrial Estate, Droitwich, Worcestershire, WR9 9AJ Tel: (01905) 797000 Fax: (01905) 797274 E-mail: marketsales@pfcgroup.co.uk
Packpost (International) Ltd, Griffin House, Griffin Lane, Aylesbury, Buckinghamshire, HP19 8BE Tel: (01296) 487493 Fax: (01296) 392369 E-mail: sales@packpost.co.uk
Pago Ltd, 7 Crown Gate, Wyncolls Road, Severalls Industrial Park, Colchester, CO4 9HZ Tel: (01206) 755206 Fax: (01206) 755210 E-mail: sales@pago.co.uk
Pointer Print, 24 The Green, Hasland, Chesterfield, Derbyshire, S41 0LJ Tel: (01246) 231970 Fax: (01246) 277298 E-mail: pointerprint@vipnet.co.uk
Precision Labelling Systems Ltd, Plows Way, Leeming Bar, Northallerton, North Yorkshire, DL7 9UL Tel: 01677 423533
Premier Labels, 100 Dalsholm Road, Glasgow, G20 0TF Tel: 0141-945 4443 Fax: 0141-945 4449 E-mail: info@premier-labels.co.uk
R B Labels Ltd, 37 Grove Road, Ilkley, West Yorkshire, LS29 9PF Tel: (01943) 468302 Fax: (01943) 850406 E-mail: sales@tradelabels.co.uk
R G S Labels, Units 7 & 8, Roman Way Small Business Park, London Road, Godmanchester, Huntingdon, Cambridgeshire, PE29 2LN Tel: (01480) 456556 Fax: (01480) 456578 E-mail: sales@rgslabels.co.uk
S Q L Ltd, Unit 1a, Stock Road, Southend-on-Sea, SS2 5QF Tel: (01702) 464978 Fax: (01702) 612929 E-mail: paul@sqlsouthend.co.uk
Scott Labels, The Old Saw Mill, Iping Road, Milland, Liphook, Hampshire, GU30 7NA Tel: (01428) 741741 Fax: (01428) 741742
South East Labels, 7 Broomers Hill Park, Broomers Hill Lane, Pulborough, West Sussex, RH20 2RY Tel: (01798) 873738 Fax: (01798) 874538 E-mail: sales@southeastlabels.co.uk
Sutterton Labels, Pinfold Road, Bourne, Lincolnshire, PE10 9HT Tel: (01778) 391637 Fax: (01778) 391638E-mail: sales@slpp.co.uk
Tamar Labels Ltd, Woodlands, Tavistock, Devon, PL19 8JE Tel: (01822) 833330 Fax: (01822) 834484 E-mail: sales@tamarlabels.co.uk
Vale Labels, Unit P Creech Business Park, Creech St. Michael, Taunton, Somerset, TA3 5PX Tel: (01823) 443902 Fax: (01823) 444188 E-mail: info@valelabels.co.uk
Vision Printers Ltd, 25 Colne Valley Business Park, Huddersfield, HD7 5QG Tel: (01484) 847307 Fax: (01484) 846581 E-mail: sales@visionprint.com
Vista Labels Limited, Vista House, Hempshaw Lane, Stockport, Cheshire, SK1 4NB Tel: 0161-477 5151 Fax: 0161-477 9203 E-mail: sales@vistalabels.com
W H P Labels Ltd, 48 Smith Street, Birmingham, B19 3EN Tel: 0121-523 0007 Fax: 0121-523 2221 E-mail: rhwhp@aol.com
Walsall Print Co. Ltd, Midland Road, Walsall, WS1 3QL Tel: (01922) 721272 Fax: (01922) 625950 E-mail: info@walsall-print.co.uk
Zebra Technologies Europe, Pittman Way, Fulwood, Preston, PR2 9ZD Tel: (01772) 797555 Fax: (01772) 693000 E-mail: zebra_ap@zebra.com

LABEL PRINTING

Cee Gee Agencies, Cee Gee House, College Road, Harrow Weald, Harrow, Middlesex, HA3 6EF Tel: (020) 8863 8596 Fax: (020) 8427 1827
Centagraphics Labels & Tags, Pitcairn Works, Pitcairn Road, Ipswich, IP1 5BX Tel: (01473) 463883 Fax: (01473) 462333 E-mail: sales@elabel.co.uk
Codeway Ltd, 13 Telford Way, Severalls Industrial Park, Colchester, CO4 9QP Tel: (01206) 756738 Fax: (01206) 756705 E-mail: sales@codeway.com
E S P Colour, Elgin Drive, Swindon, SN2 8XU Tel: (01793) 438400 Fax: (01793) 530403 E-mail: firstinitial.surname@espcolour.co.uk
▶ Ips, Executive House, Mill Lane, Blaby, Leicester, LE8 4FG Tel: 0116-277 2666 Fax: 0116-276 1199 E-mail: susan@direct-ips.co.uk
Pentagon Press Ltd, Harriot Drive, Heathcote Industrial Estate, Warwick, CV34 6TJ Tel: (01926) 833481 Fax: (01926) 314017
Premier Labels, 100 Dalsholm Road, Glasgow, G20 0TF Tel: 0141-945 4443 Fax: 0141-945 4449 E-mail: info@premier-labels.co.uk
▶ Print Search Ltd, Westinghouse Road, Trafford Park, Manchester, M17 1PJ Tel: 0161-872 8921 Fax: 0161-848 7323 E-mail: sales@princesearchpromotionalproducts.co.uk
Soabar Marking Systems, 7 Ashville Way, Whetstone, Leicester, LE8 6NU Tel: 0116-284 7000 Fax: 0116-284 7001 E-mail: sales@soabar.co.uk
Square One Advertising & Design Ltd, 134 Archer Road, Sheffield, S8 0JZ Tel: 0114-258 4557 Fax: 0114-258 3076 E-mail: info@squareone.co.uk
T H Jordan Ltd, 3 Millar Street, Belfast, BT6 8JZ Tel: (028) 9045 0866 Fax: (028) 9073 2587 E-mail: sales@thjordanltd.com

LABEL PRINTING MACHINE MANUFRS

Ab Graphic International, Carnaby Industrial Estate, Lancaster Road, Carnaby, Bridlington, North Humberside, YO15 3QY Tel: (01262) 671138 Fax: (01262) 606359 E-mail: info@abgint.com
Alpha Systems, 63-65 High Street, Standish, Wigan, Lancashire, WN6 0HD Tel: (01257) 426617 Fax: (01257) 472148 E-mail: info@alphasolutions.co.uk
B M K Industrial I D Systems, 1 Claremont Street, Aberdeen, AB10 6QP Tel: (01224) 213325 Fax: (01224) 213377 E-mail: bmk.id@talk21.com
Bulmers Business Machines Ltd, Royston House, 267 Cranmore Boulevard, Shirley, Solihull, West Midlands, B90 4QT Tel: 0121-745 5529 Fax: 0121-733 6180
Drent (UK) Ltd, 6 Blackburn Industrial Estate, Enterprise Way, Sherburn In Elmet, Leeds, LS25 6NA Tel: (01977) 685098 Fax: (01977) 681040 E-mail: duk@drentuk.com
Finecal Distributors, 2 Temple Trading Estate, Cole Road, Bristol, BS2 0UG Tel: 0117-971 1111 Fax: 0117-977 2326 E-mail: sales@finecal.co.uk
Just Plastics Ltd, The Maltings, Wayford, Norwich, NR12 9LL Tel: (01692) 581000 Fax: (01692) 581848 E-mail: martin@justplastics.co.uk
K P G Europe Ltd, Holkham Road, Orton Southgate, Peterborough, PE2 6TE Tel: 01733 235533 Fax: 01733 235117 E-mail: info@kpgeurope.com
K2 International Trading Ltd, The Kdo Business Park, Little Witley, Little Witley, Worcester, WR6 6LR Tel: (01299) 896959 Fax: (01299) 896965 E-mail: info@kdo.co.uk
Newfoil Machines, Moorhey Street, Oldham, OL4 1JE Tel: 0161-620 5688 Fax: 0161-627 0551 E-mail: sales@newfoilmachines.co.uk
Pago Ltd, 7 Crown Gate, Wyncolls Road, Severalls Industrial Park, Colchester, CO4 9HZ Tel: (01206) 755206 Fax: (01206) 755210 E-mail: sales@pago.co.uk
Weigh Control Systems Ltd, 2 Felton Mill, Felton, Morpeth, Northumberland, NE65 9HL Tel: (01670) 787177 Fax: (01670) 787179
Wood Machines Ltd, 1 Galley Hill Industrial Estate, London Road, Swanscombe, Kent, DA10 0AA Tel: (01322) 385566 Fax: (01322) 384449 E-mail: mail@uemcoltd.com

LABEL PRINTING SERVICES, GARMENT

▶ Franklins International Ltd, Scarva Road, Banbridge, County Down, BT32 3AU Tel: (028) 4062 2230 Fax: (028) 4062 3540 E-mail: info@franklinsgroup.net
▶ Tippetts Trimmings & Smallwares Ltd, 103 Knighton Fields Road West, Leicester, LE2 6LH Tel: 0116-283 5104 Fax: 0116-283 4207 E-mail: p.warren@btopenworld.com

LABEL PRINTING SERVICES, SHORT RUN

▶ ITO, Anson House, Northwick Road, Oxhey, Watford, WD19 6RS Tel: (020) 8428 0288 Fax: (020) 8420 1073 E-mail: info@itowatford.org.uk
▶ Swiss Valley Print Ltd, Unit 9 Trostre Industrial Park, Llanelli, Dyfed, SA14 9UU Tel: (01554) 758758 Fax: (01554) 758758 E-mail: cambrian@clara.net
▶ Verdi Business Forms Ltd, Harold Court House, Church Road, Harold Wood, Romford, RM3 0JX Tel: (01708) 377311 Fax: (01708) 377327 E-mail: enquiries@verdi.co.uk

LABEL PRINTING TAPES

Nuprint Trimmings Ltd, Unit 21 Springtown Industrial Estate, Springtown Road, Londonderry, BT48 0LY Tel: (028) 7128 2080 Fax: (028) 7126 0009

LABEL RIBBONS

Iml Labels & Systems Ltd, 6 Brookdale Road, Thorncliffe Park Estate, Chapeltown, Sheffield, S35 2PW Tel: 0114-246 5771 Fax: 0114-240 3410 E-mail: sales@iml-labels.co.uk

LABEL SLITTING/REWINDING MACHINES

D K Engineering Services, 7 Enterprise Industrial Estate, Enterprise Road, Waterlooville, Hampshire, PO8 0BB Tel: (023) 9259 3947 Fax: (023) 9259 3948 E-mail: sales@dkeltd.co.uk

LABEL STRINGING

A & H Europe Ltd, Unit 24 B, Star Road, Partridge Green, Horsham, West Sussex, RH13 8RA Tel: (01403) 710055 Fax: (01403) 711082 E-mail: sale@aandheurope.com
Eyetag Ltd, Albert Works, Melville Street, Bradford, West Yorkshire, BD7 1JD Tel: (01274) 721332 Fax: (01274) 740196

LABELLING MACHINE/SYSTEMS MANUFRS

Alpha Lettering Systems, 10 New Street, Ossett, West Yorkshire, WF5 8BH Tel: (01924) 275747 Fax: (01924) 275740 E-mail: sales@alphalettering.co.uk
Ashtree Label Systems, 36 Ashtree Hill, Tandragee, Craigavon, County Armagh, BT62 2HP Tel: (028) 3884 9706 Fax: (028) 3884 9706
Atwell Self-Adhesive Labellers, Unit B2 Haysbridge Business Centre, Brickhouse Lane, South Godstone, Godstone, Surrey, RH9 8JW Tel: (01342) 844146 Fax: (01342) 843666 E-mail: sales@atwell-labellers.co.uk
Bizerba UK Ltd, Eastman Way, Hemel Hempstead Industrial Estate, Hemel Hempstead, Hertfordshire, HP2 7DU Tel: (01442) 240751 Fax: (01442) 231328 E-mail: info@bizerba.co.uk
Electro Graph Ltd, 177 Lower High Street, Stourbridge, West Midlands, DY8 1TG Tel: (01384) 378436 Fax: (01384) 392542 E-mail: sales@eguk.com
Harland Machine Systems, 2 Michigan Ave, Salford, Manchester, M50 2GY Tel: 0161-848 4800 Fax: 0161-848 4830 E-mail: enquiries@harland-hms.com
Image Computer Systems Ltd, 27 Cobham Road, Ferndown Industrial Estate, Wimborne, Dorset, BH21 7PE Tel: (01202) 876064 Fax: (01202) 897682 E-mail: sales@image-cs.co.uk
Intercaps Filling Systems Ltd, 20 Lochend Road, Newbridge, Newbridge, Midlothian, EH28 8SY Tel: 0131-335 3335 Fax: 0131-335 0415 E-mail: sales@intercaps.com
Ixapack UK Ltd, Unit A, King Street, Walsall, WS1 4AF Tel: (01922) 721102 Fax: (01922) 721921 E-mail: enquiries@ixapack.com
Kroy (Europe) Ltd, Worton Drive, Worton Grange Ind Estate, Reading, RG2 0LZ Tel: 0118-986 1411 Fax: 0118-986 5205 E-mail: hamilton@kroy.com
Labelman Labels & Tags, 52b Salop Road, Oswestry, Shropshire, SY11 2RQ Tel: (01691) 679333 Fax: (01691) 679444 E-mail: sales@1abelman.demon.co.uk
Labels & Data Systems (UK) Ltd, 9 Cresswell Close, Pinchbeck, Spalding, Lincolnshire, PE11 3TY Tel: 0161-929 8828 Fax: 0161-929 8518 E-mail: labelsdata@aol.com
Lettergraph Ltd, Harvey Road, Basildon, Essex, SS13 1EP Tel: (01268) 728552 Fax: (01268) 728479 E-mail: mail@lettergraph.net
Lettering Systems Unlimited, Imex Business Centre, Abbey Road Business Park, Pity Me, Durham, DH1 5JZ Tel: 0191-386 5222 Fax: 0191-386 5444 E-mail: sales@lsu.co.uk
Norprint Ltd, Horncastle Road, Boston, Lincolnshire, PE21 9HZ Tel: (01205) 365161 Fax: (01205) 364825 E-mail: norprint@norprint.co.uk
▶ P A L S Labelling Ltd, Quebec Street, Oldham, OL9 6QJ Tel: 0161-620 0236 Fax: 0161-627 1003 E-mail: sales@palslabelling.com
▶ Packaging Services UK Ltd, Pen Court, Standard Way Industrial Estate, Northallerton, North Yorkshire, DL6 2XE Tel: (01609) 773850 Fax: (01609) 773850 E-mail: sales@packagingservicesukltd.com
Pago Ltd, 7 Crown Gate, Wyncolls Road, Severalls Industrial Park, Colchester, CO4 9HZ Tel: (01206) 755206 Fax: (01206) 755210 E-mail: sales@pago.co.uk
Piroto Labelling Ltd, 9 Pond Wood Close, Moulton Park Industrial Estate, Northampton, NN3 6RT Tel: (01604) 646600 Fax: (01604) 492090 E-mail: info@piroto-labelling.com
Precision Labelling Systems Ltd, Plows Way, Leeming Bar, Northallerton, North Yorkshire, DL7 9UL Tel: 01677 423533
Shopstuff Cash Register Services, 75 Longford Road, Longford, Coventry, CV6 6DY Tel: (024) 7683 5666 Fax: (0845) 6443075 E-mail: sales@shopstuff.co.uk
Silver Fox Ltd, Swallow Court, Swallowfields, Welwyn Garden City, Hertfordshire, AL7 1SA Tel: (01707) 373727 Fax: (01707) 372193 E-mail: sales@silfox.co.uk
Southern Pricing Systems Ltd, 28 Eastwell Close, Paddock Wood, Tonbridge, Kent, TN12 6UH Tel: (01892) 834189 Fax: (01892) 835355
Stanley Press Equipment Ltd, Sutton Mill, Byrons Lane, Macclesfield, Cheshire, SK11 7JL Tel: (01625) 619094 Fax: (01625) 619094 E-mail: sales@s-p-e.co.uk

LABELLING MACHINE/SYSTEMS, HAND HELD

Alpha Systems, 63-65 High Street, Standish, Wigan, Lancashire, WN6 0HD Tel: (01257) 426617 Fax: (01257) 472148 E-mail: info@alphasolutions.co.uk

LABELLING MACHINE/SYSTEMS, PRINT AND APPLY

Computype Ltd, Oslo Road, Hull, HU7 0YN Tel: (01482) 835366 Fax: (01482) 822441 E-mail: enquiries@compu.co.uk
Danro Ltd, 68 Station Road, Earl Shilton, Leicester, LE9 7GA Tel: (01455) 847061 Fax: (01455) 841272 E-mail: info@danroltd.co.uk
Galaxy Labels, 16 Imperial Avenue, Gedling, Nottingham, NG4 3NE Tel: 0115-956 1516 Fax: 0115-956 1516
Pentex Sales Ltd, Hamilton House Broadfields, Bicester Road, Aylesbury, Buckinghamshire, HP19 3BG Tel: (01296) 318220 Fax: (01296) 339973 E-mail: sales@pentex.co.uk
Precision Labelling Systems Ltd, Plows Way, Leeming Bar, Northallerton, North Yorkshire, DL7 9UL Tel: 01677 423533

LABELLING SWING TICKETS

Britannia Labels Ltd, 22b Centurion Way, Meridian Business Park, Leicester, LE19 1WH Tel: 0116-281 5300 Fax: 0116-281 5301 E-mail: sales@britannialabels.com
Janda Barcode Label Services, Unit 17 Progress Business Park, Orders Lane, Kirkham, Preston, PR4 2TZ Tel: (01772) 686651 Fax: (01772) 684106 E-mail: sales@jandadigital.co.uk
Partners in Print, Venture Place, 45 Lord Street, Birmingham, B7 4DQ Tel: 0121-359 0202 Fax: 0121-359 5550 E-mail: mail@partnersinprint.co.uk
▶ Paxar Apparel Group Ltd, Private Road No 1, Colwick Industrial Estate, Nottingham, NG4 2JQ Tel: 0115-989 6500 Fax: 0115-989 6622 E-mail: info@paxar-emea.com

LABELLING SYSTEMS

Concept Labelling Solutions, The Old Sunday School, Bakes Street, Bradford, West Yorkshire, BD7 3EX Tel: (01274) 404400 Fax: (01274) 405599 E-mail: sales@concept-labelling.co.uk
J A Lorrimar & Co., Lorrimar House Hatfield Hi-Tech Park, Goulton Street, Hull, HU3 4DD Tel: (01482) 228173 Fax: (01482) 214106 E-mail: info@lorrimar.co.uk

LABELLING/OVERLABELLING SERVICES

Admiral Labels & Print Ltd, Unit 16 Caldershaw Business Centre, Ings Lane, Rochdale, Lancashire, OL12 7LQ Tel: (01706) 527111 Fax: (01706) 350660 E-mail: sales@admiral-labels.co.uk
Anglo Scottish Packaging, Montrose Avenue, Hillington Industrial Estate, Glasgow, G52 4LA Tel: 0141-882 5151 Fax: 0141-882 5500 E-mail: sales@angloscottish.net
Brecon Pharmaceuticals Ltd, Pharos House Wye Valley Business Park, Brecon Road, Hay-on-Wye, Hereford, HR3 5PG Tel: (01497) 820829 Fax: (01497) 820050 E-mail: admin@brecon-pharm.co.uk
Specific Components, Unit 23, Common Bank Industrial Estate, Ackhurst Road, Chorley, Lancashire, PR7 1NH Tel: (01257) 279944 Fax: (01257) 279922 E-mail: sales@specific-components.co.uk

LABELS TO SPECIFICATION

Anotek (Nameplates) Ltd, 22 Simpson Place, Nethermains Industrial Estate, Kilwinning, Ayrshire, KA13 6PT Tel: (01294) 557932 Fax: (01294) 557809 E-mail: anotek@btconnect.com
Direct Business Supplies, 7 Terry Dicken Industrial Estate, Station Road, Stokesley, Middlesbrough, Cleveland, TS9 7AE Tel: (01642) 714715 Fax: (01642) 714715 E-mail: sales@dbsupplies.net
Ennis Labels & Print, Tower Studios, Market Street, Darwen, Lancashire, BB3 1AZ Tel: (01254) 826138 Fax: (01254) 702135 E-mail: sales@ennislabels.co.uk
Eurosoft (Leeds) Ltd, Howcroft House, 919 Bradford Road, Birstall, Batley, West Yorkshire, WF17 9JX Tel: (01924) 474732 Fax: (01924) 475729 E-mail: sales@eurosoft-leeds.co.uk
Felix Communications, 3 Phoenix Industrial Estate, Commissioners Road, Medway City Estate, Rochester, Kent, ME2 4HZ Tel: (01634) 724080 Fax: (01634) 296415 E-mail: pdc@felix.com
P S Label, 102 Vernon Road, Leicester, LE2 8GB Tel: 0116-244 0576 Fax: 0116-244 0576 E-mail: pslabels@btconnect.com

LABELS, ANTITHEFT

▶ Solutions Distributors Ltd, Unit 1 Hixon Industrial Estate, Church Lane, Hixon, Stafford, ST18 0PY Tel: (0871) 4341510 Fax: (0871) 4341514 E-mail: sales@solutions-distributors.co.uk

LABELS, BAR CODED, PRINTED

▶ Packaging Solutions Provider, 21 Pinewood Drive, Markfield Court, Markfield, Leicestershire, LE67 9RQ Tel: (01530) 243743 E-mail: bob.locke@packaginsolutionsprovider.co.uk
▶ Ryzex plc, Unit 1, Bumpers Way, Bumpers Farm, Chippenham, Wiltshire, SN14 6LH Tel: (01249) 465100 Fax: (01249) 659777 E-mail: infouk@ryzex.com
▶ Security Label, 76 High Street, Dunbar, East Lothian, EH42 1JH Tel: (01368) 869921 E-mail: enquiry@security-label.co.uk
▶ Verdi Business Forms Ltd, Harold Court House, Church Road, Harold Wood, Romford, RM3 0JX Tel: (01708) 377311 Fax: (01708) 377327 E-mail: enquiries@verdi.co.uk

LABELS, COLOUR, LITHOGRAPHICALLY PRINTED

▶ A C P, T1 The Maltings, Roydon Road, Stanstead Abbotts, Ware, Hertfordshire, SG12 8HG Tel: (01920) 870355 Fax: (01920) 870355 E-mail: admin@acprinting.co.uk
▶ Lawlor Office Supplies Ltd, 2 Agecroft Enterprise Park, Shearer Way, Swinton, Manchester, M27 8WA Tel: 0161-737 0100 Fax: 0161-737 9944 E-mail: sales@lawloroffice.co.uk

LABELS, COMPUTER, *See Computer Label Systems etc*

LABELS, FOIL BLOCK

Labelsco, 29 Moat Way, Barwell, Leicester, LE9 8EY Tel: (01455) 852400 Fax: (01455) 841444 E-mail: sales@labelsco.co.uk

LABELS, HOT FOIL PRINTED

▶ Pandora Graphics, 150-160 Dumers Lane, Radcliffe, Manchester, M26 2GF Tel: 0161-766 1774 Fax: 0161-766 1774 E-mail: info@pandoragraphics.co.uk

LABELS, LASER PRINTED

▶ ARJMK PRINT & DESIGN, 25 Sutton Lane, Eastburn, Keighley, West Yorkshire, BD20 7SL Tel: 01535 655390 Fax: 01535 655390 E-mail: roy@rjmk.co.uk

LABELS, LASER/COPIER

Bondlabels Ltd, Wollaston Way, Burnt Mills Industrial Area, Basildon, Essex, SS13 1DJ Tel: (01268) 590555 Fax: (01268) 590999 E-mail: sales@bondlabels.co.uk

LABELS, SCREEN PRINTED, ON ROLLS

Adcal Labels Ltd, Jayem Works, Gomm Road, High Wycombe, Buckinghamshire, HP13 7DJ Tel: (01494) 530761 Fax: (01494) 461651 E-mail: sales@adcal-labels.co.uk
Skanem Cardiff, Bedwas House Industrial Estate, Bedwas, Caerphilly, Mid Glamorgan, CF83 8DW Tel: (029) 2086 5567 Fax: (029) 2086 5543 E-mail: gavin.braddon@selabelimage.co.uk
Sutterton Labels, Pinfold Road, Bourne, Lincolnshire, PE10 9HT Tel: (01778) 391637 Fax: (01778) 391638E-mail: sales@slpp.co.uk

LABELS, SHORT RUN

▶ Limpet Labels UK Ltd, Russell House, Abbey Road North, Wrexham Industrial Estate, Wrexham, Clwyd, LL13 9RX Tel: (01978) 664411 Fax: (01978) 661662 E-mail: sales@limpetlabels.co.uk

LABELS, WINE BOTTLE

▶ Devine Wines, Main Road, Gwaelod-y-Garth, Cardiff, CF15 9HJ Tel: (029) 2081 1200 Fax: (029) 2081 4080 E-mail: info@devinewine.co.uk

LABELS, WOVEN/ EMBROIDERED

Adastra Label Marketing Co. Ltd, 42 Gloucester Way, London, EC1R 0BR Tel: (020) 7278 8020 Fax: (020) 7837 3770 E-mail: sales@adastralabels.com
Byways Ltd, Bramingham Business Park, Enterprise Way, Luton, LU3 4BU Tel: (01582) 524444 Fax: (01582) 491301 E-mail: info@byways.co.uk
C M C Products, Cuxham, Watlington, Oxfordshire, OX49 5NH Tel: (01491) 612676 Fax: (01491) 613771 E-mail: johncarr.cmc@myopal.net
Cash's, Torrington Avenue, Coventry, CV4 9UZ Tel: (024) 7646 6466 Fax: (024) 7646 2525 E-mail: sales@jjcash.co.uk
Genel 86 Ltd, Kent House, 9 Beech Street, Leicester, LE5 0DF Tel: 0116-251 5156 Fax: 0116-251 5159 E-mail: genel86sales@aol.com
Labelon Sales Ltd, Unit 10 Chilford Court, Rayne Road, Braintree, Essex, CM7 2QS Tel: (01376) 553030 Fax: (01376) 349437 E-mail: sales@labelon.co.uk
Willeringhaus & Co. Ltd, The Mill, 23 Saunders Copse, Mayford, Woking, Surrey, GU22 0NS Tel: (01483) 723158 Fax: (01483) 723158 E-mail: willeringhaus.co@talk21.com
Wovina Woven Labels, 1 & 3 Omaha Road, Bodmin, Cornwall, PL31 1ER Tel: (01208) 73484 Fax: (01208) 78158 E-mail: sales@wovina.com

LABELS/NAMEPLATES/BADGES

Cowen Signs, 65 Old Chester Road, Birkenhead, Merseyside, CH41 9AW Tel: 0151-647 8081 Fax: 0151-666 1087 E-mail: sales@cowen-signs.co.uk
Ditac Ltd, 1 Latton Bush Business Centre, Southern Way, Harlow, Essex, CM18 7BH Tel: (01279) 427779 Fax: (01279) 427103
Images Labels Ltd, 12 Aintree Avenue, Eckington, Sheffield, S21 4JA Tel: (01246) 436876 Fax: (01246) 435987 E-mail: info@imageslabels.com
Kedon Industrial Supplies, Oaklands Farm Industrial Estate, Goatsmoor Lane, Stock, Ingatestone, Essex, CM4 9RS Tel: (01277) 636346 Fax: (01277) 636356 E-mail: enquiries@kedonengravers.com
Langley Labels Ltd, Harthall Lane, Kings Langley, Hertfordshire, WD4 8JJ Tel: (01923) 263777 Fax: (01923) 270392 E-mail: info@langleylabels.com
M.L.P.S., PO Box 27, Grantham, Lincs, NG31 6SJ Tel: (01476) 590400 Fax: (01476) 590400 E-mail: sales@mlps.co.uk
Rudd Macnamara Ltd, Holyhead Road, Birmingham, B21 0BS Tel: 0121-523 8437 Fax: 0121-551 7032 E-mail: rudd@nameplates.co.uk
▶ Probadge, The Countyard, 27 High Street, Winslow, Buckingham, MK18 3HE Tel: (01296) 712387 Fax: (01296) 715281 E-mail: sales@probadge.com
Pryorsign, Unit 3a, Denby Way, Hellaby, Rotherham, South Yorkshire, S66 8HR Tel: (01709) 700408 Fax: (01709) 532745 E-mail: david.fordham@pryorsign.com

LABORATORY AFLATOXIN ANALYSERS

▶ Rhys International, Unit 41 42 Halliwell Industrial Estate, Rossini Street, Bolton, BL1 8DL Tel: (01204) 848430 Fax: (01294) 848431 E-mail: info@rhysinternational.co.uk

LABORATORY AIR COMPRESSORS

▶ Rhys International, Unit 41 42 Halliwell Industrial Estate, Rossini Street, Bolton, BL1 8DL Tel: (01204) 848430 Fax: (01294) 848431 E-mail: info@rhysinternational.co.uk

LABORATORY AIR CONDITIONING (AC) EQUIPMENT

A C Engineers Ltd, Unit 7, Mill Industrial Estate, Kings Coughton, Alcester, Warwickshire, B49 5QG Tel: (01789) 763956 Fax: (01789) 400565 E-mail: ace@acegroup.co.uk
Simer Environmental Services Ltd, 15 Arnside Road, Waterlooville, Hampshire, PO7 7UP Tel: (023) 9225 8059 Fax: (023) 9226 7059 E-mail: sales@simer-environmental.co.uk

LABORATORY ANALYTICAL INSTRUMENTS

▶ Ashfield Technology, 2 Ashfield Road, Cults, Aberdeen, AB15 9NQ Tel: 07803 015163 Fax: 01224 868545 E-mail: ashfield_tec@hotmail.com
Burkard Scientific (Sales) Ltd, PO Box 55, Uxbridge, Middlesex, UB8 2RT Tel: (01895) 230056 Fax: (01895) 230058 E-mail: sales@burkardscientific.co.uk
Emerson Process Management, Meridian East, Leicester, LE19 1UX Tel: 0116-282 2822 Fax: 0116-289 2896
▶ Malvern Instruments Ltd, Enigma Business Park, Grovewood Road, Malvern, Worcestershire, WR14 1XZ Tel: (01684) 892456 Fax: (01684) 892789 E-mail: info@malvern.co.uk
Perkinelmer Ltd, Chalfont Road, Seer Green, Beaconsfield, Buckinghamshire, HP9 2FX Tel: (01494) 874515 Fax: (01494) 679331 E-mail: greenca@perkin-elmer.com

LABORATORY AUTOMATION EQUIPMENT

Hasfield Systems, Yartleton Oak, Yartleton Lane, May Hill, Longhope, Gloucestershire, GL17 0RF Tel: (01452) 831881 Fax: (01452) 831881 E-mail: systems@hasfield.demon.co.uk
Zymark Ltd, 1 Wellfield, Preston Brook, Runcorn, Cheshire, WA7 3AZ Tel: (01928) 711448 Fax: (01928) 791228 E-mail: ukzymark@zymark.com

LABORATORY BALANCES

A J Cope & Son Ltd, 11-12 The Oval, London, E2 9DU Tel: (020) 7729 2405 Fax: (020) 7729 2657 E-mail: marketing@ajcope.co.uk
Electronic Weighing Services Ltd, Lytton Street, Stoke-On-Trent, ST4 2AG Tel: (01782) 416322 Fax: (01782) 413660 E-mail: sales@electronicweighing.co.uk
European Instruments, Shotover Kilns, Headington, Oxford, OX3 8ST Tel: (01865) 750375 Fax: (01865) 769985 E-mail: balances@euroinst.co.uk
Westco Bilanciai Ltd, Broadgauge House, Westridge Way, Bishops Lydeard, Taunton, Somerset, TA4 3RU Tel: (01823) 433411 Fax: (01823) 433334 E-mail: sales@westcoweigh.co.uk

LABORATORY BATHS

Nickel-Electro Ltd, Oldmixon Crescent, Weston-super-Mare, North Somerset, BS24 9BL Tel: (01934) 626691 Fax: (01934) 630300 E-mail: clifton@nickel-electro.co.uk

LABORATORY CANTILEVER SYSTEMS

▶ Complete Laboratory Installations, 5 Loughborough Technology Centre, Epinal Way, Loughborough, Leicestershire, LE11 3GE Tel: (01509) 611322 Fax: (01509) 611416 E-mail: sales@completelabs.co.uk

LABORATORY CENTRIFUGES

Electrothermal Engineering Ltd, 419 Sutton Road, Southend-on-Sea, SS2 5PH Tel: (01702) 612211 Fax: (01702) 619888 E-mail: sales@electrothermal.co.uk
Hawksley & Sons Ltd, Marlborough Road, Lancing, West Sussex, BN15 8TN Tel: (01903) 752815 Fax: (01903) 766050 E-mail: enquiries@hawksley.co.uk

LABORATORY CHEMICAL PRODUCTS

Avonchem Ltd, 10 Waterloo Street West, Macclesfield, Cheshire, SK11 6PJ Tel: (01625) 434300 Fax: (01625) 869777 E-mail: sales@avonchem.co.uk
Kemtronix UK Ltd, Churn Road, Compton, Newbury, Berkshire, RG20 6PP Tel: (01635) 578779 Fax: (01635) 578983 E-mail: ljw@kemtronix.com
Park Scientific Ltd, 24 Low Farm Place, Moulton Park Industrial Estate, Northampton, NN3 6HY Tel: (01604) 646495 Fax: (01604) 648241 E-mail: info@park.com
Precisa, Unit 4 Vermont Place, Tongwell, Pennyland, Milton Keynes, MK15 8JA Tel: (01908) 211175 Fax: (01908) 211909 E-mail: sales@precisa.co.uk
Romil Ltd, The Source, Convent Drive, Waterbeach, Cambridge, CB5 9QT Tel: (01223) 863873 Fax: (01223) 862700 E-mail: sales@romil.com
Scientific & Chemical Supplies Ltd, Carlton House, Livingstone Road, Bilston, West Midlands, WV14 0QZ Tel: (01902) 402402 Fax: (01902) 402343 E-mail: scs@scichem.com
Scipac Biosystems Ltd, Unit D7, Broad Oak Enterprise Village, Sittingbourne, Kent, ME9 8AQ Tel: (01795) 423077 Fax: (01795) 426942 E-mail: mail@scipac.com
▶ Surechem Products (Holdings) Ltd, Lion Barn Industrial Estate, Needham Market, Ipswich, IP6 8NZ Tel: (01449) 722143 Fax: (01449) 722483 E-mail: sales@surechem.co.uk

LABORATORY CHEMICAL PRODUCTS – *continued*

Thompson & Capper Ltd, Hardwick Road, Astmoor Industrial Estate, Runcorn, Cheshire, WA7 1PH Tel: (01928) 573734 Fax: (01928) 580694 E-mail: info@tablets2buy.com

Timstar Laboratory Supplies Ltd, Linea House Marshfield Bank Employment Park, Marshfield Bank, Crewe, CW2 8UY Tel: (01270) 250459 Fax: (01270) 250601 E-mail: sales@timstar.co.uk

LABORATORY CRUSHERS, JAW TYPE

Capco Test Ltd, Riverside View, Wickham Market, Suffolk, IP13 0TA Tel: (01728) 747407 Fax: (01728) 747599 E-mail: sales@capco.co.uk

LABORATORY DRAINAGE SYSTEMS

Stanfield Building Services Ltd, Imex Technology Park, Unit 7 Bellringer Road, Trentham, Stoke-on-Trent, ST4 8LJ Tel: (01782) 658877 Fax: (01782) 658899 E-mail: info@stanfieldbs.co.uk

LABORATORY ENGINEERING

Austin (UK) Ltd, Cardinal Point, Park Road, Rickmansworth, Hertfordshire, WD3 1RE Tel: (01923) 432658 Fax: (01923) 432795 E-mail: sales@austin.co.uk

M S S Clean Technology, Castle House, The Industrial Estate, York Road, York, YO60 6RZ Tel: (01347) 878877 Fax: (01347) 878878 E-mail: postbox@mss-ct.co.uk

LABORATORY ENVIRONMENTAL STANDARD TESTING

▶ Water Quality Centre, Spencer House, Manor Farm Road, Reading, RG2 0JN Tel: 0118-923 6214 Fax: 0118-923 6373 E-mail: info@materialstesting.co.uk

LABORATORY EQUIPMENT, *See also headings for particular types*

Abbott Diabetes Care, Abbott House, Norden Road, Maidenhead, Berkshire, SL6 4XE Tel: (01628) 773355 Fax: (01628) 644305

Appleton Woods Ltd, Lindon House, Heeley Road, Selly Oak, Birmingham, B29 6EN Tel: 0121-472 7353 Fax: 0121-414 1075 E-mail: info@appletonwoods.co.uk

▶ Atlas Clean Air Ltd, 5 Carrside, Lomeshaye Industrial Estate, Nelson, Lancashire, BB9 6RX Tel: (01282) 447666 Fax: (01282) 447789 E-mail: info@atlascleanair.com

▶ B S P Method Ltd, 3 Millbrook Business Centre, Floats Road, Roundthorn Industrial Estate, Manchester, M23 9YJ Tel: 0161-998 1999 Fax: 0161-946 1697 E-mail: info@bspmethod.com

Brain Power International Ltd, 3 Prospect Way, Butlers Leap, Rugby, Warwickshire, CV21 3UU Tel: (01788) 568686 Fax: (01788) 568686 E-mail: paul@callbpi.com

Christison Technology Group Ltd, Albany Road, Gateshead East Industrial Estate, Gateshead, Tyne & Wear, NE8 3AT Tel: 0191-478 8120 Fax: 0191-490 0549 E-mail: sales@christison.com

F W Parrett Ltd, 65 Ridefield Road, London, SE9 2RA Tel: (020) 8859 3254 Fax: (020) 7504 3536 E-mail: fparrett@aol.com

Glenammer Engineering, 2 Mccalls Avenue, Ayr, KA8 9AE Tel: (01292) 261444 Fax: (01292) 267222 E-mail: sales@glenammer.com

Philip Harris International, Hyde Building, Ashton Road, Hyde, Cheshire, SK14 4SH Tel: (01530) 418550 E-mail: exportsales@philipharris.co.uk

Hichrom Ltd, 1 The Markham Centre, Station Road, Theale, Reading, RG7 4PE Tel: 0118-930 3660 Fax: 0118-932 3484 E-mail: sales@hichrom.co.uk

Hurstmoor Ltd, 4 Castle Meadow, Sible Hedingham, Halstead, Essex, CO9 3PZ Tel: (01787) 463113 Fax: (01787) 462052 E-mail: sales@hurstmoor.co.uk

Icn Pharmaceuticals Ltd, Cedarwood Crockford Lane, Chineham Business Park, Chineham, Basingstoke, Hampshire, RG24 8WD Tel: (01256) 707744 Fax: (01256) 707334 E-mail: sales@valeant.com

Lab Furnishings Group, Unit 2 Malmo Park, Stockholm Road, Sutton Fields Industrial Estate, Hull, HU7 0XW Tel: (01482) 827999 Fax: (01482) 827995 E-mail: p.moran@lfplc.co.uk

▶ Lab Med, Unit 4 Brunel Way, Thetford, Norfolk, IP24 1HP Tel: (01842) 762513 Fax: (01842) 753927 E-mail: labmedemail@yahoo.co.uk

Labtech International Ltd, 1 Finger Post Cottages, The Broyle, Ringmer, Lewes, East Sussex, BN8 5NN Tel: (01273) 814888 Fax: (01273) 814999

Markes International Ltd, Unit D3 Llantrisant Business Park, Llantrisant, Pontyclun, Mid Glamorgan, CF72 8YW Tel: (01443) 230935 Fax: (01443) 231531 E-mail: enquiries@markes.com

▶ Mersey Scientific, Redstones, Mill Lane, Rainhill, Prescot, Merseyside, L35 6NH Tel: (07732) 176739 Fax: 0151-426 2876 E-mail: sales@merseyscientific.com

Nickel-Electro Ltd, Oldmixon Crescent, Weston-super-Mare, North Somerset, BS24 9BL Tel: (01934) 626691 Fax: (01934) 630300 E-mail: clifton@nickel-electro.co.uk

Optimum Developments, Optimum House, Demmings Road, Demmings Industrial Estate, Cheadle, Cheshire, SK8 2PQ Tel: 0161-491 6171 Fax: 0161-491 6345 E-mail: sales@optimumlab.co.ukl

Plastic Formers Ltd, Unit 1, King Street, Stockport Road, Denton, Manchester, M34 6PF Tel: 0161-320 7200 Fax: 0161-335 0109 E-mail: enquiries@plasticformers.co.uk

▶ QMX Laboratories Ltd, 4 Bolford Street, Thaxted, Dunmow, Essex, CM6 2PY Tel: (01371) 831611 Fax: (01371) 831622 E-mail: sales@qmxlabs.com

Scott Science & Healthcare Ltd, PO Box 83, Ashford, Kent, TN27 9XJ Tel: (01622) 765334 Fax: (01622) 765338

thepowerStore.co.uk, Unit 22, 70 Queen Elizabeth Avenue, Hillington Business Park, Hillington, Glasgow, G52 4NQ Tel: (0870) 8705522 Fax: (0870) 8705525 E-mail: sales@thepowerstore.co.uk

Thomson Scientific Sales & Services Ltd, 3 Cults Business Park, Station Road, Cults, Aberdeen, AB15 9PE Tel: (01224) 863131 Fax: (01224) 863133 E-mail: tsss@talk21.com

▶ Trafalgar Scientific, 4 Selbury Drive, Oadby, Leicester, LE2 5NG Tel: 0116-271 9010 Fax: 0116-271 4665 E-mail: sales@trafalgarscientific.co.uk

Wesbart UK Ltd, Daux Road, Billingshurst, West Sussex, RH14 9YR Tel: (01403) 782738 Fax: (01403) 784180 E-mail: wesbart@talk21.com

Zymark Ltd, 1 Wellfield, Preston Brook, Runcorn, Cheshire, WA7 3AZ Tel: (01928) 711448 Fax: (01928) 791228 E-mail: ukzymark@zymark.com

LABORATORY EQUIPMENT INSTALLATION/MAINTENANCE/ REPAIR SERVICES

Bmg Labtech Ltd, PO Box 73, Aylesbury, Buckinghamshire, HP20 2QJ Tel: (01296) 336650 Fax: (01296) 336651

Commark Air, Oaktrees, Little Warley Hall La, Little Warley, Brentwood, Essex, CM13 3EX Tel: (01277) 200309

Kemtronix UK Ltd, Churn Road, Compton, Newbury, Berkshire, RG20 6PP Tel: (01635) 578779 Fax: (01635) 578983 E-mail: ljw@kemtronix.com

Kitech Services, 38 Saddleston Close, Hartlepool, Cleveland, TS26 0EZ Tel: (01429) 276114 Fax: (01429) 276114 E-mail: alison@kitech.co.uk

▶ Lab Med, Unit 4 Brunel Way, Thetford, Norfolk, IP24 1HP Tel: (01842) 762513 Fax: (01842) 753927 E-mail: labmedemail@yahoo.co.uk

Premier Lab Serve Ltd, Gethceln House, Dawley Road, Hayes, Middlesex, UB3 1EH Tel: (020) 8581 4055 Fax: (020) 8581 4056 E-mail: info@premierlabserve.co.uk

Scientifics Ltd, 52 Offerton Industrial Estate, Hempshaw Lane, Stockport, Cheshire, SK2 5TJ Tel: 0161-477 3004 Fax: 0161-480 4642

LABORATORY EQUIPMENT (MICROBIOLOGICAL) MANUFRS

M R S Scientific Ltd, Brocks BSNS Park, Hodgson Way, Wickford, Essex, SS11 8YN Tel: (01268) 730777 Fax: (01268) 560241 E-mail: sales@mrs-scientific.com

Metlab Supplies Ltd, Unit 7, Glendale Avenue, Sandycfoft, Deeside, Clwyd, CH5 2QP Tel: (01244) 526300 Fax: (01244) 526301 E-mail: barry@metlabsupplies.co.uk

The Microbiological Supply Co., PO Box 23, Dunstable, Bedfordshire, LU5 6DW Tel: (01525) 872515 Fax: (01525) 874967

Receptor Technologies Ltd, The Barn, Crofts Lane, Adderbury, Banbury, Oxfordshire, OX17 3NB Tel: (01295) 812600 Fax: (01295) 812700 E-mail: sales@receptortechnologies.co.uk

Select Bio Sciences Ltd, 1 Bull La Industrial Estate, Bull Lane, Acton, Sudbury, Suffolk, CO10 0BD Tel: (01787) 319234 Fax: (01787) 319235E-mail: admin@selectbiosciences.com

Thermo Electron Ltd, 5 Ringway Centre, Edison Road, Basingstoke, Hampshire, RG21 6YH Tel: (01256) 817282 Fax: (01256) 817292 E-mail: info@thermols.com

Trek Diagnostic Systems Ltd, Imberhorne Lane, East Grinstead, West Sussex, RH19 1QX Tel: (01342) 318777 Fax: (01342) 318666 E-mail: info@trekds.com

LABORATORY EQUIPMENT REFURBISHMENT

▶ O'Brien Commisioning, Bridge Street, Pendlebury, Swinton, Manchester, M27 4DU Tel: 0161-728 3444 Fax: 0161-728 3555 E-mail: job.commissioning@ukonline.co.uk

LABORATORY EQUIPMENT, ANALYTICAL

▶ Colco Scientific Enterprises Ltd, 6 Peatmore Close, Pyrford, Woking, Surrey, GU22 8TQ Tel: (01932) 349141 E-mail: sales@colco.co.uk

▶ World Precision Instruments Ltd, Astonbury Farm Business Centre, Aston, Stevenage, Hertfordshire, SG2 7EG Tel: (01438) 880025 Fax: (01438) 880026 E-mail: wpiuk@wpi-europe.com

LABORATORY EQUIPMENT, CALIBRATION

K.L. Giddings Ltd, Lion Works, Station Road East, Whittlesford, Cambridge, CB22 4WL Tel: (01223) 832638 Fax: (01223) 832189 E-mail: enquires@klgiddings.co.uk

LABORATORY EQUIPMENT, MEASURING CUPS, PLASTIC

▶ O'Brien Commisioning, Bridge Street, Pendlebury, Swinton, Manchester, M27 4DU Tel: 0161-728 3444 Fax: 0161-728 3555 E-mail: job.commissioning@ukonline.co.uk

LABORATORY EQUIPMENT, PLASTIC/RUBBER PROCESS

Farrel Ltd, PO Box 27, Rochdale, Lancashire, OL11 2PF Tel: (01706) 647434 Fax: (01706) 638982 E-mail: farreluk@farrel.com

LABORATORY FUME CUPBOARD VENTILATION SYSTEMS

Commark Air, Oaktrees, Little Warley Hall La, Little Warley, Brentwood, Essex, CM13 3EX Tel: (01277) 200309

LABORATORY FURNACES

Isoheat, Unit 5, Aurillac Court, Hallcroft Industrial Estate, Aurilac Way, Retford, Nottinghamshire, DN22 7PX Tel: (01777) 708811 Fax: (01777) 708866 E-mail: isoheat@fsbdial.co.uk

Vecstar Furnaces, Unit 11-12 Dunston Trading Estate, Foxwood Road, Chesterfield, Derbyshire, S41 9RF Tel: (01246) 260094 Fax: (01246) 450213 E-mail: enquiries@vecstar.co.uk

LABORATORY FURNITURE

▶ Complete Laboratory Installations, 5 Loughborough Technology Centre, Epinal Way, Loughborough, Leicestershire, LE11 3GE Tel: (01509) 611322 Fax: (01509) 611416 E-mail: sales@completelabs.co.uk

Crossbrook Furniture Ltd, 8 Marshgate Industrial Estate, 20 Marshgate Drive, Hertford, SG13 7AJ Tel: (01992) 557000 Fax: (01992) 501666 E-mail: sales@crossbrook.co.uk

Deanestor Ltd, Deanestor Building, Warren Way, Forest Town, Mansfield, Nottinghamshire, NG19 0FL Tel: (01623) 420041 Fax: (01623) 420061 E-mail: sales@deanestor.co.uk

Kinetic Concepts Ltd, 18 Voases Lane, Anlaby, Hull, HU10 7BH Tel: (01482) 829292 Fax: (01482) 837997 E-mail: bill@kinetic.gbservices.co.uk

Klick Technology Ltd, Claverton Road, Roundthorn Industrial Estate, Manchester, M23 9FT Tel: 0161-998 9726 Fax: 0161-946 0419 E-mail: sales@klicktechnology.co.uk

Lab Furnishings Group, Unit 2 Malmo Park, Stockholm Road, Sutton Fields Industrial Estate, Hull, HU7 0XW Tel: (01482) 827999 Fax: (01482) 827995 E-mail: p.moran@lfplc.co.uk

Lab Systems Furniture Ltd, Rotary House, Bontoft Avenue, Hull, HU5 4HF Tel: (01482) 444650 Fax: (01482) 444730 E-mail: office@lab-systems.co.uk

Lab UK Furniture Ltd, Coal Pit Lane, Atherton, Manchester, M46 0RL Tel: (01942) 893223 Fax: (01942) 894141

Luntri (UK) Ltd, Trinity House, Foxes Parade, Sewardstone Road, Waltham Abbey, Essex, EN9 1PH Tel: (01992) 653065 Fax: (01992) 653165 E-mail: luntri@wxs.wl.com

Milton Laboratory Furniture Ltd, Unit 17 Birksland Industrial Estate, Bradford, West Yorkshire, BD4 8TY Tel: (01274) 395110 Fax: (01274) 395111 E-mail: paul@miltonfurniture.com

Regal Fans Ltd, Ventris House, Lakes Road, Braintree, Essex, CM7 3SS Tel: (01376) 342914 Fax: (01376) 348208 E-mail: tim@regalfans.co.uk

Rex Bousfield Ltd, Fairview Industrial Estate, Holland Road, Oxted, Surrey, RH8 9BD Tel: (01883) 717033 Fax: (01883) 717890 E-mail: john.medcraft@bousfield.com

Robinson & Gronnow Ltd, 3 Mackenzie Industrial Estate, Bird Hall Lane, Stockport, Cheshire, SK3 0SB Tel: 0161-428 1199 Fax: 0161-428 0635 E-mail: info@robinson-gronnow.co.uk

Romero UK Ltd, Sheraton House, Castle Park, Cambridge, CB3 0AX Tel: 01223 370088 Fax: 01223 370040 E-mail: ph@romero.uk.com

Safelab Systems Ltd, Unit 29, Lynx Crescent, Weston-super-Mare, Avon, BS24 9DJ Tel: (01934) 421340 Fax: (0870) 2402274 E-mail: sales@safelab.co.uk

Simmons (Patternmakers) Ltd, Station Street West Business Park, Coventry, CV6 5BP Tel: (024) 7663 7028 Fax: (024) 7663 7030 E-mail: sales@epoxyworktops.com

The Unit Joinery Co., 8-12 Totman Crescent, Rayleigh, Essex, SS6 7UY Tel: (01268) 774802 Fax: (01268) 774183

LABORATORY GAS SUPPLY SYSTEMS

Imgas Ltd, Sansom House, Portland Street, Daybrook, Nottingham, NG5 6BL Tel: 0115-966 7030 Fax: 0115-966 7031 E-mail: sales@imgas.co.uk

Medical Gases Ltd, Aztex House, Perrywood Business Park, Salfords, Redhill, RH1 5DZ Tel: (01737) 378000 Fax: (01737) 378055 E-mail: rsmith@medicalgases.uk.com

LABORATORY GLASSWARE MANUFRS

▶ Bilbate Ltd, 24 High March, High March Industrial Estate, Daventry, Northamptonshire, NN11 4HB Tel: (01327) 871467 Fax: (01327) 300619

G. Farley & Sons Ltd, Unit 6 Plaza Business Centre, Stockingswater Lane, Enfield, Middlesex, EN3 7PH Tel: (020) 8804 1367 Fax: (020) 8804 8821 E-mail: sales@g-farleyandsons.co.uk

Griffiths & Nielsen Ltd, Wyvern House, 49 Station Road, Billingshurst, West Sussex, RH14 9SE Tel: (01403) 784881 Fax: (01403) 784988 E-mail: sales@g-and-n.com

Hamilton Laboratory Glass Ltd, Unit A1 Continental Approach, Westwood Industrial Estate, Margate, Kent, CT9 4JG Tel: (01843) 232633 Fax: (01843) 232644 E-mail: sales@hamiltonlabglass.com

J A Winward & Sons, Rear of, 120 High St South, London, E6 3RW Tel: (020) 8472 5986 Fax: (020) 8503 4743 E-mail: winward@btconnect.com

Lichfield Studio Glass Ltd, Boston Industrial Estate, Power Station Road, Rugeley, Staffordshire, WS15 2HS Tel: (01889) 575551 Fax: (01889) 575551 E-mail: lich@globalnet.co.uk

Mayflower Glass Ltd, Moor Lane, East Boldon, Tyne & Wear, NE36 0AQ Tel: 0191-536 0343 Fax: 0191-536 8099 E-mail: sales@mayflower-glass.com

Poulten & Graf Ltd, 1 Alfreds Way Industrial Estate, Alfreds Way, Barking, Essex, IG11 0AS Tel: (020) 8594 4256 Fax: (020) 8594 8419 E-mail: volacjpl@aol.com

Radleys Glassworkers, Shire Hill, Saffron Walden, Essex, CB11 3AZ Tel: (01799) 513320 Fax: (01799) 513283 E-mail: sales@radleys.co.uk

Scientific & Chemical Supplies Ltd, Carlton House, Livingstone Road, Bilston, West Midlands, WV14 0QZ Tel: (01902) 402402 Fax: (01902) 402343 E-mail: scs@scichem.com

Solmedia Laboratory Supplies, 6 The Parade, Colchester Road, Romford, RM3 0AQ Tel: (01708) 343334 Fax: (01708) 372785 E-mail: labsupplies@solmedialtd.com

York Glassware Services Ltd, 9 The Crescent, York, YO24 1AW Tel: (01904) 651493 Fax: (01904) 611932 E-mail: mail@ygs.net

LABORATORY GLASSWARE WASHING MACHINES

Getinge UK Ltd, Orchard Way, Sutton-in-Ashfield, Nottinghamshire, NG17 1JU Tel: (01623) 510033 Fax: (01623) 440456

Lancer UK Ltd, 1 Pembroke Avenue, Waterbeach, Cambridge, CB25 9QP Tel: (01223) 861665 Fax: (01223) 861990 E-mail: info@lancer.co.uk

LABORATORY INSTRUMENTS

Applied Biosystems, Lingley House, 120 Birchwood Boulevard, Birchwood, Warrington, WA3 7QH Tel: (01925) 825650 Fax: (01925) 282502 E-mail: abdirect@eur.apliedbiosystems.com

Beckmass Scientific Apparatus, 25 The Brambles, Haslington, Crewe, CW1 5RA Tel: (01270) 586707 Fax: (01270) 586707

Laboratory Precision Ltd, Unit 30 Lanchester Way, Royal Oak Industrial Estate, Daventry, Northamptonshire, NN11 8PH Tel: (01327) 877774 Fax: (01327) 877444 E-mail: sales@crimpers-and-decappers.com

▶ Mersey Scientific, Redstones, Mill Lane, Rainhill, Prescot, Merseyside, L35 6NH Tel: (07732) 176739 Fax: 0151-426 2876 E-mail: sales@merseyscientific.com

Microscal Ltd, 79 Southern Row, London, W10 5AL Tel: (020) 8969 3935 Fax: (020) 8968 7302 E-mail: info@microscal.com

Nickel-Electro Ltd, Oldmixon Crescent, Weston-super-Mare, North Somerset, BS24 9BL Tel: (01934) 626691 Fax: (01934) 630300 E-mail: clifton@nickel-electro.co.uk

Ross Lab plc, Ross Lab House, Fence Avenue Industrial Estate, Macclesfield, Cheshire, SK10 1LT Tel: (01625) 610077 Fax: (01625) 619877 E-mail: sales@rosslab.com

S Murray & Co. Ltd, Holborn House, High Street, Old Woking, Woking, Surrey, GU22 9LB Tel: (01483) 740099 Fax: (01483) 755111 E-mail: sales@smurray.co.uk

LABORATORY MIXERS

Capco Test Ltd, Riverside View, Wickham Market, Suffolk, IP13 0TA Tel: (01728) 747407 Fax: (01728) 747599 E-mail: sales@capco.co.uk

LABORATORY OVENS

Electrothermal Engineering Ltd, 419 Sutton Road, Southend-on-Sea, SS2 5PH Tel: (01702) 612211 Fax: (01702) 619888 E-mail: sales@electrothermal.co.uk

LABORATORY PLASTIC WARE

B V Z Marketing Ltd, Unit 34, Meadow Lane, Ellesmere Port, CH65 4EH Tel: 0151-355 3055 Fax: 0151-355 5055

Griffiths & Nielsen Ltd, Wyvern House, 49 Station Road, Billingshurst, West Sussex, RH14 9SE Tel: (01403) 784881 Fax: (01403) 784988 E-mail: sales@g-and-n.com

Owen Mumford Holdings Ltd, Brook Hill, Woodstock, Woodstock, Oxfordshire, OX20 1TU Tel: (01993) 812021 Fax: (01993) 813466 E-mail: steve.miles@owenmumford.co.uk

Porvair Sciences Ltd, 6 Shepperton Business Park, Govett Avenue, Shepperton, Middlesex, TW17 8BA Tel: (01932) 224539 Fax: (01932) 254393 E-mail: int.sales@porvair.com

LABORATORY PRODUCT DESIGN AND PROTOTYPING SERVICES

▶ Eg Technology, 12 Kings Parade, Cambridge, CB2 1SJ Tel: (01223) 710799 Fax: (08707) 877021 E-mail: info@egtechnology.co.uk

LABORATORY REAGENTS

Abtek (Biologicals) Ltd, Unit 4, Taylor Street, Liverpool, L5 5AD Tel: 0151-298 1501 Fax: 0151-298 1758 E-mail: info@abtekbio.com

Clin-Tech Ltd, Unit G Perram Works, Merrow Lane, Guildford, Surrey, GU4 7BN Tel: (01483) 301902 Fax: (01483) 301907 E-mail: info@clin-tech.co.uk

▶ Mersey Scientific, Redstones, Mill Lane, Rainhill, Prescot, Merseyside, L35 6NH Tel: (07732) 176739 Fax: 0151-426 2876 E-mail: sales@merseyscientific.com

▶ Surechem Products (Holdings) Ltd, Lion Barn Industrial Estate, Needham Market, Ipswich, IP6 8NZ Tel: (01449) 722143 Fax: (01449) 722483 E-mail: sales@surechem.co.uk

LABORATORY ROBOTS

Zymark Ltd, 1 Wellfield, Preston Brook, Runcorn, Cheshire, WA7 3AZ Tel: (01928) 711448 Fax: (01928) 791228 E-mail: ukzymark@zymark.com

LABORATORY SERVICES

▶ Tepnel Life Sciences P.L.C., Unit 2,, Kelvin Campus, West Of Scotland Science Park, Glasgow, G20 0SP Tel: 0141-946 8889 Fax: 0141-946 4195 E-mail: jhillier@tepnel.com

LABORATORY SOLID SURFACE WORKTOPS

▶ Artisan Work Surfaces, Units 3-4, Shelton Court, Shelton Road, Willowbrook Industrial Estate, Corby, Northamptonshire, NN17 5YU Tel: (01536) 409771 Fax: (01536) 201641 E-mail: sales@artisanworksurfaces.co.uk

LABORATORY SUPPLY SERVICES

A J Cope & Son Ltd, 11-12 The Oval, London, E2 9DU Tel: (020) 7729 2405 Fax: (020) 7729 2657 E-mail: marketing@ajcope.co.uk

Alltech Associates Applied Science Ltd, 6 Kellet Road Industrial Estate, Kellet Road, Carnforth, Lancashire, LA5 9XP Tel: (01524) 734451 Fax: (01524) 733599 E-mail: sales@alltechweb.com

Anderman & Co. Ltd, 145 London Road, Kingston Upon Thames, Surrey, KT2 6NH Tel: (020) 8541 0035 Fax: (020) 8549 1617 E-mail: enquiries@earthwaterfire.com

Appleton Woods Ltd, Lindon House, Heeley Road, Selly Oak, Birmingham, B29 6EN Tel: 0121-472 7353 Fax: 0121-414 1075 E-mail: info@appletonwoods.co.uk

Beecroft & Partners Ltd, Northfield Road, Rotherham, South Yorkshire, S60 1RR Tel: (01709) 377881 Fax: (01709) 369264 E-mail: sales@beecroft-science.co.uk

Brunner Scientific, Unit 4c Hunmanby Industrial Estate, Hunmanby, Filey, North Yorkshire, YO14 0PH Tel: (01723) 891611 Fax: (01723) 890872 E-mail: sales@brunnerscientific.com

Carl Stuart, 20 Station Street, Leek, Staffordshire, ST13 8BP Tel: (0845) 2304030 Fax: (0845) 2305030 E-mail: sales@carlstuart.com

Dalon International Ltd, 12 The Spire Green Centre, Harlow, Essex, CM19 5TR Tel: (01279) 453823 Fax: (01279) 453824 E-mail: longdalon@aol.com

Davidson & Hardy (Lab Supplies) Ltd, 453-459 Antrim Road, Belfast, BT15 3BL Tel: (028) 9078 1611 Fax: (028) 9077 2801 E-mail: info@dhlab.com

Euro Lab Supplies Ltd, 43-44 Fourways, Carlyon Road Industrial Estate, Atherstone, Warwickshire, CV9 1LH Tel: (01827) 721781 Fax: (01827) 721781 E-mail: kay.cauldwell@eurolabsupplies.co.uk

Fisher Scientific Holding UK Ltd, Bishop Meadow Road, Loughborough, Leicestershire, LE11 5RG Tel: (01509) 231166 Fax: (01509) 231893 E-mail: info@fisher.co.uk

John Godrich, Pellow House, Old Street, Ludlow, Shropshire, SY8 1NU Tel: (01584) 873153 Fax: (01584) 872424 E-mail: johngodrich@johngodrich.co.uk

Gradko International Ltd, St Martins House, 77 Wales Street, Winchester, Hampshire, SO23 0RH Tel: (01962) 860331 Fax: (01962) 841339 E-mail: sales@gradko.co.uk

Iab Laboratory Specialists, Park Studios, Parkwood St, Keighley, West Yorkshire, BD21 4PJ Tel: 01535 611299 Fax: 01535 680836

Impact Test Equipment Ltd, Building 21, Stevenston Industrial Estate, Stevenston, Ayrshire, KA20 3LR Tel: (01294) 602626 Fax: (01294) 461168 E-mail: sales@impact-test.co.uk

Intergrated Scientific Ltd, 3 Centurion Business Park, Aspen Way, Rotherham, South Yorkshire, S60 1FB Tel: (01709) 830493 Fax: (01709) 830464 E-mail: sales@integsci.com

Lab 3 Ltd, 1 The Business Centre, Ross Road, Weedon Road Industrial Estate, Northampton, NN5 5AX Tel: (0870) 4445553 Fax: (0870) 1260350 E-mail: sales@lab3.co.uk

Laboratory Supplies & Instruments Ltd, 13b-14a Rathenraw Industrial Estate, Antrim, BT41 2SJ Tel: (028) 9446 3070 Fax: (028) 9446 8642 E-mail: info@labsuppliesltd.co.uk

M R S Scientific Ltd, Brocks BSNS Park, Hodgson Way, Wickford, Essex, SS11 8YN Tel: (01268) 730777 Fax: (01268) 560241 E-mail: sales@mrs-scientific.com

Mediworld Ltd, 444 - 446 Streatham High Road, London, SW16 3PX Tel: (020) 8764 1806 Fax: (020) 8679 2489 E-mail: sales@mediworld.co.uk

Owens Polyscience Ltd, 34 Chester Road, Macclesfield, Cheshire, SK11 8DG Tel: (01625) 610118 Fax: (01625) 423850

P & R Labpak Ltd, Unit 6, Ketterer Court, St. Helens, Merseyside, WA9 3AH Tel: 0870 0342055 Fax: 0870 0342056 E-mail: steve.morris@prlabs.co.uk

Quadrachem Ltd, Kingfisher House Forest Row Business Park, Station Road, Forest Row, East Sussex, RH18 5DW Tel: (01342) 820820 Fax: (01342) 820825 E-mail: sales@qclscientific.com

R & L Slaughter Ltd, Unit 11 Saxon House Upminster Trading Park, Warley Street, Upminster, Essex, RM14 3PJ Tel: (01708) 228409 Fax: (01708) 228728 E-mail: info@slaughter.co.uk

R.B. Radley & Co. Ltd, Shirehill, Saffron Walden, Essex, CB11 3AZ Tel: (01799) 513320 Fax: (01799) 513283 E-mail: sales@radleys.co.uk

Refer Scientific, Hareburn House, Bridge of Don, Aberdeen, AB23 8BT Tel: (01224) 825394 Fax: (01224) 706324 E-mail: info@referscientific.co.uk

Richardsons Of Leicester, 112a Milligan Road, Leicester, LE2 8FB Tel: 0116-283 8604 Fax: 0116-283 7109 E-mail: sales@richardsonsofleicester.co.uk

Scientific & Chemical Supplies Ltd, Carlton House, Livingstone Road, Bilston, West Midlands, WV14 0QZ Tel: (01902) 402402 Fax: (01902) 402343 E-mail: scs@scichem.com

Scientific & Chemical Supplies Ltd, 39 Back Sneddon Street, Paisley, Renfrewshire, PA3 2DE Tel: 0141-887 3531 Fax: 0141-889 8706 E-mail: paisley@scichem.co.uk

Scientific Laboratory Supplies, Unit 14 Orchard House, The Square, Hessle, North Humberside, HU13 0AE Tel: (01482) 649665 Fax: (01482) 649667 E-mail: tcherry@scientific-labs.com

Timstar Laboratory Supplies Ltd, Linea House Marshfield Bank Employment Park, Marshfield Bank, Crewe, CW2 8UY Tel: (01270) 250459 Fax: (01270) 250601 E-mail: sales@timstar.co.uk

Western Laboratory Service Ltd, Unit 8 Redan Hill Estate, Redan Road, Aldershot, Hampshire, GU12 4SJ Tel: (0870) 7879528 Fax: (0870) 7879529 E-mail: info@wls.co.uk

York Glassware Services Ltd, 9 The Crescent, York, YO24 1AW Tel: (01904) 651493 Fax: (01904) 611932 E-mail: mail@ygs.net

LABORATORY TAPS

▶ B S P Method Ltd, 3 Millbrook Business Centre, Floats Road, Roundthorn Industrial Estate, Manchester, M23 9YJ Tel: 0161-998 1999 Fax: 0161-946 1697 E-mail: info@bspmethod.com

LABORATORY TEST ANALYSIS

▶ Accelerated Weathering Laboratory Ltd, Berkeley House, Hunts Rise, South Marston Industrial Estat, Swindon, SN3 4TG Tel: (01793) 834211 Fax: (01793) 721212 E-mail: info@awlltd.co.uk

Bodycote Radiography, 1 Blackbrook Valley Industrial Estate, Narrowboat Way, Dudley, West Midlands, DY2 0XQ Tel: (01384) 455880 Fax: (01384) 457250 E-mail: dudley@bodycote-mt.com

Doctor's Laboratory plc, 60 Whitfield Street, London, W1T 4EU Tel: (020) 7460 4800 Fax: (020) 7460 4848

Global Analysis, Tappers Building, Huddersfield Road, Mirfield, West Yorkshire, WF14 9DQ Tel: (01924) 499776 Fax: (01924) 499325 E-mail: user@globalanalysis.co.uk

▶ Oilfield Chemical Technology Ltd, Craigshaw Road, West Tullos Industrial Estate, Aberdeen, AB12 3AP Tel: (01224) 248113 Fax: (01224) 248289 E-mail: octlimited@octl.co.uk

Tribologic Ltd, C/O Mechanical Engineering Dept, The University Of Leeds, Woodhouse Lane, Leeds, LS2 9JT Tel: 0113-233 2159 Fax: 0113-343 2160 E-mail: info@tribologic.co.uk

▶ University Of Leeds Farms Ltd, Financial Services, 11-84 Ec Stoner Building, Leeds, LS2 9JT Tel: 0113-234 0206 Fax: 0113-343 4058 E-mail: consulting@leeds.ac.uk

LABORATORY TEST EQUIPMENT MANUFRS, *See also headings for particular types of Analysis*

Brunner Scientific, Unit 4c Hunmanby Industrial Estate, Hunmanby, Filey, North Yorkshire, YO14 0PH Tel: (01723) 891611 Fax: (01723) 890872 E-mail: sales@brunnerscientific.com

Containment Technology Ltd, 9 Telford Road, Ferndown Industrial Estate, Wimborne, Dorset, BH21 7QW Tel: (01202) 870189 Fax: (01202) 870212

Elkay Laboratory Products UK Ltd, PO Box 6004, Basingstoke, Hampshire, RG24 8HL Tel: (01256) 811118 Fax: (01256) 811116 E-mail: sales@elkay-uk.co.uk

Engineering Systems Nottm, 1 Loach Court, Radford Bridge Road, Nottingham, NG8 1NA Tel: 0115-928 8708 Fax: 0115-928 8715 E-mail: info@engsys.co.uk

G. Farley & Sons Ltd, Unit 6 Plaza Business Centre, Stockingswater Lane, Enfield, Middlesex, EN3 7PH Tel: (020) 8804 1367 Fax: (020) 8804 8821 E-mail: sales@g-farleyandsons.co.uk

Feedback Instruments Ltd, Park Road, Crowborough, East Sussex, TN6 2QR Tel: (01892) 653322 Fax: (01892) 663719 E-mail: feedback@fdbk.co.uk

Paper Life Ltd, Unit 13 Ahed House, Sandbeds Trading Estate, Ossett, West Yorkshire, WF5 9ND Tel: (01924) 281666 Fax: (01924) 281444 E-mail: sales@paperlife.co.uk

RK Print Coat Instruments Ltd, Abington Road, Litlington, Royston, Hertfordshire, SG8 0QZ Tel: (01763) 852187 Fax: (01763) 852502 E-mail: sales@rkprint.com

Scientific & Chemical Supplies Ltd, 39 Back Sneddon Street, Paisley, Renfrewshire, PA3 2DE Tel: 0141-887 3531 Fax: 0141-889 8706 E-mail: paisley@scichem.co.uk

Westlairds Ltd, Patrixbourne, The Green, Datchet, Slough, SL3 9JH Tel: (01753) 543939 Fax: (01753) 549933 E-mail: westlairds@westlairds.co.uk

Zinsser Analytic (UK) Ltd, Howarth Road, Stafferton Way, Maidenhead, Berkshire, SL6 1AP Tel: (01628) 773202 Fax: (01628) 672199 E-mail: officeuk@zinsser-analytic.com

LABOUR RELATIONS CONSULTANCY

Organisation Resources Counsellors Inc, 127-131 Sloane Street, London, SW1X 9QP Tel: (020) 7591 5600 Fax: (020) 7591 5605 E-mail: sales@orcinc.co.uk

LACE

Alan Litman plc, Damad House, 490 Radford Road, Nottingham, NG7 7EE Tel: 0115-970 8992 Fax: 0115-942 0546 E-mail: alanlitman.plc@virgin.net

Guy Birkin & Co. Ltd, Bains Drive, Borrowash, Derby, DE72 3FS Tel: (01332) 680680 Fax: (01332) 680681

Cluny Lace Co. Ltd, Belper Street Works, Ilkeston, Derbyshire, DE7 5FJ Tel: 0115-932 5031 Fax: 0115-944 0590 E-mail: sales@clunylace.co.uk

Eurolace Ltd, 9 New Road, Stapleford, Nottingham, NG9 8GS Tel: (01332) 780042 Fax: 0115-949 1691

Excel Laces & Fabrics Ltd, 13 Rancliffe Avenue, Keyworth, Nottingham, NG12 5HY Tel: 0115-937 5030 Fax: 0115-937 6619 E-mail: clive-johnson@lineone.net

Frank P Kirk Ltd, 122 Queens Road East, Beeston, Nottingham, NG9 2FD Tel: 0115-967 7330 Fax: 0115-967 7303

Frankle Trimmings, 281-285 Bethnal Green Road, London, E2 6AH Tel: (020) 7739 0621 Fax: (020) 7739 0751 E-mail: ftrim@aol.com

Frederick Johnson, Lee House, 10 Alpine Street, Nottingham, NG6 0HS Tel: 0115-978 0767 Fax: 0115-978 2658 E-mail: fjlace@aol.com

G W & S M Mellors & Sons, 23 Meadow Road, Netherfield, Nottingham, NG4 2FR Tel: 0115-961 6213

Hansson Of Guildford, 108 Woodbridge Road, Guildford, Surrey, GU1 4PY Tel: (01483) 451625 Fax: (01483) 451602 E-mail: sales@hansson-silks.co.uk

Hurcombs Lace, Unit 38, Unity Road, Lowmoor Industrial Estate, Kirkby-In-Ashfield, Nottingham, NG17 7LE Tel: (01623) 722774 Fax: (01623) 723332

▶ Jaynies of London, 28 Upper Road, London, E13 0DH Tel: (07876) 343938 E-mail: jaynie@jayniesof london.com

Jill Leonard, Unit 2, Machins Industrial Estate Nottingham Road, Gotham, Nottingham, NG11 0HG Tel: 0115-983 1084 Fax: 0115-983 1074

M Courts Ltd, 31 Commercial Road, London, N18 1TP Tel: (020) 8884 0999 Fax: (020) 8884 4666 E-mail: mcourtsltd@btconnect.com

Malmic Lace Ltd, Malmic House, Brookside Road, Ruddington, Nottingham, NG11 6AT Tel: 0115-940 5151 Fax: 0115-984 5706 E-mail: info@malmiclace.co.uk

Morton Young & Borland Ltd, Stoneygate Road, Newmilns, Ayrshire, KA16 9AL Tel: (01560) 321210 Fax: (01560) 323153 E-mail: info@myb-ltd.com

▶ Nottingham Lace Finishing, 81A Arnold Road, Nottingham, NG6 0ED Tel: 0115-978 1979

R Chander, Alfred Street North, Nottingham, NG3 1AE Tel: 0115-950 2631 Fax: 0115-950 4668 E-mail: ashwansee@aol.com

Siegel Laces & Fabric Ltd, Maiden Lane, Nottingham, NG1 1QJ Tel: 0115-950 3210 Fax: 0115-958 3969 E-mail: sales@siegel.demon.co.uk

Silvan Ltd, 2 Coombe Road, Bushey, WD23 4SP Tel: (020) 8950 8160 Fax: (020) 8950 8163 E-mail: silvanltd@aol.com

Strella Fabrics Ltd, Radford Boulevard, Nottingham, NG7 5QG Tel: 0115-955 4444 Fax: 0115-955 4500 E-mail: enquiries@strella-fabrics.ltd.uk

Toye Kenning & Spencer Ltd, Regalia House, Newtown Road, Bedworth, Warwickshire, CV12 8QR Tel: (024) 7631 5634 Fax: (024) 7664 3018 E-mail: sales@toye.com

LACE CURTAINS

Monica Jane, Ger Y Ffynnon, Maengygroes, New Quay, Dyfed, SA45 9TH Tel: 01545 561309 Fax: 01545 560296

LACE HOME FURNISHING PRODUCTS

Bill Beaumont Textiles Ltd, Park Mills, Deighton Road, Chorley, Lancashire, PR7 2HP Tel: (01257) 263065 Fax: (01257) 241348 E-mail: sales@billbeaumont.co.uk

▶ Lifestyle Products Ltd, Talbot House, 17 Church Street, Rickmansworth, Hertfordshire, WD3 1DE Tel: (01923) 711832 Fax: (01923) 711831 E-mail: sales@life-style.co.uk

LACE IMPORT MERCHANTS OR AGENTS

Excel Laces & Fabrics Ltd, 13 Rancliffe Avenue, Keyworth, Nottingham, NG12 5HY Tel: 0115-937 5030 Fax: 0115-937 6619 E-mail: clive-johnson@lineone.net

Forever England, 51c Fore Street, Totnes, Devon, TQ9 5NJ Tel: (01803) 868149 Fax: (01803) 868149

Nottingham Laces & Trimmings, Turret E, Harrington Mills, Leopold Street, Long Eaton, Nottingham, NG10 4QE Tel: 0115-946 0766 Fax: 0115-946 0741 E-mail: sales@harrington-nlt.co.uk

LACQUER DIPPING, *See Dipping etc*

LACQUERING SERVICES

C & H Precision Finishers Ltd, Derby Road Trade Centre, Derby Road, Sandiacre, Nottingham, NG10 5HU Tel: 0115-939 4707 Fax: 0115-949 0146 E-mail: admin@chprecision.co.uk

C S Surface Coating Ltd, 2 Mackay Transport, Colonial Way, Watford, WD24 4JU Tel: (01923) 246982 Fax: (01923) 237841 E-mail: mail@cs-surface-coating.co.uk

Kirolite Products, 34-35 Dawkins Road, Poole, Dorset, BH15 4JW Tel: (01202) 676500 Fax: (01202) 681922E-mail: info@kirolite.com

Page Lacquer Co. Ltd, 3 Ferrier Industrial Estate, Ferrier Street, London, SW18 1SN Tel: (020) 8871 1235 Fax: (020) 8874 8167 E-mail: info@pagelacquer.co.uk

LACQUERS

Economy Auto Paint, 81a Main Street, Bainsford, Falkirk, FK2 7NZ Tel: (01324) 620002 Fax: (01324) 620002

Ici Packaging Coatings Ltd, Bordesley Green Road, Bordesley Green, Birmingham, B9 4TQ Tel: 0121-766 6600 Fax: 0121-766 6601 E-mail: enquiries@ici.com

Morrells Wood Finishers Ltd, 99 Mabgate Street, Leeds, LS9 7DR Tel: 0113-245 0371 Fax: (0845) 4501717 E-mail: leeds@morrells-woodfinishers.com

Smith & Rodger Ltd, 34 Elliott Street, Glasgow, G3 8EA Tel: 0141-248 6341 Fax: 0141-248 6475 E-mail: info@smithandrodger.co.uk

Sonneborn & Rieck Ltd, 91-95 Peregrine Road, Ilford, Essex, IG6 3XH Tel: (020) 8500 0251 Fax: (020) 8500 3696 E-mail: export@sonneborn-rieck.co.uk

LADDER FITTINGS

Allofts Joinery Services, 4 Ladywood Road, Old Hall, Warrington, WA5 9QR Tel: (01925) 638889 Fax: (01925) 638889 E-mail: sales@allofts.co.uk

Dudley Tool & Engineering Co. Ltd, Mill Street, Wordsley, Stourbridge, West Midlands, DY8 5SX Tel: (01384) 571181 Fax: (01384) 265435 E-mail: info@dudley-tool.co.uk

LADDER HIRE

M A C Tool Hire, 25 Park Street, Congleton, Cheshire, CW12 1EG Tel: (01260) 299751 Fax: (01260) 299698

North London Plant Hire, 4-16 Shacklewell Lane, London, E8 2EZ Tel: (020) 7254 3328 Fax: (020) 7923 4129 E-mail: sales@nlph.co.uk

S G B Rental & Sales, 104 Scrubs Lane, Willesden, London, NW10 6SF Tel: (020) 8969 3661 Fax: (020) 8960 6033

LADDERS, *See also headings for particular types under Ladders*

A1 Survey Ltd, 1 Cefn Graig, Rhiwbina, Cardiff, CF14 6SW Tel: (029) 2091 5858 Fax: (029) 2091 5858 E-mail: sales@a1survey.net

Abru Ltd, Derwentside Industrial Park, Derby Road, Belper, Derbyshire, DE56 1WE Tel: (01773) 525700 Fax: (01773) 828059 E-mail: sales@abru.co.uk

Ash Of Ancoats Ltd, 166-174 Great Ancoats Street, Manchester, M4 7AB Tel: 0161-273 6986 Fax: 0161-273 6986 E-mail: ashdiy@freenetname.co.uk

Browns Ladders & Ceilings, Glen Way, Brierfield, Nelson, Lancashire, BB9 5NH Tel: (01282) 615517 Fax: (01282) 615515 E-mail: sales@brownsladders.co.uk

Clow Group Ltd, Garratts Lane, Cradley Heath, West Midlands, B64 5AW Tel: 0121-559 5222 Fax: 0121-559 0330 E-mail: clowgroup@btconnect.com

Globe Ladders, Vincent Street, Birmingham, B12 9SG Tel: 0121-440 6636 Fax: 0121-440 5475 E-mail: info@globeladders.co.uk

J Gorstige Ltd, Unit 10 Carlton Mill, Pickering Street, Leeds, LS12 2QG Tel: 0113-279 5200 Fax: 0113-279 5200

The Ladder Man, City Ladder Works, Victoria Road, Fenton, Stoke-On-Trent, ST4 2HS Tel: 0800 197 3839 Fax: (01782) 410172 E-mail: info@theladderman.co.uk

▶ LFI Ladder & Fencing Industries (Newent) Ltd, Horsefair Lane, Newent, Glos, GL18 1RP Tel: (01531) 820541 Fax: (01531) 821161 E-mail: sales@lfi-ladders.co.uk

▶ Loadlift Ltd, Winchester House, Winchester Road, Frinton-on-Sea, Essex, CO13 9JB Tel: (01255) 671187 Fax: (01255) 672236 E-mail: sales@loadlift.com

On Site Supplies, Stephenson Way, Crawley, West Sussex, RH10 1TN Tel: (01293) 744444

Zarges (U K) Ltd, 8 Holdom Avenue, Bletchley, Milton Keynes, MK1 1QU Tel: (01908) 641118 Fax: (01908) 648176 E-mail: sales@zargesuk.co.uk

LADIES BRIEFS

▶ Scantia, 78 Rainey Street, Magherafelt, County Londonderry, BT45 5AH Tel: (028) 7930 1143 E-mail: contact@scantia.com

LADIES CORSETS

▶ Elegant Lacing, 28 Longlands Road, Halesowen, West Midlands, B62 0AZ Tel: 0121-422 6476 Fax: 0121-422 3298 E-mail: barbara@elegantlacing.co.uk

▶ Victoria Proctor, 47 Lorne Street, Liverpool, L7 0JP Tel: 0151-228 6667 E-mail: unbrokendesigns@aol.com

▶ Rawhide Corsets, Unit 209 The Custard Factory, Gibb Street, Birmingham, B9 4AA Tel: 0121-608 1220 E-mail: sales@rawhidecorsets.co.uk

▶ Scantia, 78 Rainey Street, Magherafelt, County Londonderry, BT45 5AH Tel: (028) 7930 1143 E-mail: contact@scantia.com

LADIES' FASHION MANUFRS

A & D Hope Ltd, Evelyn House, 3 Elstree Way, Borehamwood, Hertfordshire, WD6 1RN Tel: (020) 8953 7278 Fax: (020) 8953 7279 E-mail: admin@adhope.com

▶ A S Fashions Ltd, Imperial Typewriter Buildings, East Park Road, Leicester, LE5 4QD Tel: 0116-276 2780 Fax: 0116-276 2780

▶ Albert & Son Ltd, 9 Whitechapel Road, London, E1 1DU Tel: (020) 7247 3948 Fax: 0207 2476303

Alexon Group plc, 40-48 Guildford Street, Luton, LU1 2PB Tel: (01582) 723131 Fax: (01582) 724158

Amora Wear, 9 Manningtree Street, London, E1 1LG Tel: (020) 7377 8711 Fax: (020) 7377 8711

Anderson Apparel Ltd, Unit 4-5 Village Workshops, Pandy Road, Llanbrynmair, Powys, SY19 7AA Tel: (01650) 521880 Fax: (01650) 521880

Aquascutum International Ltd, Ibex House, 42-47 Minories, London, EC3N 1DY Tel: (020) 7675 9050 Fax: (020) 7675 9099 E-mail: john.harper@aquascutum.co.uk

Arcadia Group Ltd, Hudson Road, Leeds, LS9 7DN Tel: 0113-249 4949 Fax: 0113-380 6282

Banner Ltd, Banner House, Greg Street, Stockport, Cheshire, SK5 7BT Tel: 0161-474 8000 Fax: 0161-474 7655 E-mail: admin@bannergroup.co.uk

Bentwood Ltd (Sterling Group), Atlantic Street, Broadheath, Altrincham, Cheshire, WA14 5FY Tel: 0161-926 7000 Fax: 0161-926 7029 E-mail: info@stirlinggroup.com

Bianca UK, 56 Eastcastle Street, London, W1W 8EQ Tel: (020) 7580 0085 Fax: (020) 7436 3938

Brenson Fashions Ltd, 32 Fortesque Avenue, London, E8 3QB Tel: (020) 8533 1525 Fax: (020) 8533 4427

▶ Bright Look Fashions, 33-35 Mere Lane, Rochdale, Lancashire, OL11 3TD Tel: (01706) 345322 Fax: (01706) 711611

Caprice Clothing Co Ltd, Boreham Road, London, N22 6SL Tel: (020) 8888 3513 Fax: (020) 8888 5095

Carr & Westley Ltd, Bourne Mill, Carpenters Lane, Hadlow, Tonbridge, Kent, TN11 0EU Tel: (01732) 850280 Fax: (01732) 850280

Cherry Fashions, 25 Sanvey Gate, Leicester, LE1 4EP Tel: 0116-262 8420 Fax: 0116-242 5485

Christian Marcus Fashions (Nottingham), Iremonger Road, Nottingham, NG2 3HU Tel: 0115-986 7056 Fax: 0115-985 0916 E-mail: cmd@christianmarcus.co.uk

Chrysalis Clothes Ltd, L Harlow House Shelton Road, Willowbrook East Industrial Estate, Corby, Northamptonshire, NN17 5XH Tel: (01536) 269034 Fax: (01536) 269034 E-mail: blackmor@btconnect.com

Club First Ltd, Unit 51, Milmead Industrial Centre, Mill Mead Road, London, N17 9QU Tel: (020) 8493 9611

Cotswold Collections, 15 King Street, Ludlow, Shropshire, SY8 1AQ Tel: (01584) 875612 Fax: (01584) 875998

D S Fashions, Units 8-9, Albert Road, Darlington, County Durham, DL1 2PD Tel: (01325) 357144 Fax: (01325) 357144

Nigel Day, Manor Farm Buildings, Stoke Road, Martock, Somerset, TA12 6AF Tel: (01935) 824287 Fax: (01935) 825442

Dewhirst Group Ltd, Road Five, Winsford Industrial Estate, Winsford, Cheshire, CW7 3PN Tel: (01606) 555600 Fax: (01606) 555601 E-mail: linda.bradbury@dewhirst.com

Dialcrown Ltd, 90 Tollington Way, London, N7 6RY Tel: (020) 7281 8130 Fax: (020) 7281 8809

Dressy Styles Ltd, 35 Hall Street, Birmingham, B18 6BS Tel: 0121-212 3499 Fax: 0121-212 3499 E-mail: dressystyles1@activemail.co.uk

Dub Clothing Mnfrs, Thurland Chambers, 4-6 Thurland Street, Nottingham, NG1 3DR Tel: 0115-924 3166 Fax: 0115-924 3166 E-mail: sales@dubclothing.com

Dubb Fashions, 1-3 Rawlings Road, Smethwick, West Midlands, B67 5AD Tel: 0121-420 2707 Fax: 0121-434 4050

Excel London, 6-16 Arbutus Street, London, E8 4DT Tel: (020) 7241 2100 Fax: (020) 7923 0098 E-mail: info@excellondon.co.uk

Fashion Craft Ltd, 11 Dolphin Street, Ardwick, Manchester, M12 6BG Tel: 0161-273 3947 Fax: 0161-273 3947

Fashion Group Manufacturing Ltd, 21 Turle Road, London, N4 3LZ Tel: (020) 7281 5636 Fax: (020) 7281 8793

▶ Fashion-4U, 87 Woolston Avenue, Congleton, Cheshire, CW12 3ED Tel: (07708) 731770 E-mail: sales@fashion-4u.co.uk

Fashionstop Ltd, Unit 1 Redcross Mill, Redcross Street, Rochdale, Lancashire, OL12 0NZ Tel: (01706) 525304 Fax: (01706) 658983

Figen Fashions Ltd, 2-4 Tottenham Road, London, N1 4BZ Tel: (020) 7254 1610 Fax: (020) 7249 9772

Frank Usher, Unit 1 Staples Corner Retail Park, Geron Way, London, NW2 6LW Tel: (020) 8208 2881 Fax: (020) 8452 0444 E-mail: sales@frankusher.co.uk

Fudge Jeans Ltd, Queens Mill, Queen Street, Ossett, West Yorkshire, WF5 8AW Tel: (01924) 263391 Fax: (01924) 278419

Funtimz, UNIT 14 Masonfield Drive, Newton Stewart, Wigtownshire, DG8 6QA Tel: (01671) 402139 E-mail: sales@funtimz.co.uk

Goodrange Ltd, 296 Wightman Rd, London, N8 0LT Tel: 020 83477670 Fax: 020 83477670

▶ Heel2toe.co.uk Ltd, Unit 9 Meadow Heights, Fir Street, Ramsbottom, Bury, Lancashire, BL0 0BN Tel: (07779) 151881

▶ High Demand Clothing, PO BOX 58, Longfield, Kent, DA3 7YQ Tel: (020) 8123 4985 E-mail: info@hdclothing.co.uk

Ice Channel Ltd, International Building, Middleton Business Park, Cleckheaton, West Yorkshire, BD19 5LY Tel: (01274) 870600 Fax: (01274) 870222 E-mail: info@alicecollins.com

▶ Ice Clothing Co. Ltd, 13 Hessel Street, London, E1 2LR Tel: (020) 7488 3234 Fax: (020) 7488 2808 E-mail: info@ice-clothing.co.uk

In Stitches, 2 Rawstorn Road, Colchester, CO3 3JE Tel: (01206) 573356 Fax: (01206) 573356

Innovative Clothing Co. Ltd, 51 Victoria Road North, Leicester, LE4 5EX Tel: 0116-261 2803 Fax: 0116-266 5472

Interlinks Fashions Ltd, Park Royal House, Park Royal Road, London, NW10 7JH Tel: (020) 8961 8169 Fax: (020) 8963 0683

Justina Of London Ltd, 6 Lockwood Industrial Park, Mill Mead Road, London, N17 9QP Tel: (020) 8801 3663 Fax: (020) 8808 4578 E-mail: info@justinaoflondon.biz

Kesta At David Barry Ltd, 7-9 Solebay Street, London, E1 4PW Tel: (020) 7790 2525 Fax: (020) 7790 5656 E-mail: sales@kesta.co.uk

Lagenes UK Ltd, 8 Anglers Lane, London, NW5 3DG Tel: (020) 7485 3778 Fax: (020) 7284 1251

Laura Ashley Ltd, Design Centre, 27 Bagleys Lane, London, SW6 2QA Tel: (020) 7880 5100 Fax: (020) 7880 5200

Leonard Edward Dresses London Ltd, Unit 2 30a Borwick Avenue, London, E17 6RA Tel: (020) 8521 7155 Fax: (020) 8520 1444

Norman Linton Ltd, Linton House, 39-51 Highgate Road, London, NW5 1RS Tel: (020) 7267 0921 Fax: (020) 7267 0928 E-mail: email@normanlinton.co.uk

London Style Ltd, 7 Putney Hill, London, SW15 6BA Tel: (020) 7480 5705 Fax: (020) 7480 5705

M A Majid, Swan La Mill, Higher Swan Lane, Bolton, BL3 3BJ Tel: (01204) 657442 Fax: (01204) 855314

M Waldman Ltd, 8 224 Iverson Road, London, NW6 2HL Tel: (020) 7624 6527 Fax: (020) 7625 7326 E-mail: contactus@waldmanskirts.com

▶ Mac Millan, 46A Wardo Avenue, Fulham, London, SW6 6RE Tel: 0207 731 8784 Fax: 0207 731 8622 E-mail: info@mac-millan.com

Maderite Designers, 102 Greenheath Business Centre, Three Colts Lane, London, E2 6JB Tel: (020) 7739 6602 Fax: (020) 7739 6602 E-mail: victorsims@macumltd.net

Marco Trading Co. Ltd, Marco House, Tariff Street, Manchester, M1 2FF Tel: 0161-228 6765 Fax: 0161-236 3611 E-mail: info@marco-uk.com

Stephen Marks (London) Ltd, Unit B, Dolphin Way, Purfleet, Essex, RM19 1NZ Tel: (020) 7036 7000 Fax: (020) 7036 7001

Matalan Ltd, Gillibrands Road, Skelmersdale, Lancashire, WN8 9TB Tel: (01695) 552400 Fax: (01695) 552401

Medici Ltd, 17-18 Margaret Street, London, W1W 8RP Tel: (020) 7436 2882 Fax: (020) 7631 0168 E-mail: mediciltd@aol.com

Metro Clothing Co. Ltd, 96 Fonthill Road, London, N4 3HT Tel: (020) 7263 0962 Fax: (020) 7263 0962

Miss Albion Ltd, Unit 4-5 St Francis Factory Estate, Thomas Street, West Bromwich, West Midlands, B70 6LY Tel: 0121-553 2505 Fax: 0121-525 8226

Mitton & Holden Ltd, Floor 2 The Arsenel, Sutton Mill, Heapy Street, Macclesfield, Cheshire, SK11 7JL Tel: (01625) 869966 Fax: (01625) 869955 E-mail: sales@mnhltd.fsbusiness.co.uk

▶ Mobarak, 1 Harrogate Road, Rawdon, Leeds, LS19 6HW Tel: 0113-250 0880 E-mail: info@mobarak.co.uk

Mona Lisa Of London plc, Zenith House, 69 Lawrence Road, London, N15 4EY Tel: (020) 8800 7747 Fax: (020) 8802 7807 E-mail: monalisa@zenithhouse.freeserve.co.uk

Monix Ltd, 11 Solebay Street, London, E1 4PW Tel: (020) 7790 6404 Fax: (020) 7791 7296

N A K Trading Co. Ltd, 153 Dukes Rd, Western Ave, Park Royal, London, W3 0SL Tel: (020) 8752 1815 Fax: (020) 8752 1878

Jeffrey Ohrenstein Ltd, 35 Brunel Road, East Acton, London, W3 7XR Tel: (020) 8740 1100 Fax: (020) 8749 9889 E-mail: jeffrey@jogroup.co.uk

▶ Oliver Goldsmiths Sunglasses, 15 All Saints Road, London, W11 1HA Tel: (0845) 0533440 Fax: (0870) 7541899 E-mail: info@olivergoldsmith.com

Park, Davidson & Co., Ltd, 308 The White Studios, Templeton On The Green, Glasgow, G40 1DA Tel: 0141-556 3350 Fax: 0141-556 1212 E-mail: info@patdavidson.co.uk

Revelation Shirts Ltd, Bewsey Street, Warrington, WA2 7JF Tel: (01925) 634372 Fax: (01925) 418438 E-mail: infomation@revelationshirts.co.uk

Roman Originals plc, 29 Inkerman Street, Birmingham, B7 4SB Tel: 0121-380 1900 Fax: 0121-380 1912 E-mail: enquires@romanoriginal.co.uk

S M Bros Ltd, 1st Floor Union Mill, Cambrian St, Manchester, M40 7EG Tel: 0161-274 3112 Fax: 0161-274 3312

Saharastorm, 25 Charles Avenue, Harrogate, North Yorkshire, HG1 4PE Tel: (01423) 552867

Shani Ltd, 2 Greycaine Road, Watford, WD24 7GT Tel: (01923) 228395 Fax: (01923) 228373E-mail: shanimail@shani-fashions.com

Silverts Ltd, 116-120 Goswell Road, London, EC1V 7DP Tel: (020) 7253 5766 Fax: (020) 7608 2230 E-mail: sales@silverts.co.uk

▶ Swaggers, 51 St. Martins Street, Wallingford, Oxfordshire, OX10 0AJ Tel: (01491) 824022 Fax: (01491) 613039 E-mail: sales@swaggers.co.uk

Tankson Textiles, 173 Rolfe Street, Smethwick, West Midlands, B66 2AS Tel: 0121-558 1733

▶ Tec Clothing Manufacturers, 534 Stoney Stanton Road, Coventry, CV6 5FS Tel: (024) 7666 8310

▶ ThaiStyle(UK) Ladies Apparel, 23 Fleet Street, Torquay, TQ1 1DB Tel: (0845) 6440241 Fax: (0845) 2269949 E-mail: jim@thaistyle.co.uk

▶ Topclass Wedding Gowns, 1st Floor Co-op Stores, The Street, Woolpit, Bury St. Edmunds, Suffolk, IP30 9RU Tel: (01359) 241422 E-mail: topclassgowns@aol.com

Valley Fashions Ltd, Unit 2g 10-14 Hollybush Gardens, London, E2 9QP Tel: (020) 7729 7642

Verona Originals Ltd, 89-91 New Road, Whitechapel, London, E1 1HH Tel: (020) 7375 1666 Fax: (020) 7274 3025 E-mail: ray@raifashions.com

Vijay Fashions Ltd, 120 Broughton Street, Manchester, M8 8AN Tel: 0161-834 7711 Fax: 0161-833 0933 E-mail: ianq@vijayfashions.co.uk

▶ Wholesale Movie TV Music Gifts Ltd, 1St Floor, 1 Chapel Street, Bridlington, North Humberside, YO15 2DR Tel: (01262) 677730 Fax: (01262) 675702

The Windsmoor Group, Windsmoor Ho, Lawrence Rd, London, N15 4EP Tel: (020) 8800 8022 Fax: (020) 8809 6747

Gordon Wyatt Ltd, 236 Tithe Street, Leicester, LE5 4BN Tel: 0116-276 7719 Fax: 0116-246 0360

LADIES' HOSIERY

Andrea Hosiery Manufacturing Co. Ltd, 107-115 Humberstone Road, Leicester, LE5 3AN Tel: 0116-262 5543 Fax: 0116-262 8732

Burt Bros Hosiery Ltd, A-C Willow Road, Nottingham, NG7 2TA Tel: 0115-970 6133 Fax: 0115-942 0576 E-mail: burtbros@premier.co.uk

Cavendish Hosiery Ltd, 77 Cannock Street, Leicester, LE4 9HR Tel: 0116-276 6477 E-mail: cavendishhos@aol.com

▶ Cheeky Legs Wholesale Tights and Hosiery, Unit 10 Coombe Park, Ashprington, Totnes, Devon, TQ9 7DY Tel: (0845) 2576847 E-mail: admin@cheekylegs.co.uk

Coulthards UK Ltd, Haydn Road, Nottingham, NG5 1DH Tel: 0115-924 6100 Fax: 0115-924 6796

Daner Ltd, 36 Walsall Road, Willenhall, West Midlands, WV13 2EG Tel: (01902) 368788 Fax: (01902) 637584E-mail: info@daner.co.uk

Drew Brady & Co. Ltd, Dove Mill, Dove Road, Bolton, BL3 4ET Tel: (01204) 854800 Fax: (01204) 854854 E-mail: drewbrady@ruia.co.uk

LADIES' HOSIERY – *continued*

Samuel Eden & Son Ltd, Station Road, Sutton-in-Ashfield, Nottinghamshire, NG17 5FQ Tel: (01623) 553521 Fax: (01623) 552115 E-mail: sales@samueleden.co.uk

Madison Hosiery, Mill Green, Leeds, LS12 6HE Tel: 0113-244 3434 Fax: 0113-242 5634

W Brewin & Co Ltd, Eastern Boulevard, Leicester, LE2 7BE Tel: 0116-254 6372 Fax: 0116-254 2856

LADIESWEAR

▶ Armondi Ltd, Unit 2 Crusader Industrial Estate, 167 Hermitage Road, London, N4 1LZ Tel: (020) 8800 4441

▶ Barrie Lewis & Co. Ltd, Units 1 & 2, Bedwas Business Centre, Bedwas, Caerphilly, Mid Glamorgan, CF83 8DU Tel: (029) 2088 6846

▶ David Barry (London) Ltd, 7-9 Solebay St, London, E1 4PW Tel: (020) 7790 1952

▶ Beste Fashions, 10 Millers Avenue, London, E8 2DS Tel: (020) 7241 1009 Fax: (020) 7241 1011

▶ Bright Look Fashions, 33-35 Mere Lane, Rochdale, Lancashire, OL11 3TD Tel: (01706) 345322 Fax: (01706) 711611

▶ Cage Clothing, 43-68 Lower Villiers Street, Wolverhampton, WV2 4NA Tel: (01902) 717396

Captive Clothing Ltd, Great Titchfield House, 14-18 Great Titchfield Street, London, W1W 8BD Tel: (020) 7436 7744 Fax: (020) 7436 8500

▶ Charles & Patricia Lester Ltd, Old Workhouse, Union Road West, Abergavenny, Gwent, NP7 7RL Tel: (01873) 853559 Fax: (01873) 858666

▶ Clyde Kilts Ltd, 71 James Street, Glasgow, G40 1BZ Tel: 0141-554 4649

▶ Dewhirst Group, 204 Great Portland Street, London, W1W 5HU Tel: (020) 7388 7631 Fax: (020) 7383 4997

▶ Dura Manufacturing, 101 Commercial Road, London, E1 1RD Tel: (020) 7247 5820 Fax: (020) 7247 5676

▶ E Walters UK, Southern Avenue, Leominster, Herefordshire, HR6 0LY Tel: (01568) 613344 Fax: (01568) 610860 E-mail: reception@ewalters.co.uk

Feline Ltd, 48 Lord Street, Cheetham, Manchester, M3 1HN Tel: 0161-819 2717 Fax: 0161-819 2695

▶ Flame UK Ltd, 1 Mode Wheel Road, Salford, M5 5DQ Tel: 0161-737 2115 Fax: 0161-736 0871

▶ Gee Bee Fashions, 88 Crabmill Lane, Coventry, CV6 5HA Tel: (024) 7663 7022 Fax: (024) 7663 7022

▶ Ice Clothing Co. Ltd, 13 Hessel Street, London, E1 2LR Tel: (020) 7488 3234 Fax: (020) 7488 2808 E-mail: info@ice-clothing.co.uk

▶ Jacques Vert (Retail) Ltd, Webber Pavilion, Seaham Grange Industrial Estat, Seaham, County Durham, SR7 0PZ Tel: 0191-521 3555

▶ Life Tradings Ltd, 32 Mason St, Manchester, M4 5EY Tel: 0161-834 5838 Fax: 0161-834 4498 E-mail: lifetrading@yahoo.com

▶ Maxella Ltd, Cypress House, Coburg Road, London, N22 6TP Tel: (020) 8889 4686 Fax: (020) 8889 3231

▶ Mistflex Ltd, 6 5 Fountayne Road, London, N15 4QL Tel: (020) 8808 3345 Fax: (020) 8808 3324

▶ Premier Drapers, 28 Linden Street, Leicester, LE5 5EE Tel: 0116-249 0043 Fax: 0116-249 0070

▶ Princess Stores, Latteridge House, Latteridge Green, Bristol, BS37 9TS Tel: 0870 1995481 E-mail: sales@princessstores.co.uk

▶ S S Johal & Sons Ltd, 97 Monk Street, Derby, DE22 3QE Tel: (01332) 343005 Fax: (01332) 332950

▶ Saga Fashions, Clarence House, 1 Hilda Road, Chatham, Kent, ME4 5PU Tel: (01634) 826520

▶ Andrew Shane Ltd, 157 Nottingham Road, Somercotes, Alfreton, Derbyshire, DE55 4JH Tel: (01773) 541414 Fax: (01773) 541415 E-mail: andrewshane@btconnect.com

▶ Sunnyville Clothing Ltd, East Park Works, 69 St. Barnabas Road, Leicester, LE5 4BE Tel: 0116-246 1988 Fax: 0116-246 1988

▶ Sylvia Jeffreys, Queensway, Wrexham, Clwyd, LL13 8YR Tel: (01978) 360390 Fax: (01978) 361684

Westfield Manchester Ltd, Hawthorn House, 14 Manchester Road, Wilmslow, Cheshire, SK9 1BG Tel: (01625) 548100 Fax: (01625) 548200 E-mail: westfildtexuk@aol.com

LADLE DRYING/HEATING EQUIPMENT, INDUSTRIAL/ FOUNDRY

Acetarc Welding & Engineering Co. Ltd, Atley Works, Dalton Lane, Keighley, West Yorkshire, BD21 4HT Tel: (01535) 607323 Fax: (01535) 602522 E-mail: sales@acetarc.co.uk

LAKE OR POND LINER INSTALLATION CONTRACTORS

Aquatic Discount Centre, 1a Haydock Street, Newton-le-Willows, Merseyside, WA12 9AB Tel: (01925) 291439 Fax: (01925) 291439

Environmental Lining Systems Ltd, Westland Square, Leeds, LS11 5SS Tel: 0113-277 5635 Fax: 0113-277 5454 E-mail: sales@environmentallinings.co.uk

Erdington Aquatic Centre, 97 Church Road, Erdington, Birmingham, B24 9BE Tel: 0121-373 1100 Fax: 0121-373 1100

▶ Kidzone South West Ltd, Bradley Mill, Bradley Lane, Newton Abbot, Devon, TQ12 1LZ Tel: (01626) 353081 Fax: (01626) 357516 E-mail: aquaticssouthwest@hotmail.com

Landline Ltd, 1 First Avenue, Halstead, Essex, CO9 2EX Tel: (01787) 476699 Fax: (01787) 472507 E-mail: sales@landline.co.uk

LAMINAR FLOW SYSTEMS, CLEAN AIR ETC

Airfeso Ltd, 16-18 Main Street, Bolton by Bowland, Clitheroe, Lancashire, BB7 4NW Tel: (01200) 447206 Fax: (01200) 447443 E-mail: airfeso@aol.com

LAMINATE COLLAPSIBLE TUBES

Betts UK Ltd, 505 Ipswich Road, Colchester, CO4 9HE Tel: (01206) 753400 Fax: (01206) 844002 E-mail: simon.jones@betts-uk.com

LAMINATED ALUMINIUM FOIL

Novelis U.K Ltd, Castle Works, Rogerstone, Newport, Gwent, NP10 9YD Tel: (01633) 202020 Fax: (01633) 202000 E-mail: bunworth@novelis.com

LAMINATED BAGS

▶ Keep Me Promotions, 2 New Concordia Wharf, Mill Street, London, SE1 2BB Tel: (020) 7231 0001 Fax: (0870) 7605511 E-mail: steve@keepmepromotions.com

M I P Ltd, Park Lane, Halesowen, West Midlands, B63 2RE Tel: (01384) 637711 Fax: (01384) 410104

LAMINATED FLOORING

Beds Flooring Distributors, Cambridge Road, Bedford, MK42 0LH Tel: (01234) 342444 Fax: (01234) 364925 E-mail: sales@bedsflooring.co.uk

▶ The Flooring Directory, The Coach House, Lower Denbigh Road, St. Asaph, Clwyd, LL17 0EF Tel: (01745) 584868 E-mail: webmaster@carpetfitters.biz

▶ Floors 2 Go P.L.C., Microtech House, 74 New Town Row, Birmingham, B6 4HA Tel: 0121-359 0234 Fax: 0121-359 4316 E-mail: info@floors2go.co.uk

Geo Brady Flooring Ltd, Brunswick Industrial Estate, Brunswick Village, Newcastle upon Tyne, NE13 7BA Tel: 0191-217 0202 Fax: 0191-217 0202

I D E SS Ltd, 3 West Road, Harlow, Essex, CM20 2BQ Tel: (01279) 400140 Fax: (01279) 400150

Magnet Ltd, Spa Road, Bolton, BL1 4SL Tel: (01204) 521611 Fax: (01204) 364779

Magnet Ltd, Allington Way, Darlington, County Durham, DL1 4XT Tel: (01325) 481177 Fax: (01325) 744379

Montague L Meyer (Pension Trustee) Ltd, Rippleway Wharf, Barking, Essex, IG11 0DU Tel: (020) 8477 8000 Fax: (020) 8594 8255 E-mail: info@mlmuk.com

Plasman Laminate Products Ltd, Plasman Industrial Centre, Marquis Street, Manchester, M19 3JH Tel: 0161-224 0330 Fax: 0161-224 9961 E-mail: info@plasman.co.uk

St. Gobain Building Products, Unit 18 Woodford Trading Estate, Southend Road, Woodford Green, Essex, IG8 8HF Tel: (020) 8550 8899 Fax: (020) 8550 3918

Warren Insulation, Blackthorne Road, Colnbrook, Slough, SL3 0DU Tel: (01753) 687272 Fax: (01753) 681623 E-mail: heathrow@warren.co.uk

▶ Windsor Kitchens, 39 Martley Gardens, Hedge End, Southampton, SO30 2XB Tel: 01489 795489 E-mail: sales@windsorkitchens.com

LAMINATED FLOORING UNDERLAY

▶ The Laminator Flooring Company Ltd, 53 Warwick Road, Cliftonville, Margate, Kent, CT9 2JU Tel: 0800 1955196 E-mail: a1jonathanweston@hotmail.com

LAMINATED MELAMINE COMPONENTS

Bauschlinnemann UK, Widow Hill Road, Heasandford Industrial Estate, Burnley, Lancashire, BB10 2TB Tel: (01282) 686850 Fax: (01282) 412361 E-mail: armabord@armabord.co.uk

Europanel UK Ltd, 1 Gerrards Place, East Gillibrands, Skelmersdale, Lancashire, WN8 9SU Tel: (01695) 731033 Fax: (01695) 727489 E-mail: europaneluk@btconnect.co.uk

LAMINATED METAL LAMINATIONS/ASSEMBLIES, ELECTRIC MOTOR ETC

Cogent Sankey Scott Laminations (Bilston), Bankfield Works, Greenway Road, Bilston, West Midlands, WV14 0TJ Tel: (01902) 401140 Fax: (01902) 409710 E-mail: sll@cogent-power.com

Damax Electrical Laminations Ltd, Unit C Amyco Works, Doris Road, Bordesley Green, Birmingham, B9 4SJ Tel: 0121-771 3857 Fax: 0121-771 1913 E-mail: info@damaxlams.co.uk

Euro Laminations Ltd, Cromwell Road, Ellesmere Port, CH65 4DT Tel: 0151-356 1791 Fax: 0151-356 1806 E-mail: gls@cogent-power.com

LAMINATED METAL MATERIALS

Bondcote Ltd, Unit 15, Lister Road Industrial Estate, Sherrington Way, Basingstoke, Hampshire, RG22 4DQ Tel: (01256) 465983 Fax: (01256) 328818 E-mail: mail@bondcote.co.uk

Ford Component Manufacturing Ltd, East Side, Tyne Dock, South Shields, Tyne & Wear, NE33 5ST Tel: 0191-454 0141 Fax: 0191-456 0028 E-mail: sales@fordcomps.co.uk

LAMINATED PAPER OR BOARD

▶ A P I Group plc, Second Avenue, Poynton, Stockport, Cheshire, SK12 1ND Tel: (01625) 858700 Fax: (01625) 858701 E-mail: enquiries@apilaminates.com

Adlington Paper & Board Supplies Ltd, Unit 1 Adlington Industrial Estate, Adlington, Macclesfield, Cheshire, SK10 4NL Tel: (01625) 850885 Fax: (01625) 850882 E-mail: adlingtonpaper@btconnect.com

C M C Products, Cuxham, Watlington, Oxfordshire, OX49 5NH Tel: (01491) 612676 Fax: (01491) 613771 E-mail: johncarr.cmc@myopal.net

Deva Paper & Board Co. Ltd, KUS Industrial Estate, Manor Lane, Hawarden, Deeside, Flintshire, CH5 3PJ Tel: (01244) 534302 Fax: (01244) 520858 E-mail: reception@devaboard.co.uk

Duraseal, 7 27 Black Moor Road, Ebblake Industrial Estate, Verwood, Dorset, BH31 6BE Tel: (01202) 826911 Fax: (01202) 813811

International Decorative Surfaces plc, West End Approach, Morley, Leeds, LS27 0NB Tel: 0113-220 3900 Fax: 0113-220 3901

Lamboard Ltd, 228 Leads Road, Hull, HU7 0DQ Tel: (01482) 701143 Fax: (01482) 712332

S.F. Williams & Co. Ltd, Essex Works, Kenway, Southend-On-Sea, SS2 5DX Tel: (01702) 445851 E-mail: sales@sfw.co.uk

LAMINATED PLASTIC

Allied Manufacturing, Sarena House Grove Park Industrial Estate, Grove Park, London, NW9 0EB Tel: (020) 8905 8046 Fax: (020) 8200 9510 E-mail: sandra.mcguire@kingswood-allied.co.uk

B G N Boards Co. Ltd, Bromford Road, West Bromwich, West Midlands, B70 7JB Tel: 0121-552 7777 Fax: 0121-552 7722 E-mail: sales@bgn.co.uk

Baldwin Plastic Laminates Ltd, 57 Tallon Road, Hutton, Brentwood, Essex, CM13 1TG Tel: (01277) 225235 Fax: (01277) 222586

Blackheath Products Ltd, Fairfield Park, Halesowen, West Midlands, B62 9JL Tel: 0121-561 4245 Fax: 0121-561 5904 E-mail: sales@blackheathproducts.co.uk

D F Bennett & Son (Plastics), Barkers Lane, Bedford, MK41 9RU Tel: (01234) 351017 Fax: (01234) 212941

Dunstable Laminates, 47 Edward Street, Dunstable, Bedfordshire, LU6 1HE Tel: (01582) 668973 Fax: (01582) 608227 E-mail: sales@dunstablelaminates.co.uk

Formica Ltd, Block 2, Kinnoull Road, Dunisinane Industrial Estate, Dundee, DD2 3PZ Tel: (01382) 833733 Fax: (01382) 832208 E-mail: bill.lang@formica-europe.com

H S Bassett & Son Ltd, Unit 13 Coronet Way, Swansea Enterprise Park, Swansea, SA6 8RH Tel: (01792) 790022 Fax: (01792) 790033 E-mail: sonia@hsbassett.co.uk

International Decorative Surfaces plc, West End Approach, Morley, Leeds, LS27 0NB Tel: 0113-220 3900 Fax: 0113-220 3901

Ipswich Plastics Ltd, Foxtail Road, Ransomes Industrial Estate, Ipswich, IP3 9RX Tel: (01473) 270101 Fax: (01473) 721446

Mitchells Millbrook Ltd, Manor Industrial Estate, Millbrook Road, Southampton, SO15 0LD Tel: (023) 8077 1004 Fax: (023) 8070 4736 E-mail: sales@mitchellsworktops.co.uk

Modern Laminates, 179b Queens Road, Watford, WD17 2QJ Tel: (01923) 229029 Fax: (01923) 246308

Norlica Plastics Ltd, 26-29 Rutherford Close, Leigh-on-Sea, Essex, SS9 5LQ Tel: (01702) 522945 Fax: (01702) 520140

Plasman Laminate Products Ltd, Plasman Industrial Centre, Marquis Street, Manchester, M19 3JH Tel: 0161-224 0330 Fax: 0161-224 9961 E-mail: info@plasman.co.uk

Plastics & Veneers Sales Ltd, Stronghold House, 43 Fourth Street, Kirkdale, Liverpool, L20 8NL Tel: 0151-944 7150 Fax: 0151-944 7157 E-mail: sales@plasticsandveneers.co.uk

Red Rose Distribution, Parliament Street, Burnley, Lancashire, BB11 3JT Tel: (01282) 724600 Fax: (01282) 724644

S C A Ltd, Etruscan Street, Stoke-on-Trent, ST1 5PG Tel: (01782) 202122 Fax: (01782) 224200

St. Gobain Building Products, Unit 18 Woodford Trading Estate, Southend Road, Woodford Green, Essex, IG8 8HF Tel: (020) 8550 8899 Fax: (020) 8550 3918

South Western Supplies, Collett Way, Newton Abbot, Devon, TQ12 4PH Tel: (01626) 333900 Fax: (01626) 324297

Texapin Ltd, 85 Lockfield Avenue, Enfield, Middlesex, EN3 7PY Tel: (020) 8805 2275 Fax: (020) 8443 3389 E-mail: andywells@texapin.co.uk

LAMINATED PLASTIC BEARINGS

Attwater Group, PO Box 39, Preston, PR1 1TA Tel: (01772) 258245 Fax: (01772) 203361 E-mail: info@attwater.co.uk

LAMINATED PLASTIC DECORATIVE SHEET/PLASTIC LAMINATES

Bauschlinnemann UK, Widow Hill Road, Heasandford Industrial Estate, Burnley, Lancashire, BB10 2TB Tel: (01282) 686850 Fax: (01282) 412361 E-mail: armabord@armabord.co.uk

Chamberlain Plastics Ltd, Bury Close, Higham Ferrers, Rushden, Northamptonshire, NN10 8HQ Tel: (01933) 353875 Fax: (01933) 410206 E-mail: sales@chamberlain-plastics.co.uk

Countertops (Holdings) Ltd, Unit 4-5 Lymore Gardens, Bath, BA2 1AQ Tel: (01225) 424467 Fax: (01225) 448107 E-mail: worktops@btconnect.com

H S Bassett & Son Ltd, Unit 13 Coronet Way, Swansea Enterprise Park, Swansea, SA6 8RH Tel: (01792) 790022 Fax: (01792) 790033 E-mail: sonia@hsbassett.co.uk

Nu-Style Products Ltd, 25 Silverburn Crescent, Bridge Of Don Industrial Estate, Aberdeen, AB23 8EW Tel: (01224) 823000 Fax: (01224) 823111 E-mail: info@nu-styles.co.uk

LAMINATED PLASTIC FABRICATORS/FABRICATED PRODUCTS

Baldwin Plastic Laminates Ltd, 57 Tallon Road, Hutton, Brentwood, Essex, CM13 1TG Tel: (01277) 225235 Fax: (01277) 222586

Bonding Techniques (Stotfold) Ltd, Taylors Road, Stotfold, Hitchin, Hertfordshire, SG5 4AX Tel: (01462) 733120 Fax: (01462) 732822 E-mail: info@bondingtechniques.com

Countertops (Holdings) Ltd, Unit 4-5 Lymore Gardens, Bath, BA2 1AQ Tel: (01225) 424467 Fax: (01225) 448107 E-mail: worktops@btconnect.com

D F Bennett & Son (Plastics), Barkers Lane, Bedford, MK41 9RU Tel: (01234) 351017 Fax: (01234) 212941

Dunhams Of Norwich, Hellesdon Park Road, Drayton High Road, Norwich, NR6 5DR Tel: (01603) 424855 Fax: (01603) 413336

Express Bonding Services Ltd, Severn House, Western Road, Oldbury, West Midlands, B69 4LY Tel: 0121-552 0810 Fax: 0121-552 0125

GPG Sales Ltd, Unit 6, Luton Street, Liverpool, L5 9XR Tel: 0151-298 1509 Fax: 0151-298 2276 E-mail: sales@gpg-sales.com

H S Bassett & Son Ltd, Unit 13 Coronet Way, Swansea Enterprise Park, Swansea, SA6 8RH Tel: (01792) 790022 Fax: (01792) 790033 E-mail: sonia@hsbassett.co.uk

Kemlite Ltd, 25 Caker Stream Road, Alton, Hampshire, GU34 2QF Tel: (01420) 86512 Fax: (01420) 541124

Leicester Bar Fitting Co. Ltd, West Avenue, Wigston, Leicestershire, LE18 2FB Tel: 0116-288 4897 Fax: 0116-281 3122 E-mail: sales@leicesterbarfitting.co.uk

Permabond Laminates Ltd, Gibbons Street, Nottingham, NG7 2SB Tel: 0115-978 7633 Fax: 0115-942 3380 E-mail: sales@permabondlaminates.co.uk

LAMINATED PLASTIC FABRICATORS/FABRICATED PRODUCTS – *continued*

Plastics & Veneers Sales Ltd, Stronghold House, 43 Fourth Street, Kirkdale, Liverpool, L20 8NL Tel: 0151-944 7150 Fax: 0151-944 7157 E-mail: sales@plasticsandveneers.co.uk

S J Rolls Ltd, Plot 7, Wimbledon Avenue, Brandon, Suffolk, IP27 0NZ Tel: (01842) 811918 Fax: (01842) 811693

Walter Smith Joinery Ltd, Westerby Road, East Middlesbrough Industrial Estate, Middlesbrough, Cleveland, TS3 8BQ Tel: (01642) 221171 Fax: (01642) 231342 E-mail: sales@waltersmithjoineryltd.co.uk

Stockmart Plastics, 184 Kingston Road, Portsmouth, PO2 7LP Tel: (023) 9266 0736 Fax: (023) 9266 0736

W H Foster & Sons Ltd, Stourdale Road, Cradley, Cradley Heath, West Midlands, B64 7BG Tel: (01384) 415170 Fax: (01384) 415185 E-mail: sales@whfoster.co.uk

LAMINATED PLASTIC PANELS OR BOARDS

Bonding Techniques (Stotfold) Ltd, Taylors Road, Stotfold, Hitchin, Hertfordshire, SG5 4AX Tel: (01462) 733120 Fax: (01462) 732822 E-mail: info@bondingtechniques.com

Mackintosh & Partners (Properties) Ltd, The Sawmills, Small Dole, Henfield, West Sussex, BN5 9XG Tel: (01273) 497100 Fax: (01273) 497139 E-mail: sales@mackintosh.co.uk

Morland, Cain Valley Trading Estate, Llanfyllin, Powys, SY22 5DD Tel: (01691) 648626 Fax: (01691) 648560 E-mail: toby.morris@morlandpanels.co.uk

Permabond Laminates Ltd, Gibbons Street, Nottingham, NG7 2SB Tel: 0115-978 7633 Fax: 0115-942 3380 E-mail: sales@permabondlaminates.co.uk

Rex Bousfield Ltd, Fairview Industrial Estate, Holland Road, Oxted, Surrey, RH8 9BD Tel: (01883) 717033 Fax: (01883) 717890 E-mail: john.medcraft@bousfield.com

LAMINATED PLASTIC POST-FORMED PRODUCTS

Alumasc Interior Building Products Ltd, Unit C1 Halesfield 19, Telford, Shropshire, TF7 4QT Tel: (01952) 580590 Fax: (01952) 587805 E-mail: sales@alumascinteriors.com

Bristol Panel Formers, Unit 606 Central Park, Petherton Road, Bristol, BS14 9BZ Tel: (01275) 830544 Fax: (01275) 830563 E-mail: sales@bristolpanelformers.co.uk

D F Bennett & Son (Plastics), Barkers Lane, Bedford, MK41 9RU Tel: (01234) 351017 Fax: (01234) 212941

Express Bonding Services Ltd, Severn House, Western Road, Oldbury, West Midlands, B69 4LY Tel: 0121-552 0810 Fax: 0121-552 0125

Ruddy Joinery Ltd, Enterprise Way, Flitwick, Bedford, MK45 5BS Tel: (01525) 716603 Fax: (01525) 718595 E-mail: enquiries@ruddy.co.uk

LAMINATED PLASTIC, GLASS FIBRE OR FIBREGLASS BASED

Countertops (Holdings) Ltd, Unit 4-5 Lymore Gardens, Bath, BA2 1AQ Tel: (01225) 424467 Fax: (01225) 448107 E-mail: worktops@btconnect.com

LAMINATED SPRINGS

Brigg Motor Springs Ltd, 79 Bridge Street, Brigg, South Humberside, DN20 8NF Tel: (01652) 653280 Fax: (01652) 659029

Jones Springs Engineering Ltd, Gladstone Street, Wednesbury, West Midlands, WS10 8BE Tel: 0121-568 7575 Fax: 0121-568 7692 E-mail: sales@jones-springs.co.uk

Merseyside Road Springs, 97 Rimrose Road, Bootle, Merseyside, L20 4HN Tel: 0151-922 3603 Fax: 0151-944 1996

Paddington Motor Springs, Unit 46 Stadium Business Centre, North End Road, Wembley, Middlesex, HA9 0AT Tel: (020) 8795 3300 Fax: (020) 8795 5954

S & M Springs, 3-4 Benner Road, Pinchbeck, Spalding, Lincolnshire, PE11 3TZ Tel: (01775) 712125 Fax: (01775) 712126

Serck Intertruck, 293 Elland Road, Leeds, LS11 8AX Tel: 0113-242 1463 Fax: 0113-385 5811 E-mail: si.leeds@unipart.co.uk

Sperry Springs (Sussex) Ltd, Unit 4 Kingston Industrial Estate, Easton Road, Aldershot, Hampshire, GU12 4YA Tel: (01903) 762272 Fax: (01252) 327773

Springline, 20 Blacker Crescent, Netherton, Wakefield, West Yorkshire, WF4 4EY Tel: (07711) 138209 E-mail: brian.springline.@fsnet.co.uk

LAMINATED WALLBOARD

Lamboard Ltd, 228 Leads Road, Hull, HU7 0DQ Tel: (01482) 701143 Fax: (01482) 712332

Total Laminate Systems Ltd, 11 Nimrod Way, East Dorset Trade Park, Wimborne, Dorset, BH21 7SH Tel: (01202) 877600 Fax: (01202) 861638 E-mail: sales@total-laminate.co.uk

LAMINATED WINDSCREENS

▶ UK Windscreens, 44 Grassington Crescent, Liverpool, L25 9RU Tel: 0151 2844471 E-mail: info@ukwindscreens.co.uk

LAMINATING ADHESIVES

Rose Hill Polymers Ltd, Rose Hill Mill, Beech Road, Sowerby Bridge, West Yorkshire, HX6 2JT Tel: (01422) 839456 Fax: (01422) 835786 E-mail: sales@rosehill-polymers.ltd.uk

Rose Hill Polymers Ltd, Rose Hill Mill, Beech Road, Sowerby Bridge, West Yorkshire, HX6 2JT Tel: (01422) 839456 Fax: (01422) 835786 E-mail: sales@rosehill-polymers.ltd.uk

LAMINATING FILM, *See also heading for particular materials*

Librex Educational Ltd, Colwick Road, Nottingham, NG2 4BG Tel: 0115-950 4664 Fax: 0115-958 6683 E-mail: sales@librex.co.uk

LAMINATIONS, MOTORS/ TRANSFORMERS, ETC

Cogent Sankey Scott Laminations (Bilston), Bankfield Works, Greenway Road, Bilston, West Midlands, WV14 0TJ Tel: (01902) 401140 Fax: (01902) 409710 E-mail: sll@cogent-power.com

Euro Laminations Ltd, Cromwell Road, Ellesmere Port, CH65 4DT Tel: 0151-356 1791 Fax: 0151-356 1806 E-mail: gls@cogent-power.com

LAMP CRUSHERS

Balcan Engineering, Banovallum Court, Boston Road Industrial Estate, Horncastle, Lincolnshire, LN9 6JR Tel: (01507) 528500 Fax: (01507) 528528 E-mail: info@balcan.co.uk

LAMP HOLDERS

C. Quitman Ltd, Ullswater Crescent, Coulsdon, Surrey, CR5 2HR Tel: (020) 8668 5295 Fax: (020) 8660 2589 E-mail: sales@cquitman.co.uk

LAMP MOUNTING KITS

▶ Wighill Park Guns, Wighill Park Nurseries, Wighill Park, Tadcaster, North Yorkshire, LS24 8BW Tel: (01937) 833757 Fax: (01937) 530563 E-mail: info@wighillparkguns.co.uk

LAMPS, *See also headings for particular types*

Dragon, 72-74 Heol Tawe, Abercrave, Swansea, SA9 1XR Tel: (01639) 730031 Fax: (01639) 730020

▶ Envirolite Ltd, Shore Road, Perth, PH2 8BH Tel: (01738) 630731 Fax: (01738) 637150

G C Designs Ltd, Mansion House Buildings, Market Place, Crich, Matlock, Derbyshire, DE4 5DD Tel: (01773) 857388 Fax: (01773) 857388E-mail: gwyncarless@gcdesigns.co.uk

Globe Electrical Co., 25 Crown Street, Ayr, KA8 8AG Tel: (01292) 269529 Fax: (01292) 611918

▶ Nautical Antiques Center, 3a Hope Square, Weymouth, Dorset, DT4 8TR Tel: (01305) 777838 E-mail: info@nauticalantiques.org

Scaramanga Ltd, Etsome Barn, Etsome Road, Somerton, Somerset, TA11 6LU Tel: (01458) 273999 Fax: (01458) 272220 E-mail: scaramanga@mcmail.com

LAMPS, LASER ARC

▶ Laser Experience, 10 Elder Close, Bilton, Rugby, Warwickshire, CV22 7TJ Tel: (01788) 814288 Fax: (01788) 521705 E-mail: peter@laserexperience.com

LAMPS, MINERS', *See Safety Lamps etc*

LAMPS, SIGNAL, LIGHT EMITTING DIODE (LED)

▶ Fineline, The Old Quarry, Clevedon Road, Failand, Bristol, BS8 3TU Tel: 01275 395000 Fax: 01275 395001 E-mail: Dave@fineline.uk.com

LAMPS, TABLE, CRYSTAL

▶ Cavern Crystals, 376 Wakefield Road, Denby Dale, Huddersfield, HD8 8RT Tel: 01484 865427 Fax: 01484 865427 E-mail: info@crystalcavern.com

LAMPSHADE FABRICS

▶ Carolina Lighting, 1 Wandle Trading Estate, Goat Road, Mitcham, Surrey, CR4 4HW Tel: (020) 8648 6800 Fax: (020) 8648 6822 E-mail: info@carolina-lighting.co.uk

▶ e-bay-trader, 18 Saville Road, Radcliffe, Manchester, M26 4JX Tel: 0161-764 2962 E-mail: mail@e-bay-trader.co.uk

LAMPSHADE FITTINGS

▶ e-bay-trader, 18 Saville Road, Radcliffe, Manchester, M26 4JX Tel: 0161-764 2962 E-mail: mail@e-bay-trader.co.uk

LAMPSHADE FRAMES

Afterglow Lighting Ltd, Unit 4 Q, Saxby Road Industrial Estate, Melton Mowbray, Leicestershire, LE13 1BS Tel: (01664) 566377 Fax: (01664) 482139

▶ e-bay-trader, 18 Saville Road, Radcliffe, Manchester, M26 4JX Tel: 0161-764 2962 E-mail: mail@e-bay-trader.co.uk

Via Lighting, 95 St. Peters Street, Syston, Leicester, LE7 1HL Tel: 0116-260 0866 Fax: 0116-260 0944 E-mail: website@vialaghting.co.uk

LAMPSHADE TRIMMINGS

▶ Bay Design, 1 Stanways Cottage, Hatfield Broad Oak, Bishop's Stortford, Hertfordshire, CM22 7JS Tel: (01279) 718139 Fax: (01279) 718139 E-mail: michele@bay-design.co.uk

LAMPSHADES

Albany Lighting, Albany House, New Street, Congleton, Cheshire, CW12 3AH Tel: (01260) 281551 Fax: (01260) 281561

▶ Bay Design, 1 Stanways Cottage, Hatfield Broad Oak, Bishop's Stortford, Hertfordshire, CM22 7JS Tel: (01279) 718139 Fax: (01279) 718139 E-mail: michele@bay-design.co.uk

Bright Shades Manufacturer Ltd, High Road, London, NW10 2EA Tel: (020) 8830 0736 Fax: (020) 8830 0736

Bulpitts Lampshades Ltd, Jarvis House, Yarlet Bank, Stafford, ST18 9SD Tel: (01889) 508977 Fax: (01543) 508966

▶ Coconut House Ltd, Hall Street, Long Melford, Sudbury, Suffolk, CO10 9JQ Tel: (01787) 312922 E-mail: chrisandgina@coconuthouse.co.uk

Cotterell Light Centres, 28-30 Carnoustie Place, Glasgow, G5 8PH Tel: (0141) 429 5648 Fax: 0141-429 7853 E-mail: glasgow@cotterell-lightcentres.com

Derwent Lighting, Derwent Road, York Road Business Park, Malton, North Yorkshire, YO17 6YB Tel: (01653) 696444 Fax: (01653) 696965 E-mail: enquiries@derwentlighting.co.uk

J P S Lampshades, 1 Manchester Road, London, N15 6HP Tel: (020) 8800 1769

Lampshade Designs Ltd, 11-12 Sapcote Trading Centre, High Road, London, NW10 2DH Tel: (020) 8459 0367 Fax: (020) 8451 7907 E-mail: jt@lampshadedesigns.co.uk

▶ Lampshades UK, Park Road, Rhosymedre, Wrexham, LL14 3YP Tel: (01691) 774409 E-mail: sales@lampshades.uk.com

Lion Witch & Lampshade, Birmingham House, High Street, Blakeney, Gloucestershire, GL15 4EB Tel: (01594) 516552 Fax: (01594) 516422

Moss Lighting Ltd, Unit 2a Bordesley Street, Birmingham, B5 5PG Tel: 0121-643 0529 Fax: 0121-633 4576

R P Lampshades, 3 Lyttleton Road, Pershore, Worcestershire, WR10 2DF Tel: (01386) 555212 Fax: (01386) 555212

Speights Classic Lighting, Huddersfield Road, Mirfield, West Yorkshire, WF14 8BJ Tel: (01924) 494176 Fax: (01924) 480691

Tambour Shades, 21 Rose Valley, Brentwood, Essex, CM14 4HZ Tel: 01277 223960

W K Howarth, 3 Blyth Road, Halesworth, Suffolk, IP19 8EN Tel: (01986) 874417 Fax: (01986) 875518

LAND AND ENGINEERING SURVEY SERVICES

A K S Ward Ltd, 1 West Midfield, London, EC1A 9JU Tel: (020) 7236 0161 Fax: (020) 7236 3239 E-mail: consult@aksward.com

▶ ArchiTech Surveys Ltd, 86 Easton street, High Wycombe, Bucks, HP11 1LT Tel: (01494) 522455 Fax: (01494) 535667 E-mail: technical@architechsurveys.co.uk

▶ Isis Surveyors Ltd, 7 Ashurst Close, Tadley, Hampshire, RG26 4AH Tel: 0118-981 4614 Fax: 0118-981 4614 E-mail: isissurveyors@ukonline.co.uk

▶ Jfa Surveys, 36 High Street, Ashford, Kent, TN24 8TE Tel: (01233) 898439 Fax: (01233) 629300 E-mail: jfasurveys@johnfloydd.co.uk

N B Surveys Ltd, 182 Market Street, Aberdeen, AB11 5PQ Tel: (01224) 212324 Fax: (01224) 212306 E-mail: admin@nbsurveys.com

Co Ordinated Surveys, The Old Stables, Garage Street, Llandudno, Gwynedd, LL30 1DW Tel: (01492) 870277 Fax: (01492) 877759 E-mail: sales@uksurveys.com

Plowman Craven & Associates, 141 Lower Luton Road, Harpenden, Hertfordshire, AL5 5EQ Tel: (01582) 765566 Fax: (01582) 765370 E-mail: sbarnes@plowmancraven.co.uk

▶ Souterrain Archaeological Services Ltd, 50 Rectory Drive, Exhall, Coventry, CV7 9PD Tel: (024) 7631 1567 Fax: (01794) 523528 E-mail: gps@souterrain.biz

LAND DRAINAGE OR INSPECTION OR RECLAMATION OR TREATMENT CONSULTANCY OR SERVICES

Cliff Addison Drainage, Far End Cottage, Worsall Road, Kirklevington, Yarm, Cleveland, TS15 9PE Tel: (01642) 782702 Fax: (01642) 790038 E-mail: sales@cliffaddisondrainage.co.uk

Agripower Ltd, Broomfield Farm, Rignall Road, Great Missenden, Buckinghamshire, HP16 9PE Tel: (01494) 866776 Fax: (01494) 866779 E-mail: sales@agripower.co.uk

Dredging International UK Ltd, Greenstede House Wood Street, Station Road, East Grinstead, West Sussex, RH19 1UZ Tel: (01342) 323000 Fax: (01342) 326000 E-mail: diuk@dredging.com

Farm Services Ltd, Chesterton Estate Yard, Banbury Road, Lighthorne, Warwick, CV35 0AF Tel: (01926) 651540 Fax: (01926) 651540 E-mail: info@sportsdrainage.co.uk

Isle of Wight Land Drainage, Newnham Farm, Newnham Lane, Ryde, Isle Of Wight, PO33 4ED Tel: (01983) 882423 Fax: (01983) 882423 E-mail: newnhamfarm@talk21.com

Lincolnshire Drainage Co. Ltd, Fen Road, Frampton Fen, Boston, Lincolnshire, PE20 1SD Tel: (01205) 311800 Fax: (01205) 360726

May Gurney (Highways), Chalk Lane, Snetterton, Norwich, NR16 2LB Tel: (01953) 888828 Fax: (01953) 888846

P D Dixon, Pickering Fold Farm, Bezza Lane, Balderstone, Blackburn, BB2 7LQ Tel: (01772) 877289 Fax: (01772) 877479 E-mail: sales@phillipdixoncontractor.co.uk

Stanley Land Drainage Ltd, Crow Royd Farm, North Moor Lane, Huddersfield, HD5 0PZ Tel: (01924) 497283 Fax: (01924) 493481

Brian Thompson, Barrock End, Hethersgill, Carlisle, CA6 6HT Tel: (01228) 675614 Fax: (01228) 675614

▶ Viridor Waste Management Ltd, 42 Kings Hill Avenue, Kings Hill, West Malling, Kent, ME19 4AJ Tel: (01732) 229200

W A Banham & Sons Ltd, The Pipeworks, Eye Road, Hoxne, Eye, Suffolk, IP21 5BA Tel: (01379) 668268 Fax: (01379) 668268

Walsh Demolition, 257 Moorland Road, Cardiff, CF24 2LJ Tel: (029) 2046 0645 Fax: (029) 2046 0645

LAND DRAINAGE PIPE OR SYSTEMS

John Davidson Pipes Ltd, Townfoot, Longtown, Carlisle, CA6 5LY Tel: (01228) 791503 Fax: (01228) 791682 E-mail: jdpcentral@jdpipes.co.uk

Stanley Land Drainage Ltd, Crow Royd Farm, North Moor Lane, Huddersfield, HD5 0PZ Tel: (01924) 497283 Fax: (01924) 493481

Threlfall Ltd, near Moss Farm Gulf Lane, Cockerham, Lancaster, LA2 0ER Tel: (01253) 799198 Fax: (01253) 790043 E-mail: enquiry@nearmossfarm.co.uk

LAND OR SITE SURVEYING OR INVESTIGATION

Albury S I Ltd, Miltons Yard, Petworth Road, Witley, Godalming, Surrey, GU8 5LH Tel: (01428) 684836 Fax: (01428) 685261 E-mail: info@alburysi.co.uk

LAND OR SITE SURVEYING OR INVESTIGATION - *continued*

Andrews Survey, Salmon Road, Great Yarmouth, Norfolk, NR30 3QS Tel: (01493) 332111 Fax: (01493) 332265

▶ ArchiTech Surveys Ltd, 86 Easton street, High Wycombe, Bucks, HP11 1LT Tel: (01494) 522455 Fax: (01494) 535667 E-mail: technical@architechsurveys.co.uk

Colliers Cre, 15-16 Park Row, Leeds, LS1 5HD Tel: 0113-200 1800 Fax: 0113-200 1840 E-mail: leeds@colliersc re.co.uk

Robin Forestry Surveys Ltd, Coulton House, Tannery Road, Harraby Green Business Park, Carlisle, CA1 2SS Tel: (01228) 409469 Fax: (01228) 540439 E-mail: jaqs@robinsurveys.co.uk

Glen Surveys Ltd, Hatherley House, 13 Hatherley Road, Sidcup, Kent, DA14 4DS Tel: (020) 8309 5757 Fax: (020) 8309 6362 E-mail: glen@glensurveys.co.uk

Ground Engineering, Newark Road, Peterborough, PE1 5UA Tel: (01733) 568153 Fax: (01733) 315280 E-mail: admin@groundengineering.co.uk

Ground Solutions Group Ltd, Cobbs Wood Industrial Estate, Hanover Close, Ashford, Kent, TN23 1EJ Tel: (01233) 658270 Fax: (01233) 658299 E-mail: gsg@groundsolutions.co.uk

I E T G plc, Oxford House, 2 Sixth Avenue, Doncaster Finningley Airport, Doncaster, South Yorkshire, DN9 3GG Tel: (01302) 802000 Fax: (01302) 802001E-mail: sales@ietg.co.uk

▶ Jfa Surveys, 36 High Street, Ashford, Kent, TN24 8TE Tel: (01233) 898439 Fax: (01233) 629300 E-mail: jfasurveys@johnfloydd.co.uk

Laser Surveys Ltd, Brockamin House, Leigh, Worcester, WR6 5JU Tel: (01886) 833173 Fax: (01886) 833485 E-mail: worcester@lasersurveys.com

Mason Land Surveys Ltd, Dickson Street, Dunfermline, Fife, KY12 7SL Tel: (01383) 727261 Fax: (01383) 739480 E-mail: sales@mason.co.uk

Nicholls Colton & Partners Ltd, 7-11 Harding Street, Leicester, LE1 4DH Tel: 0116-253 6333 Fax: 0116-251 4709 E-mail: testing@nicholls-colton.co.uk

Oakley Soils & Concrete Engineering Ltd, Rede Hall, Chedburgh, Bury St. Edmunds, Suffolk, IP29 4UG Tel: (01284) 850555 Fax: (01284) 850345

Ocean Fix International Ltd, Waterton Grange, Stoneywood, Bucksburn, Aberdeen, AB21 9HX Tel: (01224) 714100 Fax: (01224) 714170 E-mail: pps@oceanfix-international.co.uk

▶ Shire Consulting, The Chapel, Barnsley Hall Road, Bromsgrove, Worcestershire, B61 0SZ Tel: (01527) 579933 Fax: (01527) 579537 E-mail: info@shire-uk.com

Site Data Sutton Coldfield Ltd, The Courtyard, Roman Way, Coleshill, Birmingham, B46 1HQ Tel: (01675) 430043 Fax: (01675) 430133 E-mail: site-data@dial.pipex.com

Soil Mechanics, Glossop House, Hogwood Lane, Finchampstead, Wokingham, Berkshire, RG40 4QW Tel: 0118-932 8888 Fax: 0118-932 8383 E-mail: sm@wokingham.mesgl.co.uk

South West Surveys Projects Ltd, 43 Lower Fore Street, Saltash, Cornwall, PL12 6JQ Tel: (01752) 849190 Fax: (01752) 849229 E-mail: office@swsurveys.co.uk

Sub Soil Consultancy Services Ltd, Kennedy Road, Off Chaddocks Lane, Manchester, M29 7LD Tel: (01942) 883565 Fax: (01942) 883566 E-mail: richard@subsoil.co.uk

Survey Supplies Ltd, 1-5 Bankfield Drive, Spondon, Derby, DE21 7QZ Tel: (01332) 675888 Fax: (01332) 661381 E-mail: info@surveysupplies.co.uk

▶ Vector Surveys, 24 Edwin Street, London, E16 1QA Tel: (020) 7474 3991 Fax: (020) 7474 3991 E-mail: pjwarr@btopenwolrd.com

LANDFILL SITE CHARACTERISATION OR MAPPING

▶ TerraDat Geophysics Ltd, Unit 2, Ocean Ho, Hunter St, Cardiff, CF10 5FR Tel: (0870) 7303050 Fax: (0870) 7303051 E-mail: info@terradat.co.uk

LANDFILL SITE GAS COMBUSTION SYSTEMS

▶ Hi Lo Flare Systems & Services UK Ltd, Fairewell House, Yarmouth Road, Ormesby, Great Yarmouth, Norfolk, NR29 3QB Tel: (01493) 730095 Fax: (01493) 731043 E-mail: hi-lo@hi-loflare.co.uk

The Summerleaze Waste Company Ltd, Lakeside, Summerleaze Road, Maidenhead, Berkshire, SL6 8HZ Tel: (01628) 630444 Fax: (01628) 773160 E-mail: info@summerleaze.co.uk

LANDFILL SITE GAS RECOVERY SPECIALIST SERVICES

Anglia Mechanical Environmental, Unit 38, Mere View Industrial Estate, Yaxley, Peterborough, PE7 3HS Tel: (01733) 244600 Fax: (01733) 244606 E-mail: angliamechanicle@btopenworld.com

Earth 1st Hire, 198 Cannock Road, Westcroft, Wolverhampton, WV10 8QP Tel: (01902) 861333 Fax: (01902) 864400

Enviros, Shrewsbury Business Park, Shrewsbury, SY2 6LG Tel: (01743) 284800 Fax: (01743) 245558 E-mail: marketing@enviros.com

▶ Hi Lo Flare Systems & Services UK Ltd, Fairewell House, Yarmouth Road, Ormesby, Great Yarmouth, Norfolk, NR29 3QB Tel: (01493) 730095 Fax: (01493) 731043 E-mail: hi-lo@hi-loflare.co.uk

Onyx Environmental Group P.L.C., 154A Pentonville Road, London, N1 9PE Tel: (020) 7812 5000 Fax: (020) 7812 5001

LANDFILL SITE LINING OR CAPPING CONTRACTORS

Environmental Lining Systems Ltd, Westland Square, Leeds, LS11 5SS Tel: 0113-277 5635 Fax: 0113-277 5454 E-mail: sales@environmentallinings.co.uk

LANDSCAPE ARCHITECTS

▶ Ajb Landscapes, 18 West Way, Rossett, Wrexham, LL12 0DX Tel: (01244) 579333

▶ Big Green Carpet, 31 Grange Road, Hove, East Sussex, BN3 5HU Tel: (07900) 890977 E-mail: oli@biggreencarpet.co.uk

▶ Big Green Carpet, Flat 4 Clearview House, London Road, Ashington, Pulborough, West Sussex, RH20 3DD Tel: (07810) 611236 E-mail: luke@biggreencarpet.co.uk

Cadbury Garden & Leisure, Smallway, Congresbury, Bristol, BS49 5AA Tel: (01934) 876464 Fax: (01934) 875701 E-mail: info@cadbury.g-l.co.uk

Comprehensive Planning Associates (Overseas), Bromsash House, Bromsash, Ross-On-Wye, Herefordshire, HR9 7PL Tel: (01989) 750243 Fax: (01989) 750243

E E Olley & Sons Ltd, Dartford Trade Park, Dartford, DA1 1PE Tel: (01322) 227681 Fax: (01322) 289724 E-mail: sales@eeolley.co.uk

▶ Flora Design, 106 Cromwell Road, St. Andrews, Bristol, BS6 5EZ Tel: 0117-944 1494 Fax: 0117-944 1494 E-mail: sales@floradesign.co.uk

Robin Forestry Surveys Ltd, Coulton House, Tannery Road, Harraby Green Business Park, Carlisle, CA1 2SS Tel: (01228) 409469 Fax: (01228) 540439 E-mail: jaqs@robinsurveys.co.uk

▶ Landlab Scotland, Lilac Grove, Laurieston, Castle Douglas, Kirkcudbrightshire, DG7 2PW Tel: (01556) 505970 Fax: (01556) 505975 E-mail: mail@landlab.co.uk

▶ Marc Stapleford, Unit A39 The Springboard Centre, Mantle Lane, Coalville, Leicestershire, LE67 3DW Tel: (0870) 7417314 E-mail: marc@msld.co.uk

▶ Sinclair Cleaning Services, Unit 2 Barleycroft End, Furneux Pelham, Buntingford, Hertfordshire, SG9 0LG Tel: (01279) 777115 Fax: (01279) 778006 E-mail: mail@jsld.co.uk

LANDSCAPE DESIGN SOFTWARE

▶ Cyclone Holdings Ltd, PO Box 29, Tenbury Wells, Worcestershire, WR15 8HT Tel: (01584) 811467 Fax: E-mail: admin@cyclone-chieftain.co.uk

▶ Dandys Topsoil, Yew Tree Farm, Sealand Road, Sealand, Chester, CH1 6BS Tel: (0845) 4563089 Fax: (01244) 881922 E-mail: adam@dandys.org

▶ Roots Landscaping, 83 Cecil Road, Dronfield, Derbyshire, S18 2GX Tel: (01246) 290786 E-mail: info@roots-landscaping.com

▶ T F S, 127 Cabin Lane, Oswestry, Shropshire, SY11 2PF Tel: (07811) 768841 E-mail: nostromo127@hotmail.com

LANDSCAPING MATERIALS

▶ Q Lawns, Corkway Drove, Hockwold, Thetford, Norfolk, IP26 4JR Tel: (01842) 828266 Fax: (01842) 827911 E-mail: sales@qlawns.co.uk

LANDSCAPING STONES

▶ Town & Country Turf, Howards Nursey, Handcross Road, Lower Beeding, Horsham, West Sussex, RH13 6NX Tel: (01403) 892634 Fax: (01403) 892635 E-mail: sales@tcturf.co.uk

▶ Yates Landscaping Ltd, 6 Hawthorne Business Park, Hawthorne Street, Warrington, WA5 0BT Tel: (01925) 638883 Fax: (01925) 638883 E-mail: yateslandscaping@tiscali.co.uk

LANGUAGE LABORATORIES

▶ Activa Solutions Ltd, Activa House, Commerce Way, Edenbridge, Kent, TN8 6ED Tel: (01732) 784300 Fax: (0870) 7544516 E-mail: info@activa.co.uk

Arm A-V Services, 57 St. Johns Road, Caversham, Reading, RG4 5AL Tel: 0118-948 2559 E-mail: mekka@lentil.org

▶ J T B Electronic Services, 19 Glenmore Road, Brixham, Devon, TQ5 9BT Tel: (01803) 856875 Fax: (01803) 856875 E-mail: mail@jtbelectronics.co.uk

Keith Audio Ltd, North End, Ditchling, Hassocks, West Sussex, BN6 8TG Tel: (01273) 843232 Fax: (01273) 843232

Language Technology Centre, 5&7 Kingston Hill, Kingston Upon Thames, Surrey, KT2 7PW Tel: (020) 8549 2359 Fax: (020) 8974 6994 E-mail: admin@langtec.co.uk

Magnasign Ltd, Orchard Hill, Rudgwick, Horsham, West Sussex, RH12 3EQ Tel: (01403) 822280 E-mail: languagelabsuk@aol.com

T & I Services UK Ltd, 3 Furtho Manor Farm, Northampton Road, Old Stratford, Milton Keynes, MK19 6NR Tel: (0845) 6008150 Fax: (01908) 265461 E-mail: enquiries@tiservicesuk.com

LANGUAGE SCHOOLS

All Languages Ltd, 362-364 Old Street, London, EC1V 9LT Tel: (020) 7739 6641 Fax: (020) 7739 6542 E-mail: info@alllanguages.co.uk

Basil Paterson College, 66 Queen Street, Edinburgh, EH2 4NA Tel: 0131-225 3802 Fax: 0131-226 6701 E-mail: info@basilpaterson.co.uk

Butler School Of Languages, 170 Victoria Street, London, SW1E 5LB Tel: (020) 7834 0606 Fax: (020) 7828 1184

Callan School Of English, 139 Oxford Street, London, W1D 2JB Tel: (020) 7734 5600 Fax: (020) 7494 3204E-mail: csl@callan.co.uk

Central School Of English, 1 Tottenham Court Road, London, W1T 1BB Tel: (020) 7580 2863 Fax: (020) 7255 1806 E-mail: sales@centralschool.co.uk

▶ Don Quijote, 2-4 Stoneleigh Park Road, Epsom, Surrey, KT19 0QT Tel: (020) 8786 8081 Fax: (020) 8786 8086 E-mail: info@donquijote.org

Dudley College Of Technology, The Broadway, Dudley, West Midlands, DY1 4AS Tel: (01384) 363363 Fax: (01384) 363311 E-mail: christine.richards@dudleycol.ac.uk

Evendine College, 227 Tottenham Court Road, London, W1T 7QF Tel: (020) 7580 1989 Fax: (020) 7580 1959 E-mail: evendine@evendine.com

▶ From All Around the World, 25 Warwick Road, Balderton, Newark, Notts, NG24 3QE Tel: 01636 703444 E-mail: info@fromallaroundtheworld.com

International House, 106 Piccadilly, London, W1J 7NL Tel: (020) 7518 6999 Fax: (020) 7495 0284 E-mail: info@ihlondon.co.uk

King's School of English, 25 Beckenham Road, Beckenham, Kent, BR3 4PR Tel: (020) 8650 5891 Fax: (020) 8663 3224 E-mail: info@kingslon.co.uk

Kingsway English Centre Language School, 40 Foregate Street, Worcester, WR1 1EE Tel: (01905) 619877 Fax: (01905) 613388 E-mail: info@kingsway-english.com

▶ Lancashire College, Southport Road, Chorley, Lancashire, PR7 1NB Tel: (01257) 276719 Fax: (01257) 241370 E-mail: dawn.shelton@ed.lancscc.gov.uk

▶ The Language Company, The Thistles, 9 Ramblers Close, Colwick, Nottingham, NG4 2DN Tel: 0115 8449369 E-mail: info@thelanguagecompany.co.uk

Language Studies International, 19-21 Ridgmount Street, London, WC1E 7AH Tel: (020) 7467 6500 Fax: (020) 7323 1736

Linguarama Ltd, New London Bridge House, 25 London Bridge Street, London, SE1 9SG Tel: (020) 7939 3200 Fax: (020) 7939 3230 E-mail: london@linguarama.com

Mayfair School Of English, 61-65 Oxford Street, London, W1D 2EL Tel: (020) 7437 9941 Fax: (020) 7494 3611 E-mail: info@mayfairschool.co.uk

New College, New College Drive, Swindon, SN3 1AH Tel: (01793) 436437 Fax: (01793) 436437E-mail: admissions@newcollege.ac.uk

Oxford House College, 30 Market Place, London, W1W 8AW Tel: (020) 7436 4872 Fax: (020) 7323 4582E-mail: english@oxfordhouse.co.uk

Partners In Training Ltd, 8 Marsden Park, York, YO30 4GX Tel: (01904) 691777 Fax: (01904) 691102 E-mail: info@pint.co.uk

Sels College, 64 Long Acre, London, WC2E 9JD Tel: (020) 7240 2581 Fax: (020) 7379 5793

▶ Spanish Machine, 115 Greenwich South Street, London, SE10 8NX Tel: (020) 8692 3918 E-mail: felipe@thespanishmachine.co.uk

▶ Speak Easy School Of English, 24 Chiswick High Road, London, W4 1TE Tel: (020) 8995 8772 Fax: (020) 8995 7363 E-mail: info@speakeasyschool.co.uk

Training Partnership Ltd, 450 Babbacombe Road, Torquay, TQ1 1HW Tel: (01803) 290222 Fax: (01803) 290333 E-mail: info@thetrainingpartnershipltd.com

World Language Consultants Ltd, 88 Bermondsey Street, London, SE1 3UB Tel: (020) 7357 6981 Fax: (020) 7357 7755 E-mail: worldlanguages@btconnect.com

LANGUAGE SCHOOLS, CHINESE

▶ The Language Company, The Thistles, 9 Ramblers Close, Colwick, Nottingham, NG4 2DN Tel: 0115 8449369 E-mail: info@thelanguagecompany.co.uk

LANGUAGE TUITION TAPES

▶ From All Around the World, 25 Warwick Road, Balderton, Newark, Notts, NG24 3QE Tel: 01636 703444 E-mail: info@fromallaroundtheworld.com

LAPEL PINS

Eurobelts.com, 8 Stuart Close, Darwen, Lancashire, BB3 1DP Tel: (01254) 704395 Fax: (01254) 704395 E-mail: roy@eurobelts.com

LAPIDARIES, *See also headings under Diamond*

Birmingham Stone Cutting Co. Ltd, 59 Caroline Street, Birmingham, B3 1UF Tel: 0121-236 1418 Fax: 0121-248 1418

Craftstones Europe, 52-54 Holmethorpe Avenue, Holmethorpe Industrial Estate, Redhill, RH1 2NL Tel: (01737) 767363 Fax: (01737) 768627 E-mail: craftstones@craftstones.co.uk

LAPPING ABRASIVES

▶ Lamplan Industries Ltd, Unit 5, Pettings Court Farm, Hodsoll Street, Sevenoaks, Kent, TN15 7LH Tel: (01732) 824829 Fax: (01732) 824828 E-mail: jbroad@lamsplan.com

LAPPING ABRASIVES/ ACCESSORIES/CONSUMABLES

Peter Walters (U K) Ltd, Brindley Road, Dodwells Bridge Industrial Estate, Hinckley, Leicestershire, LE10 3BY Tel: (01455) 631707 Fax: (01455) 611360 E-mail: pwuk@peter-wolters.com

LAPPING MACHINES

Boremasters, High Street, Cleobury Mortimer, Kidderminster, Worcestershire, DY14 8DS Tel: (01299) 270942 Fax: (01299) 270212 E-mail: sales@boremasters.co.uk

Kemet International Ltd, Sutton Road, Maidstone, Kent, ME15 9NJ Tel: (01622) 755287 Fax: (01622) 670915 E-mail: sales@kemet.co.uk

Ryburn Lapping, Riverside Ho, Queens Square Bus Pk, Huddersfield Rd, Honley, Huddersfield, HD9 6QZ Tel: (01484) 660878 Fax: (01484) 665373

LAPPING SERVICES

Ek Machine Tools Ltd, 14 Singer Road, Kelvin Industrial Estate, East Kilbride, Glasgow, G75 0XS Tel: (01355) 234600 Fax: (01355) 265979 E-mail: info@ekomat.co.uk

▶ Fine Glass Finishers, 1 Park Farm, Park Road, Great Chesterford, Saffron Walden, Essex, CB10 1RN Tel: (01799) 530655 Fax: (01799) 531752 E-mail: sales@fineglassfinishers.co.uk

Kemet International Ltd, Sutton Road, Maidstone, Kent, ME15 9NJ Tel: (01622) 755287 Fax: (01622) 670915 E-mail: sales@kemet.co.uk

Opticron Plastics, Unit 3 Sabre Court, Gillingham Business Park, Gillingham, Kent, ME8 0RW Tel: (01634) 366385 Fax: (01634) 366397 E-mail: info@opticron.co.uk

Precision Lapping Ltd, Unit 16 Marino Way, Finchampstead, Wokingham, Berkshire, RG40 4RF Tel: 0118-973 5989 Fax: 0118-973 7241 E-mail: paullap@aol.com

Taylor & Whiteley Ltd, Riverside House,, Queen Square Business Park, Huddersfield Road, Honley, Holmfirth, HD9 6QZ Tel: (01484) 662059 Fax: (01484) 665373

▶ U Q G Ltd, 99-101 Cambridge Road, Milton, Cambridge, CB24 6AT Tel: (01223) 425601 Fax: (01223) 420506 E-mail: sales@uqgoptics.com

Williams & Co Southampton Ltd, Victoria Street, Southampton, SO14 5QZ Tel: (023) 8022 0490 Fax: (023) 8063 8930 E-mail: sales@williams-eng.co.uk

LARGE FORMAT PLOTTERS

Tracks Cad Systems Ltd, London Road, Wokingham, Berkshire, RG40 1PD Tel: (01344) 455046 Fax: (01344) 860547 E-mail: sales@trackscad.co.uk

LARGE INSTALLATION INTRUDER DETECTORS (ID)

Berkeley Guard Ltd, The Pottery, Ham Lane, Baughurst, Tadley, Hampshire, RG26 5SD Tel: 0118-981 1428 Fax: 0118-981 0487 E-mail: info@berkeleyguard.com
Thales Underwater Systems, Ocean House, Throop Road, Templecombe, Somerset, BA8 0DH Tel: (01963) 370551 Fax: (01963) 372200 E-mail: sales@tms-ltd.com

LARGE SCALE DIGITAL DISPLAYS

Ferrograph Ltd, New York Way, New York Industrial Park, Newcastle upon Tyne, NE27 0QF Tel: 0191-280 8800 Fax: 0191-280 8810
Leuze Mayser Electronic Ltd, Generation Business Park, Barford Road, St. Neots, Cambridgeshire, PE19 6YQ Tel: (01480) 408500 Fax: (01480) 403808 E-mail: mail@leuzemayser.co.uk
London Electronics Ltd, Warren Court, Chicksands, Shefford, Bedfordshire, SG17 5QB Tel: (01462) 850967 Fax: (01462) 850968 E-mail: support@london-electronics.com

LARGE SCALE INTEGRATED FLUIDIC MICROSYSTEMS

▶ Starbridge Systems Ltd, Techneum 2, Kings Road, The Docks, Swansea, SA1 8PJ Tel: (01792) 485530 Fax: (01792) 485531 E-mail: info@labstar.co.uk

LARGE WORKPIECE TURNING

Contract Turning Ltd, Unit 27 Ventura Place, Poole, Dorset, BH16 5SW Tel: (01202) 625502 Fax: (01202) 625502 E-mail: info@contractturning.co.uk

LASER ALIGNMENT EQUIPMENT

Holderness Ship Repairers Ltd, Wassand Street, Hull, HU3 4AL Tel: (01482) 216055 Fax: (01482) 216056 E-mail: holdernessshiprepairers@compuserve.com

LASER ALIGNMENT SERVICES

A 1 Dynamic Balancing Ltd, 7-9 Hagley Road, Hayley Green, Halesowen, West Midlands, B63 1DG Tel: 0121-501 3705 Fax: 0121-501 3615 E-mail: sales@wdbltd.co.uk
Reekie Machine (Sales) Ltd, South Street, Inchinnan Industrial Estate, Inchinnan, Renfrew, PA4 9RL Tel: 0141-812 0411 Fax: 0141-812 0137 E-mail: info@reekiemachining.co.uk
Rotary Equipment Services Ltd, Unit 5-6 Castle Way, Severn Bridge Industrial Estate, Portskewett, Caldicot, Gwent, NP26 5YG Tel: (01291) 420670 Fax: (01291) 430165 E-mail: sales@reslimited.com
Rotary Equipment Services Ltd, Unit 2, Expressway Business Park, Station Road, Queensferry, Deeside, Clwyd, CH5 2TF Tel: (01244) 822402 Fax: (01244) 823960 E-mail: jeff.sheen@reslimited.com
▶ Steertrak Commercial Vehicle Servicing, Commercial House Station Road Business Park, Station Road, Tewkesbury, Gloucestershire, GL20 5DR Tel: (01684) 276900 Fax: (01684) 276500 E-mail: sales@steertrak.co.uk
▶ Warner Land Surveys, Beaumont House, 59 High Street, Theale, Reading, RG7 5AL Tel: 0118-930 3314 Fax: 0118-930 1859 E-mail: wlsl@warnerlandsurveys.com

LASER COMPONENTS

BMP Europe Ltd, Shorten Brook Drive, Altham Business Park, Altham, Accrington, Lancashire, BB5 5YH Tel: (01282) 772000 Fax: (01282) 777700 E-mail: bmp@bmp-europe.co.uk
Coherent UK Holdings Ltd, 28 St Thomas Place, The Cambridge Business Park, Ely, Cambridgeshire, CB7 4EX Tel: (01353) 658800 Fax: (01353) 659110 E-mail: sales.uk@coherent.com
▶ Global Laser Ltd, Medallion Technology Centre, Cwmtillery Industrial Estate, Cwmtillery, Abertillery, Gwent, NP13 1LZ Tel: (01495) 212213 Fax: (01495) 214004 E-mail: davidb@globallasertech.com
II-VI UK Ltd, 21 Burley road, Oakham, Leicestershire, LE15 6DH Tel: (01572) 771778 Fax: (01572) 771779 E-mail: ii-vi@oakham.uk
Laser Instrumentation Ltd, 11 Jubilee lane, Farnham, Surrey, GU10 4SZ Tel: (01252) 794918 Fax: (01252) 792810 E-mail: p.hurley@farn-ct.ac.uk
Laser S O S Ltd, 3 Burrel Road, St. Ives, Cambridgeshire, PE27 3LE Tel: (01480) 460990 Fax: (01480) 469978 E-mail: sales@lasersos.com
Laser Support Services Ltd, School Drive, Ovenstone, Anstruther, Fife, KY10 2RR Tel: (01333) 311938 Fax: (01333) 312082 E-mail: enquiries@laser-support.com
▶ Pro-Lite Technology LLP, The Cranfield Innovation Centre, University Way, Cranfield, Bedford, MK43 0BT Tel: (01234) 436110 Fax: (01234) 436111 E-mail: sales@pro-lite.uk.com

LASER COMPUTER PRINTERS

Advance Group plc, Ockley Road, Bognor Regis, West Sussex, PO21 2HW Tel: (01243) 829100 Fax: (01243) 866822 E-mail: sales@advancegroup.plc.uk
Altodigital Midlands UK Ltd, Pensnett Trading Estate, Kingswinford, West Midlands, DY6 7FZ Tel: (01384) 404660 Fax: (01384) 404665 E-mail: enquiries@altodigital.com
Anly Office Services, 1191 Middleton Road, Chadderton, Oldham, OL9 0NN Tel: 0161-627 5870 Fax: 0161-287 3945 E-mail: enquiry@anly.co.uk
Arena Business Machines, Armitage House, Thorpe Lower Lane, Robin Hood, Wakefield, West Yorkshire, WF3 3BQ Tel: 0113-288 0282 Fax: 0113-288 0671 E-mail: admin@arenagroup.net
Blazepoint Ltd, Unit 2 Tower Estate, Warpsgrove Lane, Oxford, OX44 7XZ Tel: (01865) 891666 Fax: (01865) 891118 E-mail: sales@blazepoint.co.uk
Canon UK Ltd, Cockshot Hill, Reigate, Surrey, RH2 8BF Tel: (01737) 220000 Fax: (01737) 220022
CCS Media Holdings Ltd, Old Birdholme House, Derby Road, Chesterfield, Derbyshire, S40 2EX Tel: (01246) 200200 Fax: (01246) 207048 E-mail: enquiries@ccsmedia.com
Computec Solutions Ltd, 566 Streatham High Road, London, SW16 3QQ Tel: (020) 8679 1717 Fax: (020) 8679 5245 E-mail: mail@computecltd.com
Computer Junk Shop, 10 Waterloo Road, Widnes, Cheshire, WA8 0PY Tel: 0151-420 6671 Fax: 0151-420 6671 E-mail: info@computer-junkshop.co.uk
▶ D P I Ltd, Printing House, Church Lane, Norton, Worcester, WR5 2PS Tel: (0845) 0700750 Fax: (0845) 0700751 E-mail: dclover@dpi4xerox.co.uk
Elite Contract Services Ltd, 6 Petsworth Lane, Great Notley, Braintree, Essex, CM77 7XS Tel: (0845) 2262796 E-mail: enquiries@ecsit.co.uk
Farmplan Computer Systems, Farmplan House, Rank Xerox Business Park, Mitcheldean, Gloucestershire, GL17 0SN Tel: (01594) 545011 Fax: (01594) 545012 E-mail: sales@farmplan.co.uk
Fred Johnson, Unit D2, Impirial Business Centre, West Mill, Gravesend, Kent, DA11 0DL Tel: (01474) 569919 Fax: (01474) 533261 E-mail: info@fjpaper.co.uk
▶ Mind Machine, 69 Hutton Close, Crowther, Washington, Tyne & Wear, NE38 0AH Tel: 0191-417 9295 Fax: 0191-417 0643 E-mail: admin@mindmachine.co.uk
Silicon Group, 95 Whins Road, Alloa, Clackmannanshire, FK10 3RF Tel: (01259) 725200 Fax: (01259) 725270 E-mail: info@silicon-group.co.uk
Team Group Technologies, Stammerham Business Centre, Capel Road, Rusper, Horsham, West Sussex, RH12 4PZ Tel: (01306) 713410 Fax: (01306) 713408 E-mail: sales@teamgt.co.uk
▶ Three Counties Computers, 14 Woodsage Drive, Gillingham, Dorset, SP8 4UF Tel: (01747) 823994 E-mail: sales@threecountiescomputers.co.uk
Xerox (U K) Ltd, Cheadle Place, Stockport Road, Cheadle, Cheshire, SK8 2JX Tel: 0161-931 3750 Fax: 0161-931 3751

LASER CUT STENCILS

Laser Cutting Services, Flanders Moss, Station Road, Buchlyvie, Stirling, FK8 3NB Tel: (01360) 850389 Fax: (01360) 850565 E-mail: sarahgleave@yahoo.com

LASER CUTTING MACHINE LOADING SYSTEMS

Yamazaki Machinery UK Ltd, Badgeworth Drive, Worcester, WR4 9NF Tel: (01905) 755755 Fax: (01905) 755001 E-mail: info@mazaklaser.co.uk

LASER CUTTING MACHINES

Cadcam Technology, 5 Crocus Street, Nottingham, NG2 3DE Tel: 0115-844 8050 Fax: 0115-844 8059 E-mail: info@cct-uk.com
D M G UK Ltd, Unitool House, 151 Camford Way, Luton, LU3 3AN Tel: (01582) 570661 Fax: (01582) 593700 E-mail: sales@gildemeister.com
G S I Lumonics Ltd, Cosford Lane, Swift Valley Industrial Estate, Rugby, Warwickshire, CV21 1QN Tel: (01788) 570321 Fax: (01788) 579824 E-mail: appsexpert@gsig.com
Mechtronic Industries Ltd, Innovation Centre, Kirton Lane, Stainforth, Doncaster, South Yorkshire, DN7 5DA Tel: (01302) 845000 Fax: (01302) 844440 E-mail: mechtro@aol.com
Pacer Systems Ltd, Gauntley Street, Nottingham, NG7 5HF Tel: 0115-988 7777 Fax: 0115-988 7788 E-mail: sales@pacersys.co.uk
Prima Industrie UK Ltd, Unit 1 Phoenix Park, Bayton Road Industrial Estate, Coventry, CV7 9QN Tel: (024) 7664 5588 Fax: (024) 7664 5115 E-mail: info@primauk.com
Quantum Laser Engineering Ltd, Unit 13, Albion Industrial Estate, Endemere Road, Coventry, CV6 5PY Tel: (024) 7666 3222 Fax: (024) 7666 3444 E-mail: matrixlasersltd@btconnect.com
Yamazaki Machinery UK Ltd, Badgeworth Drive, Worcester, WR4 9NF Tel: (01905) 755755 Fax: (01905) 755001 E-mail: info@mazaklaser.co.uk

LASER CUTTING MACHINES, METAL

Yamazaki Machinery UK Ltd, Badgeworth Drive, Worcester, WR4 9NF Tel: (01905) 755755 Fax: (01905) 755001 E-mail: info@mazaklaser.co.uk

LASER CUTTING SERVICES

▶ 5750 Components Ltd, 1 Overbrook Lane, Villiers Court, Knowsley Business Pk, Prescot, Merseyside, L34 9FB Tel: 0151-548 5750 Fax: 0151-548 1222 E-mail: am@5750components.co.uk
▶ A M R (Burnley) Ltd, Unit 3, Gannow Business Park, Gannow Lane, Burnley, Lancashire, BB12 6JJ Tel: (01282) 448008 Fax: (01282) 448419 E-mail: sales@lasercutters.co.uk
Advanced Sheet Metal Ltd, 6-8 Albany Road, Granby Industrial Estate, Weymouth, Dorset, DT4 9TH Tel: (01305) 771061 Fax: (01305) 752829 E-mail: info@asm-ltd.com
Alsager Precision Sheet Metal Ltd, Unit 1C Wistaston Business Centre, Wistaston Road, Crewe, CW2 7RP Tel: (01270) 251271 Fax: (01270) 215614 E-mail: alssheetmetal@talk21.com
W.R. Anderton Group, Maltings Lane, Castleton, Rochdale, Lancs, OL11 2UY Tel: (01706) 631277 Fax: (01706) 358201 E-mail: info@andertongroup.com
B & Z, O2, Cherrycourt Way, Leighton Buzzard, Bedfordshire, LU7 4UH Tel: (01525) 373018 Fax: (01525) 851439 E-mail: enquiries@bandz.co.uk
C H Barnett Ltd, 18 Tyseley Industrial Estate, Seeleys Road, Birmingham, B11 2LQ Tel: 0121-773 5222 Fax: 0121-773 7800 E-mail: sales@chbarnett.co.uk
C H K Engineering Ltd, Pyms Lane, Crewe, CW1 3PJ Tel: (01270) 255520 Fax: (01270) 211263 E-mail: sales@chk-engineering.co.uk
Caststitch Engineering Ltd, Unit 18, Daneside Business Park, Riverdane Road, Congleton, Cheshire, CW12 1UN Tel: (01260) 298188 Fax: (01260) 298188 E-mail: sales@caststitch/laser/cutting.fsnet.co.uk
Chadderton Metal Products Ltd, Unit F2 Westwood Industrial Estate, Arkwright Street, Oldham, OL9 9LZ Tel: 0161-620 7907 Fax: 0161-627 4486 E-mail: sales@cmplimited.wanadoo.co.uk
▶ Coleherne Laser, Newton Moor Industrial Estate, Lodge Street, Hyde, Cheshire, SK14 4LE Tel: 0161-366 6603 Fax: 0161-367 8239 E-mail: brian@coleherneuk.com
Corus, 11 Oldfield Lane, Leeds, LS12 4DH Tel: 0113-263 4242 Fax: 0113-231 0491 E-mail: angela.barnard@corusgroup.com
Cotswald Design & Manufacture Ltd, The Daniel Gooch Building, Whitehill Lane, Wootton Bassett, Swindon, SN4 7DB Tel: (01793) 848007 Fax: (01793) 848526 E-mail: heather@ergotec-cdm.co.uk
D C M Group Ltd, Bayton Road Industrial Estate, 41 Bayton Road, Exhall, Coventry, CV7 9EL Tel: (024) 7636 1601 Fax: (024) 7636 7914 E-mail: sales@dcm.co.uk
Electronic Metal Work Services Ltd, Hampstead Avenue, Mildenhall, Bury St. Edmunds, Suffolk, IP28 7AS Tel: (01638) 712054 Fax: (01638) 713832E-mail: info@emws.co.uk
Essex Laser Job Shop Ltd, Unit D4, Frogmore Industrial Estate, Motherwell Way, Grays, Essex, RM20 3XD Tel: (01708) 689658 Fax: (01708) 865433 E-mail: sales@essexlaser.co.uk
Eurolux Plastics Ltd, Unit 7 Station Road, Tolleshunt D'Arcy, Maldon, Essex, CM9 8TQ Tel: (01621) 868787 Fax: (01621) 868857 E-mail: euroluxplastic@ukonline.co.uk
G A P Precision Sheet Metal Work, Units 18-19, Apex Park, Diplocks Way, Hailsham, East Sussex, BN27 3JU Tel: (01323) 440024 Fax: (01323) 441183 E-mail: info@gap-metal.co.uk
G & C Engineering plc, Cobham Road, Pershore, Worcestershire, WR10 2DL Tel: (01386) 553934 Fax: (01386) 555725 E-mail: sales@gandc.co.uk
Garcross Engineering, Brandon Building, Pepper Road, Leeds, LS10 2RU Tel: 0113-271 4230 Fax: 0113-271 4240 E-mail: sales@garcross.co.uk
Intec Laser Services, Woolaston Road, Park Farm North, Redditch, Worcestershire, B98 7SG Tel: (01527) 518550 Fax: (01527) 518551 E-mail: sales@intec.uk.net
J & S Sheet Metal Products, Unit 30 South Hampshire Industrial Park, Totton, Southampton, SO40 3SA Tel: (023) 8087 2827 Fax: (023) 8086 0033 E-mail: sales@jssheetmeta1.com
Jarrobs Ltd, Units 1-5, Excalibur Industrial Estate, Fields Road, Alsager, Stoke-on-Trent, ST7 2LX Tel: (01270) 878711 Fax: (01270) 882464 E-mail: sales@jarrobs.co.uk
John Dent Engineering Co. Ltd, 1432a Clock Tower Road, Isleworth, Middlesex, TW7 6DT Tel: (020) 8560 4414 Fax: (020) 8847 4582 E-mail: info@johndentengineering.com
K J B Engineering (West Tanfield) Ltd, Unit 2 The Sawmills, West Tanfield, Ripon, North Yorkshire, HG4 5JU Tel: (01677) 470511 Fax: (01677) 470811 E-mail: sales@kjblaser.co.uk
K & R Laser Services, Unit 60A, Blackpole Trading Estate West, Worcester, WR3 8TJ Tel: (01905) 757548 Fax: (01905) 754571 E-mail: kr.lasers@virgin.net
Kram Sheet Metal, Whitacre Road Industrial Estate, Nuneaton, Warwickshire, CV11 6BZ Tel: (024) 7664 1272 Fax: (024) 7635 2520
Laser Crystal Ltd, 3 Ariel Park, Uddens Trading Estate, Wimborne, Dorset, BH21 7NL Tel: (01202) 875657 Fax: (01202) 861438 E-mail: laser_profiles@compuserve.com
Laser Line Engineering Ltd, Unit 14 Avon Business Park, Lodge Causeway, Bristol, BS16 3JP Tel: 0117-965 7002 Fax: 0117-965 7004 E-mail: sales@laser-line.net
Laser Process Ltd, Upper Keys, Keys Park Road, Hednesford, Cannock, Staffordshire, WS12 2GE Tel: (01543) 495000 Fax: (01543) 495001 E-mail: sales@laserprocess.co.uk
Laserit Ltd, Unit 26 Beeches Industrial Estate, Lavenham Road, Yate, Bristol, BS37 5QX Tel: (01454) 318585 Fax: (01454) 318541 E-mail: sales@laserit.co.uk
Laserline Dies Ltd, 6 Northumberland Court, Chelmsford, CM2 6UW Tel: (01245) 461117 Fax: (01245) 461366 E-mail: aldersc@laserlinedies.com
Malton Laser Ltd, Unit E3 The Pyramid Estate, Showfield Lane, Malton, North Yorkshire, YO17 6BT Tel: (01653) 697770 Fax: (01653) 690970 E-mail: info@maltonlaser.co.uk
Mason & King Ltd, 11 Birstall Street, Leicester, LE1 2HJ Tel: 0116-253 6491 Fax: 0116-251 2403 E-mail: ray@masonking.co.uk
Matrix Lasers North East Ltd, 5 Trafalgar Court, South Nelson Industrial Estate, Cramlington, Northumberland, NE23 1WF Tel: (01670) 739222 Fax: (01670) 739333
MBN Fabrications Ltd, Units 2-3, Northbridge Road, Berkhamsted, Hertfordshire, HP4 1EF Tel: (01442) 877888 Fax: (01442) 877862
Metals Group Ltd, Units 10-11 Walker Industrial Park, Guide, Blackburn, BB1 2QE Tel: (01254) 586700 Fax: (01254) 692063 E-mail: sales@metalsuk.com
Micro Metallic Ltd, 125 Bridge Street, Birkenhead, Merseyside, CH41 1BD Tel: 0151-647 4641 Fax: 0151-647 5012 E-mail: info@micromet.co.uk
Microkerf Ltd, 43 Boston Road, Leicester, LE4 1AW Tel: 0116-234 1500 Fax: 0116-234 1600 E-mail: sales@microkerf.com
Molyneux Engineering (Matlock) Ltd, Stancliffe Works, Molyneux Business Park, Darley Dale, Matlock, Derbyshire, DE4 2HJ Tel: (01629) 734823 Fax: (01629) 734822 E-mail: sales@molyneux-eng.co.uk
N C Laser Cutting Services, Station Approach, Cark In Cartmel, Grange-over-Sands, Cumbria, LA11 7PT Tel: (01539) 558201 Fax: (01539) 558767
N S I Group Ltd, Whitacre Road Industrial Estate, Nuneaton, Warwickshire, CV11 6BY Tel: (024) 7637 5656 Fax: (024) 7664 1191 E-mail: sales@nsigroup.co.uk
Newfield Fabrications Co. Ltd, Hall Lane, Elton, Sandbach, Cheshire, CW11 3TU Tel: (01270) 762331 Fax: (01270) 768003 E-mail: sales@newfield.co.uk
Norwest Engineering Ltd, Low Stripes, The Stripes, Cumwhinton, Carlisle, CA4 0AW Tel: (01228) 560408 Fax: (01228) 561696 E-mail: norwest@btclick.com
▶ Oxford Lasers Ltd, Moorbrook Park, Didcot, Oxfordshire, OX11 7HP Tel: (01235) 814433 Fax: (01235) 810060 E-mail: admin@oxfordlasers.com
P A G Sheet Metal Ltd, 4 River Brent Business Park, Trumpers Way, London, W7 2QA Tel: (020) 8574 3577 Fax: (020) 8893 5370 E-mail: sales@pagsheetmetal.com
Paragon Pressings, 3b Haysfield Road, Hull, HU5 4JF Tel: (01482) 462822 Fax: (01482) 462833
Pioneer Finishers, Pioneer Business Park, Princess Road, Ramsgate, Kent, CT11 7RX Tel: (01843) 596615 Fax: (01843) 580933 E-mail: pioneer.paul@talk21.com
Precision Laser Processing Ltd, Butlers Leap, Rugby, Warwickshire, CV21 3RQ Tel: (01788) 546004 Fax: (01788) 546005 E-mail: sales@prelaspro.co.uk
Press Fab Ltd, 10 Bayton Way, Exhall, Coventry, CV7 9ER Tel: (024) 7636 2509

LASER CUTTING SERVICES – *continued*

Profile & Fabrication Services, P O Box 1002, Yateley, Hampshire, GU46 6ZA Tel: (01252) 875739 Fax: (01252) 664124
▶ Quicksilver Ltd, 5 Centre Park, Marston Moor Business Park, Tockwith, York, YO26 7QF Tel: (01423) 359899 Fax: (01423) 359084 E-mail: info@profiling.co.uk
R & S Laser Cutting & Fabrications Ltd, R & S House, Clement Street, Birmingham, B1 2SW Tel: 0121-237 5646 Fax: 0121-236 9339 E-mail: sales@rs-laser-cutting.co.uk
Redditch Lasercutting Ltd, 9 Broad Ground Road, Redditch, Worcestershire, B98 8YP Tel: (01527) 510474 Fax: (01527) 510432
Reekie Steeltec Ltd, Baden Powell Road, Kirkton Industrial Estate, Arbroath, Angus, DD11 3LS Tel: (01241) 873841 Fax: (01241) 877419 E-mail: colin.cromar@reekiesteeltec.com
Sciss Ltd, Unit 9 Larkstore Park, Lodge Road, Staplehurst, Tonbridge, Kent, TN12 0QY Tel: (01580) 890582 Fax: (01580) 890583 E-mail: sales@sciss.co.uk
South Yorkshire Laser Cutting Ltd, Unit 22-23, Bookers Way, Todwick Road Industrial Estate, Dinnington, Sheffield, S25 3SH Tel: (01909) 568682 Fax: (01909) 565648 E-mail: sylc.laser@virgin.net
Sparta Ltd, Victoria Works, Hill End Lane, Rossendale, Lancashire, BB4 7AG Tel: (01706) 221111 Fax: (01706) 222309 E-mail: enquiries@sparta.co.uk
Specialised Assemblies (Wellingborough) Ltd, Engineering Works, Higham Road, Burton Latimer, Kettering, Northamptonshire, NN15 5PU Tel: (01536) 420102 Fax: (01536) 420097 E-mail: markv@specassy.com
Specialised Laser Products Ltd, Unit 6 Ford Park, Canklow Road, Rotherham, South Yorkshire, S60 2JB Tel: (01709) 720799 Fax: (01709) 837444 E-mail: sales@slp-ltd.co.uk
Spectrum Laser Ltd, 2 Aysgarth Road, Waterlooville, Hampshire, PO7 7UG Tel: (023) 9225 2900 Fax: (023) 9223 3766 E-mail: sales@spectrumlaser.co.uk
Subcon Laser Cutting Ltd, Unit 7, Trident Business Park, Park St, Nuneaton, Warwickshire, CV11 4NS Tel: (024) 7664 2221 Fax: (024) 7634 2180 E-mail: info@subconlaser.co.uk
Sygnet Signs Ltd, 129 Humberstone Rd, Leicester, LE5 3AP Tel: 0116-262 6288 Fax: 0116 262 6061
Texicoat Surface Preparation & Treatment Ltd, Derrydown Lane, St. Mary Bourne, Andover, Hampshire, SP11 6BS Tel: (01264) 738800
Universal Sheet Metal Co., Dunlop Road, Hunt End Industrial Estate, Redditch, Worcestershire, B97 5XP Tel: (01527) 402202 Fax: (01527) 403030 E-mail: usm@usmlimited.co.uk
Waterjet Profiles Ltd, Units 9, Ryder Way, Basildon, Essex, SS13 1QH Tel: (01268) 591491 Fax: (01268) 729726 E-mail: sales@waterjet-profiles.co.uk
Welded Presswork (1982) Ltd, Stafford Road, Darlaston, Wednesbury, West Midlands, WS10 8SZ Tel: 0121-526 2022 Fax: 0121-526 4905 E-mail: enquiries@weldedpresswork.co.uk
Westcom Engineers, Global Park, East Gates Industrial Estate, Colchester, CO1 2TW Tel: (01206) 794114 Fax: (01206) 792749 E-mail: admin@westcomeng.fsnet.co.uk
Westwood Automation Ltd, Bell Close, Newnham Industrial Estate, Plympton, Plymouth, PL7 4JH Tel: (01752) 202113 Fax: (01752) 202117

LASER CUTTING SYSTEMS

▶ M P Automation Ltd, 46 Europa Business Park, Bird Hall Lane, Stockport, Cheshire, SK3 0XA Tel: 0161-428 7452 Fax: 0161-428 7304

LASER CUTTING/WELDING SYSTEMS ACCESSORIES/ CONSUMABLES

Caststitch Engineering Ltd, Unit 18, Daneside Business Park, Riverdane Road, Congleton, Cheshire, CW12 1UN Tel: (01260) 298188 Fax: (01260) 298188 E-mail: sales@caststitch/laser/cutting.fsnet.co.uk
II-VI UK Ltd, 21 Burley road, Oakham, Leicestershire, LE15 6DH Tel: (01572) 771778 Fax: (01572) 771779 E-mail: ii-vi@oakham.uk
Preco Industries International Inc, St. James House, Castle Street, Canterbury, Kent, CT1 2QD Tel: (01227) 473900 Fax: (01227) 473901
Sigmatek Europe Ltd, 16 University of Warwick Science Park, Coventry, CV4 7EZ Tel: (024) 7632 3065 Fax: (024) 7632 3060 E-mail: sales@sigmanest.com

LASER DEVICES

Coherent UK Holdings Ltd, 28 St Thomas Place, The Cambridge Business Park, Ely, Cambridgeshire, CB7 4EX Tel: (01353) 658800 Fax: (01353) 659110 E-mail: sales.uk@coherent.com
Lambda Photometrics Ltd, Lambda House, Batford Mill, Lower Luton Road, Harpenden, Hertfordshire, AL5 5BZ Tel: (01582) 764334 Fax: (01582) 712084 E-mail: info@lambdaphoto.co.uk
Laser Instrumentation Ltd, 11 Jubilee lane, Farnham, Surrey, GU10 4SZ Tel: (01252) 794918 Fax: (01252) 792810 E-mail: p.hurley@farn-ct.ac.uk
Melles Griot Ltd, Sovereign Court, Lancaster Way, Ermine Business Park, Huntingdon, Cambridgeshire, PE29 6XU Tel: (01480) 420800 Fax: (01480) 420811 E-mail: info@mellesgriot.com
Sigmatek Europe Ltd, 16 University of Warwick Science Park, Coventry, CV4 7EZ Tel: (024) 7632 3065 Fax: (024) 7632 3060 E-mail: sales@sigmanest.com
Thales Optronics, 1 Linthouse Road, Glasgow, G51 4BZ Tel: 0141-440 4000 Fax: 0141-440 4001 E-mail: sales@optronics.co.uk

LASER DIODE SYSTEMS

Diomed Ltd, Diomed House 2000 Cambridge Research Park, Beach Road, Waterbeach, Cambridge, CB5 9TE Tel: (01223) 729300 Fax: (01223) 729329 E-mail: info@diomed-lasers.com
▶ Global Laser Ltd, Medallion Technology Centre, Cwmtillery Industrial Estate, Cwmtillery, Abertillery, Gwent, NP13 1LZ Tel: (01495) 212213 Fax: (01495) 214004 E-mail: davidb@globallasertech.com

LASER DISPLAY SHOW/ EXHIBITION DESIGNERS/ ORGANISERS/SERVICES

▶ Lasermatrix, 87 Ludlow Road, Woolston, Southampton, SO19 2ET Tel: 07734 206005 Fax: 07005 938915 E-mail: chris.priest@lasermatrix.co.uk
LCI Ltd, 55 Merthyr Terrace, Barnes, London, SW13 8DL Tel: (020) 8741 5747 Fax: (020) 8748 9879 E-mail: contact@lci-uk.com

LASER DRILLING MACHINES

▶ Oxford Lasers Ltd, Moorbrook Park, Didcot, Oxfordshire, OX11 7HP Tel: (01235) 814433 Fax: (01235) 810060 E-mail: admin@oxfordlasers.com

LASER ENGRAVERS

Stampreo Rubber Ltd, Plexus House, Stockholm Road, Hull, HU7 0XW Tel: (01482) 348134 Fax: (01482) 446453 E-mail: stamps@plexus-net.co.uk
Tyco Electronics Identifications, Chapel Farm Industrial Estate, Cwmcarn/Cross Keys, Cross Keys, Newport, Gwent, NP11 7ZB Tel: (01495) 273519 Fax: (01495) 272979 E-mail: sales@tycoelectronics.com

LASER ENGRAVING MACHINES

Tyco Electronics Identifications, Chapel Farm Industrial Estate, Cwmcarn/Cross Keys, Cross Keys, Newport, Gwent, NP11 7ZB Tel: (01495) 273519 Fax: (01495) 272979 E-mail: sales@tycoelectronics.com

LASER FLASH PHOTOLYSIS SPECTROMETERS

Applied Photophysics, 203 Kingston Road, Leatherhead, Surrey, KT22 7PB Tel: (01372) 386537 Fax: (01372) 386477 E-mail: sales@photophysics.com

LASER INSTRUMENTATION

Coherent UK Holdings Ltd, 28 St Thomas Place, The Cambridge Business Park, Ely, Cambridgeshire, CB7 4EX Tel: (01353) 658800 Fax: (01353) 659110 E-mail: sales.uk@coherent.com

LASER MACHINING, REFLECTIVE MATERIALS

▶ Innovation 2 Market Ltd, Kings Rd, The Docks, Swansea, SA1 8PH Tel: (01792) 295520 Fax: (01792) 295588 E-mail: sales@i2m-uk.com

LASER MACHINING/ MICROMACHINING SERVICES

Repfab Engineering Ltd, Unit 6 Whiteleather Square, Billingborough, Sleaford, Lincolnshire, NG34 0QP Tel: (01529) 240600 Fax: (01529) 240647
Sigmatek Europe Ltd, 16 University of Warwick Science Park, Coventry, CV4 7EZ Tel: (024) 7632 3065 Fax: (024) 7632 3060 E-mail: sales@sigmanest.com

LASER MARKING SERVICES, BUSINESS OR PROMOTIONAL GIFTS

CMS International Ltd, Crowborough, East Sussex, TN6 1XU Tel: (01892) 669966 Fax: (01892) 669977 E-mail: info@cmsinternational.com
George H Greensmith & Co., Hallcar Street, Sheffield, S4 7JY Tel: 0114-272 2808 Fax: 0114-272 7956 E-mail: sales@ghgreensmith.co.uk

LASER MARKING/ETCHING SERVICES

Lewmax Programming, Unit 1, Fowke Street, Rothley, Leicester, LE7 7PJ Tel: 0116-212 2133 Fax: 0116-212 2136 E-mail: sales@lewmax.co.uk

LASER MARKING/ETCHING SYSTEMS MANUFRS

Borries, 28 Coalbrookdale Road, Clayhill Light Industrial Park, Neston, CH64 3UG Tel: 0151-336 3101 Fax: 0151-336 3217 E-mail: rob@borriesuk.fsnet.co.uk
Pryor Marking Technology Ltd, Egerton Street, Sheffield, S1 4JX Tel: 0114-276 6044 Fax: 0114-276 6890 E-mail: enquiries@pryormarking.com
Quantum Laser Engineering Ltd, Unit 13, Albion Industrial Estate, Endemere Road, Coventry, CV6 5PY Tel: (024) 7666 3222 Fax: (024) 7666 3444 E-mail: matrixlaserslts@btconnect.com
Rofin Baasel UK Ltd, 3 Brunel Close, Drayton Fields Industrial Estate, Daventry, Northamptonshire, NN11 8RB Tel: (0870) 9901020 Fax: (0870) 9901030 E-mail: sales@rofin-baasel.co.uk
Rofin Sinar UK Ltd, York Way, Willerby, Hull, HU10 6HD Tel: (01482) 650088 Fax: (01482) 650022 E-mail: info@rofin-uk.com

LASER MATERIAL PROCESSING CONSULTANTS

Sonic Technologies Ltd, Ty Coch Farm, Pembrey Rd, Kidwelly, Dyfed, SA17 4TF Tel: (01554) 890612 Fax: (01554) 890612

LASER MEASURING SYSTEMS MANUFRS

C D Measurements Ltd, Chomlea, Hadfield Road, Hadfield, Glossop, Derbyshire, SK13 2ER Tel: (01457) 852929 Fax: (01457) 860619
Lasermet Ltd, 67 Portchester Road, Bournemouth, BH8 8JX Tel: (01202) 770740 Fax: (01202) 770730 E-mail: sales@lasermet.com
Powelectrics Ltd, 46 Kepler, Tamworth, Staffordshire, B79 7XE Tel: (01827) 310666 Fax: (01827) 310999 E-mail: sales@powelectrics.co.uk

LASER OPTICAL EQUIPMENT

Elliot Scientific Ltd, 3 Allied Business Centre, Coldharbour Lane, Harpenden, Hertfordshire, AL5 4UT Tel: (01582) 766300 Fax: (01582) 766340 E-mail: sales@elliotscientific.com
II-VI UK Ltd, 21 Burley road, Oakham, Leicestershire, LE15 6DH Tel: (01572) 771778 Fax: (01572) 771779 E-mail: ii-vi@oakham.uk
Lambda Photometrics Ltd, Lambda House, Batford Mill, Lower Luton Road, Harpenden, Hertfordshire, AL5 5BZ Tel: (01582) 764334 Fax: (01582) 712084 E-mail: info@lambdaphoto.co.uk
Melles Griot Ltd, Sovereign Court, Lancaster Way, Ermine Business Park, Huntingdon, Cambridgeshire, PE29 6XU Tel: (01480) 420800 Fax: (01480) 420811 E-mail: info@mellesgriot.com

LASER PLASMA PROFILING

South Yorkshire Laser Cutting Ltd, Unit 22-23, Bookers Way, Todwick Road Industrial Estate, Dinnington, Sheffield, S25 3SH Tel: (01909) 568682 Fax: (01909) 565648 E-mail: sylc.laser@virgin.net

LASER PRINTERS, COLOUR

▶ Arvanti UK Ltd, Unit 6, Morley Business Centre, Morley Road, Tonbridge, Kent, TN9 1RA Tel: (01732) 366063 Fax: (01732) 770890 E-mail: info@arvanti.co.uk

LASER PRINTING

Alpha Media Direct Marketing, 38 Second Drove, Peterborough, PE1 5XA Tel: (01733) 898023 Fax: (01733) 898324 E-mail: sales@alphamedia.co.uk
Ditac Ltd, 1 Latton Bush Business Centre, Southern Way, Harlow, Essex, CM18 7BH Tel: (01279) 427779 Fax: (01279) 427103
F E Burman Ltd, 4 Rich Industrial Estate, Crimscott Street, London, SE1 5TF Tel: (020) 7206 1000 Fax: (020) 7206 1040 E-mail: info@feburman.co.uk
Infotec UK Ltd, 1230 Arlington Business Park, Theale, Reading, RG7 4TX Tel: 0118-928 4900 Fax: 0118-928 4901
Lewis Direct Mail Marketing Ltd, 433-435 Caledonian Road, London, N7 9BG Tel: (020) 7607 6505 Fax: (020) 7607 0932 E-mail: info@ldm.co.uk
Packpost (International) Ltd, Griffin House, Griffin Lane, Aylesbury, Buckinghamshire, HP19 8BE Tel: (01296) 487493 Fax: (01296) 392369 E-mail: sales@packpost.co.uk
Paton Brown Ltd, Calico House, Printwork Lane, Manchester, M19 3JP Tel: (0870) 4445501 Fax: (0870) 4445502 E-mail: info@patonbrown.co.uk
Scan Logic Ltd, Shenstone Drive, Walsall, WS9 8TP Tel: (01922) 458158 Fax: (01922) 745110 E-mail: sales@scanlogic.co.uk
Synergie Ltd, Digital House, The Loddon Centre, Wade Road, Basingstoke, Hampshire, RG24 8QW Tel: (01256) 467771 Fax: (01256) 840383 E-mail: alison@synergie.uk.com

LASER PRINTING EQUIPMENT CARTRIDGES

Cartridge Concept, 5 Grampian Road, Elgin, Morayshire, IV30 1XN Tel: (01343) 544828 Fax: (01343) 544313 E-mail: alan@cartcon.co.uk
Laser Services Cartridge Master, 2 Woodview Business Centre, Lockwood Close, Nottingham, NG5 9JN Tel: 0115-967 3445 Fax: 0115-967 3899 E-mail: sales@laserservices.co.uk
Textone International Ltd, Atlas Works, Sedburgh Road, Halifax, West Yorkshire, HX3 9HB Tel: (01422) 320234 Fax: (01422) 357341 E-mail: sales@textone.co.uk

LASER PRINTING SYSTEMS

Document Co. Xerox Ltd, Bridge House, Oxford Road, Uxbridge, Middlesex, UB8 1HS Tel: (01895) 251133 Fax: (01895) 254095
Oki Systems UK Ltd, 550 Dundee Road, Slough, SL1 4LE Tel: (01753) 819819 Fax: (01753) 819899 E-mail: sales@okieurope.co.uk

LASER PRINTING SYSTEMS ACCESSORIES/CONSUMABLES

Keymax International Ltd, West Road, Templefields, Harlow, Essex, CM20 2AL Tel: (01279) 454455 Fax: (01279) 445550 E-mail: ttrsales@keymax.co.uk
Retone Ltd, Retone House, 60 Sherborne St, Manchester, M8 8LR Tel: 0161-839 0500 Fax: 0161-839 0600E-mail: info@retone.co.uk

LASER PRINTING SYSTEMS, DESK TOP

Ricoh UK Ltd, 1 Plane Tree Crescent, Feltham, Middlesex, TW13 7HG Tel: (020) 8261 4000 Fax: (020) 8261 4004E-mail: info@ricoh.co.uk

LASER PROFILING

▶ A M R (Burnley) Ltd, Unit 3, Gannow Business Park, Gannow Lane, Burnley, Lancashire, BB12 6JJ Tel: (01282) 448008 Fax: (01282) 448419 E-mail: sales@lasercutters.co.uk
Gen-Fab Ltd, 302 Neepsend Lane, Sheffield, S3 8AW Tel: 0114-273 0303 Fax: 0114-275 8683 E-mail: enquiry@genfab.co.uk
Hi-Tech Sheet Metal Ltd, Molyneux House, Unit B, Fort Road Ind Est, Fort Road, Littlehampton, West Sussex, BN17 7QU Tel: 01903 711222 Fax: 01903 711227 E-mail: sales@htsm-ltd.co.uk
K & R Laser Services, Unit 60A, Blackpole Trading Estate West, Worcester, WR3 8TJ Tel: (01905) 757548 Fax: (01905) 754571 E-mail: kr.lasers@virgin.net
Malton Laser Ltd, Unit E3 The Pyramid Estate, Showfield Lane, Malton, North Yorkshire, YO17 6BT Tel: (01653) 697770 Fax: (01653) 690970 E-mail: info@maltonlaser.co.uk
Matrix Lasers North East Ltd, 5 Trafalgar Court, South Nelson Industrial Estate, Cramlington, Northumberland, NE23 1WF Tel: (01670) 739222 Fax: (01670) 739333
Multishape Sheet Metal Work, 120 Camford Way, Luton, LU3 3AN Tel: (01582) 581133 Fax: (01582) 581158 E-mail: custserv@multishape.co.uk

LASER PROFILING – *continued*

Spectrum Laser Ltd, 2 Aysgarth Road, Waterlooville, Hampshire, PO7 7UG Tel: (023) 9225 2900 Fax: (023) 9223 3766 E-mail: sales@spectrumlaser.co.uk

Waterton Engineering Co. Ltd, 2 Raymond Avenue, Chadderton, Oldham, OL9 7HW Tel: 0161-624 0004 Fax: 0161-624 8276

Weland Ltd, Hardley Industrial Estate, Hardley, Southampton, SO45 3NQ Tel: (023) 8084 9747 Fax: (023) 8084 9054 E-mail: info@weland.co.uk

LASER REFRACTOMETERS

R & B Instruments Ltd, Unit 3A Farnley Low Mills, Bangor Terrace, Leeds, LS12 5PS Tel: 0113-279 1066 Fax: 0113-231 9655 E-mail: sales@rbinstruments.com

LASER SCANNING (BAR CODE) EQUIPMENT MANUFRS

Opticon Ltd, 960 Capability Green, Luton, LU1 3PE Tel: (01582) 635100 Fax: (01582) 635200 E-mail: sales@opticon.co.uk

LASER SOLDERING EQUIPMENT

D.A. Ratchford, 6 Chester Hall Lane, Basildon, Essex, SS14 3BG Tel: (01245) 322720 Fax: (01268) 534828

LASER SPORTS EQUIPMENT

Eveque Leisure Equipment Ltd, 8 Duttons Business Centre, Dock Road, Northwich, Cheshire, CW9 5HJ Tel: (01606) 45611 Fax: (01606) 421517 E-mail: info@eveque.co.uk

Laser Sport International Ltd, Building 19 Stanmore Industrial Estate, Bridgnorth, Shropshire, WV15 5HR Tel: (01746) 767186 Fax: (01746) 761312 E-mail: sales@lasersport.biz

Predator Rugby Equipment, Higher Wampford, Kings Nympton, Umberleigh, Devon, EX37 9TG Tel: (0800) 0183706 Fax: (01769) 574219 E-mail: sales@predator.co.uk

LASER STENCIL CUTTING SYSTEMS

L P K F Laser & Electronics Ltd, Coppid Beech Lane, Wokingham, Berkshire, RG40 1PD Tel: (01344) 455046 Fax: (01344) 860547 E-mail: sales@lpkf.co.uk

LASER SURVEY EQUIPMENT HIRE

Laser Plane Ltd, 6 Devonshire Business Park, Knights Park Road, Basingstoke, Hampshire, RG21 6XE Tel: (01256) 460161 Fax: (01256) 363283 E-mail: laserplaneltd@tiscali.co.uk

▶ Sentripod Survey Company Ltd, The Lodge, 13 The Hamlet, Chippenham, Wiltshire, SN15 1BY Tel: (01249) 462039 Fax: (01249) 462039 E-mail: info@sentripod.co.uk

▶ Survey Technology, Westmere Drive, Crewe, CW1 6ZG Tel: (01270) 250525 Fax: (01270) 580700 E-mail: info@surveytechnology.co.uk

LASER SYSTEMS/EQUIPMENT CONSULTANTS

Lasermet Ltd, 67 Portchester Road, Bournemouth, BH8 8JX Tel: (01202) 770740 Fax: (01202) 770730 E-mail: sales@lasermet.com

LASER SYSTEMS/EQUIPMENT MAINTENANCE/REPAIR SERVICES

Laser S O S Ltd, 3 Burrel Road, St. Ives, Cambridgeshire, PE27 3LE Tel: (01480) 460990 Fax: (01480) 469978 E-mail: sales@lasersos.com

LASER SYSTEMS/EQUIPMENT MANUFRS

Cadcam Technology, 5 Crocus Street, Nottingham, NG2 3DE Tel: 0115-844 8050 Fax: 0115-844 8059 E-mail: info@cct-uk.com

Diomed Ltd, Diomed House 2000 Cambridge Research Park, Beach Road, Waterbeach, Cambridge, CB5 9TE Tel: (01223) 729300 Fax: (01223) 729329 E-mail: info@diomed-lasers.com

Elliot Scientific Ltd, 3 Allied Business Centre, Coldharbour Lane, Harpenden, Hertfordshire, AL5 4UT Tel: (01582) 766300 Fax: (01582) 766340 E-mail: sales@elliotscientific.com

Fusion Technologies Ltd, 26 Avonbank Industrial Estate, West Town Road, Bristol, BS11 9DE Tel: 0117-982 6606 Fax: 0117-982 6616

Laser Instrumentation Ltd, 11 Jubilee lane, Farnham, Surrey, GU10 4SZ Tel: (01252) 794918 Fax: (01252) 792810 E-mail: p.hurley@farn-ct.ac.uk

Laser S O S Ltd, 3 Burrel Road, St. Ives, Cambridgeshire, PE27 3LE Tel: (01480) 460990 Fax: (01480) 469978 E-mail: sales@lasersos.com

Laserline Computer Systems, 5a The Crescent, Dunston, Gateshead, Tyne & Wear, NE11 9SJ Tel: 0191-421 1899 Fax: 0191-420 2954

N R G Management Ltd, 66 Chiltern Street, London, W1U 4AG Tel: (020) 7465 1000 Fax: (020) 7224 5740

Photonic Solutions plc, A Gracemount Business Pavilion, Captains Road, Edinburgh, EH17 8QF Tel: 0131-664 8122 Fax: 0131-664 8144 E-mail: sales@psplc.com

Prima Industrie UK Ltd, Unit 1 Phoenix Park, Bayton Road Industrial Estate, Coventry, CV7 9QN Tel: (024) 7664 5588 Fax: (024) 7664 5115 E-mail: info@primauk.com

▶ Pro-Lite Technology LLP, The Cranfield Innovation Centre, University Way, Cranfield, Bedford, MK43 0BT Tel: (01234) 436110 Fax: (01234) 436111 E-mail: sales@pro-lite.uk.com

Quantum Laser Engineering Ltd, Unit 13, Albion Industrial Estate, Endemere Road, Coventry, CV6 5PY Tel: (024) 7666 3222 Fax: (024) 7666 3444 E-mail: matrixlasersltd@btconnect.com

Rofin Baasel UK Ltd, 3 Brunel Close, Drayton Fields Industrial Estate, Daventry, Northamptonshire, NN11 8RB Tel: (0870) 9901020 Fax: (0870) 9901030 E-mail: sales@rofin-baasel.co.uk

Rofin Sinar UK Ltd, York Way, Willerby, Hull, HU10 6HD Tel: (01482) 650088 Fax: (01482) 650022 E-mail: info@rofin-uk.com

LASER TONER RECHARGE SERVICES

Cartridges UK, Corunna House, 42-44 Ousegate, Selby, North Yorkshire, YO8 4NH Tel: (01757) 212747 Fax: (01757) 212321 E-mail: nikki@cartridgesuk.com

Copyfast Photocopiers, 57 Cecil Road, Romford, RM6 6LB Tel: (020) 8599 3033 Fax: (020) 8270 9869

Surebasic Ltd, Units 2 & 3, Castlemeadows Park, Abergavenny, Gwent, NP7 7RZ Tel: (01873) 852663 Fax: (01873) 859128 E-mail: laser@change.co.uk

Team Group Technologies, Stammerham Business Centre, Capel Road, Rusper, Horsham, West Sussex, RH12 4PZ Tel: (01306) 713410 Fax: (01306) 713408 E-mail: sales@teamgt.co.uk

LASER WELDING

A B R Specialists Welding Ltd, 2 Haines Street, West Bromwich, West Midlands, B70 7DS Tel: 0121-525 1319 Fax: 0121-525 1311 E-mail: enquiries@abrspecialistwelding.co.uk

Corus, 11 Oldfield Lane, Leeds, LS12 4DH Tel: 0113-263 4242 Fax: 0113-231 0491 E-mail: angela.barnard@corusgroup.com

Laserweld 2000 Ltd, Walsall Road, Norton Canes, Cannock, Staffordshire, WS11 9TA Tel: (01543) 450099 Fax: (01543) 450098 E-mail: laserweld@aol.com

LASERS, FIVE AXIS

▶ Laser Experience, 10 Elder Close, Bilton, Rugby, Warwickshire, CV22 7TJ Tel: (01788) 814288 Fax: (01788) 521705 E-mail: peter@laserexperience.com

LATEX DIP MOULDINGS

▶ Plastic Mouldings Ltd, 4 Ailsa Road, Irvine Industrial Estate, Irvine, Ayrshire, KA12 8LP Tel: (01294) 278091 Fax: (01294) 311655 E-mail: info@plasticmouldings.com

LATEX FOAM CARPET UNDERLAY

LCW, 56 Norfolk Street, Liverpool, L1 0BE Tel: 0151-709 7034 Fax: 0151-708 6022

Underlay Direct, 1 Woodlea Gardens, Sauchie, Alloa, Clackmannanshire, FK10 3BD Tel: (07768) 588714 Fax: (01259) 218097 E-mail: sales@underlaydirectscotland.co.uk

LATEX FOAM SHOE INSOLES

Stadex Industries Ltd, Coed Aben Road, Wrexham Industrial Estate, Wrexham, Clwyd, LL13 9UH Tel: (01978) 660266 Fax: (01978) 660316 E-mail: sales@stadex.co.uk

LATEX GLOVES

▶ Fleet Electrical & Safety Direct Ltd, Unit 10, Commerce Business Centre, Commerce Close, West Wilts Trading Estate, Westbury, Wiltshire, BA13 4LS Tel: (01373) 823242 Fax: (01373) 823206 E-mail: sales@fleetelectrical.co.uk

Marigold Industrial Ltd, B2 Vantage Park, Old Gloucester Road, Hambrook, Bristol, BS16 1GW Tel: (01454) 323633 Fax: (0845) 0753356 E-mail: sales@marigold-industrial.com

LATHE CHUCKS

▶ Arc Euro Trade Ltd, 10 Archdale Street, Syston, Leicester, LE7 1NA Tel: 0116-269 5693 Fax: 0116-260 5805 E-mail: information@arceurotrade.co.uk

Pratt Burnerd International, Park Works, Lister Lane, Halifax, West Yorkshire, HX1 5JH Tel: (01422) 366371 Fax: (01422) 359379 E-mail: sales@chucksuk.co.uk

LATHE CUT SQUARE CUT WASHER SEALS

Honeycrown Ltd, Miners Road, Llay Industrial Estate, Llay, Wrexham, Clwyd, LL12 0PJ Tel: (01978) 853730 Fax: (01978) 856320 E-mail: sales@honeycrown.co.uk

LATHE CUTTING TOOLS

Ben Ford Paul Ltd, 41 West Princes Street, Glasgow, G4 9BU Tel: 0141-332 0585 Fax: 0141-333 1607 E-mail: benfordpaul@aol.com

Brooke Cutting Tools (UK) Ltd, Denby Way, Hellaby, Rotherham, South Yorkshire, S66 8HU Tel: (01709) 314500 Fax: (01709) 314501 E-mail: info@brooke.co.uk

Fairway Form Tools, Unit B1-B5 Canklow Meadows Industrial Estate, West Bawtry Road, Rotherham, South Yorkshire, S60 2XL Tel: (01709) 820055 Fax: (01709) 820066 E-mail: sales@fairwayformtools.co.uk

Grindrite Grinding Equipment Es, 14 Hertburn Estate, Hertburn, Washington, Tyne & Wear, NE37 2SF Tel: 0191-416 3654 Fax: 0191-416 3729

Rennie Tool Co. Ltd, 227 Upper Brook Street, Manchester, M13 0HB Tel: 0161-273 3901 Fax: 0161-273 3348 E-mail: rennietool@btconnect.com

Walter Maschinenbau GmbH, B13 Holly Farm Business Park, Honiley, Kenilworth, Warwickshire, CV8 1NP Tel: (01926) 485047 Fax: (01926) 485049 E-mail: info.uk@walter-machines.com

LATHE MAINTENANCE/REPAIR SERVICES

Emi Mec, 23 Avern Close, Tipton, West Midlands, DY4 7ND Tel: 0121-522 4823 Fax: 0121-522 4823 E-mail: sales@emi-mec.co.uk

LATHE TURNING, *See Turning Services, Centre Lathe*

LATHES, CENTRE/GENERAL PURPOSE

600 Lathes, Union Street, Heckmondwike, West Yorkshire, WF16 0HL Tel: (01924) 415000 Fax: (01924) 415017 E-mail: sales@600lathes.co.uk

Bracehand Ltd, Stanford Bury, Stanford Road, Shefford, Bedfordshire, SG17 5NS Tel: (01462) 817039 Fax: (01462) 816325

Colchester Lathe Co. Ltd, P O Box 20, Heckmondwike, West Yorkshire, WF16 0HN Tel: (01924) 412603 Fax: (01924) 412604 E-mail: sales@colchester.co.uk

Crawford-Swift, Rosemount Works, Huddersfield Road, Elland, West Yorkshire, HX5 0EE Tel: (01422) 379222 Fax: (01422) 379122 E-mail: mail@crawfordswift.co.uk

D M G UK Ltd, Unitool House, 151 Camford Way, Luton, LU3 3AN Tel: (01582) 570661 Fax: (01582) 593700 E-mail: sales@gildemeister.com

Fairbank Brearley International Ltd, Crown Works, Grantham Road, Halifax, West Yorkshire, HX3 6PL Tel: (01422) 360231 Fax: (01422) 355157 E-mail: mail@smarttecgroup.com

Gear Technology Ltd, 228 Lythalls Lane, Coventry, CV6 6GF Tel: (024) 7666 2556 Fax: (024) 7666 6355 E-mail: geartec@skelcher-rowe.co.uk

Star Micronics GB Ltd, Chapel Street, Melbourne, Derby, DE73 8JF Tel: (01332) 864455 Fax: (01332) 864005E-mail: sales@stargb.net

Starragheckert UK Ltd, Unit 1a-1b Haddenham Business Park, Thame Road, Haddenham, Aylesbury, Buckinghamshire, HP17 8LJ Tel: (01844) 296575 Fax: (01844) 296579 E-mail: sales@starragheckert.com

Tryax Ltd, 10 Jubilee Trading Centre, Jubilee Road, Letchworth Garden City, Hertfordshire, SG6 1NE Tel: (01462) 481295 Fax: (01462) 685275 E-mail: sales@tryax.com

LATTICE SHEET TEXTILE FEED SYSTEMS

Elliott Musgrave Ltd, Jackson Street, Bradford, West Yorkshire, BD3 9SJ Tel: (01274) 731115 Fax: (01274) 722691 E-mail: sales@elliott-musgrave.co.uk

LAUNDERING SERVICES

R L Services, 1 Bryn Road, Loughor, Swansea, SA4 6PG Tel: (01792) 897594 Fax: (01792) 416505 E-mail: ritchieslaundry@hotmail.com

LAUNDRY CHEMICAL PRODUCTS

C M R Chemical Services Ltd, Moorhey Street, Oldham, OL4 1JE Tel: 0161-626 4143 Fax: 0161-628 5081

Ideal Chemicals Ltd, Atlas House, Burton Road, Wellingborough, Northamptonshire, NN9 5HX Tel: (01933) 681616 Fax: (01933) 681042 E-mail: enquiries@idealmanufacturing.com

Kemtec Manufacturing, 1a Caddick Road, Knowsley Business Park, Prescot, Merseyside, L34 9HP Tel: 0151-549 1559 Fax: 0151-549 1729 E-mail: enquiries@kemtec.co.uk

▶ Rexodan International, PO Box 24, Widnes, Cheshire, WA8 0RB Tel: 0151-422 1100 Fax: 0151-422 1111 E-mail: export@rexodan.com

Torr-Tech Ltd, Unit 20 B-C St Helen Industrial Estate, Bishop Auckland, County Durham, DL14 9AZ Tel: (01388) 450005 Fax: (01388) 450039 E-mail: sales@torr-tech.co.uk

LAUNDRY EQUIPMENT

Armstrong Laundry Systems, Ampere Road, Newbury, Berkshire, RG14 2AE Tel: (01635) 33881 Fax: (01635) 32434 E-mail: enquiries@armstrong-laundry.co.uk

LAUNDRY INSTALLATION OR SERVICING

Cherry Tree Machines Ltd, Imperial House, Gorse Street, Blackburn, BB1 3EU Tel: (01254) 671155 Fax: (01254) 671144 E-mail: sales@cherrytreemachines.co.uk

Clay & Abbott Ltd, Unit 2 Beauchamp Industrial Park, Watling Street, Wilnecote, Tamworth, Staffordshire, B77 5BZ Tel: (01827) 288093 Fax: (01827) 288764 E-mail: clayandabbott@btconnect.com

Dunlop Design Engineering, 1 Sackville Street, Lisburn, County Antrim, BT27 4AB Tel: (028) 9267 2333 Fax: (028) 9267 2383 E-mail: info@dnet.co.uk

Powerpoint Stores Ltd, 9 The Parade, Donnington, Telford, Shropshire, TF2 8EB Tel: (01952) 604051 Fax: (01952) 606604

Scorahs Ltd, 699 Huddersfield Road, Ravensthorpe, Dewsbury, West Yorkshire, WF13 3LQ Tel: (01924) 493222 Fax: (01924) 493222

Snow White Laundries Ltd, 69 The Highway, New Inn, Pontypool, Gwent, NP4 0PN Tel: (01495) 764652 Fax: (01495) 762494

LAUNDRY INSTALLATIONS/ UNITS, MOBILE

G N X Enterprises Ltd, 55 Jameson Road, Bexhill-on-Sea, East Sussex, TN40 1EL Tel: (01424) 220986 Fax: (01424) 221343

LAUNDRY MACHINE MANUFRS

▶ Associated Laundry Systems Ltd, Broadfields Court, Broadfields, Aylesbury, Buckinghamshire, HP19 8BU Tel: (01296) 393939 Fax: (01296) 393934 E-mail: alslimited@aol.com

Bay Management Services Ltd, Applegarth House, Heversham, Milnthorpe, Cumbria, LA7 7FD Tel: (01539) 564642

C L S Laundry Equipment, Unit A17-19, Holmer Trading Estate, Hereford, HR1 1JS Tel: (01432) 275712 Fax: (01432) 275712 E-mail: intercountyservices@orange.net

Cherry Tree Machines Ltd, Imperial House, Gorse Street, Blackburn, BB1 3EU Tel: (01254) 671155 Fax: (01254) 671144 E-mail: sales@cherrytreemachines.co.uk

LAUNDRY MACHINE MANUFRS – *continued*

Joseph H Wood & Son Ltd, 15 Hemmons Road, Manchester, M12 5ST Tel: 0161-248 9814 Fax: 0161-225 2044 E-mail: wood@steamforindustry.freeserve.co.uk

M D Laundry Machines (Kendal) Ltd, Parkside Business Park, Parkside Road, Kendal, Cumbria, LA9 7EN Tel: (01539) 729090 Fax: (01539) 728298 E-mail: sales@mdlaundrymachines.com

Polymark (G B) Ltd, Unit 14, Sopwith Way, Drayton Field Industrial Estate, Daventry, Northamptonshire, NN11 8PB Tel: (01327) 308600 Fax: (01327) 308611 E-mail: polymark.sales@polymark.co.uk

Polymark (G B) Ltd, Unit 14, Sopwith Way, Drayton Field Industrial Estate, Daventry, Northamptonshire, NN11 8PB Tel: (01327) 308600 Fax: (01327) 308610

LAUNDRY SERVICES

▶ CaraClean.Com, 70 Warwick Road, London, W5 5PT Tel: (0800) 0112272 E-mail: info@caraclean.com

▶ Polzeath Linen Services, Unit 9b Pityme Industrial Estate, St. Minver, Wadebridge, Cornwall, PL27 6NS Tel: (01208) 869700 E-mail: marion@polzeathlinenservices.com

LAUNDRY SUPPLY SERVICES

Aramark Ltd, Caledonia House Lawnswood Business Park, Redvers Close, Leeds, LS16 6QY Tel: 0113-230 5300 Fax: (0870) 1118199 E-mail: client-care@aramark.co.uk

Aspley Workwear Rental, Robins Wood Road, Nottingham, NG8 3LE Tel: 0115-929 1321 Fax: 0115-929 1239

Bentley Wessex, 64 Third Avenue, Teignmouth, Devon, TQ14 9DP Tel: (01626) 770830 Fax: (01626) 770830

Besafe Protective Clothing Ltd, Somerton Works, Prince Avenue, Westcliff-on-Sea, Essex, SS0 0ER Tel: (01702) 333344 Fax: (01702) 433590 E-mail: sales@besafe.co.uk

Best Frames, 14 Clyde Drive, Livingston, West Lothian, EH54 5LS Tel: (01506) 444598

Brooks Bourne Venture, Manning Road, Bourne, Lincolnshire, PE10 9EU Tel: (01778) 394900 Fax: (01778) 394218

Brooks Service Group Plc, Bowling Hall Road, Bradford, West Yorkshire, BD4 7ST Tel: (01274) 390225 Fax: (01274) 725464

Budjit Textile Services, 53 Love Street, Paisley, Renfrewshire, PA3 2DZ Tel: 0141-887 8480 Fax: 0141-887 8480

Cornish Linen Services, The Praze, Penryn, Cornwall, TR10 8DJ Tel: (01326) 373539 Fax: (01326) 377194 E-mail: sales@cls-group.co.uk

County Luxdon Laundry Ltd, 10 Wearfield, Sunderland Enterprise Park, Sunderland, SR5 2TZ Tel: 0191-548 7676 Fax: 0191-516 0648 E-mail: countyluxdonlaundry@tiscali.co.uk

Fenland Laundries Ltd, Roman Bank, Skegness, Lincolnshire, PE25 1SQ Tel: (01754) 767171 Fax: (01754) 610344

1st Class Linen Services, Unit 9 Chapman Court, Charfleets Road Industrial Estate, Canvey Island, Essex, SS8 0PQ Tel: 01268 691222 Fax: 01268 510947 E-mail: brettbarber@fsmail.net

Floringo Ltd, Enterprise House, 133 Blyth Road, Hayes, Middlesex, UB3 1DD Tel: (020) 8587 3400 Fax: (020) 8569 1445 E-mail: floringo@globalnet.co.uk

Gochers Laundry Ltd, Alma Street, Lancing, West Sussex, BN15 8AX Tel: (01903) 753615 Fax: (01903) 763725

Innisfail Laundry Ltd, 814 Hollands Road, Haverhill, Suffolk, CB9 8HB Tel: (01440) 702061 Fax: (01440) 712331

J L A Ltd, Meadowcroft Lane, Ripponden, Sowerby Bridge, West Yorkshire, HX6 4AJ Tel: (01422) 822282 Fax: (01422) 824390 E-mail: info@jla.com

Johnson Cleaners UK Ltd, Kingsway, Team Valley Trading Estate, Gateshead, Tyne & Wear, NE11 0HB Tel: 0191-482 0088 Fax: 0191-482 1750

Laundry Supplies Ltd, Vulcan Road, Lode Lane Industrial Estate, Solihull, West Midlands, B91 2JY Tel: 0121-705 4645 Fax: 0121-711 2051 E-mail: sales@slmarketing.co.uk

Lilyplan Ltd, 31 Franklynn Road, Haywards Heath, West Sussex, RH16 4DQ Tel: (01444) 451215

Micross Electronics Ltd, Units 4-5, Great Western Court, Ashburton Industrial Estate, Ross-on-Wye, Herefordshire, HR9 7XP Tel: (01989) 768080 Fax: (01989) 768163 E-mail: sales@micross.co.uk

Oriental Linen Hire, 5 Alexander Trading Estate, Castlefield Street, Stoke-on-Trent, ST4 7AQ Tel: (01782) 205417

R L Services, 1 Bryn Road, Loughor, Swansea, SA4 6PG Tel: (01792) 897594 Fax: (01792) 416505 E-mail: ritchieslaundry@hotmail.com

Alex Reid Ltd, 128-130 Beddington Lane, Croydon, CR0 4YZ Tel: (020) 8684 7667 Fax: (020) 8683 4335 E-mail: sales@alexreid.co.uk

Scilly Linen Supplies Ltd, Porth Mellon, St. Mary's, Isles of Scilly, TR21 0JY Tel: (01720) 422211 Fax: (01720) 422211

Smelly Rug Co., Millmount Farm, Melrose, Roxburghshire, TD6 9BZ Tel: (01896) 822467 E-mail: info@thesmellyrugco.co.uk

Southern Overall Service, Unit D Foundry Close, Horsham, West Sussex, RH13 5TX Tel: (01403) 263108 Fax: (01403) 254539 E-mail: sales@horshamanddistrictlaundry.co.uk

The Sunlight Service Group Ltd, Hotel Division, 72 Thornliebank Road, Glasgow, G43 1LB Tel: 0141-632 1281 Fax: 0141-649 1151

The Sunlight Service Group, 47-49 Lomond Grove, London, SE5 7HW Tel: (020) 7701 6481 Fax: (020) 7708 5954

The Sunlight Service Group Ltd, 9 Deer Park Road, London, SW19 3UY Tel: (020) 8542 4646 Fax: (020) 8543 3984

The Sunlight Service Group Ltd, Princes Street, Penrith, Cumbria, CA11 7BQ Tel: (01768) 862744 Fax: (01768) 891881 E-mail: penrith@sunlight.co.uk

Vale Textile Services, Vale Road, Llandudno Junction, Gwynedd, LL31 9SH Tel: (01492) 581167 Fax: (01492) 593015

LAW PRINTERS/STATIONERS

Gordon Press Ltd, Caxton House, 2 Bath House Road, Croydon, CR0 4TT Tel: (020) 8684 0313 Fax: (020) 8689 6715 E-mail: sales@thegordonpress.com

O Y Z Staker Ltd, Guild House, Reddicap Trading Estate, Sutton Coldfield, West Midlands, B75 7BU Tel: 0121-241 1050 Fax: 0121-311 1778 E-mail: sales@midlandlaw.co.uk

Oyez Straker Office Supplies Ltd, 2 Didcot Road, Nuffield Industrial Estate, Poole, Dorset, BH17 0GD Tel: (01202) 681456 Fax: (01202) 665274 E-mail: david.hale@oyezstraker.co.uk

Shaw & Sons Ltd, Shaway House, 21 Bourne Park, Bourne Road, Crayford, Dartford, DA1 4BZ Tel: (01322) 621100 Fax: (01322) 550553 E-mail: sales@shaws.co.uk

Stat Plus Ltd, Greenlea Park, Prince Georges Road, London, SW19 2PU Tel: (020) 8646 5500 Fax: (020) 8640 2905 E-mail: enquiries@statplus.co.uk

Stat Plus, A1 New Pudsey Square, Bradford Road, Stanningley, Pudsey, West Yorkshire, LS28 6PX Tel: 0113-256 9494 Fax: 0113-204 7044

W.& A.Ross Ltd, 55 Days Road, St Phillips, St. Philips, Bristol, BS2 0QS Tel: 0117-955 8855 Fax: 0117-935 0518 E-mail: sales@rossofficesupplies.co.uk

LAW (PROCESS OF) ANCILLARY/FREELANCE SERVICES

Harry Counsell & Co., Cliffords Inn, Fetter Lane, London, EC4A 1LD Tel: (020) 7269 0370 Fax: (020) 7831 2526 E-mail: blandhc@aol.com

Marten Walsh Cherer Ltd, Midway House, 27-29 Cursitor Street, London, EC4A 1LT Tel: (020) 7405 5010 Fax: (020) 7405 5026 E-mail: martinwc@aol.com

Oldham Metropolitan Borough Trading Standards, North House, 130 Rochdale Road, Oldham, OL1 2JA Tel: 0161-911 4474 Fax: 0161-911 3481 E-mail: env.tradingstandard@oldham.gov.uk

LAWN BOWLS

Drakes Pride Bowls Co., 128 Richmond Row, Liverpool, L3 3BL Tel: 0151-298 1355 Fax: 0151-298 2988 E-mail: drakespride@eaclare.co.uk

Greengauge (Sports) Ltd, 5 Gateside, Commercial Park, Haddington, East Lothian, EH41 3SE Tel: (0845) 5400012 Fax: (0845) 1308029

Thurston, 110 High Street, Edgware, Middlesex, HA8 7HF Tel: (020) 8952 2002 Fax: (020) 8952 0222 E-mail: thurston@eaclare.co.uk

LAWN CARE EQUIPMENT

Bosch Lawn & Garden Limited, Suffolk Works, Stowmarket, Suffolk, IP14 1EY Tel: (01449) 742000 Fax: (01449) 675444

Wrangbrook Engineering, Sheepwalk Lane, Upton, Pontefract, West Yorkshire, WF9 1LL Tel: (01977) 648748

LAWN MOWER ATTACHMENTS

▶ Stuart Taylor, Lane Ends Cottage, Nightfield Lane, Balderstone, Blackburn, BB2 7LJ Tel: (01254) 813175 Fax: (01254) 813479 E-mail: stuarttaylor@freeola.com

LAWN MOWER BLADES

Wolverhampton Pressings Co. Ltd, Whetstone House, Fordhouse Road, Wolverhampton, WV10 9EA Tel: (01902) 307799 Fax: (01902) 721026 E-mail: sales@ralphmartindale.com

LAWN MOWER COMPONENTS

▶ Briggsbits.co.uk, Hutton Garden Centre, Banwell Road, Hutton, Weston-super-Mare, North Somerset, BS24 9UB Tel: (01934) 813261 Fax: (01934) 815356 E-mail: graham@westongm.eclipse.co.uk

▶ Stuart Taylor, Lane Ends Cottage, Nightfield Lane, Balderstone, Blackburn, BB2 7LJ Tel: (01254) 813175 Fax: (01254) 813479 E-mail: stuarttaylor@freeola.com

LAWN MOWER GRINDING MACHINES

Atterton & Ellis Ltd, Hamlet Road, Haverhill, Suffolk, CB9 8QH Tel: (01440) 702312 Fax: (01440) 712138

LAWN MOWER HIRE

▶ Stuart Taylor, Lane Ends Cottage, Nightfield Lane, Balderstone, Blackburn, BB2 7LJ Tel: (01254) 813175 Fax: (01254) 813479 E-mail: stuarttaylor@freeola.com

LAYFLAT PAPER TUBING

Stonehouse Paper & Bag Mills Ltd, Lower Mills, Stonehouse, Gloucestershire, GL10 2BD Tel: (01453) 822173 Fax: (01453) 822174 E-mail: stonehousepaper@aol.com

LEAD ACID BATTERIES

Multicell International Ltd, 6 Swannington Road, Broughton Astley, Leicester, LE9 6TU Tel: (01455) 283443 Fax: (01455) 284250 E-mail: help@multicell.co.uk

LEAD ALLOY OR LEAD SECTIONS

Heaps, Arnold & Heaps Ltd, Unit D1, Quintec Court, Barbot Hall Industrial Estate, Rotherham, South Yorkshire, S61 4RN Tel: (01709) 837669 Fax: (01709) 837671 E-mail: heaps@heapsarnold.com

LEAD ALLOY OR LEAD WIRE OR TAPES

Heaps, Arnold & Heaps Ltd, Unit D1, Quintec Court, Barbot Hall Industrial Estate, Rotherham, South Yorkshire, S61 4RN Tel: (01709) 837669 Fax: (01709) 837671 E-mail: heaps@heapsarnold.com

LEAD ALLOYS OR LEAD

Britannia Refined Metals Ltd, Britannia Works, Botany Road, Northfleet, Gravesend, Kent, DA11 9BG Tel: (01474) 538200 Fax: (01474) 538203

H J Enthoven & Sons Ltd, Darley Dale Smelter, South Darley, Matlock, Derbyshire, DE4 2LP Tel: (01629) 733291 Fax: (01629) 733092

William Rowland Ltd, 7-23 Meadow Street, Sheffield, S3 7BL Tel: 0114-276 9421 Fax: 0114-275 9429 E-mail: e-mail@william-rowland.co.uk

LEAD ANODES

Fabline Metal Finishing Services, Greenway Road, Bilston, West Midlands, WV14 0TJ Tel: (01902) 353511 Fax: (01902) 353511

Royston Lead Ltd, Pogmoor Works, Stocks Lane, Barnsley, South Yorkshire, S75 2DS Tel: (01226) 770110 Fax: (01226) 730359 E-mail: info@roystonlead.co.uk

LEAD CASTINGS

Calder Industrial Materials Ltd, Jupiter Drive, Chester West Employment Park, Chester, CH1 4EX Tel: (01244) 390093 Fax: (01244) 389191 E-mail: enquiries@caldergroup.co.uk

J D Steward Salford Ltd, Dymun Works, Missouri Avenue, Salford, M50 2NP Tel: 0161-736 1238 Fax: 0161-736 8700

Leadatom Europe Ltd, 1 Shamrock Enterprise Centre, Wingate Road, Gosport, Hampshire, PO12 4DP Tel: (023) 9252 3973 Fax: (023) 9252 3973 E-mail: sales@leadatom.co.uk

Royston Lead Ltd, Pogmoor Works, Stocks Lane, Barnsley, South Yorkshire, S75 2DS Tel: (01226) 770110 Fax: (01226) 730359 E-mail: info@roystonlead.co.uk

LEAD EXTRUSIONS

Royston Lead Ltd, Pogmoor Works, Stocks Lane, Barnsley, South Yorkshire, S75 2DS Tel: (01226) 770110 Fax: (01226) 730359 E-mail: info@roystonlead.co.uk

LEAD FABRICATORS

Calder Industrial Materials Ltd, Jupiter Drive, Chester West Employment Park, Chester, CH1 4EX Tel: (01244) 390093 Fax: (01244) 389191 E-mail: enquiries@caldergroup.co.uk

J D Steward Salford Ltd, Dymun Works, Missouri Avenue, Salford, M50 2NP Tel: 0161-736 1238 Fax: 0161-736 8700

LEAD FLASHING

British Lead Mills, Peartree Lane, Welwyn Garden City, Hertfordshire, AL7 3UB Tel: (01707) 324595 Fax: (01707) 328941 E-mail: sales@britishlead.co.uk

Leicester Glass Co. Ltd, 119-125 Bridge Road, Leicester, LE5 3QP Tel: 0116-276 8316 Fax: 0116-246 0462 E-mail: enquiries@leicesterglass.co.uk

LEAD LINED PLANT

Fabline Metal Finishing Services, Greenway Road, Bilston, West Midlands, WV14 0TJ Tel: (01902) 353511 Fax: (01902) 353511

LEAD OXIDE

Chemson Ltd, Hayhole Works, Northumberland Dock Road, Wallsend, Tyne & Wear, NE28 0PB Tel: 0191-259 7000 Fax: 0191-259 7001 E-mail: sales@chemson.co.uk

LEAD PIPES

J D Steward Salford Ltd, Dymun Works, Missouri Avenue, Salford, M50 2NP Tel: 0161-736 1238 Fax: 0161-736 8700

LEAD PRODUCTS, *See also headings for particular products*

British Lead Mills, Peartree Lane, Welwyn Garden City, Hertfordshire, AL7 3UB Tel: (01707) 324595 Fax: (01707) 328941 E-mail: sales@britishlead.co.uk

Heaps, Arnold & Heaps Ltd, Unit D1, Quintec Court, Barbot Hall Industrial Estate, Rotherham, South Yorkshire, S61 4RN Tel: (01709) 837669 Fax: (01709) 837671 E-mail: heaps@heapsarnold.com

LEAD ROOFING CONTRACTORS

A & K Services Co., 807 Lea Bridge Road, London, E17 9DS Tel: (020) 8509 2600 Fax: (020) 8520 9678 E-mail: a.kservices@btconnect.com

▶ William Stephen Everitt, 2 Highfield Road, Woodford Green, Essex, IG8 8JA Tel: (020) 8491 6994 E-mail: william.everitt@ntlworld.com

▶ Melling Roofing, 2 Fowler Street, Fulwood,, Preston, PR2 2LT Tel: 01772 461878 E-mail: mellingmark@blueyonder.co.uk

LEAD SASH WEIGHTS

Ambass-A-Door Windows & Doors Ltd, 18 Bidwell Road, Rackheath Industrial Estate, Norwich, NR13 6PT Tel: (01603) 720332 Fax: (01603) 721245 E-mail: sales@ambassadoor.fsnet.co.uk

LEAD SCRAP RECOVERY AND RECYCLING CONTRACTORS

▶ Antwerp Africa Metals and Minerals, 79 The Heights, Foxgrove Road, Beckenham, Kent, BR3 5BZ Tel: (020) 8663 0873 E-mail: antwerpafrica@yahoo.co.uk

H J Enthoven & Sons Ltd, Darley Dale Smelter, South Darley, Matlock, Derbyshire, DE4 2LP Tel: (01629) 733291 Fax: (01629) 733092

LEAD SHEET

British Lead Mills, Unit C & D Abbotsfield Rd, St. Helens, Merseyside, WA9 4HU Tel: (01744) 819126 Fax: (01744) 819335 E-mail: info@guhring.co.uk

British Lead Mills, Peartree Lane, Welwyn Garden City, Hertfordshire, AL7 3UB Tel: (01707) 324595 Fax: (01707) 328941 E-mail: sales@britishlead.co.uk

▶ indicates data change since last edition

LEAD STRIPS

North Western Lead Co Hyde Ltd, Mill Street, Newton Moor Industrial Estate, Hyde, Cheshire, SK14 4LJ Tel: 0161-368 4491 Fax: 0161-366 5103 E-mail: sales@decraled.co.uk

LEADED LIGHT GLASS CONTRACTORS OR MANUFACTURERS

Birmingham Glass Studios Ltd, Units 5 & 6 The Stained Glass Centre, 100-102 Edward Road, Balsall Heath, Birmingham, B12 9LS Tel: 0121-706 3131 Fax: 0121706 3130 E-mail: bhamglass@aol.com

Cotswold Casement Co. Ltd, Cotswold Business Village, London Road, Moreton-in-Marsh, Gloucestershire, GL56 0PS Tel: (01608) 650568 Fax: (01608) 651699 E-mail: sales@cotswold-casements.co.uk

F E Moss Glass Ltd, 678 Green Lane, Ilford, Essex, IG3 9RX Tel: (020) 8590 5180 Fax: (020) 8599 1008

Charles Lightfoot Ltd, Heywood Road, Sale, Cheshire, M33 3WB Tel: 0161-973 6565 Fax: 0161-962 5335 E-mail: clightfootltd@aol.com

Mannings, 347 Footscray Road, London, SE9 2EH Tel: (020) 8859 3908 Fax: (020) 8859 3908

Norman & Underwood Group Ltd, The Freeschool Building, 170 Scudamore Road, Leicester, LE3 1HP Tel: 0116-231 8000 Fax: 0116-231 8005E-mail: info@nandu.co.uk

Park Glass Supplies Ltd, 139 Kings Road, Kingston upon Thames, Surrey, KT2 5JE Tel: (020) 8546 8737 Fax: (020) 8546 4001

Pearsons Glass Ltd, 9-11 Maddrell Street, Liverpool, L3 7EH Tel: 0151-207 2874 Fax: 0151-207 2110 E-mail: info@pearsonsglass.co.uk

Stained Glass Experience, Studio 7 Art At Cedar Farm, Back Lane, Mawdesley, Ormskirk, Lancashire, L40 3SY Tel: (01704) 823121 Fax: (01704) 823121 E-mail: enquiries@stainedglassexperience.co.uk

Tenby & Penny Co. Ltd, 38a Beulah Road, London, E17 9LQ Tel: (020) 8520 7706 Fax: (020) 8521 1632 E-mail: tenbypenny@supanet.com

▶ Tudor Leaded Light Co., 9a Pinner Road, Watford, WD19 4EF Tel: (01923) 236932 Fax: (01923) 238210 E-mail: peter@tudorleadedlight.co.uk

Tunbridge Wells Glass Works, 10-12 Tunnel Road, Tunbridge Wells, Kent, TN1 2BT Tel: (01892) 533141 Fax: (01892) 544215 E-mail: jan@twgw.co.uk

LEADERSHIP COACHING

▶ Capita Learning & Development, 17-19 Rochester Row, London, SW1P 1LA Tel: (0870) 1648900 Fax: (0870) 1658974 E-mail: cpdwebinfo@capita.co.uk

▶ Helen Redfern, 21 Vincent Road, Croydon, CR0 6ED Tel: (020) 8405 3392 E-mail: helen@helenredfern.co.uk

▶ Stephen Ward & Company, Warwick Corner, 42 Warwick Road, Kenilworth, Warwickshire, CV8 1HE Tel: 01926 866610 Fax: 01926 851534 E-mail: mail@stephen-ward.com

LEAF SPRINGS

S M J Products, Richardshaw Lane, Stanningley, Pudsey, West Yorkshire, LS28 6BZ Tel: 0113-236 0396 Fax: 0113-261 2357

LEAFLET DELIVERY SERVICES

▶ Disperse, G 7 Academy Apartments, Elmbank Avenue, Kilmarnock, Ayrshire, KA1 3BT Tel: (01563) 574062 E-mail: info@disperse-distribution.com

▶ Red House Distribution, 57 Highcliff Drive, Leigh-on-Sea, Essex, SS9 1DQ Tel: 07775 795304 E-mail: redhousedistribution@hotmail.com

▶ S W A T Distribution, 50 Providence Place, Brighton, BN1 4GE Tel: (01273) 690573 Fax: (01273) 690573 E-mail: sales@awat-distrubution.co.uk

LEAFLET DISPENSERS

Display Containers Ltd, 19b Moor Road, Broadstone, Dorset, BH18 8AZ Tel: (01202) 658838 Fax: (01202) 698284 E-mail: sales@displaycontainers.co.uk

P.P.E. Ltd, Horsecroft Rd, The Pinnacles, Harlow, Essex, CM19 5BH Tel: (01279) 412345 Fax: (01279) 419533E-mail: sales@ppe.co.uk

▶ Rep Engineering & Manufacturing, Unit 11 Rippleside Commercial Estate, Ripple Road, Barking, Essex, IG11 0RJ Tel: (020) 8526 7711 Fax: (020) 8526 7722

UK Point Of Sale Group Ltd, Emery Court, The Embankment Business Park, Heaton Mersey, Stockport, Cheshire, SK4 3GL Tel: 0161-431 4400 Fax: 0161-431 4411 E-mail: info@ukpos.com

V K F Renzel, 20e Harris Business Park, Hanbury Road, Stoke Prior, Bromsgrove, Worcestershire, B60 4BD Tel: (01527) 878311 Fax: (01527) 878411 E-mail: sales@vkf-renzel.co.uk

LEAFLET LABELS

Denny Brothers Ltd, Kempson Way, Bury St. Edmunds, Suffolk, IP32 7AR Tel: (01284) 701381 Fax: (01284) 705575 E-mail: denny.bros@dennybros.com

Ditchling Press, Consort Way, Burgess Hill, West Sussex, RH15 9YS Tel: (01444) 243253 Fax: (01444) 242198

LEAFLET PHOTOGRAPHERS

▶ Campbell Gus, 23 Avondale Road, Rayleigh, Essex, SS6 8NJ Tel: (01268) 778519 E-mail: sales@justix.com

▶ Creative Photo Shop & Portrait Studio, Unit 16, 34 Gerard Street, Ashton-In-Makerfield, Wigan, Lancashire, WN4 9AE Tel: (01942) 725847 E-mail: info@creativephotoshop.co.uk

▶ David Hansford Photography, 17 Casterbridge Way, Gillingham, Dorset, SP8 4FG Tel: 01747 831 082 Fax: 0870 124 6166 E-mail: david@davidhansfordphoto.co.uk

▶ Edwards Photography, 16 The Vale, London, W3 7SB Tel: (020) 8749 8887 E-mail: studio@edwardsphotography.co.uk

▶ Edwards Photography, 16 The Vale, London, W3 7SB Tel: (020) 8749 8887 Fax: E-mail: studio@edwardsphotography.co.uk

▶ Jo Grant Photographer, St. Davids Road, Southsea, Hampshire, PO5 1QJ Tel: (023) 9283 9139

▶ Lewis Ronald, 5 Long Street, London, E2 8HN Tel: (020) 7033 9134 Fax:

▶ Paul Thompson-Images, 5 Edgewood Drive, Bromborough, Wirral, Merseyside, CH62 6DP Tel: 0151-327 7260 E-mail: sales@paulthompson-images.com

▶ Ian Phillips-McLaren Photographers, Orchard End, Watling Lane, Thaxted, Essex, CM6 2QY Tel: (07889) 861654 E-mail: ian@ianphillips-mclaren.com

▶ Photo Dreams, 101 Burford, Brookside, Telford, Shropshire, TF3 1LJ Tel: (01952) 279110 E-mail: ian@photodreams.co.uk

▶ Positive Pixels Photography, Stoneleigh, Bulford Road, Durrington, Salisbury, SP4 8DH Tel: (01980) 653138 E-mail: positive_pixels@tiscali.co.uk

Saban Photography, Charwell House, Wilsom Road, Alton, Hampshire, GU34 2PP Tel: (01420) 540227 E-mail: martin@saban.co.uk

Ken Shelton Photography, 10 New Walk Terrace, Fishergate, York, YO10 4BG Tel: (01904) 630112 E-mail: ken@nwt10.demon.co.uk

▶ Terry Trott, The Studio, 24 School Lane, Bapchild, Sittingbourne, Kent, ME9 9NL Tel: (01795) 472833 Fax: (01795) 475941 E-mail: info@terrytrottphotography.co.uk

▶ Vision Photographic Ltd, Unit 1 Slader Business Park, Witney Road, Nuffield Industrial Estate, Poole, Dorset, BH17 0GP Tel: (01202) 667670 Fax: (01202) 668670 E-mail: info@visionphoto.co.uk

LEAK DETECTION EQUIPMENT INSTALLATION

▶ Aquilar Ltd, Dial Post Court, Horsham Road, Rusper, Horsham, West Sussex, RH12 4QX Tel: (01293) 871874 Fax: (01293) 871717 E-mail: jwaumsley@aquilar.co.uk

Underground Location Systems Uls Ltd, 66 Hall Lane, North Walsham, Norfolk, NR28 9DU Tel: (01692) 404494 Fax: (01692) 404494 E-mail: jw@correlators.co.uk

LEAK DETECTION SERVICES

▶ Aquilar Ltd, Dial Post Court, Horsham Road, Rusper, Horsham, West Sussex, RH12 4QX Tel: (01293) 871874 Fax: (01293) 871717 E-mail: jwaumsley@aquilar.co.uk

B J Completion Services, Blackness Avenue, Altens Industrial Estate, Aberdeen, AB12 3PG Tel: (01224) 897929 Fax: (01224) 896118 E-mail: sales@bjservices.com

Fisher Leak Systems Ltd, 7 Industrial Estate, Tame Road, Birmingham, B6 7HS Tel: 0121-328 2515 Fax: 0121-327 8324 E-mail: sales@fisherleaksystems.co.uk

Ovec Systems Ltd, 5 Brown Street, Coatbridge, Lanarkshire, ML5 4AS Tel: (01236) 770699 Fax: (01236) 770898 E-mail: info@ovec.co.uk

Tuthill Vacuum Systems, Pennine Business Park, Pilsworth Road, Heywood, Lancashire, OL10 2TL Tel: (01706) 362400 Fax: (01706) 362444 E-mail: uksales@tuthill.com

Underground Location Systems Uls Ltd, 66 Hall Lane, North Walsham, Norfolk, NR28 9DU Tel: (01692) 404494 Fax: (01692) 404494 E-mail: jw@correlators.co.uk

Vacuum Engineering Services Ltd, St. Modwen Road, Stretford, Manchester, M32 0ZE Tel: 0845 5314240 Fax: 0161-866 8861 E-mail: info@vac-eng.com

LEAK DETECTION SYSTEMS

▶ Aquilar Ltd, Dial Post Court, Horsham Road, Rusper, Horsham, West Sussex, RH12 4QX Tel: (01293) 871874 Fax: (01293) 871717 E-mail: jwaumsley@aquilar.co.uk

Fisher Leak Systems Ltd, 7 Industrial Estate, Tame Road, Birmingham, B6 7HS Tel: 0121-328 2515 Fax: 0121-327 8324 E-mail: sales@fisherleaksystems.co.uk

LEAK DETECTOR TEST SYSTEMS

Fisher Leak Systems Ltd, 7 Industrial Estate, Tame Road, Birmingham, B6 7HS Tel: 0121-328 2515 Fax: 0121-327 8324 E-mail: sales@fisherleaksystems.co.uk

TQC Ltd, Hooton Street, Nottingham, NG3 2NJ Tel: 0115-950 3561 Fax: 0115-948 4642 E-mail: sales@tqc.co.uk

▶ Uson Ltd, Western Way, Bury St. Edmunds, Suffolk, IP33 3SP Tel: (01284) 760606 Fax: (01284) 763049 E-mail: info@uson.co.uk

▶ Uson Ltd, Western Way, Bury St. Edmunds, Suffolk, IP33 3SP Tel: (01284) 760606 Fax: (01284) 763049 E-mail: info@uson.co.uk

Vacuum Engineering Services Ltd, St. Modwen Road, Stretford, Manchester, M32 0ZE Tel: 0845 5314240 Fax: 0161-866 8861 E-mail: info@vac-eng.com

Weber Automatic Assembly Systems Ltd, 3 Landscape Close, Weston Business Park, Weston-On-The-Green, Oxfordshire, OX25 3SX Tel: (01869) 343688 Fax: (01869) 343699 E-mail: sales@weberautomation.com

LEAK DETECTORS, *See also headings for particular types*

Anglo Nordic Burner Products Ltd, Units 12-14, Island Farm Avenue, West Molesey, Surrey, KT8 2UZ Tel: (020) 8979 0988 Fax: (020) 8979 6961 E-mail: sales@anglonordic.co.uk

Ateq UK Ltd, Unit 71 Heming Road, The Washford Industrial Estate, Redditch, Worcestershire, B98 0EA Tel: (01527) 520011 Fax: (01527) 520022 E-mail: info@ateq.co.uk

Dean & Wood Ltd, Mole Business Park, Randalls Road, Leatherhead, Surrey, KT22 2BA Tel: (01372) 378788 Fax: (01372) 386239 E-mail: dw@dean-wood.co.uk

Girovac Ltd, Units 1 & 2, Douglas Bader Close, North Walsham, Norfolk, NR28 0TZ Tel: (01692) 403008 Fax: (01692) 404611 E-mail: enquiries@girovac.com

Ion Science Ltd, The Way, Fowlmere, Royston, Herts, SG8 7UJ Tel: (01763) 208503 Fax: (01763) 208814 E-mail: info@ionscience.com

Jola Ltd, Sprinfield Works, Lloyd St, Hopwood, Heywood, Lancs, OL10 2BP Tel: (01706) 366339 Fax: (01706) 366382 E-mail: bernie.mjola@tinyworld.co.uk

LEAK DETECTORS, AIR/GAS

Maltron International Ltd, PO Box 15, Rayleigh, Essex, SS6 9SN Tel: (01268) 778251 Fax: (01268) 745176 E-mail: maltron@msn.com

▶ Uson Ltd, Western Way, Bury St. Edmunds, Suffolk, IP33 3SP Tel: (01284) 760606 Fax: (01284) 763049 E-mail: info@uson.co.uk

Vacuum Engineering Services Ltd, St. Modwen Road, Stretford, Manchester, M32 0ZE Tel: 0845 5314240 Fax: 0161-866 8861 E-mail: info@vac-eng.com

LEAK DETECTORS, AIR/GAS, ULTRASONIC

Logis-Tech Associates, 140 Boyd Street, Crosshill, Glasgow, G42 8TP Tel: 0141-423 6911 Fax: (0870) 1276102 E-mail: hugo@logis-tech.co.uk

LEAK DETECTORS, FLUID/ LIQUID

Gotec Trading Ltd, Boulton Road, Stevenage, Hertfordshire, SG1 4QL Tel: (01438) 740400 Fax: (01438) 740005

Jola Ltd, Sprinfield Works, Lloyd St, Hopwood, Heywood, Lancs, OL10 2BP Tel: (01706) 366339 Fax: (01706) 366382 E-mail: bernie.mjola@tinyworld.co.uk

LEAK SEALING SERVICES, ON-LINE

Furmanite Engineering Ltd, 7 Colville Court, Winwick Quay, Warrington, WA2 8QT Tel: (01925) 418858 Fax: (01925) 418863 E-mail: enquiries@furmanite.com

Furmanite International Ltd, Furman House, Shap Road, Kendal, Cumbria, LA9 6RU Tel: (01539) 729009 Fax: (01539) 729359 E-mail: enquiry@furmanite.com

Leak Repairs UK, Kings Road, Immingham, South Humberside, DN40 1FN Tel: (01469) 550527 Fax: (01469) 576293 E-mail: sales@leakrepairs.co.uk

PLCS Ltd, Wartell Bank, Kingswinford, West Midlands, DY6 7QJ Tel: (01384) 298000 Fax: (01384) 400845 E-mail: sales@pressleakage.com

LEATHER

A L Maugham & Co. Ltd, 5-9 Fazakerley Street, Liverpool, L3 9DN Tel: 0151-236 1872 Fax: 0151-236 1872

A W Midgley & Son Ltd, 13 Cheddar Business Park, Wedmore Road, Cheddar, Somerset, BS27 3EB Tel: (01934) 741741 Fax: (01934) 741555 E-mail: sales@awmidgley.co.uk

Alma Leather Ltd, 12-14 Greatorex Street, London, E1 5NF Tel: (020) 7375 0343 Fax: (020) 7375 2598 E-mail: tisha.richbell@almaleather.co.uk

Charles Birch Ltd, Holly House, 43 Cavendish Street, Leeds, LS3 1LY Tel: 0113-243 1155 Fax: 0113-242 3593

Charles F Stead & Co. Ltd, Tannery, Sheepscar Street North, Leeds, LS7 2BY Tel: 0113-262 8643 Fax: 0113-262 6309 E-mail: suede@cfstead.com

Colin Cross & Co. Ltd, Fitzwilliam House, Kimbolton Road, Higham Ferrers, Rushden, Northamptonshire, NN10 8HL Tel: (01933) 358966 Fax: (01933) 410327 E-mail: adrian-alasdaire@colincrossn10.fsnet.co.uk

Dickens Bros Ltd, 69-71 Kettering Road, Northampton, NN1 4AP Tel: (01604) 636537 Fax: (01604) 636537 E-mail: dickensbrothers@btinternet.com

Doubletex Leathers Ltd, Stervon House, 1 Seaford Road, Salford, M6 6AS Tel: 0161-737 1000 Fax: 0161-737 7555 E-mail: dtxleather@aol.com

Gale Furs, 65 Regents Park Road, London, NW1 8XD Tel: (020) 7722 5870 Fax: (020) 7722 8830

A. Henry & Co., Langford Arch, London Road, Sawston, CB2 4EE Tel: (01223) 833132 Fax: (01223) 833400

Horace Battin & Co., 119 Warkton Lane, Barton Seagrave, Kettering, Northamptonshire, NN15 5AD Tel: (01536) 511464 Fax: (01536) 523455

J T Batchelor Ltd, 9-10 Culford Mews, London, N1 4DZ Tel: (020) 7254 2962 Fax: (020) 7254 0357

Marlborough Leathers, Unit A Bury Close, Higham Ferrers, Rushden, Northamptonshire, NN10 8HQ Tel: (01933) 411314 Fax: (01604) 790946 E-mail: ml@witmore-bacon.co.uk

Marshall Coppin Ltd, Unit 5 Chingford Industrial Centre, Hall Lane, London, E4 8DJ Tel: (020) 8524 1018 Fax: (020) 8524 8978

Offerclass Ltd, 73-75 Shacklewell Lane, London, E8 2EB Tel: (020) 7923 2560 Fax: (020) 7923 2692 E-mail: katrina@offerclass.com

Tricorne Leather, 13 Bell Lane, London, NW4 2BP Tel: (020) 8203 6774 Fax: (020) 8203 6145

W J & W Lang Ltd, 1 Seedhill, Paisley, Renfrewshire, PA1 1JL Tel: 0141-889 3134 Fax: 0141-889 3182 E-mail: sales@langwetblue.co.uk

LEATHER ABRASIVE WHEELS

Cheshire Leathers UK Ltd, 3 Cobden Industrial Centre, Quakers Coppice, Crewe, CW1 6FA Tel: (01270) 251556 Fax: (01270) 251557 E-mail: cheshireleather@aol.com

LEATHER BAGS

▶ Vivid Trading, Mere Farm Bell, Bell Lane, Saham Toney, Thetford, Norfolk, IP25 7HD Tel: (01953) 883264 E-mail: vividmail@hotmail.com

LEATHER BEAN BAGS

▶ Bean Bag Refill, Beanbag Filling, 11 Belgrave Court, Blackwater, Camberley, Surrey, GU17 9JE Tel: 0 870 285 1593 E-mail: info@bean-bag.co.uk

▶ Homeandleather, W9, The Innovation Centre, Festival Drive, Ebbw Vale, Gwent, NP23 8XA Tel: (01495) 356789

LEATHER BELTING

Aldersons (Northampton) Ltd, 4 William St, Northampton, NN1 3EW Tel: (01604) 639346 Fax: (01604) 638542 E-mail: aldersonsltd@aol.com

Anglo Leather Craft Ltd, Unit 4 Bellair Estate, Musker Street, Crosby, Liverpool, L23 0UB Tel: 0151-931 3177 Fax: 0151-931 4076 E-mail: angloleather@netscapeonline.co.uk

Girls Of Elegance Ltd, Office B12, Arena Business Park, Holyrood Close, Poole, Dorset, BH17 7FL Tel: 0845 8385143 Fax: 0845 8385143 E-mail: sales@girlsofelegance.co.uk

LEATHER BELTING – *continued*

▶ KSK Belts, Woodburn Road, Smethwick, West Midlands, B66 2PU Tel: 0121-565 0808 Fax: 0121-565 0808

▶ Shooterbelts.Com, Hyde House, The Hyde, London, NW9 6LH Tel: (020) 8205 7049 Fax: (020) 8975 1025 E-mail: sales@shooterbelts.com

LEATHER BINDERS

Daines & Hathaway, Shelton House, Bridgeman Street, Walsall, WS2 9PG Tel: (01922) 621823 Fax: (01922) 623393 E-mail: sales@dainesandhathaway.com

LEATHER CASES

Daines & Hathaway, Shelton House, Bridgeman Street, Walsall, WS2 9PG Tel: (01922) 621823 Fax: (01922) 623393 E-mail: sales@dainesandhathaway.com

E H Crack & Sons Ltd, High Mill, Shaw Mills, Harrogate, North Yorkshire, HG3 3HY Tel: (01423) 770226 Fax: (01423) 770188

Hanson Tower Ltd, Hanson House, Knight Road, Rochester, Kent, ME2 2JH Tel: (01634) 713363 Fax: (01634) 721099 E-mail: sales@hanson-tower.com

Oxford Leathercraft, Northfield Works Sharps Yard, Long Wittenham, Abingdon, Oxfordshire, OX14 4QW Tel: (01865) 407100 Fax: (01865) 417120

LEATHER CASH BAGS

Chiltern UK Ltd, 64 Waterloo Road, Manchester, M8 8GJ Tel: 0161-832 3206 Fax: 0161-832 7844

Peter Jones Ilg Ltd, Lower Monk Street, Abergavenny, Gwent, NP7 5NA Tel: (01873) 852742 Fax: (01873) 857573 E-mail: sales@peterjonesilg.co.uk

LEATHER COVERED BUCKLES

C A Sperati The Special Agency plc, 54 Westcombe Hill, London, SE10 0LR Tel: (020) 8858 7069 Fax: (020) 8853 5349 E-mail: enquires@casperatiplc.com

LEATHER CUSHIONS

▶ Homeandleather, W9, The Innovation Centre, Festival Drive, Ebbw Vale, Gwent, NP23 8XA Tel: (01495) 356789

LEATHER DESK STATIONERY

Filofax Time Management, Unit 3 Victoria Gardens, Burgess Hill, West Sussex, RH15 9NB Tel: (01444) 238100 Fax: (01444) 238119 E-mail: enquiries@filofax.co.uk

Hutchings & Harding Group Ltd, 163 High Street, Sawston, Cambridge, CB22 3HN Tel: (01223) 832281 Fax: (01223) 836401 E-mail: sales@chamois.com

Sebserv Business Machine Repairs, Ramsay House, 18 Vera Avenue, London, N21 1RA Tel: (020) 8360 8845 Fax: (020) 8360 6688 E-mail: info@sebserv.com

Wheeler & Oliver, 22 Cooperage Green, Royal Clarence Marina, Gosport, Hampshire, PO12 1FY Tel: (023) 9252 0091 Fax: (023) 9252 0189E-mail: info@wheelerandoliver.com

LEATHER DRESSING, *See Leather, Prepared etc*

LEATHER EQUESTRIAN PRODUCTS

Colne Saddlery, The Barn, Tewkesbury Road, Norton, Gloucester, GL2 9LH Tel: (01452) 731456 Fax: (01452) 731456 E-mail: sales@colnesaddlery.co.uk

E H Crack & Sons Ltd, High Mill, Shaw Mills, Harrogate, North Yorkshire, HG3 3HY Tel: (01423) 770226 Fax: (01423) 770188

Jabez Cliff & Co. Ltd, Globe Works, Lower Forster Street, Walsall, WS1 1XG Tel: (01922) 621676 Fax: (01922) 722575 E-mail: saddlery@barnsby.com

▶ KingswoodSaddlery.co.uk, Barleycorn Cottage, Babylon Lane, Lower Kingswood, Tadworth, Surrey, KT20 6XD Tel: (01737) 249121 Fax: (01737) 249121 E-mail: sales@kingswoodsaddlery.co.uk

Norris & Sons, Home Farm, Palace Lane, Beaulieu, Brockenhurst, Hampshire, SO42 7YG Tel: (01590) 612673 Fax: (01590) 612978

R & R Country, Hull Road, Hemingbrough, Selby, North Yorkshire, YO8 6QJ Tel: (01757) 638555 Fax: (01757) 630770 E-mail: randrcountry@btconnect.com

T & C Robinson, 4 St Marys Street, Stamford, Lincolnshire, PE9 2DE Tel: (01780) 755378 Fax: (01780) 755378 E-mail: sales@no1saddlers.co.uk

T W Bowler Ltd, Shadyoak, Marple Road, Stockport, Cheshire, SK2 5HF Tel: 0161-487 3363 Fax: 0161-487 3527 E-mail: sales@bowlers-stockport.co.uk

LEATHER EXPORT MERCHANTS OR AGENTS

Eagle Ottawa Warrington Ltd, 254 Thelwall Lane, Warrington, WA4 1NQ Tel: (01925) 650251 Fax: (01925) 655547

Wingrove & Edge Ltd, The Tannery, West Hill, Milborne Port, Sherborne, Dorset, DT9 5HL Tel: (01963) 250620 Fax: (01963) 250627 E-mail: email@whitmore-bacon.co.uk

LEATHER FLOOR COVERINGS

Hideinstyle Ltd, Dutch Barn, Church Farm, Ulcombe Hill, Ulcombe, Maidstone, Kent, ME17 1DN Tel: (01622) 892235 E-mail: info@hideinstyle.co.uk

LEATHER FURNISHING BARRELS

▶ Homeandleather, W9, The Innovation Centre, Festival Drive, Ebbw Vale, Gwent, NP23 8XA Tel: (01495) 356789

LEATHER FURNITURE

Hanson Tower Ltd, Hanson House, Knight Road, Rochester, Kent, ME2 2JH Tel: (01634) 713363 Fax: (01634) 721099 E-mail: sales@hanson-tower.com

Hideinstyle Ltd, Dutch Barn, Church Farm, Ulcombe Hill, Ulcombe, Maidstone, Kent, ME17 1DN Tel: (01622) 892235 E-mail: info@hideinstyle.co.uk

R G Collins Ltd, 43 Melton Street, Kettering, Northamptonshire, NN16 9DT Tel: (07753) 627331 Fax: (01536) 514127

Rustic Leather Co., 3 Penllwyngwent Industrial Estate, Saville Road, Ogmore Vale, Bridgend, Mid Glamorgan, CF32 7AX Tel: (01656) 842832 Fax: (01656) 841144 E-mail: sales@therusticleathercompany.co.uk

Wimborne Leather Co., Unit 2b, Sunrise Business Park, Blandford Forum, Dorset, DT11 8ST Tel: (01258) 455397 Fax: (01258) 480610

Zone Designs Ltd, Unit GG9 Gilnow Mill, Spa Road, Bolton, BL1 4LF Tel: (01204) 559500 Fax: (01204) 559500 E-mail: darren@zone-designs.co.uk

LEATHER GLOVES IMPORT

▶ Ultimate Cleaners (Industrial) Ltd, Unit 9, Cousin Street, Dudley Road, Wolverhampton, WV2 3DG Tel: (01902) 451451 E-mail: sales@ultimateindustrial.co.uk

LEATHER GOODS

▶ Alpha Leather Goods, Osbourne House, Charles Street, Walsall, WS2 9LZ Tel: (01922) 721804 Fax: (01922) 722733

▶ B Amberg, 31 Elkstone Road, London, W10 5NT Tel: (020) 8960 2000 Fax: (020) 8960 2321

British & Foreign (Exporters) Ltd, 53 Park Royal Rd, London, NW10 7LQ Tel: (020) 8965 4833 Fax: (020) 8961 3377 E-mail: leea@brit-foreign.demon.co.uk

▶ British Hide Collection, Chorley Road, Fourgates Mill, Westhoughton, Bolton, BL5 3NB Tel: (01942) 819740 Fax: (01942) 816587

▶ Burnsides Marketing Aids Ltd, 62 Station Road, Langley Mill, Nottingham, NG16 4BH Tel: (01773) 713687 Fax: (01773) 715801 E-mail: sales@burnsides.co.uk

▶ C A Cornish, 21 High Street, Street, Somerset, BA16 0EF Tel: (01458) 442746 Fax: (01458) 443850

Casson & Co. Ltd, 117 Huddersfield Road, Oldham, OL1 3NY Tel: 0161-624 2227 Fax: 0161-627 5231

▶ Dark Sensations, Chapel Works, East Street, Cannock, Staffordshire, WS11 0BU Tel: (01543) 437555 Fax: (01543) 437444 E-mail: info@darksensations.com

▶ Grapevine Trading Ltd, 5 Cloughside, Marple Bridge, Stockport, Cheshire, SK6 5BS Tel: (0870) 1620693 Fax: (0870) 1620694

Heritage Leathergoods Co. Ltd, 24-32 Princip Street, Birmingham, B4 6LE Tel: 0121-333 3339 Fax: 0121-359 3487 E-mail: inquiries@heritageleathergoods.co.uk

▶ Highland Celtic Leather Scotland, 1 Benmore House, Portnellan, Crianlarich, Perthshire, FK20 8QS Tel: (07092) 240355 Fax: (07092) 240355

▶ Kadett Car, 7 Peacock Yard, Iliffe Street, London, SE17 3LH Tel: (020) 7701 5511 Fax: (020) 7701 5511

▶ KSK Belts, Woodburn Road, Smethwick, West Midlands, B66 2PU Tel: 0121-565 0808 Fax: 0121-565 0808

Leather Studio, 5 Almond Road, Burnham, Slough, SL1 8HX Tel: (01628) 667279 Fax: (01628) 666389 E-mail: info@leatherstudio.co.uk

Peter Lewis Ltd, Unit 14, Red Lion Business Centre, Surbiton, Surrey, KT6 7QD Tel: (020) 8391 5477 Fax: (020) 8974 1650 E-mail: sales@peter-lewis.co.uk

Andrew Muirhead & Son Ltd, Unit 10 Siberia Mill, Holgate Street, Briercliffe, Burnley, Lancashire, BB10 2HQ Tel: (01282) 424040 Fax: (01282) 420209

Pelham Leather Goods Ltd, Pelham Centre, 110 Centennial Avenue, Borehamwood, Hertfordshire, WD6 3SB Tel: (020) 8731 3500 Fax: (020) 8731 3501 E-mail: sales@pelhamgroup.co.uk

▶ Rawhide Ltd, Carnaby Industrial Estate, Lancaster Road, Carnaby, Bridlington, North Humberside, YO15 3QY Tel: (01262) 400278 Fax: (01262) 401960 E-mail: enquiries@rawhidesaccesories.com

Satchel Design Ltd, Whitley Lane, Walton, Street, Somerset, BA16 9RW Tel: (01458) 442371 Fax: (01458) 841245

Start & Tremayne, 178 High Street, Burton-on-Trent, Staffordshire, DE14 1HN Tel: (01283) 563650 Fax: (01283) 561144

Tassia Ltd, 167 Hermitage Road, London, N4 1LZ Tel: (020) 8880 1833 Fax: (020) 8880 1933 E-mail: tassia@btinternet.com

Albert Thurston Ltd, 3 Frog Island, Leicester, LE3 5AG Tel: 0116-262 7515 Fax: 0116-251 3607 E-mail: sales@albertthurston.com

▶ Zodiac Industries Ltd, Kingswear Drive, Vallets Lane, Bolton, BL1 6DU Tel: (01204) 842211

LEATHER GOODS FITTINGS/ ACCESSORIES

A T H Alden Ltd, Sutherland Road, London, E17 6BU Tel: (020) 8531 3358 Fax: (020) 8527 9105 E-mail: simon@aldens.fsbusiness.co.uk

G Ettinger Ltd, 215 Putney Bridge Road, London, SW15 2NY Tel: (020) 8877 1616 Fax: (020) 8877 1146 E-mail: info@ettinger.co.uk

Town & Country, Whitwick Business Park, Stenson Road, Whitwick, Leicester, LE67 4JP Tel: (01530) 830990 Fax: (01530) 830877 E-mail: info@townandco.com

LEATHER GOODS (MADE-UP) IMPORT/EXPORT MERCHANTS OR AGENTS

Chiltern UK Ltd, 64 Waterloo Road, Manchester, M8 8GJ Tel: 0161-832 3206 Fax: 0161-832 7844

Firelog Ltd, Unit 5C-5D, Caxton Trading Estate, Printing House Lane, Hayes, Middlesex, UB3 1BE Tel: (07932) 644613 Fax: (020) 8569 1165 E-mail: firelogltd@yahoo.co.uk

G H Stafford & Son Ltd, Argyle Works, Navigation Street, Walsall, WS2 9LX Tel: (01922) 623993 Fax: (01922) 723403 E-mail: sales@ghstafford.com

Greenhaven Ltd, 11 Club Row, London, E1 6JX Tel: (020) 7613 2345 Fax: (020) 7613 5977

M Golunski & Co., Moor Street Trading Estate, Brierley Hill, West Midlands, DY5 3SS Tel: (01384) 78326 Fax: (01384) 841737 E-mail: golunski@lineone.net

LEATHER GOODS, MADE-UP

Albany Belt Co., 31-33 Beler Way, Leicester Road Industrial Estate, Melton Mowbray, Leicestershire, LE13 0DG Tel: (01664) 566055 Fax: (01664) 410205 E-mail: albany.belt@btinternet.com

Alco Leather Ltd, Crank Mills, Station Road, Morley, Leeds, LS27 8JR Tel: 0113-252 4644 Fax: 0113-238 3205

Anglo Leather Craft Ltd, Unit 4 Bellair Estate, Musker Street, Crosby, Liverpool, L23 0UB Tel: 0151-931 3177 Fax: 0151-931 4076 E-mail: angloleather@netscapeonline.co.uk

Herbert Baumann Ltd, Bago Ho, 11-15 Chase Rd, Park Royal, London, NW10 6PT Tel: (020) 8955 6400 Fax: (020) 8883 3833

Calver Ltd, 22 The Drive, Orpington, Kent, BR6 9AP Tel: (01689) 898828 Fax: (01689) 898848 E-mail: sales@calver.com

▶ Cambridge Interiors Ltd, 71 Nelson Street, Kettering, Northamptonshire, NN16 9QL Tel: (01536) 481586 Fax: (01536) 481586

Cathian Leather Goods, Compstall Mills Estate, Andrew Street, Compstall, Stockport, Cheshire, SK6 5HN Tel: 0161-427 4871 Fax: 0161-427 4871 E-mail: cathian@ukonline.co.uk

Checker Leather Ltd, The Station, Crosshouse Road, Kilmaurs, Kilmarnock, Ayrshire, KA3 2TU Tel: (01563) 541709 Fax: (01563) 537819 E-mail: sales@glenroyal.com

Daines & Hathaway, Shelton House, Bridgeman Street, Walsall, WS2 9PG Tel: (01922) 621823 Fax: (01922) 623393 E-mail: sales@dainesandhathaway.com

E J Soper Ltd, 51 Ormside Way, Redhill, RH1 2LW Tel: (01737) 762230

G Ettinger Ltd, 215 Putney Bridge Road, London, SW15 2NY Tel: (020) 8877 1616 Fax: (020) 8877 1146 E-mail: info@ettinger.co.uk

Alwyn Gloves, Crown East, Rushwick, Worcester, WR2 5TU Tel: (01905) 425624 Fax: (01905) 425624

Gostelow Advertising Ltd, 21-22 Francis Street, Hull, HU2 8DT Tel: (01482) 323459 Fax: (01482) 586325 E-mail: alec@gostelow.karoo.co.uk

Harry Irving & Co. Ltd, Hi Craft House, Sandy Road, Seaforth, Liverpool, L21 1AG Tel: 0151-928 2487 Fax: 0151-920 0617 E-mail: sales@hi-pet.com

▶ Highland Celtic Leather Scotland, 1 Benmore House, Portnellan, Crianlarich, Perthshire, FK20 8QS Tel: (07092) 240355 Fax: (07092) 240355

Hillmar Products, New Victoria Mills, Wellington Street, Bury, Lancashire, BL8 2AL Tel: 0161-763 5598 Fax: 0161-764 1368 E-mail: hilmarproducts@btopenworld.com

James Homer Ltd, 78 Mill Lane, Walsall, WS4 2BH Tel: (01922) 623683 Fax: (01922) 723747 E-mail: info.jameshomar@virgin.net

E. Hulme & Son Ltd, 13-15 Cecil Street, Walsall, WS4 2BD Tel: (01922) 622082 Fax: (01922) 722442

J A Marchant & Son Ltd, Chaddock Lane, Tyldesley, Manchester, M29 7JT Tel: (01942) 882858 Fax: (01942) 897014 E-mail: marchants2003@yahoo.co.uk

J R Tusting & Co. Ltd, The Tannery Warehouse, 29-31 Olney Road, Lavendon, Olney, Buckinghamshire, MK46 4EU Tel: (01234) 712266 Fax: (01234) 713545 E-mail: info@tusting.co.uk

Kenton Leather Products, Windmill Road, Rushden, Northamptonshire, NN10 9TN Tel: (01933) 312160 Fax: (01933) 412185

Lindy Lou, 33 George Street, Hove, East Sussex, BN3 3YB Tel: (01273) 732770

M Golunski & Co., Moor Street Trading Estate, Brierley Hill, West Midlands, DY5 3SS Tel: (01384) 78326 Fax: (01384) 841737 E-mail: golunski@lineone.net

A.D. Mackenzie, THe Old Saddlery, Cladach, Brodick, Isle Of Arran, KA27 8DE Tel: (01770) 302311 E-mail: sales@mckenzieleather.co.uk

Pelicans Manufacturing Co. Ltd, B 5 Parr Road, Stanmore, Middlesex, HA7 1NP Tel: (020) 8952 4222 Fax: (020) 8951 3639 E-mail: sales@pelicans.co.uk

Printform Direct Ltd, 8 Longbridge, Willesborough, Ashford, Kent, TN24 0TA Tel: (01233) 639898 Fax: (01233) 636866 E-mail: sales@printform.co.uk

Quality Gunslips Ltd, Sarnau, Llanymynech, Powys, SY22 6QJ Tel: (01938) 590204 Fax: (01938) 590411 E-mail: sales@gunslips.co.uk

R & F Trimmings, 185 Earlham Grove, Forest Gate, London, E7 9AP Tel: (020) 8221 1515 Fax: (020) 8221 1414 E-mail: randftrimms@aol.com

R H Leather, 36 Goulston Street, London, E1 7TP Tel: (020) 7247 5181

Regent Belt Co. Ltd, Leo House The Business Centre, Ross Road, Weedon Road Industrial Estate, Northampton, NN5 5AX Tel: (01604) 684700 Fax: (01604) 684719 E-mail: sales@regentbelt.co.uk

Sabichi Homewares Ltd, Sabichi House, 5 Wadsworth Road, Greenford, Middlesex, UB6 7JD Tel: (020) 8991 9505 Fax: (020) 8991 9218

Shilton plc, 90 Peterborough Road, London, SW6 3HH Tel: (020) 7736 7771 Fax: (020) 7731 7683 E-mail: info@janeshilton.co.uk

George Stuart Ltd, Central Drive, Walsall, WS3 2QJ Tel: (01922) 711919 Fax: (01922) 473147 E-mail: sales@georgestuart.co.uk

Swaine Adeney Brigg Ltd, Viking Way, Bar Hill, Cambridge, CB23 8EL Tel: (01799) 530521 Fax: (01799) 530320 E-mail: sales@swaine-adeney-brigg.co.uk

Tassia Ltd, 167 Hermitage Road, London, N4 1LZ Tel: (020) 8880 1833 Fax: (020) 8880 1933 E-mail: tassia@btinternet.com

Taurus Leather Ltd, Montague House, 436 Leeds Road, Robin Hood, Wakefield, West Yorkshire, WF3 3BG Tel: 0113-282 3508 Fax: 0113-282 9805

Temple Leathergoods, 45 Shaw Street, Colne, Lancashire, BB8 0DD Tel: (01282) 866367 Fax: (01282) 866367

Whitehouse Cox & Co. Ltd, 1 Morton Court Lockside, Anchor Brook Industrial Park, Aldridge, Walsall, WS9 8BZ Tel: (01922) 458881 Fax: (01922) 458889 E-mail: customerservice@whitehouse-cox.co.uk

Arnold Wills & Co. Ltd, Station Road, Uppingham, Oakham, Leicestershire, LE15 9TZ Tel: (01572) 822261 Fax: (01572) 821059 E-mail: enquiries@arnoldwills.co.uk

Peter Yates Leathergoods Ltd, Unit M2 Lockside, Anchor Brook Industrial Park, Aldridge, Walsall, WS9 8BZ Tel: (01922) 453800 Fax: (01922) 453808 E-mail: sales@peteryatesleathergoods.co.uk

York City Leather Co., Unit 7, Roland Court Industrial Estate, Huntington Road, York, YO32 9PW Tel: (01904) 765461 Fax: (01904) 765461 E-mail: lenyclyork@line1.net

LEATHER HANDLES

Oxford Leathercraft, Northfield Works Sharps Yard, Long Wittenham, Abingdon, Oxfordshire, OX14 4QW Tel: (01865) 407100 Fax: (01865) 417120

LEATHER HYDRAULIC PRODUCTS, *See Hydraulic Packings etc; also Seal etc*

LEATHER IMPORT MERCHANTS OR AGENTS

Alami International Ltd, 7 Dace Road, London, E3 2NG Tel: (020) 8533 7800 Fax: (020) 8533 0026 E-mail: sales@alami.co.uk
Alma Leather Ltd, 12-14 Greatorex Street, London, E1 5NF Tel: (020) 7375 0343 Fax: (020) 7375 2598 E-mail: tisha.richbell@almaleather.co.uk
Demolition By Trojan, 116 Knutsford Road, Grappenhall, Warrington, WA4 2PW Tel: (01925) 860039 Fax: 01925 860084
Horace Battin & Co., 119 Warkton Lane, Barton Seagrave, Kettering, Northamptonshire, NN15 5AD Tel: (01536) 511464 Fax: (01536) 523455
Leather Grace, 80 Nelson Street, London, E1 2DY Tel: (020) 7790 8000 Fax: (020) 7790 9000 E-mail: info@lloydbaker.com
Marlborough Leathers, Unit A Bury Close, Higham Ferrers, Rushden, Northamptonshire, NN10 8HQ Tel: (01933) 411314 Fax: (01604) 790946 E-mail: ml@witmore-bacon.co.uk
Edward Woodley & Sons Ltd, Newton Road, Higham Ferrers, Rushden, Northamptonshire, NN10 8HR Tel: (01933) 353373 Fax: (01933) 358275 E-mail: ewoodley@globalnet.co.uk

LEATHER INTERIOR FURNISHINGS DESIGN

Hideinstyle Ltd, Dutch Barn, Church Farm, Ulcombe Hill, Ulcombe, Maidstone, Kent, ME17 1DN Tel: (01622) 892235 E-mail: info@hideinstyle.co.uk

LEATHER JACKETS

▶ Awanstars Leather Fashion, 42 Foxton Road, Birmingham, B8 3HP Tel: (0781) 2817248 E-mail: awanstars@yahoo.co.uk

LEATHER LINGERIE

▶ Black-Thong Limited, 23 Danestone Close, Middleleaze, Swindon, SN5 5GP Tel: 07977 717893 E-mail: enquiries@black-thong.com
▶ Body Buddies Lingerie, 41 Ely Close, Southminster, Essex, CM0 7AQ Tel: (07762) 059557 E-mail: sales@bodybuddies.co.uk
▶ Horny Toys, 60 Acacia Road, London, W3 6HF Tel: 02088 961103 E-mail: info@hornytoys.co.uk
▶ Nite Life, 37 Huntly Street, Aberdeen, AB10 1TJ Tel: (01224) 561110 Fax: (01224) 561110
▶ The Passion Store, 25 Sunart Way, Hawthorn Common, Nuneaton, Warwickshire, CV10 9TB Tel: 0800 6121069 Fax: 0800 6121068 E-mail: sales@thepassionstore.co.uk
▶ The Stocking Shop Ltd, 1 Chantry Road Thornbury, Thornbury, Bristol, BS35 1ER Tel: (07771) 822972 E-mail: sales@the-stocking-shop.com

LEATHER OFFICE FURNITURE

Anthony's, 36 High Street, Stotfold, Hitchin, Hertfordshire, SG5 4LL Tel: (01462) 835452 Fax: (01462) 835452
G G I Office Furniture (UK) Ltd, Global Way, Darwen, Lancashire, BB3 0RW Tel: (01254) 778500 Fax: (01254) 778519 E-mail: info@ggieurope.com
Hands Of Wycombe, 36 Dashwood Avenue, High Wycombe, Buckinghamshire, HP12 3DX Tel: (01494) 524222 Fax: (01494) 526508
Tract Ltd, Mckay Trading Estate, Station Approach, Bicester, Oxfordshire, OX26 6BF Tel: (01869) 326300 Fax: (01869) 323430 E-mail: info@tract.ltd.uk
White Grove Group plc, Central House, Halesfield 19, Telford, Shropshire, TF7 4QT Tel: (01952) 685300 Fax: (01952) 581612 E-mail: sales@whitegrove.co.uk

LEATHER OR LEATHERETTE GARMENT BELTS

▶ A V Trading Co., 22 St Lukes Terrace, Sunderland, SR4 6NQ Tel: 0191-565 6136 Fax: 0191-565 6136 E-mail: avtrad@yahoo.co.uk
Anglo Leather Craft Ltd, Unit 4 Bellair Estate, Musker Street, Crosby, Liverpool, L23 0UB Tel: 0151-931 3177 Fax: 0151-931 4076 E-mail: angloleather@netscapeonline.co.uk
Arodix Ltd, Unit 4, 36 Greenford Road, Harrow, Middlesex, HA1 3QH Tel: (020) 8864 2272 Fax: (020) 8423 8870
Daks Simpson Ltd, 10 Old Bond Street, London, W1S 4PL Tel: (020) 7409 4000 Fax: (020) 7499 4494
E J Soper Ltd, 51 Ormside Way, Redhill, RH1 2LW Tel: (01737) 762230
Faxtip Ltd, 32 Mason Street, Manchester, M4 5EY Tel: 0161-835 3582 Fax: 0161-835 3582 E-mail: faxtip@yahoo.co.uk
Foden Ibex Ltd, Ibex House Ferrofields, Scaldwell Road, Brixworth, Northampton, NN6 9UA Tel: (01604) 880605 Fax: (01604) 880802 E-mail: sales@fodenibex.co.uk
Hunt & Holditch Ltd, Unit 12, 236-242 Lockwood Road, Huddersfield, HD1 3TG Tel: 01484 542148 Fax: 01484 549147 E-mail: hholditch@aol.com
Leathertex Ltd, 143 Bethnal Green Road, London, E2 7DG Tel: (020) 7613 4251 Fax: (020) 7613 4252 E-mail: leathertexltd@aol.com
▶ Offshore Select, 116 Weddington Road, Weddington, Nuneaton, Warwickshire, CV10 0AL Tel: (024) 7632 7582 E-mail: suedeandleather@hotmail.co.uk
Regent Belt Co. Ltd, Leo House The Business Centre, Ross Road, Weedon Road Industrial Estate, Northampton, NN5 5AX Tel: (01604) 684700 Fax: (01604) 684719 E-mail: sales@regentbelt.co.uk
▶ Shooterbelts.Com, Hyde House, The Hyde, London, NW9 6LH Tel: (020) 8205 7049 Fax: (020) 8975 1025 E-mail: sales@shooterbelts.com
Albert Thurston Ltd, 3 Frog Island, Leicester, LE3 5AG Tel: 0116-262 7515 Fax: 0116-251 3607 E-mail: sales@albertthurston.com
Village Leathers, 18 The Market, The Piazza, London, WC2E 8RB Tel: (020) 8965 2722 Fax: (020) 8965 2722 E-mail: sales@villageleathers.com
W Lees Walsall Ltd, Hatherton Works, Leamore Lane, Walsall, WS3 2BJ Tel: (01922) 476435 Fax: (01922) 407118 E-mail: sales@wlees.co.uk
Xerxes Belts, Troy Mills, Troy Road, Horsforth, Leeds, LS18 5NQ Tel: 0113-258 6675 Fax: 0113-239 0127 E-mail: sales@xerxes-belts.co.uk

LEATHER OR LEATHERETTE GLOVES

Burfield & Co Gloves Ltd, Manor Road, Martock, Somerset, TA12 6JH Tel: (01935) 823278 Fax: (01935) 826075 E-mail: burfield.gloves@btconnect.com
Chester Jefferies Ltd, Buckingham Road, Gillingham, Dorset, SP8 4QE Tel: (01747) 822629 Fax: (01747) 824092 E-mail: enquiries@chesterjefferies.co.uk
Dents, Fairfield Road, Warminster, Wiltshire, BA12 9DL Tel: (01985) 212291 Fax: (01985) 216435 E-mail: dents@dents.co.uk
Hanlin Export & Import Agents, 167a Wood Lane, Earlswood, Solihull, West Midlands, B94 5JL Tel: (01564) 702116 Fax: (01564) 703978 E-mail: hanlin.uk@btinternet.com
▶ Offshore Select, 116 Weddington Road, Weddington, Nuneaton, Warwickshire, CV10 0AL Tel: (024) 7632 7582 E-mail: suedeandleather@hotmail.co.uk
Reynolds & Kent Ltd, Unit 5 Wessex Business Centre, Meadow Lane, Westbury, Wiltshire, BA13 3EG Tel: (01373) 864767 Fax: (01373) 858697 E-mail: rnkglobes@aol.com
Southcombe Bros Ltd, Cole Lane, Stoke-sub-Hamdon, Somerset, TA14 6QD Tel: (01935) 823567 Fax: (01935) 822918 E-mail: sales@southcombe.com

LEATHER OR SUEDE CLOTHING

A & D Hope Ltd, Evelyn House, 3 Elstree Way, Borehamwood, Hertfordshire, WD6 1RN Tel: (020) 8953 7278 Fax: (020) 8953 7279 E-mail: admin@adhope.com
B Carnegie, 154 Stonhouse Street, London, SW4 6BE Tel: (020) 7627 3119
B S Fashions, 187 Plashet Rd, London, E13 0QZ Tel: 020 84720439
Bashir & Sons London Ltd, 178-180 Brick Lane, London, E1 6SA Tel: (020) 7739 0834 Fax: (020) 7739 8115
Camanchi Leathers Ltd, 184 Brick Lane, London, E1 6SA Tel: (020) 7739 5181 Fax: (020) 7256 0491
Crossbow Fashions Ltd, 4 Maryland Industrial Estate, 26 Maryland Road, London, E15 1JW Tel: (020) 8522 1652 Fax: (020) 8522 1752 E-mail: crossbowfashions@aol.com
Demolition By Trojan, 116 Knutsford Road, Grappenhall, Warrington, WA4 2PW Tel: (01925) 860039 Fax: 01925 860084
E H Crack & Sons Ltd, High Mill, Shaw Mills, Harrogate, North Yorkshire, HG3 3HY Tel: (01423) 770226 Fax: (01423) 770188
Eastman Leather Clothing, 5 Whiteoaks Industrial Unit, Filham, Ivybridge, Devon, PL21 0DW Tel: (01752) 896874 Fax: (01752) 690579
Formana Leathers, 1st Floor, 42A Fieldgate Street, London, E1 1ES Tel: (020) 7375 3113 Fax: (020) 7375 3317
Funtimz, UNIT 14 Masonfield Drive, Newton Stewart, Wigtownshire, DG8 6QA Tel: (01671) 402139 E-mail: sales@funtimz.co.uk
General Leather Co., 56 Chiltern Street, London, W1U 7QY Tel: (020) 7935 1041 Fax: (020) 7224 4312 E-mail: enquiries@generalleather.co.uk
Glyns Collections, 26 Blackfriars Street, Salford, M3 5BQ Tel: 0161-834 7581 Fax: 0161-834 7581 E-mail: martcgg@aol.com
Hidebound, Unit R1a Rocket Trading Centre, Bowring Park Rd, Liverpool, L14 3NZ Tel: 0151-252 2272 Fax: 0151 252 2273
JDL For Leather Ltd, PO Box 32, Stoke-on-Trent, ST8 7DU Tel: (01782) 518564 Fax: (01782) 522264
Joshua Kershaw & Co. Ltd, Water Street, Stockport, Cheshire, SK1 2BP Tel: 0161-480 3423 Fax: 0161-480 8106 E-mail: office@kershawleather.com
Leathertex Ltd, 143 Bethnal Green Road, London, E2 7DG Tel: (020) 7613 4251 Fax: (020) 7613 4252 E-mail: leathertexltd@aol.com
Nursey & Son Ltd, 12 Upper Olland Street, Bungay, Suffolk, NR35 1BQ Tel: (01986) 892821 Fax: (01986) 892823 E-mail: sales@nurseyleather.co.uk
Osh-gosh Ltd, 151 Bethnal Green Road, London, E2 7DG Tel: (020) 7729 3733 Fax: (020) 7613 0676
Pelle Ltd, 129 Bethnal Green Road, London, E2 7DG Tel: (020) 7729 7898 Fax: (020) 7729 7773 E-mail: pelleltd@aol.com
Rahmans Ltd, 10-14 Hollybush Gardens, London, E2 9QP Tel: (020) 7739 7790 Fax: (020) 7739 0562 E-mail: enquiries@rahmans.co.uk
Roma Leather Collection Ltd, High Street, Naseby, Northampton, NN6 6DD Tel: (01604) 740181 Fax: (01604) 740867 E-mail: info@romaleather.com
Woodland Leather, 27-33 Bethnal Green Road, London, E1 6LA Tel: (020) 7729 9494 Fax: (020) 7729 2555 E-mail: woodland_leather@btconnect.com
Woodlands Fashions, 33 Commercial Road, London, E1 1LD Tel: (020) 7247 0506 Fax: (020) 7247 7666 E-mail: sales@jeniceleather.co.uk

LEATHER PIECES

Celtic Leathers, 287 Marshfield Road, Castleton, Cardiff, CF3 2UW Tel: (01633) 680093 Fax: (01633) 680949 E-mail: sales@celtic-leathers.com

LEATHER SOFAS

The Furniture Warehouse, The Seed House, Bell Walk, Bell Lane, Uckfield, East Sussex, TN22 1AB Tel: (01825) 769202 E-mail: sales@sofasandfurniture.co.uk

LEATHER STRAPPING

Aldersons (Northampton) Ltd, 4 William St, Northampton, NN1 3EW Tel: (01604) 639346 Fax: (01604) 638542 E-mail: aldersonsltd@aol.com
Checker Leather Ltd, The Station, Crosshouse Road, Kilmaurs, Kilmarnock, Ayrshire, KA3 2TU Tel: (01563) 541709 Fax: (01563) 537819 E-mail: sales@glenroyal.com
Portch Trimmings Ltd, 2 Ireton Avenue, Leicester, LE4 9EW Tel: (0116) 276 6537 Fax: (0116) 246 0778

LEATHER TANNING

Clyde Leather Co., Broadlie Works, Neilston, Glasgow, G78 3AB Tel: 0141-881 4558 Fax: 0141-881 0522
Eagle Ottawa Warrington Ltd, 254 Thelwall Lane, Warrington, WA4 1NQ Tel: (01925) 650251 Fax: (01925) 655547
J & E Sedgwick & Co. Ltd, Reservoir Place, Walsall, WS2 9RX Tel: (01922) 622797 Fax: (01922) 724344 E-mail: sales@je-sedgwick.co.uk
W J & W Lang Ltd, 1 Seedhill, Paisley, Renfrewshire, PA1 1JL Tel: 0141-889 3134 Fax: 0141-889 3182 E-mail: sales@langwetblue.co.uk

LEATHER TRAVEL BAGS

Leather Studio, 5 Almond Road, Burnham, Slough, SL1 8HX Tel: (01628) 667279 Fax: (01628) 666389 E-mail: info@leatherstudio.co.uk
Quality Gunslips Ltd, Sarnau, Llanymynech, Powys, SY22 6QJ Tel: (01938) 590204 Fax: (01938) 590411 E-mail: sales@gunslips.co.uk

LEATHER TREATMENT CHEMICALS

British Salt Ltd, Cledford Lane, Middlewich, Cheshire, CW10 0JP Tel: (01606) 832881 Fax: (01606) 835999 E-mail: sales@british-salt.co.uk

LEATHER TRIMMINGS

T G Lewis Ltd, 15 Staveley Way, Brixworth Industrial Estate, Brixworth, Northampton, NN6 9EU Tel: (01604) 881966 Fax: (01604) 882318

LEATHER WASH BAGS

Leather Studio, 5 Almond Road, Burnham, Slough, SL1 8HX Tel: (01628) 667279 Fax: (01628) 666389 E-mail: info@leatherstudio.co.uk

LEATHER WORKING TOOLS

J T Batchelor Ltd, 9-10 Culford Mews, London, N1 4DZ Tel: (020) 7254 2962 Fax: (020) 7254 0357

LEATHERCLOTH

Colin Cross & Co. Ltd, Fitzwilliam House, Kimbolton Road, Higham Ferrers, Rushden, Northamptonshire, NN10 8HL Tel: (01933) 358966 Fax: (01933) 410327 E-mail: adrian-alasdaire@colincrossn10.fsnet.co.uk
Mark Saxby Ltd, Spring Gardens, Higham Ferrers, Rushden, Northamptonshire, NN10 8EP Tel: (01933) 312176 Fax: (01933) 413260

LEATHERS, PREPARED/ CHROME/DRESSED, *See also headings for particular usage*

Alma Leather Ltd, 12-14 Greatorex Street, London, E1 5NF Tel: (020) 7375 0343 Fax: (020) 7375 2598 E-mail: tisha.richbell@almaleather.co.uk
Colin Cross & Co. Ltd, Fitzwilliam House, Kimbolton Road, Higham Ferrers, Rushden, Northamptonshire, NN10 8HL Tel: (01933) 358966 Fax: (01933) 410327 E-mail: adrian-alasdaire@colincrossn10.fsnet.co.uk
Dickens Bros Ltd, 69-71 Kettering Road, Northampton, NN1 4AP Tel: (01604) 636537 Fax: (01604) 636537 E-mail: dickensbrothers@btinternet.com
E B Balmforth Ltd, The Old Forge, Sproxton, York, YO62 5EF Tel: (01439) 770568 Fax: (01437) 770618
Hanson Tower Ltd, Hanson House, Knight Road, Rochester, Kent, ME2 2JH Tel: (01634) 713363 Fax: (01634) 721099 E-mail: sales@hanson-tower.com
Hutchings & Harding Group Ltd, 163 High Street, Sawston, Cambridge, CB22 3HN Tel: (01223) 832281 Fax: (01223) 836401 E-mail: sales@chamois.com
J & E Sedgwick & Co. Ltd, Reservoir Place, Walsall, WS2 9RX Tel: (01922) 622797 Fax: (01922) 724344 E-mail: sales@je-sedgwick.co.uk
J & F J Baker & Co. Ltd, Hamlyns Mills, Colyton, Devon, EX24 6PD Tel: (01297) 552282 Fax: (01297) 553274
J Hewit & Sons Ltd, Kinauld Leather Works, 371 Lanark Road West, Currie, Midlothian, EH14 5RS Tel: 0131-449 2206 Fax: 0131-451 5081 E-mail: sales@hewit.com
Joshua Kershaw & Co. Ltd, Water Street, Stockport, Cheshire, SK1 2BP Tel: 0161-480 3423 Fax: 0161-480 8106 E-mail: office@kershawleather.com
James M. McQueen & Son, 180 West Regent Street, Glasgow, G2 4RU Tel: 0141-248 4865 Fax: 0141-221 4114
Andrew Muirhead & Son Ltd, 273-289 Dunn Street, Glasgow, G40 3EA Tel: 0141-554 3724 Fax: 0141-554 4741 E-mail: info@muirhead.co.uk
N C T Leather Ltd, Locher Works, Kilbarchan Road, Bridge of Weir, Renfrewshire, PA11 3RL Tel: (01505) 612182 Fax: (01505) 612123 E-mail: sales@nctleather.co.uk
Pittards P.L.C., Sherborne Road, Yeovil, Somerset, BA21 5BA Tel: (01935) 474321 Fax: (01935) 427145 E-mail: pittardsenquire@pittards.com
Tusting & Burnett (1938) Ltd, Pavenham, Bedford, MK43 7NX Tel: (01234) 826136 Fax: (01234) 824328
Village Leathers, 18 The Market, The Piazza, London, WC2E 8RB Tel: (020) 8965 2722 Fax: (020) 8965 2722 E-mail: sales@villageleathers.com
W J & W Lang Ltd, 1 Seedhill, Paisley, Renfrewshire, PA1 1JL Tel: 0141-889 3134 Fax: 0141-889 3182 E-mail: sales@langwetblue.co.uk
Thomas Ware & Sons Ltd, Coronation Road, Southville, Bristol, BS3 1RN Tel: 0117-966 4021 Fax: 0117-966 3885 E-mail: thomas.ware@btconnect.com
Wingrove & Edge Ltd, The Tannery, West Hill, Milborne Port, Sherborne, Dorset, DT9 5HL Tel: (01963) 250620 Fax: (01963) 250627 E-mail: email@whitmore-bacon.co.uk

LED DISPLAYS

Forge Europa, 35 Princes Street, Ulverston, Cumbria, LA12 7NQ Tel: (01229) 580000 Fax: (01229) 586890 E-mail: sales@forge-europa.co.uk

LED SEMICONDUCTOR DIODES

Marl International Ltd, Morcambe Road, Ulverston, Cumbria, LA12 7RY Tel: (01229) 582430 Fax: (01229) 585155 E-mail: sales@marl.co.uk

LEDS

▶ The Components Co. Ltd, Unit 30, Wem Business Park, New Street, Wem, Shrewsbury, SY4 5JX Tel: (01939) 235800 Fax: (01939) 233088 E-mail: dan@components-company.com

▶ Fiora Electronics, The Meridian, 4 Copthall House, Station Square, Coventry, CV1 2FL Tel: (0870) 7669425 Fax: (0870) 7669427 E-mail: enquiries@fioraelectronics.co.uk

LEGAL CONSULTANCY

First, Corporate Communications Macmillan House, Paddington, London, W2 1FG Tel: (020) 7291 0500 Fax: (020) 7636 1338

Secretarial Service, 43 Moselle Avenue, London, N22 6ES Tel: (020) 8889 6870 Fax: (020) 8889 6870 E-mail: emailforps@fsmail.net

LEGAL CONVEYANCING SERVICES

Baird & Co, 2 Park Place, Kirkcaldy, Fife, KY1 1XL Tel: (01592) 268608 Fax: (01592) 203369

▶ Sterling Ward, 18 Charlotte Road, London, EC2A 3PB Tel: (020) 7729 4513 Fax: (020) 7033 0589 E-mail: gary.ward@stirling-ward.com

LEGAL EXPENSE INSURANCE

▶ Randle Thomas, 2 Wendron St, Helston, Cornwall, TR13 8PP Tel: (01326) 572951 Fax: 01326 563122 E-mail: rt@randlethomas.co.uk

LEGAL INFORMATION SERVICES

A Solicitor Information Service, 4 Charles Lane, London, NW8 7SB Tel: (020) 7483 4833

Andersen, 4th Floor Forum Ho, Grenville St, St. Helier, Jersey, JE2 4UF Tel: (01534) 707100 Fax: (01534) 707101 E-mail: diane.l.porritt@uk.andersen.com

Disclaw Publishing Ltd, The Royal Hunting Lodge, York, YO30 1BD Tel: (01904) 471492 E-mail: info@emplaw.co.uk

Federation Of Crafts & Commerce, 4-5 The Briars, Waterberry Drive, Waterlooville, Hampshire, PO7 7YH Tel: (023) 9223 7010 Fax: (023) 9223 2120 E-mail: info@fcc.org.uk

▶ International Commerce Alliance, 155a Cove Road, Farnborough, Hampshire, GU14 0HQ Tel: (07766) 558748 E-mail: infouk@intnlcommerce.com

Ledingham Chalmers Solicitors Estate Agents, 1st, Rose Street, Aberdeen, AB10 1UB Tel: (01224) 408408 Fax: (01224) 408400 E-mail: mail@ledinghamchalmers.com

Lexisnexis UK, 2 Addiscombe Road, Croydon, CR9 5AF Tel: (020) 8662 2000 Fax: (020) 8662 2012 E-mail: sales@lexisnexis.co.uk

Optima Legal Services Ltd, Arndale House, Charles Street, Bradford, West Yorkshire, BD1 1UN Tel: (01274) 553150 Fax: (01274) 513718

S A S Lawyers, 30 Greek Street, Stockport, Cheshire, SK3 8AD Tel: 0161-475 7676 Fax: 0161-475 7677 E-mail: help@saslawyers.co.uk

LEGAL MATERIAL PUBLISHERS

Lexisnexis, Halsbury House, 35 Chancery Lane, London, WC2A 1EL Tel: (020) 7400 2500 Fax: (020) 7400 2611 E-mail: marketingdepartment@lexisnexis.co.uk

LEGAL SERVICES, CORPORATE

First, Corporate Communications Macmillan House, Paddington, London, W2 1FG Tel: (020) 7291 0500 Fax: (020) 7636 1338

LEGAL STAFF RECRUITMENT AGENCIES

A S A Law, Glade House, 52 Carter Lane, London, EC4V 5JL Tel: (020) 7236 2395 Fax: (020) 7246 4746

Angela Mortimer plc, 37-38 Golden Square, London, W1F 9LA Tel: (020) 7287 7788 Fax: (020) 7470 5578 E-mail: name.surname@angelamortimer.com

▶ Dilectus, Century Business Centre, Century Park, Manvers, Rotherham, South Yorkshire, S63 5DA Tel: (01709) 300216 Fax: (0870) 4602601 E-mail: kelly@dilectus.com

▶ Ortus Professional Search, 5a The Courtyard, 707 Warwick Road, Solihull, West Midlands, B91 3DA Tel: 0121 7127820

Personnel Selection, 46 West Street, Brighton, BN1 2RA Tel: (01273) 205281 Fax: (01273) 204091 E-mail: brit@persel.co.uk

Resource Group, 105 West George Street, Glasgow, G2 1PE Tel: 0141-226 1220 Fax: 0141-248 6782 E-mail: sales@trgrecruitment.net

T M P Worldwide Ltd, 53-64 Chancery Lane, Chancery House, London, WC2A 1QY Tel: (020) 7406 5000 Fax: (020) 7406 5001

LEGIONELLOSIS WATER TREATMENT CONSULTANCY

▶ Infrastructure Associates Ltd, Weir Bank, Monkey Island Lane, Bray, Maidenhead, Berkshire, SL6 2ED Tel: (01628) 762730 Fax: (01628) 762730 E-mail: scherry@infrastructureassociates.com

LEISURE MAGAZINES

▶ Ealing Life Magazine, P O Box 54909, London, W3 9WP Tel: (020) 8932 8302

▶ Your Next Magazine, Zachrome Works, Sheffield Road, Chesterfield, Derbyshire, S41 8NH Tel: (0845) 2571919 Fax: 01246 455875 E-mail: andrew@yournext.co.uk

LEISURE WEAR, *See headings for particular types, eg; Beachwear, Sports Clothing etc*

LEISURE WEAR TEXTILES

Bradley Textiles Ltd, 6 Huss Row, Belfast, BT13 1EE Tel: (028) 9032 5434 Fax: (028) 9031 5350 E-mail: bradleytextiles@btopenworld.com

Clarkewear Ltd, Marshall House, West Street, Glenfield, Leicester, LE3 8DT Tel: 0116-287 1661 Fax: 0116-232 0568 E-mail: nail@clarkewear.co.uk

Flint Casual Wear, Amundsen House, Hinckley, Leicestershire, LE10 0DP Tel: (01455) 633937 Fax: (01455) 890464

Football Kits Direct Ltd, Bridge Trading Estate, Bridge St North, Smethwick, West Midlands, B66 2BZ Tel: 0121-558 5846 Fax: 0121-555 7109 E-mail: salesunderscorefootballkitsdirect@nsn.com

Industrial Supplies Wrayson Ltd, 3-4 Brookfield Road, Cheadle, Cheshire, SK8 2PN Tel: 0161-428 0707 Fax: 0161-428 1304 E-mail: sales@wrayson.com

Josery Textiles Ltd, Unit 3 Benneworth Close, Hucknall, Nottingham, NG15 6EL Tel: 0115-963 2200 Fax: 0115-964 0223 E-mail: sales@josery.co.uk

Otterburn Mill Ltd, Otterburn, Newcastle Upon Tyne, NE19 1JT Tel: (01830) 520225 Fax: (01830) 520032 E-mail: enquiries@otterburnmill.co.uk

Price & Buckland Ltd, Benneworth Close, Hucknall, Nottingham, NG15 6EL Tel: 0115-964 0827 Fax: 0115-964 0769 E-mail: sales@price-buckland.co.uk

St. John Supplies, PO Box 707A, London, EC1V 7NE Tel: (020) 7278 7888 Fax: (020) 7278 0314 E-mail: customer-services@stjohnsupplies.co.uk

LENGTH BARS

▶ Select Gauges & Calibration Ltd, Select Works, Trevol Business Park, Torpoint, Cornwall, PL11 2PN Tel: (01752) 812147 Fax: (01752) 814892

LENS PRODUCTION EQUIPMENT, GENERATING/ POLISHING

Brain Power International Ltd, 3 Prospect Way, Butlers Leap, Rugby, Warwickshire, CV21 3UU Tel: (01788) 568686 Fax: (01788) 568686 E-mail: paul@callbpi.com

Essilor Ltd, Cooper Road, Thornbury, Bristol, BS35 3UW Tel: (01454) 417100 Fax: (01454) 281282

Gerber Coburn Optical UK Ltd, 1600 Aztec West, Almondsbury, Bristol, BS32 4UA Tel: (01454) 200780 Fax: (01454) 200787 E-mail: info@gerbercoburn.co.uk

LENSES, *See also headings for particular types*

Carclo Technical Plastics, 111 Buckingham Avenue, Slough, SL1 4PF Tel: (01753) 575011 Fax: (01753) 811359 E-mail: optics@carclo-optics.com

Crown Leisure Ltd, Gerrish Avenue, Whitehall, Bristol, BS5 9DG Tel: 0117-955 4044 Fax: 0117-955 4045 E-mail: sales@crownleisure.co.uk

▶ Stock Optics Ltd, Unit 430, Thorp Arch Estate, Wetherby, West Yorkshire, LS23 7BJ Tel: (01937) 849421 Fax: (01937) 849836 E-mail: optics1@btconnect.com

LENSES, CUSTOM MADE

Acuity Contact Lenses, Plumpton Road, Hoddesdon, Hertfordshire, EN11 0LB Tel: (01992) 445035 Fax: (01992) 451223 E-mail: enquiries@acuity-lenses.co.uk

LENSES, INFRARED/ ULTRAVIOLET (UV), OPTICAL

Comar Instruments, 70 Hartington Grove, Cambridge, CB1 7UH Tel: (01223) 245470 Fax: (01223) 410033 E-mail: mail@kyinstruments.com

Davin Optronics Ltd, Creycaine Road, Watford, WD24 7GW Tel: (01923) 206800 Fax: (01923) 234220 E-mail: sales@davinoptronics.com

LEOTARDS

▶ Baillando Dancewear, 12a Market Buildings, Maidstone, Kent, ME14 1HP Tel: (01622) 691190 E-mail: manager@baillando.co.uk

LETTER FILES

Acco Eastlight Ltd, Ashton Road, Denton, Manchester, M34 3LR Tel: 0161-336 9431 Fax: 0161-320 8012 E-mail: mark.winstanley@acco-eastlight.co.uk

G Ryder & Co. Ltd, Denbigh Road, Bletchley, Milton Keynes, MK1 1DG Tel: (01908) 375524 Fax: (01908) 373658 E-mail: john.discombe@ryderbox.co.uk

Setten & Durward Ltd, Ixl House, Waterloo Road, Llandrindod Wells, Powys, LD1 6BH Tel: (01597) 827800 Fax: (01597) 827847 E-mail: sales@ixl.uk.com

LETTER OPENING MACHINES

Pitney Bowes Office Direct, London Road, London, SE1 6LF Tel: (020) 7200 5408 Fax: (020) 7200 5432 E-mail: hassan.dayem@pb.com

LETTER SCALES

MK Scales Ltd, Cherrycourt Way, Leighton Buzzard, Bedfordshire, LU7 4UH Tel: (01525) 375519 Fax: (01525) 377290 E-mail: sales@mkscales.co.uk

LETTERING SYSTEMS

Dennis D. Evans & Co. Ltd, 391 Holywood Road, Belfast, BT4 2LS Tel: (028) 9065 2220 E-mail: materials@devans.co.uk

LETTERING, CUTOUT RELIEF

AST Signs, Unit 2, Gilwilly Road, East Lakes Business Park, Penrith, Cumbria, CA11 9BF Tel: (01768) 892292 Fax: (01768) 892294 E-mail: mark@astsigns.com

City & County Signs, 209 Pinhoe Road, Exeter, EX4 8AB Tel: (01392) 434366 Fax: (01392) 434366

Handsworth Crown Memorial Co., 283 Oxhill Road, Birmingham, B21 8EY Tel: 0121-554 3234 Fax: 0121-554 3234

LEVEL CONTROL EQUIPMENT MANUFRS, *See also headings for particular types*

E. Braude (London) Ltd, Liberta House, Scotland Hill, Sandhurst, Berkshire, GU47 8JR Tel: (01252) 876123 Fax: (01252) 875281 E-mail: sales@braude.co.uk

J S Engineering, 102 Commercial Road, Skelmanthorpe, Huddersfield, HD8 9DS Tel: (01484) 866254 Fax: (01484) 866255 E-mail: jsengineeringuk@aol.com

K S R Kuebler (UK) Level Measurement & Control Ltd, 43 Cherry Orchard Rd, West Molesey, Surrey, KT8 1QZ Tel: (020) 8941 3075 Fax: (020) 8979 4386 E-mail: ksruk@ksr-kuebler.com

Magnetrol International UK Ltd, 1 Regent Business Centre, Jubilee Road, Burgess Hill, West Sussex, RH15 9TL Tel: (01444) 871313 Fax: (01444) 871317 E-mail: sales@magnetrol.co.uk

Mercury Switch Manufacturing Co. Ltd, 26 Greenhill Cres, Watford Business Pk, Watford, WD18 8XG Tel: (01923) 240272 Fax: (01923) 228796

Pulsar Process Measurement Ltd, Oak House, Bromyard Road, Worcester, WR2 5HP Tel: (0870) 6039112 Fax: (0870) 6039114 E-mail: info@pulsar-pm.com

Sandhurst Instruments Ltd, 30 Sudley Road, Bognor Regis, West Sussex, PO21 1ER Tel: (01243) 820200 Fax: (01243) 860111 E-mail: sandhurst.instruments@freenet.co.uk

Synatel Instrumentation Ltd, Walsall Road, Norton Canes, Cannock, Staffordshire, WS11 9TB Tel: (01543) 277003 Fax: (01543) 271217 E-mail: sales@synatel.co.uk

Tav Engineering Ltd, Unit 13-14 Priory Industrial Park, Airspeed Road, Christchurch, Dorset, BH23 4HD Tel: (01425) 270444 Fax: (01425) 276766 E-mail: tavengineering@crydom.com

Wika Instruments Ltd, 4 Gatton Park Business Centre, Wells Place Merstham, Redhill, RH1 3LG Tel: (01737) 644008 Fax: 01737 644403 E-mail: info@wika.co.uk

LEVEL GAUGE MANUFRS

Calido Trading Ltd, Unit 4A, Market Hill, Maldon, Essex, CM9 4PZ Tel: (01621) 842828 Fax: (01621) 840064 E-mail: enquiries@calido.co.uk

Portway Tool & Gauge Ltd, 27 Dudley Road, Lye, Stourbridge, West Midlands, DY9 8EX Tel: (01384) 892458 Fax: (01384) 424371 E-mail: info@portwaytoolgauge.co.uk

LEVEL GAUGE SPARE PARTS

Calido Trading Ltd, Unit 4A, Market Hill, Maldon, Essex, CM9 4PZ Tel: (01621) 842828 Fax: (01621) 840064 E-mail: enquiries@calido.co.uk

Endress & Hauser, Unit 30 Northfield Way, Aycliffe Industrial Park, Newton Aycliffe, County Durham, DL5 6UF Tel: (01325) 329801 Fax: (01325) 300840 E-mail: sales@systems.endress.com

LEVEL INDICATORS OR RECORDERS

Krohne Ltd, Rutherford Drive, Park Farm Industrial Estate, Wellingborough, Northamptonshire, NN8 6AE Tel: (01933) 408500 Fax: (01933) 408501 E-mail: info@krohne.co.uk

Magnetrol International UK Ltd, 1 Regent Business Centre, Jubilee Road, Burgess Hill, West Sussex, RH15 9TL Tel: (01444) 871313 Fax: (01444) 871317 E-mail: sales@magnetrol.co.uk

Wylie Systems, Drury Lane, St. Leonards-on-Sea, East Sussex, TN38 9XS Tel: (01424) 421235 Fax: (01424) 433760 E-mail: wylie@raycowylie.com

LEVEL INDICATORS, LIQUID

Pulsar Process Measurement Ltd, Oak House, Bromyard Road, Worcester, WR2 5HP Tel: (0870) 6039112 Fax: (0870) 6039114 E-mail: info@pulsar-pm.com

▶ Solartron Mobrey Ltd, 158 Edinburgh Avenue, Slough, SL1 4UE Tel: (01753) 756600 Fax: (01753) 823589

LEVEL MEASURING EQUIPMENT

▶ P R Engineering Ltd, 6a Aizlewood Road, Sheffield, S8 0YX Tel: 0114-250 9077 E-mail: sales@laser-level.co.uk

LEVEL SENSORS

Fozmula Ltd, Berrington Road, Leamington Spa, Warwickshire, CV31 1NB Tel: (01926) 466700 Fax: (01926) 450473 E-mail: e.marketing@fozmula.com

Rechner UK Ltd, Unit 6, The Old Mill, Reading Road, Pangbourne, Reading, RG8 7HY Tel: 0118-976 6450 Fax: 0118-976 6451 E-mail: info@rechner-sensors.co.uk

LEVEL SWITCHES

P V L Ltd, 9 Lexden Lodge Industrial Estate, Crowborough Hill, Crowborough, East Sussex, TN6 2NQ Tel: (01892) 664499 Fax: (01892) 663690 E-mail: info@pd1.co.uk

Sor Europe Ltd, Farren Court, The Street, Cowfold, Horsham, West Sussex, RH13 8BP Tel: (01403) 864000 Fax: (01403) 710177 E-mail: sales@soreur.co.uk

LEVELLING MACHINES, PRECISION METAL PLATE/ SHEET

Bromley Car Audio, 50 Homesdale Road, Bromley, BR2 9LD Tel: (020) 8460 8704 Fax: (020) 8460 8704 E-mail: sales@caraudioonline.co.uk

Pearson Panke Equipment Ltd, 1 3 Halegrove Gardens, Mill Hill, London, NW7 3LR Tel: (020) 8959 3232 Fax: (020) 8959 5613 E-mail: sales@pearsonpanke.co.uk

LEVELLING MOUNTS

Nu Tech Engineering Services Ltd, Unit 7 & 14 Newtown Business Park, Albion Close, Poole, Dorset, BH12 3LL Tel: (01202) 724100 Fax: (01202) 724114 E-mail: sales@nutech-eng.com

LEVER BOX RAILWAY SIGNALLING SYSTEMS

A L A Rail Ltd, Byass Works, The Docks, Port Talbot, West Glamorgan, SA13 1RS Tel: (01639) 885435 Fax: (01639) 899842 E-mail: sales@ala-rail.com

LIBRARY EQUIPMENT SUPPLIERS

B G U Manufacturing Co., Meadow Lane, Nottingham, NG2 3JQ Tel: 0115-986 2460 Fax: 0115-986 2522 E-mail: info@bgu-man.co.uk

The British Library, The British Library STB, London, NW1 2DB Tel: (020) 7412 7000 Fax: (020) 7412 7609

Intellident, Southgate Centre Two, Wilmslow Road, Heald Green, Cheadle, Cheshire, SK8 3PW Tel: 0161-436 9950 Fax: 0161-436 8787 E-mail: sales@intellident.co.uk

Librex Educational Ltd, Colwick Road, Nottingham, NG2 4BG Tel: 0115-950 4664 Fax: 0115-958 6683 E-mail: sales@librex.co.uk

LIBRARY FURNISHING OR FITTING SERVICES

▶ A & D Joinery, Premier Partnership Estate, Leys Road, Brierley Hill, West Midlands, DY5 3UP Tel: (01384) 265165 Fax: (01384) 265464

LIBRARY FURNITURE

Crossbrook Furniture Ltd, 8 Marshgate Industrial Estate, 20 Marshgate Drive, Hertford, SG13 7AJ Tel: (01992) 557000 Fax: (01992) 501666 E-mail: sales@crossbrook.co.uk

Demco, Grange House, 2 Geddings Road, Hoddesdon, Hertfordshire, EN11 0NT Tel: (01992) 454500 Fax: (01992) 448989 E-mail: direct@gresswell.co.uk

E J Herok Ltd, Charlton Mead Lane, Hoddesdon, Hertfordshire, EN11 0DJ Tel: (01992) 462943 Fax: (01992) 464792 E-mail: info@herok.com

Librex Educational Ltd, Colwick Road, Nottingham, NG2 4BG Tel: 0115-950 4664 Fax: 0115-958 6683 E-mail: sales@librex.co.uk

Point Eight Ltd, Unit 14 Blackbrook Valley Industrial Estate, Narrowboat Way, Dudley, West Midlands, DY2 0EZ Tel: (01384) 238282 Fax: (01384) 455746 E-mail: sales@point8.co.uk

LICENSED ASBESTOS REMOVAL SCAFFOLDING

▶ C&D Industrial Services Ltd, Drovers Road, East Mains Industrial Estate, Broxburn, West Lothian, EH52 5ND Tel: (01506) 856000 Fax: (01506) 858000

▶ Cape Industrial Services Ltd, Q Fort Wallington Industrial Estate, Military Road, Fareham, Hampshire, PO16 8TT Tel: (01329) 828813 Fax: (01329) 822867

LICENSED BAR COOLER CABINETS

Weald Refrigeration, 5 Vestry Industrial Estate, Vestry Road, Sevenoaks, Kent, TN14 5EL Tel: (01732) 452050 Fax: (01732) 452122 E-mail: sales@wealdrefrigeration.com

LICENSED BAR FITTINGS

Arper Quality Products, 1 Ashwood Close, Branton, Doncaster, South Yorkshire, DN3 3UB Tel: (01302) 371133 Fax: (01302) 371777

Astore Harrison Ltd, PO Box 20, Peterborough, PE1 2DT Tel: (01733) 361361 Fax: (01733) 361360 E-mail: sales@astore-harrison.co.uk

Aubic Bar Supplies, Unit 7, Dominion Way, Rustington, Littlehampton, West Sussex, BN16 3HQ Tel: (01903) 775002 Fax: (01903) 775112 E-mail: info@aubic.co.uk

Beaumont TM Ltd, 1-4 Lyall Court, Commerce Way, Flitwick, Bedford, MK45 1UQ Tel: (01525) 722500 Fax: (01525) 718902 E-mail: info@beaumonttm.co.uk

Brassworld Bar Equipment, Unit 22 Royal Industrial Estate, Jarrow, Tyne & Wear, NE32 3HR Tel: 0191-428 2233 Fax: 0191-483 8893 E-mail: lisa@ahlpipework.co.uk

▶ Central Bar Supplies, Unit 4 1 Alice Street, Derby, DE1 2BY Tel: (01332) 296683 Fax: (01332) 296683

I M C Ltd, Unit 1, Abbey Road, Wrexham Industrial Estate, Wrexham, LL13 9RF Tel: (01978) 661155 Fax: (01978) 729990 E-mail: mail@imco.co.uk

Mitchell & Cooper Ltd, 140 Framfield Road, Uckfield, East Sussex, TN22 5AU Tel: (01825) 765511 Fax: (01825) 767173 E-mail: sales@mitchellcooper.co.uk

Swansea Bar & Catering Supplies, Unit 2 Celtic Form Business Park, Carlton Terrace, Swansea, SA1 6AE Tel: (01792) 477777 Fax: (01792) 464500

LICENSED BAR FURNISHING OR FITTING SERVICES

Abrahams & Carlisle Ltd, Carlham Works, Newman Street, Bradford, West Yorkshire, BD4 9NT Tel: (01274) 651555 Fax: (01274) 686135 E-mail: sales@abrahams-and-carlisle.co.uk

Beacon Woodcraft Ltd, Queen Street, Premier Business Park, Walsall, WS2 9NT Tel: (01922) 613255 Fax: (01922) 634720 E-mail: info@beaconwoodcraft.co.uk

Brian Matthews Licensed Trade Suppliers, 17 Malmesbury Road, Chippenham, Wiltshire, SN15 1PS Tel: (01249) 444803 Fax: (01249) 462650

Coach Trimming Coventry, Sutton Stop, Longford, Coventry, CV6 6DF Tel: (024) 7664 5488 Fax: (024) 7636 2545

Edmont Joinery Ltd, Hyde Road, Swindon, SN2 7RB Tel: (01793) 825765 Fax: (01793) 825725 E-mail: admin@edmont.co.uk

▶ Fletcher UK Ltd, PO Box 150, Houghton le Spring, Tyne & Wear, DH5 9DY Tel: 0191-526 9195 Fax: 0191-526 9195 E-mail: info@fletcheruklimited.com

Forbes West Ltd, 128 Tutbury Road, Burton-on-Trent, Staffordshire, DE13 0NU Tel: (01283) 564351 Fax: (01283) 535707

▶ Geometric Furniture Ltd, Geometric House Lark Hill, Townley Street Middleton, Middleton, Manchester, M24 1AT Tel: 0161-653 2233 Fax: 0161-653 2299 E-mail: sales@geometric-furniture.co.uk

H & J Forbes Middlesbrough Ltd, 147 Stockton Street, Middlesbrough, Cleveland, TS2 1BU Tel: (01642) 222611 Fax: (01642) 232419 E-mail: frances@forbes-group.demon.co.uk

Interbar Ltd, Unit 2 Kings Park, Primrose Hill, Kings Langley, Hertfordshire, WD4 8ST Tel: (0845) 2713216 Fax: (0845) 2713217 E-mail: sales@interbar.co.uk

John F White Cabinet Makers, Unit 6 Veasey Close, Attleborough Fields Industrial Estate, Nuneaton, Warwickshire, CV11 6RT Tel: (024) 7634 7347 Fax: (024) 7638 2077 E-mail: enquiries@jfw-cabinet.com

Keith Evans Contract Furnisher Ltd, Brackla Industrial Estate, Bridgend, Mid Glamorgan, CF31 2AE Tel: (01656) 655015 Fax: (01656) 658162 E-mail: sales@keithevans.com

Lans Fine Furnishings, 1717 London Road, Leigh-on-Sea, Essex, SS9 2SW Tel: (01702) 480591 Fax: (01702) 480591

Lynn & Jones Storefitters Ltd, Falcon House, Kenneth Street Off Ingram Road, Holbeck, Leeds, LS11 9RF Tel: 0113-234 0737 Fax: 0113-245 6130 E-mail: enquiries@lynnandjones.co.uk

Medlock Construction Ltd, Greengate Street, Oldham, OL4 1FN Tel: 0161-621 5200

Turners Bar Fitters & Joiners Ltd, Martins Mill, Pellon Lane, Halifax, West Yorkshire, HX1 5QJ Tel: (01422) 354984 Fax: (01422) 342770

Anthony Willis Shopfitters Ltd, 55 Grosvenor Street, Cardiff, CF5 1NJ Tel: (029) 2034 5582 Fax: (029) 2023 7260 E-mail: mail@anthonywillis-shopfitters.co.uk

LICENSED TRADE PUBLICATIONS

National Bartender Magazine, PO Box 9667, Nottingham, NG10 9BZ Tel: 0115-925 5227 E-mail: sb@freerbutler-gds.co.uk

LICENSED TRADE SUPPORT SERVICES

▶ GSR Services, 1 Gristmill Close, Cheltenham, Gloucestershire, GL51 0PZ Tel: (01242) 708407 Fax: 01242 708407 E-mail: sales@gsrservices.co.uk

LICENSED TRADE TRAINING

▶ GSR Services, 1 Gristmill Close, Cheltenham, Gloucestershire, GL51 0PZ Tel: (01242) 708407 Fax: 01242 708407 E-mail: sales@gsrservices.co.uk

LIDS, DIE CUT

▶ Gerhardt Ltd, Trent La Industrial Estate, Willow Road, Castle Donington, Derby, DE74 2NP Tel: (01332) 853434 Fax: (01332) 810274 E-mail: info@gerhardt.co.uk

LIFE ASSURANCE CONSULTANTS/BROKERS

▶ Birley Park Financial Advisers Ltd, 40 Chadderton Drive, Bury, Lancashire, BL9 8NL Tel: 0161 796 3383 E-mail: phillm36@aol.com

Caithness & Co. Ltd, 47 Old London Road, Kingston upon Thames, Surrey, KT2 6NG Tel: (020) 8549 8011 Fax: (020) 8547 2238 E-mail: mail@caithnessandco.com

Countrywide Principal Services, Sovereign House, Hockliffe Street, Leighton Buzzard, Bedfordshire, LU7 1GT Tel: (01525) 383084 Fax: (01525) 850285

Croucher, Reoch & Partners Ltd, 3rd Floor Babmaes Ho, 2 Babmaes St, London, SW1Y 6HD Tel: (020) 7839 5735 Fax: (020) 7930 4281 E-mail: fiztwilliamfinancial@compuserve.com

Ecclesiastical Insurance Group, Beaufort House, Brunswick Road, Gloucester, GL1 1JZ Tel: (01452) 528533 Fax: (01452) 423557 E-mail: marketing@eigmail.com

T H March & Co. Ltd, 10-12 Ely Place, London, EC1N 6RY Tel: (020) 7405 0009 Fax: (020) 7404 4629 E-mail: insurance@thmarch.co.uk

LIFE ASSURANCE SERVICES

▶ Birley Park Financial Advisers Ltd, 40 Chadderton Drive, Bury, Lancashire, BL9 8NL Tel: 0161 796 3383 E-mail: phillm36@aol.com

Britannic Assurance P.L.C., 1 Wythall Green Way, Wythall, Birmingham, B47 6WG Tel: (01564) 828888 Fax: (0870) 8870002 E-mail: info@britannic.co.uk

Clerical Medical Forestry Ltd, 33 Old Broad Street, London, EC2N 1HZ Tel: (020) 7321 1941 Fax: (020) 7321 1423

Direct Line Group Ltd, 3 Edridge Road, Croydon, CR9 1AG Tel: (020) 8686 3313 Fax: (020) 8681 0512

Friends' Provident P.L.C., Pixham End, Dorking, Surrey, RH4 1QA Tel: (0870) 6083678 Fax: (01306) 651802

Friends Provident, UK House, Castle Street, Salisbury, SP1 3SH Tel: (0870) 6071352 Fax: (0870) 5314151

▶ Lincoln, Barnett Way, Barnwood, Gloucester, GL4 3RZ Tel: (01452) 374500 Fax: (01452) 634300 E-mail: sales@lincoln-financialuk.com

London Life Ltd, Spectrum Building, Bond Street, Bristol, BS1 3AL Tel: 0117-984 7777 Fax: 0117-984 7700 E-mail: sales@amp-online.co.uk

Medical Sickness Pensions Administration Ltd, Colmore Circus Queensway, Birmingham, B4 6AR Tel: (08081) 001884 Fax: 0121-200 9140

Prudential, Laurence Pountney Hill, London, EC4R 0HH Tel: (020) 7220 7588 Fax: (020) 7548 3725

Royal National Pension Fund for Nurses, Frizzell House, County Gate, Bournemouth, BH1 2NF Tel: (01202) 292333

St. James Place, St. James Place House, Dollar Street, Cirencester, Gloucestershire, GL7 2AQ Tel: (01285) 640302 Fax: (01285) 640436

The Scottish Life Guarantee Company Ltd, 19 St. Andrew Square, Edinburgh, EH2 1AU Tel: 0131-456 7777 Fax: 0131-456 7880 E-mail: enquiries@scottishlife.co.uk

Scottish Widows Fund & Life Assurance Society, 69 Morrison Street, Edinburgh, EH3 8YF Tel: (0845) 7678910 Fax: 0131-655 6878 E-mail: info@mcuk.panasonic.co.uk

Sun Life Financial Of Canada, Head Office, Basing View, Basingstoke, Hampshire, RG21 4DZ Tel: (01256) 841414 Fax: (0870) 1611122

Windsor Life Assurance Co. Ltd, Windsor House, Telford Centre, Town Centre, Telford, Shropshire, TF3 4NB Tel: (0870) 8873333 Fax: (0870) 7091111 E-mail: sales@windsor-life.com

Winterthur Life UK Holdings Ltd, Winterthur Way, Basingstoke, Hampshire, RG21 6SZ Tel: (01256) 470707 Fax: (01256) 472682 E-mail: enquiries@winterthur-life.co.uk

LIFE COACHING CONSULTANCY

Andrew Sidebottom, 8 Overland Road, Cottingham, North Humberside, HU16 4PZ Tel: (01482) 847491 Fax: (01482) 847491 E-mail: info@psydebottom.co.uk

▶ The Butterfly Within - Life Coaching, 55 Sundridge Road, Addiscombe, Croydon, CR0 6RL Tel: (020) 8090 5007 E-mail: regine.grove@thebutterflywithin.co.uk

▶ Clairegodwincoaching.co.uk, 33 Yew Tree Gardens, Denmead, Waterlooville, Hampshire, PO7 6LH Tel: (023) 9225 5232

▶ Coaching Unlimited, Orchard Holding, The Croft, East Hagbourne, Didcot, Oxfordshire, OX11 9LS Tel: (01235) 813370 E-mail: ianclancy@coachingunlimited.co.uk

▶ Creative Mind Skills Therapeutic Training, Holden House, Holden Road, Leigh, Lancashire, WN7 1EX Tel: 08704 323423 E-mail: info@cmst.co.uk

▶ Crown Coaching, 11 Rookery Court, Marlow, Buckinghamshire, SL7 3HR Tel: (01628) 488042 E-mail: helen@crowncoaching.com

▶ Future You, Lingfield, Walnut Close, Heathfield, East Sussex, TN21 8YL Tel: 0333 4444001 E-mail: coaching@future-you.co.uk

▶ Goldeneye Executive Resourcing Ltd, Flat 6 Kings Court, 40 Hersham Road, Walton-on-Thames, Surrey, KT12 1JE Tel: (07779) 134007

▶ Jigsaw Executive Ltd, Regus House, Herald Way, Pegasus Business Park, Castle Donington, DE74 2TZ Tel: 01332 638046 Fax: 01332 638001 E-mail: info@JigsawExecutive.com

▶ Wendy Knee Life Coach, Yew Tree Cottage, Foghamshire Lane, Trudoxhill, Frome, Somerset, BA11 5DG Tel: (01373) 837247

▶ Manjit Morjaria - Life Coaching, 14 Millennium Way, Wolston, Coventry, CV8 3PE Tel: (07968) 130980 Fax: (0870) 0671850 E-mail: m_morjaria@yahoo.co.uk

▶ NOV8 Ltd, Hartham Park, Corsham, Wiltshire, SN13 0RP Tel: (01249) 700009 E-mail: kellysearch@nov8.biz

▶ Tree Of Life Coaching, 15 Hillier Close, New Barnet, Barnet, Hertfordshire, EN5 1BD Tel: (020) 8440 4925 E-mail: david@treeoflifecoaching.co.uk

▶ W L M Consulting Ltd, 21 Swan Way, Church Crookham, Fleet, Hampshire, GU51 5TU Tel: (01252) 621255 E-mail: enquiry@wlmconsulting.com

LIFE RAFTS

Jackson Yacht Services Ltd, Le Boulevard, St. Aubin, Jersey, JE3 8AB Tel: (01534) 743819 Fax: (01534) 745952 E-mail: sales@jacksonyatch.com

Tamar Inflatables, Unit 4b, Restormel Industrial Estate, Lostwithiel, Cornwall, PL22 0HG Tel: (01208) 873777 Fax: (01208) 873774 E-mail: mail@liferafts-inflatables.com

LIFE SAVING EQUIPMENT INSPECTION/MAINTENANCE SERVICES

Ropesafe, P.O. Box 115, West Wickham, Kent, BR4 9YZ Tel: 07730 677936 E-mail: ropesafe@totalise.co.uk

LIFE SAVING EQUIPMENT MANUFRS

Balcan Engineering, Banovallum Court, Boston Road Industrial Estate, Horncastle, Lincolnshire, LN9 6JR Tel: (01507) 528500 Fax: (01507) 528528 E-mail: info@balcan.co.uk

Berwyn Engineering Ltd, Euridge Works, Thickwood, Colerne, Chippenham, Wiltshire, SN14 8BG Tel: (01225) 742301 Fax: (01225) 743457 E-mail: info@jetway.co.uk

Cosalt Young, 1 Liddell Street, North Shields, Tyne & Wear, NE30 1HE Tel: 0191-257 6121 Fax: 0191-296 1431 E-mail: northshields@cosalt.co.uk

Ferguson Polycom Ltd, Windsor Mill, Hollinwood, Oldham, OL8 3RA Tel: 0161-681 2206 Fax: 0161-947 1326 E-mail: info@fergusonpolycom.co.uk

International Safety Products Ltd, 159 Hawthorne Road, Bootle, Merseyside, L20 6JU Tel: 0151-922 2202 Fax: 0151-922 5874 E-mail: sales@ispl.co.uk

Land & Marine Products Ltd, 32 Woolmer Way, Bordon, Hampshire, GU35 9QF Tel: (01420) 474484 Fax: (01420) 489002 E-mail: sales@landandmarine.co.uk

Mashford Bros Ltd, Shipbuilding Yard, Cremyll, Torpoint, Cornwall, PL10 1HY Tel: (01752) 822232 Fax: (01752) 823059 E-mail: mashfords@btconnect.com

R D F Beaufort Ltd, Kingsway, Dunmurry, Belfast, BT17 9AF Tel: (028) 9030 1531 Fax: (028) 9062 1765 E-mail: sales@rfdbeaufort.com

Umoe Schat Harding Ltd, Mumby Road, Gosport, Hampshire, PO12 1AE Tel: (023) 9258 1331 Fax: (023) 9258 2565 E-mail: sales@schat-harding.co.uk

LIFEBOAT LAUNCHING EQUIPMENT

Welin Lambie Ltd, Brittania House, Old Bush Street, Brierley Hill, West Midlands, DY5 1UB Tel: (01384) 78294 Fax: (01384) 265100 E-mail: admin@welin-lambie.co.uk

LIFEBOAT MAINTENANCE/ REPAIR SERVICES

▶ Pedro's Yacht Refinishing, Quarry House, Galmpton, Brixham, Devon, TQ5 0EH Tel: (01803) 845475 Fax: (01803) 845475 E-mail: enquiries@pedrosyachtrefinishing.co.uk

Tamar Inflatables, Unit 4b, Restormel Industrial Estate, Lostwithiel, Cornwall, PL22 0HG Tel: (01208) 873777 Fax: (01208) 873774 E-mail: mail@liferafts-inflatables.com

Tedford Rigging & Rafts, Unit 24 Ormeau Business Park, 8 Gromac Avenue, Belfast, BT7 2JA Tel: (028) 9032 6763 Fax: (028) 9023 4566 E-mail: info@tedfords.co.uk

LIFEBUOYS

Crewsaver Ltd, Clarence Square, Mumby Road, Gosport, Hampshire, PO12 1AQ Tel: (023) 9252 8621 Fax: (023) 9251 0905 E-mail: sales@crewsaver.co.uk

LIFEJACKETS

Beaufort Air Sea Equipment Ltd, Beaufort Road, Birkenhead, Merseyside, CH41 1HQ Tel: 0151-652 9151 Fax: 0151-653 6639 E-mail: cgreen@rfdbeaufort.com

Cosalt Young, 1 Liddell Street, North Shields, Tyne & Wear, NE30 1HE Tel: 0191-257 6121 Fax: 0191-296 1431 E-mail: northshields@cosalt.co.uk

Crewsaver Ltd, Clarence Square, Mumby Road, Gosport, Hampshire, PO12 1AQ Tel: (023) 9252 8621 Fax: (023) 9251 0905 E-mail: sales@crewsaver.co.uk

International Safety Products Ltd, 159 Hawthorne Road, Bootle, Merseyside, L20 6JU Tel: 0151-922 2202 Fax: 0151-922 5874 E-mail: sales@ispl.co.uk

R D F Beaufort Ltd, Kingsway, Dunmurry, Belfast, BT17 9AF Tel: (028) 9030 1531 Fax: (028) 9062 1765 E-mail: sales@rfdbeaufort.com

Remploy Ltd, 14 Alder Hills, Poole, Dorset, BH12 4AS Tel: (01202) 743445 Fax: (01202) 715337 E-mail: marine@remploy.co.uk

Seasafe Systems Ltd, Mar, Cowes, Isle of Wight, PO31 8PB Tel: (01983) 282388 Fax: (01983) 282399 E-mail: admin@seasafe.co.uk

LIFETIME STORAGE LEGAL SERVICES

Classic Legal Services Ltd, Suite 3a & 3b, Britannia House, Cowbridge, South Glamorgan, CF71 7EG Tel: (0800) 389 4137 Fax: (01446) 774000 E-mail: alun@weeks4444.fslife.co.uk

▶ Red Devil Storage Ltd, 14 - 16 Kempson Close, Gatehouse Industrial Estate, Aylesbury, Buckinghamshire, HP19 8UQ Tel: (01296) 381818 Fax: (01296) 381919 E-mail: kempsonclose@reddevilstorage.co.uk

LIFT AND SHIFT TRUCKS OR TROLLEYS

Novela Portable Trolleys, 4 Mayfield Gardens, London, NW4 2QA Tel: (020) 8202 8747 Fax: (020) 8203 3243 E-mail: novelatrolleys@aol.com

LIFT CLADDING

F S C Stainless & Alloys, Ledra Works, Reservoir Place, Walsall, WS2 9SN Tel: (01922) 612545 Fax: (01922) 637755 E-mail: sales@fscstainless.co.uk

Rimex Metals, Aden Road, Ponders End, Enfield, Middlesex, EN3 7SU Tel: (020) 8804 0633 Fax: (020) 8804 7275 E-mail: sales@rimexmetals.com

LIFT COMPONENTS

Lift Components Ltd, Units B13-14, Poplar Business Park, London, E14 9RL Tel: (020) 7515 5504 Fax: (020) 7538 2815 E-mail: sales@liftcomponents.co.uk

Liftequip Ltd, 64 Falcon Road, Battersea, London, SW11 2LR Tel: (020) 7223 9394 Fax: (020) 7228 2270 E-mail: liftequip@tiscali.co.uk

Propbrook Ltd, 389 Lichfield Road, Birmingham, B6 7SS Tel: 0121-327 7909 Fax: 0121-327 7423

Sassi Lift Systems Ltd, 5 Blackwell Drive, Braintree, Essex, CM7 2QJ Tel: (01376) 550666 Fax: (01376) 341219

Telco Sensors Ltd, The Stables, Waen Farm, Nercwys, Mold, Flintshire, CH7 4EW Tel: (0870) 9917058 Fax: (0870) 9917059 E-mail: sales@telco-sensors.co.uk

Traditional Lift Products Ltd, Unit 2 The Brambles, Lees Road, Knowsley Industrial Park, Liverpool, L33 7RW Tel: 0151-548 2121 Fax: 0151-548 2269

Windcrest (HSP Electronics) Ltd, Unit 8 Abbey Manufacturing Estate, Mount Pleasant, Wembley, Middlesex, HA0 1NR Tel: (020) 8795 0333 Fax: (020) 8795 0444 E-mail: windcrest@aol.com

LIFT CONSULTANCY OR DESIGN

Dunbar & Boardman, 91-93 Great Eastern Street, London, EC2A 3HZ Tel: (020) 7739 5093 Fax: (020) 7739 5403 E-mail: mail@dunbarboardman.com

Harding McDermott & Partners, 12 Exmouth Market, London, EC1R 4QE Tel: (020) 7833 9533 Fax: (020) 7833 3633

Steven Morrison Associates (Bromley) Ltd, 51 Tweedy Road, Bromley, BR1 3NH Tel: (020) 8466 0880 Fax: (020) 8466 7100 E-mail: steven.morrison@virgin.net

Traditional Structures Contracts Ltd, Landywood Lane, Cheslyn Hay, Walsall, WS6 7AJ Tel: (01922) 414145 Fax: (01922) 416958

LIFT CONTROL SYSTEMS

▶ Genesis Lifts Ltd, Drayton Old Lodge Business Centre, 146 Drayton High Road, Norwich, NR8 6AN Tel: 01603 861631 Fax: 0700 5850036 E-mail: trevorsherwood@dsl.pipex.com

Kone plc, 137-145 South Liberty Lane, Bristol, BS3 2TL Tel: 0117-966 2741 Fax: 0117-963 6310

Lester Control Systems Ltd, Unit D, 18 Imperial Way, Croydon, CR9 4QP Tel: (020) 8288 0668 Fax: (020) 8288 0667 E-mail: info@lestercontrols.co.uk

Lion Lift Controls Ltd, Littleton Mill, Chew Road, Winford, Bristol, BS40 8HJ Tel: (01275) 332515 Fax: (01275) 333085 E-mail: sales@lionliftcontrols.co.uk

LIFT DOORS OR GATES

Sematic UK Ltd, Meadow Gate, Valley Park Industrial Estate, Wombwell, Barnsley, South Yorkshire, S73 0UN Tel: (01226) 344800 Fax: (01226) 344811

LIFT ENGINEERS' SUPPLY SERVICES

Capstan Lift Services, 3 Marlowe Business Centre, Batavia Road, London, SE14 6BQ Tel: (020) 8694 7557 Fax: (020) 8694 6088 E-mail: capstanlifts@aol.com

FSC (Halifax) Ltd, Grantham House, Grantham Road, Halifax, West Yorkshire, HX3 6PL Tel: (01422) 347872 Fax: (01422) 321758 E-mail: kw@fscooper.com

Langham Lifts Ltd, 28 Sidney Road, London, N22 8LS Tel: (020) 8881 3337 Fax: (020) 8889 3381 E-mail: enquiries@langham-lifts.co.uk

Lift Components Ltd, Units B13-14, Poplar Business Park, London, E14 9RL Tel: (020) 7515 5504 Fax: (020) 7538 2815 E-mail: sales@liftcomponents.co.uk

▶ Murray Lift Services Ltd, 130 Station Road, Sidcup, Kent, DA15 7AB Tel: (020) 8300 0614 Fax: (020) 181 7 181 E-mail: sales@murrayliftservices.com

▶ R J Lift & Testing Services Ltd, Suite 210, Astra House, Arklow Road, London, SE14 6EB Tel: (020) 8691 5920 Fax: (020) 8691 5921 E-mail: mail@rjliftandtestingservices.co.uk

Total Lift Care Ltd, Suite 6 The Shakespeare Centre, 45-51 Shakespeare Street, Southport, Merseyside, PR8 5AB Tel: (01704) 549600 Fax: (01704) 545090 E-mail: info@totalliftcare.com

LIFT FABRICATION SERVICES

▶ Murray Lift Services Ltd, 130 Station Road, Sidcup, Kent, DA15 7AB Tel: (020) 8300 0614 Fax: (020) 181 7 181 E-mail: sales@murrayliftservices.com

LIFT INSTALLATION OR INSPECTION OR MAINTENANCE OR REPAIR OR TESTING

▶ Abbey Wedding Services, Lye Head, Bewdley, Worcestershire, DY12 2UZ Tel: (01299) 269055 Fax: (01299) 269055 E-mail: loml@lakes.wanadoo.co.uk

Accord Lift Services Ltd, Unit 5A Beechcroft Farm Industries, Chapel Wood Road, Ash, Sevenoaks, Kent, TN15 7HX Tel: (01474) 879858 Fax: (01474) 874143 E-mail: info@accordlifts.co.uk

Ace Elevators Southern Ltd, Millennium House, 74 South Street, Keighley, West Yorkshire, BD21 1DQ Tel: (01535) 602239 Fax: (01535) 661268 E-mail: sales@ace-elevators.co.uk

Allards Lifts, 3a Vectis Business Centre, Coombe Road, Paignton, Devon, TQ3 2QT Tel: (01803) 855136 Fax: (01803) 851082 E-mail: allardlifts@btconnect.com

Allott Bros & Leigh Ltd, Fullerton Road, The Ickles, Rotherham, South Yorkshire, S60 1DJ Tel: (01709) 364115 Fax: (01709) 364696 E-mail: reception@uwilperengineering.com

Blickglen Lifts Ltd, 27 Wentworth Avenue, Southbourne, Bournemouth, BH5 2EQ Tel: (01202) 429155 Fax: (01202) 429550 E-mail: info@blickglenlifts.co.uk

Caltech Lifts Servicing, Stannergate Road, Dundee, DD1 3NA Tel: (01382) 462810 Fax: (01382) 454134 E-mail: caltechlifts@btinternet.com

Capstan Lift Services, 3 Marlowe Business Centre, Batavia Road, London, SE14 6BQ Tel: (020) 8694 7557 Fax: (020) 8694 6088 E-mail: capstanlifts@aol.com

▶ Classic Lifts Ltd, Jubilee House, Altcar Road, Formby, Liverpool, L37 8DL Tel: (01704) 833255 Fax: (01704) 833880 E-mail: dave.markman@lift-engineers.co.uk

Crown Lifts Ltd, Regancy House, 33-49 Farwig Lane, Bromley, BR1 3RE Tel: (020) 8464 5000 Fax: (020) 8290 7646

E A Foulds Ltd, Clifton Street, Colne, Lancashire, BB8 9AE Tel: (01282) 861500 Fax: (01282) 869655 E-mail: info@fouldslifts.co.uk

H. Breakell & Co. (Blackburn) Ltd, P1/15 Parklands, Heywood Distribution Park, Heywood, Lancashire, OL10 2TT Tel: (01706) 369272 Fax: (01706) 629448 E-mail: enquirires@breakell-lifts.co.uk

Independent Lifts Ltd, Devonshire House, 10 Devonshire Terrace, Holmewood, Chesterfield, Derbyshire, S42 5RF Tel: (01246) 850785 Fax: (01246) 854171

Jackson Lifts Ltd, Unit 4-19, Ropery Business Park, London, SE7 7RX Tel: (020) 8293 4176 Fax: (020) 8305 0274 E-mail: sales@jacksonlifts.com

▶ Knowsley Lift Services Ltd, Cotton Exchange Building, Old Hall Street, Liverpool, L3 9LQ Tel: 0151-286 1322 Fax: 0151-286 2400 E-mail: info@knowsleylifts.com

Kone plc, 86 Broad Street, Glasgow, G40 2PX Tel: 0141-554 7604 Fax: 0141-554 6762

Langham Lifts Ltd, 28 Sidney Road, London, N22 8LS Tel: (020) 8881 3337 Fax: (020) 8889 3381 E-mail: enquiries@langham-lifts.co.uk

Lester Lift Services Ltd, 2 Torridge View, Meddon St, Bideford, Devon, EX39 2EG Tel: (01237) 478055

Lester Lift Services Ltd, 53b Winterbourne Road, Thornton Heath, Surrey, CR7 7QX Tel: (020) 8240 0059 Fax: (020) 8684 5381

Lift & Engineering Services Ltd, 16 Portersfield Road, Cradley Heath, West Midlands, B64 7BN Tel: (01384) 633115 Fax: (01384) 633119 E-mail: mailbox@lift-engineering.co.uk

LTR Lifts & Escalator Ltd, Graphic House, Druid Street, Hinckley, Leicestershire, LE10 1QH Tel: (01455) 633760 Fax: (01455) 636005 E-mail: sales@ltr-lifts.co.uk

Monarch Lifts Ltd, 5 14-16 Shore Road, London, Greater London, E9 7TA Tel: 020 89866116

Omega City Lifts Ltd, 8 Bridge Gate Centre, Martinfield, Welwyn Garden City, Hertfordshire, AL7 1JG Tel: (01707) 334962 Fax: (01707) 376594 E-mail: sanjay@omegacitylifts.co.uk

Premier Lifts, Arundel Business Centre, 49 Station Road, Harold Wood, Romford, RM3 0BS Tel: (01708) 373332 Fax: (01708) 373766

Pye London Ltd, Units 6-7, Hookers Road, London, E17 6DP Tel: (020) 8531 3334 Fax: (020) 8531 3336 E-mail: pye-london@btconnect.com

▶ R & R Lift Co. Ltd, 71a High Road, London, E18 2QP Tel: (020) 8518 8937 Fax: (020) 8518 8938

Ritchie Hart, 18 Cyprus Avenue, Belfast, BT5 5NT Tel: (028) 9065 4594 Fax: (028) 9065 6196 E-mail: ritchie.hart@charity.vfree.com

Schindler, Benwell House, Green Street, Sunbury-on-Thames, Middlesex, TW16 6QT Tel: (01932) 785281 Fax: (020) 8818 7999 E-mail: marketing@schindler.com

Stannah Stairlifts LTS, Watt Close, Andover, Hampshire, SP10 3SD Tel: (0800) 715492 E-mail: nigel_dickinson@stannah.co.uk

Telco Lifts, 5 Culmore Business Centre, Culmore Road, London, SE15 2RQ Tel: (020) 7635 5851 Fax: (020) 7639 1065

Thyssenkrupp Elevator UK Ltd, 183-185 Lower Richmond Road, Richmond, Surrey, TW9 4LN Tel: (020) 8487 1445 Fax: (020) 8487 9494 E-mail: twickenham.office@tke-uk-thyssenkrupp.com

LIFT MAINTENANCE INTERIOR PROTECTION COVERS

Kapok 1988 Ltd, Unit 13 Normanton Air Field, Long Bennington, Newark, Nottinghamshire, NG23 5FF Tel: (01949) 843020 Fax: (01949) 843719 E-mail: annable.kapok88@btclick.com

LIFT MOTOR MAINTENANCE OR REPAIR

E A Foulds Ltd, Clifton Street, Colne, Lancashire, BB8 9AE Tel: (01282) 861500 Fax: (01282) 869655 E-mail: info@fouldslifts.co.uk

LIFT SAFETY GUARDS OR SCREENS

B & M Wireworks, Prescot Trade Centre, Oliver Lyme Road, Prescot, Merseyside, L34 2SH Tel: 0151-431 0101 Fax: 0151-431 0101 E-mail: rickymartin@supanet.co.uk

LIFT SERVICING

Husbands Lift Solutions, Shelah Road, Halesowen, West Midlands, B63 3PP Tel: 0121-550 1560 Fax: 0121-585 5285 E-mail: enquiries@husbands.co.uk

▶ Murray Lift Services Ltd, 130 Station Road, Sidcup, Kent, DA15 7AB Tel: (020) 8300 0614 Fax: (020) 181 7 181 E-mail: sales@murrayliftservices.com

LIFT TABLES

Saxon Lifts Ltd, Grand Union Works, Whilton Locks, Whilton, Daventry, Northamptonshire, NN11 2NH Tel: (01327) 843355 Fax: (01327) 843887 E-mail: sales@saxonlifts.com

LIFT TABLES, SCISSOR

Manual Handling Solutions, 58, Paige Close, The Meadows, Watlington, King's Lynn, Norfolk, PE33 0TQ Tel: (01553) 811977 Fax: (01553) 811004 E-mail: sales@manualhandlingsolutions.co.uk

LIFTING CONTRACTORS OR SPECIALIST SERVICES

Alm Chesterfield, 3 North Wingfield Road, Grassmoor, Chesterfield, Derbyshire, S42 5EB Tel: (01246) 855338 Fax: (01246) 855667

Barricade Roller Shutters, 7 St. Thomas's Place, Manchester, M8 8TP Tel: 0161-833 0007 Fax: 0161-835 1546 E-mail: shutters@barricade.fsnet.co.uk

H S S Lift & Shift, Unit 12 Industrial Estate, Thomas Road, London, E14 7BN Tel: (020) 7987 4787 Fax: (020) 7987 4887

Husbands Group Ltd, Shelah Road, Halesowen, West Midlands, B63 3PP Tel: 0121-550 1560 Fax: 0121-585 5285 E-mail: sales@servicelifts.co.uk

S S C S Lifting, Harfreys Road, Harfreys Industrial Estate, Great Yarmouth, Norfolk, NR31 0LS Tel: 0845 4940724 Fax: (01493) 443390 E-mail: sales@sscsystems.com

Seward Wyon Ltd, The Old Tannery, Kelston, Bath, BA1 9AN Tel: 0117-932 7565 Fax: 0117-932 7763 E-mail: sales@sewardwyon.co.uk

Smit Salvage BV, 65 Fenchurch Street, London, EC3M 4BE Tel: (020) 7480 7648 Fax: (020) 7702 1842 E-mail: sales@smit.com

▶ Sparrows Offshore Services Ltd, Denmore Road, Bridge of Don, Aberdeen, AB23 8JW Tel: (01224) 704868 Fax: (01224) 825191 E-mail: sales@sparrows.co.uk

▶ Universal Lifting Services, Green End, Gamlingay, Sandy, Bedfordshire, SG19 3LB Tel: (01767) 651800 Fax: (01767) 650066 E-mail: info@universallifting.com

▶ Winterlift Ltd, Fairhills Industrial Estate, Woodrow Way, Irlam, Manchester, M44 6ZQ Tel: 0161-775 4400 Fax: (0845) 1309003 E-mail: andrew.winter@btinternet.co.uk

LIFTING EQUIPMENT

Brandon Hire plc, 1 Stadium Way, Leeds, LS11 0EW Tel: 0113-270 7373 Fax: 0113-270 7322

▶ Eurolifting Lifting Equipment, 15 Mountfield Road, New Romney, Kent, TN28 8LH Tel: (01797) 369494 Fax: (01797) 369151

G Taylor Midlands Ltd, 9 Haddow Street, Hamilton, Lanarkshire, ML3 7HX Tel: (01698) 283561 Fax: (01698) 457914 E-mail: enquiries@gtlifting.co.uk

H S S Lift & Shift P.L.C., Unit 4, Aquarius Business Park, Priestley Way, London, NW2 7AN Tel: (020) 8830 8080 Fax: (020) 8452 1050

▶ HSS Hire, 238 London Road, Romford, RM7 9EL Tel: (01708) 725029 Fax: (01708) 754242

▶ I M E S, Unit 4 Castle Building, Gilston Road, Saltash, Cornwall, PL12 6TW Tel: (01752) 841433 Fax: (01752) 841433

▶ Ian W Harrison, 16 Wainman Road, Peterborough, PE2 7BU Tel: (01733) 390815 Fax: (01733) 390817

LIFTING EQUIPMENT – *continued*

▶ Insight Access & Handling Ltd, Unit 6 Thornleigh Trading Estate, Dudley, West Midlands, DY2 8UB Tel: (01384) 252524 Fax: (01384) 255444 E-mail: info@insightahl.com

▶ Liko Ltd, Units 2A-2B, Brunel Centre, Brunel Way, Stonehouse, Gloucestershire, GL10 3RU Tel: (01453) 827272 Fax: (01453) 828844

▶ Linian North West Ltd, Unit 9 Shaw Street, St. Helens, Merseyside, WA10 1DQ Tel: (01744) 736330 Fax: (01744) 22013 E-mail: sales@linian.co.uk

Lloyds British Testing Co. Ltd, Sneckyeat Road Industrial Estate, Whitehaven, Cumbria, CA28 8PF Tel: (01946) 64146 Fax: (01946) 695757 E-mail: sales.whitehaven@lloydsgroup.co.uk

▶ P G Winch Repairs, Unit 14d Miller Business Park, Station Road, Liskeard, Cornwall, PL14 4DA Tel: (01579) 348146 Fax: (01579) 340613 E-mail: sales@winchrepairs.co.uk

▶ Surelift Lifting Equipment, Peterhead Offshore Supply Base, Peterhead, Aberdeenshire, AB42 2PF Tel: (01779) 477775 Fax: (01779) 477771

▶ SWL Lifting Services, 2 Nations Farm, Curdridge Lane, Curdridge, Southampton, SO32 2BH Tel: (01489) 891333 Fax: (01489) 891444

Tacklestore Ltd, Unit S3 Chittening Industrial Estate, Chittening, Bristol, BS11 0YB Tel: 0117-938 1600 E-mail: sales@tacklestore.net

▶ Tapsell Lifting Equipment, Sandy La Industrial Estate, Stourport-on-Severn, Worcestershire, DY13 9QB Tel: (01299) 827262 Fax: (01299) 828272 E-mail: sales@tapsell.com

▶ Royale Motor Factors, Tel: (07885) 768133 E-mail: mail@motor-factors.com

LIFTING EQUIPMENT, JIB

Reid Lifting Ltd, 3 Bulwark Business Park, Bulwark Road, Bulwark, Chepstow, Gwent, NP16 5JG Tel: (01291) 620796 Fax: (01291) 626490 E-mail: enquiries@reidlifting.com

LIFTING EYE BOLTS

Brooks Forgings Ltd, Doulton Road, Cradley Heath, West Midlands, B64 5QJ Tel: (01384) 566772 Fax: (01384) 637380 E-mail: sales@brooksforgings.co.uk

Harris Walton Lifting Gear Ltd, Two Woods Lane, Brierley Hill, West Midlands, DY5 1TR Tel: (01384) 74071 Fax: (01384) 74070 E-mail: sales@harriswaltonliftinggear.co.uk

John Howard & Sons Ltd, Mullineux Street, Worsley, Manchester, M28 3DZ Tel: 0161-790 2149 Fax: 0161-703 8253

Tensile Forgings, Portersfield Road, Cradley Heath, West Midlands, B64 7BN Tel: (01384) 566758

LIFTING GEAR

A D C Systems, 110 Station Road, Llandaff North, Cardiff, CF14 2FH Tel: (029) 2057 8476 Fax: (029) 2057 8477 E-mail: adcsystems@hotmail.co.uk

A P Lifting Gear, Northfield Road, Dudley, West Midlands, DY2 9JQ Tel: (01384) 250552 Fax: (01384) 250282 E-mail: apliftingsales@btconnect.com

A P Lifting Gear Co., Unit 7 Yarra Industrial Park, Ecclesfield, Sheffield, S35 9YA Tel: 0114-246 2422 Fax: 0114-246 2522 E-mail: peter.vernon@aplifting.com

A P P Lifting Services Ltd, Wrights Business Park, Stevens Road, Doncaster, South Yorkshire, DN4 0LT Tel: (01302) 367755 Fax: (01302) 855222 E-mail: sales@applifting.co.uk

A1 Ropes & Rigging Ltd, Rope House, 39a Wheatash Road, Addlestone, Surrey, KT15 2ES Tel: (01932) 561355 Fax: (01932) 561433 E-mail: info@a1ropesandrigging.ltd.uk

Abas Rope Co., Eldorado Works, Drake Avenue, Gresham Road, Staines, Middlesex, TW18 2AP Tel: (01784) 464447 Fax: (01784) 454788 E-mail: sales@splicingallied.com

Advanced Lifting Equipment, Goosens Workshop, Broadclyst, Exeter, EX5 3JQ Tel: (01392) 461393 Fax: (01392) 462393

Alm Chesterfield, 3 North Wingfield Road, Grassmoor, Chesterfield, Derbyshire, S42 5EB Tel: (01246) 855338 Fax: (01246) 855667

Ansell Jones Ltd, Satellite Industrial Park, Neachells Lane, Wolverhampton, WV11 3PQ Tel: (01902) 722117 Fax: (01902) 725533 E-mail: sales@anselljones.com

Apex Load Controls Co. Ltd, 8 Galloway Drive, Teignmouth, Devon, TQ14 9UX Tel: (01626) 776490 Fax: (01626) 770877

Applied Hoist Services, Meadows Abbey Meadows, Back Lane, Cotes, Loughborough, Leicestershire, LE12 5TA Tel: (01509) 212711 Fax: (01509) 212722 E-mail: enquire@menz.fsnet.co.uk

Barzillai Hingley & Sons Ltd, Lion Chain Works, Providence Street, Cradley Heath, West Midlands, B64 5DT Tel: (01384) 569141 Fax: (01384) 639177 E-mail: sales@barzillai.com

Bond Engineering Maintenance Ltd, Unit P-Q Little Moor Lane, North Road, Loughborough, Leicestershire, LE11 1RL Tel: (01509) 266662 Fax: (01509) 231638 E-mail: sales@cranesandhoist.co.uk

Brierley Lifting Tackle Co. Ltd, Timmis Road, Lye, Stourbridge, West Midlands, DY9 7BQ Tel: (01384) 893000 Fax: (01384) 898000 E-mail: brilift@aol.com

C A M Tyre & Welding Co. Ltd, Frome Road, Radstock, BA3 3PY Tel: (01761) 434226 Fax: (01761) 435541 E-mail: enquiries@camequipment.co.uk

Cambrian Caledonian Ltd, Llandygai Industrial Estate, Bangor, Gwynedd, LL57 4YH Tel: (01248) 370248 Fax: (01248) 370406

Camlok Lifting Clamps Ltd, 1 Knutsford Way, Chester, CH1 4NZ Tel: (01244) 375375 Fax: (01244) 377403 E-mail: sales@camlok.co.uk

Castle Lifting Gear Ltd, Porters FLD Road, Corngreaves Trading Estate, Cradley Heath, West Midlands, B64 7BL Tel: (01384) 560924 Fax: (01384) 566452 E-mail: lynn@castleliftinggear.co.uk

Catena Inspection Services, D3 Unit, Amberley Drive, Sinfin, Derby, DE24 9RE Tel: (01332) 722011 Fax: (01332) 764099 E-mail: enquiries@catenais.co.uk

Chains & Lifting Tackle Midlands Ltd, Dewsbury Road, Fenton Industrial Estate, Stoke-on-Trent, ST4 2TD Tel: (01782) 747400 Fax: (01782) 744508 E-mail: info@chainsandlifting.co.uk

Charles Pearson (Hull) Ltd, New Works, Spyvee Street, Hull, HU8 7JU Tel: (01482) 329602 Fax: (01482) 325860 E-mail: keith@cpgltd.com

Chester Chain Company Ltd, Broughton Mills Road, Bretton, Chester, CH4 0BY Tel: (01244) 663580 Fax: (01244) 663587 E-mail: admin@chesterchain.co.uk

Chester Chain Co. Ltd, 19 Greys Court, Kingsland Grange, Woolston, Warrington, WA1 4SH Tel: (01925) 838899 Fax: (01925) 811416E-mail: warrington@chesterchain.co.uk

Coventry Lifting Services Ltd, 19 Claverdon Road, Coventry, CV5 7HP Tel: (024) 7647 1972 Fax: (024) 7647 1972

Crane Services Ltd, Platts Road, Stourbridge, West Midlands, DY8 4YR Tel: (01384) 370318 Fax: (01384) 440203 E-mail: sales@craneservices.co.uk

Crosby Europe (U K) Ltd, Unit 10, Fallbank Industrial Estate, Dodworth, Barnsley, South Yorkshire, S75 3LS Tel: (01226) 290516 Fax: (01226) 240118 E-mail: sales@crosbyeurope.co.uk

CSB Lifting & Marine Products, 3 Station Road Industrial Estate, Station Road, Rowley Regis, West Midlands, B65 0JY Tel: 0121-559 5112 Fax: 0121-559 4173

Durham Lifting Ltd, Unit 12 Thames Centre, Gurney Way, Aycliffe Industrial Park, Newton Aycliffe, County Durham, DL5 6UJ Tel: (01325) 318844 Fax: (01325) 318844

E A & H Sandford Lifting Ltd, Albion Parade, Gravesend, Kent, DA12 2RN Tel: (01474) 365361 Fax: (01474) 569036

Eastwood & Dickinson Ltd, Mayflower Works, Gladstone Road, Seaforth, Liverpool, L21 1DE Tel: 0151-928 2316 Fax: 0151-474 6224 E-mail: info@eastwood-dickinson.co.uk

George Taylor & Co Lifting Gear Europe Ltd, Brickyard Road, Aldridge, Walsall, WS9 8SR Tel: (01922) 457916 Fax: (01922) 743664 E-mail: office@gtlifting.co.uk

J.A.V. Grazebrook & Co., Stourport-On-Severn, Worcestershire, DY13 0YB Tel: (01299) 827440 Fax: (01299) 827048

Gunnebo Ltd, Woolaston Road, Park Farm North, Redditch, Worcestershire, B98 7SG Tel: (01527) 522560 Fax: (01527) 510185 E-mail: sales@gunnebo.co.uk

H & H Services, 25 Albert Road, Eccles, Manchester, M30 9QJ Tel: 0161-707 6250

H S Lifting Services Ltd, 12 Canyon Road, Netherton Industrial Estate, Wishaw, Lanarkshire, ML2 0EG Tel: (01698) 327811 Fax: (01698) 327838

Hall Bros Lifting Gear Ltd, Unit 15 Olds Close, Watford, WD18 9RU Tel: (01923) 770292 Fax: (01923) 896696 E-mail: sales@halls-lifting-gear.co.uk

Harris Walton Lifting Gear Ltd, Two Woods Lane, Brierley Hill, West Midlands, DY5 1TR Tel: (01384) 74071 Fax: (01384) 74070 E-mail: sales@harriswaltonliftinggear.co.uk

HSS Lift & Shift, Hartland House, Pritchett Street, Birmingham, B6 4EX Tel: 0121-333 5704 Fax: 0121-333 5705

I & P Lifting Gear Ltd, 237 Scotia Road, Stoke-on-Trent, ST6 4PS Tel: (01782) 814411 Fax: (01782) 575510 E-mail: info@iandplifting.co.uk

Independent Lifting Services Ltd, James Court, Faraday Road, Great Yarmouth, Norfolk, NR31 0NF Tel: (01493) 650952 Fax: (01493) 657737 E-mail: mail@ilsltd.ffnet.co.uk

J D Engineering, York House, Sleaford Road, Wellingore, Lincoln, LN5 0HR Tel: (01522) 810215 Fax: (01522) 810525 E-mail: jim.dixon@eliteuk.net

J W O'Pray & Sons Ltd, Gillane Works, Wassand Street, Hull, HU3 4AL Tel: (01482) 323014 Fax: (01482) 215944 E-mail: sales@oprays.com

John Hemsley Ropes & Lifting Equipment Ltd, Unit 19 Sapcote Industrial Estate, 20 James Road, Tyseley, Birmingham, B11 2BA Tel: 0121-706 5748 Fax: 0121-706 6703

John Kesson Lifting Equipment Ltd, Unit 1 Hawick Crescent Industrial Estate, Newcastle upon Tyne, NE6 1AS Tel: 0191-265 2593 Fax: 0191-265 0498 E-mail: sales@johnkessonlifting.com

Kerswell Tooling Services Ltd, Britannic Lodge, Britannic Way, Llandarcy, Neath, West Glamorgan, SA10 6EL Tel: (01792) 812101 Fax: (01792) 814575 E-mail: sales@kerswelltoolingservices.com

Lifting Equipment Services, 2 The Trailer Centre Cottismore Farm, Newbury Road, Kingsclere, Newbury, Berkshire, RG20 4SY Tel: (01635) 297804 Fax: (01635) 297803

Lifting Equipment & Services Ltd, B6 Foundry Way, Eaton Socon, St. Neots, Cambridgeshire, PE19 8TR Tel: (01480) 217605 Fax: (01480) 407108 E-mail: info@liftingequipmenthire.com

Lifting Gear Supplies Ltd, 23 Anstey Lane, Leicester, LE4 0FF Tel: 0116-262 8023 Fax: 0116-251 4862 E-mail: sales@liftinggearsuppliesltd.co.uk

Lloyds Equipment Hire, Chain Works, Fabian Way, Crymlyn Burrows, Swansea, SA1 8PX Tel: (01792) 644460 Fax: (01792) 470559 E-mail: swansea@lloydsbritish.com

Load Monitor (U K) Ltd, The Marchoness Building, Commercial Rd, Bristol, BS1 6TG Tel: 0117-925 2300 Fax: 0117-925 2300 E-mail: sales@loadmonitor.com

M G R Wood & Clark Ltd, 133 Neilston Road, Paisley, Renfrewshire, PA2 6QL Tel: 0141-884 2000 Fax: 0141-884 4443 E-mail: mgrscotlantltd@lineone.net

Material Handling Devices Ltd, Lindeth House, 563 Bradford Road, Cleckheaton, West Yorkshire, BD19 6BU Tel: (01274) 874164 Fax: (01274) 852233 E-mail: sales.mathandlin@btclick.com

Medway Sling Co. Ltd, Knight Road, Rochester, Kent, ME2 2AH Tel: (01634) 726400 Fax: (01634) 726420 E-mail: sales@medwayslingcompany.co.uk

Neilson Hydraulics & Engineering Ltd, 22 Atlas Way, Sheffield, S4 7QQ Tel: (01709) 821002 Fax: 0114-244 0111 E-mail: sales@neilson-hydraulics.co.uk

Nene Storage Equipment Ltd, Nene House, Sopwith Way, Drayton Fields Industrial Estate, Daventry, Northamptonshire, NN11 8EA Tel: (01327) 300456 Fax: (01327) 300737 E-mail: awbrooks@nene.co.uk

New Tonne Lifting Services Ltd, 16 Sankey Valley Industrial Estate, Junction Lane, Newton-le-Willows, Merseyside, WA12 8DN Tel: (01925) 224471 Fax: (01925) 223518 E-mail: sales@lifting-engineers.co.uk

Nicoll & Jack Ltd, Locarno Works, Brown Street, Dundee, DD1 5EE Tel: (01382) 224398 Fax: (01382) 228591

Otto UK Ltd, Beacon House, Reg's Way, Bardon Hill, Coalville, Leicestershire, LE67 1GH Tel: (01530) 277900 Fax: (01530) 277911 E-mail: sales@otto.co.uk

Outreach plc, Abbots Road, Middlefield Industrial Estate, Falkirk, FK2 9AR Tel: (01324) 889000 Fax: (01324) 888901 E-mail: cmarshall@outreachltd.co.uk

Package Control (U.K.) Ltd, Unit 5 Bunas Business Park, Hollom Down Road, Lopcombe, Salisbury, SP5 1BP Tel: (01264) 782143 Fax: (0844) 8800384 E-mail: sales@package-control.co.uk

Plinth 2000 Ltd, Wetheringsett Manor, Wetheringsett, Stowmarket, Suffolk, IP14 5PP Tel: (01449) 767887 Fax: (01449) 766122 E-mail: sales@plinth2000.com

Polystrop Ltd, Bridge Road, Kingswood, Bristol, BS15 4FW Tel: 0117-970 1196 Fax: 0117-970 1205

Pro-Rol Ltd, 44 Yardley Road, Olney, Buckinghamshire, MK46 5ED Tel: (01234) 240177 Fax: (01234) 240188 E-mail: sales@projectorlisting.co.uk

Quatroserve Steel Fabricators, Bay 11 Central Works, Peartree Lane, Dudley, West Midlands, DY2 0QU Tel: (01384) 480326 Fax: (01384) 74119 E-mail: sales@quatroserve.co.uk

R & G Marine & Industrial Services, Units 1a-2a Brickmakers Industrial Estate, Castle Road, Sittingbourne, Kent, ME10 3RL Tel: (01795) 470430 Fax: (01795) 429722 E-mail: sales@randgmarine.co.uk

Riley (Lifting Equipment) Ltd, Britannia House, Greenfield Rd, Colne, Lancashire, BB8 9PD Tel: (01282) 867177 Fax: (01282) 863698 E-mail: sales@superclamp.co.uk

Rotrex Winches, Gryphon Works, Wimsey Way, Alfreton Trading Estate, Alfreton, Derbyshire, DE55 4LS Tel: (01773) 603997 Fax: (01773) 540566 E-mail: sales@rotrexwinches.co.uk

S J Humphries Ltd, Portersfield Road, Cradley Heath, West Midlands, B64 7BN Tel: (01384) 569326 Fax: (01384) 74070

Safety Welding & Lifting (International) Ltd, Site 4 Inverbreakie Industrial Estate, Invergordon, Ross-Shire, IV18 0QR Tel: (01349) 852187 Fax: (01349) 853585 E-mail: info@safetyweldinglifting.co.uk

Skidmore Lifting Equipment, 60 Sandwell Street, Walsall, WS1 3EB Tel: (01922) 613633 Fax: (01922) 626991E-mail: sales@lodar.com

Slingtak Hoists Ltd, Quarry Road, Westgate, Cleckheaton, West Yorkshire, BD19 5HP Tel: (01274) 851724 Fax: (01274) 851724 E-mail: info@slingtak.co.uk

Speedy LGH, Bentley Avenue, Cowpen Bewley Industrial Estate, Billingham, Cleveland, TS23 4BU Tel: (01642) 561611 Fax: (01642) 566032 E-mail: teeside@lgh.co.uk

Speedy LGH, Units 36-37, Millers Bridge Industrial Estate, Bootle, Merseyside, L20 1EE Tel: 0151-922 5596 Fax: 0151-922 0361 E-mail: liverpool@lgh.co.uk

Spencer Davis Handling Ltd, Glanmor Terrace, Burry Port, Dyfed, SA16 0LS Tel: (01554) 833358 Fax: (01554) 835338 E-mail: sales@sde.co.uk

Struture-flex Ltd, 24 Grove Lane, Holt, Norfolk, NR25 6EG Tel: (01263) 712911 Fax: (01263) 710015 E-mail: enquiries@structure-flex.co.uk

Talon Lifting, Unit 2 Brook Forge, Hightown Road, Cleckheaton, West Yorkshire, BD19 5JS Tel: (01274) 871242 Fax: (01274) 869716

Taunton Lifting Services, Capland, Hatch Beauchamp, Taunton, Somerset, TA3 6TR Tel: (01823) 481111 Fax: (01823) 480682

Teamwork Fabricating Ltd, C Cuxton Industrial Estate, Station Road, Cuxton, Rochester, Kent, ME2 1AJ Tel: (01634) 290551 Fax: (01634) 290021

Technique Engineering, 1 Gilmans Industrial Estate, Billingshurst, West Sussex, RH14 9EZ Tel: (01403) 784678 Fax: (01403) 784978 E-mail: info@technique-engineering.com

Techno Lift, 121 Barfillan Drive, Glasgow, G52 1BD Tel: 0141-882 4403 Fax: 0141-882 5353

Thameside Lifting Ltd, Europa Park, London Road, Grays, Essex, RM20 4DB Tel: (01375) 392333 Fax: (01375) 366889

Trafford Lifting Services Ltd, Unit 2-3 Naval Street, Manchester, M4 6AX Tel: 0161-205 9716 Fax: 0161-205 8569

W H Scott & Son, Unit 2 Elmbank Channel Commercial Park, Queens Road, Belfast, BT3 9DT Tel: (028) 9076 6700 Fax: (028) 9076 6701 E-mail: sales@gunnebo.se

LIFTING GEAR DESIGN

M.A. Carroll Engineers Ltd, Birkby, Huddersfield, HD1 5EY Tel: (01484) 510846 Fax: (01484) 425953 E-mail: macengs@cs.com

Quatroserve Steel Fabricators, Bay 11 Central Works, Peartree Lane, Dudley, West Midlands, DY2 0QU Tel: (01384) 480326 Fax: (01384) 74119 E-mail: sales@quatroserve.co.uk

Safelift Offshore Ltd, Forties Business Centre, School Road, Kintore, Inverurie, Aberdeenshire, AB51 0UX Tel: (01224) 775774 Fax: (01224) 775779 E-mail: sales@safelift.co.uk

LIFTING GEAR HIRE

Abel Foxall Lifting Gear Ltd, Wood Street, Liverpool, L1 4LA Tel: 0151-709 6882 Fax: 0151-707 0723 E-mail: allanmolloy@rossendalegroup.co.uk

Applied Hoist Services, Meadows Abbey Meadows, Back Lane, Cotes, Loughborough, Leicestershire, LE12 5TA Tel: (01509) 212711 Fax: (01509) 212722 E-mail: enquire@menz.fsnet.co.uk

B & W Lifting, Unit 2e Grangetown Centre, Stapylton Street, Middlesbrough, Cleveland, TS6 7BJ Tel: (01642) 467900 Fax: (01642) 467900 E-mail: bwlifting@hotmail.com

Bond Engineering Maintenance Ltd, Unit P-Q Little Moor Lane, North Road, Loughborough, Leicestershire, LE11 1RL Tel: (01509) 266662 Fax: (01509) 231638 E-mail: sales@cranesandhoist.co.uk

Brandon Hire plc, 63 Lyde Green, Halesowen, West Midlands, B63 2PQ Tel: (01384) 566936 Fax: (01384) 410134 E-mail: info@brandonhire.plc.uk

▶ Bridon, Denmore Road, Bridge of Don, Aberdeen, AB23 8JW Tel: (01224) 822288 Fax: (01224) 708573 E-mail: sales@bridon.com

▶ Builders Equipment Ltd, City Road, Norwich, NR1 3AN Tel: (01473) 236316 Fax: (01473) 281788E-mail: mail@builders.equipment.co.uk

C E A Towne Ship Riggers Ltd, 19 Wiltshire Road, Dairycoates Industrial Estate, Hull, HU3 6PA Tel: (01482) 572121 Fax: (01482) 504730

Castle Lifting Gear Ltd, Porters FLD Road, Corngreaves Trading Estate, Cradley Heath, West Midlands, B64 7BL Tel: (01384) 560924 Fax: (01384) 566452 E-mail: lynn@castleliftinggear.co.uk

Catena Inspection Services, D3 Unit, Amberley Drive, Sinfin, Derby, DE24 9RE Tel: (01332) 722011 Fax: (01332) 764099 E-mail: enquiries@catenais.co.uk

▶ Certex UK Ltd, 17 Gravelly Industrial Park, Birmingham, B24 8HZ Tel: 0121-327 1255 Fax: 0121-327 6966 E-mail: sales@certex.co.uk

▶ Certex UK Ltd, Unit 7a-7b, Pennine Close, Llanishen, Cardiff, CF14 5DN Tel: (029) 2068 3650 Fax: (029) 2068 3659 E-mail: sales@certex.co.uk

Certex UK Ltd, 8 Trafford Court, Doncaster, South Yorkshire, DN1 1PN Tel: (01302) 731000 Fax: (01302) 731000 E-mail: sales@certex.co.uk

▶ Certex UK Ltd, Units 1-3, Viking Way, Erith, Kent, DA8 1EW Tel: (01322) 442323 Fax: (01322) 441044 E-mail: sales@certex.co.uk

▶ Certex UK Ltd, Dukesway Court, Team Valley Trading Estate, Gateshead, Tyne & Wear, NE11 0BH Tel: 0191-491 0696 Fax: 0191-491 0787 E-mail: sales@certex.co.uk

▶ Certex UK Ltd, 125 Business Park, Llanthony Road, Gloucester, GL2 5JQ Tel: (01452) 526119 Fax: (01452) 307632 E-mail: gloucester@certex.co.uk

LIFTING GEAR HIRE – *continued*

▶ Certex UK Ltd, Ordsall Wire Mills, Ollerton Road, Retford, Nottinghamshire, DN22 7XN Tel: (01777) 708264 Fax: (01777) 705878 E-mail: glasgow@certex.co.uk
▶ Certex UK Ltd, Unit 4 Third Avenue, Southampton, SO15 0LD Tel: (023) 8070 3894 Fax: (023) 8070 3901 E-mail: admin@certex.co.uk
▶ Certex UK Ltd, Flanshaw Way Industrial Estate, Flanshaw Way, Wakefield, West Yorkshire, WF2 9LP Tel: (01924) 375431 Fax: (01924) 290538 E-mail: sales@certex.co.uk
Chester Chain Company Ltd, Broughton Mills Road, Bretton, Chester, CH4 0BY Tel: (01244) 663580 Fax: (01244) 663587 E-mail: admin@chesterchain.co.uk
Chester Chain Co. Ltd, 19 Greys Court, Kingsland Grange, Woolston, Warrington, WA1 4SH Tel: (01925) 838899 Fax: (01925) 811416E-mail: warrington@chesterchain.co.uk
Concord Lifting Equipment Ltd, Unit 4, Buzzard Creek Ind Estate, River Road, Barking, Essex, IG11 0EL Tel: (020) 8594 7529 Fax: (020) 8594 8674
County Lifting Equipment & Safety Co Ltd, Unit 2 Telford Way, Telford Way Industrial Estate, Kettering, Northamptonshire, NN16 8UN Tel: (01536) 417878 Fax: (01536) 417877
Cymru Lifting Gear Ltd, Unit 31 Abenbury Way, Wrexham Industrial Estate, Wrexham, Clwyd, LL13 9UZ Tel: (01978) 661439 Fax: (01978) 661238 E-mail: rossgrp_cog@msm.com
E A & H Sandford Lifting Ltd, Albion Parade, Gravesend, Kent, DA12 2RN Tel: (01474) 365361 Fax: (01474) 569036
Engineering & Lifting Services, Unit B Drypool Way, Hull, HU9 1NL Tel: (01482) 323812 Fax: (01482) 320550
Frank Key Nottingham Ltd, Portland Street, Daybrook, Nottingham, NG5 6BL Tel: 0115-920 8208 Fax: 0115-967 0393 E-mail: sales@frank-key.co.uk
H S S Lift & Shift, Pryme Works, Silvercroft Street, Manchester, M15 4WG Tel: 0161-839 6122
HSS Lift & Shift, 3 Triangle Business Park, Oakwell Way, Birstall, Batley, West Yorkshire, WF17 9LU Tel: (01924) 444299 Fax: (01924) 422755
HSS Lift & Shift, 265-271 Penarth Road, Cardiff, CF11 8TT Tel: (029) 2045 4544 Fax: (029) 2064 1661
HSS Lift & Shift, 240 Whifflet Street, Coatbridge, Lanarkshire, ML5 4RX Tel: (01236) 436986 Fax: (01236) 440280
HSS Lift & Shift, 8 Oakwood Industrial Park, Gatwick Road, Crawley, West Sussex, RH10 9AZ Tel: (01293) 611010 Fax: (01293) 618041
HSS Lift & Shift, 772 London Road, Alvaston, Derby, DE24 8UT Tel: (01332) 755699 Fax: (01332) 756715
HSS Lift & Shift, 760 South Street, Glasgow, G14 0SY Tel: 0141-959 0217 Fax: 0141-959 4280
HSS Lift & Shift, 765 Old Kent Road, London, SE15 1NZ Tel: (020) 7732 4558 Fax: (020) 7000 8684
HSS Lift & Shift, 148 Exeter Street, Plymouth, PL4 0AR Tel: (01752) 601225 Fax: (01752) 601225
HSS Premiere Centre, Stoneferry Road, Hull, HU8 8BZ Tel: (01482) 618007 Fax: (01482) 493189
Lifting Gear Hire plc, Hockley Way, Nixs Hill Industrial Estate, Alfreton, Derbyshire, DE55 7FA Tel: (01773) 608325 Fax: (01773) 540566 E-mail: sales@lgh.co.uk
Lifting Gear Hire Ltd, Brunel Industrial Estate, Blyth Road, Harworth, Doncaster, South Yorkshire, DN11 8QA Tel: (01302) 743600 Fax: (01302) 750697
Lifting Gear Hire plc, 17 Rosscliffe Road, Ellesmere Port, CH65 3AS Tel: 0151-357 2906 Fax: 0151-357 2380 E-mail: info@lgh.co.uk
Lifting Gear Hire plc, Unit D4 South Orbital Trading Park, Hedon Road, Hull, HU9 1NJ Tel: (01482) 223737 Fax: (01482) 219491 E-mail: hull-lifting@speedydepots.co.uk
Lifting Gear Hire Ltd, Unit 27 Boston Road, Gorse Hill Industrial Estate, Beaumont Leys, Leicester, LE4 1AW Tel: 0116-234 0255 Fax: 0116-234 0254 E-mail: leicester@lgh.co.uk
Lifting Gear Hire plc, 74 Roding Road, London, E6 6LS Tel: (020) 7511 0233 Fax: (020) 7511 1784
Lifting Gear Hire Ltd, High Yard, Wincomblee Road, Newcastle upon Tyne, NE6 3PL Tel: 0191-295 5301 Fax: 0191-295 4311 E-mail: tyneside@lgh.co.uk
Lifting Gear Hire Ltd, Unit 1, Kings Parade, Newport, Gwent, NP20 2DU Tel: (01633) 243244 Fax: (01633) 243236 E-mail: newport@lgh.co.uk
Lifting Point, 8 Warren Road, Trafford Park, Manchester, M17 1QR Tel: 0161-872 5993 Fax: 0161-872 5994 E-mail: liftingplant@hirestation.co.uk
Lloyds Equipment Hire Ltd, 3 Arrol Place, Glasgow, G40 3NY Tel: (01324) 620620 Fax: 0141-554 6531
London Lifting Gear, Buzzard Creek Industrial Estate, River Road, Barking, Essex, IG11 0EL Tel: (020) 8594 8794 Fax: (020) 8594 8795 E-mail: sales@londonliftinggear.co.uk
M F Hire Ltd, 2 Highmeres Road, Leicester, LE4 9LZ Tel: 0116-276 3807 Fax: 0116-246 0198 E-mail: enquiries@mfhgroup.co.uk
Medway Sling Co. Ltd, Knight Road, Rochester, Kent, ME2 2AH Tel: (01634) 726400 Fax: (01634) 726420 E-mail: sales@medwayslingcompany.co.uk
Midway Material Handling, 7 Pinewood Drive, Little Haywood, Stafford, ST18 0NX Tel: (01889) 882014 Fax: (01889) 882014
Bill Moore (Lifting Tackle) Ltd, 15 Woodlands Drive, Morecambe, Lancashire, LA3 1LZ Tel: (01524) 854692 Fax: (01524) 851566 E-mail: billmoreliftingtackleltd@msn.co.uk
New Tonne Lifting Services Ltd, 16 Sankey Valley Industrial Estate, Junction Lane, Newton-le-Willows, Merseyside, WA12 8DN Tel: (01925) 224471 Fax: (01925) 223518 E-mail: sales@lifting-engineers.co.uk
Plinth 2000 Ltd, Wetheringsett Manor, Wetheringsett, Stowmarket, Suffolk, IP14 5PP Tel: (01449) 767887 Fax: (01449) 766122 E-mail: sales@plinth2000.com
S S C S Lifting, Harfreys Road, Harfreys Industrial Estate, Great Yarmouth, Norfolk, NR31 0LS Tel: 0845 4940724 Fax: (01493) 443390 E-mail: sales@sscsystems.com
Safelift Offshore Ltd, Forties Business Centre, School Road, Kintore, Inverurie, Aberdeenshire, AB51 0UX Tel: (01224) 775774 Fax: (01224) 775779 E-mail: sales@safelift.co.uk
Selby Engineering & Lifting Services Ltd, 3 Lincoln Way, Sherburn in Elmet, Leeds, LS25 6PJ Tel: (01977) 684600 Fax: (01977) 685300 E-mail: sales@liftingsafety.co.uk
Specialist Services (South West) Ltd, Mardle Way, Buckfastleigh, Devon, TQ11 0JS Tel: (01364) 644101 Fax: (01364) 644080
Speedy L G H, Unit 13, Royce Road, Fleming Way, Crawley, West Sussex, RH10 2NX Tel: (01293) 615898 Fax: (01293) 615818 E-mail: crawley@lgh.co.uk
Speedy L G H, Unit 2, Crescent Industrial Park, Peartree Lane, Dudley, West Midlands, DY2 0QQ Tel: (01384) 239966 Fax: (01384) 455782 E-mail: rob.langford@lgh.co.uk
Speedy LGH, Bentley Avenue, Cowpen Bewley Industrial Estate, Billingham, Cleveland, TS23 4BU Tel: (01642) 561611 Fax: (01642) 566032 E-mail: teeside@lgh.co.uk
Speedy LGH, Units 36-37, Millers Bridge Industrial Estate, Bootle, Merseyside, L20 1EE Tel: 0151-922 5596 Fax: 0151-922 0361 E-mail: liverpool@lgh.co.uk
Speedy LGH, Long Island Park, Carlisle, CA2 5AS Tel: (01228) 599766 Fax: (01228) 599788 E-mail: info@lgh.co.uk
Speedy LGH, 100 Brook Street, Glasgow, G40 3AP Tel: 0141-554 6477 Fax: 0141-554 6162
Speedy LGH, Unit 2, 40 Adam Smith Street, Grimsby, South Humberside, DN31 1SJ Tel: (01472) 362685 Fax: (01472) 342612 E-mail: grimsby@lgh.co.uk
Speedy LGH Ltd, Unit 5, Farthing Road, Ipswich, IP1 5AP Tel: (01473) 461083 Fax: (01473) 240532 E-mail: ipswich@lgh.co.uk
Speedy LGH, West Thamesmead Business Park, 7 Kellner Road, London, SE28 0AX Tel: (020) 8854 6248 Fax: (020) 8316 0501 E-mail: south-thames@lgh.co.uk
Speedy LGH, Unit 1, Dewsbury Road, Fenton Industrial Estate, Stoke-on-Trent, ST4 2TE Tel: (01782) 272954 Fax: (01782) 260713 E-mail: stoke@lgh.co.uk
Speedy Lifting Ltd, Cronin Road, Weldon South Industrial Estate, Corby, Northamptonshire, NN18 8AQ Tel: (01536) 206306 Fax: (01536) 264513 E-mail: corby-lifting@speedydepots.co.uk
Speedy Lifting, 3 Vulcan House, Vulcan Road North, Norwich, NR6 6AQ Tel: (01603) 764642 Fax: (01603) 620839 E-mail: norwich@lgh.co.uk
Speedy Lifting, Unit 1, Llewellyns Quay, The Docks, Port Talbot, West Glamorgan, SA13 1RF Tel: (01639) 890875 Fax: (01639) 895009 E-mail: port-talbot@lgh.co.uk
Speedy Lifting, Unit 4 Meridian Park, Neptune Close, Rochester, Kent, ME2 4LE Tel: (01634) 297373 Fax: (01634) 296638 E-mail: medway@lgh.co.uk
Speedy Lifting, Unit 10, Central Trading Estate, Marine Parade, Southampton, SO14 5JP Tel: (023) 9223 8236 Fax: (023) 8063 1712 E-mail: southampton-lifting@speedydepos.co.uk
Speedy/LGH, Unit 1C, Walney Road Industrial Estate, Barrow-In-Furness, Cumbria, LA14 5UG Tel: (01229) 835407 Fax: (01229) 811236 E-mail: cumbria@lgh.co.uk
Swindon Lifting Gear Ltd, 9-11 Station Industrial Estate, Sheppard Street, Swindon, SN1 5DB Tel: (01793) 542051 Fax: (01793) 497187
Thameside Lifting Ltd, Europa Park, London Road, Grays, Essex, RM20 4DB Tel: (01375) 392333 Fax: (01375) 366889

LIFTING GEAR INSPECTION OR MAINTENANCE OR REPAIR OR TEST SERVICES

Abc Lifting Equipment Ltd, 4 Alliance Business Park, Corporation Street, Accrington, Lancashire, BB5 0RR Tel: (01254) 233349 Fax: (01254) 233533 E-mail: sales@abclifting.co.uk
Abel Foxall Lifting Gear Ltd, Wood Street, Liverpool, L1 4LA Tel: 0151-709 6882 Fax: 0151-707 0723 E-mail: allanmolloy@rossendalegroup.co.uk
Ace Elevators Ltd, Galven House, Bakewell Road, Loughborough, Leicestershire, LE11 5QY Tel: (01509) 265383 Fax: (01509) 269275E-mail: midlands@ace-elevators.co.uk
Applied Hoist Services, Meadows Abbey Meadows, Back Lane, Cotes, Loughborough, Leicestershire, LE12 5TA Tel: (01509) 212711 Fax: (01509) 212722 E-mail: enquire@menz.fsnet.co.uk
Ashdale Lifting Services Ltd, 14 Thornton Industrial Trading Estate, Milford Haven, Dyfed, SA73 2RX Tel: (01646) 695332 Fax: (01646) 693570
Austin & McLean Ltd, Unit 1, Cookesland Industrial Estate, Bodmin, Cornwall, PL31 2QB Tel: (01208) 264162 Fax: (01208) 73125
Balmoral Group Ltd, Balmoral Park, Aberdeen, AB12 3GY Tel: (01224) 859000 Fax: (01224) 859059 E-mail: group@balmoral.co.uk
▶ Bridon, Denmore Road, Bridge of Don, Aberdeen, AB23 8JW Tel: (01224) 822288 Fax: (01224) 708573 E-mail: sales@bridon.com
C I A Ltd, Froghall Road, Aberdeen, AB24 3JL Tel: (01224) 626364 Fax: (01224) 624005 E-mail: sales@c-i-a.co.uk
Camlok Lifting Clamps Ltd, 1 Knutsford Way, Chester, CH1 4NZ Tel: (01244) 375375 Fax: (01244) 377403 E-mail: sales@camlok.co.uk
Castle Lifting Gear Ltd, Porters FLD Road, Corngreaves Trading Estate, Cradley Heath, West Midlands, B64 7BL Tel: (01384) 560924 Fax: (01384) 566452 E-mail: lynn@castleliftinggear.co.uk
Catena Inspection Services, D3 Unit, Amberley Drive, Sinfin, Derby, DE24 9RE Tel: (01332) 722011 Fax: (01332) 764099 E-mail: enquiries@catenais.co.uk
Central Steel Pickling Ltd, Nomex House, Powke Lane, Cradley Heath, West Midlands, B64 5PX Tel: (01384) 566373 Fax: (01384) 566376
▶ Certex UK Ltd, 17 Gravelly Industrial Park, Birmingham, B24 8HZ Tel: 0121-327 1255 Fax: 0121-327 6966 E-mail: sales@certex.co.uk
▶ Certex UK Ltd, Unit 7a-7b, Pennine Close, Llanishen, Cardiff, CF14 5DN Tel: (029) 2068 3650 Fax: (029) 2068 3659 E-mail: sales@certex.co.uk
Certex UK Ltd, 8 Trafford Court, Doncaster, South Yorkshire, DN1 1PN Tel: (01302) 731000 Fax: (01302) 731000 E-mail: sales@certex.co.uk
▶ Certex UK Ltd, Units 1-3, Viking Way, Erith, Kent, DA8 1EW Tel: (01322) 442323 Fax: (01322) 441044 E-mail: sales@certex.co.uk
▶ Certex UK Ltd, Dukesway Court, Team Valley Trading Estate, Gateshead, Tyne & Wear, NE11 0BH Tel: 0191-491 0696 Fax: 0191-491 0787 E-mail: sales@certex.co.uk
▶ Certex UK Ltd, 125 Business Park, Llanthony Road, Gloucester, GL2 5JQ Tel: (01452) 526119 Fax: (01452) 307632 E-mail: gloucester@certex.co.uk
▶ Certex UK Ltd, Ordsall Wire Mills, Ollerton Road, Retford, Nottinghamshire, DN22 7XN Tel: (01777) 708264 Fax: (01777) 705878 E-mail: glasgow@certex.co.uk
▶ Certex UK Ltd, Unit 4 Third Avenue, Southampton, SO15 0LD Tel: (023) 8070 3894 Fax: (023) 8070 3901 E-mail: admin@certex.co.uk
▶ Certex UK Ltd, Delphwood Drive, Sherdley Road Industrial Estat, St. Helens, Merseyside, WA9 5JE Tel: (01744) 20590 Fax: (01744) 24059 E-mail: sthelens@certex.co.uk
▶ Certex UK Ltd, Flanshaw Way Industrial Estate, Flanshaw Way, Wakefield, West Yorkshire, WF2 9LP Tel: (01924) 375431 Fax: (01924) 290538 E-mail: sales@certex.co.uk
Charles Pearson (Hull) Ltd, New Works, Spyvee Street, Hull, HU8 7JU Tel: (01482) 329602 Fax: (01482) 325860 E-mail: keith@cpgltd.com
Chester Chain Company Ltd, Broughton Mills Road, Bretton, Chester, CH4 0BY Tel: (01244) 663580 Fax: (01244) 663587 E-mail: admin@chesterchain.co.uk
Coolmetal Steel Fabricators, 68-72 Bromley Street, Stourbridge, West Midlands, DY9 8JA Tel: (01384) 424424 Fax: (01384) 892810 E-mail: info@coolmetal.co.uk
Coventry Lifting Services Ltd, 19 Claverdon Road, Coventry, CV5 7HP Tel: (024) 7647 1972 Fax: (024) 7647 1972
Crane Care Ltd, 15 Avenue Road, Aston, Birmingham, B6 4DY Tel: 0121-333 3995 Fax: 0121-333 3996 E-mail: sales@cranecare.ltd.uk
Engineering Safety & Testing Ltd, P O Box 3, Saffron Walden, Essex, CB10 1RX Tel: (01799) 531040 Fax: (01799) 530917 E-mail: safety@sirdi.demon.co.uk
I M E S Ltd, Tern Place, Denmore Road, Bridge of Don, Aberdeen, AB23 8JX Tel: (01224) 705777 Fax: (01224) 824808 E-mail: marketing@imes-group.com
John Hemsley Ropes & Lifting Equipment Ltd, Unit 19 Sapcote Industrial Estate, 20 James Road, Tyseley, Birmingham, B11 2BA Tel: 0121-706 5748 Fax: 0121-706 6703
Lifting Equipment Services, 2 The Trailer Centre Cottismore Farm, Newbury Road, Kingsclere, Newbury, Berkshire, RG20 4SY Tel: (01635) 297804 Fax: (01635) 297803
Lifting Equipment & Services Ltd, B6 Foundry Way, Eaton Socon, St. Neots, Cambridgeshire, PE19 8TR Tel: (01480) 217605 Fax: (01480) 407108 E-mail: info@liftingequipmenthire.com
M G R Wood & Clark Ltd, 133 Neilston Road, Paisley, Renfrewshire, PA2 6QL Tel: 0141-884 2000 Fax: 0141-884 4443 E-mail: mgrscotlantltd@lineone.net
Medway Sling Co. Ltd, Knight Road, Rochester, Kent, ME2 2AH Tel: (01634) 726400 Fax: (01634) 726420 E-mail: sales@medwayslingcompany.co.uk
Midland Safe Load Indicators Ltd, Watling Street Works, Watling Street, Brownhills, Walsall, WS8 7JT Tel: (01543) 453166 Fax: (01543) 453167
New Tonne Lifting Services Ltd, 16 Sankey Valley Industrial Estate, Junction Lane, Newton-le-Willows, Merseyside, WA12 8DN Tel: (01925) 224471 Fax: (01925) 223518 E-mail: sales@lifting-engineers.co.uk
Olympia Testing Holdings Ltd, Oldbush Street, Off Level Street, Brierley Hill, West Midlands, DY5 1UB Tel: (01384) 573164 Fax: (01384) 265832
Plinth 2000 Ltd, Wetheringsett Manor, Wetheringsett, Stowmarket, Suffolk, IP14 5PP Tel: (01449) 767887 Fax: (01449) 766122 E-mail: sales@plinth2000.com
R & G Marine & Industrial Services, Units 1a-2a Brickmakers Industrial Estate, Castle Road, Sittingbourne, Kent, ME10 3RL Tel: (01795) 470430 Fax: (01795) 429722 E-mail: sales@randgmarine.co.uk
Rope Services Tipton Ltd, St Georges Works, Bradleys Lane, Tipton, West Midlands, DY4 9EZ Tel: 0121-557 7521 Fax: 0121-557 8921
S S C S Lifting, Harfreys Road, Harfreys Industrial Estate, Great Yarmouth, Norfolk, NR31 0LS Tel: 0845 4940724 Fax: (01493) 443390 E-mail: sales@sscsystems.com
Selby Engineering & Lifting Services Ltd, 3 Lincoln Way, Sherburn in Elmet, Leeds, LS25 6PJ Tel: (01977) 684600 Fax: (01977) 685300 E-mail: sales@liftingsafety.co.uk
Speedy LGH, 100 Brook Street, Glasgow, G40 3AP Tel: 0141-554 6477 Fax: 0141-554 6162
Street Express Ltd, Roman Ridge Road, Sheffield, S9 1GA Tel: 0114-243 1142 Fax: 0114-256 1739 E-mail: info@scx.co.uk
SWR Ltd, 3 Eastman Way, Hemel Hempstead Industrial Estate, Hemel Hempstead, Hertfordshire, HP2 7DU Tel: (01442) 219611 Fax: (01442) 259918 E-mail: sales@swrgaragedoors.com
Talon Lifting, Unit 2 Brook Forge, Hightown Road, Cleckheaton, West Yorkshire, BD19 5JS Tel: (01274) 871242 Fax: (01274) 869716
Technique Engineering, 1 Gilmans Industrial Estate, Billingshurst, West Sussex, RH14 9EZ Tel: (01403) 784678 Fax: (01403) 784978 E-mail: info@technique-engineering.com
Thameside Lifting Ltd, Europa Park, London Road, Grays, Essex, RM20 4DB Tel: (01375) 392333 Fax: (01375) 366889
Warrington Chain Ltd, Howley Quay, Howley Lane, Warrington, WA1 2DZ Tel: (01925) 630820 Fax: (01925) 631947 E-mail: sales@warringtonchain.co.uk

LIFTING GEAR SAFETY MARKERS

Chaintabs Ltd, 6 Grafton Rd, Sparkbrook, Birmingham, B11 1JP Tel: 0121-430 7957 Fax: 0121-430 7964

LIFTING GEAR TO SPECIFICATION

Able Lifting Gear Swansea Ltd, Unit 4 Clarion Close, Swansea Enterprise Park, Swansea, SA6 8QZ Tel: (01792) 771965 Fax: (01792) 773645 E-mail: sales@ableliftinggear.co.uk
Alliance Lifting Services Ltd, 95 Stockwell Road, Pembroke Dock, Dyfed, SA72 6TQ Tel: (01646) 621115 Fax: (01646) 622518
Arinsdale Ltd, Block 6 Unit A, Westmains Industrial Estate, Grangemouth, Stirlingshire, FK3 8YE Tel: (01324) 665234 Fax: (01324) 665388 E-mail: info@arinsdale.com
▶ Certex UK Ltd, Unit 7a-7b, Pennine Close, Llanishen, Cardiff, CF14 5DN Tel: (029) 2068 3650 Fax: (029) 2068 3659 E-mail: sales@certex.co.uk
Cyclone Crane Services Ltd, Water Lane, Drayton St. Leonard, Wallingford, Oxfordshire, OX10 7BE Tel: (01865) 400253 Fax: (01865) 400254 E-mail: enquiries@cyclone-cranes.co.uk
Damar Webbing Products Ltd, Unit 3 Cobnar Wood Close, Chesterfield, Derbyshire, S41 9RQ Tel: (01246) 269969 Fax: (01246) 269946 E-mail: sales@damarwebbingproducts.com
Dewsbury Lifting Services, 12 Brown La West, Leeds, LS11 0DN Tel: 0113-272 3586 Fax: 0113-272 3575 E-mail: sales@dewsburyliftingservices.co.uk
Digital Lift Controls Ltd, 14 Gresley Close, Drayton Fields Industrial Esta, Daventry, Northamptonshire, NN11 8RZ Tel: (01327) 311816 Fax: (01327) 706636
Durham Lifting Ltd, Britannia Testhouse, Forty Foot Road, Middlesbrough, Cleveland, TS2 1HB Tel: (01642) 240672 Fax: (01642) 247709
Ellesmere Port Lifting Gear, Portside North, Ellesmere Port, CH65 2HQ Tel: 0151-355 5091 Fax: 0151-357 2108

▶ indicates data change since last edition

LIFTING GEAR TO SPECIFICATION

– *continued*

Engineering Safety & Testing Ltd, P O Box 3, Saffron Walden, Essex, CB10 1RX Tel: (01799) 531040 Fax: (01799) 530917 E-mail: safety@sirdi.demon.co.uk
G S L Lift Services Ltd, Netherton Indust Estate, Netherhall Road, Netherton Industrial Estate, Wishaw, Lanarkshire, ML2 0JG Tel: (01698) 350099 Fax: (01698) 357332
Global Lifting Services, Silverburn Cresent, Bridge of Don Industrial Estate, Aberdeen, AB23 8EW Tel: (01224) 707585 Fax: (01224) 707646
H S S Lift & Shift, 169-177 Lincoln Road, Peterborough, PE1 2PN Tel: (01733) 313123 Fax: (01733) 313377
Hall Bros Lifting Gear Ltd, Unit 15 Olds Close, Watford, WD18 9RU Tel: (01923) 770292 Fax: (01923) 896696 E-mail: sales@halls-lifting-gear.co.uk
Hore Station P.L.C., D1 Armthorpe Enterprise Centre, Rands Lane, Armthorpe, Doncaster, South Yorkshire, DN3 3DY Tel: (01302) 835191 Fax: (01302) 830741
HSS Hire, 74-82 Smithfield Road, Wrexham, Clwyd, LL13 8EP Tel: (01978) 311346 Fax: (01978) 311476
HSS Lift & Shift, 2 Bilton Way, Hayes, Middlesex, UB3 3NF Tel: (020) 8561 1655 Fax: (020) 8561 0994
HSS Lift & Shift, Unit G12 Narvik Way, Tyne Tunnel Trading Estate, North Shields, Tyne & Wear, NE29 7XJ Tel: 0191-296 1126 Fax: 0191-258 2128
HSS Lift & Shift, 3 Orwell Close, Rainham, Essex, RM13 8UB Tel: (01708) 526946 Fax: (01708) 525984
HSS Lift & Shift, Unit 37, City Industrial Park Southern Road, Southampton, SO15 1HA Tel: (023) 8033 8844 Fax: (023) 8063 0730
John Kesson Lifting Equipment Ltd, Unit 1 Hawick Crescent Industrial Estate, Newcastle upon Tyne, NE6 1AS Tel: 0191-265 2593 Fax: 0191-265 0498
John Teire & Co. Ltd, 180 Rimrose Road, Bootle, Merseyside, L20 4QS Tel: 0151-944 1027 Fax: 0151-922 6739 E-mail: info@teire.co.uk
Lift Control Ltd, 89 Spottiswoode Gardens, Mid Calder, Livingston, West Lothian, EH53 0JX Tel: (01506) 880043 Fax: (01506) 880043
Lifting Equipment Services Doncaster Ltd, Unit 3b Plumtree Farm Industrial Estate, Plumtree Road, Bircotes, Doncaster, South Yorkshire, DN11 8EW Tel: (01302) 711552 Fax: (01302) 719952 E-mail: sales@lesdoncaster.co.uk
Lifting Gear Hire plc, 17 Rosscliffe Road, Ellesmere Port, CH65 3AS Tel: 0151-357 2906 Fax: 0151-357 2380 E-mail: info@lgh.co.uk
Lifting Gear Hire Ltd, High Yard, Wincomblee Road, Newcastle upon Tyne, NE6 3PL Tel: 0191-295 5301 Fax: 0191-295 4311 E-mail: tyneside@lgh.co.uk
Link Engineering Services (Manchester) Ltd, Trafford Park Road, Trafford Park, Manchester, M17 1AN Tel: 0161-848 8039 Fax: 0161-872 3553
Lloyds Equipment Hire, Chain Works, Fabian Way, Crymlyn Burrows, Swansea, SA1 8PX Tel: (01792) 644460 Fax: (01792) 470559
Mercia Lifting Gear Ltd, Dukesway, Teesside Industrial Estate, Stockton-on-Tees, Cleveland, TS17 9LT Tel: (01642) 760990 Fax: (01642) 761200
Mercian Lifting Gear Ltd, Unit 15 Trench Lock 3, Telford, Shropshire, TF1 5ST Tel: (01952) 261851 Fax: (01952) 222028
P C M, Prenton Way, North Cheshire Trading Estate, Prenton, Merseyside, CH43 3DU Tel: 0151-609 0101 Fax: 0151-609 0200
Packline Ltd, Unit 8-9 Newtown Business Park, Poole, Dorset, BH12 3LL Tel: 01202 724138
Phoenix Lifting Supplies Ltd, Unit 54 Bowen Industrial Estate, Aberbargoed, Bargoed, Mid Glamorgan, CF81 9EP Tel: (01443) 821577 Fax: (01443) 821503
Powlift Handling Systems Ltd, 3a Blackberry Lane, Halesowen, West Midlands, B63 4NX Tel: 0121-550 4750 Fax: 0121-585 5226 E-mail: sales@powlift.co.uk
Reid Lifting Ltd, 3 Bulwark Business Park, Bulwark Road, Bulwark, Chepstow, Gwent, NP16 5JG Tel: (01291) 620796 Fax: (01291) 626490 E-mail: enquiries@reidlifting.com
Rossendale Group, Roman Way, South Hykeham, Lincoln, LN6 9UH Tel: (01522) 693423 Fax: (01522) 693988
Safety Welding & Lifting International Ltd, Unit 3 Saville Street, Macclesfield, Cheshire, SK11 7LQ Tel: (01625) 422444 Fax: (01625) 618000
Site Safe Supplies Ltd, 26 Sollershott East, Letchworth Garden City, Hertfordshire, SG6 3JN Tel: 01462 685544
Speedy L G H, Unit 2, Crescent Industrial Park, Peartree Lane, Dudley, West Midlands, DY2 0QQ Tel: (01384) 239966 Fax: (01384) 455782 E-mail: rob.langford@lgh.co.uk
Sprint Lifting Equipment Ltd, 16 Pinfold Road, Thurmaston, Leicester, LE4 8AS Tel: 0116-260 4111 Fax: 0116-260 4111
Stockport Lifting Gear, Unit 14 Bamford Business Park, Whitehill Industrial Estate, Stockport, Cheshire, SK4 1PL Tel: 0161-429 0737 Fax: 0161-476 3315 E-mail: info@rossendalegroup.co.uk
Taunton Lifting Services, Capland, Hatch Beauchamp, Taunton, Somerset, TA3 6TR Tel: (01823) 481111 Fax: (01823) 480682
Ultralift Lifting Equipment, 4 Shipyard Road, Selby, North Yorkshire, YO8 8BN Tel: (01757) 213850 Fax: (01757) 700681
Wilfab UK Repair Services, Unit 2 Holmes Lane, Rotherham, South Yorkshire, S61 1AZ Tel: (01709) 553132 Fax: (01709) 553132
William Hackett Chains Ltd, Alnwick Station, Alnwick, Northumberland, NE66 2NP Tel: 01665 604200
Yorkshire Lifting Tackle, Unit 6 Wortley Moor La Trading Estate, Leeds, LS12 4HX Tel: 0113-263 3366 Fax: 0113-279 5077 E-mail: sales@yorkshire-listings-tackle.co.uk

LIFTING MAGNETS

▶ Cranequip Ltd, Cattell Road, Cape Industrial Estate, Warwick, CV34 4JN Tel: (01926) 406900 Fax: (01926) 406910 E-mail: robert.shearsby@uk.gantry.com
Hi-Flux Magnets, 9 North St Industrial Estate, Droitwich, Worcestershire, WR9 8JB Tel: (01905) 778853 Fax: (01905) 779867 E-mail: hi-fluxmagnets@aol.com

LIFTING PLATFORMS, *See also headings for particular types*

▶ Bicester Sweepers Ltd, Glebe Court, Fringford, Bicester, Oxfordshire, OX27 8RJ Tel: (01869) 277410 Fax: (01869) 277704
Power-Lifts Ltd, Marlborough House, 18 Marlborough Road, Woodthorpe, Nottingham, NG5 4FG Tel: 0115-926 9996 Fax: 0115-966 1173 E-mail: info@powerlift.co.uk

LIGHT BULBS

Martins Mill Packaging, Unit 2 Reflecting Roadstuds Induxtrial Estate, Mill Lane, Booth Town, Halifax, West Yorkshire, HX3 6TR Tel: (01422) 363935 Fax: (01422) 300800 E-mail: rmatmmp@aol.com

LIGHT BULBS, MICROSCOPE

▶ First Light Direct, 4 Bentsbrook Road, North Holmwood, Dorking, Surrey, RH5 4HW Tel: (01306) 881314 E-mail: sales@firstlightdirect.com

LIGHT BULBS, ULTRAVIOLET (UV)

▶ First Light Direct, 4 Bentsbrook Road, North Holmwood, Dorking, Surrey, RH5 4HW Tel: (01306) 881314 E-mail: sales@firstlightdirect.com
▶ Rock Electronics, 113 Glasgow Road, Dumbarton, G82 1RG Tel: (01389) 841473 Fax: (01389) 730300 E-mail: rockelectronics@fsbdial.co.uk

LIGHT IRON CASTINGS

Allen Production Services, Unit 6b Tractor Spares Industrial Estate, Strawberry Lane, Willenhall, West Midlands, WV13 3RN Tel: (01902) 366035 Fax: (01902) 601221
Leach & Thompson Ltd, Chapel Foundry, Dalton Lane, Keighley, West Yorkshire, BD21 4JU Tel: (01535) 602452 Fax: (01535) 669183 E-mail: info@smallcasting.co.uk
Ouzledale Foundry Co. Ltd, PO Box 4, Barnoldswick, Lancashire, BB18 6BN Tel: (01282) 813235 Fax: (01282) 816876
Unimetal Ltd., Bay 6B, Tractor Spares Industrial Estate, Strawberry Lane, Willenhall, West Midlands, WV13 3RS Tel: (01902) 366035 Fax: (01902) 601221 E-mail: billallen@btconnect.com

LIGHT LOAD ROAD HAULAGE

▶ Anthony Leput Ta DTS, 3 Sankey Valley Industrial Estate, Junction Lane, Newton-le-Willows, Merseyside, WA12 8DN Tel: (01925) 225760 Fax: (01925) 291014
▶ Dyce Carriers Ltd, 18 Holton Road, Holton Heath Trading Park, Poole, Dorset, BH16 6LT Tel: (01202) 820829 Fax: (01202) 620829 E-mail: lunddyce@aol.com
▶ G & K Transport, UNIT 27, HEMMING ROAD, WASHFORD IND EST, REDDITCH, WORCESTERSHIRE, B98 0DH Tel: 01527 516686 Fax: 01527 516686 E-mail: stevenkirton@blueyonder.co.uk
▶ Glh Haulage, 220 Lynn Road, Broomhill, Downham Market, Norfolk, PE38 9QY Tel: 01366 383500 Fax: 01366 381267 E-mail: glhhaulage@hotmail.co.uk
▶ News Transport, D Station Road, Ampthill, Bedford, MK45 2QY Tel: (01525) 404000 Fax: (01525) 404555 E-mail: info@newstransport.co.uk
Sheepy Farm Services Ltd, 155 Main Road, Sheepy Magna, Atherstone, Warwickshire, CV9 3QU Tel: (01827) 713142
▶ Sibley Haulage Ltd, Crabtree Lane, Lower End, Wavendon, Milton Keynes, MK17 8AP Tel: (01908) 583154 Fax: (01908) 587631

LIGHT METAL STAGING FABRICATORS

P A S M A, PO Box 168, Leeds, LS11 9WW Tel: (0845) 2304041 Fax: (0845) 2304042 E-mail: pasma@portfolio-support.co.uk
Steeldeck, Kings Cross Freight Depot, York Way, London, N1 0UZ Tel: (020) 7833 2031 Fax: (020) 7278 3403 E-mail: info@aolsteeldeck.co.uk

LIGHT PEDESTRIAN BRIDGES

Britain Fabricators Ltd, Watnall Road, Hucknall, Nottingham, NG15 6EP Tel: 0115-963 2901 Fax: 0115-968 0335 E-mail: sales@britonsltd.co.uk
Lanarkshire Welding Co. Ltd, John Street, Wishaw, Lanarkshire, ML2 7TQ Tel: (01698) 264271 Fax: (01698) 265711 E-mail: johnhett@lanarkshirewelding.co.uk

LIGHT PRECISION PRESSINGS

Friary Metal Products Ltd, 106-110 Bishop Street, Birmingham, B5 6JP Tel: 0121-622 2088 Fax: 0121-666 7277 E-mail: info@thefriarygroup.co.uk
S B Engineering (Precision) Ltd, 1 Dyke Road Mews, Brighton, BN1 3JD Tel: 01273 821397
V.C.W. Engineering Ltd, Unit 8 Ailwin Road, Morton Hall industrial Estate, Bury St. Edmunds, Suffolk, IP32 7DS Tel: (01284) 768371 Fax: (01284) 768371 E-mail: brucewhiteman@aol.com

LIGHT SENSITIVE SWITCHES

Megatron Ltd, Unit 24f1, 784-788 High Road, London, N17 0DA Tel: (020) 8365 9797 Fax: (020) 8808 6186 E-mail: sales@megatron.co.uk

LIGHT SOURCES, *See also headings for particular types*

Expert Lighting Direct Ltd, 15 Cherry Fields, Bradford, West Yorkshire, BD2 1LB Tel: (01274) 722185 Fax: (01274) 722185
Heraeous Noble Light Analytics Ltd, Unit 2-4, Nuffield Close, Cambridge, CB4 1SS Tel: (01223) 424100 Fax: (01223) 426338 E-mail:
Metwin Ltd, 1-5 Rosina Street, London, E9 6JH Tel: (020) 8985 4371 Fax: (020) 8985 6778
Newtech Lighting Ltd, Unit 27 Branbridges Industrial Estate, Branbridges Road, East Peckham, Tonbridge, Kent, TN12 5HF Tel: (0845) 6732203 Fax: (01622) 870090 E-mail: nigel@newtechltg.com

LIGHT STEEL FABRICATORS

A N Fabrication, The Old Airfield, Town Lane, Brockford, Stowmarket, Suffolk, IP14 5NF Tel: (01449) 767821 Fax: (01449) 766606
Crown Metal Fabrications, 24-26 Albert St West, Failsworth, Manchester, M35 0JN Tel: 0161-688 7571 Fax: 0161-688 7546
Evenwood Engineering Ltd, Evenwood, Bishop Auckland, County Durham, DL14 9NJ Tel: (01388) 832556 Fax: (01388) 832966
H & H Construction Co., 4 Brookhollow Way, Wollescote, Stourbridge, West Midlands, DY9 8XJ Tel: (01384) 422587 Fax: (01384) 865780
M L G Engineering, Unit 26 Small Business Centre, Penmaen Road, Pontllanfraith, Blackwood, Gwent, NP12 2DZ Tel: (01495) 220695 Fax: (01495) 220695
Nationwide Signs Ltd, Derry Street, Wolverhampton, WV2 1EY Tel: (01902) 871116 Fax: (01902) 351195 E-mail: roadframes@aol.com
R & E Engineers, Rock Channel, Rye, East Sussex, TN31 7HJ Tel: (01797) 223757 Fax: (01797) 222819
Westhead Welding Fabricators Ltd, 1 Glan Y Morfa Industrial Estate, Marsh Road, Rhyl, Clwyd, LL18 2AD Tel: (01745) 344461 Fax: (01745) 344769

LIGHTER FUEL/FUEL PRODUCTS

Keen World Marketing Ltd, 1 Northbrook Street, Newbury, Berkshire, RG14 1DJ Tel: (01635) 34600 Fax: (01635) 33360 E-mail: info@keen-newport.com

LIGHTING, *See also headings for particular types*

Alfred J Hurst, Unit 2 Duncrue Cresent, Belfast, BT3 9BW Tel: (028) 9077 0037 Fax: (028) 9077 9749 E-mail: sales@ajhurst.com
Alsigns Self Luminous, Hilland Rise, Headley, Bordon, Hampshire, GU35 8LT Tel: (01536) 201525 Fax: (01780) 479032 E-mail: douglas@surelite.co.uk
Apollo Lighting Ltd, 4 Felnex Trading Estate, Pontefract Lane, Leeds, LS9 0SL Tel: 0113-240 5511 Fax: 0113-240 5151 E-mail: sales@apollolighting.co.uk
Artemide GB Ltd, 106 Great Russell Street, London, WC1B 3NB Tel: (020) 7631 5200 Fax: (020) 7631 5222 E-mail: info@artemide.co.uk
Aurora, 6 Little Burrow, Welwyn Garden City, Hertfordshire, AL7 4SW Tel: (01707) 351820 Fax: (01707) 351821
Avon Lighting, 4 Fenbrook Close, Hambrook, Bristol, BS16 1QJ Tel: 0117-956 5511 Fax: 0117-935 3678 E-mail: avonlite@bbcopenworld.com
Avprod Lighting Mnfrs, Ravenscroft House, 39 St Annes Road, Aigburth, Liverpool, L17 6BN Tel: 0151-427 0444 Fax: 0151-427 0666
▶ Bespoke Lighting, 116 Chester Street, Birkenhead, Merseyside, CH41 5DL Tel: 0151-649 8649 Fax: 0151-649 8648
▶ Betterlight Ltd, Carey Street, Kettering, Northamptonshire, NN16 0JL Tel: (01536) 415138 Fax: (01536) 415843
▶ Blue U V, 121 Loverock Road, Reading, RG30 1DZ Tel: 0118-959 7444
Bruck Lighting Ltd, 1 Cherrytrees, Stanbridge Road Terrace, Leighton Buzzard, Bedfordshire, LU7 4QU Tel: 01525 372645 Fax: 01525 378777
C B Lighting Co., 56 Staplehill Road, Fishponds, Bristol, BS16 5BS Tel: 0117-907 4906 Fax: 0117-966 0311
Dave Camepa Lighting, Dragon Works, Leigh Upon Mendip, Radstock, BA3 5QZ Tel: (01373) 813600 Fax: (01373) 813731 E-mail: david@canepalighting.co.uk
Canatronics Delta Ltd, Unit 5, Dewhurst Row, Bamber Bridge, Preston, PR5 6SW Tel: (01772) 629429 Fax: (01772) 698611 E-mail: info@canatronics-uk.com
▶ Cimc, City House, Murraysgate Industrial Estate, Whitburn, Bathgate, West Lothian, EH47 0LE Tel: (0870) 4438280 Fax: (0870) 4438281 E-mail: mail@cimc-lighting.co.uk
▶ Clitheroe Lighting Centre, 14 Moor Lane, Clitheroe, Lancashire, BB7 1BE Tel: (01200) 423757 Fax: (01200) 423757 E-mail: lights@clitheroelightingcentre.co.uk
Collingwood, Sywell Aerodrome, Sywell, Northampton, NN6 0AW Tel: (01604) 495151 Fax: (01604) 495095 E-mail: sales@collingwoodgroup.com
Design Lighting Ltd, 9 Eagles Wood Business Park, Woodlands Lane, Bradley Stoke, Bristol, BS32 4EU Tel: (01454) 616100 Fax: (01454) 618518 E-mail: sales@designlighting.co.uk
Display Works (Scotland) Ltd, Unit 2, Polbeth Industrial Estate, Polbeth, West Calder, West Lothian, EH55 8TJ Tel: (01506) 872010 Fax: (01506) 873010 E-mail: sales@display-works.co.uk
Ebs Panels, 144b Leek Road, Endon, Stoke-on-Trent, ST9 9EW Tel: (01782) 503386 Fax: (01782) 502265 E-mail: ebspanels@btconnect.com
Edmundson Export Services, Unit 1 Skyport Drive, Harmondsworth, West Drayton, Middlesex, UB7 0LB Tel: (020) 8283 0820 Fax: (020) 8283 0821 E-mail: enquiries@edmundsonexport.com
Electrical Supplies Ltd, 7 The Broadway, Hampton Court Way, Thames Ditton, Surrey, KT7 0LX Tel: (020) 8398 9377 Fax: (020) 8398 8093
Electronic Theatre Controls Ltd, Unit 26-28 Victoria Industrial, Estate Victoria Road, London, W3 6UU Tel: (020) 8896 1000 Fax: (020) 8896 2000 E-mail: mail@etcconnect.com
Enigmex Ltd, Kestrel House, 14 Lower Brunswick Street, Leeds, LS2 7PU Tel: 0113-244 9969 Fax: 0113-244 9411
European Lamp Group Lighting Specialists, Allenby House, Knowles Lane, Bradford, West Yorkshire, BD4 9AB Tel: (01274) 473400 Fax: (0870) 4450001 E-mail: sales@europeanlamp.co.uk
Excell Metal Spinning Ltd, 27 Gunners Buildings, Limberline Road, Portsmouth, PO3 5BJ Tel: +44 (023) 9266 6456 Fax: +44 (023) 9266 5456 E-mail: excellmetal@btconnect.com
▶ Fagerult Lighting Ltd, 50 Southwark Street, London, SE1 1UN Tel: (020) 7403 4123 Fax: (020) 7378 0906
▶ First Light Lamps Ltd, Unit 23 Lancaster Way Business Park, Ely, Cambridgeshire, CB6 3NW Tel: (01353) 659922 Fax: (01353) 668883 E-mail: info@firstlightlamps.com
Firstlight Products Ltd, 22 Erica Road, Stacey Bushes, Milton Keynes, MK12 6HS Tel: (01908) 310221 Fax: (01908) 310229 E-mail: flp@firstlight-products.co.uk
▶ Flairlight Designs Ltd, 12 Hillcrest Close, Epsom, Surrey, KT18 5JY Tel: (01372) 807661 Fax: (01372) 807660 E-mail: mike@flairlight.co.uk
G C Designs Ltd, Mansion House Buildings, Market Place, Crich, Matlock, Derbyshire, DE4 5DD Tel: (01773) 857388 Fax: (01773) 857388E-mail: gwyncarless@gcdesigns.co.uk
G F E Electrical Wholesale Ltd, Enterprise House, 370-386 Farnham Road, Slough, SL2 1JD Tel: (01753) 537811 E-mail: ask@gfegroup.com
▶ Gamma Illumination Ltd, Conway House, Tenterfields, Thornhill Road, Dewsbury, West Yorkshire, WF12 9QW Tel: (01924) 482777 Fax: (01924) 438388 E-mail: sales@gamma-uk.com

LIGHTING – *continued*

▶ Granville Paul (Lamps) International, Unit 3 E, Larpool Lane Industrial Estate, Whitby, N. Yorkshire, YO22 4LX Tel: (01947) 825956 Fax: (01947) 825996

Hirepro Ltd, Unit 6 Atlas Business Centre, Oxgate La, Staples Corner, London, NW2 7HJ Tel: (020) 8438 0200 Fax: (020) 8438 0300

Hodgson Lighting, 41 High Street, Hampton Hill, Hampton, Middlesex, TW12 1NB Tel: (020) 8941 3375 Fax: (020) 8979 5178 E-mail: johnatjhlight@tiscali.co.uk

Homelec, Kings Way House, Laporte Way, Luton, LU4 8RJ Tel: (01582) 544510 Fax: (01582) 544511

▶ Ideals Lighting Mnfrs, Unit 3 Brookside, Sumpters Way, Temple Farm Industrial Estate, Southend-on-Sea, SS2 5RR Tel: (01702) 460855 Fax: (01702) 460655 E-mail: sales@idealsgb.co.uk

Illuminations Of Camberley, 66-68 High Street, Camberley, Surrey, GU15 3RS Tel: (01276) 24941 Fax: (01276) 61718 E-mail: sales@illuminationsofcamberley.co.uk

J E Wildbore Ltd, Waddington Street, Oldham, OL9 6QU Tel: 0161-624 4475 Fax: 0161-627 0930 E-mail: sales@jwildbore.co.uk

Keetch Factors 1984 Ltd, Alexandra Road, Mablethorpe, Lincolnshire, LN12 1BJ Tel: (01507) 477177 Fax: (01507) 473878 E-mail: keetchfactors@aol.com

▶ Key Lighting, 37 Dulverton Road, Birmingham, B6 7EQ Tel: 0121-322 2300 Fax: 0121-328 5050

▶ Klere Lighting, 16 Church Lane, London, SW17 9PP Tel: (020) 8772 4081

La Conch Lighting, Cranborne Industrial Estate, Cranborne Road, Potters Bar, Hertfordshire, EN6 3JN Tel: (01707) 644440 Fax: (01707) 644446 E-mail: info@laconch.co.uk

▶ Lamps & Candles Ltd, 42 Manasty Road, Orton Southgate, Peterborough, PE2 6UP Tel: (01733) 237720 Fax: (01733) 237725 E-mail: info@lampsandcandles.co.uk

Lancashire Electric Lamp Co. Ltd, 121-123 St James Street, Liverpool, L1 5HE Tel: 0151-709 1122 Fax: 0151-709 8872

Leda-Lite International Ltd, The Briars, Mayes Lane, Sandon, Chelmsford, CM2 7RP Tel: (01245) 227500 Fax: (01245) 221673 E-mail: leda-lite-international@aol.com

Leyden Electrical Supplies Ltd, Leyden Road, Stevenage, Hertfordshire, SG1 2BP Tel: (01438) 316144 Fax: (01438) 364946 E-mail: info@leydenelectrical.co.uk

The Lighthouse, 14 Station Road, Swinton, Manchester, M27 6AF Tel: 0161-727 8742 Fax: 0161-794 3562 E-mail: markalin2003@yahoon.co.uk

Linen Room, 482 Wilbraham Road, Manchester, M21 9AS Tel: 0161-860 4979 Fax: 0161-860 4979 E-mail: info@2tlr.co.uk

▶ Litecraft, 95 Seaward Street, Kinning Park, Glasgow, G41 1HJ Tel: 0141-429 0000

▶ Litetask Ltd, 1 The Courtyards, Victoria Road, Leeds, LS14 2LB Tel: 0113-265 2651 Fax: 0113-265 2652

▶ Lumasign Ltd, Unit 7, Crewe Close, Blidworth, Mansfield, Nottinghamshire, NG21 0TA Tel: (01623) 491136 Fax: (0845) 2300288 E-mail: info@lumasign.com

Lux Lighting Ltd, 100 Icknield Street, Hockley, Birmingham, B18 6RU Tel: 0121-236 7595 Fax: 0121-236 6548 E-mail: luxlight@aol.com

Malcro Lighting Ltd, Unit 13 College Fields Industrial Estate, Prince Georges Road, London, SW19 2PT Tel: (020) 8640 1001 Fax: (020) 8640 9248

Malisa Lighting Ltd, Unit 4 Conqueror Court, Spilsby Road, Harold Hill, Romford, RM3 8SB Tel: (01708) 372221 Fax: (01708) 381354 E-mail: malisa@mabeys.co.uk

▶ Mallatite (Scotland), 1 McMillan Road, Wishaw, Lanarkshire, ML2 0LA Tel: (01698) 352888 Fax: (01698) 352777

Martech UK Ltd, Conway House, Thornhill Road, Dewsbury, West Yorkshire, WF12 9QQ Tel: (01924) 482700 Fax: (01924) 438388 E-mail: sales@martech-uk.com

Medlock Electric Ltd, 605-609 Green Lanes, London, N8 0RE Tel: (020) 8348 5191 Fax: (020) 8348 3854 E-mail: sales@medlocks.demon.co.uk

Menos Lighting Equipment, 225-227 High Street, London, W3 9BY Tel: (020) 8993 7013 Fax: (020) 8992 8588

Microlights Ltd, Elcot Lane, Marlborough, Wiltshire, SN8 2BG Tel: (01672) 515611 Fax: (01672) 513816 E-mail: sales@microlightsgroup.com

▶ Millennium Lighting UK Ltd, 6 Balm Road Industrial Estate, Beza Street, Leeds, LS10 2BG Tel: 0113-277 9988 Fax: 0113-277 5697 E-mail: info@mlukltd.co.uk

J.H. Miller & Sons Ltd, Irlam Wharf Road, Irlam, Manchester, M44 5PN Tel: 0161-775 0005 Fax: 0161-775 0006 E-mail: sales@jhmiller.co.uk

▶ MS Consultants, Barton Close, South Woodham Ferrers, Chelmsford, CM3 5UB Tel: (01245) 429111 Fax: (01245) 429111

▶ Multiform Technology, Station Road, Hellingly,, Hailsham, East Sussex, BN27 4EU Tel: (01323) 848117 Fax: (01323) 441906 E-mail: sales@multiform-uk.com

Oldham Lighting Ltd, 1 James Corbett Road, Salford, M50 1DE Tel: 0161-745 8087 Fax: 0161-743 0266

Omega Lighting Ltd, 48 Potters Lane, Kiln Farm, Milton Keynes, MK11 3HQ Tel: (01908) 260015 Fax: (01908) 260019 E-mail: sales@omegalighting.co.uk

Optelma Lighting Ltd, 14 Napier Court, Barton Lane, Abingdon, Oxfordshire, OX14 3YT Tel: (01235) 553769 Fax: (01235) 523005 E-mail: sales@optelma.co.uk

▶ P O S Lighting Ltd, Unit 4 Thurmaston Court, Thurmaston, Leicester, LE4 8EB Tel: 0116-269 3500 Fax: 0116-269 3512 E-mail: poslightingltd@btopenworld.com

Palace Lamp Co. Ltd, 4 Century Building, 117 Summers Road, Brunswick Business Park, Liverpool, L3 4BL Tel: 0151-709 4000 Fax: 0151-707 0074 E-mail: duncan@palacelamp.com

▶ Louis Paulsen, 24 Barwell Business Park, Leatherhead Road, Chessington, Surrey, KT9 2NY Tel: (020) 8397 4400 Fax: (020) 8397 4455

Photon Beard Ltd, Unit K3, Cherrycourt Way, Stanbridge Road, Leighton Buzzard, Bedfordshire, LU7 4UH Tel: (01525) 850911 Fax: (01525) 850922 E-mail: info@photonbeard.com

J.F. Poynter Ltd, Unit 23 More House Farm Business Centre, Ditchling Road, Wivelsfield, Haywards Heath, West Sussex, RH17 7RE Tel: (01444) 471491 Fax: (01444) 471777 E-mail: sales@maximlamps.co.uk

▶ Precision Louvre Co. Ltd, Swinbourne Road, Burnt Mills Industrial Estate, Basildon, Essex, SS13 1EH Tel: (01268) 729554 Fax: (01268) 729563 E-mail: sales@precision-louvre.co.uk

Ring Group Ltd, Nina Works, Gelderd Road, Leeds, LS12 6NB Tel: 0113-276 7676 Fax: 0113-263 0475 E-mail: enquiries@ring.ltd.uk

Rutland Lighting, 10-12 Watergate, Grantham, Lincolnshire, NG31 6PR Tel: (01476) 591049 Fax: (01476) 591049

Samsons Transformers, 24 37 Hamilton Road, Twickenham, TW2 6SN Tel: (020) 8893 4053 Fax: (020) 8893 4054 E-mail: enquiries@samsons.co.uk

▶ Sign & Light, Unit 5 Sherwood Industrial Estate, Bonnyrigg, Midlothian, EH19 3LW Tel: 0131-654 1122 Fax: 0131-654 0808

Speights Classic Lighting, Huddersfield Road, Mirfield, West Yorkshire, WF14 8BJ Tel: (01924) 494176 Fax: (01924) 480691

R. & B. Star Ltd, 14 Kennet Road, Crayford, Dartford, DA1 4SD Tel: (01322) 555125 Fax: (01322) 522465

▶ Starscape, 7 Main Street, Lowick, Berwick-upon-Tweed, TD15 2UD Tel: (01289) 388399 E-mail: info@starceiling.co.uk

▶ Surrey Lighting Centre, 13-14 Castle Parade, Ewell By Passage, Epsom, Surrey, KT17 2PR Tel: (020) 8393 0953 Fax: (020) 8394 2181 E-mail: sales@surreylighting.co.uk

T T I Electrical Ltd, Tti House Millers Yard, Long Lane, London, N3 2QG Tel: (020) 8343 1661 Fax: (020) 8343 1771 E-mail: sales@tti-group.co.uk

▶ K.J. Tait Engineers, 15 Woodside Terrace, Glasgow, G3 7XH Tel: 0141-332 9676 Fax: 0141-332 0995 E-mail: glasgow@kjtait.com

▶ Tamtec Electronics, Stafford Park 12, Telford, Shropshire, TF3 3BJ Tel: (01952) 299399 Fax: (01952) 299300

▶ Targetti UK, Units 1-4, 11-29 Fashion Street, London, E1 6PX Tel: (020) 7377 2005 Fax: (020) 7377 0043 E-mail: office@targetti.co.uk

Tridonic Ltd, Thomas House Hampshire International Business Park, Crockford L, Chineham, Basingstoke, Hampshire, RG24 8LB Tel: (01256) 374300 Fax: (01256) 374200 E-mail: enquiries@uk.tridonic.co.uk

Valiant Lamps Ltd, European I Park, Knowles Lane, Bradford, West Yorkshire, BD4 9AD Tel: (0870) 4450000 Fax: (0870) 4450001 E-mail: wholesale@europeanlampgroup.com

▶ Vandalite, Dunkirk Mills, Dunkirk Street, Halifax, West Yorkshire, HX1 3TB Tel: (01422) 354254 Fax: (01422) 356066

▶ Wallace Whittle & Partners, 166 Great Western Road, Aberdeen, AB10 6QE Tel: (01224) 285300 Fax: (01224) 285301 E-mail: aberdeen@wallacewhittle.com

Welwyn Lighting Designs Ltd, Bessemer Road, Welwyn Garden City, Hertfordshire, AL7 1HH Tel: (01707) 255300 Fax: (01707) 255357 E-mail: sales@wewyn-lighting.co.uk

Cliff Wood Ltd, 10 Chapel Lane, Lowgate, Hull, HU1 1SB Tel: (01482) 223429 Fax: (01482) 215146 E-mail: user@cliffwoodltd.co.uk

LIGHTING ACCESSORIES

Crimway, 17 County Road, Buckingham Road Industrial Estate, Buckingham Road Industrial Estate, Brackley, Northamptonshire, NN13 7AX Tel: (01280) 840005 Fax: (01280) 704440

Delta Light, Gresham House 2a Unicorn Trading Estate, Weydown Lane, Haslemere, Surrey, GU27 1DN Tel: (01428) 651919 Fax: (01428) 644506 E-mail: sales@deltalight.co.uk

Dreamlight, 599a Prescot Road, Old Swan, Liverpool, L13 5XA Tel: 0151-228 7770 Fax: 0151-228 8612

Halo, Kings Cross Freight Depot, York Way, London, N1 0UZ Tel: (020) 7837 3300 Fax: (020) 7837 3310 E-mail: info@halo.co.uk

Hughes Light, 1 Mill Cottages, Hurcott, Kidderminster, Worcestershire, DY10 3PH Tel: (01562) 742082 Fax: 0121-440 7477

K A S Lighting Services Ltd, 39 Morton Way, London, N14 7HS Tel: (020) 8882 2500 Fax: (020) 8882 2605

Krylite Ltd, 80a Newton Road, Rushden, Northamptonshire, NN10 0HQ Tel: (01933) 312745 Fax: (01933) 410484

Light Solutions, Well House, Penn Street, Amersham, Buckinghamshire, HP7 0PY Tel: (01494) 717709 Fax: (01494) 891165 E-mail: sales@light-solutions.co.uk

Lumitron Ltd, Park House, 15-23 Greenhill Crescent, Watford Business Park, Watford, WD18 8PH Tel: (01923) 226222 Fax: (01923) 211300 E-mail: sales@lumitron.co.uk

Omega Lighting Ltd, 48 Potters Lane, Kiln Farm, Milton Keynes, MK11 3HQ Tel: (01908) 260015 Fax: (01908) 260019 E-mail: sales@omegalighting.co.uk

Profile 2000 Ltd, Units 1-3 Carey Street, Kettering, Northamptonshire, NN16 0JL Tel: (01536) 522004 Fax: (01536) 416468

Transformation Tubes, 118 Winkworth Road, Banstead, Surrey, SM7 2QR Tel: (01737) 373483 Fax: (01737) 370590 E-mail: transtubes@aol.com

Vysal Lighting Ltd, Five Acres, Morse Close, Malmesbury, Wiltshire, SN16 9UW Tel: (01666) 822059 Fax: (01666) 822422 E-mail: vysal@vysal.com

Welwyn Lighting Designs Ltd, Bessemer Road, Welwyn Garden City, Hertfordshire, AL7 1HH Tel: (01707) 255300 Fax: (01707) 255357 E-mail: sales@wewyn-lighting.co.uk

Woodside Festoon Lighting Ltd, Light House, Lancashire Hill, Stockport, Cheshire, SK4 1RR Tel: 0161-480 6448 Fax: 0161-474 1823

LIGHTING ASSEMBLY SERVICES

Baz Light Design & Installation, 6 Golden Court, Bridge Road, Lowestoft, Suffolk, NR32 3LU Tel: (01502) 501628 Fax: (01502) 501628

▶ Parkersell Lighting & Electrical Services Ltd, 1439 Clock Tower Road, Isleworth, Middlesex, TW7 6DT Tel: (020) 8569 8595 Fax: (020) 8758 9923

LIGHTING COMPONENTS

Apem Components Ltd, Drakes Drive, Long Crendon, Aylesbury, Buckinghamshire, HP18 9BA Tel: (01844) 202400 Fax: (01844) 202500 E-mail: info@apem.co.uk

B G Electrical Accessories, Unit 1 Highpoint Business Village, Henwood, Ashford, Kent, TN24 8DH Tel: (01233) 668000 Fax: (01233) 668100 E-mail: efasales@arlen.co.uk

Bonus Accessories, Citadel Trading Park, Citadel Way, Hull, HU9 1TQ Tel: (01482) 580077 Fax: (01482) 588753 E-mail: bonusacc@aol.com

Collingwood, Sywell Aerodrome, Sywell, Northampton, NN6 0AW Tel: (01604) 495151 Fax: (01604) 495095 E-mail: sales@collingwoodgroup.com

Environmental Lighting Ltd, P O Box 542, Altrincham, Cheshire, WA15 8ZU Tel: (0871) 2233320 Fax: (0871) 2233321 E-mail: envlighting@btconnect.com

▶ Inlico, Q1 Hawthorne Industrial Estate, Middlemore Road, Handsworth, Birmingham, B21 0BH Tel: 0121-515 3020 Fax: 0121-515 4629 E-mail: info@inlico.com

Masonlite Ltd, 36 Second Avenue, Chatham, Kent, ME4 5AX Tel: (01634) 812751 Fax: (01634) 811883 E-mail: neon@masonlite.com

Mode Lighting (UK) Ltd, The Maltings, 63 High Street, Ware, Hertfordshire, SG12 9AD Tel: (01920) 462121 Fax: (01920) 466882 E-mail: sales@mode-lighting.co.uk

Southgate Lighting Ltd, Southgate, Moorland Road, Drighlington, Bradford, West Yorkshire, BD11 1JY Tel: 0113-285 4000 Fax: 0113-285 3434

Touchstone Lighting Components, Unit 21-22, Emerald Way, Stone Business Park, Stone, Staffordshire, ST15 0SR Tel: (01785) 817123 Fax: (01785) 817120 E-mail: sales@touchstonelighting.co.uk

Tungsten Manufacturing Ltd, 22-28 Cambridge Street, Aylesbury, Buckinghamshire, HP20 1RS Tel: (01296) 394566 Fax: (01296) 394566 E-mail: sales@tungsten.co.uk

LIGHTING CONSULTANCY OR DESIGN

A.L.D. Lighting, Unit 6E Southbourne Business Park, Courtlands Road, Eastbourne, East Sussex, BN22 8UY Tel: (01323) 729337 Fax: (01323) 732356 E-mail: sales@aldlighting.com

B D B Marketing Ltd, D161-162 Fruit & Vegetable Market, New Covent Garden, Vauxall, London, SW8 5LL Tel: (020) 7720 4444 Fax: (020) 7720 4808 E-mail: bryan1brown@hotmail.com

Box Products Ltd, The Lodge 3 Russell House, Cambridge Street, London, SW1V 4EQ Tel: (020) 7976 6791 Fax: (020) 7828 7133 E-mail: boxproducts@btinternet.com

C L E Design Ltd, 69-71 Haydons Road, London, SW19 1HQ Tel: (020) 8540 5772 E-mail: admin@cle-design.com

Decorlight, B 68 Pier Avenue, Clacton-on-Sea, Essex, CO15 1NH Tel: (01255) 421818 Fax: (01255) 474147

Designed Architectural Lighting Ltd, 6 Conqueror Court, Spilsby Road, Harold Hill, Romford, RM3 8SB Tel: (01708) 381999 Fax: (01708) 381585

▶ Elder's Engineers, 9 Park CR, Edinburgh, EH16 6JD Tel: 0131-664 5176 Fax: 0131-664 5643

▶ Firefly Lighting Design, 4th Floor Threshold House, 65-69 Shepherds Bush Green, London, W12 8TX Tel: (020) 8746 2991 E-mail: info@fireflylightingdesign.com

▶ David Fox Design, Briars Lane, Stainforth, Doncaster, South Yorkshire, DN7 5AZ Tel: (01302) 849299 Fax: (01302) 849299 E-mail: info@davidfoxdesign.com

Hacel Lighting Ltd, Harcel House, Silverlink, Wallsend, Tyne & Wear, NE28 9ND Tel: 0191-280 9911 Fax: 0191-263 1144 E-mail: purchasing@hacel.co.uk

Illuminations Of Camberley, 66-68 High Street, Camberley, Surrey, GU15 3RS Tel: (01276) 24941 Fax: (01276) 61718 E-mail: sales@illuminationsofcamberley.co.uk

▶ Impact Arts Glasgow Ltd, The Factory, 319-321 Craigpark Drive, Glasgow, G31 2TB Tel: 0141-575 3001

Lamps & Lighting, Bridgewater Court, Network 65 Business Park, Hapton, Burnley, Lancashire, BB11 5ST Tel: (01282) 448666 Fax: (01282) 417705 E-mail: sales@lamps-lighting.co.uk

Light Matters, 6 Long Street, London, E2 8HQ Tel: (020) 7749 4770 Fax: (020) 7749 4771 E-mail: london@lightmatters.co.uk

▶ Litecraft, 95 Seaward Street, Kinning Park, Glasgow, G41 1HJ Tel: 0141-429 0000

Lloyd & Son, Copthall Farm, Breakspear Road South, Ickenham, Uxbridge, Middlesex, UB10 8HB Tel: (01895) 679000 Fax: (01895) 679000 E-mail: lloydandson640@btinternet.com

Orostream Applied Contracting Ltd, Park Road, Crowborough, East Sussex, TN6 2QT Tel: (01892) 665888 Fax: (01892) 663218 E-mail: oracl@aol.com

▶ Parkersell Lighting & Electrical Services Ltd, 17 Shield Drive, Wardley Industrial Estate, Worsley, Manchester, M28 2QB Tel: 0161-727 8205 Fax: 0161-727 7098

Puissance Computer Associates, 1 Bushey Coopers Cottage, Pond Hall Road, Hadleigh, Ipswich, IP7 5PS Tel: (01473) 822002 Fax: (01473) 829665 E-mail: sales@puissance.co.uk

Scriptus Ltd, 3 Campus Road, Listerhills Science Park, Bradford, West Yorkshire, BD7 1HR Tel: 0113-278 0367 Fax: (01274) 391973 E-mail: stylus.marketing@virgin.net

Travelling Light Birmingham, Squires Croft Business Centre, Sutton Coldfield, West Midlands, B76 2RY Tel: 0121-313 3598 Fax: 0121-313 0446 E-mail: sales@travellinglightbirmingham.co.uk

Whitecroft Lighting Ltd, Burlington Street, Ashton-under-Lyne, Lancashire, OL7 0AX Tel: (0870) 5087087 Fax: (0870) 5084210 E-mail: sales@lightshow.co.uk

LIGHTING CONTROL SYSTEM DESIGN

▶ A D V Audio Visual Installations Ltd, 12 York Place, Leeds, LS1 2DS Tel: (0870) 1995755 Fax: (0709) 2100142 E-mail: shaun@adv-installs.co.uk

▶ ISEC Solutions, Meadowcroft, Nottingham Road, Ravenshead, Nottingham, NG15 9HP Tel: 01623 792200 Fax: 01623 792293 E-mail: mark@isec-solutions.co.uk

Lightiq Ltd, 1 Rylett Studios 77 Rylett Crescent, London, W12 9RP Tel: (020) 8749 1900 Fax: (020) 8749 1999 E-mail: abby@lighting.com

LIGHTING CONTROL SYSTEMS

▶ A D V Audio Visual Installations Ltd, 12 York Place, Leeds, LS1 2DS Tel: (0870) 1995755 Fax: (0709) 2100142 E-mail: shaun@adv-installs.co.uk

Anytronics Ltd, 5-6 Hillside Industrial Estate, London Road, Horndean, Waterlooville, Hampshire, PO8 0BL Tel: (023) 9259 9410 Fax: (023) 9259 8723 E-mail: sales@anytronics.com

Avolites Ltd, Park Avenue, London, NW10 7XL Tel: (020) 8965 8522 Fax: (020) 8965 0290 E-mail: sales@avolites.com

C P Electronic Ltd, Unit 2 Abbey Manufacturing Estate, Wembley, Middlesex, HA0 1RR Tel: (020) 8900 0671 Fax: (020) 8900 0674 E-mail: enquiry@cpelectronics.co.uk

Chalmor Ltd, 1 Telmere Industrial Estate, Albert Road, Luton, LU1 3QF Tel: (01582) 748700 Fax: (01582) 748748 E-mail: sales@chalmor.co.uk

E C S Phillips Lighting Controls, Phillips Centre, Guildford Business Park, Guildford, Surrey, GU2 8XH Tel: (01483) 293235 Fax: (01483) 575534 E-mail: ecs.phillips@phillips.com

Electrak Holdings Ltd, Number One Industrial Estate, Medomsley Road, Consett, County Durham, DH8 6SR Tel: (01207) 503400 Fax: (01207) 501799 E-mail: sales@electrak.co.uk

Electronic & Technical Services Ltd, Unit 32, Price St Business Centre, Birkenhead, Merseyside, CH41 4JQ Tel: 0151-670 1897 Fax: 0151-652 9941

Huco Lightronic Ni Ltd, 3 Aghanloo Industrial Estate, Aghanloo Road, Limavady, County Londonderry, BT49 0HE Tel: (028) 7776 8567 Fax: (028) 7776 8515 E-mail: sales@huco.co.uk

LIGHTING CONTROL SYSTEMS – *continued*

Jerrards plc, Arcadia House Cairo New Road, Croydon, CR0 1XP Tel: (020) 8251 5522 Fax: (020) 8251 5500
Leax Lighting Controls, Unit 11 Mandeville Courtyard, 142 Battersea Park Road, London, SW11 4NB Tel: (020) 7501 0880 Fax: (020) 7501 0890
Lightiq Ltd, 1 Rylett Studios 77 Rylett Crescent, London, W12 9RP Tel: (020) 8749 1900 Fax: (020) 8749 1999 E-mail: abby@lighting.com
Megatron Ltd, Unit 24f1, 784-788 High Road, London, N17 0DA Tel: (020) 8365 9797 Fax: (020) 8808 6186 E-mail: sales@megatron.co.uk
Metron Energy Management Ltd, PO Box 190, Winsford, Cheshire, CW7 9AH Tel: (01606) 882722 Fax: (01606) 889440 E-mail: enquiries@demmetron.co.uk
Mode Lighting (UK) Ltd, The Maltings, 63 High Street, Ware, Hertfordshire, SG12 9AD Tel: (01920) 462121 Fax: (01920) 466882 E-mail: sales@mode-lighting.co.uk
Premier Solutions (Nottingham) Ltd, Ascot Industrial Estate, Sandiacre, Nottingham, NG10 5DL Tel: 0115-939 4122 Fax: 0115-949 0453 E-mail: info@premier-solutions.biz
Setsquare Ltd, Tonbridge Road, Hadlow, Tonbridge, Kent, TN11 0AH Tel: (01732) 851888 Fax: (01732) 851853 E-mail: sales@setsquare.co.uk
Simmtronic Ltd, Unit 3, Waterside Industrial Estate, Charlton Mead Lane, Hoddesdon, Hertfordshire, EN11 0QR Tel: (01992) 450126 Fax: (01992) 450127 E-mail: sales@simmtronic.com
Transtar, Glasgow, G52 4BL Tel: 0141-810 9644 Fax: 0141-810 8642 E-mail: sales@transtargear.co.uk
Tridonic Ltd, Thomas House Hampshire International Business Park, Crockford L, Chineham, Basingstoke, Hampshire, RG24 8LB Tel: (01256) 374300 Fax: (01256) 374200 E-mail: enquiries@uk.tridonic.co.uk
Zero 88 Lighting Ltd, Usk House, Lakeside, Llantarnam Industrial Park, Cwmbran, Gwent, NP44 3HD Tel: (01633) 838088 Fax: (01633) 867880 E-mail: sales@zero88.com

LIGHTING CORDS

Lucent Lighting (UK) Ltd, Old Station House, 7A Coppetts Road, London, N10 1NN Tel: (020) 8442 0880 Fax: (020) 8444 6998

LIGHTING DIFFUSERS

Cryselco Lighting Ltd, 274 Ampthill Road, Bedford, MK42 9QJ Tel: (01234) 273355 Fax: (01234) 210867 E-mail: sales@cryselco.co.uk
Lastolite Ltd, 1 Atlas Road, Coalville, Leicestershire, LE67 3FQ Tel: (01530) 813381 Fax: (01530) 830408 E-mail: sales@lastolite.com
▶ Shere Lighting, 5 Burrows Lea Farm, Hook Lane, Shere, Guildford, Surrey, GU5 9QQ Tel: (01483) 205333 Fax: (01483) 205334 E-mail: sherelightingltd@aol.com

LIGHTING DIMMER EQUIPMENT

Anytronics Ltd, 5-6 Hillside Industrial Estate, London Road, Horndean, Waterlooville, Hampshire, PO8 0BL Tel: (023) 9259 9410 Fax: (023) 9259 8723 E-mail: sales@anytronics.com
Avolites Ltd, Park Avenue, London, NW10 7XL Tel: (020) 8965 8522 Fax: (020) 8965 0290 E-mail: sales@avolites.com
Lightfactor Sales, 20 Greenhill Crescent, Watford Business Park, Watford, WD18 8JA Tel: (01923) 698090 Fax: (01923) 698081 E-mail: info@lightfactor.co.uk
Pulsar Light Of Cambridge, 3 Coldhams Business Park, Norman Way, Cambridge, CB1 3LH Tel: (01223) 403500 Fax: (01223) 403501 E-mail: sales@pulsarlight.com

LIGHTING (EMERGENCY) COMPONENTS

Collingwood, Sywell Aerodrome, Sywell, Northampton, NN6 0AW Tel: (01604) 495151 Fax: (01604) 495095 E-mail: sales@collingwoodgroup.com
Mackwell Electronics Ltd, Hayward Industrial Park, Vigo Place, Walsall, WS9 8UG Tel: (01922) 458255 Fax: (01922) 451263 E-mail: sales@mackwell.com
Spel Lighting Mnfrs, Beecham Close, Walsall, WS9 8UZ Tel: (0870) 5168214 Fax: (0870) 5168519 E-mail: sales@spelonline.co.uk

LIGHTING (EMERGENCY) HIRE

Golden Triangle Power Generation, Units 1-2 Weaver Park Industrial Estate, Mill Lane, Frodsham, WA6 7JB Tel: (01928) 722137 Fax: (01928) 722240E-mail: hire@gtgen.co.uk

LIGHTING (EMERGENCY) MODULES, SELF TESTING

Mackwell Electronics Ltd, Hayward Industrial Park, Vigo Place, Walsall, WS9 8UG Tel: (01922) 458255 Fax: (01922) 451263 E-mail: sales@mackwell.com

LIGHTING EQUIPMENT HIRE

▶ Impact Arts Glasgow Ltd, The Factory, 319-321 Craigpark Drive, Glasgow, G31 2TB Tel: 0141-575 3001

LIGHTING FILTERS

Cotech Ltd, Unit 13-16, Tafarnaubach Industrial Estate, Tafarnaubach, Tredegar, Gwent, NP22 3AA Tel: (01495) 711970 Fax: (01495) 725765 E-mail: sales@cotech-uk.com
Datasights Ltd, 228-234 Alma Road, Enfield, Middlesex, EN3 7BB Tel: (020) 8805 4151 Fax: (020) 8805 8084 E-mail: sales@datasights.com
Lee Filters, Unit 1-2 Kingsway, Andover, Hampshire, SP10 5LQ Tel: (01264) 364112 Fax: (01264) 355058 E-mail: sales@leefilters.com

LIGHTING FITTINGS

Abacas Electrical Supplies Ltd, Unit 3 Anthonys Way, Medway City Estate, Rochester, Kent, ME2 4NW Tel: (01634) 714468 Fax: (01634) 714480 E-mail: sales@abacuselectricalsupplies.co.uk

LIGHTING GEAR TRAYS

Peco Electrical Services, The Maltings, Roydon Road, Stanstead Abbotts, Ware, Hertfordshire, SG12 8HG Tel: (01920) 877548 Fax: (01920) 877936 E-mail: peter.coard@breathemail.net

LIGHTING IMPORT

A M C O, Tresham House, 166 High Street, Deal, Kent, CT14 6BQ Tel: (01304) 239185 Fax: (01304) 239185E-mail: ajm@emec.co.uk
Speights Classic Lighting, Huddersfield Road, Mirfield, West Yorkshire, WF14 8BJ Tel: (01924) 494176 Fax: (01924) 480691
Task Lighting Ltd, 1 Low Farm Place, Moulton Park Industrial Estate, Northampton, NN3 6HY Tel: (01604) 644875 Fax: (01604) 790016 E-mail: sales@tasklighting.co.uk

LIGHTING INTERIOR DESIGN CONSULTANCY

▶ Firefly Lighting Design, 4th Floor Threshold House, 65-69 Shepherds Bush Green, London, W12 8TX Tel: (020) 8746 2991 E-mail: info@fireflylightingdesign.com
Interiors By Design, 37 The Spinney, Pulborough, West Sussex, RH20 2AP Tel: (01798) 874969 E-mail: interiorsbydesign@ukonline.co.uk
▶ Lemon Tree Interiors, 5 Cambridge Road, Ely, Cambridgeshire, CB7 4HJ Tel: (01353) 610585 Fax: (01353) 610466 E-mail: Design@LemonTreeInteriors.Co.Uk
Steinel (UK) Ltd, 25 Manasty Road, Axis Park, Orton Southgate, Peterborough, PE2 6UP Tel: (01733) 366700 Fax: (01733) 366701 E-mail: steinel@steineluk.co.uk

LIGHTING (PHOTOGRAPHIC) CONSULTANTS OR DESIGNERS

Artseens.com Picture Library, 45 Avondale Court, Avondale Road, London, E16 4PU Tel: (020) 7476 0215 E-mail: info@artseens.com

LIGHTING RESTORATION OR REPAIR OR CLEANING SERVICES

Parkersell Lighting, 4th Floor The Connect Centre, Kingstone Crescent, Portsmouth, PO2 8AD Tel: (023) 9262 3700 Fax: (023) 9262 3720 E-mail: enquiries@parkersell.com
Weblight Lighting Contractors, Unit 14 Park Court, Sullivans Way, St. Helens, Merseyside, WA9 5GZ Tel: (01744) 455711 Fax: (01744) 455710 E-mail: sales@weblight.co.uk

LIGHTING (SPECIAL EFFECT) HIRE

Cardiff M Light & Sound, Unit 2 The Highway Man Pub, Castle View, Bridgend, Mid Glamorgan, CF31 1NJ Tel: (01656) 648170 Fax: (01656) 648412 E-mail: sales@cardiffm.co.uk
Event Lighting, 10 Palmerston Close, Kibworth, Leicester, LE8 0JJ Tel: 0116-279 3851
GDC Themed Events Ltd, 38-42 Fife Road, Kingston Upon Thames, Surrey, KT1 1SU Tel: (020) 8547 3682 Fax: (020) 8546 8461 E-mail: tim@gdc-events.co.uk
Lightech Sound & Light Ltd, Bramhall Hill Farm, Bank Lane, North Rode, Congleton, Cheshire, CW12 2PJ Tel: (01260) 223666 Fax: (01260) 223777 E-mail: mail@lightech.fsnet.co.uk
Pacific Sound & Light, 505 Bristol Road, Selly Oak, Birmingham, B29 6AU Tel: 0121-471 3110 Fax: 0121-471 3103 E-mail: enquiries@pacificsoundandlight.co.uk
Tega Office, 58 Stockholm Road, Hull, HU7 0XW Tel: (01482) 831032 Fax: (01482) 831331 E-mail: sales@tega.co.uk
Wats On Lighting & Sound Ltd, Upper House, Presteigne, Powys, LD8 2HG Tel: (01544) 260114 Fax: (01544) 267686

LIGHTING SWITCHES

▶ Beeswitched, PO Box 413, Horsham, West Sussex, RH12 2YD Tel: (01403) 242003 E-mail: info@beeswitched.com

LIGHTING TO SPECIFICATION

A.L.D. Lighting, Unit 6E Southbourne Business Park, Courtlands Road, Eastbourne, East Sussex, BN22 8UY Tel: (01323) 729337 Fax: (01323) 732356 E-mail: sales@aldlighting.com
Canatronics Delta Ltd, Unit 5, Dewhurst Row, Bamber Bridge, Preston, PR5 6SW Tel: (01772) 629429 Fax: (01772) 698611 E-mail: info@canatronics-uk.com
▶ CJ Carpets & Lighting, 53 Scotgate, Stamford, Lincolnshire, PE9 2YQ Tel: (01780) 754825 Fax: (01780) 754825
Hacel Lighting Ltd, Harcel House, Silverlink, Wallsend, Tyne & Wear, NE28 9ND Tel: 0191-280 9911 Fax: 0191-263 1144 E-mail: purchasing@hacel.co.uk
Jerrards plc, Arcadia House Cairo New Road, Croydon, CR0 1XP Tel: (020) 8251 5522 Fax: (020) 8251 5500
Luckswitch Ltd, Unit 1b St Columbe Industrial Estate, St. Columb Road, St. Columb, Cornwall, TR9 6PZ Tel: (01726) 862994 Fax: (01726) 862995
▶ Oberoi Bros Lighting Ltd, Humbleton Drive, Derby, DE22 4AU Tel: (01332) 341027 Fax: (01332) 293863 E-mail: sales@lightsuk.com
Scriptus Ltd, 3 Campus Road, Listerhills Science Park, Bradford, West Yorkshire, BD7 1HR Tel: 0113-278 0367 Fax: (01274) 391973 E-mail: stylus.marketing@virgin.net

LIGHTING TRANSFORMERS

Danbury Electronics, 20 Cutlers Road, Saltcoats Industrial Estate, South Woodham Ferrers, Chelmsford, CM3 5XJ Tel: (01245) 328174 Fax: (01245) 328963 E-mail: danburyelectx@aol.com
De Tech, Unit 36e The Lingfield Estate, Mcmullen Road, Darlington, County Durham, DL1 1RW Tel: (01325) 489001 Fax: (01325) 489001 E-mail: sales@detech.fsnet.co.uk
Mode Lighting (UK) Ltd, The Maltings, 63 High Street, Ware, Hertfordshire, SG12 9AD Tel: (01920) 462121 Fax: (01920) 466882 E-mail: sales@mode-lighting.co.uk
Torr-Tech Ltd, Unit 20 B-C St Helen Industrial Estate, Bishop Auckland, County Durham, DL14 9AZ Tel: (01388) 450005 Fax: (01388) 450039 E-mail: sales@torr-tech.co.uk

LIGHTING, AIRFIELD, PORTABLE

▶ Arbarr Electronics, Unit 14c Rathenraw Industrial Estate, Antrim, BT41 2SJ Tel: (028) 9442 9333 Fax: (028) 9442 6178 E-mail: johnpaul@arbarr.co.uk

LIGHTING, DISCO, MOBILE

▶ a Partydisco, 85 Watlands View, Porthill, Newcastle, Staffordshire, ST5 8AG Tel: (01782) 861481 E-mail: enquiries@partydisco.co.uk
▶ A2Z Disco Roadshow, Grove Street, Stoke-on-Trent, ST6 2JA Tel: (07734) 699095 E-mail: leigh@leighs.org
▶ Beach Entertainments, 89 The Ridgway, Brighton, BN2 6PB Tel: (01273) 388424
▶ Beat Route Music, 27 Branscombe Drive, Wootton Bassett, Swindon, SN4 8HS Tel: (01793) 850086 E-mail: Disco@Swindon-Disco.co.uk
▶ Discos Occasions, 12 Park Meadow, Westhoughton, Bolton, BL5 3UZ Tel: (01942) 817292 Fax: E-mail: info@occasionsdiscos.co.uk
▶ Discos Online, 29 Oaken Copse Crescent, Hawley, Farnborough, Hants, GU14 8DS Tel: 01252 661674 E-mail: andy@discosonline.co.uk
▶ DJ Hodgy! . Ltd, 54 Haig Street, Grangemouth, Falkirk, FK3 8QF Tel: (07043) 346349 Fax: (07043) 346349 E-mail: care@dj-hodgy.com
▶ Intelligent Service, Unit 13, Marino Way, Finchampstead, Wokingham, Berkshire, RG40 4RF Tel: 0118-973 5050 Fax: 0118-973 5544 E-mail: nigel@4repair.co.uk
▶ Lek Trix Enterprises, The Barn, 15 Station Street, Whetstone, Leicester, LE8 6JS Tel: 0116-286 5956 Fax: 0116-286 5956 E-mail: lektrix@aol.com
▶ Solitaire Entertainments Ltd, 11 Mitford Close, Reading, RG2 8JQ Tel: 0118-986 4595 Fax: 0118-967 2498 E-mail: info@solitaireentertainments.co.uk
▶ Soundbarrier Systems, 4 Knowsley Crescent, Portsmouth, PO6 2PJ Tel: (07709) 815242 E-mail: simon@soundbarriersystems.com
▶ Sparkys Karaoke & Disco Supplies, 5 Meadow Gardens, Portstewart, County Londonderry, BT55 7SS Tel: (028) 7083 8197 Fax: (028) 7083 8197
▶ Special FX Entertainments, Unit 3, New Found Out Farm, Whiteoak Green, Witney, Oxfordshire, OX29 9XP Tel: (07785) 266702 Fax: (08456) 106406 E-mail: enquiries@special-f-x.co.uk
▶ Supersounds Roadshow, 112 Tamarisk Road, South Ockendon, Essex, RM15 6HX Tel: (01708) 670582 E-mail: supersounds@btinternet.com
▶ Sussex Disco, The Templars, Worthing, West Sussex, BN15 0DT Tel: (01903) 200850 Fax: (01903) 200850 E-mail: info@sussexdisco.co.uk
▶ Tony Patti Entertainments, Sunrise Radio, Merrick Road, Southall, Middlesex, UB2 4AU Tel: 07961 908650 E-mail: tonypatti@sunriseradio.com

LIGHTING, EMERGENCY, PORTABLE

▶ Arbarr Electronics, Unit 14c Rathenraw Industrial Estate, Antrim, BT41 2SJ Tel: (028) 9442 9333 Fax: (028) 9442 6178 E-mail: johnpaul@arbarr.co.uk

LIGHTING, LOW LEVEL/ESCAPE

Globright Ltd, 530 Woodbridge Road, Ipswich, IP4 4PN Tel: (01473) 721561 Fax: (01473) 714069 E-mail: sales@globritephotoluminescent.com

LIGHTING, SOLAR POWERED, OUTDOOR

▶ Lighting Infocus, The Old Rectory, Jacobstowe, Okehampton, Devon, EX20 3RQ Tel: (01837) 851436 E-mail: judy@lawsondev.com
▶ Polycool Ltd, Church Lane, Kinwarton, Alcester, Warwickshire, B49 6HB Tel: (01789) 766880 Fax: (01789) 764162 E-mail: pol@polycool.co.uk
Solar Illuminations, P.O. Box 19, Rye, East Sussex, TN31 6WZ Tel: (020) 8144 0847 E-mail: sales@solarilluminations.co.uk

LIGHTNING CONDUCTOR INSTALLATION OR SERVICING

A & J Installations, 1 The Chestnuts, Codicote, Hitchin, Hertfordshire, SG4 8XR Tel: (01438) 821058 Fax: (01438) 821970
Aboval & Co. Ltd, 24 Firtrees Close, Rothershide, London, SE16 5NG Tel: (07774) 852505 Fax: (020) 7252 3793
B E S T, Morton Street, Brooke House, Middleton, Manchester, M24 6AN Tel: 0161-655 3000 Fax: 0161-655 3001 E-mail: info@bestservices.co.uk
▶ Direct Lighting Distributors Ltd, Gibbs Marsh Trading Estate, Stalbridge, Sturminster Newton, Dorset, DT10 2RY Tel: (01963) 362697 Fax: (01963) 363445
E E S London Ltd, 79 Croydon Road, Caterham, Surrey, CR3 6PD Tel: (01883) 341166 Fax: (01883) 341133
Earthing Equipment Supplies Southern Ltd, Lavender House, Church Lane, Arborfield, Reading, RG2 9JA Tel: 0118-976 0239 Fax: 0118-976 0076 E-mail: sales@earthingequip.com
Electrical Affairs Ltd, 151 Broad Lane, London, N15 4QX Tel: (020) 8808 7887 Fax: (020) 8801 5513
Eurotech Electrical Services Ltd, Green Acres, Hilton Road Seamer, Middlesbrough, Cleveland, TS9 5LX Tel: (01642) 713804 Fax: (01642) 713804 E-mail: eurotechelectricalservices@greenacres110.fsnet.co.uk

LIGHTNING CONDUCTOR INSTALLATION OR SERVICING – *continued*

Horizon Specialist Contracting Ltd, Horizon House, Criffin Enterprise Centre, Oxton Road, Eupperstone, Nottingham, NG14 6AT Tel: (0870) 0104915 Fax: (0870) 0104916 E-mail: sales@horizonsc.co.uk

Omega Red Group, 10 Brewster Square, Brucefield Industrial Estate, Livingston, West Lothian, EH54 9BJ Tel: (01506) 464620 Fax: (01506) 461382 E-mail: sales@omegaredgroup.com

Pendrich Hype Services Ltd, 78-82 Carnethie Street, Rosewell, Midlothian, EH24 9AW Tel: 0131-440 1991 Fax: 0131-448 2157 E-mail: enquiries@pendrich.com

Protectis Ltd, 12a Hazel Street, Bulwell, Nottingham, NG6 8EA Tel: 0115-975 8820 Fax: 0115-975 8821 E-mail: info@protectis.co.uk

R C Cutting & Co. Ltd, 10-12 Arcadia Avenue, London, N3 2JU Tel: (020) 8371 0001 Fax: (020) 8371 0003 E-mail: info@rccutting.co.uk

Sentinel Lightning Protection & Earthing Ltd, Sentinel House 19 Great, Northern Way Netherfield, Nottingham, NG4 2HD Tel: 0115-961 0520 Fax: 0115-961 3642 E-mail: enquiries@lightning-conductors.co.uk

Southern Lightning Engineers, Unit D2 Bearsted Green Business Centre, The Green, Bearsted, Maidstone, Kent, ME14 4DF Tel: (01622) 631312 Fax: (01622) 631313 E-mail: ian-barker@btconnect.com

Spectra Sound, Unit 1-2 The Chambers, St. Edmunds Road, Northampton, NN1 5ET Tel: (01604) 634100 Fax: E-mail: dondix@lineone.net

Tarrant S C S Ltd, 1st Floor Victoria Court, St. Pancras, Chichester, West Sussex, PO19 7GD Tel: (01243) 839992 Fax: (01243) 839993 E-mail: rita.brown.tarrant@breathemail.net

W E Harrison Sheffield Ltd, 33 Regent Terrace, Sheffield, S3 7QA Tel: 0114-272 0561 Fax: 0114-272 0564 E-mail: weh@quista.net

LIGHTNING CONDUCTORS

A N Wallis, Greasley Street, Nottingham, NG6 8NG Tel: 0115-927 1721 Fax: 0115-875 6630 E-mail: info@an-wallis.com

Best Services, M C F Complex, New Road, Kidderminster, Worcestershire, DY10 1AQ Tel: (01562) 829565 Fax: (01562) 829286

Britannia Lightning Prevectron Ltd, Longue Drive, Calverton, Nottingham, NG14 6QF Tel: 0115-847 7113 Fax: 0115-847 5185 E-mail: sales@lightninguk.fsnet.co.uk

E E S London Ltd, 79 Croydon Road, Caterham, Surrey, CR3 6PD Tel: (01883) 341166 Fax: (01883) 341133

L. Hussey & Sons Ltd, 29 Brissenden Close, Upnor, Rochester, Kent, ME2 4XW Tel: (01634) 295358

▶ L P S South, 10 Brunel Road, Gorse La Industrial Estate, Clacton-on-Sea, Essex, CO15 4LU Tel: (01255) 221369 Fax: (01255) 476754 E-mail: lpsouth@aol.com

Lightning Consultants UK Ltd, 12 Longue Drive, Calverton, Nottingham, NG14 6QF Tel: 0115-965 4124 Fax: 0115-965 4754 E-mail: sales@prevectron.com

▶ W.D. Rees Steeplejacks And Lightning Protection Ltd, Dominion Way Industrial Estate, Cardiff, CF24 1RF Tel: (029) 2047 2110 Fax: (029) 2047 2112

▶ Storm Lightning Protection, Droylsden, Manchester, M43 6XE Tel: 0161-370 9944 Fax: 0161-370 9955 E-mail: stormlighningprotection@hotmail.com

LIGHTNING ELIMINATOR OR PROTECTION EQUIPMENT

E E S Bristol Ltd, 62 Shirehampton Road, Bristol, BS9 2DL Tel: 0117-968 4002 Fax: 0117-968 3536 E-mail: kit@ees-group.co.uk

Kingsmill Industries UK Ltd, Unit 14 Hermitage Way, Mansfield, Nottinghamshire, NG18 5ES Tel: (01623) 621111 Fax: (01623) 621211 E-mail: sales@kingsmillearthing.co.uk

Omega Red Group Ltd, 28 Kansas Avenue, Salford, M50 2GL Tel: 0161-877 9881 Fax: 0161-877 9882

Omega Redgroup Ltd, 4 Avonbank Industrial Estate, West Town Road, Bristol, BS11 9DE Tel: 0117-938 1112 Fax: 0117-938 1522

Protectis Ltd, 12a Hazel Street, Bulwell, Nottingham, NG6 8EA Tel: 0115-975 8820 Fax: 0115-975 8821 E-mail: info@protectis.co.uk

Surgetech Ltd, Durlston House, North Street, Westbourne, Emsworth, Hampshire, PO10 8SN Tel: (01243) 379613 Fax: (01243) 370003 E-mail: bill.jones@surgetech.co.uk

Telematic Ltd, Pondwicks Road, Luton, LU1 3LH Tel: (01582) 429464 Fax: (01582) 459669 E-mail: admin@telematic.com

LIGHTNING PROTECTION CONTRACTORS

▶ Barsby Lightning Protection, 31 Trinity Road, Whetstone, Leicester, LE8 6JW Tel: 0116-278 7996 Fax: 0116-278 7996 E-mail: info@barsbylightning.co.uk

LIGNOSULPHONATES

Roy Dickson Wilson, Alrewas House, Main Street, Alrewas, Burton-on-Trent, Staffordshire, DE13 7ED Tel: (01283) 792255 Fax: (01283) 792041

LIME APPLICATION EQUIPMENT, SOIL STABILISATION

▶ Continental Soil Technology, The Old Dairy, Chavenage Estate, Tetbury, Gloucestershire, GL8 8XY Tel: (0845) 6034136 Fax: E-mail: info@continentalsoiltechnology.com

DNS Midlands Ltd, 1 Bridge Street, Derby, DE1 3HZ Tel: (01332) 363187 Fax: (01332) 371615 E-mail: enquiries@dnsmidlands.co.uk

LIME OR LIMESTONE

Aggregates Industries, Whitworth Quarry, Tong Lane, Whitworth, Rochdale, Lancashire, OL12 8BE Tel: (01706) 853296 Fax: (01706) 854286

Billown Lime Quarries Ltd, Billown Quarry, Ballasalla, Isle Of Man, IM9 3DW Tel: (01624) 828765 Fax: (01624) 824477

Brauncewell Quarries Ltd, Brauncewell Quarry, Brauncewell, Sleaford, Lincolnshire, NG34 8RL Tel: (01526) 832767 Fax: (01526) 833075

Buxton Lime Ltd, Tunstead Quarry, Buxton, Derbyshire, SK17 8TG Tel: (01298) 768444 Fax: (01298) 72195 E-mail: buxton.sales@buxtonlime.co.uk

C H I C Fireplaces, 116 Red Lane, Coventry, CV6 5EQ Tel: (024) 7663 8063 E-mail: chicmarbleandgranite@hotmail.co.uk

▶ Callisto Trading Ltd, 2 Duckett Mews, London, N4 1BP Tel: (07092) 008537 Fax: (07092) 020256 E-mail: info@callistotrading.co.uk

Castle Hill Quarry Co. Ltd, Cannington, Bridgwater, Somerset, TA5 2QF Tel: (01278) 652280 Fax: (01278) 653724 E-mail: sales@castlehillquarry.co.uk

Cathedral Works Organisation, Terminus Road, Chichester, West Sussex, PO19 8TX Tel: (01243) 784225 Fax: (01243) 813700 E-mail: info@cwo.uk.com

Cults Lime Ltd, Cults Hills, Cupar, Fife, KY15 7TF Tel: (01334) 652548 Fax: (01334) 657887

Francis Flower, Gurney Slade Quarry, Gurney Slade, Radstock, BA3 4TE Tel: (01749) 841146 Fax: (01749) 841285 E-mail: sales@francisflower.co.uk

J. Handford & Son Ltd, Milford House, 431 Buxton Road, Stockport, Cheshire, SK2 7HE Tel: 0161-487 3888 Fax: 0161-487 4555

Howie Minerals Ltd, Dornie Quarry, Torlundy, Fort William, Inverness-Shire, PH33 6SW Tel: (01397) 702227 Fax: (01397) 702308 E-mail: blaurie@howie-forest.co.uk

Longcliffe Quarries Ltd, Longcliffe, Brassington, Matlock, Derbyshire, DE4 4BZ Tel: (01629) 540284 Fax: (01629) 540569 E-mail: sales@longcliffe.co.uk

Alistair Mackintosh Ltd, Bannerley Road, Garretts Green Industrial Estate, Birmingham, B33 0SL Tel: 0121-784 6800 Fax: 0121-789 7068 E-mail: info@alistairmackintosh.co.uk

Keith Mount Liming Ltd, Rougham Industrial Estate, Rougham, Bury St. Edmunds, Suffolk, IP30 9ND Tel: (01359) 271033 Fax: (01359) 271151 E-mail: keith@mountliming.co.uk

Omya UK Ltd, 17 Munie Road, Glenarm, Ballymena, County Antrim, BT44 0BG Tel: (028) 2884 1333 Fax: (028) 2884 1687 E-mail: marvethblack@omya.co.uk

Singleton Birch Ltd, Melton Ross Quarries, Barnetby, South Humberside, DN38 6AE Tel: (01652) 688386 Fax: (01652) 686081

Smith & Sons (Bletchington) Ltd, Enslow, Kidlington, Oxfordshire, OX5 3AY Tel: (01869) 331281 Fax: (01869) 331734

Telling Lime Products, Primrose Avenue, Wolverhampton, WV10 8AW Tel: (01902) 789777 Fax: (01902) 398777 E-mail: m.wood@telling.co.uk

Totternhoe Lime & Stone Co. Ltd, Lower End, Totternhoe, Dunstable, Bedfordshire, LU6 2BU Tel: (01525) 220300 Fax: (01525) 221895 E-mail: tottenhoelime@btclick.com

LIME PLASTER

▶ VEN Systems Ltd, 25 Wingmore Road, London, SE24 0AS Tel: (07718) 159555 Fax: (020) 7837 8443 E-mail: info@venplaster.co.uk

LIMESTONE BATHROOM FITTINGS OR ACCESSORIES

DEVON STONE Ltd, 8 Pilot Wharf, Pierhead, Exmouth Marina, Exmouth, Devon, EX8 1XA Tel: 01395 222525 E-mail: mail@devonstone.com

LIMESTONE FIREPLACE FRONTS

▶ Thornhill Galleries, 3, 19 Osiers Road, London, SW18 1NL Tel: (020) 8874 2101 Fax: (020) 8877 0313 E-mail: sales@thornhillgalleries.co.uk

LIMESTONE FLOORING

DEVON STONE Ltd, 8 Pilot Wharf, Pierhead, Exmouth Marina, Exmouth, Devon, EX8 1XA Tel: 01395 222525 E-mail: mail@devonstone.com

▶ Lincolnshire Limestone Flooring, Stamford Road, Marholm, Peterborough, PE6 7HX Tel: (01780) 740852 Fax: (01780) 740970 E-mail: sales@lincolnshirelimestoneflooring.co.uk

LIMESTONE MOSAIC TILES

▶ Mosaic Co., Mosaic House, Phoenix Park, Eaton Socon, St. Neots, Cambridgeshire, PE19 8EP Tel: (01480) 474714 Fax: (01480) 474715 E-mail: sales@mosaiccompany.co.uk

LIMESTONE TILES

▶ Lincolnshire Limestone Flooring, Stamford Road, Marholm, Peterborough, PE6 7HX Tel: (01780) 740852 Fax: (01780) 740970 E-mail: sales@lincolnshirelimestoneflooring.co.uk

▶ Pietra Tile Distribution Ltd, 28 Silver Street, Bradford-on-Avon, Wiltshire, BA15 1JY Tel: (01225) 867678 Fax: (01225) 867678 E-mail: jakelewis@pietrastone.co.uk

Pisani plc, Unit 12 Transport Avenue, Brentford, Middlesex, TW8 9HF Tel: (020) 8568 5001 Fax: (020) 8847 3406 E-mail: sales@pisani.co.uk

LIMESTONE VANITY TOPS AND WASH BASINS

▶ Lincolnshire Limestone Flooring, Stamford Road, Marholm, Peterborough, PE6 7HX Tel: (01780) 740852 Fax: (01780) 740970 E-mail: sales@lincolnshirelimestoneflooring.co.uk

LIMIT SWITCHES

Euchner (U K) Ltd, Unit 2, Petre Drive, Sheffield, S4 7PZ Tel: 0114-256 0123 Fax: 0114-242 5333 E-mail: info@euchner.co.uk

LIMITED COMPANY ADMINISTRATION CONSULTANCY

▶ Charterhouse Group International Plc, 2nd Floor, 37 Lombard Street, London, United Kingdom, EC3V 9BQ Tel: 0800 634 4848 Fax: 0800 634 4849 E-mail: sales@charterhouseplc.com

▶ Secretariat Business Services, Suite 16, Folkestone Enterprise Centre, Shearway Business Park, Folkestone, Kent, CT19 4RH Tel: (0870) 3300615 E-mail: info@secretariatservices.net

LIMOUSINE HIRE

▶ Goldstyle Limousines, 84 Sidney Avenue, Stafford, ST17 4EN Tel: (07915) 282346 E-mail: goldstyle.limousines@ntlworld.com

LINE UP PRINTING TABLES

A & R Printing, The Gables, 160A London Road, Brandon, Suffolk, IP27 0LP Tel: (01842) 811331 Fax: (01842) 811375 E-mail: ray.boreham@btinternet.com

LINEAR ACTUATORS

C R D Devices Ltd, 3 All Saints Industrial Estate, Darlington Road, Shildon, County Durham, DL4 2RD Tel: (01388) 778400 Fax: (01388) 778800 E-mail: sales@crd-devices.co.uk

Danaher Motion, Fishleigh Road, Roundswell Business Park, Barnstaple, Devon, EX31 3UD Tel: (01271) 334500 Fax: (01271) 334502 E-mail: information@tiblmail.com

Dewert Motorised Systems, Phoenix Mecano House, 1 Faraday Road, Aylesbury, Buckinghamshire, HP19 8TX Tel: (01296) 398855 Fax: (01296) 398866 E-mail: dewertgb@phoenix-mecano.com

Ernest Fairbairn Ltd, PO Box 1410, Gerrards Cross, Buckinghamshire, SL9 8UB Tel: (01753) 882542 Fax: (01753) 882546 E-mail: ernestfairbairn@aol.com

LINAK UK Ltd, Actuation House, Crystal Drive, Sandwell Business Park, Smethwick, West Midlands, B66 1RJ Tel: 0121-544 2211 Fax: 0121-544 2552E-mail: sales@linak.co.uk

Phoenix Mecano Ltd, 6-7 Faraday Road, Aylesbury, Buckinghamshire, HP19 8TX Tel: (01296) 619100 Fax: (01296) 398866 E-mail: info@phoenix-mecano.ltd.uk

Power Jacks Ltd, South Harbour Road, Fraserburgh, Aberdeenshire, AB43 9BZ Tel: (01346) 513131 Fax: (01346) 516827 E-mail: sales@powerjacks.co.uk

▶ Robot Units UK, Woodford Park Industrial Estate, Leslie Road, Woodford Park Industrial Estat, Winsford, Cheshire, CW7 2RB Tel: (01606) 869690 Fax: (01606) 869692 E-mail: info.uk1@robotunits.com

▶ THK UK, 1 Harrison Close, Knowlhill, Milton Keynes, MK5 8PA Tel: (01908) 303050 Fax: (01908) 303070 E-mail: sales.uk@thk.co.uk

LINEAR BALL BEARINGS

A F C Linear Products, Unit 45, Llantarnam Industrial Park, Cwmbran, Gwent, NP44 3AW Tel: (01633) 861414 Fax: (01633) 872039 E-mail: afc-cwmbran@fsmail.net

Accuride International Ltd, Liliput Road, Brackmills Industrial Estate, Northampton, NN4 7AS Tel: (01604) 761111 Fax: (01604) 767190 E-mail: saleseurope@accuride-europe.com

J & M Belts Veebelts Bearings Oilseals, 72 Bridge Road, Grays, Essex, RM17 6BZ Tel: (01375) 373975 Fax: (01375) 391541 E-mail: sales@jmbelts.com

LINEAR BEARINGS

A F C Linear Products, Unit 45, Llantarnam Industrial Park, Cwmbran, Gwent, NP44 3AW Tel: (01633) 861414 Fax: (01633) 872039 E-mail: afc-cwmbran@fsmail.net

East Anglian Bearing Service Ltd, 19-21 Great Whip Street, Ipswich, IP2 8EY Tel: (01473) 602525 Fax: (01473) 688274 E-mail: sales@eabs.co.uk

Gudel Lineartec (U.K.) Ltd, Unit 5 Wickmans Drive, Banner Lane, Coventry, CV4 9XA Tel: (024) 7669 5444 Fax: (024) 7669 5666 E-mail: info@uk.gudel.com

John Handley, Unit 2 Heath Mill Bus Centre, Wombourne, Wolverhampton, WV5 8AP Tel: (01902) 898560 Fax: (01902) 898561 E-mail: sales@johnhandleybearings.com

Linear Systems & Equipment Ltd, 9 Sampson House, Arterial Road, Laindon, Basildon, Essex, SS15 6DR Tel: (01268) 419558 Fax: (01268) 417034 E-mail: linsys@btconnect.com

Midland Engineering Services Ltd, Bathville Business Centre, Armadale Indust Estate, Armadale, Bathgate, West Lothian, EH48 2ND Tel: (01501) 739081 Fax: (01501) 739083 E-mail: sales@mes4thk.sageweb.co.uk

▶ Strongbar, 2 Banningham Road, Aylsham, Norwich, NR11 6PE Tel: (01263) 734034 Fax: (01263) 734790 E-mail: sales@strongbar.co.uk

Unimatic Engineers Ltd, 130 Granville Road, London, NW2 2LN Tel: (020) 8922 1000 Fax: (020) 8922 1066 E-mail: sales@unimatic.com

LINEAR ENCODERS

Aberlink Ltd, Avening Mill, High Street, Avening, Tetbury, Gloucestershire, GL8 8LU Tel: (01453) 835737 Fax: (01453) 832574 E-mail: sales@aberlink.co.uk

H T Servo Ltd, 5 Westmarch Business Centre, River Way, Andover, Hants, SP10 1NS Tel: (01264) 355079 Fax: (01264) 337450 E-mail: info@htservo.com

Heidenhain (GB) Ltd, 200 London Road, Burgess Hill, West Sussex, RH15 9RD Tel: (01444) 247711 Fax: (01444) 870024 E-mail: sales@heidenhain.co.uk

Innovative Measurement Technology, 49 Christchurch Crescent, Bognor Regis, West Sussex, PO21 5SL Tel: (01243) 824506 Fax: (01243) 826340 E-mail: sales@imeasure.co.uk

Renishaw Plc, New Mills, Wotton-under-Edge, Gloucestershire, GL12 8JR Tel: (01453) 524126 Fax: (01453) 524201 E-mail: uk@renishaw.com

Siko Ltd, Unit 6, Cod Beck Estate, Dalton, Thirsk, North Yorkshire, YO7 3HR Tel: (01845) 578845 Fax: (01845) 577781 E-mail: sales@siko-uk.com

LINEAR FORCE ELECTRIC MOTORS

Crouzet Ltd, Intec 3, Wade Road, Basingstoke, Hampshire, RG24 8NE Tel: (01256) 318900 Fax: (01256) 318901 E-mail: sales@crouzet.com
▶ ORLIN Technologies Ltd, 50 Station Road, Ridgmont, Bedford, MK43 0UH Tel: (01525) 306100 Fax: (0871) 2477366 E-mail: sales@orlin.co.uk

LINEAR INDUCTION ELECTRIC MOTORS

Force Engineering Ltd, Old Station Close, Shepshed, Loughborough, Leicestershire, LE12 9NJ Tel: (01509) 506025 Fax: (01509) 505433 E-mail: enquiries@force.co.uk

LINEAR MOTION EQUIPMENT

▶ ORLIN Technologies Ltd, 50 Station Road, Ridgmont, Bedford, MK43 0UH Tel: (01525) 306100 Fax: (0871) 2477366 E-mail: sales@orlin.co.uk

LINEAR MOTORS

Copley Motion Systems, Luckyn Lane, Basildon, Essex, SS14 3BW Tel: (01268) 287070 Fax: (01268) 293344 E-mail: sales@copleymotion.com
Mechtronic Industries Ltd, Innovation Centre, Kirton Lane, Stainforth, Doncaster, South Yorkshire, DN7 5DA Tel: (01302) 845000 Fax: (01302) 844440 E-mail: mechtro@aol.com

LINEAR PNEUMATIC VIBRATORS

Pulse Power Process Equipment Ltd, 43 Bishops Walk, Forthampton, Gloucester, GL19 4QF Tel: (01684) 290029 Fax: (01684) 290222 E-mail: info@pulse-piv.co.uk
Tribal Automation Ltd, 6 Lodge Forge Trading Estate, Cradley Road, Cradley Heath, West Midlands, B64 7RW Tel: (01384) 562563 Fax: (01384) 562563

LINEAR SLIDE BEARING MATERIALS

Braintree Precision Components Ltd, 2-8 Blackwell Drive, Springwood Industrial Estate, Braintree, Essex, CM7 2QJ Tel: (01376) 552989 Fax: (01376) 552995 E-mail: sales@hepco.co.uk

LINEAR SLIDES

Braintree Precision Components Ltd, 2-8 Blackwell Drive, Springwood Industrial Estate, Braintree, Essex, CM7 2QJ Tel: (01376) 552989 Fax: (01376) 552995 E-mail: sales@hepco.co.uk
I K O (Nippon Thompson), 2 Vincent Ave, Crownhill, Milton Keynes, MK8 0AB Tel: (01908) 566144 Fax: (01908) 565458 E-mail: sales@iko.co.uk
Linear Systems & Equipment Ltd, 9 Sampson House, Arterial Road, Laindon, Basildon, Essex, SS15 6DR Tel: (01268) 419558 Fax: (01268) 417034 E-mail: linsys@btconnect.com

LINEAR VARIABLE DIFFERENTIAL (LVDT) TRANSFORMERS

Active Sensors Ltd, Unit 12 Sea Vixen Industrial Estate, 3 Wilverley Road, Christchurch, Dorset, BH23 3RU Tel: (01202) 480620 Fax: (01202) 480664 E-mail: sales@activesensors.com

LINEN FABRICS

W.F.B. Baird & Co, Ltd, 72 Shankbridge Road, Kells, Ballymena, County Antrim, BT42 3DL Tel: (028) 2589 8144 Fax: (028) 2589 8153
William Clark & Sons Ltd, Upperlands, Maghera, County Londonderry, BT46 5RZ Tel: (028) 7964 2214 Fax: (028) 7954 7207 E-mail: sales@wmclark.co.uk
John England (Textiles) Ltd, Portside Business Park, Airport Road West, Belfast, BT3 9ED Tel: (028) 9073 6990 Fax: (028) 9073 6989 E-mail: sales@johnenglandtextiles.com
F & Y Products, 7a Thurswood House Cranborne Industrial Estate, Cranborne Road, Potters Bar, Hertfordshire, EN6 3JN Tel: (01707) 654221 Fax: (01707) 654224
Faberhouse Online Ltd, Faber House, Ibstone, High Wycombe, Buckinghamshire, HP14 3XT Tel: (01491) 638184 Fax: (01491) 638184 E-mail: marketing@purpleandfinelinen.com
Thomas Ferguson & Co. Ltd, 54 Scarva Road, Banbridge, County Down, BT32 3QD Tel: (028) 4062 3491 Fax: (028) 4062 2453 E-mail: info@fergusonsirishlinen.com
Henry Marlow & Co. Ltd, 133 Rendlesham Road, London, E5 8PA Tel: (020) 8985 4158 Fax: (020) 8985 4301
Milliken White & Co. Ltd, 6 Huss Row, Belfast, BT13 1EE Tel: (028) 9032 2076 Fax: (028) 9031 5350 E-mail: millikenwhite@hotmail.co.uk
Ponden Mill Ltd, 23 College Walk, Keighley, West Yorkshire, BD21 3QA Tel: (01535) 610984
R N Peace & Co., 103 High Street, Witney, Oxfordshire, OX28 6HZ Tel: (01993) 702434 Fax: (01993) 702434 E-mail: mrrbpeace@aol.com
Ulster Weavers Apparel Ltd, 245 Castlewellan Road, Main Road, Moygashel, Banbridge, County Down, BT32 3SG Tel: (028) 4062 4490 Fax: (028) 4062 1100 E-mail: info@moygashel.com
Ulster Weavers Home Fashions, Unit 1-6 St Helens Business Park, Holywood, County Down, BT18 9HQ Tel: (028) 9032 9494 Fax: (028) 9032 6612 E-mail: sales@ulsterweavers.com
White House Linen Specialists, 102 Waterford Road, London, SW6 2HA Tel: (020) 7629 3521 Fax: (020) 7629 8269 E-mail: john@the-white-house.co.uk
Zedkay Textiles Ltd, 34 Charlotte Street, Manchester, M1 4FD Tel: 0161-236 4348 Fax: 0161-236 7848

LINEN GOODS, MADE-UP, *See also Textile Goods etc*

Acton's Made To Measure Bed Linen, Hamer Lane, Rochdale, Lancashire, OL16 2UL Tel: (01706) 642361 Fax: (01706) 860544 E-mail: sales@actonandactonltd.co.uk
Bolton Hemming Ltd, Halliwell Industrial Estate, Wapping Street, Bolton, BL1 8DP Tel: (01204) 492614 Fax: (01204) 492088 E-mail: enquiries@bolton-hemming.co.uk
▶ L Shailer, Hafod School House, Llanerfyl, Welshpool, Powys, SY21 0JH Tel: (01938) 820110 Fax: (01938) 820118 E-mail: info@lynshailer.co.uk
Ponden Mill Ltd, 23 College Walk, Keighley, West Yorkshire, BD21 3QA Tel: (01535) 610984
Victoria Linen Co., 2 Hargreaves St Mill, Hargreaves Street, Haslingden, Rossendale, Lancashire, BB4 5RQ Tel: (01706) 220020 Fax: (01706) 220020 E-mail: brochure@victorialinen.co.uk

LINEN HIRE

Air Linen Laundry, 4 Shentonfield Road, Sharston Industrial Area, Manchester, M22 4RW Tel: 0161-428 8099 Fax: 0161-428 8116
Blackpool Laundry Co. Ltd, Unit 6e Moor Park Industrial Estate, Kincraig Road, Blackpool, FY2 0JY Tel: (01253) 500014 Fax: (01253) 500014 E-mail: sales@blackpoollaundry.com
Catering Linen Hire, Unit E7 Aladdin Centre, Long Drive, Greenford, Middlesex, UB6 8UH Tel: (020) 8575 1844 Fax: (020) 8575 9025 E-mail: maureen.cooper@ukonline.co.uk
1st Class Linen Services, Unit 9 Chapman Court, Charfleets Road Industrial Estate, Canvey Island, Essex, SS8 0PQ Tel: 01268 691222 Fax: 01268 510947 E-mail: brettbarber@fsmail.net
Quickhire, Pemway House, Carr Lane, Hoylake, Wirral, Merseyside, CH47 4AZ Tel: 0151-632 6945 Fax: 0151-632 6946

LINEN SUPPLY SERVICES

Air Linen Laundry, 4 Shentonfield Road, Sharston Industrial Area, Manchester, M22 4RW Tel: 0161-428 8099 Fax: 0161-428 8116
Anglia Laundry & Linen Hire Services, 1a Victoria Place, Peterborough, PE1 2HB Tel: (01733) 314464 Fax: (01733) 314464
Biggleswade Linen Services Ltd, Potton Road, Biggleswade, Bedfordshire, SG18 0EJ Tel: (01767) 313159 Fax: (01767) 601958
Bolton Linen Services, Minerva Road, Farnworth, Bolton, BL4 0JR Tel: (01204) 390613 Fax: (01204) 390693
Brooks Service Group, 6 Lansdowne Hill, London, SE27 0AR Tel: (020) 8761 3001 Fax: (020) 8761 8275
Camplins Ltd, Portland Lane, Great Yarmouth, Norfolk, NR31 0JN Tel: (01493) 660000 Fax: (01493) 660006 E-mail: sales@camplings-linen.co.uk
The Caterers Linen Supply, 6-8 Jackson Way, Great Western Industrial Park, Southall, Middlesex, UB2 4SF Tel: (020) 8843 5810 Fax: (020) 8843 5865 E-mail: customerservice@caterersIinen.co.uk
Clean Linen Services Ltd, 54 Furze Platt Road, Maidenhead, Berkshire, SL6 7NL Tel: (01628) 645900 Fax: (01628) 674099 E-mail: info@cleanservices.co.uk
Cornish Linen Service, Dudnance Lane, Pool, Redruth, Cornwall, TR15 3RA Tel: (01256) 471311 Fax: (01209) 714133 E-mail: sales.camborne@cls-group.co.uk
County Luxdon Laundry Ltd, 10 Wearfield, Sunderland Enterprise Park, Sunderland, SR5 2TZ Tel: 0191-548 7676 Fax: 0191-516 0648 E-mail: countyluxdonlaundry@tiscali.co.uk
Delbanco Meyer & Co. Ltd, Portland House, Ryland Road, London, NW5 3EB Tel: (020) 7468 3000 Fax: (020) 7468 3094
Executive Linen & China Hire, Unit 3 Cockshut La Business Centre, Commerce Street, Melbourne, Derby, DE73 8FT Tel: (01332) 694333 Fax: (01332) 694333
F & Y Products, 7a Thurswood House Cranborne Industrial Estate, Cranborne Road, Potters Bar, Hertfordshire, EN6 3JN Tel: (01707) 654221 Fax: (01707) 654224
Forestbrook Linen Services Ltd, Forestbrook Ave, Rostrevor, Newry, Co. Down, BT34 3BX Tel: (028) 4173 8848
Horsham & District Laundry Ltd, Unit D, Foundry Close, Horsham, West Sussex, RH13 5TX Tel: (01403) 243340 Fax: (01403) 254539
Initial, Botany Brow, Chorley, Lancashire, PR6 0HX Tel: (01257) 272311 Fax: (01257) 233575
Initial Textile Services, Unit 10, Eldon Way, Bristol, BS4 3QQ Tel: 0117-971 2387 Fax: 0117-971 6612 E-mail: briscsu@initialtextileservices.co.uk
Innisfail Laundry Ltd, 814 Hollands Road, Haverhill, Suffolk, CB9 8HB Tel: (01440) 702061 Fax: (01440) 712331
Johnson Apparelmaster, 15 Pixmore Avenue, Letchworth Garden City, Hertfordshire, SG6 1JW Tel: (01462) 686355 Fax: (01462) 671006 E-mail: sales@apparelmaster.co.uk
Johnson Cleaners UK Ltd, Kingsway, Team Valley Trading Estate, Gateshead, Tyne & Wear, NE11 0HB Tel: 0191-482 0088 Fax: 0191-482 1750
Johnsons Apparelmaster P.L.C., Aldridge Road, Perry Barr, Birmingham, B42 2EU Tel: 0121-356 4512 Fax: 0121-344 3520
Midland Linen Services Ltd, 3 Klaxon Tysley Industrial Estate, 751 Warwick Road, Tyseley, Birmingham, B11 2HA Tel: 0121-708 1069 Fax: 0121-707 4686 E-mail: info@midlandlinen.co.uk
Richard Haworth & Co. Ltd, Kearsley Mill, Stoneclough, Radcliffe, Manchester, M26 1RH Tel: (01204) 708508 Fax: (01204) 705772 E-mail: info@richardhaworth.co.uk
S Green & Sons Ltd, Fairfield Road, London, E3 2QA Tel: (020) 8981 7940 Fax: (020) 8981 3625 E-mail: sgreen@globalnet.o.uk
Sunlight Ltd, Buckwell End, Wellingborough, Northamptonshire, NN8 4LR Tel: (01933) 279813 Fax: (01933) 274111
Sunlight Service Group Ltd, 9 Castle Road, Bournemouth, BH9 1PQ Tel: (01202) 512544 Fax: (01202) 547312 E-mail: winton@sunlight.co.uk
The Sunlight Service Group Ltd, Shap Road, Kendal, Cumbria, LA9 6DQ Tel: (01539) 723378 Fax: (01539) 740921 E-mail: kendal@sunlight.co.uk
The Sunlight Service Group Ltd, Victoria Works, Victoria Road, Sowerby Bridge, West Yorkshire, HX6 3AE Tel: (01422) 831151 Fax: (01422) 839101
Sunlight Service Group Ltd, 129 St. Leonards Road, Windsor, Berkshire, SL4 3JT Tel: (01753) 861151 Fax: (01753) 833608
Texicare Ltd, Unit 6, Lansil Industrial Estate, Caton Road, Lancaster, LA1 3PQ Tel: (01524) 39666 Fax: (01524) 841963 E-mail: stevenh@texicare.co.uk
Tibard Laundry Services Ltd, Holden Street, Ashton-under-Lyne, Lancashire, OL6 9JB Tel: 0161-330 5106 Fax: 0161-339 9995
Waveney Laundry Ltd, Clonavon Road South, Ballymena, County Antrim, BT43 5BJ Tel: (028) 2564 2131 Fax: (028) 2564 3123 E-mail: mail@waveneylaundry.com
Well Laid Table, Green Acres, Whaplode Drove, Spalding, Lincolnshire, PE12 0SP Tel: (01406) 330206 Fax: (01406) 330206

LINGERIE

A & N Resources Ltd, 8a Rowsley Avenue, West Didsbury, Manchester, M20 2XD Tel: 0161-438 0784 Fax: 0161-438 0784
Axfords Clothing Mnfrs, 82 Centurion Road, Brighton, BN1 3LN Tel: (01273) 327944 Fax: (01273) 220680
Bentwood Ltd (Sterling Group), Atlantic Street, Broadheath, Altrincham, Cheshire, WA14 5FY Tel: 0161-926 7000 Fax: 0161-926 7029 E-mail: info@stirlinggroup.com
▶ Black-Thong Limited, 23 Danestone Close, Middleleaze, Swindon, SN5 5GP Tel: 07977 717893 E-mail: enquiries@black-thong.com
▶ Body Buddies Lingerie, 41 Ely Close, Southminster, Essex, CM0 7AQ Tel: (07762) 059557 E-mail: sales@bodybuddies.co.uk
Daner Ltd, 36 Walsall Road, Willenhall, West Midlands, WV13 2EG Tel: (01902) 368788 Fax: (01902) 637584E-mail: info@daner.co.uk
Desiree Boutique, 26 High Street, Rottingdean, Brighton, BN2 7HR Tel: (01273) 303444 Fax: (01273) 303444
▶ Glamourbox, Unit 6, 9 St. Johns street, Colchester, CO2 7NN Tel: 01206 570976 E-mail: sales@glamourbox.co.uk
Halle Models Leek Ltd, Belle Vue Road, Leek, Staffordshire, ST13 8EP Tel: (01538) 399731 Fax: (01538) 399354
Holt Hosiery Co. Ltd, Deane Road Mill, Bolton, BL3 5AR Tel: (01204) 525611 Fax: (01204) 394620
▶ Horny Toys, 60 Acacia Road, London, W3 6HF Tel: 02088 961103 E-mail: info@hornytoys.co.uk
License to Frill Lingerie, 44 Fronhaul, Swiss Valle, Llanelli, Carmarthenshire, SA14 8LF Tel: (01554) 752277 E-mail: dawn@licensetofrill.co.uk
▶ Nite Life, 37 Huntly Street, Aberdeen, AB10 1TJ Tel: (01224) 561110 Fax: (01224) 561110
▶ Scantia, 78 Rainey Street, Magherafelt, County Londonderry, BT45 5AH Tel: (028) 7930 1143 E-mail: contact@scantia.com
▶ Seductive Lingerie, 14 Enderby Road, Scunthorpe, South Humberside, DN17 2HD Tel: (01724) 332874 E-mail: seller.seller@ntlworld.com
Sherwood Group P.L.C., Fields Farm Road, Long Eaton, Nottingham, NG10 1GT Tel: 0115-946 1070 Fax: 0115-946 2720 E-mail: info@sherwoodgroup.co.uk
▶ Stelladreams, 26 Wordsworth Road, Diss, Norfolk, IP22 4QA Tel: (01239) 677854
Sterling Group Ltd, Boulevard Works, Radford Boulevard, Nottingham, NG7 3AE Tel: 0115-978 2221 Fax: 0115-978 5034
Thong In Cheek, 59 Sunderland Street, Macclesfield, Cheshire, SK11 6HN Tel: (01625) 422860 E-mail: enquiries@thongincheek.com
Triumph International Ltd, Arkwright Road, Groundwell Industrial Estate, Swindon, SN25 5BE Tel: (01793) 722200 Fax: (01793) 728341

LINING FABRICS

Baylis Hargreaves Ltd, Unit 2b2 Seacroft Industrial Estate, Coal Road, Leeds, LS14 2AQ Tel: 0113-273 6689 Fax: 0113-265 0236 E-mail: sales@baylishargreaves.com
Edmund Bell & Co. Ltd, Belfry House, Roydsdale Way, Euroway Industrial Estate, Bradford, West Yorkshire, BD4 6SU Tel: (01274) 680000 Fax: (01274) 680699 E-mail: sales@edmundbell.co.uk
Evans Textile Sales Ltd, 22 Piccadilly Trading Estate, Manchester, M1 2NP Tel: 0161-274 4147 Fax: 0161-274 4070 E-mail: sales@evans-textiles.com
William Gee Ltd, William Gee House, 520-522 Kingsland Road, London, E8 4AH Tel: (020) 7254 2451 Fax: (020) 7249 8116 E-mail: wmgeetrims@aol.com
Joseph Bros Textiles Ltd, 15 Gruneisen Road, Finchley, London, N3 1LS Tel: (020) 8346 0851 Fax: (020) 8343 1773 E-mail: mjfabrics@aol.com
Shawe Hall Textiles, 85 North Western Street, Manchester, M12 6DY Tel: 0161-273 6006 Fax: 0161-273 6006
Samuel Simpson & Co. Ltd, 30 Broughton Street, Manchester, M8 8NN Tel: 0161-834 4920 Fax: 0161-834 3056 E-mail: sales@samuelsimpson.com

LINOLEUM

Armstrong Floor Products UK Ltd, Hitching Court, Abingdon Business Park, Abingdon, Oxfordshire, OX14 1RB Tel: (01235) 554848 Fax: (01235) 553583 E-mail: uk-info@armstrong.com
J De Bruyn Ltd, Units 4 & 6-7, Simonds Road, London, E10 7BN Tel: (020) 8558 4726 Fax: (020) 8539 7050 E-mail: enquiries@de-bruyne.co.uk

LINSEED OILS

Robin Appel Ltd, The Town House, The Square, Bishops Waltham, Southampton, SO32 1AF Tel: (01489) 896388 Fax: (01489) 896602 E-mail: enquiries@robin-appel.com
W.S. Lloyd Ltd, 7 Redgrove House, Stonards Hill, Epping, Essex, CM16 4QQ Tel: (01992) 572670 Fax: E-mail: jhogg@wslloyd.com

LIQUEFIED GAS CONTAINERS

Statebourne Cryogenics Ltd, 18 Parsons Road, Washington, Tyne & Wear, NE37 1EZ Tel: 0191-416 4104 Fax: 0191-415 0369 E-mail: sales@statebourne.com
Thames Cryogenics Ltd, Gooch Drive, Southmead Industrial Park, Didcot, Oxfordshire, OX11 7PR Tel: (01235) 815777 Fax: (01235) 815333 E-mail: sales@thamescryogenics.com
Wessington Cryogenics Ltd, Building 9, Philadelphia Complex, Houghton Le Spring, Tyne & Wear, DH4 4UG Tel: 0191-512 0677 Fax: 0191-512 0745 E-mail: info@wessingtoncryogenics.co.uk

LIQUEFIED PETROLEUM GAS (LPG)

Calor Gas Ltd, Dockyard Road, Ellesmere Port, CH65 4EG Tel: 0151-355 3700 Fax: 0151-357 1944 E-mail: querynw@calor.co.uk
Calor Gas Ltd, Athena House, Athena Drive, Warwick, CV34 6RL Tel: (0800) 0224199 Fax: (0870) 4006904 E-mail: commercial@calor.co.uk

LIQUEFIED PETROLEUM GAS (LPG)
– *continued*

E O Culverwell Ltd, Station Road, Robertsbridge, East Sussex, TN32 5DG Tel: (01580) 880567 Fax: (01580) 881022 E-mail: cars@eo-culverwell.ltd.uk
Lister Gases, Bridge Street, Wednesbury, West Midlands, WS10 0AW Tel: 0121-556 7181 Fax: 0121-505 1744 E-mail: primuslimited@smsuppliers.btinternet.com
North West Gases Ltd, Alma Street, St. Helens, Merseyside, WA9 3AR Tel: (01744) 753634 Fax: (01744) 24264 E-mail: sales@northwestgases.com
▶ Ozon LPG Installations Ltd, Unit 10 Miller Court Millbay Road, Millbay, Plymouth, PL1 3LQ Tel: (01752) 249915 Fax: (01752) 249915 E-mail: info@ozonlpg.com
Shell UK Ltd, M1 Markham Lane, Duckmanton, Chesterfield, Derbyshire, S44 5HS Tel: (0870) 8301100 Fax: (0870) 8301101 E-mail: enquiries@shell.com

LIQUEFIED PETROLEUM GAS (LPG) APPLIANCE/FITTINGS MANUFRS

Bullfinch (Gas Equipment) Ltd, Diadem Works, Kings Road, Tyseley, Birmingham, B11 2AJ Tel: 0121-706 6301 Fax: 0121-707 0995 E-mail: sales@bullfinch-gas.co.uk
Labro Tools & Gas Supply Co., 42-42a Nunhead Lane, London, SE15 3TU Tel: (020) 7639 9739 Fax: (020) 7252 8943
Lister Gases, Bridge Street, Wednesbury, West Midlands, WS10 0AW Tel: 0121-556 7181 Fax: 0121-505 1744 E-mail: gasses@lister.co.uk
Lister Gases, Bridge Street, Wednesbury, West Midlands, WS10 0AW Tel: 0121-556 7181 Fax: 0121-505 1744 E-mail: primuslimited@smsuppliers.btinternet.com
Widney Leisure Ltd, 5 Alfred Court Saxon Business Park, Hanbury Road, Stoke Prior, Bromsgrove, Worcestershire, B60 4AD Tel: (01527) 577800 Fax: (01527) 577900 E-mail: sales@widney-leisure.co.uk

LIQUEFIED PETROLEUM GAS (LPG) BROKERS, CARGO

Poten & Partners UK Ltd, 20 Balderton Street, London, W1K 6TL Tel: (020) 7493 7272 Fax: (020) 7629 7078E-mail: info@poten.com

LIQUEFIED PETROLEUM GAS (LPG) BROKERS, SHIPPING

Poten & Partners UK Ltd, 20 Balderton Street, London, W1K 6TL Tel: (020) 7493 7272 Fax: (020) 7629 7078E-mail: info@poten.com

LIQUEFIED PETROLEUM GAS (LPG) CARAVAN HEATING SYSTEMS

Whispair, Unit 31 Romsey Industrial Estate, Greatbridge Road, Romsey, Hampshire, SO51 0HR Tel: (01794) 523999 Fax: (01794) 519151 E-mail: info@whispaire.co.uk

LIQUEFIED PETROLEUM GAS (LPG) CONTAINERS/CYLINDERS

Automotive Tanks Ltd, Bilston Lane, Willenhall, West Midlands, WV13 2LH Tel: (01902) 604207 Fax: (01902) 606265 E-mail: sales@automotivetanks.ltd.uk
H K L Gaspower Ltd, 260 Windsor Street, Nechells, Birmingham, B7 4DX Tel: 0121-359 6131 Fax: 0121-359 8580 E-mail: shirley@hkl-gaspower.co.uk

LIQUEFIED PETROLEUM GAS (LPG) CONVERSION SERVICES

▶ EcoFuels UK Ltd, Smalleys Garage (Thorne), Selby Road, Thorne, Doncaster, South Yorkshire, DN8 4JD Tel: (0773) 0552832 Fax: (0784) 1399828 E-mail: info@EcoFuelsUK.com

LIQUEFIED PETROLEUM GAS (LPG) DISPENSERS

Pumptronics Europe Ltd, Folgate Road, North Walsham, Norfolk, NR28 0AJ Tel: (01692) 500640 Fax: (01692) 406710 E-mail: sales@pumptronics.co.uk

LIQUEFIED PETROLEUM GAS (LPG) ENGINEERING

Alternative Autom Fuel Conversions Ltd, Unit 1 Blind Pond Industrial Estate, Woburn Sands Road, Bow Brickhill, Milton Keynes, MK17 9LA Tel: (01908) 641333 Fax: (01908) 641981 E-mail: gas4cars@aol.com
▶ Ozon LPG Installations Ltd, Unit 10 Miller Court Millbay Road, Millbay, Plymouth, PL1 3LQ Tel: (01752) 249915 Fax: (01752) 249915 E-mail: info@ozonlpg.com
T E C International Ltd, Molborough House, Molborough Road, Lancing, West Sussex, BN15 8UF Tel: (01903) 851920 Fax: (01903) 851910 E-mail: paulw@tecint.co.uk
Weir Lge Process, Keith House, 2 Redheughs Rigg, Edinburgh, EH12 9DQ Tel: 0131-317 8787 Fax: 0131-452 3333 E-mail: sales@lgeprocess.com

LIQUEFIED PETROLEUM GAS (LPG) ENGINES

▶ LPG Auto Conversions, Island Cottage, Stone, Tenterden, Kent, TN30 7JL Tel: (01233) 758014 E-mail: lpg@uk2.net

LIQUEFIED PETROLEUM GAS (LPG) EQUIPMENT MAINTENANCE/REPAIR SERVICE

Liquified Gas Pumping Services Ltd, 18 Abbotsinch Road, Grangemouth, Stirlingshire, FK3 9UX Tel: (01324) 485475 Fax: (01324) 485677 E-mail: sales@lgpservices.co.uk
Spoors Ltd, Railway Street, Bishop Auckland, County Durham, DL14 7LR Tel: (01388) 603865 Fax: (01388) 608029 E-mail: spoors@onyxnet.co.uk
Wessingham Gas Vessels L.P.G. Ltd, Unit 3 Blagdon Depot, Frankland Lane, Durham, DH1 5TA Tel: 0191-384 3073 Fax: 0191-383 0615 E-mail: peterburdon@wessingham.freeserve.co.uk

LIQUEFIED PETROLEUM GAS (LPG) FUEL SYSTEMS

▶ Ozon LPG Installations Ltd, Unit 10 Miller Court Millbay Road, Millbay, Plymouth, PL1 3LQ Tel: (01752) 249915 Fax: (01752) 249915 E-mail: info@ozonlpg.com

LIQUEFIED PETROLEUM GAS (LPG) INSTALLATION CONTRACTORS

Instagas Boston Ltd, Industrial Estate, Hamilton Way, Boston, Lincolnshire, PE21 8TT Tel: (01205) 368622 Fax: (01205) 351807 E-mail: enquiries@instagas.co.uk
John Wigfull & Co Ltd, First Hangings, Blaby Road, Enderby, Leicester, LE19 4AQ Tel: 0116-286 2287 Fax: 0116-275 1232 E-mail: wigfullr@btinternet.com

LIQUEFIED PETROLEUM GAS (LPG) INSTRUMENTATION

Endress & Hauser, Unit 30 Northfield Way, Aycliffe Industrial Park, Newton Aycliffe, County Durham, DL5 6UF Tel: (01325) 329801 Fax: (01325) 300840 E-mail: sales@systems.endress.com

LIQUEFIED PETROLEUM GAS (LPG) PLANT CONTRACTORS OR DESIGNERS

Old Park Engineering Services Ltd, Woods Lane, Cradley Heath, West Midlands, B64 7AN Tel: (01384) 412550 Fax: (01384) 410784 E-mail: oldpark@blueyonder.co.uk
T E C International Ltd, Molborough House, Molborough Road, Lancing, West Sussex, BN15 8UF Tel: (01903) 851920 Fax: (01903) 851910 E-mail: paulw@tecint.co.uk
Weir Lge Process, Keith House, 2 Redheughs Rigg, Edinburgh, EH12 9DQ Tel: 0131-317 8787 Fax: 0131-452 3333 E-mail: sales@lgeprocess.com

LIQUID CONTENT GAUGES

Atkinson Equipment Ltd, Moat Road, West Wilts Trading Estate, Westbury, Wiltshire, BA13 4JF Tel: (01373) 822220 Fax: (01373) 826996 E-mail: sales@atkinsonequipment.com
Endress & Hauser, Unit 30 Northfield Way, Aycliffe Industrial Park, Newton Aycliffe, County Durham, DL5 6UF Tel: (01325) 329801 Fax: (01325) 300840 E-mail: sales@systems.endress.com
Fozmula Ltd, Berrington Road, Leamington Spa, Warwickshire, CV31 1NB Tel: (01926) 466700 Fax: (01926) 450473 E-mail: e.marketing@fozmula.com

LIQUID CRYSTAL CONTROLLERS

Hero Electronics Ltd, 10 Doolittle Mill Business Park, Froghall Road, Ampthill, Bedford, MK45 2ND Tel: (01525) 405015 Fax: (01525) 402383 E-mail: kelly@heroelec.co.uk

LIQUID CRYSTAL DISPLAY (LCD) MOUNTS

Chase AV Ltd, Unit 10, Upper Gamma, West Road, Ransomes Europark, Ipswich, IP3 9SX Tel: (01473) 279992 Fax: (01473) 279993 E-mail: sales2@chaseavdirect.co.uk

LIQUID CRYSTAL DISPLAY (LCD) PROJECTORS

Business Presentations Ltd, Hillfoot Farm, Hitchin Road, Shefford, Bedfordshire, SG17 5JD Tel: (01462) 817406 Fax: (01462) 850130 E-mail: sally@business-presentations.co.uk
▶ Communications & Sound Systems Ltd, Unit 1, Sandhurst Barn, Sandhurst Lane, Bexhill-On-Sea, East Sussex, TN39 4RH Tel: (01424) 848400 Fax: (01424) 848300 E-mail: sales@commsandsound.com

LIQUID CRYSTAL DISPLAY (LCD) TELEVISIONS

▶ Purely Plasma, Bluewater, Greenhithe, Kent, DA9 9SJ Tel: (01322) 427409 E-mail: sales@purelyplasma.com

LIQUID CRYSTAL DISPLAY (LCD) VIDEO PANELS

▶ T.J Butler (Electronics) Ltd, Unit 2 Catherine Court, Airfield View, Hawarden Industrial Park, Hawarden, Deeside, Flintshire, CH5 3NU Tel: (0871) 2224230 Fax: (01244) 538438 E-mail: service@tjbutlers.co.uk

LIQUID CRYSTAL DISPLAYS (LCD)

Inelco Ltd, Unit 3 Theale Technology Centre, Station Raod, Theale, RG7 4XX Tel: (0870) 4203561 Fax: (0870) 4203563 E-mail: sales@inelco.co.uk
Ivojo Multimedia Ltd, Newton Cross, Hayscastle, Haverfordwest, Dyfed, SA62 5HS Tel: (01348) 840080 Fax: (01348) 841081 E-mail: sales@ivojo.co.uk

LIQUID CRYSTAL MONITORS

Imp Electronics Ltd, Rocol Building, 3 Glebe Road, Huntingdon, Cambridgeshire, PE29 7DL Tel: (01480) 411822 Fax: (01480) 411833

LIQUID CRYSTAL THERMOMETERS

T L C, 1 Dock Road, Connah's Quay, Deeside, Clwyd, CH5 4DS Tel: (01244) 814066 Fax: (01244) 818502E-mail: sales@t-m-c.com

LIQUID CRYSTALS

Ginsbury Electronics Ltd, 1 Exeter House, Boufort Court, Rochester, Kent, ME2 4FE Tel: (01634) 298900 Fax: (01634) 290904 E-mail: sales@ginsbury.co.uk
Hallcrest Temperature Monitoring Systems Mnfrs, 20 Downing Road, West Meadows Industrial Estate, Derby, DE21 6HA Tel: (01332) 382421 Fax: (01332) 291208 E-mail: sales@hallcrest.com
Hallcrest Temperature Monitoring Systems Mnfrs, 20 Downing Road, West Meadows Industrial Estate, Derby, DE21 6HA Tel: (01332) 382421 Fax: (01332) 291208 E-mail: sales@hallcrest.com
T L C, 1 Dock Road, Connah's Quay, Deeside, Clwyd, CH5 4DS Tel: (01244) 814066 Fax: (01244) 818502E-mail: sales@t-m-c.com
Thermographics Measurements Ltd, Riverside Buildings, Dock Road, Connah's Quay, Deeside, Clwyd, CH5 4DS Tel: (01244) 818348 Fax: (01244) 818502 E-mail: sales@t-m-c.com

LIQUID FERTILISERS

Billericay Farm Services Ltd, School Road, Downham, Billericay, Essex, CM11 1QU Tel: (01268) 710237 Fax: (01268) 711040 E-mail: sales@bfs.uk.com
J. & H. Bunn Ltd, South Beach Parade, Great Yarmouth, Norfolk, NR30 3QA Tel: (01493) 744700 Fax: (01493) 744701 E-mail: info@jhbunn.co.uk
Contract Fertiliser & Storage Ltd, Spaldington Airfield, Bubwith Road, Spaldington, Goole, East Yorkshire, DN14 7NG Tel: (01430) 431511 Fax: (01430) 432070 E-mail: cfs@jhbunn.co.uk
John Hatcher Co. Ltd, Walton House, 218 High Street, Felixstowe, Suffolk, IP11 9DS Tel: (01394) 274321 Fax: (01394) 278600 E-mail: sales@hatcher.co.uk
Charles Mayson Ltd, The Old Rectory, Byford, Hereford, HR4 7LD Tel: (01981) 590218 Fax: (01981) 590499

LIQUID FILLING MACHINES

Accuramatic Laboratory Equipment, 42 Windsor Road, King's Lynn, Norfolk, PE30 5PL Tel: (01553) 777253 Fax: (01553) 777253 E-mail: info@accuramatic.co.uk
▶ Aerofill, 33-35 Clayton Road, Hayes, Middlesex, UB3 1RU Tel: (020) 8848 4501 Fax: (020) 8561 3308 E-mail: sales@aerofill.com

LIQUID FILLING SERVICES

Flow Tronix Ltd, Unit Vernon Place, Northern Court, Basford, Nottingham, NG6 0DE Tel: 0115-979 4886 Fax: 0115-979 4889 E-mail: info@flowtronix.co.uk

LIQUID FILLING SERVICES, CONTRACT PACKAGING

Caldo Oils Ltd, Worsley Brow, St. Helens, Merseyside, WA9 3EZ Tel: (01744) 813535 Fax: (01744) 816031E-mail: info@caldo.co.uk
Custom Packaging Ltd, Unit 1, Hortonwood 33, Telford, Shropshire, TF1 7EX Tel: (01952) 608270 Fax: (01952) 608041 E-mail: alantown@custom-pkg.co.uk
Exwold Technology, Tees Bay Business Park, Brenda Road, Hartlepool, Cleveland, TS25 2BU Tel: (01429) 230340 Fax: (01429) 232996 E-mail: sales@exwold.com
Kwikfill Ltd, Bullock Street, West Bromwich, West Midlands, B70 7HE Tel: 0121-553 0433 Fax: (0121) 553 0433 E-mail: sales@quickfill.co.uk
Lubepack Ltd, Cow Lane, Oldham, OL4 1HS Tel: 0161-620 0440 Fax: 0161-621 0801 E-mail: info@lubepack.co.uk
Reabrook Ltd, Rawdon Road, Moira, Swadlincote, Derbyshire, DE12 6DA Tel: (01283) 221044 Fax: (01283) 225731 E-mail: sales@greenhill.co.uk
S I G Combibloc Ltd, Blackthorn Way, Houghton Le Spring, Tyne & Wear, DH4 6JN Tel: 0191-385 3131 Fax: 0191-385 4713
Scholle Europe Ltd, Princesway, Team Valley Trading Estate, Gateshead, Tyne & Wear, NE11 0UT Tel: 0191-491 0066 Fax: 0191-482 6626 E-mail: sales@scholle.com

LIQUID FILLING SERVICES, CONTRACT PACKAGING, POUCHES

▶ Walters Houghton, St. Ives Way, Factory Road, Sandycroft, Deeside, Clwyd, CH5 2QS Tel: (01352) 733882 Fax: (01352) 733822 E-mail: info@waltershoughton.com

LIQUID FILTERS

▶ Airpel Filtration, Hambridge Road, Newbury, Berkshire, RG14 5TR Tel: +44 (0) 1635 263915 Fax: +44 (0) 1635 36006 E-mail: airpel@spx.com
Euro Fluid Power Ltd, St. Marys Works, Brierley Street, Stoke-on-Trent, ST6 1LB Tel: (01782) 575306 Fax: (01782) 575534 E-mail: eurofluid@aol.com
Glencoe Ltd, Glenco House, Drake Avenue, Staines, Middlesex, TW18 2AW Tel: (01784) 493555 Fax: (01784) 493222 E-mail: sales@fuelsystem.co.uk
Headline Filters Ltd, Mill Hall Business Estate, Mill Hall, Aylesford, Kent, ME20 7JZ Tel: (01622) 718927 Fax: (01622) 882448 E-mail: sales@headlinefilters.com
John Morfield Ltd, 10 Teal Court, Strathclyde Business Park, Bellshill, Lanarkshire, ML4 3NN Tel: (01698) 840888 Fax: (01698) 840234
Multiple Fabric Co. Ltd, Vulcan Mills, William Street, Tong, Bradford, West Yorkshire, BD4 9QX Tel: (01274) 682323 Fax: (01274) 651341 E-mail: info@multiplefabric.co.uk

LIQUID FILTERS – *continued*

Russell Finex Ltd, Russell House, Browells Lane, Feltham, Middlesex, TW13 7EW Tel: (020) 8818 2000 Fax: (020) 8818 2060
E-mail: enquiries@russellfinexinc.com

LIQUID FILTRATION SYSTEMS

Filterwell International Ltd, Penton, Carlisle, CA6 5QB Tel: (01228) 577339 Fax: (01228) 577442

LIQUID FLOOR COATINGS

Regal Paints Ltd, Meadow Lane Indust Estate, Meadow Lane, Alfreton, Derbyshire, DE55 7EZ Tel: (01773) 830700 Fax: (01773) 832652
E-mail: regalpaintslimited@tiscali.co.uk

LIQUID FLOW SENSORS

Rechner UK Ltd, Unit 6, The Old Mill, Reading Road, Pangbourne, Reading, RG8 7HY Tel: 0118-976 6450 Fax: 0118-976 6451
E-mail: info@rechner-sensors.co.uk

LIQUID HANDLING PLANT AND EQUIPMENT

E F D International, Unit 14 Apex Business Centre, Boscombe Road, Dunstable, Bedfordshire, LU5 4SB Tel: (01582) 666334 Fax: (01582) 664227
E-mail: sales@efd-inc.com
Newson Gale Ltd, Omega House, Private Road 8, Colwick, Nottingham, NG4 2JX Tel: 0115-940 7500 Fax: 0115-940 7501
E-mail: sales@newson-gale.co.uk

LIQUID LEVEL CONTROL EQUIPMENT

Bayham Ltd, Rutherford Road, Daneshill West, Basingstoke, Hampshire, RG24 8PG Tel: (01256) 464911 Fax: (01256) 464366
E-mail: sales@bayham.demon.co.uk
Carel Components, 24 Endeavour Way, London, SW19 8UH Tel: (020) 8946 9882 Fax: (020) 8946 6259 E-mail: ccs@carel.co.uk
Dresser Flow Control, Unit 4 Suite 1.1 Nobel House The Grand Union Office Park, Packe, Uxbridge, Middlesex, UB8 2GH Tel: (01895) 454900 Fax: (01895) 454919
E-mail: sales@dresser-valve.co.uk
Gentech International Ltd, Grangestone Eng Co, Grangestone Indust Estat E Ladywell Avenue, Maidens, Girvan, Ayrshire, KA26 9PL Tel: (01465) 713581 Fax: (01465) 714974
E-mail: enquiries@gentech-international.co.uk
Hawker Electronics Ltd, 57 The Avenue, Rubery, Rednal, Birmingham, B45 9AL Tel: 0121-453 8911 Fax: 0121-453 3777
E-mail: info@hawker-electronics.co.uk
J E Cockayne Ltd, The Exchange, Scottish Enterprise Technology Park, East Kilbride, Glasgow, G75 0QU Tel: (01355) 272305 Fax: (01355) 272306
E-mail: ian.cockayne@cockayne.co.uk
K S R Kuebler (UK) Level Measurement & Control Ltd, 43 Cherry Orchard Rd, West Molesey, Surrey, KT8 1QZ Tel: (020) 8941 3075 Fax: (020) 8979 4386
E-mail: ksruk@ksr-kuebler.com
L T H Electronics Ltd, Eltelec Works, Chaul End Lane, Luton, LU4 8EZ Tel: (01582) 593693 Fax: (01582) 598036 E-mail: sales@lth.co.uk
Frank W. Murphy Ltd, Swichgage House, Church Road, Laverstock, Salisbury, SP1 1QZ Tel: (01722) 410055 Fax: (01722) 410088
E-mail: sales@fwmurphy.co.uk
Optical Measurement Systems Ltd, Unit 6 Munro Place, Bonnyton Industrial Estate, Kilmarnock, Ayrshire, KA1 2NP Tel: (01563) 543822 Fax: (01563) 542350
E-mail: jane.savery@btclick.com
Scully UK, Unit 4 Road One, Winsford Industrial Estate, Winsford, Cheshire, CW7 3QE Tel: (01606) 553805 Fax: (01606) 553824
E-mail: sales@scullyuk.com

LIQUID LEVEL GAUGES

Bayham Ltd, Rutherford Road, Daneshill West, Basingstoke, Hampshire, RG24 8PG Tel: (01256) 464911 Fax: (01256) 464366
E-mail: sales@bayham.demon.co.uk
Burford Controls Ltd, Unit 18 Applins Park, Farrington, Blandford Forum, Dorset, DT11 8RA Tel: (01747) 811173 Fax: (01747) 811171
E-mail: information@burfordcontrols.co.uk
C G F Automation Ltd, York House, Fernie Road, Market Harborough, Leics, LE16 7PH Tel: (01858) 414616 Fax: (01858) 410196
E-mail: cgfnormondsales@veeder.co.uk
Fozmula Ltd, Berrington Road, Leamington Spa, Warwickshire, CV31 1NB Tel: (01926) 466700 Fax: (01926) 450473
E-mail: e.marketing@fozmula.com
Motherwell Control Systems Ltd, 1 St Michaels Road, St. Helens, Merseyside, WA9 4WZ Tel: (01744) 815211 Fax: (01744) 814497
E-mail: sales@motherwellcs.com
Scully UK, Unit 4 Road One, Winsford Industrial Estate, Winsford, Cheshire, CW7 3QE Tel: (01606) 553805 Fax: (01606) 553824
E-mail: sales@scullyuk.com
Tav Engineering Ltd, Unit 13-14 Priory Industrial Park, Airspeed Road, Christchurch, Dorset, BH23 4HD Tel: (01425) 270444 Fax: (01425) 276766 E-mail: tavengineering@crydom.com

LIQUID LEVEL INDICATOR/ RECORDER MANUFRS

Hawker Electronics Ltd, 57 The Avenue, Rubery, Rednal, Birmingham, B45 9AL Tel: 0121-453 8911 Fax: 0121-453 3777
E-mail: info@hawker-electronics.co.uk
Loader Fluid Engineering, Unit 4 2 Willis Way, Poole, Dorset, BH15 3SS Tel: (01202) 675220 Fax: (01202) 666890
E-mail: sales@loadereng.co.uk

LIQUID LEVEL SWITCHES

Applications Engineering Ltd, 5 Horsted Square, Bellbrook Industrial Estate, Uckfield, East Sussex, TN22 1QG Tel: (01825) 764737 Fax: (01825) 768330
E-mail: info@appeng.co.uk

LIQUID NITROGEN

Cryo Med Instruments Ltd, Cryomed House, Grove Way, Mansfield Woodhouse, Mansfield, Nottinghamshire, NG19 8BW Tel: (01623) 424200 Fax: (01623) 424777

LIQUID PACKAGING

Dayla Liquid Packing Ltd, Netherton Road, Overross Industrial Estate, Ross-on-Wye, Herefordshire, HR9 7QQ Tel: (01989) 760400 Fax: (01989) 760414
E-mail: dayla@dayla.co.uk

LIQUID PACKAGING EQUIPMENT

Dayla Liquid Packing Ltd, Netherton Road, Overross Industrial Estate, Ross-on-Wye, Herefordshire, HR9 7QQ Tel: (01989) 760400 Fax: (01989) 760414
E-mail: dayla@dayla.co.uk

LIQUID SOAPS

Castle Care Cosmetics Ltd, Invincible Road, Farnborough, Hampshire, GU14 7QP Tel: (01252) 548887 Fax: (01252) 548880
E-mail: sales@castlecare.co.uk
Diversey Lever Equipment Ltd, 4 Finway, Dallow Road, Luton, LU1 1TR Tel: (01582) 702100 Fax: (01582) 702171
James Law (Chemicals) Ltd, Crossley Street Works, Royal Street, Smallbridge, Rochdale, Lancashire, OL16 2QA Tel: (01706) 644940 Fax: (01706) 644037
Standard Soap Co. Ltd, Derby Road, Ashby-de-la-Zouch, Leicestershire, LE65 2HG Tel: (01530) 410000 Fax: (01530) 410001
E-mail: sales@standardsoap.co.uk
Tara Personal Care Ltd, 28 Ryde Avenue, Hull, HU5 1QB Tel: (01482) 444999 Fax: (01482) 473395

LIQUID WASTE INCINERATORS

Hirt Combustion Engineers Ltd, Woodford Green Works, Leslie Road, Woodford Park Industrial Estate, Winsford, Cheshire, CW7 2RB Tel: (01606) 861366 Fax: (01606) 861408
E-mail: sales@hirt.co.uk

LIQUID/GAS SEPARATORS

▶ Auxill UK Ltd, 4 Stockmers End, Capel St. Mary, Ipswich, IP9 2HQ Tel: (01473) 310659 Fax: (01473) 311740
E-mail: drewery@lineone.net

LIQUID/SOLID SEPARATORS

Ashbrook Simon-Hartley Ltd, 10/11 Brindley Court, Dalewood Road, Lymedale Business Park, Newcastle-under-Lyme, Staffordshire, ST5 9QH Tel: (01782) 578650 Fax: (01782) 260534 E-mail: enquiries@as-h.com
▶ Auxill UK Ltd, 4 Stockmers End, Capel St. Mary, Ipswich, IP9 2HQ Tel: (01473) 310659 Fax: (01473) 311740
E-mail: drewery@lineone.net
Fostech Ltd, 10 Carnreagh Road, Hillsborough, County Down, BT26 6LH Tel: (028) 9268 2652 Fax: (028) 9268 9091
E-mail: fostech@nireland.com
M & M Technical Services Ltd, Ebberns Road, Hemel Hempstead, Hertfordshire, HP3 9RD Tel: (01442) 213602 Fax: (01442) 242152
E-mail: glfoord@tiscali.co.uk

LIST BROKERS/COMPILERS

1 Stop Data Ltd, 46 High Street, Ewell, Epsom, Surrey, KT17 1RW Tel: (020) 8786 9111 Fax: (020) 8786 9115
E-mail: sales@1stopdata.com
Dudley Jenkins List Broking, City Bridge House, 57 Southwark St, London, SE1 1RU Tel: (020) 7871 9070 Fax: (020) 7871 9071
E-mail: broking@djlb.co.uk
Eagle Direct Marketing, Unit 1 Axis, Hawkfield Business Park, Whitchurch, Bristol, BS14 0BY Tel: 0117-902 0073 Fax: 0117-902 8220
E-mail: sc@eaglemailing.co.uk
Electric Marketing, 22 John Street, London, WC1N 2BY Tel: (020) 7419 7999 Fax: (020) 7419 7282
E-mail: lists@electricmarketing.co.uk
Hamilton House Mailings Ltd, Earls Trees Court, Earls Trees Road, Corby, Northamptonshire, NN17 4HH Tel: (01536) 399000 Fax: (01536) 399012 E-mail: sales@hamilton-house.com
Otto Lift (UK) Ltd, Lindon House, Lindon Road, Walsall, WS8 7BW Tel: (01543) 374777 Fax: (01543) 374141

LITHIUM BATTERIES

Argosy Ltd, Units 6-7, Ridgeway, Drakes Drive, Long Crendon, Buckinghamshire, HP18 9BF Tel: (01844) 202101 Fax: (01844) 202025
E-mail: sales@argosycable.com
Renatex Ltd, Nam House, 58 Spencer Street, Birmingham, B18 6DS Tel: 0121-233 9999 Fax: 0121-236 9295
E-mail: sales@renatex.com
Saft, River Drive, South Shields, Tyne & Wear, NE33 2TR Tel: 0191-456 1451 Fax: 0191-456 6383 E-mail: enquiries@saftbatteries.com
▶ The Small Battery Co., 70 Cromford Road, London, SW18 1NY Tel: (020) 8871 3730 Fax: (020) 8871 3686
E-mail: info@smallbattery.company.org.uk
Ultralife Batteries UK Ltd, 18 Nuffield Way, Abingdon, Oxfordshire, OX14 1TG Tel: (01235) 542642 Fax: (01235) 535766
E-mail: drichards@ultralife.co.uk
▶ Varta Microbattery GmbH, 16 Progress Business Centre, Whittle Parkway, Slough, SL1 6DQ Tel: (01628) 607930 Fax: (01628) 607939 E-mail: uksales@varta.com

LITHIUM ION BATTERIES

Alcad, 1st Floor Unit 5 Astra Centre, Edinburgh Way, Harlow, Essex, CM20 2BN Tel: (01279) 772555 Fax: (01279) 420696
E-mail: carter.sarah@alcad.com
Alexander Technologies (Europe) Ltd, 4 Doxford Drive, South West Industrial Estate, Peterlee, County Durham, SR8 2RL Tel: 0191-587 2787 Fax: 0191-587 2587
E-mail: mail@alexenergy.co.uk
Allbatteries UK Ltd, 34 The Metro Centre, Dwight Road, Watford, WD18 9SB Tel: (01923) 241500 Fax: (01923) 245700
E-mail: sales@allbatteries.com

LITHOGRAPHIC PLATE MAKERS/ PROCESSORS OR SERVICES

A P G Visual Colour Ltd, 5 Gregson Road, South Reddish, Stockport, Cheshire, SK5 7SS Tel: 0161-477 0166 Fax: 0161-476 5431
E-mail: apg@apgvisualcolour.co.uk
Abacus Lithographic Printers Ltd, 34-38 Gloucester Way, London, EC1R 0BN Tel: (020) 7278 4637 Fax: (020) 7278 8535
E-mail: sales@abacusprinting.com
Alpha Engraving Co. Ltd, Unit F1 Bounds Green Industrial Estate, South Way, London, N11 2UL Tel: (020) 8368 1674 Fax: (020) 8368 1675 E-mail: alphablocks@btconnect.com
Centrescan Ltd, Centrescan Ho, 59 Great Eastern St, London, EC2A 3HS Tel: (020) 7739 5493 Fax: (020) 7739 6509
Charter Litho Plates Ltd, Charter Ho, 51-53 Bickersteth Rd, London, SW17 9SH Tel: 020-8767 3513 Fax: 020-8767 7128
E-mail: printing@charterlitho.co.uk
Colour Assembly Ltd, 28 Thurrock Commercial Centre, Purfleet Industrial Park, Aveley, South Ockendon, Essex, RM15 4YA Tel: (01708) 891777 Fax: (01708) 891333
E-mail: info@colourassembly.co.uk
Colour Separations Ltd, 31-33 Woodford Road, Watford, WD17 1PB Tel: (01923) 245555 Fax: (01923) 241637
Colourgraphics Cambridge Ltd, 40 Clifton Road, Cambridge, CB1 7ED Tel: (01223) 213322 Fax: (01223) 212320
E-mail: colourgraphicscambridge@btconnect.com
Crown Graphic Sales Ltd, 77 Leonard Street, London, EC2A 4QS Tel: (020) 7739 7977 Fax: (020) 7739 3404
E-mail: crowngraph@aol.com
Design & Media Solutions, Tovil Hill, Maidstone, Kent, ME15 6QS Tel: (01622) 681366 Fax: (01622) 688928
E-mail: craftsmencolour@craftsmencolour.co.uk
Granville Reprographics Ltd, Demmings House, Brookfield Road, Demmings Industrial Estate, Cheadle, Cheshire, SK8 2PE Tel: 0161-428 1236 Fax: 0161-428 0418
E-mail: sales@directimaging.co.uk
Ink Slinger Ltd, Red Lion Business Centre, Red Lion Road, Surbiton, Surrey, KT6 7QD Tel: (020) 8974 2425 Fax: (020) 8974 2423
Knockout Colour Ltd, Unit 6 Shore Business Centre, 14-16 Shore Rd, London, E9 7TA Tel: (020) 8533 1177 Fax: (020) 8533 5895
Modern Colour Solutions, 2 Bullsbridge Industrial Estate, Hayes Road, Southall, Middlesex, UB2 5NB Tel: (020) 8848 4577 Fax: (020) 8848 1513
E-mail: sales@moderncoloursolutions.co.uk
Negaplate, 5 Howard Road, London, E11 3PL Tel: (020) 8558 9050 Fax: (020) 8558 9050
E-mail: negaplate@btconnect.com
Nicholson & Bass Ltd, 3 Nicholson Drive, Newtownabbey, County Antrim, BT36 4FB Tel: (028) 9034 2433 Fax: (028) 9034 2066
E-mail: sales@nicholsonbass.com
P C Graphics, Unit 1, Langley House, Middlegreen Trading Estate, Langley, Slough, SL3 6DF Tel: (01753) 571220 Fax: (01753) 692380 E-mail: sales@pcgraphics.co.uk
Pioneer Print Ltd, 8 Raven Road, London, E18 1HB Tel: (020) 8505 1552 Fax: (020) 8505 9982 E-mail: sales@pioneerprint.co.uk
Pulse Media Ltd, 32-42 Station Road, Heaton Mersey, Stockport, Cheshire, SK4 3QT Tel: 0161-432 2225 Fax: 0161-442 9096
Repro Factory Ltd, Faber House, Main Yard, 94 Wallis Road, London, E9 5LN Tel: (020) 8985 2278 Fax: (020) 8533 0755
E-mail: mail@reprofactory.com
Reprographics NI Ltd, Unit A2, 4 Westbank Drive, Belfast, BT3 9LA Tel: (028) 9037 0057 Fax: (028) 9037 0069
E-mail: reprographic@btconnect.com
S M J Graphic Services Ltd, 113 Cecil Street, Watford, WD24 5AS Tel: (01923) 222886 Fax: (01923) 218948
Schawk Ltd, Boston Court, Kansas Avenue, Salford, M50 2GN Tel: 0161-872 9449 Fax: 0161-848 8441
▶ Scopenet, Provender House, Unit Z, Paddock Wood Distribution Centre, Paddock Wood, Tonbridge, Kent, TN12 6UU Tel: (01892) 837968 Fax: (01892) 837226
Seven, 5Th Floor Big Peg, 120 Vyse Street, Hockley, Birmingham, B18 6NF Tel: 0121-236 1541 Fax: 0121-234 7775
E-mail: birmingham@sevenww.co.uk
Star Litho Plates Ltd, Unit 10 Orient Industrial Park, Simonds Road, London, E10 7DE Tel: (020) 8532 8686 Fax: (020) 8556 5568
E-mail: starlitho@btconnect.com
Studio Ninety Two Ltd, The Barns, Belmont Farm, Stud Green, Holyport, Maidenhead, Berkshire, SL6 2JH Tel: (01628) 676567 Fax: (01628) 676568
E-mail: studio92@clara.co.uk
Swaingrove Ltd, Unit 3-4 Fourwheel Drive, Rougham Industrial Estate, Rougham, Bury St. Edmunds, Suffolk, IP30 9ND Tel: (01359) 271385 Fax: (01359) 271327
E-mail: systems@swaingrove.co.uk
Technik Ltd, 2 4 Riverpark, Billet Lane, Berkhamsted, Hertfordshire, HP4 1HL Tel: (01442) 871117 Fax: (01442) 870891
E-mail: terry@technik.com
Thruxton Press Ltd, Thruxton Down House, Thruxton, Andover, Hampshire, SP11 8PR Tel: (01264) 889552 Fax: (01264) 889622
E-mail: publications@brunton.co.uk
Tower Media Solutions, 25 Holywell Row, London, EC2A 4XE Tel: (020) 7247 0876 Fax: (020) 7247 5717
E-mail: helpdesk@towermedia.co.uk
Trentgate Anglia Ltd, 35 Eastern Way, Bury St. Edmunds, Suffolk, IP32 7AB Tel: (01284) 753500 Fax: (01284) 706389
E-mail: sales@trentgate.co.uk
Vyner Litho Plates, 4 Kingside, Ruston Road, London, SE18 5BX Tel: (020) 8854 5544
E-mail: vyners@compuserve.com
Wyndeham Graphics Ltd, Unit 3-4 Maverton Road, London, E3 2JE Tel: (020) 8983 0022 Fax: (020) 8981 9802

LITHOGRAPHIC PRINTERS TO THE TRADE

A P G Visual Colour Ltd, 5 Gregson Road, South Reddish, Stockport, Cheshire, SK5 7SS Tel: 0161-477 0166 Fax: 0161-476 5431
E-mail: apg@apgvisualcolour.co.uk
▶ K Brooke & Son, 7 Broomfield Road, Marsh, Huddersfield, HD1 4QD Tel: (01484) 425286 Fax: (01484) 364727
E-mail: michael@brookeprinters.com
Buxton Press Ltd, Palace Road, Buxton, Derbyshire, SK17 6AE Tel: (01298) 212000 Fax: (01298) 212001
E-mail: sales@buxtonpress.co.uk
Centaur Communications Ltd, St. Giles House, 50 Poland Street, London, W1F 7AX Tel: (020) 7970 4000 Fax: (020) 7970 4398
City Press, The Old Courthouse, 1 The Paddock, Chatham, Kent, ME4 4RE Tel: (01634) 832820 Fax: (01634) 818741
Clearpoint Print Services Ltd, Park Lane, Nottingham, NG6 0DT Tel: 0115-979 7925 Fax: 0115-979 7958
E-mail: sales@clearpoint-print.com
Colne Press Ltd, Unit 11-12, Eastman Way, Hemel Hempstead Industrial Estate, Hemel Hempstead, Hertfordshire, HP2 7DU Tel: (01442) 212922 Fax: (01442) 265967
E-mail: info@colne.co.uk

LITHOGRAPHIC PRINTERS TO THE TRADE – *continued*

Colorprofile Printers, 4 Whitworth Road, Stevenage, Hertfordshire, SG1 4QS Tel: (01438) 724891 Fax: (01438) 720512

▶ Creative Imaging (UK) Ltd, Waterside House, 60 Wharf Road, London, N1 7SF Tel: (020) 7251 6006

Crewe Colour Printers Ltd, Millbuck Way, Sandbach, Cheshire, CW11 3SH Tel: (01270) 761113 Fax: (01270) 766386

Downland Printing Services Ltd, Unit 1 Kingley Centre, Downs Road, Weststoke, Chichester, West Sussex, PO18 9HJ Tel: (01243) 576576 Fax: (01243) 576577 E-mail: studio@downlandrepro.demon.co.uk

Dunnsprint Ltd, Clarence Works, Clarence Road, Eastbourne, East Sussex, BN22 8HJ Tel: (01323) 410902 Fax: (01323) 410573 E-mail: sales@dunnsprint.co.uk

Eden River Press Ltd, Units C-D, Charlwoods Business Centre, East Grinstead, West Sussex, RH19 2HH Tel: (01342) 313577 Fax: (01342) 324125 E-mail: mail@edenriverpress.co.uk

Europress Printers, 15-17 Green Lane, Hull, HU2 0HG Tel: (01482) 224993 Fax: (01482) 211486 E-mail: info@europresshull.co.uk

Graphicomm Ltd, 17 Willow Court, St. Modwen Road, Plymouth, PL6 8LQ Tel: (01752) 670099 Fax: (01752) 265700 E-mail: sales@graphicomm.co.uk

J W L Ltd, 1 Mundells, Welwyn Garden City, Hertfordshire, AL7 1EU Tel: (01707) 338410 Fax: (01707) 338731 E-mail: info@jwl.co.uk

▶ Loudmouth Postcards, 5 Hendon Street, Sheffield, S13 9AX Tel: (0845) 2309805 Fax: 0114-288 0044 E-mail: chet@loudworld.co.uk

Page Lithoprint Ltd, Enterprise House, Cranes Close, Basildon, Essex, SS14 3JB Tel: (01268) 464464 Fax: (01268) 464465 E-mail: sales@pagemediagroup.com

▶ Pheby Colour Litho UK, Unit A3 Newton Industrial Estate, Eastern Avenue West, Romford, RM6 5SD Tel: (020) 8599 9842 Fax: (020) 8598 1966 E-mail: ajpheby@aol.com

Piggott Printers Ltd, H The Paddocks, 347 Cherry Hinton Road, Cambridge, CB1 8DH Tel: (01223) 404800 Fax: (01223) 404801

Polestar Jowetts, Evanston Avenue, Kirkstall Road, Leeds, LS4 2HR Tel: (0113) 279 5041 Fax: (0113) 231 0193

The Print Factory Ltd, South Portway Close, Round Spinney, Northampton, NN3 8RH Tel: (01604) 790079 Fax: (01604) 492515 E-mail: info@theprintfactory.co.uk

Printing Press, 21 Clare Place, Plymouth, PL4 0JW Tel: (01752) 250580 Fax: (01752) 223855 E-mail: theprintingpress@btconnect.com

S C F Ltd, Bellbrook Industrial Estate, Uckfield, East Sussex, TN22 1QL Tel: (01825) 761166 Fax: (01825) 765836 E-mail: sales@scf-print.co.uk

St Philips Litho, Unit 2, Minto Road Industrial Centre, Bristol, BS2 9YB Tel: 0117-955 4473 Fax: 0117-955 4473

Solent Print Engineering Ltd, 1 Pytchley Close, Fareham, Hampshire, PO14 3SF Tel: (07917) 784595 E-mail: print.eng@ntlworld.com

▶ Streets Printers Ltd, Royston Road, Baldock, Hertfordshire, SG7 6NW Tel: (01462) 893771 Fax: (01462) 894660 E-mail: sales@streetsprinters.co.uk

Tranters Ltd, Markeaton Printing Works, Payne Street, Derby, DE22 3AZ Tel: (01332) 341982 Fax: (01332) 292707 E-mail: trantersales@btconnect.com

VCS Clearpoint Ltd, Salop Street, Daybrook, Nottingham, NG5 6HD Tel: 0115-967 1234 Fax: 0115-967 1154 E-mail: clearpoint@demon.co.uk

LITHOGRAPHIC PRINTERS/ LITHOGRAPHERS

▶ 21 Colour Ltd, 21 Summerlee Street, Glasgow, G33 4DB Tel: 0141-774 4455 Fax: 0141-774 3739

3 Dimensional Print Ltd, Unit 37 Acorn Industrial Park, Crayford Road, Dartford, DA1 4AL Tel: (01322) 555942 Fax: (01322) 528973 E-mail: sales@3dp.co.uk

▶ A D Garrie & Sons, 141 High Street, Auchterarder, Perthshire, PH3 1AD Tel: (01764) 662481

A D P Marketing Services, Unit 5 Carr Mills, 919 Bradford Road, Birstall, Batley, West Yorkshire, WF17 9JY Tel: (01924) 470990 Fax: (01924) 471644 E-mail: mail@adpservices.net

A D S Worldwide Ltd, West Carr Lane, Sutton Fields, Hull, HU7 0BW Tel: (01482) 820219 Fax: (01482) 831596 E-mail: sales@ads-worldwide.com

A F Litho Ltd, Grenaby Works, Grenaby Road, Croydon, CR0 2EJ Tel: (020) 8689 7849 Fax: (020) 8689 0479 E-mail: sales@aflitho.co.uk

▶ A G P Printers, 7 Colvend Street, Glasgow, G40 4DU Tel: 0141-556 4900 Fax: 0141-556 6090

A P G Visual Colour Ltd, 5 Gregson Road, South Reddish, Stockport, Cheshire, SK5 7SS Tel: 0161-477 0166 Fax: 0161-476 5431 E-mail: apg@apgvisualcolour.co.uk

A P Litho Ltd, Units 9-10 Bourne Road Industrial Park, Bourne Road, Dartford, DA1 4BZ Tel: (01322) 523289 Fax: (01322) 527343 E-mail: alan@printapl.fsnet.co.uk

▶ A S T Print Group Ltd, Ipswich Road, Cardiff, CF23 9AQ Tel: (029) 2049 7901 Fax: (029) 2045 0189

Abacus Lithographic Printers Ltd, 34-38 Gloucester Way, London, EC1R 0BN Tel: (020) 7278 4637 Fax: (020) 7278 8535 E-mail: sales@abacusprinting.com

▶ Abbey Direct Print, B2 Manor Way Business Park, Manor Way, Swanscombe, Kent, DA10 0PP Tel: (01322) 380191 Fax: (01322) 382066 E-mail: sales@abbeygroup.co.uk

Abbotts Creative Print Ltd, Turnpike Close, Bilton Way, Lutterworth, Leicestershire, LE17 4YB Tel: (01455) 552636 Fax: (01455) 551699 E-mail: info@abbottsuk.net

▶ Abel Drew Printhaus Ltd, 31 Heathfield, Stacey Bushes, Milton Keynes, MK12 6HR Tel: (01908) 227321 Fax: (01908) 227322

▶ Acanthus Press Ltd, Sylvan Road Trading Estate, Wellington, Somerset, TA21 8ST Tel: (01823) 663339 Fax: (01823) 665531

▶ Acme Printing Co. Ltd, 37 Aston Road, Waterlooville, Hampshire, PO7 7XF Tel: (023) 9282 5036 Fax: (023) 9225 9521

Acorn Design, 96 Appletree Lane, Brockhill, Redditch, Worcestershire, B97 6TS Tel: (01527) 62189

▶ Acorn Press Swindon Ltd, Westmead Industrial Estate, Westlea, Swindon, SN5 7UU Tel: (01793) 608900 Fax: (01793) 608901 E-mail: sales@acornpress.co.uk

▶ Activa, 7 Montpellier Terrace, Cheltenham, Gloucestershire, GL50 1US Tel: (01242) 230555 Fax: (01242) 231333

▶ Adcraft Ltd, Block 10, Moorfield Industrial Estate, Kilmarnock, Ayrshire, KA2 0BA Tel: (01563) 530130 Fax: (01563) 534390

▶ Admor Ltd, Jubilee Works, Kings Close, Yapton, Arundel, West Sussex, BN18 0EX Tel: (01243) 553078 Fax: (01243) 555017

Adrian Stanley, Unit 95, Imperial Trading Estate Lambs La North, Rainham, Essex, RM13 9XL Tel: (020) 8986 8232 Fax: (020) 8985 6755

▶ Advanced Images Ltd, Clydeway Skypark, 8 Elliot Place, Glasgow, G3 8EP Tel: 0141-221 4898 Fax: 0141-226 3602

▶ Aeroprinting, Unit 54B, Aidan Court, Bede Industrial Estate, Jarrow, Tyne & Wear, NE32 3EF Tel: 0191 4282428 Fax: 0191 4837266 E-mail: info@aeroprinting.co.uk

▶ Airdrie Print Services, 24-26 Flowerhill Street, Airdrie, Lanarkshire, ML6 6AP Tel: (01236) 751833 Fax: (01236) 748134

▶ Akros Print Ltd, 8 Wilson Place, East Kilbride, Glasgow, G74 4QD Tel: (01355) 226184 Fax: (01355) 248364

Albanian Press Ltd, 107 Camp Road, St. Albans, Hertfordshire, AL1 5HL Tel: (01727) 853495 Fax: (01727) 846690 E-mail: info@albanian-press.co.uk

▶ Albemarle Graphics Ltd, 35 Astbury Road, London, SE15 2NL Tel: (020) 7639 3249 Fax: (020) 7358 0754 E-mail: info@ag-online.co.uk

▶ Alexander Ritchie & Son Ltd, 163 Bonnington Road, Pilrig Industrial Estate, Edinburgh, EH6 5RE Tel: 0131-554 0431

▶ All Inc, 30 Brambles Enterprise Centre, Waterberry Drive, Waterlooville, Hampshire, PO7 7TH Tel: (023) 9224 3101 Fax: (023) 9226 2729 E-mail: info@allinc.co.uk

▶ All Ink Ltd, 30 Brambles Enterprise Centre, Waterberry Drive, Waterlooville, Hampshire, PO7 7TH Tel: (023) 9226 2715

▶ The Allesley Press Ltd, Leofric House, Waterman Road, Coventry, CV6 5TP Tel: (024) 7663 8844 Fax: (024) 7663 8890

▶ Alliance Publishing Co., 119 Talbot Road, Blackpool, FY1 3QX Tel: (01253) 751614 Fax: (01253) 292915

▶ Allprint Ltd, Llantrisant Business Park, Llantrisant, Pontyclun, Mid Glamorgan, CF72 8LF Tel: (01443) 228555 Fax: (01443) 237477 E-mail: sales@allprint2000.com

Alpha Graphics, 40 Carrmere Road, Leechmere Industrial Estate, Sunderland, SR2 9TW Tel: 0191-523 9100 Fax: 0191-523 6045

▶ Alphagraphics, 37-39 George Street, Hull, HU1 3BA Tel: (01482) 229111 Fax: (01482) 229090 E-mail: info@alphagraphics-hull.co.uk

▶ Alphagraphics Ltd, 19-21 Collingwood Street, Newcastle upon Tyne, NE1 1JE Tel: 0191-221 2030 Fax: 0191-221 2031

Alphaprint Graphic Services Ltd, 18-20 Mark Road, Hemel Hempstead Industrial Estate, Hemel Hempstead, Hertfordshire, HP2 7BN Tel: (01442) 262798 Fax: (01442) 217831

▶ Amadeus Press Ltd, Ezra House, Littlewood Drive, West 26 Industrial Estate, Cleckheaton, West Yorkshire, BD19 4TQ Tel: (01274) 863210 Fax: (01274) 863211 E-mail: info@hartandclough.co.uk

▶ Amber Press Ltd, Platt Industrial Estate, Maidstone Road, Platt, Sevenoaks, Kent, TN15 8JL Tel: (01732) 886911

▶ Anderson & Partners, 275 Kirkstall Road, Leeds, LS4 2BX Tel: 0113-231 0191

▶ Annoplanna Ltd, 12 Quarry Street, Guildford, Surrey, GU1 3UY Tel: (01483) 302727 Fax: (01483) 506108

Apd Colour Print & Design, Unit 5-6 Brookfield Farm Gravel Pit Lane, Southam Road, Cheltenham, Gloucestershire, GL52 3NQ Tel: (01242) 529132 Fax: (01242) 262311 E-mail: sales@apdprint.co.uk

▶ Applied Design, 215a Worplesdon Road, Guildford, Surrey, GU2 9XJ Tel: (01483) 232678 Fax: (01483) 237991

▶ Arc Colourprint, 16 Timber Bush, Edinburgh, EH6 6QH Tel: 0131-553 1707

Argonaut Press, 108 New Cavendish Street, London, W1W 6XP Tel: (020) 7631 1011 Fax: (020) 7631 1011

Argun Printers, 344 Mare Street, London, E8 1HA Tel: (020) 8985 7879 Fax: (020) 8985 3668 E-mail: info@argun.co.uk

Armour Print & Design, 92b Audley Street, Reading, RG30 1BS Tel: 0118-958 8957 Fax: 0118-959 4816 E-mail: dave@armourprint.co.uk

Arrow Press, 11 Riverside Park Industrial Estate, Dogflud Way, Farnham, Surrey, GU9 7UG Tel: (01252) 722790 Fax: (01252) 721874 E-mail: sales@arrowpress.co.uk

▶ Arrowhead Printing Ltd, 1 Alton Business Centre, Omega Park, Alton, Hampshire, GU34 2YU Tel: (01420) 549960 Fax: (01420) 549967

▶ Arthur Rostron & Sons Ltd, Forge Lane, Canal Road, Leeds, LS12 2PR Tel: 0113-263 8988 Fax: 0113-279 0234

▶ Ashmore Press Ltd, Unit 18 Martlets Way, Goring-by-Sea, Worthing, West Sussex, BN12 4HF Tel: (01903) 506735 Fax: (01903) 507225

▶ Ashprint Web Offset Ltd, 3 Drumhead Road, Chorley North Industrial Park, Chorley, Lancashire, PR6 7BX Tel: (01257) 230988 Fax: (01257) 230977

▶ Ashworth (Screen Printers) Ltd, Westland Square, Leeds, LS11 5SS Tel: 0113-271 7978

Aspect Design, 89 Newtown Road, Malvern, Worcestershire, WR14 1PD Tel: (01684) 561567 Fax: (01684) 560041 E-mail: help@aspect-design.net

▶ Astra Printing Services Ltd, Old Stoneywood Church, Bankhead Road, Bucksburn, Aberdeen, AB21 9HQ Tel: (01224) 715151

B & B Zinc Alloys Ltd, 233 Station Road, Knowle, Solihull, West Midlands, B93 0PU Tel: (01564) 773062 Fax: (01564) 778907

▶ B D L Litho Ltd, 3 Bat & Ball Enterprise Centre, Bat & Ball Road, Sevenoaks, Kent, TN14 5LJ Tel: (01732) 464111 Fax: (01732) 462020

▶ B & H Group, 3 Caxton Way, Watford, WD18 8UA Tel: (01923) 247466 Fax: (01923) 246476 E-mail: sales@bh-group.com

B J T Print Services Ltd, Common La, Kenilworth, Warwickshire, CV8 2EL Tel: (01926) 852085 Fax: (01926) 859591

▶ B Loony Ltd, 1 Cape House, 105 Bellingdon Road, Chesham, Buckinghamshire, HP5 2HQ Tel: (01494) 774664 Fax: (01494) 792787

B M Printers Ltd, Units 8-9, Queens Mill Road, Huddersfield, HD1 3PG Tel: (01484) 422593 Fax: (01484) 519399 E-mail: john@bmprinters.fsnet.co.uk

▶ B P S Printers, 1 Holtspur Top Lane, Beaconsfield, Buckinghamshire, HP9 1DN Tel: (01494) 678823 Fax: (01494) 674457

Baber Rollaprint Ltd, Coombs Road, Halesowen, West Midlands, B62 8AJ Tel: 0121-559 5111 Fax: 0121-559 6594 E-mail: creativity@baber-rollaprint.co.uk

▶ Bahson Colour Print, Unit 4b Adwalton Moor Bus Park, Inmoor Road, Birkenshaw, Bradford, West Yorkshire, BD11 2PS Tel: (01274) 474500 Fax: (01274) 474577

▶ Bakes & Lord Ltd, 529 Beacon Road, Bradford, West Yorkshire, BD6 3NB Tel: (01274) 521717

Barden Print Ltd, Bay Hall Print Works, Common Road, Huddersfield, HD1 5EU Tel: (01484) 422522 Fax: (01484) 435158 E-mail: design@bardenprint.com

Barham & Moore Ltd, 8 Grafton Place, Chelmsford, CM2 6TG Tel: (01245) 450554 Fax: (01245) 450845 E-mail: sales@barham-print.co.uk

▶ Barwell Litho Ltd, Unit 34 First Avenue, Westfield Industrial Estate, Midsomer Norton, Radstock, BA3 4BS Tel: (01761) 419161 Fax: (01761) 418098

▶ Bath Press, 14-18 Block 2-First Road, Blantyre Industrial Estate, Blantyre, Glasgow, G72 0ND Tel: (01698) 822727 Fax: (01698) 710105

Beaver Graphic Services, Graphic House, Wiggenhall Road, Watford, WD18 0FG Tel: (01923) 229387 Fax: (01923) 223957 E-mail: sales@beaver.co.uk

▶ Beechwood Press, 1 Park Gate Close, Bredbury Park Way, Bredbury, Stockport, Cheshire, SK6 2SZ Tel: 0161-612 0102 Fax: 0161-612 9889

▶ Belgravia Colour Printers, 12a Uplands Business Park, Blackhorse Lane, London, E17 5QJ Tel: (020) 8527 0101 Fax: (020) 8527 0105

▶ Bell Press Ltd, Jeans Lane Bells Hill, Bishop's Stortford, Hertfordshire, CM23 2NN Tel: (01279) 652976 Fax: (01279) 652770

▶ Berkshire Cutouts Ltd, Unit 7-8 Redfields Industrial Park, Church Crookham, Fleet, Hampshire, GU52 0RD Tel: (01252) 850491 Fax: (01252) 851370 E-mail: sales@chromatec.co.uk

▶ Beta Print Ltd, Unit 1c, Larkin Industrial Estate, Springfield Road, Chesham, Buckinghamshire, HP5 1PW Tel: (01494) 791463

Biddles, 24 Rollesby Road, King's Lynn, Norfolk, PE30 4LS Tel: (01553) 764728 Fax: (01553) 764633 E-mail: enquiries@biddles.co.uk

Billington Press Ltd, 20 Hepscott Road, London, E9 5HB Tel: (020) 8985 7561 Fax: (020) 8533 3692

▶ Birches Printers Ltd, 39-43 Temple Bar, Willenhall, West Midlands, WV13 1SH Tel: (01902) 605410 Fax: (01902) 637746

Bloomfield Ltd, 7b Waterloo Industrial Estate, Waterloo Road, Bidford-on-Avon, Alcester, Warwickshire, B50 4JH Tel: (01789) 490528 Fax: (01789) 490461 E-mail: info@bloomfieldprinters.co.uk

▶ Blue Design & Print, 1 Rumsey Row, The Green, Writtle, Chelmsford, CM1 3DU Tel: (01245) 423822 Fax: (01245) 423833

Bookham Print & Design, Homestead, Eastwick Road, Bookham, Leatherhead, Surrey, KT23 4BA Tel: (01372) 454506 Fax: (01372) 452087

▶ Bookmarque Printers, 110 Beddington Lane, Croydon, CR0 4TD Tel: (020) 8612 3400 Fax: (020) 8612 3401

Bosprint, Units 38 & 40, Hastings Road Industrial Estate, Hastings Road, Leicester, LE5 0LJ Tel: 0116-274 3308 Fax: 0116-276 1254 E-mail: info@bosprint.co.uk

▶ Boswell Printers & Office Supplies, Graphic House, 9 Dunlop Road, Hadleigh Road Industrial Estate, Ipswich, IP2 0UG Tel: (01473) 212000 Fax: (01473) 214000

Bowcourt Ltd, 7 Gardner Industrial Estate, Kent House Lane, Beckenham, Kent, BR3 1JR Tel: (020) 8659 1931 Fax: (020) 8676 8939 E-mail: sales@bowcourt.co.uk

Bowmans, Westland Square, Leeds, LS11 5SS Tel: 0113-272 0088 Fax: 0113-272 0261 E-mail: mail@bowmans77.co.uk

▶ BPMG Ltd, Peratone House, Gatehouse Way, Aylesbury, Buckinghamshire, HP19 8DB Tel: (01296) 436791 Fax: (01296) 380100 E-mail: sales@bpmg.co.uk

▶ Bracken Press, Print House, Swallowfields, Welwyn Garden City, Hertfordshire, AL7 1JD Tel: (01707) 896999

▶ Broad Oak Colour Printers, A-D 254 Broad Oak Road, Canterbury, Kent, CT2 7QH Tel: (01227) 767856 Fax: (01227) 762593

▶ K Brooke & Son, 7 Broomfield Road, Marsh, Huddersfield, HD1 4QD Tel: (01484) 425286 Fax: (01484) 364727 E-mail: michael@brookeprinters.com

Brown Knight & Truscott Holdings Ltd, North Farm Road, High Brooms, Tunbridge Wells, Kent, TN2 3BW Tel: (01892) 511678 Fax: (01892) 511343

▶ Buchan Observer, 28-30 Seagape, Peterhead, Aberdeenshire, AB42 1JP Tel: (01779) 472017 Fax: (01779) 871331 E-mail: sales@buchanobserver.com

▶ Buchanan Mcpherson Ltd, 2 Portland Place, Hamilton, Lanarkshire, ML3 7JU Tel: (01698) 282903

Burall, PO Box 7, Wisbech, Cambs, PE13 2SZ Tel: (0870) 728 7272 Fax: (0870) 728 7273

▶ Burall Infocard Ltd, Cromwell Road, Wisbech, Cambridgeshire, PE14 0SN Tel: (01945) 468100 Fax: (01945) 467095

▶ Burchell Design & Print, Rope Walk, Littlehampton, West Sussex, BN17 5DE Tel: 01903 717633 Fax: 01903 724823 E-mail: mark@burchell.co.uk

Burgess Printing Ltd, Unit M3 Cody Court, Salford, M50 2GE Tel: 0161-872 7881 Fax: 0161-876 0636

▶ Business Printing Co., 6 Nene Road, Bicton Industrial Park, Kimbolton, Huntingdon, Cambridgeshire, PE28 0LF Tel: (01480) 861911 Fax: (01480) 861922 E-mail: sales@theprinters.nu

▶ Busiprint Ltd, 64 Well Street, Buckingham, MK18 1EN Tel: (01280) 823000 Fax: (01280) 816464

Buxton Press Ltd, Palace Road, Buxton, Derbyshire, SK17 6AE Tel: (01298) 212000 Fax: (01298) 212001 E-mail: sales@buxtonpress.co.uk

James Byrne Printing Ltd, Unit 10 Sandleheath Industrial Estate, Old Brickyard Road, Sandleheath, Fordingbridge, Hampshire, SP6 1PA Tel: (01425) 655090 Fax: (01425) 656844 E-mail: studio@jamesbyrne.co.uk

C 3 Imaging (Glasgow), 126 Hydepark Street, Glasgow, G3 8BW Tel: 0141-226 3344

C J W Printers Ltd, South Lane, Elland, West Yorkshire, HX5 0HQ Tel: (01422) 374082 Fax: (01422) 379335

C P Offset Ltd, Kellaw Road, Darlington, County Durham, DL1 4YA Tel: (01325) 462315 Fax: (01325) 462767 E-mail: administrator@banff-buchan.ac.uk

C & R, Bruce House, Warren Park Way, Enderby, LE19 4ZW Tel: 0116-284 7464 Fax: 0116-284 7440 E-mail: info@candr.co.uk

▶ C & R Graphics Ltd, 30 Deerdykes View, Cumbernauld, Glasgow, G68 9HN Tel: (01236) 726552 Fax: (01236) 730219

C3 Imaging Ltd, Severalls Business Park, Telford Way, Colchester, CO4 9QP Tel: (01206) 845544 Fax: (01206) 845856 E-mail: jacqueline@hilocolour.co.uk

▶ Caine Douglas, Unit 2b Little Tennis St South, Nottingham, NG2 4EU Tel: 0115-958 2020 Fax: 0115-958 2030

Calendar Club, Vulcan Works, Water Lane, Exeter, EX2 8BY Tel: (01392) 207001

▶ Calf Hey Design Ltd, Unit 23, Colne Valley Business Park, Linthwaite, Huddersfield, HD7 5QG Tel: (01484) 846419 Fax: (01484) 847163

Camberley Printers Ltd, 357 London Road, Camberley, Surrey, GU15 3HQ Tel: (01276) 63048 Fax: (01276) 23477 E-mail: sales@camberleyprinters.co.uk

▶ Cambrian Printers (Aberystwyth) Ltd, Llanbadarn Road, Llanbadarn Fawr, Aberystwyth, Dyfed, SY23 3TN Tel: (01970) 627111 Fax: (01970) 615497 E-mail: info@cambrian-printers.co.uk

LITHOGRAPHIC PRINTERS/ LITHOGRAPHERS – *continued*

Castle Colour Press Ltd, 3 Morgan Way, Bowthorpe Employment Area, Norwich, NR5 9JJ Tel: (01603) 741278 Fax: (01603) 749227 E-mail: reception@castlecolour.co.uk

Celectron Printing, 18-18a Unit, Vale Business Park, Llandow, Cowbridge, South Glamorgan, CF71 7PF Tel: (01446) 774801 Fax: (01446) 775285 E-mail: info@soprint.co.uk

Central Print, 2 Swan Village Industrial Estate, Swan Lane, West Bromwich, West Midlands, B70 0NY Tel: 0121-500 6230 Fax: 0121-500 6230

Centrescan Ltd, Centrescan Ho, 59 Great Eastern St, London, EC2A 3HS Tel: (020) 7739 5493 Fax: (020) 7739 6509

Century Litho (Truro) Ltd, Kernick Industrial Estate, Penryn, Cornwall, TR10 9EP Tel: (01326) 376666 Fax: (0870) 0010305 E-mail: sales@centryprint.com

Chapel Press Ltd, Parkgate Close, Bredbury, Stockport, Cheshire, SK6 2SZ Tel: 0161-406 9495 Fax: 0161-292 0200 E-mail: info@chapelpress.com

▶ Chapman Watson & Co. Ltd, 25 Rodney Street, Edinburgh, EH7 4EL Tel: 0131-556 6275 Fax: 0131-556 8105

Charlesworth China Ltd, 254 Deighton Road, Huddersfield, HD2 1JJ Tel: (01484) 517077 Fax: (01484) 517068 E-mail: mail@charlesworth.com

▶ Chars Display London Ltd, 28 Redchurch Street, London, E2 7DP Tel: (020) 7739 3604 Fax: (020) 7739 1962

▶ Charter Print Group, Leicester Road Kingsway House, Lutterworth, Walcote, Lutterworth, Leicestershire, LE17 4JN Tel: (01455) 203600 Fax: (01455) 557979 E-mail: sales@chartergrp.co.uk

▶ Chase Colour Ltd, 2 The Sidings, Station Road, Guiseley, Leeds, LS20 8BX Tel: (01943) 874110 Fax: (01943) 870350 E-mail: info@chasecolour.com

▶ Cherith Press Ltd, 4 Craggs Industrial Park, Morven Street, Creswell, Worksop, Nottinghamshire, S80 4AJ Tel: (01909) 722411 Fax: (01909) 722811

Chord Reprographic Services, 19-20 Britton Street, London, EC1M 5NQ Tel: (020) 7253 3340 Fax: (020) 7253 5371

▶ City Press Leeds Ltd, St Anns Mill, Commercial Road, Leeds, LS5 3AE Tel: 0113-278 4286 Fax: 0113-278 6066

▶ cityview printers, 7a Bakers Yard, Alphinbrook Road, Marsh Barton Trading Estate, Exeter, EX2 8SS Tel: 01392 410222 E-mail: andy@cityviewprinters.co.uk

Clarkeprint Ltd, 45-47 Stour Street, Birmingham, B18 7AJ Tel: 0121-454 7117 Fax: 0121-454 8404 E-mail: sales@clarkeprint.co.uk

▶ Classic Printers (Peterborough) Ltd, 3 Crowland Business Centre, Crease Drove, Crowland, Peterborough, PE6 0BN Tel: (01733) 210789

Clearpoint Print Services Ltd, Park Lane, Nottingham, NG6 0DT Tel: 0115-979 7925 Fax: 0115-979 7958 E-mail: sales@clearpoint-print.com

Clearprint, 99 East Road, Sleaford, Lincolnshire, NG34 7EH Tel: (01529) 303176 Fax: (01529) 303172 E-mail: sales@clearaprint.com

M.S.O. Cleland Ltd, The Linenhall Press, 399 Castlereagh Road, Belfast, BT5 6QP Tel: (028) 9040 0200 Fax: (028) 9070 5446 E-mail: info@mso.com

▶ Clementine Oakley, 259 Water Road, Wembley, Middlesex, HA0 1HX Tel: (020) 8922 4567 Fax: (020) 8922 4568

▶ Clifford Whittaker Ltd, Britannia New Mill, Queen Street, Mossley, Ashton-under-Lyne, Lancashire, OL5 9AL Tel: (01457) 833461 Fax: (01457) 835644

Clifton Litho, 29-31 Richmond Road, Staines, Middlesex, TW18 2AA Tel: (01784) 458127 Fax: (01784) 465744

▶ Cloverleaf Press Ltd, 243 Felixstowe Road, Ipswich, IP3 9BN Tel: (01473) 274777

▶ Clunie Group Ltd, 15 Lochside St, Oban, Argyll, PA34 4HP Tel: (01631) 565485

▶ Clydebank Post, 88 Dumbarton Road, Clydebank, Dunbartonshire, G81 1UG Tel: 0141-952 1345 Fax: 0141-952 7267 E-mail: editorial@clydebankpost.co.uk

Coleridge Business Supplies, Dollis Hill Estate, Brook Road, London, NW2 7BZ Tel: (020) 8208 7711 Fax: (020) 8208 7722

▶ Collector Set Printers Ltd, Aylesford Mill, St Michaels Close, Aylesford, Kent, ME20 7BU Tel: (01622) 716636 Fax: (01622) 717515 E-mail: sales@collectorsetprinters.co.uk

College Hill Press Ltd, 37 Webber Street, London, SE1 8QW Tel: (020) 7633 0543 Fax: (020) 7633 0181 E-mail: sales@collegehillpress.co.uk

Colne Press Ltd, Unit 11-12, Eastman Way, Hemel Hempstead Industrial Estate, Hemel Hempstead, Hertfordshire, HP2 7DU Tel: (01442) 212922 Fax: (01442) 265967 E-mail: info@colne.co.uk

Colorprofile Printers, 4 Whitworth Road, Stevenage, Hertfordshire, SG1 4QS Tel: (01438) 724891 Fax: (01438) 720512

▶ Colour Direct, G Arklow Trading Estate, Arklow Road, London, SE14 6EB Tel: (020) 8305 8205 Fax: (020) 8305 8206

▶ Colourplan Design & Print Ltd, 11 Waterside Court, St. Helens, Merseyside, WA9 1UA Tel: (01744) 612636

Colourplus Print & Design, Unit 28 Monument Business Park, Warpsgrove Lane, Chalgrove, Oxford, OX44 7RW Tel: (01865) 400040 Fax: (01865) 400040 E-mail: design@colourplus.co.uk

▶ Colourprint UK Ltd, Unit Colchester Estate, Colchester Avenue, Penylan, Cardiff, CF23 9AP Tel: (029) 2046 5550 Fax: (029) 2048 2300

▶ Colourstream Litho Ltd, Riverside Court, Pride Park, Derby, DE24 8JN Tel: (01332) 224860 Fax: (01332) 224861 E-mail: sales@surrey-imaging.ik.com

Colourwise K C O Ltd, 1 Unifax, Woods Way, Goring-by-Sea, Worthing, West Sussex, BN12 4QY Tel: (01903) 242894 Fax: (01903) 506126

▶ Colprint Ltd, 2 Lower Trinity Street, Birmingham, B9 4AG Tel: 0121-766 7606 Fax: 0121-772 1350 E-mail: sales@colprint.com

Coltec Parker Ltd, Unit 3 Royd Way, Keighley, West Yorkshire, BD21 3LG Tel: (01535) 608405 Fax: (01535) 669276 E-mail: sales@coltecparker.com

▶ Communication In Print, 31 Ormside Way, Redhill, RH1 2LW Tel: (01737) 761987 Fax: (01737) 779188 E-mail: sales@ukcip.co.uk

▶ Compact Group Ltd, 4 Deacon Industrial Estate, Forstal Road, Aylesford, Kent, ME20 7SP Tel: (01622) 719365 Fax: (01622) 718831 E-mail: litho@compactlitho.co.uk

▶ Concept 2, 2B Mount Pleasant Road, London, SE13 6RB Tel: (020) 8690 3496

▶ Concert Print & Display Ltd, Unit 7, Abbey Mead Industrial Park, Brooker Road, Waltham Abbey, Essex, EN9 1HU Tel: (01992) 650555

Concorde Graphics Ltd, Units 21-23, Chiltonian Industrial Estate, Manor Lane, London, SE12 0TX Tel: (020) 8297 1115 Fax: (020) 8297 9755 E-mail: david.b@concordegraphics.co.uk

▶ Connect Colour Ltd, Unit C, Northbridge Road, Berkhamsted, Hertfordshire, HP4 1EH Tel: (01442) 879701 Fax: (01442) 879702

Connect Colour Ltd, Unit C, Northbridge Road, Berkhamsted, Hertfordshire, HP4 1EH Tel: (01442) 879701 Fax: (01442) 879702 E-mail: sales@connektcolour.com

▶ Contour Direct Ltd, Unit 40 The Metropolitan Centre, Halifax Road, Greenford, Middlesex, UB6 8XU Tel: (020) 8575 8989 Fax: (020) 8575 7553

▶ Copy Centre, 25 Rodney Street, Edinburgh, EH7 4EL Tel: 0131-556 3417 Fax: 0131-556 8105

▶ Copypoll Ltd, 9-11 Francis Court, Wellingborough Road, Rushden, Northamptonshire, NN10 6AY Tel: (01933) 411188 Fax: (01933) 411199

Copyprint UK Ltd, Ground Floor West Block Westminster Business Square, Durham Street, London, SE11 5JH Tel: (020) 7735 0956 Fax: (020) 7793 0519 E-mail: sales@copyprint.co.uk

▶ Countryside Art, The Old Rectory, Alford, Lincolnshire, LN13 0BQ Tel: (01507) 480685

County Offset, North Quays Business Park, Atlantic Street, Broadheath, Altrincham, Cheshire, WA14 5BF Tel: 0161-928 5333 Fax: 0161-927 7069 E-mail: sales@countyprint.com

▶ Cowan Print, 23 Brougham Street, Edinburgh, EH3 9JS Tel: 0131-622 1000 Fax: 0131-622 2121

▶ Cradley Digital Imaging, Chester Road, Cradley Heath, West Midlands, B64 6AB Tel: (01384) 414110

▶ Creation Greetings Ltd, Afton Road, Freshwater, Isle of Wight, PO40 9UH Tel: (01983) 758540 Fax: (01983) 758541 E-mail: sales@jarthurdixon.com

▶ Creative Copy N Colour Ltd, Unit 14c, Raleigh Hall Industrial Estate, Stafford, ST21 6JL Tel: (01785) 851183 Fax: (01785) 850445 E-mail: info@creativecopyncolour.co.uk

▶ Creative Imaging (UK) Ltd, Waterside House, 60 Wharf Road, London, N1 7SF Tel: (020) 7251 6006

▶ Creative Print & Design Wales, Unit 27 Rassau Industrial Estate, Rassau, Ebbw Vale, Gwent, NP23 5SD Tel: (01495) 307007 Fax: (01495) 309572

Creative Solutions, 197 Hagley Road, Birmingham, B16 9RD Tel: 0121-454 2222 Fax: 0121-456 2362 E-mail: pressoffice@prontaprint.com

▶ Creeds The Printers, The Gables, Broadoak, Bridport, Dorset, DT6 5NL Tel: (01308) 423411 Fax: (01308) 421511

▶ Crescent Press Ltd, 9 Wainwright Street, Birmingham, B6 5TH Tel: 0121-326 9223 Fax: 0121-326 9224 E-mail: info@crescentpress.com

▶ Cri Digital, 18 St Peters Street, Nottingham, NG7 3FF Tel: 0115-978 3337

▶ Crystal Offset, Crystal House, 17 Tariff Road, London, N17 0DY Tel: (020) 8801 1733 Fax: (020) 8365 1826

Culwick Printers Ltd, 131 Long Street, Atherstone, Warwickshire, CV9 1AD Tel: (01827) 712618 Fax: (01827) 718527 E-mail: culwicks@anchorprint.co.uk

▶ D Munro & Son, 8 Cornwall Street, Glasgow, G41 1AQ Tel: 0141-427 2633

▶ Dalton Label International Ltd, Dalton Airfield, Dalton, Thirsk, North Yorkshire, YO7 3HE Tel: (01845) 577926

Dalton & Co Printers Ltd, Oxford Court, Oxford Street, Accrington, Lancashire, BB5 1QX Tel: (01254) 871666 Fax: (01254) 871148 E-mail: info@daltons-printers.com

Danscot Print Ltd, 8 Kinnoull Street, Perth, PH1 5EN Tel: (01738) 635228 Fax: (01738) 638805

▶ Danscot Prints Ltd, Bute House, Arran Road, Perth, PH1 3DZ Tel: (01738) 622974 Fax: (01738) 620536

▶ Darlaston Printers Ltd, Reeves Street, Walsall, WS3 2DL Tel: (01922) 710671 Fax: (01922) 495652

▶ Darwin Press, Unit B Pier Road, Feltham, Middlesex, TW14 0TW Tel: (020) 8844 3780 Fax: (020) 8844 3795

▶ Dataplus Print & Design, 13 Hill Street, Dunmurry, Belfast, BT17 0AD Tel: (028) 9030 1717 Fax: (028) 9061 1292

Deanson Wilkes Forms & Systems Ltd, 1 Cramp Hill, Wednesbury, West Midlands, WS10 8ES Tel: 0121-568 7123 Fax: 0121-568 7122 E-mail: sales@deansonwilkes.co.uk

▶ Deben Print Co., 1 Bailey Close, Hadleigh Road Industrial Estat, Ipswich, IP2 0UD Tel: (01473) 210244 Fax: (01473) 217299 E-mail: sales@debenprint.co.uk

Deltor Communications Ltd, Unit C Long Acre, Saltash, Cornwall, PL12 6LZ Tel: (01752) 841717 Fax: (01752) 850450 E-mail: enquiries@deltor.co.uk

▶ Demontford Color Tech, 18 Slater Street, Leicester, LE3 5AY Tel: 0116-262 5151

▶ Denwal Press, Park House, Warren Row, Reading, RG10 8QS Tel: (01628) 824071 Fax: (01628) 825844

Design & Print Partnership, 7 Rivermead South, Rivermead Industrial Estate, Chelmsford, CM1 1PD Tel: (01245) 290516 Fax: (01245) 265137 E-mail: designandprintpartnership@btconnect.com

▶ Devon Print Proof plc, 15 Abbey Gate, Leicester, LE4 0AA Tel: 0116-251 4711 Fax: 0116-253 7984

▶ Dexter Graphics Ltd, 4-5 Sandpit Road, Dartford, DA1 5BU Tel: (01322) 288880 Fax: (01322) 287333 E-mail: enquiries@dextergraphics.com

▶ Diagraph Advertising & Display Products, Croydon Road, Nottingham, NG7 3DS Tel: 0115-924 9111 Fax: 0115-924 9222

▶ Digi Source (UK) Ltd, Chalmers Square, Deans Industrial Estate, Deans, Livingston, West Lothian, EH54 8RJ Tel: (01506) 463046

▶ Digital Typeline Publications Ltd, 2d West Telferton, Edinburgh, EH7 6UL Tel: 0131-657 1001 Fax: 0131-669 0049

▶ Direct Imaging Ltd, Demmings House, Brookfield Road, Cheadle, Cheshire, SK8 2PE Tel: 0161-491 2121

Ditchling Press, Consort Way, Burgess Hill, West Sussex, RH15 9YS Tel: (01444) 243253 Fax: (01444) 242198

▶ DKM Graphics Ltd, 132a Raceview Road, Ballymena, County Antrim, BT42 4HY Tel: (028) 2564 9239 Fax: (028) 2564 0192 E-mail: info@dkmprint.co.uk

Dobson & Crowder Ltd, Berwyn Works, Holyhead Road, Llangollen, Clwyd, LL20 8AE Tel: (01978) 862100 Fax: (01978) 860410

Dorling Print Ltd, Dorling House, 44 Wates Way, Mitcham, Surrey, CR4 4HR Tel: (020) 8685 9399 Fax: (020) 8685 9140 E-mail: info@dorling.co.uk

▶ Douglas Gauld & Co. (Tayside) Ltd, Shanwell Court Industrial Esta, Shanwell Road, Tayport, Newport-On-Tay, Fife, DD6 9EA Tel: (01382) 553494

Downland Printing Services Ltd, Unit 1 Kingley Centre, Downs Road, Weststoke, Chichester, West Sussex, PO18 9HJ Tel: (01243) 576576 Fax: (01243) 576577 E-mail: studio@downlandrepro.demon.co.uk

▶ Drakeloe Press Ltd, 7 James Way, Bletchley, Milton Keynes, MK1 1SU Tel: (01908) 271866

Edward Dudfield Ltd, 4 Whilems Works, Forest Road, Ilford, Essex, IG6 3HJ Tel: (020) 8500 4455 Fax: (020) 8500 4488 E-mail: sales@dudfields.co.uk

Dudley Print, 2 The Sling, Dudley, West Midlands, DY2 9AJ Tel: (01384) 455316 Fax: (01384) 457519 E-mail: dudley.print@virgin.net

Dunn Printing Co., 10a Beechings Way, Alford, Lincolnshire, LN13 9JE Tel: (01507) 463416 Fax: (01507) 463416 E-mail: dunnprintingco@lineone.net

▶ Dunston Printers Sheepbridge Ltd, Dunston Road, Chesterfield, Derbyshire, S41 9QD Tel: (01246) 454335 Fax: (01246) 260480

J.S. Dutton Ltd, Cale Street, Cale Green, Stockport, Cheshire, SK2 6SW Tel: 0161-480 2346 Fax: 0161-480 0728 E-mail: studio@jsdutton.co.uk

▶ Dyrlaga Thompson Print, 1c Anchor Bridge Way, Dewsbury, West Yorkshire, WF12 9QS Tel: (01924) 456655 Fax: (01924) 460986

▶ E Pilling Printers Ltd, Rose Mill, Union Street, Middleton, Manchester, M24 6DD Tel: 0161-653 9850 Fax: 0161-655 3804

▶ Earle & Ludlow, 77 Victoria Road, Cirencester, Gloucestershire, GL7 1ES Tel: (01285) 653599 Fax: (01285) 640286 E-mail: sales@earle-ludlow.co.uk

▶ East Sussex Press Ltd, Crowborough Hill, Crowborough, East Sussex, TN6 2EE Tel: (01892) 654074

▶ Eclipse Colour Print Ltd, Riley Road, Telford Way Industrial Estate, Kettering, Northamptonshire, NN16 8NN Tel: (01536) 483401 Fax: (01536) 481102 E-mail: sales@eclipsecolourprint.co.uk

▶ Educational Printing Services Ltd, Albion Mill, Water Street, Great Harwood, Blackburn, BB6 7QR Tel: (01254) 882080 Fax: (01254) 882010

▶ Ekota Printers, 114 Brick Lane, London, E1 6RL Tel: (020) 7377 2626 Fax: (020) 7377 0666

▶ The Electronic Page Co., 218-219 Springvale Industrial Estate, Cwmbran, Gwent, NP44 5BJ Tel: (01633) 875555 Fax: (01633) 871990 E-mail: sales@electronicpage.co.uk

▶ Elmar Graphics, Unit 3, 8 Becket Road, Montague Industrial Estate, London, N18 3PN Tel: (020) 8807 2350 Fax: (020) 8803 0370 E-mail: elmarhmg@globalnet.co.uk

Elpeeko Ltd, Wrightsway, Outer Circle Road, Lincoln, LN2 4JY Tel: (01522) 512111 Fax: (01522) 541796 E-mail: sales@elpeeko.com

Elsam Cross & Co., 5-6 London Road, Spalding, Lincolnshire, PE11 2TA Tel: (01775) 723758 Fax: (01775) 768575 E-mail: geoff.hemsil@virgin.net

▶ Embassy Press London Ltd, 341 Battersea Park Road, London, SW11 4LS Tel: (020) 7622 4522 Fax: (020) 7498 0173 E-mail: sales@embassypress.co.uk

▶ Emblem Print Products Ltd, 17 North Parade, Derby, DE1 3AY Tel: (01332) 362536 E-mail: sales@emblemprint.co.uk

▶ Emc Advertising Gifts, Derwent House, 1064 High Road, London, N20 0YY Tel: (020) 8492 2200 Fax: (0845) 3451065 E-mail: sales@emcadgifts.co.uk

▶ En Press Ltd, Unit 16-18 Home Farm Rural Industries, East Tytherley Road, Lockerley, Romsey, Hampshire, SO51 0JT Tel: (01794) 341425 Fax: (01794) 341424

▶ Ernest Bond Printing, 4 Kingside, Ruston Road, London, SE18 5BX Tel: (020) 8855 7788 Fax: (020) 8855 7799

▶ Esto Perpetua Ltd, 447-449 South Ordnance Road, Enfield, Middlesex, EN3 6HR Tel: (01992) 761422 Fax: (01992) 711391

▶ Europalm Services Ltd, Unit B Bouverie Mews, London, N16 0AE Tel: (020) 8211 7555 Fax: (020) 8211 7666 E-mail: sales@europalm.co.uk

Europress Printers, 15-17 Green Lane, Hull, HU2 0HG Tel: (01482) 224993 Fax: (01482) 211486 E-mail: info@europresshull.co.uk

▶ Europrint Ltd, Pigeon House Lane, Swindon, SN3 4QH Tel: (01793) 838800 Fax: (01793) 824696

▶ Evolve Print Solutions, Unit 8 Woodcock Hill Estate, Harefield Road, Rickmansworth, Hertfordshire, WD3 1PQ Tel: (01923) 774111

▶ Express Offset Ltd, Unit 4 Brickfields, Liverpool, L36 6HY Tel: 0151-449 1512 Fax: 0151-449 2817

▶ Express Print, 66 Londesborough Road, Scarborough, North Yorkshire, YO12 5AF Tel: (01723) 351464 Fax: (01723) 507955

▶ F I Printing Co Ltd, 41 Sherborne Street, Manchester, M8 8LE Tel: 0161-832 3198 Fax: 0161-832 6123 E-mail: sales@fi-printing.co.uk

▶ F M Print Ltd, Unit 5 Lennox Road Industrial Mall, Basingstoke, Hampshire, RG22 4DF Tel: (01256) 471072 Fax: (01256) 814915

▶ The Face Agency, Baron Street, London, N1 9LL Tel: (020) 7713 9700 Fax: (020) 7713 9788 E-mail: sales@thefaceagency.co.uk

▶ Fairprint Distribution Ltd, 44 West Henderson Wind, Dundee, DD1 5BT Tel: (01382) 322223

▶ Fast Forward (Scotland) Ltd, Thistle House, Caputhall Road, Deans Industrial Estate, Deans, Livingston, West Lothian, EH54 8AS Tel: (01506) 419977

▶ Field Boxmore Healthcare Leaflets, 3-4 Fairway Drive, Greenford, Middlesex, UB6 8PW Tel: (020) 8575 9119 Fax: (020) 8566 6174

▶ Fine Arts Colour Ltd, Unit 11 Boundary Business Court, 92-94 Church Road, Mitcham, Surrey, CR4 3TD Tel: (020) 8646 7007 Fax: (020) 8646 3100

Fingerprint Ltd, 7 Station Field Industrial Est, Kidlington, Oxfordshire, OX5 1JD Tel: (01865) 848080

▶ First Class Printing Ltd, Unit 3, Mugiemoss Road, Aberdeen, AB21 9US Tel: (01224) 683066

▶ Five Castles Press Ltd, Raeburn Road South, Ipswich, IP3 0ET Tel: (01473) 718719 Fax: (01473) 712122

▶ Flemings Business Printers, 20 Warwick Road, Worthing, West Sussex, BN11 3ET Tel: (01903) 211700 Fax: (01903) 211900

▶ Flowprint Ltd, E Boyn Valley Industrial Estate, Boyn Valley Road, Maidenhead, Berkshire, SL6 4EJ Tel: (01628) 778600 Fax: (01628) 773500 E-mail: sales@flowprint.com

▶ Four Point Printing & Copying, Unit 3 Fordwater Trading Estate, Ford Road, Chertsey, Surrey, KT16 8HG Tel: (01932) 561163 Fax: (01932) 568010 E-mail: info@fourpoint.co.uk

▶ Foxhill Commercial Printers, 80 Sidney Street, Cleethorpes, South Humberside, DN35 7NQ Tel: (01472) 242777 Fax: (01472) 242255 E-mail: spectrumprint@lineone.net

▶ Foxprint Printers, 1 Factory Street, Shepshed, Loughborough, Leicestershire, LE12 9AQ Tel: (01509) 505413 Fax: (01509) 650413 E-mail: print@foxprint.co.uk

Francis Anthony, Blowing House Hill, St. Austell, Cornwall, PL25 5AH Tel: (01726) 61264 Fax: (01726) 69533 E-mail: info@francis-antony.co.uk

Frank Peters Ltd, Bretton Street, Dewsbury, West Yorkshire, WF12 9BL Tel: (01924) 451881 Fax: (01924) 456864 E-mail: sales@frank-peters.co.uk

Fretwells Ltd, Oslo Road, Hull, HU7 0YN Tel: (01482) 835511 Fax: (01482) 835368 E-mail: info@fretwells.co.uk

LITHOGRAPHIC PRINTERS/ LITHOGRAPHERS – *continued*

Frewer Brothers Ltd, 3 Wealdstone Road, Sutton, Surrey, SM3 9QN Tel: (020) 8641 7171 Fax: (020) 8644 4779 E-mail: mail@frewerbrothers.co.uk

▶ Frontier Print & Design Ltd, Pickwick House, Chosen View Road, Cheltenham, Gloucestershire, GL51 9LT Tel: (01242) 573863 Fax: (01242) 511643 E-mail: sales@frontier-uk.com

▶ Future Engraving, 98 Appin Road, Birkenhead, Merseyside, CH41 9HH Tel: 0151-647 0715 Fax: 0151-647 0714 E-mail: sales@future-engraving.co.uk

▶ Futureprint Northampton Ltd, 64-72 Roe Road, Northampton, NN1 4PJ Tel: (01604) 639565 Fax: (01604) 622845 E-mail: sales@futureprint-npton.com

▶ G B Print, C2 Blaby Industrial Park, Winchester Avenue, Blaby, Leicester, LE8 4GZ Tel: 0116-247 7144 Fax: 0116-278 2723 E-mail: info@gbprint.co.uk

G & B Printers, Unit 4 Mount Road Industrial Estate, Feltham, Middlesex, TW13 6AR Tel: (020) 8755 1822 Fax: (020) 8893 3854 E-mail: info@gbprinters.co.uk

▶ G K D Litho Ltd, Origination House, 15 Strawberry Street, Hull, HU9 1EN Tel: (01482) 325313

▶ G R G Print Com, A Treefield Industrial Estate, Gelderd Road, Morley, Leeds, LS27 7JU Tel: 0113-383 3888 Fax: 0113-383 3889

G & S Jones, Unit 1e Bersham Enterprise Centre, Colliery Road, Rhostyllen, Wrexham, Clwyd, LL14 4EG Tel: (01978) 263160 Fax: (01978) 263135 E-mail: graham@gsjonesprint.co.uk

G W Belton Ltd, Heaton Street, Gainsborough, Lincolnshire, DN21 2ED Tel: (01427) 612291 Fax: (01427) 810520 E-mail: sales@gwbelton.com

▶ G W Mckane & Son, 32-34 Station Street, Keswick, Cumbria, CA12 5HF Tel: (01768) 772140 Fax: (01768) 771203

▶ Genesis Design & Print, 111 Whitby Road, Slough, SL1 3DR Tel: (01753) 696940 Fax: (01753) 696941

▶ Genesis Seven Ltd, Unit 4 Scotshaw Brook Industrial Estate, Branch Road Lower Darwen, Lower Darwen, Darwen, Lancashire, BB3 0PR Tel: (01254) 666000 Fax: (01254) 666001 E-mail: info@genesis-seven.co.uk

▶ Gilbert Sutton Ltd, Unit 9 10 16, Robin Hood Industrial Estate, Alfred Street South, Nottingham, NG3 1GE Tel: 0115-958 4942

▶ Gillies Armstrong Ltd, 97 Loanbank Quadrant, Glasgow, G51 3HZ Tel: 0141-440 0101 Fax: 0141-440 0660

Gilmour Print, Irvinehill Farm, Stewarton, Kilmarnock, Ayrshire, KA3 3EL Tel: (01294) 850217 Fax: (01294) 850444 E-mail: sales@gilmourprint.co.uk

▶ Gilt Edged Promotions Ltd, 1 Regal Close, Kings Park Road, Moulton Park Industrial Estate, Northampton, NN3 6LL Tel: (01604) 671671 Fax: (01604) 671518

Giraffe Print, PO Box 453, Epsom, Surrey, KT18 7WJ Tel: 0800 328 4712 E-mail: info@giraffeprint.com

Gladstone Press, 701 Gladstone Court Business Centre, London, SW8 4AT Tel: (020) 7498 0071 Fax: (020) 7498 0067 E-mail: nigelmason@spuk.co.uk

▶ Glencarra Textile Printers, Belford Mills, 16 Brewery Road, Kilmarnock, Ayrshire, KA1 3HZ Tel: (01563) 550978

▶ Glennleigh Associates, 14 Bateman Street, London, W1D 3AG Tel: (020) 7434 2551 Fax: (020) 7437 2222

▶ Goaters Ltd, 86A North Sherwood Street, Nottingham, NG1 4EE Tel: 0115-941 9746

▶ Goodprint UK Ltd, Stephenson Way, Thetford, Norfolk, IP24 3RU Tel: (01842) 761546 Fax: (01842) 754001

▶ Gowise Print, 4 Belmore Road, Norwich, NR7 0PT Tel: (01603) 431304

Grant Print Ltd, North Esplanades West, Aberdeen, AB11 5RJ Tel: (01224) 574329

Granville Reprographics Ltd, Demmings House, Brookfield Road, Demmings Industrial Estate, Cheadle, Cheshire, SK8 2PE Tel: 0161-428 1236 Fax: 0161-428 0418 E-mail: sales@directimaging.co.uk

Graphic Art Services, 81-82 Mackley Industrial Estate, Henfield Road, Small Dole, Henfield, West Sussex, BN5 9XR Tel: (01273) 495793 Fax: (01273) 494887 E-mail: design@graphicart.co.uk

▶ Graphic House Ltd, 83 London Road, Preston, PR1 4AS Tel: (01772) 257657 Fax: (01772) 821562 E-mail: design@graphichouse.co.uk

▶ Graphic Office Supplies Ltd, 244 Poplar High Street, London, E14 0BB Tel: (020) 7515 7162 Fax: (020) 7515 4410 E-mail: graphic@btconnect.com

▶ Graphic Press (Grimsby) Ltd, Upper Spring Street, Grimsby, South Humberside, DN31 1QP Tel: (01472) 359036

Graphicomm Ltd, 17 Willow Court, St. Modwen Road, Plymouth, PL6 8LQ Tel: (01752) 670099 Fax: (01752) 265700 E-mail: sales@graphicomm.co.uk

▶ Great Yarmouth Printing Services Ltd, Gapton Hall Road, Great Yarmouth, Norfolk, NR31 0NL Tel: (01493) 603061 Fax: (01493) 442648 E-mail: sales@midcontinentgy.com

▶ Greatwell Designs, 68 Pullman Road, Wigston, Leicestershire, LE18 2DB Tel: 0116-257 1444

Green Tree Press Ltd, Unit 1 Parham Drive, Eastleigh, Hampshire, SO50 4NU Tel: (023) 8061 1234 Fax: (023) 8064 4432 E-mail: sales@greentreepress.co.uk

Griffin Design & Print Services Ltd, 713 High Road, Leyton, London, E10 5AB Tel: (020) 8558 4721 Fax: (020) 8558 4415 E-mail: mail@griffindp.freeserve.co.uk

Griffin Print Ltd, 2-4 Belgic Square, Peterborough, PE1 5XF Tel: (01733) 553530 Fax: (01733) 555668 E-mail: info@griffinprint.co.uk

▶ Grillford Ltd, 26 Peverel Drive, Bletchley, Milton Keynes, MK1 1QZ Tel: (01908) 626700

GT Printers London Ltd, 5 Maverton Road, London, E3 2JE Tel: (020) 8981 7638 Fax: (020) 8980 1941 E-mail: sales@gtprinters.co.uk

▶ Gwasg Dinefwr Press, Rawlings Road, Llandybie, Ammanford, Dyfed, SA18 3YD Tel: (01269) 850935 Fax: (01269) 851024

▶ H E Jones Ltd, Tyseley Industrial Estate, Seeleys Road, Birmingham, B11 2LA Tel: 0121-772 0114 Fax: 0121-773 9364

▶ Hadleys Ltd, 13 Winstanley Way, Basildon, Essex, SS14 3BP Tel: (01268) 533121 Fax: (01268) 286879

▶ Haines Clark, Wellington House, 11 Merse Road, Redditch, Worcestershire, B98 9HL Tel: (01527) 61111

▶ Halcon Printing Ltd, Unit 5-7 Spurryhillock Industrial Estate, Broomhill Road, Stonehaven, Kincardineshire, AB39 2NH Tel: (01569) 762250 Fax: (01569) 766054

Halligan Direct Mail Ltd, 66 Addison Road, Bromley, BR2 9HQ Tel: (020) 8290 9000 Fax: (020) 8290 9002 E-mail: info@halligans.co.uk

▶ Hamilton Forms, 37 Westley Grange, Chartwell Drive, Wigston, Leicestershire, LE18 2FL Tel: 0116-257 1600 Fax: 0116-257 1880

Hammond Vivian Ltd, Power House, 27 Market Road, Richmond, Surrey, TW9 4LZ Tel: (020) 8876 6600 Fax: (020) 8392 1946 E-mail: info@hammondvivian.co.uk

▶ Ha'penny Press, Unit 4 Appletree Barns, Folly Lane, Copdock, Ipswich, IP8 3JQ Tel: (01473) 730055 Fax: (01473) 730169 E-mail: tickets@raffle.co.uk

▶ Harlequin Colour Press, Coedcae Lane, Pontyclun, Mid Glamorgan, CF72 9EW Tel: (01443) 222219 Fax: (01443) 226544

▶ Harris Printers, 16-18 Mary Street, Porthcawl, Mid Glamorgan, CF36 3YA Tel: (01656) 788038 Fax: (01656) 785017

▶ Harrogate Printing Ltd, Ripon Way, Harrogate, North Yorkshire, HG1 2AU Tel: (01423) 523449 Fax: (01423) 506160

Hartham Press Ltd, 5a Marshgate Trading Estate, Hertford, SG13 7AB Tel: (01992) 589334 Fax: (01992) 554826 E-mail: sales@harthampress.com

▶ Haslam Printers Ltd, Standish Street, Chorley, Lancashire, PR7 3AJ Tel: (01257) 263777 Fax: (01257) 261404 E-mail: sales@haslamprinters.co.uk

▶ Hassall & Lucking Ltd, 36 Cross Street, Long Eaton, Nottingham, NG10 1HD Tel: 0115-973 3292 Fax: 0115-946 2120

Hay Nisbet Press Ltd, 11 Dilwara Avenue, Glasgow, G14 0SQ Tel: 0141-959 3325 Fax: 0141-958 1161 E-mail: Studio@haynisbet.com

Headley Brothers Ltd, The Invicta Press, Queens Road, Ashford, Kent, TN24 8HH Tel: (01233) 623131 Fax: (01233) 612345 E-mail: printing@headley.co.uk

▶ Heath Press, Harrem House, Ogilvie Road, High Wycombe, Buckinghamshire, HP12 3DS Tel: (01494) 536117 Fax: (01494) 531298

Heathcote Press, Harriott Drive, Heathcote Industrial Estate, Warwick, CV34 6TJ Tel: (01926) 883306 Fax: (01926) 314017 E-mail: heathcotepress@freeuk.com

The Hedgehog Press, Unit B5, Imperial Bus Estate, West Mill, Gravesend, Kent, DA11 0DL Tel: (01474) 322153 Fax: (01474) 535570 E-mail: info@thehedgehogpress.co.uk

▶ Herald Graphics Ltd, Elgar Road South, Reading, RG2 0BZ Tel: 0118-931 1488

▶ Heronsgate Printers, 1 Bay Tree Avenue, Kingston Road, Leatherhead, Surrey, KT22 7UE Tel: (01372) 376635 Fax: (01372) 386521

▶ Herts & Essex Printers Ltd, Unit 14 Mead Business Centre, Mead Lane, Hertford, SG13 7BQ Tel: (01992) 554768

▶ Hickling & Squires Ltd, 1 Moorgreen Industrial Park, Engine Lane, Newthorpe, Nottingham, NG16 3QU Tel: (01773) 536400 Fax: (01773) 536444 E-mail: sales@hickling-squires.co.uk

▶ Highland Printing & Publishing Group, 13 Henderson Road, Inverness, IV1 1SP Tel: (01463) 224444

▶ Hill & Hay Ltd, 58 Rogart Street, Glasgow, G40 2AA Tel: 0141-554 2205 Fax: 0141-556 6023 E-mail: sales@hillhay.co.uk

▶ Hollinger Print Ltd, 12 Burnet Road, Sweet Briar Industrial Estate, Sweet Briar Road Industrial Es, Norwich, NR3 2BS Tel: (01603) 309000 E-mail: info@hollinger.co.uk

▶ Horizon Print & Design, Unit 4, Falkirk Enterprise Park, Falkirk, FK2 9HQ Tel: (01324) 670237

▶ Horton Print Group, Rosse Street, Bradford, West Yorkshire, BD8 9AS Tel: (01274) 777801 Fax: (01274) 777802 E-mail: sales@hortonprint.com

HSP Milners, Ironworks Road, Barrow-in-Furness, Cumbria, LA14 2PG Tel: (01229) 823392 Fax: (01229) 870274 E-mail: headoffice@hsp-milners.demon.co.uk

▶ Hugh K Clarkson & Sons Ltd, Lochiel Works, Young Street, West Calder, West Lothian, EH55 8EQ Tel: (01506) 872241 Fax: (01506) 871827

▶ Huntcard Litho Ltd, Unit 4 Platt Industrial Estate, Maidstone Road, Platt, Sevenoaks, Kent, TN15 8JL Tel: (01732) 882088 Fax: (01732) 882148

▶ I P A Print Associates Ltd, F Chiltern Commerce Centre, 45 Asheridge Road, Chesham, Buckinghamshire, HP5 2PY Tel: (01494) 791532 Fax: (01494) 783690 E-mail: sales@ipaprint.com

▶ Iain M Crosbie, Beechfield Road, Willowyard Industrial Estate, Beith, Ayrshire, KA15 1LN Tel: (01505) 504848 Fax: (01505) 504674

▶ Icon Colour Ltd, Westerham House, Fircroft Way, Edenbridge, Kent, TN8 6EL Tel: (01732) 866833 Fax: (01732) 866882

Iles Colour Print Ltd, Chase House, 1-2 Russell Town Avenue, Bristol, BS5 9LT Tel: 0117-954 7460 Fax: 0117-935 1243

▶ Image Visual Communications, Samson Close, Stephenson Industrial Estate, Newcastle upon Tyne, NE12 6DX Tel: 0191-268 8000 Fax: 0191-268 6573 E-mail: sales@image-viscom.co.uk

▶ The Image Works Ltd, 1 Carside, Lome Shay Industrial Estate, Nelson, Lancashire, BB9 6RX Tel: (01282) 447385

▶ Imagery Ltd, 3 Prince Road, Kings Norton Business Centre, Birmingham, B30 3HB Tel: 0121-486 1616 Fax: 0121-486 1282

▶ Impress Leicester Ltd, 8 Morris Road, Leicester, LE2 6BR Tel: 0116-270 0999 Fax: 0116-270 2172

▶ Impress Printers, Unit 72 Lower Bethesda Street, Stoke-on-Trent, ST1 3DE Tel: (01782) 287677 Fax: (01782) 287517 E-mail: sales@impressprinters.co.uk

Imprint, Victory House, Dalton Lane, Keighley, West Yorkshire, BD21 4JH Tel: (01535) 667954 Fax: (01535) 600072 E-mail: info@inprintkeighley.co.uk

Imprint (Bournemouth) Ltd, 2-4 Acland Road, Bournemouth, BH9 1JJ Tel: (01202) 520552 Fax: (01202) 521949

Imprint Colour Printers Ltd, Wrightsway, Lincoln, LN2 4JY Tel: (01522) 539570 Fax: (01522) 534794E-mail: guy@imprintcolourprinters.com

Imprint Offset, Unit 12A, Warrington Central Trading Estate, Bewsey Road, Warrington, WA2 7LP Tel: (01925) 651141 Fax: (01925) 651335 E-mail: sales@imprintoffset.co.uk

In Print, Seven Street, York Road Business Park, Malton, North Yorkshire, YO17 6YA Tel: (01653) 697261 Fax: (01653) 695456

Industrial Press, Oldbury Road, West Bromwich, West Midlands, B70 9DQ Tel: (024) 7663 2000 Fax: 0121-500 4994

▶ Info Tech Distribution Ltd, 11b Dawkins Road, Poole, Dorset, BH15 4JP Tel: (01202) 845989 Fax: (01202) 845985

Information Press Ltd, Southfield Road, Eynsham, Witney, Oxfordshire, OX29 4JB Tel: (01865) 882588

▶ Ink Design & Print Ltd, 1 Wessex Road, Bourne End, Buckinghamshire, SL8 5DT Tel: (01628) 524415 Fax: (01628) 529856 E-mail: info@inkltd.co.uk

▶ Inkon Printers, 63-79 Oldham Street, Hyde, Cheshire, SK14 1LL Tel: 0161-368 3444 Fax: 0161-367 8257

▶ J D Lewis & Sons Ltd, Gwasg Gomer, Llandysul, Dyfed, SA44 4JL Tel: (01559) 362371 Fax: (01559) 363758 E-mail: gwasg@gomar.co.uk

▶ J E Hacking Printer Ltd, Market Street Works, Church, Accrington, Lancashire, BB5 0DP Tel: (01254) 391222 Fax: (01254) 399827

▶ J H Davenport & Sons Ltd, Harehills Lane, Leeds, LS9 6JF Tel: 0113-249 5561 Fax: 0113-249 1381

▶ J & J Robertson, 3 Poplar Road, Dumbarton, G82 2RD Tel: (01389) 763765

▶ J M K Business Supplies, Mill Road Industrial Estate, Linlithgow Bridge, Linlithgow, West Lothian, EH49 7SF Tel: (01506) 847840 Fax: (01506) 847762

▶ J & M Publishing, 13-15 West Church St, Buckie, Banffshire, AB56 1BN Tel: (01542) 832265

▶ J Mcvicar, 97 Dykehead Street, Glasgow, G33 4AQ Tel: 0141-774 5132 Fax: 0141-774 4440

▶ J R Press, 29 Brunel Close, Drayton Fields Industrial Estate, Daventry, Northamptonshire, NN11 8RB Tel: (01327) 301566 Fax: (01327) 301410 E-mail: sales@jrpress.co.uk

▶ J T Mclaughlin Ltd, 362 Leach Place, Walton Summit Centre, Bamber Bridge, Preston, PR5 8AS Tel: (01772) 322777 Fax: (01772) 315569

J Thomson Colour Printers Ltd, 14-16 Carnoustie Place, Glasgow, G5 8PB Tel: 0141-429 1094 Fax: 0141-429 5638

▶ J W Brown (Printers) Ltd, 77a Blackheath Road, London, SE10 8PD Tel: (020) 8469 0808 Fax: (020) 8691 6556 E-mail: sales@darwinpress.co.uk

Jacee Print & Promotions Ltd, Publicity House, Station Road, Cottingham, East Yorkshire, HU16 4LL Tel: (01482) 842117 Fax: (01482) 875239 E-mail: sales@jaceeprint.co.uk

▶ James Bell & Sons Ltd, 2 Lower Auchingramont Road, Hamilton, Lanarkshire, ML3 6HW Tel: (01698) 282720 Fax: (01698) 283548 E-mail: sales@bellprinters.co.uk

James P Maginnis Ltd, 1 St. Peters Road, Portslade, Brighton, BN41 1LS Tel: (01273) 417016

Jameson Press, 21 The Fairways, New River Trading Estate, Cheshunt, Waltham Cross, Hertfordshire, EN8 0NL Tel: (01992) 635836 Fax: (01992) 636865 E-mail: info@jamesonpress.co.uk

Jayprint, 2a Douglas Road, Luton, LU4 8EB Tel: (01582) 490906 Fax: (01582) 490906

▶ John Brailsford Ltd, 30 Rawmarsh Hill, Rotherham, South Yorkshire, S62 6EU Tel: (01709) 523980 Fax: (01709) 523100 E-mail: sales@brailsfordprinters.co.uk

▶ John Brown (Printers) Ltd, Glaisdale Parkway, Bilborough, Nottingham, NG8 4JQ Tel: 0115-928 0991

▶ John Good Holbrook, 3 4 Elm Place, Old Witney Road, Eynsham, Witney, Oxfordshire, OX29 4BD Tel: (01993) 777700 Fax: (01865) 885401

▶ John Howitt Group Ltd, Oddicroft Lane, Sutton-in-Ashfield, Nottinghamshire, NG17 5FB Tel: (01623) 448000 Fax: (01623) 448001

John S Burns Ltd, 107 Coltness Lane, Queenslie Industrial Estate, Glasgow, G33 4DR Tel: 0141-766 3355 Fax: 0141-766 1991 E-mail: sales@johnsburn.co.uk

▶ John S Burns & Sons Ltd, 25 Finlas Street, Possilpark, Glasgow, G22 5DS Tel: 0141-336 8678

▶ Johnsons (Printers) Ltd, Oat Market, Nantwich, Cheshire, CW5 5AP Tel: (01270) 625207

▶ Just Forms Ltd, 72 Hammonds Drive, Eastbourne, East Sussex, BN23 6PW Tel: (01323) 732000 Fax: (01323) 732101

▶ K E P Print Group Ltd, Unit 21 Two Gates Trading Estate, Watling Street, Two Gates, Tamworth, Staffordshire, B77 5AE Tel: (01827) 280880 Fax: (01827) 285660

▶ K O J Group, Unit 6atingley Bar Industrial Estate, Tingley Common, Morley, Leeds, LS27 0HE Tel: 0113-252 3220 Fax: 0113-238 0007 E-mail: k0j@btconnect.com

K P Litho Ltd, 38 Gloucester Road, Brighton, BN1 4AQ Tel: (01273) 570173

▶ Kall Kwik Ltd, 48 Clifton Road, Cambridge, CB1 7ED Tel: (01223) 502502 Fax: (01223) 508510

▶ Kall Kwik UK Ltd, 11 The Promenade, Gloucester Road, Bristol, BS7 8AL Tel: 0117-923 2036

▶ Kall Kwik UK Ltd, 1-2 Pegler Way, Crawley, West Sussex, RH11 7AG Tel: (01293) 611116 Fax: (01293) 611119

▶ Kall Kwik UK Ltd, 95 Golders Green Road, London, NW11 8EN Tel: (020) 8458 8771 Fax: (020) 8458 9665

▶ Kall Kwik UK Ltd, Sovereign House, 13-14 Queen Street, London, W1J 5PS Tel: (020) 7491 1973 Fax: (020) 7629 0316

▶ Kall Kwik UK Ltd, 358 Kings Road, London, SW3 5UZ Tel: (020) 7351 3133 Fax: (020) 7352 5858

▶ Kall Kwik UK Ltd, Kingfisher Court, 201-203 Broadway, Salford, M50 2UE Tel: 0161-876 5111 Fax: 0161-876 5333

▶ Kall Kwik UK Ltd, 71 High Street, Winchester, Hampshire, SO23 9DA Tel: (01962) 864900 Fax: (01962) 864649

▶ Kall Kwik UK Ltd, 29 Warwick Street, Worthing, West Sussex, BN11 3DQ Tel: (01903) 820400 Fax: (01903) 821432

▶ Kay Jay Print Ltd, Park Road, Cross Hills, Keighley, West Yorkshire, BD20 8AB Tel: (01535) 632921 Fax: (01535) 636155 E-mail: sales@kjprint.co.uk

▶ Ken Girvan Printers, 90 Peterborough Road, Farcet, Peterborough, PE7 3BN Tel: (01733) 562372 Fax: (01733) 897988

▶ Kendall Press Ltd, Crown House, Trafford Park Road, Trafford Park, Manchester, M17 1HG Tel: 0161-872 9808 Fax: 0161-877 9085

Kenilworth Printers, Unit 9b Princes Dr Industrial Estate, Coventry Road, Kenilworth, Warwickshire, CV8 2FD Tel: (01926) 851180 Fax: (01926) 851173

Kent Edwards Litho Ltd, 29 Woolmer Trading Estate, Bordon, Hampshire, GU35 9QE Tel: (01420) 475666 Fax: (01420) 489004 E-mail: sales@kentedwards.co.uk

▶ Kestrel Press Irvine Ltd, 25 Whittle Place, South Newmoor Industrial Estate, Irvine, Ayrshire, KA11 4HR Tel: (01294) 222222 Fax: (01294) 222219 E-mail: sales@kestrelpress.com

▶ Kingfisher Print & Design Ltd, Wills Road, Totnes, Devon, TQ9 5XN Tel: (01803) 867087 Fax: (01803) 867088

▶ Kingsdown Commercial Stationers & Printers, Unit A Dean Street, Bristol, BS2 8SF Tel: 0117-924 4443 Fax: 0117-924 4881

Kingsway Press Ltd, Seventh Avenue, Team Valley Trading Estate, Gateshead, Tyne & Wear, NE11 0SL Tel: 0191-491 0455 Fax: 0191-491 0454 E-mail: sales@kingswaypress.co.uk

Kinmel Paper Supplies, 180 Wellington Road, Rhyl, Clwyd, LL18 1LL Tel: (01745) 354589 Fax: (01745) 354589

▶ Kirkcaldy Print Ltd, Waverley Road, Mitchelston Industrial Estate, Kirkcaldy, Fife, KY1 3NH Tel: (01592) 655590

▶ Knowledgepoint Ltd, 5 Cutbush Park, Danehill, Lower Earley, Reading, RG6 4UT Tel: 0118-918 1500 Fax: 0118-918 1501 E-mail: sales@knowledgepoint.co.uk

Kopykat Printing Ltd, 76c Rivington Street, London, EC2A 3AY Tel: (020) 7739 2451 Fax: (020) 7729 5925 E-mail: print@kopykat.co.uk

L & S Litho Printers & Designers Ltd, 15-27 Arrol Place, Glasgow, G40 3NY Tel: 0141-556 2837 Fax: 0141-554 2590 E-mail: bill.livingstone@btlslitho.com

LITHOGRAPHIC PRINTERS/ LITHOGRAPHERS – *continued*

L & S Printing Co. Ltd, Unit 10 Hazelwood Trading Estate, Hazelwood Close, Worthing, West Sussex, BN14 8NP Tel: (01903) 821005 Fax: (01903) 821006 E-mail: sue.m@ls-printing.com

▶ L S Printworks, Unit 4, Amlwch Industrial Estate, Amlwch, Gwynedd, LL68 9BX Tel: (01407) 830059

▶ Label Technology Ltd, 15 Walton Road, Pattinson North, Washington, Tyne & Wear, NE38 8QA Tel: 0191-416 7038

Labute Colour Printers Ltd, Cambridge Printing Park, Milton, Cambridge, CB4 6AZ Tel: (01223) 420000 Fax: (01223) 420860 E-mail: info@labute.co.uk

▶ Lancashire Printing Co. Ltd, Pleasington Street, Blackburn, BB2 1UF Tel: (01254) 673431 Fax: (01254) 680050

Lancastrian Labels Ltd, 183 Great Howard Street, Liverpool, L3 7DL Tel: 0151-298 1212 Fax: 0151-298 1432 E-mail: sales@lancastrian.co.uk

▶ Lanes Ltd, 16 Patricia Way, Pysons Road Industrial Estate, Broadstairs, Kent, CT10 2LF Tel: (01843) 861314 Fax: (01843) 860919

Langstane Press Ltd, Palmerston Road, Aberdeen, AB11 5QJ Tel: (01224) 212212 Fax: (01224) 210066 E-mail: sales@langstane.co.uk

▶ Lansdowne Studio (Newcastle) Ltd, 35 Moorland Way, Nelson Park, Cramlington, Northumberland, NE23 1WE Tel: (01670) 590011

▶ Larner & Weeks (Printers) Ltd, 32 Mill Green Road, Mitcham, Surrey, CR4 4HY Tel: (020) 8646 8400

▶ Laser Graphics Services Ltd, 40 Wates Way, Mitcham, Surrey, CR4 4HR Tel: (020) 8646 8877

▶ Lasting Impressions Ltd, Unit E3-E4 Barwell Business Park, Leatherhead Road, Chessington, Surrey, KT9 2NY Tel: (020) 8944 0808

▶ Launton Press Ltd, Telford Road, Bicester, Oxfordshire, OX26 4LF Tel: (01869) 242124 E-mail: sales@launtonpress.co.uk

Lear Seating UK Ltd, Gielgud Way, Cross Point Business Park, Coventry, CV2 2SA Tel: (024) 7686 7200 Fax: (024) 7686 7235

▶ Leeds Graphic Press Ltd, 24-40 Pontefract Lane, Leeds, LS9 8HY Tel: 0113-248 9262 Fax: 0113-248 9264

▶ The Lemon Press Ltd, Pipers Road, Park Farm Industrial Estate, Redditch, Worcestershire, B98 0HU Tel: (01527) 500048 Fax: (01527) 253697 E-mail: info@lemonpress.co.uk

Leopard Press UK Ltd, Foxoak Street, Cradley Heath, West Midlands, B64 5DP Tel: (01384) 410800 Fax: (01384) 410420 E-mail: enquiries@leopardpress.fsnet.co.uk

LeverPress Ltd, 12-14 Goddard Road, Whitehouse Industrial Estate, Ipswich, IP1 5NP Tel: (01473) 461464 Fax: (01473) 240118 E-mail: sales@leverpress.co.uk

▶ Lintaprint Ltd, Midland Road, Swadlincote, Derbyshire, DE11 0AN Tel: (01283) 221536 Fax: (01283) 550273 E-mail: sales@lintaprint.co.uk

▶ The Lion Press, 19 Market Square, Sandy, Bedfordshire, SG19 1EH Tel: (01767) 680368

▶ Lithgo Press Ltd, Unit 10, Ashville Way, Whetstone, Leicester, LE8 6NU Tel: 0116-284 1414 Fax: 0116-286 2302 E-mail: sales@lithgopress.co.uk

Litho Supplies, Flagship Square, Shaw Cross Business Park, Dewsbury, West Yorkshire, WF12 7TH Tel: (01924) 486130 Fax: (01924) 460502 E-mail: dewsbury@litho.co.uk

Litho Supplies Scotland Ltd, 8 Elphinstone Square, Deans Industrial Estate, Deans, Livingston, West Lothian, EH54 8RG Tel: (01506) 462555 Fax: (01506) 465678 E-mail: scotland@litho.co.uk

Lithoflow Ltd, 32 Aylesbury St, London, EC1R 0ET Tel: (020) 7017 8660 Fax: (020) 7364 6433 E-mail: info@lithoflow.co.uk

Lithograve (Birmingham) Ltd, 8-10 Lawford Close, Birmingham, B7 4HJ Tel: 0121-359 3350 Fax: 0121-359 3119 E-mail: dave@lithograve.com

Lithoprint Ltd, 4 Earl Haig Road, Hillington Park, Glasgow, G52 4RP Tel: 0141-891 8000 Fax: 0141-810 5496

▶ Lordswood Litho Ltd, Unit 10, Lordswood Industrial Estate, Revenge Road, Chatham, Kent, ME5 8UD Tel: (01634) 660611

▶ Lothian Print, 7 New Lairdship Yards, Edinburgh, EH11 3UY Tel: 0131-444 2344

Lothian Printers, 109 High Street, Dunbar, East Lothian, EH42 1ES Tel: (01368) 863785 Fax: (01368) 864908 E-mail: lothian.printers@virgin.net

▶ Loudmouth Postcards, 5 Hendon Street, Sheffield, S13 9AX Tel: (0845) 2309805 Fax: 0114-288 0044 E-mail: chet@loudworld.co.uk

▶ Lurgan Mail, 4a High Street, Lurgan, Craigavon, County Armagh, BT66 8AW Tel: (028) 3832 7777 Fax: (028) 3832 5271

Lynx D P M Ltd, Unit 35a Monument Industrial Park, Warpsgrove Lane, Chalgrove, Oxford, OX44 7RW Tel: (01865) 891989 Fax: (01865) 891164 E-mail: sales@lynxdpm.com

▶ M D Printers Ltd, 7 Phoenix Park, Coldred Road, Maidstone, Kent, ME15 9XN Tel: (01622) 755222 Fax: (01622) 752052

▶ M O S Group Ltd, Unit 2, Newby Road Industrial Estate, Newby Road, Hazel Grove, Stockport, Cheshire, SK7 5DA Tel: 0161-484 0444

M P D Offset Ltd, Unit 5 Rivergate, Westlea, Swindon, SN5 7ET Tel: (01793) 495522 Fax: (01793) 495515

▶ M P T Colour Graphics Ltd, Thames Park Business Centre, Thame, Oxfordshire, OX9 3XA Tel: (01844) 216888

▶ Mackay & Inglis Ltd, 19 Polmadie Street, Glasgow, G42 0PQ Tel: 0141-423 8866

Mackays Of Chatham Ltd, Badger Road, Chatham, Kent, ME5 8TD Tel: (01634) 864381 Fax: (01634) 867742 E-mail: macays@cpi-group.co.uk

▶ Macro Art Ltd, 3 Hardwick Road, Great Gransden, Sandy, Bedfordshire, SG19 3BJ Tel: (01767) 677946 Fax: (01767) 677916

Magazine Printing Co. P.L.C, 1082 Mollison Avenue, Brimsdown, Enfield, Middlesex, EN3 7NT Tel: (020) 8805 5000 Fax: (020) 8804 2432 E-mail: mpc@magprint.co.uk

▶ Maincolour, Hammond House, Heapy Street, Macclesfield, Cheshire, SK11 7JB Tel: (01625) 667400 Fax: (01625) 424888 E-mail: sales@maincolour.co.uk

▶ Mainstream Printing Services, 16-22 Pritchards Road, London, E2 9AP Tel: (020) 7729 4564 Fax: (020) 7739 5567

Manor Creative Ltd, 7-8 Edison Road, Eastbourne, East Sussex, BN23 6PT Tel: (01323) 514400 Fax: (01323) 509306

▶ Manor Printing Services (Wotton) Ltd, The Abbey Business Park, Charfield Road, Kingswood, Wotton-Under-Edge, Gloucestershire, GL12 8RL Tel: (01453) 843891

Mason Albums Two Trees Press Ltd, Grey Street, Denton, Manchester, M34 3RU Tel: 0161-336 2002 Fax: 0161-335 0346 E-mail: print@twotreespress.co.uk

▶ Masons Print Group Ltd, Viscount House, River Lane, Saltney, Chester, CH4 8RH Tel: (01244) 674433

▶ Matthews Print, The Courtyard, 19 Tamworth Street, Lichfield, Staffordshire, WS13 6JP Tel: (01543) 263112

▶ Maygray Graphics Ltd, Graphics House, Arundel Road, Uxbridge, Middlesex, UB8 2JX Tel: (01895) 812525

▶ Mayoh Press Ltd, Preston Street, Carnforth, Lancashire, LA5 9BY Tel: (01524) 732579

MCG Graphics Ltd, Citadel Trading Park, Citadel Way, Hull, HU9 1TQ Tel: (01482) 225835 Fax: (01482) 215077 E-mail: webmaster@mcg-graphics.com

▶ Melody Group Ltd, L'Islet, St. Sampson, Guernsey, GY2 4XN Tel: (01481) 245596 Fax: (01481) 249801

▶ Mercia Image Ltd, 8 Perkins Industrial Estate, Mansfield Road, Derby, DE21 4AW Tel: (01332) 291555 Fax: (01332) 291400

▶ Mercolour Graphics Ltd, Cherrywell House, Tamian Way, Hounslow, TW4 6BL Tel: (020) 8572 2260 Fax: (020) 8572 2262

▶ Mercury Print & Packaging, The Print Factory, Wood Lane, Off Whitehall Road, Leeds, LS12 6JY Tel: 0113-263 4463

▶ Metro Commercial Printing Ltd, 7 Mowat Industrial Estate, Sandown Road, Watford, WD24 7UY Tel: (01923) 252812 Fax: (01923) 818727

▶ Metro Press Ltd, 64-66 Albion Road, Edinburgh, EH7 5QZ Tel: 0131-661 8984

Midas Press, 3 Columbus Drive, Southwood Business Park, Farnborough, Hampshire, GU14 0NZ Tel: (01252) 517221 Fax: (01252) 516455 E-mail: sales@midaspress.co.uk

▶ Middletons Ltd, Compston Road, Ambleside, Cumbria, LA22 9DJ Tel: (01539) 432154

▶ Midland Printers, Unit3 & 4 Acre Ridge Industrial Estate, Salcombe Road, Alfreton, Derbyshire, DE55 7RG Tel: (01773) 521007 Fax: (01773) 521144

Midos Communications, 10 Heol-Y-Deri, Cardiff, CF14 6HG Tel: (029) 2069 1698 Fax: (029) 2069 1693

▶ Minta's The Printers Ltd, Palin Street, Nottingham, NG7 5AG Tel: (0808) 1550731 Fax: 0115-970 8856 E-mail: sales@mintas.co.uk

▶ Minto D P Ltd, 66 Market Place, Inverurie, Aberdeenshire, AB51 3XN Tel: (01467) 620416 Fax: (01467) 621663 E-mail: sales@mintodp.co.uk

▶ Mirage Studios Ltd, Unit 10, Adam Business Centre, Henson Way, Kettering, Northamptonshire, NN16 8PX Tel: (01536) 417707

▶ Miter Press Ltd, Miter House, 150 Rosebery Avenue, London, N17 9SD Tel: (020) 8808 9776 Fax: (020) 8885 4409 E-mail: sales@miter.co.uk

▶ MJ Impressions, 1 Montagu Mews North, London, W1H 2JS Tel: (020) 7935 5569 Fax: (020) 7935 5198

▶ Moffat Press Co. Ltd, 1-23 Queens Road West, London, E13 0PE Tel: (020) 8548 2966 Fax: (020) 8471 2494 E-mail: sales@retailweekly.com

▶ Morrish S F & Sons, Telford Road, Salisbury, SP2 7BU Tel: (01722) 336764 Fax: (01722) 414165

▶ Moschatel Transfer Printers, Unit 1, Vale Road Indust Estate, Spilsby, Lincolnshire, PE23 5HF Tel: (01790) 754775 E-mail: sales@moschatel.co.uk

▶ Mosiac Corp Ltd, 1 & 2 Bentley Court, Finedon Road Industrial Estate, Wellingborough, Northamptonshire, NN8 4BQ Tel: (01933) 229190

▶ MRN Screen Process Ltd, Unit 10 Priory Tec Park Saxon Way, Priory Park, Hessle, North Humberside, HU13 9PB Tel: (01482) 627717 Fax: (01482) 627718

▶ Multiprint, Seafield Road, Kirkcaldy, Fife, KY1 1SR Tel: (01592) 204755 Fax: (01592) 203171

▶ MWM Litho, Unit 17 Greenwich Centre Business Park, 53 Norman Road, London, SE10 9QF Tel: (020) 8858 8644 Fax: (020) 8858 8600

N S Reed Printing Supplies, 9 Dean Court, Great Western Business Park, Yate, Bristol, BS37 5NJ Tel: (01454) 323775 Fax: (01454) 326935 E-mail: nsreed.print@virgin.net

▶ N2 Visual Communications Ltd, Unit 40 Oakwood Hill Industrial Estate, Oakwood Hill, Loughton, Essex, IG10 3TZ Tel: (020) 8508 8880 Fax: (020) 8508 2331 E-mail: sales@notaprint.com

Nationwide Print, Bucklers Lane, Holmbush, St. Austell, Cornwall, PL25 3JL Tel: (01726) 63638 Fax: (01726) 67831 E-mail: sales@nationwideprint.co.uk

▶ Nayler Group Ltd, Aero Mill, Kershaw Street, Church, Accrington, Lancashire, BB5 4JS Tel: (01254) 234247 Fax: (01254) 383996

▶ The Nelson Press Ltd, Unit 9 Greatbridge Business Pa, Budds Lane, Romsey, Hampshire, SO51 0HA Tel: (01794) 515592

▶ Nevisprint, 3 Caol Industrial Estate, Ardgour Road, Caol, Fort William, Inverness-Shire, PH33 7PH Tel: (01397) 704083 Fax: (01397) 705890

▶ New Forest Printing, Riverside House, Brokenford Lane, Totton, Southampton, SO40 9DY Tel: (023) 8066 3484 Fax: (023) 8086 8549

New Goswell Printing Co., Unit 4 100 The Highway, London, E1W 2BX Tel: (020) 7481 1775 Fax: (020) 7488 9130

▶ New Vision Print & Publishing Ltd, 101 Abercorn Industrial Estate, Abercorn Street, Paisley, Renfrewshire, PA3 4AT Tel: 0141-842 1010 Fax: 0141-887 7122 E-mail: enquiries@newvisionpublishing.co.uk

Newal Print, Unit 21 Delph Road Industrial Estate, Delph Road, Brierley Hill, West Midlands, DY5 2UA Tel: (01384) 74469 Fax: (01384) 74995

Newnorth Print, College Street, Kempston, Bedford, MK42 8NA Tel: (01234) 341111 Fax: (01234) 271112 E-mail: newnorth@newnorth.co.uk

▶ Newton Press, St Cuthberts Way, Aycliffe Industrial Estate, Aycliffe Industrial Park, Newton Aycliffe, County Durham, DL5 6DX Tel: (01325) 300212 Fax: (01325) 312893 E-mail: sales@newtonpress.co.uk

▶ Nexprint Ltd, Units A, Oakfield Industrial Estate, Stanton Harcourt Road, Witney, Oxfordshire, OX29 4TH Tel: (01865) 883655

Nicro Print Services, Unit 13 Faraday Close, Washington, Tyne & Wear, NE38 8QJ Tel: 0191-417 8905 Fax: 0191-417 3496 E-mail: ray_foster@btconnect.co.uk

▶ Nightingale Press Ltd, Newark Close, Royston, Hertfordshire, SG8 5HL Tel: (01763) 248393 Fax: (01763) 245825 E-mail: sales@nightingale-press.co.uk

Northend Ltd, Clyde Road, Sheffield, S8 0TZ Tel: 0114-250 0331 Fax: 0114-250 0676 E-mail: sales@northend.co.uk

▶ Northern Illustrated Print, 141 Shakespeare Street, Southport, Merseyside, PR8 5AN Tel: (01704) 547222 Fax: (01704) 547333

▶ Norwich Colour Print Ltd, 2-3 Drayton Industrial Estate, Taverham Road, Drayton, Norwich, NR8 6RL Tel: (01603) 868862 Fax: (01603) 861371

Nova Press Printing, 3 The Old Mill, 61 Reading Road, Pangbourne, Reading, RG8 7HY Tel: 0118-984 5370 Fax: 0118-984 5370 E-mail: trevor@novapress.freeserve.co.uk

▶ Novograf Ltd, 10 Langlands Place, Kelvin South Business Park, East Kilbride, Glasgow, G75 0YF Tel: (01355) 900100 Fax: (01355) 900200

Oak Die Stamping & Engraving Co. Ltd, Tyburn Industrial Estate, Ashold Farm Road, Birmingham, B24 9QG Tel: 0121-382 4585 Fax: 0121-377 6359 E-mail: ordes-oak@btconnect.com

▶ Oasis Art & Graphics, 68 East Meadway, Birmingham, B33 0AP Tel: 0121-786 2988 Fax: 0121-789 7146 E-mail: accounts@oasisag.co.uk

Ocean Print, 70 Wood End Green Road, Hayes, Middlesex, UB3 2SL Tel: (020) 8561 3344 Fax: (020) 8561 5488 E-mail: enquiries@oceanprint.co.uk

▶ Odessa Offset Ltd, Oakfield Road Industrial Estate, Oakfield Road, London, SE20 8RA Tel: (020) 8778 7888 Fax: (020) 8776 6646 E-mail: sales@odessaoffset.com

Omega Print, Unit 8, Duns Lane, Leicester, LE3 5LX Tel: 0116-253 7388 Fax: 0116-253 7388

Optichrome Group Ltd, Maybury Road, Woking, Surrey, GU21 5HX Tel: (01483) 740290 Fax: (01483) 732609 E-mail: sales@optichrome.com

▶ Orange Advertising Ltd, 4-6 Dryden Street, London, WC2E 9NH Tel: (020) 7379 9937 Fax: (020) 7379 7679

▶ Orcadian Ltd, Hatston Industrial Estate, Kirkwall, Orkney, KW15 1DW Tel: (01856) 879000

▶ Ords Group, Progress House, Usworth Road Industrial Estate, Hartlepool, Cleveland, TS25 1PD Tel: (01429) 273456 Fax: (01429) 861948 E-mail: sales@ords.co.uk

▶ Oriel Studios, Orrell Mount, Bootle, Merseyside, L20 6NS Tel: 0151-922 2785 Fax: 0151-933 5410

▶ Orion Print Ltd, Merlin Way, Quarry Hill Industrial Estate, Ilkeston, Derbyshire, DE7 4RA Tel: 0115-930 7517 Fax: 0115-932 3353

Ormerod Developments Rochdale Ltd, Ormerod House, Caldershaw Business Park, Rochdale, Lancashire, OL12 7LQ Tel: (01706) 646808 Fax: (01706) 640694 E-mail: sales@ormerods.com

▶ Oxted Colour Printers Ltd, 6 Beadles Lane, Old Oxted, Oxted, Surrey, RH8 9JJ Tel: (01883) 712351 Fax: (01883) 717019

▶ P & A Press, P & A House, Alma Road, Chesham, Buckinghamshire, HP5 3HB Tel: (01494) 773075 Fax: (01494) 775858

▶ P A Smith & Son, Martins Grove, Whitchurch, Ross-On-Wye, Herefordshire, HR9 6BJ Tel: (01600) 890448

▶ P D Q Print Services, 93 Commercial Street, Dundee, DD1 2AF Tel: (0800) 0640794 Fax: (01382) 201776

▶ P D S Printers, 11 Kay Close, Plympton, Plymouth, PL7 4LU Tel: (01752) 343491 Fax: (01752) 343511 E-mail: sales@pdsprinters.co.uk

▶ P E C Barr (Printers) Ltd, Barr Building, Carron Place, Edinburgh, EH6 7RE Tel: 0131-554 1736

▶ P J Emmerson Ltd, 2 Bunting Road, Bury St. Edmunds, Suffolk, IP32 7BX Tel: (01284) 760751 Fax: (01284) 762368

▶ P P S Print Communication Ltd, 198 Deansgate, Manchester, M3 3NE Tel: 0161-832 4024 E-mail: sales@ppsprintcom.com

▶ Pace Print & Design, 4 Buckholt Drive, Worcester, WR4 9ND Tel: (01905) 754554 Fax: (01905) 754543 E-mail: sales@paceprintanddesign.co.uk

▶ Paceprint Printers, 4b Kenn Road, Clevedon, Avon, BS21 6EL Tel: (01275) 874238 Fax: (01275) 343733

▶ Pagefast Ltd, 4-6 Lansil Way, Lancaster, LA1 3QY Tel: (01524) 841010

▶ Palm Graphic Services Ltd, Inigma Building, Bilton Road, Bletchley, Milton Keynes, MK1 1HW Tel: (01908) 270400 Fax: (01908) 270614

▶ Panda Press Stone Ltd, 1 Newcastle Street, Stone, Staffordshire, ST15 8JU Tel: (01785) 815110

Pandaprint, 104 Park Road, Rosyth, Dunfermline, Fife, KY11 2JL Tel: (01383) 417847 Fax: (01383) 411863

▶ Paragon Design & Print, 10 Lawn Street, Paisley, Renfrewshire, PA1 1HB Tel: 0141-840 1122 Fax: 0141-887 7149 E-mail: sales@paragon-design.co.uk

▶ Paramount Print Group, Caxton Park, Wright Street, Manchester, M16 9EW Tel: 0161-872 0444 Fax: 0161-872 0514

Park Communications Ltd, Lea Mill, Eastway, London, E9 5NU Tel: (020) 8525 6200 Fax: (020) 8525 6201 E-mail: heath.mason@btinternet.com

Parkdale Press, 11-12 Tilley Road, Crowther, Washington, Tyne & Wear, NE38 0AE Tel: 0191-417 8927 Fax: 0191-419 2459 E-mail: parkdale.press@virgin.net

▶ Parker & Collinson Ltd, 42 Church Street, Lenton, Nottingham, NG7 2FH Tel: 0115-942 0140 Fax: 0115-942 0917

▶ Robert Parker Engravers, Unit 5 & 6, Dunsinane Industrial Estate, Dunsinane Avenue, Dundee, DD2 3QN Tel: (01382) 858666

Parkes Print & Design, 41 Hitchin Street, Biggleswade, Bedfordshire, SG18 8BE Tel: (01767) 603930 Fax: (01767) 603936

Parkins of Aylesbury Ltd, Unit 15, Park Street Industrial Estate, Aylesbury, Buckinghamshire, HP20 1EB Tel: (020) 8539 7559 Fax: (01296) 483018 E-mail: orders@postglow.co.uk

▶ Partners Press Ltd, Brunel Drive, Newark Industrial Estate, Newark, Nottinghamshire, NG24 2EG Tel: (01636) 702597

▶ Pearson & Brunlees Ltd, Colearine Works, Poynton Road, London, N17 9SN Tel: (020) 8808 5220 Fax: (020) 8801 3684

▶ Pearson Print Ltd, 337 Manchester Road, Denton, Manchester, M34 3QN Tel: 0161-335 0055 Fax: 0161-335 0066

▶ Peerless Literature Services, 97 Spon Lane, West Bromwich, West Midlands, B70 6AQ Tel: 0121-553 2511 Fax: 0121-525 6440

▶ Pennine Print, Widow Hill Road, Heasandford Trading Estate, Burnley, Lancashire, BB10 2BE Tel: (01282) 453716 Fax: (01282) 707276

▶ Penny Print, Hills Court, Brittania Enterprise Park, Blaydon-on-Tyne, Tyne & Wear, NE21 5NH Tel: 0191-499 0808

▶ Pentagon Colourprint Ltd, Pentagon House, Park Road, St. Helens, Merseyside, WA11 9AZ Tel: (01744) 697500 Fax: (01744) 25115

▶ Peter Scott Printers Ltd, Belshaw Court, Billington Road, Burnley, Lancashire, BB11 5UB Tel: (01282) 452221 Fax: (01282) 412353 E-mail: sales@psprintdirect.co.uk

Peterborough Printing Services Ltd, Ainsley House, Fengate, Peterborough, PE1 5XG Tel: (01733) 349881 Fax: (01733) 310711 E-mail: info@pps-print.com

Alfred Pettitt Ltd, Unit 6 Hillgate Business Centre, Swallow Street, Stockport, Cheshire, SK1 3AU Tel: 0161-476 4545 Fax: 0161-476 4505

LITHOGRAPHIC PRINTERS/ LITHOGRAPHERS – *continued*

▶ Pheby Colour Litho UK, Unit A3 Newton Industrial Estate, Eastern Avenue West, Romford, RM6 5SD Tel: (020) 8599 9842 Fax: (020) 8598 1966 E-mail: ajpheby@aol.com

Philip Bennett Lithographic Printers Ltd, Avenue Farm Industrial Estate, Birmingham Road, Stratford-upon-Avon, Warwickshire, CV37 0HR Tel: (01789) 269256 Fax: (01789) 297023

▶ Piccolo Press, 90 Harbour Street, Nairn, IV12 4PG Tel: (01667) 454508 Fax: (01667) 454509

▶ Pickles Printing Co. Ltd, Carlton Works, Savile Park Road, Halifax, West Yorkshire, HX1 2EN Tel: (01422) 353239 Fax: (01422) 353872 E-mail: sales@picklesprinters.co.uk

▶ Picton Press Ltd, Village Farm Indust Estate, Pyle, Bridgend, Mid Glamorgan, CF33 6RP Tel: (01656) 740411 Fax: (01656) 744183 E-mail: sales@pictonpressprinters.co.uk

Pioneer Print Ltd, 8 Raven Road, London, E18 1HB Tel: (020) 8505 1552 Fax: (020) 8505 9982 E-mail: sales@pioneerprint.co.uk

▶ Plan 4 Print Ltd, Goshawk Road, Quarry Hill Industrial Estate, Ilkeston, Derbyshire, DE7 4RG Tel: 0115-930 5393 E-mail: sales@plan4print.co.uk

PLP Commercial Printers, 7 Mowlem Street, London, E2 9HE Tel: (020) 8983 3439 Fax: (020) 8981 3655 E-mail: sales@plpcommercial.co.uk

Pointer Print, 24 The Green, Hasland, Chesterfield, Derbyshire, S41 0LJ Tel: (01246) 231970 Fax: (01246) 277298 E-mail: pointerprint@vipnet.co.uk

Polestar Chromoworks Ltd, Wigman Road, Nottingham, NG8 3JA Tel: 0115-900 8300 Fax: 0115-900 8320

▶ Polestar Wheatons Ltd, Hennock Road, Marsh Barton, Exeter, EX2 8RP Tel: (01392) 420222 Fax: (01392) 420300 E-mail: exeter.reception@polestar-group.com

▶ Portobello Printers Ltd, 9 Morris Road, Newtongrange, Dalkeith, Midlothian, EH22 4ST Tel: 0131-663 1292

▶ Precision Colour Printing Ltd, Halesfield 1, Telford, Shropshire, TF7 4QQ Tel: (01952) 585585 Fax: (01952) 583925

▶ Premier Impressions Ltd, Unit 10 & 11 West E Plan Estate, New Road, Newhaven, East Sussex, BN9 0EX Tel: (01273) 512512 Fax: (01273) 517518 E-mail: sales@premierimpressions.co.uk

▶ The Press, 38-42 Garman Road, London, N17 0UL Tel: (020) 8365 1595 Fax: (020) 8365 1481

Presswheel Ltd, 180 Ilderton Road, London, SE15 1NT Tel: (020) 7635 8686 Fax: (020) 7635 0414 E-mail: info@presswheel.co.uk

Price John & Sons Ltd, Brook Street, Bilston, West Midlands, WV14 0NW Tel: (01902) 353441 Fax: (01902) 404728 E-mail: sales@john-price.co.uk

▶ Priceless Print, Cross Park House, Low Green, Rawdon, Leeds, LS19 6HB Tel: 0113-239 1333 Fax: 0113-239 1444 E-mail: info@pricelessprint.co.uk

▶ Primary Print, Glynteg House, Station Terrace, Ely, Cardiff, CF5 4AA Tel: (029) 2057 3925 Fax: (029) 2057 3929 E-mail: sales@primaryprint.co.uk

Print 2000 Ltd, 54 Finnieston Square, Glasgow, G3 8ET Tel: 0141-204 2400 Fax: 0141-204 2401

▶ Print By Design, 7-9 Imperial Square, Cheltenham, Gloucestershire, GL50 1QB Tel: (01242) 216123

Print Factory, Bell Lane, Bellbrook Industrial Estate, Uckfield, East Sussex, TN22 1QL Tel: (01825) 764707 Fax: (01825) 764253

▶ Print House, 54 Notting Hill Gate, London, W11 3HT Tel: (020) 7229 1171 Fax: (020) 7727 2498 E-mail: info@printhousenottinghil1.com

▶ Print Impressions Ltd, 230 Dansom Lane North, Hull, HU8 7RS Tel: (01482) 323889

▶ Print People, 170-204 Elliot Street, Glasgow, G3 8EX Tel: 0141-248 7240 Fax: 0141-248 7771

▶ Print Plus, 126 Widemarsh Street, Hereford, HR4 9HN Tel: (01432) 272025 Fax: (01432) 353962

▶ Print Run Ltd, 28 Fulton Road, Olympic Way, Wembley, Middlesex, HA9 0TF Tel: (020) 8900 2480 Fax: (020) 8900 1455 E-mail: sales@printrun.co.uk

▶ Print Solutions, 89 St. Clair Street, Kirkcaldy, Fife, KY1 2NW Tel: (01592) 653451 Fax: (01592) 650214

▶ Print Tech Ltd, 3 Power Park, Station Approach, Banbury, Oxfordshire, OX16 5AB Tel: (01295) 262202 Fax: (01295) 271722

▶ Print Wright Ltd, 6 Boss Hall Road, Ipswich, IP1 5BN Tel: (01473) 240897 Fax: (01473) 241307

▶ Printank Ltd, 8 Bay Street, Leicester, LE1 3BX Tel: 0116-251 9797 Fax: 0116-251 9393

▶ The Printed Word Ltd, Newhouse Farm Business Centre, Old Crawley Road, Faygate, Horsham, West Sussex, RH12 4RU Tel: (01293) 851053 Fax: (01293) 851900 E-mail: info@printedword.co.uk

▶ Inc Printers, Rawmec Industrial Park, Plumpton Road, Hoddesdon, Hertfordshire, EN11 0EE Tel: (01992) 801970 Fax: (01992) 801985

▶ Print-Eze Ltd, 349 Darnick Street, Kent House, Glasgow, G21 4AX Tel: 0141-558 7829 Fax: 0141-558 9100

▶ Printfine Ltd, Unit 14-18 King Edward Industrial Estate, Gibraltar Row, Liverpool, L3 7HJ Tel: 0151-242 0000 Fax: 0151-242 0001 E-mail: sales@printfine.co.uk

▶ Printhouse Corporation Ltd, St Leonards Road, London, NW10 6ST Tel: (020) 8963 0123 Fax: (0871) 7171103 E-mail: sales@printhouse.co.uk

Printing Com (Orpington), 98 High Street, Farnborough, Orpington, Kent, BR6 7BA Tel: (01689) 870380 Fax: 01689 823590 E-mail: orpington@printing.com

▶ Printing.Com@RasLtd, Lakeland House, 10 Boughton, Chester, CH3 5AG Tel: (01244) 343333 Fax: (01244) 346120 E-mail: sales@rasgroup.co.uk

▶ Printing Place, Hanbury Road, Chelmsford, CM1 3AE Tel: (01245) 251001 Fax: (01245) 267393

Printing Press, 21 Clare Place, Plymouth, PL4 0JW Tel: (01752) 250580 Fax: (01752) 223855 E-mail: theprintingpress@btconnect.com

Printline Ltd, Unit 12, Grosvenor Way, London, E5 9ND Tel: (020) 8806 9090 Fax: (020) 8806 9434 E-mail: sales@printline.co.uk

Printus Ltd, 359 Garratt Lane, London, SW18 4DY Tel: (020) 8870 8157 Fax: (020) 8874 2236 E-mail: wandsworth@printus.co.uk

Printwise Haverhill Ltd, Homefield Road, Haverhill, Suffolk, CB9 8QP Tel: (01440) 707049 Fax: (01440) 704141 E-mail: gary@printwisegroup.com

▶ Priority Branding Ltd, Quality House, Spring Lane, Willenhall, West Midlands, WV12 4HL Tel: (01902) 607111 Fax: (01902) 633043

▶ Prontaprint Ltd, 85 New Elvet, Durham, DH1 3AQ Tel: 0191-384 3220 Fax: 0191-386 8044

▶ Prontaprint Ltd, Unit 5, Tuffley Park Lower Tuffley Lane, Gloucester, GL2 5DE Tel: (01452) 522411 Fax: (01452) 522411 E-mail: sales@gloucester.prontaprint.com

▶ Prontaprint Ltd, 367 High Street, Lincoln, LN5 7RN Tel: (01522) 530501 Fax: (01522) 538911

▶ Prontaprint Ltd, 1 Creed Lane, London, EC4V 5BR Tel: (020) 7236 7365 Fax: (020) 7248 4048

▶ Prontaprint Ltd, 25 Collingwood Street, Newcastle upon Tyne, NE1 1JE Tel: 0191-232 5500 Fax: 0191-261 4158 E-mail: mailbox@newcastle.dial.prontaprint.co.uk

▶ Prontaprint Ltd, 281 High Street, Uxbridge, Middlesex, UB8 1LQ Tel: (01895) 271939 Fax: (01895) 231551

▶ P's & Q's Ltd, Devonshire House, Devon Street, Liverpool, L3 8HA Tel: 0151-207 1777

▶ Publicity Printing Co., 986 Pollokshaws Road, Glasgow, G41 2HA Tel: 0141-649 2711 Fax: 0141-649 6087

Quadrant Offset Ltd, Riverside House, Dicker Mill, Hertford, SG13 7AE Tel: (01992) 587373 Fax: (01992) 500216 E-mail: quadsale@quadrantoffset.co.uk

▶ Quadroprint Ltd, Unit 11 Hamlet Industrial Centre, White Post Lane, London, E9 5EN Tel: (020) 8986 4818 Fax: (020) 8533 4171

▶ Quick Print UK Ltd, 1 Prince William Road, Loughborough, Leicestershire, LE11 5GU Tel: (01509) 236987 Fax: (01509) 239173 E-mail: info@quickprint.freeserve.co.uk

▶ Quintdown Printers, Trevena House, 11 Trevena Terrace, Newquay, Cornwall, TR7 1LJ Tel: (01637) 875242 Fax: (01637) 875165 E-mail: sales@quintdown.co.uk

▶ R B Print, 45-55 Bowlers Croft, Basildon, Essex, SS14 3EB Tel: (01268) 530053 Fax: (01268) 534453

▶ R S Eyre & Co. Ltd, Unit A9, Prospect Street, Erskine Industrial Estate, Liverpool, L6 1AP Tel: 0151-264 0752 Fax: 0151-263 9367 E-mail: eyrecraft@hotmail.co.uk

▶ Radclyffe & Culross & Sproston, 6-7 Glebe Road, London, E8 4BD Tel: (020) 7254 6293 Fax: (020) 7923 3862

Radford Press Ltd, Miller House, 30 Wilmot Road, London, E10 5LU Tel: (020) 8558 4814 Fax: (020) 8558 0345 E-mail: sales@radfordpress.co.uk

Rainbow Colour, 2 High St, Steventon, Abingdon, Oxfordshire, OX13 6RS Tel: (01235) 200700 Fax: (01235) 200707 E-mail: rainbow.colour@tiscali.co.uk

▶ Raiseprint Plc, Units E 1-E 2, Royd Way, Keighley, West Yorkshire, BD21 3LG Tel: (01535) 681452 E-mail: sales@raiseprint.com

Rapid Print, 3 Portland Close, Townsend Industrial Estate, Houghton Regis, Dunstable, Bedfordshire, LU5 5AW Tel: (01582) 609108 Fax: (01582) 696137

▶ Ratcliff & Roper Ltd, Kilton Road, Worksop, Nottinghamshire, S80 2EE Tel: (01909) 500444 Fax: (01909) 500614 E-mail: sales@ratcliffandroper.co.uk

Redverse, Unit 3, Benbow Business Park Harlescott Lane, Shrewsbury, SY1 3FA Tel: (01743) 466668 Fax: (01743) 466669 E-mail: info@redverse.com

▶ Reel Form Ltd, Riverside Road, Pride Park, Derby, DE24 8HY Tel: (01332) 200222 Fax: (01332) 200805

Reflex Studio Ltd, Reflex House, Bells Yew Green, Tunbridge Wells, Kent, TN3 9BQ Tel: (01892) 752888 Fax: (01892) 752889 E-mail: sales@reflex-print.co.uk

▶ Regal Litho Ltd, 352 Selbourne Road, Luton, LU4 8NU Tel: (01582) 493332

▶ Regency Press Ltd, 88 Moseley Street, Birmingham, B12 0RT Tel: 0121-622 4536 Fax: 0121-622 3307

▶ Reid Williamson Print Ltd, 26 Civic Street, Glasgow, G4 9RH Tel: 0141-332 1143

▶ Remous Ltd, Wyvern Buildings, North Street, Milborne Port, Sherborne, Dorset, DT9 5EP Tel: (01963) 250920 Fax: (01963) 251054

Renfor Four Colour, Paper Mill End Industrial Estate, Birmingham, B44 8NH Tel: 0121-356 9555 Fax: 0121-356 3555 E-mail: info@renfor.co.uk

▶ Rennie & Hodge Ltd, 47 Middlesex Street, Glasgow, G41 1EE Tel: 0141-429 6431 Fax: 0141-429 6427

▶ Reprodux Printers Ltd, Unit 7, Barrs Court Trading Estate, Station Approach, Hereford, HR1 1BB Tel: (01432) 269341 E-mail: enquiries@reprodux.co.uk

▶ Resolution Imaging, Unit 15 16, Salvesen Way, Brighton Street Industrial Estate, Hull, HU3 4UQ Tel: (01482) 212589 Fax: (01482) 211721

▶ Response, Media House, Hobson Industrial Estate, Hobson, Newcastle upon Tyne, NE16 6EA Tel: (01207) 272761 Fax: (01207) 272784

▶ Richardson Printing Ltd, Colville Road Works, Oulton Broad, Lowestoft, Suffolk, NR33 9QS Tel: (01502) 516991 Fax: (01502) 517588

▶ Riverside Press Ltd, 14-15 Riverside Industrial Park, Rapier Street, Ipswich, IP2 8JX Tel: (01473) 687679 Fax: (01473) 687690

Riverside Printing Co., 90 Wallis Road, London, E9 5LN Tel: (020) 8986 5123 Fax: (020) 8986 4776

Rollmark Dieletlit Ltd, 22 Howlett Way, Thetford, Norfolk, IP24 1HZ Tel: (01842) 754984 Fax: (01842) 761018 E-mail: roll.mark@btopenworld.com

▶ Ross Shire Journal, Dochcarty Road, Dingwall, Ross-Shire, IV15 9UD Tel: (01349) 863436 Fax: (01349) 863456

Rotaflow Ltd, Unit 16 Peterley Business Centre, 472 Hackney Road, London, E2 9EQ Tel: (020) 7739 7072 Fax: (020) 7729 9179 E-mail: rotaflow@mwfree.co.uk

▶ Rotary Printers Ltd, Mitton Street, Stourport-on-Severn, Worcestershire, DY13 9AA Tel: (01299) 823839 Fax: (01299) 826991 E-mail: sales@rotaryprinters.co.uk

▶ Rotaset Documentation, Enterprise Road, Mablethorpe, Lincolnshire, LN12 1NB Tel: (01507) 472473 Fax: (01507) 473128 E-mail: sales@rotaset.co.uk

Royal Printers Stationers & Office Furniture Co., 111a Sheen Lane, London, SW14 8AE Tel: (020) 8408 2000 Fax: (020) 8330 1221

Rubell Print Ltd, The Hollies, College Lane, Bunbury, Tarporley, Cheshire, CW6 9PQ Tel: (01829) 260420 Fax: (01829) 260426 E-mail: info@rubell.org

▶ Russell Print Services Ltd, 105 Saltley Road, Birmingham, B7 4TJ Tel: 0121-359 2723

Rustin Clark, 45 Waterloo Road, London, NW2 7TX Tel: (020) 8452 1091 Fax: (020) 8452 2008 E-mail: rustinclark@rustinclark.co.uk

▶ S.A.B. Print, 110 Albert Road, Widnes, Cheshire, WA8 6AX Tel: 0151-423 1403

S Barber & Co. Ltd, 66-68 Kitchen Street, Liverpool, L1 0AN Tel: 0151-709 7323 Fax: 0151-709 6608 E-mail: sales@barbersprn.co.uk

S F Taylor & Co. Ltd, Whitehill Industrial Estate, Haigh Avenue, Stockport, Cheshire, SK4 1NU Tel: 0161-429 7200 Fax: 0161-429 5720 E-mail: gilltress@sftaylor.com

▶ S L B Printing Services Ltd, 140 Molesey Avenue, West Molesey, Surrey, KT8 2RY Tel: (020) 8941 4115

▶ S P D Services, Birchfield Road, Kidderminster, Worcestershire, DY11 6PQ Tel: (01562) 756925 Fax: (01562) 756926

▶ St George's Press, 3 St. Georges Industrial Estate, White Hart Lane, London, N22 5QL Tel: (020) 8501 4411 Fax: (020) 8881 6658

St. Ives Direct (Edenbridge) Ltd, Enterprise Way, Edenbridge, Kent, TN8 6HF Tel: (01732) 862788 Fax: (01732) 868868 E-mail: kevin.johnson@stivesdirect.com

▶ St Ives Direct Group Ltd, The Industrial Estate, Enterprise Way, Edenbridge, Kent, TN8 6HF Tel: (01732) 862788

St Ives Direct Romford Ltd, St Ives House, Faringdon Avenue, Romford, RM3 8XL Tel: (01708) 345599 Fax: (01708) 346025

Salvo Design & Print Ltd, 4 Berrington Road, Leamington Spa, Warwickshire, CV31 1NB Tel: (01926) 429111 Fax: (01926) 450461

▶ Salvoscreen Ltd, 18b Highdown Road, Leamington Spa, Warwickshire, CV31 1XT Tel: (01926) 421402 Fax: (01926) 451447

Sarum Colourview Ltd, Unit 7-8 Woodford Centre Old Sarum Park, Lysander Way, Old Sarum, Salisbury, SP4 6BU Tel: (01722) 343600 Fax: (01722) 323604 E-mail: sales@colourview.co.uk

▶ Saxon Print Group, Saxon House, Hellesdon Park Road, Norwich, NR6 5DR Tel: (01603) 789560 Fax: (01603) 789561 E-mail: bruce.carpenter@saxongroup.com

▶ Sayles & Booth Ltd, 312 Bradford Road, Huddersfield, HD1 6LQ Tel: (01484) 420670 Fax: (01484) 435065

▶ Schwartz Ltd, 92 White Post Lane, London, E9 5EN Tel: (020) 8986 7429 Fax: (020) 8986 1125

▶ Scotish Provinsial Press Ltd, 13 Henderson Road, Inverness, IV1 1SP Tel: (01463) 224444

▶ Scotprint Bookprinters, Gateside Commerce Park, Haddington, East Lothian, EH41 3ST Tel: (01620) 828800 Fax: (01620) 828801 E-mail: sales@scotprint.co.uk

▶ Screen and Digital Printers Ltd, Unit 2 Albion Trading Estate, Cobden Street, Salford, M6 6NA Tel: 0161-745 7887 Fax: 0161-745 7421

▶ Screenplus Design Ltd, 197-201 Reid Street, Glasgow, G40 4DX Tel: 0141-550 5180 Fax: 0141-550 5189

▶ Screenprint Ltd, Sandy Lane, Lowton, Warrington, WA3 1BG Tel: (01942) 602121 Fax: (01942) 260151

▶ Security Printers Ltd, 185 Town Road, London, N9 0HQ Tel: (020) 8807 9333

▶ Selcroft Reprographics Ltd, 22 Holmethorpe Avenue, Redhill, RH1 2NL Tel: (01737) 772773 Fax: (01737) 772774

▶ Selsey Press Ltd, 84 High Street, Selsey, Chichester, West Sussex, PO20 0QH Tel: (01243) 605234 Fax: (01243) 605235

▶ Service Point, 7 Leodis Court, Leeds, LS11 5JJ Tel: 0113-244 1140 Fax: 0113-247 1183

▶ Service Point, 2 Gartons Way, London, SW11 3SX Tel: (020) 7223 6104 Fax: (020) 7924 5815

Seven Corners Communications Group, Penmark House, Woodbridge Meadows, Guildford, Surrey, GU1 1BL Tel: (01483) 576777 Fax: (01483) 567876

Severn Graphics, Unit 5, Windmill Business Park, Clevedon, Avon, BS21 6SR Tel: (01275) 879505 Fax: (01275) 340834 E-mail: richard@severngraphics.co.uk

▶ Severnprint Ltd, Unit 8-10 Ashville Industrial Estate, Ashville Road, Gloucester, GL2 5EU Tel: (01452) 416391 Fax: (01452) 307001

▶ Seville Design & Print Ltd, 10 Julian Road, Sheffield, S9 1FZ Tel: 0114-243 3995 Fax: 0114-243 8396 E-mail: sales@sevilledesign.co.uk

▶ Shaw Printing, Unit F Pegswood Industrial Estate, Pegswood, Morpeth, Northumberland, NE61 6HZ Tel: (01670) 510271 Fax: (01670) 511759E-mail: enquiries@azure-printing.co.uk

▶ Sherrens Printers, 2 Avon Court, Avon Close, Granby Industrial Estate, Weymouth, Dorset, DT4 9UX Tel: (01305) 785265 Fax: (01305) 761572

▶ Shetland Litho, Gremista, Lerwick, Shetland, ZE1 0PX Tel: (01595) 742000 Fax: (01595) 742001

▶ Shetland Times Ltd, Gremista Industrial Estate, Lerwick, Shetland, ZE1 0PX Tel: (01595) 746700 Fax: (01595) 694637

Shire Business Solutions, Shire House, Highlands Road, Shirley, Solihull, West Midlands, B90 4LR Tel: 0121-711 3030 Fax: 0121-711 3060 E-mail: sales@shire-bs.com

▶ Sholing Press, 180 Portsmouth Road, Southampton, SO19 9AQ Tel: (023) 8043 2997 Fax: (023) 8068 5907 E-mail: enquiries@sholingpress.co.uk

▶ Shout Print, 2c Merrow Business Centre, Guildford, Surrey, GU4 7WA Tel: (01483) 450009 Fax: (01483) 455009

▶ Silprint Ltd, Halifax Road, Cullingworth, Bradford, West Yorkshire, BD13 5DE Tel: (01535) 272414

Simpson's Printers, Transfer Bridge Industrial Estate, County Road, Swindon, SN1 2EL Tel: (01793) 536305 Fax: (01793) 532543 E-mail: sales@simpsonprinters.co.uk

Simpson's Printers, Transfer Bridge Industrial Estate, County Road, Swindon, SN1 2EL Tel: (01793) 536305 Fax: (01793) 532543

▶ SLP, 23 West View, Chirk, Wrexham, LL14 5HL Tel: (01691) 774778 Fax: (01691) 774849

▶ Smart Design & Print Ltd, 11 West Gorgie Parks, Edinburgh, EH14 1UT Tel: 0131-538 8020 Fax: 0131-538 8050 E-mail: sales@smartdesignandprint.com

▶ Smith Kellett Ltd, Westholme House, Westholme Road, Halifax, West Yorkshire, HX1 4ER Tel: (01422) 349029

Solent Print Engineering Ltd, 1 Pytchley Close, Fareham, Hampshire, PO14 3SF Tel: (07917) 784595 E-mail: print.eng@ntlworld.com

▶ Solway Offset Services, 11 Catherinefield Industrial Estate, Dumfries, DG1 3PQ Tel: (01387) 264959 Fax: (01387) 261112

▶ Sovereign Commercial Printers Ltd, 579 Kingston Road, London, SW20 8SD Tel: (020) 8544 9391 Fax: (020) 8542 1647 E-mail: info@sovereignprinters.co.uk

▶ Special Blue Ltd, Unit 30, Cranwell Close, Violet Road, London, E3 3QY Tel: (020) 7538 0330

Spectrum Printing Services Ltd, Hamilton Business Park, Waterside Road, Hamilton, Leicester, LE5 1TL Tel: 0116-246 1717 Fax: 0116-246 1575 E-mail: info@spectrumprinting.co.uk

▶ Speed Print, Unit 29, Dinan Way Trading Estate, Exmouth, Devon, EX8 4RS Tel: (01395) 263831 Fax: (01395) 274064

▶ Spot On Digital Imaging, Gomm Road, High Wycombe, Buckinghamshire, HP13 7DJ Tel: (01494) 435060 Fax: (01494) 443284

▶ Sprint Print Co. Ltd, 8b Okehampton Place, Exeter, EX4 1AY Tel: (01392) 276144 Fax: (01392) 420737

Stanhope Press, Railway Arch 89-90, Enid Street, London, SE16 3RA Tel: (020) 7252 3838 Fax: (020) 7232 1056

Star Litho Plates Ltd, Unit 10 Orient Industrial Park, Simonds Road, London, E10 7DE Tel: (020) 8532 8686 Fax: (020) 8556 5568 E-mail: starlitho@btconnect.com

▶ Stationery Office, Mandela Way, London, SE1 5SS Tel: (020) 7394 4200 Fax: (020) 7231 0902

LITHOGRAPHIC PRINTERS/ LITHOGRAPHERS – *continued*

▶ Status Design & Print, Pelham Street, Bolton, BL3 3JB Tel: (01204) 655995 Fax: (01204) 655229

Steve Hyde, Unit C Cophall Farm Business Park, Effingham Road, Copthorne, Crawley, West Sussex, RH10 3HZ Tel: (01342) 714230 Fax: (01342) 716760 E-mail: stevehydestudios@btconnect.com

James Stewart & Co. (Printers) Ltd, 151 Hertingfordbury Road, Hertford, SG14 1NL Tel: (01992) 582531 Fax: (01992) 500549 E-mail: sales@james-stewart.demon.co.uk

Stoate & Bishop Printers)Ltd, Shaftesbury Indust Estate, The Runnings, Cheltenham, Gloucestershire, GL51 9NH Tel: (01242) 236741 Fax: (01242) 222032 E-mail: stoatprint@btinternet.com

▶ Stockle Colour Printers Ltd, Linton Street, Bradford, West Yorkshire, BD4 7EZ Tel: (01274) 308100

Storey Evans & Co. Ltd, Robin Mills, Leeds Road, Idle, Bradford, West Yorkshire, BD10 9TE Tel: (01274) 622222 Fax: (01274) 620444 E-mail: sales@storeyevans.co.uk

Stortex (UK) Ltd, Caird Centre, Caird Park, Hamilton, Lanarkshire, ML3 0EU Tel: (01698) 455821

▶ Stratford Repro Ltd, 42 Greenhill Street, Stratford-upon-Avon, Warwickshire, CV37 6LE Tel: (01789) 269650 Fax: (01789) 414342 E-mail: sales@stratfordrepro.co.uk

▶ Streamline Press Ltd, 11 Boston Road, Leicester, LE4 1AA Tel: 0116-235 5003 Fax: 0116-235 5004 E-mail: enquiries@streamlinepress.co.uk

▶ Streets Printers Ltd, Royston Road, Baldock, Hertfordshire, SG7 6NW Tel: (01462) 893771 Fax: (01462) 894660 E-mail: sales@streetsprinters.co.uk

▶ Studio, Riverside Works, Forde Road, Newton Abbot, Devon, TQ12 4AD Tel: (01626) 358600 Fax: (01626) 358601

Sudak Printers Ltd, Unit 5A, Princess Drive Industrial Estate, Coventry Road, Kenilworth, Warwickshire, CV8 2FD Tel: (01926) 513131 E-mail: info@sudak.co.uk

Swiftprint, 186 Campden Hill Road, London, W8 7TH Tel: (020) 7229 5012 Fax: (020) 7229 3068 E-mail: mail@swiftprint.co.uk

T A (Printers) Ltd, 43-45 Milford Road, Reading, RG1 8LG Tel: 0118-957 5442 Fax: 0118-958 3899 E-mail: taprinters@i12.com

T J Offset Ltd, 6 The Mead Business Centre, Mead Lane, Hertford, SG13 7BJ Tel: (01992) 504438 Fax: (01992) 501891 E-mail: info@tjoffset.co.uk

▶ T P S Print Ltd, 5 Tunnel Avenue, London, SE10 0SL Tel: (020) 8269 1222 Fax: (020) 8269 1223

▶ T Snape & Co. Ltd, Boltons Court, Preston, PR1 3TY Tel: (01772) 254553 Fax: (01772) 204697 E-mail: sales@tsnapeprinters.co.uk

T Stephenson & Son Ltd, 5 Market Place, Prescot, Merseyside, L34 5SB Tel: 0151-426 5161 Fax: 0151-430 7738 E-mail: stephensonprint@btclick.com

▶ Tangent Printers, 52 London Road, London, SW17 9HP Tel: (020) 8648 9418

▶ Taurus Print & Design Ltd, 6 Wintersells Road, Byfleet, West Byfleet, Surrey, KT14 7LF Tel: (01932) 355511

▶ Taylor Bros Bristol Ltd, 13-25 Wilder Street, Bristol, BS2 8PY Tel: 0117-924 5452 Fax: 0117-942 7652

▶ Technical Print Services Ltd, Brentcliffe Avenue, Carlton Road, Nottingham, NG3 7AG Tel: 0115-987 3771

▶ Tewkesbury Printing Co. Ltd, Unit 16, Shannon Way, Ashchurch, Tewkesbury, Gloucestershire, GL20 8ND Tel: (01684) 850666

Thames Offset Printers, Unit 14 Epsom Business Park, Kiln Lane, Epsom, Surrey, KT17 1JF Tel: (01372) 745758 Fax: (01372) 741942 E-mail: thamesoff@aol.com

Thermofast Print Ltd, 2 Mills Road, Sudbury, Suffolk, CO10 2XX Tel: (01787) 880268 Fax: (01787) 880278 E-mail: sales@thermofast.co.uk

▶ Things Fashions Ltd, 64-66 Wallis Road, London, London, E9 5LH Tel: (020) 8985 4767

Thistle Reprographics Ltd, 55 Holburn Street, Aberdeen, AB10 6BR Tel: (01224) 213400 Fax: (01224) 213444

▶ Thomas Dornan (Printers) Ltd, Millgate, Hollings, Oldham, OL8 4JL Tel: 0161-624 4959

▶ Thomson Print & Packaging Ltd, 3 West Telferton, Edinburgh, EH7 6UL Tel: 0131-657 4066 Fax: 0131-657 4033

▶ Thorne Offset Ltd, Unit 4 Mercy Terrace, London, SE13 7UX Tel: (020) 8690 8233 Fax: (020) 8690 9860

▶ Thumbprint (Cirencester) Ltd, Wilkinson Road, Love Lane, Cirencester, Gloucestershire, GL7 1YT Tel: (01285) 656927 Fax: (01285) 659134 E-mail: frank@thumbprint.uk.net

▶ Titus Wilson & Son, Kent Works, 1 Burneside Road, Kendal, Cumbria, LA9 4RL Tel: (01539) 720244 Fax: (01539) 726677

▶ Tom Jukes Graphics Ltd, Units 5-6 First Avenue, Westfield Industrial Estate, Midsomer Norton, Radstock, BA3 4BS Tel: (01761) 416023

▶ Tom Super (Printing Supplies) Ltd, 23-31 Castle Street, Hamilton, Lanarkshire, ML3 6BU Tel: (01698) 286401

▶ Top Printers Ltd, Unit 11 Bridge Park, Harrow Road, London, NW10 0RG Tel: (020) 8961 0925 Fax: (020) 8961 9193 E-mail: sales@topprinters.co.uk

▶ Toptown Printers Ltd, Vicarage Lawn, Barnstaple, Devon, EX32 7BN Tel: (01271) 371271 E-mail: sales@toptown.co.uk

Torr Printers, Unit 2 Greg Street, Stockport, Cheshire, SK5 7BS Tel: 0161-480 9821 Fax: 0161-477 0305 E-mail: norman@torrprint.fsnet.co.uk

▶ Touraco Ltd, 6 Robert Leonard Industrial Site, Aviation Way, Southend-on-Sea, SS2 6GG Tel: (01702) 547800 Fax: (01702) 547788 E-mail: info@touraco.co.uk

▶ Tower Press Ltd, 2 Alton Road, South Warnborough, Hook, Hampshire, RG29 1RT Tel: (01256) 861886 Fax: (01256) 861887 E-mail: sales@tower-press.co.uk

▶ Trafalgar Press, 20 Robert Cort Industrial Estate, Britten Road, Reading, RG2 0AU Tel: 0118-975 0899 Fax: 0118-975 3220 E-mail: sales@trafpress.co.uk

▶ Treble M Colour Output, Production House, 205 Garnett Street, Bradford, West Yorkshire, BD3 9HA Tel: (01274) 393937 Fax: (01274) 393940

▶ Trendell Simpson Of Dundee Ltd, 3 Lintrathen Street, Dundee, DD3 8EF Tel: (01382) 825629 Fax: (01382) 832316

▶ Trueprint Litho, Unit A9 Continental Approach, Westwood Industrial Estate, Margate, Kent, CT9 4JG Tel: (01843) 220200 Fax: (01843) 292646

▶ TSC Graphics Ltd, 28 Factory Lane, Croydon, CR0 3RL Tel: (020) 8686 6553

Tuckey Print Ltd, 79 Moseley Road, Birmingham, B12 0HL Tel: 0121-773 7411 Fax: 0121-766 7339 E-mail: sales@tuckeyprint.co.uk

▶ Turnpike Press Ltd, Unit A1 Valley Link Estate, Meridian Way, Enfield, Middlesex, EN3 4TY Tel: (020) 8805 8850 Fax: (020) 8805 8851

▶ Twentyfourseven Design & Print, The New Media Centre, Old Road, Warrington, WA4 1AT Tel: (01925) 240247

▶ Ukrainian Information Service Ltd, 200 Liverpool Road, London, N1 1LF Tel: (020) 7607 6266 Fax: (020) 7607 6737

Unicorn Print & Design, 143 North Street, Romford, RM1 1ED Tel: (01708) 765017 Fax: (01708) 733491 E-mail: unicorndie@aol.com

▶ Uxbridge Press Ltd, 129 High Street, Uxbridge, Middlesex, UB8 1DL Tel: (01895) 850058 Fax: (01895) 850805 E-mail: info@drayton.co.uk

▶ Valentine Press Ltd, Valentine House, Pembroke Business Centre, Gardiners Lane South, Basildon, Essex, SS14 3AP Tel: (01268) 282555

▶ The Valley Printing Co. Ltd, Harden Beck Mill, Harden, Bingley, West Yorkshire, BD16 1BL Tel: (01535) 272861 Fax: (01535) 275332

VCS Clearpoint Ltd, Salop Street, Daybrook, Nottingham, NG5 6HD Tel: 0115-967 1234 Fax: 0115-967 1154 E-mail: clearpoint@demon.co.uk

Vertec Printing Services Ltd, 1 Swan Road, Westminster Industrial Estate, London, SE18 5TT Tel: (020) 8319 5252 Fax: (020) 8319 5275 E-mail: info@vertec-print.co.uk

▶ Victor Printing Co. Ltd, 3a Bridge Road, Felixstowe, Suffolk, IP11 7SL Tel: (01394) 274402 Fax: (01394) 276087

Vinalith Ltd, Valley House, Cray Avenue, Orpington, Kent, BR5 3RZ Tel: (01689) 878211 Fax: (01689) 833946 E-mail: sales@vinalith.co.uk

▶ Visa Press Ltd, Campbell Court, Bramley, Tadley, Hampshire, RG26 5EG Tel: (01256) 882131

▶ Vision Colour Print Ltd, 132 Wakefield Road, Drighlington, Bradford, West Yorkshire, BD11 1DR Tel: 0113-287 9962 Fax: 0113-385 6606 E-mail: studio@visioncolourprint.com

▶ Vision Print Imaging Products, 29 Ivatt Way, Peterborough, PE3 7PH Tel: (01733) 334477 Fax: (01733) 330083

▶ Visualize Printers, E Sutherland Houses, Sutherland Road, London, E17 6BU Tel: (020) 8527 6225 Fax: (020) 8523 4219

W G Harrison Ltd, Dysart Road, Grantham, Lincolnshire, NG31 7LF Tel: (01476) 402041 Fax: (01476) 566999

▶ Waddie & Co. Ltd, Dewar Square, Deans Industrial Estate, Livingston, West Lothian, EH54 8SA Tel: (01506) 419393

▶ Waddington & Ledger Ltd, Lowfields Way, Lowfields Business Park, Elland, West Yorkshire, HX5 9DA Tel: (01422) 315000 Fax: (01422) 315031 E-mail: sales@wlprint.co.uk

▶ Walker & Connell Ltd, Hastings Square, Darvel, Ayrshire, KA17 0DS Tel: (01560) 320237 Fax: (01560) 322209

The Walsall Box Co. Ltd, Bank Street, Walsall, WS1 2ER Tel: (01922) 628118 Fax: (01922) 723395 E-mail: mail@thewalsallbox.co.uk

Walsall Print Co. Ltd, Midland Road, Walsall, WS1 3QL Tel: (01922) 721272 Fax: (01922) 625950 E-mail: info@walsall-print.co.uk

▶ Waltham Litho Ltd, Unit 6, Raven Road Industrial Estate, London, E18 1HB Tel: (020) 8504 1035 Fax: (020) 8504 9365

Warnes Mail Marketing Ltd, 577 Kingston Road, London, SW20 8YA Tel: (020) 8687 3800 Fax: (020) 8545 2701 E-mail: sales@warnes.co.uk

▶ Washington Print, 24 Beswick Street, Manchester, M4 7HR Tel: 0161-273 8600 Fax: 0161-274 3708

▶ Water Side, Unit 14-15, The Griffon Centre, Vale of Leven Industrial Estat, Dumbarton, G82 3PD Tel: (01389) 755500

▶ Waverley Press (Aberdeen) Ltd, 12 Wellheads Crescent, Wellheads Industrial Estate, Aberdeen, AB21 7GA Tel: (01224) 775000 E-mail: admin@waverleypress.co.uk

Wayzgoose Holdings Ltd, Wayzgoose Ltd, East Road, Sleaford, Lincolnshire, NG34 7EH Tel: (01529) 304505 Fax: (01529) 307257 E-mail: enquiries@wayzgoose.co.uk

▶ Webmart Scotland, 16 Naughton Road, Wormit, Newport-on-Tay, Fife, DD6 8PE Tel: (01382) 542777 Fax: (01382) 542777

▶ Wessex Malthouse Direct, 24A East Reach, Taunton, Somerset, TA1 3EP Tel: (01823) 331111 Fax: (01823) 334503 E-mail: sales@wessexmalthouse.com

▶ West Printing Works Ltd, Elm Grove Lane, Steyning, West Sussex, BN44 3SA Tel: (01903) 813007 Fax: (01903) 814905

The Westdale Press Ltd, Unit 70, Portmanmoor Road Industrial Estate, Cardiff, CF24 5HB Tel: (029) 2046 1363 Fax: (029) 2066 2608 E-mail: alan@westdale.co.uk

Westheath Press Ltd, 55 Mott Street, Birmingham, B19 3HE Tel: 0121-236 0507 Fax: 0121-236 1088

▶ Westwood Press Ltd, Margate Road, Broadstairs, Kent, CT10 2PR Tel: (01843) 862864

▶ Westwood Printers, Unit C3, Willowbridge Way, Whitwood, Castleford, West Yorkshire, WF10 5NP Tel: (01977) 604647

▶ Wheatley Printers Ltd, C2 Phoenix Trading Estate, London Road, Thrupp, Stroud, Gloucestershire, GL5 2BX Tel: (01453) 731001 Fax: (01453) 731418

▶ Wheatsheaf Press, Print Works, Lacey Green, Wilmslow, Cheshire, SK9 4BQ Tel: (01625) 530530 Fax: (01625) 535898 E-mail: print@wheatsheaf.u-net.com

White, Usher Street, Ludworth, Durham, DH6 1NE Tel: (01429) 820487 Fax: (01429) 821508

▶ White House Press Ltd, Units 14-16 The Marina, Harbour Road, Lydney, Gloucestershire, GL15 5ET Tel: (01594) 842015 Fax: (01594) 841880

Whitehead & Wood Ltd, Brindley Close, Network 65 Business Park, Hapton, Burnley, Lancashire, BB11 5TD Tel: (01282) 446000 Fax: (01282) 446044 E-mail: service@wwcom.co.uk

▶ Whitmont Press, 2B Mount Pleasant Road, London, SE13 6RB Tel: (020) 8690 2696

▶ Wilgrove Express Forms Ltd, Unit 4-5 Endeavour Way, Croydon, CR0 4TR Tel: (020) 8665 7665 Fax: (020) 8689 6500

▶ William Anderson & Son Ltd, 34 Loanbank Quadrant, Glasgow, G51 3HZ Tel: 0141-440 2881 Fax: 0141-445 1480

▶ William Culross & Son Ltd, Queen Street, Coupar Angus, Blairgowrie, Perthshire, PH13 9DF Tel: (01828) 627266 Fax: (01828) 627146

▶ William Nimmo & Co. Ltd, Tennant House, 21 Tennant Street, Leith, Edinburgh, EH6 5NA Tel: 0131-554 2431

WM Print Ltd, 45-47 Frederick Street, Walsall, WS2 9NE Tel: (01922) 643008 Fax: (01922) 720149 E-mail: cooper@wmprint.co.uk

William West, 8 Kingside, Ruston Road, London, SE18 5BX Tel: (020) 8316 6966 E-mail: sales@williamwest.co.uk

▶ Wilprint Group Ltd, Ipswich Road, Cardiff, CF23 9XX Tel: (029) 2049 8484

▶ Wilton Graphics Ltd, Harnham Trading Estate, Netherhampton Road, Salisbury, SP2 8NW Tel: (01722) 320300

Wiltshire (Bristol) Ltd, First Avenue, Portbury West, Bristol, BS20 7WP Tel: (01275) 375555 Fax: (01275) 375590 E-mail: enquiries@wiltshire-print.co.uk

▶ Windles Printers, Meadow View, Drakes Drive, Long Crendon, Aylesbury, Buckinghamshire, HP18 9EQ Tel: (01844) 201683 Fax: (01844) 201695

Windmill Graphics, PO Box 11, Stroud, Gloucestershire, GL5 5BH Tel: (01453) 873758 Fax: (01453) 873699 E-mail: sales@windmillgraphics.co.uk

▶ Wirral Continuous Ltd, 26 Thursby Rd., Croft Business Park, Wirral, Merseyside, CH62 3PW Tel: 0151-334 0895

▶ Wishaw Printing Co., 84 Stewarton Street, Wishaw, Lanarkshire, ML2 8AG Tel: (01698) 357223 Fax: (01698) 351277

▶ Woking Print & Publicity Ltd, The Print Works, St. Johns Lye, Woking, Surrey, GU21 7RS Tel: (01483) 884884 Fax: (01483) 884880

▶ Woodgate-Loydor Ltd, Elmfield Avenue, Teddington, Middlesex, TW11 8BS Tel: (020) 8977 3491

▶ Woods Of Perth Ltd, 113-119 Glover Street, Perth, PH2 0JF Tel: (01738) 622244 Fax: (01738) 635234 E-mail: info@woodsofperth.co.uk

Wren Ltd, Harrier House, Aviation Way, Southend Airport, Southend-on-Sea, SS2 6UN Tel: (01702) 548044 Fax: (01702) 541463 E-mail: sales@wrenpack.co.uk

Wyke Printers Ltd, Gothenburg Way, Hull, HU7 0YD Tel: (01482) 831290 Fax: (01482) 878244 E-mail: info@wyke-printers.co.uk

Wyndham Granger, Butts Road, Southwick, Brighton, BN42 4EJ Tel: (01273) 592244 Fax: (01273) 870210 E-mail: thegrangepress@msn.com

▶ X D S Ltd, Cornishway West, Galmington Trading Estate, Taunton, Somerset, TA1 5NA Tel: (01823) 325999

▶ Xpress Print, Graphix House, Wellington Circle, Altens, Aberdeen, AB12 3JG Tel: (01224) 878799 Fax: (01224) 878713

▶ Yes Graphic Design & Print, 73 Birkmyre Road, Glasgow, G51 3HG Tel: 0141-445 8644 Fax: 0141-445 8655

▶ York City Printers Ltd, Unit 4, Birch Park, Huntington Road, York, YO31 9BL Tel: (01904) 620490

LITHOGRAPHIC PRINTING MACHINES

Allbrook Printers, 12 Fulmar Crescent, Hemel Hempstead, Hertfordshire, HP1 1SG Tel: (01442) 240748 Fax: (01442) 240748 E-mail: steve@allbrookprinters.co.uk

Colne Press Ltd, Unit 11-12, Eastman Way, Hemel Hempstead Industrial Estate, Hemel Hempstead, Hertfordshire, HP2 7DU Tel: (01442) 212922 Fax: (01442) 265967 E-mail: info@colne.co.uk

Copystatic Midlands Ltd, Northern House, Moor Knoll Lane, East Ardsley, Wakefield, West Yorkshire, WF3 2EE Tel: (01924) 823455 Fax: (01924) 820433 E-mail: headoffice@eurocopy.co.uk

Downland Printing Services Ltd, Unit 1 Kingley Centre, Downs Road, Weststoke, Chichester, West Sussex, PO18 9HJ Tel: (01243) 576576 Fax: (01243) 576577 E-mail: studio@downlandrepro.demon.co.uk

J & P Graphics International, 3, Lowerfold Drive, Shawclough, Rochdale, Lancashire, OL12 7JA Tel: (01706) 358055 Fax: 0845 280 2822 E-mail: jbrown5710@aol.com

Midos Communications, 10 Heol-Y-Deri, Cardiff, CF14 6HG Tel: (029) 2069 1698 Fax: (029) 2069 1693

Printers Partners Supplies Ltd, Unit 720 Tudor Estate, Abbey Road, London, NW10 7UN Tel: (020) 8951 9500 Fax: (020) 8963 1940 E-mail: sales@rotaprint.com

Solent Print Engineering Ltd, 1 Pytchley Close, Fareham, Hampshire, PO14 3SF Tel: (07917) 784595 E-mail: print.eng@ntlworld.com

LITHOGRAPHIC PRINTING MACHINES, OFFSET

▶ Datumpress Ltd, 87 Great North Road, Hatfield, Hertfordshire, AL9 5DA Tel: (01707) 251222 Fax: (01707) 251444

LITHOGRAPHIC PRINTING PREPRESS EQUIPMENT MANUFRS

Europress Printers, 15-17 Green Lane, Hull, HU2 0HG Tel: (01482) 224993 Fax: (01482) 211486 E-mail: info@europresshull.co.uk

▶ Graphic Line Machinery Ltd, 45 Prestongate, Hessle, North Humberside, HU13 0RD Tel: (01482) 645645 Fax: (020) 7691 7913 E-mail: info@glm.co.uk

J & P Graphics International, 3, Lowerfold Drive, Shawclough, Rochdale, Lancashire, OL12 7JA Tel: (01706) 358055 Fax: 0845 280 2822 E-mail: jbrown5710@aol.com

VCS Clearpoint Ltd, Salop Street, Daybrook, Nottingham, NG5 6HD Tel: 0115-967 1234 Fax: 0115-967 1154 E-mail: clearpoint@demon.co.uk

LITHOGRAPHIC PRINTING PREPRESS SERVICES

Advance, 18 Overbury Cres, Croydon, CR0 0LL Tel: 020 8123 0389 E-mail: info@advancestudio.co.uk

Allbrook Printers, 12 Fulmar Crescent, Hemel Hempstead, Hertfordshire, HP1 1SG Tel: (01442) 240748 Fax: (01442) 240748 E-mail: steve@allbrookprinters.co.uk

▶ Ambassador Litho Ltd, 25 Hockeys Lane, Bristol, BS16 3HH Tel: 0117-965 5252 Fax: 0117-965 3275 E-mail: info@ambassador.co.uk

Cardmaster UK, 2 Christopher Road, Leeds, LS6 2JX Tel: 0113-244 2265 Fax: 0113-244 2265 E-mail: bouncers@inname.com

Carlton Press Group N W Ltd, 3-7 Britannia Road, Sale, Cheshire, M33 2AA Tel: 0161-962 8686 Fax: 0161-969 6300 E-mail: sales@carltonpressgroup.com

Clearpoint Print Services Ltd, Park Lane, Nottingham, NG6 0DT Tel: 0115-979 7925 Fax: 0115-979 7958 E-mail: sales@clearpoint-print.com

Colorprofile Printers, 4 Whitworth Road, Stevenage, Hertfordshire, SG1 4QS Tel: (01438) 724891 Fax: (01438) 720512

Midos Communications, 10 Heol-Y-Deri, Cardiff, CF14 6HG Tel: (029) 2069 1698 Fax: (029) 2069 1693

Polestar Jowetts, Evanston Avenue, Kirkstall Road, Leeds, LS4 2HR Tel: (0113) 279 5041 Fax: (0113) 231 0193

Speedlith Ltd, Longford Trading Estate, Thomas Street, Stretford, Manchester, M32 0JT Tel: 0161-864 2233 Fax: 0161-864 5238 E-mail: speedlith@aol.com

Taylowe Ltd, Malvern Road, Furze Platt, Maidenhead, Berkshire, SL6 7RF Tel: (01628) 413333 Fax: (01628) 413397 E-mail: taylowereception@taylowe.com

LITHOGRAPHIC PRINTING PROCESSING EQUIPMENT

J & P Graphics International, 3, Lowerfold Drive, Shawclough, Rochdale, Lancashire, OL12 7JA Tel: (01706) 358055 Fax: 0845 280 2822 E-mail: jbrown5710@aol.com

LITHOGRAPHIC PRINTING TRADE SUPPLIERS/ DISTRIBUTORS/AGENTS

Central Print, 2 Swan Village Industrial Estate, Swan Lane, West Bromwich, West Midlands, B70 0NY Tel: 0121-500 6230 Fax: 0121-500 6230

Coltec Parker Ltd, Unit 3 Royd Way, Keighley, West Yorkshire, BD21 3LG Tel: (01535) 608405 Fax: (01535) 669276 E-mail: sales@coltecparker.com

Dantex Graphics Ltd, Danon House, 5 Kings Road, Bradford, West Yorkshire, BD2 1EY Tel: (01274) 777788 Fax: (01274) 777766 E-mail: dillion.c@dantex.com

Hunter Penrose Supplies Ltd, 32 Southwark Street, London, SE1 1TU Tel: (020) 7407 5051 Fax: (020) 7378 1800 E-mail: info@hunterpenrose.co.uk

I G P (UK) Ltd, Saltcoates Industrial Estate, 1-5 Cutlers Road, South Woodham Ferrers, Chelmsford, CM3 5WD Tel: (01245) 323555 Fax: (01245) 323762 E-mail: sales@igp-ukltd.co.uk

J J Huber Investments Ltd, Bellbrook, Uckfield, East Sussex, TN22 1QL Tel: (01825) 761533 Fax: (01825) 768274 E-mail: huberuk@aol.com

Norman Lane Ltd, 1 Wiggenhall Road, Watford, WD18 0FH Tel: (01923) 235231 Fax: (01923) 222569 E-mail: normanlane@easynet.co.uk

Masterange Business Services Ltd, 9 East Road, Harlow, Essex, CM20 2BJ Tel: (01279) 300600 Fax: (01279) 306911 E-mail: services@masterange.co.uk

▶ Mayday Graphic Products, Graphic House, Cratfield Road, Bury St. Edmunds, Suffolk, IP32 7DF Tel: (01284) 701571 Fax: (01284) 750553 E-mail: sales@maydaygraphics.co.uk

LITHOGRAPHIC PRINTING, OFFSET

▶ A C P, T1 The Maltings, Roydon Road, Stanstead Abbotts, Ware, Hertfordshire, SG12 8HG Tel: (01920) 870355 Fax: (01920) 870355 E-mail: admin@acprinting.co.uk

▶ Saxon Print Group, Saxon House, Hellesdon Park Road, Norwich, NR6 5DR Tel: (01603) 789560 Fax: (01603) 789561 E-mail: bruce.carpenter@saxongroup.com

LITHOGRAPHIC PROOFING SERVICES

Nicholson & Bass Ltd, 3 Nicholson Drive, Newtownabbey, County Antrim, BT36 4FB Tel: (028) 9034 2433 Fax: (028) 9034 2066 E-mail: sales@nicholsonbass.com

Qualitech Print Ltd, Bramhall Moor Industrial Park, Pepper Road, Stockport, Cheshire, SK7 5BW Tel: 0161-456 6866 Fax: 0161-487 1588 E-mail: sales@qualitech.co.uk

LITHOGRAPHIC SCANNING

Formatrix, Hayne Barton, Whitestone, Exeter, EX4 2JN Tel: (01392) 811766

Thruxton Press Ltd, Thruxton Down House, Thruxton, Andover, Hampshire, SP11 8PR Tel: (01264) 889552 Fax: (01264) 889622 E-mail: publications@brunton.co.uk

Tower Media Solutions, 25 Holywell Row, London, EC2A 4XE Tel: (020) 7247 0876 Fax: (020) 7247 5717 E-mail: helpdesk@towermedia.co.uk

LITTER PICKING HAND TOOLS

Cee Vee Engineering Ltd, Shepherds Close, Cooden Sea Road, Bexhill-on-Sea, East Sussex, TN39 4SL Tel: (01424) 845566 Fax: (01424) 842144 E-mail: sales@ceevee.co.uk

LIVE ENTERTAINMENT EVENTS CONTROL SYSTEMS

▶ Eventurous, The Water front, West Midlands Water Ski centre, Tamworth, Staffordshire, B78 2DL Tel: (0870) 6071258 E-mail: sales@eventurous.co.uk

▶ Master Blaster Disco's, 20 Pinewood, Forest Hill, Skelmersdale, Lancashire, WN8 6UZ Tel: (07769) 734126 E-mail: masterblasterdiscos@hotmail.co.uk

▶ Ventura (Jazz Band), Seafire Close, York, YO30 4UU Tel: (0776) 9504794 E-mail: yorkjazz@fmail.co.uk

Will Gray, The Magic Castle, 88 Church Lane, Whitwick, Coalville, Leicestershire, LE67 5DJ Tel: (01530) 457465 Fax: (0871) 7333318 E-mail: magic@willgray.co.uk

LIVESTOCK

▶ Arranbrook Miniature Donkeys, Mill Farm, Azerley, Ripon, North Yorkshire, HG4 3JJ Tel: (01765) 658877 E-mail: Anne@minidonks.co.uk

George Briggs & Son, Wirswall, Whitchurch, Shropshire, SY13 4LF Tel: (01948) 663733

▶ U P B Ltd, Whitehouse Distribution Centre, White House Road, Ipswich, IP1 5NX Tel: (01473) 742233 Fax: (01473) 743800

LIVESTOCK BARRIER FENCING

▶ Treefellar Scotland, 6 Brodick Avenue, Kilwinning, Ayrshire, KA13 6RJ Tel: (01294) 554472 Fax: (01294) 542825 E-mail: admin@treefellar.co.uk

LIVESTOCK EXPORT

Arbuckle Smith & Co., 106 Abercorn Street, Paisley, Renfrewshire, PA3 4AY Tel: (0141) 887 5252 Fax: (0141) 887 4461 E-mail: craig_hodgson@zieglergroup.com

LIVESTOCK HANDLING/ CONTROL EQUIPMENT

L.M. Bateman & Co. Ltd, Island Works, Cheadle Road, Chedleton, Leek, Staffordshire, ST13 7EE Tel: (01538) 361326 Fax: (01538) 360803 E-mail: info@lmbateman.co.uk

Bovingdon M.A, Stanwell Road, Ashgood Farm, Horton, Slough, SL3 9PA Tel: (01753) 682063

Cwmnant Calves Ltd, Cwmnant, Tregaron, Dyfed, SY25 6NL Tel: (01974) 298564 Fax: (01974) 298745E-mail: cwmnant.calves@farmline.com

D F E Underwood, Holly Bush Farm, Cleedownton, Ludlow, Shropshire, SY8 3EH Tel: (01584) 823270

Darlington Farmers Auction Mart Co. Ltd, Clifton Road, Darlington, County Durham, DL1 5DU Tel: (01325) 464529 Fax: (01325) 384282

Euroclip 2000 Ltd, 2 Barrington Court, Ward Road, Brackley, Northamptonshire, NN13 7LE Tel: (01280) 840900 Fax: (01280) 840904 E-mail: sales@euroclip.fsnet.co.uk

Fowler Bros, Brook Farm, Marsh Road, Burnham-on-Crouch, Essex, CM0 8NA Tel: (01621) 782877

Ian Waddington (live Stock) Ltd, Kimberly House, Mounsey Road, Preston, PR5 6LS Tel: (01772) 629988 Fax: (01772) 629988

Industrial & Agricultural Engineers, Riverside Works, Macclesfield Road, Leek, Staffordshire, ST13 8LB Tel: (01538) 399200 Fax: (01538) 373005 E-mail: sales@iae.co.uk

N Small, 7 Flush Road, Newcastle, County Down, BT33 0QF Tel: (028) 4375 1312

Nagington Farming, Doley, Adbaston, Stafford, ST20 0RQ Tel: (01785) 280466 Fax: (01785) 280466

P A Gay, Westmanton, Ashwater, Beaworthy, Devon, EX21 5HD Tel: (01409) 211245 Fax: (01409) 211483

Poultry First Ltd, The Manor House, Greenways Manor Estate, Woodhall Spa, Lincolnshire, LN10 6PY Tel: (01526) 352471 Fax: (01526) 352022

Provimi Ltd, Maple Mill, Dalton Airfield, Dalton, Thirsk, North Yorkshire, YO7 3HE Tel: (01845) 577866 Fax: (01845) 578100

Ritchey, Fearby Road, Masham, Ripon, North Yorkshire, HG4 4ES Tel: (01765) 689541 Fax: (01765) 689851 E-mail: info@ritchey.co.uk

Rugby Livestock, 1 High Street, Whittlebury, Towcester, Northamptonshire, NN12 8XH Tel: (01327) 858858 Fax: (01327) 858858

Scotch Lamb Marketing Ltd, Eastmains Farm, Newbigging, Carnwath, Lanark, ML11 8NB Tel: (01555) 840002 Fax: (01555) 840095

T R Clark, Crawl Farm, Crawl Lane, Clandown, Radstock, BA3 2XH Tel: (01761) 413120 Fax: (01761) 413120

United Auctions, Stirling Auction Market, Kildean, Stirling, FK9 4UB Tel: (01786) 473055 Fax: (01786) 450393

LIVESTOCK RADIO FREQUENCY IDENTIFICATION (RFID) TAGS

Intellident, Southgate Centre Two, Wilmslow Road, Heald Green, Cheadle, Cheshire, SK8 3PW Tel: 0161-436 9950 Fax: 0161-436 8787 E-mail: sales@intellident.co.uk

Ritchey, Fearby Road, Masham, Ripon, North Yorkshire, HG4 4ES Tel: (01765) 689541 Fax: (01765) 689851 E-mail: info@ritchey.co.uk

LIVESTOCK TRANSPORT CONTRACTORS

Davey's Livestock Transport Ltd, Council Houses, Tregadillett, Launceston, Cornwall, PL15 7EX Tel: (01566) 774251 Fax: (01566) 774251

E & S J Pearson, Felstead, Low Bentham Road, Bentham, Lancaster, LA2 7BP Tel: (01524) 261766 Fax: (01524) 263271

▶ Easycroft, 7, Bromham Mill, Giffard Park, Milton Keynes, MK14 5QP Tel: (01908) 617272

F W Hume & Sons (Contractor), Bridge Farm House, Ling Road, Palgrave, Diss, Norfolk, IP22 1AA Tel: (01379) 642620 Fax: (01379) 652738

G Harraway & Sons, Wrington Vale House, Wrington Road, Congresbury, Bristol, BS49 5AR Tel: (01934) 833000 Fax: (01934) 877330

N.S. Harvey, Station Farm, Sleaford Road, Tattershall, Lincoln, LN4 4JG Tel: (01526) 343719 Fax: (01526) 343729

J M Bell & Son, Archard Garth, Bagby, Thirsk, North Yorkshire, YO7 2PH Tel: (01845) 597205 Fax: (01845) 597971

James Kinnear Thornton Ltd, 91 Main Street, Thornton, Kirkcaldy, Fife, KY1 4AQ Tel: (01592) 774352 Fax: (01592) 771411

M F Bailey, Hartwell Stud Farm, Hartwell Lane, Stone, Staffordshire, ST15 8TL Tel: (01782) 372523

Gordon Martin & Son, The Chalet, Tresarrett, Bodmin, Cornwall, PL30 4QF Tel: (01208) 850405 Fax: (01208) 851405

Tony Monkhouse, Heatherview, Hill End, Frosterley, Bishop Auckland, County Durham, DL13 2SU Tel: (01388) 528726

P D Levi & Son, Brine Pits Cottage, Wychbold, Droitwich, Worcestershire, WR9 0BY Tel: (01527) 861580

P Monkhouse, Durham Road, Wolsingham, Bishop Auckland, County Durham, DL13 3JB Tel: (01388) 528814 Fax: (01388) 527213 E-mail: sales@monkhousehaulage.co.uk

R Davidson & Sons Ltd, South Park, Lochfoot, Dumfries, DG2 8NH Tel: (01387) 730308 Fax: (01387) 730777

S G Waite, 6 Trummery Lane, Craigavon, County Armagh, BT67 0JN Tel: (028) 9261 1527 Fax: (028) 9261 1527

W Barker & Sons, Broughton Nook, School House Lane, Abbots Bromley, Rugeley, Staffordshire, WS15 3BT Tel: (01283) 840266 Fax: (01283) 840562

Ian Walker, 58 Ettington Cl, Wellesbourne, Warwick, CV35 9RJ Tel: (01789) 840341 Fax: (01789) 840341

LIVING FLAME GAS FIRES

▶ Amgas Fires & Fireplaces Ltd, Unit 12 12 Whingate, Leeds, LS12 3BL Tel: 0113-263 0700 Fax: 0113-263 0700 E-mail: info@amgas.tk

▶ Gas Style, 374 Blackpool Road, Ashton-on-Ribble, Preston, PR2 2DS Tel: (01772) 761006 Fax: (01772) 761006

LOAD ARREST DEVICES

Globestock Engineering Ltd, Mile Oak Industrial Estate, Maesbury Road, Oswestry, Shropshire, SY10 8GA Tel: (01691) 654966 Fax: (01691) 661726 E-mail: info@globestock.co.uk

LOAD BANKS

Hillstone Products Ltd, Unit 2, Portland Industrial Estate, Portland Street, Bury, Lancashire, BL9 6EY Tel: 0161-763 3100 Fax: 0161-763 3158 E-mail: sales@hillstone.co.uk

LOAD CARRYING BALLOONS

Cameron Balloons Ltd, St Johns Street, Bedminster, Bristol, BS3 4NH Tel: 0117-963 7216 Fax: 0117-966 1168 E-mail: sales@cameronballoons.co.uk

LOAD CELL MANUFRS

Acam Instrumentation Ltd, 23 Thomas Street, Northampton, NN1 3EN Tel: (01604) 628700 Fax: (01604) 628700 E-mail: tom@acamltd.co.uk

Amber Instruments Ltd, Dunston House Sheepbridge Works, Dunston Road, Chesterfield, Derbyshire, S41 9QD Tel: (01246) 260250 Fax: (01246) 260955 E-mail: sales@amberinstruments.com

Atex Ltd, 4 Thames Park, Lester Way, Wallingford, Oxfordshire, OX10 9TA Tel: (01491) 839999 Fax: (01491) 839466 E-mail: contactuk@atex-f1.com

Cambridge Insitu Ltd, Rectory Farm, 39 High Street, Little Eversden, Cambridge, CB3 7HE Tel: (01223) 262361 Fax: (01223) 263947 E-mail: caminsitu@aol.com

Darenth Weighing Services Ltd, 75 Campbell Road, Maidstone, Kent, ME15 6PS Tel: (0870) 4436670 Fax: (0870) 4436671

Davis Decade Ltd, 30 Spring Lane, Birmingham, B24 9BX Tel: 0121-377 6292 Fax: 0121-377 6645 E-mail: dmg@decade.co.uk

Direct Weigh, 14 Milldown Avenue, Goring, Reading, RG8 0AS Tel: (01491) 872042 Fax: (01491) 873782E-mail: sales@flintec.net

Dynamic Load Monitoring UK Ltd, 3 Bridgers Farm, Nursling Street, Nursling, Southampton, SO16 0YA Tel: (023) 8074 1700 Fax: (023) 8074 1701 E-mail: info@dynaload.co.uk

Force Measurement Systems Ltd, 3-5 Lister Road, Glasgow, G52 4BH Tel: 0141-882 8858 Fax: 0141-810 3434 E-mail: sales@forcemeasurement.co.uk

Hydraulic Transmission Services Ltd, Whitehall Road, Leeds, LS12 5JB Tel: 0113-279 3017 Fax: 0113-279 5505 E-mail: hts@btinternet.com

Interface Force Measurements Ltd, Ground Floor, Unit 19 Wellington Business Park, Duke Ride, Crowthorne, Berkshire, RG45 6LS Tel: 0845 4941748 Fax: (01344) 774765 E-mail: info@interface.uk.com

M S L Oilfield Services LTD, Unit 14 Brickfield Trade Estate, Brickfield Lane, Chandler's Ford, Eastleigh, Hampshire, SO53 4DP Tel: (023) 8027 5100 Fax: (023) 8027 5200 E-mail: sales@msluk.net

Novatech Measurements Ltd, 83 Castleham Road, St. Leonards-On-Sea, East Sussex, TN38 9NT Tel: (01424) 852744 Fax: (01424) 853002 E-mail: info@novatechloadcells.co.uk

Procter & Chester (Measurements) Ltd, Dalehouse Lane, Kenilworth, Warwickshire, CV8 2UE Tel: (01926) 864444 Fax: (01926) 864888 E-mail: info@pcm-uk.com

▶ Strain Measurement Devices Ltd, Bury Road, Chedburgh, Bury St. Edmunds, Suffolk, IP29 4UQ Tel: (01284) 852000 Fax: (01284) 852371 E-mail: askus@smdsensors.co.uk

Thames Side-Maywood Ltd, 2 Collumbers Drive, Summet Avenue, Southwood, Farnborough, Hampshire, GU14 0NZ Tel: (01252) 555811 Fax: (01252) 375394 E-mail: sales@thames-side.co.uk

Vishay Measurements Group UK Ltd, 1 Cartel Units, Stroudley Road, Basingstoke, Hampshire, RG24 8FW Tel: (01256) 462131 Fax: (01256) 471441 E-mail: email@measurementsgroup.co.uk

LOAD CELL STRAIN GAUGES

Davis Decade Ltd, 30 Spring Lane, Birmingham, B24 9BX Tel: 0121-377 6292 Fax: 0121-377 6645 E-mail: dmg@decade.co.uk

Novatech Measurements Ltd, 83 Castleham Road, St. Leonards-On-Sea, East Sussex, TN38 9NT Tel: (01424) 852744 Fax: (01424) 853002 E-mail: info@novatechloadcells.co.uk

LOAD CELLS, TO CUSTOMER SPECIFICATION

Novatech Measurements Ltd, 83 Castleham Road, St. Leonards-On-Sea, East Sussex, TN38 9NT Tel: (01424) 852744 Fax: (01424) 853002 E-mail: info@novatechloadcells.co.uk

LOAD LASHING OR STRAPPING OR RESTRAINT SYSTEMS

Andrew Mitchell Co. Ltd, Bates Business Centre, Church Road, Harold Wood, Romford, RM3 0JF Tel: (01708) 370800 Fax: (01708) 377190 E-mail: info@mitco.co.uk

Flip Lock Ltd, 177 Ashby Road, Scunthorpe, South Humberside, DN16 2AQ Tel: (01724) 865692 E-mail: mgdeans@btconnect.com

M & N Canvas Services Ltd, Butterthwaite Lane, Ecclesfield, Sheffield, S35 9WA Tel: 0114-246 1293 Fax: 0114-257 0311

Matek Business Media Ltd, 4 Field Place Estate, Field Place, Broadbridge Heath, Horsham, West Sussex, RH12 3PB Tel: (01403) 276300 Fax: (01403) 276311E-mail: sales@matek.net

▶ Mudfords Sheffield Ltd, 400 Petre Street, Sheffield, S4 8LU Tel: 0114-243 3033 Fax: 0114-244 4536 E-mail: sales@mudfords.co.uk

P G S Supplies Ltd, Worthing Road, Sheffield, S9 3JB Tel: 0114-276 5566 Fax: 0114-276 5265 E-mail: sales@pgs-supplies.co.uk

Package Control (U.K.) Ltd, Unit 5 Bunas Business Park, Hollom Down Road, Lopcombe, Salisbury, SP5 1BP Tel: (01264) 782143 Fax: (0844) 8800384 E-mail: sales@package-control.co.uk

Simark Engineering Co., Griffin Industrial Estate, Rowley Regis, West Midlands, B65 0SN Tel: 0121-559 1351 Fax: 0121-559 3205 E-mail: simark.engineering@virgin.net

Technique Engineering, 1 Gilmans Industrial Estate, Billingshurst, West Sussex, RH14 9EZ Tel: (01403) 784678 Fax: (01403) 784978 E-mail: info@technique-engineering.com

Wessex Rope & Packaging, 6 20 Abingdon Road, Nuffield Industrial Estate, Poole, Dorset, BH17 0UG Tel: (01202) 661066 Fax: (01202) 661077 E-mail: sales@wrp-poole.co.uk

LOAD MONITORING SYSTEMS

Dynamic Load Monitoring UK Ltd, 3 Bridgers Farm, Nursling Street, Nursling, Southampton, SO16 0YA Tel: (023) 8074 1700 Fax: (023) 8074 1701 E-mail: info@dynaload.co.uk

Force Measurement Systems Ltd, 3-5 Lister Road, Glasgow, G52 4BH Tel: 0141-882 8858 Fax: 0141-810 3434 E-mail: sales@forcemeasurement.co.uk

Interface Force Measurements Ltd, Ground Floor, Unit 19 Wellington Business Park, Duke Ride, Crowthorne, Berkshire, RG45 6LS Tel: 0845 4941748 Fax: (01344) 774765 E-mail: info@interface.uk.com

M S L Oilfield Services LTD, Unit 14 Brickfield Trade Estate, Brickfield Lane, Chandler's Ford, Eastleigh, Hampshire, SO53 4DP Tel: (023) 8027 5100 Fax: (023) 8027 5200 E-mail: sales@msluk.net

LOAD MOVING SYSTEMS

Aerogo UK Ltd, 11a Orchard Road, Royston, Hertfordshire, SG8 6HL Tel: (01763) 249349 Fax: (0870) 4014546 E-mail: sales@aerogo-uk.co.uk

Load Moving Systems, Pitts House, Grange Road, Duxford, Cambridge, CB2 4QE Tel: (01223) 839930 Fax: (01223) 839940 E-mail: info@loadmovingsystems.co.uk

Powrwheel Ltd, 8 Queensway, New Milton, Hampshire, BH25 5NN Tel: (01425) 623123 Fax: (01425) 623111 E-mail: info@powrwheel.com

LOAD OUT HEAVY LIFTING CONTRACTORS

Doorman Long Tech, The Charles Parker Building, Midland Road, Higham Ferrers, Rushden, Northamptonshire, NN10 8DN Tel: (01933) 319133 Fax: (01933) 319135 E-mail: dlt@dormanlong.com

▶ Winterlift Ltd, Fairhills Industrial Estate, Woodrow Way, Irlam, Manchester, M44 6ZQ Tel: 0161-775 4400 Fax: (0845) 1309003 E-mail: andrew.winter@btinternet.co.uk

LOAD SAFETY TRAILER LOCKS

J Luke, 101B High Rd, Beeston, Nottingham, NG9 2LH Tel: 0115-925 5616 Fax: 0115-925 5616 E-mail: jdluke@btconect.com

LOAD SUPPORTING SLIDE BEARINGS

S K Bearings Ltd, Brewery Road, Pampisford, Cambridge, CB22 3HG Tel: (01223) 832851 Fax: (01223) 837668 E-mail: enquiries@skbearings.co.uk

LOADERS

C C T Ltd, Park Road, Holmewood, Chesterfield, Derbyshire, S42 5UY Tel: (01246) 855995 Fax: (01246) 854028 E-mail: cctltd@breathemail.net

H M Plant Ltd, Monkton Business Park North, Hebburn, Tyne & Wear, NE31 2JZ Tel: 0191-430 8400 Fax: 0191-430 8500 E-mail: info@hmplant.ltd.uk

Lewis Equipment Ltd, Waterloo Road, Bidford-on-Avon, Alcester, Warwickshire, B50 4JH Tel: (01789) 773044 Fax: (01789) 490379 E-mail: sales@lewis-equipment.co.uk

LOADING RAMPS

▶ Jorade Commercial Services Ltd, 16 Hartley Court Road, Three Mile Cross, Reading, RG7 1NS Tel: 0118-988 2852 Fax: 0118-988 3703 E-mail: debbie@byrne1718.fsnet.co.uk

LOADING RAMPS, MOBILE

▶ Loading Bay Service Ltd, Whiteheads Building, 26a Snow Hill, Wolverhampton, WV2 4AF Tel: (01902) 427472 Fax: (01902) 429374 E-mail: info@loadingbayservice.co.uk

LOAN ORIGINATION SOLUTIONS

Shakespear Finance Ltd, International House, 223 Regent Street, London, W1B 2EB Tel: (0808) 1602576 E-mail: webmaster@ adverse-credit-business-loans.co.uk

LOAN ORIGINATION SOLUTIONS, FINANCIAL

▶ Shakespeare finance ltd, 501 International House, 223 Regent Street, London, W1B 2EB Tel: (0808) 1602576 E-mail: webmaster@go4ukloans.co.uk

LOCAL AREA NETWORK (LAN) COMPUTER CABLES

▶ Acumen Accountants & Advisors Ltd, Bon Accord House, Riverside Drive, Aberdeen, AB11 7SL Tel: (01224) 573904 Fax: (01224) 572721 E-mail: enquiries@acumen.info

▶ Communications Express Ltd, 7 Grafton Place, Dukes Park Industrial Estate, Chelmsford, CM2 6TG Tel: (01245) 459490 Fax: (0845) 2000257 E-mail: sales@comms-express.com

▶ Computer Connections, 191 Donegall Street, Belfast, BT1 2FJ Tel: (028) 9032 4633 Fax: (028) 9032 4644 E-mail: matthew@computer-connections.info

▶ The Computer Shop, 69 Brockhurst Road, Gosport, Hampshire, PO12 3AR Tel: (023) 9252 2777 E-mail: sales@coppcomm.com

Conex Data Communications Ltd, Connex House, Follingsby Close, Gateshead, Tyne & Wear, NE10 8YG Tel: 0191-416 5444 Fax: 0191-416 0707 E-mail: sales@conexdata.com

Cooper Armer International Co. Ltd, Unit 2C Fernfield Farm, Whaddon Road, Milton Keynes, MK17 0PR Tel: (01908) 503018 Fax: (01908) 503811 E-mail: info@caidata.co.uk

▶ DA Internet, 128 Peckover Drive, Pudsey, Leeds, LS28 8EG Tel: 078216 11939 E-mail: sales@dainternet.net

Datasharp Voice Solutions, 50 Lonsdale Road, Notting Hill, London, W11 2DE Tel: 0207 565 9895 Fax: 0207 221 6660 E-mail: info@datasharpvoice.co.uk

▶ The Easy P C Store, 114 Moorfield Road, Widnes, Cheshire, WA8 3HX Tel: 0151-424 5671 Fax: 0151-424 5671 E-mail: info@easypcstore.co.uk

First Choice Computers West Midlands Ltd, 40 Waterloo Road, Wolverhampton, WV1 4BL Tel: (01902) 712166 Fax: (01902) 427900 E-mail: enquiries@fcc-online.co.uk

▶ TCPIP Ltd, 78 Wrentham Street, Birmingham, B5 6QP Tel: 0121-622 5000 Fax: 0121-622 5159 E-mail: sales@tcpip.ltd.uk

Westbrook Communications, Unit 9 Spectrum Industrial Estate, Bircholt Road, Maidstone, Kent, ME15 9YP Tel: (01622) 661860 Fax: (08700) 056902 E-mail: southeast@westbrookuk.com

LOCAL AREA NETWORK (LAN) PRODUCT REPAIR

D M C Products, P O Box 22, Derby, DE1 9ZU Tel: (01332) 205822 Fax: (01332) 205822 E-mail: info@dmc-systems.com

LOCAL AREA NETWORK (LAN) SYSTEM INSTALLATION

3y2k Computer Maintenance, The Coach House, Trewyn, Pandy, Abergavenny, Gwent, NP7 7PG Tel: (01873) 890002 E-mail: threey2k@hotmail.com

Archway Systems Ltd, 31 Parolles Road, London, N19 3RE Tel: (020) 7272 3530 Fax: (020) 7263 1951 E-mail: admin@arsy.co.uk

Area Networks Ltd, Sunningdale Ho, 11 George St, Altrincham, Cheshire, WA14 1RJ Tel: 0161-926 8484 Fax: 0161-926 8921

Aztech Microcentres Ltd, 322 Hemdean Road, Caversham, Reading, RG4 7QS Tel: 0118-946 6600 Fax: 0118-946 1076 E-mail: sales@aztechmicros.com

Azzurri Communications Ltd, Elmhirst Lane, Dodworth, Barnsley, South Yorkshire, S75 4LS Tel: (01226) 777111 Fax: (01226) 777100

Banbury Computers, 55 Middleton Road, Banbury, Oxon, OX16 3QR Tel: (01295) 272627E-mail: sales@banburycomputers.com

C B S L Softech, 10 Bridge Street, Hatherleigh, Okehampton, Devon, EX20 3HU Tel: (01837) 811133 Fax: (01837) 810782 E-mail: info@cbslsoftech.net

Cleanline Installations Ltd, Terminal House, Station Approach, Shepperton, Middlesex, TW17 8AS Tel: (01932) 260490 Fax: (01932) 227037 E-mail: cleanline@compuserve.com

CNS Computer Networks Ltd, Transport Hall, Gloucester Road, Avonmouth, Bristol, BS11 9AQ Tel: (0870) 7771650 Fax: (0870) 7771655 E-mail: sales@c-n-s.co.uk

Compex Computer Services, Heritage Works, First Floor Winterstoke Road, Weston-super-Mare, Avon, BS24 9AN Tel: (01934) 645044 Fax: (01934) 645077 E-mail: sales@compexcomputers.com

Complete Business Systems, Studio 3 Highfield Farm, Huncote Road, Stoney Stanton, Leicester, LE9 4DJ Tel: (01455) 271222 Fax: (01455) 271071

Computers For Schools & Education, 21 Bramble Bank, Frimley Green, Camberley, Surrey, GU16 6PN Tel: (01252) 836463 E-mail: james.findlay@lineone.net

Dacoll Ltd, Gardners Lane, Bathgate, West Lothian, EH48 1TP Tel: (01506) 815000 Fax: (01506) 656012 E-mail: sales@dacoll.co.uk

Data Strategy Ltd, 44 Kingswood Road, London, SW19 3NE Tel: (020) 8296 0643 E-mail: info@datadtrategy.com

Discovery Computer Services Ltd, Burnham Business Park, Springfield Road, Burnham-on-Crouch, Essex, CM0 8TE Tel: (01621) 786860 Fax: (01621) 786861 E-mail: info@buy-it-back.com

Doncaster Computer Exchange, 250 Great North Road, Woodlands, Doncaster, South Yorkshire, DN6 7HP Tel: (01302) 728737 Fax: (01302) 725129 E-mail: dceexchange@aol.com

Durham Computer Centre Ltd, 6 New Elvet, Durham, DH1 3AQ Tel: 0191-386 8989 Fax: 0191-384 4556 E-mail: info@durhamcomputercentre.co.uk

Elmbrook Computer Services Ltd, Alpha Place, Garth Road, Morden, Surrey, SM4 4TS Tel: (020) 8410 4444 Fax: (020) 8410 4445

Emc Computer Systems, E M C Tower, Great West Road, Brentford, Middlesex, TW8 9AN Tel: (0870) 6087777 Fax: (0870) 6087788 E-mail: sales@uk.emc.com

Equinox Meridian, 18 Haycroft Road, Surbiton, Surrey, KT6 5AU Tel: (020) 8397 7347 Fax: (020) 8397 2652 E-mail: sales@equinoxmeridian.com

G B Business Supplies, 17 Leek Road, Werrington, Stoke-on-Trent, ST9 0HX Tel: (01782) 550830 Fax: (01782) 550813 E-mail: info@gbbusiness.demon.co.uk

▶ G D S Computer Systems Ltd, 19 St. Lawrence Way, Hurstpierpoint, Hassocks, West Sussex, BN6 9SH Tel: (01273) 832841 E-mail: info@gdsit.co.uk

Information Technology Services, 4 Ashley Road, Epsom, Surrey, KT18 5AX Tel: (01372) 800466 Fax: (01372) 740544 E-mail: sales@it-services.co.uk

Intel Investments UK Ltd, Pipers Way, Swindon, SN3 1RJ Tel: (01793) 403000 Fax: (01793) 641440

Interface D C B Technolgy Ltd, Tyler Close, Normanton Industrial Estate, Normanton, West Yorkshire, WF6 1RL Tel: (01924) 224929 Fax: (01924) 224939 E-mail: general@interf.co.uk

IT Networks Ltd, 19-21 High Street, Coleshill, Birmingham, B46 1AY Tel: 0870 1616611 Fax: 0870 1616622 E-mail: info@acutec.co.uk

J T S Datacom Ltd, 2 Crossfields Close, Shinfield, Reading, RG2 9AY Tel: (0845) 6443193 Fax: (0845) 6448195 E-mail: info@jtsdata.com

Lanway Corporate Business Systems Ltd, Network 65 Business Park, Burnley, Lancashire, BB11 5TE Tel: (01282) 418888 Fax: (01282) 418861 E-mail: sales@lanway.co.uk

M K Electric, The Arnold Centre, Paycocke Road, Basildon, Essex, SS14 3EA Tel: (01268) 563000 Fax: (01268) 563405 E-mail: mkorderingenquires@hornywell.com

Microlise Business Computing, Farrington Way, Eastwood, Nottingham, NG16 3AG Tel: (01773) 535111 Fax: (01773) 537373 E-mail: enquiries@microlise.co.uk

P C Computer Services, 16 South Avenue, Bognor Regis, West Sussex, PO21 3QS Tel: (01243) 820840 Fax: (01243) 842961 E-mail: sales@pc-computers.co.uk

P R R Computers, Duckworth Street, Blackburn, BB2 2JQ Tel: (01254) 664515 Fax: (01254) 664545 E-mail: sales@prrcomputers.co.uk

Paun Computers, Unit 26 Vernon Mill, Mersey Street, Stockport, Cheshire, SK1 2HX Tel: 0161-429 8855 Fax: 0161-429 8877

Pericom P.L.C., The Priory, Cosgrove, Milton Keynes, MK19 7JJ Tel: (01908) 265533 Fax: (01908) 265534 E-mail: sales@pericom.co.uk

Powersoft Computer Services, 4 Pelham Court, Pelham Place, Crawley, West Sussex, RH11 9SH Tel: (01293) 562730 Fax: (01293) 522006 E-mail: support@powersoft-services.co.uk

Profile 2000 Plus, 16 Swadford Street, Skipton, North Yorkshire, BD23 1RD Tel: (01756) 796622 Fax: 01756 709525

▶ Pyramid Computers, Langley Road, Burscough Industrial Estate, Ormskirk, Lancashire, L40 8JR Tel: (01704) 894857 Fax: (01704) 897814 E-mail: sales@pyramid-computers.co.uk

S M T Network Solutions Ltd, 20 Park Street, Princes Risborough, Buckinghamshire, HP27 9AH Tel: (01844) 275100 Fax: (01844) 275111 E-mail: info@smtnet.co.uk

Sales Stream, Independence House, Adelaide Street, Heywood, Lancashire, OL10 4HF Tel: (01706) 647462 Fax: (01706) 347956 E-mail: n.elliott@btclick.com

Sel Computers, Palace Building, Main Street, Grange-over-Sands, Cumbria, LA11 6AB Tel: (01539) 533222 Fax: (01539) 533303

Silicon City Distribution, 50 Temple Avenue, London, N20 9EH Tel: (020) 8445 5251 Fax: (0870) 7052314E-mail: sales@silcity.com

Supportive Ltd, Old Studios, Hyde Park Road, Leeds, LS6 1RU Tel: 0113-245 7302 Fax: 0113-245 7304 E-mail: post@supportive.co.uk

Sys Dynamics Ltd, Unit 3, Burley Road, Angel Court, Leeds, LS3 1BS Tel: 0113-244 2176 Fax: 0113-244 2168

T Q S Services Ltd, Unit 3 Hartley Park Farm Business Centre, Selborne Road, Alton, Hants, GU34 3HD Tel: (01420) 511727 Fax: (01420) 511728

Talos Ltd, Prospect House, 20 High Street, Brasted, Westerham, Kent, TN16 1RG Tel: (01959) 561124 Fax: (01959) 561402 E-mail: info@quantus.co.uk

Telephone Services Ltd, Phonex House, 18 Suffolk Street, Pendleton, Salford, M6 6DU Tel: 0161-737 7055 Fax: 0161-737 7055

Teqnet Ltd, 5 Windsor Court, Clive Road, Redditch, Worcestershire, B97 4BT Tel: (01527) 592100 Fax: (01527) 592113

Tyco Electronics, Kinmel Park, Bodelwyddan, Rhyl, Clwyd, LL18 5TZ Tel: (01745) 584545 Fax: (01745) 584780 E-mail: admin@pinacl.com

Vantage Micro Systems Ltd, 2 Airfield Park, Cheddington Lane, Long Marston, Tring, Hertfordshire, HP23 4QR Tel: (01296) 668966 Fax: (01296) 662798 E-mail: sales@vantageit.co.uk

W M S Development Services P.L.C., 45 Beech St, London, EC2Y 8AD Tel: (020) 7614 4828 Fax: (020) 7614 4801

Wadsworth Electronics Ltd, Central Avenue, West Molesey, Surrey, KT8 2QB Tel: (020) 8268 7000 Fax: (020) 8268 6565 E-mail: info@wadsworth.co.uk

Xperience Peg Associates Ltd, Belmont House, Lambdon Road, London, SW20 0LW Tel: (020) 8880 4440 Fax: (020) 8880 4442 E-mail: sales@xperience-group.co.uk

LOCAL EXHAUST VENTILATION (LEV) TESTING

Ventek Ltd, Unit 5, Starcrest Industrial Estate, Talbots Lane, Brierley Hill, West Midlands, DY5 2YT Tel: (01384) 79414 Fax: (01384) 79434 E-mail: sales@ventek.co.uk

LOCATION AGENTS, FILM/ STILLS/VIDEO PHOTOGRAPHY

▶ Asvisual - Architectural Photography, 2 Eddy Street, Berkhamsted, Hertfordshire, HP4 1DQ Tel: (07747) 103334 E-mail: andy@asvisual.co.uk

▶ Beverley Foster Wedding Photographer, 14 Moorfields, Leek, Staffordshire, ST13 5LU Tel: (01538) 386403 E-mail: admin@weddingstorybook.co.uk

▶ Captured Image Photography, 7 Dunstans Croft, Mayfield, East Sussex, TN20 6UH Tel: 01435 874894 E-mail: andy@capturedimagephotography.co.uk

▶ Chris Williams Photography, 31 Manor House Road, Glastonbury, Somerset, BA6 9DF Tel: 01458 835946

David Foster Photography and Video, 4, Southfields, Leek, Staffordshire, ST13 5LR Tel: 01538 386403 E-mail: admin@weddingstorybook.co.uk

▶ Hughescrafts, Hughescrafts, 33 Thorntondale Drive, Marton Lodge, Bridlington, East Riding of Yorkshire, YO16 6GW Tel: (01262) 602180 E-mail: john@hughescrafts.com

Marcus Johnson Studios, 8 Ladywood Drive, Aboyne, Aberdeenshire, AB34 5HA Tel: (01339) 886066 Fax: (01339) 886636

▶ Lightbox Photography, 19 Lynton Drive, Southport, Merseyside, PR8 4QP Tel: (01704) 566066 E-mail: sales@the-lightbox.com

▶ Location25, 25 Clapham Common South Side, London, SW4 7AB Tel: (020) 7720 6514 Fax: (020) 7498 0040 E-mail: info@location25.com

▶ Patricia Taylor, Potter Row, Great Missenden, Buckinghamshire, HP16 9LT Tel: (01494) 868376 Fax: (01494) 868376 E-mail: patriciataylorphotography@yahoo.co.uk

Peters David Photography, Unit 14 Fordhouse Road Indust Estate, Bushbury, Wolverhampton, WV10 9XB Tel: (01902) 397739 Fax: (01902) 397001 E-mail: info@davidpeters.co.uk

▶ Scotavia Images, Birch View Cottage, High Street, Grantown-on-Spey, Morayshire, PH26 3EN Tel: (01479) 872144 E-mail: gary@smasher.demon.co.uk

▶ Wayne Paulo Photo-Stock, 14 Neville Avenue, Thornton-Cleveleys, Lancashire, FY5 3BG Tel: (01253) 864598 E-mail: wayne@photo-stock.co.uk

LOCATION FINDING COMPANIES, FILM OR TELEVISION ETC

▶ Location25, 25 Clapham Common South Side, London, SW4 7AB Tel: (020) 7720 6514 Fax: (020) 7498 0040 E-mail: info@location25.com

LOCATION PHOTOGRAPHERS

▶ Roger Askew, 14 Winterborne Road, Abingdon, Oxfordshire, OX14 1AJ Tel: (07971) 404571 E-mail: roger@rogeraskewphotography.co.uk

LOCK KEYS

Countplace Ltd, PO Box 52, Littlehampton, West Sussex, BN17 5RZ Tel: (01903) 716802 Fax: (01903) 715896 E-mail: sales@nukey.co.uk
Keys of Steel Ltd, Stringes Lane, Willenhall, West Midlands, WV13 1LF Tel: (01902) 606816 Fax: (01902) 636733 E-mail: sales@willenhall-locks.co.uk
R & R Security Services, 171 South Ealing Road, London, W5 4QP Tel: (020) 8560 3413 Fax: (020) 8560 3413 E-mail: info@randrsecurity.com

LOCK MAINTENANCE OR REPAIR

Cheshire Lock & Safe Co., Unit 3 Fence Avenue Industrial Estate, Macclesfield, Cheshire, SK10 1LT Tel: (01625) 614178 Fax: (01625) 617898 E-mail: sales@cheshirelock.co.uk
Dyno-Locks, 143 Maple Road, Surbiton, Surrey, KT6 4BJ Tel: (020) 8481 2200 Fax: (020) 8481 2288 E-mail: postmaster@dyno.com

LOCK WASHERS

Batey Metallic Packing Co. Ltd, Back Ellison Road, Gateshead, Tyne & Wear, NE11 9TR Tel: 0191-460 4167 Fax: 0191-493 2148

LOCKERS

A M P Wire Ltd, Sun Iron Works, Ward Street, Chadderton, Oldham, OL9 9EX Tel: 0161-620 7250 Fax: 0161-688 5566 E-mail: pam@ampwire.co.uk
Alkal Leisure, Unit 24, Lyon Road, Walton-on-Thames, Surrey, KT12 3PU Tel: (0845) 2305656 Fax: (0845) 2305676 E-mail: info@akc-uk.com
▶ Dyfed Industrial Developments, Graig, Burry Port, Dyfed, SA16 0BJ Tel: (01554) 832777 Fax: (01554) 832777 E-mail: did@draenog.freeserve.co.uk
Garran Lockers Ltd, Garran House, Nantgarw Road, Caerphilly, Mid Glamorgan, CF83 1AQ Tel: (0845) 6588600 Fax: (0845) 6588601 E-mail: garran@garran-lockers.co.uk
Global Industries North West Ltd, 36 Arkwright Road, Astmoor Industrial Estate, Runcorn, Cheshire, WA7 1NU Tel: (01928) 577846 Fax: (01928) 560480 E-mail: info@globalindustries.co.uk
Helmsman, Northern Way, Bury St. Edmunds, Suffolk, IP32 6NH Tel: (01284) 727600 Fax: (01284) 727601 E-mail: sales@helmsman.co.uk
Kingstonian Storage Equipment Ltd, 1 Phoenix Enterprise Park, Grovehill Road, Beverley, North Humberside, HU17 0JG Tel: (01482) 868055 Fax: (01482) 872558 E-mail: paul@kingsstorage.fsnet.co.uk
Link Lockers, Link House, Halesfield 6, Telford, Shropshire, TF7 4LN Tel: (01952) 682380 Fax: (01952) 684312 E-mail: sales@linklockers.co.uk
Locktec Ltd, Unit 7-11, Pentlandfield Business Park, Roslin, Midlothian, EH25 9RE Tel: 0131-445 7788 Fax: 0131-445 7527 E-mail: sales@locktec.net
M S Storage Equipment Ltd, 78 Park Lane, Poynton, Stockport, Cheshire, SK12 1RE Tel: (01625) 858555 Fax: (01625) 858262 E-mail: sales@msstorage.co.uk
Pow Sport & Leisure Co., PO Box 28, London, W4 4WT Tel: (0870) 3503650 Fax: (0870) 3503651 E-mail: info@pow-sport.co.uk
▶ Simply Direct, Adelphi Mill, Grimshaw Lane, Bollington, Macclesfield, Cheshire, SK10 5JB Tel: (01625) 576527 Fax: (01625) 576545 E-mail: sales@simplydirect.net

LOCKFORMING MACHINES

Bulldog Industrial Holdings Ltd, Carrington Road, Stockport, Cheshire, SK1 2JT Tel: 0161-477 0775 Fax: 0161-480 0133 E-mail: sales@bulldogprocess.com
M S Storage Equipment Ltd, 78 Park Lane, Poynton, Stockport, Cheshire, SK12 1RE Tel: (01625) 858555 Fax: (01625) 858262 E-mail: sales@msstorage.co.uk

LOCKING SYSTEMS

▶ Claymore Lock & Alarm Co., 3 Hardgate, Haddington, East Lothian, EH41 3JW Tel: (01620) 829550 Fax: (01620) 829751
▶ Lock Services Ltd, Unit 2e Queensway Enterprise Centre, Queensway, New Milton, Hampshire, BH25 5NN Tel: (01425) 623093 Fax: (01425) 638501 E-mail: sales@lock-services.co.uk

LOCKOUT KITS

▶ The Key Shop Ltd, 14D High Street, Lutterworth, Leicestershire, LE17 4AD Tel: (01455) 554999 E-mail: ian@thekeyshop.co.uk

LOCKS

Aldridge & Son Wholesale Ltd, 50 Queen Street, Salford, M3 7DQ Tel: 0161-828 0828 Fax: 0161-828 0838 E-mail: sales@e-aldridge.co.uk
Banham Security Ltd, 10 Pascal Street, London, SW8 4SH Tel: (020) 7622 5151 Fax: (020) 7498 2461 E-mail: security@banham.com
C H Wood Security Bradford Ltd, 221 Wakefield Road, Bradford, West Yorkshire, BD4 7PE Tel: (01274) 725072 Fax: (01274) 731626 E-mail: info@woodsecurity.co.uk
Campbell & Mabbs Liverpool Ltd, 1 Regent Street, Liverpool, L3 7BN Tel: 0151-236 1555 Fax: 0151-236 1698 E-mail: camabbs@aol.com
Cheshire Lock & Safe Co., Unit 3 Fence Avenue Industrial Estate, Macclesfield, Cheshire, SK10 1LT Tel: (01625) 614178 Fax: (01625) 617898 E-mail: sales@cheshirelock.co.uk
Codringtons Ltd, 38 Crawley Road, London, N22 6AG Tel: (020) 8889 8494 Fax: (020) 8889 6731 E-mail: admin@codringtons.com
Cromwell Security & Fire Services Ltd, 72 Fortune Green Road, London, NW6 1DS Tel: (020) 7435 0334 Fax: (020) 7794 3384
Door Spring Supplies Co, 25 Knox Road, Wellingborough, Northamptonshire, NN8 1HW Tel: (01933) 222431 Fax: (01933) 222531 E-mail: tony@autodoorsprings.co.uk
France Security, 176 East Street, Epsom, Surrey, KT17 1ES Tel: (01372) 726575 Fax: (01372) 726575
Hopkins, Prospect House, Jameson Road, Birmingham, B6 7SJ Tel: (0845) 4563018 Fax: (0845) 4563019 E-mail: enquires@hopkinsfittings.co.uk
J B Architectural Ironmongery Ltd, Avis Way, Newhaven, East Sussex, BN9 0DU Tel: (01273) 514961 Fax: (01273) 516764 E-mail: info@jbai.co.uk
J L M Security, 43 Rosebank Terrace, Aberdeen, AB11 6LQ Tel: (01224) 594200 Fax: (01224) 584571 E-mail: jlmlocks@aol.com
J & T Locks Bolts & Bars Ltd, Victoria Works, Victoria Street, Stoke-On-Trent, ST4 6HA Tel: (01782) 349440 Fax: (01782) 349449 E-mail: sales@storagebins.co.uk
J&T Group Ltd, PO Box 5 Victoria Works, Stoke-on-Trent, ST4 6HA Tel: (01782) 202545 Fax: (01782) 349449 E-mail: sales@storagebins.co.uk
Lockwise Lock Smiths, Border Road, Wallsend, Tyne & Wear, NE28 6RX Tel: 0191-263 0003 Fax: 0191-263 0075 E-mail: enquiries@lockwise.co.uk
Noble Integrated Systems, 211-213 Eaton Road, West Derby, Liverpool, L12 2AG Tel: 0151-228 8364 Fax: 0151-280 5145
North East Lock & Key Co., 31 Harvey Close, Crowther, Washington, Tyne & Wear, NE38 0AB Tel: 0191-416 1843 Fax: 0191-415 0995
Protectall Lock & Safe Co. Ltd, 445b Stratford Road, Sparkhill, Birmingham, B11 4LB Tel: 0121-773 1609 Fax: 0121-773 8401 E-mail: sales@protectall-security.co.uk
Wadsworth Security Products, Unit 1 Epsom Downs Metro Centre, Waterfield, Tadworth, Surrey, KT20 5EZ Tel: (01737) 360512 Fax: (01737) 370475

LOCKS, CABINET/DRAWER/ENCLOSURE

A Lewis & Sons Willenhall Ltd, 47 Church Street, Willenhall, West Midlands, WV13 1QW Tel: (01902) 605428 Fax: (01902) 601181 E-mail: lewislocksltd@aol.com
Worrall Locks Ltd, Erebus Works, Albion Road, Willenhall, West Midlands, WV13 1NH Tel: (01902) 605038 Fax: (01902) 633558 E-mail: sales@worrall-locks.co.uk

LOCKS, CAM/PUSH

A Lewis & Sons Willenhall Ltd, 47 Church Street, Willenhall, West Midlands, WV13 1QW Tel: (01902) 605428 Fax: (01902) 601181 E-mail: lewislocksltd@aol.com
Baton Lock Ltd, Baton House, 4TH Avenue The Village, Trafford Park, Manchester, M17 1DB Tel: 0161-877 4444 Fax: 0161-877 4545 E-mail: kevin.bratt@batonlockuk.com
Davenport Burgess, 47 Wednesfield Road, Willenhall, West Midlands, WV13 1AL Tel: (01902) 366448 Fax: (01902) 602472 E-mail: sales@davenport-burgess.com

LOCKS, ELECTROMAGNETIC, ACCESS CONTROL

Adams Rite Europe Ltd, 6 Moreton Industrial Estate, London Road, Swanley, Kent, BR8 8TZ Tel: (01322) 668024 Fax: (01322) 660996 E-mail: info@adamsrite.co.uk

LOCKS, ELECTRONIC/ELECTRIC

Clarke Instruments Ltd, Distloc House, Old Sarum Airfield, Old Sarum, Salisbury, SP4 6DZ Tel: (01722) 323451 Fax: (01722) 335154 E-mail: sales@clarke-inst.com
▶ Lock Services Ltd, Unit 2e Queensway Enterprise Centre, Queensway, New Milton, Hampshire, BH25 5NN Tel: (01425) 623093 Fax: (01425) 638501 E-mail: sales@lock-services.co.uk
Magnetic Solutions, Unit B7, Crabtree Road, Thorpe Industrial Estate, Egham, Surrey, TW20 8RN Tel: (01784) 438666 Fax: (01784) 438777 E-mail: trushton@magsol.co.uk
Specialized Security Products Ltd, Unit 18, Park Farm Industrial Estate, Ermine Street, Buntingford, Hertfordshire, SG9 9AZ Tel: (01763) 274223 Fax: (01763) 273515 E-mail: sales@specialized-security.co.uk
Telco Security Locks Ltd, Connaught Road, Bournemouth, BH7 6NA Tel: (01202) 420444 Fax: (01202) 432073 E-mail: sales@telcolocks.fsnet.co.uk

LOCKS, SUITCASE/BRIEFCASE/TRUNK

Wilkes Security Products Ltd, Tipton Road, Tividale, Oldbury, West Midlands, B69 3HY Tel: 0121-520 9666 Fax: 0121-520 9667

LOCKSMITH FITTING OR INSTALLATION SPECIALIST SERVICES

▶ 3 County Locksmiths, 1 Tudor Court, Gillingham, Dorset, SP8 4TF Tel: (01747) 826311 Fax: (01747) 826311 E-mail: mark@3countylocksmiths.co.uk
▶ A A Aardvark Locksmiths, Dane Road, Coventry, CV2 4JW Tel: (0845) 0710126 E-mail: ray@raygibbins.wanadoo.co.uk
A B Rooms & Son Ltd, 4 Field Street, Hull, HU9 1HS Tel: (01482) 320260 Fax: (01482) 219384 E-mail: enquiries@abrooms.co.uk
A Coventry Locksmith, 58 Beake Avenue, Coventry, CV6 3AR Tel: (024) 7660 1222 Fax: (024) 7660 1222 E-mail: coventrylockmiths@live.co.uk
A & D Lock & Key Co. Ltd, 6-7 Hockley Hill, Birmingham, B18 5AA Tel: 0121-554 7894 Fax: 0121-554 8220 E-mail: reconditionedsafes@btconnect.com
▶ A & J Locksmiths, 346 Lansbury Drive, Hayes, Middlesex, UB4 8SW Tel: (0800) 6951221 E-mail: john@a-jlocksmiths.com
▶ A & J Locksmiths, 34 Iveagh Close, Northwood, Middlesex, HA6 2TE Tel: (0800) 6951771 E-mail: john@a-jlocksmiths.com
▶ A10 Security, 78 Windmill Hill, Enfield, Middlesex, EN2 7AY Tel: (0800) 8496769 E-mail: Georgina@acornsecurity.co.uk
AAA Aardvark Locksmiths, Unit 9, Solihull Road, Shirley, Solihull, West Midlands, B90 3HB Tel: (0845) 0710128 E-mail: aardvark@raygibbins.wanadoo.co.uk
▶ AAA Aardvark Locksmiths, Unit 8, Station Road, Studley, West Midlands, B80 7HS Tel: (0845) 0760710 E-mail: molly@raygibbins.wanadoo.co.uk
Aaaa Aardvark, 24 School Lane, Solihull, West Midlands, B91 2QQ Tel: (0845) 0710125 E-mail: spud@raygibbins.wanadoo.co.uk
Aar Dee Locks & Shutters Ltd, 16 Boswell Square, Hillington, Hillington Industrial Estate, Glasgow, G52 4BQ Tel: 0141-810 3444 Fax: 0141-810 3777 E-mail: sales@aaree.co.uk
▶ Aardvark Locksmiths, 604a Bristol Road, Selly Oak, Birmingham, B29 6BQ Tel: (0845) 0760724 E-mail: buddy@raygibbins.wanadoo.co.uk
▶ Aardvark Locksmiths, Unit 19 Pochard Close, Kidderminster, Worcestershire, DY10 4UB Tel: (01562) 750077 E-mail: ray@raygibbins.wanadoo.co.uk
Abbeylocks Suffolk Locksmiths, 12 Waveney Road, Bury St. Edmunds, Suffolk, IP32 6JX Tel: (01284) 700104 E-mail: abbeylocks@chason.fsnet.co.uk
Abbra Security, 127 Charlemont Road, London, E6 6HD Tel: (020) 8552 7160
▶ Abc, 15 Goulburn Road, Norwich, NR7 9UX Tel: (01603) 438491 Fax: (01603) 466710
Abel Alarm Co Ltd, 2 Discovery House, Cook Way, Taunton, Somerset, TA2 6BJ Tel: (01823) 333868 Fax: (01823) 337852 E-mail: info.taunton@abelalarm.co.uk
Acro Security Engineers, 43 Compton Close, London, NW1 3QS Tel: (020) 7388 6300 Fax: (020) 7388 6400
▶ Addis Locksmiths, 36 lawrence close, Andover, Hampshire, SP10 3SY Tel: 01264 350980 E-mail: info@addislocksmiths.co.uk
▶ Afford-Able Locksmiths, 116 Albert Road, Epsom, Surrey, KT17 4EL Tel: 01372 725916 Fax: 07970 093934 E-mail: nick.palladino@ntlworld.com
Aldridge Holdings Ltd, Silca House, 32-34 Eagle Wharf Road, London, N1 7EG Tel: (020) 7253 5665 Fax: (020) 7251 2601 E-mail: sales@e-aldridge.co.uk
▶ Arc Locksmiths, 181 Mauldeth Road, Manchester, M19 1BA Tel: 0161-256 2551 E-mail: arclocks@yahoo.com
Associated Security Group Ltd, 59 London Road, Wallington, Surrey, SM6 7HW Tel: (020) 8669 7722 Fax: (020) 8669 9890 E-mail: sales@associatedsecuritygroup.co.uk
Barnet Lock & Security, 123-125 Baker Street, Enfield, Middlesex, EN1 3HA Tel: (020) 8342 0040 Fax: (020) 8342 0230 E-mail: barnetlock@btconnect.com
Barrs Security Locksmiths Ltd, 329 Fulham Palace Road, London, SW6 6TE Tel: (020) 7731 4502 Fax: (020) 7731 4502
Barry Bros Security, 121-123 Praed Street, London, W2 1RL Tel: (0800) 3168547 Fax: (020) 7262 5005 E-mail: info@barrybros.com
Bickers, 6 Maple Close, St. Columb, Cornwall, TR9 6SL Tel: (07977) 147294 E-mail: info@bickerslocksmiths.co.uk
Bramah Security Centres Ltd, 31 Oldbury Place, London, W1U 5PT Tel: (020) 7486 1757 Fax: (020) 7935 2779 E-mail: locksmiths@bramah.co.uk
▶ Brians Locksmiths, 125 Rotterdam Road, Lowestoft, Suffolk, NR32 2EY Tel: (01502) 572176 Fax: (01502) 572176 E-mail: brianslocksmiths@aol.com
Capital Lock & Safe Company Ltd, 91 Lancaster Road, Enfield, Middlesex, EN2 0DN Tel: (020) 8367 2775 Fax: (020) 8366 5091
Chubb Locks Custodial Services Ltd, Well Lane, Wednesfield, Wolverhampton, WV11 1TB Tel: (01902) 867730 Fax: (01902) 867789
Clares Of Croydon Ltd, 54 Tamworth Road, Croydon, CR0 1XW Tel: (020) 8688 7952 Fax: (020) 8688 1867
▶ Cobblers Bench, 128a Central Drive, Blackpool, FY1 5DY Tel: (07890) 307647 E-mail: cobblersbench@fsmail.net
▶ Combined Security, 79 Pickford Lane, Bexleyheath, Kent, DA7 4RW Tel: (020) 8304 6111 Fax: (020) 8304 6555 E-mail: info@combinedsecurity.co.uk
Cooper Kitchen, 48 Southgate, Elland, West Yorkshire, HX5 0DQ Tel: (01422) 372577 Fax: (01422) 372577
Cowper Shaw Locksmiths Ltd, 33-34 Blandford Street, Sunderland, SR1 3JJ Tel: 0191-567 2882 Fax: 0191-564 0383
D Lycett & Sons Ltd, Long Street, Premier Business Park, Walsall, WS2 9DY Tel: (01922) 625393 Fax: (01922) 616761 E-mail: donshir@tiscali.co.uk
Dockerills Brighton Ltd, 3abc Church Street, Brighton, BN1 1UJ Tel: (01273) 607434 Fax: (01273) 679771 E-mail: dockerills@dockerills.demon.co.uk
▶ Drummond Security Ltd, 44 The Broadway, Darkes Lane, Potters Bar, Hertfordshire, EN6 2HW Tel: (01707) 644454 Fax: (01707) 651314 E-mail: enquiries@drummondsecurity.com
Dyno-Locks, 143 Maple Road, Surbiton, Surrey, KT6 4BJ Tel: (020) 8481 2200 Fax: (020) 8481 2288 E-mail: postmaster@dyno.com
Em Secure, 3 Rolleston Close, Market Harborough, Leicestershire, LE16 8BZ Tel: (07891) 340168 Fax: (01858) 432756 E-mail: info@emsecure.co.uk
▶ Express Maintenance Ltd, 122 Holderness Road, Hull, HU9 1JP Tel: (01482) 325000 Fax: (01482) 325000 E-mail: maintenancecrew@aol.com
Farringdon Locksmith & Tool Supplies Ltd, 29 Exmouth Market, London, EC1R 4QL Tel: (020) 7837 5179 Fax: (020) 7278 0224
Fortress Lock & Safe Co., 107 Brixton Hill, London, SW2 1AA Tel: (020) 8674 6657 Fax: (020) 8674 6439 E-mail: info@fortresslock.co.uk
Franchi Hardware Merchants, 144-146 Kentish Town Road, London, NW1 9QB Tel: (020) 7267 3138 Fax: (020) 7485 4637 E-mail: sales@franchi.co.uk
Franchi Locks & Tools Ltd, 278 Holloway Road, London, N7 6NE Tel: (020) 7607 2200 Fax: (020) 7700 4050 E-mail: info@franchi.co.uk
Furneaux Industrial Supplies Ltd, 5 Sinclair House, Hastings Street, London, WC1H 9PZ Tel: (020) 7387 8450 Fax: (020) 7388 0197 E-mail: furnlocks@fsbdial.co.uk
G Franchi & Sons Ltd, 329-331 Grays Inn Road, London, WC1X 8BZ Tel: (020) 7278 8628 Fax: (020) 7833 9049 E-mail: tony@franchi.fsbusiness.co.uk
Greenbow Services, 17 Murhall Street, Stoke-on-Trent, ST6 4BL Tel: (01782) 867038 E-mail: esme.w@ntlworld.com
Greenlight Locksmith, 42 Preston Parade, Whitstable, Kent, CT5 4AJ Tel: (01227) 274738 E-mail: greenlightlocks@btinternet.com
Guardian Security Group (UK) Ltd, 5 Axis, Hawkfield Business Park, Hawkfield Way, Bristol, BS14 0BY Tel: 0117-946 5505 Fax: 0117-946 5506 E-mail: sales@guardiansecurity.co.uk
GWL Security Ltd, 10 Row 48, Great Yarmouth, Norfolk, NR30 1HU Tel: (01493) 857434 Fax: (01493) 857434
Harrison Locks, Pump Street, Worcester, WR1 2QX Tel: (01905) 20999 Fax: (01527) 892612 E-mail: harrison.lock@btinternet.com
Initial Fire & Security Ltd, Enterprise House, Waldeck Road, Maidenhead, Berkshire, SL6 8BR Tel: (01628) 783561 Fax: (01628) 776953 E-mail: j.sharam@ies.uk
Insafe International Ltd, Westcombe House 4th Floor, 2-4 Mount Ephraim, Tunbridge Wells, Kent, TN4 8AS Tel: (01892) 533000 Fax: (01892) 525100 E-mail: sales@insafe.co.uk
▶ Invictus Locks & Security, 10c Carnock Road, Dunfermline, Fife, KY12 9AX Tel: (07726) 012000 E-mail: invictuslocks@tiscali.co.uk
J Beattie & Son Ltd, Marlborough Place, Liverpool, L3 2BZ Tel: 0151-236 8721 Fax: 0151-236 2639 E-mail: sales@beattieslocksmith.co.uk
J L M Security, 43 Rosebank Terrace, Aberdeen, AB11 6LQ Tel: (01224) 594200 Fax: (01224) 584571 E-mail: jlmlocks@aol.com

▶ indicates data change since last edition

LOCKSMITH FITTING OR INSTALLATION SPECIALIST SERVICES – *continued*

J O'Neill & Co. Ltd, 7 Bromley Street, Hull, HU2 0PY Tel: (01482) 320146 Fax: (01482) 589968

▶ JB Locksmith, 33 Park Road, Conisbrough, Doncaster, South Yorkshire, DN12 2EQ Tel: (01709) 867361 Fax: (01709) 867361 E-mail: john@jblocksmithdoncaster.co.uk

Keyways Security Systems Ltd, Keyways House, 337 Hale Road, Hale Barns, Altrincham, Cheshire, WA15 8SX Tel: 0161-980 6655 Fax: 0161-904 0768 E-mail: info@keyways.co.uk

Kwick Key & Lock Service, 16 Westow Street, Upper Norwood, London, SE19 3AH Tel: (020) 8653 8272 Fax: (020) 8768 1214 E-mail: guythompson@yahoo.com

Lewis Security Group Ltd, 1 Hanlon Court, Royal Industrial Estate, Jarrow, Tyne & Wear, NE32 3HR Tel: 0191-496 2400 Fax: 0191-496 2401 E-mail: sales@lsgroup.com

▶ Linacre Locksmiths, 41 Linacre Avenue, Norwich, NR7 8JZ Tel: (01603) 408528 E-mail: linacrelocks@aol.com

Lincoln Security Ltd, 79-83 High Street, Lincoln, LN5 8AA Tel: (01522) 532038 Fax: (01522) 536060E-mail: enquiries@lincolnsecurity.co.uk

▶ Liverpool Locksmith, 46 Merlin Street, Liverpool, L8 8HZ Tel: 0151-281 5392 Fax: 0151-281 5392 E-mail: locksmith@safe-mail.net

Lock Assist, 139 Royal George Road, Burgess Hill, West Sussex, RH15 9TD Tel: (01444) 244344 Fax: (01444) 241324 E-mail: info@lockassist.co.uk

▶ Locks Express, Norland, Edenmount Road, Grange-over-Sands, Cumbria, LA11 6BN Tel: (0800) 7831104

▶ Locksmiths, 235 Earls Court Road, London, SW5 9FE Tel: (0800) 6951908 E-mail: john@a-jlocksmiths.com

Lockwise Lock Smiths, Border Road, Wallsend, Tyne & Wear, NE28 6RX Tel: 0191-263 0003 Fax: 0191-263 0075 E-mail: enquiries@lockwise.co.uk

London Lock & Safe Co., 10 Great Eastern Street, London, EC2A 3NT Tel: (020) 7241 3535 Fax: (020) 7650 8999 E-mail: londonlocksafe7@btconnect.com

▶ London-Locksmiths.co.uk, Stanley Road, Woodford, London, E18 Tel: (0800) 0151552 E-mail: safesecure@btinternet.com

▶ Londons Cheapest Locksmith, 9 Hurstfield Crescent, Hayes, Middlesex, UB4 8DN Tel: (0808) 1661066 E-mail: robertwells99@hotmail.co.uk

Lumsden Security, 128-130 John Street, Aberdeen, AB25 1LE Tel: (01224) 632428 Fax: (01224) 645656 E-mail: sales@lumsdensecurity.co.uk

▶ M & A Locksmiths, 31 Nelson Road, Uxbridge, Middlesex, UB10 0PU Tel: (0800) 6954195 E-mail: john@a-jlocksmiths.com

M L Banfield & Sons Ltd, 1-2 Little Western Street, Brighton, BN1 2QH Tel: (01273) 737622 Fax: (01273) 720950 E-mail: philip@banfields.co.uk

M S Services, 18 Esk Place, Aberdeen, AB16 6SQ Tel: (01224) 691742 Fax: (01224) 691742 E-mail: msservices@fsmai8l.net

▶ Andy Mace Locksmith, 67 West Hill, Portishead, Bristol, BS20 6LG Tel: (01275) 844879 E-mail: andenash@aol.com

Makesafe Ltd, 34 Balls Road, Prenton, Merseyside, CH43 5RE Tel: 0151-653 8404 Fax: 0151-653 8404

▶ Mark 1 Locks, 6 Ascot Road, Gravesend, Kent, DA12 5AL Tel: (01474) 747660 E-mail: 24hr@mark1locks.com

▶ Omega Mobile Locksmiths, 11 Wensleydale Avenue, Ilford, Essex, IG5 0NA Tel: (020) 8550 1155 Fax: (020) 8220 5810 E-mail: malcolm@omegamobilelocksmith.co.uk

▶ Oxlocks, 9 Marlborough Place, Charlbury, Chipping Norton, Oxfordshire, OX7 3SH Tel: (01608) 811418 E-mail: john@oxlocks.co.uk

P S L Access Control, 8 Curtis Road, Epsom, Surrey, KT19 0LG Tel: (020) 8337 0517 Fax: (020) 8390 6972 E-mail: paul@pslac.freeserve.co.uk

Poitdell Ltd, Slaney Place, Headcorn Road, Staplehurst, Tonbridge, Kent, TN12 0DT Tel: (01580) 891020 Fax: (01580) 890132

Reeder Lock & Safe Co. Ltd, 587 Barking Road, London, E13 9EZ Tel: (020) 7476 5450 Fax: (020) 8503 4145

Rentrifone Ltd, Premier House, 309 Ballards Lane, London, N12 8NE Tel: (020) 8455 3304 Fax: (020) 8609 0627 E-mail: rentrifone@hotmail.co.uk

Romford Securities Ltd, 34 Victoria Road, Romford, RM1 2JH Tel: (01708) 727383 Fax: (01708) 727307 E-mail: romford.security@btconect.com

S J H Sparkes & Sons Ltd, 20 Devonshire Road, Cambridge, CB1 2BH Tel: (01223) 356172 Fax: (01223) 356172

▶ St Annes, 26 St. Annes Road West, Lytham St. Annes, Lancashire, FY8 1RF Tel: (01253) 727575 Fax: (01253) 727575 E-mail: keycutters@blueyonder.co.uk

Saxon Security Locks, 208d Mitcham Road, London, SW17 9NN Tel: (020) 8767 6281 Fax: (020) 8767 7381

Securicare Systems, 45 Shore Road, East Wittering, Chichester, West Sussex, PO20 8DY Tel: (01243) 672634 Fax: (01243) 672634E-mail: securicaresystems@email.com

Security 201, 332 Goring Road, Goring-by-Sea, Worthing, West Sussex, BN12 4PE Tel: (01903) 242902 Fax: (01903) 242618 E-mail: info@security201.co.uk

Severn Valley Lock & Safe, 9-10 Comberton Road, Kidderminster, Worcestershire, DY10 1UA Tel: (01562) 829406 Fax: (01562) 864089 E-mail: sales@severnlocks.co.uk

South London Lock Service Ltd, 190 High Street, London, SE20 7QB Tel: (020) 8778 6657 Fax: (020) 8778 6657

Star Security Systems Ltd, 40E Kilburn High Road, London, NW6 5UA Tel: (020) 7625 1001 Fax: (020) 8076 5122 E-mail: enquiries@starlocks.co.uk

Steel Security Services, 121 Boothferry Road, Hull, HU4 6EX Tel: (01482) 563732 Fax: (01482) 568353

▶ TPH Locksmiths, 27 Shustoke Road, Solihull, West Midlands, B91 2NR Tel: 0121 7041999 E-mail: tomhartop@msn.com

Upton Metal Works, Magdalene Road, Torquay, TQ1 4AF Tel: (01803) 814326 Fax: (01803) 200598

V & P Fox Engravers, 23 Cecil Court, London, WC2N 4EZ Tel: (020) 7836 2902 Fax: (020) 7379 8676 E-mail: foxloxs@aol.com

W D Bishop & Sons Ltd, 9 Park Road, London, N8 8TE Tel: (020) 8348 0149 Fax: (020) 8340 0929

▶ Warrington Lock & Safe, 8 Whitfield Avenue, Paddington, Warrington, WA1 3NF Tel: (01925) 851398 Fax: (01925) 851398 E-mail: suzi@warringtonlocks.co.uk

Weare Peter 1984 Ltd, 112-116 Hazelwick Road, Crawley, West Sussex, RH10 1NH Tel: (01293) 525673 Fax: (01293) 614054

West Riding Home Securities, 13 Cross Street, Wakefield, West Yorkshire, WF1 3BW Tel: (01924) 377158 Fax: (01924) 201448

Wulfruna Locksmith Ltd, Security Centre, 198 Penn Road, Wolverhampton, WV4 4AA Tel: (01902) 337267 Fax: (01902) 337267

Young & Young, 202 King Street, Hammersmith, London, W6 0RA Tel: (020) 8762 9800 Fax: (020) 8762 9500 E-mail: sales@youngandyoung/sercurity.com

LOCKSMITHS' TOOLS

▶ Afford-Able Locksmiths, 116 Albert Road, Epsom, Surrey, KT17 4EL Tel: 01372 725916 Fax: 07970 093934 E-mail: nick.palladino@ntlworld.com

Em Secure, 3 Rolleston Close, Market Harborough, Leicestershire, LE16 8BZ Tel: (07891) 340168 Fax: (01858) 432756 E-mail: info@emsecure.co.uk

R B Medical, 2 Alton Road Industrial Estate, Ross-on-Wye, Herefordshire, HR9 5ND Tel: (01989) 563958 Fax: (01989) 768267 E-mail: a.ross@rimbros.co.uk

LOCOMOTIVE REMOTE CONTROL SYSTEMS

Cattron Theimeg UK Ltd, Riverdene Industrial Estate, Molesey Road, Hersham, Walton-On-Thames, Surrey, KT12 4RY Tel: (01932) 247511 Fax: (01932) 220937 E-mail: sales@cattronuk.com

LOCOMOTIVE REPAIR OR OVERHAUL OR MAINTENANCE

Brush Traction, PO Box 17, Loughborough, Leicestershire, LE11 1HS Tel: (01509) 617000 Fax: (01509) 617001 E-mail: sales@brushtraction.com

LOFT CONVERSION

▶ Attic Life Ltd, Unit 5 Charmborough Farm, Charlton Road, Holcombe, Radstock, BA3 5EX Tel: (01761) 239154 Fax: (01761) 233614 E-mail: contact@atticlife.co.uk

G M Conversions, 69 Staplands Road, Broadgreen, Liverpool, L14 3LJ Tel: (07740) 426233 E-mail: philma76@hotmail.com

▶ Housesmiths Ltd., 60 Hampstead House, 176 Finchley Road, London, NW3 6BT Tel: 020 7558 8693 E-mail: kellysearch@housesmiths.co.uk

▶ Loft Tec Essex, 10-12 Second Avenue, Halstead, Essex, CO9 2SU Tel: (01787) 273600 E-mail: loft_tec@yahoo.co.uk

▶ lowquote.me.uk, Rosebank, Lymm, Cheshire, WA13 0JH Tel: (01925) 758984 E-mail: please@lowquote.me.uk

▶ P.A. Taylor Plans, The Sand Quarry, Hougher Wall Road, Audley, Stoke-On-Trent, ST7 8JA Tel: (01782) 721111 Fax: (05600) 766363

▶ Total Home Build, 1 Broomhill Lane, Birmingham, B43 5LB Tel: 0121-358 1056 Fax: 0121-358 1056

▶ Upper Deck Loft Conversions, 81J Clotherholme Road, Ripon, North Yorkshire, HG4 2DN Tel: 01765 604596

LOFT CONVERSION DESIGN

▶ Aran Proplan, Aran House, Old Tarporley Road, Stretton, Warrington, WA4 4NB Tel: 01925 860002 Fax: 01925 860101 E-mail: a.newton@arangroup.com

G M Conversions, 69 Staplands Road, Broadgreen, Liverpool, L14 3LJ Tel: (07740) 426233 E-mail: philma76@hotmail.com

▶ Loft Tec Essex, 10-12 Second Avenue, Halstead, Essex, CO9 2SU Tel: (01787) 273600 E-mail: loft_tec@yahoo.co.uk

▶ Upper Deck Loft Conversions, 81J Clotherholme Road, Ripon, North Yorkshire, HG4 2DN Tel: 01765 604596

LOFT LADDERS

▶ Castle Home Products, 1 Mount Place, Boughton, Chester, CH3 5BF Tel: (0800) 3897959

Light Alloy Ltd, 85 Dales Road, Ipswich, IP1 4JR Tel: (01473) 740445 Fax: (01473) 240002 E-mail: sales@lightalloy.co.uk

▶ Loft Shop Ltd, 39 Littlehampton Road, Worthing, West Sussex, BN13 1QJ Tel: (01903) 694111 Fax: (01903) 738501

LOGISTICS AND MATERIALS HANDLING TRAINING SERVICES

Nightfreight GB Ltd, Europa House, 122 Conway Street, Birkenhead, Merseyside, CH41 6RY Tel: 0151-649 0123 Fax: 0151-649 0101 E-mail: itdepartment@nightfreight.co.uk

The Oxford Princeton Program, 1 St Floor, 59 St Aldates, Oxford, OX1 1ST Tel: (01865) 254520 Fax: (01865) 254599 E-mail: info@oxfordprinceton.com

▶ R W M Training, 3 Dunnet Place, Thurso, Caithness, KW14 8JE Tel: (01847) 894934 Fax: (07876) 844044 E-mail: info@rwm-training.co.uk

LOGISTICS CONSULTANCY

Burton & Smith Moving Ltd, Movement House Soho Mills, London Road, Wallington, Surrey, SM6 7HN Tel: (020) 8773 1122 Fax: (020) 8773 0590 E-mail: sales@burton-smith.co.uk

▶ Cosco, Unit C2 Zenith, Paycocke Road, Basildon, Essex, SS14 3DW Tel: (01268) 643000 Fax: (01268) 643019

Iveco Ltd, Iveco House, Road One, Winsford Industrial Estate, Winsford, Cheshire, CW7 3QP Tel: (01606) 541000 Fax: (01606) 541126

▶ Jigsaw Logistics Ltd, Unit 1a, Higher Bochym, Cury Cross Lanes, Helston, Cornwall, TR12 7AZ Tel: (01326) 241355 Fax: (0871) 2470904 E-mail: stuart.naish@jiglog.co.uk

▶ Key3 Partners, 12 Davy Court, Central Park, Rugby, Warwickshire, CV23 0WE Tel: 01788 540550 Fax: 01788 575484 E-mail: enquires@key3partners.com

▶ Owen (Road Services) Ltd, Dafen Industrial Estate, Dafen, Llanelli, Dyfed, SA14 8QE Tel: (01554) 754465 Fax: (01554) 770725

LOGISTICS ENGINEERING

▶ Business Direct Ltd, 2NF Floor, Somerset House, Somerset Road, Teddington, Middlesex, TW11 8RT Tel: (020) 8943 1871 Fax: (020) 8977 3048

▶ Lloyd Fraser Ltd, Furnace Lane, Nether Heyford, Northampton, NN7 3LB Tel: (01327) 349111 Fax: (01327) 349288

LOGISTICS MANAGEMENT COMPUTER SYSTEMS

Chartered Institute of Logistics & Transport (UK), Logistics & Transport Centre, Earlstrees Road, Corby, Northamptonshire, NN17 4AX Tel: (01536) 740100 Fax: (01536) 740101 E-mail: enquiry@ciltuk.org.uk

Satair Hardware Ltd, Shoreham Airport, Shoreham-by-Sea, West Sussex, BN43 5FF Tel: (01273) 441149 Fax: (01273) 464577 E-mail: enquiries@satair.com

Syncron UK Ltd, Baskerville House, Centenary Square, Birmingham, B1 2ND Tel: 0121-503 2650 Fax: 0121-503 2651

LOGISTICS MANAGEMENT SERVICES

Asco UK Ltd, Asco House, Sinclair Road, Aberdeen, AB11 9PL Tel: (01224) 580396 Fax: (01224) 576172 E-mail: info@ascoplc.com

▶ Ashworth Preece Logistics, 7 Memorial Road, Walkden, Manchester, M28 3AQ Tel: (0870) 350 1246 Fax: (0870) 350 1248

B A X Global Ltd, Unitair Centre, Great South West Road, Feltham, Middlesex, TW14 8NT Tel: (020) 8899 3000 Fax: (020) 8899 3111

B X Tech Ltd, 19 Wainright Street, Aston, Birmingham, B6 5TH Tel: 0121-327 6411 Fax: 0121-327 6681

▶ Beaky.net, 35 Vaughan Drive, Kemsley, Sittingbourne, Kent, ME10 2UB Tel: (07729) 163996 Fax: (01795) 438113

Bernard Group Ltd, Bernard House 52-54 Peregrine Road, Hainault, Ilford, Essex, IG6 3SZ Tel: (020) 8501 2599 Fax: (020) 8559 9922 E-mail: corporate@bernardgroup.plc.uk

Component Logistics Ltd, Milton Court Horsfield Way, Bredbury Park Industrial Estate, Bredbury, Stockport, Cheshire, SK6 2TD Tel: 0161-406 2800 Fax: 0161-406 2809 E-mail: cll@component-logistics.com

Crown Agents Ltd, St Nicholas House, St Nicholas Road, Sutton, Surrey, SM1 1EL Tel: (020) 8643 3311 Fax: (020) 8643 9113 E-mail: enquiries@crownagents.co.uk

Danzas AEI Intercontinental, 18-32 London Road, Staines, Middlesex, TW18 4BP Tel: (01784) 871118 Fax: (01784) 871158 E-mail: mark.oxtoby@gb.danzas.com

Dodds Ltd, Mansfield Road, Aston, Sheffield, S26 2BS Tel: 0114-287 4187 Fax: 0114-287 2251 E-mail: traffic@dodds.co.uk

▶ Edivorp Ltd, 4 Bowland Rise, Chandlers Ford, Chandler's Ford, Eastleigh, Hampshire, SO53 4QW Tel: (023) 8025 2600 E-mail: enquiries@edivorp.co.uk

▶ Europa Worldwide, Unit 2 Building 110, Castle Donington, Derby, DE74 2SA Tel: (01332) 815900 Fax: (01332) 815909 E-mail: sales@europa-worldwide.co.uk

Europa Worldwide Logistics, Europa House, 68 Hailey Rd, Erith, Kent, DA18 4AU Tel: (020) 8311 5000 Fax: (020) 8310 4805 E-mail: sales@europa-worldwide.co.uk

▶ Europa Worldwide Services, Europa House, 46 Tilton Road, Birmingham, B9 4PP Tel: 0121-766 8000 Fax: 0121-771 4669 E-mail: sales@europa-worldwide.co.uk

Exel, Harrier Parkway, Magna Park, Lutterworth, Leicestershire, LE17 4XT Tel: (01327) 308400 Fax: (01327) 308404

Exel Ltd, Solstice House, 251 Midsummer Boulevard, Central Milton Keynes, Milton Keynes, MK9 1EQ Tel: (01908) 244000 Fax: (01908) 244244 E-mail: business.enquiry@exel.com

Fabine Investments Ltd, Unit 3 Pilot Trading Estate, West Wycombe Road, High Wycombe, Buckinghamshire, HP12 3AH Tel: (01494) 462749 Fax: (01494) 522325 E-mail: pilot@pilotgroup.co.uk

Geologistics Ltd, Royal Court, 81 Tweedy Road, Bromley, BR1 1TW Tel: (020) 8460 5050 Fax: (020) 8461 8884 E-mail: prandall@geo-logistics.com

Hays Technology, Appletree Road, Chipping Warden, Banbury, Oxfordshire, OX17 1LL Tel: (01295) 663000 Fax: (01295) 660361 E-mail: logistics@haystechnology.com

▶ Gideon Hillman Consulting, 47A Lansdowne Crescent, Willes Road, Leamington Spa, Warwickshire, CV32 4PR Tel: (01926) 430883 E-mail: info@hillman-consulting.co.uk

Initial A To Z Couriers, 21a Brownlow Mews, London, WC1N 2LA Tel: (020) 7841 1741 Fax: (020) 7404 6045 E-mail: danbrown@initial-atoz.co.uk

▶ Jigsaw Logistics Ltd, Unit 1a, Higher Bochym, Cury Cross Lanes, Helston, Cornwall, TR12 7AZ Tel: (01326) 241355 Fax: (0871) 2470904 E-mail: stuart.naish@jiglog.co.uk

Kay Oneill Ltd, Unit 6, Horton Road, Colnbrook, Slough, SL3 0AT Tel: (01753) 684606 Fax: (01753) 682241 E-mail: lhr@kayoneill.com

▶ Key3 Partners, 12 Davy Court, Central Park, Rugby, Warwickshire, CV23 0WE Tel: 01788 540550 Fax: 01788 575484 E-mail: enquires@key3partners.com

Logistics Business, 17 The Crescent, Bromsgrove, Worcestershire, B60 2DF Tel: (01527) 889060 Fax: (01527) 559192 E-mail: info@logistics.co.uk

Logistics Simulation Ltd, The Capstan House, Middlewood Road, Poynton, Stockport, Cheshire, SK12 1SH Tel: (01625) 850919 Fax: (01625) 850377 E-mail: info@logsim.co.uk

Maersk Logistics, Unit 6 Orwell House, Ferry Lane, Felixstowe, Suffolk, IP11 3AQ Tel: (01394) 614600 Fax: (01394) 614636

Menlow Worldwide, Unit 19 Airlinks Industrial Estate, Spitfire Way, Heston, Hounslow, TW5 9NR Tel: (020) 8260 6000 Fax: (020) 8260 6170 E-mail: stewartinnes@menlowworldwide.com

Norman Global Logistics Ltd, 1 Griffin Centre, Staines Road, Feltham, Middlesex, TW14 0HS Tel: (020) 8893 2999 Fax: (020) 8893 1770 E-mail: pob@norman.co.uk

P & O Developments Ltd, 4 Carlton Gardens, Pall Mall, London, SW1Y 5AB Tel: (020) 7839 5611 Fax: (020) 7930 2098

▶ Park Logistics, Private Road No 4, Colwick Industrial Estate, Nottingham, NG4 2JT Tel: 0115-940 3332 Fax: 0115-940 2728 E-mail: sales@parklogistics.co.uk

Peter Brotherhood Holdings Ltd, Werrington Park Way, Peterborough, PE4 5HG Tel: (01733) 292200 Fax: (01733) 292300 E-mail: sales@peterbrotherhood.co.uk

Pinnacle International Freight Ltd, C Mortimer Road, Narborough, Leicester, LE19 2GA Tel: 0116-286 6566 Fax: 0116-286 7928 E-mail: lecmail@pif.co.uk

Redbourn International Forwarding Ltd, 43A Adelaide Street, Luton, LU1 5BD Tel: (01582) 425611 Fax: (01582) 405705 E-mail: office@redbourninternational.co.uk

LOGISTICS MANAGEMENT SERVICES – *continued*

S D International Logistics, 22 Freemans Close, Twyning, Tewkesbury, Gloucestershire, GL20 6JP Tel: (01684) 850146 Fax: (01684) 850146 E-mail: steveday@consultant.com
Satair Hardware Ltd, Shoreham Airport, Shoreham-by-Sea, West Sussex, BN43 5FF Tel: (01273) 441149 Fax: (01273) 464577 E-mail: enquiries@satair.com
ServiceTec Ltd, ServiceTec House, 3 Rutherford Close, Medway Technology Park, Stevenage, Hertfordshire, SG1 2EF Tel: (01438) 341900 Fax: (01438) 341901 E-mail: info@servicetec.com
▶ SISTech, Heriot Watt University, Edinburgh, EH14 4AS Tel: 0131-451 8162 Fax: 0131-451 8150
South Coast, The Docks, Fowey, Cornwall, PL23 1AL Tel: (01726) 832121 Fax: (01726) 833474 E-mail: agency.foy@denholm-barwil.com
Standard Motor Transport, 15 Lisle Avenue, Kidderminster, Worcestershire, DY11 7DJ Tel: (01562) 745308 Fax: (01562) 754546 E-mail: rob@standardmotortransport.co.uk
T D G European Chemicals, Euro Terminal, Westinghouse Road, Trafford Park, Manchester, M17 1PY Tel: 0161-932 6900 Fax: 0161-932 6990 E-mail: businessenquiries@tdg.co.uk
T P L Logistics Management, Lakeside House, Hindhead Road, Haslemere, Surrey, GU27 3PJ Tel: (01252) 737939 Fax: (01252) 733474 E-mail: info@tpl-logistics-management.co.uk
T P L Management Consultancy Ltd, Leigh House, Leigh Lane, Farnham, Surrey, GU9 8HP Tel: (01252) 737939 Fax: (01252) 733474 E-mail: info@tpl-logistics-management.co.uk
TDG plc, 25 Victoria Street, London, SW1H 0EX Tel: (020) 7222 7411 Fax: (020) 7222 2806 E-mail: businessenquiries@tdg.co.uk
Tri-Stor Products Ltd, 23 Weetwood Drive, Sheffield, S11 9QL Tel: 0114-236 3052 Fax: 0114-236 4429 E-mail: pdconstantine@aol.com
W B S Consulting, Grove Business Centre, Grove Technology Park, Wantage, Oxfordshire, OX12 9FF Tel: (01235) 227434 Fax: (01235) 227435 E-mail: enquiries@wwbsgroup.com
▶ World Courier, Sea Containers House, 20 Upper Ground, London, SE1 9PD Tel: (020) 7717 1400 Fax: (020) 7928 7105 E-mail: contact@worldcourier.com
▶ X2 (UK) Ltd, The Gatehouse, Fradley Distribution Park, Wood End Lane, Lichfield, Staffordshire, WS13 8NE Tel: (01543) 254597

LOGISTICS SOFTWARE

▶ C Sam, Bridge House, 1-2 Riverside Drive, Aberdeen, AB11 7LH Tel: (01224) 586855 Fax: (01244) 586866 E-mail: sales@c-sam.co.uk
Red Ledge Ltd, Red Ledge Business Centre, 289-291 Huddersfield Road, Thongsbridge, Holmfirth, HD9 3UA Tel: (01484) 686769 Fax: (01484) 687879 E-mail: sales@redledge.co.uk

LOGISTICS SUPPORT SERVICES

▶ Exel, 33 Thames Road, Barking, Essex, IG11 0HQ Tel: (020) 8532 7201 Fax: (020) 8591 1017
▶ Exel, Smoke Lane, Avonmouth, Bristol, BS11 0YA Tel: 0117-982 4541
▶ Internal Freight Auditing Ltd, 5 Keepers Close, Coleshill, Birmingham, B46 3HB Tel: (01675) 437534 E-mail: Info@IF-Audit.com
▶ MAT Network Express Ltd, Euroterminal, Unit 5 Westinghouse Circle, Trafford Park, Manchester, M17 1PY Tel: 0161-872 3222 Fax: 0161-848 9261 E-mail: bill.wyman@mat-group.com

LOGISTICS TEMPORARY STAFF RECRUITMENT AGENCIES

▶ Just Recruit (UK) Ltd, Viking Industrial Park, Tedco Business Centre, Jarrow, Tyne & Wear, NE32 3DT Tel: 0191-428 3336 Fax: 0191-428 3356 E-mail: mark@justrecruit.co.uk
▶ Redco Recruitment Group Limited, Redco House, 165 Lea Road, Pennfelds, Wolverhampton, WV3 0LQ Tel: 0845 111 0735 Fax: 0845 111 0736 E-mail: info@redcorecruitment.com

LONE WORKER ALARM SYSTEMS

▶ J P Alarms & Locksmiths Ltd, 9B Vulcans Lane, Workington, Cumbria, CA14 2NX Tel: (01900) 870941 Fax: (01900) 872807 E-mail: office@jpalarms.co.uk
Scope Communications (UK) Ltd, Quantum House, Steamer Quay Road, Totnes, Devon, TQ9 5AL Tel: (01803) 860700 Fax: (01803) 863716 E-mail: sales@scope-uk.com

LONG SERVICE RECOGNITION AWARDS

▶ Green Slate Trophies, 1 Derby Street, Burnley, Lancashire, BB11 1RL Tel: (01282) 411400 Fax: (01282) 432308

LOOM STATE LINING FABRIC CONVERTERS

J.M. Clayton & Co. Ltd, Unit 3 Phoenix Court, Hammond Avenue, Stockport, Cheshire, SK4 1PQ Tel: 0161-474 0061 Fax: 0161-474 0071 E-mail: omar@jmclayton.co.uk

LOOSE LEAF BINDERS

J.P. Charles [Binding Systems] Ltd, Units 11-12, 6 Old Church Road, London, E4 6ST Tel: (020) 8801 4222 Fax: (020) 8529 6464
Donside Plastics Welding Ltd, Drill Hall, Upper Platts, Ticehurst, Wadhurst, East Sussex, TN5 7HA Tel: (01580) 200663 Fax: (01580) 200464
Flexigate Ltd, Vicarage Lane, Hoo, Rochester, Kent, ME3 9LB Tel: (01634) 251328 Fax: (01634) 250558 E-mail: sales@flexigate.co.uk
Modern Bookbinders Ltd, Pringle Street, Blackburn, BB1 1SA Tel: (01254) 59371 Fax: (01254) 59373 E-mail: binders@btclick.com
Plasart Ltd, Chilton Industrial Estate, Windham Road, Sudbury, Suffolk, CO10 2XD Tel: (01787) 375641 Fax: (01787) 311041
Presentation For Business, L1-L2 Unit Kent Kraft Industrial Estate, Lower Road, Northfleet, Gravesend, Kent, DA11 9SR Tel: (01322) 386717 Fax: (01322) 385506 E-mail: info@p4b.co.uk
Tennant PVC, The Midway, Nottingham, NG7 2TS Tel: 0115-988 1300 Fax: 0115-988 5310 E-mail: sales@tennantpvc.co.uk

LOOSE LEAF FITTINGS/ MECHANISMS, METAL

Bensons International Systems Ltd, Bensons House, 104 Bath Road, Stroud, Gloucestershire, GL5 3TJ Tel: (01453) 755888 Fax: (01453) 753300
Harrison Products, East Gate House, Moreton Road, Longborough, Moreton-in-Marsh, Gloucestershire, GL56 0QJ Tel: (01451) 830083 Fax: (01451) 830830

LOOSE TEA

Steenbergs Organic, 1 Hallikeld Close, Melmerby, Ripon, North Yorkshire, HG4 5GZ Tel: (01765) 640101 Fax: (01765) 640101 E-mail: enquiriesl@steenbergs.co.uk

LORRIES, REFRIGERATED

▶ Glenthorpe Contracts Ltd, Flat 2, 49 West Cliff Road, Bournemouth, BH4 8BA Tel: (01202) 767926 Fax: (01202) 767948 E-mail: glenthorpecontracts@f2s.com

LORRY LOADERS

Tip N Lift UK Ltd, Boss Hall Road, Ipswich, IP1 5BN Tel: (01473) 747222 Fax: (01473) 740381 E-mail: tipnlift@aol.com
Woodfield Systems Ltd, Tyler Way, Swalecliffe, Whitstable, Kent, CT5 2RS Tel: (01227) 793351 Fax: (01227) 793625 E-mail: sales@akerkvaerner.com

LORRY MOUNTED CRANE HIRE

▶ Buckley's Crane Hire, Bryn Garth, Garth Road, Glan Conwy, Colwyn Bay, Clwyd, LL28 5TD Tel: (01492) 580227 Fax: (01492) 580725 E-mail: enquiries@buckleyscranehire.co.uk

LORRY MOUNTED CRANE INSTALLATION AND MAINTENANCE

Austin Engineering Shropshire Ltd, Cargotec Industrial Park, Ellesmere, Shropshire, SY12 9JW Tel: (01691) 622864 Fax: (01691) 622864E-mail: steve@austinengineering.co.uk

LORRY MOUNTED CRANE SPARE PARTS

Austin Engineering Shropshire Ltd, Cargotec Industrial Park, Ellesmere, Shropshire, SY12 9JW Tel: (01691) 622864 Fax: (01691) 622864E-mail: steve@austinengineering.co.uk

LORRY MOUNTED CRANES

Brade-Leigh Bodies Ltd, Albion Industrial Estate, Oldbury Road, West Bromwich, West Midlands, B70 9EH Tel: 0121-553 4361 Fax: 0121-500 6139 E-mail: sales@brade-leigh.co.uk
Fassi UK Ltd, 26 Blick Road, Heathcote Industrial Estate, Warwick, CV34 6TA Tel: (01926) 889779 Fax: (01926) 885777 E-mail: mail@fassi.co.uk
J A Chapman, The Forge, 45 Bonehurst Road, Horley, Surrey, RH6 8PJ Tel: (01293) 785060 Fax: (01293) 785060
Lancashire Tippers, Kirkhall Workshops, Bilbao Street, Bolton, BL1 4HH Tel: (01204) 493750 Fax: (01204) 847966 E-mail: lanctip@masseytruckengineering.co.uk
Plant Equipment Ltd, Clover Nook Road, Cotes Park Industrial Estate, Somercotes, Alfreton, Derbyshire, DE55 4RF Tel: (01773) 836060 Fax: (01773) 520630 E-mail: info@plantequip.co.uk
Herbert Pool Ltd, 95 Fleet Road, Fleet, Hampshire, GU51 3PJ Tel: (01252) 620444 Fax: (01252) 622292
T H White Ltd, Nursteed Road, Devizes, Wiltshire, SN10 3EA Tel: (01380) 722381 Fax: (01380) 729147 E-mail: enquiries@thwhite.co.uk
Tip N Lift UK Ltd, Boss Hall Road, Ipswich, IP1 5BN Tel: (01473) 747222 Fax: (01473) 740381 E-mail: tipnlift@aol.com
Walker Crane Services Ltd, Trading Estate, Motherwell Way, Grays, Essex, RM20 3XD Tel: (01708) 867251 Fax: (01708) 863636 E-mail: info@walkercranes.co.uk

LORRY WHEEL ALIGNMENT EQUIPMENT

▶ Steertrak Commercial Vehicle Servicing, Commercial House Station Road Business Park, Station Road, Tewkesbury, Gloucestershire, GL20 5DR Tel: (01684) 276900 Fax: (01684) 276500 E-mail: sales@steertrak.co.uk

LOSS IN WEIGHT FEEDERS

▶ Healthfarm, 23 Cumpsty Road, Liverpool, L21 9HX Tel: 0151 9206654 E-mail: stephmc.uk@hotmail.co.uk
▶ Stay Fit and Healthy, 160 Goring Road, Colchester, CO4 0DB Tel: 0207 6640538 E-mail: stayfitandhealthy@ntlworld.com

LOTTERY TICKET CONSULTANCY

▶ Tops Lotto, 64 Sherwood Street, Newton, Alfreton, Derbyshire, DE55 5SE Tel: (01773) 782215 E-mail: lozhaney@hotmail.com
▶ UK Lottery Online, Unit 142 Roslyn Road, South Tottenham, London, N15 5JJ Tel: (020) 8800 7271 Fax: (020) 8800 7277 E-mail: info@uk-lotteryonline.co.uk

LOUDSPEAKER CABINETS

M A J Electronics, Stallings Lane, Kingswinford, West Midlands, DY6 7HU Tel: (01384) 278646 Fax: (01384) 298877 E-mail: sales@majelectronic.co.uk
Rotational Mouldings Ltd, Knowles Industrial Estate, Buxton Road, Furness Vale, High Peak, Derbyshire, SK23 7PH Tel: (01663) 742897 Fax: (01663) 747584 E-mail: sales@rotationalmouldings.co.uk
Sambell Engineering Ltd, Winston Avenue, Croft, Leicester, LE9 3GQ Tel: (01455) 283251 Fax: (01455) 283908 E-mail: post@atacama-audio.co.uk
Soundlite Equipment, YBS House, Unit 3 Gladstone Terrace, Stanningley, Pudsey, West Yorkshire, LS28 6NE Tel: 0113-236 1157 Fax: 0113-236 3942

LOUDSPEAKER CHASSIS

Fane Acoustics Ltd, Unit 1, Millshaw Park Avenue, Millshaw Park Industrial Estate, Leeds, LS11 0LR Tel: 0113-277 8600 Fax: 0113-277 8700 E-mail: info@fane-acoustics.com

LOUDSPEAKER COMPONENTS

Fane Acoustics Ltd, Unit 1, Millshaw Park Avenue, Millshaw Park Industrial Estate, Leeds, LS11 0LR Tel: 0113-277 8600 Fax: 0113-277 8700 E-mail: info@fane-acoustics.com

LOUDSPEAKER DRIVERS

▶ mjbaudio, 21 Camellia Close, Three Legged Cross, Wimborne, dorset, BH21 6UD Tel: 07818 402662 E-mail: sales@mjbaudio.co.uk

▶ Phase One DJ Solutions, Station Road, Darlington, County Durham, DL3 6TA Tel: (01325) 480507 E-mail: mike@djanddiscostuff.com

LOUDSPEAKER STANDS

Power Drive Drum Co. Ltd, Unit M1 Cherrycourt Way, Leighton Buzzard, Bedfordshire, LU7 4UH Tel: (01525) 370292 Fax: (01525) 852126 E-mail: info@mypowerdrive.com

LOUDSPEAKER SYSTEMS CONSULTANTS OR DESIGNERS

Harbeth Audio Ltd, 3 Lindfield Enterprise Park, Lewes Road, Lindfield, Haywards Heath, West Sussex, RH16 2LH Tel: (01444) 484371 Fax: (01444) 487629 E-mail: sound@harbeth.co.uk

LOUDSPEAKER SYSTEMS MANUFRS

Bandor Loudspeakers, 11 Penfold Cottages, Penfold Lane, Holmer Green, High Wycombe, Buckinghamshire, HP15 6XR Tel: (01494) 714058 Fax: (01494) 715903
C I E Group, Blenheim Industrial Estate, Widdowson Close, Bulwell, Nottingham, NG6 8WB Tel: 0115-977 0075 Fax: 0115-977 0081 E-mail: marketing@cie-ltd.co.uk
D N H Worldwide Ltd, 31 Clarke Road, Mount Farm, Bletchley, Milton Keynes, MK1 1LG Tel: (01908) 275000 Fax: (01908) 275100 E-mail: dnh@dnh.co.uk
Harmen Motive Ltd, Bennett Street, Bridgend Industrial Estate, Bridgend, Mid Glamorgan, CF31 3SH Tel: (01656) 645441 Fax: (01656) 650327 E-mail: pselby@harmenbecker.com
K E F Audio UK Ltd, Eccleston Road, Tovil, Maidstone, Kent, ME15 6QP Tel: (01622) 672261 Fax: (01622) 750653 E-mail: enquiries@kef.com
Martin Audio Ltd, 2 Century Point, Halifax Road, Cressex Business Park, High Wycombe, Buckinghamshire, HP12 3SL Tel: (01494) 535312 Fax: (01494) 438669 E-mail: info@martin-audio.com
Monitor Audio Ltd, 2 Brook Road Industrial Estate, Brook Road, Rayleigh, Essex, SS6 7XL Tel: (01268) 740580 Fax: (01268) 740589 E-mail: info@monitoraudio.co.uk
Public Address Systems Ltd, Unit 5 Leestone Road Sharston, Sharston Industrial Area, Manchester, M22 4RN Tel: 0161-611 7171 Fax: 0161-611 7170 E-mail: sales@pad.co.uk
Ruark Acoustics Ltd, 59 Tailors Court, Southend-on-Sea, SS2 5TH Tel: (01702) 601410 Fax: (01702) 601414 E-mail: info@ruark.co.uk
Omar Skinner & Sons, Warfield Park, Bracknell, Berkshire, RG42 3RG Tel: (01344) 882207 Fax: (01344) 882207
Wharfedale International Ltd, I A G House, Ermine Business Park, Huntingdon, Cambridgeshire, PE29 6XU Tel: (01480) 431737 Fax: (01480) 431767 E-mail: info@wharfedale.co.uk

LOUDSPEAKER VOICE COIL COMPONENTS

Lamina Dielectrics Ltd, Daux Road, Billingshurst, West Sussex, RH14 9SJ Tel: (01403) 783131 Fax: (01403) 782237 E-mail: sales@lamina.uk.com

LOUDSPEAKERS

Boston Acoustics Distribution UK Ltd, 16 Bridge Road, Cirencester, Gloucestershire, GL7 1NJ Tel: (01285) 654432 Fax: (01285) 654430 E-mail: info@acoustic-energy.co.uk
Coles Electroacoustics Ltd, Pindar Road, Hoddesdon, Hertfordshire, EN11 0BZ Tel: (01992) 466685 Fax: (01992) 446583 E-mail: sales@coleselectroacoustics.com
Fane Acoustics Ltd, Unit 1, Millshaw Park Avenue, Millshaw Park Industrial Estate, Leeds, LS11 0LR Tel: 0113-277 8600 Fax: 0113-277 8700 E-mail: info@fane-acoustics.com
Meridian Audio Ltd, Stonehill, Stukeley Meadows Industrial Es, Huntingdon, Cambridgeshire, PE29 6EX Tel: (01480) 445678 Fax: (01480) 445686

LOUVRE BLINDS

▶ Windowcharm, Kent Road, Sheffield, S8 9RN Tel: (01709) 379092 Fax: 0114-255 8142

LOUVRE WINDOWS

Mckenzie Martin Ltd, Eton Hill Works, Eton Hill Road, Radcliffe, Manchester, M26 2US Tel: 0161-723 2234 Fax: 0161-725 9531 E-mail: general@mckenziemartin.co.uk

LOUVRE WINDOWS – *continued*

Ruskin Air Management Ltd, Stourbridge Road, Bridgnorth, Shropshire, WV15 5BB Tel: (01746) 761921 Fax: (01746) 766450 E-mail: sales@naco.co.uk

LOUVRES

▶ Avon Solar Control Ltd, Avon House, Kineton Road Industrial Estate, Southam, Warwickshire, CV47 0DR Tel: (01926) 818992 Fax: (01926) 811676 E-mail: enquiries@avonsolarcontrol.co.uk

B B S Building Components, Spon Lane, West Bromwich, West Midlands, B70 6AP Tel: 0121-553 5509 Fax: 0121-500 5425 E-mail: mail@bbsrooflights.co.uk

Cryselco Lighting Ltd, 274 Ampthill Road, Bedford, MK42 9QJ Tel: (01234) 273355 Fax: (01234) 210867 E-mail: sales@cryselco.co.uk

Lighting & Ceiling Louvres Ltd, 7-13 Cutlers Road, South Woodham Ferrers, Chelmsford, CM3 5WA Tel: (01245) 321561 Fax: (01245) 325034 E-mail: sales@lcll.co.uk

▶ Renson Fabrications, Fairfax House, Bircholt Road, Maidstone, Kent, ME15 9SF Tel: (01622) 685658 Fax: (01622) 688762 E-mail: info@rensonuk.net

LOVESPOONS

▶ Faze 3, 23 Abergele Road, Colwyn Bay, Clwyd, LL29 7RS Tel: (01492) 534294 Fax: (01492) 534294 E-mail: alan@faze3.co.uk

LOW ACTIVITY LIQUID AND SOLID NUCLEAR WASTE REPROCESSING

Smith Engineering GB Ltd, Solway Trading Estate, Maryport, Cumbria, CA15 8NF Tel: (01900) 815831 Fax: (01900) 815553 E-mail: r.smith@moonbuggy.com

LOW BED AGRICULTURAL TRAILERS

▶ Wolds Trailers, Millington Heights, Millington, York, YO42 1UB Tel: 01759 368225 Fax: 01759 369906 E-mail: millingtonheights@hotmail.com

LOW COST CALL TELEPHONE CALL SERVICE PROVIDERS

A G I S Telecom Ltd, Blairs Business Centre, South Deeside Road, Blairs, Aberdeen, AB12 5LF Tel: (01224) 864864 Fax: (0870) 1645149 E-mail: sales@agis-telecom.com

Pulse Telecoms, 106 Katherine Road, London, E6 1EN Tel: (020) 8586 0220 Fax: 0208 5860220

R G T Ltd, Chapel Road, Smallfield, Horley, Surrey, RH6 9NW Tel: (01342) 844411 Fax: (0870) 7771333 E-mail: sales@rgt.co.uk

Sprint Ltd, PO Box 2452, Hove, East Sussex, BN3 7WB Tel: (0870) 6082801 Fax: (0870) 6082802 E-mail: sales@scsl.co.uk

LOW COST REMOTELY OPERATED VEHICLES (ROV)

AC-CESS Co. UK Ltd, Tyrebagger Works, Kinellar, Aberdeen, AB21 0TT Tel: (01224) 790100 Fax: (01224) 790111 E-mail: info@ac-cess.com

LOW COST ROUTING (LCR) TELEPHONE SYSTEMS

▶ Broadband Ltd, 46 Station Road, North Harrow, Harrow, Middlesex, HA2 7SE Tel: (0845) 658 1110 Fax: (08715) 227 075 E-mail: gsmgateways@broadbandltd.co.uk

LOW EMISSION BURNERS

S I T Bray Ltd, Education Road, Meanwood Road, Leeds, LS7 2AN Tel: 0113-281 6700 Fax: 0113-281 6702 E-mail: sit.uk@sitgroup.it

LOW ENERGY LIGHTING

Steinel (UK) Ltd, 25 Manasty Road, Axis Park, Orton Southgate, Peterborough, PE2 6UP Tel: (01733) 366700 Fax: (01733) 366701 E-mail: steinel@steineluk.co.uk

LOW FRICTION COATINGS

Kal-Gard UK Ltd, Canalwood Industrial Estate, Chirk, Wrexham, LL14 5RL Tel: (01691) 772070 Fax: (01691) 778303 E-mail: tony@kal-gard.co.uk

LOW FRICTION LINEAR BEARING MATERIALS

Pentad Engineering, Unit 10, The Parkway Centre, Heneage Street, Birmingham, B7 4LY Tel: 0121-359 5190 Fax: 0121-359 4743 E-mail: sales@pentad.net

LOW LIGHT LEVEL NIGHT VISION EQUIPMENT

Fenns (Farnborough) Ltd, 77 Alexandra Road, Farnborough, Hampshire, GU14 6BN Tel: (01252) 541221 Fax: (01252) 512890 E-mail: info@fennprint.co.uk

Simrad Optronics Ltd, 3 Medowbrook Industrial Estate, Maxwell Way, Crawley, West Sussex, RH10 9SA Tel: (01293) 560413 Fax: (01293) 560418

Vistar Night Vision Ltd, 24 Doman Road, Camberley, Surrey, GU15 3DF Tel: (01276) 708800 Fax: (01276) 708807 E-mail: info@vistar.co.uk

LOW LOADERS

▶ D & S Kitching, Camwal Road, Harrogate, North Yorkshire, HG1 4PT Tel: (01423) 885632 Fax: (01423) 884800 E-mail: mai@dskplant.co.uk

LOW NOISE ANTICAVITATION VALVES

Leeds Valve Co. Ltd, Caledonia Road, Batley, West Yorkshire, WF17 5NH Tel: (01924) 428000 Fax: (01924) 428001 E-mail: sales@leedsvalve.com

LOW POWER DIRECT CURRENT (DC) ELECTRIC MOTORS

maxon motor uk ltd, Maxon House, Hogwood Lane, Finchampstead, Wokingham, Berkshire, RG40 4QW Tel: 0118-973 3337 Fax: 0118-973 7472 E-mail: salesuk@maxonmotor.com

LOW POWER MICROWAVE SOURCES

Spectral Line Systems Ltd, Units 1-3 Scott Road, Tarbert, Isle of Harris, HS3 3DL Tel: (01859) 502533 Fax: (01859) 502533 E-mail: slsltd@lineone.net

LOW PRESSURE DIE CASTINGS

M K Tool & Die Ltd, 19 Spackmans Way, Slough, SL1 2SA Tel: 01753 539159

Turner Aluminium Castings Ltd, 1 Robinson Close, Telford Way Industrial Estate, Kettering, Northamptonshire, NN16 8PU Tel: (01536) 525270 Fax: (01536) 412367

LOW PRESSURE VALVES

Marben Engineering Ltd, 3 Cobham Road, Ferndown Industrial Estate, Wimborne, Dorset, BH21 7PE Tel: (01202) 895980 Fax: (01202) 891416 E-mail: marben123@aol.com

LOW RISE BUILDING DESIGN AND CONSTRUCTION

▶ Claric Design & Build Ltd, 30 Holly Road, Golborne, Warrington, WA3 3JR Tel: (01942) 731384 Fax: (01942) 731384

▶ SC Consulting, Victoria House, 28-32 Desborough Street, High Wycombe, Buckinghamshire, HP11 2NF Tel: (01494) 601170 Fax: (01494) 601171 E-mail: mail@scceng.co.uk

LOW SMOKE ZERO HALOGEN CABLE GLANDS

C M P Products, 36 Nelson Way, Nelson Park East, Cramlington, Northumberland, NE23 1WH Tel: 0191 2657411 Fax: 0191 2650581 E-mail: cmp@cmp-products.com

LOW SMOKE ZERO HALOGEN CABLES

Allied Cables Ltd, Liverpool Road, Warrington, WA5 1AP Tel: (01925) 445764 Fax: (01925) 232880 E-mail: alliedcables@absonline.net

Amphenol Spectrastrip Ltd, Unit 21-23 Romsey Industrial Estate, Greatbridge Road, Romsey, Hampshire, SO51 0HR Tel: (01794) 517575 Fax: (01794) 516246 E-mail: info@spectra-strip.com

Capital Cables, D 20 Frogmore Industrial Estate, Motherwell Way, Grays, Essex, RM20 3XD Tel: (01708) 864464 Fax: (01708) 865385

Central Cables, Unit 15 Brindley Business Park, Chaseside Drive, Hednesford, Cannock, Staffordshire, WS11 7GD Tel: (01543) 422477 Fax: (01543) 422420 E-mail: sales@centralcables.co.uk

Lapp Ltd, 3 Perivale Park, Horsenden La South, Greenford, Middlesex, UB6 7RL Tel: (020) 8758 7800 Fax: (020) 8758 7880 E-mail: sales@lappgroup.com

▶ Sellec Special Cables Ltd, Dukeries Way, Worksop, Nottinghamshire, S81 7DW Tel: (01909) 483539 Fax: (01909) 500181 E-mail: sales@sellec.com

UK Cables Ltd, London Distribution Centre, Westlands Industrial Estate, Millington Road, Hayes, Middlesex, UB3 4AZ Tel: (020) 8561 9111 Fax: (020) 8561 6777

LOW VOLTAGE CABLE JOINTING KITS

I S P Industrial Support Products Ltd, Unit H2 Lambs Farm Business Park, Basingstoke Road, Swallowfield, Reading, RG7 1PQ Tel: 0118-988 6873 Fax: 0118-988 6576 E-mail: info@isp-cablejointing.co.uk

LOW VOLTAGE CABLES

Accent Lighting Ltd, 3 Candidus Court, Werrington, Peterborough, PE4 5DB Tel: (01733) 574524 Fax: (01733) 574524 E-mail: sales@accent-lighting.co.uk

LOW VOLTAGE ELECTRIC SCREWDRIVERS

Hixons, 45 Denton Road, Audenshaw, Manchester, M34 5BL Tel: 0161-336 3725 Fax: 0161-336 4184 E-mail: sales@hixons.com

LOW VOLTAGE FLUORESCENT LIGHTING

Homelec, Kings Way House, Laporte Way, Luton, LU4 8RJ Tel: (01582) 544510 Fax: (01582) 544511

Invertec Ltd, Whelford Road, Fairford, Gloucestershire, GL7 4DT Tel: (01285) 713550 Fax: (01285) 713548 E-mail: sales@invertec.co.uk

LOW VOLTAGE LIGHTING

Active Circuits, 14 North Street, Melton Mowbray, Leicestershire, LE13 1NL Tel: (01664) 562968 Fax: (01664) 562968

Bedsons Ltd, A1 Bodmin Road, Coventry, CV2 5DB Tel: (024) 7661 4542 Fax: (024) 7661 4523 E-mail: info@bedsons.com

Compact Lighting Ltd, Dundas Spur, Portsmouth, PO3 5RW Tel: (023) 9265 2999 Fax: (023) 9265 3053 E-mail: info@compact-lighting.co.uk

Davis Cash & Co. Ltd, Alexandra Road, Enfield, Middlesex, EN3 7EN Tel: (020) 8804 4028 Fax: (020) 8805 2896 E-mail: sales@daviscash.co.uk

Lab Craft Ltd, 22b King Street, Saffron Walden, Essex, CB10 1ES Tel: (01799) 513434 Fax: (01799) 513437 E-mail: sales@labcraft.co.uk

Light Innovation Ltd, 362 Kingston Road, Epsom, Surrey, KT19 0DT Tel: (020) 8873 1582 Fax: (020) 8224 8949

Power Equipment Design & Supplies Ltd, Lyndhurst Cottage, Seymour Road, Bath, BA1 6DZ Tel: (01225) 463721 Fax: (0845) 2804920 E-mail: info@pedsltd.co.uk

Selux UK Ltd, Harrison Way, Leamington Spa, Warwickshire, CV31 3HL Tel: (01926) 833455 Fax: (01926) 339844 E-mail: enquire@selux.co.uk

Spimin Development Ltd, Spimin House, Beacon Road, Poulton Industrial Estate, Poulton-Le-Fylde, Lancashire, FY6 8HD Tel: (01253) 881001 Fax: (01253) 881019 E-mail: sales@spimin.co.uk

Thermoforce Ltd, Wakefield Road, Cockermouth, Cumbria, CA13 0HS Tel: (01900) 823231 Fax: (01900) 825965 E-mail: sales@thermoforce.co.uk

Vitalighting Ltd, 4 Sutherland Court Moor Park Industrial Centre, Tolpits Lane, Watford, WD18 9NA Tel: (01923) 896476 Fax: (01923) 897741 E-mail: sales@vitalighting.com

LOW VOLTAGE MULTIPLE PLUGS

C E E Norm UK Ltd, Unit A1, Stafford Park 11, Telford, Shropshire, TF3 3AY Tel: (01952) 212700 Fax: (01952) 212711 E-mail: sales@ceenorm.co.uk

LOW VOLTAGE POWER SUPPLIES

Riker Ltd, Unit 12 Boat House Meadow, Salisbury, SP2 7LD Tel: (01722) 333153 Fax: (01722) 333139

LOW VOLTAGE SWITCHES

Mardix Automatic Controls Ltd, Westmorland Business Park, Gilthwaiterigg Lane, Kendal, Cumbria, LA9 6NS Tel: (01539) 720161 Fax: (01539) 724384 E-mail: switchgear@mardix.co.uk

LOW VOLTAGE SWITCHGEARS

Charnvel Ltd, Charnvel House, Canterbury Road, Nottingham, NG8 1PQ Tel: 0115-985 4000 Fax: 0115-985 5558 E-mail: info@charnvel.co.uk

Electra Switch Ltd, Unit 4 Colne Way Court, Colne Way, Watford, WD24 7NE Tel: (01923) 246154 Fax: (01923) 246482 E-mail: esl@electra-switch.co.uk

I C W Power Ltd, Joule House, 108-110 Primrose Hill, Kings Langley, Hertfordshire, WD4 8HR Tel: (01923) 266869 Fax: (01923) 264472 E-mail: sales@icwpower.com

J W & E Morris & Son Ltd, South Road, Bridgend Industrial Estate, Bridgend, Mid Glamorgan, CF31 3RB Tel: (01656) 653705 Fax: (01656) 767187 E-mail: sales@jwmorris.co.uk

M C H Eletrical Systems Ltd, Unit 7, Woodall Street, Bloxwich, Walsall, WS3 3HG Tel: (01922) 404050 Fax: (01922) 404045 E-mail: sales@mchlet.co.uk

P & B Power Engineering, Belle Vue Works, Boundary St, Manchester, M12 5NG Tel: 0161-223 5151 Fax: 0161-230 6464 E-mail: sales@pbeng.co.uk

S M Control Engineering Ltd, 1 Redhouse Industrial Estate, Middlemore Lane, Aldridge, Walsall, WS9 8DL Tel: (01922) 744020 Fax: (01922) 744001 E-mail: cbailey@smcontroleng.co.uk

LOW VOLTAGE TEST EQUIPMENT

E H P Technical Services Ltd, 6 Lincoln Road, Northborough, Peterborough, PE6 9BL Tel: (01733) 252428 Fax: (01733) 252674 E-mail: rayevans@ehpltd.freeserve.co.uk

LOW VOLTAGE TRANSFORMERS

De Tech, Unit 36e The Lingfield Estate, Mcmullen Road, Darlington, County Durham, DL1 1RW Tel: (01325) 489001 Fax: (01325) 489001 E-mail: sales@detech.fsnet.co.uk

J C C Lighting Products, Southern Cross Trading Estate, Lamplighter House, Bognor Regis, West Sussex, PO22 9TS Tel: (01243) 829040 Fax: (01243) 829051 E-mail: sales@jcc-lighting.co.uk

Jenstar Ltd, Sturmi Way, Village Farm Industrial Estate, Pyle, Bridgend, Mid Glamorgan, CF33 6BZ Tel: (01656) 745818 Fax: (01656) 745818 E-mail: sales@jenstar.co.uk

Pace Components Ltd, 38 Ballmoor, Buckingham Industrial Estate, Buckingham, MK18 1RQ Tel: (01280) 822733 Fax: (01280) 823839 E-mail: sales@pacecomponents.co.uk

Precision Windings Ltd, Unit J, Durban Road, South Bersted, Bognor Regis, West Sussex, PO22 9QT Tel: (01243) 823311 Fax: (01243) 823318E-mail: sales@precisionwindings.co.uk

Rafmi Electronics, Morrison Road, Stanley, County Durham, DH9 7RX Tel: (01207) 291300 Fax: (01207) 291304 E-mail: accounts@rasmi.com

Zeta Windings Ltd, 416-418 London Road, Isleworth, Middlesex, TW7 5XB Tel: (020) 8568 6875 Fax: (020) 8568 7194 E-mail: chris@zetacool.com

LUBRICANT BLENDING/MIXING PLANT

Mike Ward Associates, The Rodgelands, Bank Lane, Abberley, Worcester, WR6 6BQ Tel: (01299) 896654 Fax: (01299) 896955

LUBRICANT CONSULTANTS

Dynamics, Berwicks Trading Estate, Terling Hall Road, Hatfield Peverell, Chelmsford, CM3 2EY Tel: 0870 1620130 Fax: 0870 1688707 E-mail: sales@dynospill-dynamics.com

Henry Morris 1958 Ltd, Old Town Dock, Newport, Gwent, NP20 2BW Tel: (01633) 265603 Fax: (01633) 253186

The Oil Lab, 2 Little Orchard Gardens, Wolseley Road, Rugeley, Staffordshire, WS15 2ES Tel: (07050) 257431 Fax: (01889) 583682 E-mail: info@theoillab.co.uk

LUBRICANT SACHET/TUBE PACKAGING SERVICES

Lubepack Ltd, Cow Lane, Oldham, OL4 1HS Tel: 0161-620 0440 Fax: 0161-621 0801 E-mail: info@lubepack.co.uk

Packaging Services Unette Ltd, Bank Hill Street, Mount Pleasant, Oldham, OL4 1HR Tel: 0161-621 0800 Fax: 0161-621 0801 E-mail: sales@unette.co.uk

LUBRICANT (SPECIAL PURPOSE) CONSULTANTS

H & R Chempharm, Tipton Works, Dudley Road, Tipton, West Midlands, DY4 8EH Tel: 0121-522 0100 Fax: 0121-522 0115 E-mail: info@hur-chempharm.com

LUBRICANTS

A W V Turner & Co. Ltd, Rex Works, Harvest Lane, Sheffield, S3 8EB Tel: 0114-272 4162 Fax: 0114-276 9284 E-mail: awvturner@awvturner.f9.co.uk

Acrylube Technical Services, Clegg Street, Brierfield, Nelson, Lancashire, BB9 5JQ Tel: (01282) 698595 Fax: (01282) 611244 E-mail: sales@lubricantsuk.co.uk

Anthan Engineering Ltd, Watford, WD19 4EZ Tel: (01923) 249474 Fax: (01923) 249477 E-mail: anthan@anthan.co.uk

Apollo Fuels Ltd, Templeborough Depot, Sheffield Road, Tinsley, Sheffield, S9 1RT Tel: 0114-243 6814 Fax: 0114-242 3362

Aztec Oils Ltd, 31 Intake Road, Bolsover Business Park, Bolsover, Chesterfield, Derbyshire, S44 6BB Tel: (01246) 823007 Fax: (01246) 823014 E-mail: sales@aztecoils.co.uk

B S I Technology Ltd, 11 Whittle Road, Phoenix Parkway, Corby, Northants, NN17 5DX Tel: (01536) 201555 Fax: (01536) 401660 E-mail: bsilubron@netscapeonline.com

Bearing Factors, Progress Road, Whitewalls Industrial Estate, Nelson, Lancashire, BB9 8TE Tel: (01282) 693540 Fax: (01282) 691881 E-mail: sales@bearingfactors.co.uk

Border Oils, 34 Turnberry Way, Carlisle, CA3 0QL Tel: 01228 536960

Brammer Ltd, Unit A Berkeley Court Earl Russell Way, Lawrence Hill, Bristol, BS5 0BX Tel: 0117-935 0422 Fax: 0117-935 0435

C N C Fluids Ltd, Whitehall Trading Estate, Gerrish Avenue, Whitehall, Bristol, BS5 9DF Tel: 0117-935 0033 Fax: 0117-935 0440 E-mail: sales@cncfluids.co.uk

Chemodex Chemicals, Canal Road, Worksop, Nottinghamshire, S80 2EH Tel: (01909) 473301 Fax: (01909) 500961 E-mail: sales@chemodex.co.uk

Condat Ltd, Bancroft Farm, Bawtry Road, Misson Springs, Doncaster, South Yorkshire, DN10 6EZ Tel: (01302) 770088 Fax: (01302) 770776 E-mail: sales@condat.fsnet.co.uk

Cotswold Chemicals & Lubricants, Unit 16-17, Ryeford Industrial Estate, Ryeford, Stonehouse, Gloucestershire, GL10 2LB Tel: (01453) 825292 Fax: (01453) 791451 E-mail: sales@cotswoldchemicals.co.uk

Cromwell Tools Ltd, 19 Concorde Road, Norwich, NR6 6BJ Tel: (01603) 410939 Fax: (01603) 410939 E-mail: norwich@cromwell-tools.co.uk

▶ E P Specialised Fluids & Lubricants, York Street, Radcliffe, Manchester, M26 2GL Tel: 0161-766 2664 Fax: 0161-766 4778

E S B Environmental, 126 Hillcroft Crescent, Watford, WD19 4NZ Tel: (01923) 800852 Fax: (01923) 229003 E-mail: jbird@moose.co.uk

Emo Oil Ltd, Greenwich Road, Cliff Quay, Ipswich, IP3 0BZ Tel: (01473) 232931 Fax: (01473) 213126

Evesons Fuels Ltd, 456 Station Road, Dorridge, Solihull, West Midlands, B93 8EX Tel: (01564) 778877 Fax: (01564) 770655 E-mail: sales@evesons.co.uk

Exol Lubricants Ltd, All Saints Road, Wednesbury, West Midlands, WS10 9LL Tel: 0121-568 2340 Fax: 0121-568 6720 E-mail: sales@exol-lubricants.com

Express Bearings & Transmissions, Anglo Trading Estate, Shepton Mallet, Somerset, BA4 5BY Tel: (01749) 330002 Fax: (01749) 330003 E-mail: sales@expressbearings.co.uk

Forte Lubricants Ltd, Unit 4 Parbrook Close, Coventry, CV4 9XY Tel: (024) 7647 4069 Fax: (024) 7647 1213

George Broughtons & Co Ltd, Whitebirk Road, Whitebirk, Blackburn, BB1 3HZ Tel: (01254) 295509 Fax: (01254) 295501 E-mail: sales@geo-broughton.co.uk

Highspeed Lubricants Ltd, 1 Newbridge Industrial Estate, Pitt Street, Keighley, West Yorkshire, BD21 4PQ Tel: (01535) 611103 Fax: (01535) 611546 E-mail: info@highspeed.co.uk

Interflon Scotland, Woodend Industrial Estate, Cowdenbeath, Fife, KY4 8HW Tel: (01383) 515501 Fax: (01383) 515502 E-mail: scotland@interflon.fsbusiness.co.uk

▶ James Listers, 3 Riverside Industrial Estate, Meir Road, Redditch, Worcestershire, B98 7SY Tel: (01527) 500878 Fax: (01527) 510579 E-mail: redditch@lister.co.uk

Keyland Services Ltd, 7 Timbertop Road, Biggin Hill, Westerham, Kent, TN16 3QR Tel: (01959) 540670 Fax: (01959) 540670 E-mail: sales@keylandservices.com

Klenzan Ltd, 2 Cameron Court, Winwick Quay, Warrington, WA2 8RE Tel: (01925) 234696 Fax: (01925) 234693 E-mail: info@klenzan.co.uk

Laurence Industrial Oil Services Ltd, Gardner & Son, Bowerland Lane, Lingfield, Surrey, RH7 6DF Tel: (01342) 836143 Fax: (01342) 836375

Mitchell Oil Co. Ltd, Unit 4 Thornleigh Trading Estate, Dudley, West Midlands, DY2 8UB Tel: (01384) 233803 Fax: (01384) 456279 E-mail: mitchelloilltd@tiscali.co.uk

Modern Maintenance Products International, Brunel Close, Park Farm Industrial Estate, Wellingborough, Northamptonshire, NN8 6QX Tel: (01933) 670870 Fax: (01933) 670800 E-mail: info@mmp-international.co.uk

Newgate Simms Ltd, PO Box 32, Chester, CH4 0BY Tel: (01244) 660771 Fax: (01244) 661220 E-mail: info@newgatesimms.co.uk

Oak Industrial Supplies, Hamilton Road, Sutton-in-Ashfield, Nottinghamshire, NG17 5LN Tel: (01623) 442222 Fax: (01623) 441234 E-mail: sales@oakis.co.uk

The Oil Shop, 2 Little Orchard Gardens, Wolseley Road, Rugeley, Staffordshire, WS15 2ES Tel: (07050) 184420 Fax: (01889) 583682 E-mail: theoilshop@another.com

Optimum Oils Ltd, PO Box 2865, Kenilworth, Warwickshire, CV8 1YE Tel: (01452) 814476 Fax: (01452) 814476 E-mail: optimumboarders@hotmail.com

Pennine Lubricants, Unit 35 Limestone Cottage Lane, Sheffield, S6 1NJ Tel: 0114-285 2987 Fax: 0114-285 2988 E-mail: sales@penninelubricants.co.uk

Pinco Industries Ltd, 38 Hunters Way, Uckfield, East Sussex, TN22 2BB Tel: (01825) 762387 E-mail: sales@pinco.co.uk

Premier Fuels & Lubricants, Unit 1 Little Row, Fenton Industrial Estate, Stoke-on-Trent, ST4 2SQ Tel: (01782) 410389 Fax: (01782) 410684

Q8 Fuels Care, 10 Midurst Road, Fernhurst, Haslemere, Surrey, GU27 3EE Tel: (01428) 652218 Fax: (01428) 652250

R A Lubricants, Perseverance Mills, Lockwood Scar, Huddersfield, HD4 6BW Tel: (01484) 512836 Fax: (01484) 420793

R W Greeff, Tame Park, Vanguard, Wilnecote, Tamworth, Staffordshire, B77 5DY Tel: (01827) 255200 Fax: (01827) 255255 E-mail: rwgreeff@univareurope.com

Rock Oil Co. Ltd, 90 Priestley Street, Warrington, WA5 1ST Tel: (01925) 636191 Fax: (01925) 632499 E-mail: sales@rockoil.co.uk

S F R East Anglia, 22 Clements Way, Beck Row, Bury St. Edmunds, Suffolk, IP28 8AB Tel: (01638) 713758 Fax: (01638) 715541 E-mail: gary@sfrea.co.uk

Scientific Lubricants Ltd, Glendene Depot, New Hey Road, Huddersfield, HD3 3YW Tel: (01422) 375401 Fax: (01422) 379666 E-mail: sales@scientificoil.co.uk

Solar Petroleum Ltd, Ditton Road, Widnes, Cheshire, WA8 0NN Tel: 0151-424 2488 Fax: 0151-495 1007 E-mail: sales@solar-lubricants.com

Southern Counties Fuels Ltd, Colwood Lane, Warninglid, Haywards Heath, West Sussex, RH17 5UE Tel: (0845) 6004006 Fax: (0870) 7584442 E-mail: sales@scf.co.uk

Sovereign Lubricants UK Ltd, Sovereign House, Crowtrees Lane, Brighouse, West Yorkshire, HD6 3LZ Tel: (01484) 718674 Fax: (01484) 400164 E-mail: schesters@btconnect.com

Sprint Engineering Services Ltd, Unit G3 Imperial Business Estate, West Mill, Gravesend, Kent, DA11 0DL Tel: (01474) 534251 Fax: (01474) 534566 E-mail: info@sprint-uk.com

Team Flitwick, Buncefield Terminal, Green Lane, Hemel Hempstead, Hertfordshire, HP2 7HZ Tel: (01442) 430480 Fax: (01442) 430460

Team Z X 1, Millbrook Business Park, Jarvis Brook, Crowborough, East Sussex, TN6 3JZ Tel: (01892) 669828 Fax: (01892) 669832 E-mail: info@team-zx1.com

Tom-Pac (G.B.) Ltd, PO Box 8450, Prestwick, Ayrshire, KA9 1RG Tel: (01292) 471196 Fax: (01292) 471196 E-mail: tompacgb@btconnect.com

Total Butler, County House, Bayshill Road, Cheltenham, Gloucestershire, GL50 3BA Tel: (0845) 6027283 Fax: (01242) 229498 E-mail: rm.gb-mb-cssteam@totalbutler.co.uk

Total Butler Ltd, Sandy Lane, Sudbury, Suffolk, CO10 7HL Tel: (01787) 371511 Fax: (01787) 370780

Total Butler, Haybrook, Halesfield 9, Telford, Shropshire, TF7 4QW Tel: (01952) 680168 Fax: (01952) 588351

Trachem Fluid Solutions, 10 Victoria Road, Adwick-le-Street, Doncaster, South Yorkshire, DN6 7AZ Tel: (01302) 723111 Fax: (01302) 727744 E-mail: sales@oil-store.co.uk

LUBRICANTS, MOLYBDENUM DISULPHIDE

Northern Molybdenum Ltd, Samson Close, Newcastle upon Tyne, NE12 6DZ Tel: 0191-268 9478 Fax: 0191-216 0004

Spanjaard UK Ltd, PO Box 21, Huntingdon, Cambridgeshire, PE29 2EQ Tel: (01480) 457022 Fax: (01480) 457022

LUBRICANTS, TO CUSTOMER SPECIFICATION

GBR Technology Ltd, 6 Jupiter House, Calleva Park, Aldermaston, Reading, RG7 8NN Tel: 0118-982 0567 Fax: 0118-982 0590 E-mail: sales@gbrtech.co.uk

H & R Chempharm, Tipton Works, Dudley Road, Tipton, West Midlands, DY4 8EH Tel: 0121-522 0100 Fax: 0121-522 0115 E-mail: info@hur-chempharm.com

Houghton Oils & Chemicals, 19 Tandragee Road, Newry, County Down, BT35 6QE Tel: (028) 3026 7119 Fax: (028) 3026 6610

LUBRICATING ENGINEERS/ SERVICES

Scottoilers Scotland Ltd, 2 Riverside, Milngavie, Glasgow, G62 6PL Tel: 0141-955 1100 Fax: 0141-956 5896 E-mail: sales@scottoilers.com

LUBRICATING GREASE

Apiezon Products, Hibernia Way, Trafford Park, Manchester, M32 0ZD Tel: 0161-864 5419 Fax: 0161-864 5444 E-mail: sales@apiezon.com

Fuchs Lubricants (UK) Plc, P O Box 20, Stoke-on-Trent, ST1 5HU Tel: (0870) 1200400 Fax: (01782) 202072 E-mail: contact-uk@fuchs-oil.com

Ironsides Lubricants Ltd, Shield Street, Stockport, Cheshire, SK3 0DS Tel: 0161-477 5858 Fax: 0161-480 6203 E-mail: sales@ironsideslubricants.co.uk

Millers Oils Ltd, Hillside Oil Works, Rastrick, Brighouse, West Yorkshire, HD6 3DP Tel: (01484) 713201 Fax: (01484) 721263 E-mail: enquiries@millersoils.co.uk

Mitchell Oil Co. Ltd, Unit 4 Thornleigh Trading Estate, Dudley, West Midlands, DY2 8UB Tel: (01384) 233803 Fax: (01384) 456279 E-mail: mitchelloilltd@tiscali.co.uk

Molyslip Atlantic, Unit 1 Danebrook Court, Langford Lane, Kidlington, Oxfordshire, OX5 1LQ Tel: (01865) 370032 Fax: (01865) 372030 E-mail: enquiries@molyslip.co.uk

Pick Quick Service, 380 Meanwood Road, Leeds, LS7 2JF Tel: 0113-216 8811 Fax: 0113-216 8833 E-mail: sales@pickquick.co.uk

Tompion Oil Co. Ltd, Healey Road, Ossett, West Yorkshire, WF5 8LS Tel: (01924) 273295

Total Butler, County House, Bayshill Road, Cheltenham, Gloucestershire, GL50 3BA Tel: (0845) 6027283 Fax: (01242) 229498 E-mail: rm.gb-mb-cssteam@totalbutler.co.uk

Total Butler, Haybrook, Halesfield 9, Telford, Shropshire, TF7 4QW Tel: (01952) 680168 Fax: (01952) 588351

LUBRICATING OIL ADDITIVES

Afton Chemical, London Road, Bracknell, Berkshire, RG12 2UW Tel: (01344) 304141 Fax: (01344) 420666 E-mail: ethyleurope@ethyl.com

Jarmac Ltd, Stanton House, 6 Eastham Village Road, Eastham, Wirral, Merseyside, CH62 0BJ Tel: 0151-327 7511 Fax: 0151-327 7866 E-mail: sales@jarmac.u-net.com

Petro Lube, 276 Chase Road, London, N14 6HA Tel: (020) 8886 8002 Fax: (020) 8886 7716

LUBRICATING OIL DISTRIBUTORS/BLENDERS/ AGENTS

Bayford Cambria, Tir Llwyd Enterprise Park, Kinmel Bay, Rhyl, Clwyd, LL18 5JH Tel: (01745) 332121 Fax: (01745) 332122 E-mail: sales@BAYFORDCAMBRIA.co.uk

Benjamin R Vickers & Sons Ltd, Clarence Road, Leeds, LS10 1ND Tel: 0113-386 7654 Fax: 0113-386 7676 E-mail: inbox@vickers-oil.com

Caldo Oils Ltd, Unit 4 Rapier Court Sabre Close, Heathfield Industrial Estate, Newton Abbot, Devon, TQ12 6TW Tel: (01626) 835046 Fax: (01626) 836833

Carona Reuter Industrial Ltd, Coppen Road, Selinas Lane, Dagenham, Essex, RM8 1HN Tel: (020) 8592 2576 Fax: (020) 8595 8024 E-mail: carona_reuter@hotmail.com

Comma Oil & Chemicals Ltd, Comma Works, Dering Way, Gravesend, Kent, DA12 2QX Tel: (01474) 564311 Fax: (01474) 333000 E-mail: sales@commaoil.com

Contractors Equipment Sales Ltd, 1 Harrier Way, Airport Industrial Estate, Norwich, NR6 6HY Tel: (01603) 404620 Fax: (01603) 429717 E-mail: ces@ces.demon.co.uk

Crossford Oil & Tool Supplies Ltd, Unit 94 Springvale Industrial Estate, Cwmbran, Gwent, NP44 5BH Tel: (01633) 873612 Fax: (01633) 864884 E-mail: sales@crossfords.co.uk

Exol Lubricants Ltd, All Saints Road, Wednesbury, West Midlands, WS10 9LL Tel: 0121-568 2340 Fax: 0121-568 6720 E-mail: sales@exol-lubricants.com

Falcon Lubricants Ltd, Showfield Lane Industrial Estate, Malton, North Yorkshire, YO17 6BT Tel: (01653) 694019 Fax: (01653) 600283 E-mail: admin@oils.co.uk

John Clayden & Partners Lubysil Ltd, 9 Frensham Road, Sweet Briar Road Industrial Estate, Norwich, NR3 2BT Tel: (01603) 789924 Fax: (01603) 417335 E-mail: claydenlubysil@aol.com

Mobil Shipping Co. Ltd, St. Catherines House, 2 Kingsway, London, WC2B 6WJ Tel: (020) 7412 4000 Fax: (020) 7412 4084

New Era Oil UK, Bow Bridge Wharf, 1-9 High Street, London, E15 2RH Tel: (01279) 425757 Fax: (01279) 425758

▶ Oilco (Swindon) Ltd, Bagbury Green Farm, Bagbury Lane, Purton, Swindon, SN4 5LX Tel: (01793) 772437 Fax: (01793) 772437 E-mail: oilcosw.kemp@btconnect.com

Petro Lube, 276 Chase Road, London, N14 6HA Tel: (020) 8886 8002 Fax: (020) 8886 7716

Petrofer UK plc, Harcourt Business Park, Halesfield 17, Telford, Shropshire, TF7 4PW Tel: (01952) 580100 Fax: (01952) 580101 E-mail: sales@petrofer.co.uk

Production Lubricants Ltd, Progress Industrial Estate, Station Road, Rogiet, Caldicot, Monmouthshire, NP26 3UE Tel: (01291) 426900 Fax: (01291) 426940 E-mail: enquiries@severnfuels.co.uk

Rods Oils Ltd, Two Gates Trading Estate, Tamworth, Staffordshire, B77 5AE Tel: (01827) 283211 Fax: (01827) 288906 E-mail: sales@rods-oils.co.uk

S S Motors (Fuels) Ltd, 2 Honeysome Road, Chatteris, Cambridgeshire, PE16 6RZ Tel: (01354) 693181 Fax: (01354) 694181

Silgo Lubricants Ltd, 20-22-24 Thurrock Commercial Centre, Purfleet Industrial Park, Aveley, South Ockendon, Essex, RM15 4YG Tel: (01708) 865665 Fax: (01708) 868996 E-mail: sales@silgo.co.uk

Thames Lubricants Ltd, Garner Street, Stoke-on-Trent, ST4 7DE Tel: (01782) 844388 Fax: (01782) 848437 E-mail: sales@thameslubricants.co.uk

Tompion Oil Co. Ltd, Healey Road, Ossett, West Yorkshire, WF5 8LS Tel: (01924) 273295

Trachem Fluid Solutions, 10 Victoria Road, Adwick-le-Street, Doncaster, South Yorkshire, DN6 7AZ Tel: (01302) 723111 Fax: (01302) 727744 E-mail: sales@oil-store.co.uk

LUBRICATING OIL FILTERS

Chainings Ltd, Pomona Works, Newent Business Park, Newent, Gloucestershire, GL18 1DZ Tel: (01531) 822244 Fax: (01531) 821555 E-mail: sales@chainings.com

LUBRICATING OIL PRODUCERS OR REFINERS

Bretts Oils, Pipewellgate, Gateshead, Tyne & Wear, NE8 2BN Tel: 0191-477 0856 Fax: 0191-490 0360 E-mail: uksales@ovoline.co.uk

Castle Oils Ltd, Valley Works, Chemical Lane, Stoke-on-Trent, ST6 4PB Tel: (01782) 577422 Fax: (01782) 839432 E-mail: darren.tistion@castle-stoke.co.uk

Chevron & Texaco Ltd, 1 Westferry Circus, Canary Wharf, London, E14 4HA Tel: (020) 7719 3000 Fax: E-mail:

D A Stuart Ltd, Lincoln Street, Wolverhampton, WV10 0DZ Tel: (01902) 456111 Fax: (01902) 453764 E-mail: dastuart@dastuart.co.uk

Houghton Oils & Chemicals, 19 Tandragee Road, Newry, County Down, BT35 6QE Tel: (028) 3026 7119 Fax: (028) 3026 6610

John Clayden & Partners Lubysil Ltd, 9 Frensham Road, Sweet Briar Road Industrial Estate, Norwich, NR3 2BT Tel: (01603) 789924 Fax: (01603) 417335 E-mail: claydenlubysil@aol.com

Oil Inventions Ltd, Leamore Close, Walsall, WS2 7NJ Tel: (01922) 477904 Fax: (01922) 710108 E-mail: info@oilinventions.co.uk

Quaker Lubricant Distributors, Unit 6 Brunel Way, Stroudwater Business Park, Stonehouse, Gloucestershire, GL10 3SX Tel: (01453) 820800 Fax: (01453) 820820 E-mail: cindy_basile@quakerchem.com

Shell UK Ltd, Shell Centre, York Road, London, SE1 7NA Tel: (020) 7546 5000 Fax: (020) 7934 8060

Total Butler Ltd, Sandy Lane, Sudbury, Suffolk, CO10 7HL Tel: (01787) 371511 Fax: (01787) 370780

Wd-40 Co. Ltd, PO Box 44, Milton Keynes, MK11 3LJ Tel: (01908) 555400 Fax: (01908) 266900 E-mail: sales@wd40.co.uk

▶ indicates data change since last edition

LUBRICATING OIL PUMPS

Suff Marine (Europe) Ltd, 15 Allanfield Drive, Newton Stewart, Wigtownshire, DG8 6BP Tel: (01671) 401216 Fax: (01671) 401216 E-mail: sales@suffmarine.com
Varley Pumps Ltd, 1 Kimpton Road, Luton, LU1 3LD Tel: (01582) 731144 Fax: (01582) 402563E-mail: varleysales@haywardtyler.com

LUBRICATING OIL RINGS

A & A Lampkin, Greengate, Silsden, Keighley, West Yorkshire, BD20 9LA Tel: (01535) 652328 Fax: (01535) 657866

LUBRICATING SYSTEMS OR EQUIPMENT

A E Westwood Ltd, Tything Road, Kinwarton, Alcester, Warwickshire, B49 6ES Tel: (01789) 765777 Fax: (01789) 765727 E-mail: aewestwood@thesjgroup.com
A T S Electro Lube UK Ltd, Unit 383I, Jedburgh Court, Team Valley Trading Estate, Gateshead, Tyne & Wear, NE11 0BQ Tel: 0191-491 4212 Fax: 0191-491 4224 E-mail: info@ats-electro-lube.co.uk
Adams Lube Tech Ltd, Unit 6 Binns Close, Coventry, CV4 9TB Tel: (024) 7646 7941 Fax: (024) 7669 4002 E-mail: info@adamslube.com
Allube Ltd, Thorncliffe Park Estate, Chapeltown, Sheffield, S35 2PH Tel: 0114-245 4979 Fax: 0114-257 0377 E-mail: sales@allube.co.uk
Baric Systems, 11 Telford Court, Morpeth, Northumberland, NE61 2DB Tel: (01670) 505944 Fax: (01670) 505923 E-mail: sales@baricsale.co.uk
William Coulthard & Co. Ltd, Stephenson Road, Durranhill Trading Estate, Carlisle, CA1 3NS Tel: (01228) 521418 Fax: (01228) 511310 E-mail: sales@wmcoulthard.com
CTS, 41 Forge Lane, Minworth Industrial Park, Minworth, Sutton Coldfield, West Midlands, B76 1AH Tel: 0121-351 4445 Fax: 0121-351 4442 E-mail: sales@centretank.com
Dynamics, Berwicks Trading Estate, Terling Hall Road, Hatfield Peverell, Chelmsford, CM3 2EY Tel: 0870 1620130 Fax: 0870 1688707 E-mail: sales@dynospill-dynamics.com
Engineering & General Equipment Ltd, Eley Estate, Edmonton, London, N18 3BB Tel: (020) 8807 4567 Fax: (020) 8884 2229 E-mail: sales@centralube.com
Ernest H Hill Ltd, Unit 10-12, Meadowbrook Park, Halfway, Sheffield, S20 3PJ Tel: 0114-248 4882 Fax: 0114-248 9142 E-mail: sales@hillpumps.com
Fenco-Aldridge (Barton) Ltd, Lovat Court, Caldecote St, Newport Pagnell, Buckinghamshire, MK16 0YZ Tel: (01908) 614646 Fax: (01908) 214482 E-mail: fab@fenco.co.uk
G B M Products, 4 Octavian Way, Team Valley Trading Estate, Gateshead, Tyne & Wear, NE11 0HZ Tel: 0191-487 8004 Fax: 0191-487 1655 E-mail: info@gbmproducts.sagehost.co.uk
Garafit Services Ltd, Willis House, Flowers Hill, Bristol, BS4 5JJ Tel: 0117-971 1451 Fax: 0117-977 8022 E-mail: garafit.info@garafit.com
Groeneveld UK Ltd, Unit 29a Loughborough Motorway Trading Estate, Gelders Hall Road, Shepshed, Loughborough, Leicestershire, LE12 9NH Tel: (01509) 600033 Fax: (01509) 602000 E-mail: groenevel.uk@talk21.com
Interco Lubrication Services, 28 Harwood Court, Riverside Park Industrial Estate, Middlesbrough, Cleveland, TS2 1PU Tel: (01642) 247157 Fax: (01642) 247157 E-mail: chas_ophield@lineone.net
Interlube Systems Ltd, 85 St. Modwen Road, Plymouth, PL6 8LH Tel: (01752) 676000 Fax: (01752) 676001 E-mail: info@interlubesystems.co.uk
Jaco-Sumal Ltd, 8 Edwards Road, Birmingham, B24 9EP Tel: 0121-373 6988 Fax: 0121-384 7525 E-mail: jacosumal@yahoo.com
Keyland Services Ltd, 7 Timbertop Road, Biggin Hill, Westerham, Kent, TN16 3QR Tel: (01959) 540670 Fax: (01959) 540670 E-mail: sales@keylandservices.com
Kluber Lubrication, Bradford Road, Halifax, West Yorkshire, HX3 7BN Tel: (01422) 319149 Fax: (01422) 206073 E-mail: info@uk.klueber.com
Lincoln Industrial Ltd, Unit 2 Canada Close, Banbury, Oxfordshire, OX16 2RT Tel: (01295) 256611 Fax: (01295) 275771 E-mail: sales@lincolnindustrial.co.uk
Lubrication Services, 152 Oxford Road, Banbury, Oxfordshire, OX16 9BA Tel: (01295) 251821 Fax: (01295) 251821
Lumatic Ga Ltd, Theaklen Drive, St. Leonards-on-Sea, East Sussex, TN38 9AZ Tel: (01424) 436343 Fax: (01424) 429926 E-mail: sales@lumatic.co.uk
Premier Bearing Co. Ltd, Chaucer Street, Northampton, NN2 7HB Tel: (01604) 718107 Fax: (01604) 720654 E-mail: sales@premierbearing.co.uk
Samoa Ltd, Asturias House Barrs Fold Road, Wingates Industrial Estate, Westhoughton, Bolton, BL5 3XP Tel: (01942) 850600 Fax: (01204) 812160 E-mail: sales@samoa.ltd.uk
Stephens (Midlands) Ltd, Greets Green Industrial Estate, West Bromwich, West Midlands, B70 9EW Tel: 0121-522 2221 Fax: 0121-557 6861 E-mail: info@stephenslube.co.uk
Technolube Lubrication Systems, Unit 17 Calder Workshops, Gibbet Street, Halifax, West Yorkshire, HX1 4JQ Tel: (01422) 320784 Fax: (01422) 346047
Thomas Proctor & Son Ltd, Dukesway, Team Valley Trading Estate, Gateshead, Tyne & Wear, NE11 0NW Tel: 0191-491 3027 Fax: 0191-491 3028 E-mail: sales@thomasproctor.co.uk
Tribolube Ltd, Unit 4 Woodside, Thornwood, Epping, Essex, CM16 6LH Tel: (01992) 577551 Fax: (01992) 577553

LUGGAGE FITTINGS

▶ Globalbagtag.Com, Everon Centre, 58 John Street, Filey, North Yorkshire, YO14 9NT Tel: (0870) 7657280 Fax: (0870) 7657281 E-mail: sales@globalbagtag.com

LUMINAIRE LOW ENERGY LIGHTING

Ballast Tools (UK) Ltd, Unit 4 County Park Business Centre, Shrivenham Road, Swindon, SN1 2NR Tel: (01793) 697800 Fax: (01793) 527020 E-mail: btukltd@aol.com
Chalmor Ltd, 1 Telmere Industrial Estate, Albert Road, Luton, LU1 3QF Tel: (01582) 748700 Fax: (01582) 748748 E-mail: sales@chalmor.co.uk
Commercial Lighting Systems Ltd, Unit 16-17, Park Gate Business Centre, Chandlers Way, Park Gate, Southampton, SO31 1FQ Tel: (01489) 581002 Fax: (01489) 576262 E-mail: sales@commercial-lighting.co.uk
Compact Lighting Ltd, Dundas Spur, Portsmouth, PO3 5RW Tel: (023) 9265 2999 Fax: (023) 9265 3053 E-mail: info@compact-lighting.co.uk
Dextra Lighting Systems plc, 17 Brickfields Business Park, Gillingham, Dorset, SP8 4PX Tel: (01747) 826096 Fax: (01747) 858119 E-mail: sales@dextralighting.co.uk
Hodgson Lighting, 41 High Street, Hampton Hill, Hampton, Middlesex, TW12 1NB Tel: (020) 8941 3375 Fax: (020) 8979 5178 E-mail: johnatjhlight@tiscali.co.uk
Mike Smith Designs Ltd, Unit 10 Fordhouse Road Industrial Estate, Steel Drive, Wolverhampton, WV10 9XE Tel: (01902) 784400 Fax: (01902) 785980 E-mail: sales@mikesmithdesigns.com
Vitalighting Ltd, 4 Sutherland Court Moor Park Industrial Centre, Tolpits Lane, Watford, WD18 9NA Tel: (01923) 896476 Fax: (01923) 897741 E-mail: sales@vitalighting.com

LUMINAIRES

W F Electrical Distributors, 313-333 Rainham Road South, Dagenham, Essex, RM10 8SX Tel: (020) 8517 7000 Fax: (020) 8595 0519 E-mail: peter.warsap@hagemeyer.co.uk

LUMINOUS MASTERBATCHES

▶ Emsar Polymers UK Ltd, 2 The Court Stanley Green Business Park, Earl Road, Cheadle Hulme, Cheadle, Cheshire, SK8 6GN Tel: 0161-485 7772 Fax: 0161 485 7773 E-mail: info@emsarpolymers.co.uk

LUMINOUS SIGNS

▶ Andesign Sign Writers, F 11-13 Coleshill Road, Sutton Coldfield, West Midlands, B75 7AA Tel: 0121-354 2272 Fax: 0121-355 8883 E-mail: info@andesignuk.co.uk
Hilliard & Winn, 2 Sovereign House, Butterley Street, Leeds, LS10 1AW Tel: 0113-242 2542 Fax: 0113-244 4405 E-mail: hilliard@btconnect.com
London Screen Printing, St. Clare Business Park, Holly Road, Hampton, Middlesex, TW12 1PZ Tel: (020) 8941 8285 Fax: (020) 8941 8806
Sign Connections Ltd, Unit 5 Sinclair Court, Great Yarmouth, Norfolk, NR31 0NH Tel: (01493) 440285 Fax: (01493) 653888 E-mail: info@signconnections.com
Telegan Protection Ltd, 3-5 Holmethorpe Avenue, Redhill, RH1 2LZ Tel: (01737) 763800 Fax: (01737) 782727 E-mail: sales@teleganprotection.com

MACHINABLE CERAMIC MATERIALS

A G Rutter Ltd, Fitzherbert Road, Portsmouth, PO6 1RU Tel: (023) 9278 9300 Fax: (023) 9278 9500 E-mail: sales@dtw-tiles.co.uk
Arna & Farrington, Langley House, High Street, Thorpe-le-Soken, Clacton-on-Sea, Essex, CO16 0EA Tel: (01255) 862355 Fax: (01255) 862355 E-mail: sales@marisaarna.co.uk
Ceramic Substrates & Components Ltd, Lukely Works, 180 Carisbrooke Road, Newport, Isle of Wight, PO30 1DH Tel: (01983) 528697 Fax: (01983) 822252 E-mail: sales@ceramic-subtrates.co.uk
Decoritalia UK Ltd, 198 Moorland Road, Stoke-on-Trent, ST6 1EB Tel: (01782) 832662 Fax: (01782) 832651 E-mail: sales@decoritialia.co.uk
Potters Potclais Group, Pelsall Road, Walsall, WS8 7DL Tel: (01543) 377015 Fax: (01543) 372301

MACHINE CONTROL SYSTEMS

Cambridge Micro Engineering Ltd, 83 High Street, Linton, Cambridge, CB21 4JT Tel: (01223) 893872 Fax: (01223) 891760 E-mail: enquiries@cme.co.uk
R S Micro, 129 Brookfield Place, Walton Summit Centre, Bamber Bridge, Preston, PR5 8BF Tel: (01772) 628000 Fax: (01772) 628888 E-mail: rs_micro@compuserve.com

MACHINE COVERS, *See also headings for particular types*

SC Machinery, 16 Ranelagh Road, London, E6 2SL Tel: (020) 8552 9383 Fax: (020) 8552 6950 E-mail: frankcole@btconnect.com

MACHINE COVERS, CONCERTINA/TELESCOPE TYPE

Barrowfield Leather Co. Ltd, 47 Solway Street, Glasgow, G40 4JG Tel: 0141-554 7863 Fax: 0141-554 8053 E-mail: office@barrowfield.com
Blue Machenary (Scotland) Ltd, 9 Broadways Road, Spring Kerse Industrial Estate, Stirling, FK7 7ST Tel: (01786) 469444
▶ Frederick Crowther & Son Ltd, 4b High Level Way, Halifax, West Yorkshire, HX1 4PN Tel: (01422) 367788 Fax: (01422) 363802 E-mail: sales@cromar.co.uk
D Q R Precision Ltd, Unit 11 Colchester Business Centre, 1 George Williams Way, Colchester, CO1 2JS Tel: (01206) 766116 Fax: (01206) 766117 E-mail: sales@dqr.co.uk

MACHINE CUT GEARS

Carford Transmissions Ltd, 68 Rea Street South, Birmingham, B5 6LB Tel: 0121-622 7060 Fax: 0121-622 4060 E-mail: admin@carford.com
Gears in Motion, Unit 66 Rovex Business Park, Hy Hall Road, Tyseley, Birmingham, B11 2AQ Tel: 0121-706 8821 Fax: 0121-708 0512 E-mail: info@gearsinmotion.co.uk
Meldon Gears 1967 Ltd, Lees Road, Knowsley Industrial Park, Liverpool, L33 7XP Tel: 0151-546 9787 Fax: 0151-546 2861 E-mail: sales@meldongears.co.uk
The Reid Gear Co., Napier Street, Linwood, Paisley, Renfrewshire, PA3 3AN Tel: (01505) 321591 Fax: (01505) 321645 E-mail: info@reidgear.com
Sutton Gears Ltd, Unit 2 Lifford Way, Binley Industrial Estate, Binley Industrial Estate, Coventry, CV3 2RN Tel: (024) 7643 1331 Fax: (024) 7665 1000

MACHINE ENGRAVERS

A E S Engraving Co. Ltd, Unit 19, Boulton Industrial Centre, Hockley, Birmingham, B18 5AU Tel: 0121-551 9525 Fax: 0121-551 9535 E-mail: enquiries@aes-signs.com
A W Engraving, 11 Lifford Way, Binley Industrial Estate, Coventry, CV3 2RN Tel: (024) 7663 5453 Fax: (024) 7663 5486
Abbey Engraving, Unit 15 New Horizon Business Centre, Barrows Road, Harlow, Essex, CM19 5FN Tel: (01279) 626277 Fax: (01279) 626277 E-mail: info@abbeyengraving.co.uk
Accu-Rout Ltd, Maltings Lane, Castleton, Rochdale, Lancashire, OL11 2UY Tel: (01706) 631277 Fax: (01706) 646207
Ashburton Instrument Co., Western Road, Ashburton, Newton Abbot, Devon, TQ13 7ED Tel: (01364) 652579 Fax: (01364) 653978 E-mail: phil@ashins.freeserve.co.uk
Dartford Engraving Ltd, 4 Power Works Estate, Slade Green Road, Erith, Kent, DA8 2HY Tel: (01322) 340194 Fax: (01322) 347819 E-mail: mail@desp.co.uk
Deco Bishop Auckland Ltd, Roman Way Industrial Estate, Bishop Auckland, County Durham, DL14 9AW Tel: (01388) 604590 Fax: (01388) 604590
Dereham Industrial Engravers Ltd, 63 Spitalfields, Norwich, NR1 4EY Tel: (01603) 622634 Fax: (01603) 622534
Eglen Engravers Ltd, 12 Lord Street, Halifax, West Yorkshire, HX1 5AE Tel: (01422) 365556 Fax: (01422) 365564 E-mail: sales@eglenengravers.co.uk
▶ Eyre & Baxter (Stampcraft) Ltd, 229 Derbyshire Lane, Sheffield, S8 8SD Tel: 0114-250 0153 Fax: 0114-258 0856 E-mail: sales@eyreandbaxter.co.uk
F & G Lancaster, 16 Hockley Street, Birmingham, B18 6BL Tel: 0121-554 1454 Fax: 0121-554 1454
Flint & Son, 43 Nursery Road, Hockley, Birmingham, B19 2XN Tel: 0121-523 2875
Fortune UK Ltd, Wyvenhoe, Farnham Road, Farnham Royal, Slough, SL2 3AE Tel: (01753) 669471 Fax: (01753) 669472 E-mail: info@fortuneuk.com
G R C Engraving Ltd, 14 Dalkey Road, Ferndown, Dorset, BH22 8QX Tel: (01202) 861297 Fax: (01202) 861297
I & M Controls Ltd, 75 Villa Street, Birmingham, B19 2XL Tel: 0121-551 7877 Fax: 0121-554 3846 E-mail: sales@iandmcontrols.co.uk
Just Engraving, 138 St. Neots Road, Eaton Ford, St. Neots, Cambridgeshire, PE19 7AL Tel: (01480) 472715 Fax: (01480) 386716 E-mail: engraving@endersby.com
M G Engraving, 135 Somerset Road, Coventry, CV1 4EF Tel: (024) 7622 5110 Fax: (024) 7663 2894 E-mail: mg@mgengineering.fsnet.co.uk
Roger Needham & Sons Ltd, Units 15-16 Salford Enterprise Centre, Guide Street, Salford, M50 1EW Tel: 0161-745 7277 Fax: 0161-745 7826 E-mail: frankrnsl@aol.com
P J Drew Engravers Ltd, Lower Vicarage Road, Southampton, SO19 7RJ Tel: (023) 8044 6062 Fax: (023) 8042 2981 E-mail: sales@pjdrew.co.uk
Pacer Systems Ltd, Gauntley Street, Nottingham, NG7 5HF Tel: 0115-988 7777 Fax: 0115-988 7788 E-mail: sales@pacersys.co.uk
Peter's Trophies, 10 West Street, Weston-super-Mare, Avon, BS23 1JT Tel: (01934) 620206 Fax: (01934) 620206 E-mail: monty19452003@yahoo.co.uk
Plastic Formers Ltd, Unit 1, King Street, Stockport Road, Denton, Manchester, M34 6PF Tel: 0161-320 7200 Fax: 0161-335 0109 E-mail: enquiries@plasticformers.co.uk
Plastic & Metal Engravings, 9 Benson Road, Poole, Dorset, BH17 0GB Tel: (01202) 677393 Fax: (01202) 681455 E-mail: sales@plasticandmetalengraving.co.uk
Precision Units Dorset Ltd, 2a Gloucester Road, Poole, Dorset, BH12 2AP Tel: (01202) 741664 Fax: (01202) 716473 E-mail: enquiries@precisionunits.co.uk
R H Wilkins Ltd, 31-35 Kirby Street, London, EC1N 8TE Tel: (020) 7405 5187 Fax: (020) 7831 2805 E-mail: sales@rhwilkins.co.uk
Saltwell Signs (North East) Ltd, Princesway North, Team Valley Trading Estate, Gateshead, Tyne & Wear, NE11 0TU Tel: 0191-482 5555 Fax: 0191-491 0246 E-mail: sales@saltwellsigns.co.uk
Charles Smith & Reddish Ltd, 11a Lever Street, London, EC1V 3QU Tel: (020) 7253 2457 Fax: (020) 7490 4612 E-mail: info@csr-chartinstruments.co.uk
Warren & Tarry Ltd, Glenbarr Avenue, Bradgate Street, Leicester, LE4 0AE Tel: 0116-262 6056 Fax: 0116-262 6056
C.J. Watson, Hilton Chambers, Roushill, Shrewsbury, SY1 1PN Tel: (01743) 362898 Fax: (01743) 362898
William W Cope, Unit 34 Camp Hill Industrial Estate, John Kempe Way, Birmingham, B12 0HU Tel: 0121-766 8874 Fax: 0121-771 2866 E-mail: martingeer@williamcope.co.uk

MACHINE FEET

Safeload (UK)Ltd, 26, Holton Road,, Holton Heath Trading Estate, Poole, Dorset, BH16 5SL Tel: (01202) 624422 Fax: (01202) 624569

MACHINE GUARD VISION PANELS/WINDOWS

A M P Wire Ltd, Sun Iron Works, Ward Street, Chadderton, Oldham, OL9 9EX Tel: 0161-620 7250 Fax: 0161-688 5566 E-mail: pam@ampwire.co.uk
Noise Seal Ltd, Unit 20 Digby Drive, Leicester Road Industrial Estate, Melton Mowbray, Leicestershire, LE13 0RQ Tel: (01664) 480678 Fax: (01664) 480678 E-mail: sales@noiseseal.com

MACHINE GUARDS, *See also headings for particular types*

Camera Bellows, Units 3-5, St. Pauls Road, Birmingham, B12 8NG Tel: 0121-440 1695 Fax: 0121-440 0972 E-mail: sales@camerabellows.com
Industrial Controls Ltd, Unit 1 Audley Court, Lodge Way, Thetford, Norfolk, IP24 1HT Tel: (01842) 750800 Fax: (01842) 765900 E-mail: sales@industrialcontrols.co.uk
Industrial Machine Guards, 2 Dormston Trading Estate, Burton Road, Dudley, West Midlands, DY1 2UF Tel: (01902) 676485 Fax: (01902) 880987
M G Automation Ltd, 16 Stratfield Park, Elettra Avenue, Waterlooville, Hampshire, PO7 7XN Tel: (023) 9226 7727 Fax: (023) 9226 7747 E-mail: sales@mgautomation.co.uk
Morton Industrial Plastics Ltd, Cook Lane, Heckmondwike, West Yorkshire, WF16 9JG Tel: (01924) 405550 Fax: (01924) 405770 E-mail: info@mipuk.com
Powerguards Ramping Systems, Bennetts Mead, Southgate Road, Wincanton, Somerset, BA9 9EB Tel: (01963) 31206 Fax: (01963) 31904 E-mail: powerguardsinc@beeb.net

MACHINE GUARDS – *continued*

Print Guard Ltd, Unit 2, Parsonage Street, Oldbury, West Midlands, B69 4PH Tel: 0121-552 5707 Fax: 0121-552 5506 E-mail: sales@printguard.co.uk

Tapeswitch Ltd, Unit 38 Drumhead Road, Chorley North Industrial Estate, Chorley, Lancashire, PR6 7BX Tel: (01257) 249777 Fax: (01257) 246600 E-mail: sales@tapeswitch.co.uk

Troax UK Ltd, Enterprise House, Murdock Road, Dorcan, Swindon, SN3 5HY Tel: (01793) 542000 Fax: (01793) 618784 E-mail: info@troax.co.uk

MACHINE IDENTIFICATION NAMEPLATES

NBS Technologies Ltd, 7 Byfleet Technical Centre, Canada Road, West Byfleet, Surrey, KT14 7NB Tel: (01932) 351531 Fax: (01932) 351382 E-mail: sales@nbs.com

Michael Smith Engraving Services Ltd, Unit 3, Leicester, LE2 8AA Tel: 0116-283 0712 Fax: 0116-244 0198 E-mail: sales@michaelsmithswitchgear.co.uk

Stayprint Labels & Tags, Brow Lane, Shelf, Halifax, West Yorkshire, HX3 7QJ Tel: (01274) 699200 Fax: (01274) 699209 E-mail: sales@stayprint.com

MACHINE INDEX BOXES

Camco UK Ltd, 432 Perth Avenue, Slough, SL1 4TS Tel: (01753) 786100 Fax: (01753) 786101 E-mail: sales@camcoindex.com

Precision Motion (Cofil) Ltd, Unit 63, Roman Way, Longridge Road, Ribbleton, Preston, PR2 5BE Tel: (01772) 653366 Fax: (01772) 653163 E-mail: pmcofil@btconnect.com

MACHINE KNIVES

Allgrind, Unit 8 Century Street, Sheffield, S9 5DX Tel: 0114-244 4491 Fax: 0114-244 4491 E-mail: murbeck@aol.com

Colton Tooling Ltd, 4 Highmeres Road, Leicester, LE4 9LZ Tel: 0116-276 6225 Fax: 0116-276 6226 E-mail: colton@talk21.com

Fernite Of Sheffield Ltd, Fernite Works, Coleford Road, Sheffield, S9 5NJ Tel: 0114-244 0527 Fax: 0114-244 5922 E-mail: sales@fernite.co.uk

Frictec Ltd, Robinson Way, Portsmouth, PO3 5SA Tel: (023) 9266 6816 Fax: (023) 9269 0425 E-mail: sales@frictec.co.uk

Harcross Engineering Co. Ltd, Unit 1 The Ember Centre, Hersham, Walton-On-Thames, Surrey, KT12 3PU Tel: (01932) 222201 Fax: (01932) 224722 E-mail: sales@harcross-eng.co.uk

Hardy UK Ltd, 175 Fernhill Road, Bootle, Merseyside, L20 9DU Tel: 0151-922 2291 Fax: 0151-933 4164E-mail: hardyuk@aol.com

High Speed & Carbide Ltd, Freedom Works, John St, Sheffield, S2 4QT Tel: 0114-279 6197 Fax: 0114-279 7550 E-mail: sales@hscknives.co.uk

L. Hodge Engineering Ltd, Unit 12, Chiltern Business Village, Arundel Road, Uxbridge, Middlesex, UB8 2SN Tel: (01895) 813758 Fax: (01895) 812468 E-mail: john@lhodge-engineers.co.uk

Kennedy Grinding Ltd, Commerce Park, Commerce Way, Colchester, CO2 8HX Tel: (01206) 790407 Fax: (01206) 793113

Microblade Holdings Ltd, Sanderson Street, Sheffield, S9 2UA Tel: 0114-261 8855 Fax: 0114-261 9555

▶ Spear & Jackson International Ltd, The Mill Race, 346 Brightside Lane, Sheffield, S9 2SP Tel: 0114-225 0862 Fax: 0114-225 0861 E-mail: pjones@sjint.com

Swemko (UK) Ltd, 29 Bonville Road, Brislington, Bristol, BS4 5QH Tel: (0845) 0760960 Fax: 0117-972 0470 E-mail: sales@swemkoknifes.com

▶ Techform Packaging Supplies, Unit 43-51, Limestone Cottage Lane, Sheffield, S6 1NJ Tel: 0114-234 9912 Fax: 0114-234 9973

▶ V E S Precision Ltd, 10 Cropmead Industrial Estate, Crewkerne, Somerset, TA18 7HQ Tel: (01460) 270600 Fax: (01460) 270601 E-mail: enquiries@vesprecision.com

Wolstenholme Ltd, Clough Bank Works, Downgate Drive, Sheffield, S4 8BT Tel: 0114-244 5600 Fax: 0114-244 6556 E-mail: sales@wolstenholme.co.uk

Zanogen UK Ltd, Riverside Works, Buxton Road, Bakewell, Derbyshire, DE45 1GS Tel: (01629) 812582 Fax: (01629) 814494 E-mail: sales@zanogenuk.com

MACHINE METAL CLADDING

Logstrup (UK) Ltd, Units 3H & 4H Lyntown Trading Estate, Lynwell Road, Manchester, M30 9QG Tel: 0161-788 9811 Fax: 0161-789 0063 E-mail: sales@logstrupuk.co.uk

MACHINE MONITORING EQUIPMENT

Martin Trucks Ltd, 61 Battlefield Road, Shrewsbury, SY1 4AD Tel: (01743) 440205 Fax: (01743) 440205

Prism Europe Ltd, Abbey Gate One, 8 Whitewell Road, Colchester, CO2 7DE Tel: (01206) 761300 Fax: (01206) 719900 E-mail: sales@prism-uk.com

Rhombus Systems Ltd, Sumpter House, 8 Station Road, Histon, Cambridge, CB4 9LQ Tel: (01223) 568240 Fax: (01223) 566909 E-mail: sales@rhombus.co.uk

MACHINE MOUNTS

Fabreeka International Inc, Units 8-12, Jubilee Way, Shipley, West Yorkshire, BD18 1QG Tel: (01274) 531333 Fax: (01274) 531717 E-mail: info@fabreeka-uk.com

Safeload (UK)Ltd, 26, Holton Road,, Holton Heath Trading Estate, Poole, Dorset, BH16 5SL Tel: (01202) 624422 Fax: (01202) 624569

MACHINE SAFETY GUARD INSTALLATION

Total Solutions Ltd, 11 Sealand Road, Sealand, Chester, CH1 6BS Tel: (01244) 881818 Fax: (01244) 881991 E-mail: totalsols@aol.com

MACHINE SCREWS

Compass Industrial Manufacturing, Units 26-27 Izons Industrial Estate, Oldbury Road, West Bromwich, West Midlands, B70 9BS Tel: 0121-553 1298 Fax: 0121-500 6452

Namrick Ltd, 124 Portland Road, Hove, East Sussex, BN3 5QL Tel: (01273) 736963 Fax: (01273) 726708 E-mail: sales@namrick.co.uk

Threaded Fastener Supplies Ltd, 72 & 73 Heming Rd, Washford, Redditch, Worcs, B98 0EA Tel: (01527) 518533 Fax: (01527) 518527 E-mail: threaded.fastener@virgin.net

MACHINE TOOL ACCESSORIES MANUFRS

Alexander Newall Machine Tool Co. Ltd, Unit A, Brook Road, Waltham Cross, Hertfordshire, EN8 7LR Tel: (01992) 651122 Fax: (01992) 651123 E-mail: newall-london@supanet.com

Braithwaite Rebuild, Pinfold La Industrial Estate, Bridlington, North Humberside, YO16 6XS Tel: (01262) 606691 Fax: (01262) 606691

▶ L. & T.I. Brock & Co. Ltd, Unit 1 Falkland House, 19 Falkland Close, Charter Avenue Industrial Estate, Coventry, CV4 8AG Tel: (024) 7642 1200 Fax: (024) 7642 1459 E-mail: enquiries@tangi-flow.com

Butler Equipment Sales, Glovers Meadow, Maesbury Road Industrial Estate, Oswestry, Shropshire, SY10 8NH Tel: (01691) 676199 Fax: (01691) 679376

C N C Moss, Sunnyview, Chatteris Road, Somersham, Huntingdon, Cambridgeshire, PE28 3DN Tel: (01487) 840285

Cairns Machine Tool Repair Ltd, 18 Haddow Street, Hamilton, Lanarkshire, ML3 7HX Tel: (01698) 457741 Fax: (01698) 283358

Cambridge Tool Supplies Ltd, Unit 1 Brookfield Business Centre, Twentypence Road, Cottenham, Cambridge, CB4 8PS Tel: (01954) 251862 Fax: (01954) 251073 E-mail: camtool@btconnect.com

Coventry Toolholders Co. Ltd, Grovelands Estate, Longford Road, Exhall, Coventry, CV7 9ND Tel: (024) 7664 5999 Fax: (024) 7664 4081 E-mail: info@coventrytoolholders.co.uk

Cross Country Ltd, 4 Darby Gate, West Portway, Andover, Hampshire, SP10 3LF Tel: (01264) 351409 Fax: (01264) 333921

Dematic Ltd, Sir William Siemens House, Princess Road, Manchester, M20 2UR Tel: 0161-446 5292 Fax: 0161-446 5214 E-mail: sfmpost@plcman.siemens.co.uk

Digital Read Out Centre, Unit 1 53a Third Avenue, Pensnett Trading Estate, Kingswinford, West Midlands, DY6 7XG Tel: (01384) 270022 Fax: (01384) 270022

E W Equipment, 11 Worcester Road, Cheadle Hulme, Cheadle, Cheshire, SK8 5NW Tel: 0161-485 8730 Fax: 0161-485 6745 E-mail: sales@ewequipment.co.uk

Frank Bailey Machine Tools Ltd, 1 Hadfield Street, Globe Square, Dukinfield, Cheshire, SK16 4RL Tel: 0161-330 4738 Fax: 0161-343 4365

Frio UK Ltd, Whitleys, Wolfscastle, Haverfordwest, Dyfed, SA62 5DY Tel: (01437) 741755 Fax: (01437) 741781 E-mail: frio@btinternet.com

Gewefa UK Ltd, Edinburgh Way, Leafield Industrial Estate, Corsham, Wiltshire, SN13 9XZ Tel: (01453) 872074 Fax: (01225) 811388 E-mail: sales@gewefa.co.uk

▶ Giles Machine Tools Ltd, Unit A2, Brook Street Business Centre, Brook Street, Tipton, W. Midlands, DY4 9DD Tel: 0121-557 4400

▶ Henry Pels, 34 Montague Close, Walton-on-Thames, Surrey, KT12 2NQ Tel: (01932) 240707 Fax: (01932) 247638 E-mail: henrypels@btconnect.com

Inter City Machine Tools (High Wycombe) Ltd, High Wycombe, Buckinghamshire, HP14 3WZ Tel: (01494) 485701 Fax: (01494) 485716 E-mail: sales@intercmt.co.uk

Iscar Tools Ltd, Clapgate Lane, Birmingham, B32 3DE Tel: 0121-422 8585 Fax: 0121-421 8255 E-mail: sales@iscaruk.co.uk

Jaylyn Services (Midlands) Ltd, Unit 5 Shilton Industrial Estate, Coventry, CV7 9QL Tel: (024) 7661 9298 Fax: (024) 7660 2623

Kilkie Paper Mill Services, Lovesta, Gowanlea Road, Comrie, Crieff, Perthshire, PH6 2HD Tel: (01764) 670141 Fax: (0870) 1301570 E-mail: sales@kilkie.com

M M Production Services Ltd, Londonderry Farm Workshops, Keynsham Road, Willsbridge, Bristol, BS30 6EL Tel: 0117-932 6255 Fax: 0117-932 6256

M S P Ltd, Roman Way, Coleshill, Birmingham, B46 1HG Tel: (01675) 469100 Fax: (01675) 463699 E-mail: daphne@msp.ltd.uk

Maylan Engineering Co., Crucible Road, Corby, Northamptonshire, NN17 5TS Tel: (01536) 261798 Fax: (01536) 200957 E-mail: maylan@maylan.com

Millen Machine Tools Ltd, Hamilton House, 126 St. Georges Avenue, Northampton, NN2 6JF Tel: (01604) 721122 Fax: (01604) 721329 E-mail: harvey.millen@virgin.net

Portland Engineering Co. Ltd, Wide Street, Portland, Dorset, DT5 2JP Tel: (01305) 821273 Fax: (01305) 821499 E-mail: office@portlandengineering.com

Power Pipes Pendle, Maud Street Works, Maud Street, Barrowford, Nelson, Lancashire, BB9 8NX Tel: (01282) 601896 Fax: (01282) 697034 E-mail: sales@powerpipes.co.uk

Qualcot Profiling Machines Ltd, Oak Road, West Chirton North Industrial Estate, North Shields, Tyne & Wear, NE29 8SD Tel: 0191-257 5205 Fax: 0191-257 4961 E-mail: k.edmundson@qualcut.com

Quality Engineered Products, Unit 9/10, Ditchling Common, Ditchling, Hassocks, West Sussex, BN6 8SG Tel: (01444) 247906 Fax: (01444) 243720 E-mail: msaville@qep.uk.com

Slack & Parr Hydraulics Ltd, Long Lane, Kegworth, Derby, DE74 2FL Tel: (01509) 672306 Fax: (01509) 673357 E-mail: info@slack-parr.com

Standaparts Ltd, 7A South Bank, Thames Ditton, Surrey, KT7 0UD Tel: (020) 8398 7812 Fax: (020) 8398 7813 E-mail: standaparts@btclick.com

Stevenage Machine Tools Ltd, Unit 12, Ironcraft Industrial Estate, Stotfold, Hitchin, Hertfordshire, SG5 4NZ Tel: (01462) 731691 Fax: (01462) 835214

▶ Swift Machinery Maintenance, 98 Recreation Way, Kemsley, Sittingbourne, Kent, ME10 2TG Tel: (01795) 420066 Fax: (0560) 1160925

T D T Technology Ltd, Unit 20 Woodside Park, Rugby, Warwickshire, CV21 2NP Tel: (01788) 570411 Fax: (01788) 567632 E-mail: sales@tdt-technology.co.uk

T S Technology, Langwood, 87 Langley Road, Watford, WD17 4PW Tel: (01923) 221155 Fax: (01923) 218625 E-mail: sales@tstechnology.co.uk

▶ Technical Press Supplies Ltd, Unit 65 Greenway Business Centre Harlow Business Park, Greenway, Harlow, Essex, CM19 5QE Tel: (0845) 8501818 Fax: (01279) 408140

John Walton Machine Tools Ltd, Smithy Carr Lane, Brighouse, West Yorkshire, HD6 2HL Tel: (01484) 712507 Fax: (01484) 710549 E-mail: cyoung@chucks.co.uk

▶ Warwick Machine Tool, Honiley Road, Kenilworth, Warwickshire, CV8 1NQ Tel: (01676) 534534 Fax: (01676) 534548 E-mail: sales@ona-edm.co.uk

MACHINE TOOL ALIGNMENT

▶ Fortron UK Ltd, 307 Ecroyd Suite, Turner Road, Lomeshaye Business Village, Nelson, Lancashire, BB9 7DR Tel: (01282) 607893 Fax: (01282) 607894 E-mail: service@fortron.uk.com

▶ Machine Tool Technologies Ltd. (MTT), 307 Ecroyd Suite, Turner Road, Lomeshaye Business Village, Nelson, Lancashire, BB9 7DR Tel: (01282) 607854 Fax: (01282) 607894 E-mail: info@mtt.uk.com

▶ Reliant Marking Tools Co. UK, Unit 2, Benson Industrial Estate, Benson Road, Birmingham, B18 5TS Tel: 0121-523 6565 E-mail: webmaster@reliantmarkingtools.co.uk

MACHINE TOOL BAR FEEDS

K & B Machine Tool Services Ltd, 1 Farrier Road, Lincoln, LN6 3RU Tel: (01522) 687878 Fax: (01522) 687879 E-mail: service@kandbmts.com

Star Micronics GB Ltd, Chapel Street, Melbourne, Derby, DE73 8JF Tel: (01332) 864455 Fax: (01332) 864005E-mail: sales@stargb.net

MACHINE TOOL CENTRES, *See Machining Centre etc*

MACHINE TOOL CONTROL EQUIPMENT

Hewart Electronics Ltd, 2 Blakelow Bank, Macclesfield, Cheshire, SK11 7GD Tel: (01625) 422030 Fax: (01625) 422030

Jode Systems Technology Ltd, 37 High Street, Lutterworth, Leicestershire, LE17 4AY Tel: (01455) 559626 Fax: (01455) 559676 E-mail: sales@jodesystems.co.uk

Machine Control Engineers Ltd, Unit A1, Block 9a South Avenue, Blantyre Industrial Estate, Glasgow, G72 0XB Tel: (01698) 829566 Fax: (01698) 821608 E-mail: sales@mce.uk.com

MACHINE TOOL COOLANT EQUIPMENT

▶ Cromwell Tools Ltd, Thirsk Place, Derby, DE24 8JJ Tel: (01332) 360660 Fax: (01332) 204239 E-mail: derby@cromwell.co.uk

Jubilee Machine Tools, Nuns Street, Derby, DE1 3LS Tel: (01332) 348749 Fax: (01332) 342416 E-mail: sales@jubileemactools.com

Pumps & Equipment Warwick Ltd, 6 Collins Road, Heathcote Industrial Estate, Warwick, CV34 6TF Tel: (01926) 451744 Fax: (01926) 451284 E-mail: sales@pumps-equip.co.uk

MACHINE TOOL COOLING SYSTEMS

Pumps & Equipment Warwick Ltd, 6 Collins Road, Heathcote Industrial Estate, Warwick, CV34 6TF Tel: (01926) 451744 Fax: (01926) 451284 E-mail: sales@pumps-equip.co.uk

MACHINE TOOL COPYING EQUIPMENT

C S L Copy Shop, 84 St. Marys Road, Market Harborough, Leicestershire, LE16 7DX Tel: (01858) 465208 Fax: (01858) 465208

Machine Tool Attachments, 123 Kedleston Road, Derby, DE22 1FS Tel: (01332) 346948 Fax: (01332) 342360 E-mail: tony@machinetoolattachments.fsnet.co.uk

MACHINE TOOL ENGINEERING, *See also headings for particular types such as Installation; Maintenance etc*

MasseyFforgeing Ltd, Unit F, Joseph Adamson Industrial Estate, Croft Street, Hyde, Cheshire, SK14 1EE Tel: 0161-351 7364 Fax: 0161-351 7365 E-mail: sales@masseyforgeing.com

MACHINE TOOL EXPORT MERCHANTS OR AGENTS

K & C Machinery Ltd, Midland Trading Estate, Sparta Close, Rugby, Warwickshire, CV21 1PS Tel: (01788) 576381 Fax: (01788) 570182 E-mail: sales@kc-machinery.com

The Manufacturing Technologies Association, 62 Bayswater Road, London, W2 3PS Tel: (020) 7298 6400 Fax: (020) 7298 6430 E-mail: info@mta.org.uk

MS Pollard Ltd, St. Saviours Rd, Leicester, LE5 4HP Tel: 0116-276 7534 Fax: 0116-274 1547 E-mail: finn@mspollard.com

S K S Plant & Equipment Ltd, 11 Redehall Road, Smallfield, Horley, Surrey, RH6 9PY Tel: (01342) 843688 Fax: (01342) 842140 E-mail: export@fks-group.co.uk

MACHINE TOOL HIRE

▶ Blythewood Plant Hire Ltd, Fenland District Industrial Estate, Station Road, Whittlesey, Peterborough, PE7 2EY Tel: (01733) 203201 Fax: (01733) 350308 E-mail: enquiries@blythewood-plant.co.uk

Chertsey Tool Hire Ltd, 149 Upper Weybourne Lane, Farnham, Surrey, GU9 9DD Tel: (01252) 333122 Fax: (01252) 333155 E-mail: farnhamsales@chertseytoolhire.co.uk

Ebor Machine Tools Ltd, 5 Kimberlow Woods Hill, York, YO10 5HF Tel: (01904) 431611 Fax: (01904) 431622

▶ G A P Group Ltd, 79 Salamander Street, Leith, Edinburgh, EH6 7JZ Tel: 0131-554 0503 Fax: 0131-554 0861 E-mail: leith@gap-group.co.uk

▶ HSS Hire, Unit 20 Basingstoke Business Centre, Winchester Road, Basingstoke, Hampshire, RG21 8UE Tel: (01256) 461959 Fax: (01256) 331449

HSS Lift & Shift, Adam Smith Street, Grimsby, South Humberside, DN31 1SJ Tel: (01472) 250005 Fax: (01472) 250270

MACHINE TOOL HIRE – *continued*

Lord Hire Centre, Shields Road, Newcastle upon Tyne, NE6 2UD Tel: 0191-224 0044 E-mail: lord@lordhire.co.uk

Premier Tool Hire Ltd, Premier House, 34 Arthur Road, Yardley, Birmingham, B25 8HA Tel: 0121-771 4777 Fax: 0121-771 1187

Speedy Hire Centres Ltd, Tollgate House, Tollgate Lane, Bury St. Edmunds, Suffolk, IP32 6DG Tel: (01284) 766254 Fax: (01284) 700542 E-mail: customer.services@speedyhire.co.uk

Wells Hire Centre, Underwood Business Park, Wookey Hole Road, Wells, Somerset, BA5 1TU Tel: (01749) 674410 Fax: (01749) 671599 E-mail: shannonp@netcomuk.co.uk

MACHINE TOOL HOLDER SYSTEMS

Advanced Machining Technology, Unit 16 Colomendy Business Park, Rhyl Road, Denbigh, Clwyd, LL16 5TA Tel: (01745) 815888 Fax: (01745) 813222 E-mail: ben@oelheldgroup.co.uk

Coventry Toolholders Ltd, Grovelands Estate, Longford Road, Exhall, Coventry, CV7 9ND Tel: (024) 7664 5999 Fax: (024) 7664 4081 E-mail: info@coventrytoolholders.co.uk

Gewefa UK Ltd, Edinburgh Way, Leafield Industrial Estate, Corsham, Wiltshire, SN13 9XZ Tel: (01453) 872074 Fax: (01225) 811388 E-mail: sales@gewefa.co.uk

Iscar Tools Ltd, Clapgate Lane, Birmingham, B32 3DE Tel: 0121-422 8585 Fax: 0121-421 8255 E-mail: sales@iscaruk.co.uk

Rodwell Powell Ltd, Chester Hall Lane, Basildon, Essex, SS14 3DQ Tel: (01268) 286641 Fax: (01268) 286644 E-mail: info@rodwell-powell.com

MACHINE TOOL HOLDER SYSTEMS IMPORT MERCHANTS OR AGENTS

P C M Tooling UK Ltd, 825 The Ridge, St. Leonards-on-Sea, East Sussex, TN37 7PX Tel: (01424) 753174 Fax: (01424) 753089 E-mail: ukpcmtlg@aol.com

MACHINE TOOL IMPORT MERCHANTS OR AGENTS

600 Centre, Unit 18-19 Loughborough Motorway Trading Estate, Gelders Hall Road, Shepshed, Loughborough, Leicestershire, LE12 9NH Tel: (01509) 600600 Fax: (01509) 600159 E-mail: sales@600centre.co.uk

Cotswold Machinery Sales, 11 Isbourne Way, Winchcombe, Cheltenham, Gloucestershire, GL54 5NS Tel: (01242) 603907 Fax: (01242) 604059 E-mail: sales@cotswold-machinery-sales.co.uk

Dorman Machinery, 4 Percy Street, Coventry, CV1 3BY Tel: (024) 7622 6611 Fax: (024) 7622 6560 E-mail: dormansale@aol.com

Euromachine Ltd, Laund House, Beamsley, Skipton, North Yorkshire, BD23 6AW Tel: (01756) 710588 Fax: (01756) 710234 E-mail: sales@euro-machine.com

Kyal Machine Tools Ltd, Foundry Road, Stamford, Lincolnshire, PE9 2PP Tel: (01780) 765965 Fax: (01780) 765877 E-mail: office@kyalmachinetools.co.uk

The Manufacturing Technologies Association, 62 Bayswater Road, London, W2 3PS Tel: (020) 7298 6400 Fax: (020) 7298 6430 E-mail: info@mta.org.uk

Mori Seiki (UK) Ltd, 4060 Lakeside, Solihull Parkway, Birmingham Business Park, Birmingham, B37 7YN Tel: (0870) 2409500 Fax: (0870) 2409539

Tower Machine Tools Ltd, Mayflower Close, Chandler's Ford, Eastleigh, Hampshire, SO53 4AR Tel: (023) 8026 0266 Fax: (023) 8026 1012 E-mail: towermctools@compuserve.com

MACHINE TOOL INSTALLATION CONTRACTORS OR SERVICES

D N C Machine Tools Ltd, 31 Kent End, Ashton Keynes, Swindon, SN6 6PU Tel: (01285) 869199 Fax: (01285) 869199 E-mail: russ@dabsons.org

FMB UK Ltd, P O Box 5222, Leicester, LE4 8ZE Tel: 0116-260 7744 Fax: 0116-260 7222 E-mail: sales@fmbuk.co.uk

M I K Engineering, 5 Cannock Street, Leicester, LE4 9HR Tel: 0116-233 3740 Fax: 0116-233 3740

F S R Maintenance, 8 Arnside Road, Waterlooville, Hants, PO7 7UP Tel: (023) 9226 3222 Fax: (023) 9223 0946 E-mail: fsr@shaftfield.co.uk

MACHINE TOOL LIGHTING

Task Lighting Ltd, 1 Low Farm Place, Moulton Park Industrial Estate, Northampton, NN3 6HY Tel: (01604) 644875 Fax: (01604) 790016 E-mail: sales@tasklighting.co.uk

MACHINE TOOL MAINTENANCE OR REPAIR

A B D I Machine Tool Co., 67 Camden Street, Birmingham, B1 3DD Tel: 0121-236 1517 Fax: 0121-236 9342 E-mail: dereckcornock@abditools.fsnet.co.uk

A E S Enterprises Ltd, Nuffield Industrial Estate, 40 Banbury Road, Poole, Dorset, BH17 0GA Tel: (01202) 683875 Fax: (01202) 683875

Adford CNC Ltd, 96 Smirrells Road, Birmingham, B28 0LB Tel: 0121-622 2232 Fax: 0121-622 2242 E-mail: sales@adfordcnc.co.uk

Bell Machinery Ltd, PO Box 56, Tadcaster, North Yorkshire, LS24 9WS Tel: (01937) 830777 Fax: (01937) 830888E-mail: hbellmt@aol.com

Birmingham Machine Tool Services Ltd, 312-314 Bradford Street, Birmingham, B5 6ET Tel: 0121-622 6339 Fax: 0121-666 6406 E-mail: bhammctool@aol.com

C & M Machine Tools Ltd, Station Road, Coleshill, Birmingham, B46 1JN Tel: (01675) 433100 Fax: (01675) 433101 E-mail: info@candmtools.com

Coleshill Tool Service Centre, 74 Birmingham Road, Water Orton, Birmingham, B46 1TH Tel: 0121-747 2357 Fax: 0121-747 2357

Direct Machine Tools Ltd, Unit 4a Tame Valley Industrial Estate, Wilnecote, Tamworth, Staffordshire, B77 5DQ Tel: (01827) 260272 Fax: (01827) 260838 E-mail: stevedmt@aol.com

Ebor Machine Tools Ltd, 5 Kimberlow Woods Hill, York, YO10 5HF Tel: (01904) 431611 Fax: (01904) 431622

▶ Engineering Solutions 2000 Ltd, 32 Butterton Road, Rhyl, Denbighshire, LL18 1RF Tel: 07850 511707 Fax: (01745) 353184 E-mail: machinerepairs@yahoo.co.uk

Exward Services, Unit 5A, Merebrook Industrial Estate, Hanley Swan, Malvern, Worcestershire, WR13 6NP Tel: (01684) 310989 Fax: (01684) 310989

Fieldhouse Industrial Services Ltd, Unit 1 & 2, Moderna Business Park, Mytholmroyd, Hebden Bridge, West Yorkshire, HX7 5QQ Tel: (01422) 883313 Fax: (01422) 881338 E-mail: sean@fis-ltd.co.uk

Flude Machine Tools, 7 Central City Industrial Estate, Red Lane, Coventry, CV6 5RY Tel: (024) 7666 1220 Fax: (024) 7666 1220

Kelectronic, 1 Waterworks Road, Portsmouth, PO6 1NG Tel: (023) 9237 2077 Fax: (023) 9237 2077 E-mail: kelectronic.uk@aol.com

Kryle Technical Services, Ivory Buildings, Madeley Street, Stoke-on-Trent, ST6 5AT Tel: (01782) 838877 Fax: (01782) 866457 E-mail: sales@kryle.com

M F G Machinery, 6 Climax Works, Station Road, Reddish, Stockport, Cheshire, SK5 6YZ Tel: 0161-431 9125 Fax: 0161-432 2440

Machine Tool & Engineering Services Ltd, Unit 14 Quay Lane Industrial Estate, Hardway, Gosport, Hampshire, PO12 4LJ Tel: (023) 9251 1666 Fax: (023) 9251 1164 E-mail: info@mtes.co.uk

F S R Maintenance, 8 Arnside Road, Waterlooville, Hants, PO7 7UP Tel: (023) 9226 3222 Fax: (023) 9223 0946 E-mail: fsr@shaftfield.co.uk

Nigel P Jacobs, 21 Roping Road, Yeovil, Somerset, BA21 4BD Tel: (01935) 476443 Fax: (01935) 476443

P P Machine Tools Ltd, 45 The Ridgeway, Rothley, Leicester, LE7 7LE Tel: 0116-230 3050 Fax: 0116-230 4430 E-mail: pp_cnc@yahoo.com

Pentad Engineering, Unit 10, The Parkway Centre, Heneage Street, Birmingham, B7 4LY Tel: 0121-359 5190 Fax: 0121-359 4743 E-mail: sales@pentad.net

Piper Developments Ltd, Townsend House, Townsend Way, Birmingham, B1 2RT Tel: 0121-242 1194 Fax: 0121-242 1194

Power Press Repairs Ltd, 69 Kings Road, Tyseley, Birmingham, B11 2AX Tel: 0121-772 1698 Fax: 0121-772 5323 E-mail: sales@powerpressrepairs.co.uk

Selby Engineering, 28 Dinglederry, Olney, Buckinghamshire, MK46 5ES Tel: (01234) 711773 Fax: (01234) 713992

Skippy's Machine Tools, 12 Queens Road, Erdington, Birmingham, B23 7JP Tel: 0121-386 3622 Fax: 0121-386 3623 E-mail: service@skippysmt.com

David B. Swift Ltd, 63 Byward Drive, Crossgates, Scarborough, North Yorkshire, YO12 4JG Tel: (01723) 862089 E-mail: bramley_swift@btinternet.com

Uniprize Machine Tools Ltd, A3 Bankfield Industrial Estate, Sandy Lane, Stockport, Cheshire, SK5 7SE Tel: 0161-429 6161 Fax: 0161-429 0606 E-mail: uniprize@uniprize.freeserve.co.uk

D. Waterhouse & Co., Lambert Works, Luton St, Keighley, W. Yorkshire, BD21 2LE Tel: (01535) 642539 Fax: (01535) 642539

MACHINE TOOL MANUFRS, *See also headings under Machine Tools; & other headings for particular types*

600 Centre, Unit 18-19 Loughborough Motorway Trading Estate, Gelders Hall Road, Shepshed, Loughborough, Leicestershire, LE12 9NH Tel: (01509) 600600 Fax: (01509) 600159 E-mail: sales@600centre.co.uk

600 Group Plc, 600 House, Landmark Court, Revie Road, Leeds, LS11 8JT Tel: 0113-277 6100 Fax: 0113-276 5600 E-mail: sales@600group.com

600 Lathes, Union Street, Heckmondwike, West Yorkshire, WF16 0HL Tel: (01924) 415000 Fax: (01924) 415017 E-mail: sales@600lathes.co.uk

Abwood Machine Tools, 615 Princes Road, Dartford, DA2 6EF Tel: (01322) 225271 Fax: (01322) 291862 E-mail: sales@abwoodcnc.co.uk

Addison Mckee, 188 Bradkirk Place, Walton Summit Centre, Bamber Bridge, Preston, PR5 8AJ Tel: (01772) 334511 Fax: (01772) 323227 E-mail: sales@atf.co.uk

Allcut Machine Tool Ltd, Unit 12 Triangle Business Park, Quilters Way, Stoke Mandeville, Aylesbury, Buckinghamshire, HP22 5BL Tel: (01296) 615368 Fax: (01296) 615369 E-mail: dave@allcut.freeserve.co.uk

Anatric Machine Tools, 3 Sinclair Court, Bletchley, Milton Keynes, MK1 1RB Tel: (01908) 371331 Fax: (01908) 367683

Apex Industrial Ltd, 26c Orgreave CR, Sheffield, S13 9NQ Tel: 0114-254 0011 Fax: 0114-254 8002 E-mail: sheffield@apexindustrial.co.uk

Artisan Precision Engineering Co., Snatchwood Road, Abersychan, Pontypool, Gwent, NP4 7BT Tel: (01495) 772644 Fax: (01495) 773844 E-mail: artisan04@supernet.com

Avon Equipment Ltd, Unit 7-8 Dixon Business Centre, Dixon Road, Bristol, BS4 5QW Tel: 0117-972 3210 Fax: 0117-972 1120 E-mail: sales@avonequipment.com

Axe & Status Ltd, 2 Holdom Avenue, Bletchley, Milton Keynes, MK1 1QU Tel: (01908) 647707 Fax: (01908) 648087 E-mail: sales@axestatus.com

B S A Machine Tools, Mackadown Lane, Kitts Green, Birmingham, B33 0LE Tel: 0121-783 4071 Fax: 0121-789 9509 E-mail: sales@bsamachinetools.co.uk

B W Machine Tools, 4 Lyon Close, Wigston, Leicestershire, LE18 2BJ Tel: 0116-288 6070 Fax: 0116-288 0014 E-mail: toolsbw@aol.com

Bardek Precision Tools, Britten Street, Redditch, Worcestershire, B97 6HD Tel: (01527) 67358 Fax: (01527) 65145

P. Barraclough & Associates Ltd, 48 Top Lane, Copmanthorpe, York, YO23 3UJ Tel: (01904) 704065 Fax: (01904) 700496

Bell Machinery Ltd, PO Box 56, Tadcaster, North Yorkshire, LS24 9WS Tel: (01937) 830777 Fax: (01937) 830888E-mail: hbellmt@aol.com

Benchmaster Machine Tool Co., Holmfield Industrial Estate, Holmfield, Halifax, West Yorkshire, HX2 9TN Tel: (01422) 247185 Fax: (01422) 247234

Boxford Ltd, Boy Lane, Wheatley, Halifax, West Yorkshire, HX3 5AF Tel: (01422) 358311 Fax: (01422) 355924 E-mail: info@boxford.co.uk

Brierley Machine Tools Ltd, Ferry Farm Road, Llandudno Junction, Gwynedd, LL31 9SF Tel: (01492) 581777 Fax: (01492) 592558

Brookes Machine Tools Ltd, Derby Road, Kegworth, Derby, DE74 2EN Tel: (01509) 672256 Fax: (01509) 674502 E-mail: bmtlimited@aol.com

Brunner Machine Tools Ltd, 6 Colville Road, London, W3 8BL Tel: (020) 8992 6011 Fax: (020) 8992 7559 E-mail: sales@brunnermachine.co.uk

Bystronic UK Ltd, Maple Park, Lowfields Avenue, Leeds, LS12 6HH Tel: 0113-277 8112 Fax: 0113-271 9862

C & M Machine Tools Ltd, Station Road, Coleshill, Birmingham, B46 1JN Tel: (01675) 433100 Fax: (01675) 433101 E-mail: info@candmtools.com

C M S Tools Ltd, Don Pedro Close, Normanton Industrial Estate, Normanton, West Yorkshire, WF6 1TD Tel: (01924) 895999 Fax: (01924) 896999

Capital Equipment & Machinery Ltd, Mill Mead, Staines, Middlesex, TW18 4UQ Tel: (01784) 456151 Fax: (01784) 466481 E-mail: sales@capital-equipment.com

Chadwick Engineering Co. Ltd, 173-179 Tyburn Road, Erdington, Birmingham, B24 8NQ Tel: 0121-327 7997 Fax: 0121-327 7987

Chappell Machine Tools Ltd, Poultry Farm, New Road, Lambourne End, Romford, RM4 1AJ Tel: (020) 8500 6111 Fax: (020) 8500 6888

Chemtechno Ltd, 49 Queens Gardens, London, W2 3AA Tel: (020) 7723 2323 Fax: (020) 7724 9297 E-mail: chemtechno@dial.pipex.com

Chiviott Machine Tools Ltd, Unit C1 Rudford Industrial Estate, Ford Road, Ford, Arundel, West Sussex, BN18 0BD Tel: (01903) 721281 Fax: (01903) 730868 E-mail: sales@chiviott.co.uk

Cincinnati Machine Ltd, PO Box 505, Birmingham, B24 0QU Tel: 0121-351 3821 Fax: 0121-313 5379 E-mail: info@cinmach.co.uk

Cinetic Landis Grinding Ltd, Skipton Road, Cross Hills, Keighley, West Yorkshire, BD20 7SD Tel: (01535) 633211 Fax: (01535) 635493 E-mail: sales@cinetic-landis.co.uk

Clark International Machinery Ltd, PO Box 58, Stratford-upon-Avon, Warwickshire, CV37 7YF Tel: (01789) 263636 Fax: (01789) 263637 E-mail: sales@clarkintmachinery.co.uk

Collin Gladwell, Pencrennow, Tregye Road, Carnon Downs, Truro, Cornwall, TR3 6JH Tel: (01872) 864777 Fax: (01872) 870094 E-mail: cgmt@netcomuk.co.uk

Cotswold Machinery Sales, 11 Isbourne Way, Winchcombe, Cheltenham, Gloucestershire, GL54 5NS Tel: (01242) 603907 Fax: (01242) 604059 E-mail: sales@cotswold-machinery-sales.co.uk

▶ Created, Newhouses Road, Broxburn, West Lothian, EH52 5MZ Tel: (01506) 853587 Fax: (01506) 856106

Cromwell Basingstoke, Unit 5, Sherrington Way, Basingstoke, Hampshire, RG22 4DQ Tel: (01256) 355966 Fax: (01256) 477230 E-mail: info@cromwell.co.uk

Cromwell (Birmingham), 217 Chester Street, Aston, Birmingham, B6 4AE Tel: 0121-380 1700 Fax: 0121-380 1710 E-mail: birmingham@cromwell.co.uk

Cromwell Bristol Ltd, Unit E St. Vincents Trading Estate, Bristol, BS2 0UY Tel: 0117-972 1127 Fax: 0117-972 4287 E-mail: bristol@cromwell.co.uk

Cromwell Group Ltd, B Great Fenton Business Park, Grove Road, Stoke-on-Trent, ST4 4LZ Tel: (01782) 746746 Fax: (01782) 414414 E-mail: stoke@cromwell.co.uk

Cromwell Industrial Supplies, Unit 2-3 Anthonys Way, Medway City Estate, Rochester, Kent, ME2 4DN Tel: (01634) 290586 Fax: (01634) 290589 E-mail: rochester@cromwell.co.uk

Cromwell (Portsmouth), Unit 15, Admirals Park, Williams Road, Portsmouth, PO3 5NJ Tel: (023) 9266 8512 Fax: (023) 9269 9179 E-mail: portsmouth@cromwell-tools.co.uk

Cromwell Tools Ltd, 2 Murcar Industrial Estate, Denmore Road, Bridge of Don, Aberdeen, AB23 8JW Tel: (01224) 820851 Fax: (01224) 820877 E-mail: sales@kennedy-tools.co.uk

Cromwell Tools Ltd, 3-4 Tollgate Close, Cardiff, CF11 8TN Tel: (029) 2034 5888 Fax: (029) 2034 5777 E-mail: cardiff@cromwell.co.uk

Cromwell Tools Ltd, 27 Endemere Road, Coventry, CV6 5PY Tel: (024) 7666 4614 Fax: (024) 7666 6667 E-mail: coventry@cromwell-tools.co.uk

Cromwell Tools Ltd, Shaw Lane Industrial Estate, Ogden Road, Doncaster, South Yorkshire, DN2 4SQ Tel: (01302) 366600 Fax: (01302) 327556 E-mail: doncaster@cromwell-tools.co.uk

Cromwell Tools Ltd, Estate Road 6, South Humberside Industrial Estate, Grimsby, South Humberside, DN31 2TG Tel: (01472) 358741 Fax: (01472) 241433 E-mail: grimsby@cromwell-tools.co.uk

Cromwell Tools Ltd, St. James Street, Hull, HU3 2DH Tel: (01482) 326999 Fax: (01482) 213089 E-mail: hull@cromwell-tools.co.uk

Cromwell Tools Ltd, The Tool Centre, 75 St James Mill Road, Northampton, NN5 5JP Tel: (01604) 752488 Fax: (01604) 753815 E-mail: northampton@cromwell-tools.co.uk

Cromwell Tools Ltd, 131 Queens Road, Beeston, Nottingham, NG9 2FE Tel: 0115-922 3311 Fax: 0115-925 1342 E-mail: nottingham@cromwell-tools.co.uk

Cromwell Tools Ltd, Westcombe Square, Royce Road, Peterborough, PE1 5YB Tel: (01733) 555524 Fax: (01733) 311103 E-mail: peterborough@cromwell-tools.co.uk

Cromwell Tools Ltd, Ark Grove Industrial Estate, Ross Road, Stockton-on-Tees, Cleveland, TS18 2NH Tel: (01642) 673605 Fax: (01642) 671479 E-mail: stockton@cromwell.co.uk

Cromwells, Waverley House, Effingham Road, Sheffield, S4 7YR Tel: 0114-275 0631 Fax: 0114-275 4447 E-mail: sheffield@cromwell.co.uk

Cromwells Fife, Unit 4 Woodgate Way South, Glenrothes, Fife, KY7 4PF Tel: (01592) 631632 Fax: (01592) 631641 E-mail: fife@cromwell.co.uk

D M G UK Ltd, Unitool House, 151 Camford Way, Luton, LU3 3AN Tel: (01582) 570661 Fax: (01582) 593700 E-mail: sales@gildemeister.com

D S M Automation Ltd, Eel Street, Oldbury, West Midlands, B69 2BX Tel: 0121-541 1335 Fax: 0121-511 1298

Datamach Ltd, Falkland Close, Charter Avenue Industrial Estate, Coventry, CV4 8AU Tel: (024) 7647 0707 Fax: (024) 7646 4059 E-mail: enquiries@datamach.co.uk

Louis Demery & Sons Ltd, 67a Newcastle Avenue, Worksop, Nottinghamshire, S80 1LX Tel: (01909) 500358 Fax: (01909) 500637 E-mail: ldsltd@btconnect.com

Denford Ltd, Birds Royd, Brighouse, Brighouse, West Yorkshire, HD6 1NB Tel: (01484) 712264 Fax: (01484) 722160 E-mail: sales@denford.co.uk

Denis Grimshaw Machinery Ltd, PO Box 64, Droitwich, Worcestershire, WR9 0JR Tel: (01905) 621789 Fax: (01905) 621384 E-mail: sales@grimshaw.co.uk

Direct Machine Tools Ltd, Unit 4a Tame Valley Industrial Estate, Wilnecote, Tamworth, Staffordshire, B77 5DQ Tel: (01827) 260272 Fax: (01827) 260838 E-mail: stevedmt@aol.com

Dorman Machinery, 4 Percy Street, Coventry, CV1 3BY Tel: (024) 7622 6611 Fax: (024) 7622 6560 E-mail: dormansale@aol.com

Drummond Of York, Bloom House, Intake Lane, Dunnington, York, YO19 5NY Tel: (01904) 488978 Fax: (01904) 488046

▶ indicates data change since last edition

MACHINE TOOL MANUFRS – *continued*

Dudley Machine Tool Centre Ltd, High Street, Cleobury Mortimer, Kidderminster, Worcestershire, DY14 8DS Tel: (01299) 270474 Fax: (01299) 271342 E-mail: sales@dudleymachine.co.uk

Engineering Supplies Peterborough Ltd, Papyrus Road, Peterborough, PE4 5BH Tel: (01733) 577899 Fax: (01733) 321975 E-mail: engsupp@aol.com

Exe Engineering Co. Ltd, 64 Alphington Road, Exeter, EX2 8HX Tel: (01392) 275186 Fax: (01392) 260336 E-mail: sales@exeengineering.co.uk

F & R Belbin Ltd, 165-169 Whitley Road, Whitley Bay, Tyne & Wear, NE26 2DN Tel: 0191-252 4703 Fax: 0191-297 0812 E-mail: sales@frbelbin.co.uk

Farrell Engineering Ltd, Centre House, St. Leonards Road, London, NW10 6ST Tel: (020) 8965 7578 Fax: (020) 8965 7586 E-mail: farrell497@aol.com

Fast Tools Holdings Ltd, Llanthony Road, Hempsted, Gloucester, GL2 5HL Tel: (01452) 529671 Fax: (01452) 307992 E-mail: sales@fasttoolsltd.co.uk

Fendius Ltd, 20 Milverton Terrace, Leamington Spa, Warwickshire, CV32 5BA Tel: (01926) 470760 Fax: (01926) 470761 E-mail: fendiusltd@dial.pipex.com

G A C Engineering Group Ltd, New Works, Burnley Road, Sowerby Bridge, West Yorkshire, HX6 2TF Tel: (01422) 836091 Fax: (01422) 835396 E-mail: sales@gacgroup.co.uk

Garrick Ridgway Engineering Ltd, 1-4 Gerard, Tamworth, Staffordshire, B79 7UW Tel: (01827) 62948 Fax: (01827) 52717 E-mail: garrickridgeway@aol.com

Grob Machine Tools UK Ltd, Wellesbourne House, Walton Road, Wellesbourne, Warwick, CV35 9JB Tel: (01789) 470047 Fax: (01789) 470176 E-mail: grobuk@btconnect.com

H W Whiteley Engineering, Holmfield Industrial Estate, Holmfield, Halifax, West Yorkshire, HX2 9TN Tel: (01422) 244870 Fax: (01422) 248666 E-mail: gordonwhitaker@hwwhiteley.co.uk

Hambury Machine Tools, Unit 17, Malmesbury Road, Kingsditch Trading Estate, Cheltenham, Gloucestershire, GL51 9PL Tel: (01242) 690390 Fax: (01242) 690391

Harmbridge Ltd, 27 Brimble Hill, Wroughton, Swindon, SN4 0RQ Tel: (01793) 814745 Fax: (01793) 814178 E-mail: sales@harmbridge.co.uk

Hatfield Machine Tool Co. Ltd, 2 Sandiford Road, Sutton, Surrey, SM3 9RD Tel: (020) 8644 6661 Fax: (020) 8644 4233 E-mail: sales@hatmac.co.uk

Heller Machine Tools, Acanthus Road, Ravensbank Business Park, Redditch, Worcestershire, B98 9EX Tel: 0121-275 3300 Fax: 0121-275 3340 E-mail: sales@heller.co.uk

Peter Hill Machine Sales, PO Box 3402, Birmingham, B44 8DG Tel: 0121-249 7272 Fax: 0121-244 2378 E-mail: info@peterhillmachinesales.com

Holmes UK Ltd, 5 Monarch Industrial Park, Kings Road, Tyseley, Birmingham, B11 2AP Tel: 0121-706 6936 Fax: 0121-707 9913 E-mail: sales@holmesmachines.co.uk

IndustrialMachines.Net Ltd, Ipsley Street, Redditch, Worcestershire, B98 7AA Tel: (0870) 8890270 Fax: (0870) 8890271 E-mail: sales@industrialmachines.net

Inter City Machine Tools (High Wycombe) Ltd, High Wycombe, Buckinghamshire, HP14 3WZ Tel: (01494) 485701 Fax: (01494) 485716 E-mail: sales@intercmt.co.uk

J & J Tooling Services, Bridge House, Railway Street, Radcliffe, Manchester, M26 3AA Tel: 0161-724 7799 Fax: 0161-724 0722 E-mail: sales@jjtooling.co.uk

Jackson Production Services Ltd, Grangefield Road, Town Street, Stanningley, Leeds, LS28 6JP Tel: 0113-236 3366 Fax: 0113-236 3339 E-mail: salesjps@aol.com

Jaylyn Services (Midlands) Ltd, Unit 5 Shilton Industrial Estate, Coventry, CV7 9QL Tel: (024) 7661 9298 Fax: (024) 7660 2623

Jubilee Machine Tools, Nuns Street, Derby, DE1 3LS Tel: (01332) 348749 Fax: (01332) 342416 E-mail: sales@jubileemactools.com

K & C Machinery Ltd, Midland Trading Estate, Sparta Close, Rugby, Warwickshire, CV21 1PS Tel: (01788) 576381 Fax: (01788) 570182 E-mail: sales@kc-machinery.com

Larchwood Machine Tools Ltd, 61 Blue Lake Road, Dorridge, Solihull, West Midlands, B93 8BH Tel: (01564) 776234 Fax: (01564) 779270 E-mail: sales@larchwoodltd.co.uk

Laxton Tool Supplies Ltd, Royal Leamington Spa, Leamington Spa, Warwickshire, CV32 5GN Tel: (01239) 820212 Fax: (01239) 820763 E-mail: laxtontool@aol.com

Layton-Fine Machine Technologies Ltd, Units E8-E9, Park La, Castle Vale, Birmingham, B35 6LJ Tel: 0121-776 8883 Fax: 0121-776 8884 E-mail: enquiries@layton-fine.co.uk

Lead Precision Machine Tools Ltd, Calamine House, Calamine Street, Macclesfield, Cheshire, SK11 7HU Tel: (01625) 434990 Fax: (01625) 434996 E-mail: sales@leadmachinetools.co.uk

William Lees & Sons Ltd, Unit 4A Peacock Cross Estate, 32 Burnbank Road, Hamilton, Lanarkshire, ML3 9AQ Tel: (01698) 426662 Fax: (01698) 429919

Lister Machine Tools Ni Ltd, Unit 10 Boucher Business Centre, Apollo Road, Belfast, BT12 6HP Tel: (028) 9066 3804 Fax: (028) 9066 3801 E-mail: sales@listermachinetools.co.uk

Loadpoint Ltd, Unit J Chelworth Industrial Estate, Chelworth Road, Cricklade, Swindon, SN6 6HE Tel: (01793) 751160 Fax: (01793) 750155 E-mail: sales@loadpoint.co.uk

Lunn Engineering Co. Ltd, Manor Road Industrial Estate, Atherstone, Warwickshire, CV9 1RB Tel: (01827) 713228 Fax: (01827) 717624 E-mail: info@lunnengineering.co.uk

Lye Engineers Supplies Ltd, Roetan House, Thorns Road, Brierley Hill, West Midlands, DY5 2PF Tel: (01384) 424420 Fax: (01384) 424906

M M Production Services Ltd, Londonderry Farm Workshops, Keynsham Road, Willsbridge, Bristol, BS30 6EL Tel: 0117-932 6255 Fax: 0117-932 6256

Magna Machinery, Parrotts Grove Works, Aldermans Green Rd, Coventry, CV2 1NP Tel: (024) 7664 5084 Fax: (024) 7664 5085

Maidenhead Machine Tool Co. Ltd, PO Box 833, Bourne End, Buckinghamshire, SL8 5YR Tel: (01628) 526345 Fax: (01628) 810732 E-mail: mmtools@msn.com

▶ Manchester Wholesale Tools, 5 Sagar Street, Manchester, M8 8EU Tel: 0161-834 1123 Fax: 0161-834 1123

The Manufacturing Technologies Association, 62 Bayswater Road, London, W2 3PS Tel: (020) 7298 6400 Fax: (020) 7298 6430 E-mail: info@mta.org.uk

Marrill Engineering Co. Ltd, Waterman Road, Coventry, CV6 5TP Tel: (024) 7668 9221 Fax: (024) 7666 8114 E-mail: sales@marrill.co.uk

MasseyFforgeing Ltd, Unit F, Joseph Adamson Industrial Estate, Croft Street, Hyde, Cheshire, SK14 1EE Tel: 0161-351 7364 Fax: 0161-351 7365 E-mail: sales@masseyforgeing.com

Matchmaker CNC, 8 Woodland Studios, Brook Willow Farm, Woodlands Road, Leatherhead, Surrey, KT22 0AN Tel: (01372) 844999 Fax: (01372) 844998 E-mail: sales@matchmakermc.co.uk

Meddings Machine Tools, Kingsley Close, Lee Mill Industrial Estate, Ivybridge, Devon, PL21 9LL Tel: (01752) 313323 Fax: (01752) 313333 E-mail: sales@meddings.co.uk

Merit Machine Tools, Coronation Road, Cressex Business Park, High Wycombe, Buckinghamshire, HP12 3RP Tel: (01494) 522072 Fax: (01494) 529552

Monarch Machine Tools, Banbury Street, Birmingham, B5 5RH Tel: 0121-693 7051 Fax: (01543) 373888 E-mail: info@monarch-machine-tools.co.uk

N C Engineering Co. Ltd, 2 Killyrudden Road, Hamiltonsbawn, Armagh, BT61 9SF Tel: (028) 3887 1970 Fax: (028) 3887 0362 E-mail: nc.a.engineering@btinternet.com

New Century Machinery Ltd, New Century House, Victoria Road, Dukinfield, Cheshire, SK16 4XS Tel: 0161-330 4242 Fax: 0161-343 1347 E-mail: hq@newcentury.co.uk

New England Engineering Ltd, Sandy Lane Industrial Estate, Stourport-on-Severn, Worcestershire, DY13 9QB Tel: (01299) 827399 Fax: (01299) 827400 E-mail: machines@newengland.co.uk

Northern Machine Tools (Engineering) Ltd, P O Box Southbank 16, Middlesbrough, Cleveland, TS6 6LP Tel: (01642) 440551 Fax: (01642) 440141 E-mail: sales@nmt.onyxnet.co.uk

Nu Tools Machinery Sales, Rockingham Way, Redhouse Interchange, Adwick-le-Street, Doncaster, South Yorkshire, DN6 7FB Tel: (01302) 721791 Fax: (01302) 728317 E-mail: sales@nutool.co.uk

P B K Micron Ltd, Unit 6 Kingfield Industrial Estate, Coventry, CV1 4DW Tel: (024) 7622 0376 Fax: (024) 7660 7819 E-mail: sales@pbk-micron.co.uk

P S G Precision Tooling, 158 Hearsall Lane, Coventry, CV5 6HH Tel: (024) 7671 1388 Fax: (024) 7667 8617

Pennine Machine Tools Ltd, Brookwoods Industrial Estate, Burrwood Way, Holywell Green, Halifax, West Yorkshire, HX4 9BH Tel: (01422) 370109 Fax: (01422) 371338 E-mail: sales@pennine.co.uk

R A Atkins, Hunts Hill House, Hunts Hill, Normandy, Guildford, Surrey, GU3 2AH Tel: (01483) 811146 Fax: (01483) 811243

R D Barrett Small Tools, Brow Mills Industrial Estate, Brighouse Road, Hipperholme, Halifax, West Yorkshire, HX3 8DD Tel: (01422) 205828 Fax: (01422) 202358 E-mail: j.n.rushby@supanet.com

Rollo Engineering Ltd, St Andrews Works, Bonnybridge, Stirlingshire, FK4 2EJ Tel: (01324) 812469 Fax: (01324) 814040 E-mail: mail@rolloeng.co.uk

Rudolph Carne & Co Ltd, 416-418 London Road, Isleworth, Middlesex, TW7 5AE Tel: (020) 8560 1182 Fax: (020) 8568 6882 E-mail: info@carne.co.uk

S K S Plant & Equipment Ltd, 11 Redehall Road, Smallfield, Horley, Surrey, RH6 9PY Tel: (01342) 843688 Fax: (01342) 842236 E-mail: jpeters@sks-group.co.uk

Frank Salt & Co. Ltd, Sandy Lane, Stourport-on-Severn, Worcestershire, DY13 9QG Tel: (01299) 827006 Fax: (01299) 877901 E-mail: sales@franksalt.co.uk

Sedin UK Ltd, Burnley, Lancashire, BB11 5GY Tel: 01282 697979

W.M. Simpson (Oldham) Ltd, 1-3 St. Chad's High St, Uppermill, Oldham, OL3 6AP Tel: (01457) 870478 Fax: (01457) 871057

Sip (UK) Ltd, 1-2 Mercia Business Village, Torwood Close, Westwood Business Park, Coventry, CV4 8HX Tel: (024) 7647 4545 Fax: (024) 7647 0353 E-mail: peter.carnall@sipuk.com

Spectrum Robotic Systems Ltd, Spithead Business Centre, Newport Road, Sandown, Isle of Wight, PO36 9PH Tel: (01983) 401188 Fax: (01983) 408450

Staines Machine Tool Co. Ltd, 131 Ashford Road, Staines, Middlesex, TW18 1RS Tel: (01784) 245669 Fax: (01784) 241291

Stanton-Thompson (Agencies) Ltd, 14 Watcombe Road, Watlington, Oxfordshire, OX49 5QJ Tel: (01491) 613515 Fax: (01491) 613516 E-mail: diana@stanthom.freeserve.co.uk

Stirchley Machine Tool Co. Ltd, 401-407 Tyburn Road, Birmingham, B24 8HJ Tel: 0121-328 2424 Fax: 0121-327 6200

Style Machine Tools Ltd, 30a Centurion Industrial Estate, Centurion Way, Farington, Leyland, PR25 4GU Tel: (01772) 624114 Fax: (01722) 624114 E-mail: enquiries@stylemachinetools.co.uk

T & P Tooling Co., Mardyke Works, St Marys Lane, North Ockendon, Upminster, Essex, RM14 3PA Tel: (01708) 224220 Fax: (01708) 224220

Tenga Engineering Co. Ltd, Britannia House, Queensway, New Milton, Hampshire, BH25 5NN Tel: (01425) 622567 Fax: (01425) 622789

Tetroc Chambar Ltd, 3 Telford Road, Ferndown Industrial Estate, Wimborne, Dorset, BH21 7QN Tel: (01202) 871143 Fax: (01202) 897045 E-mail: sales@tetroc.com

Thomas Engineering, Units 8-10, Brinell Way, Harfreys Industrial Estate, Great Yarmouth, Norfolk, NR31 0LU Tel: (01493) 650107 Fax: (01493) 415605 E-mail: admin@stuga.co.uk

Thos P Headland (Machine Tools) Ltd, Unit 4 Blackwater Close, Fairview Industrial Park, Manor Way, Rainham, Essex, RM13 8UA Tel: (01708) 523916 Fax: (01708) 550042 E-mail: machines@tphmachinetools.co.uk

Threading Systems Ltd, Unit 11 Park Road, Dukinfield, Cheshire, SK16 5LL Tel: 0161-330 7277 Fax: 0161-330 6384

Tilgear Tool Merchants, 69 Station Road, Cuffley, Potters Bar, Hertfordshire, EN6 4HY Tel: (01707) 873434 Fax: (01707) 870383 E-mail: orders@tilgear.uk

Tooling Direct Ltd, Salford House, 535 Lichfield Road, Birmingham, B6 7SP Tel: 0121-327 1952 Fax: 0121-327 1954 E-mail: sales@tooling-direct.com

Tornos Technologies UK Ltd, Tornos House, Garden Road, Coalville, Leicestershire, LE67 4JQ Tel: (01530) 513100 Fax: (01530) 814212 E-mail: sales@tornos.co.uk

Toyoda Mitsui Europe, Matrix House, Loughborough Motorway Trading Estate, Gelders Hall Road, Shepshed, Loughborough, Leicestershire, LE12 9NH Tel: (01509) 501730 Fax: (01509) 501730 E-mail: sales@toyoda-mitsui.com

Trade-Link (EC) Ltd, 5 Carlton Gardens, Ealing, London, W5 2AN Tel: (020) 8998 1090 Fax: (020) 8810 5871 E-mail: tradelinkec@clara.net

Traktools, Old Buckenham, Old Buckenham, Attleborough, Norfolk, NR17 1PG Tel: (07860) 521375 Fax: (01953) 861126 E-mail: track.tools@virin.net

Tristar Machinery & Plant Ltd, Londonderry Works, George Street Industrial Estate, Seaham, County Durham, SR7 7SL Tel: 0191-581 3244 Fax: 0191-581 0273

Uniprize Machine Tools Ltd, A3 Bankfield Industrial Estate, Sandy Lane, Stockport, Cheshire, SK5 7SE Tel: 0161-429 6161 Fax: 0161-429 0606 E-mail: uniprize@uniprize.freeserve.co.uk

Victor Europe Ltd, Victor House, Eagle Technology Park, Queensway, Rochdale, Lancashire, OL11 1TQ Tel: (01706) 648485 Fax: (01706) 648483 E-mail: sales@victoreurope.com

Warco Machine Tools Ltd, Warco House, Fisher Lane, Chiddingfold, Godalming, Surrey, GU8 4TD Tel: (01428) 682929 Fax: (01428) 685870 E-mail: warco@warco.co.uk

West Bromwich Machine Tools, Unit 7/8 Birch Court, Crystal Drive, Smethwick, West Midlands, B66 1RB Tel: 0121-544 6503 Fax: 0121-544 6503

Whitehill Woodworking Machinery, 6 Union Street, Luton, LU1 3AN Tel: (01582) 736881 Fax: (01582) 488987 E-mail: david@whitehill-tools.com

Whitehouse Machine Tools Ltd, 7 Princes Drive Industrial Estate, Coventry Road, Kenilworth, Warwickshire, CV8 2FD Tel: (01926) 852725 Fax: (01926) 850620 E-mail: sales@wmtcnc.com

Whittingham Design & Manufacturing Co. Ltd, Chapel Works, Chapel Green, Willenhall, West Midlands, WV13 1QY Tel: (01902) 607272 Fax: (01902) 637884

Wickman Coventry Ltd, Automatic House Discovery Way, Leofric Business Park, Binley, Coventry, CV3 2TD Tel: (024) 7654 7900 Fax: (024) 7654 7420 E-mail: sales@wickman.co.uk

Wilson Machinery International Ltd, Roseberry House, Old Church Road, East Hanningfield, Chelmsford, CM3 8BG Tel: (01245) 403040 Fax: (01245) 403028 E-mail: sales@wilsonmachinery.demon.co.uk

Workrest Blades, 3 Wattville Road Industrial Estate, Wattville Road, Smethwick, West Midlands, B66 2NT Tel: 0121-558 4339 Fax: 0121-558 3666 E-mail: neal@workrestblades.co.uk

YMT Ltd, Brympton Way, Lynx West Trading Estate, Yeovil, Somerset, BA20 2HP Tel: (01935) 428375 Fax: (01935) 432684 E-mail: sales@ymtltd.co.uk

▶ Yorkshire Machine Tools Ltd, Units 5-6 Rosemount Works, Huddersfield Road, Elland, West Yorkshire, HX5 0EE Tel: (01422) 379222 Fax: (01422) 379122 E-mail: sales@ymtools.com

MACHINE TOOL NUMERICAL CONTROL (NC) SYSTEMS

B R E Europe Ltd, London Road, Feering, Colchester, CO5 9ED Tel: (01376) 572500 Fax: (01376) 572600 E-mail: sales@breltd.com

MACHINE TOOL PRESETTING EQUIPMENT

Measure-Rite Ltd, Great Central Way Industrial Estate, Great Central Way, Rugby, Warwickshire, CV21 3XH Tel: (01788) 577512 Fax: (01788) 560864 E-mail: sales@measure-rite.com

MACHINE TOOL RETROFITTING

▶ C N C Check Machine Tools Ltd, Kitchener Road, Leicester, LE5 4AT Tel: 0116-274 1044 Fax: 0116-274 1046 E-mail: mail@cnccheckmachinetools.co.uk

C S D Controls (U K), Britannia Way, Malvern, Worcestershire, WR14 1GZ Tel: (01684) 567044 Fax: (01604) 567017 E-mail: retrofit@csdcontrols.co.uk

G A C Engineering Group Ltd, New Works, Burnley Road, Sowerby Bridge, West Yorkshire, HX6 2TF Tel: (01422) 836091 Fax: (01422) 835396 E-mail: sales@gacgroup.co.uk

S2 Engineering, 4 Derwenthaugh Marina, Blaydon-on-Tyne, Tyne & Wear, NE21 5LL Tel: 0191-414 2300 Fax: 0191-414 2287 E-mail: info@s2eng.co.uk

MACHINE TOOL SPARE PARTS TO SPECIFICATION

Heenan Multiform Machines, Unit 34 Springvale Industrial Estate, Millfield Road, Bilston, West Midlands, WV14 0ST Tel: (01902) 401781 Fax: (01902) 401781

Pen Cutting Tools Ltd, Bold Street, Sheffield, S9 2LR Tel: 0114-243 0055 Fax: 0114-243 0066 E-mail: sales@pencuttingtools.co.uk

MACHINE TOOL SPINDLE RECONDITIONING SERVICES

Micron Services Ltd, Baird Close, Drayton Fields Industrial Estate, Daventry, Northamptonshire, NN11 8RY Tel: (01327) 704921 Fax: (01327) 300013

S K F Spindle Service Centre (U K) Ltd, 8 Dencora Way, Sundon Business Park, Luton, LU3 3HP Tel: (01582) 494674 Fax: (01582) 494808 E-mail: skfspindleserviceuk@skf.com

MACHINE TOOL SPINDLE TOOLING

T S Technology, Langwood, 87 Langley Road, Watford, WD17 4PW Tel: (01923) 221155 Fax: (01923) 218625 E-mail: sales@tstechnology.co.uk

MACHINE TOOL SPINDLES

H B Tools Ltd, 2 Langley Court, Langley Road, Burscough Industrial Estate, Ormskirk, Lancashire, L40 8JR Tel: (01704) 897722 Fax: (01704) 897303 E-mail: sales@hbtools.co.uk

MACHINE TOOL TAPPING ATTACHMENTS

Herbert Tooling Ltd, Roseme, Sandy Lane, Fillongley, Coventry, CV7 8DD Tel: (01676) 540040 Fax: (01676) 540040 E-mail: info@herbert-tooling.com

Railton Products Ltd, Unit 11 Ladbrook Park, Millers Road, Warwick, CV34 5AE Tel: (01926) 496351 Fax: (01926) 410574 E-mail: info@railtonproducts.co.uk

Robert Speck Ltd, Little Ridge, Whittlebury Road, Silverstone, Towcester, Northamptonshire, NN12 8UD Tel: (01327) 857307 Fax: (01327) 858166 E-mail: info@robertspeck.com

MACHINE VISION INSPECTION SYSTEMS

Cognex UK, Sunningdale House, Caldecotte Lake Drive, Caldecotte, Milton Keynes, MK7 8LF Tel: (0800) 0180018 Fax: (01908) 392463 E-mail: sales@cognex.co.uk

MACHINED CASTINGS

▶ A1 Outsource Ltd, 32 St. Ives Road, Coventry, CV2 5FZ Tel: (07903) 857799 E-mail: mitin@a1outsource.co.uk
Courtney Bell Ltd, Lawson Road, Dartford, DA1 5BP Tel: (01322) 221833 Fax: (01322) 228581
J T Barker & Sons Ltd, Leeds Foundries, Westland Square, Leeds, LS11 5SS Tel: 0113-271 6837 Fax: 0113-270 6901
William Lee Ltd, Callywhite Lane, Dronfield, Derbyshire, S18 2XU Tel: (01246) 416155 Fax: (01246) 292194 E-mail: sales@wmlee.co.uk
▶ Micro Metalsmiths Ltd, Kirkdale Road, Kirkbymoorside, York, YO62 6PX Tel: 0845 2139030 Fax: (01751) 432061 E-mail: info@micrometalsmiths.co.uk
S.J.S. Engineering, 114-116 Newhall Street, Willenhall, West Midlands, WV13 1LQ Tel: (01902) 606602 Fax: (01902) 606011
▶ Ulster Castings Ltd, 2-4 Bridge St, Comber, Newtownards, County Down, BT23 5AT Tel: (028) 9187 2372 Fax: (028) 9187 0088 E-mail: jneedham@ulstercastings.com

MACHINED PLASTIC COMPONENTS

Drymat Supplies, Top Lodge, 3 Decker Hill, Decker Hill, Shifnal, Shropshire, TF11 8QW Tel: (01952) 463747 Fax: (01952) 463905

MACHINERY ALIGNMENT SERVICES

Optimech, 14 Country Mews, Yewtree Gardens, Beardwood, Blackburn, BB2 7FJ Tel: (07710) 718593 Fax: (01282) 447111 E-mail: optimech@aol.com

MACHINERY CARRIER ROAD TRANSPORT AND HAULAGE

A B C Transport Ltd, Plot U Unswood Industrial Estate, Theaklen Drive, St. Leonards-on-Sea, East Sussex, TN38 9AZ Tel: (01424) 755059 Fax: (01424) 722234
J Bradshaw & Sons Ltd, High Street, Sturton-By-Stow, Lincoln, LN1 2BX Tel: (01427) 788223 Fax: (01427) 788498
R W Boyles Transport Ltd, Shires Road, Buckingham Road Industrial Estate, Brackley, Northamptonshire, NN13 7EZ Tel: (01280) 702690 Fax: (01280) 701619 E-mail: ron@boyles.fslife.co.uk

MACHINERY COMPONENTS, TO SPECIFICATION

Drymat Supplies, Top Lodge, 3 Decker Hill, Decker Hill, Shifnal, Shropshire, TF11 8QW Tel: (01952) 463747 Fax: (01952) 463905

MACHINERY CONTROL SYSTEMS MAINTENANCE/ REPAIR SERVICES

Alplas Plastics Machinery Services Ltd, 1 Leyside, Bromham, Bedford, MK43 8NF Tel: (01234) 823619 Fax: (01234) 825824 E-mail: sales@alplas.freeserve.co.uk
Trouble Shooter Electronics Ltd, Pear Patch, Walnut Tree Lane, Maidstone, Kent, ME15 9RQ Tel: (01622) 743196 Fax: (01622) 743196E-mail: troubleshooter@btconnect.com

MACHINERY DESIGNERS OR CONSULTANTS

Atlantic Bridge Ltd, Zenith House, 11 The Street, Chirton, Devizes, Wiltshire, SN10 3QS Tel: (01380) 848170 Fax: (01380) 840152 E-mail: sales@atlanticbridge.co.uk
Comau Estil Systems, Midland Road, Luton, LU2 0HR Tel: (01582) 817600 Fax: (01582) 817700
Jotika Midlands Software Ltd, Carmichael House, Village Green, Inkberrow, Worcester, WR7 4DZ Tel: (01386) 793415 Fax: (01386) 793407 E-mail: sales@jotika.com
Oil & Gas Systems Ltd, Gemini House, The Business Park, Ely, Cambridgeshire, CB7 4EA Tel: (01353) 666640 Fax: (01353) 666650 E-mail: mb@ogsl.com
R G P Design Innovation, 62 Cause End Road, Wootton, Bedford, MK43 9DE Tel: (01234) 767143 Fax: (01234) 767143 E-mail: rgpdesign@talk21.com
Snow Hunter Automation, PO Box 260, Scarborough, North Yorkshire, YO12 5YA Tel: (07944) 085848 Fax: (01723) 371696 E-mail: john@snowhunter.freeserve.co.uk
▶ V E S Precision Ltd, 10 Cropmead Industrial Estate, Crewkerne, Somerset, TA18 7HQ Tel: (01460) 270600 Fax: (01460) 270601 E-mail: enquiries@vesprecision.com

MACHINERY DISMANTLING OR ERECTING OR INSTALLING

Advanced Maintenance Services Ltd, Alchorne Place, The Airport, Portsmouth, PO3 5QL Tel: (023) 9267 3333 Fax: (023) 9269 3319 E-mail: ams@zoom.co.uk
B & W Machinery Installations Ltd, Eagle Iron Works, Tame Street, Stalybridge, Cheshire, SK15 1ST Tel: 0161-338 6588 Fax: 0161-338 6385
Briton Plant Installation, 8 Woodfield Road, Welwyn Garden City, Hertfordshire, AL7 1JQ Tel: (01707) 885732 Fax: (01707) 882566 E-mail: britton.plant@ntlbusiness.com
D Cave Hydraulics Ltd, Rainford Road, Bickerstaffe, Ormskirk, Lancashire, L39 0HG Tel: (01695) 735888 Fax: (01695) 725511
Elmpark Engineering Services Ltd, Washington Street Industrial Estate, Halesowen Road, Dudley, West Midlands, DY2 9RE Tel: (01384) 239301 Fax: (01384) 457378 E-mail: anything@elmparkeng.co.uk
F P Industrial Ltd, 78 Leicester Road, Wigston, Leicestershire, LE18 1DR Tel: 0116-281 2714 Fax: 0116-281 2714
Gatwick Plant Hire, Woodside, The Close, Horley, Surrey, RH6 9EB Tel: (01293) 824777 Fax: (01293) 824077 E-mail: sales@gatwickgroup.com
J Kool, Acre Holdings, Little Weighton Road, Skidby, Cottingham, North Humberside, HU16 5TP Tel: (01482) 875747 Fax: (01482) 845024 E-mail: sales@jkoo1-engineers.co.uk
Kall Kwik UK Ltd, Heaton Mersey Industrial Estate, Battersea Road, Stockport, Cheshire, SK4 3EA Tel: 0161-486 1911 Fax: 0161-431 8069 E-mail: sales@kallkwik.uk.com
Machine Tool & Engineering Services Ltd, Unit 14 Quay Lane Industrial Estate, Hardway, Gosport, Hampshire, PO12 4LJ Tel: (023) 9251 1666 Fax: (023) 9251 1164 E-mail: info@mtes.co.uk
Mechanical Engineering Services, Unit 32n The Washford Industrial Estate, Heming Road, Redditch, Worcestershire, B98 0DH Tel: (01527) 510930 Fax: (01527) 529992
J. Parrish & Son, Stanford Bury, Stanford Road, Shefford, Bedfordshire, SG17 5NS Tel: (01462) 814870 Fax: (01462) 814644 E-mail: info@jparrish.co.uk
Pro-Rol Ltd, 44 Yardley Road, Olney, Buckinghamshire, MK46 5ED Tel: (01234) 240177 Fax: (01234) 240188 E-mail: sales@projectorlisting.co.uk
Quinto Crane & Plant Ltd, Markfield Road, Groby, Leicester, LE6 0FT Tel: (01530) 244181 Fax: (01530) 244808
R P M 2000 Ltd, Millfields Road, Wolverhampton, WV4 6JE Tel: (01902) 490615 Fax: (01902) 490241
R S J Process Machinery Ltd, Phoenix House, Tame Street, Stalybridge, Cheshire, SK15 1SY Tel: 0161-338 7288 Fax: 0161-338 3574 E-mail: aquafil@btconnect.com
▶ U K A E A, Dounreay, Thurso, Caithness, KW14 7TZ Tel: (01847) 802121
Vogal Industrial Installations, Regent House, Shrewsbury Avenue, Peterborough, PE2 7WH Tel: 01733 370789
Watkinson Lifting & Transportation Ltd, Invincible Works, Marriner Road, Keighley, West Yorkshire, BD21 5LW Tel: (01535) 600151 Fax: (01535) 692249 E-mail: sales@watkinsons.com
Westside Engineering Site Services Ltd, Westside House, Pontugwindy Industrial Estate, Caerphilly, Mid Glamorgan, CF83 3HU Tel: (029) 2086 0123 Fax: (029) 2085 1122

MACHINERY EXPORT MERCHANTS OR AGENTS

Brightside Industries Ltd, Empire Works, Brewery Lane, Thornhill Lees, Dewsbury, West Yorkshire, WF12 9HQ Tel: (01924) 455717 Fax: (01924) 450220 E-mail: bsind@globalnet.co.uk
C R Cradock Tractors, Woodside, Heywood, Westbury, Wiltshire, BA13 4LW Tel: (01373) 826403 Fax: (01373) 824414
Champion Global Ltd, 33 Branbridges Industrial Estate, Branbridges Road, East Peckham, Tonbridge, Kent, TN12 5HF Tel: (01622) 873366 Fax: (01622) 873388 E-mail: a.chouchane@champion-global.co.uk
Falgard Ltd, 235 Bickenhall Mansions, Bickenhall Street, London, W1U 6BW Tel: (020) 7487 5161 Fax: (020) 7486 0939 E-mail: falgard@falgard.com
Future Technology Heat Sealers Ltd, Yew Tree Farm, Main Street, Barton In The Beans, Nuneaton, Warwickshire, CV13 0DJ Tel: (01455) 299000 E-mail: sales@futuresealers.co.uk
Kilkie Paper Mill Services, Lovesta, Gowanlea Road, Comrie, Crieff, Perthshire, PH6 2HD Tel: (01764) 670141 Fax: (0870) 1301570 E-mail: sales@kilkie.com
Mcnelis Workshop Machinery & Steel Supplies, 122 Curr Road, Beragh, Sixmilecross, Omagh, County Tyrone, BT79 0QT Tel: (028) 8075 8225 Fax: (028) 8075 8225
Maxwell Emsworth Ltd, Elsted Station, Elsted, Midhurst, West Sussex, GU29 0JT Tel: (01730) 812662 Fax: (01730) 813560
Rankinco Ltd, 4 Blades Close, Leatherhead, Surrey, KT22 7JY Tel: (01372) 276390 Fax: (01372) 276390 E-mail: ian_rankin@compuserve.com
Texel (UK) Ltd, Unit 9, 21 Wadsworth Road, Greenford, Middlesex, UB6 7LQ Tel: (020) 8998 9605 Fax: (020) 8566 7797 E-mail: texel@onetel.com
Tristar Machinery & Plant Ltd, Londonderry Works, George Street Industrial Estate, Seaham, County Durham, SR7 7SL Tel: 0191-581 3244 Fax: 0191-581 0273
Woodfield, Station Yard, Station Road, Bluntisham, Huntingdon, Cambridgeshire, PE28 3PA Tel: (01487) 843031 Fax: (01487) 843342

MACHINERY IMPORT MERCHANTS OR AGENTS

B B Services, 75 Ballyutoag Road, Belfast, BT14 8SS Tel: (028) 9082 5393 Fax: (028) 9082 5393
Bison Metalworking Machinery, Common Road, Stafford, ST16 3EQ Tel: (01785) 214242 Fax: (01785) 254232
Natural Europe Ltd, 70 Peveril Road, Beeston, Nottingham, NG9 2HU Tel: 0115-922 7284 Fax: 0115-922 7284

MACHINERY INSPECTION ENGINEERS

Heuft, Unit 24 26 Innage Park, Abeles Way, Holly Lane Industrial Estate, Atherstone, Warwickshire, CV9 2QX Tel: (01827) 717002 Fax: (01827) 716146 E-mail: dominic.metcalfe@heuft.com

MACHINERY MAINTENANCE OR REPAIR, *See also headings for particular types*

Boyerman Ltd, Unit C Chesham Close, Romford, RM7 7PJ Tel: (01708) 742854 Fax: (01708) 737737 E-mail: sales@boyerman.co.uk
Bringover Ltd, Unit 6, Boathouse Lane, Stockton-On-Tees, Cleveland, TS18 3AW Tel: (01642) 605111 Fax: (01642) 615880 E-mail: bringover@bringovr.demon.co.uk
Campbell Miller (Tools) Ltd, 16-22 Jordanvale Avenue, Clydeside Industrial Estate, Glasgow, G14 0QU Tel: 0141-954 9557 Fax: 0141-954 9979 E-mail: sales@cmtl.co.uk
Cannon Electronics & Automation Ltd, White Gates Factory, Dunmow Road, Hatfield Heath, Bishop's Stortford, Hertfordshire, CM22 7ED Tel: (01279) 730709
Casting Repairs Ltd, Hipper St South, Chesterfield, Derbyshire, S40 1SS Tel: (01246) 246700 Fax: (01246) 206519 E-mail: andrea.peck@casting-repairs.co.uk
Dorcas Engineering Ltd, Howard Road, Eaton Socon, St. Neots, Cambridgeshire, PE19 8ET Tel: (01480) 213316 Fax: (01480) 216319
Erecting & Dismantling Services Ltd, 15 Chatsworth Road, Eccles, Manchester, M30 9DZ Tel: 0161-789 1216 Fax: 0161-787 8120
Ferguson Engineering, 6 Middlefield Road, Falkirk, FK2 9AG Tel: (01324) 627352 Fax: (01324) 633672 E-mail: enquiries@smith-electrical.co.uk
Flude Machine Tools, 7 Central City Industrial Estate, Red Lane, Coventry, CV6 5RY Tel: (024) 7666 1220 Fax: (024) 7666 1220
Fourjays Machinery Services, 16 Kingsway, Nettleham, Lincoln, LN2 2QA Tel: (01522) 754880 Fax: (01522) 595269
G E M S, 31 Hatchett Street, Birmingham, B19 3NX Tel: 0121-333 4151 Fax: 0121-359 4934 E-mail: gems2@btconnet.com
▶ G W Lomas & Sons, Back Spinnerbottom, Birch Vale, High Peak, Derbyshire, SK22 1BN Tel: (01663) 742536 Fax: (01663) 742890 E-mail: info@gwlomasandsons.co.uk
HCH Engineering Ltd, Unit 4 Charlton Drive, Corngreaves Trading Estate, Cradley Heath, West Midlands, B64 7BJ Tel: (01384) 413233 Fax: (01384) 633637 E-mail: hch@ntlbusiness.com
Hillfax Ltd, Park Road, Willenhall, West Midlands, WV13 1AQ Tel: (01902) 606442 Fax: (01902) 634982 E-mail: sprint@btclick.com
▶ Hindley Engineering, Cemetery Road, Ince, Wigan, Lancashire, WN3 4NN Tel: (01942) 862894 Fax: (01942) 862894
J & W Tait Ltd, Sparrowhawk Road, Hatston Industrial Estate, Kirkwall, Orkney, KW15 1GE Tel: (01856) 872490 Fax: (01856) 873076
James E Hatch & Son, 9 Old School Lane, Adlington, Chorley, Lancashire, PR7 4DX Tel: (01257) 480064 Fax: (01257) 481213
Johnston Sweepers Ltd, 3 Heron Square, Deans Industrial Estate, Deans, Livingston, West Lothian, EH54 8QY Tel: (01506) 460563 Fax: (01506) 460564 E-mail: livingston@johnstonesweepers.com
M F H Engineering Holdings Ltd, Charlotte House, 500 Charlotte Road, Sheffield, S2 4ER Tel: 0114-279 9999 Fax: 0114-279 7501 E-mail: eng@mfhgroup.co.uk
M J Farrington Ltd, Locks Farm, Main Road, Dibden, Southampton, SO45 5TD Tel: (023) 8084 0755 Fax: (023) 8084 4588
Make Em & Break Em, Penybont Road, Pencoed, Bridgend, Mid Glamorgan, CF35 5LE Tel: (01656) 862070 Fax: (01656) 862070
Midland Safe Load Indicators Ltd, Watling Street Works, Watling Street, Brownhills, Walsall, WS8 7JT Tel: (01543) 453166 Fax: (01543) 453167
D. Morrison Machine Services, 104 Station Road, Portstewart, County Londonderry, BT55 7PU Tel: (028) 7083 5444 Fax: (028) 7083 5444
▶ Musselbrook Machine Maintenance Ltd, 136a Church Road, Croydon, CR0 1SE Tel: (020) 8686 2500 Fax: (020) 8649 9088
P M W Precision Engineering Ltd, 47-55 Alcester Street, Deritend, Birmingham, B12 0PY Tel: 0121-773 9105 Fax: 0121-773 9141
R P M 2000 Ltd, Millfields Road, Wolverhampton, WV4 6JE Tel: (01902) 490615 Fax: (01902) 490241
R & R Development, Llewellyns Quay, The Docks, Port Talbot, West Glamorgan, SA13 1SD Tel: (01639) 870330 Fax: (01639) 890317
S C S Machine Tool Services, 18 Deeming Drive, Quorn, Loughborough, Leicestershire, LE12 8NF Tel: (01509) 412108 Fax: (01509) 412108
Safety Engineers Ltd, 18 Dudley Wood Road, Dudley, West Midlands, DY2 0DB Tel: 01384 569024
Sampson Engineering Co., Stanley Road, Bradford, West Yorkshire, BD2 1AS Tel: (01274) 723299
Senior Packaging Ltd, 4 Borrowdale Road, Dewsbury, West Yorkshire, WF12 7PF Tel: (01924) 430201 Fax: (01924) 510065 E-mail: info@seniorpackaging.co.uk
Thomas, Wilch & High Ltd, Europa Way, Martineau Lane, Norwich, NR1 2EN Tel: (01603) 620644 Fax: (01603) 768334 E-mail: enquiries@thomaswilchandhigh.co.uk
William T. Wood Machinery Ltd, Bentoria Works, 395 Petre Street, Sheffield, S4 8LJ Tel: 0114-256 2200 Fax: 0114-256 1965 E-mail: sales@dronmctools.demon.co.uk

MACHINERY MERCHANTS

▶ P D E Management, 1 Berry Street, Aberdeen, AB25 1HF Tel: (01224) 841317 Fax: (0870) 1674689
▶ V Tech SMT, Bandeath Industrial Estate, Throsk, Stirling, FK7 7NP Tel: (01786) 813999 Fax: (01786) 813998 E-mail: sales@vtech-smt.co.uk

MACHINERY MODULAR FRAMEWORK SYSTEMS

Unique Design Systems Modular, Manor Farm, Pickstock, Newport, Shropshire, TF10 8AH Tel: (01952) 550037 Fax: (01952) 550037 E-mail: barryb.uds.ltd@fsmail.net

MACHINERY MOUNTING PADS AND SHEETS

Anglia Rubber & Plastics Ltd, Unit 27, Saville Road, Westwood, Peterborough, PE3 7PR Tel: (01733) 264100 Fax: (01733) 261823 E-mail: arp.sales@btconnect.com

MACHINERY PACKING SERVICES

P & M (Packing) Ltd, Unit 11, Alstam Complex, Campbell Road, Eastleigh, Hampshire, SO50 5AD Tel: (023) 8049 0440 Fax: (023) 8049 0444 E-mail: naomi@pmpacking.com

MACHINERY RECONDITIONING

Chiltern Cam Service Ltd, Unit 2a Watlington Industrial Estate, Cuxham Road, Watlington, Oxfordshire, OX49 5LU Tel: (01491) 614422 Fax: (01491) 613813 E-mail: enquiries@chilterncam.com
Charles Martin Hacker, 2 Lansdown Place Lane, Cheltenham, Gloucestershire, GL50 2JZ Tel: (01242) 522308
R.A. Jenkins, Gower Engineering Works, Station Road, Penclawdd, Swansea, SA4 3XN Tel: (01792) 851224 Fax: (01792) 851588
Metal Stitching Services Ltd, The Old Court Yard, Warwick Street, Prestwich, Manchester, M25 3HN Tel: 0161-773 6919 Fax: 0161-798 7352
Millen Machine Tools Ltd, Hamilton House, 126 St. Georges Avenue, Northampton, NN2 6JF Tel: (01604) 721122 Fax: (01604) 721329 E-mail: harvey.millen@virgin.net

MACHINERY RECONDITIONING - continued

D. Morrison Machine Services, 104 Station Road, Portstewart, County Londonderry, BT55 7PU Tel: (028) 7083 5444 Fax: (028) 7083 5444
R K L Ltd, Roland Road, Stockport, Cheshire, SK5 6TJ Tel: 0161-477 9192 Fax: 0161-480 3852
David Ricketts & Son, Court Newydd, St. Brides Major, Bridgend, M. Glam, CF32 0TG Tel: (01656) 880373
Safety Engineers Ltd, 18 Dudley Wood Road, Dudley, West Midlands, DY2 0DB Tel: 01384 569024
Spy Machinery, Albion Street, Willenhall, West Midlands, WV13 1NN Tel: (01902) 633233
Stourbridge Engineering Services Ltd, 19a Oak Street, Quarry Bank, Brierley Hill, West Midlands, DY5 2JN Tel: (01384) 561600 Fax: (01384) 561600
Tecweld Ltd, Noble Square Industrial Estate, Brynmawr, Ebbw Vale, Gwent, NP23 4BS Tel: (01495) 310796 Fax: (01495) 312383
Wayfarer Service Division, Workshop, 112 Gloucester Road, Croydon, CR0 2DE Tel: (020) 8404 1234 Fax: (020) 8689 9465

MACHINERY REFURBISHMENT

Schmidt UK Ltd, 338 Polmadie Road, Glasgow, G42 0PH Tel: 0141-423 6002 Fax: 0141-423 5518
David Stabler, 12B Salamanca Road, Long Stratton, Norwich, NR15 2PF Tel: (01508) 532122
Wayfarer Service Division, Workshop, 112 Gloucester Road, Croydon, CR0 2DE Tel: (020) 8404 1234 Fax: (020) 8689 9465

MACHINERY REMOVAL OR RELOCATION CONTRACTORS

A E T Transport Services Ltd, 8 Allens Lane, Poole, Dorset, BH16 5DA Tel: (01202) 632221 Fax: (01202) 632380 E-mail: aet-transport@btconnect.com
Abbey Transport Ltd, Concorde Road, Norwich, NR6 6BH Tel: (01603) 425928 Fax: (01603) 418333
Adams Bristow Ltd, The Old Mill, Old Malden Lane, Worcester Park, Surrey, KT4 7QS Tel: (020) 8330 3366 Fax: (020) 8330 3368
Ainscough Crane Hire Ltd, Old Mill Lane, Aylesford, Kent, ME20 7DT Tel: (01622) 716500 Fax: (01622) 716066 E-mail: maidstone@ainscough.co.uk
Ainscough Vanguard, William Thorpe Industrial Park, Park Road, Holmwood, Chesterfield, Derbyshire, S42 5UY Tel: (01246) 854644 Fax: (01246) 854161
B & W Machinery Installations Ltd, Eagle Iron Works, Tame Street, Stalybridge, Cheshire, SK15 1ST Tel: 0161-338 6588 Fax: 0161-338 6385
Allan Badman Transport Ltd, Bamfield House, Bristol, BS14 0XD Tel: (01275) 839417 Fax: (01275) 839375 E-mail: enquiries@badmantransport.co.uk
Beck & Pollitzer Engineering Ltd, 6 Locksbrook Court, Locksbrook Road, Bath, BA1 3EN Tel: (01225) 425383 Fax: (01225) 448385 E-mail: info@beck-pollitzer.com
C & M Apostolides Ltd, 257 Wood Street, Walthamstow, London, E17 3NG Tel: (020) 8923 5050 Fax: (020) 8923 6060 E-mail: mail@cama.co.uk
D J Mills, 23 Mead Road, Cheltenham, Gloucestershire, GL53 7DY Tel: (01242) 528633 Fax: (01242) 528633
Lyndon Edwards Ltd, Marlers, Pye Corner, Gilston, Harlow, Essex, CM20 2RD Tel: (01279) 414801 Fax: (01279) 450736
Factory Plant Removals UK, European Business Park, Taylors Lane, Oldbury, West Midlands, B69 2BN Tel: 0121-544 4774 Fax: 0121-552 2018 E-mail: barry.jones@factory-plant-removals.co.uk
James Garside & Son Ltd, Grantham Works, Grantham Road, Halifax, West Yorkshire, HX3 6PL Tel: (01422) 340559 Fax: (01422) 349465
Gatwick Plant Hire, Woodside, The Close, Horley, Surrey, RH6 9EB Tel: (01293) 824777 Fax: (01293) 824077 E-mail: sales@gatwickgroup.com
Hanlon & Wright Ltd, Tudor House, Park Road, Dukinfield, Cheshire, SK16 5LX Tel: 0161-330 7631 Fax: 0161-330 0436 E-mail: sales@hanlonandwright.co.uk
Hulse Engineering, Duke Street, Stoke-on-Trent, ST4 3NR Tel: (01782) 316589 Fax: (01782) 598504 E-mail: hulsefabricationsltd@hotmail.com
J A Renton & Sons, Ashby Road, Thringstone, Coalville, Leicestershire, LE67 8UH Tel: (01530) 222224 Fax: (01530) 224069 E-mail: renton.lorries@btinternet.com
▶ J H Kemp Ltd, 409 Tyburn Road, Birmingham, B24 8HJ Tel: 0121-327 3154 Fax: 0121-326 7542 E-mail: info@jhkemp.co.uk
Howard Kent, 5 Brighton Road, Shoreham-by-Sea, West Sussex, BN43 6RN Tel: (01273) 871871 Fax: (01273) 870970 E-mail: howardkent@ukonline.co.uk
M I D Services, Kilworthy Hill, Tavistock, Devon, PL19 0EP Tel: (01822) 615625 Fax: (01822) 615625
Mechanical Services (Luton) Ltd, 158A Beechwood Road, Luton, LU4 9RY Tel: (01582) 494747 Fax: (01582) 494749 E-mail: mechservluton@aol.com
Mendz Industrial Move Ltd, Abbey Meadows, Back Lane, Cotes, Loughborough, Leicestershire, LE12 5TA Tel: (01509) 212711 Fax: (01509) 212722
Midland Machinery Heavy Lift Ltd, Heath Road, Wednesbury, West Midlands, WS10 8XE Tel: 0121-526 5511 Fax: 0121-526 6846
Midland Plant Installations Ltd, Curriers Cl, Charter Avenue Industrial Estate, Coventry, CV4 8AW Tel: (024) 7646 1225 Fax: (024) 7669 4261 E-mail: info@mpi-uk.com
J. Parrish & Son, Stanford Bury, Stanford Road, Shefford, Bedfordshire, SG17 5NS Tel: (01462) 814870 Fax: (01462) 814644 E-mail: info@jparrish.co.uk
Plant Installations (Coventry) Ltd, Crondal Road, Exhall, Coventry, CV7 9NH Tel: (024) 7636 0421 Fax: (024) 7664 4303 E-mail: sales@plantinstallations.co.uk
Pro-Rol Ltd, 44 Yardley Road, Olney, Buckinghamshire, MK46 5ED Tel: (01234) 240177 Fax: (01234) 240188 E-mail: sales@projectorlisting.co.uk
Quinto Crane Hire, The Drift, Nacton Road, Ipswich, IP3 9QR Tel: (01473) 712041 Fax: (01473) 720386
Quinto Crane & Plant Ltd, Drakes Lane, Boreham, Chelmsford, CM3 3BE Tel: (01245) 360531 Fax: (01245) 362427
Quinto Crane & Plant Ltd, Admiralty Road, Great Yarmouth, Norfolk, NR30 3DY Tel: (01493) 331800 Fax: (01603) 407269
Quinto Crane & Plant Ltd, Anson Road, Norwich Airport, Norwich, NR6 6EH Tel: (01603) 410881 Fax: (01603) 404565 E-mail: cranehire@quinto.co.uk
Quinto Crane & Plant Ltd, Royce Road, Peterborough, PE1 5YB Tel: (01733) 560338 Fax: (01733) 890829 E-mail: adrian@quinto.co.uk
R E M Engineering Ltd, Unit 16, Crown Business Centre, Failsworth, Manchester, M35 9BW Tel: 0161-682 8833 Fax: 0161-682 8700 E-mail: david@remengineering.co.uk
Rex Campbell Properties Ltd, Phoenix Works, Steeley Lane, Chorley, Lancashire, PR6 0RJ Tel: (01257) 266521 Fax: (01257) 241362 E-mail: kim@rex-campbell.co.uk
Skate Systems Ltd, 55 London Road, Hurst Green, Etchingham, East Sussex, TN19 7QP Tel: (01580) 860020 Fax: (01580) 860021 E-mail: sales@skatesystems.co.uk
Stourbridge Engineering Services Ltd, 19a Oak Street, Quarry Bank, Brierley Hill, West Midlands, DY5 2JN Tel: (01384) 561600 Fax: (01384) 561600

MACHINERY VALUERS

Arrow Auctions, Bartleet Road, Washford, Redditch, Worcestershire, B98 0DQ Tel: (01527) 517707 Fax: (01527) 510924 E-mail: enquiries@arrowauction.co.uk
Hickman Shearer, 7 Buttermarket, Thame, Oxfordshire, OX9 3EW Tel: (01844) 215755 Fax: (01844) 214549 E-mail: officehs@hickman-shearer.co.uk
Ryden Property Consultants & Chartered Surveyors, Coronet House, Queen Street, Leeds, LS1 2TW Tel: 0113-243 6777 Fax: 0113-243 9323 E-mail: info@ryden.co.uk
Walker Singleton Commercial Ltd, Property House, Lister Lane, Halifax, West Yorkshire, HX1 5AS Tel: (01422) 430000 Fax: (01422) 430010 E-mail: comm@walkersingleton.co.uk
Wyles Hardy & Co. Ltd, Ley Hill Road, Bovingdon, Hemel Hempstead, Hertfordshire, HP3 0NW Tel: (01442) 832234 Fax: (01442) 834342 E-mail: enquiries@wyleshardy.com

MACHINERY, ELECTRIC MOTOR PRODUCTION

Winding Technology, Moorland House, Midway, South Crosland, Huddersfield, HD4 7DA Tel: (01484) 663389 Fax: (01484) 666783 E-mail: coil@winding.demon.co.uk

MACHINERY, PROTOTYPE OR EXPERIMENTAL

Atc Engineering Services Ltd, C1 Oak Park Estate, Northarbour Road, Portsmouth, PO6 3TJ Tel: (023) 9232 6635 Fax: (023) 9221 0907 E-mail: info@atcengineering.co.uk
William Henry Martin Ltd, Allfield Court, Condover, Shrewsbury, SY5 7AP Tel: (01743) 874550 Fax: (01743) 874650

MACHINING CENTRES, *See also headings for particular types*

George Kingsbury, Quay Lane, Hardway, Gosport, Hampshire, PO12 4LB Tel: (023) 9258 0371 Fax: (023) 9250 1741 E-mail: mtools@gkholdings.com
Grob Machine Tools UK Ltd, Wellesbourne House, Walton Road, Wellesbourne, Warwick, CV35 9JB Tel: (01789) 470047 Fax: (01789) 470176 E-mail: grobuk@btconnect.com
M Tech UK Ltd, 913a Uppingham Road, Bushby, Leicester, LE7 9RR Tel: 0116-241 5791
Machine Mart Ltd, Middleway, Thornaby, Stockton-on-Tees, Cleveland, TS17 6BZ Tel: (01642) 677881 Fax: (01642) 679896
MAKA Machinery UK Ltd, Unit 19 Queensway Link Industrial Estate, Stafford Park 17, Telford, Shropshire, TF3 3DN Tel: (01952) 270006 Fax: (01952) 270007 E-mail: info@makauk.com
S C M Group UK Ltd, Dabell Avenue, Nottingham, NG6 8WA Tel: 0115-977 0044 Fax: 0115-977 0946
▶ Teknek Manufacturing Ltd, Inchinnan Business Park, Newmains Avenue, Inchinnan, Renfrew, PA4 9RR Tel: 0141-568 8100 Fax: 0141-568 8101 E-mail: sales@teknek.com

MACHINING SERVICES, CNC, METAL

Brineton Engineering Co., Alma Street, Walsall, WS2 8JQ Tel: (01922) 620070 Fax: (01922) 722875 E-mail: sales@brineton-eng.co.uk
Fife Engineering Co. Ltd, Longrigg, Swalwell, Newcastle upon Tyne, NE16 3AW Tel: 0191-496 1133 Fax: 0191-496 5502 E-mail: admin@fife-engineering.com
Formil Engineering Ltd, Coppice Side Industrial Estate, Brownhills, Walsall, WS8 7EX Tel: (01543) 371604 Fax: (01543) 372208 E-mail: formileng@ukonline.co.uk
Harper & Simmons Ltd, 19 Howard Road, Park Farm, Redditch, Worcestershire, B98 7SE Tel: (01527) 518121 Fax: (01527) 518123 E-mail: robertsimmons@harperandsimmons.co.uk
Hyspeed CNC Ltd, Clovelly Road, Southbourne, Emsworth, Hampshire, PO10 8PE Tel: (01243) 377751 Fax: (01243) 377754 E-mail: sales@hyspeed.co.uk
Specfab (Pershore) Ltd, Unit 5A, Pershore Trading Estate, Pershore, Worcestershire, WR10 2DD Tel: (01386) 552790 Fax: (01386) 556827 E-mail: sales@specfab.co.uk
T M Engineers Midlands Ltd, Oak Lane, Kingswinford, West Midlands, DY6 7JW Tel: (01384) 400212 Fax: (01384) 296019 E-mail: sales@tmengineers.co.uk

MACHINISTS, ELECTRICAL DISCHARGE MACHINING (EDM)

D R Case & Son, 5 Lady Bee Marina Industrial Units, Albion Street, Southwick, Brighton, BN42 4EG Tel: (01273) 870850 Fax: (01273) 870855 E-mail: colin.case@btconnect.com
Travelling Wire, Unit 3 Teknol House, Victoria Road, Burgess Hill, West Sussex, RH15 9LH Tel: (01444) 239920 Fax: (01444) 239920 E-mail: twire@btconnect.com
Wines Precision Engineers, The Old Dairy, Egg Pie Lane, Weald, Sevenoaks, Kent, TN14 6NP Tel: (01732) 740542 Fax: (01732) 464440 E-mail: sales@winesweb.com

MACHINISTS, (ENGINEERS')/ GENERAL MACHINING SERVICES

3d Machine Shop Engineering Ltd, 23 The Business Centre, 20 James Road, Tyseley, Birmingham, B11 2BA Tel: 0121-628 6628 Fax: 0121-628 2008 E-mail: cliffdavies1@btconnect.com
A & A Lampkin, Greengate, Silsden, Keighley, West Yorkshire, BD20 9LA Tel: (01535) 652328 Fax: (01535) 657866
A & P Engineering Ltd, 2 Bilston Key Industrial Estate, Oxford Street, Bilston, West Midlands, WV14 7DW Tel: (01902) 408087 Fax: (01902) 408311
Accu-Rout Ltd, Maltings Lane, Castleton, Rochdale, Lancashire, OL11 2UY Tel: (01706) 631277 Fax: (01706) 646207
Ada Machining Services Ltd, Kayley Industrial Estate, Richmond Street, Ashton-under-Lyne, Lancashire, OL7 0AU Tel: 0161-339 3221 Fax: 0161-339 3981 E-mail: mail@ada-ms.co.uk
Allenfield Precision Engineering Ltd, Richs Sidings, Broadway, Didcot, Oxfordshire, OX11 8AG Tel: (01235) 816880 Fax: (01235) 811848 E-mail: trina@allenfield.co.uk
Amblecote Machine Services, 4 Junction Road, Audnam, Stourbridge, West Midlands, DY8 4YJ Tel: (01384) 374935 Fax: (01384) 373336
Andawest Engineering Ltd, Unit 2a Boardman Industrial Estate, Boardman Road, Swadlincote, Derbyshire, DE11 9DL Tel: (01283) 214182 Fax: (01283) 550909 E-mail: andawest@aol.com
Argo Products Ltd, Viola Street, Bolton, BL1 8NG Tel: (01204) 595224 Fax: (01204) 307729
Ashby Precision Engineering Drayton Ltd, Marcham Road, Drayton, Abingdon, Oxfordshire, OX14 4JH Tel: (01235) 531279 Fax: (01235) 535801 E-mail: sales@ashbyeng.com
Auto Components Ltd, 11 Coulman Road, Industrial Estate, Thorne, Doncaster, South Yorkshire, DN8 5JS Tel: (01405) 812424 Fax: (01405) 740072 E-mail: info@auto-components.co.uk
B B W Engineering Co Aston Ltd, 55 Stanhope Street, Birmingham, B12 0UX Tel: 0121-446 5223 Fax: 0121-446 5305 E-mail: m.eaton@btconnect.com
B P Newbould Ltd, 15 Hilltop Road, Hamilton, Leicester, LE5 1TT Tel: 0116-274 3303 Fax: 0116-274 3301 E-mail: sales@bpnewbould.co.uk
Berkeley Car Company Scotland Ltd, Berryfauld, Forfar Road, Arbroath, Angus, DD11 3RA Tel: (01241) 875013 Fax: (01241) 875013 E-mail: berkeleycarco@btconnect.com
BFS Sheet Metal & Engineering Ltd, 42 Woodham Lane, New Haw, Addlestone, Surrey, KT15 3NA Tel: (01932) 848142 Fax: (01932) 841937 E-mail: stephen@bfssheetmetal.co.uk
Bill Quay Engineering Co., Unit 10 Wagonway Road, Hebburn, Tyne & Wear, NE31 1SP Tel: 0191-483 7355 Fax: 0191-428 0603
Blaker Specialised Welding Repairs Ltd, Worthing Road, Dial Post, Horsham, West Sussex, RH13 8NJ Tel: (01403) 710333 Fax: (01403) 711234 E-mail: simon@blaker.co.uk
Boundary Precision Engineering Ltd, Limber Road, Lufton, Yeovil, Somerset, BA22 8RR Tel: (01935) 472094 Fax: (01935) 382488
Bracehand Ltd, Stanford Bury, Stanford Road, Shefford, Bedfordshire, SG17 5NS Tel: (01462) 817039 Fax: (01462) 816325
Brandon Precision, Holmewall Road, Leeds, LS10 4TQ Tel: 0113-277 5671 Fax: 0113-271 2161 E-mail: enquiries@brandon-medical.com
James Brown & Sons Ltd, 92 The Grove, Marton-in-Cleveland, Middlesbrough, Cleveland, TS7 8AP Tel: (01642) 318370 Fax: (01642) 318370
Brownhills Engineering Co, Progress Drive, Cannock, Staffordshire, WS11 0JE Tel: (01543) 502700 Fax: (01543) 502700
Brynmawr Tools & Engineering Co. Ltd, Heritage Court Road, Gilchrist Thomas Industrial Estate, Blaenavon, Pontypool, Gwent, NP4 9RL Tel: (01495) 790230 Fax: (01495) 792757 E-mail: wnquiries@gosengomeering.co.uk
Burrafirm Ltd, Croxstalls Road, Walsall, WS3 2XY Tel: (01922) 476836 Fax: (01922) 479442 E-mail: user@albert-jagger.co.uk
Bystone Engineers Ltd, Price Street, Bilston, West Midlands, WV14 7EE Tel: (01902) 494604 Fax: (01902) 353147
C H Sandall & Son Precision Engineers, Whiteleather Square, Billingborough, Sleaford, Lincolnshire, NG34 0QP Tel: (01529) 240277 Fax: (01529) 241543
C P A Engineering Ltd, Fircroft Way, Edenbridge, Kent, TN8 6EJ Tel: (01732) 866565 Fax: 01732 866541
Cambridge Rapid Components Ltd, Unit 4-5 Shire Hill, Saffron Walden, Essex, CB11 3AQ Tel: (01799) 522151 Fax: (01799) 521686 E-mail: sales@cambridgerapid.co.uk
Carnwood Engineering Ltd, Penn Industrial Estate, Providence Street, Cradley Heath, West Midlands, B64 5DJ Tel: (01384) 569787 Fax: (01384) 633508 E-mail: sales@carnwoodeng.co.uk
Cerberus Engineering Services Ltd, Coker Road, Weston-super-Mare, Avon, BS22 6BX Tel: (01934) 517747 Fax: (01934) 512633 E-mail: info@ceberus-eng.co.uk
Chartway Industrial Services Ltd, Faraday Drive, Bridgnorth, Shropshire, WV15 5BA Tel: (01746) 764900 Fax: (01746) 768770 E-mail: sales@chartway.co.uk
Custom Metalcraft Ltd, 36 Bennet Road, Reading, RG2 0QX Tel: 0118-986 8077 Fax: 0118-986 8078
Davison Tyne Metal Ltd, Davison Tyne Works, Bridge End, Hexham, Northumberland, NE46 4JL Tel: (01434) 604211 Fax: (01434) 602733E-mail: sales@davisontynemetal.co.uk
Dual Brown, Ross Road, Stockton-on-Tees, Cleveland, TS18 2NH Tel: (01642) 602226 Fax: (01642) 602227
E Bacon & Co. Ltd, Hutton Road, Grimsby, South Humberside, DN31 3PS Tel: (01472) 350267 Fax: (01472) 250987 E-mail: info@baconengineering.com
Engineering & Maintenance Services, Unit 75a Gibbons Industrial Park, Dudley Road, Kingswinford, West Midlands, DY6 8XF Tel: (01384) 400147 Fax: (01384) 400148
Estuary Engineering Co Ltd, Hamlin Way, King's Lynn, Norfolk, PE30 4NG Tel: (01553) 773678 Fax: (01553) 769121 E-mail: tony@estuary.demon.co.uk
F T V Proclad (UK) Ltd, Viewfield Industrial Estate, Glenrothes, Fife, KY6 2RD Tel: (01592) 772568 Fax: (01592) 775310 E-mail: sales@forthtool.co.uk
Fairwood Engineering Ltd, Dock Road, The Docks, Port Talbot, West Glamorgan, SA13 1RA Tel: (01639) 892117 Fax: (01639) 899238 E-mail: karen@fairwoodengineering.com
Formil Engineering Ltd, Coppice Side Industrial Estate, Brownhills, Walsall, WS8 7EX Tel: (01543) 371604 Fax: (01543) 372208 E-mail: formileng@ukonline.co.uk
Fox VPS Ltd, Minekeep House, Bridge Road, Camberley, Surrey, GU15 2QR Tel: (01276) 683331 Fax: (01276) 683332 E-mail: sales@foxvps.co.uk
G & B Machining Services, 55 Marlborough Road, Margate, Kent, CT9 5SU Tel: (01843) 230876
G C B Engineering Bilston Ltd, Ash Street, Bilston, West Midlands, WV14 8UP Tel: (01902) 409486 Fax: (01902) 353739 E-mail: gcb@deecon.co.uk

MACHINISTS, (ENGINEERS')/ GENERAL MACHINING SERVICES - *continued*

G K M (Aerospace) Ltd, Unit 2 Wollaston Way, Burnt Mills Industrial Estate, Basildon, Essex, SS13 1DJ Tel: (01268) 727278 Fax: (01268) 725772 E-mail: gkm@gkm-aero.demon.co.uk

Genhart Ltd, 3 Malmesbury Road, Kingsditch Trading Estate, Cheltenham, Gloucestershire, GL51 9PL Tel: (01242) 241734 Fax: (01242) 227500 E-mail: frank@genhart.co.uk

Glynnway Engineering & Welding Ltd, Salop Street, Bilston, West Midlands, WV14 0TQ Tel: (01902) 495701 Fax: (01902) 497702 E-mail: sales@glynnway.co.uk

Hawk Fasteners Ltd, Brunel Road, Middlesbrough, Cleveland, TS6 6JA Tel: (01642) 468581 Fax: (01642) 440880 E-mail: sales@hawkfast.com

A.O. Henton Engineering Co. Ltd, Cotes Road, Burbage, Hinckley, Leicestershire, LE10 2HJ Tel: (01455) 238331 Fax: (01455) 251023 E-mail: david.english@aohenton.co.uk

Hewmor Products Ltd, Unit D4 Hilton Trading Estate, Hilton Road, Lanesfield, Wolverhampton, WV4 6DW Tel: (01902) 491144 Fax: (01902) 401952 E-mail: hewmor.products@btconnect.com

Holbar Engineering, Unit 31B, Parsonage Farm Industrial Estate, Forest Hall Road, Stansted, Essex, CM24 8TY Tel: (01279) 814344 Fax: (01279) 814995 E-mail: holbar@btconnect.com

Stanley Horne & Sons Ltd, Bentley Mill Close, Walsall, WS2 0BN Tel: (01922) 611451 Fax: (01922) 726070 E-mail: sales@stanleyhorne.co.uk

Hudson's, Unit 33-35 Nailsea Trading Estate, Southfield Road, Nailsea, Bristol, BS48 1JE Tel: (01275) 857335 Fax: (01275) 810587 E-mail: hudsoneng@btconnect.com

Index Machining, James Scott Road, Halesowen, West Midlands, B63 2QT Tel: (01384) 410925 Fax: (01384) 410925

J M Fabweld Ltd, Llewellyns Quay, Port Talbot, West Glamorgan, SA13 1RF Tel: (01639) 884550 Fax: (01639) 891015 E-mail: jmfabwellltd@btconnect.com

J W Stamp & Son LLP, Holydyke, Barton On Humber, Barton-upon-Humber, South Humberside, DN18 5PS Tel: (01652) 632421 Fax: (01652) 635878

K P M Engineering, Premier Partnership Estate, Leys Road, Brierley Hill, West Midlands, DY5 3UP Tel: (01384) 75567 Fax: (01384) 75567

K S W Engineering Ltd, 7 Stirling Road, Glenrothes, Fife, KY6 2ST Tel: (01592) 774822 Fax: (01592) 772891 E-mail: stewart@kswengineering.com

Keegal Engineering Ltd, The Link Centre, Unit G Oldmixon CR, Weston-super-Mare, Avon, BS24 9AY Tel: (01934) 419659 Fax: (01934) 641185 E-mail: peter@keegal.co.uk

Kings Norton Engineering Co. Ltd, Facet Road, Birmingham, B38 9PT Tel: 0121-458 3538 Fax: 0121-458 3886 E-mail: jharper@kingsnortonengineering.co.uk

Charles Leek & Sons Ltd, Springfield Works, Ashbourne Road, Leek, Staffordshire, ST13 5AY Tel: (01538) 382066 Fax: (01538) 373153 E-mail: sales@leekgears.co.uk

Leiper Engineering, Loamo Works, Brown Street, Dundee, DD1 5EE Tel: (01382) 200240 Fax: (01382) 200240

Leonard Bowes Engineering Co. Ltd, 31 Mill Street, Brierley Hill, West Midlands, DY5 2RG Tel: (01384) 573000 Fax: (01384) 573000

Lion Engineering Services Ltd, Gapton Hall Road, Great Yarmouth, Norfolk, NR31 0NL Tel: (01493) 653642 Fax: (01493) 653353 E-mail: sales@lion-oil-tools.demon.co.uk

M F B Manufacturing Ltd, 7a The Stirling Centre, Market Deeping, Peterborough, PE6 8EQ Tel: 01778 343110

M J Raven & Son Ltd, Unit 22 Patricia Way, Pysons Road Industrial Estate, Broadstairs, Kent, CT10 2LF Tel: (01843) 866676 Fax: (01843) 866070 E-mail: sales@mjraven.co.uk

Maxspeed Engineering Ltd, Foxoak Street, Cradley Heath, West Midlands, B64 5DE Tel: (01384) 564999 Fax: (01384) 564888

Mec-Lon, 1 Enterprise Park, Etna Road, Bury St. Edmunds, Suffolk, IP33 1JZ Tel: (01284) 706334 Fax: (01284) 706334 E-mail: sales@mec-lon.co.uk

F.A. Morris (Sheffield) Ltd, 83 Headford Street, Sheffield, S3 7WA Tel: 0114-276 7327 Fax: 0114-275 3862 E-mail: sales@famorris.co.uk

Morse Systems Engineering, Unit 3, Wotton Road, Ashford, Kent, TN23 6LL Tel: (01233) 633800 Fax: (01233) 635500 E-mail: enquiries@morsesystems.co.uk

Mountwest Petroleum Engineering Ltd, Sir William Smith Road, Kirkton Industrial Estate, Arbroath, Angus, DD11 3RD Tel: (01241) 870611 Fax: (01241) 878669 E-mail: linda@mountwest-petrol.com

Newfield Engineering Co. Ltd, Hawksley Industrial Estate, Hawksley Street, Oldham, OL8 4PQ Tel: 0161-624 7222 Fax: 0161-652 1298 E-mail: sales@newfield-eng.u-net.com

Newteq Engineering Ltd, 1 Waterside Industrial Estate, Ettingshall Road, Wolverhampton, WV2 2RQ Tel: (01902) 492622 Fax: (01902) 492379 E-mail: sales@newteq.co.uk

O E S Ltd, Unit S1 Didcot Enterprise Centre, Southmead Industrial Pk, Hawksworth, Didcot, Oxon, OX11 7PH Tel: (01235) 511922 Fax: (01235) 511822

Old Oak Engineering, Unit 11, Gilchrist Thomas Industrial Estate, Blaenavon, Pontypool, Gwent, NP4 9RL Tel: (01495) 791615 Fax: (01495) 790866

PGS Engineering Ltd, Quayside Drive, Walsall, WS2 9LA Tel: (01922) 425555 Fax: (01922) 425556

Plan It, 13 Palacecraig Street, Coatbridge, Lanarkshire, ML5 4SB Tel: (01236) 421082 Fax: (01236) 424311 E-mail: peryslick@gmail.com

Plastic Machining Services, Halesfield 23, Telford, Shropshire, TF7 4NY Tel: (01952) 680369 Fax: (01952) 680371E-mail: info@p-m-s.co.uk

Precise Engineering Ltd, Cowley Road, Blyth, Northumberland, NE24 5TF Tel: (01670) 363606 Fax: (01670) 352792

Premax Engineering Ltd, 56 Porchester Street, Birmingham, B19 2LA Tel: 0121-359 5380 Fax: 0121-333 3097 E-mail: info@premax.co.uk

Premier Engineering Co. Ltd, 59a Virginia Street, Southport, Merseyside, PR8 6SJ Tel: (01704) 535955 Fax: (01704) 535955

Q P D Fabrications Ltd, Unit 2, Shelley Road, Preston, PR2 2DB Tel: (01772) 258992 Fax: (01772) 884371

Queensway Engineering Scunthorpe Ltd, 3a Banbury Road, Scunthorpe, South Humberside, DN16 1UL Tel: (01724) 851219 Fax: (01724) 849814

R D H Components Ltd, Nelson Lane, Warwick, CV34 5JB Tel: (01926) 409330 Fax: (01926) 409331

R H G Stone Engineering, 121 Main Street, Walton, Street, Somerset, BA16 9QL Tel: (01458) 442167 Fax: (01458) 447252 E-mail: info@rhgstone.co.uk

Rakeplan Engineering Co. Ltd, Unit F2 Hilton Trading Estate, Hilton Road, Lanesfield, Wolverhampton, WV4 6DW Tel: (01902) 408010 Fax: (01902) 408484

Ram Machining Ltd, Providence Street, Stourbridge, West Midlands, DY9 8HS Tel: (01384) 424144 Fax: (01384) 892396

Reekie Machine (Sales) Ltd, South Street, Inchinnan Industrial Estate, Inchinnan, Renfrew, PA4 9RL Tel: 0141-812 0411 Fax: 0141-812 0137 E-mail: info@reekiemachining.co.uk

Renown Engineering Ltd, South Cramlington Industrial Estate, Cramlington, Northumberland, NE23 7RH Tel: 0191-250 0113 Fax: 0191-250 1980 E-mail: sales@renown-engineering.co.uk

Rod Rite Engeering Ltd, Unit 15 Horsehay Works, Horsehay Estate, Telford, Shropshire, TF4 3PY Tel: (01952) 630055 Fax: (01952) 505289

Rodwell Engineering Group Ltd, 199-209 Hornchurch Road, Hornchurch, Essex, RM12 4TJ Tel: (01708) 448877 Fax: (01708) 700007

Rolls Royce Plc, PO Box 3, Barnoldswick, Lancashire, BB18 5RU Tel: (01282) 818008 Fax: (01282) 818090

Ronco Engineering Ltd, 3a-3b Unit Alderman Wood Road, Tanfield Lea Industrial Estate South, Tanfield Lea, Stanley, County Durham, DH9 9XF Tel: (01207) 284848 Fax: (01207) 290306 E-mail: enquires@ronco-engineering.co.uk

S E S Precision Engineers Ltd, 206 Bromley Road, Catford, London, SE6 2XA Tel: (020) 8461 4240 Fax: (020) 8695 6561

S G D Engineers, Unit 14c Whitebridge Industrial Estate, Whitebridge Lane, Stone, Staffordshire, ST15 8LQ Tel: (01785) 811104 Fax: (01785) 811104 E-mail: andrew.ward6@btconnect.com

Silvester Engineering Ltd, Kingsmead, Marringdean Rd, Billingshurst, West Sussex, RH14 9HE Tel: (01403) 782255 Fax: (01403) 782703 E-mail: sales@silvesterengineering.co.uk

Site Engineering Services, Reverdane Road, Congleton, Cheshire, CW12 1UN Tel: (01260) 275252 Fax: (01260) 270111 E-mail: sales@phoenixengineering.co.uk

Spectroform Engineering Services Ltd, 1a Saxby Road Industrial Estate, Hudson Road, Melton Mowbray, Leicestershire, LE13 1BS Tel: (01664) 500728 Fax: (01664) 410509 E-mail: sales@spectroform.co.uk

Speed Engineering, Station Yard, Broome, Aston-on-Clun, Craven Arms, Shropshire, SY7 0NT Tel: (01588) 660427 Fax: (01588) 660771

Stroma Engineering Ltd, 21 Bickford Road, Birmingham, B6 7EE Tel: 0121-327 5550 Fax: 0121-327 2314

Telist Engineering Services, 5 Millside Industrial Estate, Lawson Road, Dartford, DA1 5BW Tel: (01322) 291291 Fax: (01322) 291291

Thomas Engineering, Manning Road, Bourne, Lincolnshire, PE10 9HW Tel: (01778) 422720 Fax: (01778) 425530 E-mail: gecrane@totalise.co.uk

Thomson Lockhart (Engineering) Ltd, 5 Simonsburn Road, Loreny Industrial Estate, Kilmarnock, Ayrshire, KA1 5LE Tel: (01563) 527398 Fax: (01563) 522710 E-mail: info@thomsonlockhart.com

Topside Group Ltd, Daimler Drive, Cowpen Lane Industrial Estate, Billingham, Cleveland, TS23 4JD Tel: (01642) 566611 Fax: (01642) 561196

Tow Path Ltd, Unit 150 Medway Enterprise Centre, Enterprise Close, Medway City Estate, Rochester, Kent, ME2 4SY Tel: (01634) 296644 Fax: (01634) 724152

Trafalgar Engineering Co., Station Road, Station Mills, Cottingham, North Humberside, HU16 4LL Tel: (01482) 843558

Triple T Engineering Ltd, Hackworth Industrial Park, Shildon, County Durham, DL4 1HF Tel: (01388) 774444 Fax: (01388) 774444 E-mail: sales@triple-t-eng.co.uk

Twyman Engineering Ltd, Unit J, Troon Way Business Centre, Leicester, LE4 9HA Tel: 0116-276 5953 Fax: 0116-276 5953

Unilathe Ltd, Ford Green Business Park, Ford Green Road Smallthorne, Stoke-on-Trent, ST6 1NG Tel: (01782) 533300 Fax: (01782) 532013 E-mail: sales@unilathe.co.uk

W A Carr Engineering Ltd, 60 Broad Oaks, Sheffield, S9 3HJ Tel: 0114-256 2222 Fax: 0114-256 2474

W P B Machining Services Ltd, 21 Offerton Industrial Estate, Stockport, Cheshire, SK2 5TH Tel: 0161 4778500

W Stone & Sons, 20 Lodge Causeway, Bristol, BS16 3JB Tel: 0117-965 3125 Fax: 0117-965 3125

Webb Engineering Worcester Ltd, Unit 11f Shrub Hill, Worcester, WR4 9EL Tel: (01905) 29775 Fax: (01905) 726324

Whittlesey Engineering Co. Ltd, Fenland District Industrial Estate, Station Road, Whittlesey, Peterborough, PE7 2EY Tel: (01733) 203766 Fax: (01733) 350808

Wills (Engineers) Ltd, Woodside Lane, Sheffield, S3 9PB Tel: 0114-272 4334 Fax: 0114-272 4334

Wooler Ltd, North Way, Andover, Hampshire, SP10 5AZ Tel: (01264) 324181 Fax: (01264) 333554

MACHINISTS, FIVE (5) AXIS

Express Engineering Thompson Ltd, Kingsway North, Team Valley Trading Estate, Gateshead, Tyne & Wear, NE11 0EG Tel: 0191-487 2021 Fax: 0191-487 3172 E-mail: sales@express-group.co.uk

MACHINISTS, HEAVY

Valve Componets Ltd, 6 Singer Road, East Kilbride, Glasgow, G75 0XS Tel: (01355) 263884 Fax: (01355) 245146 E-mail: sales@vcl.uk.com

MACHINISTS, LIGHT

Valve Componets Ltd, 6 Singer Road, East Kilbride, Glasgow, G75 0XS Tel: (01355) 263884 Fax: (01355) 245146 E-mail: sales@vcl.uk.com

MACHINISTS, PRECISION, MILLING, CNC

A & N Engineering, 2 Emsworth Road, Southampton, SO15 3LX Tel: (023) 8031 5193 Fax: (023) 8070 4033

Allstyle Engineering Ltd, Unit 5 60 Arthur Street, Redditch, Worcestershire, B98 8JY Tel: (01527) 527687 Fax: (01527) 500467 E-mail: allstyle@tesco.net

Amicon Engineering, 24-26 Ivatt Way, Peterborough, PE3 7PG Tel: (01733) 331414 Fax: (01733) 261383 E-mail: info@amiconengineering.com

B B F CNC Machining, 31 Knowl Piece, Hitchin, Hertfordshire, SG4 0TY Tel: (01462) 432700 Fax: (01462) 431414 E-mail: bbf.cnc@btinternet.com

C P Mechanical Designs Ltd, 48 Wellington Road, Portslade, Brighton, BN41 1DT Tel: (01273) 430001 Fax: (01273) 424654 E-mail: enquiries@cpmechanical.co.uk

Copper Mill Engineering, The Mill, Bath Road, Bitton, Bristol, BS30 6LW Tel: 0117-932 2614 Fax: 0117-932 9388 E-mail: rusell@coppermillengineering.com

Dartmouth Associates Ltd, 43 Baltimore Road, Great Barr, Birmingham, B42 1DD Tel: 0121-358 0422 Fax: 0121-358 1334 E-mail: dartmouth@dartmouth-associates.co.uk

DKW Engineering, Bolde Close, Portsmouth, PO3 5RD Tel: (023) 9267 7747 Fax: (023) 9269 4335 E-mail: sales@dkwengineering.co.uk

Drillturn Engineering Ltd, Victoria Road West, Hebburn, Tyne & Wear, NE31 1UB Tel: 0191-483 5871 Fax: 0191-428 0391 E-mail: sales@drillturnengineering.co.uk

Exact Engineering Thompson Ltd, Kingsway South, Team Valley Trading Estate, Gateshead, Tyne & Wear, NE11 0JS Tel: 0191-482 6622 Fax: 0191-482 1602 E-mail: john.martin@exact-engineering.com

Hyspeed CNC Ltd, Clovelly Road, Southbourne, Emsworth, Hampshire, PO10 8PE Tel: (01243) 377751 Fax: (01243) 377754 E-mail: sales@hyspeed.co.uk

Index Precision Co., 8a Power Court, Luton, LU1 3JJ Tel: (01582) 728528 Fax: (01582) 728528

▶ Isosure Ltd, 18 Spring Terrace, Goodshawfold, Rossendale, Lancashire, BB4 8QR Tel: (01706) 225419 Fax: (01706) 230784 E-mail: info@isosure.com

K F Lever (Precision Engineering) Ltd, 56 Ash Tree Road, Southampton, SO18 1LX Tel: (023) 8055 2351 Fax: (023) 8055 3574 E-mail: klseverltd@yiscalli.co.uk

Kirkby Precision Engineering Ltd, Ashcroft Road, Liverpool, L33 7TW Tel: 0151-549 1007 Fax: 0151-549 2400 E-mail: kirkbyprecision@btclick.com

L M S Precision Engineering, 44 Wassage Way, Hampton Lovett, Droitwich, Worcestershire, WR9 0NX Tel: (01905) 779783 Fax: (01905) 779041 E-mail: roger@lmsprecision.co.uk

Linton Design & Manufacture Ltd, 6a Bessemer CR, Rabans Lane Industrial Area, Aylesbury, Buckinghamshire, HP19 8TF Tel: (01296) 429179 Fax: (01296) 392290 E-mail: linton.design@btinternet.com

Mikina Engineering, Unit 40 Downton Industrial Estate, Batten Road, Downton Industrial Estate, Salisbury, SP5 3HU Tel: (01725) 513388 Fax: (01725) 513399

Mounsey Engineering Ltd, Unit 11 North Weylands Industrial Estate, Molesey Road, Walton-on-Thames, Surrey, KT12 3PL Tel: (01932) 888555 Fax: (01932) 225388 E-mail: mounseyengineering@tiscali.co.uk

N S J Engineering, 231 Handsworth Road, Handsworth, Sheffield, S13 9BL Tel: 0114-243 1769 Fax: 0114-243 1408 E-mail: neil@nsjengineering.co.uk

Paragon Precision Products, 36 Camford Way, Luton, LU3 3AN Tel: (01582) 505005 Fax: (01582) 505010 E-mail: info@paragon-precision.co.uk

Specfab (Pershore) Ltd, Unit 5A, Pershore Trading Estate, Pershore, Worcestershire, WR10 2DD Tel: (01386) 552790 Fax: (01386) 556827 E-mail: sales@specfab.co.uk

Staffordshire Precision Engineering Ltd, 4 Red Mine Close, Newcastle, Staffordshire, ST5 9HZ Tel: (01782) 630500 Fax: (01782) 638440 E-mail: sales@staffsprecision.co.uk

Westway Precision Engineering Ltd, Henty Road, Southampton, SO16 4GF Tel: (023) 8078 9229 Fax: (023) 8070 2967

MACHINISTS, PRECISION, SUBCONTRACT

Alfred Wood & Sons Ltd, 32 Eveline Road, Mitcham, Surrey, CR4 3LE Tel: (020) 8648 3528 Fax: (020) 8640 8707 E-mail: roger.felstead@virgin.net

Ayneson Engineering Co. Ltd, Commercial Road, Wolverhampton, WV1 3RD Tel: (01902) 452862 Fax: (01902) 455383

Bracehand Ltd, Stanford Bury, Stanford Road, Shefford, Bedfordshire, SG17 5NS Tel: (01462) 817039 Fax: (01462) 816325

Cherox Precision Engineering Co., Unit 1A, Pope Iron Road, Barbourne, Worcester, WR1 3HB Tel: (01905) 21425 Fax: (01905) 25921 E-mail: john@cherox.connectfree.co.uk

Clayton Engineering Co., Church Street, Belper, Derbyshire, DE56 1EY Tel: (01773) 828955 Fax: (01773) 828243 E-mail: claytonenguk@aol.com

Groveley Engineering Ltd, Anchor Works, Groveley Road, Christchurch, Dorset, BH23 3HB Tel: (01202) 483497 Fax: (01202) 486658 E-mail: sales@groveley.co.uk

▶ H K V Engineering, 16 Crawford House, West Avenue, Wigston, Leicestershire, LE18 2FB Tel: 0116-288 7751 Fax: 0116-288 7751 E-mail: carolrobinson@aol.com

▶ Hi-Spec Precision Engineering, 1 Thistleton Road, Market Overton, Rutland, Oakham, Leicestershire, LE15 7PP Tel: (01572) 768036 Fax: (01780) 481696 E-mail: hi-spec_eng@lycos.co.uk

Howbeck Engineering, White House, London Road, Stapeley, Nantwich, Cheshire, CW5 7JU Tel: (01270) 841446 Fax: (01270) 841446 E-mail: roger.howbeck@virgin.net

▶ Jenkins Engineering Services, Waldeck House, Waldeck Road, Maidenhead, Berkshire, SL6 8BR Tel: (01628) 674080 Fax: (01628) 776648 E-mail: jenkinseng@btconnect.com

L M S Precision Engineering, 44 Wassage Way, Hampton Lovett, Droitwich, Worcestershire, WR9 0NX Tel: (01905) 779783 Fax: (01905) 779041 E-mail: roger@lmsprecision.co.uk

▶ Mendip Metalcraft, Unit 28 Underwood Business Park, Wells, Somerset, BA5 1AF Tel: (01749) 674590 Fax: (01749) 674590 E-mail: nigel.stewart@btconnect.com

MACHINISTS, SUBCONTRACT

Adminglade Ltd, Caxton House, Stoke Street, Sheffield, S9 3QH Tel: 0114-244 1932 Fax: 0114-244 1932

▶ Adr Engineering, Unit 3 Foxley Court Farm, Ascot Road, Maidenhead, Berkshire, SL6 3LA Tel: (01628) 783030 Fax: (01628) 776851 E-mail: sales@adr-engineering.co.uk

Aldersbrook Engineering, B Ajax Works, Hertford Road, Barking, Essex, IG11 8DY Tel: (020) 8591 0685 Fax: (020) 8591 9388 E-mail: enquiries@aldersbrook-engineering.com

Ayneson Engineering Co. Ltd, Commercial Road, Wolverhampton, WV1 3RD Tel: (01902) 452862 Fax: (01902) 455383

Baker Blower Engineering Co. Ltd, 39 Stanley Street, Sheffield, S3 8HH Tel: 0114-272 5527 Fax: 0114-272 7533 E-mail: bakerblower@aol.com

Cherox Precision Engineering Co., Unit 1A, Pope Iron Road, Barbourne, Worcester, WR1 3HB Tel: (01905) 21425 Fax: (01905) 25921 E-mail: john@cherox.connectfree.co.uk

MACHINISTS, SUBCONTRACT – *continued*

C.H. Clarke & Co. (Engineers) Ltd, Griffin Industrial Estate, Penncricket Lane, Rowley Regis, West Midlands, B65 0SP Tel: 0121-561 1111 Fax: 0121-559 6027 E-mail: sales@chc-machining.co.uk

▶ G D K Engineering Co. Ltd, Unit 65 Blackpole Trading Estate West, Worcester, WR3 8TJ Tel: (01905) 454261 Fax: (01905) 454231 E-mail: sales@gdk-engineering.co.uk

Harco Engineering Ltd, Canal Street, Harts Hill, Brierley Hill, West Midlands, DY5 1JJ Tel: (01384) 480280 Fax: (01384) 480399 E-mail: info@harcoeng.co.uk

Kamech Engineering Services, 7 4-6 Abingdon Road, Nuffield Industrial Estate, Poole, Dorset, BH17 0UG Tel: (01202) 669452 Fax: (01202) 669453

Machtech Press Tool Distributors, Brown Lion Street, Tipton, West Midlands, DY4 9EG Tel: 0121-522 4340 Fax: 0121-522 3860 E-mail: chris.pring@tiscali.co.uk

P.S. Marsden (Precision Engineers) Ltd, Private Road No 8, Colwick Industrial Estate, Nottingham, NG4 2JX Tel: 0115-987 9026 Fax: 0115-940 0805 E-mail: precision@psmarsden.co.uk

Mellish Engineering, Unit 14 Merchants Way, Aldridge, Walsall, WS9 8SW Tel: (01922) 457799 E-mail: mellishengineering@btopenworld.com

Neida Products Engineering Ltd, Trentham Lakes South, Stoke-on-Trent, ST4 8GQ Tel: (01782) 643643 Fax: (01782) 644220 E-mail: sales@neida.co.uk

Otto Junker (U K) Ltd, Kingsbury Road, Curdworth, Sutton Coldfield, West Midlands, B76 9EE Tel: (01675) 470551 Fax: (01675) 470645 E-mail: sales@otto-junker.co.uk

P J Metals & Plastics, Unit 4 Park Street, Kidderminster, Worcestershire, DY11 6TN Tel: (01562) 824570 Fax: (01562) 865170

Seivad Engineering Ltd, Meadow Road, Worthing, West Sussex, BN11 2RT Tel: (01903) 238845 Fax: (01903) 821529 E-mail: eng@seivad.co.uk

Sommerwest Technical Services Ltd, 32 Garrett Road, Lynx Trading Estate, Yeovil, Somerset, BA20 2TJ Tel: 01935 412595

Turntech Precision Engineers, Unit 33 Liberty Close, Woolsbridge Industrial Estate, Three Legged Cross, Wimborne, Dorset, BH21 6SY Tel: (01202) 822040 Fax: (01202) 829146 E-mail: sales@turntech-precision.co.uk

MACHINISTS, VERTICAL, CNC

Greenwood Gears Ltd, Digital House, Royd Way, Keighley, West Yorkshire, BD21 3LG Tel: (01535) 604393 Fax: (01535) 680587 E-mail: sales@hewitt-topham.co.uk

MAGAZINES, CHEMICALS

Asian Chemical News, Quadrant House, The Quadrant, Brighton Road, Sutton, Surrey, SM2 5AS Tel: (020) 8652 3500

European Chemical News, Quadrant House, The Quadrant, Sutton, Surrey, SM2 5AS Tel: (020) 8652 3500 Fax: (020) 8652 8297

Icis Lor Group Ltd, Quadrant House, The Quadrant, Sutton, Surrey, SM2 5AS Tel: (020) 8652 3535 Fax: (020) 8652 3929 E-mail: sales.uk@icislor.com

MAGAZINES, HEALTH CARE

Doctor, Quadrant House, The Quadrant, Sutton, Surrey, SM2 5AS Tel: (020) 8652 3500 Fax: (020) 8652 3793

Doctor, Quadrant House, The Quadrant, Sutton, Surrey, SM2 5AS Tel: (020) 8652 3500 Fax: (020) 8652 3793 E-mail: hospital.doctor@rbi.co.uk

▶ Find A Reflexologist Ltd, 35 Coventry Road Flushing, Flushing, Falmouth, Cornwall, TR11 5TX Tel: (0870) 2432320 E-mail: info@findareflexologist.com

Health & Beauty Salon, Quadrant House, The Quadrant, Sutton, Surrey, SM2 5AS Tel: (020) 8652 3500 Fax: (020) 8652 3793

Practice Nurse, Quadrant House, The Quadrant, Sutton, Surrey, SM2 5AS Tel: (020) 8652 3500 Fax: 020 8652845

Update, Quadrant House, The Quadrant, Brighton Road, Sutton, Surrey, SM2 5AS Tel: (020) 8652 3500

MAGNESIUM ALLOY CASTINGS

Metal Castings Ltd, Droitwich Road, Worcester, WR3 7JX Tel: (01905) 754400 Fax: (01905) 754347 E-mail: sales@metalcastingsltd.com

Rolls-Royce P.L.C., PO Box 31, Derby, DE24 8BJ Tel: (01332) 240642 Fax: (01332) 240604

Stone Foundries Ltd, Woolwich Road, London, SE7 8SL Tel: (020) 8853 4648 Fax: (020) 8305 1934 E-mail: enquiries@stone-foundries-limited.com

MAGNESIUM CARBONATE

Lehvoss UK Ltd, 20 West Road, Congleton, Cheshire, CW12 4ER Tel: (01260) 291000 Fax: (01260) 291111 E-mail: contact@lehvoss.co.uk

MAGNESIUM HYDROXIDE

Lehvoss UK Ltd, 20 West Road, Congleton, Cheshire, CW12 4ER Tel: (01260) 291000 Fax: (01260) 291111 E-mail: contact@lehvoss.co.uk

MAGNESIUM OXIDE

Hubron Sales, Albion Street, Failsworth, Manchester, M35 0WW Tel: 0161-681 2691 Fax: 0161-683 4045 E-mail: sales@hubron.com

MAGNESIUM POWDERS

Aluminium Powder Co. Ltd, Forge Lane, Minworth Industrial Park, Minworth, Sutton Coldfield, West Midlands, B76 1AH Tel: 0121-351 4686 Fax: 0121-351 7604 E-mail: enquiries@alpoco.co.uk

Harris Hart & Co. Ltd, Gregge Street Works, Gregge Street, Heywood, Lancashire, OL10 2EJ Tel: (01706) 625355 Fax: (01706) 360570 E-mail: sales@epsom-salts.com

Micro Milling, Johnsons Lane, Widnes, Cheshire, WA8 0SJ Tel: 0151-422 2970 Fax: 0151-495 1044

MAGNET (INDUSTRIAL) MANUFRS, *See also headings for particular types, eg; Lifting; Separator etc*

Cermag Ltd, 94 Holywell Road, Sheffield, S4 8AS Tel: 0114-244 6136 Fax: 0114-256 1769 E-mail: sales@cermag.co.uk

Magnapower Equipment Ltd, 11 North Street Industrial Estate, Droitwich, Worcestershire, WR9 8JB Tel: (01905) 779157 Fax: (01905) 779867 E-mail: info@magnapower.co.uk

Magnet Sales & Service Ltd, Unit 31, Blackworth Industrial Estate, Highworth, SN6 7NA Tel: (01793) 862100 Fax: (01793) 862101 E-mail: sales@magnetsales.co.uk

Magnetic Separations Ltd, 14 Meadowside Road, Sutton, Surrey, SM2 7PF Tel: (020) 8642 4413 Fax: (020) 8642 9476 E-mail: info@magneticseparations.com

Magnex Scientific Ltd, Oxford Industrial Park, 6 Mead Road, Yarnton, Oxford, OX5 1QU Tel: (01865) 853800 Fax: (01865) 842466 E-mail: sales@magnex.com

Precision Magnetics Ltd, Mangham Road, Barbot Hall Industrial Estate, Rotherham, South Yorkshire, S61 4RJ Tel: (01709) 829783 Fax: (01709) 371506 E-mail: sales@precisionmagnetics.co.uk

Ross & Catherall Ltd, Forge Lane, Killamarsh, Sheffield, S21 1BA Tel: 0114-248 6404 Fax: 0114-247 5999 E-mail: rosscatherall@doncasters.com

S G Magnets Ltd, Tesla House, 85 Ferry Lane, Rainham, Essex, RM13 9YH Tel: (01708) 558411 Fax: (01708) 554021 E-mail: sales@sgmagnets.com

Sheffield Magnet Co., Park Hill Works, Pottery Lane, Littlethorpe, Ripon, North Yorkshire, HG4 3LS Tel: (01765) 698698 Fax: (01765) 607922 E-mail: sheffield.magnet@virgin.net

Swift Levick Magnets Ltd, High Hazels Road, Barlborough, Chesterfield, Derbyshire, S43 4UZ Tel: (01246) 570500 Fax: (01246) 573000 E-mail: sales@arnoldengr.com

MAGNETIC ASSEMBLIES

Magnet Sales & Service Ltd, Unit 31, Blackworth Industrial Estate, Highworth, SN6 7NA Tel: (01793) 862100 Fax: (01793) 862101 E-mail: sales@magnetsales.co.uk

Precision Magnetics Ltd, Mangham Road, Barbot Hall Industrial Estate, Rotherham, South Yorkshire, S61 4RJ Tel: (01709) 829783 Fax: (01709) 371506 E-mail: sales@precisionmagnetics.co.uk

Swift Levick Magnets Ltd, High Hazels Road, Barlborough, Chesterfield, Derbyshire, S43 4UZ Tel: (01246) 570500 Fax: (01246) 573000 E-mail: sales@arnoldengr.com

MAGNETIC BROACHING MACHINES

Rotabroach, Imperial Works, Sheffield Road, Tinsley, Sheffield, S9 2YL Tel: 0114-221 2510 Fax: 0114-221 2563 E-mail: info@rotabroach.co.uk

MAGNETIC CARD READERS

Deister Electronic UK, Camel Gate, Spalding, Lincolnshire, PE12 6ET Tel: (01775) 717100 Fax: (01775) 717101 E-mail: info@deister.co.uk

Indala Ltd, 8-10 Clos Menter, Excelsior Business Park, Cardiff, CF14 3AY Tel: (029) 2052 0022 Fax: (029) 2052 8519 E-mail: sales@mraccess.com

Neuroscot Ltd, 8 Meadow Street, Falkirk, FK1 1RP Tel: 0131-453 3845 Fax: 0131-453 3838 E-mail: neuroscot@compuserve.com

MAGNETIC CARDS

Indala Ltd, 8-10 Clos Menter, Excelsior Business Park, Cardiff, CF14 3AY Tel: (029) 2052 0022 Fax: (029) 2052 8519 E-mail: sales@mraccess.com

Paragon Group UK Ltd, Pallion Trading Estate, Sunderland, SR4 6ST Tel: 0191-514 0716 Fax: 0191-567 1842 E-mail: enquiries@paragonuk.com

MAGNETIC COMPONENTS

Bel Fuse Europe Ltd, G 7 Unit Preston Technology Centre, Marsh Lane, Preston, PR1 8UQ Tel: (01772) 556601 Fax: (01772) 883666 E-mail: bel_europe@belfuse.com

MAGNETIC CONVEYOR SYSTEMS

Allcontrols Ltd, 20 Halifax Road, Cambridge, CB4 3PX Tel: (01223) 366164 Fax: (0870) 4580314 E-mail: info@allcontrols.co.uk

MAGNETIC DRILLING MACHINES

G & J Hall Ltd, Burgess Road, Sheffield, S9 3WD Tel: 0114-244 0562 Fax: 0114-244 9256 E-mail: sales@gjhall.co.uk

Jancy Engineering Inc, New Hall Hey Road, Rossendale, Lancashire, BB4 6HR Tel: (01706) 229490 Fax: (01706) 830496 E-mail: sales@jancy.com

MAGNETIC DRIVE PUMPS

Klaus Union (UK) Ltd, Charles Industrial Estate, Stowmarket, Suffolk, IP14 5AH Tel: (01449) 677645 Fax: (01449) 678136 E-mail: peter@klausunionltd.demon.co.uk

MAGNETIC FIELD MEASURING INSTRUMENTATION

Bartington Instruments Ltd, 10 Thorney Leys Park, Witney, Oxfordshire, OX28 4GG Tel: (01993) 706565 Fax: (01993) 774813 E-mail: sales@bartington.com

Hirst Magnetic Instruments Ltd, Pesla House, Tregoniggie Industrial Estate, Falmouth, Cornwall, TR11 4SN Tel: (01326) 372734 Fax: (01326) 378069 E-mail: dudding@hirst-magnetics.com

MAGNETIC INKJET SHEET PRINTING CONSUMABLES

Global Link, Yew Tree House, Maerway Lane, Maer, Newcastle, Staffordshire, ST5 5EN Tel: (0870) 2201626 Fax: (01630) 647524 E-mail: sales@printingconsumables.com

MAGNETIC PARTICLE INSPECTION MACHINERY MANUFRS

Advanced NDT Ltd, Orchard House, Orchard Close, Severn Stoke, Worcester, WR8 9JJ Tel: (01905) 371460 Fax: (01905) 371477 E-mail: sales@advanced-ndt.co.uk

Baugh & Weedon Ltd, Beech Business Park, Tillington Road, Hereford, HR4 9QJ Tel: (01432) 267671 Fax: (01432) 359017 E-mail: sales@bandwndt.co.uk

Bluelimit Surveys Ltd, 6 Riverside Road, Gorleston, Great Yarmouth, Norfolk, NR31 6PU Tel: (01493) 653900 Fax: (01493) 442774 E-mail: bluelimit@paston.co.uk

Fidgeon Ltd, 11 Enterprise Court, Seaham Grange Industrial Estate, Seaham, County Durham, SR7 0PS Tel: 0191-521 1233 Fax: 0191-521 1252 E-mail: sales@fidgeon.co.uk

Foerster UK Ltd, 2 Bonehill Mews, Fazeley, Tamworth, Staffordshire, B78 3QU Tel: (01827) 831290 Fax: (01827) 284982 E-mail: sales@foersteruk.com

Magnaflux, Faraday Road, Dorcan, Swindon, SN3 5HE Tel: (01793) 524566 Fax: (01793) 619498 E-mail: sales@magnaflux.co.uk

MAGNETIC RECORDING HEADS

Phi@Falmouth Ltd, Bickland Industrial Park, Falmouth, Cornwall, TR11 4RY Tel: (01326) 373134 Fax: (01326) 377249 E-mail: info@phi-falmouth.co.uk

Precision Applications Ltd, Unit 19 Lodge Hill Industrial Estate, Station Road, Westbury sub Mendip, Wells, Somerset, BA5 1EY Tel: (01749) 870525 Fax: (01749) 870525 E-mail: sales@precisionapplications.co.uk

MAGNETIC RUBBER

Magnetic Separations Ltd, 14 Meadowside Road, Sutton, Surrey, SM2 7PF Tel: (020) 8642 4413 Fax: (020) 8642 9476 E-mail: info@magneticseparations.com

MAGNETIC SEPARATORS

Hi-Flux Magnets, 9 North St Industrial Estate, Droitwich, Worcestershire, WR9 8JB Tel: (01905) 778853 Fax: (01905) 779867 E-mail: hi-fluxmagnets@aol.com

Magnetic Separations Ltd, 14 Meadowside Road, Sutton, Surrey, SM2 7PF Tel: (020) 8642 4413 Fax: (020) 8642 9476 E-mail: info@magneticseparations.com

MAGNETIC SHIELDS

Magnetic Shields Ltd, Headcorn Road, Staplehurst, Tonbridge, Kent, TN12 0DS Tel: (01580) 891521 Fax: (01580) 893345 E-mail: sales@magneticshields.co.uk

MAGNETIC SIGNS

1st Call Mercury Signs, Highfield View, Park Lane, Stokenchurch, Buckinghamshire, HP14 3TQ Tel: (01494) 482288 Fax: (01494) 483152 E-mail: mcgillsign@aol.com

Arrow Screen Print Ltd, 3 Fletcher Way, Weston Road, Norwich, NR3 3ST Tel: (01603) 485942 Fax: (01603) 485385 E-mail: sales@arrowscreenprint.co.uk

Complete Signs, 226 High Street, Croydon, CR9 1DF Tel: (0870) 8707331 Fax: (0870) 8707332 E-mail: sales@completesigns.co.uk

Curtis Screen Print, 26 Fairfax Road, Colchester, CO2 7EW Tel: (01206) 760666 Fax: (01206) 760666 E-mail: sales@curtisscreenprint.co.uk

D E Signs & Labels Ltd, Westbury Close Unit 26, Townsend Industrial Estate, Houghton Regis, Dunstable, Bedfordshire, LU5 5BL Tel: (01582) 699665 Fax: (01582) 661419 E-mail: sales@de-signsdunstable.co.uk

Graffiti Design International, Design House, Bell Lane Industrial Estate, Uckfield, East Sussex, TN22 1QL Tel: (01825) 763690 Fax: (01825) 763815 E-mail: sales@graffitidesign.co.uk

Grant's Sign Shop, 76 Croydon Road, Elmers End, Beckenham, Kent, BR3 4DF Tel: (020) 8658 7578 Fax: (020) 8663 3780

Hardy Signs, Unit 10 Falcon Close, Burton-on-Trent, Staffordshire, DE14 1SG Tel: (01283) 569102 Fax: (01283) 540001 E-mail: sales@hardysigns.co.uk

Spa Display Ltd, 23 North Street Industrial Estate, Droitwich, Worcestershire, WR9 8JB Tel: (01905) 775428 Fax: (01905) 795417 E-mail: signs@spa-display.sagehost.co.uk

MAGNETIC STRIPE CARD READERS, PORTABLE

▶ Card Scanning Solutions Ltd, 14 Coleridge Road, Finchley, London, N12 8DE Tel: (020) 7748 0818 E-mail: sales@cardscanning.com

MAGNETIC SWEEPING MACHINES

Zenith Industrial Products Ltd, Tilemans Lane, Shipston-on-Stour, Warwickshire, CV36 4PR Tel: (01608) 664366 Fax: (01608) 663951

MAGNETIC SWITCHES

Thomas White (Leicester) Ltd, Marlborough Drive, Fleckney, Leicester, LE8 8UR Tel: 0116-240 4005 Fax: 0116-240 4006 E-mail: enquiries@thomaswhitelimited.co.uk

MAGNETIC TAPE BULK ERASERS

Eyecote International Ltd, Unit 10-11 Singleton Court Business Centre, Wonastow Road Industrial Estate, Monmouth, Gwent, NP25 5JA Tel: (01600) 772433 Fax: (01600) 715749 E-mail: sales@eyecote.com

Graff of Newark Ltd, Woodhill Road, Collingham, Newark, Nottinghamshire, NG23 7NR Tel: (01636) 893036 Fax: (01636) 893317 E-mail: sales@graffofnewark.co.uk

MAGNETIC TAPE BULK ERASERS – *continued*

Weircliffe International Ltd, St Andrews Road, Exeter, EX4 2AG Tel: (01392) 272132 Fax: (01392) 413511 E-mail: sales@weircliffe.com

MAGNETIC TAPE RECORDING EQUIPMENT, *See Tape Recorder etc*

MAGNETIC TAPE STORAGE RACKS

Tandberg Data, Davenport House, Bowers Way, Harpenden, Hertfordshire, AL5 4HX Tel: (01582) 769071 Fax: (01582) 769025

MAGNETIC TAPES

Weircliffe International Ltd, St Andrews Road, Exeter, EX4 2AG Tel: (01392) 272132 Fax: (01392) 413511 E-mail: sales@weircliffe.com

MAGNETIC THERAPY PRODUCTS

▶ Dennis Regan, Suites 2 & 4, Beauford House, Serpentine Road, Cleckheaton, West Yorkshire, BD19 3HU Tel: (01274) 850940 Fax: (01274) 850940 E-mail: sales@therapyexpressltd.co.uk

MAGNETISER/MAGNETISING EQUIPMENT

Magnapower Equipment Ltd, 11 North Street Industrial Estate, Droitwich, Worcestershire, WR9 8JB Tel: (01905) 779157 Fax: (01905) 779867 E-mail: info@magnapower.co.uk

▶ Rainer Schneider Ayres, 17 Shirlock Road, London, NW3 2HR Tel: (020) 7267 0812 Fax: (020) 7284 0672 E-mail: rsa_bxt@btinternet.com

MAGNETISING/DEMAGNETISING SERVICES

Sheffield Magnet Co., Park Hill Works, Pottery Lane, Littlethorpe, Ripon, North Yorkshire, HG4 3LS Tel: (01765) 698698 Fax: (01765) 607922 E-mail: sheffield.magnet@virgin.net

MAGNETOMETERS

Allied Associates Geophysical Ltd, Concept House, Townsend Centre, Blackburn Road, Houghton Regis, Dunstable, Bedfordshire, LU5 5BQ Tel: (01582) 606999 Fax: (01582) 606991 E-mail: info@allied-associates.co.uk

Aquascan International Ltd, Aquascan House, Hill Street, Newport, Gwent, NP20 1LZ Tel: (01633) 841117 Fax: (01633) 254829 E-mail: info@aquascan.co.uk

Bartington Instruments Ltd, 10 Thorney Leys Park, Witney, Oxfordshire, OX28 4GG Tel: (01993) 706565 Fax: (01993) 774813 E-mail: sales@bartington.com

Cermag Ltd, 94 Holywell Road, Sheffield, S4 8AS Tel: 0114-244 6136 Fax: 0114-256 1769 E-mail: sales@cermag.co.uk

Foerster UK Ltd, 2 Bonehill Mews, Fazeley, Tamworth, Staffordshire, B78 3QU Tel: (01827) 831290 Fax: (01827) 284982 E-mail: sales@foersteruk.com

Pandect Instrument Laboratories Ltd, Wellington Road, Cressex Business Park, High Wycombe, Buckinghamshire, HP12 3PX Tel: (01494) 526301 Fax: (01494) 464503 E-mail: enquiries@pandect.demon.co.uk

MAGNETRONS

Aeroparts International Ltd, 2 George House, Beam Heath Way, Nantwich, Cheshire, CW5 6GD Tel: (01270) 620260 Fax: (01270) 620261 E-mail: sales@aeroparts-international.com

Gencoa Ltd, Physics Road, Liverpool, L24 9HP Tel: 0151-486 4466 Fax: 0151-486 4488 E-mail: sales@gencoa.com

MAGNETS

▶ D2, 23 High East St, Dorchester, Dorset, DT1 1HD Tel: 01305 252112 Fax: 01305 251908 E-mail: info@d2email.net

MAGNETS, CRAFTS AND HOBBIES

▶ Charmed Cards & Crafts, 22 Somerville Road, London, SE20 7NA Tel: 0208 6590737 E-mail: sales@charmedcardsandcrafts.co.uk

▶ Flutterby Designs, 12 Cypress close, Taverham, Norwich, NR8 6QG Tel: (01603) 868643E-mail: flutterbydesigns1@hotmail.com

▶ Parish Chest Ltd, Credvill,, Quakers Road, Perranwell Station, Truro, Cornwall, TR3 7PJ Tel: (01872) 864807 Fax: (01872) 870719 E-mail: forefathers@btconnect.com

▶ UK Magic - Magic Supplies & Services (Magicians & Entertainers), 1 Wakeford Cottages, Selden Lane, Worthing, West Sussex, BN11 2LQ Tel: (01903) 211785 Fax: (01903) 211519E-mail: info@natzler.com

MAGNIFIER DISTRIBUTORS OR AGENTS

Claritas Ltd, 2 Earlswood Street, London, SE10 9ES Tel: (020) 8858 2411 Fax: (020) 8305 2875 E-mail: claritasltd@amstrad.co.uk

Viking Optical Ltd, Blyth Road, Halesworth, Suffolk, IP19 8EN Tel: (01986) 875315 Fax: (01986) 874788 E-mail: viking@vikingoptical.co.uk

MAIL HANDLING EQUIPMENT

Frama UK Ltd, Unit 15 Limes Court, Conduit Lane, Hoddesdon, Hertfordshire, EN11 8EP Tel: (01992) 451125 Fax: (01992) 441013

K A S Paper Systems Ltd, Brewers Hill Road, Dunstable, Bedfordshire, LU6 1AD Tel: (01582) 662211 Fax: (01582) 664222 E-mail: mail@kaspapersystems.com

Mailing & Mechanisation UK Ltd, Thistle House, Baird Close, Drayton Fields Industrial Estate, Daventry, Northamptonshire, NN11 8RY Tel: (01327) 315031 Fax: (01327) 315231 E-mail: info@mailingandmech.com

Northern Services, 10 Albion Way, East Kilbride, Glasgow, G75 0YN Tel: (01355) 241333 Fax: (01355) 241555 E-mail: sales@northernservices.co.uk

Opex Corporation, Carrington Business Park, Carrington, Manchester, M31 4YR Tel: 0161-776 4033 Fax: 0161-776 2663 E-mail: opexhr@opex.com

MAIL HANDLING SERVICES

Arden Direct Marketing Ltd, Island House, Arthur Street, Barwell, Leicester, LE9 8AH Tel: (0870) 4025220 Fax: (01455) 852249 E-mail: sales@ardendirect.co.uk

Dawson Marketing P.L.C., The Arena, Stafferton Way, Maidenhead, Berkshire, SL6 1AY Tel: (01628) 628777 Fax: (01628) 789634 E-mail: sales@dawsonmarketing.co.uk

E C Logistics, Swallowfield Way, Hayes, Middlesex, UB3 1DQ Tel: (020) 8569 1918 Fax: (020) 8813 6564 E-mail: helpdesk@eclogistics.co.uk

F. Newman Ltd, 33 Linford St, London, SW8 4UP Tel: (020) 7720 1981 Fax: (020) 7622 0016 E-mail: fnewmans@aol.com

Postroom Suppliers Ltd, Unit D3, Lomer Farm Industrial Estate, Wrotham Road, Meopham, Gravesend, Kent, DA13 0AN Tel: (01474) 815850 Fax: (01474) 815860 E-mail: sales@europeanpostalsystems.co.uk

Royal Mail Group Ltd, 148 Old Street, London, EC1V 9HQ Tel: (020) 7250 2888 Fax: (020) 7250 2030

Royal Mail Northern Ireland, Royal Mail House, 20 Donegall Quay, Belfast, BT1 1AA Tel: (0845) 7740740 Fax: (028) 9089 2305

Teamwork Handling Ltd, Allerthorpe Business Park, Pocklington, York, YO42 1NS Tel: (01759) 322400 Fax: (01759) 303265 E-mail: magnus@teamwork-handling.co.uk

MAIL ORDER CATALOGUES

▶ Kleeneze Ltd, 80 Conniburrow Boulevard, Conniburrow, Milton Keynes, MK14 7DA Tel: (01908) 664153 E-mail: britishbiz@yahoo.co.uk

MAIL ORDER DISTRIBUTION

Bull Group Ltd, Unit D Henfield Business Park, Sussex, Henfield, West Sussex, BN5 9SL Tel: (01273) 491490 Fax: (01273) 490813 E-mail: sales@bullnet.co.uk

▶ Pure Essence, 6a Woodend Mills, South Hill, Springhead, Oldham, OL4 5DR Tel: 0161-633 9988 E-mail: info@pureessence.co.uk

▶ Queenswood Home & Garden Products, Unit 4, Southern Avenue, Leominster, Herefordshire, HR6 0QF Tel: (01568) 611281 Fax: (01568) 614143 E-mail: sales@queenswood.co.uk

Teesdale Trenchman, The Lendings, Barnard Castle, County Durham, DL12 9AB Tel: (01833) 638370 Fax: (01833) 631439 E-mail: orders@trenchermen.co.uk

MAILING LISTS, *See Direct Mail etc*

MAILING SERVICES, INTERNATIONAL

Abacus E-Solutions Ltd, Albany House, Concorde Street, Luton, LU2 0JD Tel: (01582) 702702 Fax: (01582) 452106 E-mail: sales@abacusuk.com

Acorn Mailing Services, Chaucer Business Park, Watery Lane, Kemsing, Sevenoaks, Kent, TN15 6HU Tel: (01732) 760042 Fax: (01732) 760043 E-mail: info@acornmailingservices.co.uk

NTL, Cambridge Research Park, Ely Road, Waterbeach, Cambridge, CB25 9TF Tel: (01223) 724040 Fax: (01223) 567222

P W P Direct Mail Services Ltd, A 21 Broadwater Road, Welwyn Garden City, Hertfordshire, AL7 3BQ Tel: (01707) 882255 Fax: (01707) 883322 E-mail: pwp@dial.pipex.com

▶ Regal Logistics Ltd, 7 The Gateway Centre, Coronation Road, Cressex Business Park, High Wycombe, Buckinghamshire, HP12 3SU Tel: (01494) 531100 Fax: (01494) 519123

T M B International Ltd, Platt Industrial Estate, Maidstone Road, Platt, Sevenoaks, Kent, TN15 8TB Tel: (01732) 887456 Fax: (01732) 886345 E-mail: emmac@tmbmailing.com

MAILING SERVICES, PRINTED MATTER/PERIODICAL PUBLICATIONS

Acorn Mailing Services, Chaucer Business Park, Watery Lane, Kemsing, Sevenoaks, Kent, TN15 6HU Tel: (01732) 760042 Fax: (01732) 760043 E-mail: info@acornmailingservices.co.uk

D S Print & Redesign, 7 Jute Lane, Enfield, Middlesex, EN3 7JL Tel: (020) 8805 9585 Fax: (020) 8805 2044 E-mail: re-info@ds-redesign.co.uk

John Denton Services, Unit 6 Heron Industrial Estate, Cooks Rd, Stratford, London, E15 2PW Tel: (020) 8519 3969 Fax: (020) 8519 3695

Francotyp Postalia Ltd, Unit 74 Lakeside Business Park, Hawley Road, Dartford, DA1 1EF Tel: (01322) 405000 Fax: (01322) 405040

Motivity, Unit 21 Brook Industrial Estate, Bullsbrook Road, Hayes, Middlesex, UB4 0JZ Tel: (020) 8561 5566 Fax: (020) 8561 4499 E-mail: sales@motivityuk.com

P W P Direct Mail Services Ltd, A 21 Broadwater Road, Welwyn Garden City, Hertfordshire, AL7 3BQ Tel: (01707) 882255 Fax: (01707) 883322 E-mail: pwp@dial.pipex.com

▶ Professional Van and Light Truck Magazine, Golden Hill, Leyland, PR25 3NN Tel: (01772) 433303 Fax: (01772) 433772 E-mail: info@campbelluk.com

MAILROOM EQUIPMENT

Affordable Franking Machines Q P S Ltd, Wellesbourne, Warwick, CV35 9TQ Tel: (01789) 470250 Fax: (01789) 470255

Bond R S C Associates Ltd, Unit 3 Mercy Terrace, Ladywell, London, SE13 7UX Tel: (020) 8314 1188 Fax: (020) 8314 1221 E-mail: info@bondmailrooms.com

Capital Communications, 41 Bankhead Crossway South, Edinburgh, EH11 4EP Tel: 0131-442 4314 Fax: 0131-442 2636

F P Mailing Northwest, Waterfold Park, Bury, Lancashire, BL9 7BR Tel: 0161-797 7778 Fax: 0161-799 5777

F P Mailing Systems Northern Ltd, 43 Walkington Drive, Market Weighton, York, YO43 3NR Tel: (01430) 871833 Fax: (01430) 873448

Franking People, PO Box 1579, Bristol, BS40 5LL Tel: (01934) 863428 Fax: (01934) 863406E-mail: sales@thefrankingpeople.co.uk

Kane Mailing Systems Ltd, Glamorgan House, 47 Penallta Road, Ystrad Mynach, Hengoed, Mid Glamorgan, CF82 7AN Tel: (01443) 813588 Fax: (01443) 813587 E-mail: info@kanemailing.com

Kern Ltd, Unit 5 Concorde Close, Fareham, Hampshire, PO15 5RT Tel: (01489) 564141 Fax: (01489) 565009 E-mail: info@kern.co.uk

Lones (UK) Ltd, Middlemore Lane West, Aldridge, Walsall, WS9 8BG Tel: (01922) 743833 Fax: (01922) 743760 E-mail: sales@workplace-products.co.uk

▶ N P M Ltd, Riverside Road, Pride Park, Derby, DE24 8HA Tel: (01332) 600020 Fax: (01332) 600313

Opex Corporation, Carrington Business Park, Carrington, Manchester, M31 4YR Tel: 0161-776 4033 Fax: 0161-776 2663 E-mail: opexhr@opex.com

P F E International Ltd, P F E International House, Oakwood Hill Industrial Estate, Oakwood Hill, Loughton, Essex, IG10 3TZ Tel: (020) 8502 1011 Fax: (020) 8502 4187 E-mail: marketing@pfe.co.uk

Pitney Bowes Office Direct, London Road, London, SE1 6LF Tel: (020) 7200 5408 Fax: (020) 7200 5432 E-mail: hassan.dayem@pb.com

Postroom Suppliers Ltd, Unit D3, Lomer Farm Industrial Estate, Wrotham Road, Meopham, Gravesend, Kent, DA13 0AN Tel: (01474) 815850 Fax: (01474) 815860 E-mail: sales@europeanpostalsystems.co.uk

MAIN FRAME COMPUTERS

Integranet Networking Services Ltd, 71 High Street, Harrold, Bedford, MK43 7BJ Tel: (01234) 721755 E-mail: info@integranet.co.uk

MAINS FILTERS

Reo UK Ltd, Unit 8-9 Long Lane Industrial Estate, Long Lane, Craven Arms, Shropshire, SY7 8DU Tel: (01588) 673411 Fax: (01588) 672718 E-mail: sales@reo.co.uk

Suppression Devices, Unit 8, York Street Business Centre, Clitheroe, Lancashire, BB7 2DL Tel: (01200) 444497 Fax: (01200) 444330 E-mail: sales@suppression-devices.com

MAINS SOCKET TEST EQUIPMENT

Kew Technik Ltd, Rankine Road, Basingstoke, Hampshire, RG24 8PP Tel: (01256) 864100 Fax: (01256) 864164 E-mail: sales@kewt.co.uk

MAINS SWITCHING RELAYS

Precision Relays Ltd, 3 Seafield Road, Inverness, IV1 1SG Tel: (01463) 233929 Fax: (01463) 712514 E-mail: sales@precisionrelays.co.uk

U K Solenoid Ltd, 115 London Road, Newbury, Berkshire, RG14 2AH Tel: (01635) 45991 Fax: (01635) 37807E-mail: sales@uksol.co.uk

MAINS VOLTAGE CONNECTORS

A E R C O Ltd, Units 16-17 Lawson Hunt Industrial Park, Broadbridge Heath, Horsham, West Sussex, RH12 3JR Tel: (01403) 260206 Fax: (01403) 259760 E-mail: sales@aerco.co.uk

Wieland Electric Ltd, 1 The Riverside Business Centre, Walnut Tree Close, Guildford, Surrey, GU1 4UG Tel: (01483) 531213 Fax: (01483) 505029 E-mail: info@wieland.co.uk

MAINTENANCE AND REPAIR SERVICES, AGRICULTURAL MACHINERY

▶ Agri-Care Engineering Ltd, 25 Summerhouse View, Yeovil, Somerset, BA21 4DJ Tel: (07708) 863282 E-mail: agricare276@hotmail.com

▶ Farm Machinery Ltd, The Livestock & Auction Centre, Wenlock Road, Bridgnorth, Shropshire, WV16 4QR Tel: (01746) 769812 Fax: (01746) 769813 E-mail: sales@farm-garden.co.uk

G A Stratton & Son, 4 Stoke Road, Tottenhill, King's Lynn, Norfolk, PE33 0RW Tel: (01553) 810341

McConnel Ltd, Temeside Works, Ludlow, Shropshire, SY8 1JL Tel: (01584) 873131 Fax: (01584) 876463 E-mail: sales@mcconnel.com

▶ PR Machinery Services Ltd, Unit 14 Hindley Business Centre, Hindley, Wigan, Lancashire, WN2 3PA Tel: 01942 526999

Reekie (Stirling), 19 Kerse Road, Stirling, FK7 7SY Tel: (01786) 445577 Fax: (01786) 447138

Risborough Agricultural Services Ltd, Woodway, Princes Risborough, Buckinghamshire, HP27 0NN Tel: (01844) 275275 Fax: (01844) 274264 E-mail: sales@risag.com

Sarner Ltd, Metropolis House, 16 Southsea Road, Kingston Upon Thames, Surrey, KT1 2EH Tel: (0845) 0666444 Fax: (0845) 0666555 E-mail: rmagri@sarner.com

MAINTENANCE AND SERVICING MANAGEMENT SOFTWARE

Aca Systems Ltd, Sovereign House, Ellen Terrace, Washington, Tyne & Wear, NE37 3AS Tel: 0191-417 3166 Fax: 0191-417 3288

▶ Alliband Business Services Ltd, 14a-14b Enville Road, Kingswinford, West Midlands, DY6 0JT Tel: (01384) 287483 Fax: (01384) 280186 E-mail: phil@alliband.co.uk

Alpha Business Computers Ltd, Bentley House Newby Road Industrial Estate, Newby Road, Hazel Grove, Stockport, Cheshire, SK7 5DA Tel: 0161-483 5650 Fax: 0161-483 5576 E-mail: info@alphacom.co.uk

A1 Computer Services, 6 Wheatfield Road, Westerhope, Newcastle upon Tyne, NE5 5HQ Tel: (07757) 612978 E-mail: a1computers@mail.com

MAINTENANCE AND SERVICING MANAGEMENT SOFTWARE – *continued*

Chartwell Systems, Malens, Beacon Gardens, Crowborough, East Sussex, TN6 1BG Tel: (01892) 669597 Fax: (01892) 669597 E-mail: chartwell.sys@btconnect.com
(ECSO) Express Computer Services, 636 Cathcart Road, Crosshill, Govanhill, Glasgow, G42 8AA Tel: (0871) 7890247 Fax: (0871) 7890248 E-mail: info@ecso.co.uk
▶ Epic Software Ltd, 105 Hanover Street, Edinburgh, EH2 1DJ Tel: 0131-477 2545 Fax: 0131-624 0071 E-mail: sales@epicsoftware.co.uk
Executive Software, Kings House, Cantelupe Road, East Grinstead, West Sussex, RH19 3BE Tel: (01342) 327477 Fax: (01342) 327390
Frontec (uk) Ltd, Merchants Ho, Wapping Rd, Bristol, BS1 4RW Tel: 0117-929 7309 Fax: 0117-922 1927
Interchange Group Ltd, 2 Plover Close, Interchange Park, Newport Pagnell, Buckinghamshire, MK16 9PS Tel: (01908) 618161 Fax: (0870) 0716789 E-mail: info@interchangegroup.com
Pro Cubed UK Ltd, 10 Hunters Walk, Canal Street, Chester, CH1 4EB Tel: (01244) 355295 Fax: (01244) 341488 E-mail: 20support@pro-cubed.co.uk
Xirtek, Matrix House, Langley Road, Chippenham, Wiltshire, SN15 1BT Tel: (01249) 767710 Fax: (01249) 766767 E-mail: info@matrixeng.co.uk

MAINTENANCE FREE BATTERIES

Multicell International Ltd, 6 Swannington Road, Broughton Astley, Leicester, LE9 6TU Tel: (01455) 283443 Fax: (01455) 284250 E-mail: help@multicell.co.uk

MAINTENANCE FREE CHAINS

Sedis Co. Ltd, PO Box 6529, Wellingborough, Northamptonshire, NN8 4YS Tel: (0870) 1607840 Fax: (01604) 764162 E-mail: sedisco@sedis.com
Tsubakimoto UK Ltd, Osier Drive, Annesley, Nottingham, NG15 0DX Tel: (01623) 688700 Fax: (01623) 688729 E-mail: sales@tsubaki.co.uk

MAINTENANCE MANAGEMENT CONSULTANCY

Clough & Farmer Ltd, 89 Granville Road, Sidcup, Kent, DA14 4BT Tel: (020) 8300 1436 Fax: (020) 8308 0468 E-mail: cloughandfarmer@btconnect.com
M F H Engineering Holdings Ltd, Charlotte House, 500 Charlotte Road, Sheffield, S2 4ER Tel: 0114-279 9999 Fax: 0114-279 7501 E-mail: eng@mfhgroup.co.uk
P M Consultants, 414 North Deeside Road, Cults, Aberdeen, AB15 9TD Tel: (01224) 868239 Fax: (01224) 869711 E-mail: billatpm@tiscali.co.uk
Swansea Tribology Services, Unit 5 Penrice Court, Swansea Enterprise Park, Swansea, SA6 8QW Tel: (01792) 799036 Fax: (01792) 799034 E-mail: swansea_tribology@compuserve.com

MAINTENANCE PRODUCTS

Electrocomponents U K Ltd, 5000 John Smith Drive, Oxford Business Park South, Oxford, OX4 2BH Tel: (01865) 204000 Fax: (01865) 207400E-mail: sales@electrocomponents.com
Industrial Product Solutions Ltd, Unit 3 Healey Lane Business Centre, Healey Lane, Batley, West Yorkshire, WF17 8EZ Tel: (01924) 444059 Fax: (01924) 444058 E-mail: ipsl@btinternet.com

MAKERS-UP/MACHINISTS TO THE CLOTHING TRADE

L Whitaker & Sons 1983 Ltd, Unit 4-5 Rochdale Industrial Centre, Albion Road, Rochdale, Lancashire, OL11 4HN Tel: (01706) 655611 Fax: (01706) 655611 E-mail: sales@lwhitaker.co.uk
Moon Star Garments, S M B Ho, Gipsy La, Leicester, LE4 6RE Tel: 0116-268 2322 Fax: 0116-268 2322
Northern Mens & Boyswear Ltd, 52 Lower Oxford Street, Castleford, West Yorkshire, WF10 4AF Tel: (01977) 556203 Fax: (01977) 556203
Poppetwear Ltd, Old Co-Operative Building, Newstead Road, Annesley, Nottingham, NG15 0AX Tel: (01623) 751586 Fax: (01623) 751591
Pro Sport International, 122a Wilford Grove, Nottingham, NG2 2DU Tel: 0115-986 9000 Fax: 0115-986 8000 E-mail: mail@prosportinternational.co.uk
R N Garments, Vulcan House, 8 Vulcan Road, Leicester, LE5 3EF Tel: 0116-262 0105
Trios Ironing Laundry Services, Rear of, 87 Shakespeare Drive, Westcliff-on-Sea, Essex, SS0 9AA Tel: (01702) 351418

MAKERS-UP/MACHINISTS TO THE FURNISHING TRADE, *See Soft Furnishing Goods Makers etc*

MALEIC ACID

Croda Europe Ltd, Foundry Lane, Widnes, Cheshire, WA8 8UB Tel: 0151-423 3441 Fax: 0151-423 3441

MALLEABLE IRON CASTINGS

Castings plc, Lichfield Road, Brownhills, Walsall, WS8 6JZ Tel: (01543) 374341 Fax: (01543) 377483 E-mail: mail@castings.plc.uk
▶ Charles H Coward Ltd, 540 Ecclesfield Road, Sheffield, S5 0DJ Tel: 0114-257 7666 Fax: 0114-257 7565 E-mail: ccsltd@btconnect.com
Deeleys Castings Ltd, Leamore Lane, Walsall, WS2 7BY Tel: (01922) 476898 Fax: (01922) 493507 E-mail: deeleys@fsmail.net
Feldroll Foundry Plc, Units 17 & 21, Bailey Gate, Wimborne, Dorset, BH21 4AX Tel: (01258) 857754 Fax: (01258) 857353 E-mail: mark@feldroll.co.uk
▶ Fibresec Holdings Ltd, Unit 2, Snaygill Industrial Estate, Keighley, Skipton, North Yorkshire, BD23 2QR Tel: (01756) 799822
▶ Foundry Craft Body Builders, Hick Lane Mills, Bradford Road, Batley, West Yorkshire, WF17 5LY Tel: (01924) 479020 Fax: (01924) 479020
▶ Halifax Castings Ltd, Grantham Works, Grantham Road, Halifax, West Yorkshire, HX3 6PL Tel: (01422) 364111 Fax: (01422) 321758
▶ J L Ornamental Castings, Unit 7, Old Ballynahinch Road, Lisburn, County Antrim, BT27 6TH Tel: (07710) 458636 Fax: (028) 9263 9808 E-mail: johnlavelle@btopenworld.com
Majorfax Ltd, Charles Street, Walsall, WS2 9LZ Tel: (01922) 645815 Fax: (01922) 620500 E-mail: castings@majorfax.co.uk
▶ Marshall Brass, Keeling Hall Road, Foulsham, Dereham, Norfolk, NR20 5PR Tel: (01362) 684105 Fax: (01362) 684280 E-mail: sales@marshall-brass.com
▶ Mastern Patterns, 17 Murraysgate Industrial Estate, Whitburn, Bathgate, West Lothian, EH47 0LE Tel: (01501) 744554 Fax: (01501) 743561
▶ Specialised Castings, Headswood Mill, Denny, Stirlingshire, FK6 6BL Tel: (01324) 820077 Fax: (01324) 820077 E-mail: sales@specialisedcastings.co.uk
Unimetal Ltd., Bay 6B, Tractor Spares Industrial Estate, Strawberry Lane, Willenhall, West Midlands, WV13 3RS Tel: (01902) 366035 Fax: (01902) 601221 E-mail: billallen@btconnect.com

MALLETS

H. Brettell & Sons Ltd, 20 Chestnut Ave, Forest Gate, London, E7 0JH Tel: (020) 8555 4037 Fax: (020) 8555 2106 E-mail: sales@brettells.co.uk
H Webber & Sons Ltd, Bridge House, Station Road Gomshall, Guildford, Surrey, GU5 9NP Tel: (01483) 202963 Fax: (01306) 740811 E-mail: info@hwebber.co.uk
Safety Tools Ltd, Highlands Road, Shirley, Solihull, West Midlands, B90 4NJ Tel: 0121-705 3508 Fax: 0121-713 2505 E-mail: info@safetytools.co.uk

MALT/MALT EXTRACT/MALT FLOUR

Robin Appel Ltd, The Town House, The Square, Bishops Waltham, Southampton, SO32 1AF Tel: (01489) 896388 Fax: (01489) 896602 E-mail: enquiries@robin-appel.com
Brewing-Solutions Co UK Ltd, Unit 31, Osborne Mill Osborne Street, Oldham, OL9 6QQ Tel: 0161-622 1603 Fax: 0161-622 1662 E-mail: info@brewing-solutions.co.uk
Edme Ltd, Edme House, High Street, Mistley, Manningtree, Essex, CO11 1HG Tel: (01206) 393725 Fax: (01206) 396699 E-mail: info@edme.com
Thomas Fawcett & Sons Ltd, 8 Eastfield Lane, Castleford, West Yorkshire, WF10 4LE Tel: (01977) 552490 Fax: (01977) 519076 E-mail: enquiries@fawcett-maltsters.co.uk
Greencore Malt, 24-25 Eastern Way, Bury St. Edmunds, Suffolk, IP32 7AD Tel: (01284) 772000 Fax: (01284) 753349 E-mail: greencoremalt@greencoremalt.com
Muntons Agricultural Merchants, Needham Road, Stowmarket, Suffolk, IP14 2AG Tel: (01449) 618300 Fax: (01449) 677800 E-mail: grain@muntons.com
Pure Malt Products Ltd, Victoria Bridge, Haddington, East Lothian, EH41 4BD Tel: (01620) 824696 Fax: (01620) 822018 E-mail: enquiries@puremalt.com
J.P. Simpson & Co. (Alnwick) Ltd, Tweed Valley Maltings, Tweedside Trading Estate, Berwick-upon-Tweed, TD15 2UZ Tel: (01289) 330033 Fax: (01289) 306602 E-mail: malt@simpsonsmalt.co.uk
Edwin Tucker & Sons Ltd, Teign Road, Newton Abbot, Devon, TQ12 4AA Tel: (01626) 334002 Fax: (01626) 330153 E-mail: info@tuckersmaltings.com

MAN MACHINE INTERFACE (MMI) EQUIPMENT, *See also Human Machine Interface etc*

Soft Control Ltd, Market Chambers, Market Place, Shifnal, Shropshire, TF11 9AZ Tel: (01952) 462976 Fax: (01952) 462797 E-mail: technical@softcontrol.co.uk

MAN MACHINE INTERFACE (MMI) KEYPAD SOFTWARE

T R M Electronics, 86 Moss Road, Southport, Merseyside, PR8 4JQ Tel: (01704) 563777 Fax: (01704) 565219 E-mail: keith@trminternational.com

MAN MADE STONE

▶ Amg Stone Products Ltd, Rosedale, Stonehaven Road, Aberdeen, AB12 5UT Tel: (01224) 877283 Fax: (01224 873462 E-mail: info@amgstoneproducts.com

MAN-MADE FIBRE FABRICS

William Clark & Sons Ltd, Upperlands, Maghera, County Londonderry, BT46 5RZ Tel: (028) 7964 2214 Fax: (028) 7954 7207 E-mail: sales@wmclark.co.uk
S. Dawes Weaving Ltd, Manor Mill Hallam Road, Nelson, Lancashire, BB9 8DN Tel: (01282) 612325 Fax: (01282) 690466 E-mail: info@sdawesweaving.co.uk
R A Irwin & Co. Ltd, Bannside Industrial Estate, Goban Street, Portadown, Craigavon, County Armagh, BT63 5AG Tel: (028) 3833 6215 Fax: (028) 3835 0310 E-mail: info@ra-irwin.co.uk

MAN-MADE FIBRE YARNS

E Mesrie & Sons Ltd, 3 Brazil Street, Manchester, M1 3PJ Tel: 0161-236 6274 Fax: 0161-236 8086 E-mail: yarns@mdmresourcing.com
John L Brierley Ltd, Turnbridge Mills, Huddersfield, HD1 6QT Tel: (01484) 435555 Fax: (01484) 435159 E-mail: sales@johnlbrierley.com
NGF Europe Ltd, Lea Green Road, St. Helens, Merseyside, WA9 4PR Tel: (01744) 853065 Fax: (01744) 816147 E-mail: sales@ngfeurope.com
Malcolm Ross & Sons Ltd, PO Box 4, Alderley Edge, Cheshire, SK9 7PR Tel: (01625) 583853 Fax: (01625) 586340 E-mail: sales@malcolmross.co.uk
Ullmann & Bamforth Ltd, York House, 67 Bradford Road, Brighouse, West Yorkshire, HD6 1ST Tel: (01484) 714033 Fax: (01484) 721339E-mail: sales@ullmann-bamforth.co.uk

MAN-MADE FIBRES

Texkimp Ltd, Manchester Road, Northwich, Cheshire, CW9 7NN Tel: (01606) 40345 Fax: (01606) 40366 E-mail: info@texkimp.co.uk

MAN-OVERBOARD (MOB) RECOVERY EQUIPMENT

Land & Marine Products Ltd, 32 Woolmer Way, Bordon, Hampshire, GU35 9QF Tel: (01420) 474484 Fax: (01420) 489002 E-mail: sales@landandmarine.co.uk

MANAGEMENT COACHING

▶ Helen Redfern, 21 Vincent Road, Croydon, CR0 6ED Tel: (020) 8405 3392 E-mail: helen@helenredfern.co.uk
▶ Leap Coaching Associates, 7 Hopewell Way, Crigglestone, Wakefield, West Yorkshire, WF4 3PU Tel: (01924) 254173
Unique Advantage Coaching, 11 Babylon Lane, Bishampton, Pershore, Worcestershire, WR10 2NN Tel: (0845) 6442424 Fax: (0870) 1328311 E-mail: enquiries@uniqueadvantage.co.uk

MANAGEMENT CONSULTANTS

A C T (Devon) Ltd, Barton Farmhouse, Dartington Hall, Dartington, Totnes, Devon, TQ9 6ED Tel: (01803) 864432 Fax: (01803) 868188 E-mail: actcon@btconnect.com
A I M S Elmbridge, 12 Rushett Road, Thames Ditton, Surrey, KT7 0UX Tel: (020) 8224 8107 Fax: (020) 8224 8107 E-mail: ianw@aims.co.uk
A S K Europe plc, Trent House University Way, Cranfield Technology Park, Cranfield, Bedford, MK43 0AN Tel: (01234) 757575 Fax: (01234) 757576 E-mail: mail@askeurope.com
A T Kearney Ltd, Lansdowne House, Berkeley Square, London, W1J 6ER Tel: (020) 7468 8000 Fax: (020) 7468 8001
A2z, 139 Lillie Road, London, SW6 7SX Tel: (07957) 586656 E-mail: a2zcounselling@yahoo.com
Accenture, 60 Queen Victoria Street, London, EC4N 4TW Tel: (020) 7844 4000 Fax: (020) 7844 4444
Adamson & Partners Ltd, 10 Lisbon Square, Leeds, LS1 4LY Tel: 0113-245 1212 Fax: 0113-242 0802 E-mail: stuart.adamson@adamsons.com
Aerodyne Services, 10 Hydepark Close, Newtownabbey, County Antrim, BT36 4WS Tel: (028) 9083 6333 Fax: (028) 9084 1525
Ainscough Vanguard, William Thorpe Industrial Park, Park Road, Holmwood, Chesterfield, Derbyshire, S42 5UY Tel: (01246) 854644 Fax: (01246) 854161
Alison Hodge Associates, 12 Heathfield Gardens, London, W4 4JY Tel: (020) 8995 5485 Fax: (020) 8995 4341 E-mail: alisonhodge@dial.pipex.com
Anodos Information Systems Strategy Ltd, Rangers, South Rd, Liphook, Hants, GU30 7HS Tel: (01428) 727847 E-mail: info@anodos.com
Apax Partners Ltd, 15 Portland Place, London, W1B 1PT Tel: (020) 7872 6300 Fax: (020) 7872 9449
Applied Management Techniques, 33 Harts Leap Road, Sandhurst, Berkshire, GU47 8EW Tel: (01344) 773153 Fax: (01344) 776216
Arranquote Ltd, 4 Heritage Enterprise Acres, Wakefield Road, Fitzwilliam, Pontefract, West Yorkshire, WF9 5BP Tel: (01977) 617319 Fax: (01977) 617390 E-mail: arranquote@globalnet.co.uk
Attributes Associates, 52 Harvey Rd, Guildford, Surrey, GU1 3LU Tel: (01483) 577771 Fax: (01483) 577555
Aurora Business Development Ltd, 9 Ferndown Close, Bristol, BS11 0UP Tel: 0117-962 6500 Fax: 0117-962 6500 E-mail: aurora@btinternet.com
▶ Autoview UK Ltd, Business & Innovation Centre, Wearfield, Sunderland Enterprise Park (East), Sunderland, SR5 2TA Tel: 0191 5166444 Fax: 0191 5166445 E-mail: info@autoviewsystems.co.uk
Bailie Connor Partnership Ltd, Landmark House, 5 Cromac Quay, Belfast, BT7 2JD Tel: (028) 9023 1062 Fax: (028) 9023 1273 E-mail: info@bailieconnor.co.uk
Bain & Co., 40 Strand, London, WC2N 5RW Tel: (020) 7969 6000 Fax: (020) 7969 6666
Batalas Ltd, PO Box 8770, Pershore, Worcestershire, WR10 2NU Tel: (0870) 7504400 E-mail: enquiries@batalas.co.uk
Alan Bell & Partners Ltd, Manor House, Front St South, Trimdon, Trimdon Station, County Durham, TS29 6LY Tel: (01429) 883664 Fax: (01429) 883664 E-mail: abell@criticalstrategy.com
Bennett Verby, 7 St. Petersgate, Stockport, Cheshire, SK1 1EB Tel: 0161-476 9000 Fax: 0161-476 9001 E-mail: enquiries@bennettverby.co.uk
Berkeley Partnership, 55 Blandford Street, London, W1U 7HW Tel: (020) 7224 2671 Fax: (020) 7935 1892 E-mail: sales@berkeleypartnership.com
Bourton Group Ltd, Bourton Hall, Bourton, Rugby, Warwickshire, CV23 9SD Tel: (01926) 633333 Fax: (01926) 633450 E-mail: info@bourton.co.uk
Bowman Group Ltd, 1200 Century Way, Thorpe Park Business Park, Leeds, LS15 8ZB Tel: (01422) 322211 Fax: (01325) 151100 E-mail: info@bowman-group.co.uk
John Boyes Consulting, May House, Tanners Lane, Hathern, Loughborough, Leicestershire, LE12 5JG Tel: (01509) 646530 Fax: (01509) 646530 E-mail: john@johnboyes.com
Bull & Co., 61 La Colomberie, St. Helier, Jersey, JE2 4QA Tel: (01534) 866688 Fax: (01534) 866699 E-mail: enquiries@bullandcompany.com
Business Training Partnership, 96 High Street, Burnham, Slough, SL1 7JT Tel: (01628) 664040 Fax: (01628) 660042 E-mail: dawn.oxley@btp.uk.com
C C G Corporate Consulting Group Ltd, 24 Buckingham Gate, London, SW1E 6LB Tel: (020) 7828 1123 Fax: (020) 8828 2604 E-mail: info@ccg.co.uk
C J A Group Ltd, 2 London Wall Buildings, London, EC2M 5UX Tel: (020) 7588 3588 Fax: (020) 7256 8501 E-mail: cja@cjagroup.com
C L S Europe, Heritage House, 11 Heritage Court, Chester, CH1 1RD Tel: (01244) 313022 Fax: (01244) 318455 E-mail: sales@clseurope.com

▶ indicates data change since last edition

MANAGEMENT CONSULTANTS – *continued*

C S L Recruitment & Consulting Ltd, Hurst House, 157-169 Walton Road, East Molesey, Surrey, KT8 0DX Tel: (020) 8224 9840 Fax: (020) 8941 4095 E-mail: sales@imesconsulting.com

C3 Consulting, 2 The Hawthorns, Woodbridge Road, Birmingham, B13 9DY Tel: 0121-449 8717 Fax: 0121-442 4082 E-mail: contact@c3consulting.co.uk

Campbell Birch Executive Recruitment, Broadway, Bracknell, Berkshire, RG12 1AG Tel: (01344) 424117 Fax: (01344) 360534 E-mail: info@campbellbirch.com

Campbell & Campbell, 100 University Street, Belfast, BT7 1HE Tel: (028) 9023 4541 Fax: (028) 9023 2860 E-mail: info@candc.co.uk

Charnwood Management Centre Ltd, 175 Birchwood Lane, Somercotes, Alfreton, Derbyshire, DE55 4NF Tel: (01773) 606606 Fax: (01773) 606606 E-mail: sales@thecharnwoodgroup.com

Chinal Management Services, King Charles House, 2 Castle Hill, Dudley, West Midlands, DY1 4PS Tel: (01384) 234234 Fax: (01384) 456183 E-mail: info@chinal.co.uk

Collinson Grant, Ryecroft, Aviary Road, Worsley, Manchester, M28 2WF Tel: 0161-703 5600 Fax: 0161-790 9177 E-mail: postmaster@collinsongrant.com

Computer Sciences Corporation, Euxton House, Euxton Lane, Chorley, Lancashire, PR7 6FE Tel: (01257) 265507 Fax: (01257) 242609

▶ Consultants In Quality Assurance Ltd, 215 Staines Road, Lauham, Staines, Middlesex, TW18 2RS Tel: (01784) 460563 E-mail: rhoweles@ciqa.co.uk

Control Risks, Cottons Centre, Cottons Lane, London, SE1 2QG Tel: (020) 7970 2100 Fax: (020) 7970 2222 E-mail: enquiries@control.risks.com

The Coverdale Organisation Ltd, Plestowes Farm, Hareway Lane, Barford, Warwick, CV35 8DD Tel: (01926) 625757 Fax: (01926) 625758 E-mail: info@coverdale.com

CPCR, The Charcoal, Blagdon Estate, Seaton Burn, Newcastle upon Tyne, NE13 6DB Tel: (01670) 785100 Fax: (01670) 785108 E-mail: people@cpcr.co.uk

Cripps Sears & Partners, Sardinia House, 52 Lincoln's Inn Fields, London, WC2A 3LZ Tel: (020) 7440 8999 Fax: (020) 7242 0515 E-mail: london@crippssears.com

Croner Consulting, Croner House, Wheatfield Way, Hinckley, Leicestershire, LE10 1YG Tel: (01455) 897000 Fax: (01455) 897400 E-mail: info@cronerconsulting.co.uk

Crown Business Efficiency Consultants Ltd, 41 Parsonage Road, Horsham, West Sussex, RH12 4AW Tel: (01403) 259773 Fax: (01403) 254604 E-mail: crownbec@aol.com

D C Gardner Training, Nestor House, Playhouse Yard, London, EC4V 5EX Tel: (020) 7779 8917 Fax: (020) 7779 8786

Department Of Continuing Education, Lonsdale College, Bailrigg, Lancaster, LA1 4YN Tel: (01524) 592624 Fax: (01524) 592448 E-mail: managementlearning@lancaster.ac.uk

Development Associates Group Ltd, Blenheim House, Fitzalan Court, Cardiff, CF24 0TN Tel: (029) 2049 2773 Fax: (029) 2026 4505

▶ Donna Chapman & Co., Daisy Hill, Knarr Barn Lane, Dobcross, Oldham, OL3 5RF Tel: (01457) 871533 Fax: (01457) 871533 E-mail: sales@donnachapman.com

Edward J Bows, South View, Oxhill, Warwick, CV35 0QU Tel: (01295) 680771 Fax: (01295) 688191 E-mail: 100127.1650@compuserve.com

Elmcroft Consulting Ltd, 156 Frimley Green Road, Frimley Green, Camberley, Surrey, GU16 6NA Tel: (01252) 838177

Emergent Systems Solutions Ltd, 9 Briarwood, Finchampstead, Wokingham, Berks, RG40 4XA Tel: 0118-973 6077 Fax: 0118-973 6088 E-mail: consult@emergent.co.uk

Engineering & Development Consultants Ltd, Keruing Cedar, Chess Hill, Loudwater, Rickmansworth, Hertfordshire, WD3 4HU Tel: (01923) 776567 Fax: (01923) 721438 E-mail: gmcrook@lineone.net

Enterprise Centre, Greenacre Court, Station Road, Burgess Hill, West Sussex, RH15 9DS Tel: (0845) 2301054 Fax: (0845) 2301058 E-mail: info@sussexenterprise.co.uk

Enviros Consulting Group, Waterfront Quay, Salford, M50 3XW Tel: 0161-874 3600 Fax: 0161-848 0181 E-mail: paul.bromley@enviros.com

Ernst & Young Ltd, 1 More London Place, London, SE1 2AF Tel: (020) 7951 2000 Fax: (020) 7951 1345

Ethos Partnership Limited, Suite E8, Business & Innovation Centre, Wearfield, Sunderland, SR5 2TP Tel: 0191-516 6251 Fax: (01892) 528433 E-mail: kym@ethospartnershipltd.co.uk

Eurosoft (U K) Ltd, 3 St Stephens Road, Bournemouth, BH2 6JL Tel: (01202) 297315 Fax: (01202) 558280 E-mail: info@eurosoft-uk.com

Fluor Ltd, Portland House, Bressenden Place, London, SW1E 5BH Tel: (020) 7932 1700 Fax: (020) 7932 1722

G P C International, 40 Long Acre, London, WC2E 9LG Tel: (020) 7395 7171 Fax: (020) 7395 7181 E-mail: info@gpcinternational.com

Glendinning Management Consultants Ltd, Glendinning House, 1 Station Road, Addlestone, Surrey, KT15 2AG Tel: (01932) 833600 Fax: (01932) 833601

Gustav Kaser Training International Ltd, Essex House, 118 High Street, Ongar, Essex, CM5 9EB Tel: (01277) 365335 Fax: (01277) 365277 E-mail: sales@gustavkaeser.com

▶ H D Management, 18 Claremont Crescent, Edinburgh, EH7 4HX Tel: 0131-556 9001 Fax: 0131-558 9704

H H B Management Consultants Ltd, Estate Office, Highbrook, Mertyn La, Carmel, Holywell, Clwyd, CH8 8QN Tel: (01352) 713213 Fax: (01352) 710945

Hambleden Group Ltd, PO Box 16980, London, NW8 9WP Tel: (020) 7289 4443 Fax: (020) 7289 1943 E-mail: information@hambleden.co.uk

Harmoni Its Ltd, Parklands Business Park, Forest Road, Denmead, Waterlooville, Hampshire, PO7 6XP Tel: (023) 9226 8133 Fax: (023) 9226 8160 E-mail: wci@wcigroup.com

Harris Kafton, 54-58 High Street, Edgware, Middlesex, HA8 7EJ Tel: (020) 8381 3770 Fax: (020) 8381 3470

Hay Group, Unit 2635 Kings Court, The Crescent, Birmingham Business Park, Birmingham, B37 7YE Tel: 0121-717 4600 Fax: 0121-717 4601

Hays Macintyre & Co., Fairfax House, 15 Fullwood Place, London, WC1V 6AY Tel: (020) 7969 5500 Fax: (020) 7969 5600 E-mail: sales@haysmcintyre.com

Heidrick & Struggles Ltd, 3 Burlington Gardens, London, W1S 3EP Tel: (020) 7075 4000 Fax: (020) 7075 4100 E-mail: lo@h-s.com

Henderson Management Services, 208 Henley Road, Caversham, Reading, RG4 6LR Tel: 0118-947 9159 Fax: 0118-946 4779 E-mail: hms@dial.pipex.com

Horton International UK Ltd, Audley House, 13 Palace Street, London, SW1E 5HX Tel: (020) 7630 0200 Fax: (020) 7630 0322 E-mail: london@horton-intl.com

Alexander Hughes Ltd, 14-16 Regent Street, London, SW1Y 4PH Tel: (020) 7331 1800 Fax: (020) 7331 1888 E-mail: info@alexanderhughes.co.uk

Human Factors International, 8 Staple Inn, London, WC1V 7QH Tel: (020) 7831 3123 Fax: (020) 7831 8643 E-mail: mail@humanfactors.co.uk

I A L Consultants, 109 Uxbridge Road, London, W5 5TL Tel: (020) 8832 7780 Fax: (020) 8566 4931 E-mail: ial@brg.co.uk

I T S Ltd, PO Box 331, Slough, SL2 3DQ Tel: (01753) 642144 Fax: (01753) 646461 E-mail: dir@its.ltd.uk

Ibcc, 9 Ferndown Close, Bristol, BS11 0UP Tel: 0117-968 2691 Fax: 0117-962 6500 E-mail: ibcc@btinternet.com

Indacom Group Ltd, 131 Hollywood Lane Wainscott, Rochester, Kent, ME3 8AS Tel: (01634) 716286 Fax: (01634) 724821 E-mail: adavis.indacom@btopenworld.com

Indepen Consulting Ltd, Diespeker Wharf, 38 Graham Street, London, N1 8JX Tel: (020) 7226 6336 Fax: (020) 7704 0872 E-mail: info@indepen.co.uk

Informed Solutions Ltd, The Old Bank, Old Market Place, Altrincham, Cheshire, WA14 4PA Tel: 0161-942 2000 Fax: 0161-942 2015

Innovation Centre Europe Ltd, Winton House, Winton Street, Alfriston, Polegate, East Sussex, BN26 5UH Tel: (01323) 871117 Fax: (01323) 871118 E-mail: sales@iceurope.com

Interlink Systems Engineering Ltd, Po Box 3, Leighton Buzzard, Bedfordshire, LU7 3AG Tel: (01525) 372613 Fax: (01525) 372613 E-mail: interlink.consulting@dial.pipex.com

International Training Service, Wellington Park, Belfast, BT9 6DJ Tel: (028) 9092 3388 Fax: (028) 9092 3386 E-mail: info@itsconsult.com

It World Consultants, 47 Catherine Place, London, SW1E 6DY Tel: (020) 7828 7300 Fax: (020) 7828 7990 E-mail: info@itworld.co.uk

JEMO Ltd, 11 Willowbank, Cepen Park, Chippenham, Wiltshire, SN14 6QG Tel: (01249) 447544 Fax: (01249) 661478 E-mail: jefftrain@jemoltd.plus.com

KBC Process Technology Ltd, 42-50 Hersham Road, Walton-on-Thames, Surrey, KT12 1RZ Tel: (01932) 242424 Fax: (01932) 224214 E-mail: info@kbcat.com

Kiddy & Partners 2007 Ltd, 74a Charlotte Street, London, W1T 4QH Tel: (020) 7486 6867 Fax: (020) 7486 6863 E-mail: info@kpl.co.uk

Paul Kiernan Associates Ltd, PO Box 120, London, SW3 4LU Tel: (020) 7352 5562

John Knox Ltd, 55 Rosebank Street, Leek, Staffordshire, ST13 6AG Tel: (01538) 399733 Fax: (01538) 399985 E-mail: jknox1066@aol.com

L L P, Watson House, London Road, Reigate, Surrey, RH2 9PQ Tel: (01737) 241144 Fax: (01737) 241496

Link H R Systems, Normant House, 121-123 Long Lane, Upton, Chester, CH2 1JF Tel: (01244) 399555 Fax: (01244) 399666 E-mail: general@link-hrsystems.com

Logistech Ltd, Exchange House, 494 Midsummer Boulevard, Milton Keynes, MK9 2EA Tel: (01908) 255985 E-mail: info@logistech.co.uk

M F Business Services, 10 Bodington Road, Sutton Coldfield, West Midlands, B75 5ET Tel: (07973) 639660 Fax: 0121-308 3003 E-mail: enquiries@mfbusiness.co.uk

Macgregor Associates Consulting, Sherwood House, 7 Gregory, Nottingham, NG7 6LB Tel: 0115-962 0222 Fax: 0115-962 2144 E-mail: info@macgregorassociates.co.uk

Mckinsey & Co. (UK), 1 Jermyn Street, London, SW1Y 4UH Tel: (020) 7839 8040 Fax: (020) 7339 5000

Management Advisory Ltd, 5 - 8 Edwards Centre, The Horsefair, Hinckley, Leicestershire, LE10 0AN Tel: (01455) 444222 Fax: (01455) 891251 E-mail: admin@managementadvisory.net

Management Horizons Europe Ltd, Europa House, Church Street, Isleworth, Middlesex, TW7 6DA Tel: (020) 8560 9393 Fax: (020) 8580 8310 E-mail: info@mheurope.com

Management Process Development Ltd, 30 Chantreys Drive, Elloughton, Brough, North Humberside, HU15 1LH Tel: (01482) 665675 E-mail: richard-grafton@supanet.com

▶ Marchaven Consulting Ltd, 8 Daisy Lane, Overseal, Swadlincote, Derbyshire, DE12 6JH Tel: (01283) 761813 E-mail: jarvis.whitehead@marchaven.co.uk

Mast International Group plc, Hermitage House, Bath Road, Taplow, Maidenhead, Berkshire, SL6 0AR Tel: (01628) 784062 Fax: (01628) 773061 E-mail: info@mast.co.uk

Mercuri International UK Ltd, 6 Olton Bridge, 245 Warwick Road, Solihull, West Midlands, B92 7AH Tel: 0121-706 3400 Fax: 0121-706 3900 E-mail: admin.london@mercuri.co.uk

Metra Martech Ltd, 7 Chiswick High Road, London, W4 2ND Tel: (020) 8742 7888 Fax: (020) 8742 8558 E-mail: research@metra-martech.com

Michael Rigby Associates, 15 Market Street, Wotton-under-Edge, Gloucestershire, GL12 7AE Tel: (01453) 521621 Fax: (01453) 521681 E-mail: results@521621.,com

Mitre Group Ltd, Molyneux Business Park, Whitworth Road, Darley Dale, Matlock, Derbyshire, DE4 2HJ Tel: (01629) 733900 Fax: (01629) 735666 E-mail: mail@mitregroup.co.uk

Modulus Management Consultancy Ltd, 188 Washway Road, Sale, Cheshire, M33 6RN Tel: 0161-905 1089 Fax: 0161-905 3588 E-mail: mmc@modulus-ltd.co.uk

Moore Stephens International Ltd, St Paul's, 8-12 Warwick Lane, London, EC4P 4BN Tel: (020) 7248 4499 Fax: (020) 7334 7976 E-mail: postmaster@moorestephens.com

N B Information Ltd, 570 Lanark Road West, Balerno, Midlothian, EH14 7BN Tel: 0131-449 7922 E-mail: support@-info.co.uk

Nelson Securities, View House, Rochester Way, Crowborough, East Sussex, TN6 2DR Tel: (01892) 652544

New Work Trust Co. Ltd, Station Road Workshops, Station Road, Kingswood, Bristol, BS15 4PJ Tel: 0117-957 5577 Fax: 0117-956 8776 E-mail: newworktrust@btconnect.com

Newburgh Management Services Ltd, 13 Cobbs Brow Lane, Newburgh, Wigan, Lancashire, WN8 7ND Tel: 0161-746 8582 Fax: (08700) 549489 E-mail: nmsl.ewj@btinternet.com

Newchurch Computer Systems, Causeway House, 13 The Causeway, Teddington, Middlesex, TW11 0JR Tel: (020) 8783 3300 Fax: (020) 8977 8198 E-mail: info@newchurch.co.uk

Nifes Consulting Group Ltd, 8 Woodside Terrace, Glasgow, G3 7UY Tel: 0141-332 2453 Fax: 0141-333 0402 E-mail: glasgow@nifes.co.uk

Nigel Wright Consultancy, 78 Grey Street, Newcastle upon Tyne, NE1 6AF Tel: 0191-222 0770 Fax: 0191-222 1786 E-mail: enquiries@nwc.co.uk

Oakfield Consultancy Partnership, 1 Farndon Hall, Church Lane, Farndon, Chester, CH3 6QF Tel: (01925) 491234 Fax: (01925) 480088 E-mail: enquiries@oakfieldconsultancy.com

O'Neill Management Ltd, 9 Albany Drive, Bishops Waltham, Southampton, SO32 1GE Tel: (0787) 9463824 E-mail: sales@oneill-management.com

Oranvale Ltd, Central Chambers, 4 Market Place, Ramsbottom, Bury, Lancashire, BL0 9HT Tel: (01706) 827327 Fax: (01706) 821488 E-mail: oranvale@telpark.co.uk

Orr & Boss & Partners Ltd, Landmark House, Station Road, Cheadle Hulme, Cheadle, Cheshire, SK8 7BS Tel: (0870) 3216501 Fax: (0870) 3216502E-mail: orrboss@aol.com

Orridge & Co. Ltd, Astra Centre, Edinburgh Way, Harlow, Essex, CM20 2BN Tel: (01279) 620800 Fax: (01279) 620806 E-mail: info@orridge.net

P A International Consulting Group Ltd, 123 Buckingham Palace Road, London, SW1W 9SR Tel: (020) 7730 9000 Fax: (020) 7333 5050 E-mail: info@paconsulting.com

P D A Ltd, Woodfield, Holmfirth Road, New Mill, Holmfirth, HD9 7LX Tel: (01484) 685879 Fax: (01484) 682775 E-mail: pda.international@easynet.co.uk

P M Consultants, 414 North Deeside Road, Cults, Aberdeen, AB15 9TD Tel: (01224) 868239 Fax: (01224) 869711 E-mail: billatpm@tiscali.co.uk

Pamela Neave, 18 St. Augustines Parade, Bristol, BS1 4UL Tel: 0117-921 1831 Fax: 0117-925 1019 E-mail: enquiries@pamela-neave.co.uk

Charles Paterson Search & Selection, 31 Ranelagh Grove, London, SW1W 8PA Tel: (020) 7730 6555 Fax: (020) 7730 6555 E-mail: charles@charlespaterson.com

People Agenda Ltd, 167 Watling St West, Towcester, Northamptonshire, NN12 6BX Tel: (01327) 354871 Fax: (01327) 358799 E-mail: sales@peopleagenda.com

Pi Ally Ltd, 24 Merton Road, Benfleet, Essex, SS7 5QJ Tel: (01268) 569190 Fax: (01268) 565517 E-mail: johnhall@pially.com

Pielle & Co. Ltd, Museum House, 25 Museum St, London, WC1A 1PL Tel: (020) 7323 1587 Fax: (020) 7631 0029 E-mail: team@pielleconsulting.com

Pierce Management Services, Essex House Cromwell Park, Banbury Road, Chipping Norton, Oxfordshire, OX7 5SR Tel: (01608) 647100 Fax: (01608) 641881

Pims Associates Ltd, 15-16 Basinghall Street, London, EC2V 5BR Tel: (020) 7776 2800 Fax: (020) 7776 2828 E-mail: info@pimsconsulting.com

PML Programme Management Ltd, Unit 34, Threadneedle Street, London, EC2R 8AY Tel: (020) 7256 2216 Fax: (020) 7510 0061 E-mail: kim_newman@pmlgroup.com

Pressure Systems International Ltd, 124 Victoria Road, Farnborough, Hampshire, GU14 7PW Tel: (01252) 510000 Fax: (01252) 510099 E-mail: sales@pressure-systems.com

Process Management International Ltd, Barclays Venture Centre Sir William Lyons Road, University of W, Coventry, CV4 7EZ Tel: (024) 7641 9089 Fax: (024) 7641 9480 E-mail: sales@pmi.co.uk

The Profit Partnership Ltd, White Gates, Oldway, Upton St. Leonards, Gloucester, GL4 8AF Tel: (01452) 372540 Fax: (01452) 372540

Project Systems Support Ltd, Chatelaine, Gazing Lane, West Wellow, Romsey, Hampshire, SO51 6BS Tel: (01794) 322755 Fax: (01794) 323964 E-mail: robert_toogood@projectsystemssupport.co.uk

PRTM Ltd, Kirkhill House, Broom Road East, Newton Mearns, Glasgow, G77 5LL Tel: 0141-616 2616 Fax: 0141-616 2555 E-mail: info@prtm.com

Psychometric Research & Development Ltd, Brewmaster House, The Maltings, St. Albans, Hertfordshire, AL1 3HT Tel: (01727) 841455 Fax: (01727) 847846 E-mail: steve@prd.co.uk

R C H Quality & Design, The Glen, Trevor Road, Llangollen, Clwyd, LL20 7UH Tel: (01978) 860706 E-mail: roberrt.hicks@btclick.com

Rab Personnel Management Services, 18 Dolphin Close, London, SE28 8PY Tel: (020) 8311 1261 Fax: (020) 8311 1261 E-mail: sales@rabpms.co.uk

▶ Red Seal, Technium Business Park, Kings Road, Swansea, SA1 8PH Tel: (01792) 295004 Fax: (01792) 485577 E-mail: studio@red-seal.com

Reed Employment Ltd, 31 Wheeler Gate, Nottingham, NG1 2NA Tel: 0115-947 6301 Fax: 0115-947 6135 E-mail: nottingham.employment@reed.co.uk

Regan Consulting Practice Ltd, Choni Cottage, Manor Road, South Wingfield, Alfreton, Derbyshire, DE55 7NH Tel: (01773) 521528 Fax: (01773) 830688 E-mail: helpdesk@reganconsulting.co.uk

Research Associates UK Ltd, 99 Oulton Road, Stone, Staffordshire, ST15 8DX Tel: (01785) 813164 Fax: (01785) 813268 E-mail: sales@research-associates.co.uk

Resource Management Associates Ltd, 4 Western Road, Romford, RM1 3JT Tel: (01708) 735888 Fax: (01708) 735999 E-mail: charleskeep@rma-uk.org

Reynolds & Associates, Mendota, Stonehouse Lane, Cookham, Maidenhead, Berkshire, SL6 9TP Tel: (01628) 471680 Fax: (01628) 471680 E-mail: br@reynoldsconsult.co.uk

Right Management Consultants, Augustine House, 6A Austin Friars, London, EC2N 2HA Tel: (020) 7448 8750 Fax: (020) 7588 2114 E-mail: rightaugustine@right.com

Rundle Brownswood Ltd, Leigh Court, Pill Road, Abbots Leigh, Bristol, BS8 3RA Tel: (01275) 374994 Fax: (01275) 374681 E-mail: info@rundlebrownswood.com

S T T Associates, PO Box 18, Ledbury, Herefordshire, HR8 2YR Tel: (01531) 633604 Fax: (01531) 632790

Kurt Salmon Associates Ltd, Bruce Court, 25a Hale Road, Altrincham, Cheshire, WA14 2EY Tel: 0161-925 2727 Fax: 0161-927 7135 E-mail: manchester@kurtsalmon.com

Sapphire One Consulting Ltd, 5 Wordsworth Road, Addlestone, Surrey, KT15 2SW Tel: (01932) 857109 Fax: (0870) 0562324 E-mail: info@sapphireone.co.uk

Sciteb Ltd, 18 Newton Man, Queens Club Gardens, London, W14 9RR Tel: (020) 7381 1481 Fax: (020) 7499 9253 E-mail: nicholas.beale@sciteb.com

Anne Shaw Consultants Ltd, Adelphi Mill, Grimshaw Lane, Bollington, Macclesfield, Cheshire, SK10 5JB Tel: (01625) 576225 Fax: (01625) 576262 E-mail: consult@anneshaw.com

Sheppard Moscow Personal Development Ltd, Enterprise House, 59-65 Upper Ground, London, SE1 9PQ Tel: (020) 7929 9650 Fax: (020) 7620 2200 E-mail: sml@sheppardmoscow.com

Sigma Consultancy Scotland Ltd, 18 Overton Crescent, Dyce, Aberdeen, AB21 7FW Tel: (01224) 723947 Fax: (01224) 773754

Stanton Chase International, 56 Haymarket, London, SW1Y 4RN Tel: (020) 7930 6314 Fax: (020) 7930 9539 E-mail: london@stantonchase.com

Stirling Business Solutions Ltd, Lasyard House, Underhill Street, Bridgnorth, Shropshire, WV16 4BB Tel: (01746) 769301 Fax: (01746) 769302 E-mail: sales@tmssolutions.co.uk

MANAGEMENT CONSULTANTS – *continued*

Strategem Ltd, Hough End Hall, 95 Nell Lane, Manchester, M21 7AZ Tel: 0161-860 0344 Fax: 0161-860 0888 E-mail: strategem@strategem.co.uk
Strategy International Ltd, The Ivory Ho, St. Katherine Docks, London, E1W 1BN Tel: (020) 7480 5652 Fax: (020) 7488 9643 E-mail: ej@dgroup.co.uk
T E K Group, Millennium House, 30 Junction Road, Sheffield, S11 8XB Tel: 0114-263 1000 Fax: 0114-263 1991
T M P Worldwide, Kinnaird, 1 Pall Mall, London, SW1Y 5AU Tel: (020) 7451 9400 Fax: (020) 7451 9401
T P L Logistics Management, Lakeside House, Hindhead Road, Haslemere, Surrey, GU27 3PJ Tel: (01252) 737939 Fax: (01252) 733474 E-mail: info@tpl-logistics-management.co.uk
▶ Talking Chalk Ltd, Eastwood House, Chalk Lane, East Horsley, Leatherhead, Surrey, KT24 6TH Tel: (0845) 6586914 Fax: (020) 7681 1332 E-mail: information@talkingchalk.co.uk
Taylor Clarke Partnership Ltd, 4 Fitzroy Place, Glasgow, G3 7RH Tel: 0141-221 1707 Fax: 0141-221 6266 E-mail: info@taylorclarke.co.uk
Tenon P.L.C., Sumner House, St. Thomass Road, Chorley, Lancashire, PR7 1HP Tel: (01257) 518000 Fax: (01257) 518001 E-mail: chorley@tenongroup.com
Thomson Partners Ltd, 14 Sandyford Place, Glasgow, G3 7NB Tel: 0141-248 3666 Fax: 0141-248 3404
Tmi, 50 High Street, Henley-in-Arden, West Midlands, B95 5AN Tel: (01527) 851741 Fax: (01527) 851777 E-mail: sales@tmi.co.uk
Towers Perrin, 71 High Holborn, London, WC1V 6TP Tel: (020) 7170 2000 Fax: (020) 7170 2222
Towers Perrin, 71 High Holborn, London, WC1V 6TP Tel: (020) 7170 2000 Fax: (020) 7170 2222
Transition Support Ltd, Vantage Point Business Village, 7/4, Mitcheldean, Gloucestershire, GL17 0DD Tel: (01594) 546151 Fax: (01594) 546153 E-mail: mail@transition-support.com
Turner & Coates Ltd, PO Box 91, Salford, M6 6XG Tel: (0845) 8909870 Fax: (0845) 8909871 E-mail: info@turnerandcoates.com
Turpin Smale Foodservice Consultancy, Blackfriars Foundry, 156 Blackfriars Road, London, SE1 8EN Tel: (020) 7620 0011 Fax: (0870) 141 0397 E-mail: chris.brown@turpinsmale.co.uk

MANAGEMENT INFORMATION PUBLICATIONS

Atex Media Command Ltd, Woodside House, Latimer, Chesham, Buckinghamshire, HP5 1UQ Tel: (01494) 546500 Fax: (01494) 766761 E-mail: info@atex.com
Cimtech, College Lane, Hatfield, Hertfordshire, AL10 9AB Tel: (01707) 281060 Fax: (01707) 281061 E-mail: c.cimtech@herts.ac.uk

MANAGEMENT INFORMATION SERVICES

Accurate Business Solutions Ltd, 80 Peach Street, Wokingham, Berkshire, RG40 1XH Tel: 0118-977 3880 Fax: 0118-977 1260 E-mail: info@accurate.co.uk
Communisis Security Products Ltd, Trafford Wharf Road, Trafford Park, Manchester, M17 1HE Tel: 0161-869 1000 Fax: 0161-869 1010
Esmerk, Thames Tower, Station Road, Reading, RG1 1LX Tel: 0118-956 5820 Fax: 0118-956 5850 E-mail: response@esmerk.com
Facet Publishing, 7 Ridgmount Street, London, WC1E 7AE Tel: (020) 7255 0594 Fax: (020) 7255 0591 E-mail: info@facetpublishing.co.uk
Glass's Information Services Ltd, 1 Princes Road, Weybridge, Surrey, KT13 9TU Tel: (01932) 823823 Fax: (01932) 846564 E-mail: enquiries@glass.co.uk
Imprint Business Systems Ltd, Poplars, High Easter, Chelmsford, CM1 4RB Tel: (01245) 231670 Fax: (01245) 231789 E-mail: sales@imprint-mis.co.uk
Infologistix Ltd, 4 Wesleyan Chapel Walk, Stapleford, Nottingham, NG9 8BQ Tel: 0115-939 9907 Fax: 0115-939 9117 E-mail: info@infologistix.co.uk
Printpak Ltd, Lacey House, Holly Road, Hampton Hill, Hampton, Middlesex, TW12 1QQ Tel: (020) 8941 0952 Fax: (020) 8979 9367 E-mail: sales@printpak.com
Williams Lea, Clifton House, 75-77 Worship Street, London, EC2A 2EJ Tel: (020) 7772 4400 Fax: (020) 7772 4468 E-mail: sales@williamslea.com

MANAGEMENT OUTPLACEMENT CONSULTANCY

H D A International, 4 Park Place, 12 Lawn Lane, Vauxhall, London, SW8 1UD Tel: (020) 7820 9199 Fax: (020) 7735 8175 E-mail: admin@hda.co.uk

MANAGEMENT SOLUTIONS SOFTWARE

Compelsolve Ltd, Bishops Court, Solihull Parkway, Birmingham Business Park, Birmingham, B37 7YD Tel: 0121-329 0200 Fax: 0121-329 0201 E-mail: birmingham.reception@compelsolve.com
▶ Hebron (UK) Ltd, Oxford Road, Yeovil, Somerset, BA21 5HR Tel: (01935) 403000 Fax: (01935) 403025 E-mail: info@hebron.co.uk
▶ Norton Waste Services, The Heath Business & Technical Park, Runcorn, Cheshire, WA7 4QX Tel: (01928) 511655 Fax: (01928) 511656 E-mail: enquires@mortongreen.com
Xilinx Ltd, Benchmark House, 203 Brooklands Road, Weybridge, Surrey, KT13 0RH Tel: (01932) 820821 Fax: (0870) 7350601 E-mail: sales@xilinx.com

MANAGEMENT TRAINING QUALIFICATIONS

▶ Barfil Management Centre, Barfil Farm, Crocketford, Dumfries, DG2 8RW Tel: (01387) 266079 Fax: (01387) 266118
▶ Creative Educationltd, 89 Sanderstead Road, South Croydon, Surrey, CR2 0PF Tel: (020) 8666 0234 Fax: (020) 8666 0414 E-mail: sales@creativeeducation.co.uk
Department Of Continuing Education, Lonsdale College, Bailrigg, Lancaster, LA1 4YN Tel: (01524) 592624 Fax: (01524) 592448 E-mail: managementlearning@lancaster.ac.uk
▶ Harris Management Training, Teviotbank Gardens, Denholm, Hawick, Roxburghshire, TD9 8PB Tel: (01450) 870688 Fax: (01450) 870688
▶ OCTG Procter, Peregrine Road, Westhill Business Park, Westhill, Aberdeen, AB32 6JL Tel: (01224) 748600 Fax: (01224) 746676
▶ Scottish Training Consultants, 28 Oldmill Crescent, Belmedie, Aberdeen, AB23 8WA Tel: (01358) 742470 Fax: (01358) 742775
▶ Christopher Swann, 408-410 Corn Exchange Building, Fenwick Street, Liverpool, L2 7QS Tel: (0845) 1259010 Fax: (0845) 1259014 E-mail: sales@christopherswann.com

MANAGEMENT TRAINING ROLEPLAY ACTOR HIRE

▶ R.C_Annie Ltd, 34 Pullman Place, Eltham, London, SE9 9EG Tel: (07811) 390313 Fax: (0802) 3782880 E-mail: ruth@arty-annie.com

MANAGEMENT TRAINING SPECIALISTS/SCHOOLS

Alison Hodge Associates, 12 Heathfield Gardens, London, W4 4JY Tel: (020) 8995 5485 Fax: (020) 8995 4341 E-mail: alisonhodge@dial.pipex.com
Answers Training International Ltd, Rose Lodge, Old Potbridge Road, Winchfield, Hook, Hampshire, RG27 8BT Tel: (01252) 845500 Fax: (01252) 845585 E-mail: info@answers-group.com
Marcus Bohn Associates Ltd, Studio House, Delamare Road, Cheshunt, Waltham Cross, Hertfordshire, EN8 9SH Tel: (01992) 633882 Fax: (01992) 627831 E-mail: sales@marcusbohn.co.uk
C G Resources Ltd, 62 Wellington Street West, Broughton, Manchester, M7 2FD Tel: 0161-792 8234 Fax: 0161-792 7080 E-mail: enq@cgresources.com
▶ Cambridge Online Learning Ltd, Barnsley Business & Innovation Centre, Innovation Way, Barnsley, South Yorkshire, S75 1JL Tel: (01226) 321717 Fax: (01226) 290888 E-mail: info@cambridge-online-learning.co.uk
Catalyst, 175 Tottenham Court Road, London, W1T 7NU Tel: (020) 7436 3636 Fax: (020) 7580 7449 E-mail: newbuisness@cgsuk.com
Cert Consultancy & Training, Dairy Farm, Little Gringley, Retford, Nottinghamshire, DN22 0DU Tel: (01777) 860835 Fax: (01777) 702353 E-mail: cert@certuk.com
Charnwood Management Centre Ltd, 175 Birchwood Lane, Somercotes, Alfreton, Derbyshire, DE55 4NF Tel: (01773) 606606 Fax: (01773) 606606 E-mail: sales@thecharnwoodgroup.com
Chartwell Learning & Development Ltd, Old Orchard, Bickley Road, Bromley, BR1 2NE Tel: (020) 8467 1956 Fax: (020) 8467 1754 E-mail: info@chartwell-learn.co.uk
Cullen Scholefield Ltd, Maxwelton House, 41 Boltro Road, Haywards Heath, West Sussex, RH16 1BJ Tel: (01444) 455052 Fax: (01444) 459221 E-mail: enquiries@csgconsult.com
Dale Carnegie Training, 1200 Century Way, Thorpe Park, Leeds, LS15 8ZA Tel: 0113-251 5116
Department Of Continuing Education, Lonsdale College, Bailrigg, Lancaster, LA1 4YN Tel: (01524) 592624 Fax: (01524) 592448 E-mail: managementlearning@lancaster.ac.uk
Development Associates Group Ltd, Blenheim House, Fitzalan Court, Cardiff, CF24 0TN Tel: (029) 2049 2773 Fax: (029) 2026 4505
Development Dimensions International Ltd, B Sefton Park, Bells Hill, Stokes Poges, Slough, SL2 4JS Tel: (01753) 616000 Fax: (01753) 616099 E-mail: info@ddi-europe.com
Executive Development, Fairlawns, Normans Green, Plymtree, Cullompton, Devon, EX15 2LA Tel: (01884) 277122 Fax: (01884) 277122 E-mail: info@execdevelop.com
Gustav Kaser Training International Ltd, Essex House, 118 High Street, Ongar, Essex, CM5 9EB Tel: (01277) 365335 Fax: (01277) 365277 E-mail: sales@gustavkaeser.com
Hadley Park Training, 163 Hadley Park Road, Leegomery, Telford, Shropshire, TF1 6QF Tel: (01952) 257343 Fax: (01952) 257343 E-mail: maggiepoole1@aol.com
▶ J S B Training & Consulting, Dove House, Arcadia Avenue, London, N3 2JU Tel: (020) 8371 7000 Fax: (020) 8371 7001 E-mail: enquiries@jsbonline.com
LCT, 7 Acorn Mews, Harlow, Essex, CM18 6NA Tel: (01279) 411331 Fax: (01279) 412864 E-mail: sales@lctinternational.com
The Leadership Trust Training Ltd, Weston Under Penyard, Weston under Penyard, Ross-on-Wye, Herefordshire, HR9 7YH Tel: (01667) 455811 Fax: (01989) 768133 E-mail: enquiries@leadership.co.uk
▶ M H L Corrporate, Claremont CR, Edinburgh, EH7 4HX Tel: 0131-557 4633
Mantra Consultancy Group, 25 Ellington Street, London, N7 8PN Tel: (020) 7609 9055 Fax: (020) 7609 9447
Maritech Consultants Ltd, 10 South Quay, Great Yarmouth, Norfolk, NR30 2QH Tel: (01493) 331822 Fax: (01493) 331687 E-mail: sales@maritech.co.uk
Mast International Group plc, Hermitage House, Bath Road, Taplow, Maidenhead, Berkshire, SL6 0AR Tel: (01628) 784062 Fax: (01628) 773061 E-mail: info@mast.co.uk
New College, New College Drive, Swindon, SN3 1AH Tel: (01793) 436437 Fax: (01793) 436437E-mail: admissions@newcollege.ac.uk
▶ Oxford Management College, Eynsham Hall, North Leigh, Witney, Oxfordshire, OX29 6PN Tel: (01865) 514106 Fax: (01993) 883986 E-mail: info@oxfordmanagementcollege.com
Partners In Training Ltd, 8 Marsden Park, York, YO30 4GX Tel: (01904) 691777 Fax: (01904) 691102 E-mail: info@pint.co.uk
Paul Temple Associates Ltd, Laurel Cottage, 15a Hillside Road, Haslemere, Surrey, GU27 3RL Tel: (01428) 656150 Fax: (01428) 642676 E-mail: paul@paultempleassociates.com
▶ Primary Tuition, 40 Gilderdale Close, Birchwood, Warrington, WA3 6TH Tel: (01925) 821995 E-mail: mary@cottam.freeserve.co.uk
Roffey Park Institute, Forest Road, Colgate, Horsham, West Sussex, RH12 4TD Tel: (01293) 851644 Fax: (01293) 851565 E-mail: sales@roffeypark.com
Scottish Enterprise Dunbartonshire, Spectrum House, 1a North Avenue, Clydebank Business Park, Clydebank, Dunbartonshire, G81 2DR Tel: 0141-951 2121 Fax: 0141-951 1907 E-mail: dunbartonshire@scotent.co.uk
Sigta Ltd, 26 Abinger Road, Portslade, Brighton, BN41 1RZ Tel: (01273) 420029 Fax: (01273) 423982 E-mail: sales@sigta.co.uk
Smallpiece Enterprises, 27 Newbold Terrace, Leamington Spa, Warwickshire, CV32 4ES Tel: (01926) 336423 Fax: (01926) 450679 E-mail: train@smallpeice.co.uk
▶ Spence Associates, 41 Francis Gardens, Winchester, Hampshire, SO23 7HD Tel: (01962) 867425 Fax: (01962) 841425 E-mail: sales@spencea.com

MANAGEMENT/EXECUTIVE SELECTION RECRUITMENT AGENCIES/CONSULTANTS/ SERVICES

Adamson & Partners Ltd, 10 Lisbon Square, Leeds, LS1 4LY Tel: 0113-245 1212 Fax: 0113-242 0802 E-mail: stuart.adamson@adamsons.com
▶ Alexander James Executive Search Ltd, Winslow House, 16 Rumford Court, Rumford Place, Liverpool, L3 9DG Tel: 0151 236 1875 Fax: 0151 258 2018 E-mail: info@alexanderjamesltd.co.uk
James Allen & Associates, PO Box 8, York, YO41 4YE Tel: (01904) 607227 Fax: (01904) 607337 E-mail: james_allen.associates@lineone.net
▶ Altmore General Recruitment, Office 15 Townsend Enterprise Park, 28 Townsend Street, Belfast, BT13 2ES Tel: (028) 9032 8411 Fax: (028) 9032 8400 E-mail: cr@altmore.co.uk
Deven Anderson Ltd, George House, 121 High Street, Henley-in-Arden, West Midlands, B95 5AU Tel: (01564) 795565 Fax: (01564) 795122 E-mail: headhunt@devenanderson.co.uk
Angela Mortimer plc, 37-38 Golden Square, London, W1F 9LA Tel: (020) 7287 7788 Fax: (020) 7470 5578 E-mail: name.surname@angelamortimer.com
Ashbrittle Ltd, Ashbrittle House, Lower Dagnall Street, St. Albans, Hertfordshire, AL3 4PA Tel: (01727) 854054 Fax: (01727) 865557 E-mail: mail@ashbrittle.com
▶ Baldock Advanced Motorcycle Training, 31 Bush Spring, Baldock, Hertfordshire, SG7 6QT Tel: (01462) 641775 Fax: (0871) 4335485 E-mail: tclarke@evprecruit.com
Bullus & Co., Rumbolds House, Hammonds Road, Sandon, Chelmsford, CM2 7RS Tel: (01245) 474035 Fax: (01245) 477175 E-mail: search@bullus.co.uk
C C G Corporate Consulting Group Ltd, 24 Buckingham Gate, London, SW1E 6LB Tel: (020) 7828 1123 Fax: (020) 8828 2604 E-mail: info@ccg.co.uk
▶ Call Centre Recruitment Experts Ltd, Greyfriars Chambers, Greyfriars, Bedford, MK40 1HJ Tel: (01234) 400233 Fax: (01234) 272155 E-mail: sian@callrecruit.co.uk
Careers In Design Recruitment Ltd, 28 New Road, Ware, Hertfordshire, SG12 7BU Tel: (01920) 486125 Fax: (01920) 412599 E-mail: recruit@careersindesign.com
▶ Cathedral Appointments, 33 Southernhay East, Exeter, EX1 1NX Tel: (01392) 413577 Fax: (01392) 425690 E-mail: sales@cathedralappointments.co.uk
Charnwood Management Centre Ltd, 175 Birchwood Lane, Somercotes, Alfreton, Derbyshire, DE55 4NF Tel: (01773) 606606 Fax: (01773) 606606 E-mail: sales@thecharnwoodgroup.com
Christopher Beale Associates Ltd, 14 Queen Anne's Gate, London, SW1H 9AA Tel: (020) 7976 7701 Fax: (020) 7976 7265
Concept Staffing Ltd, 11 Boutport Street, Barnstaple, Devon, EX31 1RW Tel: (01271) 321666 Fax: (01271) 326280 E-mail: headoffice@conceptstaffing.co.uk
Connaught Partners Ltd, 111 Hagley Road, Birmingham, B16 8LB Tel: 0121-452 5117 Fax: 0121-452 5118 E-mail: sales@connaughtpartners.com
Courtenay Stewart Ltd, 3 Hanover Square, London, W1S 1HB Tel: (0871) 2227616 Fax: (0871) 2227626 E-mail: sales@courtenayhr.com
Digital Video Interview Services, The City Arc, Curtain Court, 7 Curtain Road, London, EC2A 3LT Tel: 0207 1009270 Fax: 0207 1009310 E-mail: info@digitalvideointerview.co.uk
Diligencia Ltd, The Maltings, 100 Wilderspool Causeway, Warrington, WA4 6PU Tel: (01925) 241444 Fax: (01925) 241666 E-mail: info@diligencia.co.uk
E G Recruitment Ltd, 56 Meldon Terrace, Newbiggin-by-the-Sea, Northumberland, NE64 6XH Tel: (01670) 858834 Fax: (01865) 400166 E-mail: eddie@egrecruitment.co.uk
Executives Online, Dolphin House, St. Peter Street, Winchester, Hampshire, SO23 8BW Tel: (01962) 829705 Fax: (01962) 866116 E-mail: info@executivesonline.co.uk
▶ Firth Ross Martin, 7 Castle Street, Edinburgh, EH2 3AH Tel: 0131-220 6669 Fax: 0131-225 8180
▶ Global Automotive Recruitment, 28 Springbourne Court, Beckenham, Kent, BR3 5ED Tel: (0845) 330 9317 Fax: (0845) 330 9318 E-mail: info@garecruitment.com
Global Executives Ltd, 18 Stoneleigh Court, Frimley, Camberley, Surrey, GU16 8XH Tel: (01276) 671535 Fax: (01276) 671536 E-mail: sales@globalexecutives.com
Helix Recruitment Limited, George Street, Hailsham, East Sussex, BN27 1AD Tel: (01323) 445464 Fax: (01323) 440814 E-mail: kelly@helixrecruitment.co.uk
Highfield Human Solutions Ltd, 1 London Road, Newbury, Berkshire, RG14 1JL Tel: (01635) 33923 Fax: (01635) 38837 E-mail: admin@highfielduk.co.uk
▶ HighVeld Select, P O Box 196, Morpeth, Northumberland, NE61 6WQ Tel: (01670) 789965
Horizon Recruitment Ltd, 6 Piccadilly, Bradford, West Yorkshire, BD1 3LW Tel: (01274) 744991 Fax: (01274) 744992
Human Factors International, 8 Staple Inn, London, WC1V 7QH Tel: (020) 7831 3123 Fax: (020) 7831 8643 E-mail: mail@humanfactors.co.uk
Paul Kiernan Associates Ltd, PO Box 120, London, SW3 4LU Tel: (020) 7352 5562
▶ Grant Lawson Ltd, Albany House, 14 Shute End, Wokingham, Berkshire, RG40 1BJ Tel: 0118-979 6023 Fax: (07092) 382965
Listgrove Ltd, 16 The Courtyard, Timothys Bridge Road, Stratford-upon-Avon, Warwickshire, CV37 9NP Tel: (01789) 207070 Fax: (01789) 207096 E-mail: contact@listgrove.co.uk
Lloyds TSB Autolease Ltd, Blake House, Hatchford Way, Birmingham, B26 3RZ Tel: (0870) 6006333 Fax: 0121-700 6030
Motor Trade Selection, Parkway House, Sheen Lane, London, SW14 8LS Tel: (020) 8392 1818 Fax: (020) 8876 4631 E-mail: recruit@mtselect.co.uk
Non Executive Directorship Exchange, Hurst House, City Road, Radnage, High Wycombe, Buckinghamshire, HP14 4DW Tel: (01494) 483728 E-mail: nedexchange@netscape.net
Orion Engineering Services Ltd, 21 Albert Street, Aberdeen, AB25 1XX Tel: (01224) 632121 Fax: (01224) 640046 E-mail: abz@orioneng.co.uk
P S D Contracts Ltd, 28 Essex Street, London, WC2R 3AT Tel: (020) 7970 9700 Fax: (020) 7936 3976
Pamela Neave, 18 St. Augustines Parade, Bristol, BS1 4UL Tel: 0117-921 1831 Fax: 0117-925 1019 E-mail: enquiries@pamela-neave.co.uk
Pendleton Consultants Ltd, Stuart House, The Back, Chepstow, Gwent, NP16 5HH Tel: (01291) 620290 Fax: (01291) 628030 E-mail: mlp@pendleton-consultants.co.uk
Penna plc, Regent Arcade House, 19-25 Argyll Street, London, W1F 7TS Tel: (020) 7663 6633 Fax: (020) 7663 7261 E-mail: londonwest@e-penna.com

MANAGEMENT/EXECUTIVE SELECTION RECRUITMENT AGENCIES/CONSULTANTS/ SERVICES – *continued*

People & Property Ltd, 18 Coulson Street, London, SW3 3NB Tel: (020) 7225 1313 Fax: (020) 7225 2765 E-mail: peopleandproperty@btinternet.com

Redford Cairns Ltd, PO Box 17252, London, SE19 3ZN Tel: (020) 8653 6365 Fax: (020) 8653 1001 E-mail: rrcl@redfordcairns.com

Rochester Partnership Ltd, 7 St Helens Place, London, EC3A 6AU Tel: (020) 7256 9000 Fax: (020) 7256 9111

Russam G M S Ltd, 48 High St North, Dunstable, Bedfordshire, LU6 1LA Tel: (01582) 666970 Fax: (01582) 471757 E-mail: hq@russam-gms.co.uk

Russell Reynolds Associates Inc, 24 St James's Square, London, SW1Y 4HZ Tel: (020) 7839 7788 Fax: (020) 7839 9295

Salesvacancies.Com, Charter House, Unit 1 South Bourne Business Park, Eastbourne, East Sussex, BN22 8UY Tel: (01323) 739995 Fax: (01323) 721990 E-mail: sales@salesvacancies.com

Sciteb Ltd, 18 Newton Man, Queens Club Gardens, London, W14 9RR Tel: (020) 7381 1481 Fax: (020) 7499 9253 E-mail: nicholas.beale@sciteb.com

▶ Search & Supply Recruitment, The Sanctuary, Shelley Close, Armitage, Staffordshire, WS15 4UW Tel: 01543 304583 Fax: 01543 304583 E-mail: enquiry@searchandsupply.co.uk

Star Executives Ltd, 7 Fitz Roy Mews, London, W1T 6DQ Tel: (020) 7387 6999 Fax: (020) 7387 6999 E-mail: info@starexecutives.com

▶ Stephens Associates, 14 Buckingham Street, London, WC2N 6DF Tel: (020) 7925 0200 Fax: (020) 7925 0235 E-mail: stephens@stephens.co.uk

▶ Talking Chalk Ltd, Eastwood House, Chalk Lane, East Horsley, Leatherhead, Surrey, KT24 6TH Tel: (0845) 6586914 Fax: (020) 7681 1332 E-mail: information@talkingchalk.co.uk

Technology Project Services International Ltd, 1 Warwick Row, London, SW1E 5ER Tel: (020) 7963 1234 Fax: (020) 7963 1299 E-mail: mail@tps.co.uk

▶ Technology Resourcing, Unit 29, Surrey Technology Centre, Occam Road, Guildford, Surrey, GU2 7YG Tel: (01483) 302211 Fax: (01483) 301222 E-mail: recruit@tech-res.co.uk

John Thompson Associates Ltd, Compton House, 20 Selsdon Road, South Croydon, Surrey, CR2 6PA Tel: (020) 7378 6884 Fax: (020) 8680 9773 E-mail: compton@tal-hwt.co.uk

Tyzack Associates Ltd, Medius House, 2 Sheraton Street, London, W1F 8BH Tel: (020) 7758 4000 Fax: (020) 7758 4001 E-mail: info@tyzackassociates.com

Ward Executive Ltd, High Street, Epsom, Surrey, KT19 8EH Tel: (020) 8332 0555 Fax: (020) 8405 7701 E-mail: ward@wardexec.co.uk

▶ WayGoose, 45 Skylines Village, Limeharbour, London, E14 9TS Tel: (020) 7537 0700 Fax: (020) 7515 4545 E-mail: info@waygoose.com

Whitehead Man G K R & Associates, Queensbury House, 3 Old Burlington Street, London, W1S 3AE Tel: (020) 7534 0000 Fax: (020) 7290 2050 E-mail: mail@wmann.com

Jonathan Wren & Co. Ltd, 34 London Wall, London, EC2M 5RU Tel: (020) 7309 3550 Fax: (020) 7309 3552 E-mail: career@jwren.com

MANEGE MANAGER EQUESTRIAN ARENA LEVELLERS

▶ Maple Arenas, 41 Newlands Road, Riddings, Alfreton, Derbyshire, DE55 4EQ Tel: (01773) 606068 Fax: (01773) 606068 E-mail: info@maneges.co.uk

MANGANESE STEEL PLATE

Universal Steel, 9 Lindholme Gardens, Owlthorpe, Sheffield, S20 6TD Tel: (07870) 575523 Fax: 0114-248 4139 E-mail: peterjwatters@tiscali.co.uk

MANHOLE COVERS OR FRAMES, *See also headings for particular types*

▶ Arcova Manhole Cover Manufacturers, Willow Tree Farm, Main Street, Laneham, Retford, Nottinghamshire, DN22 0NG Tel: (01777) 228931 Fax: (01777) 228504 E-mail: sales@arcova.co.uk

▶ Fibresec Holdings Ltd, Unit 2, Snaygill Industrial Estate, Keighley, Skipton, North Yorkshire, BD23 2QR Tel: (01756) 799822

MANHOLE LIDS/HATCHES, TANKER ETC

Progressive Engineers Ltd, Groby Road, Audenshaw, Manchester, M34 5HT Tel: 0161-371 0440 Fax: 0161-371 0444 E-mail: info@progressive-eng.com

MANHOLE SHUTTER SYSTEMS

Industrial Encoders Direct Ltd, D1 Dutton Road, Redwither Business Park, Wrexham, Clwyd, LL13 9UL Tel: (01978) 664722 Fax: (01978) 664733 E-mail: sales@industrialencodersdirect.co.uk

MANICURE PRODUCTS

▶ The Beauty Preference, 33 Lyon Close, Maidenbower, Crawley, West Sussex, RH10 7ND Tel: (01293) 883716 E-mail: rose@beautypref.com

▶ Chakir Hairdressing, 62 High Street, Linlithgow, West Lothian, EH49 7AQ Tel: (01506) 671800 E-mail: info@chakirhair.co.uk

MANIFOLD VALVES

▶ Alco Valves Ltd, Mission Works, Birds Royd Lane, Brighouse, West Yorkshire, HD6 1LQ Tel: 01484 710511 Fax: 01484 713009 E-mail: uk@alco-valves.com

MANIFOLDS, *See also headings for particular types*

▶ Rovtech Ltd, Rovtech House Cothal View Kirkton Avenue, Pitmedden Industrial Estate, Dyce, Aberdeen, AB21 0BA Tel: (01224) 775527 Fax: (01224) 775547

Siemens V D O Automotive Systems, Halesfield 25, Telford, Shropshire, TF7 4LP Tel: (01952) 683600 Fax: (01952) 580626 E-mail: sales@siemens.auto.com

MANIPULATORS

▶ Cyba Manufacturing Technology Ltd, Unit 5 Hattersely Industrial, Estate Stockport Road, Hyde, Cheshire, SK14 3QT Tel: 0161-367 8789 Fax: 0161-367 8785 E-mail: info@cybamantech.co.uk

Dalmek Ltd, 2 Ringway Centre, Edisin Road, Basingstoke, Hampshire, RG21 6YH Tel: (01256) 814420 Fax: (01256) 814434 E-mail: info@dalmecltd.co.uk

MANOMETERS

Abbirko UK Ltd, 4 Manor Works, Station Road South, Totton, Southampton, SO40 9HP Tel: (023) 8066 8833 Fax: (023) 8066 7777 E-mail: sales@abbirko.co.uk

Poddymeter Ltd, Unit 2 Park Works, Borough Road, Kingston Upon Thames, Surrey, KT2 6BD Tel: (020) 8546 9311 Fax: (020) 8547 2325 E-mail: poddy.ltd@virgin.net

MANUAL BREAK GLASS FIRE ALARM CALL POINTS

Fulleon, Llantarnam Industrial Park, Cwmbran, Gwent, NP44 3AW Tel: (01633) 628500 Fax: (01633) 866346 E-mail: sales@fulleon.co.uk

Kac Alarm Co. Ltd, Kac House, Thorn Hill Road, Moons Moat North Industrial Es, Redditch, Worcestershire, B98 9ND Tel: (01527) 406655 Fax: (01527) 406677 E-mail: marketing@kac.co.uk

MANUAL DISPENSING SYRINGE GUNS

Kaycee Veterinary Products, Unit 14 Lindfield Enterprise Park, Lewes Road, Lindfield, Haywards Heath, West Sussex, RH16 2LH Tel: (01444) 482888 Fax: (01444) 483383 E-mail: tds@kaycee.co.uk

MANUAL LASER MARKING MACHINES AND SYSTEMS

H K Technologies Ltd, Unit 7 Hadrians Way, Glebe Farm Industrial Estate, Rugby, Warwickshire, CV21 1ST Tel: (01788) 577288 Fax: (01788) 562808 E-mail: admin@hktechnologies.com

MANUAL METAL ARC (MMA) WELDING EQUIPMENT

Migatronic Welding Equipment Ltd, 21 Jubilee Drive, Loughborough, Leicestershire, LE11 5XS Tel: (01509) 211492 Fax: (01509) 231959 E-mail: sales@migatronic.co.uk

MANUAL METAL ARC (MMA) WELDING INVERTER HIRE

▶ Welder Equipment Services Ltd, Redfield Road, Lenton Lane Industrial Estate, Nottingham, NG7 2UJ Tel: 0115-986 8181 Fax: 0115-985 1936

MANUAL OR HAND WIND CABLE REELING DRUMS OR REELS

Jo-El Electric Ltd, Stafford Park 5, Telford, Shropshire, TF3 3AS Tel: (01952) 209001 Fax: (01952) 238090 E-mail: info@jo-el.com

T E L Engineering Ltd, Newby Road, Hazel Grove, Stockport, Cheshire, SK7 5DA Tel: 0161-456 6545 Fax: 0161-456 3810 E-mail: mail@trolexengineering.co.uk

Youldon, 7 West Road, Harlow, Essex, CM20 2BU Tel: (01279) 774300 Fax: (01279) 774310 E-mail: sales@collins-youldon.com

MANUAL OR HAND WIND HOSE REELS

Fluid Transfer Ltd, Nailsworth Mills Estate, Avening Road, Nailsworth, Stroud, Gloucestershire, GL6 0BT Tel: (01453) 833381 Fax: (01453) 833529 E-mail: sales@fluid-transfer.co.uk

Haselden Manufacturing Co., PO Box 349A, Surbiton, Surrey, KT5 9YG Tel: (020) 8337 7284 Fax: (020) 8337 7284

MANUAL PAINT SPRAY GUNS

Airbrush Co Ltd, 7 Marlborough Road, Lancing, West Sussex, BN15 8UF Tel: (0870) 0660445 Fax: (08700) 660817 E-mail: sales@airbrushes.com

MANUALLY OPERATED HANDLING EQUIPMENT

Oak Industrial Supplies, Hamilton Road, Sutton-in-Ashfield, Nottinghamshire, NG17 5LN Tel: (01623) 442222 Fax: (01623) 441234 E-mail: sales@oakis.co.uk

MANUALLY OPERATED HYDRAULIC VALVES

Hi-Press Hydraulics Ltd, Riverside Works, Forge Road, Whaley Bridge, High Peak, Derbyshire, SK23 7HY Tel: (01663) 735089 Fax: (01663) 735090 E-mail: sales@hi-press.co.uk

MANUFACTURERS' AGENTS/ REPRESENTATIVES

3m UK plc, Gorseinon Road, Penllergaer, Swansea, SA4 9GD Tel: (01792) 893021 Fax: (01792) 890427

A C S Thermal Engineers Ltd, 264 Trafford Road, Eccles, Manchester, M30 0JJ Tel: 0161-787 9084 Fax: 0161-787 9116 E-mail: a.c.s.@thermal.com

Allied Wall Ties, Blade Works, Marriner Road, Keighley, West Yorkshire, BD21 5LW Tel: (01535) 690555 Fax: (01535) 606031

Atlantis Trading Co, Unit 12 Workplace, Highfield Street, Coalville, Leicestershire, LE67 3BZ Tel: (01530) 830840 Fax: (01530) 830850 E-mail: info@atlantisclassics.co.uk

Aurum Ltd, 1A Crab La, New Invention, Willenhall, W. Midlands, WV12 5BJ Tel: (01922) 404394 Fax: (01922) 338212

Bartholomew C & Son Ltd, 15 Hatton Place, London, EC1N 8RU Tel: (020) 7405 9557 Fax: (020) 7404 4706

Beeversales Components Ltd, Aurillac Way, Retford, Nottinghamshire, DN22 7PX Tel: (01777) 700611 Fax: (01777) 701799 E-mail: sales@beeversales.com

Big Egg Designs, 1 Parade Mews, Norwood Road, London, SE27 9AX Tel: (020) 8674 3600 Fax: (020) 8674 3600

Bowling Finishing Services Ltd, Bowling Mill, Lonsdale Street, Nelson, Lancashire, BB9 9HQ Tel: (01282) 612336

British Bakeries Ltd, Belmont Road, Erith, Kent, DA8 1JZ Tel: (01322) 341144 Fax: (01322) 350249

BW Plastics Ltd, Acton Holdings, Long Lane, Essington, Wolverhampton, WV11 2AA Tel: (01922) 405114 Fax: (01922) 405114

Chase Manufacturing Ltd, Unit 52 Enterprise Way, Newport, Gwent, NP20 2AQ Tel: (01633) 841088 Fax: (01633) 243087 E-mail: sales@chaseladders.co.uk

Citibase Ltd, 100 Wellington Street, Leeds, LS1 4LT Tel: 0113-242 2444 Fax: 0113-242 2433 E-mail: leeds.ws@citibase.co.uk

Cobolt Systems Ltd, Mill Road, Reedham, Norwich, NR13 3TL Tel: (01493) 700172 Fax: (01493) 701037 E-mail: cobolt@compusreve.co.uk

Corenso UK Ltd, Corenso House, 2 Patriot Drive, Rooksley, Milton Keynes, MK13 8LN Tel: (01908) 678111 Fax: (01908) 690067

Corus Ltd, Ashorne Hill Management College, Ashorne Hill, Leamington Spa, Warwickshire, CV33 9PY Tel: (01926) 488029 Fax: (01926) 488024

Direct Commissioning Services, 8 Ashfields, Loughton, Essex, IG10 1SB Tel: (020) 8418 9996 Fax: (020) 8418 9914 E-mail: directcommissioning@btinternet.com

Dominic Evans Electronics, Woodhall Farm, Fox Lane, Kempsey, Worcester, WR5 3QD Tel: (01905) 820860

Equinomic Products Ltd, Passfield House Farm, Headley Lane, Passfield, Liphook, Hampshire, GU30 7RN Tel: (01428) 751110 Fax: (01428) 751140

European Infopoint Ltd, Premier House, 11 Marlborough Place, Brighton, BN1 1UB Tel: (01273) 608311 Fax: (01273) 609040 E-mail: kelly@premier-house.com

Fastsigns, 630-642 Chesterfield Road, Sheffield, S8 0SA Tel: 0114-255 2553 Fax: 0114-258 8444

Fibretek UK Ltd, Brick Kiln Lane, Long Stratton, Norwich, NR15 2LH Tel: (01508) 473077 Fax: (01508) 471377 E-mail: sales@fibretekuk.co.uk

Forum Executive Bureau Ltd, Orwell House, Cowley Road, Cambridge, CB4 0PP Tel: (01223) 506850 Fax: (01223) 420251 E-mail: info@forumexecutive.com

G Pack Manufacturing Ltd, 1 The Green, Glossop, Derbyshire, SK13 6LT Tel: (01457) 858535

George Barker & Co Leeds Ltd, Highfield Works, Highfield Road, Idle, Bradford, West Yorkshire, BD10 8RF Tel: (01274) 703200 Fax: (01274) 615916

Gillian & Baines, Common Lane, Knottingley, West Yorkshire, WF11 8BN Tel: (01977) 672322 Fax: (01977) 677088

Glass Fibre Workshop Ltd, Unit 2 Drury Square, Beeston, King's Lynn, Norfolk, PE32 2NA Tel: (01328) 701901 Fax: (01328) 701196

Goodman (Direct Marketing) Ltd, 37 Blenheim Terrace, London, NW8 0EJ Tel: (020) 7328 3961 Fax: (020) 7328 3962 E-mail: peter_gdm@btinternet.com

Robert Hellin Ltd, 5 Mill Street, London, W1S 2AY Tel: (020) 7499 5777 Fax: (020) 7409 2727

High Oak Auto Salvage, High Oak Works, High Oak Road, Wicklewood, Wymondham, Norfolk, NR18 9QP Tel: (01953) 601156 Fax: (01953) 601156

Intellect, Russell Square House, 10-12 Russell Square, London, WC1B 5EE Tel: (020) 7331 2000 Fax: (020) 7331 2040 E-mail: info@intellectuk.org

Interspace Communications Ltd, Fourth Floor Trafalgar House, 11 Waterloo Place, London, SW1Y 4AU Tel: (020) 7930 8001 Fax: (020) 7930 0465 E-mail: isclon@msn.com

Isca, Unit 29 Nine Mile Point Industrial Estate, Ynysddu, Newport, Gwent, NP11 7HZ Tel: (01495) 200747 Fax: (01495) 200757 E-mail: kharris@iscauk.com

J F Payne, Enterprise House, Herbert Road, Newport, Gwent, NP19 7BH Tel: (01633) 223959 Fax: (01633) 266927 E-mail: jfp@ukonline.co.uk

J K (England) Ltd, Third Floor Walmar House, 296 Regent St, London, W1B 3AW Tel: (020) 7255 1900 Fax: (020) 7255 1991 E-mail: jke@jkengland.u-net.com

J & T Partnership, Red House Barn, Mickfield Road, Stownham Aspal, Stowmarket, Suffolk, IP14 5LT Tel: (01449) 711010 Fax: (01449) 711010

Cliff Jackson, 97 Cottage Lane, Ormskirk, Lancashire, L39 3NF Tel: (07946) 434999 Fax: (01695) 571114 E-mail: cliffjackson@btinternet.com

Jays Of Yorkshire, Green Lane, Featherstone, Pontefract, West Yorkshire, WF7 6EH Tel: (01977) 792431 Fax: (01977) 600334 E-mail: info@jaysofyorkshire.co.uk

Jersey Farmers (Trading) Union Ltd, 20 Commercial Buildings, St. Helier, Jersey, JE2 3NB Tel: (01534) 733277 Fax: (01534) 768916 E-mail: jstusth@jasonmiles.co.uk

Kings Worldwide Ltd, 34 Junction Rd, London, N19 5RE Tel: (020) 7263 0963 Fax: (020) 7281 3966 E-mail: info@kingsww.com

L & P Springs UK Ltd, Ravenscroft Way, Barnoldswick, Lancashire, BB18 6JA Tel: (01282) 814054 Fax: (01282) 814064 E-mail: sales@leggett.com

J.B. Landers, 6 Stonebridge Centre, 51 Rangemoor Rd, London, N15 4LP Tel: (020) 8808 0066 Fax: (020) 8808 0066

Mondy Packaging & Bromborough, Old Hall Industrial Estate, Wirral, Merseyside, CH62 3QH Tel: 0151-334 1060 Fax: 0151-334 4443

Monton Fencing Ltd, Montonfields Road, Eccles, Manchester, M30 8AW Tel: 0161-788 7838 Fax: 0161-707 5525

▶ indicates data change since last edition

MANUFACTURERS' AGENTS/ REPRESENTATIVES – *continued*

MRI Polytech P.L.C., Nab Works, Long Lane, Pott Shrigley, Macclesfield, Cheshire, SK10 5SD Tel: (01625) 575737 Fax: (01625) 575720 E-mail: karen@mri-polytech.com
Norton Castings, 18 Oaklands, Old Buckenham, Attleborough, Norfolk, NR17 1SA Tel: (01953) 860998 Fax: (01953) 860998 E-mail: enquiries@nortoncastings.co.uk
Nottage Forge, 4 Locks Lane, Nottage, Porthcawl, Mid Glamorgan, CF36 3HY Tel: (01656) 783180
Octopus Instruments Ltd, 2 Sussex Street, Bedale, North Yorkshire, DL8 2AJ Tel: (01677) 424213 Fax: (01677) 424597 E-mail: peter@octopus-instruments.co.uk
Penclawdd Forge, Station Square, Penclawdd, Swansea, SA4 3XT Tel: (01792) 850124 Fax: (01792) 416267
Phill's Model Shop, 41-42 Nile Street, North Shields, Tyne & Wear, NE29 0BB Tel: 0191-272 8443 Fax: 0191-272 8443 E-mail: sales@phillsmodels.com
Powys Windows, 1 Enterprise Works, Trawsffordd Road, Ystradgynlais, Swansea, SA9 1BS Tel: (01639) 849243 Fax: (01639) 849243
Products To Europe Ltd, The Office On The Green, Wraysbury, Staines, Middlesex, TW19 5NA Tel: (01784) 488400 Fax: (01784) 488401
Race Products, Unit 1 Parkview, Gallamore Lane Industrial Estate, Market Rasen, Lincolnshire, LN8 3HZ Tel: (01673) 842704 Fax: (01673) 842470 E-mail: raceproducts@aol.com
Right Track Ltd, 15 34 Union Road, Macclesfield, Cheshire, SK11 7BN Tel: (01625) 618581 Fax: (01625) 616586 E-mail: right@tract1534.freeserve.co.uk
Ro Dor Ltd, Stevens Drove, Houghton, Stockbridge, Hampshire, SO20 6LP Tel: (01794) 388080 Fax: (01794) 388090 E-mail: info@ro-dor.co.uk
Rushall Protective Clothing Co. Ltd, 501 Bloxwich Road, Walsall, WS3 2XA Tel: (01922) 710055 Fax: (01922) 407885
S K B Sails, The Sail Loft, Commercial Road, Penryn, Cornwall, TR10 8AG Tel: (01326) 372107 Fax: (01326) 373792
S T S Signals Ltd, Unit 2 Teilo Works, Tyn Y Bonau Road, Pontarddulais, Swansea, SA4 8SA Tel: (01792) 885995 Fax: (01792) 885913
Sca Packaging Exeter, Kingfisher Way, Sowton Industrial Estate, Exeter, EX2 7LE Tel: (01392) 445141 Fax: (01392) 445125 E-mail: sales@scapackaging.co.uk
Simon West Interiors Ltd, Hendon Street, Sunderland, SR1 2NF Tel: 0191-514 3052 Fax: 0191-514 1989
Smurfit Corrugated, Lattersey Hill Trading Estate, Benwick Road, Whittlesey, Peterborough, PE7 2JA Tel: (01733) 206050 Fax: (01733) 202770 E-mail: mike.dench@smurfitkappa.co.uk
Somar International Ltd, Somar House, Heron Way, Newham, Truro, Cornwall, TR1 2XN Tel: (01872) 223000 Fax: (01872) 264325 E-mail: enquiries@somar.co.uk
South West Business Centre Ltd, Queensgate House, 48 Queen Street, Exeter, EX4 3SR Tel: (01392) 215541 Fax: (01392) 410436 E-mail: mpurton@swbus.co.uk
Stackright Services Ltd, P O Box 456, Derby, DE24 8UP Tel: 0870 428 2479 Fax: 01332 830132E-mail: sales@stackrightservices.co.uk
T S I S Engineering Ltd, 14 Waterloo Place, London, SW1Y 4AR Tel: (020) 7930 1562 Fax: (020) 7939 6569 E-mail: tsis.eng@onetel.net
Tashglen Ltd, 3 Mountington Park Close, Harrow, Middlesex, HA3 0NW Tel: (020) 8907 9428 Fax: 020) 8909 1661 E-mail: tashglen@compuserve.com
Thermo Designs Ltd, 64 Duff Street, Edinburgh, EH11 2HW Tel: 0131-313 3131 Fax: 0131-313 2772
Tivoli Manufacturing Ltd, Howfield Lane, Chartham, Canterbury, Kent, CT4 7HG Tel: (01227) 731156 Fax: (01227) 730137
Viva Science Ltd, Unit 31, Stroud Business Centre, Stonehouse, Gloucestershire, GL10 3RQ Tel: (01453) 821972 Fax: (01453) 827928
Wessington Cabins Ltd, Wessington Avenue, Calne, Wiltshire, SN11 0AP Tel: (01249) 812153 Fax: (01249) 817652 E-mail: sales@wessingtoncabins.co.uk
Westaway Sails Ltd, Erme Bridge, Ivybridge, Devon, PL21 9DU Tel: (01752) 892560 Fax: (01752) 895575 E-mail: sales@westawaysails.co.uk
Willis European, Dock Meadow Drive, Wolverhampton, WV4 6LE Tel: (01902) 490895 Fax: (01902) 490896 E-mail: info@williseuropean.com
Peter Wylie, 26 Noel Street, London, W1F 8GY Tel: (020) 7734 6140 Fax: (020) 7734 4904 E-mail: ptrwylie@aol.com
Yajima UK Ltd, Unit 17, Rassau Industrial Estate, Rassau, Ebbw Vale, Gwent, NP23 5SD Tel: (01495) 307190 Fax: (01495) 308677 E-mail: adams@yajima-uk.co.uk

MANUFACTURING CHEMISTS

Anglian Pharma Sales & Marketing Ltd, Titmore Court, Titmore Green, Little Wymondley, Hitchin, Hertfordshire, SG4 7XJ Tel: (01438) 743070 Fax: (01438) 743080 E-mail: admin@anglianpharma.com
Chemisphere, 3, Trafford Park, Manchester, M17 1RE Tel: 0161-874 7200 Fax: 0161-874 7201
Harvey Scruton, North Lane, Huntington, York, YO32 9SU Tel: (01904) 400878 Fax: (01904) 400120
J.M. Loveridge Ltd, Southbrook Road, Southampton, SO15 1BH Tel: (023) 8022 2008 Fax: (023) 8063 9836 E-mail: admin@jmloveridge.com
Michie Charles Pharmaceutical Chemist, 391 Union Street, Aberdeen, AB11 6BX Tel: (01224) 585312 Fax: (01224) 574264 E-mail: info@michies.co.uk
J. Pickles Healthcare, Beech Ho, 62 High St, Knaresborough, N. Yorkshire, HG5 0EA Tel: (01423) 867314 Fax: (01423) 869177 E-mail: enquiries@jpickleshealthcare.com
William Ransom & Son P.L.C., Alexander House, 40a Wilbury Way, Hitchin, Hertfordshire, SG4 0AP Tel: (01462) 437615 Fax: (01462) 420528 E-mail: info@williamransom.com
Rodette International Ltd, 19 Sturges Road, Ashford, Kent, TN24 8NE Tel: (01233) 611660 Fax: (01233) 011722 E-mail: sales@orbaorginals.com
Rutpen Ltd, Lambourn Woodlands, Hungerford, Berkshire, RG17 7TJ Tel: (01488) 71926 Fax: (01488) 71947E-mail: mail@rutpen.co.uk
Tell Products Ltd, 93 Cobbold Road, London, NW10 9SU Tel: (020) 8459 6873 Fax: (020) 8830 4977
Thornton & Ross Ltd, Linthwaite, Huddersfield, HD7 5QH Tel: (01484) 842217 Fax: (01484) 847301 E-mail: mail@thorntonross.com
Weleda U K Ltd, Heanor Road, Ilkeston, Derbyshire, DE7 8DR Tel: 0115-944 8200 Fax: 0115-944 8210 E-mail: weledauk@compuserve.com
Wyeth Laboratories, Bath Road, Taplow, Maidenhead, Berkshire, SL6 0AP Tel: (01628) 604377 Fax: (01628) 666368

MANUFACTURING CONTROL COMPUTER SYSTEMS

Active Controls, 6 Court Yard Workshops, Bath Street, Market Harborough, Leicestershire, LE16 9EW Tel: (01858) 466504 Fax: (01858) 463650 E-mail: activecontrols@ukonline.co.uk
Advantec Systems Ltd, 39 Westfield Close, Dorridge, Solihull, West Midlands, B93 8DY Tel: (01564) 739134
Ohm Electronics Ltd, 515 Pinner Road, Harrow, Middlesex, HA2 6EH Tel: (020) 8427 0545 Fax: (020) 8863 7930 E-mail: sales@ohmelectronics.co.uk

MANUFACTURING INDUSTRY RECRUITMENT

▶ G & T Associates, William Knox House, Britannic Way, Llandarcy, Neath, West Glamorgan, SA10 6EL Tel: (01792) 321202 Fax: (01792) 321295 E-mail: info@gtassociates.co.uk

MANUFACTURING MANAGEMENT CONSULTANTS

Baillie Associates Ltd, 50 Main Street, Lowdham, Nottingham, NG14 7BE Tel: 0115-966 3929 Fax: 0115-966 4745 E-mail: binfo@baillies.com
Bourton Group Ltd, Bourton Hall, Bourton, Rugby, Warwickshire, CV23 9SD Tel: (01926) 633333 Fax: (01926) 633450 E-mail: info@bourton.co.uk
Data Technology Group Ltd, Unit 3-4 The Long Room, Coppermill Lock, Uxbridge, Middlesex, UB9 6JA Tel: (01895) 829300 Fax: (01895) 820555 E-mail: general.information@datatechnology.co.uk
Fastsigns, 630-642 Chesterfield Road, Sheffield, S8 0SA Tel: 0114-255 2553 Fax: 0114-258 8444
Indacom Group Ltd, 131 Hollywood Lane Wainscott, Rochester, Kent, ME3 8AS Tel: (01634) 716286 Fax: (01634) 724821 E-mail: adavis.indacom@btopenworld.com
▶ Machan Consulting, 1 Belvedere Close, Keyworth, Nottingham, NG12 5JF Tel: 07780 646142 Fax: 0115 9375407 E-mail: enquiries@machan.co.uk
N I S Holdings Ltd, Ackhurst Road, Chorley, Lancashire, PR7 1NH Tel: (01257) 265656 Fax: (01257) 275501 E-mail: info@nisltd.com
Newburgh Management Services Ltd, 13 Cobbs Brow Lane, Newburgh, Wigan, Lancashire, WN8 7ND Tel: 0161-746 8582 Fax: (08700) 549489 E-mail: nmsl.ewj@btinternet.com
PHS Associates Ltd, 38 Ashworth Park, Knutsford, Cheshire, WA16 9DL Tel: (01565) 653330 E-mail: sales@p-h-s.co.uk
Andrew Reid & Partners, 36-37 Furnival Street, London, EC4A 1JQ Tel: (020) 7430 1611 Fax: (020) 7404 0553 E-mail: general@andrewreid.co.uk
Resource Management Systems, Mexborough Business Centre, College Road, Mexborough, South Yorkshire, S64 9JP Tel: (01709) 578300 Fax: (01709) 578010 E-mail: sales@rmsuk.co.uk
Scottoilers Scotland Ltd, 2 Riverside, Milngavie, Glasgow, G62 6PL Tel: 0141-955 1100 Fax: 0141-956 5896 E-mail: sales@scottoilers.com
Sumark Services, 221 Ware Road, Hoddesdon, Hertfordshire, EN11 9AF Tel: (01992) 421756 Fax: (01992) 421756
W B S Consulting, Grove Business Centre, Grove Technology Park, Wantage, Oxfordshire, OX12 9FF Tel: (01235) 227434 Fax: (01235) 227435 E-mail: enquiries@wwbsgroup.com
▶ Wilson Alexander, Queen Caroline House, 3 High, Windsor, Berkshire, SL4 1LD Tel: (01753) 850540 Fax: 01753 850490 E-mail: info@wilsonalexander.com

MANUFACTURING OR PROCESS DESIGN SOFTWARE

▶ Solweb Ltd, Suite 8a Bourne Gate, 25 Bourne Valley Road, Poole, Dorset, BH12 1DY Tel: (01202) 269879 Fax: 01202 762233 E-mail: info@solweb.co.uk

MANUFACTURING STATIONERS

Aerodex Flloyd Ltd, Aerodex Floyd, Tinge Wick Road Industrial Park, Buckingham, MK18 1FY Tel: (01280) 813095 Fax: (01280) 813095 E-mail: aerodex.floyd@talk21.com
Baddeley Brothers London Ltd, Bayford St Indust Units, Bayford Street, London, E8 3SE Tel: (020) 8986 2228 Fax: (020) 8986 4383 E-mail: enquiries@baddeleybrothers.com
Jean Barrington, 32 Dove Way, Kirkby Mills Industrial Estate, Kirkbymoorside, York, YO62 6QR Tel: (01751) 430081 Fax: (01751) 430081 E-mail: nigelboyes@onetel.com
Bowcourt Ltd, 7 Gardner Industrial Estate, Kent House Lane, Beckenham, Kent, BR3 1JR Tel: (020) 8659 1931 Fax: (020) 8676 8939 E-mail: sales@bowcourt.co.uk
Collins Debden, Westerhill Road, Bishopbriggs, Glasgow, G64 2QT Tel: 0141-300 8500 Fax: 0141-300 8600 E-mail: sales@collinsdebden.com
Deacon Bros Printers Ltd, Old Mill Park, Kirkintilloch, Glasgow, G66 1SW Tel: 0141-776 5272 Fax: 0141-776 1094 E-mail: sales@deacon-brothers.com
Drawing Office Supplies & Photocopying South Wales Ltd, 4 North Point, Western Avenue, Bridgend Industrial Estate, Bridgend, Mid Glamorgan, CF31 3RX Tel: (01656) 654744 Fax: (01656) 646609 E-mail: drawing.os@btconnect.com
George Girwood & Company Dundee Ltd, 2 Lower Pleasance, Dundee, DD1 5QU Tel: (01382) 322435
Hamelin Stationery Ltd, River Street, Brighouse, West Yorkshire, HD6 1LU Tel: (01484) 385600 Fax: 01484 385602 E-mail: sales@oxfordstationery.com
Harveys Ltd, Edgefield Road Industrial Estate, Loanhead, Midlothian, EH20 9SX Tel: 0131-440 0074 Fax: 0131-440 3478 E-mail: sales@harveys.ltd.uk
The Hedgehog Press, Unit B5, Imperial Bus Estate, West Mill, Gravesend, Kent, DA11 0DL Tel: (01474) 322153 Fax: (01474) 535570 E-mail: info@thehedgehogpress.co.uk
Impakt Stationers, Unit 12 Endeavour Way, Croydon, CR0 4TR Tel: (020) 8684 5777 Fax: (020) 8684 5999 E-mail: sales@impakt.co.uk
Jenkinson Marshall & Co. Ltd, 103 Neepsend Lane, Sheffield, S3 8AT Tel: 0114-272 1311 Fax: 0114-276 6240
Johnston Printing Ltd, Mill Road, Kilrea, Coleraine, County Londonderry, BT51 5RJ Tel: (028) 2954 0312 Fax: (028) 2954 1070 E-mail: service@johnston-printing.co.uk
K L Goddard, 1 Lambton Road, London, SW20 0LW Tel: (020) 8946 9494 Fax: (020) 8947 5675
KRS Ltd, Westfield House, Broad Lane, Leeds, LS13 3HA Tel: 0113-239 3088 Fax: 0113-257 7582
Links Labels & Tapes Ltd, Pinfold Road, Bourne, Lincolnshire, PE10 9HT Tel: (01778) 426282 Fax: (01778) 425003 E-mail: enquiries@linkslabels-tapes.co.uk
▶ M H T Group, 10 Arkwright Road, Reading, RG2 0LU Tel: 0118-975 5557 Fax: 0118-920 5180
Marland Paper & Plastics Ltd, Whiteleather Square, Billingborough, Sleaford, Lincolnshire, NG34 0QP Tel: (01529) 240637 Fax: (01529) 240638 E-mail: sales@marland.co.uk
Newton Print, 27a Coleshill Road, Sutton Coldfield, West Midlands, B75 7AX Tel: 0121-378 3711 Fax: 0121-311 1779 E-mail: david.deere@virgin.net
North Account Book Manufacturing Co., 23 Oldfield Lane, Heckmondwike, West Yorkshire, WF16 0JE Tel: (01924) 402309 Fax: (01924) 412070 E-mail: sales@northaccountprinters.co.uk
Parbury Brothers Ltd, The Vicarage, Great Wolford, Shipston-On-Stour, Warwickshire, CV36 5NQ Tel: (07973) 696524 E-mail: sales@parbury.co.uk
Pegasus National Ltd, Pegasus House, Battersea Road, Stockport, Cheshire, SK4 3EA Tel: 0161-432 0575 Fax: 0161-442 2388 E-mail: info@adocsystem.com
Quinn's The Printers, 181 Donegall Street, Belfast, BT1 2FJ Tel: (028) 9032 3552 Fax: (028) 9031 9166 E-mail: desgin@quinnstheprinters.com
Ryman The Stationer, 336 North End Road, London, SW6 1NB Tel: (020) 7381 8885 Fax: (020) 7381 8885
Setten & Durward Ltd, Ixl House, Waterloo Road, Llandrindod Wells, Powys, LD1 6BH Tel: (01597) 827800 Fax: (01597) 827847 E-mail: sales@ixl.uk.com
South Eastern Printing & Stationery Co. Ltd, Unit 5H Horndon Industrial Park, Station Road, West Horndon, Brentwood, Essex, CM13 3XL Tel: (01277) 812111 Fax: (01277) 811388
Spirax Binding (Scotland) Ltd, Inveralmond Road, Inveralmond Estate, Perth, PH1 3XA Tel: (01738) 626281 Fax: (01738) 630575 E-mail: sales@spirax.co.uk
T W G Packaging, King Edward Industrial Estate, Gibraltar Row, Liverpool, L3 7HJ Tel: 0151-227 1045 Fax: 0151-236 2114 E-mail: mygpackaging@compuserve.com
Victor Stationery Ltd, 4 Marshalls Road, Belfast, BT5 6QU Tel: (028) 9040 1555 Fax: 028 90704872 E-mail: sales@victorstationery.com
F.W. Wallen & Sons Ltd, Welkin Road, Lower Bredbury, Stockport, Cheshire, SK6 2BH Tel: 0161-494 9766 Fax: 0161-406 7580 E-mail: info@egertonstationery.co.uk
▶ Wessex Malthouse Direct, 24A East Reach, Taunton, Somerset, TA1 3EP Tel: (01823) 331111 Fax: (01823) 334503 E-mail: sales@wessexmalthouse.com
William Sinclair & Sons Stationers Ltd, PO Box 1, Otley, West Yorkshire, LS21 1QF Tel: (01943) 461144 Fax: (01943) 850017 E-mail: sales@silvine.com
Witherby & Co. Ltd, 32-36 Aylesbury Street, London, EC1R 0ET Tel: (020) 7253 5413 Fax: (020) 7336 7493 E-mail: briandoors@witherbys.co.uk
Worktown Office Supplies Ltd, 1 Park Court, Premier Way, Abbey Park, Romsey, Hants, SO51 9AQ Tel: (01794) 525065 Fax: (01794) 525025 E-mail: orders@worktown.com

MANURE BAGS

Gardenscape, Rye Road, Newenden, Cranbrook, Kent, TN18 5QG Tel: (0800) 854663 Fax: (01797) 253554 E-mail: gerald@bourne.uk.com

MAP DRAWERS/ CARTOGRAPHERS

Harper Collins Publisher Ltd, Westerhill Rd, Glasgow, G64 2QT Tel: 0141-772 3200 Fax: 0141-306 3104 E-mail: vivion.mccormack@harpercollins.co.uk
Harpercollins Pubrs Ophelia House, Fulham Palace Road, London, W6 8JA Tel: (020) 8741 7070 Fax: (020) 8307 4440 E-mail: vibecke.olsen@harpercollins.co.uk
Lovell Johns Ltd, 10 Hanborough Business Park, Lodge Road, Long Hanborough, Witney, Oxfordshire, OX29 8RU Tel: (01993) 883161 Fax: (01993) 883096 E-mail: enquiries@lovelljohns.com
▶ Nicolson Maps, 3 Frazer Street, Largs, Ayrshire, KA30 9HP Tel: (01475) 689242 Fax: (01475) 689242 E-mail: enquiries@nicolsonmaps.com
▶ P C Graphics (UK) Ltd, 1 Westminster Court, Hipley Street, Woking, Surrey, GU22 9LG Tel: (01483) 770691 Fax: (01483) 729281 E-mail: info@pcgraphics.uk.com
S D Graphics, (c/o Complete Print), 3 Rawstorne Place, London, EC1V 7NL Tel: (020) 7837 4555 Fax: (020) 7837 4555

MAP MAKING OR CARTOGRAPHY SOFTWARE

Cosmographics, 1 Mowat Industrial Estate, Sandown Road, Watford, WD24 7UY Tel: (01923) 210909 Fax: (01923) 211657 E-mail: enquiries@cosmographics.co.uk
Dotted Eyes Ltd, Hanbury Court Harris Business Park, Hanbury Road, Stoke Prior, Bromsgrove, Worcestershire, B60 4JJ Tel: (01527) 556920 Fax: (01527) 556939 E-mail: info@dottedeyes.com
▶ Isis Surveyors Ltd, 7 Ashurst Close, Tadley, Hampshire, RG26 4AH Tel: 0118-981 4614 Fax: 0118-981 4614 E-mail: isissurveyors@ukonline.co.uk

MAP PUBLISHERS

Geographer's A - Z Map Co. Ltd, Fairfield Road, Borough Green, Sevenoaks, Kent, TN15 8PP Tel: (01732) 781000 Fax: (01732) 780677 E-mail: sales@a-zmaps.co.uk
Harper Collins Publisher Ltd, Westerhill Rd, Glasgow, G64 2QT Tel: 0141-772 3200 Fax: 0141-306 3104 E-mail: vivion.mccormack@harpercollins.co.uk
Harpercollins Pubrs Ophelia House, Fulham Palace Road, London, W6 8JA Tel: (020) 8741 7070 Fax: (020) 8307 4440 E-mail: vibecke.olsen@harpercollins.co.uk

MAP PUBLISHERS – *continued*

Imray Laurie Norie & Wilson Ltd, Wych House, 20 Broadway, St. Ives, Cambridgeshire, PE27 5BT Tel: (01480) 462114 Fax: (01480) 496109 E-mail: enquiries@imray.com

▶ Nicolson Maps, 3 Frazer Street, Largs, Ayrshire, KA30 9HP Tel: (01475) 689242 Fax: (01475) 689242 E-mail: enquiries@nicolsonmaps.com

Oilfield Publications, 15 The Homend, Ledbury, Herefordshire, HR8 1BN Tel: (01531) 634561 Fax: (01531) 634239 E-mail: sales@oilpubs.com

▶ P C Graphics (UK) Ltd, 1 Westminster Court, Hipley Street, Woking, Surrey, GU22 9LG Tel: (01483) 770691 Fax: (01483) 729281 E-mail: info@pcgraphics.uk.com

Redbooks, Bridewell House, Bridewell Lane, Tenterden, Kent, TN30 6EP Tel: (01580) 764225 Fax: (01580) 763720 E-mail: sales@estate-publications.co.uk

MAP SELLERS/DISTRIBUTORS/ AGENTS/SPECIALIST SERVICES

Cook Hammond & Kell Ltd, Whittington House, 764-768 Holloway Road, London, N19 3JQ Tel: (020) 7281 2161 Fax: (020) 7281 4117

Kenroy Thompson Ltd, 25 Cobourg Street, Plymouth, PL1 1SR Tel: (01752) 227693 Fax: (0800) 7836322 E-mail: sales@kenroythompson.co.uk

Map Marketing Ltd, 92-104 Carnwath Road, London, SW6 3HW Tel: (020) 7526 2322 Fax: (020) 7371 0473 E-mail: sales@mapmarketing.com

▶ Nicolson Maps, 3 Frazer Street, Largs, Ayrshire, KA30 9HP Tel: (01475) 689242 Fax: (01475) 689242 E-mail: enquiries@nicolsonmaps.com

▶ P C Graphics (UK) Ltd, 1 Westminster Court, Hipley Street, Woking, Surrey, GU22 9LG Tel: (01483) 770691 Fax: (01483) 729281 E-mail: info@pcgraphics.uk.com

Polymaps, 41 Truro Rd, St. Austell, Cornwall, PL25 5JE Tel: (01726) 66666 Fax: (01726) 64797

Stanfords Digital, 12-14 Long Acre, London, WC2E 9LP Tel: (020) 7836 2260 Fax: (020) 7379 4776 E-mail: sales@stanfords.co.uk

MARBLE

Aurora Marble Ltd, Green Lea Mills, Cross Green Road, Huddersfield, HD5 9XX Tel: (01484) 510470 Fax: (01484) 538943

Bannocks Of Solihull, 117 Streetsbrook Road, Shirley, Solihull, West Midlands, B90 3PF Tel: 0121-744 1727 Fax: 0121-733 1651

Blyth Marble Ltd, Lawn Road, Carlton-in-Lindrick, Worksop, Nottinghamshire, S81 9LB Tel: (01909) 730807 Fax: (01909) 730114 E-mail: admin@blyth-marble.co.uk

Borg & Ranalli Ltd, 364a Clapham Road, London, SW9 9AR Tel: (020) 7627 3962 Fax: (020) 8947 1501

▶ Callisto Trading Ltd, 2 Duckett Mews, London, N4 1BP Tel: (07092) 008537 Fax: (07092) 020256 E-mail: info@callistotrading.co.uk

Felix Campania Ltd, 42 Ditton Hill Road, Surbiton, Surrey, KT6 5JD Tel: (020) 8339 0011 Fax: (020) 8398 5495 E-mail: felix.campania@btinternet.com

▶ Francis N Lowe Ltd, New Road, Middleton, Matlock, Derbyshire, DE4 4NA Tel: (01629) 822216 Fax: (01629) 824348

Granite Granite Ltd, Russell Gardens, Wickford, Essex, SS11 8QG Tel: (01268) 761214 Fax: (01268) 560088

H Butterfield Ltd, Selbourne Road, Luton, LU4 8QF Tel: (01582) 491100 Fax: (01582) 490969 E-mail: enquiries@butterfieldnatstone.co.uk

J & R Marble Company Ltd, Unit 9, Period Works, London, E10 7QT Tel: (020) 8539 6471 Fax: (020) 8539 9264 E-mail: sales@jrmarble.co.uk

Alistair Mackintosh Ltd, Bannerley Road, Garretts Green Industrial Estate, Birmingham, B33 0SL Tel: 0121-784 6800 Fax: 0121-789 7068 E-mail: info@alistairmackintosh.co.uk

Maple Aggregates UK Ltd, 50 Preston Road, Brighton, BN1 4QF Tel: (01273) 699001 Fax: (01273) 670977

Marbonyx Ltd, Welton Way, Purdeys Indust Estate, Purdeys Industrial Estate, Rochford, Essex, SS4 1LA Tel: (01702) 543235 Fax: (01702) 543266 E-mail: sales@marbonyx.com

▶ Medusa Creations, Unit 2b Carnaby Industrial Estate, Lancaster Road, Carnaby, Bridlington, North Humberside, YO15 3QY Tel: (01262) 605222 Fax: (01262) 605654

Minilco Specialities Ltd, Bowesfield Industrial Estate, Bowesfield Lane, Stockton-on-Tees, Cleveland, TS18 3HJ Tel: (01642) 674375 Fax: (01642) 614379

Phillips & Sons, 110-111 Lewes Road, Brighton, BN2 3QB Tel: (01273) 682751 Fax: (01273) 677469

Pisani plc, Unit 12 Transport Avenue, Brentford, Middlesex, TW8 9HF Tel: (020) 8568 5001 Fax: (020) 8847 3406 E-mail: sales@pisani.co.uk

Premier Marble Ltd, 3 Dewing Road, Rackheath Industrial Estate, Rackheath, Norwich, NR13 6PS Tel: (01603) 721995 Fax: (01603) 721948 E-mail: premarble@aol.com

Prestige Marble Co., Armoury Works, Armoury Way, London, SW18 1EZ Tel: (020) 8874 7100 Fax: (020) 8870 0025 E-mail: prestigemarble@aol.com

Scottish Natural Stones Ltd, Westwood Estate, West Calder, West Lothian, EH55 8PN Tel: (01506) 874222 Fax: (01506) 874285

Shackerley (Holdings) Group Ltd, 139 Wigan Road, Euxton, Chorley, Lancashire, PR7 6JH Tel: (01257) 273114 Fax: (01257) 262386 E-mail: sales@shackerley.co.uk

Studio 2, 5 Sizes Court, Henshaw Lane, Yeadon, Leeds, LS19 7DP Tel: 0113-239 1859 Fax: 0113-250 9688

Stylecharm Fireplaces, 14 Bowlers Croft, Basildon, Essex, SS14 3EE Tel: (01268) 287673 Fax: (01268) 287710 E-mail: carl@beeb.net

Sussex Marble Co. Ltd, 16 Wainwright Close, St. Leonards-on-Sea, East Sussex, TN38 9PP Tel: (01424) 852575 Fax: (01424) 852798 E-mail: sales@sussexmarble.co.uk

▶ Tabounchik Trading, 1a Maxim Cottages, Hophurst Lane, Crawley Down, Crawley, West Sussex, RH10 4LJ Tel: (01342) 717188 E-mail: tabounchik@fsmail.net

UK Marble Ltd, 21 Burcott Road, Hereford, HR4 9LW Tel: (01432) 352178 Fax: (01432) 352112 E-mail: sales@ukmarble.co.uk

Zanetti & Bailey, Verona House, Filwood Road, Bristol, BS16 3RY Tel: 0117-965 6565 Fax: 0117-965 1236 E-mail: info@marbleflooring.com

MARBLE BOWLS

Zarka Marble Ltd, 41a Belsize Lane, London, NW3 5AU Tel: (020) 7431 3042 Fax: (020) 7431 3879 E-mail: enquiries@zarkamarble.co.uk

MARBLE FIRE SURROUNDS

▶ W J Lafford Ltd, 21 Harmondsworth Road, West Drayton, Middlesex, UB7 9JJ Tel: (01895) 442441 Fax: (01895) 421596 E-mail: alexis@memorialsculpture.com

MARBLE FIREPLACE FRONTS

Stylecharm Fireplaces, 14 Bowlers Croft, Basildon, Essex, SS14 3EE Tel: (01268) 287673 Fax: (01268) 287710 E-mail: carl@beeb.net

West Wales Marble & Granite, Units 9-11 Industrial Estate, Church Road, Gorslas, Llanelli, Dyfed, SA14 7NN Tel: (01269) 832868 Fax: (01267) 238525 E-mail: mail@westwalesmarbleandgranite.com

MARBLE FIREPLACES

▶ Mann's Fireplaces, 96-98 Scotland Road, Nelson, Lancashire, BB9 7XJ Tel: (01282) 614789 Fax: (01282) 614789 E-mail: info@mannsfireplaces.co.uk

▶ Stone Installations.co.uk, 9 Talbot Road, Rushden, Northamptonshire, NN10 6DQ Tel: 01933 387059 Fax: 01933 387059

▶ Thornhill Galleries, 3, 19 Osiers Road, London, SW18 1NL Tel: (020) 8874 2101 Fax: (020) 8877 0313 E-mail: sales@thornhillgalleries.co.uk

▶ W J Lafford Ltd, 21 Harmondsworth Road, West Drayton, Middlesex, UB7 9JJ Tel: (01895) 442441 Fax: (01895) 421596 E-mail: alexis@memorialsculpture.com

West Wales Marble & Granite, Units 9-11 Industrial Estate, Church Road, Gorslas, Llanelli, Dyfed, SA14 7NN Tel: (01269) 832868 Fax: (01267) 238525 E-mail: mail@westwalesmarbleandgranite.com

MARBLE FLOOR TILES

▶ Martin & Sons, 103-109 Efford Road, Plymouth, PL3 6NG Tel: (01752) 771586 Fax: (01752) 706388 E-mail: martinsandsons@plymstonewannado.co.uk

MARBLE VANITY TOPS AND WASH BASINS

▶ W J Lafford Ltd, 21 Harmondsworth Road, West Drayton, Middlesex, UB7 9JJ Tel: (01895) 442441 Fax: (01895) 421596 E-mail: alexis@memorialsculpture.com

MARBLE WASH BASINS

C H I C Fireplaces, 116 Red Lane, Coventry, CV6 5EQ Tel: (024) 7663 8063 E-mail: chicmarbleandgranite@hotmail.co.uk

Rocktops Ltd, Matts Hill Farm, Matts Hill Road, Hartlip, Sittingbourne, Kent, ME9 7UY Tel: (01634) 264606 Fax: (01322) 349251

MARGARINE

ADM Pura Foods Ltd, Erith Oil Works, Church Manorway, Erith, Kent, DA8 1DL Tel: (01322) 443000 Fax: (01322) 443027

MARINE AERIALS

▶ Shipmates, 2 Newcomen Road, Dartmouth, Devon, TQ6 9AF Tel: (01803) 839292 Fax: (01803) 832538 E-mail: admin@chandlery.co.uk

MARINE AIR COMPRESSORS

Britannia Marine Services, Unit 11 50 Windsor Avenue, London, SW19 2TJ Tel: (020) 8408 6020 Fax: (020) 8408 6040 E-mail: sales@britannia.com

MARINE AIR CONDITIONING (AC) EQUIPMENT

Atlantic Refrigeration Ltd, Peel Street, Northam, Southampton, SO14 5QT Tel: (023) 8033 9141 Fax: (023) 8022 9840 E-mail: grantwest@atlantic-refrig.co.uk

P H Services Ltd, 37 Limberline Spur, Portsmouth, PO3 5DX Tel: (023) 9269 3448 Fax: (023) 9263 9094 E-mail: huntphill@aol.com

Stream Environmental, 100-102 Headstone Road, Harrow, Middlesex, HA1 1PF Tel: (020) 8933 6611 Fax: (020) 8424 8001 E-mail: sales@streamenvironmental.co.uk

MARINE ALUMINIUM FABRICATORS

Design Engineering & Fabrications International Ltd, 14 Newbridge Way, Pennington, Lymington, Hampshire, SO41 8BH Tel: (01590) 671411 Fax: (01590) 676021 E-mail: info@defint.com

MARINE ANCHOR HANDLING EQUIPMENT

Bruce Anchor Ltd, Royston Road, Deans Industrial Estate, Livingston, West Lothian, EH54 8AH Tel: (01506) 415454 Fax: (01506) 461202 E-mail: bruceanchor@lineone.net

MARINE ANCHORS

Bembridge & Jenkins Ltd, Moland Forge, Central Trading Estate, Shaw Road, Dudley, West Midlands, DY2 8QX Tel: (01384) 243833 Fax: (01384) 455628

Gael Force Ltd, 136 Anderson Street, Longman, Inverness, IV3 8DH Tel: (01463) 229448 Fax: (01463) 229421 E-mail: sales@gaelforce.net

MARINE ANTIFOULING SYSTEMS

▶ MCPS Ltd, Tedco BSNS Works, Tedco Business Works, Henry Robson Way, South Shields, Tyne & Wear, NE33 1RF Tel: 0191-454 4444 Fax: 0191-427 4607 E-mail: sales@mcpsltd.com

MARINE AUTOMATIC PILOT AND STEERING GEAR

C-Tronix UK Ltd, 185a Lower Blandford Road, Broadstone, Dorset, BH18 8DH Tel: (01202) 695500 E-mail: ap9000mart@aol.com

Raymarine Ltd, Quaypoint, North Harper Road, Portsmouth, PO6 3TD Tel: (023) 9269 3611 Fax: (023) 9269 4642 E-mail: info@raymarine.com

V T Marine Products Ltd, Hamilton Road, Cosham, Portsmouth, PO6 4PX Tel: (023) 9253 9750 Fax: (023) 9253 9764

MARINE AUTOMATION CONTROLS

I Y S Control Systems, 15e West Station Yard, Spital Road, Maldon, Essex, CM9 6TW Tel: (01621) 858185 Fax: (01621) 893769 E-mail: design_john@europe.com

M J R Controls Ltd, Unit 85, Willows Court, Thornaby, Stockton-on-Tees, Cleveland, TS17 9PP Tel: (01642) 762151 Fax: (01642) 762502 E-mail: enquiries@mjrcontrols.com

Radamec Control Systems Ltd, Euro House, Abex Road, Newbury, Berkshire, RG14 5EY Tel: (01635) 40528 Fax: (01635) 47453 E-mail: sales@radamec-controls.co.uk

MARINE BATTERIES

Alcad, 1st Floor Unit 5 Astra Centre, Edinburgh Way, Harlow, Essex, CM20 2BN Tel: (01279) 772555 Fax: (01279) 420696 E-mail: carter.sarah@alcad.com

Bristol Batteries, Axis Business Centre, Westmead Trading Estate, Westmead, Swindon, SN5 7YS Tel: (01793) 616646 Fax: (01793) 490011 E-mail: sales@bristolbatteries.com

Manbat Ltd, Water Street, Abergele, Clwyd, LL22 7SL Tel: (01745) 832174 Fax: (01745) 833503 E-mail: sales@manbat.co.uk

Manbat Ltd, Unit 1-5 Chancel Place, Store Street, Manchester, M1 2WB Tel: 0161-273 2235 Fax: 0161-273 7368 E-mail: sale@manbat.co.uk

Manbat Ltd, Lancaster Road, Shrewsbury, SY1 3LG Tel: (01743) 460792 E-mail: sales@manbat.co.uk

Mastervolt UK Ltd, Winchester Hill, Romsey, Hampshire, SO51 7ND Tel: (01794) 516443 Fax: (01794) 516453 E-mail: sales@mastervolt.com

MARINE BOILERS

Whispair, Unit 31 Romsey Industrial Estate, Greatbridge Road, Romsey, Hampshire, SO51 0HR Tel: (01794) 523999 Fax: (01794) 519151 E-mail: info@whispaire.co.uk

MARINE BOLLARDS

Ansell Jones Ltd, Satellite Industrial Park, Neachells Lane, Wolverhampton, WV11 3PQ Tel: (01902) 722117 Fax: (01902) 725533 E-mail: sales@anseljones.com

MARINE BROKERS, *See Ship Brokers*

MARINE BUOYS

A B Pharos Marine Ltd, Steyning Way, Hounslow, TW4 6DL Tel: (020) 8538 1100 Fax: (020) 8577 4170 E-mail: sales@pharosmarine.com

Cotesi Ltd, 5-7 Mill Fold, Sowerby Bridge, West Yorkshire, HX6 4DJ Tel: (01422) 821000 Fax: (01422) 821007 E-mail: enquiries@cotesi.co.uk

Crewsaver Ltd, Clarence Square, Mumby Road, Gosport, Hampshire, PO12 1AQ Tel: (023) 9252 8621 Fax: (023) 9251 0905 E-mail: sales@crewsaver.co.uk

Hippo Marine Ltd, 1 Gilston Road, Saltash, Cornwall, PL12 6TW Tel: (01752) 843333 Fax: (01752) 843333

P P S Glassfibre Ltd, Harlaw Way, Harlaw Road Industrial Estate, Inverurie, Aberdeenshire, AB51 4SG Tel: (01467) 621907 Fax: (01467) 620265 E-mail: ppsglassfibre@btconnect.com

MARINE CAPSTANS

Lebus International Engineers Ltd, Dane Works, Crown Quay Lane, Sittingbourne, Kent, ME10 3HU Tel: (01795) 475324 Fax: (01795) 428004 E-mail: enquiries@lebusintengineers.com

North Sea Winches Ltd, Dunslow Road, Eastfield, Scarborough, North Yorkshire, YO11 3UT Tel: (01723) 584080 Fax: (01723) 581605 E-mail: sales@nswinches.co.uk

MARINE CATERING EQUIPMENT

B E K Engineering Ltd, Unit C1, New St, Charfield, Wotton-under-Edge, Gloucestershire, GL12 8ES Tel: (01453) 844372 Fax: (01453) 842050 E-mail: bek@harris-pye.com

Promart Manufacturing Ltd, Caddick Road, Knowsley Industrial Park South, Knowsley Business Park, Prescot, Merseyside, L34 9HP Tel: 0151-547 4666 Fax: 0151-546 6152 E-mail: sales@promart.co.uk

MARINE CHAINS

Bradney Chain & Engineering Co. Ltd, Quarry Road, Dudley, West Midlands, DY2 0EB Tel: (01384) 636233 Fax: (01384) 634289 E-mail: sales@bradneychain.co.uk

F P M Henderson Ltd, 35 Halley Street, Glasgow, G13 4DJ Tel: 0141-941 1211 Fax: 0141-941 2011 E-mail: sales@fpmhenderson.co.uk

X J F Plastics Ltd, Unit 1 & 2, Southfield Lane Industrial Estate, Whitwell, Worksop, Nottinghamshire, S80 4SB Tel: (01909) 724211 Fax: (01909) 724582 E-mail: enquiries@xjfplastics.co.uk

MARINE CLEANING CONTRACTORS

Boat Care UK, 1Turpins Ride, Welwyn, Herts, AL6 0QS Tel: 0845 6521415. E-mail: enquires@boatcareuk.com

MARINE CLOSED CIRCUIT TELEVISION (CCTV) EQUIPMENT

Connectic Synx Ltd, The Flarepath, Elsham Wolds Industrial Estate, Brigg, South Humberside, DN20 0SP Tel: (01652) 688908 Fax: (01652) 688928 E-mail: sales@synx.ltd.uk

MARINE COMMUNICATION EQUIPMENT

A N D & Group, Tanners Bank, North Shields, Tyne & Wear, NE30 1JH Tel: (01233) 635278 Fax: (0870) 4449680 E-mail: info@and-group.net

Greenham Regis Ltd, Kings Saltern Road, Lymington, Hampshire, SO41 3QD Tel: (01590) 671144 Fax: (01590) 679517 E-mail: lymington@greenham-regis.com

MARINE COMMUNICATION SYSTEMS

Thales Land & Joint Systems, Newton Road, Crawley, West Sussex, RH10 9TS Tel: (01293) 518855 Fax: (01293) 446340 E-mail: jon.bye@uk.thalesgroup.com

MARINE COMPONENT PACKING BOXES

East Lancashire Box, Spring Street, Rishton, Rishton, Blackburn, BB1 4LL Tel: (01254) 889820 Fax: (01254) 889927

MARINE COMPUTER SOFTWARE SYSTEMS

Global Maritime, Friars Bridge Court 41-45 Blackfriars Road, London, SE1 8NZ Tel: (020) 7922 8900 Fax: (020) 7922 8901 E-mail: gm@globalmaritime.com

Maritime Progress Ltd, 3-5 Holmethorpe Avenue, Redhill, RH1 2LZ Tel: (01737) 763400 Fax: (01737) 782818 E-mail: info@maritimeprogress.com

MARINE CONSULTANCY OR CONSULTING ENGINEERS

B M T Defence Services Ltd, 210 Lower Bristol Road, Bath, BA2 3DQ Tel: (01225) 448712 Fax: (01225) 448714 E-mail: info@bmtdsl.co.uk

BMTGroup Ltd, Goodrich House, 1 Waldegrave Road, Teddington, Middlesex, TW11 8LZ Tel: (020) 8943 5544 Fax: (020) 8943 5347 E-mail: enquiries@bmtmail.com

Bowen Barrack & Co., 9 SMM Business Park, Dock Road, Birkenhead, Merseyside, CH41 1DT Tel: 0151-653 7948 Fax: 0151-653 7990

Brookes Bell Jarrett Kirman LLP, Martins Building, Exchange Flags, Liverpool, L2 3PG Tel: 0151-236 0083 Fax: 0151-236 2945 E-mail: liv@brookesbell.com

Burness Corlett & Partners, 12-20 Camomile Street, London, EC3A 7PT Tel: (020) 7621 2943 Fax: (020) 7929 4167 E-mail: enquiries@bctq.com

Burnison Engineering plc, PO Box 24, Newbury, Berkshire, RG14 5GZ Tel: (01635) 552255 Fax: (01635) 552944

▶ Caudle Contracts & Design Ltd, Everglades, Maiden St, Weston, Hitchin, Hertfordshire, SG4 7AA Tel: (01462) 790580 Fax: (01462) 790398 E-mail: sales@caudle.co.uk

Caudles, 23 West One House, St. Georges Road, Cheltenham, Gloucestershire, GL50 3DT Tel: (01242) 222307 Fax: (01242) 222665

Chains North West Ltd, 180 Rimrose Road, Bootle, Merseyside, L20 4QS Tel: 0151-933 2633 Fax: 0151-922 6739

Global Maritime, Friars Bridge Court 41-45 Blackfriars Road, London, SE1 8NZ Tel: (020) 7922 8900 Fax: (020) 7922 8901 E-mail: gm@globalmaritime.com

Ics Installations Ltd, 5 Bates Close, Larkfield, Aylesford, Kent, ME20 6TG Tel: (01732) 848550 Fax: (01732) 848550 E-mail: lloyd.porter@ics-installations.com

L G S A Marine, 67-83 Mariners House Queens Dock Commercial Centre, Norfolk S, Liverpool, L1 0BG Tel: 0151-707 2233 Fax: 0151-707 2170 E-mail: liverpool@lgsamarine.co.uk

London Offshore Consultants Ltd, 20 St Dunstans Hill, London, EC3R 8NP Tel: (020) 7283 5544 Fax: (020) 7600 0562 E-mail: loc@londonoffshore.co.uk

Marine & Offshore Consultants Ltd, Magellan House, James Watt Close, Great Yarmouth, Norfolk, NR31 0NX Tel: (01493) 440166 Fax: (01493) 658490 E-mail: support@modgy.co.uk

Maritime Consulting Associates Ltd, Owl Building, Battery Green Road, Lowestoft, Suffolk, NR32 1DH Tel: (01502) 730791 Fax: (01502) 508001 E-mail: marineconsult@compuserve.com

Medina Yacht Services, Marvel Lane, Newport, Isle of Wight, PO30 3DT Tel: (01983) 822691 Fax: (01983) 822692 E-mail: s@mys.com

Minton Treharne & Davies Ltd, Merton House The Avenue Industrial Park, Croescadarn Close, Cardiff, CF23 8HF Tel: (029) 2054 0000 Fax: (029) 2054 0111 E-mail: mtd@minton.co.uk

Noble Denton Consultants Ltd, Noble House, 39 Tabernacle Street, London, EC2A 4AA Tel: (020) 7812 8700 Fax: (020) 7812 8701 E-mail: marketing@nobledenton.co.uk

Peter Fraenkel Maritime Ltd, 21-37 South Street, Dorking, Surrey, RH4 2JZ Tel: (01306) 879797 Fax: (01306) 879798 E-mail: contact@fraenkel.co.uk

Qinetiq, Cody Technology Park, Ively Road, Farnborough, Hampshire, GU14 0LX Tel: 08700 100942 Fax: (01252) 393399 E-mail: contactus@qinetiq.com

R & J Maritime Ltd, 89 Durnford Street, Plymouth, PL1 3QW Tel: (01752) 671586 Fax: (01752) 265744 E-mail: rjmedler@supanet.com

Seaspeed Technology Ltd, 2 City Business Centre, Basin Road, Chichester, West Sussex, PO19 8DU Tel: (01243) 784222 Fax: (01243) 784333 E-mail: info@seaspeed.co.uk

Shipping Guides Ltd, 75 Bell Street, Reigate, Surrey, RH2 7AN Tel: (01737) 242255 Fax: (01737) 222449 E-mail: info@portinfo.co.uk

Shiptech (U K) Ltd, St. Andrews House, 33 Beverley Road, Hull, HU3 1XH Tel: (01482) 324964 Fax: (01482) 226679 E-mail: info@shiptech.co.uk

T M C Marine Consultants Ltd, Lloyds Wharf, Mill Street, London, SE1 2BD Tel: (020) 7237 2617 Fax: (020) 7231 8069 E-mail: info@tmcmarine.co.uk

T M G (Europe) Ltd, Whitestones House, 2 Kidderpore Avenue, London, NW3 7SB Tel: (01322) 861959 Fax: (0870) 7525490 E-mail: info@tmgeurope.co.uk

W J Marine Analytical Services Ltd, Unit 4, Marine Park, Tapton Hall Industrial Estate, Great Yarmouth, Norfolk, NR31 0NL Tel: (01493) 600600 Fax: (01493) 652099 E-mail: wjmarine@btinternet.com

White Young Green Ltd, The Mill Yard, Nursling Street, Nursling, Southampton, SO16 0AJ Tel: (0870) 6091084 E-mail: southampton@wyg.com

MARINE CONTROL SYSTEMS

Aker Kvaerner Subsea Ltd, Unit 59, Clivemont Road, Cordwallis Industrial Estate, Maidenhead, Berkshire, SL6 7BZ Tel: (01628) 506560 Fax: (01628) 506501 E-mail: info@kvaerner.com

▶ European Marine & Machinery Agencies, Nutsey House, Nutsey Lane, Totton, Southampton, SO40 3NB Tel: (023) 8058 0020 Fax: (023) 8058 0021 E-mail: sales@europeanmarine.co.uk

M J R Controls Ltd, Unit 85, Willows Court, Thornaby, Stockton-on-Tees, Cleveland, TS17 9PP Tel: (01642) 762151 Fax: (01642) 762502 E-mail: enquiries@mjrcontrols.com

Matrix Controls, 4 Zan Industrial Park, Crewe Road, Wheelock, Sandbach, Cheshire, CW11 4QD Tel: (01270) 753066 Fax: (01270) 753066 E-mail: sales@matrixcontrols.co.uk

Ocean Technical Systems Ltd, Oceantech House, Station Approach, Cheam, Sutton, Surrey, SM2 7AU Tel: (020) 8643 2233 Fax: (020) 8643 6444 E-mail: ots@oceantechsys.com

S M M Propeller Services Ltd, Wharf Road, Gravesend, Kent, DA12 2RU Tel: (01474) 320192 Fax: (01474) 335047

Sea Technik Ltd, Court House, 15 Glynne Way, Hawarden, Deeside, Clwyd, CH5 3NS Tel: (01244) 535787 Fax: (01244) 538908 E-mail: admin@seatechnik.com

MARINE DRILLING AND BLASTING CONTRACTORS

Seacore Ltd, Lower Quay, Gweek, Helston, Cornwall, TR12 6UD Tel: (01326) 221771 Fax: (01326) 221553 E-mail: sales@seacore.co.uk

MARINE ELECTRIC CABLES

Apex Cables Ltd, St Johns Road, Meadowfield Industrial Estate, Durham, DH7 8RJ Tel: 0191-378 7900 Fax: 0191-378 7909 E-mail: apex@apexcables.co.uk

MARINE ELECTRICAL CONTRACTORS

ABB Ltd, 21-25 Commerce Street, Maritime Centre, Aberdeen, AB11 5FE Tel: (01224) 592123 Fax: (01224) 592690 E-mail: lynn.boyne@gb.abb.com

Marine Radio Services Ltd, 50 Merton Way, West Molesey, Surrey, KT8 1PQ Tel: (020) 8979 7979 E-mail: marineradio@f2s.com

▶ Moidart Engineering, Mingarry, Acharacle, Argyll, PH36 4JX Tel: (07880) 706439 Fax: (01967) 431515 E-mail: jaz.maclellan@tiscali.co.uk

MARINE ELECTRICAL EQUIPMENT

ABB Ltd, 21-25 Commerce Street, Maritime Centre, Aberdeen, AB11 5FE Tel: (01224) 592123 Fax: (01224) 592690 E-mail: lynn.boyne@gb.abb.com

Armstrong Electrical, 109 Hatch Road, Pilgrims Hatch, Brentwood, Essex, CM15 9QA Tel: (01277) 375511 Fax: (01277) 375511 E-mail:

Atec Hampshire Ltd, Peel Street, Southampton, SO14 5QT Tel: (023) 8063 1391 Fax: (023) 8033 8931 E-mail: sales@atec-hants.co.uk

Consilium Marine UK Branch, 23 Saffron Court, Southfields, Laindon, Basildon, Essex, SS15 6SS Tel: (020) 8508 1702 Fax: (020) 8508 1703

Diverse Yacht Services, Unit 12 Hamble Yacht Services, Port Hamble, Hamble, Southampton, SO31 4NN Tel: (023) 8045 3399 Fax: (023) 8045 5288 E-mail: phil@diverseyachts.com

Emoos Consultants Ltd, 8 Battery Green Road, Lowestoft, Suffolk, NR32 1DE Tel: (01502) 587696 Fax: (01502) 589159 E-mail: navtronicks@rya-online.net

Energy Solutions UK Ltd, Property Services House, George Summers Close, Medway City Estate, Rochester, Kent, ME2 4NS Tel: (01634) 290772 Fax: (01634) 290773 E-mail: mail@energy-solutions.co.uk

Furuno UK Ltd, Ocean House Parklands Business Park, Forest Road, Denmead, Waterlooville, Hampshire, PO7 6XP Tel: (023) 9223 0303 Fax: (023) 9223 0101 E-mail: denmead@furunouk.freeserve.co.uk

Navico UK Ltd, Premier Way, Abbey Park, Romsey, Hampshire, SO51 9DH Tel: (01794) 510010 Fax: (01794) 510006 E-mail: sales.uk@navico.com

Norcontrol It Ltd, 12 High Street, Winterbourne, Bristol, BS36 1JN Tel: (01454) 774466 Fax: (01454) 774488

PDM Neptec Ltd, 4-6 Alton Business Centre, Omega Park, Alton, Hampshire, GU34 2YU Tel: (01420) 85848 Fax: (01420) 84288 E-mail: sales@pdmneptec.com

Pole Star Space Applications, Whiteleys Centre, 301-303 Queensway, London, W2 4YN Tel: (020) 7313 7400 Fax: (020) 7313 7401

▶ Precision Navigation Ltd, 12 Court Farm, Stutton Road, Brantham, Manningtree, Essex, CO11 1PW Tel: (01473) 327813 Fax: (01473) 326859

Simrad Marine Electrical Services, Fish Market Quay, Commercial Road, Buckie, Banffshire, AB56 1UR Tel: (01542) 834888 Fax: (01542) 839005

Tacktick Marine Electrical, 22 North Street, Emsworth, Hampshire, PO10 7DG Tel: (01243) 379331 Fax: (01243) 379199 E-mail: sales@tacktick.com

Taplin International Ltd, Unit 3 Lower William Street, Southampton, SO14 5QE Tel: (023) 8023 2304 Fax: (023) 8023 2305 E-mail: mail@switchcraft.info

MARINE ELECTRONIC ENGINEERING SERVICES

Boat Care UK, 1Turpins Ride, Welwyn, Herts, AL6 0QS Tel: 0845 6521415. E-mail: enquires@boatcareuk.com

Boat Electrics & Electronics Ltd, Harbour Road, Troon, Ayrshire, KA10 6DJ Tel: (01292) 315355 Fax: (01292) 315825 E-mail: sales@boatelectronics.com

C P C Communications, 56 Clive Road, Cardiff, CF5 1HG Tel: (029) 2066 5213 Fax: (01639) 646003

Denbridge Marine Ltd, Cammell Lairds Waterfront Park, Campbell Town Road, Birkenhead, Merseyside, CH41 9HP Tel: 0151-649 4080 Fax: (0870) 0518953 E-mail: info@denbridgemarine.com

F.T. Everard & Sons Ltd, Blake House, Admiral Park, Crossway, Dartford, DA2 6QQ Tel: (01322) 394500 Fax: (01322) 311943

Everard Shipping Companies, Peninsular House, 36 Monument Street, London, EC3R 8LJ Tel: (020) 7398 4450 Fax: (020) 7398 4480

Furuno (U K) Ltd, South Breakwater, Fraserburgh, Aberdeenshire, AB11 5QA Tel: (01346) 518300 Fax: (01346) 512545 E-mail: sales@furuno.co.uk

Mantsbrite Ltd, 19F Spital Road, Maldon, Essex, CM9 6DY Tel: (01621) 853003 Fax: (01621) 850877 E-mail: sales@mantsbrite.com

Maricom Ltd, Hamble Point Marina, School Lane, Hamble, Southampton, SO31 4JD Tel: (023) 8045 4263 Fax: (023) 8045 6910 E-mail: sales@maricom.co.uk

Maritime Solutions, 87 Cauldwell Hall Road, Ipswich, IP4 4QG Tel: (0777) 6347360 E-mail: info@maritimesolutionsipswich.com

Selex Communications Ltd, Unit 26, Byker Business Development Centre, Albion Row, Byker, Newcastle Upon Tyne, NE6 1LQ Tel: 0191-265 0374 Fax: 0191-265 0382 E-mail: newcastle-marine@selexcomms.com

H. Williamson & Sons Ltd, Main Street, Scalloway, Shetland, ZE1 0TR Tel: (01595) 880645 Fax: (01595) 880535 E-mail: mail@hwilliamson.co.uk

MARINE ELECTRONIC EQUIPMENT MANUFRS

A V O Systems Ltd, Unit 3 Dodnor Lane, Newport, Isle Of Wight, PO30 5XA Tel: (01983) 526527 Fax: (01983) 526524 E-mail: sales@avosystems.com

C-Max Ltd, Unit B1 Roman Hill Business Park, Broadmayne, Dorchester, Dorset, DT2 8LY Tel: (01305) 853005 Fax: (01305) 852136 E-mail: mail@cmaxsonar.com

Diverse Yacht Services, Unit 12 Hamble Yacht Services, Port Hamble, Hamble, Southampton, SO31 4NN Tel: (023) 8045 3399 Fax: (023) 8045 5288 E-mail: phil@diverseyachts.com

Echopilot Ltd, 1 Endeavour Park, Crow Arch Lane, Ringwood, Hampshire, BH24 1SF Tel: (01425) 476211 Fax: (01425) 474300 E-mail: info@echopilot.com

F.T. Everard & Sons Ltd, Blake House, Admiral Park, Crossway, Dartford, DA2 6QQ Tel: (01322) 394500 Fax: (01322) 311943

Everard Shipping Companies, Peninsular House, 36 Monument Street, London, EC3R 8LJ Tel: (020) 7398 4450 Fax: (020) 7398 4480

Greenham Regis Ltd, Kings Saltern Road, Lymington, Hampshire, SO41 3QD Tel: (01590) 671144 Fax: (01590) 679517 E-mail: lymington@greenham-regis.com

A.H. Latham Marine, Highfield Business Centre, 1 Simmonds Road, Wincheap Industrial Estate, Canterbury, Kent, CT1 3RA Tel: (01227) 472822 Fax: (01227) 768597 E-mail: sales@zincsmart.com

Nasa Marine, Boulton Road, Stevenage, Hertfordshire, SG1 4QG Tel: (01438) 354033 Fax: (01438) 741498 E-mail: nasa.marine@aol.com

Navico UK Ltd, Premier Way, Abbey Park, Romsey, Hampshire, SO51 9DH Tel: (01794) 510010 Fax: (01794) 510006 E-mail: sales.uk@navico.com

Raymarine Ltd, Quaypoint, North Harper Road, Portsmouth, PO6 3TD Tel: (023) 9269 3611 Fax: (023) 9269 4642 E-mail: info@raymarine.com

Sea Technik Ltd, Court House, 15 Glynne Way, Hawarden, Deeside, Clwyd, CH5 3NS Tel: (01244) 535787 Fax: (01244) 538908 E-mail: admin@seatechnik.com

Simutech Electronics Ltd, Unit 42 Louis Pearlman Centre, Goulton Street, Hull, HU3 4DL Tel: (01482) 212961 Fax: (01482) 585608 E-mail: simutechpt@compuserve.com

T P Electronics, White House Drakes View, Staddon Heights, Plymouth, PL9 9SP Tel: (01752) 482722 Fax: (01752) 482744 E-mail: info@tpelectronics.co.uk

Wema, Horton Court, Horton, Bristol, BS37 6QR Tel: (01454) 316103 Fax: (01454) 310510

Woodsons Of Aberdeen Ltd, Goval House, Dyce, Aberdeen, AB21 0HT Tel: (01224) 722884 Fax: (01224) 722859 E-mail: sales@woodsons.co.uk

MARINE ELECTRONIC TUBES

Furuno UK Ltd, Ocean House Parklands Business Park, Forest Road, Denmead, Waterlooville, Hampshire, PO7 6XP Tel: (023) 9223 0303 Fax: (023) 9223 0101 E-mail: denmead@furunouk.freeserve.co.uk

MARINE ENGINE CONTROL OR STEERING CABLES

Kongsberg Auto Motive, Christopher Martin Road, Basildon, Essex, SS14 3ES Tel: (01268) 522861 Fax: (01268) 282994 E-mail: m.dickason@morse-controls.co.uk

MARINE ENGINE MANUFRS

American Marine Imports, Waterloo Park, Bidford-on-Avon, Alcester, Warwickshire, B50 4JG Tel: (01789) 491673 Fax: (01789) 778377 E-mail: ami1.ltd@btconnect.com

D B Marine, Cookham Bridge, Cookham On Thames, Cookham, Maidenhead, Berkshire, SL6 9SN Tel: (01628) 526032 Fax: (01628) 520564 E-mail: sales@dbmarine.co.uk

Dale Sailing Co Ltd, Brunel Quay, Neyland, Milford Haven, Dyfed, SA73 1PY Tel: (01646) 601061 Fax: (01646) 601061 E-mail: enquiries@dale-sailing.co.uk

Finning Mak Ltd, Rennell House, 40-42 Mill Place, Kingston upon Thames, Surrey, KT1 2RL Tel: (020) 8541 4747 Fax: (020) 8541 4371

H W Richmond & Sons, Swanston Road, Great Yarmouth, Norfolk, NR30 3NQ Tel: (01493) 842066

MARINE ENGINE MANUFRS – *continued*

Hewson & Turrell Ltd, Robinson Lane, Grimsby, South Humberside, DN31 3SF Tel: (01472) 351475 Fax: (01472) 242611 E-mail: sales@hewsonandturrell.co.uk

Kelpie Boats, Hobbs Point, Pembroke Dock, Dyfed, SA72 6TR Tel: (01646) 683661 Fax: (01646) 621398 E-mail: martin@kelpieboats.com

Lancing Marine, 51 Victoria Road, Portslade, Brighton, BN41 1XY Tel: (01273) 411765 Fax: (01273) 430290 E-mail: mail@lancingmarine.com

▶ Marlec Marine Ltd, 11 Military Road, Ramsgate, Kent, CT11 9LG Tel: (01843) 852452 Fax: (01843) 596280 E-mail: alan@marlecmarine.com

Mermaid Marine Ltd, 70-72 Cobham Road, Ferndown Industrial Estate, Wimborne, Dorset, BH21 7RN Tel: (01202) 891824 Fax: (01202) 895882 E-mail: engines@mermaid-marine.co.uk

Rye Harbour Marine, The Point, Rye Harbour Village, Rye, East Sussex, TN31 7PU Tel: (01797) 227667 Fax: (01797) 227667

Sabre Engines Ltd, 22 Cobham Road, Ferndown Industrial Estate, Wimborne, Dorset, BH21 7PW Tel: (01202) 893720 Fax: (01202) 851700 E-mail: post@sabre-engines.co.uk

Slinden Services, 3 Riverside Court, Westminster Industrial Estate, Measham, Swadlincote, Derbyshire, DE12 7DS Tel: (01530) 274646 Fax: (01530) 274647 E-mail: info@slindenservices.co.uk

MARINE ENGINE REPAIR

▶ I S S Machinery Services Ltd, 37 Eastcheap, London, EC3M 1DT Tel: (020) 7626 3505 Fax: (020) 7626 3606

▶ MMS Scotland Ltd, Clyde Marina, The Harbour, Ardrossan, Ayrshire, KA22 8DB Tel: (01294) 604831 E-mail: info@mmsscotland.co.uk

▶ Quayside Marine, 56 Grange Road, Torquay, TQ1 1LF Tel: (01803) 293370 E-mail: sales@quaysidemarine.co.uk

MARINE ENGINE SPARE PARTS/ WEARING PARTS

Amc Diesel Engineering Ltd, Beverley House, Hall Lane, Longton, Preston, PR4 5ZD Tel: (01772) 613003 Fax: (01772) 616364 E-mail: sales@amcdiesel.co.uk

Britannia Marine Services, Unit 11 50 Windsor Avenue, London, SW19 2TJ Tel: (020) 8408 6020 Fax: (020) 8408 6040 E-mail: sales@britannia.com

Chera Marine, 3 Overmoor Fold, Idle, Bradford, West Yorkshire, BD10 8UT Tel: (07976) 741327 Fax: (01274) 619663

Diesel Injector Services, 8 Staveley Way, Brixworth Industrial Estate, Brixworth, Northampton, NN6 9EU Tel: (01604) 880546 Fax: (01604) 880704 E-mail: info@dieselinjectors.co.uk

Diesel Marine International Ltd, Gloucester Road, North Shields, Tyne & Wear, NE29 8RQ Tel: 0191-257 5577 Fax: 0191-258 6398 E-mail: sales@dmiuk.co.uk

Donovan Diesel Engine Equipment, St. Bartholomew Building, Nelson Street, Bolton, BL3 2AH Tel: (01204) 527520 Fax: (01204) 524348 E-mail: donovanandson@aol.com

Keller Bryant Shipping Ltd, Ibex House, Minories, London, EC3N 1DY Tel: (020) 7481 8833 Fax: (0870) 4104312 E-mail: keller-bryant@dial.pipex.com

Marine Electronic Supplies, Unit 14 Westwood Court, Brunel Road, Totton, Southampton, SO40 3WX Tel: (023) 8066 3316 Fax: (023) 8066 3241 E-mail: sales@mesuk.com

▶ Marlec Marine Ltd, 11 Military Road, Ramsgate, Kent, CT11 9LG Tel: (01843) 852452 Fax: (01843) 596280 E-mail: alan@marlecmarine.com

Perkins Engines Co. Ltd, Perkins Powerpart Distribution Centre, Frank Perkins Way, Irlam, Manchester, M44 5PP Tel: 0161-776 5000 Fax: 0161-776 5100

Skandiaverken Ltd S K V, Cartside Avenue, Inchinnan, Renfrew, PA4 9RW Tel: 0141-812 8121 Fax: 0141-812 8124 E-mail: spares@skvuk.com

MARINE ENGINE STARTER MOTORS

▶ Starter Mart, 994 Astley Street, Globe Square, Dukinfield, Cheshire, SK16 4QS Tel: (0870) 8034101 Fax: 0161-343 5755 E-mail: enquires@startermart.co.uk

MARINE ENGINE TEST BED EQUIPMENT

C P Engineering, Sandys Road, Malvern, Worcestershire, WR14 1JJ Tel: (01684) 584850 Fax: (01684) 573088 E-mail: sales@cpengineering.com

MARINE ENGINEERING CONSULTANTS

Burls Gordon & Rolland Ltd, 7 Loxford Way, Caterham, Surrey, CR3 6BX Tel: (01883) 331288 Fax: (01883) 342181 E-mail: surveyor@burlsgordon.demon.co.uk

Burness Corlett & Partners, 12-20 Camomile Street, London, EC3A 7PT Tel: (020) 7621 2943 Fax: (020) 7929 4167 E-mail: enquiries@bctq.com

Challenger Marine Ltd, Freemans Wharf, Falmouth Road, Penryn, Cornwall, TR10 8AD Tel: (01326) 377222 Fax: (01326) 377800 E-mail: sales@challengermarine.co.uk

▶ Imes, Clyde Submarine Base, Faslane, Helensburgh, Dunbartonshire, G84 8HL Tel: (01436) 811000 Fax: (01436) 811477

Lola Cars Ltd, 12 Glebe Road, St Peters Hill, Huntingdon, Cambridgeshire, PE29 7DY Tel: (01480) 456722 Fax: (01480) 482970 E-mail: lola@lolacars.com

Penton Service Centre Ltd, Penton Hook Marina, Mixnams Lane, Chertsey, Surrey, KT16 8QR Tel: (01932) 568772 Fax: (01932) 568967 E-mail: sales@pentonservicecentre.co.uk

River Tees Engineering & Welding Ltd, Slipways, Normanby Wharf, Middlesbrough, Cleveland, TS3 8AT Tel: (01642) 226226 Fax: (01642) 245544 E-mail: river-tees@the-slipways.fsnet.co.uk

MARINE ENGINEERING DESIGN CONSULTANCY

Boyd Line, The Orangery Hesslewood Country Office Park, Ferriby Road, Hessle, North Humberside, HU13 0LH Tel: (01482) 324024 Fax: (01482) 323737 E-mail: info@boydline.co.uk

Denray Cables & Controls, Edwards House, 327 Whapload Road, Lowestoft, Suffolk, NR32 1UL Tel: (01502) 516971 Fax: (01502) 537045

Doxford Design Engineering Ltd, 3 Fellside, Ponteland, Newcastle upon Tyne, NE20 9JW Tel: 0191-519 1433

MARINE ENGINEERING EQUIPMENT, *See also headings for particular types*

A G B Diesels Ltd, 20 Blaris Industrial Estate, Altona Road, Lisburn, County Antrim, BT27 5QB Tel: (028) 9266 1010 Fax: (028) 9266 7711 E-mail: enquiries@aves.co.uk

A V O Systems Ltd, Unit 3 Dodnor Lane, Newport, Isle Of Wight, PO30 5XA Tel: (01983) 526527 Fax: (01983) 526524 E-mail: sales@avosystems.com

B F S International, Willowbrook, 20 Bray Road, Bray, Maidenhead, Berkshire, SL6 1UE Tel: (01628) 671458 Fax: (01628) 784337 E-mail: sales@bfs-international.co.uk

Bainbridge International Ltd, 8 Flanders Park, Flanders Road, Hedge End, Southampton, SO30 2FZ Tel: (01489) 776000 Fax: (01489) 776005 E-mail: mail@bainbridgeint.co.uk

Be Spares Marine, 9 Town Quay Wharf, Abbey Road, Barking, Essex, IG11 7BZ Tel: (020) 8594 9409 Fax: (020) 8594 9429 E-mail: sales@besparesmarine.co.uk

▶ Cardiff Craftsmen Ltd, Unit S1 Cardiff Bay Business Centre, Titan Road, Cardiff, CF24 5EL Tel: (029) 2049 5312 Fax: (029) 2048 8182E-mail: info@cardiffcraftsmen.co.uk

Central Diesel, Unit 15 Hawksley Industrial Estate, Hawksley Street, Oldham, OL8 4PQ Tel: 0161-620 7070 Fax: 0161-620 6007 E-mail: steve.kay@central-diesel.co.uk

C-Max Ltd, Unit B1 Roman Hill Business Park, Broadmayne, Dorchester, Dorset, DT2 8LY Tel: (01305) 853005 Fax: (01305) 852136 E-mail: mail@cmaxsonar.com

D.F. Coulam & Sons, Northfields Industrial Estate, 3 Stirling Way, Market Deeping, Peterborough, PE6 8LG Tel: (01778) 346518 Fax: (01778) 380495 E-mail: sales@dfcspares.com

D Steer Fabrication, 4 Riverside Avenue West, Lawford, Manningtree, Essex, CO11 1UN Tel: (01206) 391767 Fax: (01206) 391767 E-mail: thesteers@virgin.net

Donovan Diesel Engine Equipment, St. Bartholomew Building, Nelson Street, Bolton, BL3 2AH Tel: (01204) 527520 Fax: (01204) 524348 E-mail: donovanandson@aol.com

E T Marine & Industrial Engineering Co Ltd, Manor Way, Grays, Essex, RM17 6BJ Tel: (01375) 378282 Fax: (01375) 385804 E-mail: works@etmarine.com

Hardy Engineering, Unit D Foundry Lane, Burnham-on-Crouch, Essex, CM0 8SH Tel: (01621) 782726 Fax: (01621) 785645 E-mail: email@hardyengineering.com

Hepworths Shipyard Ltd, Main Street, Paull, Hull, HU12 8AN Tel: (01482) 338817 Fax: (01482) 338820 E-mail: hepworths@rix.co.uk

Hutton & Co. (Ships Chandlers) Ltd, Connaught Road, Kingswood, Hull, HU7 3AP Tel: (01482) 329925 Fax: (01482) 580588 E-mail: sales@huttons-chandlers.com

Inverlane Marine Services Ltd, 15 Lintlaw Drive, Glasgow, G52 2NS Tel: 0141-883 4834 Fax: 0141-882 8874 E-mail: sales@inverlane-marine.co.uk

Lincoln Diesels plc, Great Northern Terrace, Lincoln, LN5 8HJ Tel: (01522) 511512 Fax: (01522) 512935 E-mail: ld@lincolndiesels.com

Macgregor GBR Ltd, Powerhouse, Silverlink, Wallsend, Tyne & Wear, NE28 9ND Tel: 0191-295 2180 Fax: 0191-295 2188 E-mail: info@macgregor-group.com

Re Trem & Co. Ltd, Old Bawtry Road, Finningley, Doncaster, South Yorkshire, DN9 3BX Tel: (01302) 770203 Fax: (01302) 770868 E-mail: sales@enginesandgenerators.com

Seaeye Marine Ltd, Seaeye House, Lower Quay Road, Fareham, Hampshire, PO16 0RQ Tel: (01329) 289000 Fax: (01329) 289001

Sea-Quipment International Sales Ltd, Bassett Road, Park Lane Industrial Estate, Halesowen, West Midlands, B63 2RE Tel: (01384) 562999 Fax: (01384) 568217

SSAB Swedish Steel UK (Dobel), Unit 17 Narrowboat Way, Hurst Business Park, Brierley Hill, West Midlands, DY5 1UF Tel: (01384) 74660 Fax: (01384) 77575 E-mail: sales@dobel.co.uk

W. Stowell (Shipping) Ltd, 37 Coleridge Avenue, Low Fell, Gateshead, Tyne & Wear, NE9 6EN Tel: 0191-487 3222 Fax: 0191-491 0056 E-mail: sparestan@stowellshipping.co.uk

V T Marine Products Ltd, Hamilton Road, Cosham, Portsmouth, PO6 4PX Tel: (023) 9253 9750 Fax: (023) 9253 9764

Watermota Ltd, Cavalier Road, Heathfield Industrial Estate, Newton Abbot, Devon, TQ12 6TQ Tel: (01626) 830910 Fax: (01626) 830911 E-mail: mike@watermota.co.uk

MARINE ENGINEERS OR ENGINEERING SERVICES

A & P Tyne, Wagonway Road, Hebburn, Tyne & Wear, NE31 1SP Tel: 0191-430 8600 Fax: 0191-428 6228 E-mail: tyne@ap-group.co.uk

Aalmar Surveys Ltd, 32-38 Dukes Place, London, EC3A 7LP Tel: (020) 7929 1401 Fax: (020) 7626 3775 E-mail: info@aalmar.com

A. Adamson, 81 Iona Way, Tirantilloch, Glasgow, G66 3PU Tel: (0141) 552 5749 Fax: (0141) 552 4917

Air Vehicles Design & Engineering Ltd, Unit 4 Three Gates Road, Cowes, Isle of Wight, PO31 7UT Tel: (01983) 293194 Fax: (01983) 291987 E-mail: info@airvehicles.co.uk

B Sinclair, Kirkton Cottage, Auchterless, Turriff, Aberdeenshire, AB53 8BA Tel: (01888) 511406 Fax: (01888) 511406

Barclay & Purvis Ltd, 8 Baker St, Weybridge, Surrey, KT13 8AU Tel: (01932) 845247 Fax: (01932) 850448

John Bridger Marine, Haven Road, Exeter, EX2 8DP Tel: (01392) 250970 Fax: (01392) 410955E-mail: bridgermarine@btconnect.com

Brixham Marine Services Ltd, Unit 21 Northfields Industrial Estate, Brixham, Devon, TQ5 8UA Tel: (01803) 854224 Fax: (01803) 857363 E-mail: salesandservice@bmslimited.co.uk

Burgess Marine Services, Channel View Road, Dover, Kent, CT17 9TJ Tel: (01304) 207707 Fax: (01304) 207727 E-mail: info@burgessengineering.co.uk

Burls Gordon & Rolland Ltd, 7 Loxford Way, Caterham, Surrey, CR3 6BX Tel: (01883) 331288 Fax: (01883) 342181 E-mail: surveyor@burlsgordon.demon.co.uk

C V S Pentapower, St. Andrews Road, Northampton, NN1 2LF Tel: (01604) 638537 Fax: (01604) 634927 E-mail: sales@pentapower.com

▶ Cardiff Craftsmen Ltd, Unit S1 Cardiff Bay Business Centre, Titan Road, Cardiff, CF24 5EL Tel: (029) 2049 5312 Fax: (029) 2048 8182E-mail: info@cardiffcraftsmen.co.uk

M.A. Carroll Engineers Ltd, Birkby, Huddersfield, HD1 5EY Tel: (01484) 510846 Fax: (01484) 425953 E-mail: macengs@cs.com

Challenger Marine Ltd, Freemans Wharf, Falmouth Road, Penryn, Cornwall, TR10 8AD Tel: (01326) 377222 Fax: (01326) 377800 E-mail: sales@challengermarine.co.uk

Chera Marine, 3 Overmoor Fold, Idle, Bradford, West Yorkshire, BD10 8UT Tel: (07976) 741327 Fax: (01274) 619663

Crouch Engineering Co. (Burnham-on-Crouch) Ltd, 150 Station Rd, Burnham-on-Crouch, Essex, CM0 8HQ Tel: (01621) 782130 Fax: (01621) 782130

D B Marine, Cookham Bridge, Cookham On Thames, Cookham, Maidenhead, Berkshire, SL6 9SN Tel: (01628) 526032 Fax: (01628) 520564 E-mail: sales@dbmarine.co.uk

D D Z Marine, Largs Yacht Haven, Irvine Road, Largs, Ayrshire, KA30 8EZ Tel: (01475) 686072 Fax: (01475) 672887 E-mail: sales@ddzmarine.com

Darthaven Marina Ltd, Brixham Road, Kingswear, Dartmouth, Devon, TQ6 0SG Tel: (01803) 752733 Fax: (01803) 752722

E T Marine & Industrial Engineering Co Ltd, Manor Way, Grays, Essex, RM17 6BJ Tel: (01375) 378282 Fax: (01375) 385804 E-mail: works@etmarine.com

Eurotex International Ltd, Unit 20 Shipyard Estate, Brightlingsea, Colchester, CO7 0AR Tel: (01206) 304063 Fax: (01206) 304026 E-mail: terry.kershaw@virgin.net

Felixarc Marine, Ground Floor, Wickenden House, The Dock, Felixstowe, Suffolk, IP11 3TZ Tel: (01394) 676497 Fax: (01394) 674039

Freedom Marine Ltd, 3 Westfield Industrial Estate, Westfield Lane, Etchinghill, Folkestone, Kent, CT18 8BX Tel: (01303) 862215 Fax: (01303) 863066 E-mail: freedom@engines10.freeserve.co.uk

G Heyn & Sons Ltd, 1 Corry Place, Belfast, BT3 9AH Tel: (028) 9035 0000 Fax: (028) 9035 0011 E-mail: info@heyn.co.uk

Garvel Clyde, James Watt Dock, Greenock, Renfrewshire, PA15 2AJ Tel: (01475) 725372 Fax: (01475) 725377

Goodchild Marine Services, Burgh Castle Yacht Station, Butt Lane, Burgh Castle, Great Yarmouth, Norfolk, NR31 9PZ Tel: (01493) 782301 Fax: (01493) 782306 E-mail: info@goodchildmarine.co.uk

▶ Gordon Giles & Co. Ltd, Rennie House, 57-60 Aldgate High Street, London, EC3N 1AL Tel: (020) 7709 0011 Fax: (020) 7709 0022 E-mail: info@newmangiles.com

Hamilton Jet UK Ltd, Unit 4a Birches Industrial Estate, East Grinstead, West Sussex, RH19 1XZ Tel: (01342) 313437 Fax: (01342) 313438 E-mail: info@hamjetuk.com

Hart Fenton & Co. Ltd, First Floor Norman House, Kettering Terrace, Portsmouth, PO2 7AE Tel: (023) 9287 5277 Fax: (023) 9287 5280 E-mail: hf@hart-fenton.co.uk

Hartman Marine Services, Unit C2 The Boatyard, Stonar Industrial Estate, Sandwich, Kent, CT13 9LY Tel: (01304) 614121 Fax: (01304) 615070 E-mail: hartman.marine@virgin.net

Hedley (Engineering Services) Ltd, West Havelock Street, South Shields, Tyne & Wear, NE33 5DZ Tel: 0191-456 0250 Fax: 0191-455 6040 E-mail: info@hedley.co.uk

High Line Yachting Ltd, Mansion Lane, Iver, Buckinghamshire, SL0 9RG Tel: (01753) 651496 Fax: (01753) 630095 E-mail: sales@high-line.co.uk

Hilsea Engineering Ltd, 3 St Georges Indust Estate, Rodney Road, Southsea, Hampshire, PO4 8SS Tel: (023) 9273 1676 Fax: (023) 9282 7801 E-mail: hilseaeng@fsbdial.co.uk

Hythe Marine Services, Prospect Place, Hythe, Southampton, SO45 6AU Tel: (023) 8084 8782 Fax: (023) 8084 6760 E-mail: raymithchener@btconnect.com

Irvings Engineering, Denton I, Newhaven, East Sussex, BN9 9BA Tel: (01273) 513032 Fax: (01273) 513032 E-mail: info@plmarine.com

John H Whitaker Holdings, Crown Dry Dock, Tower Street, Hull, HU9 1TY Tel: (01482) 595300 Fax: (01482) 226270

Judge & Dalton, 6 College Road, Northfleet, Gravesend, Kent, DA11 9AU Tel: (01474) 564504 Fax: (01474) 535809 E-mail: knjudg@aol.com

K & K Mouldings Ltd, Bridge Road, Ely, Cambridgeshire, CB7 4DY Tel: (01353) 663726 Fax: (01353) 668766 E-mail: sales@bridgeboatyard.com

Kishorn Mechanical, Russel Workshop, Kishorn, Strathcarron, Ross-Shire, IV54 8XF Tel: (01520) 733261 Fax: (01520) 733261

M M S Ship Repair & Dry Dock Co. Ltd, Alexandra Dock, Hull, HU9 1TA Tel: (01482) 219278 Fax: (01482) 588061 E-mail: sales@mms-shiprepair.co.uk

Mactaggart Scott (Holdings) Ltd, PO Box 1, Loanhead, Midlothian, EH20 9SP Tel: 0131-440 0311 Fax: 0131-440 4493

Marine & General Engineers Ltd, PO Box 470, Guernsey, GY1 6AT Tel: (01481) 245808 Fax: (01481) 248765

Marine Power Ltd, Deacons Boatyard, Bridge Road, Bursledon, Southampton, SO31 8AW Tel: (023) 8040 3918 Fax: (023) 8040 4491 E-mail: peter@marine-power.co.uk

Markwell Ltd, 24-25 Littlewood Lane, Hoveton, Norwich, NR12 8DZ Tel: (01603) 783053 Fax: (01603) 783053

Matatec, Station Road, Seaton Delaval, Seaton Delaval, Whitley Bay, Tyne & Wear, NE25 0PT Tel: 0191-237 9900 Fax: 0191-237 9999 E-mail: msl@matatec.co.uk

Melec Trading, 24 Parkshiel, South Shields, Tyne & Wear, NE34 8BU Tel: 0191-454 5585 E-mail: ka@melec.co.uk

▶ Milford Haven Ship Repairers, The Docks, Milford Haven, Dyfed, SA73 3DJ Tel: (01646) 696320 Fax: (01646) 696321 E-mail: mhsr@milford-docks.co.uk

Motortech Marine Engineering Ltd, 4-5 The Slipway, Marina Keep, Port Solent, Portsmouth, PO6 4TR Tel: (023) 9220 1171 Fax: (023) 9220 1172 E-mail: enquiries@motortechmarine.co.uk

Mouchel Parkman plc, West Hall, Parvis Road, West Byfleet, Surrey, KT14 6EZ Tel: (01932) 337000 Fax: (01932) 340673 E-mail: info@mouchelparkman.com

Mounts Bay Engineering Ltd, North Pier, Newlyn, Penzance, Cornwall, TR18 5JB Tel: (01736) 363095 Fax: (01736) 332010

Mulco Engineering Ltd, 9-10 St Machar Road, Aberdeen, AB24 2UU Tel: (01224) 481215 Fax: (01224) 486041 E-mail: info@mulco.co.uk

North Western Automarine, Largs Yacht Haven, Irvine Road, Largs, Ayrshire, KA30 8EZ Tel: (01475) 687139 Fax: (01475) 687139

▶ P T Marine, Metalstock House, Vanguard Way, Shoeburyness, Southend-On-Sea, SS3 9RE Tel: (07973) 780930 Fax: (07814) 182901 E-mail: service@marine-eng.co.uk

Porter & Haylett Ltd, Viaduct Works, Wroxham, Norwich, NR12 8RX Tel: (01603) 782472 Fax: (01603) 783089 E-mail: sales@connoisseurafloat.com

MARINE ENGINEERS OR ENGINEERING SERVICES – *continued*

Poseidon Maritime (UK) Ltd, 480 Union Street, Aberdeen, AB10 1TS Tel: (01224) 561133 Fax: (01224) 561144 E-mail: info@poseidonuk.com

George Prior Engineering Ltd, ABC Wharf, Southgates Road, Great Yarmouth, Norfolk, NR30 3LQ Tel: (01493) 852311 Fax: (01493) 330074

▶ Quayside Precision Engineering, Unit 14-15 Vancouver Wharf, Hazel Road, Southampton, SO19 7BN Tel: (023) 8043 9700 Fax: (023) 8043 9701

R H P Marine, Shepards Wharf, Medina Road, Cowes, Isle of Wight, PO31 7HT Tel: (01983) 290421 Fax: (01983) 290114 E-mail: rhpmarine@aol.com

R W Davis & Son Ltd, Junction Dry Dock, Canal Bank, Saul, Gloucester, GL2 7LA Tel: (01452) 740233 Fax: (01452) 741307 E-mail: sales@rwdavis.co.uk

R Wright & Son Marine Engineers Ltd, Church Broughton Road, Foston, Derby, DE65 5PW Tel: (01283) 812177 Fax: (01283) 812052

Retreat Boatyard Topsham Ltd, Retreat Drive, Topsham, Exeter, EX3 0LS Tel: (01392) 874720 Fax: (01392) 876182 E-mail: sales@retreatboatyard.co.uk

RHP Marine, Shepards Wharf, Medina Road, Cowes, Isle of Wight, PO31 7HT Tel: (01983) 200036 Fax: (01983) 299114

Royle Jackson Ltd, 1 Granville Street, Southampton, SO14 5FQ Tel: (023) 8033 1288 Fax: (023) 8033 9022

Scarborough Marine Engineers Ltd, 35-36 Sandside, Scarborough, North Yorkshire, YO11 1PQ Tel: (01723) 375199 Fax: (01723) 379734E-mail: info@scarboroughmarine.co.uk

Seacor Marine International Ltd, Columbus Buildings, Waveney Road, Lowestoft, Suffolk, NR32 1BN Tel: (01502) 573366 Fax: (01502) 581500 E-mail: alan@bpos1.fsbusiness.co.uk

Sesmarine Ltd, 19A Harraton Terrace, Birtley, Chester Le Street, County Durham, DH2 2QG Tel: 0191-411 1141 Fax: 0191-411 4211

Shipaid Diesel Services Ltd, 9 Marjorie Avenue, Lincoln, LN6 7SD Tel: (01522) 533990 Fax: (01522) 544355 E-mail: shipaid.deisel@globaluk.net

Sillette Sonic, 2 Beverley Trading Estate, Garth Road, Morden, Surrey, SM4 4LU Tel: (020) 8337 7543 Fax: (020) 8330 9014 E-mail: sales@sillette.co.uk

Topper International Ltd, Kingsnorth Industrial Estate, Wotton Road, Ashford, Kent, TN23 6LN Tel: (01233) 629186 Fax: (01233) 645897 E-mail: info@toppersailboats.com

Troon Marine Services Ltd, Harbour Road, Troon, Ayrshire, KA10 6DJ Tel: (01292) 316180 Fax: (01292) 316180

Veeanco Ltd, 20-22 Dunston Trading Estate, Foxwood Road, Chesterfield, Derbyshire, S41 9RF Tel: (01246) 452152 Fax: (01246) 455940 E-mail: sales@veeanco.com

W Bertram & Sons Ltd, Walpole Street, South Shields, Tyne & Wear, NE33 5EF Tel: 0191-455 6727 Fax: 0191-455 6727

W J Marine Analytical Services Ltd, Unit 4, Marine Park, Tapton Hall Industrial Estate, Great Yarmouth, Norfolk, NR31 0NL Tel: (01493) 600600 Fax: (01493) 652099 E-mail: wjmarine@btinternet.com

Watermota Ltd, Cavalier Road, Heathfield Industrial Estate, Newton Abbot, Devon, TQ12 6TQ Tel: (01626) 830910 Fax: (01626) 830911 E-mail: mike@watermota.co.uk

West End Marine, Stocks Lane, Batley, West Yorkshire, WF17 8PA Tel: (01924) 478060 Fax: (01924) 478060 E-mail: westendmarine1@aol.com

Wilman Marine Ltd, 510 Victoria Road, Feltham, Middlesex, TW13 7DR Tel: (020) 8890 4000 Fax: (020) 8751 4128 E-mail: wilmanuniversal@msn.com

Wooberry Engineering & Marine Co, 21 Parvis Road, West Byfleet, Surrey, KT14 6HD Tel: (01932) 352070 Fax: (01932) 353479

MARINE EQUIPMENT

Air Vehicles Design & Engineering Ltd, Unit 4 Three Gates Road, Cowes, Isle of Wight, PO31 7UT Tel: (01983) 293194 Fax: (01983) 291987 E-mail: info@airvehicles.co.uk

Anglo Eastern Ship Management UK Ltd, The Parks, 107-115 Milton Street, Glasgow, G4 0DN Tel: 0141-353 1020 Fax: 0141-353 2366 E-mail: supplies@tandh.co.uk

Aquamarine, 216 Fair Oak Road, Eastleigh, Hampshire, SO50 8HU Tel: (023) 8060 0473 Fax: (023) 8060 1381 E-mail: admin@aqua-marine.co.uk

Atec Hampshire Ltd, Peel Street, Southampton, SO14 5QT Tel: (023) 8063 1391 Fax: (023) 8033 8931 E-mail: sales@atec-hants.co.uk

Bath Marina & Caravan Park, Brassmill Lane, Bath, BA1 3JT Tel: (01225) 424301 Fax: (01225) 424301 E-mail: sales@bwml.co.uk

Be Spares Marine, 9 Town Quay Wharf, Abbey Road, Barking, Essex, IG11 7BZ Tel: (020) 8594 9409 Fax: (020) 8594 9429 E-mail: sales@besparesmarine.co.uk

Blacknor Technology Ltd, 1d South Way, Southwell Business Park, Portland, Dorset, DT5 2NJ Tel: (01305) 860922 Fax: (01305) 860912 E-mail: enquiries@blacknor.com

Bloctube Marine Services Ltd, 5 Felnex Close, Leeds, LS9 0SR Tel: 0113-248 4827 Fax: 0113-240 3351 E-mail: enquiries@bloctube.co.uk

Boat & Jet Ski World, 94 Newhall Street, Willenhall, West Midlands, WV13 1LQ Tel: 0121-323 5335 Fax: (01902) 366136 E-mail: post@boatandjetskiworld.co.uk

Bosuns Locker, 10 Military Road, Ramsgate, Kent, CT11 9LG Tel: (01843) 597158 Fax: (01843) 597158

Briggs Marine Contractors Ltd, West Dock, Seaforth Place, Burntisland, Fife, KY3 9AU Tel: (01592) 872939 Fax: (01592) 873975

Chas Newens Marine Co. Ltd, The Boathouse, Embankment, London, SW15 1LB Tel: (020) 8788 4587 Fax: (020) 8780 2339 E-mail: sales@chastheboat.co.uk

Crayford Special Vehicle Ltd, Lyon Way, St. Albans, Hertfordshire, AL4 0LQ Tel: (01727) 851222 Fax: (01727) 859222 E-mail: sales@crayford.co.uk

D S B Offshore Ltd, Eden House, 59 Fulham High Street, London, SW6 3JJ Tel: (020) 7384 2882 Fax: (020) 7731 8163 E-mail: sales@dsboffshore.com

Furneaux Riddall & Co. Ltd, Alchorne Place, Portsmouth, PO3 5PA Tel: (023) 9266 8621 Fax: (023) 9269 0521 E-mail: info@furneauxriddall.com

Interworld, Avenue Road, Lasham, Alton, Hampshire, GU34 5SU Tel: (01256) 381641 Fax: (01256) 381378

L D C Racing Sail Boats, Trafalgar Close, Chandler's Ford, Eastleigh, Hampshire, SO53 4BW Tel: (023) 8027 4500 Fax: (023) 8027 4800 E-mail: info@ldcracingsailboats.co.uk

Leda-Lite International Ltd, The Briars, Mayes Lane, Sandon, Chelmsford, CM2 7RP Tel: (01245) 227500 Fax: (01245) 221673 E-mail: leda-lite-international@aol.com

Make Fast Ltd, 31 Mochdre Industrial Estate, Mochdre, Newtown, Powys, SY16 4LE Tel: (01686) 629010 Fax: (01686) 626700 E-mail: sales@makefast.com

Maricom Ltd, Hamble Point Marina, School Lane, Hamble, Southampton, SO31 4JD Tel: (023) 8045 4263 Fax: (023) 8045 6910 E-mail: sales@maricom.co.uk

Marine Equipment Supply Co. Ltd, Enterprise House, Harveys Lane, Seething, Norwich, NR15 1EN Tel: (01508) 483702 Fax: (01508) 482710 E-mail: enquiries@marine-equipment.co.uk

Marine Ventures Ltd, Marven House, 1 Field Road, Reading, RG1 6AP Tel: 0118-950 3707 Fax: 0118-950 4066 E-mail: info@marineventures.co.uk

Mermaid Marine Ltd, 70-72 Cobham Road, Ferndown Industrial Estate, Wimborne, Dorset, BH21 7RN Tel: (01202) 891824 Fax: (01202) 895882 E-mail: engines@mermaid-marine.co.uk

Ninefields Holdings Ltd, 1 & 2 Bruce Grove, Heron Trading Estate, Wickford, Essex, SS11 8DB Tel: (01268) 732148 Fax: (01268) 764394 E-mail: info@ninefields.co.uk

Ocean Safety Ltd, Saxon Wharf, Lower York Street, Southampton, SO14 5QF Tel: (023) 8072 0800 Fax: (023) 8072 0801

Outboard & Hydroplane Services Ltd, 12 Springfield Road, Aughton, Ormskirk, Lancashire, L39 6ST Tel: (01695) 422350 Fax: (01695) 424106 E-mail: frank.lynch1@btconnect.com

Plastimo Ltd, Hamilton Business Park, Botley Road, Hedgend, Southampton, SO30 2HE Tel: (01489) 778850 Fax: (0870) 7511950 E-mail: sales@plastimo.co.uk

S E S Ltd, Unit 3 6 Clarence Street, Aberdeen, AB11 5DB Tel: (01224) 212132 Fax: (01224) 213031 E-mail: sales@ses-marine.com

Sternpower Marine Drives Ltd, 51 Victoria Road, Portslade, Brighton, BN41 1XY Tel: (01273) 411765 Fax: (01273) 430290 E-mail: sternpower@lancingmarine.com

W Christie & Co. Ltd, 22 Crownpoint Road, Glasgow, G40 2BS Tel: 0141-951 1265 Fax: 0141-556 1444 E-mail: sales@wchristie.co.uk

Walkers Yacht Chandlery, 1 Brunel Road, Leigh-on-Sea, Essex, SS9 5JL Tel: (01702) 421321 Fax: (01702) 421321

Water Sports, 6A Red Road, West Mersea, Colchester, CO5 8QT Tel: (01206) 384296

Whitstable Marine, Sea Wall, Whitstable, Kent, CT5 1BX Tel: (01227) 262525 Fax: (01227) 772750 E-mail: sales@thedinghystore.co.uk

Woodsons Of Aberdeen Ltd, Goval House, Dyce, Aberdeen, AB21 0HT Tel: (01224) 722884 Fax: (01224) 722859 E-mail: sales@woodsons.co.uk

MARINE FABRICATORS

Ab Light Engineering, Hollygrove Farm, Upper Northam Drive, Hedge End, Southampton, SO30 4BG Tel: (023) 8046 6657 Fax: (023) 8046 6657

B F S Enterprise Fabrications Ltd, 6 Ellough Industrial Estate, Ellough, Beccles, Suffolk, NR34 7TD Tel: (01502) 716383 Fax: (01502) 717416 E-mail: m.spence@bfs-fabs.co.uk

Hewson & Turrell Ltd, Robinson Lane, Grimsby, South Humberside, DN31 3SF Tel: (01472) 351475 Fax: (01472) 242611 E-mail: sales@hewsonandturrell.co.uk

MARINE FILTERS

K & N Filters Europe Ltd, John Street, Warrington, WA2 7UB Tel: (01925) 636950 Fax: (01925) 418948E-mail: kn@knfilters.com

Separ Distribution, 428 Whippendell Road, Watford, WD18 7QU Tel: (01923) 819041 Fax: (01923) 255052 E-mail: filtration@separ.co.uk

MARINE FIXED BLADE PROPELLERS

Clements Engineering (St. Neots) Ltd, Unit 120 Westgate, Airfield Industrial Park, Little Staughton, Bedford, MK44 2BN Tel: (01234) 378814 Fax: (01234) 376779 E-mail: sales@clementsmarine.co.uk

▶ Ringprop plc, Haslar Road, Gosport, Hampshire, PO12 2AU Tel: (023) 9233 5788 Fax: (023) 9233 5787 E-mail: info@ringprop.com

MARINE FLUORESCENT LIGHTING

Marine Lighting UK Ltd, 80 Dunster Road, Chelmsley Wood, Birmingham, B37 7UU Tel: 0121-770 8522 Fax: 0121-770 0505 E-mail: marlux@btconnect.com

Sondia Lighting Ltd, 45 Portland Place, Hull, HU2 8QP Tel: (01482) 223353 Fax: (01482) 225681 E-mail: sales@sondialighting.com

MARINE FUEL INJECTION INSTALLATION OR SERVICING

Peter Fraenkel Maritime Ltd, 21-37 South Street, Dorking, Surrey, RH4 2JZ Tel: (01306) 879797 Fax: (01306) 879798 E-mail: contact@fraenkel.co.uk

MARINE FUEL OIL WASTE RECOVERY OR PROCESSORS OR SERVICES OR MERCHANTS

▶ Oil Salvage Ltd, Lyster Road, Bootle, Merseyside, L20 1AS Tel: 0151-933 4084 Fax: 0151-922 8488 E-mail: sales@oilsalvage.com

MARINE GEARS

Newbrook Engineering Co. Ltd, Church Street, Donington, Spalding, Lincolnshire, PE11 4UA Tel: (01775) 820583 Fax: (01775) 820487 E-mail: newbrook.eng@virgin.net

MARINE GENERATOR SETS

Allam Marine Ltd, 10-12 Lime Street, Hull, HU8 7AB Tel: (01482) 224861 Fax: (01482) 226680

MARINE GRADE HARDWOODS

▶ Lewis, Unit 92 Dolphin House Stephenson Way, Formby Business Park, Formby, Liverpool, L37 8EG Tel: (01704) 831142 Fax: (01704) 879767 E-mail: enquiries@ablewis.co.uk

MARINE HARDWARE

C F E Fasteners Ltd, Unit 18, Central Trading Estate, Cable Street, Wolverhampton, WV2 2HX Tel: (01902) 871777 Fax: (01902) 351410 E-mail: sales@cfe.co.uk

CSB Lifting & Marine Products, 3 Station Road Industrial Estate, Station Road, Rowley Regis, West Midlands, B65 0JY Tel: 0121-559 5112 Fax: 0121-559 4173

Diverse Yacht Services, Unit 12 Hamble Yacht Services, Port Hamble, Hamble, Southampton, SO31 4NN Tel: (023) 8045 3399 Fax: (023) 8045 5288 E-mail: phil@diverseyachts.com

▶ Dorset Marine Services Ltd, Unit C51, Block B, Winfrith Technology Centre, Winfrith, Dorchester, Dorset, DT2 8DH Tel: (0845) 3452493 Fax: (0845) 3452494 E-mail: sales@dorsetmarineservices.co.uk

Gowen Ocean Sailmakers Ltd, 130 Coast Road, West Mersea, Colchester, CO5 8PG Tel: (01206) 384412 Fax: (01206) 382834 E-mail: sales@gosails.com

Hawk Mouldings, Mill Rythe Lane, Hayling Island, Hampshire, PO11 0QG Tel: (023) 9246 3864 Fax: (023) 9246 7204 E-mail: sales@hawkmouldings.co.uk

MARINE HATCH COVERS

Lewmar Ltd, Southmoor Lane, Havant, Hampshire, PO9 1JJ Tel: (023) 9247 1841 Fax: (023) 9248 5720 E-mail: info@lewmar.com

Trend Marine Products Ltd, Sutton Road, Catfield, Great Yarmouth, Norfolk, NR29 5BG Tel: (01692) 581307 Fax: (01692) 582993 E-mail: enquiry@trendmarine.com

MARINE HEAT EXCHANGERS

A M I Exchanges Ltd, Apex Workshops, Graythorp Industrial Estate, Hartlepool, Cleveland, TS25 2DF Tel: (01429) 860187 Fax: (01429) 860673 E-mail: sales@ami-exchangers.co.uk

Abbey Heat Transfer Ltd, Unit 6 Parham Drive, Eastleigh, Hampshire, SO50 4NU Tel: (023) 8065 3331 Fax: (023) 8065 3332 E-mail: hugh@abbeyheat.co.uk

Cov Rad Heat Transfer, Canley Works, Sir Henry Parkes Road, Coventry, CV5 6BN Tel: (024) 7671 3316 Fax: (024) 7671 3316 E-mail: glen.hurst@covrad.co.uk

UK Exchangers Ltd, Unit 13 StileBrook Road, Olney, Buckinghamshire, MK46 5EA Tel: (01234) 244320 Fax: (01234) 714978 E-mail: sales@uk-exchangers.com

MARINE HULL SURVEYORS

YachtScan Ltd, 52 Gifford Terrace Road, Plymouth, PL3 4JE Tel: 0845 873 6335 Fax: 07790 320492 E-mail: info@yachtscan.co.uk

MARINE INFORMATION SERVICES, *See also Shipping Information Services*

BMT Cordah Ltd, Grove House, 7 Ocean Way, Southampton, SO14 3TJ Tel: (023) 8023 2222 Fax: (023) 8023 2891 E-mail: jenny.bell@bmtcordah.com

Parsons Brinckerhoff Ltd, 29 Cathedral Road, Cardiff, CF11 9HA Tel: (029) 2082 7000 Fax: (029) 2082 7001

MARINE INSTRUMENTATION

Fred Allen Products Ltd, Number 16, Balena Close, Creekmoore Trading Estate, Poole, Dorset, BH17 7DB Tel: (01202) 657740 Fax: (01202) 667778 E-mail: sales@fredallenproducts.com

Bond Instrumentation & Process Control Ltd, Woodrope Building, Woodrolfe Road, Tollesbury, Essex, CM9 8SE Tel: (01621) 862140 Fax: (01621) 862141 E-mail: bond@bond.ipc.com

Echopilot Ltd, 1 Endeavour Park, Crow Arch Lane, Ringwood, Hampshire, BH24 1SF Tel: (01425) 476211 Fax: (01425) 474300 E-mail: info@echopilot.com

▶ John Lawrie Demolition Ltd, Hareness Road, Altens Industrial Estate, Aberdeen, AB12 3LE Tel: (01224) 871844 Fax: (01224) 898053 E-mail: info@johnlawrie.com

Simrad Ltd, Star Lane, Margate, Kent, CT9 4NP Tel: (01843) 290290 Fax: (01843) 290471

MARINE INSTRUMENTATION DESIGN ENGINEERS

Thomas Gunn Navigation Services Ltd, Anchor House, 62 Regent Quay, Aberdeen, AB11 5AR Tel: (01224) 595045 Fax: (01224) 584702 E-mail: info@thomasgunn.com

MARINE INSURANCE BROKERS

Heath Lambert Overseas Ltd, 133 Houndsditch, London, EC3A 7AH Tel: (020) 7560 3000 Fax: (020) 7560 3000 E-mail: info@heathgroup.com

St Margarets, 11 Tower View, Kings Hill, West Malling, Kent, ME19 4UY Tel: (01732) 223820 Fax: (01732) 223821 E-mail: yachts@stminsurance.co.uk

Seascope Insurance Services Ltd, 57 Mansell Street, London, E1 8AN Tel: (020) 7488 3288 Fax: (020) 7481 4499 E-mail: enquiries@seains.com

MARINE INSURANCE COMPANIES

Ace European Group, The Ace Building, 100 Leadenhall Street, London, EC3A 3BP Tel: (020) 7173 7000 Fax: (020) 7173 7800 E-mail: info@ace-ina.com

Britannia Steam Ship Insurance Association Ltd, New City Court, 20 St Thomas Street, London, SE1 9RR Tel: (020) 7407 3588 Fax: (020) 7403 3942

MARINE INSURANCE COMPANIES – *continued*

C N A Europe Holdings Ltd, 77 Gracechurch Street, London, EC3V 0DL Tel: (020) 7548 1171

Cornish Fishing Vessels Insurance Society Ltd, Fish Market, Newlyn, Penzance, Cornwall, TR18 5DS Tel: (01736) 360720 Fax: (01736) 331079

Das Legal Expenses Insurance Co. Ltd, D A S House Quay Side, Temple Back, Bristol, BS1 6NH Tel: 0117-934 2000 Fax: 0117-934 2109 E-mail: sales@das.co.uk

Liverpool & London P & I Management Ltd, Royal Liver Building, Pier Head, Liverpool, L3 1QR Tel: 0151-236 3777 Fax: 0151-236 0053 E-mail: info@livlon.co.uk

North Of England P & I, 100 Quayside, Newcastle upon Tyne, NE1 3DU Tel: 0191-232 5221 Fax: 0191-261 0540 E-mail: general@nepia.com

United Kingdom Mutual War Risks Association Ltd, International House, 26 Creechurch Lane, London, EC3A 5BA Tel: (020) 7283 4646 Fax: (020) 7929 3918

W.K. Webster & Co. Ltd, 10 Fen Church Avenue, London, EC3M 5BN Tel: (020) 8300 7744 Fax: (020) 8309 1266 E-mail: info@wkwebster.com

MARINE INSURANCE MANAGERS

Thomas Miller & Co. Ltd, International House, 26 Creechurch Lane, London, EC3A 5BA Tel: (020) 7283 4646 Fax: (020) 7283 5614

MARINE INTERIOR DESIGN

Hollis Design LLP, 30 St Catherines Road, Winchester, Hampshire, SO23 0PS Tel: (0845) 8382034 E-mail: architect@hollisdesign.co.uk

MARINE LAMPS, *See Safety Lamps etc*

MARINE LAUNCH AND RECOVERY SYSTEMS

▶ All Oceans Engineering Ltd, Tyrebagger Works, Kinellar, Aberdeen, AB21 0TT Tel: (01224) 791001 Fax: (01224) 791002 E-mail: admin@alloceans.co.uk

MARINE LIGHTING

Francis Searchlights, Union Road, Bolton, BL2 2HJ Tel: (01204) 527196 Fax: (01204) 558979 E-mail: sales@francis.co.uk

Lab Craft Ltd, 22b King Street, Saffron Walden, Essex, CB10 1ES Tel: (01799) 513434 Fax: (01799) 513437 E-mail: sales@labcraft.co.uk

Marine Lighting UK Ltd, 80 Dunster Road, Chelmsley Wood, Birmingham, B37 7UU Tel: 0121-770 8522 Fax: 0121-770 0505 E-mail: marlux@btconnect.com

MARINE LIQUID CARGO LOADING ARMS

Industrial Flow Control Ltd, Unit 1, Askews Farm Lane, Grays, Essex, RM17 5XR Tel: (01375) 387155 Fax: (01375) 387420 E-mail: sales@inflow.co.uk

Woodfield Systems Ltd, Tyler Way, Swalecliffe, Whitstable, Kent, CT5 2RS Tel: (01227) 793351 Fax: (01227) 793625 E-mail: sales@akerkvaerner.com

MARINE LUBRICANTS

Benjamin R Vickers & Sons Ltd, Clarence Road, Leeds, LS10 1ND Tel: 0113-386 7654 Fax: 0113-386 7676 E-mail: inbox@vickers-oil.com

Claymore Lubricants (Midlands) Ltd, 48 Heming Road, Washford, Redditch, Worcestershire, B98 0EA Tel: (01527) 502252 Fax: (01527) 502253 E-mail: sales@claymore-lubricants.co.uk

Valvoline Oil Co., Dock Road, Birkenhead, Merseyside, CH41 1DR Tel: 0151-652 1551 Fax: 0151-653 8900 E-mail: sales@valvolineuk.com

MARINE MAIN SHAFT BEARINGS

Countrose Bearings, PO Box 376, Birmingham, B42 2TB Tel: 0121-356 7220 Fax: 0121-356 7322 E-mail: c.bennett@tufnol.co.uk

Orkot Composites, Dodds Close, Rotherham, South Yorkshire, S60 1BX Tel: (01709) 789800 Fax: (01709) 374819

MARINE MASTS

▶ Freewing Masts, Clachnaharry Works Lock, Clachnaharry Road, Inverness, IV3 8RA Tel: (01463) 243161 Fax: (01463) 794506

▶ Freewing Masts, 17 Birchwood Road, Westhill, Inverness, IV2 5DW Tel: (01463) 791101 Fax: (01463) 794506 E-mail: richard@freewingmasts.co.uk

Hood Yacht Spars Ltd, Wick Road, Burnham-on-Crouch, Essex, CM0 8LT Tel: (01621) 782821 Fax: (01621) 785162 E-mail: hoodsparuk@aol.com

Needlespar Ltd, Harvey Crescent, 207 Warsash Road, Warsash, Southampton, SO31 9JE Tel: (01489) 573406

Selden Masts Ltd, Lederle Lane, Gosport, Hampshire, PO13 0FZ Tel: (01329) 504000 Fax: (01329) 504049 E-mail: info@seldenmast.co.uk

South Ferriby Marina Ltd, South Ferriby Marina, Red Lane, South Ferriby, Barton-Upon-Humber, South Humberside, DN18 6JH Tel: (01652) 635620 Fax: (01652) 660517 E-mail: tfertuson_ie@yahoo.co.uk

Z Spars International Ltd, Unit 2, Pond Hall Road, Hadleigh, Ipswich, IP7 5PW Tel: (01473) 820610 Fax: (01473) 827354 E-mail: sales@zsparsuk.com

MARINE MODELS

Brookite Ltd, Brightly Mill, Okehampton, Devon, EX20 1RR Tel: (01837) 53315 Fax: (01837) 53223 E-mail: enquiries@brookite.com

Deans Marine, Conquest Drove, Farcet, Peterborough, PE7 3DH Tel: (01733) 244166 Fax: (01733) 244166 E-mail: deansmarine@yahoo.co.uk

MARINE NAVIGATIONAL INSTRUMENTS

Fred Allen Products Ltd, Number 16, Balena Close, Creekmoore Trading Estate, Poole, Dorset, BH17 7DB Tel: (01202) 657740 Fax: (01202) 667778 E-mail: sales@fredallenproducts.com

B Cooke & Son Ltd, 58-59 Market Place, Hull, HU1 1RH Tel: (01482) 224412 Fax: (01482) 219793 E-mail: bcs@cooke.karoo.co.uk

B & G Ltd, Premier Way, Abbey Park, Romsey, Hampshire, SO51 9DH Tel: (01794) 518448 Fax: (01794) 518077 E-mail: sales@bandg.co.uk

Bloctube Marine Services Ltd, 5 Felnex Close, Leeds, LS9 0SR Tel: 0113-248 4827 Fax: 0113-240 3351 E-mail: enquiries@bloctube.co.uk

Chelton Desant Comunications Ltd, Emblem House, Pynes Hill, Exeter, EX2 5BA Tel: (01392) 667777 Fax: (01392) 667778 E-mail: info@whiskyalpha.com

Greenham Regis Ltd, Kings Saltern Road, Lymington, Hampshire, SO41 3QD Tel: (01590) 671144 Fax: (01590) 679517 E-mail: lymington@greenham-regis.com

Kelvin Hughes Ltd, New North Road, Hainault, Ilford, Essex, IG6 2UR Tel: (020) 8502 6887 Fax: (020) 8500 0837 E-mail: sales@kelvinhughes.co.uk

M S I Defence Systems Ltd, Salhouse Road, Norwich, NR7 9AY Tel: (01603) 484065 Fax: (01603) 415649 E-mail: contact@msi-dsl.com

Marine Electronic Supplies, Unit 14 Westwood Court, Brunel Road, Totton, Southampton, SO40 3WX Tel: (023) 8066 3316 Fax: (023) 8066 3241 E-mail: sales@mesuk.com

Charles Smith & Reddish Ltd, 11a Lever Street, London, EC1V 3QU Tel: (020) 7253 2457 Fax: (020) 7490 4612 E-mail: info@csr-chartinstruments.co.uk

Sperry Marine Systems, Burlington House, 118 Burlington Road, New Malden, Surrey, KT3 4NR Tel: (020) 8942 2464 Fax: (020) 8329 2415

MARINE OR SHIP OR WATERTIGHT DOORS

Ansell Jones, Unit 1 Satellite Industrial Estate, Neachells Lane, Wolverhampton, WV11 3PQ Tel: (01902) 722117 Fax: (01902) 725533 E-mail: sales@anselljones.com

▶ Pensher-Skytech, Felling Works, William Street, Gateshead, Tyne & Wear, NE10 0JP Tel: 0191-438 0455 Fax: 0191-438 2328 E-mail: sales@pensher.co.uk

Trans-Global Engineering Ltd, Camlock Works, 13-15 Bridlington Road, Hunmanby, Filey, North Yorkshire, YO14 0LR Tel: (01723) 892122 Fax: (01723) 891554 E-mail: trans@beckgroup.co.uk

MARINE OUTBOARD ENGINES

American Marine Imports, Waterloo Park, Bidford-on-Avon, Alcester, Warwickshire, B50 4JG Tel: (01789) 491673 Fax: (01789) 778377 E-mail: ami1.ltd@btconnect.com

▶ Ely Boat Chandlers, 21 Waterside, Ely, Cambridgeshire, CB7 4AU Tel: (01353) 663095 Fax: (01353) 664514 E-mail: sales@elyboatchandlers.co.uk

▶ Marlec Marine Ltd, 11 Military Road, Ramsgate, Kent, CT11 9LG Tel: (01843) 852452 Fax: (01843) 596280 E-mail: alan@marlecmarine.com

MARINE PAINTING CONTRACTORS

▶ painting@decorating, 35 Phoenix Road, Chatham, Kent, ME5 8SY Tel: (01634) 306379 E-mail: keithnegus@blueyonder.co.uk

MARINE PAINTS

Camrex Chugoku Ltd, Norris House, 4 Norris Street, London, SW1Y 4RJ Tel: (020) 7925 2535 Fax: (020) 7925 2447 E-mail: mailbox@chugoku.co.uk

▶ Ely Boat Chandlers, 21 Waterside, Ely, Cambridgeshire, CB7 4AU Tel: (01353) 663095 Fax: (01353) 664514 E-mail: sales@elyboatchandlers.co.uk

Hempel UK Ltd, Ty Coch Way, Llantarnam Industrial Park, Cwmbran, Gwent, NP44 3XF Tel: (01633) 874024 Fax: (01633) 489089 E-mail: sales@hempel.com

MARINE PILE DRILLING CONTRACTORS

French Equipment, Runnymede Boat House, Windsor Road, Old Windsor, Windsor, Berkshire, SL4 2JL Tel: (01784) 439626 Fax: (01784) 433309

MARINE PROPELLER SHAFTS

Friedenthals Ltd, Marine Propeller Works, Croft Street, Preston, PR1 8XD Tel: (01772) 254255 Fax: (01772) 204829

J B Stainless Ltd, 61 Washford Road, Sheffield, S9 3XW Tel: 0114-242 0042 Fax: 0114-243 0043 E-mail: michael@jbstainless.co.uk

MARINE PROPELLERS

Bruntons Propellers Ltd, Oakwood Business Park, Stephenson Road West, Clacton-on-Sea, Essex, CO15 4TL Tel: (01255) 420005 Fax: (01255) 427775 E-mail: info@bruntons-propellers.com

Clements Engineering (St. Neots) Ltd, Unit 120 Westgate, Airfield Industrial Park, Little Staughton, Bedford, MK44 2BN Tel: (01234) 378814 Fax: (01234) 376779 E-mail: sales@clementsmarine.co.uk

Friedenthals Ltd, Marine Propeller Works, Croft Street, Preston, PR1 8XD Tel: (01772) 254255 Fax: (01772) 204829

J Crowther Royton Ltd, Eden Works Belgrave Mill, Honeywell Lane, Oldham, OL8 2JP Tel: 0161-652 4234 Fax: 0161-627 4265 E-mail: crowther.marine@tiscali.co.uk

Kart Propulsion Co. Ltd, Bank Chambers, 70 Pier Road, Erith, Kent, DA8 1BA Tel: (01322) 346346 Fax: (01322) 347346 E-mail: info@kortpropulsion.com

▶ Ringprop plc, Haslar Road, Gosport, Hampshire, PO12 2AU Tel: (023) 9233 5788 Fax: (023) 9233 5787 E-mail: info@ringprop.com

Stone Manganese Marine Ltd, Dock Road, Birkenhead, Merseyside, CH41 1DT Tel: 0151-652 2372 Fax: 0151-652 2377 E-mail: sales@stonemanganese.co.uk

Teignbridge Propellers Ltd, Great Western Way, Forde Road, Newton Abbot, Devon, TQ12 4AW Tel: (01626) 333377 Fax: (01626) 360783 E-mail: sales@teignbridge.co.uk

MARINE PROPULSION GEAR/ SYSTEMS/UNIT MANUFRS

Hamilton Jet UK Ltd, Unit 4a Birches Industrial Estate, East Grinstead, West Sussex, RH19 1XZ Tel: (01342) 313437 Fax: (01342) 313438 E-mail: info@hamjetuk.com

Kart Propulsion Co. Ltd, Bank Chambers, 70 Pier Road, Erith, Kent, DA8 1BA Tel: (01322) 346346 Fax: (01322) 347346 E-mail: info@kortpropulsion.com

Protocol Control Systems Ltd, 2 Knighton Enterprise Park, Ludlow Road, Knighton, Powys, LD7 1HJ Tel: (01547) 529238 Fax: (01547) 529090 E-mail: info@protocolcontrolsystems.co.uk

Rolls Royce, Nucleus, London Science & Business Park, Brunel Way, Dartford, DA1 5GA Tel: (01322) 312028 Fax: (01322) 312054

Sillette Sonic, 2 Beverley Trading Estate, Garth Road, Morden, Surrey, SM4 4LU Tel: (020) 8337 7543 Fax: (020) 8330 9014 E-mail: sales@sillette.co.uk

MARINE PUMPS

Aquafax Ltd, Unit 14 Dencora Way, Sundon Business Park, Luton, LU3 3HP Tel: (01582) 568700 Fax: (01582) 583913 E-mail: sales@aquafax.co.uk

Britannia Marine Services, Unit 11 50 Windsor Avenue, London, SW19 2TJ Tel: (020) 8408 6020 Fax: (020) 8408 6040 E-mail: sales@britannia.com

Desmi Ltd, Unit 6A, Rosevale Business Park, Parkhouse Industrial Estate West, Newcastle, Staffordshire, ST5 7UB Tel: (01782) 566900 Fax: (01782) 563666 E-mail: desmi_ltd@desmi.com

Mack Engineering, Montrose Avenue, Hillington Industrial Estate, Glasgow, G52 4LA Tel: 0141-882 1030 Fax: 0141-882 7330 E-mail: mackengineering@btinternet.com

Sigma Engineering Ltd, 26 Church Street, Altrincham, Cheshire, WA14 4DW Tel: 0161-928 9988 Fax: 0161-926 8726 E-mail: sigmapumps@aol.com

MARINE RUDDERS

Clements Engineering (St. Neots) Ltd, Unit 120 Westgate, Airfield Industrial Park, Little Staughton, Bedford, MK44 2BN Tel: (01234) 378814 Fax: (01234) 376779 E-mail: sales@clementsmarine.co.uk

Weardale Steel (Wolsingham) Ltd, Durham Road, Wolsingham, Bishop Auckland, County Durham, DL13 3HX Tel: (01388) 527201 Fax: (01388) 527838 E-mail: les.graham@weardalecastings.co.uk

MARINE SAFETY SERVICES

Boat Care UK, 1Turpins Ride, Welwyn, Herts, AL6 0QS Tel: 0845 6521415. E-mail: enquires@boatcareuk.com

Myton Systems Ltd, 3 West End, Lund, Driffield, North Humberside, YO25 9TN Tel: (01377) 217364 Fax: (01377) 217364 E-mail: sales@mytonsystems.co.uk

MARINE SALVAGE CONTRACTORS

Donarm Construction Ltd, Viewfield Industrial Estate, Glenrothes, Fife, KY6 2RS Tel: (01592) 775201 Fax: (01592) 771751 E-mail: donarm_construction@compuserve.com

Klyne Tugs Lowestoft Ltd, Cumberland Place, Whapooad Road, Lowestoft, Suffolk, NR32 1UQ Tel: (01502) 515250 Fax: (01502) 500225 E-mail: enquiries@klyne-tugs.demon.co.uk

Offshore Shipbrokers Holdings Ltd, 9 11 Folgate Street, London, E1 6BX Tel: (020) 7377 9774 Fax: (020) 7377 9775 E-mail: london@offshore-shipbrokers.co.uk

Smit Salvage BV, 65 Fenchurch Street, London, EC3M 4BE Tel: (020) 7480 7648 Fax: (020) 7702 1842 E-mail: sales@smit.com

Svitzer Towage Ltd, 11 Marina Court, Castle Street, Hull, HU1 1TJ Tel: (01482) 337650 Fax: (01482) 337683 E-mail: info@adsteamuk.co.uk

United Salvage Ltd, 5 Quay Middle, King George Dock,, Hull, HU9 5PR Tel: (01482) 224181 Fax: (01482) 324669 E-mail: svitzersalvage@svitzer.co.uk

MARINE SECURITY SYSTEMS

Blacknor Technology Ltd, 1d South Way, Southwell Business Park, Portland, Dorset, DT5 2NJ Tel: (01305) 860922 Fax: (01305) 860912 E-mail: enquiries@blacknor.com

MARINE SITE INVESTIGATION SERVICES

Planit EOD Ltd, The Old Granary, Radwinter Road, Saffron Walden, ESSEX, CB10 2ET Tel: (0870) 7663210 Fax: (0870) 7663230 E-mail: sales@planiteod.com

Seacore Ltd, Lower Quay, Gweek, Helston, Cornwall, TR12 6UD Tel: (01326) 221771 Fax: (01326) 221553 E-mail: sales@seacore.co.uk

MARINE SLIPWAYS

Crinan Boatyard Ltd, Crinan, Lochgilphead, Argyll, PA31 8SW Tel: (01546) 830232 Fax: (01546) 830281 E-mail: info@crinanboatyard.co.uk

Hythe Marine Services, Prospect Place, Hythe, Southampton, SO45 6AU Tel: (023) 8084 8782 Fax: (023) 8084 6760 E-mail: raymithchener@btconnect.com

MARINE STEEL FABRICATORS

B F S Enterprise Fabrications Ltd, 6 Ellough Industrial Estate, Ellough, Beccles, Suffolk, NR34 7TD Tel: (01502) 716383 Fax: (01502) 717416 E-mail: m.spence@bfs-fabs.co.uk

Design Engineering & Fabrications International Ltd, 14 Newbridge Way, Pennington, Lymington, Hampshire, SO41 8BH Tel: (01590) 671411 Fax: (01590) 676021 E-mail: info@defint.com

▶ Milford Haven Ship Repairers, The Docks, Milford Haven, Dyfed, SA73 3DJ Tel: (01646) 696320 Fax: (01646) 696321 E-mail: mhsr@milford-docks.co.uk

MARINE SURVEYORS

Aalmar Surveys Ltd, 32-38 Dukes Place, London, EC3A 7LP Tel: (020) 7929 1401 Fax: (020) 7626 3775 E-mail: info@aalmar.com

A. Adamson, 81 Iona Way, Tirantilloch, Glasgow, G66 3PU Tel: (0141) 552 5749 Fax: (0141) 552 4917

▶ All Points Marine Services, 232 - 5 Charter House, Lord Montgomery Way, Portsmouth, PO1 2SN Tel: (07854) 454826 Fax: (01983) 249576 E-mail: marineboatsurveyor@yahoo.co.uk

BMT Murray Fenton Ltd, 70 Newcomen Street, London, SE1 1YT Tel: (020) 7234 9160 Fax: (020) 7234 9161 E-mail: enquiries@bmtmarcon.com

BMT The Salvage Association, 37-39 Lime Street, London, EC3M 7AY Tel: (020) 7648 9650 Fax: (020) 7234 9187 E-mail: sales@wreckage.org

Bowen Barrack & Co., 9 SMM Business Park, Dock Road, Birkenhead, Merseyside, CH41 1DT Tel: 0151-653 7948 Fax: 0151-653 7990

Brookes Bell Jarrett Kirman LLP, Martins Building, Exchange Flags, Liverpool, L2 3PG Tel: 0151-236 0083 Fax: 0151-236 2945 E-mail: liv@brookesbell.com

Burls Gordon & Rolland Ltd, 7 Loxford Way, Caterham, Surrey, CR3 6BX Tel: (01883) 331288 Fax: (01883) 342181 E-mail: surveyor@burlsgordon.demon.co.uk

Bushell Nicol Wawn & Son, Howden Terminal, Willington Quay, Wallsend, Tyne & Wear, NE28 6UL Tel: 0191-263 1213 Fax: 0191-263 0987

A.W. Byrde & Associates, Stonefield, Kimmeridge, Wareham, Dorset, BH20 5PE Tel: (01929) 480064 Fax: (01929) 481304 E-mail: yachtsurvey@btopenworld.com

Casebourne Leach & Co., Room 506, Coppergate House 16 Brune Street, London, E1 7NJ Tel: (020) 7375 2575 Fax: (020) 7953 8411 E-mail: office@casebourne-leach.co.uk

Charles Taylor Consulting, International House, 1 St.Katherines Way, London, E1W 1UT Tel: (020) 7759 4955 Fax: (020) 7481 9545 E-mail: info@charlestaylorconsulting.com

▶ E L Johnson Sons & Mowatt, Charter House 7th Floor, 450 High Road, Ilford, Essex, IG1 1UF Tel: (020) 8514 2456 Fax: (020) 8478 5760 E-mail: surveys@elj.co.uk

Global Maritime, Friars Bridge Court 41-45 Blackfriars Road, London, SE1 8NZ Tel: (020) 7922 8900 Fax: (020) 7922 8901 E-mail: gm@globalmaritime.com

Graham & Woolnough, Suite 9, SMM Business Park, Dock Road, Birkenhead, Merseyside, CH41 1DT Tel: 0151-653 7948 Fax: 0151-653 7990 E-mail: information@grahamwoolnough.com

Hart Fenton & Co. Ltd, First Floor Norman House, Kettering Terrace, Portsmouth, PO2 7AE Tel: (023) 9287 5277 Fax: (023) 9287 5280 E-mail: hf@hart-fenton.co.uk

Inchcape Shipping Services UK Ltd, Main Gate, 1 Sheerness Docks, Sheerness, Kent, ME12 1RT Tel: (01795) 660556 Fax: (01795) 580121

Industrial Safety Inspections Ltd, Lea Lodge, Ansley, Nuneaton, Warwickshire, CV10 0QU Tel: (01675) 481779 Fax: (01675) 481780 E-mail: sales@isi-uk.net

J Mckee & Partners Ltd, 34 South Quay, Great Yarmouth, Norfolk, NR30 2RG Tel: (01493) 850131 Fax: (01493) 330149 E-mail: mckeeships@aol.com

James Maxton & Co, Calor Gas Building, Airport Road West, Belfast, BT3 9EE Tel: (028) 9045 8238 Fax: (028) 9045 6428 E-mail: jmaxton@aol.com

John Gargan Chartering Ltd, Trident House, 105 Derby Road, Bootle, Merseyside, L20 8LZ Tel: 0151-922 0066 Fax: 0151-922 5006 E-mail: john@johngargan.co.uk

L G S A Marine, 67-83 Mariners House Queens Dock Commercial Centre, Norfolk S, Liverpool, L1 0BG Tel: 0151-707 2233 Fax: 0151-707 2170 E-mail: liverpool@lgsamarine.co.uk

▶ Mcneil Marine, 1 Tan Y Banc, Graig, Burry Port, Dyfed, SA16 0DT Tel: (01554) 833233 E-mail: surveys@mcneilmarine.com

Marine & Offshore Consultants Ltd, Magellan House, James Watt Close, Great Yarmouth, Norfolk, NR31 0NX Tel: (01493) 440166 Fax: (01493) 658490 E-mail: support@modgy.co.uk

▶ Marine Surveys, 8 Queens Park Gardens, Seaford, East Sussex, BN25 2QE Tel: 01323 873267 E-mail: info@marine-surveys.org

Maritime Consulting Associates Ltd, Owl Building, Battery Green Road, Lowestoft, Suffolk, NR32 1DH Tel: (01502) 730791 Fax: (01502) 508001 E-mail: marineconsult@compuserve.com

Maritime Surveyors Ltd, 27 Acton Road, Lowestoft, Suffolk, NR33 7LG Tel: (01502) 563081 Fax: (01502) 586650 E-mail: lesleyholland@maritimesurveyors.fsnet.co.uk

Noble Denton Consultants Ltd, Noble House, 39 Tabernacle Street, London, EC2A 4AA Tel: (020) 7812 8700 Fax: (020) 7812 8701 E-mail: marketing@nobledenton.co.uk

▶ Pedro's Yacht Refinishing, Quarry House, Galmpton, Brixham, Devon, TQ5 0EH Tel: (01803) 845475 Fax: (01803) 845475 E-mail: enquiries@pedrosyachtrefinishing.co.uk

▶ Pegasus Marine Surveys, 12 Rockfield Road, Tobermory, PA75 6PN Tel: (01688) 302112 Fax: (01688) 302112 E-mail: surveys@pegasusmarine.co.uk

R Brumwell & Co., Compton House, Walnut Tree Close, Guildford, Surrey, GU1 4TX Tel: (01483) 302276 Fax: (01483) 302292 E-mail: brumwell@btinternet.com

Robert Lyon & Co, 39-40 Longbridge Road, Barking, Essex, IG11 8TS Tel: (020) 8591 5600 Fax: (020) 8591 2785 E-mail: rlyonlondon@compuserve.com

S Roberts Marine Ltd, Coburg Wharf, Liverpool, L3 4BP Tel: 0151-707 8300 Fax: 0151-707 8300E-mail: stephen@robmar.freeserve.co.uk

▶ Warner Land Surveys, Beaumont House, 59 High Street, Theale, Reading, RG7 5AL Tel: 0118-930 3314 Fax: 0118-930 1859 E-mail: wlsl@warnerlandsurveys.com

YachtScan Ltd, 52 Gifford Terrace Road, Plymouth, PL3 4JE Tel: 0845 873 6335 Fax: 07790 320492 E-mail: info@yachtscan.co.uk

MARINE SWITCHGEARS

Elecsis Ltd, Yeo Road, Bridgwater, Somerset, TA6 5NA Tel: (01278) 453198 Fax: (01278) 453198 E-mail: chris.pratt@elecsis.com

Whippendell Electrical Ltd, 477-479 Whippendell Road, Watford, WD18 7PU Tel: (01923) 228201 Fax: (01923) 228007 E-mail: kevin@wippendale-marine.co.uk

MARINE TANK OPERATORS

Athenian Tankers UK Ltd, 2 Dartmouth Street, London, SW1H 9BP Tel: (020) 7222 2742 Fax: (020) 7222 4824 E-mail: chartering@athenian.co.uk

John H Whitaker Holdings, Crown Dry Dock, Tower Street, Hull, HU9 1TY Tel: (01482) 595300 Fax: (01482) 226270

MARINE ULTRASONIC THICKNESS MEASUREMENT SURVEYORS

YachtScan Ltd, 52 Gifford Terrace Road, Plymouth, PL3 4JE Tel: 0845 873 6335 Fax: 07790 320492 E-mail: info@yachtscan.co.uk

MARINE UNIVERSAL AUTOMATIC IDENTIFICATION SYSTEMS (UAIS)

Tideland Signal Ltd, Unit B Kendal House, Victoria Way, Burgess Hill, West Sussex, RH15 9NF Tel: (01444) 872240 Fax: (01444) 872241 E-mail: sales@tidelandsignal.ltd.uk

MARINE VALVES

H E Lupton & Sons 1952 Ltd, Quebec Works, Elland Lane, Elland, West Yorkshire, HX5 9DU Tel: (01422) 370349 Fax: (01422) 370349 E-mail: sales@lupton1952.wanado.co.uk

John Mills & Sons (Newcastle) Ltd, 509 Shields Road, Walkergate, Newcastle upon Tyne, NE6 4PX Tel: 0191-265 6550 Fax: 0191-265 1002 E-mail: sales@johnmillsnewcastleltd.co.uk

Radlett Valve & Engineering Co. Ltd, 38 Watling Street, Radlett, Hertfordshire, WD7 7NN Tel: (01923) 852131 Fax: (01923) 854484 E-mail: sales@radlettvalve.co.uk

Peter Smith Valve Co. Ltd, Occupation Road, Nottingham, NG6 8RX Tel: 0115-927 2831 Fax: 0115-977 0233 E-mail: sales@petersmithvalve.co.uk

MARINE WINCHES

Able Engineering, Dunslow Road, Eastfield, Scarborough, North Yorkshire, YO11 3UT Tel: (01723) 585639 Fax: (01723) 581605 E-mail: admin@nswinches.co.uk

Lewmar Ltd, Southmoor Lane, Havant, Hampshire, PO9 1JJ Tel: (023) 9247 1841 Fax: (023) 9248 5720 E-mail: info@lewmar.com

W J Marine Analytical Services Ltd, Unit 4, Marine Park, Tapton Hall Industrial Estate, Great Yarmouth, Norfolk, NR31 0NL Tel: (01493) 600600 Fax: (01493) 652099 E-mail: wjmarine@btinternet.com

Welin Lambie Ltd, Brittania House, Old Bush Street, Brierley Hill, West Midlands, DY5 1UB Tel: (01384) 78294 Fax: (01384) 265100 E-mail: admin@welin-lambie.co.uk

MARINE WINDOWS

Branchsound Ltd, Unit 9, Springfield Road Industrial Estate, Burnham-on-Crouch, Essex, CM0 8TE Tel: (01621) 782964 Fax: (01621) 783314 E-mail: tecnauticwindow@btclick.com

Chadwell Safety Glass Ltd, Maldon Road, Latchingdon, Chelmsford, CM3 6LF Tel: (01621) 743084 Fax: (01621) 742977

▶ Houdini Marine Windows Ltd, 1 Hallmark Industrial Estate, Hall Road, Southminster, Essex, CM0 7EH Tel: (01621) 773293 Fax: (01621) 773852 E-mail: sales@houdini-marine.co.uk

Seaglaze Marine Windows Ltd, Wendover Road, Rackheath, Norwich, NR13 6LH Tel: (01603) 720745 Fax: (01603) 721770 E-mail: sales@seaglaze.co.uk

Trend Marine Products Ltd, Sutton Road, Catfield, Great Yarmouth, Norfolk, NR29 5BG Tel: (01692) 581307 Fax: (01692) 582993 E-mail: enquiry@trendmarine.com

MARINE WIRE ROPES

The Dinghy Store, Sea Wall, Whitstable, Kent, CT5 1BX Tel: (01227) 274168 Fax: (01227) 772750 E-mail: sales@thedinghystore.co.uk

MARINE WOODWORKERS

Kirolite Products, 34-35 Dawkins Road, Poole, Dorset, BH15 4JW Tel: (01202) 676500 Fax: (01202) 681922E-mail: info@kirolite.com

MARKERS

Pryor Marking Technology Ltd, Egerton Street, Sheffield, S1 4JX Tel: 0114-276 6044 Fax: 0114-276 6890 E-mail: enquiries@pryormarking.com

MARKET INNOVATION/ DEVELOPMENT CONSULTANTS

Beetham Engineering Systems Ltd, 5 Hutchwns Close, Porthcawl, Mid Glamorgan, CF36 3LD Tel: (01656) 784882 Fax: (01656) 773332 E-mail: h.howard@btconnect.com

C D S & Co., 245 New Road, Croxley Green, Rickmansworth, Hertfordshire, WD3 3HE Tel: (01923) 441122 Fax: (01923) 440799 E-mail: david@cds-co.co.uk

D R P Group, 252 Ikon Industrial Estate, Droitwich Road, Hartlebury, Kidderminster, Worcestershire, DY10 4EU Tel: (01299) 250531 Fax: (01299) 250173 E-mail: sales@drp.co.uk

Elliott Independent Ltd, 28 Spring Lane, Great Horwood, Milton Keynes, MK17 0QW Tel: (01296) 714745 Fax: (01296) 711957 E-mail: ann@elliottindependent.com

Gala Marketing Ltd, Farrier House, 221-223 High Street, Henley-In-Arden, West Midlands, B95 5BG Tel: (01564) 794005 Fax: (01564) 793301

▶ Really Useful Research, 9 Balmoral Grange, Prestwich, Manchester, M25 0GZ Tel: 0161-720 9924 Fax: 0161-740 0561 E-mail: sales@forensic-marketing.com

MARKET MAKERS

Gala Marketing Ltd, Farrier House, 221-223 High Street, Henley-In-Arden, West Midlands, B95 5BG Tel: (01564) 794005 Fax: (01564) 793301

Gerrard, 29 Windsor Place, Cardiff, CF10 3BZ Tel: (029) 2082 9600 Fax: (029) 2022 1061 E-mail: sales@gerrard.com

L M P Market Supplies, 4 Marine Industrial Estate, Marine Street, Cwm, Ebbw Vale, Gwent, NP23 7TB Tel: (01495) 370052 Fax: (01495) 370052

Royal Bank Of Scotland, 135 Bishopsgate, London, EC2M 3UR Tel: (020) 7085 0000 Fax: (020) 7375 5050 E-mail: enquiries@rbsmarkets.com

Smith & Williamson Investment Management, 25 Moorgate, London, EC2R 6AY Tel: (020) 7776 8700 Fax: (020) 7131 4001 E-mail: info@smith.williamson.co.uk

MARKET RESEARCH

A C Nielsen Ltd, Nielsen House, London Road, Headington, Oxford, OX3 9RX Tel: (01865) 742742 Fax: (01865) 742222 E-mail: graham.northfield@acnielsen.co.uk

▶ Aspect Studio Ltd, 14 Woodland Drive, Watford, WD17 3BX Tel: (01923) 213989 Fax: 01923 213980 E-mail: info@aspectstudio.co.uk

Autopower Car Alarms & Hi Fi Centre, 345 Vicarage Road, Kings Heath, Birmingham, B14 7NN Tel: 0121-441 1856 Fax: 0121-441 5551 E-mail: bobgihair@aol.com

▶ B D S Marketing & Research Ltd, Lonsdale, Single Hill, Shoscombe, Bath, BA2 8LZ Tel: (01761) 433035 Fax: (01761) 434579 E-mail: julian.clapp@bdsmarketing.co.uk

Baloris Ltd, Oakfield House, 35 Perrymount Road, Haywards Heath, West Sussex, RH16 3BW Tel: (01444) 441252 Fax: (01444) 452107 E-mail: seanhickey@valoris.com

BMRB Ltd, Ealing Gate Way, 26-30 Uxbridge Road, Ealing, London, W5 2VP Tel: (020) 8566 5000 Fax: (020) 8579 9208 E-mail: mailbox@bmrb.co.uk

C P I UK Ltd, 107 Boston Road, Gorse Hill, Leicester, LE4 1AW Tel: 0116-234 0600 Fax: 0116-235 2592 E-mail: uk.info@cpiglobal.com

Canadean Ltd, Unit 9-12 Faraday Court, Rankine Road, Basingstoke, Hampshire, RG24 8PF Tel: (01256) 394200 Fax: (01256) 394201 E-mail: sales@canadean.com

▶ Channel Strategy Research, European Communication Centre, Flag Business Exchange, Vicarage Farm Road, Fengate, Peterborough, PE1 5TX Tel: 01733 704070 Fax: 01733 704080 E-mail: marketing@channelstrategy.co.uk

Colbear Advertising Ltd, Unit 8, Durham Lane, Armthorpe, Doncaster, South Yorkshire, DN3 3FE Tel: (01302) 302414 Fax: (01302) 836171 E-mail: emma@colbear.co.uk

Consensus Research International Ltd, 61 Southwark Street, London, SE1 0HL Tel: (020) 7803 4050 Fax: (020) 7803 4051 E-mail: mail@consensus-research.com

▶ Covent Garden Connection, 18-20 York Buildings, London, WC2N 6JU Tel: 0207 8399700 Fax: 0207 8399720 E-mail: info@cgc.uk.com

Critical Research Ltd, Crown Life House, 41-43 Alma Street, Luton, LU1 2PL Tel: (01582) 480588 Fax: (01582) 485015 E-mail: mail@critical.co.uk

▶ Customer Research Technology Ltd, Business Innovation Centre Binley Business Park, Harry Weston R, Coventry, CV3 2TX Tel: (024) 7643 0295 Fax: (024) 7643 0291 E-mail: info@opinionmeter.co.uk

David Lewis Consultancy Ltd, 31b High Street, Tunbridge Wells, Kent, TN1 1XL Tel: (01892) 542825 Fax: (01892) 708700 E-mail: sales@dlcltd.com

Diagnostics Social & Market Research Ltd, 109 Gloucester Road, London, SW7 4SS Tel: (020) 7373 7111 Fax: (020) 7370 2580 E-mail: reception@diagnostics.co.uk

Doner Cardwell Hawkins, 26 Emerald Street, London, WC1N 3QS Tel: (020) 7405 4611 Fax: (020) 7437 3961 E-mail: doner@donermail.co.uk

▶ Engage Surveys, 5 Howbridge Close, Ellenbrook, Worsley, Manchester, M28 7XZ Tel: 0161-799 8992 E-mail: craig@engage-surveys.com

Epic Marketing Services, Point Road, Canvey Island, Essex, SS8 7RT Tel: (01268) 514290 Fax: (01268) 695891 E-mail: sales@epictelemarketing.co.uk

Euromonitor plc, 60-61 Britton Street, London, EC1M 5UX Tel: (020) 7251 0985 Fax: (020) 7608 3149 E-mail: info@euromonitor.com

Experian, Talbot House, Talbot Street, Nottingham, NG80 1TH Tel: (0870) 0121111 Fax: (01753) 594001

F D S International Ltd, The Ground Floor, Hill House, London, N19 5NA Tel: (020) 7272 7766 Fax: (020) 7272 4468 E-mail: enquiries@fdf.co.uk

Facts International Ltd, Facts Centre, 3 Henwood, Ashford, Kent, TN24 8FL Tel: (01233) 637000 Fax: (01233) 626950 E-mail: facts@facts.uk.com

The Gallup Organisation Ltd, Drapers Court, Kingston Hall Road, Kingston upon Thames, Surrey, KT1 2BG Tel: (020) 8939 7000 Fax: (020) 8939 7039

▶ GfK NOP, Ludgate House, 245 Blackfriars Road, London, SE1 9UL Tel: 020 7890 9000 Fax: 020 7890 9001 E-mail: ukinfo@gfk.com

Gyrographic Communications, 603 The Chambers, Chelsea Harbour, London, SW10 0XF Tel: (020) 7351 1550 Fax: (020) 7351 3318

Harris Interactive, International House, Pepper Road, Hazel Grove, Stockport, Cheshire, SK7 5BW Tel: 0161-615 2300 Fax: 0161-615 2394

Heron Marketing Services Ltd, First Floor, 61-65 High Street, Standish, Wigan, Lancashire, WN6 0HD Tel: (01257) 472148 Fax: (01257) 472148 E-mail: info@heronmarketing.co.uk

Hi Europe, Hattori House, Vanwall Road, Maidenhead, Berkshire, SL6 4UB Tel: (01628) 770077 Fax: (01628) 785433 E-mail: sales@hieurope.com

Hill Taylor Partnership, Alexandra House, Pound Lane, Exmouth, Devon, EX8 4NP Tel: (01395) 222242 Fax: (01395) 225858 E-mail: enquiries@hilltaylor.co.uk

▶ Howard Consultancy, 26 The Loont, Winsford, Cheshire, CW7 1EU Tel: (01606) 552189 Fax: (01606) 552189 E-mail: roberthoward@onetel.net

I A L Consultants, 109 Uxbridge Road, London, W5 5TL Tel: (020) 8832 7780 Fax: (020) 8566 4931 E-mail: ial@brg.co.uk

MARKET RESEARCH – *continued*

I R B Ltd, Harlin House, 4th Floor, 47-51 Great Suffolk Street, London, SE3 9RQ Tel: (020) 8265 5000 Fax: (020) 6333 0315 E-mail: info@irb.co.uk

Ias Smarts Ni Ltd, 157 /159 High Street Citigate, Holywood, County Down, BT18 9HU Tel: (028) 9039 5500 Fax: (028) 9039 5600

Illuma Research Ltd, Richmond Bridge House, 419 Richmond Road, Twickenham, TW1 2EX Tel: (020) 8296 6600 Fax: (01935) 841693 E-mail: info@illumaresearch.co.uk

International Marketing Partners, 6 Lower Grosvenor Place, London, SW1W 0EN Tel: (020) 7828 9400 Fax: (020) 7828 9466 E-mail: info@intermarketingonline.com

Intex Management Services Ltd, 6 Regent Park, Booth Drive, Wellingborough, Northamptonshire, NN8 6GR Tel: (01933) 402255 Fax: (01933) 402266 E-mail: enquiries@imsresearch.com

Ipsos UK Ltd, Kings House, Kymberley Road, Harrow, Middlesex, HA1 1PT Tel: (020) 8861 8000 Fax: (020) 8861 5515 E-mail: ian.catchpole@ipsos.com

Andrew Irving Associates, Lloyds Bank Building, Muswell Hill Broadway, London, N10 3RZ Tel: (020) 8444 5678 Fax: (020) 8444 9221 E-mail: aia@aiaresearch.co.uk

Jupiter B2B Marketing, 82 Beech Farm Drive, Macclesfield, Cheshire, SK10 2ER Tel: (01625) 431166 Fax: (01625) 431177 E-mail: karriegrant@jupiterb2b.co.uk

▶ Kids Industries, 65 Leonard Street, London, EC2A 4QS Tel: (020) 7684 3795 Fax: 020 7684 3801E-mail: bertie@kidsindustries.co.uk

▶ Andrew Lester & Associates, 9 Thames Park, Lester Way, Wallingford, Oxfordshire, OX10 9TA Tel: (01491) 824181 Fax: (01491) 824180 E-mail: marketing@andrew-lester.com

Linkbridge Ltd, 173 Quemerford, Calne, Wiltshire, SN11 8JX Tel: (01249) 811476 Fax: (01249) 811854 E-mail: lars@linkbridge.co.uk

M P S Group, 207 Desborough Road, High Wycombe, Buckinghamshire, HP11 2QL Tel: (01494) 452600 Fax: (01494) 449122 E-mail: bbi@bbi.co.uk

M V A Consultancy, Sunley Tower, Piccadilly Plaza, Manchester, M1 4BT Tel: 0161-236 0282 Fax: 0161-236 0095

Market Research (Northern Ireland) Ltd, 44-46 Elmwood Avenue, Belfast, BT9 6AZ Tel: (028) 9066 1037 Fax: (028) 9068 2007 E-mail: info@mrni.co.uk

Marketing Assistance Ltd, Grange Road, Tiptree, Colchester, CO5 0QQ Tel: (01621) 818555 Fax: (01621) 810884 E-mail: sales@marketing-assistance.co.uk

▶ Marketwise Strategies Ltd, Adamson House, 65 Westgate Road, Newcastle upon Tyne, NE1 1SG Tel: 0191-261 4426 E-mail: info@marketwisestrategies.com

Robert Marshall Marketing Consultancy, 194 Richmond Road, Kingston Upon Thames, Surrey, KT2 5HE Tel: (020) 8546 1711 Fax: (020) 8974 6120 E-mail: rmarshal@netcomuk.co.uk

G.F.K. Martin Hamblin, Ludgate House, 245 Blackfriars Road, London, SE1 9UL Tel: (020) 7222 8181 Fax: (020) 7890 9001 E-mail: info@gfk.com

Maxwell Stamp Group plc, Abbots Court, 34 Farringdon Lane, London, EC1R 3AX Tel: (020) 7251 0147 Fax: (020) 7251 0140 E-mail: london@maxwellstamp.com

MBS International Marketing, Olympic House, 142 Queen Street, Glasgow, G1 3BU Tel: 0141-221 3298 Fax: 0141-221 3409 E-mail: sales@mbs-int-marketing.com

Metra Martech Ltd, 7 Chiswick High Road, London, W4 2ND Tel: (020) 8742 7888 Fax: (020) 8742 8558 E-mail: research@metra-martech.com

Michael Rigby Associates, 15 Market Street, Wotton-under-Edge, Gloucestershire, GL12 7AE Tel: (01453) 521621 Fax: (01453) 521681 E-mail: results@521621.,com

Millward Brown UK Ltd, Olympus Avenue, Tachbrook Park, Warwick, CV34 6RJ Tel: (01926) 452233 Fax: (01926) 833600 E-mail: info@uk.millwardbrown.com

Mintel Group Ltd, 18-19 Long Lane, London, EC1A 9PL Tel: (020) 7606 4533 Fax: (020) 7606 5932 E-mail: info@mintel.com

Mori, 77-81 Borough Road, London, SE1 1FY Tel: (020) 7347 3000 Fax: (020) 7347 3800 E-mail: mori@mori.com

Msi Marketing Research, Viscount House, River Lane, Saltney, Chester, CH4 8RH Tel: (0800) 1956756 Fax: (0800) 1956757 E-mail: enquiries@msi-marketingresearch.co.uk

North East One Ltd, 48 Leazes Park Road, Newcastle Upon Tyne, NE1 4PG Tel: 0191-261 5261 Fax: 0191-232 0637 E-mail: general@northeastone.co.uk

Northern Survey Service, 199 Marlborough Avenue, Princes Avenue, Hull, HU5 3LG Tel: (01482) 342240 Fax: (01482) 448905

▶ Novacheck Ltd, 438 London Road, High Wycombe, Buckinghamshire, HP11 1LP Tel: (01494) 526553 Fax: (01494) 526553 E-mail: contactus@novacheck.com

Opinion Research Corporation International, 1 Islington High Street, London, N1 9AH Tel: (020) 7675 1000 Fax: (020) 7675 1900 E-mail: website@orc.co.uk

P M Consultants, 414 North Deeside Road, Cults, Aberdeen, AB15 9TD Tel: (01224) 868239 Fax: (01224) 869711 E-mail: billatpm@tiscali.co.uk

Perspective Marketing, 18 Manor Way, Hail Weston, St. Neots, Cambridgeshire, PE19 5LG Tel: (01480) 477990 E-mail: research@perspective-marketing.co.uk

▶ Pescado Ltd, Wingham Business Centre, Goodnestone Road, Wingham, Canterbury, Kent, CT3 1AR Tel: (01227) 723130 Fax: (01227) 723149 E-mail: info@pescado.co.uk

Price Direct Ltd, 505A Norwood Road, London, SE27 9DL Tel: (020) 8761 7612 Fax: (020) 8761 7514 E-mail: info@pricedirect.com

▶ Really Useful Research, 9 Balmoral Grange, Prestwich, Manchester, M25 0GZ Tel: 0161-720 9924 Fax: 0161-740 0561 E-mail: sales@forensic-marketing.com

Research Associates UK Ltd, 99 Oulton Road, Stone, Staffordshire, ST15 8DX Tel: (01785) 813164 Fax: (01785) 813268 E-mail: sales@research-associates.co.uk

The Research House Ltd, 124 Wigmore St, London, W1U 3RY Tel: (020) 7935 4979 Fax: (020) 7224 2494 E-mail: researchhouse@btinternet.com

Research International Group Ltd, 6-7 Grosvenor Place, London, SW1X 7SH Tel: (020) 7656 5500 Fax: (020) 7235 0202 E-mail: riuk@research-int.com

Research & Marketing Ltd, Trefor House, Galdames Place, Cardiff, CF24 5RE Tel: (029) 2043 5800 Fax: (029) 2048 3540 E-mail: info@rmltd.net

▶ Research247.com, 23 Riverford Close, Harpenden, Hertfordshire, AL5 4LX Tel: (01582) 469699 E-mail: info@research247.com

Rocket Science, Trident Bus Centre, 3 Startforth Road, Riverside Park Industrial Estate, Middlesbrough, Cleveland, TS2 1PJ Tel: (01642) 808888 Fax: (01642) 249049 E-mail: enquiries@rocketscience-crm.co.uk

Rosslyn Research Ltd, 112 Boundary Road, St Johns Wood, London, NW8 0RH Tel: (020) 7328 8823 Fax: (020) 7624 1242 E-mail: admin@rosslyn-research.co.uk

Sigma Ltd, 143 Westmoreland Road, Bromley, BR2 0TY Tel: (020) 8460 9191 Fax: (020) 8460 3969 E-mail: groupsigma@aol.com

Sintercast Ltd, 30 Anyards Road, Cobham, Surrey, KT11 2LA Tel: (01932) 862100 Fax: (01932) 862146 E-mail: info@sintercast.com

Snap Survey Software Mercator Research Group Ltd, 5 Mead Court, Cooper Road, Thornbury, Bristol, BS35 3UW Tel: (01454) 280800 Fax: (01454) 281216 E-mail: info@snapsurveys.com

▶ Strategic Insight, Orchard Lodge, Roydon, Diss, Norfolk, IP22 5XL Tel: 01379 641168 E-mail: m.lawton@strategic-insight.org

▶ Survey Analysis (UK) Ltd, Old School House, 89 Main Road, Glengarnoch, Beith, Ayrshire, KA14 3AH Tel: 01505 682582 Fax: 01505 682681 E-mail: info@surveyanalysis.co.uk

Surveyplan Market Research, Summit House, Tower Hill, Dorking, Surrey, RH4 2AN Tel: (01306) 876211 Fax: (01306) 740643 E-mail: info@surveyplan.co.uk

Taylor Nelson Sofres plc, 66 Wilson Street, London, EC2A 2JX Tel: (020) 7868 6500 Fax: (020) 7868 6501

Taylor Nelson Sofres, West Gate, London, W5 1UA Tel: (020) 8967 0007 Fax: (020) 8967 4060

Taylor Nelson Sofres plc, 66 Wilson Street, London, EC2A 2JX Tel: (020) 7868 6500 Fax: (020) 7868 6501 E-mail: christine.davidson@tnsofres.com

TNS Research & Consultancy Ltd, 4-5 Bonhill Street, London, EC2A 4SR Tel: (020) 7891 1200 Fax: (020) 7891 1299

▶ Twelfth Man Marketing, 38 Garth Road, Bangor, Gwynedd, LL57 2SE Tel: (020) 7871 1781 E-mail: info@twelfth-man.com

Weeks Computing Services, 6 Langley Street, London, WC2H 9JA Tel: (020) 7379 3548 Fax: (020) 7240 8870 E-mail: office@weekscomputing.com

MARKET RESEARCH ANALYSIS

▶ Aspect Studio Ltd, 14 Woodland Drive, Watford, WD17 3BX Tel: (01923) 213989 Fax: 01923 213980 E-mail: info@aspectstudio.co.uk

▶ B D S Marketing & Research Ltd, Lonsdale, Single Hill, Shoscombe, Bath, BA2 8LZ Tel: (01761) 433035 Fax: (01761) 434579 E-mail: julian.clapp@bdsmarketing.co.uk

Critical Research Ltd, Crown Life House, 41-43 Alma Street, Luton, LU1 2PL Tel: (01582) 480588 Fax: (01582) 485015 E-mail: mail@critical.co.uk

David Lewis Consultancy Ltd, 31b High Street, Tunbridge Wells, Kent, TN1 1XL Tel: (01892) 542825 Fax: (01892) 708700 E-mail: sales@dlcltd.com

▶ Engage Surveys, 5 Howbridge Close, Ellenbrook, Worsley, Manchester, M28 7XZ Tel: 0161-799 8992 E-mail: craig@engage-surveys.com

Eurodata Computer Services Ltd, 8 Westmead Corner, Carshalton, Surrey, SM5 2NZ Tel: (020) 8643 0933 Fax: (020) 8643 1886 E-mail: eurodatacs@aol.com

▶ GfK NOP, Ludgate House, 245 Blackfriars Road, London, SE1 9UL Tel: 020 7890 9000 Fax: 020 7890 9001 E-mail: ukinfo@gfk.com

Heron Marketing Services Ltd, First Floor, 61-65 High Street, Standish, Wigan, Lancashire, WN6 0HD Tel: (01257) 472148 Fax: (01257) 472148 E-mail: info@heronmarketing.co.uk

Impress Solutions Ltd, 268-272 North Street, Romford, RM1 4QN Tel: (01708) 759760 Fax: (01708) 759761 E-mail: accounts@impress-solutions.com

Intex Management Services Ltd, 6 Regent Park, Booth Drive, Wellingborough, Northamptonshire, NN8 6GR Tel: (01933) 402255 Fax: (01933) 402266 E-mail: enquiries@imsresearch.com

Ipsos UK Ltd, Kings House, Kymberley Road, Harrow, Middlesex, HA1 1PT Tel: (020) 8861 8000 Fax: (020) 8861 5515 E-mail: ian.catchpole@ipsos.com

Key Data Group Ltd, Lincoln Street, Old Basford, Nottingham, NG6 0FT Tel: 0115-942 2266 Fax: 0115-942 0065 E-mail: info@keydatagroup.co.uk

Millward Brown UK Ltd, Olympus Avenue, Tachbrook Park, Warwick, CV34 6RJ Tel: (01926) 452233 Fax: (01926) 833600 E-mail: info@uk.millwardbrown.com

Mintel Group Ltd, 18-19 Long Lane, London, EC1A 9PL Tel: (020) 7606 4533 Fax: (020) 7606 5932 E-mail: info@mintel.com

Perspective Marketing, 18 Manor Way, Hail Weston, St. Neots, Cambridgeshire, PE19 5LG Tel: (01480) 477990 E-mail: research@perspective-marketing.co.uk

▶ Strategic Insight, Orchard Lodge, Roydon, Diss, Norfolk, IP22 5XL Tel: 01379 641168 E-mail: m.lawton@strategic-insight.org

▶ Survey Analysis (UK) Ltd, Old School House, 89 Main Road, Glengarnoch, Beith, Ayrshire, KA14 3AH Tel: 01505 682582 Fax: 01505 682681 E-mail: info@surveyanalysis.co.uk

MARKET RESEARCH STAFF RECRUITMENT AGENCIES

▶ Bluemonday Recruitment, 18 Soho Square, London, W1D 3QL Tel: (020) 7025 8747 Fax: (020) 7025 8100 E-mail: sales@bluemondayrecruitment.com

Edward Drummond & Co Ltd., Westpoint 78 Queens Road, Clifton, Bristol, BS8 1QX Tel: 0117 9858755 E-mail: info@edwarddrummond.com

▶ Research247.com, 23 Riverford Close, Harpenden, Hertfordshire, AL5 4LX Tel: (01582) 469699 E-mail: info@research247.com

Spring Group Ltd, Hazlitt House, 4 Bouverie Street, London, EC4Y 8AX Tel: (020) 7300 9000 Fax: (020) 7300 9090 E-mail: info@spring.com

MARKET RESEARCH, FOOD AND BEVERAAGE INDUSTRY

Canadean Ltd, Unit 9-12 Faraday Court, Rankine Road, Basingstoke, Hampshire, RG24 8PF Tel: (01256) 394200 Fax: (01256) 394201 E-mail: sales@canadean.com

MARKETING COMMUNICATION SERVICES

▶ Adeptus Marketing & Design, 20 Station Road, Parkstone, Poole, Dorset, BH14 8UB Tel: 01202 711416 Fax: 07092 236937 E-mail: info@adeptusdesign.com

▶ Another Late Night, 19 Hope Street, Liverpool, L1 9BQ Tel: 0151-708 7103 E-mail: enquiries@anotherlatenight.biz

▶ Athene Communications, 26 Priestgate, Peterborough, PE1 1WG Tel: (01733) 865040 Fax: (01733) 865013 E-mail: jane@athene-communications.co.uk

▶ Campbell Pryde, 10 Hampton Gardens, Sawbridgeworth, Hertfordshire, CM21 0AN Tel: (01279) 425283 E-mail: sales@campbellpryde.com

Captive Minds, Studio 23, The London Fruit & Wool Exchange, 56 Brushfield Street, London, E1 6HB Tel: (020) 7392 2662 Fax: E-mail: info@captiveminds.co.uk

▶ The Gate Marketing & Design Ltd, Murlain Business Centre, Union Street, Chester, CH1 1QP Tel: 01244 357 242 Fax: 01244 357 215 E-mail: anna@thegatemarketing.com

▶ Hothouse Integrated Marketing Ltd, 8 Tenby Street, Birmingham, B1 3AJ Tel: 0121-233 0533 Fax: 0121-200 2567

▶ Immaculate UK Ltd, Centre 500, 500 Chiswick High Road, London, W4 8RG Tel: (020) 8987 8900 Fax: (020) 8956 2402 E-mail: info@immaculateuk.com

▶ LoewyBe, 147A Grosvenor Road, London, SW1V 3JY Tel: (020) 7798 2100 Fax: (020) 7798 2022 E-mail: enquire@loewybe.com

▶ McKinty Marketing Services, 56 Stoke Fields, Guildford, Surrey, GU1 4LS Tel: (01483) 852815 E-mail: alexandra@mckinty.com

▶ Manifest Communications, The Media Centre, Northumberland Street, Huddersfield, HD1 1RL Tel: (01484) 483088 Fax: (01484) 483089 E-mail: info@manifestcomms.co.uk

▶ Martyn Wilson & Associates, 52 Abbotswood Road, London, SW16 1AW Tel: 0844 484 9727 Fax: 0870 855 5365 E-mail: Kelly@martynwilson.co.uk

▶ Messaging Warehouse UK, Paragon House, 48 Seymour Grove, Manchester, M16 0LN Tel: 0161-888 3333 Fax: 0161-877 7991 E-mail: sales@messagingwarehouse.com

▶ Nigel Beale, Woodlands, Forton, Chard, Somerset, TA20 4HB Tel: 01468 61824 Fax: 0870 770 9440 E-mail: nigel@thebeales.co.uk

▶ Panda Distribution, Unit 11, Windrush Millennium Centre, 70 Alexandra Road, Manchester, M16 7WD Tel: (0870) 7772971 Fax: (0870) 7772973 E-mail: kellyenquiries@pandadistribution.co.uk

▶ Prospect Research, Gwydir Street, Cambridge, CB1 2LG Tel: (0870) 4604501 Fax: (0870) 1377425 E-mail: chris.walthew@prospectresearch.co.uk

Realia, Godmersham Park, Godmersham, Canterbury, Kent, CT4 7DT Tel: (01227) 731210 Fax: (01227) 731209 E-mail: paul.williamson@realia-marketing.com

▶ Tall Poppy, 11-12 Merchants Crescent, Wharf Street Victoria Quays, Sheffield, S2 5SY Tel: 0114-272 7077 Fax: (0871) 6618601 E-mail: info@tall-poppy.com

▶ Two Heads Global Design Ltd, Kit Lane, Checkendon, Reading, RG8 0TY Tel: (01491) 681061 Fax: (01491) 682095 E-mail: victoria@2heads.tv

MARKETING CONSULTANCY, BRAND CREATION, INTERNET

▶ Metro Research Ltd, 118 The Chandlery, 50 Westminster Bridge Road, London, SE1 7QY Tel: (0870) 9979777 Fax: (020) 7953 7450 E-mail: vinesh@metroresearch.com

MARKETING CONSULTANTS,

See also specialist services

A D C Marketing Ltd, Unit 4, Richardson Way, Crosspoint Business Park, Coventry, CV2 2TY Tel: (0870) 7525252 Fax: (0870) 7525251 E-mail: enquiries@adc-uk.com

Adare Carwin, Unit B Wellington Gate, Silverthorne Way, Waterlooville, Hampshire, PO7 7XY Tel: (023) 9224 5000 Fax: (023) 9224 5060 E-mail: info@adare.com

Adfield-Harvey Ltd, The Granary, Beckbury, Shifnal, Shropshire, TF11 9DG Tel: (01952) 752500 Fax: (01952) 752510 E-mail: info@adfield.co.uk

Advision Advertising, Vision House, Main Cross Road, Great Yarmouth, Norfolk, NR30 3NZ Tel: (01493) 854000 Fax: (01493) 330016 E-mail: advision@btconnect.com

Amethyst Ltd, Amherst House, Ferring Street, Worthing, West Sussex, BN12 5JR Tel: (01903) 700444 Fax: (01903) 700455 E-mail: production@amethystmailing.co.uk

Applied Management Techniques, 33 Harts Leap Road, Sandhurst, Berkshire, GU47 8EW Tel: (01344) 773153 Fax: (01344) 776216

Arthur Wood Advertising Ltd, 69 Dane Road, Sale, Cheshire, M33 7BP Tel: 0161-968 6900 Fax: 0161-968 6939 E-mail: info@awa.uk

Askquith Industrial Marketing Services, PO Box 10, Corbridge, Northumberland, NE45 5BY Tel: (01434) 633068 Fax: (01434) 633068 E-mail: bill@ask-marketing.co.uk

Astron Marketing Technology, Crawford House, Crawford Way, Liverpool, L7 9NG Tel: 0151-228 8003 Fax: 0151-259 6129

Autopower Car Alarms & Hi Fi Centre, 345 Vicarage Road, Kings Heath, Birmingham, B14 7NN Tel: 0121-441 1856 Fax: 0121-441 5551 E-mail: bobgihair@aol.com

B C Marketing Ltd, 7 Eastway Business Village, Olivers Place, Fulwood, Preston, PR2 9WT Tel: (01772) 654654 Fax: (01772) 652233 E-mail: mail@bcmarketing.co.uk

B D S Sponsorship Ltd, 19 Waterside, 44-48 Wharf Road, London, N1 7UX Tel: (020) 7689 3333 Fax: (020) 7689 3344 E-mail: bds@sponsorship.co.uk

Baloris Ltd, Oakfield House, 35 Perrymount Road, Haywards Heath, West Sussex, RH16 3BW Tel: (01444) 441252 Fax: (01444) 452107 E-mail: seanhickey@valoris.com

Blackwood Communications, 2a New Road, Mytholmroyd, Hebden Bridge, West Yorkshire, HX7 5DZ Tel: (01422) 883688 Fax: (01422) 881376 E-mail: info@blackwood-pr.co.uk

Brand Development Co., 50 Long Acre, London, WC2E 9JR Tel: (020) 7497 9727 Fax: (020) 7497 3581 E-mail: info@brandevo.com

Brittan Design Partnership, 7 The Old Fire Station Annexe, Fairfield Road, Market Harborough, Leicestershire, LE16 9QJ Tel: (01858) 466950 Fax: (01858) 434632 E-mail: enquiry@goto-bdp.co.uk

C S L Recruitment & Consulting Ltd, Hurst House, 157-169 Walton Road, East Molesey, Surrey, KT8 0DX Tel: (020) 8224 9840 Fax: (020) 8941 4095 E-mail: sales@imesconsulting.com

C T C, 12 Whiteladies Road, Bristol, BS8 1PD Tel: 0117-311 9009 Fax: 0117-311 9010 E-mail: info@ctcuk.com

Caburn Hope, Unit D Rusbridge Lane, Lewes, East Sussex, BN7 2XX Tel: (01273) 480404 Fax: (01273) 480505 E-mail: info@caburnhope.co.uk

Cambashi Ltd, 52 Mawson Road, Cambridge, CB1 2HY Tel: (01223) 460439 Fax: (01223) 461055 E-mail: info@cambashi.com

Carlson Companies (U K) Ltd, Performance Improvement Belgrave House, 1 Greyfriars, Northampton, NN1 2LQ Tel: (01604) 234300 Fax: (01604) 230219 E-mail: sales@carlson-europe.com

▶ indicates data change since last edition

MARKETING CONSULTANTS - *continued*

Caters Advertising, The Old Mill, Sunfield Place, Stanningley, Pudsey, West Yorkshire, LS28 6DR Tel: 0113-257 5757 Fax: 0113-255 5100 E-mail: info@caters.net

Cato Associates Ltd, 13 Chelsea Crescent Chelsea Harbour, Chelsea Harbour, London, SW10 0XB Tel: (020) 7352 1406 Fax: (020) 7326689 E-mail: mac@cato.co.uk

Celebration File Ltd, Oakwood House, Spa Road, Melksham, Wiltshire, SN12 7TA Tel: (01225) 705582 Fax: (01225) 700277 E-mail: direct@cflmarketing.co.uk

Charles Millward Partnership Ltd, Old Angel Cottage, Main Road, Flax Bourton, Bristol, BS48 3QQ Tel: (01275) 464868 Fax: (01275) 464868 E-mail: cmp.ltd@btinternet.com

Chartered Institute Of Marketing, Moor Hall, The Moor, Cookham, Maidenhead, Berkshire, SL6 9QH Tel: (01628) 427500 Fax: (01628) 427499 E-mail: marketing@cim.co.uk

Chilworth Communications, 106 Star Street, London, W2 1QF Tel: (020) 7706 1014 Fax: (020) 7258 3852 E-mail: enquiries@chilworthcommunications.com

Citygate Dewe Rogerson Ltd, 3 London Wall Buildings, London, EC2M 5SY Tel: (020) 7638 9571 Fax: (020) 7628 3444

▶ Client Appeal, 13 Crutchley Road, Wokingham, Berkshire, RG40 1XA Tel: 0118-977 6775 E-mail: sales@clientappeal.co.uk

Consilium, The Old Stables, Onehouse Hall, Lower Road, Onehouse, Stowmarket, Suffolk, IP14 3BY Tel: (01449) 676435 Fax: (01449) 676436 E-mail: sb@exclusiveheritagevenues.co.uk

Crisp Marketing Associates Ltd, 45 Queen Street, Exeter, EX4 3SR Tel: (01392) 412582 Fax: (01392) 421942 E-mail: office@crisp-uk.com

▶ CWP, 37 38 The Old Woodyard, Hall Drive, Hagley, Stourbridge, West Midlands, DY9 9LQ Tel: (01562) 730066 Fax: (01562) 730066 E-mail: chris@cwppr.u-net.com

D A Marketing & Communications Ltd, Prince Consort House, 109-111 Farringdon Road, London, EC1R 3BW Tel: (020) 7841 0088 E-mail: enquiries@damarketing.co.uk

Da Ltd, Bridge House, Marsh Lane, Shepley, Huddersfield, HD8 8AE Tel: (01484) 609609 Fax: (01484) 609600 E-mail: sales@dacreative.com

Dawndeal Ltd, 7 Hunsdon Drive, Sevenoaks, Kent, TN13 3AX Tel: (01732) 455386 Fax: (01732) 740002E-mail: bdl@fsbdial.co.uk

DDB Ltd, 12 Bishops Bridge Road, London, W2 6AA Tel: (01446) 795264 Fax: (020) 7402 4871 E-mail: sales@bmpddb.com

Deeson Group Ltd, Ewell House, Graveney Road, Goodnestone, Faversham, Kent, ME13 8UP Tel: (01795) 535468 Fax: (01795) 535469 E-mail: enquiries@deeson.co.uk

Direct Know How, 17 St. Annes Court, London, W1F 0BQ Tel: (020) 7734 3532 Fax: (020) 7734 1779 E-mail: postmaster@tsm-direct.co.uk

Earl & Thompson Marketing Ltd, The Creative Centre, 1 Hucclecote Road, Gloucester, GL3 3TH Tel: (01452) 627100 Fax: (01452) 627101 E-mail: info@earl-thompson.co.uk

The Edge, 3 Wolseley Terrrence, Cheltenham, Gloucestershire, GL50 1TH Tel: (01242) 580365 Fax: (01242) 261816 E-mail: design@theedge.co.uk

Elliott Independent Ltd, 28 Spring Lane, Great Horwood, Milton Keynes, MK17 0QW Tel: (01296) 714745 Fax: (01296) 711957 E-mail: ann@elliottindependent.com

▶ Elygra Ltd, 6 The Quad, Mercury Court, Chester, CH1 4QP Tel: (01244) 399900 Fax: (01244) 399904 E-mail: mail@elygra.co.uk

Fearon Design & Marketing, 3 Brook Lane, Berkhamsted, Hertfordshire, HP4 1SX Tel: (01442) 386135 Fax: (01442) 386529 E-mail: andy@fearon-design.co.uk

Focal Design Ltd, The Old Bakery, Albion Road, New Mills, High Peak, Derbyshire, SK22 3EX Tel: (01663) 746100 Fax: (01663) 746920 E-mail: sales@focaldesign.co.uk

Freestyle Marketing Communications Ltd, 3 Pelham Road, Nottingham, NG5 1AP Tel: 0115-985 6954 Fax: 0115-985 6955 E-mail: ed@freestyleuk.com

G M S Marketing Ltd, 44 Albert Street, Newark, Nottinghamshire, NG24 4BQ Tel: (01636) 702961 Fax: (01636) 674876

▶ GaP Management Ltd, PO Box 292, Barnsley, South Yorkshire, S75 3YB Tel: 01226 290288 E-mail: info@gapmanagement.co.uk

GGH Marketing Communications, 1 West Street, Titchfield, Fareham, Hampshire, PO14 4DH Tel: (01329) 846166 Fax: (01329) 512063 E-mail: geoff@ggh.co.uk

The Grass Roots Group UK Ltd, Pennyroyal, Station Road, Tring, Hertfordshire, HP23 5QY Tel: (01442) 829400 Fax: (01442) 829405 E-mail: contactus@grg.com

Grove Advertising Services Ltd, 104 Kennerley Road, Stockport, Cheshire, SK2 6EY Tel: 0161-483 9000 Fax: 0161-483 9669

H B A Creative Ltd, Mortimer Hall, 1 Birmingham Road, Kidderminster, Worcestershire, DY10 2BU Tel: (01562) 822208 Fax: (01562) 754639

Halpen Marketing Management Ltd, 44 Fulham Road, London, SW3 6HH Tel: (020) 7581 9911 Fax: (020) 7581 8151 E-mail: mail@halpen.com

Harris Interactive, International House, Pepper Road, Hazel Grove, Stockport, Cheshire, SK7 5BW Tel: 0161-615 2300 Fax: 0161-615 2394

Harvest Marketing Communications, 35 Havant Business Centre, Harts Farm Way, Havant, Hampshire, PO9 1HU Tel: (023) 9244 9655 Fax: (023) 9248 1760 E-mail: info@harvestpr.co.uk

The Henley Centre, 9 Bridewell Place, Bridewell Gate, London, EC4V 6AW Tel: (020) 7955 1800 Fax: (020) 7353 2899 E-mail: future@henleycentre.com

I A S Smarts, Clarence Mill, Clarence Road, Bollington, Macclesfield, Cheshire, SK10 5JZ Tel: (01625) 578578 Fax: (01625) 578579 E-mail: sue@iasbranding.co.uk

I T S Ltd, PO Box 331, Slough, SL2 3DQ Tel: (01753) 642144 Fax: (01753) 646461 E-mail: dir@its.ltd.uk

Ibcc, 9 Ferndown Close, Bristol, BS11 0UP Tel: 0117-968 2691 Fax: 0117-962 6500 E-mail: ibcc@btinternet.com

Image Advertising & Promotions Ltd, 7 The Circle, Tredegar, Gwent, NP22 3PS Tel: (01495) 712900 Fax: (01495) 712905 E-mail: info@imagead.net

Imarco Ltd, Herkomer House, 156 High Street, Bushey, WD23 3HF Tel: (020) 8420 4599 Fax: (020) 8420 4273 E-mail: vision@imarco.co.uk

Industry Direct Ltd, 5 Kinsbourne Court, 96-100 Luton Road, Harpenden, Hertfordshire, AL5 3BL Tel: (01582) 462266 Fax: (01582) 461874 E-mail: sales@idlworldwide.com

▶ Integer Research, 55 Farringdon Road, London, EC1M 3JB Tel: (020) 7092 8100 Fax: (020) 7503 1266 E-mail: sales@integer-research.com

Inter World Marketing, 17 Windermere Road, West End, Southampton, SO18 3PE Tel: (023) 8047 4243 Fax: (023) 8047 6821 E-mail: sales@interworldmarketing.net

International Marketing Partners, 6 Lower Grosvenor Place, London, SW1W 0EN Tel: (020) 7828 9400 Fax: (020) 7828 9466 E-mail: info@intermarketingonline.com

Intex Management Services Ltd, 6 Regent Park, Booth Drive, Wellingborough, Northamptonshire, NN8 6GR Tel: (01933) 402255 Fax: (01933) 402266 E-mail: enquiries@imsresearch.com

Jobs In Marketing Ltd, Dale House, 35 Dale Street, Manchester, M1 2HF Tel: 0161-950 8901 Fax: 0161-950 8903 E-mail: enquiries@jobs-in-marketing.co.uk

John M Davis & Associates, East Riding Small Business Centre, Annie Reed Road, Beverley, North Humberside, HU17 0LF Tel: (01482) 865766 Fax: (01482) 865766 E-mail: pr@nilspin.com

KLP, 109 Wardour Street, London, W1F 0UH Tel: (020) 7478 3400 Fax: (020) 7478 3578 E-mail: sales@klpeuroscd.co.uk

Kubiak Creative Ltd, 1 Farleigh Court, Old Weston Road, Flax Bourton, Bristol, BS48 1UR Tel: (01275) 464836 Fax: (01275) 461295 E-mail: sales@kubiakcreative.com

L A Marketing Ltd, The Old Chapel, Lane End, Chapeltown, Sheffield, S35 2UH Tel: 0114-284 4484 Fax: 0114-286 9447 E-mail: info@la-mktg.demon.co.uk

L M A Ltd, LMA House, Third Avenue, Southampton, SO15 0LD Tel: (023) 8077 2888 Fax: (023) 8077 2999 E-mail: create@lma.co.uk

Lebury Metals, The Fields, Kingsland Road, Shrewsbury, SY3 7AF Tel: (01743) 233215 Fax: (01743) 233215

Leo Burnett, Warwick Building, Avonmore Road, London, W14 8HQ Tel: (020) 7751 1800 Fax: (020) 7348 3855

M V I Systems Ltd, Appian House, 4 Wessex Road, Bourne End, Buckinghamshire, SL8 5TD Tel: (01344) 426844

Macgregor Associates Consulting, Sherwood House, 7 Gregory, Nottingham, NG7 6LB Tel: 0115-962 0222 Fax: 0115-962 2144 E-mail: info@macgregorassociates.co.uk

Main Street Marketing, 1-3 Bachelors Walk, Lisburn, County Antrim, BT28 1XJ Tel: (028) 9268 2059 Fax: (028) 9267 1555

Marber Promotions & Marketing Ltd, 30b Park Road, Hale, Altrincham, Cheshire, WA15 9NN Tel: 0161-927 9085 Fax: 0161-927 9087 E-mail: enquiries@marber.co.uk

Marcus Ltd, 39 Outram Street, Darlington, County Durham, DL3 7DP Tel: (01325) 353882 Fax: (01325) 358408 E-mail: sales@newpc.co.uk

Marketing for Profits Ltd, Top Floor, 33 Southbourne Grove, Southbourne, Bournemouth, BH6 3QT Tel: 01202 257423 Fax: 01202 257423 E-mail: accounts@consultancymarketing.co.uk

Marketing Services Travel & Tourism Ltd, High Holborn House, 52-54 High Holborn, London, WC1V 6RB Tel: (020) 7242 3131 Fax: (020) 7242 2838 E-mail: info@supereps.com

Markland Advertising & Marketing Ltd, The Old Chapel, 13 Victoria Road, Chester, CH2 2AX Tel: (01244) 651951 Fax: (01244) 651952

Coleman Moore Partner Agency Network Ltd, 53A Main Road, Duston, Northampton, NN5 6JN Tel: (01604) 598989 Fax: (01604) 598979 E-mail: info@colemanmoore.com

Moreton Baker & Co. Ltd, March House, Keepers Gate, Sutton Coldfield, West Midlands, B74 2NL Tel: 0121-355 0049 Fax: 0121-355 0254

Morris Nicholson Cartwright Ltd, 161-163 Ashley Road, Hale, Altrincham, Cheshire, WA15 9SD Tel: 0161-928 9489 Fax: 0161-928 6091 E-mail: mail@mnc-advertising.co.uk

Mountain View Ltd, 18 Soho Square, London, W1D 3QL Tel: (020) 7025 8013 Fax: (020) 7025 8113 E-mail: georgia@mountainview.co.uk

Msi Marketing Research, Viscount House, River Lane, Saltney, Chester, CH4 8RH Tel: (0800) 1956756 Fax: (0800) 1956757 E-mail: enquiries@msi-marketingresearch.co.uk

Northern Survey Service, 199 Marlborough Avenue, Princes Avenue, Hull, HU5 3LG Tel: (01482) 342240 Fax: (01482) 448905

Orchestra Bristol Ltd, 17-19 Emery Road, Bristol, BS4 5PF Tel: 0117-972 4400 Fax: 0117-972 4501 E-mail: sales@orchestra.co.uk

P D A, Manor House, Main Road, Wycombe, Melton Mowbray, Leicestershire, LE14 4QG Tel: 0116-230 1997 Fax: (01664) 444530

P & M Associates, 6 Brendan Close, Coleshill, Birmingham, B46 3EF Tel: (01675) 465566 Fax: (01675) 464440 E-mail: marketing@pmassoc.co.uk

P R Plus Ltd, 196 Barker Butts Lane, Coventry, CV6 1ER Tel: (024) 7659 0721 Fax: (024) 7659 0700

Perspective Marketing, 18 Manor Way, Hail Weston, St. Neots, Cambridgeshire, PE19 5LG Tel: (01480) 477990 E-mail: research@perspective-marketing.co.uk

Pims Associates Ltd, 15-16 Basinghall Street, London, EC2V 5BR Tel: (020) 7776 2800 Fax: (020) 7776 2828 E-mail: info@pimsconsulting.com

Presight Marketing Consultants, 4 Addison Avenue, London, W11 4QR Tel: (020) 7603 6553 Fax: (020) 7602 8089 E-mail: presight@presight.co.uk

Priority Services Ltd, The Lodge, Castle Bromwich Hall, Birmingham, B36 9DE Tel: (0121) 748 8710 Fax: (0121) 748 8711 E-mail: enquiries@priorityservices.co.uk

Profile Marketing Services, Profile House, 2 Hartfield Close, Kents Hill, Milton Keynes, MK7 6HN Tel: (01908) 605099 Fax: (01908) 672499 E-mail: services@profilemarketing.co.uk

Projects Advertising & Marketing Ltd, Unit B5 Southways Park, London Road, Lowfield Heath, Crawley, West Sussex, RH10 9TQ Tel: (01293) 446949 Fax: (01293) 455071 E-mail: sales@projectsadv.co.uk

Race, 10 Manchester Road, Wilmslow, Cheshire, SK9 1BG Tel: (01625) 521100 E-mail: design@race-international.com

Richardson Carpenter, Manor Farm, Cliddesden, Basingstoke, Hampshire, RG25 2JB Tel: (01256) 353700 Fax: (01256) 358100

Rocket Science, Trident Bus Centre, 3 Startforth Road, Riverside Park Industrial Estate, Middlesbrough, Cleveland, TS2 1PJ Tel: (01642) 808888 Fax: (01642) 249049 E-mail: enquiries@rocketscience-crm.co.uk

Roskill Information Services, 27a Leopold Road, London, SW19 7BB Tel: (020) 8944 0066 Fax: (020) 8947 9568 E-mail: info@roskill.co.uk

Shaw Marketing & Design Ltd, 18 Albany Street, Edinburgh, EH1 3QB Tel: 0131-557 5663 Fax: 0131-556 7379 E-mail: enquiries@shawltd.demon.co.uk

▶ Sitel UK Ltd, Sitel House, Timothys Bridge Road, Stratford-upon-Avon, Warwickshire, CV37 9HY Tel: (01789) 299622 Fax: (01789) 292341 E-mail: info@sitel.com

Springboard Marketing Ltd, 1 Tonbridge Chambers, Pembury Road, Tonbridge, Kent, TN9 2HZ Tel: (01732) 363399 Fax: (01732) 352304 E-mail: info@springboard-marketing.co.uk

Square One Advertising & Design Ltd, 134 Archer Road, Sheffield, S8 0JZ Tel: 0114-258 4557 Fax: 0114-258 3076 E-mail: info@squareone.co.uk

Staffordshire Marketing Ltd, Charrington House, 17 Market Street, Lichfield, Staffordshire, WS13 6JX Tel: (01543) 263942 Fax: (01543) 415249E-mail: info@stratford-marketing.co.uk

Stopford Graham & Co. Ltd, Chapel House, 1 Borough Road, Altrincham, Cheshire, WA15 9RA Tel: 0161-941 1024 Fax: 0161-926 9773

Sudatek Ltd, 59 Barn Meadow Lane, Bookham, Leatherhead, Surrey, KT23 3EZ Tel: (01372) 450008 Fax: (01372) 450006 E-mail: sales@sudatek.com

Take One Media, Unit 4 Century Point, Halifax Road, High Wycombe, Buckinghamshire, HP12 3SL Tel: (01494) 888500 Fax: (01494) 436914

Tandem Consultancy, Top Executive Suite, 55 West Street, Chichester, West Sussex, PO19 1RU Tel: (01243) 778822 Fax: (01243) 779951 E-mail: creatorbiz@tandemuk.com

Tangram Ltd, Lane House, Main Road, Fyfield, Abingdon, Oxfordshire, OX13 5LN Tel: (01865) 390380 Fax: (01865) 390001

Taylor Alden Ltd, 92-94 Toynbee Road, London, SW20 8SL Tel: (020) 8543 3866 Fax: (020) 8543 2841 E-mail: pr@tayloralden.co.uk

Tecnon Orbichem Ltd, 12 Calico House, Clove Hitch Quay, London, SW11 3TN Tel: (020) 7924 3955 Fax: (020) 7978 5307 E-mail: sales@orbichem.com

Triad Creative Marketing, Randolph House, 37-41 Longshut Lane West, Stockport, Cheshire, SK2 6RX Tel: 0161-480 2482 Fax: 0161-480 8926 E-mail: mail@triadcreative.com

▶ Upthejunction.Com, 3 Saxon Road, Hoylake, Wirral, Merseyside, CH47 3AE Tel: 0151-632 2451 E-mail: info@upthejunction.com

Wakefield Taffarello Associates, 54 Old Street, London, EC1V 9AL Tel: (020) 7250 0500 Fax: (020) 7250 1553 E-mail: wta@wtadspr.demon.co.uk

Mike Ward Associates, The Rodgelands, Bank Lane, Abberley, Worcester, WR6 6BQ Tel: (01299) 896654 Fax: (01299) 896955

Windsor Creative Communications, Anglesey Lodge, Farnborough Road, Aldershot, Hampshire, GU11 3BJ Tel: (0845) 4503407 Fax: (0845) 4503409 E-mail: windsor@windsor-creative.com

Winkler International Ltd, Po Box 104, Peacehaven, E. Sussex, BN10 7WD Tel: (01273) 585010 Fax: (01273) 587981 E-mail: john.winkler@winkler.co.uk

Word Link Ltd, 121a Godolphin Road, London, W12 8JN Tel: (020) 8749 3388 Fax: (020) 8749 8398 E-mail: sales@wordlink.demon.co.uk

Writing Machine, 19 City Business Centre, Hyde Street, Winchester, Hampshire, SO23 7TA Tel: (01962) 841250 Fax: (01962) 870558 E-mail: sales@writingmachine.com

Wunderman Ltd, Fourth Floor, Greater London House, Hampstead Road, London, NW1 7QP Tel: (020) 7611 6666 Fax: (020) 7611 6668

Yes City Ltd, 12 Carthusian Street, London, EC1M 6EZ Tel: (020) 7600 4600 Fax: (020) 7600 7424 E-mail: richard.amphlett@yescity.biz

MARKETING CONSULTANTS, STRATEGIC

A D C Marketing Ltd, Unit 4, Richardson Way, Crosspoint Business Park, Coventry, CV2 2TY Tel: (0870) 7525252 Fax: (0870) 7525251 E-mail: enquiries@adc-uk.com

The Edge, 3 Wolseley Terrrence, Cheltenham, Gloucestershire, GL50 1TH Tel: (01242) 580365 Fax: (01242) 261816 E-mail: design@theedge.co.uk

Infotrends Ltd, Sceptre House, 7-9 Castle Street, Luton, LU1 3AJ Tel: (01582) 400120 Fax: (01582) 411001 E-mail: info@capv.com

Management Process Development Ltd, 30 Chantreys Drive, Elloughton, Brough, North Humberside, HU15 1LH Tel: (01482) 665675 E-mail: richard-grafton@supanet.com

▶ Nigel Beale, Woodlands, Forton, Chard, Somerset, TA20 4HB Tel: 01468 61824 Fax: 0870 770 9440 E-mail: nigel@thebeales.co.uk

▶ River Communications, 9 The Terrace, Woodford Green, Essex, IG8 0XS Tel: (020) 8504 4009 Fax: (020) 8504 4454 E-mail: info@river-communications.com

▶ Synergy Coaching Ltd, 1 Ryding Close, Farington Moss, Leyland, PR26 6QZ Tel: (01772) 641234 Fax: (01772) 641234

MARKETING GRAPHIC DESIGN

▶ 2 C F Communications Ltd, 42c Barrack Square, Martlesham Heath, Ipswich, IP5 3RF Tel: (01473) 622263 Fax: (01473) 622515 E-mail: info@2cf.com

▶ 4Consultancy Ltd, 45 Grange Avenue, Highbridge, Somerset, TA9 3AJ Tel: (01278) 785919 E-mail: Brad@4consultancy.net

▶ About Turn Creative, Somerford Business Court, Holmes Chapel Road, Somerford, Congleton, Cheshire, CW12 4SN Tel: (01260) 281431 Fax: (01260) 289362 E-mail: info@aboutturncreative.co.uk

▶ Absolute Marketing, 115 Elmdon Lane, Marston Green, Birmingham, B37 7DN Tel: 0121 688 7686 Fax: 0121 688 7686 E-mail: absolutemarketing@blueyonder.co.uk

▶ Accappella, Nightingale Farm, Whiteacre Lane, Waltham, Canterbury, Kent, CT4 5SR Tel: (01227) 700725 E-mail: emma@accappellastudio.co.uk

▶ Adeptus Marketing & Design, 20 Station Road, Parkstone, Poole, Dorset, BH14 8UB Tel: 01202 711416 Fax: 07092 236937 E-mail: info@adeptusdesign.com

▶ Aloof Design, 5 Fisher Street, Lewes, East Sussex, BN7 2DG Tel: (01273) 470887 E-mail: michellekostyrka@aloofdesign.com

▶ Altered Image, St. Helier, Jersey, JE2 3GH Tel: (01534) 767323

▶ Another Late Night, 19 Hope Street, Liverpool, L1 9BQ Tel: 0151-708 7103 E-mail: enquiries@anotherlatenight.biz

▶ Artlines Media Ltd, 54 Cressex Buissness Park, Lincoln Road, High Wycombe, Buckinghamshire, HP12 3RL Tel: (01494) 614600 Fax: (01494) 614601 E-mail: tom@artlines.co.uk

Bang Communications Ltd, The Black Barn, Farleigh Road, Cliddesden, Basingstoke, Hampshire, RG25 2JL Tel: (01256) 370900 Fax: (01256) 370901 E-mail: info@bang-on.net

▶ Base Creative Ltd, 46 Parkway, Dorking, Surrey, RH4 1EU Tel: (01306) 875447 E-mail: info@base-creative.co.uk

Bda, The Studio, Pipits Croft, Bicester, Oxfordshire, OX26 6XW Tel: (01869) 322158 Fax: (01869) 322158E-mail: info@bda-uk.com

▶ Clear Design Services, 44 Seaford Road, Wokingham, Berkshire, RG40 2EL Tel: 0118 9894455 E-mail: info@cleardesignservices.co.uk

▶ Comfy Graphics, 8 Metcalf Mews, Uppermill, Oldham, OL3 6DN Tel: (01457) 810734 E-mail: info@comfygraphics.co.uk

▶ The Conservatory, Spitfire Studios, 63-71 Collier Street, London, N1 9BE Tel: (020) 7278 3222 E-mail: studio@theconservatory.co.uk

MARKETING GRAPHIC DESIGN - *continued*

▶ CreaCom Design, 181 High Street, Invergordon, Ross-Shire, IV18 0AL Tel: (01349) 853003 E-mail: info@creacomdesign.com
▶ The Creative Business, 37 Deans Walk, Gloucester, GL1 2PX Tel: (01452) 545076 E-mail: davidn@thecreativebiz.com
▶ D C Group, Corsley, Corsley, Warminster, Wiltshire, BA12 7QH Tel: (01373) 832288 Fax: (01373) 832589 E-mail: stefen@dcgroup.uk.net
▶ D-Face Design, Studio, 104 Kensal Road, Kensal Rise, London, W10 5BZ Tel: (020) 8959 3125 Fax: (020) 8959 3125 E-mail: design@d-face.co.uk
▶ Evolve, 35 Townfield Road, Mobberley, Knutsford, Cheshire, WA16 7HG Tel: (01565) 872683 Fax: (01565) 872534
▶ Exposure, Marketing and Design Services, 12 FieldFare, Billericay, Essex, CM11 2PA Tel: 01277 621474 E-mail: paula@exposureonline.co.uk
▶ Eye For Design, PO BOX 4657, Shrewsbury, SY1 9AD Tel: 01743 353536 E-mail: sales@eyefor.co.uk
▶ Fernleigh Design Ltd, Unit 5 Parc Ty Glas, Llanishen, Cardiff, CF11 7BF Tel: 02920 763524 Fax: 02920 763525 E-mail: amanda@fernleighdesign.co.uk
▶ Fingertip Designs, 17 Hildenley Close, Scarborough, North Yorkshire, YO12 5DU Tel: (01723) 351668 E-mail: fingertipdesigns@yahoo.co.uk
Fir Tree Design Co., 2 Turpyn Court, Woughton on the Green, Milton Keynes, MK6 3BW Tel: (01908) 661100 Fax: (01908) 670055 E-mail: info@firtreedesign.com
First Impression (Doncaster), PO Box 812, Doncaster, South Yorkshire, DN1 9AE Tel: 01302 874381 E-mail: contact@firstimpression.co.uk
▶ Fli Backward Ltd, 557 Wilmslow Road, Manchester, M20 4GJ Tel: 0161-445 0273
▶ Fresh Biz Marketing, 1 Oban Close, Wakefield, West Yorkshire, WF3 1JU Tel: 0870 284 6180 Fax: 0870 284 6181 E-mail: info@freshbizmarketing.com
▶ Fruitcake Design Associates Ltd, Flat 8, Aquatico, Walnut Tree Close, Guildford, Surrey, GU1 4UL Tel: (07855) 576565 E-mail: clee@fruitcake.co.uk
▶ G D Sign, 62 West Street, Gorseinon, Swansea, SA4 4AF Tel: (01792) 549172 E-mail: sales@gdsign.co.uk
▶ G3 Creative Solutions, 7 Woodside Crescent, Glasgow, G3 7UL Tel: (01389) 875889 Fax: 0141-332 2233 E-mail: mail@g3creative.co.uk
GIA Design Ltd, 46a Pevensey Road, Eastbourne, East Sussex, BN21 3HP Tel: (01323) 722131 Fax: (01323) 642940 E-mail: greg@duvacourt.co.uk
Giant, 36 Queen Square, Bristol, BS1 4QS Tel: 0117 9086666 Fax: 0117 9085566 E-mail: info@gianteffect.co.uk
▶ Greensplash Ltd, 308 Chester Road, Hartford, Northwich, Cheshire, CW8 2AB Tel: (01606) 884123 Fax: (01606) 884212 E-mail: enquiries@greensplash.com
▶ Horrex Davis Design Associates Ltd, 6 Dorset Street, London, W1U 6QL Tel: (020) 7486 8132 Fax: (020) 7487 2936 E-mail: design@hdda.co.uk
▶ Hypermania Design, Woodmancote, Clay Lane, Fishbourne, Chichester, West Sussex, PO18 8DW Tel: (01243) 780385 E-mail: sean@hypermania.com
ican DESIGN LTD, ST PETER'S GATE, CHARLES ST, SUNDERLAND, SR6 0AN Tel: 0191 5561074 Fax: 0191 5561001 E-mail: STUDIO@ICANDESIGN.CO.UK
▶ Ice Age Media, The Cottage, Old Mold Road, Gwersyllt, Wrexham, LL11 4SB Tel: (01978) 758071 E-mail: andy@theiceage.co.uk
▶ Idealogic, Focal Point, 88 Coronation Avenue, Bath, BA2 2JP Tel: 01225 483322 Fax: 01225 483322 E-mail: kirstie@idealogicuk.com
▶ Image Directors, Power House, Powerscroft Road, Sidcup, Kent, DA14 5EA Tel: (0870) 4584475 Fax: (0870) 4584476 E-mail: steve@imagedirectors.co.uk
▶ Immaculate UK Ltd, Centre 500, 500 Chiswick High Road, London, W4 8RG Tel: (020) 8987 8900 Fax: (020) 8956 2402 E-mail: info@immaculateuk.com
▶ Jamie Ambler Studio, 34 Headlands, Kettering, Northamptonshire, NN15 7HP Tel: (01536) 525467 Fax: 01536 312535 E-mail: sales@bluemoonstudios.uk.com
▶ Kreative Juice, 24 Martholme Close, Blackburn, BB6 7TZ Tel: (01254) 884917 E-mail: info@kreativejuice.co.uk
▶ Daniel Lowton Designs, Rochester Avenue, Rochester, Kent, ME1 2DS Tel: (01634) 880754 E-mail: daniel@dldesigns.biz
▶ McHardy Media Ltd, The Media Centre, 6 North Isla Street, Dundee, DD3 7JQ Tel: (01382) 423248 E-mail: sales@mchardymedia.co.uk
▶ McKinty Marketing Services, 56 Stoke Fields, Guildford, Surrey, GU1 4LS Tel: (01483) 852815 E-mail: alexandra@mckinty.com
▶ Mainsail Ltd, Medina Yard, Arctic Road, Cowes, Isle of Wight, PO31 7PG Tel: (01983) 200901 Fax: (01983) 200902 E-mail: beth@mainsail.co.uk
▶ Merge Design Consultancy, 37 Dinorben Avenue, Fleet, Hampshire, GU52 7SQ Tel: (07980) 626443 E-mail: nick.green@mergedc.co.uk
▶ Mill Design & Marketing, Hilliard House, Lester Way, Wallingford, Oxfordshire, OX10 9TA Tel: (01491) 833822 Fax: (01491) 833002 E-mail: steve@millmarketing.co.uk
MMV Design, 30 Rosewood Court, Rothwell, LEEDS, LS26 0XG Tel: 0113 2825831 E-mail: enquiries@mmvdesign.co.uk
▶ Morse Brown, 517 Hagley Road, Smethwick, West Midlands, B66 4AX Tel: 0121-429 7770 E-mail: mail@morsebrowndesign.co.uk
▶ Mushroom Marketing Ltd, Melbury House, Oxford Road, Bournemouth, BH8 8ES Tel: (01202) 315538 Fax: (01202) 961351 E-mail: info@mushroommarketing.co.uk
▶ Nigel Beale, Woodlands, Forton, Chard, Somerset, TA20 4HB Tel: 01468 61824 Fax: 0870 770 9440 E-mail: nigel@thebeales.co.uk
Origin One UK Ltd, Dukes Yard Shakespeare Industrial Estate, Acme Road, Watford, WD24 5AL Tel: (01923) 246116 Fax: (01923) 246113 E-mail: info@origin-1.co.uk
▶ Profile Design, 10 West Pallant, Chichester, West Sussex, PO19 1TF Tel: (01243) 537444 Fax: (01243) 537440 E-mail: sales@profiledesign.net
▶ Punctum, Unit 57, Enterprise Way, Newport, Gwent, NP20 2AQ Tel: (01633) 843237 E-mail: enquiries@punctumphotographic.co.uk
Realia, Godmersham Park, Godmersham, Canterbury, Kent, CT4 7DT Tel: (01227) 731210 Fax: (01227) 731209 E-mail: paul.williamson@realia-marketing.com
▶ RT Media Ltd, Allen House, 2a East Borough, Wimborne, Dorset, BH21 1PF Tel: (01202) 888192 Fax: (01202) 888192 E-mail: info@rtmedia.com
▶ Rye Design, 107-109 High Street, Rochester, Kent, ME1 1JS Tel: (01634) 818168 Fax: (01634) 818178 E-mail: sales@ryedesign.co.uk
▶ Scott Britten, 16 Pheonix House, Hyssop Close, Cannock, Staffordshire, WS11 7GA Tel: (01543) 579977 Fax: 01543 467260 E-mail: info@scottbritten.co.uk
▶ Simcoemedia, 14 Romans Court, Old Basford, Nottingham, NG6 0HF Tel: 07704 629906 E-mail: design@simcoe.co.uk
Slave to Design, Suite 5, Unit 9, Oldham Street Business Centre, Hanley, Stoke-on-Trent, ST1 3EY Tel: (01782) 207884 Fax: (01782) 207884 E-mail: info@slavetodesign.com
▶ SM Creative Ltd, 4 Raven Close, Chorley, Lancashire, PR7 2RE Tel: (01257) 232392 Fax: (01257) 232392 E-mail: design@smcreative.co.uk
▶ Stik-Chik Agency, Old Straw Barn, 5 Greenacre Drive, Rushden, Northamptonshire, NN10 0TQ Tel: (07866) 718132 E-mail: enquiries@ntlworld.co.uk
▶ Studiohope, 2 Oolite Grove, Bath, BA2 2UF Tel: (01225) 830634 Fax: (01225) 830634 E-mail: mcmaster@studiohope.co.uk
▶ Subcircle Creative, 5 Luther Mews, Brighton, BN2 9YR Tel: 01273 675428
▶ Swimming Hippo Design, Eagle Tower, Montpellier Drive, Cheltenham, Gloucestershire, GL50 1TA Tel: (01242) 263102 Fax: (01242) 262491 E-mail: create@swimminghippo.co.uk
▶ Touch Marketing & Design, Unit 21 Trident Park, Trident Way, Blackburn, BB1 3NU Tel: (01254) 602260 Fax: (01254) 602260 E-mail: info@touchmarketing.co.uk
▶ Twentytwo Design, 1 Down Close, Portishead, Bristol, BS20 8BX Tel: (01275) 842768 E-mail: info@twentytwo.co.uk
Twisted Octopus Ltd, 4 Spring Gardens, Watery Lane, Wooburn Green, High Wycombe, Buckinghamshire, HP10 0NZ Tel: (01628) 523159 Fax: (01628) 523159 E-mail: sales@twistedoctopus.com
▶ Urbansoul Design, Kingfisher Centre, Futures Park, Bacup, Lancashire, OL13 0BB Tel: (01706) 877899 Fax: (01706) 877899 E-mail: info@urbansouldesign.co.uk
▶ The Vector Studio, 44 High Oakham Close, Sutton-in-Ashfield, Nottinghamshire, NG17 4JS Tel: (07931) 934479 E-mail: thevectorstudio@hotmail.com
▶ VMAL, Unit B3 Connaught Business Centre, London, NW9 6JL Tel: (0845) 1082356 Fax: (0845) 1082357 E-mail: info@vmal.co.uk
▶ Benjamin H.W. Wills, Argoed Uchaf Farm, Sunnyview, Argoed, Blackwood, Gwent, NP12 0AJ Tel: (07980) 019849 E-mail: theartist@bhww.co.uk
▶ Wooden House Design & Media, Upton House, Baldock Street, Royston, Hertfordshire, SG8 5AY Tel: 01763 247288 E-mail: kelly@woodenhouse.com
▶ The Workroom Ltd, 28 Waterside, 44-48 Wharf Road, London, N1 7UX Tel: (020) 7608 0840 Fax: (020) 7608 0850 E-mail: admin@workroom.co.uk
Ziggurat Design, Hall Farm Barn, Carleton Forehoe, Norwich, NR9 4AL Tel: (01603) 757600 E-mail: info@zigguratdesign.co.uk

MARKETING INFORMATION SERVICES

▶ Activnet Biz, Little Gaddesden, Berkhamsted, Hertfordshire, HP4 1PA Tel: (01442) 843516 Fax: (0870) 7060164 E-mail: marika.woods@activnet.biz
Austrian National Tourist Office, 13-14 Cork Street, London, W1S 3NS Tel: (020) 7629 0461 Fax: (020) 7499 6038 E-mail: info@anto.co.uk
Glass's Information Services Ltd, 1 Princes Road, Weybridge, Surrey, KT13 9TU Tel: (01932) 823823 Fax: (01932) 846564 E-mail: enquiries@glass.co.uk
Hi Europe, Hattori House, Vanwall Road, Maidenhead, Berkshire, SL6 4UB Tel: (01628) 770077 Fax: (01628) 785433 E-mail: sales@hieurope.com
I H S Global Insight, Wimbledon Bridge House, 1 Hartfield Road, London, SW19 3RU Tel: (020) 8544 7800 Fax: (020) 8544 7801 E-mail: receptionist.london@globalinsight.com
▶ Really Useful Research, 9 Balmoral Grange, Prestwich, Manchester, M25 0GZ Tel: 0161-720 9924 Fax: 0161-740 0561 E-mail: sales@forensic-marketing.com
Signature Industries Ltd, Unit 19 Atlas Industrial Estate, Foundry Street, Glasgow, G21 4PR Tel: 0141-558 7272 Fax: 0141-558 9696 E-mail: info@sigcom.co.uk
Taylor Nelson Sofres, West Gate, London, W5 1UA Tel: (020) 8967 0007 Fax: (020) 8967 4060

MARKETING OR SALES CONSULTANCY

1 Solutions, 15 Royston Road, St. Albans, Hertfordshire, AL1 5NF Tel: (01727) 869020 E-mail: 101@another.com
▶ A & C Management Consultants Ltd, 13a Harben Parade, Finchley Road, London, NW3 6LH Tel: (020) 7564 7050 Fax: (020) 7564 8764 E-mail: acmanagement@tiscali.co.uk
▶ Amber Green, 135 George Street, Edinburgh, EH2 4JS Tel: 0131-514 4000 Fax: 0131-514 4001 E-mail: info@ambergreen.co.uk
▶ Client Appeal, 13 Crutchley Road, Wokingham, Berkshire, RG40 1XA Tel: 0118-977 6775 E-mail: sales@clientappeal.co.uk
▶ E-active Marketing, PO Box 332, Bushey, WD23 3XZ Tel: 07092 369840 Fax: 07092 369840 E-mail: john@e-active.co.uk
Itdynamics Ltd, Lion Court, Staunton Harold, Ashby-de-la-Zouch, Leicestershire, LE65 1RT Tel: (01332) 695090 Fax: (01332) 695009 E-mail: info@itdynamics.co.uk
Made in Portugal, Unit 4, Mews House, Princes Lane, Muswell Hill, London, N10 3LU Tel: (0845) 232 0001 Fax: (0845) 232 0007 E-mail: info@madeinportugal.co.uk
▶ Market Synergies Ltd, 65 Cannon Court Road, Maidenhead, Berkshire, SL6 7QP Tel: (0790) 9993682 E-mail: enquiries@marketsynergies.co.uk
▶ Pilot House, Globe Park, Broxburn, West Lothian, EH52 6EF Tel: (01506) 855727 E-mail: tim@pilothouse.co.uk
▶ River Communications, 9 The Terrace, Woodford Green, Essex, IG8 0XS Tel: (020) 8504 4009 Fax: (020) 8504 4454 E-mail: info@river-communications.com
Sales Plus, PO Box 50, Knebworth, Hertfordshire, SG3 6UE Tel: (01438) 811657 Fax: (01438) 813320 E-mail: smedalsj@aol.com
▶ Stewart Miller Associates, Na Mara, Innellan, Dunoon, Argyll, PA23 7QN Tel: (01369) 830000
▶ Tactical MarComms, 16 Blythe Road, Corfe Mullen, Wimborne, Dorset, BH21 3LR Tel: (01202) 699967 Fax: (01202) 699967 E-mail: eddie.palmer@tacticalmarcomms.com
▶ Viatris, Building 2000, Cambridge Research Park, Beach Road, Waterbeach, Cambridge, CB5 9PD Tel: (01223) 205999

MARKETING OR SALES SOFTWARE

▶ Advanced Solutions International Europe, The Old Pump House, The Stables, Pettaugh Road, Stonham Aspal, Stowmarket, Suffolk, IP14 6AU Tel: 08705 887700 Fax: 01473 892032 E-mail: info-eu@advsol.com
Aw Computer Systems Ltd, 16 Dundry Lane, Winford, Bristol, BS40 8AN Tel: (01275) 474591 Fax: (0870) 9004911 E-mail: awcs@dial.pipex.com
▶ Business Systems UK Ltd, 462 London Road, Isleworth, Middlesex, TW7 4ED Tel: (020) 8326 8200 Fax: (020) 8326 8400 E-mail: sales@businesssystemsuk.com
▶ Cobault Computer Systems, 29 Great George Street, Bristol, BS1 5QT Tel: 0117-920 0123 Fax: 0117-920 0124E-mail: info@cobault.com
European Automation Intelligence Ltd, 124 Warwick Street, Leamington Spa, Warwickshire, CV32 4QY Tel: (01926) 889393 Fax: (01926) 888378
▶ Gamma Dataware, Hillington Park Innovation Centre, 1 Ainslie Road, Glasgow, G52 4RU Tel: 0141-585 6338
H C C M Systems Ltd, 3 Church Street, Leamington Spa, Warwickshire, CV31 1EG Tel: (01926) 451551 Fax: (01926) 451556 E-mail: sales@hccm.co.uk
▶ Integrate Software, 18 Knightsbridge, Northwich, Cheshire, CW9 8GE Tel: (0845) 1249800
Adrian Moss Associates, PO Box 473, Chichester, West Sussex, PO18 8BT Tel: (01243) 574500 Fax: (01243) 528923 E-mail: adrian@business-initiatives.com
Pythagoras Communications Ltd, Clivemont Road, Maidenhead, Berkshire, SL6 7BZ Tel: (01628) 590700 Fax: (01628) 590717
Star Computer Group plc, King Edward Court, 23 High Street, Sutton Coldfield, West Midlands, B72 1XS Tel: 0121-355 6171 Fax: 0121-354 4656 E-mail: info@starplc.co.uk
▶ Techdivision, 118 St. Margarets Road, Twickenham, TW1 2AA Tel: (020) 8891 3010 Fax: (020) 8288 2591 E-mail: info@techdivison.co.uk

MARKETING PHOTOGRAPHERS

▶ John Wilson, Ground Floor, 6 Madeira Road, London, SW16 2DF Tel: 020 8516 9582 E-mail: info@jcwilson.net

MARKETING STAFF RECRUITMENT

Garrett Lloyd Ltd, Unit 39-40 Derwent Business Centre, Clarke Street, Derby, DE1 2BU Tel: (01332) 206219 Fax: (01332) 206225 E-mail: recruitment@garrett-lloyd.com
▶ The Media Agency, 1 Brewery Hill, Arundel, West Sussex, BN18 9DQ Tel: 01903 882836 Fax: 01903 882836 E-mail: themediaagency@hotmail.co.uk

MARKETING SUPPORT SERVICES

▶ Activnet Biz, Little Gaddesden, Berkhamsted, Hertfordshire, HP4 1PA Tel: (01442) 843516 Fax: (0870) 7060164 E-mail: marika.woods@activnet.biz
Celebration File Ltd, Oakwood House, Spa Road, Melksham, Wiltshire, SN12 7TA Tel: (01225) 705582 Fax: (01225) 700277 E-mail: direct@cflmarketing.co.uk
▶ CWP, 37 38 The Old Woodyard, Hall Drive, Hagley, Stourbridge, West Midlands, DY9 9LQ Tel: (01562) 730066 Fax: (01562) 730066 E-mail: chris@cwppr.u-net.com
D R P Group, 252 Ikon Industrial Estate, Droitwich Road, Hartlebury, Kidderminster, Worcestershire, DY10 4EU Tel: (01299) 250531 Fax: (01299) 250173 E-mail: sales@drp.co.uk
H G A Creative Communications, The Old Exchange, 514 Liverpool Road, Irlam, Manchester, M44 6AJ Tel: 0161-775 7890 Fax: 0161-775 7916 E-mail: info@hgacreative.com
N C H Marketing Services Ltd, Earls Tree Industrial Estate, Corby, Northamptonshire, NN17 4DU Tel: (01536) 400123 Fax: (01536) 443319 E-mail: shagan@nchmarketing.co.uk
Novation International Ltd, 5 Minister's Park, East Kilbride, Glasgow, G74 5BX Tel: (01355) 268437 Fax: (01355) 260915 E-mail: novation.int@virgin.net
Pos Direct Ltd, 99 Boston Road, Leicester, LE4 1AW Tel: 0116-234 4400 Fax: 0116-235 8947 E-mail: sales@pos-direct.co.uk
▶ Storage Direct Ltd, 6 Russell Place, Trinity, Edinburgh, EH5 3HA Tel: 01506 871757 Fax: 01506 873400 E-mail: sales@mgk-storagedirect.co.uk

MARKETING TRAINING, INTERNATIONAL

▶ Big Fish Training, Huntingdon House, 35 Field Road, Reading, RG1 6AP Tel: 0845 833 0072 Fax: 0870 705 8562
▶ Spectrum Marketing Ltd, PO Box 274, Blackburn, BB1 8XB Tel: 01254 249991 Fax: 01254 249417 E-mail: info@spectrummarketing.co.uk
▶ Strategy Consulting Ltd, The Haven Scotland House Farm, Stockwood Road, Bristol, BS4 5LU Tel: (0845) 8386906 Fax: (0870) 1369549 E-mail: info@strategyconsultinglimited.co.uk

MARKETING, SMALL BUSINESS

▶ 1 Onion Ltd, 20 Abbeville Mews, London, SW4 7BX Tel: (07004) 166466 E-mail: info@1onion.com
2nd Chance Ltd, Basepoint Business & Innovation Centre, East Portway, Caxton Close, Andover, Hampshire, SP10 5HS Tel: 0800 0112164 Fax: 01264 353124 E-mail: info@2ndchance.co.uk
▶ 4Consultancy Ltd, 45 Grange Avenue, Highbridge, Somerset, TA9 3AJ Tel: (01278) 785919 E-mail: Brad@4consultancy.net
▶ Adeptus Marketing & Design, 20 Station Road, Parkstone, Poole, Dorset, BH14 8UB Tel: 01202 711416 Fax: 07092 236937 E-mail: info@adeptusdesign.com
▶ Ashley Hastings, 20 Manor Heath, Copmanthorpe, York, YO23 3SL Tel: (01904) 700847 E-mail: ashley@ashleyhastings.co.uk
▶ Bee Online Ltd, 24 Taphouse Avenue Witney, Witney, Oxfordshire, OX28 1JJ Tel: (01993) 200852 Fax: (01993) 200852 E-mail: info@buzzonline.biz
▶ Budget Marquees, 18 Cliff Hill, Gorleston, Great Yarmouth, Norfolk, NR31 6DQ Tel: (01493) 300721 E-mail: info@BudgetMarquees.co.uk

MARKETING, SMALL BUSINESS – *continued*

Captive Minds, Studio 23, The London Fruit & Wool Exchange, 56 Brushfield Street, London, E1 6HB Tel: (020) 7392 2662 Fax: E-mail: info@captiveminds.co.uk

▶ Consult TM Ltd, Avon Lodge, Watery Lane, Sherbourne, Warwick, CV35 8AL Tel: (0845) 4085960 Fax: (0845) 4085961 E-mail: tonym@cosulttm.co.uk

▶ Eurekastep, Exchange House, Worthing Road, Horsham, West Sussex, RH12 1SQ Tel: (01403) 219600 Fax: (01403) 273679 E-mail: info@eurekastep.com

▶ The Gate Marketing & Design Ltd, Murlain Business Centre, Union Street, Chester, CH1 1QP Tel: 01244 357 242 Fax: 01244 357 215 E-mail: anna@thegatemarketing.com

Imstra Ltd, 63 Church Lane Oldton, Oulton, Stone, Staffordshire, ST15 8UB Tel: (01785) 816110 E-mail: gayle@imstra.co.uk

▶ Ingenius One, Express Courtyard, Luke Lane, Brailsford, Ashbourne, DE6 3BY Tel: (01335) 361199 Fax: (01335) 361188 E-mail: enquiries@ingeniusone.com

▶ KJW Resources Ltd, 12 Main Street, Scarcliffe, Chesterfield, Derbyshire, S44 6SZ Tel: (01246) 827703 E-mail: info@kjw-resources.com

▶ McCormack & Kent Consulting Ltd, PO Box 49, Ashford, Kent, TN24 9WF Tel: (0845) 0573257 Fax: (01622) 338900 E-mail: team@mccormack-kent.co.uk

▶ McKinty Marketing Services, 56 Stoke Fields, Guildford, Surrey, GU1 4LS Tel: (01483) 852815 E-mail: alexandra@mckinty.com

▶ Martyn Wilson & Associates, 52 Abbotswood Road, London, SW16 1AW Tel: 0844 484 9727 Fax: 0870 855 5365 E-mail: Kelly@martynwilson.co.uk

▶ Panda Distribution, Unit 11, Windrush Millennium Centre, 70 Alexandra Road, Manchester, M16 7WD Tel: (0870) 7772971 Fax: (0870) 7772973 E-mail: kellyenquiries@pandadistribution.co.uk

▶ pharos technology ltd, Ground Floor, Ashe Hill, Ashe, Basingstoke, Hampshire, RG25 3AE Tel: 01256 770566 E-mail: info@pharostechnology.co.uk

▶ Positive Business Partners Ltd, 6 Sussex Mews, The Pantiles, Tunbridge Wells, Kent, TN2 5QJ Tel: (01892) 616262 Fax: (01892) 513118 E-mail: info@positive-business.com

▶ Powerview Consulting Services, 44 Rectory Avenue, Corfe Mullen, Wimborne, Dorset, BH21 3EZ Tel: (01202) 699977 Fax: (01202) 699977 E-mail: business.growth@powerview-services.com

▶ Prospect Research, Gwydir Street, Cambridge, CB1 2LG Tel: (0870) 4604501 Fax: (0870) 1377425 E-mail: chris.walthew@prospectresearch.co.uk

▶ Strategy Consulting Ltd, The Haven Scotland House Farm, Stockwood Road, Bristol, BS4 5LU Tel: (0845) 8386906 Fax: (0870) 1369549 E-mail: info@strategyconsultinglimited.co.uk

MARKING DEVICE MANUFRS

Ash Rubber Stamp Co Ltd, 149 Barford Street, Birmingham, B5 6AS Tel: 0121-622 4040 Fax: 0121-622 6600 E-mail: sales@ashstamp.co.uk

Birmingham Rubber Stamp Co Ltd, 209 Streetly Road, Erdington, Birmingham, B23 7AH Tel: 0121-377 7757 Fax: 0121-377 7718 E-mail: sales@britishstamp.com

Borries, 28 Coalbrookdale Road, Clayhill Light Industrial Park, Neston, CH64 3UG Tel: 0151-336 3101 Fax: 0151-336 3217 E-mail: rob@borriesuk.fsnet.co.uk

Davidson & Co. Ltd, 92 Harwood Street, Sheffield, S2 4SE Tel: 0114-272 4584 Fax: 0114-279 7309

Decon Laboratories Ltd, Conway Street, Hove, East Sussex, BN3 3LY Tel: (01273) 739241 Fax: (01273) 722088 E-mail: sales@decon.co.uk

▶ Eyre & Baxter (Stampcraft) Ltd, 229 Derbyshire Lane, Sheffield, S8 8SD Tel: 0114-250 0153 Fax: 0114-258 0856 E-mail: sales@eyreandbaxter.co.uk

Hamilton Rand, Paper Mill End Industrial Estate, Birmingham, B44 8NH Tel: 0121-344 3202 Fax: 0121-344 3202

Pakmark, Units 1-2 Benson Industrial Estate, Benson Rd, Birmingham, B18 5TS Tel: 0121-523 0665 Fax: 0121-523 5343 E-mail: pakmark@btconnect.com

Pryor Marking Technology Ltd, Egerton Street, Sheffield, S1 4JX Tel: 0114-276 6044 Fax: 0114-276 6890 E-mail: enquiries@pryormarking.com

Sauven Marking, 4 Wintersells Road, Byfleet, West Byfleet, Surrey, KT14 7LF Tel: (01932) 355191 Fax: (01932) 354511 E-mail: sales@sauven-marking.co.uk

Supreme Rubber Stamp Co., 1 Valley End Business Centre, Nunn Brook Road, Huthwaite, Sutton-in-Ashfield, Nottinghamshire, NG17 2HU Tel: (01623) 514942 Fax: (01623) 559849 E-mail: faststampsuk@yahoo.co.uk

Synnex Information Technology Ltd, Synnex House, Nedge Hill, Telford, Shropshire, TF3 3AH Tel: (01952) 207200 E-mail: enquiries@smartwater.com

William W Cope, Unit 34 Camp Hill Industrial Estate, John Kempe Way, Birmingham, B12 0HU Tel: 0121-766 8874 Fax: 0121-771 2866 E-mail: martingeer@williamcope.co.uk

MARKING DIES

C A Grant, Orgreave Crescent, Sheffield, S13 9NQ Tel: 0114-269 5498 Fax: 0114-269 5412 E-mail: sales@cagrant.co.uk

I C S (Industrial & Consumer Supplies), Tor-Y-Mynydd Farm, Devauden, Chepstow, Gwent, NP16 6NU Tel: (01600) 860869 Fax: (01600) 860869

MARKING INKS

Dia-Nielsen UK Ltd, Enfield Lock, South Ordnance Road, Enfield, Middlesex, EN3 6JG Tel: (01992) 787110

Industrial Services York Ltd, Station Estate, Station Road, Tadcaster, North Yorkshire, LS24 9SG Tel: (01937) 832761 Fax: (01937) 833012 E-mail: info@suremark.ltd.uk

Kuretake UK Ltd, 14 Broad Ground Road, Redditch, Worcestershire, B98 8YP Tel: (01527) 523799 Fax: (01527) 523815 E-mail: zig33uk@kuretake.ne.jp

Roger Needham & Sons Ltd, Unit 2b, Civic Industrial Park, Waymills, Whitchurch, Shropshire, SY13 1TT Tel: (01948) 662629 Fax: (01948) 665045 E-mail: info@rnsl.co.uk

▶ Onink Ltd, Unit G Meadowside Industrial Estate, Meadowside Street, Renfrew, PA4 8YE Tel: 0141-886 6732 Fax: 0141-886 6733 E-mail: enquiries@onink-ltd.com

Rollers' Inks & Marking Ltd, PO Box 69, Hull, HU2 8HS Tel: (01482) 218172 Fax: (01482) 214999 E-mail: info@markcbrown.co.uk

Tolbest Ltd, 10 Aston Court, Kingsland Grange, Woolston, Warrington, WA1 4SG Tel: (01925) 825335 Fax: (01925) 825336 E-mail: info@tolbest.co.uk

XL Marking Systems, Unit 405 Thorp Arch Trading Estate, Thorp Arch, Wetherby, West Yorkshire, LS23 7BJ Tel: (01937) 844014 Fax: (01937) 842137

MARKING MACHINE/SYSTEMS MANUFRS

Brandone Machine Tool Ltd, Unit 1, 57 Bushey Grove Road, Bushey, WD23 2JW Tel: (01923) 637893 Fax: (01923) 248055 E-mail: brandone@btconnect.com

I E L Identequip Ltd, Tenmat Buildings, Ashburton Road West, Trafford Park, Manchester, M17 1RU Tel: 0161-876 4679 Fax: 0161-876 0009 E-mail: iel@identequip.com

Markall Machines Ltd, PO Box 1948, Loughton, Essex, IG10 2BE Tel: (01992) 575355 Fax: (01992) 575553

Sauven Marking, 4 Wintersells Road, Byfleet, West Byfleet, Surrey, KT14 7LF Tel: (01932) 355191 Fax: (01932) 354511 E-mail: sales@sauven-marking.co.uk

Telesiseagle Ltd, Dolphin Street, Colyton, Devon, EX24 6LU Tel: (01297) 551313 Fax: (01297) 551319 E-mail: sales@telesiseagle.co.uk

White & Street International Ltd, Unit 17-18, Enfield Industrial Estate, Redditch, Worcestershire, B97 6BN Tel: (01527) 67881 Fax: (01527) 69966 E-mail: enquiries@whiteandstreet.com

MARKING MACHINE/SYSTEMS, ELECTROCHEMICAL

Etch Mark Ltd, 5 Romford Road, Stafford, ST16 3DZ Tel: (01785) 253143 Fax: (01785) 223282 E-mail: info@etchmark.co.uk

MARKING/IDENTIFICATION SERVICES

A S G Services Ltd, 8 Easter Court, Europa Boulevard, Westbrook, Warrington, WA5 7ZB Tel: (01925) 710923 Fax: (01925) 712966 E-mail: info@asgservices.co.uk

Engraving Services, 102 Chester Road, Talke, Stoke-on-Trent, ST7 1SD Tel: (01782) 782270 Fax: (01782) 787020 E-mail: engravingservices@tinyworld.co.uk

MARMALADES

▶ Gillies Fine Foods Ltd, Inchrory Drive, Dingwall, Ross-Shire, IV15 9XH Tel: (01349) 861100 Fax: (01349) 864400 E-mail: info@gilliesfinefoods.co.uk

MARQUEE DESIGN SERVICES

GDC Themed Events Ltd, 38-42 Fife Road, Kingston Upon Thames, Surrey, KT1 1SU Tel: (020) 8547 3682 Fax: (020) 8546 8461 E-mail: tim@gdc-events.co.uk

Roder UK Ltd, Unit 16 Earith Business Park, Meadow Drove, Earith, Huntingdon, Cambridgeshire, PE28 3QF Tel: (01487) 840840 Fax: (01487) 840843 E-mail: sales@roderuk.com

MARQUEE HIRE

▶ A & M Marquees, 11 Stanley Road, Knutsford, Cheshire, WA16 0DE Tel: (07866) 580529 Fax: (01565) 633977 E-mail: info@ammarquees.com

▶ Alfresco Mini Marquee Hire, 12 Valley Road, Newbury, Berkshire, RG14 6ER Tel: (0800) 9706753 E-mail: info@alfrescomarqueehire.co.uk

▶ Apple Marquees Ltd, Cranford House, 20 Harborough Rd, Kingsthorpe, Northampton, NN2 7AZ Tel: 01604 627290 E-mail: info@applemarquees.co.uk

Aquila Shelters Ltd, Claremont House, St Georges Road, Bolton, BL1 2BY Tel: (01204) 522424 Fax: (01204) 365110 E-mail: sales@aquila-shelters.co.uk

Away & Away, The Stables, Goulds Green, Hillingdon, Uxbridge, Middlesex, UB8 3DG Tel: (01895) 442260 Fax: (01895) 447561

▶ Bags Of Fun, 9 Crofton Avenue, Corringham, Stanford-le-Hope, Essex, SS17 7TD Tel: (01375) 404716 E-mail: sales@rodeobullrides.co.uk

C.F. Barker & Sons (Marquees) Ltd, 47 Osborne Road, Thornton Heath, Surrey, CR7 8PD Tel: (01883) 337099 Fax: (020) 8653 2932

Blithfield Events Ltd, Cawarden Springs Farm, Blithbury Road, Rugeley, Staffordshire, WS15 3HL Tel: (01889) 582228 Fax: (01889) 575695 E-mail: marquees@blthfieldevents.co.uk

▶ Brooks Marquee Hire, Chart Hill Road, Staplehurst, Tonbridge, Kent, TN12 0DE Tel: (0800) 7837089 Fax: (01622) 844662

Owen Brown, Station Road, Castle Donington, Derby, DE74 2NL Tel: (01332) 850000 Fax: (01332) 850005 E-mail: info@owen-brown.co.uk

Burgoynes Lyonshall Ltd, Lyonshall, Kington, Herefordshire, HR5 3JR Tel: (01544) 340283 Fax: (01544) 340228 E-mail: enquiries@burgoynes-lyonshall.co.uk

Carter's, 99-113 Caversham Road, Reading, RG1 8AR Tel: 0118-959 9022 Fax: 0118-950 0618 E-mail: info@carterse.com

Chichester Canvas, Chichester Road, Sidlesham Common, Chichester, West Sussex, PO20 7PY Tel: (01243) 641164 Fax: (01243) 641888 E-mail: sales@chicanvas.co.uk

Compass Marquees, East Oakdene, Headcorn, Ashford, Kent, TN27 9JF Tel: (01622) 892254 Fax: (01622) 891473 E-mail: tents@compass-marquees.co.uk

▶ Complete Events, Events House Red Shute Hill Industrial Estate, Red Shute Hill, Hermitage, Thatcham, Berkshire, RG18 9QL Tel: (01635) 202466 Fax: (01635) 202467 E-mail: sales@completeevents.co.uk

The Devon Marquee Co., Fairview, Murchington, Chagford, Newton Abbot, Devon, TQ13 8HJ Tel: (01647) 433530 Fax: (01647) 433530

Dover Marquee Co. Ltd, 30 Mayfield Avenue, Dover, Kent, CT16 2PL Tel: (01304) 215315 Fax: (01304) 202086 E-mail: sales@dover-marquee.co.uk

Event Hire, Stuart Road, Bredbury Park Industrial Estate, Bredbury, Stockport, Cheshire, SK6 2SR Tel: 0161-494 5213 Fax: 0161-494 5213 E-mail: info@mcmeventhire.co.uk

Fiesta, Farley Farms Bridge Farm, Reading Road, Arborfield, Reading, RG2 9HT Tel: 0118-976 2310 Fax: 0118-976 2311 E-mail: enquiries@fiestamarqueehire.co.uk

▶ Finedining.co.uk, 9a Ty Draw, Little Mill, Pontypool, Gwent, NP4 0HR Tel: (01495) 785449 E-mail: tracey@finedining.co.uk

Florida Marquees, Bradbury Street, Sheffield, S8 9QQ Tel: 0114-258 9626 Fax: 0114-250 7527 E-mail: rmitchell@apex-marquees.u-net.com

Four Jays Site A Loo, Barling Farm, East Sutton, Maidstone, Kent, ME17 3DX Tel: (01622) 843135 Fax: (01622) 844410 E-mail: sales@fourjays.co.uk

G L Events Alfred Bull, 2c Cathedral Hill Industrial Estate, Guildford, Surrey, GU2 7YB Tel: (01483) 575492 Fax: (01483) 573448 E-mail: info@alfredbullmarquees.co.uk

G L Events Snowdens, Second Drove, Eastern Industry, Fengate, Peterborough, PE1 5XA Tel: (01733) 344110 Fax: (01733) 314985 E-mail: info@snowdens.co.uk

Gala Occasions Ltd, Hurcott Hall Farm, Hurcott, Kidderminster, Worcestershire, DY10 3PH Tel: (01562) 825882 Fax: (01562) 741000 E-mail: galaltd@lineone.net

Hart & Co Windsor, 151 St Leonards Road, Windsor, Berkshire, SL4 3DW Tel: (01753) 864075 Fax: (01753) 830251 E-mail: sales@hartstents.co.uk

Humberside Marquees, 400 Wincolmlee, Hull, HU2 0QL Tel: (01482) 610102 Fax: (01482) 609955 E-mail: info@humbersidemarquees.com

J B Cater Hire, Unit 10 Nursteed Road Trading Estate, William Road, Devizes, Wiltshire, SN10 3EW Tel: (01380) 729192 Fax: (01380) 729192 E-mail: info@wallismarquees.co.uk

▶ Leicester Marquee Hire, PO Box 7741, Leicester, LE5 2FD Tel: 0116-254 3879 E-mail: info@lmhire.co.uk

Leith (U K) Ltd, Pier Road, Berwick-upon-Tweed, TD15 1JB Tel: (01289) 307264 Fax: (01289) 330517 E-mail: enquiries@wleithmarquees.co.uk

Lewis Marquees Westbourne Ltd, Unit 20 The Wren Centre, Westbourne Road, Emsworth, Hampshire, PO10 7SU Tel: (01243) 372242 Fax: (01243) 372265 E-mail: admin@lewismarquees.com

Mar-Key Marquees Ltd, 427c Aviation Park West, Bournemouth Int Airport, Hurn, Christchurch, Dorset, BH23 6NW Tel: (01202) 577111 Fax: (01202) 573014 E-mail: sales@mar-key.com

Markham Marquees, Morrow House, Morrow Lane, Ardleigh, Colchester, CO7 7NG Tel: (01206) 231084 Fax: (01206) 230713 E-mail: info@markham-marquees.co.uk

▶ Marldon Marquees, 111 Winner Street, Paignton, Devon, TQ3 3BP Tel: (01392) 433633 Fax: (01803) 666888 E-mail: info@marldonmarquees.co.uk

Marshall Marquees, Watercress Farm, Upton Lane, Dundry, Bristol, BS41 8NS Tel: 0117-964 6528 E-mail: info@marshallmarquees.co.uk

M. Nicol & Co. Ltd, Unit 5, Slaidburn Crescent, Southport, Merseyside, PR9 9YF Tel: (01704) 509667 Fax: (01704) 509669

The Party People, 41 Croydon Road, Beckenham, Kent, BR3 4AB Tel: (020) 8658 1110 Fax: (020) 8658 1548

Peppers Marquees Ltd, Crosshill, Snaith, Goole, North Humberside, DN14 9JT Tel: (01405) 860249 Fax: (01405) 862098 E-mail: info@peppersmarquees.co.uk

Purvis Marquee Hire, East Mains Holdings, Ingliston, Newbridge, Midlothian, EH28 8NB Tel: 0131-335 3685 Fax: 0131-335 0294 E-mail: sales@purvis-maquees.co.uk

Regency Marquees Ltd, Bilsington Road, Willow Court, Ruckinge, Ashford, Kent, TN26 2PB Tel: (01233) 732130 Fax: (01233) 733757 E-mail: info@regencymarquees.co.uk

▶ Rent A Tent Marquees, 7 Nobles Close, Grove, Wantage, Oxfordshire, OX12 0NR Tel: (01235) 760026E-mail: info@rentatentmarquees.co.uk

▶ Sawtry Marquees, 4 Shawley Road, Sawtry, Cambridgeshire, PE28 5UH Tel: 01487 831852 E-mail: sawtrymarquees@btinternet.com

▶ Simpers Ltd, 17 Mercers Row, Cambridge, CB5 8HY Tel: (01223) 351729 Fax: (01223) 311818 E-mail: info@simpers.co.uk

Tents & Marquees Ltd, Haughton Farm, Haughton, Shrewsbury, SY4 4GB Tel: (01743) 709246 Fax: (01743) 709106 E-mail: info@tentsandmarquees.com

MARQUEES

Aquila Shelters Ltd, Claremont House, St Georges Road, Bolton, BL1 2BY Tel: (01204) 522424 Fax: (01204) 365110 E-mail: sales@aquila-shelters.co.uk

C.F. Barker & Sons (Marquees) Ltd, 47 Osborne Road, Thornton Heath, Surrey, CR7 8PD Tel: (01883) 337099 Fax: (020) 8653 2932

Burgoynes Lyonshall Ltd, Lyonshall, Kington, Herefordshire, HR5 3JR Tel: (01544) 340283 Fax: (01544) 340228 E-mail: enquiries@burgoynes-lyonshall.co.uk

Crocker Bros, 8-18 Station Road, Chellaston, Derby, DE73 5SU Tel: (01332) 700699 Fax: (01332) 705655 E-mail: sales@crockerbros.co.uk

Custom Covers 1984 Ltd, Quayside Road, Southampton, SO18 1AD Tel: (023) 8033 5744 Fax: (023) 8022 5581 E-mail: sales@customcovers.co.uk

Florida Marquees, Bradbury Street, Sheffield, S8 9QQ Tel: 0114-258 9626 Fax: 0114-250 7527 E-mail: rmitchell@apex-marquees.u-net.com

Grays Traditional Marquees, Southbank, Blackwater, Newport, Isle Of Wight, PO30 3BG Tel: (01983) 525221 Fax: (01983) 529296 E-mail: info@islandmarquees.co.uk

J & J Carter Ltd, 8 Lion Court, Basingstoke, Hampshire, RG24 8QU Tel: (01256) 811455 Fax: (01256) 811458 E-mail: sales@jjcarter.com

J & S Franklin Holdings & Management Services Ltd, Franklin House, 151 Strand, London, WC2R 1HL Tel: (020) 7836 2762 Fax: (020) 7836 2784 E-mail: defence@franklin.co.uk

▶ Leicester Marquee Hire, PO Box 7741, Leicester, LE5 2FD Tel: 0116-254 3879 E-mail: info@lmhire.co.uk

Leith (U K) Ltd, Pier Road, Berwick-upon-Tweed, TD15 1JB Tel: (01289) 307264 Fax: (01289) 330517 E-mail: enquiries@wleithmarquees.co.uk

Mar-Key Marquees Ltd, 427c Aviation Park West, Bournemouth Int Airport, Hurn, Christchurch, Dorset, BH23 6NW Tel: (01202) 577111 Fax: (01202) 573014 E-mail: sales@mar-key.com

▶ Marldon Marquees, 111 Winner Street, Paignton, Devon, TQ3 3BP Tel: (01392) 433633 Fax: (01803) 666888 E-mail: info@marldonmarquees.co.uk

Marshall Marquees, Watercress Farm, Upton Lane, Dundry, Bristol, BS41 8NS Tel: 0117-964 6528 E-mail: info@marshallmarquees.co.uk

Milton Leicester Ltd, North Street, Wigston, Leicestershire, LE18 1PR Tel: 0116-288 5871 Fax: 0116-288 0116 E-mail: sales@miltons.ltd.uk

G. Mudford & Sons Ltd, Aurillac Way, Hallcroft Road, Retford, Nottinghamshire, DN22 7PX Tel: (01777) 703489 Fax: (01777) 704743 E-mail: info@mudfordmarquees.co.uk

MARQUEES – *continued*

M. Nicol & Co. Ltd, Unit 5, Slaidburn Crescent, Southport, Merseyside, PR9 9YF Tel: (01704) 509667 Fax: (01704) 509669

Purvis Marquee Hire, East Mains Holdings, Ingliston, Newbridge, Midlothian, EH28 8NB Tel: 0131-335 3685 Fax: 0131-335 0294 E-mail: sales@purvis-maquees.co.uk

R L Trim, 9 Acreman Street, Cerne Abbas, Dorchester, Dorset, DT2 7LD Tel: (01300) 341209 Fax: (01300) 341815

Roder UK Ltd, Unit 16 Earith Business Park, Meadow Drove, Earith, Huntingdon, Cambridgeshire, PE28 3QF Tel: (01487) 840840 Fax: (01487) 840843 E-mail: sales@roderuk.com

▶ Sawtry Marquees, 4 Shawley Road, Sawtry, Cambridgeshire, PE28 5UH Tel: 01487 831852 E-mail: sawtrymarquees@btinternet.com

MARQUETRY CUTTERS/ MANUFRS

Aaronson Veneers, 56 Dennis Lane, Stanmore, Middlesex, HA7 4JW Tel: (020) 8954 1555 Fax: (020) 8954 1555

MARTIAL ARTS EQUIPMENT

Levenshulme Karate Club, Klondyke Club, Burnage Range, Levenshulme, Manchester, M19 2UG Tel: 0161-221 2676 E-mail: shukokaikarate2000@yahoo.co.uk

▶ London Martial Arts Club, Miles St, London, SW8 1SD Tel: 0207 352 7716

Murrain Sports, 289 Walsall Road, Perry Barr, Birmingham, B42 1TY Tel: 0121-356 6090 Fax: 0121-344 3447 E-mail: sales@murrainsports.co.uk

▶ Warriors World Ltd, Unit 12, Pembroke Business Centre, Gardiners Lane South, Basildon, Essex, SS14 3HY Tel: (07970) 004098 E-mail: sales@warriorsworld.co.uk

MASKING CAP/PLUG (SCREW THREAD PROTECTION) MANUFRS

Caplugs Ltd, Unit 7, Overfield Industrial Estate, Off Thorpe Way, Banbury, Oxfordshire, OX16 4XR Tel: (01295) 263753 Fax: (01295) 263788 E-mail: support@caplugs.co.uk

Dbi Plastics, Cottage La Industrial Estate, Broughton Astley, Leicester, LE9 6PD Tel: (01455) 283380 Fax: (01455) 283384 E-mail: info@dbiplastics.com

Hi Tek Products Ltd, 2a Dawkins Road, Poole, Dorset, BH15 4JP Tel: (01202) 661300 Fax: (01202) 661230 E-mail: gjb@hitekproducts.com

MASKING TAPES, *See also headings for particular types*

Davis & Moore, 5 Bute Street, Salford, M50 1DU Tel: 0161-737 1166 Fax: 0161-736 4038

Hi Tek Products Ltd, 2a Dawkins Road, Poole, Dorset, BH15 4JP Tel: (01202) 661300 Fax: (01202) 661230 E-mail: gjb@hitekproducts.com

Shand Higson & Co. Ltd, Lees Road, Knowsley Industrial Park North, Knowsley, Liverpool, L33 7SE Tel: 0151-549 2210 Fax: 0151-549 1405 E-mail: sales@shandhigson.co.uk

MASONIC REGALIA

A R Fabb Bros Ltd, 29-31 Risborough Road, Maidenhead, Berkshire, SL6 7BJ Tel: (01628) 623533 Fax: (01628) 622705 E-mail: sales@fabb.co.uk

Benton & Johnson Ltd, Regalia House, Newtown Road, Bedworth, Warwickshire, CV12 8QR Tel: (024) 7684 8800 Fax: (024) 7664 3018 E-mail: bentonandjohnson@toye.com

Ensign Flag, 42 Dunes Way, Liverpool, L5 9RJ Tel: 0151-298 1007 Fax: 0151-298 1006 E-mail: enquiries@ensignflags.com

▶ Filton Masonic Hall Ltd, 140 Park Road, Stapleton, Bristol, BS16 1DT Tel: 0117-965 5541 E-mail: secretary@fmhcl.org.uk

Merit Badge & Regalia Co. Ltd, Merit House, Stanhope Street, Highgate, Birmingham, B12 0UX Tel: 0121-440 6861 Fax: 0121-440 1037 E-mail: sales@fcparry.com

Rodwell Regalia, 2 Shires Road, Trimmingham House, Buckingham Road Industrial Estate, Brackley, Northamptonshire, NN13 7EZ Tel: (01280) 701180 Fax: (01280) 704799

Stephen Simpson, 50 Manchester Road, Preston, PR1 3YH Tel: (01772) 556688 Fax: (01772) 204738

MASONRY CONTRACTORS, *See Stone Masonry etc*

MASONRY DRILLS

Corroy Products Ltd, 25 Queen Street, Premier Business Park, Walsall, WS2 9NT Tel: (01922) 644884 Fax: (01922) 471370 E-mail: sales@corroy.co.uk

MASONRY FIXINGS

Helifix Ltd, 21 Warple Way, London, W3 0RX Tel: (020) 8735 5200 Fax: (020) 8735 5201 E-mail: info@helifix.co.uk

MASONRY REPAIR PRODUCTS

Helifix Ltd, 21 Warple Way, London, W3 0RX Tel: (020) 8735 5200 Fax: (020) 8735 5201 E-mail: info@helifix.co.uk

Tensid UK plc, 70a Wheatash Road, Addlestone, Surrey, KT15 2ES Tel: (01932) 564133 Fax: (01932) 562046 E-mail: info@tensid.com

MASONRY STONE

▶ St Mary's Cathedral Workshop Ltd, 28 Manor Place, Edinburgh, EH3 7EB Tel: 0131-220 2227

Suffolk Masonery Services, 31 Woolner Close, Barham, Ipswich, IP6 0DL Tel: (01473) 831719 E-mail: r.templeton@ntlworld.com

MASONRY SUPPORT SYSTEMS

B R C Special Products, Carver Road, Astonfields Industrial Estate, Stafford, ST16 3BP Tel: (01785) 222288 Fax: (01785) 240029

MASS FLOW CONTROLLERS

▶ Chell Instruments Ltd, Folgate House, Folgate Road, North Walsham, Norfolk, NR28 0AJ Tel: (01692) 500555 Fax: (01692) 500088 E-mail: info@chell.co.uk

MASS SPECTROMETERS

Bruker BioSpin Ltd, Banner Lane, Coventry, CV4 9GH Tel: (024) 7685 5200 Fax: (024) 7646 5317 E-mail: admin@bruker.co.uk

F E I, Philips House Cambridge Business Park, Cowley Road, Cambridge, CB4 0HF Tel: (01223) 468555 Fax: (01223) 468599

Hiden Analytical Ltd, 420 Europa Boulevard, Westbrook, Warrington, WA5 7UN Tel: (01925) 445225 Fax: (01925) 416518 E-mail: info@hiden.co.uk

Jeol UK Ltd, Silver Court, Watchmead, Welwyn Garden City, Hertfordshire, AL7 1LT Tel: (01707) 377117 Fax: (01707) 373254 E-mail: uk.sales@jeoleuro.com

MASS TRANSFER PLANT CONTRACTORS OR DESIGNERS

Koch Glitsch (U K), Hobson Lane, Kirkby Stephen, Cumbria, CA17 4RN Tel: (01768) 374400 Fax: (01768) 374401

MASSAGE EQUIPMENT

▶ Equilibrium Complementary Health Centre, 16 Station Street, Lewes, East Sussex, BN7 2DB Tel: (01273) 470955 E-mail: info@equilibrium-clinic.com

Living Fountains Detox Clinic, 10 Hemlock Close, Oakwood, Derby, DE21 2NZ Tel: 0870 027 3656 Fax: 0870 1334836 E-mail: info@livingfountains.org

MASTER GEARS

Frenco International, 11 Fortnum Close, Birmingham, B33 0LG Tel: 0121-789 7895 Fax: 0121-789 7050 E-mail: sales@frenco.co.uk

Precision Technologies International Ltd, 22 Mariner, Tamworth, Staffordshire, B79 7UL Tel: (01827) 54371 Fax: (01827) 310406 E-mail: sales@ptiltd.co.uk

MASTER MODELS

4 D Model Shop Ltd, 120 Leman Street, London, E1 8EU Tel: (020) 7264 1288 Fax: (020) 7264 1299 E-mail: info@modelshop.co.uk

A E Blanchard, 144 Station Road, Ratby, Leicester, LE6 0JP Tel: 0116-239 3831 Fax: 0116-239 3831

Victorian Model Workshop, The Ferrers Centre, Melbourne Road, Staunton Harold, Ashby-de-la-Zouch, Leicestershire, LE65 1RU Tel: (01332) 864436 E-mail: info@modelworkshop.co.uk

MASTER OF CEREMONIES

Peter Moore, 18 College Gardens, London, SW17 7UG Tel: (020) 8767 2103 Fax: (020) 8767 2103 E-mail: peter@toastmasterlondon.com

MASTERBATCH

▶ Emsar Polymers UK Ltd, 2 The Court Stanley Green Business Park, Earl Road, Cheadle Hulme, Cheadle, Cheshire, SK8 6GN Tel: 0161-485 7772 Fax: 0161 485 7773 E-mail: info@emsarpolymers.co.uk

Steritouch, Unit 15 Roseheyworth Business, Abertillery, Gwent, NP13 1SP Tel: (01495) 211400 E-mail: info@steritouch.com

MASTERBATCH ADDITIVES

Douglas Baker Plastics Ltd, Doubak Works Barton Industrial Estate, Mount Pleasant, Bilston, West Midlands, WV14 7LH Tel: (01902) 353800 Fax: (01902) 353855 E-mail: sales@dbplastics.co.uk

Begg & Co Thermoplastics Ltd, 71 Hailey Road, Erith, Kent, DA18 4AW Tel: (020) 8310 1236 Fax: (020) 8310 4371 E-mail: darrenw@fsmail.net

Collords Ltd, Kirkby Bank Road, Knowsley Industrial Park, Liverpool, L33 7SY Tel: 0151-546 9222 Fax: 0151-549 0489 E-mail: sales@colloids.co.uk

Performance Master Batches Ltd, Blaenant Industrial Estate, Blaenavon Road, Brynmawr, Ebbw Vale, Gwent, NP23 4BX Tel: (01495) 310583 Fax: (01495) 312158 E-mail: customer.service@pmb.co.uk

Spectra Masterbatch Ltd, 5 Blyth Road, Halesworth, Suffolk, IP19 8EN Tel: (01986) 875100 Fax: (01986) 875700 E-mail: sales@spectra-masterbatch.co.uk

MASTERBATCH ENGINEERING

Begg & Co Thermoplastics Ltd, 71 Hailey Road, Erith, Kent, DA18 4AW Tel: (020) 8310 1236 Fax: (020) 8310 4371 E-mail: darrenw@fsmail.net

Collords Ltd, Kirkby Bank Road, Knowsley Industrial Park, Liverpool, L33 7SY Tel: 0151-546 9222 Fax: 0151-549 0489 E-mail: sales@colloids.co.uk

MASTERBATCH, COLOUR/ PIGMENT

Eclipse Colours, Hillam Road, Bradford, West Yorkshire, BD2 1QN Tel: (01274) 731552 Fax: (01274) 738118 E-mail: sales@eclipsecolours.co.uk

Holland Colours UK Ltd, Unit 16 Sabre Court, Gillingham Business Park, Gillingham, Kent, ME8 0RW Tel: (01634) 388727 Fax: (01634) 388910 E-mail: hcuk@hollandcolours.com

▶ Meridian Colour Co., Unit 3g Black Dyke Mills, Brighouse Road, Queensbury, Bradford, West Yorkshire, BD13 1QA Tel: (01274) 884900 Fax: (0871) 2216425 E-mail: info@meridiancolour.com

Metaflake Ltd, Station Road, Anstruther, Fife, KY10 3JA Tel: (01333) 313440 Fax: (01333) 313044 E-mail: enq@metaflake.com

▶ Positive Associates Ltd, PO Box 354, Dorking, Surrey, RH5 6FU Tel: (01306) 731482 Fax: (01306) 731534 E-mail: sales@positive-associates.com

Spectra Masterbatch Ltd, 5 Blyth Road, Halesworth, Suffolk, IP19 8EN Tel: (01986) 875100 Fax: (01986) 875700 E-mail: sales@spectra-masterbatch.co.uk

MASTERBATCH, COLOUR/ PIGMENT FOR PLASTIC

Americhem Ltd, Cawdor Street, Eccles, Manchester, M30 0QF Tel: 0161-789 7832 Fax: 0161-787 7832

Ampacet UK Ltd, Unit F1, Halesfield 21, Telford, Shropshire, TF7 4NX Tel: (01952) 581814 Fax: (01952) 581815

Douglas Baker Plastics Ltd, Doubak Works Barton Industrial Estate, Mount Pleasant, Bilston, West Midlands, WV14 7LH Tel: (01902) 353800 Fax: (01902) 353855 E-mail: sales@dbplastics.co.uk

Cabot G B Ltd, Gate Street, Dukinfield, Cheshire, SK16 4RU Tel: 0161-934 4500 Fax: 0161-934 4502 E-mail: webmaster@cabot-corp.com

Colourmaster, Stock Lane, Peel St, Chadderton, Oldham, OL9 9EY Tel: 0161-624 9479 Fax: 0161-678 8877 E-mail: sales@colour-master.co.uk

Eclipse Colours, Hillam Road, Bradford, West Yorkshire, BD2 1QN Tel: (01274) 731552 Fax: (01274) 738118 E-mail: sales@eclipsecolours.co.uk

Ferro Great Britain Ltd, Westgate, Aldridge, Walsall, WS9 8YH Tel: (01922) 458300 Fax: (01922) 741399

Gabriel-Chemie UK Ltd, Transfesa Road, Paddock Wood, Tonbridge, Kent, TN12 6UT Tel: (01892) 836566 Fax: (01892) 836979 E-mail: info@gabriel-chemie.com

Hampton Colours Ltd, Toadsmoor Mills, Brimscombe, Stroud, Gloucestershire, GL5 2UH Tel: (01453) 731555 Fax: (01453) 731234 E-mail: sales@hamptoncolours.co.uk

Holland Colours UK Ltd, Unit 16 Sabre Court, Gillingham Business Park, Gillingham, Kent, ME8 0RW Tel: (01634) 388727 Fax: (01634) 388910 E-mail: hcuk@hollandcolours.com

Hubron Sales, Albion Street, Failsworth, Manchester, M35 0WW Tel: 0161-681 2691 Fax: 0161-683 4045 E-mail: sales@hubron.com

I C O UK Ltd, 24 Norris Way, Wellingborough Road, Rushden, Northamptonshire, NN10 6BP Tel: (01933) 315500 Fax: (01933) 313300

Matrix Plastics Ltd, 141 Edinburgh Avenue, Slough, SL1 4SS Tel: (01753) 551177 Fax: (01753) 551166 E-mail: sales@matrix-plastics.co.uk

Metaflake Ltd, Station Road, Anstruther, Fife, KY10 3JA Tel: (01333) 313440 Fax: (01333) 313044 E-mail: enq@metaflake.com

Performance Master Batches Ltd, Blaenant Industrial Estate, Blaenavon Road, Brynmawr, Ebbw Vale, Gwent, NP23 4BX Tel: (01495) 310583 Fax: (01495) 312158 E-mail: customer.service@pmb.co.uk

Performance Master Batches Ltd, Blaenant Industrial Estate, Blaenavon Road, Brynmawr, Ebbw Vale, Gwent, NP23 4BX Tel: (01495) 310583 Fax: (01495) 312158 E-mail: customer.service@pmb.co.uk

PolyONE Corporation UK Ltd, Langley Road South, Salford, M6 6SN Tel: 0161-737 1717 Fax: 0161-737 3611

▶ Positive Associates Ltd, PO Box 354, Dorking, Surrey, RH5 6FU Tel: (01306) 731482 Fax: (01306) 731534 E-mail: sales@positive-associates.com

Prisma Colour Ltd, Hole House Mill, Marple Road, Chisworth, Glossop, Derbyshire, SK13 5DH Tel: (01457) 856505 Fax: (01457) 856505 E-mail: sales@prismacolour.com

▶ Rite Systems, 43 The Stripe, Stokesley, Middlesbrough, Cleveland, TS9 5PX Tel: (01642) 713140 E-mail: jgreen@ritesystems.com

Silvergate Plastics, Unit 53 Clywedog Road South, Wrexham Industrial Estate, Wrexham, Clwyd, LL13 9XS Tel: (01978) 661496 Fax: (01978) 660462 E-mail: sales@silvergate-plastics.co.uk

Spectra Masterbatch Ltd, 5 Blyth Road, Halesworth, Suffolk, IP19 8EN Tel: (01986) 875100 Fax: (01986) 875700 E-mail: sales@spectra-masterbatch.co.uk

Thane Dispersions Ltd, Spedding Road, Fenton Industrial Estate, Stoke-on-Trent, ST4 2ST Tel: (01782) 412217 Fax: (01782) 744769 E-mail: enquiries@thane.uk.com

MASTERBATCH, COLOUR/ PIGMENT FOR RUBBER

Eclipse Colours, Hillam Road, Bradford, West Yorkshire, BD2 1QN Tel: (01274) 731552 Fax: (01274) 738118 E-mail: sales@eclipsecolours.co.uk

▶ Positive Associates Ltd, PO Box 354, Dorking, Surrey, RH5 6FU Tel: (01306) 731482 Fax: (01306) 731534 E-mail: sales@positive-associates.com

MASTIC APPLICATORS

Proseal Adhesives & Sealants, 4 Nuttall Avenue, Great Harwood, Blackburn, BB6 7ER Tel: (01254) 888646 Fax: (01254) 888646

Technaseal Concrete Repairing Services, 11 Marriott Close, Heigham Street, Norwich, NR2 4UX Tel: (01603) 667106 Fax: (01603) 612636 E-mail: info@technasel.co.uk

MASTIC ASPHALT

Permanite, Cawder Quarry, Matlock, Derbyshire, DE4 2JH Tel: (01629) 580680 Fax: (01629) 57099 E-mail: info@permanite-asphalt.co.uk

MASTIC ASPHALT CONTRACTORS

Atkin John Construction Ltd, Viking Place, Cardiff, CF10 4UU Tel: (029) 2044 2060 Fax: (029) 2044 2065 E-mail: atkintrade@atkingroup.co.uk

North Herts Asphalt Ltd, Unit 15 The Cuttings, Station Approach, Hitchin, Hertfordshire, SG4 9UW Tel: (01462) 434877 Fax: (01462) 421539

Rock Asphalte, Latymer House, 2 Ravenscourt Road, London, W6 0UX Tel: (020) 8748 7881 Fax: (020) 8748 7225 E-mail: enquiries@rockasphalte.com

Sussex Asphalte, Clarendon Place, Portslade, Brighton, BN41 1DJ Tel: (01273) 417315 Fax: (01273) 422304 E-mail: info@sussexasphalte.co.uk

MASTIC ASPHALT CONTRACTORS

– continued

W G Walker & Co Ayr Ltd, Hawkhill Works, Somerset Road, Ayr, KA8 9NF Tel: (01292) 263122 Fax: (01292) 611691 E-mail: enquiries@wgwalker.co.uk

Woodhull Roofing Ltd, Unit S3 Olton Wharf, Richmond Road, Solihull, West Midlands, B92 7RN Tel: 0121-707 3111 Fax: 0121-708 1222 E-mail: woodhull.roofing@ic24.net

MATCHBOX/BOOKMATCH PUBLICITY CONSULTANTS OR CONTRACTORS

Matchmakers International, Richmond Street, Sheepfolds Industrial Estate, Sunderland, SR5 1BQ Tel: 0191-514 4199 Fax: 0191-565 6416 E-mail: matchfactory@edward-thompson.com

Octavius Hunt Ltd, Dove Lane, Redfield, Bristol, BS5 9NQ Tel: 0117-955 5304 Fax: 0117-955 7875 E-mail: info@octavius-hunt.co.uk

Promo Branding Ltd, New Southgate Industrial Estate, Lower Park Road, London, N11 1QD Tel: (020) 8361 8820 Fax: (020) 8361 8821 E-mail: sales@promobranding.co.uk

MATCHES

Octavius Hunt Ltd, Dove Lane, Redfield, Bristol, BS5 9NQ Tel: 0117-955 5304 Fax: 0117-955 7875 E-mail: info@octavius-hunt.co.uk

MATERIAL COST REDUCTION CONSULTANCY

▶ Auger Productions, Suite F16, Scope House, Weston Road, Crewe, CW1 6DD Tel: (01270) 258111 Fax: (01270) 258161 E-mail: info@auger-productions.com

▶ Optimus Business Practice, The Manzar Centre, Whitlenge Lane, Hartlebury, Kidderminster, Worcestershire, DY10 4HD Tel: (01299) 250745 Fax: (01299) 250240 E-mail: info@optimusbp.co.uk

▶ Purchasing Assistance Ltd, The Spinney 2 Park Road, Norton, Malton, North Yorkshire, YO17 9EA Tel: (01653) 696226 Fax: 01653 696226 E-mail: info@purchasing-assistance.co.uk

MATERIAL GRINDING MILL SERVICES

Micron Technologies Ltd, Crossways Boulevard, Crossways, Dartford, DA2 6QY Tel: (01322) 425200 Fax: (01322) 425201 E-mail: info@microntech.com

MATERIAL HANDLING CONTROL COMPUTER SYSTEMS

▶ Advanced Control Systems Ltd, 140 Aberford Road, Woodlesford, Leeds, LS26 8LG Tel: 0113-282 7123 Fax: 0113-282 5252 E-mail: office@xcl.co.uk

MATERIAL HANDLING EQUIPMENT

Action Handling Equipment Ltd, Maltings Industrial Estate, Station Road, Sawbridgeworth, Hertfordshire, CM21 9JY Tel: (01279) 724989 Fax: (01279) 600224 E-mail: sales@actionhandling.co.uk

Autotrack (Birmingham) Ltd, Ball Unit House Station Road Industrial Estate, Station Road, Woodchester, Stroud, Gloucestershire, GL5 5EQ Tel: (01453) 873155 Fax: (01453) 878500 E-mail: info@autotrack.co.uk

B B Conveyors Ltd, 5 Hallcroft Industrial Estate, Aurilac Way, Retford, Nottinghamshire, DN22 7PX Tel: (01777) 711111 Fax: (01777) 711501

B C Barton & Son Ltd, Granville Iron Works, Oldbury, West Midlands, B69 2NJ Tel: 0121-557 2272 Fax: 0121-557 2276 E-mail: pressworkers@b-c-b.co.uk

Bache Pallets Ltd, Bromley Street, Stourbridge, West Midlands, DY9 8HU Tel: (01384) 897799 Fax: (01384) 891351 E-mail: sales@bache-pallets.co.uk

Base Handling Products Ltd, Unit 20 Barleyfield Industrial Estate, Barleyfield Way, Nantyglo, Ebbw Vale, Gwent, NP23 4LU Tel: (01495) 312172 Fax: (01495) 312089 E-mail: info@baseproducts.co.uk

▶ Brandon Hire plc, Long Wood Road, Trafford Park, Manchester, M17 1PZ Tel: 0161-877 7720 Fax: 0161-877 7741

Brighouse Engineering Ltd, Martin House, 2 Martin Street, Brighouse, West Yorkshire, HD6 1DA Tel: (01484) 719999 Fax: (01484) 720422 E-mail: brigeng@compuserve.com

Bryant Plastic Products Ltd, Walk Mills, The Walk, Coney Lane, Keighley, West Yorkshire, BD21 5AR Tel: (01535) 606676 Fax: (01535) 602966 E-mail: sales@bryantplastics.co.uk

Caledonian Storage Ltd, Broadhouse Lea, Cleghorn, Lanark, ML11 8PA Tel: (0870) 2406115 Fax: (0870) 2401146

Caterpillar UK Ltd, Peckleton Lane, Desford, Leicester, LE9 9JU Tel: (01455) 826826 Fax: (01455) 826900

Chase Equipment Ltd, 53A Wellington Industrial Estate, Coseley, Bilston, West Midlands, WV14 9EE Tel: (01902) 675835 Fax: (01902) 674998 E-mail: sales@chaseequipment.com

Clark Handling Ltd, Hobson Industrial Estate, Hobson, Newcastle upon Tyne, NE16 6EA Tel: (01207) 270825 Fax: (01207) 271393 E-mail: sales@clarkhandling.co.uk

Coningsby Metals Ltd, 47-49 Silver Street, Coningsby, Lincoln, LN4 4SG Tel: (01526) 342141 Fax: (01526) 343382 E-mail: sales@cml-gt.co.uk

Conveyors Direct, Unit 6, Fishburn Industrial Estate, Fishburn, Stockton-on-Tees, Cleveland, TS21 4AJ Tel: 01740 623338 Fax: 01740 622504 E-mail: sales@conveyorsdirect.co.uk

Craemer UK Ltd, Craemer House, Hortonwood 1, Telford, Shropshire, TF1 7GN Tel: (01952) 641366 Fax: (01952) 607801 E-mail: sales@craemer.co.uk

Crossfield Engineering Co., Barrow Road, Sheffield, S9 1JZ Tel: 0114-243 8441 Fax: 0114-243 9266 E-mail: sales@crossfielduk.com

Dalmek Ltd, 2 Ringway Centre, Edisin Road, Basingstoke, Hampshire, RG21 6YH Tel: (01256) 814420 Fax: (01256) 814434 E-mail: info@dalmecltd.co.uk

Dosco Overseas Engineering Ltd, Dosco Industrial Estate, Ollerton Road, Tuxford, Newark, Nottinghamshire, NG22 0PQ Tel: (01777) 870621 Fax: (01777) 871580 E-mail: sales@dosco.co.uk

Ease-E-Load Trolleys Ltd, Saunders House, Moor Lane, Birmingham, B6 7HH Tel: 0121-356 2228 Fax: 0121-356 2220 E-mail: info@ease-e-load.co.uk

Egemin UK Ltd, 369 Wellingborough Road, Northampton, NN1 4EU Tel: (01604) 234994 Fax: (01604) 234483 E-mail: info@egemin.co.uk

Ensign Associates, 75 Bourn Lea, Houghton le Spring, Tyne & Wear, DH4 4PF Tel: 0191-385 5188 Fax: 0191-385 5188

▶ Euroquipment Ltd, Mallard House, Avon Way, Newbury Business Park, Newbury, Berkshire, RG14 2RF Tel: (0870) 1630077 Fax: (0870) 1630099 E-mail: sales@euroquipment.co.uk

Ewab Engineering Ltd, Stafford Park 16, Telford, Shropshire, TF3 3BS Tel: (01952) 239200 Fax: (01952) 239258 E-mail: pam.berry@ewab.net

Fairport Engineering Group Ltd, Market Place, Adlington, Chorley, Lancashire, PR7 4EZ Tel: (01257) 484000 Fax: (01257) 483312 E-mail: info@fairport.co.uk

Fort Jason Ltd, Stourvale Trading Estate, Banners Lane, Halesowen, West Midlands, B63 2AX Tel: (01384) 567165 Fax: (01384) 567626

G P C Industries Ltd, Market St, Spilsby, Lincolnshire, PE23 5JT Tel: (01790) 753835 Fax: (01790) 752109 E-mail: sales@gpcind.co.uk

General Bridge & Engineering Ltd, Fleming Road, Earlstrees Industrial Estate, Corby, Northamptonshire, NN17 4SW Tel: (01536) 205744 Fax: (01536) 402456 E-mail: email@genbridge.fsnet.co.uk

Goddard & Co 1992 Ltd, Copley Mill, Demesne Drive, St. Pauls Trading Estate, Stalybridge, Cheshire, SK15 2QF Tel: 0161-304 9690 Fax: 0161-304 9694 E-mail: goddardco1992@btinternet.com

J.A.V. Grazebrook & Co., Stourport-On-Severn, Worcestershire, DY13 0YB Tel: (01299) 827440 Fax: (01299) 827048

Grimmitt Holdings Ltd, Woodgate Business Park, Kettleswood Drive, Birmingham, B32 3GH Tel: 0121-421 7000 Fax: 0121-421 9081

H C Slingsby plc, Otley Road, Shipley, West Yorkshire, BD17 7LW Tel: (01274) 535030 Fax: (01274) 535033 E-mail: sales@slingsby.com

Hallam Materials Handling Ltd, 232-234 Woodbourn Road, Sheffield, S9 3LQ Tel: 0114-275 3000 Fax: 0114-275 3222 E-mail: hallam-mh@btconnect.com

K. Hartwall Ltd, Green Lane Industrial Estate, Spennymoor, County Durham, DL16 6BP Tel: (01388) 824700 Fax: (01388) 824724

▶ Hirata Corporation Of Europe, Grafton Road, Burbage, West Grafton, Marlborough, Wiltshire, SN8 3BA Tel: (01672) 811728 Fax: (01672) 811666 E-mail: sales@hirata.co.uk

Hooper Knight & Co., St Albans Road, Gloucester, GL2 5FW Tel: (01452) 502888 Fax: (01452) 502960 E-mail: intray@hooperknight.com

Indumat Systems Ltd, 25 Campbell Court Business Park, Bramley, Tadley, Hampshire, RG26 5EG Tel: (01256) 880228 Fax: (01256) 880338 E-mail: info.uk@ek-automation.com

Intern Transport Systems (U K) Ltd, 421 Nottingham Road, Ilkeston, Derbyshire, DE7 5BP Tel: 0115-930 7724 Fax: 0115-930 1742 E-mail: sales@itsuk.org.uk

J C B Landpower Ltd, Lakeside Works, Denstone Road, Rocester, Uttoxeter, Staffordshire, ST14 5JP Tel: (01889) 590312 Fax: (01889) 590588 E-mail: enq@jcbinfo.co.uk

Jenco Control & Export Ltd, Roebuck Road Trading Estate, 41-43 Roebuck Road, Ilford, Essex, IG6 3TU Tel: (020) 8501 5522 Fax: (020) 8501 5533 E-mail: info@jenco.co.uk

Joloda (International) Ltd, 51 Speke Road, Liverpool, L19 2NY Tel: 0151-427 8954 Fax: 0151-427 1393 E-mail: info@joloda.com

Joy Mining Machinery Ltd, Seaman Way, Ince, Wigan, Lancashire, WN1 3DD Tel: (0870) 2526000 Fax: (0870) 2526888 E-mail: rbailey@joy.co.uk

L F E Material Handling, Units 3-5 Hibberd House, Curriers Close, Charter Avenue Industrial Esta, Coventry, CV4 8AW Tel: (024) 7647 0170 Fax: (024) 7669 4521 E-mail: lfemh@btconnect.com

L M S Constructional Engineers Ltd, 8 Swinton Meadows Industrial Estate, Meadow Way, Swinton, Mexborough, South Yorkshire, S64 8AB Tel: (01709) 571001 Fax: (01709) 571021 E-mail: sales@lmskan.co.uk

Linde Material Handling Scotland, Unit 11 Barrett Trading Estate, Denmore Road, Bridge of Don, Aberdeen, AB23 8JW Tel: (01224) 707020 Fax: (01224) 707066 E-mail: enquiries@linde-mh-scotland.co.uk

Lintec Systems Ltd, Unit 11 Maguire Industrial Estate, Torrington Avenue, Coventry, CV4 9HN Tel: 0121-442 4434 Fax: 0121-442 4160 E-mail: peter@justhandling.fsnet.co.uk

Logitrans UK Ltd, Unit 5 Ascot Industrial Estate, Icknield Way, Letchworth Garden City, Hertfordshire, SG6 1TD Tel: (01462) 678444 Fax: (01462) 678555

M G K Engineering (Northern) Ltd, Polbeth Industrial Estate, Polbeth, West Calder, West Lothian, EH55 8TJ Tel: (01506) 871757 Fax: (01506) 873400 E-mail: sales@mgkscot.co.uk

M S I Forks Ltd, Carr Hill, Doncaster, South Yorkshire, DN4 8DH Tel: (01302) 366961 Fax: (01302) 340663

McConnell Equipment Ltd, 16 Ballycraigy Road, Antrim, BT41 1PL Tel: (028) 9446 3921 Fax: (028) 9446 7102 E-mail: macquip@btinternet.com

Material Handling Devices Ltd, Lindeth House, 563 Bradford Road, Cleckheaton, West Yorkshire, BD19 6BU Tel: (01274) 874164 Fax: (01274) 852233 E-mail: sales.mathandlin@btclick.com

Mechandling Ltd, 11b Greenfield Farm Industrial Estate, Congleton, Cheshire, CW12 4TR Tel: (01260) 299411 Fax: (01260) 299032 E-mail: sales@mechandling.co.uk

Mercia Mechanical Handling Ltd, Unit C4-C6, Guy Motors Industrial Park, Park Lane, Wolverhampton, WV10 9QF Tel: (01902) 739852 Fax: (01902) 739547 E-mail: merciamech@btconnect.com

Middlehurst Ltd, 103 Boyn Valley Road, Maidenhead, Berkshire, SL6 4EA Tel: (01628) 628044 Fax: (01628) 773143 E-mail: office@middlehurstlimited.com

▶ Molenaar, 32, Buckingham Close, Northampton, NN4 0RR Tel: (01604) 701367 Fax: (01604) 701514

Motan Ltd, Unit 10 Blacklands Way, Abingdon Business Park, Abingdon, Oxfordshire, OX14 1RD Tel: (01235) 550011 Fax: (01235) 550033 E-mail: sales.ltd@motan.com

Nasus Mechanical Handling Ltd, Unit 3 Monkmoor Trading Estate, Monkmoor Road, Shrewsbury, SY2 5TZ Tel: (01743) 355496 Fax: (01743) 235443

Nelson Sheetmetal Fabricators Ltd, Walton St Works, Walton St, Colne, Lancashire, BB8 0EW Tel: (01282) 866966 Fax: (01282) 866990 E-mail: nsc@fsmail.net

Nene Mechanical Equipment, Nene House, Drayton Way, Drayton Fields Industrial Estate, Daventry, Northamptonshire, NN11 5EA Tel: (01327) 300456 Fax: (01327) 300737 E-mail: sales@nene.co.uk

Oakway Mechanical Equipment, 42 Oliver Street, Northampton, NN2 7JJ Tel: (01604) 792255

P A Loading Systems Ltd, 9 Kineton Road, Kenilworth, Warwickshire, CV8 2AW Tel: (01926) 851619 Fax: (01926) 850478 E-mail: davidparry@mash-b.co.uk

P.J. Parmiter & Sons Ltd, Station Works, Tisbury, Salisbury, SP3 6QZ Tel: (01747) 870821 Fax: (01747) 871171 E-mail: mail@parmiter.co.uk

Pipe Coil Technology, Hadrian Road, Wallsend, Tyne & Wear, NE28 6HF Tel: 0191-295 9910 Fax: 0191-295 9911

Planned Storage Systems Ltd, Murdock Road, Dorcan, Swindon, SN3 5HY Tel: (01793) 694071 Fax: (01793) 610516 E-mail: mail@hi-lo.co.uk

Powerail Ltd, High Road, Finchley, London, N12 8PT Tel: (020) 8446 0350 Fax: (020) 8446 7054

Powerscreen International Distribution Ltd, Coalisland Road, Dungannon, County Tyrone, BT71 4DR Tel: (028) 8774 0701 Fax: (028) 8774 7231 E-mail: sales@powerscreen.co.uk

▶ Rhewum GB, 3 The Point Business Park, Market Harborough, Leicestershire, LE16 7QU Tel: (01858) 468088 Fax: (01858) 433934 E-mail: info@rhewum.de

S M C Euro Clamps Ltd, Demmings Road, Cheadle, Cheshire, SK8 2PP Tel: 0161-428 8323 Fax: 0161-428 4513 E-mail: purchasing@smceuroclamps.com

Sev, 356d Dukesway Court, Gateshead, Tyne & Wear, NE11 0BH Tel: 0191-487 1311 Fax: 0191-482 0243 E-mail: sales@sev.co.uk

Solitec Engineering, Unit 8 Gilchrist Thomas Industrial Estate, Blaenavon, Pontypool, Gwent, NP4 9RL Tel: (01453) 828727 Fax: (01495) 790666 E-mail: solitec@aol.com

Spencer Davis Handling Ltd, Glanmor Terrace, Burry Port, Dyfed, SA16 0LS Tel: (01554) 833358 Fax: (01554) 835338 E-mail: sales@sde.co.uk

Spring Vale Engineering (Brighouse) Ltd, Spring Vale Industrial Estate, Elland Road, Brighouse, West Yorkshire, HD6 2RA Tel: (01484) 720205 Fax: (01484) 400056 E-mail: enquiries@springvalegroup.com

Still Materials Handling, Aston Way, Moss Side Industrial Estate, Leyland, PR26 7UX Tel: (01772) 644300 Fax: (01772) 454668 E-mail: sales@still.co.uk

Stor Tech, Unit A Castle Park Industrial Estate, Bower Street, Oldham, OL1 3LN Tel: 0161-678 8597 Fax: 0161-665 0579 E-mail: info@stortech.ltd.uk

Swisslog Digitron Ltd, Regents Court, Farmoor Lane, Redditch, Worcestershire, B98 0SD Tel: (01527) 517333 Fax: (01527) 517344 E-mail: info@digitron.ltd.uk

Thornton Industries (UK) Ltd, Thornton Ho, Dock La, Shipley, W. Yorkshire, BD17 7BE Tel: (01274) 598694 Fax: (01274) 531577 E-mail: sales@tiukltd.net

Thyssenkrupp Materials Handling Equipment, Nene House, Sopwith Way, Drayton Fields Industrial Esta, Daventry, Northamptonshire, NN11 8PB Tel: (01327) 301199 Fax: (01327) 300681 E-mail: david@tkmh.co.uk

▶ Transdek UK Ltd, PO Box 76, Retford, Nottinghamshire, DN22 8ST Tel: (01777) 705958 Fax: (01777) 706756 E-mail: info@transdek.com

Translift Holdings plc, 22 Padgets Lane, Redditch, Worcestershire, B98 0RB Tel: (01527) 527411 Fax: (01527) 510177 E-mail: sales@translift.co.uk

Ultra Contract Services, Camford Way, Luton, LU3 3AN Tel: (01582) 490000 Fax: (01582) 597038 E-mail: mail@ultracs.co.uk

Upm Machinery Sales Ltd, 5 Elder Way, Waterside Drive, Langley, Slough, SL3 6EP Tel: (01753) 548801 Fax: (01753) 544115 E-mail: royf@upm.co.uk

Van Der Lande Industries, 59 Marsh Lane, Hampton-in-Arden, Solihull, West Midlands, B92 0AJ Tel: (01675) 443801 Fax: (01675) 443169 E-mail: roger.peart@vanderlande.co.uk

Variant Systems UK Ltd, Unit S1 The Old Brickyard, Ashton Keynes, Swindon, SN6 6QR Tel: (01285) 861870 Fax: (01285) 862110 E-mail: s.ascroft@variantsystems.co.uk

Vertex Precision Engineering Ltd, 7 Armoury Road, Lufton Trading Estate, Yeovil, Somerset, BA22 8RL Tel: (01935) 477310 Fax: (01935) 706212 E-mail: vertex@vertexeng.demon.co.uk

W K D Storage Systems Ltd, 3-4 Bourne Industrial Estate, Wrotham Road, Borough Green, Sevenoaks, Kent, TN15 8DF Tel: (01732) 882042 Fax: (01732) 885763 E-mail: sales@wkdstorage.co.uk

W S Barrett & Son Ltd, Riverside Industrial Estate, Marsh Lane, Boston, Lincolnshire, PE21 7PJ Tel: (01205) 362585 Fax: (01205) 310831 E-mail: info@wsbarrett.co.uk

A. & G. Walden Bros Ltd, 34 Wimbledon Avenue, Brandon, Suffolk, IP27 0NZ Tel: (01842) 811776 Fax: (01842) 814603 E-mail: trucks@walden.co.uk

Weldwork Ltd, Central Way, Feltham, Middlesex, TW14 0XJ Tel: (020) 8890 4141 Fax: (020) 8751 5793 E-mail: info@cmf.co.uk

Alan E. Wheeler & Son, Unit 90, Condover Industrial Estate, Condover, Shrewsbury, SY5 7NH Tel: (01743) 718426 Fax: (01743) 718224 E-mail: sales@vacuumlifting.com

Wiland Wines Ltd, Regent House, Ellis Street, Anstey, Leicester, LE7 7FG Tel: 0116-236 3479 Fax: 0116-234 0262

Wilmat Handling Company Ltd, 43 Steward Street, Birmingham, B18 7AE Tel: 0121-454 7514 Fax: 0121-456 1792 E-mail: info@wilmat-handling.co.uk

Wise Handling Ltd, Haworth Road, Cullingworth, Bradford, West Yorkshire, BD13 5DU Tel: (01535) 272033 Fax: (01535) 275774 E-mail: sales@wiseboathoists.co.uk

Wyvern Handling & Storage Equipment Ltd, PO Box 5483, Stourport-on-Severn, Worcestershire, DY13 3BG Tel: (01299) 829300 Fax: (01299) 825799 E-mail: sales@wyvernhandling.co.uk

Yale Europe, Flagship House, Reading Road North, Fleet, Hampshire, GU51 4WD Tel: (01252) 770700 Fax: (01252) 770890

MATERIAL HANDLING SYSTEM BELT CONVEYORS

Aegis Security, Dane Road, Bletchley, Milton Keynes, MK1 1JQ Tel: (01908) 375451 Fax: (01908) 375044 E-mail: info@kemco-aegis.com

J White Fabrications, South Cowton, Northallerton, North Yorkshire, DL7 0JB Tel: (01325) 378207 Fax: (01325) 378271

Megadyne U K Ltd, Gildersome Spur, Gildersome, Leeds, LS27 7JZ Tel: 0113-238 2910 Fax: 0113-238 3870 E-mail: sales@megadyne.co.uk

Tek Machinery Ltd, 9 Stadium Court, Barbot Hall Industrial Estate, Parkgate, Rotherham, South Yorkshire, S62 6EW Tel: (01709) 820820 Fax: (01709) 382504 E-mail: info@tekmachinery.co.uk

▶ Total Maintenance Solutions, Unit 94 Silverbriar, Business & Innovation Centre, Sunderland Enterprise Park, Sunderland, SR5 2TQ Tel: 0191-516 6489 Fax: 0191-516 6499 E-mail: sales@online-tms.com

MATERIAL MAGNETIC PARTICLE TESTING

Bluelimit Surveys Ltd, 6 Riverside Road, Gorleston, Great Yarmouth, Norfolk, NR31 6PU Tel: (01493) 653900 Fax: (01493) 442774 E-mail: bluelimit@paston.co.uk

MATERIAL TECHNOLOGY INFORMATION SERVICES

Double Dean Ltd, Fallowfields, Dummer, Basingstoke, Hants, RG25 2AG Tel: (01256) 398550

Green It Solutions Ltd, Unit 1 King George Court, High Street, Billericay, Essex, CM12 9BY Tel: (01277) 844940 Fax: (01277) 844941 E-mail: info@greenit.co.uk

Institute Of Sheet Metal Engineering, 48 Holloway Head, Birmingham, B1 1NG Tel: 0121-622 2860 Fax: 0121-666 6316 E-mail: admin@instituteofmetalfinishing.org

MATERIAL TEST EQUIPMENT

Blacks Equipment Ltd, Barton La, Armthorpe, Doncaster, S. Yorkshire, DN3 3AA Tel: (01302) 834444 Fax: (01302) 831834 E-mail: sales@blacksequipment.com

D F D Instruments, Northpoint House, 52 High Street, Knaphill, Woking, Surrey, GU21 2PY Tel: (01483) 799333 Fax: (01483) 480199 E-mail: tore@dfdinstruments.co.uk

Engineering Systems Nottm, 1 Loach Court, Radford Bridge Road, Nottingham, NG8 1NA Tel: 0115-928 8708 Fax: 0115-928 8715 E-mail: info@engsys.co.uk

Instron, Coronation Road, High Wycombe, Buckinghamshire, HP12 3SY Tel: (01494) 464646 Fax: (01494) 456123 E-mail: info_news@instron.com

Messmer Instruments Ltd, Unit F1 Imperial Business Estate, West Mill, Gravesend, Kent, DA11 0DL Tel: (01474) 566488 Fax: (01474) 560310 E-mail: sales@messmerinstruments.com

Nortest Scientific Apparatus, Unit 1 The Woodyard, Castle Ashby, Northampton, NN7 1LF Tel: (01604) 696192 Fax: (01604) 696198 E-mail: brian@nortest.co.uk

Pro Test Panels Ltd, Unit 38 Padgets Lane, South Moons Moat, Redditch, Worcestershire, B98 0RD Tel: (01527) 514404 Fax: (05601) 149560 E-mail: sales@testpanels.com

▶ Q A Equipment Ltd, Hutton Place, Grasslot, Maryport, Cumbria, CA15 8ED Tel: (01900) 812777 Fax: (0870) 7598333 E-mail: sales@qaequipment.co.uk

R & H Testing Services Ltd, Cannel Road, Burntwood Business Park, Burntwood, Staffordshire, WS7 3FU Tel: (01543) 677400 Fax: (01543) 677477 E-mail: sales@randhtesting.com

Tinius Olsen Ltd, Unit 6, Perrywood Business Park, Honeycrock Lane, Salfords, Redhill, RH1 5DZ Tel: (01737) 765001 Fax: (01737) 764768 E-mail: sales@tiniusolsen.co.uk

MATERIAL VIBRATORY COMPACTION

Orthos (Engineering) Ltd, No 2, 2 The Point, Market Harborough, Leicestershire, LE16 7QU Tel: (01858) 464246 Fax: (01858) 434480 E-mail: sales@orthos.uk.com

MATERIALS ADVISORY AND CONSULTING SERVICES

Metaltech Consulting Services, 2 Talisman Business Centre, Duncan Road, Park Gate, Southampton, SO31 7GA Tel: (01489) 885483 Fax: (01489) 589372 E-mail: info@metaltechconsulting.co.uk

MATERIALS HANDLING CONSULTANTS OR DESIGNERS

Amek Conveyors, 17 Bergen Way, Hull, HU7 0YQ Tel: (01482) 838605 Fax: (01482) 838705 E-mail: sales@amek.co.uk

Hardie Secure Products Ltd, 17 Station Road, Flitwick, Bedford, MK45 1JT Tel: (01525) 716736 Fax: (01525) 716736 E-mail: hsfabrications@msn.com

Kelk Engineering, Unit 4 Kelleythorpe Industrial Estate, Kellythorpe, Driffield, North Humberside, YO25 9DJ Tel: (01377) 252313 Fax: (01377) 232846 E-mail: enquiries@kelkeng.co.uk

Spring Vale Engineering (Brighouse) Ltd, Spring Vale Industrial Estate, Elland Road, Brighouse, West Yorkshire, HD6 2RA Tel: (01484) 720205 Fax: (01484) 400056 E-mail: enquiries@springvalegroup.com

▶ Transdek UK Ltd, PO Box 76, Retford, Nottinghamshire, DN22 8ST Tel: (01777) 705958 Fax: (01777) 706756 E-mail: info@transdek.com

Western Industrial, Linhay Business Park, Eastern Road, Ashburton, Devon, TQ13 7UP Tel: (01364) 651860 Fax: (01364) 651861 E-mail: sales@westernindustrial.co.uk

Western Mechanical Handling UK Ltd, Celtic Road, Moss Side Industrial Estate, Callington, Cornwall, PL17 7SD Tel: (01579) 383788 Fax: (01579) 383923

MATERIALS HANDLING EQUIPMENT HIRE

Dawson Rentals Ltd, Aberford Road, Garforth, Leeds, LS25 2ET Tel: 0113-287 4874 Fax: 0113-286 9158 E-mail: info@dawsongroup.co.uk

HSS Lift & Shift, 399 York Road, Leeds, LS9 6TA Tel: 0113-240 7707 Fax: 0113-240 9944

Nene Storage Equipment Ltd, Nene House, Sopwith Way, Drayton Flelds Indusrial Estate, Daventry, Northamptonshire, NN11 8EA Tel: (01327) 300456 Fax: (01327) 300737 E-mail: awbrooks@nene.co.uk

Stephensons Enterprise Fork Trucks, Unit 1, Great Bank Road, Westhoughton, Bolton, BL5 3XU Tel: (01942) 276711 Fax: (01942) 276728 E-mail: enterpriseforktruck@lineone.net

MATERIALS HANDLING EQUIPMENT INSTALLATION OR SERVICING

B & I Fabrications, Farrington Place, Rossendale Road Industrial Estate, Burnley, Lancashire, BB11 5TY Tel: (01282) 411434 Fax: (01282) 838963

Jenco Control & Export Ltd, Roebuck Road Trading Estate, 41-43 Roebuck Road, Ilford, Essex, IG6 3TU Tel: (020) 8501 5522 Fax: (020) 8501 5533 E-mail: info@jenco.co.uk

Johnson's Chopwell Ltd, Tollbridge Road, Blaydon-on-Tyne, Tyne & Wear, NE21 5TB Tel: 0191-414 2455 Fax: 0191-414 1640 E-mail: johnsonschopwell@b&k.co.uk

Joloda (International) Ltd, 51 Speke Road, Liverpool, L19 2NY Tel: 0151-427 8954 Fax: 0151-427 1393 E-mail: info@joloda.com

Lincoln Industrial Ltd, Unit 2 Canada Close, Banbury, Oxfordshire, OX16 2RT Tel: (01295) 256611 Fax: (01295) 275771 E-mail: sales@lincolnindustrial.co.uk

Richardson & Co. Ltd, Smithfold Lane, Worsley, Manchester, M28 0GP Tel: 0161-702 7002

S T B Engineering Ltd, Toadsmoor Road, Brimscombe, Stroud, Gloucestershire, GL5 2UF Tel: (01453) 885353 Fax: (01453) 886824 E-mail: sales@stbengineering.com

MATERIALS HANDLING EQUIPMENT, USED

▶ K C Handling, 47 Kirkwood Close, New Springs, Aspull, Wigan, Lancashire, WN2 1DZ Tel: (01942) 230054 Fax: (01942) 230054 E-mail: kc.handling@lycos.co.uk

MATERIALS HANDLING PLANT, BULK, *See Bulk etc*

MATERIALS HANDLING PROJECT MANAGEMENT

Fairport Engineering Group Ltd, Market Place, Adlington, Chorley, Lancashire, PR7 4EZ Tel: (01257) 484000 Fax: (01257) 483312 E-mail: info@fairport.co.uk

Game Engineering Ltd, Camp Road, Witham St. Hughs, Lincoln, LN6 9TW Tel: (01522) 868021 Fax: (01522) 868027 E-mail: sales@game-security-engineering.com

MATERIALS HANDLING SERVICES

D B Controls Ltd, 9 Station Road, Adwick-Le-Street, Doncaster, South Yorkshire, DN6 7BE Tel: (01302) 330837 Fax: (01302) 724731 E-mail: sales@dbcontrols.co.uk

MATERIALS TESTING LABORATORY EQUIPMENT

Engineering Systems Nottm, 1 Loach Court, Radford Bridge Road, Nottingham, NG8 1NA Tel: 0115-928 8708 Fax: 0115-928 8715 E-mail: info@engsys.co.uk

Hanatek Services Ltd, 10 Sunny Close, Goring-By-Sea, Worthing, West Sussex, BN12 4BD Tel: (01903) 246418 Fax: (01903) 506815 E-mail: info@hanatek.co.uk

▶ Water Quality Centre, Spencer House, Manor Farm Road, Reading, RG2 0JN Tel: 0118-923 6214 Fax: 0118-923 6373 E-mail: info@materialstesting.co.uk

Zwick Ltd, Main Enquiries, Southern Avenue, Leominster, Herefordshire, HR6 0QH Tel: (01568) 615201 Fax: (01568) 616626 E-mail: sales.info@zwick.co.uk

MATERNITY CLOTHING

▶ Bumps Maternity Wear, 19 Frederick Street, Sunderland, SR1 1LT Tel: 0191-565 3232 Fax: 0191 5520988 E-mail: info@bumpsmaternity.com

▶ J J Clothing Ltd, 219 Western Road, Leicester, LE3 0EA Tel: 0116-275 6252

MATHEMATICAL INSTRUMENTS

Helix Group plc, Lye, Engine Lane, Stourbridge, West Midlands, DY9 7AJ Tel: (01384) 424441 Fax: (01384) 892617 E-mail: info@helixhq.com

MATS, *See also headings for particular types*

Beaver Mats, PO Box 305, Eastleigh, Hampshire, SO53 3XR Tel: (023) 8062 0304

Cosmos Motor Products Ltd, Unit 3A Neptune Industrial Estate, Neptune Road, Harrow, Middlesex, HA1 4HX Tel: (020) 8863 8666 Fax: (020) 8427 3689 E-mail: salescomopro@cs.com

Javah Ltd, Warwick Mills, Howard Street, Batley, West Yorkshire, WF17 6JH Tel: (01924) 452156 Fax: (01924) 455015 E-mail: sales@javah.com

Kopak-Walker Ltd, PO Box 65, Hitchin, Hertfordshire, SG4 0TW Tel: (01462) 452487 Fax: (01462) 452249 E-mail: sales@kopak-walker.co.uk

L.Nicot & Company Ltd, 7 Beeches Avenue, Carshalton Beeches, Carshalton, Surrey, SM5 3LB Tel: (020) 8773 8050 Fax: (020) 8773 8070

Selected Rug & Matting Ltd, 74 Long Lane, London, SE1 4AU Tel: (020) 7407 8471 Fax: (020) 7378 0540 E-mail: srmlondon@aol.com

Bruce Starke & Co. Ltd, Langton Green, Eye, Suffolk, IP23 7HL Tel: (01379) 870209 Fax: (01379) 871232 E-mail: info@bruce-starke.com

MATTING/MATS, ANIMAL HOUSING

Davies & Co. (Kettering), Beatrice Road, Kettering, Northamptonshire, NN16 9QS Tel: (01536) 513456 Fax: (01536) 310080 E-mail: david@davieskett.co.uk

MATTING/MATS, PROMOTIONAL, COIR

Designer Logo Matting, 56 Southbury Road, Enfield, Middlesex, EN1 1YB Tel: (020) 8342 2020 Fax: (020) 8342 2021

MATTRESS ACCESSORIES

BFL Trading Ltd, 314 Regents Park Road, London, N3 2LT Tel: (020) 8371 6000 Fax: (020) 8371 6010 E-mail: info@bfl.com

Inva Care Ltd, M S S House, Taffs Fall Road, Treforest Industrial Estate, Pontypridd, Mid Glamorgan, CF37 5TT Tel: (01443) 849222 Fax: (01656) 649016 E-mail: uk@inva-care.com

MATTRESS COVERS

Britton Gelplas Ltd, Venture House, 5th Avenue, Letchworth Garden City, Herts, SG6 1JT Tel: (01462) 480808 Fax: (01462) 481398 E-mail: roger.young@britton-group.com

Cumulus Mattress Protectors, Selinas Lane, Dagenham, Essex, RM8 1ES Tel: (020) 8592 2233 Fax: (020) 8593 3787 E-mail: enquiries@abbey-quilting.co.uk

Durasak, Stansfeld Street, Blackburn, BB2 2NG Tel: (01254) 51733 Fax: (01254) 51833 E-mail: sales@durasat.co.uk

MATTRESS FILLINGS, *See Fillings etc*

MATTRESS INTERIOR SPRINGS

Charles Blyth & Co. Ltd, Carnival Way, Castle Donington, Derby, DE74 2NJ Tel: (01332) 810283 Fax: (01332) 855810 E-mail: info@charlesblyth-co.co.uk

Wade Spring Ltd, Bennett Street, Long Eaton, Nottingham, NG10 4HL Tel: 0115-946 3000 Fax: 0115-946 1361 E-mail: mchiltern@wade-spring.com

MATTRESS PRODUCTION MACHINERY

Gateway Textiles Ltd, Northgate Terrace, Unit 3 Northern Road, Newark, Nottinghamshire, NG24 2EU Tel: (01636) 676194 Fax: (01636) 611367 E-mail: sales@gatewaysystems.co.uk

Mattress Production Technology Ltd, New Line Industrial Estate, The Sidings, Bacup, Lancashire, OL13 9RW Tel: (01706) 878558 Fax: (01706) 878288 E-mail: enquiries@mptg.demon.co.uk

MATTRESS PROTECTORS

Fogarty Ltd, Havenside, Fishtoft Road, Boston, Lincolnshire, PE21 0AH Tel: (01205) 361122 Fax: (01205) 353202 E-mail: info@fogarty.co.uk

MATTRESSES

▶ Abberley Ltd, Unit 7, Roach View, Millhead Way, Rochford, Essex, SS4 1LB Tel: (01702) 533761 Fax: (01702) 533760

▶ Cockett's Bespoke Beds, 32-34 High Street, Herne Bay, Kent, CT6 5LH Tel: (0870) 7552343 E-mail: mail@cockets.com

▶ Ed's Beds, 26A Front Street, Framwellgate Moor, Durham, DH1 5EJ Tel: 0191-375 7275 Fax: 0191-375 7275

First Technicare Co. Ltd, Unit 10 Acorn Production Centre, 105 Blundell Street, London, N7 9BN Tel: (020) 7609 8761 Fax: (020) 7607 1062E-mail: tripos3@aol.com

▶ Memflex, Calder House, Saville Road, Castleford, West Yorkshire, WF10 1HH Tel: (01977) 669690 Fax: (01977) 669693 E-mail: sales@memflex.co.uk

▶ Norian Mattress Manufacturers, Unit 4-6 Millfield, Chard, Somerset, TA20 2DA Tel: (01460) 239988

▶ Twinkle Nights, 79 Bennetts Castle Lane, Dagenham, Essex, RM8 3YB Tel: (020) 8599 0741

MEASUREMENT BEARINGS

Plastigauge, Unit 2, Gaugemaster Way, Ford, Arundel, West Sussex, BN18 0RX Tel: (01903) 882822 Fax: (01903) 884962 E-mail: sales@plastigauge.co.uk

MEASUREMENT GEARS

Frenco International, 11 Fortnum Close, Birmingham, B33 0LG Tel: 0121-789 7895 Fax: 0121-789 7050 E-mail: sales@frenco.co.uk

MEASURING EQUIPMENT MANUFRS, *See also headings for particular types*

Afriso Eurogauge Ltd, Imberhorne Lane, East Grinstead, West Sussex, RH19 1RF Tel: (01342) 323641 Fax: (01342) 315513 E-mail: sales@eurogauge.co.uk

Aja Ltd, 6 Heathlands Close, Twickenham, TW1 4BP Tel: (020) 8892 8900 Fax: (020) 8892 8901

Grapevine Instruments, PO Box 598, Canterbury, Kent, CT4 7GW Tel: (07010) 707940 Fax: (01227) 730892 E-mail: sfigures@netcomuk.co.uk

Icon Research Ltd, Raw Holdings, East Calder, Livingston, West Lothian, EH53 0HY Tel: (01506) 885000 Fax: (01506) 885501

Keithley Instruments Ltd, 2 Commerce Park, Brunel Road, Theale, Reading, RG7 4AB Tel: 0118-929 7500 Fax: 0118-929 7519 E-mail: enquiries@keithley.com

Kipp & Zonen Ltd, PO Box 819, Lincoln, LN6 0WY Tel: (01522) 695403 Fax: (01522) 696598 E-mail: kipp.uk@kippzonen.com

Mayer International (UK) Ltd, 18 Monnach Way, Winchester, Hampshire, SO22 5QU Tel: (01962) 625618 E-mail: johnmayer@tunnel-lighting-control.com

Measure-Rite Ltd, Great Central Way Industrial Estate, Great Central Way, Rugby, Warwickshire, CV21 3XH Tel: (01788) 577512 Fax: (01788) 560864 E-mail: sales@measure-rite.com

▶ Practical Metrology, 6a Station Parade, South Street, Lancing, West Sussex, BN15 8AA Tel: (01903) 525000 Fax: (01903) 525001

Price & Weston, Orchard St, Worcester, WR5 3DY Tel: (01905) 360463 Fax: (01905) 763040 E-mail: enquiries@price-weston.co.uk

R D P Group Ltd, Grove Street, Heath Town, Wolverhampton, WV10 0PY Tel: (01902) 457512 Fax: (01902) 452000 E-mail: sales@rdpelectronics.com

T W L Force Systems, 15 Old Farm Lane, Fareham, Hampshire, PO14 2DB Tel: (01329) 665186 Fax: (01329) 668177 E-mail: sales@twlforce.co.uk

Taylor Hobson, P O Box 36, Leicester, LE4 9JQ Tel: 0116-276 3771 Fax: 0116-274 1350 E-mail: sales@taylor-hobson.com

MEASURING EQUIPMENT, ONE/ TWO/THREE DIMENSIONAL (1D/ 2D/3D)

J.H. Barclay & Co., 53 Burnfield Road, Giffnock, Glasgow, G46 7PY Tel: 0141-638 9382 Fax: 0141-638 9848 E-mail: solutions@jhbarclay.co.uk

▶ Eley Metrology Ltd, Beaufort House Beaufort Court Industrial Estate, Mansfield Road, Derby, DE21 4FS Tel: (01332) 367475 Fax: (01332) 371435 E-mail: email@eleymet.com

C.E. Johansson Ltd, Metrology House, Halesfield 13, Telford, Shropshire, TF7 4PL Tel: 0870 4462667 Fax: 0870 4462668 E-mail: enquiry@hexmet.co.uk

Pi Tape Ltd, Dean Court, Upper Dean, Huntingdon, Cambridgeshire, PE28 0NL Tel: (01234) 708882 Fax: (01234) 708677 E-mail: sales@pitape.co.uk

MEASURING INSTRUMENT/ SYSTEMS, *See Electronic Measuring etc; also other headings for particular types*

MEAT

▶ Campbell Bros Ltd, Sherwood Industrial Estate, Bonnyrigg, Midlothian, EH19 3LW Tel: 0131-654 0050 Fax: 0131-654 0080 E-mail: sales@campbellbrothers.co.uk

MEAT CUTTING/MINCING EQUIPMENT, INDUSTRIAL

John Kirk Supplies Ltd, 145 Guildford Road, Ash, Aldershot, Hampshire, GU12 6DF Tel: (01252) 334774 Fax: (01252) 315946 E-mail: sales@johnkirksupplies.com

MEAT PACKAGING NETS

Keymesh Ltd, Premier Business Centre, Attwood Street, Stourbridge, West Midlands, DY9 8RY Tel: (01384) 898899 Fax: (01384) 898775 E-mail: sales@keymesh.com

▶ Scobies & Junor, 1 Singer Road, Kelvin Industrial Estate, East Kilbride, Glasgow, G75 0XS Tel: (01355) 237041 Fax: (01355) 263585 E-mail: info@scobie-junor.co.uk

MEAT PROCESSING

▶ The Arran Lamb Co., The Abattoir, Blackwaterfoot, Isle of Arran, KA27 8EZ Tel: (01770) 850264 Fax: (01770) 850264 E-mail: iain@arranlamb.com

MEAT PROCESSING EQUIPMENT

A M C Food Machinery Ltd, 55-57 Waverley Road, Yate, Bristol, BS37 5QR Tel: (01454) 322315 Fax: (01454) 323144 E-mail: sales@amcfoodmachinery.com

B Brooks Norwich Ltd, Beckhithe, Little Melton, Norwich, NR9 3NP Tel: (01603) 810137 Fax: (01603) 812272 E-mail: sales@ppcsfoodservice.co.uk

Boyd Food Machinery, Ramas, Buckie, Banffshire, AB56 4BA Tel: (01542) 835885 Fax: (01542) 835080 E-mail: boyd@boydfood.com

Falcon Food Equipment Ltd, Unit 3 The Old Station, Wells Road, Hallatrow, Bristol, BS39 6EN Tel: (01761) 453010 Fax: (01761) 452975 E-mail: sales@falconfoodequipment.com

Matrix Machinery, Bermar House Unit 38 Rumer Hill Business Estate, Rumer Hill Road, Cannock, Staffordshire, WS11 0ET Tel: (01543) 466256 Fax: (01543) 466320 E-mail: jpl@matrixmachinery.fsnet.co.uk

Orbital Food Machinery, 2 Cavendish Road, Bury St. Edmunds, Suffolk, IP33 3TE Tel: (01284) 725255 Fax: (01284) 725335

▶ Scobies & Junor, 1 Singer Road, Kelvin Industrial Estate, East Kilbride, Glasgow, G75 0XS Tel: (01355) 237041 Fax: (01355) 263585 E-mail: info@scobie-junor.co.uk

MEAT PRODUCTS, PROCESSED/COOKED

A B P Scotland Ltd, Whitburn Road, Bathgate, West Lothian, EH48 2HR Tel: (01506) 632722 Fax: (01506) 632802

A D M UK Ltd, Pondswood Industrial Estate, Drury Lane, St. Leonards-on-Sea, East Sussex, TN38 9XL Tel: (01424) 456900 Fax: (01424) 426483

Abramsons Kosher Food Products, 61 Bury Old Road, Prestwich, Manchester, M25 0FG Tel: 0161-773 2020 Fax: 0161-798 6550

Anglo Beef Processors Ltd, The Abbatoir, Battlefield Road, Harlescott, Shrewsbury, SY1 4AH Tel: (01743) 442322 Fax: (01743) 446326 E-mail: stevenfeehan@abpltd.com

Apetito, Crackley Way, Peartree Lane Industrial Estate, Dudley, West Midlands, DY2 0UW Tel: (01384) 254389 Fax: (01384) 456334

Apex Bacon Co., Milk Street, Leek, Staffordshire, ST13 6BE Tel: (01538) 387363 Fax: (01538) 382204

Berigood Cooked Meats, 23 Preston Old Road, Freckleton, Preston, PR4 1PB Tel: (01772) 632215

Boston Sausage, 13 High Street, Boston, Lincolnshire, PE21 8SH Tel: (01205) 362167

Brooks Ltd, Beckhithe, Little Melton, Norwich, NR9 3NP Tel: (01603) 810137 Fax: (01603) 812272

Stevie Broons Ltd, Murraysgate Industrial Estate, Whitburn, Bathgate, West Lothian, EH47 0LE Tel: (01501) 745607 Fax: (01501) 745819

Cherry Valley Farms Ltd, Rothwell, Market Rasen, Lincolnshire, LN7 6BJ Tel: (01472) 371271 Fax: (01472) 362422 E-mail: admin@cherryvalley.co.uk

Chicken Joes, Empire Industrial Estate, Brickyard Road, Aldridge, Walsall, WS9 8UR Tel: (0870) 0601240 E-mail: mail@chickenjoes.net

Church's Pork Butchers Ltd, 224 High Street, Epping, Essex, CM16 4AQ Tel: (01992) 573231 Fax: (01992) 561525

Cornish Farmhouse Bacon, West Balsdon Farm, Whitstone, Holsworthy, Devon, EX22 6LE Tel: (01288) 341171 Fax: (01288) 341075 E-mail: justin_uglow@btconnent.com

DBC Foodservice Ltd, Denmark House, Parkway, Welwyn Garden City, Hertfordshire, AL8 6JN Tel: (01707) 323421 Fax: (01707) 320143 E-mail: info@dbc.foodservice.co.uk

▶ Elite Foods, Unit 3g Aireworth Mills, Aireworth Road, Keighley, West Yorkshire, BD21 4DH Tel: (01535) 661188 Fax: (01535) 661188

Estuary Fine Foods Ltd, Unit 3 Station Yard, Duddon Road, Askam-in-Furness, Cumbria, LA16 7AL Tel: (01229) 466828 Fax: (01229) 462343

Fleur D E Leys Pies Ltd, Baxenden, Accrington, Lancashire, BB5 2SA Tel: (01706) 221993 Fax: (01706) 228044

Flowfood Ltd, South Street, Ashton-under-Lyne, Lancashire, OL7 0PH Tel: 0161-330 0411 Fax: 0161-343 2193 E-mail: sales@flowfood.co.uk

Fred C Robinson Ltd, 40 Hillhead Road, Ballyclare, County Antrim, BT39 9DS Tel: (028) 9334 0455 Fax: (028) 9335 2393 E-mail: info@fcrobinson.co.uk

Fresh Bacon Co., Ty Verlon Industrial Estate, Cardiff Road, Barry, South Glamorgan, CF63 2BE Tel: (01446) 700900

Global Group plc, Park Lane, Wolverhampton, WV10 9QD Tel: (01902) 865714 Fax: (01902) 866316

Grampian Country Pork Suffolk Ltd, Little Wratting, Haverhill, Suffolk, CB9 7TD Tel: (01440) 704444 Fax: (01440) 762120 E-mail: grampian@gcfg.com

Ingram Foods Ltd, 4 Blackbrook Valley Industrial Estate, Narrowboat Way, Dudley, West Midlands, DY2 0XQ Tel: (01384) 237551 Fax: (01384) 240017 E-mail: ingramfoodslimited@btinternet.com

J W Fidler & Sons, Nile Street, Bolton, BL3 6BW Tel: (01204) 529948 Fax: (01204) 365263

K & J Cooked Meats, Unit 12 Phoenix Int Industrial Estate, Charles Street, West Bromwich, West Midlands, B70 0AY Tel: 0121-557 8430 Fax: 0121-522 3368

Kerry Foods Ltd, 76 Mosley Street, Burton-on-Trent, Staffordshire, DE14 1DS Tel: (01283) 561661 Fax: (01283) 511048

London Burger Co Ltd, Redlands, Lower Street, Great Addington, Kettering, Northamptonshire, NN14 4BL Tel: (01536) 330551 Fax: (01536) 330552 E-mail: info@londonburger.fsnet.co.uk

▶ Longday Foods Ltd, 98 Pottergate, Norwich, NR2 1EQ Tel: (01603) 612000 Fax: (01603) 664777 E-mail: mike@longday.co.uk

M J C Distribution, 50 Icknield Street, Hockley, Birmingham, B18 5AY Tel: 0121-551 3549 Fax: 0121-554 9097

MKL Meats, 45b Saul Road, Downpatrick, County Down, BT30 6PA Tel: (028) 4461 2123 Fax: (028) 4461 7009 E-mail: mklmeat@btconnect.com

Oakley Bros, 93 Greenfield Road, Flitton, Bedford, MK45 5DR Tel: (01525) 717171 Fax: (01525) 717171

Pioneer Food Service, PO Box 30, Carlisle, CA1 2RR Tel: (01228) 523474 Fax: (01228) 512906 E-mail: sales@pioneerfoodservice.co.uk

Pork Farm Bowyers, 55 Stallard Street, Trowbridge, Wiltshire, BA14 8HH Tel: (01225) 777367 Fax: (01225) 777367 E-mail: mike.godley@pork-farms.co.uk

Pork Farms Bowyers, Longmead, Shaftesbury, Dorset, SP7 8PL Tel: (01747) 851511 Fax: (01747) 853401

R Bedford & Sons Cooked Meats, Cunliffe Road, Blackburn, BB1 5SU Tel: (01254) 52553 Fax: (01254) 583701

R M Gearings, Milber Down, Coffinswell, Newton Abbot, Devon, TQ12 4SE Tel: (01803) 872651 Fax: (01392) 257057

Raymond Miller Butchers Ltd, Strathspey Industrial Estate, Grantown On Spey, Grantown-on-Spey, Morayshire, PH26 3NB Tel: (01479) 872520 Fax: (01479) 872892

Saxby Brothers Ltd, PO Box 15, Wellingborough, Northamptonshire, NN8 1LH Tel: (01933) 221700 Fax: (01933) 221702 E-mail: info@saxbys.co.uk

Jack Scaife, Stanfield Road, Waterfoot, Rossendale, Lancashire, BB4 7LR Tel: (0870) 1126881 Fax: (0870) 1126882 E-mail: sales@jackscaife.co.uk

Scotbeef Ltd, 27 Glenburn Road, East Kilbride, Glasgow, G74 5BA Tel: (01355) 225381 Fax: (01355) 264327 E-mail: longleys@scotbeef.com

Stella Foods Holding Ltd, 6 Tileyard Road, London, N7 9AH Tel: (020) 7692 4455 Fax: (020) 7692 4470 E-mail: info@negroni.co.uk

Tulip Ltd, Mantle Lane, Coalville, Leicestershire, LE67 3DU Tel: (01530) 836501 Fax: (01530) 510708

Tulip Ltd, Beveridge Way, Hardwick Narrows Estate, King's Lynn, Norfolk, PE30 4NB Tel: (01553) 771937 Fax: (01553) 777139

W.A. Turner Ltd, Broadwater Lane, Tunbridge Wells, Kent, TN2 5RD Tel: (01892) 515215 Fax: (01892) 510028 E-mail: sales@waturner.co.uk

Vale Of Mowbray Ltd, 5-6 Mowbray Terrace, Leeming Bar, Northallerton, North Yorkshire, DL7 9BL Tel: (01677) 422661 Fax: (01677) 424986 E-mail: sales@valeofmowbray.com

▶ W J Pearce & Sons, High Street, Chew Magna, Bristol, BS40 8PW Tel: (01275) 332417 Fax: (01275) 332417 E-mail: suepearce2003@yahoo.co.uk

Whistler's Farm, 4 Lorenzo Drive, Liverpool, L11 1BW Tel: 0151-256 0340 Fax: 0151-256 0653

MEAT SLICERS

▶ Grote International, Wrexham Technology Park, Wrexham, Clwyd, LL13 7YP Tel: (01978) 362243 Fax: (01978) 362255 E-mail: sales@intl.grotecompany.com

MEAT, HALAL

▶ Abdullah Musa & Sons Ltd., Head Office: Musa House, 262 Deepdale Road, Preston, PR1 6QB Tel: 01772 700005 Fax: 01772 705550 E-mail: info@musagroup.co.uk

MECHANICAL CAN OPENERS

Ambit Projects Ltd, North Lynn Industrial Estate, King's Lynn, Norfolk, PE30 2JL Tel: (01553) 692977 Fax: (01553) 692997 E-mail: ambit@btinternet.com

D C Norris & Co Engineering Ltd, Sand Road Industrial Estate, Sand Road, Great Gransden, Sandy, Bedfordshire, SG19 3AH Tel: (01767) 677515 Fax: (01767) 677956 E-mail: mail@dcnorris.co.uk

Henry Squire & Sons Ltd, Unit 2 Hilton Cross Business Park, Cannock Road, Wolverhampton, WV10 7QZ Tel: (01902) 308050 E-mail: info@henry-squire.co.uk

MECHANICAL CLEAN ASSEMBLY

Reliance Precision Mechatronics LLP, Rowley Mills, Penistone Road, Lepton, Huddersfield, HD8 0LE Tel: (01484) 601000 Fax: (01484) 601001 E-mail: sales@reliance.co.uk

MECHANICAL CLUTCHES

Broadbent Drives, Britannia Mills, Portland Street, Bradford, West Yorkshire, BD5 0DW Tel: (01274) 783434 Fax: (01274) 390527 E-mail: sales@broadbent-drives.co.uk

L U K A S (Hereford) Ltd, Holme Lacy Road, Rotherwas, Hereford, HR2 6LA Tel: (01432) 265265 Fax: (01432) 275146

MECHANICAL COMPONENT DESIGN

Warwick Design Consultants Ltd, Unit 12, Waterloo Park, Bidford-on-Avon, Alcester, Warwickshire, B50 4JG Tel: (01789) 490591 Fax: (01789) 490592 E-mail: wdc@warwickdesign.com

MECHANICAL COMPONENTS, *See also headings for particular types*

Ace Interactive Ltd, Roe Garage, Charlton Road, Andover, Hampshire, SP10 3JZ Tel: (01264) 350424 Fax: (01264) 356281

MECHANICAL CONSULTANCY OR CONSULTING ENGINEERS OR DESIGNERS

Arup, 13 Fitzroy Steet, London, W1T 4BQ Tel: (020) 7636 1531 Fax: (020) 7755 3716 E-mail: corporate@arup.com

Norman Bromley Partnership, Bridge House, 99-101 High Street, Tonbridge, Kent, TN9 1DR Tel: (01732) 773737 Fax: (01732) 773353 E-mail: mail@normanbromley.co.uk

Caldwell Consulting Engineers, 8 Lorne Street, Belfast, BT9 7DU Tel: (028) 9066 9456 Fax: (028) 9066 2219 E-mail: admin@caldwellconsulting.net

▶ Capita Symonds Ltd, Edwinstowe House, High Street, Edwinstowe, Nottinghamshire, NG21 9PR Tel: (01623) 821506 Fax: (01623) 821507

Carl Bro Group, Grove House, Mansion Gate Drive, Leeds, LS7 4DN Tel: 0113-262 0000 Fax: 0113-262 0737 E-mail: enquiries@carlbro.com

Caudles, 23 West One House, St. Georges Road, Cheltenham, Gloucestershire, GL50 3DT Tel: (01242) 222307 Fax: (01242) 222665

Cogan & Shackleton, 35 Railway Road, Coleraine, County Londonderry, BT52 1PE Tel: (028) 7034 4036 Fax: (028) 7035 7028 E-mail: admin@coshack.co.uk

Cundell, Saffron House, 6-10 Kirby Street, London, EC1N 8TS Tel: (020) 7438 1600 Fax: (020) 7438 1601 E-mail: info@cundall.com

Defra Design, Bradley Farm, Cumnor, Oxford, OX2 9QU Tel: (01865) 863937 Fax: (01865) 865878 E-mail: design@defra.co.uk

▶ Elmec Systems Ltd, Bowbridge La, New Balderton, Newark, Nottinghamshire, NG24 3BY Tel: (01636) 676666 Fax: (01636) 676667

▶ The Engineering Practice, Gunnery House, Gunnery Terrace, Leamington Spa, Warwickshire, CV32 5PE Tel: (01926) 436010 Fax: (01926) 470326

Faber Maunsell Ltd, Marlborough House, 18 Upper Marlborough Road, St. Albans, Hertfordshire, AL1 3UT Tel: (020) 8784 5784 Fax: (020) 8784 5700 E-mail: enquiries@fabermaunsell.com

Frazer Nash Consultancy Ltd, Stonebridge The Dorking Business Park, Station Road, Dorking, Surrey, RH4 1HJ Tel: (01306) 885050 Fax: (01306) 886464 E-mail: info@fnc.co.uk

Gemini Technology Reading Ltd, 1 34 Bennet Road, Reading, RG2 0QX Tel: 0118-931 4206 Fax: 0118-931 4213 E-mail: tonybates@gemini-tech.demon.co.uk

Helix Services Consultancy, 5 Saturn House, Calleva Park, Aldermaston, RG7 3PW Tel: 0118-981 9000 Fax: 0118-981 9001 E-mail: mail@helixconsultancy.com

Integrated Building Services Design Partnership plc, Newton House Cambridge Business Park, Cowley Road, Cambridge, CB4 0WZ Tel: (01223) 436600 Fax: (01223) 436601 E-mail: mail@ibs-plc.co.uk

JCP Consulting, Lomond House, 85 - 87 Holywood Road, Belfast, BT4 3BD Tel: (028) 9065 9299 Fax: (028) 9022 1101 E-mail: consult@jcpconsulting.co.uk

M G Bennett & Associates Ltd, Bennett House, Pleasley Road, Whiston, Rotherham, South Yorkshire, S60 4HQ Tel: (01709) 373782 Fax: (01709) 363730 E-mail: mgb@bennettmg.co.uk

Medtec Design Services Ltd, Unit 34, JS White Eastate, Cowes, Isle Of Wight, PO31 7LP Tel: (01983) 294974 Fax: (01983) 290255 E-mail: design@medtec.co.uk

N H P Romsey Ltd, Tadburn Road, Romsey, Hampshire, SO51 5HS Tel: (01794) 523678 Fax: (01794) 515468

Neale Consulting Engineers Ltd, Highfield, Pilcot Hill, Dogmersfield, Hook, Hampshire, RG27 8SX Tel: (01252) 629199 Fax: (01252) 815625 E-mail: ncel@tribology.co.uk

R W Gregory & Partners, Cathedral Buildings, Dean Street, Newcastle upon Tyne, NE1 1PJ Tel: 0191-232 6306 Fax: 0191-232 5359 E-mail: newcastle@rwgregory.co.uk

▶ Services Management Ltd, Seymour House, 51 Praed Street, London, W2 1NR Tel: (020) 7565 5763 Fax: (020) 7565 5754 E-mail: c.bower@sml-ltd.com

▶ Staff Solution Limited, Lasyard House, Underhill Street, Bridgnorth, Shropshire, WV16 4BB Tel: 01746 767107 Fax: 01746 769217 E-mail: sales@staffsolution.co.uk

D.C. White & Partners Ltd, Highfield, Pilcot Hill, Dogmersfield, Hook, Hampshire, RG27 8SX Tel: 0845 4941739 Fax: (01252) 815625 E-mail: blair.white@dcwhite.co.uk

Williams & Shaw Ltd, Agar House, 31 Ballynahinch Road, Carryduff, Belfast, BT8 8BB Tel: (028) 9081 3075 Fax: (028) 9081 4135 E-mail: info@williams-shaw.co.uk

Woodside Air Conditioning Ltd, 81 Woodside Business Park, Shore Road, Birkenhead, Merseyside, CH42 1EP Tel: 0151-650 2369 Fax: 0151-650 2375 E-mail: desau@merseymail.com

Wulstan Design & Controls Ltd, 98c Blackpole Trading Estate, Worcester, WR3 8TJ Tel: (01905) 458555 Fax: (01905) 454325 E-mail: malcolm@wulstandesigns.fsbusiness.co.uk

MECHANICAL CONTRACT MANUFACTURING SERVICES

Asmec Electronics Solutions Ltd, 64-68 Wilbury Way, Hitchin, Hertfordshire, SG4 0TP Tel: (01462) 441155 Fax: (01462) 441150 E-mail: nashr@asmec.com

Capital Vehicle Maintenance Ltd, 207-209 Worton Road, Isleworth, Middlesex, TW7 6DS Tel: (020) 8758 0888 Fax: (020) 8758 0777

MECHANICAL CONTRACT MANUFACTURING SERVICES – *continued*

H Humphrey & Co Ltd, Church Road, Romford, RM3 0JA Tel: (01708) 377000 Fax: (01708) 377343 E-mail: services@h-humphrey.com
R E S Services Ltd, Unit 16 Ilford Trading Estate, Paycocke Road, Basildon, Essex, SS14 3DR Tel: (01268) 531153 Fax: (01268) 525227 E-mail: janeryan@resservices.co.uk
Wheeler's (Westbury) Ltd, 31D Link Road, West Wilts Trading Estate, Westbury, Wiltshire, BA13 4JB Tel: (01373) 823755 Fax: (01373) 858045 E-mail: info@wheelers-westbury.co.uk

MECHANICAL DESIGN SERVICES, COMPUTER AIDED (CAD)

▶ CADVanced Ltd, 5 Thorne Rd, Doncaster, S. Yorkshire, DN1 2HJ Tel: (01909) 506655 Fax: (01909) 506655 E-mail: info@cadvancedltd.co.uk
Digital Metal Ltd, The Church Gatehouse, Skinner Lane, Pontefract, West Yorkshire, WF8 1HG Tel: (01977) 706121 Fax: (01977) 705226
Frazer-Nash Consultancy Ltd, Quay Head House, Colston Ave., Bristol, BS1 1EB Tel: 0117-922 6242 Fax: 0117-922 6524 E-mail: sales@fnc.co.uk
Gemini Technology Reading Ltd, 1 34 Bennet Road, Reading, RG2 0QX Tel: 0118-931 4206 Fax: 0118-931 4213 E-mail: tonybates@gemini-tech.demon.co.uk
Heron Conversions, 45 Herons Way, Pembury, Tunbridge Wells, Kent, TN2 4DW Tel: (01892) 823891 Fax: (01892) 825287 E-mail: bdwhero@aol.com
Precision CAE, 6 Catholic Road, Brynmawr, Ebbw Vale, Gwent, NP23 4EF Tel: (01495) 313216 Fax: (0871) 661 5891 E-mail: abarnes@precisioncae.com
▶ Projex Design, Van Alloys Industrial Estate, Busgrove Lane, Stoke Row, Henley-on-Thames, Oxfordshire, RG9 5QW Tel: (01491) 682757 Fax: (01491) 681778 E-mail: andy@projexdesign.co.uk

MECHANICAL DOOR BELLS

Dereve Flow Control Ltd, Park Lane, Handsworth, Birmingham, B21 8LE Tel: 0121-553 7021 Fax: 0121-525 5664 E-mail: sales@dereve.co.uk

MECHANICAL ENGINEERING DESIGN SERVICES

Able Engineering Design, 8 Macaulay Road, Rugby, Warwickshire, CV22 6HE Tel: (01788) 817010 E-mail: danny@200300.co.uk
Amek Conveyors, 17 Bergen Way, Hull, HU7 0YQ Tel: (01482) 838605 Fax: (01482) 838705 E-mail: sales@amek.co.uk
Black & Veatch Group Ltd, Grosvenor House 69 London Road, Redhill, RH1 1LQ Tel: (01737) 789918 Fax: (01737) 772767 E-mail: bvcs@bv.com
Capro Europe, Building 54, Second Avenue, Pensnett Trading Estate, Kingswinford, West Midlands, DY6 7XJ Tel: (01384) 276300 Fax: (01384) 402010
Defra Design, Bradley Farm, Cumnor, Oxford, OX2 9QU Tel: (01865) 863937 Fax: (01865) 865878 E-mail: design@defra.co.uk
▶ Delta Motorsport, Litchlake Barns, Buckingham Road, Silverstone, Towcester, Northamptonshire, NN12 8TJ Tel: (01327) 858200 Fax: (01327) 858134 E-mail: enquiries@delta-motorsport.com
Doxford Design Engineering Ltd, 3 Fellside, Ponteland, Newcastle upon Tyne, NE20 9JW Tel: 0191-519 1433
Drake & Scull Engineering Ltd, Drake Scull Ho, 86 Talbot Rd, Old Trafford, Manchester, M16 0QD Tel: 0161-874 4800 Fax: 0161-874 4900
Eoin Technology Ltd, 35 Warwick Terrace, East Street, Olney, Buckinghamshire, MK46 4BU Tel: (07775) 935422 Fax: (0871) 2564641 E-mail: postbox@eointech.co.uk
Ergro Mechanical Services, Wallgrove House, Hooley Lane, Redhill, RH1 6DG Tel: (01737) 770001 Fax: (01737) 771900 E-mail: info@ergro.co.uk
G E D Designs, 400 Aviation Park West, Bournemouth Int Airp, Hurn, Christchurch, Dorset, BH23 6NW Tel: (01202) 578537 Fax: (01202) 578537
▶ G M Design, Nightingale House, 8 Taylor Street, Liverpool, L5 5AD Tel: 0151-207 5595 Fax: 0151- 207 5601 E-mail: mattjack@agjengineering.co.uk
Gemini Technology Reading Ltd, 1 34 Bennet Road, Reading, RG2 0QX Tel: 0118-931 4206 Fax: 0118-931 4213 E-mail: tonybates@gemini-tech.demon.co.uk
▶ GML Design Engineering Ltd., Cutting House, Pampisford Road, Abington, Cambridge, CB1 6AH Tel: 01223 897905
H M Skenfield Ltd, Laneside Mills, Laneside, Morley, Leeds, LS27 7NR Tel: 0113-253 4120 Fax: 0113-253 4120
Mott Macdonald Ltd, St Anne House, 20-26 Wellesley Road, Croydon, CR9 2UL Tel: (020) 8774 2000 Fax: (020) 8681 5706 E-mail: marketing@mottmac.com
R W Gregory & Partners, Cathedral Buildings, Dean Street, Newcastle upon Tyne, NE1 1PJ Tel: 0191-232 6306 Fax: 0191-232 5359 E-mail: newcastle@rwgregory.co.uk
Roemac Services Ltd, M90 Lathalmond, Dunfermline, Fife, KY12 0SJ Tel: (01383) 625553 Fax: (01383) 625554 E-mail: sales@roemac.co.uk

MECHANICAL ENGINEERING RECRUITMENT

▶ Car Design Jobs, PO Box 8208, Colchester, CO3 3WU Tel: 0845 838 1598
▶ E T S Technical Sales, Phoenix House, Phoenix Way, Cirencester, Gloucestershire, GL7 1QG Tel: (0870) 0702246 E-mail: mark@ets-technical-sales.co.uk

MECHANICAL ENGINEERS OR ENGINEERING CONTRACTORS

A B B Ltd, Deben House, 1 Selsdon Way, City Harbour, London, NW10 6DH Tel: (020) 7515 5551 Fax: (020) 7515 5551 E-mail: abb.buildingtechnology@gb.abb.com
▶ Abbey Contractors Ltd, Haydock Park Road, Derby, DE24 8HT Tel: (01332) 291646
Air Technology, Unit 1 Oaks Industrial Estate, Festival Drive, Loughborough, Leicestershire, LE11 5XN Tel: (01509) 264900 Fax: (01509) 264800 E-mail: office@airtechnology.co.uk
Aker Kvaerner Engineering Services Ltd, Phoenix House, 3 Surtees Way, Surtees Business Park, Stockton-on-Tees, Cleveland, TS18 3HR Tel: (01642) 334000 Fax: (01642) 334001
Albon Engineering & Munfacturing plc, Roche Hall Way, Rochford, Essex, SS4 1JU Tel: (01702) 530500 Fax: (01702) 547618 E-mail: malcolm-webster@albonplc.com
Alex Bonar & Co. Ltd, Pennybridge Industrial Estate, Ballymena, County Antrim, BT42 3HB Tel: (028) 2565 2449 Fax: (028) 2564 1838 E-mail: info@alexanderbonar.com
Anglia Pipework Ltd, 27 Manor Farm Close, Drayton, Norwich, NR8 6EE Tel: (01603) 260199 Fax: (01603) 400722 E-mail: angliaparkwork@aol.com
Anglo Standard Pipework, Arisdale Avenue, South Ockendon, Essex, RM15 5DP Tel: (01708) 858800 Fax: (01708) 858811 E-mail: sales@anglostandard.com
Autumn Engineering Co. Ltd, 58 Bath Street, Gravesend, Kent, DA11 0DF Tel: (01474) 560446 Fax: (01474) 535510
William Bailey Ltd, Merlin Court, Ripley Road, Ambergate, Belper, Derbyshire, DE56 2EP Tel: (01773) 853703 Fax: (01773) 856930 E-mail: enquiries@williambailey.co.uk
Beaumont & Blackburn Ltd, 21 Wellington Road, Dewsbury, West Yorkshire, WF13 1HL Tel: (01924) 461067 Fax: (01924) 430971
▶ Beddis Kenley Engineering Ltd, Unit 6, Astra Park, Parkside Lane, Leeds, LS11 5TD Tel: 0113-270 9674
Blackbourne Electrical Co. Ltd, Springfarm Industrial Estate, Antrim, BT41 4NZ Tel: (028) 9446 4231 Fax: (028) 9446 7109 E-mail: bec@karl.co.uk
Bradmeres Engineering Ltd, Unit 42 Wilford Industrial Estate, Ruddington Lane, Wilford, Nottingham, NG11 7EP Tel: 0115-981 7814 Fax: 0115-981 9782 E-mail: bradmeres@btconnect.com
Brittons Ltd, Waterlip Works, Cranmore, Shepton Mallet, Somerset, BA4 4RW Tel: (01749) 880371 Fax: (01749) 880347 E-mail: sales@brittons-uk.com
Broughton Mechanical & Civil Engineering Ltd, Ditton Road, Widnes, Cheshire, WA8 0TH Tel: 0151-423 5273 Fax: 0151-495 1390 E-mail: enquiries@jep-engineering.co.uk
Brownings Electric Co. Ltd, 11 Thames Road, Barking, Essex, IG11 0HG Tel: (020) 8591 3030 Fax: (020) 8594 7708 E-mail: enquiries@browningselectric.co.uk
▶ Building Environmental Services P.L.C., The Church House, Kneesworth Street, Royston, Hertfordshire, SG8 5AB Tel: (01763) 248752
C W T Ltd, Hempstalls Lane, Newcastle, Staffordshire, ST5 0SW Tel: (01782) 625222 Fax: (01782) 625333 E-mail: cwtlimited@aol.com
Camco Engineering Ltd, Malvito House, Dale Street, Bilston, West Midlands, WV14 7JX Tel: (01902) 404090 Fax: (01902) 402070 E-mail: sales@camcoengineering.co.uk
▶ Capri Mechanical Services Ltd, 53-55 Cutlers Road, South Woodham Ferrers, Chelmsford, CM3 5WA Tel: (01245) 321144 E-mail: info@caprimechanical.co.uk
Carkeek Engineers, 15 Valley Road, Plympton, Plymouth, PL7 1RS Tel: (01752) 517460 Fax: (01752) 347470
Charles Andrews, The Corner House, Fourth Avenue, Trafford Park, Manchester, M17 1DB Tel: 0161-848 9955 Fax: 0161-848 9966 E-mail: info@charlesandrews.co.uk
Cleeve Engineering Ltd, 38 Evesham Rd, Bishops Cleeve, Cheltenham, Glos, GL52 8SA Tel: (01242) 673223 Fax: (01242) 677282
Colchester Rewind & Repairs Ltd, Moss Road, Stanway, Colchester, CO3 0LE Tel: (01206) 768886 Fax: (01206) 768915 E-mail: sales@colchesterrewinds.co.uk
Commercial Vehicle Enterprises, Redhouse Industrial Estate, Middlemore Lane, Aldridge, Walsall, WS9 8DL Tel: (01922) 457992
CSS Ltd, Road Three, Winsford Industrial Estate, Winsford, Cheshire, CW7 3PD Tel: (01606) 861809 Fax: (01606) 559337 E-mail: sales@chemicalsupport.co.uk
Digitimer Ltd, 37 Hydeway, Welwyn Garden City, Hertfordshire, AL7 3BE Tel: (01707) 328347 Fax: (01707) 373153 E-mail: bcooper@digitimer.com
▶ Dodd Group, Unit 8-9 Gate Centre, Bredbury Park Way, Bredbury, Stockport, Cheshire, SK6 2SN Tel: 0161-406 1720 Fax: 0161-406 1729
Doddgroup Eastern Ltd, Oldmedow Road, King's Lynn, Norfolk, PE30 4LB Tel: (01553) 772423 Fax: (01553) 691343 E-mail: kings-lynn@doddgroup.com
Doncasters Amtech, Weycroft Avenue, Axminster, Devon, EX13 5HU Tel: (01297) 34567 Fax: (01297) 631110 E-mail: dgage@doncasters.com
Dowding & Mills plc, Camp Hill, Birmingham, B12 0JJ Tel: 0121-766 6161 Fax: 0121-773 2345 E-mail: group.birmingham@dowdingandmills.com
Dowding & Mills Engineering Services Ltd, Third Way, Avonmouth, Bristol, BS11 9HL Tel: 0117-938 1188 Fax: 0117-938 0066
Dowding & Mills Southern Ltd, 24-26 White Post Lane, London, E9 5EP Tel: (020) 8985 8351 Fax: (020) 8985 9615 E-mail: engineering.london@dowdingandmills.com
Dunham Engineering Services Ltd, The Burton Business Park, Hudson Road, Leeds, LS9 7DN Tel: 0113-248 4422 Fax: 0113-235 0809 E-mail: info@dunhamengineering.co.uk
E I W H S, 69-72 High Street, Croydon, CR0 1PA Tel: (020) 8680 7071 Fax: (020) 8680 9818 E-mail: eiwhs@davishouse.co.uk
E M S Ltd, 15-29 Eyre Street Hill, London, EC1R 5LB Tel: (020) 7837 4707 Fax: (020) 7833 8299 E-mail: enquiries@ems-maintenance.co.uk
Ei WHS, Staveley House, Fort Street, Blackburn, BB1 5EG Tel: (01254) 670261 Fax: (01254) 680832 E-mail: blackburn@eiwhs.co.uk
Eiwhs, 1 London Road, Great Shelford, Cambridge, CB22 5DB Tel: (01223) 845776 Fax: (01223) 842910 E-mail: cambridge.eiwhs@staveley.co.uk
Eiwhs, 23 Dunlop Way, Queensway Industrial Estate, Scunthorpe, South Humberside, DN16 3RN Tel: (01724) 282328 Fax: (01724) 282321 E-mail: rchallis.eiwhs@staveley.co.uk
Eiwhs, Unit 10, President Buildings Savile St East, Sheffield, S4 7UQ Tel: 0114-275 0012 Fax: 0114-276 1402 E-mail: sheffield.eiwhs@staveley.co.uk
Eiwhs, 21 Allensway, Thornaby, Stockton-on-Tees, Cleveland, TS17 9HA Tel: (01642) 769085 Fax: (01642) 761137 E-mail: eiwhs.thornaby@staveley.co.uk
Esmanco Engineering Ltd, Hadfield Industrial Estate, Waterside, Hadfield, Glossop, Derbyshire, SK13 1BS Tel: (01457) 861673 Fax: (01457) 864044 E-mail: esmanco@btconnect.com
F & H Engineering Ltd, Victoria Works Industrial Estate, Accrington Road, Burnley, Lancashire, BB11 5EF Tel: (01282) 433178 Fax: (01282) 832247
F W Marsh Electrical & Mechanical Ltd, Ryde Business Park, Nicholson Road, Ryde, Isle of Wight, PO33 1BF Tel: (01983) 562109 Fax: (01983) 615592
Felgoron Ltd, North Street Industrial Estate, Droitwich, Worcestershire, WR9 8JB Tel: (01905) 771938 Fax: (01905) 774677
Fire Systems Ltd, Station House, 5 Ridsdale Road, London, SE20 8AG Tel: (020) 8659 7235 Fax: (020) 8659 7237 E-mail: enquiries@firesystems.co.uk
G.W. Franklin & Son Ltd, 4 Drakes Courtyard, 291 Kilburn High Road, London, NW6 7JR Tel: (020) 7328 6611 Fax: (020) 7328 4932
G E Oil & Gas, Badentoy Crescent, Badentoy Park, Aberdeen, AB12 4YD Tel: (01224) 785100 Fax: (01224) 785120
▶ G W F Engineering Ltd, Woodhouse Road, Scunthorpe, South Humberside, DN16 1BD Tel: (01724) 868646 Fax: (01724) 867747 E-mail: enquiries@gwf.co.uk
Gallagher & Mckinney, Carrakeel Drive, Maydown, Londonderry, BT47 6UQ Tel: (028) 7186 1068 Fax: (028) 7186 1069 E-mail: paula@gmck.com
Glenaber Engineers Ltd, Denfield House, 5 Smeaton Road, Kirkcaldy, Fife, KY1 2EY Tel: (01592) 651940 Fax: (01592) 651963 E-mail: admin-glenaberengineers@ecosse.net
J.M. Grail (General Engineers) Ltd, Newtown Road, Steam Mills, Cinderford, Gloucestershire, GL14 3JE Tel: (01594) 822054 Fax: (01594) 826654 E-mail: info@grail.eu.com
▶ H Clarke & Sons Ltd, Linton, Skipton, North Yorkshire, BD23 5HH Tel: (01756) 752319 Fax: (01756) 752319
Hay-Tech Engineering, 12 Market Street, Bracknell, Berkshire, RG12 1JG Tel: (01344) 868011 Fax: (01344) 867979 E-mail: wood.c@btconnect.com
Heavy Machining Services Ltd, 19 Ashville Way, Cambridge Road, Whetstone, Leicester, LE8 6NU Tel: 0116-275 2225 Fax: 0116-275 2005
Helical Components Coventry Ltd, Telford Road, Exhall, Coventry, CV7 9ES Tel: (024) 7636 1058 Fax: (024) 7636 7270
Hensall Mechanical Services (Holdings) Ltd, Roall, Goole, North Humberside, DN14 0NA Tel: (01977) 661318 Fax: (01977) 662127 E-mail: enquiries@hensall.com
▶ Heraldlink Ltd, 25 East Hill, Dartford, DA1 1RX Tel: (01322) 294488
Horley Metal Productions Ltd, 30 Balcombe Road, Horley, Surrey, RH6 9AA Tel: (01293) 820234 Fax: (01293) 820235
Howard Motors, 2 Aqueduct St Industrial Estate, Aqueduct Street, Preston, PR1 7JJ Tel: (01772) 727552 Fax: (01772) 727552
Itec Power Services Ltd, Itec House, 2 Berkeley Street, Ashton-under-Lyne, Lancashire, OL6 7DT Tel: 0161-343 1595 Fax: 0161-343 2341 E-mail: sales@itecpower.co.uk
J R Powell, Rectory Farm, Poundon, Bicester, Oxfordshire, OX27 9BE Tel: (01869) 278877 Fax: (01869) 278067
Jackson Consultants, 9 Forest Court, Barlborough, Chesterfield, Derbyshire, S43 4UW Tel: (01246) 810155 Fax: (01246) 810155
Jones, PO Box 141, Wallingford, Oxfordshire, OX10 6AF Tel: (01491) 835032 Fax: (01491) 834765
▶ Jpsa Manufacturing, 28 Castleham Road, St. Leonards-on-Sea, East Sussex, TN38 9NS Tel: (01424) 852221 Fax: (01424) 852135 E-mail: jpsa@btconnect.com
K A Wing Ltd, 13 Stapledon Road, Orton Southgate, Peterborough, PE2 6TD Tel: (01733) 370448 Fax: (01733) 370488 E-mail: kawing@btinternet.com
▶ Kelo & Co. Ltd, Market Hill, St. Ives, Cambridgeshire, PE27 5AL Tel: (01480) 466805 Fax: (01480) 495173 E-mail: mail@kelopipelines.com
H. King & Sons Ltd, Acreman Street, Sherborne, Dorset, DT9 3PA Tel: (01935) 812185 Fax: (01935) 812034
Knowlton & Newman (Portsmouth) Ltd, Unit 4, Admiral Park, Portsmouth, PO3 5RQ Tel: (023) 9265 0100 Fax: (023) 9265 1097 E-mail: sales@knports.co.uk
Lacegold Electrical & Mechanical Services, 1 Aerial House, School Aycliffe, Newton Aycliffe, County Durham, DL5 6QF Tel: (01325) 315316 Fax: (01325) 329940 E-mail: lacegoldems@upexgroup.co.uk
Land & Marine, Lawrence House, Lower Bristol Road, Bath, BA2 9ET Tel: (01225) 331116 Fax: (01225) 445057 E-mail: steveholton@landandmarine.co.uk
Lister Precision Components Ltd, 27 Benedict Square, Werrington, Peterborough, PE4 6GD Tel: (01733) 573700 Fax: (01733) 326224 E-mail: keith@listerprecision.co.uk
Litton Group Ltd, 38 Young Street, Lisburn, County Antrim, BT27 5EB Tel: (028) 9267 2325 Fax: (028) 9260 7473 E-mail: mechanical@litton.co.uk
M E H Group Services P.L.C., 1 Thornham Grove, Stratford, London, E15 1DN Tel: (020) 8534 4441 Fax: (020) 8519 1933 E-mail: mwood@mehltd.co.uk
Mcgill Services Ltd, Vinci House Macklin Avenue, Cowpen Lane Industrial Estate, Billingham, Cleveland, TS23 4HF Tel: (01642) 379400 Fax: (01642) 379429 E-mail: mcgill@mcgillservices.co.uk
Mckiernan Group Ltd, Crown St Works, Crown Street, Accrington, Lancashire, BB5 0RW Tel: (01254) 398532 Fax: (01254) 392157 E-mail: design@themckiernangroup.co.uk
Marlborough Four Wheel Drive, Unit B, Smiths Yard, Axford, Marlborough, Wiltshire, SN8 2EY Tel: (01672) 516041 Fax: (01672) 519189
Mechanical & Ferrous Ltd, 1 Church Road, Erith, Kent, DA8 1PG Tel: (01322) 447714 Fax: (01322) 436228 E-mail: mechferrous@aol.com
Medway T & G Services Ltd, 2 & 3 Victory Park, Medway City Estate, Rochester, Kent, ME2 4ER Tel: 01634 717766
Mendip Engineering Ltd, Mendip House, Pows Orchard, Midsomer Norton, Radstock, BA3 2HY Tel: (01761) 413698 Fax: (01761) 416172 E-mail: enquiries@mendipengineering.co.uk
Morson Projects Ltd, 37 Liverpool Road, Irlam, Manchester, M44 6TB Tel: 0161-777 4000 Fax: 0161-777 4001 E-mail: enquiries@morson-projects.co.uk
Norstead, Metnor House, Mylord Crescent, Newcastle upon Tyne, NE12 5YD Tel: 0191-268 4000 Fax: 0191-268 6650 E-mail: engineering@norstead.co.uk
North Heath Motors Horsham, North Heath Industrial Estate, North Heath Lane, Horsham, West Sussex, RH12 5QE Tel: (01403) 255035
▶ Nutford Engineering Ltd, 11 Hales Road, Leeds, LS12 4PL Tel: 0113-231 1478 Fax: 0113-231 1469
Orwin (North East) Ltd, 1-3 Brockwell Road, Crowther Industrial Estate, District 3, Washington, Tyne & Wear, NE38 0AF Tel: 0191-417 7092 Fax: 0191-416 7277
P E M E, Rayfern House, Newark Road, Peterborough, PE1 5DE Tel: (0870) 8449393 Fax: (01753) 539156 E-mail: enquries@peme.co.uk
Pipework & Mechanical Contracts Ltd, Ty Verlon Industrial Estate, Cardiff Road, Barry, South Glamorgan, CF63 2BE Tel: (01446) 748611 Fax: (01446) 746906
Plant Life Controls Ltd, Unit 1c Causeway Park, Central Road, Warrington, WA4 6RF Tel: (01925) 234788 Fax: (01925) 234781 E-mail: enquiries@plc1.co.uk
Powerminster Ltd, 20 Don Road, Sheffield, S9 2UB Tel: 0114-282 0220 Fax: 0114-282 0221 E-mail: info@powerminster.co.uk

MECHANICAL ENGINEERS OR ENGINEERING CONTRACTORS – *continued*

Precision Products, 2a Penner Road, Havant, Hampshire, PO9 1QH Tel: (023) 9248 1848 Fax: (023) 9245 5024 E-mail: salesppp@aol.com

Progressive Engineers Ltd, Groby Road, Audenshaw, Manchester, M34 5HT Tel: 0161-371 0440 Fax: 0161-371 0444 E-mail: info@progressive-eng.com

Pye London Ltd, Units 6-7, Hookers Road, London, E17 6DP Tel: (020) 8531 3334 Fax: (020) 8531 3336 E-mail: pye-london@btconnect.com

Qualter Hall & Co. Ltd, Johnson Street, Barnsley, South Yorkshire, S75 2BY Tel: (01226) 205761 Fax: (01226) 286269 E-mail: admin@qualterhall.co.uk

R E Page Engineering Co. Ltd, Winterstoke Road, Weston-super-Mare, Avon, BS23 3YS Tel: (01934) 628547 Fax: (01934) 643265

R E S Services Ltd, Unit 16 Ilford Trading Estate, Paycocke Road, Basildon, Essex, SS14 3DR Tel: (01268) 531153 Fax: (01268) 525227 E-mail: janeryan@resservices.co.uk

R K L Ltd, Roland Road, Stockport, Cheshire, SK5 6TJ Tel: 0161-477 9192 Fax: 0161-480 3852

▶ R P E Mechanical Engineers Ltd, Unit 7 Off Low Mills Lane, Ravensthorpe Industrial Estate, Dewsbury, West Yorkshire, WF13 3LN Tel: (01924) 494549 Fax: (01924) 480874

▶ R R Pullen, Frying Pan Farm, Melksham Lane, Broughton Gifford, Melksham, Wiltshire, SN12 8LL Tel: (01225) 702343 Fax: (01225) 793652 E-mail: rpbp@dsl.pipex.com

▶ John Rainey & Co., Wattstown Indust Estate, Newbridge Road, Coleraine, County Londonderry, BT52 2LB Tel: (028) 7035 7774

Renoco Engineering Ltd, Unit 36, Station Lane Industrial Estate, Old Whittington, Chesterfield, Derbyshire, S41 9QX Tel: (01246) 454725 Fax: (01246) 454599 E-mail: renocoeng@aol.com

Rex Campbell Properties Ltd, Phoenix Works, Steeley Lane, Chorley, Lancashire, PR6 0RJ Tel: (01257) 266521 Fax: (01257) 241362 E-mail: kim@rex-campbell.co.uk

Riber Engineering Ltd, Brindley Way, Speedwell Industrial Estate, Staveley, Chesterfield, Derbyshire, S43 3JF Tel: (01246) 471244 Fax: (01246) 471233 E-mail: ribereng@aol.com

▶ RMD Contracts, 4 Outram Road, Dukinfield, Cheshire, SK16 4XE Tel: 0161-339 9910 Fax: 0161-343 2015 E-mail: info@rmdcontracts.com

Rotary North West Ltd, Rotary House, Chantry Court, Chester West Employment Park, Chester, CH1 4QN Tel: (01244) 382233 Fax: (01244) 382458

Rotary Southern Ltd, Rotary House, Breakspear Road, Ruislip, Middlesex, HA4 7ST Tel: (01895) 674264 Fax: (01895) 630673 E-mail: info@rotarysouthern.co.uk

▶ Rotating Machinery Services, 126 Fletcher Road, Stoke-on-Trent, ST4 4AJ Tel: (01782) 747580 Fax: (01782) 749647

S M P Security Ltd, Halesfield 24, Telford, Shropshire, TF7 4NZ Tel: (01952) 585673 Fax: (01952) 582816

Sheetfabs (Nottingham) Ltd, Nottingham Road, Attenborough, Beeston, Nottingham, NG9 6DR Tel: 0115-925 8101 Fax: 0115-943 0872 E-mail: sheetfabs@sheetfabs.co.uk

Skanska Construction, Maple Cross House, Denham Way, Maple Cross, Rickmansworth, Hertfordshire, WD3 9SW Tel: (01923) 776666 Fax: (01923) 777834 E-mail: skanska.construction@skanska.co.uk

Skanska Rashleigh Weatherfoil Ltd, West Lodge, Station Approach, West Byfleet, Surrey, KT14 6NG Tel: (01932) 791800 Fax: (01932) 791810 E-mail: krw.receptionist@skanska.co.uk

Soron Ltd, Unit 2d Payne Street, Glasgow, G4 0LE Tel: 0141-333 9518 Fax: 0141-332 2711

Sotham Engineering Services Ltd, Home End, Fulbourn, Cambridge, CB21 5BS Tel: (01223) 881081 Fax: (01223) 880169 E-mail: info@sotham.co.uk

Stead & Wilkins Fabrications Ltd, Jolly Farmers Wharf, Thames Road, Crayford, Dartford, DA1 4QH Tel: (01322) 529134 Fax: (01322) 550314 E-mail: alanbaynton@steadandwilkins.co.uk

Stelex Construction Equipment Ltd, Prees Industrial Estate, Shrewsbury Rd, Prees, Whitchurch, Shropshire, SY13 2DJ Tel: (01948) 840840 Fax: (01948) 841147 E-mail: info@stelex.co.uk

▶ T C Power Ltd, Unit 23 Priory Tec Park Saxon Way, Priory Park, Hessle, North Humberside, HU13 9PB Tel: (01482) 629550 Fax: (01482) 350670 E-mail: sales@turbinecontrols.com

Taylor Hydraulics & Mechanical Services, 36 Long Ridge, Brighouse, West Yorkshire, HD6 3RZ Tel: (01484) 717552 Fax: (01484) 717552

Thomson Ltd, Monk Fryston Park, Betteras Hill Road, Hillam, Leeds, LS25 5PF Tel: (01977) 686100 Fax: (01977) 686149 E-mail: main@thomson-group.co.uk

TML Precision Engineers, Potash Lane, Hethel, Norwich, NR14 8EY Tel: (01953) 601700 Fax: (01953) 603505E-mail: info@tmlcnc.com

Turnshire Engineering Ltd, Unit 3, Acacia Close, Cherry Court Way, Leighton Buzzard, Bedfordshire, LU7 8QE Tel: (01525) 851202 Fax: (01525) 851202

Upfield Engineering, Rutherfords Business Park, Marley Lane, Battle, East Sussex, TN33 0TY Tel: (01424) 775373 Fax: (01424) 777164 E-mail: enquiries@upfieldengineering.co.uk

Vaughan Engineering Group Ltd, Aercon Works, 556 Antrim Road, Newtownabbey, County Antrim, BT36 4RF Tel: (028) 9083 7441 Fax: (028) 9034 2469 E-mail: info@vaughan-group.co.uk

Vogal Industrial Installations, Regent House, Shrewsbury Avenue, Peterborough, PE2 7WH Tel: 01733 370789

W D M, North View, Soundwell, Bristol, BS16 4NX Tel: 0117-956 7233 Fax: 0117-957 0351

W H K (Walton) Ltd, Walton Business Centre, 44-46 Terrace Road, Walton-on-Thames, Surrey, KT12 2SD Tel: (01932) 247979 Fax: (01932) 245948 E-mail: colin@whk.co.uk

▶ Weir Street Light Engineering Co. Ltd, Weir Street, Blackburn, BB2 2AN Tel: (01254) 59544 Fax: (01254) 698767

Weldatube Mechanical Services Ltd, 74 Fryerning Lane, Ingatestone, Essex, CM4 0NN Tel: (01277) 353306 Fax: (01277) 354903 E-mail: keepincall@btopenworld.com

West Cumberland Engineering Ltd, Joseph Noble Road, Lillyhall Industrial Estate, Lillyhall, Workington, Cumbria, CA14 4JX Tel: (01900) 872787 Fax: (01900) 872789 E-mail: wcel@wcel.vhe.co.uk

Willas Engineering Ltd, 9-10 Village Farm Road, Village Farm Industrial Estate, Pyle, Bridgend, Mid Glamorgan, CF33 6BL Tel: (01656) 745000 Fax: (01656) 745175 E-mail: ian@willas.co.uk

Wright Engineering Co Nottingham Ltd, Colwickwood Works, Colwick Road, Nottingham, NG2 4BG Tel: 0115-950 2284 Fax: 0115-948 4967 E-mail: wright@wright-engineers.co.uk

Wycliff Services Ltd, Godwin Road, Earlstrees Industrial Estate, Corby, Northamptonshire, NN17 4DS Tel: (01536) 406500 Fax: (01536) 406800 E-mail: johnh@wycliff-services.co.uk

MECHANICAL HANDLING BIN DISCHARGERS

▶ F C E Materials Handling Ltd, Taylor Stiles Building, Methilhaven Road, Methil, Leven, Fife, KY8 3LA Tel: (01333) 429434 Fax: (01333) 423582 E-mail: info@fcegroup.com

Solitec Engineering, Unit 8 Gilchrist Thomas Industrial Estate, Blaenavon, Pontypool, Gwent, NP4 9RL Tel: (01453) 828727 Fax: (01495) 790666 E-mail: solitec@aol.com

MECHANICAL HANDLING EQUIPMENT

A & M Engineering Hull Ltd, Unit 30 B, Foster Street, Hull, HU8 8BT Tel: (01482) 820806 Fax: (01482) 824614 E-mail: sales@am-engineering.co.uk

▶ Austin Design & Manufacture Ltd, Unit 2 Warish Hall, Warish Hall Road, Takeley, Bishop's Stortford, Hertfordshire, CM22 6NZ Tel: (01279) 871527 Fax: (01279) 871544 E-mail: keith@admfloors.com

B & B Attachments Ltd, Guildgate House, Pelican Lane, Newbury, Berkshire, RG14 1NX Tel: (01635) 232000 Fax: (01635) 237444 E-mail: info@bandbattachments.com

Base Handling Products Ltd, Unit 20 Barleyfield Industrial Estate, Barleyfield Way, Nantyglo, Ebbw Vale, Gwent, NP23 4LU Tel: (01495) 312172 Fax: (01495) 312089 E-mail: info@baseproducts.co.uk

Braham & Dixon Ltd, 88 Hodgson Street, Hull, HU8 7JB Tel: (01482) 211853 Fax: (01482) 211865 E-mail: eric@bd-eng.co.uk

Clansman Dynamics Ltd, The Stephenson Building, Nasmyth Avenue, Scottish Enterprise Technology Park, East Kilbride, Glasgow, G75 0QR Tel: (01355) 579900 Fax: (01355) 579901 E-mail: info@clansmandynamics.com

Conveyor & Elevator Co., Grange Works, Wellington Street, Accrington, Lancashire, BB5 2NT Tel: (01254) 390727 Fax: (01254) 390521

FCE Engineering Ltd, Methilhaven Road, Methil, Leven, Fife, KY8 3LA Tel: (01333) 423557 Fax: (01333) 423582

Fredenhagen Ltd, Keynes House, Alfreton Road, Derby, DE21 4AS Tel: (01332) 340077 Fax: (01332) 340614 E-mail: sales@fredenhagen.co.uk

Game Engineering Ltd, Camp Road, Witham St. Hughs, Lincoln, LN6 9TW Tel: (01522) 868021 Fax: (01522) 868027 E-mail: sales@game-security-engineering.com

Glomac Engineering Ltd, Little End Road, Eaton Socon, St. Neots, Cambridgeshire, PE19 8JH Tel: (01480) 215533 Fax: (01480) 405952 E-mail: sales@glomac.co.uk

Haith Industrial, Cowhouse Lane, Armthorpe, Doncaster, South Yorkshire, DN3 3EE Tel: (01302) 831911 Fax: (01302) 300173 E-mail: sales@haith.co.uk

Halifax Process Engineering Ltd, 4 Shay Lane Works, Shay Lane, Ovenden, Halifax, West Yorkshire, HX3 6SF Tel: (01422) 367931 Fax: (01422) 349023 E-mail: sales@halifaxprocess.co.uk

Hallam Materials Handling Ltd, 232-234 Woodbourn Road, Sheffield, S9 3LQ Tel: 0114-275 3000 Fax: 0114-275 3222 E-mail: hallam-mh@btconnect.com

Hallanshire Engineering Holdings Ltd, Unit 14, North Anston Trading Estate, Dinnington, Sheffield, S25 4JJ Tel: (01909) 562091 Fax: (01909) 550206E-mail: sales@heh.co.uk

John M Henderson & Co. Ltd, Kings Works, Sir William Smith Road, Kirkton Industrial Estate, Arbroath, Angus, DD11 3RD Tel: (01241) 870774 Fax: (01241) 875559 E-mail: contracts@johnmhenderson.co.uk

Law-Denis Engineering Ltd, Fengate, Peterborough, PE1 5PE Tel: (01733) 563000 Fax: (01733) 563300 E-mail: info@lawdenis.com

Lawson Engineers Ltd, Barras Lane, Dalston, Carlisle, CA5 7ND Tel: (01228) 711470 Fax: (01228) 711255 E-mail: sales@lawson-engineers.com

Lee Beesley Ltd, Merthyr Tydfil Industrial Estate, Dowlais, Merthyr Tydfil, CF48 2SS Tel: (01685) 385524 Fax: (01685) 723006 E-mail: enq@leebeesley.co.uk

Lunn Engineering Co. Ltd, Manor Road Industrial Estate, Atherstone, Warwickshire, CV9 1RB Tel: (01827) 713228 Fax: (01827) 717624 E-mail: info@lunnengineering.co.uk

Harry Major Machine UK Ltd, 3 Gosforth Close, Middlefield Industrial Estate, Sandy, Bedfordshire, SG19 1RB Tel: (01767) 689500 Fax: (01767) 680893 E-mail: sales@hmm-uk.com

Mechandling Ltd, 11b Greenfield Farm Industrial Estate, Congleton, Cheshire, CW12 4TR Tel: (01260) 299411 Fax: (01260) 299032 E-mail: sales@mechandling.co.uk

Noble Engineering Ltd, Greenhey Place, Skelmersdale, Lancashire, WN8 9SA Tel: (01695) 724764 Fax: (01695) 557573 E-mail: mail@nobleeng.co.uk

Oakland Elevators Ltd, 6 Mandervell Road, Oadby, Leicester, LE2 5LL Tel: 0116-272 0800 Fax: 0116-272 0904 E-mail: sales@oakland-elevators.co.uk

Orthos Projects Ltd, Fernie Road, Market Harborough, Leicestershire, LE16 7PH Tel: (01858) 462806 Fax: (01858) 464403 E-mail: sales@orthos.uk.com

Herbert Pool Ltd, 95 Fleet Road, Fleet, Hampshire, GU51 3PJ Tel: (01252) 620444 Fax: (01252) 622292

▶ Probst North West Ltd, 26 Whitelegge Street, Bury, Lancashire, BL8 1SW Tel: 0161-272 0111 Fax: 0161-705 2525

R B Engineering Services, Unit 43 College Street, Kempston, Bedford, MK42 8LU Tel: (01234) 211263 Fax: (01234) 328835

Ratcliff Tail Lifts Ltd, Bessemer Road, Welwyn Garden City, Hertfordshire, AL7 1ET Tel: (01707) 325571 Fax: (01707) 327752 E-mail: info@ratcliffpalfinger.co.uk

S M C Euro Clamps Ltd, Demmings Road, Cheadle, Cheshire, SK8 2PP Tel: 0161-428 8323 Fax: 0161-428 4513 E-mail: purchasing@smceuroclamps.com

Squires, Closglas, Llanarthney, Carmarthen, Dyfed, SA32 8HJ Tel: (01558) 668005 Fax: (01558) 668005

Stantone Mechanical Handling Ltd, 3 Rothersthorpe Avenue, Rothersthorpe Avenue Industrial Estate, Northampton, NN4 8JW Tel: (01604) 761001 Fax: (01604) 762318

Stothert & Pitt, Lower Bristol Road, Bath, BA2 3DJ Tel: (01225) 314400 Fax: (01225) 332529

Street Express Ltd, Roman Ridge Road, Sheffield, S9 1GA Tel: 0114-243 1142 Fax: 0114-256 1739 E-mail: info@scx.co.uk

T J Mechanical Handling (manea) Ltd, 12 East Street, Manea, March, Cambridgeshire, PE15 0JJ Tel: (01354) 680007

Toyota Material Handling UK, 705-707 Stirling Road, Trading Estate, Slough, SL1 4SY Tel: 0870 850 1400 E-mail: we.deliver@uk.toyota-industries.eu

Wright Engineering Rainham Ltd, Imperial Trading Estate, Lambs La North, Rainham, Essex, RM13 9XL Tel: (01708) 554618 Fax: (01708) 553395 E-mail: wright0458@aol.com

MECHANICAL HANDLING EQUIPMENT CONSULTANTS OR DESIGNERS

Attwood Evans Consultancy, 10 Olivers Battery Road North, Winchester, Hants, SO22 4JA Tel: (01962) 869672

Central Mechanical Handling Services Ltd, 7 Hanley Terrace, Malvern, Worcestershire, WR14 4PF Tel: (01684) 891042 Fax: (01684) 891042

Crossfield Engineering Co., Barrow Road, Sheffield, S9 1JZ Tel: 0114-243 8441 Fax: 0114-243 9266 E-mail: sales@crossfielduk.com

Custom Enclosures Ltd, Concorde House, Concorde Street, Luton, LU2 0JD Tel: (01582) 480425 Fax: (01582) 414372 E-mail: custom.enclosures@btconnect.com

John M Henderson & Co. Ltd, Kings Works, Sir William Smith Road, Kirkton Industrial Estate, Arbroath, Angus, DD11 3RD Tel: (01241) 870774 Fax: (01241) 875559 E-mail: contracts@johnmhenderson.co.uk

Street Express Ltd, Roman Ridge Road, Sheffield, S9 1GA Tel: 0114-243 1142 Fax: 0114-256 1739 E-mail: info@scx.co.uk

MECHANICAL HANDLING EQUIPMENT HIRE

Beck & Pollitzer, Rochester Way, Dartford, DA1 3QT Tel: (01322) 528291 Fax: (01322) 525461 E-mail: info@beck-pollitzer.com

MECHANICAL HANDLING EQUIPMENT MAINTENANCE OR REPAIR

A T Best Handlers Ltd, 114 Main Street, Chapelhall, Airdrie, Lanarkshire, ML6 8SB Tel: (01236) 607077 Fax: (01236) 607079 E-mail: info@atbesthandlers.co.uk

▶ M. & E. Baldwins, Finmere Road, Eastbourne, East Sussex, BN22 8QG Tel: (01323) 417101 Fax: (01323) 417102

Felgoron Ltd, North Street Industrial Estate, Droitwich, Worcestershire, WR9 8JB Tel: (01905) 771938 Fax: (01905) 774677

MECHANICAL LEATHER PRODUCTS, *See Hydraulic Packings etc; also Seal etc*

MECHANICAL LOADING SHOVEL SPARE PARTS

Lloyd Loaders MH Ltd, Hipperholme, Halifax, West Yorkshire, HX3 8PJ Tel: (01422) 201164 Fax: (01422) 205872 E-mail: muir-hill@lloydsmh.fsnet.co.uk

MECHANICAL LOADING SHOVELS

Lloyd Loaders MH Ltd, Hipperholme, Halifax, West Yorkshire, HX3 8PJ Tel: (01422) 201164 Fax: (01422) 205872 E-mail: muir-hill@lloydsmh.fsnet.co.uk

MECHANICAL MOTOR CAR PARKING SYSTEMS

Wohr Parking Sytems, Aston Works, Back Lane, Aston, Bampton, Oxfordshire, OX18 2DQ Tel: (01993) 851791 Fax: (01993) 851793 E-mail: sales@woehr.de

MECHANICAL OPERATION PNEUMATIC VALVES

Trutorq Actuators, 1 The Anchorage, Gosport, Hampshire, PO12 1LY Tel: (023) 9251 1123 Fax: (023) 9250 2272 E-mail: leon@trutorq-actuators.com

MECHANICAL PACKING RINGS

John Crane, Nash Road, Trafford Park, Manchester, M17 1SS Tel: 0161-872 2484 Fax: 0161-872 1654

MECHANICAL PLATING

Interserve Industrial Services Ltd, PO Box 3, Redditch, Worcestershire, B98 0FH Tel: (01527) 507500 Fax: (01527) 507501

West Bromwich Central Plating Co. Ltd, Great Bridge St, West Bromwich, West Midlands, B70 0DA Tel: 0121-557 5352

MECHANICAL PRESSES UP TO 100 TONNES CAPACITY

▶ Formost Machinery Services, Holly Lane Industrial Estate, Atherstone, Warwickshire, CV9 2QX Tel: (01827) 721010 Fax: (01827) 721012

M B Techniques Ltd, Douglas Street, Hamilton, Lanarkshire, ML3 0BU Tel: (01698) 457222 Fax: (01698) 891924

MECHANICAL REMOTE CONTROL SYSTEMS

Crown Surveillance, 11 Huss's Lane, Long Eaton, Nottingham, NG10 1GS Tel: 0115-946 5422 Fax: 0115-946 5433 E-mail: info@crown-cctv.co.uk

Gills Cables, 25 Apollo, Lichfield Road Industrial Estate, Tamworth, Staffordshire, B79 7TA Tel: (01827) 304777 Fax: (01827) 314568 E-mail: kevinhatton@gillscables.com

MECHANICAL ROAD SWEEPERS

Scarab Holdings Ltd, Pattenden Lane, Marden, Tonbridge, Kent, TN12 9QD Tel: (01622) 831006 Fax: (01622) 831417 E-mail: scarab@scarab-sales.com

Schmidt Holdings Ltd, Southgate Way, Orton Southgate, Peterborough, PE2 6GP Tel: (01733) 363300 Fax: (01733) 363333 E-mail: sales@schmidt.co.uk

Williams Plant Hire Ltd, Henfaes Lane, Welshpool, Powys, SY21 7BE Tel: (01938) 552337 Fax: (01938) 555650

MECHANICAL SEAL SEALANT SYSTEMS

Flowserve Ltd, Dakota Avenue, Salford, M50 2PU Tel: 0161-869 1200 Fax: 0161-869 1235

Tekhniseal Ltd, Unit 1 Priestley Road, Worsley, Manchester, M28 2LY Tel: 0161-794 6063 Fax: 0161-794 4773 E-mail: tekhniseal@btconnect.com

MECHANICAL SERVICES, *See Building Engineering Services, Mechanical*

MECHANICAL SYSTEM DESIGN

Ibex Geo-tech Ltd, Ibex House, Malt Mill Lane, Halesowen, W. Midlands, B62 8JJ Tel: 0121-559 3862 Fax: 0121-559 9404 E-mail: jane.palmer@ibexgeotech.com

Practical Designs, South Road, Harlow, Essex, CM20 2AS Tel: (01279) 432509 Fax: (01279) 431971 E-mail: sales@practical-design.co.uk

MECHANICAL TEST EQUIPMENT

F Worrall, Purdy Road, Batmans Hill Industrial Estate, Bilston, West Midlands, WV14 8UB Tel: (01902) 491366 Fax: (01902) 491366 E-mail: fworreluk@yahoo.com

MECHANICAL VARIABLE SPEED POWER TRANSMISSION EQUIPMENT

Berges UK Ltd, 3 Nelson Business Centre, Nelson Street, Denton, Manchester, M34 3ET Tel: (0161) 335 0995 Fax: 0161-335 0935

Heynau, Unit 43, Britannia Way, Enterprise Industrial Park, Lichfield, Staffordshire, WS14 9UY Tel: (01543) 255995 Fax: (01543) 250316 E-mail: acdcpowerdrives@aol.com

MECHANICALLY OR ELECTRONICALLY OPERATED BARRIERS

A Markham & Sons Ltd, London Road, Bowers Gifford, Basildon, Essex, SS13 2DT Tel: (01268) 553748 Fax: (01268) 584502 E-mail: info@markhams.co.uk

Access Control Automation Ltd, Arun Business Park, Bognor Regis, West Sussex, PO22 9SX Tel: (01243) 830641 Fax: (01243) 830738 E-mail: sales@accesscontrolautomation.com

Arkas Ltd, Nubal House, Headcorn Road, Sutton Valence, Maidstone, Kent, ME17 3EH Tel: 0845 5314195 Fax: (01622) 843488 E-mail: danny@arkas.co.uk

Automatic Systems Equipment UK Ltd, Unit G4, Middlesex Business Centre, Bridge Road, Southall, Middlesex, UB2 4AB Tel: (020) 8744 7669 Fax: (020) 8744 7670 E-mail: sales@automaticsystems.co.uk

Clarke Instruments Ltd, Distloc House, Old Sarum Airfield, Old Sarum, Salisbury, SP4 6DZ Tel: (01722) 323451 Fax: (01722) 335154 E-mail: sales@clarke-inst.com

Delta Scientific Corporation UK Ltd, Delta House, 70 South View Avenue, Caversham, Reading, RG4 5BB Tel: 0118-948 1133 Fax: 0118-948 1122 E-mail: deltascuk@aol.com

Faac Security Equipment, Unit 6 Hamilton Close, Basingstoke, Hampshire, RG21 6YT Tel: (01256) 318100 Fax: (01256) 318101 E-mail: sales@faac.co.uk

Gate A Mation Ltd, 8 Boundary Business Centre, Boundary Way, Woking, Surrey, GU21 5DH Tel: (01483) 747373 Fax: (01483) 776688 E-mail: sales@gate-a-mation.com

Gunnebo Entrance Control Ltd, Optimus, Bell Lane, Bellbrook Industrial Estate, Uckfield, East Sussex, TN22 1QL Tel: (01825) 761022 Fax: (01825) 763835 E-mail: info@gunneboe.co.uk

Gunnebo Perimiter Protection (UK) Ltd, Bishops Hull, Taunton, Somerset, TA1 5EA Tel: (01823) 271911 Fax: (01823) 335763 E-mail: info@gunnebo.co.uk

Heda, Unit D5, Chaucer Business Park, Kemsing, Sevenoaks, Kent, TN15 6YU Tel: (01732) 765474 Fax: (01732) 765478

Hi-Tec Controls (Bolton) Ltd, Unit 4 Riverside, Waters Meeting Road, The Valley, Bolton, BL1 8TU Tel: (01204) 392172 Fax: (01204) 391660 E-mail: info@hitecontrols.co.uk

Kaba Garog, 9 Eagle Park Drive, Warrington, WA2 8JA Tel: (01925) 401555 Fax: (01925) 401551 E-mail: sales@kgw.kaba.co.uk

Newgate (Newark) Ltd, Brunel Drive, Newark, Nottinghamshire, NG24 2DE Tel: (01636) 700172 Fax: (01636) 605400 E-mail: sales@newgate.uk.com

Sidac Systems Ltd, New Road, Chorley, Bridgnorth, Shropshire, WV16 6PP Tel: (01746) 718737 Fax: (01746) 718737 E-mail: marie@cook120136.fsnet.co.uk

Simplex Security Systems, PO Box 33903, London, NW9 6ER Tel: (020) 8200 9991 Fax: (020) 8200 6598 E-mail: sales@simplex.org.uk

MEDAL BOXES

H.B. Sale Ltd, 390 Summer Lane, Birmingham, B19 3PN Tel: 0121-236 5661 Fax: 0121-233 3817

MEDAL PRODUCERS/ MEDALLISTS

B J Dawson Coins, 52 St Helens Road, Bolton, BL3 3NH Tel: (01204) 63732 Fax: (01204) 63732

Bigbury Mint Ltd, Ermington Mill, Ermington, Ivybridge, Devon, PL21 9NT Tel: (01548) 830717 Fax: (01548) 830046 E-mail: sales@bigburymint.com

Bullseye Awards & Garments Ltd, 1-2 Norbbeck Parade, Hanger Lane, London, NW10 7HR Tel: (0844) 8009047 Fax: (020) 8997 3840 E-mail: sales@bullseyeuk.com

C & J Medals, 14 Fairford Road, Tilehurst, Reading, RG31 6QB Tel: 0118-942 5356 Fax: 0118-942 5356

▶ Mark Carter Ltd, Slough, SL3 6RR Tel: (01753) 534777 E-mail: markgcarter@bulldoghome.com

Classic Miniatures Ltd, 8 Heathlands Close, Twickenham, TW1 4BP Tel: (020) 8892 3686 Fax: (020) 8744 1142 E-mail: sales@classicminiatures.co.uk

Coincraft Coins, PO Box 112, London, WC1B 3PH Tel: (020) 7636 1188 Fax: (020) 7323 2860 E-mail: info@coincraft.com

Colborne Ltd, Park Road, Trowbridge, Wiltshire, BA14 8AP Tel: (01225) 764101 Fax: (01225) 762009 E-mail: sales@awards.uk.com

Colmet Plus, The Morgans, Lower Road, Little Hallingbury, Bishop's Stortford, Hertfordshire, CM22 7RA Tel: (01279) 722400 Fax: (01279) 726901 E-mail: mr@colmetplus.co.uk

Fine Ceramic Trophies, 26 Chain St, Stoke-on-Trent, ST6 1NA Tel: 01782 577255 Fax: 01782 577255

G H Rainey & Sons Ltd, 81 Spencer Street, Birmingham, B18 6DE Tel: 0121-236 8060

Geoff Happs Trophies, 21 High Street, Bentley, Doncaster, South Yorkshire, DN5 0AA Tel: (01302) 872296

John Harrison Sports Ltd, 79 Hough Lane, Leyland, PR25 2YD Tel: (01772) 423054 Fax: (01772) 456294 E-mail: sales@jhsports.co.uk

Alexander Kirkwood & Son, 13 Albany Street, Edinburgh, EH1 3PY Tel: 0131-556 7843 Fax: 0131-556 4779

Military Mart, 151 Throston Grange Lane, Hartlepool, Cleveland, TS26 0TX Tel: (01429) 868428 Fax: (01429) 299029

Munich 72 Trophies, 6a Bombay Street, London, SE16 3UX Tel: (020) 7231 7095 Fax: (020) 7231 7095 E-mail: sales@munichtrophies.co.uk

Neate Militarian Antiques, PO Box 3794, Sudbury, Suffolk, CO10 9LX Tel: (01787) 248168 Fax: (01787) 248363

R & B Trophies, 16 St Nicholas Street, Weymouth, Dorset, DT4 8AA Tel: (01305) 776826 Fax: (01305) 776826 E-mail: rbtrophys@tiscali.co.uk

▶ Selcraft Ltd, Leigh Sinton, Malvern, Worcestershire, WR13 5XS Tel: (01886) 834850 Fax: (01886) 834851 E-mail: info@selcraft.com

Skelton T.J Ltd, 16 Well Street, Birmingham, B19 3BJ Tel: 0121-554 0487 Fax: 0121-523 3585 E-mail: info@whderby.co.uk

Southend Sports Trophies, 536 Sutton Road, Southend-on-Sea, SS2 5PW Tel: (01702) 616046 Fax: (01702) 616046

Spink & Son Ltd, 69 Southampton Row, London, WC1B 4ET Tel: (020) 7563 4000 Fax: (020) 7563 4066 E-mail: sales@spink-online.com

Tower Mints Ltd, 1-21 Carew Street, London, SE5 9DF Tel: (020) 7733 7268 Fax: (020) 7274 0151 E-mail: info@towermint.co.uk

U Deserve a Medal, Tawel, Ely Valley Road, Coed Ely, Tonyrefail, Porth, Rhondda Cynon Taff, CF39 8PX Tel: (01443) 671174 E-mail: Enquiries@u-deserve-a-medal.co.uk

W H Darby Ltd, 16 Well Street, Birmingham, B19 3BJ Tel: 0121-554 9817 Fax: 0121-523 3585 E-mail: info@whdarby.co.uk

MEDIA COMPUTERS

Zebra Studios, 52 Eldon St North, Barnsley, South Yorkshire, S71 1LG Tel: (01226) 299238 Fax: (01226) 299238 E-mail: sales@zebrastudios.co.uk

MEDIA PRESS CUTTINGS

Durrants Press Cuttings Ltd, Discovery House, 28-42 Banner Street, London, EC1Y 8QE Tel: (020) 7674 0200 Fax: (020) 7674 0222 E-mail: contact@durrants.co.uk

MEDIA SALES MANAGEMENT

Stanton Media Sales, 10 Grazing Lane, Redditch, Worcestershire, B97 5PE Tel: (01527) 404295 Fax: (01527) 540503 E-mail: sales@stantonmedia.co.uk

MEDIATION SERVICES

▶ Afirm Ltd, 10 Windsor Road, Lindford, Bordon, Hampshire, GU35 0RY Tel: (01420) 473573 Fax: (01420) 473573 E-mail: afirm@freenet.co.uk

Berrymans Lace Mawer, Salisbury House, London Wall, London, EC2M 5QN Tel: (020) 7638 2811 Fax: (020) 7920 0361 E-mail: damian.greiff@blm-law.com

Brindley Twist Tafft & James, Lowick Gate Coventry Trading Estate, Siskin Drive, Middlemarch Business Park, Coventry, CV3 4FJ Tel: (024) 7653 1532 Fax: (024) 7630 1300 E-mail: admin@bttj.com

▶ Compromitto, 151 West George St, Glasgow, G2 2JJ Tel: 0141 2284737

MEDIATION TRAINING

▶ Afirm Ltd, 10 Windsor Road, Lindford, Bordon, Hampshire, GU35 0RY Tel: (01420) 473573 Fax: (01420) 473573 E-mail: afirm@freenet.co.uk

MEDICAL AIR CUSHIONS

Alsamex Products Ltd, 1 Protea Way, Pixmore Avenue, Letchworth Garden City, Hertfordshire, SG6 1JT Tel: (01462) 672951 Fax: (01462) 480660 E-mail: sales@alsamex.co.uk

▶ Central Health Care Midlands, Unit 46 Rumer Hill Business Estate, Rumer Hill Road, Cannock, Staffordshire, WS11 0ET Tel: (01543) 467407 Fax: (01543) 469741 E-mail: sales@centralhealthcare.net

MEDICAL AND HEALTHCARE MARKETING RECRUITMENT

▶ eMedCareers, Jobsite UK (Worldwide) Ltd., Langstone Technology Park, Havant, Hampshire, PO9 1SA Tel: 0870 774 8732

▶ Hyndman Consultants, Kyrle Grange, Peterstow, Ross-on-Wye, Herefordshire, HR9 6JZ Tel: (01989) 768767 Fax: (01989) 768766 E-mail: john@hyndman.co.uk

MEDICAL AND HEALTHCARE PORTALS

Healthsites, Annexe House, 6 Shinfield Road, Reading, RG2 7BW Tel: 0118-942 0993 E-mail: t.underwood@healthsites.co.uk

MEDICAL AND HEALTHCARE SALES RECRUITMENT

▶ eMedCareers, Jobsite UK (Worldwide) Ltd., Langstone Technology Park, Havant, Hampshire, PO9 1SA Tel: 0870 774 8732

▶ Futurefind Sales Recruitment, Wira House, Ring Road, West Park, Leeds, LS16 6EB Tel: 0113-275 5656 Fax: 0113-278 2181 E-mail: recruitment@futurefind.co.uk

▶ Hyndman Consultants, Kyrle Grange, Peterstow, Ross-on-Wye, Herefordshire, HR9 6JZ Tel: (01989) 768767 Fax: (01989) 768766 E-mail: john@hyndman.co.uk

▶ Kirkham Young Ltd, Suite 4, 17 High Street, Battle, East Sussex, TN33 0AE Tel: (0870) 7873134 Fax: (01424) 777746 E-mail: info@kirkhamyoung.co.uk

▶ New Line Sales Recruitment Ltd, Clay House, 5 Horninglow Street, Burton-on-Trent, Staffordshire, DE14 1NG Tel: (01283) 500077 Fax: (08701) 163370 E-mail: sales@newlinesales.co.uk

▶ Salestarget.co.uk, Holden House, 57 Rathbone Place, London, W1T 1JU Tel: (020) 7769 9147 Fax: (020) 7769 9205 E-mail: sales@salestarget.co.uk

▶ Twenty Four Seven, 1 Marsel House, Stephensons Way, Ilkley, West Yorkshire, LS29 8DD Tel: (01943) 604777 Fax: (01943) 604800 E-mail: enquiries@247recruitment.org.uk

MEDICAL AND SURGICAL APRONS

▶ Dorset Nursing Supplies Co., 3 Wickham Road, Bournemouth, BH7 6JX Tel: (01202) 425070 Fax: (01202) 418332 E-mail: sales@dorsetnursing.co.uk

MEDICAL CABINETS

Hospital Metalcraft Ltd, Blandford Heights, Blandford Forum, Dorset, DT11 7TG Tel: (01258) 451338 Fax: (01258) 455056 E-mail: sales@bristolmaid.com

MEDICAL CHAIRS

C P L, 2 St. James Road, Brackley, Northamptonshire, NN13 7XY Tel: (01280) 706661 Fax: (01280) 706671 E-mail: canonbury@canonbury.com

▶ James Upholstery, 3 Booth Road, Little Lever, Bolton, BL3 1JY Tel: (01204) 408993 E-mail: jamesupholstery@ntlworld.com

MEDICAL DIAGNOSTIC EQUIPMENT

Abbott Diabetes Care, Abbott House, Norden Road, Maidenhead, Berkshire, SL6 4XE Tel: (01628) 773355 Fax: (01628) 644305

Axis Shield plc, Dundee Technology Park, Dundee, DD2 1XA Tel: (01382) 422000 Fax: (01382) 422088 E-mail: shield@uk.axis-shield.com

Chirus Ltd, Park House, 15-19 Greenhill Crescent, Watford, WD18 8PH Tel: (01923) 212744 Fax: (01923) 244751

Keeler Ltd, Clewer Green Works, Clewer Hill Road, Windsor, Berkshire, SL4 4AA Tel: (01753) 857177 Fax: (01753) 830247 E-mail: info@keeler.co.uk

Morton Medical Ltd, Unit 3 College Farm Buildings, Tetbury Road, Cirencester, Gloucestershire, GL7 6PY Tel: (01285) 655210 Fax: (0845) 8693116 E-mail: sales@mortonmedical.co.uk

Oakfield Instruments Ltd, Oakfield Industrial Estate, Eynsham, Witney, Oxfordshire, OX29 4AN Tel: (01865) 882532 Fax: (01865) 883970 E-mail: info@flexilog.net

Unipath Ltd, Priory Business Park, Bedford, MK44 3UP Tel: (01234) 835000 Fax: (01234) 835001 E-mail: info@unipath.com

MEDICAL ELECTRONIC EQUIPMENT

Anaesthesia Technology Ltd, Walshford, Wetherby, West Yorkshire, LS22 5JJ Tel: (01937) 587001 Fax: (01937) 587002 E-mail: sales@anaetech.co.uk

Applied Medical Technical Ltd, 4-5 Orwell Furlong, Cambridge, CB4 0WY Tel: (01223) 420415 Fax: (01223) 420797 E-mail: sales@applied-medical.co.uk

Charter-Kontron Ltd, Avant BSNS Centre, Avant Business Centre, First Avenue, Bletchley, Milton Keynes, MK1 1DL Tel: (01908) 646070 Fax: (01908) 646030 E-mail: sales@charter-kontron.co.uk

Commercial Science, 11 Hylands Close, Crawley, West Sussex, RH10 6RX Tel: (01293) 446244 Fax: (01293) 446244

Digitimer Ltd, 37 Hydeway, Welwyn Garden City, Hertfordshire, AL7 3BE Tel: (01707) 328347 Fax: (01707) 373153 E-mail: bcooper@digitimer.com

E M E (Electro Medical Equipment) Ltd, 60 Gladstone Pl, Brighton, BN2 3QD Tel: (01273) 654100 Fax: (01273) 654101 E-mail: info@eme-med.co.uk

Ectron Ltd, Knap Close, Letchworth Garden City, Hertfordshire, SG6 1AQ Tel: (01462) 682124 Fax: (01462) 481463 E-mail: ectronltd@btconnect.com

G M Instruments Ltd, 6 Ashgrove Workshops, Kilwinning, Ayrshire, KA13 6PU Tel: (01294) 554664 Fax: (01294) 551154 E-mail: gminstruments@aol.com

Huntleigh Healthcare Ltd, 35 Portmanmoor Road Industrial Estate, East Moors, Cardiff, CF24 5HN Tel: (029) 2048 5885 Fax: (029) 2049 2520 E-mail: info@huntleigh-diagnostics.co.uk

Industrial & Medical Electronics Ltd, 140 Rocky Lane, Perry Barr, Birmingham, B42 1QF Tel: 0121-356 0061 Fax: 0121-356 0061

Instrumentation Laboratory UK Ltd, Kelvin Close, Birchwood, Warrington, WA3 7PB Tel: (01925) 810141 Fax: (01925) 826708 E-mail: sales@il.com

Medipost (UK) Ltd, 17 Surrey Close, Granby Industrial Estate, Weymouth, Dorset, DT4 9TY Tel: (01305) 760750 Fax: (01305) 776917 E-mail: info@medipost.co.uk

MEDICAL ELECTRONIC EQUIPMENT

– continued

Miltech International Ltd, Unit 3 Magellan Close, Walworth Industrial Estate, Andover, Hampshire, SP10 5NT Tel: (01264) 323233 Fax: (01264) 400905 E-mail: info@miltech-international.com
Morgan Automation Ltd, Rake Heath House, Hill Brow, Liss, Hampshire, GU33 7NT Tel: (01730) 895900 Fax: (01730) 895922 E-mail: sales@morgan-automation.com
Oak Medical Services Ltd, Unit 5-6 Island Carr Industrial Estate, Island Carr Road, Brigg, South Humberside, DN20 8PD Tel: (01652) 657200 Fax: (01652) 657009 E-mail: sales@oakmedicalservices.co.uk
Oakfield Instruments Ltd, Oakfield Industrial Estate, Eynsham, Witney, Oxfordshire, OX29 4AN Tel: (01865) 882532 Fax: (01865) 883970 E-mail: info@flexilog.net
S L E Ltd, Twin Bridges Business Park, 232 Selsdon Road, South Croydon, Surrey, CR2 6PL Tel: (020) 8681 1414 Fax: (020) 8649 8570 E-mail: admin@sle.co.uk
Trim Tone Ltd, 8 Coastguard Way, Christchurch, Dorset, BH23 3NR Tel: (01202) 482514 E-mail: trimtone@onetel.net.uk
Ultrasound Technologies Ltd, Lodge Way, Severn Bridge Industrial Estate, Portskewett, Caldicot, Gwent, NP26 5PS Tel: (01291) 425425 Fax: (01291) 427093 E-mail: ultratech@doppler.co.uk
Y D T Medical Ltd, 92 Hartley Down, Purley, Surrey, CR8 4EB Tel: (020) 8763 9777 Fax: (020) 8763 9444 E-mail: ydtlimited@aol.com

MEDICAL EQUIPMENT, *See also headings for particular types; also Medical Supply etc*

Apollo Dental Ltd, Tempest House, Lyon Road, Walton-on-Thames, Surrey, KT12 3PU Tel: (01932) 240950 Fax: (01932) 246606
Applied Cytometry Systems, Unit 2 Brooklands Way, Brooklands Park Industrial Estate, Dinnington, Sheffield, S25 2JZ Tel: (01909) 566982 Fax: (01909) 561463 E-mail: acs@appliedcytometry.com
Arrow Medical Ltd, Unit B1 Hatton Gardens Industrial Estate, Kington, Herefordshire, HR5 3RB Tel: (01544) 231760 Fax: (01544) 231640 E-mail: info@arrowmedical.co.uk
▶ Astric Medical, 36 Blatchington Road, Hove, East Sussex, BN3 3YN Tel: (01273) 716516 Fax: (01273) 716516 E-mail: astricmed@aol.com
Axis Shield plc, Dundee Technology Park, Dundee, DD2 1XA Tel: (01382) 422000 Fax: (01382) 422088 E-mail: shield@uk.axis-shield.com
Baxa Ltd, Radius Court, Eastern Road, Bracknell, Berkshire, RG12 2UP Tel: (01344) 890916 Fax: (01344) 890917
Baxter Healthcare Ltd, Wallingford Road, Compton, Newbury, Berkshire, RG20 7QW Tel: (01635) 206000 Fax: (01635) 206115 E-mail: admin@baxterhealthcare.co.uk
Biasys Health Care, Manor Way, Woking, Surrey, GU22 9JU Tel: (01483) 770331 Fax: (01483) 727193
C H Medical Ltd, 8 Oaktree Place, Matford Business Park, Marsh Barton, Exeter, EX2 8WA Tel: (01392) 824668 Fax: (01392) 823747 E-mail: sales@chmedical.com
▶ Central Health Care Midlands, Unit 46 Rumer Hill Business Estate, Rumer Hill Road, Cannock, Staffordshire, WS11 0ET Tel: (01543) 467407 Fax: (01543) 469741 E-mail: sales@centralhealthcare.net
Chambers Medical Care Ltd, Unit 5, Beresford Gate, South Way, Andover, Hampshire, SP10 5BN Tel: (01264) 332172 Fax: (01264) 332247 E-mail: derek@chambers-medical.co.uk
▶ Charnwood Healthcare Ltd, Unit B7, 46 Holton Heath Training Park, Holton Road, Poole, Dorset, BH16 6LT Tel: (01202) 620839 Fax: (01202) 620839 E-mail: charnwood.healthcare@virgin.net
Chelmer Surgical Supply, PO Box 1424, Braintree, Essex, CM77 8XH Tel: (01376) 550501 Fax: (01376) 550501 E-mail: chelmer@talk21.com
Consort Engineering (Ashton-under-Lyne) Ltd, Commercial Brow, Hyde, Cheshire, SK14 2JR Tel: 0161-366 6883 Fax: 0161-366 9703
▶ Corinthean Surgical, Mill, Unit B2f The Business Park, Pleasley Vale, Mansfield, Nottinghamshire, NG19 8RL Tel: (01623) 819741 Fax: (01623) 819742
Coronet Medical Technologies Ltd, The Coach House, Phoenix Business Centre, Low Mill Road, Ripon, North Yorkshire, HG4 1NS Tel: (01765) 605551 Fax: (01765) 608476
Cryo Med Instruments Ltd, Cryomed House, Grove Way, Mansfield Woodhouse, Mansfield, Nottinghamshire, NG19 8BW Tel: (01623) 424200 Fax: (01623) 424777
▶ CTL, Princes Business Centre, 26 Mostyn Road, Colwyn Bay, Clwyd, LL29 8PB Tel: (01492) 535986 Fax: (01492) 534958 E-mail: ian.mclaughlin3@btopenworld.com
Cuneiform, Coxford Abbey Farm, Coxford, King's Lynn, Norfolk, PE31 6TB Tel: (01485) 528050 Fax: (01485) 528380
Cuneiform Medical Equipment Mnfrs, The Old Post Office, Weasenham Road, Great Massingham, King's Lynn, Norfolk, PE32 2EY Tel: (01485) 520309 Fax: (01485) 528380 E-mail: cuneiform@freenet.co.uk
▶ Cytyc UK Ltd, 2 Link 10, Napier Way, Crawley, West Sussex, RH10 9RA Tel: (01293) 522080 Fax: (01293) 528010
Dankroy Ltd, 129 Mayfield Avenue, London, N12 9HY Tel: (020) 8445 2157 Fax: (020) 8445 0538
Dansac Ltd, Victory House, Vision Park, Histon, Cambridge, CB4 9ZR Tel: (01223) 235100 Fax: (01223) 235145 E-mail: dansac.ltd@dansac.com
Datex Ohmeda Ltd, 71 Great North Road, Hatfield, Hertfordshire, AL9 5EN Tel: (01707) 263570 Fax: (01707) 260065
Deltex Medical Ltd, Terminus Road, Chichester, West Sussex, PO19 8TX Tel: (01243) 774837 Fax: (01243) 532534 E-mail: info@deltexmedical.com
Dynamic Imaging Ltd, 9 Cochrane Square, Brucefield Industrial, Livingston, West Lothian, EH54 9DR Tel: (01506) 415282 Fax: (01506) 410603 E-mail: marketing@dynamicimaging.co.uk
E P L Medical Ltd, 4 Yardley Road, Knowsley Industrial Park, Liverpool, L33 7SS Tel: 0151-548 1494 Fax: 0151-549 2046 E-mail: info@eplmedical.com
▶ Easi Care Mobility, 18 Village Farm Industrial Estate, Pyle, Bridgend, Mid Glamorgan, CF33 6NU Tel: (01656) 670472 Fax: (01656) 670492
Endoscopic Manufacturing & Services Ltd, Unit 14 Alliance Court, Alliance Road, London, W3 0RB Tel: (020) 8896 1002 Fax: (020) 8752 1030 E-mail: info@endoscopiclondon.com
▶ Espiner Medical Products, Unit 8, Carey Development, Tweed Road, Clevedon, Somerset, BS21 6RR Tel: (01275) 341072 Fax: (01275) 341073 E-mail: mail@espenermedical.com
Eurosurgical Ltd, Merrow Business Centre, Guildford, Surrey, GU4 7WA Tel: (01483) 456007 Fax: (01483) 456008 E-mail: sales@eurosurgical.co.uk
Exmoor Plastics, Unit 2 4 Trinity Business Centre, South Street, Taunton, Somerset, TA1 3AQ Tel: (01823) 276837 Fax: (01823) 334154 E-mail: sales@exmoorplastics.co.uk
Female Health Co. (UK) P.L.C., 1 Sovereign Park, Coronation Road, Park Royal, London, NW10 7QP Tel: (020) 8965 2813 Fax: (020) 8453 0324 E-mail: info@female.condom.org
G E Ultrasound Ltd, 2 Napier Road, Bedford, MK41 0JW Tel: (01234) 340881 Fax: (01234) 266261
Gyrus International Ltd, 410 Wharfedale Road, Wokingham, Berkshire, RG41 5RA Tel: 0118-921 9700 Fax: 0118-921 9800
Helica Instruments Ltd, 1 Heriot-Watt Research Park, Riccarton, Currie, Midlothian, EH14 4AP Tel: 0131-449 4933 Fax: 0131-449 2204
Howorth Airtech Ltd, Victoria Works, Lorne Street, Farnworth, Bolton, BL4 7LZ Tel: (01204) 700900 Fax: (01204) 862378 E-mail: info@howorthairtech.co.uk
Huntleigh Healthcare Ltd, 35 Portmanmoor Road Industrial Estate, East Moors, Cardiff, CF24 5HN Tel: (029) 2048 5885 Fax: (029) 2049 2520 E-mail: info@huntleigh-diagnostics.co.uk
Huntleigh Healthcare Ltd, 310-312 Dallow Road, Luton, LU1 1TD Tel: (01582) 413104 Fax: (01582) 459100 E-mail: sales.admin@huntleigh-healthcare.com
▶ In Futuro, 23 Badger Walk, Broxburn, West Lothian, EH52 5TW Tel: (01506) 853353
Integra Neurosciences, Newbury Road, Andover, Hampshire, SP10 4DR Tel: (01264) 345700 Fax: (01264) 332113 E-mail: sales@integra-is.com
Invacare Ltd, South Road, Bridgend Industrial Estate, Bridgend, Mid Glamorgan, CF31 3PY Tel: (01656) 664321 Fax: (01656) 667532 E-mail: sales@invacare.com
John Preston & Co Belfast Ltd, Blaris Industrial Estate, Altona Road, Lisburn, County Antrim, BT27 5QB Tel: (028) 9267 7077 Fax: (028) 9267 7099 E-mail: info@jphealthcare.co.uk
Johnson & Johnson Finance Ltd, Coronation Road, Ascot, Berkshire, SL5 9EY Tel: (01344) 864140 Fax: (01344) 871133 E-mail: enquiries@johnsonandjohnson.com
Keymed Ltd, Keymed House, Stock Road, Southend-on-Sea, SS2 5QH Tel: (01702) 616333 Fax: (01702) 465677 E-mail: keymed@keymed.co.uk
Kimal P.L.C., Arundel Road, Uxbridge Industrial Estate, Uxbridge, Middlesex, UB8 2SA Tel: (01895) 270951 Fax: (01895) 274035
M I E Medical Research Ltd, 6 Wortley Moor Road, Leeds, LS12 4JF Tel: 0113-279 3710 Fax: 0113-231 0820 E-mail: sales@mie-uk.com
Medezine & Medica, 7 Station Approach, Stoneleigh, Epsom, Surrey, KT19 0QZ Tel: (020) 8873 3033 Fax: (020) 8873 3034 E-mail: medimed@easynet.co.uk
Medical Device Consultancy, 6 Bessborough Drive, Cardiff, CF11 8NE Tel: (029) 2022 1640 Fax: (029) 2022 1579 E-mail: lewlink@btclick.com
Medical & Industrial Manufacturing Co. Ltd, Broadway, Dukinfield, Cheshire, SK16 4UU Tel: 0161-339 6028 Fax: 0161-330 0944 E-mail: mimcoltd@compuserve.com
Medivance Instrumnets Ltd, Barretts Green Road, London, NW10 7AP Tel: (020) 8965 2913 Fax: (020) 8963 1270 E-mail: enquiries@velopex.com
▶ Mediwatch Ltd, Swift House, Cosford Lane, Swift Valley Industrial Estate, Rugby, Warwickshire, CV21 1QN Tel: (01788) 547888 Fax: (01788) 538434 E-mail: info@mediwatch.com
Mediwrap, Birchwood House, 55 Vanguard Way, Shoeburyness, Southend-On-Sea, SS3 9QY Tel: (01702) 291878 Fax: (01702) 290013 E-mail: sales@mediwrap.com
▶ Medline Scientific Ltd, Tower Estate, Warpsgrove Lane, Stadhampton, Oxford, OX44 7XZ Tel: (01865) 400321 Fax: (01865) 400736
Mercury Products South Ltd, 36 Carpenters, Billingshurst, West Sussex, RH14 9RB Tel: (01403) 786639 Fax: (01403) 786637 E-mail: merprod@yahoo.co.uk
Micro Precision Instruments Ltd, The Welsh Mill, Park Hill Drive, Frome, Somerset, BA11 2LE Tel: (01373) 461057 Fax: (01373) 451835
▶ Mirada Solutions, Beaver House, 23-38 Hythe Bridge Street, Oxford, OX1 2ET Tel: (01865) 265500 Fax: (01865) 265501
MSS, Taffs Fall Road, Treforest Industrial Estate, Pontypridd, Mid Glamorgan, CF37 5TT Tel: (01443) 849200 Fax: (01443) 843377 E-mail: info@medsys.co.uk
▶ MTS International, Daisyfield Street, Darwen, Lancashire, BB3 0AT Tel: (01254) 707621 Fax: (08707) 661463
Owen Mumford Holdings Ltd, Brook Hill, Woodstock, Woodstock, Oxfordshire, OX20 1TU Tel: (01993) 812021 Fax: (01993) 813466 E-mail: info@owenmumford.co.uk
▶ N. H. S. Edinburgh, Nine Mile Burn, Penicuik, Midlothian, EH26 9LT Tel: (01968) 679333 Fax: (01968) 679222
Nightingale Care Beds, Unit 20 Abenbury Way, Wrexham Industrial Estate, Wrexham, Clwyd, LL13 9UZ Tel: (01978) 661699 Fax: (01978) 661705
Nikomed Ltd, Stuart Court, Salisbury Road, Romsey, Hampshire, SO51 6DJ Tel: (01794) 525100 Fax: (01794) 525101 E-mail: sales@nikomed.co.uk
Nuromed Ltd, Unit 17A, Makerfield Way, Ince, Wigan, Lancashire, WN2 2PR Tel: (01942) 238259 Fax: (01942) 498491 E-mail: info@nuromed.com
Oak Medical Services Ltd, Unit 5-6 Island Carr Industrial Estate, Island Carr Road, Brigg, South Humberside, DN20 8PD Tel: (01652) 657200 Fax: (01652) 657009 E-mail: sales@oakmedicalservices.co.uk
Oakfield Instruments Ltd, Oakfield Industrial Estate, Eynsham, Witney, Oxfordshire, OX29 4AN Tel: (01865) 882532 Fax: (01865) 883970 E-mail: info@flexilog.net
Old Rocket plc, Imperial Way, Watford, WD24 4XX Tel: (01923) 651400 Fax: (01923) 240334 E-mail: sales@rocketmedical.com
Omega Diagnostics Ltd, Hillfoots Business Village, Alva Industrial Estate, Alva, Clackmannanshire, FK12 5DQ Tel: (01259) 763030 Fax: (01259) 761853
▶ Oncology Imaging Systems, Kennett House The Office Village, River Way, Uckfield, East Sussex, TN22 1SL Tel: (01825) 744063 Fax: (01825) 749557
▶ Opcare Ltd, Unit 3, Princeville Road Industrial Estate, Duncombe Street, Bradford, West Yorkshire, BD8 9AJ Tel: (01274) 481122 Fax: (01274) 481139 E-mail: info@opcare.co.uk
Orthos Ltd, The Stables, Leigh Court Business Centre, Abbots Leigh, Bristol, BS8 3RA Tel: (01275) 376377 Fax: (01275) 376378
Owen Mumford Holdings Ltd, Brook Hill, Woodstock, Woodstock, Oxfordshire, OX20 1TU Tel: (01993) 812021 Fax: (01993) 813466 E-mail: steve.miles@owenmumford.co.uk
Oxylitre Ltd, Morton House, 43-45 Skerton Road, Manchester, M16 0WJ Tel: 0161-872 6322 Fax: 0161-848 7914 E-mail: sales@oxylitre.co.uk
Peacock's Medical Group Ltd, Benfield Business Park, Benfield Road, Newcastle upon Tyne, NE6 4NQ Tel: 0191-276 9600 Fax: 0191-276 9696
Philips Medical Systems, PO Box 263, Reigate, Surrey, RH2 0FY Tel: (01737) 230400 Fax: (01737) 230401 E-mail: claire.daynes@philips.com
Phoenix Healthcare Distribution Ltd, Eddison Road, Hamshall Distribution Park, Coleshill, Birmingham, B46 1DA Tel: (01675) 436500 Fax: (01675) 436502
▶ Polymorit Ltd, Unit B1 Little Heath Industrial Estate, Old Church Road, Coventry, CV6 7NB Tel: (024) 7670 5522 Fax: (024) 7670 5533 E-mail: sales@polymorit.com
Rescue & Medical Equipment, Field House, Blackrock, Clydach, Abergavenny, Gwent, NP7 0LW Tel: (01873) 830031 Fax: (01873) 831748 E-mail: sales@rescueandmedical.com
S M S Technologies Ltd, Elizabeth House, Elizabeth Way, Harlow, Essex, CM19 5TL Tel: (01279) 406000 Fax: (01279) 406001 E-mail: admin@smstl.com
Scimed Ltd, Unit 5, Avon Business Park, Lodge Causeway, Fishponds, Bristol, BS16 3JP Tel: 0117-958 3754 Fax: 0117-958 4089 E-mail: enquiries@scimed-uk.com
Smiths Medical International Ltd, Bramingham Business Park, Enterprise Way, Luton, LU3 4BU Tel: (01582) 430000 Fax: (01582) 430001 E-mail: info@pneupac.co.uk
Spacelabs Healthcare Ltd, 3 Chiltern Court Asheridge Road Industrial Estate, Asheridge Road, Chesham, Buckinghamshire, HP5 2PX Tel: (01494) 784422 Fax: (01494) 791497 E-mail: advsales@spacelabs.com
▶ Sunflower Medical, Headway Business Centre, Knowles Lane, Bradford, West Yorkshire, BD4 9SW Tel: (01274) 684004 Fax: (01274) 684006 E-mail: info@sunflowermedical.co.uk
Support Stool, 13 Madeley Road, Aylesbury, Buckinghamshire, HP21 8BP Tel: (01296) 581764 Fax: (01296) 586583 E-mail: sales@supportstool.co.uk
S. Teasdale (Hospital Equipment) Ltd, Unit 1 & 2, Brighton Road, Stockport, Cheshire, SK4 2BE Tel: 0161-219 0080 Fax: 0161-219 0081
▶ Technical Medical Services, 8 Merlin Way, Quarry Hill Industrial Estate, Ilkeston, Derbyshire, DE7 4RA Tel: 0115-932 3242 Fax: 0115-944 1618 E-mail: tmsderby@aol.com
Technical Service Consultants Ltd, The Rope Walk, Schofield Street, Heywood, Lancashire, OL10 1DS Tel: (01706) 620600 Fax: (01706) 620445 E-mail: sales@tsc-ltd.demon.co.uk
▶ Tyco Health Care UK Ltd, Ashwood Crockford Lane, Chineham Business Park, Chineham, Basingstoke, Hampshire, RG24 8EH Tel: (01256) 708880 E-mail: info@kendallhq.com
▶ UK Care Products, Petre Street, Sheffield, S4 8LJ Tel: 0114-243 3377 Fax: 0114-243 3377 E-mail: mail@options4health.co.uk
Vitalograph Ltd, Maids Moreton House, Vitalograph Business Park, Maids Moreton, Buckingham, MK18 1SW Tel: (01280) 827100 Fax: (01280) 823302 E-mail: sales@vitalograph.co.uk
Wimpole International Ltd, 113 Colney Heath Lane, St. Albans, Hertfordshire, AL4 0TN Tel: (01727) 868057 Fax: (01727) 847116 E-mail: wimpoleint@mcmail.com

MEDICAL EQUIPMENT DESIGN SERVICES

Ceema Technology, 4 The Omega Centre, Stratton Business Park, Biggleswade, Bedfordshire, SG18 8QB Tel: (01767) 319800 Fax: (01767) 317621 E-mail: reception@ceema.co.uk

MEDICAL EQUIPMENT HIRE

Shopmobility, 6 Morris Mews, Leominster, Herefordshire, HR6 8LZ Tel: (01568) 616755

MEDICAL EQUIPMENT IMPORT/ EXPORT MERCHANTS OR AGENTS

▶ Engine Spares, 82 Mitcham Road, London, SW17 9NG Tel: (020) 8767 5990 Fax: (020) 8767 5991 E-mail: smithaustin01@btconnect.com
Frannan International Ltd, 1 Chiswick Square, London, W4 2QG Tel: (020) 8994 7475 Fax: (020) 8994 1393 E-mail: office@frannan.com
Hermes Medical, Kilburn Park Road, London, NW6 5XD Tel: (020) 7625 8014 Fax: (020) 7487 2986 E-mail: marketing@hermesmed.co.uk
▶ Simply Medical, 315 Centennial Park, Centennial Avenue, Elstree, Borehamwood, Hertfordshire, WD6 3TJ Tel: (020) 8236 3900 Fax: (020) 8953 4453 E-mail: info@simplymedical.co.uk

MEDICAL EQUIPMENT MAINTENANCE/REPAIR SERVICES

▶ Lab Med, Unit 4 Brunel Way, Thetford, Norfolk, IP24 1HP Tel: (01842) 762513 Fax: (01842) 753927 E-mail: labmedemail@yahoo.co.uk
▶ Simply Medical, 315 Centennial Park, Centennial Avenue, Elstree, Borehamwood, Hertfordshire, WD6 3TJ Tel: (020) 8236 3900 Fax: (020) 8953 4453 E-mail: info@simplymedical.co.uk

MEDICAL EQUIPMENT PACKAGING MACHINES

Packaging Automation Ltd, 1 Montgomery Close, Parkgate Industrial Estate, Knutsford, Cheshire, WA16 8XW Tel: (01565) 755000 Fax: (01565) 751015 E-mail: sales@pal.co.uk

MEDICAL EQUIPMENT PACKAGING MATERIALS

▶ Amcor Flexibles Winterbourne, Winterbourne Road, Stoke Gifford, Bristol, BS34 6PT Tel: 0117-987 2000 Fax: 0117-987 2002 E-mail: healthcare_info@amcor-flexibles.com
Nelipak Thermoforming, PO Box 28, Bristol, BS31 1XT Tel: 0117-986 7163 Fax: 0117-986 7197

MEDICAL EQUIPMENT, DURABLE

Convatec Ltd, Milton Road, Uxbridge, Middlesex, UB10 8EF Tel: (01895) 628400 Fax: (01895) 628456

MEDICAL GAS ANALYSERS

Drew Scientific Group plc, Unit 4 Peter Green Way Furness Business Park, Barrow-in-Furness, Cumbria, LA14 2PE Tel: (01229) 432089 Fax: (01229) 432096 E-mail: sales@drew-scientific.com

Specialty Gases Ltd, Buiding 940 Kent Science Park, Sittingbourne, Kent, ME9 8PS Tel: (01795) 599099 Fax: (01795) 411525 E-mail: sales@specialty-gases.com

MEDICAL GAS CONTROL SYSTEMS

Gas Arc Group Ltd, Vinces Road, Diss, Norfolk, IP22 4WW Tel: (01379) 652263 Fax: (01379) 644235 E-mail: mail@gas-arc.co.uk

▶ Medaes Ltd, Telford Cresent, Speedwell Industrial Estate, Staveley, Chesterfield, Derbyshire, S43 3PF Tel: (01246) 474242 Fax: (01246) 472982 E-mail: sales@medaes.co.uk

MEDICAL GAS SUPPLY SYSTEMS

Imgas Ltd, Sansom House, Portland Street, Daybrook, Nottingham, NG5 6BL Tel: 0115-966 7030 Fax: 0115-966 7031 E-mail: sales@imgas.co.uk

MEDICAL GASES

▶ Bellcraig Medical Ltd, 8 Muriel Street, Barrhead, Glasgow, G78 1QB Tel: 0141-880 4141 Fax: 0141-876 0301

▶ Medaes Ltd, Telford Cresent, Speedwell Industrial Estate, Staveley, Chesterfield, Derbyshire, S43 3PF Tel: (01246) 474242 Fax: (01246) 472982 E-mail: sales@medaes.co.uk

Nothern Gas Installation, 7 Alder Road, Failsworth, Manchester, M35 0GH Tel: 0161-682 8323 Fax: 0161-682 0043 E-mail: info@northerngasinstallations.com

MEDICAL GLASSWARE

Labco, Brow Works, Copyground Lane, High Wycombe, Buckinghamshire, HP12 3HE Tel: (01494) 459741 Fax: (01494) 465101 E-mail: sales@labco.co.uk

S Murray & Co. Ltd, Holborn House, High Street, Old Woking, Woking, Surrey, GU22 9LB Tel: (01483) 740099 Fax: (01483) 755111 E-mail: sales@smurray.co.uk

MEDICAL INDUSTRY PACKAGING

Amcor Flexibles, 1 Gass Close, Highbridge, Somerset, TA9 4JT Tel: (01278) 793232 Fax: (01278) 794996 E-mail: sales@amcor.com

▶ Amcor Flexibles Winterbourne, Winterbourne Road, Stoke Gifford, Bristol, BS34 6PT Tel: 0117-987 2000 Fax: 0117-987 2002 E-mail: healthcare_info@amcor-flexibles.com

▶ Flexible Medical Packaging Ltd, Unit 8, Hightown, White Cross Industrial Estate, Lancaster, LA1 4XS Tel: (01524) 68737 Fax: (01524) 67110 E-mail: sales@flexible-medical.com

Sealed Air Ltd, Clifton House, 1 Marston Road, St. Neots, Cambridgeshire, PE19 2HN Tel: (01480) 224000 Fax: (01480) 224063

MEDICAL INDUSTRY STAFF RECRUITMENT

A S A Law, Glade House, 52 Carter Lane, London, EC4V 5JL Tel: (020) 7236 2395 Fax: (020) 7246 4746

▶ Adjuvant Recruitment Ltd, P.O. Box 65, Tenterden, Kent, TN30 7WD Tel: 0845 33 12395 E-mail: info@adjuvantrecruitment.com

▶ eMedCareers, Jobsite UK (Worldwide) Ltd., Langstone Technology Park, Havant, Hampshire, PO9 1SA Tel: 0870 774 8732

MEDICAL INSTRUMENTS, *See also headings for particular types*

Bedfont Scientific Ltd, 105 Rochester Airport Industrial Estate, Laker Road, Rochester, Kent, ME1 3QX Tel: (01634) 673720 Fax: (01634) 673721 E-mail: info@bedfont.com

MEDICAL MICROPLATE FILTRATION EQUIPMENT

Porvair plc, 50 Bergen Way, North Lynn Industrial Estate, King's Lynn, Norfolk, PE30 2JG Tel: (01553) 765500 Fax: (01553) 765599 E-mail: lclare@porvair.com

MEDICAL MOULDS

A 4 Engineering Ltd, 7 Manor Park, 35 Willis Way, Poole, Dorset, BH15 3SZ Tel: (01202) 676047 Fax: (01202) 684675 E-mail: a4eng@a4eng.com

Medtex Ltd, 9 139 Oldbury Road, Smethwick, West Midlands, B66 1JE Tel: 0121-558 1398 Fax: 0121-565 1910

MEDICAL OR SURGICAL FABRICS

Acordis Services Ltd, Po Box 111, Coventry, CV6 5RS Tel: (024) 7658 2288 Fax: (024) 7668 2737 E-mail: enquiries@acordisservices.com

Altimed Ltd, 74 Sullington Road, Shepshed, Loughborough, Leicestershire, LE12 9JJ Tel: (01509) 501720 Fax: (01509) 501721 E-mail: enquiries@altimed.co.uk

MEDICAL OR SURGICAL GOODS, SILICONE RUBBER MOULDINGS

Rubber Engineering Services, 4 Gorton Cresent, Windmill Lane Industrial Estate, Denton, Manchester, M34 3RB Tel: 0161-320 9900 Fax: 0161-320 9940 E-mail: sales@rubberengineering.co.uk

MEDICAL OXYGEN CONCENTRATOR MACHINES

Rimer-Alco Ltd, Cardiff Bay Business Centre, Titan Road, Cardiff, CF24 5EJ Tel: (029) 2049 9969 Fax: (029) 2049 2223 E-mail: rimer@rimeralco.co.uk

Smiths Medical International Ltd, Bramingham Business Park, Enterprise Way, Luton, LU3 4BU Tel: (01582) 430000 Fax: (01582) 430001 E-mail: info@pneupac.co.uk

MEDICAL PIPELINE ENGINEERS, INSTALLATION OR SERVICE, GAS SUPPLY

Medical Gases Ltd, Aztex House, Perrywood Business Park, Salfords, Redhill, RH1 5DZ Tel: (01737) 378000 Fax: (01737) 378055 E-mail: rsmith@medicalgases.uk.com

Medical & Industrial Manufacturing Co. Ltd, Broadway, Dukinfield, Cheshire, SK16 4UU Tel: 0161-339 6028 Fax: 0161-330 0944 E-mail: mimcoltd@compuserve.com

Nothern Gas Installation, 7 Alder Road, Failsworth, Manchester, M35 0GH Tel: 0161-682 8323 Fax: 0161-682 0043 E-mail: info@northerngasinstallations.com

Penlon Ltd, 8 Salford Enterprise Centre, Guide Street, Salford, M50 1EW Tel: 0161-745 7952 Fax: 0161-745 7953 E-mail: east.healthcare@penlon.co.uk

MEDICAL PLASTIC INJECTION MOULDINGS

Central Mouldings Ltd, Reform Street Industrial Estate, Reform Street, Sutton-In-Ashfield, Nottinghamshire, NG17 5DB Tel: (01623) 553005 Fax: (01623) 440370 E-mail: bcadman@ypm.net

Forteq UK Ltd, Tandem Industrial Estate, Wakefield Road, Tandem, Huddersfield, HD5 0QR Tel: (01484) 424384 Fax: (01484) 535053

MEDICAL SALES STAFF RECRUITMENT

▶ Futurefind Sales Recruitment, Wira House, Ring Road, West Park, Leeds, LS16 6EB Tel: 0113-275 5656 Fax: 0113-278 2181 E-mail: recruitment@futurefind.co.uk

▶ New Line Sales Recruitment Ltd, Clay House, 5 Horninglow Street, Burton-on-Trent, Staffordshire, DE14 1NG Tel: (01283) 500077 Fax: (08701) 163370 E-mail: sales@newlinesales.co.uk

MEDICAL SOFTWARE

Acropolis Computers Ltd, 2D Dolphin Way, Stapleford, Cambridge, CB2 5DW Tel: (01223) 841700 Fax: (01223) 841802 E-mail: info@biosoft.com

Advanced Expert Systems Ltd, Woburn House, Vernon Gate, Derby, DE1 1UL Tel: (01332) 383521 Fax: (01332) 383532

Anglia Health Care Ltd, Oak Lodge, School Lane, Little Melton, Norwich, NR9 3LB Tel: (01603) 819600 Fax: (01603) 812811

Bluespier International Ltd, Wood End House, Grafton Flyford, Worcester, WR7 4PH Tel: (01905) 391120 Fax: (01905) 391121 E-mail: susan.williams@bluespier.com

Capstone Systems, Oak Mead, Honington, Bury St. Edmunds, Suffolk, IP31 1RE Tel: (01359) 268711 Fax: (01359) 268870 E-mail: dcg@capstonesystems.co.uk

Compucorp Ltd, Unit 37 Watford Metro Centre, Dwight Road, Watford, WD18 9SB Tel: (01923) 220121 E-mail: info@compucorp.co.uk

Deltace Systems Ltd, Pierremont Hall, Pierremont Avenue, Broadstairs, Kent, CT10 1JX Tel: (01843) 861888 Fax: (01843) 865006

E M I S, 77 Back Lane, Horsforth, Leeds, LS18 4RF Tel: 0113-259 1122 Fax: 0113-239 0162 E-mail: emis@e-mis.com

Hudson House, 8 Albany Street, Edinburgh, EH1 3QB Tel: 0131-473 2300 Fax: 0131-473 2309 E-mail: info@jupsys.co.uk

Jupiter Systems, 82 Meadrow, Godalming, Surrey, GU7 3HT Tel: (01483) 410001 Fax: (01483) 422866 E-mail: info@jupitersystems.net

Practiceworks Ltd, Elopak House, Rutherford Close, Stevenage, Hertfordshire, SG1 2PR Tel: (01438) 245000 Fax: (01438) 245001

Streets Heaver Computer Systems Ltd, 4 Low Moor Road, Lincoln, LN6 3JY Tel: (01522) 872000 Fax: (01522) 872255 E-mail: control@streetsheaver.com

MEDICAL STAFF RECRUITMENT

▶ Adjuvant Recruitment Ltd, P.O. Box 65, Tenterden, Kent, TN30 7WD Tel: 0845 33 12395 E-mail: info@adjuvantrecruitment.com

Bridgewater International Recruitment Direct, 109 Bodmin Road, Astley, Tyldesley, Manchester, M29 7PE Tel: (01942) 873158 Fax: (01942) 896946 E-mail: birdrecruit@blueyonder.co.uk

MEDICAL SUPPLY/SURGICAL SUPPLY MANUFRS

A & A Traders, 11 Devonshire Mews, Chiswick, London, W4 2HA Tel: (020) 8994 1333 Fax: (020) 8994 5291 E-mail: aat1@aol.com

▶ Abacus Healthcare Services Ltd, Radway Green Venture Park, Radway Green Road, Crewe, CW2 5PR Tel: (01270) 844260

▶ Abbey Dental Laboratory, 56 Orford Lane, Warrington, WA2 7AF Tel: (01925) 232032 Fax: (01925) 629558

Addaction Scotland, Nethergate Business Centre, Dundee, DD1 4ER Tel: (01382) 206888 Fax: (01382) 229870 E-mail: salt@salts.co.uk

Adrian Armstrong Medical Equipment, 46 Newbolt Avenue, Sutton, Surrey, SM3 8EE Tel: (020) 8641 0099 Fax: (020) 8641 0031

▶ Advanced Medical Products, 10 Brindley Road, Clacton-on-Sea, Essex, CO15 4XL Tel: (01255) 421634 Fax: (01255) 432149

Advanced Medical Supplies Ltd, Freemantle House, Kingsclere Park, Kingsclere, Newbury, Berkshire, RG20 4SW Tel: (01635) 299857 Fax: (01635) 297546 E-mail: sales@ams-med.com

▶ Aesthetic Dental Services Ltd, 201 Bristol Avenue, Blackpool, FY2 0JF Tel: (01253) 594245 Fax: (01253) 500592 E-mail: andypheland@firstdental.co.uk

▶ Aesthetic Dental Services Ltd, 112 Wetherby Road, Harrogate, North Yorkshire, HG2 7AB Tel: (01423) 885268 Fax: (01423) 880036

▶ Aldersley Battery Chairs Ltd, New Cross Street, Wednesbury, West Midlands, WS10 7ST Tel: 0121-568 8999

Ansell Ltd, Ansell House, 119 Ewell Road, Surbiton, Surrey, KT6 6AL Tel: (020) 8481 1800 Fax: (020) 8481 1828 E-mail: info@ansell.com

Applied Medical Technical Ltd, 4-5 Orwell Furlong, Cambridge, CB4 0WY Tel: (01223) 420415 Fax: (01223) 420797 E-mail: sales@applied-medical.co.uk

Asher Andell Ltd, Midway House, Main Road, Upper Broughton, Melton Mowbray, Leicestershire, LE14 3BG Tel: (01664) 822131 Fax: (01664) 823332 E-mail: medical@asher-andell.co.uk

▶ Astor-Bannerman Medical Ltd, Unit 11f Coln Park, Andoversford Industrial Estate, Andoversford, Cheltenham, Gloucestershire, GL54 4HJ Tel: (01242) 820820 Fax: (01242) 821110 E-mail: sales@astorbannerman.co.uk

Athrodax Healthcare International Ltd, Hawthorn Business Park, Puddlebrook, Drybrook, Gloucestershire, GL17 9HP Tel: (01594) 544440 Fax: (01594) 545800 E-mail: sales@athrodax.co.uk

B. Braun Medical Ltd, Brookdale Road, Thorncliffe Park Estate, Chapeltown, Sheffield, S35 2PW Tel: 0114-225 9000 Fax: 0114-225 9111 E-mail: info@bbraun.com

▶ B D G Ceramics, Ure Street, Dundee, DD1 5JD Tel: (01382) 225985 Fax: (01382) 229866

B D UK Ltd, 21 Between Towns Road, Cowley, Oxford, OX4 3LY Tel: (01865) 748844 Fax: (01865) 717313

▶ Bath Knight, Paladin, Atlas Street, Stoke-on-Trent, ST4 3AL Tel: (01782) 840840 Fax: (01782) 209243

Beaver Healthcare Equipment, Beaver House, 1 Vale Rise, Tonbridge, Kent, TN9 1TB Tel: (01732) 367777

Beckman Coulter (UK) Ltd, Oakley Court, Kingsmead Business Park, London Road, High Wycombe, Buckinghamshire, HP11 1JU Tel: (01494) 441181 Fax: (01494) 447558

▶ Benchmark Dental Laboratories Ltd, Renwick House, Brixham Road, Paignton, Devon, TQ4 7RE Tel: (01803) 555741 Fax: (01803) 664273 E-mail: mail@1stdental.co.uk

▶ Bolton Bros Shoe & Appliance Makers Ltd, Penn Street, Newcastle upon Tyne, NE4 7BG Tel: 0191-273 2012 Fax: 0191-226 0143

Boots, 32 The Broadway, Joel Street, Northwood, Middlesex, HA6 1PF Tel: (01923) 820841 Fax: (01923) 825555

Bullen Health Care Group, 85-87 Kempston Street, Liverpool, L3 8HE Tel: 0151-207 1239 Fax: 0151-207 3804E-mail: info@bullens.com

C M E, 6 Ascot Park Estate, Lenton Street, Sandiacre, Nottingham, NG10 5DL Tel: 0115-949 9066 Fax: 0115-939 3102 E-mail: gcb@cme.globalnet.co.uk

Camlon, Camlon House, Unit 10 D, The Grip Industrial Estate, Linton, Cambridge, CB21 4NR Tel: (01223) 897989 Fax: (01223) 897904 E-mail: sales@camlon.com

Care Centres Ltd, 75 Rowlands Road, Worthing, West Sussex, BN11 3JN Tel: (01903) 821515 Fax: (01903) 235132 E-mail: carecentresltd@supanet.com

▶ Careflex Ltd, 1-2 Anchor Buildings 5 Battle Road, Heathfield Industrial Estate, Newton Abbot, Devon, TQ12 6RY Tel: (01626) 836440 Fax: (01626) 836441 E-mail: sales@careflex.co.uk

Cartier Communications International, 7 Hazelbury Rd, High Wycombe, Bucks, HP13 7RZ Tel: 01494 538354 Fax: 01494 443468

Caterham Surgical Supplies Ltd, 89A Gloucester Road, Croydon, CR0 2DN Tel: (020) 8683 1103 Fax: (020) 8683 1105 E-mail: info@caterhamsurgical.co.uk

Centromed International Ltd, Anglo House, Wotton Road, Ashford, Kent, TN23 6LN Tel: (01233) 635353 Fax: (01233) 635351 E-mail: info@centromed.com

▶ Chas A Blatchfords, 11 Atlas Way, Sheffield, S4 7QQ Tel: 0114-263 7900 Fax: 0114-263 7901

▶ Chelmsford Dental Laboratories Ltd, 65 Victoria Road, Chelmsford, CM1 1PA Tel: (01245) 287535 Fax: (01245) 600008

▶ Chingford Dental Laboratories, 118 Chingford Mount Road, London, E4 9AA Tel: (020) 8531 1212 Fax: (020) 8926 2685 E-mail: mandy@chingford.com

Coloplast Ltd, Peterborough Business Park, Lynch Wood, Peterborough, PE2 6FX Tel: (01733) 392000 Fax: (01733) 233348 E-mail: gbcareteam@coloplast.com

Consolidated Supply Services, Unit 7, Hastingwood Business Centre, Hastingwood, Harlow, Essex, CM17 9GD Tel: (01279) 641131 Fax: (01279) 635438

Convatec Ltd, Milton Road, Uxbridge, Middlesex, UB10 8EF Tel: (01895) 628400 Fax: (01895) 628456

Credenhill Ltd, 10 Cossall Industrial Estate, Cossall Industrial Estate, Ilkeston, Derbyshire, DE7 5UG Tel: 0115-932 0144 Fax: 0115-944 0437 E-mail: sales@credenhill.co.uk

▶ Dentafix UK Ltd, Unit 11-13, Helix Business Park, Camberley, Surrey, GU15 2QT Tel: (01276) 691821 Fax: (01276) 23490 E-mail: info@dentafix.co.uk

▶ Diagnostic Ultrasound UK Ltd, The Granary, Aston Sandford, Aylesbury, Buckinghamshire, HP17 8LP Tel: (01844) 299207 Fax: (01844) 299218

▶ Draeger Ltd, 2 The Willows, Mark Road, Hemel Hempstead Industrial Estate, Hemel Hempstead, Hertfordshire, HP2 7BN Tel: (01442) 211110 Fax: (01442) 240327

Durbin P.L.C., Unit 5, Redlands Business Centre, Redlands, Coulsdon, Surrey, CR5 2UN Tel: (020) 8660 2220 Fax: (020) 8668 0751 E-mail: catalogesales@durbin.co.uk

▶ E S L Healthcare Ltd, Sandown Court, Station Road, Glenfield, Leicester, LE3 8BT Tel: 0116-231 8900 Fax: 0116-233 1000 E-mail: uksales@pressalitcare.com

▶ The Electrode Co., Llangwm, Usk, Gwent, NP15 1HJ Tel: (01291) 650279 E-mail: keltic@electo.co.uk

Endoscopic Manufacturing & Services Ltd, Unit 14 Alliance Court, Alliance Road, London, W3 0RB Tel: (020) 8896 1002 Fax: (020) 8752 1030 E-mail: info@endoscopiclondon.com

Eurosurgical Ltd, Merrow Business Centre, Guildford, Surrey, GU4 7WA Tel: (01483) 456007 Fax: (01483) 456008 E-mail: sales@eurosurgical.co.uk

Farnhurst Medical Ltd, Unit 16 Alfold Craft & Business Centre, Loxwood Road, Alfold, Cranleigh, Surrey, GU6 8HP Tel: (01403) 752775 Fax: (01403) 752261 E-mail: sales@farnhurst-medical.co.uk

▶ Finsbury Instruments Ltd, Unit 13 Mole Business Park, Randalls Road, Leatherhead, Surrey, KT22 7BA Tel: (01372) 360830 Fax: (01372) 360779 E-mail: sales@finsbury.org

MEDICAL SUPPLY/SURGICAL SUPPLY MANUFRS – *continued*

▶ Fleinns Medicare, Phoenix Park, Chickenhall Lane, Eastleigh, Hampshire, SO50 6RP Tel: (023) 8061 3333 Fax: (023) 8065 0230
▶ Fleinns Medicare Ltd, Unit 5-6 The Boatyard Industrial Estate, Mill Road, Fareham, Hampshire, PO16 0TA Tel: (01329) 823258 Fax: (01329) 822353
▶ Footlogic Ltd, 571 Southmead Road, Westbury-On-Trym, Bristol, BS10 5NL Tel: 0117-969 7600
G E Bridge & Co. Ltd, 123-125 Old Christchurch Road, Bournemouth, BH1 1HF Tel: (01202) 204802 Fax: (01202) 204800
▶ G S Halligan, 175 Knightlow Road, Birmingham, B17 8PY Tel: 0121-420 2227 Fax: 0121-434 3967
▶ General Anaesthetic Services, Ingrow Bridge Works, Keighley, West Yorkshire, BD21 5EF Tel: (01535) 609615
▶ Gilbey Orthopaedic Footwear Ltd, 29 Shuna Place, Glasgow, G20 9ED Tel: 0141-946 4782
Giltech Ltd, 12 North Harbour Industrial Estate, Ayr, KA8 8BN Tel: (01292) 264406 Fax: (01292) 611900 E-mail: innovation@giltech.demon.co.uk
▶ Glasgow Disabled Aid Specialists, 300 Blantyre Ferme Road, Uddingston, Glasgow, G71 7RN Tel: 0141-641 3656 Fax: 0141-641 3656
▶ Gloucestershire Industrial Services, Unit 26 Severnside Trading Estate, Gloucester, GL2 5HS Tel: (01452) 520438 Fax: (01452) 300850
▶ Gowllands Ltd, 3 Gladstone Road, Croydon, CR0 2BQ Tel: (020) 8689 4125 Fax: (020) 8684 2525 E-mail: sales@gowlands.co.uk
Gta UK Ltd, 34 Nottingham South Estate, Ruddington Lane Wilford, Nottingham, NG11 7EP Tel: 0115-981 5703 Fax: 0115-945 5106 E-mail: mail@gtauk.demon.co.uk
Harmony Centre, 26 Lower Hillgate, Stockport, Cheshire, SK1 1JE Tel: 0161-480 8030 Fax: 0161-480 8030
▶ Health Care Centre, Alexandra Buildings, The Roe, St. Asaph, Clwyd, LL17 0NA Tel: (01745) 584818 Fax: (01754) 584775
Henleys Medical Supplies Ltd, Brownfields, Welwyn Garden City, Hertfordshire, AL7 1AN Tel: (01707) 333164 Fax: (01707) 334795 E-mail: sales@henleysmed.com
Hne Huntleigh Ltd, Unit 11b Brooklands Way, Boldon Business Park, Boldon Colliery, Tyne & Wear, NE35 9LZ Tel: 0191-536 1291 Fax: 0191-536 1307
▶ Humanware Europe Ltd, Russell Smith House Unit 2, Bullmatt Business Centre, Northampton Road, Rushden, Northamptonshire, NN10 6AR Tel: (01933) 415800 Fax: (01933) 411029 E-mail: eu.info@humanware.com
▶ Hunter Scientific Ltd, Unit 1 Priors Hall, Widdington, Saffron Walden, Essex, CB11 3SB Tel: (01799) 541688 Fax: (01799) 541703 E-mail: sales@hunterscientific.com
Hypoguard Ltd, Dock Lane, Melton, Woodbridge, Suffolk, IP12 1PE Tel: (01394) 387333 Fax: (01394) 380152 E-mail: enquiries@hypoguard.co.uk
▶ Implants International Simco 708 Ltd, 71 Jay Avenue, Teesside Industrial Estate, Stockton-on-Tees, Cleveland, TS17 9LZ Tel: (01642) 769080 Fax: (01642) 765848 E-mail: enquiries@implantsinternational.com
Instrumentation Laboratory UK Ltd, Kelvin Close, Birchwood, Warrington, WA3 7PB Tel: (01925) 810141 Fax: (01925) 826708 E-mail: sales@il.com
Intavent Orthofix Ltd, Burney Court, Cordwallis Park, Maidenhead, Berkshire, SL6 7BZ Tel: (01628) 594500 Fax: (01628) 789400 E-mail: enquiries@intaventorthofix.com
John Preston & Co Belfast Ltd, Blaris Industrial Estate, Altona Road, Lisburn, County Antrim, BT27 5QB Tel: (028) 9267 7077 Fax: (028) 9267 7099 E-mail: info@jphealthcare.co.uk
Joint Replacement Instrumentation Ltd, 8 Broadstone Place, London, W1U 7EP Tel: (020) 7487 4477 Fax: (020) 7224 2862 E-mail: jri@jri-ltd.co.uk
Judd Medical Ltd, Highfield House, 53 Worcester Road, Bromsgrove, Worcestershire, B61 7DN Tel: (01527) 559010 Fax: (01527) 559080
▶ Kare Orthopaedic Ltd, Gareloch Road, Port Glasgow, Renfrewshire, PA14 5XH Tel: (01475) 730020 Fax: (01475) 730040
▶ Koehler Chemie Ltd, Astley Way, Astley La Industrial Estate, Swillington, Leeds, LS26 8XT Tel: 0113-287 1122 Fax: 0113-287 3087
▶ Lance Paragon Ltd, Owlerton Green, Sheffield, S6 2BJ Tel: 0114- 255 1063 E-mail: info@lance-paragon.co.uk
Lifescan Scotland, Beechwood Park North, Inverness, IV2 3ED Tel: (01463) 721000 Fax: (01463) 722000
▶ Lpe Medical Ltd, Gordleton Industrial Centre, Hannah Way, Pennington, Lymington, Hampshire, SO41 8JD Tel: (01590) 681258 Fax: (01590) 681251 E-mail: sales@lpemedical.com
Lyall Willis & Co. Ltd, 49 Cooden Sea Road, Bexhill-on-Sea, East Sussex, TN39 4SL Tel: (01424) 848388 Fax: (01424) 848399 E-mail: info@lyallwillis.co.uk
▶ Mccue plc, Unit 27, Shamblehurst Lane, Hedge End, Southampton, SO30 2FY Tel: (01489) 795668 Fax: (01489) 795670
▶ Marine Dental Practice, 36 Marine Parade, Worthing, West Sussex, BN11 3QA Tel: (01903) 234136 Fax: (01903) 216195
Median Systems Ltd, Unit 26 Bailey Gate, Sturminster Marshall, Wimborne, Dorset, BH21 4DB Tel: (01258) 858999 Fax: (01258) 857714
Medifix Adhesive Products Ltd, Cosgrove Way, Luton, LU1 1XL Tel: (01582) 488499 Fax: (01582) 488100 E-mail: medifix@btinternet.com
▶ Medrad UK Ltd, Unit 25 Lancaster Way Business Park, Ely, Cambridgeshire, CB6 3NW Tel: (01353) 645024 E-mail: info@medrad.com
▶ Munro W Rehab Ltd, Unit 8-10 Dunrobin Court, 14 North Avenue, Clydebank Business Park, Clydebank, Dunbartonshire, G81 2QP Tel: 0141-952 2323
Myco Falcon, 8 Stanley Centre, Kelvin Way, Crawley, West Sussex, RH10 9SE Tel: (01293) 544533 Fax: (01293) 402737 E-mail: enquiries@rapidcare.com
Navrish Ltd, Navrish Nivas, 17 Bishops Close, Mays Lane, Arkley, Barnet, Hertfordshire, EN5 2QH Tel: (020) 8440 0803 Fax: (020) 8441 6813 E-mail: sales@navrish.co.uk
Nealbourne Ltd, PO Box 10, Keighley, West Yorkshire, BD21 4PP Tel: (01535) 667535 Fax: (01535) 609199
▶ Op Care, Hills Road, Cambridge, CB2 2DA Tel: (01223) 243391 Fax: (01225) 416564
Ostomed Ltd, Summit House, Kellet Lane, Bamber Bridge, Preston, PR5 6AN Tel: (01772) 626688 Fax: (01772) 626699
▶ Othy Ltd, Ashville Trading Estate, The Runnings, Cheltenham, Gloucestershire, GL51 9PT Tel: (01242) 246250
Overseas Medical Supplies UK Ltd, 14 Cumberland Avenue, London, NW10 7QL Tel: (020) 8965 9711 Fax: (020) 8965 6894 E-mail: oms@overseasmedical.com
▶ P R Cooper Footline Ltd, Sycamore Works, Melton Road, Tilton on the Hill, Leicester, LE7 9LG Tel: 0116-259 7263 Fax: 0116-259 7489
Peacock's Medical Group Ltd, Benfield Business Park, Benfield Road, Newcastle upon Tyne, NE6 4NQ Tel: 0191-276 9600 Fax: 0191-276 9696
Peacock's Medical Group Ltd, Benfield Business Park, Benfield Road, Newcastle upon Tyne, NE6 4NQ Tel: 0191-276 9600 Fax: 0191-276 9696
▶ Phoenix, 14 Pindar Road, Hoddesdon, Hertfordshire, EN11 0BZ Tel: (01992) 479444 Fax: (01992) 478878
Pilgrim Technology, 53 Carlton Road, Boston, Lincolnshire, PE21 8PA Tel: (01205) 363833 Fax: (01205) 363833
▶ Platts & Nisbett Ltd, Woodfold Works, Sheffield, S3 9PE Tel: 0114-275 0387 Fax: 0114-279 8434
▶ Portsmouth Surgical Equipment Ltd, 38 New Lane, Havant, Hampshire, PO9 2NF Tel: (023) 9249 9922 Fax: (023) 9249 8899
▶ Rehabilitation Services Ltd, Unit 51 Riverside Estate, Sir Thomas Longley Road, Medway City Estate, Rochester, Kent, ME2 4DP Tel: (01634) 297010 Fax: (01634) 297011
Research Instruments Ltd, Kernick Road, Penryn, Cornwall, TR10 9DQ Tel: (01326) 372753 Fax: (01326) 378783 E-mail: sales@research-instruments.com
Richardsons Of Leicester, 112a Milligan Road, Leicester, LE2 8FB Tel: 0116-283 8604 Fax: 0116-283 7109 E-mail: sales@richardsonsofleicester.co.uk
▶ Richley Dental Studio, 1 Nimmings Road, Halesowen, West Midlands, B62 9JQ Tel: 0121-561 4444 Fax: 0121-561 4563
Rocialle Medical Ltd, Dales Manor Business Park, Grove Road, Sawston, Cambridge, CB22 3TJ Tel: (01223) 495700 Fax: (01223) 495701 E-mail: info@rocialle.com
▶ Ross Care Centres Ltd, 3 Royal London Industrial Estate, Old Lane, Leeds, LS11 8AG Tel: 0113-277 7007 Fax: 0113-277 7040
Salt Healthcare, 7 Connel Court, Ardconnel Street, Inverness, IV2 3EY Tel: (01463) 241756 Fax: (01463) 710345 E-mail: sales@salt.com
Salt & Son Ltd, Blatchford Road, Horsham, West Sussex, RH13 5QR Tel: (01403) 274197 Fax: (01403) 218933E-mail: salts@salts.co.uk
Salt & Son Ltd, 15 Harlesden Road, London, NW10 2BY Tel: (020) 8451 3348 Fax: (020) 8830 0635 E-mail: info@salt.co.uk
Salts Healthcare Ltd, Unit 2 Richard Street, Birmingham, B7 4AA Tel: 0121-333 2000 Fax: 0121-359 0830 E-mail: salt@salts.co.uk
Frank Sammeroff Ltd, 131 Woodhead Road, Glasgow, G53 7NN Tel: 0141-881 5701 Fax: 0141-881 4919 E-mail: info@sammeroff.co.uk
Scala Surgical Ltd, 200 Church Road, London, NW10 9NP Tel: (020) 8459 1816 Fax: (020) 8459 3416 E-mail: scala_impex@yahoo.co.uk
Schuco International London Ltd, Lyndhurst Avenue, London, N12 0NE Tel: (020) 8368 1642 Fax: (020) 8361 3761 E-mail: sales@schuco.co.uk
▶ Sheppey Dental Laboratory, 1a-2a Railway Terrace, Queenborough, Kent, ME11 5AY Tel: (01795) 662025 Fax: (01795) 583593
▶ Shiloh Active Care, Greensward House, 12 Brook Road, Rayleigh, Essex, SS6 7UR Tel: (01268) 771191 Fax: (01268) 771192
▶ Siemens Medical Solutions, Nasmyth Building, Nasmyth Avenue, East Kilbride, Glasgow, G75 0QU Tel: (01355) 353030 Fax: (01355) 353031
Sterilox Technologies International Ltd, Montrose House, Montrose Street, Stoke-on-Trent, ST4 3PB Tel: (01782) 595969 Fax: (01782) 595979
▶ Karl Storz Endoscopy UK Ltd, Ninewells, Thomas Wise Place, Dundee, DD2 1UB Tel: (01382) 647500 Fax: (01382) 644999 E-mail: sales@karlstorz-uk.com
Thackraycare Ltd, Unit 1 The Links, Bakewell Road, Orton Southgate, Peterborough, PE2 6ZX Tel: (0800) 590916 Fax: (01733) 392849
Timesco of London, 3 Carnival Close, Basildon, Essex, SS14 3WN Tel: (01268) 297700 Fax: (01268) 297800 E-mail: info@timesco.com
Tricomed Surgical Ltd, 10 Tenterden Road, Croydon, CR0 6NN Tel: (020) 8656 1924 Fax: (020) 8656 7026 E-mail: tricomed@btconnect.com
▶ Vacsax Ltd, Western Wood Way, Plympton, Plymouth, PL7 5BG Tel: (01752) 337000
▶ Voxar Ltd, Bonnington Bond, 2 Anderson Place, Edinburgh, EH6 5NP Tel: 0131-472 4792
▶ W & H (U K) Ltd, 6 Stroud Wood Bus Centre, Park St, St. Albans, Hertfordshire, AL2 2NJ Tel: (01727) 874990
Walk Easy Sales, 2 Vicarage Field, Broom Street, Great Cornard, Sudbury, Suffolk, CO10 0JT Tel: (01787) 311559 E-mail: enquiries@walkeasy.co.uk
▶ Walton Dental Arts Ltd, Kinawley, 3 Station Road, Leatherhead, Surrey, KT22 7AA Tel: (01372) 377154 Fax: (01372) 362369 E-mail: sales@waltondentalarts.co.uk
▶ Ways & Means, Findel House, Excelsior Road, Ashby-de-la-Zouch, Leicestershire, LE65 1NG Tel: (0845) 6060911 Fax: (01530) 419150
▶ Wessex Dental Laboratory, Unit 10 Holes Bay Park, Sterte Avenue West, Poole, Dorset, BH15 2AA Tel: (01202) 674486 Fax: (01202) 674486 E-mail: wessex.dental@virgin.net
West Salts Medilink, Salts House, 53 Valley Road, Plymouth, PL7 1RF Tel: (01752) 346027 Fax: (01752) 346027
▶ Westley Dental Laboratories Ltd, 430 Stratford Road, Sparkhill, Birmingham, B11 4AD Tel: 0121-772 5313 Fax: 0121-772 5313
▶ Wheelchair Care Ltd, Unit 2, Greshop Industrial Estate, Forres, Morayshire, IV36 2GW Tel: (01309) 676677 Fax: (01309) 674479 E-mail: enquiries@wheelchaircare.co.uk
Whitehouse Plastics Ltd, Unit 4 Tiber Way, Glebe Farm Industrial Estate, Rugby, Warwickshire, CV21 1ED Tel: (01788) 541042 Fax: (01788) 552314 E-mail: sales@whitehouseplastics.co.uk
D.M. Wood Medical Ltd, Units 6-7, 1 Kirkhill Place, Kirkhill Industrial Estate, Dyce, Aberdeen, AB21 0GU Tel: (01224) 723388 Fax: (01224) 770670 E-mail: admin@dmwood-medical.com
Carl Zeiss Ltd, PO Box 78, Welwyn Garden City, Hertfordshire, AL7 1LU Tel: (01707) 331144 Fax: (01707) 330237 E-mail: info@zeiss.co.uk

MEDICAL SWAB STICKS, PLASTIC/PAPER

Papersticks Ltd, Govett Avenue, Shepperton, Middlesex, TW17 8AB Tel: (01932) 228491 Fax: (01932) 242828 E-mail: sales@papersticks.co.uk
John Weiss & Son Ltd, 89 Alston Drive, Bradwell Abbey, Milton Keynes, MK13 9HF Tel: (01908) 318017 Fax: (01908) 318708 E-mail: sales@johnweiss.com

MEDICAL TAPES

▶ ATC (Application Tape Co.) Ltd, Calf Hey South, Rochdale, Lancashire, OL11 2JS Tel: (01706) 633043 Fax: (01706) 710086 E-mail: sales@apptape.co.uk

MEDICAL TRANSCRIPTION SERVICES

Audio Experts, Springboard Business Centre, Ellerbeck Way, Middlesbrough, Cleveland, TS9 5JZ Tel: (01642) 715345 Fax: (01642) 715344 E-mail: office@audio-experts.co.uk
Voicescript, 31 Rickford Road, Nailsea, Bristol, BS48 4QB Tel: 01275 791184 E-mail: enquiries@voicescript.co.uk

MEDICAL USAGE MAGNETS

Siemens Magnet Technology Ltd, Wharf Road, Eynsham, Witney, Oxfordshire, OX29 4BP Tel: (01865) 880880 Fax: (01865) 850176

MEDICAL VIDEO IMAGE CAMERAS

Brian Reece Scientific Ltd, 12 West Mills, Newbury, Berkshire, RG14 5HG Tel: (01635) 32827 Fax: (01635) 34542 E-mail: brian@brsl.co.uk

MEDICINAL TABLETS

Custom Pharmaceuticals Ltd, Gill House, Conway Street, Hove, East Sussex, BN3 3LW Tel: (01273) 323513 Fax: (01273) 729483
▶ Life Healthcare, Freepost JE723, St. Helier, Jersey, JE1 1AF Tel: (0845) 1667070 E-mail: help@elixireurope.com

MEDIUM DENSITY FIBREBOARD (MDF)

Albion Extrusions Ltd, Penrose Works, Penrose Street, Bolton, BL2 6DX Tel: (01204) 385803 Fax: (01204) 385816 E-mail: info@albionextrusions.co.uk
Arnold Laver, Manningham Sawmills, Canal Road, Bradford, West Yorkshire, BD2 1AR Tel: (01274) 732861 Fax: (01274) 737060 E-mail: sales@bradford.timberworld.co.uk
Gower Timber Ltd, Crofty Indust Estate, Crofty, Swansea, SA4 3SW Tel: (01792) 851140 Fax: (01792) 850128 E-mail: classact@gowertimberltd.fsnet.co.uk
▶ L F P (UK) Ltd, LFP House, 1 Grange Meadows, Elmswell, Bury St. Edmunds, Suffolk, IP30 9GE Tel: (01359) 242900 Fax: (01359) 242121 E-mail: info@lfpuk.co.uk
Neat Concepts Ltd, F25 Hastingwood Trading Estate, 35 Harbet Road, London, N18 3HU Tel: (020) 8807 5805 Fax: (020) 8884 4963 E-mail: sales@neatform.com
Pfleiderer Industry, Oakfield House, Springwood Way, Tytherington Business Park, Macclesfield, Cheshire, SK10 2XA Tel: (01625) 660410 Fax: (01625) 617301 E-mail: info@pfleiderer.co.uk

MEDIUM HAULAGE LORRIES

Gerry Webb Transport Services Ltd, 4 Shelson Parade, Ashford Road, Feltham, Middlesex, TW13 4QZ Tel: (020) 8867 0000 Fax: (020) 8867 0088 E-mail: gerrywebbtpt@talk21.com

MEDIUM STRENGTH ALUMINIUM ALLOY EXTRUSIONS

Alserco (UK) Ltd, 111 Fazeley Street, Digbeth, Birmingham, B5 5RR Tel: 0121 643 2421 Fax: 0121 633 3140 E-mail: philip.relph@tkmuk.thyssenkrupp.com

MEDIUM VOLTAGE SWITCHGEARS

Abb, Rossmore Road East, Ellesmere Port, CH65 3DD Tel: 0151-357 8400 Fax: 0151-355 9137
Merlin Gerin, 123 Jack Lane, Leeds, LS10 1BS Tel: 0113-290 3500 Fax: 0113-290 3710 E-mail:

MEDIUM VOLTAGE TEST EQUIPMENT

T. & R. Test Equipment Ltd, 15-16 Woodbridge Meadows, Guilford, Guildford, Surrey, GU1 1BJ Tel: (01483) 207428 Fax: (01483) 235759 E-mail: sales@trtest.com

MELAMINE FACED CHIPBOARD

Blackheath Products Ltd, Fairfield Park, Halesowen, West Midlands, B62 9JL Tel: 0121-561 4245 Fax: 0121-561 5904 E-mail: sales@blackheathproducts.co.uk
Europanel UK Ltd, 1 Gerrards Place, East Gillibrands, Skelmersdale, Lancashire, WN8 9SU Tel: (01695) 731033 Fax: (01695) 727489 E-mail: europaneluk@btconnect.co.uk
▶ Lawcris Panel Products Ltd, Unit C Cross Green Close, Leeds, LS9 0RY Tel: 0113-217 7177 Fax: 0113-240 5588 E-mail: sales@lawcris.co.uk
Red Rose Distribution, Parliament Street, Burnley, Lancashire, BB11 3JT Tel: (01282) 724600 Fax: (01282) 724644

MELAMINE LAMINATES

Impressions, J1 Dunkerswell Business Park, Dunkerswell Airfield, Honiton, Devon, EX14 4LE Tel: (01404) 891850 Fax: (01404) 891850 E-mail: rob@impressions1990.co.uk
International Decorative Surfaces plc, West End Approach, Morley, Leeds, LS27 0NB Tel: 0113-220 3900 Fax: 0113-220 3901
Pfleiderer Industry, Oakfield House, Springwood Way, Tytherington Business Park, Macclesfield, Cheshire, SK10 2XA Tel: (01625) 660410 Fax: (01625) 617301 E-mail: info@pfleiderer.co.uk

MELAMINE TRAYS

Melamaster, Bodmin Road, Coventry, CV2 5DB Tel: (024) 7672 4919 Fax: (024) 7672 4920 E-mail: sales@melamaster.co.uk

MELTING FURNACES

Inductotherm Europe Ltd, The Furlong, Berry Hill Industrial Estate, Droitwich, Worcestershire, WR9 9AH Tel: (01905) 795100 Fax: (01905) 795138 E-mail: sales@inductotherm.co.uk

Monometer Holdings Ltd, Monometer House, Rectory Grove, Leigh-on-Sea, Essex, SS9 2HN Tel: (01702) 472201 Fax: (01702) 715112 E-mail: sales@monometer.co.uk

MELTING POTS/TANKS, INDUSTRIAL

Controlled Equipment, 17 The Mead Business Centre, Mead Lane, Hertford, SG13 7BJ Tel: (01992) 584404 Fax: (01992) 500177 E-mail: sales@meltingtank.com

MEMBERSHIP CARDS

D & M Business Cards, 4 Foxley Court, Oakwood, Derby, DE21 2EU Tel: (01332) 668468 Fax: (01332) 668462 E-mail: sales@dmbusinesscards.co.uk

Identilam plc, Faygate Business Centre, Faygate Lane, Faygate, Horsham, West Sussex, RH12 4DN Tel: (01293) 851711 Fax: (01293) 851742 E-mail: sales@indentilam.co.uk

Liberty Printers Ltd, Willett Road, Thornton Heath, Surrey, CR7 6AA Tel: (020) 8684 1486 Fax: (020) 8689 3202 E-mail: service@libertyprinters.co.uk

MEMBRANE BIOREACTOR (MBR) WASTE WATER TREATMENT SYSTEMS

▶ Micro-Membrane Systems Ltd, 9 Cork Terrace, Bath, BA1 3BE Tel: (01225) 444290 Fax: (01225) 461060 E-mail: info@micromembrane.co.uk

W2O Environment, 58 Cecil Road, Northampton, NN2 6PQ Tel: (01604) 478415 Fax: (01604) 478415 E-mail: wolfram@w2oenvironment.net

MEMBRANE BIOREACTOR SYSTEMS

Ultratech Services, 73C Stevens Road, Stourbridge, West Midlands, DY9 0XW Tel: (01384) 373926 Fax: (01384) 393785 E-mail: ultratech@btinternet.com

MEMBRANE FILTER SYSTEMS

▶ Memprotech, 9, Crane Way,, Woolsbridge Industrial Estate,, Three Legged Cross, Wimborne, Dorset, BH21 6FA Tel: (01202) 823699 Fax: (01202) 813863 E-mail: info@memprotech.com

MEMBRANE FILTERS

Koch Membrane Systems, The Granary, Telegraph Street, Stafford, ST17 4AT Tel: (01785) 272500 Fax: (01785) 223149

▶ Memprotech, 9, Crane Way,, Woolsbridge Industrial Estate,, Three Legged Cross, Wimborne, Dorset, BH21 6FA Tel: (01202) 823699 Fax: (01202) 813863 E-mail: info@memprotech.com

Millipore (UK) Ltd, Units 3-5 The Court Yard, Hattes Lane, Watford, WD18 8YH Tel: (0870) 9004645 Fax: (0870) 9004646 E-mail: csr_uk@millipore.com

Pti Technologies UK Ltd, Orgreave Lane, Handsworth, Sheffield, S13 9NZ Tel: 0114-269 3999 Fax: 0114-269 1409 E-mail: filters@ptitechnologies.co.uk

MEMBRANE FILTRATION PLANT AND EQUIPMENT

Desal Supplies, Unit 4 Fletcher Street, Rochdale, Lancashire, OL11 1AE Tel: (01706) 869777 Fax: (01706) 713095 E-mail: sales@desal.co.uk

Ultratech Services, 73C Stevens Road, Stourbridge, West Midlands, DY9 0XW Tel: (01384) 373926 Fax: (01384) 393785 E-mail: ultratech@btinternet.com

MEMBRANE KEYBOARDS

Touch Panel Products Ltd, Short Way, Thornbury, Bristol, BS35 3UT Tel: (01454) 417307 Fax: (01454) 413708 E-mail: sales@touchpanels.co.uk

MEMBRANE KEYPADS

Customdesigntechnologies Ltd, Greatworth Park, Welsh Lane, Greatworth, Banbury, Oxfordshire, OX17 2HB Tel: (01280) 845530 Fax: (01295) 768888 E-mail: sales@customdesigntechnologies.com

Electro Serigraphic Products Ltd, Unit 8 Colliers Way, Reepham, Norwich, NR10 4SW Tel: (01603) 871227 Fax: (01603) 871237 E-mail: esp@membrane-switches.co.uk

MEMBRANE PRESSINGS

David Clouting Ltd, 7B Perry Road, Witham, Essex, CM8 3UD Tel: (01376) 518037 Fax: (01376) 500104 E-mail: sales@davidclouting.co.uk

MEMBRANE SWITCH PANELS

Parlex Europe Ltd, Taylor Road, Newport, Isle of Wight, PO30 5LG Tel: (01983) 526535 Fax: (01983) 524964 E-mail: sales@uk.parlex.com

MEMO PADS

▶ Officepoint Fivestar, 326 Kensal Road, London, W10 5BZ Tel: (020) 8969 8348 Fax: (020) 8969 8349 E-mail: sales@officepointfivestar.com

MEMORY CARD READERS/ WRITERS

Digital Depot, 13 High Street, Stevenage, Hertfordshire, SG1 3BG Tel: (01438) 367619 Fax: (01438) 359020 E-mail: sales@digitaldepot.co.uk

MEMORY CHIPS

A R M Ltd, 110 Fulbourn Road, Cherry Hinton, Cambridge, CB1 9NJ Tel: (01223) 400400 Fax: (01223) 400410 E-mail: info@arm.com

Atmel UK Ltd, Coliseum Business Centre, Riverside Way, Camberley, Surrey, GU15 3YL Tel: (01344) 390060 Fax: (01344) 390070 E-mail: jane.sorrell@atmel.com

Megabytes, 90 Central Road, Worcester Park, Surrey, KT4 8HU Tel: (020) 8335 4224 Fax: (020) 8715 0914 E-mail: sales@megabytes.co.uk

MEMORY SYSTEMS

Active Network Systems Ltd, 5 Coneygear Road, Hartford, Huntingdon, Cambridgeshire, PE29 1QL Tel: (01480) 437997 Fax: (01480) 436031 E-mail: sales@ans-ltd.co.uk

Astute Electronics Ltd, Church House, Church Street, Ware, Hertfordshire, SG12 9EN Tel: (01920) 483800 Fax: (01920) 486399 E-mail: insales@astute.co.uk

MEMORY, FLASH, UNIVERSAL SERIAL BUS (USB)

Blue Goose Systems, 44 Whitebridge Road, Onchan, Isle of Man, IM3 4HR Tel: (01624) 671719 Fax: (01624) 620179 E-mail: enquiries@bluegoosesystems.co.uk

Faisal, C517 New Providence Wharf, 1 Fairmont Avenue, London, UK, E14 9PF Tel: 07976 289139 Fax: 0870 4586531 E-mail: sales@flashdrive-direct.com

▶ Netshop Ltd, Grays Place, Slough, SL2 5AF Tel: (01753) 691661 Fax: (01753) 691037 E-mail: sales@netshop.co.uk

▶ Ware247 Ltd, 16 Castle Grove Drive, Leeds, LS6 4BR Tel: (0845) 3457859 E-mail: sales@ware247.co.uk

X2m Ltd, 2 The Acorns, Redehall Road, Smallfield, Horley, Surrey, RH6 9QJ Tel: (0870) 7704626 Fax: (0870) 7704626 E-mail: info@x2muk.co.uk

MEMORY, HIGH DENSITY

▶ Ware247 Ltd, 16 Castle Grove Drive, Leeds, LS6 4BR Tel: (0845) 3457859 E-mail: sales@ware247.co.uk

MENS LIFESTYLE MAGAZINES

▶ 4mags, 30B Grosvenor Road, Caversham, Reading, RG4 5EN Tel: 07939 084481 E-mail: sales@4mags.co.uk

MENS SHOES

Bacup Shoe Co. Ltd, Atherton Holme Mill, Railway Street, Bacup, Lancashire, OL13 0UF Tel: (01706) 873304 Fax: (01706) 873216 E-mail: admin@bacupshoe.co.uk

Barker Shoes Sales Ltd, 3 Station Road, Earls Barton, Northampton, NN6 0NT Tel: (01604) 810387 Fax: (01604) 812350 E-mail: barker@barkersshoes.co.uk

Beaconsfield Footwear Ltd, 2 Peel Road, Skelmersdale, Lancashire, WN8 9PT Tel: (01695) 712720 Fax: (01695) 712715 E-mail: info@hotter.co.uk

Brevitt Rieker Ltd, 37 Tenter Road, Moulton Park Industrial Estate, Northampton, NN3 6AX Tel: (01604) 491222 Fax: (01604) 499512 E-mail: sales@rieker.net

W.J. Brookes Sraigh Devine, 44 King Street, Earls Barton, Northampton, NN6 0LQ Tel: (01604) 810217 Fax: (01604) 812511 E-mail: providerwb@aol.com

Joseph Cheaney & Sons Ltd, PO Box 1 69 Rushton Road, Kettering, Northamptonshire, NN14 2RZ Tel: (01536) 760383 Fax: (01536) 761354 E-mail: info.cheaney@cheaney.co.uk

Chuckle Shoes, 3 New Bridge Street, Exeter, EX4 3JW Tel: (01392) 270321 Fax: (01392) 207003

Church & Co (Footwear Ltd), St James, Northampton, NN5 5JB Tel: (01604) 593333 Fax: (01604) 754405 E-mail: sales@church-footwear.com

C. & J. Clark International Ltd, 40 High Street, Street, Somerset, BA16 0YA Tel: (01458) 443131 Fax: (01458) 447547 E-mail: john.keery@clarks.com

Cox Geo J Ltd, Westfield Road, Wellingborough, Northamptonshire, NN8 3HD Tel: (01933) 224181 Fax: (01933) 277892 E-mail: info@georgecox.co.uk

D B Shoes Ltd, Irchester Road, Rushden, Northamptonshire, NN10 9XF Tel: (01933) 359217 Fax: (01933) 410218 E-mail: denton@dbshoes.freeserve.co.uk

Edward Green & Co., Cliftonville Road, Northampton, NN1 5BU Tel: (01604) 626880 Fax: (01604) 626889 E-mail: enquiries@edwardgreen.com

Grenson Shoes Ltd, Queen Street, Rushden, Northamptonshire, NN10 0AB Tel: (01933) 358734 Fax: (01933) 410106 E-mail: enquiries@grenson.com

Lambert Howarth Group P.L.C., Healeywood Road, Burnley, Lancashire, BB11 2HL Tel: (01282) 471200 Fax: (01282) 471279

Loake Bros Ltd, Wood Street, Kettering, Northamptonshire, NN16 9SN Tel: (01536) 415411 Fax: (01536) 410190 E-mail: enquiries@loake.co.uk

N P S Shoes, South St, Wollaston, Wellingborough, Northamptonshire, NN29 7RY Tel: (01933) 664207 Fax: (01933) 664699 E-mail: npsshoes@eurotellbroadband.com

H. Orton & Sons Ltd, 2 Oxford Street, Earl Shilton, Leicester, LE9 7BB Tel: (01455) 844373 Fax: (01455) 848849 E-mail: ortonshoes@aol.com

Sanders & Sanders Ltd, Spencer Works, Spencer Road, Rushden, Northamptonshire, NN10 6AE Tel: (01933) 353066 Fax: (01933) 410355 E-mail: mail@sanders-uk.com

Alfred Sargent & Sons Ltd, Portland Road, Rushden, Northamptonshire, NN10 0DQ Tel: (01933) 312065 Fax: (01933) 410207

R.E. Tricker Ltd, St. Michaels Road, Northampton, NN1 3JX Tel: (01604) 630595 Fax: (01604) 624978 E-mail: sales@trickers.com

White & Co. Ltd, 50a Main Road, Hackleton, Northampton, NN7 2AB Tel: (01604) 870982 Fax: (01604) 870529 E-mail: shoes@whiteeb.co.uk

MENSWEAR ACCESSORIES TO SPECIFICATION

Burberry Ltd, Abergorki Industrial Estate, Ynyswen Road, Treorchy, Mid Glamorgan, CF42 6EF Tel: (01443) 772020 Fax: (01443) 775956 E-mail: info@burberry.com

MENSWEAR IMPORT MERCHANTS OR AGENTS, *See Clothing Import Merchants or Agents*

MENSWEAR MANUFRS

28 Black London, Unit 3A, Trafalgar Business Park, Broughton Lane, Manchester, M8 9TZ Tel: 0161-839 2224 Fax: 0161-839 6661

▶ A B Clothing Ltd, 63 Britannia Street, Leicester, LE1 3LE Tel: 0116-251 2518 Fax: 0116-251 2518

Afay Ltd, 6 Stoddart Street, South Shields, Tyne & Wear, NE34 0JT Tel: 0191-456 1253 Fax: 0191-454 2808

▶ Alex Scott & Co Kiltmakers Ltd, 43 Schoolhill, Aberdeen, AB10 1JT Tel: (01224) 643924 Fax: (01224) 626061 E-mail: sales@kiltmakers.co.uk

Aquascutum International Ltd, Ibex House, 42-47 Minories, London, EC3N 1DY Tel: (020) 7675 9050 Fax: (020) 7675 9099 E-mail: john.harper@aquascutum.co.uk

B M B Menswear Ltd, Canal Granary Buildings, Canal Wharf, Holbeck, Leeds, LS11 5BB Tel: 0113-259 5500 Fax: 0113-259 5512

Banner Ltd, Banner House, Greg Street, Stockport, Cheshire, SK5 7BT Tel: 0161-474 8000 Fax: 0161-474 7655 E-mail: admin@bannergroup.co.uk

Bindra Bros Ltd, 6-8 Hazel Street, Leicester, LE2 7JN Tel: 0116-247 0116 Fax: 0116-247 0126 E-mail: hazelfashion@hotmail.com

▶ Blue Star Jeans Ltd, Chesterfield Road, Leicester, LE5 5LF Tel: 0116-273 3533

Bonart Ltd, 19 Stilebrook Road, Olney, Buckinghamshire, MK46 5EG Tel: (01234) 711171 Fax: (01234) 711979 E-mail: hq@bonart.co.uk

▶ Brennand Clothing Ltd, Halliwell Industrial Estate, Rossini Street, Bolton, BL1 8DL Tel: (01204) 493160 Fax: (01204) 493190

▶ Caledonia Textiles, Bridgeton Business Centre, 285 Abercromby Street, Glasgow, G40 2DD Tel: 0141-556 2705 Fax: 0141-564 5123

Christies Agencies Ltd, Symal House, Edgware Road, London, NW9 0HU Tel: (020) 8200 9584 Fax: (020) 8200 6592 E-mail: info@christiesagencies.com

Chrysalis Clothes Ltd, L Harlow House Shelton Road, Willowbrook East Industrial Estate, Corby, Northamptonshire, NN17 5XH Tel: (01536) 269034 Fax: (01536) 269034 E-mail: blackmor@btconnect.com

▶ Clan Albanach Kiltmakers, 24 High Street, South Queensferry, West Lothian, EH30 9PP Tel: 0131-331 2221 Fax: 0131-319 2221

S. Corman (Calverton) Ltd, Mancor House, Bolsover Street, Hucknall, Nottingham, NG15 7TZ Tel: 0115-963 2268 Fax: 0115-963 2062

D Gurteen & Sons Ltd, Chauntry Mills, Haverhill, Suffolk, CB9 8AZ Tel: (01440) 702601 Fax: (01440) 703394 E-mail: sales@gurteen.co.uk

T. Deas & Sons Ltd, 27-29 Wilder Street, Bristol, BS2 8QA Tel: 0117-924 6967

▶ Diadora (UK) Ltd, Sovereign Court, King Edward Street, Macclesfield, Cheshire, SK10 1AA Tel: (01625) 421212

Doon Trading Co., 55 Westfield Road, Smethwick, West Midlands, B67 6AW Tel: 0121-555 5398 Fax: 0121-555 5398

Douglas & Grahame Ltd, Wellington House, 322 Donegall Road, Belfast, BT12 6FX Tel: (028) 9056 7777 Fax: (028) 9032 7700 E-mail: sales@douglasandgrahame.com

Douglas & Grahame UK Ltd, Shenstone Business Park, Lynn Lane, Shenstone, Lichfield, Staffordshire, WS14 0SB Tel: (0870) 8507777 Fax: (0870) 2077700

E C Snaith & Son Ltd, 20 Vale Street, Denbigh, Clwyd, LL16 3BE Tel: (01745) 812218 Fax: (01745) 816367

▶ Equi Brief Ltd, Pinmore Mains, Pinmore, Girvan, Ayrshire, KA26 0TD Tel: (01465) 841161 Fax: (01465) 841161

▶ Fabricville Ltd, 83 Mortimer Street, London, W1W 7SL Tel: (020) 7636 2201 Fax: (020) 7631 5399

▶ Finesse Ltd, 7 St. Pancras Commercial Centre, Pratt Street, London, NW1 0BY Tel: (020) 7485 7766 Fax: (020) 7485 7799

Firstneat Ltd, 99 Mabgate, Leeds, LS9 7DR Tel: 0113-245 4039 Fax: 0113-245 4039

▶ Flaxstyle Factory Outlet, Tariff Road, London, N17 0DY Tel: (020) 8808 4088 Fax: (020) 8885 3139 E-mail: info@flaxstyle.co.uk

▶ Fyfe & Allan, 90-96 Dykehead Street, Glasgow, G33 4AQ Tel: 0141-774 5900 Fax: 0141-774 7360

▶ The Gap, 167-201 Argyle Street, Glasgow, G2 8DJ Tel: 0141-221 0629

Geko Fashion Marketing Ltd, Geko House, Kimberley Road, London, NW6 7SG Tel: (020) 7624 0164 Fax: (020) 7372 5733

▶ Gymphlex Ltd, Stamford Buildings, Stamford Street, Leicester, LE1 6NJ Tel: 0116-255 6326 Fax: 0116-247 1215 E-mail: enquiries@gymphlex.co.uk

Herbie Frogg Group Ltd, 2nd Floor, 125 New Bond Street, London, W1S 1DY Tel: (020) 7629 0446 Fax: (020) 7629 0423 E-mail: admin@herbie-frogg.co.uk

▶ Hobby Casuals, The Sanderson Centre, Lees Lane, Gosport, Hampshire, PO12 3UL Tel: (023) 9258 3826 Fax: (023) 9251 0287

Innocence Clothing Ltd, 103 Wantz Road, Dagenham, Essex, RM10 8PS Tel: (020) 8593 0593 Fax: (020) 8593 0587 E-mail: info@innocenceclothing.com

▶ J J Clothing Ltd, 219 Western Road, Leicester, LE3 0EA Tel: 0116-275 6252

J K (England) Ltd, Third Floor Walmar House, 296 Regent St, London, W1B 3AW Tel: (020) 7255 1900 Fax: (020) 7255 1991 E-mail: jke@jkengland.u-net.com

J S Marketing, 7 Wheler Road, Seven Stars Industrial Estate, Coventry, CV3 4LJ Tel: (024) 7651 1155 Fax: (024) 7651 8877 E-mail: sales@jsmarketing.com

▶ Keela (International) Ltd, 53 Nasmyth Road, Glenrothes, Fife, KY6 2SD Tel: (01592) 771241

Kilgour, 7-8 Savile Row, London, W1S 3PE Tel: (020) 7734 6905 Fax: (020) 7287 8147 E-mail: kilgour@8savilerow.com

MENSWEAR MANUFRS - *continued*

Lambourne Clothing International, 18 Dunlop Road, Hadleigh Road Industrial Estate, Hadleigh Road, Ipswich, IP2 0UG Tel: (01473) 250404 Fax: (01473) 222282 E-mail: lambourneint3@aol.com

▶ Lambton Tailoring, Unit 25g Springfield Commercial Centre, Bagley Lane, Farsley, Pudsey, West Yorkshire, LS28 5LY Tel: 0113-257 0841 Fax: 0113-239 4472

Lipman & Sons, 22 Charing Cross Road, London, WC2H 0HR Tel: (020) 7379 3872 Fax: (020) 7497 8733

Mabro Trading Ltd, Rebond House, 98-124 Brewery Road, London, N7 9PG Tel: (020) 7609 4181 Fax: (020) 7607 4828 E-mail: mail@mabro.co.uk

Magee Clothing Ltd, Unit 5-25 Woodside Road Industrial Estate, Woodside Road, Ballymena, County Antrim, BT42 4QJ Tel: (028) 2564 6211 Fax: (028) 2564 5111 E-mail: mageesales@aol.com

▶ Mardale Clothing Ltd, Unit 101 Oystons Mill, Strand Road, Preston, PR1 8UR Tel: (01772) 722513 Fax: (01772) 726715 E-mail: sales@mardale.com

Stephen Marks (London) Ltd, Unit B, Dolphin Way, Purfleet, Essex, RM19 1NZ Tel: (020) 7036 7000 Fax: (020) 7036 7001

Matalan Ltd, Gillibrands Road, Skelmersdale, Lancashire, WN8 9TB Tel: (01695) 552400 Fax: (01695) 552401

▶ Moette Leisurewear Ltd, The Old Chapel, Quebec Street, Langley Park, Durham, DH7 9XA Tel: 0191-373 5995 Fax: 0191-373 6318 E-mail: mail@moette.co.uk

▶ New Meuro Design, 99 Bridge Road, Leicester, LE5 3LD Tel: 0116-276 8988 Fax: 0116-276 8988

Newrooss Impex Ltd, New Skopes House, 2 Cross Green Garth, Cross Green Industrial Estate, Leeds, LS9 0SF Tel: 0113-240 2211 Fax: 0113-248 9544 E-mail: sales@skopes.com

Norseman (Rainwear) Ltd, Viking Mill, Standish Street, Chorley, Lancs, PR7 3BB Tel: (01257) 262733 Fax: (01257) 261071 E-mail: general@norseman.fsbusiness.co.uk

Painter & Peart, 15 Holmethorpe Avenue, Redhill, RH1 2NB Tel: (01737) 773777 Fax: (01737) 773932 E-mail: sales@thesuitcentre.co.uk

▶ Paramo Ltd, Durgates Industrial Estate, Durgates, Wadhurst, East Sussex, TN5 6DF Tel: (01892) 786444 Fax: (01892) 784961

▶ Parmar Clothing, 9 Wanlip Street, Leicester, LE1 2JS Tel: 0116-251 5820

Perry Ellis Europe Ltd, Crittall Road, Witham, Essex, CM8 3DJ Tel: (01376) 502345 Fax: (01376) 500733 E-mail: custserv@farah.co.uk

▶ Polaris Apparel Ltd, Business Park, Station Road, Bolsover, Chesterfield, Derbyshire, S44 6BH Tel: (01246) 240218 Fax: (01246) 241560

▶ R Cundle, 12 Whinbrook Crescent, Leeds, LS17 5PN Tel: 0113-288 8390 Fax: 0113-288 8390

▶ R & O Textiles, Unit 1 Frederick Street, Walsall, WS2 9NJ Tel: (01922) 613183 Fax: (01922) 613183

▶ Rair International Ltd, 2 Brougham Street, Leicester, LE1 2BA Tel: 0116-253 3078 Fax: 0116-253 3078

▶ Real Clothing Co. Ltd, Unit 19 Lockwood Industrial Park, Mill Mead Road, London, N17 9QP Tel: (020) 8885 9500 Fax: (020) 8365 1926

Rockgreen Ltd, 128 Whitechapel Road, London, E1 1JE Tel: (020) 7377 9552 Fax: (020) 7375 0549 E-mail: rockgreenltd@btinternet.com

▶ Rostrum Sportswear Ltd, Princes Street, Lochmaben, Lockerbie, Dumfriesshire, DG11 1PQ Tel: (01387) 811315 Fax: (01387) 811990 E-mail: info@rostrumsportswear.co.uk

Saville Heaton Ltd, Heaton House, Bradford Road, Dewsbury, West Yorkshire, WF13 2EE Tel: (01924) 466333 Fax: (01924) 456654 E-mail: sales@oakman.co.uk

Shapero Agencies Ltd, Salts Mill, Victoria Road, Shipley, West Yorkshire, BD18 3LB Tel: (01274) 531210 Fax: (01274) 531259

Sterling Group Ltd, Boulevard Works, Radford Boulevard, Nottingham, NG7 3AE Tel: 0115-978 2221 Fax: 0115-978 5034

▶ Stewart Christie & Co. Ltd, 63 Queen Street, Edinburgh, EH2 4NA Tel: 0131-225 6639 Fax: 0131-220 2397

Strom International Ltd, Unit B3 Connaught Business Centre, Edgware Road, London, NW9 6JL Tel: (020) 8205 9697 Fax: (020) 8905 8189 E-mail: sales@strom.co.uk

Vijay Fashions Ltd, 120 Broughton Street, Manchester, M8 8AN Tel: 0161-834 7711 Fax: 0161-833 0933 E-mail: ianq@vijayfashions.co.uk

MENTORING CONSULTANCY

▶ Business Advisor Partnership, Hamlet House, 63 High Street, Eccleshall, Stafford, ST21 6BW Tel: (01785) 851536 Fax: (01785) 859437 E-mail: pat@thebusinessadvisor.org

▶ Manjit Morjaria - Life Coaching, 14 Millennium Way, Wolston, Coventry, CV8 3PE Tel: (07968) 130980 Fax: (0870) 0671850 E-mail: m_morjaria@yahoo.co.uk

▶ Proficio Solutions Ltd, 2 Cleaver Cottages Appleshaw, Andover, Hampshire, SP11 9AD Tel: (01264) 772047 Fax: (01264) 772047 E-mail: info@proficiosolutions.co.uk

Unique Advantage Coaching, 11 Babylon Lane, Bishampton, Pershore, Worcestershire, WR10 2NN Tel: (0845) 6442424 Fax: (0870) 1328311 E-mail: enquiries@uniqueadvantage.co.uk

MENU DISPLAY CASES

Menu Shop, 38 High Street, Warminster, Wiltshire, BA12 9AF Tel: (01985) 217000 Fax: (01985) 218000 E-mail: sales@menushop.co.uk

Silvercases, Daux Road, Billingshurst, West Sussex, RH14 9SR Tel: (01403) 784671 Fax: (01403) 785353 E-mail: info@woodcon.co.uk

MENU SYSTEMS, ILLUMINATED, FAST FOOD OUTLETS ETC

▶ C J G, Box Bush Farm, Oxenhall Lane, Gorsley, Ross-on-Wye, Herefordshire, HR9 7BJ Tel: (01989) 720788 Fax: (01989) 720788 E-mail: cathy@cjgcatering.co.uk

Dan Display & Imaging Ltd, Harlequin House, Coedcad Lane, Pontyclun, Mid Glamorgan, CF72 9EW Tel: (01443) 225656 Fax: (01443) 226544 E-mail: info@dandisplay.co.uk

Sign Fit, 482 Barking Road, London, E6 2LT Tel: (020) 8552 1194 Fax: (020) 8548 1047

MERCHANDISING DISPLAYS, *See Point of Sale/Purchase etc*

MERCHANT BANKING

B N P Leasing Ltd, 10 Hareward Avenue, London, NW1 6AA Tel: (020) 7595 2000 Fax: (020) 7595 2555

Barclays Capital, 7th Floor, 5 North Colonnade, London, E14 4BB Tel: (020) 7623 2323 Fax: (020) 7621 5290

The British Linen Bank Ltd, PO Box 49, Edinburgh, EH3 7NZ Tel: (0131) 243 8386 Fax: (0131) 243 8393 E-mail: blb@blb.co.uk

Butterfield Private Bank, 99 Gresham Street, London, EC2V 7NG Tel: (020) 7776 6700 Fax: (020) 7776 6701 E-mail: info@butterfieldprivatebank.co.uk

GML International Ltd, Knighton House, 56 Mortimer Street, London, W1W 7RT Tel: (020) 7580 8588 Fax: (020) 7580 8688 E-mail: info@gml.net

Investec 1 Ltd, 2 Gresham Street, London, EC2V 7QP Tel: (020) 7597 4000 Fax: (020) 7597 4070 E-mail: info@investec.com

Kleinwort Benson Gilts Ltd, 20 Fenchurch St, London, EC3M 3BY Tel: (020) 7623 8000 Fax: (020) 7623 4069

Legg Mason Investments, 32 Harbour Exchange Square, London, E14 9JX Tel: (020) 7537 0000 Fax: (020) 7070 7505

Moscow Narodny Bank Ltd, 81 King William Street, London, EC4N 7BG Tel: (020) 7623 2066 Fax: (020) 7283 4840

N M Rothschild & Sons Leasing Ltd, New Court Street, Swithins Lane, London, EC4P 4DU Tel: (020) 7280 5000 Fax: (020) 7929 1643 E-mail: infouk@rothschild.co.uk

U B S Investment Bank, 100 Liverpool Street, London, EC2M 2RH Tel: (020) 7567 8000 Fax: (020) 7568 4800

Wintrust Securities Ltd, 21 New Street, Bishopsgate, London, EC2M 4HR Tel: (020) 7523 5230 Fax: (020) 7523 5233 E-mail: info@wintrust.co.uk

MERCURY

Quicksilver Refiners Ltd, 225a Finchley Road, London, NW3 6LP Tel: (020) 7431 0330 Fax: (020) 7435 6572

MERCURY THERMOMETERS

James Scientific Instruments Ltd, PO Box 18134, London, EC1R 4WD Tel: (020) 7837 1154 Fax: (020) 7278 7293 E-mail: sales@jamessciinst.com

MERGER AND ACQUISITION CONSULTANCY

A Anthony, Rose Hill House, Pygons Hill Lane, Liverpool, L31 4JF Tel: 0151-526 4008 Fax: 0151-526 1673

Bearwood Finance Services, 39 Friar Street, Reading, RG1 1DX Tel: 0118-958 5880 Fax: 0118-958 5599 E-mail: mail@bearwood.co.uk

▶ Chesham Amalgamations & Investments Ltd, 19 Woodsyre, London, SE26 6SS Tel: (0870) 9032748 Fax: (020) 7060 4462 E-mail: confidential@chesham.ltd.uk

Diverco Ltd, 4 Bank Street, Worcester, WR1 2EW Tel: (01905) 23383 Fax: (01905) 613523

KPMG UK Ltd, Peat House, 1 Waterloo Way, Leicester, LE1 6LP Tel: 0116-256 6000 Fax: 0116-256 6050

Resource Management Associates Ltd, 4 Western Road, Romford, RM1 3JT Tel: (01708) 735888 Fax: (01708) 735999 E-mail: charleskeep@rma-uk.org

MESH FABRICS, *See Net Fabrics etc*

MESH LOCKERS

▶ Simply Direct, Adelphi Mill, Grimshaw Lane, Bollington, Macclesfield, Cheshire, SK10 5JB Tel: (01625) 576527 Fax: (01625) 576545 E-mail: sales@simplydirect.net

MESH, ELECTROFORMED, ULTRA FINE

Gilder Grids, Unit 11 Withambrook Park Industrial Estate, Grantham, Lincolnshire, NG31 9ST Tel: (01476) 560052 Fax: (01476) 568165 E-mail: sales@gildergrids.co.uk

MESH, FLY SCREEN

▶ Environmental Hygiene Services, 66a North Street, Wetherby, West Yorkshire, LS22 6NR Tel: (01937) 589220 Fax: (01937) 587999 E-mail: info@ehs-uk.co.uk

Exclusive Screens Ltd, PO Box 183,, Bishop Auckland, County Durham, DL15 8WW Tel: 01388 762377 Fax: 01388 762377 E-mail: info@exclusivescreens.co.uk

MESSENGER SERVICES

Connection Delivery Service Ltd, 6 Domingo Street, London, EC1Y 0TA Tel: (020) 7253 2211 Fax: (020) 7251 3381

Fastway Flyers Ltd, 78 Rivington Street, London, EC2A 3AY Tel: (020) 7729 3333 Fax: (020) 7729 3806 E-mail: fastwayflyers@1tel.net.uk

Fleet Street Flyers, 21a Brownlow Mews, London, WC1N 2LA Tel: (020) 7242 6666 Fax: (020) 7404 6045

Greater London Hire, GLH House, 12-18 High Road, London, N2 9PJ Tel: (020) 8883 5000 Fax: (020) 8444 2026

Lewis Day Transport plc, 76 East Road, London, N1 6AB Tel: (020) 7014 1000 Fax: (020) 7014 1001

Point To Point Couriers Ltd, Eve Road, Woking, Surrey, GU21 5JS Tel: (01483) 723511 Fax: (01483) 750427

Special Delivery Ltd, 531 Kings Road, London, SW10 0TZ Tel: (020) 7351 5133 Fax: (020) 7351 6076

Speedlaw Services, 43 Ainsdale Road, Ealing, London, W5 1JY Tel: (020) 8991 1111

World's End Couriers, Unit 6b Farm Lane Trading Estate, Farm Lane, London, SW6 1QJ Tel: (020) 7381 8991 Fax: (020) 7385 4468

MESSENGERS-AT-ARMS

David K. Bell, 12 Church Street, Coatbridge, Lanarkshire, ML5 3ER Tel: (01236) 424617 Fax: (01236) 433866 E-mail: general@dkbell.co.uk

James Orr, Room 17 Dalziel Workspace, Mason Street, Motherwell, Lanarkshire, ML1 1YE Tel: (01698) 267408 Fax: (01698) 259567

James Reid & Son, 10 Bon Accord Square, Aberdeen, AB11 6DJ Tel: (01224) 588309 Fax: (01224) 584598 E-mail: aberdeen@jamesreidandson.co.uk

Rutherford & Macpherson, 102 Bath Street, Glasgow, G2 2EP Tel: 0141-332 3223 Fax: 0141-332 3225 E-mail: administrator@arandem.co.uk

George Walker & Co., 81-83 Glasgow Road, Dumbarton, G82 1RE Tel: (01389) 733933 Fax: (01389) 742305 E-mail: admin_dept@georgewalker.co.uk

METAL ALLOY CATALYSTS

Johnson Matthey Plc, 40-42 Hatton Garden, London, EC1N 8EE Tel: (020) 7269 8400 Fax: (020) 7269 8433 E-mail: jmpr@matthey.com

METAL ALLOYS, *See Alloy Metal etc*

METAL ANALYSIS EQUIPMENT

Metal Scan Ltd, 16 The Brunel Centre, Newton Road, Manor Royal, Crawley, West Sussex, RH10 9TU Tel: (01293) 513123 Fax: (01293) 521507 E-mail: sales@aruntechnology.com

METAL BADGES

▶ Badge UK, 58 Crossgate, Cupar, Fife, KY15 5HS Tel: (01334) 656677 Fax: (01334) 656678 E-mail: mail@badgeuk.co.uk

C & C Sales, 18 Nelson Place, Stirling, FK7 7PA Tel: (01786) 474439 Fax: (01786) 474439

Classic Miniatures Ltd, 8 Heathlands Close, Twickenham, TW1 4BP Tel: (020) 8892 3686 Fax: (020) 8744 1142 E-mail: sales@classicminiatures.co.uk

G S M Primographic, Unit 2b Ffrwdgrech Industrial Estate, Ffrwdgrech Road, Brecon, Powys, LD3 8LA Tel: (01874) 624433 Fax: (01874) 624575 E-mail: info@gsmprimographic.co.uk

I4c Publicity, 3 Broad Street, Coventry, CV6 5AX Tel: (024) 7666 7440 Fax: (024) 7666 3736 E-mail: sales@i4cpublicity.co.uk

Lewis W O, 39 Howard Street, Birmingham, B19 3HP Tel: 0121-236 4240 Fax: 0121-233 3057 E-mail: sales@lewisbadges.co.uk

Merit Badge & Regalia Co. Ltd, Merit House, Stanhope Street, Highgate, Birmingham, B12 0UX Tel: 0121-440 6861 Fax: 0121-440 1037 E-mail: sales@fcparry.com

Premier Badges, Unit 8 Little Hyde Farm, Ingatestone, Essex, CM4 0DU Tel: (01277) 355078 Fax: (01277) 355092 E-mail: sales@premierbadges.co.uk

R E V Gomm Ltd, 31 Commercial St, Birmingham, B1 1RJ Tel: 0121-643 7427 Fax: 0121-633 3394 E-mail: gomms@shawmunstergroup.co.uk

Skelton T.J Ltd, 16 Well Street, Birmingham, B19 3BJ Tel: 0121-554 0487 Fax: 0121-523 3585 E-mail: info@whderby.co.uk

Stylex, 49 Berwick Street, London, W1F 8SH Tel: (020) 7437 2428 Fax: (020) 7437 0649 E-mail: sales@style-x.co.uk

Universal Button Co. Ltd, 10-12 Witan Street, London, E2 6JX Tel: (020) 7739 5750 Fax: (020) 7739 1961

W Downing, 79 Spencer Street, Birmingham, B18 6DE Tel: 0121-236 7353 Fax: 0121-200 2429

W H Darby Ltd, 16 Well Street, Birmingham, B19 3BJ Tel: 0121-554 9817 Fax: 0121-523 3585 E-mail: info@whdarby.co.uk

W Reeves Badges Ltd, 34-35 Tenby Street, Birmingham, B1 3EE Tel: 0121-236 3731 Fax: 0121-236 3731 E-mail: sales@reevesbadges.co.uk

METAL BALERS

Planters Clayton Ltd, Unit 6, Rivington House, Horwich Business Park, Chorley New Road, Horwich, Bolton, BL6 5UE Tel: (01204) 690003 Fax: (01204) 690170 E-mail: office@plantersclayton.com

METAL BANDSAWS

Crescent Machinery Ltd, Unit 1 Moderna Business Park, Moderna Way, Mytholmroyd, Hebden Bridge, West Yorkshire, HX7 5QQ Tel: (01422) 884888 Fax: (01422) 881338 E-mail: info@crescentmachinery.co.uk

▶ Dakin-Flathers Ltd, Dakin-Flathers Ltd Boothroyds, Way, Featherstone, Pontefract, West Yorkshire, WF7 6RA Tel: (01977) 705600 Fax: (01977) 705700 E-mail: sales@dakin-flathers.com

Harrison Saw & Tool Ltd, Underbank Way, Carrs Industrial Estate, Haslingden, Rossendale, Lancashire, BB4 5HR Tel: (01706) 225221 Fax: (01706) 831409 E-mail: sales@harrisonsaw.co.uk

Sharpening & Supply (Midlands) & Co., 1 Queen Street, Darlaston, Wednesbury, West Midlands, WS10 8JF Tel: 0121-526 6800 Fax: 0121-526 2256 E-mail: sharpsupplytool@westmids.fsbusiness.co.uk

METAL BAR FABRICATION

Delph Developments Ltd, 55 Bamford Street, Clayton, Manchester, M11 4FE Tel: 0161-231 6444 Fax: 0161-231 8555 E-mail: stan@delph-uk.com

Deva Forge Fabrication, Hoole Bank, Hoole Village, Chester, CH2 4ES Tel: (01244) 301730 Fax: (01244) 300421

L H W Engineering Ltd, Iremonger Road, London Road, Nottingham, NG2 3HU Tel: 0115-986 1247 Fax: 0115-986 0684 E-mail: sales@lhw.co.uk

James Matthews, 17 Glebe Road, Downpatrick, County Down, BT30 7AW Tel: (028) 4488 1619 Fax: (028) 4488 1619

Pollards Engineering, Mundy Street, Ilkeston, Derbyshire, DE7 8EU Tel: 0115-932 4787 Fax: 0115-930 3559 E-mail: info@pollardengineering.com

Technical Fabrications, Unit 28 Rowfant Business Centre, Wallage Lane, Rowfant, Crawley, West Sussex, RH10 4NQ Tel: (01342) 717523 Fax: (01342) 715392

Warbla Forge, Lowtown, Pudsey, West Yorkshire, LS28 9AY Tel: 0113-255 2538 Fax: 0113-290 9112

▶ indicates data change since last edition

METAL BASED CHEMICALS

Heraeus Silica & Metals Ltd, Cinderhill Industrial Estate, Stoke-on-Trent, ST3 5LB Tel: (01782) 599423 Fax: (01782) 599802
E-mail: enquiries@4cmd.com

Shepherd Widnes Ltd, Moss Bank Road, Widnes, Cheshire, WA8 0RU Tel: 0151-424 9156 Fax: 0151-495 1446
E-mail: sales@shepwidnes.co.uk

METAL BATTERY CONTAINERS

Hawker Ltd, Rake Lane, Clifton Junction, Swinton, Manchester, M27 8LR Tel: 0161-794 4611

METAL BED FRAMES

Blindcraft, 2 Peffer Place, Edinburgh, EH16 4BB Tel: 0131-661 1205 Fax: 0131-652 2095
E-mail: sales@blindcraft.co.uk

Huntleigh Nesbit Evans Ltd, Woodsbank Trading Estate, Woden Road West, Wednesbury, West Midlands, WS10 7BL Tel: 0121-556 1511 Fax: 0121-502 2092
E-mail: sales@huntcare.co.uk

▶ Loungearound, 33 Station Road, New Milton, Hampshire, BH25 6HR Tel: (01425) 639212 Fax: (01425) 639213
E-mail: sales@loungearound.co.uk

▶ Loungearound Furniture, 40-42 Ashley Road, Bournemouth, BH1 4LJ Tel: (01202) 720777 Fax: (01202) 720888
E-mail: Sales@loungearound.co.uk

▶ Arshad Rashid, 145 West Street, Banbury, Oxfordshire, OX16 3HE Tel: (0871) 2006250 Fax: (0871) 2006251
E-mail: enquiries@yourhomefurniture.co.uk

Victorian Brass Bedstead Co., Hoe Copse, Cocking, Midhurst, West Sussex, GU29 0HL Tel: (01730) 812287
E-mail: toria@netcomuk.co.uk

METAL BEDSTEADS

Charterbrae Ltd, Unit 3 Coneygre Industrial Estate, Tipton, West Midlands, DY4 8XP Tel: 0121-520 5353 Fax: 0121-522 2018
E-mail: sales@cbbeds.u-net.com

Simmons Bedding Group P.L.C., Knight Road, Strood, Kent, ME2 2BP Tel: (01634) 723557 Fax: (01634) 290257

METAL BELLOWS

Heitz GmbH, 8 Priory Close, Deeping St. James, Peterborough, PE6 8PR Tel: (01778) 347164 Fax: (01778) 349240
E-mail: heitzbellows@yahoo.co.uk

Nutberry Ltd, Unit 12 Apex Park, Diplocks Way, Hailsham, East Sussex, BN27 3JU Tel: (01323) 442070 Fax: (01323) 442071
E-mail: nutberry@easynet.co.uk

Palatine Precision Ltd, Airport Industrial Estate, 45 Laker Road, Rochester, Kent, ME1 3QX Tel: (01634) 684571 Fax: (01634) 200836
E-mail: sales@palatineprecision.co.uk

Teddington Engineered Solutions, Heol Cropin, Dafen, Llanelli, Dyfed, SA14 8QW Tel: (01554) 744500 Fax: (01792) 885843
E-mail: sales@tes.uk.com

METAL BELTING

Belt Technologies Europe, Pennine House, Washington, Tyne & Wear, NE37 1LY Tel: 0191-415 3010 Fax: 0191-415 0333
E-mail: sales@bte.co.uk

METAL BENDING MACHINES

Addison Mckee, 188 Bradkirk Place, Walton Summit Centre, Bamber Bridge, Preston, PR5 8AJ Tel: (01772) 334511 Fax: (01772) 323227 E-mail: sales@atf.co.uk

METAL BENDING/FORMING SERVICES

A L Spinnings - CNC Punch Weld, Unit 499-101 Newhall Street, Willenhall, West Midlands, WV13 1LQ Tel: (01902) 601318 Fax: (01902) 601318 E-mail: adacncpunch@aol.com

Accurate Section Benders Ltd, Dawley Brook Road, Kingswinford, West Midlands, DY6 7AU Tel: (01384) 402402 Fax: (01384) 402462
E-mail: sales@accuratesectionbenders.co.uk

Dyke Engineering, Unit 4, Vastre Industrial Estate, Newtown, Powys, SY16 1DZ Tel: (01686) 624412 Fax: (01686) 623236
E-mail: dykeengineering@mid-wales.net

Industrial & Tractor Ltd, Navigation Road, Worcester, WR5 3DF Tel: (01905) 763777 Fax: (01905) 763008
E-mail: sales@intrac.co.uk

JMR Section Benders Ltd, Unit 8 Sterling Industrial Estate, Rainham Road South, Dagenham, Essex, RM10 8TX Tel: (020) 8593 7324 Fax: (020) 8595 6139
E-mail: sales@jmrsectionbenders.co.uk

Qualitetch Components Ltd, Century Way, March, Cambridgeshire, PE15 8QW Tel: (01354) 658787 Fax: (01354) 650385
E-mail: sales@qualitetch.co.uk

METAL BOTTLE CAPS OR CLOSURES

A E Chapman & Son Ltd, Timbermill Way, Gauden Road, London, SW4 6LY Tel: (020) 7622 4414 Fax: (020) 7720 0189
E-mail: aecsonltd@aol.com

Croxson William & Son Ltd, Alpha Place, Garth Road, Morden, Surrey, SM4 4LX Tel: (020) 8337 2945 Fax: (020) 8337 6783
E-mail: exports@croxsons.com

Metal Closures Huddersfield Ltd, Tandem Industrial Estate, Wakefield Road, Tandem, Huddersfield, HD5 0BL Tel: (01484) 533216 Fax: (01484) 543203
E-mail: sales@metal-closures.co.uk

Specialist Anodising Ltd, New Hall Works, Elm Street, Burnley, Lancashire, BB10 1NY Tel: (01282) 412500 Fax: (01282) 422804
E-mail: saco@sacoltd.com

METAL BROKERS

B & B Zinc Alloys Ltd, 233 Station Road, Knowle, Solihull, West Midlands, B93 0PU Tel: (01564) 773062 Fax: (01564) 778907

B M I Engineering Ltd, Vernon Road, Halesowen, West Midlands, B62 8HN Tel: 0121-559 3406 Fax: 0121-561 2603
E-mail: sales@bmi-engineering.co.uk

J B Schofield & Sons Ltd, Greenhead, Linthwaite, Huddersfield, HD7 5TS Tel: (01484) 842766 Fax: (01484) 843638

Natexis (Metals) Ltd, 47-53 Cannon Street, London, EC4M 5SH Tel: (020) 7648 4950 Fax: (020) 7248 5262

METAL BUCKLES

Active Springs, Redditch Road, Studley, Warwickshire, B80 7AY Tel: (01527) 854932 Fax: (01527) 854969
E-mail: robert@active-springs.co.uk

Bodill Parker Group Ltd, Barnfield Industrial Estate, Speed Road, Tipton, West Midlands, DY4 9DY Tel: 0121-557 4164 Fax: 0121-557 4177 E-mail: sales@bodill-parker.co.uk

Dalman & Narborough Ltd, 38-40 Lombard Street, Birmingham, B12 0QN Tel: 0121-772 2008 Fax: 0121-771 4182
E-mail: sales@dalman-narborough.co.uk

Stanley Bros, Long Street, Premier Business Park, Walsall, WS2 9DX Tel: (01922) 621788 Fax: (01922) 723560
E-mail: info@stanley-brothers.com

Tanside Ltd, Back Lane Farm, High London Lane, Winfarthing, Diss, Norfolk, IP22 2EF Tel: (01953) 861444 Fax: (01953) 861440
E-mail: tansideltd@btconnect.com

Thomas Walker Pensions Trust Ltd, 39 St Paul's Square, Birmingham, B3 1QY Tel: 0121-236 5565 Fax: 0121-236 6725
E-mail: sales@thomaswalker.co.uk

Tomkins Buckle, Brockhurst CR, Walsall, WS5 4QG Tel: (01922) 723003 Fax: (01922) 723149 E-mail: sales@fhtomkins.com

Walter Melville Ltd, Fanshaws Lane, Brickendon, Hertford, SG13 8PG Tel: (01992) 511285 Fax: (01992) 511286
E-mail: melville_trimmings@yahoo.co.uk

METAL BUTTONS

A M J Engineering, 38 Towerfield Road, Shoeburyness, Southend-on-Sea, SS3 9QT Tel: (01702) 295331 Fax: (01702) 296862
E-mail: info@amjbuttons.com

James Grove & Sons Ltd, PO Box 5, Halesowen, West Midlands, B63 3UW Tel: 0121-550 4015 Fax: 0121-501 3905
E-mail: sales@jamesgroveandsons.co.uk

Toye Kenning Spencer Stadden, 77 Warstone Lane, Birmingham, B18 6NL Tel: 0121-236 3253 Fax: 0121-236 7217
E-mail: sales@toyebirm.demon.co.uk

METAL CABINETS

Acco UK Ltd, Bretton Way, Bretton, Peterborough, PE3 8YE Tel: (01733) 264711 Fax: (01733) 269910

Burgess & Co. Ltd, New North Road, Heckmondwike, West Yorkshire, WF16 9DP Tel: (01924) 402406 Fax: (01924) 410175
E-mail: info@cburgess.co.uk

Cyphermet Ltd, Bone Lane, Newbury, Berkshire, RG14 5SH Tel: (01635) 34099 Fax: (01635) 528623 E-mail: sales@cyphermet.co.uk

Dynamica Ltd, Enterprise Road, Mablethorpe, Lincolnshire, LN12 1NB Tel: (01507) 473052 Fax: (01507) 478832

James Bedford & Co. Ltd, Pennine View, Birstall, Batley, West Yorkshire, WF17 9NF Tel: (01924) 442048 Fax: (01924) 472117
E-mail: sales@jbedford.co.uk

William G. Fuller & Co. Ltd, 43 Earl Street, Hastings, East Sussex, TN34 1SG Tel: (01424) 426094 Fax: (01424) 444763
E-mail: sales@fullermedical.co.uk

METAL CABLE GLANDS

Cembre Ltd, Fair View Industrial Estate, Kingsbury Road, Curdworth, Sutton Coldfield, West Midlands, B76 9EE Tel: (01675) 470440 Fax: (01675) 470220
E-mail: sales@cembre.co.uk

Kec Ltd, Orpheus House, Calleva Park, Aldermaston, Reading, RG7 8TA Tel: 0118-981 1571 Fax: 0118-981 1570
E-mail: sales@kec.co.uk

METAL CASES/BOXES/ CONTAINERS, *See also headings for particular usage*

Pensteel Ltd, Unit 1, Horndon Industrial Park, West Horndon, Essex, CM13 3XL Tel: (01277) 810211 Fax: (01277) 811971
E-mail: sales@pensteel.co.uk

METAL CASES/BOXES/ CONTAINERS, INDUSTRIAL

J Burton, Bings Heath, Astley, Shrewsbury, SY4 4BZ Tel: (01939) 250266

Savill Cases, Units 14-17, Willow Farm Business Park, Rickinghall, Diss, Norfolk, IP22 1LQ Tel: (01379) 898898 Fax: (01379) 898466
E-mail: savillcases@aol.com

METAL CHAMFERING MACHINES

Hydrafeed Ltd, Talgarth House, Bond Avenue, Bletchley, Milton Keynes, MK1 1JD Tel: (01908) 376630 Fax: (01908) 647843
E-mail: info@hydrafeed.co.uk

Seco Engineering Co. Ltd, 32 Reading Road South, Fleet, Hampshire, GU52 7QL Tel: (01252) 622333 Fax: (01252) 623888
E-mail: sales@secoeng.co.uk

METAL CHEMICAL ETCHING

AES Science Ltd, The Old Laundry, 15 Barratt Street, Easton, Bristol, BS5 6DE Tel: 0117-951 0234 Fax: 0117-952 0234
E-mail: aes@aessigns.co.uk

H.M. Avison & Co. Ltd, 305 Feltham Hill Road, Ashford, Middlesex, TW15 1LT Tel: (01784) 253130 Fax: (01784) 253130

C & G Industrial Chemicals Ltd, Sovereign Works, Deep Dale Lane, Lower Gornal, Dudley, West Midlands, DY3 2AF Tel: (01384) 455225 E-mail: angiegroves@tiscali.co.uk

Etch Components, Unit 3 58 Caroline Street, Birmingham, B3 1UF Tel: 0121-233 4409 Fax: 0121-233 9282

Greengate Engraving Ltd, 292 High Street, Stoke-on-Trent, ST6 5TY Tel: (01782) 822884 Fax: (01782) 815345

Modern Engraving Ltd, Leese Street, Stoke-on-Trent, ST4 1AL Tel: (01782) 849055 Fax: (01782) 744565
E-mail: sales@modernengraving.co.uk

Multitechnic Ltd, Coopies Lane, Morpeth, Northumberland, NE61 6JQ Tel: (01670) 512090 Fax: (01670) 503143
E-mail: sales@multitechnic.com

METAL CHEMICAL MILLING

Etch Components, Unit 3 58 Caroline Street, Birmingham, B3 1UF Tel: 0121-233 4409 Fax: 0121-233 9282

Photofabrication Services Ltd, 14 Cromwell Road, St Neots, St. Neots, Cambridgeshire, PE19 2HP Tel: (01480) 475831 Fax: (01480) 475801 E-mail: sales@photofab.co.uk

Precision Micro, Vantage Way, Erdington, Birmingham, B24 9GZ Tel: 0121-380 0100 Fax: 0121-359 3313
E-mail: sales@precisionmicro.com

Qualitetch Components Ltd, Century Way, March, Cambridgeshire, PE15 8QW Tel: (01354) 658787 Fax: (01354) 650385
E-mail: sales@qualitetch.co.uk

Tecan Ltd, Tecan Way, Granby Industrial Estate, Weymouth, Dorset, DT4 9TU Tel: (01305) 765432 Fax: (01305) 780194
E-mail: info@tecan.co.uk

METAL CLEANING OR DERUSTING

Chemsquad Ltd, 23 Izons Industrial Estate, Oldbury Road, West Bromwich, West Midlands, B70 9BS Tel: 0121-553 1340 Fax: 0121-525 2077

Clayton Thermal Processes Ltd, 2 Summerton Road, Oldbury, West Midlands, B69 2EL Tel: 0121-511 1203 Fax: 0121-511 1192
E-mail: claytonthermal@claytonholdings.com

Lenton Treatment Holdings Ltd, 68 Cannock Street, Barkby Thorpe Road, Leicester, LE4 9HR Tel: 0116-276 7162 Fax: 0116 2767446 E-mail: mail@lentontreatments.co.uk

Thomson Pettie, Canal Bank Estate, Seabegs Road, Bonnybridge, Stirlingshire, FK4 2BP Tel: (01324) 815747 Fax: (01324) 819072

METAL CLOSURES

Bericap (U K) Ltd, Oslo Road, Hull, HU7 0YN Tel: (01482) 826666 Fax: (01482) 832839
E-mail: info.uk@bericap.com

Greif UK Ltd, Merseyside Works, Oil Sites Road, Ellesmere Port, CH65 4EZ Tel: 0151-373 2000 Fax: 0151-373 2072
E-mail: kathy.turton@tri-sure.com

METAL COATINGS

Advanced Colour Coatings Ltd, Bannerley Road, Garretts Green, Birmingham, B33 0SL Tel: +44 (0) 121-789 6991 Fax: +44 (0) 121-789 6992
E-mail: enquiry@accoatings.co.uk

B A S S Hydro Coatings Ltd, Unit 101 Tenth Avenue, Deeside Industrial Park, Deeside, Clwyd, CH5 2UA Tel: (01244) 281315 Fax: (01244) 281316
E-mail: coil-coatings-uk@coatings.basf.org

Ici Packaging Coatings Ltd, Bordesley Green Road, Bordesley Green, Birmingham, B9 4TQ Tel: 0121-766 6600 Fax: 0121-766 6601
E-mail: enquiries@ici.com

Strip Tinning Ltd, Heath Street South, Springhill, Birmingham, B18 7PY Tel: 0121-454 8008 Fax: 0121-454 7600
E-mail: richard@stuk.demon.co.uk

Tamworth Heat Treatment Ltd, 7 Darwell Park, Mica Close, Tamworth, Staffordshire, B77 4DR Tel: (01827) 318030 Fax: (01827) 318039

The Valspar UK Holding Corporation Ltd, Unit 2-3 Avenue One, Witney, Oxfordshire, OX28 4XR Tel: (01993) 707400 Fax: (01993) 775579

METAL COMPONENTS

Catenate Consulting Ltd, Beech Leigh, Rectory Hill, Berrynarbor, Ilfracombe, Devon, EX34 9SE Tel: (01271) 882460 Fax: (01271) 882460
E-mail: sales@catenate-consulting.co.uk

Hydram Engineering Ltd, Avenue Two, Chilton Industrial Estate, Chilton, Ferryhill, County Durham, DL17 0SG Tel: (01388) 720222 Fax: (01388) 721025
E-mail: hydram@hydram.co.uk

▶ Plastic Design Solutions Ltd, 80 Church Road, Stockton-on-Tees, Cleveland, TS18 1TW Tel: (01642) 671711 Fax: (01642) 671762
E-mail: admin@plastic-design-solutions.freeserve.co.uk

SSD Drives Ltd, New Courtwick Lane, Wick, Littlehampton, West Sussex, BN17 7RZ Tel: (01903) 737000 Fax: (01903) 737100
E-mail:

METAL COMPONENTS, PRECISION, IT INDUSTRY

Cambridge Rapid Components Ltd, Unit 4-5 Shire Hill, Saffron Walden, Essex, CB11 3AQ Tel: (01799) 522151 Fax: (01799) 521686
E-mail: sales@cambridgerapid.co.uk

METAL COMPONENTS, SMALL TURNED

▶ Armstrong Blacksmiths & Engineers, Lichfield Road Industrial Estate, Tamworth, Staffordshire, B79 7TA Tel: (01827) 316663 Fax: (01827) 66833
E-mail: armstrong.blacksmiths@btopenworld.com

METAL CONDUITS

Flexicon Ltd, Roman Way, Coleshill, Birmingham, B46 1HG Tel: (01675) 466900 Fax: (01675) 466901 E-mail: sales@flexicon.uk.com

METAL CONTROL PANELS

939 Engineering Co., Lodgefield Road, Halesowen, West Midlands, B62 8AX Tel: 0121-559 1133 Fax: 0121-559 0321

Estil Ltd, Charlotte Street, Dudley, West Midlands, DY1 1TD Tel: (01384) 243643 Fax: (01384) 243644E-mail: sales@estil.co.uk

Keraplate Ltd, 46 Holton Road, Holton Heath Trading Park, Poole, Dorset, BH16 6LT Tel: (01202) 622882 Fax: (01202) 632438
E-mail: sales@keraplate.co.uk

West Coast Controls Ltd, Crossveggate Industrial Estate, Milngavie, Glasgow, G62 6RA Tel: 0141-956 4327 Fax: 0141-956 6639
E-mail: wcc@westcoastcontrols.co.uk

METAL CROPPING MACHINES

Kingsland Engineering Co. Ltd, Weybourne Road, Sheringham, Norfolk, NR26 8HE Tel: (01263) 822153 Fax: (01263) 825667 E-mail: info@kingsland.com

METAL CUBICLE SWITCHBOARDS

Cubic Modular Systems (UK) Ltd, Unit 8 Boston Court, Kansas Avenue, Salford, M50 2GN Tel: 0161-876 4742 Fax: 0161-876 4746 E-mail: info@cubic-uk.co.uk

▶ Salem Automation Ltd, Sycamore Road, Eastwood Trading Estate, Rotherham, South Yorkshire, S65 1EN Tel: (01709) 538200 Fax: (01709) 376903 E-mail: sales@salemautomation.net

METAL CULVERTS

Wells Spiral Tubes Ltd, Prospect Works, Airedale Road, Keighley, West Yorkshire, BD21 4LW Tel: (01535) 664231 Fax: (01535) 664235 E-mail: sales@wells-spiral.co.uk

METAL CUPBOARDS

Bott Ltd, Bude-Stratton Business Park, Bude, Cornwall, EX23 8LY Tel: (01288) 357788 Fax: (01288) 352692 E-mail: info@bottltd.co.uk

James Bedford & Co. Ltd, Pennine View, Birstall, Batley, West Yorkshire, WF17 9NF Tel: (01924) 442048 Fax: (01924) 472117 E-mail: sales@jbedford.co.uk

Redditek Systems Ltd, Unit 53 South Moons Moat Industrial Estate, Padgets Lane, Redditch, Worcestershire, B98 0RD Tel: (01527) 501687 Fax: (01527) 510320 E-mail: sales@redditek.co.uk

METAL CURTAIN RAIL OR POLE OR FITTINGS

Briman Contracts Ltd, Unit 2b Building B Wembley Commercial Centre, East Lane, Wembley, Middlesex, HA9 7UR Tel: (020) 8908 0102 Fax: (020) 8904 0664 E-mail: info@briman.co.uk

Cameron Fuller Ltd, Duchy Road, Heathpark Industrial Estate, Honiton, Devon, EX14 1YD Tel: (01404) 47568 Fax: (01404) 44425 E-mail: sales@cameronfuller.co.uk

▶ Fit-ex.com, 36 Hobhouse Close, Great Barr, Birmingham, B42 1HB Tel: 0121 2411164 E-mail: steve.burns@fit-ex.com

▶ Fit-Ex.Com, 30 Hans Apel Drive, Brackley, Northamptonshire, NN13 6HD Tel: (01280) 701090 Fax: (01280) 701090 E-mail: fitex@btinternet.com

Hunter & Hyland Ltd, 201-205 Kingston Road, Leatherhead, Surrey, KT22 7PB Tel: (01372) 378511 Fax: (01372) 370038 E-mail: enquiries@hunterandhyland.co.uk

McCormick Weeks Ltd, Unit 2, Springfield Farm, Perrotts Brook, Cirencester, Gloucestershire, GL7 7DT Tel: (01285) 831771 Fax: (01285) 831881 E-mail: enquiries@mccormickweeks.com

▶ Poles4curtains, 4 Manywells Industrial Estate, Cullingworth, Bradford, West Yorkshire, BD13 5DX Tel: (01535) 273355 Fax: (01535) 273344 E-mail: info@poles4curtains.co.uk

Charles Rowley & Co. Ltd, 22 Athole Street, Birmingham, B12 0DA Tel: 0121-440 7711 Fax: 0121-440 4837 E-mail: sales@charlesrowley.co.uk

Silent Gliss Ltd, Pyramid Business Park, Poorhole Lane, Broadstairs, Kent, CT10 2PT Tel: (01843) 863571 Fax: (01843) 864503 E-mail: info@silentgliss.co.uk

METAL CUTTING GUILLOTINES

Crescent Machinery Ltd, Unit 1 Moderna Business Park, Moderna Way, Mytholmroyd, Hebden Bridge, West Yorkshire, HX7 5QQ Tel: (01422) 884888 Fax: 01422 881338 E-mail: info@crescentmachinery.co.uk

Morgan Rushworth Ltd, Bromley Street, Lye, Stourbridge, West Midlands, DY9 8HS Tel: (01384) 895491 Fax: (01384) 424448 E-mail: sales@morganrushworth.com

Pearson Production Systems Ltd, Stargate Industrial Estate, Ryton, Tyne & Wear, NE40 3EX Tel: 0191-413 8080 Fax: 0191-413 8822

Press & Shear Machinery Ltd, 12/14 Ninian Park Ninian Way, Wilnecote, Tamworth, Staffordshire, B77 5ES Tel: (01827) 250000 Fax: (01827) 250022 E-mail: sales@pressandshear.com

R M T-Gabro Ltd, Hilton Road, Cobbs Wood Industrial Estate, Ashford, Kent, TN23 1EW Tel: (01233) 628976 Fax: (01233) 631888 E-mail: sales@mjallen.co.uk

METAL CUTTING PRESSWORK TRAYS

Panilet Tables, 17 Dragon Court, Crofts End Road, Bristol, BS5 7XX Tel: 0117-951 1858 Fax: 0117-951 1858 E-mail: info@panilettables.co.uk

METAL DEBURRING, *See also Metal Finishing etc*

Anotronic Ltd, Stewkley Road, Soulbury, Leighton Buzzard, Bedfordshire, LU7 0DF Tel: (01525) 270261 Fax: (01525) 270235 E-mail: sales@anotronic.co.uk

Ewen Engineering, Roscoe Road, Sheffield, S3 7DZ Tel: 0114-273 0327 Fax: 0114-275 1955 E-mail: sales@ewenengineering.co.uk

Poligrat (UK) Ltd, 2 Holder Road, Aldershot, Hampshire, GU12 4RH Tel: (01252) 336337 Fax: (01252) 322791 E-mail: info@poligratuk.co.uk

METAL DIAPHRAGMS

Ashridge Engineering Ltd, 58 North Road Indust Estate, Okehampton, Devon, EX20 1BQ Tel: (01837) 53381 Fax: (01837) 55022 E-mail: sales@ash-eng.co.uk

Martins Instrumentation, Wellington Road, Tharston Industrial Estate, Long Stratton, Norwich, NR15 2PE Tel: (01508) 531813 Fax: (01508) 531758

METAL DISINTEGRATION SERVICES

Aks Machining Ltd, 5 Wistaston Road Business Centre, Wistaston Road, Crewe, CW2 7RP Tel: (01270) 585554 Fax: (01270) 586606

Furmanite International Ltd, Furman House, Shap Road, Kendal, Cumbria, LA9 6RU Tel: (01539) 729009 Fax: (01539) 729359 E-mail: enquiry@furmanite.com

METAL DISTRIBUTORS/AGENTS/ STOCKHOLDERS

▶ Aggregate Industries Ltd, Old Station Yard, Beauly, Inverness-Shire, IV4 7BG Tel: (01463) 782868 Fax: (01463) 782873

Aggregate Industries Ltd, Toms Forest Quarry, Kintore, Inverurie, Aberdeenshire, AB51 0YU Tel: (01467) 644200 Fax: (01467) 644250 E-mail: enquiries@aggregates.com

Alstain Metal Services Ltd, Sapcote Trading Centre, Small Heath Highway, Birmingham, B10 0HR Tel: 0121-773 5655 Fax: 0121-773 5220 E-mail: sales@alstain.co.uk

▶ Bardon Aggregate, Fledmyre Quarry, Forfar, Angus, DD8 2HX Tel: (01307) 464728

▶ Bonnar Sand & Gravel Co. Ltd, Clachan Gravel Pit, Cairndow, Argyll, PA26 8BL Tel: (01499) 600269

▶ Border Fine Arts, Townfoot, Langholm, Dumfriesshire, DG15 0ET Tel: (01387) 383027 Fax: (01387) 383020 E-mail: norman.maxwell@enesco.co.uk

▶ Ciba Speciality Chemicals Colours plc, Hawkhead Road, Paisley, Renfrewshire, PA2 7BG Tel: 0141-887 1144 Fax: 0141-840 2283

▶ Cloburn Quarry Co Ltd, Pettinain, Lanark, ML11 8SR Tel: (01555) 663444 Fax: (01555) 664111

▶ Doosanbabcock, Porterfield Road, Renfrew, PA4 8DJ Tel: 0141-886 4141

▶ Edmund Nuttall Ltd, Glasgow Road, Kilsyth, Glasgow, G65 9BL Tel: (01236) 467050 Fax: (01236) 467072

▶ Ennstone Thistle Ltd, Cloddach Quarry, Elgin, Morayshire, IV30 8TW Tel: (01343) 559830

▶ Ennstone Thistle Ltd, Craigenlow Quarry, Dunecht Westhill, Skene, Aberdeenshire, AB32 7ED Tel: (01330) 833361

▶ Enstil & Thistle, Banavie Quarry, Banavie, Fort William, Inverness-Shire, PH33 7LX Tel: (01397) 772267 Fax: (01397) 772389

▶ Glenside, Block 2 Unit 4 Bandeath Industrial Estate, Throsk, Stirling, FK7 7NP Tel: (01786) 816655 Fax: (01786) 816100

▶ Heraeus Quartz Ltd, 5 Langlands Place, Kelvin South Business Park, East Kilbride, Glasgow, G75 0YF Tel: (01355) 244456

▶ Hunting Oilfield Services International Ltd, Badentoy Avenue, Badentoy Industrial Estate Portlethen, Aberdeen, AB12 4SQ Tel: (01224) 787000

▶ Laird Bros Forfar Ltd, Old Brechin Road, Lunanhead, Forfar, Angus, DD8 3NQ Tel: (01307) 466577 Fax: (01307) 468642

▶ M G Supplies Ltd, Unit Y Smarden Business Estate, Smarden, Ashford, Kent, TN27 8QL Tel: (01233) 770500 Fax: (01233) 770100 E-mail: sales@mgsupplies.com

▶ McArthur, Waverley Street, Court Bridge, Coatbridge, Lanarkshire, ML5 2BE Tel: (01236) 449266 Fax: (01236) 442100

Metal Technology Ltd, Steeple Road Industrial Estate, Antrim, BT41 1AB Tel: (028) 9448 7777 Fax: (028) 9448 7878 E-mail: info@metaltechnology.com

Milton Keynes Metals Ltd, Ridge Hill Farm, Nash, Milton Keynes, MK17 0EH Tel: (01296) 713631 Fax: (01296) 714155 E-mail: sales@mkmetals.co.uk

▶ Nobel Enterprises, P O Box 2, Stevenston, Ayrshire, KA20 3LN Tel: (01294) 487000 Fax: (01294) 487111

Rhodia Pharma Solutions, Three Trees Road, Newbie, Annan, Dumfriesshire, DG12 5QH Tel: (01461) 203661

▶ Roderick Macaskill Contractor, Ardhasaig, Isle of Harris, HS3 3AJ Tel: (01859) 502066

▶ Rom Ltd, Murraysgate Industrial Estate, Whitburn, Bathgate, West Lothian, EH47 0LE Tel: (01501) 740661 E-mail: sales@rom.co.uk

▶ Ski Slope Services Ltd, Woodlands, Woodlands Road, Blairgowrie, Perthshire, PH10 6JU Tel: (01250) 873028 Fax: (01250) 874723 E-mail: info@sss.uk

▶ Tarmac Ltd, Upper Cruiks, Inverkeithing, Fife, KY11 1HH Tel: (01383) 413241 Fax: (01383) 413244

▶ Tarmac Ltd, New Bigging Quarry, Carnwath, Lanark, ML11 8NE Tel: (01555) 840361

▶ Tayside Contracts, Collace Quarry, Collace, Perth, PH2 6JB Tel: (01821) 650222 Fax: (01821) 650440

▶ William Tracey Ltd, Dunniflats Depot, Lugton, Kilmarnock, Ayrshire, KA3 4EA Tel: (01505) 850343 Fax: (01505) 850102 E-mail: dunniflats@wmtracey.co.uk

Unicorn Metals, 3 Belper Road, Kilburn, Belper, Derbyshire, DE56 0LQ Tel: (01332) 882000 Fax: (01332) 880141

▶ W R Simmers Ltd, Backmuir, Keith, Banffshire, AB55 5PE Tel: (01542) 882543 Fax: (01542) 886065

▶ Tom Young Ltd, Wishaw Low Road, Cleland, Motherwell, Lanarkshire, ML1 5QU Tel: (01698) 860516 Fax: (01698) 861529

METAL DOOR FRAMES

Doors & Hardware Ltd, Taskmaster Works, Maybrook Road, Minworth, Sutton Coldfield, West Midlands, B76 1AL Tel: 0121-351 5276 Fax: 0121-313 1228 E-mail: sales@doors-and-hardware.com

METAL DRIVE TAPES

Belt Technologies Europe, Pennine House, Washington, Tyne & Wear, NE37 1LY Tel: 0191-415 3010 Fax: 0191-415 0333 E-mail: sales@bte.co.uk

METAL DUCT FRAMES OR COVERS

▶ Arcova Manhole Cover Manufacturers, Willow Tree Farm, Main Street, Laneham, Retford, Nottinghamshire, DN22 0NG Tel: (01777) 228931 Fax: (01777) 228504 E-mail: sales@arcova.co.uk

Durey Castings Ltd, Shell Garage, Hawley Road, Dartford, DA1 1PU Tel: (01322) 272424 Fax: (01322) 288073 E-mail: sales@dureycastings.co.uk

H & V Fabrications, Church Road, Stockton-on-Tees, Cleveland, TS18 2LZ Tel: (01642) 670813 Fax: (01642) 670813 E-mail: h.andv@hotmail.co.uk

Hotchkiss Air Supply, 6 Sovereign Park, Coronation Road, London, NW10 7QP Tel: (020) 8965 2066 Fax: (020) 8965 2088 E-mail: has.london@virgin.net

Surespan Ltd, Leamore Industrial Estate, Leamore Close, Walsall, WS2 7NL Tel: (01922) 711185 Fax: (01922) 497943

METAL DUCTING CONNECTORS

Drum Closures Ltd, Borwick Rails, Millom, Cumbria, LA18 4JT Tel: (01229) 772101 Fax: (01229) 774972 E-mail: sales@drum-closures.co.uk

METAL EXTRUSION DIES

Cumbria Extrusion Dies Ltd, Unit 4, Buddle Road, Clay Flatts Industrial Estate, Workington, Cumbria, CA14 3YD Tel: (01900) 66952 Fax: (01900) 66761

Eroga Die Co. Ltd, 6a Eastbrook Road Trading Estate, Eastbrook Road, Gloucester, GL4 3DB Tel: (01452) 524039 Fax: (01452) 500615 E-mail: mail@erogadie.com

Minium Tool Co. Ltd, Unit 1 & 2, Malmesbury Road, Kingsditch Trading Estate, Cheltenham, Gloucestershire, GL51 9PL Tel: (01242) 529352 Fax: (01242) 521737 E-mail: miniumtool@btconnect.com

Service Aluminium Co Ltd, Eastbrook Road, Gloucester, GL4 3DD Tel: (01452) 423541 Fax: (01452) 501643 E-mail: office@serval.co.uk

METAL FABRICATIONS TO SPECIFICATION

A D J Fabrications Ltd, Unit 8a Bowes Road, Riverside Park Industrial Estate, Middlesbrough, Cleveland, TS2 1LU Tel: (01642) 225726 Fax: (01642) 242738

A J Fabrications, 28A Somerset Street, Northampton, NN1 3LW Tel: (01604) 628070 Fax: (01604) 627929

Abbott Fabrications Ltd, Unit 1b Woodleys Yard, Newton Road, Higham Ferrers, Rushden, Northamptonshire, NN10 8HW Tel: (01933) 419942 Fax: (01933) 411619 E-mail: enquiries@abbott-fabrications.co.uk

Compton Engineering Ltd, Cheapside, Bridgend Industrial Estate, Bridgend, Mid Glamorgan, CF31 3UN Tel: (01656) 654341 Fax: (01656) 669936 E-mail: comptoneng@aol.com

▶ Fab Tech Automotive Ltd, Unit 5-6 Lichfield Trading Estate, Lagrange, Tamworth, Staffordshire, B79 7XD Tel: (01827) 66602 Fax: (01827) 66168 E-mail: sales@fabtechauto.co.uk

G T Pressing Co. Ltd, 46 Freehold Terrace, Brighton, BN2 4AB Tel: (01273) 601222 Fax: (01273) 682367 E-mail: enquiries@gtpressing.co.uk

▶ Metal Fabrications Systems, Metal House, Hobson Industrial Estate, Hobson, Newcastle upon Tyne, NE16 6EA Tel: (01207) 271199 Fax: (01207) 272299 E-mail: john@metal-fabrication.co.uk

Neptune Fabrications Ltd, 5 Ibrox Industrial Estate, Carmichael Street, Glasgow, G51 2QU Tel: 0141-427 3773 Fax: 0141-427 3703 E-mail: nepfab@btconnect.co.uk

▶ Osborne Business Enterprises Ltd, Selsey Road, Sidlesham, Chichester, West Sussex, PO20 7NE Tel: 01243 641974

Whitwell & Sons, 1 Laycock Gate, Blackpool, FY3 8AT Tel: (01253) 395172 Fax: (01253) 395176

Wilbar Engineers, Patterson Street, Blaydon-on-Tyne, Tyne & Wear, NE21 5TL Tel: 0191-414 5697 Fax: 0191-499 0174 E-mail: wilbarengineer@aol.com

METAL FABRICATORS, *See also headings for particular metals*

A & S Fabrications Nottingham, Unit E1 County Business Park, Eastcroft, Nottingham, NG2 3HS Tel: 0115-986 8382 Fax: 0115-986 9238

Active Security UK Ltd, 7 Little Hereford Street, Bromyard, Herefordshire, HR7 4DE Tel: (01885) 488994 Fax: (01885) 482194 E-mail: sales@activesecurityuk.com

▶ Allmec Engineering Ltd, 8 Guardian Street Industrial Estate, Guardian Street, Warrington, WA5 1SJ Tel: (01925) 575820 Fax: (01925) 637796 E-mail: allmec@aol.com

Amtec Ltd, Throop Business Park, Throop Road, Bournemouth, BH8 0DW Tel: (01202) 533557 Fax: (01202) 533567 E-mail: info@amteccorrosion.co.uk

Autoscroll Engineering, 5 Morley Street, Daybrook, Nottingham, NG5 6JX Tel: 0115-967 0327

Avon, 28 Charlton Road, Kingswood, Bristol, BS15 1HB Tel: 0117-935 2061 Fax: 0117-947 7533

B James, Green Park, West Moore, Diptford, Totnes, Devon, TQ9 7PE Tel: (01364) 73501 Fax: (01364) 73501

Bartek Engineering Ltd, 24 Industrial Estate, Cornwall Road, Smethwick, West Midlands, B66 2JS Tel: 0121-555 8885 Fax: 0121-555 8885

Bennett & Skelland Ltd, 306 Liverpool Road, Warrington, WA5 1DP Tel: (01925) 634066 Fax: (01925) 445505 E-mail: bennettandskelland@tiscali.co.uk

Bickerton Bros, 8 Arden Road, Alcester, Warwickshire, B49 6HN Tel: (01789) 763834 Fax: (01789) 400512 E-mail: bickbros@aol.com

Birmingham Stopper, 235 Icknield Street, Hockley, Birmingham, B18 6QU Tel: 0121-551 7781 Fax: 0121-554 4567 E-mail: robertp@birminghamstopper.co.uk

Chiffon Engineering Services Ltd, 11 Almond Rd, Bermondsey, London, SE16 3LR Tel: (020) 7231 8831 Fax: (020) 7231 1997

Cogent Contracts Ltd, Limekiln Lane, Birmingham, B14 4SP Tel: 0121-474 2500 Fax: 0121-474 6163 E-mail: cogentcontracts@hotmail.com

Corby Mechanical Services Ltd, Unit C1 Priors Court, Priors Haw Road, Corby, Northamptonshire, NN17 5JG Tel: (01536) 408866 Fax: (01536) 408811 E-mail: sales@corby-mechanical.co.uk

Crossfield Excalibur Ltd, Unit 21 Woolfold Trading Estate, Mitchell Street, Bury, Lancashire, BL8 1SF Tel: 0161-763 4377 Fax: 0161-763 4926 E-mail: enquiry@excalibur-irm.co.uk

D & A Fabrications, Unit 23 Landgate Industrial Estate, Wigan Road, Ashton-in-Makerfield, Wigan, Lancashire, WN4 0BW Tel: (01942) 717183 Fax: (01942) 719880

Dehavilland, 10 Stonehouse Commercial Centre, Bristol Road, Stonehouse, Gloucestershire, GL10 3RD Tel: (01453) 828272 Fax: (01453) 821945

METAL FABRICATORS – *continued*

Developlant Ltd, Unit 37, Clocktower Business Centre, Works Road, Hollingwood, Chesterfield, Derbyshire, S43 2PE Tel: (01246) 471982 Fax: (01246) 471886 E-mail: sales@developlant.co.uk

▶ Ditech Metal Products, 17 Alrewas Road, Kings Bromley, Burton-on-Trent, Staffordshire, DE13 7HW Tel: (01543) 473633 Fax: (01543) 473634 E-mail: info@ditechltd.co.uk

DTM Olympic, Unit 10a Griffin Industrial Estate, Rowley Regis, West Midlands, B65 0SN Tel: 0121-559 8431 Fax: 0121-559 7551

E M Hunt, Whitehirst Park Works, Kilwinning, Ayrshire, KA13 6PF Tel: (01294) 552682 Fax: (01294) 557949

Eden Fabrication Ltd, Primrose Hall, Green End, Threeholes, Wisbech, Cambridgeshire, PE14 9JD Tel: (01354) 638446 Fax: (01354) 638467

Elmgate Engineering Co. Ltd, Cattedown Road, Plymouth, PL4 0RW Tel: (01752) 222285 Fax: (01752) 222285

Empire Process Engineers Ltd, Ryder Close, Swadlincote, Derbyshire, DE11 9EU Tel: (01283) 226599 Fax: (01283) 210160

▶ Euromech, Unit 4, Stewart House, Kingsway East, Dundee, DD4 7RE Tel: (01382) 454447 Fax: (01382) 454088

F C R Metal Fabrications, Summerfield, Chacley, Gloucester, GL19 4EE Tel: (01684) 274756 Fax: (01684) 274756

▶ F L S Metalwork Ltd, PO Box 54, Ipswich, IP7 6WB Tel: (01473) 827263 Fax: (01473) 829762 E-mail: mark@fls1.fsnet.co.uk

F Mace & Son Ltd, 13a Victoria Avenue, Camberley, Surrey, GU15 3HP Tel: (01276) 65798 Fax: (01276) 686525 E-mail: fmacesons@btconnect.com

▶ Feenix Fabs Ltd, Unit 51 Wellington Industrial Estate, Bilston, West Midlands, WV14 9EE Tel: (01902) 676780 Fax: (01902) 663397

Feorge Plant & Fabrications Ltd, Unit 4 Transport Depot, Thorney, Langport, Somerset, TA10 0DW Tel: (01458) 253140 Fax: (01458) 253309

G & M Engineering, The Stores, Ffostrasol, Llandysul, Dyfed, SA44 4TE Tel: (01239) 851682 Fax: (01239) 851682

G T Pressing Co. Ltd, 46 Freehold Terrace, Brighton, BN2 4AB Tel: (01273) 601222 Fax: (01273) 682367 E-mail: enquiries@gtpressing.co.uk

Gateweld Metal, Villiers Drive, Oldham, OL8 1ED Tel: 0161-628 5551 Fax: (01706) 370240

Griffiths Fabrications, Unit A10 Dovers Corner Industrial Estate, New Road, Rainham, Essex, RM13 8QT Tel: (01708) 523797 Fax: (01708) 522698

H A D Metal Ltd, 7 Grosvenor Drive, Loughton, Essex, IG10 2JX Tel: (020) 8508 8842 Fax: (020) 8508 8842

Dennis Hawkins Welding, Westside Farm, High Street, Stoke Goldington, Newport Pagnell, Buckinghamshire, MK16 8NP Tel: (01908) 551400

Hawksley Engineering Ltd, Burringham Road, Gunness, Scunthorpe, South Humberside, DN17 3LT Tel: (01724) 782511 Fax: (01724) 783577 E-mail: hawkeng@ic24.net

Hydro Aluminium Extrusion, Durham Road, Birtley, Chester le Street, County Durham, DH3 2AH Tel: 0191-301 1200 Fax: 0191-301 1234 E-mail: sales@hydro.com

Interlink Fabrications Ltd, Interlink House, Commerce Way, Lancing, West Sussex, BN15 8TA Tel: (01903) 763663 Fax: (01903) 762621 E-mail: interlink@interlink-fabs.co.uk

Iron & Steel Fabrications Ltd, PO Box 666, Dunmow, Essex, CM6 1WA Tel: (01371) 876054 Fax: (0870) 7626996 E-mail: sales@ironandsteel.co.uk

The Iron Works, 138 Stamford Brook Arches, Ravenscourt Park, London, W6 0TQ Tel: (020) 8748 6535 Fax: (020) 8748 5735

J Colburn, Aldrington Basin South, Basin Road South, Portslade, Brighton, BN41 1WF Tel: (01273) 413190 Fax: (01273) 423684

J & J Carter Ltd, 8 Lion Court, Basingstoke, Hampshire, RG24 8QU Tel: (01256) 811455 Fax: (01256) 811458 E-mail: sales@jjcarter.com

J Mortimer Fabrications Ltd, Old Station Yard, Kirkby Lonsdale, Carnforth, Lancashire, LA6 2HP Tel: (01524) 271700 Fax: (01524) 272290 E-mail: john@mortimerfabrications.co.uk

K T B Engineering Ltd, 14 Northwood Road, Thornton Heath, Surrey, CR7 8HQ Tel: (020) 8771 9541 Fax: (020) 8771 3896 E-mail: sales@ktbengineering.co.uk

KB Fabrications (Dewsbury) Ltd, Ravenswharfe Road, Dewsbury, West Yorkshire, WF13 3RD Tel: (01924) 438803 Fax: (01924) 438803

M J R Fabrications, B Cranborne Industrial Estate, Cranborne Road, Potters Bar, Hertfordshire, EN6 3JN Tel: (01707) 646825 Fax: (01707) 649089

M R K Services, Unit 97 Northwick Business Centre, Northwick Park, Blockley, Moreton-in-Marsh, Gloucestershire, GL56 9RF Tel: (01386) 700912 Fax: (01386) 700922 E-mail: sales@mrkservices.co.uk

Masterford Ltd, Lyon Road, Bletchley, Milton Keynes, MK1 1EX Tel: (01908) 373106 Fax: (01908) 377181 E-mail: john-forder@btconnect.com

MBS, 53-59 Southcote Road, Bournemouth, BH1 3SH Tel: (01202) 589314 Fax: (01202) 587974

Metal Fabrication, Unit 13 Waterside Business Park, Waterside, Hadfield, Glossop, Derbyshire, SK13 1BE Tel: (01457) 862043 Fax: (01457) 868961

▶ Metal Solutions South West Ltd, B Estover Trading Estate, Estover Road, Plymouth, PL6 7PY Tel: (01752) 770555 Fax: (01752) 775444

▶ Metal Works UK Ltd, Greenman Yard, Boreham Street, Hailsham, East Sussex, BN27 4SF Tel: (01323) 833333 Fax: (01323) 833740

▶ Mid Cornwall Metal Fabrications, Treloggan Industrial Estate, Newquay, Cornwall, TR7 2SX Tel: (01637) 879474 Fax: (01637) 877278

▶ Mig Antig Workshops, 28 Business Village, Wexham Road, Slough, SL2 5HF Tel: (01753) 529961 Fax: (01753) 529961

▶ Olema Engineering, M J F Yard, Chiddingfold Road, Dunsfold, Godalming, Surrey, GU8 4PB Tel: (01483) 200700 Fax: (01483) 200700

Ornamental Metals, 7 West Mills, Mill Street, Kirkcaldy, Fife, KY1 1SD Tel: (01592) 206335 Fax: (01592) 641507

▶ P J D Engineering Ltd, 4 Henlow Industrial Estate, Henlow, Bedfordshire, SG16 6DS Tel: (01462) 815544 Fax: (01462) 816677

P J T Engineering, Unit 3 367 Bryn Road, Ashton-in-Makerfield, Wigan, Lancashire, WN4 8BS Tel: (01942) 712022 Fax: (01942) 712022 E-mail: sales@pjtengineering.gbr.cc

P P Systems, Unit 23, Enterprise Centre, Bryn Road, Bridgend, Mid Glamorgan, CF32 9BS Tel: (01656) 724859 Fax: (01656) 724859

P T Marine & General Fabrications, North Parade, Falmouth, Cornwall, TR11 2TD Tel: (01326) 311004 Fax: (01326) 311004

Pendle Metal Craft, 7-9 Rookery Road, Barnoldswick, Lancashire, BB18 6YH Tel: (01282) 817333 Fax: (01282) 852751

▶ Pentland Tech, 8 Hardengreen Industrial Estate, Dalkeith, Midlothian, EH22 3NX Tel: 0131-561 9373 Fax: 0131-561 9374

Phoenix Fabrications Ltd, Unit 11 Meadow Drove, Earith, Huntingdon, Cambridgeshire, PE28 3QF Tel: (01487) 843888 Fax: (01487) 843905

Profab Fabrications, Unit 3, 10 Coldside Road, Dundee, DD3 8DF Tel: (01382) 832711

R P Shaw Fabrications, Rendova Farm, Powey Lane, Mollington, Chester, CH1 6LH Tel: (01244) 881043 Fax: (01244) 881023

R Strachan, Harbour Road, Fraserburgh, Aberdeenshire, AB43 9BN Tel: (01346) 510800 Fax: (01346) 511801

Rainham Healthy Living Centre, 103-107 High Street, Rainham, Gillingham, Kent, ME8 8AA Tel: (01634) 337706

Remal Thermal Cycling Ltd, 4 Pinfold Place, Skelmersdale, Lancashire, WN8 9PQ Tel: (01695) 720462 Fax: (01695) 50414 E-mail: sales@remal-thorid.com

Renown Engineering Ltd, South Cramlington Industrial Estate, Cramlington, Northumberland, NE23 7RH Tel: 0191-250 0113 Fax: 0191-250 1980 E-mail: sales@renown-engineering.co.uk

Robert Flannigan Engineering, 1 Flemington Industrial Park, Craigneuk Street, Motherwell, Lanarkshire, ML1 2NT Tel: (01698) 309307 Fax: (01698) 309312 E-mail: rfeconveyors@aol.com

S & S Engineering, Unit 21 Such Close, Letchworth Garden City, Hertfordshire, SG6 1JF Tel: (01462) 675983 Fax: (01462) 675983

▶ S T S Defence, 12-20 Sharlands Road, Fareham, Hampshire, PO14 1RD Tel: (01329) 231310 Fax: (01329) 231300

Scottys Gates Ltd, Dixon Business Centre, 27 Dixon Road, Bristol, BS4 5QW Tel: 0117-977 8865 Fax: 0117-907 4698 E-mail: sales@scottys-gate.sagenet.co.uk

Spectrum Engineering & Transmission Co. Ltd, Unit 43 Purfleet Industrial Park, London Road, Aveley, South Ockendon, Essex, RM15 4YA Tel: (01708) 861718 Fax: (01708) 867540 E-mail: bob@spectrum-engineering.co.uk

SPJ Enterprises Ltd, Unit 14-15 Oakleigh Trading Estate, Anchor Road, Bilston, West Midlands, WV14 9NA Tel: (01902) 491818 Fax: (01902) 491818

Sykes Fabrications, West Street, Morley, Leeds, LS27 9EU Tel: 0113-238 3079 Fax: 0113-238 3081

Telford Polishers Ltd, Charlton Forge Church Street, Oakengates, Telford, Shropshire, TF2 6BY Tel: (01952) 614441 Fax: (01952) 612229 E-mail: sales@cmfc.freeserve.co.uk

The Towel House Co. Ltd, 120 Glover Street, Birmingham, B9 4EY Tel: 0121-766 6644 Fax: 0121-771 0446 E-mail: info@polehousecompany.co.uk

Turnmil Engineering, Riverside Industrial Estate, Glanamman, Ammanford, Dyfed, SA18 1LQ Tel: (01269) 825684 Fax: (01269) 824650 E-mail: ceri@turnmil.co.uk

Union Fabrications, Unit 12 & 13 Garden Mill Industrial Estate, Derby Road, Kingsbridge, Devon, TQ7 1SA Tel: (01548) 852922 Fax: (01548) 852922

Update Products Ltd, The Westway, Alvechurch Road, Birmingham, B31 3PU Tel: 0121-477 7777 Fax: 0121-477 6880

Warmglade Ltd, 2 College Farm, Church Street, Whaddon, Royston, Hertfordshire, SG8 5RU Tel: (01223) 208788

Welding Services Dundee Ltd, 2 Eagle Mills, Brown Constable Street, Dundee, DD4 6QZ Tel: (01382) 223760 Fax: (01382) 225085

Westdale Products Ltd, 56 Blackpole Road, Worcester, WR3 8SQ Tel: (01905) 457959 Fax: (01905) 458047

▶ Westmans Engineering, Westmans Trading Estate, Love Lane, Burnham-on-Sea, Somerset, TA8 1EY Tel: (01278) 781666 Fax: (01278) 781666

Wisbech Fabrications Ltd, Unit 3, 62 Weasenham Lane, Wisbech, Cambridgeshire, PE13 2RU Tel: (01945) 466477 Fax: (01945) 466456 E-mail: wisfabltd@aol.com

A. & B. Woodberry Ltd, 156 Crow Lane, Romford, RM7 0ES Tel: (01708) 737979 Fax: (01708) 737918 E-mail: abwoodberry@go-plus.net

Wragg Bros Ltd, Robert Way, Wickford, Essex, SS11 8DQ Tel: (01268) 732607 Fax: (01268) 768499 E-mail: wragg.bros@btclick.com

Wye Valley Engineering Ltd, Unit 260 Netherwood Road Rotherwas Indust Estate, Rotherwas Industrial Estate, Hereford, HR2 6JU Tel: (01432) 266507 Fax: (01432) 341645 E-mail: enquries@durabase.co.uk

METAL FABRICATORS, TO SPECIFICATION

▶ Ditech Metal Products, 17 Alrewas Road, Kings Bromley, Burton-on-Trent, Staffordshire, DE13 7HW Tel: (01543) 473633 Fax: (01543) 473634 E-mail: info@ditechltd.co.uk

G R C Extraction Systems, Unit 13 Forbes Court, Billington Road, Burnley, Lancashire, BB11 5UB Tel: (01282) 421130 Fax: (01282) 425971 E-mail: grceng@aol.com

Griffiths Fabrications, Unit A10 Dovers Corner Industrial Estate, New Road, Rainham, Essex, RM13 8QT Tel: (01708) 523797 Fax: (01708) 522698

▶ K O Engineering Services, 1 Daniels Farm, Wash Road, Basildon, Essex, SS15 4AZ Tel: (01268) 281500 Fax: (01268) 281500 E-mail: info@koengineeringservices.com

SPJ Enterprises Ltd, Unit 14-15 Oakleigh Trading Estate, Anchor Road, Bilston, West Midlands, WV14 9NA Tel: (01902) 491818 Fax: (01902) 491818

Welding Services Dundee Ltd, 2 Eagle Mills, Brown Constable Street, Dundee, DD4 6QZ Tel: (01382) 223760 Fax: (01382) 225085

METAL FENCING

Bucks Metal Finishers Ltd, 19 March Place, Gatehouse Industrial Area, Aylesbury, Buckinghamshire, HP19 8UG Tel: (01296) 420301 Fax: (01296) 420302 E-mail: jacqui.carlisle@btconnect.com

Darfen Durafencing, Herons Way, Carr Hill, Doncaster, South Yorkshire, DN4 8WA Tel: (01302) 360242 Fax: (01302) 364359 E-mail: mail@darfen.co.uk

Hill & Smith Holdings plc, Unit 2 Highlands Court, Cranmore Avenue, Shirley, Solihull, West Midlands, B90 4LE Tel: 0121-704 7430 Fax: 0121-704 7439 E-mail: enquiries@hsholdings.co.uk

N K Fencing, 40 Trailcock Road, Carrickfergus, County Antrim, BT38 7NU Tel: (028) 9335 1172 Fax: (028) 9333 6433 E-mail: sales@nkfencing.com

Safeguard Security Fencing Ltd, Safeguard House, Coldaville Road, Horbury Junction, Wakefield, West Yorkshire, WF4 5ER Tel: (01924) 264949 Fax: (01924) 264913

METAL FENCING POSTS

Darfen Durafencing, Herons Way, Carr Hill, Doncaster, South Yorkshire, DN4 8WA Tel: (01302) 360242 Fax: (01302) 364359 E-mail: mail@darfen.co.uk

Heras UK Fencing Systems, Herons Way, Balby, Doncaster, South Yorkshire, DN4 8WA Tel: (01302) 364551 Fax: (01302) 322401 E-mail: heras.sales@heras.co.uk

METAL FERRULES

Austin Wolstencroft & Co. Ltd, 56 Broadbent Road, Oldham, OL1 4HY Tel: 0161-624 5236 Fax: 0161-620 8413 E-mail: avrilbrooks20944@aol.com

Stroud Metal Co. Ltd, Dudbridge, Stroud, Gloucestershire, GL5 3EZ Tel: (01453) 763331 Fax: (01453) 753804 E-mail: enquiries@stroudmetal.co.uk

METAL FILLED EPOXY RESINS

I T W Devcon, Unit 3 Shipton Way, Express Business Park, Rushden, Northamptonshire, NN10 6GL Tel: (0870) 4587388 Fax: (0870) 4589077 E-mail: sales@itw-devcon.co.uk

METAL FILTER CLOTHS

▶ G Bopp & Co. Ltd, Grange Close, Clover Nook Industrial Park, Somercotes, Alfreton, Derbyshire, DE55 4QT Tel: (01773) 521266 Fax: (01773) 521163 E-mail: info@gbopp.com

Potter & Soar Ltd, Beaumont Road, Banbury, Oxfordshire, OX16 1SD Tel: (01295) 253344 Fax: (01295) 272132 E-mail: potter.soar@btinternet.com

R Cadisch & Sons, Unit 1, 879 High Road, London, N12 8QA Tel: (020) 8492 0444 Fax: (020) 8492 0333 E-mail: info@cadisch.com

METAL FILTER COMPONENTS

Albany Metal Spinners, 18 Stirling Close, Washington, Tyne & Wear, NE38 8QD Tel: 0191-419 4588 Fax: 0191-416 3700 E-mail: sales@albanymetalspinners.co.uk

J. Walsh Spinnings, Unit 2, 58 Caroline Street, Hockley, Birmingham, B3 1UF Tel: 0121-233 3258 Fax: 0121-233 3258

METAL FINISHING CHEMICALS

Access Chemicals Ltd, Hedging Lane, Wilnecote, Tamworth, Staffordshire, B77 5EX Tel: (01827) 289000 Fax: (01827) 289080 E-mail: sales@accesschemicals.co.uk

Armack Chemicals, 52-53 Brook Street, Lye, Stourbridge, West Midlands, DY9 8SL Tel: (01384) 897531 Fax: (01384) 892448 E-mail: sales@armack.co.uk

C & G Industrial Chemicals Ltd, Sovereign Works, Deep Dale Lane, Lower Gornal, Dudley, West Midlands, DY3 2AF Tel: (01384) 455225 E-mail: angiegroves@tiscali.co.uk

En Mach Services, Unit 11 Lythalls Lane Industrial Estate, Lythalls Lane, Coventry, CV6 6FJ Tel: (024) 7668 1403 Fax: (024) 7668 1403 E-mail: yanhunt@tiscali.co.uk

Poligrat (UK) Ltd, 2 Holder Road, Aldershot, Hampshire, GU12 4RH Tel: (01252) 336337 Fax: (01252) 322791 E-mail: info@poligratuk.co.uk

▶ Wirral Fospray Ltd, Hawarden Business Park, Clwyd Close Manor Lane, Hawarden, Deeside, Clwyd, CH5 3NS Tel: (01244) 520202 Fax: (01244) 520363 E-mail: sales@wirralfospray.com

METAL FINISHING SERVICES, POWDER COAT PAINTING

Alpha Stove Enamelling Ltd, Unit 17 Green Lane Industrial Estate, Green Lane, Letchworth Garden City, Hertfordshire, SG6 1HP Tel: (01462) 670761 Fax: (01462) 684466 E-mail: alphastoveltd@aol.com

Armadillo Coatings, Unit 3A, Victor Business Centre, Arthur Street, Redditch, Worcestershire, B98 8JY Tel: (01527) 526855 Fax: (01527) 502856E-mail: msalter@aol.com

Britannia Powder & Plastic Coating Ltd, Unit 8 Thistlebrook Industrial Estate, Eynsham Drive, London, SE2 9RB Tel: (020) 8311 0991 Fax: (020) 8311 0773

D J B Associates Ltd, 4-6 Roman Court, Watling Street, Bridgtown, Cannock, Staffordshire, WS11 0BN Tel: (01543) 574162 Fax: (01543) 574282

Hankoe Advanced Surface Treatments Ltd, 823 Yeovil Road, Slough Trading Estate, Slough, SL1 4JA Tel: (01753) 522779 Fax: (01753) 539320 E-mail: hankoe@btconnect.com

METAL FINISHING/POLISHING PLANT/EQUIPMENT/SUPPLIES DISTRIBUTORS OR AGENTS

▶ A L P Plants, Unit 26b Central Industrial Estate, Cable Street, Wolverhampton, WV2 2RJ Tel: (01902) 455592 Fax: (01902) 455586

Access Chemicals Ltd, Hedging Lane, Wilnecote, Tamworth, Staffordshire, B77 5EX Tel: (01827) 289000 Fax: (01827) 289080 E-mail: sales@accesschemicals.co.uk

Asbury Brodie & Co. Ltd, 1 Dover Street, Birmingham, B18 5HN Tel: 0121-554 7000 Fax: 0121-554 0242 E-mail: sales@asburybrodie.co.uk

Aspentech Ltd, Unit 1 Century Court, Tolpits La, Watford, WD18 9RS Tel: (01923) 254499 Fax: (01923) 816456

Bender Machine Services Ltd, Manchester Road, Haslingden, Rossendale, Lancashire, BB4 5SL Tel: (01706) 225521 Fax: (01706) 218844 E-mail: info@bendermachine.com

Crauford Technology Ltd, 135B Edinburgh Avenue Trading Estate, Slough, SL1 4SW Tel: (01753) 531462 Fax: (01753) 552580 E-mail: davidd@craufurd.com

Equip (Midlands) Ltd, Byron Street, Buxton, Derbyshire, SK17 6NT Tel: (01298) 22233 Fax: (01298) 72097

▶ Macarron Electroplaters, Orchardbank Industrial Estate, Forfar, Angus, DD8 1UQ Tel: (01307) 460999 Fax: (01307) 469810

Plasticraft Ltd, Godiva Place, Coventry, CV1 5PN Tel: (024) 7625 3099 Fax: (024) 7655 1402 E-mail: sales@plasticraft.co.uk

R J Plastics, 83-84 Buckingham Street, Birmingham, B19 3HU Tel: 0121-233 1077 Fax: 0121-236 6355

RJH Morrisflex Holdings Ltd, Artillery Street, Heckmondwike, West Yorkshire, WF16 0NR Tel: (01924) 402490 Fax: (01924) 404635 E-mail: sales@rjheng.co.uk

Rodway & Taylor Birmingham Ltd, 85 Buckingham Street, Birmingham, B19 3HU Tel: 0121-236 4027 Fax: 0121-233 2972 E-mail: paul.rodway@virgin.net

METAL FINISHING/POLISHING PLANT/EQUIPMENT/SUPPLIES DISTRIBUTORS OR AGENTS –

continued

Titanium Engineering Ltd, Unit 42 Great Western Industrial Estate, Great Western Close, Birmingham, B18 4QF Tel: 0121-523 6932 Fax: 0121-523 5991 E-mail:

▶ Turton Plating Services, 9 Quarry Road, Chorley, Lancashire, PR6 0LR Tel: (01257) 264532 Fax: (01257) 241654

METAL FINISHING/POLISHING PROCESS CHEMICAL PRODUCTS

Armack Chemicals, 52-53 Brook Street, Lye, Stourbridge, West Midlands, DY9 8SL Tel: (01384) 897531 Fax: (01384) 892448 E-mail: sales@armack.co.uk

Rem, 5 Stockton End, Sandy, Bedfordshire, SG19 1RY Tel: (01767) 691592 Fax: (01767) 691599 E-mail: mmorse@remchem.co.uk

METAL FINISHING/POLISHING SERVICES

A & D Webb Metal Polishing Specialists, 3 Standard Works, Orchard Place, Stonehouse, Gloucestershire, GL10 2PL Tel: (01453) 825573 Fax: (01453) 825573 E-mail: sales@adwebbmetalpolishers.co.uk

A & K Metal Polishing, Bourne Mills, London Road, Brimscombe, Stroud, Gloucestershire, GL5 2TA Tel: (01453) 883747 Fax: (01453) 883747

Advanced Colour Coatings Ltd, Bannerley Road, Garretts Green, Birmingham, B33 0SL Tel: +44 (0) 121-789 6991 Fax: +44 (0) 121-789 6992 E-mail: enquiry@accoatings.co.uk

Advanced Surface Treatments Ltd, Unit 11, Alpha Business Park, Deedmore Road, Coventry, CV2 1EQ Tel: (024) 7660 3232 Fax: (024) 7661 1776 E-mail: sales@astec-uk.com

All Metal Polishers, Unit 41 65 Caroline Street, Birmingham, B3 1UG Tel: 0121-236 1162

Allbrite Metal Polishers, 13 Shelah Road, Halesowen, West Midlands, B63 3PG Tel: 0121-550 3819 Fax: 0121-550 4747

Almond & Mellor Services Ltd, Hampden Mill, Grimshaw Street, Darwen, Lancashire, BB3 2QJ Tel: (01254) 705498 Fax: (01254) 873680 E-mail: sales@almondmellor.freeserve.co.uk

Alstain Metal Services Ltd, Sapcote Trading Centre, Small Heath Highway, Birmingham, B10 0HR Tel: 0121-773 5655 Fax: 0121-773 5220 E-mail: sales@alstain.co.uk

▶ Anopol Ltd, PO Box 177, Birmingham, B5 5QA Tel: 0121-693 0280 Fax: 0121-631 2274 E-mail: info@anapol.co.uk

▶ Avon Polishing Ltd, Unit 4 & 5 Rollingmill Business Park, Rollingmill Street, Walsall, WS2 9EQ Tel: (01922) 633937 Fax: (01922) 633937

B T & G Midson, 39 Mere View Industrial Estate, Yaxley, Peterborough, PE7 3HS Tel: (01733) 243833 Fax: (01733) 243833

Ber Polishing Co. Ltd, 8 A1 Trading Estate, Lewisham Road, Smethwick, West Midlands, B66 2BN Tel: 0121-565 2735 Fax: 0121-565 2735

W. Birch & Son (Polishers) Ltd, 42-50 Bissell Street, Birmingham, B5 7HP Tel: 0121-666 6164 Fax: 0121-622 1218 E-mail: sales@badgeranodising.co.uk

Bodycote Metallurgical Coatings Ltd, Shakespeare Street, Wolverhampton, WV1 3LR Tel: (01902) 452915 Fax: (01902) 352917 E-mail: sales.bmc@bodycote.co.uk

Bodycote Metallurgical Coatings Uxbridge Ltd, 5 Carleton House, 549 Eskdale Road, Uxbridge, Middlesex, UB8 2RT Tel: (01895) 252185 Fax: (01895) 810755

▶ BOMBER COUNTY CUSTOMS, Drakes holdings, Ferry Road, Fiskerton, Lincoln, LN3 4HU Tel: (07958) 018368 E-mail: petescustom24@yahoo.co.uk

Bradleys (Stowmarket) Ltd, 49 Knightsdale Road, Ipswich, IP1 4JJ Tel: (01473) 461400 Fax: (01473) 461490

C & H Precision Finishers Ltd, Derby Road Trade Centre, Derby Road, Sandiacre, Nottingham, NG10 5HU Tel: 0115-939 4707 Fax: 0115-949 0146 E-mail: admin@chprecision.co.uk

Caerphilly Metal Polishers, 1 The Rhos, Bedwas Road, Caerphilly, Mid Glamorgan, CF83 3AU Tel: (029) 2086 7837 Fax: (029) 2086 7837

Caliba Spraying, Wallet Street, Nottingham, NG2 3EL Tel: 0115-986 9200 Fax: 0115-986 9204 E-mail: sales@surface-coating.co.uk

Ceratex Engineering Ltd, Church La Works, Church Lane, Kelbrook, Barnoldswick, Lancashire, BB18 6UF Tel: (01282) 842900 Fax: (01282) 844093 E-mail: sales@ceratex.co.uk

Colonnade UK, Unit 41 Hallmark Trading Estate, Fourth Way, Wembley, Middlesex, HA9 0LB Tel: (020) 8902 7722 Fax: (020) 8795 4187 E-mail: info@colonnadeuk.com

Colourite Anodisers Ltd, Selinas Lane, Dagenham, Essex, RM8 1ET Tel: (020) 8592 1172 Fax: (020) 8592 1171 E-mail: info@colourite.net

Cort Surface Coating Ltd, 26 Britten Rd, Elgar Road South, Reading, RG2 0AU Tel: 0118-975 6338 Fax: 0118-975 6350

Croydon Electroplaters Ltd, 2 Bridge Parade, Waddon Road, Croydon, CR0 4JH Tel: (020) 8688 4709

Crystal Polishing Ltd, Century Park, Garrison Lane, Birmingham, B9 4NZ Tel: 0121-766 6733 Fax: 0121-766 6733

Deansfield Metal Finishing Co. Ltd, Colliery Road, Wolverhampton, WV1 2RD Tel: (01902) 351811 Fax: (01902) 458165 E-mail: admin@deansfield.fsbusiness.co.uk

The Diamond Metal Finishing Company Ltd, 6 Newfields Industrial Estate, High Street, Stoke-on-Trent, ST6 5PD Tel: (01782) 822442 Fax: (01782) 839125 E-mail: stevependo@aol.com

DMS Metal Spinning, 6 Grafton Road, Birmingham, B11 1JP Tel: 0121-773 8885 Fax: 0121-773 3141 E-mail: adriandms@aol.com

E A E Polishing Services Ltd, Green Street, Oldham, OL8 1TA Tel: 0161-678 8273 Fax: 0161-628 5144 E-mail: sales@eaepolishingservices.co.uk

E C Hopkins, Unit 34 Stretford Motorway Estate, Stretford, Manchester, M32 0ZH Tel: 0161-866 9122 Fax: 0161-866 9121 E-mail: sales@echopkins.com

E T Flower & Co. Ltd, 26-30 Theobald Street, Borehamwood, Hertfordshire, WD6 4SG Tel: (020) 8953 2343 Fax: (020) 8905 1845

Elland Metal Finishers, Woodman Works, South Lane, Elland, West Yorkshire, HX5 0PA Tel: (01422) 375974 Fax: (01422) 375974

Ellison Metal Finishing Ltd, 8 Acorn Business Park, Keighley Road, Skipton, North Yorkshire, BD23 2UE Tel: (01756) 796805 Fax: (01535) 630942 E-mail: sales@ellisonmf.co.uk

Emp Tooling Services Ltd, Brockhampton Lane, Havant, Hampshire, PO9 1LU Tel: (023) 9249 2626 Fax: (023) 9249 2582 E-mail: info@e-m-p.biz

Empress Promotions Ltd, 6 Holkham Road, Orton Southgate, Peterborough, PE2 6TE Tel: (01733) 391133 Fax: (01733) 370738 E-mail: sales@empresspromo.com

▶ Euro Polishing Technology, 83 Moorhey Street, Oldham, OL4 1JE Tel: 0161-628 4466 Fax: 0161-628 4477 E-mail: europolishing@hotmail.co.uk

▶ Ferrari Electroplating, C Station Works, Bury Road, Radcliffe, Manchester, M26 2UA Tel: 0161-723 0202 Fax: 0161-724 8699

Forg Welding & Engineering Co. Ltd, 4 Block 2 Mariner Way, Felnex Industrial Estate, Newport, Gwent, NP19 4PQ Tel: (01633) 274690 Fax: (01633) 270975 E-mail: sales@forg.co.uk

Four Ways Engineering Co., Unit 18 Bennerley Court, Blenheim Industrial Estate, Sellars Wood Drive, Bulwell, Nottingham, NG6 8UT Tel: 0115-977 0018 Fax: 0115-977 0018

H & S Enamelling (U K) Ltd, Unit 10, Highbridge Industrial Estate, Oxford Rd, Uxbridge, Middlesex, UB8 1LX Tel: (01895) 233251 Fax: (01895) 810800 E-mail: sales@hsenamelling.co.uk

Hampshire Electroplating Co Ltd, 69-75 Empress Road, Southampton, SO14 0JW Tel: (023) 8022 5639 Fax: (023) 8063 9874 E-mail: enquiries@hepcoltd.co.uk

Hi-Brite Polishing, 160 Clayton Road, Hayes, Middlesex, UB3 1AN Tel: (020) 8561 5102 Fax: (020) 8561 6949

Isleworth Polishing & Plating Ltd, 273 High Street, Brentford, Middlesex, TW8 0JL Tel: (020) 8560 7440 Fax: (020) 8560 7440

J.W.Rudge & Co.Limited, Anne Road, Smethwick, West Midlands, B66 2NZ Tel: 0121-558 5519 Fax: 0121-558 0053 E-mail: millssteve@btconnect.co.uk

K G Coating Ltd, Unit 8-9 Canal Wood Industrial Estate, Chirk, Wrexham, LL14 5RL Tel: (01691) 778070 Fax: (01691) 778303 E-mail: sales@kgcoating.co.uk

K S M Metal Finishing Ltd, Newhall Street, Willenhall, West Midlands, WV13 1LQ Tel: (01902) 607176 Fax: (01902) 607176

▶ K & S Metal Polishers, Unit G10 Rudford Industrial Estate, Ford Road, Ford, Arundel, West Sussex, BN18 0BD Tel: (01903) 718180 Fax: (01903) 718180 E-mail: ksmetal@talk21.com

Kypol Ltd, Suven House, 55 Gosforth Close, Middlefield Industrial Estate, Sandy, Bedfordshire, SG19 1RB Tel: (01767) 682424 Fax: (01767) 681180 E-mail: info@kypol.co.uk

L B Parkes Co. Ltd, Station Street, Walsall, WS2 9JZ Tel: (01922) 720720 Fax: (01922) 723400 E-mail: sales@lbparkes.co.uk

L Bingham Ltd, 36 Malinda Street, Sheffield, S3 7EJ Tel: 0114-272 1525 Fax: 0114-249 3397 E-mail: lbinghamltd@aol.com

Lazenby Metal Services, Unit 34 Calder Wharf Mills, Huddersfield Road, Dewsbury, West Yorkshire, WF13 3JW Tel: (01924) 457777 Fax: (01924) 457755 E-mail: enquiries@lazenbymetal.com

Malcolm Enamellers Midlands Ltd, Lawley Middleway, Birmingham, B4 7XT Tel: 0121-359 7553 Fax: 0121-359 8309 E-mail: sales@malcolms.co.uk

Merridale Polishing & Plating Co. Ltd, Friar Street, Wednesbury, West Midlands, WS10 0RE Tel: 0121-556 3636 Fax: 0121-556 8886

Metal Finishing Ltd, Station Street, Town Wharf Business Park, Walsall, WS2 9JZ Tel: (01922) 720720 Fax: (01922) 723400 E-mail: sales@lbparkes.net

Metal Finishing Supplies Ltd, 99a North Street, Cannock, Staffordshire, WS11 0AZ Tel: (01543) 505771 Fax: (01543) 466011

▶ Midland Finishing Ltd, Eel Street, Oldbury, West Midlands, B69 2BX Tel: 0121-544 9494 Fax: 0121-544 4540 E-mail: info@midlandfinishing.co.uk

Moss Vernon Electroplating Ltd, Churchfields Works, Churchfields Road, Brighouse, West Yorkshire, HD6 1DH Tel: (01484) 710153 Fax: (01484) 720329

Newman Ltd, 219 Moseley Street, Birmingham, B5 6LE Tel: 0121-622 2884 Fax: 0121-622 1986 E-mail: singhsatnam@btconnect.com

Norman Hay plc, Godiva Place, Coventry, CV1 5PN Tel: (024) 7622 9373 Fax: (024) 7622 4420 E-mail: info@normanhay.com

Nottingham Zinc Group Ltd, Byron Avenue, Lowmoor Business Park, Kirkby-in-Ashfield, Nottingham, NG17 7LA Tel: (01623) 752107 Fax: (01623) 721453 E-mail: clive@nottinghamzinc.co.uk

Nu-Pro Surface Treatments, Eagle Works, London Road, Thrupp, Stroud, Gloucestershire, GL5 2BA Tel: (01453) 883344 Fax: (01453) 731597 E-mail: sales@nu-pro.com

Pabco (UK) Ltd, Unit 2, Balnea Creekmoor Industrial Estate, Poole, Dorset, BH17 7EB Tel: (01202) 696365 Fax: (01202) 696365

Polish Inc, 4 Justin Business Park, Sandford Lane, Wareham, Dorset, BH20 4DY Tel: (01929) 554037 Fax: (01929) 555262

Proclean Alloy Wheel Refurbishment, 61-63 Houghton Street, Prescot, Merseyside, L34 5RS Tel: 0151-292 5525 Fax: 0151-426 1885

▶ Profile 7000 Ltd, Station St West Business Park, Coventry, CV6 5BP Tel: 024 76683366

Propak Sheet Metal Ltd, Unit C-D Gunnels Wood Park, Gunnels Wood Road, Stevenage, Hertfordshire, SG1 2BH Tel: (01438) 728885 Fax: (01438) 740298 E-mail: bruce@propak.co.uk

RCJ Metal Finishers Ltd, 3 Pindar Road, Hoddesdon, Hertfordshire, EN11 0BZ Tel: (01992) 467931 Fax: (01992) 471547 E-mail: john@rcjmf.co.uk

Rem, 5 Stockton End, Sandy, Bedfordshire, SG19 1RY Tel: (01767) 691592 Fax: (01767) 691599 E-mail: mmorse@remchem.co.uk

Rhodes Barrellings, Unit 4, Victoria Avenue, Borrowash, Derby, DE72 3HE Tel: (07718) 160144 Fax: (01332) 666090 E-mail: rhodesbarrelling@aol.com

Robins Metal Polishers Ltd, Unit 4, Fleming Way, Cressex Business Park, High Wycombe, Buckinghamshire, HP12 3TS Tel: (01494) 536446

Roundcroft Metal Finishing, Unit 1 Roundcroft, Willenhall, West Midlands, WV13 2PN Tel: (01902) 606962 Fax: (01902) 606962

Sandy Powder Coating, 14 Howard Road, Eaton Socon, St. Neots, Cambridgeshire, PE19 8ET Tel: (01480) 470555 Fax: (01480) 477155

Senior Aluminium Systems, Eland Road, Denaby Main, Doncaster, South Yorkshire, DN12 4HA Tel: (01709) 772600 Fax: 01709 772601 E-mail: enquiries@senioraluminium.co.uk

Sherwood Services Ltd, Bolina Road, London, SE16 3LD Tel: (020) 7252 1293

Sillavan Metal Polishes, Sillavan Works, Wood Street, Bury, Lancashire, BL8 2SL Tel: 0161-797 6666 Fax: 0161-797 3454 E-mail: bury@sillavan.co.uk

Somerco Industrial Ltd, 34 Tollpark Road, Cumbernauld, Glasgow, G68 0LW Tel: (01236) 728445 Fax: (01236) 728445 E-mail: somerco@aol.com

South Staffs Group Ltd, Churchfield House, 36 Vicar Street, Dudley, West Midlands, DY2 8RG Tel: (01384) 458300 Fax: (01384) 233670 E-mail: sales@southstaffsindustries.com

South West Metal Finishing Ltd, Alphinbrook Road, Marsh Barton Trading Estate, Exeter, EX2 8TJ Tel: (01392) 258234 Fax: (01392) 421538 E-mail: swmf@eicgroup.co.uk

Sparton Metal Polishers, Unit 11 Croydon Street, Leeds, LS11 9RT Tel: 0113-244 6975 Fax: 0113-244 5629 E-mail: ash@amsspartan.com

Specialised Polishing Services, 10 Lodge Way, Thetford, Norfolk, IP24 1HE Tel: (01842) 762700 Fax: (01842) 762700

Stainless Equipment Co. (Metal Finishers) Ltd, Alma Road, Ponders End, Enfield, Middx, EN3 7BB Tel: (020) 8805 0884 Fax: (020) 8804 8167 E-mail: david@stainlesssteelpolishers.co.uk

Star Polishing, Graiseley House, Graiseley Row, Wolverhampton, WV2 4HJ Tel: (01902) 421137 Fax: (01902) 421137

Sussex Blast Cleaning Ltd, 35 Industrial Estate, Station Road, Hailsham, East Sussex, BN27 2ER Tel: (01323) 849229 Fax: (01323) 442442

Tanfield Group plc, Vigo Centre, Birtley Road, Washington, Tyne & Wear, NE38 9DA Tel: 0191-417 2170 Fax: (0845) 1557756 E-mail: sales@tanfieldgroup.com

Telford Polishers Ltd, Charlton Forge Church Street, Oakengates, Telford, Shropshire, TF2 6BY Tel: (01952) 614441 Fax: (01952) 612229 E-mail: sales@cmfc.freeserve.co.uk

Thomas H Gee & Co. Ltd, 271 Summer Lane, Birmingham, B19 2PX Tel: 0121-359 1279 Fax: 0121-359 7686 E-mail: sales@thomashgee.co.uk

Total Finishing Solutions, 67-70 Mott Street, Birmingham, B19 3HE Tel: 0121-233 3505 Fax: 0121-233 9207 E-mail: wesley.jenkinson@totalfinishingsolutions.co.uk

Townhead Electroplating Services, Unit E3 Fieldhouse Industrial Estate, Fieldhouse Road, Rochdale, Lancashire, OL12 0AA Tel: (01706) 647802 E-mail: townheadelectroplating@yahoo.com

Tring Metal Polishing, Unit 13 Brook Street, Tring, Hertfordshire, HP23 5EF Tel: (01442) 824151

Tromans Bros, 6 Troman Industrial Estate, 212 Halesowen Road, Netherton, Dudley, West Midlands, DY2 9PD Tel: (01384) 569495 Fax: (01384) 569495

Twickenham Plating Group Ltd, 7-9 Edwin Road, Twickenham, TW1 4JJ Tel: (020) 8744 1800 Fax: (020) 8744 2001 E-mail: info@twickenham.co.uk

Wasp Metal Polishing Ltd, Unit 4 Beaver Industrial Estate, Southmoor Lane, Havant, Hampshire, PO9 1JW Tel: (023) 9245 0011 Fax: (023) 9245 0011 E-mail: director@waspmetalpolishing.com

▶ Watson & Lewis Ltd, 5 Cullen Way, London, NW10 6JZ Tel: (020) 8961 3000 Fax: (020) 8965 1990

Wellbrite Plating Co., 24 Lansdown Place Lane, Cheltenham, Gloucestershire, GL50 2LB Tel: (01242) 523790

E. Williams Plating Ltd, Unit 3, The Dean, Alresford, Hampshire, SO24 9BQ Tel: (01962) 733199 Fax: (01962) 735146 E-mail: enquiries@ewp-hants.co.uk

N.L. Williams Group Ltd, Westside Industrial Estate, Jackson Street, St. Helens, Merseyside, WA9 3AT Tel: (01744) 26526 Fax: (01744) 22551 E-mail: enquiries@safetysurfacing.uk.com

METAL FIRE ESCAPES

Caroway Fabrications Ltd, 40 Aston Road, Waterlooville, Hampshire, PO7 7XF Tel: (023) 9226 7614 Fax: (023) 9226 2290

Iron Designs Ltd, 117-119 Victoria Road, Portslade, Brighton, BN41 1XD Tel: (01273) 423685 Fax: (01273) 418927

K & R Fabrications Ltd, Old Station Close, Shepshed, Loughborough, Leicestershire, LE12 9NJ Tel: (01509) 506996 Fax: (01509) 506996 E-mail: kandrfabs@btconnect.com

L H W Engineering Ltd, Iremonger Road, London Road, Nottingham, NG2 3HU Tel: 0115-986 1247 Fax: 0115-986 0684 E-mail: sales@lhw.co.uk

METAL FITTINGS/ ACCESSORIES, LEATHER GOODS

Buxactic Ltd, Sedgwick Lane, Horsham, West Sussex, RH13 6QE Tel: (01403) 218880 Fax: (01403) 274111 E-mail: chris@buxatic.co.uk

METAL FITTINGS/EDGINGS/ ACCESSORIES, PACKING OR TRANSIT CASE/BOX TRADE

Ames Stokes Stevens & Son, Hanley Works, Hanley Street, Birmingham, B19 3SP Tel: 0121-359 5561 Fax: 0121-359 2336 E-mail: sales@amesstokes.com

METAL FOAM MECHANICAL ENGINEERING COMPONENTS

Menrica Engineering Ltd, 17 Paynes Lane, Rugby, Warwickshire, CV21 2UH Tel: (01788) 572434

METAL FOLDING

Byworth Engineering Ltd, Albion Works, Royd Ings Ave, Keighley, W. Yorkshire, BD21 4BZ Tel: (01535) 602780 Fax: (01535) 611319

Colmet Precision Ltd, Unit 15 Upper Wingbury Courtyard Business Centre, Leighton Road, Wingrave, Aylesbury, Buckinghamshire, HP22 4LW Tel: (01296) 681658 Fax: (01296) 681726 E-mail: sales@colmet.co.uk

Colval Engineering, Unit 1a Bury Farm, Curbridge, Botley, Southampton, SO30 2HB Tel: (01489) 799100 Fax: (01489) 799100

Enterprise Fabrication Co., Virginia Street, Southport, Merseyside, PR8 6RZ Tel: (01704) 541544 Fax: (01704) 544260 E-mail: enterprise@e-fabs.co.uk

METAL FRAMED DOUBLE GLAZED WINDOWS

▶ H & P Double Glazing Ltd, Kelsall Street, Oldham, OL9 6HR Tel: 0161-678 9144 E-mail: enquires@hpdoubleglazing.co.uk

METAL FRAMED WINDOWS

Albann Mckinney Window Co Ltd, Hyde Park, Mallusk, Newtownabbey, County Antrim, BT36 4PX Tel: (028) 9084 2611 Fax: (028) 9034 2317 E-mail: mailbox@mcneill-mcmanus.com

METAL FRAMING SYSTEMS

Metsec plc, Broadwell Works, Birmingham Road, Oldbury, West Midlands, B69 4HE Tel: 0121-552 1541 E-mail: windows@metsec.com

Rose & Krieger, Phoenix Mecano House, 6-7 Faraday Road, Rabans Lane Industrial Estate, Aylesbury, Buckinghamshire, HP19 8TX Tel: (01296) 398865 Fax: (01296) 398866 E-mail: rkgb@phoenix-mecano.ltd.uk

Unistrut Holdings Ltd, Unistrut House, Edison Road, Bedford, MK41 0HU Tel: (01234) 220400 Fax: (01234) 216004 E-mail: cmathews@tyco-bspd.com

Universal Fixings Ltd, Unit 1 2 Balds Lane, Jubilee Business Park, Lye, Stourbridge, West Midlands, DY9 8SH Tel: (01384) 422284

METAL FURNITURE

▶ Artistry In Iron Ltd, Unit D2 Commercial Avenue, Cheadle Hulme, Cheadle, Cheshire, SK8 6QH Tel: 0161-482 8022 Fax: 0161-482 8023 E-mail: sales@artistryuk.com

D F Barber, Bunwell Road, Besthorpe, Attleborough, Norfolk, NR17 2NZ Tel: (01953) 452422 Fax: (01953) 452422

▶ Eikon Creations, 5 Black Lake Industrial Estate, Black Lake, West Bromwich, West Midlands, B70 0PG Tel: 0121-525 6876 Fax: 0121-525 6577 E-mail: sales@eikoncreations.co.uk

Formlo Leisure Products Ltd, Cleadon House, Church Lane, Tibberton, Droitwich, Worcestershire, WR9 7NW Tel: (01905) 345496 Fax: (01905) 345827 E-mail: formlo.leisure@virgin.net

▶ Geometric Furniture Ltd, Geometric House Lark Hill, Townley Street Middleton, Middleton, Manchester, M24 1AT Tel: 0161-653 2233 Fax: 0161-653 2299 E-mail: sales@geometric-furniture.co.uk

Radford Customer Guidance & Checkouts Division, Sherbourne Drive, Tilbrook, Milton Keynes, MK7 8BA Tel: (01908) 366688 Fax: (01908) 368811 E-mail: sales@radford.co.uk

G.S. Smart & Co. Ltd, Ardath Road, Birmingham, B38 9PN Tel: 0121-459 0983 Fax: 0121-459 8559 E-mail: info@metalrax-group.co.uk

Steelware Co. UK Ltd, 36 Normandy Way, Walker Lines Industrial Estate, Bodmin, Cornwall, PL31 1EX Tel: (01208) 77766 Fax: (01208) 77779

A. & B. Woodberry Ltd, 156 Crow Lane, Romford, RM7 0ES Tel: (01708) 737979 Fax: (01708) 737918 E-mail: abwoodberry@go-plus.net

METAL FURNITURE COMPONENTS

A Howe Light Engineering, 1 Priory Works, Priory Cresent, Southend-on-Sea, SS2 6LD Tel: (01702) 611451 Fax: (01702) 469078 E-mail: david.knight@steelfabricators1.co.uk

B G B Services & Supply Ltd, Unit 52, Sovereign Road, Kings Norton Business Centre, Birmingham, B30 3HN Tel: 0121-458 5424 Fax: 0121-459 4756 E-mail: ian@bgbservices.co.uk

Calmels Design Ltd, 3-7 Southville, London, SW8 2PR Tel: (020) 7622 6181 Fax: (020) 7498 2889 E-mail: lois@calmels.co.uk

▶ Clockwork Components Ltd, 6 Network Point, Range Road, Witney, Oxfordshire, OX29 0YN Tel: (01993) 775767 Fax: (01993) 892313

Fabrication & Design Excellence Ltd, Pegasus Buildings, Olympus Business Park, Quedgeley, Gloucester, GL2 4JA Tel: (01452) 722944 Fax: (01452) 722825 E-mail: sales@fdproducts.co.uk

J A Kinnersley & Co. Ltd, Copenhagen Road, Hull, HU7 0XQ Tel: (01482) 826020 Fax: (01482) 878447 E-mail: sales@j-kinnersley.co.uk

Paragon Business Furniture, Sturmer Road, Haverhill, Suffolk, CB9 7UU Tel: (01440) 712160 Fax: (01440) 712157 E-mail: enquiries@paragon-businessfurn.com

METAL GARDEN BENCHES

▶ Event Prop Hire, Unit 1, Green Park Business Centre, Eastmoor, Sutton on the Forrest, York, YO61 1ET Tel: (01347) 811713 Fax: (0845) 0940817E-mail: enquiries@eventprophire.com

▶ Supergreenthumb, London, London, N22 6SD Tel: 0800 917 4252

METAL GARDEN FURNITURE

Brambley Furniture, 108 Westmoor Street, Charlton, London, SE7 8NQ Tel: (020) 8293 6662 Fax: (020) 8305 0907

English Hurdle, Curload, Stoke St. Gregory, Taunton, Somerset, TA3 6JD Tel: (01823) 698418 Fax: (01823) 698859 E-mail: hurdle@enterprise.net

Formlo Leisure Products Ltd, Cleadon House, Church Lane, Tibberton, Droitwich, Worcestershire, WR9 7NW Tel: (01905) 345496 Fax: (01905) 345827 E-mail: formlo.leisure@virgin.net

Hemington Rustics, Cheneys Farm, Romsey Road, Ower, Romsey, Hampshire, SO51 6AF Tel: (023) 8073 9217

Nova Garden Furniture Ltd, Graveney Road, Faversham, Kent, ME13 8UN Tel: (01795) 535511 Fax: (01795) 539215 E-mail: sales@novagardenfurniture.co.uk

Oxleys Furniture Ltd, Lapstone Farn, Westington Hill, Chipping Campden, Gloucestershire, GL55 6UR Tel: (01386) 840466 Fax: (01386) 840455

▶ Smartwood Lesiure Products, Belle Vue Barn, Mansergh, Carnforth, Lancashire, LA6 2EJ Tel: (01524) 273333 Fax: (01524) 273303

Wessex Forge, Unit 5, Lodgehill Industrial Estate, Westbury-Sub-Mendip, Wells, Somerset, BA5 1EY Tel: (01749) 672984 Fax: (01749) 670150 E-mail: info@wessexforge.co.uk

METAL GATES

Albion Fencing Ltd, 2239 London Road, Glasgow, G32 8XL Tel: 0141-778 1672 Fax: 0141-778 6688 E-mail: info@albionfencing.co.uk

B F Elton, The Bungalow, Bristol Road, Rooksbridge, Axbridge, Somerset, BS26 2TF Tel: (01934) 750433

Bedford Fencing Co. Ltd, 8 Sargeant Turner Trading Estate, Bromley Street, Stourbridge, West Midlands, DY9 8HZ Tel: (01384) 422688 Fax: (01384) 422688

▶ Brook Metal Design Ltd, Brook Farm Industrial Estate, Stapleford Road, Romford, RM4 1EJ Tel: (01708) 687420

Burbage Gates Ltd, Sapcote Road, Burbage, Hinckley, Leicestershire, LE10 2AU Tel: (01455) 613844 Fax: (01455) 611333 E-mail: sales@burbagegates.co.uk

Burbage Iron Craft Ltd, Unit 16, Sketchley Industrial Estate, Hinckley, Leicestershire, LE10 3ER Tel: (01455) 251656 Fax: (01455) 614136 E-mail: sales@burbageironcraft.co.uk

William Burns & Sons, 1 School Road, Millisle, Newtownards, County Down, BT22 2DZ Tel: (028) 9048 4140 Fax: (028) 9048 4140

Ceto Engineering Ltd, Howard Road, Eaton Socon, St. Neots, Cambridgeshire, PE19 8ET Tel: (01480) 406646 Fax: (01480) 406605

City Gate Automation, 32 Hetherington Road, Shepperton, Middlesex, TW17 0SP Tel: (01932) 786464 Fax: (01932) 766199

Country Forge, Kidderminster Road, Dodford, Bromsgrove, Worcestershire, B61 9DU Tel: (01527) 575765 Fax: (01527) 575761 E-mail: sales@metalartproducts.co.uk

Craig & Buchanan Ltd, 23 Lochburn Road, Glasgow, G20 9AE Tel: 0141-946 2007 Fax: 0141-945 2100 E-mail: shona@craigbuchanan.co.uk

Cumbrian Implement Co. Ltd, 4 King Street, Aspatria, Wigton, Cumbria, CA7 3ET Tel: (01697) 320269 Fax: (01697) 322677 E-mail: newdale@btconnect.com

D & E Fabrications Ltd, Latteridge Road, Iron Acton, Bristol, BS37 9TL Tel: (01454) 228810 Fax: (01454) 228810

Dowlings Ltd, Duttons Farm, Bangors Road South, Iver, Buckinghamshire, SL0 0AY Tel: (01753) 630653 Fax: (0870) 2201684 E-mail: dowlingsltd@aol.com

F Kitchen Lancaster Ltd, Unit 6 Forestgate, Whiteland Industrial Estate, Morecambe, Lancashire, LA3 3PD Tel: (01524) 63835 Fax: 01524 63835 E-mail: sales@fkitchen.co.uk

Fylde Coast Gate, Amy Johnson Way, Blackpool, FY4 2RP Tel: (01253) 347000 Fax: (01253) 407518

Gate Place, 140 Poulton Road, Southport, Merseyside, PR9 7DB Tel: (01704) 224365 Fax: (01704) 507500

A.A. Gates Ltd, Culver Garden Centre, Cattlegate Road, Crews Hill, Enfield, Middlesex, EN2 9DS Tel: (020) 8367 3500 Fax: (020) 8342 1115 E-mail: argonarc@aol.com

Gateways Northwest Ltd, 2 St. James Street, Southport, Merseyside, PR8 5AE Tel: (01704) 500056 Fax: (01704) 546080

Gaytsmaid Wrought Ironwork, Unit 1 St. Johns Lane, Bewdley, Worcestershire, DY12 2QY Tel: (01299) 405153 Fax: (01299) 405153 E-mail: enquiries@gaytsmaid.co.uk

Holt Bros Horwich, Brunel Works, Brunel Street, Horwich, Bolton, BL6 5NX Tel: (01204) 697393 Fax: (01204) 697393

Hyders 1994 Ltd, Landway House, Basted Lane, Borough Green, Sevenoaks, Kent, TN15 8PY Tel: (01732) 886988 Fax: (01732) 886988

Marton Gateway Engineers, 96 Vicarage Lane, Blackpool, FY4 4EL Tel: 01253 692611

Noble Gates Ltd, Ivy House Farm, Whiston, Penkridge, Stafford, ST19 5QH Tel: (01785) 714148 Fax: (01785) 714148

Oadby Wrought Iron, Chapel Street, Oadby, Leicester, LE2 5AD Tel: 0116-271 5040

Oak Tree Forge, Oak Tree Yard, Upper Manor Road, Paignton, Devon, TQ3 2TP Tel: (01803) 550436 Fax: (01803) 529277

Gary Paul Engineering, 4 Rosewood Park, St. James's Road, Blackburn, BB1 8ET Tel: (01254) 582263 Fax: (01254) 582263

Pembury Fencing, Unit, Church Farm, Collier Street, Tonbridge, Kent, TN12 9RT Tel: (0870) 2423707 Fax: (0870) 2423708 E-mail: pemburyfencing@tiscali.co.uk

Renzland Forge Ltd, 83A London Road, Copford, Colchester, CO6 1LG Tel: (01206) 210212 Fax: (01206) 211290

▶ Rowley Engineering Co. Ltd, Tollgate Industrial Estate, Stafford, ST16 3HS Tel: (01785) 223831 Fax: (01785) 222764 E-mail: sales@roweng.com

Russell Shutters Ltd, Unit 6 Sterling Industrial Estate, Dagenham, Essex, RM10 8TX Tel: (020) 8592 4545 Fax: (020) 8984 0378 E-mail: sales@lbsgroup.co.uk

S Buck, 36 Stanley Road, Warmley, Bristol, BS15 4NX Tel: 0117-967 4740 Fax: 0117-961 8050

S Burvill & Son Ltd, The Forge Cossins Farm, Downside Road, Downside, Cobham, Surrey, KT11 3LZ Tel: (01932) 589666 Fax: (01932) 589669

Sablon Fabrications, Unit 6 Laches Close, Four Ashes, Wolverhampton, WV10 7DZ Tel: (01902) 798894 Fax: (01902) 798895

H. Scrowcroft & Sons, Daisyfield Works, Rosslyn Avenue, Preesall, Poulton-Le-Fylde, Lancashire, FY6 0HE Tel: (01253) 810451

Singer & James Ltd, 33 Roebuck Road, Ilford, Essex, IG6 3TZ Tel: (020) 8500 4115 Fax: (020) 8501 2456 E-mail: info@singerandjames.co.uk

Steelcraft Ltd, Unit 2-6 Drum Industrial Estate, Chester le Street, County Durham, DH2 1AG Tel: 0191-410 9996 Fax: 0191-410 9228 E-mail: sales@steelcraft.ltd.uk

Thames Forge Ltd, Fullers Yard, Sheephouse Road, Maidenhead, Berkshire, SL6 8HA Tel: (01628) 622423 Fax: (01628) 622423

Thing Ama Jigs Ltd, 136 Oyster Lane, Byfleet, West Byfleet, Surrey, KT14 7JQ Tel: (01932) 340764 Fax: (01932) 351280

Wellform Ltd, Unit E14, Cumberland Road Trading Estate, Loughborough, Leicestershire, LE11 5DE Tel: (01509) 264000 Fax: (01509) 611891

Wideacre Metal Gates Ltd, 15 Buttress Way, Smethwick, West Midlands, B66 3DL Tel: 0121-558 4263 Fax: 0121-558 5735 E-mail: gailkaren@msn.com

Woking Forge Ltd, 126A High Street, Old Woking, Woking, Surrey, GU22 9JN Tel: (01483) 760313 Fax: (01483) 756332

METAL GUILLOTINE CUTTING SERVICES

Crew Stainless & Special Alloys, Unit 17 Coneygre Industrial Estate, Tipton, West Midlands, DY4 8XP Tel: 0121-520 1066 Fax: 0121-520 7600 E-mail: sales@crewstainless.co.uk

Cudlow Steel Services Ltd, Unit H4 Rudford Industrial Estate, Ford Road, Ford, Arundel, West Sussex, BN18 0BD Tel: (01903) 714545 Fax: (01903) 716151 E-mail: cudlow@fsbdial.co.uk

London Engineering Co. Ltd, 9-13 Valentia Place, London, SW9 8PJ Tel: (020) 7738 7338 Fax: (020) 7924 0331 E-mail: londonendco@aol.com

Parson & Crosland Ltd, PO Box 10, Middlesbrough, Cleveland, TS2 1HG Tel: (01642) 244161 Fax: (01642) 230487 E-mail: sales@parson-crosland.co.uk

William Hinsley Engineers Ltd, 1 Croft Street, Sowerby Bridge, West Yorkshire, HX6 2AJ Tel: (01422) 839968

METAL HALIDE LAMPS

Accent Lighting Ltd, 3 Candidus Court, Werrington, Peterborough, PE4 5DB Tel: (01733) 574524 Fax: (01733) 574524 E-mail: sales@accent-lighting.co.uk

Newey & Eyre Ltd, Unit 15 17, Whittle Way, Crawley, West Sussex, RH10 9RW Tel: (01293) 517500 Fax: (01293) 561362 E-mail: neweyandeyre@hagemeyer.co.uk

Newey & Eyre Ltd, 62 Manners View, Newport, Isle of Wight, PO30 5FA Tel: (01983) 523481 Fax: (01983) 520723

Newionaire, 10 Cofton Road, Marsh Barton Trading Estate, Marsh Barton Trading Estate, Exeter, EX2 8QW Tel: (01392) 829180 Fax: (01392) 410358

Primarc Ltd, 816 Leigh Road, Slough, SL1 4BD Tel: (01753) 558001 Fax: (01753) 811678 E-mail: uv@primarc.com

METAL HANDRAILS

Bennetts Of Bromsgrove Ltd, 53 Sherwood Road, Aston Fields Industrial Estate, Bromsgrove, Worcestershire, B60 3DR Tel: (01527) 870440 Fax: (01527) 575595 E-mail: sales@bennettsbathrooms.co.uk

Handrail Design Ltd, Sail & Colour Loft, The Historic Dockyard, Chatham, Kent, ME4 4TE Tel: (01634) 817800 Fax: (01634) 817711 E-mail: enquiries@handraildesign.co.uk

Mainframe Fabrications Hereford Ltd, Unit 6A Thorn Business Park, Rotherwas, Hereford, HR2 6JT Tel: (01432) 353703 Fax: (01432) 340588

METAL HANGING BASKET BRACKETS

▶ Flairmet, Unit 1 2, Ladfordfields Industrial Park, Seighford, Stafford, ST18 9QE Tel: (01785) 282301 Fax: (01785) 282626 E-mail: flairmet@weathervane.uk.com

▶ PHS Greenleaf, Western Industrial Estate, Lon-Y-Llyn, Caerphilly, Mid Glamorgan, CF83 1XH Tel: (029) 2085 1000 Fax: (029) 2080 9064 E-mail: enquiries@phs.co.uk

METAL HARDWARE FURNITURE FITTINGS

Crofts & Assinder, Standard Brass Works, Lombard Street, Deritend, Birmingham, B12 0QX Tel: 0121-622 1074 Fax: 0121-622 1074 E-mail: general@crofts.co.uk

Daro Factors Ltd, 80-84 Wallis Road, London, E9 5LW Tel: (020) 8510 4000 Fax: (020) 8510 4001 E-mail: sales@daro.com

Dudley Tool & Engineering Co. Ltd, Mill Street, Wordsley, Stourbridge, West Midlands, DY8 5SX Tel: (01384) 571181 Fax: (01384) 265435 E-mail: info@dudley-tool.co.uk

Fabrication & Design Excellence Ltd, Pegasus Buildings, Olympus Business Park, Quedgeley, Gloucester, GL2 4JA Tel: (01452) 722944 Fax: (01452) 722825 E-mail: sales@fdproducts.co.uk

G & T Furniture Fittings, Upper Rainham Road, Hornchurch, Essex, RM12 4ES Tel: (07860) 802481 Fax: (01708) 470211

J Shiner & Sons Ltd, 8 Windmill Street, London, W1T 2JE Tel: (020) 7636 0740 Fax: (020) 7580 0740 E-mail: info@j-shiner.co.uk

Martin Co. Ltd, 160 Dollman Street, Duddeston, Birmingham, B7 4RS Tel: 0121-359 2111 Fax: 0121-359 4698 E-mail: sales@martin.co.uk

Page Castor Ltd, Blakemore Road, West Bromwich, West Midlands, B70 8JF Tel: 0121-553 1710 Fax: 0121-525 0631

Paragon Business Furniture, Sturmer Road, Haverhill, Suffolk, CB9 7UU Tel: (01440) 712160 Fax: (01440) 712157 E-mail: enquiries@paragon-businessfurn.com

R P Hardware Ltd, 6 Parkside Industrial Estate, Hickman Avenue, Wolverhampton, WV1 2EN Tel: (01902) 351161 Fax: (01902) 871434 E-mail: sales@rp-hardware.co.uk

METAL HEAT TREATMENT

▶ 3m Hillington, Johnstone Avenue, Hillington Industrial Estate, Glasgow, G52 4NZ Tel: 0141-891 4300

▶ Alpha Plating Technologies Ltd, Unit 1 2, Block 3, Wednesbury Trading Estate, Wednesbury, West Midlands, WS10 7JN Tel: 0121-506 1720

▶ Applied Precison Coatings Ltd, 1 Lessarna Court, Bowling Back Lane, Bradford, West Yorkshire, BD4 8ST Tel: (01274) 724897 Fax: (01274) 738306

▶ Bredero Shaw Ltd, Bredero House, Imperial Dock, Leith, Edinburgh, EH6 7DT Tel: 0131-553 9700 Fax: 0131-553 9604

▶ Bredero Shaw Ltd, Castle Street, Castlepark Industrial Estate, Ellon, Aberdeenshire, AB41 9RF Tel: (01358) 723435 Fax: (01358) 723371 E-mail: ellon.reception@brederoshaw.shawcor.com

▶ C3 Emulet Ltd, Caledonian House, High Street, Dingwall, Ross-Shire, IV15 9RY Tel: (01349) 865554 Fax: (01349) 865558 E-mail: enquires@c3emulet.com

▶ Eastside Surface Coatings Ltd, 18 Eastmuir Street, Glasgow, G32 0HS Tel: 0141-778 6541 Fax: 0141-764 0882

▶ Fab Chrome Ltd, 58-60 Tannoch Drive, Lenzie Mills Industrial Estate, Cumbernauld, Glasgow, G67 2XX Tel: (01236) 458451 Fax: (01236) 458581

▶ Ferrari Electroplating, C Station Works, Bury Road, Radcliffe, Manchester, M26 2UA Tel: 0161-723 0202 Fax: 0161-724 8699

▶ Forfar Galvanisers Ltd, Carseview Road, Forfar, Angus, DD8 3BT Tel: (01307) 460222 Fax: (01307) 460444

▶ GMF Bradford, Bowling Ironworks, Bowling Back Lane, Bradford, West Yorkshire, BD4 8YY Tel: (01274) 306830 Fax: (01274) 728679

▶ Highland Metal Developments Ltd, 3 Pinefield Parade, Elgin, Morayshire, IV30 6FG Tel: (01343) 548855 Fax: (01343) 545551 E-mail: enquiries@higalv.co.uk

▶ Leeds Galvanizing Co. Ltd, Albion Park, Armley Road, Leeds, LS12 2EJ Tel: 0113-243 1111

▶ M M P Polishers, Clovelly Road, Southbourne, Emsworth, Hampshire, PO10 8PE Tel: (01243) 379204 Fax: (01243) 378145

▶ Perry Plating Jigs & Co. Ltd, 71a Lifford Lane, Birmingham, B30 3DY Tel: 0121 4591800

Praxair Surface Technologies Ltd, 2 Oldmixon CR, Weston-super-Mare, Avon, BS24 9AX Tel: (01934) 411300 Fax: (01934) 411301 E-mail: sales@praxair.com

▶ Surface Treatment Specialists Ltd, 1B Nelson Street, Widnes, Cheshire, WA8 0QD Tel: 0151-424 1200

METAL HEAT TREATMENT – *continued*

Syntena & North East Ltd, Unit B8, Tyne Tunnel Trading Estate, North Shields, Tyne & Wear, NE29 7XB Tel: 0191-258 4564 Fax: 0191-258 2568

▶ Weatherguard Systems, Cardenden, Lochgelly, Fife, KY5 0AU Tel: (01592) 782828

METAL HEAT TREATMENT INCLUDING ON SITE, *See also Induction Heat Treatment*

Agra Heat Treatment, 15 Ure Street, Dundee, DD1 5JD Tel: (01382) 201600 Fax: (01382) 226918

Alpha Rowen Treatments Ltd, 3-4 & 7 Brymill Industrial Units, Brown Lion Street, Tipton, West Midlands, DY4 9EG Tel: 0121-557 2376 Fax: 0121-557 2580

Barton Forge & Ironwork Ltd, 48 Alexandra Road, Enfield, Middlesex, EN3 7EH Tel: (020) 8804 1752

Beccles Heat Treatments, Gosford Road, Beccles, Suffolk, NR34 9QP Tel: (01502) 717738 Fax: (01502) 711001 E-mail: admin@b-h-t.co.uk

Beta Heat Treatment Ltd, Summerton Road, Oldbury, West Midlands, B69 2EL Tel: 0121-511 1190 Fax: 0121-511 1192 E-mail: beta@claytonholdings.com

Body Coat Heat Treatment, Stillington, Stockton-on-Tees, Cleveland, TS21 1LD Tel: (01740) 630353 Fax: (01740) 630075

Body Coating Treatments Ltd, Cranbourne Road, Gosport, Hampshire, PO12 1RW Tel: (023) 9258 0946 Fax: (023) 9251 0292 E-mail: markdavies@bodycoat.com

Bodycote Birmingham, Britannia House, Austin Way, Hampstead Industrial Estate, Birmingham, B42 1DU Tel: 0121-358 7266 Fax: 0121-358 0478 E-mail: info@bodycote.co.uk

Bodycote Birmingham, Britannia House, Austin Way, Hampstead Industrial Estate, Birmingham, B42 1DU Tel: 0121-358 7266 Fax: 0121-358 0478 E-mail: sales@bodycote.com

Bodycote Heat Treatment Ltd, 11 Bamfurlong Industrial Park, Staverton, Cheltenham, Gloucestershire, GL51 6SX Tel: (01452) 714440 Fax: (01452) 856097 E-mail: sales@bodycote.co.uk

Bodycote Heat Treatment Ltd, Field Way, Rotherham, South Yorkshire, S60 1QG Tel: (01709) 361047 Fax: (01709) 828529 E-mail: sales@bodycote.co.uk

Bodycote Heat Treatment Ltd, 437 Chester Road, Woodford, Stockport, Cheshire, SK7 1QP Tel: 0161-440 0288 Fax: 0161-440 8017 E-mail: sales@bodycote.co.uk

Bodycote Heat Treatment Ltd, Macclesfield Road, Hazel Grove, Stockport, Cheshire, SK7 5EN Tel: 0161-483 0511 Fax: 0161-483 5450 E-mail: sales@bodycote.co.uk

Bodycote Heat Treatments Ltd, Springwood Court, Springwood Close, Tytherington Business Park, Macclesfield, Cheshire, SK10 2XF Tel: (01625) 505300 Fax: (01625) 505320 E-mail: info@bodycote.co.uk

Bodycote Heating Treatment Ltd, 18 Westgate, Skelmersdale, Lancashire, WN8 8AZ Tel: (01695) 716500 Fax: (01695) 50105 E-mail: sales@bodycote.co.uk

Bodycote (Somerset) Ltd, Leach Road, Chard Business Park, Chard, Somerset, TA20 1FA Tel: (01460) 67957 Fax: (01460) 67962 E-mail: sales@bodycote.co.uk

British Heat Treatments, 40 Milton Road, East Kilbride, Glasgow, G74 5BU Tel: (01355) 225288 Fax: (01355) 265845 E-mail: jbridges@ajt-engineering.co.uk

Brockmoor Foundry, The Leys, Brierley Hill, West Midlands, DY5 3UJ Tel: (01384) 480026 Fax: (01384) 480032 E-mail: sales@brockmoor.co.uk

Charlwood Aquatics, Horley Road, Charlwood, Horley, Surrey, RH6 0BJ Tel: (01293) 776377 Fax: (01293) 786730

Coventry Heat Treatment Ltd, Unit A-B, Brindley Road, Bayton Road Industrial Estate, Coventry, CV7 9EP Tel: (024) 7636 0099 Fax: (024) 7636 6222 E-mail: covheat@aol.com

Diffusion Alloys Ltd, 160-162 Great North Road, Hatfield, Hertfordshire, AL9 5JW Tel: (01707) 266111 Fax: (01707) 276669

Doon Valley (Heat Treatment) Ltd, Unit 6, Block 7 Chapelhall Industrial Estate, Stirling Road, Airdrie, Lanarkshire, ML6 8QX Tel: (01236) 756668 Fax: (01236) 756646 E-mail: doon.valley@talk21.com

E Stokes, 55 Wharf Road, Tyseley, Birmingham, B11 2DX Tel: 0121-707 2615 Fax: 0121-707 2615

Essex Heat Treatments Ltd, Unit C2, Perry Road, East Industrial Estate, Witham, Essex, CM8 3UX Tel: (01376) 515229 Fax: (01376) 518701 E-mail: eht@withamcm83ux.fsnet.co.uk

Flame Hardeners Ltd, Shorter Works, Bailey Lane, Sheffield, S1 3BL Tel: 0114-276 8167 Fax: 0114-273 8657

Gloucester Heat Treatment Specialists Ltd, Unit 7 Venture Business Centre, Madleaze Road, Gloucester, GL1 5SJ Tel: (01452) 526434 Fax: (01452) 303680 E-mail: heat-treat@ghtl.co.uk

Hartek Engineers Ltd, Hadrian Works, Wellington Road, Dunston, Gateshead, Tyne & Wear, NE11 9JL Tel: 0191-460 0672 Fax: 0191-460 1555 E-mail: techservices.ne@btinternet.com

Heasons Heat Treatment Co, Commerce Way, Lancing, West Sussex, BN15 8TQ Tel: (01903) 755038 Fax: (01903) 767046 E-mail: heasons@btopenworld.com

Heat Treatment 2000 Ltd, Brandon Way, West Bromwich, West Midlands, B70 9PQ Tel: 0121-526 2000 Fax: 0121-500 0809 E-mail: heattreat2000@aol.com

Heat Treatments Northampton Ltd, Sheaf Close, Lodge Farm Industrial Estate, Northampton, NN5 7UL Tel: (01604) 586920 Fax: (01604) 759286 E-mail: sales@heat-treatment.co.uk

HHT Midlands Ltd, Heath Road, Darlaston, West Midlands, WS10 8LU Tel: 0121-526 4771 Fax: 0121-526 4153 E-mail: sales@hht.co.uk

High Speed Hardening Sheffield Ltd, Naseby Street, Sheffield, S9 1BR Tel: 0114-244 1516 Fax: 0114-244 1516

Howco Quality Alloys Ltd, Carbrook Street, Sheffield, S9 2JN Tel: 0114-244 6711 Fax: 0114-244 7469 E-mail: sales@howcogroup.com

Huyton Heat Treatments Ltd, Unit 6 Brickfields, Liverpool, L36 6HY Tel: 0151-480 4135 Fax: 0151-480 7336 E-mail: sales@huyton-heat-treat.co.uk

Induction Heating Service Ltd, Unit 28, Watery Lane Industrial Estate, Willenhall, West Midlands, WV13 3SU Tel: (01902) 605578 Fax: (01902) 605652 E-mail: sales@david-finch.fsnet.co.uk

Inidam Ltd, Budds Lane Industrial Estate, Romsey, Hampshire, SO51 0HA Tel: (01794) 830388 Fax: (01794) 830066 E-mail: ndt@inidam.com

Kemwell Thermal Ltd, Roma Road, Birmingham, B11 2JH Tel: 0121-708 1188 Fax: 0121-706 3390 E-mail: enquiries@kemwellthermal.com

Kiveton Park Holdings Ltd, Kiveton Park, Sheffield, S26 6NQ Tel: (01909) 770252 Fax: (01909) 772949 E-mail: sales@kpsteel.co.uk

Lush Heat Treatment Ltd, 128 Great North Road, Hatfield, Hertfordshire, AL9 5JN Tel: (01707) 264104 Fax: (01707) 274850

Metric Group Ltd, Metric House, 5 Love Lane, Cirencester, Gloucestershire, GL7 1YG Tel: (01285) 651441 Fax: (01285) 653944 E-mail: postmaster@metricgroup.co.uk

Middleton Heat Treatments Ltd, 315 Whapload Road, Lowestoft, Suffolk, NR32 1UL Tel: (01502) 561721 Fax: (01502) 517712

Midland Heat Treatments Ltd, Chillington Works, Hickman Avenue, Wolverhampton, WV1 2BU Tel: (01902) 450757 Fax: (01902) 459093 E-mail: induction@midland-heat.co.uk

Multijet Hardening Ltd, 8 West Don Street, Sheffield, S6 3BH Tel: 0114-234 5592 Fax: 0114-231 4772

R.J. Nash Ltd, 74 Livery Street, Birmingham, B3 1RG Tel: (0121) 200 3900 Fax: (0121) 200 3906 E-mail: brookwelding@btinternet.com

P B A Heat Treating Ltd, Unit 7-8, Bevan Industrial Estate, Brierley Hill, West Midlands, DY5 3TF Tel: (01384) 480331 Fax: (01384) 78381 E-mail: sales@pbaheattreatment.co.uk

Quality Heat Treatments Ltd, Chesterton Way, Eastwood Trading Estate, Rotherham, South Yorkshire, S65 1ST Tel: (01709) 379188 Fax: (01709) 829849 E-mail: j.mcconaghy@qhtltd.com

Quantum Heat Treatment & Brazing Ltd, 43 Barton Road, Bletchley, Milton Keynes, MK2 3DE Tel: (01908) 642242 Fax: (01908) 368629 E-mail: quantumheat@hotmail.com

Redditch Electro Plating Co. Ltd, Arrow Road North, Redditch, Worcestershire, B98 8NT Tel: (01527) 63858 Fax: (01527) 591504

Scottish Night Riding Services Ltd, 138 Clydeholm Road, Glasgow, G14 0QQ Tel: 0141-959 0668 Fax: 0141-959 0668

Servis Heat Treatment Co. Ltd, 258b Ipswich Road, Trading Estate, Slough, SL1 4EP Tel: (01753) 521823 Fax: (01753) 531094 E-mail: sales@servisheattreatment.com

Special Steels Ltd, Woodbourn Hill, Attercliffe, Sheffield, S9 3NE Tel: 0114-272 0321 Fax: 0114-275 8354

Techniques Surfaces (UK) Ltd, Wood Lane, Erdington, Birmingham, B24 9QL Tel: 0121-382 8060 Fax: 0121-377 8928 E-mail: info@ts-uk.com

Thermal Hire Ltd, Unit A Bedewell Industrial Park, Hebburn, Tyne & Wear, NE31 2HQ Tel: 0191-428 0423 Fax: 0191-428 0061 E-mail: enquiries@thermalhire.com

Thomas C Wild, Vulcan Works, Tinsley Park Road, Sheffield, S9 5DP Tel: 0114-244 2471 Fax: 0114-244 2052E-mail: info@tc-wild.co.uk

Tti Group Ltd, 39-43 Bilton Way, Luton, LU1 1UU Tel: (01582) 486644 Fax: (01582) 481148 E-mail: sales@ttigroup.co.uk

Wallwork Heat Treatment Birmingham Ltd, Sydenham Road, New Shires Industrial Estate, Birmingham, B11 1DQ Tel: 0121-771 2467 Fax: 0121-628 1555 E-mail: enquiries@wallworkht.com

Walton Heat Treatment Ltd, 143 Hersham Road, Walton-on-Thames, Surrey, KT12 1RR Tel: (01932) 241975 Fax: (01932) 241975

Wilson Tool & Engineering Co Essex Ltd, 2-4 Parsons Road, Manor Trading Estate, Benfleet, Essex, SS7 4PY Tel: (01268) 752836 Fax: (01268) 565323 E-mail: sales@wilson-tool.co.uk

Zotic Ltd, 26-30 Highgate Square, Highgate, Birmingham, B12 0DU Tel: 0121-440 3130 Fax: 0121-440 6646

METAL HOOKS

Olympia Triumph International Ltd, 5 Queens Road, Swanage, Dorset, BH19 2EQ Tel: (01929) 424326 Fax: (01929) 427403 E-mail: sales@olympia-triumph.co.uk

▶ Younger Enterprizes, Newton Bank, St. Andrews, Fife, KY16 9TY Tel: (07903) 841590 Fax: (01334) 478905 E-mail: jmdy@sol.co.uk

METAL INERT GAS (MIG) AND TUNGSTEN INERT GAS (TIG) WELDING

Cameo Engineering Ltd, Unit 20 Brookside Business Park, Cold Meece, Stone, Staffordshire, ST15 0RZ Tel: (01785) 761134 Fax: (01785) 761837

Cladburn Engineering Co., C Block 17 South Avenue, Blantyre Industrial Estate, Blantyre, Glasgow, G72 0XB Tel: (01698) 822550 Fax: (01698) 825130

Fastweld '93 Welding Services, Unit 8, Old Farm Buildings, Maiden Lane, Crayford, Dartford, DA1 4LX Tel: (01322) 553145 Fax: (01322) 553145

Flexbore, Pontygwindy Industrial Estate, Caerphilly, Mid Glamorgan, CF83 3HU Tel: (029) 2088 3552 Fax: (029) 2086 6410

Greenberry Bros Engineers Ltd, Brunel Drive, Newark, Nottinghamshire, NG24 2EG Tel: (01636) 676694 Fax: (01636) 675830 E-mail: sales@greenberrybros.co.uk

W H Hannaford, 100 Chester Road, Watford, WD18 0RE Tel: (01923) 223669 Fax: (01923) 223669

METAL INJECTION MOULDINGS (MIM)

Arburg Ltd, Tachbrook Park Drive, Warwick, CV34 6RH Tel: (01926) 457000 Fax: (01926) 457030 E-mail: uk@arburg.com

Metal Injection Mouldings Ltd, Davenport Lane, Broadheath, Altrincham, Cheshire, WA14 5DS Tel: 0161-928 4247 Fax: 0161-927 7023

METAL INJECTION MOULDINGS (MIM), AEROSPACE INDUSTRY

Metal Injection Mouldings Ltd, Davenport Lane, Broadheath, Altrincham, Cheshire, WA14 5DS Tel: 0161-928 4247 Fax: 0161-927 7023

METAL INJECTION MOULDINGS (MIM), DEFENCE INDUSTRY

Metal Injection Mouldings Ltd, Davenport Lane, Broadheath, Altrincham, Cheshire, WA14 5DS Tel: 0161-928 4247 Fax: 0161-927 7023

METAL JAR CLOSURES

Carnaud Metalbox Closures Europe UK, Lake Road, Hamworthy, Poole, Dorset, BH15 4LJ Tel: (01202) 774200 Fax: (01202) 774390

METAL JOINING SYSTEMS

▶ A.I. Welders, Unit 16, Dalcross Industrial Estate, Inverness, IV2 7XB Tel: (01667) 461383 Fax: (01667) 462520 E-mail: sales@ai-welders.co.uk

B T M Automation Products (UK) Ltd, Unit 6, Stephenson Road, St. Ives, Cambridgeshire, PE27 3WJ Tel: 0845 5314209 Fax: (01480) 497479 E-mail: btmautomation@btconnect.com

METAL KITCHEN UNITS

▶ Bespoke Kitchens, 1 Hillcrest, Stoodleigh, Tiverton, Devon, EX16 9PJ Tel: (01398) 351467

▶ Brighton & Hove Removals, 190 Portland Road, Hove, East Sussex, BN3 5QN Tel: (01273) 735111 E-mail: sales@brightonandhovekitchens.com

▶ Essex Specialised Joinery, Essexquay House, Quayside Industrial Estate, Maldon, Essex, CM9 5FA Tel: (01621) 843384 Fax: (01621) 843411

▶ Kitchen Heaven, 26 Nibley Lane, Iron Acton, Bristol, BS37 9UP Tel: (01454) 228100 E-mail: sales@kitchenheaven.co.uk

Niche Kitchens, 28 Kay Street, Rossendale, Lancashire, BB4 7LS Tel: (01706) 217121 Fax: (01706) 212893 E-mail: info@nichekitchens.co.uk

Rubber Duck Home Improvements, 361 Holburn Street, Aberdeen, AB10 7FQ Tel: (01224) 212397

▶ Verona Kitchens Ltd, 24 Grasgarth Close, London, W3 9HS Tel: (020) 8993 1540 Fax: (020) 8993 1540 E-mail: sales@veronakitchens.co.uk

METAL LABELS

Chaintabs Ltd, 6 Grafton Rd, Sparkbrook, Birmingham, B11 1JP Tel: 0121-430 7957 Fax: 0121-430 7964

Coventry Nameplate Co., 5 Watercall Ave, Styvechale, Coventry, CV3 5AW Tel: (024) 7669 3212 Fax: (024) 7669 3288 E-mail: markcove@dsl.pipex.com

A.J. Gilbert (Birmingham) Ltd, 66-77 Buckingham Street, Birmingham, B19 3HU Tel: 0121-236 7774 Fax: 0121-236 6024 E-mail: lucysox@aol.com

Metalprint Signs & Nameplates, 37 The Pentlands, Kintbury, Hungerford, Berkshire, RG17 9XB Tel: (01488) 658670 Fax: (01488) 658670 E-mail: fp@metalplaques.co.uk

Mockridge Labels (Sales) Ltd, Viaduct Works, Cavendish Street, Ashton-under-Lyne, Lancashire, OL6 7QL Tel: 0161-308 2331 Fax: 0161-343 1958 E-mail: mike.graham@mockridge.com

Panel Print Industrial Screen Printers, 7-12 Morris Road, Poole, Dorset, BH17 0GG Tel: (01202) 686575 Fax: (01202) 675733 E-mail: panelprint@btconnect.com

Peninsular Nameplates, Peninsular House, Carr Lane, Hoylake, Wirral, Merseyside, CH47 4AY Tel: 0151-632 5814 Fax: 0151-632 1090 E-mail: info@peninsular-nameplates.co.uk

Plastic Metal & Profiles Ltd, Unit 99 14 North Tyne Industrial Estate, Whitley Road, Benton, Newcastle upon Tyne, NE12 9SZ Tel: 0191-266 5050 Fax: 0191-266 5724 E-mail: sales@pmpnamesplates.co.uk

R C Perry & Co. Ltd, Unit 4 Worthington Way, Wigan, Lancashire, WN3 6XE Tel: (01942) 494012 Fax: (01942) 494021 E-mail: inquiries@rcperry.co.uk

S O S Talisman, 21 Grays Corner, Ley Street, Ilford, Essex, IG2 7RQ Tel: (020) 8554 5579 Fax: (020) 8554 1090 E-mail: sostalisman@btinternet.com

Trade Advertising Services, The Bungalow Manor Lane, Unit 11 K U S Industrial Estate, Hawarden, Deeside, Clwyd, CH5 3DP Tel: (01244) 520351 Fax: (01244) 536363 E-mail: tradeadvertising@aol.com

METAL LASER PROFILE CUTTING

A D J Fabrications Ltd, Unit 8a Bowes Road, Riverside Park Industrial Estate, Middlesbrough, Cleveland, TS2 1LU Tel: (01642) 225726 Fax: (01642) 242738

Caststitch Engineering Ltd, Unit 18, Daneside Business Park, Riverdane Road, Congleton, Cheshire, CW12 1UN Tel: (01260) 298188 Fax: (01260) 298188 E-mail: sales@caststitch/laser/cutting.fsnet.co.uk

▶ Cybercut Laser Profiling Ltd, 7 Manford Industrial Estate, Manor Road, Erith, Kent, DA8 2AJ Tel: (01322) 344890 Fax: (01322) 344899 E-mail: sales@cybercut.co.uk

J M J Precision Sheet Metal Ltd, 11 Boulton Road, Stevenage, Hertfordshire, SG1 4QX Tel: (01438) 360711 Fax: (01438) 360721

▶ Laser Products UK Ltd, Phoenix Works, Hope Bank Honley, Holmfirth, HD9 6PR Tel: (01484) 665870 Fax: (01484) 663581 E-mail: sales@laserproductsuk.com

▶ Prima Lasers, 121 Boundary Road, Wooburn Green, Buckinghamshire, HP10 0DJ Tel: (07841) 414839 E-mail: mail@primalasers.co.uk

Roscope Ltd, Telford Way, Telford Way Industrial Estate, Kettering, Northamptonshire, NN16 8UN Tel: (01536) 415644 Fax: (01536) 316929E-mail: roscope.sales@btconnect.com

Subcon Laser Cutting Ltd, Unit 7, Trident Business Park, Park St, Nuneaton, Warwickshire, CV11 4NS Tel: (024) 7664 2221 Fax: (024) 7634 2180 E-mail: info@subconlaser.co.uk

▶ Trim Profiles Ltd, C Fleming Way, Coronation Road, Cressex Business Park, High Wycombe, Buckinghamshire, HP12 3TS Tel: (01494) 440352 Fax: (01494) 448933

METAL LIGHTING EQUIPMENT SPINNERS

Ashford Metal Spinners Ltd, Unit E, Chilmington Works, Chilmington Green, Great Chart, Ashford, Kent, TN23 3DR Tel: (01233) 610404 E-mail: ams@ashfordmetalspinning.co.uk

METAL LIGHTING REFLECTORS

Lastolite Ltd, 1 Atlas Road, Coalville, Leicestershire, LE67 3FQ Tel: (01530) 813381 Fax: (01530) 830408 E-mail: sales@lastolite.com

R C Beresford Ltd, 48 St. Georges Street, Birmingham, B19 3QU Tel: 0121-236 8455 Fax: 0121-236 8493

Steel Spinnings Ltd, 94-96 Steward Street, Birmingham, B18 7AF Tel: 0121-456 3737 Fax: 0121-452 1616 E-mail: info@steelspinnings.com

Stockfield Manufacturing Co. Ltd, Sherbourne Road, Balsall Heath, Birmingham, B12 9DJ Tel: 0121-440 1333 Fax: 0121-440 8221 E-mail: info@stockfield.com

METAL LIQUID POURING FUNNELS

Hartle I G E Ltd, Unit 5, Ilford Trading Estate, Paycocke Road, Basildon, Essex, SS14 3DR Tel: (01268) 520496 Fax: (01268) 285477 E-mail: sales@hartleige.com

METAL LITTER BINS OR CONTAINERS

Main Event Sales & Hire, Unit 25, Coleshill Industrial Estate, Station Road, Coleshill, Birmingham, B46 1JP Tel: (01675) 464224 Fax: (01675) 466082 E-mail: sales@mainevent.co.uk
S M P Playgrounds Ltd, Thorpe Industrial Estate, Ten Acre Lane, Egham, Surrey, TW20 8RJ Tel: (01784) 489100 Fax: (01784) 431079 E-mail: sales@smp.co.uk
Wybone Ltd, Mason Way, Hoyland, Barnsley, South Yorkshire, S74 9TF Tel: (01226) 744010 Fax: (01226) 350105 E-mail: sales@wybone.co.uk

METAL LOUVRES

Air Marks Systems Ltd, A3-A4 Salcombe Road, Alfreton, Derbyshire, DE55 7RG Tel: (01773) 832228 Fax: (01773) 830186 E-mail: sales@airmarkssystems.ltd.uk
Brooke Air, J C House, Hurricane Way, Wickford, Essex, SS11 8YB Tel: (01268) 572266 Fax: (01268) 560606 E-mail: jcv@jchouse.freeserve.co.uk
Environmental Technology Ltd, Entech House, London Road, Woolmer Green, Knebworth, Hertfordshire, SG3 6JR Tel: (01438) 812812 Fax: (01438) 814224 E-mail: admin@etl-entech.co.uk
J C Vents Ltd, J.C. House, Hurricane Way, Wickford Business Park, Wickford, Essex, SS11 8YB Tel: (01268) 561122 Fax: (01268) 560606 E-mail: sales@jcvents.co.uk
Jordan Reflectors Ltd, 9-10 Seax Way, Basildon, Essex, SS15 6SW Tel: (01268) 415828 Fax: (01268) 410985 E-mail: sday@jordonreflectors.co.uk
Lighting & Ceiling Louvres Ltd, 7-13 Cutlers Road, South Woodham Ferrers, Chelmsford, CM3 5WA Tel: (01245) 321561 Fax: (01245) 325034 E-mail: sales@lcll.co.uk

METAL MACHINED COMPONENTS

Albion Automotive Ltd, Lancashire Enterprises Business Park, Centurian Way, Leyland, PR26 6TZ Tel: (01772) 831400 Fax: (01772) 831401
Select Engineering, Broad Ground Road, Redditch, Worcestershire, B98 8YP Tel: (01527) 517157 Fax: (01527) 517145 E-mail: info@select-engineering.co.uk

METAL MACHINING OR PLANING OR TURNING INCLUDING ON SITE

Andover Precision Ltd, Marriott Road, Dudley, West Midlands, DY2 0JZ Tel: (01384) 212655 Fax: (01384) 235863 E-mail: dave.andover@btconnect.com
Beard Engineering Co. Ltd, Pye Hill Road, Jacksdale, Nottingham, NG16 5LR Tel: (01773) 602535 Fax: (01773) 540185 E-mail: admin@beardengineering.co.uk
H.E. Butters & Co., Baldwins Gate, Newcastle, Staffordshire, ST5 5DA Tel: (01782) 680253
Croft Engineering Co. Ltd, Unit 7A, Parnall Road, Fishponds, Bristol, BS16 3JH Tel: 0117-958 3286 Fax: 0117-958 4390
Destec Engineering Ltd, Five Mile Lane, Washingborough, Lincoln, LN4 1AF Tel: (01522) 791721 Fax: (01522) 790033 E-mail: sales@destec.co.uk
F Worrall, Purdy Road, Batmans Hill Industrial Estate, Bilston, West Midlands, WV14 8UB Tel: (01902) 491366 Fax: (01902) 491366 E-mail: fworreluk@yahoo.com
Furmanite International Ltd, Furman House, Shap Road, Kendal, Cumbria, LA9 6RU Tel: (01539) 729009 Fax: (01539) 729359 E-mail: enquiry@furmanite.com
H C S Tools Ltd, Unit T, Millmeade Industrial Estate, Staines, Middlesex, TW18 4UK Tel: (01895) 257265 Fax: (01895) 235630 E-mail: alan@hcstools.fsnet.co.uk
Harrisons Pipeline Engineering Ltd, Curtis Road, Norwich, NR6 6RB Tel: (01603) 426928 Fax: (01603) 414225 E-mail: darren@harrisons-eng.com
Hay Metal Craft, Elemore House, Easington Lane, Houghton Le Spring, Tyne & Wear, DH5 0QT Tel: 0191-517 1284 Fax: 0191-517 1284
J J Service, Star Trading Estate, Ponthir, Newport, Gwent, NP18 1PQ Tel: (01633) 420552 Fax: (01633) 430224
Kerry Engineering, Unit 12 Isis Trading Estate, Swindon, SN1 2PG Tel: (01793) 423333 Fax: (01793) 423888
Nicol & Andrew plc, 2 Mossland Road, Hillington Industrial Estate, Glasgow, G52 4XZ Tel: 0141-882 4724 Fax: 0141-883 3350 E-mail: info@nicolandandrew.com
P R V Engineering Ltd, Pegasus House, Polo Grounds, New Inn, Pontypool, Gwent, NP4 0TW Tel: (01495) 769697 Fax: (01495) 769776 E-mail: enquiries@prv-engineering.co.uk
Reekie Machine (Sales) Ltd, South Street, Inchinnan Industrial Estate, Inchinnan, Renfrew, PA4 9RL Tel: 0141-812 0411 Fax: 0141-812 0137 E-mail: info@reekiemachining.co.uk
RWE npower, TS Ferrybridge, Old Great North Road, Knottingley, West Yorkshire, WF11 8PR Tel: (01977) 632201 Fax: (01977) 632311 E-mail: tsg@rwe.com
Simaron Engineering, Sunny Hill Road, Barnfields Industrial Estate, Leek, Staffordshire, ST13 5RG Tel: (01538) 386301
Thorne Engineers Ltd, Millfield Industrial Estate, York, YO19 6NA Tel: 01904 448890

METAL MANUFACTURERS' AGENTS/REPRESENTATIVES/ TRADING SUBSIDIARIES

▶ Booth Wire Products, Springvale Works, Elland Road, Brookfoot, Brighouse, West Yorkshire, HD6 2RN Tel: (01484) 714837 Fax: (01484) 710515 E-mail: sales@boothwire.co.uk
Bull Tubes Ltd, Unit 4, Park Road, Willenhall, West Midlands, WV13 1AH Tel: (01902) 608881 Fax: (01902) 602221 E-mail: enquiries@bulltube.com
Claydon Architectural Ltd, 11-12 Claydon Industrial Park, Great Blakenham, Ipswich, IP6 0NL Tel: (01473) 831000 Fax: (01473) 832154 E-mail: sales@cam-ltd.co.uk
Cotswold Tool & Press, Bromag Industrial Estate, Minster Lovell, Witney, Oxfordshire, OX29 0SR Tel: (01993) 772923 Fax: (01993) 779615 E-mail: sales@ctap.co.uk
Fab 24 Ltd, 326 Drumoyne Road, Glasgow, G51 4DX Tel: 0141-810 5656 Fax: 0141-810 5000 E-mail: info@fab24.co.uk
Newlyn Forge, 70 Bushey Hall Road, Bushey, WD23 2EQ Tel: (01923) 251660 Fax: (01923) 251660
Rack Systems (Engineering) Ltd, Kirkby Mills Industrial Estate, Kirkby Mills, Kirkbymoorside, York, YO62 6QR Tel: (01751) 432647 E-mail: info@racksystems.co.uk
Skytrex Model Makers, 1 Charnwood Business Park, North Road, Loughborough, Leicestershire, LE11 1LE Tel: (01509) 213789 Fax: (01509) 230874 E-mail: sales@skytrex.com

METAL MARKERS

I E L Identequip Ltd, Tenmat Buildings, Ashburton Road West, Trafford Park, Manchester, M17 1RU Tel: 0161-876 4679 Fax: 0161-876 0009 E-mail: iel@identequip.com
Industrial Services York Ltd, Station Estate, Station Road, Tadcaster, North Yorkshire, LS24 9SG Tel: (01937) 832761 Fax: (01937) 833012 E-mail: info@suremark.ltd.uk

METAL MERCHANTS IMPORTERS, EXPORTERS OR TRADERS, INTERNATIONAL

Aero Metals International, 53 Furze Hill Court, Furze Hill, Hove, East Sussex, BN3 1PG Tel: (01273) 383000 Fax: (01273) 387387 E-mail: info@aerometals.co.uk
Austin Trumanns Steel Ltd, Moss Lane, Worsley, Manchester, M28 3NH Tel: 0161-799 8882 Fax: 0161-790 1848 E-mail: sales@austin-trumanns.co.uk
C F Booth Engineering Ltd, Clarence Metal Works, Armer Street, Rotherham, South Yorkshire, S60 1AF Tel: (01709) 559198 Fax: (01709) 561859 E-mail: enquiries@cfboothltd.com
C G Rees Stainless Ltd, 325 North Road, Cardiff, CF14 3BP Tel: (029) 2061 5911 Fax: (029) 2061 8612 E-mail: cgrees@netcomuk.co.uk
Consolidated Stainless Recycling Ltd, 5-6 Station Road, Warley, Rowley Regis, West Midlands, B65 0JY Tel: 0121-561 4282 Fax: 0121-561 4708 E-mail: enquiries@consolidateduk.com
Derek Raphael, 6 York Street, London, W1U 6PL Tel: (020) 7535 1690 Fax: (020) 7535 1691
Hempel Metals UK Ltd, Primrose Park, Greasbrough Road, Rotherham, South Yorkshire, S60 1RH Tel: (01709) 376966 Fax: (01709) 361589 E-mail: info@hempel-wire.com
Lambert Metals International Ltd, Laburnum House, 1 Spring Villa Road, Edgware, Middlesex, HA8 7EB Tel: (020) 8951 4844 Fax: (020) 8951 1151 E-mail: howardmasters@lambert-metals.co.uk
M D International Ltd, 45 Circus Road, St. John's Wood, London, NW8 9JH Tel: (020) 7266 2939 Fax: (020) 7286 8291
Metal Enterprises & Co. Ltd, 150 Buckingham Palace Road, London, SW1W 9TR Tel: (020) 7730 6134 Fax: (020) 7730 0740
Mormet Alloys Ltd, Tamworth Road, Two Gates, Tamworth, Staffordshire, B77 1EA Tel: (01827) 285555 Fax: (01827) 286286 E-mail: sales@mormet.co.uk
Pritt & Co. Ltd, 23 Pembridge Square, London, W2 4DR Tel: (020) 7221 0909 Fax: (020) 7727 4837 E-mail: sales@pritt.co.uk
C.L. Prosser & Co. Ltd, 7 Parkfield Road, Stockton-On-Tees, Cleveland, TS18 3DJ Tel: (01642) 676043 Fax: (01642) 617418 E-mail: lenabain@freeserve.co.uk
Rugeley Aluminium Products Ltd, 5a Knighton Road, Sutton Coldfield, West Midlands, B74 4NY Tel: 0121-353 0006 Fax: 0121-353 5586 E-mail: teakandco@aol.com
Simportex, 452a Finchley Road, London, NW11 8DG Tel: (020) 8457 8770 Fax: (020) 8457 7484 E-mail: sales@simportex.com
Steel Plate & Sections Ltd, Mill House Forge Lane, Minworth Industrial Park, Minworth, Sutton Coldfield, West Midlands, B76 1AH Tel: 0121-313 4300 Fax: 0121-351 7924 E-mail: sales@steelplate.co.uk
Williamson & Co., Hill Street Works, Hill Street, Elgin, Morayshire, IV30 1AL Tel: (01343) 542260 Fax: (01343) 548107

METAL MERCHANTS SURPLUS/ LIQUIDATED/REDUNDANT JOB AND STOCK BUYERS, *See also individual metals*

Argent Independant Steel (UK) Ltd, Lake Road, Leeway Industrial Estate, Newport, Gwent, NP19 4WN Tel: (01633) 290260 Fax: (01633) 290911 E-mail: info@argentindependantsteel.ltd.uk
J S Bamforth & Co. Ltd, Top Vale Works, Colne Vale Road, Huddersfield, HD3 4NY Tel: (01484) 652777 Fax: (01484) 461460
Metal & Waste Recycling, Kenninghall Road, London, N18 2PD Tel: (020) 8807 4268 Fax: (020) 8884 0381

METAL MIRROR FRAMES

▶ Framework, 5 Station Parade, Ashford, Middlesex, TW15 2RX Tel: (01784) 258800 Fax: (01784) 250503 E-mail: sales@jandmframework.com

METAL MUSICAL INSTRUMENT COMPONENTS

A P Woolrich, Canalside, Huntworth, Bridgwater, Somerset, TA7 0AJ Tel: (01278) 663020 Fax: (01278) 663913 E-mail: sales@ap-woolrich.co.uk

METAL NAMEPLATES

A Weston, 23 Marsh St South, Stoke-on-Trent, ST1 1JA Tel: (01782) 214580 Fax: (01782) 214581
Abbey Craftsmen, 127 Haslemere Road, Liphook, Hampshire, GU30 7BX Tel: (01428) 727187 Fax: (0800) 0561362 E-mail: terry@abbey.go-plus.net
Alamode Engraving & Sign Co. Ltd, 3 Reform Street, Hull, HU2 8EF Tel: (01482) 323704 Fax: (01482) 216403 E-mail: sales@alamode.freeserve.co.uk
Autosigns Ltd, North Mills, Frog Island, Leicester, LE3 5DH Tel: 0116-262 9526 Fax: 0116-251 2889 E-mail: enquiries@autosigns.co.uk
B M G Industries Ltd, Amwell Lane, Stanstead Abbotts, Ware, Hertfordshire, SG12 8EB Tel: (01920) 870240 Fax: (01920) 870652 E-mail: bmgprint@aol.com
Beta Engravers (Northampton) Ltd, Clarence Avenue, Northampton, NN2 6NY Tel: (01604) 715152 Fax: (01604) 717131
C & S Nameplate Co. Ltd, 37 Vale Road, Portslade, Brighton, BN41 1GD Tel: (01273) 419646 Fax: (01273) 411316 E-mail: sales@candsnameplate.com
Chaintabs Ltd, 6 Grafton Rd, Sparkbrook, Birmingham, B11 1JP Tel: 0121-430 7957 Fax: 0121-430 7964
Commercial Nameplate Manufacturing Co., Butt End Mills, Chadwick Fold Lane, Mirfield, West Yorkshire, WF14 8PW Tel: (01924) 498652 Fax: (01924) 491167 E-mail: sales@commercialnameplates.co.uk
Ellis Rees & Co., The Old Foundry, Grove Road, Northfleet, Gravesend, Kent, DA11 9AX Tel: (01474) 567861 Fax: (01474) 537056
F & G Lancaster, 16 Hockley Street, Birmingham, B18 6BL Tel: 0121-554 1454 Fax: 0121-554 1454
Fife Signs Screen Printers, 3 Waverley Road, Kirkcaldy, Fife, KY1 3NH Tel: (01592) 655646 Fax: (01592) 655330 E-mail: sales@caledoniasigns.co.uk
G S M Graphic Art, Castlegarth Works, Masonic Lane, Thirsk, North Yorkshire, YO7 1PS Tel: (01845) 522184 Fax: (01845) 522206 E-mail: gsmgrapicarts@gsmgroup.co.uk
Good Acre Engraving, 120 Main Street, Sutton Bonington, Loughborough, Leicestershire, LE12 5PF Tel: (01509) 673082 Fax: (01509) 673082 E-mail: goodacre@ndirect.co.uk
Hitech Signmakers Ltd, 65-81 Townsend St, Glasgow, G4 0LA Tel: 0141-332 4111 Fax: 0141-331 1906 E-mail: sales@hitechsigns.co.uk
Hockerill Engraving, 2d Willis Vean Industrial Estate, Mullion, Helston, Cornwall, TR12 7DF Tel: (01326) 240400 Fax: (01326) 240620 E-mail: hockerill@dial.pipex.com
Howdens Signs Ltd, 94 Burley Road, Leeds, LS3 1JP Tel: 0113-245 7752 Fax: 0113-242 6993 E-mail: sales@howdenssigns.com
Links Engraving, 150 Duke Street, Edinburgh, EH6 8HR Tel: 0131-554 5156 Fax: 0131-553 6827 E-mail: sales@linksengraving.co.uk
M T M Products Ltd, Dunston Trading Estate, Foxwood Road, Sheepbridge, Chesterfield, Derbyshire, S41 9RF Tel: (01246) 450228 Fax: (01246) 455635 E-mail: sales@mtmlabels.co.uk
Rudd Macnamara Ltd, Holyhead Road, Birmingham, B21 0BS Tel: 0121-523 8437 Fax: 0121-551 7032 E-mail: rudd@nameplates.co.uk
The Manchester Rubber Stamp Company Ltd, 63 Red Bank, Manchester, M8 8RD Tel: 0161-834 1988 Fax: 0161-835 1529 E-mail: geoff@mrsengravers.co.uk
Mercury Engraving & Diesinking Ltd, Unit A5 Up Ringway, Bounds Green Industrial Estate, London, N11 2UD Tel: (0800) 1077118 Fax: (020) 8368 9018 E-mail: sales@mercuryengraving.co.uk
Multisigns, 31 Levellers Lane, Eynesbury, St. Neots, Cambridgeshire, PE19 2JL Tel: (01480) 471717 Fax: (01480) 471747 E-mail: sales@multisigns.co.uk
Paul Spencer Ltd, Consulate House, Sheffield Street, Stockport, Cheshire, SK4 1RU Tel: 0161-477 1688 Fax: 0161-480 4950 E-mail: sales@paulspencersigns.com
Plastic Metal & Profiles Ltd, Unit 99 14 North Tyne Industrial Estate, Whitley Road, Benton, Newcastle upon Tyne, NE12 9SZ Tel: 0191-266 5050 Fax: 0191-266 5724 E-mail: sales@ppnameplates.co.uk
The Principle Nameplate Company Ltd, Unit 19 St. Michaels Trading Estate, Bridport, Dorset, DT6 3RR Tel: (01308) 459900 Fax: (01308) 459911 E-mail: sales@platesandplaques.com
F.J. Rogers Engravers, 10 Tacket Street, Ipswich, IP4 1AY Tel: (01473) 251836
SJH Engraving, 74 Cecil Street, Birmingham, B19 3SU Tel: 0121-359 1321 Fax: 0121-333 4668
Trade Advertising Services, The Bungalow Manor Lane, Unit 11 K U S Industrial Estate, Hawarden, Deeside, Clwyd, CH5 3DP Tel: (01244) 520351 Fax: (01244) 536363 E-mail: tradeadvertising@aol.com
Trafalgar House Engraving, 4 Trafalgar Street, Brighton, BN1 4EQ Tel: (01273) 603498 Fax: (01273) 680181
Trapex Hardware Ltd, Pindar Road, Hoddesdon, Hertfordshire, EN11 0DE Tel: (01992) 462150 Fax: (01992) 446736 E-mail: info@trapex.com
Winken (Marking) Ltd, Eyre Street, Birmingham, B18 7AA Tel: 0121-456 3141 Fax: 0121-456 3151

METAL OFFICE FURNITURE

Bramwell Furniture Ltd, Unit 50 Crayford Industrial Estate, Swaisland Drive, Crayford, Dartford, DA1 4HS Tel: (01322) 556223 Fax: (01322) 550900 E-mail: sales@bramwellfurniture.co.uk
Caledonian Furniture Co. Ltd, 17 Glencryan Road, Cumbernauld, Glasgow, G67 2UH Tel: (01236) 735180 Fax: (01236) 734670 E-mail: sales@calfurn.co.uk
Dams International Ltd, Gores Road, Knowsley Industrial Park, Liverpool, L33 7XS Tel: 0151-548 7111 Fax: 0151-548 7071
DAMS International (Office Equipment) Ltd, Sefton Retail Park, Dunnings Bridge Road, Bootle, Merseyside, L30 6YL Tel: 0151-525 7222 Fax: 0151-530 1164
Diamik Solutions Ltd, A W Nielsen Road, Goole, North Humberside, DN14 6UE Tel: (0845) 1300690 Fax: (0845) 1300691 E-mail: sales@diamikbymorris.co.uk
Educational & Municipal Equipment Scotland, Blackaddie Road, Sanquhar, Dumfriesshire, DG4 6DE Tel: (01659) 50404 Fax: (01659) 50107 E-mail: sales@emescotland.co.uk
Emergent Crown Contract Office Furnishings Ltd, 59 Pellon Lane, HX, Halifax, West Yorkshire, HX1 5BE Tel: (01422) 349119 Fax: (01422) 206033 E-mail: sales@emergent-crown.co.uk
Evertaut, Lions Drive, Shadsworth Business Park, Blackburn, BB1 2QS Tel: (01254) 297880 Fax: (01254) 274859 E-mail: sales@evertaut.co.uk
F C Brown Steel Equipment Ltd, 17 Queens Road, Bisley, Woking, Surrey, GU24 9BJ Tel: (01483) 474577 Fax: (01483) 489962
Falcon Office Furniture, 1-2 Stillington Road, Easingwold, York, YO61 3JE Tel: (01347) 822911 Fax: (01347) 823503 E-mail: sales@falconfurniture.co.uk
Ernest Gill & Son, Holmfield Industrial Estate, Holmfield, Halifax, West Yorkshire, HX2 9TN Tel: (01422) 246286 Fax: (01422) 240716
Harling Fabrications Ltd, Bunns Bank, Attleborough, Norfolk, NR17 1QD Tel: (01953) 453682 Fax: (01953) 453758 E-mail: harlingfabs@btconnect.com
Herman Ltd, Herman Miller Estate, Bath Road, Chippenham, Wiltshire, SN14 0AT Tel: (01249) 657011 Fax: (01249) 654942

METAL OFFICE FURNITURE – *continued*

J R Bourne Powder Coatings Ltd, Beckingham Road, Great Totham, Maldon, Essex, CM9 8EA Tel: (01621) 892972 Fax: (01621) 893299 E-mail: sales@jrbourne.co.uk

Komfort Office Environments Plc, Units 1-10, Whittle Way, Crawley, West Sussex, RH10 9RW Tel: (01293) 592500 Fax: (01293) 553271 E-mail: general@komfort.com

Mercol (Office Furniture) Ltd, Primrose Mill, Ratcliffe Street, Darwin, Blackburn, BB3 2BZ Tel: (01254) 775500 Fax: (01254) 774911

Metal Office Equipment Ltd, 52a Chiswick Avenue, Mildenhall, Bury St. Edmunds, Suffolk, IP28 7AY Tel: (01638) 716960 Fax: (01638) 717875

John Pulsford Associates Ltd, 4 Sphere Industrial Estate, Campfield Road, St. Albans, Hertfordshire, AL1 5HT Tel: (01727) 840800 Fax: (01727) 840083 E-mail: info@jpa-furniture.com

▶ R M D Office Solutions, 1 Montrose Terrace, Old Wrexham Road, Gresford, Wrexham, Clwyd, LL12 8UN Tel: (01978) 853721 Fax: (01978) 856470 E-mail: enquiries@officesols.co.uk

Remploy Furniture Group Ltd, Bank Top, Blackburn, BB2 1TH Tel: (01254) 52271 Fax: (01254) 618419 E-mail: blackburn@remploy.co.uk

Roc Furniture Ltd, Austin Way, Birmingham, B42 1DF Tel: 0121-358 2436 Fax: 0121-358 6016 E-mail: sales@roc-office.co.uk

Smiths Office & Commercial Furniture, Windsor Road, Redditch, Worcestershire, B97 6DJ Tel: (01527) 66663 Fax: (01527) 69333 E-mail: info@smithseating.co.uk

Souness & Boyne Interiors Ltd, Suite 8, Adam Ferguson House, Station Road, Musselburgh, Midlothian, EH21 7PQ Tel: 0131-653 2228 Fax: 0131-653 2229

TBS (South Wales) Ltd, Triumph Works, The Willows, Merthyr Tydfil, Mid Glamorgan, CF48 1YH Tel: (01685) 384041 Fax: (01685) 352202 E-mail: sales@triumph-tbs.com

Tract Ltd, Mckay Trading Estate, Station Approach, Bicester, Oxfordshire, OX26 6BF Tel: (01869) 326300 Fax: (01869) 323430 E-mail: info@tract.ltd.uk

Tubular Furniture Ltd, Unit F1-F3, Coedcae Industrial Estate, Pontyclun, Mid Glamorgan, CF72 9HG Tel: (01443) 229326 Fax: (01443) 230493 E-mail: sales@tubular-furniture.co.uk

Wake Industries Ltd, Basin Lane, Tamworth, Staffordshire, B77 2AH Tel: (01827) 65864 Fax: (01827) 53326 E-mail: info@wakeindustries.co.uk

METAL OFFICE FURNITURE COMPONENTS

Amerson Ltd, 9 Albany Road, Granby Industrial Estate, Weymouth, Dorset, DT4 9TH Tel: (01305) 206101 Fax: (01305) 206106 E-mail: amersonsales@amerson.co.uk

Harling Fabrications Ltd, Bunns Bank, Attleborough, Norfolk, NR17 1QD Tel: (01953) 453682 Fax: (01953) 453758 E-mail: harlingfabs@btconnect.com

▶ R M D Office Solutions, 1 Montrose Terrace, Old Wrexham Road, Gresford, Wrexham, Clwyd, LL12 8UN Tel: (01978) 853721 Fax: (01978) 856470 E-mail: enquiries@officesols.co.uk

S R Tubular Systems, Pioneer Mill, Kelly Street, Blackburn, BB2 4PJ Tel: (01254) 689922 Fax: (01254) 689933

Woodstock Leabank Office Furniture, Corrie Way, Bredbury, Stockport, Cheshire, SK6 2ST Tel: 0161-494 1242 Fax: 0161-494 4409 E-mail: sales@woodstockleabank.co.uk

METAL OXIDE SEMICONDUCTOR (MOS) INTEGRATED CIRCUITS (IC) TO SPECIFICATION

Oxford Semiconductor Ltd, 25 Milton Park, Milton, Abingdon, Oxfordshire, OX14 4SH Tel: (01235) 824900 Fax: (01235) 821141 E-mail: sales@oxsemi.com

St Microelectronics, 1000 Aztec West, Almondsbury, Bristol, BS32 4SQ Tel: (01454) 616616 Fax: (01454) 617910 E-mail: postmaster@st.com

METAL PALLET OR STILLAGES

K. Hartwall Ltd, Green Lane Industrial Estate, Spennymoor, County Durham, DL16 6BP Tel: (01388) 824700 Fax: (01388) 824724

K. Hertwall Ltd, Flemington Road, Glenrothes, Fife, KY7 5QJ Tel: (01592) 753745 Fax: (01592) 753747

Kenneth Whitehouse, Mill Lane, Fazeley, Tamworth, Staffordshire, B78 3QD Tel: (01827) 261678 Fax: (01827) 251469 E-mail: kenw@clara.co.uk

METAL PEN NIBS

D Leonardt & Co., New Road, Highley, Bridgnorth, Shropshire, WV16 6NN Tel: (01746) 861203 Fax: (01746) 862296 E-mail: sales@leonardt.com

METAL PICKLING

Alkemi M F Technologies, Clwyd Close, Manor Lane, Hawarden, Deeside, Clwyd, CH5 3PZ Tel: (01244) 536299 Fax: (01244) 520363 E-mail: simonn@alkemimetalfinishing.co.uk

METAL PICTURE FRAME MOULDINGS

▶ Alderglade Picture Framers, The Alderglade, Harefield Road, Uxbridge, Middlesex, UB8 1PN Tel: (01895) 231205 E-mail: john@alderglade.com

D J Simons & Sons Ltd, 122-150 Hackney Road, London, E2 7QL Tel: (020) 7739 3744 Fax: (020) 7739 4452 E-mail: dsimons@djsimons.co.uk

METAL PIPES, *See individual metal or application sometimes called Tube*

METAL PLATE ROLLING

Accurate Section Benders Ltd, Dawley Brook Road, Kingswinford, West Midlands, DY6 7AU Tel: (01384) 402402 Fax: (01384) 402462 E-mail: sales@accuratesectionbenders.co.uk

Barnshaw Plate Rollers Ltd, Anchor Lane, Coseley, Bilston, West Midlands, WV14 9NE Tel: (01902) 880250 Fax: (01902) 880505

J J Haslam Ltd, Park Works, Clegg Street, Bolton, BL2 6DU Tel: (01204) 527342 Fax: (01204) 388259 E-mail: malcolm.green@jjhaslam.com

JMR Section Benders Ltd, Unit 8 Sterling Industrial Estate, Rainham Road South, Dagenham, Essex, RM10 8TX Tel: (020) 8593 7324 Fax: (020) 8595 6139 E-mail: sales@jmrsectionbenders.co.uk

T H E Section Bending Co. Ltd, Houghton Road, North Anston Trading Estate, North Anston, Sheffield, S25 4JJ Tel: (01909) 550080 Fax: (01909) 550114 E-mail: sales@thebending.co.uk

Wyko Tubes, Vauxhall Street, Queens Cross, Dudley, W. Midlands, DY1 1TA Tel: (01384) 237816 Fax: (01384) 457463 E-mail: sales@wyko-tubes.co.uk

METAL POLISHING, *See also Metal Finishing etc*

▶ BOMBER COUNTY CUSTOMS, Drakes holdings, Ferry Road, Fiskerton, Lincoln, LN3 4HU Tel: (07958) 018368 E-mail: petescustom24@yahoo.co.uk

Caerphilly Metal Polishers, 1 The Rhos, Bedwas Road, Caerphilly, Mid Glamorgan, CF83 3AU Tel: (029) 2086 7837 Fax: (029) 2086 7837

E T Flower & Co. Ltd, 26-30 Theobald Street, Borehamwood, Hertfordshire, WD6 4SG Tel: (020) 8953 2343 Fax: (020) 8905 1845

▶ Euro Polishing Technology, 83 Moorhey Street, Oldham, OL4 1JE Tel: 0161-628 4466 Fax: 0161-628 4477 E-mail: europolishing@hotmail.co.uk

High Class Metal Polishing, Unit 1-2 Lower Mills, Bridgend, Stonehouse, Gloucestershire, GL10 2BB Tel: (01453) 825464 Fax: (01453) 825464

J S D Polishers Ltd, 19-21 Hatchett Street, Hockley, Birmingham, B19 3NX Tel: 0121-359 4880 Fax: 0121-359 4880

▶ K & S Metal Polishers, Unit G10 Rudford Industrial Estate, Ford Road, Ford, Arundel, West Sussex, BN18 0BD Tel: (01903) 718180 Fax: (01903) 718180 E-mail: ksmetal@talk21.com

▶ Mirror Finish Metal Polishing, 2 Fryers Road, Walsall, WS2 7LZ Tel: (01922) 402080

Wasp Metal Polishing Ltd, Unit 4 Beaver Industrial Estate, Southmoor Lane, Havant, Hampshire, PO9 1JW Tel: (023) 9245 0011 Fax: (023) 9245 0011 E-mail: director@waspmetalpolishing.com

METAL POLISHING, SHEET, MIRROR FINISH

▶ Oxford Instruments Analytical Ltd, Halifax Road, High Wycombe, Buckinghamshire, HP12 3SE Tel: (01494) 442255 Fax: (01494) 524129 E-mail: analytical@oxinst.co.uk

METAL POWDER MANUFRS, *See also headings for particular types*

Active Metals, Unit F Holbrook Green, Holbrook Industrial Estate, Holbrook, Sheffield, S20 3FE Tel: 0114-247 3662 Fax: 0114-247 8372 E-mail: mlee@active-metals.freeserve.co.uk

Aluminium Powder Co. Ltd, Forge Lane, Minworth Industrial Park, Minworth, Sutton Coldfield, West Midlands, B76 1AH Tel: 0121-351 4686 Fax: 0121-351 7604 E-mail: enquiries@alpoco.co.uk

Richard Cooke Engineering Steels Ltd, 38 Moorgate Road, Rotherham, South Yorkshire, S60 2AG Tel: (01709) 830214 Fax: (01709) 830216 E-mail: sales@rces.co.uk

Debdale Metal Powders Ltd, Waterhouse Road, Manchester, M18 7HZ Tel: 0161-231 1504 Fax: 0161-223 2763 E-mail: info@debdale.com

Makin Metal Powers Ltd, Buckley Road, Rochdale, Lancashire, OL12 9DT Tel: (01706) 717317 Fax: (01706) 717303 E-mail: mmp@makin-metals.com

PBW Metal Products Ltd, Bridge End Mills, Tong Lane, Whitworth, Rochdale, Lancashire, OL12 8BG Tel: (01706) 854354 Fax: (01706) 854330 E-mail: sales@pbwmetal.com

Pometon Ltd, 5, Queensway Link Industrial Estate, Telford, Shropshire, TF3 3DN Tel: (01952) 299777 Fax: (01952) 299008 E-mail: sales@pometon.demon.co.uk

METAL PRESSINGS

Bridgford Pressings Ltd, Building No. 3 Gotham Business Complex, Leake Road, Gotham, Nottingham, NG11 0LB Tel: 0115-983 0884 Fax: 0115-983 0155 E-mail: enquiries@bridgfordpressings.co.uk

▶ Bristol Bending Sanoh Ltd, Quedgeley Court, Shepherd Road, Gloucester, GL2 5EL Tel: (01452) 303062 Fax: (01452) 300575

Broadway Stamping Ltd, Denbigh Road, Bletchley, Milton Keynes, MK1 1DT Tel: (01908) 647703 Fax: (01908) 649279 E-mail: broadways@broadwaystampings.co.uk

Cefn Strain Gauges, Unit E26 Hirwaun Industrial Estate, Hirwaun, Aberdare, Mid Glamorgan, CF44 9UP Tel: (01685) 814451 Fax: (01685) 814342 E-mail: rob@cefn-sg.sfnet.co.uk

Dene Spring UK Ltd, Bridge Works, Allum Lane, Borehamwood, Hertfordshire, WD6 3LT Tel: (020) 8953 6888 Fax: (020) 8207 5872 E-mail: deor@denespringuk.co.uk

European Springs & Pressings Ltd, Chaffinch Business Park, Croydon Road, Beckenham, Kent, BR3 4DW Tel: (020) 8663 1800 Fax: (020) 8663 1900 E-mail: sales@europeansprings.com

Fowkes & Danks Ltd, Howard Road, Park Farm Industrial Estate, Redditch, Worcestershire, B98 7SE Tel: (01527) 830800 Fax: (01527) 830801 E-mail: enquiries@fowkes&danks.co.uk

G & O Springs Ltd, Broad Ground Road, Lakeside, Redditch, Worcestershire, B98 8YP Tel: (01527) 523764 Fax: (01527) 527920 E-mail: steve@g-o-springs.com

Harlow Pressings Ltd, 57-60 Llantarnam Industrial Park, Cwmbran, Gwent, NP44 3AW Tel: (01633) 487400 Fax: (01633) 863010

Holdfast Manufacturing Ltd, Platts Road, Amblecote, Stourbridge, West Midlands, DY8 4YR Tel: (01384) 397575 Fax: (01384) 390458

Jeffark Engineering & Metal Pressings Ltd, 2 Lane End Road, Sands Industrial Estate, High Wycombe, Buckinghamshire, HP12 4HG Tel: (01494) 471454 Fax: (01494) 471131 E-mail: enquiries@jeffark.co.uk

Juraise (Springs) Ltd, Sugarbrook Mill, Buntsford Hill, Stoke Pound, Bromsgrove, Worcestershire, B60 3AR Tel: (01527) 878811 Fax: (01527) 877537 E-mail: adrian@juraise.com

Prestige Engineering, 27 Thornleigh Trading Estate, Dudley, West Midlands, DY2 8UB Tel: (01384) 234488 Fax: (01384) 238884 E-mail: prestigeengineering@btconnect.com

Prestision Engineers, 15-16 St Andrews Industrial Estate, Sydney Road, Birmingham, B9 4QB Tel: 0121-772 4414 Fax: 0121-771 0472 E-mail: geoff@prestision.co.uk

Roscope Ltd, Telford Way, Telford Way Industrial Estate, Kettering, Northamptonshire, NN16 8UN Tel: (01536) 415644 Fax: (01536) 316929E-mail: roscope.sales@btconnect.com

Thornbury Manufacturing Ltd, Darklake View, Estover, Plymouth, PL6 7TL Tel: (01752) 696697 Fax: (01752) 696698 E-mail: sales@tml-ltd.com

METAL PRESSINGS TO SPECIFICATION

G & O Springs Ltd, Broad Ground Road, Lakeside, Redditch, Worcestershire, B98 8YP Tel: (01527) 523764 Fax: (01527) 527920 E-mail: steve@g-o-springs.com

Holdfast Manufacturing Ltd, Platts Road, Amblecote, Stourbridge, West Midlands, DY8 4YR Tel: (01384) 397575 Fax: (01384) 390458

METAL PRETREATMENT CHEMICALS

Kluthe, 314 Midsummer Boulevard, Milton Keynes, MK9 2UB Tel: (01908) 440120 Fax: (01908) 440121 E-mail: info@kluthe.co.uk

Rem, 5 Stockton End, Sandy, Bedfordshire, SG19 1RY Tel: (01767) 691592 Fax: (01767) 691599 E-mail: mmorse@remchem.co.uk

METAL PRETREATMENT SERVICES

Aerospace Systems & Technologies Group Ltd, Unit 24 Number One Industrial Estate, Consett, County Durham, DH8 6SR Tel: (01207) 582811 Fax: (01207) 582812 E-mail: enquiries@cav-aerospace.net

Barley Chalu Ltd, Ayton Road, Wymondham, Norfolk, NR18 0QH Tel: (01953) 602771 Fax: (01953) 606631 E-mail: sales@barleychalu.co.uk

METAL PRINTING

B S P Ltd, 26 Balmer Cut, Buckingham Industrial Estate, Buckingham, MK18 1UL Tel: (01280) 813881 Fax: (01280) 822429 E-mail: sales@buckscreenprint.co.uk

Exel Engraving Ltd, 19 Brickfields Industrial Estate, Finway Road, Hemel Hempstead, Hertfordshire, HP2 7QA Tel: (01442) 270510 Fax: (01442) 270520 E-mail: exelsales@aol.com

Hyspec Screen Process Printers, Brunel Road, Bedford, MK41 9TG Tel: (01234) 217972 Fax: (01234) 328182 E-mail: info@hyspec.co.uk

Metalprint Signs & Nameplates, 37 The Pentlands, Kintbury, Hungerford, Berkshire, RG17 9XB Tel: (01488) 658670 Fax: (01488) 658670 E-mail: fp@metalplaques.co.uk

METAL PRINTING TYPE

▶ J Jays Ltd, Unit 4, Baron Court, Chandlers Way, Southend-On-Sea, SS2 5SE Tel: (01702) 461777 Fax: (01702) 465176 E-mail: adverts@jjays.com

METAL PRODUCT DESIGN AND DEVELOPMENT SERVICES

Metal Art Co., Cadgerhill, Glendaveny, Peterhead, Aberdeenshire, AB42 3DY Tel: (01779) 838888 Fax: (01779) 838333 E-mail: info@classicmetalart.co.uk

R & G Metal Products, 172-174 Colne Road, Twickenham, TW2 6RE Tel: (020) 8893 3300

S M J Sheetmetal Fabrications, Wild Street, Dukinfield, Cheshire, SK16 4DL Tel: 0161-343 3109 Fax: 0161-343 3109

J. Walsh Spinnings, Unit 2, 58 Caroline Street, Hockley, Birmingham, B3 1UF Tel: 0121-233 3258 Fax: 0121-233 3258

METAL PRODUCTS

▶ Adamant Safe & Lock Co. Ltd, Adamant House Unit 1, Princeville Road Industrial Estate, Duncombe Street, Bradford, West Yorkshire, BD8 9AJ Tel: (01274) 726698 Fax: (01274) 543358

▶ Architectural Security & Protection Ltd, 22c Orgreave CR, Sheffield, S13 9NQ Tel: 0114-288 0041 Fax: 0114-288 0041

▶ Aspect Metalcraft, Unit 8, Potts Marsh Industrial Estate, Eastbourne Road, Westham, Pevensey, East Sussex, BN24 5NH Tel: (01323) 735537 Fax: (01323) 765666 E-mail: sales@aspectmetalcraft.com

Avonstar Trading Co. Ltd, 44 Barn Street, Digbeth, Birmingham, B5 5QB Tel: 0121-643 0408 Fax: 0121-643 1104 E-mail: kevin.taylor@avonstar.co.uk

▶ B I Z Engineering Ltd, Millmarsh Lane, Brunsdown, Enfield, Middlesex, EN3 7QA Tel: (020) 8443 3300 Fax: (020) 8804 6672 E-mail: sales@bizengineering.com

Carpet Accessory Trims Ltd, Unit 24c Park Avenue Estate, Sundon Park Road, Luton, LU3 3BP Tel: (01582) 561500 Fax: (01582) 561900 E-mail: sales@tat-accs.com

▶ China Project Management Ltd, 1 Lady Place, Livingston, West Lothian, EH54 6TB Tel: (01506) 411866 E-mail: info@chinapro.co.uk

▶ Citysafe Wholesale Ltd, Unit 1-4 Mortimers Farm Industrial Estate, Romsey Road, Ower, Romsey, Hampshire, SO51 6AF Tel: (023) 8081 4181 Fax: (023) 8081 2771 E-mail: admin@citysafe.co.uk

▶ D K T Group Ltd, Albany Court Blenheim Road, Airfield Industrial Estate, Ashbourne, Derbyshire, DE6 1HA Tel: (01335) 300222 Fax: (01335) 300353

▶ Discount Store, 53 Westmuir Street, Glasgow, G31 5EL Tel: 0141-556 7321 Fax: 0141-556 7188

METAL PRODUCTS – *continued*

▶ Dmi Fabrications, 2 Derby Works, Derby Road, Bootle, Merseyside, L20 8LQ Tel: 0151-922 4015 Fax: 0151-922 4019

▶ Environmental Hygiene Products Ltd, Unit 1 & 3, & 8 Blairlaith Industrial Estate, Tain, Ross-Shire, IV19 1EB Tel: (01862) 893978 Fax: (01862) 894455

▶ Glengowan Engineering Ltd, Block 5, Chapelhall Industrial Estate, Chapelhall, Airdrie, Lanarkshire, ML6 8QH Tel: (01236) 753355 Fax: (01236) 767610 E-mail: sales@glengowan.co.uk

▶ Greenfarm Engineering, The Bungalow, Station Road, Wath-upon-Dearne, Rotherham, South Yorkshire, S63 7DG Tel: (01709) 876711 Fax: (01709) 875899

▶ Henley Metal Products, Whitley, Edge Lane, Henley-in-Arden, West Midlands, B95 5DT Tel: (01564) 795389 Fax: (01564) 795171

▶ J & M Fabrications, 1c Saxby Road Industrial Estate, Hudson Road, Melton Mowbray, Leicestershire, LE13 1BS Tel: (01664) 560118 Fax: (01664) 560119

▶ K O Engineering Services, 1 Daniels Farm, Wash Road, Basildon, Essex, SS15 4AZ Tel: (01268) 281500 Fax: (01268) 281500 E-mail: info@koengineeringservices.com

▶ MB Fabrications, Unit 18, Yeoman Business Estate, Wharf Road, Burton-on-Trent, Staffordshire, DE14 1PZ Tel: 01283 516026 Fax: 01283 516026

▶ Needham Electrical Ltd, Maitland Road, Lion Barn Industrial Estate, Needham Market, Ipswich, IP6 8NZ Tel: (01449) 722642 Fax: (01449) 722182

▶ Peglar, Belmont Works, St. Catherines Avenue, Doncaster, South Yorkshire, DN4 8DF Tel: (0870) 1200285 Fax: (01302) 367661

▶ Plan Engineers, 1 Ashton Grange Industrial Estate, Bryn Road, Ashton-in-Makerfield, Wigan, Lancashire, WN4 8BX Tel: (01942) 271299 Fax: (01942) 721756

▶ Powder Process Technology Ltd, Unit 18 Tardebigge Court, Hewell Lane, Redditch, Worcestershire, B97 6QJ Tel: (01527) 540404

▶ Ramsay & Sons Forfar Ltd, 61 West High Street, Forfar, Angus, DD8 1BG Tel: (01307) 462255 Fax: (01307) 466956

▶ Robert Dyas Holdings Ltd, 2 Old Basing Mall, Basingstoke, Hampshire, RG21 7AW Tel: (01256) 329153

▶ S R Fabrications Ltd, Holm Industrial Estate, Barterholm Road, Paisley, Renfrewshire, PA2 6PF Tel: 0141-840 4934 Fax: 0141-840 4935

▶ Stikatak Ltd, J Braintree Industrial Estate, Braintree Road, Ruislip, Middlesex, HA4 0EJ Tel: (020) 8839 4405 Fax: (020) 8842 1387 E-mail: enquiry@stikatak.co.uk

▶ T R Fabrications Ltd, Houghton Road North Anston Estate, North Anston Trading Estate, North Anston, Sheffield, S25 4JJ Tel: (01909) 568777 Fax: (01909) 550630

▶ Total Hygiene Ltd, Bank House, 182-186 Washway Road, Sale, Cheshire, M33 6RN Tel: 0161-969 1199 Fax: 0161-973 2711 E-mail: info@total-hygiene.co.uk

▶ Window Fitters Mate, Unit 27 Riverside Estate, Sir Thomas Longley Road, Medway City Estate, Rochester, Kent, ME2 4DP Tel: (01634) 717714 Fax: (01634) 717714

▶ X Met, 106 107, Newhouse Industrial Estate, Newhouse, Motherwell, Lanarkshire, ML1 5RX Tel: (01698) 733533 Fax: (01698) 734617

METAL PROTECTION PAINTS

Avenue Coatings, 3 David Road, Colnbrook, Slough, SL3 0TW Tel: (01753) 686888 Fax: (01753) 684684 E-mail: paint@avenue-group.co.uk

Green Speed Power Coating, Slack Street, Macclesfield, Cheshire, SK11 7JP Tel: (01625) 439993 Fax: (01625) 439993

Hempel UK Ltd, Ty Coch Way, Llantarnam Industrial Park, Cwmbran, Gwent, NP44 3XF Tel: (01633) 874024 Fax: (01633) 489089 E-mail: sales@hempel.com

Industrial Paint Services S W Ltd, 1 Lyte Building, Wern Trading Estate, Rogerstone, Newport, Gwent, NP10 9FQ Tel: (01633) 897766 Fax: (01633) 897716

METAL PUNCH TOOLS

Rydal Precision Tools Ltd, Unit 5 The Technology Centre, London Road, Swanley, Kent, BR8 7AN Tel: (01322) 614661 Fax: (01322) 614760 E-mail: sales@rydal.co.uk

METAL PURLINS

Albion Section Ltd, Albion Road, West Bromwich, West Midlands, B70 8BD Tel: 0121-553 1877 Fax: 0121-553 5507 E-mail: albionsections@enterprise.net

Bridge Steel Sections, PO Box 92, Smethwick, West Midlands, B66 2PA Tel: 0121-555 1460 Fax: 0121-555 1461 E-mail: sales.ssl@hadleygroup.co.uk

Hi-Span Ltd, Ayton Road, Wymondham, Norfolk, NR18 0RD Tel: (01953) 603081 Fax: (01953) 607842 E-mail: sales@hi-span.com

Metsec plc, Broadwell Works, Birmingham Road, Oldbury, West Midlands, B69 4HE Tel: 0121-552 1541 E-mail: windows@metsec.com

Ward Insulated Panels Ltd, Sherburn, Malton, North Yorkshire, YO17 8PQ Tel: (01944) 710591 Fax: (01944) 710777 E-mail: wbc@wards.co.uk

METAL RAILINGS

▶ A & H Wrought Iron Work, 14b Smeaton Industrial Estate, Hayfield Road, Kirkcaldy, Fife, KY1 2HE Tel: (07949) 501853 E-mail: adam.guthrie@sky.com

Arc Fabrication Ltd, 2 Gourley Place, London, N15 5NF Tel: (020) 8800 2557 Fax: (020) 7706 1248 E-mail: sales@arcfabrications.com

▶ Brook Metal Design Ltd, Brook Farm Industrial Estate, Stapleford Road, Romford, RM4 1EJ Tel: (01708) 687420

Caroway Fabrications Ltd, 40 Aston Road, Waterlooville, Hampshire, PO7 7XF Tel: (023) 9226 7614 Fax: (023) 9226 2290

▶ Rowley Engineering Co. Ltd, Tollgate Industrial Estate, Stafford, ST16 3HS Tel: (01785) 223831 Fax: (01785) 222764 E-mail: sales@roweng.com

T J Blackburn & Son, Victoria, Ableton Lane, Severn Beach, Bristol, BS35 4PR Tel: (01454) 632905 Fax: (01454) 632905

METAL REFINING SERVICES

Metallic Extractors (Non-Ferrous) Ltd, Marsh Lane, Water Orton, Birmingham, B46 1NS Tel: 0121-747 3611 Fax: 0121-749 3769 E-mail: srap@beavermetals.com

METAL REPAIR MATERIALS

T M S UK Ltd, Knightswood Terrace, Blantyre, Glasgow, G72 9BQ Tel: (01698) 711103 Fax: (01698) 711103 E-mail: enquiries@tmsuk.org

METAL RESTORATION

P.J. Miller Ltd, The Old Baths, Main Road, Far Cotton, Northampton, NN4 8EN Tel: (01604) 767710 Fax: (01604) 764884

METAL ROOF CLADDING

Ash & Lacy Building Systems, Bromford Lane, West Bromwich, West Midlands, B70 7JJ Tel: 0121-525 1444 Fax: 0121-524 8435 E-mail: kay.hall@ashandlacy.com

BCC Stockholders Ltd, Pontardulais Road, Gorseinon, Swansea, SA4 4FQ Tel: (01792) 893985 Fax: (01792) 893124 E-mail: sales@rollaclad.com

▶ Cheshire Rooffix, 6 St. Augustines Road, Stockport, Cheshire, SK3 0JN Tel: (01614) 771449 Fax: (01614) 771449 E-mail: john.h.carroll@btinternet.com

Corus Building Systems, Units 1-3 Fishwicks Industrial Estate, Kilbuck Lane, St. Helens, Merseyside, WA11 9SZ Tel: (01942) 295500 Fax: (01942) 272136E-mail: info@kalzip.co.uk

▶ Coverworld UK Ltd, Mansfield Road, Bramley Vale, Chesterfield, Derbyshire, S44 5GA Tel: (01246) 454711 Fax: (01246) 858223 E-mail: sales@coverworld.co.uk

Gleno Industries Ltd, Mansfield Road, Bramley Vale, Chesterfield, Derbyshire, S44 5GA Tel: 01246 858224 Fax: 01246 858223 E-mail: scott.wall@coverworld.co.uk

Rigidal Systems Ltd, Unit 62 Blackpole Trading Estate West, Worcester, WR3 8ZJ Tel: (01905) 750500 Fax: (01905) 750555 E-mail: info@rigidal.co.uk

Ruukki UK Ltd, The Old Granary, Riccall Grange King Rudding Lane, Riccall, York, YO19 6QL Tel: (01757) 249334 Fax: (01757) 249335 E-mail: claddingsalesuk@ruukki.com

Ward Insulated Panels Ltd, Sherburn, Malton, North Yorkshire, YO17 8PQ Tel: (01944) 710591 Fax: (01944) 710777 E-mail: wbc@wards.co.uk

METAL ROOF FITTINGS OR FASTENINGS OR ACCESSORIES

Building Product Design Ltd, 2 Brooklands Road, Sale, Cheshire, M33 3SS Tel: 0161-905 5700 Fax: 0161-905 2085 E-mail: postmaster@buildingproductdesign.com

▶ Cheshire Rooffix, 6 St. Augustines Road, Stockport, Cheshire, SK3 0JN Tel: (01614) 771449 Fax: (01614) 771449 E-mail: john.h.carroll@btinternet.com

Construction Fastener Techniques, C F T House, Mill Race Lane, Stourbridge, West Midlands, DY8 1JN Tel: (01384) 442277 Fax: (01384) 442999 E-mail: sales@cftltd.co.uk

D Fix Bridgend Ltd, Newton Yard, Cemetery Road, Bridgend, Mid Glamorgan, CF31 1NA Tel: (01656) 669609 Fax: (01656) 767584 E-mail: mikecoleman@datapowertool.co.uk

Fixfast Fasteners & Fixing Devices Ltd, Forge Works, Horsham Road, Mid Holmwood, Dorking, Surrey, RH5 4EJ Tel: (01306) 880299 Fax: (01306) 880038 E-mail:

Lafarge Roofing Technical Centers Ltd, Sussex Manor Business Park, Gatwick Road, Crawley, West Sussex, RH10 9NZ Tel: (01293) 618418 Fax: (01293) 614548

Matthews Of Keynsham Ltd, Keynsham Road, Keynsham, Bristol, BS31 2DE Tel: 0117-986 4356 Fax: 0117-986 7491 E-mail: sales@matthewsofkeynsham.com

Powell Gee & Co Ltd, PO Box 15, Wednesbury, West Midlands, WS10 0UF Tel: 0121-556 6729 Fax: 0121-556 6729 E-mail: sales@powellgee.co.uk

SFS Intec Ltd, 153 Kirkstall Road, Leeds, LS4 2AT Tel: 0113-208 5500 Fax: 0113-208 5519 E-mail: gb.leeds@sfsintec.biz

METAL ROOFING MATERIALS

Haironville T A C Ltd, Abbotsfield Road, Abbotsfield Road, Abbotsfield Industrial Park, St. Helens, Merseyside, WA9 4HU Tel: (01744) 818181 Fax: (01744) 851555 E-mail: technical@haironvilletac.co.uk

▶ Planwell Roofing Supplies Ltd, The Roofing Centre, March Road East, Buckie, Banffshire, AB56 4BY Tel: (01542) 832170 Fax: (01542) 832182 E-mail: sales@planwell.co.uk

METAL SAFETY CONTAINERS

Hartle I G E Ltd, Unit 5, Ilford Trading Estate, Paycocke Road, Basildon, Essex, SS14 3DR Tel: (01268) 520496 Fax: (01268) 285477 E-mail: sales@hartleige.com

METAL SANITARY WARE FITTINGS

Polypipe Bathroom & Kitchen Products Ltd, Edlington Lane, Warmsworth, Doncaster, South Yorkshire, DN4 9LS Tel: (01302) 310666 Fax: (01302) 856421

Sanitary Appliances Ltd, 3 Sandiford Road, Sutton, Surrey, SM3 9RN Tel: (020) 8641 0310 Fax: (020) 8641 6426 E-mail: info@sanitaryappliances.co.uk

METAL SAWING ENGINEERS/ SERVICES

Aks Machining Ltd, 5 Wistaston Road Business Centre, Wistaston Road, Crewe, CW2 7RP Tel: (01270) 585554 Fax: (01270) 586606

Contracut Cutting Services, Unit 19 Mill House Lane, Triangle, Sowerby Bridge, West Yorkshire, HX6 3LN Tel: (01422) 835313 Fax: (01422) 835320 E-mail: scott.thewlis@tiscali.co.uk

Economic Cutting Ltd, 1 Orgreave Crescent, Sheffield, S13 9NQ Tel: 0114-254 9222 Fax: 0114-254 9333 E-mail: sales@economiccutting.co.uk

Effingham Steel Services Ltd, Butterthwaite Lane, Ecclesfield, Sheffield, S35 9WA Tel: 0114-246 8977 Fax: 0114-245 4272 E-mail: sales@effinghamsteel.co.uk

Patent Ferrule Co. Ltd, 2 Palmers Road, Redditch, Worcestershire, B98 0RF Tel: (01527) 528925 Fax: (01527) 510533 E-mail: sales@patentferrule.co.uk

Precision Sawing Services Ltd, Union Road, Oldbury, West Midlands, B69 3EX Tel: 0121-544 9233 Fax: 0121-544 8846 E-mail: pssl2@aol.com

METAL SAWING EQUIPMENT OR SYSTEMS

Crescent Machinery Ltd, Unit 1 Moderna Business Park, Moderna Way, Mytholmroyd, Hebden Bridge, West Yorkshire, HX7 5QQ Tel: (01422) 884888 Fax: (01422) 881338 E-mail: info@crescentmachinery.co.uk

Meba Saw Co Ltd, 27 Palmer Road, Retford, Nottinghamshire, DN22 6SS Tel: (01777) 860102 Fax: (01777) 860306 E-mail: mebasaw@btconnect.com

Meddings Machine Tools, Kingsley Close, Lee Mill Industrial Estate, Ivybridge, Devon, PL21 9LL Tel: (01752) 313323 Fax: (01752) 313333 E-mail: sales@meddings.co.uk

Prosaw Ltd, Telford Way, Kettering, Northamptonshire, NN16 8UN Tel: (01536) 410999 Fax: (01536) 410080 E-mail: sales@prosaw.co.uk

METAL SCULPTURE POLISHING

▶ Butterfly Bronze, 2 Bons Farm Cottages, Stapleford Road, Stapleford Tawney, Romford, RM4 1RP Tel: (020) 8500 3037 Fax: (01708) 687 488 E-mail: links@butterflybronze.com

METAL SEATED BALL VALVES

L G Ball Valves Ltd, Units 5-6, Westgate Trading Estate, Aldridge, Walsall, WS9 8EX Tel: (01922) 459999 Fax: (01922) 458688 E-mail: sales@lgball-valves.co.uk

METAL SEATED BUTTERFLY VALVES

Kurvers International Supply Services Ltd, Unit 14 Northfields Prospect Business Centre, Northfields, London, SW18 1PE Tel: (020) 8877 1355 Fax: (020) 8874 7266 E-mail: info@ukkurvers.com

METAL SHEARING MACHINES

Bystronic UK Ltd, Chard Junction, Chard, Somerset, TA20 4QR Tel: (01460) 222100 Fax: (01460) 222108 E-mail: sales@bystronic.com

Morgan Rushworth Ltd, Bromley Street, Lye, Stourbridge, West Midlands, DY9 8HS Tel: (01384) 895491 Fax: (01384) 424448 E-mail: sales@morganrushworth.com

Joseph Rhodes Ltd, Bell Vue, Elm Tree Street, Wakefield, West Yorkshire, WF1 5EQ Tel: (01924) 371161 Fax: (01924) 370928 E-mail: sales@joseph-rhodes.co.uk

METAL SHIMS

Attewell Ltd, 4 Southbridge Way, Southall, Middlesex, UB2 4BY Tel: (020) 8571 0055 Fax: (020) 8571 7139 E-mail: sales@attewell.co.uk

Lock Engineering Co Ltd, Western Trading Estate, 22 Trading Estate Road, London, NW10 7LY Tel: (020) 8961 6649 Fax: (020) 8961 1036 E-mail: ss@lockeng.co.uk

Photofabrication Services Ltd, 14 Cromwell Road, St Neots, St. Neots, Cambridgeshire, PE19 2HP Tel: (01480) 475831 Fax: (01480) 475801 E-mail: sales@photofab.co.uk

Rayhome Manufacturers, Walshaw Road, Bury, Lancashire, BL8 1PY Tel: 0161-761 1132 Fax: 0161-764 6015 E-mail: sales@rayshim.co.uk

METAL SIGN BLANKS

1st Vinyl Demand Signs, 80-82 Beckenham Lane, Bromley, BR2 0DW Tel: (020) 8313 9199 Fax: (020) 8313 9979

20 Twenty Graphics Ltd, Unit 2, Parkfield Industrial Estate, London, SW11 5BA Tel: (020) 8541 4526 Fax: (020) 7819 9922 E-mail: graphics@20twentygraphics.co.uk

A B C Signs & Engraving, 17 Whitehall, Christchurch, Dorset, BH23 1DE Tel: (01202) 488444 Fax: (01202) 488822 E-mail: info@florassecret.co.uk

Admiral Signs & Graphics, Clough Street, Stoke-on-Trent, ST1 4BA Tel: (01782) 206065 Fax: (01782) 264200 E-mail: admiral.sings@btinternet.com

Advanced Signs, Unit 1 Langhaugh Industrial Estate, Galashiels, Selkirkshire, TD1 2AJ Tel: (01896) 757203 Fax: (01896) 758521 E-mail: advanced-signs@hotmail.com

Allsigns, 1-1A Havelock Crescent, Bridlington, East Yorkshire, YO16 4JH Tel: (01262) 400700 Fax: (01262) 400701 E-mail: rob@allsigns-bridlington.co.uk

Aph Signs, 1 Pinfold Lane, Llay Industrial Estate, Llay, Wrexham, Clwyd, LL12 0PX Tel: (01978) 856565 Fax: (01978) 856568

Appleton Signs Signwriters, Waterloo Indust Estate, Flanders Road, Hedge End, Southampton, SO30 2QT Tel: (01489) 787203 Fax: (01489) 788281

Applied Lettering, 2 Junction Road, Andover, Hampshire, SP10 3QT Tel: (01264) 357438 Fax: (01264) 357438

Ashby Trade Sign Supplies Ltd, Youngs Industrial Estate, Aldermaston, Reading, RG7 4PW Tel: 0118-981 5343 Fax: 0118-981 5335 E-mail: sales@ashbytrade.co.uk

Bomphray Signs, 38 Central Avenue, Troon, Ayrshire, KA10 7AZ Tel: (01292) 319555 Fax: (01292) 319444

C D T Signs, 9 Woodlands Road, Cirencester, Gloucestershire, GL7 1SP Tel: (01285) 640680 Fax: (01285) 652346

Cee-Jay, 4-6 Beeching Close, Bexhill-on-Sea, East Sussex, TN39 3YF Tel: (01424) 734126 Fax: (01424) 734126

Central Signs, 4 Glentye Gardens, Falkirk, FK1 5NT Tel: (01324) 610070 Fax: (01324) 610070

Citisigns Ltd, 2a Church Lane, Dinnington, Sheffield, S25 2LY Tel: (01909) 567474 Fax: (01909) 564141 E-mail: mail@citysigns.co.uk

City Sign Centre, Ockley Road, Bognor Regis, West Sussex, PO21 2HW Tel: (01243) 774833 Fax: (01243) 539114 E-mail: info@cmlsigns.co.uk

Complete Sign Experience Ltd, 20 Fox Croft, Tibshelf, Alfreton, Derbyshire, DE55 5QR Tel: (01773) 590163 Fax: (01773) 590163

Computer Print, 23 West View, Chirk, Wrexham, LL14 5HL Tel: 01691 778320 Fax: 01691 774849

Daw Signs Ltd, Unit 7 Edgefauld Avenue, Glasgow, G21 4UR Tel: 0141-557 2223 Fax: 0141-558 9333 E-mail: sales@dawsigns.com

Fastsigns, 86 Walcot Street, Bath, BA1 5BD Tel: (01225) 447797 Fax: (01225) 444010

METAL SIGN BLANKS - *continued*

Fastsigns, 222 St Albans Road, Watford, WD24 4AU Tel: (01923) 211777 Fax: (01923) 219191 E-mail: watford@fastsigns.com
Franklin Cooper, 7 Derrydown Road, Birmingham, B42 1RZ Tel: 0121-356 8184
Fuhrmann Signs, Old Station Road, Ventnor, Isle of Wight, PO38 1DX Tel: (01983) 854520 Fax: (01983) 852118
Graphic Engravers, 354 Halliwell Road, Bolton, BL1 8AP Tel: (01204) 844159 Fax: (01204) 849445 E-mail: graphicengravers@btconnect.com
Hutsons Ltd, 65 Wide Bargate, Boston, Lincolnshire, PE21 6SG Tel: (01205) 362107 Fax: (01205) 358030 E-mail: signs@hutsons.ltd.co.uk
Ideal Signs, Lerburn Place, The Lerburne, Wedmore, Somerset, BS28 4ED Tel: (01934) 712888 Fax: (01934) 713777
Impress Express, Unit 10 Merlin Park, Fred Dannatt Road, Mildenhall, Bury St. Edmunds, Suffolk, IP28 7RD Tel: (01638) 718878 Fax: (01638) 711887 E-mail: info@impressexpress.co.uk
Invictor Neon Signs Ltd, Unit 3, Vernon Works, Nottingham Road, Nottingham, NG6 0FU Tel: 0115-911 3113 Fax: 0115-978 0880
Mcgowan Signs Ltd, 42 Marriner Road, Keighley, West Yorkshire, BD21 5LW Tel: (01535) 210011 Fax: (01535) 210012
N & N Signs, 353 Green Lanes, London, N4 1DZ Tel: (020) 8802 4929 Fax: (020) 8880 2591
Nichols Sign Ltd, Units 1 & 14 Treeton Enterprise, Rother Crescent, Treeton, Rotherham, South Yorkshire, S60 5QY Tel: 0114-288 9998 Fax: 0114-288 9998
Omega Signs Ltd, Newmarket Approach, Leeds, LS9 0RJ Tel: 0113-240 3000 Fax: 0113-249 2228 E-mail: sales@omega-signs.co.uk
Osprey Co., Guards Road, Coldstream, Berwickshire, TD12 4EE Tel: (01890) 883127 Fax: (01890) 882138 E-mail: sales@signsbynature.co.uk
Pearce Signs Central, 5 Ninian Park, Ninian Way, Wilnecote, Tamworth, Staffordshire, B77 5ES Tel: (01827) 281555 Fax: (01827) 287555 E-mail: central@pearcegroup.com
Prosign, Unit 13 Hoddesdon Industrial Centre, Pindar Road, Hoddesdon, Hertfordshire, EN11 0DD Tel: (01992) 461145 Fax: (01992) 461143
Ranyard Signs Ltd, Brigg Road, Caistor, Market Rasen, Lincolnshire, LN7 6RX Tel: (01472) 852528 Fax: (01472) 851516 E-mail: sales@ranyard-signs.co.uk
Riada Signs, Unit 4d Ballybrakes Industrial Estate, Ballybrakes Road, Ballymoney, County Antrim, BT53 6LW Tel: (028) 2766 2845 Fax: (028) 2766 2228 E-mail: enquiries@riadasigns.co.uk
J. Rigg, 43 Bolton Road, Bury, Lancashire, BL8 2AB Tel: 0161-763 9903 Fax: 0161-763 9903 E-mail: jrsigns@aol.com
Simon Russell, 5 The Hill, Kings Lane, Snitterfield, Stratford-upon-Avon, Warwickshire, CV37 0QB Tel: (01789) 730011 Fax: (01789) 730011
Scancad Services Ltd, Sussex House, Ewhurst Road, Cranleigh, Surrey, GU6 7AE Tel: (01483) 273770 Fax: (01483) 275931 E-mail: rbennet@btconnect.com
Sign A Rama, 35-36 Auster Road, York, YO30 4XA Tel: (0800) 0272588 Fax: (01904) 692155
The Sign Factory, 86 Oxford Road, Clacton-on-Sea, Essex, CO15 3TG Tel: (01255) 429242 Fax: (01255) 429242
Sign Right Rugby, 47 High Street, Welford, Northampton, NN6 6HT Tel: (01858) 575715 Fax: (01858) 575705
Signature Signs, Unit 79 Brasenose Road, Bootle, Merseyside, L20 8HJ Tel: 0151-933 7327 Fax: 0151-933 7323
Signbox Ltd, 3 Egham Business Village, Crabtree Road, Egham, Surrey, TW20 8RB Tel: (01784) 438688 Fax: (01784) 471694
Signcraft, 172 St Sepulchre Gate West, Doncaster, South Yorkshire, DN1 3AQ Tel: (01302) 361078 Fax: (01302) 321804 E-mail: info@signcraft-doncaster.com
Signmaster E D Ltd, Pinnaclehill Industrial Estate, Kelso, Roxburghshire, TD5 8DW Tel: (01573) 223227 Fax: (01573) 225014
Signs & Designs, Riverside House, Lock Lane, Castleford, West Yorkshire, WF10 2JZ Tel: (01977) 512095 Fax: (01977) 603695 E-mail: sales@signs-designs.co.uk
Signs & Designs Of Perth, 17 Main Street, Bridgend, Perth, PH2 7HD Tel: (01738) 633355 Fax: (01738) 577001 E-mail: sales@signsperth.co.uk
Signs Direct, Commerce House, Bank Street, Long Eaton, Nottingham, NG10 1GY Tel: 0115-972 5001 Fax: 0115-972 3111 E-mail: sales@signsdirect-midlands.co.uk
▶ Signs Express Ltd, 1 2 The Old Church, St. Matthews Road, Norwich, NR1 1SP Tel: (01603) 625925 Fax: (01603) 613136 E-mail: sales@signsexpress.co.uk
Signs Of The Times, 43 Sidcup Hill, Sidcup, Kent, DA14 6HJ Tel: (020) 8309 5577 Fax: (020) 8309 5574 E-mail: mark@signsofthetimesuk.com
Signway Supplies (Datchet) Ltd, Signway House, Stroudley Road, Basingstoke, Hampshire, RG24 8UG Tel: (01256) 811234 Fax: (01256) 811299
Soanes Signs, Unit 15 Woodland Park Industrial Estate, Shortthorn Road, Stratton Strawless, Norwich, NR10 5NU Tel: (01603) 754544 Fax: (01603) 754127
Solent Sign Ltd, 174 The Dale, Waterlooville, Hampshire, PO7 5JD Tel: (023) 9264 5796 Fax: (023) 9264 5796 E-mail: sales@solent-signs.co.uk
South West Highways Signs, Upcott Avenue, Barnstaple, Devon, EX31 1HN Tel: 01271 342607
Spectrum Menu Systems Ltd, Units 12 &13, Hixon Industrial Estate, Church Lane, Hixon, Stafford, ST18 0PY Tel: (01889) 271440 Fax: (01889) 271449
Speedy Signs, 1 Moor Lane, Dungannon, County Tyrone, BT71 6HS Tel: (028) 8772 7511 Fax: (028) 8772 9511
Spencer Signs Ltd, Courtney Street, Hull, HU8 7QF Tel: (01482) 325797 Fax: (01482) 323077
Swift Signs, 26 Stradey Park Avenue, Llanelli, Dyfed, SA15 3EF Tel: (01554) 757781 Fax: (01554) 774024
Teal Signs Ltd, 545 Stanningley Road, Leeds, LS13 4EN Tel: 0113-255 6363 Fax: 0113-236 0593 E-mail: sales@tealsigns.co.uk
Trade Signs, 150 London Road, Bedford, MK42 0PS Tel: (01234) 211782 Fax: (01234) 340200 E-mail: sales@tradesigns229.ffnet.co.uk
Viz Biz Design, 4 Ings Road, Wakefield, West Yorkshire, WF1 1DZ Tel: (01924) 377888 Fax: (01924) 385573 E-mail: vizbiz@btconnect.com

METAL SIGNS

1st Call Rotosign Ltd, Pressmetal House, St Augustines Business Park, Whitstable, Kent, CT5 2QJ Tel: (01227) 794490 Fax: (01227) 794488 E-mail: sales@amp-uk.co.uk
A Finch & Co., 1-21 Bedminster Down Road, Bristol, BS13 7AB Tel: 0117-963 2763 Fax: 0117-963 2826
Alacrity Signs, Woodrolfe Road, Tollesbury, Maldon, Essex, CM9 8SE Tel: (01621) 860579 Fax: (01621) 868522
Alpha Sign Systems, Oakwood Bussiness Park, Oldmixon Crescent, Weston-Super-Mare, Avon, BS24 9AY Tel: (01934) 625444 Fax: (01934) 625358 E-mail: sales@alphasignsystems.com
Ashford Signmakers Ltd, Unit 11q Godinton Way Industrial Estate, Godinton Way, Ashford, Kent, TN23 1JB Tel: (01233) 621447 Fax: (01233) 624327 E-mail: coneysigns@aol.com
B M G Industries Ltd, Amwell Lane, Stanstead Abbotts, Ware, Hertfordshire, SG12 8EB Tel: (01920) 870240 Fax: (01920) 870652 E-mail: bmgprint@aol.com
Brilliant Signs & Fabrications, Unit 2 Forty Green, Bledlow, Princes Risborough, Buckinghamshire, HP27 9PN Tel: (01844) 273602 Fax: (0871) 4330112 E-mail: peter.snellgrove@brilliant-signs.com
Centre Signs Ltd, 14 Iliffe Avenue, Oadby, Leicester, LE2 5LH Tel: 0116-271 4247 Fax: 0116-272 0260 E-mail: graphics@centresigns.co.uk
Citisigns Ltd, 2a Church Lane, Dinnington, Sheffield, S25 2LY Tel: (01909) 567474 Fax: (01909) 564141 E-mail: mail@citysigns.co.uk
Commercial Signs & Displays Ltd, Commercial Road, Devizes, Wiltshire, SN10 1EH Tel: (01380) 721068 Fax: (01380) 721068 E-mail: commercialsigns@btconnect.com
Elmtree Signs, 62 Empress Road, Southampton, SO14 0JU Tel: (023) 8023 0903 Fax: (023) 8023 0904 E-mail: rod@elmtreesigns.co.uk
Exel Engraving Ltd, 19 Brickfields Industrial Estate, Finway Road, Hemel Hempstead, Hertfordshire, HP2 7QA Tel: (01442) 270510 Fax: (01442) 270520 E-mail: exelsales@aol.com
Fastsigns, 449 Cowbridge Road East, Cardiff, CF5 1JH Tel: (029) 2034 4455 Fax: (029) 2034 4488 E-mail: 868@fastsigns.com
G R Design Sign, 119 The Glade, Croydon, CR0 7QP Tel: (020) 8239 7025 Fax: (020) 8239 7023
Graffiti Design International, Design House, Bell Lane Industrial Estate, Uckfield, East Sussex, TN22 1QL Tel: (01825) 763690 Fax: (01825) 763815 E-mail: sales@graffitidesign.co.uk
Harper Signs Ltd, 12-20 Diana Street, Newcastle upon Tyne, NE4 6DA Tel: 0191-232 4926 Fax: 0191-261 0676 E-mail: sales@harpersigns.co.uk
Jenter Engraving Ltd, Unit 4F, Lansbury Estate, 102 Lower Guildford Road, Knaphill, Woking, Surrey, GU21 2EP Tel: (01483) 289100 Fax: (01483) 289200
Maxwell Jones Studios Ltd, 58K Arthur Street, Redditch, Worcestershire, B98 8JY Tel: (01527) 502900 Fax: (01527) 510265 E-mail: sales@maxwelljones.com
Metalline Signs Ltd, Barton Hill Trading Estate, Maze Street, Bristol, BS5 9TE Tel: 0117-955 5291 Fax: 0117-955 7518 E-mail: sales@metalline-signs.co.uk
National Sign Co., Alleysbank Road, Rutherglen, Glasgow, G73 1LX Tel: 0141-647 4348 Fax: 0141-613 1309 E-mail: info@nationalsign.co.uk
Nuneaton Signs, 3 Kelsey Close, Attleborough Fields Industrial Estate, Nuneaton, Warwickshire, CV11 6RS Tel: (024) 7634 1922 Fax: (024) 7664 1305 E-mail: sales@nuneatonsigns.co.uk
Olympic Sign Services, Unit 5, Bradbauy Drive, Springwood Indutrial Estate, Braintree, Essex, CM7 2SD Tel: (01376) 551300 Fax: (01376) 328121 E-mail: sales@olypicsignservices.co.uk
Peter Tipper Signs & Plates Ltd, 33 Purdeys Industrial Estate, Purdeys Way, Rochford, Essex, SS4 1ND Tel: (01702) 549830 Fax: (01702) 549831 E-mail: info@tipper-signs.co.uk
Phoenix Signs Ltd, Unit 7, Continental Approach, Westwood Industrial Estate, Margate, Kent, CT9 4JG Tel: (01843) 228682 Fax: (01843) 227373 E-mail: vince@phoenixsignsuk.ltd.uk
Plastisigns, Oak Tre Farm, Escrick Road, Wheldrake, York, YO19 6BQ Tel: (01904) 449970 Fax: (01904) 449970 E-mail: plastisigns@supanet.com
R G Services, PO Box 1864, Radstock, BA3 3ZA Tel: (01761) 435858 Fax: (01761) 435858 E-mail: sales@rgservices.co.uk
Raysigns Ltd, 11-13 Tower Hamlets Road, Dover, Kent, CT17 0BJ Tel: (01304) 214506 Fax: (01304) 202915 E-mail: andrew@raysigns.fsnet.co.uk
Royal British Legion Industries, Royal British Legion Village, Hall Road, Aylesford, Kent, ME20 7NL Tel: (01622) 795900 Fax: (01622) 882195 E-mail: enquries@rbli.co.uk
Royle & Gemmell, Booth House, Suthers Street, Oldham, OL9 7TQ Tel: 0161-628 9292 Fax: 0161-628 9292
Sign Designs, 147-149 Hutcheon Street, Aberdeen, AB25 3RY Tel: (01224) 645361 Fax: (01224) 643647 E-mail: dundee@signdesigns.co.uk
Sign Workshop The, Doods Road, Reigate, Surrey, RH2 0NT Tel: (01737) 240479 Fax: (01737) 223694
Signcraft (Cheltenham) Ltd, Unit 40 Lansdale Industrial Estate, Gloucester Road, Cheltenham, Gloucestershire, GL51 8PL Tel: (01242) 513133 Fax: (01242) 227074 E-mail: sales@signcraftcheltenham.co.uk
Sign-Maker.Net, Little Knowle Farm, High Bickington, Umberleigh, Devon, EX37 9BJ Tel: (01769) 560675 Fax: (01769) 560819 E-mail: enquiries@sign-maker.net
Signwise, Unit 26 Enterprise Way, Newport, Gwent, NP20 2AQ Tel: (01633) 841766 Fax: (01633) 841766 E-mail: info@signwise.net
Simplex Ltd, Unit C Peter Road, Lancing, West Sussex, BN15 8TH Tel: (01903) 750333 E-mail: sales@simplexltd.com
Techniform Graphics Ltd, 172 Bexley Road, London, SE9 2PH Tel: (020) 8850 9191 Fax: (020) 7703 6001 E-mail: sales@techniformgraphics.co.uk

METAL SLITTING

J & J Slitting Services Ltd, 217 Sams Lane, West Bromwich, West Midlands, B70 7EX Tel: 0121-553 1131 Fax: 0121-525 2411
Roberts Steels Ltd, Unit 2, Bay 3 Sovereign Works, Deepdale Lane, Dudley, West Midlands, DY3 2AF Tel: (01384) 259549 Fax: (01384) 456851 E-mail: sales@robertssteelsgroup.co.uk
Stafford Stainless Steels, Meaford Power Station, Meaford, Stone, Staffordshire, ST15 0UU Tel: (01782) 796868 Fax: (01782) 374410 E-mail: sales@stainless.st

METAL SLOTTING

Interkey Engineers, The Workshop, Leigh Sinton, Malvern, Worcestershire, WR13 5EQ Tel: (01886) 830222 Fax: (01886) 830222
Stanton Engineering Coventry 1999 Ltd, 9 Lythalls La Industrial Estate, Lythalls Lane, Coventry, CV6 6FL Tel: (024) 7668 8552

METAL SMALLWARES

Autospin, Castle Trading Estate, Fareham, Hampshire, PO16 9SE Tel: (023) 9237 7737 Fax: (023) 9221 9544 E-mail: mariacrawley180@hotmail.com

METAL SPINNERS/SPINNINGS

A L Spinnings - CNC Punch Weld, Unit 499-101 Newhall Street, Willenhall, West Midlands, WV13 1LQ Tel: (01902) 601318 Fax: (01902) 601318 E-mail: adacncpunch@aol.com
A M S Corporation Ltd, 58-59 Haampton St, Birmingham, B19 3LU Tel: 0121-200 1633 Fax: 0121-200 1685
A1 Metal Spinners Ltd, Clovelly Road, Southbourne, Emsworth, Hampshire, PO10 8PF Tel: (01243) 378401 Fax: (01243) 374219 E-mail: info@metalspinners-in.co.uk
Acme Spinning Co. Ltd, Garratts Lane, Cradley Heath, West Midlands, B64 5RE Tel: 0121-559 1648 Fax: 0121-559 1299 E-mail: info@acmespinning.com
Albany Metal Spinners, 18 Stirling Close, Washington, Tyne & Wear, NE38 8QD Tel: 0191-419 4588 Fax: 0191-416 3700 E-mail: sales@albanymetalspinners.co.uk
Ashford Metal Spinners Ltd, Unit E, Chilmington Works, Chilmington Green, Great Chart, Ashford, Kent, TN23 3DR Tel: (01233) 610404 E-mail: ams@ashfordmetalspinning.co.uk
Autospin, Castle Trading Estate, Fareham, Hampshire, PO16 9SE Tel: (023) 9237 7737 Fax: (023) 9221 9544 E-mail: mariacrawley180@hotmail.com
Ball Spinning Co. Ltd, Unit 34 Park Farm Industrial Estate, Ermine Street, Buntingford, Hertfordshire, SG9 9AZ Tel: (01763) 273506 Fax: (01763) 273509 E-mail: enquiries@ballspinning.co.uk
Barkwood Ltd, 5 Erb Buildings, Claybank Road, Portsmouth, PO3 5NQ Tel: (023) 9265 2078 Fax: (023) 9265 2063 E-mail: barkwoodmetalspinners@hotmail.com
▶ C G Metal Spinners, Unit 34 Fairways Business Park, Lammas Road, London, E10 7QB Tel: (020) 8558 6233 Fax: (020) 8558 4568 E-mail: spincraft1@yahoo.co.uk
Calder Metal Spinning Co. Ltd, Victoria Mills, Wharfe St, Mill Lane, Brighouse, West Yorkshire, HD6 1PP Tel: (01484) 713061 Fax: (01484) 400096 E-mail: david@caldermetspin.co.uk
Catering-Suppliers.com, PO Box 12976, Witton, B6 7AP Tel: 0121-331 4200 E-mail: cateringsuppliers@gmail.com
Craft Metal Spinning (Warrington) Ltd, Howley Tannery, Howley Lane, Warrington, WA1 2DN Tel: (01925) 630985 Fax: (01925) 235187 E-mail: craft@metalspinning.co.uk
▶ Denn UK Ltd, 22 Hither Mead, Bishops Lydeard, Taunton, Somerset, TA4 3NT Tel: (01823) 432893 Fax: (01823) 430037 E-mail: dennuk@btopenworld.com
DMS Metal Spinning, 6 Grafton Road, Birmingham, B11 1JP Tel: 0121-773 8885 Fax: 0121-773 3141 E-mail: adriandms@aol.com
Dorset Metal Spinning Services, Blue Zone Aviation Park West, Bournemouth International Airport, Hurn, Christchurch, Dorset, BH23 6NW Tel: (01202) 593670 Fax: (01202) 593670
E T Martin & Son Edmonton Ltd, Unit 21 Landmark Commercial Centre, Commercial Road, London, N18 1UB Tel: (020) 8884 2060 Fax: (020) 8807 7046 E-mail: sales@etmartinson.co.uk
Excell Metal Spinning Ltd, 27 Gunners Buildings, Limberline Road, Portsmouth, PO3 5BJ Tel: +44 (023) 9266 6456 Fax: +44 (023) 9266 5456 E-mail: excellmetal@btconnect.com
F E M, Bradware Industrial Park, Leonard Street, Bingley, West Yorkshire, BD16 1DP Tel: (01274) 511911 Fax: (01274) 511913
G B Metal Spinnings Ltd, 68a Glover Street, Birmingham, B9 4EL Tel: 0121-773 5444 Fax: 0121-773 5666 E-mail: lee@gb-metalspinnings.com
Gawthorpe Metal Spinning, 4 Drakes Industrial Estate, Shay Lane, Ovenden, Halifax, West Yorkshire, HX3 6RL Tel: (01422) 330519
Hebden Metal Spinners, Melbourne Works, Melbourne Street, Hebden Bridge, West Yorkshire, HX7 6AS Tel: (01422) 843804 Fax: (01422) 843804
Hi Trim Ltd, Meadow Mill, Water Street, Stockport, Cheshire, SK1 2BY Tel: 0161-480 4366 Fax: 0161-480 4366 E-mail: sales@hi-trim.co.uk
J Hipwell & Son Ltd, 427 Warwick Road, Greet, Birmingham, B11 2JU Tel: 0121-706 5471 Fax: 0121-706 0502
J & J Metalspin, 10 Hack Street, Birmingham, B9 4AH Tel: 0121-772 8968 Fax: 0121-772 8968
Jacksons Metal Spinners, 1 Noke Lane Business Centre, Noke Lane, St. Albans, Hertfordshire, AL2 3NY Tel: (01727) 846038 Fax: (01727) 846658 E-mail: gaallen@freenet.co.uk
John Trafford, Unit 16 Phoebe La Industrial Estate, Halifax, West Yorkshire, HX3 9EX Tel: (01422) 345575 Fax: (01422) 356300 E-mail: spintraff@aol.com
King & Rawlings, 278-284 High Street, Waltham Cross, Hertfordshire, EN8 7EA Tel: (01992) 623575 Fax: (01992) 640570
Lloyd & Son, Copthall Farm, Breakspear Road South, Ickenham, Uxbridge, Middlesex, UB10 8HB Tel: (01895) 679000 Fax: (01895) 679000 E-mail: lloydandson640@btinternet.com
Metal Spinners Group Ltd, Clough Road, Manchester, M9 4FP Tel: 0161-205 2286 Fax: 0161-203 4376 E-mail: msg@metal-spinners.co.uk
Metal Spinners Group Ltd, Newburn Industrial Estate, Shelley Road, Newcastle upon Tyne, NE15 9RT Tel: 0191-267 1011 Fax: 0191-264 7137 E-mail: sales@metal-spinners.co.uk
Metspin Ltd, Clovelly Road, Southbourne, Emsworth, Hampshire, PO10 8PF Tel: (01243) 378401 Fax: (01243) 374219 E-mail: sales@metspin.com
Middleton Metal Spinning, Clough Road, Manchester, M9 4FP Tel: 0161 2058687
Midland Spinanpress Co. Ltd, 5 Sydney Road, Bordesley Green, Birmingham, B9 4QB Tel: 0121-772 6804 Fax: 0121-766 8580
J.T. Morris & Co., Downing Street, Smethwick, West Midlands, B66 2QG Tel: 0121-558 9388 Fax: 0121-558 2487
Partscale Ltd, 42 Hutton Close, Crowther, Washington, Tyne & Wear, NE38 0AH Tel: 0191-416 3440 Fax: 0191-416 2665
Powlett & Loach, 20 Western Road, Stratford-upon-Avon, Warwickshire, CV37 0AH Tel: (01789) 269879 Fax: (01789) 299892 E-mail: powlett@aol.com
R C Beresford Ltd, 48 St. Georges Street, Birmingham, B19 3QU Tel: 0121-236 8455 Fax: 0121-236 8493
Rochdale Metal Spinning Co., 6 Bury Road, Rochdale, Lancashire, OL11 4AU Tel: (01706) 365309 Fax: (01706) 367077 E-mail: rochspin@ukonline.co.uk

METAL SPINNERS/SPINNINGS - *continued*

Spinamex, Unit 2 B B W Estates, Oldmixon CR, Weston-super-Mare, Avon, BS24 9BA Tel: (01934) 635077 Fax: (01934) 635077 E-mail: deedazfinn@aol.com
Steel Spinnings Ltd, 94-96 Steward Street, Birmingham, B18 7AF Tel: 0121-456 3737 Fax: 0121-452 1616 E-mail: info@steelspinnings.com
Stockfield Manufacturing Co. Ltd, Sherbourne Road, Balsall Heath, Birmingham, B12 9DJ Tel: 0121-440 1333 Fax: 0121-440 8221 E-mail: info@stockfield.com
Walford Metal Spinning Co. Ltd, 13 Morris Road, Nuffield Industrial Estate, Poole, Dorset, BH17 7RS Tel: (01202) 678848 Fax: (01202) 678848
Waywood Products, 27 Brownlow Business Centre, Ulster Street, Lurgan, Craigavon, County Armagh, BT67 9AN Tel: (028) 3834 8153 Fax: (028) 3834 8153
Wilkinson & Son, 14a Hall Street North, Boothtown, Halifax, West Yorkshire, HX3 6TS Tel: (01422) 349630 Fax: (01422) 349630
Willis & Bates, Reservoir Road, Halifax, West Yorkshire, HX2 0ES Tel: (01422) 361228 Fax: (01422) 340480 E-mail: sales@bairstowbrothers.co.uk

METAL SPINNERS/SPINNINGS, SPECIAL METALS

Metal Spinners Group Ltd, Clough Road, Manchester, M9 4FP Tel: 0161-205 2286 Fax: 0161-203 4376 E-mail: msg@metal-spinners.co.uk

METAL SPINNING, COMPUTER AIDED DESIGN, COMPUTER AIDED MANUFACTURING (CADCAM) DESIGN

Metspin Ltd, Clovelly Road, Southbourne, Emsworth, Hampshire, PO10 8PF Tel: (01243) 378401 Fax: (01243) 374219 E-mail: sales@metspin.com

METAL SPRAYING CONSUMABLES AND SUPPLIES

Humark Engineering, Cavendish Bridge, Shardlow, Derby, DE72 2HL Tel: (01332) 799999 Fax: (01332) 799999
Thermal Spray Material Services Ltd, Brook Street Business Centre, Brook Street, Tipton, West Midlands, DY4 9DD Tel: 0121-520 0720 Fax: 0121-520 3002 E-mail: thermalsprayuk@aol.com

METAL SPRAYING CONTRACTORS OR SERVICES

Agra (Precision Engineering) Co. Ltd, 15 Ure Street, Dundee, DD1 5JD Tel: (01382) 229333 Fax: (01382) 226918 E-mail: info@agra-eng.co.uk
Alban Engineering Services Ltd, Wood Street Passage, Wood Street, Kettering, Northamptonshire, NN16 9SQ Tel: (01536) 513225 Fax: (01536) 513225
B G Penny & Co. Ltd, Unit 3, Three Spires Industrial Estate, Ibstock Road, Coventry, CV6 6JR Tel: (024) 7636 7636 Fax: (024) 7636 7636
F. Bemrose Ltd, Manby Road, Immingham, South Humberside, DN40 2LL Tel: (01469) 572961 Fax: (01469) 571498 E-mail: frankbemrose@aol.com
Bootham Engineers Mechanical Services, Amy Johnson Way, Clifton Moor, York, YO30 4WT Tel: (01904) 477670 Fax: (01904) 691826 E-mail: engineering.location@dowdingandmills.com
Bradleys (Stowmarket) Ltd, 49 Knightsdale Road, Ipswich, IP1 4JJ Tel: (01473) 461400 Fax: (01473) 461490
Brian Plant, Wickham Road, Grimsby, South Humberside, DN31 3SL Tel: (01472) 241342 Fax: (01472) 354329
C F Smith Precision Grinding, The Station, Station Hill, Overton, Basingstoke, Hampshire, RG25 3JH Tel: (01256) 770457 Fax: (01256) 771701 E-mail: cfsmith@btconnect.com
Celcoat Ltd, 3 Crown Works, Rotherham Road, Beighton, Sheffield, S20 1AH Tel: 0114-269 0771 Fax: 0114-254 0495 E-mail: celcoatltd@tiscali.co.uk
Cotswold Blast Cleaning, Linenfields, Old Boars Hill, Oxford, OX1 5JJ Tel: (07831) 705205 Fax: (01865) 326134
Croboride Engineering Ltd, Little Burton West, Burton-on-Trent, Staffordshire, DE14 1PP Tel: (01283) 511188 Fax: (01283) 530845 E-mail: info@croboride.co.uk
ESP Coatings Ltd, Units A5-E13, Hastingwood Trading Estate, Harbet Road, Edmonton, London, N18 3HT Tel: (020) 8803 1115 Fax: (020) 8035 567 E-mail: espcoatings@btconnect.com
Ferrous Protection Ltd, Hanson House, Grains Road, Delph, Oldham, OL3 5RN Tel: (01457) 873419 Fax: (01457) 871091 E-mail: ferrous_protection@yahoo.com
G & G Powder Coatings Ltd, 3 Rippleside Commercial Estate, Ripple Road, Barking, Essex, IG11 0RJ Tel: (020) 8592 4555 Fax: (020) 8592 4777 E-mail: info@gg-powdercoating.com
Gardwell Coatings Ltd, Ellough Airfield, Ellough, Beccles, Suffolk, NR34 7TE Tel: (01502) 712793 Fax: (01502) 711636 E-mail: sales@gardwellcoatings.co.uk
Hastie & Co, Morfa Road, Swansea, SA1 2EP Tel: (01792) 651541 Fax: (01792) 468119 E-mail: steven.miller@hastiegroup.co.uk
▶ Austin Hayes Ltd, Cemetery Road, Yeadon, Leeds, LS19 7BD Tel: 0113-250 2255 Fax: 0113-250 2200 E-mail: info@austinhayes.co.uk
Humark Engineering, Cavendish Bridge, Shardlow, Derby, DE72 2HL Tel: (01332) 799999 Fax: (01332) 799999
Hunprenco Group of Companies Ltd., Hunmanby Industrial Estate, Bridlington Road, Hunmanby, Filey, North Yorkshire, YO14 0PH Tel: (01723) 890105 Fax: (01723) 890018 E-mail: hunprenco@btinternet.com
Le Carousel, 35 Easter Park, Benyon Road, Silchester, Reading, RG7 2PQ Tel: 0118-970 0228 Fax: 0118-970 1944
Metallizers (Heckmondwike) Ltd, Old White Lee Colliery, Leeds Road, Heckmondwike, West Yorkshire, WF16 9BH Tel: (01924) 473840 Fax: (01924) 473794
North Kent Shot Blasting Co. Ltd, Grove Road, Northfleet, Gravesend, Kent, DA11 9AX Tel: (01474) 350030 Fax: (01474) 327329 E-mail: info@nksb.co.uk
Penfold Metalising Co. Ltd, Barnham Road, Barnham, Bognor Regis, West Sussex, PO22 0ES Tel: (01243) 552178 Fax: (01243) 554472 E-mail: info@penmet.co.uk
Plasma Coatings Ltd, 3 Meverill Road, Tideswell, Buxton, Derbyshire, SK17 8PY Tel: (01298) 873700 Fax: (01298) 873708 E-mail: info@plasma-group.co.uk
Possilpark Shotblasting Co. Ltd, 73 Dunn Street, Glasgow, G40 3PE Tel: 0141-556 6221 Fax: 0141-551 0714 E-mail: admin@possilparks.co.uk
Pwe Coatings, 9 Nobel Square, Burnt Mills Industrial Estate, Basildon, Essex, SS13 1LS Tel: (01268) 729983 Fax: (01268) 727955
R W G Engineering Ltd, Unit 5, Portlands Centre, Sutton Road, St. Helens, Merseyside, WA9 3DR Tel: (01744) 454225 Fax: (01744) 454226
Silvey Engineering Ltd, Redstones, Haywicks Lane, Hardwick, Gloucester, GL2 3QE Tel: (01452) 720439
South Staffs Group Ltd, Churchfield House, 36 Vicar Street, Dudley, West Midlands, DY2 8RG Tel: (01384) 458300 Fax: (01384) 233670 E-mail: sales@southstaffsindustries.com
▶ South Staffs Industries Ltd, Bloomfield Road, Tipton, West Midlands, DY4 9EE Tel: 0121-522 2373 Fax: 0121-522 3528
Surface Engineers Manchester Ltd, Globe Works Off Astley Street, Dukinfield, Cheshire, SK16 4QZ Tel: 0161-330 9224 Fax: 0161-343 2650
Sussex Pattern Co. Ltd, 70 Victoria Road, Burgess Hill, West Sussex, RH15 9LY Tel: (01444) 245292 Fax: (01444) 247168 E-mail: info@sussexpattern.co.uk
Jack Tighe Coatings Ltd, Sandall Stones Road, Kirk Sandall Industrial Estate, Doncaster, South Yorkshire, DN3 1QR Tel: (01302) 880360 Fax: (01302) 880370
Universal Applied Coatings Ltd, Parish Lane, Pease Pottage, Crawley, West Sussex, RH10 5NY Tel: (01293) 514943 Fax: (01293) 552619

METAL SPRAYING EQUIPMENT

Electro Mechanical Services Ltd, 24B Portman Road, Reading, RG30 1EA Tel: 0118-956 1222 Fax: 0118-956 1220 E-mail: info@emssolutions.co.uk
I E L Identequip Ltd, Tenmat Buildings, Ashburton Road West, Trafford Park, Manchester, M17 1RU Tel: 0161-876 4679 Fax: 0161-876 0009 E-mail: iel@identequip.com
MCP, 8 Whitebridge Industrial Estate, Whitebridge Lane, Stone, Staffordshire, ST15 8LQ Tel: (01785) 815651 Fax: (01785) 812115 E-mail: equipment@mcp-group.co.uk
Sulzer Metco (UK) Ltd, Suflex Estate, Newport Road, Risca, Newport, Gwent, NP11 6YD Tel: (01633) 600970 Fax: (01633) 601717 E-mail: simon.hiiemal@sulzer.com

METAL SPRAYING WIRE

Metra Non-Ferrous Metals Ltd, Pindar Road, Hoddesdon, Hertfordshire, EN11 0DE Tel: (01992) 460455 Fax: (01992) 451207 E-mail: enquiries@metra-metals.co.uk

METAL STAIR NOSINGS

Gradus Carpets Ltd, Chapel Mill, Park Green, Macclesfield, Cheshire, SK11 7LZ Tel: (01625) 859000 Fax: (01625) 850352 E-mail: sales@gradusworld.com
Permadeck Systems Ltd, Unit 12 Westside Industrial Estate, Jackson Street, St. Helens, Merseyside, WA9 3AT Tel: (01744) 751869 Fax: (01744) 22551 E-mail: enquiries@safteysurfacing.uk.com

METAL STAIR TREADS

Trimplex, Mulberry Way, Belvedere, Kent, DA17 6AN Tel: (020) 8312 0400 Fax: (020) 8312 1400 E-mail: saftytread@btconnect.com

METAL STAIRCASES

Audenshaw Steel Ltd, Unit 12 Wharf Parade, Lower Wharf Street, Ashton-under-Lyne, Lancashire, OL6 7PE Tel: 0161-343 8550 Fax: 0161-343 8550
B & D Willett Fabrications Ltd, 131 Mereside, Soham, Ely, Cambridgeshire, CB7 5EG Tel: (01353) 721374 Fax: (01353) 722567 E-mail: rujwillett@bdwillett.co.uk
British Standard Gratings, 2 Springhill Trading Eastate, Aston Street, Shifnal, Shropshire, TF11 8DR Tel: (01952) 277777 Fax: (01952) 277778
▶ Brook Metal Design Ltd, Brook Farm Industrial Estate, Stapleford Road, Romford, RM4 1EJ Tel: (01708) 687420
Cambrian Foundry Ltd, Unit 34 Vastre Indust Estate, Kerry Road, Newtown, Powys, SY16 1DZ Tel: (01686) 626209 Fax: (01686) 629500 E-mail: camfound@hotmail.com
Cambridge Structures Ltd, 2 Huntingdon Street, St. Neots, Cambridgeshire, PE19 1BG Tel: (01480) 477700 Fax: (01480) 477766 E-mail: contact@cambridgestructures.com
Ceto Engineering Ltd, Howard Road, Eaton Socon, St. Neots, Cambridgeshire, PE19 8ET Tel: (01480) 406646 Fax: (01480) 406605
Cornish Stairways Ltd, Kernick Industrial Estate, Penryn, Cornwall, TR10 9DQ Tel: (01326) 374662 Fax: (01326) 376596 E-mail: mikejordan@cornishstairways.co.uk
D G N Design, Unit 7 270 Lakey Lane, Birmingham, B28 8RA Tel: 0121-778 6878 Fax: 0121-778 6878
D & R Structures Ltd, 7 Lidsey Road, Woodgate, Chichester, West Sussex, PO20 3SU Tel: (01243) 544838 Fax: (01243) 544840
Davey & Jordan, 3 Jennings Road, Kernick Industrial Estate, Penryn, Cornwall, TR10 9AA Tel: (01326) 372282 Fax: (01326) 376596
Edwin Clarke, Francis House, George Street, Lincoln, LN5 8LG Tel: (01522) 530912 Fax: (01522) 510929
Fabrenco Ltd, Wilton Road, Humberston, Grimsby, South Humberside, DN36 4AW Tel: (01472) 814845 Fax: (01472) 210412 E-mail: fabrenco@quista.net
Fellows, 1 Wattville Road, Smethwick, West Midlands, B66 2NU Tel: 0121-555 8550 Fax: 0121-555 8660 E-mail: trevor@hsfellowsltd.com
Fenweld Steel Fabricators, Bramley Road, St. Ives, Cambridgeshire, PE27 3WS Tel: (01480) 300877 Fax: (01480) 492120
Fire Escapes Unlimited, Unit 2 Atlas Trading Estate, Colebrook Road, Birmingham, B11 2NT Tel: 0121-772 4443 Fax: 0121-753 4222 E-mail: feunlimited@aol.com
Form Weld Ltd, Unit 3C, Cutters Close, Narborough, Leicester, LE19 2FZ Tel: 0116-286 6654 Fax: 0116-275 0877 E-mail: formweld@btconnect.com
Frixos Metal Works Ltd, Unit 4, 30 Aden Road, Brimsdown, Enfield, Middlesex, EN3 7SY Tel: (020) 8443 1050 Fax: (020) 8440 1233 E-mail: jimmy@frixosmetalworks.co.uk
G C W Fabrications Ltd, Unit 23, James Carter Road, Bury St. Edmunds, Suffolk, IP28 7DE Tel: (01638) 515478 Fax: (01638) 717554
General Services Fabrications Ltd, Sudmeadow Road, Gloucester, GL2 5HS Tel: (01452) 304515 Fax: (01452) 504729
Hough Engineering, 138A High Street, Silverdale, Newcastle, Staffordshire, ST5 6LX Tel: (01782) 633984 Fax: (01782) 715987 E-mail: houghengineering@supnet.com
Hubbard Architectural Metalwork Ltd, 3 Hurricane Way, Norwich, NR6 6HS Tel: (01603) 424817 Fax: (01603) 487158 E-mail: tony.hubbard@hubbardsmetalwork.co.uk
J & B Novak Metalcraft Ltd, White Cottage Farm, Lucas Green Road, West End, Woking, Surrey, GU24 9LZ Tel: (01483) 474979 Fax: (01483) 472487
J P Fabrications, C 4 Belcon Industrial Estate, Geddings Road, Hoddesdon, Hertfordshire, EN11 0NT Tel: (01992) 444428 Fax: (01992) 444428 E-mail: jpfabs@aol.com
L M Engineering Services Ltd, Unit 226D, Redwither Industrial Complex, Wrexham, Clwyd, LL13 9XU Tel: (01978) 660111 Fax: (01978) 660227 E-mail: steel@lmeng.fsbusiness.co.uk
Luton Fabrications Ltd, Tring Road, Dunstable, Bedfordshire, LU6 2JX Tel: (01582) 663330 Fax: (01582) 662333
Mecright Contractors Ltd, Unit 10 Prospect Business Park, Longford Road, Cannock, Staffordshire, WS11 0LG Tel: (01543) 469222 Fax: (01543) 469444 E-mail: patrick@mecright.co.uk
K.C. Milner Engineering Ltd, Unit 7 Shepherd Cross Street, Bolton, BL1 3DE Tel: (01204) 843540 Fax: (01204) 493480
P J T Engineering, Unit 3 367 Bryn Road, Ashton-in-Makerfield, Wigan, Lancashire, WN4 8BS Tel: (01942) 712022 Fax: (01942) 712022 E-mail: sales@pjtengineering.gbr.cc
P & M Decorative Metal Work Ltd, Unit 1, Park Street, Oldbury, West Midlands, B69 4LQ Tel: 0121-544 8880 Fax: 0121-544 4617 E-mail: pmdeco@aol.com
Perdaw Engineering Co. Ltd, 4 Liverpool Road, Cadishead, Manchester, M44 5AF Tel: 0161-775 4133 Fax: 0161-777 9634 E-mail: sales@perdaw.co.uk
Peter Marshall Ltd, Gelderd Road, Morley, Leeds, LS27 7LL Tel: 0113-307 6730 Fax: 0113-307 5968
▶ Powerdeck Ltd, Unit 4, Blackhill Industrial Estate, Black Hill, Stratford-upon-Avon, Warwickshire, CV37 0PH Tel: (01789) 730444 Fax: (01789) 730888 E-mail: sales@powerdeck.co.uk
Roberts Engineering, Bergen Way, Hull, HU7 0YQ Tel: (01482) 838240 Fax: (01482) 830697 E-mail: admin@robertsengineering.co.uk
Safety Stairways Ltd, Unit 45 Owen Road Industrial Estate, Willenhall, West Midlands, WV13 2PX Tel: 0121-526 3133 Fax: 0121-526 2833 E-mail: info@safety-stairways.com
Staircase & Balustrades Ltd, Slaney Street, Oakengates, Telford, Shropshire, TF2 6ET Tel: (01952) 610370 Fax: (01952) 610370
Stronga Ltd, Ashendene Farm, White Stubbs Lane, Bayford, Hertford, SG13 8PZ Tel: (01992) 519000 Fax: (01992) 519011 E-mail: info@stronga.co.uk
Walker Metalwork (Elland) Ltd, Castle Mills, Elland, West Yorkshire, HX5 0RY Tel: 01422 310011

METAL STRAIGHTENING

Macnab, Stringes Lane, Willenhall, West Midlands, WV13 1LD Tel: (01902) 631159 Fax: (01902) 606922
Phoenix Ironworks Co. Ltd, Newall Street, Littleborough, Lancashire, OL15 9DL Tel: (01706) 378102 Fax: (01706) 379937 E-mail: sales@phoenix-ironworks.co.uk

METAL STRAPPING CLIPS

A D Engineering Co., Edward Street, Redditch, Worcestershire, B97 6HA Tel: (01527) 60355 Fax: (01527) 63639

METAL STRESS RELIEVING EQUIPMENT

V S R Co., Unit 13A, Shrub Hill Industrial Estate, Worcester, WR4 9EL Tel: (01905) 452800 Fax: (01905) 731811E-mail: sales@v-s-r.co.uk

METAL STRIP SLITTING MACHINES

McMillan Conroy Machinery, PO Box 3081, Walsall, WS2 9SS Tel: (01922) 725444 Fax: (01922) 640336 E-mail: sales@mcmillanconroy.co.uk

METAL SWAGING

Hallen Engineering Ltd, PO Box 27, Wednesbury, West Midlands, WS10 7SZ Tel: 0121-556 3324 Fax: 0121-502 0194 E-mail: sales@hallen.co.uk
Lutley Manufacturing Ltd, Unit H, 100 Dudley Road East, Oldbury, West Midlands, B69 3DY Tel: 0121-552 2456 Fax: 0121-544 3545 E-mail: richardsweeney.lutley@btinternet.com
Oil States MCS Ltd, Bouthwood Road, Sowerby Woods Industrial Estate, Barrow-in-Furness, Cumbria, LA14 4RD Tel: (01229) 825080 Fax: (01229) 839791 E-mail: owen-osmotherly@osmcs-bat.co.uk
Peter Randle & Son Grinding, 9 The Washford Industrial Estate, Heming Road, Redditch, Worcestershire, B98 0DH Tel: (01527) 528891 Fax: (01527) 528891

METAL TELECOMMUNICATION COMPONENTS

E.J. Watts Engineering Group, Faldo Road, Barton-le-Clay, Bedford, MK45 4RJ Tel: (01582) 881601 Fax: (01582) 881075 E-mail: info@ejwatts.co.uk

METAL TELECOMMUNICATION EQUIPMENT ENCLOSURES

A T Communications, Canon House, Thame Road, Haddenham, Aylesbury, Buckinghamshire, HP17 8LH Tel: (01844) 266266 Fax: (01844) 266262
Eurocraft Trustees Ltd, Cinderbank, Netherton, Dudley, West Midlands, DY2 9AE Tel: (01384) 230101 Fax: (01384) 256883 E-mail: sales@eurocraft.co.uk

METAL TELECOMMUNICATION EQUIPMENT ENCLOSURES – *continued*

Genesis Scotland Ltd, The Douglas Centre, Marchmont Crescent, Buckie, Banffshire, AB56 4BT Tel: (01542) 834947 Fax: (0870) 3835549E-mail: genesisltd@btopenworld.com

K P Equipe Communications Ltd, 1-3 Faraday Close, Drayton Fields Industrial Estate, Daventry, Northamptonshire, NN11 8RD Tel: (01327) 871187 Fax: (01327) 871188

Murphy Telecommunications, 293 Salisbury Road, Totton, Southampton, SO40 3LZ Tel: (023) 8086 1479 Fax: (023) 8086 8483 E-mail: murtel@talktalk.net

P C D Products Ltd, Cleveland Road, Hemel Hempstead Industrial Estate, Hemel Hempstead, Hertfordshire, HP2 7EY Tel: (01442) 248565 Fax: (01442) 241033 E-mail: sales@pcdproducts.co.uk

METAL TENT PEGS

Hampton Works Ltd, Twyning Road, Stirchley, Birmingham, B30 2XZ Tel: 0121-458 2901 Fax: 0121-433 3819 E-mail: sales@hampton-works.co.uk

W4 Ltd, Unit B, Ford Lane Industrial Estate, Arundel, West Sussex, BN18 0DF Tel: (01243) 553355 Fax: (01243) 553540 E-mail: enquiries@w4limited.com

METAL TENT POLES

Ultramatrix Production Services Ltd, Farfield Works, Birds Green, Romsley, Bridgnorth, Shropshire, WV15 6HJ Tel: (01746) 780360 Fax: (01746) 780933

METAL TIME RECORDER CARD RACKS

A M Time Services, 8 Ivyside Close, Killamarsh, Sheffield, S21 1JT Tel: 0114-248 5855 Fax: 0114-248 5855 E-mail: info@amtime.co.uk

▶ South Wales Time Recorders Sales & Services Ltd, Time House, Regent Street, Barry, South Glamorgan, CF62 8DT Tel: (01446) 721446 Fax: (01446) 744678 E-mail: sales@swtr.co.uk

METAL TOOL BOXES OR CABINETS OR CASES OR CHESTS

Birchfield Sheet Metal Sheet Metal, 15 Hadfield Industrial Estate, Waterside, Hadfield, Glossop, Derbyshire, SK13 1BS Tel: (01457) 865536 Fax: (01457) 865536

Britool Ltd, Churchbridge Works, Walsall Road, Cannock, Staffordshire, WS11 3JR Tel: (01922) 702100 Fax: (01922) 702101 E-mail: uk_sales@britool.co.uk

Lista (UK) Ltd, 17 Alston Drive, Bradwell Abbey, Milton Keynes, MK13 9HA Tel: (01908) 222333 Fax: (01908) 222433 E-mail: info.uk@lista.com

M A C Tools, Gowerton Road, BlackMills, Northampton, NN4 7BW Tel: (01604) 827351 Fax: (01604) 661654

Scooter Store Ltd, Unit 11 Italstyle Buildings, Cambridge Road, Harlow, Essex, CM20 2HE Tel: (01279) 453565 Fax: (01279) 454030 E-mail: albertwass@site-safe.co.uk

METAL TREATMENT SERVICES, RUBBER BONDING

Bromley Enterprises UK Ltd, Unit 7 Bruntingthorpe Industrial Estate, Upper Bruntingthorpe, Lutterworth, Leicestershire, LE17 5QZ Tel: 0116-247 8912 Fax: 0116-247 8969 E-mail: bromleyenterprises@googlemail.com

METAL TUBE CUTTING MACHINES

▶ B E W O (UK) Ltd, Unit 3 Bay 2, Eastacre, The Willenhall Estate, Willenhall, West Midlands, WV13 2JZ Tel: (01902) 635027 Fax: (01902) 635843E-mail: info@bewo.co.uk

Langbow Ltd, 222 Wolseley Court Towers Plaza, Wheelhouse Road, Rugeley, Staffordshire, WS15 1UW Tel: (01889) 575380 Fax: (01889) 578872 E-mail: sales@langbow.com

Rotostock (Sales) Ltd, Porte Marsh Road, Calne, Wiltshire, SN11 8BW Tel: (01249) 822222 Fax: (01249) 822300 E-mail: sales@rotostock.co.uk

METAL TUBE CUTTING SERVICES

Duright Engineering Co., Portway Road, Wednesbury, West Midlands, WS10 7DZ Tel: 0121-556 7718 Fax: 0121-556 7745 E-mail: sales@duright.co.uk

M P Manipulated Tubes Ltd, 40 Bracebridge Street, Aston, Birmingham, B6 4PJ Tel: 0121-359 0478 Fax: 0121-333 3082

Microkerf Ltd, 43 Boston Road, Leicester, LE4 1AW Tel: 0116-234 1500 Fax: 0116-234 1600 E-mail: sales@microkerf.com

Voestalpine Elmsteel Ltd, Dodwells Bridge Industrial Estate, Jacknell Road, Hinckley, Leicestershire, LE10 3BS Tel: (01455) 620300 Fax: (01455) 620320

METAL TUBE ENDS

▶ Brophy Castings, Building 15 Soho Mills, Wooburn Green, High Wycombe, Buckinghamshire, HP10 0PF Tel: (01628) 525068 Fax: (01628) 525129 E-mail: info@brophycastings.co.uk

Guy Raymond Engineering Company Ltd, Rollesby Road, King's Lynn, Norfolk, PE30 4LX Tel: (01553) 761401 Fax: (01553) 767459 E-mail: info@guy-raymond.co.uk

METAL VAPOUR DEGREASING

▶ Serfice Engineering Consulting, 37 Leys Avenue, Desborough, Kettering, Northamptonshire, NN14 2PY Tel: (01536) 763567

METAL WATERING CANS

Haws Watering Cans, 120 Beakes Road, Smethwick, West Midlands, B67 5AB Tel: 0121-420 2494 Fax: 0121-429 1668 E-mail: sales@haws.demon.co.uk

METAL WHEELBARROWS

Bescot Constuction, Besot Crescent, Walsall, WS1 4NX Tel: (01922) 621286 Fax: (01922) 621321 E-mail: enquiries@chillingtonbarrows.co.uk

Maingate Ltd, PO Box 330, Woking, Surrey, GU22 9XS Tel: (0845) 2306585 Fax: (0845) 2307585

Thacker Barrows Ltd, Conduit Road, Norton Canes, Cannock, Staffordshire, WS11 9TE Tel: (01543) 279056 Fax: (01543) 276079 E-mail: sales@thackerbarrows.co.uk

METALLIC EFFECT PAINTS

Eckart UK, Unit C The Sidings, Station Road, Ampthill, Bedford, MK45 2QY Tel: (01525) 409520 Fax: (01525) 409521 E-mail: sales@eckart.co.uk

METALLIC FIGURINES

Kitney & Co., Unit 12 Crystal Business Centre, Sandwich, Kent, CT13 9QX Tel: (01304) 611968 Fax: (01304) 614642 E-mail: sales@kitneyandco.com

▶ www.321Deco.co.uk, 14 Bridgeway Centre, Wrexham Industrial Estate, Wrexham, LL13 9QS Tel: (01978) 661572 Fax: (01978) 661572 E-mail: sd@ukmemory.com

METALLIC GASKETS

Nicholsons Sealing Technologies Ltd, Hamsterley, Newcastle upon Tyne, NE17 7SX Tel: (01207) 560505 Fax: (01207) 561004 E-mail: info@nicholsons.co.uk

METALLIC OR SHOT BLASTING ABRASIVE MATERIALS

Associated Wire Products, Hendre Mine, The Nant, Rhydymwyn, Mold, Clwyd, CH7 5QD Tel: (01352) 741222 Fax: (01352) 741666

B C Abrasives Ltd, Cleeton Cottage, Cleeton St. Mary, Kidderminster, Worcestershire, DY14 0QU Tel: (01584) 891202 Fax: (01584) 891002 E-mail: bcabrasives2@btconnect.com

Conqueror Industries Ltd, Units 3-9, Royston Trading Estate, South Close, Royston, Hertfordshire, SG8 5UH Tel: (01763) 249535 Fax: (01763) 247276E-mail: info@c-i-ltd.co.uk

Ervin Amasteel Ltd, George Henry Road, Tipton, West Midlands, DY4 7BZ Tel: 0121-522 2777 Fax: 0121-522 2927 E-mail: info@ervinamasteel.com

▶ Fastback (UK), 31 Hill Road, Fareham, Hampshire, PO16 8LA Tel: (07931) 568823 E-mail: brnmonks@aol.com

▶ Industrial Coating Services Ltd, 370 Farm Street, Birmingham, B19 2UA Tel: 0121-551 1984 Fax: 0121-523 4157 E-mail: info@industrial-coating-services.ltd.uk

Metalltechnik UK Ltd, 8 Mere Close, Shifnal, Shropshire, TF11 9QA Tel: (01952) 461242 Fax: (01952) 417489 E-mail: metuk@dialstart.net

Pometon Ltd, 5, Queensway Link Industrial Estate, Telford, Shropshire, TF3 3DN Tel: (01952) 299777 Fax: (01952) 299008 E-mail: sales@pometon.demon.co.uk

Scangrit, Eastfield Road, South Killingholme, Immingham, South Humberside, DN40 3NF Tel: (01469) 574715 Fax: (01469) 571644 E-mail: sales@scangrit.co.uk

Sivil & Marine Ltd, Gibson Lane, Melton, North Ferriby, East Yorkshire, HU14 3HN Tel: (01482) 633305 Fax: (01482) 634835 E-mail: info@sivilandmarine.co.uk

Wolverhampton Abrasives, Orgreave Drive, Sheffield, S13 9NR Tel: (0800) 0853085 Fax: 0114-254 0913E-mail: gritsales@aol.com

METALLIC PACKINGS AND JOINTINGS

Grange Gaskets (Bradford) Ltd, Carnarvon Works, Bolton Lane, Bradford, West Yorkshire, BD2 1AE Tel: (01274) 734238 Fax: (01274) 306594

Harrison, J.A. & Co. Ltd, Britain Works, Sherborne Street, Manchester, M8 8HP Tel: 0161-832 2282 Fax: 0161-832 3263 E-mail: enquiries@jaharrison.co.uk

Klinger Ltd, Klinger Building, Wharfedale Road, Euroway Industrial Estate, Bradford, West Yorkshire, BD4 6SG Tel: (01274) 688222 Fax: (01274) 688962 E-mail: enquiries@klingeruk.co.uk

METALLIC PAINTS

R C Stiven & Co., Unit 31 Faraday Street, Dryburgh Industrial Estate, Dundee, DD2 3QQ Tel: (01382) 833322 Fax: (01382) 889133 E-mail: aws@rcstiven.sol.co.uk

METALLIC PIGMENTS

Metaflake Ltd, Station Road, Anstruther, Fife, KY10 3JA Tel: (01333) 313440 Fax: (01333) 313044 E-mail: enq@metaflake.com

Silberline Ltd, Banbeath Industrial Estate, Leven, Fife, KY8 5HD Tel: (01333) 424734 Fax: (01333) 421369 E-mail: info@silberline.co.uk

METALLIC SCREWED BANDING

Silver Fox Ltd, Swallow Court, Swallowfields, Welwyn Garden City, Hertfordshire, AL7 1SA Tel: (01707) 373727 Fax: (01707) 372193 E-mail: sales@silfox.co.uk

METALLIC STATIONERY SUNDRIES

Bensons International Systems Ltd, Bensons House, 104 Bath Road, Stroud, Gloucestershire, GL5 3TJ Tel: (01453) 755888 Fax: (01453) 753300

METALLIC WASHERS, *See also other nearby headings for individual metal*

N D Jig & Gauge Co.Ltd, Bush Works, Leabrook Road, Wednesbury, West Midlands, WS10 7NB Tel: 0121-556 0824 Fax: 0121-556 8177 E-mail: sqplatewashers@aol.com

Pressex Engineers, Express Technical Centre, Kingsway, Team Valley Trading Estate, Gateshead, Tyne & Wear, NE11 0JL Tel: 0191-497 3430 Fax: 0191-497 3431 E-mail: pressex@responsive-engioneering.com

METALLISED BAGS

Brayford Plastics, Horncastle Lane, Dunholme, Lincoln, LN2 3QF Tel: (01522) 530557 Fax: (01522) 730372 E-mail: info@brayfordplastics.com

METALLISED FILM CAPACITORS

Europtronic Group, 5 Kerry Avenue, Stanmore, Middlesex, HA7 4NJ Tel: (020) 8954 9798 Fax: (020) 8954 8918 E-mail: evelina.huang@europtronic.com

Industrial Capacitors Wrexham Ltd, Miners Road, Llay Industrial Estate, Llay, Wrexham, Clwyd, LL12 0PJ Tel: (01978) 853805 Fax: (01978) 853785 E-mail: sales@icwltd.co.uk

METALLISED PAPER

▶ A P I Group plc, Second Avenue, Poynton, Stockport, Cheshire, SK12 1ND Tel: (01625) 858700 Fax: (01625) 858701 E-mail: enquiries@apilaminates.com

Metalised Products Ltd, Pontygwindy Industrial Estate, Caerphilly, Mid Glamorgan, CF83 3HU Tel: (029) 2088 5988 Fax: (029) 2086 3718

METALLISED POLYCARBONATE CAPACITORS

M F D Capacitors (1991) Ltd, Lion Lane, Penley, Wrexham, LL13 0LY Tel: (01978) 710551 Fax: (01978) 710501 E-mail: sales@mfdcapacitors.co.uk

Radiotronic, Advance Park Rhonymedre, Wrexham, Clwyd, LL14 3YR Tel: (01978) 823900 Fax: (01978) 822913 E-mail: sales@aslgroup.uk.com

METALLISING PROCESSORS OR SERVICES

A P Metalising, Dunsford Road, Meadow Lane Industrial Estate, Alfreton, Derbyshire, DE55 7RH Tel: (01773) 835398 Fax: (01773) 521229

Amcor Flexibles Camvac, Burrell Way, Thetford, Norfolk, IP24 3QY Tel: (01842) 755021 Fax: (0845) 0822426 E-mail: steve.jackson@amcor-flexibles.com

Dibro Ltd, Unit 2, Bechers Drive, Aintree Racecourse Retail & Business Park, Liverpool, L9 5AY Tel: 0151-525 0365 Fax: 0151-525 0342 E-mail: tom@dibro.com

Ionbond Ltd, Factory 36 Number One Industrial Estate, Medomsley Road, Consett, County Durham, DH8 6TS Tel: (01207) 500823 Fax: (01207) 590254 E-mail: info@ionbond.com

Selectrobuild Precision Plating Ltd, Meadowside, Cultercullen, Udny, Ellon, Aberdeenshire, AB41 6QQ Tel: (01651) 842533 Fax: (01651) 842533

METALLURGICAL ANALYSIS EQUIPMENT

Benetec Cutting Tools, Unit 5b Midland Trading Estate, Consul Road, Rugby, Warwickshire, CV21 1PB Tel: (01788) 561133 Fax: (01788) 560223 E-mail: sales@benetecmetlab.com

Metal Scan Ltd, 16 The Brunel Centre, Newton Road, Manor Royal, Crawley, West Sussex, RH10 9TU Tel: (01293) 513123 Fax: (01293) 521507 E-mail: sales@aruntechnology.com

Metprep Ltd, Curriers Close, Charter Avenue Industrial Estate, Coventry, CV4 8AW Tel: (024) 7642 1222 Fax: (024) 7642 1192 E-mail: sales@metprep.co.uk

METALLURGICAL ANALYSTS/ ASSAYERS/METALLURGISTS

A S A M S Ltd, Marine Building Owen Road, Harfreys Industrial Estate, Great Yarmouth, Norfolk, NR31 0NA Tel: (01493) 653535 Fax: (01493) 653254 E-mail: sales@asams.co.uk

▶ Alex Stewart Assayers Ltd, Caddick Road, Knowsley Business Park, Prescot, Merseyside, L34 9HP Tel: 0151-548 7777 Fax: 0151-548 0714 E-mail: info@alexstewart.com

The Birmingham Assay Office, P O Box 151, Birmingham, B3 1SB Tel: 0121-236 6951 Fax: (0121) 236 9032

Bodycote Materials Testing, 12 High March, High March Industrial Estate, Daventry, Northamptonshire, NN11 4HB Tel: (01327) 702964 Fax: (01327) 871119 E-mail: daventry@bodycote.com

Central Metallurgical Laboratory, 53 Sussex Street, Sheffield, S4 7YY Tel: 0114-272 1735 Fax: 0114-275 6797 E-mail: neilellis@centralmet.co.uk

Coleshill Laboratories Ltd, Gorsey Lane, Coleshill, Birmingham, B46 1JU Tel: (01675) 462313 Fax: (01675) 463748

Ductile Steel Processors, Planetary Industrial Estate, Planetary Road, Willenhall, West Midlands, WV13 3XP Tel: (01902) 303230 Fax: (01902) 303231

Dunelm Testing Service Ltd, 3 Phoenix Road, Crowther Industrial Estate, Washington, Tyne & Wear, NE38 0AD Tel: 0191-417 9911 Fax: 0191-419 3070 E-mail: dunelmtest@btconnect.com

E White, Watling Street, Clifton upon Dunsmore, Rugby, Warwickshire, CV23 0AQ Tel: (01788) 860526 Fax: (01788) 860150 E-mail: sales@ericwhite.co.uk

G T G Engineering Co. Ltd, 1 Albert Street, Loughborough, Leicestershire, LE11 2DW Tel: (01509) 215077 Fax: (01509) 234810 E-mail: martingeorge@gtgeng.co.uk

Imperial Innovations Ltd, Imperial College, London, SW7 2AZ Tel: (020) 7581 4949 Fax: (020) 7589 3553 E-mail: sales@imperial.ac.uk

Kitto Laboratories Ltd, Christy House, Church Lane, Braintree, Essex, CM7 5RX Tel: (01376) 552554 Fax: (01376) 552923

London & Scandinavian Metallurgical Co. Ltd, Fullerton Road, Rotherham, South Yorkshire, S60 1DL Tel: (01709) 828500 Fax: (01709) 833772 E-mail: enquiries@lsm.co.uk

M B Inspections Ltd, PO Box 4, Motherwell, Lanarkshire, ML1 3NP Tel: (01698) 262277 Fax: (01698) 269774

METALLURGICAL ANALYSTS/ ASSAYERS/METALLURGISTS – *continued*

Marple Laboratories Birmingham Ltd, 19 Northampton Street, Birmingham, B18 6DU Tel: 0121-233 1504 Fax: 0121-236 3287 E-mail: info@marplelabs.co.uk

Co Mech Ltd, Victory House, Victory Road, Derby, DE24 8EL Tel: (01332) 275820 Fax: (01332) 275817 E-mail: sales@comech.co.uk

Metals Technology (Testing) Ltd, Unit 1 Byron House, 6 Finchwell Close, Sheffield, S13 9DF Tel: 0114-243 7271 Fax: 0114-243 7288 E-mail: sales@metalstechnology.co.uk

P M I Services, Glen Villa, Ashbrooke Range, Sunderland, SR2 9BP Tel: 0191-528 1469 Fax: 0191-511 0369

Scientifics Ltd, 2-6 Langlands Place, Kelvin South Business Park, East Kilbride, Glasgow, G75 0YF Tel: (01355) 225488 Fax: (01355) 249669 E-mail: east.kilbride@scientifics.com

Sheffield Assay Office, 137 Portobello Street, Sheffield, S1 4DR Tel: 0114-275 5111 Fax: 0114-275 6473 E-mail: jarvisd@assayoffice.co.uk

METALLURGICAL LABORATORY SERVICES

Incotest, Holmer Road, Hereford, HR4 9SL Tel: (01432) 352230 Fax: (01432) 353545 E-mail: info@incotest.co.uk

METALLURGICAL MICROSCOPES

Imaging Associates Ltd, 6 Avonbury Business Park, Howes Lane, Bicester, Oxfordshire, OX26 2UA Tel: (01869) 356240 Fax: (01869) 356241 E-mail: sales@imas.co.uk

METALLURGICAL PLANT ENGINEERS/DESIGN SERVICES

Siemens V A I Metals Technologies Ltd, Loewy House 11 Enterprise Way, Aviation Park, Hurn, Christchurch, Dorset, BH23 6EW Tel: (01202) 331000 Fax: (01202) 581851 E-mail: sales@vai.co.at

METALS INDUSTRY SUPPORT SERVICES

Heckett, Harsco House, Regent Park, Leatherhead, Surrey, KT22 7SG Tel: (01372) 381400 Fax: (01372) 381499

Multiserv UK Ltd, Wortley Road, Rotherham, South Yorkshire, S61 1LT Tel: (01709) 321000 Fax: (01709) 321003

METALWORK, ART/ DECORATIVE/ORNAMENTAL

Anvil Engineering, Aiskew Ironworks, Sandhill Lane, Bedale, North Yorkshire, DL8 1DU Tel: (01677) 427362 Fax: (01677) 427364 E-mail: info@anvileng.co.uk

Broomecupboard.com, Knole Ho, Otham La, Bearsted, Maidstone, Kent, ME15 8SJ Tel: (01622) 738006 E-mail: info@broomecupboard.com

Bruce & Hyslop (Brucast) Ltd, 1 Well Lane, Bootle, Merseyside, L20 3BS Tel: 0151-922 2404 Fax: 0151-922 5994 E-mail: colin.appleton@bruceandhyslop.com

Calmels Design Ltd, 3-7 Southville, London, SW8 2PR Tel: (020) 7622 6181 Fax: (020) 7498 2889 E-mail: lois@calmels.co.uk

Cameo Engineering Ltd, Unit 20 Brookside Business Park, Cold Meece, Stone, Staffordshire, ST15 0RZ Tel: (01785) 761134 Fax: (01785) 761837

Peter Crownshaw, St. Michaels Forge, Tenbury Wells, Worcestershire, WR15 8TG Tel: (01584) 811371 Fax: (01584) 811094

D J Williams & Son, H Peblig Mill, Llanbeblig Road, Caernarfon, Gwynedd, LL55 2SE Tel: (01286) 673254 Fax: (01286) 672007

Davey & Jordan, 3 Jennings Road, Kernick Industrial Estate, Penryn, Cornwall, TR10 9AA Tel: (01326) 372282 Fax: (01326) 376596

Fotheringhay Forge & Woodburners, The Old Forge, Fotheringhay, Peterborough, PE8 5HZ Tel: (01832) 226323 Fax: (01832) 226323 E-mail: enquiries@woodburnersat fotheringhay.co.uk

Iron Designs Ltd, 117-119 Victoria Road, Portslade, Brighton, BN41 1XD Tel: (01273) 423685 Fax: (01273) 418927

Irony Creative Metalwork, Units 20-28 Avenue B, Sneinton, Nottingham, NG1 1DV Tel: 0115-911 7008 Fax: 0115-911 7008 E-mail: enquiries@ironycreative.co.uk

L A Richardson & Son Ltd, Putney Bridge Arches, 75-76 Station Approach, London, SW6 3UH Tel: (020) 7736 1566 Fax: (020) 7736 1566

Louis Lejeune Ltd, The Rectory, 71 High Street, Wilburton, Ely, Cambridgeshire, CB6 3RA Tel: (01353) 740444 Fax: (01353) 741599

David Lewin Metal Craft, P O Box 753, St. Albans, Hertfordshire, AL2 3WU Tel: (01727) 868300 Fax: (01727) 868300 E-mail: delewin@theiet.org

P W Crispin, 117-119 Marlborough Road, Romford, RM7 8AP Tel: (01708) 732880 Fax: (01708) 732880

Reekie Steeltec Ltd, Baden Powell Road, Kirkton Industrial Estate, Arbroath, Angus, DD11 3LS Tel: (01241) 873841 Fax: (01241) 877419 E-mail: colin.cromar@reekiesteeltec.com

S K Metal Works Ltd, 190 Courtauld Road, London, N19 4BA Tel: (020) 7263 1575 Fax: (020) 7263 1575

S.P Forming & Welding, Northwood Street, Birmingham, B3 1TT Tel: 0121-236 0582 Fax: (0121) 236 0582

Sherborne Metal Masters, Ash Lane, Little London, Tadley, Hampshire, RG26 5EL Tel: (01256) 880096 Fax: (01256) 880096

METALWORKING LUBRICANTS

C P Lubricants, Drivers Wharf, Northam Road, Southampton, SO14 0YD Tel: (023) 8033 7800 Fax: (023) 8033 7801 E-mail: cp@cplubricants.co.uk

Kluthe, 314 Midsummer Boulevard, Milton Keynes, MK9 2UB Tel: (01908) 440120 Fax: (01908) 440121 E-mail: info@kluthe.co.uk

METALWORKING MACHINERY IMPORT MERCHANTS OR AGENTS

A G Shepherd Machinery Ltd, Toledo Works, Neepsend Lane, Sheffield, S3 8AW Tel: 0114-270 6146 Fax: 0114-270 6147 E-mail: sales@agshepherd.com

Advantage Automation Ltd, 21 Broadway, Maidenhead, Berkshire, SL6 1NJ Tel: (01628) 777759 Fax: (01628) 778681

Jancy Engineering Inc, New Hall Hey Road, Rossendale, Lancashire, BB4 6HR Tel: (01706) 229490 Fax: (01706) 830496 E-mail: sales@jancy.com

METALWORKING SAW BLADES

Quicksharp Services, Signal Hill Farm, Lenborough Road, Gawcott, Buckingham, MK18 4JG Tel: (01280) 822062 Fax: (08707) 778463

METALWORKING TO SPECIFICATION

Central Steel Fabrications North West, Unit 5 Brickfields, Wilson Road Huyton, Liverpool, L36 6HY Tel: 0151-480 7504 Fax: 0151-480 7504 E-mail: enquiries@centralsteel.co.uk

Design Engineering, 169 Railway Arches, Midland Road, London, E10 6JT Tel: (020) 8925 3003 Fax: (020) 8925 3013

The Iron Works, 138 Stamford Brook Arches, Ravenscourt Park, London, W6 0TQ Tel: (020) 8748 6535 Fax: (020) 8748 5735

M K Trueman, 4 Murphys Yard, Railway Road, Idle, Bradford, West Yorkshire, BD10 9RJ Tel: (01274) 612492

S M L Engineering Co. Ltd, Benlow Works, Silverdale Road, Hayes, Middlesex, UB3 3BW Tel: (020) 8573 5907 Fax: (020) 8561 5033

Teversham Engineering Ltd, Hall Farm, Church Road, Teversham, Cambridge, CB1 9AP Tel: 01223 293904

METALWORKING WELDING FABRICATION

▶ John Rich Fabrications Ltd, Unit 2-3 Lakeside Works, Oare Road, Faversham, Kent, ME13 7TJ Tel: (01795) 591178 Fax: (01795) 538889 E-mail: john.rich@eurotellonline.com

METEOROLOGICAL/ ENVIRONMENTAL INSTRUMENT/ SYSTEMS MANUFRS

Environmental Measurements Ltd, Business & Innovation Centre, Wearfield, Sunderland Enterprise Park, Sunderland, SR5 2TA Tel: 0191-501 0064 Fax: 0191-501 0065 E-mail: sales@emltd.net

▶ Met Engineering Ltd, Unit 3, Mode Wheel Road, Salford, M5 5DQ Tel: 0161-737 2627 Fax: 0161-737 2628 E-mail: info@metenguk.com

Muir Matheson, Aberlan House, Blackburn Industrial Estate, Kinellar, Aberdeen, AB21 0RX Tel: (01224) 791222 Fax: (01224) 791555 E-mail: sales@muir-matheson.com

Read Scientific Ltd, 32 Brancaster Way, Swaffham, Norfolk, PE37 7RY Tel: (01760) 724546 Fax: (01760) 724340 E-mail: bill.read@ntlworld.com

S T S Defence Ltd, Amery House, Steeple Drive, Alton, Hampshire, GU34 1TN Tel: (01420) 88683 Fax: (01420) 89190 E-mail: sts@spacetechsys.co.uk

▶ Star Environmental Systems Ltd, Gaia Lodge, Blairs, Aberdeen, AB12 5YT Tel: (01224) 860260 Fax: (01224) 860265

Vector Instruments, 115 Marsh Road, Rhyl, Clwyd, LL18 2AB Tel: (01745) 350700 Fax: (01745) 344206 E-mail: admin@windspeed.co.uk

METEOROLOGICAL/ ENVIRONMENTAL STUDIES

Environmental Measurements Ltd, Business & Innovation Centre, Wearfield, Sunderland Enterprise Park, Sunderland, SR5 2TA Tel: 0191-501 0064 Fax: 0191-501 0065 E-mail: sales@emltd.net

METER BOARDS

R H Ling, 82 Forest Road, Frome, Somerset, BA11 2TQ Tel: (01373) 467592 Fax: (01373) 467592

METER MAINTENANCE/REPAIR SERVICES

Bulk Meter Services, 3 Faversham Road, Challock, Ashford, Kent, TN25 4BQ Tel: (0845) 2307887 Fax: (01233) 740943 E-mail: sales@bms-ltd.com

Nimbus Meters, 20 2a Ringwood Road, Eastbourne, East Sussex, BN22 8TA Tel: (01323) 639609

SLK Engineering & Manufacturing Services Ltd, 4 Castle Road, Ellon, Aberdeenshire, AB41 9EY Tel: (01358) 724002 Fax: (01358) 720166 E-mail: sales@sltengineering.co.uk

Westwood Meters & Timers Ltd, Torre Station Yard, Newton Road, Torquay, TQ2 5DD Tel: (01803) 297179 Fax: (01803) 299080 E-mail: sales@electricmeters.co.uk

METER TEST EQUIPMENT

▶ Tecnisis Ltd, Unit 3 Martlesham Creek Industrial Estate, Sandy Lane, Martlesham, Woodbridge, Suffolk, IP12 4SD Tel: (01394) 389098 Fax: (01394) 389062 E-mail: sales@tecnisis.co.uk

METERING PUMPS

Clyde Associated Engineers Ltd, Block 5, 76 Beardmore Way, Clydebank Industrial Estate, Clydebank, Dunbartonshire, G81 4HT Tel: 0141-951 1331 Fax: 0141-951 3460 E-mail: lac@caeltd.co.uk

Enraf Fluid Technology Ltd, 6 Pennant Park, Standard Way, Fareham, Hampshire, PO16 8XU Tel: (01329) 825823 Fax: (01329) 825824 E-mail: info@enraf.com

Gee & Co Effluent Control & Recovery Ltd, Gee House, Holbourn Hill, Birmingham, B7 5JR Tel: 0121-326 1700 Fax: 0121-326 1779 E-mail: info@geeco.co.uk

Milton Roy UK Ltd, Oaklands Business Centre, Oaklands Park, Wokingham, Berkshire, RG41 2FD Tel: 0118-977 1066 Fax: 0118-977 1198 E-mail: contact@dosapro.com

Morgans Products, 7 Myreside Drive, Inverkeilor, Arbroath, Angus, DD11 5PZ Tel: (01241) 830267 Fax: (01241) 830435 E-mail: dosher@inverkeilor.rapiddial.co.uk

ProMinent Fluid Controls (UK) Ltd, Resolution Road, Ashby-de-la-Zouch, Leicestershire, LE65 1DW Tel: (01530) 560555 Fax: (01530) 560777 E-mail: sales@prominent.co.uk

Seepex UK Ltd, Unit 3 Armtech Row, Houndstone Business Park, Yeovil, Somerset, BA22 8RW Tel: (01935) 472376 Fax: (01935) 479836 E-mail: sales@seepex.co.uk

Sera Dosing UK Ltd, 7 Woodland Drive, Alma Park Road, Grantham, Lincolnshire, NG31 9SR Tel: (01476) 565512 Fax: (01476) 590171 E-mail: enquiries@liquiddosing.co.uk

Williams Instruments, 29E Station Road, Desborough, Desborough, Kettering, Northamptonshire, NN14 2RL Tel: (01536) 762674 Fax: (01536) 761973 E-mail: pumppackage@btconnect.com

METERING SYSTEMS/ EQUIPMENT MANUFRS

Saddleworth Meter Services, 62 Delph Lane, Delph, Oldham, OL3 5HX Tel: (01457) 871387 Fax: (01457) 871387

Skeltonhall Systems Ltd, 70 Carwood Road, Sheffield, S4 7SD Tel: 0114-243 1332 Fax: 0114-244 9579 E-mail: info@skeltonhall-systems.com

METERS

▶ 4 Advantage Metering Solutions Ltd, Westside House, Old Great North Road, Sutton-On-Trent, Newark, Nottinghamshire, NG23 6QS Tel: (01636) 822860 Fax: (01636) 823066 E-mail: juliec@4advantage.co.uk

Metering Technology Solutions Ltd, Dogmore, Stoke Row, Henley-on-Thames, Oxfordshire, RG9 5PD Tel: (01491) 681688 Fax: (01491) 681076 E-mail: mts@meter.co.uk

Nimbus Meters, 20 2a Ringwood Road, Eastbourne, East Sussex, BN22 8TA Tel: (01323) 639609

P & J W Meters, Unit 1, Salisbury House, Salisbury Road, Newton Abbot, Devon, TQ12 2DF Tel: (0800) 5875540 Fax: (0800) 216905

Switch 2 Energy Solutions Ltd, High Mill, Mill Street, Cullingworth, Bradford, West Yorkshire, BD13 5HA Tel: (01535) 270266 Fax: (01535) 270282 E-mail: sales@switch2.com

METERS, DIGITAL PANEL

The ST. Albans Meter Company Ltd, Lombardy House, The Ridgeway, St. Albans, Hertfordshire, AL4 9AL Tel: (01727) 899911 Fax: (01727) 899922 E-mail: stalbansmeters@ukgateway.net

METHYLENE DIPHENYLENE DIISOCYANATE (MDI) BINDERS

Rose Hill Polymers Ltd, Rose Hill Mill, Beech Road, Sowerby Bridge, West Yorkshire, HX6 2JT Tel: (01422) 839456 Fax: (01422) 835786 E-mail: sales@rosehill-polymers.ltd.uk

Rose Hill Polymers Ltd, Rose Hill Mill, Beech Road, Sowerby Bridge, West Yorkshire, HX6 2JT Tel: (01422) 839456 Fax: (01422) 835786 E-mail: sales@rosehill-polymers.ltd.uk

METROLOGY CONSULTANTS

Dimensional Inspection Services, Unit 19 Wombourne Enterprise Park, Bridgnorth Road, Wombourne, Wolverhampton, WV5 0AL Tel: (01902) 326225 Fax: (01902) 326225 E-mail: sales@diserv.free-online.co.uk

National Physical Laboratory, Hampton Road, Teddington, Middlesex, TW11 0LW Tel: (020) 8977 3222 Fax: (020) 8943 6458 E-mail: enquiry@npl.co.uk

METROLOGY EQUIPMENT

Diatest UK Ltd, 18 Avondale Avenue, Hinchley Wood, Esher, Surrey, KT10 0DA Tel: (020) 8398 1100 Fax: (020) 8398 9887 E-mail: sales@diatest.co.uk

Instro Precision Ltd, Hornet Close, Pysons Road Industrial Estate, Broadstairs, Kent, CT10 2YD Tel: (01843) 604455 Fax: (01843) 861032 E-mail: marketing@instro.com

▶ Select Gauges & Calibration Ltd, Select Works, Trevol Business Park, Torpoint, Cornwall, PL11 2PN Tel: (01752) 812147 Fax: (01752) 814892

Taylor Hobson, P O Box 36, Leicester, LE4 9JQ Tel: 0116-276 3771 Fax: 0116-274 1350 E-mail: sales@taylor-hobson.com

METROLOGY EQUIPMENT, USED

▶ 1st Call ProWeigh (Yorkshire) Ltd (Scales), 8 The Sycamores, Doncaster, South Yorkshire, DN5 7UH Tel: 01302 787176 Fax: 01302 787176 E-mail: info@proweigh.co.uk

MEZZANINE FLOOR OR PLATFORM DESIGN AND INSTALLATION

Allen Mezzanines, 42 Croft Lane, Letchworth Garden City, Hertfordshire, SG6 1AP Tel: (01462) 484022 Fax: (01462) 484022 E-mail: allenmezzanines@ntlworld.com

Bradfield Storage Handling Ltd, Forty Horse Close, Codnor Gate Business Park, Ripley, Derbyshire, DE5 3ND Tel: (01773) 748748 Fax: (01773) 749998 E-mail: sales@bradfield-storage.co.uk

MEZZANINE FLOORS OR PLATFORMS

Aarcweld Scotland Ltd, 7 Rennie Place, East Kilbride, Glasgow, G74 5HD Tel: (01355) 244545 Fax: (01355) 244589 E-mail: sales@aarcweld.co.uk

Adex Interiors For Industry Ltd, 5 Avebury Court, Hemel Hempstead, Hertfordshire, HP2 7TA Tel: (01442) 232327 Fax: (01442) 262713 E-mail: adex@msn.com

MEZZANINE FLOORS OR PLATFORMS – *continued*

Advanced Handling & Storage Ltd, Staindrop Road, West Auckland, Bishop Auckland, County Durham, DL14 9JY Tel: (01388) 832287 Fax: (01388) 832297 E-mail: advancedracking@aol.com

Allen Mezzanines, 42 Croft Lane, Letchworth Garden City, Hertfordshire, SG6 1AP Tel: (01462) 484022 Fax: (01462) 484022 E-mail: allenmezzanines@ntlworld.com

Amracks Ltd, 2 Cockerell Road, Corby, Northamptonshire, NN17 5DU Tel: (01536) 401361 Fax: (01536) 275909 E-mail: info@amracks.co.uk

▶ Ancar Installations, 208 Amblecote Road, Brierley Hill, West Midlands, DY5 2PP Tel: (01384) 485000 Fax: (01384) 485000

Anglia Partitions Ltd, Unit 3 Freisian Way, King's Lynn, Norfolk, PE30 4JQ Tel: (01553) 691202 Fax: (01553) 769808 E-mail: info@angliapartitions.demon.co.uk

▶ Atlas Handling Ltd, Unit 15, Bondor Business Centre, London Road, Baldock, Hertfordshire, SG7 6HP Tel: (01462) 491700 Fax: (01462) 491666 E-mail: john.p.johnson@btconnect.com

▶ Base Line, 4 The Square, Notley Green, Great Notley, Braintree, Essex, CM77 7WT Tel: (01376) 551030 Fax: (01376) 551251 E-mail: sales@base-line.co.uk

Bromag Structures Ltd, Burford Road, Witney, Oxfordshire, OX29 0RE Tel: (01993) 703584 Fax: (01993) 772149 E-mail: jo@bromag.demon.co.uk

Corbett Storage Solutions, Enterprise House, Enterprise Way, Edenbridge, Kent, TN8 6HF Tel: (0800) 3165656 Fax: (01732) 862430 E-mail: customerservice@paulcorbett.co.uk

▶ Csi, Harris Business Park, Hanbury Road, Stoke Prior, Bromsgrove, Worcestershire, B60 4BD Tel: (01527) 559900 Fax: (01527) 559901

Davicon Structural Engineers, The Wallows Industrial Estate, Fens Pool Avenue, Brierley Hill, West Midlands, DY5 1QA Tel: (01384) 572851 Fax: (01384) 265098 E-mail: sales@davicon.com

Design Masters Ltd, 2 Marlows Court, Marlows, Hemel Hempstead, Hertfordshire, HP1 1LE Tel: (01442) 256756 Fax: (01442) 260602 E-mail: designmasters@aol.com

Dexion Storage Centre Anglia Ltd, 43 Hurricane Way, Norwich, NR6 6HE Tel: (01603) 418121 Fax: (01603) 418124 E-mail: sales@dexion-anglia.co.uk

Doity Engineering Ltd, Isherwood Street, Rochdale, Lancashire, OL11 1JF Tel: (01706) 345515 Fax: (01706) 640454 E-mail: sales@doity.com

Down & Francis Industrial Products Ltd, Ardath Road, Kings Norton, Birmingham, B38 9PN Tel: 0121-433 3300 Fax: 0121-433 3325 E-mail: reception@downandfrancis.co.uk

▶ E A C Group Of Companies, Jubilee House, Broadway, Silver End, Witham, Essex, CM8 3RQ Tel: (01376) 585855 Fax: (01376) 587910 E-mail: mail@eacgroup.net

Ek Partitions & Ceilings Ltd, 15 Arden Business Centre, Arden Road, Alcester, Warwickshire, B49 6HW Tel: (01789) 400404 Fax: (01789) 400505 E-mail: sales@ekpartitions.com

Fab Vent Engineering, North Road, Stoke-on-Trent, ST6 2BZ Tel: (01782) 219995 Fax: (01782) 219995

G B H Services Ltd, 17-18 Mercia Way, Bells Close Industrial Estate, Newcastle Upon Tyne, NE15 6UF Tel: 0191-229 0488 Fax: 0191-264 4095 E-mail: sales@gbhservices.co.uk

Gardner Engineering Co. Ltd, Vale Rise, Tonbridge, Kent, TN9 1TB Tel: (01732) 350100 Fax: (01732) 362409 E-mail: sales@gardnerfloors.com

Greenoaks Ltd, Greenoaks House, Siemens Road, Irlam, Manchester, M44 5AH Tel: 0161-775 0956 Fax: 0161-776 1951 E-mail: info@greenoaks.ltd.uk

H & R Interiors, 155 High Street, Rhyl, Clwyd, LL18 1UF Tel: (01745) 344443 Fax: (01745) 343303

▶ Hallamshire Manufacturing, Unit 2 Dannemora Drive, Sheffield, S9 5DF Tel: 0114-256 1330 Fax: 0114-256 1332 E-mail: sales@hm-limited.co.uk

Hampshire Mezzanine Floors Ltd, Hawkeswood Road, Southampton, SO18 1AB Tel: (023) 8063 1888 Fax: (023) 8023 0033 E-mail: sales@hmf-uk.com

Headway Storage Systems Ltd, 142 Bath Road, Totterdown, Bristol, BS4 3EF Tel: 0117-971 2222 Fax: 0117-972 4912

Hertfordshire Storage Systems Ltd, 6 Winton Road, Ware, Hertfordshire, SG12 7AX Tel: (01920) 467027 Fax: (01920) 462563 E-mail: info@hertfordshirestorage.co.uk

Hi-Store Ltd, Station Approach, Four Marks, Alton, Hampshire, GU34 5HN Tel: (01420) 562522 Fax: (01420) 564420 E-mail: sales@hi-store.com

Peter Howell Office Interiors, 105 Dockfield Road, Shipley, West Yorkshire, BD17 7BE Tel: (01274) 592337 Fax: (01274) 531595 E-mail: info@peter-howell.com

Lauren Industries, Loxley Green, Uttoxeter, Staffordshire, ST14 8QF Tel: (01889) 568000 Fax: (01889) 567116 E-mail: info@laurenindust.co.uk

Linco PC Ltd, Edge Lane Street, Royton, Oldham, OL2 6DS Tel: 0161-624 7098 Fax: 0161-678 6162 E-mail: info@lincopc.com

Lyntech Systems Ltd, Unit 11 Maguire Industrial Estate, Torrington Avenue, Coventry, CV4 9HN Tel: (024) 7646 8710 Fax: (024) 7646 6111 E-mail: sales@lyntech-systems.ltd.uk

Main Welding Co. Ltd, Shawclough Road, Shawclough, Rochdale, Lancashire, OL12 6LN Tel: (01706) 655131 Fax: (01706) 655135 E-mail: enquiries@mainltd.co.uk

▶ Make Space Mezzanine Floors Ltd, 1-5 Mill Field Road, Donington, Spalding, Lincolnshire, PE11 4UR Tel: (01775) 822060 Fax: (01775) 822061

Maxi Storage Systems Ltd, Walkley Mills, Spen Vale Street, Heckmondwike, West Yorkshire, WF16 0PS Tel: (01924) 411706 Fax: (01924) 411711 E-mail: keith@maxistorage.co.uk

The Mezzanine Floor Co. Ltd, Unit 2B, 9 Cannon Lane, Tonbridge, Kent, TN9 1PP Tel: (01732) 356085 Fax: (01732) 361278 E-mail: sales@mezzanine.co.uk

Nor-Rak Systems Ltd, Unit 103 Batley Enterprise Centre, 513 Bradford Rd, Batley, W. Yorkshire, WF17 8LL Tel: (0800) 0776169 Fax: (01924) 442777 E-mail: sales@nor-raksystems.co.uk

Partitioning Plus Ltd, 342b Farnham Rd, Slough, SL2 1BT Tel: 01753 572373 Fax: 01753 694422

Pba Interiors, 119 Chiltern Drive, Surbiton, Surrey, KT5 8LS Tel: (020) 8390 6855 Fax: (020) 8399 0653

Peter Evans Ltd, Wickwar Road, Chipping Sodbury, Bristol, BS37 6BQ Tel: (01278) 793339 Fax: (01278) 793251 E-mail: mail@peforktrucks.co.uk

Pheonix Systems, Phoenix House, 15-19 Norway Street, Portslade, Brighton, BN41 1GN Tel: (01273) 418874 Fax: (01273) 418363 E-mail: info@phoenix-sys.co.uk

▶ Powerdeck Ltd, Unit 4, Blackhill Industrial Estate, Black Hill, Stratford-upon-Avon, Warwickshire, CV37 0PH Tel: (01789) 730444 Fax: (01789) 730888 E-mail: sales@powerdeck.co.uk

The Redditch Partitions & Storage Co. Ltd, Unit 1 Old Forge Business Centre, Little Forge Road, Park Farm North, Redditch, Worcestershire, B98 7SF Tel: (01527) 517055 Fax: (01527) 517025 E-mail: info@redditch-partitions.co.uk

South West Storage Equipment, Unit 1-2 Rowan Court, Armstrong Way, Yate, Bristol, BS37 5NG Tel: (01454) 310536 Fax: (01454) 322090 E-mail: enquiries@southweststorage.co.uk

Sovereign Commercial Installation, Avenue Lane, Eastbourne, East Sussex, BN21 3UL Tel: (01323) 439090 Fax: (01323) 721967

Stomet Industries Ltd, Thorpe House, Thorpe Way, Banbury, Oxfordshire, OX16 4SP Tel: (01295) 257565 Fax: (01295) 271762 E-mail: sales@oastdeck.com

Stor Tech, Unit A Castle Park Industrial Estate, Bower Street, Oldham, OL1 3LN Tel: 0161-678 8597 Fax: 0161-665 0579 E-mail: info@stortech.ltd.uk

Storage Concepts Ltd, Pate Road, Melton Mowbray, Leicestershire, LE13 0RG Tel: (01664) 410414 Fax: (01664) 569969 E-mail: sales@storageconcepts.co.uk

Storage Equipment Systems, A Bumpers Farm Industrial Estate, Bristol Road, Bumpers Farm, Chippenham, Wiltshire, SN14 6LH Tel: (01249) 445593 Fax: (01249) 658779 E-mail: aashelving@aol.com

Systems Storage, 125 Back Road, Linton, Cambridge, CB1 6UJ Tel: (01223) 892433 Fax: (01223) 893864 E-mail: alfhughes@aol.com

Technirack Systems Ltd, Unit 18 Avenue One, Witney, Oxfordshire, OX28 4XZ Tel: (01993) 893602 Fax: (01993) 893601

Tedwood Storage Systems Ltd, 1489 Melton Road, Queniborough, Leicester, LE7 3FP Tel: 0116-269 3838

Trills, Enterprise House, 21 Sherwood Road, Bromsgrove, Worcestershire, B60 3DR Tel: (01527) 874920 Fax: (01527) 876857 E-mail: enquiries@trills.co.uk

Tri-Stor Products Ltd, 23 Weetwood Drive, Sheffield, S11 9QL Tel: 0114-236 3052 Fax: 0114-236 4429 E-mail: pdconstantine@aol.com

Tyler Storage Ltd, 2 Compton Drive, Poole, Dorset, BH14 8PW Tel: (01202) 733344 Fax: (01202) 730228

West Mercia Sections Ltd, Nicholls Road, Tipton, West Midlands, DY4 9LG Tel: 0121-557 9927 Fax: 0121-520 3133 E-mail: sales@westmerciasections.freeserve.co.uk

Wickens Engineering Ltd, 1 Shire Business Park, Wainwright Road, Worcester, WR4 9FA Tel: (01905) 456780 Fax: (01905) 456073 E-mail: info@wickens.co.uk

▶ Working Space Solutions, 32 Selbourne Road, Weston-super-Mare, Avon, BS23 4LU Tel: 0117-925 1899 Fax: 0117-925 1913 E-mail: workingspace@btopenworld.com

MEZZANINE SYSTEM EXHIBITION STAND HIRE

Images Storage & Partitioning Ltd, 68 Iron Mill Lane, Dartford, DA1 4RR Tel: (01322) 525975 Fax: (01322) 558032 E-mail: mrimages@globalnet.co.uk

MICA

Startin & Co. Ltd, 2 Sylvan Road, Wanstead, London, E11 1QN Tel: (020) 8989 5125 Fax: (020) 8989 5657

MICA POWDER/GRANULES

Dean & Tranter, Rockbourne Road, Sandleheath, Fordingbridge, Hampshire, SP6 1RA Tel: (01425) 654011 Fax: (01425) 654141 E-mail: office@deantranter.co.uk

MICA PRODUCTS

Calido Trading Ltd, Unit 4A, Market Hill, Maldon, Essex, CM9 4PZ Tel: (01621) 842828 Fax: (01621) 840064 E-mail: enquiries@calido.co.uk

Dean & Tranter, Rockbourne Road, Sandleheath, Fordingbridge, Hampshire, SP6 1RA Tel: (01425) 654011 Fax: (01425) 654141 E-mail: office@deantranter.co.uk

MICRO OR MINI PILING

Cofra UK Ltd, PO Box 154, Horsham, West Sussex, RH12 3PJ Tel: (01403) 754422 Fax: (01403) 754433 E-mail: cofra.uk@cofra.com

MICRO SWITCHES

Camis Electronics Ltd, Platts Road, Amblecote, Stourbridge, West Midlands, DY8 4YR Tel: (01384) 441402 Fax: (01384) 370354 E-mail: sales@camis.demon.co.uk

MICROBIOLOGICAL ANALYSTS/ CONSULTANTS

Herd Mundy Richardson Ltd, Oak House Bredbury Parkway, Ashton Road, Bredbury Park Industrial Estate, Stockport, Cheshire, SK6 2QN Tel: 0161-406 6767 Fax: 0161-494 8400 E-mail: sue.richardson@hmrlabs.com

I D G (U K) Plc, Topley House, 52 Wash Lane, Bury, Lancashire, BL9 6AU Tel: 0161-797 5729 Fax: 0161-762 9322 E-mail: labm@idgplc.com

Invicta Analytical Services, Alexandra House, 5 Blyth Road, Bromley, BR1 3RS Tel: (020) 8290 5629 Fax: (020) 8290 4443 E-mail: admin@invictaas.co.uk

M S Laboratories Ltd, 33 Sanders Road, Finedon Road Industrial Estate, Wellingborough, Northamptonshire, NN8 4NL Tel: (01933) 276668 Fax: (01933) 273841 E-mail: enquiries@mslabs.co.uk

Micro Search Laboratories Ltd, Burnley Road, Mytholmroyd, Hebden Bridge, West Yorkshire, HX7 5LH Tel: (01422) 885087 Fax: (01422) 883721 E-mail: mail@micro-search.com

Oil Plus Ltd, Unit E Dominion House, Kennet Side, Newbury, Berkshire, RG14 5PX Tel: (01635) 30226 Fax: (01635) 49618 E-mail: m.bowyer@oilplus.co.uk

Oxoid Holdings Ltd, Wade Road, Kingsland Industrial Park, Basingstoke, Hampshire, RG24 8PW Tel: (01256) 841144 Fax: (01256) 463388 E-mail: oxoid@oxoid.com

P M S Micro Ltd, 3 Brown Avenue, Leeds, LS11 0DS Tel: 0113-277 3523 Fax: 0113-277 6867 E-mail: mail@pmsmicro.co.uk

R H M Technology Ltd, Lord Rank Centre, Lincoln Road, High Wycombe, Buckinghamshire, HP12 3QR Tel: (01494) 526191 Fax: (01494) 428080 E-mail: enquiries@rhmtech.co.uk

MICROBIOLOGICAL CONTAINMENT CABINETS

▶ Atlas Clean Air Ltd, 5 Carrside, Lomeshaye Industrial Estate, Nelson, Lancashire, BB9 6RX Tel: (01282) 447666 Fax: (01282) 447789 E-mail: info@atlascleanair.com

MICROBIOLOGICAL LABORATORY CONSUMABLES

Dako Ltd, Denmark House, Angel Drove, Ely, Cambridgeshire, CB7 4ET Tel: (01353) 669911 Fax: (01353) 668989

Mast Group Ltd, Mast House, Derby Road, Bootle, Merseyside, L20 1EA Tel: 0151-933 7277 Fax: 0151-944 1332 E-mail: sales@mastgrp.com

MICROBIOLOGICAL SAFETY CABINETS

Medical Air Technology, Mars Street, Oldham, OL9 6LY Tel: 0161-621 6200 Fax: 0161-624 7547E-mail: sales@medicalairtechnology.com

MICROBIOLOGICAL TEST KITS

Dako Ltd, Denmark House, Angel Drove, Ely, Cambridgeshire, CB7 4ET Tel: (01353) 669911 Fax: (01353) 668989

I D G (U K) Plc, Topley House, 52 Wash Lane, Bury, Lancashire, BL9 6AU Tel: 0161-797 5729 Fax: 0161-762 9322 E-mail: labm@idgplc.com

MICROBIOLOGICAL WATER TESTING

City Water Pre-Com Ltd, Maidenhead Yard, The Wash, Hertford, SG14 1PX Tel: (01992) 505353 Fax: (01992) 554852 E-mail: enquiries@city-water.com

MICROCIRCUIT CONSULTANTS/ DESIGNERS/PRODUCTION SERVICES

Dialog Semiconductor UK Ltd, Windmill Hill Business Park, Whitehill Way, Swindon, SN5 6PJ Tel: (01793) 875327 Fax: (01793) 875328 E-mail: mixed_signal@diasemi.com

Technograph Microcircuits Ltd, Railway Triangle Industrial Estate, Walton Road, Portsmouth, PO6 1TN Tel: (023) 9232 1654 Fax: (023) 9237 5353 E-mail: info@technographmicro.com

MICROCIRCUITS, THICK FILM/ HYBRID

Corintech Ltd, Ashford Mill, 118-122 Station Road, Fordingbridge, Hampshire, SP6 1DZ Tel: (01425) 655655 Fax: (01425) 652756 E-mail: info@corintech.co.uk

MICROCOMPUTER CASSETTE BLANKS

Downsoft Ltd, Downsway House, Epsom Road, Ashtead, Surrey, KT21 1LD Tel: (01372) 272422 Fax: (01372) 276122 E-mail: sales@downsoft.co.uk

MICROCOMPUTERS

Intermec Technologies UK Ltd, Reading International Business Park, Reading, RG2 6DD Tel: 0118-923 0800 Fax: 0118-923 0801 E-mail: infoeurope@intermec.com

Nectar, Artemis Court, St. Johns Road, Meadowfield Industrial Estate, Durham, DH7 8TZ Tel: 0191-378 1946 Fax: 0191-378 1469 E-mail: sales@nectar.uk.com

R M P.L.C., New Mill House, 183 Milton Park, Abingdon, Oxfordshire, OX14 4SE Tel: (01235) 826000 Fax: (01235) 826999 E-mail: salesdesk@rm.com

Wyse Technology (U K) Ltd, 1 The Pavilions, Ruscombe Park, Twyford, Reading, RG10 9NN Tel: 0118-934 5345 Fax: (01734) 340749 E-mail: sales@wyse.com

MICROCONTROLLER DESIGN AND DEVELOPMENT SERVICES

A D Developments Ltd, 5a London Road, Loughton, Milton Keynes, MK5 8AB Tel: (01908) 222606 E-mail: enquiries@addevelopments.com

MICROCONTROLLERS

Advanced Micro Devices UK Ltd, Amd House, Frimley Business Park, Frimley, Camberley, Surrey, GU16 7SL Tel: (01276) 803100 Fax: (01276) 803102 E-mail: info@amd.com

Emulation Technology UK Ltd, 78 Asheridge Road, Chesham, Buckinghamshire, HP5 2PY Tel: (01494) 791336 Fax: (01494) 792336

Hitex (UK) Ltd, University of Warwick Science Park, Sir William Lyons Road, Coventry, CV4 7EZ Tel: (024) 7669 2066 Fax: (024) 7669 2131 E-mail: sales@hitex.co.uk

Lloyd Research Ltd, 7-7A Brook Lane, Warsash, Southampton, SO31 9FH Tel: (01489) 885515 Fax: (01489) 885853 E-mail: progs@lloydres.co.uk

MICROELECTRONIC COMPONENT PACKING SERVICES

I P L, Unit 16, Llys y Fedwen, Parc Menai, Poundbury, Bangor, Gwynedd, LL57 4BN Tel: (01248) 672122 E-mail: sales@ipl-int.com

MICROELECTRONIC COMPONENT PLACEMENT EQUIPMENT

M B Technology, Benfieldside, Milton Road, Wokingham, Berkshire, RG40 1DD Tel: 0118-977 6039 Fax: 0118-978 9386

MICROELECTRONIC COMPONENTS

Sabre Advanced Micro Electronics Ltd, Unit 11 The Pines Trading Estate, Broad Street, Guildford, Surrey, GU3 3BH Tel: (01483) 535444 Fax: (01483) 535888 E-mail: sales@sabreadv.com
Thick Film Microcircuits Ltd, Unit 4 Wickford Way, London, E17 6JD Tel: (020) 8531 7226 Fax: (020) 8527 5521 E-mail: sales@thickfilm.co.uk

MICROELECTRONIC CONSULTANTS/DESIGNERS/ PRODUCTION SERVICES

Automated Entry Systems Ltd, Automation House, 61 East Street, Warminster, Wiltshire, BA12 9BZ Tel: (01985) 215827 Fax: (01985) 219299 E-mail: aeswinchcombe@aol.com
Cammax Precima Ltd, 4 Brunel Way, Severalls Industrial Park, Colchester, CO4 9QX Tel: (01206) 855542 Fax: (01206) 855543 E-mail: sales@cammax.co.uk
Y D T Medical Ltd, 92 Hartley Down, Purley, Surrey, CR8 4EB Tel: (020) 8763 9777 Fax: (020) 8763 9444 E-mail: ydtlimited@aol.com

MICROELECTRONIC DISTRIBUTORS OR AGENTS

Die Technology Ltd, Corbrook Road, Chadderton, Oldham, OL9 9SD Tel: 0161-626 3827 Fax: 0161-627 2341E-mail: info@ditech.co.uk
Mintech Semiconductors Ltd, 2 Hellesdon Park Road, Drayton High Road, Norwich, NR6 5DR Tel: (01603) 788967 Fax: (01603) 788920 E-mail: sales@mintech.co.uk
S M Group (Europe) Ltd, Mercator House, Brest Road, Plymouth, PL6 5XP Tel: (01752) 662129 Fax: (01752) 241040 E-mail: sales@smgeurope.com

MICROELECTRONIC EQUIPMENT/SYSTEMS

Cammax Precima Ltd, 4 Brunel Way, Severalls Industrial Park, Colchester, CO4 9QX Tel: (01206) 855542 Fax: (01206) 855543 E-mail: sales@cammax.co.uk

MICROELECTRONIC (HYBRID) PRODUCTION EQUIPMENT

Disco Hi-Tec, Second Floor, 151 London Road, East Grinstead, West Sussex, RH19 1ET Tel: (01342) 313165 Fax: (01342) 313177 E-mail: sales.uk@discoeurope.com
M B Technology, Benfieldside, Milton Road, Wokingham, Berkshire, RG40 1DD Tel: 0118-977 6039 Fax: 0118-978 9386

MICROELECTRONIC PRODUCTION TEST EQUIPMENT

▶ Saintel (UK) Ltd, Floor One, Meadowside, Lower Road, Cookham, Maidenhead, Berkshire, SL6 9HF Tel: (01628) 523666 Fax: (0870) 1315214 E-mail: saintel@dial.pipex.com

MICROENCAPSULATION EQUIPMENT

Lsi Logic Europe Ltd, Greenwood House, London Road, Bracknell, Berkshire, RG12 2UB Tel: (01344) 413200 Fax: (01344) 413329

MICROENCAPSULATION SERVICES, FLUID ETC

Hallcrest Temperature Monitoring Systems Mnfrs, 20 Downing Road, West Meadows Industrial Estate, Derby, DE21 6HA Tel: (01332) 382421 Fax: (01332) 291208 E-mail: sales@hallcrest.com

MICROFICHE BUREAU SERVICES

Asm Data Ltd, Unit 9-12, Faraday Park, Andover, Hampshire, SP10 3SA Tel: (01264) 336007 Fax: (01264) 336100 E-mail: admin@asmdata.co.uk
Bottom Line Technologies Ltd, Ground Floor, Cromwell House, Bartley Wood Business Park, Bartley Way, Hook, Hampshire, RG27 9XA Tel: (01252) 618600 Fax: 0118-956 9988 E-mail: info@bottomline.com
Datascan Solutions Group Ltd, 424 Kingtson Road, Raynes Pk, London, SW20 8LL Tel: (020) 8542 5151 Fax: (020) 8544 0108 E-mail: enqiures@imagingandarchiving.co.uk
Dectel Information Systems, Swinbourne Road, Burnt Mills Industrial Estate, Basildon, Essex, SS13 1EF Tel: (01268) 727586 Fax: (01268) 591422 E-mail: sales@dectel.co.uk
Docscan Ltd, 23 Cater Road, Bishopsworth, Bristol, BS13 7TW Tel: 0117-935 9818 Fax: 0117-935 9828 E-mail: docscan@servicepointuk.com

MICROFICHE/MICROFILM/ OPTICAL DISC SUPPLIES (CONSUMABLES/EQUIPMENT) DISTRIBUTORS OR AGENTS

Datascan Solutions Group Ltd, 424 Kingtson Road, Raynes Pk, London, SW20 8LL Tel: (020) 8542 5151 Fax: (020) 8544 0108 E-mail: enqiures@imagingandarchiving.co.uk
The Genus Group, 15/16 Hammond Close, Nuneaton, Warwickshire, CV11 6RY Tel: (024) 7625 4955 Fax: (024) 7638 2319 E-mail: info@genusit.com
Line Scan, Unit 2, Seeking Road, Bartlett Court, Lynx Trading Estate, Yeovil, Somerset, BA20 2NZ Tel: (01935) 471440 Fax: (01935) 475285 E-mail: enquiries@linescan.co.uk
M C2 Micrographic, 19 Heron Road, Belfast, BT3 9LE Tel: (028) 9046 6337 Fax: (028) 9046 6397

MICROFILM BUREAU/OPTICAL DISC BUREAU SERVICES

Applied Office Imaging Ltd, Moat Farm, Vicarage Road, Pitstone, Leighton Buzzard, Bedfordshire, LU7 9EY Tel: (01296) 661002
Asm Data Ltd, Unit 9-12, Faraday Park, Andover, Hampshire, SP10 3SA Tel: (01264) 336007 Fax: (01264) 336100 E-mail: admin@asmdata.co.uk
Bottom Line Technologies Ltd, Ground Floor, Cromwell House, Bartley Wood Business Park, Bartley Way, Hook, Hampshire, RG27 9XA Tel: (01252) 618600 Fax: 0118-956 9988 E-mail: info@bottomline.com
Castle Data Imaging Ltd, 2a Mandalay Street, Nottingham, NG6 0BH Tel: 0115-927 4122 Fax: 0115-927 4122 E-mail: imaging@castledata.freeserve.co.uk
▶ Compact Data Management Ltd, 6 Leons Way, Tollgate Drive, Tollgate Industrial Estate, Stafford, ST16 3HS Tel: (01785) 220846 Fax: (01785) 220876 E-mail: sales@compact.uk.com
Cosmo Imaging Ltd, Systems House, Ocean Street, Altrincham, Cheshire, WA14 5DP Tel: 0161-928 6042 Fax: 0161-929 7327 E-mail: info@cgil.co.uk
Docscan Ltd, 23 Cater Road, Bishopsworth, Bristol, BS13 7TW Tel: 0117-935 9818 Fax: 0117-935 9828 E-mail: docscan@servicepointuk.com
E D M Group Ltd, Woden Road, Wolverhampton, WV10 0AY Tel: (01902) 459907 Fax: (01902) 351243 E-mail: docman@edm.co.uk
East Midlands Micro Imaging, 46 Tenter Road, Moulton Park Industrial Estate, Northampton, NN3 6AX Tel: (01604) 644665 Fax: (01604) 643673 E-mail: sales@em-micro-imaging.co.uk
Godiva Imaging Ltd, Little Heath Industrial Estate, Old Church Road, Coventry, CV6 7ND Tel: (024) 7663 7192 Fax: (024) 7663 7192
Graphic Data UK Ltd, 550 Broadway, Salford, M50 2UE Tel: 0161-877 1099 Fax: 0161-877 1151 E-mail: gary_newbury@graphicdata.co.uk
H M S L Group Ltd, Mayflower House, 11 Caxton Hill, Hertford, SG13 7NE Tel: (01992) 500555 Fax: (01992) 554241 E-mail: sales@hmsl.co.uk
Iron Mountain Ltd, Mill Way, Sittingbourne, Kent, ME10 2PT Tel: (01795) 479241 Fax: (01795) 427224 E-mail: info@ironmountain.co.uk
Line Scan, Unit 2, Seeking Road, Bartlett Court, Lynx Trading Estate, Yeovil, Somerset, BA20 2NZ Tel: (01935) 471440 Fax: (01935) 475285 E-mail: enquiries@linescan.co.uk
M C2 Micrographic, 19 Heron Road, Belfast, BT3 9LE Tel: (028) 9046 6337 Fax: (028) 9046 6397
▶ Mcpherson Document Solutions, 102-112 Main Road, Elderslie, Johnstone, Renfrewshire, PA5 9AX Tel: (01505) 331534 Fax: (01505) 328266 E-mail: sales@trmcpherson.co.uk
Mail Source, 3a St Leonards Industrial Estate, Aston Road, Bedford, MK42 0LJ Tel: (01234) 405555 Fax: (01234) 363025
Marathon Microfilming Ltd, St. Marys Place, Southampton, SO14 3HY Tel: (023) 8022 0481 Fax: (023) 8023 0452 E-mail: sales@marathonmicro.com
Micro Services (Eastern) Ltd, Unit 4 Craven Way Industrial Estate, Newmarket, Suffolk, CB8 0BW Tel: (01638) 661055 Fax: (01638) 664098
Microform Imaging Ltd, Main Street, East Ardsley, Wakefield, West Yorkshire, WF3 2AP Tel: (01924) 825700 Fax: (01924) 871005 E-mail: info@microform.co.uk
Microformat UK Ltd, 344 High Street, Rochester, Kent, ME1 1JE Tel: (01634) 813751 Fax: (01634) 831557 E-mail: sales@microformat.co.uk
Microstat, Unit 17, Crown Road, King Norton Business Centre, Birmingham, B30 3HY Tel: 0121-486 2020 Fax: 0121-486 2424 E-mail: enquiry@microstat.co.uk
Optical Record Systems, Eagle Close, Chandler's Ford, Eastleigh, Hampshire, SO53 4NF Tel: (023) 8026 7755 Fax: (023) 8061 8861 E-mail: info@orsgroup.com
Storofile, Shirewood Store, Woodlands, Wimborne, Dorset, BH21 8LX Tel: (01202) 822115 Fax: (01202) 822866 E-mail: sales@storofile.com
Vintage Archives, LT Braxted Hall, Witham Road, Little Braxted, Witham, Essex, CM8 3EU Tel: (01376) 503111 Fax: (01376) 504982 E-mail: mail@vintagearchives.co.uk

MICROFILM CAMERAS

The Genus Group, 15/16 Hammond Close, Nuneaton, Warwickshire, CV11 6RY Tel: (024) 7625 4955 Fax: (024) 7638 2319 E-mail: info@genusit.com

MICROFILM DOCUMENT IMAGING

Dectel Information Systems, Swinbourne Road, Burnt Mills Industrial Estate, Basildon, Essex, SS13 1EF Tel: (01268) 727586 Fax: (01268) 591422 E-mail: sales@dectel.co.uk
H M S L Group Ltd, Mayflower House, 11 Caxton Hill, Hertford, SG13 7NE Tel: (01992) 500555 Fax: (01992) 554241 E-mail: sales@hmsl.co.uk
Micro Services (Eastern) Ltd, Unit 4 Craven Way Industrial Estate, Newmarket, Suffolk, CB8 0BW Tel: (01638) 661055 Fax: (01638) 664098

MICROFILM EQUIPMENT MAINTENANCE/REPAIR SERVICES

Solar Microfilm Equipment Ltd, 1 Laser Quay, Culpeper Close, Medway City Estate, Rochester, Kent, ME2 4HU Tel: (01634) 290099 Fax: (01634) 290110 E-mail: info@solar-imaging.com

MICROFILM READER/PRINTER EQUIPMENT

The Genus Group, 15/16 Hammond Close, Nuneaton, Warwickshire, CV11 6RY Tel: (024) 7625 4955 Fax: (024) 7638 2319 E-mail: info@genusit.com

MICROFILM STORAGE OF DATA SYSTEMS

Document Imaging Services Ltd, Image House, Radford Way, Billericay, Essex, CM12 0BT Tel: (01277) 625000 Fax: (01277) 624999 E-mail: sales@document-imaging.co.uk
Microgen P.L.C., Fleet House Fleetwood Park, 3 Barley Way, Fleet, Hampshire, GU51 2QJ Tel: (01252) 772300 Fax: (01252) 772301 E-mail: marketing@microgen.co.uk

MICROFLOW CONNECTORS

S G E (Europe) Ltd, 1 Potters Lane, Kiln Farm, Milton Keynes, MK11 3LA Tel: (01908) 568844 Fax: (01908) 566790 E-mail: uk@sge.com

MICROFLUIDIC TECHNOLOGY CONSULTANCY

▶ Starbridge Systems Ltd, Techneum 2, Kings Road, The Docks, Swansea, SA1 8PJ Tel: (01792) 485530 Fax: (01792) 485531 E-mail: info@labstar.co.uk

MICROMANIPULATORS

Intracel Ltd, 4 Station Road, Shepreth, Royston, Hertfordshire, SG8 6PZ Tel: (01763) 262680 Fax: (01763) 262676 E-mail: intracel@intracel.co.uk

MICROPHONES, *See also headings for particular types*

Audio Technica Ltd, 2 Royal London Ind Estate, Old Lane, Beeston, Leeds, LS11 8AG Tel: 0113-277 1441 Fax: 0113-270 4836 E-mail: sales@audio-technica.co.uk
B B M Electronics Group Ltd, Kestral House, Garth Road, Morden, Surrey, SM4 4LP Tel: (020) 8330 3111 Fax: (020) 8330 3222 E-mail: enquiries@trantec.co.uk
Fulcrum Systems, Hillbottom Road, Sands Industrial Estate, High Wycombe, Buckinghamshire, HP12 4HJ Tel: (0845) 4304060 Fax: (01494) 473324 E-mail: sales@fulcrum-systems.co.uk
Retell, 53 Thames Street, Sunbury-on-Thames, Middlesex, TW16 5QH Tel: (01932) 779755 Fax: (01932) 780383 E-mail: sales@retell.co.uk
Star Computer Services (U K) Ltd, Unit 21 Woodside Park, Rugby, Warwickshire, CV21 2NP Tel: (01788) 551522 Fax: (01788) 551523

MICROPROCESSOR BASED CONTROL SYSTEMS

Cambridge Micro Engineering Ltd, 83 High Street, Linton, Cambridge, CB21 4JT Tel: (01223) 893872 Fax: (01223) 891760 E-mail: enquiries@cme.co.uk
Cambridge Microprocessor Systems Ltd, 17-18 Zone D, Chelmsford Road Industrial Estate, Great Dunmow, Dunmow, Essex, CM6 1XG Tel: (01371) 875644 Fax: (01371) 876077 E-mail: info@cms.uk.com
Cougar Automation Ltd, Cougar House Parklands Business Park, Forest Road, Denmead, Waterlooville, Hampshire, PO7 6XP Tel: (023) 9226 9960 Fax: (023) 9226 9968 E-mail: info@cougar-automation.com
Forward Microsystems Leicester Ltd, 40 Northgate Street, Leicester, LE3 5BY Tel: 0116-262 7974 Fax: 0116-262 4864 E-mail: sales@formicro.co.uk
Golconda, Links House, Southglade Business Park, Hucknall Road, Nottingham, NG5 9RA Tel: 0115-977 1101 Fax: 0115-977 0047 E-mail: golconda@golconda.co.uk
Hine Engineering Ltd, 149 Bolton Hall Road, Bolton Woods, Bradford, West Yorkshire, BD2 1BQ Tel: (01274) 401850 Fax: (01274) 401850 E-mail: rod@akili.demon.co.uk
Micro Robotics Ltd, 135 Ditton Walk, Cambridge, CB5 8QB Tel: (01223) 523100 Fax: (01223) 524242 E-mail: sales@microrobotics.co.uk
Mott Macdonald Group, Spring Bank House, 33 Stamford Street, Altrincham, Cheshire, WA14 1ES Tel: 0161-926 4000 Fax: 0161-926 4100 E-mail: manchester@mottmac.com
Pennine Machine Tools Ltd, Brookwoods Industrial Estate, Burrwood Way, Holywell Green, Halifax, West Yorkshire, HX4 9BH Tel: (01422) 370109 Fax: (01422) 371338 E-mail: sales@pennine.co.uk
Pi Technology, Milton Hall, Ely Road, Milton, Cambridge, CB4 6WZ Tel: (01223) 441434 Fax: (01223) 203999 E-mail: enquiries@pitechnology.com
Proconics Ltd, 43 Hipper St South, Chesterfield, Derbyshire, S40 1SS Tel: (01246) 221210 Fax: (01246) 563923 E-mail: petel@cathelco.co.uk
Scotland Electronics (International) Ltd, 28 West Road, Greshop Industrial Estate, Forres, Morayshire, IV36 2GW Tel: (01309) 678900 Fax: (01309) 678909 E-mail: sales@scotlandelectronics.co.uk
Storm Power, 13 Pendyffryn Road, Rhyl, Clwyd, LL18 4RU Tel: (01745) 354405 Fax: (01745) 361219 E-mail: sales@stormpower.co.uk
Tactical Controls Ltd, Unit 4 Parkland Business Centre, Chartwell Road, Lancing, West Sussex, BN15 8UE Tel: (01903) 750800 Fax: (01903) 750678 E-mail: email@tacticalcontrols.co.uk
Tebbs Engineering Development Ltd, 7 Maltings Close, Cranfield, MK43 0BY Tel: (01234) 750099 Fax: (01234) 750896 E-mail: martin@tebbseng.co.uk
Trio Motion Technology Ltd, Shannon Way, Tewkesbury, Gloucestershire, GL20 8ND Tel: (01684) 292333 Fax: (01684) 297929 E-mail: sales@triomotion.com

MICROPROCESSOR CHIP CONSULTANTS OR DESIGNERS

Die Technology Ltd, Corbrook Road, Chadderton, Oldham, OL9 9SD Tel: 0161-626 3827 Fax: 0161-627 2341E-mail: info@ditech.co.uk
St Microelectronics, 1000 Aztec West, Almondsbury, Bristol, BS32 4SQ Tel: (01454) 616616 Fax: (01454) 617910 E-mail: postmaster@st.com

MICROPROCESSOR CONTROL INSTRUMENTS

Hine Engineering Ltd, 149 Bolton Hall Road, Bolton Woods, Bradford, West Yorkshire, BD2 1BQ Tel: (01274) 401850 Fax: (01274) 401850 E-mail: rod@akili.demon.co.uk

MICROPROCESSOR DEVELOPMENT SYSTEMS

Computer Solutions Ltd, 1A New Haw Road, Addlestone, Surrey, KT15 2BZ Tel: (01932) 829460 Fax: (01932) 840603 E-mail: sales@computer-solutions.co.uk

Hitex (UK) Ltd, University of Warwick Science Park, Sir William Lyons Road, Coventry, CV4 7EZ Tel: (024) 7669 2066 Fax: (024) 7669 2131 E-mail: sales@hitex.co.uk

MICROPROCESSOR EMULATORS

Ashling Microsystems Ltd, Studio 9 Intec 2, Wade Road, Basingstoke, Hampshire, RG24 8NE Tel: (01256) 811998 Fax: (01256) 811761 E-mail: ian.harry@ashling.com

MICROPROCESSOR REAL TIME SYSTEMS

Ashling Microsystems Ltd, Studio 9 Intec 2, Wade Road, Basingstoke, Hampshire, RG24 8NE Tel: (01256) 811998 Fax: (01256) 811761 E-mail: ian.harry@ashling.com

MICROPROCESSOR SYSTEM DEVELOPMENT

Hitex (UK) Ltd, University of Warwick Science Park, Sir William Lyons Road, Coventry, CV4 7EZ Tel: (024) 7669 2066 Fax: (024) 7669 2131 E-mail: sales@hitex.co.uk

MICROPROCESSOR SYSTEMS CONSULTANTS OR DESIGNERS

Clover Systems, 7 Endsleigh Gardens, Long Ditton, Surbiton, Surrey, KT6 5JL Tel: (020) 8399 1822 Fax: (020) 8770 0556 E-mail: cloversystems@btconnect.com

Custom Micro Products Ltd, 450 Blandford Road, Poole, Dorset, BH16 5BN Tel: (01202) 631733 Fax: (01202) 632036 E-mail: sales@custom-micro.com

E I B M Electronics Ltd, Unit B2 Greengate Industrial Estate, Greenside Way, Middleton, Manchester, M24 1SW Tel: 0161-653 8181 Fax: 0161-653 8282 E-mail: jacki.eibm@boltblue.net

Limrose Group Ltd, Aerial Road, Llay Industrial Estate, Llay, Wrexham, Clwyd, LL12 0TU Tel: (01978) 855555 Fax: (01978) 855556 E-mail: limrose@aol.com

Omega Research Ltd, 32 Wissey Way, Ely, Cambridgeshire, CB6 2WW Tel: (01353) 612520 Fax: (01353) 612520 E-mail: sales@omega-research.co.uk

Sabre Technology (Hull) Ltd, 3a Newlands Science Park, Newlands Centre, Inglemire Lane, Hull, HU6 7TQ Tel: (01482) 801003 Fax: (01482) 801078 E-mail: info@sabretechnology.co.uk

MICROPROCESSOR SYSTEMS MANUFRS

Cherlyn Electronics Ltd, Brookmount Court, Kirkwood Road, Cambridge, CB4 2QH Tel: (01223) 424169 Fax: (01223) 426543 E-mail: mail@cherlyn.co.uk

Custom Micro Products Ltd, 450 Blandford Road, Poole, Dorset, BH16 5BN Tel: (01202) 631733 Fax: (01202) 632036 E-mail: sales@custom-micro.com

Hewart Electronics Ltd, 2 Blakelow Bank, Macclesfield, Cheshire, SK11 7GD Tel: (01625) 422030 Fax: (01625) 422030

Intel Investments UK Ltd, Pipers Way, Swindon, SN3 1RJ Tel: (01793) 403000 Fax: (01793) 641440

Peterson Electronics Ltd, Academy Street, Forfar, Angus, DD8 2HA Tel: (01307) 462591 Fax: (01307) 462591

Quality Measurement Systems Ltd, 55 Manor Road, East Preston, Littlehampton, West Sussex, BN16 1QA Tel: (01903) 850040 Fax: (01903) 786837

Transmitton Ltd, Coalfield Way, Ashby-de-la-Zouch, Leicestershire, LE65 1JD Tel: (01530) 258000 Fax: (01530) 258008 E-mail: sales@transmitton.co.uk

Warren Point Ltd, Pixmore House, Pixmore Centre, Pixmore Avenue, Letchworth Garden City, Hertfordshire, SG6 1JG Tel: (01462) 483733 Fax: (01462) 786103

Wellgates, Unit 6 Junction 7 Business Park, Blackburn Road, Clayton Le Moors, Lancashire, BB5 5JW Tel: (01254) 395379 Fax: (01254) 395379

MICROSCOPE ACCESSORIES

Agar Scientific Ltd, 66a Cambridge Road, Stansted, Essex, CM24 8DA Tel: (01279) 813519 Fax: (01279) 815106 E-mail: sales@agarscientific.com

Deben UK, Brickfields Business Park, Old Stowmarket Road, Woolpit, Bury St. Edmunds, Suffolk, IP30 9QS Tel: (01359) 244870 Fax: (01359) 244879 E-mail: web@deben.co.uk

Gilder Grids, Unit 11 Withambrook Park Industrial Estate, Grantham, Lincolnshire, NG31 9ST Tel: (01476) 560052 Fax: (01476) 568165 E-mail: sales@gildergrids.co.uk

MICROSCOPE MANUFRS

British Diamond Wire Die Co. Ltd, 66 Old Wareham Road, Poole, Dorset, BH12 4QS Tel: (01202) 745104 Fax: (01202) 746125 E-mail: sales@bdwd.freeserve.co.uk

Claritas Ltd, 2 Earlswood Street, London, SE10 9ES Tel: (020) 8858 2411 Fax: (020) 8305 2875 E-mail: claritasltd@amstrad.co.uk

GX Microscopes, Hazelstub Depot, Camps Road, Haverhill, Suffolk, CB9 9AF Tel: (01440) 714737 Fax: (01440) 709421 E-mail: eurosales@gxmicroscopes.com

Meiji Techno UK Ltd, The Vineyard, Hillside, Axbridge, Somerset, BS26 2AN Tel: (01934) 733655 Fax: (01934) 733660 E-mail: enquiries@meijitechno.co.uk

Prior Scientific Instruments Ltd, Unit 3-4 Fielding Industrial Estate, Wilbraham Road, Fulbourn, Cambridge, CB21 5ET Tel: (01223) 881711 Fax: (01223) 881710 E-mail: sales@prior.com

Stockport Binocular & Telescope Centre, Mercian Way, Stockport, Cheshire, SK3 9DF Tel: 0161-429 8002 Fax: 0161-474 0440 E-mail: tloptics@aol.com

Yorkshire Scientific Instruments, Garth House, 3 Garth Avenue, Leeds, LS17 5BH Tel: 0113-268 3206 Fax: 0113-269 6047 E-mail: yorkinsts@aol.com

MICROSCOPE SLIDE DYESTUFFS

Gainland International Ltd, Factory Road, Sandycroft, Deeside, Clwyd, CH5 2QJ Tel: (01244) 536326 Fax: (01244) 531254 E-mail: sandralewis@gccdiagnostics.com

MICROSCOPES, STEREOSCOPIC

Optical Vision Ltd, Unit 3 Woolpit Business Park, Windmill Avenue, Woolpit, Bury St. Edmunds, Suffolk, IP30 9UP Tel: (01359) 244200 Fax: (01359) 244255 E-mail: info@opticalvision.co.uk

MICROWAVE AMPLIFIERS

Microwave Amplifiers Ltd, 4 High Street, Nailsea, Bristol, BS48 1BT Tel: (01275) 853196 Fax: (01275) 858502 E-mail: sales@maltd.com

MICROWAVE AND RADAR TECHNOLOGY SERVICES

▶ Arrow Geophysics, 14 The Fridays, East Dean, Eastbourne, East Sussex, BN20 0DH Tel: (01323) 423556 Fax: (01323) 423556 E-mail: enquiries@arrowgeophysics.co.uk

MICROWAVE ANTENNAS

Precision Antennas Ltd, Masons Road, Stratford-upon-Avon, Warwickshire, CV37 9NU Tel: (01789) 266131 Fax: (01789) 298497 E-mail: sales@precision-antennas.co.uk

MICROWAVE ATTENUATORS

Credowan Ltd, 148 Stocks Lane, East Wittering, Chichester, West Sussex, PO20 8NT Tel: (01243) 670711 Fax: (01243) 672907 E-mail: sales@credowan.co.uk

MICROWAVE CABLE ASSEMBLIES

Atlantic Microwave Ltd, 40a Springwood Drive, Braintree, Essex, CM7 2YN Tel: (01376) 550220 Fax: (01376) 552145 E-mail: sales@atlanticmicrowave.co.uk

R F S UK Ltd, 9 Haddenham Business Park, Thame Road, Haddenham, Aylesbury, Buckinghamshire, HP17 8LJ Tel: (01844) 294900 Fax: (01844) 294944 E-mail: sales@rfsworld.com

Rhophase Microwaves Ltd, Earlstrees Court, Earlstrees Industrial Estate, Corby, Northamptonshire, NN17 4RH Tel: (01536) 263440 Fax: (01536) 260764 E-mail: sales@rhophase.co.uk

MICROWAVE CAPACITORS

Microwave & Commercial Services, PO Box 145, Worksop, Nottinghamshire, S81 8YA Tel: (01909) 569000 Fax: (07976) 208744 E-mail: microwaveservices@yahoo.co.uk

MICROWAVE COMBINATION OVENS

Microwave & Commercial Services, PO Box 145, Worksop, Nottinghamshire, S81 8YA Tel: (01909) 569000 Fax: (07976) 208744 E-mail: microwaveservices@yahoo.co.uk

MICROWAVE COMPONENT MANUFRS

Alroy Microwaves & Electronics Ltd, Boulton Road, Stevenage, Hertfordshire, SG1 4QX Tel: (01438) 314753 Fax: (01483) 367430 E-mail: sales@alroymicrowave.co.uk

Anaren Microwave Europe Inc, Suites 16-17, Somerset House, Hussar Court, Waterlooville, Hampshire, PO7 7SG Tel: (023) 9223 2392 Fax: (023) 9225 1369 E-mail: anareneurope@anaren.com

Anglia Microwaves Ltd, 5 Chandlers Quay, Maldon, Essex, CM9 4LF Tel: (01621) 841420 E-mail: sales@anglia-micro.co.uk

Atlantic Microwave Ltd, 40a Springwood Drive, Braintree, Essex, CM7 2YN Tel: (01376) 550220 Fax: (01376) 552145 E-mail: sales@atlanticmicrowave.co.uk

Castle Microwave Ltd, 5 Park Street, Newbury, Berkshire, RG14 1EA Tel: (01635) 271300 Fax: (01635) 271301 E-mail: sales@castlemicrowave.com

Chelton Ltd, 4th Avenue, Chelton Centre Fieldhouse Lane, Marlow, Buckinghamshire, SL7 1TF Tel: (01628) 472072 Fax: (01628) 482255 E-mail: mkt@chelton.co.uk

Credowan Ltd, 148 Stocks Lane, East Wittering, Chichester, West Sussex, PO20 8NT Tel: (01243) 670711 Fax: (01243) 672907 E-mail: sales@credowan.co.uk

M/A-com Ltd, Featherstone Road, Wolverton Mill, Milton Keynes, MK12 5EW Tel: (01908) 574200 Fax: (01908) 574300

Milmega Ltd, Ryde Business Park, Nicholson Road, Ryde, Isle Of Wight, PO33 1BQ Tel: (01983) 616863 Fax: (01983) 616864 E-mail: sales@milmega.co.uk

Mircro Networks Ltd, Unit 5, Dorcan Bus Village, Murdoch Road, Swindon, SN3 5HY Tel: (01793) 613991 Fax: (01793) 613977 E-mail: sales@mnc.com

Mitech Telecom, Arenson Centre, Arenson Way, Houghton Regis, Dunstable, Bedfordshire, LU5 5UL Tel: (01582) 445000 Fax: 01582 445060

▶ Morgan, Vauxhall Industrial Estate, Ruabon, Wrexham, Clwyd, LL14 6HY Tel: (01978) 810456 Fax: (01978) 824303 E-mail: ruabon.sales@morganplc.com

Powerwave (UK) Ltd, Enterprise Drive, Station Road, Four Ashes, Wolverhampton, WV10 7DF Tel: (01902) 798204 Fax: (01902) 798205

Q Par Angus Ltd, Barons Cross Laboratories, Barons Cross Road, Barons Cross, Leominster, Herefordshire, HR6 8RS Tel: (01568) 612138 Fax: (01568) 616373 E-mail: sales@q-par.com

Rhophase Microwaves Ltd, Earlstrees Court, Earlstrees Industrial Estate, Corby, Northamptonshire, NN17 4RH Tel: (01536) 263440 Fax: (01536) 260764 E-mail: sales@rhophase.co.uk

SJ Technologie, 10 Westminster Drive, Barton Seagrave, Kettering, Northamptonshire, NN15 6GE Tel: (08451) 304640 Fax: (08451) 304650 E-mail: sales@sjtechnologie.co.uk

H.R. Smith Technical Development Ltd, Street Court, Kingsland, Leominster, Herefordshire, HR6 9QA Tel: (01568) 708744 Fax: (01568) 708713 E-mail: sales@hr-smith.com

Spectral Line Systems Ltd, Units 1-3 Scott Road, Tarbert, Isle of Harris, HS3 3DL Tel: (01859) 502533 Fax: (01859) 502533 E-mail: slsltd@lineone.net

TMD Technologies Ltd, Intercraft House, Swallowfield Way, Hayes, Middlesex, UB3 1AW Tel: (020) 8573 5555 Fax: (020) 8569 1839 E-mail: wecare@tmd.co.uk

Trak Microwave Ltd, Dunsinane Avenue, Dunsinane Industrial Estate, Dundee, DD2 3QF Tel: (01382) 833411 Fax: (01382) 833599

MICROWAVE EQUIPMENT

Caprock UK Ltd, Caprock Building, Denmore Road, Bridge Of Don, Aberdeen, AB23 8JW Tel: (01224) 707377 Fax: (01224) 707254 E-mail: info@caprock.co.uk

MICROWAVE FILTERS

BSC Filters Ltd, Jorvik House, Outgang Lane, Osbaldwick, York, YO19 5UP Tel: (01904) 438438 Fax: (01904) 438123 E-mail: sales@bscfilters.com

Microwave & Commercial Services, PO Box 145, Worksop, Nottinghamshire, S81 8YA Tel: (01909) 569000 Fax: (07976) 208744 E-mail: microwaveservices@yahoo.co.uk

MICROWAVE HYBRID COMPONENTS

SJ Technologie, 10 Westminster Drive, Barton Seagrave, Kettering, Northamptonshire, NN15 6GE Tel: (08451) 304640 Fax: (08451) 304650 E-mail: sales@sjtechnologie.co.uk

MICROWAVE INSTRUMENTATION MAINTENANCE/REPAIR SERVICES

Electronic Services, 15 Cherry Tree Road, Wakefield, West Yorkshire, WF2 6LJ Tel: (01924) 256397 Fax: (01924) 256397 E-mail: john@jelecserv.wanadoo.co.uk

J U L Services, 53 Canons Drive, Edgware, Middlesex, HA8 7RG Tel: (020) 8951 5199 Fax: (020) 8905 6448

Link Microtek Ltd, Intec 4.1, Wade Road, Basingstoke, Hampshire, RG24 8NE Tel: (01256) 355771 Fax: (01256) 355118 E-mail: sales@linkmicrotek.com

Microwave Hospital, 90 Oxford Road, Waterloo, Liverpool, L22 7RF Tel: 0151-931 4221

MICROWAVE OVEN MAINTENANCE/REPAIR SERVICES

Anglia Microwave Centre, 51-53 Argyle St, Cambridge, CB1 1AS Tel: 01223 416276

Commercial Microwave Repairs Ltd, Cobbetts Lane, Hill Farm, Blackwater, Camberley, Surrey, GU17 9LW Tel: (01252) 879752 Fax: (01252) 879307

Electronic Services, 15 Cherry Tree Road, Wakefield, West Yorkshire, WF2 6LJ Tel: (01924) 256397 Fax: (01924) 256397 E-mail: john@jelecserv.wanadoo.co.uk

Gloucestershire Microwave Services, 2-4 Kingsholm Road, Gloucester, GL1 3AT Tel: (01452) 525070 Fax: (01452) 384095 E-mail: gloucestershiremicrowave@svcsfsnet.co.uk

Industrial Microwave Services Ltd, Swannington Road, Cottage Lane Industrial Estate, Broughton Astley, Leicester, LE9 6TU Tel: (01455) 285666 Fax: (01455) 285599 E-mail: sales@industrialmicrowaveservices.com

Ipswich Microwave Centre, 420 Spring Road, Ipswich, IP4 5NE Tel: (01473) 725699 Fax: (01473) 727952 E-mail: ipswich@microwavecentre.fsnet.co.uk

Jai Electronics, 155 High Street, London, NW10 4TR Tel: (020) 8965 5080 Fax: (020) 8961 2924 E-mail: jai@beeb.net

Kwik Kook, 73 Main Street, Hillend, Dunfermline, Fife, KY11 9ND Tel: (01383) 410041 Fax: (01383) 414817

R & M Microwave Ovens, 8 The Cloisters, Fareham, Hampshire, PO15 5PU Tel: (01329) 844517 Fax: (01329) 843522

Silverthorn Services, 73 Whitehall Gardens, London, E4 6EJ Tel: (020) 8524 8481 Fax: (020) 8524 8481

South Wales Microwaves, 47 St. Helens Road, Swansea, SA1 4BD Tel: (01792) 651422 Fax: (01792) 475205

MICROWAVE OVEN MANUFRS

Apuro Ltd, Unit 21a Monkspath Business Park, Highlands Road, Shirley, Solihull, West Midlands, B90 4NZ Tel: 0121-744 0968 Fax: 0121-744 0974 E-mail: enquiries@apuro.co.uk

Masterwaves, 131 Maiden Lane, Dartford, DA1 4NF Tel: (020) 8312 1000 Fax: (01322) 525488 E-mail: masterwaves@aol.com

Merrychef, 5E Langley Business Centre, Station Road, Langley, SL3 8DS Tel: 01753 485 900 (01753) 485900 Fax: (01753) 485901 E-mail: info@enodis.com

South Wales Microwaves, 47 St. Helens Road, Swansea, SA1 4BD Tel: (01792) 651422 Fax: (01792) 475205

Wessex Servicing, 22 Maureen Close, Poole, Dorset, BH12 3HG Tel: (01202) 718818 Fax: (01202) 718818 E-mail: service@wessexservicing.co.uk

MICROWAVE SUBASSEMBLIES

Anaren Microwave Europe Inc, Suites 16-17, Somerset House, Hussar Court, Waterlooville, Hampshire, PO7 7SG Tel: (023) 9223 2392 Fax: (023) 9225 1369 E-mail: anareneurope@anaren.com

MICROWAVE SYSTEM ENGINEERING

Berkshire Microwave Services, 3 Cavendish Meads, Sunninghill, Ascot, Berkshire, SL5 9TB Tel: (01344) 623867 Fax: (01344) 623867

Hitek Electronic Materials Ltd, 15 Wentworth Road, Scunthorpe, South Humberside, DN17 2AX Tel: (01724) 851678 Fax: (01724) 280586 E-mail: sales@hitek-ltd.co.uk

Industrial Microwave Services Ltd, Swannington Road, Cottage Lane Industrial Estate, Broughton Astley, Leicester, LE9 6TU Tel: (01455) 285666 Fax: (01455) 285599 E-mail: sales@industrialmicrowaveservices.com

Kwik Kook, 56 Higher Road, Liverpool, L25 0QQ Tel: 0151-448 1201 Fax: 0151-281 2508 E-mail: howie@kwikkook.co.uk

MICROWAVE TEST EQUIPMENT

Aeroflex Co. Ltd, Long Acres House, 6 Hills Way, Stevenage, Hertfordshire, SG1 2AN Tel: (01438) 742200 Fax: (01438) 727601 E-mail: deb.stockman@ifrsys.com

MILD STEEL FABRICATIONS

Primarc Engineering Ltd, Unit 4 Esslemont Industrial Estate, Ellon, Aberdeenshire, AB41 8PA Tel: (01358) 724543 Fax: (01358) 724550

▶ Roberts & Lyons, 59 A Wymeswold Industrial Estate, Wymeswold Lane, Burton On The Wolds, Loughborough, Leicestershire, LE12 5TY Tel: (01509) 881207 Fax: (01509) 880668 E-mail: sales@robertsandlyons.co.uk

Support Systems Nottingham Ltd, Nottingham Road, Beeston, Nottingham, NG9 6DP Tel: 0115-922 9067 Fax: 0115-925 5555

Welded Presswork (1982) Ltd, Stafford Road, Darlaston, Wednesbury, West Midlands, WS10 8SZ Tel: 0121-526 2022 Fax: 0121-526 4905 E-mail: enquiries@weldedpresswork.co.uk

MILD STEEL FABRICATORS

A M P S Fabrications Ltd, Arch 36 Miles Street, London, SW8 1RY Tel: (020) 7587 1444 Fax: (020) 7587 5141 E-mail: ampsfabs@aol.com

▶ Broplant Fabrications Ltd, Moorfield Industrial Estate, Cotes Heath, Stafford, ST21 6QY Tel: (01782) 791232 Fax: (01782) 791611 E-mail: broplantfabs@ukonline.co.uk

▶ Bute Blacksmiths, 88 High Street, Rothesay, Isle of Bute, PA20 9BB Tel: (01700) 504235 Fax: (01700) 504235 E-mail: enquiries@buteblacksmiths.fsnet.co.uk

▶ Exmouth Engineering Ltd, Unit 4, Pound Lane, Exmouth, Devon, EX8 4NP Tel: (01395) 267600 Fax: (01395) 223888 E-mail: sales@exmouthengerneering.co.uk

Web Fabrications Ltd, Gledholt Business Park, Allen Row, Paddock, Huddersfield, HD1 4SB Tel: (01484) 545333 Fax: (01484) 422194

MILD STEEL SECURITY GATES

Atlantic Security, Unit 462 Robeson Street, Bow Common Lane, London, E3 4JA Tel: (020) 8981 5559 Fax: (020) 8981 5559 E-mail: atlansecur@yahoo.co.uk

MILD STEEL STAIRCASES

Lowe Engineering Midland Ltd, Stone Road, Bramshall, Uttoxeter, Staffordshire, ST14 8SH Tel: (01889) 563244 Fax: (01889) 563554 E-mail: sales@loweengineering.co.uk

Metafab Solutions, Marine Shed, Cu Lighting Estate, Broadwell, Coleford, Gloucestershire, GL16 7EG Tel: (01594) 839220 Fax: (01594) 827878 E-mail: sales@metafabs.com

MILD STEEL WELDING FABRICATION

A & B Fabrications, 1 Morrell Street, Maltby, Rotherham, South Yorkshire, S66 7LL Tel: (01709) 816402

A D R Art Metalwork, 109 Railway Arches, Cannon Street Road, London, E1 2LY Tel: (020) 7488 3776 Fax: (020) 7488 3776

Advance Fabrications Ltd, 1 Harrow Garage, Newbury Road, Headley, Thatcham, Berkshire, RG19 8LG Tel: (01635) 268234 Fax: (01635) 268704

Alfreton Fabrications Ltd, Unit 5b Wimsey Way, Somercotes, Alfreton, Derbyshire, DE55 4LS Tel: (01773) 608163 Fax: (01773) 608163 E-mail: sales@alfertonfabs.co.uk

Arc Engineering Fabrication Ltd, 311 Bexhill Road, St. Leonards-on-Sea, East Sussex, TN38 8AJ Tel: (01424) 715220 Fax: (01424) 442344 E-mail: steelwork@arcfab.freeserve.co.uk

Archer Engineering (Leeds) Ltd, Pepper Road, Hunslet, Leeds, LS10 2RU Tel: 0113-270 5478 Fax: 0113-271 9886 E-mail: richard@archereng.co.uk

Arden Fabrications, Packwood Road, Lapworth, Solihull, West Midlands, B94 6EJ Tel: (01564) 770966 Fax: (01564) 771052 E-mail: guy@ardenfabrications.co.uk

Arminhall Engineering, Shire Hill Industrial Estate, Saffron Walden, Essex, CB11 3AQ Tel: (01799) 524510 Fax: (01799) 526680

B B & W W Erectors Ltd, 51 Uckfield Road, Enfield, Middlesex, EN3 6AS Tel: (01992) 717417 Fax: (01992) 767894

Beam Structural Services Ltd, Creek Road, March, Cambridgeshire, PE15 8RE Tel: (01354) 660895 Fax: (01354) 661361 E-mail: sales@bssmarchltd.co.uk

Bebbington Steps Ltd, Unit 1-2 Finnimore Industrial Estate, Ottery St. Mary, Devon, EX11 1NR Tel: (01404) 813817 Fax: (01404) 813817E-mail: martin@bebbingtonsteps.co.uk

Birchall Engineering Ltd, Birchwood Park Old School, Cottingham Street, Goole, North Humberside, DN14 5RR Tel: (01405) 767930 Fax: (01405) 767876

Brightarc Welding, Newlands Farm, Canterbury Road, Selsted, Dover, Kent, CT15 7HL Tel: (01303) 844319 Fax: (01303) 844666

Brookside Services Ltd, Station Road, Harrietsham, Maidstone, Kent, ME17 1JA Tel: (01622) 858995 Fax: (01622) 859793

Cadnam Metalcraft, Southampton Road, Cadnam, Southampton, SO40 2NB Tel: (023) 8081 2489 Fax: (023) 8081 2976 E-mail: cadnammetalcraft@btconnect.com

Tab Fabs Ltd, Unit 4 Lower Wield, Alresford, Hampshire, SO24 9AJ Tel: (01256) 389123 Fax: (01256) 389188

Trentham Fencing & Contractors Ltd, 17-19 Church Lane, Stoke-on-Trent, ST4 4QB Tel: (01782) 644165 Fax: (01782) 644490 E-mail: sales@trenthamfencing.co.uk

Wilbar Engineers, Patterson Street, Blaydon-on-Tyne, Tyne & Wear, NE21 5TL Tel: 0191-414 5697 Fax: 0191-499 0174 E-mail: wilbarengineer@aol.com

MILD STEEL, HOT ROLLED

▶ Franklin Steel Stockholders plc, Heathhall Industrial Estate, Heathhall, Dumfries, DG1 3PH Tel: (01387) 268877 Fax: (01387) 259101

MILITARY BADGES

▶ militarybadges.co.uk, 27 Post House Wynd, Darlington, County Durham, DL3 7LP Tel: (01325) 489820 E-mail: diamondmerchants@btopenworld.com

Jeremy Tenniswood, 36 St. Botolphs Street, Colchester, CO2 7EA Tel: (01206) 368787 Fax: (01206) 367836 E-mail: info@militaria.co.uk

▶ Ben Worsley, 14 Foster Avenue, Beaumont Park, Huddersfield, HD4 5LN Tel: (01484) 326669 Fax: (01484) 326669 E-mail: info@ben-worsley.com

MILITARY BUTTONS

N Schahid Ltd, Unit 3 Knoll Business Centre, Old Shoreham Road, Hove, East Sussex, BN3 7GS Tel: (01273) 424200 Fax: (01273) 424204 E-mail: nschahid@aol.com

MILITARY COUNTERMEASURE PRODUCTS, CHAFF ETC

Pains Wessex Ltd, High Post, Salisbury, SP4 6AS Tel: (01722) 411611 Fax: (01722) 428798 E-mail: info@chemringcm.com

MILITARY ELECTRONIC DEFENCE EQUIPMENT

Com Development Europe Ltd, Unit 10 Triangle Business Park, Quilters Way, Stoke Mandeville, Aylesbury, Buckinghamshire, HP22 5SX Tel: (01296) 616400 Fax: (01296) 616500 E-mail: info@comdev.co.uk

M T H Ltd, 42 Queens Road, Farnborough, Hampshire, GU14 6DT Tel: (01252) 519251 Fax: (01252) 524494 E-mail: mthltd@nildram.co.uk

MILITARY EQUIPMENT, *See headings for particular types*

MILITARY FOOTWEAR

Global Military Supplies, Unit 2, Deben Way off Wilford Bridge Road, Woodbridge, Suffolk, IP12 1RS Tel: 01394 611051 Fax: 01394 388551 E-mail: info@globalmilitarysupplies.co.uk

Haynes & Cann Ltd, 1-9 Overstone Road, Northampton, NN1 3JL Tel: (01604) 626143 Fax: (01604) 604721

Sanders & Sanders Ltd, Spencer Works, Spencer Road, Rushden, Northamptonshire, NN10 6AE Tel: (01933) 353066 Fax: (01933) 410355 E-mail: mail@sanders-uk.com

MILITARY HELMETS

C M R International (UK) Military Firearms & Antiquities, 53 High Street, Ashford, Kent, TN24 8SG Tel: (0871) 2301318 Fax: (0871) 2301318 E-mail: cmrinternational@aol.com

▶ John Marshall Armour Systems Ltd, 578 Coldhams Lane, Cambridge, CB1 3JR Tel: (01223) 516814 Fax: (01223) 516813 E-mail: sales@marshallarmour.com

N P Aerospace Ltd, 473 Foleshill Road, Coventry, CV6 5AQ Tel: (024) 7663 8464 Fax: (024) 7668 7313 E-mail: info@np-aerospace.co.uk

MILITARY LOGISTICS SUPPORT SERVICES

Aviation Jersey Ltd, Beaumont, St. Peter, Jersey, JE3 7BR Tel: (01534) 725301 Fax: (01534) 759449 E-mail: sales@aviationjersey.com

MILITARY MODELS

Amerang Ltd, 15b Commerce Way, Lancing, West Sussex, BN15 8TA Tel: (01903) 765496 Fax: (01903) 765178 E-mail: sales@amerang-group.com

MILITARY PYROTECHNICS

Pains Wessex Ltd, High Post, Salisbury, SP4 6AS Tel: (01722) 411611 Fax: (01722) 428798 E-mail: info@chemringcm.com

MILITARY SIMULATORS

C A E UK plc, Innovation Drive, York Road, Burgess Hill, West Sussex, RH15 9TW Tel: (01444) 247535 Fax: (01444) 244895 E-mail: cae_plc@cae.co.uk

MILITARY TRAILERS

The Boughton Group, Graycar Business Park, Barton Turn, Barton under Needwood, Burton-on-Trent, Staffordshire, DE13 8EN Tel: (01283) 711771 Fax: (01283) 711669 E-mail: enquiries@reynoldsboughton.com

MILITARY VEHICLES

Agricultral & Cross Country Vehicle, Drayton Mount Farm, Barrow Hill, Belbroughton, Stourbridge, West Midlands, DY9 0BL Tel: (01562) 730404

MILITARY WEBBING

Amsafe Bridport, The Court, West Street, Bridport, Dorset, DT6 3QU Tel: (01308) 456666 Fax: (01308) 456605 E-mail: david.rumney@amsafe.com

MILK

▶ Allarburn Holdings Ltd, Edgar Road, Elgin, Morayshire, IV30 6XQ Tel: (01343) 547455 Fax: (01343) 552297

▶ Braziers Dairies, Bellingdon Road, Chesham, Buckinghamshire, HP5 2NN Tel: (01494) 784232 Fax: (01494) 792500

▶ Caldwells Dairy, 72 Inglefield Street, Glasgow, G42 7AW Tel: 0141-422 1828

▶ Claymore Dairies Ltd, 4a Dochcarty Road, Dingwall, Ross-Shire, IV15 9UG Tel: (01349) 863120 Fax: (01349) 861921

Dairy Crest Ltd, Pelton Road, Basingstoke, Hampshire, RG21 6XD Tel: (01256) 321329 Fax: (01256) 810833

▶ Dairy Crest Ltd, 4 Alexandra Road, Epsom, Surrey, KT17 4BJ Tel: (01372) 726551 Fax: (01372) 747231 E-mail: epson.depot@dairycrest.co.uk

▶ Dairy Crest Ltd, 10 George Edwards Road, Fakenham, Norfolk, NR21 8NL Tel: (01328) 862025 Fax: (01328) 855704

▶ Dairy Crest Ltd, Stenner House, Brinell Way, Great Yarmouth, Norfolk, NR31 0LU Tel: (01493) 660400 Fax: (01493) 657289

▶ Dairy Crest Ltd, Barn Hawe, Church Hill, Orpington, Kent, BR6 0HE Tel: (01689) 827511

▶ Dairy Crest Ltd, Tavistock Road, West Drayton, Middlesex, UB7 7QX Tel: (01895) 443611

Dairy Crest, Units 1B, Weir Lane, Worcester, WR2 4AY Tel: (01905) 748100 Fax: (01905) 748483

▶ Drakemire Dairy Ltd, 1 Argyle Crescent, Hillhouse Park Industrial Estate, Hamilton, Lanarkshire, ML3 9BQ Tel: (01698) 423236

▶ East Of England Developments Ltd, Felixstowe Road, Nacton, Ipswich, IP10 0DE Tel: (01473) 659911 E-mail: dairy@eastofengland.coop

▶ Express Dairies Ltd, Reform Road, Maidenhead, Berkshire, SL6 8BY Tel: (01628) 638892 Fax: (01628) 770650

▶ Express Dairies Milk, Hanson Road, Liverpool, L9 7BP Tel: 0151-525 9857

▶ Grahams Dairies, Changue Farm, Cumnock, Ayrshire, KA18 2QU Tel: (01290) 421155 Fax: (01290) 425988

▶ Great Hookley Farm, Hookley Lane, Elstead, Godalming, Surrey, GU8 6JD Tel: (01252) 702121 Fax: (01252) 703716

▶ Ipswich & Norwich Co-Operative Society, Ormond Road, Great Yarmouth, Norfolk, NR30 1QB Tel: (01493) 856750 Fax: (01493) 331810

▶ John Kerr & Son (Dairymen) Ltd, Unit M 207, Strathmartine Road, Dundee, DD3 8PH Tel: (01382) 825018

▶ Langage Farm Dairy Produce, Langage Farm, Higher Chalonsleigh, Smithaleigh, Plymouth, PL7 5AY Tel: (01752) 337723 E-mail: sales@langagefarm.com

▶ Long Clawson Dairy, 7 Langar Lane, Harby, Melton Mowbray, Leicestershire, LE14 4BL Tel: (01949) 860405 Fax: (01949) 860259

▶ Robert Wiseman Dairies Ltd, Minto Avenue, Altens Industrial Estate, Aberdeen, AB12 3JZ Tel: (01224) 890444 Fax: (01224) 894844

▶ Robert Wiseman Dairies Ltd, 12 Brunthill Road, Kingstown Industrial Estate, Carlisle, CA3 0EH Tel: (01228) 511006 Fax: (01228) 511008

▶ Watsons Dairy, Bere Farm, Heath Road, Soberton, Southampton, SO32 3QH Tel: (01329) 832127 Fax: (01329) 834502

▶ Robert Wiseman Dairies Ltd, 3 Noremac Way, Bellshill Industrial Estate, Bellshill, Lanarkshire, ML4 3NY Tel: (01698) 749356 Fax: (01698) 746739

MILK POWDERED/PROCESSED PRODUCTS

Adams Food Ingredients Ltd, Prince St, Leek, Staffordshire, ST13 6DB Tel: (01538) 399686 Fax: (01538) 399766 E-mail: sales@adams-food-ingredients.co.uk

Armaghdown Creameries Ltd, Greenbank Industrial Estate, Newry, County Down, BT34 2SJ Tel: (028) 3026 2224 Fax: (028) 3026 9565 E-mail: contact@fanevalley.co.uk

J W Fidler & Sons, Nile Street, Bolton, BL3 6BW Tel: (01204) 529948 Fax: (01204) 365263

Pritchitt Foods Ltd, Kingfisher House, 21-23 Elmfield Road, Bromley, BR1 1LT Tel: (020) 8290 7020 Fax: (020) 8290 7030 E-mail: sales@pritchitts.com

Staple Dairy Products Ltd, Main Road, Orpington, Kent, BR5 3HS Tel: (01689) 888700 Fax: (01689) 888710 E-mail: sales@stapledairy.co.uk

Robert Wiseman Dairies Ltd, Craigshaw Drive, West Tullos, Aberdeen, AB12 3XB Tel: (01224) 896969 Fax: (01224) 871948 E-mail: rwiseman@wiseman-dairies.co.uk

MILK PRODUCTS, *See Dairy Products/Produce etc, also headings for particular types*

MILK, POWDERED

▶ Synthetic Polybulk UK, Unit 4 Brandon House, 23-25 Brandon Street, Hamilton, Lanarkshire, ML3 6DA Tel: (01698) 527122 Fax: (01698) 527127 E-mail: jim.mccreadie@polybulk.com

MILKING MACHINES AND COMPONENTS

Blyford Dairy Services, Oakley, Primes Lane, Blyford, Halesworth, Suffolk, IP19 9JS Tel: (01986) 872578 Fax: (01986) 875569

David Birch Milking Equipment, Milliganton Farm, Auldgirth, Dumfries, DG2 0JX Tel: (01387) 740219 Fax: (01387) 740667

Electro Mech Agri Ltd, 7 Tulnagall Road, Dungannon, County Tyrone, BT70 3LR Tel: (028) 8776 7376 Fax: (028) 8776 7034

Fullwood Ltd, Grange Road, Ellesmere, Shropshire, SY12 9DF Tel: (01691) 627391 Fax: (01691) 627361 E-mail: sales@fullwood.com

MILKING MACHINES AND COMPONENTS – *continued*

Green Oak Equipment Ltd, 11 Boleyn Court, Manor Park, Runcorn, Cheshire, WA7 1SR Tel: (01928) 579971 Fax: (01928) 579269 E-mail: greenoak.runcorn@fsbdial.co.uk
Vaccar Ltd, Beaulieu Park, Staunton, Coleford, Gloucestershire, GL16 8PB Tel: (01600) 716216 Fax: (01600) 785183 E-mail: info@vaccar.com
Venture Dairy Services, Dobles Lane Industrial Estate, Holsworthy, Devon, EX22 6HN Tel: (01409) 254413 Fax: (01409) 254304 E-mail: sales@venturedairyservices.co.uk
Wessex Farm Installations, Mill Road, High Ham, Langport, Somerset, TA10 9DJ Tel: (01458) 250292 Fax: (01458) 259102
Westfalia Surge Ltd, 30 Tanners Drive, Blakelands, Milton Keynes, MK14 5BN Tel: (01908) 589600 Fax: (01908) 589650 E-mail: sales@westfaliasurgeltd.com

MILLED PARTS

▶ Helix Precision Machining, Unit 18, Unitfactory Estate, Hull, HU8 7QF Tel: (01482) 323131 Fax: (01482) 226639 E-mail: office@helixprecision.co.uk

MILLIMETRIC MICROWAVE COMPONENTS

Q Par Angus Ltd, Barons Cross Laboratories, Barons Cross Road, Barons Cross, Leominster, Herefordshire, HR6 8RS Tel: (01568) 612138 Fax: (01568) 616373 E-mail: sales@q-par.com

MILLING CHUCKS

Goodwood Engineering, Enterprise Way, King's Lynn, Norfolk, PE30 4LJ Tel: (01553) 766574 Fax: (01553) 766574 E-mail: andy@goodwoodeng.co.uk

MILLING CUTTERS, *See also headings for particular types*

Burcas Ltd, Park Lane, Handsworth, Birmingham, B21 8LT Tel: 0121-553 2777 Fax: 0121-553 1284 E-mail: info@burcas.co.uk
Richard Lloyd Ltd, Cromwell Works, Tenbury Wells, Worcestershire, WR15 8LF Tel: (01584) 810381 Fax: (01584) 810080 E-mail: sales@galtona.co.uk
M R Tool (Atherstone) Ltd, Unit 1, Netherwood Industrial Estate, Ratcliffe Road, Atherstone, Warwickshire, CV9 1HY Tel: (01827) 713097 Fax: (01827) 718518 E-mail: mrtoolsales@btconnect.com
Presto International Ltd, Penistone Road, Sheffield, S6 2FN Tel: 0114-234 9361 Fax: 0114-234 7446 E-mail: kevin.blackwell@presto-tools.com
W.J. Quinn Cutting Tools Ltd, 9 Wainwright Street, Aston, Birmingham, B6 5TH Tel: 0121-328 4640 E-mail: sales@quinntoolsgroup.co.uk
Rapid Grinding Services Ltd, 3 Bilston Key Industrial Estate, Oxford Street, Bilston, West Midlands, WV14 7DW Tel: (01902) 354040 Fax: (01902) 354055
Steloc Tooling Co, 3 Brunswick Trading Estate, Hertford Street, Sparkbrook, Birmingham, B12 8NP Tel: 0121-440 3467 Fax: 0121-440 5194
Sumitomo Electric Hardmetal Ltd, 50 Summerleys Road, Princes Risborough, Buckinghamshire, HP27 9PW Tel: (01844) 342081 Fax: (01844) 342415 E-mail: enquiries@sumitomo-hardmetal.co.uk
Walter Maschinenbau GmbH, 813 Holly Farm Business Park, Honiley, Kenilworth, Warwickshire, CV8 1NP Tel: (01926) 485047 Fax: (01926) 485049 E-mail: info.uk@walter-machines.com

MILLING ENGINEERING SERVICES

Adm Milling Ltd, 1 King Edward Road, Brentwood, Essex, CM14 4HG Tel: (01277) 262525 Fax: (01277) 694358
Alford Engineering, Fen Lane, Maltby le Marsh, Alford, Lincolnshire, LN13 0JT Tel: (01507) 450566 Fax: (01507) 450327
Alton Precision Engineering Ltd, Unit 27a Chemical Lane, Stoke-on-Trent, ST6 4PB Tel: (01782) 813753 Fax: (01782) 813752 E-mail: altonpre@clara.co.uk
B K Engineering Services, 4 Eye Green Industries, Crowland Road, Eye, Peterborough, PE6 7SZ Tel: (01733) 222711 Fax: (01733) 222711
Beard Engineering Co. Ltd, Pye Hill Road, Jacksdale, Nottingham, NG16 5LR Tel: (01773) 602535 Fax: (01773) 540185 E-mail: admin@beardengineering.co.uk
Biddlecombe Engineering Ltd, Unit 18 Landford Common Farm, New Road, Landford, Salisbury, SP5 2AZ Tel: (01794) 322992 Fax: (01794) 323001
Bollin Dale Engineering Ltd, Pownall Square, Macclesfield, Cheshire, SK11 8DT Tel: (01625) 422620 Fax: (01625) 614322 E-mail: sales@bollineng.co.uk
Braefield Precision Engineers Ltd, High Lane, Stanstead, Stansted, Essex, CM24 8LQ Tel: (01279) 815686 Fax: (01279) 815647 E-mail: braefield@tiscali.co.uk
Bromfield Precision Engineering Ltd, 905 Uxbridge Road, Uxbridge, Middlesex, UB10 0NH Tel: (020) 8573 8422 Fax: (020) 8569 2589
C Churchfield, Unit 7 Howsell Road Industrial Estate, Malvern, Worcestershire, WR14 1UJ Tel: (01684) 892150 Fax: (01684) 892150
Camm Precision Engineers Ltd, 45 Winpenny Road, Parkhouse Industrial Estate East, Parkhouse Industrial Estate East, Newcastle, Staffordshire, ST5 7RH Tel: (01782) 565611 Fax: (01782) 562747
Clydeview Engineering Cleland Ltd, 24 Bellside Road, Cleland, Motherwell, Lanarkshire, ML1 5NP Tel: (01698) 860287 Fax: (01698) 861866 E-mail: clydeview@btconnect.com
CMJ Mould Tools, 22 Benfield Way, Braintree, Essex, CM7 3YS Tel: (01376) 347776 Fax: (01376) 347776 E-mail: sales@cmjmouldtools.co.uk
Contract Engineering Ltd, Meadow Mill, Water Street, Stockport, Cheshire, SK1 2BY Tel: 0161-480 5673 Fax: 0161-477 2687
Croboride Engineering Ltd, Little Burton West, Burton-on-Trent, Staffordshire, DE14 1PP Tel: (01283) 511188 Fax: (01283) 530845 E-mail: info@croboride.co.uk
Crusherform Grinding Co., 30 Kennington Road, Nuffield Industrial Estate, Poole, Dorset, BH17 0GF Tel: (01202) 679363 Fax: (01202) 682970
D C Hall Ltd, Woburn Lane, Aspley Guise, Milton Keynes, MK17 8JJ Tel: (01908) 583888 Fax: (01908) 582041E-mail: ray@dchall.co.uk
Dart Precision Engineering, 41 Eton Wick Road, Eton Wick, Windsor, Berkshire, SL4 6LU Tel: (01753) 831110 Fax: (01753) 831110
Dixi & Associates, Unit 3 Riverstone Middlemarch Business Park, Coventry Tradin, Middlemarch Business Park, Coventry, CV3 4FJ Tel: (024) 7688 2108 Fax: (024) 7688 2115
Dowling & Fransen (Engineers) Ltd, North End Road, Wembley, Middlesex, HA9 0AN Tel: (020) 8903 2155 Fax: (020) 8903 2158 E-mail: dowling@fransen.fsbusiness.co.uk
Excel Precision Engineering Ltd, 32 High St, Drayton, Abingdon, Oxon, OX14 4JW Tel: (01235) 538333 Fax: (01235) 538303 E-mail: neiltyler@btconnect.com
Farnworth Grinding Co. Ltd, 20 Gladstone Road, Farnworth, Bolton, BL4 7EH Tel: (01204) 571853 Fax: (01204) 574613
G B Precision Engineering Co., 1 Port Hope Road, Birmingham, B11 1JS Tel: 0121-766 7008 Fax: 0121-773 2824 E-mail: info@gbprecision.co.uk
G S W Haswell, The Workshop, Winchester Street, Botley, Southampton, SO30 2AA Tel: (01489) 785293
Goldburn Engineering Co. Ltd, Unit 12, Uddens Trading Estate, Wimborne, Dorset, BH21 7LL Tel: (01202) 893100 Fax: (01202) 861666
Green Engineering, Cheethams Mill, Park Street, Stalybridge, Cheshire, SK15 2BT Tel: 0161-303 7129 Fax: 0161-303 7129
Allan Hayes Engineering Ltd, Charlwoods Road, East Grinstead, West Sussex, RH19 2HR Tel: (01342) 324536 Fax: (01342) 312556
Hayward Engineering, Unit 6 11-15 Francis Avenue, Bournemouth, BH11 8NX Tel: (01202) 573235 Fax: (01202) 581903 E-mail: sales@haywardeng.co.uk
Highbank Tools Ltd, Unit 7 Reliance Trading Estate, Manchester, M40 3AG Tel: 0161-681 2506 Fax: 0161-683 4937
Holbar Engineering, Unit 31B, Parsonage Farm Industrial Estate, Forest Hall Road, Stansted, Essex, CM24 8TY Tel: (01279) 814344 Fax: (01279) 814995 E-mail: holbar@btconnect.com
Index Precision Co., 8a Power Court, Luton, LU1 3JJ Tel: (01582) 728528 Fax: (01582) 728528
Jan Engineering Ltd, Cheethams Mill, Park Street, Stalybridge, Cheshire, SK15 2BT Tel: 0161-338 6024 Fax: 0161-338 6024
Jem Sheet Metal & Engineering Ltd, Borron Street, Portwood, Stockport, Cheshire, SK1 2JD Tel: 0161-480 2347 Fax: 0161-480 6210 E-mail: info.jem@btinternet.com
Kathglade Ltd, 20 Aston Road, Waterlooville, Hampshire, PO7 7XE Tel: (023) 9226 9777 Fax: (023) 9226 2190
King Engineering, Bell Farm, Royston, Hertfordshire, SG8 8ND Tel: (01763) 848899 Fax: (01763) 848899
Krouse Precision Engineering Ltd, Carterton Industrial Estate, Black Bourton Road, Carterton, Oxfordshire, OX18 3EZ Tel: (01993) 843683 Fax: (01993) 840539 E-mail: sales@jdkrouse.co.uk
Last Engineering Ltd, St. Thomas Place, Ely, Cambridgeshire, CB7 4EX Tel: (01353) 669000 Fax: (01353) 668999 E-mail: mail@lastengineering.com
M C F Services Ltd, Units 4-5, Camden Drive, Hockley, Birmingham, B1 3LR Tel: 0121-236 8956 Fax: 0121-236 8048
M P Engineering, 7 Locke Place, Birmingham, B7 4HH Tel: 0121-359 5854 Fax: 0121-359 5854
Mac Machining Ltd, Unit 26, Hoobrook Enterprise Centre, Worcester Road, Kidderminster, Worcestershire, DY10 1HY Tel: (01562) 67619 Fax: (01562) 861243 E-mail: morris@macmachining.freeserve.co.uk
Machtech Press Tool Distributors, Brown Lion Street, Tipton, West Midlands, DY4 9EG Tel: 0121-522 4340 Fax: 0121-522 3860 E-mail: chris.pring@tiscali.co.uk
Magchucks (UK), 16-22 Lodge Road, Hockley, Birmingham, B18 5PN Tel: 0121-551 1566 Fax: 0121-523 9188
P.S. Marsden (Precision Engineers) Ltd, Private Road No 8, Colwick Industrial Estate, Nottingham, NG4 2JX Tel: 0115-987 9026 Fax: 0115-940 0805 E-mail: precision@psmarsden.co.uk
Marvic Textiles Ltd, Chelsea Harbour Design Centre, London, SW10 0XE Tel: (020) 7352 3119 Fax: (020) 8879 3448
Media Resources, Church Croft House, Station Road, Rugeley, Staffordshire, WS15 2HE Tel: (01889) 503100 Fax: (01889) 503100 E-mail: info@media-resources.co.uk
NS Engineering Solutions, Units 23/24, Snibston Drive, Coalville, Leicestershire, LE67 3NQ Tel: (01530) 835400 Fax: (01530) 510947 E-mail: sales@nsengineering.co.uk
Presto Engineering, Unit 11 Lakeside Industrial Estate, Stanton Harcourt, Witney, Oxfordshire, OX29 5SL Tel: (01865) 883508 Fax: (01865) 881228
R K R Engineering, Northpoint, Enterprise Close, Medway City Estate, Rochester, Kent, ME2 4LY Tel: (01634) 723565 Fax: (01634) 712912
Reldale Ltd, 60 Dunster Street, Northampton, NN1 3JY Tel: (01604) 632438 Fax: (01604) 632438 E-mail: enquiries@reldaleltd.co.uk
S J Products, Unit 2 Trench Lock 3, Telford, Shropshire, TF1 5ST Tel: (01952) 240656 Fax: (01952) 242281 E-mail: info@sjproductstoolanddie.co.uk
▶ S W S Machining Ltd, Progress Drive, Cannock, Staffordshire, WS11 0JE Tel: (01543) 504181 Fax: (01543) 573834 E-mail: sales@swsmachining.co.uk
Shanick Engineering Co. Ltd, Byfield Place, Bognor Regis, West Sussex, PO22 9QY Tel: (01243) 863666 Fax: (01243) 827629 E-mail: shannick.eng@surfree.co.uk
Speedform Tools (Midlands) Ltd, Windmill Street, Walsall, WS1 3EE Tel: (01922) 635499 Fax: (01922) 722878 E-mail: info@speedform.co.uk
Sprite Engineering Ltd, 10 Lenziemill Road, Cumbernauld, Glasgow, G67 2RL Tel: (01236) 457970 Fax: (01236) 457970
Unicut, 6 Tewin Court, Welwyn Garden City, Hertfordshire, AL7 1AU Tel: (01707) 331227 Fax: (01707) 390382 E-mail: sales@unicutprecision.com
Upton & Scott, Huntspill Road, Highbridge, Somerset, TA9 3DE Tel: (01278) 783279 Fax: (01278) 783279
Widenoble Services Ltd, Tower House Unit 25 Baldock Industrial Estate, London Road, Baldock, Hertfordshire, SG7 6NG Tel: (01462) 895431 Fax: (01462) 895096 E-mail: eileen@widenoble.freeserve.co.uk
Wines Precision Engineers, The Old Dairy, Egg Pie Lane, Weald, Sevenoaks, Kent, TN14 6NP Tel: (01732) 740542 Fax: (01732) 464440 E-mail: sales@winesweb.com

MILLING ENGINEERING SERVICES, 5 AXIS

Rojac Patterns Ltd, Automotive Components Park, Hallens Drive, Wednesbury, West Midlands, WS10 7DD Tel: 0121-556 0909 Fax: 0121-556 4343 E-mail: sales@rojac.com

MILLING MACHINES, *See also headings for particular types*

Boxford Ltd, Boy Lane, Wheatley, Halifax, West Yorkshire, HX3 5AF Tel: (01422) 358311 Fax: (01422) 355924 E-mail: info@boxford.co.uk
Ingersoll International UK Ltd, 7 Sopwith Way, Drayton Fields, Daventry, Northamptonshire, NN11 5PB Tel: (01327) 313500 Fax: (01327) 313509 E-mail: inggmbh@ingersoll-uk.co.uk
▶ S I M Machine Tools Ltd, 5-6a Unit, London Terrace, Darwen, Lancashire, BB3 3DF Tel: (01254) 777117 Fax: (01254) 774841 E-mail: sales@simmachinetools.com
Turner Grain Engineering Ireland Ltd, 1 Station Road, Moira, Craigavon, County Armagh, BT67 0NE Tel: (028) 9261 1590 Fax: (028) 9261 2797
W R Tooling Ltd, Armytage Road Industrial Estate, Armytage Road, Brighouse, West Yorkshire, HD6 1QF Tel: (01484) 719642 Fax: (01484) 716854 E-mail: info@wrtooling.co.uk

MILLS, CASING, OILWELL

Vallourec Mannesmann Oil & Gas UK Ltd, 4 Prospect Place, Westhill, Aberdeenshire, AB32 6SY Tel: (01224) 279340 Fax: (01224) 279341 E-mail: info@vmog.co.uk

MIMIC PANELS/DIAGRAMS

Betrix Industrial Models Ltd, 18-20 Waterloo Road, Stockport, Cheshire, SK1 3BD Tel: 0161-477 1766 Fax: 0161-474 7052 E-mail: betrixmodels@aol.com
Eglen Engravers Ltd, 12 Lord Street, Halifax, West Yorkshire, HX1 5AE Tel: (01422) 365556 Fax: (01422) 365564 E-mail: sales@eglenengravers.co.uk
Greengate Engraving Ltd, 292 High Street, Stoke-on-Trent, ST6 5TY Tel: (01782) 822884 Fax: (01782) 815345
I D C Signs & Engraving, 26 Harwood Street, Blackburn, BB1 3BS Tel: (01254) 263679 Fax: (01254) 263699 E-mail: sales@idcsigns.co.uk
▶ Palm Signs Systems, 35a Greenfield Business Park, Bagillt Road, Greenfield, Holywell, Clwyd, CH8 7HJ Tel: (01352) 712222 Fax: (01352) 712255 E-mail: info@palmsigns.co.uk
Plumridge & Peters Ltd, Unit 5, Gillmans Industrial Estate, Natts Lane, Billingshurst, West Sussex, RH14 9EY Tel: (01403) 783762 Fax: (01403) 784288 E-mail: plumridge@ndirect.co.uk
Swiss Mimic Co Ltd, 26 Highfield Road, Chertsey, Surrey, KT16 8BU Tel: (01932) 569100 Fax: (01932) 569100 E-mail: swiss.mimic@tiscarly.co.uk

MINCEMEAT

F. Duerr & Sons Ltd, Float Road, Roundthorn Industrial Estate, Manchester, M23 9DR Tel: 0161-226 2251 Fax: 0161-945 0143 E-mail: admin@duerrs.co.uk
W T Mather Ltd, Lockett Road South Lancashire Industrial Estate, South Lancashire Industrial Es, Ashton-in-Makerfield, Wigan, Lancashire, WN4 8DE Tel: (01942) 711615 Fax: (01942) 271290 E-mail: sales@wt-mather.co.uk

MINE ELECTRICAL EQUIPMENT

Baldwin & Francis, President Park, Sheffield, S4 7UQ Tel: 0114-286 6000 Fax: 0114-286 6059 E-mail: enquiries@baldwinandfrancis.com
Chalmit Lighting, 388 Hillington Road, Hillington Industrial Estate, Glasgow, G52 4BL Tel: 0141-882 5555 Fax: 0141-883 3704 E-mail: sales@chalmit.com

MINE OR TUNNEL BLASTING CONTRACTORS

Saxton Drilling Ltd, Cardrew Industrial Estate, Redruth, Cornwall, TR15 1SS Tel: (01209) 315100 Fax: (01209) 315000

MINE RAILWAY EQUIPMENT

Holywell Engineering Ltd, Station Road, Backworth, Newcastle Upon Tyne, NE27 0AE Tel: 0191-268 4365 Fax: 0191-268 9506 E-mail: eng@holywell.com
Railway Mine & Plantation Equipment Ltd, 4 Grosvenor Place, London, SW1X 7DG Tel: (020) 7201 3399 Fax: (020) 7201 3311

MINERAL DRESSING/PRESSING/ PREPARATION/PROCESSING PLANT

Bradley Pulverizer Co., 15 Kennet Road, Crayford, Crayford, Dartford, DA1 4QN Tel: (01322) 559106 Fax: (01322) 528690 E-mail: bradley.pulverizer@btinternet.com
M E P Ltd, PO Box 1824, Salisbury, SP2 0AH Tel: (01722) 744799 Fax: (0870) 7052951 E-mail: enquiries@mep.uk.com

MINERAL EXPLORATION SERVICES

Peter Bennie Ltd, Oxwich Close, Brackmills Industrial Estate, Northampton, NN4 7BH Tel: (01604) 766101 Fax: (01604) 760671 E-mail: admin@peter.bennie.co.uk

MINERAL MERCHANTS IMPORTERS, EXPORTERS, OR TRADERS, INTERNATIONAL

Tuchkin Enterprises Ltd, PO Box 88, Hatfield, Hertfordshire, AL9 5DU Tel: (01707) 278436 Fax: (01707) 269347 E-mail: tuchkin@ntlworld.com

MINERAL MERCHANTS, GRINDERS/PROCESSORS OR SERVICES

Cults Lime Ltd, Cults Hills, Cupar, Fife, KY15 7TF Tel: (01334) 652548 Fax: (01334) 657887
Fine Grinding Ltd, Blackhole Mine, Foolow Road, Eyam, Hope Valley, Derbyshire, S32 5QS Tel: (01433) 630827 Fax: (01433) 631554 E-mail: finegrind@btconnect.com

MINERAL MERCHANTS, GRINDERS/ PROCESSORS OR SERVICES – *continued*

Francis Flower, Gurney Slade Quarry, Gurney Slade, Radstock, BA3 4TE Tel: (01749) 841146 Fax: (01749) 841285 E-mail: sales@francisflower.co.uk

Hines Milling & Processing Ltd, Scott Lidgett Industrial Estate, Scott Lidgett Road, Longport, Stoke-On-Trent, ST6 4NQ Tel: (01782) 819616 Fax: (01782) 837174 E-mail: hines@iclwebkite.co.uk

M E P Mineral Engineers Processors Ltd, Unit 4 PWS Industrial Estate, Tunstall Road, Knypersley Viddleph, Stoke-On-Trent, ST8 7BE Tel: (01782) 511244 Fax: (0870) 7052951

North Cape Minerals Ltd, Pentagon House, Bucknall New Road, Stoke-on-Trent, ST1 2BA Tel: (01782) 208718 Fax: (01782) 286529 E-mail: alan.moseley@ncm.no

Scott Health & Safety Ltd, Pimbo Road, West Pimbo, Skelmersdale, Lancashire, WN8 9RA Tel: (01695) 727171 Fax: (01695) 711775 E-mail: plarge@tycoint.com

Vitabiotics Health Foods, 1 Apsley Way, London, NW2 7HF Tel: (020) 8955 2600 Fax: (020) 8955 2601

Western Minerals Ltd, 253 Cranbrook Road, Ilford, Essex, IG1 4TQ Tel: (020) 8554 0102 Fax: (020) 8518 2920

MINERAL PROCESSING PLANT AND EQUIPMENT

South West Metallurgical Services, Sancreed Business Centre, Grumbla, Sancreed, Penzance, Cornwall, TR20 8QU Tel: (01736) 810812 Fax: (01736) 810810 E-mail: swmet@swmet.com

MINERAL SEPARATION PLANT

Holman-Wilfley Ltd, Wheal Jane Mine, Baldhu, Truro, Cornwall, TR3 6EE Tel: (01872) 561163 Fax: (01872) 561162 E-mail: mail@holmanwilfley.co.uk

MINERAL SUPPLEMENTS

▶ Enzyme Process UK, 4 Broadgate House, Westlode Street, Spalding, Lincolnshire, PE11 2AF Tel: (01775) 761927 Fax: (01775) 761104 E-mail: enquiries@enzymepro.com

▶ myNaturalife.com, 3 Horncastle Cottages, Plawhatch Lane, Sharpthorne, East Grinstead, West Sussex, RH19 4JH Tel: (020) 7990 7744 Fax: (020) 7990 7744

▶ Vsiblehealth, Cheviot Way, Verwood, Dorset, BH31 6UG Tel: (01202) 813572

MINERAL WATER

Buxton Mineral Water, Station Road, Buxton, Derbyshire, SK17 6AQ Tel: (01298) 766000 Fax: (01298) 72088

▶ Devonia Water, Lipton Farm, Totnes, Devon, TQ9 7RN Tel: (01548) 521506 Fax: (01548) 521321

▶ Peckam Springs, 3 Waterside Road, Haslingden, Rossendale, Lancashire, BB4 5EN Tel: (01706) 230969 Fax: (01706) 223595 E-mail: info@peckamsprings.com

Purely Scottish Ltd, Woollands, Cockburnspath, Berwickshire, TD13 5XW Tel: (01368) 860600 Fax: (01368) 861960 E-mail: sales@purelyscottish.com

▶ Royal Springs, Unit 1 Goulbourne Street, Keighley, West Yorkshire, BD21 1JR Tel: (01535) 667990 Fax: (01535) 603700

MINERAL WOOL INSULATION PRODUCTS

▶ 1st Insulation Partners Ltd, Insulation House, Shaw Road, Eastwood Trading Estate, Rotherham, South Yorkshire, S65 1SG Tel: (01709) 365785 Fax: 01709 365786 E-mail: office@firstinsulation.com

Wilhams Insulation Export Division Ltd, 117 Bohemia Road, St. Leonards-on-Sea, East Sussex, TN37 6RL Tel: (01424) 201000 Fax: (01424) 201000 E-mail: sales@wilhams.-insulation.co.uk

MINERALOGICAL SPECIMEN SUPPLY SERVICES

Gregory, Bottley & Lloyd, 13 Seagrave Road, London, SW6 1RP Tel: (020) 7381 5522 Fax: (020) 7381 5512

MINI COMPUTERS

Baydel Ltd, Brook Way, Leatherhead, Surrey, KT22 7NA Tel: (01372) 378811 Fax: (01372) 386960 E-mail: enquiry@baydel.com

Concurrent UK Ltd, Chiltern House, Broad Lane, Bracknell, Berkshire, RG12 9GU Tel: (01344) 403280 Fax: (01344) 403283

O B S Computer Maintenance & Sales, 113 Beech Hill Ave, Wigan, Lancs, WN6 7RP Tel: (01257) 421278 E-mail: sales@obscomputers.com

Pericom P.L.C., The Priory, Cosgrove, Milton Keynes, MK19 7JJ Tel: (01908) 265533 Fax: (01908) 265534 E-mail: sales@pericom.co.uk

MINI CRANES

▶ UNIC Cranes Europe Ltd, Unit 10, Ridgeway, Drakes Drive, Long Crendon, Aylesbury, Buckinghamshire, HP18 9BF Tel: (01844) 202071 Fax: (01844) 202075 E-mail: sales@unic-cranes.co.uk

MINI EXCAVATOR HIRE

▶ Crescent Plant Hire, South Street, Braintree, Essex, CM7 3QQ Tel: (01376) 344871

M A C Tool Hire, 25 Park Street, Congleton, Cheshire, CW12 1EG Tel: (01260) 299751 Fax: (01260) 299698

▶ Plant Parts International Ltd, 10 High Street, Pensnett, Kingswinford, West Midlands, DY6 8XD Tel: (01384) 408950 Fax: (01384) 404600 E-mail: sales@dig-dog.com

MINI EXCAVATORS

Arnold Plant Hire Ltd, Bredbury Park Way, Bredbury Park Industrial Estate, Bredbury, Stockport, Cheshire, SK6 2SN Tel: 0161-406 8734 Fax: 0161-406 8804 E-mail: hire@arnold-plant.co.uk

Beddoes Bros, Pentre Hyling, Church Stoke, Montgomery, Powys, SY15 6HU Tel: (01588) 620199 Fax: (01588) 620499 E-mail: paul@beddoesplant.co.uk

J C B Cab Systems Ltd, Riverside, Rugeley, Staffordshire, WS15 2WA Tel: (01889) 572700 Fax: (01889) 585999 E-mail: enquiries@jcb.com

Kubota (UK) Ltd, Dormer Road, Thame, Oxfordshire, OX9 3UN Tel: (01844) 214500 Fax: (01844) 216685 E-mail: sales@kubota.co.uk

▶ MTS Nationwide, Ablow Street, Wolverhampton, WV2 4ER Tel: (01902) 422479 Fax: (01902) 422481 E-mail: craig.colley@mtsbobcat.co.uk

▶ Sandhurst Equipment Rental, Thames House, College Road, Northfleet, Gravesend, Kent, DA11 9AU Tel: (0845) 120 6622 Fax: (01474) 567611 E-mail: info@sandhurst-rent.co.uk

▶ Sandhurst Plant, The Whitewall Centre, Whitewall Road, Medway City Estate, Rochester, Kent, ME2 4DZ Tel: (01634) 739590 Fax: (0845) 1206644 E-mail: info@sandhurst.co.uk

Strickland Direct Ltd, 5 Main Road, Cropthorne, Pershore, Worcestershire, WR10 3NE Tel: (01386) 860349 Fax: (01386) 860057

MINI MOTOCROSS PIT BIKES

▶ Pocket Bike Imports, 1 Looseleigh Park, Plymouth, PL6 5JL Tel: 01752 360066 Fax: 01752 360066

MINI SKIPS

A R C, Ripley Drive, Normanton Business Park, Normanton Industrial Estate, Normanton, West Yorkshire, WF6 1QT Tel: (01924) 223333 Fax: (0871) 4330708 E-mail: sales@arccomputers.co.uk

Thomson Engineering, 66 Whitehill Road, Glenrothes, Fife, KY6 2RP Tel: 01592 774345

Webb Truck Equipment, Acton Place, Melford Road, Acton, Sudbury, Suffolk, CO10 0BB Tel: (01787) 377368 Fax: (01787) 880618 E-mail: sales@web-extrareach.co.uk

MINIATURE CIRCUIT BREAKER (CB) ACCESSORIES

▶ Spares-Direct-2-U, 20 Allerton Grange Gardens, Moortown, Leeds, LS17 6LL Tel: 0113 2263384 Fax: 0113 2955753 E-mail: info@sparesdirect2u.com

MINIATURE CIRCUIT BREAKERS (CB)

Eaton Electric Ltd, Reddings Lane, Tyseley, Birmingham, B11 3EZ Tel: 0121-685 2100 Fax: 0121-706 2012 E-mail: meminfo@eaton.com

G E Power Controls Ltd, East Lancashire Road, Liverpool, L10 5HB Tel: 0151-524 1122 Fax: 0151-523 7007 E-mail: gepcuk.sales@gepc.ge.com

Hager Engineering Ltd, 50 Horton Wood, Telford, Shropshire, TF1 7FT Tel: (0870) 2402400 Fax: (0870) 2400400E-mail: info@hager.co.uk

Hte Controls, 4 Cala Trading Estate, Ashton Vale Road, Bristol, BS3 2HA Tel: 0117-966 5925 Fax: 0117-966 1940 E-mail: sales@htecontrols.co.uk

Otter Controls Ltd, Hardwick Square South, Buxton, Derbyshire, SK17 6LA Tel: (01298) 762300 Fax: (01298) 72664 E-mail: sales@ottercontrols.com

Raytech International, Coldnose Road, Rotherwas Industrial Estate, Hereford, HR2 6JL Tel: (01432) 340833 Fax: (01432) 340844 E-mail: sales@raytech.uk.com

Schneider Electric Ltd, 120 New Cavendish Street, London, W1W 6XX Tel: (0870) 6088608 Fax: (0870) 6088606

MINIATURE ELECTRIC MOTORS

maxon motor uk ltd, Maxon House, Hogwood Lane, Finchampstead, Wokingham, Berkshire, RG40 4QW Tel: 0118-973 3337 Fax: 0118-973 7472 E-mail: salesuk@maxonmotor.com

Mellor Electrics Ltd, Sett End Road, Shadsworth Business Park, Blackburn, BB1 2NW Tel: (01254) 53854 Fax: (01254) 678625 E-mail: info@mellorelectrics.co.uk

MINIATURE FUSES

▶ Europa Components, Europa House, Airport Way, Luton, LU2 9NH Tel: (01582) 692440 Fax: (01582) 692450 E-mail: sales@europacomponents.com

MINIATURE GAS TURBINE ENGINES

Bowman Power Group Ltd, Ocean Quay, Belvidere Road, Southampton, SO14 5QY Tel: (023) 8023 6700 Fax: (023) 8035 2565 E-mail: sales@bowmanpower.co.uk

MINIATURE INSTRUMENT BALL BEARINGS

I E C Ltd, 41 Harwell Road, Nuffield Industrial Estate, Poole, Dorset, BH17 0BD Tel: (01202) 680333 Fax: (01202) 680101 E-mail: info@iecltd.co.uk

P B I International Ltd, Unit 29-30, Roper Close, Canterbury, Kent, CT2 7EP Tel: (01227) 455800 Fax: (01227) 458838 E-mail: sales@ball-bearings.co.uk

MINIATURE LOUDSPEAKERS

Bandor Loudspeakers, 11 Penfold Cottages, Penfold Lane, Holmer Green, High Wycombe, Buckinghamshire, HP15 6XR Tel: (01494) 714058 Fax: (01494) 715903

MINIATURE OR SUBMINIATURE LAMPS

C J Harris Electronic Components, Rosebank, Chafford Lane, Fordcombe, Tunbridge Wells, Kent, TN3 0SH Tel: (01892) 740000 Fax: (01892) 740100 E-mail: chrisharris2@btconnect.com

Wilkes Lighting Ltd, Lyric House, 113-115 Tong Road, Leeds, LS12 1QJ Tel: 0113-231 9076 Fax: 0113-231 9078 E-mail: mick.wilkes@virgin.net

MINIATURE POWER TOOLS

Hilti Centre (Belfast), Unit 7 Loughside Industrial Park, Dargan Cresent, Belfast, BT3 9JP Tel: (0870) 4281024 Fax: (0800) 886200

M Power Tools Ltd, Manor Farm, Newton Tony, Salisbury, SP4 0HA Tel: (01980) 629526

MINIATURE PRECISION TUBES

Accellent, Unit E3 Brookside Business Park, Greengate, Middleton, Manchester, M24 1GS Tel: 0161-643 0018 Fax: 0161-643 0019 E-mail: susan.ward@accellent.com

MINIATURE RELAYS

Precision Relays Ltd, 3 Seafield Road, Inverness, IV1 1SG Tel: (01463) 233929 Fax: (01463) 712514 E-mail: sales@precisionrelays.co.uk

MINIATURE STEAM BOILERS

Controlled Flame Boilers Ltd, Gorse Lane Industrial Estate, Brunel Road, Clacton-on-Sea, Essex, CO15 4LU Tel: (01255) 224500 Fax: (01255) 224555 E-mail: sales@steamboilers.co.uk

MINIATURE SWITCHES

C & K Systems Ltd, Cunliffe Drive, Northfield Ave., Kettering, Northamptonshire, NN16 8LF Tel: (01536) 410595 Fax: (01536) 416602

Lorlin Electronics, Enterprise Unit A-C, Harwood Road, Littlehampton, West Sussex, BN17 7AT Tel: (01903) 725121 Fax: (01903) 723919 E-mail: lorlin@btconnect.com

MINIATURE TRANSDUCERS

Atex Ltd, 4 Thames Park, Lester Way, Wallingford, Oxfordshire, OX10 9TA Tel: (01491) 839999 Fax: (01491) 839466 E-mail: contactuk@atex-f1.com

Kulite Sensors Ltd, Kulite House, Stroudley Road, Basingstoke, Hampshire, RG24 8UG Tel: (01256) 461646 Fax: (01256) 479510 E-mail: sales@kulite.co.uk

MINIBUS HIRE

▶ Air-2-There.Co.Uk, 55 Leighswood Avenue, Walsall, WS9 8AT Tel: (01922) 864248 E-mail: enquires@air-2-there.co.uk

▶ Airline Cars & Coaches, Drumshoreland Road, Fernlea, Broxburn, West Lothian, EH52 5PF Tel: (01506) 852473 Fax: (01506) 857274 E-mail: aircab1@aol.com

▶ Aminibus.co.uk, 92 Grange Lane, Barnsley, South Yorkshire, S71 5QQ Tel: (01226) 246445 Fax: (01226) 246101 E-mail: info@aminibus.co.uk

▶ Pauls Mini Bus, 14 Cross Walk, Bristol, BS14 0RX Tel: (01275) 542422 Fax: (01275) 831476 E-mail: info@paulsminibus.co.uk

MINING CHEMICALS

Ciba Specialty Chemicals plc, Charter Road, Macclesfield, Cheshire, SK10 2NX Tel: (01625) 665000 Fax: (01625) 619637

Ciba Specialty Chemicals plc, Charter Road, Macclesfield, Cheshire, SK10 2NX Tel: (01625) 665000 Fax: (01625) 619637

MINING COMPANY OVERSEAS UK OFFICES

Scarborough Minerals P.L.C., 1 Grosvenor Crescent, London, SW1X 7EF Tel: (020) 7152 6230 Fax: (020) 7152 6231 E-mail: info@scrbmin.com

MINING CONSULTING ENGINEERS/CONSULTANTS/ TECHNOLOGISTS

Amalgamated Construction Co. Ltd, Whaley Road, Barnsley, South Yorkshire, S75 1HT Tel: (01226) 243413 Fax: (01226) 320202 E-mail: info@amco-construction.co.uk

Anderson Associates, 5 Station Road, Parbold, Wigan, Lancashire, WN8 7NU Tel: (01257) 463149 Fax: (01257) 463149

Bryco Ltd, Greystones, Langwith Road, Scarcliffe, Chesterfield, Derbyshire, S44 6TH Tel: (01246) 823407 Fax: (01246) 827899 E-mail: brycoltd@btinternet.com

Butterley Ltd, Langthwaite Grange Industrial Estate, South Kirkby, Pontefract, West Yorkshire, WF9 3AP Tel: (01977) 643461 Fax: (01977) 655353

Cementation Skanska, Bentley House, Jossey Lane, Doncaster, South Yorkshire, DN5 9ED Tel: (01302) 821100 Fax: (01302) 821111

Herbert Tooling Ltd, Rosne, Sandy Lane, Fillongley, Coventry, CV7 8DD Tel: (01676) 540040 Fax: (01676) 542093 E-mail: info@herbert-tooling.com

IMC Group Consulting Ltd, PO Box 18, Nottingham, NG15 0DT Tel: (01623) 726166 Fax: (01623) 729359 E-mail: mining@imcgcl.com

Mccormick Macnaughton Ni Ltd, Blaris Industrial Estate, Altona Road, Lisburn, County Antrim, BT27 5QB Tel: (028) 9266 1221 Fax: (028) 9266 1355 E-mail: sales@mccormickmacnaughton.com

J.W.H. Ross & Co., 10 Annfield Place, Glasgow, G31 2XN Tel: 0141-554 2166 Fax: 0141-554 7639 E-mail: info@jwhross.co.uk

Lorne Stewart P.L.C., Stewart House, Kenton Road, Harrow, Middlesex, HA3 9TU Tel: (020) 8759 9988 Fax: (020) 8759 9987

UK Coal plc, Harworth Park Industrial Estate, Blyth Road, Harworth, Doncaster, South Yorkshire, DN11 8DB Tel: (01302) 751751 Fax: (01302) 752420

MINING CONTRACTORS

Cementation Skanska, Bentley House, Jossey Lane, Doncaster, South Yorkshire, DN5 9ED Tel: (01302) 821100 Fax: (01302) 821111

Lonmin plc, 4 Grosvenor Place, London, SW1X 7YL Tel: (020) 7201 6000 Fax: (020) 7201 6100 E-mail: contact@lonmin.com

MINING CONVEYOR CHAINS

Mec A Tec Services Ltd, Boleness Road, Wisbech, Cambridgeshire, PE13 2RB Tel: (01945) 474685 Fax: (01945) 474687 E-mail: mecatec@aol.com
Reilloc Chain Ltd, Stourport Road, Kidderminster, Worcestershire, DY11 7BQ Tel: (01562) 820717 Fax: (01562) 820377

MINING CONVEYOR SYSTEMS

Continental Conveyor Ltd, West Quay Road, Sunderland Enterprise Park, Sunderland, SR5 2TD Tel: 0191-516 5353 Fax: 0191-516 5399 E-mail: sales@continental-conveyor.co.uk
Joy Mining Machinery Ltd, Meco Works, Bromyard Road, Worcester, WR2 5EG Tel: (01905) 422291 Fax: (0870) 2521888 E-mail: worcester@joy.co.uk
MATO Ltd, Church Bank Works, Kirk Road, Church, Accrington, Lancashire, BB5 4JW Tel: (01254) 235411 Fax: (01254) 238023 E-mail: info@mato.co.uk

MINING LOCOMOTIVES

Clayton Equipment Ltd, Unit 2a, Second Avenue, Centrum One Hundred, Burton-on-Trent, Staffordshire, DE14 2WF Tel: (01283) 524470 Fax: (0870) 1129192 E-mail: info@claytonequipment.com

MINING OR CONSTRUCTION DRILL RODS

D C M Drillquip Ltd, Hazel Way, Bermuda Road, Nuneaton, Warwickshire, CV10 7QG Tel: (024) 7634 8328 Fax: (024) 7634 8329 E-mail: sales@drillquip.co.uk

MINING PLANT AND EQUIPMENT, *See also headings for particular types some listed under Mine*

Arbra Instruments, Advance Park, Park Road, Rhosymedre, Wrexham, Clwyd, LL14 3YR Tel: (01978) 823900 Fax: (01978) 822913 E-mail: sales@aslgroup.uk
▶ Castlebridge Plant, Ketley Business Park, Ketley, Telford, Shropshire, TF1 5JD Tel: (01952) 254422 Fax: (01952) 254433
Clayton Equipment Ltd, Unit 2a, Second Avenue, Centrum One Hundred, Burton-on-Trent, Staffordshire, DE14 2WF Tel: (01283) 524470 Fax: (0870) 1129192 E-mail: info@claytonequipment.com
▶ Controlled Systems Ltd, Unit 1, Ryder Close, Swadlincote, Derbyshire, DE11 9EU Tel: (01283) 216231
Coronet Rail Ltd, Castor Road, Sheffield, S9 2TL Tel: 0114-256 2225 Fax: 0114-261 7826 E-mail: sales@coronetrail.co.uk
D B T GB Ltd, Hallam Fields Road, Ilkeston, Derbyshire, DE7 4BS Tel: 0115-930 2603 Fax: 0115-932 9683
Dosco Overseas Engineering Ltd, Dosco Industrial Estate, Ollerton Road, Tuxford, Newark, Nottinghamshire, NG22 0PQ Tel: (01777) 870621 Fax: (01777) 871580 E-mail: sales@dosco.co.uk
F M C Technologies (UK) Ltd, Queensferry Road, Dunfermline, Fife, KY11 8UD Tel: (01383) 731531 Fax: (01383) 731297
▶ Halliburton Manufacturing & Services Ltd, Forties Road, Montrose, Angus, DD10 9ET Tel: (01674) 675959
Hausherr (U K) Ltd, High St, Clay Cross, Chesterfield, Derbyshire, S45 9PF Tel: (01246) 252000 Fax: (01246) 865077 E-mail: hausherr@btconnect.com
Holman-Wilfley Ltd, Wheal Jane Mine, Baldhu, Truro, Cornwall, TR3 6EE Tel: (01872) 561163 Fax: (01872) 561162 E-mail: mail@holmanwilfley.co.uk
Joy Mining Machinery Ltd, Kirkby La, Pinxton, Nottingham, NG16 6HX Tel: (01773) 515200 Fax: (01773) 515300E-mail: rbailey@joy.co.uk
Joy Mining Machinery Ltd, Seaman Way, Ince, Wigan, Lancashire, WN1 3DD Tel: (0870) 2526000 Fax: (0870) 2526888 E-mail: rbailey@joy.co.uk
Joy Mining Machinery Ltd, Meco Works, Bromyard Road, Worcester, WR2 5EG Tel: (01905) 422291 Fax: (0870) 2521888 E-mail: worcester@joy.co.uk
MATO Ltd, Church Bank Works, Kirk Road, Church, Accrington, Lancashire, BB5 4JW Tel: (01254) 235411 Fax: (01254) 238023 E-mail: info@mato.co.uk
▶ National Oilwell UK Ltd, 266 Auchmill Road, Bucksburn, Aberdeen, AB21 9NB Tel: (01224) 714499 Fax: (01224) 714599
▶ Plant Glazing Ltd, Ruthvenfield Place, Inveralmond Industrial Estate, Perth, PH1 3XU Tel: (01738) 626421
Qualter Hall & Co. Ltd, Johnson Street, Barnsley, South Yorkshire, S75 2BY Tel: (01226) 205761 Fax: (01226) 286269 E-mail: admin@qualterhall.co.uk
Railway Mine & Plantation Equipment Ltd, 4 Grosvenor Place, London, SW1X 7DG Tel: (020) 7201 3399 Fax: (020) 7201 3311
Simm Engineering Group, Gilbertson Works, Jessell Street, Sheffield, S9 3HY Tel: 0114-244 0764 Fax: 0114-244 2725 E-mail: sales@simmengineeringgroup.co.uk
▶ U W G Ltd, 1 Chalk Hill House, 19 Rosary Road, Norwich, NR1 1SZ Tel: (01603) 767438 Fax: (01603) 767441
Volvo Construction Equipment, First Avenue, Minworth, Sutton Coldfield, West Midlands, B76 1BA Tel: 0121-351 7711 Fax: 0121-313 1480

MINING TOOLS

Drill Sharp, Unit 22a Orgreave Crescent, Handsworth, Sheffield, S13 9NQ Tel: 0114-269 1664 Fax: 0114-288 0266 E-mail: rog@moorlandeng.co.uk
Fisher Engineering Ltd, Main Street, Ballinamallard, Enniskillen, County Fermanagh, BT94 2FY Tel: (028) 6638 8521 Fax: (028) 6638 8706 E-mail: info@fisher-engineering.co.uk
P & H Minepro Services Ltd, Seaman Way, Ince, Wigan, Lancashire, WN1 3DD Tel: (01942) 614400 Fax: (01942) 614419 E-mail: ph-min@phmining.com

MIRROR FRAMING

Chesham Glass Co., 1 Broad Street, Chesham, Buckinghamshire, HP5 3EA Tel: (01494) 792266 Fax: (01494) 782377
▶ Frames, 6 Ladbroke Park, Millers Road, Warwick, CV34 5AN Tel: (01926) 419784 Fax: (01926) 419784 E-mail: info@framesuk.co.uk
▶ Framework, 5 Station Parade, Ashford, Middlesex, TW15 2RX Tel: (01784) 258800 Fax: (01784) 250503 E-mail: sales@jandmframework.com
Memory Lane Prints, 43 Park Road, Hartlepool, Cleveland, TS24 7PW Tel: (01429) 234268 Fax: (01429) 281007

MIRROR HEATING PADS

Bocco Ltd, Fitzroy House, Lynwood Park, Worcester Park, Surrey, KT4 7AT Tel: (020) 8330 7007 Fax: (020) 8330 3351 E-mail: bocco@lineone.net

MIRRORS, *See also headings for particular types*

▶ A W Morris Ltd, Unit 4 6 & 7 West Mews, West Road Tottenham, London, N17 0QT Tel: (020) 8880 9191 Fax: (020) 8801 8736 E-mail: sales@morrismirrors.com
Belvedere, Kite Hill Studios, Kite Hill, Selborne, Alton, Hampshire, GU34 3LA Tel: (01420) 511524 Fax: (01420) 511491 E-mail: m.hackman@btclick.com
▶ Bigstudio Glass Design Ltd, Hunter House Farm, Tees Road, Hartlepool, Cleveland, TS25 2DX Tel: (01429) 270777 Fax: (01429) 270888 E-mail: sales@big-studio.co.uk
Bradley Furniture Kent Ltd, Bradley House, Park Farm Close, Park Farm Industrial Estate, Folkestone, Kent, CT19 5ED Tel: (01303) 850011 Fax: (01303) 244028 E-mail: info@bradleyfurniture.co.uk
Cameo Mirror & Glass, Anglian Road, Walsall, WS9 8EP Tel: (0845) 1709881 Fax: (0845) 1709882 E-mail: enquiries@cameoglass.co.uk
Chelsea Glass Ltd, 650 Portslade Road, London, SW8 3DH Tel: (020) 7720 6905 Fax: (020) 7978 2827
Chiswick Lane Glass Ltd, 44 Chiswick Lane, London, W4 2JQ Tel: (020) 8994 5779 Fax: (020) 8742 1467 E-mail: sales@chiswickglass.co.uk
Diamond Glass Works, Brown Street, Bolton, BL1 1TY Tel: (01204) 527853 Fax: (01204) 527853
Dutton Glass & Mirrors Ltd, 66 Holloway Head, Birmingham, B1 1NG Tel: 0121-622 1221 Fax: 0121-643 5520
Fancy Metal Goods Ltd, 71 Lifford Lane, Birmingham, B30 3DY Tel: 0121-459 9777 Fax: 0121-459 9595 E-mail: fancymetalgoods@btconnect.com
Hanwell Glass Co. Ltd, 183 Uxbridge Road, London, W7 3TH Tel: (020) 8567 2186 Fax: (020) 8840 0042
JP Glass & Decor Ltd, 3 Eastcote Industrial Estate, Field End Road, Ruislip, Middlesex, HA4 9XG Tel: (020) 8429 2999 Fax: (020) 8868 4314 E-mail: sales@jpglass.com
▶ Linthorpe Frames, Rear of Haymore Street, Middlesbrough, Cleveland, TS5 6JD Tel: (07841) 944417 Fax: (01642) 816596
Lombards Of Cheshunt Ltd, 25 High Street, Cheshunt, Waltham Cross, Hertfordshire, EN8 0BS Tel: (01992) 623160 Fax: (01992) 622422
Mirrors & Glass Stockport Ltd, 84 Wellington Road North, Stockport, Cheshire, SK4 1HW Tel: 0161-480 1875 Fax: 0161-480 7008 E-mail: sales@mirrorsandglass.co.uk
Northolt Glass Co. Ltd, 151-159 Church Road, Northolt, Middlesex, UB5 5AG Tel: (020) 8841 6989 Fax: (020) 8842 1944 E-mail: n.glass@talk21.com
Park Glass Supplies Ltd, 139 Kings Road, Kingston upon Thames, Surrey, KT2 5JE Tel: (020) 8546 8737 Fax: (020) 8546 4001
Pearsons Glass Ltd, 9-11 Maddrell Street, Liverpool, L3 7EH Tel: 0151-207 2874 Fax: 0151-207 2110 E-mail: info@pearsonsglass.co.uk
▶ Pinetree Workshop, 57A Southfield Road, Hinckley, Leicestershire, LE10 1UB Tel: (01455) 613298 Fax: (01455) 613298
▶ Reflections Mirrors Ltd, 128b Station Road, Sidcup, Kent, DA15 7AB Tel: (020) 8302 3004 Fax: (020) 8302 3004 E-mail: sales@reflections-mirrors.com
Specialist Mirror Shop, Mediterranean Village, Metrocentre, Gateshead, Tyne & Wear, NE11 9XG Tel: 0191-460 9328
Tower Glass Ltd, Yeomans Industrial Park, Yeomans Way, Bournemouth, BH8 0BJ Tel: (01202) 518555 Fax: (01202) 539015 E-mail: sales@towerglass.co.uk
Vencel Resil Ltd, Infinity House, Anderson Way, Belvedere, Kent, DA17 6BG Tel: (020) 8320 9100 Fax: (020) 8320 9110 E-mail: sales@vencel.co.uk

MIRRORS, PICTORIAL/ ADVERTISING

Mitreprize Ltd, Mitre House, 96-98 Braemar Avenue, South Croydon, Surrey, CR2 0QB Tel: (020) 8668 4999 Fax: (020) 8668 1487 E-mail: info@mitreprize.co.uk

MIRRORS, SAFETY/SECURITY

Ashtree Glass Ltd, Ashtree Works, Brownroyd Street, Bradford, West Yorkshire, BD8 9AF Tel: (01274) 546732 Fax: (01274) 548525 E-mail: sales@ashtree.yorks.com
Mawby & King Ltd, Upperton Road, Leicester, LE2 7AY Tel: 0116-204 6000 Fax: 0116-204 6001 E-mail: sales@mawbyandking.co.uk

MIRRORS, SURFACE COATED FOR INSTRUMENTS

Optometrics (UK) Ltd, Unit C6, Cross Green Garth, Leeds, LS9 0SF Tel: 0113-249 6973 Fax: 0113-235 0420 E-mail: optouk@aol.com
▶ Scientific Optical Ltd, Drury Lane, Pondswood Industrial Estate, St. Leonards-on-Sea, East Sussex, TN38 9YA Tel: (01424) 430371 Fax: (01424) 441639 E-mail: sales@scientificoptical.com

MIRRORS, WROUGHT IRON FRAME

Framepak Ltd, 21 Robjohns Road, Widford Industrial Estate, Chelmsford, CM1 3AG Tel: (01245) 266633 Fax: (01245) 266933 E-mail: info@framepakltd.com
▶ L & L Welding, Unit E 1, St. Davids Industrial Estate, Pengam, Blackwood, Gwent, NP12 3SW Tel: (01443) 832000 Fax: (01443) 832000 E-mail: marklewiswales@yahoo.co.uk

MISCELLANEOUS IRON CASTINGS

James Hoyle & Son, 50 Andrews Road, London, E8 4RL Tel: (020) 7254 2335 Fax: (020) 7254 8811 E-mail: jameshoyle@btclick.com

MIXER TAPS

KWC UK Ltd, 149 Balham Hill, London, SW12 9DJ Tel: (020) 8675 9335 Fax: (020) 8675 8568 E-mail: kwcuk@globalnet.co.uk

MIXERS, *See also headings for particular types*

Advanced Engineering Middleton Ltd, Unit 5D, Transpennine Trading Estate, Gorells way, Rochdale, Lancashire, OL11 2PX Tel: (01706) 759003 Fax: (01706) 759004 E-mail: info@aemixers.com
Clyde Associated Engineers Ltd, Block 5, 76 Beardmore Way, Clydebank Industrial Estate, Clydebank, Dunbartonshire, G81 4HT Tel: 0141-951 1331 Fax: 0141-951 3460 E-mail: lac@caeltd.co.uk
▶ Kemutec Powder Technologies Ltd, Springwood Way, Macclesfield, Cheshire, SK10 2ND Tel: (01625) 412000 Fax: (01625) 412001 E-mail: sales@kemutec.com
Morton Machine Co. Ltd, Atlantic Works, Newhouse Industrial Estate, Motherwell, Lanarkshire, ML1 5SW Tel: (01698) 732021 Fax: (01698) 732546 E-mail: info@morton-machines.co.uk
Orthos (Engineering) Ltd, No 2, 2 The Point, Market Harborough, Leicestershire, LE16 7QU Tel: (01858) 464246 Fax: (01858) 434480 E-mail: sales@orthos.uk.com
Plenty Filters, Plenty House, Hambridge Road, Newbury, Berkshire, RG14 5TR Tel: +44 (0) 1635 42363 Fax: +44 (0) 1635 49758 E-mail: filters@plenty.co.uk
▶ Synergy Devices Ltd, Unit 2 Network 4, Lincon Road, Cressex Business Park, High Wycombe, Buckinghamshire, HP12 3RF Tel: (01494) 769020 Fax: (01494) 528611 E-mail: sales@speedmixer.co.uk

MIXERS, FLUID/LIQUID

Advanced Engineering Middleton Ltd, Unit 5D, Transpennine Trading Estate, Gorells way, Rochdale, Lancashire, OL11 2PX Tel: (01706) 759003 Fax: (01706) 759004 E-mail: info@aemixers.com
Meter Mix Systems Ltd, Unit 1 Brindley Close, Rushden, Northamptonshire, NN10 6EN Tel: (01933) 354500 Fax: (01933) 354506
Mixing Solutions Ltd, Unit G Venture House, Bone Lane, Newbury, Berkshire, RG14 5SH Tel: (01635) 275300 Fax: (01635) 275375 E-mail: sales@mixingsolutions.com
Premier Colloid Mills, Building A302 Vickers Drive, Brooklands Industrial Park, Weybridge, Surrey, KT13 0YU Tel: (01932) 355366 Fax: (01932) 352660 E-mail: sales@bptskerman.com
▶ Refina Ltd, Unit 7 Upton Industrial Estate, Factory Road, Poole, Dorset, BH16 5SL Tel: (01202) 632270 Fax: (01202) 632432 E-mail: sales@refina.co.uk
Silverson Machines Ltd, Waterside, Chesham, Buckinghamshire, HP5 1PQ Tel: (01494) 786331 Fax: (01494) 791452 E-mail: sales@silverson.co.uk
Trojan Mixers, 1191 Stratford Road, Hall Green, Birmingham, B28 8BX Tel: 0121-777 5555 Fax: 0121-777 5555 E-mail: trojanmixers@hotmail.com

MIXERS, PAINT COLOUR/TINT

Merris Development Engineers Ltd, Howarth Road, Maidenhead, Berkshire, SL6 1AP Tel: (01628) 785371 Fax: (01628) 670339 E-mail: brendan@merris.co.uk

MIXING VALVES

Reliance Water Controls Ltd, Worcester Road, Evesham, Worcestershire, WR11 4RA Tel: (01386) 47148 Fax: (01386) 47028 E-mail: sales@rwc.co.uk

MIXING VESSEL LINERS/ COVERS

Chiltern Plastics Ltd, Unit 31, Jubilee Trade Centre, Jubilee Road, Letchworth Garden City, Hertfordshire, SG6 1SP Tel: (01462) 676262 Fax: (01462) 481075 E-mail: carrol@chilternplastics.co.uk

MOBILE AIR COMPRESSORS

W. Bateman & Co., Garstang Rd, Barton, Preston, PR3 5AA Tel: (01772) 862948 Fax: (01772) 861639 E-mail: sales@bateman-sellarc.co.uk
Oswald Record Plant Sales (Midlands) Ltd, Whittington Way, Whittington Moor, Chesterfield, Derbyshire, S41 9AG Tel: (01246) 451057 Fax: (01246) 454078 E-mail: sales@oswaldrecord.co.uk

MOBILE AIR CONDITIONING (AC) EQUIPMENT

Agricultural & Mobile Air Conditioning Ltd, Avening Road, Nailsworth, Stroud, Gloucestershire, GL6 0BS Tel: (01453) 832884 Fax: (01453) 832040 E-mail: sales@ama-airconditioning.co.uk

MOBILE BUILDING HIRE

A1 Accommodation, Hunts Plant Yard, Great North Road, Buckden, St. Neots, Cambridgeshire, PE19 5UL Tel: (01480) 810013 Fax: (01480) 810868 E-mail: sales@a1-accommodation.co.uk
Mobile Storage UK, New Millerdam Industrial, Barnsley Road, Newmillerdam, Wakefield, West Yorkshire, WF2 6QW Tel: (01924) 254254 Fax: (01924) 249249
Pennine Services, Bredbury Park Way, Bredbury Park Industrial Estate, Bredbury, Stockport, Cheshire, SK6 2SN Tel: 0161-406 7555 Fax: 0161-406 7555
Rovacabin, Williams Shipping Yard, Andes Road, Nursling, Southampton, SO16 0YZ Tel: (023) 8074 1345 Fax: (023) 8074 0108 E-mail: drice@sgb.co.uk

MOBILE CATERING VEHICLES

▶ Corporate Food Co. Ltd, Unit 6 Queensferry Industrial Estate, Chester Road, Pentre, Deeside, Flintshire, CH5 2DJ Tel: (01244) 536273 Fax: (01244) 537999 E-mail: info@cfccaterers.co.uk

MOBILE COMMERCE (MCOMMERCE) SOFTWARE

▶ Gempro Website Design and Development Services, 249 Beaver Lane, Ashford, Kent, TN23 5PA Tel: 01233 334069 E-mail: info@gempro.co.uk

Hyperion Systems Ltd, 12 The Mount, Guildford, Surrey, GU2 4HN Tel: (01483) 301793 Fax: (01483) 561657 E-mail: glor.benson@chyp.com

▶ Italik, 2B Rudgate Court, Walton, Wetherby, West Yorkshire, LS23 7BF Tel: (01937) 848380 Fax: (01937) 848381 E-mail: info@italik.co.uk

MOBILE COMMUNICATION NETWORK FOR MOBILE TELEPHONE EQUIPMENT

02 UK, 260 Bath Road, Slough, SL1 4DX Tel: (01753) 565000 Fax: (01753) 565010

▶ 2u phones, 5 Avon House,, York Close,, Northam,, Southampton, SO14 5SE Tel: 02380 943371 E-mail: im_with_cheryl@yahoo.com

MOBILE COMMUNICATION PRODUCTS

▶ 2u phones, 5 Avon House,, York Close,, Northam,, Southampton, SO14 5SE Tel: 02380 943371 E-mail: im_with_cheryl@yahoo.com

MOBILE COMMUNICATION SYSTEMS

▶ 2u phones, 5 Avon House,, York Close,, Northam,, Southampton, SO14 5SE Tel: 02380 943371 E-mail: im_with_cheryl@yahoo.com

Action Business Systems, 8 The Broadway, Hampton Court Way, Thames Ditton, Surrey, KT7 0LX Tel: (0870) 1607911 Fax: (0870) 1607933 E-mail: customercare@action-plc.co.uk

C A Clase (UK) Ltd, 20 Woolmer Way, Bordon, Hampshire, GU35 9QF Tel: (01420) 488422 Fax: (01420) 488522 E-mail: sales@caclase.co.uk

C T S, 17 Pages Walk, London, SE1 4SB Tel: (020) 7252 1849 Fax: (020) 7252 3241 E-mail: sales@ctslimited.co.uk

Commontime Ltd, 568 Burton Road, Derby, DE23 6DG Tel: (01332) 368500 Fax: (01332) 366880 E-mail: sales@commontime.com

Digital Dispatch Ltd, 38-39 Bar Hill Business Park, Saxon Way, Bar Hill, Cambridge, CB23 8SL Tel: (01954) 780888 Fax: (01954) 781612 E-mail: sales@digitaldispatch.com

DS Developments, Unit 41a Hobbs Industrial Estate, Newchapel, Lingfield, Surrey, RH7 6HN Tel: (01342) 835444 Fax: (01342) 832277 E-mail: sales@dsdevelopments.co.uk

HNC Electronics, 70 Oxford Street, London, W1D 1BP Tel: (020) 7436 0844

Motorola Ltd, Viables Industrial Estate, Jays Close, Basingstoke, Hampshire, RG22 4PD Tel: (01256) 358211 Fax: (01256) 469838 E-mail: sales@mot.com

Radio Service, Unit 129 Brookfield Place, Walton Summit Industrial Estate, Bamber Bridge, Preston, PR5 8BF Tel: (01772) 628000 Fax: (01772) 628888 E-mail: ians@rstechnology.co.uk

▶ Roke Manor Research, Roke Manor, Old Salisbury Lane, Romsey, Hampshire, SO51 0ZN Tel: (01794) 833000 Fax: (01794) 833433 E-mail: info@roke.co.uk

SELEX Communications, Green Park Business Centre, Sutton-On-Forest, York, YO61 1ET Tel: (01347) 811881 Fax: (01347) 811991 E-mail: davies.sales@selex-comms.com

MOBILE COMPUTING SYSTEMS

▶ Lucid It Ltd, 26 St. Leonards Way, Ashley Heath, Ringwood, Hampshire, BH24 2HS Tel: (01425) 475060 E-mail: info@lucidit.co.uk

▶ Micromatter Technology Solutions Ltd, 21 Victoria Terrace, Dunfermline, Fife, KY12 0LY Tel: (01383) 733467 E-mail: alan.craig@micromatter.co.uk

MOBILE CONCRETE PUMPS

Aintree Concrete Pumping, 21 Aintree Close, Gravesend, Kent, DA12 5AS Tel: (01474) 333616 Fax: (01474) 333616 E-mail: info@aintreeconcretepumping.co.uk

▶ Median Enterprises, PO Box 32, Southampton, SO31 6UH Tel: (01489) 885174 Fax: (01489) 574847 E-mail: info@median.co.uk

MOBILE CONTAINERISED REFRIGERATION UNITS

Accessible Hire & Refrigeration Ltd, Masters House, 46 Bridgnorth Road, Wollaston, Stourbridge, West Midlands, DY8 3QG Tel: (01384) 446000 Fax: (01384) 375242 E-mail: hire@ahrltd.co.uk

MOBILE CRANE HIRE

A Jardine & Sons, Northgate, White Lund Industrial Estate, Morecambe, Lancashire, LA3 3PA Tel: (01524) 33113 Fax: (01524) 843262

A W Plant Services Ltd, Eurocentre, North River Road, Great Yarmouth, Norfolk, NR30 1TE Tel: (01493) 330209 Fax: (01493) 843470

Abbey Transport Ltd, Concorde Road, Norwich, NR6 6BH Tel: (01603) 425928 Fax: (01603) 418333

Ainscough Crane Hire Ltd, Old Mill Lane, Aylesford, Kent, ME20 7DT Tel: (01622) 716500 Fax: (01622) 716066 E-mail: maidstone@ainscough.co.uk

Ainscough Crane Hire Ltd, Ipswich Road, Cardiff, CF23 9AQ Tel: (029) 2049 5455 Fax: (029) 2049 3967 E-mail: cardiff@inc.co.uk

Ainscough Crane Hire Ltd, Harewood Works, Middlesbrough Road, Thornaby, Stockton-on-Tees, Cleveland, TS17 7BN Tel: (01642) 661111 Fax: (01642) 612422 E-mail: general@ainscough.co.uk

▶ Baldwins Crane Hire Ltd, 52-54 River Road, Barking, Essex, IG11 0DW Tel: (020) 8591 9901 Fax: (020) 8591 9981 E-mail: info@baldwinscranehire.co.uk

William Birch & Sons Ltd, 1 Link Road Court, Osbaldwick, York, YO10 3JQ Tel: (01904) 411411 Fax: (01904) 428428 E-mail: info@williambirch.co.uk

Brookfields Garden Centre, 431 Mapperley Plains, Nottingham, NG3 5RW Tel: 0115-926 8200 Fax: 0115-967 3261

▶ Buckley's Crane Hire, Bryn Garth, Garth Road, Glan Conwy, Colwyn Bay, Clwyd, LL28 5TD Tel: (01492) 580227 Fax: (01492) 580725 E-mail: enquiries@buckleyscranehire.co.uk

C & S Crane Hire, 54 Pondhills Lane, Arnold, Nottingham, NG5 8DS Tel: 0115-926 3273 Fax: 0115-967 6491

Cadman Cranes Ltd, Moss Road, Stanway, Colchester, CO3 0LF Tel: (01206) 543232 Fax: (01206) 763231 E-mail: info@cadmancontracts.com

Cheshire Crane Hire, 12 Nant Road, Connah's Quay, Deeside, Clwyd, CH5 4AL Tel: (01244) 814164 Fax: (01244) 815265

City Lifting, Purfleet Industrial Park, Aveley, South Ockendon, Essex, RM15 4YA Tel: (01708) 805550 Fax: (01708) 805558 E-mail: hire@citylifting.co.uk

Curtis Power & Co. Ltd, Carter La Farm, 5 Carterhall Lane, Sheffield, S12 3XD Tel: 0114-239 8764 Fax: 0114-265 4441

Davies Crane Hire Ltd, Pensarn Road, Carmarthen, Dyfed, SA31 2BS Tel: (01267) 234660 Fax: (01267) 232346 E-mail: enquiries@daviescranehire.co.uk

Davies Crane Hire Ltd, Phoenix Wharf, Harbour Road, The Docks, Port Talbot, West Glamorgan, SA13 1RA Tel: (01639) 883474 Fax: (01639) 897028 E-mail: enquiries@daviescrane.co.uk

Dewsbury & Proud Ltd, Biddings Lane, Bilston, West Midlands, WV14 9NN Tel: (01902) 405553 Fax: (01902) 354420 E-mail: operations@cranehiremidlands.com

G Cox Oldbury Ltd, 146 Dudley Road East, Oldbury, West Midlands, B69 3EB Tel: 0121-552 4413 Fax: 0121-552 1883

G R Carr Essex Ltd, Archers Fields, Burnt Mills Industrial Estate, Basildon, Essex, SS13 1DN Tel: (01268) 522226 Fax: (01268) 522126 E-mail: grc@grcarr.com

J Exley Ltd, Park Works, 644 Bradford Road, Batley, West Yorkshire, WF17 8HG Tel: (01924) 472353 Fax: (01924) 440007 E-mail: greg@jexley.co.uk

Machinery Installations (Birmingham) Ltd, Unit 12A, Middlemore Lane West, Aldridge, Walsall, WS9 8BG Tel: (01922) 743187 Fax: (01922) 743206 E-mail: mibham@aol.com

Macsalvors Plant Hire Ltd, Newham Road, Truro, Cornwall, TR1 2SU Tel: (01872) 277123 Fax: (01872) 223340 E-mail: caneron@macsalvors.co.uk

Marsh Plant Hire Ltd, Wallingford Road, Uxbridge, Middlesex, UB8 2SS Tel: (01895) 231291 Fax: (01895) 811650

Midland Machinery Heavy Lift Ltd, Heath Road, Wednesbury, West Midlands, WS10 8XE Tel: 0121-526 5511 Fax: 0121-526 6846

Newcastle & Gateshead Crane Hire, The Ferry House, Ryton Village, Ryton, Tyne & Wear, NE40 3QJ Tel: 0191-413 3763 Fax: 0191-413 5424 E-mail: nclcrane@aol.com

P Burley & Son, Magna Mile, Ludford, Market Rasen, Lincolnshire, LN8 6AH Tel: (01507) 313620 Fax: (01507) 313620

P P Engineering, Charles Street, Kilnhurst, Mexborough, South Yorkshire, S64 5TG Tel: (01709) 578877 Fax: (01709) 578555 E-mail: ppengineering@talk21.com

Rileys Crane Hire, Grove House, Cloford, Frome, Somerset, BA11 4PH Tel: (01373) 836366

Sangwin Concrete Products Ltd, Dansom Lane, Hull, HU8 7LN Tel: (01482) 329921 Fax: (01482) 215353 E-mail: info@sangwin.co.uk

Savage Cranes Ltd, West Street, Hunton, Maidstone, Kent, ME15 0RR Tel: (01622) 820611 Fax: (01622) 820807

▶ Shires Crane Hire Ltd, Sheepbridge Lane, Chesterfield, Derbyshire, S41 9RX Tel: (01246) 452296 Fax: (01246) 451015 E-mail: louise@shirescrane.fsnet.co.uk

▶ Simmons Industrial Services, C Anchor Business Centre, 102 Beddington Lane, Croydon, CR0 4YX Tel: (020) 8688 3553 Fax: (020) 8667 9241 E-mail: info@simmons-industrial.co.uk

Telford Crane Hire Ltd, Halesfield 22, Telford, Shropshire, TF7 4QX Tel: (01952) 586304 Fax: (01952) 587848 E-mail: sales@telfordcrane.co.uk

Telford Crane Hire Ltd, Halesfield 22, Telford, Shropshire, TF7 4QX Tel: (01952) 586304 Fax: (01952) 587848 E-mail: sales@telfordcrane.co.uk

▶ J. Thomas (Southern) Ltd, Bankside House, Henfield Road, Small Dole, Henfield, West Sussex, BN5 9XQ Tel: (01273) 494848 Fax: (01273) 497804 E-mail: cranes@jthomas.co.uk

MOBILE CRANES

Davies Crane Hire Ltd, Phoenix Wharf, Harbour Road, The Docks, Port Talbot, West Glamorgan, SA13 1RA Tel: (01639) 883474 Fax: (01639) 897028 E-mail: enquiries@daviescrane.co.uk

James Industrial & Aviation Supplies Ltd, Stowmarket, Suffolk, IP14 2EU Tel: (01449) 673902 Fax: (01449) 677394

P Hird & Sons Ltd, English Street, Hull, HU3 2BT Tel: (01482) 227333 Fax: (01482) 587710 E-mail: sales@peter-hird.co.uk

Rig Lift UK Ltd, Richmer Road, Erith, Kent, DA8 2HN Tel: (01322) 341166 Fax: (01322) 341165

Severnside Machinery Ltd, Unit 57, Ditton Priors, Bridgnorth, Shropshire, WV16 6SS Tel: 01746 712433

▶ Shires Crane Hire Ltd, Sheepbridge Lane, Chesterfield, Derbyshire, S41 9RX Tel: (01246) 452296 Fax: (01246) 451015 E-mail: louise@shirescrane.fsnet.co.uk

MOBILE ELECTROSTATIC AIR FILTER UNITS

Westbury Financial Management, Hall Farm Estate, Gadbrook Road, Betchworth, Surrey, RH3 7AH Tel: (01306) 611611 Fax: (01306) 611613 E-mail: sales@westburyfilters.co.uk

MOBILE EXHIBITIONS, *See Exhibition, Mobile etc*

MOBILE GENERATOR SETS

Arc-Gen Ltd, Station Road, Four Ashes Industrial Estate, Four Ashes, Wolverhampton, WV10 7DB Tel: (01902) 790824 Fax: (01902) 790355 E-mail: andymunford@arc-gen.co.uk

Generated Power Services Ltd, Argosons Hunsdon Stud, Eastwick Road, Hunsdon, Ware, Hertfordshire, SG12 8PP Tel: (01920) 877171 Fax: (01920) 877128

Mastervolt UK Ltd, Winchester Hill, Romsey, Hampshire, SO51 7ND Tel: (01794) 516443 Fax: (01794) 516453 E-mail: sales@mastervolt.com

Noconn Electrical Contacts Ltd, Unit 71, Storforth Lane Trading Estate, Chesterfield, Derbyshire, S41 0QZ Tel: (01246) 209556 Fax: (01246) 201440 E-mail: info@electricalcontacts.com

Sandhurst Manufacturing, Belchmire Lane, Gosberton, Spalding, Lincolnshire, PE11 4HG Tel: (01775) 840020 Fax: (01775) 843063 E-mail: info@sandhurst-mfg.com

MOBILE HOME STATIC CARAVANS

▶ Anthony Percival, 22 Swale Drive, Wellingborough, Northamptonshire, NN8 5ZL Tel: (01933) 405449 Fax: 01933 400310 E-mail: anthony@percival69.freeserve.co.uk

MOBILE INFORMATION SYSTEMS

Applabs Ltd, Preston Technology Centre, Marsh Lane, Preston, PR1 8UQ Tel: (01772) 885850 Fax: (01772) 558881 E-mail: info@isintegration.com

MOBILE PARTITIONING

C P Supplies Ltd, 1-3 Brixton Road, London, SW9 6DE Tel: (020) 7582 2911 Fax: (020) 7582 0271 E-mail: bmkennington@cpsupplies.co.uk

Dividers Ltd, Unit 1, Llanelli Gate, Dafen, Llanelli, Dyfed, SA14 8LQ Tel: (01269) 844877 Fax: (01269) 831112 E-mail: sales@esperowalls.com

I D M Southern Ltd, Unit 1, Lavernham Road, Brent Eleigh, Sudbury, Suffolk, CO10 9PB Tel: (01449) 740040 Fax: (01449) 744950 E-mail: mail@idmsouthern.co.uk

MOBILE RADIO TRANSMISSION EQUIPMENT

▶ Cam Com Radio, Gusto Mills, Huntingdon Road, Cambridge, CB3 0DL Tel: (01223) 277274 Fax: (01223) 277207 E-mail: camcom@metronet.co.uk

MOBILE SCREENS

▶ Connectafone Mobile Phones, 184 Brownhill Road, London, SE6 2DJ Tel: (020) 8244 6666 Fax: (020) 8698 9417 E-mail: enquiries@konnectafone.co.uk

Powerscreen International Distribution Ltd, Coalisland Road, Dungannon, County Tyrone, BT71 4DR Tel: (028) 8774 0701 Fax: (028) 8774 7231 E-mail: sales@powerscreen.co.uk

MOBILE SHELVING

Link 51 Ltd, Link House, Halesfield 6, Telford, Shropshire, TF7 4LN Tel: (0800) 515600 Fax: (01952) 682452 E-mail: enquiries@link51.co.uk

Link 51 (Shelving Storage) Ltd, 16 Mill St, Brierley Hill, West Midlands, DY5 2TB Tel: (01384) 472500 Fax: (01384) 472599 E-mail: shelving@link51.co.uk

▶ Production Lines Northern Ltd, 14 Pleasant Row, Queensbury, Bradford, West Yorkshire, BD13 2BW Tel: (01274) 812035 E-mail: philip@productionlines.co.uk

MOBILE STORAGE EQUIPMENT OR SYSTEMS

Britannia Storage Systems, Airfield, Earls Colne, Colchester, CO6 2NS Tel: (01787) 223884 Fax: (01787) 223038 E-mail: enquires@britannia-storage.co.uk

Mobile Base Co Shropshire Ltd, Unit E1 Stafford Park 15, Telford, Shropshire, TF3 3BB Tel: (01952) 200018 Fax: (01952) 291119

Polstore Storage Systems Ltd, PO Box 408, Dorking, Surrey, RH5 5YF Tel: (0870) 8504012 Fax: (0870) 8504013 E-mail: info@polstore.co.uk

Rackline Systems Storage Ltd, Oaktree Lane, Talke Pits, Stoke-on-Trent, ST7 1RX Tel: (01782) 777666 Fax: (01782) 777444 E-mail: sales@rackline.co.uk

Remploy Furniture Group, Baglan Energy Park, Central Avenue, Baglan, Port Talbot, West Glamorgan, SA12 7AX Tel: (01639) 824637 Fax: (01639) 424685 E-mail: furniture@remploy.co.uk

Sono UK Ltd, Enterprise House, Murdock Road, Dorcan, Swindon, SN3 5HY Tel: (01793) 488488 Fax: (01793) 522868 E-mail: info@sono-uk.com

TSD Wakefield, Keys Road, Mixs Hill, Somercoates, Alfreton, Derbyshire, DE55 7FQ Tel: (0870) 6090111 Fax: (01773) 521015 E-mail: sales@wakefields.co.uk

MOBILE STORAGE RACKS

Mobilrax International Ltd, Arch Unit 1138 Bath Factory Estate, 41 Norwood Road, London, SE24 9AJ Tel: (020) 8674 0131 Fax: (020) 8678 6270 E-mail: info@mobilrax.com

Storage Logic, 24 High Street, Bovingdon, Hemel Hempstead, Hertfordshire, HP3 0HG Tel: (01442) 831133 Fax: (01442) 831144 E-mail: info@storage-logic.co.uk

MOBILE TELEPHONE ACCESSORIES

A-B Accessories, 93 Ilchester Rd, Yeovil, Somerset, BA21 3BJ Tel: (08707) 450976 Fax: (01935) 434100 E-mail: andy@abaccessories.co.uk

Angels (Cwas) Ltd, 100 Rooley Avenue, Bradford, West Yorkshire, BD6 1DB Tel: (01274) 731532 Fax: (01274) 308290 E-mail: sales@angel-mobile-phones.co.uk

Corporate Telecom Systems Ltd, 3 College St Mews, Northampton, NN1 2QF Tel: (01604) 603009 Fax: (01604) 637838 E-mail: sales@corporate-telecom.co.uk

▶ EMobilesdirect, 892 Chester Road, Stretford, Manchester, M32 0PA Tel: 0161-283 8727 E-mail: info@e-mobilesdirect.co.uk

▶ GOSIM, Concord House, 10 Great North Way, York Business Park, York, YO26 6RB Tel: (0870) 1023400 Fax: (0870) 1023401 E-mail: sales@gosim.com

▶ Handsfree Warehouse, 25 Portland Road, Kilmarnock, Ayrshire, KA1 2BT Tel: (01563) 521000 E-mail: david@telecom3.co.uk

Phoneline, 26 High Street, Long Eaton, Nottingham, NG10 1LL Tel: 0115-946 5656 Fax: 0115-946 4188 E-mail: jgcomms@msn.com

MOBILE TELEPHONE ACCESSORIES

– *continued*

▶ Phones-GB, 6 Hathaway Close, Balsall Common, Coventry, CV7 7EP Tel: 01676 530407 E-mail: stevemorris@uk2.net
Protech Ltd, 4 Nuffield Road, St. Ives, Cambridgeshire, PE27 3LX Tel: (01325) 310520 Fax: (01480) 300670 E-mail: sales@pro-tech-ltd.co.uk
▶ Spiky, 116A Fillongley Road, Meriden, Meriden, Coventry, CV7 7LT Tel: 01676 523759 Fax: 01676 523759 E-mail: spiky@myspiky.co.uk
▶ TMD-UK Ltd, 28B High Street, Sunninghill, Ascot, Berkshire, SL5 9NE Tel: (0870) 9906001 Fax: (0870) 9906002 E-mail: service@tmd-uk.co.uk

MOBILE TELEPHONE CASES

A-B Accessories, 93 Ilchester Rd, Yeovil, Somerset, BA21 3BJ Tel: (08707) 450976 Fax: (01935) 434100 E-mail: andy@abaccessories.co.uk
Angels (Cwas) Ltd, 100 Rooley Avenue, Bradford, West Yorkshire, BD6 1DB Tel: (01274) 731532 Fax: (01274) 308290 E-mail: sales@angel-mobile-phones.co.uk
▶ Connectafone Mobile Phones, 184 Brownhill Road, London, SE6 2DJ Tel: (020) 8244 6666 Fax: (020) 8698 9417 E-mail: enquiries@konnectafone.co.uk
Corporate Telecom Systems Ltd, 3 College St Mews, Northampton, NN1 2QF Tel: (01604) 603009 Fax: (01604) 637838 E-mail: sales@corporate-telecom.co.uk
▶ EMobilesdirect, 892 Chester Road, Stretford, Manchester, M32 0PA Tel: 0161-283 8727 E-mail: info@e-mobilesdirect.co.uk
Purvers International Ltd, Gateway House, Fareham Road, Gosport, Hampshire, PO13 0FW Tel: (01329) 238111 Fax: (01329) 825888 E-mail: mail@purvers.co.uk
▶ TMD-UK Ltd, 28B High Street, Sunninghill, Ascot, Berkshire, SL5 9NE Tel: (0870) 9906001 Fax: (0870) 9906002 E-mail: service@tmd-uk.co.uk

MOBILE TELEPHONE CLEANING CLOTHS

▶ brettonmobiles.2u.co.uk, 172 Kirkmeadow, Bretton, Peterborough, PE3 8JN Tel: (01733) 332390 E-mail: brettoncomputers@ukonline.co.uk

MOBILE TELEPHONE CONSULTANCY

▶ Air Business Communication Ltd, Riverside Business Centre, Riverside Road, Lowestoft, Suffolk, NR33 0TQ Tel: 08700 420675 E-mail: sales@airmobiles.co.uk
Paul Strachan Consulting Ltd, 30 Turfbeg Drive, Forfar, Angus, DD8 3LH Tel: (01307) 460667 Fax: (0870) 420 3597 E-mail: info@strachanconsulting.co.uk

MOBILE TELEPHONE CONTENT PROVIDERS

▶ Celebrity Voices Ltd, 23 Springfeilds, Waltham Abbey, Essex, EN9 1UD Tel: (01992) 611097 E-mail: stuart@celebrityvoices.co.uk

MOBILE TELEPHONE CONTENT PROVIDERS, JAVA GAMES

▶ Spiky, 116A Fillongley Road, Meriden, Meriden, Coventry, CV7 7LT Tel: 01676 523759 Fax: 01676 523759 E-mail: spiky@myspiky.co.uk

MOBILE TELEPHONE EQUIPMENT

Ablemail Electronics Ltd, Unit 17 Christie St Industrial Estate, Christie Street, Stockport, Cheshire, SK1 4LR Tel: 0161-480 6910 Fax: 0161-480 8686 E-mail: info@ablemail.co.uk
▶ Air Business Communication Ltd, Riverside Business Centre, Riverside Road, Lowestoft, Suffolk, NR33 0TQ Tel: 08700 420675 E-mail: sales@airmobiles.co.uk
Angels (Cwas) Ltd, 100 Rooley Avenue, Bradford, West Yorkshire, BD6 1DB Tel: (01274) 731532 Fax: (01274) 308290 E-mail: sales@angel-mobile-phones.co.uk
Anglia Telecom Centres plc, 166 Handford Road, Ipswich, IP1 2BH Tel: (01473) 382000 Fax: (01473) 225617 E-mail: mandy.stafford@angliatelecom.co.uk
Bleepers, PO Box 71, Barnet, Hertfordshire, EN4 0QD Tel: (07000) 253373 Fax: (020) 8440 8024 E-mail: sales@bleepers.co.uk
C & M Installations, 11 Craven Close, Longwell Green, Bristol, BS30 7BX Tel: 0117-983 0310
Champ Telephones Holdings Ltd, 11-15 Station Street, Coventry, CV6 5FL Tel: (024) 7666 7757 Fax: (024) 7668 2290 E-mail: gary@champtel.co.uk
Corporate Telecom Systems Ltd, 3 College St Mews, Northampton, NN1 2QF Tel: (01604) 603009 Fax: (01604) 637838 E-mail: sales@corporate-telecom.co.uk
Daewoo International Ltd, 10TH Floor C I Tower, St. Georges Square, New Malden, Surrey, KT3 4HH Tel: (020) 8336 9130 Fax: (020) 8949 3783 E-mail: kelliedodds@daewoo.co.uk
Fone Installations, Unit 2 Douglas Buildings, Lodge Road, Staplehurst, Tonbridge, Kent, TN12 0QZ Tel: (01580) 893377 Fax: (01580) 893434 E-mail: mail@foneinstallations.co.uk
▶ Mobile Phones 4U, 10 Langhurst Court, Wenlock Close, Loundsley Green, Chesterfield, Derbyshire, S40 4PE Tel: (01246) 237267 E-mail: dallsop@mobile-phones4u.net
Motorola Ltd, Redwood, Crockford Lane, Basingstoke, Hampshire, RG24 8WQ Tel: (01256) 790790 Fax: (01256) 817481
Nokia (U K) Ltd, Summet Avenue, Farmborough, Farmborough, Farnborough, Hampshire, GU14 0NG Tel: (01252) 866000 Fax: (01252) 866001
Panasonic Mobile Communicationdevelopment Of Eu, Daytona Drive, Colthorpe, Thatcham, Berkshire, RG19 4ZD Tel: (01635) 871466 Fax: (01635) 871345
Parris Wolfe Communications Ltd, Trade Tower, Coral Row, London, SW11 3UF Tel: (020) 7738 1111 Fax: (020) 7738 0111
Phoneline, 26 High Street, Long Eaton, Long Eaton, Nottingham, NG10 1LL Tel: 0115-946 5656 Fax: 0115-946 4188 E-mail: jgcomms@msn.com
Procom Ltd, Unit I3, Springhead Enterprise Park, Springhead Road, Northfleet, Gravesend, Kent, DA11 8HL Tel: (01474) 322244 Fax: (01474) 322135 E-mail: info@procom-pescot.co.uk
Radiocoms Systems Ltd, 170a Oval Road, Croydon, ,Hounslow, Hounslow, TW6 2BG Tel: (0870) 4604600 Fax: (020) 8759 1411
Relcom Communications, Unit 1, Oliver Business Park, Oliver Road, London, NW10 7JB Tel: (020) 8965 2333 Fax: (020) 8965 2323 E-mail: info@relcom.co.uk
R's Electrics, 815 High Road, London, N17 8ER Tel: (0870) 7746333 Fax: (020) 8808 4955 E-mail: sales@rs-electrics.co.uk
Talk Telecom Ltd, Unit 35 City Industrial Park, Southern Road, Southampton, SO15 1HG Tel: (023) 8071 8730 Fax: (023) 8071 8738

MOBILE TELEPHONE EQUIPMENT HIRE

▶ Adam Phones Ltd, 2-3 Dolphin Square, Edensor Road, London, W4 2ST Tel: (0800) 123000 Fax: (0500) 001230 E-mail: info@fonehire.com
Cellhire plc, Park House, Clifton Park Avenue, York, YO30 5PB Tel: (01904) 610610 Fax: (01904) 611028 E-mail: rentals@cellhire.com
Nine Hundred Communications, White Rose Way, Doncaster, South Yorkshire, DN4 5JH Tel: (01302) 368866 Fax: (01302) 340363 E-mail: sales@gbcomms.co.uk

MOBILE TELEPHONE EQUIPMENT MAINTENANCE OR HIRE

▶ Dancap Electronics, 24 Trent Crescent, Thatcham, Berkshire, RG18 3DN Tel: (01635) 866394 Fax: (01635) 869589 E-mail: dancap@btinternet.com
Premiere Eurocom Ltd, The Courtyard, 9 Waterside Drive, Langley, Slough, SL3 6EZ Tel: (01753) 543712 Fax: (01753) 583536 E-mail: admin@premeuro.com

MOBILE TELEPHONE HOLDERS

Lancewich Promotional Items, Unit 14 Wellington Business Park, Dukes Ride, Crowthorne, Berkshire, RG45 6LS Tel: (01344) 753550 Fax: (01344) 753551 E-mail: sales@lancewich.co.uk

MOBILE TELEPHONE KITS, HANDS FREE, VEHICLE, BLUETOOTH

▶ Trim Wizard, 3 Trelawne Drive, Cranleigh, Surrey, GU6 8BS Tel: (07748) 963904 E-mail: andy@trimwizard.co.uk

MOBILE TELEPHONE KITS, HANDS FREE, VEHICLE, PLUG IN

▶ Blue Mobiles, 6 Hampson Gardens, Edenthorpe, Doncaster, South Yorkshire, DN3 2TN Tel: 07921 996869 E-mail: bluemobiles@tiscali.co.uk
▶ Trim Wizard, 3 Trelawne Drive, Cranleigh, Surrey, GU6 8BS Tel: (07748) 963904 E-mail: andy@trimwizard.co.uk

MOBILE TELEPHONES

▶ Air Business Communication Ltd, Riverside Business Centre, Riverside Road, Lowestoft, Suffolk, NR33 0TQ Tel: 08700 420675 E-mail: sales@airmobiles.co.uk
▶ Ayudar, Sheraton House, Castle Park, Cambridge, CB3 0AX Tel: (08709) 9 01090
▶ Barclay Communications, Grove House, 145-149 Donegall Passage, Belfast, BT7 1DT Tel: (028) 9096 0366 Fax: (028) 9023 2679 E-mail: info@barclaycomms.com
▶ Blue Mobiles, 6 Hampson Gardens, Edenthorpe, Doncaster, South Yorkshire, DN3 2TN Tel: 07921 996869 E-mail: bluemobiles@tiscali.co.uk
▶ Connectafone Mobile Phones, 184 Brownhill Road, London, SE6 2DJ Tel: (020) 8244 6666 Fax: (020) 8698 9417 E-mail: enquiries@konnectafone.co.uk
▶ Fone Options UK, Kingsbury House 468 Church Lane, Kingsbury, London, NW9 8UA Tel: 0800 1804814 E-mail: sales@foneoptions.co.uk
▶ Networx Ltd, PO Box 8812, Lanark, ML11 9YQ Tel: (0870) 3501345 Fax: (0870) 3501346
▶ Soneric Communications, Unit 24 Wren Court, Strathclyde Business Park, Bellshill, Lanarkshire, ML4 3NQ Tel: (01698) 742210 Fax: (01698) 840080 E-mail: sales@soneric.com
Talk Group, Suite 57, Century House, Leeds, LS14 1BS Tel: (0870) 7550300 Fax: (0870) 7550305 E-mail: info@talkgroup.co.uk
Tekeda Telecom, Cygnet Court, Hawthorn Street, Wilmslow, Cheshire, SK9 5EL Tel: (01625) 416200 Fax: (01625) 539042 E-mail: enq@takeda-telecom.co.uk

MOBILE TELEPHONES, HANDS FREE

▶ Alternative Mobiles, 20 Fletcher Gate, Nottingham, NG1 2FZ Tel: (0870) 1203233
▶ Mobile Phones 4U, 10 Langhurst Court, Wenlock Close, Loundsley Green, Chesterfield, Derbyshire, S40 4PE Tel: (01246) 237267 E-mail: dallsop@mobile-phones4u.net
▶ On Air Telecom Ltd, West Point, 501 Chester Road, Manchester, M16 9HU Tel: 0161-906 9060 Fax: 0161-906 9061 E-mail: sales@onairtelecom.com
The Utility Warehouse, PO Box 407, Huntingdon, Cambridgeshire, PE29 2ZG Tel: (0845) 1242201 Fax: (0870) 7773753

MOBILE VEHICLE LIFTING EQUIPMENT

Joloda International, Joloda Hydraroll Division, Gaerwen, Gwynedd, LL60 6BH Tel: (01248) 421454 Fax: (01248) 421748 E-mail: sales@transpotech.co.uk
Somers Totalkare Ltd, Unit 15 Forge Trading Estate, Mucklow Hill, Halesowen, West Midlands, B62 8TR Tel: 0121-585 2700 Fax: 0121-501 1458 E-mail: sales@somerstotalkare.co.uk

MOBILE WELDING

A & W Fabrications & Structural Services, Old Bush Street, Brierley Hill, West Midlands, DY5 1UB Tel: (01384) 573676 Fax: (01384) 573676
C & M Welding Services, Crabtree Road, Thorpe Industrial Estate, Egham, Surrey, TW20 8RN Tel: (01784) 438127 Fax: (01784) 470223
D Mcinnes, Clayslap, Kilmarnock, Ayrshire, KA1 5LN Tel: (01563) 522774 Fax: (01563) 571530 E-mail: enquires@duncanmcinnes.com
Linkweld Engineering & Construction Ltd, 56 High Street, Edenbridge, Kent, TN8 5AJ Tel: (01732) 864376
Nelsons Birstall Ltd, Perseverance Works, Gelderd Road, Batley, West Yorkshire, WF17 9PX Tel: (01924) 474981 Fax: (01924) 440871 E-mail: sales@nelsonseng.co.uk
P J Welding & Fabricating, Unit 12, Summerhill Industrial Estate, Goodman Street, Birmingham, B1 2SS Tel: 0121-236 8152 Fax: 0121-212 1705
J.L. Pinder & Son Ltd, 138 Hanbury Road, 8-11 The Old Basin, Stoke Prior, Bromsgrove, Worcestershire, B60 4JZ Tel: (01527) 876438 Fax: (01527) 576435 E-mail: sales@jlpindersandsons.co.uk

MOBILITY STAIR CLIMBERS

▶ Baronmead International Ltd, 1 Flansham Business Centre, Hoe Lane, Flansham, Bognor Regis, West Sussex, PO22 8NJ Tel: (01243) 586692 Fax: (01243) 586312 E-mail: info@baronmead.com
Sparks Fire Protection, 89 Llewellyn Street, Port Talbot, West Glamorgan, SA12 8SG Tel: (01639) 885837 E-mail: kevin@sparksfire.org.uk

MODAL ANALYSIS SYSTEMS

Data Physics (UK) Ltd, South Rd, Hailsham, East Sussex, BN27 3JJ Tel: (01323) 846464 Fax: (01323) 847550 E-mail: sales@dataphysics.com

MODEL AGENCY BOOKS

▶ Eyecandy Model & Promotions Agency, 11-13 Derby Street, Manchester, M8 8QE Tel: 0161-833 3888 E-mail: info@eyecandy-promo.co.uk
▶ The Model Academy Ltd, 1 Atworth Grove, Littleover, Derby, DE23 3WZ Tel: (01332) 540446 Fax: (01332) 549017 E-mail: ra@themodelacademy.co.uk
▶ Nottingham Girls Model Agency, 49 Penrhyn Cresent, Nottingham, NG9 5PA Tel: 0115 841 9685 E-mail: agency@nottinghamgirls.co.uk

MODEL ENGINES

▶ Honeywell Spark Plugs, Unit D6, Treforest Industrial Estate, Pontypridd, Mid Glamorgan, CF37 5YP Tel: (01443) 844992 Fax: (01443) 842275 E-mail: sparkplugs@honeywell.com

MODEL FITTINGS AND MATERIALS

D K G Hobbies UK, 14 Princes Street, Southport, Merseyside, PR8 1EZ Tel: (01704) 500630 Fax: (01704) 500630
J Perkins, Ashford Road, Lenham, Maidstone, Kent, ME17 2DL Tel: (01622) 854300 Fax: (01622) 854301 E-mail: jpmail@jpmodels.co.uk
P O P Enterprises, 34 Southwark St, Nottingham, NG6 0DA Tel: 0115-913 0233 Fax: 0870 0520990
Panda Model Wholesale, Unit 8A, Bramley Hedge Farm, Redhill Road, Cobham, Surrey, KT11 1EQ Tel: (01932) 865388 Fax: (01932) 865388 E-mail: sales@panda-models.demon.co.uk
Reeves 2000, Appleby Hill, Austrey, Atherstone, Warwickshire, CV9 3ER Tel: (01827) 830894 Fax: (01827) 830631 E-mail: sales@ajreeves.com

MODEL MAKING ACCESSORIES

ACS Engineering, 2 Cairndubh Cottages, Cairnbaan, Lochgilphead, Argyll, PA31 8SQ Tel: (01546) 603849 E-mail: acs-engineering@wargyll.fsnet.co.uk

MODEL MAKING BOILERS

ACS Engineering, 2 Cairndubh Cottages, Cairnbaan, Lochgilphead, Argyll, PA31 8SQ Tel: (01546) 603849 E-mail: acs-engineering@wargyll.fsnet.co.uk

MODEL MAKING KITS

John Adams Trading Co. Ltd, The Barn, 3 Deanes Close, Steventon, Abingdon, Oxfordshire, OX13 6SZ Tel: (01235) 833066 Fax: (01235) 861116 E-mail: trading@johnadams.co.uk
Antics, 16 St Swithins Street, Worcester, WR1 2PS Tel: (01905) 22075
Deans Marine, Conquest Drove, Farcet, Peterborough, PE7 3DH Tel: (01733) 244166 Fax: (01733) 244166 E-mail: deansmarine@yahoo.co.uk
Hewitt & Booth Ltd, St Andrews Road, Huddersfield, HD1 6RZ Tel: (01484) 546621 Fax: (01484) 450580 E-mail: sales@hewittandbooth.com
The Network Modelmakers, Arch 9, 67A St Marks Road, London, W11 1RE Tel: (020) 7243 1816 Fax: (020) 7243 1809 E-mail: mail@networkmodelmakers.com
The Prop Shop, Unit 5 The Stable Yard, Alscot Pk, Atherstone on Stour, Stratford-upon-Avon, Warwickshire, CV37 8BL Tel: (01789) 450905 Fax: (01789) 450905
RTF, Little Brixham, Ashford Road, Bethersden, Ashford, Kent, TN26 3AX Tel: (01233) 820718 Fax: (01233) 820718
Scale Models Weston, The Wheel House, 10 Alfred St, Weston-super-Mare, Avon, BS23 1PU Tel: (01934) 413462 Fax: (01934) 643301 E-mail: workshop@scalemodelswestern.sfnet.co.uk
South Eastern Finecast, Glenn House, Hartfield Row, Forest Row, East Sussex, RH18 5DZ Tel: (01342) 824711 Fax: (01342) 822270

MODEL (SCALE) IMPORT/ EXPORT MERCHANTS OR AGENTS

Amerang Ltd, 15b Commerce Way, Lancing, West Sussex, BN15 8TA Tel: (01903) 765496 Fax: (01903) 765178 E-mail: sales@amerang-group.com

Irvine Ltd, Green Street, Enfield, Middlesex, EN3 7FJ Tel: (020) 8361 1123 Fax: (020) 8361 8684 E-mail: sales@irvineltd.com

MODELLING HANDICRAFT MATERIAL/SETS/KITS

▶ The Crafthouse, 118-120 Outram Street, Sutton-in-Ashfield, Nottinghamshire, NG17 4FT Tel: (01623) 550011 Fax: (01623) 550011

▶ Netmerchants, Unit 53 Ledcom Industrial Estate, Bank Road, Larne, County Antrim, BT40 3AW Tel: (028) 2827 7440 Fax: (028) 2826 7977 E-mail: info@netmerchants.co.uk

Pisces, Westwood Studios, Marshfield Bank, Crewe, CW2 8UY Tel: (01270) 216211 Fax: (01270) 586150 E-mail: info@pisces-art.co.uk

RW Racing, 19a Bridge Industries, Fareham, Hampshire, PO16 8SX Tel: (01329) 236640 Fax: (01329) 236640 E-mail: neil@rwracing.freeserve.co.uk

Stadium Chalk & Crayon Co. Ltd, Endle Street, Southampton, SO14 5AW Tel: (023) 8022 6765 Fax: (023) 8063 0304 E-mail: sales@stadium-chalk.fsnet.co.uk

MODELS, ADVERTISING/FILM/ TELEVISION ETC

3DD, 3 Marlow Workshops, Arnold Circus, London, E2 7JN Tel: (020) 7739 7933 Fax: (020) 7739 7195 E-mail: sales@3dd.co.uk

Brandbright Ltd, The Old School, Cromer Road, Bodham, Holt, Norfolk, NR25 6QG Tel: (01263) 588755 E-mail: sales@brandbright.co.uk

Complete Fabrication Ltd, Unit B1, Faircharm Studios, 8-12 Creekside, London, SE8 3DX Tel: (020) 8694 9666 Fax: (020) 8694 9669 E-mail: mail@completefabrication.com

▶ JSM Industrial Model Making, Unit 5 Home Farm House Works, Mildenhall, Marlborough, Wiltshire, SN8 2LR Tel: (01672) 512305 Fax: (01672) 512305 E-mail: studio@jsmmodelmakers.freeserve.co.uk

Rainford Models Ltd, Bingswood Industrial Estate, Whaley Bridge, High Peak, Derbyshire, SK23 7LY Tel: (01663) 719119 Fax: (01663) 719109 E-mail: sales@rainfordmodels.co.uk

MODELS, INDUSTRIAL/ INDUSTRIAL PROCESS

A E Blanchard, 144 Station Road, Ratby, Leicester, LE6 0JP Tel: 0116-239 3831 Fax: 0116-239 3831

B & H Precision Tooling Ltd, Unit 14 Glover Estate, Egmont Street, Mossley, Ashton-Under-Lyne, Lancashire, OL5 9PY Tel: (01457) 833434 Fax: (01457) 835685 E-mail: sales@bh-precision.co.uk

Berry Place Models Ltd, 1 Berry Place, Sebastian Street, London, EC1V 0HE Tel: (020) 7490 8222 Fax: (020) 7336 8482 E-mail: enquiries@berryplace.co.uk

D & M Connell, Shay Dene, Shaw Lane, Queensbury, Bradford, West Yorkshire, BD13 2LD Tel: (01274) 881099 Fax: (01274) 881099

David Fawcett Ltd, Tynyronnen, Mynytho, Pwllheli, Gwynedd, LL53 7RT Tel: (01758) 740720 Fax: (01758) 740722 E-mail: fawcett@pipemedia.co.uk

G B Models, 119 Church Road, Urmston, Manchester, M41 9ET Tel: 0161-747 2900 Fax: 0161-747 2901

Metropolis, Grange Business Centre, Belasis Avenue, Billingham, Cleveland, TS23 1LG Tel: (01642) 361255 Fax: (01642) 365700 E-mail: sales@metropolisdevelopments.co.uk

Optimus Models, 115 Crosshall Road, Eaton Ford, St. Neots, Cambridgeshire, PE19 7AB Tel: (01480) 473831 Fax: (01480) 384098

Space Models Ltd, Pier Road, North Feltham Trading Estate, Feltham, Middlesex, TW14 0TW Tel: (020) 8890 5542 Fax: (020) 8751 1731 E-mail: enq@spacemodels.co.uk

MODELS, SCALE, FIGURES

Uncle Tom's Dolls Houses Factory, 49 Ansty Road, Wyken, Coventry, CV2 3FG Tel: 0247 6278104 Fax: 0247 6278104 E-mail: info@dollshouses.atspace.com

MODELS, STEAM ENGINE

ACS Engineering, 2 Cairndubh Cottages, Cairnbaan, Lochgilphead, Argyll, PA31 8SQ Tel: (01546) 603849 E-mail: acs-engineering@wargyll.fsnet.co.uk

▶ Sussex Steam Co., 94 North Lane, East Preston, West Sussex, BN16 1HE Tel: 01903 770848 Fax: 01903 770848 E-mail: john@sussexsteam.co.uk

MODEM SOFTWARE

Coherent Technologies Ltd, Vyne House, 2 Hardwicks Way, London, SW18 4AJ Tel: (020) 8871 3515 Fax: (020) 8877 3683 E-mail: sales@coherent-tech.co.uk

MODEMS

Coherent Technologies Ltd, Vyne House, 2 Hardwicks Way, London, SW18 4AJ Tel: (020) 8871 3515 Fax: (020) 8877 3683 E-mail: sales@coherent-tech.co.uk

Computing Needs Ltd, 9-11 Manor Road, Felixstowe, Suffolk, IP11 2EJ Tel: (01394) 278067 Fax: (01394) 458140 E-mail: sales@computingneeds.co.uk

Sascal Displays Ltd, Unit 1 Hayes Metro Centre, Springfield Road, Hayes, Middlesex, UB4 0LE Tel: (020) 8573 0303 Fax: (020) 8569 1515 E-mail: sales@sascal.com

SeNd Technology Ltd, Hunters End, Cox Green Lane, Maidenhead, Berkshire, SL6 3EU Tel: (0870) 4587363 Fax: (07092) 383861 E-mail: sales@sendtech.co.uk

Westermo Data Communications Ltd, Talisman Business Centre, Duncan Road, Park Gate, Southampton, SO31 7GA Tel: (01489) 580585 Fax: (01489) 580586 E-mail: sales@westermo.co.uk

MODULAR AIR FILTRATION CONTAINMENT SYSTEMS

Applied Containment Engineering Ltd, Unit 4, Shaw Cross Business Park, Dewsbury, West Yorkshire, WF12 7RF Tel: (01924) 455339 Fax: (01924) 452295 E-mail: applied.containment@ace-ltd.com

MODULAR CONVEYOR SYSTEMS

Bevpak Ltd, 27-28 Arkwright Road, Astmore Industrial Estate, Runcorn, Cheshire, WA7 1NU Tel: (01928) 574815 Fax: (01928) 589487 E-mail: bevpak@hotmail.co.uk

MODULAR DISPLAY SYSTEMS

▶ arken P-O-P Ltd, Studlands Park Avenue, Newmarket, Suffolk, CB8 7EA Tel: (01638) 565656 Fax: (01638) 662770 E-mail: info@arken-pop.com

Clip International Ltd, Avon Works, Church Road, Bristol, BS30 5RD Tel: 0117-937 2636 Fax: 0117-937 3172 E-mail: info@clipdisplay.com

Contract Sign Services, The Old Chapel, Sandfield Road, Churchdown, Gloucester, GL3 2HD Tel: (01452) 857017 Fax: (01452) 713706 E-mail: sales@contractsignservices.co.uk

Display Matrix, Unit 14, Dixon Business Centre Dixon Road, Bristol, BS4 5QW Tel: 0117-300 9925 Fax: 0117-977 2457 E-mail: info@displaymatrix.co.uk

Driscoll Bros Group Ltd, 59 Grasmere Road, Gatley, Cheadle, Cheshire, SK8 4RS Tel: 0161-428 2109 Fax: (01625) 548466 E-mail: glynn@driscollbros.co.uk

Fastlane Displays Ltd, 19 Arkwright Court, Astmoor Industrial Estate, Runcorn, Cheshire, WA7 1NX Tel: (01928) 569846 Fax: (01928) 569846

QK Honeycomb Products Ltd, Creeting Road, Stowmarket, Suffolk, IP14 5AS Tel: (01449) 612145 Fax: (01449) 677604 E-mail: sales@qkhoneycomb.co.uk

R T Display Systems Ltd, 10 Lyon Road, South Wimbledon, London, SW19 2RL Tel: (020) 8545 2945 Fax: (020) 8545 2955 E-mail: sales@octanorm.co.uk

SD Displays Ltd, 157 Boyn Valley Road, Maidenhead, Berkshire, SL6 4EG Tel: (01628) 673864 Fax: (01628) 674803 E-mail: sales@sd-displays.co.uk

Supertube, Darby House, Darby Way, Narborough, Leicester, LE19 2GP Tel: 0116-286 6611 Fax: 0116-275 0216

MODULAR FIXTURING SYSTEMS

Metris UK Ltd, Argosy Road, Nottingham EMA, Castle Donnington, Derby, DE74 2SA Tel: (01332) 811349 Fax: (01332) 850149 E-mail: sales@lkuk.co.uk

MODULAR PLATFORM OR RAISED FLOORING

Bathgate Flooring Ltd, 1 Fir Tree Lane, Rotherwas, Hereford, HR2 6LA Tel: (01432) 353003 Fax: (01432) 353004

Bromag Structures Ltd, Burford Road, Witney, Oxfordshire, OX29 0RE Tel: (01993) 703584 Fax: (01993) 772149 E-mail: jo@bromag.demon.co.uk

C P Supplies Ltd, 95 Chester Street, Aston, Birmingham, B6 4AE Tel: 0121-380 1600 Fax: 0121-380 1616 E-mail: admin@cpsupplies.co.uk

Davicon Structural Engineers, The Wallows Industrial Estate, Fens Pool Avenue, Brierley Hill, West Midlands, DY5 1QA Tel: (01384) 572851 Fax: (01384) 265098 E-mail: sales@davicon.com

Hatmet Ltd, Interiors House, Lynton Road, London, N8 8SL Tel: (020) 8341 0200 Fax: (020) 8341 9878 E-mail: info@hatmet.co.uk

The Mezzanine Floor Co. Ltd, Unit 2B, 9 Cannon Lane, Tonbridge, Kent, TN9 1PP Tel: (01732) 356085 Fax: (01732) 361278 E-mail: sales@mezzanine.co.uk

Raised Floor Systems, Peak House, Works Road, Letchworth Garden City, Hertfordshire, SG6 1GB Tel: (01582) 734161 Fax: (01582) 400946 E-mail: sales@raisedfloorsystems.co.uk

Veitchi (Scotland) Ltd, Unit 7, Hareness Circle, Altens Industrial Estate, Aberdeen, AB12 3LY Tel: (01224) 896333 Fax: (01224) 890354 E-mail: aberdeen@veitchi.com

MODULAR PORTABLE BUILDINGS

ACS Cabins, Midlands Farm, Mill Lane, Headley, Bordon, Hampshire, GU35 0PB Tel: (01428) 714900

MODULAR SOFAS

Nabru Ltd, Unit 12, Sarum Complex, Salisbury Road, Uxbridge, Middlesex, UB8 2RZ Tel: (01895) 256868 Fax: (01895) 239214 E-mail: service@nabru.co.uk

MODULAR SYSTEM SIGNS

▶ Sign Directory, 38 Sandport Street, Edinburgh, EH6 6EP Tel: 0131-553 4224 Fax: 0131-554 5797 E-mail: signdirectory@btclick.com

Signconex Ltd, St. Johns Works, Fern Street, Bury, Lancashire, BL9 5BP Tel: 0161-764 9500 Fax: 0161-764 9600 E-mail: sales@signconex.co.uk

MODULATORS

Advent Communications, Preston Hill House, Preston Hill, Chesham, Buckinghamshire, HP5 3HE Tel: (01494) 774400 Fax: (01494) 791127 E-mail: sales@vislink.com

MODULATORS, CLOSED CIRCUIT TELEVISION (CCTV) CAMERAS

Barrier Surveillance Services, 77 Main Street, Shildon, County Durham, DL4 1AN Tel: (01388) 776833 Fax: (01388) 775886

MODULE CONTROL SYSTEMS

Counting Solutions Ltd, 1-3 Bowling Green Road, Kettering, Northamptonshire, NN15 7QW Tel: (01536) 511010 Fax: (01536) 513653 E-mail: sales@counting-solutions.co.uk

MOHAIR

Laycock International Ltd, Stanley Mills, Whitley Street, Bingley, West Yorkshire, BD16 4JH Tel: (01274) 562563 Fax: (01274) 562823 E-mail: mohair@legend.co.uk

MOHAIR FABRICS

Gamma Beta Holdings Ltd, Briggella Mills, Bradford, West Yorkshire, BD5 0QA Tel: (01274) 525508 Fax: (01274) 521157 E-mail: furnishing@hield.co.uk

Moxon, Yew Tree Mills, Holmbridge, Holmfirth, HD9 2NN Tel: (01484) 691500 Fax: (01484) 691505 E-mail: sales@moxon.co.uk

William Halstead & Co Dudley Hill Ltd, Stanley Mills, Edward Street, Bradford, West Yorkshire, BD4 9RS Tel: (01274) 682921 Fax: (01274) 685698 E-mail: sales@williamhalstead.co.uk

MOISTURE ANALYSERS

Allcontrols Ltd, 20 Halifax Road, Cambridge, CB4 3PX Tel: (01223) 366164 Fax: (0870) 4580314 E-mail: info@allcontrols.co.uk

Cem Microwave Technology Ltd, 2 Middle Slade, Buckingham Industrial Estate, Buckingham, MK18 1WA Tel: (01280) 822873 Fax: (01280) 822342 E-mail: info.uk@cem.com

Metrohm UK Ltd, 2 Buckingham Industrial Park, Top Angel, Buckingham Industrial Estate, Buckingham, MK18 1TH Tel: (01280) 824824 Fax: (01280) 824800 E-mail: enquiry@metrohm.co.uk

▶ Moisture Control & Measurement Ltd, Thorp Arch Trading Estate, Thorp Arch, Wetherby, West Yorkshire, LS23 7BJ Tel: (01937) 843927 Fax: (01937) 842524 E-mail: sales@mcm-moisture.com

Shaw Moisture Meters (UK) Ltd, Rawson Road, Westgate, Bradford, West Yorkshire, BD1 3SQ Tel: (01274) 733582 Fax: (01274) 370151 E-mail: mail@shawmeters.com

Thermo Electron, 2a Swift Park, Old Leicester Road, Rugby, Warwickshire, CV21 1DZ Tel: (01788) 820300 Fax: (01788) 820419 E-mail: tewi@thermo.com

MOISTURE METERS

K P M Moisture Meters Aqua Boy, Manndalin, Harrogate View, Leeds, LS17 8AZ Tel: 0113-268 5054 Fax: 0113-268 5054 E-mail: kpmmeters@aol.com

▶ Moisture Control & Measurement Ltd, Thorp Arch Trading Estate, Thorp Arch, Wetherby, West Yorkshire, LS23 7BJ Tel: (01937) 843927 Fax: (01937) 842524 E-mail: sales@mcm-moisture.com

Paper Life Ltd, Unit 13 Ahed House, Sandbeds Trading Estate, Ossett, West Yorkshire, WF5 9ND Tel: (01924) 281666 Fax: (01924) 281444 E-mail: sales@paperlife.co.uk

Protimeter plc, Meter House, Fieldhouse Lane, Marlow, Buckinghamshire, SL7 1LW Tel: (01628) 472722 Fax: (01628) 474312 E-mail: sales@protometer.com

Sinar Technology Ltd, Unit 8 Camberley Business Centre, Bracebridge, Camberley, Surrey, GU15 3DP Tel: (01276) 63957 Fax: (01276) 29941 E-mail: office@sinar.co.uk

Verus Instruments Ltd, Clare House, Pinewood Road, High Wycombe, Buckinghamshire, HP12 4DA Tel: (01494) 558206 Fax: (01494) 558383 E-mail: sales@verus.co.uk

MOISTURE RESISTANT TELECOMMUNICATIONS CONNECTORS

Viking Ltd, Chatsworth House, Portland Close, Houghton Regis, Dunstable, Bedfordshire, LU5 5AW Tel: (01582) 603600 Fax: (01582) 471114 E-mail: accounts@vikingltd.co.uk

MOISTURE TEST INSTRUMENTS

Protimeter plc, Meter House, Fieldhouse Lane, Marlow, Buckinghamshire, SL7 1LW Tel: (01628) 472722 Fax: (01628) 474312 E-mail: sales@protometer.com

MOLECULAR BIOLOGY RESEARCH EQUIPMENT

Cochranes of Oxford Ltd, Grove Farm Barns, High Street, Shipton-under-Wychwood, Chipping Norton, Oxfordshire, OX7 6DG Tel: (01993) 832868 Fax: (01993) 832578 E-mail: cochranes@mailbox.co.uk

MOLING OR PIPE LAYING CONTRACTORS

Mole Plumbers, 123 Arrowe Park Road, Wirral, Merseyside, CH49 5PB Tel: 0151-605 1469 Fax: 0151-605 1472 E-mail: sales@moleuk.com

MOLYBDENUM CHEMICAL PRODUCTS

Climax Molybdenum UK Ltd, Needham Road, Stowmarket, Suffolk, IP14 2AE Tel: (01449) 674431 Fax: (01449) 675972 E-mail: climax@phelpsdodge.com

MOLYBDENUM COMPONENTS

British Refractory Metals, 27 Nobel Square, Burnt Mills Industrial Estate, Basildon, Essex, SS13 1LP Tel: (01268) 591386 Fax: (01268) 591389 E-mail: pcurtisbrm@aol.com

Burcas Ltd, Park Lane, Handsworth, Birmingham, B21 8LT Tel: 0121-553 2777 Fax: 0121-553 1284 E-mail: info@burcas.co.uk

MOLYBDENUM COMPONENTS - *continued*

Duckworth & Kent Reading Ltd, 113 Armour Road, Tilehurst, Reading, RG31 6HB Tel: 0118-942 9828 Fax: 0118-945 1191 E-mail: duckworth.kent@btconnect.com
Plansee Metals Ltd, 3 Lidstone Court, Uxbridge Road, George Green, Slough, SL3 6AG Tel: (01753) 576959 Fax: (01753) 577591
H C Starck Ltd, Unit 1 Harris Road, Calne, Wiltshire, SN11 9PT Tel: (01249) 822122 Fax: (01249) 823800 E-mail: sally.field@hcstarck.co.uk
Thermal Spray Material Services Ltd, Brook Street Business Centre, Brook Street, Tipton, West Midlands, DY4 9DD Tel: 0121-520 0720 Fax: 0121-520 3002 E-mail: thermalsprayuk@aol.com
Tungsten Manufacturing Ltd, 22-28 Cambridge Street, Aylesbury, Buckinghamshire, HP20 1RS Tel: (01296) 394566 Fax: (01296) 394566 E-mail: sales@tungsten.co.uk

MOLYBDENUM DISULPHIDE COATING PROCESSORS OR SERVICES

Climax Molybdenum UK Ltd, Needham Road, Stowmarket, Suffolk, IP14 2AE Tel: (01449) 674431 Fax: (01449) 675972 E-mail: climax@phelpsdodge.com

MOLYBDENUM DISULPHIDE ENGINE OIL ADDITIVES

United Oil Products Ltd, Unit 2 Wonastow Road Industrial Estate East, Monmouth, Gwent, NP25 5JB Tel: (01600) 772110 Fax: (01600) 772660 E-mail: unitedoil@hotmail.com

MOLYBDENUM POWDER

British Refractory Metals, 27 Nobel Square, Burnt Mills Industrial Estate, Basildon, Essex, SS13 1LP Tel: (01268) 591386 Fax: (01268) 591389 E-mail: pcurtisbrm@aol.com

MOLYBDENUM SCRAP

Jack Sharkey & Co. Ltd, 2 Middlemore Road, Smethwick, West Midlands, B66 2DR Tel: 0121-558 7444 Fax: 0121-558 9810

MOLYBDENUM STOCKHOLDERS

Burcas Ltd, Park Lane, Handsworth, Birmingham, B21 8LT Tel: 0121-553 2777 Fax: 0121-553 1284 E-mail: info@burcas.co.uk

MONITORING SYSTEMS

▶ A & R Designs Ltd, Unit 21, Stevenston Industrial Estate, Stevenston, Ayrshire, KA20 3LR Tel: (01294) 601042 Fax: (01294) 601400 E-mail: ardgas@aol.com

MONITORING SYSTEMS, TO CUSTOMER SPECIFICATION, *See also headings under Control Systems; and other heading for particular application*

Datapaq Ltd, Deanland House, 160 Cowley Road, Cambridge, CB4 0GU Tel: (01223) 423141 Fax: (01223) 423306 E-mail: sales@datapaq.co.uk
Isoscan UK Ltd, Unit 1 Portelant Barns, Cowdown Farm, Micheldever, Winchester, Hampshire, SO21 3DN Tel: (01962) 774411 Fax: (01962) 774477 E-mail: sales@isoscan.co.uk

MONITORS, GAS, CONFINED SPACE

▶ IMS (Cheshire) Ltd, Ion Path, Road Three, Winsford Industrial Estate, Winsford, Cheshire, CW7 3GE Tel: (01606) 550099 Fax: (01606) 556418 E-mail: enquiries@imscheshire.com

MONITORS, HEART BEAT

Cardionetics Ltd, Centaur House, Ancells Road, Fleet, Hampshire, GU51 2UJ Tel: (01252) 761040 Fax: (01252) 761117 E-mail: sales@cardionetics.com
▶ Fitness Equipment Clearance, Boland House, Nottingham South & Wilford Industrial Estate, Nottingham, NG11 7EP Tel: 0115-982 2844 Fax: 0115-982 6775 E-mail: sales@fitness-equipment-clearance.co.uk
▶ Thenewyou Net Ltd, Butterflies 19 Alston Mews, Thatcham, Berkshire, RG19 3XF Tel: (01635) 862239

MONITORS, PLASMA DISPLAY

▶ Visual Service Centre, Unit 1 Derby Trading Estate, Stores Road, Derby, DE21 4BE Tel: (01332) 291119 Fax: (01332) 291119 E-mail: info@visualservicecentre.co.uk

MONITORS, PLASMA SCREEN

Business Presentations Ltd, Hillfoot Farm, Hitchin Road, Shefford, Bedfordshire, SG17 5JD Tel: (01462) 817406 Fax: (01462) 850130 E-mail: sally@business-presentations.co.uk

MONOCLONAL BLOOD REAGENTS

Millipore UK Ltd, Fleming Road, Kirkton Campus, Livingston, West Lothian, EH54 7BN Tel: (01506) 404000 Fax: (01506) 404001 E-mail:

MONUMENTAL OR ARCHITECTURAL MASONS OR CRAFTSMEN OR MANUFACTURERS

A Elfes Ltd, 155-157 Green Lane, Ilford, Essex, IG1 1XW Tel: (020) 7788 3290 Fax: (020) 8478 7979
A & J Robertson Granite Ltd, Church Street, Irvine, Ayrshire, KA12 8PE Tel: (01294) 279558 Fax: (01294) 279558
James Beresford & Sons, Bridge Street, Belper, Derbyshire, DE56 1BA Tel: (01773) 822117 Fax: (01773) 822117
▶ Blackwells Stone Craft, Overleigh Road, Chester, CH4 7HW Tel: (01244) 680704 Fax: (01244) 671772
Blake & Horlock, 286 Church Street, London, N9 9HJ Tel: (020) 8807 3992 Fax: (020) 8807 3992
Browns Glass & Glazing, 6 Silver Street, Bridgwater, Somerset, TA6 3EG Tel: (01278) 423157 Fax: (01278) 423157
C.J.Jordan & Son Ltd, Zero, Alfred Road, London, W3 6LH Tel: (020) 8992 0638 Fax: (020) 8992 0073
Davis Memorials, 56a Station Road, Cradley Heath, West Midlands, B64 6NU Tel: (01384) 566958 Fax: (01384) 569708
Davis Memorials, 1 Park Street, Kidderminster, Worcestershire, DY11 6TN Tel: (01384) 566958 Fax: (01562) 861160
J. Day & Son Ltd, Station Road, Bishop's Stortford, Hertfordshire, CM23 3BJ Tel: (01279) 653450 Fax: (01279) 503637 E-mail: jdayandson@tiscali.co.uk
F J Cambridge & Co. Ltd, 75 Stroud Road, Gloucester, GL1 5AQ Tel: (01452) 523581 Fax: (01452) 523581
Galloway Granite Works, Sorbie, Newton Stewart, Wigtownshire, DG8 8EW Tel: (01988) 850350 Fax: (01988) 850340 E-mail: galloway-granite@btconect.com
Geere & Co., 233 Dunstable Road, Luton, LU4 8BN Tel: (01582) 730313 Fax: (01582) 727691 E-mail: info@memorialgroup.co.uk
H G Blatcher Memorial Masons Ltd, 409 Sutton Road, Southend-on-Sea, SS2 5PQ Tel: (01702) 468950 Fax: (01702) 600274 E-mail: info@memorialmasons.co.uk
Handsworth Crown Memorial Co., 283 Oxhill Road, Birmingham, B21 8EY Tel: 0121-554 3234 Fax: 0121-554 3234
John Hardman Trading Co. Ltd, Lightwoods House, Lightwoods Park, Hagley Road West, Birmingham, B67 5DP Tel: 0121-429 7609 Fax: 0121-420 2316 E-mail: info@hardmantrading.com
Inigo Jones & Co. Ltd, Tudor Slate Works, Caernarfon, Gwynedd, LL54 7ST Tel: (01286) 830242 Fax: (01286) 831247 E-mail: slate@inigojones.co.uk
J & G Mossman Ltd, 284 High Street, Glasgow, G4 0QT Tel: 0141-552 2161 Fax: 0141-552 2161
▶ James Long Masons Ltd, Timbrell Street, Trowbridge, Wiltshire, BA14 8PN Tel: (01225) 763074 Fax: (01225) 774654
Jersey Monumental Co, 82 New Street, St. Helier, Jersey, JE2 3TE Tel: (01534) 730252 Fax: (01534) 731374 E-mail: jmco@jerseymail.co.uk
John Hood & Son Sculptors Ltd, Station Road, Wick, Caithness, KW1 5LB Tel: (01955) 603102 Fax: (01955) 603102
William Kent Memorials (March) Ltd, 11 Upwell Rd, March, Cambs, PE15 9DT Tel: (01354) 652030 Fax: (01354) 652030
Kingston Masonry, 19 Cambridge Road, Kingston upon Thames, Surrey, KT1 3NG Tel: (020) 8546 3504 Fax: (020) 8547 3493
Lancashire Stone Cutters Ltd, Unit 3, Ramsbottom Mill Crow Lane, Ramsbottom, Bury, Lancashire, BL0 9BR Tel: (01706) 827799 Fax: (01706) 827799
Landers Quarries Ltd, Kingston Road, Worth Matravers, Swanage, Dorset, BH19 3JP Tel: (01929) 439205 Fax: (01929) 439268 E-mail: landers@purbeckstone.co.uk
Larcombes Memorials, 14-16 Mount Charles Road, St. Austell, Cornwall, PL25 3LD Tel: (01726) 73618 Fax: (01726) 69900
London Stone Conservation, 42 Sekforde Street, Clerkenwell, London, EC1R 0HA Tel: (020) 7251 0592 Fax: (020) 7251 0592 E-mail: lsc@londonstoneconservation.co.uk
William Loxley Ltd, 1 Weoley Avenue, Birmingham, B29 6PP Tel: 0121-472 0834 Fax: 0121-472 8658
Meredith Jones, Parry Road, Llanrwst, Gwynedd, LL26 0DG Tel: (01492) 640348 Fax: (01492) 640348 E-mail: rwroberts@enterprise.net
Nettlebank Monumental Masons Ltd, 26 Chapel Street, Cheadle, Stoke-on-Trent, ST10 1DY Tel: (01538) 750051 Fax: (01538) 750599
Phillips & Sons, 110-111 Lewes Road, Brighton, BN2 3QB Tel: (01273) 682751 Fax: (01273) 677469
R Mccann, 405 Oxhill Road, Birmingham, B21 8JT Tel: 0121-554 3232 Fax: 0121-554 3232
Symm & Co. Ltd, Osney Mead, Oxford, OX2 0EQ Tel: (01865) 254900 Fax: (01865) 254935 E-mail: mailbox@symm.co.uk
Turner & Co., 240 Sebert Road, London, E7 0NP Tel: (020) 8534 1843 Fax: (020) 8519 0057
Universal Engine Power Ltd, 9 Flitch Industrial Estate, Chelmsford Road, Dunmow, Essex, CM6 1XJ Tel: (01371) 875331 Fax: (01371) 874777 E-mail: sales@unipower.uk.com
W J Haysom & Son, St Adhelms Quarry, Swanage, Dorset, BH19 3LN Tel: (01929) 439217 Fax: (01929) 439215 E-mail: haysom@purbeckstone.co.uk
W S Moore, 160 Malpas Road, Newport, Gwent, NP20 5PN Tel: (01633) 855902 Fax: (01633) 855902
▶ Walkers Bros Cockermouth Ltd, 6 Market Place, Cockermouth, Cumbria, CA13 9NQ Tel: (01900) 823302 Fax: (01900) 823302
William Loxley Ltd, 1 Weoley Avenue, Birmingham, B29 6PP Tel: 0121-472 0834 Fax: 0121-472 0834 E-mail: williamloxley@blueyonder.co.uk

MOORING BUOYS

▶ Lindon Lewis Marine Ltd, Shepperton Marina, Felix Lane, Shepperton, Middlesex, TW17 8NS Tel: 01932 247427 Fax: 01932 223934 E-mail: info@pushtheboatout.com

MOORING REPAIR

Cox's Boatyard Ltd, Staithe Road, Barton Turf, Norwich, NR12 8AZ Tel: (01692) 536206 Fax: (01692) 536206 E-mail: info@coxsboatyard.co.uk
Kelpie Marine Boat Yard, Kelpie Marine, Great North Road, Roxton, Bedford, MK44 3DS Tel: (01234) 870249

MOORING SYSTEMS (MARINE) MANUFRS

D N Consultancy Services, 60 Southover, London, N12 7ES Tel: (020) 8446 6001 Fax: (020) 8445 3711 E-mail: chains@dnconsultancy.com
Eltonsford Ltd, 106 Palmerston Road, Southsea, Hampshire, PO5 3PT Tel: (023) 9282 6926 Fax: (023) 9282 4338
F P M Henderson Ltd, 35 Halley Street, Glasgow, G13 4DJ Tel: 0141-941 1211 Fax: 0141-941 2011 E-mail: sales@fpmhenderson.co.uk
Griffin Woodhouse, Greenfields, Romsley Lane, Shatterford, Bewdley, Worcestershire, DY12 1RS Tel: (01299) 861829 Fax: (01299) 861830E-mail: sales@griffin-woodhouse.co.uk
Holtite Ltd, Jubilee Works, Woods Lane, Cradley Heath, West Midlands, B64 7AW Tel: (01384) 560611 Fax: (01384) 410214 E-mail: holtite@aol.com
M S L Oilfield Services LTD, Unit 14 Brickfield Trade Estate, Brickfield Lane, Chandler's Ford, Eastleigh, Hampshire, SO53 4DP Tel: (023) 8027 5100 Fax: (023) 8027 5200 E-mail: sales@msluk.net
Redhill Marine Ltd, Ratcliffe On Soar, Nottingham, NG11 0EB Tel: (01509) 672770

MOPED ACCESSORIES, *See Motor Cycle Accessories etc*

MOPS, *See also headings for particular types*

Cherry Tree Products Ltd, Barn Meadow House, Barnmeadow Lane, Great Harwood, Blackburn, BB6 7AB Tel: (01254) 882544 Fax: (01254) 882550
Ewood Products, Barnmeadow House, Barnmeadow Lane, Great Harwood, Blackburn, BB6 7AB Tel: (01254) 882550 Fax: (01254) 882550
Farrar Bros, 49 Haugh Shaw Road, Halifax, West Yorkshire, HX1 3AR Tel: (01422) 352198 Fax: (01422) 349539 E-mail: farrarbros@aol.com
P. Gerratt Ltd, Baring Road, Northampton, NN5 7BA Tel: (01604) 758545 Fax: (01604) 588755 E-mail: sales@gerratt.com
Robert Scott & Sons, Oakview Mills, Manchester Road, Greenfield, Oldham, OL3 7HG Tel: (01457) 873931 Fax: (01457) 819490 E-mail: admin@robert-scott.co.uk

MORTGAGE BROKERS OR AGENTS OR CONSULTANCY

A S C Partnership plc, 3 Park Road, London, NW1 6AS Tel: (020) 7616 6628 Fax: (020) 7616 6634 E-mail: central@asc.co.uk
Agri Web, Enterprise House, 2-4 Balloo Avenue, Bangor, County Down, BT19 7QT Tel: (028) 9127 5913 Fax: (028) 9127 5563
Aman.Smart-Finance, Ammanford, Carmarthenshire, SA18 1JF Tel: (01269) 826643 E-mail: aman@smart-finance.co.uk
▶ Central Capital Mortgages, 2nd Floor, Edward Hyde Building, 38 Clarendon Road, Watford, WD17 1JJ Tel: 0800 032 23 20 E-mail: contact.us@centralcapital.com
Chase De Vere Mortgage Management Ltd, St James House, 23 Kings Street, London, SW1Y 6QY Tel: (020) 7930 7242 Fax: (020) 7930 3691 E-mail: simon.tyler@cdvmm.co.uk
▶ Clear Cut Mortgages, St. James House, St. James Square, Cheltenham, Gloucestershire, GL50 3WD Tel: (0845) 0698000 E-mail: info@clearcutmortgages.com
Coin & Leisure, Unit 1, Station Enterprises, Station Road, Abergavenny, Gwent, NP7 5HY Tel: (01873) 853360
▶ Commercial Factoring Ltd, Belle Grove House, Manor Court, Rogiet, Caldicot, Gwent, NP26 3TU Tel: (0845) 1235696 E-mail: admin@factoringadvice.com
Croucher, Reoch & Partners Ltd, 3rd Floor Babmaes Ho, 2 Babmaes St, London, SW1Y 6HD Tel: (020) 7839 5735 Fax: (020) 7930 4281 E-mail: fiztwilliamfinancial@compuserve.com
Ecclesiastical Insurance Group, Beaufort House, Brunswick Road, Gloucester, GL1 1JZ Tel: (01452) 528533 Fax: (01452) 423557 E-mail: marketing@eigmail.com
▶ Finance Direct, PO Box 127, Birmingham, B20 2XB Tel: (0800) 1973707
▶ Financial Consultancy, 244a Broadway, Bexleyheath, Kent, DA6 8AS Tel: (0845) 4668866 Fax: (0845) 4668877 E-mail: sales@thefinancialconsultancy.com
Gemini Consultants Ltd, The Gemini Building, Houghton Hall Park, Houghton Regis, Dunstable, Bedfordshire, LU5 5GB Tel: (01582) 868621 Fax: (01582) 868622 E-mail: mail@geminiconsultants.com
Humberts, Mansfield House, Silver Street, Taunton, Somerset, TA1 3DN Tel: (01823) 331234 Fax: (01823) 332034 E-mail: taunton.ag@humberts.co.uk
Mortgage Shop Ltd, King Georges Chambers, 1 St. James Square, Bacup, Lancashire, OL13 9AA Tel: (01706) 875746 Fax: (01706) 875122 E-mail: mortgageshopltd@btconnect.com
Norwich Union P.L.C., St. Helen's, 1 Undershaft, London, EC3P 3DQ Tel: (020) 7283 7500
O'Riordan Bond Estate Agents, St. Edmunds House, St. Edmunds Road, Northampton, NN1 5DY Tel: (01604) 632805 Fax: (01604) 609306
Arvin Parmar, 23 Queniborough Road, Leicester, LE4 6GW Tel: (07941) 360350 E-mail: agentarvin@hotmail.com
▶ Personal Touch Leicester, 111 Belvior Road, Coalville, Leicestershire, LE67 3PH Tel: 0871 750 4330 Fax: 0871 750 4327 E-mail: enquires@ptimortgages.co.uk
▶ Russell Young Ifa Ltd, 18 Front Street, Low Pittington, Durham, DH6 1BQ Tel: 0191-372 3319 Fax: 0191-372 3319 E-mail: info@russellyoung-ifa.com
▶ Smaart Associates, 1 Farnham Road, Guildford, Surrey, GU2 4RG Tel: (01483) 549815 Fax: (01483) 549115 E-mail: info@smaart.info
▶ South West Mortgage Solutions, 12 Court View, Brixton, Plymouth, PL8 2NY Tel: (01752) 881647 Fax: (01752) 881647 E-mail: enquiry@justmortgagesplus.com
▶ Surrex Financial Management, 2 Paddock Road, Ashford, Kent, TN23 5WH Tel: (01233) 665812 Fax: (01903) 261550 E-mail: walterb@surrexfm.com
▶ Think Smart Finance Ltd, 778 High Road, London, N12 9QR Tel: (020) 8445 5428
▶ Tudor Associates Ltd, Stallington Hall Farm, Stallington Road, Blythe Bridge, Stoke-On-Trent, ST11 9QJ Tel: (01782) 388439 Fax: (01782) 399737 E-mail: rosiepatterson@hotmail.com
▶ Wholesale Mortgages, Lluest Pentre, Pentre Lane, Rhuddlan, Rhyl, Clwyd, LL18 6HY Tel: (01745) 590006 Fax: (01745) 590016

MORTGAGE BROKERS, REMORTGAGING

Aman.Smart-Finance, Ammanford, Carmarthenshire, SA18 1JF Tel: (01269) 826643 E-mail: aman@smart-finance.co.uk
▶ Finance Direct, PO Box 127, Birmingham, B20 2XB Tel: (0800) 1973707
▶ LGI Consulting, 2nd Floor, 41A Church Street, Weybridge, Surrey, KT13 8DG Tel: 01932 856699 E-mail: info@lgiconsulting.co.uk

MORTGAGE BROKERS, REMORTGAGING – *continued*

▶ Mortgage Simplicity, Inglewood House, Inglewood, Alloa, Clackmannanshire, FK10 2HU Tel: (0845) 8381502 E-mail: info@mortgagesimplicity.co.uk

▶ Wholesale Mortgages, Lluest Pentre, Pentre Lane, Rhuddlan, Rhyl, Clwyd, LL18 6HY Tel: (01745) 590006 Fax: (01745) 590016

MORTGAGE BROKERS, REMORTGAGING, BAD CREDIT

▶ Central Capital Mortgages, 2nd Floor, Edward Hyde Building, 38 Clarendon Road, Watford, WD17 1JJ Tel: 0800 032 23 20 E-mail: contact.us@centralcapital.com

▶ LGI Consulting, 2nd Floor, 41A Church Street, Weybridge, Surrey, KT13 8DG Tel: 01932 856699 E-mail: info@lgiconsulting.co.uk

MORTUARY EQUIPMENT AND ACCESSORIES

County Hospital & Mortuary Equipment, 13 Westfield Crescent, Brighton, BN1 8JB Tel: (01273) 885441 Fax: (01273) 240954 E-mail: county@pavilion.co.uk

MOSAIC PATTERN GLASS

▶ Azurra Mosaics, PO Box 2801, Purley, Surrey, CR8 1WX Tel: (0845) 0908110 Fax: (0870) 1313319 E-mail: info@mosaics.co.uk

MOSAIC WORKERS OR CONTRACTORS

A Andrews & Sons Ltd, 324-330 Meanwood Road, Leeds, LS7 2JE Tel: 0113-262 4751 Fax: 0113-262 3337 E-mail: contracts@andrews-tiles.co.uk

Birmingham Tile & Mosaic Co. Ltd, Ceramic House, 198 Kings Road, Tyseley, Birmingham, B11 2AP Tel: 0121-707 4505 Fax: 0121-707 5585 E-mail: mail@btandm.co.uk

Marriott & Price Ltd, Station House Station Yard, Waterhouse Lane, Kingswood, Tadworth, Surrey, KT20 6EN Tel: (01737) 352735 Fax: (01737) 359192 E-mail: info@marriottandprice.co.uk

O Toffolo & Son Ltd, 42 Temple Street, Hull, HU5 1AE Tel: (01482) 342674 Fax: (01482) 441344 E-mail: carl@toffolo.co.uk

Swedecor Ltd, Manchester Street, Hull, HU3 4TX Tel: (01482) 329691 Fax: (01482) 212988 E-mail: info@swedecor.com

MOSAICS

▶ Azurra Mosaics, PO Box 2801, Purley, Surrey, CR8 1WX Tel: (0845) 0908110 Fax: (0870) 1313319 E-mail: info@mosaics.co.uk

Contelec Engravings Ltd, Spring Lane, Willenhall, West Midlands, WV12 4JG Tel: (01902) 369307 Fax: (01902) 369309 E-mail: engrave@contelec.co.uk

Mosaic Arts, 18 Buckland Cresent, London, NW3 5DX Tel: (020) 7722 1505 Fax: (020) 7722 9674

Tower Ceramics, 91 Parkway, London, NW1 7PP Tel: (020) 7485 7192 Fax: (020) 7267 9571

Udny Edgar & Co. Ltd, 314 Balham High Road, London, SW17 7AA Tel: (020) 8767 8181 Fax: (020) 8767 7709

MOTIF EMBROIDERERS

Brentwood Marketing, Lockhill Mills, Holmes Road, Sowerby Bridge, West Yorkshire, HX6 3LD Tel: (01422) 831185 Fax: (01422) 831186 E-mail: info@brentwoodmarketing.co.uk

▶ Hand & Lock, 86 Margaret Street, London, W1W 8TE Tel: (020) 7580 7488 Fax: (020) 7580 7499 E-mail: enquiries@handembroidery.com

M G A Corporation Ltd, Unit 6 Britannia Business Park, Mills Road Quarrywood, Quarry Wood, Aylesford, Kent, ME20 7NT Tel: (01622) 717332 Fax: (01622) 715508 E-mail: goldstaruk@ukonline.co.uk

MOTION CONTROL EQUIPMENT

Micromech Systems Ltd, Units 7 & 8, Chilford Court, Braintree, Essex, CM7 2QS Tel: (01376) 333300 Fax: (01376) 552600 E-mail: sales@micromech.co.uk

MOTION CONTROL SYSTEMS

Micromech Systems Ltd, Units 7 & 8, Chilford Court, Braintree, Essex, CM7 2QS Tel: (01376) 333300 Fax: (01376) 552600 E-mail: sales@micromech.co.uk

Syscom Motion Solution Ltd, Unit 19 Barnsley Business & Innovation Centre, Innovation Way, Barnsley, South Yorkshire, S75 1JL Tel: (01226) 771630 Fax: (01226) 771696 E-mail: info@automation.co.uk

MOTION SIMULATORS

Cuesim Ltd, 2-4 Highfield Park, Highfield Road, Oakley, Bedford, MK43 7TA Tel: (01234) 828000 Fax: (01234) 828001 E-mail: sales@cuesim.com

Quadrant Systems Ltd, Victoria Gardens, Burgess Hill, West Sussex, RH15 9NB Tel: (01444) 246226 Fax: (01444) 870172 E-mail: pmasters@quadrant-systems.co.uk

MOTIVATIONAL TRAINING

▶ Pinnacle Academy of Martial Arts, Sir Charles Lucas School, Acacia Avenue, Colchester, CO4 3JL Tel: 01206 323343 E-mail: enquiries@pinnacleacademy.co.uk

MOTIVE POWER BATTERIES

▶ DBS Brand Factors, Unit 5, Haydock Lane, Haydock, St. Helens, Merseyside, WA11 9UY Tel: (01942) 276657 Fax: (01942) 722067 E-mail: enquiries@dbsbrandfactors.co.uk

Manbat Ltd, Unit 4D, Temple Gate Distribution Centre, Mead Street, Bristol, BS3 4RP Tel: 0117-977 6477 Fax: 0117-977 8481 E-mail: bristol@manbat.co.uk

Manbat Ltd, Unit 1-5 Chancel Place, Store Street, Manchester, M1 2WB Tel: 0161-273 2235 Fax: 0161-273 7368 E-mail: sale@manbat.co.uk

Manbat Ltd, Lancaster Road, Shrewsbury, SY1 3LG Tel: (01743) 460792 E-mail: sales@manbat.co.uk

MOTOCROSS MOTORCYCLES

▶ Pembrokeshire Classics (Motorcycles), Bromleigh, Reynalton, Kilgetty, Dyfed, SA68 0PH Tel: (01834) 891685 Fax: (01834) 891685 E-mail: mail@pembrokeshireclassics.com

MOTOR CAR MANUFRS/ CONCESSIONAIRES/SOLE IMPORTERS

Aston Martin Lagonda Ltd, Tickford Street, Newport Pagnell, Buckinghamshire, MK16 9AN Tel: (01908) 610620 Fax: (01908) 613708 E-mail: enquiry@astonmartin.com

Auto Imaginations, Ranmore Common, Dorking, Surrey, RH5 6SX Tel: (01483) 284114

Bentley Insurance Services Ltd, Pyms Lane, Crewe, CW1 3PL Tel: (01270) 255155 Fax: (01270) 586548 E-mail: recruitment@bentley.co.uk

BMW (GB) Ltd, Ellesfield Avenue, Bracknell, Berkshire, RG12 8TA Tel: (01344) 426565 Fax: (01344) 480203 E-mail: customer.service@bmw.co.uk

Bristol Cars Ltd, 368-370 Kensington High Street, London, W14 8NL Tel: (020) 7603 5554

C 2 P Automotive Ltd, Bradbourne Drive, Tilbrook, Milton Keynes, MK7 8AT Tel: (01908) 362400 Fax: (01908) 362401

Caterham Cars Ltd, 32 Station Avenue, Caterham, Surrey, CR3 6LB Tel: (01883) 333700 Fax: (01883) 333707 E-mail: sales@caterham.co.uk

Citroen UK Ltd, 221 Bath Road, Slough, SL1 4BA Tel: (0870) 6069000 Fax: (01753) 748100

Daihatsu Vehicle Distributors, Ryder Street, West Bromwich, West Midlands, B70 0EJ Tel: 0121-520 5000 Fax: (01304) 206317

Eagle Specialist Vehicles Ltd, 105 Manchester Road, West Houghton, Bolton, BL5 3QH Tel: (01942) 850200 Fax: (01942) 819745 E-mail: eaglespecial@aol.com

Fiat Auto UK, Fiat House, 240 Bath Road, Slough, SL1 4DX Tel: (01753) 511431 Fax: (01753) 511471

Allen Ford, London Road, Coventry, CV3 4AA Tel: (024) 7650 7000 Fax: (024) 7650 4393

Ford Motor Co. Ltd, Central Head Office, Eagle Way, Brentwood, Essex, CM13 3BW Tel: (023) 8058 7300

Ginetta G4 & G12 UK Ltd, 2 The Retreat, West Bergholt, Colchester, CO6 3HN Tel: (01206) 241864 Fax: (01206) 241875

Grinnall Specialist Cars, Westridge House, Jennings Wood Lane, Heightington, Bewdley, Worcestershire, DY12 2YJ Tel: (01299) 822862 Fax: (01299) 822889 E-mail: mark@grinnallcars.com

Group Lotus P.L.C., Potash Lane, Hethel, Norwich, NR14 8EZ Tel: (01953) 608000 Fax: (01953) 608127 E-mail: group@lotuscars.co.uk

Hyundai Motors UK Ltd, St. Johns Court, Easton Street, High Wycombe, Buckinghamshire, HP11 1JX Tel: (01494) 428600 Fax: (01494) 428699

Import My Vehicle Ltd, Currie House, Herbert Walker Avenue, Western Docks, Southampton, SO15 1HJ Tel: (023) 8033 6635 Fax: (023) 8033 8833E-mail: info@importmyvehicle.co.uk

J B A Engineering Ltd, Unit 56b Bradley Hall Trading Estate, Bradley Lane, Standish, Wigan, Lancashire, WN6 0XQ Tel: (01257) 424549 Fax: (01257) 424549

Light Car Co. Ltd, 1 White Horse Business Park, Faringdon Road, Stanford in the Vale, Faringdon, Oxfordshire, SN7 8NP Tel: (01367) 710377 Fax: (01367) 710219

Lynx Motors (International) Ltd, 68 Castleham Road, St. Leonards-on-Sea, East Sussex, TN38 9NU Tel: (01424) 851277 Fax: (01424) 853771 E-mail: enquiries@lynxmotors.co.uk

Mclaren Cars Ltd, Horsell Common, Woking, Surrey, GU21 4YH Tel: (01483) 261500 Fax: (01483) 261502 E-mail: mcl.reception@mclaren.com

Morgan Motor Co. Ltd, Pickersleigh Road, Malvern, Worcestershire, WR14 2LL Tel: (01684) 573104 Fax: (01684) 892295 E-mail: sales@morgan-motor.co.uk

Peugeot Motor Co Plc, P O Box 25, Coventry, CV3 1BD Tel: (024) 7688 6000 Fax: (024) 7688 4001

Pilgrim Cars (U K) Ltd, Unit 14 Mackley Industrial Estate, Henfield Road, Small Dole, Henfield, West Sussex, BN5 9XR Tel: (01273) 493860 Fax: (01273) 494889 E-mail: sales@pilgrimcars.com

Renault UK Ltd, Rivers Office Park, Denham Way, Maple Cross, Rickmansworth, Hertfordshire, WD3 9YS Tel: (01923) 895000 Fax: (01923) 895101 E-mail: enquiries@renault.co.uk

Seward, 400 Poole Road, Branksome, Poole, Dorset, BH12 1DD Tel: (01202) 545700 Fax: (01202) 752934

Specialist Sports Cars Ltd, Old School Yard, Smithfield Street, Llanidloes, Powys, SY18 6EJ Tel: (01686) 413000 Fax: (01686) 413000

Suzuki GB P.L.C., Steinbeck Crescent, Snelshall West, Milton Keynes, MK4 4AE Tel: (01908) 336600 Fax: (01908) 336719

T H White Ltd, Tetbury Road, Cirencester, Gloucestershire, GL7 1US Tel: (01285) 653354 Fax: (01285) 885175

Tiger Racing Ltd, The Echo New Toll Service Station, Wisbech Road, Thorney Toll, Wisbech, Cambridgeshire, PE13 4AX Tel: (01733) 271131 Fax: (01733) 271131

Toyota (G B) plc, Great Burgh, Burgh Heath, Epsom, Surrey, KT18 5UX Tel: (01737) 363633 Fax: (01737) 367700 E-mail: info@toyota.com

Toyota Motor Manufacturing UK Ltd, Deeside Industrial Park, Deeside, Clwyd, CH5 2TW Tel: (01244) 282121 Fax: (01244) 282901

Vauxhall Motors Ltd, North Road, Ellesmere Port, CH65 1AL Tel: 0151-355 3777 Fax: 0151-350 2911

Vauxhall Motors Ltd, Griffin House, Osborne Road, Luton, LU1 3YT Tel: (01582) 721122 Fax: (01582) 427400

MOTOR CAR OR VEHICLE AERIALS

▶ newcar4me.com, Camelot House, Bredbury Park Way, Bredbury Park Industrial Estate, Bredbury, Stockport, Cheshire, SK6 2SN Tel: (0870) 9905583 Fax: (0870) 9905584 E-mail: alex.hamilton@newcar4me.com

Nippon Antenna Europe, Venture House, Bone Lane, Newbury, Berkshire, RG14 5SH Tel: (01635) 30001 Fax: (01635) 35406 E-mail: nae@nippon-antenna.co.uk

MOTOR CAR OR VEHICLE AIR CONDITIONING (AC) EQUIPMENT

A C C Automatic Transmission, 24 The Fairways, New River Trading Estate, Cheshunt, Waltham Cross, Hertfordshire, EN8 0NL Tel: (01992) 639678 Fax: (01992) 634544

Advanced Radiators Ltd, Unit 6 Bells Close Industrial Estate, Newcastle upon Tyne, NE15 6UF Tel: 0191-267 3312 Fax: 0191-264 2707 E-mail: info@adrad.co.uk

Auto Electrical Services, Unit 34-36 Harmill Industrial Estate, Grovebury Road, Leighton Buzzard, Bedfordshire, LU7 4FF Tel: (01525) 372330 Fax: (01525) 851685 E-mail: info@aes2.co.uk

▶ Automotive Parts Distribution Ltd, Unit 2, Ash, Kembrey Park, Swindon, SN2 8UN Tel: (01793) 433933 Fax: (01793) 614965 E-mail: swindon@apd.co.uk

Bergstrom Inc., Hengoed, Mid Glamorgan, CF82 7YH Tel: (01443) 865100 Fax: (01443) 865157

Cardair, 7 Fieldon Court, Lower Gravenhurst, Gravenhurst, Bedford, MK45 4NL Tel: (07836) 378640 Fax: (01525) 861890 E-mail: d.skinner545@btinternet.com

Carrier Sutrak, Unit 6, The IO Centre, Lodge Farm Industrial Estate, Northampton, NN5 7UW Tel: (01604) 581468 Fax: (01604) 758132

Coldlink, 18 Wellesley Road, Tharston, Norwich, NR15 2PD Tel: (01508) 532277 Fax: (01508) 532377

Coolair UK Ltd, Kingsley Road, Lincoln, LN6 3TA Tel: (01522) 682288 Fax: (01522) 681197

Eberspacher UK Ltd, Unit 10 Headlands Business Park, Salisbury Road, Blashford, Ringwood, Hampshire, BH24 3PB Tel: (01425) 480151 Fax: (01425) 480152 E-mail: enquiries@eberspacher.com

Gallay Ltd, Paterson Road, Finedon Road Industrial Estate, Wellingborough, Northamptonshire, NN8 4BZ Tel: (01933) 224801 Fax: (01933) 279902 E-mail: sales@gallay.co.uk

▶ newcar4me.com, Camelot House, Bredbury Park Way, Bredbury Park Industrial Estate, Bredbury, Stockport, Cheshire, SK6 2SN Tel: (0870) 9905583 Fax: (0870) 9905584 E-mail: alex.hamilton@newcar4me.com

NRF (UK) Ltd, Lamport Drive, Heartlands Business Park, Daventry, Northamptonshire, NN11 5YH Tel: (01327) 300242 Fax: (01327) 300225 E-mail: sales@nrf.co.uk

Sanden International Europe Ltd, Hampshire Int Business Park, Crockford Lane, Chineham, Basingstoke, Hampshire, RG24 8WH Tel: (01256) 708888 Fax: (01256) 708883 E-mail: sales@sanden-europe.com

MOTOR CAR OR VEHICLE BADGES

▶ Creative Graphics International, Unit 21, Weston Road Industrial Estate, Stratford-upon-Avon, Warwickshire, CV37 0AH Tel: (01789) 415141 Fax: (01789) 414160

Spar Plastics, 7 Park Trading Estate, Park Road, Hockley, Birmingham, B18 5HB Tel: 0121-551 6220 Fax: 0121-551 6220

W Reeves Badges Ltd, 34-35 Tenby Street, Birmingham, B1 3EE Tel: 0121-236 3731 Fax: 0121-236 3731 E-mail: sales@reevesbadges.co.uk

MOTOR CAR OR VEHICLE CARPETS

▶ David Nightingale, 20 Gastard Lane, Gastard, Corsham, Wiltshire, SN13 9QN Tel: (01249) 701271 Fax: (01249) 701271 E-mail: david.nightingale@coachtrimming.co.uk

▶ Scottish Motor Trimmers, Glenhead Road, Lenzie, Glasgow, Glasgow, G66 5AJ Tel: 07721 309744 Fax: 0141 578 7870 E-mail: p.james37@ntlworld.com

Unique Car Mats UK Ltd, 2 Hassall Road, Skegness, Lincolnshire, PE25 3TB Tel: (01754) 761334 Fax: (01754) 767355 E-mail: info@uniqueproductsuk.com

MOTOR CAR OR VEHICLE FINANCE

▶ Deal Detective, Knavesmire House, 4 Campleshon Road, York, YO23 1PE Tel: (01904) 632615 Fax: (01904) 629825 E-mail: deals@thedealdetectives.com

▶ Godfrey Davis Contract Hire Ltd, Tryford House, High Street, Bushey, WD23 3XX Tel: (020) 8950 0950 Fax: (020) 8950 6145

▶ Hiltingbury Motors Ltd, 72 Hiltingbury Road, Chandlers Ford, Eastleigh, Hampshire, SO53 5SS Tel: (023) 8026 6688 Fax: (023) 8026 6680 E-mail: sales@hiltingburymazda.com

▶ Platinum Motor Group, 16-17 The Causeway, Chippenham, Wiltshire, SN15 3DA Tel: (01249) 654321 Fax: (01249) 462683 E-mail: platinum.chippenham.sales@net.vauxhall.co.uk

▶ Platinum Nissan, Meridian Motor Park, North Bradley, Trowbridge, Wiltshire, BA14 0BJ Tel: (01225) 759510 Fax: (01225) 759501 E-mail: d17115man@uk.nissan.biz

▶ Platinum Nissan Box, St Martins Garage, Bath Road, Box, Corsham, Wiltshire, SN13 8AE Tel: (01225) 744444 Fax: (01225) 744477 E-mail: sales@platinumnissan.co.uk

▶ Platinum Renault, Meridian Business Park, North Bradley, Trowbridge, Wiltshire, BA14 0BJ Tel: (01225) 759525 Fax: (01225) 759526

▶ Platinum Renault Bath, Lower Bristol Road, Bath, BA2 3DN Tel: (01225) 485410 Fax: (01225) 338653

▶ Platinum Renault Chippenham, London Road, Chippenham, Wiltshire, SN15 3BB Tel: (01249) 651131 Fax: (01249) 658813

▶ Platinum Skoda, Lower Bristol Road, Bath, BA2 3DR Tel: (01225) 324910 Fax: (01225) 324919 E-mail: enquiries@platinumskoda.co.uk

▶ Platinum Toyota, Meridian Motor Park, North Bradley, Trowbridge, Wiltshire, BA14 0BJ Tel: (01225) 759560 Fax: (01225) 759551

▶ Platinum Toyota Bath, Lower Bristol Road, Bath, BA2 3DN Tel: (01225) 486200 Fax: (01225) 420815 E-mail: im-pb@platinum.toyota.co.uk

▶ Platinum Vauxhall, 8 Meridian Business Park, North Bradley, Trowbridge, Wiltshire, BA14 0BJ Tel: (01225) 759585 Fax: (01225) 759576

▶ Platinum Vauxhall Frome, Manor Road, Marston Trading Estate, Warminster, Wiltshire, BA12 6HR Tel: (01373) 463351 Fax: (01373) 462001 E-mail: platinum.frome.sales@net.vauxhall.co.uk

MOTOR CAR OR VEHICLE FINANCE

– continued

▶ Renrod Financial Solutions, 36 Victoria Road, Warminster, Wiltshire, BA12 8HF Tel: (0800) 3281188 Fax: (01985) 211857 E-mail: sales@platinumfinancialsolutions.co.uk

▶ Southampton Mazda, Bursledon Road, Southampton, SO19 7LW Tel: (023) 8042 2777 Fax: (023) 8044 3320 E-mail: sales@southamptonmazda.co.uk

▶ Wellsway BMW, Lower Bristol Road, Bath, BA2 3DR Tel: (01225) 448145 Fax: (01225) 420794

▶ Wellsway Mini, Lower Bristol Road, Bath, BA2 3DR Tel: (01225) 448555 Fax: (01225) 420794 E-mail: sales@wellswaymini.co.uk

MOTOR CAR OR VEHICLE SEAT COVERS

▶ C E Moore Ltd, 37 Disraeli Road, London, NW10 7AX Tel: (020) 8961 2225 Fax: (020) 8963 0122

Scot Seats Direct, Gainford Business Centre, Fenwick, Kilmarnock, Ayrshire, KA3 6AR Tel: (01560) 600100 Fax: (01560) 600100 E-mail: gainford@lineone.net

▶ SmartDent Paintless Dent Removal Training Ltd, Unit 5, Ashwyn Business Centre, Marchants Way, Sheddingdean Industrial Estate, Burgess Hill, West Sussex, RH15 8QY Tel: (01444) 257342 Fax: (01444) 257673 E-mail: colm@smartwise.com

Trim Technology & Services Ltd, 9-14 Colliery Lane, Exhall, Coventry, CV7 9NW Tel: (024) 7664 6000 Fax: (024) 7664 6001 E-mail: sales@trim-technology.com

MOTOR CAR OR VEHICLE SEATS

Cobra Seats Ltd, Units D1-D2 Halesfield 23, Telford, Shropshire, TF7 4NY Tel: (01952) 684020 Fax: (01952) 581777 E-mail: enquiries@cobraseats.com

The Comfy Seat Co., George Baylis Road, Berry Hill Industrial Estate, Droitwich, Worcestershire, WR9 9RB Tel: (01905) 795955 Fax: (01905) 794683 E-mail: sales@comfyseating.co.uk

Denormo Technics Ltd, 8 Teal Business Pk, Dudwell Bridge, Hinckley, Leics, LE10 3BZ Tel: (01455) 250153 Fax: (01455) 617061

Elap Engineering Ltd, Fort Street, Accrington, Lancashire, BB5 1QG Tel: (01254) 871599 Fax: (01254) 389992 E-mail: mail@elap.co.uk

Faurecina Midlands Ltd, PO Box 200, Coventry, CV3 1LU Tel: (024) 7663 5533 Fax: (024) 7688 5075

Intier Automotive Seating Ltd, Newmanleys Road, New Eastwood, Nottingham, NG16 3JG Tel: (01773) 716131 Fax: (01773) 712587

Johnson Control, Cherry Blossom Way, Sunderland, SR5 3TW Tel: 0191-415 6000 Fax: 0191-415 3857 E-mail: sales@ikedahoover.com

Kab Seating Ltd, Stone Circle Road Round Spinney Indust Estate, Round Spinney Industrial Estat, Northampton, NN3 8RF Tel: (01604) 790500 Fax: (01604) 790155 E-mail: marketing@kabseating.com

Keiper UK Ltd, Woodgate Business Park, Clapgate Lane, Birmingham, B32 3BZ Tel: 0121-423 2828 Fax: 0121-423 2561

Motor Drive Seats, Ebury Street, Radcliffe, Manchester, M26 4BL Tel: 0161-724 5176 Fax: 0161-725 9265 E-mail: sales@motordrive.com

Restall Bros Ltd, Colliery Road, West Bromwich, West Midlands, B71 4JT Tel: 0121-500 1300 Fax: 0121-500 1301 E-mail: contact@restallgroup.co.uk

Scot Seats Direct, Gainford Business Centre, Fenwick, Kilmarnock, Ayrshire, KA3 6AR Tel: (01560) 600100 Fax: (01560) 600100 E-mail: gainford@lineone.net

▶ Star Seating Ltd, 5 Two Woods Trading Estate, Talbots Lane, Brierley Hill, West Midlands, DY5 2YX Tel: (01384) 485672 Fax: (01384) 485673 E-mail: sales@starseating.com

T E K Seating Ltd, 7 Spa Industrial Park, Longfield Road, Tunbridge Wells, Kent, TN2 3EN Tel: (01892) 515028 Fax: (01892) 529751 E-mail: sales@tekseating.co.uk

Tees Tarpaulins Ltd, Skinner Street, Stockton-on-Tees, Cleveland, TS18 1EG Tel: (01642) 607772 Fax: (01642) 607633

MOTOR CAR OR VEHICLE WHEELS

Components Automotive (73) Ltd, 4-6 Wulfrun Industrial Estate, Stafford Road, Wolverhampton, WV10 6HG Tel: (01902) 311499 Fax: (01902) 715213 E-mail: sales@comp.co.uk

K N Wheels Ltd, Holyhead Road, Ketley, Telford, Shropshire, TF1 5DS Tel: (01952) 613757 Fax: (01952) 613757 E-mail: knwheels@bt.co.uk

UK Racing Castings, Unit 1-2 Argent Business Park, Argent Road, Queenborough, Kent, ME11 5JP Tel: (01795) 585454 Fax: (01795) 585488 E-mail: sales@uk-racing-castings.co.uk

MOTOR CAR POLISHING

▶ Pro-Shine Valeting, 2 Myers Way, Charlton, Banbury, Oxfordshire, OX17 3DY Tel: (07944) 035810 E-mail: enquiries@Pro-ShineValeting.com

MOTOR CAR STORAGE

▶ Archive Attic Ltd, The Farm Office, Grooms Lane, Creaton, Northampton, NN6 8NN Tel: (01604) 505715 E-mail: sales@archiveattic.co.uk

MOTOR CAR SUSPENSION SYSTEMS

Firestone Industrial Products Inc, Church Street, Staines, Middlesex, TW18 4EP Tel: (01784) 462326 Fax: (01784) 462327 E-mail: sales@firestoneindustrial.com

Granning Engineering Ltd, 37 Melford Court, Hardwick Grange, Woolston, Warrington, WA1 4RZ Tel: (01925) 810400 Fax: (01925) 817153 E-mail: sales@grannings.com

MOTOR CAR TRANSPORTER SPARE PARTS

▶ E V Automotive Ltd, Padstow Road, Coventry, CV4 9XB Tel: (024) 7649 6666 Fax: (024) 7649 6677 E-mail: info@evukcarpanels.co.uk

MOTOR CAR WASHING

▶ Pro-Shine Valeting, 2 Myers Way, Charlton, Banbury, Oxfordshire, OX17 3DY Tel: (07944) 035810 E-mail: enquiries@Pro-ShineValeting.com

MOTOR CARS, USED

▶ John Grose Group Ltd, Ipswich Road, Woodbridge, Suffolk, IP12 4BX Tel: (01394) 383333 Fax: (01394) 384501

MOTOR CHASSIS

A B T Products Ltd, Ashburton Industrial Estate, Ross-on-Wye, Herefordshire, HR9 7BW Tel: (01989) 563656 Fax: (01989) 566824 E-mail: abtproducts@clara.net

Chassis Developments Ltd, Grovebury Road, Leighton Buzzard, Bedfordshire, LU7 4SL Tel: (01525) 374151 Fax: (01525) 370127 E-mail: david.brain@chasisdevelopments.co.uk

Westfield Sports Cars Ltd, 1 Gibbons Industrial Park, Dudley Road, Kingswinford, West Midlands, DY6 8XF Tel: (01384) 400077 Fax: (01384) 288781 E-mail: info@westfield-sportscars.co.uk

MOTOR COMPONENTS

Automotive Distributors Ltd, Unit 9 Wheelbarrow Park Estate, Pattenden Lane, Marden, Tonbridge, Kent, TN12 9QJ Tel: (01622) 833007 Fax: (01622) 833001 E-mail: info@blueprint-adl.co.uk

D Trippier, The Mill, Mill Lane, Bury, Lancashire, BL8 1TB Tel: 0161-764 4050 Fax: 0161-764 5050

Evans Halshaw Ltd, Estate Garage, Treforest Industrial Estate, Pontypridd, Mid Glamorgan, CF37 5YA Tel: (01443) 842376 Fax: (01443) 842687 E-mail: justin.brown@pendragon.uk.com

Peugeot Motor Co. P.L.C., Torrington Avenue, Tile Hill, Coventry, CV4 0UX Tel: (024) 7688 3000 Fax: (024) 7688 3551

MOTOR COMPUTER SYSTEMS

▶ Garrards Transport, 7 Argonaut Park, Galleymead Road, Colnbrook, Slough, SL3 0EN Tel: (01753) 685006 Fax: (01753) 680109E-mail: office@garrardstransport.co.uk

MAM Software Ltd, 1 Station Road, Deepcar, Sheffield, S36 2SQ Tel: (0870) 7667012 Fax: (0870) 7667023

Zytek Systems Ltd, Fradley Distribution Park, Wood End Lane, Fradley, Lichfield, Staffordshire, WS13 8NE Tel: (01543) 412789

MOTOR CONTROL CENTRE ENCLOSURES

Cheltenham Controls, 183 Westgate Street, Gloucester, GL1 2RN Tel: (01452) 503390 Fax: (01452) 503630 E-mail: info.cheltcontrols@dis-ltd.co.uk

Halton Panelcraft Ltd, 2 Gavin Road, Widnes, Cheshire, WA8 8RE Tel: 0151-424 0022 Fax: 0151-424 2058 E-mail: panelcraft@lineone.net

MOTOR CONTROL CENTRES

Blackburn Starling & Co. Ltd, Queens Drive, Nottingham, NG2 3AY Tel: 0115-986 6331 Fax: 0115-986 0301 E-mail: sales@blackburn-starling.co.uk

Control & Power Engineering Ltd, Fox Covert Lane, Misterton, Doncaster, South Yorkshire, DN10 4ER Tel: (01427) 891256 Fax: (01427) 891307 E-mail: capeuk@aol.com

Huggett Electrical Ltd, Twerton Mill, Lower Bristol Road, Bath, BA2 1EW Tel: (01225) 426271 Fax: (01225) 448154 E-mail: mail@huggettelectrical.co.uk

Kane Engineering Ltd, Glenford Road, Newtownards, County Down, BT23 4AU Tel: (028) 9181 4465 Fax: (028) 9181 8900 E-mail: info@kane-engineering.co.uk

▶ M H Automation International Ltd, 8 Swift Business Centre East Moors Industrial Estate, Keen Road, Cardiff, CF24 5JR Tel: (029) 2025 3300 Fax: (029) 2025 3303 E-mail: mail@mhai.co.uk

Pandelco Ltd, Canal Street, Burton-on-Trent, Staffordshire, DE14 3TB Tel: (01283) 542738 Fax: (01283) 511774 E-mail: sales@pandelco.co.uk

MOTOR CONTROL GEAR MANUFRS

Dold Industries, 11 Hamberts Road, Blackall Industrial Estate, South Woodham Ferrers, Chelmsford, CM3 5UW Tel: (01245) 324432 Fax: (01245) 325570 E-mail: admin@dold.co.uk

G E Power Controls Ltd, East Lancashire Road, Liverpool, L10 5HB Tel: 0151-524 1122 Fax: 0151-523 7007 E-mail: gepcuk.sales@gepc.ge.com

Gibbons Drive Systems Ltd, Woodrolfe Road, Tollesbury, Maldon, Essex, CM9 8RY Tel: (01621) 868138 Fax: (01621) 868188 E-mail: sales@gibbonsdrives.co.uk

MOTOR CONTROL GEAR PANELS

Switchgear International Ltd, Farthing Road Industrial Estate, Ipswich, IP1 5AP Tel: (01473) 240280 Fax: (01473) 242929 E-mail: sales@switchgearinternational.co.uk

MOTOR CONTROL SENSORS

The Grant Group Ltd, 47A Linfield Industrial Estate, Belfast, BT12 5LA Tel: (028) 9032 3329 Fax: (028) 9032 3218 E-mail: info@thegrantgroup.com

MOTOR ENGINE COOLING FANS

Pacet Manufacturing Ltd, Wyebridge, Cores End Road, Bourne End, Buckinghamshire, SL8 5HH Tel: (01628) 526754 Fax: (01628) 810080 E-mail: enquiries@pacet.co.uk

MOTOR ENGINE VALVES

G & S Valves Ltd, Catteshall Lane, Godalming, Surrey, GU7 1JS Tel: (01483) 415444 Fax: (01483) 426891 E-mail: gsvalves@aol.com

MOTOR FINANCE

▶ New Car Discount.com Ltd, Unit 7A, Kayley Industrial Estate, Richmond Street, Ashton-under-Lyne, Lancashire, OL7 0AU Tel: (08703) 500144 Fax: (08703) 500244 E-mail: sales@new-car-discount.com

The Paragon Group Of Companies plc, St Catherine S Court, Herbert Road, Solihull, West Midlands, B91 3QE Tel: 0121-712 2505 Fax: 0121-712 2555 E-mail: marketing@paragon-group.co.uk

▶ Renrod Financial Solutions, 36 Victoria Road, Warminster, Wiltshire, BA12 8HF Tel: (0800) 3281188 Fax: (01985) 211857 E-mail: sales@platinumfinancialsolutions.co.uk

Sequent Ltd, Kushi Koti, Court Road, Maidenhead, Berkshire, SL6 8LQ Tel: (01628) 628190 Fax: (01628) 623336 E-mail: seq1989@aol.com

MOTOR INDUSTRY RUBBER PRODUCTS

Avon Rubber P.L.C., European Headquarters, Hampton Park West, Melksham, Wiltshire, SN12 6NB Tel: (01225) 896800 Fax: (01225) 896302 E-mail: enquiries@avon-rubber.com

D E C Rubber Co. Ltd, Unit 20, Fordhouse Road Industrial Estate, Fordhouses, Wolverhampton, WV10 9XD Tel: (01902) 780046 Fax: (01902) 780076

Essential Equipment Ltd, Unit 24 Planetary Industrial Estate, Planetary Road, Willenhall, West Midlands, WV13 3XA Tel: (01902) 725055 Fax: (01902) 862684 E-mail: enquiries@essentialequipment.co.uk

MOTOR OIL MEASURES

Hartle I G E Ltd, Unit 5, Ilford Trading Estate, Paycocke Road, Basildon, Essex, SS14 3DR Tel: (01268) 520496 Fax: (01268) 285477 E-mail: sales@hartleige.com

MOTOR PROTECTION RELAYS

Megacon Controls Ltd, 21 Oldends Industrial Estate, Oldends, Stonehouse, Gloucestershire, GL10 3RQ Tel: (01453) 824471 Fax: (01453) 825234 E-mail: sales@megacon.co.uk

P & B Engineering Ltd, Bell Vue Works, Boundary St, Manchester, M12 5NG Tel: 0161-230 6363 Fax: 0161-230 6464 E-mail: mail@pbeng.co.uk

MOTOR SCRAPERS

ASM Metal Recycling Ltd, Griffin Lane, Aylesbury, Buckinghamshire, HP19 8BB Tel: (01296) 337711 Fax: (01296) 337751 E-mail: asm@asm-recycling.co.uk

MOTOR STARTERS

▶ Starter Mart, 994 Astley Street, Globe Square, Dukinfield, Cheshire, SK16 4QS Tel: (0870) 8034101 Fax: 0161-343 5755 E-mail: enquires@startermart.co.uk

MOTOR VEHICLE ACCESSORIES/COMPONENTS/ SPARE PARTS IMPORT/EXPORT MERCHANTS OR AGENTS

▶ Ace Motors, Victoria Mill, Alliance Street, Accrington, Lancashire, BB5 2RT Tel: (01254) 232662 E-mail: info@acemotorsbaxenden.co.uk

Alphalube Lubricant Distributors, Lincoln Road, Newark, Nottinghamshire, NG24 2DR Tel: (01636) 673705 Fax: (01636) 686660 E-mail: allwoodssales@lineone.net

Automotive Distributors Ltd, Unit 9 Wheelbarrow Park Estate, Pattenden Lane, Marden, Tonbridge, Kent, TN12 9QJ Tel: (01622) 833007 Fax: (01622) 833001 E-mail: info@blueprint-adl.co.uk

Automotive Technology Ltd, 3 Morton Street, Leamington Spa, Warwickshire, CV32 5SY Tel: (01926) 882201 Fax: (01926) 420934 E-mail: sidaway@atl-uk.com

Border Holdings UK Ltd, The Grove, Craven Arms, Shropshire, SY7 8DA Tel: (01588) 672711 Fax: (01588) 672660 E-mail: info@britparc.co.uk

Borgwarner Trustees Ltd, Borg Warner Ltd, Kenfig Industrial Estate, Margam, Port Talbot, West Glamorgan, SA13 2PG Tel: (01656) 741001 Fax: (01656) 745811

Capitan (Europe) Ltd, Capitan House, 1C Church Road, Croydon, CR0 1SG Tel: (020) 8688 2617 Fax: (020) 8688 2821 E-mail: sales@capitan.co.uk

Classic, Hildersley, Ross-on-Wye, Herefordshire, HR9 7NW Tel: (01989) 769191 Fax: (01989) 769191

Colchester Motor Factors, 3a Hawkins Road, Colchester, CO2 8JY Tel: (01206) 799503 Fax: (01206) 790915

Cranes Of Hollesley Ltd, The Street, Hollesley, Woodbridge, Suffolk, IP12 3QU Tel: (01394) 411687 Fax: (01394) 410238 E-mail: enquiries@cranesford.co.uk

D & J Export Ltd, 33 Valkyrie Road, Westcliff-on-Sea, Essex, SS0 8BY Tel: (01702) 348340 Fax: (01702) 331080 E-mail: don@d-jexports.com

English Ford, 1 Yarrow Road, Poole, Dorset, BH12 4QA Tel: (01202) 715577 Fax: (01202) 715973 E-mail: brettsanstleben@evanshalshaw.com

European Autoparts Ltd, 5 Kimber Road, London, SW18 4NR Tel: (020) 8640 9335 Fax: (020) 8877 0359

F & J Exports Ltd, Unit 14, Thornleigh Trading Estate, Blowers Green, Dudley, West Midlands, DY2 8UB Tel: (01384) 213186 Fax: (01384) 456990

Frenco Ltd, 24 Worcester Street, Kidderminster, Worcestershire, DY10 1ED Tel: (01562) 69442 Fax: (01562) 820410

German Swedish & French, 8 Boss Hall Road, Ipswich, IP1 5BN Tel: (01473) 748166 Fax: (01473) 463814 E-mail: ipswich@gsfcarparts.com

GT Exhaust Ni Ltd, Carran Business Park, Enniskillen, County Fermanagh, BT74 4RZ Tel: (028) 6632 2282 Fax: (028) 6632 3391 E-mail: sales@gtexhausts.co.uk

Kris Motors, Withy Road, Ladymore, Bilston, West Midlands, WV14 0RX Tel: (01902) 492995 Fax: (01902) 494626

MOTOR VEHICLE ACCESSORIES/ COMPONENTS/SPARE PARTS IMPORT/EXPORT MERCHANTS OR AGENTS – *continued*

M & F Components, Marlbrough Road, Accrington. Lancashire, BB5 5BE Tel: (01254) 301121 Fax: (01254) 391416 E-mail: ucount@mafcobell.co.uk

Mackie Automotive Systems UK Ltd, North Road, Ellesmere Port, CH65 1BL Tel: 0151-356 4004 Fax: 0151 356 3281 E-mail: sales@mackieautomotive.com

Macpower Ltd, 167 Cheviot Gardens, London, NW2 1PY Tel: (020) 8458 2793 Fax: (020) 8458 8484

Majorsell International Ltd, Unit G Springhill Business Park, 111 Steward Street, Birmingham, B18 7AF Tel: 0121-455 0200 Fax: 0121-455 0272 E-mail: sales@majorsell.co.uk

Mercedes Benz (UK) Ltd, Tongwell, Delaware Drive, Milton Keynes, MK15 8BA Tel: (01908) 245000

▶ P T Co., Greensleeves, Green Bottom, Wimborne, Dorset, BH21 2LW Tel: (01202) 639243 Fax: (01202) 639243 E-mail: sales@ptcompany.co.uk

▶ Panaf Car Accessories, 174 Enterprise Court, Eastways, Witham, Essex, CM8 3YS Tel: (01376) 511550 Fax: (01376) 515131 E-mail: panaf@btclick.com

Power Steering Specialists, Unit 1-2 Brocklebank Industrial Estate, Brocklebank Road, London, SE7 7SX Tel: (020) 8858 0168 Fax: (020) 8858 7595E-mail: sales@powersteering.co.uk

Reliant Parts World Ltd, Unit C, Orbital Way, Cannock, Staffordshire, WS11 8XW Tel: (01543) 431941 Fax: (01543) 431966 E-mail: info@reliant-motors.co.uk

XRN Engineering Ltd, Unit 2-3, A V S Trading Park, Chapel Lane, Milford, Godalming, Surrey, GU8 5HE Tel: (01483) 861777 Fax: (01483) 425841 E-mail: xrn.eng@btinternet.com

MOTOR VEHICLE ACCESSORIES/COMPONENTS/ SPARE PARTS WHOLESALE DISTRIBUTORS/FACTORS/ AGENTS

A B M Motor Factors Ltd, 65 Plumstead High Street, London, SE18 1SB Tel: (020) 8316 0400 Fax: (020) 8317 2621 E-mail: sales@abmmotorspares.co.uk

A F Smith & Son, Fengate, Peterborough, PE1 5XB Tel: (01733) 319595 Fax: (01733) 898370

Aashish Motors, 374 High Road, London, N17 9HY Tel: (020) 8808 2407 Fax: (020) 8885 3127

Adroit Accessories Ltd, Henry Street, Walsall, WS2 9XU Tel: (01922) 632839 Fax: (01922) 629154 E-mail: sales@adroit-accessories.co.uk

▶ Ajay Autoparts, 3 St. Johns Court Foster Road, Ashford Business Park, Sevington, Ashford, Kent, TN24 0SJ Tel: (01233) 501000 Fax: (01233) 501111

Aldon Automotive Ltd, Breener Industrial Estate, Station Drive, Brierley Hill, West Midlands, DY5 3JZ Tel: (01384) 572553 Fax: (01384) 480418 E-mail: alden@yesit.co.uk

Allmakes Ltd, 176 Milton Park, Milton, Abingdon, Oxfordshire, OX14 4SW Tel: (01235) 821122 Fax: (01235) 821133 E-mail: allmakes@allmakes.co.uk

Anglia Battery & Filter Co., 834 London Road, Leigh-on-Sea, Essex, SS9 3NH Tel: (01702) 470262 Fax: (01702) 470335 E-mail: sales@angliabattery.co.uk

Anthony & Associates, 2 Thorn Road, Poole, Dorset, BH17 9AX Tel: (01202) 380500 Fax: (01202) 380510

Apd Ltd, 69-71 Lower Bristol Road, Bath, BA2 3BE Tel: (01225) 424221 Fax: (01225) 444357 E-mail: orders@apd.co.uk

Apec Ltd, Armstrong Way, Bristol, BS37 5NG Tel: (01454) 324644 Fax: (01454) 311414 E-mail: info@apecbraking.co.uk

▶ Auto Craft Engineering, Unit 1 St. Davids Industrial Estate, Pengam, Blackwood, Gwent, NP12 3SW Tel: (01443) 831748 Fax: (01443) 831758 E-mail: info@autocraftengineering.co.uk

Auto Europe Parts Ltd, Unit 11 Betchworth Works, Ifield Road, Charlwood, Horley, Surrey, RH6 0DX Tel: (01293) 863777 Fax: (01293) 863888 E-mail: info@autoeurope.co.uk

Auto Spares & Salvage, Station House, Station Road, Raunds, Wellingborough, Northamptonshire, NN9 6BX Tel: (01933) 626166 Fax: (01933) 625339 E-mail: admin@autospares-salvage.com

Automotive Industrial Partnerships Ltd, 52 Heming Road, Redditch, Worcestershire, B98 0EA Tel: (01527) 504200 Fax: (01527) 516195 E-mail: sales@aip.demon.co.uk

Autonational Ltd, Troy Industrial Estate, Jill Lane, Sambourne, Redditch, Worcestershire, B96 6ES Tel: (01527) 892003 Fax: (01527) 893310 E-mail: autonational@aol.com

Autoquip Ltd, 2-4 Church Rd, Lawrence Hill, Bristol, BS5 9JA Tel: 0117-955 6789 Fax: 0117-954 1925 E-mail: autoquip@aol.com

Autoquip Factors Ltd, 2-3 Woodland Close, Torquay, TQ2 7BD Tel: (01803) 612260 Fax: (01803) 618119

B J Ashpole Ltd, Southmill Road, Bishop's Stortford, Hertfordshire, CM23 3DJ Tel: (01279) 653211 Fax: (01279) 651694

Beadles Group Ltd, 370 Princes Road, Dartford, DA1 1LN Tel: (01322) 222201 Fax: (01322) 289896 E-mail: info@beadles-dartford.volkswagen.co.uk

Bedford Battery Co. Ltd, 1-3 & 2-12 Wellington Street, Bedford, MK40 2HZ Tel: (01234) 340661 Fax: (01234) 217205

Bennett & Sons, Mowlem Trading Estate, Leeside Road, London, N17 0QJ Tel: (020) 8365 0033 Fax: (020) 8836 5161 E-mail: tottenham@bennetts.com

Bennett's, Chapel Pond Hill, Bury St. Edmunds, Suffolk, IP32 7HT Tel: (01284) 766166 Fax: (01284) 769634 E-mail: burystedmunds@bennetts.com

Biggleswade Auto Supplies Ltd, 132 Shortmead Street, Biggleswade, Bedfordshire, SG18 0BH Tel: (01767) 316666 Fax: (01767) 318362 E-mail: biggsautosupplies@ntlworld.com

▶ Bill Carver Ltd, Unit 2 Turner Industrial Estate, Turner Street, Denton, Manchester, M34 3EG Tel: 0161-320 3400 Fax: 0161-320 3433

▶ Black Diamond Ltd, Units 2-7 Guardian St Industrial Estate, Guardian Street, Warrington, WA5 1SJ Tel: (01925) 416619 Fax: (01925) 230472

Border Holdings UK Ltd, The Grove, Craven Arms, Shropshire, SY7 8DA Tel: (01588) 672711 Fax: (01588) 672660 E-mail: info@britparc.co.uk

Borough Motor Services Ltd, 226 Cleveland Street, Birkenhead, Merseyside, CH41 3QJ Tel: 0151-647 8019 Fax: 0151-650 0666 E-mail: bmsltd@btinternet.com

Brake Direct Ltd, PO Box 11, Bordon, Hampshire, GU35 9YR Tel: (01420) 474834 Fax: (01420) 474834

Bransby Components, Unit 7, Minafon Yard, Betws Yn Rhos, Abergele, Clwyd, LL22 8AW Tel: 01492 680682 Fax: 01492 680286

▶ Brink (UK) Ltd, Unit 7 Centrovell Industrial E, Caldwell Road, Nuneaton, Warwickshire, CV11 4NG Tel: (024) 7635 2353

BRT Bearings Ltd, 9 Common Bank Industrial Estate, Ackhurst Road, Chorley, Lancashire, PR7 1NH Tel: (01257) 264266 Fax: (01257) 274698

C & C Auto Services Ltd, 13 Kingston Road, London, SW19 1JX Tel: (020) 8540 8871 Fax: (020) 8542 8903

C D Bramall Plc, Etherstone Avenue, Newcastle upon Tyne, NE7 7LQ Tel: 0191-266 3311 Fax: 0191-215 0762 E-mail: newcastlehyundaisales@evanshalshaw.com

C H B Engineering, Mantra House, South Street, Keighley, West Yorkshire, BD21 1SX Tel: (01535) 607741 Fax: (01535) 690539

C T P Wipac Ltd, London Road, Buckingham, MK18 1BH Tel: (01280) 822800 Fax: (01280) 822802 E-mail: sales@wipac.com

Caerbont Automotive Instruments Ltd, Caerbont, Abercrave, Swansea, SA9 1SH Tel: (01639) 732200 Fax: (01639) 732201

Camberley Auto Factors Ltd, Units 6-7, 196 Old Shoreham Road, Hove, East Sussex, BN3 3TW Tel: (01273) 775488 Fax: (01273) 822821 E-mail: sales@camberleyautofactors.co.uk

Capitan (Europe) Ltd, Capitan House, 1C Church Road, Croydon, CR0 1SG Tel: (020) 8688 2617 Fax: (020) 8688 2821 E-mail: sales@capitan.co.uk

▶ Car & Commercial Components, Freckleton St, Blackburn, BB2 2AL Tel: (01254) 670121

Car Spares Cheshunt Ltd, Delamare Road, Cheshunt, Waltham Cross, Hertfordshire, EN8 9AP Tel: (01992) 639844 Fax: (01992) 623871 E-mail: sales@carspares.co.uk

Car Spares (Stony Stratford), 98 High Street, Stony Stratford, Milton Keynes, MK11 1AH Tel: (01908) 564333 Fax: (01908) 568386

Carlex Ltd, Unit 19 Rivington Court, Hardwick Grange, Woolston, Warrington, WA1 4RT Tel: (01925) 811073 Fax: (01925) 817235 E-mail: sales@carlex.co.uk

▶ Carparts, 3 Sentry Lane, Newtownabbey, County Antrim, BT36 4XU Tel: (028) 9084 8218 Fax: (028) 9083 5490 E-mail: admin@carpartsuk-ire.com

Central Car Paints, 93 Crafton St East, Leicester, LE1 2DG Tel: 0116-262 9727 E-mail: info@centralcarparts.co.uk

Cobra Seats Ltd, Units D1-D2 Halesfield 23, Telford, Shropshire, TF7 4NY Tel: (01952) 684020 Fax: (01952) 581772 E-mail: enquiries@cobraseats.com

Continental Teves UK Ltd, Waun-Y-Pound Industrial Estate, Ebbw Vale, Gwent, NP23 6PL Tel: (01495) 350350 Fax: (01495) 350351

Corbeau Seats Ltd, 17 Wainwright Close, St. Leonards-on-Sea, East Sussex, TN38 9PP Tel: (01424) 854499 Fax: (01424) 854488 E-mail: mat@corbeau'seats.co.uk

Cosmos Motor Products Ltd, Unit 3A Neptune Industrial Estate, Neptune Road, Harrow, Middlesex, HA1 4HX Tel: (020) 8863 8666 Fax: (020) 8427 3689 E-mail: salescomopro@cs.com

D J Lockhart Ltd, Ballycastle Road, Coleraine, County Londonderry, BT52 2DY Tel: (028) 7035 1121 Fax: (028) 7035 1124

David Huggett Commercial Motor Factors Ltd, D Brittania Road, Waltham Cross, Hertfordshire, EN8 7NH Tel: (01992) 762519 Fax: (01992) 718472

Dick Lovett Bristol Ltd, Laurel Court, Cribbs Causeway, Bristol, BS10 7TU Tel: 0117-905 0000 Fax: 0117-905 0090

Dingbro Ltd, 1 Merchant Place, Mitchelston Industrial Estate, Kirkcaldy, Fife, KY1 3NJ Tel: (01592) 652400 Fax: (01592) 653989

Dinnages Car Dealers, Brougham Road, Worthing, West Sussex, BN11 2NR Tel: (01903) 820505 Fax: (01903) 212523 E-mail: marketing@dinnages.co.uk

DLS UK, Water Lane, Wirksworth, Matlock, Derbyshire, DE4 4AA Tel: (01629) 822185 Fax: (01629) 825683 E-mail: sales@dls-uk.co.uk

Dodgsons Of Preston Ltd, 143-155 Fylde Road, Preston, PR1 2XP Tel: (01772) 258353 Fax: (01772) 555937

▶ Don Hoods Trimming Co. Ltd, 2a Hampton Road, Erdington, Birmingham, B23 7JJ Tel: 0121-373 1313 Fax: 0121-377 7631 E-mail: sales@donhoods.com

Dunstonian Holdings Ltd, 28a Station Square, Petts Wood, Orpington, Kent, BR5 1LS Tel: (01689) 832545 Fax: (01689) 878258 E-mail: enquiries@dunstonian.co.uk

E B C Brakes, EBC Building, Countess Road, Northampton, NN5 7EA Tel: (01604) 583344 Fax: (01604) 583744 E-mail: info@ebcbrackesuk.com

E U (Colchester) Ltd, Unit B1 Cowdray Centre, Cowdray Avenue, Colchester, CO1 1BL Tel: (01206) 548582 Fax: (01206) 579584

Elmet Fascia Design Ltd, Unit 3 Blackburn Industrial Estate, Enterprise Way, Sherburn In Elmet, Leeds, LS25 6NF Tel: (01977) 681441 Fax: (01977) 681428

English Ford, 1 Yarrow Road, Poole, Dorset, BH12 4QA Tel: (01202) 715577 Fax: (01202) 715973 E-mail: brettsanstleben@evanshalshaw.com

European Autoparts Ltd, 5 Kimber Road, London, SW18 4NR Tel: (020) 8640 9335 Fax: (020) 8877 0359

Evans Halshaw Motors Ltd, The Vauxhall Centre, Crownhill, Milton Keynes, MK8 0AE Tel: (01908) 568601 Fax: (01908) 261020 E-mail: vauxhallcentre@crownhillgm.demon.co.uk

Evolution Automotive Components Ltd, 17 Lythalls Lane, Coventry, CV6 6FN Tel: (024) 7663 7337 Fax: (024) 7663 7351 E-mail: sales@eacparts.com

F A I Automotive plc, Chiltern Trading Estate, Grovebury Road, Leighton Buzzard, Bedfordshire, LU7 4TU Tel: (0870) 8391800 Fax: (0870) 8391804 E-mail: sales@faiauto.com

F G Barnes, Cuxton Road, Parkwood Industrial Estate, Maidstone, Kent, ME15 9YF Tel: (01622) 755531 Fax: (01622) 692216 E-mail: sales@fgbarnes.co.uk

F & J Exports Ltd, Unit 14, Thornleigh Trading Estate, Blowers Green, Dudley, West Midlands, DY2 8UB Tel: (01384) 213186 Fax: (01384) 456990

Fast Lane Auto Ltd, Callywith Gate Industrial Estate, Launceston Road, Bodmin, Cornwall, PL31 2RQ Tel: (01208) 264546 Fax: (01208) 264547 E-mail: sales@fastlaneauto.co.uk

Fischer Group Of Companies, Whiteley Road, Hithercroft Industrial Estate, Wallingford, Oxfordshire, OX10 9AT Tel: (01491) 827919 Fax: (01491) 827953 E-mail: sales@fischer.co.uk

▶ Ford Motor Co. Ltd, Royal Oak Way South, Royal Oak Industrial Estate, Daventry, Northamptonshire, NN11 8NT Tel: (01327) 305300

Frenco Ltd, 24 Worcester Street, Kidderminster, Worcestershire, DY10 1ED Tel: (01562) 69442 Fax: (01562) 820410

Friction Linings Southampton Ltd, Unit 2 Easton La Business Park, Easton Lane, Winchester, Hampshire, SO23 7RQ Tel: (01962) 867666 E-mail: info@frictionlinings.co.uk

Gee & Garnham Ltd, 1-6 Crescent Mews, London, N22 7GG Tel: (020) 8888 4982 Fax: (020) 8881 1353 E-mail: gg@geeandgarnham.com

GKN Driveline, 5 Kingsbury Business Park, Kingsbury Road, Minworth, Sutton Coldfield, West Midlands, B76 9DL Tel: 0121-313 1661 Fax: 0121-313 2074 E-mail: ids.Minworth@gkndriveline.com

▶ Gloucester Road Gear Boxes, Barton Manor, Midland Road, Bristol, BS2 0RL Tel: 0117-954 1424 Fax: 0117-941 1596

▶ Gravell Holdings Ltd, 6 Banc Pendre, Kidwelly, Dyfed, SA17 4TA Tel: (01554) 890436 Fax: (01554) 891338

GSF, 21-23 Fort Industrial Park, Chester Road, Castle Vale, Birmingham, B35 7AR Tel: 0121-749 8800 Fax: 0121-749 8801 E-mail: enquiries@uro.co.uk

Gunson Ltd, Bristol Road, Bridgwater, Somerset, TA6 4BX Tel: (01278) 436240 Fax: (01278) 450567 E-mail: gunson@globalnet.co.uk

H G H Components Ltd, 77 River Road, Barking, Essex, IG11 0DS Tel: (020) 8594 7500 Fax: (020) 8594 7533

Halfords Ltd, Icknield St Drive, Redditch, Worcestershire, B98 0DE Tel: (01527) 517601 Fax: (01527) 513201

Hayling Industrial Ltd, Units 8-9 Hayling Billy Business Centre, Furniss Way, Hayling Island, Hampshire, PO11 0ED Tel: (023) 9246 3868 Fax: (023) 9246 3831 E-mail: sales@haylingindustrial.com

Highland Motor Parts Ltd, 21 Henderson Road, Inverness, IV1 1SN Tel: (01463) 223700 Fax: (01463) 711351 E-mail: sales@highlandmotorparts.co.uk

Hitachi Automotive Systems (Europe) Ltd, Aspinall Way, Middlebrook Business Park, Bolton, BL6 6JH Tel: (01204) 469879 Fax: (01204) 469748

▶ Hitachi Cable UK Ltd, Unit 39-40, Rassau Industrial Estate, Rassau, Ebbw Vale, Gwent, NP23 5SD Tel: (01495) 308304 Fax: (01495) 356809

▶ Hi-Ton (International) Ltd, Montgomery Street, Sparkbrook, Birmingham, B11 1DY Tel: 0121-772 2711

Intier Automotive Ltd, Golden Valley Mill, Mill Lane, Bitton, Bristol, BS30 6HL Tel: 0117-932 5656 Fax: 0117-932 7525

Iron Stores Jersey Ltd, 10-12 Commercial Buildings, St. Helier, Jersey, JE1 3UD Tel: (01534) 877755 Fax: (01534) 727449

J H Lightbody & Son Ltd, 437 Townmill Road, Glasgow, G31 3AN Tel: 0141-550 0666 Fax: 0141-550 0330 E-mail: lightbody@iris-web.co.uk

▶ Jaystock Distribution, Unit A3 Empress Park, Empress Road, Southampton, SO14 0JX Tel: (023) 8063 9000 Fax: (023) 8023 5325

Johnson Controls UK Automotive Ltd, 10 Hedera Road, Redditch, Worcestershire, B98 9EY Tel: (01527) 507100 Fax: (01527) 507101

Johnson Motor Accessories, 29 Central Parade, New Addington, Croydon, CR0 0JB Tel: (01689) 842151 Fax: (01689) 842151

K & J Brakes & Hoses Ltd, Alamein Road, Morfa Industrial Estate, Landore, Swansea, SA1 2HY Tel: (01792) 460582 Fax: (01792) 642675

Kaid Ltd, 36B Sandbed Lane, Belper, Derbyshire, DE56 0SH Tel: (01773) 882461 Fax: (0870) 7062237

Kongsberg Automotive, Callister Way, Burton-on-Trent, Staffordshire, DE14 2SY Tel: (01283) 492000 Fax: (01283) 492003 E-mail: info@ka-group.com

Kris Motors, Withy Road, Ladymore, Bilston, West Midlands, WV14 0RX Tel: (01902) 492995 Fax: (01902) 494626

L A P Electrical Ltd, 52 Enterprise Drive, Aldridge Road, Sutton Coldfield, West Midlands, B74 2DZ Tel: 0121-353 5181 Fax: 0121-353 5206

L Bennett & Son Ltd, 43 Normandy Road, St. Albans, Hertfordshire, AL3 5PR Tel: (01727) 855879 Fax: (01727) 847409 E-mail: enquiries@bennetts.com

L C Davis & Sons Ltd, Drury Lane, St. Leonards-on-Sea, East Sussex, TN38 9BA Tel: (01424) 430787 Fax: (01424) 721006 E-mail: hastings@lcdavis.com

L C P Automotive Components, Unit 3 Ebbsfleet Industrial Estate, Northfleet, Gravesend, Kent, DA11 9DZ Tel: (01474) 320300 Fax: (01474) 320595

L R Centre, Bridge Industrial Estate, Speke Hall Road, Speke, Liverpool, L24 9HB Tel: 0151-486 9800 Fax: 0151-486 5986 E-mail: info@lrparts.net

Lancashire Daf Ltd, Four Oaks Road, Walton Summit Centre, Bamber Bridge, Preston, PR5 8BW Tel: (01772) 338111 Fax: (01772) 332665E-mail: enquiries@lancashiredaf.co.uk

LCP, 3 Mill Road, Portslade, Brighton, BN41 1PD Tel: (01273) 430730 Fax: (01273) 430901 E-mail: sales@lcp-automotive.co.uk

LCP Automotive Components, Bridge Road, Ashford, Kent, TN23 1BB Tel: (01233) 623113 Fax: (01233) 631366

LCP Automotive Components, Prospect House, Broad Oak Road, Canterbury, Kent, CT2 7PX Tel: (01227) 766001 Fax: (01227) 769425

LCP Automotive Components, 15 Acorn Industrial Park, Crayford Road, Dartford, DA1 4AL Tel: (01322) 557825 Fax: (01322) 557829

LCP Automotive Components, 555 Canterbury Street, Gillingham, Kent, ME7 5LF Tel: (01634) 575506 Fax: (01634) 855573

LCP Automotive Components, St. Peter Street, Maidstone, Kent, ME16 0SN Tel: (01622) 672222 Fax: (01622) 672227

LCP Automotive Components, 3 Lamberts Road, Tunbridge Wells, Kent, TN2 3EH Tel: (01892) 544829 Fax: (01892) 548131

Lifestyle Ford, 3 Mount Ephraim, Tunbridge Wells, Kent, TN4 8AG Tel: (01892) 515666 Fax: (01892) 548441 E-mail: mail@lifestyleford.co.uk

Linco Components, 2 Redstone Industrial Estate, Redstone Road, Boston, Lincolnshire, PE21 8EA Tel: (01205) 352516 Fax: (01205) 310205

Linde Material Handling Scotland Ltd, 3 Milton Road, East Kilbride, Glasgow, G74 5DH Tel: (01355) 233601 Fax: (01355) 235833 E-mail: enquiries@linde-mh-scotland.co.uk

Linings & Hoses Ltd, 95 Cooperative Street, Stafford, ST16 3DA Tel: (01785) 254634 Fax: (01785) 222802 E-mail: peterjackson@liningsandhoses.co.uk

Llanrad Distribution plc, Unit 26 Bookers Way, Dinnington, Sheffield, S25 3SH Tel: (01909) 550944 Fax: (01909) 568403 E-mail: cool@llanrad.co.uk

Lloyds Motor Spares Ltd, 96 Bilton Road, Perivale, Greenford, Middlesex, UB6 7BN Tel: (020) 8902 1188 Fax: (020) 8795 1327

Mann & Overton Ltd, 39-41 Brewery Road, London, N7 9QH Tel: (020) 7700 0888 Fax: (020) 7700 6676 E-mail: info@mannandoverton.com

Mercury Motors Ltd, 5-7 Strawberry Vale, Twickenham, TW1 4RX Tel: (020) 8892 4604 Fax: (020) 8892 4454 E-mail: enquiries@mercurymotors.co.uk

▶ Mobiletron Car Component Mnfrs, 80 Roman Way Industrial Estate, Ribbleton, Preston, PR2 5BE Tel: (01772) 693780 Fax: (01772) 693790 E-mail: sales@mobiletron.co.uk

▶ indicates data change since last edition

MOTOR VEHICLE ACCESSORIES/ COMPONENTS/SPARE PARTS WHOLESALE DISTRIBUTORS/ FACTORS/AGENTS – *continued*

Mont Blanc Industri UK Ltd, Eden Way, Pages Industrial Park, Leighton Buzzard, Bedfordshire, LU7 4TZ Tel: (01525) 850800 Fax: (01525) 850808 E-mail: sales@montblancuk.co.uk

▶ Motion Engineering Ltd, 38 Sandy Way, Amington Industrial Estate, Tamworth, Staffordshire, B77 4DS Tel: (01827) 66047

Movac Group Ltd, Unit 8 Brookside, Sumpters Way, Southend-on-Sea, SS2 5RR Tel: (01702) 602020 Fax: (01702) 602080

Movac Romford Ltd, 21a Bates Road, Romford, RM3 0JH Tel: (01708) 374227 Fax: (01708) 386877 E-mail: info@movac.com

Mr Tyre Ltd, Fairfield Industrial Estate, Louth, Lincolnshire, LN11 0YF Tel: (01507) 602484 Fax: (01507) 606404

Multipart Universal, 8 Stevenson Way, Sheffield, S9 3WZ Tel: 0114-261 1122 Fax: 0800 834500 E-mail: uksales@ucukltd.com

N G K Spark Plugs UK Ltd, Maylands Avenue, Hemel Hempstead, Hertfordshire, HP2 4SD Tel: (01442) 281000 Fax: (01442) 281001 E-mail: enquiries@ngk.co.uk

Norfolk Truck Enfield Ltd, Mollison Avenue, Enfield, Middlesex, EN3 7NE Tel: (020) 8804 1266 Fax: (020) 8443 2590

Northwood Spares & Accessories Ltd, 87 Newington Causeway, London, SE1 6DH Tel: (020) 7407 9681 Fax: (020) 7940 0820 E-mail: info@northwoods-ltd.com

Omega Automotive Ltd, 4 Europa Way, Britannia Enterprise Park, Lichfield, Staffordshire, WS14 9TZ Tel: (01543) 490628 Fax: (01543) 493421 E-mail: info@omega-automotive.com

Onexe Products, Unit 7 Shutterton Industrial Estate, Dawlish, Devon, EX7 0NH Tel: (01626) 865568 Fax: (01626) 865568

Oscott Equipments Ltd, 25 Great Lister Street, Birmingham, B7 4LS Tel: 0121-333 3200 Fax: 0121-333 2991

▶ P T Co., Greensleeves, Green Bottom, Wimborne, Dorset, BH21 2LW Tel: (01202) 639243 Fax: (01202) 639243 E-mail: sales@ptcompany.co.uk

Andrew Page Ltd, Apson House, Colton Mill, Bullerthorpe Lane, Leeds, LS15 9JL Tel: 0113-397 0200 Fax: 0113-397 0295 E-mail: accounts@andrewpage.com

Partco Autoparts Ltd, Redstone Caravan Park, Boston, Lincolnshire, PE21 8AL Tel: (01205) 365984 Fax: (01205) 352716 E-mail: ap.boston.m@unipart.co.uk

Partco Autoparts Ltd, Unit 11 Gatwick Int Distribution Centre, Cobham Way, Crawley, West Sussex, RH10 9RX Tel: (01293) 524211 Fax: (01293) 518187

Partco Autoparts Ltd, Ellen Street, Hove, East Sussex, BN3 3LZ Tel: (01273) 779973 Fax: (01273) 326086 E-mail: ap.hove.m/ead/unipart@unipart.com

Parts 4 Cars Ltd, 991 Wolverhampton Road, Oldbury, West Midlands, B69 4RJ Tel: 0121-544 4040 Fax: 0121-544 5558 E-mail: info@davidmanners.co.uk

Pearl Products, 2 Manor Trading Estate, Armstrong Road, Benfleet, Essex, SS7 4PW Tel: (01268) 756216 Fax: (01268) 565589 E-mail: info@pearlproducts.co.uk

Pennant Automotive & Industrial Supplies, University Farm, Wasthill Lane, Kings Norton, Birmingham, B38 9EP Tel: 0121-459 4276 Fax: 0121-451 2488

▶ Pilot Industries UK Ltd, Swinbourne Road, Burnt Mills Industrial Estate, Basildon, Essex, SS13 1EF Tel: (01268) 590570 Fax: (01268) 590580

Pirtek, 2 Oxford Court, Oxford Street, Birmingham, B5 5NF Tel: 0121-633 0101 Fax: 0121-633 0043 E-mail: info@pirtekbirmingham.co.uk

Pirtek, Unit 35 Seymour Street, Millers Bridge Industrial Estate, Bootle, Merseyside, L20 1EE Tel: 0151-933 9000 Fax: 0151-933 5333 E-mail: info@pirtekuk.com

Pirtek, St. Andrews Road, Avonmouth, Bristol, BS11 9HQ Tel: 0117-982 0056 Fax: 0117-982 4361 E-mail: info@pirtekbristol.co.uk

Pirtek, Unit 35, Acton Park Industrial Estate, The Vale, Acton, London, W3 7QE Tel: (020) 8749 8444 Fax: (020) 8749 8333 E-mail: info@pirtek.co.uk

Pirtek, 6 Westbrook Trading Estate, Westbrook Road, Trafford Park, Manchester, M17 1AY Tel: 0161-877 0000 Fax: 0161-877 8899 E-mail: pirtek-manchester@supanet.com

Pirtek, 337 Ranglet Road, Walton Summit Centre, Bamber Bridge, Preston, PR5 8AR Tel: (01772) 620111 Fax: (01772) 629996 E-mail: preston@pirtekcentre.co.uk

Pirtek, 5 Bergland Park, Maritime Close, Medway City Estate, Rochester, Kent, ME2 4AD Tel: (01634) 297080 Fax: (01634) 297087 E-mail: zen24815@zen.co.uk

Pirtek, 3 Alert House, Dannemora Drive, Sheffield, S9 5DF Tel: 0114-249 3666 Fax: 0114-249 3667 E-mail: sheffield@pirtekcentre.co.uk

Pirtek, Unit 8 Westmill Street, Stoke-on-Trent, ST1 3EL Tel: (01782) 206206 Fax: (01782) 206306 E-mail: stoke@pirtekcentre.co.uk

Pirtek (Nottingham) Ltd, Unit 4 Trentview Court, Moreland Street, Nottingham, NG2 3FX Tel: 0115-985 0081 Fax: 0115-985 0132 E-mail: info@pirteknottingham.co.uk

Poolec Automotive Products Ltd, Fourth Way, Bristol, BS11 8DL Tel: 0117-982 9109 Fax: 0117-982 7690 E-mail: poolec.bristol@btconnect.com

Precision Engine Services (Inverness), Units 1-4, 48 Seafield Road, Inverness, IV1 1SG Tel: (01463) 235537 Fax: (01463) 712684

Premier Cars Ltd, Ffordd Maelgwyn, Tremarl Industrial Estate, Llandudno Junction, Gwynedd, LL31 9PL Tel: (01492) 582999 Fax: (01492) 582599 E-mail: mail@premiercars.bmw-net.co.uk

Premier Supply Co., Perram Works, Merrow Lane, Guildford, Surrey, GU4 7BN Tel: (01483) 534346 Fax: (01483) 303992 E-mail: countylr@aol.com

▶ Prestige Number Plates & Signs Ltd, 283 Duke Street, Glasgow, G31 1HX Tel: 0141-550 1323 Fax: 0141-550 1324

Provincial Motor Factors, William Street, Sunderland, SR1 1TW Tel: 0191-565 8141 Fax: 0191-565 9296 E-mail: sales@provincialtyres.co.uk

Quinton Hazell Automotive Ltd, Conway Road, Colwyn Bay, Clwyd, LL28 5BS Tel: (01492) 544201 Fax: (01492) 542202

R Biller & Co., 22-36 Charles Street, Rochester, Kent, ME2 2BL Tel: (01634) 290666 Fax: (01634) 296700

R Charnock, 1 Adswood Industrial Estate, Adswood Road, Stockport, Cheshire, SK3 8LF Tel: 0161-477 3082 Fax: 0161-480 9854 E-mail: sales@rickcharnockcomponents.co.uk

R G Ergonomics Ltd, 7 Princewood Road, Earlstrees Industrial Estate, Corby, Northamptonshire, NN17 4AP Tel: (01536) 263691 Fax: (01536) 274988 E-mail: enquires@rgergonomics.co.uk

▶ R S Piper Ltd, 2 St. Johns Court Foster Road, Ashford Business Park, Sevington, Ashford, Kent, TN24 0SJ Tel: (01233) 500200 Fax: (01233) 500300 E-mail: sales@pipercams.co.uk

Randstad Ltd, Unit 37 Crow Hall Road, Nelson Park East, Cramlington, Northumberland, NE23 1WH Tel: (01670) 735575 Fax: (01670) 590739 E-mail: enquiries@ranstadltd.co.uk

Red Dot Ltd, Unit 4, Blueprint Commercial Centre, Imperial Way, Watford, WD24 4JD Tel: (0870) 3002354

Riders Landrover, Threemilestone Industrial Estate, Threemilestone, Truro, Cornwall, TR4 9LD Tel: (01872) 263377 Fax: (01872) 261606 E-mail: sales@riders-landrover.co.uk

Rolls Royce Marine Power plc, PO Box 2000, Derby, DE21 7XX Tel: (01332) 248167

Russels Automotive, 16 Bunyon Road, Kempston, Bedford, MK42 8HA Tel: (01234) 840655 Fax: (01234) 851358

S A S Components Ltd, 4 Saxon Business Park, Hanbury Road, Stoke Prior, Bromsgrove, Worcestershire, B60 4AD Tel: (01527) 575502 Fax: (01527) 575276 E-mail: sales@sascomponents.co.uk

▶ S B Components International Ltd, Millennium Works, Enterprise Way, Wisbech, Cambridgeshire, PE14 0SB Tel: (01945) 475234 Fax: (01945) 476251

S P A Bristol Ltd, Unit 22, Barton Hill Trading Estate, Bristol, BS5 9RD Tel: 0117-955 3166 Fax: 0117-955 6053

S & W Services (Yorkshire) Ltd, 129/133 Manningham Lane, Bradford, West Yorkshire, BD8 7JA Tel: (01274) 722388 Fax: (01274) 722380

Sargents Factors Ltd, Birches Industrial Estate, East Grinstead, West Sussex, RH19 1XZ Tel: (01342) 321456 Fax: (01342) 321598

Savilles Motor Factors Ltd, 15 Elders Street, Scarborough, North Yorkshire, YO11 1DZ Tel: (01723) 375010 Fax: (01723) 353798

Scorpion Vehicle Security Systems Ltd, Unit 1 Siemens Road, North Bank Industrial Estate, Manchester, M44 5AH Tel: 0161-777 9666 Fax: 0161-777 9473 E-mail: sales@selecto-parts.co.uk

▶ Sec Ltd, 6-8 Howard Chase, Basildon, Essex, SS14 3BE Tel: (01268) 533316 Fax: (01268) 531454

Securon Amersham Ltd, Winchmore Hill, Amersham, Buckinghamshire, HP7 0NZ Tel: (01494) 434455 Fax: (01494) 726499 E-mail: sales@securon.co.uk

▶ Serck Intertruck, 104 Hydepark Street, Glasgow, G3 8BW Tel: 0141-221 1127 Fax: 0141-248 1221

Sews Europe, Unit 1, Woodlands Business Pk, Ystradgynlais, Swansea, SA9 1JW Tel: (01639) 842281 Fax: (01639) 849853 E-mail: info@sewse.com

South Eastern Auto Ltd, Bridge Industrial Centre, Wharf Road, Tovil, Maidstone, Kent, ME15 6RR Tel: (01622) 690010 Fax: (01622) 690683 E-mail: seaes@aol.com

South West Glassfibre, The Former Mine Compressor House, Dolcoath, Camborne, Cornwall, TR14 8RR Tel: (01209) 613033 Fax: (01209) 613033

▶ Southern Exhaust Supplies Ltd, Avonside Indust Estate, St. Philips Marsh, Bristol, BS2 0TS Tel: 0117-972 8844 Fax: 0117-971 7112

Southern Motor Factors Ltd, 25 Lower Gravel Road, Bromley, BR2 8LR Tel: (020) 8462 6372 Fax: (020) 8462 7919E-mail: info@smfuk.com

SSP Powar Forge Ltd, 1A Denaby Main Industrial Estate, Coalpit Lane, Denaby Main, Doncaster, South Yorkshire, DN12 4LH Tel: 0114-244 8371 Fax: 0114-242 6714 E-mail: ssppowarforge@btconnect.com

Starbuck Distribution Ltd, Queen Street, Walsall, WS2 9NS Tel: (01922) 612194 Fax: (01922) 630503

Stockwell Motor Accessories, 226-236 Clapham Road, London, SW9 0PZ Tel: (020) 7582 3666 Fax: (020) 7735 6484

Stoneridge Pollak Ltd, The Moors, Tewkesbury Road, Cheltenham, Gloucestershire, GL51 9BP Tel: (01242) 283000 Fax: (01242) 283023 E-mail: stuart.felton@stoneridgepollak.co.uk

Stormont Truck & Van Ltd, Ellen Street, Portslade, Brighton, BN41 1DW Tel: (01273) 430828 Fax: (01273) 411490

Stratstone Of Mayfair, 14 Berkeley Street, London, W1J 8DX Tel: (020) 7514 0400 Fax: (020) 7491 1410 E-mail: sales-mayfair@pendragon.uk.com

Summit Accessories, 1 Lombard Way, Banbury, Oxfordshire, OX16 4TJ Tel: (01295) 275469 Fax: (01295) 270249 E-mail: sales@summit-auto.com

Supreme Distributing Co. Ltd, 235-237 Coldharbour Lane, London, SW9 8RR Tel: (020) 7274 2516 Fax: (020) 7737 5377

Sureparts Motor Component Distribution, 12 Howard Road, Park Farm Industrial Estate, Redditch, Worcestershire, B98 7SE Tel: (01527) 501333 Fax: (01527) 522848

T D Fitchett, Redland Industrial Estate, Station Hill, St. Georges, Telford, Shropshire, TF2 9JX Tel: (01952) 620434 Fax: (01952) 610510

▶ T I Group, Glover Industrial Estate, Spire Road, Washington, Tyne & Wear, NE37 3ES Tel: 0191-451 5700 Fax: 0191-451 5730

Thames Valley Pressings Ltd, Transteel Layton Road, Brentford, Middlesex, TW8 0QJ Tel: (020) 8847 3636 Fax: (020) 8758 1236 E-mail: info@tvpressings.co.uk

Thule Ltd, Five C Business Centre, Concorde Drive, Clevedon, Avon, BS21 6UH Tel: (01275) 340404 Fax: (01275) 340686 E-mail: sales@thule.co.uk

Tri Fen Engineering, Unit 28 Boston Industrial Estate, Power Station Road, Rugeley, Staffordshire, WS15 2HS Tel: (01889) 577871 Fax: (01889) 585093

Truck-Lite Co. Ltd, Waterfall Lane, Cradley Heath, West Midlands, B64 6QB Tel: 0121-561 7000 Fax: 0121-561 1415 E-mail: birminghamsales@truck-lite.com

Truckstop Hawkes, Unit 9 Brook Street, Redditch, Worcestershire, B98 8NG Tel: (01527) 68279 Fax: (01527) 60026 E-mail: info@truckstophawkes.co.uk

Truepart Ltd, Decoy Bank, Doncaster, South Yorkshire, DN4 5JD Tel: (01302) 344919 Fax: (01302) 327191 E-mail: info@wst.co.uk

Unipart Automotive Ltd, Windsor Road, Bedford, MK42 9SU Tel: (01234) 350601 Fax: (01234) 261647

Unipart Automotive Ltd, Unit 5 - 7, Shepcote Enterprise Park 2, Europa Drive, Sheffield, S9 1XT Tel: 0114-243 0301 Fax: 0114-261 7745 E-mail: bb.sheffieldnorth.m@unipart.co.uk

Universal Products Leicester Ltd, 46 Main Street, Kirby Muxloe, Leicester, LE9 2AU Tel: 0116-239 3625 Fax: 0116-239 3625

V C Saunders Engineering Ltd, 20 Weir Road, London, SW19 8UG Tel: (020) 8947 5262 Fax: (020) 8944 1812

Visteon, Basildon Plant, Christopher Martin Road, Basildon, Essex, SS14 3HG Tel: (01268) 705300 Fax: (01268) 533970 E-mail: sales@visteon.com

W M Rollings Ltd, 49 Brook Street, Wrexham, Clwyd, LL13 7LR Tel: (01978) 364956 Fax: (01978) 359659 E-mail: wmrollings@aol.com

Walsall Brake Services Ltd, Middlemore Lane West, Aldridge, Walsall, WS9 8BG Tel: (01922) 744625 Fax: (01922) 744626

Warwickshire Ignition Services Ltd, 5 Colletts Drive, Cheltenham, Gloucestershire, GL51 8JQ Tel: (01242) 523500 Fax: (01242) 524117

Waterloo Motor Trade Ltd, Main Street, Hull, HU2 0JX Tel: (01482) 328308 Fax: (01482) 212398 E-mail: sales@waterloo-mt.co.uk

Webbs Spare Parts, 127-129 High Street, Stevenage, Hertfordshire, SG1 3HS Tel: (01438) 312669 Fax: (01438) 729867 E-mail: web21.stevenage@autonetplus.co.uk

Weiler-Knight (UK) Ltd, 17 Glebe Road, Groby, Leicester, LE6 0GT Tel: 0116-287 6963 Fax: 0116-287 8099 E-mail: mel.knight@pipemedia.co.uk

Wilson Lendrum & Weir Ltd, Derrychara Road, Enniskillen, County Fermanagh, BT74 6JF Tel: (028) 6632 2720 Fax: (028) 6632 2212

Zobra Auto Centre, 1a Hazelbury Cresent, Luton, LU1 1DF Tel: (01582) 724883 Fax: (01582) 705533

MOTOR VEHICLE AIRBAGS

Airbags International Ltd, Viking Way, Congleton, Cheshire, CW12 1TT Tel: (01260) 294300 Fax: (01260) 294301

MOTOR VEHICLE AXLES

ArvinMeritor HVS Ltd, Park Lane, Great Alne, Alcester, Warwickshire, B49 6HT Tel: (01789) 768236 Fax: (01789) 488031

Daf Trucks Ltd, Eastern By Passage, Thame, Oxfordshire, OX9 3FB Tel: (01844) 261111 Fax: (01844) 217111 E-mail: info@daftrucks.com

Dana Spicer Axle Europe Ltd, Birch Road, Witton, Birmingham, B6 7JR Tel: 0121-249 2500 Fax: 0121-249 2599 E-mail: pete.yale@dana.com

Granning Engineering Ltd, 37 Melford Court, Hardwick Grange, Woolston, Warrington, WA1 4RZ Tel: (01925) 810400 Fax: (01925) 817153 E-mail: sales@grannings.com

Jaguar Axle Supplies, 23 Spencer Walk, Tilbury, Essex, RM18 8XH Tel: (01375) 846986 Fax: (01375) 408017 E-mail: ed@ward-engineering.co.uk

Nicol Transmission Services, Coppice Trading Estate, Kidderminster, Worcestershire, DY11 7QY Tel: (01562) 752651 Fax: (01562) 823128

Oldbury UK Ltd, Bulliol Buisiness Park, Wobaston Road, Wolverhampton, WV9 5EU Tel: (01902) 397216 Fax: (01902) 878265 E-mail: sales@oldburyuk.co.uk

MOTOR VEHICLE BODY BUILDERS, *See also Commercial Vehicle Body Builders*

A S Whitaker & Sons, Stephenson Avenue, Pinchbeck, Spalding, Lincolnshire, PE11 3SW Tel: (01775) 722789 Fax: (01775) 710519 E-mail: phil@whitakers-bodyshop.co.uk

B A S Systems Land Systems Weapons & Vehicles, PO Box 106, Telford, Shropshire, TF1 6QW Tel: (01952) 224500 Fax: (01952) 243910

Jack Barclay Ltd, 18 Berkeley Square, London, W1J 6AE Tel: (020) 7629 7444 Fax: (020) 7629 8258 E-mail: administration@jackbarclay.co.uk

A.G. Bracey Ltd, Unit 13, Pucklechurch Trading Estate, Pucklechurch, Bristol, BS16 9QH Tel: 0117-937 2705 Fax: 0117-937 4243

Bradshaws Body Repairs Ltd, 329 London Road, Hemel Hempstead, Hertfordshire, HP3 9AN Tel: (01442) 211711 Fax: (01442) 251788

Bulkrite Commercial Vehicle Bodybuilders, Dorrington, Shrewsbury, SY5 7EB Tel: (01743) 718232 Fax: (01743) 718293 E-mail: bulkrite_1@lineone.net

▶ ChipsAway (AshBruch) Ltd, 1 Kingfisher Business Park, London Road, Bedford, MK42 0NY Tel: (01234) 360300 Fax: (01234) 360300 E-mail: lucie@chips-away.com

▶ ChipsAway Leamington Spa, 8 Markham Drive, Leamington Spa, Warwick, CV31 2PP Tel: 01926 330561

Coleman Milne, Wigan Road, Westhoughton, Bolton, BL5 2EE Tel: (01942) 815600 Fax: (01942) 815115 E-mail: sales@woodall-nicholson.co.uk

D C W Accided Repairs Ltd, Cornhill Close, Lodge Farm Industrial Estate, Harlestone Road, Northampton, NN5 7UQ Tel: (01604) 753208 Fax: (01604) 759718

Dalblair of Ayr Ltd, 127 Prestwick Road, Ayr, KA8 8ND Tel: (01292) 269123 Fax: (01292) 280290 E-mail: dalblair@yahoo.com

Donovan Kendell Ltd, 18-20 Catherine Street, St. Albans, Hertfordshire, AL3 5BY Tel: (01727) 841717 Fax: (01727) 860859

E T Tucker Ltd, 87 Severn Road, Cardiff, CF11 9EA Tel: (029) 2022 9842

East Anglian Motor & Sheet Metal Co. Ltd, 10 Garden Street, Norwich, NR1 1QX Tel: (01603) 625664 Fax: (01603) 760545 E-mail: sales@ea-arc.co.uk

Fleck Bros, 85 Templepatrick Road, Ballyclare, County Antrim, BT39 9RQ Tel: (028) 9332 3866 Fax: (028) 9335 2830

Fred Smith & Sons Motor Bodies Ltd, Sams Lane, West Bromwich, West Midlands, B70 7EG Tel: 0121-525 8359 Fax: 0121-553 0578 E-mail: james@fredsmithandsons.co.uk

G Broughton & Sons, Ferneries Road, Barnetby, South Humberside, DN38 6HN Tel: (01652) 688652 Fax: (01652) 688069

Gormac Coachworks, 5 Thomson Street, Renfrew, PA4 8HQ Tel: 0141-886 4072 Fax: 0141-885 2821 E-mail: gormac@btconnect.com

Griffin Mill Garages Ltd, Upper Boat, Pontypridd, Mid Glamorgan, CF37 5YE Tel: (01443) 842216 Fax: (01443) 842584 E-mail: info@griffinmill.co.uk

JM Accident Repair Centre, 9 St Machar Drive, Aberdeen, AB24 3YJ Tel: (01224) 488441 Fax: (01224) 497989

K & I Ltd, Hardengreen Coachworks, Dalkeith, Midlothian, EH22 3LD Tel: 0131-663 4545 Fax: 0131-654 2373 E-mail: info@k-and-i.co.uk

Lynch Truck Services Ltd, Barnfield Way, Altham, Accrington, Lancashire, BB5 5YT Tel: (01282) 773377 Fax: (01282) 779933 E-mail: enquiries@lynchtrucks.com

Mccomb Coachwork, 22 Market Place, Tattershall, Lincoln, LN4 4LJ Tel: (01526) 342292 Fax: (01526) 344411 E-mail: mail@mccombcoachwork.co.uk

Marshall Specialist Vehicles Ltd, The Airport, Cambridge, CB5 8RX Tel: (01223) 373900 Fax: (01223) 373064 E-mail: info@marshallsv.com

Medcalf & Co. (Coachbuilders) Ltd, Fordwater Trading Estate, Fordwater Road, Chertsey, Surrey, KT16 8HG Tel: (01932) 563026 Fax: (01932) 571086

MKG Motor Group Ltd, Cavendish Road, Stevenage, Hertfordshire, SG1 2ET Tel: (01438) 365663 Fax: (01438) 318318

Nationwide Crash Repair Centres Ltd, Axe Road, Bridgwater, Somerset, TA6 5LN Tel: (01278) 422238 Fax: (01278) 427939

Nationwide Crash Repair Centres Ltd, 171 Maxwell Road, Glasgow, G41 1TG Tel: 0141-429 5371 Fax: 0141-420 1084

MOTOR VEHICLE BODY BUILDERS

– continued

Park Sheet Metal Co. Ltd, Bayton Road, Exhall, Coventry, CV7 9DJ Tel: (024) 7636 1606 Fax: (024) 7664 4078 E-mail: office@parksheetmetal.co.uk

Penman Engineering Ltd, Heathhall Industrial Estate, Heathhall, Dumfries, DG1 3NY Tel: (01387) 252784 Fax: (01387) 267332 E-mail: info@penman.co.uk

Popplewells Coach Works Ltd, High Road, Thornwood, Epping, Essex, CM16 6LP Tel: (01992) 574040 Fax: (01992) 576653

R Hind, Durranhill Trading Estate, Carlisle, CA1 3NQ Tel: (01228) 523647 Fax: (01228) 512712

Jack Rob Motors Ltd, East Lane Business Park, 2 Bell Lane, Wembley, Middlesex, HA9 7RB Tel: (020) 8908 5577 Fax: (020) 8904 8515 E-mail: jackrob@motormenu.co.uk

S E Ison & Sons, Ebberns Road, Hemel Hempstead, Hertfordshire, HP3 9QS Tel: (01442) 264104 Fax: (01442) 233611 E-mail: office@seison.co.uk

S F Vehicle Builders Ltd, Crossways, Church Stretton, Shropshire, SY6 6PG Tel: (01694) 722804 Fax: (01694) 723583

S Macneillie & Son Ltd, Stockton Close, Walsall, WS2 8LD Tel: (01922) 725560 Fax: (01922) 720916

▶ Smart Alloys, Unit 5 Harrison Street, Blackburn, BB2 2JN Tel: (01254) 589626 Fax: (0845) 3891161 E-mail: info@smartalloys.co.uk

Spafax International Ltd, Kingsland Industrial Park, Stroudley Road, Basingstoke, Hampshire, RG24 8UG Tel: (01256) 814400 Fax: (01256) 814141 E-mail: sales@spafaxmirrors.com

Tanker & General Ltd, Hedley Avenue, West Thurrock, Grays, Essex, RM20 4EL Tel: (01375) 370660 Fax: (0870) 8723134 E-mail: mgeary@tankergeneral.com

Welford Thomas Ltd, Unit 35 Thornleigh Trading Estate, Dudley, West Midlands, DY2 8UB Tel: (01384) 451340 Fax: (01384) 451345 E-mail: welford.bodies@btinternet.co.uk

Transbus International Ltd, Hydepark Industrial Estate, Mallusk, Newtownabbey, County Antrim, BT36 8NP Tel: (028) 9034 2006 Fax: (028) 9034 2678 E-mail: phaveron@walexander.co.uk

Whites Accident Repair Centre, 10 Imperial Way, Croydon, CR0 4RR Tel: (020) 8686 0055 Fax: (020) 8688 1102

Wigan Trailer Centre Ltd, Cricket St Business Park, Cricket Street, Wigan, Lancashire, WN6 7TP Tel: (01942) 248373 Fax: (01942) 821317 E-mail: info@wtcltd.co.uk

Wimpole Garages Ltd, Portland Street South, Ashton-under-Lyne, Lancashire, OL6 7RE Tel: 0161-330 9551 Fax: 0161-339 0141

MOTOR VEHICLE BODY BUILDERS, GLASS FIBRE OR FIBREGLASS

B B Beresford, Goods Road, Belper, Derbyshire, DE56 1UU Tel: (01773) 825959 Fax: (01773) 821213 E-mail: beresford@btconnect.com

▶ ChipsAway (AshBruch) Ltd, 1 Kingfisher Business Park, London Road, Bedford, MK42 0NY Tel: (01234) 360300 Fax: (01234) 360300 E-mail: lucie@chips-away.com

Delta Styling.co.uk, Unit 12, Carlton Industrial Estate, Albion Road, Carlton, Barnsley, South Yorkshire, S71 3HW Tel: (01226) 722761

Smith & Deakin Plastics, 75 Blackpole Trading Estate West, Worcester, WR3 8TJ Tel: (01905) 458886 Fax: (01905) 458889 E-mail: sales@smithanddeakin.co.uk

Truckman Ltd, Chosen View Road, Cheltenham, Gloucestershire, GL51 9LT Tel: (01242) 580033 Fax: (01242) 580044 E-mail: sales@truckman.co.uk

Westfield Sports Cars Ltd, 1 Gibbons Industrial Park, Dudley Road, Kingswinford, West Midlands, DY6 8XF Tel: (01384) 400077 Fax: (01384) 288781 E-mail: info@westfield-sportscars.co.uk

MOTOR VEHICLE BODY COMPONENTS

E C Hopkins Ltd, Barton Industrial Estate, Mount Pleasant, Bilston, West Midlands, WV14 7LH Tel: (01902) 401755 Fax: (01902) 495097 E-mail: bhopkins@echopkins.co.uk

Evans Halshaw Ltd, Estate Garage, Treforest Industrial Estate, Pontypridd, Mid Glamorgan, CF37 5YA Tel: (01443) 842376 Fax: (01443) 842687 E-mail: justin.brown@pendragon.uk.com

Stadco Ltd, 21 Renaissance Way, Liverpool, L24 9PX Tel: 0151-728 4500

MOTOR VEHICLE BODY CONSULTANTS OR DESIGNERS

Lynx Motors (International) Ltd, 68 Castleham Road, St. Leonards-on-Sea, East Sussex, TN38 9NU Tel: (01424) 851277 Fax: (01424) 853771 E-mail: enquiries@lynxmotors.co.uk

MOTOR VEHICLE BODY FITTINGS

Bott, Unit 9 Ivanhoe Industrial Estate, Tournament Way, Ashby-de-la-Zouch, Leicestershire, LE65 2UU Tel: (01530) 410600 Fax: (01530) 410629 E-mail: v-sales@bottltd.co.uk

William Hawkes Ltd, 183 & 184 High St, Deritend, Birmingham, B12 0LH Tel: 0121-772 2694 Fax: 0121-772 2694

Huf UK Ltd, Neptune Industrial Estate, Owen Road, Willenhall, West Midlands, WV13 2PZ Tel: (01902) 366023 Fax: (01902) 366424

Polytec Holden Ltd, Porthouse Industrial Estate, Bromyard, Herefordshire, HR7 4NS Tel: (01885) 485153 Fax: (01885) 483057 E-mail: gareth.anderson@polytec-holden.com

Sears Seating, Unit 33, Rassau Industrial Estate, Ebbw Vale, Gwent, NP23 5SD Tel: (01495) 304518 Fax: (01495) 304452 E-mail: info@searsseating.co.uk

MOTOR VEHICLE BODY INSULATION MATERIALS/ PRODUCTS

Rieter Automotive Great Britain Ltd, Keller House, Hereward Rise, Halesowen, West Midlands, B62 8AN Tel: 0121-504 4500 Fax: 0121-504 4521 E-mail: steve.nash@rieterauto.com

MOTOR VEHICLE BODY KITS

▶ Christian I D Coachworks, Russell Hill Place, Purley, Surrey, CR8 2LH Tel: (020) 8660 6444 Fax: (020) 8668 0116 E-mail: ian@idcoachworks.fsnet.co.uk

J B A Engineering Ltd, Unit 56b Bradley Hall Trading Estate, Bradley Lane, Standish, Wigan, Lancashire, WN6 0XQ Tel: (01257) 424549 Fax: (01257) 424549

MOTOR VEHICLE BODY MAINTENANCE OR REPAIR

▶ Ace Motors, Victoria Mill, Alliance Street, Accrington, Lancashire, BB5 2RT Tel: (01254) 232662 E-mail: info@acemotorsbaxenden.co.uk

▶ Bowron Motor Care, Hatton House, Flaunden Lane, Flaunden, Hemel Hempstead, Hertfordshire, HP3 0PQ Tel: (01442) 834634 Fax: (01442) 834488 E-mail: sales@bowron-motorcare.co.uk

▶ Croft Bros UK Ltd, Unit D1 Riverside Way, Cowley, Uxbridge, Middlesex, UB8 2YF Tel: (01895) 850700 Fax: (01895) 270584 E-mail: info@croftbrothers.co.uk

▶ Dashtech Services (UK), Delta Street, New Basford, Nottingham, NG7 7GJ Tel: (07980) 213377 E-mail: m_ali1972@hotmail.com

▶ Lady Royd Garage, 507 Thornton Road, Bradford, West Yorkshire, BD8 9RB Tel: (01274) 545304 Fax: (01274) 498176 E-mail: fiona@ladyroyd.co.uk

Parry & Blockwell Ltd, Magdelene Street, Haverfordwest, Dyfed, SA61 1JJ Tel: (01437) 763129 Fax: (01437) 766713

▶ PCT Porsche Specialists, Fast Lane Building, A45 Dunchurch Highway, Allesley, Coventry, CV5 9QA Tel: (0845) 6444993 E-mail: info@pctcars.co.uk

▶ Smart Refinishers (Aberdeen) Ltd, Kirkhill Indust Estate, Aberdeen, AB21 0HP Tel: (01224) 772999 Fax: (01224) 772007 E-mail: sales@smartrefinishers.co.uk

MOTOR VEHICLE BODY PANELS

Ex Pressed Steel Panels Ltd, Ickornshaw Mill, Ickornshaw, Cowling, Keighley, West Yorkshire, BD22 0DB Tel: (01535) 632721 Fax: (01535) 636977 E-mail: sales@steelpanels.co.uk

Lye Panels Ltd, 41 Delph Road, Brierley Hill, West Midlands, DY5 2TW Tel: (01384) 70032 Fax: (01384) 70032

Surepart S V G Ltd, Morda Mill Business Centre, Beaconsfield Terrace, Morda, Oswestry, Shropshire, SY10 9PE Tel: (01691) 655300 Fax: (01691) 653838

MOTOR VEHICLE BODY PRESSINGS

London Taxis (International) Plc, Holyhead Road, Coventry, CV5 8JJ Tel: (024) 7657 2000 Fax: (024) 7657 2001 E-mail: exports@lti.co.uk

Ogihara Europe Ltd, Hortonwood Industrial Estate, Queensway, Telford, Shropshire, TF1 7LL Tel: (01952) 222111 Fax: (01952) 222050 E-mail: sales@ogihara.co.uk

▶ Stadco Ltd, Harlescott Lane, Shrewsbury, SY1 3AS Tel: (01743) 462227 Fax: (01743) 447709 E-mail: info@stadco.co.uk

T K A Body Stampings Ltd, Wolverhampton Road, Cannock, Staffordshire, WS11 1LY Tel: (01543) 466664 Fax: (01543) 466665 E-mail: info@tkbs.thyssenkrupp.com

Widney Pressings, Scotswood Road, Newcastle upon Tyne, NE15 6BZ Tel: 0191-273 9117 Fax: 0191-272 3492 E-mail: awingfield@bodyinwhitepressings.co.uk

MOTOR VEHICLE BODY REFINISHING/PANEL BEATING/ SPRAYING SPECIALIST SERVICES

A Lloyd & Son, Urban Road, Kirkby-in-Ashfield, Nottingham, NG17 8AP Tel: (01623) 752965 Fax: (01623) 752965

Alex Morrison Ltd, 56 Gilwilly Road, Gilwilly Industrial Estate, Penrith, Cumbria, CA11 9BL Tel: (01768) 863037 Fax: (01768) 890950

Arch Services, Bodymoor Green Farm, Coventry Road, Kingsbury, Tamworth, Staffordshire, B78 2DZ Tel: (01827) 875558 Fax: (01827) 875539

Autocrafts, Brimscombe Mills, Brimscombe, Stroud, Gloucestershire, GL5 2SB Tel: (01453) 882468 Fax: (01453) 882182

BBS, Unit 2-3 Cauldwell Walk, Bedford, MK42 9DT Tel: (01234) 268838 Fax: (01234) 359071

Bill Heaney Ltd, Hume Street, Newcastle upon Tyne, NE6 1LN Tel: 0191-265 8511 Fax: 0191-209 0203 E-mail: heaneyacc@aol.com

Bindon Auto Body Centre Ltd, Cook Way, Bindon Road, Taunton, Somerset, TA2 6BJ Tel: (01823) 338582 Fax: (01823) 321854

R. Boyle Motor Engineering Ltd, Blackwall Way, London, E14 9QG Tel: (020) 7987 2683 Fax: (020) 7987 2683

Bracebridge Motor Body Works Ltd, 246 Newark Road, Lincoln, LN6 8RP Tel: (01522) 520383 Fax: (01522) 537137

Bristol Street Motors, Southam Road, Banbury, Oxfordshire, OX16 2RS Tel: (01295) 253511 Fax: (01295) 261325 E-mail: mja49@bristolstreet.co.uk

Martin Brown Paints Ltd, 265 Dickson Road, Blackpool, FY1 2JJ Tel: (01253) 626907 Fax: (01253) 753494 E-mail: enquiries@martinbrownpaints.com

Car Clinic Co. Ltd, Cannal Road, Bradford, West Yorkshire, BD1 4AJ Tel: (01274) 386400 Fax: (01274) 735185

Car Comm Aid Ltd, 47-49 Henshall Road, Parkhouse Industrial Estate, Parkhouse Industrial Estate West, Newcastle, Staffordshire, ST5 7RY Tel: (01782) 563474 Fax: (01782) 563550 E-mail: mail@carcommaid.co.uk

Carbody Banbury Ltd, Thorpe Lane, Banbury, Oxfordshire, OX16 4UT Tel: (01295) 273945 Fax: (01295) 270226 E-mail: philatcbl@aol.com

Chandlers Garage Holdings Ltd, B M W House, Water Lane, Littlehampton, West Sussex, BN16 4EH Tel: (01903) 784147 Fax: (01903) 785289 E-mail: enquiries@chandlers-bmw.co.uk

▶ Christian I D Coachworks, Russell Hill Place, Purley, Surrey, CR8 2LH Tel: (020) 8660 6444 Fax: (020) 8668 0116 E-mail: ian@idcoachworks.fsnet.co.uk

Colchester Accident Repairs, 105 Gosbecks Road, Colchester, CO2 9JT Tel: (01206) 578242 Fax: (01206) 762616

Crosbie Cain & Kennish, South Quay Industrial Estate, Douglas, Isle of Man, IM1 5AT Tel: (01624) 673156 Fax: (01624) 676354

D D Evans & Co Ltd, The Garage, New Road, Pontarddulais, Swansea, SA4 8TB Tel: (01792) 882637

D Reed & Son, Churchill Road, Cheltenham, Gloucestershire, GL53 7EG Tel: (01242) 523637

Dick Lovett Bristol Ltd, Laurel Court, Cribbs Causeway, Bristol, BS10 7TU Tel: 0117-905 0000 Fax: 0117-905 0090

Donovan Kendell Ltd, 18-20 Catherine Street, St. Albans, Hertfordshire, AL3 5BY Tel: (01727) 841717 Fax: (01727) 860859

F G Barnes, Cuxton Road, Parkwood Industrial Estate, Maidstone, Kent, ME15 9YF Tel: (01622) 755531 Fax: (01622) 692216 E-mail: sales@fgbarnes.co.uk

Factory Lane Autos Ltd, 9-11 Broton Drive, Halstead, Essex, CO9 1HB Tel: (01787) 474446 Fax: (01787) 475616

Fieldhouse & Husbands, Cemetery Road, Houghton Regis, Dunstable, Bedfordshire, LU5 5BZ Tel: (01582) 867709 Fax: (01582) 861255 E-mail: dnoel@freewire.net

F.J. Fildes, Stourbridge Road, Lye, Stourbridge, West Midlands, DY9 7BU Tel: (01384) 892939 Fax: (01384) 892903 E-mail: postmaster@rmgroup.co.uk

Garlics Ltd, Sandpits Acacia Road, Bourneville, Birmingham, B30 2AH Tel: 0121-472 3848 Fax: 0121-414 0065

Pete Garth Autorefinishing Ltd, Riverview Road, Beverley, North Humberside, HU17 0LD Tel: (01482) 882747 Fax: (01482) 865423

Gribben Motors, 159 Keady Road, Armagh, BT60 3AE Tel: (028) 3752 4614 Fax: (028) 3752 4614

Groom & Hornsby Ltd, 496 Cowley Road, Oxford, OX4 2DP Tel: (01865) 455400 Fax: (01865) 776236 E-mail: info@groom-hornsby.co.uk

H E Marshalls of Slough, Petersfield Avenue, Slough, SL2 5EF Tel: (01753) 522421 Fax: (01753) 531233

Harborne Garage Ltd, 2 Ewhurst Avenue, Birmingham, B29 6EY Tel: 0121-472 4300 Fax: 0121-472 4400 E-mail: admin@harbornegarage.co.uk

I M Refinishers, 2 Northampton Road, Brixworth, Northampton, NN6 9DY Tel: (01604) 880880 Fax: (01604) 881222 E-mail: ideal.motors@virgin.net

Impact Refinishers Ltd, Main Street, Hull, HU2 0LF Tel: (01482) 327690 Fax: (01482) 328036 E-mail: enquiries@impactrefinishers.co.uk

L.E. Jackson (Coachworks) Ltd, Vehicle Body Centre, Queens Road, Loughborough, Leicestershire, LE11 1HD Tel: (01509) 230811 Fax: (01509) 230812

K Brotherton, Unit 23 Honeybourne Airfield Trading Estate, Honeybourne, Evesham, Worcestershire, WR11 7QF Tel: (01386) 833429 Fax: (01386) 833429

Leighton Coach Works, Buzzard Works, Billington Road, Leighton Buzzard, Bedfordshire, LU7 4TN Tel: (01525) 373365 Fax: (01525) 853365

Roy Lloyd Ltd, 1 Hall Street, Southport, Merseyside, PR9 0SF Tel: (01704) 537333 Fax: (01704) 548543

Frank Ludlow Ltd, 71 Windmill Road, Luton, LU1 3XL Tel: (01582) 414441 Fax: (01582) 483618

M B Motors, Wedglen Park, Midhurst, West Sussex, GU29 9RE Tel: (01730) 813000 Fax: (01730) 812227 E-mail: mbmotors@pchowne.freeserve.co.uk

Marlboro' Motors Ltd, 10 Watson, 10 Watsons Walk, St. Albans, Hertfordshire, AL1 1PA Tel: (01727) 850601 Fax: (01727) 844245

Marsh Barton Coachworks Ltd, Grace Road, Marsh Barton, Exeter, EX2 8PU Tel: (01392) 202224 Fax: (01392) 423576 E-mail: admin@marshbartoncoachworks.co.uk

MKG Motor Group Ltd, Cavendish Road, Stevenage, Hertfordshire, SG1 2ET Tel: (01438) 365663 Fax: (01438) 318318

Nationwide Crash Repair Centres Ltd, 11-13 York Street, Ayr, KA8 8AN Tel: (01292) 267142 Fax: (01292) 610307

Oval Bodyshop, Broadway North, West Wilts Trading Estate, Westbury, Wiltshire, BA13 4JX Tel: (01373) 855866 Fax: (01373) 858103

Penfold Motors, 345 Lee High Road, London, SE12 8RU Tel: (020) 8355 8000 Fax: (020) 8355 8018 E-mail: sales@penfolds-vauxhall.co.uk

Premier Bodyshops Ltd, 15 Bilton Way, Luton, LU1 1UU Tel: (01582) 424100 Fax: (01582) 483615 E-mail: info@premierbodyshops.co.uk

Progress Panels, Stoke Mill, Mill Road, Sharnbrook, Bedford, MK44 1NP Tel: (01234) 781007

R & B Autos, Hackhurst Lane, Lower Dicker, Hailsham, East Sussex, BN27 4BW Tel: (01323) 845487

R S Dawe Motor Body Repair Centre, Norfolk Road, Gravesend, Kent, DA12 2PS Tel: (01474) 365840 Fax: (01474) 350900

R W Burt & Co Ltd, 47 Swindon Road, Cheltenham, Gloucestershire, GL50 4AH Tel: (01242) 525051 Fax: (01242) 525051

Riverside Motors Selby Ltd, Maltings Yard, Ousegate, Selby, North Yorkshire, YO8 8BL Tel: (01757) 704999 Fax: (01757) 704999

S Macneillie & Son Ltd, Stockton Close, Walsall, WS2 8LD Tel: (01922) 725560 Fax: (01922) 720916

S V R Coachworks, Unit U10, Rudford Industrial Estate, Ford Road, Ford, Arundel, West Sussex, BN18 0BF Tel: (01903) 734929 Fax: (01243) 545133

Solus Norwich Union, 16 Blenheim Road, Epsom, Surrey, KT19 9AP Tel: (01372) 727133 Fax: (01372) 745048 E-mail: info@longmead.co.uk

▶ Station Garage, Wilbraham Road, Fulbourn, Cambridge, CB21 5ET Tel: (01223) 880747 Fax: (01223) 880885 E-mail: mail@stationgaragefulbourn.co.uk

Stevens & Gill Panelcraft, Unit 54, Barking Industrial Park, Alfreds Way, Barking, Essex, IG11 0TJ Tel: (020) 8594 0357 Fax: (020) 8594 0357

Supertune Automotive Ltd, 291 Elland Road, Leeds, LS11 8AX Tel: 0113-277 4311 Fax: 0113-272 0400

Technik Motors Ltd, 2a Langdale Avenue, Mitcham, Surrey, CR4 4AE Tel: (020) 8648 8162 Fax: (020) 8648 8162

Tenby Coachworks Ltd, The Green, Tenby, Dyfed, SA70 8EU Tel: (01834) 842016 Fax: (01834) 843283

Tony Bone Crash Repairs, Grace Road Central, Marsh Barton Trading Estate, Exeter, EX2 8QA Tel: (01392) 252277

Tregoning Ford, Tollgate, St. Breock, Wadebridge, Cornwall, PL27 7HT Tel: (01208) 893000 Fax: (01208) 815320 E-mail: sales@tregoningford.co.uk

Trewick Coachworks Ltd, Benton Square Indust Estate, Wesley Drive, Newcastle upon Tyne, NE12 9UN Tel: 0191-266 3581 Fax: 0191-270 0597 E-mail: repairs@trewicks.co.uk

Trinder Brothers, 3 Beaver Units, Quarry Lane Industrial Estate, Chichester, West Sussex, PO19 7NY Tel: (01243) 783504 Fax: (01243) 783504

C. Twigg & Son, Hope Street, Rotherham, South Yorkshire, S60 1LH Tel: (01709) 373146 Fax: (01709) 362747 E-mail: btwigg@btconnect.com

Vigurs Torquay Ltd, Vigurs Yard, Forest Road, Torquay, TQ1 4JS Tel: (01803) 327535 Fax: (01803) 316940 E-mail: info@virgus.co.uk

MOTOR VEHICLE BODY REFINISHING/PANEL BEATING/ SPRAYING SPECIALIST SERVICES

– continued

Whatley & Co (Pewsley) Ltd, Avonside Works, Pewsey, Wiltshire, SN9 5AS Tel: (01672) 562404 Fax: (01672) 563091 E-mail: whatley.pewsey@lineone.net

Wright Bus Ltd, Galgorm Industrial Estate, Fenaghy Road, Galgorm, Ballymena, County Antrim, BT42 1PY Tel: (028) 2564 1212 Fax: (028) 2564 9703 E-mail: sales@wright-bus.com

MOTOR VEHICLE BODY REFINISHING/SPRAYING PRODUCTS

Atex Factors Ltd, Canal Street, Brierley Hill, West Midlands, DY5 1JR Tel: (01384) 480500 Fax: (01384) 74820

Brown Brothers, Unit 2, Wild Street, Lowestoft, Suffolk, NR32 1XH Tel: (01502) 573196 Fax: (01502) 508076

E M M UK Ltd, Old Road, Southam, Warwickshire, CV47 1RA Tel: (01926) 812419 Fax: (01926) 817425 E-mail: sales@emm.co.uk

General Express Motor Supplies (Leicester) Ltd, Pullman Road, Wigston, Leicestershire, LE18 2DB Tel: 0116-288 1344 Fax: 0116-257 0290

Kent Car Panel & Paint Ltd, Units 2-3, Willow Industries, Tyland Lane, Sandling, Maidstone, Kent, ME14 3BN Tel: (01622) 752821 Fax: (01622) 754254 E-mail: kentcarpanels@aol.com

Key Paint Ltd, 1 Eldon Road, Luton, LU4 0AZ Tel: (01582) 572627 Fax: (01582) 593489

L E Went Ltd, 52-56 Burlington Road, New Malden, Surrey, KT3 4NU Tel: (020) 8949 0626 Fax: (020) 8715 1116 E-mail: iew.paint@virgin.net

Mallaband Motor Factors Ltd, Unit 2, Lansell Industrial Estate, Caton Road, Lancaster, LA1 3PD Tel: (01524) 60861 Fax: (01524) 843556

Milton Keynes Paint & Equipment Ltd, Unit K, Lyon Road, Denbigh West, Bletchley, Milton Keynes, MK1 1EX Tel: (01908) 371441 Fax: (01908) 367030 E-mail: sales@mkpe.co.uk

Morelli Equipment Ltd, 1 City Road, Norwich, NR1 3AJ Tel: (01603) 760037 Fax: (01603) 760017 E-mail: headoffice@morelli.co.uk

Morelli Group Ltd, Unit 2 Baird Road, Enfield, Middlesex, EN1 1SJ Tel: (07956) 385795 Fax: (020) 8351 5172 E-mail: headoffice@morelli.co.uk

Movac Group Ltd, 135 Ditton Walk, Cambridge, CB5 8QB Tel: (01223) 240568 Fax: (01223) 412459

Movac Group Ltd, 11 Portman Road, Ipswich, IP1 2BP Tel: (01473) 213763 Fax: (0870) 8358601 E-mail: info@movac.com

Provincial Motor Factors, William Street, Sunderland, SR1 1TW Tel: 0191-565 8141 Fax: 0191-565 9296 E-mail: sales@provincialtyres.co.uk

Scarborough Laquers Co., Merry Lees, Staxton, Scarborough, North Yorkshire, YO12 4NN Tel: (01944) 710349 Fax: (01944) 710470 E-mail: sales@scarboroughlacquers.co.uk

Totnes Radiators, Burke Road, Totnes, Devon, TQ9 5XL Tel: (01803) 863123 Fax: (01803) 863123 E-mail: admin@carradiator.co.uk

MOTOR VEHICLE BODY REPAIR

▶ Bowron Motor Care, Hatton House, Flaunden Lane, Flaunden, Hemel Hempstead, Hertfordshire, HP3 0PQ Tel: (01442) 834634 Fax: (01442) 834488 E-mail: sales@bowron-motorcare.co.uk

▶ Dashtech Services (UK), Delta Street, New Basford, Nottingham, NG7 7GJ Tel: (07980) 213377 E-mail: m_ali1972@hotmail.com

▶ Lady Royd Garage, 507 Thornton Road, Bradford, West Yorkshire, BD8 9RB Tel: (01274) 545304 Fax: (01274) 498176 E-mail: fiona@ladyroyd.co.uk

▶ PCT Porsche Specialists, Fast Lane Building, A45 Dunchurch Highway, Allesley, Coventry, CV5 9QA Tel: (0845) 6444993 E-mail: info@pctcars.co.uk

▶ Smart Refinishers (Aberdeen) Ltd, Kirkhill Indust Estate, Aberdeen, AB21 0HP Tel: (01224) 772999 Fax: (01224) 772007 E-mail: sales@smartrefinishers.co.uk

▶ Trim Wizard, 3 Trelawne Drive, Cranleigh, Surrey, GU6 8BS Tel: (07748) 963904 E-mail: andy@trimwizard.co.uk

▶ UV Refinish Technology Ltd, 15 Jasmine Road, Great Bridgeford, Stafford, ST18 9PT Tel: 01785 281171 Fax: 01785 281171 E-mail: mproctor@uv-refinishtechnology.co.uk

MOTOR VEHICLE BODY REPAIR EQUIPMENT

▶ UV Refinish Technology Ltd, 15 Jasmine Road, Great Bridgeford, Stafford, ST18 9PT Tel: 01785 281171 Fax: 01785 281171 E-mail: mproctor@uv-refinishtechnology.co.uk

MOTOR VEHICLE BODY REPAIR/ FILLER PRODUCTS

Bondaglass Voss Ltd, Sunderland Road, Sandy, Bedfordshire, SG19 1QY Tel: (01767) 681432 Fax: (01767) 691720

Bracebridge Motor Body Works Ltd, 246 Newark Road, Lincoln, LN6 8RP Tel: (01522) 520383 Fax: (01522) 537137

Brownlow Way Garage, Topping Street, Off Brownlow Way, Bolton, BL1 3UB Tel: (01204) 533300 Fax: (01204) 533300

Continental Service Station Ltd, Brecon Road, Caerbont, Abercrave, Swansea, SA9 1SW Tel: (01639) 730279 Fax: (01639) 730282 E-mail: continentalss@aol.com

Ensign Engineering Co., Station Road, Baldock, Hertfordshire, SG7 5BT Tel: (01462) 892931 Fax: (01462) 893667

Factory Lane Autos Ltd, 9-11 Broton Drive, Halstead, Essex, CO9 1HB Tel: (01787) 474446 Fax: (01787) 475616

Gladwins Ltd, Church Road, Warboys, Huntingdon, Cambridgeshire, PE28 2RJ Tel: (01487) 822427 Fax: (01487) 823142 E-mail: gladwinsbodyshop@aol.com

Greens Accident Repair Centre, 1 Mercer Road, Warnham, Horsham, West Sussex, RH12 3RL Tel: (01403) 254506 Fax: (01403) 254695

John Hitchin Cars, Unit 3 Dean Street, Bedford, MK40 3EQ Tel: (01234) 348527 Fax: (01234) 348753

R.C. Jones (Motor Bodies) Ltd, Claycliffe Road, Barugh Green, Barnsley, South Yorkshire, S75 1HS Tel: (01226) 205123 Fax: (01226) 292202 E-mail: reception@rcjones.net

Motor Body Care (Northwich) Ltd, Denton Drive, Northwich, Cheshire, CW9 7LU Tel: (01606) 331438 Fax: (01606) 331440

N & V Motors, 13-14 Oakwood Industrial Park, Gatwick Road, Crawley, West Sussex, RH10 9AZ Tel: (01293) 547541 Fax: (01293) 611917

Pond & Sharman Ltd, Browells Lane, Feltham, Middlesex, TW13 7EQ Tel: (020) 8890 8222 Fax: (020) 8751 0179 E-mail: pond@cogg.co.uk

Popplewells Coach Works Ltd, High Road, Thornwood, Epping, Essex, CM16 6LP Tel: (01992) 574040 Fax: (01992) 576653

Starkie & Palmer, 16 Fairfield Road, Market Harborough, Leicestershire, LE16 9QQ Tel: (01858) 469508 Fax: (01858) 469508

Tip Top Accident Repairs Ltd, Worcester Road, Kidderminster, Worcestershire, DY10 1HY Tel: (01562) 822081 Fax: (01562) 825922

▶ UV Refinish Technology Ltd, 15 Jasmine Road, Great Bridgeford, Stafford, ST18 9PT Tel: 01785 281171 Fax: 01785 281171 E-mail: mproctor@uv-refinishtechnology.co.uk

Wimpole Garages Ltd, Portland Street South, Ashton-under-Lyne, Lancashire, OL6 7RE Tel: 0161-330 9551 Fax: 0161-339 0141

MOTOR VEHICLE BODY TOOLING

Modern Machinery Supplies Ltd, Rathdown Road, Lissue Industrial Estate West, Lisburn, County Antrim, BT28 2RE Tel: (028) 9262 2011 Fax: (028) 9262 2181 E-mail: sales@modernmachinerysupplies.co.uk

MOTOR VEHICLE BREAKERS/ SALVAGE CONTRACTORS

Anthony & Associates, 2 Thorn Road, Poole, Dorset, BH17 9AX Tel: (01202) 380500 Fax: (01202) 380510

Borough Motor Services Ltd, 226 Cleveland Street, Birkenhead, Merseyside, CH41 3QJ Tel: 0151-647 8019 Fax: 0151-650 0666 E-mail: bmsltd@btinternet.com

H W Taroni Metals Ltd, Aston Church Road, Saltley, Birmingham, B8 1QF Tel: 0121-327 2959 Fax: 0121-327 4140 E-mail: paul@h-taroni.fsnet.co.uk

J Spindler & Sons Ltd, Joma Roma, The Common, Metfield, Harleston, Norfolk, IP20 0LP Tel: (01986) 785335 Fax: (01986) 785472 E-mail: martin@srts.fsnet.co.uk

▶ Sharples Street Salvage, Sharples Street, Blackburn, BB2 3QT Tel: (01254) 696824 Fax: (01254) 696824 E-mail: info@sssalvage.com

Taroni Bros, Unit 14 Rocky La Trading Estate, William Henry Street, Birmingham, B7 5ER Tel: 0121-333 3330 Fax: 0121-333 6080

Z B Motors, Old Maidstone Road, Sidcup, Kent, DA14 5BB Tel: (020) 8300 2783 Fax: (020) 8309 7539

MOTOR VEHICLE BUMPERS

Hope Technical Developments Ltd, High Street, Ascot, Berkshire, SL5 7HP Tel: (01344) 624855 Fax: (01344) 626237 E-mail: info@hope-tecdev.com

MOTOR VEHICLE COMPONENT IMPORT/EXPORT MERCHANTS OR AGENTS

Motor Parts Direct Ltd, Unit 4 The Cobden Centre, Hawksworth, Didcot, Oxfordshire, OX11 7HL Tel: (01235) 817890 Fax: (01235) 813897

MOTOR VEHICLE COMPONENT PRESSINGS

A E Oscroft & Sons, 49d Pipers Road, Park Farm Industrial Estate, Redditch, Worcestershire, B98 0HU Tel: (01527) 502203 Fax: (01527) 510378 E-mail: info@aeoscroft.co.uk

Bacol Fine Blanking Ltd, Tramway, Oldbury Road, Smethwick, West Midlands, B66 1NY Tel: (01527) 874205 Fax: (01527) 833761 E-mail: info@bacolfineblanking.co.uk

Baylis Automotive, Unit 49g, Pipers Road, Park Farm Industrial Estate, Redditch, Worcestershire, B98 0HU Tel: (01527) 517220 Fax: (01527) 517114 E-mail: tclews@baylisautomotive.com

Fowkes & Danks Ltd, Howard Road, Park Farm Industrial Estate, Redditch, Worcestershire, B98 7SE Tel: (01527) 830800 Fax: (01527) 830801 E-mail: enquiries@fowkes&danks.co.uk

Jenks & Cattell Engineering Ltd, Neachells Lane, Wolverhampton, WV11 3PU Tel: (01902) 305530 Fax: (01902) 305529 E-mail: sales@jenks-cattell.co.uk

Metal Pressings Group Ltd, Howard Road, Redditch, Worcestershire, B98 7SE Tel: (01527) 526933 Fax: (01527) 510009 E-mail: cmp@metal-pressings.com

Presscraft Components Ltd, 3 Woodburn Road, Smethwick, West Midlands, B66 2PU Tel: 0121-558 1888 Fax: 0121-555 5498 E-mail: info@presscraft-limited.co.uk

Romo (Engineering) Ltd, Unit 12B, Waterfall Lane Trading Estate, Waterfall Lane, Cradley Heath, West Midlands, B64 6PU Tel: 0121-559 5966 Fax: 0121-559 5952 E-mail: press@romo.co.uk

▶ Stadco Ltd, Harlescott Lane, Shrewsbury, SY1 3AS Tel: (01743) 462227 Fax: (01743) 447709 E-mail: info@stadco.co.uk

Taylor Pressform Ltd, 21 Rigby Close, Heathcote Industrial Estate, Warwick, CV34 6TH Tel: (01926) 339507 Fax: (01926) 451306

Wagon Automotive Wantage Plant, Main Street, East Challow, Wantage, Oxfordshire, OX12 9SY Tel: (01235) 770770 Fax: (01235) 770017 E-mail: wantage@wagonautomotive.com

MOTOR VEHICLE COMPONENT REMANUFACTURING

Caterpillar Remanufacturing Services, Lancaster Road, Shrewsbury, SY1 3NX Tel: (01743) 212000 Fax: (01743) 212700

A.W.D. Dwight & Sons (Engineers) Ltd, Delamare Road, Cheshunt, Waltham Cross, Hertfordshire, EN8 9UD Tel: (01992) 634255 Fax: (01992) 626672 E-mail: sales@imperialengineering.co.uk

The Hutson Motor Company Ltd, Pawson Street, Bradford, West Yorkshire, BD4 8DF Tel: (01274) 669052 Fax: (01274) 669685 E-mail: hutsonmc@talk21.com

Kwik-Fit GB Ltd, 216 West Main Street, Broxburn, West Lothian, EH52 5AS Tel: (01506) 864000 Fax: (01506) 864141 E-mail: info@kwik-fit.com

Q H Auto Electrics, Lichfield Road, Brownhills, Walsall, WS8 6LH Tel: (01543) 377281 Fax: (01543) 361062

Shaftec Automotive Components Ltd, 2 Cato Street, Birmingham, B7 4TS Tel: 0121-333 3555 Fax: 0121-359 3003 E-mail: shaftec@automotive8.freeserve.co.uk

MOTOR VEHICLE COMPONENTS

Auto Europe Parts Ltd, Unit 11 Betchworth Works, Ifield Road, Charlwood, Horley, Surrey, RH6 0DX Tel: (01293) 863777 Fax: (01293) 863888 E-mail: info@autoeurope.co.uk

Avon Automotive, Bumbers Farm Industrial Estate, Bumpers Way, Chippenham, Wiltshire, SN14 6NF Tel: (01249) 667000 Fax: (01249) 667001 E-mail: enquiries@avonauto.com

Borgwarner Holdings Ltd, Roydsdale Way, Euroway Industrial Estate, Bradford, West Yorkshire, BD4 6SE Tel: (01274) 684915 Fax: (01274) 689671

Robert Bosch Ltd, Cardiff Plant, Miskin Industrial Park, Miskin, Pontyclun, Mid Glamorgan, CF72 8XQ Tel: (01443) 221000 Fax: (01443) 221201

C T P Wipac Ltd, London Road, Buckingham, MK18 1BH Tel: (01280) 822800 Fax: (01280) 822802 E-mail: sales@wipac.com

Cummins Turbo Technologies Ltd, St. Andrews Road, Huddersfield, HD1 6RA Tel: (01484) 422244 Fax: (01484) 511680 E-mail: enquiries@cummins.co.uk

Dave Mac Supplies, 1-3 Northey Road, Coventry, CV6 5NF Tel: (024) 7668 3239 Fax: (024) 7658 1852

E C Hopkins Ltd, Barton Industrial Estate, Mount Pleasant, Bilston, West Midlands, WV14 7LH Tel: (01902) 401755 Fax: (01902) 495097 E-mail: bhopkins@echopkins.co.uk

European After Market Management Ltd, 22 The Parchments, Newton-le-Willows, Merseyside, WA12 0DY Tel: (01925) 223515 Fax: (01925) 223515 E-mail: phil@pjwipers.co.uk

Falcon Automotive Engineering, Unit 8 Victoria Way, Pride Park, Derby, DE24 8AN Tel: (01332) 227280 Fax: (01332) 227289 E-mail: sales@falcon-automotive.co.uk

Faurecina Midlands Ltd, PO Box 200, Coventry, CV3 1LU Tel: (024) 7663 5533 Fax: (024) 7688 5075

Firstek, Harvey Road, Burnt Mills Industrial Estate, Basildon, Essex, SS13 1EP Tel: (01268) 727472 Fax: (01268) 729872

G K N Export Services Ltd, PO Box 55, Redditch, Worcestershire, B98 0TL Tel: (01527) 517715 Fax: (01527) 517700 E-mail: information@gkn.com

Harmon Precision Grinding, 55 Haviland Road, Ferndown Industrial Estate, Ferndown Industrial Estate, Wimborne, Dorset, BH21 7PY Tel: (01202) 654198 Fax: (01202) 654199 E-mail: info@harmon.co.uk

Johnson Control Telford Interiors, Unit E, Halesfield 10, Telford, Shropshire, TF7 4QP Tel: (01952) 686000 Fax: (01952) 686001

Johnson Controls Automotive UK Ltd, Unit B Stafford Park 6, Telford, Shropshire, TF3 3BQ Tel: (01952) 209300

Kautex Unipart Ltd, Renown Avenue, Coventry, CV5 6UD Tel: (024) 7667 1100 Fax: (024) 7667 1101

Kenlowe Accessories & Co. Ltd, Burchetts Green, Maidenhead, Berkshire, SL6 6QU Tel: (01628) 823303 Fax: (01628) 823451 E-mail: sales@kenlowe.com

Lynwood Engineering, Albert House, High Street, Tipton, West Midlands, DY4 9HG Tel: 0121-522 6600 Fax: 0121-522 6601 E-mail: lynwoodengineering@qualtronyc.co.uk

Meritor Light Vehicle Systems (U K) Ltd, Roof Systems, Fordhouse Lane, Birmingham, B30 3BW Tel: 0121-459 1166 Fax: 0121-459 9808 E-mail: marco.foley@arvinmeritor.com

Midland Vehicle Components Ltd, Oban Road, Coventry, CV6 6HH Tel: (024) 7664 4255 Fax: (024) 7636 4747

Millvale Engineering Ltd, Millvale House, Selsley Hill, Dudbridge, Stroud, Gloucestershire, GL5 3HF Tel: (01453) 766396 Fax: (01453) 759630 E-mail: clive.millward@millvaleltd.co.uk

Mont Blanc Industri UK Ltd, Eden Way, Pages Industrial Park, Leighton Buzzard, Bedfordshire, LU7 4TZ Tel: (01525) 850800 Fax: (01525) 850808 E-mail: sales@montblancuk.co.uk

Motaquip Ltd, Torrington Avenue, Torrington Avenue, Tile Hill, Coventry, CV4 9UX Tel: (024) 7688 3000 Fax: (024) 7647 3235 E-mail: customer.services@motamail.net

N Thompson, Unit J & K Cardigan Workspace, Lennox Road, Leeds, LS4 2BL Tel: 0113-289 0819

Omega Automotive Ltd, 4 Europa Way, Britannia Enterprise Park, Lichfield, Staffordshire, WS14 9TZ Tel: (01543) 490628 Fax: (01543) 493421 E-mail: info@omega-automotive.com

▶ Panaf Car Accessories, 174 Enterprise Court, Eastways, Witham, Essex, CM8 3YS Tel: (01376) 511550 Fax: (01376) 515131 E-mail: panaf@btclick.com

Partco Autoparts Ltd, Unit 11 Gatwick Int Distribution Centre, Cobham Way, Crawley, West Sussex, RH10 9RX Tel: (01293) 524211 Fax: (01293) 518187

R D H Components Ltd, Nelson Lane, Warwick, CV34 5JB Tel: (01926) 409330 Fax: (01926) 409331

Serck Intertruck, 293 Elland Road, Leeds, LS11 8AX Tel: 0113-242 1463 Fax: 0113-385 5811 E-mail: si.leeds@unipart.co.uk

Siemens V D O Automotive Systems, Halesfield 25, Telford, Shropshire, TF7 4LP Tel: (01952) 683600 Fax: (01952) 580626 E-mail: sales@siemens.auto.com

T R W Fastening Systems, Buckingham Road, Aylesbury, Buckinghamshire, HP19 9QA Tel: (01296) 717000 Fax: (01296) 717100 E-mail: gil.swash@trw.com

Technical Services UK Ltd, Highfield Works, Intake Road, Bradford, West Yorkshire, BD2 3JR Tel: (01274) 637851 Fax: (01274) 637852

Trelleborg Stanton Ltd, 853 London Road, Grays, Essex, RM20 3LG Tel: (01708) 685685 Fax: (01708) 685686 E-mail: sales@stanton-uk.com

Troy Components Ltd, Troy Industrial Estate, Jill Lane, Sambourne, Redditch, Worcestershire, B96 6ES Tel: (01527) 892941 Fax: (01527) 893310

Vegem Ltd, PO Box 9, Leeds, LS27 0QN Tel: 0113-253 0451 Fax: 0113-252 1161 E-mail: enquiries@vegem.co.uk

R.L. Walsh & Sons (Coventry) Ltd, 17 Lythalls Lane, Coventry, CV6 6FN Tel: (024) 7668 7241 Fax: (024) 7666 2870 E-mail: office@rlwalsh.co.uk

Z F Trading, Eldon Way, Crick, Northampton, NN6 7SL Tel: (01788) 822353 Fax: (01788) 823829 E-mail: sales@zf.com

MOTOR VEHICLE CONTROL CABLES

Fast Lane Auto Ltd, Callywith Gate Industrial Estate, Launceston Road, Bodmin, Cornwall, PL31 2RQ Tel: (01208) 264546 Fax: (01208) 264547 E-mail: sales@fastlaneauto.co.uk

MOTOR VEHICLE CONVERSION

Cowal Mobility Aid Ltd, Cowal Court, Heath End Road, Great Kingshill, High Wycombe, Buckinghamshire, HP15 6HL Tel: (01494) 714400 Fax: (01494) 714818
E-mail: sales@cowalmobility.co.uk
D S A, 4-5 Edison Road, Rabans Lane Industrial Area, Aylesbury, Buckinghamshire, HP19 8TE Tel: (01296) 486911 Fax: (01296) 334335
E-mail: hq@gforcemotorsport.co.uk
▶ K C Mobility Services Ltd, Unit 2, Carlinghow Mills, 501 Bradford Road, Batley, West Yorkshire, WF17 8LL Tel: (01924) 442386
Leo Engineering Ltd, Bingswood Industrial Estate, Whaley Bridge, High Peak, Derbyshire, SK23 7LY Tel: (01663) 735344 Fax: (01663) 735352 E-mail: info@minibusoptions.co.uk

MOTOR VEHICLE DELIVERY/ COLLECTION SERVICES

▶ Alan-Peters Group, 38 Newton Road, Isleworth, Middlesex, TW7 6QD Tel: 020 8569 9006 Fax: 020 8569 7789
E-mail: info@alan-petersgroup.co.uk
▶ Broughtons Distribution Ltd, Brailwood Road, Bilsthorpe, Newark, Nottinghamshire, NG22 8UA Tel: (01623) 411114 Fax: (01623) 411010
E-mail: sales@broughtonsdistribution.co.uk
Dunn & Webster, 4 Hever Close, Dudley, West Midlands, DY1 2SY Tel: (07850) 750089
Fax: (01384) 233224
▶ Eclipse Vehicle Management, Unit 15 Rectory La Trading Estate, Kingston Bagpuize, Abingdon, Oxfordshire, OX13 5AS Tel: (01865) 823113 Fax: (01865) 823115
Mainland Car Deliveries Ltd, Mainland House, Bootle, Merseyside, L20 3EF Tel: 0151-933 9612 Fax: 0151-933 4751
E-mail: contactus@mcd-ltd.co.uk
Tibbett & Britten Group P.L.C., Centennial Park, Centennial Avenue, Elstree, Borehamwood, Hertfordshire, WD6 3TL Tel: (020) 8327 2000
Fax: (020) 8327 2199
E-mail: info@tandb.co.uk

MOTOR VEHICLE DOG GUARDS

M M G Guards, 1 Station Street, Holbeach, Spalding, Lincolnshire, PE12 7LF Tel: 01406 426047

MOTOR VEHICLE DRIVING TUITION SIMULATORS

▶ Ashby's Driving School, 29 Acres Gardens, Tadworth, Surrey, KT20 5LP Tel: (01737) 358430 Fax: (01737) 358430
E-mail: info@ashbysdrivingschool.gbr.cc
▶ Southern Driver Training, 87 Wrestwood Road, Bexhill-on-Sea, East Sussex, TN40 2LP
Tel: (01424) 732952
E-mail: southerndrivertraining@hotmail.com

MOTOR VEHICLE ELECTRICAL ACCESSORIES

▶ Cartel Uk Ltd, 20 Colwell Road, Leicester, LE3 9AX Tel: (07977) 777742 Fax: 0116-223 9702 E-mail: cartel_uk@hotmail.co.uk

MOTOR VEHICLE ENGINE COMPONENTS

Power Assemblies Ltd, Cooper Street, Wolverhampton, WV2 2JL Tel: (01902) 456767
Fax: (01902) 456761
S M S Diesel Spares Ltd, Cabot Works, Bilton Way, Enfield, Middlesex, EN3 7NH Tel: (020) 8443 4442 Fax: (020) 8443 3667
E-mail: sales@smsdiesel.co.uk

MOTOR VEHICLE ENGINE TEST EQUIPMENT

C P Engineering, Sandys Road, Malvern, Worcestershire, WR14 1JJ Tel: (01684) 584850 Fax: (01684) 573088
E-mail: sales@cpengineering.com
▶ Performance Automotive, Unit 5 Bridgeway, St. Leonards-On-Sea, East Sussex, TN38 8AP
Tel: 01424 200825
E-mail: performanceautomotive@hotmail.co.uk
Sun Diagnostic, Unit 12 Horsleys Fields, King's Lynn, Norfolk, PE30 5DD Tel: (01553) 692422
Fax: (01553) 691844
E-mail: uksales@snapon.com

MOTOR VEHICLE ENGINE TUNING

Classic Performance Ltd, 7 Trent Industrial Estate, Wetmore Road, Burton-on-Trent, Staffordshire, DE14 1QY Tel: (01283) 531122
Fax: (01283) 531328
E-mail: sales@classicperformance.co.uk
▶ Hillside Garage, Laundry Lane, Ingleton, Carnforth, Lancashire, LA6 3DA Tel: (01524) 241595 Fax: (01524) 241595
E-mail: sales@hillsidegarage.f9.co.uk
Port-Formance, 59 Canberra Square, Warrington, WA2 0DY Tel: (01925) 724278 Fax: (01925) 724278 E-mail: steveposo@ntlworld.com

MOTOR VEHICLE ENGINEERING

A C C Automatic Transmission, 24 The Fairways, New River Trading Estate, Cheshunt, Waltham Cross, Hertfordshire, EN8 0NL Tel: (01992) 639678 Fax: (01992) 634544
Aldon Automotive Ltd, Breener Industrial Estate, Station Drive, Brierley Hill, West Midlands, DY5 3JZ Tel: (01384) 572553 Fax: (01384) 480418 E-mail: alden@yesit.co.uk
Andrew Young Auto Electrical & Air Con Specialists, 4 Prospect Business Park, Langston Road, Loughton, Essex, IG10 3TR
Tel: (020) 8508 5880 Fax: (020) 8502 3530
Ashbrook Garage Ltd, Ashbrook Garage, Clyro, Hereford, HR3 5SD Tel: (01497) 821046
Fax: (01497) 821182
E-mail: poleposition@lineone.net
B A Kirk, Tadwell Farm, Elm Lane, Minster on Sea, Sheerness, Kent, ME12 3SQ Tel: (01795) 876723 Fax: (01795) 876723
B S Motors, 42 Tyne Road, Sandy, Bedfordshire, SG19 1SA Tel: (01767) 682206 Fax: (01767) 682208 E-mail: sales@bsmotors.com
Bartons Of Bawtry Ltd, Market Place, Bawtry, Doncaster, South Yorkshire, DN10 6JL
Tel: (01302) 710212 Fax: (01302) 710212
Carparts, Hyberry, Ashlands Meadow, Crewkerne, Somerset, TA18 7NN Tel: (01460) 74600
Crouch Engineering Co. (Burnham-on-Crouch) Ltd, 150 Station Rd, Burnham-on-Crouch, Essex, CM0 8HQ Tel: (01621) 782130
Fax: (01621) 782130
J. Douthwaite & Sons Ltd, Forest Street, Blackburn, BB1 3BB Tel: (01254) 675115
Fax: (01254) 297255
E-mail: info@jdstrucks.co.uk
E T Tucker Ltd, 87 Severn Road, Cardiff, CF11 9EA Tel: (029) 2022 9842
Emanuel Bros Ltd, Wexham Road, Slough, SL1 1RW Tel: (01753) 524153 Fax: (01753) 530775 E-mail: sales@emanuelbrothers.co.uk
F J Payne & Son Ltd, Oakfield Industrial Estate, Eynsham, Witney, Oxfordshire, OX29 4AW
Tel: (01865) 882299 Fax: (01865) 882309
E-mail: sales@fjpayne.com
G B B UK Ltd, Manchester Road, Burnley, Lancashire, BB11 1JZ Tel: (01282) 419903
Fax: (01282) 410239 E-mail: info@gbb.com
Hartwell Truck, London Road, Dunstable, Bedfordshire, LU6 3DT Tel: (01582) 597575
Fax: (01582) 582650
A. Hemingway & Sons Ltd, Whitley Lane, Grenoside, Sheffield, S35 8RP Tel: 0114-246 7676 Fax: 0114-257 0264
▶ Hillside Garage, Laundry Lane, Ingleton, Carnforth, Lancashire, LA6 3DA Tel: (01524) 241595 Fax: (01524) 241595
E-mail: sales@hillsidegarage.f9.co.uk
▶ Lowhall Motors, Woodbottom Mills, Low Hall Road, Horsforth, Leeds, LS18 4EF
Tel: 0113-250 4411
M B Motors, Wedglen Park, Midhurst, West Sussex, GU29 9RE Tel: (01730) 813000
Fax: (01730) 812227
E-mail: mbmotors@pchowne.freeserve.co.uk
Marlborough Four Wheel Drive, Unit B, Smiths Yard, Axford, Marlborough, Wiltshire, SN8 2EY
Tel: (01672) 516041 Fax: (01672) 519189
Mercury Motors Ltd, 5-7 Strawberry Vale, Twickenham, TW1 4RX Tel: (020) 8892 4604
Fax: (020) 8892 4454
E-mail: enquiries@mercurymotors.co.uk
Millbrook Proving Ground Ltd, Station Lane, Millbrook, Bedford, MK45 2JQ Tel: (01525) 404242 Fax: (01525) 403420
E-mail: test@millbrook.co.uk
Mittens Vehicle Servicing, The Council Depot, Swindon Road, Cheltenham, Gloucestershire, GL51 9JZ Tel: (01242) 526445 Fax: (01242) 526445
Moserve Auto Engineers, 9 Avon Industrial Estate, Butlers Leap, Rugby, Warwickshire, CV21 3UY Tel: (01788) 561099 Fax: (01788) 337099
Motech Garages, Delph Industrial Estate, Delph Road, Brierley Hill, West Midlands, DY5 2UA
Tel: (01384) 75599 Fax: (01384) 262474
Motortune, 41 Carrhill Road, Mossley, Ashton-under-Lyne, Lancashire, OL5 0SE
Tel: (01457) 832798 Fax: (01457) 831500
MTC Northwest Ltd, Gores Road, Knowsley Industrial Park, Liverpool, L33 7XS
Tel: 0151-545 4750 Fax: 0151-545 4760
E-mail: sales@mtc-northwest.co.uk
Overdrive Auto Services, A 5 Dalton Street, Hull, HU8 8BB Tel: (01482) 222441 Fax: (01482) 222441 E-mail: paul@overdrive.karoo.co.uk
Peartree Engine & Clutch Centre, 1 Peartree Farm, Welwyn Garden City, Hertfordshire, AL7 3UW Tel: (01707) 322026 Fax: (01707) 322026
R Allen Tonbridge Ltd, 18 Lyons Cresent, Tonbridge, Kent, TN9 1EX Tel: (01732) 353499
Rex Caunt, 6 Kings Court, Kingsfield Road, Barwell, Leicester, LE9 8NZ Tel: (01455) 846963 Fax: (01455) 846963
E-mail: rex@rexcauntracing.com
▶ Roye Peters Motor Engineers, 1A Drygate Street, Larkhall, Lanarkshire, ML9 2AJ
Tel: 01698 884037
E-mail: roye@royesgarage.co.uk
Ryan Car Services, C Taplow Road, Taplow, Maidenhead, Berkshire, SL6 0ND Tel: (01628) 669047 Fax: (01628) 605148
Scott Gibbin Ltd, Padholme Road, Peterborough, PE1 5XP Tel: (01733) 561569 Fax: (01733) 552065
Stalham Engineering Co. Ltd, The Green, Stalham, Norwich, NR12 9QG Tel: (01692) 580513 Fax: (01692) 581770
E-mail: mgn@stalhameng.co.uk
Storrington Auto Repairs, M J House, Old Mill Drive, Storrington, Pulborough, West Sussex, RH20 4RH Tel: (01903) 746694 Fax: (01903) 741101
Tennant Motor Services (Leeds) Ltd, Parkspring Coachworks Garage, Swinnow Lane, Leeds, LS13 4LZ Tel: 0113-256 3411 Fax: 0113-236 0430
Thurlow Nunn, Cromer Road, Holt, Norfolk, NR25 6EU Tel: (01263) 713206 Fax: (01263) 713207
Tonge Fold Engineers Ltd, Ainsworth Lane, Bolton, BL2 2PP Tel: (01204) 521917
Fax: (01204) 521917

MOTOR VEHICLE EXHAUST BRACKETS

▶ Lo Cost Tyre & Exhaust, Unit 6, Wotton Road, Ashford, Kent, TN23 6LL Tel: (01233) 666636

MOTOR VEHICLE EXHAUST REPAIR

▶ Ellis Motors, 6 Sheddingdean Business Centre, Marchants Way, Burgess Hill, West Sussex, RH15 8QY Tel: (01444) 480606
Fax: (01444) 480606
E-mail: fixit@ellismotors.co.uk
▶ Lady Royd Garage, 507 Thornton Road, Bradford, West Yorkshire, BD8 9RB
Tel: (01274) 545304 Fax: (01274) 498176
E-mail: fiona@ladyroyd.co.uk

MOTOR VEHICLE FINANCE PACKAGES, CONTRACT HIRE

▶ Bluroc Leasing4u, 4 Mallard Way, Crewe, CW1 6ZQ Tel: (01270) 617540 Fax: (0870) 0941442 E-mail: info@leasing4u.co.uk
▶ J. Charles (Auto Advantage) Ltd, 1 Shallcross Mill Road, Whaley Bridge, High Peak, Derbyshire, SK23 7JQ Tel: (0845) 3303545
Fax: (0845) 3303543
E-mail: virgin.surfer@virgin.net
▶ Direct Vehicle Leasing (Coventry) Ltd, Sovereign Court, 230 Upper Fifth Street, Milton Keynes, MK9 2HR Tel: (0870) 2424628
Fax: (0870) 0514667
E-mail: sales@dvl-coventry.net
▶ E Z Credit, 34 Sudley Road, Bognor Regis, West Sussex, PO21 1ER Tel: (01243) 841818
Fax: (01243) 840180
▶ Eland Business Services Ltd, 57 Eland Way, Cherry Hinton, Cambridge, CB1 9XQ
Tel: (0800) 4589941
E-mail: contact@ebslfinance.co.uk
▶ GCH 2000, 3-5 High Street, Evington, Leicester, LE5 6FH Tel: 0116-273 4759
Fax: (0845) 1235856
E-mail: vehicles@gch2000.co.uk
Key Vehicle Solutions, 80a Main Street, Cherry Burton, Beverley, North Humberside, HU17 7RF Tel: (0845) 1662405 Fax: (0845) 1662406
E-mail: sales@key-vehicle-solutions.co.uk
▶ L C V Leasing & Finance Ltd, Unit 1a Basepoint Enterprise Centre, Stroudley Road, Basingstoke, Hampshire, RG24 8UP
Tel: (0845) 4665599 Fax: (01256) 406739
E-mail: info@lcvleasing.co.uk
▶ UK Automotive Finance Ltd, 3 Alfred St Garage, Alfred Street, Newton-le-Willows, Merseyside, WA12 8BH Tel: (01925) 227777
Fax: (01925) 226655
E-mail: dave@ukautomotivefinance.co.uk
▶ VehicleOptions (Wales), Redwither Business Centre, Redwither Business Park, Wrexham, LL13 9XR Tel: (01978) 664516 Fax: (01978) 661494E-mail: nickcarlton@vehicleoptions.biz
▶ Vipul Dave, 72 Portswood Road, Southampton, SO17 2FW Tel: 0845 8382737
Fax: 0845 8382736
E-mail: info@motordriven.co.uk

MOTOR VEHICLE FINANCE PACKAGES, FINANCE LEASE

▶ J. Charles (Auto Advantage) Ltd, 1 Shallcross Mill Road, Whaley Bridge, High Peak, Derbyshire, SK23 7JQ Tel: (0845) 3303545
Fax: (0845) 3303543
E-mail: virgin.surfer@virgin.net
▶ E Z Credit, 34 Sudley Road, Bognor Regis, West Sussex, PO21 1ER Tel: (01243) 841818
Fax: (01243) 840180
▶ Eland Business Services Ltd, 57 Eland Way, Cherry Hinton, Cambridge, CB1 9XQ
Tel: (0800) 4589941
E-mail: contact@ebslfinance.co.uk
▶ GCH 2000, 3-5 High Street, Evington, Leicester, LE5 6FH Tel: 0116-273 4759
Fax: (0845) 1235856
E-mail: vehicles@gch2000.co.uk
▶ Independent Cars Ltd, Hydra Business Park, Nether Lane, Ecclesfield, Sheffield, S35 9ZX
Tel: (0845) 4303020 Fax: 0114-232 9130
E-mail: info@independentcars.co.uk
L 4 Lease Ltd, Keystone House, 30 Exeter Road, Bournemouth, BH2 5AR Tel: (0870) 4462407
Fax: (07005) 804365
E-mail: info@myfleet.co.uk
▶ L C V Leasing & Finance Ltd, Unit 1a Basepoint Enterprise Centre, Stroudley Road, Basingstoke, Hampshire, RG24 8UP
Tel: (0845) 4665599 Fax: (01256) 406739
E-mail: info@lcvleasing.co.uk
▶ UK Automotive Finance Ltd, 3 Alfred St Garage, Alfred Street, Newton-le-Willows, Merseyside, WA12 8BH Tel: (01925) 227777
Fax: (01925) 226655
E-mail: dave@ukautomotivefinance.co.uk

MOTOR VEHICLE FINANCE PACKAGES, LEASE PURCHASE

▶ E Z Credit, 34 Sudley Road, Bognor Regis, West Sussex, PO21 1ER Tel: (01243) 841818
Fax: (01243) 840180

MOTOR VEHICLE FLEET INSURANCE

▶ Insurance for Car Hire, Trans-World House, 0 City Road, London, EC1Y 2BP Tel: (020) 7012 6300 Fax: (020) 7012 6315
E-mail: iskra@webfactory.bg
▶ Taxi insurance from WYN Group Insurance Services, WYN House, 4 Eve Road, Woking, Surrey, GU21 5JT Tel: 01483 722266
E-mail: info@wyngroup.co.uk

MOTOR VEHICLE FLEET MAINTENANCE SERVICES

Bramall Quicks Ltd, Lower Bridge Street, Chester, CH1 1DX Tel: (01244) 320444
Fax: (01244) 349536
▶ Christian I D Coachworks, Russell Hill Place, Purley, Surrey, CR8 2LH Tel: (020) 8660 6444
Fax: (020) 8668 0116
E-mail: ian@idcoachworks.fsnet.co.uk
Whittaker Fleet Care Ltd, Bordesley Street, Birmingham, B5 5PN Tel: 0121-643 6211
Fax: 0121-643 8299
E-mail: info@wfleetcare.com

MOTOR VEHICLE FUEL SYSTEMS

T I Group Automotive Systems Ltd, Unit 110 Tenth Avenue, Deeside Industrial Park, Deeside, Clwyd, CH5 2UA Tel: (01244) 280488 Fax: (01244) 283640
▶ T I Group Automotive Systems UK Ltd, Halesfield 9, Telford, Shropshire, TF7 4ET
Tel: (01952) 651000 Fax: (01952) 651166
E-mail: mdebono@uk.tiauto.com
Toyoda Gosei Fluid Systems UK Ltd, Rockingham Road, Market Harborough, Leicestershire, LE16 7QE Tel: (01858) 439800
Fax: (01858) 410191

MOTOR VEHICLE HANDLING/ MANOEUVRING MACHINES

Rod Brown Engineering Ltd, Western Villa 58 The Dean, Alresford, Hampshire, SO24 9BD
Tel: (01962) 735220 Fax: (01962) 735239
E-mail: sales@rodbrowneng.co.uk

MOTOR VEHICLE HEATERS/ HEATING EQUIPMENT

Carrier Sutrak, Unit 6, The IO Centre, Lodge Farm Industrial Estate, Northampton, NN5 7UW Tel: (01604) 581468 Fax: (01604) 758132
Foursome Vehicle Heaters Ltd, Brockhill Works, Windsor Road, Redditch, Worcestershire, B97 6DJ Tel: (01527) 64126 Fax: (01527) 584611 E-mail: info@vehicleheaters.co.uk
Mikuni Heating UK Ltd, Unit 6 Second Avenue, Southampton, SO15 0LP Tel: (023) 8052 8777
Fax: (023) 8052 8800
E-mail: sales@mikuniheating.com

▶ indicates data change since last edition

MOTOR VEHICLE HEAVY DUTY CABS

A B T Products Ltd, Ashburton Industrial Estate, Ross-on-Wye, Herefordshire, HR9 7BW Tel: (01989) 563656 Fax: (01989) 566824 E-mail: abtproducts@clara.net

MOTOR VEHICLE HIGH PERFORMANCE EQUIPMENT

D S A, 4-5 Edison Road, Rabans Lane Industrial Area, Aylesbury, Buckinghamshire, HP19 8TE Tel: (01296) 486911 Fax: (01296) 334335 E-mail: hq@gforcemotorsport.co.uk

MMV Performance Ltd, 111 Drip Road, Raploch, Stirling, FK8 1RW Tel: (01786) 448800 Fax: (01786) 448808

Ricardo UK Ltd, Midlands Technical Centre, Southam Road, Leamington Spa, Warwickshire, CV31 1FQ Tel: (01926) 319319 Fax: (01926) 319300

MOTOR VEHICLE HOODS

M L C Monsoon Ltd, Northfield Business Park, London Road, Lower Dicker, Hailsham, East Sussex, BN27 4BZ Tel: (01323) 440422 Fax: (01323) 845705

MOTOR VEHICLE INSTRUMENTS

Instrument Repair Service, 35 Radcliffe Road, West Bridgford, Nottingham, NG2 5FF Tel: 0115-981 9988 Fax: 0115-945 5358 E-mail: info@irs-gb.com

MOTOR VEHICLE INSURANCE

Allianz Cornhill Insurance plc, 57 Ladymead, Guildford, Surrey, GU1 1DB Tel: (01483) 568161 Fax: (01483) 300952 E-mail: cornhill@gho.cornhill.co.uk

Axa Insurance, 1 Aldgate, London, EC3N 1RE Tel: (020) 7702 3109 Fax: (020) 7369 3909

Car Care Plan, Mid Point, Thornbury, Bradford, West Yorkshire, BD3 7AG Tel: (0870) 7527000 Fax: (0870) 7527100

Cheltenham Insurance Brokers Ltd, Herriot House, North Place, Cheltenham, Gloucestershire, GL50 4DS Tel: (01242) 517787

▶ i4insurance, Ipswich, IP1 Tel: (01473) 268210 E-mail: advertising@i4insurance.co.uk

M M A Insurance plc, 2 Norman Place, Reading, RG1 8DA Tel: 0118-955 2222 Fax: 0118-955 2211 E-mail: info@mma-insurance.com

Major Travel plc, Fortress Grove, 28-34 Fortress Road, London, NW5 2HB Tel: (020) 7393 1088 Fax: (020) 7393 1096 E-mail: info@majortravel.co.uk

Milne Friend & Partners, Suite 2-5 Renslade House, Bonhay Road, Exeter, EX4 3AY Tel: (01392) 430097 Fax: (01392) 218696 E-mail: rodmilne@milnefriend.co.uk

Provident Financial Management Services, Colonnade, Sunbridge Road, Bradford, West Yorkshire, BD1 2LQ Tel: (01274) 304044 Fax: (01274) 727300 E-mail: info@provident.co.uk

Steveni Kessler Insurance Services Ltd, Steveni Kessler House Dominion Business Park, Goodwin Road, London, N9 0BG Tel: (020) 8345 5500 Fax: (020) 8482 2000 E-mail: sales@steveni-kessler.co.uk

UKI Partnerships, Green Flag House, Cote Lane, Pudsey, West Yorkshire, LS28 5GF Tel: 0113-236 3236 Fax: 0113-257 3111 E-mail: rcroucher@directline.com

MOTOR VEHICLE INTERIOR ACCESSORIES

ALBRI FASHION ACCESSORIES, 69 Thornham Street, Greenwich, London, SE10 9SB Tel: (07957) 254825 Fax: (0870) 242 0473 E-mail: info@albrifashion.com

▶ P T Co., Greensleeves, Green Bottom, Wimborne, Dorset, BH21 2LW Tel: (01202) 639243 Fax: (01202) 639243 E-mail: sales@ptcompany.co.uk

▶ Remploy Ltd, Bede Trading Estate, Jarrow, Tyne & Wear, NE32 3EG Tel: 0191-489 7528 Fax: 0191-483 3087

MOTOR VEHICLE LAMPS

Cambridge (Auto Bulbs) Ltd, Unit 30 Over Industrial Park, Norman Way, Over, Cambridge, CB24 5QE Tel: (01954) 231611 Fax: (01954) 230552 E-mail: cabulbs@tesco.net

Lucas Aftermarket Operations, Stratford Road, Shirley, Solihull, West Midlands, B90 4LA Tel: 0121-506 5000 Fax: 0121-506 5001 E-mail: enquiries@lucasestateagents.co.uk

Mccroft Lighting, 54a Woods Lane, Derby, DE22 3UD Tel: (01332) 299100 Fax: (01332) 200365

Normalec Ltd, Kingsley House, 1 Kingsley Street, Leicester, LE2 6DY Tel: 0116-288 9922 Fax: 0116-288 8463 E-mail: sales@normalitefsnet.co.uk

Perei Group Ltd, Sunbury House 4 Christy Estate, Ivy Road, Aldershot, Hampshire, GU12 4TX Tel: (01252) 350833 Fax: (01252) 350875 E-mail: enquiries@perei.co.uk

Truck-Lite Co. Ltd, Waterfall Lane, Cradley Heath, West Midlands, B64 6QB Tel: 0121-561 7000 Fax: 0121-561 1415 E-mail: birminghamsales@truck-lite.com

MOTOR VEHICLE LIGHTING

Cambridge (Auto Bulbs) Ltd, Unit 30 Over Industrial Park, Norman Way, Over, Cambridge, CB24 5QE Tel: (01954) 231611 Fax: (01954) 230552 E-mail: cabulbs@tesco.net

Ceag Ltd, Zenith Park, Whaley Road, Barnsley, South Yorkshire, S75 1HT Tel: (01226) 206842 Fax: (01226) 731645 E-mail: sales@ceag.co.uk

Flexible Lamps Ltd, Barrows Road, Pinnacles Estate, Harlow, Essex, CM19 5FA Tel: (01279) 406406 Fax: (01279) 406407 E-mail: admin@flexible-lamps.co.uk

Francis Searchlights, Union Road, Bolton, BL2 2HJ Tel: (01204) 527196 Fax: (01204) 558979 E-mail: sales@francis.co.uk

Hella Manufacturing, Wildmere Road, Banbury, Oxfordshire, OX16 3EY Tel: (01295) 272211 Fax: (01295) 278025

Invertec Ltd, Whelford Road, Fairford, Gloucestershire, GL7 4DT Tel: (01285) 713550 Fax: (01285) 713548 E-mail: sales@invertec.co.uk

Lab Craft Ltd, 22b King Street, Saffron Walden, Essex, CB10 1ES Tel: (01799) 513434 Fax: (01799) 513437 E-mail: sales@labcraft.co.uk

Normalec Ltd, Kingsley House, 1 Kingsley Street, Leicester, LE2 6DY Tel: 0116-288 9922 Fax: 0116-288 8463 E-mail: sales@normalitefsnet.co.uk

Perei Group Ltd, Sunbury House 4 Christy Estate, Ivy Road, Aldershot, Hampshire, GU12 4TX Tel: (01252) 350833 Fax: (01252) 350875 E-mail: enquiries@perei.co.uk

▶ Stirling, 7 Cunningham Road, Stirling, FK7 7SW Tel: (01786) 445349 Fax: (01786) 445349 E-mail: sales@fergusons450222.com

MOTOR VEHICLE LOCKS

C E Marshall Wolverhampton Ltd, Church Street, Willenhall, West Midlands, WV13 1QW Tel: (01902) 364500 Fax: (01902) 634908

MOTOR VEHICLE NUMBERPLATE NUMBERS

▶ G T Grafix, PO Box 154, Ashton-Under-Lyne, Lancashire, OL6 6WB Tel: (0845) 8385167 E-mail: info@gtgrafix.com

▶ Global Registrations Ltd, PO Box 911, Exeter, EX2 5NZ Tel: (01392) 207008 Fax: (01392) 250321 E-mail: info@globalreg.co.uk

▶ Marks 4 Cars, Hall Farm Cottage, The Hill, Worlaby, Brigg, North Lincolnshire, DN20 0NP Tel: (01652) 618317 E-mail: sales@marks4cars.co.uk

▶ The One Stop Print Group, 123 Spring Bank, Hull, HU3 1BH Tel: (01482) 324752 Fax: (01482) 606847 E-mail: info@theonestop.co.uk

▶ The Private Plate Co., PO Box 77, Swansea, SA7 9YR Tel: (01639) 888833 Fax: (01639) 888844 E-mail: sales@myownplate.co.uk

MOTOR VEHICLE NUMBERPLATES

Auto Plates, Unit 1 Chessington Trade Park, Cox Lane, Chessington, Surrey, KT9 1TW Tel: (020) 8391 9070 Fax: (020) 8391 9075

Colton Signs, Castlegate Mills, Spa Mews, Harrogate, North Yorkshire, HG2 7LF Tel: (01423) 886461 Fax: (01423) 881141 E-mail: coltonsigns@harrogatespa.fsn.co.uk

▶ First Plate, Metro House, Darlaston Road, Wednesbury, West Midlands, WS10 7SW Tel: 0121-505 7878 Fax: 0121-505 6550

Hills Numberplate Holdings plc, Unit 6 Electric Avenue, Birmingham, B6 7JJ Tel: 0121-623 8050 Fax: 0121-623 8011 E-mail: orders@hillsnumberplates.com

Jepson Signs Ltd, Unit 2 North Road Industrial Estate, Meynell Road, Darlington, County Durham, DL3 0YQ Tel: (01325) 463547 Fax: (01325) 381172

M V I Systems Ltd, Appian House, 4 Wessex Road, Bourne End, Buckinghamshire, SL8 5TD Tel: (01344) 426844

▶ Marks 4 Cars, Hall Farm Cottage, The Hill, Worlaby, Brigg, North Lincolnshire, DN20 0NP Tel: (01652) 618317 E-mail: sales@marks4cars.co.uk

P M A Group, Unit 8, Waterside Road, Hamilton Industrial Park, Leicester, LE5 1TL Tel: 0116-246 1400 Fax: 0116-246 1659 E-mail: sales@pmagroup.co.uk

▶ PG's Cherished Numbers, Weir Wood, Spring Hill Farm, Forest Row, East Sussex, RH18 5HT Tel: (01342) 824444

Scotrad Car Radiator Repairs, 410 Gorgie Road, Edinburgh, EH11 2RN Tel: 0131-337 8887 Fax: 0131-337 9998 E-mail: sales@scotrad.co.uk

Signam Ltd, Harris Road, Warwick, CV34 5FY Tel: (01926) 417300 Fax: (01926) 417333 E-mail: sales@signam.co.uk

▶ Tennant UK Ltd, Mount Street, New Basford, Nottingham, NG7 7HX Tel: 0115-973 8080 Fax: 0115-973 8090 E-mail: sales@tennantsuk.com

Totnes Radiators, Burke Road, Totnes, Devon, TQ9 5XL Tel: (01803) 863123 Fax: (01803) 863123 E-mail: admin@carradiator.co.uk

MOTOR VEHICLE OIL LEVELLING SYSTEMS

Groeneveld UK Ltd, Unit 29a Loughborough Motorway Trading Estate, Gelders Hall Road, Shepshed, Loughborough, Leicestershire, LE12 9NH Tel: (01509) 600033 Fax: (01509) 602000 E-mail: groenevel.uk@talk21.com

MOTOR VEHICLE OIL PRODUCTS

Comma Oil & Chemicals Ltd, Comma Works, Dering Way, Gravesend, Kent, DA12 2QX Tel: (01474) 564311 Fax: (01474) 333000 E-mail: sales@commaoil.com

Granville Oil & Chemicals Ltd, Unit 29 Goldthorpe Industrial Estate, Commercial Road, Goldthorpe, Rotherham, South Yorkshire, S63 9BL Tel: (01709) 890099 Fax: (01709) 891121 E-mail: info@granvilleoilchem.co.uk

Valvoline Oil Co., Dock Road, Birkenhead, Merseyside, CH41 1DR Tel: 0151-652 1551 Fax: 0151-653 8900 E-mail: sales@valvolineuk.com

MOTOR VEHICLE OIL SUMP GUARDS

Press Fab Ltd, 10 Bayton Way, Exhall, Coventry, CV7 9ER Tel: (024) 7636 2509

MOTOR VEHICLE PAINTS

Broomstick Car & Commercials Ltd, Willow Farm, Ivinghoe Aston, Leighton Buzzard, Bedfordshire, LU7 9DF Tel: (01525) 220123 Fax: (01525) 221351

MOTOR VEHICLE POWER TRANSMISSION EQUIPMENT, *See headings for particular types*

MOTOR VEHICLE PRODUCTION ASSEMBLY LINES

Thyssenkrupp Krause Ltd, 2 Wells Place, Gatton Park Business Centre, Redhill, RH1 3LG Tel: (01737) 284000 Fax: (01737) 284111 E-mail: sales@krause.co.uk

MOTOR VEHICLE RADIATOR CAPS

Llanrad Distribution plc, Unit 26 Bookers Way, Dinnington, Sheffield, S25 3SH Tel: (01909) 550944 Fax: (01909) 568403 E-mail: cool@llanrad.co.uk

MOTOR VEHICLE RADIATORS

Boston Radiator Services Ltd, Maud Street, Boston, Lincolnshire, PE21 6TP Tel: (01205) 369555 Fax: (01205) 364829

County Radiators Ltd, 21 Nobel Square, Burnt Mills Industrial Estate, Basildon, Essex, SS13 1LP Tel: (01268) 728314 Fax: (01268) 728314

Denson Marston Ltd, Otley Road, Baildon, Shipley, West Yorkshire, BD17 7JR Tel: (01274) 582266 Fax: (01274) 597165 E-mail: enquiries@denso.co.jp

G & M Radiator, 23 Fordneuk Street, Glasgow, G40 2TA Tel: 0141-550 5800 Fax: 0141-550 5858 E-mail: sales@gm-radiator.com

Lancashire Motor Radiator Co Ltd, 2-28 Great Homer Street, Liverpool, L5 3LE Tel: 0151-207 1048 Fax: 0151-207 0996 E-mail: nell@chemdirect.co.uk

Llanrad Distribution plc, Unit 26 Bookers Way, Dinnington, Sheffield, S25 3SH Tel: (01909) 550944 Fax: (01909) 568403 E-mail: cool@llanrad.co.uk

Midshires Radiator Services Ltd, 5 Orleton Road, Ludlow Business Park, Ludlow, Shropshire, SY8 1XF Tel: (01584) 874495 Fax: (01584) 874495

Newquay Radiators, Victoria Business Park, Roche, St. Austell, Cornwall, PL26 8JF Tel: (01726) 890922 Fax: (01726) 890974

Northern Radiators Ltd, 3 Dolly Lane, Leeds, LS9 7TU Tel: 0113-245 5051 Fax: 0113-245 7486 E-mail: info@radiatorsonline.co.uk

P M A Group, Unit 8, Waterside Road, Hamilton Industrial Park, Leicester, LE5 1TL Tel: 0116-246 1400 Fax: 0116-246 1659 E-mail: sales@pmagroup.co.uk

Serck Intertruck, Worrall Street, Salford, M5 4TA Tel: 0161-872 5726 Fax: 0161-873 8074 E-mail: si.manchester732@unipart.co.uk

Serck Intertruck, Neachells Lane, Willenhall, West Midlands, WV13 3SH Tel: (01902) 862520 Fax: (01902) 306335

Serck Services, Units 9 & 10, Brook Industrial Estate, Bullsbrook Road, Hayes, Middlesex, UB4 0JZ Tel: (020) 8813 7470 Fax: (020) 8813 7499 E-mail: si@unipart.co.uk

Sussex Radiators, Stephenson Way, Crawley, West Sussex, RH10 1TN Tel: (01293) 528225

Terry Radiators, Bay 2, 198 Derby Road, Chesterfield, Derbyshire, S40 2EP Tel: (01246) 234401

Totnes Radiators, Burke Road, Totnes, Devon, TQ9 5XL Tel: (01803) 863123 Fax: (01803) 863123 E-mail: admin@carradiator.co.uk

Wessex Radiator, Portsmouth Road, Bursledon, Southampton, SO31 8EP Tel: (023) 8040 2848 Fax: (023) 8040 2848

MOTOR VEHICLE RADIO ALARM SYSTEMS, *See Alarm, Motor Car etc*

MOTOR VEHICLE RAMPS

Deans Systems Ltd, Borwick Drive, Grovehill, Beverley, North Humberside, HU17 0HQ Tel: (01482) 868111 Fax: (01482) 881890 E-mail: info@deanssystems.com

MOTOR VEHICLE RECOVERY

A1 Marsden Recovery Specialists Ltd, Musgrave Park Industrial Estate, Stockmans Way, Belfast, BT9 7ET Tel: (028) 9068 2892 Fax: (028) 9038 1319 E-mail: linda@a1marsden.com

Arm Services, The Willows, Crays Hill Road, Crays Hill, Billericay, Essex, CM11 2YP Tel: (01268) 530470 Fax: (01268) 530470

B A E, 8 Eagle Estate, Brookers Road, Billingshurst, West Sussex, RH14 9RZ Tel: (01403) 782696

B M Commercials, Firbank Industrial Estate, Dallow Road, Luton, LU1 1TW Tel: (01582) 400262 Fax: (01525) 406089

Bushey Hall Garage, Bushey Hall Drive, Bushey, WD23 2QE Tel: (01923) 237135 Fax: (01923) 235372 E-mail: bushey.hall@virgin.net

▶ Clark Motor Engineering, 1 & 2 Charlwood Park Cottages, Charlwood Road, Horley, Surrey, RH6 0AJ Tel: 01293 772202 E-mail: recovery@clarkmotorengineering.co.uk

▶ Devon Truck Centre, Woodbury Salterton, Exeter, EX5 1EL Tel: (01395) 239399 Fax: (01395) 239399

Dorking Autos Ltd, 6 Reading Arch Road, Redhill, RH1 1HG Tel: (01737) 780040 Fax: (01737) 779986

First Assist Group Ltd, 32-42 High Street, Purley, Surrey, CR8 2PP Tel: (020) 8763 3000 Fax: (020) 8668 1262 E-mail: corporate.info@firstassist.co.uk

Fred Smith & Sons Motor Bodies Ltd, Sams Lane, West Bromwich, West Midlands, B70 7EG Tel: 0121-525 8359 Fax: 0121-553 0578 E-mail: james@fredsmithandsons.co.uk

Gosling Of Kidderminster, Unit 208 Foley Industrial Estate, Kidderminster, Worcestershire, DY11 7DH Tel: (01562) 68427 Fax: (01562) 68427 E-mail: sales@goslings.co.uk

Greens Accident Repair Centre, 1 Mercer Road, Warnham, Horsham, West Sussex, RH12 3RL Tel: (01403) 254506 Fax: (01403) 254695

Heybeck Garage Ltd, Leeds Road, Dewsbury, West Yorkshire, WF12 7RB Tel: (01924) 472660

Kenfield Recovery Southern Ltd, 124-126 Nathan Way, London, SE28 0AU Tel: (020) 8855 5544 Fax: (020) 8317 2471

R S Dawe Motor Body Repair Centre, Norfolk Road, Gravesend, Kent, DA12 2PS Tel: (01474) 365840 Fax: (01474) 350900

Tip Top Accident Repairs Ltd, Worcester Road, Kidderminster, Worcestershire, DY10 1HY Tel: (01562) 822081 Fax: (01562) 825922

UKI Partnerships, Green Flag House, Cote Lane, Pudsey, West Yorkshire, LS28 5GF Tel: 0113-236 3236 Fax: 0113-257 3111 E-mail: rcroucher@directline.com

Whatley & Co (Pewsley) Ltd, Avonside Works, Pewsey, Wiltshire, SN9 5AS Tel: (01672) 562404 Fax: (01672) 563091 E-mail: whatley.pewsey@lineone.net

▶ Wiltshire Recovery, Hopton Park Industrial Estate, Hopton Road, Devizes, Wiltshire, SN10 2EY Tel: (01380) 735055 Fax: (01380) 730252 E-mail: admin@wiltshire-recovery.com

Wimhall Ltd, Creswell Road, Clowne, Chesterfield, Derbyshire, S43 4LT Tel: (01246) 810619

Wykebeck Recoveries, Selby Road, Leeds, LS9 0EW Tel: 0113-248 4735 Fax: 0113-249 5122

MOTOR VEHICLE RECOVERY EQUIPMENT

Tip N Lift UK Ltd, Boss Hall Road, Ipswich, IP1 5BN Tel: (01473) 747222 Fax: (01473) 740381 E-mail: tipnlift@aol.com

Winchmaster Lifting Equipment, 6 South Orbital Trading Park, Hedon Road, Hull, HU9 1NJ Tel: (01482) 223663 Fax: (01482) 218285 E-mail: sales@winchmaster.co.uk

MOTOR VEHICLE RECOVERY VEHICLE HIRE

▶ Autosort, Pier Garage, Fairlie, Ayrshire, KA29 0AU Tel: (01475) 560088 E-mail: webmaster@autosort.co.uk

MOTOR VEHICLE RECOVERY VEHICLES

▶ S & B Recovery, 118 Rossend Terrace, Burntisland, Fife, KY3 0DJ Tel: (0783) 2106600 E-mail: recovery1@hotmail.co.uk

V W Panels Ltd, 302 Ampthill Road, Bedford, MK42 9QS Tel: (01234) 352021 Fax: (01234) 305390 E-mail: enquiries@vwpanels.co.uk

MOTOR VEHICLE REPAIR/ RESTORATION SERVICES

A Pile & Son Ltd, St Vincents Road, Dartford, DA1 1UU Tel: (01322) 224346 Fax: (01322) 277321

A S Whitaker & Sons, Stephenson Avenue, Pinchbeck, Spalding, Lincolnshire, PE11 3SW Tel: (01775) 722789 Fax: (01775) 710519 E-mail: phil@whitakers-bodyshop.co.uk

Ajl, 5-6 Bankside, Kidlington, Oxfordshire, OX5 1JE Tel: (01865) 375262 Fax: (01865) 370839

Alan Myerscough, The Ellers, Ulverston, Cumbria, LA12 0AA Tel: (01229) 584444 Fax: (01229) 581213 E-mail: alanmyerscoughford@ic24.net

Alan's Autos, Chapel La, Anslow, Burton-on-Trent, Staffs, DE13 9QA Tel: (01283) 567000

Aldrington Body Care, 8 Basin Road North, Portslade, Brighton, BN41 1WA Tel: (01273) 411312 Fax: (01273) 430836 E-mail: juliagraeme@aol.com

Allspeed Clutches & Brakes, Unit 14c Birches Industrial Estate, East Grinstead, West Sussex, RH19 1XZ Tel: (01342) 322829 Fax: (01342) 300464

Am Car Care, A4 Bolney Road, Cowfold, Horsham, West Sussex, RH13 8AZ Tel: (01403) 864638 Fax: (01403) 864638

Antelope Garage Ltd, Swan Close Road, Banbury, Oxfordshire, OX16 5AQ Tel: (01295) 265435 Fax: (01295) 269208

Arter Bros Ltd, Barham Services, Folkestone Road, Barham, Canterbury, Kent, CT4 6EX Tel: (01227) 831356 Fax: (01227) 832060 E-mail: sales@arterbros.co.uk

Ashbrook Garage Ltd, Ashbrook Garage, Clyro, Hereford, HR3 5SD Tel: (01497) 821046 Fax: (01497) 821182 E-mail: poleposition@lineone.net

Ashford Coachworks Ltd, Ashford Road, Ashford, Middlesex, TW15 1XB Tel: (01784) 888600 Fax: (01784) 888620

Associated Vehicle Services, 222 Main Rd, Hawkwell, Hockley, Essex, SS5 4EG Tel: 01702 201869

Auto 2000, 24 College Street, Kempston, Bedford, MK42 8LU Tel: (01234) 210012

Auto Crash Repairs Ltd, Lorita House, Barkers Lane, Brunel Road, Bedford, MK41 9TG Tel: (01234) 266881 Fax: (01234) 351601 E-mail: acrbedford@btconnect.com

Auto Guard Security Centre Ltd, Unit 3 Sandy La Industrial Estate, Stourport-on-Severn, Worcestershire, DY13 9QB Tel: (01299) 878111 Fax: (01299) 871990

▶ Auto Repairs & Recovery, Unit C1 Riverside Industrial Estate, Bridge Road, Littlehampton, West Sussex, BN17 5DF Tel: (01903) 726635 Fax: (01903) 733013 E-mail: autorepair2001@yahoo.com

Auto Services, 26 Arden Business Centre, Arden Road, Alcester, Warwickshire, B49 6HW Tel: (01789) 763327 Fax: (01789) 763327 E-mail: enquiries@autoservices.co.uk

Autocrafts, Brimscombe Mills, Brimscombe, Stroud, Gloucestershire, GL5 2SB Tel: (01453) 882468 Fax: (01453) 882182

Autorite Ltd, 60-61 Leslie Park Road, Croydon, CR0 6TP Tel: (020) 8654 8977 Fax: (020) 8656 8277

Avon Autopoint, Charles Martin Business Park, Arrow Road North, Redditch, Worcestershire, B98 8NT Tel: (01527) 68109 Fax: (01527) 61264 E-mail: avonautopoint@tiscali.co.uk

B A E, 8 Eagle Estate, Brookers Road, Billingshurst, West Sussex, RH14 9RZ Tel: (01403) 782696

B & G Repairs, Ditchling Common, Ditchling, Hassocks, West Sussex, BN6 8SG Tel: (01444) 245691 Fax: (01444) 236041

B H Panels Ltd, 4 Waterloo Avenue, Fordbridge, Birmingham, B37 6RE Tel: 0121-779 6971 Fax: 0121-779 6217

Baker Auto Care, 18 Bankside, Station Approach, Kidlington, Oxfordshire, OX5 1JE Tel: (01865) 376008 Fax: (01865) 841511

Bath Panel Beating Co. Ltd, Roseberry Road, Bath, BA2 3DX Tel: (01225) 320060 Fax: (01225) 320062 E-mail: bodyshop@bathpanel.sagehost.co.uk

Beaumont H Landrover Specialist, Square Mill, Wainstalls, Halifax, West Yorkshire, HX2 7UG Tel: (01422) 244823 Fax: (01422) 247397 E-mail: info@beaumontlandrovers.co.uk

Blackmore Commercials, Little Tennis Street, Nottingham, NG2 4EL Tel: 0115-958 6696 Fax: 0115-979 9698

R. Boyle Motor Engineering Ltd, Blackwall Way, London, E14 9QG Tel: (020) 7987 2683 Fax: (020) 7987 2683

Bradbury's Engineering, The Crossways, Loggerheads, Market Drayton, Shropshire, TF9 4BX Tel: (01630) 672900 Fax: (01630) 673858 E-mail: bradburyeng@aol.com

Bramall Quicks Ltd, Lower Bridge Street, Chester, CH1 1DX Tel: (01244) 320444 Fax: (01244) 349536

Brownlow Way Garage, Topping Street, Off Brownlow Way, Bolton, BL1 3UB Tel: (01204) 533300 Fax: (01204) 533300

Butler Engineering, Fen Road Garage, Fen Road, Heighington, Lincoln, LN4 1JH Tel: (01522) 790375 Fax: (01522) 790375

C Goodman & Son Ltd, Pensbury Place, London, SW8 4TR Tel: (020) 7622 6444 Fax: (020) 7498 3842 E-mail: goodmangarage@aol.com

Carparts, Hyberry, Ashlands Meadow, Crewkerne, Somerset, TA18 7NN Tel: (01460) 74600

Chandlers Garage Holdings Ltd, B M W House, Water Lane, Littlehampton, West Sussex, BN16 4EH Tel: (01903) 784147 Fax: (01903) 785289 E-mail: enquiries@chandlers-bmw.co.uk

Arnold Clark Automobiles Ltd, 527 Queensferry Road, Edinburgh, EH4 7QD Tel: 0131-312 4444 Fax: 0131-312 4445 E-mail: barnton@arnoldclark.co.uk

Clarke Bros Auto Factors Ltd, 161/163 Cromac Street, Belfast, BT2 8JE Tel: (028) 9024 8444 Fax: (028) 9023 8094

Classic & Modern & Paint & Bodywork, Unit 2 Manor Park, Windsor Road, Bedford, MK42 9HW Tel: (01234) 341410

Classic Performance Ltd, 7 Trent Industrial Estate, Wetmore Road, Burton-on-Trent, Staffordshire, DE14 1QY Tel: (01283) 531122 Fax: (01283) 531328 E-mail: sales@classicperformance.co.uk

Colchester Accident Repairs, 105 Gosbecks Road, Colchester, CO2 9JT Tel: (01206) 578242 Fax: (01206) 762616

Colliers Garage, 133b Upper Street, London, N1 1QP Tel: (0870) 7772757 Fax: (020) 7354 5106

Colwick Vale Coachworks Ltd, Colwick Road, Nottingham, NG2 4BG Tel: 0115-950 2670 Fax: 0115-941 4398

Commercial Repairs, Derber House Old Newton Road, Heathfield Industrial Estate, Heathfield, Newton Abbot, Devon, TQ12 6SL Tel: (01626) 834789 Fax: (01626) 835425

Continental Service Station Ltd, Brecon Road, Caerbont, Abercrave, Swansea, SA9 1SW Tel: (01639) 730279 Fax: (01639) 730282 E-mail: continentalss@aol.com

Cranes Of Hollesley Ltd, The Street, Hollesley, Woodbridge, Suffolk, IP12 3QU Tel: (01394) 411687 Fax: (01394) 410238 E-mail: enquiries@cranesford.co.uk

Cranks & Bearings, 1A Rotherfield Road, Enfield, Middlesex, EN3 6AL Tel: (01992) 763279 Fax: (01992) 650840

Crockerhill Cars, Unit 10 Quarry Lane, Chichester, West Sussex, PO19 8QA Tel: (01243) 528731 Fax: (01243) 533343 E-mail: rbjervis@aol.com

Crossle Car Co. Ltd, 217 Old Holywood Road, Holywood, County Down, BT18 9QS Tel: (028) 9076 3332 Fax: (028) 9076 0676 E-mail: arnie@crossle.fsnet.co.uk

D C Baxter Motors Ltd, The Garage, Rectory Road, Ruskington, Sleaford, Lincolnshire, NG34 9AB Tel: (01526) 832321 Fax: (01526) 833662 E-mail: peterbaxter4@btinternet.com

D C W Accided Repairs Ltd, Cornhill Close, Lodge Farm Industrial Estate, Harlestone Road, Northampton, NN5 7UQ Tel: (01604) 753208 Fax: (01604) 759718

D J Garages, 46 St. Andrews Road, Carshalton, Surrey, SM5 2DY Tel: (020) 8669 2344 Fax: (020) 8669 2344

Dakar Cars Ltd, Stanhill Farm, Birchwood Road, Dartford, DA2 7HD Tel: (01322) 614044 Fax: (01322) 668500 E-mail: sales@dakar.co.uk

Davey Motor Engineering, High Street, Hawkesbury Upton, Badminton, Avon, GL9 1AU Tel: (01454) 238294

W.G. Davies (Landore) Ltd, Unit 11, St. Davids Road, Morriston, Swansea, SA6 8QL Tel: (01792) 795705 Fax: (01792) 797823 E-mail: wgdavies@telnet.co.uk

Denis Welch Motors Ltd, Sudbury Road, Yoxall, Burton-on-Trent, Staffordshire, DE13 8NA Tel: (01543) 472214 Fax: (01543) 472339 E-mail: sales@bighealey.co.uk

Denney Diving, Esplanade Garage, 50-55 Esplanade, Redcar, Cleveland, TS10 3AG Tel: (01642) 486666 Fax: (01642) 483507

Diesel Recon, 2 Napier Place, Wardpark North Cumbernauld, Dullatur, Glasgow, G68 0BP Tel: (01236) 505600 Fax: (01236) 724517

Diesel Service Centre, Mount Pleasant, Peterborough, PE2 8HW Tel: (01733) 558600

Dinnages Car Dealers, Brougham Road, Worthing, West Sussex, BN11 2NR Tel: (01903) 820505 Fax: (01903) 212523 E-mail: marketing@dinnages.co.uk

Dovercourt Ford Ltd, 30 Robjohns Road, Widford Industrial Estate, Chelmsford, CM1 3AQ Tel: (01245) 706600 E-mail: simon.beament@dovercourt.com

E T Tucker Ltd, 87 Severn Road, Cardiff, CF11 9EA Tel: (029) 2022 9842

Eames Motor Repairs, 18 St James Industrial Estate, Westhampnett Road, Chichester, West Sussex, PO19 7JU Tel: (01243) 775968 Fax: (01243) 775968

Eccles Wing & Radiator Company Ltd, 3 Chadwick Road, Eccles, Manchester, M30 0NZ Tel: 0161-789 1126 Fax: 0161-789 1126

Eden Garage, Temple Sowerby, Penrith, Cumbria, CA10 1RS Tel: (01768) 361212 Fax: (01768) 361550 E-mail: enquire@eden-garage.co.uk

▶ Ellis Motors, 6 Sheddingdean Business Centre, Marchants Way, Burgess Hill, West Sussex, RH15 8QY Tel: (01444) 480606 Fax: (01444) 480606 E-mail: fixit@ellismotors.co.uk

Eltham Executive Charter, Crown Woods Way, London, SE9 2NL Tel: (020) 8850 2011 Fax: (020) 8850 5210E-mail: eec@cwcom.net

Emanuel Bros Ltd, Wexham Road, Slough, SL1 1RW Tel: (01753) 524153 Fax: (01753) 530775 E-mail: sales@emanuelbrothers.co.uk

Ensign Engineering Co., Station Road, Baldock, Hertfordshire, SG7 5BT Tel: (01462) 892931 Fax: (01462) 893667

Enterprise Garage, Units 1 & 2, Fitzalan Road, Arundel, West Sussex, BN18 9JS Tel: (01903) 882278 E-mail: sales@enterprisegarage.com

Essential Motor Services Ltd, 5 Sugarbrook Road, Aston Fields Industrial Estate, Bromsgrove, Worcestershire, B60 3DN Tel: (01527) 870757 Fax: (01527) 870757

Evans Hallshaw Newport Ltd, Turner Street, Newport, Gwent, NP19 7XH Tel: (01633) 244442 Fax: (01633) 243041

F J Glass & Co. Ltd, The Workshop, Mill Road, Okehampton, Devon, EX20 1PR Tel: (01837) 52255

F Short Ltd, Green Lane, Felling, Gateshead, Tyne & Wear, NE10 0EZ Tel: 0191-469 4627 Fax: 0191-438 4680

Factory Lane Autos Ltd, 9-11 Broton Drive, Halstead, Essex, CO9 1HB Tel: (01787) 474446 Fax: (01787) 475616

Fiennes Restoration Ltd, Clanfield Mill, Little Clanfield, Bampton, Oxfordshire, OX18 2RX Tel: (01367) 810438 Fax: (01367) 810532 E-mail: enquiries@fiennes.co.uk

Fred Smith & Sons Motor Bodies Ltd, Sams Lane, West Bromwich, West Midlands, B70 7EG Tel: 0121-525 8359 Fax: 0121-553 0578 E-mail: james@fredsmithandsons.co.uk

Frost & Smith, Tweesden, Cray Road, Sidcup, Kent, DA14 5BZ Tel: (020) 8300 2242 Fax: (020) 8309 6964

Fussell Wadman Ltd, Hopton Industrial Estlondon Road, Devizes, Wiltshire, SN10 2EU Tel: (01380) 731970 Fax: (01380) 731971 E-mail: fussell_wadman@dealers.peugeot.co.uk

G.B. Bracket Hire & Jig Sales, 15 Hasse Road, Soham, Ely, Cambridgeshire, CB7 5UN Tel: (01353) 624406 Fax: 01353 624671

G F Williams & Sons Risca Garages Ltd, 89 Cromwell Road, Risca, Newport, Gwent, NP11 7AD Tel: (01633) 612412 Fax: (01495) 270408

G W Commercials, Balklands, Five Ashes, Mayfield, East Sussex, TN20 6JJ Tel: (01825) 830788 Fax: (01825) 830788

Garlics Ltd, Sandpits Acacia Road, Bourneville, Birmingham, B30 2AH Tel: 0121-472 3848 Fax: 0121-414 0065

Pete Garth Autorefinishing Ltd, Riverview Road, Beverley, North Humberside, HU17 0LD Tel: (01482) 882747 Fax: (01482) 865423

Gateway Autos Ltd, Units 2-6 Trafford Distribution Centre, Tenax Road, Trafford Park, Manchester, M17 1JT Tel: 0161-872 9559 Fax: 0161-872 9536

John Gordon Motors Ltd, Rear of, 117a London Road, St. Albans, Hertfordshire, AL1 1LR Tel: (01727) 855096 Fax: (01727) 841966 E-mail: jgordonmotors@aol.com

Gosling Of Kidderminster, Unit 208 Foley Industrial Estate, Kidderminster, Worcestershire, DY11 7DH Tel: (01562) 68427 Fax: (01562) 68427 E-mail: sales@goslings.co.uk

James Graham, 85 Derryloughan Road, Loughgall, Armagh, BT61 8PH Tel: (028) 3889 1312 Fax: (028) 3889 1843

▶ Gravell Holdings Ltd, 6 Banc Pendre, Kidwelly, Dyfed, SA17 4TA Tel: (01554) 890436 Fax: (01554) 891338

Great Yarmouth Coach Works, 15 Queens Road, Great Yarmouth, Norfolk, NR30 3HT Tel: (01493) 843835 Fax: (01493) 330800 E-mail: ian@greatyarmouthcoachworks.co.uk

Hammond of Hendon Ltd, 189c Brent Crescent, London, NW10 7XR Tel: (020) 8965 5339 Fax: (020) 8965 5338 E-mail: hammondofhendon@btconnect.com

Hardings, Old Express Yard, Corwen Road, Pontybodkin, Mold, Clwyd, CH7 4TG Tel: (01352) 771575

Hayes Engineering & Garage Services, Unit 2a Europa Trading Estate, Fraser Road, Erith, Kent, DA8 1QL Tel: (01322) 440332 Fax: (01322) 439930 E-mail: sales@hayescharters.com

Holland Brothers Ltd, Tawney Street, Boston, Lincolnshire, PE21 6RS Tel: (01205) 355566 Fax: (01205) 358172 E-mail: enquiries@hollandbrothers.co.uk

Howard Basford Ltd, Portside North, Ellesmere Port, CH65 2HQ Tel: 0151-357 6000 Fax: 0151-357 1026

Humphreys Garage Bearwood Ltd, Anderson Road, Smethwick, West Midlands, B67 5DR Tel: 0121-429 1741 Fax: 0121-429 1741

I M Services, 2 Premier Way, Ampfield, Romsey, Hampshire, SO51 9DQ Tel: (01794) 518866 Fax: (01794) 518877

J & J Motor Engineers Ltd, 405 New Kings Road, London, SW6 4RL Tel: (020) 7736 8161

J Mccartney Ltd, 168 Park View Road, London, N17 9BL Tel: (020) 8808 0582 Fax: (020) 8365 1884 E-mail: jmccartneylimited@parkviewroad.fsnet.co.uk

J R Pitchers Ltd, Selby Place, Great Yarmouth, Norfolk, NR30 3LG Tel: (01493) 843947 Fax: (01493) 857172 E-mail: jrpitchersltd@btconnect.com

J W J Car & Commercial Repairs, 113-115 Codicote Road, Welwyn, Hertfordshire, AL6 9TY Tel: (01438) 820351

L.E. Jackson (Coachworks) Ltd, Vehicle Body Centre, Queens Road, Loughborough, Leicestershire, LE11 1HD Tel: (01509) 230811 Fax: (01509) 230812

Jeakins Motor Ltd, Noble House, Wrexham Road, Basildon, Essex, SS15 6PX Tel: (01268) 542464 Fax: (01268) 493593 E-mail: jeakins@lineone.net

Jordans Garage Ltd, Flambard Way, The Wharf, Godalming, Surrey, GU7 1JF Tel: (01483) 415201 Fax: (01483) 424533

K & I Ltd, Hardengreen Coachworks, Dalkeith, Midlothian, EH22 3LD Tel: 0131-663 4545 Fax: 0131-654 2373 E-mail: info@k-and-i.co.uk

Karaglow Ltd, 32 The Spires, Dromore, County Down, BT25 1QE Tel: (028) 9269 3641

Kar-Aid, Barclays Bungalow, West Chiltington Lane, Coneyhurst, Billingshurst, West Sussex, RH14 9DN Tel: (01403) 783999

Kenfield Recovery Southern Ltd, 124-126 Nathan Way, London, SE28 0AU Tel: (020) 8855 5544 Fax: (020) 8317 2471

Kennington Motors, Unit 52 Sandford Lane, Kennington, Oxford, OX1 5RP Tel: (01865) 739064 Fax: (01865) 730007

Kettering Bodycraft Ltd, Henson Way, Telford Way Industrial Estate, Kettering, Northamptonshire, NN16 8PX Tel: (01536) 483739 Fax: (01536) 511500

Knight Motors, Unit G, Bakers Wharf, Millbank Street, Southampton, SO14 5QQ Tel: (023) 8023 4008 Fax: (023) 8023 4008 E-mail: richard@knightmotors.com

KWR UK Ltd, KWR (Uk) Ltd Whessoe Road, Darlington, County Durham, DL3 0QP Tel: (01325) 284422 Fax: (01325) 284422 E-mail: kevin@kwr.biz

Lakshmi Collison Care, 290a Ampthill Road, Bedford, MK42 9QL Tel: (01234) 261930 Fax: (01234) 353372

▶ Leaves Green Garage, Biggin Hill Garage, Leaves Green Road, Keston, Kent, BR2 6DU Tel: (01959) 571903

Lincs Auto Services 1986 Ltd, 136-140 Roman Bank, Skegness, Lincolnshire, PE25 1SE Tel: (01754) 767463 Fax: (01754) 762290 E-mail: rrsbfm@aol.com

Lindfield Rover, 2 Bridge Road, Haywards Heath, West Sussex, RH16 1UA Tel: (01444) 458641 Fax: (01444) 458644

Liphook Coachworks Ltd, Unit 3, Bleachers Yard Industrial Estate, Station Road, Liphook, Hampshire, GU30 7DR Tel: (01428) 722363 Fax: (01428) 725255 E-mail: lee@liphookcoachworks.freeserve.co.uk

Lowood Garage Ltd, 12 Kings Avenue, London, SW4 8BQ Tel: (020) 7622 7174 Fax: (020) 7720 9095

Lynn Road Motors Ltd, 28-30 Lynn Road, Ilford, Essex, IG2 7DS Tel: (020) 8554 5670 Fax: (020) 8518 2426

▶ M A C Motors Ltd, Unit E, Curzon Business Centre, Curzon Street, Burton-on-Trent, Staffordshire, DE14 2DH Tel: (01283) 534230 E-mail: sales@macmotors.co.uk

M Gaze, Thurlton, Norwich, NR14 6NZ Tel: (01508) 548910 Fax: (01508) 548920

The M O T Welding Service (Auto Weld) Of Worthing, Unit 14 Ivy Arch Road, Worthing, West Sussex, BN14 8BX Tel: (01903) 230634

M & S Accident Repair Centre, Unit 21 Slingsby Close, Attleborough Fields Industrial Estate, Nuneaton, Warwickshire, CV11 6RP Tel: (024) 7632 8239 Fax: (024) 7632 8239

M & W Motors Hayes Ltd, Printing House Lane, Hayes, Middlesex, UB3 1AP Tel: (020) 8573 1082 Fax: (020) 8561 9330

Main Ford Car Dealership, Hopping Hill, New Duston, Northampton, NN5 6PD Tel: (01604) 581121 Fax: (01604) 582969

Meakins & Son Ltd, 17 St. James Industrial Estate, Westhampnett Road, Chichester, West Sussex, PO19 7JU Tel: (01243) 774343 Fax: (01243) 780223 E-mail: meakins@fsmail.net

Medcalf & Co. (Coachbuilders) Ltd, Fordwater Trading Estate, Fordwater Road, Chertsey, Surrey, KT16 8HG Tel: (01932) 563026 Fax: (01932) 571086

Mercury Motors Ltd, 5-7 Strawberry Vale, Twickenham, TW1 4RX Tel: (020) 8892 4604 Fax: (020) 8892 4454 E-mail: enquiries@mercurymotors.co.uk

Merseyside Rustproofing Co., 84 Seel Street, Liverpool, L1 4BH Tel: 0151-709 2409

MOTOR VEHICLE REPAIR/ RESTORATION SERVICES – *continued*

Midhurst Garage, Wedglen Industrial Estate, Midhurst, West Sussex, GU29 9RE Tel: (01730) 814032 Fax: (01730) 814032 E-mail: infomidhurst@motormouse.net

Mill Garage Ltd, 19 Crown Road, Kings Norton Business Centre, Birmingham, B30 3HY Tel: 0121-486 3486 Fax: 0121-486 3486

Morland Jones Lotus Repairs, 226 Railway Arches, Trussley Road, London, W6 7PP Tel: (020) 8741 2303 Fax: (020) 8741 3116 E-mail: info@morlandjones.co.uk

Moserve Auto Engineers, 9 Avon Industrial Estate, Butlers Leap, Rugby, Warwickshire, CV21 3UY Tel: (01788) 561099 Fax: (01788) 337099

Mossley, Unit 89 Earls Road, Grangemouth, Stirlingshire, FK3 8XE Tel: (01324) 474555 Fax: (01324) 474555 E-mail: mossleyautos@aol.com

Myers & Bowman Ltd, Lillyhall West, Workington, Cumbria, CA14 4PE Tel: (01946) 832282 Fax: (01946) 832596 E-mail: info@myers-and-bowman.toyota.co.uk

N W S Services Ltd, Mayswood Road, Wootton Wawen, Henley-in-Arden, West Midlands, B95 6AL Tel: (01564) 792546

Nashil Automotive Engineers Ltd, 22 Burners Lane, Kiln Farm, Milton Keynes, MK11 3HB Tel: (01908) 307777 Fax: (01908) 307444 E-mail: arif@nashil-automotive.co.uk

Nationwide Autocentres Ltd, 10 Duncombe Street, Bletchley, Milton Keynes, MK2 2LY Tel: (01908) 270476 Fax: (01908) 642121

Nationwide Crash Repair Centres Ltd, Axe Road, Bridgwater, Somerset, TA6 5LN Tel: (01278) 422238 Fax: (01278) 427939

Nationwide Crash Repair Centres Ltd, Smeaton Road, West Gourdie Industrial Estate, Dundee, DD2 4UT Tel: (01382) 623133 Fax: (01382) 612962

Nationwide Crash Repair Centres Ltd, Unit 1c Pentland Industrial Estate, Loanhead, Midlothian, EH20 9QH Tel: 0131-440 2323 Fax: 0131-440 4323

Newbourne Automobile Engineers, New Street, Luton, LU1 5DE Tel: (01582) 722522 Fax: (01582) 732800 E-mail: newbourne-arc@barclays.net

Niall Cars, 5 Fort Road, Wick, Littlehampton, West Sussex, BN17 7QU Tel: (01903) 722510 Fax: (01903) 722510

Ooops! Net, 4 K & B Estate, Holyrood Close, Poole, Dorset, BH17 7BP Tel: (01202) 695999 Fax: (01202) 696333 E-mail: mail@ooops.net

P G C Motors, Unit 1, High Street, Arlesey, Bedfordshire, SG15 6TB Tel: (01462) 834544

Park Row Garage Ltd, 61 Hoskins Street, London, SE10 9PB Tel: (020) 8305 0870 Fax: (020) 8305 0870 E-mail: sales@parkrowgarage.co.uk

Pearce Engineering, Fishmore Road, Fishmore, Ludlow, Shropshire, SY8 3DP Tel: (01584) 876016 Fax: (01584) 876016 E-mail: sales@pearcecycles.co.uk

Penfold Motors, 345 Lee High Road, London, SE12 8RU Tel: (020) 8355 8000 Fax: (020) 8355 8018 E-mail: sales@penfolds-vauxhall.co.uk

Cecil Penney Ltd, Sheffield Road Garage, Penistone, Sheffield, S36 6HF Tel: (01226) 763102 Fax: (01226) 370346

Premier Bodyshops Ltd, 15 Bilton Way, Luton, LU1 1UU Tel: (01582) 424100 Fax: (01582) 483615 E-mail: info@premierbodyshops.co.uk

R & C Motor Co. Ltd, White Hart Road, Slough, SL1 2SF Tel: (01753) 529454 Fax: (01753) 517021

R S Dawe Motor Body Repair Centre, Norfolk Road, Gravesend, Kent, DA12 2PS Tel: (01474) 365840 Fax: (01474) 350900

Reed Of Trowbridge Ltd, Canal Road Industrial Estate, Trowbridge, Wiltshire, BA14 8RL Tel: (01225) 752525 Fax: (01225) 751089

Reliance Garage Ltd, Turnlee Road, Glossop, Derbyshire, SK13 6PW Tel: (01457) 853222

Renfrew Motor Engineers, Unit 2 Brown Street, Renfrew, PA4 8HW Tel: 0141-886 6667 Fax: 0141-561 1019

Ric Woods, Unit 6-7 The Capri Centre, Oakfield Road, Stockport, Cheshire, SK3 8SG Tel: 0161-483 4810 Fax: 0161-483 6817 E-mail: sales@ricwood.com

Riders Jaguar, 53 Dracaena Avenue, Falmouth, Cornwall, TR11 2EL Tel: (01326) 212222 Fax: (01326) 212006

Riders Landrover, Threemilestone Industrial Estate, Threemilestone, Truro, Cornwall, TR4 9LD Tel: (01872) 263377 Fax: (01872) 261606 E-mail: sales@riders-landrover.co.uk

Ristes Motor Co. Ltd, Gamble Street, Nottingham, NG7 4EY Tel: 0115-978 5834 Fax: 0115-942 4351 E-mail: info@ristes.zee-web.co.uk

Rosendale Motor Engineering Ltd, 4A-4C Tyrrell Road, East Dulwich, London, SE22 9NA Tel: (020) 8693 9511 Fax: (020) 8299 0968 E-mail: info@rosendale-motors.co.uk

Round Tyres, 4 Grey Friars, Grantham, Lincolnshire, NG31 6PG Tel: (01476) 573273 Fax: (01476) 573273

RSG, 6 Arunside Industrial Estate, Fort Road, Arunside Industrial Estate, Littlehampton, West Sussex, BN17 7QU Tel: (01903) 715550 Fax: (01903) 715550

Ryder Coachworks Ltd, Birchanger Industrial Estate, Bishop's Stortford, Hertfordshire, CM23 2TH Tel: (01279) 659059 Fax: (01279) 758460

Ryders Autoservice International Ltd, 215 Knowsley Road, Bootle, Merseyside, L20 4NW Tel: 0151-933 4338 Fax: 0151-944 1424 E-mail: customerservices@ryders.co.uk

Saxon Gate Motorist Centre, London Road Trading Estate, London Road, Biggleswade, Bedfordshire, SG18 8PS Tel: (01767) 314125 Fax: (01767) 314011

Shaftesbury Garage Ltd, 65b East Barnet Road, Barnet, Hertfordshire, EN4 8RN Tel: (020) 8449 9111 Fax: (020) 8449 9922 E-mail: andy@shaftesburygarage.co.uk

Sheen Lane Motors Ltd, 194-198 Sheen Lane, London, SW14 8LF Tel: (020) 8876 1011 Fax: (020) 8392 2092

Sherwood Truck & Van Ltd, Berristow Lane, Blackwell, Alfreton, Derbyshire, DE55 5HP Tel: (01773) 863311 Fax: (01773) 580271 E-mail: enquiries@sherwoodtruckandvan.com

Silurian Scania, Whitchurch, Ross-On-Wye, Herefordshire, HR9 6EG Tel: (01600) 891257 Fax: (01600) 891251

Sipson Group Ltd, Stone Close, West Drayton, Middlesex, UB7 8JU Tel: (01895) 441661 Fax: (01895) 431140

Skylark Motor Services, The Ridge, Woodfalls, Salisbury, SP5 2LW Tel: (01725) 510282 Fax: (01725) 512844

Solus Norwich Union, 16 Blenheim Road, Epsom, Surrey, KT19 9AP Tel: (01372) 727133 Fax: (01372) 745048 E-mail: info@longmead.co.uk

South West Motors Ltd, 1 Cornishway North, Galmington Trading Estate, Taunton, Somerset, TA1 5LY Tel: (01823) 327805 Fax: (01823) 321791

▶ Station Garage, Wilbraham Road, Fulbourn, Cambridge, CB21 5ET Tel: (01223) 880747 Fax: (01223) 880885 E-mail: mail@stationgaragefulbourn.co.uk

Stone Acre, Barnby Dun Road, Doncaster, South Yorkshire, DN2 4QP Tel: (01302) 327111 Fax: (01302) 340460 E-mail: sales@stoneacre.com

Subway, 6a Friargate Arches, Derby, DE1 1BU Tel: (01332) 347472

Taunton Motor Co. Ltd, 35-39 Priory Bridge Road, Taunton, Somerset, TA1 1QD Tel: (01823) 278171 Fax: (01823) 338201 E-mail: info@tauntonmotorcompany.co.uk

Tip Top Accident Repairs Ltd, Worcester Road, Kidderminster, Worcestershire, DY10 1HY Tel: (01562) 822081 Fax: (01562) 825922

Tomlin International, Europa Trading Centre, London Road, Grays, Essex, RM20 4DB Tel: (01375) 372952 Fax: (01375) 372952

Tregoning Ford, Tollgate, St. Breock, Wadebridge, Cornwall, PL27 7HT Tel: (01208) 893000 Fax: (01208) 815320 E-mail: sales@tregoningford.co.uk

Tressler Coachworks Ltd, Unit 44 Bell Lane, Bellbrook Industrial Estate, Uckfield, East Sussex, TN22 1QL Tel: (01825) 762262 Fax: (01825) 767446

Trewick Coachworks Ltd, Benton Square Indust Estate, Wesley Drive, Newcastle upon Tyne, NE12 9UN Tel: 0191-266 3581 Fax: 0191-270 0597 E-mail: repairs@trewicks.co.uk

Trinder Brothers, 3 Beaver Units, Quarry Lane Industrial Estate, Chichester, West Sussex, PO19 7NY Tel: (01243) 783504 Fax: (01243) 783504

Trumbar Truck Care Ltd, 57 Victoria Road, Diss, Norfolk, IP22 4JD Tel: (01379) 652161 Fax: (01379) 641500

Peter Turner Fork Lifts Ltd, Wistons Lane, Elland, West Yorkshire, HX5 9DT Tel: (01422) 378900 Fax: (01422) 372492 E-mail: sales@peterturner-forklifts.co.uk

Veefix Auto Centre, Stephenson Way, Crawley, West Sussex, RH10 1TN Tel: (01293) 545980

Vehicle Body Services, 56 Arthur Street, Redditch, Worcestershire, B98 8JY Tel: (01527) 529188 Fax: (01527) 514317

Vehicle & Tail Lift Repairs, 2 Churchward, Didcot, Oxfordshire, OX11 7HB Tel: (01235) 818922 Fax: (01235) 510236

Vye's Hove Ltd, 17-26 Carlton Terrace, Portslade, Brighton, BN41 1XF Tel: (01273) 412191 Fax: (01273) 415659

W C Commercials Ltd, Stanbridge Road, Great Billington, Leighton Buzzard, Bedfordshire, LU7 9JH Tel: (01525) 851797 Fax: (01525) 851798 E-mail: wccom@fsbdial.co.uk

W H Whittingham & Sons Ltd, 84-86 West Street, Rochford, Essex, SS4 1AS Tel: (01702) 544146 Fax: (01702) 542326

W J King Garages Ltd, Albany Park Garage, 10-16 Steynton Avenue, Bexley, Kent, DA5 3HP Tel: (020) 8300 4466

Walton Coachworks (Kingswood) Ltd, Kingswood Station, Kingswood, Tadworth, Surrey, KT20 6EB Tel: (01737) 355050 Fax: (01737) 373327

Warren P & Co. Ltd, The Garage, Frimley Green Road, Frimley Green, Camberley, Surrey, GU16 6LD Tel: (01252) 835436 Fax: (01252) 835711

Wayne Bassford, 12 Kepler, Lichfield Road Industrial Estate, Tamworth, Staffordshire, B79 7XE Tel: (01827) 55000

Weiler-Knight (UK) Ltd, 17 Glebe Road, Groby, Leicester, LE6 0GT Tel: 0116-287 6963 Fax: 0116-287 8099 E-mail: mel.knight@pipemedia.co.uk

Whalley John Ltd, 5 Stort Valley Industrial Estate, Stansted Road, Bishop's Stortford, Hertfordshire, CM23 2TU Tel: (01279) 654181 Fax: (01279) 654424 E-mail: john@whalley-integrale.ukclara.com

Wimhall Ltd, Creswell Road, Clowne, Chesterfield, Derbyshire, S43 4LT Tel: (01246) 810619

Woodbourne Garage, 1 Cuckmere Way, Brighton, BN1 8GB Tel: (01273) 561581 Fax: (01273) 555694

Wrights Garage Ullesthorpe Ltd, Claybrooke Road, Ullesthorpe, Lutterworth, Leicestershire, LE17 5AD Tel: (01455) 209171

York, Ward & Rowlatt Ltd, St. Johns Street, Wellingborough, Northamptonshire, NN8 4LG Tel: (01933) 443403 Fax: (01933) 445044 E-mail: info@yorkward.co.uk

MOTOR VEHICLE REVERSING AID CAMERAS

▶ EasyVision Camera Systems, 82 St Benedict Rd, Brandon, Suffolk, IP27 0UN Tel: 01842 811985 E-mail: sales@easy-vision.co.uk

MOTOR VEHICLE SAFETY BELTS

Airbags International Ltd, Viking Way, Congleton, Cheshire, CW12 1TT Tel: (01260) 294300 Fax: (01260) 294301

Key Safety Systems UK Ltd, Norfolk Street, Carlisle, CA2 5HX Tel: (01228) 591711 Fax: (01228) 546994 E-mail: reception@keysafetyinc.com

Reflex Safety Systems Ltd, Inertia House, Lowther Road, Stanmore, Middlesex, HA7 1EP Tel: (020) 8204 0200 Fax: (020) 8204 1100 E-mail: enq@reflexsafety.co.uk

Securon Amersham Ltd, Winchmore Hill, Amersham, Buckinghamshire, HP7 0NZ Tel: (01494) 434455 Fax: (01494) 726499 E-mail: sales@securon.co.uk

Stockbridge Racing Ltd, Grosvenor Garage, High Street, Stockbridge, Hampshire, SO20 6HE Tel: (01264) 810712 Fax: (01264) 810247 E-mail: sales@willansharness.co.uk

MOTOR VEHICLE SECURITY LOCKS

Saxon Industries, Everland Road, Hungerford, Berkshire, RG17 0DX Tel: (01488) 684545 Fax: (01488) 684317 E-mail: sales@saxonind.co.uk

MOTOR VEHICLE SHOCK ABSORBERS

E X B Ltd, Unit 15 Eldonwell Trading Estate, Eldon Way, Bristol, BS4 3QQ Tel: 0117-972 8380 Fax: 0117-972 3615

Quantum Racing Services Ltd, Unit 9 Station Approach Industrial Estate, Pulborough, West Sussex, RH20 1AQ Tel: (01798) 875199 Fax: (01798) 875899 E-mail: quantum.racing@argonet.co.uk

MOTOR VEHICLE STEERING COLUMNS

NSK Steering Systems Europe Ltd, Silverstone Drive, Gallagher Business Park, Coventry, CV6 6PA Tel: (024) 7658 8588 Fax: (024) 7658 8599 E-mail: surman@nsk.com

MOTOR VEHICLE SUNROOFS

Auto Glass York Ltd, Layerthorpe, York, YO31 7YW Tel: (01904) 644723 Fax: (01904) 611624

Executive Autocare Centre, 70 Bury Road, Hemel Hempstead, Hertfordshire, HP1 1HW Tel: (01442) 260796 Fax: (01442) 233294 E-mail: executiveautocare@bt.com

MOTOR VEHICLE TEST EQUIPMENT

Cirrus Technologies Ltd, Heming Road, Washford Industrial Estate, Redditch, Worcestershire, B98 0DN Tel: (01527) 527882 Fax: (01527) 502074 E-mail: sales@cirrustesting.com

MOTOR VEHICLE TRADE IMPORT/EXPORT MERCHANTS OR AGENTS

Allmakes Ltd, 176 Milton Park, Milton, Abingdon, Oxfordshire, OX14 4SW Tel: (01235) 821122 Fax: (01235) 821133 E-mail: allmakes@allmakes.co.uk

R.H. Collier & Co. Ltd, 1-41 Sutton Road, Erdington, Birmingham, B23 6QH Tel: 0121-377 8888 Fax: 0121-377 6907 E-mail: fleetsales@colliers.co.uk

Colt Car Company Ltd, Watermoor, Cirencester, Gloucestershire, GL7 1LF Tel: (01285) 655777 Fax: (01285) 658026 E-mail: enquiries@mitsubishi-cars.co.uk

Drumstar Ltd, Omega House, 17a Dereham Road, Mattishall, Dereham, Norfolk, NR20 3AA Tel: (01362) 858888 Fax: (01362) 858884 E-mail: sales@drumstar.fsnet.co.uk

Hotbray Ltd, 16 Jubilee Way, London, SW19 3GZ Tel: (020) 8545 0011 Fax: (020) 8545 0020 E-mail: sales@hotbray.co.uk

Isuzu (UK) Ltd, Ryder Street, Great Bridge, West Bromwich, West Midlands, B70 0EJ Tel: 0121-522 2000 Fax: 0121-520 5025

Kia, 2 The Heights, Brooklands, Weybridge, Surrey, KT13 0NY Tel: (0800) 775777 E-mail: pcarter@kia.co.uk

Lixmere Ltd, Lixmere House, 211 Kenton Road, Harrow, Middlesex, HA3 0HD Tel: (020) 8907 1177 Fax: (020) 8909 2777 E-mail: enquiries@lixmere.co.uk

Mercedes Benz (UK) Ltd, Tongwell, Delaware Drive, Milton Keynes, MK15 8BA Tel: (01908) 245000

Sequent Ltd, Kushi Koti, Court Road, Maidenhead, Berkshire, SL6 8LQ Tel: (01628) 628190 Fax: (01628) 623336 E-mail: seq1989@aol.com

Shinehill Ltd, 127 Ettingshall Road, Wolverhampton, WV2 2JP Tel: (01902) 451322 Fax: (01902) 870621 E-mail: shinehill@fsnet.co.uk

MOTOR VEHICLE TRIMMING/ UPHOLSTERY SERVICES

▶ Auto Trim, 36 Dorset Close, Bletchley, Milton Keynes, MK3 7HZ Tel: (01908) 368542 E-mail: sales@autotrimmer.co.uk

Barton & Sons (Coach Trimmers), 2 New Town Trading Estate, Chase Street, Luton, LU1 3QZ Tel: (01582) 412932 Fax: (01582) 726867 E-mail: sales@carinteriors.net

Guilford (Europe) Ltd, Cotes Park Lane, Somercotes, Alfreton, Derbyshire, DE55 4NJ Tel: (01773) 841200 Fax: (01773) 547315

J M Grant, 73 New Road, Rednal, Birmingham, B45 9JT Tel: 0121-453 8783 Fax: 0121-453 8783

▶ J & S Upholstery, 43 Askern Industrial Estate Moss Road, Askern, Doncaster, South Yorkshire, DN6 0DD Tel: (01302) 709926 Fax: (01302) 789112 E-mail: joanne@thetrimshack.fsnet.co.uk

Maidstone Trimming Co., 12 The Downs, Chatham, Kent, ME5 9RA Tel: (01622) 690707 E-mail: maidstonetrim@aol.com

Michael Figgitt Upholstery Upholstery, Orleans Close, Unit 3, Four Pools Industrial Estate, Evesham, Worcestershire, WR11 2FP Tel: (01386) 45120 Fax: (01386) 45264 E-mail: sales@figgittupholstery.co.uk

MOTOR VEHICLE TRIMMINGS

A F Smith & Son, Fengate, Peterborough, PE1 5XB Tel: (01733) 319595 Fax: (01733) 898370

Bourbon Fabi UK Ltd, North Portway Close, Round Spinney Industrial Estate, Northampton, NN3 8RE Tel: (01604) 493126 Fax: (01604) 644547 E-mail: simon.t@bourbonfabi.co.uk

C M I Plastics Ltd, Wood Street Works, Wood Street, Burnley, Lancashire, BB10 1QH Tel: (01282) 420021 Fax: (01282) 831387 E-mail: sales@cmi-ltd.com

Cass Bros, 153 Hastings Road, Bromley, BR2 8NQ Tel: (020) 8462 2387 Fax: (020) 8462 2387

Faurecina Midlands Ltd, PO Box 200, Coventry, CV3 1LU Tel: (024) 7663 5533 Fax: (024) 7688 5075

John Skinner Manufacturing Ltd, 82b Chesterton Lane, Cirencester, Gloucestershire, GL7 1YD Tel: (01285) 657410 Fax: (01285) 650013 E-mail: sales@john-skinner.co.uk

W. Marston Ltd, 70 Fazeley Street, Birmingham, B5 5RD Tel: 0121-643 0852 Fax: 0121-643 9534 E-mail: info@williammarstonltd.co.uk

Pianoforte Supplies Ltd, Simplex Works, Ashton Road, Roade, Northampton, NN7 2LG Tel: (01604) 862441 Fax: (01604) 862427 E-mail: sales@psluk.co.uk

R Tek Ltd, Unit 1 Triangle Business Park, Pentrebach, Merthyr Tydfil, Mid Glamorgan, CF48 4TQ Tel: (01685) 373159 Fax: (01685) 373204 E-mail: maindesk@r-tek.co.uk

MOTOR VEHICLE VALETING

▶ 1st Dirt Busters, 20 Clarendon Road, Southsea, Hampshire, PO5 2EE Tel: (023) 9282 9429 E-mail: dirt.busters@virgin.net

▶ Aautoclean Car Valet Services, 30 Oakdale Road, Oldbury, West Midlands, B68 8AY Tel: (07776) 194420 Fax: 0121-544 3276 E-mail: aautoclean@blueyonder.co.uk

▶ ACS Mobile Valeting, Wilthorpe, Barnsley, South Yorkshire, S75 1JW Tel: 07913 504999 E-mail: valeting@acsmobile.co.uk

▶ Autogleam Mobile Valeting, 76 Birkdale, Warmley, Bristol, BS30 8GH Tel: 0117-961 8666 Fax: 0117-914 0777 E-mail: info@autogleam.net

Car Care, 153 St. Johns Road, Kettering, Northamptonshire, NN15 5AZ Tel: (01536) 524512 E-mail: sales@carcare-mvs.co.uk

▶ G R Valeting, 35 Rutland Close, Catterick Garrison, North Yorkshire, DL9 3HJ Tel: (01748) 833434 E-mail: gordon@grvaleting.com

MOTOR VEHICLE VALETING – *continued*

▶ K G B Car Valeting, 12 Stuchbury Close, Aylesbury, Buckinghamshire, HP19 8GD Tel: (01296) 436444 Fax: (01296) 436444 E-mail: info@kgbcarvaleting.co.uk

▶ Lellers Valeting Centres Ltd, 159 Turners Hill, Cheshunt, Waltham Cross, Hertfordshire, EN8 9BH Tel: (01992) 641383 Fax: E-mail: valet@lellers.co.uk

▶ M A C Motors Ltd, Unit E, Curzon Business Centre, Curzon Street, Burton-on-Trent, Staffordshire, DE14 2DH Tel: (01283) 534230 E-mail: sales@macmotors.co.uk

▶ Pro Shine Valeting Services, 2 Metcalf Close, Sweet Briar Road Industrial Es, Norwich, NR3 2BP Tel: (01603) 487879 E-mail: info@pro-shine.co.uk

Professional Mobile Valet Service, 31 Brimbleworth Lane, St. Georges, Weston-super-Mare, Avon, BS22 7XS Tel: (07811) 158953 E-mail: professionalmobilevaletservice@hotmail.co.uk

▶ Waterless Detailers (Derby) Ltd, 20 Victoria Drive, Woodville, Swadlincote, Derbyshire, DE11 8DY Tel: (07970) 607166 E-mail: derby@waterlessdetailers.co.uk

MOTOR VEHICLE VALETING, MOBILE

▶ Aautoclean Car Valet Services, 30 Oakdale Road, Oldbury, West Midlands, B68 8AY Tel: (07776) 194420 Fax: 0121-544 3276 E-mail: aautoclean@blueyonder.co.uk

▶ ACS Mobile Valeting, Wilthorpe, Barnsley, South Yorkshire, S75 1JW Tel: 07913 504999 E-mail: valeting@acsmobile.co.uk

▶ Auto Valeting Services, 7 Ham Close, Collingbourne Kingston, Marlborough, Wiltshire, SN8 3SB Tel: 01264 850621 E-mail: mike@autovaletingservices.co.uk

▶ Autogleam Mobile Valeting, 76 Birkdale, Warmley, Bristol, BS30 8GH Tel: 0117-961 8666 Fax: 0117-914 0777 E-mail: info@autogleam.net

Car Care, 153 St. Johns Road, Kettering, Northamptonshire, NN15 5AZ Tel: (01536) 524512 E-mail: sales@carcare-mvs.co.uk

▶ Car Treat (Mobile Car Valeting), 135 Rylands Road, Kennington, Kennington, Ashford, Kent, TN24 9LU Tel: (01233) 629247 E-mail: jonathan4reeves@uk2.net

▶ carvalet.co.uk Limited, Iron Walls, Tutbury, Burton-on-Trent, Staffordshire, DE13 9NH Tel: 08006 985589 Fax: 08702 646647 E-mail: info@carvalet.co.uk

▶ Drive 'n' Shine, 427 Leatherhead Road, Chessington, Surrey, KT9 2NQ Tel: (0796) 0781193 E-mail: info@driveandshine.co.uk

▶ Elbow Grease Mobile Valeting, 23 Bolyfant Crescent, Whitnash, Leamington Spa, Warwickshire, CV31 2RH Tel: (07863) 219378

▶ F1 Mobile Valeting, Hollins Lane, Bury, Lancashire, BL9 8BS Tel: (07766) 526153 E-mail: enquiries@f1mobilevaleting.co.uk

▶ G R Valeting, 35 Rutland Close, Catterick Garrison, North Yorkshire, DL9 3HJ Tel: (01748) 833434 E-mail: gordon@grvaleting.com

▶ Get Valeted, Gainsborough House, 17-23 High Street, Slough, SL1 1DY Tel: 0845 0529771 E-mail: info@getvaleted.co.uk

▶ K G B Car Valeting, 12 Stuchbury Close, Aylesbury, Buckinghamshire, HP19 8GD Tel: (01296) 436444 Fax: (01296) 436444 E-mail: info@kgbcarvaleting.co.uk

▶ Lellers Valeting Centres Ltd, 159 Turners Hill, Cheshunt, Waltham Cross, Hertfordshire, EN8 9BH Tel: (01992) 641383 Fax: E-mail: valet@lellers.co.uk

M J Macaulay, 4 Webster Place, Rosyth, Dunfermline, Fife, KY11 2TU Tel: (07708) 854378 E-mail: mac@macaulay2560.freeserve.co.uk

Posh Wosh - Mobile Car Valeting Ashford Kent, Unit 19, Dunnock Road, Kennington, Ashford, Kent, TN25 4QJ Tel: (07811) 547041 Fax: (01233) 630537 E-mail: posh_wosh2003@hotmail.com

▶ Smart Valeting, 28 Cosby Road, Littlethorpe, Leicester, LE19 2HF Tel: 0116-286 6338 E-mail: spencer@smartvaleting.co.uk

▶ Squeaky Clean, 34 Dean Road, Wrexham, Clwyd, LL13 9EH Tel: (07713) 922158 E-mail: info@squeaky-clean.me.uk

▶ Valet Magic, 6 High Street, Stanwell, Staines, Middlesex, TW19 7JS Tel: (01753) 680395 Fax: (01753) 680395 E-mail: info@valetmagic.com

▶ Valetmaster Mobile Car Valeting Service, Unit 8, Westerleigh Road, Pucklechurch, Bristol, BS16 9RB Tel: 07966 022209 E-mail: robert01@fsmail.net

MOTOR VEHICLE VALETING/ CLEANING/WASHING/ CHEMICALS/PRODUCTS

▶ 1st Dirt Busters, 20 Clarendon Road, Southsea, Hampshire, PO5 2EE Tel: (023) 9282 9429 E-mail: dirt.busters@virgin.net

Anglia Battery & Filter Co., 834 London Road, Leigh-on-Sea, Essex, SS9 3NH Tel: (01702) 470262 Fax: (01702) 470335 E-mail: sales@angliabattery.co.uk

▶ Atomiza Ltd, Provident House, 6-20 Burrell Row, Beckenham, Kent, BR3 1AT Tel: (0845) 0066006 Fax: (020) 8402 1221 E-mail: info@atomiza.co.uk

▶ LBVALETING, 55 Walnut Crescent, Kettering, Northamptonshire, NN16 9PX Tel: (01536) 501217 E-mail: lbvaleting@hotmail.com

▶ Prestige Car Valeting, 8 The Oaks, West Byfleet, Surrey, KT14 6RL Tel: (07811) 111999 Fax: (01932) 402124 E-mail: prestigecarvaleting@yahoo.co.uk

▶ Pro Shine Valeting Services, 2 Metcalf Close, Sweet Briar Road Industrial Es, Norwich, NR3 2BP Tel: (01603) 487879 E-mail: info@pro-shine.co.uk

Professional Mobile Valet Service, 31 Brimbleworth Lane, St. Georges, Weston-super-Mare, Avon, BS22 7XS Tel: (07811) 158953 E-mail: professionalmobilevaletservice@hotmail.co.uk

Ryko International Ltd, Unit 11, Broadoak Industrial Estate, Broadbridge Heath, Horsham, West Sussex, RH12 3JR Tel: (01403) 240364 Fax: (01403) 246955 E-mail: sales@ryko.com

Sterling Products Ltd, Richmond Street, West Bromwich, West Midlands, B70 0DD Tel: 0121-557 0022 Fax: 0121-557 0222

▶ Valetmaster Mobile Car Valeting Service, Unit 8, Westerleigh Road, Pucklechurch, Bristol, BS16 9RB Tel: 07966 022209 E-mail: robert01@fsmail.net

▶ Waterless Detailers (Derby) Ltd, 20 Victoria Drive, Woodville, Swadlincote, Derbyshire, DE11 8DY Tel: (07970) 607166 E-mail: derby@waterlessdetailers.co.uk

▶ The Waterless Valeting Co. Edinburgh, 1A Lansdowne Crescent, Edinburgh, EH12 5EQ Tel: 0131-225 3220 E-mail: brian.anderson22@btopenworld.com

MOTOR VEHICLE WASHING SYSTEMS

Air Services, Redgate Road South Lancashire Industrial Estate, South Lancashire Industrial Es, Ashton-in-Makerfield, Wigan, Lancashire, WN4 8DT Tel: (01942) 722333 Fax: (01942) 725716 E-mail: sales@air-serv.co.uk

Ryko International Ltd, Unit 11, Broadoak Industrial Estate, Broadbridge Heath, Horsham, West Sussex, RH12 3JR Tel: (01403) 240364 Fax: (01403) 246955 E-mail: sales@ryko.com

Smith Bros & Webb Ltd, 22 Tything Road East, Kinwarton, Alcester, Warwickshire, B49 6EX Tel: (01789) 400096 Fax: (01789) 400231 E-mail: sales@vehicle-washing-systems.co.uk

Wash Shop, 1 Hartford Way, Sealand Industrial Estate, Chester, CH1 4NT Tel: (01244) 520916 Fax: (01244) 526022

▶ Washtec UK Ltd, 14a Oak Industrial Park, Chelmsford Road, Dunmow, Essex, CM6 1XN Tel: (01371) 878800 Fax: (01371) 878810 E-mail: sales@washtec-uk.com

Wickham Auto Wash Ltd, Norton Road, Stevenage, Hertfordshire, SG1 2BB Tel: (01438) 314041 Fax: (01438) 740140 E-mail: all@wickham-autowash.co.uk

Wilcomatic Ltd, 123 Beddington Lane, Croydon, CR0 4YL Tel: (020) 8649 9760 Fax: (020) 8680 9791 E-mail: sales@wilcomatic.co.uk

MOTOR VEHICLE WHEEL CLAMPS

A H Hanson Ltd, Marley Street, Keighley, West Yorkshire, BD21 5JX Tel: (01535) 604112 Fax: (01535) 610085 E-mail: sales@wheel-clamp.com

MOTOR VEHICLE WINDOW ETCHING KITS

Retainagroup Ltd., 134-136 Buckingham Palace Road, London, SW1W 9SA Tel: (020) 7823 6868 Fax: (020) 7823 6864 E-mail: general.sales@retainagroup.co.uk

MOTOR VEHICLE WINDOWS

Chadwell Safety Glass Ltd, Maldon Road, Latchingdon, Chelmsford, CM3 6LF Tel: (01621) 743084 Fax: (01621) 742977

Cheshire Vehicle Windows Ltd, Unit 3 Phoenix Centre, Road One Winsford Indust Estate, Winsford Industrial Estate, Winsford, Cheshire, CW7 3PZ Tel: (01606) 557114 Fax: (01606) 861250 E-mail: cvwindows@ukonline.co.uk

Percy Lane Ltd, Lichfield Road, Tamworth, Staffordshire, B79 7TL Tel: (01827) 63821 Fax: (01827) 310159 E-mail: sales@percy-lane.co.uk

Seaglaze Marine Windows Ltd, Wendover Road, Rackheath, Norwich, NR13 6LH Tel: (01603) 720745 Fax: (01603) 721770 E-mail: sales@seaglaze.co.uk

Stanway Screens Ltd, Oil Croft Orchard, Main Road, Bredon, Tewkesbury, Gloucestershire, GL20 7LX Tel: (01684) 772378 Fax: (01684) 772013 E-mail: marcuspriest@hotmail.com

MOTORCYCLE ACCESSORIES

▶ Bob Heath Visors Ltd, 6 Birmingham Road, Walsall, WS1 2NA Tel: (01922) 614747 Fax: (01922) 644956 E-mail: b.heath@virgin.net

▶ Falcon Shock Absorbers Ltd, 5 Ryan Business Park, Sandford Lane, Wareham, Dorset, BH20 4DY Tel: (01929) 554545 Fax: (01929) 550550 E-mail: falconshockabsorbers@speed-mail.co.uk

Harris Performance Products Ltd, 6 Marshgate Drive, Hertford, SG13 7AQ Tel: (01992) 532500 Fax: (01992) 587052 E-mail: sales@harris-performance.com

M C A (Aston) Ltd, 38-50 Victoria Road, Aston, Birmingham, B6 5HF Tel: 0121-554 6644 Fax: 0121-554 7854

Metmachex Engineering Ltd, 9 Monk Road, Alfreton, Derbyshire, DE55 7RL Tel: (01773) 836241 Fax: (01773) 520109 E-mail: sales@metmachex.com

Motor Cycle Clothing Centre, 36 Norwich Road, Wymondham, Norfolk, NR18 0NS Tel: (01953) 606922 Fax: (01953) 606922 E-mail: enquiries@motorcycle-clothing.co.uk

P F K Ling Ltd, 55 Mendham Lane, Harleston, Norfolk, IP20 9DW Tel: (01379) 853213 Fax: (01379) 854373 E-mail: power@lings.com

P & P Seating, 429 Meadway, Birmingham, B33 0DZ Tel: 0121-784 9441 Fax: 0121-789 7061 E-mail: info@ppseat.co.uk

Pyramid Plastics Ltd, Unit 22 Corringham Road Industrial Estate, Corringham Road, Gainsborough, Lincolnshire, DN21 1QB Tel: (01427) 810473 Fax: (01427) 612204 E-mail: david@pyramid-plastics.co.uk

Renntec, 69 Woolsbridge Industrial Estate, Three Legged Cross, Wimborne, Dorset, BH21 6SP Tel: (01202) 826722 Fax: (01202) 826747 E-mail: info@renntec.com

Skidmarx, 16-18 Cambridge Road, Granby Industrial Estate, Weymouth, Dorset, DT4 9TJ Tel: (01305) 780808 Fax: (01305) 787499 E-mail: info@skidmarx.co.uk

▶ Thorncraft Motorcycles, 258a Whalley New Road, Blackburn, BB1 9SR Tel: (01254) 264230 Fax: (01254) 680156 E-mail: sales@thorncraft.co.uk

MOTORCYCLE ALARM SYSTEMS

Bridgwater Electronics Ltd, Unit 15 Westmans Industrial Estate, Love Lane, Burnham-on-Sea, Somerset, TA8 1EY Tel: (01278) 789552 Fax: (01278) 789782 E-mail: sales@bridgwater-electronics.co.uk

Tri-State Electronics, Unit 4, Bumpers Enterprise Centre, Bumpers Farm Industrial Estate, Chippenham, Wiltshire, SN14 6QA Tel: (01249) 464650 Fax: (01249) 445414 E-mail: mikenickless@msn.com

MOTORCYCLE COMPONENTS

Alpha Bearings Ltd, Kingsley St, Dudley, West Midlands, DY2 0QA Tel: (01384) 255151 Fax: (01384) 457509 E-mail: info@alpha-bearings.com

D M W Motor Cycles Ltd, Tynesbank Works, Walkden, Manchester, M28 0SF Tel: 0161-790 5277 Fax: 0161-703 8170 E-mail: dctomkinson@hotmail.com

▶ Falcon Shock Absorbers Ltd, 5 Ryan Business Park, Sandford Lane, Wareham, Dorset, BH20 4DY Tel: (01929) 554545 Fax: (01929) 550550 E-mail: falconshockabsorbers@speed-mail.co.uk

Harris Performance Products Ltd, 6 Marshgate Drive, Hertford, SG13 7AQ Tel: (01992) 532500 Fax: (01992) 587052 E-mail: sales@harris-performance.com

Norman Hyde Ltd, Rigby Close, Heathcote Industrial Estate, Warwick, CV34 6TL Tel: (01926) 497375 Fax: (01926) 832352 E-mail: sales@normanhyde.co.uk

M C A (Aston) Ltd, 38-50 Victoria Road, Aston, Birmingham, B6 5HF Tel: 0121-554 6644 Fax: 0121-554 7854

Roger Maughfling Engineering Ltd, Station Works, Knucklas, Knighton, Powys, LD7 1PN Tel: (01547) 528201 Fax: (01547) 520392 E-mail: supersprox@supersprox.demon.co.uk

P F K Ling Ltd, 55 Mendham Lane, Harleston, Norfolk, IP20 9DW Tel: (01379) 853213 Fax: (01379) 854373 E-mail: power@lings.com

Skidmarx, 16-18 Cambridge Road, Granby Industrial Estate, Weymouth, Dorset, DT4 9TJ Tel: (01305) 780808 Fax: (01305) 787499 E-mail: info@skidmarx.co.uk

Sprint Manufacturing, 30b, Upton Lovell, Warminster, Wiltshire, BA12 0JW Tel: (01985) 850821 Fax: (01985) 850821 E-mail: enquiries@sprintmanufacturing.co.uk

T Ireson, Gas Lane, Cricklade, Swindon, SN6 6BY Tel: (01793) 750044 Fax: (01793) 750044

MOTORCYCLE COURIER SERVICES

Astral Max Couriers, 90a High Street, Rickmansworth, Hertfordshire, WD3 1AQ Tel: (01923) 711444 Fax: (01923) 711714 E-mail: sales@maxinternational.co.uk

▶ FETCH, BIRMINGHAM, WEST MIDLANDS, BIRMINGHAM, B20 3RN Tel: 07725 441306 E-mail: eric@fetch.cc

▶ Mr D's Couriers Ltd, Gothic House, Barker Gate, Nottingham, NG1 1JU Tel: (0870) 7506396 Fax: (0870) 7506397 E-mail: mrdscouriers@hotmail.com

MOTORCYCLE ENGINEERING SPECIALIST SERVICES

Alpha Bearings Ltd, Kingsley St, Dudley, West Midlands, DY2 0QA Tel: (01384) 255151 Fax: (01384) 457509 E-mail: info@alpha-bearings.com

Biggleswade Sheet Metal Co, The Old Forge, Rose Lane, Biggleswade, Bedfordshire, SG18 0JT Tel: (01767) 318509 Fax: (01767) 318509

Bradbury's Engineering, The Crossways, Loggerheads, Market Drayton, Shropshire, TF9 4BX Tel: (01630) 672900 Fax: (01630) 673858 E-mail: bradburyeng@aol.com

Burnbank Garage, Burnbank Street, Campbeltown, Argyll, PA28 6JD Tel: (01586) 552772 Fax: (01586) 551414 E-mail: accounts@burnbankgarage.com

Custom Tanks & Designs, Unit 23a Pershore Trading Estate, Pershore, Worcestershire, WR10 2DD Tel: (01386) 554136

D M W Motor Cycles Ltd, Tynesbank Works, Walkden, Manchester, M28 0SF Tel: 0161-790 5277 Fax: 0161-703 8170 E-mail: dctomkinson@hotmail.com

▶ Falcon Shock Absorbers Ltd, 5 Ryan Business Park, Sandford Lane, Wareham, Dorset, BH20 4DY Tel: (01929) 554545 Fax: (01929) 550550 E-mail: falconshockabsorbers@speed-mail.co.uk

Harthills Motor Cycles, 10 Caledonia Street, Bilston, West Midlands, WV14 6AE Tel: (01902) 492481

Surrey Harley Davidson Buell, 285-293 High Street, Dorking, Surrey, RH4 1RL Tel: (01306) 883825 Fax: (01306) 881397

Tritan Engineering Ltd, Bondgate, Green Lane, Ripon, North Yorkshire, HG4 1QQ Tel: (01765) 601608 Fax: (01765) 606800

MOTORCYCLE FAIRING REPAIR SERVICES

▶ Stephen Marrs Bike Art, 9 loan road, Cullybackey, Ballymena, County Antrim, BT42 1er Tel: (028) 2588 1865 E-mail: stephen@marrs101.freeserve.co.uk

▶ ZNR paintwork Ltd, 12 Burgess Road, Ivyhouse Lane Industrial Estate, Hastings, East Sussex, TN35 4NR Tel: 01424 432465

MOTORCYCLE SEATS

P & P Seating, 429 Meadway, Birmingham, B33 0DZ Tel: 0121-784 9441 Fax: 0121-789 7061 E-mail: info@ppseat.co.uk

R K Leighton, 2 Partridge Court, Price Street, Birmingham, B4 6JZ Tel: 0121-359 0514 Fax: 0121-333 3130 E-mail: sales@rk-leighton.co.uk

MOTORCYCLE SECURITY CAGES

▶ Y anchor, 19 Earsdon Terrace, West Allotment, Newcastle Upon Tyne, NE27 0DY Tel: 0191 2159738

MOTORCYCLE SIDECARS

Unit Sidecars Ltd, Wethersfield Road, Sible Hedingham, Halstead, Essex, CO9 3LB Tel: (01787) 461000 Fax: (01787) 461000 E-mail: sales@unitsidecars.co.uk

MOTORCYCLE SPARE PARTS

B & C Express Ltd, Station Road, Potterhanworth, Lincoln, LN4 2DX Tel: (01522) 791369 Fax: (01522) 794262 E-mail: sales@bandcexpress.co.uk

Feridax 1957 Ltd, Park Lane, Halesowen, West Midlands, B63 2NT Tel: (01384) 410384 Fax: (01384) 638287E-mail: info@feridax.com

Norman Hyde Ltd, Rigby Close, Heathcote Industrial Estate, Warwick, CV34 6TL Tel: (01926) 497375 Fax: (01926) 832352 E-mail: sales@normanhyde.co.uk

Milverton Motor Cycle Parts, 21-23 Kyotts Lake Road, Birmingham, B11 1JX Tel: 0121-772 4517 Fax: 0121-771 1904

MOTORCYCLE SPARE PARTS – *continued*

Surrey Harley Davidson Buell, 285-293 High Street, Dorking, Surrey, RH4 1RL Tel: (01306) 883825 Fax: (01306) 881397

The Velocette Motor Cycle Co., Meriden Works, Birmingham Road, Millisons Wood, Coventry, CV5 9AZ Tel: (01676) 522066 Fax: (01676) 522331

Waffell Ltd, 111 Sadler Road, Doddington Road, Lincoln, LN6 3RS Tel: (01522) 888444 Fax: (01522) 888400 E-mail: sales@totalbikebits.com

MOTORCYCLE TRAINING

▶ Acer Motorcycle Training, 18 Severn Oaks, Quedgeley, Gloucester, GL2 4YX Tel: (01452) 720975 E-mail: sales@acermotorcycles.com

▶ Easyrider Motorcycle Training School, rear of Stafford Cricket Club Riverway, Stafford, ST18 9BH Tel: (01785) 254542 Fax: (01785) 254542 E-mail: antonionarcisi@tiscali.co.uk

▶ RideRight UK, 47 Leafields, Houghton Regis, Dunstable, Bedfordshire, LU5 5LT Tel: (07932) 746662 E-mail: info@riderightuk.co.uk

MOTORCYCLE TYRES

Bridgestone UK Ltd, Athena Drive, Tachbrook Park, Warwick, CV34 6UX Tel: (01926) 488500 Fax: (01926) 488600 E-mail: bfuk.reception@bridgestone-eu.com

Continental Tyre Group Ltd, Continental House, 191 High Street, Yiewsley, West Drayton, Middlesex, UB7 7XW Tel: (01895) 425900 Fax: (01895) 425982

Cooper Tyre & Rubber Co UK Ltd, Bath Road, Melksham, Wiltshire, SN12 8AA Tel: (01225) 703101 Fax: (01225) 707880

Feltham Tyres, Green Man Lane, Feltham, Middlesex, TW14 0QD Tel: (020) 8890 7138 Fax: (020) 8751 4428 E-mail: sales@felthamtyre.co.uk

▶ Goodyear Dunlop, Tyrefort, 88-98 Wingfoot Way, Erdington, Birmingham, B24 9HY Tel: 0121-306 6166

Kalvin Tyre Co. Ltd, 259 High Road, Broxbourne, Hertfordshire, EN10 6PZ Tel: (01992) 462728

MOTORCYCLE VISOR CLEANING CLOTHS

▶ Lameduck Enterprises, 27 Duxford Close, Redditch, Worcestershire, B97 5BY Tel: 01527) 542269 Fax: 01527) 540299 E-mail: lameduck@hotmail.com

MOTORCYCLE WHEELS

Central Wheel Components Ltd, Station Road Industrial Estate, Station Road, Coleshill, Birmingham, B46 1HT Tel: (01675) 462264 Fax: (01675) 466412 E-mail: info@central-wheel.co.uk

MOTORCYCLES

▶ 3g Distribution, Marshalls Court, Shrewsbury, SY1 2HX Tel: (01743) 270470 Fax: (01743) 270470

▶ Adventure Motorcycle Holidays, Bryn Alyn, Denbigh Road, Rhydymwyn, Mold, Flintshire, CH7 5HF Tel: (01352) 742122 E-mail: sales@amch.co.uk

Colin Appleyard Ltd, Worth Way, Keighley, West Yorkshire, BD21 5AJ Tel: (01535) 606311 Fax: (01535) 602585 E-mail: bikes@colinappleyard.co.uk

Chris Appleby Engineering, Homestead Farm, Great Burches Road, Benfleet, Essex, SS7 3NG Tel: (01268) 776642 Fax: (01268) 776645 E-mail: enquiries@applebee.co.uk

Easy Rider (Europe) Ltd, Wright Street, Stafford, ST16 3AY Tel: (01785) 250353 Fax: (01785) 257048 E-mail: info@easyridereurope.co.uk

Flitwick Motor Cycles, Station Road, Flitwick, Bedford, MK45 1JR Tel: (01525) 750380 Fax: (01525) 750390 E-mail: sales@flitwickmotorcycles.co.uk

Harris Performance Products Ltd, 6 Marshgate Drive, Hertford, SG13 7AQ Tel: (01992) 532500 Fax: (01992) 587052 E-mail: sales@harris-performance.com

Kawasaki Motors UK, 1 Dukes Meadow, Millboard Road, Bourne End, Buckinghamshire, SL8 5XF Tel: (01628) 856750 Fax: (01628) 856796 E-mail: customerservice@kawasaki.co.uk

▶ Metamorphicycles, The Old Foundry, Chawston Lane, Chawston, Bedford, MK44 3BH Tel: (01480) 216510 Fax: (01480) 216510

Moore Large & Co. Ltd, Grampian Buildings, Sinfin Lane, Derby, DE24 9GL Tel: (01332) 274200 Fax: (01332) 270635

▶ North Leicester Motor Cycles Ltd, 64 Whitehill Road, Ellistown, Coalville, Leicestershire, LE67 1EL Tel: (01530) 263381 Fax: (01530) 262960 E-mail: sales@motomorini.co.uk

P F K Ling Ltd, 55 Mendham Lane, Harleston, Norfolk, IP20 9DW Tel: (01379) 853213 Fax: (01379) 854373 E-mail: power@lings.com

▶ Pembrokeshire Classics (Motorcycles), Bromleigh, Reynalton, Kilgetty, Dyfed, SA68 0PH Tel: (01834) 891685 Fax: (01834) 891685 E-mail: mail@pembrokeshireclassics.com

▶ Qbike Ltd, 18 Conglass Drive, Inverurie, Aberdeenshire, AB51 4LB Tel: (07815) 746035 E-mail: info@qbike.biz

Ride On Motor Cycles, 19-21 Nithsdale Street, Glasgow, G41 2PZ Tel: 0141-424 0404 Fax: 0141-423 4685 E-mail: sales@ride-on-motorcycles.co.uk

▶ Robinsons Foundry Ltd, Broad Oak Road, Canterbury, Kent, CT2 7QG Tel: (01227) 378400 Fax: (01227) 454726 E-mail: sales@robinsonsfoundry.co.uk

Suzuki GB P.L.C., Steinbeck Crescent, Snelshall West, Milton Keynes, MK4 4AE Tel: (01908) 336600 Fax: (01908) 336719

Vehicletrademaster, PO Box 5347, Northampton, NN3 7YT Tel: (08702) 405445 Fax: (08702) 405445 E-mail: vtmoffice@btinternet.com

MOTORCYCLES, FOUR WHEELED, ROUGH TERRAIN

▶ Adventure Motorcycle Holidays, Bryn Alyn, Denbigh Road, Rhydymwyn, Mold, Flintshire, CH7 5HF Tel: (01352) 742122 E-mail: sales@amch.co.uk

Gerald Dinnis Ltd, Tedburn Road, Whitestone, Exeter, EX4 2HF Tel: (01392) 811581 Fax: (01392) 811722 E-mail: info@whitehorsemotors.co.uk

The Quad Centre, 12 Hillcrest Way, Buckingham Industrial Park, Buckingham, MK18 1HJ Tel: (01280) 817350 Fax: (01280) 817351 E-mail: info@thequadcentre.com

MOTORCYCLES, MINI

▶ Pocket Bike Imports, 1 Looseleigh Park, Plymouth, PL6 5JL Tel: 01752 360066 Fax: 01752 360066

MOTORCYCLES, POLICE

▶ RideRight UK, 47 Leafields, Houghton Regis, Dunstable, Bedfordshire, LU5 5LT Tel: (07932) 746662 E-mail: info@riderightuk.co.uk

MOTORCYCLES, ROUGH TERRAIN

▶ Adventure Motorcycle Holidays, Bryn Alyn, Denbigh Road, Rhydymwyn, Mold, Flintshire, CH7 5HF Tel: (01352) 742122 E-mail: sales@amch.co.uk

▶ Lameduck Enterprises, 27 Duxford Close, Redditch, Worcestershire, B97 5BY Tel: 01527) 542269 Fax: 01527) 540299 E-mail: lameduck@hotmail.com

▶ Pembrokeshire Classics (Motorcycles), Bromleigh, Reynalton, Kilgetty, Dyfed, SA68 0PH Tel: (01834) 891685 Fax: (01834) 891685 E-mail: mail@pembrokeshireclassics.com

Quad Bike Tours, Keepers Cottage, Inverlair, Fersit, Roy Bridge, Inverness-Shire, PH31 4AR Tel: (01397) 732371 E-mail: info@quadbiketours.co.uk

▶ RideRight UK, 47 Leafields, Houghton Regis, Dunstable, Bedfordshire, LU5 5LT Tel: (07932) 746662 E-mail: info@riderightuk.co.uk

MOTORCYCLIST'S HELMETS

Feridax 1957 Ltd, Park Lane, Halesowen, West Midlands, B63 2NT Tel: (01384) 410384 Fax: (01384) 638287E-mail: info@feridax.com

Helmet Integrated Systems, 3 Focus 4, Fourth Avenue, Letchworth Garden City, Hertfordshire, SG6 2TU Tel: (01462) 478000 Fax: (01462) 478010 E-mail: sales@helmets.co.uk

MOTORCYCLISTS' CLOTHING

Feridax 1957 Ltd, Park Lane, Halesowen, West Midlands, B63 2NT Tel: (01384) 410384 Fax: (01384) 638287E-mail: info@feridax.com

Scott Leathers Ltd, Unit 11 12, Industrial Estate, Stainton Grove, Barnard Castle, County Durham, DL12 8UJ Tel: (01833) 638913 Fax: (01833) 690375

Frank Thomas Ltd, Station Road, Finedon, Wellingborough, Northamptonshire, NN9 5NT Tel: (01933) 682260 Fax: (01933) 682261

MOTORCYCLISTS' CLOTHING, OFF ROAD

▶ Beck Powersports, Suite 2, 27 Colmore Row, Birmingham, B3 2EW Tel: 0121 557 8837 Fax: 08701 257572 E-mail: info@beckpowersports.co.uk

▶ Gaz Bikes, Beckfield Arabians, Midville Lane, Stickney, Boston, Lincolnshire, PE22 8DN Tel: 08456 434310 Fax: 08456 434310 E-mail: sales@gazbikes.co.uk

MOTORISED CARAVANS

Auto Sleepers Ltd, Orchard Works Indust Estate, Broadway, Worcestershire, WR12 7QF Tel: (01386) 853338 Fax: (01386) 858343 E-mail: sales@auto-sleepers.co.uk

Autocruise Group Holdings Ltd, Swinton Meadows Industrial Estate, Meadow Way, Swinton, Mexborough, South Yorkshire, S64 8AB Tel: (01709) 571411 Fax: (01709) 579292 E-mail: sales@autocruise.co.uk

Carlight Caravans Ltd, Unit 5-7 Tamson Way, Church Lane, Sleaford, Lincolnshire, NG34 7DE Tel: (01529) 302120 Fax: (01529) 302240 E-mail: mail@carlight.co.uk

Jabez Barker, Coneygre Industrial Estate, Tipton, West Midlands, DY4 8XP Tel: 0121-520 7058 Fax: 0121-522 3229

Murvi Motor Caravans Ltd, 4 East Way, Lee Mill Industrial Estate, Ivybridge, Devon, PL21 9GE Tel: (01752) 892200 Fax: (01752) 892202 E-mail: sales@murvi.co.uk

Swift Holdings Ltd, Dunswell Road, Cottingham, North Humberside, HU16 4JX Tel: (01482) 847332 Fax: (01482) 876335 E-mail: enquire@swiftleisure.co.uk

MOTORISED CONVEYOR BELT DRUMS

Van Der Graaf UK Ltd, 23 The Metro Centre, Peterborough, PE2 7UH Tel: (01733) 391777 Fax: (01733) 391044 E-mail: paul@vandergraaf.co.uk

MOTORISED METAL GOLF TROLLEYS

▶ Remotecontrolgolf.com, Fairfax, Paignton, Devon, TQ4 5LH Tel: (01803) 402668

MOTORS, SLIDING GATE

Darfen Durafencing, Bradman Road, Knowsley Industrial Park, Liverpool, L33 7UR Tel: 0151-547 3626 Fax: 0151-549 1205 E-mail: northwest@darfen.co.uk

MOTORSPORT COMPONENT CNC MILLING TO SPECIFICATION

Linton Design & Manufacture Ltd, 6a Bessemer CR, Rabans Lane Industrial Area, Aylesbury, Buckinghamshire, HP19 8TF Tel: (01296) 429179 Fax: (01296) 392290 E-mail: linton.design@btinternet.com

MRW Engineering Ltd, Unit 23a Hoo Farm Industrial Estate, Worcester Road, Kidderminster, Worcestershire, DY11 7RA Tel: (01562) 745042 Fax: (01562) 746472 E-mail: sales@mrwe.co.uk

MOTORSPORT MOTORCYCLES

Cryogenics International Ltd, 7 Brunel Way, Fareham, Hampshire, PO15 5TX Tel: (01489) 886722 Fax: (01489) 575229 E-mail: alan.rjones@cryogenicsinternational.co.uk

MOULD ENGRAVERS

B.H.R. Precision Engraving, Units 215 Victory Business Centre, Somers Road North, Portsmouth, PO1 1PJ Tel: (023) 9281 6613 Fax: (023) 9281 6613

Plumridge & Peters Ltd, Unit 5, Gillmans Industrial Estate, Natts Lane, Billingshurst, West Sussex, RH14 9EY Tel: (01403) 783762 Fax: (01403) 784288 E-mail: plumridge@ndirect.co.uk

MOULD REPAIR WELDING EQUIPMENT

Aps Welding Services, 215 Kirk Road, Wishaw, Lanarkshire, ML2 7DD Tel: (01698) 361601 Fax: (01698) 292555

MOULD (RUBBER) PRODUCTION COMPOUND SUPPLIERS

W P Notcutt Ltd, Homewood Farm, Newark Lane, Ripley, Woking, Surrey, GU23 6DJ Tel: (01483) 223311 Fax: (01483) 479594 E-mail: sales@notcutt.com

MOULD TOOLS/TOOLING

Jackson Engineering Stoke On Trent Ltd, Scott Lidgett Road, Stoke-on-Trent, ST6 4LX Tel: (01782) 812139 Fax: (01782) 824374 E-mail: sales@jacksonengineering.co.uk

North Notts Tool Makers Ltd, Unit 1 Fox Covert Way, Crown Farm Industrial Estate, Forest Town, Mansfield, Nottinghamshire, NG19 0FR Tel: (01623) 621188 Fax: (01623) 622662 E-mail: info@nntools.co.uk

MOULDED CASE CIRCUIT BREAKERS (CB)

A F Switchgear & Control Panels Ltd, Nunn Brook Road, Huthwaite, Sutton-in-Ashfield, Nottinghamshire, NG17 2HU Tel: (01623) 555600 Fax: (01623) 555800 E-mail: e-mail@afswitchgear.co.uk

Hager Engineering Ltd, 50 Horton Wood, Telford, Shropshire, TF1 7FT Tel: (0870) 2402400 Fax: (0870) 2400400E-mail: info@hager.co.uk

MOULDED PAPER PULP BOTTLE PACKAGING FOR POSTAL

▶ Cullen Packaging, 10 Dalsholm Avenue, Glasgow, G20 0TS Tel: 0141-945 2222 Fax: 0141-945 3567 E-mail: jamesg@cullen.co.uk

▶ Exel, PO Box 7, Barnsley, South Yorkshire, S71 2QG Tel: (01226) 710025

MOULDED PLUGS AND CONNECTORS

Murrelektronik Ltd, Albion Street, Pendlebury, Swinton, Manchester, M27 4FG Tel: 0161-728 3133 Fax: 0161-728 3130 E-mail: sales@murrelektronik.co.uk

MOULDED POLYSTYRENE (PS) BOXES

Peterhead Box Co. Ltd, Balmoor Industrial Estate, Peterhead, Aberdeenshire, AB42 1QG Tel: (01779) 470676 Fax: (01779) 473952

MOULDED PULP PRODUCTS

Omni-Pac UK Ltd, South Denes, Great Yarmouth, Norfolk, NR30 3QH Tel: (01493) 855381 Fax: (01493) 858464

MOULDING MATERIALS, *See also headings for particular types*

South Western Industrial Plasters, 63 Netherstreet, Bromham, Chippenham, Wiltshire, SN15 2DP Tel: (01380) 850616

MOULDING OR CERAMIC PLASTER

Aristocast Originals Ltd, 2 Wardsend Road, Sheffield, S6 1RQ Tel: 0114-269 0900 Fax: 0114-234 4885 E-mail: sales@troikaam.co.uk

D P Mouldings, 4 Station Hill, Maesteg, Mid Glamorgan, CF34 9AE Tel: (01656) 737033

Myra Plaster Mouldings, 24 Myra Road, Downpatrick, County Down, BT30 7JX Tel: (028) 4488 1676 Fax: (028) 4488 1676

Thredgards Ltd, Milne House, Ward Street, Alloa, Clackmannanshire, FK10 1ET Tel: (01259) 218181 Fax: (01259) 212777 E-mail: david.haswell@thredgards.com

MOULDING POWDERS, *See Plastic Moulding Materials etc*

MOULDINGS, *See also headings for particular types*

Abbeystone Stone Merchants, Harbury Lane, Heathcote, Warwick, CV34 6SL Tel: (01926) 450111 Fax: (01926) 336354

Diamond Paste & Mould Co., 78 Battle Road, St. Leonards-on-Sea, East Sussex, TN37 7AG Tel: (01424) 201505 Fax: (01424) 421359 E-mail: sales@sugarcity.co.uk

Lakeland Mouldings, Soulby, Penrith, Cumbria, CA11 0JE Tel: (01768) 486989 Fax: (01768) 486989 E-mail: ann@lakelandmouldings.co.uk

▶ M & M Picture Frames Mouldings Ltd, Humber Road, Barton-upon-Humber, South Humberside, DN18 5BN Tel: (01652) 632632 Fax: (01652) 660451 E-mail: sales@pinewrap.co.uk

Omco UK Ltd, New St Mills, Carlisle Road, Pudsey, West Yorkshire, LS28 8LW Tel: 0113-257 3172

Penspell Ltd, 1 Bradfield Road, Finedon Road Industrial Estate, Wellingborough, Northamptonshire, NN8 4HB Tel: (01933) 443605 Fax: (01933) 271489 E-mail: penspell@btclick.com

MOULDINGS – *continued*

Pro Mould Plastics, School Lane, Pendock, Gloucester, GL19 3PR Tel: (01684) 833048 Fax: (01684) 833049

Rotary Products Ltd, Box Bush, Upper Redbrook, Monmouth, Gwent, NP25 4LU Tel: (01600) 715723 Fax: (01600) 716215

S & C Moulds, Southfield Lodge, Burnham Road, Althorne, Chelmsford, CM3 6DP Tel: (01621) 744165 Fax: (01621) 744165

T M T Engineering Co., 11a Portway, Warminster, Wiltshire, BA12 8QG Tel: (01985) 216015 Fax: (01985) 216015

Tavishelm Tools Ltd, 10-12 Stacey Avenue, London, Greater London, N18 3PL Tel: 020 88039747

▶ Triton Tooling, Unit 11 Harmill Industrial Estate, Grovebury Road, Leighton Buzzard, Bedfordshire, LU7 4FF Tel: (01525) 376007 Fax: (01525) 372007

MOULDINGS, RUBBER MOULDINGS, GENERAL

Kingfisher Rubber & Plastics, Unit 1alfred Court Saxon Business Park, Hanbury Road, Stoke Prior, Bromsgrove, Worcestershire, B60 4AD Tel: (01527) 570570 Fax: (01527) 575200 E-mail: marklewis.kingfisher@virgin.net

Midhope Products, Unit 26-27 Albion Mills, Miry Lane, Thongsbridge, Holmfirth, HD9 7HP Tel: (01484) 688646 Fax: (01484) 688648 E-mail: midprod@btinternet.com

Reevite Ltd, 16 Murdock Road, Bicester, Oxfordshire, OX26 4PP Tel: (01869) 252520 Fax: (01869) 241394 E-mail: info@reevite.co.uk

Rubber Engineering Services, 4 Gorton Cresent, Windmill Lane Industrial Estate, Denton, Manchester, M34 3RB Tel: 0161-320 9900 Fax: 0161-320 9940 E-mail: sales@rubberengineering.co.uk

S R M Peakland Ltd, Vulcan Way, Coalville, Leicestershire, LE67 3AP Tel: (01530) 838317 Fax: (01530) 835122 E-mail: sales@srmpeakland.co.uk

MOULDINGS, WOOD, DECORATIVE

▶ Wild Goose Carvings, Unit 2E Delaware Road Industrial Estate, Delaware Road, Gunnislake, Cornwall, PL18 9AR Tel: (01822) 833764 Fax: (01822) 833801 E-mail: info@buycarvings.com

MOUNTED PLAIN BEARINGS

Criptic-Arvis Ltd, Croft Grange Works, Bridge Park Road, Thurmaston, Leicester, LE4 8BL Tel: 0116-260 9700 Fax: 0116-264 0147 E-mail: sales@arvis.co.uk

MOUNTS, *See Levelling etc; also Antivibration etc*

MOUTH WHISTLES

J. Hudson & Co. (Whistles) Ltd, 244 Barr Street, Hockley, Birmingham, B19 3AH Tel: 0121-554 2124 Fax: 0121-551 9293 E-mail: sale@acmewhistles.co.uk

MOVABLE FLOORING SYSTEMS

▶ Austin Design & Manufacture Ltd, Unit 2 Warish Hall, Warish Hall Road, Takeley, Bishop's Stortford, Hertfordshire, CM22 6NZ Tel: (01279) 871527 Fax: (01279) 871544 E-mail: keith@admfloors.com

MOZZARELLA CHEESE

▶ Fior D I Latte, Unit 22, Jubilee Drive, Loughborough, Leicestershire, LE11 5XS Tel: (01509) 211310

MP3 AUDIO SYSTEMS

▶ iPod Power, Spring Road, Ettingshall, Wolverhampton, WV4 6JX Tel: (0845) 1259520 Fax: (0845) 1259520 E-mail: webmaster@ipodpower.co.uk

▶ Think4 Ltd, Block P1 Unit, Heywood Distribution Park, Pilsworth Road, Heywood, Lancashire, OL10 2TT Tel: (0870) 1644446 Fax: (01706) 620000

Toad plc, National Control Centre, Drake Road, Mitcham, Surrey, CR4 4HQ Tel: (020) 8710 7770 Fax: (020) 8710 7708 E-mail: info@toad.co.uk

MUD CHEMICALS

Morrison Mud Engng Services, Sandford Lane, Everdene House, Wareham, Dorset, BH20 4DY Tel: (01929) 551245 Fax: (01929) 554245 E-mail: enquiries@morrisonmud.co.uk

Richkeen Chemicals Ltd, 33 Chapmans Cresent, Chesham, Buckinghamshire, HP5 2QT Tel: (01494) 786669 Fax: (01494) 786503 E-mail: richkeenc@aol.com

MUD PUMPS

Denhaolm Oilfield Services, Greenbank Place, East Tullos Industrial Estate, Aberdeen, AB12 3BT Tel: (01224) 249424 Fax: (01224) 249496

MUD SEPARATORS

Hampco Ltd, Blairs College, South Deeside Road, Blairs, Aberdeen, AB12 5LF Tel: (01224) 860300 Fax: (01224) 860301 E-mail: admin@hampco.com

MUDGUARDS

B J C Mudguards Ltd, 14 Floodgate Street, Birmingham, B5 5ST Tel: 0121-643 3295

Glenshiel Manufacturing Co., 3 Seaview, Kyle, Ross-Shire, IV40 8AS Tel: (01599) 534857 Fax: (01599) 534757 E-mail: stan@glenshiel.co.uk

Parlok UK Ltd, Cornwall Street, Parr Industrial Estate, St. Helens, Merseyside, WA9 1PT Tel: (01744) 639191 Fax: (01744) 612870 E-mail: sales@parlok.co.uk

MUFFINS

▶ Baking Solutions Ltd, Avenue Two, Witney, Oxfordshire, OX28 4YQ Tel: (01993) 864777 Fax: (01993) 777440 E-mail: info@bakingsolutions.co.uk

MUGS, BONE CHINA

Data Impex Ltd, 58 Beakes Road, Smethwick, West Midlands, B67 5RU Tel: (01902) 456619 Fax: 0121-533 0154 E-mail: sales@dataimpex.com

MULTIAXIS LASER CUTTING SERVICES

Subcon Laser Cutting Ltd, Unit 7, Trident Business Park, Park St, Nuneaton, Warwickshire, CV11 4NS Tel: (024) 7664 2221 Fax: (024) 7634 2180 E-mail: info@subconlaser.co.uk

Sygnet Signs Ltd, 129 Humberstone Rd, Leicester, LE5 3AP Tel: 0116-262 6288 Fax: 0116 262 6061

MULTIAXIS LASER PROCESSING

Waterjet Profiles Ltd, Units 9, Ryder Way, Basildon, Essex, SS13 1QH Tel: (01268) 591491 Fax: (01268) 729726 E-mail: sales@waterjet-profiles.co.uk

MULTICHIP LED LAMPS

C J Harris Electronic Components, Rosebank, Chafford Lane, Fordcombe, Tunbridge Wells, Kent, TN3 0SH Tel: (01892) 740000 Fax: (01892) 740100 E-mail: chrisharris2@btconnect.com

MULTICORE CABLES

Anixter UK Ltd, Anixter House, 1 York Road, Uxbridge, Middlesex, UB8 1RN Tel: (0845) 6041301 Fax: (01895) 818182

MULTIFUNCTION STEEL WORKING MACHINES

Ar Fabrications Ltd, 21 Rigg Street, Stewarton, Kilmarnock, Ayrshire, KA3 5AG Tel: (01560) 483777 Fax: (01560) 483777

Unimach Machine Tools Ltd, Folgate Road, North Walsham, Norfolk, NR28 0AJ Tel: 01692 409706

MULTILATERAL COMPLETION EQUIPMENT, OILWELL

National Oilwell Varco, Holton Road, Holton Heath Trading Park, Poole, Dorset, BH16 6LT Tel: (01202) 631817 Fax: (01202) 631708 E-mail: pcesales@nov.com

MULTILAYER OPTICAL COATINGS

▶ Siltint Ind Ltd, 124 Longley Lane, Sharston, Manchester, M22 4SP Tel: 0161-945 4000 Fax: 0161-945 4040 E-mail: info@siltint.com

MULTILAYER PRINTED CIRCUITS

Advanced Interconnection Technology Ltd, Business & Technology Centre, Green Lane, Eccles, Manchester, M30 0RJ Tel: 0161-787 3143 Fax: 0161-787 3144 E-mail: sales@ait-ltd.com

K C E Europe, Ashcombe House, Queen Street, Godalming, Surrey, GU7 1BA Tel: (01483) 528080 Fax: (01483) 528090 E-mail: sales@kce-europe.com

Lyncolec Ltd, 2 Abingdon Road, Nuffield Industrial Estate, Poole, Dorset, BH17 0UG Tel: (01202) 679797 Fax: (01202) 684530 E-mail: pcb@lyncolec.co.uk

Mho Trak Ltd, Blackhorse Road, Letchworth Garden City, Hertfordshire, SG6 1HB Tel: (01462) 480123 Fax: (01462) 480246 E-mail: data@mhotrak.co.uk

Printech Circuit Laboratories Ltd, 31-35 Haltwhistle Road, South Woodham Ferrers, Chelmsford, CM3 5ZA Tel: (01245) 323244 Fax: (01245) 329472 E-mail: sales@pcll.co.uk

Quassia Electronics Ltd, Bearwalden Business Park, Wendens Ambo, Saffron Walden, Essex, CB11 4JX Tel: (01799) 541174 Fax: (01799) 541937 E-mail: info@quassiaelectronics.co.uk

Quick Circuits Ltd, 1 Loverock Road, Reading, RG30 1DZ Tel: 0118-950 8921 Fax: 0118-956 8237 E-mail: sales@quick-circuits.com

Stevenage Circuits Ltd, Caxton Way, Stevenage, Hertfordshire, SG1 2DF Tel: (01438) 751800 Fax: (01438) 728103 E-mail: sales@stevenagecircuits.co.uk

Tru-Lon Printed Circuits (Royston) Ltd, Newark Close, York Way Industrial Estate, Royston, Hertfordshire, SG8 5HL Tel: (01763) 248922 Fax: (01763) 249281 E-mail: info@tru-lon.co.uk

MULTILEVEL ARRAY LED DISPLAYS

Infotec Ltd, The Maltings, Tamworth Road, Ashby-de-la-Zouch, Leicestershire, LE65 2PS Tel: (01530) 560600 Fax: (01530) 560111 E-mail: sales@infotech.co.uk

MULTIMEDIA BUREAU SERVICES

Acxiom, Counting House, 53 Tooley Street, London, SE1 2QN Tel: (020) 7526 5100 Fax: (020) 7526 5200

MULTIMEDIA ENTERTAINMENT COMPUTER SYSTEMS

Creative Computers Ltd, 258 Old Christchurch Road, Bournemouth, BH1 1PS Tel: (01202) 775600 Fax: (01202) 775559 E-mail: sales@creativegroup.co.uk

J B Communications Group Ltd, 15 Brackenbury Road, London, W6 0BE Tel: (020) 8749 6036 Fax: (020) 8749 9676 E-mail: interest@jbcommunications.co.uk

Siren Technology, 167 Radcliffe New Road, Whitefield, Manchester, M45 7RG Tel: 0161-796 5279 Fax: 0161-796 3208 E-mail: enquiries@sirentechnology.co.uk

Sony Music Entertainment UK Ltd, 10 Great Marlborough Street, London, W1F 7LP Tel: (020) 7911 8400 Fax: (020) 7911 8600

▶ WaveFX - Video & Multimedia Production, The Barn, 19 Edward Street, Cambridge, CB1 2LS Tel: (07779) 240169 E-mail: jamie@wavefx.co.uk

MULTIMEDIA MESSAGING (MMS) MOBILE TELEPHONES

▶ Phil Handsaker, 2 St. Johns Road, Tipton, West Midlands, DY4 9PB Tel: (07834) 689399 Fax: 0121-530 2049 E-mail: info@fourfootsnake.com

▶ Mobile Phones 4U, 10 Langhurst Court, Wenlock Close, Loundsley Green, Chesterfield, Derbyshire, S40 4PE Tel: (01246) 237267 E-mail: dallsop@mobile-phones4u.net

MULTIMEDIA PRODUCTION GRAPHIC DESIGN

▶ Creative Rage Ltd, Wassell Wood House, Habberley Road, Bewdley, Worcestershire, DY12 1LD Tel: (01299) 409062 E-mail: contact@creativerage.co.uk

▶ G13:Graphics & Multimedia, 47 Clarence Square, Cheltenham, Gloucestershire, GL50 4JR Tel: (01242) 210519 Fax: E-mail: mail@gavinpalmer.com

▶ Gem Stone Graphics Ltd, 4 Highdown Court, Forestfield, Crawley, West Sussex, RH10 6PR Tel: (01293) 524546E-mail: info@gsg-ltd.co.uk

▶ The Right Service, Bradford Road, Birmingham, B36 9AA Tel: 0121-246 8490 Fax: 0121-246 8490 E-mail: questions@therightservice.com

▶ Subcircle Creative, 5 Luther Mews, Brighton, BN2 9YR Tel: 01273 675428

▶ Surrey Films Ltd, Valley Farm, Green Lane, Churt, Farnham, Surrey, GU10 2LT Tel: (01428) 609532 E-mail: pete@surreyfilms.co.uk

▶ Tom Wakefield, Holly Tree Cottage, Woodmancote, Cirencester, Glos, GL7 7EF Tel: (0776) 6604866 Fax: E-mail: info@furryfeetstudios.com

MULTIMEDIA PROJECTOR HIRE

Av2hire.com (Manchester) Ltd, 22 Hardwick Street, Buxton, Derbyshire, SK17 6DH Tel: (0845) 0705168 E-mail: manchester@av2hire.com

Smart Visual Presentation Products Ltd, Unit 18, Kempton Road, Pershore, Worcestershire, WR10 2TA Tel: (0870) 0800612 Fax: (0870) 0800613 E-mail: sales@smartvisual.co.uk

MULTIMEDIA SERVICES

▶ Incognito Visual Communications, 2 Sheraton Street, London, W1F 8BH Tel: (020) 7851 4470 Fax: (01832) 733875 E-mail: lance@ivcltd.co.uk

▶ Lunar Interactive Multimedia Design, 2 Robincroft, Gressingham, Lancaster, LA2 8LP Tel: (01524) 222335 E-mail: john@lunar.co.uk

Ncube UK, 8 The Square, Stockley Park, Uxbridge, Middlesex, UB11 1FW Tel: (020) 8899 1706 Fax: (020) 8610 6869

Pollen Recording Studios, 97 Main Street, Bishop Wilton, York, YO42 1SP Tel: (01759) 368223 E-mail: enquiries@pollenstudio.co.uk

MULTIMEDIA SOFTWARE

Aquila Computer Services Ltd, 8-11 Waveney Road, Lowestoft, Suffolk, NR32 1BN Tel: (01502) 562555 Fax: (01502) 538149 E-mail: enquiries@aquila.uk.com

Autodesk Ltd, 1 Meadow Gate Avenue, Farnborough Business Park, Farnborough, Hampshire, GU14 6FG Tel: (01252) 456600 Fax: (01252) 456601

▶ Craig Jones Video Jockey, Breckland House, Hanbury Road, Hanbury, Bromsgrove, Worcestershire, B60 4DA Tel: (01527) 821303 Fax: (01527) 821303 E-mail: craigjones@clubberuk.com

ILX Group P.L.C., George House, Princes Court, Beam Heath Way, Nantwich, Cheshire, CW5 6GD Tel: (01270) 611600 Fax: (01270) 628513 E-mail: sales@ilxgroup.com

Iris Co Systems, Integra House, 138-140 Alexandra Road, London, SW19 7JY Tel: (020) 8879 3939 Fax: (020) 8879 7880 E-mail: info@computersoftware.com

Steelsoft Computing, Willowdene, Thornton-Cleveleys, Lancashire, FY5 3NB Tel: (01253) 828000 Fax: (01253) 867821 E-mail: sales@steelsoft.co.uk

MULTIMEDIA SYSTEMS

A T C Ltd, Greenway House, Greenway Business Centre, Harlow, Essex, CM19 5QD Tel: 0161-406 1000 Fax: (0870) 0558081 E-mail: sales@atc.co.uk

Connect It, Aizlewoods Mill, Nursery Street, Sheffield, S3 8GG Tel: 0114-282 3307 Fax: 0114-282 3302

Novus Interactive Ltd, 48 Rose Hill, Rednal, Birmingham, B45 8RT Tel: 0121-457 8008

MULTIMETERS, *See also headings for particular types*

Agilent Technologies UK Ltd, Eskdale Road, Winnersh, Wokingham, Berkshire, RG41 5DZ Tel: (07004) 666666 Fax: (07004) 444555 E-mail: contactcenter_uk@agilent.com

Di-Log, Unit 28 Wheel Forge Way, Trafford Park, Manchester, M17 1EH Tel: 0161-877 0322 Fax: 0161-877 1614E-mail: sales@dilog.co.uk

Instrotech Ltd, Unit A Penfold Trading Estate, Imperial Way, Watford, WD24 4YY Tel: (01923) 442244 Fax: (01923) 252959 E-mail: sales@instrotech.com

MULTIMETERS - *continued*

Servo & Electronic Sales Ltd, Unit 1/5 Harden Road Industrial Estate, Harden Road, Lydd, Romney Marsh, Kent, TN29 9LX Tel: (01797) 322500 Fax: (01797) 321569 E-mail: servo@plugs.demon.co.uk

MULTIPIN CONNECTORS

Ceep Ltd, Unit 7 Weydown Industrial Estate, Haslemere, Surrey, GU27 1DW Tel: (01428) 661515 Fax: (01428) 644147 E-mail: sales@ceep.co.uk

MULTIPLATFORM OPERATING SYSTEMS

Intrinsyc Europe, Fountain House, Great Cornbow, Halesowen, West Midlands, B63 3BL Tel: 0121-501 6000 Fax: 0121-501 6035

MULTIPLEXERS

Advent Communications, Preston Hill House, Preston Hill, Chesham, Buckinghamshire, HP5 3HE Tel: (01494) 774400 Fax: (01494) 791127 E-mail: sales@vislink.com

Dee Communications, 453 Brook Lane, Birmingham, B13 0BT Tel: 0121-702 2552 Fax: 0121-778 3633 E-mail: sales@deecomms.co.uk

Vocality International Ltd, Lydling Barn Lydling Farm, Puttenham Lane, Shackleford, Godalming, Surrey, GU8 6AP Tel: (01483) 813120 Fax: (01483) 813121 E-mail: sales@vocality.com

MULTIPURPOSE ABS BOXES

Boxes Kelvin Fenton Ltd, George Street, Burnley, Lancashire, BB11 1LX Tel: (01282) 477047 Fax: (01282) 477048 E-mail: boxeskf@discali.co.uk

Carmo Ltd, 11-19 Bancrofts Road, Eastern Industrial Area, South Woodham Ferrers, Chelmsford, CM3 5UG Tel: (01245) 322130 Fax: (01245) 328695 E-mail: brian@carmo.co.uk

D S Smith Packaging Wessex, 86 Livingstone Road, Andover, Hampshire, SP10 5NS Tel: (01264) 350753 Fax: (01264) 353315 E-mail: sales@danisco.com

Marish Packaging Ltd, Riverside Way, Cowley, Uxbridge, Middlesex, UB8 2YF Tel: (01895) 256885 Fax: (01895) 256905 E-mail: sales@marishpackaging.co.uk

Pitney Press, 50 Main Road, Middlezoy, Bridgwater, Somerset, TA7 0NN Tel: (01823) 698181 Fax: (01823) 698605

David S. Smith Norpack, Unit 4, 3A West Chirton Trading Estate, North Shields, Tyne & Wear, NE29 7UD Tel: 0191-257 1141 Fax: 0191-258 6193

MULTIPURPOSE WOODWORKING MACHINES

Craft Supplies Ltd, Newburgh Works, Netherside, Bradwell, Hope Valley, Derbyshire, S33 9NT Tel: (01433) 622550 Fax: (01433) 622552 E-mail: sales@craft-supplies.co.uk

MULTISKILLED CONTRACT LABOUR, ELECTRICAL AND MECHANICAL ENGINEERING

▶ E & A Site Services, 34 Kingsman Road, Stanford-le-Hope, Essex, SS17 0JW Tel: (01375) 644400 Fax: (01375) 644400 E-mail: eass@approvedtrading.com

▶ P G Services, 84 Tyron Way, Sidcup, Kent, DA14 6AZ Tel: 0208 3005738 Fax: 0208 3026330 E-mail: p.gservices@btinternet.com

MULTISPINDLE DRILLING AND TAPPING ATTACHMENTS

Gy Roll Ltd, Sand Road Industrial Estate, Sand Road, Great Gransden, Sandy, Bedfordshire, SG19 3AH Tel: (01767) 677377 Fax: (01767) 677900 E-mail: sales@gyroll.com

MULTISPINDLE DRILLING MACHINE MANUFRS

B R E Europe Ltd, London Road, Feering, Colchester, CO5 9ED Tel: (01376) 572500 Fax: (01376) 572600 E-mail: sales@breltd.com

Slack & Parr Hydraulics Ltd, Long Lane, Kegworth, Derby, DE74 2FL Tel: (01509) 672306 Fax: (01509) 673357 E-mail: info@slack-parr.com

MULTISTAGE CENTRIFUGAL PUMPS

Kinder Janes Engineers Ltd, Porters Wood, St. Albans, Hertfordshire, AL3 6HU Tel: (01727) 844441 Fax: (01727) 844247 E-mail: info@kinder-janes.co.uk

Union Pumps Union Pumps, Green Road, Penistone, Sheffield, S36 6BJ Tel: (01226) 763311 Fax: (01226) 766535 E-mail: bkearsley@unionpump.textron.com

MULTIWAY FIBRE OPTIC CONNECTORS

N F I Ltd, 259 York Town Road, College Town, Sandhurst, Berkshire, GU47 0RT Tel: (01276) 600200 Fax: (01276) 600161 E-mail: info@nfi.uk.com

MUNICIPAL SERVICE EQUIPMENT AND VEHICLES

Geesink Norba Ltd, Llantrisant Business Park, Llantrisant, Pontyclun, Mid Glamorgan, CF72 8XZ Tel: (01443) 222301 Fax: (01443) 237192 E-mail: sales@pdegeesink.co.uk

▶ Hopkinsons Fairdeals Ltd, Mayfield Farm, Doncaster Road, East Hardwick, Pontefract, West Yorkshire, WF8 3EQ Tel: (01977) 620418 Fax: (01977) 620419 E-mail: sales@hopdeals.com

Johnston Sweepers Ltd, Curtis Road, Dorking, Surrey, RH4 1XF Tel: (01306) 884722 Fax: (01306) 884151 E-mail: enquiries@johnstonsweepers.com

Lamberhurst Engineering Ltd, Priory Farm, Parsonage Lane, Lamberhurst, Tunbridge Wells, Kent, TN3 8DS Tel: (0845) 6121141 Fax: (0845) 6121142 E-mail: info@lameng.com

MUNICIPAL SERVICE EQUIPMENT/VEHICLE SPARE PARTS/WEARING PARTS

Londonderry Garage Ltd, New Garage, Londonderry, Northallerton, North Yorkshire, DL7 9NB Tel: (01677) 422185 Fax: (01677) 428311

Munitech Ltd, Hoo Marina Industrial Estate, Vicarage Lane, Hoo, Rochester, Kent, ME3 9LB Tel: (01634) 250771 Fax: (01634) 250388 E-mail: info@munitech.co.uk

MURDER MYSTERY PARTY GAMES

▶ How About Now, 10 Waynflete Lane, Farnham, Surrey, GU9 7BH Tel: (01252) 891790 Fax: E-mail: adam@howaboutnow.co.uk

MUSEUM DESIGNERS/FITTERS

Absolute Museum & Gallery Products, 66 Leonard Street, London, EC2A 4LW Tel: (020) 7729 5817 Fax: (020) 7613 4224 E-mail: info@absoluteproduct.com

Dauphin Museum Services, PO Box 602, Oxford, OX44 9LU Tel: (01865) 343542 Fax: (01865) 343307 E-mail: sales@dauphin.co.uk

EDM Ltd, Brunel House, 1 Thorp Road, Newton Heath, Manchester, M40 5BJ Tel: 0161-203 3150 Fax: 0161-202 2500 E-mail: reception@edm.ltd.uk

▶ V & W Animatronics, Unit 2, Cockles Lane, Weymouth, Dorset, DT4 9LT Tel: (01305) 768959 Fax: (01305) 768959 E-mail: info@animatronica.co.uk

MUSHROOM CULTIVATION EQUIPMENT

Traymaster Ltd, New Road, Catfield, Great Yarmouth, Norfolk, NR29 5BQ Tel: (01692) 582100 Fax: (01692) 582211

MUSHROOMS

▶ Surrey Downs Food, Units 79-80, Dunsfold Park, Stovolds Hill, Cranleigh, Surrey, GU6 8TB Tel: (01483) 273000 Fax: (01483) 273022 E-mail: info@surreydownsfoods.com

MUSIC AGENCIES/LIBRARIES/ SEARCH SERVICES

▶ AffordaBand, 275 Rotherhithe Street, London, SE16 5EY Tel: (020) 7237 7886

▶ Beat Suite, Studio 1, 5-7 Pink Lane, Newcastle upon Tyne, NE1 5DW Tel: 0191-221 2400 Fax: 0191-261 5746 E-mail: info@beatsuite.com

E Flat Minor Ltd, 1 Sheppy Race, Long Street, Croscombe, Wells, Somerset, BA5 3QL Tel: (01749) 343484 E-mail: info@eflatminor.co.uk

Peters Edition Ltd, 2-6 Bachers Street, London, N1 6DN Tel: (020) 7553 4000 Fax: (020) 7490 4921 E-mail: sales@uk.edition-peters.com

▶ The Theme Team Production Music, The Theme Team, 1 Leigh Rd, Gravesend, Kent, DA11 7PS Tel: (01474) 320460 E-mail: info@thethemeteam.biz

MUSIC AND ENTERTAINMENT MAGAZINES

▶ David Lancaster, 23 Borrowdale Road, Lancaster, LA1 3HF Tel: (01524) 66913 Fax: 01524 66913 E-mail: david@davidlancaster.co.uk

▶ Funtastic Entertainment, 55 Friars Lane, Barrow-in-Furness, Cumbria, LA13 9NS Tel: (01229) 820718 E-mail: funadmin@funtastic-entertainment.co.uk

▶ UK Magic - Magic Supplies & Services (Magicians & Entertainers), 1 Wakeford Cottages, Selden Lane, Worthing, West Sussex, BN11 2LQ Tel: (01903) 211785 Fax: (01903) 211519E-mail: info@natzler.com

MUSIC COMPOSING

Elite, Forest Row, East Sussex, RH18 5ES Tel: (01342) 822292 E-mail: info@elitespage.co.uk

MUSIC COMPUTERS

▶ ComputerDJ, Unit 5 The Shine, St. Marks Street, Hull, HU8 7FB Tel: (01482) 319700 Fax: (01482) 319701 E-mail: info@comptuerdj.net

MUSIC ENGRAVERS

Caligraving Ltd, Brunel Way, Thetford, Norfolk, IP24 1HP Tel: (01842) 752116 Fax: (01842) 755512

Fencing Co., 3 Morgan Street, Llanbradach, Caerphilly, Mid Glamorgan, CF83 3LW Tel: (029) 2088 5976 Fax: (029) 2088 5976

MUSIC ON HOLD TELEPHONE SYSTEMS

▶ The Theme Team Production Music, The Theme Team, 1 Leigh Rd, Gravesend, Kent, DA11 7PS Tel: (01474) 320460 E-mail: info@thethemeteam.biz

MUSIC PUBLISHERS

Caritas Music Publishing, Achmore, Moss Road, Ullapool, Ross-Shire, IV26 2TF Tel: (01854) 612 236 Fax: (01854) 612 236 E-mail: caritas@caritas-music.co.uk

Cramer Music Ltd, 23 Garrick Street, London, WC2E 9RY Tel: (020) 7240 1612 Fax: (020) 7240 2639

Kassner Associated Publishers Ltd, 11 Wyfold Road, London, SW6 6SE Tel: (020) 7385 7700 Fax: (020) 7385 3402 E-mail: songs@kassner-music.co.uk

▶ Music 4, 41-42 Berners Street, London, W1T 3NB Tel: (020) 7016 2000 Fax: (020) 7016 2001 E-mail: office@music4.com

Music Exchange (Manchester) Ltd, Claverton Road, Wythenshawe, Manchester, M23 9ZA Tel: 0161-946 1234 Fax: 0161-946 1195 E-mail: sales@music-exchange.co.uk

New Notations Computer Services Ltd, 7 Duncombe Hill, London, SE23 1QY Tel: (07968) 312032 Fax: (0870) 7604795

Peters Edition Ltd, 2-6 Bachers Street, London, N1 6DN Tel: (020) 7553 4000 Fax: (020) 7490 4921 E-mail: sales@uk.edition-peters.com

▶ Sunrise Music Group, 11 Redstock Close, Westhoughton, Bolton, BL5 3UX Tel: 01942-810 820 E-mail: sales@sunrisemusicgroup.co.uk

Wright & Round Ltd, PO Box 157, Gloucester, GL1 1LW Tel: (01452) 523438 Fax: (01452) 385631 E-mail: wright-and-round@interactive-sciences.co.uk

MUSIC SYSTEMS, DIGITAL

▶ xum music service, 28 Floriston Court, Northolt, Middlesex, UB5 4JX Tel: (07704) 345414 E-mail: info@xum-music.co.uk

MUSICAL ENTERTAINMENT VIDEO FILM PRODUCTION

▶ Ambient Light Productions Ltd, 6 Shipquay Street, Londonderry, BT48 6DN Tel: (028) 7136 3525 E-mail: info@ambient-light.co.uk

▶ Benben, 5 Trafalgar Road, Cambridge, CB4 1EU Tel: (07771) 902020 E-mail: benben@benben.co.uk

▶ Bird-e Video, The Old Granary, Scotterthorpe, Gainsborough, Lincolnshire, DN21 3JL Tel: (01724) 761101 Fax: (01724) 761101 E-mail: steve.bird-e@virgin.net

▶ Digital Media Music, 61 Birkbeck Road, Mill Hill, London, NW7 4BP Tel: 020881 67775 E-mail: info@digitalmediamusic.co.uk

Disc Wizards, 3 Oakleigh Court, Edgware, Middlesex, HA8 5JB Tel: (020) 8931 0001 Fax: (020) 8931 0001 E-mail: info@discwizards.com

▶ Grasshopper Films Ltd, 3rd Floor 14 Bacon Street, London, E1 6LF Tel: (020) 7739 7154 Fax: (020) 7739 6359 E-mail: info@grasshopperfilms.com

▶ Minion A V, 44 Dunraven Parade, Belfast, BT5 6BT Tel: (07799) 558787 Fax: E-mail: nathanmateer@minionvideo.co.uk

▶ MLK Music, 5 Madeline Grove, Ilford, Essex, IG1 2RG Tel: 07951 302734 E-mail: info@mlkmusic.co.uk

▶ On The River Film & Video Production, 2/1 5 McIntyre Place, Paisley, Renfrewshire, PA2 6EE Tel: 0141-889 2411 Fax: 0141-889 2411 E-mail: info@concepttoscreen.com

▶ Orbital Productions, 38 Burnfoot Road, Hawick, Roxburghshire, TD9 8EN Tel: (01450) 378212 E-mail: sg1@orbital-productions.com

▶ Schtum Ltd, 11 Osram Road, East Lane Business Park, Wembley, Middlesex, HA9 7NG Tel: (020) 8904 4422 Fax: (020) 8904 3777 E-mail: info@schtum.co.uk

▶ Surrey Films Ltd, Valley Farm, Green Lane, Churt, Farnham, Surrey, GU10 2LT Tel: (01428) 609532 E-mail: pete@surreyfilms.co.uk

▶ WV Entertainment Limited, C/O The Suite, 3 Goldthorn Avenue, Wolverhampton, WV4 5AA Tel: 07939 930781

MUSICAL INSTRUMENT ACCESSORIES

▶ Blake-Robson Northumbria Tuning Machines, Low Lambton Farm, Penshaw, Houghton le Spring, Tyne & Wear, DH4 7NQ Tel: 0191-246 2007 Fax: 0191-385 8013 E-mail: tuningmachines@aol.com

D J M Music Ltd, Unit 2 Archers Park, Branbridges Road, East Peckham, Tonbridge, Kent, TN12 5HP Tel: 0845 4584581 Fax: 0845 4584581 E-mail: sales@djmmusic.com

H J Fletcher & Newman Ltd, 5 Bourne Enterprise Centre, Wrotham Road, Borough Green, Sevenoaks, Kent, TN15 8DG Tel: (01732) 886555 Fax: (01732) 884789 E-mail: enquiries@fletcher-newman.co.uk

▶ Henry Nurdin Instrument Repairs, 51 Garth Owen, Newtown, Powys, SY16 1JL Tel: (07779) 755814 E-mail: info@guitar-repairs.co.uk

Paxman (Cases) Ltd, 252 Mawney Road, Romford, RM7 8DH Tel: (01708) 766363 Fax: (01708) 766363

▶ String Clean, Unit 2 Quarry Farm, Bodiam, Robertsbridge, East Sussex, TN32 5RA Tel: (01580) 831804 E-mail: sales@stringclean.com

William Shaw Scholes Ltd, 273 Whitechapel Road, Scholes, Cleckheaton, West Yorkshire, BD19 6HN Tel: (01274) 873157 Fax: (01274) 874777

MUSICAL INSTRUMENT CASES/ BAGS

D J M Music Ltd, Unit 2 Archers Park, Branbridges Road, East Peckham, Tonbridge, Kent, TN12 5HP Tel: 0845 4584581 Fax: 0845 4584581 E-mail: sales@djmmusic.com

▶ Freestyle Case Co. Ltd, Dale House, Brewery Lane, Thornhill, Dewsbury, West Yorkshire, WF12 9HU Tel: (01924) 455414

Paxman (Cases) Ltd, 252 Mawney Road, Romford, RM7 8DH Tel: (01708) 766363 Fax: (01708) 766363

MUSICAL INSTRUMENT DESIGN AND DEVELOPMENT SERVICES

▶ Henry Nurdin Instrument Repairs, 51 Garth Owen, Newtown, Powys, SY16 1JL Tel: (07779) 755814 E-mail: info@guitar-repairs.co.uk

▶ John Ward, 48 Albert Road, Sheffield, S8 9QW Tel: 0114-281 1475 E-mail: drumsrdangerous@blueyonder.co.uk

MUSICAL INSTRUMENT REPAIR

▶ Bonners Music Superstore, 56 Langney Road, Eastbourne, East Sussex, BN21 3JN Tel: (01323) 639335 Fax: (01323) 649100 E-mail: info@bonnersmusic.co.uk

▶ D M Guitars, 2 37 Brook Road, Rayleigh, Essex, SS6 7XJ Tel: (01268) 777356 E-mail: sales@dm-guitars.co.uk

▶ Guitar Spares & Repairs, 89 Old Snow Hill, Next to Sound Control, Birmingham, B4 6HW Tel: 0121 2455867 E-mail: info@guitarsparesandrepairs.com

MUSICAL INSTRUMENT RESTORATION

▶ Guitar Spares & Repairs, 89 Old Snow Hill, Next to Sound Control, Birmingham, B4 6HW Tel: 0121 2455867 E-mail: info@guitarspareandrepairs.com

▶ Michael Eeley & Son, Hose Street Works, Hose Street, Stoke-on-Trent, ST6 5AL Tel: (01782) 813383 Fax: (01782) 813383

MUSICAL INSTRUMENT WIRE STRINGS

H W Audio Ltd, 180-198 St. Georges Road, Bolton, BL1 2PH Tel: (01204) 385199 Fax: (01204) 364057 E-mail: sales@hwaudio.co.uk

S. Parke & Co. Ltd, Station Road, Stalbridge, Sturminster Newton, Dorset, DT10 2RZ Tel: (01963) 363377 Fax: (01963) 363640 E-mail: sales@wmhughes.co.uk

MUSICAL INSTRUMENTS, INCLUDING MUSICAL SUPPLIES, *See also headings for particular types*

Acoustic Arts, The Old Laundry, Kingswood Foundation Est Britannia Rd, Kingswood, Bristol, BS15 8DB Tel: 0117-935 2034 Fax: 0117-935 2034

Arbiter Group Ltd, 2nd Floor, Atlantic House, Stirling Way, Borehamwood, London, Hertfordshire, WD6 2BT Tel: (020) 8207 7860 Fax: (020) 8953 6221 E-mail: sales@arbitergroup.com

▶ Bluemoon Bottle Neck Co., 2 Lintonville Terrace, Ashington, Northumberland, NE63 9UN Tel: (01670) 858888 E-mail: sales@bluemoonbottleneck.co.uk

Brandoni Music Ltd, Unit 3-6 Wembley Commercial Centre, East Lane, Wembley, Middlesex, HA9 7XJ Tel: (020) 8908 2323 Fax: (020) 8908 2323

The British Piano Manufacturing Co., Woodchester Mill, Selsley Road, North Woodchester, Stroud, Gloucestershire, GL5 5NN Tel: (01453) 872871 Fax: (01453) 872822

▶ Class A, 14 Mccoy's Arcade, Fore Street, Exeter, EX4 3AN Tel: (01392) 494988 Fax: (01392) 496335 E-mail: sales@classadistribution.co.uk

D J M Music Ltd, Unit 2 Archers Park, Branbridges Road, East Peckham, Tonbridge, Kent, TN12 5HP Tel: 0845 4584581 Fax: 0845 4584581 E-mail: sales@djmmusic.com

Digital Village, St. Mary Street, Southampton, SO14 1NR Tel: (023) 8023 3444 Fax: (023) 8023 3266

E Flat Minor Ltd, 1 Sheppy Race, Long Street, Croscombe, Wells, Somerset, BA5 3QL Tel: (01749) 343484 E-mail: info@eflatminor.co.uk

F H Browne & Sons Ltd, The Street, Ash, Canterbury, Kent, CT3 2AA Tel: (01304) 813146 Fax: (01304) 812142 E-mail: brownefh@aol.com

T.W. Fern, Unit 1 Sulivan Enterprises, Sulivan Rd, London, SW6 3DJ Tel: (020) 7371 5191

Fylde Guitars, Hartness Road, Gilwilly Industrial Estate, Penrith, Cumbria, CA11 9BD Tel: (01768) 891515 Fax: (01768) 868998 E-mail: sales@fyldeguitars.com

▶ George Lowden, Down Business Park, 46 Belfast Road, Downpatrick, County Down, BT30 9UP Tel: (028) 4461 9161 Fax: (028) 4461 7043 E-mail: sales@georgelowden.com

H J Fletcher & Newman Ltd, 5 Bourne Enterprise Centre, Wrotham Road, Borough Green, Sevenoaks, Kent, TN15 8DG Tel: (01732) 886555 Fax: (01732) 884789 E-mail: enquiries@fletcher-newman.co.uk

▶ Harmonic Solutions Ltd, Unit 5C, Millwey Rise Industrial Estate, Axminster, Devon, EX13 5HU Tel: (01297) 34344 Fax: (01297) 34344 E-mail: richard@harmsol.co.uk

Hughes & Mcleod, 5 Black Causeway Road, Strangford, Downpatrick, County Down, BT30 7LX Tel: (028) 4488 1880 Fax: (028) 4488 1880 E-mail: info@bagpipers.co.uk

▶ Iceni Music, The Surridge, 2 Stepfield, Witham, Essex, CM8 3TH Tel: (01376) 500820 Fax: (01376) 585636 E-mail: sales@zootbass.co.uk

J Thibouville Lamy & Co. Ltd, Gilbert House, 406 Roding La South, Woodford Green, Essex, IG8 8EY Tel: (020) 8551 1282 Fax: (020) 8550 8377 E-mail: sales@jtlamy.co.uk

▶ K Seabourne, 17 Bath Road, Worcester, WR5 3AA Tel: (01905) 350234 Fax: (01905) 350234 E-mail: info@bassurgery.com

Korg UK Ltd, 9 Newmarket Court, Kingston, Milton Keynes, MK10 0AU Tel: (01908) 857100 Fax: (01908) 857199 E-mail: info@korg.co.uk

▶ L M S Music Supplies, PO Box 7, Exeter, EX1 1WB Tel: (01392) 428108 Fax: (01392) 412521 E-mail: lmsmusic@compuserve.com

Mccallum Bagpipes, Moorfield Indus Estate, Troon Road, Kilmarnock, Ayrshire, KA2 0BA Tel: (01563) 527002 Fax: (01563) 530260

Macmurchie Bagpipe Makers, 47e West End, West Calder, West Lothian, EH55 8EJ Tel: (01506) 872333 Fax: (01506) 885220 E-mail: sales@macmurchiebagpipes.co.uk

Malcolm Rose & Karin Richter, English Passage, Lewes, East Sussex, BN7 2AP Tel: (01273) 481010 Fax: (01273) 481010 E-mail: info@malcolm-rose.com

Microvox Musical Instrument, 248 Huddersfield Road, Thongsbridge, Holmfirth, HD9 3JL Tel: (01484) 684049 Fax: (01484) 684049 E-mail: sales@microvox.co.uk

Music & Design Ltd, 12 Linnell Road, Redhill, RH1 4DH Tel: (01737) 768272 E-mail: chris.bayley@virgin.net

Music Education Supplies Ltd, Unit 1 Bentinck Workshops, Park Lane, Kirkby-in-Ashfield, NG17 9LE Tel: (0845) 0264703 Fax: (01623) 726871 E-mail: sales@mesdirect.com

▶ Osborne Mandolins, Star Gallery, Castle Ditch Lane, Lewes, East Sussex, BN7 1YJ Tel: (01273) 473883 E-mail: info@osborne.co.uk

Paxman (Cases) Ltd, 252 Mawney Road, Romford, RM7 8DH Tel: (01708) 766363 Fax: (01708) 766363

▶ Pearl UK Ltd, 11 Presley Way, Crownhill, Milton Keynes, MK8 0ES Tel: (01908) 260055 Fax: (01908) 262545

Pipers Cave, 138 Dungannon Road, Cookstown, County Tyrone, BT80 9BD Tel: (028) 8676 3615 Fax: (028) 8676 2983

George Potter & Co. (Musical Instruments) Ltd, 26-28 Grosvenor Road, Aldershot, Hampshire, GU11 3DP Tel: (01252) 323226 Fax: (01252) 342921 E-mail: pottersdrums@aol.com

Premier Percussion Ltd, Blaby Road, Wigston, Leicestershire, LE18 4DF Tel: 0116-277 3121 Fax: 0116-277 6627 E-mail: info@premier-percussion.com

Roland UK Ltd, Atlantic House, Atlantic Close, Swansea Enterprise Park, Swansea, SA7 9FJ Tel: (01792) 702701 Fax: (01792) 600520 E-mail: sales@roland.co.uk

Rotosound Manufacturing Ltd, Unit 3B, Morewood Close, Sevenoaks, Kent, TN13 2HU Tel: (01732) 450838 Fax: (01732) 458994 E-mail: jason@rotosound.com

▶ Shuker Bass, 72 Arundel Street, Sheffield, S1 2NS Tel: 0114-275 8380

Gordon Smith, 9 Manchester Road, Partington, Manchester, M31 4FB Tel: 0161-777 9438 Fax: 0161-777 6871 E-mail: gordonsmith@tesco.net

Status Graphite, Unit 6a, Commerce Way, Colchester, CO2 8HR Tel: (01206) 868150 Fax: (01206) 868160

Strings & Things Ltd, Unit 3, 202-210 Brighton Road, Shoreham-By-Sea, West Sussex, BN43 6RJ Tel: (01273) 440442 Fax: (01273) 440278E-mail: strings@stringsandthings.co.uk

Sutherland Trading Co., Bedwas House Industrial Estate, Bedwas, Caerphilly, Mid Glamorgan, CF83 8XQ Tel: (029) 2088 7337 Fax: (029) 2085 1056E-mail: info@sutherlandtrading.com

▶ Suzuki Europe, Unit 18 Lodge Farm Business Centre, Wolverton Road, Castlethorpe, Milton Keynes, MK19 7ES Tel: (01908) 511488 Fax: (01908) 511904

T W Howarth & Co. Ltd, 31-35 Chiltern Street, London, W1U 7PN Tel: (020) 7935 2407 Fax: (020) 7224 2564 E-mail: sales@howarth.uk.com

▶ Teampro Music, 16 Wick Drive, Wickford, Essex, SS12 9AS Tel: (01268) 573273 E-mail: sales@teampromusic.co.uk

Teijeiro Juan Music Co. Ltd, 5 The Campsbourne, London, N8 7PN Tel: (020) 8348 9191 Fax: (020) 8348 0562 E-mail: enquiries@juanteijeiro.com

▶ David Van Edwards, The Smokehouse, 6 Whitwell Road, NORWICH, NR1 4HB Tel: (01603) 629899 E-mail: lutes@vanedwards.co.uk

Yamaha Kemble Music U K Ltd, Sherbourne Drive, Tilbrook, Milton Keynes, MK7 8BL Tel: (01908) 366700 Fax: (01908) 368872

MUSICAL INSTRUMENTS, PERCUSSION, EDUCATIONAL

Music Education Supplies Ltd, Unit 1 Bentinck Workshops, Park Lane, Kirkby-in-Ashfield, NG17 9LE Tel: (0845) 0264703 Fax: (01623) 726871 E-mail: sales@mesdirect.com

▶ Totally Ratted Productions, 95 Ewart Road*Forest Fields, Forest Fields, Nottingham, NG7 6HG Tel: 0115 8330457 E-mail: productions@totallyratted.com

MUSICAL INSTRUMENTS, STRING, BOWED

▶ David Van Edwards, The Smokehouse, 6 Whitwell Road, NORWICH, NR1 4HB Tel: (01603) 629899 E-mail: lutes@vanedwards.co.uk

MUSLIN LEMON WRAPS

J S D Products (UK) Ltd, 84 Tippendell Lane, Park Street, St. Albans, Hertfordshire, AL2 2HD Tel: (01727) 875660 Fax: (01727) 875659 E-mail: info@jsdproducts.co.uk

NAIL GUNS

Fixings & Power Tools Direct Ltd, Tunbridge Wells Tool Room Stag Trade Park, Longfield Road, Tunbridge Wells, Kent, TN2 3BF Tel: (0800) 365598 Fax: (01892) 520888 E-mail: sales@fixings-direct.co.uk

▶ Martin Plant Hire Ltd, Unit 12 Howard Court, Nerston Industrial Estate, East Kilbride, Glasgow, G74 4QZ Tel: (01355) 245600 Fax: (01355) 244066

P A Hill Fasteners Ltd, 25 Sherwood Road, Bromsgrove, Worcestershire, B60 3DR Tel: (01527) 575838 Fax: (01527) 870419 E-mail: sales@pahillfasteners.co.uk

Unimerco Ltd, Nanscawen Road, Fradley, Lichfield, Staffordshire, WS13 8LH Tel: (01543) 267777 Fax: (01543) 267778 E-mail: info@unimerco.com

NAILING MACHINE MANUFRS

Betco Packaging Supplies, 12 Gregston Industrial Estate, Birmingham Road, Oldbury, West Midlands, B69 4EX Tel: 0121-552 8400 Fax: 0121-511 1324 E-mail: sales@betcofasteners.co.uk

Danum Supplies, Kelham Street, Doncaster, South Yorkshire, DN1 3RE Tel: (01302) 344475

Galino Ltd, 2 South Caldeen Road, Coatbridge, Lanarkshire, ML5 4EG Tel: (01236) 449898 Fax: (01236) 449899 E-mail: galino.ltd@virgin.net

NAILS, *See also headings for particular types*

A H Hanson Ltd, Marley Street, Keighley, West Yorkshire, BD21 5JX Tel: (01535) 604112 Fax: (01535) 610085 E-mail: sales@wheel-clamp.com

Fincham Fasteners, 18 Industrial Estate, Sanders Road, Bromsgrove, Worcestershire, B61 7DG Tel: (01527) 875413 Fax: (01527) 875413 E-mail: sales@finchamfasteners.com

John George & Sons Ltd, 2-4 Deacon Way, Reading, RG30 6AZ Tel: 0118-941 1234 Fax: 0118-945 1059 E-mail: sales@johngeorge.co.uk

Lazer Vix Ltd, Turner Buildings, Russell Road, Birkenhead, Merseyside, CH42 1LU Tel: 0151-644 8860 Fax: 0151-643 1204

P A Hill Fasteners Ltd, 25 Sherwood Road, Bromsgrove, Worcestershire, B60 3DR Tel: (01527) 575838 Fax: (01527) 870419 E-mail: sales@pahillfasteners.co.uk

Plastestrip Profiles Ltd, Trenance Mill, St. Austell, Cornwall, PL25 5LZ Tel: (01726) 74771 Fax: (01726) 69238 E-mail: sales@plaspro.force9.co.uk

Powernail Fasteners & Fixing Devices, Lancaster Fields, Crewe, CW1 6FF Tel: (01270) 588839 Fax: (01270) 500669 E-mail: enquiries@powernail.co.uk

Secure Bolts, Unit 18 Blenheim Way, Liverpool, L24 1YH Tel: 0151-486 3154 Fax: 0151-486 3154

Frank Shaw (Bayonet) Ltd, Merse Road, North Moons Moat, Redditch, Worcestershire, B98 9HL Tel: (01527) 66241 Fax: (01527) 584455 E-mail: sales@frankshaw.co.uk

▶ Soewitos Hair And Beauty Salon, Brunel Centre, Bletchley, Milton Keynes, MK2 2ES Tel: 01908 642985

Southern Nail Supplies, Ikon House, 3 Arkwright Road, Reading, RG2 0LU Tel: 0118-987 3344

Willenhall Fasteners Holdings Ltd, Frederick William Street, Willenhall, West Midlands, WV13 1NE Tel: (01902) 630760 Fax: (01902) 636447 E-mail: sales@willenfast.co.uk

▶ www.topgun.co.uk, 18 Derby Road, Blackpool, FY1 2JF Tel: (01253) 296000 Fax: (01253) 296001 E-mail: topgun@nildram.co.uk

Young Black Industrial Stapling Ltd, Radway Road, Swindon, SN3 4ND Tel: (01793) 838400 Fax: (01793) 838401 E-mail: info@youngblack.co.uk

NAME BADGES

B I S Trent Rosettes, 7 Railway Enterprise Centre, Shelton New Road, Stoke-on-Trent, ST4 7SH Tel: (01782) 279797 Fax: (01782) 279797

▶ Badge UK, 58 Crossgate, Cupar, Fife, KY15 5HS Tel: (01334) 656677 Fax: (01334) 656678 E-mail: mail@badgeuk.co.uk

Badgemans Recognition Express, 8 Hillside Industrial Estate, London Road, Horndean, Waterlooville, Hampshire, PO8 0BL Tel: (023) 9259 5509 Fax: (023) 9259 5528 E-mail: sales@re-southern.co.uk

Computerised Exhibition Services Badges Ltd, 31 Highbridge Road, Sutton Coldfield, West Midlands, B73 5QB Tel: 0121-354 9595 Fax: 0121-354 6227 E-mail: badgereg@aol.com

Durable UK Ltd, East Dorset Trade Park, 10 Nimrod Way, Wimborne, Dorset, BH21 7SH Tel: (01202) 897071 Fax: (01202) 873381 E-mail: marketing@durable-uk.com

Express Services, Henson Way, Telford Way Industrial Estate, Kettering, Northamptonshire, NN16 8PX Tel: (01536) 481778 Fax: (01536) 521412 E-mail: sales@express-services.uk.com

High Profile, 9 Haslemere Way, Banbury, Oxfordshire, OX16 5RW Tel: (01295) 267966 Fax: (01295) 272477 E-mail: sales@high-profile.co.uk

K P Badges & Trophies, 4 Antrim Road, Bristol, BS9 4BS Tel: 0117-962 0191 Fax: 0117-975 4264 E-mail: sales@trophiesuk.biz

▶ Probadge, The Countyard, 27 High Street, Winslow, Buckingham, MK18 3HE Tel: (01296) 712387 Fax: (01296) 715281 E-mail: sales@probadge.com

▶ Quick Thermal Transfer Ltd, 32 Cricketers Close, Ashington, Pulborough, West Sussex, RH20 3JQ Tel: (01903) 893308 E-mail: sales@qtt.info

▶ Recognition Express, Unit 2b Boundary Business Park, Wheatley Road, Garsington, Oxford, OX44 9EJ Tel: (0844) 8004265 Fax: 01865 368080 E-mail: sales@re-oxford.co.uk

Target Badges, 134 Watnall Road, Hucknall, Nottingham, NG15 7NH Tel: 0115-956 0047 Fax: 0115-956 0047 E-mail: info@targetbadges.co.uk

TCE Ltd, Newstead Industrial Estate, Trentham, Stoke-On-Trent, ST4 8HX Tel: (01782) 643278 Fax: (01782) 657766 E-mail: tce@tcelabels.co.uk

Westway Business Services, 2 St. Marys Way, Baldock, Hertfordshire, SG7 6JF Tel: (01462) 490900 Fax: (01462) 490411

NAMEPLATE MARKING MACHINES, *See Marking Machines/Systems etc*

NAMEPLATE PRODUCTION SERVICES

Ashley Industrial, South Wraxall, Bradford-on-Avon, Wiltshire, BA15 2RL Tel: (01225) 868083 Fax: 01225 868089 E-mail: japapps@aol.com

Coventry Nameplate Co., 5 Watercall Ave, Styvechale, Coventry, CV3 5AW Tel: (024) 7669 3212 Fax: (024) 7669 3288 E-mail: markcove@dsl.pipex.com

Initial Monogram Co. Ltd, 18 Capel Road, Watford, WD19 4AE Tel: (01923) 255540 Fax: (01923) 819003 E-mail: initialmonogram@ntlworld.com

P C Engravers World Of Trophies, 29 Lower Addiscombe Road, Croydon, CR0 6PQ Tel: (020) 8680 1354 Fax: (020) 8686 8706 E-mail: pcengravers@btconnect.com

NAMEPLATES, *See also headings for particular types*

Abbey Signs, Unit 1, The Yarn Barn, Upper Manor Road, Preston, Paignton, Devon, TQ3 2TP Tel: (01803) 559029 Fax: (01803) 666010 E-mail: sales@abbey4signs.com

Advertising Signs, 11 Teal Court, Strathclyde Business Park, Bellshill, Lanarkshire, ML4 3NN Tel: (01698) 844114 Fax: (01698) 844377

Class 1 Signs Ltd, 69 Breck Road, Anfield, Liverpool, L4 2QS Tel: 0151-264 0003 Fax: 0151-263 5996 E-mail: sales@class1signs.co.uk

G & A Kirsten Ltd, 11 Amwell End, Ware, Hertfordshire, SG12 9HP Tel: (01920) 487300 Fax: (01920) 487304 E-mail: gakirsten@btclick.com

Graphic Engineering Northern Ltd, Sheaf Bank Business Park, Prospect Road, Heeley, Sheffield, S2 3EN Tel: 0114-250 0151 Fax: 0114-255 5161 E-mail: sales@graphicengineering.co.uk

Hotline Signs, 18a Bridge Street, Buxton, Derbyshire, SK17 6BS Tel: (01298) 25491 Fax: (01298) 78452

Jepson Signs Ltd, Unit 2 North Road Industrial Estate, Meynell Road, Darlington, County Durham, DL3 0YQ Tel: (01325) 463547 Fax: (01325) 381172

Jepson Signs Ltd, 2 Morley Road, London, SE13 6DQ Tel: (020) 8318 5528 Fax: (020) 8297 9121

Leek Signs & Graphics, Unit 10 Town Yard Industrial Estate, Station Street, Leek, Staffordshire, ST13 8BF Tel: (01538) 385262 Fax: (01538) 385262

Marking Service Signs Ltd, King Street Works, King Street, Drighlington, Bradford, West Yorkshire, BD11 1EJ Tel: 0113-285 2745 Fax: 0113-285 4748 E-mail: marserve@fsnet.co.uk

Mockridge Labels (Sales) Ltd, Viaduct Works, Cavendish Street, Ashton-under-Lyne, Lancashire, OL6 7QL Tel: 0161-308 2331 Fax: 0161-343 1958 E-mail: mike.graham@mockridge.com

Nameplate Services, The Iron Works, Union Street, Royton, Oldham, OL2 5JD Tel: 0161-620 4702 Fax: 0161-620 0503 E-mail: holt@nameplateservices.co.uk

Nu Lite, 22 Ayloffs Walk, Hornchurch, Essex, RM11 2RJ Tel: (01708) 442232 Fax: (01708) 451696

The Principle Nameplate Company Ltd, Unit 19 St. Michaels Trading Estate, Bridport, Dorset, DT6 3RR Tel: (01308) 459900 Fax: (01308) 459911 E-mail: sales@platesandplaques.com

NAMEPLATES – *continued*

Signet Signs Ltd, 45 West Town Road, Backwell, Bristol, BS48 3HG Tel: (01275) 463601 Fax: (01275) 462990 E-mail: mail@signetsigns.co.uk
Taylor & Pickles Ltd, Bushell St Mills, Bushell Street, Preston, PR1 2SP Tel: (01772) 251520 Fax: (01772) 561610 E-mail: info@taylorandpickles.co.uk
Torbay Signs, Ashfield Road, Torquay, TQ2 6HE Tel: (01803) 605981 Fax: (01803) 605913
Willprint Screen Process Printers, 7 Pomeroy Drive, Oadby, Leicester, LE2 5NE Tel: 0116-271 0574 Fax: 0116-271 0550 E-mail: sales@willprints.co.uk

NAMEPLATES TO SPECIFICATION

Cowen Signs, 65 Old Chester Road, Birkenhead, Merseyside, CH41 9AW Tel: 0151-647 8081 Fax: 0151-666 1087 E-mail: sales@cowen-signs.co.uk
Fastsigns Ltd, 36 High St, New Malden, Surrey, KT3 4HE Tel: 020 83360802 Fax: 020 83360914
Willprint Screen Process Printers, 7 Pomeroy Drive, Oadby, Leicester, LE2 5NE Tel: 0116-271 0574 Fax: 0116-271 0550 E-mail: sales@willprints.co.uk

NAPHTHENIC PETROLEUM BASE OILS

▶ Ellita Ltd, 6 Rushout Avenue, Harrow, Middlesex, HA3 0AR Tel: (020) 8446 7401 Fax: (020) 8445 6335E-mail: info@ellita.co.uk

NARROW FABRICS

Altimed Ltd, 74 Sullington Road, Shepshed, Loughborough, Leicestershire, LE12 9JJ Tel: (01509) 501720 Fax: (01509) 501721 E-mail: enquiries@altimed.co.uk
▶ Atlas Transfer Printers Ltd, 9 Wanstead Road, Leicester, LE3 1TR Tel: 0116-231 4500 Fax: 0116-231 4600 E-mail: atpl@btconnect.com
Barford Bros Ltd, 111 North Street, Luton, LU2 7QG Tel: (01582) 720371 Fax: (01582) 611098
Bowmer Bond Narrow Fabrics Ltd, Hanging Bridge Mills, Ashbourne, Derbyshire, DE6 2EA Tel: (01335) 342244 Fax: (01335) 300651 E-mail: sales@bowmerbond.co.uk
H Seal & Co. Ltd, Church Lane, Whitwick, Coalville, Leicestershire, LE67 5DJ Tel: (01530) 832351 Fax: (01530) 813382 E-mail: sales@hseal.co.uk
Hattersley Aladdin UK, Greengate, Keighley, West Yorkshire, BD21 5JL Tel: (01639) 730997 Fax: (01535) 610195 E-mail: info@hattersley.co.uk
Rykneld Tean Ltd, Hansard Gate, West Meadows Industrial Estate, Derby, DE21 6RR Tel: (01332) 542700 Fax: (01332) 542710 E-mail: sales@rykneldtean.co.uk
Transfra Graphics Ltd, Stadium Place, Leicester, LE4 0JS Tel: 0116-234 0440 Fax: 0116-235 1881 E-mail: sales@transfragraphics.com

NARROW GAUGE OR INDUSTRIAL OR PORTABLE RAILWAY SYSTEMS

Balfour Beatty Rail Track Systems Ltd, Osmaston Street, Sandiacre, Nottingham, NG10 5AN Tel: 0115-921 8218 Fax: 0115-541 8219 E-mail: phil.bean@bbrail.com
Mardyke Miniature Railway, 1 Imperial Trading Estate, Lambs La North, Rainham, Essex, RM13 9XL Tel: (01708) 520264 Fax: (01708) 553395

NARROW GAUGE RAILWAY POINTS OR SWITCHES

A L A Rail Ltd, Byass Works, The Docks, Port Talbot, West Glamorgan, SA13 1RS Tel: (01639) 885435 Fax: (01639) 899842 E-mail: sales@ala-rail.com

NARROW WEB CUTTING MACHINES

Scan Relation, 2 The Mews, 15a Liverpool Road, Southport, Merseyside, PR8 4AS Tel: (01704) 550500 Fax: (01704) 566958 E-mail: smithage@btinternet.com

NATURAL CEMENT

Lime Green Products Ltd, The Coates Kiln, Stretton Road, Much Wenlock, Shropshire, TF13 6DG Tel: (01952) 728611 Fax: (01952) 728361 E-mail: enquire@lime-green.co.uk

NATURAL DECORATORS SPONGES

Crown Brolac Decorator Centre, 5 London Road, Bedford, MK42 0PB Tel: (01234) 360541 Fax: (01234) 360551 E-mail: cdc406.bedford@dwn.akzonobel.com
Medisponge, 35 Water Drive, Standish, Wigan, Lancashire, WN6 0EH Tel: (01257) 473175 Fax: (01257) 473175

NATURAL DRAINAGE CONTRACTORS

▶ Drain Doctor Plumbing, Station House, Macnaghten Road, Southampton, SO18 1GG Tel: (023) 8033 3312 Fax: (023) 8033 2600 E-mail: j-rook@btconnect.com

NATURAL GAS AND TOTAL ENERGY FISCAL METERING

Effectech Ltd, Dovefields Road, Dovefields Industrial Estate, Uttoxeter, Staffordshire, ST14 8HU Tel: (01889) 569220 Fax: (01889) 569220 E-mail: sharon.foster@effectech.co.uk

NATURAL GAS DISTRIBUTION

BG Group, 100 Thames Valley Park Drive, Reading, RG6 1PT Tel: 0118-935 3222 Fax: 0118-929 3710 E-mail: admin@bg-group.com

NATURAL GAS EXPLORATION SERVICES

Petro-Canada, Bowater House, 114 Knightsbridge, London, SW1X 7LD Tel: (020) 7225 7100 Fax: (020) 7584 6459

NATURAL GASES

A4 Cryogenics, 10 Carlisle Road, Templepatrick, Ballyclare, County Antrim, BT39 0AW Tel: (028) 9443 3408 Fax: (028) 9443 3408
British Gas Trading, Bridge St, Leeds, LS2 7PE Tel: (0845) 609 1122
Chevron & Texaco Ltd, 1 Westferry Circus, Canary Wharf, London, E14 4HA Tel: (020) 7719 3000 Fax: E-mail:
Fargo Ltd, Toddington Lane, Wick, Littlehampton, West Sussex, BN17 7QR Tel: (01903) 721591 Fax: (01903) 730737 E-mail: sales@fargro.co.uk
Mobil Services Co. Ltd, Mobil Court, 3 Clements Inn, London, WC2A 2EB Tel: (020) 7412 4000 Fax: (020) 7412 4084
Scottish & Southern Energy P.L.C., Centenary House, 10 Winchester Road, Basingstoke, Hampshire, RG21 8UQ Tel: (0845) 7210220 Fax: (01256) 304269 E-mail: national.sales@scottish-southern.co.uk
Scottish & Southern Energy plc, Inveralmond House, 200 Dunkeld Road, Perth, PH1 3AQ Tel: (01738) 456000 Fax: (01738) 456520 E-mail: info@scottish-southern.co.uk
Southern Counties Fuels Ltd, Colwood Lane, Warninglid, Haywards Heath, West Sussex, RH17 5UE Tel: (0845) 6004006 Fax: (0870) 7584442 E-mail: sales@scf.co.uk
Taylor Edwards & Co., Royal Buildings, Mosley Street, Manchester, M2 3AN Tel: 0161-907 3488

NATURAL GUM, *See also headings for particular types*

Arthur Bramwell & Co. Ltd, Bronte House, 58-62 High Street, Epping, Essex, CM16 4AE Tel: (01992) 577333 Fax: (01992) 561138 E-mail: arthurbranwell@branwell.com
Cray Valley Ltd, Laporte Road, Stallingborough, Grimsby, South Humberside, DN41 8DR Tel: (01469) 572464 Fax: (01469) 572988 E-mail: martin.brewer@crayvalley.com
T.M. Duche & Sons Ltd, 16A Hall Road, Wilmslow, Cheshire, SK9 5BN Tel: (01625) 538530 Fax: (01625) 538540 E-mail: info@tmduche.com
Thew, Arnott & Co. Ltd, Newman Works, 270 London Road, Wallington, Surrey, SM6 7DJ Tel: (020) 8669 3131 Fax: (020) 8669 7747 E-mail: sales@thewarnott.co.uk

NATURAL RESINS

Altro Ltd, Works Road, Letchworth Garden City, Hertfordshire, SG6 1NW Tel: (01462) 707604 Fax: (01462) 707504 E-mail: leisure@altro.co.uk
B I P (Oldbury) Ltd, PO Box 3180, Oldbury, West Midlands, B69 4PG Tel: 0121-544 2333 Fax: 0121-552 4267 E-mail: enquiries@bip.co.uk

P P Composites Ltd, Unit 39c Vale Business Park, Llandow, Cowbridge, South Glamorgan, CF71 7PF Tel: (01446) 775885 Fax: (01446) 775822 E-mail: sales@ppcomposites.ltd.uk
Solvay Speciality Chemicals Ltd, Lostock Works, Works Lane, Northwich, Cheshire, CW9 7ZR Tel: (01606) 723331 Fax: (01606) 723336 E-mail: sales@solvay.com

NATURAL SPONGES

Sydney Heath & Son Ltd, P O Box 1 Bycars Road, Stoke-on-Trent, ST6 4SH Tel: (01782) 839121 Fax: (01782) 839124 E-mail: sales@sydney-heath.co.uk
Medisponge, 35 Water Drive, Standish, Wigan, Lancashire, WN6 0EH Tel: (01257) 473175 Fax: (01257) 473175
Rubberlast (Britain) Ltd, Unit 2 Gelderd Trading Estate, Brown Lane West, Leeds, LS12 6BD Tel: 0113-245 5234 Fax: 0113-244 8293 E-mail: sales@rubberlast.com

NATURAL STONE

A Robinson & Son, 14 Main Street, Annalong, Newry, County Down, BT34 4TR Tel: (028) 4376 8213 Fax: (028) 4376 8872 E-mail: enquiries@arobinson.co.uk
Bannocks Of Solihull, 117 Streetsbrook Road, Shirley, Solihull, West Midlands, B90 3PF Tel: 0121-744 1727 Fax: 0121-733 1651
Bath Patio Slab Centre, Whiteway Road, Bath, BA2 2RG Tel: (01225) 319334 Fax: (01225) 319334 E-mail: info@bathslabs.com
J. Battle, Pipers Drier Studio, Clarendon Park, Salisbury, SP5 3ES Tel: (01722) 711770 Fax: (01722) 506707 E-mail: jay.battle@ntlworld.com
C E D Ltd, 728 London Road, Grays, Essex, RM20 3LU Tel: (01708) 867237 Fax: (01708) 867230 E-mail: sales@ced.ltd.uk
Caledonian Stone Co., Marchlands, Lonmay, Fraserburgh, Aberdeenshire, AB43 8RN Tel: (01346) 532747 Fax: (01346) 532547 E-mail: sales@caledonianstone.com
Cemex (NI) Ltd, 41 Manse Road, Carrowdore, Newtownards, County Down, BT22 2EZ Tel: (028) 9186 1450 Fax: (028) 9186 1555
Davis Memorials, 56a Station Road, Cradley Heath, West Midlands, B64 6NU Tel: (01384) 566958 Fax: (01384) 569708
Elite Tiles Ltd, Elite House, The Broadway, London, NW9 7BP Tel: (020) 8202 1806 Fax: (020) 8202 8608 E-mail: info@elitetiles.co.uk
Ennstone Building Products Ltd, Stainton Quarry, Barnard Castle, County Durham, DL12 8RB Tel: (01833) 690444 Fax: (01833) 690377 E-mail: ennstone@ukonline.co.uk
Ennstone Thistle Ltd, Quarry Road, Balmullo, St. Andrews, Fife, KY16 0BH Tel: (01334) 870208 Fax: (01334) 870893
George Farrar (Quarries) Ltd, Bradford Street, Keighley, West Yorkshire, BD21 3EB Tel: (01535) 602344 Fax: (01535) 606247 E-mail: sales@farrar.co.uk
Granit Ops Ltd, West Dean Road, West Tytherley, Salisbury, SP5 1QG Tel: (01980) 862253 Fax: (01980) 863073 E-mail: stone@granit-ops.co.uk
H Butterfield Ltd, Selbourne Road, Luton, LU4 8QF Tel: (01582) 491100 Fax: (01582) 490969 E-mail: enquiries@butterfieldnatstone.co.uk
J Day Stoneworks, Church Lane, Colney Heath, St. Albans, Hertfordshire, AL4 0NH Tel: (01727) 823326 Fax: (01727) 827710 E-mail: jdaystoneworks@btinternet.com
J Oldham & Co. Ltd, Tearne House, Hollington, Stoke-on-Trent, ST10 4HR Tel: (01889) 507353 Fax: (01889) 507212 E-mail: enquiries@joldham.co.uk
Johnsons Wellfield Quarries Ltd, Crosland Hill, Huddersfield, HD4 7AB Tel: (01484) 652311 Fax: (01484) 460007 E-mail: sales@johnson-wellfield.co.uk
Landers Quarries Ltd, Kingston Road, Worth Matravers, Swanage, Dorset, BH19 3JP Tel: (01929) 439205 Fax: (01929) 439268 E-mail: landers@purbeckstone.co.uk
D. & P. Lovell Quarries Ltd, Downs Quarry, Kingston Road, Langton Matravers, Swanage, Dorset, BH19 3JP Tel: (01929) 439255 Fax: (01929) 439324
Marbonyx Ltd, Welton Way, Purdeys Indust Estate, Purdeys Industrial Estate, Rochford, Essex, SS4 1LA Tel: (01702) 543235 Fax: (01702) 543266 E-mail: sales@marbonyx.com
Miles Stone, Quarry Yard, Woodside Avenue, Eastleigh, Hampshire, SO50 9ES Tel: (023) 8061 3178
Natural Stone Co., Elm Cottage, Ockham Road North, Ockham, Woking, Surrey, GU23 6NW Tel: (01483) 211111 Fax: (01483) 211555
Pickard Group, Fagley Lane, Eccleshill, Bradford, West Yorkshire, BD2 3NT Tel: (01274) 637307 Fax: (01274) 626146 E-mail: sales@pickard.co.uk
▶ The Quarry Stonehouse, Caswell's Yard, 215 Aylesbury Road, Wendover, Buckinghamshire, HP22 6BA Tel: (01296) 622750 Fax: (01296) 622750 E-mail: bert.roberts@thequarry.co.uk
Ross Hillman Ltd, Station Road, Westbury, Wiltshire, BA13 3JP Tel: (01373) 822447 Fax: (01373) 824492

▶ Rustic Stone House Signs, 8 Burstow Park Business Centre, Antlands Lane, Shipley Bridge, Horley, Surrey, RH6 9TF Tel: (01293) 823673 Fax: (01293) 821462 E-mail: stone@rusticstone.net
▶ S Mcconnell & Sons, 184 Carrigenagh Road, Kilkeel, Newry, County Down, BT34 4QA Tel: (028) 4176 3717 Fax: (028) 4176 5019
Salop Sand & Gravel Supply Co. Ltd, Station Road, Admaston, Telford, Shropshire, TF5 0AN Tel: (01952) 254101 Fax: (01952) 223932 E-mail: info@gravel.co.uk
Shipley Quarries, Rose Cottage, Lartington, Barnard Castle, County Durham, DL12 9BP Tel: (01833) 650529 Fax: (01833) 650529
Silverland Stone Ltd, Holloway Hill, Lyne, Chertsey, Surrey, KT16 0AE Tel: (01932) 569277 Fax: (01932) 563558 E-mail: gskilbeck@btinternet.com
▶ Stanleys Quarry, Westington Hill, Broad Campden, Chipping Campden, Gloucestershire, GL55 6UR Tel: (01386) 841236 Fax: (01386) 841845
Stoke Hall Quarry (Stone Sales) Ltd, Eyam Road, Grindleford, Hope Valley, Derbyshire, S32 2HW Tel: (01433) 630313 Fax: (01433) 631353 E-mail: design@stokehallquarry.co.uk
Stonemarket Driveway Contractors Ltd, Old Gravel Quarry, Oxford Road, Ryton on Dunsmore, Coventry, CV8 3EJ Tel: (024) 7651 8700 Fax: (024) 7651 8777 E-mail: sales@stonemarket.co.uk
W J Haysom & Son, St Adhelms Quarry, Swanage, Dorset, BH19 3LN Tel: (01929) 439217 Fax: (01929) 439215 E-mail: haysom@purbeckstone.co.uk
W S Moore, 160 Malpas Road, Newport, Gwent, NP20 5PN Tel: (01633) 855902 Fax: (01633) 855902
▶ Wudo Ltd, 2 Stanley Road, Hertford, SG13 7LQ Tel: (01992) 504014 Fax: (01992) 537388 E-mail: rachelwu@lineone.net

NATURAL STONE AGGREGATES

▶ Cemex Materials, Forcegarth Quarry, Middleton, Barnard Castle, County Durham, DL12 0EP Tel: (01833) 622255

NATURAL STONE KITCHEN WORKTOPS

▶ Silestone Of London, Unit 2 Octinum Business Park, Albert Drive, Woking, Surrey, GU21 5RW Tel: (01483) 757345 Fax: (01483) 757346 E-mail: sales@silestoneoflondon.co.uk

NATURAL STONE PRODUCTS

▶ Fairhaven of Anglesey Abbey Ltd, Northfield Farm, Lode Road, Bottisham, Cambridge, CB5 9DN Tel: (01223) 812555
▶ Hanson Bath & Portland Stone, Avon Mill Lane, Keynsham, Bristol, BS31 2UG Tel: 0117-986 9631 Fax: 0117-986 7115
▶ The Quarry Stonehouse, Caswell's Yard, 215 Aylesbury Road, Wendover, Buckinghamshire, HP22 6BA Tel: (01296) 622750 Fax: (01296) 622750 E-mail: bert.roberts@thequarry.co.uk

NATURAL VEGETABLE COLOURS

Chr. Hansen (UK) Ltd, 2 Tealgate, Charnham Park, Hungerford, Berkshire, RG17 0YT Tel: (01488) 689800 Fax: (01488) 685436 E-mail: contactus-gb@gb.chr-hansen.com

NAVAL ARCHITECTS

B M T Defence Services Ltd, 210 Lower Bristol Road, Bath, BA2 3DQ Tel: (01225) 448712 Fax: (01225) 448714 E-mail: info@bmtdsl.co.uk
Laurent Giles Naval Architects Ltd, PO Box 130, Lymington, Hampshire, SO41 0TX Tel: (01590) 641777 Fax: (01590) 641888 E-mail: info@laurentgiles.co.uk
Graham & Woolnough, Suite 9, SMM Business Park, Dock Road, Birkenhead, Merseyside, CH41 1DT Tel: 0151-653 7948 Fax: 0151-653 7990 E-mail: information@grahamwoolnough.com
Hart Fenton & Co. Ltd, First Floor Norman House, Kettering Terrace, Portsmouth, PO2 7AE Tel: (023) 9287 5277 Fax: (023) 9287 5280 E-mail: hf@hart-fenton.co.uk
The Mccombie Napier Company Ltd, Newburgh, Ellon, Aberdeenshire, AB41 6BW Tel: (01358) 789987 Fax: (01358) 789877 E-mail: mccombienapier@aol.com
Seadrec Ltd, Blackhall House, Blackhall Lane, Paisley, Renfrewshire, PA1 1TA Tel: 0141-887 4131 Fax: 0141-887 6437 E-mail: info@lobnitz.com
Shiptech (U K) Ltd, St. Andrews House, 33 Beverley Road, Hull, HU3 1XH Tel: (01482) 324964 Fax: (01482) 226679 E-mail: info@shiptech.co.uk
T M C Marine Consultants Ltd, Lloyds Wharf, Mill Street, London, SE1 2BD Tel: (020) 7237 2617 Fax: (020) 7231 8069 E-mail: info@tmcmarine.co.uk

NAVAL CRAFT BUILDERS

B A E Systems plc, Stirling Square, 6 Carlton Gardens, London, SW1Y 5AD Tel: (01252) 373232 Fax: (01252) 383000

NAVIGATION POSITION FIXING EQUIPMENT CONSULTANTS/ SERVICES

▶ Del Norte Technology Ltd, Unit 20 Hunts Rise, South Marston Industrial Estat, Swindon, SN3 4TG Tel: (01793) 827982 Fax: (01793) 827984 E-mail: lsmith@del-norte.co.uk

NAVIGATIONAL AIDS

A B Pharos Marine Ltd, Steyning Way, Hounslow, TW4 6DL Tel: (020) 8538 1100 Fax: (020) 8577 4170 E-mail: sales@pharosmarine.com

B Cooke & Son Ltd, 58-59 Market Place, Hull, HU1 1RH Tel: (01482) 224412 Fax: (01482) 219793 E-mail: bcs@cooke.karoo.co.uk

F P M Henderson Ltd, 35 Halley Street, Glasgow, G13 4DJ Tel: 0141-941 1211 Fax: 0141-941 2011 E-mail: sales@fpmhenderson.co.uk

Fernau Avionics Ltd, Unit C Airport Executive Park, President Way, Luton, LU2 9NY Tel: (01582) 483111 Fax: (01582) 484404 E-mail: info@fernau.com

Kelvin Hughes Ltd, Kilgraston House, 11-13 Southampton Street, Southampton, SO15 2ED Tel: (023) 8063 4911 Fax: (023) 8033 0014 E-mail: southampton@kelvinhughes.co.uk

Orga, A1 Kingsway Business Park, Oldfield Road, Hampton, Middlesex, TW12 2HD Tel: (0870) 6092452 Fax: (020) 8941 6683 E-mail: sales@orga.nl

Silva Ltd, Fleming Road, Kirkton Campus, Livingston, West Lothian, EH54 7BN Tel: (01506) 419555 Fax: (01506) 415906 E-mail: info@silva.ltd.uk

Tideland Signal Ltd, Unit B Kendal House, Victoria Way, Burgess Hill, West Sussex, RH15 9NF Tel: (01444) 872240 Fax: (01444) 872241 E-mail: sales@tidelandsignal.ltd.uk

NAVIGATIONAL BUOYS

Hydrosphere UK Ltd, Units C & D, Westend Centre, Colt House Lane, Upper Froyle, Alton, Hampshire, GU34 4JR Tel: (01420) 520374 Fax: (01420) 520373 E-mail: sales@hydrosphere.co.uk

X J F Plastics Ltd, Unit 1 & 2, Southfield Lane Industrial Estate, Whitwell, Worksop, Nottinghamshire, S80 4SB Tel: (01909) 724211 Fax: (01909) 724582 E-mail: enquiries@xjfplastics.co.uk

NAVIGATIONAL INSTRUMENT/ SYSTEMS ENGINEERING SERVICES

Fenns (Farnborough) Ltd, 77 Alexandra Road, Farnborough, Hampshire, GU14 6BN Tel: (01252) 541221 Fax: (01252) 512890 E-mail: info@fennprint.co.uk

Thomas Gunn Navigation Services Ltd, Anchor House, 62 Regent Quay, Aberdeen, AB11 5AR Tel: (01224) 595045 Fax: (01224) 584702 E-mail: info@thomasgunn.com

Jeppesen UK Ltd, Alteon House, Crawley Business Quarter, Manor Royal, Crawley, West Sussex, RH10 9AD Tel: (01293) 842400 E-mail: david.forsythe@jeppesen.com

London Navaids Ltd, Unit 29 Sheraton Business Centre, 20 Wadsworth Road, Greenford, Middlesex, UB6 7JB Tel: (020) 8997 6599 Fax: (020) 8997 6899

NAVIGATIONAL INSTRUMENTS,

See also headings for particular types

Ships Electronic Services Ltd, Chichester House Waterside Court, Neptune Way, Medway City Estate, Rochester, Kent, ME2 4NZ Tel: (01634) 295500 Fax: (01634) 295537 E-mail: sales@ses-marine.com

NAVIGATIONAL LIGHTING

Hydrosphere UK Ltd, Units C & D, Westend Centre, Colt House Lane, Upper Froyle, Alton, Hampshire, GU34 4JR Tel: (01420) 520374 Fax: (01420) 520373 E-mail: sales@hydrosphere.co.uk

NAVIGATIONAL SYSTEMS

Sound & Secure Ltd, 454-456 Thornton Road, Bradford, West Yorkshire, BD8 9BS Tel: (01274) 775005 Fax: (01274) 770051

NEBOSH HEALTH AND SAFETY TRAINING

▶ Safety Training Unit Ltd, 1062 Cornforth Drive, Sittingbourne Research Centre, Sittingbourne, Kent, ME9 8HL Tel: (01795) 438841 Fax: (0870) 131920 E-mail: enquiries@stunit.co.uk

NECKTIE FABRICS

City Fax Ltd, 1 Cronin Road, Weldon South Industrial Estate, Corby, Northamptonshire, NN18 8AQ Tel: (01536) 402242 Fax: (01536) 402201 E-mail: cityfax.corby@cityfaxltd.com

DPT Wear Ltd, 17-20 Martinfield Business Centre, Martinfield, Welwyn Garden City, Hertfordshire, AL7 1HG Tel: (01707) 373838 Fax: (01707) 332288 E-mail: admin@dptwear.com

Stephen Walters & Sons Ltd, Sudbury Silk Mills, Sudbury, Suffolk, CO10 2XB Tel: (01787) 372266 Fax: (01787) 880126 E-mail: sales@stephenwalters.co.uk

D.H.J. Weisters Ltd, Anchor Mill, Darwen, Lancashire, BB3 0AH Tel: (01254) 873333 Fax: (01254) 873659 E-mail: customer-services@weisters.co.uk

NECKTIE INTERLININGS

City Fax Ltd, 1 Cronin Road, Weldon South Industrial Estate, Corby, Northamptonshire, NN18 8AQ Tel: (01536) 402242 Fax: (01536) 402201 E-mail: cityfax.corby@cityfaxltd.com

DPT Wear Ltd, 17-20 Martinfield Business Centre, Martinfield, Welwyn Garden City, Hertfordshire, AL7 1HG Tel: (01707) 373838 Fax: (01707) 332288 E-mail: admin@dptwear.com

Richards James Weldon, 5-6 The Mews, Hatherley Road, Sidcup, Kent, DA14 4BH Tel: (020) 8300 7878 Fax: (020) 8300 9709

NECKTIES

Richard Atkinson & Co. Ltd, 10 Nicholson Drive, Mallusk, Newtownabbey, County Antrim, BT36 4FD Tel: (028) 9084 3323 Fax: (020) 8908 4850 E-mail: info@atkinsons-irishpoplin-ties.com

Beckford Silk Ltd, Ashton Road, Beckford, Tewkesbury, Gloucestershire, GL20 7AU Tel: (01386) 881507 Fax: (01386) 882019 E-mail: sales@beckfordsilk.co.uk

C B Collections Ltd, 11 Grosvenor Road, Batley, West Yorkshire, WF17 0LX Tel: (01924) 476977 Fax: (01924) 478315 E-mail: silks@dial.pipex.com

Charnwood Ties Ltd, 91 Farndale Drive, Loughborough, Leicestershire, LE11 2RG Tel: (01509) 215378 Fax: (01509) 215378 E-mail: mail@charnwoodties.co.uk

City Fax Ltd, 1 Cronin Road, Weldon South Industrial Estate, Corby, Northamptonshire, NN18 8AQ Tel: (01536) 402242 Fax: (01536) 402201 E-mail: cityfax.corby@cityfaxltd.com

Creative Club Ties, The Whitehouse, 84 Cromley Road, High Lane, Stockport, Cheshire, SK6 8BU Tel: (01663) 762173 Fax: (01663) 810243 E-mail: karen9702@hotmail.co.uk

Creative Club Ties, The Whitehouse, 84 Cromley Road, High Lane, Stockport, Cheshire, SK6 8BU Tel: (01663) 762173 Fax: (01663) 810243 E-mail: julian.hyde@talk21.com

Criag Mill Of Scotland, 17 Station Road, Biggar, Lanarkshire, ML12 6BS Tel: (01899) 220289 Fax: (01899) 221182E-mail: calzeat@aol.com

DPT Wear Ltd, 17-20 Martinfield Business Centre, Martinfield, Welwyn Garden City, Hertfordshire, AL7 1HG Tel: (01707) 373838 Fax: (01707) 332288 E-mail: admin@dptwear.com

Ernex Group, P O Box 53967, London, SW15 3UY Tel: (020) 7731 6707 Fax: (020) 7731 6703 E-mail: ties@ernex.co.uk

I4c Publicity, 3 Broad Street, Coventry, CV6 5AX Tel: (024) 7666 7440 Fax: (024) 7666 3736 E-mail: sales@i4cpublicity.co.uk

Interlogo London Ltd, High Street, Newport, Isle of Wight, PO30 1BQ Tel: (01983) 522470 Fax: (01983) 532891 E-mail: sales@interlogo.co.uk

Maccravats Ltd, Byrons Lodge, Byrons Lane, Macclesfield, Cheshire, SK11 7JW Tel: (01625) 422079 Fax: (01625) 614641 E-mail: maccravats@yahoo.com

McDade Neckware Ltd, Unit 20, Imex Bussiness Centre, 198 Swanston Street, Glasgow, G40 3HH Tel: 0141-554 0448 Fax: 0141-556 2403 E-mail: mcdadeties@cwcom.net

Mark Handford & Co., 78 Coleswood Road, Harpenden, Hertfordshire, AL5 1EQ Tel: (01582) 762065 Fax: (01582) 623317

Munday C H Ltd, 8 St. Johns Road, Woking, Surrey, GU21 7SE Tel: (01483) 771588 Fax: (01483) 756627 E-mail: enquiries@chmunday.co.uk

Network Promotions, 5 Braehead Business Units, Braehead Road, Linlithgow, West Lothian, EH49 6EP Tel: (01506) 845797 Fax: (01506) 845149

O H Hewett Ltd, 21 Farncombe Street, Godalming, Surrey, GU7 3AY Tel: (01483) 426917 Fax: (01483) 424810 E-mail: enquiries@ohhewett.co.uk

Pam Ties Ltd, Pam House, Milk Street, Tyldesley, Manchester, M29 8DQ Tel: (01942) 887920 Fax: (01942) 887921 E-mail: pamties@btconnect.com

Rael Brook (Group) Ltd, Grosvenor Street, Ashden Underline, Ashton-Under-Lyne, Lancashire, OL7 0JY Tel: 0161-344 5618 Fax: 0161-308 5060 E-mail: admin@raelbrookshirts.com

Seppi, 28 High Street, Meldreth, Royston, Hertfordshire, SG8 6JU Tel: (01763) 260326 Fax: (01763) 260035 E-mail: sales@seppities.co.uk

Tie Rack Corporate Neckwear Ltd, Capital Interchange Way, Brentford, Middlesex, TW8 0EX Tel: (020) 8230 2300 Fax: (020) 8230 2350 E-mail: corpsales@tie-rack.co.uk

Tie & Scarf Co. Ltd, Warth Park, Radcliffe Road, Bury, Lancashire, BL9 9NB Tel: 0161-761 5151 Fax: 0161-762 0202 E-mail: tieandscarf@chaytow.com

Woodstock Neckwear Ltd, Telford Road, Glenrothes, Fife, KY7 4NX Tel: (01592) 771777 Fax: (01592) 631717

NECKWEAR

▶ Phormium Ltd, Braehead Cottage, Finavon, Forfar, Angus, DD8 3PX Tel: (01307) 850715 Fax: (01307) 850756 E-mail: p.s.ingham@btinternet.com

NEEDLE BEARINGS

I K O (Nippon Thompson), 2 Vincent Ave, Crownhill, Milton Keynes, MK8 0AB Tel: (01908) 566144 Fax: (01908) 565458 E-mail: sales@iko.co.uk

NEEDLE VALVES

Conoflow Ltd, 18 Brook Road, Wimborne, Dorset, BH21 2BH Tel: (01202) 888010 Fax: (01202) 842009

Euro Carb Ltd, 256 Kentwood Hill, Tilehurst, Reading, RG31 6DR Tel: 0118-943 1180 Fax: 0118-943 1190 E-mail: sales@dellorto.co.uk

Oliver Valves Ltd, Haig Road, Parkgate Industrial Estate, Knutsford, Cheshire, WA16 8DX Tel: (01565) 632636 Fax: (01565) 654089 E-mail: sales@valves.co.uk

Oppenheimer Engineering Services, 20 Vanguard Way, Shoeburyness, Southend-on-Sea, SS3 9RA Tel: (0870) 8722752 Fax: (0870) 8722750 E-mail: oes@oppenheimers.co.uk

NEEDLES, KNITTING/HOSIERY MACHINE

Groz-Beckert UK Ltd, Groz-Beckert House, Gloucester Crescent, Wigston, Leicestershire, LE18 4YL Tel: 0116-264 3500 Fax: 0116-264 3505

Mitchell Grieve Ltd, Wolsey Road, Coalville, Leicestershire, LE67 3TS Tel: (01530) 510565 Fax: (01530) 510458 E-mail: sales@mitchell-grieve.co.uk

NEEDLES, SEWING MACHINE, INDUSTRIAL

▶ Gur Sewing Machine Co., 162 Halesowen Street, Rowley Regis, West Midlands, B65 0ES Tel: 0121-561 5169 Fax: 0121-559 3449 E-mail: sales@gur.co.uk

▶ pro-stitch.co.uk, 4th floor, constellation mill, hardman st, radcliffe, manchester, M26 4GY Tel: 0161 767 9494 Fax: 0161 737 7258 E-mail: lhcassidy@aol.com

NEEDLEWORK KITS/ REQUISITES/SETS

Fred Aldous Ltd, Handicraft Centre, 37 Lever Street, Manchester, M1 1LW Tel: 0161-236 2477 Fax: 0161-236 6075 E-mail: aldous@btinternet.com

W H I Tapestry Shop, 85 Pimlico Road, London, SW1W 8PH Tel: (020) 7730 5366

NEODYMIUM MAGNETS

Swift Levick Magnets Ltd, High Hazels Road, Barlborough, Chesterfield, Derbyshire, S43 4UZ Tel: (01246) 570500 Fax: (01246) 573000 E-mail: sales@arnoldengr.com

NEON LAMP ASSEMBLIES

Cranfield Electrical Ltd, 2 Adams Close, Kempston, Bedford, MK42 7JE Tel: (01234) 853044 Fax: (01234) 853054 E-mail: sales@cranfieldelectrical.com

NEON LAMPS

Cranfield Electrical Ltd, 2 Adams Close, Kempston, Bedford, MK42 7JE Tel: (01234) 853044 Fax: (01234) 853054 E-mail: sales@cranfieldelectrical.com

NEON SIGNS

A Weston, 23 Marsh St South, Stoke-on-Trent, ST1 1JA Tel: (01782) 214580 Fax: (01782) 214581

Abacus Neon Sign Maker, 30 Greenfield Road, Atherton, Manchester, M46 9LW Tel: (01942) 883622

Acme Neon, Fitzroy Terrace, Grafton Street, Northampton, NN1 2NU Tel: (01604) 631068 Fax: (01604) 631068 E-mail: sales@acmeneon.co.uk

Blaze Neon Ltd, Patricia Way, Pysons Road Industrial Estate, Broadstairs, Kent, CT10 2XZ Tel: (01843) 601075 Fax: (01843) 867924 E-mail: chrisa@blazeneon.com

D B Sign Associates Ltd, Dukeries Industrial Estate, Claylands Avenue, Worksop, Nottinghamshire, S81 7BQ Tel: (01909) 472922 Fax: (01909) 478698 E-mail: office@dbsigns.com

Electro Signs Ltd, 97 Vallentin Road, London, E17 3JJ Tel: (020) 8521 8066 Fax: (020) 8520 8127 E-mail: info@electrosigns.co.uk

Elite Signs, 8 Cavendish Road, Salford, M7 4WW Tel: 0161-792 0232 Fax: 0161-792 0232 E-mail: elitesignsprint@aol.com

Futurama Ltd, Island Farm House, Island Farm Road, West Molesey, Surrey, KT8 2TR Tel: (020) 8941 1999 Fax: (020) 8783 1687 E-mail: postbox@futurama.ltd.uk

Gothard Neon Ltd, 11 Chorley Road, Blackpool, FY3 7XQ Tel: (01253) 390049 Fax: (01253) 390049 E-mail: dgothard@neon.signs.net

Hendon Sign Co., 25-27 The Burroughs, London, NW4 4AR Tel: (020) 8202 8900 Fax: (020) 8202 4071

J G Neon Signs, 639 Walsall Road, Great Barr, Birmingham, B42 1EH Tel: 0121-357 4033 Fax: 0121-357 4033

Kemps Neon Ltd, 2 Matrix Court, Leeds, LS11 5WB Tel: 0113-271 5777 Fax: 0113-271 5666 E-mail: sales@kempsneon.com

Marneon Signs Ltd, 11 Pontyglasdwr Street, Swansea, SA1 2BH Tel: (01792) 646949 Fax: (01792) 652227 E-mail: andrew-cotford@marneonsigns.com

Neon Signs Northampton Ltd, 1 Colwyn Road, Northampton, NN1 3PZ Tel: (01604) 636341 Fax: (01604) 636341

Nu Lite, 22 Ayloffs Walk, Hornchurch, Essex, RM11 2RJ Tel: (01708) 442232 Fax: (01708) 451696

Peter Tipper Signs & Plates Ltd, 33 Purdeys Industrial Estate, Purdeys Way, Rochford, Essex, SS4 1ND Tel: (01702) 549830 Fax: (01702) 549831 E-mail: info@tipper-signs.co.uk

Rye Signs Ltd, 4 11 Fieldings Road, Cheshunt, Waltham Cross, Hertfordshire, EN8 9TL Tel: (01992) 636348 Fax: (01992) 621579 E-mail: dave@ryesigns.demon.co.uk

S & N Signs, 133 Masons Hill, Bromley, BR2 9HT Tel: (020) 8460 8777 Fax: (020) 8460 8777

Sapsford Signs, 4 Mitre Avenue, London, E17 6QG Tel: (020) 8520 3739 Fax: (020) 8520 3739

Sign 2000 Ltd, Maidstone Road, Paddock Wood, Tonbridge, Kent, TN12 6QJ Tel: (01892) 834383 Fax: (01892) 838349 E-mail: info@sign2000.co.uk

Sign Connections Ltd, Unit 5 Sinclair Court, Great Yarmouth, Norfolk, NR31 0NH Tel: (01493) 440285 Fax: (01493) 653888 E-mail: info@signconnections.com

Sign Factory, 1333 London Road, Leigh-on-Sea, Essex, SS9 2AD Tel: (01702) 716161 Fax: (01702) 716141 E-mail: sales@signfactory.ws

Sign Services, Unit A4 Maidstone Industrial Centre, St Peter Street, Maidstone, Kent, ME16 0ST Tel: (01622) 681135 Fax: (01622) 678330 E-mail: sales@signservicesonline.co.uk

Signflair Ltd, 10-54 Ainsworth Avenue, Belfast, BT13 3EN Tel: (028) 9032 6007 Fax: (028) 9033 1936 E-mail: signflair@dnet.co.uk

Southern Neon Lights, 57a Rockstone Lane, Southampton, SO14 6JA Tel: (023) 8071 0300 Fax: (023) 8033 8481 E-mail: sales@southernneon.com

Stalite Signs Ltd, 7 Apple Lane, Exeter, EX2 5GL Tel: (01392) 447001 Fax: (01392) 447002 E-mail: sales@stalite.co.uk

Taylor Electronics Manchester Ltd, 287 Chester Road, Manchester, M15 4EY Tel: 0161-834 5050 Fax: 0161-834 5051

Tubeolight Signcraft C I, 1 Landes Du Marche, La Grande Route De St. Pierre, St. Peter, Jersey, JE3 7AY Tel: (01534) 485591 Fax: (01534) 485592 E-mail: sales@signtechjersey.co.uk

W A Ellwood Signs, 1 Ferry Lane, Rainham, Essex, RM13 9YH Tel: (01708) 521703 Fax: (01708) 521703

NEON TRANSFORMERS

Tunewell Transformers, 2 Maple Park, Essex Road, Hoddesdon, Hertfordshire, EN11 0EX Tel: (01992) 801300 Fax: (01992) 801301 E-mail: sales@tunewell.com

NEST BOXES

The Nestbox Company Ltd, Bolton Farm Lyonshall, Lyonshall, Kington, Herefordshire, HR5 3JY Tel: (01544) 340657 Fax: (01544) 340672 E-mail: sales@nestbox.co.uk

NET BAGS

BAG Supplies Ltd, Unit J, East Lakes Business Park, Cowper Road, Gilwilly Industrial Estate, Penrith, Cumbria, CA11 9BN Tel: (07798) 723040 Fax: (01786) 892779 E-mail: info@bagsupplies.com

NET CURTAINS

Ado UK Ltd, Abex Road, Newbury, Berkshire, RG14 5EY Tel: (01635) 521261 Fax: (01635) 529005

John Aird & Co. Ltd, Greenbank Mills, East Main Street, Darvel, Ayrshire, KA17 0JB Tel: (01560) 323600 Fax: (01560) 323601 E-mail: johnaird@compuserve.com

Blinds Direct Solar Control Systems, 20 Blue Chalet Industrial Park, West Kingsdown, Sevenoaks, Kent, TN15 6BQ Tel: (01474) 854156 Fax: (01474) 855361 E-mail: woodblinds@btconnect.com

D&B Tracks & Blinds, 1 Caistor Close, Calcot, Reading, RG31 7AY Tel: 0118-943 2757

Deyron Ltd, 32 Southgate Avenue, Mildenhall, Bury St. Edmunds, Suffolk, IP28 7AT Tel: (01638) 716340 Fax: (01638) 515707

Filigree Ltd, Carter Lane East, South Normanton, Alfreton, Derbyshire, DE55 2EG Tel: (01773) 811619 Fax: (01773) 862777 E-mail: enquiries@filigree.demon.co.uk

Grays Blinds, 44 Bridge Road, Grays, Essex, RM17 6BU Tel: (01375) 379022 Fax: (01375) 390109

▶ H D Chadwick & Sons, Gorton Road, Manchester, M11 2DZ Tel: 0161-223 1701 Fax: 0161-231 6752 E-mail: roger.chadwick@tesco.net

Krams Ugo Ltd, 18 Deans Drive, Edgware, Middlesex, HA8 9NU Tel: (020) 8906 8656 Fax: (020) 8906 8822 E-mail: enquiries@kramsugo.co.uk

Morton Young & Borland Ltd, Stoneygate Road, Newmilns, Ayrshire, KA16 9AL Tel: (01560) 321210 Fax: (01560) 323153 E-mail: info@myb-ltd.com

▶ Net Curtains Direct, 14 Alder Close, Dibden Purlieu, Southampton, SO45 5SJ Tel: (023) 8084 6946

NET FABRICS, CURTAIN/DRESS/ FURNISHING

Frank P Kirk Ltd, 122 Queens Road East, Beeston, Nottingham, NG9 2FD Tel: 0115-967 7330 Fax: 0115-967 7303

▶ Sherwoods Fabrics, 39 Church Street, Malvern, Worcestershire, WR14 2AA Tel: (01684) 572379 Fax: (01684) 563295 E-mail: info@sherwoodsfabrics.co.uk

NETS, AGRICULTURAL/ HORTICULTURAL/ ARBORICULTURAL

▶ Capatex Ltd, 127 North Gate, Nottingham, NG7 7FZ Tel: 0115-978 6111 Fax: 0115-978 6222 E-mail: info@capatex.com

Henry Cowls & Sons, Gilly Gabben Industrial Estate, Mawgan, Helston, Cornwall, TR12 6BB Tel: (01326) 221514 Fax: (01326) 221382

Knowle Nets Ltd, 20 East Road, Bridport, Dorset, DT6 4NX Tel: (01308) 424342 Fax: (01308) 458186 E-mail: sales@knowlenets.co.uk

W Oliver Allen & Sons, Loe Bar Road, Porthleven, Helston, Cornwall, TR13 9EN Tel: (01326) 562222 Fax: (01326) 562222 E-mail: woallen@porth-leven.com

NETTING/NETS, *See also headings for particular types*

Aaask Innobative Solutions, The Gap, Hafod Moor, Gwernaffield, Mold, Clwyd, CH7 5ET Tel: 0141-616 3333 Fax: 0141-639 5895 E-mail: sales@aaask.com

E F E & G B Nets, Bodmin, Cornwall, PL31 1YJ Tel: (01208) 873945 Fax: (01208) 873945 E-mail: sales@efe-uk.com

House & Co., 6 Gordleton Industrial Estate, Hannah Way, Pennington, Lymington, Hampshire, SO41 8JD Tel: (01590) 682285 Fax: (01590) 683553 E-mail: saleshouseandco@aol.com

Palmhive Technical Textiles Ltd, NTG House, Willow Road, Nottingham, NG7 2TA Tel: 0115-970 7900 Fax: 0115-970 7999 E-mail: enquiries@palmhive.co.uk

NETWORK ANALYSERS/ MEASUREMENT SYSTEMS DISTRIBUTORS OR AGENTS

Access It Ltd, The Old Grain Store, Brenley Lane, Boughton-under-Blean, Faversham, Kent, ME13 9LY Tel: (01227) 750555 Fax: (01227) 750070 E-mail: sales@accessit.co.uk

Annodata Business Communications, Shannon House, Station Road, Kings Langley, Hertfordshire, WD4 8SE Tel: (01923) 261733 Fax: (01923) 261678

G Tech UK Ltd, Link House, 19 Colonial Way, Watford, WD24 4JL Tel: (01923) 474800 Fax: (01923) 474830 E-mail: first.surname@gtech.com

Hydra P.L.C., 145 Cannon Street, London, EC4N 5BQ Tel: (020) 7337 2777 Fax: (020) 7337 2772 E-mail: sales@hydranet.co.uk

J M D Systems Ltd, 7 St. Pauls Yard, Silver Street, Newport Pagnell, Buckinghamshire, MK16 0EG Tel: (01908) 217033 Fax: (01982) 217044

Loftus Computer Consultancy, First Quarter, Blenheim Road, Epsom, Surrey, KT19 9QN Tel: (01372) 748874 Fax: (01372) 739307 E-mail: info@loftusitns.co.uk

Montague Tate Ltd, PO Box 179, Cirencester, Gloucestershire, GL7 7YT Tel: (0870) 4030007 Fax: (0870) 4030008 E-mail: admin@montague-tate.co.uk

Network Technologies & Associates Ltd, 38 High Street, Newmarket, Suffolk, CB8 8LB Tel: (01638) 668633 Fax: (01638) 561924 E-mail: info@networktechnologies.co.uk

Sabrefame Ltd, Brook House, Duck Street, Wendens Ambo, Saffron Walden, Essex, CB11 4JU Tel: (01799) 542287 Fax: (01799) 541954 E-mail: sabrefame@aol.com

Stoneleigh Consultancy Ltd, The Ditches Hall, Ellesmere Road, Wem, Shrewsbury, SY4 5TX Tel: (01939) 238800 Fax: (01939) 235123 E-mail: sales@stoneleigh.co.uk

Strategy Partners International Ltd, Chappell House, The Green, Datchet, Slough, SL3 9EH Tel: (01753) 592787 Fax: (01753) 592789

Telecom Ltd, 12 Richmond Tce, Gateshead, Tyne & Wear, NE8 1RN Tel: 0191-477 2961 Fax: 0191 497 5226

NETWORK COMPUTER INTERFACE CARDS (CIC)

Adax Europe Ltd, Reada Court, Vachel Road, Reading, RG1 1NY Tel: 0118-952 2800 Fax: 0118-957 1530 E-mail: info@adax.co.uk

K S Computers, 3 Dyneley Road, Blackburn, BB1 3AB Tel: (01254) 505500 Fax: (01254) 691466 E-mail: purchasing@javelincomputers.co.uk

NETWORK HARDWARE SUPPORT

▶ Advantech Ltd, 5 Clarence Road, Grays, Essex, RM17 6QA Tel: (01375) 392822 Fax: (01375) 392399 E-mail: enquiries@advantechltd.co.uk

▶ Anything It, 14 Mary Seacole Road, Plymouth, PL1 3JY Tel: (01752) 667771 Fax: (01752) 667771 E-mail: sales@anything-it.biz

▶ Blue Box Technology Ltd, Unit 54, Works Road, Hollingwood, Chesterfield, Derbyshire, S43 2PE Tel: (01246) 472233 Fax: (01246) 477788 E-mail: sales@bb24.co.uk

▶ C H C Solutions, Thorley Health Centre, Villiers-Sur-Marne, Bishop's Stortford, Hertfordshire, CM23 4EG Tel: (01279) 210088 Fax: (0870) 1417242 E-mail: contactus@chcsolutions.co.uk

▶ Cambit Support, 16 Chesterton Hall CR, Cambridge, CB4 1AP Tel: (01223) 576705 E-mail: sales@cambit.net

▶ Exeye, 20 Denmark Street, London, WC2H 8NA Tel: (0845) 1303291

▶ The Gosport PC Clinic, 69 Brockhurst Road, Gosport, Hampshire, PO12 3AR Tel: (023) 9252 2777 Fax: (023) 9252 2777 E-mail: support@coppcomm.com

Ilkley It Services Ltd, Nat West Bank Chambers The, Grove Ilkley, Ilkley, West Yorkshire, LS29 9LS Tel: (01943) 601601 E-mail: info@ilkleyitservices.co.uk

▶ Impact Computing & Consulting, Oak Mount, Blackpool Road, Newton, Preston, PR4 3RE Tel: (01772) 684282 Fax: (01772) 681597 E-mail: sales@impactcomputing.co.uk

▶ Infinity Business Solutions, Shinfield Grange, Cutbush Lane, Shinfield, Reading, RG2 9AF Tel: 0118-988 2777 E-mail: sales@infinity-bf.com

▶ Infinity Technologies Ltd, Hamlet House, 366-368 London, Westcliff-on-Sea, Essex, SS0 7HZ Tel: (01268) 777050 Fax: (08700) 548697 E-mail: bpb@inftech.co.uk

▶ Isys Computer Services Ltd, 4 Charlotte Street, Dumbarton, G82 4JB Tel: (0845) 1434040 Fax: (0845) 1434039 E-mail: info@isys-computers.co.uk

▶ ITC Service Ltd, 45 Wedderlaw, Cramlington, Northumberland, NE23 6PA Tel: (07919) 154375 Fax: 0191-416 3003 E-mail: info@itcservive.co.uk

▶ Khipu Networks Ltd, Infineon House, Minley Road, Fleet, Hampshire, GU51 2RD Tel: (01252) 773184 Fax: (01252) 629008 E-mail: sales@khipu-networks.com

▶ LinWin Computer Services, 123 Tradewinds, Wards Wharf Appproach, London, London, E16 2ER Tel: 079 71695701 Fax: 0870 7064637 E-mail: info@linwin.co.uk

▶ Liquid It Ltd, 22 Heron Court Road, Bournemouth, BH9 1DG Tel: (08707) 547843 Fax: 08707 627843

▶ No Wires Networks, 4 Laxton Close, Luton, LU2 8SJ Tel: (0845) 0093781 Fax: (0870) 1162823 E-mail: info@nowiresnetworks.co.uk

▶ OffSight IT Services Ltd, Unit 3, Cannock Chase Enterprise Centre, Hednesford, Cannock, Staffordshire, WS12 0QU Tel: (01543) 426142 E-mail: enquiries@offsight.co.uk

▶ Ooh It, 49 Westcroft Gardens, Morden, Surrey, SM4 4DJ Tel: (020) 8543 6769 Fax: (0870) 705 8270 E-mail: Info@oohit.com

▶ PC Response, 3 Heathlands Court, Wokingham, Berkshire, RG40 3AY Tel: 01344 761880 E-mail: help@pcresponse.net

▶ Peach Data Services P.L.C., Lakeside, Festival Park, Stoke-on-Trent, ST1 5RY Tel: (01782) 267484 Fax: (01782) 267454 E-mail: john.burnett@peachdata.co.uk

▶ Pi Computers, Unit 17 Rosebridge Court, Rosebridge Way, Ince, Wigan, Lancashire, WN1 3DP Tel: (01942) 244959 Fax: (01942) 244966 E-mail: picomp@f2s.com

▶ Premier Management, 18 Balmoral CR, Oswestry, Shropshire, SY11 2XG Tel: (01691) 653505 E-mail: carl.palmer@premierconsultancy.com

Premier Networks UK, Garsett House, St. Andrews Hall Plain, Norwich, NR3 1AU Tel: (01603) 305659 E-mail: info@premiernetworks.co.uk

▶ S R S Computer Systems Ltd, 1 Dewar House, 1 Enterprise Way, Dunfermline, Fife, KY11 8PY Tel: (01383) 624446 Fax: (01383) 840880 E-mail: kellyanne@srsnet.co.uk

▶ Sapath Systems, 145 Vaughan Road, Harrow, Middlesex, HA1 4EG Tel: (0870) 9502936 Fax: (0870) 1281422E-mail: info@sapath.com

▶ Sebolis Ltd, Swindon Innovation Centre, University of Bath in Swindon, Oakfield Campus, Marlowe Avenue, Swindon, SN3 3JR Tel: 01793 329927 E-mail: enquiries@sebolis.co.uk

▶ Seca PCS Ltd, Unit E 7 Craigend Place, Anniesland, Glasgow, G13 2UN Tel: 0141-959 1440 E-mail: info@secapcs.co.uk

▶ SGP Computing Ltd, 1 Hinckley Road, Earl Shilton, Leicester, LE9 7LG Tel: (01455) 449372 Fax: (01455) 449372 E-mail: enquiries@sgpcomputing.com

▶ Springdot Ltd, 14 Barham Close, Bromley, BR2 8LU Tel: (020) 8462 0682 E-mail: enquiries@springdot.co.uk

▶ Virus & Adware Removal, Woodpeckers, 19 Wildcroft Drive, Wokingham, Berkshire, RG40 3HY Tel: 0118-977 5957 Fax: 0118-977 5957 E-mail: aardy@btinternet.com

NETWORK MANAGEMENT SERVICES

▶ Logicomm 2000 Ltd, 174 Watling Street, Bridgtown, Cannock, Staffordshire, WS11 0BD Tel: (0845) 2255816 Fax: (0845) 2255817 E-mail: sales@logicomm-2000.com

NETWORK PLANNING SOFTWARE

G E Netwrok Solutions, Elizabeth House, 1 High Street, Chesterton, Cambridge, CB4 1WR Tel: (01223) 301144 Fax: (01223) 311145

NETWORK PRODUCTS

Adax Europe Ltd, Reada Court, Vachel Road, Reading, RG1 1NY Tel: 0118-952 2800 Fax: 0118-957 1530 E-mail: info@adax.co.uk

Electronics 2000 Ltd, Grafton House, Grafton Street, High Wycombe, Buckinghamshire, HP12 3AJ Tel: (01494) 444044 Fax: (01494) 470499 E-mail: sales@e2000.com

Euronetwork Ltd, 1 Horwood Court, Bletchley, Milton Keynes, MK1 1RD Tel: (01908) 371909 Fax: (01908) 378239 E-mail: info@euronetwork.co.uk

NETWORK SERVICE PROVIDERS

Datel Solutions, 71 Elgin Street, Dunfermline, Fife, KY12 7SA Tel: (01383) 742752 Fax: (01383) 432223 E-mail: info@datel-solutions.co.uk

▶ Realsys Technology, 24 Velsheda Road, Shirley, Solihull, West Midlands, B90 2JN Tel: 0121-244 2936 Fax: (0871) 2422788 E-mail: sales@realis8ion.com

▶ Smarttalk Communications, 23 Burlington Lane, London, W4 2RN Tel: (020) 8742 0321 Fax: 0870 2854888 E-mail: solutions@smarttalkuk.com

NETWORK SYSTEMS

▶ N D S 8 Ltd, 11 Bankhead Broadway, Edinburgh, EH11 4DB Tel: (0845) 2260070 Fax: 0131-538 8202 E-mail: david.ashton@nds8.co.uk

Tertio Ltd, 3000 Manchester Business Park, Manchester, M22 5TG Tel: 0161-266 1016 Fax: 0161-266 1396

NETWORK TEST EQUIPMENT

▶ Fluke Networks, Egale 1, 80 St. Albans Road, Watford, WD17 1RP Tel: (01923) 281300 Fax: (01923) 281301 E-mail: sales-uk@flukenetworks.com

NETWORKING SERVICES

▶ Logicomm 2000 Ltd, 174 Watling Street, Bridgtown, Cannock, Staffordshire, WS11 0BD Tel: (0845) 2255816 Fax: (0845) 2255817 E-mail: sales@logicomm-2000.com

NEURO LINGUISTIC PROGRAMMING (NLP) PSYCHOLOGY CONSULTANTS

▶ Executive Coaching & Mentoring Ltd, 67 Hampton Road, Southport, Merseyside, PR8 6QA Tel: (01704) 530821 E-mail: info@ecam.nu

NEURO LINGUISTIC PROGRAMMING (NLP) TRAINING

▶ At The Source, 192 Clarendon Park Road, Leicester, LE2 3AF Tel: 0116-270 6255 E-mail: beverley@atthesource.co.uk

NEWSPAPER HANDLING EQUIPMENT

Macdermid plc, Cale Lane, New Springs, Wigan, Lancashire, WN2 1JR Tel: (01942) 501000 Fax: (01942) 501110 E-mail: wigansales@macdermid.com

▶ Muller Martini Ltd, The Ridgeway, Iver, Buckinghamshire, SL0 9JQ Tel: (01753) 657700 Fax: (01753) 655658 E-mail: enquiries@mullermartini.co.uk

NEWSPAPER PRESS CONVEYOR SYSTEMS

Heidelberg Graphic Equipment Ltd, Intercity Way, Leeds, LS13 4LX Tel: 0113-224 8300 Fax: 0113-239 3118

WRH Marketing UK Ltd, 6 Stanstead Courtyard, Parsonage Road, Takeley, Bishop's Stortford, Hertfordshire, CM22 6PU Tel: (01279) 635657 Fax: (01279) 445666 E-mail: productinfo@wrh-marketing-uk.com

NEWSPAPER PRINTING

Central Independent Newspapers Ltd, Ventura Park Road, Tamworth, Staffordshire, B78 3LZ Tel: (01827) 848586 Fax: (01827) 848640

Chester Chronicle, Chronicle House, Commonhall Street, Chester, CH1 2AA Tel: (0870) 7021234

Derry Journal Newspapers Ltd, 22 Buncrana Road, Londonderry, BT48 8AA Tel: (028) 7127 2200 Fax: (028) 7127 2218 E-mail: editorial@jerryjernonal.com

Wilfred Edmunds Ltd, 37 Station Road, Chesterfield, Derbyshire, S41 7XD Tel: (01246) 504500 Fax: (01246) 504580 E-mail: editorial@derbyshiretimes.co.uk

Mail News & Media Ltd, Blundells Corner, Beverley Road, Hull, HU3 1XS Tel: (01482) 327111 Fax: (01482) 584314

Milap Weekly, Masbro Centre, 87 Masbro Road, London, W14 0LR Tel: (020) 7385 8966 Fax: (020) 7385 8966

Mortons of Horncastle Ltd, Morton Way, Boston Road, Horncastle, Lincolnshire, LN9 6JR Tel: (01507) 523456 Fax: (01507) 527840 E-mail: admin@mortons.co.uk

NCJ Media Ltd, Groat Market, Newcastle Upon Tyne, NE1 1ED Tel: 0191-232 7500 Fax: 0191-230 4144

North London & Herts Newspaper Ltd, 9-10 Riverside, Enfield, Middlesex, EN1 3SZ Tel: (020) 8367 2345 Fax: (020) 8366 4013 E-mail: newsenfield@trinitysight.co.uk

Peterborough Web, Oundle Road, Peterborough, PE2 9QH Tel: (01733) 342525 Fax: (01733) 896514

Sharman & Co. Ltd, Newark Road, Peterborough, PE1 5TD Tel: (01733) 424949 Fax: (01733) 424948

NEWSPAPER PRINTING – *continued*

Western Morning News Co. Ltd, 17 Brest Road, Derriford, Plymouth, PL6 5AA Tel: (01752) 765500 Fax: (01752) 765515 E-mail: plymouthfrontcounter@westcountrypublications.co.uk

NEWSPAPER/COURIER BAGS

Bolton Metropolitan Borough Council Commercial Services Bolmoor I, St Helens Road, Bolton, BL3 3NS Tel: (01204) 336855 Fax: (01204) 658072 E-mail: sales@bolmoor.co.uk

Mail News & Media Ltd, Blundells Corner, Beverley Road, Hull, HU3 1XS Tel: (01482) 327111 Fax: (01482) 584314

S M B Couriers, 683 Tonbridge Road, Barming, Maidstone, Kent, ME16 9DQ Tel: (07930) 281229 E-mail: info@smbcouriers.com

NEWSPAPERS

▶ The Ashford Advertiser, PO Box 1, Ashford, Kent, TN23 4ZU Tel: (01233) 624538 Fax: (01233) 641900 E-mail: theadvertiser@aol.com

Guernsey Press, PO Box 57, Guernsey, GY1 3BW Tel: (01481) 240240 Fax: (01481) 240235 E-mail: newsroom@guernsey-press.com

NEWTONIAN REFLECTOR TELESCOPES

▶ Sussex Astronomy Centre, 16 Mulberry Lane, Goring By Sea, Worthing, West Sussex, BN12 4JL Tel: (01903) 247317 E-mail: worthingastronomy@tiscali.co.uk

NI-HARD IRON CASTINGS

Ductile Castings Ltd, Trent Foundary, Dawes Lane, Scunthorpe, South Humberside, DN15 6UW Tel: (01724) 862152 Fax: (01724) 280461 E-mail: info@ductile.co.uk

Durham Foundry (Sheffield) Ltd, Durham Foundry, Harleston Street, Sheffield, S4 7QB Tel: 0114-249 4977 Fax: 0114-249 4910 E-mail: castings@durhamfoundry.com

NICKEL ALLOY BARS

Haynes International Ltd, Parkhouse St, Openshaw, Manchester, M11 2ER Tel: 0161-230 7777 Fax: 0161-223 2412 E-mail: memarycz@haynesint.co.uk

Valbruan UK Ltd, 36a Walworth Road, Andover, Hampshire, SP10 5LH Tel: (01264) 333390 Fax: (01264) 333315

NICKEL ALLOY CASTINGS

Investment Castings Congleton Ltd, Greenfield Farm Industrial Estate, Congleton, Cheshire, CW12 4TR Tel: (01260) 280181 Fax: (01260) 298208 E-mail: info@investment-castings.co.uk

▶ Precision Products (Cumberland) Ltd, Highmill, Alston, Cumbria, CA9 3HT Tel: (01434) 381228 Fax: (01434) 381038 E-mail: sales@shawprocess.co.uk

Taylormade Castings Ltd, Cobridge Road, Stoke-on-Trent, ST1 5JP Tel: (01782) 261537 Fax: (01782) 261262 E-mail: tmcstoke@ukonline.co.uk

NICKEL ALLOY FABRICATIONS

Fabwell Ltd, Unti J Balds Lane, Stourbridge, West Midlands, DY9 8TE Tel: (01384) 898288 Fax: (01384) 898289 E-mail: sales@fabwell.co.uk

Langfields Ltd, 158 Liverpool Street, Salford, M5 4LJ Tel: 0161-736 4506 Fax: 0161-745 7108 E-mail: sales@langfields.com

NICKEL ALLOY FLANGES/ FITTINGS MANUFRS

CML Alloys, Buildings 8 9, 8 First Avenue, Pensnett Trading Estate, Kingswinford, West Midlands, DY6 7TG Tel: (01384) 282400 Fax: (01384) 270800 E-mail: sales@amari-international.com

Haynes International Ltd, Parkhouse St, Openshaw, Manchester, M11 2ER Tel: 0161-230 7777 Fax: 0161-223 2412 E-mail: memarycz@haynesint.co.uk

Hytemp Ltd, Lowther Rd, Sheffield, S6 2DQ Tel: 0114-233 8163 Fax: 0114-233 8211 E-mail: sales@hytemp.com

Non-Corrosive Control Lines Ltd, 25 Blake House, Gunwharf Quays, Portsmouth, PO1 3TH Tel: (023) 9273 1178 Fax: (023) 9273 1196 E-mail: nccl@btconnect.com

NICKEL ALLOY RODS/WIRES

Omega Resistance Wire Ltd, Hadley Works, Cranborne Road, Potters Bar, Hertfordshire, EN6 3JL Tel: (01707) 620111 Fax: (01707) 649225 E-mail: sales@omega-wire.com

Thyssenkrupp V D M UK Ltd, VDM House, 111 Hare Lane, Claygate, Esher, Surrey, KT10 0QY Tel: (01372) 467137 Fax: (01372) 466388

NICKEL ALLOY SHEETS

Thyssenkrupp V D M UK Ltd, VDM House, 111 Hare Lane, Claygate, Esher, Surrey, KT10 0QY Tel: (01372) 467137 Fax: (01372) 466388

NICKEL ALLOY SPRINGS

Valley Spring Co. Ltd, Pottery Lane East, Chesterfield, Derbyshire, S41 9BH Tel: (01246) 451981 Fax: (01246) 454327 E-mail: sales@valleyspring.com

NICKEL ALLOY STOCKHOLDERS

Byworth Material Services, 12 Stonehouse Commercial Centre, Bristol Road, Stonehouse, Gloucestershire, GL10 3RD Tel: (01453) 821609 Fax: (01453) 821471 E-mail: byworth@aol.com

C M L Alloys Ltd, Units 44-45 Stretford Motorway Estate, Barton Dock Road, Trafford Park, Manchester, M32 0ZH Tel: 0161-864 5001 Fax: 0161-865 5751 E-mail: sales@cmlimited.com

CML Alloys, Buildings 8 9, 8 First Avenue, Pensnett Trading Estate, Kingswinford, West Midlands, DY6 7TG Tel: (01384) 282400 Fax: (01384) 270800 E-mail: sales@amari-international.com

Columbia Metals Ltd, Union Street South, Halifax, West Yorkshire, HX1 2LA Tel: (01422) 343026 Fax: (01422) 346587 E-mail: export@columbiametals.co.uk

Enpar Special Alloys Ltd, Station Road, Ecclesfield, Sheffield, S35 9YR Tel: 0114-219 3002 Fax: 0114-219 1145 E-mail: sales.esa@firthrixson.com

Goodwin Alloy Products, Goodwin House, Leek Road, Hanley, Stoke-On-Trent, ST1 3NR Tel: (01782) 220260 Fax: (01782) 228060 E-mail: goodwinplc@goodwin.co.uk

Haynes International Ltd, Parkhouse St, Openshaw, Manchester, M11 2ER Tel: 0161-230 7777 Fax: 0161-223 2412 E-mail: memarycz@haynesint.co.uk

Hytemp Ltd, Lowther Road, Sheffield, S6 2DQ Tel: 0114-233 8163 Fax: 0114-233 8211 E-mail: sales@hytemp.com

Maher Ltd, 2 Brightside Way, Sheffield, S9 2RQ Tel: 0114-290 9200 Fax: 0114-290 9290 E-mail: sales@maher.co.uk

Orchard Materials Ltd, 7 Brunel Way, Thornbury, Bristol, BS35 3UR Tel: (01454) 415222 Fax: (01454) 415333 E-mail: sales@orchardmaterials.com

Philip Cornes & Co. Ltd, Lanner Building, Clews Road, Redditch, Worcestershire, B98 7ST Tel: (01527) 555000 Fax: (01527) 547000 E-mail: philipcornes.sales@twmetals.co.uk

Quest 4 Alloys Ltd, Alloys House, Dale Street, Bilston, West Midlands, WV14 7JY Tel: (01902) 409316 Fax: (01902) 409304 E-mail: info@quest4alloys.co.uk

Resistalloy International Ltd, 36 Wheatacre Road, Stocksbridge, Sheffield, S36 2GB Tel: 0114-288 3872

Ross & Catherall Ltd, Forge Lane, Killamarsh, Sheffield, S21 1BA Tel: 0114-248 6404 Fax: 0114-247 5999 E-mail: rosscatherall@doncasters.com

Special Piping Materials Ltd, Broadway, Dukinfield, Cheshire, SK16 4UU Tel: 0161-343 7005 Fax: 0161-343 7011 E-mail: sales@spm.co.uk

Special Quality Alloys Ltd, Colwall St, Sheffield, S9 3WP Tel: 0114-243 4366 Fax: 0114-244 1199 E-mail: sales@specialqualityalloys.com

Ugitech UK Ltd, Units 14-15 Erdington Industrial Park, Chester Road, Birmingham, B24 0RD Tel: 0121-382 9494 Fax: 0121-386 1328 E-mail: sales@uginesavoie.usinor.com

NICKEL ALLOY STRIPS

Thyssenkrupp V D M UK Ltd, VDM House, 111 Hare Lane, Claygate, Esher, Surrey, KT10 0QY Tel: (01372) 467137 Fax: (01372) 466388

NICKEL ALLOY TUBES

C M L Alloys Ltd, Units 44-45 Stretford Motorway Estate, Barton Dock Road, Trafford Park, Manchester, M32 0ZH Tel: 0161-864 5001 Fax: 0161-865 5751 E-mail: sales@cmlimited.com

CML Alloys, Buildings 8 9, 8 First Avenue, Pensnett Trading Estate, Kingswinford, West Midlands, DY6 7TG Tel: (01384) 282400 Fax: (01384) 270800 E-mail: sales@amari-international.com

Kay Electronics & Materials, 52 Albany Park Road, Kingston Upon Thames, Surrey, KT2 5SU Tel: (020) 8546 3235 Fax: (020) 8549 5712 E-mail: jaqueline_babinet@hotmail.com

Le Guellec, Stone Road, Tittensor, Stoke-On-Trent, ST12 9HA Tel: (01782) 374111 Fax: (01782) 373488 E-mail: info@wlmetals.co.uk

Metal Sections Ltd, Broadwell Road, Oldbury, West Midlands, B69 4HE Tel: 0121-601 6000 Fax: 0121-601 6121 E-mail: metsecplc@metsec.com

Non-Corrosive Control Lines Ltd, 25 Blake House, Gunwharf Quays, Portsmouth, PO1 3TH Tel: (023) 9273 1178 Fax: (023) 9273 1196 E-mail: nccl@btconnect.com

NICKEL ANODES

Asbury Brodie & Co. Ltd, 1 Dover Street, Birmingham, B18 5HN Tel: 0121-554 7000 Fax: 0121-554 0242 E-mail: sales@asburybrodie.co.uk

NICKEL BRONZE SINTERED FILTERS

Sintamesh Ltd, Unit 2, Bentinck Workshops, Park Lane, Kirkby-in-Ashfield, Nottingham, NG17 9LE Tel: (01623) 753401 Fax: (01623) 753408 E-mail: sinta@btconnect.com

NICKEL CADMIUM (NICD) BATTERIES

Bristol Batteries Ltd, 3 Dove Lane, St. Pauls, Bristol, BS2 9HP Tel: 0117-955 0536 Fax: 0117-935 1791 E-mail: admin@bristolbatteries.com

Saft Ltd, 6th Floor Westgate House, West Gate, Harlow, Essex, CM20 1JN Tel: (01279) 772550 Fax: (01279) 420909 E-mail: sarah.carter@saftbatteries.com

NICKEL CADMIUM (NICD) BATTERY CHARGERS

Edw Controls, Birch Park, Huntington Road, York, YO31 9BL Tel: (01904) 643908 Fax: (01904) 623494 E-mail: info@edwcontrols.co.uk

NICKEL CADMIUM (NICD) RECHARGEABLE OR SEALED BATTERIES

Alexander Technologies (Europe) Ltd, 4 Doxford Drive, South West Industrial Estate, Peterlee, County Durham, SR8 2RL Tel: 0191-587 2787 Fax: 0191-587 2587 E-mail: mail@alexenergy.co.uk

Ni-Cd Services, 4 Queens Park Road, Bournemouth, BH8 9BP Tel: (01202) 395404 Fax: (01202) 398393 E-mail: russellfrederick@mac.com

Pulsar Developments Ltd, Spracklen House, Dukes Place, Marlow, Buckinghamshire, SL7 2QH Tel: (01628) 473555 Fax: (01628) 474325 E-mail: sales@pulsardevelopments.com

Ripmax Ltd, Ripmax Corner, Green Street, Enfield, Middlesex, EN3 7SJ Tel: (020) 8282 7500 Fax: (020) 8282 7501 E-mail: mail@ripmax.com

S E C Industrial Battery Co. Ltd, Thorney Weir House, Thorney Mill Road, Iver, Buckinghamshire, SL0 9AQ Tel: (01895) 431543 Fax: (01895) 431880 E-mail: info@secbattery.com

Saft Ltd, 6th Floor Westgate House, West Gate, Harlow, Essex, CM20 1JN Tel: (01279) 772550 Fax: (01279) 420909 E-mail: sarah.carter@saftbatteries.com

Saft, River Drive, South Shields, Tyne & Wear, NE33 2TR Tel: 0191-456 1451 Fax: 0191-456 6383 E-mail: enquiries@saftbatteries.com

Westgate Developments, Derby House, 11 Rosebery Road, Langley Vale, Epsom, Surrey, KT18 6AF Tel: (01372) 800404 Fax: (01372) 800407 E-mail: west-gate@ntlworld.com

NICKEL CHROME COBALT ALLOYS

Firth Rixson Superalloys Ltd, Shepley Street, Glossop, Derbyshire, SK13 7SA Tel: (01457) 854351 Fax: (01457) 855529 E-mail: lbrierley@firthrixson.com

NICKEL CHROME TAPES

Omega Resistance Wire Ltd, Hadley Works, Cranborne Road, Potters Bar, Hertfordshire, EN6 3JL Tel: (01707) 620111 Fax: (01707) 649225 E-mail: sales@omega-wire.com

NICKEL FORGINGS MANUFRS

Firth Rixson Forgings Ltd, Dale Road North, Darley Dale, Matlock, Derbyshire, DE4 2JB Tel: 0114-219 3005 E-mail: info@firthrixson.com

Maher Ltd, 2 Brightside Way, Sheffield, S9 2RQ Tel: 0114-290 9200 Fax: 0114-290 9290 E-mail: sales@maher.co.uk

NICKEL METAL HYDRIDE BATTERIES

Alexander Technologies (Europe) Ltd, 4 Doxford Drive, South West Industrial Estate, Peterlee, County Durham, SR8 2RL Tel: 0191-587 2787 Fax: 0191-587 2587 E-mail: mail@alexenergy.co.uk

Allbatteries UK Ltd, 34 The Metro Centre, Dwight Road, Watford, WD18 9SB Tel: (01923) 241500 Fax: (01923) 245700 E-mail: sales@allbatteries.co.uk

▶ Budget, 13 865 Ringwood Road, Bournemouth, BH11 8LW Tel: (01202) 582700 Fax: (01202) 573200 E-mail: info@budgetbatteries.co.uk

Saft Ltd, 6th Floor Westgate House, West Gate, Harlow, Essex, CM20 1JN Tel: (01279) 772550 Fax: (01279) 420909 E-mail: sarah.carter@saftbatteries.com

▶ Varta Microbattery GmbH, 16 Progress Business Centre, Whittle Parkway, Slough, SL1 6DQ Tel: (01628) 607930 Fax: (01628) 607939 E-mail: uksales@varta.com

NICKEL PLATING SERVICES

Clark Electro-Plating (Wrexham) Ltd, The Old Foundry, Hill Street, Rhostyllen, Wrexham, Clwyd, LL14 4AT Tel: (01978) 355803 Fax: (01978) 291321

Derby Plating Services Ltd, 148 Abbey Street, Derby, DE22 3SS Tel: (01332) 382408 Fax: (01332) 382408

Hastings Metal Finishers, Unit 7-8 Prince Consort Industrial Estate, Hebburn, Tyne & Wear, NE31 1EH Tel: 0191-483 9213 Fax: 0191-483 9213 E-mail: hmf.sales@tiscali.co.uk

New Tech Finishing, Commercial Road, Walsall, WS2 7NQ Tel: (01922) 404604 Fax: (01922) 711083 E-mail: enquiries@ntfltd.co.uk

Nuneaton Fine Finishers, Maguire Industrial Estate, Unit 3 Torrington Avenue, Coventry, CV4 9HN Tel: (024) 7642 2002 Fax: (024) 7647 1460

Satchrome Ltd, Unit 19 Birchills House Industrial Estate, Green Lane, Walsall, WS2 8LF Tel: (01922) 622721 Fax: (01922) 625353 E-mail: satchrome@yahoo.co.uk

Thomas HG & Co. Ltd, 78 Steward Street, Birmingham, B18 7AF Tel: 0121-454 0677 Fax: 0121-454 0677 E-mail: markf@thomashgee.co.uk

Twickenham Plating Group Ltd, 12-13 Balena Close, Poole, Dorset, BH17 7DB Tel: (01202) 692416 Fax: (01202) 600628 E-mail: info@pender.co.uk

NICKEL RECYCLING/RESIDUAL METAL RECOVERY SERVICES/ MERCHANTS OR AGENTS

Albert Alderton, Town Cross Avenue, Bognor Regis, West Sussex, PO21 2DP Tel: (01243) 824700 Fax: (01243) 821482

Jack Sharkey & Co. Ltd, 2 Middlemore Road, Smethwick, West Midlands, B66 2DR Tel: 0121-558 7444 Fax: 0121-558 9810

O B Metals Co. Ltd, Watery Lane Industrial Estate, Watery Lane, Willenhall, West Midlands, WV13 3SU Tel: (01902) 608691 Fax: (01902) 603312

NICKEL SILVER

Aldruscilla, 8 Deer Park Road, London, SW19 3UU Tel: (020) 8543 8710 Fax: (020) 8543 0605 E-mail: metal@aldruscilla.co.uk

NICKEL STOCKHOLDERS

Metals Group Ltd, Units 10-11 Walker Industrial Park, Guide, Blackburn, BB1 2QE Tel: (01254) 586700 Fax: (01254) 692063 E-mail: sales@metalsuk.com

Vicsteels Ltd, Suite 20 London House, 266 Fulham Road, London, SW10 9EL Tel: (020) 7795 2345 Fax: (020) 7795 0460 E-mail: vicsteels@aol.com

NIGHT VISION EQUIPMENT

▶ Action Optics, 16 Butts Ash Gardens, Hythe, Southampton, SO45 3BL Tel: (023) 8084 2801 Fax: (023) 8084 2801 E-mail: richard@actionoptics.co.uk

IntroVision, Units 6-7, The Glover Centre, 23-25 Bury Mead Road, Hitchin, Hertfordshire, SG4 1RP Tel: (01462) 459400 Fax: (01462) 459500 E-mail: introvision@ukonline.co.uk

NIGHT VISION EQUIPMENT – *continued*

Thomas Jacks Ltd, Unit B/2, The Bridge Business Centre, Timothys Bridge Road, Stratford Enterprise Park, Stratford-upon-Avon, Warwickshire, CV37 9HW Tel: (01789) 264100 Fax: (01789) 264200 E-mail: info@thomasjacks.co.uk

NIGHTDRESSES

Bentwood Ltd (Sterling Group), Atlantic Street, Broadheath, Altrincham, Cheshire, WA14 5FY Tel: 0161-926 7000 Fax: 0161-926 7029 E-mail: info@stirlinggroup.com

Direct Alarms, 11 Croft House Drive, Morley, Leeds, LS27 8NU Tel: 0113-289 7897 Fax: 0113-255 6919

Maun Hosiery Ltd, Intake Business Centre, Kirkland Avenue, Mansfield, Nottinghamshire, NG18 5QP Tel: (01623) 621860 Fax: (01623) 621860E-mail: nightwear@maunhosiery.co.uk

NIGHTWEAR

▶ Fimex Ltd, 4 Fimex Industrial Park, Victoria Road, Leeds, LS14 2LA Tel: 0113-218 8855 Fax: 0113-218 8866

▶ Glamourbox, Unit 6, 9 St. Johns street, Colchester, CO2 7NN Tel: 01206 570976 E-mail: sales@glamourbox.co.uk

▶ P J Heaven, PO Box 164, Beverley, North Humberside, HU17 7AP Tel: (01482) 860777 Fax: (01482) 860777 E-mail: sales@pjheaven.co.uk

▶ The Sleep Factory, PO Box 28859, London, SW13 0YX Tel: (020) 8332 7467

NIMONIC ALLOY STOCKHOLDERS, *See Nickel Alloy Stockholders*

NIOBIUM

Plansee Metals Ltd, 3 Lidstone Court, Uxbridge Road, George Green, Slough, SL3 6AG Tel: (01753) 576959 Fax: (01753) 577591

NITRIDE CASE HARDENING SERVICES

Beta Heat Treatment Ltd, Summerton Road, Oldbury, West Midlands, B69 2EL Tel: 0121-511 1190 Fax: 0121-511 1192 E-mail: beta@claytonholdings.com

Body Coat Heat Treatment, Stillington, Stockton-on-Tees, Cleveland, TS21 1LD Tel: (01740) 630353 Fax: (01740) 630075

NITRILE RUBBER (NBR) CABLE GLANDS

▶ Eland Cables Ltd, 120 Highgate Studios, 53-79 Highgate Road, London, NW5 1TL Tel: (020) 7241 8787 Fax: (020) 7241 8700 E-mail: sales@eland.co.uk

NITROGEN PRODUCTION PLANT

Boc Ltd, The Priestley Centre, 10 Priestley Road, Surrey Research Park, Guildford, Surrey, GU2 7XY Tel: (01483) 579857 Fax: (01483) 244658

Linde Cryoplants Ltd, Blackwater Way, Aldershot, Hampshire, GU12 4DR Tel: (01252) 331351 Fax: (01252) 343062 E-mail: info@linde-lcl.com

Linde Gas UK Ltd, Newfield Industrial Estate, High Street, Stoke-on-Trent, ST6 5PD Tel: (01782) 822058 Fax: (01782) 822350

NITROGEN SERVICES

B J Completion Services, Blackness Avenue, Altens Industrial Estate, Aberdeen, AB12 3PG Tel: (01224) 897929 Fax: (01224) 896118 E-mail: sales@bjservices.com

B J Services Co (U K) Ltd, Marine Base, Southtown Road, Great Yarmouth, Norfolk, NR31 0JJ Tel: (01493) 680680 Fax: (01493) 680780

NO LIGHT SECURITY CAMERAS

Soneck Electronics Ltd, 3A Cumberland Works, Wintersells Road, Byfleet, Surrey, KT14 7LF Tel: (01932) 355925 Fax: (01932) 336675 E-mail: soneck@tesco.net

NOISE ANALYSIS VIBRATION EQUIPMENT

Acsoft Ltd, Unit 8B, Wingbury Courtyard, Leighton Road, Wingrave, Aylesbury, Buckinghamshire, HP22 4LW Tel: (01296) 682686 Fax: (01296) 682860 E-mail: sales@acsoft.co.uk

NOISE AND VIBRATION CONTROL CONSULTANCY

Integrated Computer Services (Scotland) Ltd, 105a Shore Rd, Innellan, Dunoon, Argyll, PA23 7SR Tel: (01369) 830647 Fax: (01369) 830783 E-mail: ics_ltd@netcomuk.co.uk

▶ Isvr Consulting, University Road, Southampton, SO17 1BJ Tel: (023) 8059 2162 Fax: (023) 8059 2728 E-mail: consultancy@isvr.co.uk

Noise & Vibration Engineering Ltd, 1 Rothesay Avenue, London, SW20 8JU Tel: (020) 8542 9226 Fax: (020) 8540 8481 E-mail: enquiries@noise-vibration.co.uk

NOISE AND VIBRATION TRAINING

▶ Lessnoise Acoustic Engineers, Pheonix House, Sussex Close, Knaphill, Woking, Surrey, GU21 2RB Tel: (01483) 487575 Fax: (01483) 487575 E-mail: mail@lessnoise.net

NOISE ASSESSMENT OR AUDIOMETRY CONSULTANCY

Acoustic Control Systems, 64 Cromley Road, High Lane, Stockport, Cheshire, SK6 8BU Tel: (01663) 764409 Fax: (01663) 764409 E-mail: sales@acousticcontrol.co.uk

Acoustical Investigation & Research Organisation Ltd, Duxons Turn, Hemel Hempstead, Hertfordshire, HP2 4SB Tel: (01442) 247146 Fax: (01442) 256749 E-mail: airo@bcs.org.uk

Auricle Screening, 27 High Street, Petersfield, Hampshire, GU32 3JR Tel: (0800) 1804097 Fax: (01252) 720820 E-mail: iatkinson@noiseatwork.org

Equus Partnership Ltd, Park House, 15-19 Greenhill CR, Watford, WD18 8PH Tel: (01923) 213625 Fax: (01923) 213863 E-mail: acoustix@equuspartnership.co.uk

Hearing & Healthcare, 376 Buxton Road, Macclesfield, Cheshire, SK11 7ES Tel: (01625) 433108 Fax: (01625) 502323 E-mail: hearinghc@aol.com

Industrial Safety Inspections Ltd, Lea Lodge, Ansley, Nuneaton, Warwickshire, CV10 0QU Tel: (01675) 481779 Fax: (01675) 481780 E-mail: sales@isi-uk.net

▶ Isvr Consulting, University Road, Southampton, SO17 1BJ Tel: (023) 8059 2162 Fax: (023) 8059 2728 E-mail: consultancy@isvr.co.uk

MACAW Engineering Ltd, 1 Park Road, Gosforth Business Park, Newcastle upon Tyne, NE12 8DG Tel: 0191-216 4930 E-mail: info@macawengineering.com

NOISE CONTROL ACOUSTIC EQUIPMENT

Air Technology & Acoustics Ltd, 1451 Stratford Road, Hall Green, Birmingham, B28 9HT Tel: 0121-777 1847 Fax: 0121-777 3468

Cullum Detuners Ltd, Adams Close, Heanor Gate Industrial Park, Heanor, Derbyshire, DE75 7SW Tel: (01773) 717341 Fax: (01773) 760601 E-mail: sales.enquiries@cullum.co.uk

Keiss Contracts (UK) Ltd, 9-10 Cooper Drive, Braintree, Essex, CM7 2RF Tel: (01376) 326962 Fax: (01376) 322555 E-mail: keiss-contracts@btconnect.com

NOISE CONTROL CONSULTANTS OR DESIGNERS

A G S Noise Control Ltd, 16 Digby Drive, Melton Mowbray, Leicestershire, LE13 0RQ Tel: (01664) 568728 Fax: (01664) 481190 E-mail: sales@agsnoisecontrol.co.uk

Acia Engineering, 39 Garners Lane, Stockport, Cheshire, SK3 8SD Tel: 0161-487 2225 Fax: (0871) 9941778 E-mail: ian@acia-acoustics.co.uk

Acoustic Consultancy Services, 2 Belhaven Terrace Lane, Glasgow, G12 9LZ Tel: 0141-339 7536 Fax: 0141-339 7536 E-mail: andywatson@talk21.com

Acoustic Control Systems, 64 Cromley Road, High Lane, Stockport, Cheshire, SK6 8BU Tel: (01663) 764409 Fax: (01663) 764409 E-mail: sales@acousticcontrol.co.uk

Acoustic Design Consultancy, Aldham House, Lady La Industrial Estate, Hadleigh, Ipswich, IP7 6BQ Tel: (01473) 824452 Fax: (01473) 824408 E-mail: adc@acoustic.co.uk

Acoustic & Engineer Consultants Ltd, 1 Stockport Road, Marple, Stockport, Cheshire, SK6 6BD Tel: 0161-449 5900 Fax: 0161-449 5901 E-mail: kaw@aecltd.co.uk

Acoustic & Noise Partnership, Penburn House, 25a Upper Dock Street, Newport, Gwent, NP20 1DL Tel: (01633) 252957 Fax: (01633) 252958 E-mail: paul@acoustics-and-noise.co.uk

Air Technology & Acoustics Ltd, 1451 Stratford Road, Hall Green, Birmingham, B28 9HT Tel: 0121-777 1847 Fax: 0121-777 3468

ATCO Noise Management Ltd, PO Box 3, Newcastle Upon Tyne, NE20 9WY Tel: (01661) 825379 Fax: (01661) 825379 E-mail: jerry.kinver@atconoise.com

Belair Research Ltd, Broadway, Bourne, Cambridge, CB23 2TA Tel: (01954) 718366 Fax: (01954) 718355 E-mail: brl@acoustical.co.uk

Burau Verater Ltd, 91 Winchester Road, Chandlers Ford, Eastleigh, Hampshire, SO53 2GG Tel: (023) 8024 2300 Fax: (023) 8024 2399

C A D (Sales) Ltd, Unit 6, Waldegraves Business Park, West Mersea, Colchester, CO5 8SE Tel: (01206) 386611 Fax: (01206) 385959

Cole Jarman Associates, John Cree House, 24b High Street, Addlestone, Surrey, KT15 1TN Tel: (01932) 829007 Fax: (01932) 829003 E-mail: info@colejarman.com

Denis R Robinson & Associates, 169 Sherwood Avenue, Northampton, NN2 8TB Tel: (01604) 843807 Fax: (01604) 843807 E-mail: denis-rr@skynet.co.uk

Equus Partnership Ltd, Park House, 15-19 Greenhill CR, Watford, WD18 8PH Tel: (01923) 213625 Fax: (01923) 213863 E-mail: acoustix@equuspartnership.co.uk

Hann Tucker Associates Ltd, Duke House, Duke Street, Woking, Surrey, GU21 5BA Tel: (01483) 770595 Fax: (01483) 729565 E-mail: enquiries@hanntucker.co.uk

Hearing & Healthcare, 376 Buxton Road, Macclesfield, Cheshire, SK11 7ES Tel: (01625) 433108 Fax: (01625) 502323 E-mail: hearinghc@aol.com

Hepworth Acoustics Ltd, 5 Bankside, Crosfield Street, Warrington, WA1 1UP Tel: (01925) 579100 Fax: (01925) 579150 E-mail: enquiries@hepworth-acoustics.co.uk

I A C (Industrial Acoustics Company) Ltd, I A C House, Moorside Road, Winchester, Hampshire, SO23 7US Tel: (01962) 873000 Fax: (01962) 873123 E-mail: info@iacl.co.uk

Keiss Contracts (UK) Ltd, 9-10 Cooper Drive, Braintree, Essex, CM7 2RF Tel: (01376) 326962 Fax: (01376) 322555 E-mail: keiss-contracts@btconnect.com

Martec Environmental Consultants Ltd, Waterbrow Wood, Gressingham, Lancaster, LA2 8LX Tel: (01524) 222000 Fax: (07970) 137469 E-mail: sales@noise.sh

Midland Environmental Laboratories, Unit D17 Forge Lane, Minworth Industrial Park, Minworth, Sutton Coldfield, West Midlands, B76 1AH Tel: 0121-351 6469 Fax: 0121-351 6469

Peter Moore, 20 Holland Close, Shorne, Gravesend, Kent, DA12 3EH Tel: (01474) 824177 Fax: (01474) 824177

Noise & Vibration Engineering Ltd, 1 Rothesay Avenue, London, SW20 8JU Tel: (020) 8542 9226 Fax: (020) 8540 8481 E-mail: enquiries@noise-vibration.co.uk

▶ Peninsular Acoustics, 114 Shrewsbury Road, Prenton, Merseyside, CH43 8SP Tel: 0151-652 6270 Fax: 0151-652 6270 E-mail: noise@btconnect.com

R M S Vibration Test Laboratory, 26 Coder Road, Ludlow Business Park, Ludlow, Shropshire, SY8 1XE Tel: (01584) 861395 Fax: (01584) 861395 E-mail: rms.vibes@avignon.enta.net

Thornavon Ltd, Unit 4 Brook Street Business Centre, Brook Street, Colchester, CO1 2UZ Tel: (01206) 796888 Fax: (01206) 796889 E-mail: thornavon@tiscali.co.uk

NOISE CONTROL ENGINEERING

Euro Acoustics Holdings Ltd, 54 Trevean Way, Newquay, Cornwall, TR7 1TW Tel: (01637) 852172 Fax: (01637) 853960 E-mail: alan@euro-acoustics.com

NOISE CONTROL EQUIPMENT OR SYSTEMS ENGINEERS OR FABRICATORS

A G S Noise Control Ltd, 16 Digby Drive, Melton Mowbray, Leicestershire, LE13 0RQ Tel: (01664) 568728 Fax: (01664) 481190 E-mail: sales@agsnoisecontrol.co.uk

A1 Metal Fabrications, 22 Boston Road, Leicester, LE4 1AU Tel: 0116-235 0444 Fax: 0116-235 0444

Alter Air, 6 Holly Grove, Basildon, Essex, SS16 6SB Tel: (01268) 540862 Fax: (01268) 540862

ATCO Noise Management Ltd, PO Box 3, Newcastle Upon Tyne, NE20 9WY Tel: (01661) 825379 Fax: (01661) 825379 E-mail: jerry.kinver@atconoise.com

Bradgate Containers Ltd, Leicester Road, Shepshed, Loughborough, Leicestershire, LE12 9EG Tel: (01509) 508678 Fax: (01509) 503224 E-mail: sales@bradgate.co.uk

C A D (Sales) Ltd, Unit 6, Waldegraves Business Park, West Mersea, Colchester, CO5 8SE Tel: (01206) 386611 Fax: (01206) 385959

Contrasound Ltd, Unit 15 Rye Industrial Park, Rye Harbour Road, Rye, East Sussex, TN31 7TE Tel: (01797) 227070 Fax: (01797) 225969

Cullum Detuners Ltd, Adams Close, Heanor Gate Industrial Park, Heanor, Derbyshire, DE75 7SW Tel: (01773) 717341 Fax: (01773) 760601 E-mail: sales.enquiries@cullum.co.uk

D 4 S Fabrications Ltd, 19 Morses Lane, Brightlingsea, Colchester, CO7 0SF Tel: (01206) 303668 Fax: (01206) 304835 E-mail: ab@d4sfabrication.co.uk

Environmental Silencing Ltd, D5 Fleming Road, Hinckley, Leicestershire, LE10 3DU Tel: (01455) 617067 Fax: (01455) 615633 E-mail: contact@enviromental-silencing.fsnet.co.uk

Envirosound Ltd, 8 Murrell Green Business Park, London Road, Hook, Hampshire, RG27 9GR Tel: (01256) 760775 Fax: (01256) 760754 E-mail: sales@envirosound.co.uk

Galloway Acoustics, Low Mill Lane, Ravensthorpe Industrial Estate, Dewsbury, West Yorkshire, WF13 3LN Tel: (01924) 498818 Fax: (01924) 498414 E-mail: sales.dewsbury@gallowaygroup.co.uk

Hodgson & Hodgson Group, Audio House, Progress Road, Sands Industrial Estate, High Wycombe, Buckinghamshire, HP12 4JD Tel: (01494) 519000 Fax: (01494) 465274 E-mail: ecomax@easynet.co.uk

I A C (Industrial Acoustics Company) Ltd, I A C House, Moorside Road, Winchester, Hampshire, SO23 7US Tel: (01962) 873000 Fax: (01962) 873123 E-mail: info@iacl.co.uk

Krantz Systems Ltd, 61-67 Rectory Road, Wivenhoe, Colchester, CO7 9ES Tel: (01206) 827171 Fax: (01206) 826936 E-mail: kjr@d4s.co.uk

Noico Ltd, Patrick House, Station Road, Hook, Hampshire, RG27 9HU Tel: (01256) 766207 Fax: (01256) 768413 E-mail: sales@noico.co.uk

Noise Insulation & Measurement Services, High Darkdale House, Slaggyford, Brampton, Cumbria, CA8 7NW Tel: (01434) 381394 Fax: (01434) 382634 E-mail: noise@cwcom.net

Noise Seal Ltd, Unit 20 Digby Drive, Leicester Road Industrial Estate, Melton Mowbray, Leicestershire, LE13 0RQ Tel: (01664) 480678 Fax: (01664) 480678 E-mail: sales@noiseseal.com

Pennine Forge, Peel Park Works, Peel Park View, Bradford, West Yorkshire, BD3 0JY Tel: (01274) 642248 Fax: (01274) 634132

Powertherm Contracts Insulation Ltd, C Crown Works, Rotherham Road, Beighton, Sheffield, S20 1AH Tel: 0114-288 9119 Fax: 0114-288 9882 E-mail: powertherm@aol.com

Proto Associates, 26 Fox Lane, Hilltop, Bromsgrove, Worcestershire, B61 7NL Tel: (01527) 831567 Fax: (01527) 831567 E-mail: aturchyn@globalnet.co.uk

Thornavon Ltd, Unit 4 Brook Street Business Centre, Brook Street, Colchester, CO1 2UZ Tel: (01206) 796888 Fax: (01206) 796889 E-mail: thornavon@tiscali.co.uk

NOISE CONTROL EXHAUST SYSTEMS

A & I (Peco) Acoustics Ltd, 100 Sandford Street, Birkenhead, Merseyside, CH41 1AZ Tel: 0151-647 9015 Fax: 0151-666 1805 E-mail: sales@peco.co.uk

NOISE CONTROL MATERIALS OR PRODUCTS

Acoustic Enclosures Co. Ltd, Unit 3 Waldergraves Business Park, Waldergraves Lane, West Mersey, Colchester, CO5 8SE Tel: (01206) 384377 Fax: (01206) 384611 E-mail: acoustic.enclosures@btinternet.com

▶ Acousticabs Industrial Noise Control Ltd, Unit 52, Pocklington Industrial Estate, Pocklington, York, YO42 1NR Tel: (01759) 305266 Fax: (01759) 305268 E-mail: info@acousticabs.com

Alkie Ltd, Millwood View, Stalybridge, Cheshire, SK15 3AU Tel: 0161-338 8070 Fax: 0161-338 3191 E-mail: alkie.ltd@virgin.net

C E P Cladding Ltd, Wainwright Close, St. Leonards-On-Sea, East Sussex, TN38 9PP Tel: (01424) 852641 Fax: (01424) 852797 E-mail: claddings@cepgroup.co.uk

Contrasound Ltd, Unit 15 Rye Industrial Park, Rye Harbour Road, Rye, East Sussex, TN31 7TE Tel: (01797) 227070 Fax: (01797) 225969

Envirosound Ltd, 8 Murrell Green Business Park, London Road, Hook, Hampshire, RG27 9GR Tel: (01256) 760775 Fax: (01256) 760754 E-mail: sales@envirosound.co.uk

SilentCel, 137 Percy Avenue, Kingsgate, Broadstairs, Kent, CT10 3LE Tel: (07855) 358230 Fax: (01843) 603142 E-mail: enquiries@silentcel.co.uk

Web Fabrications Ltd, Gledholt Business Park, Allen Row, Paddock, Huddersfield, HD1 4SB Tel: (01484) 545333 Fax: (01484) 422194

NOISE CONTROL SERVICES

A G S Noise Control Ltd, 16 Digby Drive, Melton Mowbray, Leicestershire, LE13 0RQ Tel: (01664) 568728 Fax: (01664) 481190 E-mail: sales@agsnoisecontrol.co.uk

Acia Engineering, 39 Garners Lane, Stockport, Cheshire, SK3 8SD Tel: 0161-487 2225 Fax: (0871) 9941778 E-mail: ian@acia-acoustics.co.uk

▶ Acousticabs Industrial Noise Control Ltd, Unit 52, Pocklington Industrial Estate, Pocklington, York, YO42 1NR Tel: (01759) 305266 Fax: (01759) 305268 E-mail: info@acousticabs.com

Allaway Acoustics Ltd, 1 Queens Road, Hertford, SG14 1EN Tel: (01992) 550825 Fax: (01992) 554982 E-mail: enquiries@allawayacoustics.co.uk

Contrasound Ltd, Unit 15 Rye Industrial Park, Rye Harbour Road, Rye, East Sussex, TN31 7TE Tel: (01797) 227070 Fax: (01797) 225969

Deane Austin Associates, PO Box 274, Aldershot, Hampshire, GU11 1TT Tel: (01252) 333727 Fax: (01252) 337266 E-mail: daa@tacitus.co.uk

Gill Insulation Eastern Ltd, 39 Boss Hall Road, Ipswich, IP1 5BN Tel: (01473) 462822 Fax: (01473) 241153 E-mail: jon@gilleastern.co.uk

Hodgson & Hodgson Group, Audio House, Progress Road, Sands Industrial Estate, High Wycombe, Buckinghamshire, HP12 4JD Tel: (01494) 519000 Fax: (01494) 465274 E-mail: ecomax@easynet.co.uk

Nendle Acoustics Ltd, 153 High Street, Aldershot, Hampshire, GU11 1TT Tel: (01252) 344222 Fax: (01252) 333782 E-mail: info@nendle.co.uk

Noico Ltd, Patrick House, Station Road, Hook, Hampshire, RG27 9HU Tel: (01256) 766207 Fax: (01256) 768413 E-mail: sales@noico.co.uk

Noise & Pulsation Control Ltd, 5 King Edwards Road, Ruislip, Middlesex, HA4 7AE Tel: (01895) 676215 Fax: (01895) 676215 E-mail: noiseandpulsationuk@btinternet.com

Pennine Forge, Peel Park Works, Peel Park View, Bradford, West Yorkshire, BD3 0JY Tel: (01274) 642248 Fax: (01274) 634132

Sound Research Laboratories Ltd, Holbrook House, Holbrook Hall Park, Little Waldingfield, Sudbury, Suffolk, CO10 0TH Tel: (01787) 247595 Fax: (01787) 248420 E-mail: srl@soundresearch.co.uk

Sypol Ltd, Elsinore House, Buckingham Street, Aylesbury, Buckinghamshire, HP20 2NQ Tel: (01296) 415715 Fax: (01296) 397106 E-mail: helpme@sypol.com

Vibronoise Ltd, 62 Talbot Rd, Old Trafford, Manchester, M16 0PN Tel: 0161-428 3100 Fax: 0161-428 1198 E-mail: info@virbronoise.co.uk

NOISE CONTROL VISION PANELS OR WINDOWS

Noise Seal Ltd, Unit 20 Digby Drive, Leicester Road Industrial Estate, Melton Mowbray, Leicestershire, LE13 0RQ Tel: (01664) 480678 Fax: (01664) 480678 E-mail: sales@noiseseal.com

Selectaglaze Ltd, 1 Campfield Road, St. Albans, Hertfordshire, AL1 5HT Tel: (01727) 837271 Fax: (01727) 844053 E-mail: enquiries@selectaglaze.co.uk

NOISE INSULATION WINDOWS

Griffin Windows Ltd, Unit 37 Abergorki Industrial Estate, Treorchy, Mid Glamorgan, CF42 6DL Tel: (01443) 777333 Fax: (01443) 776773 E-mail: suzm@griffinwindows.co.uk

Selectaglaze Ltd, 1 Campfield Road, St. Albans, Hertfordshire, AL1 5HT Tel: (01727) 837271 Fax: (01727) 844053 E-mail: enquiries@selectaglaze.co.uk

NOISE MEASUREMENT EQUIPMENT

24 Acoustics, 24 Bell Street, Romsey, Hampshire, SO51 8GW Tel: 01794 515999 Fax: (0871) 2420156 E-mail: info@24acoustics.co.uk

NOISE MONITORING/ MEASURING INSTRUMENTATION/EQUIPMENT

Acsoft Ltd, Unit 8B, Wingbury Courtyard, Leighton Road, Wingrave, Aylesbury, Buckinghamshire, HP22 4LW Tel: (01296) 682686 Fax: (01296) 682860 E-mail: sales@acsoft.co.uk

PC Werth, 45 Nightingale Lane, London, SW12 8SP Tel: (020) 8675 5151 Fax: (020) 8772 2701 E-mail: pcwerth@pcwerth.co.uk

NON CHEMICAL PAINT STRIPPING EQUIPMENT

Benflow UK, 395 Crewe Road, Wistaston, Nantwich, Cheshire, CW5 6NW Tel: (07813) 158317 Fax: (01270) 664551 E-mail: enquiries@belflow.co.uk

N.A. Robson Ltd, Robson Way, Highfurlong, Blackpool, FY3 7PP Tel: (01253) 393406 Fax: (01253) 300160 E-mail: sales@robson.uk.com

Surface Dynamics (UK) Ltd, 348 SPON LANE SOUTH, WEST BROMWICH, WEST MIDLANDS, B70 6AZ Tel: (0121) 553 7772 Fax: (0121) 553 4746 E-mail: sales@surfacedynamics.co.uk

NON CHEMICAL WATER CONDITIONING PLANT

Bio-Claire International Ltd, 48 Bathurst Walk, Iver, Buckinghamshire, SL0 9BH Tel: (01753) 774778 Fax: (01753) 774788

▶ Calmag Ltd, Unit 3-6, Crown Works, Bradford Road, Sandbeds, Keighley, West Yorkshire, BD20 5LN Tel: (01535) 210320 Fax: (01535) 210321 E-mail: sales@calmagltd.com

NON CONTACT INSPECTION EQUIPMENT

Cognex UK, Sunningdale House, Caldecotte Lake Drive, Caldecotte, Milton Keynes, MK7 8LF Tel: (0800) 0180018 Fax: (01908) 392463 E-mail: sales@cognex.co.uk

Inex Inspection System, Unit 14 First Avenue, Trafford Park, Manchester, M17 1JZ Tel: 0161-876 1700 Fax: 0161-876 1701

Planer plc, 110 Windmill Road, Sunbury-on-Thames, Middlesex, TW16 7HD Tel: (01932) 755000 Fax: (01932) 755001 E-mail: sales@planer.co.uk

Wyko Industrial Distribution Ltd, Venture Way, Priorswood Industrial Estate, Taunton, Somerset, TA2 8DE Tel: (01823) 271221 Fax: (01823) 289675 E-mail: scantron@scantron-net.co.uk

NON CONTACT MEASURING EQUIPMENT

Hexagon Metrology, Halesfield 13, Telford, Shropshire, TF7 4PL Tel: (01952) 681300 Fax: (01952) 681311 E-mail: enquiry@hexmet.co.uk

Wyko Industrial Distribution Ltd, Venture Way, Priorswood Industrial Estate, Taunton, Somerset, TA2 8DE Tel: (01823) 271221 Fax: (01823) 289675 E-mail: scantron@scantron-net.co.uk

NON CONTACT TEMPERATURE MEASURING INSTRUMENTS

Instruments Direct (Services) Ltd, Unit 8 The Courtyard, Stenson Road, Coalville, Leicestershire, LE67 4jp Tel: (01530) 832500 Fax: (01530) 817087E-mail: sales@inds.co.uk

NON CONTACT THERMOCOUPLES

Exergen Corp, Tollgate House, 69-71 High Street, Harpenden, Hertfordshire, AL5 2SL Tel: (01582) 461123 Fax: (01582) 461117 E-mail: sales@qhigroup.com

NON DESTRUCTIVE TEST (NDT) EQUIPMENT/SYSTEMS MANUFRS

A D I Supplies & Services, Block 2, Rosendale Way, Blantyre, Glasgow, G72 0NJ Tel: (01698) 829991 Fax: (01698) 829992 E-mail: sales@adi-supplies.co.uk

Ardrox Engineering, Godiva Place, Coventry, CV1 5PN Tel: (024) 7655 9986 Fax: (024) 7655 1402 E-mail: sales@ardroxengineering.com

Baugh & Weedon Ltd, Beech Business Park, Tillington Road, Hereford, HR4 9QJ Tel: (01432) 267671 Fax: (01432) 359017 E-mail: sales@bandwndt.co.uk

Bodycote, Unit 6-7 Furlong Business Centre, The Furlong, Berry Hill Industrial Estate, Droitwich, Worcestershire, WR9 9AH Tel: (01905) 774861 Fax: (01905) 776598 E-mail: droitwich@bodycote-mt.com

E M Inspection Co Ltd, 11-18 Victoria Street, Wigston, Leicestershire, LE18 1AJ Tel: 0116-288 3974

Fischer Instrumentation (GB) Ltd, Department K, Gordleton Industrial Park, Hannah Way, Pennington, Lymington, Hampshire, SO41 8JD Tel: (01590) 684100 Fax: (01590) 684110 E-mail: mail@fischergb.co.uk

G E Inspection Technologies, Inspec Ho, 129-135 Camp Rd, St. Albans, Herts, AL1 5HL Tel: (01727) 795500 Fax: (01727) 795400

Indentec Hardness Testing Machines Ltd, Lye Valley Industrial Estate, Bromley Street, Lye, Stourbridge, West Midlands, DY9 8HX Tel: (01384) 896949 Fax: (01384) 424470 E-mail: mail@indentec.demon.co.uk

J M E Ltd, Electron House, Old Nelson St, Lowestoft, Suffolk, NR32 1EQ Tel: (01502) 500969 Fax: (01502) 511932 E-mail: sales@jme.co.uk

Johnson & Allen Ltd, Neocol Works, Smithfield, Sheffield, S3 7AR Tel: 0114-273 8066 Fax: 0114-272 9842 E-mail: info@johnsonandallen.co.uk

Magnaflux, Faraday Road, Dorcan, Swindon, SN3 5HE Tel: (01793) 524566 Fax: (01793) 619498 E-mail: sales@magnaflux.co.uk

Marposs Ltd, Leofric Business Park, Progress Way, Binley Industrial Estate, Coventry, CV3 2TJ Tel: (024) 7688 4950 Fax: (024) 7663 6622 E-mail: sales@uk.marposs.com

Merit Lowson & French Ltd, The Barn, Wharfe Bank Terrace, Tadcaster, North Yorkshire, LS24 9AN Tel: (01937) 835225 Fax: (01937) 530225 E-mail: lowson@mlfltd.fsbussines.co.uk

Meritronics Ltd, Otterden Place, Otterden, Faversham, Kent, ME13 0BT Tel: (01795) 890341 Fax: (01795) 890341 E-mail: contact@meritronics.co.uk

Olympus N D T Ltd, 12 Nightingale Court, Nightingale Close, Rotherham, South Yorkshire, S60 2AB Tel: (01709) 836115 Fax: (01709) 835177 E-mail: info.uk@olympusndt.com

Phoenix Inspection Systems Ltd, 46 Melford Court, Hardwick Grange, Woolston, Warrington, WA1 4RZ Tel: (01925) 826000 Fax: (01925) 838788 E-mail: pryan@phoenixisl.co.uk

Rhopoint Instrumentation, 12 Beeching Road, Bexhill-on-Sea, East Sussex, TN39 3LG Tel: (01424) 730600 Fax: (01424) 730600 E-mail: enquiries@rhopointinstruments.com

Sibert Technology, 2a Merrow Business Centre, Merrow Lane, Guildford, Surrey, GU4 7WA Tel: (01483) 440724 Fax: (01483) 440727 E-mail: NDT@sibtec.com

Staveley NDT Technologies, 3 Cromwell Park, Banbury Road, Chipping Norton, Oxfordshire, OX7 5SR Tel: (01608) 642001 Fax: (01608) 644752 E-mail: sales@sndt.co.uk

T W L Force Systems, 15 Old Farm Lane, Fareham, Hampshire, PO14 2DB Tel: (01329) 665186 Fax: (01329) 668177 E-mail: sales@twlforce.co.uk

Technology Design Ltd, Wharton Park House, Nat Lane, Winsford, Cheshire, CW7 3BS Tel: (01606) 590123 Fax: (01606) 591253 E-mail: sales@technologydesign.com

Testrade Ltd, Unit 22 Olds Close, Watford, WD18 9RU Tel: (01923) 720222 Fax: (01923) 720444 E-mail: sales@testrade.co.uk

Ultrafine Technology Ltd, Unit 14 Brook Lane Business Centre, Brook Lane North, Brentford, Middlesex, TW8 0PP Tel: (020) 8569 9920 Fax: (020) 8569 9649 E-mail: sales@ultrafinetechnology.co.uk

Validation Centre, Unit 9 Sinclair Court, Great Yarmouth, Norfolk, NR31 0NH Tel: (01493) 443800 Fax: (01493) 443900 E-mail: sales@tvcalx.co.uk

NON DESTRUCTIVE TESTING (NDT)

▶ Insight NDT Ltd, 3 Kilnhurst Business Park, Glasshouse Road, Kilnhurst, Mexborough, South Yorkshire, S64 5TH Tel: (01709) 571710 Fax: (01709) 571712 E-mail: info@insightndt.co.uk

▶ Resource N D T, 5 Sideley, Kegworth, Derby, DE74 2FJ Tel: (01509) 673084

NON DESTRUCTIVE TESTING (NDT) AND INSPECTION

A W L Inspection & N D T Services Ltd, Unit 34, Royal Industrial Estate, Jarrow, Tyne & Wear, NE32 3HR Tel: 0191-430 0837 Fax: 0191-430 0837 E-mail: awl_ndt@btconnect.com

Argos Inspection Co. Ltd, Tower Road, Washington, Tyne & Wear, NE37 2SH Tel: 0191-417 7707 Fax: 0191-415 4979 E-mail: ndt@argosinspection.com

Ashton & Moore Ltd, 12 Smith Street, Hockley, Birmingham, B19 3EX Tel: 0845 618 8196 Fax: 0845 618 8197 E-mail: sales@ashton-moore.co.uk

Axiom NDT Services Ltd, 72-74 Clifford Lane, Glasgow, G51 1NR Tel: 0141-427 3302 Fax: 0141-427 7240 E-mail: enquiries@axiomndt.co.uk

Bodycote, Unit 6-7 Furlong Business Centre, The Furlong, Berry Hill Industrial Estate, Droitwich, Worcestershire, WR9 9AH Tel: (01905) 774861 Fax: (01905) 776598 E-mail: droitwich@bodycote-mt.com

Bodycote Materials Testing, 12 High March, High March Industrial Estate, Daventry, Northamptonshire, NN11 4HB Tel: (01327) 702964 Fax: (01327) 871119 E-mail: daventry@bodycote.com

C A N (Offshore) Ltd, Hareness Road, Altens, Aberdeen, AB12 3LE Tel: (01224) 870100 Fax: (01224) 876015 E-mail: mailserve@cangroup.net

C M L Group Ltd, Unit 5 Wheatland Business Park, Wheatland Lane, Wallasey, Merseyside, CH44 7ER Tel: (0151-631 5600 Fax: 0151-631 5601 E-mail: enquiries@cml-group.com

Capital Inspection Services, 3 Poyle Technical Centre, Willow Road, Colnbrook, Slough, SL3 0DP Tel: (01753) 684896 Fax: (01753) 681739E-mail: cap.inspection@btconnect.com

Charlwood Aquatics, Horley Road, Charlwood, Horley, Surrey, RH6 0BJ Tel: (01293) 776377 Fax: (01293) 786730

Cobalt NDT Ltd, 2 Eccleston Park Trade Centre, Prescot Road, St. Helens, Merseyside, WA10 3BZ Tel: (01744) 734321 Fax: (01744) 734321

Dinsley Devices Ltd, Ivy House, Streatlam, Barnard Castle, County Durham, DL12 8TZ Tel: (01388) 710734 Fax: (01833) 637971 E-mail: dinsearch@hotmail.com

Ductile Steel Processors, Planetary Industrial Estate, Planetary Road, Willenhall, West Midlands, WV13 3XP Tel: (01902) 303230 Fax: (01902) 303231

E M & I (Marine) Ltd, 18 Fairburn Terrace, Dyce, Aberdeen, AB21 7DT Tel: (01224) 771077 Fax: (01224) 771049E-mail: info@emiall.co.uk

E M Inspection Co Ltd, 11-18 Victoria Street, Wigston, Leicestershire, LE18 1AJ Tel: 0116-288 3974

Engineering Test Services Ltd, Tofts Farm Industrial Estate West, Brenda Road, Hartlepool, Cleveland, TS25 2BQ Tel: (01429) 233951 Fax: (01429) 865447 E-mail: inspection@engtestservicesltd.fsnet.co.uk

Format Quality Assurance Services Ltd, 25-27 Brindley Road, Reginald Road Industrial Estate, St. Helens, Merseyside, WA9 4HY Tel: (01744) 816225 Fax: (01744) 820161 E-mail: bjjformat@msn.com

Frazer-Nash NDT Ltd, Bradshaw Street, Heywood, Lancashire, OL10 1PL Tel: (01706) 628794 Fax: (01706) 627289 E-mail: enquiries@frazer-nash-btconnect.com

Haworth Castings Ltd, Budds Lane, Romsey, Hampshire, SO51 0HA Tel: (01794) 512685 Fax: (01794) 830086 E-mail: sales@haworthcastings.com

I M F Technical Services Ltd, Unit 5 50 Cotton Street, Aberdeen, AB11 5EE Tel: (01224) 210147 Fax: (01224) 572752 E-mail: ian@imftech.freeserve.co.uk

Inidam Ltd, Budds Lane Industrial Estate, Romsey, Hampshire, SO51 0HA Tel: (01794) 830388 Fax: (01794) 830066 E-mail: ndt@inidam.com

▶ Insight NDT Ltd, 3 Kilnhurst Business Park, Glasshouse Road, Kilnhurst, Mexborough, South Yorkshire, S64 5TH Tel: (01709) 571710 Fax: (01709) 571712 E-mail: info@insightndt.co.uk

J D Jackson (Electronics), Eastfield Labs, Danethorpe Hill, Newark, Nottinghamshire, NG24 2PD Tel: (01636) 705718 Fax: (01636) 610120 E-mail: sales@jacksonelectronics.co.uk

James Fisher Inspection & Measurement Services Ltd, Factory Road, Sandycroft, Deeside, Clwyd, CH5 2QJ Tel: (01244) 520058 Fax: (01244) 535440 E-mail: sales@ndt-inspection.co.uk

JPB Trading Ltd, Martindale, Cannock, Staffordshire, WS11 7XN Tel: (01543) 462676 Fax: (01543) 571368 E-mail: sales@eurospection.co.uk

Lloyds Register, Denburn House, Union Terrace, Aberdeen, AB10 1NN Tel: (01224) 267400 Fax: (01224) 267401 E-mail: enquiries@lr.org

Material Inspection Ltd, Wincomblee Road, Walker, Newcastle upon Tyne, NE6 3QQ Tel: 0191-295 4733 Fax: 0191-295 4723 E-mail: office@materialinspection.co.uk

Material Measurements Ltd, Avenue One, Witney, Oxfordshire, OX28 4XS Tel: (01993) 778522 Fax: (01993) 708673 E-mail: ph@material-measurements.co.uk

Material Measurements Group Ltd, 61 Albert Road North, Reigate, Surrey, RH2 9RS Tel: (01737) 222211 Fax: (01737) 224333 E-mail: enquiries@material-measurements.co.uk

Co Mech Ltd, Victory House, Victory Road, Derby, DE24 8EL Tel: (01332) 275820 Fax: (01332) 275817 E-mail: sales@comech.co.uk

Medcrest Ltd, Valley Road, Wombwell, Barnsley, South Yorkshire, S73 0BS Tel: (01226) 759360 Fax: (01226) 757392 E-mail: general@medcrest.co.uk

N D T Consultants Ltd, Siskin Drive, Middlemarch Business Park, Coventry, CV3 4FJ Tel: (024) 7651 1151 Fax: (024) 7651 1696 E-mail: sales@ndt-consultants.co.uk

N D T Electronics, 30 Royal Industrial Estate, Jarrow, Tyne & Wear, NE32 3HR Tel: 0191-428 0962 Fax: 0191-428 0904 E-mail: ian.armson@ndtelectronicservices.com

NDT Services Ltd, 5 Side Ley, Kegworth, Derby, DE74 2FJ Tel: (01509) 680088 Fax: (01509) 680080 E-mail: sales@ndtservices.co.uk

Oilfield Testing Services, Viking Road, Great Yarmouth, Norfolk, NR31 0NU Tel: (01493) 440555 Fax: (01493) 440737 E-mail: ots@oilfieldtesting.com

Omiran Ltd, Units 1-2, James Carter Road, Mildenhall, Bury St. Edmunds, Suffolk, IP28 7DE Tel: (01638) 716748 Fax: (01638) 716779 E-mail: sales@omiran.co.uk

P M I Services, Glen Villa, Ashbrooke Range, Sunderland, SR2 9BP Tel: 0191-528 1469 Fax: 0191-511 0369

P T S - Total Quality Management, Verulam Road, Stafford, ST16 3EA Tel: (01785) 250706 Fax: (01785) 250906

NON DESTRUCTIVE TESTING (NDT) AND INSPECTION – *continued*

Physical Acoustics Ltd, Norman Way, Over, Cambridge, CB24 5QE Tel: (01954) 231612 Fax: (01954) 231102E-mail: info@pacuk.co.uk
Scientific & Technical Services Ltd, 3 Summerhill, Blaydon-on-Tyne, Tyne & Wear, NE21 4JR Tel: 0191-414 7801 Fax: 0191-414 1245 E-mail: sts@stsltd.fsnet.co.uk
Scot Test Ltd, 12 Thomas Street, Paisley, Renfrewshire, PA1 2RE Tel: 0141-887 7925 Fax: 0141-889 0665 E-mail: scot-testltd@btconnect.com
Sendt Ltd, Littlebrook Business Centre, Littlebrook Manorway, Dartford, DA1 5PZ Tel: (01322) 287347 Fax: (01322) 287493 E-mail: tony.blake@sendt.freeserve.co.uk
Spree Engineering Ltd, The Laboratory, Castle Road, Sittingbourne, Kent, ME10 3RL Tel: (01795) 421441 Fax: (01795) 470479
Technical Inspection Services UK Ltd, 11 Somerset Road, Clevedon, Avon, BS21 6DP Tel: (01275) 871130 Fax: (01275) 875917 E-mail: info@tis-uk.co.uk
Ultrarad Technical Services Hull Ltd, Holderness House, Staithes Road, Hedon, Hull, HU12 8DX Tel: (01482) 324495 Fax: (01482) 620016 E-mail: uts.hull@virgin.net
Ultrascan Non-Destructive Testing Ltd, Unit 39, Canal Bridge Enterprise Centre, Meadow Lane, Ellesmere Port, CH65 4EH Tel: 0151-357 3069 Fax: 0151-355 2490 E-mail: scantek@ultrascan-ndt.com
Ultraspection Ltd, 13 St. Josephs Close, Olney, Buckinghamshire, MK46 5HD Tel: (01234) 714092 Fax: (01234) 714192 E-mail: ultraspection@btinternet.com
United Bright Bar Co. Ltd, Station Road, Four Ashes, Wolverhampton, WV10 7DG Tel: (01902) 791010 Fax: (01902) 790044 E-mail: sales@unitedbrightbar.co.uk
Visual Testing Services Ltd, PO Box 424, Peterborough, PE3 9DH Tel: (01733) 267285 Fax: (01733) 261356 E-mail: insight@vtservices.co.uk

NON DESTRUCTIVE TESTING (NDT), EDDY CURRENT

G E Inspection Technologies, Inspec Ho, 129-135 Camp Rd, St. Albans, Herts, AL1 5HL Tel: (01727) 795500 Fax: (01727) 795400
Independent Integrity Inspection, Unit 13 Oak Tree Business Park, Spitfire Way, South Marston, Swindon, SN3 4TX Tel: (01793) 836150 Fax: (01793) 836151 E-mail: problem.solved@indei.co.uk

NON DESTRUCTIVE TESTING (NDT), SUBSEA/UNDERWATER

Nevis Centre, An Aird, Fort William, Inverness-Shire, PH33 6AN Tel: (01397) 700707 Fax: (01397) 700708 E-mail: info@theunderwatercentre.co.uk

NON EXECUTIVE DIRECTOR SEARCH OR RECRUITMENT

▶ Barnett Consulting Services Ltd, Providence House, River Street, Windsor, Berkshire, SL4 1QT Tel: (01753) 856723 Fax: (01753) 866297 E-mail: barnettgp@aol.com
Digital Video Interview Services, The City Arc, Curtain Court, 7 Curtain Road, London, EC2A 3LT Tel: 0207 1009270 Fax: 0207 1009310 E-mail: info@digitalvideointerview.co.uk
Edward Drummond & Co Ltd., Westpoint 78 Queens Road, Clifton, Bristol, BS8 1QX Tel: 0117 9858755 E-mail: info@edwarddrummond.com
▶ Goldeneye Executive Resourcing Ltd, Flat 6 Kings Court, 40 Hersham Road, Walton-on-Thames, Surrey, KT12 1JE Tel: (07779) 134007

NON FERROUS METAL BUSHES

M & C Engineering, Unit 12 West Bowhouse Workshops, Girdle Toll, Irvine, Ayrshire, KA11 1BU Tel: (01294) 215986 Fax: (01294) 215986

NON FERROUS METAL CASTINGS, *See also headings for particular types*

Alfa, Rockwood, Keldholme, York, YO62 6NB Tel: (01751) 432953 Fax: (01751) 432518
Archibald Young Brassfounders Ltd, Motherwell Business Centre, Albert Street, Motherwell, Lanarkshire, ML1 1PR Tel: (01698) 263165 Fax: (01698) 263211 E-mail: enquiries@archibaldyoung.co.uk
Archway Brown Ltd, 43 Bury Mead Road, Hitchin, Hertfordshire, SG5 1RT Tel: (01462) 432139 Fax: (01462) 420102
B & C Non-Ferrous Foundry Ltd, Unit 3, Bedwas House Industrial Estate, Caerphilly, Mid Glamorgan, CF83 8DW Tel: (029) 2088 6871 Fax: (029) 2086 9916 E-mail: ceri@bcfoundry.co.uk
British Engines Ltd, St Peters, Newcastle upon Tyne, NE6 1BS Tel: 0191-265 9091 Fax: 0191-276 3244 E-mail: sales@bel.co.uk
Brooks Crownhill Patternmakers Ltd, North Way, Andover, Hampshire, SP10 5AZ Tel: (01264) 355136 Fax: (01264) 332145 E-mail: info@bcplimited.co.uk
Brooks Crownhill Patternmakers Ltd, North Way, Andover, Hampshire, SP10 5AZ Tel: (01264) 355136 Fax: (01264) 332145 E-mail: info@bcplimited.co.uk
Canlin Castings Ltd, Star Foundry, North Street, Langley Mill, Nottingham, NG16 4BS Tel: (01773) 715412 Fax: (01773) 530434 E-mail: sales@canlincastings.co.uk
Cannop Foundry 1981 Ltd, Forest Vale Indust Estate, Crabtree Road, Forest Vale Industrial Estate, Cinderford, Gloucestershire, GL14 2YQ Tel: (01594) 822143 Fax: (01594) 824200 E-mail: sales@cannop.co.uk
Cerdic Foundries Ltd, Beeching Close, Chard, Somerset, TA20 1BB Tel: (01460) 64301 Fax: (01460) 63961 E-mail: sales@cerdicfoundries.co.uk
Charter Castings Ltd, Bagnall Street, Great Bridge, Tipton, West Midlands, DY4 7BS Tel: 0121-557 9831 Fax: 0121-520 4761 E-mail: mail@chartercastings.co.uk
D Harper Non Ferrous Foundry, Airedale Works, New Works Road, Low Moor, Bradford, West Yorkshire, BD12 0QN Tel: (01274) 691842 Fax: (01274) 691842 E-mail: sales@dhfoundries.co.uk
Devon Metalcrafts Ltd, 2 Victoria Way, Exmouth, Devon, EX8 1EW Tel: (01395) 272846 Fax: (01395) 276688 E-mail: info@devonmetalcrafts.co.uk
Draycast Foundries Ltd, Bellingdon Road, Chesham, Buckinghamshire, HP5 2NR Tel: (01494) 786077 Fax: (01494) 791337 E-mail: sales@draycast.co.uk
East Coast Castings Co. Ltd, The Foundry, Norwich Road, Carbrooke, Thetford, Norfolk, IP25 6TL Tel: (01953) 881741 Fax: (01953) 884769 E-mail: ecc@fsbdial.co.uk
Essex Replica Castings (Basildon) Ltd, 108-112 Westmoor Street, Charlton, London, SE7 8NQ Tel: (020) 8858 6110 Fax: (020) 8305 0907 E-mail: nicktownsend@jardineinternational.com
F Bullett & Co., Island Farm Road, West Molesey, Surrey, KT8 2UU Tel: (020) 8979 1573 Fax: (020) 8941 7352 E-mail: nickbullet@fbullet.com
Fabricast Multi Metals Ltd, Main Street, Hull, HU2 0LF Tel: (01482) 327944 Fax: (01482) 216670 E-mail: sales@fabricast.co.uk
Feldaroll Foundry Ltd, Units 14-21A, Bailie Gate Industrial Estate, Sturminster Marshall, Wimborne, Dorset, BH21 4DB Tel: (01258) 857754 Fax: (01258) 857353
Fox VPS Ltd, Minekeep House, Bridge Road, Camberley, Surrey, GU15 2QR Tel: (01276) 683331 Fax: (01276) 683332 E-mail: sales@foxvps.co.uk
G K N Ltd, Sheepbridge Works, Sheepbridge Lane, Chesterfield, Derbyshire, S41 9QD Tel: (01246) 260026 Fax: (01246) 260022
Glenmore Foundry Ltd, 7 Pinfold Road, Thurmaston, Leicester, LE4 8AS Tel: 0116-269 7094 Fax: 0116-269 7411
Haworth Castings Ltd, Budds Lane, Romsey, Hampshire, SO51 0HA Tel: (01794) 512685 Fax: (01794) 830086 E-mail: sales@haworthcastings.com
Holders Ltd, 55-59 Bensham Grove, Thornton Heath, Surrey, CR7 8DD Tel: (07802) 377122 Fax: (020) 8653 3011 E-mail: sales@holders.ltd.uk
Ideal Sand & Die Casting Co., Unit 5, New Field Industrial Estate, High St, Stoke-on-Trent, ST6 5PB Tel: (01782) 818866 Fax: (01782) 836750 E-mail: sales@idealcasting.co.uk
Longton Light Alloys Ltd, Foxley Lane, Stoke-on-Trent, ST2 7EH Tel: (01782) 536615 Fax: (01782) 533415 E-mail: info@aluminium-castings.com
Madeley Brass Castings, Unit B8 Court Works Industrial Estate, Bridgnorth Road, Madeley, Telford, Shropshire, TF7 4JB Tel: (01952) 583004 Fax: (01952) 583004
Majorfax Ltd, Charles Street, Walsall, WS2 9LZ Tel: (01922) 645815 Fax: (01922) 620500 E-mail: castings@majorfax.co.uk
Manor Foundry Ilkeston Ltd, Lower Granby Street, Ilkeston, Derbyshire, DE7 8DJ Tel: 0115-932 0097 Fax: 0115-930 4548 E-mail: john@manor-foundry.wanadoo.co.uk
Meltcharm Ltd, 4 Enterprise Works, Lockfield Avenue, Enfield, Middlesex, EN3 7PX Tel: (020) 8804 5779 Fax: (020) 8443 3814
Monkman Brass Founders, 3 Broom Street, Bradford, West Yorkshire, BD4 7AP Tel: (01274) 732117 Fax: (01274) 732117
Morris Singer Ltd, Unit 10 Highfield Industrial Estate, Church Lane, Lasham, Alton, Hampshire, GU34 5SQ Tel: (01256) 381033 Fax: (01256) 381565 E-mail: info@morrissinger.co.uk
New Pro Foundries Ltd, Unit C, Horton Close, West Drayton, Middlesex, UB7 8EB Tel: (01895) 443194 Fax: (01895) 442968 E-mail: info@newpro.co.uk
Noirit Ltd, 17-18 Hatherton Street, Walsall, WS4 2LE Tel: (01922) 625471 Fax: (01922) 722339 E-mail: sales@noirit.com
Non Ferrous Founders Ltd, Paudy Lane, Thrussington, Leicester, LE7 4TA Tel: (01509) 889483 Fax: (01509) 889484 E-mail: nfsleicester@aol.com
P & H Castings, Greenfield Road, Colne, Lancashire, BB8 9PD Tel: (01282) 871449 Fax: (01282) 859199
Premiere Castings Ltd, The Old Foundry, Green Street, Oldham, OL8 1TA Tel: 0161-620 6605 Fax: 0161-678 6552 E-mail: premier.castings@btconnect.com
Read Foundry Ltd, Meeting Lane, Brierley Hill, West Midlands, DY5 3LB Tel: (01384) 79399 Fax: (01384) 79399
Sime Foundry Ltd, Stafford Street, Wednesbury, West Midlands, WS10 7JX Tel: 0121-502 5559 Fax: 0121-556 8079E-mail: simefdy@aol.com
F. Smithson, Anchor Mills Foundry, Watergate, Dewsbury, W. Yorkshire, WF12 9DY Tel: (01924) 462439
South Lincs Patterns, Ivanhoe, Spalding Common, Spalding, Lincolnshire, PE11 3AS Tel: (01775) 722988 Fax: (01775) 760386 E-mail: sales@southlincsfoundry.co.uk
Springlynn, Manor Road, Woodley, Stockport, Cheshire, SK6 1RT Tel: 0161-430 6719 Fax: 0161-406 6193 E-mail: david@springlynn.fsbusiness.co.uk
Stone Foundries Ltd, Woolwich Road, London, SE7 8SL Tel: (020) 8853 4648 Fax: (020) 8305 1934 E-mail: enquiries@stone-foundries-limited.com
Taylormade Castings Ltd, Cobridge Road, Stoke-on-Trent, ST1 5JP Tel: (01782) 261537 Fax: (01782) 261262 E-mail: tmcstoke@ukonline.co.uk
Techcast Foundries Ltd, Pigott House, Parkway Avenue, Sheffield, S9 4WA Tel: 0114-272 9741 Fax: 0114-278 1585 E-mail: sales@techcast.co.uk
Tremelling Pattern Co., 3 Lisle Road, High Wycombe, Buckinghamshire, HP13 5SH Tel: (01494) 533897 Fax: (01494) 472777
V T L Automotors Ltd, Ellen Holme, Luddendenfoot, Halifax, West Yorkshire, HX2 6EL Tel: (01422) 882561 Fax: (01422) 883323
Waterfit Ltd, 293 Birmingham New Road, Dudley, West Midlands, DY1 4SJ Tel: 0121-520 7987 Fax: 0121-557 0357 E-mail: enquires@waterfit.co.uk
Westland Casting Co. Ltd, 4-5 Vaux Road, Finedon Road Industrial Estate, Wellingborough, Northamptonshire, NN8 4TG Tel: (01933) 276718 Fax: (01933) 442185 E-mail: info@westlandcastings.co.uk
Wilstead Patterns & Castings, Brickyard House, Mill Lane, Arlesey, Bedfordshire, SG15 6RF Tel: (01462) 835559
Wrekin Shell Mouldings Ltd, Unit D1 & D2, Halesfield 21, Telford, Shropshire, TF7 4NX Tel: (01952) 580946 Fax: (01952) 582546 E-mail: wsm@dynafluid.com

NON FERROUS METAL FABRICATORS

DMI Young & Cunningham Ltd, West Chirton Industrial Estate, Gloucester Road, North Shields, Tyne & Wear, NE29 8RQ Tel: 0191-270 4690 Fax: 0191-270 4691 E-mail: newcastle@yandc.co.uk
Skilled Manufacturing Ltd, Victoria Road, Halesowen, West Midlands, B62 8HY Tel: 0121-559 0776 Fax: 0121-559 0801
The Towel House Co. Ltd, 120 Glover Street, Birmingham, B9 4EY Tel: 0121-766 6644 Fax: 0121-771 0446 E-mail: info@polehousecompany.co.uk
Welding Services Dundee Ltd, 2 Eagle Mills, Brown Constable Street, Dundee, DD4 6QZ Tel: (01382) 223760 Fax: (01382) 225085

NON FERROUS METAL PRESSINGS

A E Harris & Co Birmingham Ltd, 109-138 Northwood Street, Birmingham, B3 1SZ Tel: 0121-233 2386 Fax: 0121-200 3702 E-mail: sales@aeharris.co.uk
BMR Presswork, Market Street, Draycott, Derby, DE72 3NB Tel: (01332) 875384 Fax: (01332) 874022
Fourjay Ltd Presswork, Royal Works, Coleshill Street, Sutton Coldfield, West Midlands, B72 1SJ Tel: 0121-354 1115 Fax: 0121-354 1205 E-mail: enquiries@fourjay.co.uk
H T Brigham & Co. Ltd, Station Road, Coleshill, Birmingham, B46 1JQ Tel: (01675) 463882 Fax: (01675) 467441 E-mail: admin@htbrigham.co.uk
Metal Pressings Group Ltd, Howard Road, Redditch, Worcestershire, B98 7SE Tel: (01527) 526933 Fax: (01527) 510009 E-mail: cmp@metal-pressings.com
Phoenix Pressings Ltd, Wakefield Road, Brighouse, West Yorkshire, HD6 1PE Tel: (01484) 712422 Fax: (01484) 716471 E-mail: sales@phoenixpressings.co.uk
Precision Machining Engineers (Harrow) Ltd, Brember Road, Harrow, Middlesex, HA2 8UN Tel: (020) 8590 5959 Fax: (020) 8422 5077 E-mail: info@cakedecoration.co.uk
Prescient Engineering Ltd, 25 Mereside, Soham, Ely, Cambridgeshire, CB7 5EE Tel: (01353) 720787 Fax: (01353) 723356 E-mail: contact@prescientengineeringltd.co.uk
T W Stamping Ltd, 112-117 Charles Henry Street, Birmingham, B12 0SJ Tel: 0121-622 2600 Fax: 0121-622 2700 E-mail: sales@gueststamping.co.uk
Waterhouse Pressings Ltd, Unit 4f Snaygill Industrial Estate, Keighley Road, Skipton, North Yorkshire, BD23 2QR Tel: (01756) 794577 Fax: (01756) 701481

NON FERROUS METAL SCRAP/ WASTE/RESIDUE RECOVERY/ RECYCLING CONTRACTORS/ MERCHANTS/PROCESSORS OR SERVICES

A E Burgess & Sons Ltd, Ulverscroft Road, Leicester, LE4 6BY Tel: 0116-262 0065 Fax: 0116-251 0501
A J & L M Perrett, 19a Cotton End, Northampton, NN4 8BS Tel: (01604) 761249 Fax: (01604) 767095
Accrington Non Ferrous Metals, Argyle Street, Accrington, Lancashire, BB5 1DQ Tel: (01254) 234550 Fax: (01254) 234550
Albert Alderton, Town Cross Avenue, Bognor Regis, West Sussex, PO21 2DP Tel: (01243) 824700 Fax: (01243) 821482
Ampthill Metal Co. Ltd, Station Road Industrial Estate, Ampthill, Bedford, MK45 2QY Tel: (01525) 403388 Fax: (01525) 404908 E-mail: mick@ampthillmetal.co.uk
▶ Antwerp Africa Metals and Minerals, 79 The Heights, Foxgrove Road, Beckenham, Kent, BR3 5BZ Tel: (020) 8663 0873 E-mail: antwerpafrica@yahoo.co.uk
Apm Metals Ltd, Plantation Works, Eurolink Way, Sittingbourne, Kent, ME10 3HH Tel: (01795) 426021 Fax: (01795) 421858 E-mail: apmmetalsltd@btconnect.com
B & J Alloys Ltd, The Leys, Brierley Hill, West Midlands, DY5 3UJ Tel: (01384) 485533
Bates & Davis 1998, 82 Pikehelve Street, West Bromwich, West Midlands, B70 0TU Tel: 0121-557 3346 Fax: 0121-557 4162 E-mail: sales@wpmgroupltd.co.uk
Belstan Metals Non-Ferrous Ltd, 21-27 Hunters Road, Hockley, Birmingham, B19 1DP Tel: 0121-554 5531 Fax: 0121-515 2824
Benfleet Scrap Co. Ltd, 16 Brunel Road, Manor Trading Estate, Benfleet, Essex, SS7 4PS Tel: (01268) 756525 Fax: (01268) 566121
Bidwell Metals Ltd, Tiger Works, Clandown, Radstock, BA3 3BR Tel: (01761) 432391 Fax: (01761) 432522
Bruce Bishop & Sons Ltd, Lake Avenue, Slough, SL1 3BZ Tel: (01753) 525206 Fax: (01753) 532801
W. Bloy & Son, King Edward Street, Grimsby, North East Lincolnshire, DN31 3JP Tel: (01472) 354069 Fax: (01472) 354069
Bradford Moor Iron & Steel Co. Ltd, Cow Lane, Newark, Nottinghamshire, NG24 1HQ Tel: (01636) 703645 Fax: (01636) 672167
Bridge Metals Birmingham Ltd, 4 Landor Street, Birmingham, B8 1AE Tel: 0121-359 6991
Burke Bros Cheltenham Ltd, Hayricks Wharf, Tewkesbury Road, Cheltenham, Gloucestershire, GL51 9AH Tel: (01242) 519227 Fax: (01242) 231293
C Gearing & Son, 28-30 Seabeach Lane, Eastbourne, East Sussex, BN22 7NZ Tel: (01323) 726029 Fax: (01323) 726029
Clarkes Metal Merchants, 39 Livingstone Place, Newport, Gwent, NP19 8EW Tel: (01633) 259178 E-mail: iancl2@aol.com
Cliftongrade Ltd, 262 Newport Road, Cowes, Isle of Wight, PO31 8PE Tel: (01983) 292611 Fax: (01983) 292612
Coleshill Metals, 234 Station Road, Nether Whitacre, Coleshill, Birmingham, B46 2BY Tel: (01675) 464533
Corus Engineering Steels, Station Works, 680 Warwick Rd, Tyseley, Birmingham, B11 2HL Tel: 0121-706 1110 Fax: 0121-706 8459 E-mail: enquiries.ces@corusgroup.com
Cramlington & District Metals Ltd, Appleby Street, North Shields, Tyne & Wear, NE29 6TE Tel: 0191-257 2049 Fax: 0191-257 9907
Crossley & Craven Halifax Ltd, Exmoor Street, Halifax, West Yorkshire, HX1 3QP Tel: (01422) 352027 Fax: (01422) 358122
Albert Draper & Son Ltd, Black 5 Works, Ravenstreet, Hull, HU9 1PP Tel: (01482) 320712 Fax: (01482) 585312 E-mail: info@adraper.co.uk
▶ Drapers Developments Ltd, Black Five Works, Raven Street, Hull, HU9 1PP Tel: (01482) 323223 Fax: (01482) 585312
E Platt & Sons, Waterloo Street, Bolton, BL1 8HU Tel: (01204) 526304 Fax: (01204) 526330
E & S Metals, Cadwell Lane, Hitchin, Hertfordshire, SG4 0SA Tel: (01462) 455171 Fax: (01462) 453037
European Metal Recycling Ltd, Stoney Stanton Road, Coventry, CV1 4FF Tel: (024) 7668 9051 Fax: (024) 7663 8827
European Metal Recycling Ltd, Sirius House, Delta CR, Westbrook, Warrington, WA5 7NS Tel: (01925) 715400 Fax: (01925) 713480
European Metals Recycling Ltd, Willows, Station Road, East Tilbury, Tilbury, Essex, RM18 8QR Tel: (01375) 856902 Fax: (01375) 843880
Europian Metal Recycling Ltd, Longbeck Trading Estate, Marske-By-The-Sea, Redcar, Cleveland, TS11 6HB Tel: (01642) 482386 Fax: (01642) 243566

NON FERROUS METAL SCRAP/ WASTE/RESIDUE RECOVERY/ RECYCLING CONTRACTORS/ MERCHANTS/PROCESSORS OR SERVICES – *continued*

F J Church Holdings Ltd, Centenary Works, Manor Way, Rainham, Essex, RM13 8RH Tel: (01708) 522651 Fax: (01708) 522786 E-mail: dave@fjchurch.co.uk

F W Singleton Scrap Metal Merchants Ltd, Score Street, Manchester, M11 2SN Tel: 0161-220 8058 Fax: 0161-220 8059 E-mail: scrap@fwsingleton.freeserve.co.uk

Finebran Ltd, Units 5-6, Curran Road, Cardiff, CF10 5DF Tel: (029) 2039 8211 Fax: (029) 2064 1193

G H Newbery & Son Ltd, 4 Ashton Road, Marsh Barton Industrial Estate, Exeter, EX2 8LN Tel: (01392) 275377 Fax: (01392) 435249 E-mail: ghnewbery@btconnect.com

▶ Global Allianz UK Ltd, Trocall House, Wakering Road, Barking, Essex, IG11 8PD Tel: (020) 8507 3222 Fax: 0208 5073444 E-mail: ram@globalallianz.com

▶ Griffin Stringer Ltd, Allenway, Sunningdale Road, Leicester, LE3 1UX Tel: 0116-231 2840 Fax: 0116-231 2840

H F Bates & Sons, 94 Fairfield Road, London, E3 2QP Tel: (020) 8980 1133 Fax: (020) 8980 1797

Peter Hanratty, Albion Street, Whitehaven, Cumbria, CA28 9AA Tel: (01946) 693954 Fax: (01946) 693954 E-mail: phanratty2003@yahoo.co.uk

Henderson Kerr Ltd, Kirklee Road, Bellshill, Lanarkshire, ML4 2QW Tel: (01563) 541325 Fax: (01563) 541325 E-mail: info@hendersonkerr.com

Heppenstall Metal Co. Ltd, Heppenstall Lane, Sheffield, S9 3XB Tel: 0114-244 1839 Fax: 0114-244 3861

Hicks Metals & Alloys, 170-176 Fazeley Street, Birmingham, B5 5SE Tel: 0121-772 1896 Fax: 0121-771 2085

Houston & Sons Ltd, Victoria Avenue, Crewe, CW2 7SR Tel: (01270) 500312 Fax: (01270) 587428 E-mail: info@houston-and-sons.co.uk

J J Crowhurst Ltd, 4 Vincent Street, Birmingham, B12 9SG Tel: 0121-446 4386 Fax: 0121-446 5188 E-mail: jjcrowhurst.ltd@virgin.net

J Lawrence, 1 Alma Street, Walsall, WS2 8JQ Tel: (01922) 628759 Fax: (01922) 639969

J Smith Metals Ltd, Parkfield Road, Wolverhampton, WV4 6EL Tel: (01902) 492120 Fax: (01902) 353398 E-mail: chris@jsmithmetals.com

J & W Robinson Glasgow Ltd, 719 South Street, Glasgow, G14 0BX Tel: 0141-950 1812 Fax: 0141-950 1944

Jighand Ltd, 5c Thames Road, London, E16 2EZ Tel: (020) 7473 1400 Fax: (020) 7473 1372 E-mail: patsy@jighand.com

John Hill & Son (Walsall) Ltd, Wolverhampton Road, Park Brook, Walsall, WS2 8TB Tel: (01922) 622309 Fax: (01922) 622309

C.D. Jordans & Sons Ltd, Dundas Spur, Dundas Lane, Copnor, Portsmouth, PO3 5NX Tel: (023) 9266 1391 Fax: (023) 9267 9503 E-mail: michelle@cdjordan.co.uk

C. Keay Ltd, 21 Leopold Street, Birmingham, B12 0UP Tel: 0121-440 1894 Fax: 0121-440 2500

L & D Mortimer, Birch Street, Bury, Lancashire, BL9 5AL Tel: 0161-764 1362 Fax: 0161-761 6836

LT Mumford, 223 Gascoigne Road, Barking, Essex, IG11 7LN Tel: (020) 8594 1187

Mason Metals Ltd, Two Woods Lane, Mill Street, Brierley Hill, West Midlands, DY5 1TA Tel: (01384) 79841 Fax: (01384) 76414 E-mail: info@masonmetals.co.uk

Metal & Waste Recycling, Powke Lane, Cradley Heath, West Midlands, B64 5PT Tel: 0121-559 1156 Fax: 0121-561 5371 E-mail: enquires@nbrookes.co.uk

Microspot Ltd, Concorde House, 10-12 London Road, Maidstone, Kent, ME16 8QA Tel: (01622) 687771 Fax: (01622) 690801 E-mail: microspot@microspot.co.uk

Mountstar Metal Corporation Ltd, Buckland Road, Pen Mill Trading Estate, Yeovil, Somerset, BA21 5HA Tel: (01935) 423061 Fax: (01935) 432069 E-mail: yeovil@mountstar.com

O B Metals Co. Ltd, Watery Lane Industrial Estate, Watery Lane, Willenhall, West Midlands, WV13 3SU Tel: (01902) 608691 Fax: (01902) 603312

Par Metals Ltd, Unit 68 Birch Road East Industrial Estate, Birch Road East, Birmingham, B6 7DB Tel: 0121-327 2891 Fax: 0121-327 2765

C.L. Prosser & Co. Ltd, 7 Parkfield Road, Stockton-On-Tees, Cleveland, TS18 3DJ Tel: (01642) 676903 Fax: (01642) 617418 E-mail: lenabain@freeserve.co.uk

R O B A Metals Ltd, Kinwarton Farm Road, Kinwarton, Alcester, Warwickshire, B49 6EH Tel: (01789) 763232 Fax: (01789) 400660 E-mail: info@robametals.co.uk

Ray Pillinger, Aldred Close, Norwood Industrial Estate, Killamarsh, Sheffield, S21 2JH Tel: 0114-248 3739 Fax: 0114-248 8081

Reg Morris (Brierley Hill) Ltd, Canal Street, Brierley Hill, West Midlands, DY5 1JJ Tel: (01384) 78187 Fax: (01384) 75361

Reliance Scrap Metal Merchants Ltd, 78-86 Nuffield Road, Nuffield Industrial Estate, Poole, Dorset, BH17 0RS Tel: (01202) 673539 Fax: (01202) 669509

Robert Gibbs Contracting Co. Ltd, Bridge Works, Rye Park Industrial Estate, Hoddesdon, Hertfordshire, EN11 0EW Tel: (01992) 441585 Fax: (01992) 463932 E-mail: sales@gibbsscrap.co.uk

Robin Hood Metals Ltd, Robin Hood Place, Church Gresley, Swadlincote, Derbyshire, DE11 9NL Tel: (01283) 217540

Rykneld Metals Ltd, Derby Road, Burton-on-Trent, Staffordshire, DE14 1RS Tel: (01283) 562745 Fax: (01283) 562745

S B Wheeler & Sons Ltd, 16 Commerce Way, Colchester, CO2 8HH Tel: (01206) 791559 Fax: (01206) 791500

S Norton & Co., Bankfield Site, Regent Road, Bootle, Merseyside, L20 8RQ Tel: 0151-955 3300 Fax: 0151-955 3399 E-mail: s.norton@s-norton.co.uk

S V R Coachworks, Unit U10, Rudford Industrial Estate, Ford Road, Ford, Arundel, West Sussex, BN18 0BF Tel: (01903) 734929 Fax: (01243) 545133

Isaac Shaw Ltd, Doulton Works, Marlborough Way, Tamworth, Staffordshire, B77 2HA Tel: (01827) 260915 Fax: (01827) 261039 E-mail: isl@tecweb.com

Sims Group (U K) Ltd, Whitelands Road, Ashton-under-Lyne, Lancashire, OL6 6UG Tel: 0161-343 2316 Fax: 0161-343 3272

Sims Metal UK Ltd, Gatton Road, Bristol, BS2 9SH Tel: 0117-955 7767 Fax: 0117-955 8098 E-mail: info@simsmetal.com.au

Sims Metal UK Ltd, 7 Christow Road, Marsh Barton Trading Estate, Exeter, EX2 8QT Tel: (01392) 276292 Fax: (01392) 422420 E-mail: sales@sims-group.com

Sims Metal UK Ltd, Blackbushe House, Vigo Lane, Yateley, Hampshire, GU46 6ED Tel: (01252) 873222 Fax: (01252) 876072

Andrew & Mark Smith Metals Ltd, Darbishire Street, Bolton, BL1 2TN Tel: (01204) 533662 Fax: (01204) 392480 E-mail: mark@smithmetals.co.uk

Springvale Metals, 55 Springvale Street, Willenhall, West Midlands, WV13 1EJ Tel: (01902) 606562 Fax: (01902) 606619

Stevens Metal Co Ltd, 33-35 Overton Road, Leicester, LE5 0JB Tel: 0116-276 7418 Fax: 0116-276 7418

Stone Bros, Unit 9 Withy Road Trading Estate, Bilston, West Midlands, WV14 0RX Tel: (01902) 496651 Fax: (01902) 496651

Summit Solder Products, Rail Works, Railway Sidings, Biggleswade, Bedfordshire, SG18 8BD Tel: (01767) 318999 Fax: (01767) 318912 E-mail: summit@mountstar.com

Taylor Metals, 244 Bernard Street, Glasgow, G40 3NX Tel: 0141-556 1903 Fax: 0141-556 1903

H.L. Thorne & Co. Ltd, Hainge Road, Tividale, Oldbury, West Midlands, B69 2PA Tel: 0121-557 6155 Fax: 0121-557 3747 E-mail: info@thorneltd.co.uk

Tilbury Metals Ltd, Old Reservoir Road, Portsmouth, PO6 1SU Tel: (023) 9221 0008 Fax: (023) 9220 1184

W N Thomas & Sons Ltd, Stoke Gardens, Slough, SL1 3QA Tel: (01753) 524575 Fax: (01753) 694765 E-mail: info@thomasmetalrecycling.co.uk

Wallhurst Metals Ltd, 97 Holborn Hill, Birmingham, B6 7QX Tel: 0121-327 3597 Fax: 0121-327 3597

Warwick Street Metal Works Ltd, 77 Warwick Street, Birmingham, B12 0NH Tel: 0121-773 5181 Fax: 0121-766 7104

William Waugh Edinburgh Ltd, Custom House, 11 West Harbour Road, Edinburgh, EH5 1PH Tel: 0131-552 7758 Fax: 0131-552 7758 E-mail: recycle@williamwaugh.co.uk

Weymouth Scrap Co., 20 Cambridge Road, Granby Industrial Estate, Weymouth, Dorset, DT4 9TJ Tel: (01305) 785538 Fax: (01305) 777595

White Bros, Rear 2 & 3, Ruskin Road, Stanford-le-Hope, Essex, SS17 0LF Tel: (01375) 672259 Fax: (01375) 361028 E-mail: whitebros1950@aol.com

Wimbledon Metal Co. Ltd, 105-107 Brighton Road, Surbiton, Surrey, KT6 5NF Tel: (020) 8399 2178

Wirral Metals Ltd, 2 Carlton Road, Birkenhead, Merseyside, CH42 9NQ Tel: 0151-652 2115 E-mail: sales@wirralmetals.com

NON FERROUS METAL SECTIONS

A W S, Nelsons Wharf, Sandy Lane Industrial Estate, Stourport-on-Severn, Worcestershire, DY13 9QB Tel: (01299) 829202 Fax: (01299) 829203 E-mail: sales@aws-services.co.uk

Brian Mccance Steel Ltd, 1 Dargan Road, Belfast, BT3 9JU Tel: (028) 9077 2326 Fax: (028) 9077 9698 E-mail: admin@mccancesteel.com

Bridge Steel Sections Ltd, Ridgeacre Road, West Bromwich, West Midlands, B71 1BB Tel: 0121-553 6771 Fax: 0121-556 6325 E-mail: sales.bss@hadleygroup.co.uk

Compound Sections Ltd, Bond Avenue, Bletchley, Milton Keynes, MK1 1JS Tel: (01908) 622400 Fax: (01908) 622421

Fortress Industries Ltd, 6 Trench Road, Newtownabbey, County Antrim, BT36 4TY Tel: (028) 9034 2655 Fax: (028) 9034 2651 E-mail: info@fortressindustries.com

Stewart Fraser Ltd, Henwood Industrial Estate, Ashford, Kent, TN24 8DR Tel: (01233) 625911 Fax: (01233) 633149 E-mail: sales@stewartfraser.com

Mattersons Ltd, Kingfield Road, Coventry, CV6 5AS Tel: (024) 7670 3713 Fax: (024) 7666 8156 E-mail: sales@matterson.co.uk

Pianoforte Supplies Ltd, Simplex Works, Ashton Road, Roade, Northampton, NN7 2LG Tel: (01604) 862441 Fax: (01604) 862427 E-mail: sales@psluk.co.uk

Rollform Sections Ltd, PO Box 92, Smethwick, West Midlands, B66 2PA Tel: 0121-555 1310 Fax: 0121-555 1311 E-mail: sales.rs@hadleygroup.co.uk

Rowen Structures Ltd, Fulwood Road South, Sutton-in-Ashfield, Nottinghamshire, NG17 2JW Tel: (01623) 558558 Fax: (01623) 558866 E-mail: sales@rowenstructures.co.uk

Maurice Walsah & Co. Ltd, Drumaness Industrial Estate, Old Park Road, Drumaness, Ballynahinch, County Down, BT24 8SE Tel: (028) 9756 2842 Fax: (028) 9756 2592 E-mail: info@mauricewalsh.com

NON FERROUS METAL STAMPINGS

Bowler Group Ltd, Bowler House Harvey Road, Burnt Mills Industrial Estate, Basildon, Essex, SS13 1DD Tel: (01268) 470700 Fax: (01268) 470900

T W Stamping Ltd, 112-117 Charles Henry Street, Birmingham, B12 0SJ Tel: 0121-622 2600 Fax: 0121-622 2700 E-mail: sales@gueststamping.co.uk

NON FERROUS METAL TUBE FITTINGS, *See also headings for particular types*

Dreh Ltd, Duncombe Road, Bradford, West Yorkshire, BD8 9TB Tel: (01793) 533262 Fax: (01793) 619510 E-mail: sales@dreh.co.uk

I B P Conex Ltd, Alexander Street, Dundee, DD3 7DT Tel: (01382) 221301 Fax: (01382) 201292 E-mail: salesuk@ibpgroup.com

Rabco Fittings Ltd, Unit 15 Palmers Road, East Moons Moat, Redditch, Worcestershire, B98 0RF Tel: (01527) 510733 Fax: (01527) 510735 E-mail: admin@rabco-fittings.com

NON FERROUS METAL TUBES, *See also individual metal*

Outokumpu Copper Metal Supplies Ltd, Mill Road, Sharnbrook, Bedford, MK44 1NP Tel: (01234) 781234 Fax: (01234) 781915 E-mail: andrew.smith@outokumpu.com

Tiverton Fabrications Ltd, Tiverton Business Park, Tiverton Way, Tiverton, Devon, EX16 6TG Tel: (01884) 255701 Fax: (01884) 253047

NON FERROUS METALS, *See also headings for individual metals*

Ace Metal, 10 Morgan Way, Bowthorpe Employment Area, Norwich, NR5 9JJ Tel: (01603) 731935 Fax: (01603) 748421 E-mail: acemetalsupplies@aol.com

▶ Antwerp Africa Metals and Minerals, 79 The Heights, Foxgrove Road, Beckenham, Kent, BR3 5BZ Tel: (020) 8663 0873 E-mail: antwerpafrica@yahoo.co.uk

Bidwell Metals Ltd, Tiger Works, Clandown, Radstock, BA3 3BR Tel: (01761) 432391 Fax: (01761) 432522

Bristol Steel Stockholders Ltd, Unit 13-14 Avonbridge Trading Estate, Atlantic Road, Bristol, BS11 9QD Tel: 0117-982 8131 Fax: 0117-982 8137 E-mail: steel@bristolsteel.co.uk

C G Rees Stainless Ltd, 325 North Road, Cardiff, CF14 3BP Tel: (029) 2061 5911 Fax: (029) 2061 8612 E-mail: cgrees@netcomuk.co.uk

▶ Christie & Son (Metal Merchants) Ltd, Lobnitz Dock, Meadowside Street, Renfrew, PA4 8SY Tel: 0141-885 1253 Fax: 0141-885 1937 E-mail: info@christieandson.com

Coleshill Metals, 234 Station Road, Nether Whitacre, Coleshill, Birmingham, B46 2BY Tel: (01675) 464533

E.R. Coley (Steel) Ltd, James Scott Road, Off Park Lane, Halesowen, West Midlands, B63 2QT Tel: (01384) 567121 Fax: (01384) 411259

Danson Steel Ltd, C Kingsbridge Wharf, Kingsbridge Road, Barking, Essex, IG11 0BD Tel: (020) 8507 8921 Fax: (020) 8507 8746 E-mail: danson@barking57.fsnet.co.uk

Direct Plastics Ltd, Unit 12 Portland Business Park, Richmond Park Road, Sheffield, S13 8HS Tel: 0114-256 0889 Fax: 0114-256 0809 E-mail: paul@directplastics.co.uk

Durbin Metal Industries Ltd, Unit 0, Lawrence Drive, Stover Trading Estate, Bristol, BS37 5PG Tel: (01454) 322668 Fax: (01454) 317415 E-mail: sales@durbinmetals.co.uk

Edwards Metals Ltd, Unit 37 Birch Road East Industrial Estate, Birch Road East, Birmingham, B6 7DA Tel: 0121-322 2366 Fax: 0121-326 9369

Eggleston Bros Ltd, Centurion Way Business Park, Alfreton Road, Derby, DE21 4AY Tel: (01332) 341536 Fax: (01332) 295715 E-mail: info@egglestonbros.co.uk

Fabricast Multi Metals Ltd, Main Street, Hull, HU2 0LF Tel: (01482) 327944 Fax: (01482) 216670 E-mail: sales@fabricast.co.uk

Fays Metals Ltd, 3 37 Colville Road, London, W3 8BL Tel: (020) 8993 8883 Fax: (020) 8993 7200 E-mail: sales@fays-metals.co.uk

Franklin Steel Stockholders P.L.C., Franklin Park, Patterson Street, Blaydon-On-Tyne, Tyne & Wear, NE21 5TL Tel: 0191-499 0222 Fax: 0191-499 0223 E-mail: sales@franklinsteel.co.uk

G W Metals & Tools, Unit O & Q Newtown Road Trading Estate, Newtown Road, Worcester, WR5 1HA Tel: (01905) 612342 Fax: (01905) 25544

▶ Grimley Smith Associates, Bramble Island, Great Oakley, Harwich, Essex, CO12 5JW Tel: (01255) 886613 Fax: (01255) 886612

H.C Turk Engineering Services Ltd, 4a The Mews, Bentley Street, Gravesend, Kent, DA12 2DH Tel: (01474) 325331 Fax: (01474) 353140

John Hood & Co., 55 Cheapside Street, Glasgow, G3 8BH Tel: 0141-221 2433 Fax: 0141-221 0508

J T P (Non-Ferrous Stockholders) Ltd, Rope Street, Shelton New Road, Hartshill, Stoke-on-Trent, ST4 6DJ Tel: (01782) 711755 Fax: (01782) 717301 E-mail: dgreer@jtpnonferrous.co.uk

Jade Non Ferrous Metals Ltd, Metallum House, Arthur Drive, Hoo Farm Industrial Estate, Kidderminster, Worcestershire, DY11 7RA Tel: (01562) 746454 Fax: (01562) 820465 E-mail: sales@metalwarehouse.com

Jighand Ltd, 5c Thames Road, London, E16 2EZ Tel: (020) 7473 1400 Fax: (020) 7473 1372 E-mail: patsy@jighand.com

John Keatley (Metals) Ltd, 33-35 Shadwell Street, Birmingham, B4 6HD Tel: 0121-236 4300 Fax: 0121-236 8576 E-mail: lynley@johnkeatleymetals.com

Kelvin Steels Ltd, Spiersbridge Lane, Thornliebank Industrial Estate, Thornliebank, Glasgow, G46 8JT Tel: 0141-638 7988 Fax: 0141-638 1097 E-mail: info@kelvinsteels.com

L Clancey & Sons, Murton Lane, Murton, York, YO19 5UF Tel: (01904) 489169 Fax: (01904) 489508 E-mail: clancey.l@btconnect.com

Luvaca Wolverhampton Ltd, Unit B, Smeston Bridge Industrial Estate, Bridgnorth Road, Wombourne, Wolverhampton, WV5 8AY Tel: (01902) 324747 Fax: (01902) 324501 E-mail: sales@thatcher-alloys.com

William McCormac & Henderson & Co. Ltd, 9 Broomhead Drive, Dunfermline, Fife, KY12 9DR Tel: (01383) 721882

▶ Macedonia Steel Ltd, 93-99 Upper Richmond Road, London, SW15 2TG Tel: (020) 8780 5577 Fax: (020) 8780 5455 E-mail: macsteel@onetel.net.uk

Maxim Industries Ltd, Bankfield Road, Tyldesley, Manchester, M29 8QH Tel: 0161-703 2244 Fax: 0161-702 6454 E-mail: info@themssgroup.co.uk

Maxpower Automotive Ltd, Bank Street, West Bromwich, West Midlands, B71 1HB Tel: 0121-567 0200 Fax: 0121-588 6828 E-mail: jgarner@maxaut.co.uk

Metals South West, 10 Bradley Lane, Newton Abbot, Devon, TQ12 1LZ Tel: (01626) 362026 Fax: (01626) 332220

Metropes Metals Ltd, Estate Road 3, South Humberside Industrial Estate, Grimsby, South Humberside, DN31 2TB Tel: (01472) 342440 Fax: (01472) 267815

Milton Keynes Metals Ltd, Ridge Hill Farm, Nash, Milton Keynes, MK17 0EH Tel: (01296) 713631 Fax: (01296) 714155 E-mail: sales@mkmetals.co.uk

Multi Metal Stockholders, 7-19 Hulme Street, Salford, M5 4PY Tel: 0161-736 0918 Fax: 0161-745 7423 E-mail: sales@multimetals.fsnet.co.uk

Nefco Multi Metals Ltd, Unit 19 Maun Valley Industrial Estate, Junction Road, Sutton-in-Ashfield, Nottinghamshire, NG17 5GS Tel: (01623) 551313 Fax: (01623) 551195 E-mail: nefco@btconnect.com

Oldbury Aluminium Alloys Ltd, Amberway, Halesowen, West Midlands, B62 8AY Tel: 0121-504 3880 Fax: 0121-504 3889 E-mail: oaaltd@aol.com

P & P Non Ferrous (Stockists) Ltd, 47B Premier Trading Estate, The Leys, Brierley Hill, West Midlands, DY5 3UP Tel: (01384) 482888 Fax: (01384) 482088 E-mail: sales@ppnonferrous.co.uk

Righton Ltd, Unit 7-10 Beeches Trading Estate, Waverley Road, Yate, Bristol, BS37 5FF Tel: (01454) 318601 Fax: (01454) 273392 E-mail: bristol@righton.co.uk

Righton Ltd, Unit 13b Anniesland Industrial Estate, Glasgow, G13 1EU Tel: 0141-954 8962 Fax: 0141-959 3467 E-mail: info@righton.co.uk

Smiths Metal Centres Ltd, 42-56 Tottenham Road, London, N1 4BZ Tel: (020) 7241 2430 Fax: (020) 7254 9608

Southern Metals, 29 St. James Industrial Estate, Westhampnett Road, Chichester, West Sussex, PO19 7JU Tel: (01243) 781814 Fax: (01243) 781814

Steel Stop Ltd, Methley Road, Castleford, West Yorkshire, WF10 1LX Tel: (01977) 555333 Fax: (01977) 603960

Thames Stockholders Ltd, Unit 5w Redburn Industrial Estate, Woodall Road, Enfield, Middlesex, EN3 4LQ Tel: (020) 8805 3282 Fax: (020) 8804 8164

Villamead, 203 Inkerman Street, Birmingham, B7 4SA Tel: 0121-359 7498 Fax: 0121-359 7498 E-mail: villamead@aol.com

NON FERROUS METALS – *continued*

W Collins, Cupola Works, Masbrough Street, Rotherham, South Yorkshire, S60 1EX Tel: (01709) 382556
Watts Clift Holdings Ltd, Westgate, Aldridge, Walsall, WS9 8DJ Tel: (01922) 743360 Fax: (01922) 743362
Weldit, 25-27 Bilton Way, Luton, LU1 1UU Tel: (01582) 727840 Fax: (01582) 727841
West Yorkshire Steel Co. Ltd, Sandbeck Works, Sandbeck Industrial Estate, Wetherby, West Yorkshire, LS22 7DN Tel: 01937 584440 Fax: (0845) 658 1305 E-mail: sales@westyorkssteel.com
Wrekin Steel Ltd, Unit A4 Hortonwood 10, Telford, Shropshire, TF1 7ES Tel: (01952) 677600 Fax: (01952) 677900

NON FERROUS NAILS

Stone Fasteners Ltd, Woolwich Road, London, SE7 8SL Tel: (020) 8293 5080 Fax: (020) 8293 4935 E-mail: sales@stonefasteners.com
Yvens Decroupet UK Ltd, 28 Thrift Wood, Bicknacre, Chelmsford, CM3 4HT Tel: (01245) 227172 Fax: (01245) 227182

NON FERROUS PRODUCTS

Bayliss Patterns Walsall Ltd, Rollingmill Street, Walsall, WS2 9EG Tel: (01922) 626972 Fax: (01922) 633748

NON FERROUS ROLLED METAL PRODUCTS, *See also headings for particular types*

Alcoa Europe Flat Rolled Products, Clark Street, Dolgarrog, Conwy, Gwynedd, LL32 8JH Tel: (01492) 614200 Fax: (01492) 614294 E-mail: info@dolgarrog.com
B Mason & Sons Ltd, Wharf Street, Aston, Birmingham, B6 5SA Tel: 0121-327 0181 Fax: 0121-322 8341 E-mail: sales@bmason.co.uk

NON FERROUS WIRE MESH

Multi Weldmesh Ltd, Heasandford Industrial Estate, Widow Hill Road, Burnley, Lancashire, BB10 2TJ Tel: (01282) 425300 Fax: (01282) 422204

NON GEOGRAPHICAL NUMBER TELEPHONE CALL SERVICE PROVIDERS

▶ Alphatalk Ltd, 109 Digbeth, Birmingham, B5 6DT Tel: 0121-633 5200 Fax: (0870) 2005200 E-mail: info@alphatalk.com
▶ Lamtha2 Telecom, Fairford Leys Way, Aylesbury, Buckinghamshire, HP19 7FQ Tel: (0871) 9190134
▶ Charles Stuart Phone Services, 18 Harewood Avenue, Newark, Nottinghamshire, NG24 4BE Tel: (01636) 705313 Fax: (01636) 335235 E-mail: sales@charles-stuart.com
▶ Zimo Communications, 26 York Street, London, W1U 6PZ Tel: (0800) 3213000 E-mail: sales@ewcoms.com

NON INDUCTIVE FIXED RESISTORS

V T M U K Ltd, 8 Corinium Centre, Raans Road, Amersham, Buckinghamshire, HP6 6JQ Tel: (01494) 738600 Fax: (01494) 738610 E-mail: admin@vtm.co.uk

NON INDUSTRIAL MINIATURE RAILWAY SYSTEMS

Mardyke Miniature Railway, 1 Imperial Trading Estate, Lambs La North, Rainham, Essex, RM13 9XL Tel: (01708) 520264 Fax: (01708) 553395

NON INTRUSIVE IN DRUM MIXERS

Calmore Machinery Co. Ltd, 4 28 Black Moor Road, Ebblake Industrial Estate, Verwood, Dorset, BH31 6BB Tel: (01202) 827701 Fax: (01202) 813053 E-mail: info@calmorehinges.co.uk

NON MECHANICAL PLANT HIRE

Deedman Tropical Plant Hire Co., 3k Longcauseway, Farnworth, Bolton, BL4 9BS Tel: (01204) 577000 Fax: (01204) 577770 E-mail: sales@deedman.co.uk
▶ Mabey Hire Ltd, Stag Industrial Estate, Oxford Street, Bilston, West Midlands, WV14 7HZ Tel: (01902) 404512 Fax: (01902) 494942

NON METALLIC SHIMS

Plastic Shims & Gaskets Co. Ltd, 49-53 Glengall Road, Peckham, London, SE15 6NF Tel: (020) 7740 9705 Fax: (020) 7635 9791 E-mail: sales@psggroup.co.uk

NON METALLIC WASHERS, *See also other nearby headings for individual material*

Godfrey Insulations Ltd, Siddons Factory Estate, Howard Street, West Bromwich, West Midlands, B70 0SZ Tel: 0121-556 0011 Fax: 0121-556 9553
R.H. Nuttall Ltd, Century Works, Great Brook Street, Nechells Green, Birmingham, B7 4EN Tel: 0121-359 2484 Fax: 0121-359 4439 E-mail: sales@rhnuttall.co.uk

NON ORGANIC COMPOST FERTILISERS

▶ Joseph Metcalf Ltd, Nook Lane, Lower Green, Astley, Manchester, M29 7LW Tel: (01942) 896668 Fax: (01942) 897485 E-mail: rgrice@gemweb.co.uk

NON PRECIOUS METAL MENSWEAR ACCESSORIES

necktiesonline.co.uk Ltd, Daymer, Ashmore Green Road, Ashmore Green, Thatcham, Berkshire, RG18 9ER Tel: (01635) 872499 E-mail: sales@necktiesonline.co.uk
▶ Wholesale Movie TV Music Gifts Ltd, 1St Floor, 1 Chapel Street, Bridlington, North Humberside, YO15 2DR Tel: (01262) 677730 Fax: (01262) 675702

NON REFLECTIVE PICTURE FRAME GLASS

▶ Britannia Mounts Co. Ltd, Unit E3-E4, Meltham Mills Industrial Estate, Meltham, Holmfirth, HD9 4DS Tel: (01484) 854444 Fax: (01484) 854433 E-mail: sales@britannia-mounts.co.uk
▶ Evergreen Gallery, 12 Sheaf Street, Daventry, Northamptonshire, NN11 4AB Tel: (01327) 878117 E-mail: info@evergreengallery.co.uk
▶ Framing Fantastic, 149 Seven Mile Straight, Muckamore, Antrim, BT41 4QT Tel: (028) 9443 9287 Fax: (028) 9443 9287 E-mail: info@framingfantastic.com
▶ Taurus Colour Laboratories, 6 Kelvin Business Centre, Kelvin Way, Crawley, West Sussex, RH10 9SF Tel: (01293) 553427 Fax: (01293) 553429 E-mail: LES@TAURUSCOLOURLABS.CO.UK

NON RETURN VALVES

Aquaflow Ltd, Onneley Works, Newcastle Road, Woore, Crewe, CW3 9RU Tel: (01630) 647111 Fax: (01630) 647734 E-mail: response@aquaflowvalves.com
Arrow Valves Ltd, 68 High Street, Tring, Hertfordshire, HP23 4AG Tel: (01442) 823123 Fax: (01442) 823234 E-mail: info@arrowvalves.co.uk
Goodwin International Ltd, Ivy House Foundry, Hanley, Stoke-on-Trent, ST1 3NR Tel: (01782) 220000 Fax: (01782) 208060 E-mail: goodwinplc@goodwin.co.uk
Ham Baker Hartley, Garner Street, Etruria, Stoke-on-Trent, ST4 7BH Tel: (01782) 202300 Fax: (01782) 203639 E-mail: enquiries@hambaker.co.uk

NON RETURN WATER VALVES

Barnes & Gannon Ltd, Charles House, Royle Barn Road, Rochdale, Lancashire, OL11 3DT Tel: (01706) 344997 Fax: (01706) 641653 E-mail: sales@aqua-check.co.uk

NON SKID CHAINS

R U D Chains Ltd, Units 10-14, John Wilson Business Park, Thanet Way, Whitstable, Kent, CT5 3QT Tel: (01227) 276611 Fax: (01227) 276586 E-mail: sales@rud.co.uk

NON SLIP CONCRETE FLOORING

▶ Hi-Tec Roofing, 4 Gallowhill Road, Paisley, Renfrewshire, PA3 4TF Tel: 0141-887 5775 Fax: 0141-887 5775 E-mail: sales@hi-tecroofing.co.uk

NON SLIP FLOOR COVERINGS

▶ Hi-Tec Roofing, 4 Gallowhill Road, Paisley, Renfrewshire, PA3 4TF Tel: 0141-887 5775 Fax: 0141-887 5775 E-mail: sales@hi-tecroofing.co.uk

NON SPARKING ALLOY CASTINGS

Brock Metal Co., Walsall Road, Norton Canes, Cannock, Staffordshire, WS11 9NR Tel: (01543) 276666 Fax: (01543) 276418 E-mail: brock@brock-metal.co.uk

NON STACKABLE LOAD ROAD TRANSPORT AND HAULAGE

▶ Clive's Light Removals, 4 Coastguard Cottages, Isle of Grain, Rochester, Kent, ME3 0DS Tel: 0777 8872492 E-mail: clive@fsmail.net

NON STANDARD BOLTS AND NUTS

A C T (Fasteners & Components) Ltd, Units 13 & 16, Four Ashes Industrial Estate, Station Road, Four Ashes, Wolverhampton, WV10 7DB Tel: (01902) 791880 Fax: (01902) 791884 E-mail: info@actfasteners.co.uk
Arnold Wragg Ltd, Unit 2, Parkway One, Parkway Drive, Sheffield, S9 4WU Tel: 0114 2519050 Fax: 0114 2446635 E-mail: sales@arnold-wragg.com
Cotswold Autoflo Ltd, Unit 2, Willow Park, Hinton Road, Childswickham, Broadway, Worcestershire, WR12 7HY Tel: (01386) 853284 Fax: (01386) 854636 E-mail: sales@autoflo.co.uk
Doran Engineering Co Holdings Ltd, Planetary Industrial Estate, Planetary Road, Willenhall, West Midlands, WV13 3XW Tel: (01902) 866000 Fax: (01902) 866222
Elmor Supplies Ltd, 104 Branbridges Road, East Peckham, Tonbridge, Kent, TN12 5HH Tel: (01622) 871870 Fax: (01622) 872024
Eurofast Petrochemical Supplies Ltd, Unit 30 Planetary Industrial Estate, Planetary Road, Willenhall, West Midlands, WV13 3TA Tel: (01902) 307788 Fax: (01902) 307744 E-mail: eps-sales@eurofast.co.uk
Ivyplus Fasteners & Fixing Devices, 41 Colmore Flats, Henrietta Street, Birmingham, B19 3PT Tel: 0121-212 2485 Fax: 0121-212 2485
Lydford Precision Engineering Ltd, Sutherland Avenue, Monmore Green, Wolverhampton, WV2 2JH Tel: (01902) 351353 Fax: (01902) 351616 E-mail: sales@lydford-eng.co.uk
Nuts & Bolts (Cannock) Ltd, Unit 40 Rumer Hill Business Estate, Rumer Hill Rd, Cannock, Staffordshire, WS11 0ET Tel: (01543) 466100 Fax: (01543) 466699 E-mail: sales@nutsandbolts-staffs.co.uk
P R D Fasteners Ltd, Unit 10 Monmer Close Industrial Estate, Willenhall, West Midlands, WV13 1JR Tel: (01902) 636246 Fax: (01902) 605759 E-mail: sales@prdfasteners.co.uk
P R D Holdings Ltd, Unit 13, Monmer Close, Willenhall, West Midlands, WV13 1JR Tel: (01902) 639360 Fax: (01902) 639365 E-mail: info@prdholdings.com
Ralin Group Ltd, Brierley Lane, Bilston, West Midlands, WV14 8TU Tel: (01902) 491954 Fax: (01902) 357299 E-mail: sales@ralingroup.co.uk
Rollstud Ltd, 5 Denmore Industrial Estate, Denmore Road, Denmore Industrial Estate, Aberdeen, AB23 8JW Tel: (01224) 425300 Fax: (01224) 425333
SKM Products Ltd, Unit N3 Troon Way Business Centre, Humberstone Lane, Leicester, LE4 9HA Tel: 0116-246 1727 Fax: 0116-246 0313
Specthread Ltd, Unit 20, Field Close, Bloxwich, Walsall, WS3 3JS Tel: (01922) 710180 Fax: (01922) 710181
Spensall Engineering Ltd, Kitson Road, Leeds, LS10 1NR Tel: 0113-245 0726 Fax: 0113-242 0047
Stainless Steel Fasteners Ltd, Broombank Road, Chesterfield, Derbyshire, S41 9QJ Tel: (01246) 451818 Fax: (01246) 455268 E-mail: sales@ssfast.co.uk
Triplefast International Ltd, Unit 13 Monmer Close Industrial Estate, Willenhall, West Midlands, WV13 1JR Tel: (01902) 636399 Fax: (01902) 609880 E-mail: sales@triplefast.co.uk
Trojan Special Fasteners Ltd, 18 Fortnum Close, Tile Cross, Birmingham, B33 0LG Tel: 0121-789 8586 Fax: 0121-789 8006 E-mail: sales@trojanspecialfastenersltd.co.uk
Turbo Engineering Ltd, Unit 14, Prince Consort Industrial Estate, Hebburn, Tyne & Wear, NE31 1EH Tel: (0845) 4941706 Fax: 0191-483 6745 E-mail: dominic.rutherford@btinternet.com
W J L Engineering, 30-31 Sapcote Trading Centre, Powke Lane, Cradley Heath, West Midlands, B64 5QR Tel: (01384) 567782 Fax: (01384) 412692 E-mail: wjlengineering@btconnect.com
Wirth Engineering, Birch House, Fraser Road, Erith, Kent, DA8 1QX Tel: (01322) 434345 Fax: (01322) 434346

NON STANDARD INDEXABLE CUTTING TOOLS

Logtek C N C Cut, 12a Church Road, Formby, Liverpool, L37 8BQ Tel: (01704) 873222 Fax: (01704) 873222 E-mail: deslogan@supanet.com

NON STANDARD INSERT PANEL DOORS

Young's Doors, 24 City Road, Norwich, NR1 3AN Tel: (01603) 629889 Fax: (01603) 764650 E-mail: mail@youngs-doors.co.uk

NON STATIC CARPETS

Rawson Carpets Ltd, Castlebank Mills, Portobello Road, Wakefield, West Yorkshire, WF1 5PS Tel: (01924) 382860 Fax: (01924) 290334 E-mail: sales@rawsoncarpets.co.uk

NON STATUS MORTGAGE BROKERS

▶ LGI Consulting, 2nd Floor, 41A Church Street, Weybridge, Surrey, KT13 8DG Tel: 01932 856699 E-mail: info@lgiconsulting.co.uk

NON STICK COATING PROCESSORS OR SERVICES

Product Release Europe Ltd, Cusson Road, Knowsley Industrial Park, Liverpool, L33 7BY Tel: 0151-549 1491 Fax: 0151-548 4035

NON STICK COATINGS

Kal-Gard UK Ltd, Canalwood Industrial Estate, Chirk, Wrexham, LL14 5RL Tel: (01691) 772070 Fax: (01691) 778303 E-mail: tony@kal-gard.co.uk
Whitford Plastics Ltd, Christleton Court, Manor Park, Runcorn, Cheshire, WA7 1ST Tel: (01928) 571000 Fax: (01928) 571010 E-mail: sales@whitfordww.co.uk

NON TEXTILE MENSWEAR ACCESSORIES

Concept Covers Ltd, 1 Monarch Works, Balds Lane, Stourbridge, West Midlands, DY9 8TE Tel: (01384) 897101 Fax: (01384) 891171 E-mail: concept-covers@supanet.com

NON VOLATILE COMPUTER MEMORY

Alpine Technology Ltd, Unit 12 Tungsten Building, George Street, Portslade, Brighton, BN41 1RA Tel: (01273) 425290 Fax: (0870) 8901087 E-mail: sales@alpinetech.co.uk

NON WOVEN DISPOSABLE PRODUCTS

Orvec International Ltd, Malmo Road, Hull, HU7 0YF Tel: (01482) 879146 Fax: (01482) 625325 E-mail: service@orvec.com

NON WOVEN FABRICS

B F F Technical Fabric Ltd, Bath Road, Bridgwater, Somerset, TA6 4NZ Tel: (01278) 428500 Fax: (01278) 429499 E-mail: information@bff-technicalfabric.com
Camtex Fabrics Ltd, Blackwood Road, Lillyhall Industrial Estate, Lillyhall, Workington, Cumbria, CA14 4JJ Tel: (01900) 602646 Fax: (01900) 66827 E-mail: info@cambrelle.com
James Dewhurst Ltd, Altham Lane, Altham, Accrington, Lancashire, BB5 5YA Tel: (01282) 775311 Fax: (01282) 774717 E-mail: sales@james-dewhurst.co.uk
Hanes International UK, Unit 11 Trans Pennine Trading Estate, Gorrells Way, Rochdale, Lancashire, OL11 2PX Tel: (01706) 514250 Fax: (01706) 712848 E-mail: sales@hanesindustries.com
Lantor (UK) Ltd, 73 St. Helens Road, Bolton, BL3 3PP Tel: (01204) 855000 Fax: (01204) 61722 E-mail: sales@lantor.co.uk

NON WOVEN FILTER MEDIA

P G Lawton, Caldene Business Park, Burnley Road, Mytholmroyd, Hebden Bridge, West Yorkshire, HX7 5QJ Tel: (01422) 883903 Fax: (01422) 884278 E-mail: pg.lawton@uk.sglcarbon.de

Portways, Sedgley Road East, Tipton, West Midlands, DY4 7UY Tel: 0121-557 7641 Fax: 0121-522 2012 E-mail: sales@vitafibres.com

Porvair Technology Ltd, Clywedog Road South, Wrexham Industrial Estate, Wrexham, Clwyd, LL13 9XS Tel: (01978) 661144 Fax: (01978) 664554E-mail: enquiries@porvairfiltration.com

Purification Products Ltd, Reliance Works, Saltaire Road, Shipley, West Yorkshire, BD18 3HL Tel: (01274) 530155 Fax: (01274) 580453 E-mail: sales@purification.co.uk

NON WOVEN INTERLININGS

Vilene Interlinings, PO Box 3, Elland, West Yorkshire, HX5 9DX Tel: (01422) 327900 Fax: (01422) 327999 E-mail: vilenesales@freudenberg-nw.com

NON WOVEN WIPES

Whitminster International Ltd, Dudbridge Road, Stroud, Gloucestershire, GL5 3HF Tel: (01453) 762266 Fax: (01453) 762277 E-mail: mailroom@whitminster.co.uk

NON-FERROUS METAL PRODUCTS, *See individual metal used*

NOTARIES PUBLIC

Saville & Co., 1 Carey Lane, London, EC2V 8AE Tel: (020) 7920 0000 Fax: (020) 7920 0088 E-mail: mail@savillenotaries.com

NOTICE BOARDS

▶ Andesign Sign Writers, F 11-13 Coleshill Road, Sutton Coldfield, West Midlands, B75 7AA Tel: 0121-354 2272 Fax: 0121-355 8883 E-mail: info@andesignuk.co.uk

GBC UK Holdings Ltd, Rutherford Road, Basingstoke, Hampshire, RG24 8PD Tel: (01256) 842828 Fax: (01256) 842581 E-mail: sales@gbcuk.co.uk

Harewood Products Ltd, Unit 1, Union Road, The Valley, Bolton, BL2 2DT Tel: (01204) 395730 Fax: (01204) 388018 E-mail: info@adboards.com

Magiboards Ltd, Unit F, Stafford Park 12, Telford, Shropshire, TF3 3BJ Tel: (01952) 292111 Fax: (01952) 292280 E-mail: sales@magiboards.co.uk

Signwise Sign Services Ltd, 4 Challenger Way, Peterborough, PE1 5EX Tel: (01733) 565770 Fax: (01733) 563384 E-mail: info@signwisesignservices.co.uk

Vista Visuals UK, Unit 4 Old Mill Industrial Estate, Bamber Bridge, Preston, PR5 6SY Tel: (01772) 696725 Fax: (01772) 696726 E-mail: danny@vistavisuals.co.uk

NOVELTY AEROSOLS

G A C (UK) Ltd, 56 Llantarnam Park, Cwmbran, Gwent, NP44 3AW Tel: (01633) 861411 Fax: (01633) 838306

NOVELTY GOLFING ITEM GIFTWARE

▶ Golfsim, 30 Elvington, King'S Lynn, King's Lynn, Norfolk, PE30 4TA Tel: (07956) 090436 E-mail: info@golfsimulation.co.uk

▶ Interknickers Ltd, 21 Claremont Drive, Coalville, Coalville, Leicestershire, LE67 2ND Tel: (01530) 460316 E-mail: interknickers@btinternet.com

NOVELTY T SHIRTS

▶ The Jump Shop, C/o Skydive UK Ltd, Dunkeswell Airfield, Dunkeswell, Honiton, Devon, EX14 4LG Tel: (07939) 030339 Fax: (01246) 203487 E-mail: sales@thejumpshop.co.uk

Talking T's, 1 149b Histon Road, Cambridge, CB4 3JD Tel: (01223) 304104 Fax: (01223) 304110 E-mail: sales@t-shirts.co.uk

NUCLEAR CONTAINMENT SYSTEMS

Chesim Engineering Ltd, 7 Brunel Way, Fareham, Hampshire, PO15 5TX Tel: (01489) 885994 Fax: (01489) 885931 E-mail: sales@chesim.co.uk

NUCLEAR DECONTAMINATION/ DECOMMISSIONING SERVICES

Holemasters Demtech, Unit 2-4 Dixon Street, Westhoughton, Bolton, BL5 3PX Tel: (01942) 840600 Fax: (01942) 840700 E-mail: enquiries@holemasters.co.uk

NSG Enviromental Ltd, Scientia House Matrix Park, Western Avenue, Buckshaw Village, Chorley, Lancashire, PR7 7NB Tel: (01772) 458818 Fax: (01772) 458819 E-mail: mailbox@nsgenvironmental.co.uk

Nukem Nuclear Ltd, Kelburn Court, Daten Park, Warrington, WA3 6TW Tel: (01925) 858200 Fax: (01925) 811866 E-mail: info@nukem.co.uk

Richardson, Courville House, 1 Ellerbeck Court, Stokesley, Middlesbrough, Cleveland, TS9 5PT Tel: (01642) 714791 Fax: (01642) 714387 E-mail: enquiries@pcrichardson.co.uk

NUCLEAR EQUIPMENT DESIGN SERVICES

Chesim Engineering Ltd, 7 Brunel Way, Fareham, Hampshire, PO15 5TX Tel: (01489) 885994 Fax: (01489) 885931 E-mail: sales@chesim.co.uk

Gravatom Engineering Systems Ltd, William Kelvin Building, Claylands Road, Bishops Waltham, Southampton, SO32 1BH Tel: (01489) 896010 Fax: (01489) 894382 E-mail: sales@gravatom.com

NUCLEAR INDUSTRY CONSULTANTS

▶ Intelligent Risk Management Ltd, PO Box 148, Kendal, Cumbria, LA9 7WY Tel: (01539) 736126 Fax: (01539) 736286 E-mail: david.arnold@i-rm.com

▶ World Nuclear Association, 22a St. James's Square, London, SW1Y 4JH Tel: (020) 7451 1520 Fax: (020) 7839 1501 E-mail: wna@world-nuclear.org

NUCLEAR INDUSTRY SPECIALIST ALLOYS

Heymark Metals Ltd, Becklands Close, Bar Lane, Roecliffe, York, YO51 9NR Tel: (01423) 323388 Fax: (01423) 326888 E-mail: enquiries@heymark.co.uk

NUCLEAR INFORMATION SERVICES

Nuclear Industry Association, First Floor Whitehall House, 41 Whitehall, London, SW1A 2BY Tel: (020) 7766 6640 Fax: (020) 7839 4695 E-mail: info@niauk.org

▶ World Nuclear Association, 22a St. James's Square, London, SW1Y 4JH Tel: (020) 7451 1520 Fax: (020) 7839 1501 E-mail: wna@world-nuclear.org

NUCLEAR LEAD SHIELDING

Delfield Precision Engineering Co. Ltd, Apex House, Stonefield Close, Ruislip, Middlesex, HA4 0XT Tel: (020) 8842 0527 Fax: (020) 8845 7796

NUCLEAR LEADWORK, *See Leadwork etc*

NUCLEAR MAGNETIC RESONANCE SPECTROMETERS

Bruker BioSpin Ltd, Banner Lane, Coventry, CV4 9GH Tel: (024) 7685 5200 Fax: (024) 7646 5317 E-mail: admin@bruker.co.uk

NUCLEAR PLANT CONTRACTORS OR DESIGNERS

BNFL, Birchwood Park Avenue, Birchwood, Warrington, WA3 6GR Tel: (01925) 832000 Fax: (01925) 822711 E-mail: sales@britishnucleargroup.com

Simon-Carves Ltd, PO Box 17, Cheadle, Cheshire, SK8 5BR Tel: 0161-486 4000 Fax: 0161-486 1302 E-mail: simon.carves@simoncarves.com

NUCLEAR PLANT EQUIPMENT

Corus Process Engineering, Old Frame RM, Derwent Howe, Workington, Cumbria, CA14 3YZ Tel: (01900) 68000 Fax: (01900) 601111 E-mail: cpe@corusgroup.com

Jordan Division Ltd, Millbrook Road, Yate, Bristol, BS37 5PB Tel: (01454) 328300 Fax: (01454) 325866 E-mail: sales@jordanengineering.co.uk

NUCLEAR PLANT MANUFRS OR ENGINEERS

BNFL, Birchwood Park Avenue, Birchwood, Warrington, WA3 6GR Tel: (01925) 832000 Fax: (01925) 822711 E-mail: sales@britishnucleargroup.com

Leopold Grove Engineering Co. Ltd, Amy Johnson Way, Blackpool, FY4 2RP Tel: (01253) 342144 Fax: (01253) 349667 E-mail: office@leopoldeng.co.uk

Sse Pipe Fittings Ltd, Pedmore Road, Dudley, West Midlands, DY2 0RE Tel: (01384) 480333 Fax: (01384) 480805 E-mail: sales@ssepipefittings.co.uk

NUCLEAR RESEARCH AND DEVELOPMENT SERVICES

BNFL, Birchwood Park Avenue, Birchwood, Warrington, WA3 6GR Tel: (01925) 832000 Fax: (01925) 822711 E-mail: sales@britishnucleargroup.com

NUCLEAR WASTE CONTAINERS

Deva Manufacturing Services, Unit 3 Chester Gates, Dunkirk, Chester, CH1 6LT Tel: (01244) 851183 Fax: (01244) 851187 E-mail: sales@deva-uk.com

NUCLEAR WASTE MANAGEMENT SERVICES

Aker Kvaerner Engineering Services Ltd, Phoenix House, 3 Surtees Way, Surtees Business Park, Stockton-on-Tees, Cleveland, TS18 3HR Tel: (01642) 334000 Fax: (01642) 334001

Furness Engineering & Technology, Ellers Mill, The Ellers, Ulverston, Cumbria, LA12 0AQ Tel: (01229) 584043 Fax: (01229) 586440 E-mail: mail@fetl.co.uk

NSG Enviromental Ltd, Scientia House Matrix Park, Western Avenue, Buckshaw Village, Chorley, Lancashire, PR7 7NB Tel: (01772) 458818 Fax: (01772) 458819 E-mail: mailbox@nsgenvironmental.co.uk

Nukem Nuclear Ltd, Kelburn Court, Daten Park, Warrington, WA3 6TW Tel: (01925) 858200 Fax: (01925) 811866 E-mail: info@nukem.co.uk

NUCLEAR WASTE STORAGE EQUIPMENT

Non Entry Systems Ltd, Bruce Road, Fforestfach, Swansea, SA5 4HS Tel: (01792) 580455 Fax: (01792) 578610 E-mail: sales@nonentrysystems.com

NUCLEONIC INSTRUMENTS

Alrad Instruments Ltd, Alder House, Turnpike Road Industrial Estate, Newbury, Berkshire, RG14 2NS Tel: (01635) 30345 Fax: (01635) 32630 E-mail: sales@alrad.co.uk

Perkinelmer Ltd, Chalfont Road, Seer Green, Beaconsfield, Buckinghamshire, HP9 2FX Tel: (01494) 874515 Fax: (01494) 679331 E-mail: cc.uk@perkinelmer.com

Ronan Engineering Ltd, Factory 1-2 Tilley Road, Crowther, Washington, Tyne & Wear, NE38 0AE Tel: 0191-416 1689 Fax: 0191-416 5856 E-mail: sales@ronan.com

NUMBERED AND BAR CODED LABELS

Arc Labels Ltd, The Maltings Industrial Estate, Doncaster Road, Whitley Bridge, Goole, North Humberside, DN14 0HH Tel: (01977) 663063 Fax: (01977) 663064 E-mail: sales@arclabels.com

Aztec Labels, Kidderminster Industrial Estate, Spennells Valley Road, Kidderminster, Worcestershire, DY10 1XS Tel: (01562) 66518 Fax: (01562) 69802 E-mail: sales@azteclabel.co.uk

▶ Bar Code Systems (London) Ltd, Lakeside House, 1 Furzeground Way, Stockley Park, Uxbridge, Middlesex, UB11 1BD Tel: (0870) 3516496 Fax: (020) 8622 3249 E-mail: robertmoorman@barcode-systems.com

Bemrosebooth Ltd, Stockholm Road, Hull, HU7 0XY Tel: (01482) 826343 Fax: (01482) 826667 E-mail: contact@bemrosebooth.co.uk

Crown Labels, 102 Walkley Rd, Sheffield, S6 2XP Tel: 0114-232 1152 Fax: 0114-232 1301 E-mail: sales@crownlabels.co.uk

Ennis Labels & Print, Tower Studios, Market Street, Darwen, Lancashire, BB3 1AZ Tel: (01254) 826138 Fax: (01254) 702135 E-mail: sales@ennislabels.co.uk

Icon Labels Ltd, 1 Lower Oakham Way, Oakham Business Park, Mansfield, Nottinghamshire, NG18 5BU Tel: (01623) 421241 Fax: (01623) 421251 E-mail: sales@iconlabels.co.uk

Ovalring Ltd, 60 Prince of Wales Lane, Birmingham, B14 4JY Tel: 0121-436 6060 Fax: 0121-436 6061

▶ Robstock Ltd, Unit 9-10, Rope Walk, Ilkeston, Derbyshire, DE7 5HX Tel: 0115-930 3308 Fax: 0115-932 4726 E-mail: sales@robstock.co.uk

S L Conyers & Son Ltd, Hawthorns Industrial Estate, Middlemore Road, Handsworth, Birmingham, B21 0BH Tel: 0121-551 2875 Fax: 0121-554 5267 E-mail: webmaster@conyers-labels.com

NUMBERING MACHINES

Lethaby Numbering Systems, Central Way, Walworth Industrial Estate, Andover, Hampshire, SP10 5AL Tel: (01264) 365951 Fax: (01264) 356303 E-mail: sales@atlanticzeiser.com

Rollem Patent Products Ltd, The Common, Ecclesfield, Sheffield, S35 9WN Tel: 0114-246 8981 Fax: 0114-246 5487 E-mail: sales@rollem.co.uk

NUMERICAL CONTROL (NC) LATHES

600 Lathes, Union Street, Heckmondwike, West Yorkshire, WF16 0HL Tel: (01924) 415000 Fax: (01924) 415017 E-mail: sales@600lathes.co.uk

Boxford Ltd, Boy Lane, Wheatley, Halifax, West Yorkshire, HX3 5AF Tel: (01422) 358311 Fax: (01422) 355924 E-mail: info@boxford.co.uk

Cincinnati Machine Ltd, PO Box 505, Birmingham, B24 0QU Tel: 0121-351 3821 Fax: 0121-313 5379 E-mail: info@cinmach.co.uk

Colchester Lathe Co. Ltd, P O Box 20, Heckmondwike, West Yorkshire, WF16 0HN Tel: (01924) 412603 Fax: (01924) 412604 E-mail: sales@colchester.co.uk

George Kingsbury, Quay Lane, Hardway, Gosport, Hampshire, PO12 4LB Tel: (023) 9258 0371 Fax: (023) 9250 1741 E-mail: mtools@gkholdings.com

Lead Precision Machine Tools Ltd, Calamine House, Calamine Street, Macclesfield, Cheshire, SK11 7HU Tel: (01625) 434990 Fax: (01625) 434996 E-mail: sales@leadmachinetools.co.uk

Matchmaker CNC, 8 Woodland Studios, Brook Willow Farm, Woodlands Road, Leatherhead, Surrey, KT22 0AN Tel: (01372) 844999 Fax: (01372) 844998 E-mail: sales@matchmakermc.co.uk

Pfiffner UK Ltd, 9 Manor Courtyard, Hughenden Avenue, High Wycombe, Buckinghamshire, HP13 5RE Tel: (01494) 510166 Fax: (01494) 510211

NURSING HOME COMMUNICATION SYSTEMS

Bell System Telephones Ltd, Presley Way, Crownhill, Milton Keynes, MK8 0ET Tel: (01908) 261106 Fax: (01908) 261116 E-mail: sales@bellsystem.co.uk

Initial Attendo Ltd, Shadsworth Business Park, Blackburn, BB1 2PR Tel: (01254) 688688 Fax: (01254) 696460 E-mail: info@attendo.co.uk

NUT TAPPING

Tapping Services, 18-19 Broad Lanes, Bilston, West Midlands, WV14 0RY Tel: (01902) 404882 Fax: (01902) 403692

NUTRITION CONSULTANCY

Living Fountains Detox Clinic, 10 Hemlock Close, Oakwood, Derby, DE21 2NZ Tel: 0870 027 3656 Fax: 0870 1334836 E-mail: info@livingfountains.org

▶ SlimSeekers, 11 Huntleys Park, Tunbridge Wells, Kent, TN4 9TD Tel: (01892) 535300 Fax: (01892) 535311 E-mail: suehay@slimseekers.co.uk

Vitrition UK Ltd, 7 Victoria Spring Business Park, Wormald Street, Liversedge, West Yorkshire, WF15 6RA Tel: (01924) 410400 Fax: (01924) 410500 E-mail: jo.pollard@btconnect.com

NUTRITIONAL FOOD SUPPLEMENTS

Aloevera Co UK, PO Box 15, Towcester, Northamptonshire, NN12 8DJ Tel: (01327) 830855 Fax: (01327) 831000

Ardern Healthcare Ltd, Pipers Brook Farm, Eastham, Tenbury Wells, Worcestershire, WR15 8NP Tel: (01584) 781777 Fax: (01584) 781788 E-mail: info@ardernhealthcare.com

Aviform Ltd, Unit 4, G-K Wellesley Road, Tharston Industrial Estate, Long Stratton, Norwich, NR15 2PD Tel: (01508) 530813 Fax: (01508) 530873 E-mail: sales@aviform.co.uk

Balham Wholefoods & Health Store, 8 Bedford Hill, London, SW12 9RG Tel: (020) 8673 4842

Biocare Ltd, Lakeside Centre, 180 Lifford Lane, Birmingham, B30 3NU Tel: 0121-433 3727 Fax: 0121-433 3879 E-mail: info@biocare.co.uk

▶ Cambridge Nutrtional Sciences Ltd, Eden Research Park, Henry Crabb Road, Littleport, Ely, Cambridgeshire, CB6 1SE Tel: (01353) 862220 Fax: (01353) 863330 E-mail: mike@elisa.co.uk

▶ FeelAmazing, Marvell Rise, Harrogate, North Yorkshire, HG1 3LT Tel: (07976) 533827 E-mail: feelamazing@earnyourdream.co.uk

▶ The Forever Aloe Store, 1 Argyle Street, Gorse Hill, Swindon, SN2 8BP Tel: (01793) 641732 E-mail: sales@theforeveraloestore.co.uk

Fullwell Mill Ltd, Unit 5d Southwick Industrial Estate, Sunderland, SR5 3TX Tel: 0191-548 0050 Fax: 0191-516 9946 E-mail: info@fmfoods.co.uk

▶ Global Nutrition, 1 Furness Close, South Wootton, King's Lynn, Norfolk, PE30 3TR Tel: (01553) 671467 E-mail: kath@wellness4all.org.uk

▶ Healing Within (Herbalife), 5 Bentham Hill House, Stockland Green Road, Tunbridge Wells, Kent, TN3 0TJ Tel: 01892 541621 E-mail: rachel.scriven@btopenworld.com

Herbalife Independent Distributor, 9 Willenhall Close, Luton, LU3 3XX Tel: (01582) 591906

▶ Nutrafx Ltd, P.O. Box 157, Sandbach, Cheshire, CW11 4WY Tel: 08707 607551 Fax: 01270 766439 E-mail: lee@nutrafx.com

Science In Sport Ltd, Ashwood, Brockhall Village, Old Langho, Blackburn, BB6 8BB Tel: (01254) 246060 Fax: (01254) 246061 E-mail: info@scienceinsport.com

Vitrition UK Ltd, 7 Victoria Spring Business Park, Wormald Street, Liversedge, West Yorkshire, WF15 6RA Tel: (01924) 410400 Fax: (01924) 410500 E-mail: jo.pollard@btconnect.com

Wholesale Nutrition Ltd, Aztec House, Delta Business Park, Salterns Lane, Fareham, Hampshire, PO16 0JL Tel: 0800 174545 Fax: (01329) 289222

▶ www.herbalcare4u.com, 65 Mayfield Park South, Fishponds, Bristol, BS16 3NF Tel: 0117 9586577 E-mail: danielle.saunders@kingitsolutions.com

▶ www.Nutritionzone.co.uk, Unit 5, Mill Road Industrial Estate, Linlithgow Bridge, Linlithgow, West Lothian, EH49 7QY Tel: (01506) 848968 E-mail: admin@nutrtionzone.co.uk

NUTRITIONAL LABORATORY SERVICES

▶ Cambridge Nutrtional Sciences Ltd, Eden Research Park, Henry Crabb Road, Littleport, Ely, Cambridgeshire, CB6 1SE Tel: (01353) 862220 Fax: (01353) 863330 E-mail: mike@elisa.co.uk

NUTS, *See also Bolt and Nut Distributors etc: also other headings for particular types*

Buckinghamshire Fastener Co. Ltd, 14 Wilverley Road, Christchurch, Dorset, BH23 3RU Tel: (01202) 488202 Fax: (01202) 474442 E-mail: sales@buckfastener.co.uk

D S Fasteners Ltd, Unit 7, Hill Fort Close, Fison Way Industrial Estate, Thetford, Norfolk, IP24 1HS Tel: (01842) 763000 Fax: (01842) 764055

Fairways Fasteners Ltd, Unit 6 Starvale Road Industrial Estate, Lye, Stourbridge, West Midlands, DY9 8PP Tel: (01384) 897535 Fax: (01384) 423611 E-mail: sales@screwsandbolts.co.uk

High Tensile Bolts Ltd, Imperial Works, 93 Lockfield Avenue, Enfield, Middlesex, EN3 7PY Tel: (020) 8805 8510 Fax: (020) 8805 1553 E-mail: kebrell@montal-internet.co.uk

Mid Essex Fasteners Ltd, Beehive Lane Works, Beehive Lane, Chelmsford, CM2 9TE Tel: (01245) 257323 Fax: (01245) 252460 E-mail: midessexfasteners@btinternet.com

NUTS, CAPTIVE/BLIND

Bolhoff Fastenings Ltd, Midacre, Willenhall, West Midlands, WV13 2JW Tel: (01902) 637161 Fax: (01902) 609495 E-mail: enquiries@bollhoff.co.uk

Normandy Air Compressors, Unit 1d Cranborne Industrial Estate, Cranborne Road, Potters Bar, Hertfordshire, EN6 3JN Tel: (01707) 662248

Torque Control Ltd, 60 Alstone Lane, Cheltenham, Gloucestershire, GL51 8HE Tel: (01242) 261233 Fax: (01242) 221115 E-mail: torquecontrolltd@btinternet.com

NUTS, LOCK

Cotswold Autoflo Ltd, Unit 2, Willow Park, Hinton Road, Childswickham, Broadway, Worcestershire, WR12 7HY Tel: (01386) 853284 Fax: (01386) 854636 E-mail: sales@autoflo.co.uk

Fairchild Fasteners UK Ltd, Unit 6 Bardon 22 Industrial Estate, Bardon Hill, Coalville, Leicestershire, LE67 1TE Tel: (01530) 518900 Fax: (01530) 518910 E-mail: sales@fairchildfasteners.com

Trojan Special Fasteners Ltd, 18 Fortnum Close, Tile Cross, Birmingham, B33 0LG Tel: 0121-789 8586 Fax: 0121-789 8006 E-mail: sales@trojanspecialfastenersltd.co.uk

NUTSCHE PRESSURE FILTERS

Howard Filter Systems, East Skirdle, Waterrow, Taunton, Somerset, TA4 2AY Tel: (01984) 623112 Fax: (01984) 624770 E-mail: hfsl@btconnect.co.uk

NYLON BELTING

Chiorino UK, Phoenix Avenue, Featherstone, Pontefract, West Yorkshire, WF7 6EP Tel: (01977) 691880 Fax: (0870) 6065061 E-mail: sales@chiorino.co.uk

Whitaker Transmissions, 2 Heys Lane, Oswaldtwistle, Accrington, Lancashire, BB5 3BJ Tel: (01254) 382791 Fax: (01254) 239062

NYLON BOLTS AND NUTS

Allthread Plastics Ltd, Ridley Road, Burnt Mills Industrial Estate, Basildon, Essex, SS13 1EG Tel: (01268) 726559 Fax: (01268) 725287 E-mail: sales@allthread.co.uk

Micro Plastics (International) Ltd, Unit 2, Henley Industrial Park, Henley Road, Coventry, CV2 1SR Tel: (024) 7661 4320 Fax: (024) 7661 4831 E-mail: microplas@aol.com

Nylon & Alloys Ltd., 74 Half Acre Road, Hanwell, London, W7 3JJ Tel: (020) 8579 5166 Fax: (020) 8579 6986 E-mail: na@nylonalloys.co.uk

Plastic Parts Centre, Unit 12 Old Forge Trading Estate, Dudley Road, Stourbridge, West Midlands, DY9 8EL Tel: (01384) 424248 Fax: (01384) 424348 E-mail: sales@mossplastics.co.uk

NYLON CASTOR WHEELS

▶ Midland Wheels and Castors, The Die-Pat Centre, Broad March, Daventry, Northamptonshire, NN11 4HE Tel: (01327) 313111 Fax: (01327) 871821 E-mail: rayh@die-pat.co.uk

NYLON COATING PROCESSORS OR SERVICES

Omnikote Ltd, Chamberlain Road, Aylesbury, Buckinghamshire, HP19 8DY Tel: (01296) 483266 Fax: (01296) 392285 E-mail: sales@omnikote.co.uk

Sureline Finishing, 1-2 Quarry CR, Pennygillam Industrial Estate, Launceston, Cornwall, PL15 7PF Tel: (01566) 776630 Fax: (01566) 777773

NYLON COATINGS

▶ G & L Coatings, 8 Wallace Way, Hitchin, Hertfordshire, SG4 0SE Tel: (01462) 436668 Fax: (01462) 438982 E-mail: george.cooney@talk21.com

NYLON FABRICS

Frederick Beardsley & Co. Ltd, 1 Cotmanhay Road, Ilkeston, Derbyshire, DE7 8HR Tel: 0115-932 4502 Fax: 0115-944 1298 E-mail: sales@frederickbeardsley.com

J.F. Hodgett & Co. Ltd, 66 Bedford Street South, Leicester, LE1 3JR Tel: 0116-251 0705 Fax: 0116-251 2877 E-mail: jfhodgett@hotmail.com

Intercontinental Mercantile Ltd, 23 Dollis Hill Estate, 105 Brook Road, London, NW2 7BZ Tel: (020) 8830 7388 Fax: (020) 8830 7388

Maytex Fabrics Ltd, Curzon Works, Curzon Street, Leicester, LE1 2HH Tel: 0116-262 4422 Fax: 0116-262 4447 E-mail: maytexfab@aol.com

NYLON FIBRES

EMS-CHEMIE (UK) Ltd, Darfin House, Priestly Court, Stafford Technology Park, Stafford, ST18 0AR Tel: (01785) 283739 Fax: (01785) 283722 E-mail: welcome@uk.emsgrivory.com

▶ H T Gaddum & Co. Ltd, 3 Jordangate, Macclesfield, Cheshire, SK10 1EF Tel: (01625) 427666 Fax: (01625) 511331 E-mail: sales@gaddum.co.uk

NYLON HANDRAILS

Handrail Design Ltd, Sail & Colour Loft, The Historic Dockyard, Chatham, Kent, ME4 4TE Tel: (01634) 817800 Fax: (01634) 817711 E-mail: enquiries@handraildesign.co.uk

John Monaghan (Midlands) Ltd, Unit 5 Cavendish, Lichfield Road Industrial Estate, Tamworth, Staffordshire, B79 7XH Tel: (01827) 302480 Fax: (01827) 62164 E-mail: info@monaghanmidlands.co.uk

NYLON NUTS

Harrison & Clough Ltd, PO Box 9, Keighley, West Yorkshire, BD21 4EG Tel: (0870) 8892222 Fax: (0870) 8892233

Nylon & Alloys Ltd., 74 Half Acre Road, Hanwell, London, W7 3JJ Tel: (020) 8579 5166 Fax: (020) 8579 6986 E-mail: na@nylonalloys.co.uk

NYLON PACKAGING FILM

Brand Packaging Ltd, Bridge Mills, Holland Street, Pendleton, Salford, M6 6EL Tel: 0161-736 8941 Fax: 0161-745 7141

NYLON RAW MATERIALS

Longfield Chemicals Ltd, Hawthorne Farm, Tarvin Road, Frodsham, WA6 6UZ Tel: (01928) 739977 Fax: (01928) 739553 E-mail: enquiries@longchem.co.uk

NYLON SEWING THREAD

Barbra Coats Ltd, Hilden Mill, Lisburn, County Antrim, BT27 4RR Tel: (028) 9267 2231 Fax: (028) 9267 8048E-mail: mail@coats.com

Donisthorpe, PO Box 137, Leicester, LE4 1BF Tel: 0116-234 7920 Fax: 0116-234 7901 E-mail: sales@amann.com

Somac Threads Manufacturing Ltd, Unit 2-3 Brymau Four Trading Estate, River Lane, Saltney, Chester, CH4 8RF Tel: (01244) 680506 Fax: (01244) 680202 E-mail: sales@somac.co.uk

NYLON STOCKHOLDERS

Durbin Metal Industries Ltd, Unit 0, Lawrence Drive, Stover Trading Estate, Bristol, BS37 5PG Tel: (01454) 322668 Fax: (01454) 317415 E-mail: sales@durbinmetals.co.uk

Metals South West, 10 Bradley Lane, Newton Abbot, Devon, TQ12 1LZ Tel: (01626) 362026 Fax: (01626) 332220

NYLON YARN

Conti Fibre UK Ltd, Hulley Road, Macclesfield, Cheshire, SK10 2LT Tel: (01625) 429636 Fax: (01625) 610974

O RING DISTRIBUTORS OR AGENTS

M. Barnwell Services Ltd, 5 Bessemer Crescent, Rabans Lane Industrial Estate, Aylesbury, Buckinghamshire, HP19 8TF Tel: (01296) 431429 Fax: (01296) 435716 E-mail: aylesbury@barnwell.co.uk

Ceetak Ltd, Fraser Road, Priory Business Park, Bedford, MK44 3WH Tel: (01234) 832200 Fax: (01234) 832299 E-mail: ceetakltd@ceetak.com

Clarendon Engineering Ltd, 30 High Street, Earl Shilton, Leicester, LE9 7DG Tel: (01455) 841200 Fax: (01455) 841110 E-mail: sales@clarendoneng.co.uk

D E L Industrial Fastenings Ltd, Elvetham Bridge, Fleet, Hampshire, GU51 1AE Tel: (01252) 626425 Fax: (01252) 811741 E-mail: info@delindustrial.co.uk

O Rings Ltd, Gravel Lane, Chichester, West Sussex, PO19 8PQ Tel: (01243) 787817 Fax: (01243) 530440 E-mail: sales@oringslimited.co.uk

Supaseal (U K) Ltd, PO Box 5329, Market Harborough, Leicestershire, LE16 7PT Tel: (01858) 434141 Fax: (01858) 434717 E-mail: admin@supaseal.co.uk

O RINGS

Claron Plastics Ltd, Alders Way, Yalberton Industrial Estate, Paignton, Devon, TQ4 7QL Tel: (01803) 528677 Fax: (01803) 525134 E-mail: services@claron.co.uk

Dichtomatik Ltd, Donington House, Riverside Road, Pride Park, Derby, DE24 8HY Tel: (01332) 202121 Fax: (01332) 524404 E-mail: mail@dichtomatik.co.uk

▶ E A P International Ltd, Junction 19 Industrial Park, Green Lane, Heywood, Lancashire, OL10 1NB Tel: (01706) 624422 Fax: (01706) 624455 E-mail: sales@eapseals.com

Greene Tweed & Co. Ltd, Mere Way, Ruddington, Nottingham, NG11 6JS Tel: 0115-931 5777 Fax: 0115-931 5888 E-mail: mktng@gtweed.com

Grommets Ltd, Unit 2 Hollands La Industrial Estate, Henfield, West Sussex, BN5 9QY Tel: (01273) 493355 Fax: (01273) 493388 E-mail: sales@grommets.co.uk

Meadex Mouldings Ltd, Units 1-2, Tanyard Lane, Ross-On-Wye, Herefordshire, HR9 7BH Tel: (01989) 567999 Fax: (01989) 768022 E-mail: sales@meadex.co.uk

Northern Engineering Sheffield Ltd, Haigh Moor Drive, Dinnington, Sheffield, S25 2JY Tel: (01909) 560203 Fax: (01909) 560184 E-mail: sales@northerneng.co.uk

Precision Polymer Engineering Ltd, Greenbank Road, Blackburn, BB1 3EA Tel: (01254) 295400 Fax: (01254) 680182 E-mail: sales@prepol.com

Ramsay Services Ltd, Unit C Bamburgh Court, Team Valley Trading Estate, Gateshead, Tyne & Wear, NE11 0TX Tel: 0191-422 4200 Fax: 0191-422 4222

Superior Seals, 7 Nimrod Way, East Dorset Trade Park, Wimborne, Dorset, BH21 7SH Tel: (01202) 854300 Fax: (01202) 854313 E-mail: sales.seals@superiorltd.com

Derek Timms Seals Ltd, 90 Evelyn Road, Birmingham, B11 3JJ Tel: 0121-773 7666 Fax: 0121-766 5590 E-mail:

O RINGS, PTFE

Trelleborg Sealing Solutions, 1 Cranbrook Way, Shirley, Solihull, West Midlands, B90 4GT Tel: 0121-744 1221 Fax: 0121-733 2442 E-mail: tssuk@trelleborg.com

OAK

Mccurdy & Co. Ltd, Manor Farm, Stanford Dingley, Reading, RG7 6LS Tel: 0118-974 4866 Fax: 0118-974 4375 E-mail: jobs@mccurdyco.com

OAK DINING FURNITURE

▶ Timberline Pine Ltd, 1-2 Kingswalk, Winchester, Hampshire, SO23 8AF Tel: (01962) 861133 Fax: (01962) 884231 E-mail: sales@timberlinepine.co.uk

OAK FRAMED BUILDINGS

▶ Holmsley Mill Ltd, Holmsley, Burley, Ringwood, Hampshire, BH24 4HY Tel: (01425) 402507 Fax: (01425) 403516 E-mail: sales@holmsleymill.co.uk

▶ Oakwrights Country Buildings, The Lakes, Swainshill, Hereford, HR4 7PU Tel: (0845) 2309560 Fax: (01432) 357733

OAK FRAMES

▶ Oak-Apple Frames, Widcombe Farm, Culmhead, Taunton, Somerset, TA3 7DX Tel: (01823) 421395 Fax: (01823) 421395 E-mail: enquiries@oakappleframes.co.uk

Wills Mill, mobile sawmilling and timber, The Woodshed, Home Farm, Baynards Park, Cranleigh, Surrey, GU6 8EQ Tel: 01483 548000 Fax: 01483 548000 E-mail: will@wills-mill.co.uk

OATMEAL

European Oat Millers Ltd, Mile Road, Bedford, MK42 9TB Tel: (01234) 327922 Fax: (01234) 353892 E-mail: sales@oatmillers.com

Grampian Oat Products, Boyndie, Boyndie, Banff, AB45 2LR Tel: (01261) 843330 Fax: (01261) 843394

John Hogarth Ltd, PO Box 6, Kelso, Roxburghshire, TD5 7HR Tel: (01573) 224224 Fax: (01573) 225461 E-mail: johnhogarth@kelsomills.freeserve.co.uk

Morning Foods Ltd, North Western Mills, Crewe, CW2 6HP Tel: (01270) 213261 Fax: (01270) 500291 E-mail: sales@morningfoods.com

OBSERVATION CLASS REMOTELY OPERATED VEHICLES (ROV)

AC-CESS Co. UK Ltd, Tyrebagger Works, Kinellar, Aberdeen, AB21 0TT Tel: (01224) 790100 Fax: (01224) 790111 E-mail: info@ac-cess.com

OBSOLETE BALL BEARINGS

Goldline F1 Ltd, Stafford Park 17, Telford, Shropshire, TF3 3DG Tel: (01952) 292401 Fax: (01952) 292403 E-mail: info@goldlinebearings.co.uk

OBSOLETE ELECTRONIC COMPONENTS

A Tec International Ltd, 109-111 St. Johns Hill, Sevenoaks, Kent, TN13 3PE Tel: (01732) 743737 Fax: (01732) 743838 E-mail: vic@a-tecuk.com

Abacus Eiger Northeast, Hall Mews, Clifford Road, Boston Spa, Wetherby, West Yorkshire, LS23 6DT Tel: (01937) 841312 Fax: (01937) 841062

Amelec Ltd, 101 Moreton Street, Cannock, Staffordshire, WS11 5HN Tel: (01543) 466191 Fax: (01543) 467339 E-mail: info@amelec.co.uk

Austin Semiconductor (Europe) Ltd, Test House, 1 Mill Lane, Alton, Hampshire, GU34 2QG Tel: (01420) 88022 Fax: (01420 87259 E-mail: sales@austinsemi.com

Geoff Bullen Electronics, Unit 1-2 Woods Way, Goring-by-Sea, Worthing, West Sussex, BN12 4QY Tel: (01903) 244500 Fax: (01903) 700715 E-mail: sales@gbelectronics.com

Component Forum Ltd, PO Box 20, Towcester, Northamptonshire, NN12 7XJ Tel: (01908) 543808 Fax: (01908) 543909 E-mail: enquiries@componentforum.co.uk

Contact Components Ltd, 5 Parkend, Harlow BSNS Park, Harlow, Essex, CM19 5QF Tel: (01279) 424211 Fax: (01279) 424213

Contact Electronics Ltd, Unit 4 Westmead House, 123 Westmead Road, Sutton, Surrey, SM1 4JH Tel: (020) 8643 3000 Fax: (020) 8643 5777 E-mail: contact@contact-electronics.co.uk

Genalog Ltd, Gills Green Oast, Gills Green, Cranbrook, Kent, TN18 5ET Tel: (01580) 753754 Fax: (01580) 752979 E-mail: sales@genalog.com

Greenweld, C/O Permex Ltd, Riverside House, Plumpton Road, Hoddesdon, Hertfordshire, EN11 0PA Tel: (01992) 452980 Fax: (01992) 452981 E-mail: bargains@greenweld.co.uk

P R S Invistech, The Technology Centre, Easting Close, Worthing, West Sussex, BN14 8HQ Tel: (01903) 217337 Fax: (01903) 217713 E-mail: sales@prsl.co.uk

Pro Found Electronics Ltd, The Forge, 31a The Broadway, Thatcham, Berkshire, RG19 3HX Tel: (01635) 872986 Fax: (01635) 872986

OBSOLETE SEMICONDUCTOR DIODES

W W E Semiconductors Ltd, The Beeches, Grange Rd, Uckfield, E. Sussex, TN22 1QU Tel: (01825) 746900 Fax: (01825) 746911

OBSOLETE SEMICONDUCTORS

Ace Components Ltd, 4 Priory Gardens, Scorton, Preston, PR3 1AQ Tel: (01524) 793893 Fax: (01524) 793894 E-mail: colinbabbs.ace@ukonline.co.uk

Alpine Technology Ltd, Unit 12 Tungsten Building, George Street, Portslade, Brighton, BN41 1RA Tel: (01273) 425290 Fax: (0870) 8901087 E-mail: sales@alpinetech.co.uk

OBSTACLE WARNING LIGHTING

▶ F & L Accessories Ltd, 4 5 Chosen View Road, Cheltenham, Gloucestershire, GL51 9LT Tel: (01242) 571409 Fax: (01242) 574240 E-mail: sales@flacc.co.uk

OCCASIONAL FURNITURE

▶ Ancholme Discount Furniture, Unit 7 Island Carr Industrial Estate, Island Carr Road, Brigg, South Humberside, DN20 8PD Tel: (01652) 653644 Fax: (01652) 653644 E-mail: chizel@btopenworld.com

Be Modern Ltd, Head Office, Western Approach, South Shields, Tyne & Wear, NE33 5QZ Tel: 0191-455 3571 Fax: 0191-456 5556 E-mail: justina.hathaway@bemodern.co.uk

Furniture Fusion, Bedford Road, Apsley Guise, Milton Keynes, MK17 8DJ Tel: (01908) 586334 Fax: (01908) 586332 E-mail: info@furniturefusion.co.uk

▶ In Focus Interiors, Oxenwood, Westhill Road South, South Wonston, Winchester, Hampshire, SO21 3HP Tel: (01962) 883092 Fax: (01962) 885144

Mayers & Shaw Ltd, Unit 6 Bunns Bank, Old Buckenham, Attleborough, Norfolk, NR17 1QD Tel: (01953) 453225 Fax: (01953) 456055 E-mail: sales@mayersandshaw.co.uk

▶ Northcroft Ltd, Argall Works, Argall Avenue, London, E10 7QE Tel: (020) 8558 6919 Fax: (020) 8556 1097 E-mail: info@northcroft.uk.com

▶ Shimu Oriental Furniture Ltd, 3C-3D Harrogate Road, Rawdon, Leeds, LS19 6HW Tel: (0870) 2071433 Fax: 0113-250 8284 E-mail: info@shimu.co.uk

G.S. Smart & Co. Ltd, Ardath Road, Birmingham, B38 9PN Tel: 0121-459 0983 Fax: 0121-459 8559 E-mail: info@metalrax-group.co.uk

Teemo Designs Ltd, Roman Bank, Cherry Holt Road, Bourne, Lincolnshire, PE10 9LQ Tel: (01778) 421421 Fax: (01778) 393135 E-mail: teemo@globalnet.co.uk

Whiteleaf Ltd, Po Box 2, Princes Risborough, Buckinghamshire, HP27 9DP Tel: (01844) 261199 Fax: (01844) 342337 E-mail: sales@whiteleaffurniture.co.uk

OCCUPANCY CONTROLS, LIGHTING

▶ Reality Logic Ltd, 28 Harsfold Road, Rustington, Littlehampton, West Sussex, BN16 2QE Tel: (01903) 775352 Fax: (0870) 4589021 E-mail: jeremy.aston@realitylogic.com

OCCUPATIONAL HEALTH OR HYGIENE OR SAFETY CONSULTANCY

▶ A F Consulting, 19 Waylands, Cricklade, Swindon, SN6 6BT Tel: (01793) 751398 Fax: (01793) 751398 E-mail: info@afcons.co.uk

Aberdeen Medical Services, 6 Rubislaw Terrace, Aberdeen, AB10 1XE Tel: (01224) 625766 Fax: (01224) 646612

▶ Artemia Ltd, Keystone House, Grateley, Andover, Hampshire, SP11 8HZ Tel: (01264) 889020 E-mail: pajohnson@doctors.org.uk

C P A Laboratories Ltd, 318 Worple Road, London, SW20 8QU Tel: (020) 8946 8621 Fax: (020) 8947 1206 E-mail: admincpa@eurofins.com

Complete Projects CDM Ltd, 25 Cadman Street, Mosborough, Sheffield, S20 5BU Tel: 0114-251 4106 Fax: 0114-251 4106 E-mail: info@completeprojectscdm.co.uk

Corporate Health Ltd, 30 Bradford Road, Slough, SL1 4PG Tel: (01753) 781600 Fax: (01753) 517889 E-mail: enquiries@corporatehealth.co.uk

▶ Cottam Parkinson Consulting Ltd, Unit 5, Thomas Street, Congleton, Cheshire, CW12 1QU Tel: (01260) 289229 Fax: (01260) 289221 E-mail: info@cottamparkinson.co.uk

E R M Risks, 8 Cavendish Square, London, W1G OER Tel: (020) 7465 7349 Fax: (020) 7465 7270 E-mail: tawg@ermuk.com

Environmental Services, 48 Shillingford Road, Exeter, EX2 8UB Tel: (01392) 438251 Fax: (01392) 435623 E-mail: tmayne@environmentuk.com

▶ Everwell Occupational Health Ltd, The Rowans, Holmes Chapel Road, Somerford, Congleton, Cheshire, CW12 4SP Tel: (01477) 544306 E-mail: enquiries@everwelloh.co.uk

Gipping Occupational Health Ltd, Mill Lodge, Mendlesham Green, Stowmarket, Suffolk, IP14 5RB Tel: (01449) 766913 Fax: (01449) 766891 E-mail: advice@gipping.co.uk

▶ Grosvenor Health, Grosvenor House, Prospect Hill, Redditch, Worcestershire, B97 4DL Tel: (01527) 532100 Fax: (01527) 592732 E-mail: info@grosvenorhealth.com

Mabbett & Associates Ltd, Mabbett House, 11 Sandyford Place, Glasgow, G3 7NB Tel: 0141-227 2300 Fax: 0141 227 2301 E-mail: bradley@mabbett.com

North Sea Medical Centre Ltd, 3 Lowestoft Road, Gorleston, Great Yarmouth, Norfolk, NR31 6SG Tel: (01493) 414141 Fax: (01493) 441988 E-mail: occhealth@northseamedical.demon.co.uk

O H S Ltd, 11-17 Campus Road, Listerhills Science Park, Bradford, West Yorkshire, BD7 1HR Tel: (01274) 735848 Fax: (01274) 392280 E-mail: info@ohs.co.uk

R P S Consultants Ltd, Executive Freight Building, Kirkhill Drive, Kirkhill Industrial Estate, Aberdeen, AB21 0EU Tel: (01224) 773734 Fax: (01224) 724220 E-mail: rpsad@rpsplc.co.uk

Safety First Aid Group Ltd, Unit 15-17 Garrick Industrial Centre, Irving Way, London, NW9 6AQ Tel: (020) 8202 7447 Fax: (0800) 281655 E-mail: sales@safetyfirstaid.co.uk

▶ Scotcare Health Solutions, 21 Carron Way, Paisley, Renfrewshire, PA3 4NW Tel: (07940) 223619 Fax: 0141-887 7197 E-mail: info@scotcare.co.uk

▶ TCH Safety Consultants, Cobblers Cottage, Packet Lane, Rosudgeon, Penzance, Cornwall, TR20 9QD Tel: 01736 762016 Fax: 01736 762016 E-mail: info@tchsafety.co.uk

OCCUPATIONAL HEALTH/ HYGIENE/SAFETY PRODUCTS,

See also headings for particular products

Industrial Catering Industries Ltd, Sterling Works, Clarence Road, Cardiff, CF10 5FA Tel: (029) 2049 8498 Fax: (029) 2048 8838 E-mail: sales@phoenix-saxton.com

McConnell Equipment Ltd, 16 Ballycraigy Road, Antrim, BT41 1PL Tel: (028) 9446 3921 Fax: (028) 9446 7102 E-mail: macquip@btinternet.com

Quantitech Ltd, 3 Old Wolverton Road, Old Wolverton, Milton Keynes, MK12 5NP Tel: (01908) 227722 Fax: (01908) 227733 E-mail: quant@quantitech.co.uk

Safetymark Consultancy Services, Sydney Cottages, Elm Road, Claygate, Esher, Surrey, KT10 0EJ Tel: (01372) 462277 Fax: (01372) 462288 E-mail: mark.snelling@safetymark.net

▶ Safewell, 31 Teesdale Avenue, Hull, HU9 3UG Tel: (01482) 792159 E-mail: sales@safewell.com

OCCUPATIONAL SAFETY AND HEALTH ACT (OSHA) STANDARD OVENS

▶ Everwell Occupational Health Ltd, The Rowans, Holmes Chapel Road, Somerford, Congleton, Cheshire, CW12 4SP Tel: (01477) 544306 E-mail: enquiries@everwelloh.co.uk

OCEANOGRAPHIC INSTRUMENT HIRE

Ashtead Technology Ltd, Unit 3, Kirkton Avenue, Pimedden Road Industrial Estate, Aberdeen, AB21 0BF Tel: (01224) 771888 Fax: (01224) 770129 E-mail: rentals@ashtead-technology.com

G S E Rentals Ltd, Unit 32, Wellheads Industrial Estate, Aberdeen, AB21 7GA Tel: (01224) 771247 Fax: (01224) 723116 E-mail: info@gserentals.co.uk

OCEANOGRAPHIC INSTRUMENT MANUFRS

Valeport Ltd, St. Peters Quay, Totnes, Devon, TQ9 5EW Tel: (01803) 869292 Fax: (01803) 869293 E-mail: sales@valeport.co.uk

OCEANOGRAPHIC SERVICES/ SURVEYS

Andrews Survey, Salmon Road, Great Yarmouth, Norfolk, NR30 3QS Tel: (01493) 332111 Fax: (01493) 332265

BMT Cordah Ltd, Grove House, 7 Ocean Way, Southampton, SO14 3TJ Tel: (023) 8023 2222 Fax: (023) 8023 2891 E-mail: jenny.bell@bmtcordah.com

Fugro Ltd, Hithercroft Road, Wallingford, Oxfordshire, OX10 9RB Tel: (0870) 4021300 Fax: (0870) 4021599 E-mail: uk@geos.com

Proudman Oceanographic Laboratory, Bidston Observatory, Bidston Hill, Prenton, Merseyside, CH43 7RA Tel: 0151-653 8633 Fax: 0151-653 6269 E-mail: sales@pol.ac.uk

ODOUR CONTROL BIOLOGICAL PRODUCTS

▶ Branova Cleaning Services, Meadow Mills, Carlton Road, Dewsbury, West Yorkshire, WF13 2BA Tel: (01924) 486000 Fax: (01924) 486010 E-mail: sales@branova.com

ODOUR CONTROL COLUMNS

Brooks Composites Ltd, Percival Lane, Runcorn, Cheshire, WA7 4DS Tel: (01928) 574776 Fax: (01928) 577067 E-mail: sales@brooks-composites.co.uk

ODOUR CONTROL SYSTEMS

Armfibre Ltd, Unit 7, Wilstead Industrial Park, Kenneth Way, Wilstead, Bedford, MK45 3PD Tel: (01234) 741444 Fax: (01767) 651901 E-mail: sales@armfibre.com

E A West, Pyewipe, Grimsby, South Humberside, DN31 2SW Tel: (01472) 232000 Fax: (01472) 232020 E-mail: hmats_uk@huntsman.com

Odour Control Systems Ltd, Manor Lane, Hawarden, Deeside, Clwyd, CH5 3PP Tel: (01244) 536700 Fax: (01244) 535184 E-mail: mail@odourcontrolsystems.ltd.co.uk

P M G Technical Services Ltd, Unit 9, Walton Industrial Estate, Beacon Road, Stone, Staffordshire, ST15 0NN Tel: (01785) 818857 Fax: (01785) 816587 E-mail: info@pmgtech.co.uk

Sly Filters Europe Ltd, 16 The Warren, East Goscote, Leicester, LE7 3XA Tel: 0116-260 8187 Fax: 0116-264 0543 E-mail: sly@ridgep.fsbusiness.co.uk

OFF ROAD LORRIES

▶ TruckSmart Ltd, Lancaster New Road, Cabus, Preston, PR3 1AD Tel: (01524) 791999 Fax: 01524 792999 E-mail: sales@trucksmart.co.uk

OFF ROAD TRAILERS

Artcom Tradebridge Ltd, Unit 2E, South Bridgend, Crieff, Perthshire, PH7 4DJ Tel: (01764) 654666 Fax: (0560) 1163109 E-mail: enquiries@scot-track.co.uk

Dewi A Jones, 9 Groesffordd, Llanddoged, Llanrwst, Gwynedd, LL26 0UA Tel: (01492) 640399 Fax: (01492) 641905 E-mail: sales@burtech-daj-trailers.co.uk

Rolling Transport Systems Ltd, Unit 21 Old Yarn Mills, Westbury, Sherborne, Dorset, DT9 3RQ Tel: (01935) 814390 Fax: (01935) 815720

OFF ROAD VEHICLES

A T Landquip, Lonmay, Fraserburgh, Aberdeenshire, AB43 8RN Tel: (01346) 532492 Fax: (01346) 532547 E-mail: sales@atlandquip.com

A U S A (UK) Ltd, Unit 6-7 Alma Industrial Estate, Regent Street, Rochdale, Lancashire, OL12 0HQ Tel: (01706) 649691 Fax: (01706) 649720 E-mail: ausa@comel.demon.co.uk

Artcom Tradebridge Ltd, Unit 2E, South Bridgend, Crieff, Perthshire, PH7 4DJ Tel: (01764) 654666 Fax: (0560) 1163109 E-mail: enquiries@scot-track.co.uk

R.H. Collier & Co. Ltd, 1-41 Sutton Road, Erdington, Birmingham, B23 6QH Tel: 0121-377 8888 Fax: 0121-377 6907 E-mail: fleetsales@colliers.co.uk

Crayford Special Vehicle Ltd, Lyon Way, St. Albans, Hertfordshire, AL4 0LQ Tel: (01727) 851222 Fax: (01727) 859222 E-mail: sales@crayford.co.uk

Gerald Dinnis Ltd, Tedburn Road, Whitestone, Exeter, EX4 2HF Tel: (01392) 811581 Fax: (01392) 811722 E-mail: info@whitehorsemotors.co.uk

L W Vass Holdings Ltd, Station Road, Ampthill, Bedford, MK45 2RB Tel: (01525) 403255 Fax: (01525) 404194 E-mail: sales@vass.co.uk

OFFICE ACCOMMODATION OR BUSINESS CENTRES OR OFFICE LETTING AGENTS

Acorns Lettings and Property Management, High Street, Stanwell Village, Staines, Middlesex, TW19 7JS Tel: 01784 254596 E-mail: info@acorns-lettings.co.uk

Action Team For Jobs, Belasis Business Centre, Coxwold Way, Belasis Hall Technology Park, Billingham, Cleveland, TS23 4EA Tel: (01642) 343434 Fax: (01642) 370328 E-mail: lynn.hitchin@dbh-officers.com

Adams & Adams Ltd, Adams House, Dickerage Lane, New Malden, Surrey, KT3 3SF Tel: (020) 8949 1121 Fax: (020) 8336 1126 E-mail: adamsnewmalden@aol.com

Anglia Textile Manufacturers Ltd, Holly Park Mills, Calverley, Pudsey, West Yorkshire, LS28 5QS Tel: 0113-257 0861 Fax: 0113-257 2391 E-mail: fabrics@angliat.free.online.co.uk

BMF Business Services, 211 Piccadilly, London, W1J 9HF Tel: (020) 7353 8688 Fax: (020) 7895 1353 E-mail: info@211piccadilly.co.uk

Bond Estates Ltd, Bond Avenue, Bletchley, Milton Keynes, MK1 1JJ Tel: (01908) 270900 Fax: (01908) 270052 E-mail: info@terrapin-ltd.co.uk

▶ Brennan Lettings & Property Management, Weddington Road, Nuneaton, Warwickshire, CV10 0EG Tel: (024) 7635 2537

Brookfield Business Centre Ltd, 333 Crumlin Road, Belfast, BT14 7EA Tel: (028) 9074 5241 Fax: (028) 9074 8025

▶ Castle Properties, 7-9 Portland Street, Cheltenham, Gloucestershire, GL52 2NZ Tel: 0870 240 7113 E-mail: info@castleprop.co.uk

Citibase Ltd, 100 Wellington Street, Leeds, LS1 4LT Tel: 0113-242 2444 Fax: 0113-242 2433 E-mail: leeds.ws@citibase.co.uk

Collingwood Houses Sevices Ltd, Collingwood House, 367 Croydon Road, Wallington, Surrey, SM6 7NY Tel: (020) 8773 2411 Fax: (020) 8669 3013 E-mail: collingwoodhouse@btinternet.com

▶ Derby Just Lets, 2 Foxfields Drive, Oakwood, Derby, DE21 2ND Tel: 0870 027 3654 Fax: 0870 1334836 E-mail: derby@justlets.com

▶ Derby Lets, 18 Maidenshaw Road, Epsom, Surrey, KT19 8HE Tel: (0845) 6023008 E-mail: office@derbylets.wanadoo.co.uk

▶ Emerald Bay Ltd, 50 Gorsey Lane, Warrington, WA1 3PS Tel: (01925) 243366 Fax: (01925) 243377

Executive Communications Centres, 252-256 Kings Road, Reading, RG1 4HP Tel: 0118-956 6660 Fax: 0118-956 6415

OFFICE ACCOMMODATION OR BUSINESS CENTRES OR OFFICE LETTING AGENTS – *continued*

First Base, Enterprise House, Ocean Way, Southampton, SO14 3XB Tel: (023) 8033 1666 Fax: (023) 8033 2050 E-mail: southampton@fbase.com

▶ Gainsborough Business Centres, 100 Pall Mall, St. James's, London, SW1Y 5HP Tel: (0800) 3282668 E-mail: sales@gainsbc.co.uk

▶ GO HAVEN LTD, 72A WESTBOURNE RD, HUDDERSFIELD, HD1 4LE Tel: 01484 544300 E-mail: enquire@gohaven.com

Hampton Leasing Ltd, 7 Mount Mews, High Street, Hampton, Middlesex, TW12 2SH Tel: (020) 8979 2262 Fax: (020) 8941 2645 E-mail: info@messagebase.com

▶ Isherwoods, 12 Imperial Square, Cheltenham, Gloucestershire, GL50 1QB Tel: (01242) 226999 Fax: (01242) 227444

J Clarke & Sons Enterprises, 213 Muswell Hill Broadway, London, N10 3RS Tel: (020) 8883 9946 Fax: (020) 8883 9947 E-mail: sales@clarkepropertygroup.co.uk

John Grout & Co. Ltd, Dallow Street, Burton-on-Trent, Staffordshire, DE14 2PQ Tel: (01283) 813454

▶ Joseph's Well Office Space, Josephs Well, Hanover Walk, Leeds, LS3 1AB Tel: 0113-271 7221 Fax: 0113-246 1454 E-mail: mtaylor@pullans.com

K G Business Centre, KG Business Centre, Kingsfield Way, Northampton, NN5 7QS Tel: (01604) 750777 Fax: (01604) 580011 E-mail: sales@kgbc.co.uk

▶ Liberty Business Centres, Sybrig House, Ridge Way, Donibristle Industrial Park, Hillend, Dunfermline, Fife, KY11 9JN Tel: (01383) 823030 Fax: (01383) 820003 E-mail: info@libertybusinesscentres.co.uk

London Offices & Properties Ltd, 35 Piccadilly, London, W1J 0DW Tel: (020) 7734 7282 Fax: (020) 7734 4561 E-mail: offices@35piccadilly.co.uk

▶ lookingforaproperty.com, 18 Grosvenor Wharf Road, Isle of Dogs, London, E14 3EF Tel: (020) 7538 1915 Fax: (01322) 226 047 E-mail: info@lookingforaproperty.com

Mascot Letting Agent, 351 A Whitehorse Road, Croydon, CR0 2HS Tel: (020) 8665 6683 Fax: (020) 8665 6683 E-mail: mascot.croydon@btinternet.com

▶ MLS Business Centres South West, 66 Queen Square, Bristol, BS1 4JP Tel: 0117-987 6200 Fax: 0117-987 6201 E-mail: tom.endacott@mlsbusinesscentres.com

▶ Passion for Property Ltd, 66 Lower Bridge Street, Chester, CH1 1RU Tel: (01244) 350300 Fax: (01244) 350311 E-mail: info@passionforproperty.com

Penn Studios, Penn Farm Studios, Harston Road, Haslingfield, Cambridge, CB23 1JZ Tel: (01487) 773282

Regus (Central London), 1 Northumberland Avenue, London, WC2N 5BW Tel: (020) 7872 5500 Fax: (020) 7872 5611 E-mail: karl.newman@regus.com

▶ Royston Estate Agents, 118-120 Glenthorne Road, London, W6 0LP Tel: (020) 8563 7100 Fax: (020) 8563 7045 E-mail: kellysearch.com@roystonw6.co.uk

Saracen's House Business Centre, Saracens House, 25 ST. Margarets Green, Ipswich, IP4 2BN Tel: (01473) 225951 Fax: (01473) 211508 E-mail: reception@saracens.co.uk

▶ Saturn Facilities Ltd, Bedford Heights, Brickhill Drive, Bedford, MK41 7PH Tel: (01234) 244500 Fax: (01234) 244511 E-mail: tjordan@saturnfacilities.com

▶ Saturn Facilities Ltd, 101 Lockhurst Lane, Coventry, CV6 5SF Tel: (024) 7658 2000 Fax: (024) 7658 2401 E-mail: sales@saturnfacilities.com

Saturn Facilities Ltd, 8-10 Grosvenor Gardens, London, SW1W 0DH Tel: (020) 7861 0550 Fax: (020) 7861 0551 E-mail: enquiries@saturnfacilities.com

▶ Saturn Facilities, Saturn Centre, Spring Road, Ettingshall, Wolverhampton, WV4 6JX Tel: (01902) 493192 Fax: (01902) 402553 E-mail: tjordan@saturnfacilities.com

▶ Saturn Facilities Birmingham, Ephraim Phillips House, Bissell Street, Birmingham, B5 7UP Tel: 0121 6221366 E-mail: tjordan@saturnfacilities.com

▶ Saturn Facilities Mayfair, 5-6 Carlos Place, Mayfair, London, W1K 3AP Tel: (020) 7907 9700 E-mail: tjordan@saturnfacilities.com

▶ Saturn Facilities Worthing, Columbia House, Columbia Drive, Worthing, West Sussex, BN13 3hd Tel: (01903) 262663 E-mail: tjordan@saturnfacilities.com

Signature House Ltd, Signature House, 232A Rainhill Road, Rainhill, Prescot, Merseyside, L35 4LD Tel: 0151-430 7114 Fax: 0151-431 0515 E-mail: laurataylor@psignature.com

Skillion Ltd, Southbank Commercial Centre, 140 Battersea Park Road, London, SW11 4NB Tel: (020) 7622 5511 Fax: (020) 7738 8272 E-mail: southbankcc@easynet.co.uk

Stevenage Business Initiative, The Business & Technology Centre, Bessemer Drive, Stevenage, Hertfordshire, SG1 2DX Tel: (01438) 315733 Fax: (01438) 313001 E-mail: sbienq@stevbtc.demon.co.uk

▶ T L B Homes, 40 Royle Green Road, Manchester, M22 4NG Tel: 0161-945 5777 Fax: 0161-945 5536

▶ Whitchurch Business Centre, Green End, Whitchurch, Shropshire, SY13 1AD Tel: (01948) 660550 Fax: (01948) 660560 E-mail: james.archer@whitchurchbc.co.uk

▶ Wilkinson Estates, 1 High Street, Maidenhead, Berkshire, SL6 1JN Tel: (01628) 777075 Fax: (01628) 788007 E-mail: post@wilkinsons.co.uk

OFFICE ACCOMMODATION WITH FACILITIES ETC, *See Business Centres etc*

OFFICE AGENTS OR PROPERTY CONSULTANCY

Acre Investments Ltd, Short Acre Street, Walsall, WS2 8HW Tel: (01922) 623360 Fax: (01922) 623360

James Andrew International Ltd, 72-75 Marylebone High Street, London, W1U 5JW Tel: (020) 7224 4436 Fax: (020) 7486 5277 E-mail: hms@jamesandrew.co.uk

City Partitions, 13 Chesterfield Road, Ashford, Middlesex, TW15 2NB Tel: (01784) 255552

Cluttons P.L.C., Portman House, 2 Portman Street, London, W1H 6DU Tel: (020) 7408 1010 Fax: (020) 7629 3263 E-mail: ph@cluttons.co.uk

Colliers Cre, 15-16 Park Row, Leeds, LS1 5HD Tel: 0113-200 1800 Fax: 0113-200 1840 E-mail: leeds@colliers cre.co.uk

Alan Croft Property Services, 48 Conduit Street, London, W1S 2YR Tel: (020) 7434 9799 Fax: (020) 7734 0217

D E & J Levy, Dukes Court, 32 Duke Street, London, SW1Y 6DF Tel: (020) 7930 1070 Fax: (020) 7930 3028 E-mail: info@dejlevy.co.uk

▶ Donaldsons, 48 Warwick Street, London, W1B 5NL Tel: (020) 7534 5000 Fax: (020) 7424 0045

Dunster & Morton, 92 London Street, Reading, RG1 4SJ Tel: 0118-955 1700 Fax: 0118-955 1725 E-mail: info@dunsterandmorton.co.uk

Garner & Sons, 15 St Petersgate, Stockport, Cheshire, SK1 1EB Tel: 0161-480 3013 Fax: 0161-477 9125 E-mail: enquiries@garnerandsons.co.uk

Hampton Leasing Ltd, 7 Mount Mews, High Street, Hampton, Middlesex, TW12 2SH Tel: (020) 8979 2262 Fax: (020) 8941 2645 E-mail: info@messagebase.com

Edwin Hill, 18 Saville Row, London, W1S 3PW Tel: (020) 7287 2020 Fax: (020) 7734 1255 E-mail: ehlondon@edwinhill.co.uk

Hurst Warne Ltd, 323 Kingston Road, Leatherhead, Surrey, KT22 7TU Tel: (01372) 360190 Fax: (01372) 360211 E-mail: enquiries@hurstwarne.co.uk

Robert Irving & Burns, 23-24 Margaret St, London, W1W 8LF Tel: (020) 7637 0821 Fax: (020) 7637 8827E-mail: props@rib.co.uk

▶ Kingsley Commercial, Chenil House, 181-183 Kings Road, London, SW3 5EB Tel: (020) 7352 3130 Fax: (020) 7352 5111 E-mail: sales@kingsleycommercial.co.uk

▶ London Apartment Rentals, 17 Queensborough Terr, Bayswater, London, W2 3SS Tel: (020) 7727 2828 Fax: (020) 7229 9816 E-mail: brian@london-apartment-rentals.com

Mellersh & Harding, 43 St. James'S Place, London, SW1A 1NS Tel: (020) 7499 0866 Fax: (020) 7522 8501 E-mail: info@mellersh.co.uk

Nai Gooch Webster, 4 Albemarle Street, London, W1S 4BW Tel: (020) 7409 5100 Fax: (020) 7409 5199

Smith Melzack Pepper Angliss Services Ltd, 7-10 Chandos Street, Cavendish Square, London, W1G 9AJ Tel: (020) 7546 1996 Fax: (020) 7546 1900 E-mail: enquiries@sm-pa.co.uk

Teacher Marks Ltd, 23 Princes Street, London, W1B 2LX Tel: (020) 7493 4422 Fax: (020) 7497 7773 E-mail: offices@teachermarks.co.uk

Titanic Off Licence, Russell Lane, London, N20 0BB Tel: (020) 8368 9339

Daniel Watney, 25 Hosier Lane, London, EC1A 9DW Tel: (020) 7246 5000 Fax: (020) 7248 7001 E-mail: info@danwat.com

John D. Wood International Ltd, 19 Berkeley Street, London, W1J 8ED Tel: (020) 7629 9050 Fax: (020) 7493 9815 E-mail: property@johndwood.com

OFFICE AIR CONDITIONING (AC) SYSTEMS

A C J Industrial Ltd, Longbeck Trading Estate, Marske-By-The-Sea, Redcar, Cleveland, TS11 6HB Tel: (01642) 483045 Fax: (01642) 487588 E-mail: garbut@globalnet.co.uk

Breeze Cool Air Conditioning & Refrigeration Ltd, 37 Amberley Road, Macclesfield, Cheshire, SK11 8LX Tel: (01625) 511336 Fax: (01625) 511288 E-mail: enquiries@breezecool.co.uk

Cool Heat Services, 167 Hullbridge Road, South Woodham Ferrers, Chelmsford, CM3 5LN Tel: (01245) 321615 Fax: (01245) 328981

Haywood Office Services, Trafalgar Close, Chandlers Ford Industrial Estate, Chandler's Ford, Eastleigh, Hampshire, SO53 4BW Tel: (023) 8025 4454 Fax: (023) 8026 7986 E-mail: sales@haywoodofficeservices.co.uk

Jackson Refrigeration, Unit 19, Cossall Industrial Estate, Solomon Road, Ilkeston, Derbyshire, DE7 5UA Tel: 0115-944 4898 Fax: 0115-944 4981 E-mail: katejackson@jacksonrefrigeration.co.uk

Max Fordham & Partners, 42-43 Gloucester Cresent, London, NW1 7PE Tel: (020) 7267 5161 Fax: (020) 7482 0329 E-mail: post@maxfordham.com

OFFICE AUTOMATION SYSTEM COMPUTERS

Ikon Office Solutions plc, Ikon Court, 150 Great Cambridge Road, Enfield, Middlesex, EN1 1PW Tel: (020) 8366 9666 Fax: (020) 8367 6729

Synergistic Software Co Ltd, Hughenden House, Main Street, Collingham, Wetherby, West Yorkshire, LS22 5AS Tel: (01937) 573446 Fax: (01937) 574211 E-mail: tony@syn.co.uk

OFFICE CHAIRS

A C F Office Seating Collection, Wellington Street, Bury, Lancashire, BL8 2BD Tel: 0161-761 6889 Fax: 0161-761 6853

Alpha Marketing plc, 53 Dargan Road, Belfast, BT3 9JU Tel: (028) 9078 1531 Fax: (028) 9037 0053 E-mail: alphamarketing@msn.com

Anthony's, 36 High Street, Stotfold, Hitchin, Hertfordshire, SG5 4LL Tel: (01462) 835452 Fax: (01462) 835452

Bowyers Office Equipment, Church Road, Penn, High Wycombe, Buckinghamshire, HP10 8LP Tel: (01494) 816585 Fax: (01494) 813684 E-mail: charles.bowyer@bowyersoffice.co.uk

▶ Brent Cross, Sayer House, Oxgate Lane, London, NW2 7JN Tel: (020) 8208 2626 Fax: (020) 8208 2012 E-mail: sales@brentxofficefurniture.co.uk

Claughton Office Equipment Ltd, 53 Beverley Road, Hull, HU3 1XL Tel: (01482) 323235 Fax: (01482) 224201 E-mail: sales@claughtons.com

Frames & Fabric Ltd, Unit D1 West End Mills, Leopold Street, Long Eaton, Nottingham, NG10 4QD Tel: 0115-972 6282 Fax: 0115-946 1697

Girsberger London, 140 Old Street, London, EC1V 9BJ Tel: (020) 7490 3223 Fax: (020) 7490 5665 E-mail: sales@girsberger.com

▶ Inter County Office Furniture, 20-21 Woodside Industrial Park, Works Road, Letchworth Garden City, Hertfordshire, SG6 1LA Tel: (01462) 675609 Fax: (01462) 687025 E-mail: sales@intercounty.com

KAB Seating Ltd, Round Spinney, Northampton, NN3 8RS Tel: (01604) 790500 Fax: (01604) 648176E-mail: gailthompson@kabseating.com

Komac, Unit 17-18, Narrowboat Way, Blackbrook Valley Indusrial Estate, Dudley, West Midlands, DY2 0XQ Tel: (01384) 481396 Fax: (01384) 481397

Laporta Office Furniture & Equipment, 26-30 Prescott Place, London, SW4 6BU Tel: (020) 7720 6006 Fax: (020) 7720 6116 E-mail: info@laporta.co.uk

Lones (UK) Ltd, Middlemore Lane West, Aldridge, Walsall, WS9 8BG Tel: (01922) 743833 Fax: (01922) 743760 E-mail: sales@workplace-products.co.uk

Herman Miller Ltd, 61 Aldwych, London, WC2B 4AE Tel: (0845) 226 7202 Fax: (0845) 430 9260 E-mail: info_uk@hermanmiller.com

Office Depot UK, Guilbert House, Greenwich Way, Andover, Hampshire, SP10 4JZ Tel: (0870) 7556611 Fax: (0870) 4114735 E-mail: name@officedepot.com

Offizone Office Stationery Supplies, 1-15 Middle Hillgate, Stockport, Cheshire, SK1 3AY Tel: 0161-480 2010 Fax: 0161-480 4133 E-mail: sales@offizone.co.uk

Pledge Office Chairs Ltd, Millstream Works, Mill Road, Leighton Buzzard, Bedfordshire, LU7 1BA Tel: (01525) 376181 Fax: (01525) 382392 E-mail: sales@pledgechairs.co.uk

Of Quest Ltd, Irton House, Tower Estate, Warpsgrove Lane, Chalgrove, Oxford, OX44 7TH Tel: (01865) 891444 Fax: (01865) 893722 E-mail: customerservice@ofquest.co.uk

RCD Projects Ltd, 62 Portman Road, Reading, RG30 1EA Tel: 0118-950 2021 Fax: 0118-950 2036 E-mail: sales@rcdprojects.co.uk

Seatco Sales Ltd, Imperial Ho, Kings Court, King St, Leyland, PR25 2LE Tel: (01772) 434361

Stenochair Ltd, 30 Stilebrook Road, Industrial Estate, Olney, Buckinghamshire, MK46 5EA Tel: (01234) 711354 Fax: (01234) 713652 E-mail: sales@stenochair.co.uk

▶ Tetras Interiors Ltd, 55 Lincoln Road, Poole, Dorset, BH12 2HT Tel: (01202) 566480 Fax: (01202) 386403 E-mail: tetrasinteriors@aol.com

▶ Traditional Values Ltd, 10-14 West Street, Southend-on-Sea, SS2 6HJ Tel: (01702) 300087 Fax: (01702) 390766 E-mail: info@traditional-values.co.uk

Vector Seating Ltd, Raleigh Road, Bedminster, Bristol, BS3 1QU Tel: 0117-953 2000 Fax: 0117-953 2005 E-mail: sales@vector-seating.co.uk

Verco Office Furniture Ltd, Chapel Lane, High Wycombe, Buckinghamshire, HP12 4BG Tel: (01494) 448000 Fax: (01494) 464216 E-mail: sales@verco.co.uk

▶ Visual-Q Ltd, The Corner House, Willow Walk, Englefield Green, Egham, Surrey, TW20 0DQ Tel: (0870) 2401059 Fax: (01784) 472143 E-mail: tgates@visual-q.co.uk

Wallis Office Furniture Ltd, 8-18 Fowler Road, Hainault Industrial Estate, Ilford, Essex, IG6 3UT Tel: (020) 8500 9991 Fax: (020) 8500 1949 E-mail: sales@wallisoffice.com

Wheatley Dyson & Son Ltd, 1 Quarry Court, Beacon Hill Road, Halifax, West Yorkshire, HX3 6AQ Tel: (0800) 6342010 Fax: (0800) 0424329 E-mail: sales@wheatley-dyson.co.uk

OFFICE CLEANING CONTRACTORS/SERVICES

A M Cleaning Services, West Lodge, Beckenham Place Park, Beckenham, Kent, BR3 5BP Tel: (020) 8658 8181 E-mail: info@amcleaning.info

Able Cleaning Services Ltd, Kemp House, 152-160 City Road, London, EC1V 2NP Tel: (020) 7250 3722 Fax: (020) 7608 3424

▶ Ablib, 1 Foresters Cottages, Mead Road, Edenbridge, Kent, TN8 5DE Tel: (01732) 867879 E-mail: ablibcleaners@hotmail.co.uk

Action Industrial Cleaning Services UK Ltd, Bridge House, 1 Bridge Close, Romford, RM7 0AU Tel: (01708) 725356 Fax: (01708) 737117

▶ Advanced Cleaning Services, Chapel Street, Exning, Newmarket, Suffolk, CB8 7HA Tel: (01638) 578444 Fax: (01638) 578542 E-mail: adrian@actltd.co.uk

▶ The All Clear Co., 15 Rigg Approach, London, E10 7QN Tel: (0800) 1693633 Fax: (020) 8539 9462 E-mail: enquiries@theallclearcompany.co.uk

Ambassador Cleaning Services Company, 18 Ashwin Street, London, E8 3DL Tel: (020) 7241 0937 Fax: (020) 7249 9583

Arise N Shine Cleaning Services & Supplies, 68 Icknield Close, Ickleford, Hitchin, Hertfordshire, SG5 3TE Tel: (01462) 675525 Fax: (01462) 456288

Avac, 38 Comiston Road, Edinburgh, EH10 5QQ Tel: 0131-452 8455 Fax: 0131-664 9085 E-mail: avac@netscapeonline.co.uk

Avocet Cleaning Services, 210 Queen Ediths Way, Cambridge, CB1 8NL Tel: (01223) 244038 Fax: (01223) 244038

Aztec Plant Displays, 18 Eden Way, Pages Industrial Estate, Leighton Buzzard, Bedfordshire, LU7 4TZ Tel: (01525) 372322 Fax: (01525) 379426E-mail: info@aztec.co.uk

B & C Office Cleaning Services, 25 Castlereagh St, London, W1H 5YR Tel: (020) 7636 0519

B-G Kleen, 94 Radegund Road, Cambridge, CB1 3RS Tel: (01223) 242677 Fax: (01223) 242677

Birkin Cleaning Services Ltd, Unit 8 Little Mundells, Welwyn Garden City, Hertfordshire, AL7 1EW Tel: (01707) 322228 Fax: (01707) 387666 E-mail: sales@birkinclean.co.uk

Blue Diamond Services, 106 Pembroke Road, Ruislip, Middlesex, HA4 8NW Tel: (01895) 671500 Fax: (01895) 671509 E-mail: info@blued.co.uk

Blue Sparkle Cleaning Contractors, 2 Clarenden Place, Dartford, DA2 7HL Tel: (01322) 669494

Bonsers Cleaning Nottingham, 19a Forester Street, Netherfield, Nottingham, NG4 2LJ Tel: 0115-988 7520 Fax: (01636) 815926 E-mail: contact@bonsersrestoration.co.uk

Broadway Computer Cleaning Service, 45 Broadway, Gillingham, Kent, ME8 6BA Tel: (01634) 232974

▶ Browns Associated Cleaners, Tamarind House, 41 Marshall Avenue, Bridlington, North Humberside, YO15 2DT Tel: (01262) 606779 E-mail: brownscleaners@btinternet.com

Cameron Industrial Services Ltd, 351 Hale Road, Widnes, Cheshire, WA8 8TS Tel: 0151-423 3892 Fax: 0151-423 3892 E-mail: enquiries@cameronltd.co.uk

Churchills Cleaning Contractors, Unit 45, Woolsbridge Industrial Park, Three Legged Cross, Wimborne, Dorset, BH21 6SZ Tel: (01202) 825284 Fax: (01202) 828229

Cleanforce Contracting Ltd, Force Group House, 31-33 Albion Street, Stoke-on-Trent, ST1 1QF Tel: (01782) 213333 Fax: (01782) 284555 E-mail: info@clean-force.biz

Cleaning Contractors Services Group Ltd, 253 Alcester Road South, Kings Heath, Birmingham, B14 6DT Tel: 0121-444 4232 Fax: 0121-443 1117 E-mail: contractcleaning@kingsheathb14.wannadoo.co.uk

Complete Cleaning Services Scotland, 6 Muriel Street, Barrhead, Glasgow, G78 1QB Tel: 0141-880 8118 Fax: 0141-880 6673 E-mail: info@completecleaningservices.com

Consistent Cleaning Services Ltd, 78 North End Road, London, W14 9ES Tel: (020) 7602 6981 Fax: (020) 7602 1306

Corina Cleaning Services, Unit M The Old Bakery, Bakery Lane, Bognor Regis, West Sussex, PO21 1UR Tel: (01243) 868302 Fax: (01243) 868302 E-mail: adrienne@corinacleaning.co.uk

Courtesy Cleaning Services Ltd, Courtesy House 35 Redburn Industrial Estate, Woodall Road, Enfield, Middlesex, EN3 4LQ Tel: (020) 8805 8586 Fax: (020) 8805 5868

▶ Crawley Office Cleaning Services, 69 Gatwick Road, Crawley, West Sussex, RH10 9RD Tel: (01293) 619975 Fax: (01293) 619975 E-mail: crawleyoffice@cleaningservices.net

OFFICE CLEANING CONTRACTORS/ SERVICES – *continued*

▶ Crystal Clean Southwest, Carrick Business Centre, Commercial Road, Penryn, Cornwall, TR10 8AR Tel: (01326) 377999 Fax: 01326 377999
E-mail: crystal_cleaning@btconnect.com

D & R Services, 36 Eastfield Road, Wellingborough, Northamptonshire, NN8 1QU Tel: (01933) 278921 Fax: (01933) 278921

▶ Delmar Corporation Ltd, 167 Watling Road, Castleford, West Yorkshire, WF10 2QY Tel: (01977) 519529
E-mail: brian@delmar-cleaning.co.uk

Design & Care Cleaning Services Ltd, 89 Walcot Square, London, SE11 4UB Tel: (020) 7261 1502 Fax: (020) 7820 0032
E-mail: design.care@virgin.net

English Cleaning Co., 272 Latimer Industrial Estate, Latimer Road, London, W10 6RQ Tel: (020) 8960 0000 Fax: (020) 8969 7077
E-mail: info@english-cleaning.co.uk

Enviroclean Services Ltd, Unit A 5 Colville Road, London, W3 8BL Tel: (020) 8896 0088 Fax: (020) 8896 2676

Essex Cleaning Services Ltd, 6 Alderman Avenue, Barking, Essex, IG11 0LX Tel: (020) 8594 2155 E-mail: ecsltd@arfoster.fsnet.co.uk

Fernley Airport Services Ltd, Concorde House, Colndale Road, Colnbrook, Slough, SL3 0HQ Tel: (0870) 8400611 Fax: (0870) 8400622

General & Industrial Window Cleaning Co. Ltd, 203-209 Gateford Road, Worksop, Nottinghamshire, S81 7BB Tel: (01909) 472967 Fax: (01909) 472967

Green Bros Ltd, 44 High Street, Corby, Northamptonshire, NN17 1UU Tel: (01536) 265754 Fax: (01536) 206460
E-mail: enquiries@greenbros.co.uk

▶ Greenserve Cleaning Services, 63 Tenter Road, Moulton Park Industrial Estate, Moulton Park Industrial Estate, Northampton, NN3 6AX Tel: (01604) 494605 Fax: (01604) 645786
E-mail: enquiries@greenservecleaning.co.uk

I S S Support Services, Strathdon Drive, London, SW17 0PS Tel: (020) 8947 9045 Fax: (020) 8947 9732

Initial Cleaning Services, Unit 2, Rhymney River Bridge Road, Cardiff, CF3 7AF Tel: (029) 2046 4243 Fax: (029) 2048 7248
E-mail: initialcleaning@rentokilinitial.com

Inverclean Services Ltd, Port Glasgow Road, Greenock, Renfrewshire, PA15 2UD Tel: (01475) 744223 Fax: (01475) 744224
E-mail: sales@inverclean.co.uk

ISS Facility Services Ltd, 15A Huntingdon Street, St. Neots, Cambridgeshire, PE19 1BL Tel: (01480) 403404 Fax: (01480) 408579

Kilbey Cleaning & Maintenance Services, 104 Mansfield Road, London, NW3 2HX Tel: (020) 7267 8829 Fax: (020) 7284 4525

Lawrence & Tester Ltd, Property Services House, George Summers Close, Medway City Estate, Rochester, Kent, ME2 4NS Tel: (01306) 886313 Fax: (01634) 290777
E-mail: reception@lawrenceandtester.co.uk

Lombard Cleaning Services Ltd, Kemp House, 152-160 City Road, London, EC1V 2NP Tel: (020) 7251 2182 Fax: (020) 7251 2444

London Independent Office Cleaning Ltd, 32-38 Scrutton Street, London, EC2A 4RQ Tel: (020) 7377 8487 Fax: (020) 7655 8444

London Property Maintenance Cleaning Ltd, 245 Main Road, Sidcup, Kent, DA14 6QS Tel: (020) 8269 8480 Fax: (020) 8269 8481
E-mail: lpm@lpm-cleaning.co.uk

▶ Magic Bean & Cow Ltd., 93-97 Gowe Street, London, WC1E 6AD Tel: 07841 841319 Fax: 0207 9169686
E-mail: info@magicbeanandcow.co.uk

▶ Martin, 8 Walnut Tree Avenue, Martham, Great Yarmouth, Norfolk, NR29 4QS Tel: (01493) 740746
E-mail: martin@procleaning-office.co.uk

The Mayfair Cleaning Company Ltd, 374 Wandsworth Road, London, SW8 4TD Tel: (020) 7720 6447 Fax: (020) 7498 8246
E-mail: info@mayfaircleaning.co.uk

Nottingham Industrial Cleaners Ltd, Elizabeth House, Wigman Road, Bilborough, Nottingham, NG8 3HY Tel: 0115-900 7300 Fax: 0115-900 7310

O C S Group, Servia Road, Leeds, LS7 1NJ Tel: 0113-246 1281 Fax: 0113-234 1682
E-mail: ecleaning@ocs.co.uk

Office Angels Commercial Cleaning, 12 Armstrong Close, Halstead, Sevenoaks, Kent, TN14 7BS Tel: (0845) 1084241
E-mail: officeangelscleaning@googlemail.com

▶ Office Care, Collate House, Victoria Way, Pride Park, Derby, DE24 8AN Tel: (01332) 332331 Fax: (01332) 200212
E-mail: sales@officecare.uk.com

Orion Cleaning & Support Services, Unit 12 Parmiter Industrial Centre, Parmiter Street, London, E2 9HZ Tel: (020) 8880 7222 Fax: 0208 880 7080

P & H Cleaning Co. Ltd, 72-74 Gipsy Hill, London, SE19 1PD Tel: (020) 8761 5324 Fax: (020) 8761 7306
E-mail: admin@pandhcleaning.co.uk

Poppy, 91 Allerton Road, Shrewsbury, SY1 4QW Tel: (01743) 369800

PSK, 42 Benington Road, Aston, Stevenage, Hertfordshire, SG2 7DY Tel: (01438) 880922 Fax: (01438) 880923
E-mail: kim.aston@btinternet.com

R E L Contracts, Springfield, Brumstead Road, Stalham, Norwich, NR12 9DE Tel: (01692) 582238

R J P Royal Cleaning Contractors, 5 Ermine Street, Buntingford, Hertfordshire, SG9 9AZ Tel: (01763) 272912

R P C Cleaning Services Ltd, 201 Acton Lane, London, W4 5DA Tel: (020) 8994 4778 Fax: (020) 8994 4178

Sawston Cleaning Services Ltd, 25 Brookfield Road, Sawston, Cambridge, CB22 3EH Tel: (01223) 832922 Fax: (01223) 830031
E-mail: enquiries@sawstoncleaning.co.uk

Sloane Cleaning Services, Anerley Town Hall, Anerley Road, London, SE20 8BD Tel: (020) 7584 6500 Fax: (020) 7527 7918

South Central Cleaning Services, 7 Acorn Workshops, Empress Road, Southampton, SO14 0JY Tel: (023) 8032 2752 Fax: (023) 8032 2752E-mail: russellbowley@hotmail.com

South Midlands Group plc, 48 Oakley Road, Luton, LU4 9PU Tel: (01582) 490606 Fax: (01582) 581305
E-mail: info@smgplc.co.uk

South Western Flooring Services, 145-147 Park Lane, Frampton Cotterell, Bristol, BS36 2ES Tel: (01454) 880982 Fax: (01454) 880982
E-mail: swflooring@blueyonda.co.uk

Sovereign Cleaning Services, 56 Silverknowes Parkway, Edinburgh, EH4 5LA Tel: 0131-336 2492 Fax: 0131-336 2492

▶ Spotless Cleaning Services, 317 Coalburn Road, Coalburn, Lanark, ML11 0NF Tel: (01555) 820032 Fax: (01555) 820032
E-mail: spotless@email.com

Supacleen Ltd, 1 Bessemer Close, Cardiff, CF11 8DL Tel: (029) 2066 6663 Fax: (029) 2066 6663 E-mail: supacleen@onetel.net.uk

Swallow Cleaning Contractors, Spa Road, Lincoln, LN2 5TB Tel: (01522) 540056 Fax: (01522) 546846
E-mail: enquiries@swallowcleaning.com

Thames Cleaning Co. Ltd, 14 Hatherley Road, Sidcup, Kent, DA14 4BG Tel: (020) 8302 6633 Fax: (020) 8300 7779
E-mail: jenny.mclaren@thamescleaning.co.uk

Thames Valley Cleaning Contractors (Reading) Ltd, Unit 5A, Bridgewater Close, Reading, RG30 1JT Tel: 0118-959 9141 Fax: 0118-953 3838 E-mail: thamesvalleycing@aol.com

▶ Thoroughclean Services, 4 Deemouth Business Centre, South Esplanade East, Aberdeen, AB11 9PB Tel: (01224) 891570 Fax: (01224) 891540
E-mail: sales@thoroughclean.co.uk

Trustclean Ltd, Queens Court, Doncaster, South Yorkshire, DN5 9QH Tel: (01302) 783193 Fax: (01302) 781556
E-mail: info@trustclean.co.uk

Turners Industrial Cleaning Systems Ltd, Leyden Works, Leyden Road, Stevenage, Hertfordshire, SG1 2BP Tel: (01438) 352802 Fax: (01438) 314188
E-mail: turners.carole@talk21.com

Ultra Clean, Hillside Cottage, Croesau Bach, Oswestry, Shropshire, SY10 9AY Tel: (01691) 670837 Fax: (01691) 670837
E-mail: philevo@btinternet.com

Vacman Specialist Cleaning, Budmhor, Portree, Isle of Skye, IV51 9DJ Tel: (01478) 613111 Fax: (01478) 613321
E-mail: info@vacman.co.uk

Victoria Medical & General Cleaning Services Ltd, Victoria House, Skeltons Lane, London, E10 5BZ Tel: (020) 8556 0141 Fax: (020) 8558 9437

Wetton Cleaning Services Ltd, 278-280 St James's Road, London, SE1 5JX Tel: (020) 7237 2007 Fax: (020) 7252 3277
E-mail: wcs@wetton.co.uk

Wright Way Cleaning & Maintenance Services, Bosserts End, 11a Bosserts Way, Highfields Caldecote, Cambridge, CB23 7PA Tel: (01954) 212405 Fax: (01954) 212406
E-mail: wright-way@btconnect.com

OFFICE CLEANING CONTRACTORS/SERVICES, HIGH TECHNOLOGY

Capital Cleaning Service, 25 Camps Rigg, Livingston, West Lothian, EH54 8PD Tel: (01506) 440333 Fax: (01506) 431318

Daily Office Cleaning, 30 West Gorgie Parks, Edinburgh, EH14 1UT Tel: 0131-455 7364 Fax: 0131-455 7364
E-mail: info@scotdoc.co.uk

Dunedin Contract Cleaning Services, 2 Pitt Street, Edinburgh, EH6 4BU Tel: 0131-554 9879 Fax: 0131-554 9879

Harwoods Cleaning Contractors Ltd, Unit 3 Block 13 Whiteside Industrial Estate, Bathgate, West Lothian, EH48 2RX Tel: (01506) 633584 Fax: (01506) 636868 E-mail: harcc@aol.com

Hy Tec East London, 303 Higham Hill Road, London, E17 5RG Tel: (020) 8925 0400 Fax: (020) 8925 0411
E-mail: sales@hy-tec.co.uk

Initial Cleaning Services, Unit 2, Rhymney River Bridge Road, Cardiff, CF3 7AF Tel: (029) 2046 4243 Fax: (029) 2048 7248
E-mail: initialcleaning@rentokilinitial.com

▶ Office Care, Collate House, Victoria Way, Pride Park, Derby, DE24 8AN Tel: (01332) 332331 Fax: (01332) 200212
E-mail: sales@officecare.uk.com

Olscot, 40 Dryden Road, Loanhead, Midlothian, EH20 9LZ Tel: 0131-448 2257 Fax: 0131-440 1359

O'Neill Cleaning Ltd, Unit 5 Mitchelston Drive, Mitchelston Industrial Estate, Kirkcaldy, Fife, KY1 3NF Tel: (01592) 655777 Fax: (01592) 655777 E-mail: sales@oneillcleaning.com

OFFICE COMPLIMENT SLIPS

Multisets Ltd, Suite 2B, Second Floor, Eastheath House, Eastheath Avenue, Wokingham, Berkshire, RG41 2PR Tel: 0118-936 7600 Fax: 0118-936 7601
E-mail: info@multisets.co.uk

Winstanley & Watkins, 104 Duke Street, Liverpool, L1 5AG Tel: 0151-709 0808 Fax: 0151-709 3060
E-mail: info@wwprint.co.uk

OFFICE DESIGN OR PLANNING OR REFURBISHMENT OR FITTING SERVICES

A.Davies & Co.(Shopfitters)Limited, Chiswick Studios, Power Road, London, W4 5PY Tel: (020) 8987 4100 Fax: (020) 8987 2647
E-mail: info@daviesshopfitters.com

A1 Partitions, Fairview, Vicarage Close, Ravensden, Bedford, MK44 2RW Tel: (01234) 771144 Fax: (01234) 772080
E-mail: info@a1-partitions.co.uk

Abstract Office Interiors Ltd, 3 Forest Industrial Park, Forest Road, Hainault, Ilford, Essex, IG6 3HL Tel: (020) 8501 6633 Fax: (020) 8501 6634

▶ Accent Office Interiors, 53-55 Cardiff Road, Luton, LU1 1PP Tel: (01582) 722211

Ardmac Performance Contracting Ltd, Annesborough Industrial Area, 15 Annesborough Road, Lurgan, Craigavon, County Armagh, BT67 9JD Tel: (028) 3834 7093 Fax: (028) 3834 1604
E-mail: info@ardmac.com

Ashwell Construction Co. Ltd, 158 Victoria Rise, Clapham, London, SW4 0NW Tel: (020) 7622 0688 Fax: (020) 7627 1336
E-mail: enquiries@ashwell-interiors.co.uk

B C L Construction Ltd, 263 Haydons Road, London, SW19 8TY Tel: (020) 8543 6221 Fax: (020) 8543 9725
E-mail: sales@bclltdconstruction.co.uk

Bolts Of Hereford, 5-7 Perseverance Road, Hereford, HR4 9SN Tel: (01432) 269508 Fax: (01432) 263835
E-mail: nick.bolt@btclick.com

Bridger & Co Office Interiors, South Ease Cottage, Send Marsh Road, Ripley, Woking, Surrey, GU23 6JQ Tel: (01483) 224920 Fax: (01483) 211599

▶ C J Design, 47 St. Dunstans Road, Bristol, BS3 5NZ Tel: (07798) 808594 Fax: (0870) 8555366

C L C Contractors Ltd, Northbrook Industrial Estate, Vincent Avenue, Southampton, SO16 6PQ Tel: (023) 8070 1111 Fax: (023) 8070 1171 E-mail: mail@clcgroup.com

C P D Distribution P.L.C., Units 11-12, Stadium Industrial Estate, Craddock Road, Luton, LU4 0JF Tel: (01582) 594222 Fax: (01582) 595222

Caledonian Contracts (Aberdeen) Ltd, 8 Holland Place, Aberdeen, AB25 3UW Tel: (01224) 630355 Fax: (01224) 639504

City Office Interiors Ltd, Albany House, 31 Hurst Street, Birmingham, B5 4BD Tel: 0121-622 4811 Fax: 0121-622 5756
E-mail: contact@cityofficeinteriors.co.uk

City Office Interiors Ltd, 1 Duchess Street, London, W1W 6AN Tel: (0870) 2203772 Fax: (020) 7079 5929
E-mail: sales@cityofficeinteriors.co.uk

Claremont Business Environment, Design Studio 2 Quay Side Commerce Centre, Lower Quay, Fareham, Hampshire, PO16 0XR Tel: (01329) 220123 Fax: (01329) 221322
E-mail: info@claremontgi.com

Contract Services Renovation & Refurbishing Ltd, Lombardian House Liverpool Road, Cadishead, Manchester, M44 5DD Tel: 0161-777 8278 Fax: 0161-777 6298
E-mail: general@contracts-svcs.co.uk

CPS Interiors Ltd, 1 Prince William Way, Loughborough, Leicestershire, LE11 5DD Tel: (01509) 230429 Fax: (01509) 610617
E-mail: cpsinteriors@btconnect.com

Craftwork Industries Ltd, 98 Lower Richmond Road, London, SW15 1LN Tel: (020) 8780 1798 Fax: (020) 8780 1861
E-mail: sales@craftwork-interiors.co.uk

Custom Design, Southview, Rhodes Minnis, Canterbury, Kent, CT4 6XU Tel: (01303) 862888 Fax: (0871) 7503757
E-mail: highbarn@globalnet.co.uk

Charles Dean Partnership Ltd, Brasted Lodge, Westerham Road, Westerham, Kent, TN16 1QH Tel: (01959) 565909 Fax: (01959) 565606 E-mail: sales@charlesdean.co.uk

Demountable Partitions Ltd, 4 Twin Bridges Business Park, 232 Selsdon Road, South Croydon, Surrey, CR2 6PL Tel: (020) 8410 3800 Fax: (020) 8239 0083
E-mail: sales@demountables.co.uk

Dunelm Office Interiors, 149 Kells Lane, Gateshead, Tyne & Wear, NE9 5HR Tel: 0191-491 5080 Fax: 0191-420 0197

Factory & Office Consultants Ltd, Stuart House, 5-7 Wellington Street, Long Eaton, Nottingham, NG10 4LY Tel: 0115-972 5686 Fax: 0115-946 0842
E-mail: sales@fando.co.uk

Fray Design Ltd, Ghyll Way Airedale Business Centre, Keighley Road, Skipton, North Yorkshire, BD23 2TZ Tel: (01756) 704040 Fax: (01756) 704041
E-mail: sales@fraydesign.co.uk

General Partitioning Ltd, 632 Eastern Avenue, Ilford, Essex, IG2 6PG Tel: (020) 8554 5010 Fax: (020) 8554 5012

Glenside Commercial Interiors, Glenside House, Kitchener Road, High Wycombe, Buckinghamshire, HP11 2SW Tel: (01494) 529803 Fax: (01494) 452212

Grosvenor Workspace Solutions, Compass House, Chivers Way, Histon, Cambridge, CB24 9AD Tel: (01223) 475555 Fax: (01223) 475566 E-mail: info@grosvenor.uk.com

Halstead Associates, 27 Windsor Pl, Cardiff, CF10 3BZ Tel: (029) 2066 6505 Fax: (029) 2066 5584

Harrington Associates Ltd, Unit 1 Bright St., Coventry, CV6 5EB Tel: (024) 7666 2731 Fax: (024) 7663 8058
E-mail: sales@harringtonassociates.co.uk

Heaton Shopfitters Ltd, 88 Tatton Road South, Stockport, Cheshire, SK4 4LX Tel: 0161-442 5786 Fax: 0161-718 3519

▶ Hodge Ltd, 4 North Howard Street, Belfast, BT13 2AS Tel: (028) 9024 1812 Fax: (028) 9024 6866

Inline Logistics Ltd, The Grange, Brixworth, Northampton, NN6 9DL Tel: (01604) 882200 Fax: (01604) 882323

Integra Contracts Ltd, 119-123 Hackford Road, London, SW9 0QT Tel: (020) 7820 1800 Fax: (020) 7820 1182
E-mail: icl@integracontracts.co.uk

Interior Contracts Group, Ethos House, 52 Tanners Drive, Blakelands, Milton Keynes, MK14 5BW Tel: (01908) 216766 Fax: (01908) 216744

Interior Property Specialists Ltd, Interplan House, Chelmsford Road Industrial Estate, Dunmow, Essex, CM6 1HE Tel: (01371) 874241 Fax: (01371) 873848
E-mail: contact@ips-interiors.co.uk

Irwins Ltd, Low Hall Road, Horsforth, Leeds, LS18 4EW Tel: 0113-250 6811 Fax: 0113-250 6933 E-mail: sales@irwins.co.uk

JBL Office, 168-170 Cumnor Road, Boars Hill, Oxford, OX1 5JS Tel: (01865) 739056 Fax: (01865) 326754 E-mail: sales@jbl.co.uk

Jennor Electrical, 57-59 Brynn Street, St. Helens, Merseyside, WA10 1JB Tel: (01744) 730717 Fax: (01744) 759657
E-mail: general@jennor.co.uk

K A Moon & Co., 29 Bingley Grove, Woodley, Reading, RG5 4TT Tel: 0118-969 1683 Fax: 0118-969 1683

Kestrel Building Services Ltd, George Street, High Wycombe, Buckinghamshire, HP11 2RZ Tel: (01494) 474398 Fax: (01494) 472540
E-mail: info@kestreloffice.com

Kinnarps UK Ltd, 8 Lindsay Square, Deans Industrial Estate, Deans, Livingston, West Lothian, EH54 8RL Tel: (01506) 415885 Fax: (01506) 411447
E-mail: sales@kinnarps.co.uk

L P B Contracts, 4 Matthews Green Road, Wokingham, Berkshire, RG41 1JU Tel: 0118-978 3424 Fax: 0118-978 3424

Larchbond Facilities Ltd, Ongar Hall Farm, Brentwood Road, Orsett, Grays, Essex, RM16 3HU Tel: (01375) 892929 Fax: (01375) 892624 E-mail: sales@larchbond.co.uk

Leicester Office Furnishers, 9-11 Cannock Street, Leicester, LE4 9HR Tel: 0116-246 3686 Fax: 0116-246 3681
E-mail: enquiries@leicesteroffice.com

Logic Office Group, Vestry Industrial Estate, Vestry Road, Sevenoaks, Kent, TN14 5EL Tel: (01732) 457636 Fax: (01732) 740706
E-mail: contracts.admin@logic-office.co.uk

M J F Interdec Ltd, Greenford, Middlesex, UB18 9YS Tel: (01895) 909090 Fax: (01895) 909010 E-mail: hotline@interdec.co.uk

M K Contracts Ltd, 50 Buntingbridge Road, Ilford, Essex, IG2 7LR Tel: (020) 8518 2100 Fax: (020) 8518 2984

Mccarthy Design, Ladygrove Court, Preston, Hitchin, Hertfordshire, SG4 7SA Tel: (01462) 440957 Fax: (01462) 440961
E-mail: peter@mccarthydesign.co.uk

Mccarthy Developments 2000 Ltd, Systems House, Broad Lane, Coventry, CV5 7AX Tel: (024) 7646 8866 Fax: (024) 7669 4486
E-mail: sales@mccarthygroup.co.uk

Mcfeggan Brown Ltd, Unit 1, 38 Midland Road, Staplehill, Bristol, BS16 4NW Tel: 0117-957 3355 Fax: 0117-956 7221

Mcof Ltd, 3 Station Road, Brompton on Swale, Richmond, North Yorkshire, DL10 7SN Tel: (01748) 812612 Fax: (01748) 812618
E-mail: thomaslinckh@btconnect.com

Material Matters, 2 Ninian Park, Ninian Way, Wilnecote, Tamworth, Staffordshire, B77 5ES Tel: (01827) 262527 Fax: (01827) 262530

Matrix Interior Systems Ltd, Crombie Mews, Abercrombie Street, London, SW11 2JB Tel: (020) 7924 7574 Fax: (020) 7924 7270
E-mail: matrixinteriors@aol.com

Mentha & Halsall (Shopfitters) Ltd, 95a Linaker St, Southport, Merseyside, PR8 5BU Tel: (01704) 530800 Fax: (01704) 500601
E-mail: info@mentha-halsall.com

Mirage Interiors Ltd, 12 Sand Road, Kewstoke, Weston-super-Mare, Avon, BS22 9UH Tel: (01934) 612439 Fax: (01934) 641900
E-mail: walls@mirage-interiors.com

Morgan Lovell P.L.C., 16 Noel Street, London, W1F 8DA Tel: (020) 7734 4466 Fax: (020) 7734 2968 E-mail: info@morganlovell.co.uk

Moss Projects Ltd, Victoria House, 28-32 Desborough Street, High Wycombe, Buckinghamshire, HP11 2NF Tel: (01494) 535238 Fax: (01494) 535248
E-mail: info@moss.ltd.uk

Nason Foster Ltd, Moor Lane, Birmingham, B6 7HH Tel: 0121-356 5693 Fax: 0121-356 3818 E-mail: sales@nasonfoster.co.uk

OFFICE DESIGN OR PLANNING OR REFURBISHMENT OR FITTING SERVICES – *continued*

▶ North Wilts Office Supplies, Ford, Chippenham, Wiltshire, SN14 8RT Tel: (01225) 742569 Fax: (01249) 783207 E-mail: sales@nwos.co.uk

Office Economy, Camden House, Bridge Road, Kingswood, Bristol, BS15 4FW Tel: 0117-915 9990 Fax: 0117-957 3591

Overbury P.L.C., 77 Newman Street, London, W1T 3EW Tel: (020) 7307 9000 Fax: (020) 7307 9001 E-mail: info@overbury.co.uk

Paramount Office Interiors, Paramount House, Pascal Close, St. Mellons, Cardiff, CF3 0LW Tel: (029) 2083 9800 Fax: (029) 2083 9801 E-mail: sales@paramountinteriors.com

Partitioning Plus Ltd, 342b Farnham Rd, Slough, SL2 1BT Tel: 01753 572373 Fax: 01753 694422

R Carslaw, Chelsea Reach, 79-89 Lots Road, London, SW10 0RN Tel: (020) 7376 4440 Fax: (020) 7351 3258 E-mail: sales@robertcarslaw.com

S M Group (Europe) Ltd, Mercator House, Brest Road, Plymouth, PL6 5XP Tel: (01752) 662129 Fax: (01752) 241040 E-mail: sales@smgeurope.com

Saunders & Associates Ltd, PO Box 6504, Basingstoke, Hampshire, RG22 4YZ Tel: (01256) 328881 E-mail: saceilings@btconnect.com

Scotwood Interiors Ltd, 48 Milton Road, East Kilbride, Glasgow, G74 5BU Tel: (01355) 241727 Fax: (01355) 241601 E-mail: sales@scotwood.com

Shepherd Interiors, Unit 4, 10 First Avenue, Bletchley, Milton Keynes, MK1 1DN Tel: (01908) 644688 Fax: (01908) 646606 E-mail: info@rgnsltd.co.uk

Shopfittings & Equipment, Waterloo Industrial Estate, Waterloo Road, Bidford-on-Avon, Alcester, Warwickshire, B50 4JH Tel: (01789) 778497 Fax: (01789) 490132 E-mail: sales@shopfittingsandequipment.co.uk

Southridge Interiors Ltd, The Kiln, Pencroft, Crondall, Farnham, Surrey, GU10 5PX Tel: (01252) 852010 Fax: (01252) 852015

Southwark & Boon Ltd, 23 Tallon Road, Hutton, Brentwood, Essex, CM13 1TE Tel: (01277) 225661 Fax: (01277) 233620 E-mail: sales@southwarkandboon.com

Stroud Office Interiors Ltd, Alder Ho, Inchbrook Trading Estate, Woodchester, Stroud, Glos, GL5 5EY Tel: (01453) 834867 Fax: (01453) 835818 E-mail: derek@stroudofficeinteriors.co.uk

Task Systems Ltd, W H House, 32 Bethnal Green Road, London, E1 6HZ Tel: (020) 7729 5088 Fax: (020) 7729 4709 E-mail: marketing@tasksystems.co.uk

Thurnham Contracts, Coldharbour Farm, Cold Harbour Lane, Thurnham, Maidstone, Kent, ME14 3LS Tel: (01622) 880427 Fax: (01622) 880698

Waterhouse Building Refurbishment & Interiors, 98 Bradford Road, East Ardsley, Wakefield, West Yorkshire, WF3 2JL Tel: (01924) 822274 Fax: (01924) 823951 E-mail: info@waterhouse-ideas.co.uk

Anthony Willis Shopfitters Ltd, 55 Grosvenor Street, Cardiff, CF5 1NJ Tel: (029) 2034 5582 Fax: (029) 2023 7260 E-mail: mail@anthonywillis-shopfitters.co.uk

▶ Workscape Ltd, 1-2 Westpoint Business Park, Bumpers Farm, Chippenham, Wiltshire, SN14 6RB Tel: (01249) 447200 Fax: (01249) 447400

OFFICE EQUIPMENT DESIGN SERVICES

Alpha Marketing plc, 53 Dargan Road, Belfast, BT3 9JU Tel: (028) 9078 1531 Fax: (028) 9037 0053 E-mail: alphamarketing@msn.com

Copyright Office Furniture & Equipment, 150 Conway Road, Colwyn Bay, Clwyd, LL29 7LR Tel: (01492) 534807 Fax: (01492) 534807 E-mail: sales@copyrite.net

▶ Digital Products, 59 Imperial Way, Croydon, CR0 4RR Tel: (0845) 1306251 E-mail: sales@dmcplc.co.uk

Ikon Office Solutions plc, Ikon House Angels Wing, Hunslet Road, Leeds, LS10 1AF Tel: 0113-244 5050 Fax: 0113-244 9191

Pennine Drawing Office Services, Unit X1 2 Keighley Business Centre, South Street, Keighley, West Yorkshire, BD21 1AG Tel: (01535) 667422 Fax: (01535) 610130 E-mail: pennine@totalise.co.uk

Rapidos Ltd, Unit 11 Steyning Way, Hounslow, TW4 6DL Tel: (020) 8570 9393 Fax: (020) 8577 3450 E-mail: printroom@repropoint.com

Repropoint Ltd, 332 London Road, Portsmouth, PO2 9JY Tel: (023) 9266 9941 Fax: (023) 9269 6514 E-mail: info@repropoint.com

OFFICE EQUIPMENT HIRE

▶ The Desk Warehouse, Beersbridge Road, Belfast, BT5 5DX Tel: (028) 9058 0900 Fax: (028) 9058 0900 E-mail: sales@deskwarehouse.co.uk

OFFICE EQUIPMENT KEYS

▶ Fast Key Services Ltd, 5c Russell Court, Russell Gardens, Wickford, Essex, SS11 8QU Tel: (01268) 562562 Fax: (01268) 570121 E-mail: marc@fastkeys.co.uk

OFFICE EQUIPMENT MAINTENANCE/REPAIR SPECIALIST SERVICES

Abc Axworthy's Ltd, Cotswold House, Kingsland Trading Estate, St Phillips Road, Bristol, BS2 0JZ Tel: 0117-927 2700 Fax: 0117-927 3345 E-mail: abc@axworthys.co.uk

Acorn Business Machines, Unit 4 Crossley Mills, New Mill Road, Honley, Holmfirth, HD9 6QB Tel: (0800) 5429405 Fax: (01484) 660076 E-mail: mark@acornbuisnessmachines.co.uk

Action Business Systems, 8 The Broadway, Hampton Court Way, Thames Ditton, Surrey, KT7 0LX Tel: (0870) 1607911 Fax: (0870) 1607933 E-mail: customercare@action-plc.co.uk

Advanced Technology Systems Ltd, 1 Russetts, Basildon, Essex, SS16 6SH Tel: (01268) 491900 E-mail: sales@atsweb.co.uk

▶ Atherton & Co., 15 Cheapside, Liverpool, L2 2DY Tel: 0151-236 7977 Fax: 0151-236 7977

Bates Office Service Ltd, Unit 26-29 Ropery Business Park, Anchor & Hope Lane, London, SE7 7RX Tel: (020) 8858 0988 Fax: (020) 8858 1136 E-mail: sales@thestationers.co.uk

Bison Supplies, 31 Garland Avenue, Belfast, BT8 6YH Tel: (028) 9040 2292 Fax: (028) 9040 2292

Border Office Equipment, 4 Block 14 Amber Business Centre, Greenhill Lane, Riddings, Alfreton, Derbyshire, DE55 4BR Tel: (01773) 608039 Fax: (01773) 609145 E-mail: borderofficeriddings@btopenworld.com

Boswell & Davis, 1 Sunbury Workshops, Swanfield Street, London, E2 7LF Tel: (020) 7739 5738

▶ Caldic Services Ltd, 20 Lightwoods Hill, Smethwick, West Midlands, B67 5EA Tel: 0121-420 4267 Fax: 0121-420 4267 E-mail: caldic@talktalk.net

CCS, Peashill Farm, Peashill Lane, Cotgrave, Nottingham, NG12 3HD Tel: 0115-989 2423 Fax: 0115-989 4951

Clarity Copiers Cornwall & Co, Unit 5d 5d Carminnow Road Industrial Estate, Bodmin, Cornwall, PL31 1EP Tel: (01208) 78201 Fax: (01208) 75916

Clark Office Electronics, 18 Willoughby Road, Tamworth, Staffordshire, B79 8NH Tel: (01827) 53520 Fax: (01827) 58557 E-mail: clark.office@ntlworld.com

Copyfax Ltd, Unit C, Burnham Trading Park, Burnley, Lancashire, BB11 4AA Tel: (01282) 453935 Fax: (01282) 416071 E-mail: sales@copifax.co.uk

Crailcrest Ltd, Coach House, Birch Grove, Horsted Keynes, Haywards Heath, West Sussex, RH17 7DJ Tel: (01825) 740190 Fax: (01825) 740178 E-mail: sales@crailcrest.com

Currie Business Services Ltd, 244-252 Price Street, Birkenhead, Merseyside, CH41 3PS Tel: 0151-343 9196 Fax: 0151-647 7627 E-mail: cbssupply@aol.com

▶ Digital Office Solutions, 2 Hyders Farm, Bonnetts Lane, Ifield, Crawley, West Sussex, RH11 0NY Tel: (01293) 537827 Fax: (01293) 619934 E-mail: sales@digital-office-solutions.co.uk

Executive Communications, Hi Tech House, 18 Beresford Avenue, Wembley, Middlesex, HA0 1YP Tel: (020) 8903 3425 Fax: (01784) 431560 E-mail: executivecomm@execs.com

▶ Exiserv Ltd, 1 Page Heath Lane, Bromley, BR1 2DR Tel: (07931) 970900 Fax: (01474) 873589 E-mail: sales@exiserv.com

Granada Typewriters & Copiers, 38 Cardinal Ave, Kingston upon Thames, Surrey, KT2 5SB Tel: (020) 8549 9785 Fax: (020) 8549 9785

Hardwicks, 32 Greenfield Road, Newport Pagnell, Buckinghamshire, MK16 8DA Tel: (01908) 217315 Fax: (01908) 617617

Inpace Ltd, 100 Brize Norton Road, Minster Lovell, Witney, Oxfordshire, OX29 0SG Tel: (01993) 706303 Fax: (01993) 706305 E-mail: info@inpace.com

J D M Office Equipment Services, 66 Harborne Road, Oldbury, West Midlands, B68 9JB Tel: 0121-429 3805 Fax: 0121-554 4627

Ludgate Office Equipment Ltd, 7 Stevens Lane, Claygate, Esher, Surrey, KT10 0TD Tel: (01372) 466091 Fax: (01372) 464960 E-mail: sales@ludgateoe.co.uk

Mcgregor Business Equipment, Unit 2 Fence Avenue, Macclesfield, Cheshire, SK10 1LT Tel: (01625) 618182 Fax: (01625) 618545 E-mail: officesupplies@mcgregors.co.uk

Metrik Office Supplies, 20 Market Square, Dumfries, DG2 7AB Tel: (01387) 253844 Fax: (01387) 257343 E-mail: scallender@metrik.co.uk

N R G Group Ltd, 4 Rushmills, Northampton, NN4 7YB Tel: (01604) 732700

▶ Oceanside Business Machines, 18 Town Farm, Redruth, Cornwall, TR15 2XG Tel: (01209) 210697 Fax: (01209) 210697 E-mail: mark@oceansidebizmachines.co.uk

Office Services, 1 Isaacs Yard, Wrafton Road, Braunton, Devon, EX33 2BT Tel: (01271) 817429 Fax: (01271) 816655

Offstat Office Supplies Ltd, 2nd Floor, 41 Dace Road, London, E3 2NG Tel: (020) 8525 7707 Fax: (020) 8525 7708 E-mail: office-services@offstat.sagehost.co.uk

Premier Office Automation, 137 Middle Road, Shoreham-By-Sea, West Sussex, BN43 6LL Tel: (01273) 455571 Fax: (01273) 455573

Premier Reprographics, Marblemand House, 25 Yarm Road, Stockton-on-Tees, Cleveland, TS18 3NJ Tel: (01642) 806680 Fax: (01642) 806680

▶ S C H Digital, Hoghton Avenue, Bacup, Lancashire, OL13 9RD Tel: (01706) 870034 Fax: (01706) 870034 E-mail: steven.houghton1@ntlworld.com

▶ S R S Shredder Repair Services, PO Box 4279, Dunstable, Bedfordshire, LU6 1WX Tel: (01582) 536346 Fax: (01582) 601448 E-mail: info@shredderrepair.co.uk

Service Copier Supplies, 1 Swan Lane, Harleston, Norfolk, IP20 9AN Tel: (01379) 853713 Fax: (01379) 852158 E-mail: enq@servicesupplies.com

Stafford Ltd, Overbrook Court, Overbrook Lane, Knowsley, Prescot, Merseyside, L34 9FB Tel: 0151-907 0027 Fax: 0151-907 0028 E-mail: paul.spooner@staffords.ltd.uk

Tasktron Ltd, 3 Wintonlea, Monument Way West, Woking, Surrey, GU21 5EN Tel: (01483) 776060 Fax: (01483) 721389 E-mail: sales@crc.uk.com

Toms Office Technology Ltd, 26 Adelaide Road, Leamington Spa, Warwickshire, CV31 3PL Tel: (01926) 425842 Fax: (01926) 832017 E-mail: sales@tomsoffice.co.uk

Wight Business Services, 3 Daish Way, Newport, Isle of Wight, PO30 5XB Tel: (01983) 822229 Fax: (01983) 521899 E-mail: wbs@freenet.co.uk

OFFICE EQUIPMENT MANUFRS,

See also headings for particular equipment

A A A Stationery, 15-19 Benwell Road, London, N7 7BL Tel: (020) 7700 4246 Fax: (020) 7700 3150 E-mail: info@galaxywholesalers.com

A Healey Office Equipment Ltd, The Meadows, 2 Waterberry Drive, Waterlooville, Hampshire, PO7 7XX Tel: (023) 9226 9711 Fax: (023) 9226 9722 E-mail: sales@ahealey.co.uk

A Kelly Ltd, Mita House, Wester Gourdie Industrial Estate, West Gourdie Industrial Estate, Dundee, DD2 4UH Tel: (01382) 623311 Fax: (01382) 611910 E-mail: admin@kellyscopiers.co.uk

▶ A M P M Office Equipment Ltd, 12 South Street, Braunton, Devon, EX33 2AA Tel: (01271) 815859 Fax: (01271) 815858 E-mail: darren@ampmofficeequipment.co.uk

Abacus Leewell, 30b High Street, Langford, Biggleswade, Bedfordshire, SG18 9RR Tel: (01462) 700229 Fax: (01462) 701291 E-mail: sales@abacus-leewell.co.uk

Abbey Business Machines, 13-15 Oakford, Kingsteignton, Newton Abbot, Devon, TQ12 3EQ Tel: (01626) 202502 Fax: (01626) 202503 E-mail: sales@abbeybusinessmachines.co.uk

Abc Axworthy's Ltd, Cotswold House, Kingsland Trading Estate, St Phillips Road, Bristol, BS2 0JZ Tel: 0117-927 2700 Fax: 0117-927 3345 E-mail: abc@axworthys.co.uk

Acco UK Ltd, Gatehouse Road, Aylesbury, Buckinghamshire, HP19 8DT Tel: (01296) 397444 Fax: (01296) 311000 E-mail: info@acco-uk.co.uk

Acorn Business Machines, Unit 4 Crossley Mills, New Mill Road, Honley, Holmfirth, HD9 6QB Tel: (0800) 5429405 Fax: (01484) 660076 E-mail: mark@acornbuisnessmachines.co.uk

Acorn Business Supplies Ltd, Acorn House Motorway Industrial Estate, Forstal, Aylesford, Kent, ME20 7AF Tel: (01622) 882233 Fax: (01622) 882101 E-mail: sales@acorn-business-supplies.co.uk

Action Business Systems, 8 The Broadway, Hampton Court Way, Thames Ditton, Surrey, KT7 0LX Tel: (0870) 1607911 Fax: (0870) 1607933 E-mail: customercare@action-plc.co.uk

Advanced Computer Furniture, Unit 2 Masons Road Industrial Estate, Masons Road, Stratford-upon-Avon, Warwickshire, CV37 9NF Tel: (01789) 414449 Fax: (01789) 415553

Allen Lyman Office Equipment Ltd, 213 Wellingborough Road, Northampton, NN1 4EF Tel: (01604) 639586 Fax: (01604) 231249 E-mail: allen.lyman@virgin.net

Alpha Business Centre Ltd, 12 Princes Drive, Colwyn Bay, Clwyd, LL29 8LA Tel: (01492) 531813 Fax: (01492) 531708 E-mail: sales@alpha-business-centre.co.uk

Alpha Business Machines Ltd, 5 Chorley West Business Park, Ackhurst Road, Chorley, Lancashire, PR7 1NL Tel: (01257) 279000 Fax: (01257) 231010 E-mail: alpha@copfax.freeserve.co.uk

Altodigital Midlands UK Ltd, Pensnett Trading Estate, Kingswinford, West Midlands, DY6 7FZ Tel: (01384) 404660 Fax: (01384) 404665 E-mail: enquiries@altodigital.com

Amazon Business Communications Ltd, Amazon House 2, Pitters Piece, Long Crendon, Aylesbury, Buckinghamshire, HP18 9PP Tel: (01844) 202035 Fax: (01844) 202031 E-mail: info@amazon-business.com

Anca, Leyton Avenue, Mildenhall, Bury St. Edmunds, Suffolk, IP28 7BL Tel: (01638) 717611 Fax: (01638) 717711

▶ Antler Office Furniture Ltd, Seedbed Centre, Langston Road, Loughton, Essex, IG10 3TQ Tel: (020) 8787 7097 Fax: (020) 8787 7066 E-mail: enquiries@antleroffice.co.uk

Aquarius Back Care, The Old Dairy, Broom Hill, Bristol, BS16 1DN Tel: 0117-965 8555 Fax: 0117-965 8444 E-mail: info@backcare.co.uk

Arena Business Machines, Armitage House, Thorpe Lower Lane, Robin Hood, Wakefield, West Yorkshire, WF3 3BQ Tel: 0113-288 0282 Fax: 0113-288 0671 E-mail: admin@arenagroup.net

Avenue Office Supplies, 3 David Road, Colnbrook, Slough, SL3 0TW Tel: (01753) 687687 Fax: (01753) 681681 E-mail: admin@avenue-group.co.uk

Azzurri Communications Ltd, Elmhirst Lane, Dodworth, Barnsley, South Yorkshire, S75 4LS Tel: (01226) 777111 Fax: (01226) 777100

B C L, 12 The Square, Caterham, Surrey, CR3 6QA Tel: (01883) 340311 Fax: (01883) 342144 E-mail: solutions@bclsystems.com

Barkshire Group, 40 Ivanhoe Road, Hogwood Industrial Estate, Finchampstead, Wokingham, Berkshire, RG40 4QQ Tel: 0118-973 2919 Fax: 0118-973 0899 E-mail: sales@barkshiregroup.co.uk

Barry Bennett Ltd, Unit 15a Bankfield Business Park, Quebec Street, Bolton, BL3 5JN Tel: (01204) 534311 Fax: (01204) 362783 E-mail: info@baarybennett.co.uk

Beith Printing Co. Ltd, 1-7 Earl Haig Road, Hillington Industrial Estate, Glasgow, G52 4JU Tel: 0141-882 9088 Fax: 0141-882 3204 E-mail: mail@beith-printing.co.uk

Belmonte Business Equipment Ltd, Carlton House, 230 Manchester Road, Stockport, Cheshire, SK4 1NN Tel: 0161-480 5556 Fax: 0161-480 6546 E-mail: sales@belmonte.co.uk

Bennett Sykes Group, 84 Vaughan Way, Leicester, LE1 4SH Tel: 0116-253 0454 Fax: 0116-253 6127 E-mail: enquiries@bennettsykes.co.uk

Beta Electronics Ltd, 11 Indescon Court, Docklands, London, E14 9TN Tel: (020) 7531 2828 Fax: (020) 7531 2929

Bi-Silque UK Ltd, 72c Noramn Way Industrial Estate, Longbridge Road, Preston, PR2 5BB Tel: (01772) 655353 Fax: (01772) 655525

Blundell Harling Ltd, 9 Albany Road, Granby Industrial Estate, Weymouth, Dorset, DT4 9TH Tel: (01305) 206000 Fax: (01305) 760598 E-mail: sales@blundellharling.co.uk

Border Office Equipment, 4 Block 14 Amber Business Centre, Greenhill Lane, Riddings, Alfreton, Derbyshire, DE55 4BR Tel: (01773) 608039 Fax: (01773) 609145 E-mail: borderofficeriddings@btopenworld.com

Boston Office Solutions, Moor La Trading Estate, Sherburn in Elmet, Leeds, LS25 6ES Tel: (01977) 681068 Fax: (01977) 681619 E-mail: sales@bostonoffice.co.uk

Bradford Business Machines, 155 Bradford Road, Cleckheaton, West Yorkshire, BD19 3SX Tel: (01274) 879608 Fax: (01274) 879608 E-mail: bradfordbusiness@aol.com

Brian Green, D B H House, Boundary Street, Liverpool, L5 9YJ Tel: 0151-207 5225 Fax: 0151-207 3300 E-mail: sales@brian-green.co.uk

Britim Computer Products Ltd, Broadway Unit 1, Horseshoe Yard, Crowland, Peterborough, PE6 0BJ Tel: (01733) 212121 Fax: (01733) 212122 E-mail: sales@britim.biz

Bullock & Bosson, Unit 6, Victoria Road, Stoke-on-Trent, ST4 2HS Tel: (01782) 747222 Fax: (01782) 746200 E-mail: phillips@bullockandbosson.co.uk

C B S Office Supplies Ltd, 1 Winship Road, Milton, Cambridge, CB4 6BQ Tel: (01223) 225555 Fax: (01223) 225550 E-mail: mail@cbsofficesupplies.co.uk

▶ C C M South West Ltd, 6 Crown Close, Crown Industrial Estate, Taunton, Somerset, TA2 8RX Tel: (01823) 331166 Fax: (01823) 270393

C C M Sussex Ltd, PO Box 2004, Peacehaven, East Sussex, BN10 7HZ Tel: (01273) 586963 Fax: (01273) 584000 E-mail: sales@ccm.gb.com

C R Business Equipment Ltd, Unit 11 Stephenson Way, Formby Business Park, Formby, Liverpool, L37 8EG Tel: (01704) 834083 Fax: (01704) 834083

Cartridges UK, Corunna House, 42-44 Ousegate, Selby, North Yorkshire, YO8 4NH Tel: (01757) 212747 Fax: (01757) 212321 E-mail: nikki@cartridgesuk.com

Central Business Machines Ltd, 112-118 Kingsland Road, London, E2 8DJ Tel: (020) 7729 5588 Fax: (020) 7729 9137

Charnwood Publishing Co. Ltd, Vaughan Street, Coalville, Leicestershire, LE67 3GG Tel: (01530) 832288 Fax: (01530) 510390 E-mail: chardwoodp@aol.com

Chrystal & Hill Ltd, 14-30 Woodhead Road, South Nitshill Industrial Estate, Glasgow, G53 7WA Tel: 0141-880 6600 Fax: 0141-880 6611 E-mail: sales@chrystal-hill.co.uk

City Office Audio London Ltd, Superstore, 303-309 Camberwell New Road, London, SE5 0TF Tel: (020) 7703 6032 Fax: (020) 7703 5500 E-mail: grm@cityoffice.co.uk

City Office Ni Ltd, 67 Boucher Cresent, Belfast, BT12 6HU Tel: (028) 9038 1838 Fax: (028) 9038 1954 E-mail: info@cityofficni.com

Claughton Office Equipment Ltd, 53 Beverley Road, Hull, HU3 1XL Tel: (01482) 323235 Fax: (01482) 224201 E-mail: sales@claughtons.com

OFFICE EQUIPMENT MANUFRS – *continued*

Club Copying Co. Ltd, 10-18 Sandgate Street, London, SE15 1LE Tel: (020) 7635 5252 Fax: (020) 7635 5714 E-mail: jacquidalton@clubcopying.co.uk

Cluine Group Ltd, 15 Lochside Street, Oban, Argyll, PA34 4HP Tel: (01631) 562572 Fax: (01631) 565286 E-mail: info@officesupplies-printing.co.uk

Coffee Supply Co., 3 Sunnylaw Road, Bridge of Allan, Stirling, FK9 4QD Tel: (01786) 834242 Fax: (01786) 833988

Colemans Office Supplies, 8a Berrington Road, Leamington Spa, Warwickshire, CV31 1NB Tel: (01926) 451751 Fax: (01926) 450973 E-mail: info@colemansofficesupplies.co.uk

▶ Combined Colour Solutions Ltd, 9 Holme Road, Ramsey, Huntingdon, Cambridgeshire, PE26 2SS Tel: (01733) 844285

Commercial Business Equipment Ltd, 1-3 Chorley Road, Walton-le-Dale, Preston, PR5 4JA Tel: 0151-495 2359 Fax: 0151-495 2827

Communications South Ltd, 284 Hayling Avenue, Portsmouth, PO3 6EF Tel: (023) 9283 3993 Fax: (023) 9283 3288 E-mail: sales@commsouth.co.uk

Concorde Business Machines Ltd, 4 Dye House Lane, London, E3 2TB Tel: (020) 8983 0777 Fax: (020) 8983 0689

Cooper Office Supplies Ltd, 61c Lord Avenue, Thornaby, Stockton-on-Tees, Cleveland, TS17 9JX Tel: (01642) 760414 Fax: (01642) 750991 E-mail: sales@cooperoffice.co.uk

Copi Stationers, Lower Cardiff Road, Pwllheli, Gwynedd, LL53 5BY Tel: (01758) 614364 Fax: (01758) 614364

Copylogic Ltd, The Palmerston Centre, Oxford Road, Wealdstone, Harrow, Middlesex, HA3 7RG Tel: (020) 8863 4483 Fax: (020) 8861 1620 E-mail: mail@copylogic.co.uk

Corporate Business Systems, 11 Shotts St, Glasgow, G33 4JB Tel: 0141-774 5000 Fax: 0141-774 2256

Corporate Express, Tameside Drive, Birmingham, B6 7AY Tel: 0121-331 3400 Fax: 0121-331 3002 E-mail: dylan.jones@cexp.co.uk

Crest Reprographics (Northern) Ltd, Crest House, Gibralter Row, Liverpool, L3 7HJ Tel: 0151-236 2642 Fax: 0151-236 2726 E-mail: info@crest-reprographics.co.uk

Crombie Office Equipment Ltd, Unit 9 Wellington Business Park, Wellington Circle, Nigg, Aberdeen, AB12 3JG Tel: (01224) 630082 Fax: (01224) 632168 E-mail: sales@gfofficesupplies.co.uk

Currie Business Services Ltd, 244-252 Price Street, Birkenhead, Merseyside, CH41 3PS Tel: 0151-343 9196 Fax: 0151-647 7627 E-mail: cbssupply@aol.com

D M W Copier Services, 431 Oakleigh Road North, London, N20 0RU Tel: (020) 8361 4833 Fax: (020) 8368 6229

Danka (UK) P.L.C., Carlisle, CA4 8LL Tel: (01228) 562935 Fax: (01228) 562936 E-mail: bcowen@danka.co.uk

▶ Danwood Group, 14 The Courtyard, Buntsford Drive, Bromsgrove, Worcestershire, B60 3DJ Tel: (01527) 571571 Fax: (01527) 571572 E-mail: sales@englands.co.uk

Danwood Group, Seymour House, Little Money Road, Loddon, Norwich, NR14 6JD Tel: (01508) 521300 Fax: (01508) 521319 E-mail: mail@danwood.co.uk

▶ Denovo Interiors, Units 1-2, Lock Way, Dewsbury, West Yorkshire, WF13 3SX Tel: (01924) 491887 Fax: (01924) 496591 E-mail: lcameron@denovo-int.co.uk

▶ Digital Vision Technologies Ltd, Langdale House, Gadbrook Business Centre, Rudheath, Northwich, Cheshire, CW9 7TN Tel: (01606) 331234 Fax: (01606) 338640 E-mail: info@dutl.co.uk

Document House, Viscount House Queensway Court Business Park, Arkwright Way, Scunthorpe, South Humberside, DN16 1AD Tel: (01482) 370470 Fax: (01724) 271041 E-mail: sherralee.thompson@documenthouse.co.uk

Don Ruffles, 53 Bell Street, Reigate, Surrey, RH2 7AQ Tel: (01737) 245755 Fax: (01737) 244095 E-mail: sales@rufflesstationery.com

Draw Write, 72-74 Sandgate, Ayr, KA7 1BX Tel: (01292) 610735 Fax: (01292) 263877 E-mail: dwrite7274@aol.com

Edwards, Glyn Office Equipment Ltd, 4 Charles Street, Milford Haven, Dyfed, SA73 2AJ Tel: (01646) 698833 Fax: (01646) 698837 E-mail: mark@gedwards-office.demon.co.uk

Egan Reid Stationery Co. Ltd, Horsfield Way, Bredbury Park Industrial Estate, Bredbury, Stockport, Cheshire, SK6 2SU Tel: 0161-406 6000 Fax: 0161-406 6591 E-mail: sales@eganreid.co.uk

Electronic Business Systems Ltd, 852 Tyburn Road, Birmingham, B24 9NT Tel: 0121-384 2513 Fax: 0121-377 6014 E-mail: info@e-b-s.co.uk

▶ Electronic Document Services Ltd, 54 Bankhead Crossway South, Edinburgh, EH11 4EP Tel: 0131-442 3000

Ensiform Type Products Ltd, 2 Nafcot Street, Watford, WD17 4RB Tel: (01923) 442020 Fax: (0800) 838097

Entwisle Paddon Ltd, 11 King Street West, Stockport, Cheshire, SK3 0DX Tel: 0161-480 2879 Fax: 0161-476 1325

Equipu, Unit M1, The Maltings, Lodway Business Centre, Pill, Bristol, BS20 0DH Tel: (01275) 813838 Fax: (01275) 813122 E-mail: equipu@eurocopy.co.uk

Eximedia UK Ltd, 4 Black Swan Yard, London, SE1 3XW Tel: (020) 7403 1555 Fax: (020) 7403 8524 E-mail: info@eximedia.co.uk

F B Jesper & Son Ltd, 14 Oxford St, Harrogate, North Yorkshire, HG1 1PU Tel: (01423) 503998 E-mail: harrogate@jespers.co.uk

F P Mailing Systems (Services) Ltd, 2 Manor Farm Close, Windsor, Berkshire, SL4 4DJ Tel: (01753) 621868 Fax: (01753) 862566

▶ F S C Ltd, Bronte Works, Chesham Street, Keighley, West Yorkshire, BD21 4LG Tel: (0845) 2305332 Fax: (01535) 683301

Fax (UK) Ltd, Timber House, Standford Place, Church Stretton, Shropshire, SY6 6DY Tel: (01694) 722333 Fax: (0870) 3665760 E-mail: sales@shopuk.co.uk

First Copy Ltd, 187 High Street, Bottisham, Cambridge, CB5 9BB Tel: (0800) 592566 Fax: (01223) 813850 E-mail: info@firstcopy.co.uk

G&T, 9 Orwell Court, Hurricane Way, Wickford, Essex, SS11 8YJ Tel: (01268) 766500 Fax: (01268) 766530 E-mail: info@gtoffice.co.uk

GB Copier Systems Ltd, Waterloo Road, Stoke-on-Trent, ST6 2EU Tel: (01782) 814444 Fax: (01782) 814455

Global Direct, 2 Cartsdyke, Greenock, Renfrewshire, PA15 1DT Tel: (01475) 500011 Fax: (01475) 500022 E-mail: scotland@micsco.co.uk

Group Business Services Ltd, Wincheap Indust Estate, Simmonds Road, Canterbury, Kent, CT1 3RA Tel: (01227) 478377 E-mail: sandra@groupbusiness.co.uk

H A Office Supplies, 25 Pittfield Street, London, N1 6HB Tel: (020) 7608 3670 Fax: (020) 7608 3670

Harewood Products Ltd, Unit 1, Union Road, The Valley, Bolton, BL2 2DT Tel: (01204) 395730 Fax: (01204) 388018 E-mail: info@adboards.com

Hatherway Office Furniture Ltd, The Farmhouse On The Green, Upper Quinton, Stratford-Upon-Avon, Warwickshire, CV37 8SX Tel: (01789) 721113 Fax: (01789) 721220 E-mail: fbs@freeola.com

High-Tech Business Machines, 18 Kirkgate, Birstall, Batley, West Yorkshire, WF17 9PB Tel: (01924) 420803 Fax: (01924) 420804 E-mail: info@hi-techbm.co.uk

▶ Hodge Ltd, 4 North Howard Street, Belfast, BT13 2AS Tel: (028) 9024 1812 Fax: (028) 9024 6866

I O T P.L.C., Crompton Close, Basildon, Essex, SS14 3AZ Tel: (01268) 523366 Fax: (01268) 527135 E-mail: eoe@eurocopy.co.uk

Ikon Office Solutions Dublin Ltd, Ikon House, 30 Cowcross Street, London, EC1M 6DQ Tel: (020) 7253 4545 Fax: (020) 7250 3690

Index Business Supplies Ltd, 127-129 Becontree Avenue, Dagenham, Essex, RM8 2UL Tel: (020) 8598 9912 Fax: (020) 8598 8658 E-mail: info@indexbs.com

Infotec UK Ltd, 1230 Arlington Business Park, Theale, Reading, RG7 4TX Tel: 0118-928 4900 Fax: 0118-928 4901

Inglis Allen Ltd, 40 Townsend Place, Kirkcaldy, Fife, KY1 1HF Tel: (01592) 267201 Fax: (01592) 206049 E-mail: info@scottishcalendars.com

Integrated Office Systems Ltd, Unit 89 Willows Court, Thornaby, Stockton-on-Tees, Cleveland, TS17 9PP Tel: (01642) 751444 Fax: (01642) 761444 E-mail: enquiries@iosltd.co.uk

▶ Intermec International Inc, Sovereign House, Vastern Road, Reading, RG1 8BT Tel: 0118-987 9400 Fax: 0118-987 9401

▶ J K Office Supplies, 21 Rufford Rise, Sothall, Sheffield, S20 2DW Tel: 0114-247 1515 Fax: 0114-247 1515

JBL Office, 168-170 Cumnor Road, Boars Hill, Oxford, OX1 5JS Tel: (01865) 739056 Fax: (01865) 326754 E-mail: sales@jbl.co.uk

Jim Barlow Stationers Ltd, 18 Park Road, Worsley, Manchester, M28 7DA Tel: 0161-799 9558 Fax: 0161-703 8789 E-mail: sales@jimbarlows.co.uk

Ben Johnson Office Equipment Ltd, Sterling Park, York, YO30 4WU Tel: (01904) 698698 Fax: (01904) 698699 E-mail: info@benjohnson.co.uk

K T D Colourcraft Ltd, 7 Lowther Street, Carlisle, CA3 8ES Tel: (01228) 528559 Fax: (01228) 819799

Kami Office Supplies, 620 Western Avenue, London, W3 0TE Tel: (020) 8896 9399

Kendal Business Equipment Ltd, Kendal House, The Street, Shadoxhurst, Ashford, Kent, TN26 1LU Tel: (01233) 733267 Fax: (01233) 733221 E-mail: kendalbusinessequipment@hotmail.com

Kingfield Heath Ltd, 17 Trench Road, Hydepark Industrial Estate, Newtownabbey, County Antrim, BT36 4TY Tel: (028) 9084 3511 Fax: (028) 9083 5133

Konica Business Machines UK Ltd, 2 Wharfside, Oldbury, West Midlands, B69 2BU Tel: 0121-544 3344 Fax: 0121-544 3130 E-mail: info@bs.konicaminolta.co.uk

KTC Office Stationery Supplies, 21 Pudding Lane, Maidstone, Kent, ME14 1TY Tel: (01622) 758853 Fax: (01622) 753741 E-mail: ktcoffice@btconnect.com

Langstane Press Ltd, Palmerston Road, Aberdeen, AB11 5QJ Tel: (01224) 212212 Fax: (01224) 210066 E-mail: sales@langstane.co.uk

Lasercare Bristol Ltd, 8 Bromley Heath Avenue, Bristol, BS16 6JS Tel: 0117-908 3463 Fax: 0117-907 7538 E-mail: sales@lasercarebristol.co.uk

Lemark Office Equipment North Ltd, Unit 2-3 Universal Cresent, North Anston Trading Estate, North Anston, Sheffield, S25 4JJ Tel: (01909) 566328 Fax: (01909) 567771

Linconshire Office Friends Ltd, Unit 1 Viking Court, Gilbey Road, Grimsby, North East Lincolnshire, DN31 2UJ Tel: (01472) 341493 Fax: (01472) 341600 E-mail: sales@officefriends.com

Lion House UK Ltd, 1 Old Parsonage Yard, Horton Road, Horton Kirby, Dartford, DA4 9BN Tel: (01322) 868606 Fax: (01322) 866441 E-mail: howardelkins@lionhouse.co.uk

London Business Equipment, 529 High Road Leytonstone, London, E11 4PB Tel: (020) 8558 0024 Fax: (020) 8556 4865 E-mail: sales@1ondonbusinessequipment.com

Ludgate Office Equipment Ltd, 7 Stevens Lane, Claygate, Esher, Surrey, KT10 0TD Tel: (01372) 466091 Fax: (01372) 464960 E-mail: sales@ludgateoe.co.uk

M J Farmer, 50 Wolverhampton Road, Wednesfield, Wolverhampton, WV11 1UJ Tel: (01902) 728827 Fax: (01902) 728827

Ma Interiors, St Jude's Church, Dulwich Road, London, SE24 0PB Tel: (020) 7737 1371 Fax: (020) 7274 2023 E-mail: sales@mainteriors.co.uk

Mccarthy Developments 2000 Ltd, Systems House, Broad Lane, Coventry, CV5 7AX Tel: (024) 7646 8866 Fax: (024) 7669 4486 E-mail: sales@mccarthygroup.co.uk

▶ Macro Business Equipment (UK) Ltd, 10 Clarke Street, Derby, DE1 2BU Tel: (01332) 227630 Fax: (0870) 7412899

Manton Office Equipment Ltd, 4 Clipstone Brook Industrial Estate, Cherrycourt Way, Leighton Buzzard, Bedfordshire, LU7 4GP Tel: (01525) 852350 Fax: (01525) 852352 E-mail: info@mantonoffice.com

Margolis Business Systems, Unit 4.02 Crayfield Business Park, New Mill Road, Orpington, Kent, BR5 3QA Tel: (01689) 891000 Fax: (01689) 890555 E-mail: sales@margolis.co.uk

Mather K.G Office Supplies, 1a Higher Common Way, Buckley, Clwyd, CH7 3PW Tel: (01244) 548393 Fax: (01244) 548393

Metrik Office Supplies, 20 Market Square, Dumfries, DG2 7AB Tel: (01387) 253844 Fax: (01387) 257343 E-mail: scallender@metrik.co.uk

MicroMedia UK Ltd, 74 Gloucester Road, London, E17 6AE Tel: (07762) 660697 Fax: (020) 8527 3302

Midland Business Equipment Ltd, Unit 4 Highlands House, Stirling Road, Shirley, Solihull, West Midlands, B90 4NE Tel: (01675) 470061 Fax: 01675 470889 E-mail: info@m-b-e.co.uk

Midshire Business Systems Northern Ltd, Jones Court, Jones Square, Stockport, Cheshire, SK1 4LJ Tel: 0161-477 3277 Fax: 0161-477 3340 E-mail: info@midshire.co.uk

Modern Typewriting Supplies Ltd, 69 Choumert Road, London, SE15 4AS Tel: (020) 7639 6317 Fax: (020) 7358 1079 E-mail: modern@btconnect.com

Mondi Reprographics, 7 Glebe House, 110 Church La East, Aldershot, Hampshire, GU11 3HN Tel: (01252) 313830

Moray Business & Computer Centre, 20 Commerce Street, Elgin, Morayshire, IV30 1BS Tel: (01343) 552000 Fax: (01343) 552020 E-mail: sales@moray-business.co.uk

N R G Group Ltd, 4 Rushmills, Northampton, NN4 7YB Tel: (01604) 732700

Neat Ideas Ltd, Sandall Stones Road, Kirk Sandall Industrial Estate, Doncaster, South Yorkshire, DN3 1QU Tel: (01302) 890089 Fax: (01302) 886605 E-mail: sales@neat-ideas.com

Nexus Computer & Office Supplies, 64 Edward Road, Shaw, Oldham, OL2 7EY Tel: (01706) 846131 Fax: (01706) 846131 E-mail: peterradcliffefree@btopenworld.com

Normid Plan Filing Systems, 476 London Road, High Wycombe, Buckinghamshire, HP11 1LP Tel: (01494) 474775 Fax: (01494) 474796 E-mail: sales@normid.co.uk

North West Drawing & Office Supplies, 19 Priory Lane, Penwortham, Preston, PR1 0AR Tel: (01772) 751481 Fax: (01772) 751946 E-mail: nwdrawing@ukonline.co.uk

O K I (Europe) Ltd, Central House, Balfour Road, Hounslow, TW3 1HY Tel: (020) 8219 2190 Fax: (020) 8219 2199

Office Equipment Selection Ltd, Mylord CR, Camperdown Industrial Estate, Newcastle upon Tyne, NE12 5RF Tel: 0191-268 3333 Fax: 0191-268 0344 E-mail: sales@oesltd.co.uk

Office Equipment UK Ltd, Unit 3, Blowick Business Park, Crowland Street, Southport, Merseyside, PR9 7RU Tel: (01704) 539133 Fax: (01704) 539180 E-mail: oeukltd@btopenworld.com

Office Way, 64 Derby Road, Long Eaton, Nottingham, NG10 4QP Tel: 0115-849 1777 Fax: 0115-946 9801 E-mail: theofficeway@aol.com

Orchard Drawing Boards, Union Square, Wakefield, West Yorkshire, WF1 1TT Tel: (01924) 291333 Fax: (01924) 290909

Orchard Stationary, 6 High Street, Stanstead Abbotts, Ware, Hertfordshire, SG12 8AB Tel: (01920) 870900 Fax: (01920) 871860 E-mail: sales@orchardstationery.co.uk

Osborne Stationers Ltd, 27 Market Street, Wolverhampton, WV1 3AG Tel: (01902) 427071 Fax: (01902) 771070

Oyez Straker Office Supplies Ltd, Guild House, Wesley Drive, Newcastle upon Tyne, NE12 9UP Tel: 0191-215 0844 Fax: 0191-266 8450

P S Office Supplies Ltd, 40 Great Lister Street, Birmingham, B7 4LS Tel: 0121-333 5000 Fax: 0121-333 5001 E-mail: sales@psonline.co.uk

Paper Flow Ltd, Unit 5 & 6, 20 Bugsby Way, London, SE7 7SJ Tel: (020) 8331 2090 Fax: (020) 8331 2001 E-mail: sales@paperflowonline.com

PDQ Direct, Sureline House, Easting Close, Worthing, West Sussex, BN14 8HQ Tel: (01903) 282500 Fax: (01903) 282599 E-mail: sales@pdqdirect.co.uk

Penketh's Ltd, Bassendale Road, Croft Business Park, Wirral, Merseyside, CH62 3QL Tel: 0151-334 4417 Fax: 0151-737 5001 E-mail: enquiries@penkeths.co.uk

Pennine Drawing Office Services, Unit X1 2 Keighley Business Centre, South Street, Keighley, West Yorkshire, BD21 1AG Tel: (01535) 667422 Fax: (01535) 610130 E-mail: pennine@totalise.co.uk

▶ Photocopier Sales, 137 Kings Road, Kingston upon Thames, Surrey, KT2 5JE Tel: (020) 8547 1222 Fax: (020) 8547 3666 E-mail: info@kingsofficesupplies.com

Photostatic Copiers Anglia & Co., 39-41 West End Street, Norwich, NR2 4NA Tel: (01603) 613969 Fax: (01603) 667373 E-mail: sales@photostatic.com

Pricebusters, Unit 5b Petergreen Way, Furness Business Park, Barrow-in-Furness, Cumbria, LA14 2PE Tel: (01229) 432720 Fax: (01229) 432720

Prime Systems, Brickbarn House, Knowle Lane, Cranleigh, Surrey, GU6 8JL Tel: (01483) 276442 E-mail: sales@primecouk.com

Printel, 43 Cross Road, Croydon, CR0 6TE Tel: (020) 8681 2262 Fax: (020) 8688 5883 E-mail: printel@btinernet.com

Redworth Products Ltd, Church Farm Barns, Church Farm Lane, Marsworth, Tring, Hertfordshire, HP23 4ND Tel: (01296) 662882 Fax: (01296) 660880 E-mail: redworth-products@lineone.net

Research Micro Systems Ltd, Radclyffe House, 66-68 Hagley Road, Birmingham, B16 8PF Tel: 0121-410 5860

Royal Printers Stationers & Office Furniture Co., 111a Sheen Lane, London, SW14 8AE Tel: (020) 8408 2000 Fax: (020) 8330 1221

S.D.I Plotter Supplies Sigma Graphics, Higher Hillgate, Stockport, Cheshire, SK1 3QY Tel: 0161-429 7404 Fax: 0161-402 9425

S K D Office Supplies Ltd, 71-75 Railway Road, Leigh, Lancashire, WN7 4AD Tel: (01942) 603326 Fax: (01942) 674961 E-mail: sales@skdoffice.co.uk

S M Group (Europe) Ltd, Mercator House, Brest Road, Plymouth, PL6 5XP Tel: (01752) 662129 Fax: (01752) 241040 E-mail: sales@smgeurope.com

▶ S R S Shredder Repair Services, PO Box 4279, Dunstable, Bedfordshire, LU6 1WX Tel: (01582) 536346 Fax: (01582) 601448 E-mail: info@shredderrepair.co.uk

Saber Office Furniture Ltd, 21 Bath Lane, Leicester, LE3 5BF Tel: 0116-251 1121 Fax: 0116-251 2625 E-mail: sales@ukofficefurniture.co.uk

Santiki Ltd, Unit A4 The Connaught Business Centre, 22 Willow Lane, Mitcham, Surrey, CR4 4NA Tel: (020) 8685 0550 Fax: (020) 8640 7414 E-mail: sales@santiki.co.uk

Satellite Business Systems Ltd, 11-13 Wakley Street, London, EC1V 7LT Tel: (020) 7417 2020 Fax: (020) 7417 2093 E-mail: sales@xenith.uk.com

▶ Sciamed Ltd, Mart Road, Alford, Aberdeenshire, AB33 8BZ Tel: (01975) 564111 Fax: (01975) 564222

Scott Computer Supplies, Unit A3, Sumervell Street, Cambuslang, Glasgow, G72 7EB Tel: 0141-646 2690 Fax: 0141-646 2838 E-mail: info@scottcomputersupplies.co.uk

Set (Cardiff) Ltd, 6-7 Duke St, Cardiff, CF10 1AY Tel: (029) 2037 3328 Fax: (029) 2038 3344

Shepshed Knight Printing Service Ltd, 91 Charnwood Road, Shepshed, Loughborough, Leicestershire, LE12 9NL Tel: (01509) 502246 Fax: (01509) 503179 E-mail: sales@shepshedknight.com

Sidney Graham Business Supplies Ltd, 236-240 Station Road, Kings Heath, Birmingham, B14 7TE Tel: 0121-443 3377 Fax: 0121-441 1456 E-mail: matt@sidneygraham.plus.com

Sigma Group, PO Box 302, Guernsey, GY1 3SD Tel: (01481) 241111 Fax: (01481) 246391 E-mail: sales@sigma-aztec.com

▶ Spacesaver Furniture, 149-153 High Holborn, London, WC1V 6PJ Tel: (020) 7404 7552 Fax: (020) 7404 7442

Stafford Ltd, Overbrook Court, Overbrook Lane, Knowsley, Prescot, Merseyside, L34 9FB Tel: 0151-907 0027 Fax: 0151-907 0028 E-mail: paul.spooner@staffords.ltd.uk

Stationery Express, 15 The Metro Centre, St. Johns Road, Isleworth, Middlesex, TW7 6NJ Tel: (020) 8568 1771 Fax: (020) 8569 8168 E-mail: sales@stationeryexpress.net

Stevenson Office Furniture, 863-865 Harrow Road, London, NW10 5NG Tel: (020) 8969 3850 Fax: (020) 8968 1790

Stewarts of Edinburgh Ltd, Meadowbank Works, 67 Marionville Road, Edinburgh, EH7 6AJ Tel: 0131-659 6010 Fax: 0131-652 1348 E-mail: mail@stewarts.eu.com

Swift Business Equipment Ltd, Northgate, Aldridge, Walsall, WS9 8TR Tel: (01922) 743454 Fax: (01922) 743134 E-mail: sales@swiftbe.co.uk

OFFICE EQUIPMENT MANUFRS – *continued*

Tab Business Machines & Equipment Ltd, 2-3 London Road, London, SE1 6JZ Tel: (020) 7620 3366 Fax: (020) 7633 0206 E-mail: sales@tab.uk.com

Talbot Office Products Equipment Ltd, 5 Gunnery Terrace, The Royal Arsnal, Woolwich, London, SE18 6SW Tel: (020) 7231 7020 Fax: (020) 7231 8087

Tannas Office Supplies Ltd, 76 High Road, London, NW10 2PU Tel: (020) 8459 0521 Fax: (020) 8459 8603 E-mail: info@tannas.co.uk

Tattersalls, 46 Warner Street, Accrington, Lancashire, BB5 1HN Tel: (01254) 232244 Fax: (01254) 386454

Todds Of Lincoln Ltd, Centenary House, Whisby Way, Lincoln, LN6 3LQ Tel: (01522) 884000 Fax: (01522) 884411 E-mail: sales@toddslinc.co.uk

Toms Office Technology Ltd, 26 Adelaide Road, Leamington Spa, Warwickshire, CV31 3PL Tel: (01926) 425842 Fax: (01926) 832017 E-mail: sales@tomsoffice.co.uk

▶ Top Office Products, Greenway Centre, Doncaster Road, Bristol, BS10 5PY Tel: 0117-959 1111 Fax: 0117-959 1112 E-mail: topofficeproducts@btconnect.com

Trio Systems, 14 Hampton Road, Twickenham, TW2 5QB Tel: (020) 8893 4455 Fax: (020) 8893 4456 E-mail: sales@triosystems.co.uk

Unicorn Office Products Ltd, Unit 25 Station Road Workshops, Station Road, Bristol, BS15 4PJ Tel: 0117-907 6662 Fax: 0117-907 6663 E-mail: sales@unicornonline.net

Vitesse plc, Excelda House, 15 Tennis Street, London, SE1 1YD Tel: (020) 7357 7888 Fax: (020) 7357 8855 E-mail: sales@vitesse.plc.uk

W A Hutton & Co. Ltd, 37 School Lane, Stockport, Cheshire, SK4 5DE Tel: 0161-431 5500 Fax: 0161-442 1318 E-mail: sales@wahutton.co.uk

Wagstaff Office Interiors, Unit 12-15 Wharfeside, Rosemont Road, Wembley, Middlesex, HA0 4PE Tel: (020) 8432 1000 Fax: (020) 8432 1111 E-mail: interiors@wagstaffgroup.co.uk

Walrus Office Group Ltd, Barton Fields Centre, Church Broughton, Derby, DE65 5AP Tel: (01283) 733339 Fax: (01283) 733399 E-mail: info@walrus.co.uk

Walters Office World Ltd, 19 Royce Road, Peterborough, PE1 5YB Tel: (01733) 707000 Fax: (01733) 708000 E-mail: info@walters.co.uk

▶ Wasp Barcode Technologies, 20 Churchill Square, Kings Hill, West Malling, Kent, ME19 4YU Tel: (0845) 4301971 Fax: (0845) 6001973

WB Office Equipment Ltd, 16 Mandervell Road, Oadby, Leicester, LE2 5LQ Tel: 0116-271 1033 Fax: 0116-271 1022

West End Stationers Ltd, 231 Kentish Town Road, London, NW5 2JT Tel: (020) 7485 4472 Fax: (020) 7267 5231

West Midland Office Supplies, Cherry Tree Walk, Farrier Street, Worcester, WR1 3BH Tel: (0870) 3330933 Fax: (0870) 9001449

Western Office Equipment, 53 Omaha Road, Walker Lines Industrial Estate, Bodmin, Cornwall, PL31 1ES Tel: (01208) 72042 Fax: (01208) 79642 E-mail: western@office54.fsbusiness.co.uk

Whittaker Office Supplies Ltd, Weldon Road, Loughborough, Leicestershire, LE11 5TE Tel: (01509) 235888 Fax: (01509) 610511 E-mail: smart@whittaker-os.co.uk

Wilcox Desk Top Equipment, Unison House, 46 George Street, Kidderminster, Worcestershire, DY10 1PY Tel: (01562) 824470 Fax: (01562) 829867 E-mail: sales@wilcoxdesktop.co.uk

Williams Office Concept Ltd, 1 Arthur Street, Derby, DE1 3EF Tel: (01332) 371311 Fax: (01332) 364797

Dan Wood Scotland, Grampian House, Virginia Street, Aberdeen, AB11 5AU Tel: (01224) 211900 Fax: (01224) 212828 E-mail: reception.aberdeen@sctland.co.uk

Worktown Office Supplies Ltd, 1 Park Court, Premier Way, Abbey Park, Romsey, Hants, SO51 9AQ Tel: (01794) 525065 Fax: (01794) 525025 E-mail: orders@worktown.com

Zonal Retail Data Systems Ltd, Unit 5a The Scotway Centre, Newton Village, Dalkeith, Midlothian, EH22 1SP Tel: 0131-654 4800 Fax: 0131-654 4801

OFFICE FILES

David Connolly Ltd, 3 Stanley Mills Business Park, Britannia Road, Huddersfield, HD3 4QS Tel: (01484) 641832 Fax: (01484) 462011 E-mail: davidconnolly@btconnect.com

Sabell & Co., Saxon Way, Birmingham, B37 5AX Tel: 0121-770 1389 Fax: 0121-788 1970

OFFICE FURNISHERS AND FURNITURE, *See also headings for particular types*

A & B Office Furnishers, 4 Charlton Mead Lane, Hoddesdon, Hertfordshire, EN11 0DJ Tel: (0870) 0502040

A F I Ltd, Unit 17-20, Greenfield, Royston, Hertfordshire, SG8 5HN Tel: (01763) 241007 Fax: (01763) 241040 E-mail: sales@phase.co.uk

A S G, 15 Wharfside, Bletchley, Milton Keynes, MK2 2AZ Tel: (01908) 375020 Fax: (01908) 375145 E-mail: sales@asgoffice.co.uk

A50 Office Furniture, Unit 4, The Old Boatyard, Church Broughton Road, Foston, Derby, DE65 5PW Tel: (01283) 810015 Fax: (01283) 814474E-mail: sales@a50officefurniture.co.uk

Abacus, Unit 29, Ardent Way, Mountheath Industrial Park, Prestwich, Manchester, M25 9WE Tel: 0161-773 7594 Fax: 0161-773 0093 E-mail: info@abacusweighing.com

Abbey Central, 90 Croydon Road, Beckenham, Kent, BR3 4DF Tel: (020) 8650 2456 Fax: (020) 8650 2456

Abbotts Office Solutions, Station Yard, Thame, Oxfordshire, OX9 3UH Tel: (01844) 268360 Fax: (01844) 268370 E-mail: abbott@officesolutions.co.uk

▶ Accent Office Interiors, 53-55 Cardiff Road, Luton, LU1 1PP Tel: (01582) 722211

Accord Office Supplies Ltd, Unit 22 Bridge Mead, Westmead Industrial Estate, Westlea, Swindon, SN5 7TL Tel: (0800) 7311133 Fax: (0800) 7311133 E-mail: sales@accordoffice.co.uk

Acorn Partition & Storage Systems, Kingsley Road, Lincoln, LN6 3TA Tel: (01522) 688771 Fax: (01522) 680404 E-mail: sales@apss.co.uk

Alpha Business Centre Ltd, 12 Princes Drive, Colwyn Bay, Clwyd, LL29 8LA Tel: (01492) 531813 Fax: (01492) 531708 E-mail: sales@alpha-business-centre.co.uk

Anthony's, 36 High Street, Stotfold, Hitchin, Hertfordshire, SG5 4LL Tel: (01462) 835452 Fax: (01462) 835452

Austin Office Furniture Ltd, 19 Millicent Road, London, E10 7LG Tel: (020) 8558 6489 Fax: 0208 558 6499 E-mail: sales@austinoffice.co.uk

Axis Scotland Ltd, 12 Auchingramont Road, Hamilton, Lanarkshire, ML3 6JT Tel: (01698) 785000 Fax: (01698) 785111 E-mail: enquiries@axis.gb.com

Barkshire Group, 40 Ivanhoe Road, Hogwood Industrial Estate, Finchampstead, Wokingham, Berkshire, RG40 4QQ Tel: 0118-973 2919 Fax: 0118-973 0899 E-mail: sales@barkshiregroup.co.uk

Baron Contracts Ltd, 72 Cross Road, Maldon, Essex, CM9 5ED Tel: (01621) 856991 Fax: (01621) 850326

Barry Bennett Ltd, Unit 15a Bankfield Business Park, Quebec Street, Bolton, BL3 5JN Tel: (01204) 534311 Fax: (01204) 362783 E-mail: info@baarybennett.co.uk

Bennett Sykes Group, 84 Vaughan Way, Leicester, LE1 4SH Tel: 0116-253 0454 Fax: 0116-253 6127 E-mail: enquiries@bennettsykes.co.uk

▶ Blue Light Office Supplies Ltd, 1 Cedar Wood Drive, Watford, WD25 0RR Tel: (01923) 677005 Fax: (01923) 673584 E-mail: sales@bluelightoffice.com

Blue Line Office Furniture, Endeavour House, London Stansted Airport, Stansted, Essex, CM24 1SJ Tel: (01279) 669470 Fax: (01279) 669471 E-mail: sales@blueline.uk.com

Border Office Equipment, 4 Block 14 Amber Business Centre, Greenhill Lane, Riddings, Alfreton, Derbyshire, DE55 4BR Tel: (01773) 608039 Fax: (01773) 609145 E-mail: borderofficeriddings@btopenworld.com

▶ Brent Cross, Sayer House, Oxgate Lane, London, NW2 7JN Tel: (020) 8208 2626 Fax: (020) 8208 2012 E-mail: sales@brentxofficefurniture.co.uk

Brewers Business Solutions Ltd, Water-Ma-Trout, Helston, Cornwall, TR13 0LW Tel: (01326) 563424 Fax: (01326) 563606

▶ Bristol Business Interiors, CastleMead, Lower Castle Street, Bristol, BS1 3AG Tel: 08450 090514 E-mail: info@bristol-business-interiors.com

Bristol Office Products, Woodview House, 47 Woodleaze, Bristol, BS9 2HX Tel: 0117-968 5016 Fax: 0117-968 5993 E-mail: sales@bop.uk.com

▶ Business Interiors Direct Ltd, Unit C19, Alison Centre, 39 Alison Crescent, Sheffield, S2 1AS Tel: (0845) 4300880 Fax: (0845) 4300990 E-mail: sales@businessinteriorsdirect.co.uk

▶ C I S Office Furniture Ltd, Furniture House, Potters Lane, Wednesbury, West Midlands, WS10 7LP Tel: 0121-556 8741 Fax: 0121-556 9588 E-mail: sales@cisoffice.co.uk

C Silverman Office Furniture Centre, Fen Road, Cambridge, CB4 1UN Tel: (01223) 425168 Fax: (01223) 424826 E-mail: info@silvermanfurniture.co.uk

Central London Office Supplies, 182 Parkview Road, Welling, Kent, DA16 1ST Tel: (020) 8303 2679 Fax: (020) 3223 0068

▶ Channel, The Praze, Penryn, Cornwall, TR10 8AA Tel: (01326) 375657 Fax: (01326) 375676E-mail: enquiries@channelgroup.co.uk

▶ Cicada Interiors Limited, 64 Knightsbridge, London, United Kingdom, SW1X 7JF Tel: (020) 7590 3095 Fax: (020) 7590 9601 E-mail: peter@cicadainteriors.com

City Office Audio London Ltd, Superstore, 303-309 Camberwell New Road, London, SE5 0TF Tel: (020) 7703 6032 Fax: (020) 7703 5500 E-mail: grm@cityoffice.co.uk

Claremont Business Environment, Design Studio 2 Quay Side Commerce Centre, Lower Quay, Fareham, Hampshire, PO16 0XR Tel: (01329) 220123 Fax: (01329) 221322 E-mail: info@claremontgi.com

Clark Office Furniture Ltd, Unit 8, Cannock Chase Enterprise Centre, Walkers Rise, Hednesford, Staffordshire, WS12 0QW Tel: (01543) 423456 Fax: (01543) 426565 E-mail: sales@clarkofficefurniture.com

▶ Commercial & Industrial Interiors Ltd, 1e Princess Court, Princess Way, Prudhoe, Northumberland, NE42 6PL Tel: (01661) 836304 Fax: (0845) 3454229 E-mail: john@ciinteriors.com

Complete Interiors, Ansell Road, Inscape House, Dorking, Surrey, RH4 1QN Tel: (01306) 882198 Fax: (01306) 876427 E-mail: info@completeinteriors.co.uk

Craigavon Office Supplies, 1 Moores Lane, Lurgan, Craigavon, County Armagh, BT66 8DW Tel: (028) 3832 7231 Fax: (028) 3832 1801 E-mail: info@jameshamiltongroup.com

Creative Interior Projects Ltd, 4 Denham Walk, Chalfont St. Peter, Gerrards Cross, Buckinghamshire, SL9 0EN Tel: (01494) 873347 Fax: (01494) 873353 E-mail: sales@creativeinteriorprojects.co.uk

Crescent Office Ltd, 71-73 Beverley Road, Hull, HU3 1XL Tel: (01482) 224444 Fax: (01482) 213505 E-mail: user@crescent-office.com

Dartex Office Furniture, Unit 6 Crayside Industrial Estate, Thames Road, Crayford, Dartford, DA1 4RF Tel: (01322) 521545 Fax: (01322) 558685 E-mail: sales@dartexofficefurniture.co.uk

Delta Business Equipment, Unit G3 Meadow Mill, Water Street, Stockport, Cheshire, SK1 2BY Tel: 0161-480 1222 Fax: 0161-480 0022 E-mail: sales@deltaoffice.co.uk

Dialstat Office Supplies, 1 Sovereign Business Park, 46-48 Willis Way, Poole, Dorset, BH15 3TB Tel: (01202) 774400 Fax: (01202) 666818 E-mail: info@dialstat.co.uk

▶ DKF Iinteriors, Royce Road, Peterborough, PE1 5YB Tel: (0845) 6443145 Fax: (0845) 6443146 E-mail: info@dkfiinteriors.com

Dudley H B S Ltd, Suite 1 Beaufighter House, Alpha 319, Churtsey Road, Chobham, Surrey, GU24 8HW Tel: (0870) 4442884 Fax: (0870) 4442885 E-mail: steve@howarine.co.uk

Dunelm Office Interiors, 149 Kells Lane, Gateshead, Tyne & Wear, NE9 5HR Tel: 0191-491 5080 Fax: 0191-420 0197

Egan Reid Stationery Co. Ltd, Horsfield Way, Bredbury Park Industrial Estate, Bredbury, Stockport, Cheshire, SK6 2SU Tel: 0161-406 6000 Fax: 0161-406 6591 E-mail: sales@eganreid.co.uk

Emergent Crown Contract Office Furnishings Ltd, 59 Pellon Lane, HX, Halifax, West Yorkshire, HX1 5BE Tel: (01422) 349119 Fax: (01422) 206033 E-mail: sales@emergent-crown.co.uk

Entwisle Paddon Ltd, 11 King Street West, Stockport, Cheshire, SK3 0DX Tel: 0161-480 2879 Fax: 0161-476 1325

Ergonom Ltd, Whittington House, 19-30 Alfred Place, London, WC1E 7EA Tel: (020) 7323 2325 Fax: (020) 7323 2032 E-mail: enquiry@ergonom.com

Excel Office Equipment, 24 Mannamead Road, Plymouth, PL4 7AA Tel: (01752) 660151 Fax: (01752) 225778 E-mail: sales@exeloffice.co.uk

▶ G & B Office Services Group Limited, G & B Corner, Blackbird Road, Leicester, LE4 0BX Tel: 0116-251 7777 Fax: 0116-251 1854 E-mail: peter@gboffice.com

G G I Office Furniture (UK) Ltd, Global Way, Darwen, Lancashire, BB3 0RW Tel: (01254) 778500 Fax: (01254) 778519 E-mail: info@ggieurope.com

G W B Ltd, 113-115 Codicote Road, Welwyn, Hertfordshire, AL6 9TY Tel: (01438) 821088 Fax: (01438) 821421 E-mail: sales@gwbltd.co.uk

Glenside Commercial Interiors, Glenside House, Kitchener Road, High Wycombe, Buckinghamshire, HP11 2SW Tel: (01494) 529803 Fax: (01494) 452212

Green Standards Ltd, Green Standards House, Lower Ledge Farm, Dyrham, Chippenham, Wiltshire, SN14 8EY Tel: (0870) 2401445 E-mail: admin@greenstandards.org

H W Dansies, 409 Chatsworth Road, Chesterfield, Derbyshire, S40 2DH Tel: (01246) 235455 Fax: (01246) 220862 E-mail: sales@dansies.co.uk

Hattons Office Furniture, 2-8 Borough Road, St. Helens, Merseyside, WA10 3SY Tel: (01744) 753337 Fax: (01744) 611976

Hawk Furniture Ltd, Holme Industrial Estate, Skiff Lane, Holme-on-Spalding-Moor, York, YO43 4BB Tel: (01430) 861229 Fax: (01430) 861225E-mail: enquiries@hawkfurniture.co.uk

Haywood Office Services, Trafalgar Close, Chandlers Ford Industrial Estate, Chandler's Ford, Eastleigh, Hampshire, SO53 4BW Tel: (023) 8025 4454 Fax: (023) 8026 7986 E-mail: sales@haywoodofficeservices.co.uk

▶ Hodge Ltd, 4 North Howard Street, Belfast, BT13 2AS Tel: (028) 9024 1812 Fax: (028) 9024 6866

Index Business Supplies Ltd, 127-129 Becontree Avenue, Dagenham, Essex, RM8 2UL Tel: (020) 8598 9912 Fax: (020) 8598 8658 E-mail: info@indexbs.com

Integra Contracts Ltd, 119-123 Hackford Road, London, SW9 0QT Tel: (020) 7820 1800 Fax: (020) 7820 1182 E-mail: icl@integracontracts.co.uk

▶ Inter County Office Furniture, 20-21 Woodside Industrial Park, Works Road, Letchworth Garden City, Hertfordshire, SG6 1LA Tel: (01462) 675609 Fax: (01462) 687025 E-mail: sales@intercounty.com

Interior & Facility Contracts Ltd, Excelsior House, Buntsford Park Road, Bromsgrove, Worcestershire, B60 3DX Tel: (01527) 573000 Fax: (01527) 573001 E-mail: enquiries@interior-facility.com

Interline UK, Greenacre Farm, Smallgains La, Stock, Ingatestone, Essex, CM4 9PR Tel: (01245) 477922 Fax: (01245) 475539 E-mail: sales@interlineuk.com

J Thompson, 78a Pall Mall, Liverpool, L3 7EN Tel: 0151-227 3600 Fax: 0151-231 1160

▶ Jigsaw Business Interiors Limited, RVL House, 6 Elphinstone Square, Deans South West Industrial Estate, Livingston, West Lothian, EH54 8RG Tel: 01506 417177 Fax: (01506) 418970 E-mail: info@jigsawbi.com

Jim Barlow Stationers Ltd, 18 Park Road, Worsley, Manchester, M28 7DA Tel: 0161-799 9558 Fax: 0161-703 8789 E-mail: sales@jimbarlows.co.uk

Just Seating International Ltd, Croxdale, Durham, DH6 5HT Tel: (01325) 300123 Fax: (01388) 812416 E-mail: sales@justseating.co.uk

K & N International Office Systems Ltd, 52 Britton Street, London, EC1M 5UQ Tel: (020) 7490 9340 Fax: (020) 7490 9349 E-mail: sales@kn-international.co.uk

Kestrel Building Services Ltd, George Street, High Wycombe, Buckinghamshire, HP11 2RZ Tel: (01494) 474398 Fax: (01494) 472540 E-mail: info@kestreloffice.com

Kinnarps UK Ltd, 8 Lindsay Square, Deans Industrial Estate, Deans, Livingston, West Lothian, EH54 8RL Tel: (01506) 415885 Fax: (01506) 411447 E-mail: sales@kinnarps.co.uk

Knoll International, 1 Lindsey Street, London Central Markets, London, EC1A 9PQ Tel: (020) 7236 6655 Fax: (020) 7248 1744

Laporta Office Furniture & Equipment, 26-30 Prescott Place, London, SW4 6BU Tel: (020) 7720 6006 Fax: (020) 7720 6116 E-mail: info@laporta.co.uk

Le-Al (Associates) Ltd, Zenith House, Cromwell Road, Bredbury, Stockport, Cheshire, SK6 2RF Tel: 0161-406 9899 Fax: 0161-406 9880 E-mail: info@le-al.co.uk

Leicester Office Furnishers, 9-11 Cannock Street, Leicester, LE4 9HR Tel: 0116-246 3686 Fax: 0116-246 3681 E-mail: enquiries@leicesteroffice.com

▶ Lightning Technology Ltd, 38 Stafford Road, Wallington, Surrey, SM6 9AA Tel: (0800) 3288727 Fax: (020) 8647 1115 E-mail: kevin@lightningofficesupplies.co.uk

Lion House UK Ltd, 1 Old Parsonage Yard, Horton Road, Horton Kirby, Dartford, DA4 9BN Tel: (01322) 868606 Fax: (01322) 866441 E-mail: howardelkins@lionhouse.co.uk

Martin Luck Ltd, Rowdown House Rowdown Close, Langage Business Park, Plympton, Plymouth, PL7 5EY Tel: (01752) 336699 Fax: (01752) 330022 E-mail: sales@martinluck.co.uk

M & A Office Supplies Ltd, Unit 12 Westwood Court, Brunel Road, Totton, Southampton, SO40 3WX Tel: (023) 8066 7110 Fax: (023) 8066 7136 E-mail: simon@maoffice.demon.co.uk

M J Farmer, 50 Wolverhampton Road, Wednesfield, Wolverhampton, WV11 1UJ Tel: (01902) 728827 Fax: (01902) 728827

Ma Interiors, St Jude's Church, Dulwich Road, London, SE24 0PB Tel: (020) 7737 1371 Fax: (020) 7274 2023 E-mail: sales@mainteriors.co.uk

Mccarthy Developments 2000 Ltd, Systems House, Broad Lane, Coventry, CV5 7AX Tel: (024) 7646 8866 Fax: (024) 7669 4486 E-mail: sales@mccarthygroup.co.uk

Mcof Ltd, 3 Station Road, Brompton on Swale, Richmond, North Yorkshire, DL10 7SN Tel: (01748) 812612 Fax: (01748) 812618 E-mail: thomaslinckh@btconnect.com

Magnum Office Products, 4-5 Priestley Way, Crawley, West Sussex, RH10 9NT Tel: (01293) 547220 Fax: (01293) 543572 E-mail: ray.butler@magnumoffice.co.uk

Margolis Business Systems, Unit 4.02 Crayfield Business Park, New Mill Road, Orpington, Kent, BR5 3QA Tel: (01689) 891000 Fax: (01689) 890555 E-mail: sales@margolis.co.uk

Martin Reprographics Ltd, Wrightsway, Lincoln, LN2 4JY Tel: (01522) 526268 Fax: (01522) 546514 E-mail: martinrepro@talk21.com

E.F.G. Matthews Ltd, Northfield Drive, Milton Keynes, MK15 0DQ Tel: (01908) 665643 Fax: (01908) 609948

▶ Melbro Ltd, 109 London Road, Crayford, Dartford, DA1 4DS Tel: (01322) 523645 Fax: 01322 523257 E-mail: brian.morgan@melbro.net

Herman Miller Ltd, 61 Aldwych, London, WC2B 4AE Tel: (0845) 226 7202 Fax: (0845) 430 9260 E-mail: info_uk@hermanmiller.com

▶ Netstationers, 57 Water Lane, Wilmslow, Cheshire, SK9 5BQ Tel: (0800) 0833178 Fax: (0800) 0833179 E-mail: phil.hopkins@netstationers.co.uk

New Look Office Furniture, Chester Street, Saltney, Chester, CH4 8RD Tel: (01244) 682568 Fax: (01244) 671465

North Wilts Office Supplies, Ford, Chippenham, Wiltshire, SN14 8RT Tel: (01225) 742569 Fax: (01249) 783207 E-mail: sales@nwos.co.uk

O E S (London) Ltd, Chadwell Heath Lane, Romford, RM6 4NP Tel: (020) 8597 7641 Fax: (020) 8599 5083 E-mail: sales@oes-london.demon.co.uk

▶ indicates data change since last edition

OFFICE FURNISHERS AND FURNITURE – *continued*

Oaktree Interiors Ltd, Frederick House, 498 Reading Road, Winnersh, Wokingham, Berkshire, RG41 5EX Tel: 0118-979 6600 Fax: 0118-979 4044 E-mail: sales@oaktreeoffice.com

Office 21 Projects Ltd, Whitby Oliver, 31 Hospital Fields Road, Fulford Industrial Estate, Fulford Road, York, YO10 4FS Tel: (01904) 655106 E-mail: info@office21.co.uk

The Office Centre, 24 Queen Street, Gravesend, Kent, DA12 2EE Tel: (01474) 560271 Fax: (01474) 334484

Office Wise, 73 New Crane Street, Chester, CH1 4JE Tel: (01244) 317505 Fax: (01244) 343413 E-mail: office.wise@virgin.net

▶ OfficeGiant, Unit 1, Empress Business Centre, Chester Road, Manchester, M16 9EB Tel: (0800) 7317931 Fax: 0161-877 7772 E-mail: sales@officegiant.co.uk

Osco Office Supplies Ltd, H E M House, Kirkstall Road, Leeds, LS4 2BT Tel: 0113-279 3511 Fax: 0113-231 0926 E-mail: sales@oscodirect.com

Paramount Office Interiors, Paramount House, Pascal Close, St. Mellons, Cardiff, CF3 0LW Tel: (029) 2083 9800 Fax: (029) 2083 9801 E-mail: sales@paramountinteriors.com

Pars Office Systems, 57 High Street, Tetsworth, Thame, Oxfordshire, OX9 7BS Tel: (01844) 280100 Fax: (01844) 281373 E-mail: anne@parsoffice.com

Pedder & Summers Ltd, 2a Ashton Road, Hartwell, Northampton, NN7 2HW Tel: (01604) 863881 Fax: (01604) 863755 E-mail: sales@pedderandsummers.co.uk

Penketh's Ltd, Bassendale Road, Croft Business Park, Wirral, Merseyside, CH62 3QL Tel: 0151-334 4417 Fax: 0151-737 5001 E-mail: enquiries@penkeths.co.uk

Platt Office Equipment Ltd, 65 Minchenden Crescent, London, N14 7EP Tel: (020) 8886 9632 Fax: (020) 8886 2142 E-mail: melvyn@plattoffice.co.uk

Portsdown Office Ltd, 1 Warrior Business Centre, Fitzherbert Road, Portsmouth, PO6 1TX Tel: (023) 9232 4611 Fax: (023) 9221 0164 E-mail: sales@portsdown.co.uk

Premier Logistics International, 6 Ballard Business Park, Cuxton Road, Rochester, Kent, ME2 2NY Tel: (01634) 304403 Fax: (01634) 403408 E-mail: sales@premier-logistics.com

Principal Corporation Ltd, Principal House, Parsonage Business Park, Horsham, West Sussex, RH12 4AL Tel: (01403) 258486 Fax: (01403) 210131 E-mail: solutions@principalcorp.co.uk

R B S Office Supplies, Tollgate Business Centre, Tollgate Drive, Tollgate Industrial Estate, Stafford, ST16 3HS Tel: (01785) 254859 Fax: (01785) 220400 E-mail: sales@rbsofficesupplies.co.uk

RCD Projects Ltd, 62 Portman Road, Reading, RG30 1EA Tel: 0118-950 2021 Fax: 0118-950 2036 E-mail: sales@rcdprojects.co.uk

Restall Brown & Clennell Ltd, 21 North Street, Lewes, East Sussex, BN7 2PE Tel: (01273) 473612 Fax: 01273 477783 E-mail: sales@rbc-furniture.co.uk

Rochdale Equipment Centre Ltd, Howard Street, Rochdale, Lancashire, OL12 0LU Tel: (01706) 656092 Fax: (01706) 641825 E-mail: sales@officefurniture-online.co.uk

S E T Office Supplies Ltd, Asset House, 63 Penarth Road, Cardiff, CF10 5RA Tel: (029) 2022 5555 Fax: (029) 2022 1922 E-mail: sales@setofficesupplies.co.uk

Saber Office Furniture Ltd, 21 Bath Lane, Leicester, LE3 5BF Tel: 0116-251 1121 Fax: 0116-251 2625 E-mail: sales@ukofficefurniture.co.uk

Scotforms Computer Stationery Ltd, 3 Hatton Square, Livingston, West Lothian, EH54 9BJ Tel: (01506) 410871 Fax: (01506) 416805 E-mail: info@scotforms.co.uk

Scott Howard, Unit 15 Handlemaker Road, Frome, Somerset, BA11 4RW Tel: (01373) 466656 Fax: (01373) 47223 E-mail: scotthoward@compuserve.com

Sigma Group, PO Box 302, Guernsey, GY1 3SD Tel: (01481) 241111 Fax: (01481) 246391 E-mail: sales@sigma-aztec.com

Smiths Office & Commercial Furniture, Windsor Road, Redditch, Worcestershire, B97 6DJ Tel: (01527) 66663 Fax: (01527) 69333 E-mail: info@smithseating.co.uk

Solent Business Supplies, 2 Marples Way, Havant, Hampshire, PO9 1UH Tel: (023) 9248 9933 Fax: (023) 9248 9934 E-mail: sales@solentbs.co.uk

Spacetime Interiors Ltd, Unit 1, Sunderleigh Farm, Bampton, Tiverton, Devon, EX16 9DT Tel: (0845) 8620326 Fax: (0845) 8689369 E-mail: sales@space-time.co.uk

Spacewise, Unit 2, The Business Center, Corinium Industrial Estate, Raans Road, Amersham, Buckinghamshire, HP6 6FB Tel: (01494) 431200 Fax: (01494) 431203 E-mail: sales@quintoncav.co.uk

Steelcase Strafor plc, Second Floor 2 Carriage Row, 183 Eversholt St, London, NW1 1BU Tel: (020) 7874 0000 Fax: (020) 7380 0153

Stevenson Office Furniture, 863-865 Harrow Road, London, NW10 5NG Tel: (020) 8969 3850 Fax: (020) 8968 1790

Supreme Seating & Desking Ltd, 4 40 Wilton Road, Reading, RG30 2SS Tel: 0118-959 5535 Fax: 0118-950 3271 E-mail: info@supremeseating.com

Swift Business Equipment Ltd, Northgate, Aldridge, Walsall, WS9 8TR Tel: (01922) 743454 Fax: (01922) 743134 E-mail: sales@swiftbe.co.uk

T D O C Ltd, 63-71 Roe Road, Northampton, NN1 4PH Tel: (01604) 233777 Fax: (01604) 234437

Task Systems Ltd, W H House, 32 Bethnal Green Road, London, E1 6HZ Tel: (020) 7729 5088 Fax: (020) 7729 4709 E-mail: marketing@tasksystems.co.uk

Trademark Interiors, 8 March Monte Gate, Hemel Hempstead, Hertfordshire, HP2 7BF Tel: (01442) 260022 Fax: (01442) 232244 E-mail: info@tmark.co.uk

Typewriter & Equipment Co. Ltd, Teco House, High Street, Lye, Stourbridge, West Midlands, DY9 8LU Tel: (01384) 424416 Fax: (01384) 423423 E-mail: info@tecoltd.co.uk

V C I Office Furniture, 183 Brighton Road, South Croydon, Surrey, CR2 6EG Tel: (020) 8680 5244 Fax: (020) 8680 7081 E-mail: vci@btconnect.com

▶ Viscount Interiors, 5 Thorley Hall Stables, Thorley, Bishop's Stortford, Hertfordshire, CM23 4BE Tel: (01279) 654309 Fax: (01279) 654309 E-mail: sales@viscountinteriors.co.uk

Vitra Ltd, 30 Clerkenwell Road, London, EC1M 5PG Tel: (020) 7608 6200 Fax: (020) 7499 1967 E-mail: info_uk@vitra.com

WB Office Equipment Ltd, 16 Mandervell Road, Oadby, Leicester, LE2 5LQ Tel: 0116-271 1033 Fax: 0116-271 1022

Webber Office Solutions Inc Blare It Out Biographi, 117 Marsh Road, Rhyl, Clwyd, LL18 2AB Tel: (01745) 337066 Fax: (01745) 337072 E-mail: sales@officerus.com

Wheatley Dyson & Son Ltd, 1 Quarry Court, Beacon Hill Road, Halifax, West Yorkshire, HX3 6AQ Tel: (0800) 6342010 Fax: (0800) 0424329 E-mail: sales@wheatley-dyson.co.uk

Whitegrove Group P.L.C., Units 5-7, Goodwood Road, Boyatt Wood Industrial Estate, Eastleigh, Hampshire, SO50 4NT Tel: (023) 8064 2643 Fax: (023) 8064 2647

Wight Business Services, 3 Daish Way, Newport, Isle of Wight, PO30 5XB Tel: (01983) 822229 Fax: (01983) 521899 E-mail: wbs@freenet.co.uk

Withy Grove Stores Ltd, 35-39 Withy Grove, Manchester, M4 2BJ Tel: 0161-834 0044

Worktown Office Supplies Ltd, 1 Park Court, Premier Way, Abbey Park, Romsey, Hants, SO51 9AQ Tel: (01794) 525065 Fax: (01794) 525025 E-mail: orders@worktown.com

▶ Your Home Furniture, 145 West Street, Banbury, Oxfordshire, OX16 3HE Tel: (0871) 2006251 Fax: (0871) 2006251 E-mail: enquiries@yourhomefurniture.co.uk

OFFICE FURNITURE

925 Ltd, Unit 46-47 Monument Business Park, Warpsgrove Lane, Chalgrove, Oxford, OX44 7RW Tel: (01865) 891925 Fax: (01865) 891929 E-mail: enquiries@925ltd.co.uk

A Plus Office Furniture & Interiors, 363 Dunstable Road, Luton, LU4 8BY Tel: (01582) 707272 E-mail: sales@aplusoffice.co.uk

Aaron, Waltham Business Park, Brickyard Road, Swanmore, Southampton, SO32 2SA Tel: (01489) 892111 Fax: (01489) 892117

Acorn Partition & Storage Systems, Kingsley Road, Lincoln, LN6 3TA Tel: (01522) 688771 Fax: (01522) 680404 E-mail: sales@apss.co.uk

▶ Active Seating, 1 35 Brook Road, Rayleigh, Essex, SS6 7XJ Tel: (01268) 779991 Fax: (01268) 773289 E-mail: info@arrowoffice.co.uk

▶ Apple Display Systems Ltd, Units 1-9, Nelson Business Centre, Nelson Street, Manchester, M34 3ET Tel: 0161-335 0660

B F C Brava Ltd, 26 Store Street, London, WC1E 7BT Tel: (020) 7631 1501

▶ Beck Interiors Ltd, Victory House, Cox Lane, Chessington, Surrey, KT9 1SG Tel: (020) 8974 0500 Fax: (020) 8974 0555 E-mail: mail@beckinteriors.com

▶ Beechgrove Woodworking Ltd, 7-8 Lancaster Park Industrial Estate, Bowerhill, Melksham, Wiltshire, SN12 6TT Tel: (01225) 792920 Fax: (01225) 792131 E-mail: sales@beechgrovefurniture.co.uk

▶ Bingham Pine Furniture, Grantham Road, Radcliffe-on-Trent, Nottingham, NG12 2JP Tel: 0115-933 2555 Fax: 0115-933 2555 E-mail: binghampine@aol.com

▶ Bissett & Taylor Ltd, Unit 29-31, Tyock Industrial Estate, Elgin, Morayshire, IV30 1XY Tel: (01343) 544055 Fax: (01343) 548422

▶ Blevins Ltd, 189 Old Shettleston Road, Glasgow, G32 7HN Tel: 0141-764 3733 Fax: 0141-764 3734

▶ Britannia Pine, Unit 9b Watling St Business Park, Watling Street, Cannock, Staffordshire, WS11 9XG Tel: (01543) 379888 Fax: (01543) 276901

▶ Bulmer Interior Contracts Ltd, Lauren House, 164 Brinkburn Street, Newcastle upon Tyne, NE6 2AR Tel: 0191-276 4781 Fax: 0191-276 2663

▶ C J Carpentry & Design, Unit 12 Hybris Business Park, Warmwell Road, Crossways, Dorchester, Dorset, DT2 8BF Tel: (01305) 854555 Fax: (01305) 854555

▶ C J Design, 47 St. Dunstans Road, Bristol, BS3 5NZ Tel: (07798) 808594 Fax: (0870) 8555366

▶ Carlton Screens Ltd, 1 Real Workshops, Westfield Road, Parkgate, Rotherham, South Yorkshire, S62 6EY Tel: (01709) 525414 Fax: (01709) 710158

▶ Carlton Shopfitting Ltd, Carlton House, Carlton Road, Dewsbury, West Yorkshire, WF13 2AT Tel: (01924) 454612 Fax: (01924) 460042

▶ Central Shopfitters Ltd, Palm Street, New Basford, Nottingham, NG7 7HS Tel: 0115-942 2671 Fax: 0115-919 1993

▶ Clive Christian, 10 Phoenix Place, Lewes, East Sussex, BN7 2QJ Tel: (01273) 483080 Fax: (01273) 483639 E-mail: sales@clivechristian.com

▶ Commercial Envelopes, 158 Lichfield Road, Sandhills, Walsall, WS9 9PF Tel: (01543) 452326 Fax: (01543) 821509 E-mail: denise@commercialenvelopes.co.uk

▶ Peter Craig, Wallyford Industrial Estate, Wallyford, Musselburgh, Midlothian, EH21 8QJ Tel: 0131-665 4517 Fax: 0131-653 1969

▶ Das Business Furniture Ltd, 12 Appold Street, London, EC2A 2AW Tel: (020) 7655 4933 Fax: (020) 7247 3613

Data Spectrum, Sycamore House, Wendlebury, Bicester, Oxfordshire, OX25 2PB Tel: (01869) 325266E-mail: enquiries@dataspectrum.co.uk

Discount Desk Centre, Kilsyth Road, Longcroft, Bonnybridge, Stirlingshire, FK4 1HD Tel: (0870) 2407817 Fax: (0870) 2407814 E-mail: sales@discountdeskcentre.co.uk

▶ Dovetail Contract Furniture, 1 St. Georges Court, St. Georges Road, Bristol, BS1 5UG Tel: 0117-930 4442 Fax: 0117-976 0014 E-mail: info@dovetail.com

▶ Eastlake Group Ltd, Unit 1, Philipshill Industrial Estate, East Kilbride, Glasgow, G74 5PG Tel: (01355) 593200 Fax: (01355) 593201 E-mail: info@eastlakegroup.com

Tim Ecote, 31 Warner Drive, Springwood Industrial Estate, Braintree, Essex, CM7 2YW Tel: (01376) 528112 Fax: (01376) 528114

Eves Joinery, Edwards Lane, Liverpool, L24 9HX Tel: 0151-486 1896 Fax: 0151-448 1548

▶ G G I Furniture (UK) Ltd, Global Way, Lower Eccleshill Road, Darwen, Lancashire, BB3 0RW Tel: (01254) 778500 Fax: (01254) 778519 E-mail: info@ggieurope.com

▶ Glover, Unit 13, Chivenor, Barnstaple, Devon, EX31 4AY Tel: (01271) 815321 Fax: (01271) 815321

Green Standards Ltd, Green Standards House, Lower Ledge Farm, Dyrham, Chippenham, Wiltshire, SN14 8EY Tel: (0870) 2401445 E-mail: admin@greenstandards.org

Greenfield Stationery, Unit 7 Northside Business Centre, Wellington Street, Birmingham, B18 4NR Tel: 0121-515 5100 Fax: 0121-515 5101 E-mail: mail@greenfieldstationery.com

▶ Gresham Office Furniture, Lynstock Way, Lostock, Bolton, BL6 4SA Tel: (01204) 664400 Fax: (01204) 664433 E-mail: info@gof.co.uk

Haagensen Wardrobes, F A Would, Ladysmith Road, Grimsby, South Humberside, DN32 9SH Tel: (01472) 343030 Fax: (01472) 341333 E-mail: adrian@haaggensonwardrobes.com

▶ Harris Office Furniture Ltd, 41 Grove Street, Edinburgh, EH3 8AF Tel: 0131-229 3180 Fax: 0131-228 3767

▶ Harte Electrical Ltd, Springfield Mill, Spa Street, Ossett, West Yorkshire, WF5 0HW Tel: (01924) 280000 Fax: (01924) 263836

▶ Havelock (Europa) Plc, Moss Way, Hill End Industrial Estate, Dalgety Bay, Dunfermline, Fife, KY11 9JH Tel: (01383) 820044 Fax: (01383) 820064

▶ I P E C Furniture Ltd, Lodge Mill, Victoria Street, Accrington, Lancashire, BB5 0PG Tel: (01254) 235487 Fax: (01254) 871035 E-mail: info@ipecfurniture.co.uk

▶ I R W (Enclosures) Ltd, Unit 7, Liskeard Enterprise Centre, Station Road, Liskeard, Cornwall, PL14 4DA Tel: (01579) 344334

K C Office Services Ltd, The Relocation Centre, Blenheim Road, Lancing, West Sussex, BN15 8UQ Tel: (01903) 600400 Fax: (01903) 607082 E-mail: ops@kcos.co.uk

Lamb Macintosh Ltd, The Ten Building, 10 Wellcroft Road, Slough, SL1 4AQ Tel: (01753) 522369 Fax: (01753) 517216 E-mail: sales@lambmacintosh.com

▶ Logic Office Interiors Ltd, 748 London Road, Hounslow, TW3 1PD Tel: (020) 8572 7474

▶ Luv It Furniture, Unit 6, Deacon Trading Estate, Earle Street, Newton-Le-Willows, Merseyside, WA12 9XD Tel: (01925) 298788 Fax: (01925) 298736

Mccarthy Design, Ladygrove Court, Preston, Hitchin, Hertfordshire, SG4 7SA Tel: (01462) 440957 Fax: (01462) 440961 E-mail: peter@mccarthydesign.co.uk

▶ Simon Manners, The Street, Croxton, Thetford, Norfolk, IP24 1LN Tel: (01842) 755922 Fax: (01842) 755922

▶ Martins Shop & Bar Fitters Ltd, 2-8 West Bowling Green Street, Edinburgh, EH6 5PQ Tel: 0131-553 4777

MDS Interiors Ltd, Willows, St.James's Place, Cranleigh, Surrey, GU6 8RR Tel: (01483) 276206 Fax: (01483) 278227 E-mail: mail@mds-services.demon.co.uk

Metalen Products Ltd, The Winnowing Barn, Sherington, Newport Pagnell, Buckinghamshire, MK16 9QP Tel: (01908) 327100 Fax: (01908) 327101 E-mail: sales@metalen.co.uk

▶ Metalliform Holdings, Chambers Road, Hoyland, Barnsley, South Yorkshire, S74 0EZ Tel: (01226) 350555 Fax: (01226) 350112 E-mail: sales@metalliform.co.uk

▶ Midas Contract Systems, 1 Airth Drive, Glasgow, G52 1JU Tel: 0141-849 1001 Fax: 0141-840 2112

Office 21 Projects Ltd, Whitby Oliver, 31 Hospital Fields Road, Fulford Industrial Estate, Fulford Road, York, YO10 4FS Tel: (01904) 655106 E-mail: info@office21.co.uk

Office Innovations, 1-3 Factory Lane, Beeston, Beeston, Nottingham, NG9 4AA Tel: 0115-925 7898 Fax: 0115-925 7899 E-mail: salesandenquires@officeinnovations.co.uk

▶ Ollerton Ltd, Samlesbury Mill, Goosefoot Lane, Samlesbury Bottoms, Preston, PR5 0RN Tel: (01254) 852127

▶ Opm Ltd, 219a Westminster Industrial Estate, London, SE18 5TS Tel: (020) 8316 6080 Fax: (020) 8316 6079 E-mail: info@opmfurniture.co.uk

▶ Orion, 6 Astley Way, Astley La Industrial Estate, Swillington, Leeds, LS26 8XT Tel: 0113-232 0555 Fax: 0113-232 0505

▶ Parr Engineering, Unit 22-25 Lodge Farm Business Centre, Wolverton Road, Castlethorpe, Milton Keynes, MK19 7ES Tel: (01908) 510822 Fax: (01908) 510937

▶ Plan It Contracts Ltd, 37 Colquhoun Avenue, Glasgow, G52 4PL Tel: 0141-883 8741 Fax: 0141-882 7071

▶ Prestige Shop Fitting Installations, 79 Carron Place, East Kilbride, Glasgow, G75 0YL Tel: (01355) 244540 Fax: (01355) 235080 E-mail: lindadesign@prestigeinstalations.net

▶ Queensbury Shelters Ltd, Fitzherbert Road, Portsmouth, PO6 1SE Tel: (023) 9221 0052 Fax: (023) 9221 0059

▶ R A P Industries Ltd (Sheet Metal), Welbeck Way, Peterborough, PE2 7WH Tel: (01733) 394941 Fax: (01733) 391825

Rabbitt Recycling, 27-29 New Street, Charfield, Wotton-under-Edge, Gloucestershire, GL12 8ES Tel: (01453) 844343 Fax: (01453) 521330 E-mail: info@rabbittrecycling.co.uk

▶ Redferns Furniture, 2 Glover Centre, Egmont Street, Mossley, Ashton-under-Lyne, Lancashire, OL5 9PY Tel: (01457) 839282 Fax: (01457) 839282

Riverside Office Supplies, 1 Apex Centre, Clywedog Road South, Wrexham Industrial Estate, Wrexham, Clwyd, LL13 9XS Tel: (01978) 660066 Fax: (01978) 661767

▶ Rutland Woodcraft, The Workshop, 31 Great North Road, Stibbington, Peterborough, PE8 6LS Tel: (01780) 784500 Fax: (01780) 784500 E-mail: info@rutlandwoodcraft.co.uk

▶ Ryan, Sandars Road, Heapham Road Industrial Estate, Gainsborough, Lincolnshire, DN21 1RZ Tel: (01427) 677556 Fax: (01427) 617773 E-mail: info@martinryan.co.uk

▶ S Barber & Co Shopfitters Ltd, Bangor Terrace, Leeds, LS12 5PS Tel: 0113-263 9996 Fax: 0113-279 0158 E-mail: info@sbarber.co.uk

▶ Sandywood Furniture, 8 Boundary Business Court, Church Road, Mitcham, Surrey, CR4 3TD Tel: (020) 8687 7070 Fax: (020) 8648 7020 E-mail: sandywoodfurnitureltd@gmill.com

Screen Solutions Ltd, Beaufort House, Newton Road, Peacehaven, East Sussex, BN10 8JQ Tel: (01273) 589922 Fax: (01273) 589921 E-mail: sales@screensolutions.co.uk

Trojan Aluminium Ltd, 7 Burton Close, Falcon Road Industrial Estate, Norwich, NR6 6AY Tel: (01603) 426024 Fax: (01603) 417882 E-mail: sale@trojanaluminium.co.uk

▶ Tube & Wire Display Ltd, Middle Mill, Oxford Street East, Ashton-under-Lyne, Lancashire, OL7 0NE Tel: 0161-339 4877 Fax: 0161-343 2596

▶ Walker & Kitching Ltd, Sandall Stones Road, Kirk Sandall Estate, Kirk Sandall, Doncaster, South Yorkshire, DN3 1QR Tel: (01302) 880044

▶ Wolfram 74, 148 Tooley Street, London, SE1 2TU Tel: (020) 7357 9581

The Woodcutter, Receptional 7, Station Square, High Street, Flitwick, Bedford, MK45 1DP Tel: (01525) 715520

▶ Yorkshire Business Equipment Ltd, 3 Cornish Way, 2 Barbot Hall Industrial Estate, Mangham Road, Rotherham, South Yorkshire, S62 6EG Tel: (01709) 515000 Fax: (01709) 364812 E-mail: united@yb.co.uk

OFFICE FURNITURE COMPONENTS

▶ Blandford Office Furniture, 20a Sunrise Business Park, Higher Shaftesbury Road, Blandford Forum, Dorset, DT11 8ST Tel: (01258) 450006 Fax: (01258) 459933 E-mail: ian@officefurniture.demon.co.uk

OFFICE FURNITURE FITTINGS

▶ Tangent Furniture, 36-42 New Inn Yard, London, EC2A 3EY Tel: (0870) 9904150 Fax: (0870) 9904199 E-mail: enquiries@tangentsales.co.uk

OFFICE FURNITURE HIRE

▶ Brent Cross, Sayer House, Oxgate Lane, London, NW2 7JN Tel: (020) 8208 2626 Fax: (020) 8208 2012 E-mail: sales@brentxofficefurniture.co.uk

Dartex Office Furniture, Unit 6 Crayside Industrial Estate, Thames Road, Crayford, Dartford, DA1 4RF Tel: (01322) 521545 Fax: (01322) 558685 E-mail: sales@dartexofficefurniture.co.uk

OFFICE FURNITURE HIRE – *continued*

▶ Jigsaw Business Interiors Limited, RVL House, 6 Elphinstone Square, Deans South West Industrial Estate, Livingston, West Lothian, EH54 8RG Tel: 01506 417177 Fax: 01506 418970 E-mail: info@jigsawbi.com

Spacewise, Unit 2, The Business Center, Corinium Industrial Estate, Raans Road, Amersham, Buckinghamshire, HP6 6FB Tel: (01494) 431200 Fax: (01494) 431203 E-mail: sales@quintoncav.co.uk

OFFICE FURNITURE INSTALLATION/ASSEMBLY SERVICES

Access Interiors Ltd, 140 Science Park Milton Road, Cambridge, CB4 0GF Tel: (01223) 506441 Fax: 01223 506441

Bowyers Office Equipment, Church Road, Penn, High Wycombe, Buckinghamshire, HP10 8LP Tel: (01494) 816585 Fax: (01494) 813684 E-mail: charles.bowyer@bowyersoffice.co.uk

Creative Interior Projects Ltd, 4 Denham Walk, Chalfont St. Peter, Gerrards Cross, Buckinghamshire, SL9 0EN Tel: (01494) 873347 Fax: (01494) 873353 E-mail: sales@creativeinteriorprojects.co.uk

Haagensen Wardrobes, F A Would, Ladysmith Road, Grimsby, South Humberside, DN32 9SH Tel: (01472) 343030 Fax: (01472) 341333 E-mail: adrian@haaggensonwardrobes.com

Hertsmere Group Services, 2 Chartmoor Road, Leighton Buzzard, Bedfordshire, LU7 4WG Tel: (01525) 219227 Fax: (01525) 219220 E-mail: sales@hgs-uk.com

I D M Southern Ltd, Unit 1, Lavernham Road, Brent Eleigh, Sudbury, Suffolk, CO10 9PB Tel: (01449) 740040 Fax: (01449) 744950 E-mail: mail@idmsouthern.co.uk

Larchbond Facilities Ltd, Ongar Hall Farm, Brentwood Road, Orsett, Grays, Essex, RM16 3HU Tel: (01375) 892929 Fax: (01375) 892624 E-mail: sales@larchbond.co.uk

MDS Interiors Ltd, Willows, St.James's Place, Cranleigh, Surrey, GU6 8RR Tel: (01483) 276206 Fax: (01483) 278227 E-mail: mail@mds-services.demon.co.uk

Nottingham Office Equipment Co. Ltd, Castle Boulevard, Nottingham, NG7 1FN Tel: 0115-950 5117 Fax: 0115-950 4880 E-mail: noe@tinyworld.co.uk

Overbury P.L.C., 77 Newman Street, London, W1T 3EW Tel: (020) 7307 9000 Fax: (020) 7307 9001 E-mail: info@overbury.co.uk

John Pulsford Associates Ltd, 4 Sphere Industrial Estate, Campfield Road, St. Albans, Hertfordshire, AL1 5HT Tel: (01727) 840800 Fax: (01727) 840083 E-mail: info@jpa-furniture.com

Serota Furniture, 92 Hilliard Road, Northwood, Middlesex, HA6 1SW Tel: (01923) 840697 E-mail: michael@serota.co.uk

Spacewise, Unit 2, The Business Center, Corinium Industrial Estate, Raans Road, Amersham, Buckinghamshire, HP6 6FB Tel: (01494) 431200 Fax: (01494) 431203 E-mail: sales@quintoncav.co.uk

OFFICE FURNITURE OR EQUIPMENT CLEANING PRODUCTS

▶ Coleman Property Care Ltd, 29 Harley Street, London, W1G 9QR Tel: 0845 095 1280 Fax: 0845 095 1290 E-mail: info@colemanfm.com

Derby Office Machines Ltd, 16 Prime Enterprise Park, Prime Park Way, Derby, DE1 3QB Tel: (01332) 371500 Fax: (01332) 385001 E-mail: sales@derbyofficemachines.co.uk

Essex Cleaning Services Ltd, 6 Alderman Avenue, Barking, Essex, IG11 0LX Tel: (020) 8594 2155 E-mail: ecsltd@arfoster.fsnet.co.uk

HK Wentworth Ltd, Kingsbury Park, Midlington Road, Swadlincote, Derbyshire, DE11 0AN Tel: (01283) 222111 Fax: (01283) 550177 E-mail: afsales@hkw.co.uk

Office Angels Commercial Cleaning, 12 Armstrong Close, Halstead, Sevenoaks, Kent, TN14 7BS Tel: (0845) 1084241 E-mail: officeangelscleaning@googlemail.com

▶ Red Apple, 2 Wrawby Road, Brigg, South Humberside, DN20 8DL Tel: (01652) 653704 Fax: (01652) 657777 E-mail: Sales@redapplecleaning.co.uk

▶ Tetras Interiors Ltd, 55 Lincoln Road, Poole, Dorset, BH12 2HT Tel: (01202) 566480 Fax: (01202) 386403 E-mail: tetrasinteriors@aol.com

OFFICE FURNITURE REPAIR/ RENOVATION SERVICES

Austin Office Furniture Ltd, 19 Millicent Road, London, E10 7LG Tel: (020) 8558 6489 Fax: 0208 558 6499 E-mail: sales@austinoffice.co.uk

Baron Contracts Ltd, 72 Cross Road, Maldon, Essex, CM9 5ED Tel: (01621) 856991 Fax: (01621) 850326

Business Seating Manufacturing Supplies Ltd, 8 Bridgewater Close, Reading, RG30 1JT Tel: (0800) 9179848 Fax: 0118-951 4505 E-mail: sales@businessandseating.co.uk

▶ C I S Office Furniture Ltd, Furniture House, Potters Lane, Wednesbury, West Midlands, WS10 7LP Tel: 0121-556 8741 Fax: 0121-556 9588 E-mail: sales@cisoffice.co.uk

▶ Gilletts Upholstrey, 15 Cranbrook Terrace, Cranleigh, Surrey, GU6 7ES Tel: (01483) 274897E-mail: gillettsupholstrey@yahoo.co.uk

Hurst Interior Contracts Ltd, Hurst House, Fordcombe Road, Fordcombe, Tunbridge Wells, Kent, TN3 0RT Tel: (01892) 740586 Fax: (01892) 740660

Overbury P.L.C., 77 Newman Street, London, W1T 3EW Tel: (020) 7307 9000 Fax: (020) 7307 9001 E-mail: info@overbury.co.uk

RCD Projects Ltd, 62 Portman Road, Reading, RG30 1EA Tel: 0118-950 2021 Fax: 0118-950 2036 E-mail: sales@rcdprojects.co.uk

Supreme Seating & Desking Ltd, 4 40 Wilton Road, Reading, RG30 2SS Tel: 0118-959 5535 Fax: 0118-950 3271 E-mail: info@supremeseating.com

▶ Suretech Services Ltd, 12 Florence Road, Codsall, Wolverhampton, WV8 1JD Tel: (01902) 840684 Fax: (01902) 847088 E-mail: info@suretechservices.co.uk

Trident Interiors, 7 The Glade, Croydon, CR0 7QG Tel: (020) 8656 1207 Fax: (020) 8655 1992 E-mail: contacts@tridentinteriors.co.uk

OFFICE FURNITURE ROLLER SHUTTERS

Alpha Marketing plc, 53 Dargan Road, Belfast, BT3 9JU Tel: (028) 9078 1531 Fax: (028) 9037 0053 E-mail: alphamarketing@msn.com

The Tambour Company Ltd, Warren Road, Green Lane Business Park, Featherstone, Pontefract, West Yorkshire, WF7 6EL Tel: (01977) 600026 Fax: (01977) 600991

Waivis Co. Ltd, 14 Minerva Road, London, NW10 6HJ Tel: (020) 8965 6818 Fax: (020) 8965 6287 E-mail: info@waivis.co.uk

OFFICE FURNITURE TO SPECIFICATION

▶ Bamber's Special Projects, 5 Challenge Court, Love La Industrial Estate, Bishops Castle, Shropshire, SY9 5DW Tel: (01588) 638111 Fax: (01588) 638111 E-mail: info@specialprojects.co.uk

Brazier Interior Systems Ltd, Medino House Rushington Business Park, Rushington Lane, Totton, Southampton, SO40 9LU Tel: (023) 8058 0000 Fax: (023) 8066 1900

▶ Dimension Furniture, Church Lane, OXTED, Surrey, RH8 9LH Tel: 07860 809104 E-mail: martin.parsons@dimensionfurniture.co.uk

Ideal Business Supplies Ltd, Marsh Lanelords Meadow Industrial Estate, Lords Meadow Industrial Estate, Crediton, Devon, EX17 1ES Tel: (01363) 775999 Fax: (01363) 775996 E-mail: info@idealbusinesssupplies.co.uk

OFFICE FURNITURE, SYSTEMS

Aided Design & Draughting Supplies, Spreadeagle Court, Northgate Street, Gloucester, GL1 1SL Tel: (01452) 505040 Fax: (01452) 505040

Avenue Office Supplies, 3 David Road, Colnbrook, Slough, SL3 0TW Tel: (01753) 687687 Fax: (01753) 681681 E-mail: admin@avenue-group.co.uk

Blue Line Office Furniture, Endeavour House, London Stansted Airport, Stansted, Essex, CM24 1SJ Tel: (01279) 669470 Fax: (01279) 669471 E-mail: sales@blueline.uk.com

Broadstock Office Furniture Ltd, Brunel Road, Lyme Green Business Park, London Road, Macclesfield, Cheshire, SK11 0TA Tel: (01625) 431979 Fax: (01625) 511136 E-mail: enquire@broadstock.co.uk

▶ Dovetail Contract Furniture, 1 St. Georges Court, St. Georges Road, Bristol, BS1 5UG Tel: 0117-930 4442 Fax: 0117-976 0014 E-mail: info@dovetail.com

Emergent Crown Contract Office Furnishings Ltd, 59 Pellon Lane, HX, Halifax, West Yorkshire, HX1 5BE Tel: (01422) 349119 Fax: (01422) 206033 E-mail: sales@emergent-crown.co.uk

Flexiform Business Furniture Ltd, The Office Furniture Centre, 1392 Leeds Road, Bradford, West Yorkshire, BD3 7AE Tel: (01274) 656013 Fax: (01274) 665760 E-mail: sales@flexiform.co.uk

Godfrey Syrett Ltd, Littleburn Industrial Estate, Langley Moor, Durham, DH7 8HE Tel: 0191-268 1010 Fax: 0191-378 1660 E-mail: sales@godfreysyrett.co.uk

Green Standards Ltd, Green Standards House, Lower Ledge Farm, Dyrham, Chippenham, Wiltshire, SN14 8EY Tel: (0870) 2401445 E-mail: admin@greenstandards.org

Howe UK Ltd, 22 Jaggard Way, London, SW12 8SG Tel: (020) 8673 9777 Fax: (020) 8675 9111 E-mail: sales@howeuk.co.uk

John Sheridan & Sons, 72 Old Rossorry Road, Enniskillen, County Fermanagh, BT74 7LF Tel: (028) 6632 2510 Fax: (028) 6632 3895 E-mail: shaunsheridan@email.com

Neville Johnson Ltd, 4 Broadoak Business Park, Ashburton Road West, Trafford Park, Manchester, M17 1RW Tel: 0161-873 8333 Fax: 0161-873 8335 E-mail: info@nevillejohnson.co.uk

Lurejumbo Ltd, Unit 2 Darwin Road, Off Steel Road, Corby, Northamptonshire, NN17 5XZ Tel: (01536) 401971 Fax: (01536) 401972 E-mail: info@metalico.org.uk

Pentos Office Furniture Ltd, Asher Lane, Pentrich, Ripley, Derbyshire, DE5 3RE Tel: (01773) 570700 Fax: (01773) 570160 E-mail: email@pentos-plc.co.uk

Portsdown Office Ltd, 1 Warrior Business Centre, Fitzherbert Road, Portsmouth, PO6 1TX Tel: (023) 9232 4611 Fax: (023) 9221 0164 E-mail: sales@portsdown.co.uk

Premier Seating International Ltd, Parkside Mill, Walter Street, Blackburn, BB1 1TL Tel: (01254) 673400 Fax: (01254) 665571 E-mail: sales@premierseating.co.uk

Remploy Furniture Group, Baglan Energy Park, Central Avenue, Baglan, Port Talbot, West Glamorgan, SA12 7AX Tel: (01639) 824637 Fax: (01639) 424685 E-mail: furniture@remploy.co.uk

Senator International Ltd, Sykeside Drive, Altham Business Park, Altham, Accrington, Lancashire, BB5 5YE Tel: (01282) 725000 Fax: (01282) 775039 E-mail: sales@senatorinternational.co.uk

Sigma Group, 12 Don Road, St. Helier, Jersey, JE2 4QD Tel: (01534) 733561 Fax: (01534) 768546 E-mail: cdpsigma@itl.net

Spacetime Interiors Ltd, Unit 1, Sunderleigh Farm, Bampton, Tiverton, Devon, EX16 9DT Tel: (0845) 8620326 Fax: (0845) 8689369 E-mail: sales@space-time.co.uk

Task Systems Ltd, W H House, 32 Bethnal Green Road, London, E1 6HZ Tel: (020) 7729 5088 Fax: (020) 7729 4709 E-mail: marketing@tasksystems.co.uk

▶ Viscount Interiors, 5 Thorley Hall Stables, Thorley, Bishop's Stortford, Hertfordshire, CM23 4BE Tel: (01279) 654309 Fax: (01279) 654309 E-mail: sales@viscountinteriors.co.uk

▶ Tony Walker Interiors, Whitehall Court, 14 Telford Road, Edinburgh, EH4 2BA Tel: 0131-343 6151 Fax: 0131-332 4366 E-mail: enquiries@tonywalker.co.uk

Watts Systems Ltd, Church Street, Old Basford, Nottingham, NG6 0GA Tel: 0115-970 5566 Fax: 0115-970 6688

West Midland Office Supplies, Cherry Tree Walk, Farrier Street, Worcester, WR1 3BH Tel: (0870) 3330933 Fax: (0870) 9001449

White Grove Group plc, Central House, Halesfield 19, Telford, Shropshire, TF7 4QT Tel: (01952) 685300 Fax: (01952) 581612 E-mail: sales@whitegrove.co.uk

Workspace Office Solutions Ltd, 1 Swanick Court, Alfreton, Ripley, Derbyshire, DE5 57AF Tel: (01773) 523080 Fax: (01773) 523099 E-mail: email@pentos-plc.co.uk

OFFICE PARTITIONS

▶ Accent Office Interiors, 53-55 Cardiff Road, Luton, LU1 1PP Tel: (01582) 722211

▶ Bloc Interiors, 25 Lodge Road, Little Houghton, Northampton, NN7 1AE Tel: (01604) 891110 Fax: (01604) 899478 E-mail: alisonparker@blocinteriors.co.uk

▶ Connect Exhibitions Ltd, 73 Lynton Road, Acton, London, W3 9HL Tel: (0845) 0170820 Fax: (020) 8896 2064 E-mail: info@connectexhibitions.com

Craftwork Industries Ltd, 98 Lower Richmond Road, London, SW15 1LN Tel: (020) 8780 1798 Fax: (020) 8780 1861 E-mail: sales@craftwork-interiors.co.uk

▶ F R S, 20 Winchcombe Street, Cheltenham, Gloucestershire, GL52 2LY Tel: (01242) 709501 Fax: (01242) 709502 E-mail: info@frs.uk.com

▶ P.J. Gallagher Suspended Ceilings, 61 Berkeley Heights, Killyclogher, Omagh, County Tyrone, BT79 7PR Tel: (028) 8224 4845 Fax: (028) 8224 1670 E-mail: info@pjgallagher.co.uk

▶ London & Essex Interiors Ltd, 30 Sawney Brook, Writtle, Chelmsford, CM1 3JH Tel: (07863) 349830 Fax: (01245) 423074 E-mail: londonandessex@btinternet.com

M S T Interiors, 27 Gelli Gwyn Road, Morriston, Swansea, SA7 9TF Tel: 0870 803 4847 E-mail: info@partitionsandceilings.co.uk

▶ Syd Pollard Commercial Interiors, 98 Marlowe Road, Worthing, West Sussex, BN14 8EZ Tel: (01903) 533483 Fax: (01903) 533483 E-mail: info@partitions.org.uk

▶ Storage Equipment Centre, Entrance Two, Gunnels Wood Road, Stevenage, Hertfordshire, SG1 2BT Tel: (0870) 2410872 Fax: (0870) 2410873 E-mail: info@sec-online.co.uk

▶ Style Midlands, Unit 3, Phoenix Park, Telford Way, Stephenson Industrial Estate, Coalville, Leicestershire, LE67 3HB Tel: (01530) 831144 Fax: (01530) 831184 E-mail: midlands@style-partitions.co.uk

▶ Working Space Solutions, 32 Selbourne Road, Weston-super-Mare, Avon, BS23 4LU Tel: 0117-925 1899 Fax: 0117-925 1913 E-mail: workingspace@btopenworld.com

OFFICE RELOCATION

▶ Elephant Removals, Unit 1 53 Wandle Way, London, SW18 4UJ Tel: (020) 8877 9263 Fax: (0845) 0091801 E-mail: info@elephantremovals.co.uk

OFFICE REMOVAL CONTRACTORS

▶ A B C Removals & Storage, High Peaks, Church Lane, Bledlow Ridge, High Wycombe, Buckinghamshire, HP14 4AX Tel: (01494) 481277 E-mail: info@abcremovalsandstorage.com

Arrowpak Transport & Warehousing Ltd, Norwood Road, Brandon, Suffolk, IP27 0PB Tel: (01842) 812165 Fax: (01842) 813051 E-mail: sales@arrowpak.co.uk

Badgers Removals, Unit 11 Nathan Way, London, SE28 0BQ Tel: (020) 8317 4500 Fax: (020) 8317 3539

Bishop's Blatchpack, Kestrel Way, Sowton Industrial Estate, Exeter, EX2 7PA Tel: (01392) 202040 Fax: (01392) 201251 E-mail: blatchpack@bishops-move.co.uk

Bishops Move Wokingham Ltd, Oaklands Business Centre, Oaklands Park, Wokingham, Berkshire, RG41 2FD Tel: (01276) 685515 Fax: 0118-977 3183 E-mail: wokingham@bishopsmove.co.uk

C & M Apostolides Ltd, 257 Wood Street, Walthamstow, London, E17 3NG Tel: (020) 8923 5050 Fax: (020) 8923 6060 E-mail: mail@cama.co.uk

Commercial & Personal Relocations Ltd, Space Centre, Legg Brothers Industrial Estate, Spring Road, Wolverhampton, WV4 6JT Tel: (01902) 491001 Fax: (01902) 491002 E-mail: liz@cpr-uk.com

F R Hackworthy & Sons, Depository, Elliott Road, Plymouth, PL4 0SB Tel: (01752) 228815 Fax: (01752) 600615

Garrards Removals & Storage, Unit 9b Mill Lane Trading Estate, Mill Lane, Croydon, CR0 4AA Tel: (020) 8688 4979 Fax: (020) 8686 4140

Harrow Green Ltd, Cooks Road, London, E15 2PW Tel: (020) 8522 0101 Fax: (020) 8522 0252 E-mail: info@harrowgreen.com

Hartgrove Bros, Station Road, Redcar, Cleveland, TS10 1RD Tel: (01642) 489937 Fax: (01642) 489937

K C Office Services Ltd, The Relocation Centre, Blenheim Road, Lancing, West Sussex, BN15 8UQ Tel: (01903) 600400 Fax: (01903) 607082 E-mail: ops@kcos.co.uk

M J F Interdec Ltd, Greenford, Middlesex, UB18 9YS Tel: (01895) 909090 Fax: (01895) 909010 E-mail: hotline@interdec.co.uk

▶ Martins Removal Service Ltd, 198 Colinton Road, Edinburgh, EH14 1BP Tel: 0131-443 1056

Masons Moving Group Ltd, Storage House, Priority Business Park, Barry, South Glamorgan, CF63 2BG Tel: (01446) 733330 Fax: (01446) 733827 E-mail: enquiries@masonsmovinggroup.co.uk

Moving Home Co. Ltd, Serin House, Hindsley Place, London, SE23 2NF Tel: (020) 8699 6766 Fax: (020) 8699 5067 E-mail: services@movinghomecompany.com

▶ Pinnacle Commercial Solutions Ltd, Unit 6, Canal Lane, Tunstall, Stoke-on-Trent, ST6 4PA Tel: (01782) 834800 Fax: (01782) 822033 E-mail: enquiries@pinnaclecommercialsolutions.com

R Open & Son Ltd, Unit 15 Oakwood Hill, Oakwood Hill Inustrial Estate, Loughton, Essex, IG10 3TZ Tel: (020) 8989 5741 Fax: (020) 8508 2115 E-mail: ropenremovals@aol.co.uk

Smarts Of Northolt, Unit 15 The Metropolitan Centre, Derby Road, Greenford, Middlesex, UB6 8UJ Tel: (0500) 030609 Fax: (020) 8575 8804 E-mail: sales@smartsremovals.co.uk

Taylors Removals Ltd, The Potters, 13 Central Way, Cwmbran, Gwent, NP44 5HT Tel: (01633) 276555 Fax: (01633) 290888

▶ The-Big-Move.Com, 60 Wyken Way, Wyken, Coventry, CV2 3HG Tel: (0700) 5102727 E-mail: info@the-big-move.com

▶ Town & Country, Water Eaton Lane, Penkridge, Stafford, ST19 5QE Tel: (01785) 714600 Fax: (01785) 711221 E-mail: andycoombs@townandcountry.uk.com

▶ Town & Country, Water Eaton Lane, Penkridge, Stafford, ST19 5QE Tel: (01785) 714600 Fax: (01785) 711221 E-mail: andycoombs@townandcountry.uk.com

U T S Johnsons Removals Storage, Unit 1 Parker Industrial Estate, Mansfield Road, Derby, DE21 4SZ Tel: (01332) 371452 Fax: (01332) 298803 E-mail: moves@johnsons-rs.co.uk

OFFICE SHELVING

A W Interiors Ltd, 4 Streetgate Park, Sunniside, Newcastle upon Tyne, NE16 5LD Tel: 0191-488 9910 Fax: 0191-488 9920 E-mail: bill@awinteriors.freeserve.co.uk

▶ UK Shelving Ltd, Faraday Building, 136-144a Queen Victoria Street, London, EC4V 4BU Tel: (020) 7357 6489 Fax: (01268) 510829 E-mail: sales@ukshelving.co.uk

OFFICE STAFF RECRUITMENT AGENCIES

Aberdeen Appointments Agency Ltd, 461 Union Street, Aberdeen, AB11 6DB Tel: (01224) 211211 Fax: (01224) 211411 E-mail: info@aaa.uk.com

OFFICE STAFF RECRUITMENT AGENCIES – *continued*

Ace Appointments, 4 Market Square, Northampton, NN1 2DL Tel: (01604) 630781 Fax: (01604) 620495 E-mail: recruit@aceappsnorth.co.uk

▶ Action Drive Ltd, 15 Grove Market Place, Court Yard, London, SE9 5PU Tel: (020) 8850 3763 Fax: (020) 8850 4113 E-mail: actiondrive@hotmail.com

▶ Agency Staff Ltd, PO Box 8315, Birmingham, B31 2AL Tel: 0121-476 8337 Fax: 0121-476 8337 E-mail: agency.staff@virgin.net

August P A's & Personnel, 8 Gobbitts Yard, Woodbridge, Suffolk, IP12 1DD Tel: (01394) 388828 E-mail: enquiries@august-pas.com

▶ Austin Banks Ltd, Hutton Business Centre, Suite 1a High Street, Bentley, Doncaster, South Yorkshire, DN5 9QP Tel: (01302) 822228 Fax: 01302 822237 E-mail: james@austinbanks.co.uk

Blue Arrow, Portland House, Longbrook Street, Exeter, EX4 6AB Tel: (01392) 424733 Fax: (01392) 490486 E-mail: enquiries@bluearrow.co.uk

▶ Bond Williams Professional Recruitment, 23 Hinton Road, Bournemouth, BH1 2EF Tel: (01202) 201700 Fax: (01202) 201645 E-mail: enquiry@bondwilliams.co.uk

▶ Chameleon Personnel Services Ltd, 1 West Street, Leighton Buzzard, Bedfordshire, LU7 1DA Tel: (01525) 218068 Fax: (01525) 218067 E-mail: info@chameleonpersonnel.co.uk

▶ Corinium Language Associates, Wadham Close, Southrop, Lechlade, Gloucestershire, GL7 3NR Tel: (01367) 851100 E-mail: info@coriniumlanguage.co.uk

▶ D I Recruitment, 8 Dig Street, Ashbourne, Derbyshire, DE6 1GF Tel: (01335) 342354 Fax: (01335) 300179 E-mail: info@direcruitment.co.uk

▶ Employment Enjoyment Ltd, 6 Shurdington Road, Cheltenham, Gloucestershire, GL53 0DJ Tel: 01242 252337 Fax: 01242 580451 E-mail: info@employment-enjoyment.co.uk

▶ Employment4students, 16 Spicers Field, Oxshott, Leatherhead, Surrey, KT22 0UT Tel: 01483 855528 Fax: 01483 855528 E-mail: nick.thompson@e4s.co.uk

▶ FinanceCVs.co.uk, 18 Bedfordshire Down, Warfield, Bracknell, Berkshire, RG42 3UA Tel: (07006) 300980 E-mail: info@financecvs.co.uk

▶ Friendly People Ltd, The Old Post Office, 2, Church Street, Brigstock, Kettering, Northamptonshire, NN14 3EX Tel: (01536) 373648 E-mail: info@friendly-people.co.uk

▶ The Harris Lord Group Ltd, 45a Carfax, Horsham, West Sussex, RH12 1EQ Tel: (01403) 273370 Fax: (01403) 273364

▶ Just Recruit (UK) Ltd, Viking Industrial Park, Tedco Business Centre, Jarrow, Tyne & Wear, NE32 3DT Tel: 0191-428 3336 Fax: 0191-428 3356 E-mail: mark@justrecruit.co.uk

MDS Consultants, Tribune Avenue, Broadheath, Altrincham, Cheshire, WA14 5RX Tel: 0161-927 7744 Fax: 0161-927 7612

▶ Parker Robinson Recruitment Ltd, The Imex Business Park, Shobnall Road, Burton-On-Trent, Staffordshire, DE14 2AU Tel: (01283) 543406 Fax: (01283) 519191 E-mail: owen@parkerrobinson.co.uk

▶ The People Consultancy, 18 Clapgate Road, Bushey, WD23 3NF Tel: (020) 8950 2876 E-mail: rachel@peopleconsultancy.com

▶ Red Eagle, 38 Bouverie Square, Folkestone, Kent, CT20 1BA Tel: (01303) 851133 Fax: (01303) 851134 E-mail: jobs@red-eagle.co.uk

▶ Redco Recruitment Group Limited, Redco House, 165 Lea Road, Pennfelds, Wolverhampton, WV3 0LQ Tel: 0845 111 0735 Fax: 0845 111 0736 E-mail: info@redcorecruitment.com

▶ S D W Recruitment, 33 Currie House, Herbert Walker Avenue, Southampton, SO15 1HJ Tel: (023) 8033 6633 Fax: (023) 8033 6633 E-mail: info@sdwrecruitment.co.uk

▶ Specialist Appointments, Unit 1 The Old Bakery, South Road, Reigate, Surrey, RH2 7LB Tel: (01737) 223305 Fax: (08704) 296873 E-mail: recruit@specialistappointments.co.uk

Stafflink (UK) Ltd, 138 Lower Road, London, SE16 2UG Tel: (020) 7252 2212 Fax: (020) 7252 2901 E-mail: info@staff-link.co.uk

▶ TMP & Associates Ltd, Sedgecombe House, Garfield Road, Camberley, Surrey, GU15 2JG Tel: 01276 684007 Fax: 01276 684010 E-mail: mike@tmpandass.com

▶ Try Temps Ltd, Unit A2 Imex Business Park, Kings Road, Tyseley, Birmingham, B11 2AL Tel: 0121-693 3311 Fax: 0121-693 3355 E-mail: sales@trytemps.co.uk

▶ Helen Watson, PO Box 565, East Grinstead, West Sussex, RH19 1WQ Tel: (07799) 645907 E-mail: jobs@networking4you.net

▶ Paul Wells Consultants, 32 Catharine Close, Chafford Hundred, Grays, Essex, RM16 6QH Tel: (01375) 484044 E-mail: paulwellsconsult@btinternet.com

OFFICE STATIONERY PRODUCTS

A B Copyright Ltd, Whitehall Chambers, Halifax Road, Hipperholme, Halifax, West Yorkshire, HX3 8EN Tel: (01422) 200200 Fax: (01422) 200150 E-mail: enquiries@abcopyright.co.uk

▶ A D M Office Supplies Ltd, PO Box 1, Yateley, Hampshire, GU46 6WY Tel: (01252) 876494 Fax: (01252) 879505 E-mail: admin@admoffice.co.uk

▶ Business Envelopes, 11 Juniper Grove, Livingston, West Lothian, EH54 5JF Tel: (07790) 439975

C O S, Unit 9, Hastingwood Business Centre, Hastingwood, Harlow, Essex, CM17 9GD Tel: (0845) 3893030 Fax: (0845) 3893031 E-mail: sales@colouroffset.co.uk

▶ Commercial Envelopes, 158 Lichfield Road, Sandhills, Walsall, WS9 9PF Tel: (01543) 452326 Fax: (01543) 821509 E-mail: denise@commercialenvelopes.co.uk

The Computer Broker/Direct Stationery Ltd, 80 Cricklade Street, Cirencester, Gloucestershire, GL7 1JN Tel: (0870) 2860891 Fax: (0870) 0632949 E-mail: sales@directstationery.net

▶ Direct-Inks, 18 The Island, Midsomer Norton, Radstock, BA3 2HQ Tel: (01761) 410222

G H UK Distribution Ltd, 13 York House, Langston Road, Loughton, Essex, IG10 3TQ Tel: (020) 8502 0100 Fax: (020) 8508 2114 E-mail: ghukdistribution@btconnect.com

iStationers Ltd, Suite 1, 18a Ropergate, Pontefract, West Yorkshire, WF8 1LP Tel: 01226 715194 E-mail: Sales@iStationers.com

▶ Speedbird Supplies, 15 Thistledown Drive, Ixworth, Bury St. Edmunds, Suffolk, IP31 2NH Tel: (01359) 235170 Fax: (01359) 232015 E-mail: sales@speedbird-supplies.co.uk

▶ Yate Express Stationers, 250 Longs Drive, Yate, Bristol, BS37 5XR Tel: (01454) 880080 Fax: (01454) 880081 E-mail: y.e.s@blueyonder.co.uk

OFFICE VACUUM CLEANERS

▶ An Other Cleaning Company, 11 Pembrook Road, Holbrook, Coventry, CV6 4FD Tel: (024) 7666 5921 Fax: (024) 7666 5921 E-mail: rob@aocc.co.uk

▶ Companyclean Ltd, Unit 2A 83 Prestbury Road, Cheltenham, Gloucestershire, GL52 2DR Tel: (01242) 572918 E-mail: sales@companyclean.co.uk

▶ Crystal Clean Southwest, Carrick Business Centre, Commercial Road, Penryn, Cornwall, TR10 8AR Tel: (01326) 377999 Fax: 01326 377999 E-mail: crystal_cleaning@btconnect.com

Hy Tec East London, 303 Higham Hill Road, London, E17 5RG Tel: (020) 8925 0400 Fax: (020) 8925 0411 E-mail: sales@hy-tec.co.uk

Industrial Cleaning Supplies Liverpool Ltd, 7-29 Brasenose Road, Liverpool, L20 8HL Tel: 0151-922 2000 Fax: 0151-922 3733 E-mail: sales@theicsgroup.co.uk

OFFSHORE BASKETS

C T C Container Trading (U.K.) Ltd, Hillview Base, Hillview Rd, East Tullos, Aberdeen, AB12 3HB Tel: (01224) 879111 Fax: (01224) 879015 E-mail: information@ctccontainers.com

OFFSHORE CERTIFICATION/ VERIFICATION AUTHORITIES

Lloyds Register, 71 Fenchurch Street, London, EC3M 4BS Tel: (020) 7709 9166 Fax: (020) 7488 4796 E-mail: lloydsreg@lr.org

OFFSHORE COMPUTER SOFTWARE

Bristlecone UK Ltd, Fulton House, Fulton Road, Wembley, Middlesex, HA9 0TF Tel: (0870) 7368880 Fax: (0870) 7368889 E-mail: sunilk@bcone.co.uk

OFFSHORE CONSULTANTS

Dreh Ltd, Duncombe Road, Bradford, West Yorkshire, BD8 9TB Tel: (01793) 533262 Fax: (01793) 619510 E-mail: sales@dreh.co.uk

Dron & Dickson Group, Craigshaw Road, West Tullos Industrial Estate, Aberdeen, AB12 3AR Tel: (01224) 874554 Fax: (01224) 895220 E-mail: info@drondickson.co.uk

E P C, PO Box 2229, London, W14 0JA Tel: (020) 7602 2979 Fax: (020) 7371 6431 E-mail: aboi@bmec.org.uk

Marine & Offshore Consultants Ltd, Magellan House, James Watt Close, Great Yarmouth, Norfolk, NR31 0NX Tel: (01493) 440166 Fax: (01493) 658490 E-mail: support@modgy.co.uk

Micropack Engineering Ltd, Fir Training Centre, Portlethen, Aberdeen, AB12 4RR Tel: (01224) 784055 Fax: (01224) 784056 E-mail: info@micropack.co.uk

South West Surveys Projects Ltd, 43 Lower Fore Street, Saltash, Cornwall, PL12 6JQ Tel: (01752) 849190 Fax: (01752) 849229 E-mail: office@swsurveys.co.uk

OFFSHORE COORDINATION AND PORT SERVICES

Seletar Services, Queens Road, Great Yarmouth, Norfolk, NR30 3NW Tel: (01493) 857313 Fax: (01493) 332202

OFFSHORE ENGINEERING

Babcock Scientific Services, Rosyth Dockyard, Rosyth, Dunfermline, Fife, KY11 2YD Tel: (01383) 412131 Fax: (01383) 422699 E-mail: bs-info@babcock.co.uk

Control Equipment Ltd, Tyco Park, Grimshaw Lane, Newton Heath, Manchester, M40 2WL Tel: 0161-455 4232 Fax: 0161-455 4441 E-mail: tycocontrolsystems.uk@tycoint.com

Marinetronix Ltd, Unit 1, Airside Business Park, Dyce Drive, Kirkhill Industrial Estate, Dyce, Aberdeen, AB21 0GT Tel: (01224) 774423 Fax: (01224) 724396 E-mail: info@marinetronix.co.uk

▶ SeaMark Systems Ltd, Uphall Depot, Broxburn, West Lothian, EH52 5NT Tel: (01506) 435888 Fax: (01506) 432520

Shaw Group UK Ltd, Stores Road, Derby, DE21 4BG Tel: (01332) 291122 Fax: (01332) 291123 E-mail: info@shawgrp.com

Swan Hunter Tyneside Ltd, Station Road, Wallsend, Tyne & Wear, NE28 6EQ Tel: 0191-295 0295 Fax: 0191-262 0374 E-mail: john.mitchell@swanhunter.com

Westerngeco, Schlumberger House, Buckingham Gate, London Gatwick Airport, Gatwick, West Sussex, RH6 0NZ Tel: (01293) 556000 Fax: (01293) 556080 E-mail: sales@westerngeco.co.uk

Ziebel UK Ltd, Wardes Road, Inverurie, Aberdeenshire, AB51 3TT Tel: (01467) 622332 Fax: (01467) 625235

OFFSHORE GEOTECHNICAL GROUND INVESTIGATION

▶ Lusted Consulting Ltd, 5 Alliance Way, Paddock Wood, Tonbridge, Kent, TN12 6TY Tel: (01892) 835937 E-mail: info@lustedconsulting.ltd.uk

Seacore Ltd, Lower Quay, Gweek, Helston, Cornwall, TR12 6UD Tel: (01326) 221771 Fax: (01326) 221553 E-mail: sales@seacore.co.uk

OFFSHORE HEALTH AND SAFETY CONSULTANCY

▶ Intelligent Risk Management Ltd, PO Box 148, Kendal, Cumbria, LA9 7WY Tel: (01539) 736126 Fax: (01539) 736286 E-mail: david.arnold@i-rm.com

R P S Engineering & Safety, Dalton House, 105 Dalton Avenue, Birchwood, Warrington, WA3 6YF Tel: (01925) 831000 Fax: (01925) 831231 E-mail: rpswa@rpsgroup.com

OFFSHORE MAINTENANCE CABINS

Labtech Modular Engineering, Blackness Road, Altens Industrial Estate, Aberdeen, AB12 3LH Tel: (01224) 337777 Fax: (01224) 337770 E-mail: sales@labtech.co.uk

OFFSHORE OR SUBSEA OR UNDERWATER MAINTENANCE OR REPAIR CONTRACTORS

Aberdeen Fabrication Ltd, Links Place, Aberdeen, AB11 5DY Tel: (01224) 588321 Fax: (01224) 583898 E-mail: sales@afab.co.uk

Aker Maritime, McNulty Quay, Commercial Rd, South Shields, Tyne & Wear, NE33 1RZ Tel: 0191-401 5977 Fax: 0191-401 5958

C A N (Offshore) Ltd, Hareness Road, Altens, Aberdeen, AB12 3LE Tel: (01224) 870100 Fax: (01224) 876015 E-mail: mailserve@cangroup.net

Cansco Pressure Control Ltd, Badentoy Road, Portlethen, Aberdeen, AB12 4YA Tel: (01224) 782211 Fax: (01224) 782266 E-mail: sales@3plus.co.uk

Mcnulty Offshore Ltd, 16-17 Corstorphine Town, South Shields, Tyne & Wear, NE33 1RZ Tel: 0191-401 5800 Fax: 0191-401 5802 E-mail: mcnulty@mcnultyoffshore.com

Wood Group Pressure Control Ltd, Blackhouse Circle, Blackhouse Industrial Estate, Peterhead, Aberdeenshire, AB42 1BN Tel: (01779) 474293 Fax: (01779) 474298

OFFSHORE PLATFORM GRATINGS

Lionweld Kennedy Ltd, Marsh Road, Middlesbrough, Cleveland, TS1 5JS Tel: (01642) 245151 Fax: (01642) 224710 E-mail: sales@lk-uk.com

OFFSHORE STORAGE CONTAINERS

Containercare Ltd, Dock Road, Liverpool, L19 2JW Tel: 0151-427 1771 Fax: 0151-427 1772 E-mail: sales@concare.co.uk

Transmit Containers Ltd, Bessemer Way, Harfreys Industrial Estate, Great Yarmouth, Norfolk, NR31 0LX Tel: (01493) 650792 Fax: (01493) 443500

Vertec Engineering, 4 Pitmedden Road, Dyce, Aberdeen, AB21 0DP Tel: (01224) 772969 Fax: (01224) 772528 E-mail: info@vertec-eng.co.uk

OFFSHORE TRUST SERVICES

▶ Andersen Offshore Company Formations, PO Box 8188, Colchester, CO3 3WW Tel: (020) 8123 1493 E-mail: idpnd@yahoo.co.uk

▶ Worldwide Corporate Services, 5 Angelica Way, Whiteley, Fareham, Hampshire, PO15 7HY Tel: (0700) 5946936 E-mail: info@worldcorporate.co.uk

OIL, *See also other headings for particular types, some under oil*

Apollo Fuels Ltd, Templeborough Depot, Sheffield Road, Tinsley, Sheffield, S9 1RT Tel: 0114-243 6814 Fax: 0114-242 3362

Caldo Oils Ltd, Worsley Brow, St. Helens, Merseyside, WA9 3EZ Tel: (01744) 813535 Fax: (01744) 816031E-mail: info@caldo.co.uk

Maxol Oil, 48 Trench Road, Mallusk, Newtownabbey, County Antrim, BT36 4TY Tel: (028) 9050 6000 Fax: (028) 9050 6500 E-mail: info@maxoldirect.com

National Grid Co. P.L.C., Littlebrook Manorway, Dartford, DA1 5PS Tel: (01322) 295160 Fax: (01322) 295040 E-mail: robin.greaves@ngc.co.uk

Pride Oil plc, Crown Road, Enfield, Middlesex, EN1 1DZ Tel: (020) 8345 8100 Fax: (020) 8804 9977 E-mail: info@pride-oils.co.uk

Top Oil Products Ltd, Eastway, London, E9 5NR Tel: (020) 8548 3636 E-mail: online*@aol.com

OIL ABSORBENTS

B & D Clays & Chemicals Ltd, 10 Wandle Way, Willow Lane Trading Estate, Mitcham, Surrey, CR4 4NB Tel: (020) 8640 9221 Fax: (020) 8648 5033 E-mail: sales@bdclays.co.uk

C.P. Burns & Associates Ltd, Peter's Farm, Helmdon, Brackley, Northants, NN13 5QH Tel: (01295) 768271 Fax: (01295) 768298 E-mail: enquiries@burnsassociates.demon.co.uk

Oil Dri UK Ltd, Bannisters Row, Wisbech, Cambridgeshire, PE13 3HZ Tel: (01945) 581244 Fax: (01945) 581250 E-mail: sales@oil-dri.co.uk

▶ Sorbican Distribution, 27 Priory Lane, Hartley Wintney, Hook, Hampshire, RG27 8EX Tel: (01256) 762435

OIL ADDITIVES

Afton Chemical, London Road, Bracknell, Berkshire, RG12 2UW Tel: (01344) 304141 Fax: (01344) 420666 E-mail: ethyleurope@ethyl.com

Hornett Bros & Co. Ltd, Ferry Lane, Rainham, Essex, RM13 9YH Tel: (01708) 556041 Fax: (01708) 557546 E-mail: sales@hornett.net

OIL AND GAS CEMENTING PRODUCTS

Ray Oil Tool Co. Ltd, Unit 48 Howe Moss Avenue, Dyce, Aberdeen, AB21 0GP Tel: (01224) 773313 Fax: (01224) 773304 E-mail: sales@rayoiltool.co.uk

OIL AND GAS COMPLETION SERVICES

Baker Hughes Ltd, Campus 1, Aberdeen Science And Technology Centre, Bridge Of Don, Aberdeen, AB22 8GT Tel: (01224) 226000 Fax: (01224) 226006

OIL AND GAS CONDITION MONITORING

Bureau Veritas, Pavilion 1 Craig Shaw Business Park, Craig Shaw Road, Tullos, Aberdeen, AB12 3AR Tel: (01224) 892100 Fax: (01224) 898437

The Oil Lab, 2 Little Orchard Gardens, Wolseley Road, Rugeley, Staffordshire, WS15 2ES Tel: (07050) 257431 Fax: (01889) 583682 E-mail: info@theoillab.co.uk

Silgo Lubricants Ltd, 20-22-24 Thurrock Commercial Centre, Purfleet Industrial Park, Aveley, South Ockendon, Essex, RM15 4YG Tel: (01708) 865665 Fax: (01708) 868996 E-mail: sales@silgo.co.uk

OIL AND GAS EXPLORATION AND PRODUCTION EQUIPMENT, *See also headings for particular types*

Carrack Ltd, Badentoy Crescent, Badentoy Industrial Estate, Portlethen, Aberdeen, AB12 4YD Tel: (01224) 783100 Fax: (01224) 783400 E-mail: sandym@carrackltd.com

OIL AND GAS EXPLORATION OR PRODUCTION COMPANIES

Amerada Hess Ltd, 33 Grosvenor Place, London, SW1X 7HY Tel: (020) 7823 2626 Fax: (020) 7887 2199

B P, Burnside Road, Farburn Industrial Estate, Dyce, Aberdeen, AB21 7PB Tel: (01224) 832000 Fax: (01224) 725273

B P Exploration, Britannic House, 1 Finsbury Circus, London, EC2M 7BA Tel: (020) 7496 4000 Fax: (020) 7496 4630

B P Exploration Operating Co. Ltd, Wytch Farm, Wytch, Corfe Castle, Wareham, Dorset, BH20 5JR Tel: (01929) 476000 Fax: (01929) 476072

BG Group, 100 Thames Valley Park Drive, Reading, RG6 1PT Tel: 0118-935 3222 Fax: 0118-929 3710 E-mail: admin@bg-group.com

British Petroleum Co. P.L.C., 1 St. James's Square, London, SW1Y 4PD Tel: (020) 7496 4000 Fax: (020) 7496 4630

Cairn Energy plc, 50 Lothian Road, Edinburgh, EH3 9BY Tel: 0131-475 3000 Fax: 0131-475 3030 E-mail: pr@cairn-energy.plc.uk

Chevron & Texaco Ltd, 1 Westferry Circus, Canary Wharf, London, E14 4HA Tel: (020) 7719 3000 Fax: E-mail:

Conoco (UK) Ltd, Rubislaw House, Anderson Drive, Rubislaw Ho, Aberdeen, AB15 6FZ Tel: (01224) 205000 Fax: (01224) 205222

Conocophillips Ltd, 2 Portman Street, London, W1H 6DU Tel: (020) 7408 6000 Fax: (020) 7408 6660

E N I UK Ltd, 10 Ebury Bridge Road, London, SW1W 8PZ Tel: (020) 7344 6000 Fax: (020) 7344 6044 E-mail: sales@eni.co.uk

Exon Mobile House, Ermyn Way, Leatherhead, Surrey, KT22 8UX Tel: (01372) 222000 Fax: (01372) 222556

Exxon Mobil Group, Exxon Mobil House, Ermyn Way, Leatherhead, Surrey, KT22 8UX Tel: (01372) 222000 Fax: (01372) 222556

Marathon International Petroleum G B Ltd, Capital House, 25 Chapel Street, London, NW1 5DQ Tel: (020) 7298 2500 Fax: (020) 7298 2501

Nexen Energy Services (International) Ltd, Mallard Court, Market Square, Staines, Middlesex, TW18 4RH Tel: (01784) 429500 Fax: (01784) 429550

O M V UK Ltd, 14 Ryder Street, London, SW1Y 6QB Tel: (020) 7333 1600 Fax: (020) 7333 1610 E-mail: info@omv.com

Petro-Canada, Bowater House, 114 Knightsbridge, London, SW1X 7LD Tel: (020) 7225 7100 Fax: (020) 7584 6459

Premier Oil & Gas Services Ltd, 23 Lower Belgrave Street, London, SW1W 0NR Tel: (020) 7730 1111 Fax: (020) 7730 4696 E-mail: premier@premier-oil.com

Shell UK Ltd, Shell Centre, York Road, London, SE1 7NA Tel: (020) 7546 5000 Fax: (020) 7934 8060

Sigma Exploration Ltd, 21 Chipstead Street, London, SW6 3SR Tel: (020) 7608 3883 Fax: (020) 7608 3883 E-mail: johnkiller@aol.com

Statoil (U K) Ltd, 11 Regent St, London, SW1Y 4ST Tel: (020) 7766 7777 Fax: (020) 7766 7862 E-mail: info@statoil.com

Svenska Petroleum Exploration, 1 Hamilton Mews, London, W1J 7HA Tel: (020) 7647 2500 Fax: (020) 7647 2501 E-mail: info@speuk.co.uk

Total E And P UK P.L.C., Crawpeel Road, Altens, Aberdeen, AB12 3FG Tel: (01224) 297000 Fax: (01224) 298999

OIL AND GAS INDUSTRY CEMENTING SERVICES

B J Services Co UK Ltd, Badentoy Avenue, Badentoy Industrial Estate, Portlethen, Aberdeen, AB12 4YB Tel: (01224) 401401 Fax: (01224) 401501

OIL AND GAS INDUSTRY CONSULTANTS

O I E Services Ltd, Centurion Court, North Esplanade West, Aberdeen, AB11 5QH Tel: (01224) 256400 Fax: (01224) 256444 E-mail: info@optima-energy.com

Smith Rea, 78 Carden Place, Aberdeen, AB10 1UL Tel: (01224) 612400 Fax: (01224) 612401 E-mail: info@srel.co.uk

T M Services Ltd, 5 Charterhouse Square, London, EC1M 6PX Tel: (020) 7867 8600 Fax: (020) 7867 8787 E-mail: tmservices@tmworldwide.co.uk

OIL AND GAS INDUSTRY SUPPLY SERVICES

Aberdeen Web Ltd, Unit 5a Wellheads Crescent, Wellheads Indust Estate, Dyce, Aberdeen, AB21 7HG Tel: (01224) 723111 Fax: (01224) 774141

Lloyd & Jones Engineers Ltd, Langton House, 74 Regent Road, Bootle, Merseyside, L20 1EJ Tel: 0151-955 4700 Fax: 0151-922 5418 E-mail: sales@lloyd-jones.com

Vetco Gray Controls Ltd, Harness Road, Altens Industrial Estate, Aberdeen, AB12 3LE Tel: (01224) 872211 Fax: (01224) 894840

▶ Visintini-Jones, Capel Barn, Capel Road, Orlestone, Ashford, Kent, TN26 2EH Tel: (01233) 733617 Fax: (01233) 733511 E-mail: rayjones@talktalk.net

OIL AND GAS PRODUCTION VALVE TRIM COMPONENTS

Valve Componets Ltd, 6 Singer Road, East Kilbride, Glasgow, G75 0XS Tel: (01355) 263884 Fax: (01355) 245146 E-mail: sales@vcl.uk.com

OIL BLENDING, *See headings for particular types of Oil*

OIL BROKERS

Bunkerfuels UK Ltd, 21-24 Mill Bank Tower, London, SW1P 4QP Tel: (020) 7828 3299 Fax: (020) 7834 4951 E-mail: bunkers@bunkerfuels.co.uk

▶ Cawl Bunker Services, Albion Mills, 18 East Tenter St, London, E1 8DM Tel: (020) 7216 2000 Fax: (020) 7216 2001 E-mail: bunkers@cawl-group.com

OIL BUNKERING AGENTS, *See Bunkering Agents*

OIL BURNER CONTROLS

Hotfrost, 72-76 Brighton Road, Surbiton, Surrey, KT6 5PP Tel: (020) 8399 7151 Fax: (020) 8399 9549

OIL BURNER INSTALLATION OR SERVICING

High-Fire Ltd, 37a Cyprus Rd, Leicester, LE2 8QP Tel: 0116-232 7980

S & S Burner Services Ltd, Unit 14 193 The Garth Road Industrial Centre, Garth Road, Morden, Surrey, SM4 4LZ Tel: (020) 8330 7992 Fax: (020) 8330 7993

OIL COOLED TRANSFORMERS

International Transformers, Longley Lane, Sharston Industrial Area, Manchester, M22 4RU Tel: 0161-428 9507 Fax: 0161-428 0052 E-mail: info@int-transformers.co.uk

OIL COOLER MANUFRS

Becool Radiators Ltd, Paterson Road, Wellingborough, Northamptonshire, NN8 4BZ Tel: (01933) 230420 Fax: (01933) 279902 E-mail: sales@gallay.co.uk

Fawcett Christie Hydraulics Ltd, Sandycroft Industrial Estate, Chester Road, Sandycroft, Deeside, Clwyd, CH5 2QP Tel: (01244) 535515 Fax: (01244) 533002 E-mail: sales@fch.co.uk

OIL DISPERSANT SPRAYING SYSTEMS

Ayles Fernie International Ltd, Unit D5 Chaucer Business Park, Watery Lane, Kemsing, Sevenoaks, Kent, TN15 6YU Tel: (01732) 762962 Fax: (01732) 761961 E-mail: sales@aylesfernie.co.uk

Ro-Clean Desmi Ltd, Unit 24 Shamrock Quay, William Street, Southampton, SO14 5QL Tel: (02380) 829751 Fax: (02380) 339190 E-mail: uk.ro-clean@desmi.com

OIL DIVING SUITS

Respirex, F Kingsfield Business Centre, Philanthropic Road, Redhill, RH1 4DP Tel: (01737) 778600 Fax: (01737) 779441 E-mail: sales@respirex.co.uk

OIL EXPLORATION ELECTRONIC EQUIPMENT

Avalon Sciences, Unit 6-7 Wessex Buildings, Bancombe Road, Somerton, Somerset, TA11 6SB Tel: (01458) 270000 Fax: (01458) 270088 E-mail: sales@avalonsciences.com

OIL EXPLORATION SERVICES

Amerada Hess Ltd, 33 Grosvenor Place, London, SW1X 7HY Tel: (020) 7823 2626 Fax: (020) 7887 2199

B P Chemicals Marketing Ltd, 1 St James Square, London, SW1Y 4PD Tel: (020) 7496 4000 Fax: (020) 7496 4630

B P Exploration Operating Co. Ltd, Wytch Farm, Wytch, Corfe Castle, Wareham, Dorset, BH20 5JR Tel: (01929) 476000 Fax: (01929) 476072

Cairn Energy plc, 50 Lothian Road, Edinburgh, EH3 9BY Tel: 0131-475 3000 Fax: 0131-475 3030 E-mail: pr@cairn-energy.plc.uk

OIL FILTER/FILTRATION EQUIPMENT

Carlson Filtration Ltd, The Buttmill, Barnoldswick, Lancashire, BB18 5HP Tel: (01282) 811000 Fax: (01282) 811001 E-mail: sales@carlson.co.uk

Filterall Ltd, PO Box 29, Daventry, Northamptonshire, NN11 1AQ Tel: (01327) 877624 Fax: (01327) 705749 E-mail: filterall@btconnect.com

OIL FILTRATION EQUIPMENT/ SYSTEMS, INDUSTRIAL

Haesler Machine Tools, 14 Leyden Road, Stevenage, Hertfordshire, SG1 2BW Tel: (01438) 350835 Fax: (01438) 229482 E-mail: ben.haesler@ntlworld.com

National Grid Co. P.L.C., Littlebrook Manorway, Dartford, DA1 5PS Tel: (01322) 295160 Fax: (01322) 295040 E-mail: robin.greaves@ngc.co.uk

OIL FIRED AIR HEATERS

Bering Heating Supplies Ltd, Unit 9 Station Industrial Estate, Oxford Road, Wokingham, Berkshire, RG41 2YQ Tel: 0118-978 9886 Fax: 0118-978 7460

Comtherm Ltd, Comenco Works, Union Lane, Droitwich, Worcestershire, WR9 9AZ Tel: (01905) 775783 Fax: (01905) 794195 E-mail: sales@comtherm.co.uk

William May Ltd, Cavendish Street, Ashton-under-Lyne, Lancashire, OL6 7QW Tel: 0161-330 3838 Fax: 0161-339 1097 E-mail: mwm@william-may.com

OIL FIRED BOILERS

Crossling, 2 Kingstown Broadway, Kingstown Industrial Estate, Carlisle, CA3 0HA Tel: (01228) 541101 Fax: (01228) 539288 E-mail: marketing@crossling.co.uk

▶ Midland Fuel Services Ltd, 62 Primrose Way, Kidderminster, Worcestershire, DY10 1NG Tel: 01562 748991

Warmflow Engineering Co. Ltd, Lissue Industrial Estate, Moira Road, Lisburn, County Antrim, BT28 2RF Tel: (028) 9262 1515 Fax: (028) 9262 1199 E-mail: mail@warmflow.co.uk

OIL FIRED CENTRAL HEATING BOILERS

Adept Heating & Mechanical Services Ltd, Raidons, Nutbourne Lane, Nutbourne, Pulborough, West Sussex, RH20 2HS Tel: (01798) 875239 Fax: (01798) 875239 E-mail: daveblaber@aol.com

▶ bjsedgwick.com, 23 Meadowbrook Close, Norwich, NR1 2HJ Tel: (01603) 618514 E-mail: barry@supasedg.freeserve.co.uk

The Heating People Ltd, 1 Brooklands, Filey, North Yorkshire, YO14 9BA Tel: (0845) 8382732 Fax: (01723) 513981 E-mail: enquiries@theheatingpeople.co.uk

▶ J H S Plumbing & Heating Ltd, Tamsui, Sevenoaks Road, Ightham, Sevenoaks, Kent, TN15 9DS Tel: (01732) 884949 Fax: (01322) 860922 E-mail: korina@draindoctors.biz

▶ Wolf Heating Uk Ltd, 8 Brunel Court, Rudheath Way, Gadbrook Business Park, Northwich, Cheshire, CW9 7EG Tel: 01606 354371 Fax: 01606 44805 E-mail: info@wolfheatinguk.co.uk

OIL FIRED WARM AIR APPLIANCES

Benson Heating, Ludlow Road, Knighton, Powys, LD7 1LP Tel: (01547) 529245 Fax: (01547) 520399 E-mail: information@bensonheating.co.uk

OIL FLARE SYSTEMS

Process Equipment Parts (UK) Ltd, Kershaw House, 449 Great West Road, Hounslow, TW5 0BU Tel: (020) 8754 3999 Fax: (020) 8754 3990 E-mail: mail@process-equipment.co.uk

OIL FREE AIR COMPRESSORS

Fini (UK) Ltd, Unit A5 & A6, Greenwood Court, Veasey Close, Attleborough Fields Industrial Estate, Nuneaton, Warwickshire, CV11 6RT Tel: (024) 7632 2850 Fax: (024) 7634 9607 E-mail: finicompressors@yahoo.co.uk

Silgo Lubricants Ltd, 20-22-24 Thurrock Commercial Centre, Purfleet Industrial Park, Aveley, South Ockendon, Essex, RM15 4YG Tel: (01708) 865665 Fax: (01708) 868996 E-mail: sales@silgo.co.uk

OIL FREE COMPRESSORS

Northey Technologies Ltd, Nortech House, Allens Lane, Poole, Dorset, BH16 5DG Tel: (01202) 668600 Fax: (01202) 668500 E-mail: info@northey.net

OIL GREENHOUSE HEATERS

Two Wests & Elliott Ltd, Carrwood Road, Chesterfield, Derbyshire, S41 9RH Tel: (01246) 451077 Fax: (01246) 260115 E-mail: sales@twowests.co.uk

OIL IN WATER MONITORING INSTRUMENTS

Rivertrace Engineering Ltd, P Kingsfield Business Centre, Philanthropic Road, Redhill, RH1 4DP Tel: (0870) 7702721 Fax: (0870) 7702722 E-mail: info@rivertrace.com

OIL INDUSTRY INFORMATION SERVICES

Aberdeen City Libraries, Rosemount Viaduct, Aberdeen, AB25 1GW Tel: (01224) 634622 Fax: (01224) 636811 E-mail: bustech@-rec.aberdeen.net.uk

D D Group UK Ltd, 35 Bo'ness Road, Grangemouth, Stirlingshire, FK3 8AN Tel: (01324) 472442 Fax: (01324) 474002 E-mail: mailroom@dbgroup.uk.com

Infield Systems Ltd, 15 London Fruit Exchange, Brushfield Street, London, E1 6HB Tel: (020) 7426 9660 Fax: (020) 7247 5035 E-mail: data@infield.com

OIL INDUSTRY PERFORATING SERVICES

Weatherford, Crawpeel Road, Altens Industrial Estate, Aberdeen, AB12 3LG Tel: (01224) 380280 Fax: (01224) 380088

OIL LAMPS

▶ Nautical Antiques Center, 3a Hope Square, Weymouth, Dorset, DT4 8TR Tel: (01305) 777838 E-mail: info@nauticalantiques.org

OIL MANAGEMENT AND FILTRATION

Falcon Lubricants Ltd, Showfield Lane Industrial Estate, Malton, North Yorkshire, YO17 6BT Tel: (01653) 694019 Fax: (01653) 600283 E-mail: admin@oils.co.uk

OIL MANAGEMENT AND FILTRATION – *continued*

Oil Cleanse, Julius Caesar House, 66 High Street, Alton, Hampshire, GU34 1ET Tel: (01420) 542027 Fax: (01420) 542027 E-mail: malcolm.woods.oil@talk21.com

OIL METERS

Ranger Instrument Co. Ltd, Rutherford Road, Basingstoke, Hampshire, RG24 8PG Tel: (01256) 464911 Fax: (01256) 464366 E-mail: ranger@bayham.demon.co.uk

OIL (MINERAL) INDUSTRIAL PRODUCTS DISTRIBUTORS/ BLENDERS/AGENTS

Aztec Oils Ltd, 31 Intake Road, Bolsover Business Park, Bolsover, Chesterfield, Derbyshire, S44 6BB Tel: (01246) 823007 Fax: (01246) 823014 E-mail: sales@aztecoils.co.uk

British Benzol, Roentgen Road, Staineshill East, Basingstoke, Hampshire, RG24 8NT Tel: (01256) 811020 Fax: (01256) 355151

Evesons Fuels Ltd, 456 Station Road, Dorridge, Solihull, West Midlands, B93 8EX Tel: (01564) 778877 Fax: (01564) 770655 E-mail: sales@evesons.co.uk

Falcon Lubricants Ltd, Showfield Lane Industrial Estate, Malton, North Yorkshire, YO17 6BT Tel: (01653) 694019 Fax: (01653) 600283 E-mail: admin@oils.co.uk

Gleaner Oil & Gas, Milnfield, Elgin, Morayshire, IV30 1UZ Tel: (01343) 557477 Fax: (01343) 548534 E-mail: oilgas@gleaner.co.uk

Mid Ulster Proteins Ltd, 47 Seagoe Industrial Estate, Craigavon, County Armagh, BT63 5QD Tel: (028) 3833 7217 Fax: (028) 3833 6114 E-mail: atrfood@btinternet.com

Millers Oils Ltd, Hillside Oil Works, Rastrick, Brighouse, West Yorkshire, HD6 3DP Tel: (01484) 713201 Fax: (01484) 721263 E-mail: enquiries@millersoils.co.uk

Minster Fuels Ltd, Three Cross Road, West Moors, Wimborne, Dorset, BH21 6QW Tel: (01202) 897771 Fax: (01202) 891155 E-mail: sales@minsterfuels.co.uk

▶ Oilco (Swindon) Ltd, Bagbury Green Farm, Bagbury Lane, Purton, Swindon, SN4 5LX Tel: (01793) 772437 Fax: (01793) 772437 E-mail: oilcosw.kemp@btconnect.com

Rock Chemicals Ltd, 90 Priestley Street, Warrington, WA5 1ST Tel: (01925) 636191 Fax: (01925) 632499 E-mail: sales@rockoil.co.uk

Rye Oil Ltd, Rye Harbour Road, Rye, East Sussex, TN31 7TE Tel: (01797) 223374 Fax: (01797) 226991 E-mail: sales@rye-oil.ltd.uk

Smith & Allan, 1a Valley St, Darlington, County Durham, DL1 1QE Tel: (01325) 462228 Fax: (01325) 368122 E-mail: stevearcher@smithandallan.com

Swan Petroleum, Wood Lane, Ellesmere, Shropshire, SY12 0HY Tel: (01691) 626201 Fax: (01691) 626365 E-mail: swanpetroleum@tggroup.co.uk

Total Butler Ltd, Seven Brethren Bank, Sticklepath, Barnstaple, Devon, EX31 2AS Tel: (01271) 345977 Fax: (01271) 346756 E-mail: barnstaple.depot@totalbutler.co.uk

OIL (MINERAL) INDUSTRIAL PRODUCTS PRODUCERS OR REFINERS

Great Yarmouth Pottery, 18-19 Trinity Place, Great Yarmouth, Norfolk, NR30 3HA Tel: (01493) 850585

Inios, PO Box 21, Grangemouth, Stirlingshire, FK3 9XH Tel: (01324) 483422

Mid Ulster Proteins Ltd, 47 Seagoe Industrial Estate, Craigavon, County Armagh, BT63 5QD Tel: (028) 3833 7217 Fax: (028) 3833 6114 E-mail: atrfood@btinternet.com

Nynas UK Ab, East Camperdown Street, Dundee, DD1 3LG Tel: (01382) 462211 Fax: (01382) 456846

Oil Inventions Ltd, Leamore Close, Walsall, WS2 7NJ Tel: (01922) 477904 Fax: (01922) 710108 E-mail: info@oilinventions.co.uk

Smith & Allan, 1a Valley St, Darlington, County Durham, DL1 1QE Tel: (01325) 462228 Fax: (01325) 368122 E-mail: stevearcher@smithandallan.com

Total UK Ltd - Lindsey Oil Refinery, Eastfield Road, North Killingholme, Immingham, North Lincolnshire, DN40 3LW Tel: (01469) 563300 Fax: (01469) 563766

OIL MIST DETECTORS

Quality Monitoring Instruments Ltd, 5 Hampstead West, 224 Iverson Road, London, NW6 2HL Tel: (020) 7328 3121 Fax: (020) 7328 5888 E-mail: qmi@oilmist.com

OIL OR PETROLEUM HOSES

Dantec Ltd, Tarran Way, Tarran Industrial Estate, Wirral, Merseyside, CH46 4TL Tel: 0151-678 2222 Fax: 0151-606 0188 E-mail: sales@dantec.ltd.uk

Elaflex Ltd, Riverside House, Plumpton Road, Hoddesdon, Hertfordshire, EN11 0PA Tel: (01992) 452950 Fax: (01992) 452911 E-mail: info@elaflex.co.uk

Merseyflex Ltd, 46 Mason Street, Edge Hill, Liverpool, L7 3EW Tel: 0151-707 1652 Fax: 0151-708 0128 E-mail: sales@merseyflex.co.uk

OIL OR PETROLEUM LABORATORY SERVICES

Core Laboratories, 17 Howe Moss Drive, Kirkhill Industrial Estate, Dyce, Aberdeen, AB21 0GL Tel: (01224) 421000 Fax: (01224) 421003 E-mail: sales@corelab.co.uk

Its Testing Services UK Ltd, Wellheads Crescent, Wellheads Industrial Estate, Aberdeen, AB21 7GA Tel: (01224) 723242 Fax: (01224) 722894

S G S (U K) Ltd, Rossmore Business Park, Ellesmere Port, CH65 3EN Tel: 0151-350 6666 Fax: 0151-350 6600 E-mail: ukenquiries@sgs.com

Saybolt UK Ltd, Oliver Close, Grays, Essex, RM20 3EE Tel: (01708) 862611 Fax: (01708) 867401

OIL PREHEATERS

A K Waugh Ltd, 49 Dalsetter Avenue, Glasgow, G15 8TE Tel: 0141-944 3303 Fax: 0141-944 4750 E-mail: sales@akwaugh.com

OIL PRODUCTION CHEMICALS

Baker Petrolite, Howe Moss Avenue, Kirkhill Industrial Estate, Dyce, Aberdeen, AB21 0GP Tel: (01224) 405700 Fax: (01224) 405705

Champion Technolgies Ltd, W Sam White Building, Peter Seat Drive, Altens, Aberdeen, AB12 3HT Tel: (01224) 879022 Fax: (01224) 876022 E-mail: champion@champion-servo.com

M I Drilling Fluids Ltd, Pocra Quay, Aberdeen, AB11 5DQ Tel: (01224) 584336 Fax: (01224) 576119

Schlumberger Evaluation & Production Services UK Ltd, Westhill Industrial Estate, Enterprise Drive, Westhill, Aberdeen, AB32 6TQ Tel: (01224) 741424 Fax: (01224) 840406

Tower Chemicals Ltd, First Avenue, Grangefield Industrial Estate, Pudsey, West Yorkshire, LS28 6QN Tel: 0113-256 8111 Fax: 0113-256 9111 E-mail: sales@towerchemicals.co.uk

OIL PUMPS

Airtex Products Ltd, Hanworth Trading Estate, Hampton Road West, Feltham, Middlesex, TW13 6EH Tel: (020) 8755 4400 Fax: (020) 8894 3026 E-mail: info@airtex.co.uk

Concentric Pumps Ltd, Unit 10 Gravelly Park, Tyburn Road, Birmingham, B24 8HW Tel: 0121-327 2081 Fax: 0121-327 6187 E-mail: general@concentric-pumps.co.uk

Hydrovern Ltd, Unit 21, Wilden Industrial Estate, Wilden Lane, Stourport-On-Severn, Worcestershire, DY13 9JY Tel: (0870) 7706222 Fax: (0870) 7706223 E-mail: info@hydrovern.co.uk

Varley Pumps Ltd, 1 Kimpton Road, Luton, LU1 3LD Tel: (01582) 731144 Fax: (01582) 402563E-mail: varleysales@haywardtyler.com

OIL RE-REFINING SERVICES TO THE TRADE

Midland Oil Refinery Ltd, Shelah Road, Halesowen, West Midlands, B63 3PN Tel: 0121-585 6006 Fax: 0121-585 5405

OIL RECOVERY COMPANIES/ OPERATORS

Chemical Recoveries, Rockingham Works Smoke Lane, Bristol, BS11 0YA Tel: 0117-982 0303 Fax: 0117-982 0301 E-mail: info@chemrec.co.uk

Envirosol Ltd, Unit 28 Thornleigh Trading Estate, Dudley, West Midlands, DY2 8UB Tel: (01384) 241808 Fax: (01384) 237519 E-mail: sales@envirosol.co.uk

Oikos Storage Ltd, Hole Haven Wharf, Canvey Island, Essex, SS8 0NR Tel: (01268) 682206 Fax: (01268) 510095E-mail: info@oikos.co.uk

▶ Oil Salvage Ltd, Lyster Road, Bootle, Merseyside, L20 1AS Tel: 0151-933 4084 Fax: 0151-922 8488 E-mail: sales@oilsalvage.com

OIL RECOVERY PLANT

Non Entry Systems Ltd, Bruce Road, Fforestfach, Swansea, SA5 4HS Tel: (01792) 580455 Fax: (01792) 578610 E-mail: sales@nonentrysystems.com

Willacy Oil Services Ltd, Whittle Close, Engineer Park, Deeside, Clwyd, CH5 2QE Tel: (01244) 520122 Fax: (01244) 520283 E-mail: sales@willacyoil.com

OIL REFINING, *See headings for particular types of Oil*

OIL REFINING PLANT MANUFRS OR ENGINEERS

Nynas Ltd, Wallis House, 76 North Street, Guildford, Surrey, GU1 4AW Tel: (01483) 506953 Fax: (01483) 506954

Snamprogetti Ltd, Snamprogetti House, Basingview, Basingstoke, Hampshire, RG21 4YY Tel: (01256) 461211 Fax: (01256) 482211 E-mail: sales@snampro.co.uk

OIL REMOVAL FILTERS

Master Filtration Ltd, 7 Arden Press Way, Letchworth Garden City, Hertfordshire, SG6 1LH Tel: (01462) 675844 Fax: (01462) 480852 E-mail: sales@master-filtration.co.uk

OIL RIG CONSTRUCTION, *See headings under Rig etc*

OIL RIG PLATFORMS, *See Rig etc*

OIL RIG SPECIALIST TRANSMISSION SERVICES

Lee, Crossley Hall Works, York Street, Bradford, West Yorkshire, BD8 0HR Tel: (01274) 496487 Fax: (01274) 487081

OIL SEALS

▶ Action Seals Ltd, Westfield Road, Wallasey, Merseyside, CH44 7JA Tel: 0151-652 6661 Fax: 0151-653 4994 E-mail: sales@actionseals.co.uk

Advanced Products (Seals & Gaskets) Ltd, Unit 25C, Number One Industrial Estate, Consett, Co. Durham, DH8 6SR Tel: (01207) 500317 Fax: (01207) 501210 E-mail: gc@advancedproducts.co.uk

Aldona Seals, 1 Brindley Road, South West Industrial Estate, Peterlee, County Durham, SR8 2LT Tel: 0191-518 1555 Fax: 0191-518 0555 E-mail: gtsm@gtgroup.co.uk

Arefco Special Products Ltd, Jubilee Industrial Estate, Ashington, Northumberland, NE63 8UA Tel: (01670) 819513 Fax: (01670) 816132 E-mail: sales@arefco.co.uk

Autospin (Oil Seals) Ltd, Birkdale Avenue, Selly Oak, Birmingham, B29 6UB Tel: 0121-472 1243 Fax: 0121-471 3348 E-mail: sales@autospin.co.uk

Blue Diamond Bearings Ltd, Rolwey House, School Close, Chandler's Ford, Eastleigh, Hampshire, SO53 4BY Tel: (023) 8025 8966 Fax: (023) 8025 8925 E-mail: bdsales@rolwey.com

City Seals & Bearings Ltd, Stevenson Road, Sheffield, S9 3XG Tel: 0114-244 3030 Fax: 0114-244 0044 E-mail: info@cityseals.co.uk

D E L Industrial Fastenings Ltd, Elvetham Bridge, Fleet, Hampshire, GU51 1AE Tel: (01252) 626425 Fax: (01252) 811741 E-mail: info@delindustrial.co.uk

Dowty Engineered Seals Ltd, Ashchurch, Tewkesbury, Gloucestershire, GL20 8JS Tel: (01684) 299111 Fax: (01684) 852210

Flowseal Ltd, 34h Aston Road, Waterlooville, Hampshire, PO7 7XQ Tel: (023) 9226 5031 Fax: (023) 9224 0382 E-mail: sales@flowseal.co.uk

Force Seven Bearings, First Avenue, Team Valley Trading Estate, Gateshead, Tyne & Wear, NE11 0NU Tel: 0191-487 2421 Fax: 0191-491 0842 E-mail: force7@nbcgroup.com

GMS, 175 Booth Street, Birmingham, B21 0NU Tel: 0121-551 5440 Fax: 0121-554 5344 E-mail: enquiries@gmspolymer.co.uk

Industrial Marine Rubber, 3 Spurryhillock Industrial Estate, Broomhill Road, Stonehaven, Kincardineshire, AB39 2NH Tel: (01569) 766344 Fax: (01569) 766419

Interseals Engineers' Merchants, Lowlands Industrial Estate, Braye Road, Vale, Guernsey, GY3 5XG Tel: (01481) 246364 Fax: (01481) 248235 E-mail: sales@interseals.co.uk

Pioneer Weston, Smithfold Lane, Worsley, Manchester, M28 0GP Tel: 0161-703 2000 Fax: 0161-703 2025 E-mail: info@pwi-ltd.com

Rubbertec International Ltd, Maydown Industrial Estate, Londonderry, BT47 6UQ Tel: (028) 7186 0005 Fax: (028) 7186 1411 E-mail: info@rubbertecinternational.com

Sampson Gaskets Ltd, Unit 22, Leigh Road, Ramsgate, Kent, CT12 5EU Tel: (01843) 854800 Fax: (01843) 851804 E-mail: uksales@sampsons.co.uk

Scorpion H.T. Ltd, Unit 1 Ogles Yard, Victoria Road, Ripley, Derbyshire, DE5 3FW Tel: (01773) 570600 Fax: (01773) 570200

Sealmac Technology Ltd, 1645 Pershore Road, Kings Norton, Birmingham, B30 3DR Tel: 0121-459 4944 Fax: 0121-459 8420 E-mail: sales@sealmac.co.uk

Wyko Seals Ltd, Hereward Rise, Halesowen Industrial Park, Halesowen, West Midlands, B62 8AN Tel: 0121-501 2021 Fax: 0121-501 3014 E-mail: sales@dichta.com

OIL SEPARATORS, *See Separator, Oil/Gas/Liquid etc*

OIL SERVICE COMPANIES

Cebo UK Ltd, Boundary Road, Great Yarmouth, Norfolk, NR31 0LY Tel: (01493) 656100 Fax: (01493) 650020 E-mail: nick@cebo-yarmouth.fsnet.co.uk

Metrol Technology Ltd, Unit 24 Kirkhill Place, Dyce, Aberdeen, AB21 0GU Tel: (01224) 772771 Fax: (01224) 772660

Scotvalve Services Ltd, Howemoss Cresent, Kirkhill Industrial Estate, Dyce, Aberdeen, AB21 0GN Tel: (01224) 722993 Fax: (01224) 723750 E-mail: sales@scotvalves.co.uk

Willbros (Overseas) Ltd, The Old Rechtory, Barkston, Grantham, Lincolnshire, NG32 2NB Tel: (020) 8549 4471 Fax: (020) 8974 8536 E-mail: arthur.west@willbros.com

OIL SKIMMING EQUIPMENT

Russell Benussi Associates, 3 Pebble Close, Tamworth, Staffordshire, B77 4RD Tel: (01827) 68008 Fax: (01827) 69265 E-mail: sales@benussi.com

OIL SPILLAGE CONTAINMENT BOOMS

Ayles Fernie International Ltd, Unit D5 Chaucer Business Park, Watery Lane, Kemsing, Sevenoaks, Kent, TN15 6YU Tel: (01732) 762962 Fax: (01732) 761961 E-mail: sales@aylesfernie.co.uk

G T Pollution Technology Ltd, 3 Medina Court, Arctic Road, Cowes, Isle Of Wight, PO31 7XD Tel: (01983) 280185 Fax: (01983) 280056 E-mail: info@lamor.com

New Pig Ltd, Hogs Hill, Watt Place, Hamilton International Technology Park, Blantyre, Glasgow, G72 0AH Tel: (0800) 919900 Fax: (0800) 7315071 E-mail: pigpen@newpig.com

Ro-Clean Desmi Ltd, Unit 24 Shamrock Quay, William Street, Southampton, SO14 5QL Tel: (02380) 829751 Fax: (02380) 339190 E-mail: uk.ro-clean@desmi.com

OIL SPILLAGE CONTROL EQUIPMENT

Ayles Fernie International Ltd, Unit D5 Chaucer Business Park, Watery Lane, Kemsing, Sevenoaks, Kent, TN15 6YU Tel: (01732) 762962 Fax: (01732) 761961 E-mail: sales@aylesfernie.co.uk

G T Pollution Technology Ltd, 3 Medina Court, Arctic Road, Cowes, Isle Of Wight, PO31 7XD Tel: (01983) 280185 Fax: (01983) 280056 E-mail: info@lamor.com

OIL SPILLAGE CONTROL EQUIPMENT, INTERCEPTOR

Klargester Environmental Ltd, College Road, Aston Clinton, Aylesbury, Buckinghamshire, HP22 5EW Tel: (01296) 633000 Fax: (01296) 633001 E-mail: sales@kingspanec.com

Oil Pollution Environmental Control Ltd, 1 Nab Lane, Birstall, Batley, West Yorkshire, WF17 9NG Tel: (01924) 442701 Fax: (01924) 471925 E-mail: sales@opec.co.uk

Thames Lubricants Ltd, Garner Street, Stoke-on-Trent, ST4 7DE Tel: (01782) 844388 Fax: (01782) 848437 E-mail: sales@thameslubricants.co.uk

OIL SPILLAGE OR POLLUTION DISPERSAL OR CLEAN UP CONTRACTORS OR SERVICES

Briggs Environmental Services Ltd, Leading Light Building, 142 Sinclair Road, Aberdeen, AB11 9PR Tel: (01224) 898666 Fax: (01224) 896950 E-mail: marketing@briggsmarine.com

OIL SPILLAGE OR POLLUTION DISPERSAL OR CLEAN UP CONTRACTORS OR SERVICES – *continued*

Eurotech Environmental Ltd, Northern Road, Newark, Nottinghamshire, NG24 2EU Tel: (0800) 0281786 Fax: (01636) 611727 E-mail: sales@eurotechenvironmental.com

Fosse, 12 Enderby Road Industrial Estate, Whetstone, Leicester, LE8 6HZ Tel: 0116-286 7844 Fax: (0870) 2247842 E-mail: sales@fosse.co.uk

D.V. Howells Ltd, The MPSC, Milford Haven, Dyfed, SA73 3AQ Tel: (01646) 697041 Fax: (01646) 696345 E-mail: info@dvhowells.com

OIL SPILLAGE/POLLUTION ABSORBENT MATERIALS

New Pig Ltd, Hogs Hill, Watt Place, Hamilton International Technology Park, Blantyre, Glasgow, G72 0AH Tel: (0800) 919900 Fax: (0800) 7315071 E-mail: pigpen@newpig.com

Oil Pollution Environmental Control Ltd, 1 Nab Lane, Birstall, Batley, West Yorkshire, WF17 9NG Tel: (01924) 442701 Fax: (01924) 471925 E-mail: sales@opec.co.uk

▶ Sorbican Distribution, 27 Priory Lane, Hartley Wintney, Hook, Hampshire, RG27 8EX Tel: (01256) 762435

Steetley Bentonite & Absorbents Ltd, Woburn Road, Woburn Sands, Milton Keynes, MK17 8TU Tel: (01908) 583939 Fax: (01908) 585231

▶ Syntec Manufacturing Ltd, 6 Mid Road, Blairlinn Industrial Estate, Cumbernauld, Glasgow, G67 2TT Tel: (01236) 739696 Fax: (01236) 727955 E-mail: sales@syntecchemicals.com

OIL STORAGE CONTRACTORS

Oikos Storage Ltd, Hole Haven Wharf, Canvey Island, Essex, SS8 0NR Tel: (01268) 682206 Fax: (01268) 510095E-mail: info@oikos.co.uk

Rotherham Waste Oils, Quarry Oil Depot, Kilnhurst Road, Kilnhurst, Mexborough, South Yorkshire, S64 5TL Tel: (01709) 527131 Fax: (01709) 719729 E-mail: sales@rwoil.co.uk

▶ Sem Logistics Milford Haven Ltd, Waterston Road, Milford Haven, Dyfed, SA73 1DR Tel: (01646) 692461 Fax: (01646) 695837

Simon Storage Immingham West Ltd, West Riverside, Immingham Dock, Immingham, North East Lincolnshire, DN40 2QU Tel: (01469) 572615 Fax: (01469) 577019

OIL STORAGE TANK MAINTENANCE/REPAIR SERVICES

▶ Silocare Ltd, Grayingham Road, Blyborough, Gainsborough, Lincolnshire, DN21 4EY Tel: (01427) 668061 Fax: (01427) 668062 E-mail: silocare@aol.com

OIL TANK INSTALLATION

▶ FlameFix Ltd, Charlton House, 32 High Street, Cullompton, Devon, EX15 1AE Tel: (07883) 037667 E-mail: ksales@flamefix.co.uk

OIL TANKS

Allied Tank & Fabrications Ltd, Phoenix Works Industrial Estate, Richards Street, Wednesbury, West Midlands, WS10 8BZ Tel: 0121-568 8166 Fax: 0121-568 8177 E-mail: sales@alliedtanks.co.uk

Balmoral Tanks Ltd, Wellington Road, Aberdeen, AB12 3GY Tel: (01224) 859100 Fax: (01224) 859123 E-mail: tanks@balmoral.co.uk

Castle Engineering Resources Ltd, 4 Central Works, Peartree Lane, Dudley, West Midlands, DY2 0QU Tel: (01384) 230233 Fax: (01384) 230757 E-mail: castle.eng@btclick.com

D & S Services, Unit H2 & Unit H3 Rudford Industrial Estate, Ford Road, Ford, Arundel, West Sussex, BN18 0BD Tel: (01903) 732732 Fax: (01903) 716151 E-mail: sales@dandsservices.co.uk

Easiflo Engineering Ltd, Providence Street, Stourbridge, West Midlands, DY9 8HR Tel: (01384) 894811 Fax: (01384) 422447 E-mail: easiflo.eng@btconnect.com

Koronka Agriculture & Tanks Ltd, Bridgend, Kinross, KY13 8EN Tel: (01577) 862189 Fax: (01577) 864773 E-mail: sales@koronka.co.uk

L A Wiles & Sons, The Conifers, Aisthorpe, Lincoln, LN1 2SG Tel: (01522) 730351 Fax: (01522) 730900 E-mail: sales@wilestanks.co.uk

Land & Marine Project Engineering, Dock Road North, Wirral, Merseyside, CH62 4TQ Tel: 0151-641 5600 Fax: 0151-644 9990 E-mail: matthew.osullivan@landandmarine.com

North Hunts Welding & Engineering Co., America Farm Cottage, Oxney Road, Peterborough, PE1 5YR Tel: (01733) 222632 Fax: (01733) 222732

Telford Tanks Ltd, Unit 3c Central Works, Peartree Lane, Dudley, West Midlands, DY2 0QU Tel: (01384) 212167 Fax: (01384) 457757

W H Dale Ltd, Main Street, Thornton Curtis, Ulceby, South Humberside, DN39 6XW Tel: (01469) 531229 Fax: (01469) 530611 E-mail: sales@whdale.co.uk

▶ Wefco (Gainsborough) Ltd, Brittania Works, Spring Gardens, Gainsborough, Lincolnshire, DN21 2AZ Tel: (01427) 611000 Fax: (01427) 612000 E-mail: glennb@wefco.net

OIL TERMINAL OPERATORS

Conoco Phillips, Seal Sands, Middlesbrough, Cleveland, TS2 1UH Tel: (01642) 546411 Fax: (01642) 546096

OIL TESTING SERVICES

High Voltage Maintenance Services, Littlebrook Business Centre, Littlebrook Manorway, Dartford, DA1 5PZ Tel: (01322) 273100 Fax: (01322) 294413 E-mail: enquiries@hvms.co.uk

OIL WASTE RECYCLING OR DISPOSAL OR RECOVERY OR MERCHANTS OR PROCESSORS OR SERVICES

Arrow Environmental Services Ltd, Exchange Works, Kelvin Way, West Bromwich, West Midlands, B70 7JW Tel: 0121-525 0757 Fax: 0121-525 1179 E-mail: arrow.environmental@virgin.net

Associated Reclaimed Oils, 165 Tunnel Avenue, London, SE10 0PW Tel: (020) 8858 9907 Fax: (020) 8858 9907

Central Waste Oil Collections Ltd, 143 Queen Street, Walsall, WS2 9NT Tel: (01922) 725966 Fax: (01922) 721966

Enba NI Ltd, The Old Mill, Drumaness, Ballynahinch, County Down, BT24 8LS Tel: (028) 9756 1574 Fax: (028) 9756 1576 E-mail: sales@enbani.com

Hall & Campey Enviromental Services Ltd, Cavendish Works, Cavendish St, Nottingham, NG7 2TJ Tel: 0115-978 0321 Fax: 0115-942 3973 E-mail: sales@hallandcampey.co.uk

Hitech Equipment Ltd, 36 Clark Street, Paisley, Renfrewshire, PA3 1RB Tel: 0141-887 5689 Fax: 0141-887 7846 E-mail: gaynor@hitech-env.co.uk

Hurn Waste Oil Ltd, 20 Winkham Business Park, Shaftesbury, Dorset, SP7 9QJ Tel: (01747) 858561 Fax: (01747) 858562 E-mail: oilwaterltd@hotmail.com

O S S Group Ltd, Valley Road, Morley, Leeds, LS27 8ES Tel: (0870) 8702088 Fax: 0113-252 7009 E-mail: sales@ossgroupltd.com

▶ Oil Salvage Ltd, Lyster Road, Bootle, Merseyside, L20 1AS Tel: 0151-933 4084 Fax: 0151-922 8488 E-mail: sales@oilsalvage.com

Rotherham Waste Oils, Quarry Oil Depot, Kilnhurst Road, Kilnhurst, Mexborough, South Yorkshire, S64 5TL Tel: (01709) 527131 Fax: (01709) 719729 E-mail: sales@rwoil.co.uk

Tank Cleaners (Glasgow) Ltd, Robslee Drive, Giffnock, Glasgow, G46 7TY Tel: 0141-638 0906 Fax: 0141-638 9014 E-mail: simon@mitchellthomson.fsnet.co.uk

Valve Grove, Unit 15 16 Withy Road Industrial Estate, Withy Road, Bilston, West Midlands, WV14 0RX Tel: (01902) 498560 Fax: (01902) 498474

OIL WASTE RECYCLING/ DISPOSAL/RECOVERY EQUIPMENT

▶ DJB Recycling Machinery Ltd, 37 Cotswold Road, Sheffield, S6 4QY Tel: 0114-233 3058 Fax: 01142 333058

Hall & Campey Enviromental Services Ltd, Cavendish Works, Cavendish St, Nottingham, NG7 2TJ Tel: 0115-978 0321 Fax: 0115-942 3973 E-mail: sales@hallandcampey.co.uk

Willacy Oil Services Ltd, Whittle Close, Engineer Park, Deeside, Clwyd, CH5 2QE Tel: (01244) 520122 Fax: (01244) 520283 E-mail: sales@willacyoil.com

OIL WELL CEMENTING SIMULATORS

Drilling Systems UK Ltd, Hurnview House, Bournemouth International Airport, Hurn, Christchurch, Dorset, BH23 6EW Tel: (01202) 582255 Fax: (01202) 582288 E-mail: info@drillingsystems.com

OIL WELL COMPLETION EQUIPMENT

National Oilwell Varco, Holton Road, Holton Heath Trading Park, Poole, Dorset, BH16 6LT Tel: (01202) 631817 Fax: (01202) 631708 E-mail: pcesales@nov.com

OIL WELL COMPLETION FLUID SERVICES

Baker Hughes Ltd, Campus 1, Aberdeen Science And Technology Centre, Bridge Of Don, Aberdeen, AB22 8GT Tel: (01224) 226000 Fax: (01224) 226006

OIL WELL COMPLETION PRODUCTS

Elmar Services Ltd, Westhill Industrial Estate, Westhill, Aberdeenshire, AB32 6TQ Tel: (01224) 740261 Fax: (01224) 743138 E-mail: sales@elmar.co.uk

OIL WELL DRILLING CHEMICALS

Melbray Chemicals Ltd, Chemical House, Durham Lane Industrial Park, Stockton-on-Tees, Cleveland, TS16 0RG Tel: (01642) 790483 Fax: (01642) 790486 E-mail: melbraychemicals@btconnect.com

Richkeen Chemicals Ltd, 33 Chapmans Cresent, Chesham, Buckinghamshire, HP5 2QT Tel: (01494) 786669 Fax: (01494) 786503 E-mail: richkeenc@aol.com

▶ Weatherford UK Ltd, 76-78 Charlotte Street, London, Greater London, W1T 4QW Tel: 020 74624930

OIL WELL DRILLING CONSULTANCY

Geoscience Ltd, Falmouth Business Park, Bickland Water Road, Falmouth, Cornwall, TR11 4SZ Tel: (01326) 211070 Fax: (01326) 212754 E-mail: batchelor@geoscience.co.uk

Houlder Ltd, 59 Lafone Street, London, SE1 2LX Tel: (020) 7357 7317 Fax: (020) 7403 8201 E-mail: mail@houlder-offshore.co.uk

OIL WELL DRILLING CONTRACTORS OR ENGINEERS

Boldon Drilling Ltd, Private Road 3, Colwick Industrial Estate, Nottingham, NG4 2BB Tel: 0115-961 1250 Fax: 0115-961 7338 E-mail: drill@bds.co.uk

British American Offshore Ltd, 39 Upper Brook Street, London, W1K 7QW Tel: (020) 7499 2957 Fax: (020) 7409 2738

British Drilling and Freezing Co. Ltd, Private Road No 3, Colwick Industrial Estate, Colwick, Nottingham, NG4 2BB Tel: 0115-961 1300 Fax: 0115-961 7338 E-mail: drill@bdf.co.uk

Diamond Offshore, Howe Moss Drive, Kirkhill Industrial Estate, Dyce, Aberdeen, AB21 0GL Tel: (01224) 727500 Fax: (01224) 722873

Dolphin Drilling Ltd, Howe Moss Drive, Kirkhill Industrial Estate, Dyce, Aberdeen, AB21 0GL Tel: (01224) 411411 Fax: (01224) 723627

Globalsantafe Holding Company North Sea Ltd, Greenbank Crescent, East Tullos Industrial Estate, Aberdeen, AB12 3BG Tel: (01224) 404200 Fax: (01224) 404300

K C A Deutag Drilling Ltd, Minto Drive, Altens Industrial Estate, Aberdeen, AB12 3LW Tel: (01224) 299600 Fax: (01224) 895813 E-mail: info@kcadeutag.com

Noble Drilling UK Ltd, Wellheads Road, Farburn Industrial Estate, Dyce, Aberdeen, AB21 7HG Tel: (01224) 401600 Fax: (01224) 771176 E-mail: mpope@noblecorp.com

Scientific Drilling Controls Ltd, Dyce Industrial Park, Wellheads Industrial Estate, Aberdeen, AB21 7GA Tel: (01224) 724535 Fax: (01224) 770581 E-mail: sales@scientific-drilling.co.uk

Stena Drilling, Greenbank Crescent, East Tullos Industrial Estate, Aberdeen, AB12 3BG Tel: (01224) 401180 Fax: (01224) 897089 E-mail: stena.commercial@sdlabz.com

E.G. Thompson (Bulk Carriers) Ltd, Suite 7 Bonnington Bond, 2 Anderson Place, Edinburgh, EH6 5NP Tel: 0131-555 5222 Fax: 0131-557 4742

Transocean, Crawpeel Road, Altens Industrial Estate, Aberdeen, AB12 3LG Tel: (01224) 427700 Fax: (01224) 427800

OIL WELL DRILLING EQUIPMENT

Black Gold Oil Tools Ltd, Souter Head Road, Altens Industrial Estate, Aberdeen, AB12 3LF Tel: (01224) 894019 Fax: (01224) 879731 E-mail: info@blackgoldoiltools.co.uk

Brewis Engineering, Handlemaker Road, Frome, Somerset, BA11 4RW Tel: (01373) 451387 Fax: (01373) 452714 E-mail: sales@brewisdirect.com

Cansco Equipment & Rentals Ltd, Units 2-3 Teesland Development, Hareness Circle, Altens, Aberdeen, AB12 3LY Tel: (01224) 872228 Fax: (01224) 897541 E-mail: enquiries@cansco.com

Darren Sbo, Canklow Meadows Industrial Estate, Rotherham, South Yorkshire, S60 2XL Tel: (01709) 722600 Fax: (01709) 722657 E-mail: info@darron-sbo.com

Dril-Quip (Europe) Ltd, Stoneywood Park, Stoneywood Road, Dyce, Aberdeen, AB21 7DZ Tel: (01224) 727000 Fax: (01224) 727070

Hunting Energy Services, Silverburn Place, Bridge of Don Industrial Estate, Aberdeen, AB23 8EG Tel: (01224) 820909 Fax: (01224) 823123 E-mail: dave@cromar.com

I O E S Ltd, 6 Princeton Court, Felsham Road, London, SW15 1AZ Tel: (020) 8780 1222 Fax: (020) 8780 1812 E-mail: sales@ioes.net

K C H Drilling Supplies Ltd, 35 York Place, Aberdeen, AB11 5FW Tel: (01224) 211820 Fax: (01224) 213065 E-mail: mudvac@ifb.co.uk

Mid Continent Great Yarmouth Ltd, Gapton Hall Road, Harfreys Industrial Estate, Great Yarmouth, Norfolk, NR31 0HX Tel: (01493) 655269 Fax: (01493) 601512 E-mail: sales@midcontinentgy.com

Montex Ltd, 109 Clarence Gate Gardens, Glentworth Street, London, NW1 6AL Tel: (020) 7724 3207 Fax: (020) 7724 3831 E-mail: cmshah@marmon.co.uk

Mountwest Petroleum Engineering Ltd, Sir William Smith Road, Kirkton Industrial Estate, Arbroath, Angus, DD11 3RD Tel: (01241) 870611 Fax: (01241) 878669 E-mail: linda@mountwest-petrol.com

National Oilwell (UK) Ltd, Badentoy Crescent, Badentoy Industrial Estate, Portlethen, Aberdeen, AB12 4YD Tel: (01224) 334960

Oilfield Material Management Ltd, 34 Abbotswell Road, Aberdeen, AB12 3AB Tel: (01224) 891011 Fax: (01224) 891012 E-mail: sales@omm.net

Pioneer Oil Tools Ltd, Sir William Smith Road, Kirkton Industrial Estate, Arbroath, Angus, DD11 3RD Tel: (01241) 877776 Fax: (01241) 871037 E-mail: sales@pioneeroiltools.com

Reed Hycalog, 6 Abbotswell Road, Aberdeen, AB12 3AF Tel: (01224) 877688 Fax: (01224) 898651

Security D B S, Clyde Facilities, Howemoss Crescent, Kirkhill Industrial Estate, Dyce, Aberdeen, AB21 0EN Tel: (01224) 728400 Fax: (01224) 728487

SlimDril Ltd, Unit 4 Marine Park, Gapton Hall Road, Great Yarmouth, Norfolk, NR31 0NL Tel: (01493) 656145 Fax: (01493) 601772 E-mail: sdi@slimdril.co.uk

OIL WELL DRILLING EQUIPMENT HIRE

Andergauge Ltd, Hareness Road, Altens Industrial Estate, Aberdeen, AB12 3LE Tel: (01224) 336500 Fax: (01224) 336505 E-mail: sales@andergauge.com

Cansco Equipment & Rentals Ltd, Units 2-3 Teesland Development, Hareness Circle, Altens, Aberdeen, AB12 3LY Tel: (01224) 872228 Fax: (01224) 897541 E-mail: enquiries@cansco.com

Dril-Quip (Europe) Ltd, Stoneywood Park, Stoneywood Road, Dyce, Aberdeen, AB21 7DZ Tel: (01224) 727000 Fax: (01224) 727070

M S I Oilfield Products, Units 5-6 Murcar Industrial Estate, Denmore Road, Bridge of Don, Aberdeen, AB23 8JW Tel: (01224) 708011 Fax: (01224) 708022 E-mail: bherd@msiproducts.com

OIL WELL DRILLING EQUIPMENT MAINTENANCE OR REPAIR

Amec Group Ltd, City Gate, Altens Farm Road, Nigg, Aberdeen, AB12 3LB Tel: (01224) 291000 Fax: (01224) 291001

Moduspec Engineering UK Ltd, 2 Craigshaw Road, West Tullos Industrial Estate, Aberdeen, AB12 3AQ Tel: (01224) 248144 Fax: (01224) 284125 E-mail: sales@moduspec.com

Mountwest Petroleum Engineering Ltd, Sir William Smith Road, Kirkton Industrial Estate, Arbroath, Angus, DD11 3RD Tel: (01241) 870611 Fax: (01241) 878669 E-mail: linda@mountwest-petrol.com

Tricore Ltd, Blackburn Industrial Estate, Kinellar, Aberdeen, AB21 0RX Tel: (01224) 790338 Fax: (01224) 790660 E-mail: info@tricore.co.uk

Venture Oilfield Services Ltd, 11 Faraday Road, Southfields, Glenrothes, Fife, KY6 2RU Tel: (01592) 772176 Fax: (01592) 775455 E-mail: mail@ventureoil.com

OIL WELL DRILLING JACK UP EQUIPMENT

Abb Vetco Gray UK Ltd, Gapton Hall Road, Great Yarmouth, Norfolk, NR31 0NL Tel: (01493) 444777 Fax: (01493) 414221 E-mail: shaun.bradley@vetco.com

OIL WELL DRILLING MONITORING OR CONTROL SYSTEMS

Rigserv Ltd, Unit 9 Wellheads Crescent, Wellheads Industrial Estate, Aberdeen, AB21 7GA Tel: (01224) 724212 Fax: (01224) 724282 E-mail: information@rigserv.com

OIL WELL DRILLING PROJECT MANAGEMENT

Cutting & Wear Resistant Development Ltd, Greasbrough Road, Rotherham, South Yorkshire, S60 1RW Tel: (01709) 361041 Fax: (01709) 374211E-mail: sales@cwuk.com

Norwell Oil & Gas Exploration, Norwell House, 78 Queens Road, Aberdeen, AB15 4YE Tel: (01224) 498400 Fax: (01224) 208300 E-mail: samantha@norwellengineering.com

OIL WELL DRILLING SOFTWARE

M I Drilling Fluids Ltd, Pocra Quay, Aberdeen, AB11 5DQ Tel: (01224) 584336 Fax: (01224) 576119

Paradigm Geo-Physical UK Ltd, Mackenzie Buildings, 168 Skene Street, Aberdeen, AB10 1PE Tel: (01224) 649555 Fax: (01224) 649496

OIL WELL FISHING OR RETRIEVAL TOOL

Bowen Tools Div I R I International, Kirkton Avenue, Pitmedden Road Industrial Estate, Dyce, Aberdeen, AB21 0BF Tel: (01224) 771339 Fax: (01224) 723034

Pioneer Oil Tools Ltd, Sir William Smith Road, Kirkton Industrial Estate, Arbroath, Angus, DD11 3RD Tel: (01241) 877776 Fax: (01241) 871037 E-mail: sales@pioneeroiltools.com

OIL WELL FISHING OR RETRIEVAL TOOL HIRE

Boyer Leisure Ltd, Ford Lane, Iver, Buckinghamshire, SL0 9LL Tel: (01753) 630302 Fax: (01753) 630302 E-mail: tackleshop@boyer.co.uk

OIL WELL MUD LOGGING

Robertson Geologging Ltd, York Road, Deganwy, Conwy, Gwynedd, LL31 9PX Tel: (01492) 582323 Fax: (01492) 582322 E-mail: sales@geologging.com

OIL WELL PRODUCTION LOGGING MASTS

Zone Power Ltd, High Road, Bressingham, Diss, Norfolk, IP22 2AT Tel: (01379) 687796 Fax: (01379) 687437 E-mail: sales@zonepower.com

OIL WELL PRODUCTION LOGGING SERVICES

Schlumberger Evaluation & Production Services UK Ltd, Unit 46 Howe Moss Terrace, Kirkhill Industrial Estate, Dyce, Aberdeen, AB21 0GR Tel: (01224) 406000 Fax: (01224) 723257

OIL WELL SOLID CONTROL SERVICES

Brandt, Badentoy Way, Badentoy Park, Portlethen, Aberdeen, AB12 4YS Tel: (01224) 787700 Fax: (01224) 784555 E-mail: sales@brandt-uk.com

▶ Solids Control Services Ltd, 4 International Base, Greenwell Road, East Tullos Industrial Estate, Aberdeen, AB12 3AX Tel: (01224) 249220 Fax: (01224) 249221

OIL/GAS/LIQUID SEPARATORS

Hodge Separators Ltd, 1 Jennings Road, Kernick Road Industrial Estate, Penryn, Cornwall, TR10 9LY Tel: (01326) 375388 Fax: (01326) 377235 E-mail: sales@hodge-separators.com

Natco Group, C/O Axsia Howmar Ltd, Albany Park Estate, Frimley Road, Camberley, Surrey, GU16 7QQ Tel: (01276) 681101 Fax: (01276) 681107 E-mail: ahl@axsia.com

Parmatic Esplen Ltd, Second Avenue, Flixborough Industrial Estate, Scunthorpe, South Humberside, DN15 8SD Tel: (01724) 281202 Fax: (01724) 858365 E-mail: info@parmaticfilter.co.uk

OIL/WATER INTERCEPTOR TANKS

Conder Products Ltd, Whitehouse Way, South West Industrial Estate, Peterlee, County Durham, SR8 2HZ Tel: 0191-587 8660 Fax: 0191-586 1274 E-mail: sales@conderproducts.co.uk

OILCANS

A E Westwood Ltd, Tything Road, Kinwarton, Alcester, Warwickshire, B49 6ES Tel: (01789) 765777 Fax: (01789) 765727 E-mail: aewestwood@thesjgroup.com

OILFIELD EQUIPMENT

Cansco Equipment & Rentals Ltd, Units 2-3 Teesland Development, Hareness Circle, Altens, Aberdeen, AB12 3LY Tel: (01224) 872228 Fax: (01224) 897541 E-mail: enquiries@cansco.com

Cansco Pressure Control Ltd, Badentoy Road, Portlethen, Aberdeen, AB12 4YA Tel: (01224) 782211 Fax: (01224) 782266 E-mail: sales@3plus.co.uk

Craig International Supplies Ltd, 219 Albert Quay, Aberdeen, AB11 5QA Tel: (01224) 591555 Fax: (01224) 212558 E-mail: cis@craig-group.com

Crux Products Ltd, Paddock Wood, Carlton Road, South Godstone, Godstone, Surrey, RH9 8LE Tel: (01342) 892260 Fax: (01342) 893878 E-mail: mblandcrux@aol.com

Flexitallic Scotland Ltd, Unit 18d Wellheads Crescent, Aberdeen, AB21 7GA Tel: (01224) 725241 Fax: (01224) 722911

Guralp Systems Ltd, 3 Midas House, Calleva Park, Reading, RG7 8QZ Tel: 0118-981 9056 Fax: 0118-981 9943 E-mail: guralp@guralp.com

I B N, 138-140 Wapping High Street, London, E1 9NQ Tel: (020) 7369 1200 Fax: (020) 7369 1217

I O E S Ltd, 6 Princeton Court, Felsham Road, London, SW15 1AZ Tel: (020) 8780 1222 Fax: (020) 8780 1812 E-mail: sales@ioes.net

Inprojex International UK Ltd, 58 Uxbridge Road, London, W5 2ST Tel: (020) 8567 9680 Fax: (020) 8579 5241 E-mail: inprojex@inprojex.co.uk

ITS Environmental Services Ltd, Woodside, Sauchen, Inverurie, Aberdeenshire, AB51 7LP Tel: 01330 830240 Fax: 01330 830249 E-mail: lbarron@its-uk.co.uk

K C H Drilling Supplies Ltd, 35 York Place, Aberdeen, AB11 5FW Tel: (01224) 211820 Fax: (01224) 213065 E-mail: mudvac@ifb.co.uk

M S I Oilfield Products, Units 5-6 Murcar Industrial Estate, Denmore Road, Bridge of Don, Aberdeen, AB23 8JW Tel: (01224) 708011 Fax: (01224) 708022 E-mail: bherd@msiproducts.com

Mid Continent Great Yarmouth Ltd, Gapton Hall Road, Harfreys Industrial Estate, Great Yarmouth, Norfolk, NR31 0HX Tel: (01493) 655269 Fax: (01493) 601512 E-mail: sales@midcontinentgy.com

Montex Ltd, 109 Clarence Gate Gardens, Glentworth Street, London, NW1 6AL Tel: (020) 7724 3207 Fax: (020) 7724 3831 E-mail: cmshah@marmon.co.uk

National Oilwell Varco, Holton Road, Holton Heath Trading Park, Poole, Dorset, BH16 6LT Tel: (01202) 631817 Fax: (01202) 631708 E-mail: pcesales@nov.com

Oil States Industries (U K) Ltd, Blackness Road, Aberdeen, AB12 3LH Tel: (01224) 290000 Fax: (01224) 290110 E-mail: sales@oilstates-uk.com

Scotech International Services, Craigshaw Road, West Tullos Industrial Estate, Aberdeen, AB12 3AR Tel: (01224) 248450 Fax: (01224) 248023 E-mail: sales@scotech.co.uk

Trade-Link (EC) Ltd, 5 Carlton Gardens, Ealing, London, W5 2AN Tel: (020) 8998 1090 Fax: (020) 8810 5871 E-mail: tradelinkec@clara.net

Well Service, West Brent, Forties Road Industrial Estate, Hillside, Montrose, Angus, DD10 9ET Tel: (01674) 677177 Fax: (01674) 677277 E-mail: sales@wellservice.com

Yardbury Engineering & Oil Filled Products Ltd, Greenhole Place, Bridge of Don Industrial Estate, Aberdeen, AB23 8EU Tel: (01224) 826677 Fax: (01224) 826310 E-mail: admin@yardbury.com

OILFIELD EQUIPMENT HIRE

Hewden Hire Centres, Unit 2, 4-14 Commerce Street, Aberdeen, AB11 5EB Tel: (01224) 595102 Fax: (01224) 584611

OILFIELD SERVICING OR MAINTENANCE OR REPAIR OR TEST SERVICES

Dolphin Drilling Ltd, Howe Moss Drive, Kirkhill Industrial Estate, Dyce, Aberdeen, AB21 0GL Tel: (01224) 411411 Fax: (01224) 723627

I B N, 138-140 Wapping High Street, London, E1 9NQ Tel: (020) 7369 1200 Fax: (020) 7369 1217

O I E Services Ltd, Centurion Court, North Esplanade West, Aberdeen, AB11 5QH Tel: (01224) 256400 Fax: (01224) 256444 E-mail: info@optima-energy.com

OLEINES

H. Foster & Co. Ltd, 103 Kirkstall Road, Leeds, LS3 1JL Tel: 0113-243 9016 Fax: 0113-242 2418 E-mail: sales@hfoster.co.uk

OLEOCHEMICALS

Meade King Robinson & Company Ltd, 501 Tower Building, 22 Water Street, Liverpool, L3 1BL Tel: 0151-236 3191 Fax: 0151-236 4431 E-mail: info@mkr.co.uk

Oleotec Ltd, Rossfield Road, Ellesmere Port, CH65 3BS Tel: 0151-357 1778 Fax: 0151-357 1857 E-mail: sales@oleotec.com

ON LAND DRILLING

Amco Drilling International, PO Box 1, Barnsley, South Yorkshire, S75 1HT Tel: (01226) 243413 Fax: (01226) 320202 E-mail: info@amco-constrction.co.uk

K C A Deutag Drilling Ltd, Minto Drive, Altens Industrial Estate, Aberdeen, AB12 3LW Tel: (01224) 299600 Fax: (01224) 895813 E-mail: info@kcadeutag.com

ON LAND DRILLING RIGS

▶ Dando Drilling International Ltd, Old Customs House, Wharf Road, Littlehampton, West Sussex, BN17 5DD Tel: (01903) 731312 Fax: (01903) 730305 E-mail: info@dando.co.uk

I O E S Ltd, 6 Princeton Court, Felsham Road, London, SW15 1AZ Tel: (020) 8780 1222 Fax: (020) 8780 1812 E-mail: sales@ioes.net

▶ Sandhurst Plant, The Whitewall Centre, Whitewall Road, Medway City Estate, Rochester, Kent, ME2 4DZ Tel: (01634) 739590 Fax: (0845) 1206644 E-mail: info@sandhurst.co.uk

ON LINE HOTEL DIRECTORIES

▶ The Beeches, Boston Road, Heckington, Sleaford, Lincolnshire, NG34 9JQ Tel: (01529) 462059 E-mail: thebeeches@lycos.co.uk

▶ Bull Hotel, Bulkley Square, Llangefni, Gwynedd, LL77 7LR Tel: (01248) 722119 Fax: (01248) 750488 E-mail: bull@welsh-historic-inns.com

▶ Chy Garth Guest House, P.O. Box 4, St. Ives, Cornwall, TR26 2JX Tel: (01736) 795677

▶ Hyde Park West Hotel, 25-26 Pembridge Square, Hyde Park, Bayswater, London, W2 4DR Tel: (020) 7229 3400 Fax: (020) 7229 5933 E-mail: info@majestic-london.co.uk

▶ Langton House, 46 Alma Road, Windsor, Berkshire, SL4 3HA Tel: 01753 858299 Fax: 01753 858299 E-mail: paul@langtonhouse.co.uk

▶ Room Rates, 85 Cavendish Drive, Northampton, NN3 3HL Tel: 0870 1439055

▶ Xcapewithus, Southbridge House, Southbridge Place, Croydon, CR0 4HA Tel: (0870) 6093484 E-mail: sales@xcapewithus.com

ON SITE BORING

Sub Soil Consultancy Services Ltd, Kennedy Road, Off Chaddocks Lane, Manchester, M29 7LD Tel: (01942) 883565 Fax: (01942) 883566 E-mail: richard@subsoil.co.uk

ON SITE BUILDING OR STRUCTURE FIBREGLASS COATING SERVICES

Castle Mouldings, 1 Dew Farm, Church Lane, Peasmarsh, Rye, East Sussex, TN31 6XD Tel: (01797) 230734 E-mail: castlemouldings@hotmail.com

ON SITE CARPET CLEANING SERVICES

▶ A Fleming, 19 Laurel Braes, Bridge of Don, Aberdeen, AB22 8XY Tel: (01224) 820333 E-mail: info@aflemingcarpetclean.com

Access Cleaning Solutions, 321 Blythswood Court, Glasgow, G2 7PH Tel: 0141-221 7355 E-mail: info@accesscleaningsolutions.co.uk

Acclaim Carpet Cleaners, 20 Graydon Avenue, Chichester, West Sussex, PO19 8RF Tel: (01243) 780381 Fax: (01243) 780381 E-mail: info@1aacclaim.co.uk

▶ Advanced Cleaning Services, Chapel Street, Exning, Newmarket, Suffolk, CB8 7HA Tel: (01638) 578444 Fax: (01638) 578542 E-mail: adrian@actltd.co.uk

▶ Angel Chemdry, 53 Goodwood Avenue, Hutton, Brentwood, Essex, CM13 1QD Tel: (01277) 217776 Fax: (01277) 217776 E-mail: angelchemdry@talktalk.net

▶ Atlas Carpetcare, 93 Heath End Road, Flackwell Heath, High Wycombe, Buckinghamshire, HP10 9ES Tel: (01628) 533329 Fax: E-mail: paul@wiseman250.fsnet.co.uk

▶ Aurora Services, 58 Kinnaird Close, Slough, SL1 6AS Tel: (0870) 9504617 Fax: 07732 103565 E-mail: aurora.services@tiscali.co.uk

B & C Office Cleaning Services, 25 Castlereagh St, London, W1H 5YR Tel: (020) 7636 0519

▶ Clean Tech, 35 Church Close, Grimston, King's Lynn, Norfolk, PE32 1BN Tel: (01485) 609223 Fax: (01485) 600475 E-mail: mikebarrett@genie.co.uk

Cleaning Contractors Services Group Ltd, 253 Alcester Road South, Kings Heath, Birmingham, B14 6DT Tel: 0121-444 4232 Fax: 0121-443 1117 E-mail: contractcleaning@kingsheathb14.wannadoo.co.uk

▶ D B Services, 194 West Street, Fareham, Hampshire, PO16 0HF Tel: (01329) 288464 Fax: (01329) 825815 E-mail: southern@dbservices.co.uk

▶ Fabtec Upholstery Cleaners, Plevna Place, Alton, Hampshire, GU34 2DS Tel: (01420) 87199 E-mail: michael@fabteccleaning.co.uk

Lombard Cleaning Services Ltd, Kemp House, 152-160 City Road, London, EC1V 2NP Tel: (020) 7251 2182 Fax: (020) 7251 2444

▶ M & L Carpets Ltd, 54 Crouch End Hill, London, N8 8AA Tel: (020) 8341 0914 Fax: (020) 8341 0914 E-mail: info@mlcarpets.com

▶ Master Clean, 41 Willows Lane, Rochdale, Lancashire, OL16 4BQ Tel: (01706) 710426 Fax: (01706) 710426 E-mail: master_clean@walla.com

▶ MCS Flooring & Fabric Cleaning, Rundells, Harlow, Essex, CM18 7HB Tel: (01279) 866838 E-mail: chamois.leathers@ntlworld.com

Orion Cleaning & Support Services, Unit 12 Parmiter Industrial Centre, Parmiter Street, London, E2 9HZ Tel: (020) 8880 7222 Fax: 0208 880 7080

▶ Outright Cleaning, 52 Edderston Ridge, Peebles, EH45 9NA Tel: (01721) 729066 E-mail: neil@outrightcleaning.co.uk

▶ PH Cleaning Ltd, 5 Green Place, Links Road Flackwell Heath, High Wycombe, Buckinghamshire, HP10 9LW Tel: (01628) 530157 Fax: (01628) 530157 E-mail: info@phcleaning.co.uk

▶ Pinnacle Cleaning, 41 Bramble Court, Ferndown, Bournemouth, BH22 0HL Tel: 0870 345 5757 E-mail: webenquiries@pinnacle-cleaning.co.uk

▶ The Red Carpet, 21 Morris Court, Waltham Abbey, Essex, EN9 3DX Tel: 01992 619469 E-mail: theredcarpet@hotmail.co.uk

Sawston Cleaning Services Ltd, 25 Brookfield Road, Sawston, Cambridge, CB22 3EH Tel: (01223) 832922 Fax: (01223) 830031 E-mail: enquiries@sawstoncleaning.co.uk

▶ Servicemaster Ltd, The Cleaning & Restoration Centre, Lime Avenue, Torquay, TQ2 5JL Tel: (01803) 200985 Fax: (01803) 200985 E-mail: office@cleanandrestore.co.uk

▶ Smith's Cleaning, 17 Lytchett Way, Poole, Dorset, BH16 5LS Tel: (01202) 620895 E-mail: smithscleaning@ntlworld.com

Square 1 Cleaning Services, Botany Bay Ii, Playhatch, Reading, RG4 9QU Tel: 0118-946 1503 E-mail: square1@botanybayii.freeserve.co.uk

▶ Straker Cleaning, 41 Abbotts Road, Sutton, Surrey, SM3 9SJ Tel: (020) 8644 8892 E-mail: chris@strakercleaning.co.uk

Vacman Specialist Cleaning, Budmhor, Portree, Isle of Skye, IV51 9DJ Tel: (01478) 613111 Fax: (01478) 613321 E-mail: info@vacman.co.uk

ON SITE MACHINE TOOL SERVICING

▶ CB CNC UK Ltd, Apartment 113, Whitfield Mill, Meadow Road, Apperley Bridge, Bradford, West Yorkshire, BD10 0LP Tel: (07881) 922680 Fax: (01274) 612808 E-mail: cc.silv-birch@fsmail.net

ON SITE RECYCLING

▶ Glenside Recycling Ltd, Colliery, Coalpit Lane, Rugeley, Smethwick, West Midlands, B66 2JN Tel: (01889) 574045 Fax: 0121-565 0646 E-mail: mikekillett@glensiderecycling.co.uk

ONE WAY CLUTCHES

Stieber Brakes, Wichita Building, Ampthill Road, Bedford, MK42 9RD Tel: (01234) 355499 Fax: (01234) 214264 E-mail: diane.lawman@wichita.co.uk

ONLINE INFORMATION SERVICES

B Plan Information Sytems, The Square, Basing View, Basingstoke, Hampshire, RG21 4EB Tel: (01256) 691111 Fax: (01256) 692450 E-mail: enquiries@fiinfo.com
Kompass Publishers, Windsor Court, East Grinstead House, East Grinstead, West Sussex, RH19 1XA Tel: (0800) 0185882 Fax: (01342) 335747 E-mail: sales@kompass.co.uk

ONSHORE OR OFFSHORE CABIN HIRE

A Plant Accommodation, 659 Eccles New Road, Salford, M50 1AY Tel: 0161-787 9041 Fax: 0161-787 8291 E-mail: manchesteraccomm@aplants.com
Labtech Modular Engineering, Blackness Road, Altens Industrial Estate, Aberdeen, AB12 3LH Tel: (01224) 337777 Fax: (01224) 337770 E-mail: sales@labtech.co.uk
Mcleod Cabins Ltd, The Saw Mill, Ipsden, Wallingford, Oxfordshire, OX10 6AS Tel: (01491) 871502 Fax: (01491) 871504
Rentacom Ltd, Hart Hill Farm, Hart Hill, Charing, Ashford, Kent, TN27 0HP Tel: (01233) 713555 Fax: (01233) 713511
Wernick Hire Ltd, Pipe Lane, Banbury, Oxfordshire, OX16 2RP Tel: (01295) 275315 Fax: (01295) 709827

ONSHORE OR OFFSHORE CABINS

Connect Building Systems Ltd, Barmston Road, Beverley, North Humberside, HU17 0LA Tel: (01482) 330430 Fax: (01482) 330431
Containercare Ltd, Dock Road, Liverpool, L19 2JW Tel: 0151-427 1771 Fax: 0151-427 1772 E-mail: sales@concare.co.uk
John Horsfall & Sons Greetland Ltd, West Vale Works, Halifax, West Yorkshire, HX4 8BB Tel: (01422) 372237 Fax: (01422) 310105 E-mail: sales@johnhorsfall.com
Labtech Modular Engineering, Blackness Road, Altens Industrial Estate, Aberdeen, AB12 3LH Tel: (01224) 337777 Fax: (01224) 337770 E-mail: sales@labtech.co.uk
Rovacabin, Powke Lane, Cradley Heath, West Midlands, B64 5PZ Tel: 0121-561 4003 Fax: 0121-561 4811
Transmit Containers Ltd, Bessemer Way, Harfreys Industrial Estate, Great Yarmouth, Norfolk, NR31 0LX Tel: (01493) 650792 Fax: (01493) 443500
Vertec Engineering, 4 Pitmedden Road, Dyce, Aberdeen, AB21 0DP Tel: (01224) 772969 Fax: (01224) 772528 E-mail: info@vertec-eng.co.uk

OPEN DIE FORGINGS

Forged Products, Venture House, Cross Street, Macclesfield, Cheshire, SK11 7PG Tel: (01625) 428399 Fax: (01625) 508200 E-mail: forgedproducts@dial.pipex.com
Formet Division Ltd, Wincomblee Road, Low Walker, Newcastle Upon Tyne, NE6 3QQ Tel: 0191-263 8686 Fax: 0191-262 6428 E-mail: sales@hipg.co.uk
M S I - Quality Forgings Ltd, Balby Carr Bank, Balby, Doncaster, South Yorkshire, DN4 8DH Tel: (01302) 325906 Fax: (01302) 760511 E-mail: sales@msi-forge.com
Newlo International Ltd, Market Place, Chapel-en-le-Frith, High Peak, Derbyshire, SK23 0EN Tel: (01298) 812973 Fax: (01298) 813282
North West Forgings Ltd, Unit F2 Nasmyth Business Park, James Nasmyth Way, Eccles, Manchester, M30 0SN Tel: 0161-785 2785 Fax: 0161-785 2777 E-mail: sales@nationalforge.com
P T S Ltd, 2 Academy Street, Coatbridge, Lanarkshire, ML5 3AU Tel: (01236) 431277 Fax: (01236) 431052 E-mail: mailbox@pts.ltd.uk

OPEN PLAN OFFICE SCREENS

C & M Partitioning Ltd, 10-12 Stirling Road, London, E17 6BT Tel: (020) 8531 3834 Fax: (020) 8531 3837
E C O Manufacturing Ltd, St. Marys Road, Ramsey, Huntingdon, Cambridgeshire, PE26 2SR Tel: (01487) 710800 Fax: (01487) 710900 E-mail: sales@ecomanufacturing.com
Komfort Workspace P.L.C., Reith Way, West Portway Industrial Estate, Andover, Hampshire, SP10 3TY Tel: (01264) 332166 Fax: (01264) 333560 E-mail: velosity@komfort.com
▶ Panelscreens, 18 Lower Road, Breachwood Green, Hitchin, Hertfordshire, SG4 8NS Tel: (01438) 833728 Fax: (01438) 833728 E-mail: paulfurse@panelscreens.co.uk

OPERATING TABLES, OPTHALMIC

Rastrick Engineering Ltd, 7 Martin Street, Brighouse, West Yorkshire, HD6 1DA Tel: (01484) 715748 Fax: (01484) 720639

OPHTHALMIC INSTRUMENT MANUFRS

Carleton Optical Equipment Ltd, Pattisson House, Addison Road, Chesham, Buckinghamshire, HP5 2BD Tel: (01494) 775811 Fax: (01494) 774371 E-mail: carleton@carletonltd.com
Dixey Instruments, 5 High Street, N Hykeham, Northampton, NN6 9DD Tel: (01522) 683152 Fax: (01604) 882488 E-mail: info@dixeyinstruments.com
E T H Metals Ltd, Unit 2B, 2 Bowyer Street, Birmingham, B10 0SA Tel: 0121-753 1673 Fax: 0121-753 1674 E-mail: zircon@onetel.net.uk
Keeler Ltd, Clewer Green Works, Clewer Hill Road, Windsor, Berkshire, SL4 4AA Tel: (01753) 857177 Fax: (01753) 830247 E-mail: info@keeler.co.uk
Edward Marcus Ltd, Unit 3 Marrtree Business Park, Kirkwood Close, Oxspring, Sheffield, S36 8ZP Tel: (01226) 764082 Fax: (01226) 764082 E-mail: sales@edwardmarcus.co.uk
Opthalmedica Ltd, Old Bury Hill Garden, Milton Street, Westcott, Dorking, Surrey, RH4 3PX Tel: (01306) 875255 Fax: (01306) 875255 E-mail: maureen.wright@btconnect.com
Sterimedix Ltd, Unit 6/7, Kingfisher Business Park, Arthur Street, Redditch, Worcestershire, B98 8LG Tel: (01527) 501480 Fax: (01527) 501491 E-mail: sales@sterimedix.com
Surgical Instrument Group Holdings Ltd, 89a Gloucester Road, Croydon, CR0 2DN Tel: (020) 8683 1103 Fax: (020) 8683 1105
United Optical Industries Ltd, 583 Moseley Road, Birmingham, B12 9BL Tel: 0121-442 2222 Fax: 0121-449 9993 E-mail: sales@bog.co.uk
Unomedical Ltd, 26-27 Thornhill Road, Redditch, Worcestershire, B98 9NL Tel: (01527) 587700 Fax: (01527) 592111 E-mail: redditch@unomedical.com
John Weiss & Son Ltd, 89 Alston Drive, Bradwell Abbey, Milton Keynes, MK13 9HF Tel: (01908) 318017 Fax: (01908) 318708 E-mail: sales@johnweiss.com

OPHTHALMIC LENS, *See Lenses etc*

OPHTHALMOSCOPES

Keeler Ltd, Clewer Green Works, Clewer Hill Road, Windsor, Berkshire, SL4 4AA Tel: (01753) 857177 Fax: (01753) 830247 E-mail: info@keeler.co.uk
Medscope Ltd, 68 Hardy Street, Maidstone, Kent, ME14 2SJ Tel: (01622) 204743 Fax: (01622) 202362

OPTICAL ACCESSORIES MANUFRS

Dunelm Optical Co Ltd, 9 Enterprise Way, Spennymoor, County Durham, DL16 6YP Tel: (01388) 420420 Fax: (01388) 810102

OPTICAL CHARACTER RECOGNITION EQUIPMENT/ SYSTEMS MANUFRS

Cognitronics Ltd, Claylands Avenue, Worksop, Nottinghamshire, S81 7DJ Tel: (01909) 477272 Fax: (01909) 486260 E-mail: sales@cognitronics.co.uk
Data & Research Services plc, Sunrise Parkway, Linford Wood, Milton Keynes, MK14 6LR Tel: (01908) 666088 Fax: (01908) 607668 E-mail: enquiries@drs.co.uk
Scan Optics Ltd, 5 Brookside, Colne Way, Watford, WD24 7QJ Tel: (01923) 819581 Fax: (01923) 212633

OPTICAL CHOPPERS

Scitec Instruments, Bartles Industrial Estate, North Street, Redruth, Cornwall, TR15 1HR Tel: (01209) 314608 Fax: (01209) 314609 E-mail: info@scitec.uk.com

OPTICAL COATING MATERIALS

▶ Vista Optics Ltd, Cheshire Science Centre, Gorsey Lane, Widnes, Cheshire, WA8 0RP Tel: (0870) 0111620 Fax: (0870) 0111630 E-mail: sales@vista-optics.com

OPTICAL COATING SERVICES

Image Optics Components, Harvey Road, Basildon, Essex, SS13 1ES Tel: (01268) 728477 Fax: (01268) 590445 E-mail: sales@image-optics.fsnet.co.uk
Kaypul Optics Ltd, Unit 4 West Docks, Harbour Place, Burntisland, Fife, KY3 9DW Tel: (01592) 874140 Fax: (01592) 874140 E-mail: kaypulltd@aol.com

OPTICAL COATING/THIN FILM

D & A, Conference Centre Aston Cross Business Park, 50 Rocky Lane, Aston, Birmingham, B6 5RQ Tel: 0121-706 6133 Fax: 0121-697 2700 E-mail: contactus@danda.co.uk
Datasights Ltd, 228-234 Alma Road, Enfield, Middlesex, EN3 7BB Tel: (020) 8805 4151 Fax: (020) 8805 8084 E-mail: sales@datasights.com
Oxford Instruments Plasma Technology Ltd, North End Road, Yatton, Bristol, BS49 4AP Tel: (01934) 837000 Fax: (01934) 837001 E-mail: plasma.technology@oxinst.co.uk

OPTICAL COMPONENT MANUFRS

B A E Systems Avionics Ltd, Christopher Martin Road, Basildon, Essex, SS14 3EL Tel: (01268) 522822 Fax: (01268) 883140
Comar Instruments, 70 Hartington Grove, Cambridge, CB1 7UH Tel: (01223) 245470 Fax: (01223) 410033 E-mail: mail@kyinstruments.com
Datasights Ltd, 228-234 Alma Road, Enfield, Middlesex, EN3 7BB Tel: (020) 8805 4151 Fax: (020) 8805 8084 E-mail: sales@datasights.com
Dunelm Optical Co Ltd, 9 Enterprise Way, Spennymoor, County Durham, DL16 6YP Tel: (01388) 420420 Fax: (01388) 810102
Elwen Eos Ltd, PO Box 261, Shefford, Bedfordshire, SG17 5PW Tel: (01462) 814708 Fax: (01462) 814708 E-mail: elweneos@aol.com
Gooch & Housego plc, Cornhill, Ilminster, Somerset, TA19 0AB Tel: (01460) 52271 Fax: (01460) 54972 E-mail: info@goochandhousego.com
I C Optical Systems Ltd, 190-192 Ravenscroft Road, Beckenham, Kent, BR3 4TW Tel: (020) 8778 5094 Fax: (020) 8676 9816 E-mail: sales@icopticalsystems.com
Instrument Plastics Ltd, 33-37 Kings Grove Industrial Estate, Kings Grove, Maidenhead, Berkshire, SL6 4DP Tel: (01628) 770018 Fax: (01628) 773299 E-mail: sales@instrumentplastics.co.uk
L G Optical (Mfg) Ltd, 25 Brunel Road, St. Leonards-on-Sea, East Sussex, TN38 9RT Tel: (01424) 851878 Fax: (01424) 853368 E-mail: info@lgoptical.co.uk
Melles Griot Ltd, Sovereign Court, Lancaster Way, Ermine Business Park, Huntingdon, Cambridgeshire, PE29 6XU Tel: (01480) 420800 Fax: (01480) 420811 E-mail: info@mellesgriot.com
Moritex Europe Ltd, 14 Signet Court, Swann Road, Cambridge, CB5 8LA Tel: (01223) 301148 Fax: (01223) 301149 E-mail: moritex.europe@dial.pipex.com
Optical Instruments Balham Ltd, Unit 39 Neville Court, 23 Neville Road, Croydon, CR0 2DS Tel: (020) 8664 9799 Fax: (020) 8664 9771 E-mail: info@optil.co.uk
Optiglass Ltd, 52-54 Fowler Road, Hainault, Ilford, Essex, IG6 3UT Tel: (020) 8500 1264 Fax: (020) 8500 1955 E-mail: info@optiglass.co.uk
Optometrics (UK) Ltd, Unit C6, Cross Green Garth, Leeds, LS9 0SF Tel: 0113-249 6973 Fax: 0113-235 0420 E-mail: optouk@aol.com
Plasmon Data Systems, Whiting Way, Melbourn, Royston, Hertfordshire, SG8 6EN Tel: (01763) 261516 Fax: (01763) 264444 E-mail: sales@plasmon.co.uk
▶ Scientific Optical Ltd, Drury Lane, Pondswood Industrial Estate, St. Leonards-on-Sea, East Sussex, TN38 9YA Tel: (01424) 430371 Fax: (01424) 441639 E-mail: sales@scientificoptical.com
Specac Ltd, River House, 97 Cray Avenue, Orpington, Kent, BR5 4HE Tel: (01689) 873134 Fax: (01689) 878527 E-mail: sales@specac.co.uk
Speirs Robertson Ltd, 42 Bedford Road, London, N2 9DA Tel: (01234) 823410 Fax: (0870) 7624234 E-mail: sales@robertson.co.uk
▶ U Q G Ltd, 99-101 Cambridge Road, Milton, Cambridge, CB24 6AT Tel: (01223) 425601 Fax: (01223) 420506 E-mail: sales@uqgoptics.com
F. Wiggins (Meakins), 106 Brook Farm Road, Saxmundham, Suffolk, IP17 1WL Tel: (07887) 751801

OPTICAL CONTACT LENSES

Acuity Contact Lenses, Plumpton Road, Hoddesdon, Hertfordshire, EN11 0LB Tel: (01992) 445035 Fax: (01992) 451223 E-mail: enquiries@acuity-lenses.co.uk
CIBA Vision (UK) Ltd, Flanders Road, Hedge End, Southampton, SO30 2LG Tel: (01489) 785580 Fax: (01489) 786802 E-mail: parkwest.reception@cibavision.com
County Laboratories, 78 Sitwell Street, Spondon, Derby, DE21 7FG Tel: (01332) 678411 Fax: (01332) 678411
Look Now Optical, 5 Skinner Street, Gillingham, Kent, ME7 1HD Tel: (01634) 852600 Fax: (01634) 852600 E-mail: sales@easylenses.co.uk
Microsoft Research Ltd, 7 JJ Thomson Avenue, Madingley Road, Cambridge, CB3 0FB Tel: (01223) 479700 Fax: (01223) 479999
▶ Samantha Nolan, 18 Walton Road, Southampton, SO19 0JB Tel: (023) 8042 0916

OPTICAL DESIGN ENGINEERS

Davin Optronics Ltd, Creycaine Road, Watford, WD24 7GW Tel: (01923) 206800 Fax: (01923) 234220 E-mail: sales@davinoptronics.com
Elwen Eos Ltd, PO Box 261, Shefford, Bedfordshire, SG17 5PW Tel: (01462) 814708 Fax: (01462) 814708 E-mail: elweneos@aol.com

OPTICAL EMISSION SPECTROMETERS

Metal Scan Ltd, 16 The Brunel Centre, Newton Road, Manor Royal, Crawley, West Sussex, RH10 9TU Tel: (01293) 513123 Fax: (01293) 521507 E-mail: sales@aruntechnology.com

OPTICAL EQUIPMENT, *See also headings for particular types*

Dunelm Optical Co Ltd, 9 Enterprise Way, Spennymoor, County Durham, DL16 6YP Tel: (01388) 420420 Fax: (01388) 810102
Microscopy Supplies & Consultants Ltd, Park House, 6a Carneil Road, Carnock, Dunfermline, Fife, KY12 9JH Tel: (01383) 851434 Fax: (01383) 851434
Topcon Great Britain Ltd, Topcon House, Kennet Side, Newbury, Berkshire, RG14 5PX Tel: (01635) 551120 Fax: (01635) 551170

OPTICAL FIBRE CABLE MARKING EQUIPMENT

▶ N I Europe Ltd, 1 Beverley Road, Market Weighton, York, YO43 3JN Tel: (01430) 803355 Fax: (01430) 803356 E-mail: sales@networkinstallations.co.uk

OPTICAL FIBRE FOR FIBRE OPTICS

Alker Optical Equipment Ltd, Alker House, 190 North Gate, New Basford, Nottingham, NG7 7FT Tel: 0115-942 0290 Fax: 0115-978 8190 E-mail: sales@alker.co.uk
Bruce Data Networks, 22 Duthie Road, Tarves, Ellon, Aberdeenshire, AB41 7JX Tel: (01651) 851568 Fax: (01651) 851416 E-mail: jim.bruce@btinternet.com
Diomed Ltd, Diomed House 2000 Cambridge Research Park, Beach Road, Waterbeach, Cambridge, CB5 9TE Tel: (01223) 729300 Fax: (01223) 729329 E-mail: info@diomed-lasers.com
Endoscan Ltd, 58 Acacia Road, St. Johns Wood, London, NW8 6AG Tel: (020) 7483 2300 Fax: (020) 7483 2900 E-mail: sales@endoscan.co.uk
▶ Lucid Optical Services Ltd, Lucid Training Centre, Garsdale, Sedbergh, Cumbria, LA10 5PE Tel: (01539) 621219 Fax: (01539) 621205 E-mail: annette@lucidos.co.uk
Sumitomo Electric Europe Ltd, Unit 220 Centennial Park, Elstree, Hertfordshire, WD6 3SL Tel: (020) 8953 4489 Fax: (020) 8207 5950 E-mail: a.bayram@sumielectric.com
Universal Fibre Optics (Old Co) Ltd, 6 Home Place, Coldstream, Berwickshire, TD12 4DT Tel: (01890) 883416 Fax: (01890) 883062 E-mail: info@universal-fibre-optics.com

OPTICAL FILTERS

Instrument Plastics Ltd, 33-37 Kings Grove Industrial Estate, Kings Grove, Maidenhead, Berkshire, SL6 4DP Tel: (01628) 770018 Fax: (01628) 773299 E-mail: sales@instrumentplastics.co.uk
Kaypul Optics Ltd, Unit 4 West Docks, Harbour Place, Burntisland, Fife, KY3 9DW Tel: (01592) 874140 Fax: (01592) 874140 E-mail: kaypulltd@aol.com
Northumbria Optical Coatings Ltd, Unit 10 Burford Way, Boldon Business Park, Boldon Colliery, Tyne & Wear, NE35 9PZ Tel: 0191-537 4888 Fax: 0191-537 4777 E-mail: sales@noc-ltd.com
F. Wiggins (Meakins), 106 Brook Farm Road, Saxmundham, Suffolk, IP17 1WL Tel: (07887) 751801

OPTICAL FINISHING/POLISHING SERVICES

Reliable Techniques Ltd, Unit 59 Parkhouse Industrial Estate West, Brick Kiln Lane, Newcastle, Staffordshire, ST5 7AS Tel: (01782) 565002 Fax: (01782) 565001 E-mail: optics@reliabletechniques.fsnet.co.uk

OPTICAL GLASS

D & E Optics Ltd, 163-164 Rolfe Street, Smethwick, West Midlands, B66 2AU Tel: 0121-565 2333 Fax: 0121-565 1658

H V Skan Ltd, 425-433 Stratford Road, Shirley, Solihull, West Midlands, B90 4AE Tel: 0121-733 3003 Fax: 0121-733 1030 E-mail: info@skan.co.uk

Tintometer Ltd, Palmers Way, Trenant Industrial Estate, Wadebridge, Cornwall, PL27 6HB Tel: (01208) 812719 Fax: (01208) 812719

United Optical Ltd, 44-46 Corporation Street, Belfast, BT1 3DE Tel: (028) 9024 1351 Fax: (028) 9032 3594

OPTICAL GRATICULES

Optics Asia (UK) Ltd, Unit 430, Thorp Arch Trading Estate, Thorp Arch, Wetherby, West Yorkshire, LS23 7BJ Tel: (01937) 849932 Fax: (01937) 849836 E-mail: opticsasiaukltd@aol.com

OPTICAL INFORMATION DISPLAYS

Nexus Alpha Ltd, Unit 8 Beaufort Ho, Beaufort Court, Sir Thomas Longley Rd, Rochester, Kent, ME2 4FB Tel: (01634) 304226 Fax: (01634) 301315

OPTICAL INSPECTION EQUIPMENT, PROFILE PROJECTOR

Optical Services, 15 Barkestone Close, Emerson Valley, Milton Keynes, MK4 2AT Tel: (01908) 526100 Fax:

OPTICAL INSTRUMENT MANUFRS

Agar Scientific Ltd, 66a Cambridge Road, Stansted, Essex, CM24 8DA Tel: (01279) 813519 Fax: (01279) 815106 E-mail: sales@agarscientific.com

▶ Berkshire Opthalmic Laboratories Ltd, Unit 6 Pipers Court, Berkshire Drive, Thatcham, Berkshire, RG19 4ER Tel: (01635) 865050 E-mail: sales@berkshirelabs.com

Cerium Group Ltd, Cerium Industrial Park, Appledore Road, Tenterden, Kent, TN30 7DE Tel: (01580) 765211 Fax: (01580) 765573 E-mail: ceriumgrp@aol.com

Coates Optical Supplies, Gretton Road, Winchcombe, Cheltenham, Gloucestershire, GL54 5EE Tel: (01242) 603888 Fax: (01242) 603828 E-mail: info@coates-optical.demon.co.uk

Elwen Eos Ltd, PO Box 261, Shefford, Bedfordshire, SG17 5PW Tel: (01462) 814708 Fax: (01462) 814708 E-mail: elweneos@aol.com

Henri Picard & Frere, 8 Pixham Court, Pixham Lane, Dorking, Surrey, RH4 1PG Tel: (020) 8949 3142 Fax: (020) 8949 3142 E-mail: sales@picard.co.uk

▶ Humberside Optical Services, 11 Antelope Road, Humber Bridge Industrial Estate, Barton-upon-Humber, South Humberside, DN18 5RS Tel: (01652) 660070 Fax: (01652) 660084 E-mail: sales@lensnet.co.uk

Keymed Ltd, Keymed House, Stock Road, Southend-on-Sea, SS2 5QH Tel: (01702) 616333 Fax: (01702) 465677 E-mail: keymed@keymed.co.uk

▶ Lensfast, Seath Road, Rutherglen, Glasgow, G73 1RW Tel: 0141-643 1135 Fax: 0141-643 1219

▶ Lenstec Ltd, Unit 8 Bedwas Business Centre, Bedwas, Caerphilly, Mid Glamorgan, CF83 8DU Tel: (029) 2088 3009 Fax: (029) 2088 9798 E-mail: sales@lenstec.co.uk

Metax Ltd, 77 Capital Business Centre, Carlton Road, South Croydon, Surrey, CR2 0BS Tel: (020) 8916 2077 Fax: (01689) 889994 E-mail: sales@metax.co.uk

▶ Norville Optical Co. Ltd, 8 Grange Road, Houstoun Industrial Estate, Livingston, West Lothian, EH54 5DE Tel: (01506) 434261 Fax: (01506) 431851

Opthalmedica Ltd, Old Bury Hill Garden, Milton Street, Westcott, Dorking, Surrey, RH4 3PX Tel: (01306) 875255 Fax: (01306) 875255 E-mail: maureen.wright@btconnect.com

Optical Instruments Balham Ltd, Unit 39 Neville Court, 23 Neville Road, Croydon, CR0 2DS Tel: (020) 8664 9799 Fax: (020) 8664 9771 E-mail: info@optil.co.uk

Optimax, 36 Douglas Road, Halesowen, West Midlands, B62 9HX Tel: 0121-561 1122 Fax: 0121-559 0541

▶ Portland Optical Laboratories Ltd, 7 New Street, Bridgtown, Cannock, Staffordshire, WS11 0DD Tel: (01543) 579442 Fax: (01543) 579055

▶ Rodenstock (UK) Midland Division Ltd, Bridge Business Park, Bridge Park Road, Thurmaston, Leicester, LE4 8BL Tel: 0116-269 4060

RPD Precision Drawings, Unit 7 North Lynn Industrial Estate, King's Lynn, Norfolk, PE30 2HZ Tel: (01553) 774765 Fax: (01553) 764816 E-mail: rpd@mywebpage.net

Simden Optical Ltd, Haugh Lane, Blaydon-on-Tyne, Tyne & Wear, NE21 4SA Tel: 0191-499 0122 Fax: 0191-414 4723

Simrad Optronics Ltd, 3 Medowbrook Industrial Estate, Maxwell Way, Crawley, West Sussex, RH10 9SA Tel: (01293) 560413 Fax: (01293) 560418

▶ Sinclair Ltd, Corse Industrial Estate, Gloucester Road, Corse, Gloucester, GL19 3RD Tel: (01452) 840771 Fax: (01452) 840315 E-mail: sales@hirose.co.uk

▶ Vision Express (UK) Ltd, 81-83 Russell Way, Metrocentre, Gateshead, Tyne & Wear, NE11 9XX Tel: 0191-460 0644 Fax: 0191-460 0097

Warwick Evans Optical Co. Ltd, 22 Palace Road, London, N11 2PS Tel: (020) 8888 0051 Fax: (020) 8888 9055 E-mail: sales@keystonevision.com

OPTICAL INTERFEROMETERS

I C Optical Systems Ltd, 190-192 Ravenscroft Road, Beckenham, Kent, BR3 4TW Tel: (020) 8778 5094 Fax: (020) 8676 9816 E-mail: sales@icopticalsystems.com

OPTICAL LENSES

American Optical UK Ltd, Unit 76-77 Capitol Industrial Park, Capitol Way, London, NW9 0EW Tel: (020) 8205 6575 Fax: (020) 8200 9749

▶ Berkshire Opthalmic Laboratories Ltd, Unit 6 Pipers Court, Berkshire Drive, Thatcham, Berkshire, RG19 4ER Tel: (01635) 865050 E-mail: sales@berkshirelabs.com

Carclo Technical Plastics, 111 Buckingham Avenue, Slough, SL1 4PF Tel: (01753) 575011 Fax: (01753) 811359 E-mail: optics@carclo-optics.com

Comar Instruments, 70 Hartington Grove, Cambridge, CB1 7UH Tel: (01223) 245470 Fax: (01223) 410033 E-mail: mail@kyinstruments.com

Crown Leisure Ltd, Gerrish Avenue, Whitehall, Bristol, BS5 9DG Tel: 0117-955 4044 Fax: 0117-955 4045 E-mail: sales@crownleisure.co.uk

D J Newson Ltd, 2 Bunkell Road, Rackheath Industrial Estate, Rackheath, Norwich, NR13 6PX Tel: (01603) 720904 Fax: (01603) 720756

Davin Optronics Ltd, Creycaine Road, Watford, WD24 7GW Tel: (01923) 206800 Fax: (01923) 234220 E-mail: sales@davinoptronics.com

Draford Optical Ltd, Abford Works, 12 Crittall Road, Industrial Estate West, Witham, Essex, CM8 3AT Tel: (01376) 512040 Fax: (01376) 515817

Essex Optical Co. Ltd, 172 Enterprise Court, Eastways, Witham, Essex, CM8 3YS Tel: (01376) 512630 Fax: (01376) 515154 E-mail: enquiries@essexoptical.co.uk

Essilor Ltd, Cooper Road, Thornbury, Bristol, BS35 3UW Tel: (01454) 417100 Fax: (01454) 281282

Eyeline Of England, 1 South Orbital Trading Park, Hedon Road, Hull, HU9 1NJ Tel: (01482) 327512 Fax: (01482) 224279 E-mail: info@eyelineuk.com

Hoya Lens UK Ltd, Wrexham Industrial Estate, Wrexham, Clwyd, LL13 9UA Tel: (01978) 663400 Fax: (01978) 663135 E-mail: enquiries@hoya.co.uk

▶ Humberside Optical Services, 11 Antelope Road, Humber Bridge Industrial Estate, Barton-upon-Humber, South Humberside, DN18 5RS Tel: (01652) 660070 Fax: (01652) 660084 E-mail: sales@lensnet.co.uk

I C Optical Systems Ltd, 190-192 Ravenscroft Road, Beckenham, Kent, BR3 4TW Tel: (020) 8778 5094 Fax: (020) 8676 9816 E-mail: sales@icopticalsystems.com

▶ Independent Optics Ltd, 20 Norman Way Industrial Estate, Norman Way, Cambridge, CB2 1NS Tel: (01954) 231545 Fax: (01954) 231340

▶ Leicester Optical Ltd, Unit 9, Victoria Mills, Fowke Street, Rothley, Leicester, LE7 7PJ Tel: 0116-237 5646 Fax: 0116-237 6449 E-mail: info@leicesteroptical.co.uk

▶ Lensfast, Seath Road, Rutherglen, Glasgow, G73 1RW Tel: 0141-643 1135 Fax: 0141-643 1219

▶ Lenstec Ltd, Unit 8 Bedwas Business Centre, Bedwas, Caerphilly, Mid Glamorgan, CF83 8DU Tel: (029) 2088 3009 Fax: (029) 2088 9798 E-mail: sales@lenstec.co.uk

Lentoid Group, PO Box 21, Otley, West Yorkshire, LS21 1HA Tel: (01943) 461613 Fax: (01943) 464018 E-mail: sales@lentoid.com

Mersona Ltd, PO Box 12, Halesowen, West Midlands, B62 8AP Tel: 0121-559 5683 Fax: 0121-559 7487

Newbold & Davis Ltd, PO Box 282, Newcastle, Staffordshire, ST5 9HU Tel: (01782) 622305 Fax: (01782) 623043 E-mail: newbold-davis@nusyte.co.uk

▶ Norville Optical Co. Ltd, 8 Grange Road, Houstoun Industrial Estate, Livingston, West Lothian, EH54 5DE Tel: (01506) 434261 Fax: (01506) 431851

▶ Norville Optical Co. Ltd, Chevychase Court, Seaham Grange Industrial Estate, Seaham, County Durham, SR7 0PR Tel: 0191-523 8023 Fax: 0191-523 8024

Optics Asia (UK) Ltd, Unit 430, Thorp Arch Trading Estate, Thorp Arch, Wetherby, West Yorkshire, LS23 7BJ Tel: (01937) 849932 Fax: (01937) 849836 E-mail: opticsasiaukltd@aol.com

Optiglass Ltd, 52-54 Fowler Road, Hainault, Ilford, Essex, IG6 3UT Tel: (020) 8500 1264 Fax: (020) 8500 1955 E-mail: info@optiglass.co.uk

Optimax, 36 Douglas Road, Halesowen, West Midlands, B62 9HX Tel: 0121-561 1122 Fax: 0121-559 0541

Optometrics (UK) Ltd, Unit C6, Cross Green Garth, Leeds, LS9 0SF Tel: 0113-249 6973 Fax: 0113-235 0420 E-mail: optouk@aol.com

Pentax UK Ltd, Pentax House, Heron Drive, Slough, SL3 8PN Tel: (01753) 792792 Fax: (01753) 792794 E-mail: contactus@.pentax.co.uk

▶ Portland Optical Laboratories Ltd, 7 New Street, Bridgtown, Cannock, Staffordshire, WS11 0DD Tel: (01543) 579442 Fax: (01543) 579055

▶ Rodenstock (UK) Midland Division Ltd, Bridge Business Park, Bridge Park Road, Thurmaston, Leicester, LE4 8BL Tel: 0116-269 4060

S B Optical Ltd, 1 Mill Square, Catrine, Mauchline, Ayrshire, KA5 6QZ Tel: (01290) 551339 Fax: (01290) 552635 E-mail: hughk@sboptical.freeserve.co.uk

▶ Scientific Optical Ltd, Drury Lane, Pondswood Industrial Estate, St. Leonards-on-Sea, East Sussex, TN38 9YA Tel: (01424) 430371 Fax: (01424) 441639 E-mail: sales@scientificoptical.com

▶ Sinclair Ltd, Corse Industrial Estate, Gloucester Road, Corse, Gloucester, GL19 3RD Tel: (01452) 840771 Fax: (01452) 840315 E-mail: sales@hirose.co.uk

▶ U Q G Ltd, 99-101 Cambridge Road, Milton, Cambridge, CB24 6AT Tel: (01223) 425601 Fax: (01223) 420506 E-mail: sales@uqgoptics.com

Ultra Vision International Ltd, Commerce Way, Leighton Buzzard, Bedfordshire, LU7 4RW Tel: (01525) 381112 Fax: (01525) 370091 E-mail: lenses@ultravision.co.uk

United Optical Ltd, 44-46 Corporation Street, Belfast, BT1 3DE Tel: (028) 9024 1351 Fax: (028) 9032 3594 E-mail: unitedoptical@lineone.net

Vectis Optical Laboratories Ltd, 81a High Street, Newport, Isle of Wight, PO30 1BG Tel: (01983) 525272 Fax: (01983) 525272

Vision Labs Ltd, 2 Foley Grove, Foley Business Park, Kidderminster, Worcestershire, DY11 7PT Tel: (01562) 820333 Fax: (01562) 820500

▶ Vista Optics Ltd, Cheshire Science Centre, Gorsey Lane, Widnes, Cheshire, WA8 0RP Tel: (0870) 0111620 Fax: (0870) 0111630 E-mail: sales@vista-optics.com

OPTICAL MACHINERY MANUFRS

Cerium Group Ltd, Cerium Industrial Park, Appledore Road, Tenterden, Kent, TN30 7DE Tel: (01580) 765211 Fax: (01580) 765573 E-mail: ceriumgrp@aol.com

Gerber Coburn Optical UK Ltd, 1600 Aztec West, Almondsbury, Bristol, BS32 4UA Tel: (01454) 200780 Fax: (01454) 200787 E-mail: info@gerbercoburn.co.uk

Lamda Polytech Ltd, 1 Lincoln Park, Borough Road, Buckingham Road Industrial Est, Brackley, Northamptonshire, NN13 7BE Tel: (01280) 705500 Fax: 01280 706868 E-mail: sales@lamdapolytech.co.uk

OPTICAL MANUFACTURING SERVICES/MANUFACTURING OPTICIANS

Apollo Optical Manufacturing Ltd, 12b Carvers Trading Estate, Southampton Road, Ringwood, Hampshire, BH24 1JS Tel: (01425) 479593 Fax: (01425) 479963

▶ Barnsley Optical, Unit 16 Zenith Park, Whaley Road, Barnsley, South Yorkshire, S75 1HT Tel: (01226) 284646 Fax: (01226) 205306 E-mail: info@barnsleyoptical.co.uk

Brenal Optical Services, Great Western Street, Wednesbury, West Midlands, WS10 7LL Tel: 0121-556 1506 Fax: 0121-556 9792

▶ Burgess Optical, 22 Northfield Avenue, Knottingley, West Yorkshire, WF11 0JE Tel: (01977) 670395 Fax: (01977) 670394 E-mail: burgessoptical@btinternet.com

Clyde Optical Co. Ltd, Optics House, Seath Road, Rutherglen, Glasgow, G73 1RW Tel: 0141-643 0639 Fax: 0141-643 1219

County Laboratories, 78 Sitwell Street, Spondon, Derby, DE21 7FG Tel: (01332) 678411 Fax: (01332) 678411

D & E Optics Ltd, 163-164 Rolfe Street, Smethwick, West Midlands, B66 2AU Tel: 0121-565 2333 Fax: 0121-565 1658

Derby Optical Co. Ltd, 18 Agard Street, Derby, DE1 1YS Tel: (01332) 349527 Fax: (01332) 292462

Executive Optics (Holdings), 205 Trafalgar Road, London, SE10 9EQ Tel: (020) 8858 8585 Fax: (020) 8293 5818

Eyeline Of England, 1 South Orbital Trading Park, Hedon Road, Hull, HU9 1NJ Tel: (01482) 327512 Fax: (01482) 224279 E-mail: info@eyelineuk.com

Gilco Optics Ltd, North Farm Road, Tunbridge Wells, Kent, TN2 3DH Tel: (01892) 542844 Fax: (01892) 548847 E-mail: gilco.optics@talk21.com

Oliver Goldsmith Eyewear Ltd, The Studio, St Nicholas Close, Elstree, Borehamwood, Hertfordshire, WD6 3EW Tel: (020) 8207 5153 Fax: (020) 8207 2747 E-mail: oliver@ogspecs.force9.net

H T S Optical Group Ltd, Industrial House, Conway Street, Hove, East Sussex, BN3 3LU Tel: (01273) 773918 Fax: (01273) 737246

Halifax Optical 1992 Ltd, 3 Clover Hill Road, Halifax, West Yorkshire, HX1 2YG Tel: (01422) 365969 Fax: (01422) 381225

Leith Optical Co., Unit 12-14 Stewartfield, Edinburgh, EH6 5RQ Tel: 0131-554 8355 Fax: 0131-553 4318

Liverpool R.X. Co. Ltd, Liverpool, L69 1UZ Tel: 0151-709 1643 Fax: 0151-709 1643

The Manor Optical Co. Ltd, Manor House, Dudley Road, Halesowen, West Midlands, B63 4LS Tel: 0121-550 2609 Fax: 0121-550 5915 E-mail: sales@manor-optical.co.uk

Northern Optical Manchester Co. Ltd, 1 Edwin Road, Manchester, M11 3NQ Tel: 0161-273 5222 Fax: 0161-274 3591

Norville Optical Group Ltd, Magdala Road, Gloucester, GL1 4DG Tel: (01452) 528686 Fax: (01452) 411094 E-mail: sales@norville.co.uk

Oakhill Optical Laboratory Ltd, PO Box 3, Stourbridge, West Midlands, DY9 8DA Tel: (01384) 894035 Fax: (01384) 423701

▶ Posh Eyes, Westbury House, 52 French Laurence Way, Chalgrove, Oxford, OX44 7YF Tel: 01865 400384 E-mail: message@posheyes.co.uk

Premier Optical Services Ltd, 104 Oxford Road, Clacton-on-Sea, Essex, CO15 3TH Tel: (01255) 424999 Fax: (01255) 426646 E-mail: enquires@premieropticals.co.uk

Progressive Optical Co. Ltd, 165 North Street, Barking, Essex, IG11 8LA Tel: (020) 8594 0160 Fax: (020) 8594 0139 E-mail: jgreen@btconnect.com

Quality Lenses Ltd, 89A King Street, Southport, Merseyside, PR8 1LQ Tel: (01704) 534108 Fax: (01704) 544132

Roundford Ltd, The Old Co-Op, Croft Lane, Adderbury, Banbury, Oxfordshire, OX17 3NB Tel: (01295) 810137 Fax: (01295) 812056 E-mail: rdfd@walford-and-round.co.uk

Sherwin & Oliver Ltd, Midleton Industrial Estate, Guildford, Surrey, GU2 8XW Tel: (01483) 569241 Fax: (01483) 578232

Smart Vision, 40 Hamlet Court Road, Westcliff-on-Sea, Essex, SS0 7LX Tel: (01702) 343260 Fax: (01702) 343260

South Coat Optical Ltd, 26 Highcroft Industrial Estate, Enterprise Road, Waterlooville, Hampshire, PO8 0BT Tel: (023) 9259 9411 Fax: (023) 9259 9011

Tant Laboratories Ltd, 17 Twyford Business Centre, London Road, Bishop's Stortford, Hertfordshire, CM23 3YT Tel: (0870) 8770100 Fax: (01279) 713170 E-mail: sales@tantlabs.com

S. & H.C. Taylor Ltd, Devon House, Tan Lane, Exeter, EX2 8EG Tel: (01392) 421500 Fax: (01392) 423889

United Optical Industries Ltd, 583 Moseley Road, Birmingham, B12 9BL Tel: 0121-442 2222 Fax: 0121-449 9993 E-mail: sales@bog.co.uk

▶ Vision Express (UK) Ltd, 81-83 Russell Way, Metrocentre, Gateshead, Tyne & Wear, NE11 9XX Tel: 0191-460 0644 Fax: 0191-460 0097

White Hart Optical Co. Ltd, Redburn Road, Newcastle upon Tyne, NE5 1PQ Tel: 0191-286 0441 Fax: 0191-271 0721

Williams Harris Optical Supplies, 4 Stanley Green Road, Poole, Dorset, BH15 3AF Tel: (01202) 686622 Fax: (01202) 674020

Wyvern Optical Ltd, 87 Narborough Road, Leicester, LE3 0LF Tel: 0116-254 8431 E-mail: wyvern1947@aol.com

OPTICAL MEASURING INSTRUMENTS

Coates Optical Supplies, Gretton Road, Winchcombe, Cheltenham, Gloucestershire, GL54 5EE Tel: (01242) 603888 Fax: (01242) 603828 E-mail: info@coates-optical.demon.co.uk

Optical Tools For Industry, Brickfield Lane, Denbigh Road, Ruthin, Clwyd, LL15 2TN Tel: (01824) 704991 Fax: (01824) 705075 E-mail: info@optical-tools.co.uk

RPD Precision Drawings, Unit 7 North Lynn Industrial Estate, King's Lynn, Norfolk, PE30 2HZ Tel: (01553) 774765 Fax: (01553) 764816 E-mail: rpd@mywebpage.net

OPTICAL PRISMS

Optics Asia (UK) Ltd, Unit 430, Thorp Arch Trading Estate, Thorp Arch, Wetherby, West Yorkshire, LS23 7BJ Tel: (01937) 849932 Fax: (01937) 849836 E-mail: opticsasiaukltd@aol.com

OPTICAL PROJECTORS

Baty International, Victoria Road, Burgess Hill, West Sussex, RH15 9LB Tel: (01444) 235621 Fax: (01444) 246985E-mail: sales@baty.co.uk
▶ G P S Installations, Morgan Business Centre, Mylord CR, Camperdown Industrial Estate, Newcastle upon Tyne, NE12 5UJ Tel: 0191-216 1200 Fax: 0191-216 1200 E-mail: sales@gpsinstallations.co.uk
Optical Technology Training Ltd, Carleton Business Park, Carleton New Road, Skipton, North Yorkshire, BD23 2AA Tel: (01756) 797155 Fax: (01756) 797112

OPTICAL SCANNER MANUFRS

Data & Research Services plc, Sunrise Parkway, Linford Wood, Milton Keynes, MK14 6LR Tel: (01908) 666088 Fax: (01908) 607668 E-mail: enquiries@drs.co.uk

OPTICAL SUBSTRATES

Kaypul Optics Ltd, Unit 4 West Docks, Harbour Place, Burntisland, Fife, KY3 9DW Tel: (01592) 874140 Fax: (01592) 874140 E-mail: kaypulltd@aol.com

OPTICAL SUPPLY SERVICES

Arthur Hayes Opticians Ltd, 1070 Whitgift Centre, Croydon, CR0 1UX Tel: (020) 8686 0707
Cambridge Optical Group Ltd, PO Box 76, Cambridge, CB3 8SH Tel: (01954) 781259 Fax: (01954) 789807 E-mail: admin@cambridge-optical.com
Cerium Group Ltd, Cerium Industrial Park, Appledore Road, Tenterden, Kent, TN30 7DE Tel: (01580) 765211 Fax: (01580) 765573 E-mail: ceriumgrp@aol.com
Dolland & Aitchison Ltd, 35 Wigmore Street, London, W1U 1PW Tel: (020) 7580 4343 Fax: (020) 7580 3966
Gerber Coburn Optical UK Ltd, 1600 Aztec West, Almondsbury, Bristol, BS32 4UA Tel: (01454) 200780 Fax: (01454) 200787 E-mail: info@gerbercoburn.co.uk
Grafton Optical Co. Ltd, 2a Cherry Tree Walk, London, EC1Y 8NX Tel: (020) 7628 7358 Fax: (020) 7628 7359 E-mail: frames@graftonop.fsnet.co.uk
In Focus Ltd, Wild Fowl Trust Newgrounds, Slimbridge, Gloucester, GL2 7BT Tel: (01453) 890978 Fax: (01453) 890267 E-mail: infocus@netcomuk.co.uk
Medirex Opticans, 28-29 Wilcox Close, London, SW8 2UD Tel: (020) 7622 1893 Fax: (020) 7652 0033 E-mail:
Menrad Optics Ltd, Unit 4, Bone Lane, Newbury, Berkshire, RG14 5SH Tel: (01635) 32123 Fax: (01635) 38442 E-mail: jenny@menrad.co.uk
Microsoft Research Ltd, 7 JJ Thomson Avenue, Madingley Road, Cambridge, CB3 0FB Tel: (01223) 479700 Fax: (01223) 479999
P G Allder & Partners Ltd, 3a Peacock Alley, Leighton Buzzard, Bedfordshire, LU7 1HF Tel: (01525) 372664 Fax: (01525) 372996 E-mail: headoffice@alldersopticians.com
J.J. Vickers & Sons Ltd, Unit 9, 35 Revenge Road, Lordswood, Chatham, Kent, ME5 8DW Tel: (01634) 201284 Fax: (01634) 201286 E-mail: sales@jjvickers.co.uk
Wyvern Optical Ltd, 87 Narborough Road, Leicester, LE3 0LF Tel: 0116-254 8431 E-mail: wyvern1947@aol.com

OPTICAL TELESCOPES

Optical Vision Ltd, Unit 3 Woolpit Business Park, Windmill Avenue, Woolpit, Bury St. Edmunds, Suffolk, IP30 9UP Tel: (01359) 244200 Fax: (01359) 244255 E-mail: info@opticalvision.co.uk
Simden Optical Ltd, Haugh Lane, Blaydon-on-Tyne, Tyne & Wear, NE21 4SA Tel: 0191-499 0122 Fax: 0191-414 4723

OPTOELECTRONIC COMPONENT MANUFRS

Centronic Ltd, Centronic House, King Henrys Drive, New Addington, Croydon, CR9 0BG Tel: (01689) 808000 Fax: (01689) 841822 E-mail: info@centronic.co.uk
Chromatechnic Ltd, 35 Princes Street, Ulverston, Cumbria, LA12 7NQ Tel: (01229) 581551 E-mail: edavidson@chromatechnic.com
Electron Technologies Ltd, Bury Street, Ruislip, Middlesex, HA4 7TA Tel: (01895) 630771 Fax: (01895) 635953 E-mail: info@electron-tubes.co.uk
IsoCom Components Ltd, Unit 25B, Park View Road West, Park View Industrial Estate, Brenda Road, Hartlepool, Cleveland, TS25 1UD Tel: (01429) 863609 Fax: (01429) 863581 E-mail: sales@isocom.co.uk
Livewire Electronic Components Ltd, CWM Farm Barn, Llantrisant, Usk, Gwent, NP15 1LG Tel: (01291) 673003 Fax: (01291) 671001 E-mail: info@livewire.uk.com
O M C UK Ltd, Candela House, Cardrew Industrial Estate, Redruth, Cornwall, TR15 1SS Tel: (01209) 215424 Fax: (01209) 215197 E-mail: omc-sales@omc-uk.com
P R P Optoelectronics Ltd, Woodburcote Way, Towcester, Northamptonshire, NN12 6TF Tel: (01327) 359135 Fax: (01327) 359602 E-mail: sales@prpopto.co.uk
Pacer Components plc, Unit 4 Horseshoe Park, Pangbourne, Reading, RG8 7JW Tel: 0118-984 5280 Fax: 0118-984 5425 E-mail: pacer@pacer.co.uk
Photek Ltd, 26 Castleham Road, St. Leonards-On-Sea, East Sussex, TN38 9NS Tel: (01424) 850555 Fax: (01424) 850051 E-mail: sales@photek.co.uk
Selectronic Ltd, Book End, Witney, Oxfordshire, OX29 0YE Tel: (01993) 778000 Fax: (01993) 772512 E-mail: sales@selectronic-ltd.co.uk
Thales Optronics, 1 Linthouse Road, Glasgow, G51 4BZ Tel: 0141-440 4000 Fax: 0141-440 4001 E-mail: sales@optronics.co.uk

OPTOELECTRONIC EQUIPMENT

Photek Ltd, 26 Castleham Road, St. Leonards-On-Sea, East Sussex, TN38 9NS Tel: (01424) 850555 Fax: (01424) 850051 E-mail: sales@photek.co.uk
Thales Optronics, 1 Linthouse Road, Glasgow, G51 4BZ Tel: 0141-440 4000 Fax: 0141-440 4001 E-mail: sales@optronics.co.uk

OPTOELECTRONIC SWITCHES

IsoCom Components Ltd, Unit 25B, Park View Road West, Park View Industrial Estate, Brenda Road, Hartlepool, Cleveland, TS25 1UD Tel: (01429) 863609 Fax: (01429) 863581 E-mail: sales@isocom.co.uk

ORBITAL WELDING

▶ Orbimatic UK, 7 The Manor Grove Centre, Vicarage Farm Road, Peterborough, PE1 5UH Tel: (01733) 555285 Fax: (01733) 555831
Rideout Engineering Ltd, 197 South Liberty Lane, Bristol, BS3 2TN Tel: 0117-953 8900 Fax: 0117-953 8800

ORBITAL WELDING EQUIPMENT

▶ Orbimatic UK, 7 The Manor Grove Centre, Vicarage Farm Road, Peterborough, PE1 5UH Tel: (01733) 555285 Fax: (01733) 555831

ORDER PICKING EQUIPMENT

Digitron Translift Ltd, Hallcroft Road, Retford, Nottinghamshire, DN22 7PT Tel: (01777) 707511 Fax: (01777) 860778
Vanriet UK Ltd, W Riverside Industrial Estate, Atherstone Street, Fazeley, Tamworth, Staffordshire, B78 3RW Tel: (01827) 288871 Fax: (01827) 250810 E-mail: sales@vanriet.co.uk

ORGANIC BAKERY PRODUCTS

▶ Rebecca Rayner, Glebe Farm, Kings Ripton, Huntingdon, Cambridgeshire, PE28 2NL Tel: 01487 773282

ORGANIC CERTIFIED FLOUR

▶ Rebecca Rayner, Glebe Farm, Kings Ripton, Huntingdon, Cambridgeshire, PE28 2NL Tel: 01487 773282

ORGANIC CERTIFIED FOOD INGREDIENTS

Eco Health & Grainstore, 50 Hillfoot Street, Dunoon, Argyll, PA23 7DT Tel: (01369) 705106
▶ Elysium Natural Products Ltd, Unit 12, Moderna Business Park, Moderna Way, Mytholmroyd, Hebden Bridge, West Yorkshire, HX7 5QQ Tel: (01422) 885523 Fax: (01422) 884629 E-mail: elysiumproducts@aol.com
▶ Going Organic, Ware, Hertfordshire, SG12 Tel: (01920) 484856 E-mail: info@goingorganic.co.uk
▶ Local Farmers Markets, 29 Compton Street, Chesterfield, Derbyshire, S40 4TA Tel: 01246 230302
MotherHemp Ltd, Spring Dale Farm, Rudston, Diffield, East Riding of Yorkshire, YO25 4DJ Tel: (01262) 421100 Fax: (020) 7691 7475 E-mail: contact@motherhemp.com
▶ Rebecca Rayner, Glebe Farm, Kings Ripton, Huntingdon, Cambridgeshire, PE28 2NL Tel: 01487 773282
Wild Thymes, 2 Hughenden Yard, High Street, Marlborough, Wiltshire, SN8 1LT Tel: (01672) 516373 Fax: (01672) 516373

ORGANIC CERTIFIED FRUIT

Cornflower Wholefoods, 49 High Street, Brightlingsea, Colchester, CO7 0AQ Tel: (01206) 306679 Fax: (01206) 308515 E-mail: cornflowerbsea@aol.com
The East India Shipping Co., 7 Norfolk Cottages, Kings Cross Lane, South Nutfield, Redhill, RH1 5NG Tel: (07866) 638288 E-mail: theeastindiashippingcompany@yahoo.co.uk
Eco Health & Grainstore, 50 Hillfoot Street, Dunoon, Argyll, PA23 7DT Tel: (01369) 705106
▶ Going Organic, Ware, Hertfordshire, SG12 Tel: (01920) 484856 E-mail: info@goingorganic.co.uk

ORGANIC CERTIFIED VEGETABLES

Cornflower Wholefoods, 49 High Street, Brightlingsea, Colchester, CO7 0AQ Tel: (01206) 306679 Fax: (01206) 308515 E-mail: cornflowerbsea@aol.com
The East India Shipping Co., 7 Norfolk Cottages, Kings Cross Lane, South Nutfield, Redhill, RH1 5NG Tel: (07866) 638288 E-mail: theeastindiashippingcompany@yahoo.co.uk
Eco Health & Grainstore, 50 Hillfoot Street, Dunoon, Argyll, PA23 7DT Tel: (01369) 705106
▶ Going Organic, Ware, Hertfordshire, SG12 Tel: (01920) 484856 E-mail: info@goingorganic.co.uk

ORGANIC FERTILISERS

John Hatcher Co. Ltd, Walton House, 218 High Street, Felixstowe, Suffolk, IP11 9DS Tel: (01394) 274321 Fax: (01394) 278600 E-mail: sales@hatcher.co.uk
Timac UK Ltd, Bath Road Industrial Estate, Bath Road, Chippenham, Wiltshire, SN14 0AB Tel: (01249) 467100 Fax: (01249) 660232

ORGANIC FOOD PRODUCTS

▶ The Olive Oil Store, 1 Saffron Road, Chafford Hundred, Grays, Essex, RM16 6NA Tel: 01375 483863 E-mail: sales@oliveoilstore.co.uk

ORGANIC PEST CONTROL

▶ Peter Cox Ltd, John O Gaunts Trading Estate, Leeds Road, Rothwell, Leeds, LS26 0JB Tel: 0113-282 5316 Fax: 0113-393 4927 E-mail: petercox.leeds@ecolab.com

ORGANISATIONAL DEVELOPMENT (OD) HUMAN RESOURCES (HR) COMPUTER SOFTWARE

▶ Lasa Development UK Ltd, Little Manor, Itlay, Daglingworth, Cirencester, Gloucestershire, GL7 7HZ Tel: (01285) 643469 E-mail: info@lasadev.com

ORGANISATIONAL RESOURCES CONSULTANCY

AMJ (UK), Epps Buildings, Bridge Road, Ashford, Kent, TN23 1BB Tel: (01233) 663205 Fax: (01233) 664181E-mail: info@amj-uk.com
Hay Group, Unit 2635 Kings Court, The Crescent, Birmingham Business Park, Birmingham, B37 7YE Tel: 0121-717 4600 Fax: 0121-717 4601
Jay Engineering Consultancy Ltd, 178 Aldridge Road, Streetly, Sutton Coldfield, West Midlands, B74 3TP Tel: 0121-353 6400 Fax: 0121-353 9600 E-mail: john.butler@iee.org

ORGANOMETALLIC COMPOUNDS

▶ Alfa Aesar, Shore Road, Port Of Heysham Industrial Park, Heysham, Morecambe, Lancashire, LA3 2XY Tel: (01524) 850506 Fax: (01524) 850608 E-mail: uksales@alfa.com

ORIENTAL GOODS IMPORT MERCHANTS OR AGENTS

Joseph Lavian, Oriental Carpet Centre, 105 Eade Road, London, N4 1TJ Tel: (020) 8800 0707 Fax: (020) 8800 0404 E-mail: lavian@lavian.com

ORIENTATED POLYPROPYLENE (OPP) FILM

Precision Formes Ltd, 13 Glegg Street, Liverpool, L3 7DX Tel: 0151-207 2446 Fax: 0151-298 1539 E-mail: info@pfl3.co.uk
Skymark Packaging International Ltd, Southern Avenue, Leominster, Herefordshire, HR6 0QF Tel: (01568) 611393 Fax: (01568) 611602 E-mail: info@skymark.co.uk

ORIFICE FLANGES

Folglade Pipe & Fittings Ltd, Penlake Industrial Estate, Reginald Road, Sutton, St. Helens, Merseyside, WA9 4JA Tel: (01744) 820119 Fax: (01744) 811412 E-mail: sales@folglade.co.uk

ORIGINAL DESIGN ARTWORK

▶ A Anthony Art, 4 Stanhope Road, Horncastle, Lincolnshire, LN9 5DG Tel: (01507) 526487 Fax: (01507) 526487 E-mail: tonyfield@btinternet.com
Simon Birtall, West Kirby, Wirral, Merseyside, CH48 2HL Tel: (0779) 0471098 E-mail: simon@birtall.co.uk
▶ Digital Design Canvas UK, 10, churchbury rd, enfield, middx, EN1 3HR Tel: 0208 3646205 E-mail: enquiries@digitaldesignuk.co.uk
▶ Flameboy Graphix, 9 Halliday Drive, Armley, Leeds, LS12 3PA Tel: 01132 891205 Fax: 0113 891205 E-mail: info@flameboygraphix.co.uk
▶ My Modern Art, 81 Beveley Road, Oakengates, Telford, Shropshire, TF2 6SD Tel: (07740) 338778 E-mail: sales@mymodernart.co.uk
▶ Snout Ltd, 9 The Lime Kilns, Barrow upon Soar, Loughborough, Leicestershire, LE12 8YF Tel: (01509) 415643 E-mail: info@snoutthings.co.uk

ORNAMENTAL CONCRETE PRODUCTS

Albion Architectural Concrete Ltd, Newbrook Works, Pound Lane, Upper Beeding, Steyning, West Sussex, BN44 3JD Tel: (01903) 815262 Fax: (01903) 815619 E-mail: mike@albionart.co.uk

ORNAMENTAL GATES

Adams Sandy Engng, Fordoun Aerodrome, Fordoun, Laurencekirk, Kincardineshire, AB30 1JR Tel: (01561) 320800 Fax: (01561) 320811 E-mail: info@sandyadamsengineering.co.uk
Ag Con Products Ltd, 45 Newtown Road, Rostrevor, Newry, County Down, BT34 3BZ Tel: (028) 4173 8963 Fax: (028) 4173 8971 E-mail: brian@ag.con.fsnet.co.uk
Arc Fabrication Ltd, 2 Gourley Place, London, N15 5NF Tel: (020) 8800 2557 Fax: (020) 7706 1248 E-mail: sales@arcfabrications.com
City Gate Automation, 32 Hetherington Road, Shepperton, Middlesex, TW17 0SP Tel: (01932) 786464 Fax: (01932) 766199
Cruddas Security Services Ltd, 1 Oak Street Industrial Park, Oak Street, Cradley Heath, West Midlands, B64 5JY Tel: (01384) 569307 Fax: (01384) 569307
Forge Fabrications, 8 South Street, Crowland, Peterborough, PE6 0AJ Tel: (01733) 211441 Fax: (01733) 211258 E-mail: justin@forgefabrications.co.uk
Forge Group, Holbrook Commerce Park, Holbrook Close Holbrook Indust Estate, Holbrook, Sheffield, S20 3FJ Tel: 0114-248 2222 Fax: 0114-248 2222
Gate Place, 16 Boston Road, Leicester, LE4 1AU Tel: 0116-236 6525 Fax: 0116-236 6525
Iron Awe, Unit 24 Lansil Walk, Lansil Industrial Estate, Lancaster, LA1 3PQ Tel: (01524) 845511 Fax: (01524) 845511 E-mail: petersmalley@ironawe.com
J A Roskelly & Son, The Forge, 19 Penmare Terrace, Hayle, Cornwall, TR27 4PH Tel: (01736) 753160
Leicester Wrought Iron Co., 25-27 Thurcaston Road, Leicester, LE4 5PG Tel: 0116-266 3566 Fax: 0116-266 3566
R Ekin, Claylands Avenue, Worksop, Nottinghamshire, S81 7BE Tel: (01909) 472638 Fax: (01909) 472638
Reddick Forge, Crawley Down Road, Felbridge, East Grinstead, West Sussex, RH19 2PS Tel: (01342) 302055 Fax: (01342) 302055 E-mail: sales@reddickforge.co.uk

ORNAMENTAL GATES – *continued*

S Burvill & Son Ltd, The Forge Cossins Farm, Downside Road, Downside, Cobham, Surrey, KT11 3LZ Tel: (01932) 589666 Fax: (01932) 589669

Scroll Gates, Southampton Road, Eastleigh, Hampshire, SO50 5QT Tel: (023) 8061 2028 Fax: (023) 8061 2028 E-mail: sales@scrollgates.com

Steeltech Kinetix Ltd, Dancroft Works, Gauxholme Fold, Todmorden, Lancashire, OL14 7PW Tel: (01706) 817144 Fax: (01706) 817522 E-mail: mail@steeltech-kinetix.co.uk

Town & Country Gates & Railings, Unit 6e Waterloo Industrial Estate, Gorsey Mount Street, Stockport, Cheshire, SK1 3BU Tel: 0161-429 7325 Fax: 0161-480 4388 E-mail: philbohen@aol.com

W B Engineering, 13 Paynes Lane, Rugby, Warwickshire, CV21 2UH Tel: (01788) 565225 Fax: (01788) 565225

ORNAMENTAL IRON CASTINGS

Cast Metal Repairs Ltd, High Street Mills, High St, Heckmondwike, W. Yorkshire, WF16 0DL Tel: (01924) 403444 Fax: (01924) 410164 E-mail: tranter@rhodesengineering.co.uk

Coyle Fabrications, Culdee House, Culdee Drive, Armagh, BT61 7RJ Tel: (028) 3752 3753 Fax: (028) 3751 1526 E-mail: info@coylefabrications.com

Hathern Forge, Hathern Nurseries, Derby Road, Hathern, Loughborough, Leicestershire, LE12 5LD Tel: (01509) 646990 Fax: (01509) 646990 E-mail: sales@hathernforge.co.uk

Iron Art, Unit 1, Birch Industrial Estate, Eastbourne, East Sussex, BN23 6PH Tel: (01323) 722784 Fax: (01323) 722784 E-mail: info@iron-art.co.uk

ORNAMENTAL WROUGHT IRON GATES

▶ Distinctive Gates & Railings, Enterprise House, 260 Chorley New Road, Horwich, Bolton, BL6 5NY Tel: (01204) 699675 Fax: (01204) 668300 E-mail: enquiries@bendtube.co.uk

▶ Sillars Iron Art, 42 Rannoch Place, Castlepark, Irvine, Ayrshire, KA12 9NQ Tel: (01294) 230774 E-mail: briansillars810@msn.com

ORTHODONTIC EQUIPMENT

▶ Hotwire Orthodontics, Highgate Works, Tomtits Lane, Forest Row, East Sussex, RH18 5AT Tel: (01342) 827750

ORTHOPAEDIC APPLIANCE/ EQUIPMENT

A C Tonks Orthopaedics Ltd, 5 Riverside Industrial Estate, Meir Road, Redditch, Worcestershire, B98 7SY Tel: (01527) 518611 Fax: (01527) 518612 E-mail: office@actonks.co.uk

Consort Engineering (Ashton-under-Lyne) Ltd, Commercial Brow, Hyde, Cheshire, SK14 2JR Tel: 0161-366 6883 Fax: 0161-366 9703

Cox Orthopaedic, 108 Whitechapel Road, London, E1 1JD Tel: (020) 7247 1178 Fax: (020) 7247 0622 E-mail: enquiries@coxortho.com

E Smith & Co, Albion Street, Hull, HU1 3TE Tel: (01482) 324599 Fax: (01482) 588266

▶ Finsbury Instruments Ltd, Unit 13 Mole Business Park, Randalls Road, Leatherhead, Surrey, KT22 7BA Tel: (01372) 360830 Fax: (01372) 360779 E-mail: sales@finsbury.org

Gilbert & Mellish Ltd, 3 Lightning Way, Birmingham, B31 3PH Tel: 0121-475 1101 Fax: 0121-478 0163 E-mail: sales@gilbert-mellish.co.uk

Kettering Surgical Appliances Ltd, 73 Overstone Road, Northampton, NN1 3JW Tel: (01604) 622886 Fax: (01604) 629689 E-mail: paul@ketteringsurgical.com

Prescription Footwear Associates Ltd, P F A House, Lake Lane, Barnham, Bognor Regis, West Sussex, PO22 0JB Tel: (01243) 554407 Fax: (01243) 554407 E-mail: sales@pfa.sageweb.co.uk

Promedics Ltd, Moorgate Street, Blackburn, BB2 4PB Tel: (01254) 619000 Fax: (01254) 619001 E-mail: sales@promedics.co.uk

ORTHOPAEDIC CHAIRS

Will Beck Ltd, Kitchener Road, High Wycombe, Buckinghamshire, HP11 2SW Tel: (0845) 4500444 Fax: (0845) 4500445 E-mail: sales@wil.co.uk

Electric Mobility Euro Ltd, Canal Way, Ilminster, Somerset, TA19 9DL Tel: (01460) 258100 Fax: (01460) 258125 E-mail: sales@electricmobility.co.uk

▶ Thomas Doran Parkanaur Trust, 57 Parkanaur Road, Dungannon, County Tyrone, BT70 3AA Tel: (028) 8776 1272 Fax: (028) 8776 9428 E-mail: info@parkupholstery.plus.com

ORTHOPAEDIC CUTTING/ THREADING TOOLS

T-Tech Tooling Ltd, 70 Prince Of Wales Lane, Yardley Wood, Birmingham, B14 4JZ Tel: 0121-474 2255 Fax: 0121-474 2066 E-mail: sales@t-tech.co.uk

ORTHOPAEDIC GOODS, *See Surgical etc*

ORTHOPAEDIC INDUSTRY MATERIALS

Depuy International Holdings Ltd, St Anthonys Road, Beeston, Leeds, LS11 8DT Tel: 0113-270 0461 Fax: 0113-272 4101 E-mail: depuy@dpygb.jnj.com

ORTHOPAEDIC INSTRUMENTS

Surgical Holdings Ltd, 8 Parkside Centre, Potters Way, Southend-on-Sea, SS2 5SJ Tel: (01702) 602050 Fax: (01702) 460006 E-mail: office@surgicalholdings.co.uk

ORTHOPHOTOGRAPHIC MAPPING

3di International, Brighton Road, Shoreham-by-Sea, West Sussex, BN43 6RE Tel: (01273) 464883 Fax: (01273) 454238 E-mail: sussex@3dillc.com

B K S Survey Group Ltd, Ballycairn Road, Coleraine, County Londonderry, BT51 3HZ Tel: (028) 7035 2311 Fax: (028) 7035 7637 E-mail: sales@bks.co.uk

Simmons Aerofilms, 32-34 Station Close, Potters Bar, Hertfordshire, EN6 1TL Tel: (01707) 648390 Fax: (01707) 648399 E-mail: library@aerofilms.com

OSCILLATORS

Total Frequency Control Ltd, Units 3-4 Mill Lane, Storrington, West Sussex, RH20 4NF Tel: (01903) 740000 Fax: (01903) 742208 E-mail: sales@tfc.co.uk

Vitec Group Communications Ltd, 7400 Beach Drive, Cambridge Research Park, Cambridge, CB25 9TP Tel: (01223) 815000 Fax: (01223) 815001 E-mail: vgc.uk@vitecgroup.com

OSCILLOSCOPES, *See also headings for particular types*

Hameg UK Ltd, 18 Glebe Lane, Buckden, St. Neots, Cambridgeshire, PE19 5TG Tel: (01480) 812100 Fax: (01480) 819187 E-mail: hameguk@btopenworld.com

Pico Technology Ltd, The Mill House, Cambridge Street, St. Neots, Cambridgeshire, PE19 1QB Tel: (01480) 396395 Fax: (01480) 396296 E-mail: vikki@picotech.com

▶ S J Electronics, Unit 3 Vernon Court, Henson Way, Telford Way Industrial Estate, Kettering, Northamptonshire, NN16 8PX Tel: (01536) 416200 Fax: (01536) 416300 E-mail: sales@sjelectronics.co.uk

OSIER

▶ Musgrove Willows, Lakewall, Westonzoyland, Bridgwater, Somerset, TA7 0LP Tel: (01278) 691105 Fax: (01278) 699107 E-mail: info@musgrovewillows.co.uk

OUTBOARD ENGINE ACCESSORIES

▶ Aqua Marine Ltd, Units 14 & 15 Penton Hook Marina, Staines Road, Chertsey, Surrey, KT16 8PY Tel: 01932 570202 Fax: (01932) 570222 E-mail: info@aquamarineuk.com

▶ NB Marine, Ainwee, Rahane, Helensburgh, Dunbartonshire, G84 0QW Tel: (020) 7870 6247 E-mail: mail@nbmairne.co.uk

OUTDOOR ADVERTISING COLUMNS

▶ John Comaish Advertising Services, Unit 17, Sefton Lane Industrial Estate, Maghull, L31 8BX Tel: 0151-520 4330 E-mail: enquires@comaish.co.uk

▶ Marketing Force Ltd, Cliff House, Chevalier Road, Felixstowe, Suffolk, IP11 7EJ Tel: (01394) 672467 Fax: (01394) 672468 E-mail: marketingforce@digitalflair.co.uk

OUTDOOR ADVERTISING FLAGS

▶ John Comaish Advertising Services, Unit 17, Sefton Lane Industrial Estate, Maghull, L31 8BX Tel: 0151-520 4330 E-mail: enquires@comaish.co.uk

▶ Marketing Force Ltd, Cliff House, Chevalier Road, Felixstowe, Suffolk, IP11 7EJ Tel: (01394) 672467 Fax: (01394) 672468 E-mail: marketingforce@digitalflair.co.uk

OUTDOOR ADVERTISING LIGHT BOXES

▶ John Comaish Advertising Services, Unit 17, Sefton Lane Industrial Estate, Maghull, L31 8BX Tel: 0151-520 4330 E-mail: enquires@comaish.co.uk

OUTDOOR CATERING

▶ Occasions Caterers Ltd, Unit 22 Bow Triangle Business, Centre Eleanor Street Bow, London, E3 4UR Tel: (020) 8980 2770

OUTDOOR CHRISTMAS FESTIVE LIGHTING

Target Animations & Lighting, Fairlands, Main Road, Westerfield, Ipswich, IP6 9AA Tel: (01473) 255670 Fax: (0871) 9943275

OUTDOOR EVENT ORGANISING

▶ IN GEAR EVENT SUPPORT, Unit 7 Coppen Road, Dagenham, Essex, RM8 1HJ Tel: 020 8593 0550 Fax: 020 8593 0552 E-mail: Glenn@ingearevents.fsbusiness.co.uk

OUTDOOR EVENTS ELECTRICAL CONTRACTORS

▶ Craigs Electrical Co., 203 Kersey Crescent, Speen, Newbury, Berkshire, RG14 1SW Tel: (07876) 550331 Fax: (01635) 820308 E-mail: craig@youhirewewire.co.uk

OUTDOOR FURNITURE ACCESSORIES

▶ Budget Marquees, 18 Cliff Hill, Gorleston, Great Yarmouth, Norfolk, NR31 6DQ Tel: (01493) 300721 E-mail: info@BudgetMarquees.co.uk

▶ GoAfrica, 34 St. Barnabas Street, Wellingborough, Northamptonshire, NN8 3HB Tel: (0845) 6447984 E-mail: gwen@goafrica.co.uk

Mode Lifestyle, Winsham, Chard, Somerset, TA20 4BZ Tel: (0870) 2403606 E-mail: e@mode.co.uk

▶ North East Outdoor, 27A Skinner Street, Whitby, North Yorkshire, YO21 3AH Tel: (01947) 600616 E-mail: sales@neoutdoor.co.uk

▶ Supergreenthumb, London, London, N22 6SD Tel: 0800 917 4252

OUTDOOR GARDEN OR LEISURE LIGHTING

▶ Babylon Garden Design, 5 Linksway, Leigh-on-Sea, Essex, SS9 4QY Tel: (01702) 527242 E-mail: discover@babylon-gardens.co.uk

Brilliant (UK) Ltd, Hanworth Trading Estate, Hampton Road West, Feltham, Middlesex, TW13 6DR Tel: (020) 8898 3131 Fax: (020) 8898 3232 E-mail: sales@brilliant-ag.com

▶ Lighting for Gardens Ltd, 20 Furmston Court, Letchworth Garden City, Hertfordshire, SG6 1UJ Tel: (01462) 486777 Fax: (01462) 480344 E-mail: sales@lightingforgardens.com

Litex Design, Unit 4 Empire Centre, Imperial Way, Watford, WD24 4YH Tel: (01923) 247254 Fax: (01923) 226772 E-mail: joshea@litex.demon.co.uk

Turnock Ltd, Reaymer Close, Walsall, WS2 7QZ Tel: (01922) 710422 Fax: (01922) 710428

Woodhouse UK plc, Harrison Way, Leamington Spa, Warwickshire, CV31 3HL Tel: (01926) 314313 Fax: (01926) 883778 E-mail: enquires@woodhouse.co.uk

OUTDOOR PLANT POTS

Dingley Dell Enterprises, Kidderminster, Worcestershire, DY14 9ZE Tel: (01905) 621636 Fax: (01905) 620311

OUTDOOR SEATING

Lyngrade Lancashire Ltd, Unit 23 Hardmans Business Centre, New Hall Hey Road, Rossendale, Lancashire, BB4 6HH Tel: (01706) 212780 Fax: (01706) 212816 E-mail: info@lyngrade.co.uk

OUTDOOR SMOKING SHELTERS

▶ Nim (Ltd Engineering), Yardley House, 100 Chase Park Road, Yardley Hastings, Northampton, NN7 1HF Tel: (01604) 696120 Fax: (01604) 696122 E-mail: info@nimltdengineering.com

OUTERWEAR

▶ Barrie Lewis & Co. Ltd, Units 1 & 2, Bedwas Business Centre, Bedwas, Caerphilly, Mid Glamorgan, CF83 8DU Tel: (029) 2088 6846

▶ David Barry (London) Ltd, 7-9 Solebay St, London, E1 4PW Tel: (020) 7790 1952

▶ Beste Fashions, 10 Millers Avenue, London, E8 2DS Tel: (020) 7241 1009 Fax: (020) 7241 1011

▶ Charles & Patricia Lester Ltd, Old Workhouse, Union Road West, Abergavenny, Gwent, NP7 7RL Tel: (01873) 853559 Fax: (01873) 858666

▶ Clyde Kilts Ltd, 71 James Street, Glasgow, G40 1BZ Tel: 0141-554 4649

▶ Dewhirst Group, 204 Great Portland Street, London, W1W 5HU Tel: (020) 7388 7631 Fax: (020) 7383 4997

▶ E Walters UK, Southern Avenue, Leominster, Herefordshire, HR6 0LY Tel: (01568) 613344 Fax: (01568) 610860 E-mail: reception@ewalters.co.uk

▶ Flame UK Ltd, 1 Mode Wheel Road, Salford, M5 5DQ Tel: 0161-737 2115 Fax: 0161-736 0871

▶ Gee Bee Fashions, 88 Crabmill Lane, Coventry, CV6 5HA Tel: (024) 7663 7022 Fax: (024) 7663 7022

▶ Life Tradings Ltd, 32 Mason St, Manchester, M4 5EY Tel: 0161-834 5838 Fax: 0161-834 4498 E-mail: lifetrading@yahoo.com

▶ Mistflex Ltd, 6 5 Fountayne Road, London, N15 4QL Tel: (020) 8808 3345 Fax: (020) 8808 3324

▶ S S Johal & Sons Ltd, 97 Monk Street, Derby, DE22 3QE Tel: (01332) 343005 Fax: (01332) 332950

▶ Saga Fashions, Clarence House, 1 Hilda Road, Chatham, Kent, ME4 5PU Tel: (01634) 826520

▶ Andrew Shane Ltd, 157 Nottingham Road, Somercotes, Alfreton, Derbyshire, DE55 4JH Tel: (01773) 541414 Fax: (01773) 541415 E-mail: andrewshane@btconnect.com

▶ Sunnyville Clothing Ltd, East Park Works, 69 St. Barnabas Road, Leicester, LE5 4BE Tel: 0116-246 1988 Fax: 0116-246 1988

OUTERWEAR, LADIES'

▶ Armondi Ltd, Unit 2 Crusader Industrial Estate, 167 Hermitage Road, London, N4 1LZ Tel: (020) 8800 4441

▶ Barrie Lewis & Co. Ltd, Units 1 & 2, Bedwas Business Centre, Bedwas, Caerphilly, Mid Glamorgan, CF83 8DU Tel: (029) 2088 6846

▶ David Barry (London) Ltd, 7-9 Solebay St, London, E1 4PW Tel: (020) 7790 1952

▶ Beste Fashions, 10 Millers Avenue, London, E8 2DS Tel: (020) 7241 1009 Fax: (020) 7241 1011

▶ Bright Look Fashions, 33-35 Mere Lane, Rochdale, Lancashire, OL11 3TD Tel: (01706) 345322 Fax: (01706) 711611

▶ Charles & Patricia Lester Ltd, Old Workhouse, Union Road West, Abergavenny, Gwent, NP7 7RL Tel: (01873) 853559 Fax: (01873) 858666

▶ Clyde Kilts Ltd, 71 James Street, Glasgow, G40 1BZ Tel: 0141-554 4649

▶ Dewhirst Group, 204 Great Portland Street, London, W1W 5HU Tel: (020) 7388 7631 Fax: (020) 7383 4997

▶ E Walters UK, Southern Avenue, Leominster, Herefordshire, HR6 0LY Tel: (01568) 613344 Fax: (01568) 610860 E-mail: reception@ewalters.co.uk

▶ Flame UK Ltd, 1 Mode Wheel Road, Salford, M5 5DQ Tel: 0161-737 2115 Fax: 0161-736 0871

▶ Gee Bee Fashions, 88 Crabmill Lane, Coventry, CV6 5HA Tel: (024) 7663 7022 Fax: (024) 7663 7022

▶ Jacques Vert (Retail) Ltd, Webber Pavilion, Seaham Grange Industrial Estat, Seaham, County Durham, SR7 0PZ Tel: 0191-521 3555

▶ Life Tradings Ltd, 32 Mason St, Manchester, M4 5EY Tel: 0161-834 5838 Fax: 0161-834 4498 E-mail: lifetrading@yahoo.com

▶ Maggie Carol Ltd, Unit 1 & 2, Fallbarn Road, Rossendale, Lancashire, BB4 7NT Tel: (01706) 228879

▶ Mistflex Ltd, 6 5 Fountayne Road, London, N15 4QL Tel: (020) 8808 3345 Fax: (020) 8808 3324

▶ S S Johal & Sons Ltd, 97 Monk Street, Derby, DE22 3QE Tel: (01332) 343005 Fax: (01332) 332950

OUTERWEAR, LADIES' – *continued*

▶ Saga Fashions, Clarence House, 1 Hilda Road, Chatham, Kent, ME4 5PU Tel: (01634) 826520

▶ Andrew Shane Ltd, 157 Nottingham Road, Somercotes, Alfreton, Derbyshire, DE55 4JH Tel: (01773) 541414 Fax: (01773) 541415 E-mail: andrewshane@btconnect.com

▶ Sunnyville Clothing Ltd, East Park Works, 69 St. Barnabas Road, Leicester, LE5 4BE Tel: 0116-246 1988 Fax: 0116-246 1988

▶ Sylvia Jeffreys, Queensway, Wrexham, Clwyd, LL13 8YR Tel: (01978) 360390 Fax: (01978) 361684

OUTPLACEMENT CONSULTANCY

▶ Lifescales, Spectrum House, Dunstable Road, Redbourn, St. Albans, Hertfordshire, AL3 7PR Tel: (0845) 6381330 E-mail: info@workscales.co.uk

Mobifax UK Ltd, Units 3-4 Ash Court, Crystal Drive, Sandwell Business Park, Smethwick, West Midlands, B66 1QG Tel: 0121-541 1604 Fax: 0121-541 1605

▶ Oakwell Consultants, Billing Arbours House, Heather Lane, Northampton, NN3 8EY Tel: (01604) 413888 Fax: (0870) 1304049 E-mail: sales@oakwell-consultants.fsnet.co.uk

OUTSIDE BROADCAST MICROPHONE WINDSHIELDS

Rycote Microphone Windshields Ltd, Libbys Drive, Stroud, Gloucestershire, GL5 1RN Tel: (01453) 759338 Fax: (01453) 764249 E-mail: info@rycote.com

OUTSIDE CATERING

Penni Black Ltd, 14 Lyminge Gardens, Wandsworth, London, SW18 3JS Tel: (0800) 3896107 Fax: (020) 8870 9422 E-mail: charlotte@penniblack.co.uk

▶ C J G, Box Bush Farm, Oxenhall Lane, Gorsley, Ross-on-Wye, Herefordshire, HR9 7BJ Tel: (01989) 720788 Fax: (01989) 720788 E-mail: cathy@cjgcatering.co.uk

The Cook & The Butler Event Company Ltd, Blackfriars Foundry Annexe, 65 Glasshill Street, London, SE1 0QR Tel: (020) 7620 1818 Fax: (020) 7620 1820 E-mail: cookandbutler@btconnect.com

Creative Canapes, Unit D12, Barwell Business Park, Leatherhead Road, Chessington, Surrey, KT9 2NY Tel: (0845) 3668811 E-mail: enquiries@creativecanapes.co.uk

▶ Fodder Mongers, 3 Barratt Industrial Park, Whittle Avenue, Fareham, Hampshire, PO15 5SL Tel: (01489) 565040 Fax: (01489) 564041E-mail: enquiries@foddermongers.com

▶ Frenchy's Kitchen, 1 Cypress Close, Caerleon, Newport, NP18 3RN Tel: (01633) 431428 E-mail: pascal@frenchyskitchen.co.uk

▶ Great Taste, 5 Garfield Road, Netley Abbey, Southampton, SO31 5DN Tel: (023) 8045 3181 E-mail: enquiries@great-taste.co.uk

K2 Catering Ltd, PO Box 49808, London, NW5 2YA Tel: (07970) 425285 Fax: (020) 7284 1325 E-mail: ian@k2catering.com

▶ Minghella Isle Of Wight Ltd, High Street, Wootton Bridge, Ryde, Isle of Wight, PO33 4PL Tel: (01983) 883545 Fax: (01983) 883242 E-mail: sales@minghella.co.uk

▶ MRI Catering, 45 Bishops Way, Andover, Hampshire, SP10 3EH Tel: (01264) 339006 Fax: (01264) 363487 E-mail: kieran@mricatering.co.uk

▶ Peter Stuart, Falkners, Rectory Lane, Bramshott, Liphook, Hampshire, GU30 7QZ Tel: (01428) 727089

OUTSOURCING MANAGEMENT CONSULTANCY

▶ Biztech Business Consultants, Field Farm, Ashton Road, Minety, Malmesbury, Wiltshire, SN16 9QP Tel: (01666) 862000 Fax: (01666) 860594

OUTSOURCING PROPERTY CONSULTANCY

American Appraisal (UK) Ltd, Portland Buildings, 127-129 Portland Street, Manchester, M1 4PZ Tel: 0161-237 9907 Fax: 0161-237 9908

Land Securities Finance Ltd, 5 Strand, London, WC2N 5HR Tel: (020) 7413 9000 Fax: (020) 7920202 E-mail: landsecurities@landsecurites.com

▶ Tradesmen Recommended, Unit 10B, Dinting Lane Industrial Estate, Glossop, Derbyshire, SK13 7NU Tel: (01457) 856270 Fax: (01457) 862214 E-mail: enquiries@tradesmen-recommended.co.uk

OVEN CLEANING PRODUCTS

▶ Cookerburra Oven Cleaning Services, 18 Monterey Street, Manselton, Swansea, SA5 9PE Tel: 01792 475551 Fax: 01792 467765 E-mail: neil.cox@cookerburra.co.uk

OVEN CLEANING SERVICES

▶ Cookerburra Oven Cleaning Services, 18 Monterey Street, Manselton, Swansea, SA5 9PE Tel: 01792 475551 Fax: 01792 467765 E-mail: neil.cox@cookerburra.co.uk

Easycleaning-London Ltd, Unit 5, Egerton Court, Old Brompton Road, London, SW7 3HT Tel: (0800) 7312341 E-mail: easycleaning-london@lycos.com

▶ Kooka-Kleen, 27 Hayman Road, Ipswich, IP3 0HB Tel: 01473 429485 E-mail: chris@kookakleen.com

▶ Oven Butler, 17 Sheffield Road, Anston, Sheffield, S25 5DT Tel: (01909) 564411 E-mail: paul.allen15@btinternet.com

▶ Oven Master, 12 Fuchsia Close, Priorslee, Telford, Shropshire, TF2 9PG Tel: (01952) 210067 Fax: (01952) 210067 E-mail: ovenmaster@tiscali.co.uk

▶ Spotless Cleaning Services, 317 Coalburn Road, Coalburn, Lanark, ML11 0NF Tel: (01555) 820032 Fax: (01555) 820032 E-mail: spotless@email.com

OVEN ENGINEERS/ INSTALLATION/MAINTENANCE OR REPAIR, INDUSTRIAL

Boden Clark Ltd, George Henry Rd, Greatbridge, Tipton, W. Midlands, DY4 7BZ Tel: 0121-557 1700 Fax: 0121-557 3788

John Norton & Son Ltd, 169 Rutland Road, Sheffield, S3 9PT Tel: 0114-272 1294 Fax: 0114-276 6336 E-mail: sales@nortons.co.uk

OVEN MITTS/GLOVES

J W Martin Ltd, Prince Regent Road, Belfast, BT5 6QR Tel: (028) 9070 2021 Fax: (028) 9070 5566 E-mail: mail@jwmartin.co.uk

McCaw Allan & Co. Ltd, Victoria Street, Lurgan, Craigavon, County Armagh, BT67 9DU Tel: (028) 3834 1412 Fax: (028) 3834 3095 E-mail: sales@mccaw-allan.com

OVEN TO TABLEWARE

The Poole Pottery, 49 Wyatts Lane, Corfe Mullen, Wimborne, Dorset, BH21 3SQ Tel: (01202) 600838 E-mail: chris@mrpottery.co.uk

OVENS, *See also headings for particular types under Ovens*

Hedinair Ovens Ltd, 3 Pilot Close, Fulmar Way, Wickford, Essex, SS11 8YW Tel: (01268) 761777 Fax: (01268) 760210 E-mail: sales@hedinair.co.uk

OVER SPEED SWITCHES

Hubner Elektromaschinen A.G., PO Box 4022, Reading, RG8 8UD Tel: 0118-984 5351 Fax: 0118-984 3979 E-mail: sales@powertronic.co.uk

OVERHEAD CONVEYOR SYSTEMS

Acetarc Welding & Engineering Co. Ltd, Atley Works, Dalton Lane, Keighley, West Yorkshire, BD21 4HT Tel: (01535) 607323 Fax: (01535) 602522 E-mail: sales@acetarc.co.uk

Amber Industries, Amber House, Crompton Street, Chadderton, Oldham, OL9 9AA Tel: 0161-284 2222 Fax: 0161-627 0075 E-mail: sales@amber-industries.ltd.uk

Jack Burrows & Sons, Unit 10 Field Gate Works, New Street, Walsall, WS1 3DN Tel: (01922) 644150 Fax: (01922) 724375

Digitron Translift Ltd, Hallcroft Road, Retford, Nottinghamshire, DN22 7PT Tel: (01777) 707511 Fax: (01777) 860778

The Handling Conceps, Unit E, Swallow Court, Bromsgrove, Worcestershire, B60 4FE Tel: (01527) 570900 Fax: (01527) 570947 E-mail: sales@handlingconcepts.co.uk

John Morgan Conveyors Ltd, 1 Purbrook Road, Wolverhampton, WV1 2EJ Tel: (01902) 455755 Fax: (01902) 452245 E-mail: jmconveyors@btinternet.com

Midland Handling Equipment Ltd, Stretton Road, Great Glen, Leicester, LE8 9GN Tel: 0116-259 3175 Fax: 0116-259 2820 E-mail: sales@mhel.co.uk

Opto International Ltd, Bayley Street, Stalybridge, Cheshire, SK15 1QQ Tel: 0161-330 9136 Fax: 0161-343 7332 E-mail: enquiry@optoint.co.uk

OVERHEAD CRANES

Abc Lifting Equipment Ltd, 4 Alliance Business Park, Corporation Street, Accrington, Lancashire, BB5 0RR Tel: (01254) 233349 Fax: (01254) 233533 E-mail: sales@abclifting.co.uk

Acorn Lifting Services Ltd, Northern Court, Off Vernon Road, Nottingham, NG6 0BJ Tel: 0115-976 2862 Fax: 0115-976 1406 E-mail: als@acorn-lifting.co.uk

Brookfields Garden Centre, 431 Mapperley Plains, Nottingham, NG3 5RW Tel: 0115-926 8200 Fax: 0115-967 3261

Butterley Nuclear Engineering Ltd, Engineering Works, Ripley, Derbyshire, DE5 3BQ Tel: (01773) 573573 Fax: (01773) 749898 E-mail: admin@butterley.com

Cobal Cranes Ltd, Doctor Lane, Sheffield, S9 5AP Tel: 0114-261 8003 Fax: 0114-261 9003 E-mail: steven.hides@btconnect.com

Delph Electrical Lifting Services Ltd, 3 The Wallows Industrial Estate, Fens Pool Avenue, Brierley Hill, West Midlands, DY5 1QA Tel: (01384) 76222 Fax: (01384) 75524

J Barnsley Cranes Ltd, Unit 16 Pedmore Road Industrial Estate, Pedmore Road, Brierley Hill, West Midlands, DY5 1TJ Tel: (01384) 484811 Fax: (01384) 484333 E-mail: jsatch@jbarnsleycranes.com

Midland Cranes Ltd, Church La, Seisdon, Wolverhampton, WV5 7EZ Tel: 01902 897018 Fax: 01902 898491

Morris Material Handling Ltd, PO Box 7, Loughborough, Leicestershire, LE11 1RL Tel: (01509) 643200 Fax: (01509) 610666 E-mail: info@morriscranes.co.uk

Morris Material Handling, Lodge Way, Thetford, Norfolk, IP24 1HE Tel: (01842) 750252 Fax: (01842) 750909

Norcrane Ltd, Unit E, Bedewell Industrial Park, Hebburn, Tyne & Wear, NE31 2XQ Tel: 0191-489 5066 Fax: 0191-483 9702 E-mail: norcrane@norcrane.co.uk

▶ Pelloby Engineering Ltd, Halesfield 19, Telford, Shropshire, TF7 4QT Tel: (01952) 586626 Fax: (01952) 587871 E-mail: sales@pelloby.com

Quatroserve Steel Fabricators, Bay 11 Central Works, Peartree Lane, Dudley, West Midlands, DY2 0QU Tel: (01384) 480326 Fax: (01384) 74119 E-mail: sales@quatroserve.co.uk

R Stahl Ltd, Unit 43 Stahl House Elmdon Trading Estate, Bickenhill Lane, Birmingham, B37 7HE Tel: 0121-767 6400 Fax: 0121-767 6480 E-mail: info@rstahl.co.uk

United Crane Services Ltd, Niagara Works, Beeley Wood Rd, Sheffield, S6 1NH Tel: 0114-285 2801 Fax: 0114-232 5626 E-mail: unitedcranes@aol.com

OVERHEAD FAULT LOCATION EQUIPMENT

Bowden Bros Ltd, Brickworks House, Spook Hill, North Holmwood, Dorking, Surrey, RH5 4HR Tel: (01306) 743355 Fax: (01306) 876768 E-mail: info@bowdon-bros.com

OVERHEAD LINE WINCHES

J.M. Loveridge P.L.C., Higher Merley Lane, Corfe Mullen, Wimborne, Dorset, BH21 3EQ Tel: (01202) 882306 Fax: (01202) 880059

OVERHEAD RADIANT ELECTRIC HEATERS

Scanlock Overseas Property Agents, 208 Pensby Road, Heswall, Wirral, Merseyside, CH60 7RJ Tel: 0151-342 6530 Fax: 0151-342 6530 E-mail: sales@scanlock.com

OVERHEAD SECTIONAL DOORS

Emmerson Industrial Doors Ltd, Enterprise Way, Sherburn in Elmet, Leeds, LS25 6NA Tel: (01977) 685566 Fax: (01977) 681981 E-mail: sales@emmerson-doors.co.uk

Faltec Doors Ltd, Statham Street, Stoke-on-Trent, ST1 4HB Tel: (01782) 205205

Lambourn Valley Projects Ltd, 13 Prospect Road, Hungerford, Berkshire, RG17 0JL Tel: (01488) 680680 Fax: (01488) 681258 E-mail: sales@dock-levellers.co.uk

Welding Engineers (Hertford) Ltd, Unit 1, Lower Road, Great Amwell, Ware, Hertfordshire, SG12 9TA Tel: (01920) 468634 Fax: (01920) 487463 E-mail: hertford@weldingengineers.co.uk

OVERHEAD TRANSMISSION FITTINGS

Mosdorfer C C L Systems Ltd, Unit B6, Market Overton Industrial Estate, Thistleton Road, Market Overton, Oakham, Leicestershire, LE15 7PP Tel: (01572) 768381 Fax: (01572) 767531 E-mail: office@mosdorferccl.co.uk

Overhead Line Fittings (U.K.) Ltd, 12 Wood Lane, Norton Juxta Twycross, near Atherstone, Atherstone, Warwickshire, CV9 3QB Tel: (01827) 880210 Fax: (01827) 880811 E-mail: sales@overheadlinefittings.co.uk

Preformed Line Products GB Ltd, East Portway, Andover, Hampshire, SP10 3LH Tel: (01264) 366234 Fax: (01264) 356714 E-mail: sales@preformed.com

OVERHEAD TRANSMISSION SUPPLIES

Balfour Beatty Rail Projects Ltd, Acornfield Road, P O Box 12, Kirby Industrial Estate, Liverpool, L33 7TY Tel: 0151-548 5000 Fax: 0151-548 5320

OVERLOAD RELEASE CLUTCHES

British Autogard Ltd, Siddington, Cirencester, Gloucestershire, GL7 6EU Tel: (01285) 640333 Fax: (01285) 659476 E-mail: sales@autogard.co.uk

Broadbent Drives, Britannia Mills, Portland Street, Bradford, West Yorkshire, BD5 0DW Tel: (01274) 783434 Fax: (01274) 390527 E-mail: sales@broadbent-drives.co.uk

Howdon Power Transmission Ltd, Paganhill Lane, Stroud, Gloucestershire, GL5 4JT Tel: (01453) 750814 Fax: (01453) 765320 E-mail: sales@howdon.co.uk

OVERPRINTING MACHINES, *See Label Overprinting etc*

OVERSEAS COURIER SERVICES

▶ A N Logistics, 18 Canal Side, Beeston, Nottingham, NG9 1NG Tel: (0800) 8818167 Fax: 0845 4660167 E-mail: alan@anlogistics.co.uk

Adur Packaging Ltd, 1 Brook Farm, Horsham Road, Cowfold, Horsham, West Sussex, RH13 8AH Tel: (01403) 864994 Fax: (01403) 864774 E-mail: adurpackaging@aol.com

Ai International Couriers Ltd, 17 Vicarage Lane, Horley, Surrey, RH6 8AR Tel: (01293) 776875 Fax: (01293) 820950 E-mail: ailgw@clara.net

B A X Global Ltd, Unitair Centre, Great South West Road, Feltham, Middlesex, TW14 8NT Tel: (020) 8899 3000 Fax: (020) 8899 3111

▶ CHILLFREEZE DIRECT LTD, UNIT 6C BASSET COURT, LOAKE CLOSE, GRANGE PARK, NORTHAMPTON, NN4 5EZ Tel: 0870 2407998 Fax: 0870 7202733 E-mail: enquires@chillfreezedirect.co.uk

City Air Express Ni Ltd, West Bank Drive, Belfast, BT3 9LA Tel: (028) 9078 1878 Fax: (028) 9078 1788 E-mail: sales@cityairexpress.com

City Sprints, 58-62 Scrutton Street, London, EC2A 4PH Tel: (020) 7880 1100 Fax: (020) 7466 4901

▶ Courier Please Ltd, Suite 44, 468 Walton Road, West Molesey, Surrey, KT8 8AE Tel: 07890 454428 Fax: 0208 3390859 E-mail: info@acourierplease.co.uk

▶ D & R Couriers, Building 2, 47 Skelwith Road, Marton, Blackpool, FY3 9UL Tel: 01253 312713 Fax: 01253 312713 E-mail: richard@dandrcouriers.co.uk

Dale Express Transport Ltd, Dale House, 232 Selsdon Road, Croydon, CR2 6PL Tel: (020) 8760 5000 Fax: (020) 8760 0202 E-mail: service@daleexpress.co.uk

DHL Express (UK) Ltd, Orbital Pk, 178-188 Great South West Road, Hounslow, TW4 6JS Tel: (08701) 100300

Direct Despatch International Ltd, D D I House, 1-21 Elkstone Road, London, W10 5NT Tel: (020) 7724 4000 Fax: (020) 8964 8244 E-mail: sales@ddi.co.uk

Direct Link South, 38 Millbrook Road East, Southampton, SO15 1HY Tel: (023) 8033 1541 E-mail: louis.roe@dirlinks.freeserve.co.uk

Express 2000 Ltd, Pembley Green, Copthorne Common, Copthorne, Crawley, West Sussex, RH10 3LF Tel: (01342) 713500 Fax: (01342) 713520 E-mail: sales@express2000.co.uk

▶ Express Courier Services, Unit 8d Northwood Business Park, Newport Road, Cowes, Isle of Wight, PO31 8PE Tel: (01983) 299944 Fax: (01983) 299944 E-mail: info@ecs-iow.co.uk

Federal Express Corporation, Federal Express House Bond Gate Chambers, Bond Gate, Nuneaton, Warwickshire, CV11 4AL Tel: (024) 7634 3333 Fax: (024) 7637 5257

▶ The Great British Courier Co., 33 Harris Crescent, Needingworth, St. Ives, Cambridgeshire, PE27 4TE Tel: (01480) 465450 E-mail: gbcc@btinternet.com

Initial A To Z Couriers, 21a Brownlow Mews, London, WC1N 2LA Tel: (020) 7841 1741 Fax: (020) 7404 6045 E-mail: danbrown@initial-atoz.co.uk

Initial City Link Ltd, Wellington House, 61-73 Staines Road West, Sunbury-On-Thames, Middlesex, TW16 7AH Tel: (01932) 822622 Fax: (01932) 785560 E-mail: enquiries@city-link.co.uk

OVERSEAS COURIER SERVICES – *continued*

▶ KP Couriers (Cambs) Ltd, Keepers Lodge, Gamlingay Road, Waresley, Sandy, Bedfordshire, SG19 3DD Tel: (01767) 651717 Fax: (01767) 652062 E-mail: kpcambs@hotmail.co.uk
Parceline Ltd, Roebuck Lane, Smethwick, West Midlands, B66 1BY Tel: (0845) 9505505 Fax: 0121-500 2646 E-mail: info@parceline.com
Pegasus, 86-92 Stewarts Road, London, SW8 4UG Tel: (020) 7622 2222 Fax: (020) 7622 1616 E-mail: sales@pegasus-couriers.com
Pegasus, 86-92 Stewarts Road, London, SW8 4UG Tel: (020) 7622 2222 Fax: (020) 7622 1616 E-mail: sales@pegasus-couriers.com
Quickshift UK Ltd, Gatwick Buisness Centre, Unit 10 Kennel Lane, Hookwood, Horley, Surrey, RH6 0AH Tel: (01293) 541215 Fax: (01293) 539067 E-mail: info@quickshift-couriers.com
Samfreight Ltd, Bath Road, West Drayton, Middlesex, UB7 0DB Tel: (020) 8750 2300 Fax: (020) 8750 2301 E-mail: lee.george@samfreight.co.uk
Skynet Worldwide Express, Unit 8-9 Maple Grove Business Centre, Lawrence Road, Hounslow, TW4 6DR Tel: (020) 8538 1988 Fax: (020) 8538 1921 E-mail: tustserv@deltec-international.com
S M B Couriers, 683 Tonbridge Road, Barming, Maidstone, Kent, ME16 9DQ Tel: (07930) 281229 E-mail: info@smbcouriers.com
▶ Southern Despatch, 87 Palmerston Road, Bournemouth, BH1 4HP Tel: (01202) 394357 Fax: (01202) 398954 E-mail: sales@southerndespatch.co.uk
Streetwise Courier Services, 25 Johns Mews, London, WC1N 2NS Tel: (020) 7404 6161 Fax: (020) 7404 6045 E-mail: mach1ltd@aol.com
▶ Andy Theaker Ltd, 49 Wordsworth Road, Stockport, Cheshire, SK5 6JH Tel: 0161-221 1296 Fax: 0161-221 1178
▶ Time Express Swiss Couriers Ltd, Unit 20, Trident Industrial Estate, Blackthorne Road, Colnbrook, Slough, SL3 0AX Tel: (01753) 686830

OVERSEAS EXHIBITION CONTRACTORS

Adams Exhibitions, 6 Rose Green Road, Bristol, BS5 7XE Tel: 0117-952 1000 Fax: 0117-952 2000 E-mail: joe@adams-exhibitions.co.uk
▶ Arena Display Ltd, 3 Scotch George Lane, Knaresborough, North Yorkshire, HG5 9EH Tel: (01423) 770900 Fax: (01423) 770400 E-mail: steve@arenadisplay.co.uk
Aspect Exhibitions Ltd, 1 Ashton Lodge Farm, Hartwell Road, Ashton, Northampton, NN7 2JT Tel: (01604) 864999 Fax: (01604) 864888 E-mail: sales@aspectexhib.co.uk
Central Display Production, B Gresham Way Industrial Estate, Gresham Way, London, SW19 8ED Tel: (020) 8944 5156 Fax: (020) 8944 5950 E-mail: dudley@centraldisplay.com
Cobb Group Exhibition Services Ltd, PO Box 37, Luton, LU1 1YW Tel: (01582) 453308 Fax: (01582) 417528 E-mail: info@cobbgroup.co.uk
Crown Exhibitions & Displays, 3 Partons Road, Kings Heath, Birmingham, B14 6TA Tel: 0121-441 2822 Fax: 0121-441 2772 E-mail: info@crownexhibition.co.uk
Devonshire House Associates Ltd, Gainsborough Trading Estate, Rufford Road, Stourbridge, West Midlands, DY9 7ND Tel: (01384) 442322 Fax: (01384) 440949
Display Maintenance Ltd, Old Bank Mills, Old Bank Road, Earlsheaton, Dewsbury, West Yorkshire, WF12 7AA Tel: (01924) 469664 Fax: (0870) 8508511 E-mail: enquiries@displaymaintenance.co.uk
Equinox Design Ltd, Equinox Park, 100 Jack Lane, Leeds, LS10 1BW Tel: 0113-244 1300 Fax: 0113-242 4533 E-mail: equinoxdesign@compuserve.com
The Exhibition & Interiors Co. Ltd, Station Road, Irthlingborough, Wellingborough, Northamptonshire, NN9 5QE Tel: (01933) 650222 Fax: (01933) 655688 E-mail: sales@exhibitionandinteriors.co.uk
Fairs & Exhibitions (1992) Ltd, Manor House, 1 The Crescent, Leatherhead, Surrey, KT22 8DH Tel: (020) 8391 0999 Fax: (020) 8391 0220 E-mail: info@fairs-exhibs.com
Finesse Group, Cobbswood Industrial Estate, Brunswick Road, Ashford, Kent, TN23 1EH Tel: (01233) 663399 Fax: (01233) 665599 E-mail: info@finessegroup.com
Global Displays Ltd, Global House, Berry Hill, Berry Hill Industrial Estate, Droitwich, Worcestershire, WR9 9RB Tel: (01905) 797978 Fax: (01905) 797919 E-mail: sales@globaldisplays.co.uk
Highfield International Exhibition Services Ltd, Unit 1A, Worcester Trading Estate, Blackpole Rd, Worcester, WR3 8HR Tel: (01905) 754158 Fax: (01905) 456218
Nortex Ltd, 73 Arthur Street, Lakeside, Redditch, Worcestershire, B98 8JY Tel: (01527) 500742 Fax: (01527) 502999 E-mail: nortex.exhibitions@virgin.net
Oakmace Exhibitions Ltd, Aimes Green Farm, Galley Hill, Waltham Abbey, Essex, EN9 2AU Tel: (01992) 893768 Fax: (01992) 893981 E-mail: display@oakmace.com
▶ Scenic Effect, Eyreswood Farm, Astwood Road, Cranfield, Bedford, MK43 0AU Tel: (01234) 750777 Fax: (01234) 752172 E-mail: martin@sceniceffects.com
Standpoint Ltd, Unit 22A, Park Avenue Estate, Sundon Park, Luton, LU3 3BP Tel: (01582) 561754 Fax: (01582) 563296 E-mail: info@standpoint.uk.com

OVERSEAS MANAGEMENT/ MARKETING/DEVELOPMENT,

See Export Management etc

OVERSEAS PROPERTY BROKERS

▶ 4 Homes Abroad, 6 Henley Close, Chardstock, Axminster, Devon, EX13 7SX Tel: (01454) 777686 E-mail: sales@4homesabroad.com

OVERSEAS PROPERTY CONSULTANCY

▶ Greenwood Overseas, 25 Regent Street, Rugby, Warwickshire, CV21 2PE Tel: (01788) 552050 Fax: (01788) 579164 E-mail: zlf@greenwoodoverseas.com
▶ Hilton International Properties (UK) Ltd., 1 Bury Old Road, Manchester, M25 0FQ Tel: 0161 7735916 Fax: 0161 7735916 E-mail: info@propertyforsaleinspain.com
▶ Inmoshop Limited, 14 Bryony Road, Bicester, Oxfordshire, OX26 3WY Tel: 01869 329932 E-mail: enquiries@inmoshop.co.uk
▶ Rosefame Properties, West Cottage, Church Street, Ticehurst, Wadhurst, East Sussex, TN5 7DL Tel: (01580) 201319 Fax: (01580) 201604 E-mail: info@rosefame.co.uk
▶ Spanish Costa Properties, 9 Castle Hill Court, 21-23 Castle Hill Avenue, Folkestone, Kent, CT20 2QU Tel: 01303 240125

OVERSEAS REMOVAL CONTRACTORS

▶ A & L Movers, 87 Burnell Avenue, Welling, Kent, DA16 3HP Tel: (020) 8309 8005 E-mail: sales@aandlmovers.co.uk

OXYACETYLENE WELDING OR CUTTING EQUIPMENT

Bryant Welding Supplies, PO Box 100, Southampton, SO40 9LA Tel: (023) 8086 7789 Fax: (023) 8066 3688 E-mail: sales@bryantwelding.co.uk
Cutting & Welding Supplies Ltd, 15-16 Lower High Street, Cradley Heath, West Midlands, B64 5AB Tel: (01384) 567874 Fax: (01384) 567064 E-mail: cutweld@btconnect.com
East Midland Welding Supply Co. Ltd, Baker Brook Industrial Estate, Wigwam Lane, Hucknall, Nottingham, NG15 7SZ Tel: 0115-964 2000 Fax: 0115-964 1651 E-mail: sales@eastmidwelding.freeserve.co.uk
Eltham Welding Supplies Ltd, 2-12 Parry Place, London, SE18 6AN Tel: (020) 8854 1226 Fax: (020) 8854 2720 E-mail: sales.woolwich@elthamweldingsupplies.co.uk
▶ Flame-Equip Ltd, 8 Mandervelle Road, Oadby, Leicester, LE2 5LQ Tel: 0116-271 3364 Fax: 0116-272 0126 E-mail: sales@flame-equip.demon.co.uk
Goodwin Air Plasma Ltd, Unit 18 Kernan Drive, Loughborough, Leicestershire, LE11 5JF Tel: (01509) 237369 Fax: (01509) 234942 E-mail: goodwinplasma@aol.com
Grahams Machinery Sales Ltd, Deva House, Knutsford Way, Sealand Industrial Estate, Chester, CH1 4NX Tel: (01244) 376764 Fax: (01244) 377177 E-mail: sales@grahams-machinery.co.uk
Wescol Ltd, PO Box 41, Wolverhampton, WV1 2RZ Tel: (01902) 351283 Fax: (01902) 871937 E-mail: sales@wescol.com
Westermans Welding Equipment, 2 Brook Street, Syston, Leicester, LE7 1GD Tel: 0116-269 6941 Fax: 0116-269 6942 E-mail: welding@westermans.com
J. Weston & Partners Ltd, Cudgamoor Farm, East Putford, Holsworthy, Devon, EX22 7XR Tel: (01237) 451838 Fax: (01237) 451553 E-mail: nigel.moulder@hotmail.co.uk

OXYACETYLENE WELDING/ CUTTING ENGINEERS/ SERVICES/SUBCONTRACTORS

David Williams Llandudno Ltd, 4 Builder Street, Llandudno, Gwynedd, LL30 1DR Tel: (01492) 876869 Fax: (01492) 870664
J O'Neill & Co. Ltd, 7 Bromley Street, Hull, HU2 0PY Tel: (01482) 320146 Fax: (01482) 589968
▶ Plasurf Engineering, Park Farm, Feckenham Road, Hanbury, Bromsgrove, Worcestershire, B60 4DH Tel: (01527) 821038 Fax: (01527) 821038 E-mail: vic@plasurf.co.uk
W H Hannaford, 100 Chester Road, Watford, WD18 0RE Tel: (01923) 223669 Fax: (01923) 223669

OXYGEN ANALYSERS

▶ Albion Water Management Ltd, 30/31 Station Close, Potters Bar, Hertfordshire, EN6 1TL Tel: (01707) 607230 Fax: (01707) 607235 E-mail: water@albiongroup.co.uk
▶ Enotec UK Ltd, PO Box 9026, Dumfries, DG1 3YH Tel: (0870) 3500102 Fax: (0870) 3500302 E-mail: enotec.uk@enotec.com
Ultramedic Ltd, Wavertree Boulevard South, Liverpool, L7 9PF Tel: 0151-228 0354 Fax: 0151-252 1673

OXYGEN CUTTING MACHINES

Gega Lotz Ltd, Kiln Way, Woodville, Swadlincote, Derbyshire, DE11 8EA Tel: (01283) 214281 Fax: (01283) 222108 E-mail: sales@gegalotz.co.uk

OXYGEN PRODUCTION PLANT

Boc Ltd, The Priestley Centre, 10 Priestley Road, Surrey Research Park, Guildford, Surrey, GU2 7XY Tel: (01483) 579857 Fax: (01483) 244658
Linde Cryoplants Ltd, Blackwater Way, Aldershot, Hampshire, GU12 4DR Tel: (01252) 331351 Fax: (01252) 343062 E-mail: info@linde-lcl.com

OXYGEN THERAPY/MEDICAL EQUIPMENT

Med Tech, Riverside Works, Miller Row, Edinburgh, EH4 3BQ Tel: 0131-225 4295 Fax: 0131-220 4065 E-mail: med-tech@tiscali.co.uk
Oxylitre Ltd, Morton House, 43-45 Skerton Road, Manchester, M16 0WJ Tel: 0161-872 6322 Fax: 0161-848 7914 E-mail: sales@oxylitre.co.uk
Respironics (UK) Ltd, Unit 8, Cityfields Business Park, City Fields Way, Tangmere, Chichester, West Sussex, PO20 2FT Tel: (0800) 1300840 Fax: (0800) 1300846 E-mail: info@respironics.com

OZONE GENERATING/ OZONISATION EQUIPMENT

Hampden Test Equipment Ltd, Satra House, Rockingham Road, Kettering, Northamptonshire, NN16 9JH Tel: (01536) 518563 Fax: (01536) 519256 E-mail: hampden-test@satra.co.uk
ProMinent Fluid Controls (UK) Ltd, Resolution Road, Ashby-de-la-Zouch, Leicestershire, LE65 1DW Tel: (01530) 560555 Fax: (01530) 560777 E-mail: sales@prominent.co.uk
Severn Trent Water Ltd, Park Lane, Minworth, Sutton Coldfield, West Midlands, B76 9BL Tel: 0121-722 4000 Fax: 0121-313 1938 E-mail: salesenq@severntrentservices.co.uk
Triogen Ltd, Triogen House, 117 Barfillan Drive, Glasgow, G52 1BD Tel: 0141-810 4861 Fax: 0141-810 5561 E-mail: sales@triogen.com

OZONE SAFE AEROSOLS

New Guard Coatings Ltd, Sandbeck Way, Wetherby, West Yorkshire, LS22 7DN Tel: (01937) 586311 Fax: (01937) 580041 E-mail: sales@newguard.co.uk

OZONE SYSTEM WATER TREATMENT PLANT AND EQUIPMENT

Silkstream Water Treatment Equipment, 36 Spencer Close, Potton, Sandy, Bedfordshire, SG19 2QY Tel: (01767) 261942 E-mail: sales@silkstream.co.uk
Triogen Ltd, Triogen House, 117 Barfillan Drive, Glasgow, G52 1BD Tel: 0141-810 4861 Fax: 0141-810 5561 E-mail: sales@triogen.com

PACKAGE INTEGRITY TEST EQUIPMENT

Hanatek Sevices Ltd, 10 Sunny Close, Goring-By-Sea, Worthing, West Sussex, BN12 4BD Tel: (01903) 246418 Fax: (01903) 506815 E-mail: info@hanatek.co.uk

PACKAGED AIR CONDITIONING (AC) UNITS

A A F-Mcquay UK Ltd, Bassington Lane, Cramlington, Northumberland, NE23 8AF Tel: (01670) 713477 Fax: (01670) 714370
Anchor Ventilation Co Britair Ltd, Malt Lane, Stoke-on-Trent, ST3 1RR Tel: (01782) 312809 Fax: (01782) 311138
Artic Air Refrigeration & Air Conditioning, 14 Bell Mead, Studley, Warwickshire, B80 7SH Tel: (01527) 857578 Fax: (01527) 857578
Beta Air, Unit 6, Cheltenham Trade Park, Arle Road, Cheltenham, Gloucestershire, GL51 8LZ Tel: (01242) 570995 Fax: (01242) 226131 E-mail: betaair.storacall@btinternet.com
Clivet UK, Unit 4 Kingdom Close, Segenworth East, Fareham, Hampshire, PO15 5TJ Tel: (01489) 550621 Fax: (01489) 573033 E-mail: info@clivet-uk.co.uk
▶ Dalair Ltd, Southern Way, Wednesbury, West Midlands, WS10 7BU Tel: 0121-556 9944 Fax: 0121-502 3124 E-mail: sales@dalair.co.uk
Direct Building Maintenance Services Ltd, 1 Nelmes Close, Hornchurch, Essex, RM11 2QA Tel: (01708) 447373 Fax: (01708) 445888
E C E Environmental Control Equipment Ltd, Harvel Works, Harvel, Meopham, Gravesend, Kent, DA13 0BT Tel: (01474) 814432 Fax: (01474) 812488 E-mail: richardbarnes@ece.uk.com
Eaton-Williams Holdings Ltd, Station Road, Edenbridge, Kent, TN8 6EG Tel: (01732) 866055 Fax: (01732) 863461 E-mail: peter.dewdney@eaton-williams.com
Edenaire Ltd, Station Road, Edenbridge, Kent, TN8 6EG Tel: (01732) 866066 Fax: (01732) 866653
Fujitsu General UK Co Ltd, Unit 150 Centennial Park, Centennial Avenue, Elstree, Borehamwood, Hertfordshire, WD6 3SG Tel: (020) 8731 3450 Fax: (020) 8731 3451
Lennox Industries, PO Box 174, Northampton, NN4 7EX Tel: (01604) 669100 Fax: (01604) 669150 E-mail: sales@lennoxuk.com
P.M. Luft, Essex House, Astra Centre, Edinburgh Way, Harlow, Essex, CM20 2BN Tel: (01279) 416087 Fax: (01279) 416076
Shorts Industries Ltd, PO Box 258, Bradford, West Yorkshire, BD2 1QR Tel: (01274) 305066 Fax: (01274) 736212 E-mail: sales@shorts-lifts.co.uk

PACKAGED BOILERS

Rogan Heating Services, 4 Reach Road Industrial Estate, Reach Road, Burwell, Cambridge, CB5 0AH Tel: (01638) 743500 Fax: (01638) 743843 E-mail: roganhs@globalnet.co.uk

PACKAGED PUMPING SETS

Kinder Janes Engineers Ltd, Porters Wood, St. Albans, Hertfordshire, AL3 6HU Tel: (01727) 844441 Fax: (01727) 844247 E-mail: info@kinder-janes.co.uk

PACKAGED VENTILATION UNITS

Aircare Ventilation Engineers Ltd, Unit 3d Newbattle Abbey Annexe, Newbattle Road, Newbattle, Dalkeith, Midlothian, EH22 3LJ Tel: 0131-660 9555 Fax: 0131-660 9666 E-mail: aircare@fsbdial.co.uk
Airduct Ltd, Raywell Street, Hull, HU2 8EP Tel: (01482) 326868 Fax: (01482) 589991 E-mail: airduct@hull92.freeserve.co.uk
Colt International Ltd, 13 Dormer Place, Leamington Spa, Warwickshire, CV32 5AA Tel: (01926) 450650 Fax: (01926) 450651
Euro Filter, Hare Park Mills, 46 Hare Park Lane, Liversedge, West Yorkshire, WF15 8EP Tel: (01623) 412412 Fax: (01274) 869956 E-mail: info@ecsfiltration.com
Fans & Spares Ltd, Dakota South, 1 Dakota Avenue, Salford, M50 2PU Tel: 0161-873 7212 Fax: 0161-848 7293 E-mail: pattyduncan@fansandspares.co.uk
Mansfield, Pollard & Co. Ltd, Edward House, Parry Lane, Bradford, West Yorkshire, BD4 8TL Tel: (01274) 774050 Fax: (01274) 775424 E-mail: admin@manpo.co.uk
Marshalls Sheetmetal Blackrow Barns, Short Thorn Road, Blackrow Barns, Felthorpe, Norwich, NR10 4DE Tel: (01603) 755473 Fax: (01603) 754040 E-mail: enquiries@marshallssheetmetal.co.uk
Silavent Environmental, Pine Works, Pine Street, Hyde, Cheshire, SK14 4TG Tel: 0161-366 5903 Fax: 0161-367 8105
Uniflo Systems Ltd, 9 Neptune Industrial Estate, Neptune Close, Medway City Estate, Rochester, Kent, ME2 4LT Tel: (01634) 716117 Fax: (01634) 290235 E-mail: sales@uniflo.co.uk

PACKAGED WATER BOOSTER PUMPING SETS

Brooks Ltd, Causeway Park Manchester Road, Audenshaw, Manchester, M34 5UU Tel: 0161-666 5000 Fax: 0161-666 5050 E-mail: sales@brooks.ltd.uk
H R Holfeld Belfast Ltd, Altona Road, Lisburn, County Antrim, BT27 5RU Tel: (028) 9267 7523 Fax: (028) 9266 0263
Harton Services Ltd, Unit 6 Thistlebrook Industrial Estate, Eynsham Drive, London, SE2 9RB Tel: (020) 8310 0421 Fax: (020) 8310 6785 E-mail: hartons@globalnet.co.uk
Pressmain (Pressurisation) Co. Ltd, Opal Works, Denhill Road Industrial Estate, Moss Side, Manchester, M15 5NR Tel: 0161-226 4727 Fax: 0161-226 5848 E-mail: sales@pressmain.com
Stuart Turner Ltd, Market Place, Henley-on-Thames, Oxfordshire, RG9 2AD Tel: (01491) 572655 Fax: (01491) 573704 E-mail: sales@stuart-turner.co.uk

PACKAGING ADHESIVE TAPES

3M Tapes & Adhesives Group, 3M Centre, Cain Road, Bracknell, Berkshire, RG12 8HT Tel: (01344) 858000 Fax: (01344) 858278
Acre Packaging Supplies Ltd, 15 Kepler, Lichfield Road Industrial Estate,, Tamworth, Staffordshire, B79 7XE Tel: (01827) 310330 Fax: (01827) 310337 E-mail: sales@acrepackaging.co.uk
Anca Industrial Supplies Ltd, Unit 16 Forge Trading Estate, Mucklow Hill, Halesowen, West Midlands, B62 8TP Tel: 0121-503 0919 Fax: 0121-585 5483 E-mail: admin@anca.co.uk
Boyce & Co., Exeter Airport Industrial Estate, Exeter Airport, Clyst Honiton, Exeter, EX5 2LJ Tel: (01392) 368891 Fax: (01392) 365598
▶ Cardboard Boxes, 1 Ivanhoe Street, Leicester, LE3 9GX Tel: 0116-275 2039
Lesta Packaging plc, 21 Nedham Street, Leicester, LE2 0HD Tel: (0116) 2624448 Fax: (0116) 2624449 E-mail: enquiries@lestapackaging.co.uk
Morrison Adhesive Tapes Ltd, PO Box 2279, Glasgow, G33 9AE Tel: 0141-779 5648 E-mail: morrisontapes@tiscali.co.uk
Saffron Tape Design, Epsilon House, 27 Fulfen Way, Saffron Walden, Essex, CB11 4DW Tel: (01799) 520170 Fax: (01799) 520170 E-mail: saffrontapedesign@tiscali.co.uk
▶ Tec Pak, Unit 7, Uddens Trading Estate, Wimborne, Dorset, BH21 7LQ Tel: (01202) 870060
Viking Industrial Products Ltd, 1 Coronation Business Centre, Hard Ings Road, Keighley, West Yorkshire, BD21 3ND Tel: (01535) 610373 Fax: (01535) 616231 E-mail: sales@vikingtapes.co.uk
Weller Packaging Ltd, Birchbrook Industrial Park, Lynn Lane, Shenstone, Lichfield, Staffordshire, WS14 0DJ Tel: (01543) 482100 Fax: (01543) 482140 E-mail: sales@wellerpackaging.co.uk

PACKAGING ALUMINIUM FOIL

Novelis UK Ltd, Stourbridge Road, Bridgnorth, Shropshire, WV15 6AW Tel: (01746) 765757 Fax: (01746) 761860

PACKAGING BAG CLOSURES

Deakins Packing Co., 3 Osman House, Prince Street, Bolton, BL1 2NP Tel: (01204) 393211 Fax: (01204) 381282 E-mail: deakinspackaging@yahoo.co.uk
F D W Packaging, Allerton Mills, Allerton Road, Allerton, Bradford, West Yorkshire, BD15 7QX Tel: (01274) 491013 Fax: (01274) 481752
Zip Pack Packaging Technology, Unit 17, Shaw Wood Business Park, Doncaster, South Yorkshire, DN2 5TB Tel: (01302) 344119 Fax: (01302) 321703 E-mail: enquiries@zippack.co.uk

PACKAGING BAG TIES

G T Products Europe Ltd, Unit 14 Ford La Business Park, Ford, Arundel, West Sussex, BN18 0UZ Tel: (01243) 555303 Fax: (01243) 555304 E-mail: enquiries@gtproductseurope.com

PACKAGING CONTROL SYSTEMS

C-Trak Ltd, 6 Greaves Indust Estate, Leighton Buzzard, Bedfordshire, LU7 4UB Tel: (01525) 850316 Fax: (01525) 854050 E-mail: sales@ctrak.fsnet.co.uk
Industrial Automation Systems Ltd, Unit 1, Springwater Park, Crews Hole Road, St. George, Bristol, BS5 8AN Tel: 0117-954 1212 Fax: 0117-954 1321 E-mail: sales@accupac.co.uk

PACKAGING DESIGNERS OR CONSULTANTS

▶ Aloof Design, 5 Fisher Street, Lewes, East Sussex, BN7 2DG Tel: (01273) 470887 E-mail: michellekostyrka@aloofdesign.com
▶ Ambassador Litho Ltd, 25 Hockeys Lane, Bristol, BS16 3HH Tel: 0117-965 5252 Fax: 0117-965 3275 E-mail: info@ambassador.co.uk
Arrowsacks Packaging, PO Box 234, Dover, Kent, CT15 6GD Tel: (01304) 853604 Fax: (01304) 852540 E-mail: arrowsacks@isleoak.freeserve.co.uk
Bda, The Studio, Pipits Croft, Bicester, Oxfordshire, OX26 6XW Tel: (01869) 322158 Fax: (01869) 322158E-mail: info@bda-uk.com
Bridgeshire Packaging Ltd, 1 Wimsey Way, Alfreton Trading Estate, Somercotes, Alfreton, Derbyshire, DE55 4LS Tel: (01773) 601000 Fax: (01773) 606075 E-mail: sales@bridgeshire.co.uk
Century Box & Packaging Ltd, The Tunnels Elms Farm, Gretton Fields, Cheltenham, Gloucestershire, GL54 5HQ Tel: (01242) 620895 Fax: (01242) 620999 E-mail: sales@centurybox.co.uk
Comtext Services Ltd, 2 Chatsworth Technology Park, Dunston Road, Whittington Moor, Chesterfield, Derbyshire, S41 8XA Tel: (01246) 260650 Fax: (01246) 260613 E-mail: info@comtextservices.co.uk
Continental Polymers Ltd, PO Box 983, Swindon, SN5 5WJ Tel: (01793) 875161 Fax: (01793) 887281 E-mail: cpl@contpoly.co.uk
Design Bridge Ltd, 18 Clerkenwell Close, London, EC1R 0QN Tel: (020) 7814 9922 Fax: (020) 7814 9024 E-mail: info@designbridge.co.uk
Design packaging Solutions Ltd, Grove Farm, The Grove, Moulton, Northampton, NN3 7UF Tel: (01604) 645334 Fax: (01604) 644920 E-mail: suden@fsbdial.co.uk
Edwards' Analytical, Rose Cottage, Walker Hall, Winston, Darlington, County Durham, DL2 3PN Tel: (01325) 730766 Fax: (01325) 730911 E-mail: davidjhe@aol.com
Elmwood Design Ltd, 40-44 Thistle Street, Edinburgh, EH2 1EN Tel: 0131-225 1181 Fax: 0131-718 0390 E-mail: enquiries@elmwood.co.uk
▶ Farish Associates, 94 Sutton Court, Chiswick, London, W4 3JF Tel: (020) 8742 3223 Fax: (020) 8742 3226 E-mail: sales@farish.com
Fir Tree Design Co., 2 Turpyn Court, Woughton on the Green, Milton Keynes, MK6 3BW Tel: (01908) 661100 Fax: (01908) 670055 E-mail: info@firtreedesign.com
Fourth Dimension Integrated Design Solutions, 36-38 Mill Green Road, Mitcham, Surrey, CR4 4HZ Tel: (020) 8240 2244 Fax: (020) 8240 2223 E-mail: 4d@combined.uk.com
Graphic Results, 99 Bridge Street, Belper, Derbyshire, DE56 1BA Tel: (01773) 599159 Fax: (01773) 599259 E-mail: sales@graphic-results.co.uk
Hanmere Polythene Ltd, Blackhorse Road, Letchworth Garden City, Hertfordshire, SG6 1HD Tel: (01462) 482222 Fax: (01462) 481096 E-mail: sales@hanmere.co.uk
▶ Image + (Imageplus + plus), Unit 1 The Depot, Electric Wharf, Coventry, CV1 4JP Tel: (024) 7683 4780 Fax: (024) 7683 4781 E-mail: info@image-plus.co.uk
Insit Moulded Packaging Ltd, Aintree Avenue, White Horse Business Park, Trowbridge, Wiltshire, BA14 0XB Tel: (01225) 767985 Fax: (01225) 777405E-mail: sales@insit.co.uk
Kiwiplan, Unit 5, Crompton Court, Burntwood Business Park, Burntwood, Staffordshire, WS7 3GG Tel: (01543) 273073 Fax: (01543) 273074 E-mail: info@kiwiplan-europe.com
Link Design Development, 17 Brownfields, Welwyn Garden City, Hertfordshire, AL7 1AN Tel: (01707) 331991 Fax: (01707) 327918
▶ Lucid Innovation Group, PO Box 180, Manchester, M21 9XW Tel: 0161-860 0058 E-mail: ideas@lucidinnovation.com
M R Designs, 6 Lower Farm, 130 High Street, Irchester, Wellingborough, Northamptonshire, NN29 7AB Tel: (01933) 410016 Fax: (01933) 419929 E-mail: mr-designs@btconnect.com
▶ Marchant Design Associates, 28/29 Woodside Close, Amersham, Buckinghamshire, HP6 5EF Tel: 01494 725093 E-mail: business@marchantassociates.com
P I Design International, 1-5 Colville Mews, London, W11 2AR Tel: (020) 7727 3226 Fax: (020) 7908 0809 E-mail: hello@piglobal.com
Pak Wraps Ltd, Unit 16 Sefton Lane Industrial Estate, Liverpool, L31 8BX Tel: 0151-924 0767 Fax: 0151-924 6555
Pira International, Cleeve Road, Leatherhead, Surrey, KT22 7RU Tel: (01372) 802000 Fax: (01372) 802238 E-mail: membership@pira-international.co.uk
Precision Printing Plates Ltd, Philips Park Road, Beswick, Manchester, M11 3FU Tel: 0161-274 4010 Fax: 0161-274 3542 E-mail: sales@ppp-digital.co.uk
▶ Principal Image, Cherry Tree Lane, Rostherne, Altrincham, Cheshire, WA14 3RZ Tel: (01565) 830213 Fax: (01565) 830214 E-mail: info@principalimage.com
Product Stream Ltd, 65 Oxford Street, Hull, HU2 0QP Tel: (01482) 327755 Fax: (01482) 327766 E-mail: info@productstream.co.uk
Professional Packaging Services Ltd, 1 The Barn, Hawksworth Lane, Guiseley, Leeds, LS20 8HD Tel: (01943) 882400 Fax: (01943) 878191 E-mail: sales@p-p-s-ltd.com
PSW Packaging Ltd, 1 Creslands, Oldmixon CR, Weston-super-Mare, Avon, BS24 9AX Tel: (01934) 418183 Fax: (01934) 626953 E-mail: pswpackagingltd@fsbdial.co.uk
▶ Red Seal, Technium Business Park, Kings Road, Swansea, SA1 8PH Tel: (01792) 295004 Fax: (01792) 485577 E-mail: studio@red-seal.com
Sharp Interpack, Colley Lane, Bridgwater, Somerset, TA6 5YS Tel: (01278) 435000 Fax: (01278) 423019 E-mail: info@sharpinterpack.co.uk
Siebert Head Ltd, 80 Goswell Road, London, EC1V 7DB Tel: (020) 7689 9090 Fax: (020) 7689 9080 E-mail: info@sieberthead.com
Spotlight Design Services Ltd, 118 Queens Road, Walton-on-Thames, Surrey, KT12 5LL Tel: (01932) 245934
Springetts Brand Design Consultants, 13 Salisbury Place, London, W1H 1FJ Tel: (020) 7486 7527 Fax: (020) 7487 3033 E-mail: all@springetts.co.uk
Volume Design Associates, The Studio, 22 Kings Road, High Wycombe, Buckinghamshire, HP11 1SA Tel: (01494) 459989 Fax: (01494) 459089 E-mail: info@vda.co.uk
Watershed Design, 31 Freegrove Road, Islington, London, N7 9RG Tel: (020) 7700 1759 Fax: (020) 7700 1692 E-mail: peter@watershed-uk.com

PACKAGING EQUIPMENT COMPONENTS/SEALING ELEMENTS

Everest Packaging, 52 Wellington Road, Edgbaston, Birmingham, B15 2ER Tel: 0121-236 3573

PACKAGING EQUIPMENT ENGINEERS, INSTALLATION OR SERVICE

Ancholme Machinery Co. Ltd, Units 3-4, Albert Street, Brigg, North Lincolnshire, DN20 8HQ Tel: (01652) 657521 Fax: (01652) 650073 E-mail: ancholme1@aol.com
Carmichael Engineering Ltd, 62 Burkitt Road, Earlstrees Industrial Estate, Corby, Northamptonshire, NN17 4DT Tel: (01536) 261431 Fax: (01536) 201477 E-mail: mail@carmichael-eng.co.uk
Everest Packaging, 52 Wellington Road, Edgbaston, Birmingham, B15 2ER Tel: 0121-236 3573
Ilapak Ltd, Chalfont House, Silverdale Road, Hayes, Middlesex, UB3 3BN Tel: (020) 8797 2000 Fax: (020) 8797 2050 E-mail: sales@ilapak.co.uk
Wright Machinery Ltd, Stonefield Way, Ruislip, Middlesex, HA4 0JU Tel: (020) 8842 2244 Fax: (020) 8842 1113 E-mail: sales@wright.co.uk
Yorkshire Packaging Supplies Ltd, Quarry Lane, Dewsbury, West Yorkshire, WF12 7JJ Tel: (01924) 441355 Fax: (01924) 440686 E-mail: info@yps.co.uk

PACKAGING EQUIPMENT MANUFRS

A M P Rose, Heapham Road, Gainsborough, Lincolnshire, DN21 1QU Tel: (01427) 611969 Fax: (01427) 616854 E-mail: admin@amp-rose.com
Aaron Packaging Machinery, Leeds 12 Business Park, Barras Garth Road, Leeds, LS12 4JY Tel: (07802) 886250 E-mail: sales@aaron-pack-mart.co.uk
Abpac, Wessex Way, Wincanton Business Park, Wincanton, Somerset, BA9 9RR Tel: (01963) 32913 Fax: (01963) 34358 E-mail: sales@abpac.co.uk
Adpak Machinery Systems Ltd, 3 Pendleside, Lomeshaye Industrial Estate, Nelson, Lancashire, BB9 6RY Tel: (01282) 601444 Fax: (01282) 612201 E-mail: info@adpak.co.uk
Ancholme Machinery Co. Ltd, Units 3-4, Albert Street, Brigg, North Lincolnshire, DN20 8HQ Tel: (01652) 657521 Fax: (01652) 650073 E-mail: ancholme1@aol.com
Anchor Plastics Machinery, The Watermill, Royal Quay, Harefield, Uxbridge, Middlesex, UB9 6SA Tel: (01895) 824301 Fax: (01895) 825344 E-mail: info@anchor-pm.co.uk
Astrapac Midlands Ltd, Mount Road, Burntwood, Staffordshire, WS7 0AJ Tel: (01543) 677262 Fax: (01543) 672718 E-mail: sales@astrapac.co.uk
Autobox Ltd, Unit S1 Cherrycourt Way, Leighton Buzzard, Bedfordshire, LU7 4UH Tel: (01525) 852831 Fax: (01525) 382353 E-mail: enquiries@autobox.co.uk
Autotape Systems Ltd, Quakers Coppice, Crewe, CW1 6FA Tel: (01270) 254737
Bernley Packaging, Unit 13 Wilton Industrial Court, 851 Bradford Road, Batley, West Yorkshire, WF17 8NN Tel: (01924) 471188 Fax: (01924) 471199 E-mail: burnpack@aol.com
CDS, Belvoir Way, Fairfield Industrial Estate, Louth, Lincolnshire, LN11 0LQ Tel: (01507) 610555 Fax: (01507) 610500
Ceetak Ltd, Fraser Road, Priory Business Park, Bedford, MK44 3WH Tel: (01234) 832200 Fax: (01234) 832299 E-mail: ceetakltd@ceetak.com
Cermex UK Ltd, PO Box 12, Huntingdon, Cambridgeshire, PE29 6EF Tel: (01480) 455919 Fax: (01480) 451520 E-mail: sales@cermexuk.com
Crosland V K Ltd, Unit 4, Lyons Road, Trafford Park, Manchester, M17 1RN Tel: 0161-877 8668 Fax: 0161-876 5234 E-mail: sales@croslandvk.com
Custom Enclosures Ltd, Concorde House, Concorde Street, Luton, LU2 0JD Tel: (01582) 480425 Fax: (01582) 414372 E-mail: custom.enclosures@btconnect.com
D I G Corrugated Machinery Ltd, Masterlord Industrial Park, Station Road, Leiston, Suffolk, IP16 4JD Tel: (01728) 832755 Fax: (01728) 832764 E-mail: sales@dig-group.co.uk
The Dabarr Group Ltd, The Packhouse, Parsonage Farm Heath Road, Boughton Monchelsea, Maidstone, Kent, ME17 4JB Tel: (01622) 747450 Fax: (01622) 746812 E-mail: info@dabarr.co.uk
E D L Packaging, Oswald Street, Burnley, Lancashire, BB12 0BY Tel: (01282) 429305 Fax: (01282) 429350 E-mail: sales@johnquinn.co.uk
Easiweigh Ltd, Unit 1b Shrub Hill Industrial Estate, Worcester, WR4 9EL Tel: (01905) 28075 Fax: (01905) 22229 E-mail: sales@easiweigh.co.uk
Endoline Machinery Ltd, Stratton Business Park, London Road, Biggleswade, Bedfordshire, SG18 8QB Tel: (01767) 316422 Fax: (01767) 318033 E-mail: info@endoline.co.uk
Euro Pack, Common Lane North, Beccles, Suffolk, NR34 9BP Tel: (01502) 716540 Fax: (01502) 716814 E-mail: europacksales@gei-int.com
Eurograv Ltd, Sprint Industrial Estate, Chertsey Road, Byfleet, West Byfleet, Surrey, KT14 7BD Tel: (01932) 336262 Fax: (01932) 336271 E-mail: sales@eurograv.co.uk
Everest Packaging, 52 Wellington Road, Edgbaston, Birmingham, B15 2ER Tel: 0121-236 3573
Gainsborough Craftsmen Ltd, Jennifer Works, Gainsborough, Lincolnshire, DN21 1HU Tel: (01427) 613994 Fax: (01427) 611949
Gainsborough Engineering Co., Corringham Road Industrial Estate, Corringham Road, Gainsborough, Lincolnshire, DN21 1QB Tel: (01427) 617677 Fax: (01427) 810443 E-mail: info@gains-eng.co.uk
▶ GB Packaging Supplies Ltd, Unit 4 Carrside Park, Hatfield, Doncaster, South Yorkshire, DN7 6AZ Tel: (01302) 351751 Fax: (01302) 845178
▶ Goddard C H & Co Cartons Ltd, Unit 1-2 Church Trading Estate, Slade Green Road, Erith, Kent, DA8 2JA Tel: (01322) 358940 Fax: (01322) 358949 E-mail: info@chgoddard.com
H Erben Ltd, Lady Lane, Hadleigh, Ipswich, IP7 6AS Tel: (01473) 823011 Fax: (01473) 828252 E-mail: enquiries@urban.co.uk
Harcross Engineering Co. Ltd, Unit 1 The Ember Centre, Hersham, Walton-On-Thames, Surrey, KT12 3PU Tel: (01932) 222201 Fax: (01932) 224722 E-mail: sales@harcross-eng.co.uk
I D Machinery Ltd, 78 Alston Drive, Bradwell Abbey, Milton Keynes, MK13 9HG Tel: (01908) 321778 Fax: (01908) 322707 E-mail: sales@idmachinery.com
I M A (UK) Ltd, 3 Arden Road, Alcester, Warwickshire, B49 6HN Tel: (01789) 400880 Fax: (01789) 400880 E-mail: hotdesk@imauk.co.uk
▶ Isbir Bulk Bag, G The Granary Business Centre, Coal Road, Cupar, Fife, KY15 5YQ Tel: (01334) 650088 Fax: (01334) 650072
R.A. Jones Europak, Unit 30 Concourse House, Leeds, LS11 7DF Tel: 0113 2765842
Kemwall Engineering Co., 52 Bensham Grove, Thornton Heath, Surrey, CR7 8DA Tel: (020) 8653 7111 Fax: (020) 8653 9669 E-mail: sales@kemwall.co.uk
Kite Packaging, 8 Stirling Road, Glenrothes, Fife, KY6 2ST Tel: (01592) 630536 Fax: (01592) 630936
Lachenmeier (UK) Ltd, Wilsons Park, Monsall Road, Newton Heath, Manchester, M40 8PA Tel: 0161-205 3666 Fax: 0161-205 3777 E-mail: kl@lachenmeier.com
▶ Lawtons Group Ltd, 60 Vauxhall Road, Liverpool, L3 6DL Tel: 0151-479 3000 Fax: 0151-479 3001 E-mail: info@lawtonsgroup.co.uk
M A P Systems Ltd, Unit 22 Sarum Complex, Salisbury Road, Uxbridge, Middlesex, UB8 2RZ Tel: (01895) 811234 Fax: (01895) 238681
M & A Packaging Services Ltd, Spring Lane North, Malvern, Worcestershire, WR14 1BU Tel: (01684) 560099 Fax: (01684) 560095 E-mail: info@mapexinspection.co.uk
Mac Pac Ltd, 5 Barton Road, Stockport, Cheshire, SK4 3EG Tel: 0161-442 1642 Fax: 0161-442 1643 E-mail: sales@macpac.co.uk
Marden Edwards Ltd, 2 East Dorset Trade Park, Nimrod Way, Wimborne, Dorset, BH21 7SH Tel: (01202) 861200 Fax: (01202) 861400 E-mail: sales@mardenedwards.com
Meco Pak (UK) Ltd, Greenway House, Sugarswell Business Park, Shenington, Banbury, Oxfordshire, OX15 6HW Tel: (01295) 688910 Fax: (01295) 688911 E-mail: info@mecopak.co.uk

PACKAGING EQUIPMENT MANUFRS

– continued

Motoman Robotics UK Ltd, Unit 2 Johnson Park, Wildmere Road, Banbury, Oxfordshire, OX16 3JU Tel: (01295) 272755 Fax: (01295) 267127
E-mail: derekpasquire@motoman.co.uk

▶ Newrap, 11 Castle Clough, Hapton, Burnley, Lancashire, BB12 7LN Tel: (01282) 777953 Fax: (01282) 778558
E-mail: info@newrap.co.uk

▶ Nissen Packaging Ltd, Unit 31 Jubilee Trade Centre, Jubilee Road, Letchworth Garden City, Hertfordshire, SG6 1SP Tel: (01462) 676262 Fax: (01462) 481075
E-mail: info@nissenpackaging.co.uk

Norden UK Ltd, Church Street, Baldock, Hertfordshire, SG7 5AF Tel: (01462) 895245 Fax: (01462) 895683
E-mail: enquiries@norden.co.uk

Novopac (UK) Ltd, Fieldhead Broomers Corner, Shipley, Horsham, West Sussex, RH13 8PR Tel: (01403) 740003 Fax: (01403) 740071
E-mail: richard@novopac.co.uk

O K International Europe Ltd, Shepherds Grove Industrial Estate, Stanton, Bury St. Edmunds, Suffolk, IP31 2AR Tel: (01359) 250705 Fax: (01359) 250165
E-mail: sales@okinteurope.co.uk

P F M Packaging Machinery Ltd, P F M House, 2 Pilgrim Way, Stanningley, Pudsey, West Yorkshire, LS28 6LU Tel: 0113-239 3401 Fax: 0113-239 3402
E-mail: pfm@pfm-ltd.co.uk

Packaging Aids Ltd, 1 Lords Way, Basildon, Essex, SS13 1TN Tel: (01268) 885858 Fax: (01268) 885860
E-mail: sales@packer-products.co.uk

Packaging Engineers Automation Ltd, Unit 10 Sandown Estate, Sandown Road, Watford, WD24 7UB Tel: (01923) 237121 Fax: (01923) 236125

▶ Packaging First, Nash Hall, Chelmsford Road, High Ongar, Ongar, Essex, CM5 9NL Tel: (01277) 363656 Fax: (01277) 362277

Pharma Machines Ltd, 64 Windsor Avenue, London, SW19 2RJ Tel: (020) 8542 9966 Fax: (020) 8540 1600
E-mail: sales@pharma-machines.com

▶ Plas Tek, Delamare Road, Cheshunt, Waltham Cross, Hertfordshire, EN8 9SB Tel: (01992) 781800 Fax: (01992) 781811
E-mail: info@plas-tek.co.uk

▶ Procorr Packaging, Uppingham Road, Skeffington, Leicester, LE7 9YE Tel: 0116-259 9302

Proco-STS Ltd, Unit 3, Castle Road, Chelston Business Park, Wellington, Somerset, TA21 9JQ Tel: (01823) 663535 Fax: (01823) 663373 E-mail: info@proco-sts.com

Propack Automation Machinery Ltd, Unit 8 Binns Close, Coventry, CV4 9TB Tel: (024) 7647 0074 Fax: (024) 7647 1190
E-mail: sales@propack.co.uk

Quickpack UK Ltd, 14 Linnell Way, Telford Way Industrial Estate, Kettering, Northamptonshire, NN16 8PS Tel: (01536) 510910 Fax: (01536) 410568 E-mail: quickpackuk@quickpack.com

Raupack Ltd, 131 High Street, Old Woking, Woking, Surrey, GU22 9LD Tel: (01483) 736800 Fax: (01483) 736810

Remploy Ltd, Gordon Banks Drive, Trentham Lakes North, Stoke-on-Trent, ST4 4TJ Tel: (01782) 658438 Fax: (01782) 643492

▶ Robatech UK Ltd, The Street, Broughton Gifford, Melksham, Wiltshire, SN12 8PH Tel: (01225) 783456 Fax: (01225) 783400
E-mail: sales@robatech.co.uk

Robatech UK Ltd, The Street, Broughton Gifford, Melksham, Wiltshire, SN12 8PH Tel: (01225) 783456 Fax: (01225) 783400
E-mail: sales@robatech.co.uk

Rovema Packaging Machines, The Coach House The Firs, High Street, Whitchurch, Aylesbury, Buckinghamshire, HP22 4SJ Tel: (01296) 642060 Fax: (01296) 641550
E-mail: sales@rovema.co.uk

▶ S C Packaging Supplies, Unit D 11 Seedbed Centre, Langston Road, Loughton, Essex, IG10 3TQ Tel: (020) 8418 9652 Fax: (020) 8521 7058

S Kempner Ltd, 498 Honeypot Lane, Stanmore, Middlesex, HA7 1JZ Tel: (020) 8952 5262 Fax: (020) 8952 8061
E-mail: sales@kempner.co.uk

Samarose Engineering Services Ltd, Unit 3 West Side, Ash Industrial Estate, Flex Meadow, Harlow, Essex, CM19 5TJ Tel: (01279) 421395 Fax: (01279) 421612
E-mail: ses@samarose.co.uk

Sandiacre Packaging Machinery Ltd, 101 Lilac Grove, Beeston, Nottingham, NG9 1PF Tel: 0115-967 8787 Fax: 0115-967 8707
E-mail: sandiacre.uk@molins.com

Selo UK Ltd, Mulberry Road, Rock Ferry, Birkenhead, Merseyside, CH42 3YA Tel: 0151-644 9393 Fax: 0151-645 2202
E-mail: info@selo.co.uk

Shrinkwrap Machinery Co. Ltd, 145 Sterte Road, Poole, Dorset, BH15 2AF Tel: (01202) 674944 Fax: (01202) 671891
E-mail: sales@shrinkwrap.co.uk

Sidel (UK) Ltd, Lowesden Works, Lambourn Woodlands, Hungerford, Berkshire, RG17 7RU Tel: (01488) 72525 Fax: (01488) 72302

Sontex Machinery Ltd, 61 Westgate, Cleckheaton, West Yorkshire, BD19 5JZ Tel: (01274) 872299 Fax: (01274) 862829
E-mail: info@sontex.co.uk

▶ Strong Team, Marsden House, Elmdon Lane, Birmingham, B37 7DL Tel: 0121-505 5520 Fax: 0121-505 4333

Sunset Packaging Supplies Ltd, Unit 4 Witan Park, Avenue Two, Witney, Oxfordshire, OX28 4FN Tel: (01993) 776641 Fax: (01993) 779834
E-mail: enquiries@sunsetpackaging.co.uk

Supreme Plastics Group plc, Supreme House, 300 Regents Park Road, London, N3 2JX Tel: (020) 8346 3291 Fax: (020) 8346 1624
E-mail: info@supremeplastics.com

▶ Sutton's Packaging, Unit 33 Dinan Way Trading Estate, Concorde Road, Exmouth, Devon, EX8 4RS Tel: (01395) 223405 Fax: (01395) 446546
E-mail: sales@suttonswrap.co.uk

Swissvac (G B) Ltd, Marish Wharf, St Marys Road, Middlegreen, Slough, SL3 6DA Tel: (01753) 546777 Fax: (01753) 585564
E-mail: mail@swissvac.co.uk

Taurus Packaging, Meadow Lane, Little Houghton, Northampton, NN7 1AH Tel: (01604) 891707 Fax: (01604) 891708
E-mail: tauruspackaging@hotmail.com

▶ Trio Packaging Ltd, Unit 8 Station Road, Ampthill, Bedford, MK45 2QP Tel: (01525) 841313 Fax: (01525) 841515

▶ UNSA UK Ltd, Number One The Beehive, Lions Drive, Shadsworth Business Park, Blackburn, BB1 2QS Tel: (01254) 699469 Fax: (01254) 699569

Wantzen Ltd, Anton House, South Park, Sevenoaks, Kent, TN13 1EB Tel: (01732) 458185 Fax: (01732) 458188
E-mail: info@wantzen.co.uk

Watershed Packaging Ltd, 30 Chapman Way, Tunbridge Wells, Kent, TN2 3EF Tel: (01892) 515777 Fax: (01892) 510852
E-mail: enquiries@kent.watershed-packaging.co.uk

Wipak UK Ltd, Unit 3 Buttington Cross Enterprise Park, Buttington, Welshpool, Powys, SY21 8SL Tel: (01938) 555255 Fax: (01938) 555277 E-mail: sales@wipak.com

Wraps UK, 2 Nimrod Way, East Dorset Trade Park, Wimborne, Dorset, BH21 7SH Tel: (01202) 880204 Fax: (01202) 842632
E-mail: sales@wrapsuk.com

Wright Machinery Ltd, Stonefield Way, Ruislip, Middlesex, HA4 0JU Tel: (020) 8842 2244 Fax: (020) 8842 1113
E-mail: sales@wright.co.uk

PACKAGING EQUIPMENT TO SPECIFICATION

Senior Packaging Ltd, 4 Borrowdale Road, Dewsbury, West Yorkshire, WF12 7PF Tel: (01924) 430201 Fax: (01924) 510065
E-mail: info@seniorpackaging.co.uk

PACKAGING EQUIPMENT, CASE ERECTING/LOADING AND SEALING

The Dabarr Group Ltd, The Packhouse, Parsonage Farm Heath Road, Boughton Monchelsea, Maidstone, Kent, ME17 4JB Tel: (01622) 747450 Fax: (01622) 746812
E-mail: info@dabarr.co.uk

PACKAGING EQUIPMENT, WRAPAROUND, CASE/TRAY

Euro Pack, Common Lane North, Beccles, Suffolk, NR34 9BP Tel: (01502) 716540 Fax: (01502) 716814
E-mail: europacksales@gei-int.com

Waller Eurosel, 43 Bridgeman Terrace, Wigan, Lancashire, WN1 1TT Tel: (01942) 234897 Fax: (01942) 496276
E-mail: info@waller-eurosel.co.uk

PACKAGING FANCY ACCESSORIES, RIBBONS/BOWS ETC

Berisfords Ltd, Thomas Street, Congleton, Cheshire, CW12 1EF Tel: (01260) 274011 Fax: (01260) 274014
E-mail: office@berisfords-ribbons.co.uk

Brooklyn Bow & Ribbon Co. Ltd, Herald Business Park, Golden Acres Lane, Coventry, CV3 2RT Tel: (024) 7663 5599 Fax: (024) 7663 5525
E-mail: sales@brooklynbow.co.uk

Fashion Ribbon Ltd, Manners Avenue, Manners Industrial Estate, Ilkeston, Derbyshire, DE7 8EF Tel: 0115-930 8699 Fax: 0115-930 4555 E-mail: chris@fashionribbon.co.uk

PACKAGING ICE PACKS

Hydropac Ltd, Unit 76, Lincoln Road, Cressex Business Park, High Wycombe, Bucks, HP12 3RH Tel: (01494) 530182 Fax: (01494) 538539 E-mail: sales@hydropac.co.uk

PACKAGING INDUSTRY STAFF RECRUITMENT

D K Associates Ltd, 26-34 Friar Lane, Nottingham, NG1 6DQ Tel: 0115-947 3500 Fax: 0115-985 9007
E-mail: office@dk-recruit.co.uk

▶ Mercury Search & Selection Ltd, Redhill House, Hope Street, Chester, CH4 8BU Tel: (01244) 677219 Fax: (01244) 682710
E-mail: info@mercurysearch.co.uk

PACKAGING LASER PRINTERS

▶ Printec Consultants, 19-20 Berners Street, London, W1T 3LW Tel: (020) 7636 6264

PACKAGING MACHINE BLADES

Carmichael Engineering Ltd, 62 Burkitt Road, Earlstrees Industrial Estate, Corby, Northamptonshire, NN17 4DT Tel: (01536) 261431 Fax: (01536) 201477
E-mail: mail@carmichael-eng.co.uk

PACKAGING MACHINE DESIGN

A C C Systems Ltd, 6 Vulcan Court, Vulcan Way, Coalville, Leicestershire, LE67 3FW Tel: (01530) 814151 Fax: (01530) 814152
E-mail: sales@accsystems.co.uk

Gainsborough Craftsmen Ltd, Jennifer Works, Gainsborough, Lincolnshire, DN21 1HU Tel: (01427) 613994 Fax: (01427) 611949

GIGA Systems Ltd, 71 Watercall Avenue, Coventry, CV3 5AX Tel: (0870) 7525515
E-mail: info@gigasystems.co.uk

P L F International, Riverside House Iconfield Park, Freshfields Road, Parkeston, Harwich, Essex, CO12 4EN Tel: (01255) 552994 Fax: (01255) 552995
E-mail: sales@plfinternational.com

PACKAGING MACHINES, *See also headings for particular types*

Argosy Machinery Ltd, Unit F6, Southwell Road, Horsham St. Faith, Norwich, NR10 3JU Tel: (01603) 893987 Fax: (01603) 893988
E-mail: info@argosymachineryltd.co.uk

Campak Ltd, Burkitt Road, Earlstrees Industrial Estate, Corby, Northamptonshire, NN17 4DT Tel: (01536) 261501 Fax: (01536) 443656
E-mail: sales@campak.freeserve.co.uk

Carmichael Engineering Ltd, 62 Burkitt Road, Earlstrees Industrial Estate, Corby, Northamptonshire, NN17 4DT Tel: (01536) 261431 Fax: (01536) 201477
E-mail: mail@carmichael-eng.co.uk

Comcount Ltd, Unit 16 Cranham Estate, Shipston Close, Worcester, WR4 9XN Tel: (01905) 454710 Fax: (01905) 455849
E-mail: mail@comcount.co.uk

Formech International Ltd, 4 Thrales End Farm, Thrales End Lane, Harpenden, Hertfordshire, AL5 3NS Tel: (01582) 469797 Fax: (01582) 469646 E-mail: sales@formech.com

I M A (UK) Ltd, 3 Arden Road, Alcester, Warwickshire, B49 6HN Tel: (01789) 400880 Fax: (01789) 400880
E-mail: hotdesk@imauk.co.uk

Ilapak Ltd, Chalfont House, Silverdale Road, Hayes, Middlesex, UB3 3BN Tel: (020) 8797 2000 Fax: (020) 8797 2050
E-mail: sales@ilapak.co.uk

▶ Newrap, 11 Castle Clough, Hapton, Burnley, Lancashire, BB12 7LN Tel: (01282) 777953 Fax: (01282) 778558
E-mail: info@newrap.co.uk

▶ North West Packaging, 34 Kempton Park Fold, Southport, Merseyside, PR8 5PL Tel: (01704) 544733 Fax: (01704) 544733
E-mail: info@nwp.co.uk

Remploy Ltd, Gordon Banks Drive, Trentham Lakes North, Stoke-on-Trent, ST4 4TJ Tel: (01782) 658438 Fax: (01782) 643492

▶ Sandiacre Packaging Machinery Ltd, 101 Lilac Grove, Beeston, Nottingham, NG9 1PF Tel: 0115-967 8787 Fax: 0115-967 8707
E-mail: sandiacre.uk@molins.com

▶ Dick Smith Services Ltd, 3 Shannon Centre, Shannon Way, Canvey Island, Essex, SS8 0PE Tel: (01268) 510963 Fax: (01268) 510977E-mail: sales@dicksmithservices.co.uk

▶ Tekpak (UK), Unit 203, 57 Great George Street, Leeds, LS1 3AJ Tel: (0845) 0537622 Fax: 0113-242 9176
E-mail: andrew.jackson@tekpak.co.uk

PACKAGING MATERIAL/GOODS/ PRODUCTS MANUFRS

A & A Packaging Company Unlimited, 16B Westfield Industrial Estate, Off Portsmouth Road, Horndean, Waterlooville, Hampshire, PO8 9JX Tel: (023) 9259 7792 Fax: (023) 9259 0049
E-mail: sales@aandapackaging.co.uk

A B L Perpack 1985 Ltd, 7 Baron Avenue, Telford Way Industrial Estate, Kettering, Northamptonshire, NN16 8UW Tel: (01536) 412744 Fax: (01536) 412752
E-mail: sales@ablperpack.co.uk

A & J Brooks, 37-39 North Acton Road, London, NW10 6PF Tel: (020) 8965 1440 Fax: (020) 8965 1440

A.M. Agencies, 81 Bargery Road, London, SE6 2LP Tel: (020) 8698 8896 Fax: (020) 8461 3627

A O N Converters Ltd, Unit 2 Hoblens Lane, Liverpool, L21 6PL Tel: 0151-920 7329 Fax: 0151-949 0483
E-mail: aonfoam@aol.com

A R Wilson Packaging, 151 Nottingham Road, Nottingham, NG6 0FU Tel: 0115-978 1047 Fax: 0115-942 2302
E-mail: arwilson@proweb.co.uk

A Warne & Co. Ltd, Nelson Trading Estate, 11 The Path, London, SW19 3BL Tel: (020) 8543 3045 Fax: (020) 8543 6089
E-mail: sales@awarne.com

Abpac, Wessex Way, Wincanton Business Park, Wincanton, Somerset, BA9 9RR Tel: (01963) 32913 Fax: (01963) 34358
E-mail: sales@abpac.co.uk

Acacia, 37 Shoebury Avenue, Shoeburyness, Southend-on-Sea, SS3 9BH Tel: (01702) 297555 Fax: (01702) 298015

Acorn Trading Co., 101 Shakespeare Road, London, W3 6SA Tel: (020) 8992 6366 Fax: (020) 8992 9660

Adam Adams Ltd, 1 Chapel Road, Portslade, Brighton, BN41 1PF Tel: (01273) 431100 Fax: (01273) 431110
E-mail: adam-adams@cwcom.net

Adams Packaging Ltd, Timberlaine Estate, Quarry Lane, Chichester, West Sussex, PO19 8PP Tel: (01243) 783474 Fax: (01243) 815960 E-mail: adams-adams@cwcom.net

Adpak Machinery Systems Ltd, 3 Pendleside, Lomeshaye Industrial Estate, Nelson, Lancashire, BB9 6RY Tel: (01282) 601444 Fax: (01282) 612201
E-mail: info@adpak.co.uk

Alcan Packaging Corby Ltd, 5 Adderlade House, Corby Gate Business Park, Corby, Northamptonshire, NN17 5JG Tel: (01536) 400500 Fax: (01536) 400333

Allied Packaging Ltd, Brabant House, Portsmouth Road, Thames Ditton, Surrey, KT7 0EY Tel: (020) 8398 8882 Fax: (020) 8398 4485
E-mail: sales@alliedpackaging.co.uk

Amasec Airfil Ltd, Unit 1 Colliery Lane, Exhall, Coventry, CV7 9NW Tel: (07739) 974027 Fax: (024) 7664 4325E-mail: sales@airfil.com

Ambassador Packaging, Tundry Way, Chainbridge Road, Blaydon-On-Tyne, Tyne & Wear, NE21 5ST Tel: (0870) 6099888 Fax: 0191-414 6627
E-mail: ambassador.blaydon@pactiv.com

Ambassador Packaging, Unit 2 Venture Park, Stirling Way, Bretton, Peterborough, PE3 8YD Tel: (0870) 6099888 Fax: (01733) 330954
E-mail: ambassador.@pactiv.com

Ambassador Packaging Ltd, Road One, Winsford Industrial Estate, Winsford, Cheshire, CW7 3QB Tel: (01606) 567000 Fax: (01606) 567001 E-mail: ambassador@pregis.com

Amcor Ltd, Denmark House, Brick Close, Kiln Farm, Milton Keynes, MK11 3DP Tel: (01908) 261333 Fax: (01908) 261334

Amico Packaging Supplies, 4 Robinson Road, Leicester, LE5 4NS Tel: 0116-276 2786 Fax: 0116-276 9786

Amipak Ltd, 16-18 Factory Lane, Croydon, CR0 3RL Tel: (020) 8681 8611 Fax: (020) 8688 5314 E-mail: sales@amipak.co.uk

Answerpak Ltd, Unit M, Fircroft Way, Edenbridge, Kent, TN8 6EL Tel: (01732) 869930 Fax: (01732) 869939
E-mail: sales@answerpak.co.uk

Apperley Business Supplies Ltd, 1 St Andrews Road, Montpelier, Bristol, BS6 5EH Tel: 0117-942 4972 Fax: 0117-942 4400
E-mail: marklaval@blueyonder.co.uk

Applewade Packaging Ltd, Park House, 15-19 Greenhill CR, Watford, WD18 8PH Tel: (01923) 250202 Fax: (01923) 251101
E-mail: sales@applewade.co.uk

▶ Ardmair Enterprises Ltd, 82 Brown Edge Road, Buxton, Derbyshire, SK17 7AF Tel: (01298) 78926 Fax: (01298) 25122
E-mail: mail@ardmairenterprises.co.uk

Armour Supplies Ltd, Units 2-3, Brunel Road, Churchfield Industrial Estate, St. Leonards-on-Sea, East Sussex, TN38 9RT Tel: (01424) 853717 Fax: (01424) 853719

B B S Packaging, Wakeford Farm, Aldermaston Road, Pamber End, Tadley, Hampshire, RG26 5QN Tel: (01256) 851281 Fax: (01256) 850429

B J Industrial Supplies Ltd, 6 Harwood Street, Blackburn, BB1 3BD Tel: (01254) 675244 Fax: (01254) 663061
E-mail: info@thetradeshop.co.uk

B P B Paperboard Ltd, B P B UK Service Centre, East Leake, Loughborough, Leicestershire, LE12 6JU Tel: 0115-945 1000 Fax: 0115-945 1199

BCP Fluted Packaging Ltd, Crompton House, Nuttall Way Shadsworth, Shadsworth Business Park, Blackburn, BB1 2JT Tel: (01254) 677790 Fax: (01254) 681736
E-mail: info@bcpflute.com

Berkshire Pallets Ltd, Unit 2 Membury Business Park, Lambourn Woodlands, Hungerford, Berkshire, RG17 7TJ Tel: (01488) 73700 Fax: (01488) 73701

Betco Packaging Supplies, 12 Gregston Industrial Estate, Birmingham Road, Oldbury, West Midlands, B69 4EX Tel: 0121-552 8400 Fax: 0121-511 1324
E-mail: sales@betcofasteners.co.uk

Birmingham Packaging Co., 40 Rushey Lane, Tyseley, Birmingham, B11 2BL Tel: 0121-706 9171 Fax: 0121-708 2565
E-mail: sales@birminghampackaging.co.uk

PACKAGING MATERIAL/GOODS/ PRODUCTS MANUFRS – *continued*

Bischof & Klein UK Ltd, Unit C Hortonwood 2, Telford, Shropshire, TF1 7XX Tel: (01952) 606848 Fax: (01952) 606698 E-mail: info@bk-packaging.co.uk

Bloomfield Supplies, Naas Lane, Gloucester, GL2 5RG Tel: (01452) 883354 Fax: (01452) 725115 E-mail: info@bloomfieldsupplies.co.uk

Boyce & Co., Exeter Airport Industrial Estate, Exeter Airport, Clyst Honiton, Exeter, EX5 2LJ Tel: (01392) 368891 Fax: (01392) 365598

Braythorn Ltd, Phillips Street, Birmingham, B6 4PT Tel: 0121-359 8800 Fax: 0121-359 8412 E-mail: sales@braythorn.co.uk

Breamfold Packaging Ltd, 129 Richmond Road, London, E8 3NJ Tel: (020) 7249 6735 Fax: (020) 7249 6737 E-mail: sales@breamfoldpackaging.co.uk

Bretby Nurseries Ltd, Bretby Lane, Bretby, Burton-on-Trent, Staffordshire, DE15 0QS Tel: (01283) 703355 Fax: (01283) 704035 E-mail: bretby.nurseries@virgin.net

Bristol Packaging Co., 29 Stoneberry Road, Bristol, BS14 0UA Tel: (01275) 540800 Fax: (01275) 541266

British Polythene Industries, 96 Port Glasgow Road, Greenock, Renfrewshire, PA15 2UL Tel: (01475) 501000 Fax: (01475) 743143 E-mail: carolanderson@bpipoly.com

Brooks Packaging Ltd, 37-39 North Acton Road, London, NW10 6PF Tel: (020) 8961 2733 Fax: (020) 8965 9841 E-mail: sales@brookpackaging.co.uk

Bunzl Ltd, 5 Bonnington Road Lane, Edinburgh, EH6 5BJ Tel: 0131-553 5555 Fax: 0131-554 6068 E-mail: service@bunzlcleaningsupplies.co.uk

Bunzl Retail Supplies Ltd, Lamplight Way, Swinton, Manchester, M27 8UJ Tel: 0161-743 2222 Fax: 0161-743 2233 E-mail: info@bunzlretail.com

▶ Burgopak Ltd, 64 Great Suffolk Street, London, SE1 0BL Tel: (020) 7593 1444 Fax: (020) 7593 1414 E-mail: info@burgopak.com

C & B Co., Wholesale Warehouse, Chappell Drive, Doncaster, South Yorkshire, DN1 2RF Tel: (01302) 361357 Fax: (01302) 361357

C E D O Ltd, Halesfield 11, Telford, Shropshire, TF7 4LZ Tel: (01952) 272727 Fax: (01952) 274102

C L F Packaging, Orchard House, Heath Road, Warboys, Huntingdon, Cambridgeshire, PE28 2UW Tel: (01487) 823222 Fax: (01487) 824011 E-mail: sales@clfpack.co.uk

C L Plastics Ltd, Furnace Road, Oakenshaw, Bradford, West Yorkshire, BD12 7BH Tel: (01274) 603344 Fax: (01274) 691541 E-mail: sales@clplastics.com

C & S Packaging, Vestry Industrial Estate, Vestry Road, Sevenoaks, Kent, TN14 5EL Tel: (01732) 456663 Fax: (01732) 459296

Campsie Paper Co. Ltd, Courtauld Way, Eglinton, Londonderry, BT47 3DN Tel: (028) 7181 1243 Fax: (028) 7181 1626

Captain Packaging Ltd, 5 Clarence Wharf, Mumby Road, Gosport, Hampshire, PO12 1AJ Tel: (023) 9251 1125 Fax: (023) 9252 5844 E-mail: sales@captain.co.uk

Cardboard Box Co. Ltd, Clayton Park Enterpsise Centre, Petre Road, Clayton Le Moors, Accrington, Lancashire, BB5 5JB Tel: (01254) 232223 Fax: (01254) 232636 E-mail: info@thecardboardbox.co.uk

Cargo Packing Services Ltd, Portland Works, Hill Street, Ashton-under-Lyne, Lancashire, OL7 0PZ Tel: 0161-343 4737 Fax: 0161-343 4738 E-mail: contact@cargopack.co.uk

Carters Packaging Ltd, Station Road, Pool, Redruth, Cornwall, TR15 3QJ Tel: (01209) 612333 Fax: (01209) 612444 E-mail: info@carterpackaging.com

Castle Packaging Ltd, Bott Lane, Walsall, WS1 2JG Tel: (01922) 625451 Fax: (01922) 722202 E-mail: sales@castlepackaging.co.uk

Challenge Packaging Ltd, Ridgewood Indust Park, New Road, Ridgewood, Uckfield, East Sussex, TN22 5SX Tel: (01825) 761836 Fax: (01825) 768408 E-mail: sales@chalpak.co.uk

Chello Chemicals, Homme Castle, Shelsley Walsh, Worcester, WR6 6RR Tel: (01886) 812877 Fax: (01886) 812899 E-mail: sales@chellochemicals.co.uk

Clingfoil Ltd, Unit 1 Second Avenue, Poynton, Stockport, Cheshire, SK12 1ND Tel: (01625) 878953 Fax: (01625) 859005 E-mail: sales@clingfoil.co.uk

Colt Staplers, 10 Bunting Close, Mitcham, Surrey, CR4 4ND Tel: (020) 8687 5500 Fax: (020) 8687 5501 E-mail: sales@coltstaplers.co.uk

Contact Packaging, Unit 5-17, Prince Road, Kings Norton Business Centre, Birmingham, B30 3HB Tel: 0121-458 5060

Coogan & Watts Ltd, Central Park, Newtownabbey, County Antrim, BT36 4FS Tel: (028) 9084 5800 Fax: (028) 9034 2739 E-mail: info@cooganwatts.co.uk

T. Cooper & Co. (Macclesfield) Ltd, Hobson Street, Macclesfield, Cheshire, SK11 8BB Tel: 01625 422953

Copac, 14 Aylesbury Business Centre, Chamberlain Road, Aylesbury, Buckinghamshire, HP19 8DY Tel: (01296) 398844 Fax: (01296) 431153

Costerwise Ltd, Studio A Royalty Studios, 105 Lancaster Road, London, W11 1QF Tel: (020) 7221 0666 Fax: (020) 7229 7000 E-mail: costerwise@talk21.com

Cotswold Industrial Products, Westmead Drive, Westmead Industrial Estate, Swindon, SN5 7YT Tel: (01793) 610880 Fax: (01793) 616941 E-mail: sales@cpkgg.com

Cutts Box Co. Ltd, Lion Works, Mowbray Street, Sheffield, S3 8EZ Tel: 0114-272 8673 Fax: 0114-276 5757

D S Smith, Muir Road, Houstoun Industrial Estate, Livingston, West Lothian, EH54 5DP Tel: (01506) 432841 Fax: (01506) 438347

Dalziel Ltd, Afon Aboo Road, Rogerstone, Newport, Gwent, NP10 9HZ Tel: (01633) 898150 Fax: (01633) 898160 E-mail: claire.warren@dalziel..co.uk

Danda UK Packaging Ltd, 8 Drury Way Industrial Estate, Laxcon Close, London, NW10 0TG Tel: (020) 8459 5500 Fax: (020) 8459 2351

Davis Group, 48 Watersfield Way, Edgware, Middlesex, HA8 6RZ Tel: (020) 8951 4264 Fax: (020) 8951 4342 E-mail: rdavis7054@aol.com

Day Paper Sales Ltd, 15 Silverwell Street, Bolton, BL1 1PP Tel: (01204) 398222 Fax: (01204) 362370 E-mail: sales@daypapersales.co.uk

Dayworth Packaging, Unit Q1, Trecenydd Industrial Estate, Caerphilly, Mid Glamorgan, CF83 2RZ Tel: (029) 2085 4860 Fax: (029) 2085 4861 E-mail: enquiries@dayworthpackaging.co.uk

De Maeyer International, Office, 77 Winchester Road, Four Marks, Alton, Hampshire, GU34 5HR Tel: (01420) 562776 Fax: (01420) 562874 E-mail: admin@demaeyer.co.uk

Deakins Packing Co., 3 Osman House, Prince Street, Bolton, BL1 2NP Tel: (01204) 393211 Fax: (01204) 381282 E-mail: deakinspackaging@yahoo.co.uk

Doric Anderton, Fifth Avenue, Trafford Park, Trafford Park, Manchester, M17 1TN Tel: 0161-848 0156 Fax: 0161-872 1652 E-mail: info@doricanderton.com

E P S Products Ltd, Units 5-6, Govan Road, Fenton Industrial Estate, Stoke-on-Trent, ST4 2RS Tel: (01782) 749662 Fax: (01782) 749757

Easypack Ltd, Unit 1, The Io Centre, Arlington Business Park, Stevenage, Hertfordshire, SG1 2BD Tel: (0845) 8380168 Fax: (0845) 8380160 E-mail: info@easypack.net

Euro Packaging plc, Unit 14 Elderpark Workspace, 100 Elderpark Street, Glasgow, G51 3TR Tel: 0141-445 3003 Fax: 0141-445 5111 E-mail: info@europackaging.co.uk

Excel Packaging & Insulation Co. Ltd, Unit 9, Woodcock Hill Estate, Harefield Road, Rickmansworth, Hertfordshire, WD3 1PQ Tel: (01923) 770247 Fax: (01923) 770248 E-mail: enquiries@excelpackaging.co.uk

F D W Packaging, Allerton Mills, Allerton Road, Allerton, Bradford, West Yorkshire, BD15 7QX Tel: (01274) 491013 Fax: (01274) 481752

F F P Packaging Solutions Ltd, 1-7 Tenter Road, Moulton Park Industrial Estate, Northampton, NN3 6PZ Tel: (01604) 643535 Fax: (01604) 790042 E-mail: sales@ffppkg.co.uk

F P Cartons Ltd, Ironmould Lane, Bristol, BS4 5SA Tel: 0117-972 3233 Fax: 0117-971 0381 E-mail: fpcartonltd@freeuk.com

Fast-Pak Packaging Ltd, Unit 1 Kayley Industrial Estate, Richmond Street, Ashton-under-Lyne, Lancashire, OL7 0AU Tel: 0161-339 0697 Fax: 0161-339 4700 E-mail: fastpak@talk21.com

Fillmore Packaging Ltd, Unit 15, Bowthorpe Industrial Estate, Norwich, NR5 9JE Tel: (01603) 745911 Fax: (01603) 747519 E-mail: sales.norwich@fillmorepackaging.co.uk

Firn Overseas Packaging Ltd, Firn House, 61 Church Street, Hungerford, Berkshire, RG17 0JH Tel: (01488) 683193 Fax: (01488) 684701 E-mail: sales@firn.org

Fletchers Packaging, Wilsom Road, Omega Park, Alton, Hampshire, GU34 2QE Tel: (020) 8684 4201 Fax: (020) 8681 5453 E-mail: sales@fletchers-packaging.co.uk

Forton Packaging Ltd, 11 Brookgate, Bristol, BS3 2UN Tel: 0117-953 7222 Fax: 0117-953 7456 E-mail: sales@fortonpack.com

Fortress Packaging Ltd, 21 Lake Road, Tunbridge Wells, Kent, TN4 8XT Tel: (01892) 545769 Fax: (01892) 545769

FPF Packaging & Tubes, 8 Leafield Industrial Estate, Leafield Way, Corsham, Wiltshire, SN13 9SW Tel: (01225) 810103 Fax: (01225) 810663 E-mail: enquires@fpf.com

G & T Packaging Ltd, Unit 10A, Factory Lane, Warminster, Wiltshire, BA12 8LT Tel: (01985) 216441 Fax: (01985) 216491 E-mail: enquiries@gtpack.btopenworld.com

G T Paper & Packaging Ltd, Lingard Street, Stoke-on-Trent, ST6 1ED Tel: (01782) 577328 Fax: (01782) 577068 E-mail: sam@gtpaper.co.uk

General Packaging Co., Unit 3 Cooksland Industrial Estate, Bodmin, Cornwall, PL31 2QB Tel: (01208) 265870 Fax: (01208) 72457 E-mail: enquiries@generalpackaging.co.uk

George Danby & Son Ltd, Bank Terrace, Barwell, Leicester, LE9 8GG Tel: (01455) 845522 Fax: (01455) 846633 E-mail: info@phonefirst.co.uk

Glen Pac Southern Ltd, 11 The Forty, Cricklade, Swindon, SN6 6HW Tel: (01793) 751527 Fax: (01793) 750551 E-mail: sales@glenpac.com

Global Packaging Ltd, 9 Lockwood Way, Black Horse Lane, London, E17 5RB Tel: (020) 8531 3130 Fax: (020) 8503 2319

Graham's Cartons, Garston Quays, Blackburn Street, Liverpool, L19 8EL Tel: 0151-427 6565 Fax: 0151-427 5123 E-mail: colin.graham@grahams-cartons.co.uk

Grove Packaging, Unit 2c Old Park Industrial Estate, Old Park Road, Wednesbury, West Midlands, WS10 9LR Tel: 0121-556 4735 Fax: 0121-556 4579

▶ Hasan Hangers Ltd, 3 Mousell Street, Manchester, M8 8HY Tel: 0161-819 1001 Fax: 0161-819 1002

Hewpack Industries Ltd, 35 Stapledon Road, Orton Southgate, Peterborough, PE2 6TD Tel: (01733) 239639 Fax: (01733) 370967

Hills Packaging, Lincoln Street, Rochdale, Lancashire, OL11 1LB Tel: (01706) 352398 Fax: (01706) 657808 E-mail: sales@hillspackaging.co.uk

Hobson Paragon UK Ltd, Commercial Way, Oakengates, Telford, Shropshire, TF2 6SG Tel: (01952) 619111 Fax: (01952) 616921

C.A. Holbrook Ltd, St. Georges Works, Faire Street, Derby, DE22 3WB Tel: (01332) 347021 Fax: (01332) 380750 E-mail: info@presteagebinders.com

Holman & Williams Packaging Ltd, Riverside Road, London, SW17 0BA Tel: (020) 8879 1010 Fax: (020) 8944 5162 E-mail: sales@hwpackaging.co.uk

Hurst Packaging Ltd, Unit 6, Cromwell Centre, Stepfield, Witham, Essex, CM8 3BZ Tel: (01376) 520642 Fax: (01376) 501757 E-mail: sales@hurstpackaging.co.uk

I L P Protective Packaging, 75 Woodburn Road, Carrickfergus, County Antrim, BT38 8PS Tel: (028) 9336 8448 Fax: (028) 9335 1447 E-mail: sales@ilp-plaswood.co.uk

I Palmer & Son Ltd, 106 Lower Parliament Street, Nottingham, NG1 1EH Tel: 0115-950 3458 Fax: 0115-941 3458

▶ Indigo Concept Packaging, Knowll House Union Wharf, Leicester Road, Market Harborough, Leicestershire, LE16 7UW Tel: (01858) 410710 Fax: (01858) 410810 E-mail: sales@indigocp.com

Initial Packaging Solutions Ltd, Unit 16 Westgate, Everite Industrial Estate, Widnes, Cheshire, WA8 8RA Tel: 0151-420 4333 Fax: 0151-423 4451 E-mail: sales@initialpackaging.co.uk

Insit Moulded Packaging Ltd, Aintree Avenue, White Horse Business Park, Trowbridge, Wiltshire, BA14 0XB Tel: (01225) 767985 Fax: (01225) 777405E-mail: sales@insit.co.uk

▶ Iretex NI Ltd, 75 Woodburn Road, Carrickfergus, County Antrim, BT38 8PS Tel: (028) 9336 8448 Fax: (028) 9335 1447

Isca-Bags, 47 Marsh Green Road, Marsh Barton, Exeter, EX2 8PN Tel: (01392) 275906 Fax: (01392) 435028 E-mail: info@isca-bags.com

J P Hygiene Supplies, Britannia Estate, Leagrave Road, Luton, LU3 1RJ Tel: (01582) 488851 Fax: (01582) 410005 E-mail: sales@jphygiene.co.uk

Jaffabox Ltd, Starley Way, Birmingham, B37 7HB Tel: 0121-250 2000 Fax: 0121-250 2001 E-mail: sales@jaffabox.com

Jason Plastics Ltd, Prettywood, Bury New Road, Heap Bridge, Bury, Lancashire, BL9 7HZ Tel: 0161-763 8000 Fax: 0161-763 8052 E-mail: sales@jasonpackaging.co.uk

Jaycee Packaging Ltd, 8 Fairefield Crescent, Glenfield, Leicester, LE3 8EH Tel: 0116-231 4994 Fax: 0116-231 4989

Jayfour Packaging, 93 Charles Henry Street, Birmingham, B12 0SJ Tel: 0121-622 4451 Fax: 0121-666 6502 E-mail: sales@jayfourpkg.com

John C Brow Ltd, Prince Regent Road, Belfast, BT5 6SA Tel: (028) 9079 8171 Fax: (028) 9040 1095 E-mail: sales@browpack.com

John Darvell, 1 Westfield Farm, Henley Road, Medmenham, Marlow, Buckinghamshire, SL7 2TA Tel: (01491) 575286 Fax: (01491) 579617 E-mail: johndarvellpackaging@tiscali.co.uk

John Gray Paper & Twine Ltd, 48 Thomas Street, Manchester, M4 1ER Tel: 0161-832 3313 Fax: 0161-839 7068 E-mail: sales@johngray-packaging.co.uk

July Packaging, Unit 8 Manford Industrial Estate, Manor Road, Erith, Kent, DA8 2AJ Tel: (01322) 342123 Fax: (01322) 334479 E-mail: charlesdavies@zyworld.com

K & A Polystyrene, 30 Lavell Mews, Bradford, West Yorkshire, BD2 3HW Tel: (01274) 631341 Fax: (01274) 641781

K E B Packaging Ltd, Mills Hill Road, Middleton, Manchester, M24 2FT Tel: 0161-655 3464 Fax: 0161-655 3460 E-mail: sales@keb.co.uk

K P Packaging, Eastwood Avenue, Grimsby, South Humberside, DN34 5BE Tel: (01472) 750006 Fax: (01472) 349975

▶ K & S Packaging, 33-37 Garman Road, London, N17 0UL Tel: (020) 8885 6677 Fax: (020) 8885 6678 E-mail: info@kspackaging.com

Kay Metzeler Ltd, Wellington Road, Bollington, Macclesfield, Cheshire, SK10 5JJ Tel: (01625) 573366 Fax: (01625) 574075 E-mail: info@kay-metzeler.co.uk

Kendon Packaging Group, Bow Paper Works, Bridgwater Road, London, E15 2JZ Tel: (020) 7249 9645 Fax: (020) 8519 4333 E-mail: sales@kendon.co.uk

Keymesh Ltd, Premier Business Centre, Attwood Street, Stourbridge, West Midlands, DY9 8RY Tel: (01384) 898899 Fax: (01384) 898775 E-mail: sales@keymesh.com

Kingfisher Tapes Ltd, Unit 3 Kents Avenue, Hemel Hempstead, Hertfordshire, HP3 9XH Tel: (01442) 212624 Fax: (01442) 241057

Kingpak Plastic Sheeting Supplies, Unit 11-12, Waterside Business Park, Hadfield, Glossop, Derbyshire, SK13 1BE Tel: (01457) 862521 Fax: (01457) 862138 E-mail: enquiries@kingpak.co.uk

Kingsmoor Packaging Ltd, Cary Court, Bancombe Road, Somerton, Somerset, TA11 6SB Tel: (01458) 273001 Fax: (01458) 273350

Kite Packaging, PO Box 50, Blackwood, Gwent, NP12 2XF Tel: (01495) 230976 Fax: (01495) 230080 E-mail: southwales@packwithkite.com

Kite Packaging, 186 Torrington Avenue, Coventry, CV4 9AJ Tel: (024) 7642 0088 Fax: (024) 7642 0062 E-mail: sales@packwithkite.com

Kite Packaging, H Park 34, Collett, Didcot, Oxfordshire, OX11 7WB Tel: (01235) 815615 Fax: (01235) 750760 E-mail: thamesvalley@packwithkite.com

Kite Packaging, 2 Crammond Park, Lovet Road, Harlow, Essex, CM19 5TF Tel: (01279) 406160 Fax: (01279) 406161 E-mail: southeast@packwithkite.com

Kite Packaging, Unit 24-28, Stakehill Industrial Estate, Middleton, Manchester, M24 2RW Tel: 0161-643 1001 Fax: 0161-643 1122 E-mail: manchester@packwithkite.com

Kite Packaging, Portfield Road, Portsmouth, PO3 5SF Tel: (023) 9265 2676 Fax: (023) 9265 2677 E-mail: southcoast@packwithkite.com

Kite Packaging Ltd (Sheffield), Unit 3, Grange Mill Lane, Sheffield, S9 1HW Tel: (01709) 565010 Fax: (01709) 565011 E-mail: sheffield@packwithkite.com

Leicester Polythene Packaging Ltd, 93a Gwendolen Road, Leicester, LE5 5FL Tel: 0116-273 4235 Fax: 0116-273 4410 E-mail: sales@lppl.co.uk

Leroy Packaging Ltd, Heasandford Mill, Netherwood Road, Burnley, Lancashire, BB10 2EJ Tel: (01282) 438016 Fax: (01282) 430289 E-mail: learoyd@learoyd.co.uk

Liberty Plastics Ltd, Riversleigh Business Centre, 20 Harcourt Road, Dorney Reach, Maidenhead, Berkshire, SL6 0DU Tel: (01628) 773943 Fax: (01628) 788031 E-mail: tony@libertyplastics.freeserve.co.uk

LINPAC Moulded Foams Ltd, 5-7 Menasha Way, Queensway Industrial Estate, Brigg Road, Scunthorpe, North Lincolnshire, DN16 3RT Tel: (01724) 868153 Fax: (01724) 270021

Lo Cost Packaging Ltd, 32 Stephenson Street, London, E16 4SA Tel: (020) 7474 3786 Fax: (020) 7474 5786

Locpac Suppliers, 2 Queensway Business Centre, Waterloo Road, Widnes, Cheshire, WA8 0FD Tel: 0151-423 2828 Fax: 0151-495 2630 E-mail: enquiries@locpac.co.uk

The London Fancy Box Company Ltd, Poulton Close, Coombe Valley, Dover, Kent, CT17 0XB Tel: (01304) 242001 Fax: (01304) 240229 E-mail: a.darrall@londonfancybox.co.uk

Longs Packaging Ltd, 5-8 Rutherford Close, Leigh-on-Sea, Essex, SS9 5LQ Tel: (01702) 524342 Fax: (01702) 420257 E-mail: peterwood145@supanet.com

M F Manufacturing Ltd, Unit 1 Foundry Lane, Bristol, BS5 7XH Tel: 0117-965 1100 Fax: 0117-965 1188 E-mail: sales@mf-manufacturing.co.uk

Macfarlane Group Ltd, Siskin Parkway East, Middlemarch Business Park, Coventry, CV3 4PE Tel: (024) 7651 1511 Fax: (024) 7651 1302 E-mail: enquiries@national-packaging.co.uk

Macfarlane Group UK Ltd, Unit 2, Concorde Road, Patchway, Bristol, BS34 5TB Tel: (0870) 8500542 Fax: (0870) 8500543 E-mail: bristol@macfarlanegroup.net

Macfarlane Packaging P.L.C., The Water Front, Kingfisher Boulevard, Mewburn Riverside, Newcastle Upon Tyne, NE15 8NZ Tel: (0870) 6086100 Fax: (0870) 6086101

Magson Stationery, Bluestem Road, Ransomes Industrial Estate, Ipswich, IP3 9RR Tel: (01473) 727667 Fax: (01473) 727863

Marland Paper & Plastics Ltd, Whiteleather Square, Billingborough, Sleaford, Lincolnshire, NG34 0QP Tel: (01529) 240637 Fax: (01529) 240638 E-mail: sales@marland.co.uk

Marshall Wilson, Units 4 a-c Blochairn Industrial Estate, 16-24 Siemens Place, Glasgow, G21 2BN Tel: 0141-552 7577 Fax: 0141-552 5434

Martins Mill Packaging, Unit 2 Reflecting Roadstuds Induxtrial Estate, Mill Lane, Booth Town, Halifax, West Yorkshire, HX3 6TR Tel: (01422) 363935 Fax: (01422) 300800 E-mail: rmatmmp@aol.com

Mason & Jones Packaging, Unit 7, Aston Road, Aston Fields Industrial Estate, Bromsgrove, Worcestershire, B60 3EX Tel: (01527) 577123 Fax: (01527) 577248 E-mail: sales@masonandjones.com

Mid Glam Packing Supplies Ltd, Unit 8 Nine Mile Point Industrial Estate, Ynysddu, Newport, Gwent, NP11 7HZ Tel: (01495) 200555 Fax: (01495) 200876 E-mail: sales@midglam-packing.co.uk

Molygran & Co. Ltd, 115-119 Bury Road, Radcliffe, Manchester, M26 2UT Tel: 0161-724 4771 Fax: 0161-724 8855 E-mail: sales@molygran.com

Morris Packaging Ltd, 3a Telford Road, Ferndown Industrial Estate, Wimborne, Dorset, BH21 7QN Tel: (01202) 892623 Fax: (01202) 894903 E-mail: sales@packaging-uk.co.uk

Nicholas Packaging Ltd, Ham Lane, Kingswinford, West Midlands, DY6 7JJ Tel: (01384) 400500 Fax: (01384) 270943 E-mail: sales@nicholaspackaging.com

Nicholl Packaging Ltd, 4 Thackley Court, Thackley Old Road, Shipley, West Yorkshire, BD18 1BW Tel: (01274) 580563 Fax: (01274) 531675 E-mail: info@nichollpackaging.co.uk

North West Fire Ltd, Ross Road, Ellesmere Port, CH65 3DB Tel: 0151-355 6822 Fax: (01978) 751646

PACKAGING MATERIAL/GOODS/ PRODUCTS MANUFRS – *continued*

Northdown Packaging, 13c Quarry Wood Industrial Estate, Mills Road, Aylesford, Kent, ME20 7NA Tel: (01622) 710695 Fax: (01622) 790889 E-mail: sales@northdownpackaging.co.uk

Northern Corrugated Cases Ltd, 16 Middlewich Road, Byley, Middlewich, Cheshire, CW10 9NX Tel: (01606) 836811 Fax: (01606) 836088 E-mail: sales@northcorr.co.uk

Northern Packaging Ltd, Selby Place, Stanley Industrial Estate, Skelmersdale, Lancashire, WN8 8EF Tel: (01695) 731445 Fax: (01695) 51865 E-mail: sales@northern-packaging.co.uk

O Kahn Printers Ltd, 10 Timberwharf Road, London, N16 6DB Tel: (020) 8800 9941 Fax: (020) 8809 4896 E-mail: samkahn@freenet.co.uk

Omni-Pac UK Ltd, South Denes, Great Yarmouth, Norfolk, NR30 3QH Tel: (01493) 855381 Fax: (01493) 858464

Ozbox, Herald Way, Binley Industrial Estate, Binley Industrial Estate, Coventry, CV3 2RQ Tel: (024) 7656 1561 Fax: (024) 7656 1555 E-mail: tena.snell@ozbox.co.uk

Packaging, Flemming Way, Crawley, West Sussex, RH10 9JY Tel: (01293) 611111 Fax: (01293) 550555

Packaging Co., 195 Scudamore Road, Leicester, LE3 1UQ Tel: 0116-231 3444 Fax: 0116-231 3344 E-mail: sales@thepackagingcompany.co.uk

Palagan Ltd, Tavistock Street, Dunstable, Bedfordshire, LU6 1NE Tel: (01582) 600234 Fax: (01582) 601636 E-mail: mail@palagan.co.uk

PBL Packaging, 6 Maple Business Park, Walter Street, Birmingham, B7 5ET Tel: 0121-327 7757 Fax: 0121-328 3382

Peter Beyson Packaging Ltd, 2 Duchess Industrial Estate, Sievewright Street, Rutherglen, Glasgow, G73 1QS Tel: 0141-613 0001 Fax: 0141-613 1526 E-mail: sales@peterbrysonpackaging.com

▶ Pinnacle Print & Packaging Ltd, J Tyburn Industrial Estate, Ashold Farm Road, Birmingham, B24 9QG Tel: 0121-694 8800 Fax: 0121-694 8822 E-mail: sales@pinnaclepp.co.uk

Planned Packaging Ltd, 20 High Street, Great Budworth, Northwich, Cheshire, CW9 6HF Tel: (01606) 891432 Fax: (01606) 891466 E-mail: plannedpackagingltd@btinternet.com

Pleatwise Packaging Sussex Ltd, 27 Albert Drive, Burgess Hill, West Sussex, RH15 9TN Tel: (01444) 870654 Fax: (01444) 244171

Porter Packaging Co. Ltd, Hardwick Grange, Woolston, Warrington, WA1 4RT Tel: (01925) 822828 Fax: (01925) 837593

Premier Sacks & Packaging Ltd, Dean Farm, King St Woodford, Woodford, Stockport, Cheshire, SK7 1RL Tel: (01625) 521971 Fax: (01625) 521972 E-mail: info@premiersacks.co.uk

Promens, Unit 1, The Trident Centre, Armstrong Road, Basingstoke, Hampshire, RG24 8NU Tel: (01256) 844700 Fax: (01256) 844988 E-mail: jeremy.wilson@promens.com

Quality Films Ltd, Hoks Green Business Park, Martindale, Cannock, Staffordshire, WS11 7XL Tel: (01543) 577814 Fax: (01543) 577807 E-mail: sales@quality-films.co.uk

Que Packaging, 14 Chapel Street, Bradford, West Yorkshire, BD1 5DL Tel: (01274) 728498 Fax: (01274) 728498 E-mail: sales@quepackaging.com

R H Fibreboard Containers Ltd, 18 Knights Road, Chelston Business Park, Wellington, Somerset, TA21 9JH Tel: (01823) 663918 Fax: (01823) 665560 E-mail: enquiries@r-h-f.co.uk

Rainbow Bag UK Ltd, 3A Bess Park Road, Trenant Industrial Estate, Wadebridge, Cornwall, PL27 6HB Tel: (01208) 812442 Fax: (01208) 816181 E-mail: sales@rainbowbags.co.uk

Rajapack, Unit 1, Marston Gate, Bridgemont, Bedford, MK43 0YL Tel: (0800) 5424428 Fax: (0800) 5424429 E-mail: sales@rajapack.co.uk

Rapid Packaging Supplies Ltd, 26 Bayton Road, Exhall, Coventry, CV7 9EJ Tel: (024) 7636 0800 Fax: (024) 7664 4322 E-mail: sales@rapidpackaging.co.uk

RCL Sales, 55 Throgmorton Road, Yateley, Hampshire, GU46 6FA Tel: (01252) 890047 Fax: (01252) 861220

Remploy Ltd, Croespenmaen Industrial Estate, Kendon, Crumlin, Newport, Gwent, NP11 3AG Tel: (01495) 246505 Fax: (01495) 248334 E-mail: john.lundie@remploy.co.uk

E. Revell & Sons Ltd, Unit 1C Joesph Wilson Industrial Estate, Mill Strood Road, Whitstable, Kent, CT5 3PS Tel: (01227) 277020 Fax: (01227) 770839

Reymar Ltd, 9 Reynolds Close, London, NW11 7EA Tel: (020) 8905 5261 Fax: (020) 8905 5263

C.S. Robertson (Packaging) Ltd, 4 Young Place, Kelvin Industrial Estate, East Kilbride, Glasgow, G75 0TD Tel: (01355) 244656 Fax: (01355) 265163 E-mail: csrobertsonpkg@btinternet.com

Robin Packaging Ltd, Unit 3c Quarryfield Industrial Estate, Mere, Warminster, Wiltshire, BA12 6LA Tel: (01747) 861500 Fax: (01747) 861600 E-mail: sales@printedcarriers.com

RPC Containers Ltd, Grove Street, Raunds, Wellingborough, Northamptonshire, NN9 6ED Tel: (01933) 623311 Fax: (01933) 622126 E-mail: sales@rpc-raunds.co.uk

Sadlers Carton Stockholders Ltd, 10 Tilton Road, Small Heath, Birmingham, B9 4PE Tel: 0121-772 5200 Fax: 0121-771 4368 E-mail: sales@sadlers.co.uk

Sai Pac UK Ltd, Poly House, 88 Park Road, Ilford, Essex, IG1 1SF Tel: (020) 8553 4050 Fax: (020) 8553 5151

St Vincents Insulation Ltd, 19 St Vincents Road, Dartford, DA1 1XF Tel: (01322) 225174 Fax: (01322) 221474 E-mail: sales@stvincents.co.uk

Sca Packaging Ltd, UK Central Office, Papyrus Way, Larkfield, Aylesford, Kent, ME20 7TW Tel: (01622) 883000 Fax: (01622) 716308

Shand Higson & Co. Ltd, Lees Road, Knowsley Industrial Park North, Knowsley, Liverpool, L33 7SE Tel: 0151-549 2210 Fax: 0151-549 1405 E-mail: sales@shandhigson.co.uk

Sherwood Packaging Ltd, Amber Drive, Langley Mill, Nottingham, NG16 4BE Tel: (01773) 760101 Fax: (01773) 530527 E-mail: sales@sherwoodpkg.com

Skymark Packaging International Ltd, Southern Avenue, Leominster, Herefordshire, HR6 0QF Tel: (01568) 611393 Fax: (01568) 611602 E-mail: info@skymark.co.uk

Smart Packaging Ltd, Units 15-16, Beeches Industrial Estate, Lavenham Road, Yate, Bristol, BS37 5QX Tel: (01454) 311811 Fax: (01454) 311822 E-mail: smartpackaging@breathemail.net

Smiths & Bateson Ltd, Kitling Road, Knowsley Business Park, Prescot, Merseyside, L34 9JA Tel: 0151-547 1801 Fax: 0151-547 7171 E-mail: sales@smithbateson.co.uk

Smurfit Townsend Hook, Paper Mills, Mill Street, Snodland, Kent, ME6 5AX Tel: (01634) 240205 Fax: (01634) 243458 E-mail: sales@smurfit-europe.com

Sonoco Consumer Products Ltd, Stokes Street, Manchester, M11 4QX Tel: 0161-230 7000 Fax: 0161-230 1200E-mail: info@sonoco.com

Sontex Machinery Ltd, 61 Westgate, Cleckheaton, West Yorkshire, BD19 5JZ Tel: (01274) 872299 Fax: (01274) 862829 E-mail: info@sontex.co.uk

Springfield Cartons Ltd, Cottenham Lane, Salford, M7 1TW Tel: 0161-833 9857 Fax: 0161-832 1831

Springpack, New Road, Pershore, Worcestershire, WR10 1BY Tel: (01386) 552550 Fax: (0870) 7747402

Storm Cutting Formes, Unit 2 Roe Street, Congleton, Cheshire, CW12 1PS Tel: (01260) 291793 Fax: (01260) 291794

Styropack UK Ltd, Unit A Rudford Industrial Estate, Ford Road, Ford, Arundel, West Sussex, BN18 0BD Tel: (01903) 725282 Fax: (01903) 731628 E-mail: ford@styropack.co.uk

Styropack UK Ltd, 1 Stephenson Street, Hillington Industrial Estate, Glasgow, G52 4JD Tel: 0141-882 9166 Fax: 0141-882 7022 E-mail: glasgow@styropack.co.uk

▶ Sudpack UK Ltd, 40 High Park Drive, Wolverton Mill, Milton Keynes, MK12 5TT Tel: (01908) 525720 Fax: (01908) 525721 E-mail: info@suedpack.com

Sundolitt Ltd, 8 Broomfield Road, Montrose, Angus, DD10 8SY Tel: (01674) 676006 Fax: (01674) 676686

Supapak Ltd, 24 Jubilee Way, Shipley, West Yorkshire, BD18 1QG Tel: (01274) 531314 Fax: (01274) 532008 E-mail: sales@supapak.com

Superfine Tapes Co. Ltd, Batford Mill, Lower Luton Road, Harpenden, Hertfordshire, AL5 5ES Tel: (01582) 460808 Fax: (01582) 766535

T Leighton & Sons, Unit 1a Albion Trading Estate, Mossley Road, Ashton-under-Lyne, Lancashire, OL6 6NQ Tel: 0161-330 4933 Fax: 0161-343 7025 E-mail: tlsbox@aol.com

Tams Packaging Ltd, Sopers Road, Cuffley, Potters Bar, Hertfordshire, EN6 4TP Tel: (01707) 876777 Fax: (01707) 872233 E-mail: tams.packaging@talk21.com

Thorpe Packaging Ltd, Ripley Drive, Normanton Industrial Estate, Normanton, West Yorkshire, WF6 1QT Tel: (01924) 898802 Fax: (01924) 898803 E-mail: peter@thorpepackaging.sagehost.co.uk

▶ Tipografic, Unit 1B, Squires Gate Industrial Estate, Squires Gate Lane, Blackpool, FY4 3RN Tel: (01253) 404142 Fax: (01253) 402882 E-mail: iesthomas@tipgrafic.co.uk

Transatlantic Plastics Ltd, Unit 6 Lulworth Business Centre, Nutwood Way, Totton, Southampton, SO40 3WW Tel: (023) 8086 9999 Fax: (023) 8066 6622 E-mail: sales@transpack.co.uk

Travelstock Packaging Ltd, 20 & 21 The Arches, South College St, Aberdeen, AB11 6JX Tel: (01224) 582657 Fax: (01224) 584303 E-mail: sales@travelstockpackaging.co.uk

▶ Treadstone Technology, Galleon House, 4-10 Guildford Road, Chertsey, Surrey, KT16 9BJ Tel: (01932) 567527 Fax: (01932) 570772 E-mail: info@treadstone.co.uk

Trench Packaging Ltd, Unit C, New Farm, Froyle Lanw, South Warnborough, Hook, Hampshire, RG29 1SH Tel: (01256) 861333 Fax: (01256) 861334 E-mail: sales@trenchpack.co.uk

▶ Tri Pac Logistics, 3 49-51 Nurseries Road, Baillieston, Glasgow, G69 6UL Tel: 0141-773 2942 Fax: 0141-773 2507 E-mail: enquiries@tripaclogistics.co.uk

Turner & Co., Hamlin Way, Hardwick Narrows Industrial Estate, King's Lynn, Norfolk, PE30 4NG Tel: (01553) 692822

▶ Tyler Packaging Ltd, Fosse Way, Chesterton, Leamington Spa, Warwickshire, CV33 9JY Tel: (01926) 651451 Fax: (01926) 651691 E-mail: info@tylerpackaging.co.uk

UK Packaging, 36-38 Nansen Road, Leicester, LE5 5FX Tel: 0116-273 4141 Fax: 0116-273 8181 E-mail: fardinsattar@hotmail.com

Unita Packaging Ltd, Unit 15 Bloomsgrove Industrial Estate, Ilkeston Rd, Nottingham, NG7 3JG Tel: 0115-978 6172 Fax: 0115-978 6776 E-mail: sales@unita.co.uk

Universal Packaging Ltd, Units 3-4, Capitol Industrial Centre, Fulmar Way, Wickford, Essex, SS11 8YW Tel: (01268) 561400 Fax: (01268) 572900 E-mail: admin@uplgroupltd.com

V A Whitley & Co. Ltd, Milward House, Fir Street, Heywood, Lancashire, OL10 1NW Tel: (01706) 364211 Fax: (01706) 366828 E-mail: mine@vawhitley.co.uk

Valenbeck Ltd, Bailey Industrial Estate, Ellison Street, Jarrow, Tyne & Wear, NE32 3JU Tel: 0191-483 2290 Fax: 0191-483 3574 E-mail: sales@valenbeck.co.uk

W & M Watson, Unit 1a Clyde Industrial Estate, Glasgow, G73 1PP Tel: (01506) 852324 Fax: (01506) 855210

W. Ridley & Co. Ltd, 12-16 Bean Street, Hull, HU3 2PQ Tel: (01482) 224691 Fax: (01482) 587098 E-mail: info@wridley.co.uk

West Packaging Ltd, Cornish Street, Sheffield, S6 3AA Tel: 0114-276 0555 Fax: 0114-275 7590 E-mail: info@westpack.co.uk

Wilmot Packaging Ltd, Rutherford Way, Swindon Village, Cheltenham, Gloucestershire, GL51 9TU Tel: (01242) 245151 Fax: (01242) 245155

▶ Wooderson Packaging Ltd, Alexander House, Christy Court, Basildon, Essex, SS15 6TL Tel: (01268) 548200 Fax: (01268) 541878 E-mail: info@woodersonpackaging.co.uk

Woods Packaging, Unit D4 Whitwood Enterprise Park, Whitwood Lane, Whitwood, Castleford, West Yorkshire, WF10 5PX Tel: (01977) 604050 Fax: (01977) 604400 E-mail: sales@woods-packaging.co.uk

Woodway Packaging Ltd, 25-27 Mallard Close, Earls Barton, Northampton, NN6 0JF Tel: (01604) 812678 Fax: (01604) 810678

Yorkshire Packaging Supplies Ltd, Quarry Lane, Dewsbury, West Yorkshire, WF12 7JJ Tel: (01924) 441355 Fax: (01924) 440686 E-mail: info@yps.co.uk

PACKAGING MATERIALS

▶ A D Stretch Wrap Ltd, 1 Hermitage Way, Mansfield, Nottinghamshire, NG18 5ES Tel: (01623) 648845 Fax: (01623) 608846

Advanced Protective Packaging Ltd, 25 Towerfield Road, Shoeburyness, Southend-on-Sea, SS3 9QT Tel: (01702) 293312 Fax: (01702) 298556 E-mail: salessouth@advanced-pp.co.uk

▶ All-Pac, Trevilson Business Park, St. Newlyn East, Newquay, Cornwall, TR8 5JF Tel: (01872) 510065 Fax: (01872) 510765 E-mail: sales@all-pac.co.uk

▶ Arrow Film Convertors, Sterling Industrial Park, Carr Wood Road, Castleford, West Yorkshire, WF10 4PS Tel: (01977) 556551 Fax: (01977) 556552

▶ Bambe Ltd, 3 Granville Industrial Estate, Granville Road, London, NW2 2LD Tel: (020) 8381 4567 Fax: (020) 8381 4589 E-mail: sales@bambeltd.co.uk

▶ Bettapack, 37 Portland Drive, Biddulph, Stoke-on-Trent, ST8 6RY Tel: (01782) 510833 Fax: (01782) 510833

▶ Box Clever Wholesale, 1e Britannia Estate, Leagrave Road, Luton, LU3 1RJ Tel: (01582) 722990 Fax: (01582) 450030

▶ Boxes And Packaging (Cambridge)Ltd, Edison Road, St. Ives Industrial Estate, St. Ives, Cambridgeshire, PE27 3LF Tel: (01480) 467633 Fax: (01480) 309100 E-mail: cambridge@boxesandpackaging.com

▶ Complete Polythene Packaging, Hanney Road, Steventon, Abingdon, Oxfordshire, OX13 6AP Tel: (01235) 820610 Fax: (01235) 820710 E-mail: compolypack@tiscali.co.uk

Dochart Packaging & Hygiene Supplies Ltd, 46-48 Maurice Gaymer Road, Attleborough, Norfolk, NR17 2QZ Tel: (01953) 456040 Fax: (01953) 455144

▶ Dynamic Packaging, St. Davids Close, Stevenage, Hertfordshire, SG1 4UZ Tel: (01438) 313161 Fax: (01438) 313161

Edulan Ltd, Unit M North Stage, 92 Broadway, Salford, M50 2UW Tel: 0161-876 8040 Fax: 0161-876 8041 E-mail: sales@edulan.com

Elmwood Design Ltd, 40-44 Thistle Street, Edinburgh, EH2 1EN Tel: 0131-225 1181 Fax: 0131-718 0390 E-mail: enquiries@elmwood.co.uk

▶ Global Packaging Sources Irm Ltd, 6 West Street, Ramsey, Isle of Man, IM8 1DB Tel: (01624) 812444 Fax: (01624) 812555 E-mail: sales@gpsiom.com

▶ Hamson Engineering, 18 Braefoot Avenue, Milngavie, Glasgow, G62 6JZ Tel: 0141-956 4144 Fax: 0141-956 6946

▶ I C S Europe, Multi Media Exchange, 72-80 Corporation Road, Middlesbrough, Cleveland, TS1 2RF Tel: (01642) 230676 Fax: (01642) 219636

▶ Igneous Products Ltd, Aquaduct Works, Marple Bridge, Stockport, Cheshire, SK6 5LD Tel: 0161-449 7666 Fax: 0161-449 7666

▶ Inter Pack, 9 Cradock Road, Luton, LU4 0JF Tel: (01582) 570050 Fax: (01582) 570060 E-mail: sales@interpackltd.co.uk

▶ Interbags, PO Box 2083, Hockley, Essex, SS5 4QW Tel: (01702) 205750 Fax: (01702) 204596

▶ Islepac, 1a Macaulay Road, Stornoway, Isle of Lewis, HS1 2HD Tel: (01851) 706911 Fax: (01851) 706911 E-mail: info@islepac.co.uk

▶ J Eastwood & Son, Holme Iron Works, Sowerby Bridge, West Yorkshire, HX6 3LE Tel: (01422) 835550 Fax: (01422) 836067

Kite Packaging, 2 Newbridge Road Industrial Estate, Pontllanfraith, Blackwood, Gwent, NP12 2XF Tel: (01495) 230976 Fax: (01495) 230080

Laserpack Cartons & Cases Ltd, Unit 4, Llandygai Industrial Estate, Bangor, Gwynedd, LL57 4YH Tel: (0845) 2575758 Fax: (0845) 2575759 E-mail: sales@laserpack.co.uk

▶ LCP Packaging Materials, Unit 4a Tanfield Lea Industrial Estate South, Tanfield Lea, Stanley, County Durham, DH9 9QX Tel: (01207) 237666 Fax: (01207) 238666 E-mail: enquiries@lcp.linst.ac.uk

Light Alloy Ltd, Barney Hayes Lane, Cadnam, Southampton, SO40 2ND Tel: (023) 8081 1180 Fax: (023) 8081 1197

▶ Macfarlene Group, Unit A2, The Waterfront, Kingfisher Boulevard, Newcastle Upon Tyne, NE15 8NZ Tel: (0870) 6086100 Fax: (0870) 6086101

▶ Malvern Packaging, Unit 24 Bourne Road Industrial Park, Bourne Road, Dartford, DA1 4BZ Tel: (01322) 524780 Fax: (01322) 524780 E-mail: enquiries@malvernpackaging.co.uk

▶ Manor Packaging Ltd, 30-31 Maxwell Road, Peterborough, PE2 7JN Tel: (01733) 233884 Fax: (01733) 233885 E-mail: sales@manorpackaging.co.uk

▶ Now Plastics, Salters Lane, Sedgefield, Stockton-on-Tees, Cleveland, TS21 3EE Tel: (01740) 625228 Fax: (01740) 625204 E-mail: sales@nowplastics.com

▶ P C Packaging Ltd, P C House, Vulcan Road, Bilston, West Midlands, WV14 7HT Tel: (01902) 495200 Fax: (01902) 495275

▶ P P P UK Ltd, Orchard House, Henwood, Ashford, Kent, TN24 8DH Tel: (01233) 665597 Fax: (01233) 665598 E-mail: hassansard@aol.com

▶ Packaging Direct, Lock House, The Meads, Hertford, SG13 7BD Tel: (01992) 505056 Fax: (01992) 505777

Parkside Packaging Ltd, Willenhall Lane, Binley, Coventry, CV3 2AS Tel: (024) 7645 5455 Fax: (024) 7645 6056 E-mail: sales@parkside-pkg.co.uk

Pioneer Packaging Ltd, Unit 16, Dunsinan Industrial Estate, Dunsinan Avenue, Dundee, DD2 3QT Tel: (01382) 833233 Fax: (01382) 832256E-mail: sales@pioneerpackaging.co.uk

▶ Pro-Pac Contract Packaging Ltd, 30 Springwell Road, Leeds, LS12 1AW Tel: (0870) 4322567 Fax: (0870) 4322568

▶ Propack Film, Unit 88 Leyland Trading Estate, Irthlingborough Road, Wellingborough, Northamptonshire, NN8 1RA Tel: (01933) 275111

Samuel Grant Midlands Ltd, 22 Willow Road, Castle Donington, Derby, DE74 2NP Tel: (01332) 858200 Fax: (01332) 858292

Simpsons, Clapper Lane, Staplehurst, Tonbridge, Kent, TN12 0JS Tel: (01580) 890747 Fax: (01580) 890667 E-mail: simpsonssolutions@supanet.com

Thompson Packaging, Unit 5, Kenyons Farm, Gough Lane, Walton Summit, Preston, PR5 6AR Tel: (01772) 620768 Fax: (01772) 620764 E-mail: info@arranmarketing.co.uk

Total Spectrum Ltd, 11 Intec 2, Wade Road, Basingstoke, Hampshire, RG24 8NE Tel: (01256) 814114 Fax: (01256) 814115 E-mail: sales@totalspectrum.co.uk

Willpack Case Mnfrs, Unit 1a Blackheath Trading Estate, Cakemore Road, Rowley Regis, West Midlands, B65 0QN Tel: 0121-559 4949 Fax: 0121-559 4545 E-mail: sales@willpack.net

PACKAGING PLASTIC PRODUCTS, *See also headings for particular items or materials*

Agentdraw Ltd, 42 Great Central Street, Leicester, LE1 4JT Tel: 0116-251 9990 Fax: 0116-251 9997 E-mail: kevin@agentdraw.co.uk

Anson Packaging Ltd, 62 Station Road, Haddenham, Ely, Cambridgeshire, CB6 3XD Tel: (01353) 740990 Fax: (01353) 741365 E-mail: anson@avroind.com

B P I Stretchville, Bath Road, Bridgwater, Somerset, TA6 4BF Tel: (01278) 446262 Fax: (01278) 452252 E-mail: pswexports@brithene.com

Bell Packaging Ltd, Barratt Industrial Park, Airport Way, Luton, LU2 9NH Tel: (01582) 459292 Fax: (01582) 450181 E-mail: info@bellpackaging.com

Cambrian Containers, Unit 32 Mochdre Industrial Estate, Mochdre, Newtown, Powys, SY16 4LE Tel: (01686) 611360 Fax: (01686) 611361

Central Tin Canister Co. Ltd, Orrell Mount, Bootle, Merseyside, L20 6NS Tel: 0151-933 6704 Fax: 0151-933 5315 E-mail: centralplastic@freenetname.co.uk

PACKAGING PLASTIC PRODUCTS - *continued*

Esterform Packaging Ltd, Boraston Lane, Tenbury Wells, Worcestershire, WR15 8LE Tel: (01584) 810600 Fax: (01584) 810213 E-mail: paulw@esterform.com

Huhtamaki (UK) Ltd, Rowner Road, Gosport, Hants, PO13 0PR Tel: (023) 9251 2434 Fax: (023) 9251 2330 E-mail: sales@gb.huhtamaki.com

Jiffy Packaging Co. Ltd, Road Four, Winsford Industrial Estate, Winsford, Cheshire, CW7 3QR Tel: (01606) 551221 Fax: (01606) 592634 E-mail: sales@jiffy.co.uk

John Darvell, 1 Westfield Farm, Henley Road, Medmenham, Marlow, Buckinghamshire, SL7 2TA Tel: (01491) 575286 Fax: (01491) 579617 E-mail: johndarvellpackaging@tiscali.co.uk

Leeds Vacuum Formers Ltd, 4 National Road, Hunslet Business Park, Leeds, LS10 1TD Tel: 0113-277 3800 Fax: 0113-277 5263 E-mail: sales@leedsvacform.com

M S K Packaging Ltd, 13 Prince William Road, Loughborough, Leicestershire, LE11 5GU Tel: (01509) 264338 Fax: (01509) 233427

Manuplastics Ltd, Lombard Road, London, SW19 3TZ Tel: (020) 8542 3421 Fax: (020) 8540 0594 E-mail: sales@manuplastics.co.uk

Mongoose Plastics Ltd, 57-58 Nasmyth Road, Glenrothes, Fife, KY6 2SD Tel: (01592) 774800 Fax: (01592) 775032 E-mail: george@mongoose-plastics.co.uk

Moss Products Plastics Ltd, Isle of Wight Lane, Kensworth, Dunstable, Bedfordshire, LU6 2PP Tel: (01582) 873366 Fax: (01582) 873399 E-mail: sales@mossproducts.co.uk

Ongropack UK, 46 Gray's Inn Road, London, WC1X 8LP Tel: (020) 7831 4225 Fax: (020) 7831 9578 E-mail: allen@ongropack.fsnet.co.uk

Pactiv Europe Ltd, 4 Young Square, Brucefield Industrial Estate, Livingston, West Lothian, EH54 9BX Tel: (01506) 462247 Fax: (01506) 415458 E-mail: sales@pactiv.com

Polimoon Ltd, Babbage Road, Engineer Park, Sandycroft, Deeside, Clwyd, CH5 2QD Tel: (01244) 537555 Fax: (01244) 526645 E-mail: sales@polimoon.com

Polyan Covers, 5 Bainbridge Wharf, Farnhill, Keighley, West Yorkshire, BD20 9BX Tel: (01535) 631212 Fax: (01535) 631313

▶ Sudpack UK Ltd, 40 High Park Drive, Wolverton Mill, Milton Keynes, MK12 5TT Tel: (01908) 525720 Fax: (01908) 525721 E-mail: info@suedpack.com

Superfos Runcorn Ltd., Edison Road, Astmoor Industrial Estate, Runcorn, Cheshire, WA7 1PY Tel: (01928) 575051 Fax: (01928) 572038 E-mail: steve.winstanley@superfos.co.uk

Supreme Plastics Ltd, Stainsacre Lane, Whitby, North Yorkshire, YO22 4PT Tel: (01947) 604161 Fax: (01947) 606168 E-mail: sales@supremeplastics.com

Suttons Performance Packaging, 16 Albert Way, Chatteris, Cambridgeshire, PE16 6US Tel: (01354) 693171 Fax: (01354) 695430 E-mail: info@suttonspp.co.uk

Thermoform Ltd, The Larches Moor Farm Road, Airfield Industrial Estate, Ashbourne, Derbyshire, DE6 1HD Tel: (01335) 343757 Fax: (01335) 300096 E-mail: enquiries@thermoform-limited.co.uk

Tpi Plastic Sheeting Supplies, Scott Lidgett Road, Stoke-on-Trent, ST6 4NQ Tel: (01782) 837141 Fax: (01782) 575154 E-mail: info@tpi-polythene.co.uk

William Beckett Plastics Ltd, Unit 5a, Tinsley Industrial Park, Shepcote Way, Sheffield, S9 1TH Tel: 0114-243 4399 Fax: 0114-256 0196 E-mail: sales@beckettplastics.co.uk

PACKAGING POLYSTYRENE (PS) CUT PIECES

Adur Packaging Ltd, 1 Brook Farm, Horsham Road, Cowfold, Horsham, West Sussex, RH13 8AH Tel: (01403) 864994 Fax: (01403) 864774 E-mail: adurpackaging@aol.com

C S Manufacturing Ltd, 13-14 Feeder Road, St. Phillips, Bristol, BS2 0SB Tel: 0117-977 3388 Fax: 0117-977 3397 E-mail: csmanufacturing@btconnect.com

E P S Products Ltd, Units 5-6, Govan Road, Fenton Industrial Estate, Stoke-on-Trent, ST4 2RS Tel: (01782) 749662 Fax: (01782) 749757

Excel Packaging & Insulation Co. Ltd, Unit 9, Woodcock Hill Estate, Harefield Road, Rickmansworth, Hertfordshire, WD3 1PQ Tel: (01923) 770247 Fax: (01923) 770248 E-mail: enquiries@excelpackaging.com

Expanded Polystyrene Supplies, Denton Island, Newhaven, East Sussex, BN9 9BA Tel: (01273) 612303 Fax: (01273) 517306 E-mail: sales@pabrico.co.uk

K & A Polystyrene, 30 Lavell Mews, Bradford, West Yorkshire, BD2 3HW Tel: (01274) 631341 Fax: (01274) 641781

K B Packaging & Insulation, The Warehouse, Foggathorpe, Selby, North Yorkshire, YO8 6PR Tel: (01757) 289131 Fax: (01757) 289142 E-mail: enquiries@kbpackagingandinsulation.co.uk

Molygran & Co. Ltd, 115-119 Bury Road, Radcliffe, Manchester, M26 2UT Tel: 0161-724 4771 Fax: 0161-724 8855 E-mail: sales@molygran.com

Polyscot Polystyrene, 4 Craigluscar Road, Dunfermline, Fife, KY12 9JA Tel: (01383) 732296 Fax: (01383) 620365 E-mail: eps@polyscot.co.uk

S & B E P S Ltd, Dudley, Cramlington, Northumberland, NE23 7PY Tel: 0191-250 0818 Fax: 0191-250 0548 E-mail: company@sandbeps.com

St Vincents Insulation Ltd, 19 St Vincents Road, Dartford, DA1 1XF Tel: (01322) 225174 Fax: (01322) 221474 E-mail: sales@stvincents.co.uk

Tylex Products Ltd, Ashton Works, Cunliffe Road, Blackpool, FY1 6SD Tel: (01253) 765046 Fax: (01253) 791676 E-mail: tylex.polystyrene@btinternet.com

Weald Polyproducts Ltd, Unit 1, Heron Bussiness Park, White Field Avenue, Sundon Park, Luton, LU3 3BB Tel: (01582) 508517 Fax: (01582) 570188 E-mail: sales.wheels@btconnect.com

Wevax Ltd, Prospect Close, Lowmoor Business Park, Kirkby-in-Ashfield, Nottingham, NG17 7LF Tel: (01623) 754268 Fax: (01623) 723447

PACKAGING PRINTING

P & P Print & Packing, F 7 Gore Road, Burnham, Slough, SL1 8AA Tel: (01628) 666249 Fax: (01628) 602471 E-mail: printandpacking@btconnect.com

S G Print Ltd, PO Box 6068, Basildon, Essex, SS14 3WJ Tel: (01621) 773610 Fax: (01621) 773271 E-mail: sales@sgprint.ltd.uk

PACKAGING REEL TO REEL FLEXOGRAPHIC PRINTING

Clifton Packaging Group P.L.C., Maridian Business Park, Centurion Way, Leicester, LE19 1WH Tel: 0116-289 3355 Fax: 0116-289 1113 E-mail: info@cliftonpackaging.co.uk

E B R Ltd, West Quay Road, Enterprise Park, Sunderland, SR5 2TE Tel: 0191-501 1777 Fax: 0191-501 1700 E-mail: info@ebr.co.uk

Norman Knights Ltd, 1 Russell Court, Russell Gardens, Wickford, Essex, SS11 8QU Tel: (01268) 733722 Fax: (01268) 764537 E-mail: sales@normanknights.com

Modern Packaging UK Ltd, Unit 26 Lansdown Industrial Estate, Gloucester Road, Cheltenham, Gloucestershire, GL51 8PL Tel: (01242) 262002 Fax: (01242) 261919 E-mail: sales@modern-packaging.co.uk

Polyprint Mailing Films Ltd, Mackintosh Road, Rackheath Industrial Estate, Rackheath, Norwich, NR13 6LJ Tel: (01603) 721807 Fax: (01603) 721813 E-mail: jneville@polyprint.co.uk

Printpack Ltd, Bridge Hall Mills, Bridge Hall Lane, Bury, Lancashire, BL9 7PA Tel: 0161-764 5441 Fax: 0161-705 1624 E-mail: bbleasdale@printpack.com

QC Packaging Films Ltd, Technology House, Heage Road Industrial Estate, Ripley, Derbyshire, DE5 3GH Tel: (01773) 740300 Fax: (01773) 740301 E-mail: info@qcpackagingfilms.com

Roberts,Mart & Co.Limited, Aire Valley House, Thornes Farm Way, Leeds, LS9 0AN Tel: 0113-202 6500 Fax: 0113-202 6550 E-mail: info@roberts-mart.co.uk

Skymark Packaging Solutions, Manners Avenue, Manners Industrial Estate, Ilkeston, Derbyshire, DE7 8EF Tel: 0115-930 2020 Fax: 0115-907 1525 E-mail: admin@skymark.co.uk

PACKAGING SACHETS

A.P. Sachets Ltd, Stafford Park 6, Telford, Shropshire, TF3 3AT Tel: (01952) 234100 Fax: (01952) 234111 E-mail: sales@sachets.co.uk

Guardpack Ltd, 12 & 14 Grafton Place, Dukes Park Industrial Estate, Chelmsford, CM2 6TG Tel: (01245) 451770 Fax: (01245) 451710 E-mail: jeremy@guardpack.co.uk

Heinz Foodservice, South Building, Hayes Park, Hayes, Middlesex, UB4 8AL Tel: (0800) 575755 E-mail: foodservice.enquiry@uk.hjheinz.com

Moore & Buckle Ltd, 3 Lancots Lane, St. Helens, Merseyside, WA9 3EX Tel: (01744) 733066 Fax: (01744) 451000 E-mail: info@mooreandbuckle.com

PACKAGING SERVICES/ CONTRACT PACKAGING, *See also headings for particular types*

Allgo Ltd, Unit 9c Bank Hall Park, Wharf Street, Warrington, WA1 2DG Tel: (01925) 570150 Fax: (01925) 570155 E-mail: david.snitch@allgo.biz

Allport Overland, Allport House, Thurrock Park Way, Tilbury, Essex, RM18 7HZ Tel: (01375) 487800 Fax: (01375) 487890 E-mail: info@allport.co.uk

▶ Alternative Packaging Solutions Ltd, The Studio Prospect Place, Mill Lane, Alton, Hampshire, GU34 2SX Tel: (01420) 544800 Fax: (01420) 544850

Belgrave Press Ltd, 320 Melton Road, Leicester, LE4 7SL Tel: 0116-266 2516 Fax: 0116-261 0053 E-mail: sales@belgravepress.co.uk

Belgrave Shipping Co. Ltd, Fishers Way, Belvedere, Kent, DA17 6BS Tel: (020) 8310 1890 Fax: (020) 8312 3505 E-mail: belgrave@ukfraite.co.uk

Blue Boar, Unit D3 New Yatt Business Centre, Kite Lane, New Yatt, Witney, Oxfordshire, OX29 6TJ Tel: (01993) 868878 Fax: (01993) 868878 E-mail: helen.cook@virgin.net

Brecon Pharmaceuticals Ltd, Pharos House Wye Valley Business Park, Brecon Road, Hay-on-Wye, Hereford, HR3 5PG Tel: (01497) 820829 Fax: (01497) 820050 E-mail: admin@brecon-pharm.co.uk

Budelpack March Ltd, Martin Avenue, March, Cambridgeshire, PE15 0BJ Tel: (01354) 660400 Fax: (01354) 661270 E-mail: info@budelpack.com

Caps Cases Ltd, Studlands Park Industrial Estate, Newmarket, Suffolk, CB8 7AU Tel: (01638) 667326 Fax: (01638) 667407 E-mail: info@capscases.co.uk

Cargo Packing Services Ltd, Portland Works, Hill Street, Ashton-under-Lyne, Lancashire, OL7 0PZ Tel: 0161-343 4737 Fax: 0161-343 4738 E-mail: contact@cargopack.co.uk

Catalent Pharma Solutions, Lancaster Way, Wingates Industrial Estate, Westhoughton, Bolton, BL5 3XX Tel: (01942) 790000 Fax: (01942) 799799

Coburn Fasteners, Unit 1-3 Brunel Way, Stroudwater Business Park, Stonehouse, Gloucestershire, GL10 3SX Tel: (01453) 828515 Fax: (01453) 791040 E-mail: andy@coburnfasteners.co.uk

Contract Blending & Packing Ltd, Heys Lane, Great Harwood, Blackburn, BB6 7UA Tel: (01254) 877870 Fax: (01254) 877871

Contract Packers (Midlands) Ltd, Kiln Way, Woodville, Swadlincote, Derbyshire, DE11 8ED Tel: (01283) 224489 Fax: (01283) 224030 E-mail: barrypresscott@vitax.co.uk

County Enterprises Sheltered Workshop, St Pauls Street, Worcester, WR1 2BA Tel: (01905) 23819 Fax: (01905) 27832 E-mail: countyentepriees@worcestershire.gov.uk

Custom Packaging Ltd, Unit 1, Hortonwood 33, Telford, Shropshire, TF1 7EX Tel: (01952) 608270 Fax: (01952) 608041 E-mail: alantown@custom-pkg.co.uk

Eurocare Impex Services Ltd, Units 9-10 Holme Industrial Estate, Ballplay Road, Moffat, Dumfriesshire, DG10 9JU Tel: (01683) 221336 Fax: (01683) 221335

Eurohill Traders Ltd, 195 Vale Road, Tonbridge, Kent, TN9 1SU Tel: (01732) 770777 Fax: (01732) 770757 E-mail: sales@apac.co.uk

Excelsior Packers, Brookside Lane, Oswaldtwistle, Accrington, Lancashire, BB5 3NY Tel: (01254) 356622 Fax: (01254) 356677 E-mail: sales@gemweb.co.uk

Field Group Ltd, Misbourne House Badminton Court, Church Street, Amersham, Buckinghamshire, HP7 0DD Tel: (01494) 720200 Fax: (01494) 431138 E-mail: marketing@fieldgroup.com

L.P. Foreman & Sons Ltd, Farrow Road, Wigford Industrial Estate, Chelmsford, CM1 3TH Tel: (01245) 264521 Fax: (01245) 495232 E-mail: sales@lpforeman.co.uk

Friars & Co., Unit 2b Shakespeare Industrial Estate, Shakespeare Street, Watford, WD24 5RU Tel: (01923) 249420 Fax: (01923) 818142 E-mail: friars@ukf.net

G N N International Ltd, Unit 70, Woolsbridge Industrial Estate, Three Legged Cross, Wimborne, Dorset, BH21 6SU Tel: (01202) 823012 Fax: (01202) 821754 E-mail: info@contractpackers.net

Graham Lloyd Bedford Ltd, Ampthill Road, Bedford, MK42 9JN Tel: (01234) 267810 Fax: (01234) 212942 E-mail: graham@grahamlloyd.co.uk

Green Cuisine Food Products Ltd, Unit 3 Threxton Industrial Estate, Watton, Thetford, Norfolk, IP25 6NG Tel: (01953) 882991 Fax: (01953) 885401 E-mail: greencuisine@btinternet.com

Growing Success Ltd, Unit 8 Oakwell Brewery, Barnsley, South Yorkshire, S71 1HJ Tel: (01226) 289966 Fax: (01226) 733711

Hanworth Laboratories Ltd, The Grip, Hadstock Road, Linton, Cambridge, CB21 4XN Tel: (01223) 892217 Fax: (01223) 893623 E-mail: sales@hanworthlabs.co.uk

Hewpack Industries Ltd, 35 Stapledon Road, Orton Southgate, Peterborough, PE2 6TD Tel: (01733) 239639 Fax: (01733) 370967

Hurst Packaging Ltd, Unit 6, Cromwell Centre, Stepfield, Witham, Essex, CM8 3BZ Tel: (01376) 520642 Fax: (01376) 501757 E-mail: sales@hurstpackaging.co.uk

I B L Bulk Liquids, Lime Street, Hull, HU8 7AS Tel: (01482) 320736 Fax: (01482) 226162 E-mail: phil@intbl.co.uk

J K J Manufacturing Ltd, Amsterdam Road, Hull, HU7 0XF Tel: (01482) 825868 Fax: (01482) 878659 E-mail: mail@e-pac.co.uk

J R S Packaging Ltd, Unit 6, The Vineyards Industrial Estate, Gloucester Road, Cheltenham, Gloucestershire, GL51 8NJ Tel: (01242) 226269 Fax: (01242) 261954 E-mail: jrspackaging@lineone.net

Jak-Pak, Spring Bank Buildings, Every St, Nelson, Lancashire, BB9 7BS Tel: (01282) 698654 Fax: (01282) 611330

Jaxpal Ltd, Unit 37 Planetary Industrial Estate, Planetary Road, Willenhall, West Midlands, WV13 3XB Tel: (01902) 721066 Fax: (01902) 865839 E-mail: sales@jaxpal.co.uk

Justinor Products Ltd, St. Johns Business Park, St. Johns Grove, Hull, HU9 3RL Tel: (01482) 799321 Fax: (01482) 799470 E-mail: sales@justinor.co.uk

Kwikfill Ltd, Bullock Street, West Bromwich, West Midlands, B70 7HE Tel: 0121-553 0433 Fax: (0121) 553 0433 E-mail: sales@quickfill.co.uk

L C S London Ltd, 65-85 Grosvenor Road, Hanwell, London, W7 1HR Tel: (020) 8567 4884 Fax: (020) 8567 2803

Laboratory Facilities Ltd, 24 Britwell Road, Burnham, Slough, SL1 8AG Tel: (01628) 604149 Fax: (01628) 667920 E-mail: officelabfacs@btconnect.com

Lenpack Contract Packing & Warehousing, Pretoria Road, Chertsey, Surrey, KT16 9LW Tel: (01932) 567997 Fax: (01932) 564070 E-mail: sales@lenpack.co.uk

The London Fancy Box Company Ltd, Poulton Close, Coombe Valley, Dover, Kent, CT17 0XB Tel: (01304) 242001 Fax: (01304) 240229 E-mail: a.darrall@londonfancybox.co.uk

Lubepack Ltd, Cow Lane, Oldham, OL4 1HS Tel: 0161-620 0440 Fax: 0161-621 0801 E-mail: info@lubepack.co.uk

M T Box, 8 Plough Estate, Blandford Heights, Blandford Forum, Dorset, DT11 7UG Tel: (01258) 459837 Fax: (01258) 480132

Mac Pac Ltd, 5 Barton Road, Stockport, Cheshire, SK4 3EG Tel: 0161-442 1642 Fax: 0161-442 1643 E-mail: sales@macpac.co.uk

Marbal Pre Packing, 22-28 Clough Road, Rotherham, South Yorkshire, S61 1RD Tel: (01709) 553900 Fax: (01709) 553803 E-mail: sales@marbal.com

Marsden Packaging Ltd, Peter Street, Blackburn, BB1 5LW Tel: (01254) 56453 Fax: (01254) 581090

Midlands Direct Mail & Packaging Services Ltd, Bellamy Road, Mansfield, Nottinghamshire, NG18 4LN Tel: (01623) 636337 Fax: (01623) 420917 E-mail: sales@mdmuk.co.uk

Motivity, Unit 21 Brook Industrial Estate, Bullsbrook Road, Hayes, Middlesex, UB4 0JZ Tel: (020) 8561 5566 Fax: (020) 8561 4499 E-mail: sales@motivityuk.com

North Downs International Ltd, Saxon Way, Wincanton Business Park, Wincanton, Somerset, BA9 9RT Tel: (01963) 828828 Fax: (01963) 828833

Northampton Finishing Centre Ltd, Barn Way, Lodge Farm Industrial Estate, Northampton, NN5 7UW Tel: (01604) 580704 Fax: (01604) 757701

P & A Packing (Northern) Ltd, Huntsman Drive, Irlam, Manchester, M44 5PA Tel: 0161-777 8199 Fax: 0161-777 8089 E-mail: papack@globalnet.co.uk

Packaging Services Unette Ltd, Bank Hill Street, Mount Pleasant, Oldham, OL4 1HR Tel: 0161-621 0800 Fax: 0161-621 0801 E-mail: sales@unette.co.uk

Pactiv Europe Ltd, 4 Young Square, Brucefield Industrial Estate, Livingston, West Lothian, EH54 9BX Tel: (01506) 462247 Fax: (01506) 415458 E-mail: sales@pactiv.com

Pennine Packaging Co Ltd, Dell Road, Rochdale, Lancashire, OL12 6BZ Tel: (01706) 655787 Fax: (01706) 860418 E-mail: penninepackaging@hotmail.com

▶ Pharmaceutical Development & Manufacturing Services (PDMS) Ltd, 22 Seagoe Industrial Estate, Craigavon, County Armagh, BT63 5QD Tel: (028) 3836 3363 Fax: (028) 3836 3300 E-mail: info@pdms-almac.com

J. Pickles Healthcare, Beech Ho, 62 High St, Knaresborough, N. Yorkshire, HG5 0EA Tel: (01423) 867314 Fax: (01423) 869177 E-mail: enquiries@jpickleshealthcare.com

Pleatwise Packaging Sussex Ltd, 27 Albert Drive, Burgess Hill, West Sussex, RH15 9TN Tel: (01444) 870654 Fax: (01444) 244171

Plymouth Agencies Ltd, Oakfield Press, Elliott Road, Plymouth, PL4 0SG Tel: (01752) 262323 Fax: (01752) 228764 E-mail: sales@plymouthagencies.co.uk

Plymouth Packaging Services Ltd, Baird House, Darklake Close, Estover, Plymouth, PL6 7TJ Tel: (01752) 696330 Fax: (01752) 695589

Plymouth Packaging Services Ltd, Baird House, Darklake Close, Estover, Plymouth, PL6 7TJ Tel: (01752) 696330 Fax: (01752) 695589

▶ Primepac Solutions Ltd, Unit 36, Rassau Industrial Estate, Rassau, Ebbw Vale, Gwent, NP23 5SD Tel: (01495) 309367 Fax: 01495 309367 E-mail: sales@primepacsolutions.co.uk

Printcut Boxfast Ltd, 144 Charles Henry Street, Birmingham, B12 0SD Tel: 0121-622 4353 Fax: 0121-622 1254 E-mail: sales@pcbf.co.uk

Quality Packing, 16-18 Ogmore Crescent, Bridgend Industrial Estate, Bridgend, Mid Glamorgan, CF31 3TE Tel: (01656) 669888 Fax: (01656) 656284 E-mail: qualitypacking@btinternet.com

Queen Elizabeth's Foundation, Bradmere House, Kingston Road, Leatherhead, Surrey, KT22 7NA Tel: (01372) 389940 Fax: (01372) 361386 E-mail: bradhouse@bradhouse.demon.co.uk

Recon Services, Unit 3 Barratt Industrial Park, St. Oswalds Road, Gloucester, GL1 2SH Tel: (01452) 415116 Fax: (01452) 415124 E-mail: reconservi@aol.com

Rojay World Freight Ltd, 3 Eastern Road, Aldershot, Hampshire, GU12 4TD Tel: (01252) 354200 Fax: (01252) 354210

Rossendale Packaging Services Ltd, Unit 24a Victoria Industrial Centre, Victoria Street, Accrington, Lancashire, BB5 0PH Tel: (01254) 382030 Fax: (01254) 382030

PACKAGING SERVICES/CONTRACT PACKAGING – *continued*

S C A, Riverbank Works, Riverford Road, Glasgow, G43 1RP Tel: 0141-632 0999 Fax: 0141-632 8111

Set In Hand, Unit 1-2 Combs Tannery, Tannery Road, Combs, Stowmarket, Suffolk, IP14 2EN Tel: (01449) 675599 Fax: (01449) 678392 E-mail: james@setinhand.com

Sheffield Packaging Services Ltd, Sheffield Road, Woodhouse Mill, Sheffield, S13 9WH Tel: 0114-269 3977 Fax: 0114-269 3980 E-mail: sheffpack@btopenworld.com

Springdew Ltd, Unit 9 10, Woodlands Business Park, Ystradgynlais, Swansea, SA9 1JW Tel: (01639) 849676 Fax: (01639) 845662 E-mail: mail@springdewfreeserve.co.uk

Strategic Sourcing International Limited, Unit A46, Western Avenue, Bridgend Industrial Estate, Bridgend, Mid Glamorgan, CF31 3RT Tel: 0870 2111195 Fax: 0870 2111197 E-mail: sales@sourcewithus.com

Total Packing Services Ltd, Unit 1, Newton Park, Andover, Hampshire, SP10 3SH Tel: (01264) 334243 Fax: (01264) 334119

Vacuum Forming Scotland, Newmains Avenue, Inchinnan, Renfrew, PA4 9RR Tel: 0141-812 5075 Fax: 0141-812 5058 E-mail: info@vacfs.co.uk

Venturpak Ltd, 11-16 & 19-22 Willow Road, Pen-Y-Fan Industrial Estate, Crumlin, Newport, Gwent, NP11 4EG Tel: (01495) 241700 Fax: (01495) 241710 E-mail: office@venturpak.co.uk

Wasdell Packaging Machines Ltd, Upper Mills Trading Estate, Stonehouse, Gloucestershire, GL10 2BJ Tel: (01453) 828383 Fax: (01453) 828687 E-mail: reception@wasdell.co.uk

Watford Sheltered Workshops Ltd, Century Park, Dalton Way, Watford, WD17 2SF Tel: (01923) 220256 Fax: (01923) 245311 E-mail: richard@watfordworkshop.co.uk

The Ways & Means Trust Ltd, 2 Paddock Road, Caversham, Reading, RG4 5BY Tel: 0118-948 1944 Fax: 0118-946 1176 E-mail: mail@waysandmeans.org.uk

Westons Development, Pickering Street, Maidstone, Kent, ME15 9RT Tel: 01622 740418 Fax: 01622 743911 E-mail: dbwestons@aol.com

Wilmot Packaging Ltd, Rutherford Way, Swindon Village, Cheltenham, Gloucestershire, GL51 9TU Tel: (01242) 245151 Fax: (01242) 245155

Wincanton Logistics Ltd, Central Way, Feltham, Middlesex, TW14 0XQ Tel: (020) 8831 1500 Fax: (020) 8831 1518

Winpack Ltd, Unit A1 Lattersey Hill Trading Estate, Benwick Road, Whittlesey, Peterborough, PE7 2JA Tel: (01733) 208799 Fax: (01733) 204007

Wordsworth UK Ltd, Grimshaw Lane, Middleton, Manchester, M24 2AE Tel: 0161-653 9006 Fax: 0161-653 2613

Wrapid Holdings Ltd, 250 Thornton Road, Bradford, West Yorkshire, BD1 2LB Tel: (01274) 220220 Fax: (01274) 736195 E-mail: mail@wrapid.co.uk

PACKAGING SHRINK WRAPPING SERVICES

Aaron Packaging Machinery, Leeds 12 Business Park, Barras Garth Road, Leeds, LS12 4JY Tel: (07802) 886250 E-mail: sales@aaron-pack-mart.co.uk

Bluebird Packaging Machines Ltd, 43 Boulton Road, Reading, RG2 0NU Tel: 0118-987 4611 Fax: 0118-987 4575 E-mail: sales@bluebird-machines.co.uk

J R S Packaging Ltd, Unit 6, The Vineyards Industrial Estate, Gloucester Road, Cheltenham, Gloucestershire, GL51 8NJ Tel: (01242) 226269 Fax: (01242) 261954 E-mail: jrspackaging@lineone.net

John C Brow Ltd, Prince Regent Road, Belfast, BT5 6SA Tel: (028) 9079 8171 Fax: (028) 9040 1095 E-mail: sales@browpack.com

Pennine Packaging Co Ltd, Dell Road, Rochdale, Lancashire, OL12 6BZ Tel: (01706) 655787 Fax: (01706) 860418 E-mail: penninepackaging@hotmail.com

Plymouth Packaging Services Ltd, Baird House, Darklake Close, Estover, Plymouth, PL6 7TJ Tel: (01752) 696330 Fax: (01752) 695589

Skincross (Cheshire) Ltd, 6 Riverside, Dukinfield, Cheshire, SK16 4HE Tel: 0161-343 7323 Fax: 0161-343 7324

Winpack Ltd, Unit A1 Lattersey Hill Trading Estate, Benwick Road, Whittlesey, Peterborough, PE7 2JA Tel: (01733) 208799 Fax: (01733) 204007

PACKAGING SIZE CHANGE PARTS

Harcross Engineering Co. Ltd, Unit 1 The Ember Centre, Hersham, Walton-On-Thames, Surrey, KT12 3PU Tel: (01932) 222201 Fax: (01932) 224722 E-mail: sales@harcross-eng.co.uk

PACKAGING TO SPECIFICATION

Brand Packaging Ltd, Bridge Mills, Holland Street, Pendleton, Salford, M6 6EL Tel: 0161-736 8941 Fax: 0161-745 7141

Bretby Nurseries Ltd, Bretby Lane, Bretby, Burton-on-Trent, Staffordshire, DE15 0QS Tel: (01283) 703355 Fax: (01283) 704035 E-mail: bretby.nurseries@virgin.net

C & B Co., Wholesale Warehouse, Chappell Drive, Doncaster, South Yorkshire, DN1 2RF Tel: (01302) 361357 Fax: (01302) 361357

Charlesworth China Ltd, 254 Deighton Road, Huddersfield, HD2 1JJ Tel: (01484) 517077 Fax: (01484) 517068 E-mail: mail@charlesworth.com

Hobson Paragon UK Ltd, Commercial Way, Oakengates, Telford, Shropshire, TF2 6SG Tel: (01952) 619111 Fax: (01952) 616921

Jiffy Packaging Co. Ltd, Road Four, Winsford Industrial Estate, Winsford, Cheshire, CW7 3QR Tel: (01606) 551221 Fax: (01606) 592634 E-mail: sales@jiffy.co.uk

Printhouse Group, 8 Albert Drive, Burgess Hill, West Sussex, RH15 9TN Tel: (01444) 871776 Fax: (01444) 871731 E-mail: info@printhousegroup.com

Saffron Tape Design, Epsilon House, 27 Fulfen Way, Saffron Walden, Essex, CB11 4DW Tel: (01799) 520170 Fax: (01799) 520170 E-mail: saffrontapedesign@tiscali.co.uk

PACKAGING TRADE ENGINEERING SUPPLIERS/ DISTRIBUTORS/AGENTS

Samuel Grant (North East) Ltd, Unit 13-16, Tanfield Lea South Industrial Estate, Tanfield Lea, Stanley, County Durham, DH9 9QX Tel: (01207) 283510 Fax: (01207) 290063 E-mail: nesales@samuelgrant.com

John Fenwick Rossendale Ltd, Vine Grove Works, Commerce Street, Haslingden, Rossendale, Lancashire, BB4 5JT Tel: (01706) 210300 Fax: (01706) 210325 E-mail: dwrudd@lineone.net

PACKAGING TWINE

Fleming's Ropes & Twines Woolston Ltd, Bridge Road, Woolston, Warrington, WA1 4AT Tel: (01925) 499955 Fax: (01925) 492208

Kite Packaging, 2 Crammond Park, Lovet Road, Harlow, Essex, CM19 5TF Tel: (01279) 406160 Fax: (01279) 406161 E-mail: southeast@packwithkite.com

PACKAGING, AIR BUBBLE/ CONVERTERS

Amasec Airfil Ltd, Unit 1 Colliery Lane, Exhall, Coventry, CV7 9NW Tel: (07739) 974027 Fax: (024) 7664 4325E-mail: sales@airfil.com

The Bubble Factory Ltd, Grove Road, Preston, Canterbury, Kent, CT3 1EF Tel: (01227) 722228 Fax: (01227) 722399 E-mail: thebubble.factory@yahoo.co.uk

Hobson Paragon UK Ltd, Commercial Way, Oakengates, Telford, Shropshire, TF2 6SG Tel: (01952) 619111 Fax: (01952) 616921

Morris Packaging Ltd, 3a Telford Road, Ferndown Industrial Estate, Wimborne, Dorset, BH21 7QN Tel: (01202) 892623 Fax: (01202) 894903 E-mail: sales@packaging-uk.co.uk

PACKAGING, BAG-IN-BOX

Dupont Liquid Packaging Systems LB Europe Ltd, Oakwood Road, Romiley, Stockport, Cheshire, SK6 4DZ Tel: 0161-406 8880 Fax: 0161-406 8881

Flomotion Rental Ltd, 7 Wilton Close, Partridge Green, Horsham, West Sussex, RH13 8RX Tel: (01403) 711170 Fax: (01403) 711059

Kliklok Woodman International Ltd, Western Drive, Bristol, BS14 0AY Tel: (01275) 836131 Fax: (01275) 891754 E-mail: sales@kliklok-woodman-int.com

O K International Europe Ltd, Shepherds Grove Industrial Estate, Stanton, Bury St. Edmunds, Suffolk, IP31 2AR Tel: (01359) 250705 Fax: (01359) 250165 E-mail: sales@okinteurope.co.uk

PACKAGING, BAGS, LAMINATED JUTE

Paper Bag Co., Units 8 & 9 Oakfield Business Centre, Northacre Industrial Estate, Stephenson Road, Westbury, Wiltshire, BA13 4WF Tel: 01373 825834 Fax: 01373 865984 E-mail: sales@paperbagco.co.uk

▶ WineBag.co.uk, 4 Melcombe Gardens, Harrow, HA3 9RH Tel: (0701) 0704731 E-mail: sales@winebag.co.uk

PACKAGING, CLEAR PLASTIC FORMINGS

Tony Chapman Electronics Ltd, Hayleys Manor, Epping Upland, Epping, Essex, CM16 6PQ Tel: (01992) 578231 Fax: (01992) 576139 E-mail: sales@tceltd.co.uk

PACKAGING, FLEXIBLE/ PRODUCTS

A A Packaging Ltd, The Light Industrial Estate, Hesketh Bank, Preston, PR4 6SP Tel: (01772) 617481 Fax: (01772) 614856 E-mail: info@aapackaging.co.uk

Aarison Packaging, Townfoot Industrial Estate, Brampton, Cumbria, CA8 1SW Tel: (0845) 1301864 Fax: (0845) 1301864 E-mail: enq@aarison.co.uk

Alcan Packaging (Cumbria), Salterbeck Trading Estate, Salterbeck, Workington, Cumbria, CA14 5DX Tel: (01946) 839600 Fax: (01946) 830199 E-mail: sales@alcanpackaging.com

Alcan Packaging Materials, The Sawmill, Eridge Road, Eridge Green, Tunbridge Wells, Kent, TN3 9JR Tel: (01892) 509100 Fax: (01892) 509190

Amcor, Digby Street, Ilkeston, Derbyshire, DE7 5TS Tel: 0115-932 4391 Fax: 0115-932 7506

Amcor Ltd, Denmark House, Brick Close, Kiln Farm, Milton Keynes, MK11 3DP Tel: (01908) 261333 Fax: (01908) 261334

Amcor Flexibles, 1 Gass Close, Highbridge, Somerset, TA9 4JT Tel: (01278) 793232 Fax: (01278) 794996 E-mail: sales@amcor.com

Amcor Flexibles Europe, Crompton Road, Ilkeston, Derbyshire, DE7 4BZ Tel: 0115-932 1443 Fax: 0115-944 0644 E-mail: info@amcor-flexibles.com

Amcor Flexibles S & R, Intaglio House, Brucefield Park West, Livingston, West Lothian, EH54 9ES Tel: (01506) 412845 Fax: (01506) 417344

Amcore Flexibles, Hawkfield Way, Hawkfield Business Park, Bristol, BS14 0BD Tel: 0117-975 3200 Fax: 0117-975 3311 E-mail: sales@amcore.com

Arteb Printing Ltd, Unit 13 Lyon Industrial Estate, Brindley Road, Reginald Road Industrial Estate, St. Helens, Merseyside, WA9 4HY Tel: (01744) 820933 Fax: (01744) 815154 E-mail: info@arteb.co.uk

Allan Austin Ltd, Crystal Drive, Smethwick, West Midlands, B66 1QG Tel: 0121-552 8513 Fax: 0121-552 1480 E-mail: allan@austinltd.freeserve.co.uk

B P I Stretchville, Bath Road, Bridgwater, Somerset, TA6 4BF Tel: (01278) 446262 Fax: (01278) 452252 E-mail: pswexports@brithene.com

Bailey Packaging Ltd, PO Box 64, Solihull, West Midlands, B93 9NZ Tel: (01564) 774259 Fax: (01564) 777859

Barrier Foil Products, Unit 9, Sutton Fold Sullivans Way, St. Helens, Merseyside, WA9 5GL Tel: 0161-480 4007 Fax: (01744) 451000 E-mail: barrierfoil@aol.com

Bemis Packaging Ltd, The Flarepath, Elsham Wolds Industrial Estate, Brigg, South Humberside, DN20 0SP Tel: (01652) 680680 Fax: (01652) 680630

Border Converters, Second Avenue, Deeside Industrial Park, Deeside, Clwyd, CH5 2NX Tel: (01244) 289988 Fax: (01244) 289300 E-mail: admin@borderconverters.co.uk

Brand Packaging Ltd, Bridge Mills, Holland Street, Pendleton, Salford, M6 6EL Tel: 0161-736 8941 Fax: 0161-745 7141

Dale Products Plastics Ltd, Barnsley Road, Hoyland, Barnsley, South Yorkshire, S74 0QW Tel: (01226) 742511 Fax: (01226) 350496 E-mail: dale.products@fsbdial.co.uk

F F P Packaging Solutions Ltd, 1-7 Tenter Road, Moulton Park Industrial Estate, Northampton, NN3 6PZ Tel: (01604) 643535 Fax: (01604) 790042 E-mail: sales@ffpkg.co.uk

Flexell, Unit 3, Bypass Park Estate, Sherburn in Elmet, Leeds, LS25 6EP Tel: (01977) 685755 Fax: (01977) 685778

Fretfoil Ltd, 13-15 Izons La Industrial Estate, West Bromwich, West Midlands, B70 9BY Tel: 0121-525 6588 Fax: 0121-525 6735 E-mail: fretfoilltd@aol.com

▶ Harris & Spilsbury Ltd, 131 St Margarets Road, Ward End, Birmingham, B8 2BD Tel: 0121-327 1095 Fax: 0121-326 0818 E-mail: sales@harris-and-spilsbury.co.uk

Huhtamaki (UK) Ltd, Rowner Road, Gosport, Hants, PO13 0PR Tel: (023) 9251 2434 Fax: (023) 9251 2330 E-mail: sales@gb.huhtamaki.com

Imperial Polythene Products Ltd, Unit 3 Lakeside Industrial Estate, Colnbrook, Slough, SL3 0ED Tel: (01753) 686336 Fax: (01753) 682793

Norman Knights Ltd, 1 Russell Court, Russell Gardens, Wickford, Essex, SS11 8QU Tel: (01268) 733722 Fax: (01268) 764537 E-mail: sales@normanknights.com

Longulf Ltd, Prince Albert House, 2 Kingsmill Terrace, London, NW8 6BN Tel: (020) 7722 7733 Fax: (020) 7722 9028 E-mail: info@longulf.com

Modern Packaging UK Ltd, Unit 26 Lansdown Industrial Estate, Gloucester Road, Cheltenham, Gloucestershire, GL51 8PL Tel: (01242) 262002 Fax: (01242) 261919 E-mail: sales@modern-packaging.co.uk

Moore & Buckle Ltd, 3 Lancots Lane, St. Helens, Merseyside, WA9 3EX Tel: (01744) 733066 Fax: (01744) 451000 E-mail: info@mooreandbuckle.com

N G C Consultancy Ltd, Unit 1A, The Mayfields, Southcrest, Redditch, Worcestershire, B98 7DU Tel: (01527) 404739 Fax: (01527) 404739

Novelis UK Ltd, Stourbridge Road, Bridgnorth, Shropshire, WV15 6AW Tel: (01746) 765757 Fax: (01746) 761860

Panmer Plastics Ltd, 5 Delta Centre, Mount Pleasant, Wembley, Middlesex, HA0 1UX Tel: (020) 8903 7733 Fax: (020) 8903 3036 E-mail: info@panmer.com

Premier Flexible Packaging Ltd, 14 Aber Road, Flint, Clwyd, CH6 5EX Tel: (01352) 733365 Fax: (01352) 733152 E-mail: info@premierflexible.co.uk

Printpack Ltd, Bridge Hall Mills, Bridge Hall Lane, Bury, Lancashire, BL9 7PA Tel: 0161-764 5441 Fax: 0161-705 1624 E-mail: bbleasdale@printpack.com

▶ Riverside Packaging Printers Ltd, Roughmoor, Williton Industrial Estate, Taunton, Somerset, TA4 4RF Tel: (01984) 631757 Fax: (01984) 635910 E-mail: sales@rppl.co.uk

Suface Specialists P.L.C., Bath Road, Bridgwater, Somerset, TA6 4PA Tel: (01278) 424321 Fax: (01278) 421999

Tech Folium Ltd, Triumph Trading Park, Speke Hall Road, Speke, Liverpool, L24 9GQ Tel: 0151-486 4300 Fax: 0151-486 3335

Tmec UK Ltd, 6 Sidenhill Close, Shirley, Solihull, West Midlands, B90 2QD Tel: 0121-733 8726 Fax: 0121-733 8726 E-mail: enquiries@tmec.co.uk

Tyco Plastics Ltd, Unit 2 Westland Square, Leeds, LS11 5SS Tel: 0113-270 3737 Fax: 0113-270 0778

Weald Ltd, High Street, Buxted, Uckfield, East Sussex, TN22 4LA Tel: (01825) 732000 Fax: (01825) 732722 E-mail: tony@wealdpackaging.freeserve.uk

Wilson Packaging Products, 38 Hatherley Road, Manchester, M20 4RU Tel: 0161-434 0454 Fax: 0161-448 1070 E-mail: wilsonpackaging@btconnect.com

PACKAGING, GIFT BOX

BoxMart Ltd, Unit 1C, Ringway Industrial Estate, Eastern Avenue, Lichfield, Staffordshire, WS13 7SF Tel: (01543) 411574 Fax: (01543) 258952 E-mail: enquiries@boxmart.co.uk

▶ Expatboxes, Robyn's Way, Edenbridge, Kent, TN8 5SE Tel: (07840) 891880 E-mail: info@expatboxes.com

▶ Slipped Discs, 2 Broomfield Court, Broomfield Park, Ascot, Berkshire, SL5 0JP Tel: (01344) 622131 Fax: (01344) 622131 E-mail: sales@slipped-discs.com

Uncle Tom's Dolls Houses Factory, 49 Ansty Road, Wyken, Coventry, CV2 3FG Tel: 0247 6278104 Fax: 0247 6278104 E-mail: info@dollshouses.atspace.com

PACKAGING, GLASSINE/ GREASEPROOF, CONFECTIONERY, BISCUIT ETC

CRP Print & Packaging Ltd, Cooks Road, Weldon North Industrial Estate, Corby, Northamptonshire, NN17 5JT Tel: (01536) 200333 Fax: (01536) 403329 E-mail: sales@crpprint.co.uk

PACKAGING, MODIFIED ATMOSPHERE (MAP)

British Polythene Industries, 96 Port Glasgow Road, Greenock, Renfrewshire, PA15 2UL Tel: (01475) 501000 Fax: (01475) 743143 E-mail: carolanderson@bpipoly.com

PACKAGING, PALLETWRAP

Acre Packaging Supplies Ltd, 15 Kepler, Lichfield Road Industrial Estate,, Tamworth, Staffordshire, B79 7XE Tel: (01827) 310330 Fax: (01827) 310337 E-mail: sales@acrepackaging.co.uk

Bernley Packaging, Unit 13 Wilton Industrial Court, 851 Bradford Road, Batley, West Yorkshire, WF17 8NN Tel: (01924) 471188 Fax: (01924) 471199 E-mail: burnpack@aol.com

G & T Packaging Ltd, Unit 10A, Factory Lane, Warminster, Wiltshire, BA12 8LT Tel: (01985) 216441 Fax: (01985) 216491 E-mail: enquiries@gtpack.btopenworld.com

Garden City Packaging Ltd, 10 Blackhorse Road, Letchworth Garden City, Hertfordshire, SG6 1HB Tel: (01462) 686200 Fax: (01462) 677042 E-mail: gcp@idnet.co.uk

Gottlieb Packaging Materials Ltd, Unit 1-3 Harp Trading Estate, Guinness Road, Trafford Park, Manchester, M17 1SR Tel: 0161-872 0983 Fax: 0161-872 0984 E-mail: phil_doherty@btconnect.com

Thorpe Packaging Ltd, Ripley Drive, Normanton Industrial Estate, Normanton, West Yorkshire, WF6 1QT Tel: (01924) 898802 Fax: (01924) 898803 E-mail: peter@thorpepackaging.sagehost.co.uk

Viking Industrial Products Ltd, 1 Coronation Business Centre, Hard Ings Road, Keighley, West Yorkshire, BD21 3ND Tel: (01535) 610373 Fax: (01535) 616231 E-mail: sales@vikingtapes.co.uk

PACKAGING, PROMOTIONAL/ CUSTOM MAKERS

Crown Speciality Packaging U K Ltd, Rock Valley, Mansfield, Nottinghamshire, NG18 2EZ Tel: (01623) 622651 Fax: (01623) 624626

Ideal Packaging Co, Unit 49, Queens Court Trading Estate Greets Green Road, West Bromwich, West Midlands, B70 9EL Tel: 0121-557 3624 Fax: 0121-520 5316 E-mail: sales@idealpackaging.co.uk

Insit Moulded Packaging Ltd, Aintree Avenue, White Horse Business Park, Trowbridge, Wiltshire, BA14 0XB Tel: (01225) 767985 Fax: (01225) 777405E-mail: sales@insit.co.uk

P O S Packaging Ltd, Cressex Business Park, 30A Wellington Road, High Wycombe, Buckinghamshire, HP12 3PR Tel: (01494) 473701 Fax: (01494) 473801 E-mail: unique.pkg@online.rednet.co.uk

Printhouse Group, 8 Albert Drive, Burgess Hill, West Sussex, RH15 9TN Tel: (01444) 871776 Fax: (01444) 871731 E-mail: info@printhousegroup.com

Promocan, Plaistow Road, Loxwood, Billingshurst, West Sussex, RH14 0TS Tel: (01403) 753453 Fax: 0845 6120655 E-mail: tmursell@promocan.co.uk

Suttons Performance Packaging, 16 Albert Way, Chatteris, Cambridgeshire, PE16 6US Tel: (01354) 693171 Fax: (01354) 695430 E-mail: info@suttonspp.co.uk

Walsh & Jenkins plc, Power House, Powerscroft Road, Sidcup, Kent, DA14 5EA Tel: (020) 8308 6300 Fax: (020) 8308 6340 E-mail: bags@walsh-jenkins.co.uk

PACKAGING, TINPLATE, PROMOTIONAL/PRODUCTS

▶ Bowler Group Ltd, Bowler House Harvey Road, Burnt Mills Industrial Estate, Basildon, Essex, SS13 1DD Tel: (01268) 470700 Fax: (01268) 477717 E-mail: info@hjbowlerandsons.com

PACKERS/PACKING (CONTRACT) SERVICES, *See also headings for particular types*

Air Sea Packing Group Ltd, Air Sea House, Third Cross Road, Twickenham, TW2 5EB Tel: (020) 8893 3303 Fax: (020) 8893 3068 E-mail: sales@airseapacking.com

Allgo Ltd, Unit 9c Bank Hall Park, Wharf Street, Warrington, WA1 2DG Tel: (01925) 570150 Fax: (01925) 570155 E-mail: david.snitch@allgo.biz

Allpac, Beck View Road, Beverley, North Humberside, HU17 0JT Tel: (01482) 881255 Fax: (01482) 863537 E-mail: sales@allpac.co.uk

Allport Packaging Ltd, Brokenford Lane, Totton, Southampton, SO40 9TF Tel: (023) 8066 3111 Fax: (023) 8066 3049 E-mail: info@allport.co.uk

Aqua Det Sales Co. Ltd, Bowles House, Blackthorne Road, Colnbrook, Slough, SL3 0AL Tel: (01753) 684282 Fax: (01753) 680305

Blisters Ltd, Second Avenue, Midsomer Norton, Radstock, BA3 4AR Tel: (01761) 418277 Fax: (01761) 418900 E-mail: enquiries@blisters.ltd.uk

Blue Boar, Unit D3 New Yatt Business Centre, Kite Lane, New Yatt, Witney, Oxfordshire, OX29 6TJ Tel: (01993) 868878 Fax: (01993) 868878 E-mail: helen.cook@virgin.net

BMT, Chapel Street, Wincham, Northwich, Cheshire, CW9 6DA Tel: (01606) 43886 Fax: (01606) 49059 E-mail: crosswarehouse@btconnect.com

▶ Bowlen Packaging Ltd, Castle Clough Mill, Hapton, Burnley, Lancashire, BB12 7LN Tel: (01282) 770770

Carefields Ltd, 5 Atherton Way, Brigg, South Humberside, DN20 8AR Tel: (01652) 653584 Fax: (01652) 650417 E-mail: carefields@carefields.ltd.uk

Chelsea Foods Ltd, Ferry Lane Industrial Estate, Lamson Road, Rainham, Essex, RM13 9YY Tel: (01708) 521378 Fax: (01708) 525662 E-mail: sales@chelseafoods.co.uk

Conway Packing Services Ltd, Central Works, Groveland Road, Tipton, West Midlands, DY4 7UD Tel: 0121-520 1144 Fax: 0121-520 2670 E-mail: admin@conwaypack.co.uk

Copras Specialities Ltd, Copperas House Terrace, Todmorden, Lancashire, OL14 7PU Tel: (01706) 817899 Fax: (01706) 813671 E-mail: copras@packing.fsbusiness.co.uk

Corby Bottlers P.L.C., Clarke House, Brunel Road, Earlstrees Industrial Estate South, Corby, Northamptonshire, NN17 4JW Tel: (01536) 446000 Fax: (01536) 446001

Cotswold Perfumery Ltd, Victoria Street, Bourton-on-the-Water, Cheltenham, Gloucestershire, GL54 2BU Tel: (01451) 820698 Fax: (01451) 821717 E-mail: sales@cotswold-perfumery.co.uk

Craigton Packaging Ltd, 43 Scotts Road, Paisley, Renfrewshire, PA2 7AN Tel: 0141-887 0244 Fax: 0141-887 5462 E-mail: info@craigton.com

Crate Co. Ltd, Unit 7 Green Role Estate, Howe Moss Drive, Kirkhill Industrial Estate, Dyce, Aberdeen, AB21 0GL Tel: (01224) 771494 Fax: (01224) 775140

Dynamic Packaging Ltd, 18-20 Cater Road, Bishopworth, Bristol, BS13 7TW Tel: 0117-978 1222 Fax: (0117) 978 1333 E-mail: sales@dymanicpackaging.co.uk

Elmlead Services Ltd, Unit 1, Riverside Court, Colne Road, Huddersfield, HD1 3ER Tel: (01484) 425565 Fax: (01484) 425418 E-mail: elmlead@yahoo.co.uk

Exwold Technology, Tees Bay Business Park, Brenda Road, Hartlepool, Cleveland, TS25 2BU Tel: (01429) 230340 Fax: (01429) 232996 E-mail: sales@exwold.com

F T Short Ltd, Fitton Road, St Germans, King's Lynn, Norfolk, PE34 3AX Tel: (01553) 617344 Fax: (01553) 617020 E-mail: info@ftshort.co.uk

Fleet Shipping International Ltd, 41-47 Blue Anchor Lane, London, SE16 3UL Tel: (020) 7232 0777 Fax: (020) 7232 2600 E-mail: sales@fwwshipping.com

▶ Flexible Packing Services Ltd, Unit 4, Cedab Road, Ellesmere Port, CH65 4FE Tel: 0151-355 2333 Fax: 0151-355 3332 E-mail: enquiries@flexpackservices.co.uk

G N N International Ltd, Unit 70, Woolsbridge Industrial Estate, Three Legged Cross, Wimborne, Dorset, BH21 6SU Tel: (01202) 823012 Fax: (01202) 821754 E-mail: info@contractpackers.net

Glen Pac Southern Ltd, 11 The Forty, Cricklade, Swindon, SN6 6HW Tel: (01793) 751527 Fax: (01793) 750551 E-mail: sales@glenpac.com

Global Vacuum Forming Ltd, Vedonis Works, Leicester Road, Lutterworth, Leicestershire, LE17 4HD Tel: (01455) 556891 Fax: (01455) 556099 E-mail: sales@gvf.co.uk

Good Packing Co. Ltd, Mariner, Lichfield Road Industrial Estate, Tamworth, Staffordshire, B79 7TJ Tel: (01827) 65911 Fax: (01827) 59310 E-mail: info@goodpackaging.co.uk

Graham Lloyd Bedford Ltd, Ampthill Road, Bedford, MK42 9JN Tel: (01234) 267810 Fax: (01234) 212942 E-mail: graham@grahamlloyd.co.uk

Growing Success Ltd, Unit 8 Oakwell Brewery, Barnsley, South Yorkshire, S71 1HJ Tel: (01226) 289966 Fax: (01226) 733711

Heritage Packaging, 3 Whitebridge Industrial Estate, Whitebridge Lane, Stone, Staffordshire, ST15 8LQ Tel: (01785) 819189 Fax: (01785) 819089 E-mail: heripak@hotmail.com

Horley Services Ltd, Salfords Industrial Estate, Salfords, Redhill, RH1 5ES Tel: (01293) 771481 Fax: (01293) 786701 E-mail: sales@horleysg.demon.co.uk

Inca Co-Packing Services Ltd, Unit 2g Nelson Way, Nelson Park West, Cramlington, Northumberland, NE23 1WG Tel: (01670) 590428

Innovo Chemicals Ltd, The Common, Cranleigh, Surrey, GU6 8RY Tel: (01483) 277219 Fax: (01483) 268030 E-mail: sales@innovochem.co.uk

Jacques Products, Greengate Industrial Estate, Greenside Way, Middleton, Manchester, M24 1SW Tel: 0161-688 7744 Fax: 0161-688 6060

Jet Removal Services, Plantation Road, Burscough Industrial Estate, Burscough, Lancashire, L40 8JT Tel: (01704) 895206 Fax: (01704) 896890 E-mail: sales@jetremovals.co.uk

Kammac plc, Gladden Place, Skelmersdale, Lancashire, WN8 9SY Tel: (01695) 727272 Fax: (01695) 720854 E-mail: info@kammac.com

Leeways Packaging Services Ltd, Lobstock, Churcham, Gloucester, GL2 8AN Tel: (01452) 750487 Fax: (01452) 750653 E-mail: info@leeways.co.uk

Lenpack Contract Packing & Warehousing, Pretoria Road, Chertsey, Surrey, KT16 9LW Tel: (01932) 567997 Fax: (01932) 564070 E-mail: sales@lenpack.co.uk

Lightwood plc, Hangar 2, North Weald Airfield, North Weald, Epping, Essex, CM16 6AA Tel: (01992) 524237 Fax: (01992) 524501 E-mail: store@lightwoodplc.demon.co.uk

Metokote U K Ltd, Hackwood Road, High March Industrial Estate, Daventry, Northamptonshire, NN11 4ES Tel: (01327) 703745 Fax: (01327) 300141

Natures Way Foods Ltd, Park Farm, Chichester Road, Selsey, Chichester, West Sussex, PO20 9HP Tel: (01243) 603111 Fax: (01243) 605777E-mail: natureswayfoods@nwfltd.co.uk

Nichols plc, Laurel House 3 Woodlands Park, Ashton Road, Newton-le-Willows, Merseyside, WA12 0HH Tel: (01925) 222222 Fax: (01925) 222233

Nordis Industries, Cornhill Close, Lodge Farm Industrial Estate, Northampton, NN5 7UB Tel: (01604) 596910 Fax: 01604 758470

Norfolk Industries For The Blind, Oak Street, Norwich, NR3 3BP Tel: (01603) 667957 Fax: (01603) 624265 E-mail: sales@norfolk-industries.co.uk

Co Ordinated Packaging Ltd, 3-4 Robert Way, Wickford, Essex, SS11 8DD Tel: (01268) 570600 Fax: (01268) 570611

P & D Case Making, Unit 12 Ventura Place, Poole, Dorset, BH16 5SW Tel: (01202) 632181 Fax: (01202) 621041

P D Q Packing, 4-6 Shaw Road, Dudley, West Midlands, DY2 8TP Tel: (01384) 242242 Fax: (01384) 242212

Packaging Ltd, Dierden St Works, Dierden Street, Winsford, Cheshire, CW7 3DL Tel: (01606) 594149 Fax: (01606) 861390

Professional Packaging Services Ltd, 1 The Barn, Hawksworth Lane, Guiseley, Leeds, LS20 8HD Tel: (01943) 882400 Fax: (01943) 878191 E-mail: sales@p-p-s-ltd.com

R S B Services, 16a Verney Rd, London, SE16 3DH Tel: (020) 7277 5161 Fax: (020) 7277 5115

▶ Reactive Solutions, 6 Lakeside Business Park, Pinfold Road, Thurmaston, Leicester, LE4 8AT Tel: 0116-260 3930 Fax: 0116-260 3931 E-mail: dean@reactive-solutions.com

Relga Ltd, 31 Mexborough Road, Bolton Woods, Bradford, West Yorkshire, BD2 1BL Tel: (01274) 591677 Fax: (01274) 591677

Smithz Pac, Unit 33, Darwin Enterprise Centre, Railway Road, Darwen, Lancashire, BB3 3EH Tel: (01254) 703311 E-mail: smithzpac@yahoo.co.uk

South Devon & Cornwall Institution For The Blind, 2 Stonehouse Street, Plymouth, PL1 3PY Tel: (01752) 662317 Fax: (01752) 662317 E-mail: sdcib@zoom.co.uk

Speedpac, Sywell Airport Business Park, Wellingborough Road, Sywell, Northampton, NN6 0BN Tel: (01604) 746999 Fax: (01604) 746900 E-mail: sales@speedpac.co.uk

Spiro GB Ltd, Harlescott Lane, Shrewsbury, SY1 3AR Tel: (01743) 443051 Fax: (01743) 443053 E-mail: steve@spirogb.enta.net

Tara Personal Care Ltd, 28 Ryde Avenue, Hull, HU5 1QB Tel: (01482) 444999 Fax: (01482) 473395

Tuplin Ltd, Unit 7-8 Bridge Industrial Estate, Balcombe Road, Horley, Surrey, RH6 9HU Tel: (01293) 433433 Fax: (01293) 433438 E-mail: sales@tuplin.co.uk

R.C. Warren Packers Ltd, Unit C Valley Park, Tolpits Lane, Watford, WD18 9LT Tel: (01923) 770747 Fax: (01923) 770731 E-mail: twarren@warrenpackers.co.uk

Richard Whittaker Ltd, Unit 28 Transpennine Industrial Estate, Gorrels Way, Queensway, Rochdale, Lancashire, OL11 2QR Tel: (01706) 341700 Fax: (01706) 341357 E-mail: sales@richard-whittaker.com

A.C. Willis & Co. Ltd, 25-29 Robert St, Northampton, NN1 3BL Tel: (01604) 631826 Fax: (01604) 631826 E-mail: canto_ltd@btinternet.com

Wrapid Contract Services Ltd, Astley Park Industrial Estate, Chaddock Lane, Astley, Manchester, M29 7JY Tel: (01942) 894132 Fax: (01942) 894983

Yateley Industries For The Disabled Ltd, Mill Lane, Yateley, Hampshire, GU46 7TF Tel: (01252) 872337 Fax: (01252) 860620

PACKING BOXES, WOODEN

▶ Acorn Packaging Services Ltd, Joinery Works, Butts Road, Stanford-le-Hope, Essex, SS17 0JH Tel: (01375) 643277 Fax: (01375) 643277 E-mail: sales@acornpackaging.co.uk

PACKING CASE LINERS

Catesby Packing Case Co Ltd, 647 Melton Road, Thurmaston, Leicester, LE4 8EB Tel: 0116-269 3503 Fax: 0116-269 3503

Protective Packaging Ltd, Dane Road Industrial Estate, Sale, Cheshire, M33 7BH Tel: 0161-976 2006 Fax: 0161-976 3330 E-mail: info@protpack.com

PACKING CASES, *See also Export Packing Case Manufrs*

Abbey Case Co. Ltd, Britannia Road, Waltham Cross, Hertfordshire, EN8 7NZ Tel: (01992) 715996 Fax: (01992) 719852 E-mail: sales@abbeycase.co.uk

Allport Packaging Ltd, Brokenford Lane, Totton, Southampton, SO40 9TF Tel: (023) 8066 3111 Fax: (023) 8066 3049 E-mail: info@allport.co.uk

Barnes & Woodhouse Cases, Commercial Street, Middlesbrough, Cleveland, TS2 1JT Tel: (01642) 224092 Fax: (01642) 251272

Basingstoke Packaging, 24 London Road, Thatcham, Berkshire, RG18 4LQ Tel: (01635) 863783 Fax: (01635) 861675

Bolam & Shaw Ltd, Red Doles Works, Red Doles Lane, Huddersfield, HD2 1YF Tel: (01484) 425705 Fax: (01484) 430480 E-mail: sales@bolamandshaw.co.uk

Catesby Packing Case Co Ltd, 647 Melton Road, Thurmaston, Leicester, LE4 8EB Tel: 0116-269 3503 Fax: 0116-269 3503

Chilfen Joinery Ltd, 1 Flint Road, Letchworth Garden City, Hertfordshire, SG6 1HJ Tel: (01462) 705390 Fax: (01462) 674327 E-mail: michelled@chilfen.co.uk

Con-Lloyd Ltd, Chapter Street, Manchester, M40 2AY Tel: 0161-203 4660 Fax: 0161-205 4518 E-mail: info@con-lloyd.com

Crate Co. Ltd, Unit 7 Green Role Estate, Howe Moss Drive, Kirkhill Industrial Estate, Dyce, Aberdeen, AB21 0GL Tel: (01224) 771494 Fax: (01224) 775140

D R S Cases Ltd, Unit 17, Forest Business Park, Argall Avenue, London, E10 7FB Tel: (020) 8520 7500 Fax: (020) 8520 9385

Doncaster Packaging Ltd, Units 4/5 Shaw Lane Indust Estate Ogden Road, Long Sandall, Doncaster, South Yorkshire, DN2 4SQ Tel: (01302) 365334 Fax: (01302) 329012

E Abrahams & Co. Ltd, 1 Crown Close, London, E3 2JH Tel: (020) 8980 1937 Fax: (020) 8980 3762 E-mail: info@abrahamscases.co.uk

E Hammond Case & Pallets Ltd, Noose Lane, Willenhall, West Midlands, WV13 3AZ Tel: (01902) 606391 Fax: (01902) 604331 E-mail: sales@ehammond.co.uk

E W Hoe Export Packers Ltd, Violet Road, London, E3 3QH Tel: (020) 7987 2444 Fax: (020) 7987 0497 E-mail: sales@ewhoe.co.uk

E W Turner & Co. Ltd, Tame Street, West Bromwich, West Midlands, B70 0QP Tel: 0121-556 1141 Fax: 0121-556 3911 E-mail: accounts@ewturner.co.uk

Factory Reconstruction Co. (Manchester) Ltd, Paradise Mill, Bell Street, Oldham, OL1 3PY Tel: 0161-624 5988 Fax: 0161-665 1994 E-mail: ukpallets@aol.com

T. Ginder (Packaging) Ltd, Upper Brook Street, Walsall, WS2 9PE Tel: (01922) 622251 Fax: (01922) 643265

H S G Packing Cases Ltd, Long Row, New Works Road, Low Moor, Bradford, West Yorkshire, BD12 0QN Tel: (01274) 601137 Fax: (01274) 678597 E-mail: sales@hsg-packing-cases.co.uk

George Hill Ltd, Biddings Lane, Bilston, West Midlands, WV14 9NW Tel: (01902) 403631 Fax: (01902) 492308 E-mail: sales@g-hill2000.co.uk

Hilton Industrial Services Ltd, The Old Cheese Factory, Stone Road, Hill Chorlton, Newcastle, Staffordshire, ST5 5DR Tel: (01782) 680680 Fax: (01782) 680546

I P S Fencing Supplies, 65 Toms Lane, Kings Langley, Hertfordshire, WD4 8NJ Tel: (01923) 268431 Fax: (01923) 261459 E-mail: info@ipsfencing.com

J K Francis & Son Ltd, 16 Fortnum Close, Birmingham, B33 0JY Tel: 0121-783 7568 Fax: 0121-789 7140

J Nicklin & Sons Ltd, 36 Erskine Street, Birmingham, B7 4LL Tel: 0121-359 8101 Fax: 0121-359 6673 E-mail: sales@nicklin.co.uk

Johnson & Akam Ltd, Old Park Court, Harris Street, Bradford, West Yorkshire, BD1 5HW Tel: (01274) 726375 Fax: (01274) 307946 E-mail: general@johnsonandakam.co.uk

Frederick Jones (Belfast) Ltd, 17 Napier Street, Belfast, BT12 5FE Tel: (028) 9032 4467 Fax: (028) 9032 5252 E-mail: sales@fjones.com

Joseph H Lines & Sons Ltd, Eagle Road, Moons Moat North Industrial Es, Redditch, Worcestershire, B98 9HF Tel: (01527) 63078 Fax: (01527) 63294 E-mail: j.h.lines@dial.pipex.com

Langlands & Mcainsh (Packaging) Ltd, 133 Seagate, Dundee, DD1 2HP Tel: (01382) 224657 Fax: (01382) 201969

Edwin Lawton Ltd, Old Quarry, Uttoxeter Road, Blythe Bridge, Stoke-on-Trent, ST11 9ND Tel: (01782) 393631 Fax: (01782) 388221 E-mail: pallets@edwinlawton.com

M A & C E Hathaway, 7 Blackmoor Road, Ebblake Industrial Estate, Verwood, Dorset, BH31 6AX Tel: (01202) 824067 Fax: (01202) 821301

M G Cases Ltd, Unit 8 Neills Road, Bold Industrial Park, St. Helens, Merseyside, WA9 4TU Tel: (01744) 821630 Fax: (01744) 821630

M Musgrove Ltd, 1 Gunnersbury Mews, London, W4 4AP Tel: (020) 8994 2941 Fax: (020) 8994 4484

M S Shirts Box Ltd, 45 Finchwell Road, Sheffield, S13 9AS Tel: 0114-244 2591 Fax: 0114-244 3909 E-mail: msshirtsbox@ssbdial.co.uk

Mcwiltons Ltd, 4 Basin Road North, Portslade, Brighton, BN41 1WA Tel: (01273) 423733 Fax: (01273) 430836

Mailway Northern Holdings Ltd, 12-16 Pitcliffe Way, West Bowling, Bradford, West Yorkshire, BD5 7SG Tel: (01274) 720019 Fax: (01274) 370132 E-mail: reception@mailway.co.uk

Mobile Pallets Ltd, 1 Woodend Mill, Manchester Road, Mossley, Ashton-under-Lyne, Lancashire, OL5 9AY Tel: (01457) 837725 Fax: (01457) 837804

Musson Wood Products Ltd, Common La Industrial Estate, Kenilworth, Warwickshire, CV8 2EL Tel: (01926) 859616 Fax: (01926) 850844

N & R Manufacturing Ltd, Lawrence House Apollo, Lichfield Road Industrial Estate, Tamworth, Staffordshire, B79 7TA Tel: (01827) 57218 Fax: (01827) 60289

Nefab Packaging UK Ltd, 151 Silbury Boulevard, Milton Keynes, MK9 1LH Tel: (01908) 424300 Fax: (01908) 424301 E-mail: helen.coffin@nefab.se

Newfields Timber Yard Co. Ltd, 420 High Street, Stoke-on-Trent, ST6 5ES Tel: (01782) 834057 Fax: (01782) 839772

Northern Corrugated Cases Ltd, 16 Middlewich Road, Byley, Middlewich, Cheshire, CW10 9NX Tel: (01606) 836811 Fax: (01606) 836088 E-mail: sales@northcorr.co.uk

P & D Case Making, Unit 12 Ventura Place, Poole, Dorset, BH16 5SW Tel: (01202) 632181 Fax: (01202) 621041

Packaging Industries Ltd, Beaumont Way, Aycliffe Industrial Pk, Newton Aycliffe, Co. Durham, DL5 6SN Tel: (01325) 313444 Fax: (01325) 300246 E-mail: sales@pi-box.co.uk

Pine Products Ltd, 1 Hope Carr Way, Leigh, Lancashire, WN7 3DE Tel: (01942) 604999 Fax: (01942) 260734 E-mail: info@pine-products.net

PACKING CASES – *continued*

Rapid Packaging Supplies Ltd, 26 Bayton Road, Exhall, Coventry, CV7 9EJ Tel: (024) 7636 0800 Fax: (024) 7664 4322 E-mail: sales@rapidpackaging.co.uk

Rosewood Maufacturing Co. Ltd, Bede Trading Estate, Jarrow, Tyne & Wear, NE32 3EN Tel: 0191-428 1214 Fax: 0191-428 1021 E-mail: sales@rosewoodpackaging.co.uk

Rowlinson Packaging Ltd, Unit 1 Green Lane, Wardle, Nantwich, Cheshire, CW5 6BN Tel: (01829) 260571 Fax: (01829) 260718 E-mail: packaging@rowlinson.co.uk

S C A Packaging, Brook Road, Speedwell, Bristol, BS5 7TD Tel: 0117-951 7415 Fax: 0117-935 4260

Showell Packing Ltd, Showell Road, Wolverhampton, WV10 9JY Tel: (01902) 725895 Fax: (01902) 862962 E-mail: peterhoward@hoship.com

Star Pac Ltd, 23 Fernwood Close, Redditch, Worcestershire, B98 7TN Tel: (01527) 850022 Fax: (01527) 850033 E-mail: sales@starpac.co.uk

Strong Holdings plc, Caspian Wharf, Violet Road, London, E3 3QQ Tel: (020) 7987 7113 Fax: (020) 7987 9060 E-mail: info@strongcases.com

T R Price & Son, Unit F3 Dudley Central Trading Estate, Hope Street, Dudley, West Midlands, DY2 8RS Tel: (01384) 237629

Raymond Tisdale & Co. Ltd, Common Lane, Kenilworth, Warwickshire, CV8 2EL Tel: (01926) 852227 Fax: (01926) 850844

J. Walters & Co. Ltd, 47 & 49 Howard Street, Birmingham, B19 3HL Tel: 0121-236 5937

Whirlowdale Trading Co. Ltd, Canklow Meadows Industrial Estate, West Bawtry Road, Rotherham, South Yorkshire, S60 2XL Tel: (01709) 829061 Fax: (01709) 378947 E-mail: sales@whirlowdale.com

PACKING CASES, WOODEN

▶ Acorn Packaging Services Ltd, Joinery Works, Butts Road, Stanford-le-Hope, Essex, SS17 0JH Tel: (01375) 643277 Fax: (01375) 643277 E-mail: sales@acornpackaging.co.uk

Gordano Packaging Ltd, 2a Lansdown Industrial Estate, Gloucester Road, Cheltenham, Gloucestershire, GL51 8PL Tel: (01242) 263765 Fax: (01242) 263768 E-mail: jeb@gordano-packaging.co.uk

PACKINGS, *See also headings for particular types*

▶ Deverall Services Ltd, S1 Unit Rudford Industrial Estate, Ford Road, Ford, Arundel, West Sussex, BN18 0BD Tel: (01903) 725123 Fax: (01903) 725456

PAD PRINTERS/PRINTING SERVICES

Abm Labels & Print, Blaenant Industrial Estate, Blaenavon Road, Brynmawr, Ebbw Vale, Gwent, NP23 4BX Tel: (01495) 312835 Fax: (01495) 312819 E-mail: info@abmlabels.co.uk

Econoprint UK Ltd, Cooper Drive, Springwood Industrial Estate, Braintree, Essex, CM7 2RF Tel: (01376) 349955 Fax: (01376) 346853 E-mail: sales@econoprint.co.uk

▶ FX Direct Ltd, Unit 6c Manor Way, Woking, Surrey, GU22 9JX Tel: (01483) 776676 Fax: (01483) 740447 E-mail: sales@fxdirect.co.uk

Golding Products Ltd, Unit 24 Hortonwood 33, Telford, Shropshire, TF1 7YQ Tel: (01952) 606667 Fax: (01952) 670267 E-mail: sales@goldingproducts.com

Jaro Screens Ltd, Unit 20 Shaftmoor Industrial Estate, 226 Shaftmoor Lane, Hall Green, Birmingham, B28 8SP Tel: 0121-702 2157 Fax: 0121-778 6995 E-mail: sales@jaroscreensltd.co.uk

Kingsway Print, The Old Chapel, Peterborough Road, Whittlesey, Peterborough, PE7 1PJ Tel: (01733) 350550

Multicolour Developments, 67a Foxhill Road, Reading, RG1 5QR Tel: 0118-935 1676 Fax: 0118-935 2258 E-mail: printsplate@aol.com

Padtec Ltd, 14 Balmercut, Buckingham Industrial Estate, Buckingham, MK18 1SQ Tel: (01280) 822251 Fax: (01280) 822958 E-mail: sales@padtec.co.uk

Purley Plastics, 41 Haviland Road, Ferndown Industrial Estate, Wimborne, Dorset, BH21 7RY Tel: (01202) 892255 Fax: (01202) 892255

Stadium Plastics Midlands Ltd, Unit 4-6 Southways Industrial Estate, Coventry Road, Hinckley, Leicestershire, LE10 0NJ Tel: (01455) 234202 Fax: (01455) 234191 E-mail: chris@spfd.fsbusiness.co.uk

Totalprint Ltd, Station Road, Gedney Hill, Spalding, Lincolnshire, PE12 0NP Tel: (01406) 330122 Fax: (01406) 330123 E-mail: info@totalprintltd.co.uk

Walsall Gold Blocking Service, John Street, Walsall, WS2 8AF Tel: (01922) 630031 Fax: (01922) 722855

PAD PRINTING ACCESSORIES/ CONSUMABLES

A M A Plastics, Unit 1 Moreton Park Industrial Estate, Moreton Road South, Luton, LU2 0TL Tel: (01582) 734630 Fax: (01582) 419260

Tampoprint UK Ltd, Oaklands Park, Wokingham, Berkshire, RG41 2FD Tel: 0118-973 0500 Fax: 0118-973 0725 E-mail: sales@tampoprint.co.uk

PAD PRINTING MACHINE MANUFRS

Multicolour Developments, 67a Foxhill Road, Reading, RG1 5QR Tel: 0118-935 1676 Fax: 0118-935 2258 E-mail: printsplate@aol.com

PADDED COVER TARPAULINS

A J S Tarpaulin Services, Mariner Way, Felnex Industrial Estate, Newport, Gwent, NP19 4PQ Tel: (01633) 290387 Fax: (01633) 277317 E-mail: ajstarpaulins@tinyworld.co.uk

J Clemishaw & Company Ltd, Barnbrook Building, Barnbrook Street, Bury, Lancashire, BL9 7DT Tel: 0161-764 4614 Fax: 0161-764 4615

PADDED FILM AND TELEVISION EQUIPMENT BAGS

Custom Bags, Unit 2b 102 Throckley Way, Middlefields Industrial Estate, South Shields, Tyne & Wear, NE34 0NU Tel: 0191-427 7766 Fax: 0191-427 7755 E-mail: sales@custombags.co.uk

Euro Packaging plc, 118 Amington Road, Yardley, Birmingham, B25 8JZ Tel: 0121-706 6181 Fax: 0121-706 6514 E-mail: info@europackaging.co.uk

PADDLE BLADE FANS

Fans & Spares Ltd, 6 Brookmead Industrial Estate, Beddington Lane, Croydon, CR0 4TB Tel: (020) 8683 1241 Fax: (020) 8689 0043 E-mail: croydon@fansandspares.co.uk

Fans & Spares Ltd, Unit 2 Rosevale Road, Parkhouse Industrial Estate We, Newcastle, Staffordshire, ST5 7EF Tel: (01782) 579076 Fax: (01782) 563592 E-mail: stoke@fansandspares.co.uk

Fercell Engineering Ltd, Unit 1, Old Mill Lane, Aylesford, Kent, ME20 7DT Tel: (01622) 791414 Fax: (01622) 791515 E-mail: info@fercell.com

PADLOCK MANUFRS

B & G Lock & Tool Co. Ltd, Chapel Green, Willenhall, West Midlands, WV13 1RD Tel: (01902) 630290 Fax: (01902) 633794 E-mail: sales@bgpadlocks.co.uk

Dorplan Architectural Ironmongers, 434-436 Mutton Lane, Potters Bar, Hertfordshire, EN6 3AT Tel: (01707) 647647 Fax: (01707) 647378

Hiatt Hardware Ltd, Hiatt Industrial Estate, Baltimore Road, Great Barr, Birmingham, B42 1HZ Tel: 0121-358 4970 Fax: 0121-357 6033 E-mail: sales@hiatt-hardware.com

Pinson, 44a-44b Pinson Road, Willenhall, West Midlands, WV13 2PR Tel: (01902) 606302 Fax: (01902) 609327

Willenhall Locks Ltd, Stringes Lane, Willenhall, West Midlands, WV13 1LF Tel: (01902) 636041 Fax: (01902) 636733 E-mail: sales@willenhall-locks.co.uk

Worrall Locks Ltd, Erebus Works, Albion Road, Willenhall, West Midlands, WV13 1NH Tel: (01902) 605038 Fax: (01902) 633558 E-mail: sales@worrall-locks.co.uk

PAELLA PANS

Paellastore.com, 32 Moray Close, Hinckley, Leicestershire, LE10 0UY Tel: (01455) 459585 E-mail: info@paellastore.com

PAGING SYSTEMS

Direct Telecommunications Systems Ltd, Direct House, 16 Commercial Road, Skelmanthorpe, Huddersfield, HD8 9DA Tel: (01484) 867867 Fax: (01484) 867860 E-mail: info@direct-telecom.co.uk

Dove Technology UK Ltd, 8 London Road, Worcester, WR5 2DL Tel: (01905) 353153 Fax: (01905) 352863 E-mail: sales@dovetech.co.uk

Multitone Electronics plc, Multitone House, Shortwood Copse Lane, Kempshott, Basingstoke, Hampshire, RG23 7NL Tel: (01256) 320292 Fax: (01256) 462643 E-mail: info@multitone.com

Mustang Communications Ltd, Dunslow Road, Eastfield, Scarborough, North Yorkshire, YO11 3UT Tel: (01723) 582555 Fax: (01723) 581673 E-mail: kelly@mustang.co.uk

Scope Communications (UK) Ltd, Quantum House, Steamer Quay Road, Totnes, Devon, TQ9 5AL Tel: (01803) 860700 Fax: (01803) 863716 E-mail: sales@scope-uk.com

▶ Sensorium Ltd, 9 Nethertown Broad Street, Dunfermline, Fife, KY12 7DS Tel: (01383) 720600 Fax: (01383) 739793 E-mail: info@sensorium.co.uk

Toa Corporation, Unit 2 Hook Rise South Industrial Park, Hook Rise South, Surbiton, Surrey, KT6 7LD Tel: (0870) 7740987 Fax: (0870) 7770839 E-mail: info@toa.co.uk

PAGING SYSTEMS CONTRACTORS/INSTALLATION/ RENTAL/SERVICE/SUPPLIERS

2CL Communications Ltd, Unit 3 The Crosshouse Centre, Crosshouse Road, Southampton, SO14 5GZ Tel: (023) 8033 6411 Fax: (023) 8072 0038 E-mail: sales@2cl.co.uk

Bleepers, PO Box 71, Barnet, Hertfordshire, EN4 0QD Tel: (07000) 253373 Fax: (020) 8440 8024 E-mail: sales@bleepers.co.uk

Pageone Communications Ltd, 2 Brentside Executive Centre, Great West Road, Brentford, Middlesex, TW8 9DA Tel: (0870) 0555300 Fax: (020) 8914 5212 E-mail: customerservices@pageone.co.uk

Radio Links Communications Ltd, Eaton House, Great North Road, Eaton Socon, St. Neots, Cambridgeshire, PE19 8EG Tel: (01480) 217220 Fax: (01480) 406667 E-mail: info@radio-links.co.uk

Senator Communications Ltd, 5 Newton Court, Wavertree Technology Park, Liverpool, L13 1EJ Tel: 0151-259 5959 Fax: 0151-259 0099 E-mail: sales@senatorinternational.uk

▶ Sensorium Ltd, 9 Nethertown Broad Street, Dunfermline, Fife, KY12 7DS Tel: (01383) 720600 Fax: (01383) 739793 E-mail: info@sensorium.co.uk

Shipton Communications Ltd, 1 Frogmore Road, Hemel Hempstead, Hertfordshire, HP3 9TG Tel: (01442) 345600 Fax: (01442) 345663

West London Electric Acton Ltd, 9-11 High Street, London, W3 6NQ Tel: (020) 8992 2155 Fax: (020) 8992 4067E-mail: sales@wle.co.uk

PAINT ADDITIVES

B S B, 28 Heathfield Road, Bexleyheath, Kent, DA6 8NP Tel: (020) 8303 0196 Fax: (020) 8303 6466

Alister Brown, Unit 3 Huddersfield Street, Galashiels, Selkirkshire, TD1 3BF Tel: (01896) 758668 Fax: (01896) 758668

PAINT AND POWDER COATING CONSULTANTS

Trade Paint Supplies Ltd, Grove Road, Northfleet, Gravesend, Kent, DA11 9AX Tel: (01474) 560382 Fax: (01474) 362926 E-mail: sales@tradepaintsupplies.ltd.uk

PAINT APPLICATOR PADS

Flock Development & Research Co. Ltd, Clarence Mill, Clarence Street, Stalybridge, Cheshire, SK15 1QF Tel: 0161-339 4946 Fax: 0161-343 2045 E-mail: flock@flockdev.co.uk

PAINT BRUSHES

Bee Gee Brushes Ltd, Unit 3c Saxon Business Park, Hanbury Road, Stoke Prior, Bromsgrove, Worcestershire, B60 4AD Tel: (01527) 837001 Fax: (01527) 837001 E-mail: mar_r_goddard@hotmail.com

Hamilton Acorn Ltd, Halford Road, Attleborough, Norfolk, NR17 2HZ Tel: (01953) 453201 Fax: (01953) 454943 E-mail: sales@hamilton-acorn.co.uk

Hamilton Acorn Ltd, Callywhite Lane, Dronfield, Derbyshire, S18 2XP Tel: (01246) 418306 Fax: (01246) 410334 E-mail: info@hamilton-acorn.co.uk

James Laird Gold Leaf Ltd, 18 Craig Road, Glasgow, G44 3DR Tel: 0141-637 8288 Fax: 0141-637 8288 E-mail: goldleaf@jameslaird.com

L G Harris & Co. Ltd, Hanbury Road, Stoke Prior, Bromsgrove, Worcestershire, B60 4AE Tel: (01527) 575441 Fax: (01527) 575366 E-mail: enquiries@lgharris.co.uk

Samuel Latham Ltd, 475 Evesham Rd, Crabbs Cross, Redditch, Worcs, B97 5JQ Tel: (01527) 543238 Fax: (01527) 550824

▶ The Traditional Paint Co., 1 North End, Bury Mead Road, Hitchin, Hertfordshire, SG5 1RT Tel: 0845 8903434 Fax: 01462 421337 E-mail: traditionalpaint@yahoo.co.uk

PAINT CHEMICALS

Akcros Chemicals, PO Box 1, Manchester, M30 0BH Tel: 0161-785 1111 Fax: 0161-788 7886 E-mail: info.eccles@akcros.com

Collinda Investments Ltd, 25 Ottways Lane, Ashtead, Surrey, KT21 2PL Tel: (01372) 278416 Fax: (01372) 278559 E-mail: info@collinda.co.uk

E Wood Ltd, Standard Way Industrial Estate, Northallerton, North Yorkshire, DL6 2XA Tel: (01609) 778907 Fax: (01609) 783762 E-mail: thortex@ewood.co.uk

Kansai Paint Europe Ltd, Wembley Point, 1 Harrow Road, Wembley, Middlesex, HA9 6DE Tel: (020) 8900 5933 Fax: (020) 8900 5966 E-mail: info@kansaipaint.co.uk

Specialised Industrial Chemicals Ltd, 44 Henver Road, Newquay, Cornwall, TR7 3BN Tel: (01637) 850643 Fax: (01637) 880040 E-mail: sales@sic-uk.com

Tetrosyl Ltd, Bevis Green Works, Mill Road, Walmersley, Bury, Lancashire, BL9 6RE Tel: 0161-764 5981 Fax: 0161-797 5899 E-mail: info@tetrosyl.com

Wilfrid Smith Group plc, Elm House, Medlicott Close, Corby, Northamptonshire, NN18 9NF Tel: (01536) 460020 Fax: (01536) 462400 E-mail: info@wilfrid-smith.co.uk

PAINT DIPPING, *See Dipping etc*

PAINT FINISHING CONTRACTORS

Cleftbridge Coatings Ltd, Unit 8a, Lower Road Trading Estate, Ledbury, Herefordshire, HR8 2DH Tel: (01531) 633771 Fax: (01531) 633719 E-mail: enquiries@cleftbridge.co.uk

Gainsthorpe Furniture Ltd, Unit 5 Cromwell Centre, Roebuck Road, Ilford, Essex, IG6 3UG Tel: (020) 8501 3712 Fax: (020) 8501 5448 E-mail: info@gainsthorpe.co.uk

Mason & King Ltd, 11 Birstall Street, Leicester, LE1 2HJ Tel: 0116-253 6491 Fax: 0116-251 2403 E-mail: ray@masonking.co.uk

▶ painting@decorating, 35 Phoenix Road, Chatham, Kent, ME5 8SY Tel: (01634) 306379 E-mail: keithnegus@blueyonder.co.uk

South West Industrial Finishers Co. Ltd., 117-119 Severn Road, Weston-Super-Mare, Avon, BS23 1DS Tel: (01934) 414613 Fax: (01934) 636243

PAINT FINISHING SYSTEMS ENGINEERS, INSTALLATION OR SERVICE

Industrial Powder & Paint Services, 9a Boss Hall Road, Ipswich, IP1 5BN Tel: (01473) 463333 Fax: (01473) 747153 E-mail: sales@ippsltd.co.uk

Powda Paint Finishing Plant Ltd, p.o. box 60, Dudley, West Midlands, DY3 1TP Tel: (01902) 677033 Fax: (01902) 678319 E-mail: info@pfpltd.co.uk

Three Spires Finishing Systems Ltd, 45 Lanes Close, Kings Bromley, Burton-on-Trent, Staffordshire, DE13 7JS Tel: (01543) 473069 Fax: (01543) 473069 E-mail: info@threespiresfinishing.co.uk

PAINT PRODUCTION PLANT

Eiger Torrance Ltd, 253 Europa Boulevard Westbrook, Westbrook, Warrington, WA5 7TN Tel: (01925) 232455 Fax: (01925) 237767 E-mail: sales@eiger-torrance.com

PAINT REMOVERS

Hammerite Products Ltd, Eltringham Works, Prudhoe, Northumberland, NE42 6LP Tel: (01661) 830000 Fax: (01661) 835760 E-mail: sales@hammerite.com

PAINT ROLLERS

Earlex Ltd, Opus Park Moorfield Road, Slyfield Industrial Estate, Guildford, Surrey, GU1 1SZ Tel: (01483) 454666 Fax: (01483) 454548 E-mail: enquiries@earlex.co.uk

Flock Development & Research Co. Ltd, Clarence Mill, Clarence Street, Stalybridge, Cheshire, SK15 1QF Tel: 0161-339 4946 Fax: 0161-343 2045 E-mail: flock@flockdev.co.uk

Hamilton Acorn Ltd, Halford Road, Attleborough, Norfolk, NR17 2HZ Tel: (01953) 453201 Fax: (01953) 454943 E-mail: sales@hamilton-acorn.co.uk

Hamilton Acorn Ltd, Callywhite Lane, Dronfield, Derbyshire, S18 2XP Tel: (01246) 418306 Fax: (01246) 410334 E-mail: info@hamilton-acorn.co.uk

Edward Jackson Ltd, Red Hall, Red Hall Lane, Southburgh, Thetford, Norfolk, IP25 7TG Tel: (01362) 820145 Fax: (01362) 820192 E-mail: info@edwardjacksonltd.com

PAINT SPRAYING CONTRACTORS OR SERVICES INCLUDING ON SITE

Aim Aviation Ltd, Building 138, Bournemouth International, Airport, Christchurch, Dorset, BH23 6NW Tel: (01202) 599666 Fax: (01202) 599677 E-mail: enquiries@aim-aviation.co.uk
Armacoating North West Ltd, Moores Mill, Cathrine Street East, Denton, Manchester, M34 3RQ Tel: 0161-320 9856 Fax: 0161-320 0772
Asdec Ltd, Unit 7-8 Building 33, Second Avenue, Pensnett Trading Estate, Kingswinford, West Midlands, DY6 7UG Tel: (01384) 402463 Fax: (01384) 402662 E-mail: asdecc@hotmail.com
Brookside Refurbishers, Unit 1/2, Brookside Garage, Wellingborough Road, Wellingborough, Northamptonshire, NN8 4BW Tel: (01933) 279288
Cape Industrial Services Ltd, Kirkton Drive, Dyce, Aberdeen, AB21 0BG Tel: (01224) 215800 Fax: (01224) 722879 E-mail: sales@capeindustrialservices.co.uk
▶ CeilCote, 26 Fenlake Business Centre, Fengate, Peterborough, PE1 5BQ Tel: (01733) 558251 Fax: (01733) 558251 E-mail: lloyd@ceilcote.com
Cement Glaze Decorators Ltd, 5 Barry Parade, Barry Road, London, SE22 0JA Tel: (020) 8299 2553 Fax: (020) 8299 2346
Cotswold Blast Cleaning, Linenfields, Old Boars Hill, Oxford, OX1 5JJ Tel: (07831) 705205 Fax: (01865) 326134
Cyphermet Ltd, Bone Lane, Newbury, Berkshire, RG14 5SH Tel: (01635) 34099 Fax: (01635) 528623 E-mail: sales@cyphermet.co.uk
European Coatings Ltd, Sandwich Industrial Estate, Ramsgate Road, Sandwich, Kent, CT13 9LY Tel: (01304) 621121 Fax: (01304) 621535
▶ Austin Hayes Ltd, Cemetery Road, Yeadon, Leeds, LS19 7BD Tel: 0113-250 2255 Fax: 0113-250 2200 E-mail: info@austinhayes.co.uk
▶ Icom Spray Paint Systems, Penn Road, Hazlemere, High Wycombe, Buckinghamshire, HP15 7PB Tel: (01494) 812733 E-mail: mail@icomsps.freeserve.co.uk
Interplas Coatings Ltd, Lygon Buildings, Peartree Lane, Dudley, West Midlands, DY2 0QU Tel: (01384) 236327 Fax: (01384) 255428 E-mail: sales@interplascoatings.com
J Hambleton Stove Enamellers, Egerton Street, Droylsden, Manchester, M43 7EL Tel: 0161-301 4444 Fax: 0161-371 0944
Liverpool Auto Service, Unit 12b Weaver Industrial Estate, Blackburne Street, Liverpool, L19 8JA Tel: 0151-427 5707 Fax: 0151-427 5707
Marawise Treatments Ltd, Unit 17 Relton Mews, Eden Street, Coventry, CV6 5HE Tel: (024) 7668 7121 Fax: (024) 7668 7121
Metalion Ltd, North Acton Road, London, NW10 6PD Tel: (020) 8965 4677 Fax: (020) 8965 3142
Morplate Ltd, Hammerton Street, Burnley, Lancashire, BB11 1LE Tel: (01282) 428571 Fax: (01282) 413600
R.J. Nash Ltd, 74 Livery Street, Birmingham, B3 1RG Tel: (0121) 200 3900 Fax: (0121) 200 3906 E-mail: brookwelding@btinternet.com
Nationwide Coatings UK Ltd, 5 Canal Estate, Station Road, Langley, Slough, SL3 6EG Tel: (01753) 671612 Fax: (01753) 671613 E-mail: sales@nationwidecoatings.co.uk
New Tech Finishing, Commercial Road, Walsall, WS2 7NQ Tel: (01922) 404604 Fax: (01922) 711083 E-mail: enquiries@ntfltd.co.uk
Paraid Ltd, Unit 4 Bond Street, West Bromwich, West Midlands, B70 7DQ Tel: 0121-580 0111 Fax: 0121-580 0222
Penfold Metalising Co. Ltd, Barnham Road, Barnham, Bognor Regis, West Sussex, PO22 0ES Tel: (01243) 552178 Fax: (01243) 554472 E-mail: info@penmet.co.uk
Possilpark Shotblasting Co. Ltd, 73 Dunn Street, Glasgow, G40 3PE Tel: 0141-556 6221 Fax: 0141-551 0714 E-mail: admin@possilparks.co.uk
Pwe Coatings, 9 Nobel Square, Burnt Mills Industrial Estate, Basildon, Essex, SS13 1LS Tel: (01268) 729983 Fax: (01268) 727955
R M H Refinishing, 2 Rutland Court, Manners Avenue, Manners Industrial Estate, Ilkeston, Derbyshire, DE7 8EF Tel: 0115-944 1528 Fax: 0115-944 1526
Rednal Polishing & Spraying Co. Ltd, Station Works, 17-19 Station Road, Northfield, Birmingham, B31 3TE Tel: 0121-475 4826 Fax: 0121-475 2712
Rollem Fabrications Ltd, The Common, Ecclesfield, Sheffield, S35 9WN Tel: 0114 2468119
S J C Shopfitters, 3 Britannia Road, Waltham Cross, Hertfordshire, EN8 7NY Tel: (01992) 711151 Fax: (01992) 714441 E-mail: sales@sjcshopfitters.co.uk
S S Central Coating Ltd, Unit 5 Oakhill Trading Estate, Euston Street, Freemens Common, Leicester, LE2 7ST Tel: 0116-255 4748 Fax: 0116-255 4769 E-mail: satu@sscoatings.com
Toricourt Ltd, 38 Westbury Road, Southampton, SO15 4JP Tel: (023) 8051 0982 Fax: (023) 8078 0363 E-mail: info@spectruminteriors.co.uk
Ucl Coatings, Peartree Lane, Dudley, West Midlands, DY2 0QY Tel: (01384) 262747 Fax: (01384) 480262
Willow Stove Enamellers, Unit 11 Eagle Trading Estate, Willow Lane, Mitcham, Surrey, CR4 4UY Tel: (020) 8646 7169 Fax: (020) 8646 7169

PAINT SPRAYING EQUIPMENT

Air Power Centre, Unit B4 Anchorage Business Park, Chain Caul Way, Ashton-on-Ribble, Preston, PR2 2YL Tel: (01772) 728513 Fax: (01772) 736506 E-mail: apcpreston@airpowercentre.com
Covercat Spray Systems, 2 Whorlton Road, Riverside Park, Middlesbrough, Cleveland, TS2 1QJ Tel: (01642) 243844 Fax: (01642) 240343 E-mail: sales@covercat.com
Danum Supplies, Kelham Street, Doncaster, South Yorkshire, DN1 3RE Tel: (01302) 344475
Durr Ltd, Broxell Close, Warwick, CV34 5QF Tel: (01926) 418800 Fax: (01926) 400679 E-mail: sales@durr.com
Eurolok Ltd, Tame Park, Vanguard, Wilnecote, Tamworth, Staffordshire, B77 5DY Tel: (01827) 287439 Fax: (01827) 287485 E-mail: sales@eurolok.com
F S L Electrostatic Systems Ltd, 5 A K Business Park, Russell Road, Southport, Merseyside, PR9 7SA Tel: (01704) 506439 Fax: (01704) 505043 E-mail: salesfsl@aol.com
Finishing Connect Ltd, 865 Plymouth Road, Slough, SL1 4LP Tel: (01753) 676788 Fax: (01753) 676790 E-mail: fincon@technocom.com
Garafit Services Ltd, Willis House, Flowers Hill, Bristol, BS4 5JJ Tel: 0117-971 1451 Fax: 0117-977 8022 E-mail: garafit.info@garafit.com
Gray Campling Ltd, 91a Southcote Road, Bournemouth, BH1 3SN Tel: (01202) 291828 Fax: (01202) 297304 E-mail: sales@graycampling.co.uk
ITW Automotive Finishing UK, Lockside, Anchor Brook Industrial Estate, Aldridge, Walsall, WS9 8EG Tel: (01922) 423700 Fax: (01922) 423705 E-mail: info@itwautofin.co.uk
Kleinmichel, Birds Hill, Letchworth Garden City, Hertfordshire, SG6 1JE Tel: (01462) 677611 Fax: (0870) 7626539 E-mail: uk-sales@kleinmichel.com
Minden Industrial Ltd, Saxham Business Park, Little Saxham, Bury St. Edmunds, Suffolk, IP28 6RX Tel: (01284) 760791 Fax: (01284) 702156 E-mail: sales@minden-ind.co.uk
Movac Group Ltd, 135 Ditton Walk, Cambridge, CB5 8QB Tel: (01223) 240568 Fax: (01223) 412459
Movac Group Ltd, 11 Portman Road, Ipswich, IP1 2BP Tel: (01473) 213763 Fax: (0870) 8358601 E-mail: info@movac.com
Nordson (UK) Ltd, Ashurst Drive, Cheadle Heath, Stockport, Cheshire, SK3 0RY Tel: 0161-495 4200 Fax: 0161-428 6716
Oscott Air Ltd, Sherlock Street, Birmingham, B5 6LT Tel: 0121-622 2789 Fax: 0121-666 6012 E-mail: sales@oscottair.com
Scarborough Laquers Co., Merry Lees, Staxton, Scarborough, North Yorkshire, YO12 4NN Tel: (01944) 710349 Fax: (01944) 710470 E-mail: sales@scarboroughlacquers.co.uk

PAINT SPRAYING PLANT

Capital Design Services Ltd, Bridge Buildings, 11A Ladybridge Road, Cheadle Hulme, Cheadle, Cheshire, SK8 5LL Tel: 0161-486 9524 Fax: 0161-485 8605

PAINT SPRAYING SYSTEMS INSTALLATION CONTRACTORS/ SERVICES

Rod Brown Engineering Ltd, Western Villa 58 The Dean, Alresford, Hampshire, SO24 9BD Tel: (01962) 735220 Fax: (01962) 735239 E-mail: sales@rodbrowneng.co.uk
Three Spires Finishing Systems Ltd, 45 Lanes Close, Kings Bromley, Burton-on-Trent, Staffordshire, DE13 7JS Tel: (01543) 473069 Fax: (01543) 473069 E-mail: info@threespiresfinishing.co.uk

PAINT SPRAYING, WET

▶ Pristine Ceilings, Unit 10 Phoenix Workshops, Station Road, Mochdre, Colwyn Bay, Clwyd, LL28 5EF Tel: (01492) 544777 Fax: (01492) 544094 E-mail: robert.pierce@btconnect.com
▶ Woodspray Timber Preservation Services, 21 Hillhead Road, Toomebridge, Antrim, BT41 3SF Tel: (028) 7965 1794 Fax: (028) 7965 1795 E-mail: info@woodsprayltd.com

PAINT STRIPPING CHEMICALS

Eco Solutions Ltd, Summerleaze, Church Road, Winscombe, Avon, BS25 1BH Tel: (01934) 844484 Fax: (01934) 844119 E-mail: info@ecosolutions.co.uk

PAINT STRIPPING CONTRACTORS

Almit Metal Finishing, Whinfield Drive, Aycliffe Industrial Estate, Aycliffe Industrial Park, Newton Aycliffe, County Durham, DL5 6AU Tel: (01325) 311777 Fax: (01325) 316472
Benflow UK, 395 Crewe Road, Wistaston, Nantwich, Cheshire, CW5 6NW Tel: (07813) 158317 Fax: (01270) 664551 E-mail: enquiries@belflow.co.uk
Halls Specialised Services, Brooklyn Farm, North Hill, Horndon-on-the-Hill, Stanford-le-Hope, Essex, SS17 8QA Tel: (01375) 361408 Fax: (01375) 361448 E-mail: enquiries@hallsspecialisedservices.co.uk
Mill At Gordleton, Silver Street, Sway, Lymington, Hampshire, SO41 6DJ Tel: (01590) 682219 Fax: (01590) 683073 E-mail: sales@gordletonmill.co.uk
Park Engineering, Manor Farm, Manor Road, South Hinksey, Oxford, OX1 5AS Tel: (01865) 327050 Fax: (01865) 327050
Ultrasonic Cleaning Services UK Ltd, 10 Pepper Road, Leeds, LS10 2EU Tel: 0113-271 5807 Fax: 0113-271 5722 E-mail: sales@ucs-uk-ltd.co.uk

PAINT TEST EQUIPMENT

Fischer Instrumentation (GB) Ltd, Department K, Gordleton Industrial Park, Hannah Way, Pennington, Lymington, Hampshire, SO41 8JD Tel: (01590) 684100 Fax: (01590) 684110 E-mail: mail@fischergb.co.uk
Rhopoint Instrumentation, 12 Beeching Road, Bexhill-on-Sea, East Sussex, TN39 3LG Tel: (01424) 730600 Fax: (01424) 730600 E-mail: enquiries@rhopointinstruments.com

PAINT TEST/RESEARCH SERVICES/LABORATORIES

John Ashworth & Partners Ltd, PO Box 160, Bacup, Lancashire, OL13 0BW Tel: (01706) 879544 Fax: (01706) 647767 E-mail: johnashworth.paint@virgin.net
E E F, Broadway House, Cothill Street, London, SW1H 9NQ Tel: (020) 7222 7777 Fax: (020) 7343 3190 E-mail: enquires@eef-fed.org.uk
Paint Research Association, 14 Castle Mews, High Street, Hampton, Middlesex, TW12 2NP Tel: (020) 8487 0800 Fax: (020) 8487 0801 E-mail: coatings@pra.org.uk
Scientific & Technical Services Ltd, 3 Summerhill, Blaydon-on-Tyne, Tyne & Wear, NE21 4JR Tel: 0191-414 7801 Fax: 0191-414 1245 E-mail: sts@stsltd.fsnet.co.uk

PAINT THINNERS

C K Chemicals, Unit 16 Lady La Industrial Estate, Hadleigh, Ipswich, IP7 6BQ Tel: (01473) 822836 Fax: (01473) 824044 E-mail: sales@ckchemicals.co.uk
Hammerite Products Ltd, Eltringham Works, Prudhoe, Northumberland, NE42 6LP Tel: (01661) 830000 Fax: (01661) 835760 E-mail: sales@hammerite.com
Intercoat Industrial Paints & Lacquers Ltd, Bridgeman Street, Walsall, WS2 9NW Tel: (01922) 638821 Fax: (01922) 722952

PAINT TOLL MANUFACTURE

Brewers Ltd, Priory Bridge Road, Taunton, Somerset, TA1 1QD Tel: (01823) 284532 Fax: (01823) 353712
Dispersion Technology Ltd, Factory Lane, Brantham, Manningtree, Essex, CO11 1NJ Tel: (01206) 395000 Fax: (01206) 392872 E-mail: christine@dispersion-technology.co.uk

PAINTBALL CLEANING EQUIPMENT

▶ Holmbush Paintball, C/O Holmbush Farm, Crawley Road, Faygate, Horsham, West Sussex, RH12 4SE Tel: (01293) 852261 E-mail: euenquiries@holmbushpaintballshop.com

PAINTERS' TOOLS

C Brewer & Sons Ltd, 49 New England Street, Brighton, BN1 4GQ Tel: (01273) 570243 Fax: (01273) 693592 E-mail: brighton@brewers.co.uk
Clifton Paints Ltd, 92-100 North Street, Bedminster, Bristol, BS3 1HF Tel: 0117-966 0321 Fax: 0117-963 1301 E-mail: sales@dacrylate.co.uk

PAINTING CONTRACTORS

A1 Blasting Cleaning & Painting, Riverside House Wallerscote Island, Winnington Lane, Northwich, Cheshire, CW8 4YF Tel: (01606) 783203 Fax: (01606) 781581
Aldeby Painting Services Ltd, Britannia Way, Thurmaston, Leicester, LE4 8JY Tel: 0116-269 5699 Fax: 0116-260 2887 E-mail: kevin.aldeby@virgin.net
Alfred Bagnall & Sons London Ltd, 4 Udney Park Road, Teddington, Middlesex, TW11 9BG Tel: (020) 8977 4474 Fax: (020) 8943 5389
Angus Decorating, Kings Works, Sir William Smith Road, Kirkton Industrial Estate, Arbroath, Angus, DD11 3RD Tel: (01241) 435238 Fax: (01241) 879474
▶ Balkany Enterprise Ltd, 144 Page Road, Feltham, Feltham, Middlesex, TW14 8DN Tel: (07951) 767106 Fax: (020) 8707 6636 E-mail: bobbi_mk@yahoo.com
F. Bemrose Ltd, Manby Road, Immingham, South Humberside, DN40 2LL Tel: (01469) 572961 Fax: (01469) 571498 E-mail: frankbemrose@aol.com
Blastreat Arundel Ltd, 14 Fitzalan Road, Arundel, West Sussex, BN18 9JS Tel: (01903) 883262 Fax: (01903) 884185 E-mail: blastreat@btconnect.com
Robert Bruce Construction Ltd, Unit 40 Thornleigh Trading Estate, Blowers Green Road, Dudley, West Midlands, DY2 8UB Tel: (01384) 457780 Fax: (01384) 259921
C L C Contractors Ltd, 21 Oswin Road, Leicester, LE3 1HR Tel: 0116-254 4105 Fax: 0116-254 2784 E-mail: leicester@clcgroup.com
C L C Contractors Ltd, Northbrook Industrial Estate, Vincent Avenue, Southampton, SO16 6PQ Tel: (023) 8070 1111 Fax: (023) 8070 1171 E-mail: mail@clcgroup.com
C L C Contractors Anglia, 7 Station Way, Brandon, Suffolk, IP27 0BH Tel: (01842) 813972 Fax: 01842 813113 E-mail: brandon@clcgroup.com
Carkeek Engineers, 15 Valley Road, Plympton, Plymouth, PL7 1RS Tel: (01752) 517460 Fax: (01752) 347470
CLC Contractors Ltd, 212 Manchester Road, Warrington, WA1 3BD Tel: (01925) 417200 Fax: (01925) 417201
Collins Contractors Ltd, 31 Gillian Street, London, SE13 7AJ Tel: (020) 8690 0077 Fax: (020) 8690 4077 E-mail: info@collins-contractors.co.uk
Colorlites, Unit 23 Lordswood Industrial Estate, Revenge Road, Chatham, Kent, ME5 8UD Tel: (01634) 862839 Fax: (01634) 865285 E-mail: salesdesk@colorlites.com
Cosmos Decorators Ltd, 580 Lawmoor Street, Glasgow, G5 0TX Tel: 0141-429 8171 Fax: 0141-420 1143 E-mail: sales@cosmosdecorators.co.uk
▶ D J Bryant, 59 Queen Victoria Avenue, Hove, East Sussex, BN3 6XA Tel: (01273) 707300 Fax: (01273) 541005
Daly (Painting Contractors) Ltd, Decor House Terracotta Drive, Clay Lane, Coventry, CV2 4LG Tel: (024) 7665 0033 Fax: (024) 7665 0056 E-mail: sales@dalypaintings.co.uk
David Hobdell Building Ltd, Cheltenham House, Grange Road, London, N17 0ER Tel: (020) 8801 5244 Fax: (020) 8885 2876
Decorative Specialist Ltd, 14 Kensington Church Street, London, W8 4EP Tel: (020) 7937 3483 Fax: (020) 7376 2182
Donald Humberstone & Co. Ltd, Brackenborough Road, Louth, Lincolnshire, LN11 0AG Tel: (01507) 603003 Fax: (01507) 603003
E G Lewis & Co. Ltd, Tank Farm Road, Llandarcy, Neath, West Glamorgan, SA10 6EN Tel: (01792) 323288 Fax: (01792) 323255 E-mail: timl@eglewis.com
Edinburgh Painting Contractors, 30 Christiemiller Avenue, Edinburgh, EH7 6ST Tel: (0131) 669 4691 Fax: (0131) 669 4691
F K Electrical Services Ltd, Hyde Park Corner, Leeds, LS6 1AE Tel: 0113-275 9044 Fax: 0113-230 4631 E-mail: fkelectrical@fsmail.net
Fairhurst Ward Abbotts Ltd, 225 London Road, Greenhithe, Kent, DA9 9RR Tel: (01322) 387000 Fax: (01322) 370235 E-mail: works@fwa.dart.co.uk
Fields Reading Ltd, 5 Metro Centre, Toutley Road, Wokingham, Berkshire, RG41 1QW Tel: 0118-977 6066 Fax: 0118-940 1195
Finlaysons, Botany Mill, Roxburgh Street, Galashiels, Selkirkshire, TD1 1PB Tel: (01896) 752673 Fax: (01896) 751239
G I Sykes Ltd, The Hayes, Lye, Stourbridge, West Midlands, DY9 8NX Tel: (01384) 891341 Fax: (01384) 894773
G & N Shotblasting Ltd, Brindley Close, Drayton Fields Industrial Estate, Daventry, Northamptonshire, NN11 8RP Tel: (01327) 872569 Fax: (01327) 300878 E-mail: sales@shotblast.co.uk
Garness & Pearson Decorating Contractors Ltd, Summer Lane, Birmingham, B19 3NG Tel: 0121-359 3711 Fax: 0121-359 7311
H B Pearce Contractors Ltd, Grey Gables, Pytchley Road, Kettering, Northamptonshire, NN15 6NE Tel: (01536) 310234 Fax: (01536) 310638
▶ Austin Hayes Ltd, Cemetery Road, Yeadon, Leeds, LS19 7BD Tel: 0113-250 2255 Fax: 0113-250 2200 E-mail: info@austinhayes.co.uk
James Hodgins & Sons Ltd, 77 Coustonholm Road, Glasgow, G43 1UF Tel: 0141-632 6241 Fax: 0141-636 1184

PAINTING CONTRACTORS – *continued*

Ian Williams, Station Road, Warmley, Bristol, BS30 8XG Tel: 0117-960 9510 Fax: 0117-935 3772E-mail: lynne.westcott@ianwilliams.co.uk

Ipf, 37 Whitehill Road, Glenrothes, Fife, KY6 2RW Tel: (01592) 771805 Fax: (01592) 771805

J D Painting Contractors Ltd, High Street, Newburn, Newcastle upon Tyne, NE15 8LN Tel: 0191-264 5131 Fax: 0191-264 0485 E-mail: jd.painting@virgin.net

J J Williams Painting Services Ltd, 75 Village Farm Road, Pyle, Bridgend, Mid Glamorgan, CF33 6BN Tel: (01656) 744311 Fax: (01656) 744617 E-mail: enquiries@jjwilliamsltd.com

Jack Tighe Decorating Ltd, Redbourne Mere, Kirton Lindsey, Gainsborough, Lincolnshire, DN21 4NW Tel: (01652) 649215 Fax: (01652) 648159

JMS Coatings Ltd, Units 8-9, Harlaw Business Centre, Inverurie, Aberdeenshire, AB51 4FR Tel: (01467) 622385 Fax: (01467) 624431

▶ John Hill Building Contractor, 11 Goslipgate, Pickering, North Yorkshire, YO18 8DQ Tel: (07890) 942046 Fax: (01751) 477975 E-mail: info@countrywidedecorators.co.uk

John Stedeford & Sons Ltd, Unit 68b Sapcote Trading Centre, Wyrley Road, Birmingham, B6 7BN Tel: 0121-328 3218 Fax: 0121-327 4965

▶ K & N Finishers Southern Ltd, Castle Trading Estate, Fareham, Hampshire, PO16 9SF Tel: (023) 9237 0591 Fax: (023) 9238 0130 E-mail: kandnfinishers@bt.com

The Lord Group Ltd, Oak Mill Mellor Street, Rochdale, Lancashire, OL12 6UY Tel: (01706) 341311 Fax: (01706) 861810 E-mail: info@thelordgroup.co.uk

Mackay Decorators Perth Ltd, 1 Riverside, Perth, PH2 7TR Tel: (01738) 623227 Fax: (01738) 623228 E-mail: enquiries@mackaydecorators.co.uk

Maclean & Speirs Group Ltd, East Fulton Farm, Darluith Road, Linwood, Paisley, Renfrewshire, PA3 3TP Tel: (01505) 324777 Fax: (01505) 335482 E-mail: info@macleanandspeirs.co.uk

Midland Painting Contractors, 34 College Street, Kempston, Bedford, MK42 8LU Tel: (01234) 354097 Fax: (01234) 267478 E-mail: helen@midlandpainters.co.uk

Milhench Painting Contractors Ltd, Lyceum Works, George Street, Chadderton, Oldham, OL9 9HY Tel: 0161-624 2868 Fax: 0161-628 5569

John Miller & Sons (Painters) Ltd, 52 Main Street, Barrhead, Glasgow, G78 1RE Tel: 0141-881 1516 Fax: 0141-880 8113

Mitie Property Services Eastern Ltd, Davey Close, Colchester, CO1 2XL Tel: (01206) 871954 Fax: (01206) 863818 E-mail: property.colchester@mitie.co.uk

Mitie Property Services London Ltd, Mitie House, Eskdale Road, Uxbridge, Middlesex, UB8 2RT Tel: (01895) 206850 Fax: (01895) 206851

Mitie Property Services (Midlands) Ltd, Coppice Side Industrial Estate, Brownhills, Walsall, WS8 7HF Tel: (01543) 375461 Fax: (01543) 378194

Mitie Property Services North East Ltd, 1 Redesdale Court, Middlesbrough, Cleveland, TS2 1RL Tel: (01642) 247956 Fax: (01642) 223378 E-mail: prop@mitie.co.uk

Norman Rew Decorations, 22 Sycamore Close, Wellington, Telford, Shropshire, TF1 3NH Tel: (01952) 255951

Peake & Son Ltd, Welch Street, Stoke-on-Trent, ST4 4DF Tel: (01782) 847496 Fax: (01782) 847496 E-mail: chris@speakeandson.fsnet.co.uk

Peveril Decorators Ltd, Peveril House, Alfreton Road, Derby, DE21 4AG Tel: (01332) 344739 Fax: (01332) 368622 E-mail: sales@perverildecorators.co.uk

Pipeline & Metal Coatings Ltd, Atlantic Shed South Dock, Alexandra Docks, Newport, Gwent, NP20 2NQ Tel: (01633) 256031 Fax: (01633) 840285

R E Martin Manchester Ltd, Unit 8-9-Spring Road Industrial Estate, Lanesfield Drive, Wolverhampton, WV4 6UA Tel: (01902) 496342 Fax: (01902) 404760 E-mail: info@remartin.com

Reed & Sons Ltd, Brittleware Farm Buildings, Norwood Hill Road, Charlwood, Horley, Surrey, RH6 0EB Tel: (01293) 863333 Fax: (01293) 863334 E-mail: reedandsonsltd@yahoo.com

Reilly & Warnock, 2 Pokelly Place, Stewarton, Kilmarnock, Ayrshire, KA3 5PF Tel: (01560) 484279

Roften Galvanising Ltd, North Road, Ellesmere Port, CH65 1AB Tel: 0151-355 4257 Fax: 0151-355 0753 E-mail: creditacc_roften@yahoo.co.uk

S C Grover Ltd, Grover House Burntmill Industrial Estate, Elizabeth Way, Harlow, Essex, CM20 2JH Tel: (01279) 420763 Fax: (01279) 416535

Seddon Stoke Ltd, PO Box 13, Stoke-on-Trent, ST4 3NN Tel: (01782) 599511 Fax: (01782) 599682 E-mail: transport@seddonstoke.co.uk

Sharrocks Ltd, 143-153 Whitehorse Road, Croydon, CR0 2LJ Tel: (020) 8684 4218 Fax: (020) 8689 6244 E-mail: sharrockslondon@btclick.com

Arnold Sharrocks Ltd, 229 Spotland Road, Rochdale, Lancashire, OL12 7AQ Tel: (01706) 655411 Fax: (01706) 642452 E-mail: arnold-sharrocks@2binternet.co.uk

Supablast Nationwide Ltd, 17 Gorsey Lane, Coleshill, Birmingham, B46 1JU Tel: (01675) 464446 Fax: (01675) 464447 E-mail: enquiries@supablast.co.uk

Surface Technik (Tamworth) Ltd, Ninian Way, Wilnecote, Tamworth, Staffordshire, B77 5ES Tel: (01827) 250736 Fax: (01827) 283384

T C & D Technical Services Ltd, Kirkcroft Farm, Thorpe Hesley, Rotherham, South Yorkshire, S61 2RP Tel: 0114-246 9410 Fax: 0114-257 7935

▶ T I Protective Coatings, Unit 6, Lodge Bank, Crown Lane, Horwich, Bolton, BL6 5HY Tel: (01204) 468080 Fax: (01204) 695188 E-mail: sales@ticoatings.co.uk

Turner Maintenance Ltd, Bessemer Road, Norwich, NR4 6DQ Tel: (01603) 626609 Fax: (01603) 626090

Valrene Ltd, 234 Highfield Road, Washwood Heath, Birmingham, B8 3QR Tel: 0121-327 5388 Fax: 0121-328 3197

Wallis Ltd, 47 Homesdale Road, Bromley, BR2 9TN Tel: (020) 8464 3377 Fax: (020) 8464 5847 E-mail: gen@wallisb.kier.co.uk

Warley Painters Ltd, Winchester Works, Malt Mill Lane, Halesowen, West Midlands, B62 8JF Tel: 0121-561 5665 Fax: 0121-561 5556 E-mail: wp@warleypaint.co.uk

Whittle Painting, 170a Monton Road, Eccles, Manchester, M30 9GA Tel: 0161-787 7667 Fax: 0161-787 8841 E-mail: sales@whittlepaintinggroup.co.uk

Whittle Painting Group Ltd, Daybrook House, Merchant Street, Nottingham, NG6 8GT Tel: 0115-977 0311 Fax: 0115-977 1472 E-mail: sales@whittlegroup.co.uk

Wilfred Lord Ltd, Oak Mill, Mellor St, Rochdale, Lancashire, OL12 6UY Tel: (01706) 341311 Fax: (01706) 861810

PAINTS, *See also headings for particular types*

3p Paint Co Stockport Ltd, Hallam Mill, Hallam Street, Stockport, Cheshire, SK2 6PT Tel: 0161-477 4202 Fax: 0161-477 4202 E-mail: 3ppaintcompany@tiscali.co.uk

A D P (Lancashire) Ltd, Unit 1, Apian Way Industrial Estate, Salford, M7 4WZ Tel: 0161-792 1034 Fax: 0161-792 6811 E-mail: adppaints@aol.com

Akzo Nobel Industrial Coatings Ltd, Crown House, Hollins Road, Darwen, Lancashire, BB3 0BG Tel: (01254) 760760 Fax: (01254) 701092 E-mail:

Bailey Paints Ltd, London Road, Thrupp, Stroud, Gloucestershire, GL5 2AZ Tel: (01453) 882237 Fax: (01453) 731413 E-mail: info@baileypaints.demon.co.uk

Bradite Ltd, Ogwen Valley Works, Bethesda, Bangor, Gwynedd, LL57 4YP Tel: (01248) 600315 Fax: (01248) 602782 E-mail: sales@bradite.co.uk

▶ Bristol (UK) Ltd, 3 Sutherland Court, Tolpits Lane, Watford, WD18 9SP Tel: (01923) 779333 Fax: (01923) 779666 E-mail: tech.sales@bristolpaint.com

C Brewer & Sons Ltd, 5 Sphere Industrial Estate, Campfield Road, St. Albans, Hertfordshire, AL1 5HT Tel: (01727) 844737 Fax: (01727) 846672

C S Marine, Newmet House, Rue De St. Lawrence, Waltham Abbey, Essex, EN9 1PF Tel: (01992) 703403 Fax: (01992) 768393 E-mail: materials@newmet.co.uk

Car Colour Services Ltd, 92-94 Mawney Road, Romford, RM7 7JB Tel: (01708) 705005 Fax: (01708) 732618 E-mail: ccsromford@aol.com

Central Car Paints, 93 Crafton St East, Leicester, LE1 2DG Tel: 0116-262 9727 E-mail: info@centralcarpaints.co.uk

▶ Colorite Paint Co. Ltd, 169 Boston Road, Hanwell, London, W7 3QJ Tel: (020) 8579 3381 Fax: (020) 8567 5158 E-mail: info@colorite.co.uk

County Decorating, 134 Crossbrook Street, Cheshunt, Waltham Cross, Hertfordshire, EN8 8JH Tel: (01992) 628265 Fax: (01992) 628265 E-mail: countydecs_@cheshotmail.com

Dale, Herriot Way, Scunthorpe, South Humberside, DN15 8XU Tel: (01724) 855645 Fax: (01724) 278278 E-mail: sales@daleuk.co.uk

Dexter Paints Ltd, Albert Works, Trafalgar Street, Burnley, Lancashire, BB11 1RE Tel: (01282) 423361 Fax: (01282) 414573

Dulux Ltd, Manchester Road, West Timperley, Altrincham, Cheshire, WA14 5PG Tel: 0161-968 3000 Fax: 0161-973 4202

Dulux Ltd, 66 Burleys Way, Leicester, LE1 3BD Tel: 0116-262 9471 Fax: 0116-251 2985

E Hague Furnace Compounds, 31 Chorley Drive, Sheffield, S10 3RQ Tel: 0114-230 2707 Fax: 0114-230 2707

Envirocoat Industrial Paints, Northumberland Avenue, Fountain Road, Hull, HU2 0LN Tel: (01482) 585162 Fax: (01482) 327273 E-mail: envirocoat@aol.com

Foxell & James, 57 Farringdon Road, London, EC1M 3JB Tel: (020) 7405 0152 Fax: (020) 7405 3631 E-mail: sales@foxellandjames.co.uk

John Frackelton & Son Ltd, 25 Imperial Drive, Belfast, BT6 8JH Tel: (028) 9073 2231 Fax: (028) 9073 1764 E-mail: tiles@frackeltons.co.uk

Ici Paints plc T/As Dulux, Wexham Road, Slough, SL2 5DS Tel: (01753) 550000 Fax: (01753) 578218 E-mail: sales@dulux.com

Indestructible Paint Ltd, 23-25 Pentos Drive, Sparkhill, Birmingham, B11 3TA Tel: 0121-702 2485 Fax: 0121-778 4338 E-mail: sales@indestructible.co.uk

Industrial Paint & Powder Ltd, 45 Lanark Road, Edinburgh, EH14 1TL Tel: 0131-443 8793 Fax: 0131-455 7806 E-mail: sales@indpaintandpowder.co.uk

Industrial Paint Services S W Ltd, 1 Lyte Building, Wern Trading Estate, Rogerstone, Newport, Gwent, NP10 9FQ Tel: (01633) 897766 Fax: (01633) 897716

Industrial Powder & Paint Services, 9a Boss Hall Road, Ipswich, IP1 5BN Tel: (01473) 463333 Fax: (01473) 747153 E-mail: sales@ippsltd.co.uk

Irving Little & Co. Ltd, 213 Cleveland Street, Birkenhead, Merseyside, CH41 3QE Tel: 0151-666 1004 Fax: 0151-666 1013

J H Lightbody & Son Ltd, 437 Townmill Road, Glasgow, G31 3AN Tel: 0141-550 0666 Fax: 0141-550 0330 E-mail: lightbody@iris-web.co.uk

H.I.S. Lawson Ltd, 84-88 Millbrook Road East, Southampton, SO15 1BG Tel: (023) 8063 2927 Fax: (023) 8033 9878 E-mail: enquiries@lawson-his.co.uk

Marrs Cross & Wilfrid Fairbairns Ltd, Hardwood House, 1 Oglander Road, London, SE15 4EH Tel: (020) 7639 5106 Fax: (020) 7639 5106 E-mail: mxf@ukgateway.net

Metalflake Motor Factors, 15d Oakcroft Road, Chessington, Surrey, KT9 1RH Tel: (020) 8397 6198 Fax: (020) 8974 2850 E-mail: sales@metalflake.co.uk

Morelli Central Ltd, 414 Stoney Stanton Road, Coventry, CV6 5DG Tel: (024) 7668 1143 Fax: (024) 7663 7464 E-mail: headoffice@morelli.co.uk

Movac Group Ltd, 11 Portman Road, Ipswich, IP1 2BP Tel: (01473) 213763 Fax: (0870) 8358601 E-mail: info@movac.com

N W E Paints Ltd, 66-70 Ffordd Las, Rhyl, Clwyd, LL18 2EA Tel: (01745) 342342 Fax: (01745) 334746 E-mail: admin@nwepaints.co.uk

Orion Paints Ltd, Unit 22 Manor Complex, Kirkby Bank Road, Knowsley Industrial Park, Liverpool, L33 7SY Tel: 0151-548 6756 Fax: 0151-549 1572 E-mail: sales@orionpaints.co.uk

▶ Permanent Coatings, 33 Normandy Way, Bodmin, Cornwall, PL31 1HA Tel: (01208) 264999 Fax: (01208) 264998

R C Stiven & Co., Unit 31 Faraday Street, Dryburgh Industrial Estate, Dundee, DD2 3QQ Tel: (01382) 833322 Fax: (01382) 889133 E-mail: aws@rcstiven.sol.co.uk

Rapidpaint Birmingham Ltd, 197-199 Bradford Street, Birmingham, B12 0JD Tel: 0121-693 4020 Fax: 0121-693 5665

SigmaKalon, 16D 16F Kilroot Business Park, Larne Road, Carrickfergus, County Antrim, BT38 7PR Tel: (028) 9335 1567 Fax: (028) 9335 1569

Simpson's Paints Ltd, 122-124 Broadley Street, London, NW8 8BB Tel: (020) 7723 6657 Fax: (020) 7706 4662

Smith & Allan, 1a Valley St, Darlington, County Durham, DL1 1QE Tel: (01325) 462228 Fax: (01325) 368122 E-mail: stevearcher@smithandallan.com

Startmaze Ltd, Unit 2, Glaholm Industrial Estate, Glaholm Road, Hendon, Sunderland, SR1 2NX Tel: 0191-567 3649 Fax: 0191-510 3917

Thos Kelly & Co., Dromore Street, Ballynahinch, County Down, BT24 8AG Tel: (028) 9756 2380 Fax: (028) 9756 1564

Trade Paint Supplies Ltd, Grove Road, Northfleet, Gravesend, Kent, DA11 9AX Tel: (01474) 560382 Fax: (01474) 362926 E-mail: sales@tradepaintsupplies.ltd.uk

PALISADE FENCING

Chase Timber Products Ltd, Twickenham Avenue, Brandon, Suffolk, IP27 0PD Tel: (01842) 810690 Fax: (01842) 812987 E-mail: mail@chasetimberproducts.co.uk

▶ Corus Special Profiles Ltd, Skinningrove, Saltburn-By-The-Sea, Cleveland, TS13 4ET Tel: (01287) 640212 Fax: (01287) 643467

Lanlee Supplies Ltd, Red Scar Works, Burnley Road, Colne, Lancashire, BB8 8ED Tel: (01282) 868204 Fax: (01282) 870116 E-mail: sales@lanleesupplies.co.uk

Roc Fencing Ltd, Firs Indust Estate, Kidderminster, Worcestershire, DY11 7QN Tel: (01562) 69440 Fax: (01562) 823718 E-mail: sales@rocfencing.co.uk

PALISADE GATES

Darfen Durafencing, 15-21 Speedwell Road, Yardley, Birmingham, B25 8HU Tel: 0121-772 8666 Fax: 0121-772 8648 E-mail: central@darfen.co.uk

Darfen Durafencing, Bradman Road, Knowsley Industrial Park, Liverpool, L33 7UR Tel: 0151-547 3626 Fax: 0151-549 1205 E-mail: northwest@darfen.co.uk

▶ F Peart & Co. Ltd, Baltic Works, Baltic Street, Hartlepool, Cleveland, TS25 1PW Tel: (01429) 860308 Fax: (01302) 770051 E-mail: sales@fpeart.com

▶ Gibbs Bros, Kitesbridge Farm, Asthall, Burford, Oxfordshire, OX18 4HL Tel: (01993) 878600 E-mail: info@gibbsbrothers.co.uk

PALLET COLLARS

Anglo European Pallets, Unit 1 Old Airfield Farm, Moreton Valence, Gloucester, GL2 7NG Tel: (01452) 883305 Fax: (01452) 723082 E-mail: mac@aepallet.demon.co.uk

H G Timber Ltd, Three Ways Wharf, Rigby Lane, Hayes, Middlesex, UB3 1ET Tel: (020) 8561 3311 Fax: (020) 8569 2122 E-mail: sales@hgtimber.co.uk

Hilton Industrial Services Ltd, The Old Cheese Factory, Stone Road, Hill Chorlton, Newcastle, Staffordshire, ST5 5DR Tel: (01782) 680680 Fax: (01782) 680546

Nefab Packaging UK Ltd, 151 Silbury Boulevard, Milton Keynes, MK9 1LH Tel: (01908) 424300 Fax: (01908) 424301 E-mail: helen.coffin@nefab.se

Trafalgar Cases Ltd, Stanhope Works, Primrose Hill, Kings Langley, Hertfordshire, WD4 8HS Tel: (01923) 261155 Fax: (01923) 268064 E-mail: sales@trafalgarcases.com

PALLET CONVERTER EQUIPMENT/SYSTEMS

Palletower (GB) Ltd, Pallet Centre Europe, Dane Road Industrial Estate, Sale, Cheshire, M33 7BH Tel: 0161-905 2233 Fax: 0161-972 0922 E-mail: info@palletower.com

Simons Reeve Holdings Ltd, Private Road No 2, Colwick Industrial Estate, Nottingham, NG4 2JR Tel: 0115-987 0970 Fax: 0115-961 1737 E-mail: mail@simons-reeve.co.uk

PALLET COVERS OR HOODS

▶ Cliffe Industrial Packaging Ltd, Marshfield Bank Employment Park, Marshfield Bank, Crewe, CW2 8UY Tel: (01270) 212136 Fax: (01270) 212145

Controlla Covers Ltd, Brunswick Industrial Park, Hannah Street, Darwen, Lancashire, BB3 3HL Tel: (01254) 772020 Fax: (01254) 773030 E-mail: controlla@aol.com

Humber Europe Ltd, Shorten Brook Drive, Altham Business Park, Altham, Accrington, Lancashire, BB5 5YH Tel: (01282) 770333 Fax: (01282) 776888 E-mail: info@humberbigbag.com

Derek Lambert (Polythene) Ltd, Keighley Road, Bingley, West Yorkshire, BD16 2RD Tel: (01274) 560423 Fax: (01274) 561833 E-mail: sales@dereklambert.co.uk

Palagan Ltd, Tavistock Street, Dunstable, Bedfordshire, LU6 1NE Tel: (01582) 600234 Fax: (01582) 601636 E-mail: mail@palagan.co.uk

Philton Polythene Converters Ltd, Charfleets Road, Canvey Island, Essex, SS8 0PQ Tel: (01268) 696331 Fax: (01268) 510517 E-mail: sales@philton.co.uk

R P Whitehead Ltd, Gelderd Road, Leeds, LS12 6NB Tel: 0113-263 0613 Fax: 0113-263 0602

Sherwood Packaging Ltd, Amber Drive, Langley Mill, Nottingham, NG16 4BE Tel: (01773) 760101 Fax: (01773) 530527 E-mail: sales@sherwoodpkg.com

Shrinkfast Ltd, Bridgewater Close, Hawkesworth TRDG Estate, Hawkesworth Trading Estate, Swindon, SN2 1ED Tel: (01793) 612072 Fax: (01793) 534649 E-mail: sales@shrinkfast.co.uk

Tyco Plastics Ltd, Armytage Road, The Industrial Estate, Brighouse, West Yorkshire, HD6 1PT Tel: (01484) 714313 Fax: (01484) 720452 E-mail: info@tycoplastics.com

Xtex Polythene Ltd, Spring Mills, Main Street, Wilsden, Bradford, West Yorkshire, BD15 0DX Tel: (01535) 272871 Fax: (01535) 275702 E-mail: sales@xtec.co.uk

PALLET EDGING GUARDS

I T W Angleboard, Crackley Way, Peartree Lane, Dudley, West Midlands, DY2 0UW Tel: (01384) 253290 Fax: (01384) 253321 E-mail: uksales@itwangleboard.net

PALLET FEET

Kenneth Whitehouse, Mill Lane, Fazeley, Tamworth, Staffordshire, B78 3QD Tel: (01827) 261678 Fax: (01827) 251469 E-mail: kenw@clara.co.uk

PALLET GATE MANUFRS

Crockett & Son, Aylesbury Road, Askett, Princes Risborough, Buckinghamshire, HP27 9LY Tel: (01844) 344175 Fax: (01844) 343509

Tyne & Weir Timber, Lanesley Sawmill, Lanesley, Gateshead, Tyne & Wear, NE11 0EX Tel: 0191-491 3988 Fax: 0191-491 4054

PALLET HANDLING EQUIPMENT OR SYSTEMS

Industrial Automation Ltd, 8 The Midway, Nottingham, NG7 2TS Tel: 0115-840 0500 Fax: 0115-840 5959 E-mail: sales@ind-auto.com

Sperrin Metal Products Ltd, Cahore Road, Draperstown, Magherafelt, County Londonderry, BT45 7AP Tel: (028) 7962 8362 Fax: (028) 7962 8972 E-mail: sales@sperrin-metal.com

PALLET HIRE

Chep, Unit 2,, Weybridge Business Park, Addlestone Road, Addlestone, Surrey, KT15 2UP Tel: (01932) 850085 Fax: (01932) 850144

Flomotion Rental Ltd, 7 Wilton Close, Partridge Green, Horsham, West Sussex, RH13 8RX Tel: (01403) 711170 Fax: (01403) 711059

M S Shirts Box Ltd, 45 Finchwell Road, Sheffield, S13 9AS Tel: 0114-244 2591 Fax: 0114-244 3909 E-mail: msshirtsbox@ssbdial.co.uk

Palletower (GB) Ltd, Pallet Centre Europe, Dane Road Industrial Estate, Sale, Cheshire, M33 7BH Tel: 0161-905 2233 Fax: 0161-972 0922 E-mail: info@palletower.com

Simons Reeve Holdings Ltd, Private Road No 2, Colwick Industrial Estate, Nottingham, NG4 2JR Tel: 0115-987 0970 Fax: 0115-961 1737 E-mail: mail@simons-reeve.co.uk

PALLET INVERTER SYSTEMS

Payne Pallet Inverters Ltd, Dereham Road, Beeston, King's Lynn, Norfolk, PE32 2NQ Tel: (01328) 700138 Fax: (01328) 701879 E-mail: david@paynepalletinverters.co.uk

PALLET LOADING EQUIPMENT

Joloda (International) Ltd, 51 Speke Road, Liverpool, L19 2NY Tel: 0151-427 8954 Fax: 0151-427 1393 E-mail: info@joloda.com

PALLET MAINTENANCE OR REPAIR

J B J Pallets Ltd, Hedingham Road, Wethersfield, Braintree, Essex, CM7 4EQ Tel: (01371) 850035 Fax: (01371) 850420

P H Pallet Services, Broadway, Globe Lane Industrial Estate, Dukinfield, Cheshire, SK16 4UJ Tel: 0161-351 1333 Fax: 0161-366 9322 E-mail: sales@phpallets.com

Palick Ltd, The Mill, Silverdale Road, Newcastle, Staffordshire, ST5 2TA Tel: (01782) 661600 Fax: (01782) 630404 E-mail: sales@palick.co.uk

Stanlow Pallets Ltd, Indigo Road, Ellesmere Port, CH65 4AJ Tel: 0151-356 3932 Fax: 0151-357 2667

R.W. Whittaker (Pallets) Ltd, Booth Street, Middleton Junction, Manchester, M24 1SF Tel: 0161-643 1718 Fax: 0161-643 0556 E-mail: robwhit@palcase.fastnet.co.uk

PALLET NAILS

▶ MC Technical Services, Unit 4 A6 Business Centre, Telford Way Telford Industrial, Telford Way Industrial Estate, Kettering, Northamptonshire, NN16 8UN Tel: (01536) 410201 Fax: (01536) 412189 E-mail: sales@mctechnicalservices.com

P & C Pallets Ltd, Timber Yard, Llandowlais Street, Oakfield, Cwmbran, Gwent, NP44 7HD Tel: (01633) 870055 E-mail: michelle@pcpallets.co.uk

PALLET OR STILLAGES, *See also headings for particular types*

B & I Fabrications, Farrington Place, Rossendale Road Industrial Estate, Burnley, Lancashire, BB11 5TY Tel: (01282) 411434 Fax: (01282) 838963

Glenrothes Industrial Packing Ltd, 75-76 Whitecraigs Road, Glenrothes, Fife, KY6 2RX Tel: (01592) 771052 Fax: (01592) 620158

Kenneth Whitehouse, Mill Lane, Fazeley, Tamworth, Staffordshire, B78 3QD Tel: (01827) 261678 Fax: (01827) 251469 E-mail: kenw@clara.co.uk

Manchester Drums Ltd, Bower Street, Newton Heath, Manchester, M40 2AS Tel: 0161-203 4611 Fax: 0161-203 5404

P H Pallet Services, Broadway, Globe Lane Industrial Estate, Dukinfield, Cheshire, SK16 4UJ Tel: 0161-351 1333 Fax: 0161-366 9322 E-mail: sales@phpallets.com

Palick (Wolverhampton) Ltd, Hilton Main Industrial Estate, Bognop Road, Essinton, Wolverhampton, WV11 2BE Tel: (01902) 727691 E-mail: sales@palick.co.uk

Planned Storage Systems Ltd, Castle House, Victoria St, Englefield Green, Egham, Surrey, TW20 0QL Tel: (01784) 471471 Fax: (01784) 471343 E-mail: sales@planned-storage.co.uk

R Elliott & Sons Ltd, 21 Bridge Street, Uttoxeter, Staffordshire, ST14 8AR Tel: (01889) 565241 Fax: (01889) 563203

Staffs Timber Products Ltd, New Park House, Newstead Industrial Trading Estate, Stoke-on-Trent, ST4 8HX Tel: (01782) 641241 Fax: (01782) 642982 E-mail: info@pallets4u.com

Star Pallets, Shawlands Farm, Newchapel Road, Lingfield, Surrey, RH7 6BL Tel: (01342) 833704 Fax: (01342) 833704

Theaker recycling Ltd, Heanor Road, Loscoe, Heanor, Derbyshire, DE75 7JT Tel: (01773) 710071 Fax: (01773) 710077 E-mail: office@theakerrecycling.co.uk

▶ Zenick Group Ltd, 184 Stanley Green Road, Poole, Dorset, BH15 3AH Tel: (01202) 673744 Fax: (01202) 678798 E-mail: jane@zenickgroup.fsnet.co.uk

PALLET RACKING

Aarcweld Scotland Ltd, 7 Rennie Place, East Kilbride, Glasgow, G74 5HD Tel: (01355) 244545 Fax: (01355) 244589 E-mail: sales@aarcweld.co.uk

Action Handling Equipment Ltd, Maltings Industrial Estate, Station Road, Sawbridgeworth, Hertfordshire, CM21 9JY Tel: (01279) 724989 Fax: (01279) 600224 E-mail: sales@actionhandling.co.uk

Advanced Handling & Storage Ltd, Staindrop Road, West Auckland, Bishop Auckland, County Durham, DL14 9JY Tel: (01388) 832287 Fax: (01388) 832297 E-mail: advancedracking@aol.com

Corbett Storage Solutions, Enterprise House, Enterprise Way, Edenbridge, Kent, TN8 6HF Tel: (0800) 3165656 Fax: (01732) 862430 E-mail: customerservice@paulcorbett.co.uk

Cornish Maintenance Co, 4 Bilton Road, Perivale, Greenford, Middlesex, UB6 7FB Tel: (020) 8998 9247 Fax: (020) 8998 9149 E-mail: d.cornish@theshelvingcentre.co.uk

F Eastwood & Sons plc, London Works, Ripple Road, Barking, Essex, IG11 0SY Tel: (020) 8591 7200 Fax: (020) 8591 4193 E-mail: sales@feastwood.co.uk

Flowstore Systems plc, 39 Frogmore Industrial Estate, Clayton Road, Hayes, Middlesex, UB3 1AU Tel: (020) 8581 5555 Fax: (020) 8581 5575 E-mail: sales@flowstore.co.uk

Greenoaks Ltd, Greenoaks House, Siemens Road, Irlam, Manchester, M44 5AH Tel: 0161-775 0956 Fax: 0161-776 1951 E-mail: info@greenoaks.ltd.uk

Hertfordshire Storage Systems Ltd, 6 Winton Road, Ware, Hertfordshire, SG12 7AX Tel: (01920) 467027 Fax: (01920) 462563 E-mail: info@hertfordshirestorage.co.uk

Invicta (Borough Green Sawmills) Ltd, Invicta Business Centre, Beach Hill Way, Gillingham, Kent, ME8 6PT Tel: (01732) 882012 Fax: (01732) 883062 E-mail: enquiries@invictabgs.co.uk

Link 51 Ltd, Link House, Halesfield 6, Telford, Shropshire, TF7 4LN Tel: (0800) 515600 Fax: (01952) 682452 E-mail: enquiries@link51.co.uk

Lintec Systems Ltd, Unit 11 Maguire Industrial Estate, Torrington Avenue, Coventry, CV4 9HN Tel: 0121-442 4434 Fax: 0121-442 4160 E-mail: peter@justhandling.fsnet.co.uk

M H Group, M H House, Madeley Street, Hull, HU3 2AH Tel: (01482) 328896 Fax: (01482) 225867 E-mail: sales@mhindustrial.co.uk

Maxi Storage Systems Ltd, Walkley Mills, Spen Vale Street, Heckmondwike, West Yorkshire, WF16 0PS Tel: (01924) 411706 Fax: (01924) 411711 E-mail: keith@maxistorage.co.uk

Mobilrax International Ltd, Arch Unit 1138 Bath Factory Estate, 41 Norwood Road, London, SE24 9AJ Tel: (020) 8674 0131 Fax: (020) 8678 6270 E-mail: info@mobilrax.com

Monarch Shelving Ltd, Unit 7, Moss Lane Industrial Estate, Heyside, Oldham, OL2 6HR Tel: (01706) 880355 Fax: (0870) 7505477 E-mail: sales@monarchdirect.co.uk

▶ Norfolk Storage Equipment Ltd, 15 Maurice Gaymer Road, Attleborough, Norfolk, NR17 2QZ Tel: (01953) 458800 Fax: (01953) 458819 E-mail: sales@nsel.biz

Pallett Racking Systems Ltd, Fryer Works, Ann Street, Willenhall, West Midlands, WV13 1EN Tel: (01902) 606205 Fax: (01902) 606681 E-mail: pallettrackingsys@aol.com

Randall Storage Systems Ltd, 5 Beaucroft Road, Wimborne, Dorset, BH21 2QW Tel: (01202) 848059 Fax: (01202) 848059

John Riddel & Son Ltd, 1A Dagger Road, Lisburn, County Antrim, BT28 2TJ Tel: (028) 9262 0810 Fax: (028) 9262 0811 E-mail: sales@riddel.co.uk

Rochdale Equipment Centre Ltd, Howard Street, Rochdale, Lancashire, OL12 0LU Tel: (01706) 656092 Fax: (01706) 641825 E-mail: sales@officefurniture-online.co.uk

Ssi Schaefer Ltd, 83-84 Livingstone Road, Walworth Industrial Estate, Andover, Hampshire, SP10 5QZ Tel: (01264) 386600 Fax: (01264) 386611 E-mail: solutions@ssi-schaefer.co.uk

Stockport Racking Co. Ltd, 12 Hammond Avenue, Whitehill Industrial Estate, Stockport, Cheshire, SK4 1PQ Tel: 0161-477 0155 Fax: 0161-477 0159

Storage Equipment Systems, A Bumpers Farm Industrial Estate, Bristol Road, Bumpers Farm, Chippenham, Wiltshire, SN14 6LH Tel: (01249) 445593 Fax: (01249) 658779 E-mail: aashelving@aol.com

Systems Storage, 125 Back Road, Linton, Cambridge, CB1 6UJ Tel: (01223) 892433 Fax: (01223) 893864 E-mail: alfhughes@aol.com

▶ Ultimate Storage Equipment Ltd, Unit 2, Northside Industrial Park, Whitley Bridge, Goole, North Humberside, DN14 0GH Tel: (0800) 0284377 Fax: (0800) 0284388 E-mail: info@useltd.co.uk

West Pennine Storage Equipment Ltd, West Pennine Business Park, Burnley Road, Bacup, Lancashire, OL13 8PJ Tel: (01706) 875500 Fax: (01706) 875600 E-mail: westpenninesd@aol.com

PALLET RECOVERY

Anglo European Pallets, Unit 1 Old Airfield Farm, Moreton Valence, Gloucester, GL2 7NG Tel: (01452) 883305 Fax: (01452) 723082 E-mail: mac@aepallet.demon.co.uk

Avonmouth Pallets Ltd, King Road Avenue, Avonmouth, Bristol, BS11 9HG Tel: 0117-982 9012 Fax: 0117-982 5108 E-mail: sales@avonmouthpallets.co.uk

Bridgwater Pallets Ltd, 13 Parrett Way, Colley Lane Industrial Estate, Bridgwater, Somerset, TA6 5LB Tel: (01278) 444039 Fax: (01278) 446888

E S Harverson & Son Transport Ltd, Unit 3 Abbey Industrial Estate, Mitcham, Surrey, CR4 4NA Tel: (020) 8648 5553 Fax: (020) 8646 7009 E-mail: bharverson@aol.com

Industrial Pallet & Transport Services, Kirkhaw Lane, Knottingley, West Yorkshire, WF11 8RD Tel: (01977) 671886 Fax: (01977) 671995

Palick Ltd, The Mill, Silverdale Road, Newcastle, Staffordshire, ST5 2TA Tel: (01782) 661600 Fax: (01782) 630404 E-mail: sales@palick.co.uk

▶ RPS Ltd, Wilton Centre, Wilton, Redcar, Cleveland, TS10 4RF Tel: 01642 465556 Fax: 01642 465929 E-mail: info@rpsltd.com

PALLET STORAGE

Encase Packers Ltd, Scout Hill Mills, Broad Street, Dewsbury, West Yorkshire, WF13 3SA Tel: (01924) 502030 Fax: (01924) 520062

PALLET STRAPPING SYSTEMS

Cordstrap Ltd, Paddock Road, Skelmersdale, Lancashire, WN8 9PL Tel: (01695) 554700 Fax: (01695) 556644 E-mail: sales@cordstrap.net

PALLET STRETCH/CLING/ SHRINK WRAPPING FILM

▶ Cobden, 4-5 Laundry Street, Salford, M6 6WJ Tel: 0161-745 7744 Fax: 0161-745 9027 E-mail: info@cobdensupplies.co.uk

I G Industries plc, The Flarepath, Elsham Wolds Industrial Estate, Brigg, South Humberside, DN20 0SP Tel: (01652) 688888 Fax: (01652) 688808 E-mail: sales@igindustries.co.uk

July Packaging, Unit 8 Manford Industrial Estate, Manor Road, Erith, Kent, DA8 2AJ Tel: (01322) 342123 Fax: (01322) 334479 E-mail: charlesdavies@zyworld.com

PALLET STRETCH/CLING/ SHRINK WRAPPING FILM, POLYETHYLENE (PE)

I G Industries plc, The Flarepath, Elsham Wolds Industrial Estate, Brigg, South Humberside, DN20 0SP Tel: (01652) 688888 Fax: (01652) 688808 E-mail: sales@igindustries.co.uk

PBL Packaging, 6 Maple Business Park, Walter Street, Birmingham, B7 5ET Tel: 0121-327 7757 Fax: 0121-328 3382

Shrinkfast Ltd, Bridgewater Close, Hawkesworth TRDG Estate, Hawkesworth Trading Estate, Swindon, SN2 1ED Tel: (01793) 612072 Fax: (01793) 534649 E-mail: sales@shrinkfast.co.uk

Total Polyfilm Ltd, Unit 95, Seedlee Road, Walton Summit Industrial Estate, Bamber Bridge, Preston, PR5 8AE Tel: (01772) 322229 Fax: (01772) 314276

PALLET STRETCH/CLING/ SHRINK WRAPPING MACHINES

Campak Ltd, Burkitt Road, Earlstrees Industrial Estate, Corby, Northamptonshire, NN17 4DT Tel: (01536) 261501 Fax: (01536) 443656 E-mail: sales@campak.freeserve.co.uk

Euro Pack, Common Lane North, Beccles, Suffolk, NR34 9BP Tel: (01502) 716540 Fax: (01502) 716814 E-mail: europacksales@gei-int.com

Hampshire Packaging Services Ltd, Unit 3, International House, Spring Hall Road, Burnley, Lancashire, BB11 2LQ Tel: (01282) 434446 Fax: (01282) 484452

S Kempner Ltd, 498 Honeypot Lane, Stanmore, Middlesex, HA7 1JZ Tel: (020) 8952 5262 Fax: (020) 8952 8061 E-mail: sales@kempner.co.uk

Total Polyfilm Ltd, Unit 95, Seedlee Road, Walton Summit Industrial Estate, Bamber Bridge, Preston, PR5 8AE Tel: (01772) 322229 Fax: (01772) 314276

PALLET TRANSPORTATION OR HAULAGE

▶ CRS 24: 7, 6 Whitburn Road, Bathgate, West Lothian, EH48 1HH Tel: (0870) 7665 206 Fax: (01506) 637562 E-mail: gary@crs247.com

▶ G & T Transport, Unit 6 Llwyn Y Graig, Gorseinon, Swansea, SA4 9WG Tel: (01792) 899499 Fax: (01792) 899898 E-mail: info@gandttransport.co.uk

▶ TK Direct (Light Haulage) Coventry, 20 Springfield Crescent, Bedworth, Warwickshire, CV12 8NX Tel: (07970) 151944 Fax: (024) 7673 1422 E-mail: info@tkdirect.co.uk

TKA Distribution Ltd, 11 Church Meadows, Bocking, Braintree, Essex, CM7 5SL Tel: (01376) 340170 Fax: (01376) 349163 E-mail: trevor@tkadistribution.co.uk

▶ W H Barley Transport & Storage Ltd, Old Wolverton Road, Old Wolverton, Milton Keynes, MK12 5NL Tel: (01908) 227222 Fax: (01908) 227370 E-mail: sales@whbarley.co.uk

PALLET TRUCK COMPONENTS

Eaton Clutch Transmission, Norfolk Street, Worsley Estate North, Worsley, Manchester, M28 3GJ Tel: (01204) 797077 Fax: (01204) 797090

PALLET TRUCK MAINTENANCE OR REPAIR

Essex Pallet Truck Services, 16 Fennel Close, Tiptree, Colchester, CO5 0TF Tel: (07949) 091271 Fax: (01621) 810867 E-mail: essexpallettrucks.services@virgin.net

Pallet Truck Services, 11 Moorfield Road, Irlam, Manchester, M44 6JT Tel: 0161-775 1716 Fax: 0161-775 1716

PALLET TRUCKS

Essex Pallet Truck Services, 16 Fennel Close, Tiptree, Colchester, CO5 0TF Tel: (07949) 091271 Fax: (01621) 810867 E-mail: essexpallettrucks.services@virgin.net

G P C Industries Ltd, Market St, Spilsby, Lincolnshire, PE23 5JT Tel: (01790) 753835 Fax: (01790) 752109 E-mail: sales@gpcind.co.uk

Manual Handling Solutions, 58, Paige Close, The Meadows, Watlington, King's Lynn, Norfolk, PE33 0TQ Tel: (01553) 811977 Fax: (01553) 811004 E-mail: sales@manualhandlingsolutions.co.uk

Mobile Pallet Truck Services, The Watermill, Barton Mill Lane, Faldo Road, Barton-le-Clay, Bedford, MK45 4RF Tel: (01582) 769971 Fax: (01582) 763665

Oakway Mechanical Equipment, 42 Oliver Street, Northampton, NN2 7JJ Tel: (01604) 792255

Polymathic Trucks Ltd, Coolie House, Unit 2 Anders, Lichfield Road Industrial Estate, Tamworth, Staffordshire, B79 7TA Tel: (01827) 63441 Fax: (01827) 310765 E-mail: sales@coolie.co.uk

PALLET TRUCKS, HYDRAULIC

Aaa Fabrication, 1 Pottery Demolition SD, Burnham Street, Stoke-on-Trent, ST4 3EZ Tel: (01782) 332493 Fax: (01782) 327091 E-mail: aaafabricationukltd@hotmail.co.uk

Equip4work Ltd, 1st Floor, 1 St. Michael Street, Dumfries, DG1 2QD Tel: (0844) 4999222 Fax: (0844) 4999322 E-mail: sales@equip4work.co.uk

Howard Pallet Truck Services, 4 Bridgwater Court, Oldmixon CR, Weston-super-Mare, Avon, BS24 9AY Tel: (01934) 621777 Fax: (01934) 621888 E-mail: sales@howardhandling.co.uk

PALLET TRUCKS, USED

Howard Pallet Truck Services, 4 Bridgwater Court, Oldmixon CR, Weston-super-Mare, Avon, BS24 9AY Tel: (01934) 621777 Fax: (01934) 621888 E-mail: sales@howardhandling.co.uk

▶ WarehouseEquipment.co.uk, 58 Gleneagles Ave, Leicester, LE4 7GB Tel: 0116-266 4478 Fax: 0116-266 4478 E-mail: sales@warehouseequipment.co.uk

PALLET/STILLAGE MAINTENANCE/REPAIR SERVICES

G B Fabrication & Welding Services, Bunkers Hill, Bunkers Hill, Kidlington, Oxfordshire, OX5 3EL Tel: (07770) 761599 Fax: (01869) 331759 E-mail: julian.gbfabf@virgin.net

PALLET/STILLAGE MAINTENANCE/ REPAIR SERVICES – *continued*

Symonds Trolley Services Ltd, Wern Trading Estate, Rogerstone, Newport, Gwent, NP10 9XX Tel: (01633) 892362 Fax: (01633) 896618 E-mail: symonds@symondshydroclean.co.uk

Wheatley Pallet Services Ltd, Sandall Stones Road, Kirk Sandall, Doncaster, South Yorkshire, DN3 1QR Tel: (01302) 885683 Fax: (01302) 884218 E-mail: wpspallet@aol.com

PALLET/STILLAGES, RECONDITIONED

A.M Pallet Services Ltd, Goods Yard, Bryanstone Road, Waltham Cross, Hertfordshire, EN8 7PJ Tel: (01992) 652700 Fax: (01992) 651185 E-mail: sales@prpallets.com

Ady, Antrim Road, Warrington, WA2 8JT Tel: (01925) 419933 Fax: (01925) 419944 E-mail: sales@bulkbags.co.uk

Avonmouth Pallets Ltd, King Road Avenue, Avonmouth, Bristol, BS11 9HG Tel: 0117-982 9012 Fax: 0117-982 5108 E-mail: sales@avonmouthpallets.co.uk

Bridgwater Pallets Ltd, 13 Parrett Way, Colley Lane Industrial Estate, Bridgwater, Somerset, TA6 5LB Tel: (01278) 444039 Fax: (01278) 446888

Central Pallet Company Ltd, 36-51 Lower Dartmouth Street, Bordesley, Birmingham, B9 4LG Tel: 0121-772 5620 Fax: 0121-766 5778

E S Harverson & Son Transport Ltd, Unit 3 Abbey Industrial Estate, Mitcham, Surrey, CR4 4NA Tel: (020) 8648 5553 Fax: (020) 8646 7009 E-mail: bharverson@aol.com

Industrial Pallet & Transport Services, Kirkhaw Lane, Knottingley, West Yorkshire, WF11 8RD Tel: (01977) 671886 Fax: (01977) 671995

Larner Pallets Recycling Ltd, Jute Lane, Brimsdown, Enfield, Middlesex, EN3 7PJ Tel: (020) 8804 1494 Fax: (020) 8804 1164 E-mail: admin@larnerpallets.com

M&M, Unit 4-5 Phoenix Centre, Road One, Winsford Industrial Estate, Winsford, Cheshire, CW7 3PZ Tel: (01606) 861869 Fax: (01606) 861497

Oldfield Solutions Ltd, Oldfield House, Damery Lane, Woodford, Berkeley, Gloucestershire, GL13 9JR Tel: (01454) 261122 Fax: (01454) 261253

P H Pallet Services, Broadway, Globe Lane Industrial Estate, Dukinfield, Cheshire, SK16 4UJ Tel: 0161-351 1333 Fax: 0161-366 9322 E-mail: sales@phpallets.com

P R Pallet Services, Macdermott Road, Widnes, Cheshire, WA8 0PF Tel: 0151-495 1422 Fax: 0151-495 1123

P & R Pallets & Cases, 2 Bridge Industrial Estate, Hot Lane, Stoke-on-Trent, ST6 2DL Tel: (01782) 822555 Fax: (01782) 822555

Palick Ltd, The Mill, Silverdale Road, Newcastle, Staffordshire, ST5 2TA Tel: (01782) 661600 Fax: (01782) 630404 E-mail: sales@palick.co.uk

Palick (Wolverhampton) Ltd, Hilton Main Industrial Estate, Bognop Road, Essinton, Wolverhampton, WV11 2BE Tel: (01902) 727691 E-mail: sales@palick.co.uk

Pine Products Ltd, 1 Hope Carr Way, Leigh, Lancashire, WN7 3DE Tel: (01942) 604999 Fax: (01942) 260734 E-mail: info@pine-products.net

Rapid Packaging Supplies Ltd, 26 Bayton Road, Exhall, Coventry, CV7 9EJ Tel: (024) 7636 0800 Fax: (024) 7664 4322 E-mail: sales@rapidpackaging.co.uk

Stanlow Pallets Ltd, Indigo Road, Ellesmere Port, CH65 4AJ Tel: 0151-356 3932 Fax: 0151-357 2667

Star Pallets, Shawlands Farm, Newchapel Road, Lingfield, Surrey, RH7 6BL Tel: (01342) 833704 Fax: (01342) 833704

Theaker recycling Ltd, Heanor Road, Loscoe, Heanor, Derbyshire, DE75 7JT Tel: (01773) 710071 Fax: (01773) 710077 E-mail: office@theakerrecycling.co.uk

W P S Logistics Ltd, The Old Power Ho, Rhossdu Industrial Estate, Wrexham, Clwyd, LL11 4YL Tel: (01978) 261043 Fax: (01978) 312695

R.W. Whittaker (Pallets) Ltd, Booth Street, Middleton Junction, Manchester, M24 1SF Tel: 0161-643 1718 Fax: 0161-643 0556 E-mail: robwhit@palcase.fastnet.co.uk

Wrexham Pallet Services, Rhosddu Industrial Estate, Main Road, Rhosrobin, Wrexham, Clwyd, LL11 4YL Tel: (01978) 261043 Fax: (01978) 312695

PALLET/STILLAGES, RECYCLED WOOD

▶ Worldcare Wales Ltd, Ffordd Maelgwyn, Tremarl Industrial Estate, Llandudno Junction, Gwynedd, LL31 9PL Tel: (01492) 593080 E-mail: john@worldcarewaste.fsnet.co.uk

PALLET/STILLAGES, ROLLING TYPE

M & J Enterprises, Cuckoo Lane, Winterbourne Down, Bristol, BS36 1AG Tel: 0117-957 2440 Fax: (01454) 318710

PALLETISED GOODS ROAD TRANSPORT AND HAULAGE

▶ Crowfoot Carriers Ltd, Gosforth Rd, Ascot Drive, Derby, DE24 8HU Tel: (01332) 372621 Fax: (01332) 346171

▶ Crowfoots Carriers (Manchester) Ltd, Park Street, Stalybridge, Cheshire, SK15 2BT Tel: 0161-303 7133 Fax: 0161-304 8226

▶ T & A Logistics Newcastle Ltd, 8 Holystone Grange, Stonelea, Holystone, Newcastle upon Tyne, NE27 0UX Tel: (07968) 725110 Fax: 0191-215 1300 E-mail: sales@talogistics.co.uk

PALLETISERS OR DEPALLETISERS

Chronos Richardson Ltd, Unit 1 Centurion Business Centre, Dabell Avenue, Nottingham, NG6 8WN Tel: 0115-935 1351 Fax: 0115-935 1353 E-mail: info@chronos-richardson.com

Iain Glass, Wrangham, Philips Lane, Darrington, Pontefract, West Yorkshire, WF8 3BH Tel: (01977) 795497 Fax: (01977) 790777 E-mail: iainglass@btclick.com

M J Maillis UK Ltd, Monarch House, Chrysalis Way, Eastwood, Nottingham, NG16 3RY Tel: (01773) 539000 Fax: (01773) 539090 E-mail: info@mallis.co.uk

Shrinkwrap Machinery Co. Ltd, 145 Sterte Road, Poole, Dorset, BH15 2AF Tel: (01202) 674944 Fax: (01202) 671891 E-mail: sales@shrinkwrap.co.uk

W J Morray Engineering Ltd, Anglia Way, Braintree, Essex, CM7 3RG Tel: (01376) 322722 Fax: (01376) 323277 E-mail: sales@morray.com

PALLETS OR ROLL PALLETS

KDM International plc, The Havens, Ransomes Europark, Ipswich, IP3 9SJ Tel: (01473) 276900 Fax: (01473) 276911 E-mail: sales@kdm.co.uk

Simons Reeve Holdings Ltd, Private Road No 2, Colwick Industrial Estate, Nottingham, NG4 2JR Tel: 0115-987 0970 Fax: 0115-961 1737 E-mail: mail@simons-reeve.co.uk

PAN HEAD MACHINE SCREWS

Anglian Fasteners Ltd, 16 Millbrook Close, Northampton, NN5 5JF Tel: (01604) 758585 Fax: (01604) 758565 E-mail: anglianf@micromat.net

Arkwell Fasteners Ltd, Unit 1, Chapel Street, Long Eaton, Nottingham, NG10 1EQ Tel: 0115-973 1181 Fax: 0115-946 1123 E-mail: sales@arkwell.co.uk

PANAMA HATS

▶ Talulah & Fox, 27 Barnham Road, Barnham, Bognor Regis, West Sussex, PO22 0ER Tel: (01243) 551733 E-mail: info@talulahandfox.co.uk

▶ The Whiteley H A T Co. Ltd, Unitb 1, Bramingham Business Park, Enterprise Way, Luton, LU3 4BU Tel: (01582) 493393 Fax: (01582) 491838 E-mail: sales@whiteley-hat.co.uk

PANEL ADHESIVES

Adhesive & Coating Supplies, Sherborne St West, Salford, M3 7LF Tel: 0161-835 1420 Fax: 0161-839 3543 E-mail: sales@chemipat.co.uk

PANEL HEAT EXCHANGERS

Cov Rad Heat Transfer, Canley Works, Sir Henry Parkes Road, Coventry, CV5 6BN Tel: (024) 7671 3316 Fax: (024) 7671 3316 E-mail: glen.hurst@covrad.co.uk

Omega Thermo Engineering Ltd, Unit 30, Globe Industrial Estate, Rectory Road, Grays, Essex, RM17 6ST Tel: (01375) 898400 Fax: (01375) 898420

▶ Tranter Ltd, Unit 50, Monckton Road Industrial Estate, Wakefield, West Yorkshire, WF2 7AL Tel: (01924) 298393 Fax: (01924) 291596 E-mail: sales@tranterphe.com

PANEL INDICATORS

BEKA Associates Ltd, Old Charlton Road, Hitchin, Hertfordshire, SG5 2DA Tel: (01462) 438301 Fax: (01462) 453971 E-mail: sales@beka.co.uk

Panel Technology Ltd, Whittle Road, Hinckley, Leicestershire, LE10 3DW Tel: (01455) 631622 Fax: (01455) 615693 E-mail: enquiries@certec.co.uk

PANEL MOUNTED LED INDICATORS

C M L Innovative Technologies Ltd, Beetons Way, Bury St. Edmunds, Suffolk, IP32 6RA Tel: (01284) 762411 Fax: (01284) 754406 E-mail: sales@cml-it.com

Marl International Ltd, Morcambe Road, Ulverston, Cumbria, LA12 7RY Tel: (01229) 582430 Fax: (01229) 585155 E-mail: sales@marl.co.uk

P R P Optoelectronics Ltd, Woodburcote Way, Towcester, Northamptonshire, NN12 6TF Tel: (01327) 359135 Fax: (01327) 359602 E-mail: sales@prpopto.co.uk

PANEL MOUNTING CONNECTORS

Multi-Contact (UK) Ltd, 3 Presley Way, Crownhill, Milton Keynes, MK8 0ES Tel: (01908) 265544 Fax: (01908) 262080 E-mail: uk@multi-contact.com

Wieland Electric Ltd, 1 The Riverside Business Centre, Walnut Tree Close, Guildford, Surrey, GU1 4UG Tel: (01483) 531213 Fax: (01483) 505029 E-mail: info@wieland.co.uk

PANEL SIZING MACHINES

Avontech Machines, Park Yard, Old Down, Tockington, Bristol, BS32 4PB Tel: (0845) 070 4343 Fax: (0845) 070 4346 E-mail: avontech@blueyonder.co.uk

PANEL SWITCHBOARDS

M C R Electrical Services, 2 Factory Estate, English Street, Hull, HU3 2BE Tel: (01482) 589062 Fax: (01482) 589525 E-mail: mcr@unit2.fslife.co.uk

PANELS, COLD ROOM

▶ Coldhold Systems Ltd, Albright Road, Widnes, Cheshire, WA8 8FY Tel: 0151-423 0023 Fax: 0151-423 0043 E-mail: info@coldhold.com

▶ Isotek, Unit 3, Bode Business Park, Ball Haye Green, Leek, Staffordshire, ST13 6BW Tel: (01538) 384008 Fax: (01538) 384016 E-mail: info@cooltrailers.co.uk

Storer Refrigeration & Catering Manufacturers Ltd, Newstead Industrial Estate, Brookfield Road, Arnold, Nottingham, NG5 7ER Tel: 0115-920 0329 Fax: 0115-967 0676 E-mail: tedblake@supanet.com

PANELS, TO SPECIFICATION/ CUSTOM BUILT

Ex Pressed Steel Panels Ltd, Ickornshaw Mill, Ickornshaw, Cowling, Keighley, West Yorkshire, BD22 0DB Tel: (01535) 632721 Fax: (01535) 636977 E-mail: sales@steelpanels.co.uk

PANORAMIC PHOTOGRAPHY

▶ Digital Imaging Services & Photography, 8 Odense Court, East Kilbride, G75 0SA Tel: 07855 669213 E-mail: alex_disp@yahoo.co.uk

Image Aviation, 12A Court Park, Thurlestone, Kingsbridge, Devon, TQ7 3LX Tel: (01548) 562324 E-mail: fotos967@hotmail.com

▶ Lightbox Photography, 19 Lynton Drive, Southport, Merseyside, PR8 4QP Tel: (01704) 566066 E-mail: sales@the-lightbox.com

▶ Warren Photographic, Warren House, Albury Heath, Guildford, Surrey, GU5 9DB Tel: (01483) 203354 E-mail: us@warrenphoto.freeserve.co.uk

PAPER AGENTS

Arctic Paper UK Ltd, Quadrant House, 47 Croydon Road, Caterham, Surrey, CR3 6PB Tel: (01883) 331800 Fax: (01883) 330560 E-mail: info-uk@arcticpaper.com

Aylesford Paper Sales, Consolidated Paper House, Forstal Road, Aylesford, Kent, ME20 7AE Tel: (01622) 716353 Fax: (01622) 716663 E-mail: sales@aylesfordpaper.co.uk

City Paper Ltd, Xerox House, Maylands Avenue, Hemel Hempstead, Hertfordshire, HP2 7DE Tel: (0870) 2410472 Fax: (0870) 2410473 E-mail: sales@citypaper.com

Contract Paper Ltd, Sovereign House, Rhosili Road, Brackmills, Northampton, NN4 7JE Tel: (0870) 6082374 Fax: (0870) 6082375 E-mail: marketing@hspg.com

H H Pegg Ltd, Elsinore House, 77 Fulham Palace Road, London, W6 8JA Tel: (020) 8237 6000 Fax: (020) 8237 6049

John Heyer Paper Ltd, Langwood House, 63-81 High Street, Rickmansworth, Hertfordshire, WD3 1EQ Tel: (0870) 2423355 Fax: (0870) 2421114 E-mail: sales@johnheyerpaper.co.uk

▶ Jensen Barker Technical Services Ltd, Fowlswick Industrial Estate, Fowlswick Lane, Allington, Chippenham, Wiltshire, SN14 6QE Tel: (01249) 783844 Fax: (01249) 783306 E-mail: info@jensen-barker.com

M-Real (U K) Ltd, Kings Chase, 107 King St, Maidenhead, Berkshire, SL6 1DP Tel: (01628) 411611 Fax: (01628) 411666

P Gray Ltd, PO Box 299, Croydon, CR9 6EQ Tel: (020) 8681 6637 Fax: (020) 8681 6630 E-mail: pgraylimited@aol.com

Palm Paper Ltd, The Former Courthouse, County Court Road, King's Lynn, Norfolk, PE30 5EJ Tel: (01553) 818570 Fax: (01553) 692397 E-mail: derek.harman@palmpaper.co.uk

Storaenso, Enso House, New Mill Road, Orpington, Kent, BR5 3TW Tel: (01689) 892700 Fax: (01689) 897290

Storaenso UK Ltd, 1 Phoenix Place, Nottingham, NG8 6BA Tel: 0115-964 7100 Fax: 0115-964 7170

Talk Paper Ltd, 1 Canada Road, Byfleet, West Byfleet, Surrey, KT14 7JL Tel: (01932) 335577 Fax: (01932) 335580

Torras Paper Ltd, Creator House, Maidstone Road, Kingston, Milton Keynes, MK10 0BD Tel: (01908) 288000 Fax: (01908) 288001 E-mail: info@torraspapel.es

U P M Kymmene Ltd, 2 Victoria Street, Altrincham, Cheshire, WA14 1ET Tel: (0870) 6000876 Fax: (0870) 6060876

Victor Tandberg & Co. Ltd, Bridge House, Restmor Way, Wallington, Surrey, SM6 7AH Tel: (020) 8773 1431 Fax: (020) 8715 1119 E-mail: sales@victortandberg.co.uk

PAPER BACKED ALUMINIUM FOIL

S.F. Williams & Co. Ltd, Essex Works, Kenway, Southend-On-Sea, SS2 5DX Tel: (01702) 445851 E-mail: sales@sfw.co.uk

PAPER BAG MANUFRS

Border Converters, Second Avenue, Deeside Industrial Park, Deeside, Clwyd, CH5 2NX Tel: (01244) 289988 Fax: (01244) 289300 E-mail: admin@borderconverters.co.uk

A.P. Burt & Sons Ltd, Severn Paper Mill, Harbour Road, Portishead, Bristol, BS20 7DJ Tel: (01275) 842454 Fax: (01275) 849613 E-mail: tdavies@apburt.co.uk

Chichester Paper Bag Co., 5 St. James Industrial Estate, Westhampnett Road, Chichester, West Sussex, PO19 7JU Tel: (01243) 773742 Fax: (01243) 538898 E-mail: martin@chipack.co.uk

Coogan & Watts Ltd, Central Park, Newtownabbey, County Antrim, BT36 4FS Tel: (028) 9084 5800 Fax: (028) 9034 2739 E-mail: info@cooganwatts.co.uk

Dempson Packaging, Hermitage Mills, Hermitage Lane, Maidstone, Kent, ME16 9NP Tel: (01622) 727027 Fax: (01622) 720768 E-mail: sales@dempson.co.uk

Euro Packaging plc, Unit 14 Elderpark Workspace, 100 Elderpark Street, Glasgow, G51 3TR Tel: 0141-445 3003 Fax: 0141-445 5111 E-mail: info@europackaging.co.uk

Fleetbest UK, Northgate, White Lund Trading Estate, Morecambe, Lancs, LA3 3AY Tel: (01524) 61818 Fax: (01524) 67014

Gardners, 149 Commercial Street, London, E1 6BJ Tel: (020) 7247 5119

Medina Packaging, 123 Station Road, Kings Heath, Birmingham, B14 7TA Tel: 0121-444 1425 Fax: 0121-624 3956 E-mail: medinapackaging@blueyonder.co.uk

William Montgomery & Sons, 79 Ladas Drive, Belfast, BT6 9FR Tel: (028) 9040 1593 Fax: (028) 9040 1593

Plymouth Agencies Ltd, Oakfield Press, Elliott Road, Plymouth, PL4 0SG Tel: (01752) 262323 Fax: (01752) 228764 E-mail: sales@plymouthagencies.co.uk

Poly Print, 59 High St, London, E17 7AD Tel: (020) 8521 4408 Fax: (020) 8521 4568 E-mail: polyprint@carrierbag.freeserve.co.uk

Rainbow Bag UK Ltd, 3A Bess Park Road, Trenant Industrial Estate, Wadebridge, Cornwall, PL27 6HB Tel: (01208) 812442 Fax: (01208) 816181 E-mail: sales@rainbowbags.co.uk

C.S. Robertson (Packaging) Ltd, 4 Young Place, Kelvin Industrial Estate, East Kilbride, Glasgow, G75 0TD Tel: (01355) 244656 Fax: (01355) 265163 E-mail: csrobertsonpkg@btinternet.com

Sapphire Packaging, 28 Eldon Way, Hockley, Essex, SS5 4AD Tel: (01702) 205999 Fax: (01702) 562107 E-mail: sales@sapphirepackaging.com

PAPER BAG MANUFRS – *continued*

South Wales Sack & Bag, 4 Rhymney River Bridge Road, Cardiff, CF23 9AF Tel: (029) 2049 5060 Fax: (029) 2049 5055 E-mail: andrew_manuel@amserve.net
Southend Paper Bag Co., 90 Archer Avenue, Southend-on-Sea, SS2 4QT Tel: (01702) 463830
Springpack, New Road, Pershore, Worcestershire, WR10 1BY Tel: (01386) 552550 Fax: (0870) 7747402
Stonehouse Paper & Bag Mills Ltd, Lower Mills, Stonehouse, Gloucestershire, GL10 2BD Tel: (01453) 822173 Fax: (01453) 822174 E-mail: stonehousepaper@aol.com
Tidmas Townsend Ltd, 208-210 Seaside, Eastbourne, East Sussex, BN22 7QS Tel: (01323) 734240 Fax: (01323) 416894
Travelstock Packaging Ltd, 20 & 21 The Arches, South College St, Aberdeen, AB11 6JX Tel: (01224) 582657 Fax: (01224) 584303 E-mail: sales@travelstockpackaging.co.uk
Unita Packaging Ltd, Unit 15 Bloomsgrove Industrial Estate, Ilkeston Rd, Nottingham, NG7 3JG Tel: 0115-978 6172 Fax: 0115-978 6776 E-mail: sales@unita.co.uk
Paul White Ltd, 69 Upper Accomodation Road, Leeds, LS9 8LS Tel: 0113-248 9898 Fax: 0113-248 4863 E-mail: leeds@paulwhiteltd.co.uk
Wyatt & Ackerman Ltd, 30 North Street, Bedminster, Bristol, BS3 1HW Tel: 0117-966 1675 Fax: 0117-966 1775 E-mail: sales@wyattandackerman.co.uk

PAPER BAGS, PRINTED/ ADVERTISING/PROMOTIONAL

Chichester Paper Bag Co., 5 St. James Industrial Estate, Westhampnett Road, Chichester, West Sussex, PO19 7JU Tel: (01243) 773742 Fax: (01243) 538898 E-mail: martin@chipack.co.uk
Markapac, 37-41 Finchley Park, London, N12 9JY Tel: (0800) 2300301 Fax: (0800) 2300302 E-mail: info@detsafe.co.uk

PAPER BALERS

Bollegraaf UK Ltd, 93-96 William Street, West Bromwich, West Midlands, B70 0BG Tel: 0121-557 9700 Fax: 0121-557 9800 E-mail: info@bollegraaf.co.uk
Lyndex Recycling Systems Ltd, Stafford Park 10, Telford, Shropshire, TF3 3BP Tel: (01952) 290333 Fax: (01952) 290229 E-mail: info@lindexrecycling.com
▶ Middleton Engineering Ltd, Ashcott Road, Meare, Glastonbury, Somerset, BA6 9SU Tel: (01458) 860264 Fax: (01458) 860311 E-mail: middletonadmin@btconnect.com

PAPER CARRIER BAGS

Airborne Packaging Ltd, Pegasus House, Beatrice Road, Leicester, LE3 9FH Tel: 0116-253 6136 Fax: 0116-251 4485 E-mail: sales@airbornebags.co.uk
Alphawrap Printers, 13 Miners Road, Llay Industrial Estate, Llay, Wrexham, Clwyd, LL12 0PJ Tel: (01978) 856109 Fax: (01978) 852077 E-mail: admin@alphawrap.co.uk
Chichester Paper Bag Co., 5 St. James Industrial Estate, Westhampnett Road, Chichester, West Sussex, PO19 7JU Tel: (01243) 773742 Fax: (01243) 538898 E-mail: martin@chipack.co.uk
Creation Carriers, Vista Business Centre, 50 Salisbury Road, Hounslow, TW4 6JQ Tel: (020) 8538 0204 Fax: (020) 8538 0207 E-mail: creationcarriers@btconnect.com
Dempson Packaging, Hermitage Mills, Hermitage Lane, Maidstone, Kent, ME16 9NP Tel: (01622) 727027 Fax: (01622) 720768 E-mail: sales@dempson.co.uk
Jason Plastics Ltd, Prettywood, Bury New Road, Heap Bridge, Bury, Lancashire, BL9 7HZ Tel: 0161-763 8000 Fax: 0161-763 8052 E-mail: sales@jasonpackaging.co.uk
Kyme Packaging Ltd, The Dairy, 2, Culverthorpe, Grantham, Lincolnshire, NG32 3NQ Tel: (01529) 455777 Fax: (01529) 455787 E-mail: kyme.packaging@virgin.net
Progressive Supplies Paper Ltd, 18 Crawford Place, London, W1H 5AY Tel: (020) 7563 7330 Fax: (020) 7706 3058 E-mail: sales@progressivesupplies.com
Sapphire Packaging, 28 Eldon Way, Hockley, Essex, SS5 4AD Tel: (01702) 205999 Fax: (01702) 562107 E-mail: sales@sapphirepackaging.com
Thomas Norman, Unit 1 Moreton Industrial Estate, London Road, Swanley, Kent, BR8 8DE Tel: (01322) 611600 Fax: (01322) 611609 E-mail: info@thomasnorman.co.uk

PAPER CHEMICALS

Bin UK Ltd, Prince Street, Bolton, BL1 2NP Tel: (01204) 366997 Fax: (01204) 366998 E-mail: uk_sales@binkemi.com
Buckman Laboratories Ltd, Millbank House, Bollin Walk, Wilmslow, Cheshire, SK9 1BJ Tel: (01625) 524875 Fax: (01625) 525988
Euram Chemicals Ltd, PO Box 346, Marlow, Buckinghamshire, SL7 1WH Tel: (01628) 472848 Fax: (01628) 890095 E-mail: sales@euramchemicals.co.uk
Feralco (UK) Ltd, Ditton Road, Widnes, Cheshire, WA8 0PH Tel: 0151-802 2940 Fax: 0151-802 2999 E-mail: info@feralco.com
G E Water & Process Technologies Ltd, Foundry Lane, Widnes, Cheshire, WA8 8UD Tel: 0151-424 5351 Fax: 0151-423 2722
Stephenson Group Ltd, PO Box 305, Bradford, West Yorkshire, BD7 1HY Tel: (01274) 723811 Fax: (01274) 370108 E-mail: src@stephensongroup.co.uk

PAPER CLOSURES

Zip Pack Packaging Technology, Unit 17, Shaw Wood Business Park, Doncaster, South Yorkshire, DN2 5TB Tel: (01302) 344119 Fax: (01302) 321703 E-mail: enquiries@zippack.co.uk

PAPER COATING EQUIPMENT

Dixon, Unit C, 3 Fen End, Astwick Road, Stotfold, Hitchin, Hertfordshire, SG5 4BA Tel: (01462) 834911 Fax: (01462) 834911 E-mail: sales@dixontechnologies.com
Longfield Coating & Engineering Products Ltd, 21 Humes Avenue, London, W7 2LJ Tel: (020) 8567 1852 Fax: (020) 8579 3399 E-mail: ans@longfield-coating.com

PAPER COATINGS

Smith & McLaurin Ltd, Cartside Mill, Kilbarchan, Renfrewshire, PA10 2AF Tel: (01505) 707700 Fax: (01505) 704992 E-mail: info@smcl.co.uk
Venex Technical Developments Ltd, Unit 3, Mount Pleasant Farm, Moorend Road, Yardley Gobion, Towcester, Northamptonshire, NN12 7UF Tel: (01908) 543158 Fax: (01908) 543052 E-mail: chris@venex.biz

PAPER COLLATING, *See Collating etc*

PAPER CONSULTANTS/ ADVISORY SERVICES

Firn Overseas Packaging Ltd, Firn House, 61 Church Street, Hungerford, Berkshire, RG17 0JH Tel: (01488) 683193 Fax: (01488) 684701 E-mail: sales@firn.org
Poyry Forest Industry Consulting Ltd, 2 Station Way, Sutton, Surrey, SM3 8SW Tel: (020) 8770 2144 Fax: (020) 8770 2115
Premier Paper Ltd, Premier House, Faringdon Avenue, Harold Hill, Romford, RM3 8SP Tel: (01708) 330330 Fax: (01708) 330325

PAPER CONVERTERS

A R Paper Convertors Ltd, 20 River Road, Barking, Essex, IG11 0DG Tel: (020) 8591 7868 Fax: (020) 8591 7083 E-mail: sales@arpaper.co.uk
Accrol Papers Ltd, Roman Road Indust Estate, Blackburn, BB1 2LU Tel: (01254) 278844 Fax: (01254) 278855 E-mail: info@accrol.co.uk
Arteb Printing Ltd, Unit 13 Lyon Industrial Estate, Brindley Road, Reginald Road Industrial Estate, St. Helens, Merseyside, WA9 4HY Tel: (01744) 820933 Fax: (01744) 815154 E-mail: info@arteb.co.uk
▶ B K H Paper Converters Ltd, Unit 1, Eurolink Industrial Estate, Sittingbourne, Kent, ME10 3RN Tel: (01795) 479534
Bondlabels Ltd, Wollaston Way, Burnt Mills Industrial Area, Basildon, Essex, SS13 1DJ Tel: (01268) 590555 Fax: (01268) 590999 E-mail: sales@bondlabels.co.uk
Border Converters, Second Avenue, Deeside Industrial Park, Deeside, Clwyd, CH5 2NX Tel: (01244) 289988 Fax: (01244) 289300 E-mail: admin@borderconverters.co.uk
Canarycliff Co. Ltd, Maple Works, Old Shoreham Road, Hove, East Sussex, BN3 7ED Tel: (01273) 726325 Fax: (01273) 203070 E-mail: sales@ticketmedia.com
▶ Cobden, 4-5 Laundry Street, Salford, M6 6WJ Tel: 0161-745 7744 Fax: 0161-745 9027 E-mail: info@cobdensupplies.co.uk
Corpak Film Converters, Unit 19 Dinting Lane Industrial Estate, Glossop, Derbyshire, SK13 7NU Tel: (01457) 860758 Fax: (01457) 856008
Crimped Paper Works(M/C) Ltd, Bowden Park, Chapel-En-Le-Frith, High Peak, Derbyshire, SK23 0JX Tel: (01298) 812181 Fax: (01298) 815905 E-mail: sales@crimpedpaper.co.uk
D S Smith, Windsor Road, Louth, Lincolnshire, LN11 0YG Tel: (01507) 609393 Fax: (01507) 600478
Dane Paper Products Ltd, Rushenden Road, Queenborough, Kent, ME11 5HL Tel: (01795) 669933 Fax: (01795) 669909 E-mail: suenightingale@dane-paper.co.uk
Disposable Supplies, Movement House Soho Mills, London Road, Wallington, Surrey, SM6 7HN Tel: (020) 8773 2692 Fax: (020) 8669 1907 E-mail: sales@disposablesupplies.co.uk
Doric Anderton, Fifth Avenue, Trafford Park, Trafford Park, Manchester, M17 1TN Tel: 0161-848 0156 Fax: 0161-872 1652 E-mail: info@doricanderton.com
Fairfield Graphics Ltd, 34 Station Road, Liphook, Hampshire, GU30 7DS Tel: (01428) 726500 Fax: (01428) 725008 E-mail: fairfield@inkjetsupplies.com
G W Chadwick Ltd, Unit 40 Chorley North Industrial Park, Chorley, Lancashire, PR6 7BX Tel: (01257) 234242 Fax: (01257) 234213 E-mail: email@gwchadwick.co.uk
Gould Design & Manufacture Ltd, Sefton Street, Heywood, Lancashire, OL10 2JF Tel: (01706) 898000 Fax: (01706) 364426 E-mail: sales@goulds-ltd.com
Harver Packaging Co. Ltd, 479 Chester Road, Manchester, M16 9HF Tel: 0161-786 3900 Fax: 0161-848 8656 E-mail: sales@harverpac.co.uk
K P P Converters Ltd, Site 72, Units 1-4, Manners Industrial Estate, Ilkeston, Derbyshire, DE7 8EF Tel: 0115-930 5777 Fax: 0115-932 9184 E-mail: enquiries@kpptissue.co.uk
Kruger Tissue Industrial Division, Penygroes Industrial Estate, Penygroes, Caernarfon, Gwynedd, LL54 6DB Tel: (01286) 880969 Fax: (01286) 880026 E-mail: customer.service@kruger.co.uk
L & S Middleton Paper Co., Eagle Works, Somerford Place, Willenhall, West Midlands, WV13 3EA Tel: (01902) 635551 Fax: (01902) 636728 E-mail: middletonpaper@compuserve.com
Limehouse Boardmills Ltd, 26 Crittall Road, Witham, Essex, CM8 3DR Tel: (01376) 519519 Fax: (01376) 514520 E-mail: sales@limehouse-board.co.uk
Listan Paper Converters Ltd, Old Wharf Industrial Estate, Old Wharf Road, Grantham, Lincolnshire, NG31 7AA Tel: (01476) 570052 Fax: (01476) 565542 E-mail: sales@listan.freeserve.co.uk
Lynvale Ltd, Unit 6, Lime Grove Estate, Falconer Road, Haverhill, Suffolk, CB9 7XU Tel: (0870) 1609255 Fax: (0870) 1609256 E-mail: info@lynvale.co.uk
M6 Paper Group Ltd, Motorway House, Charter Way, Macclesfield, Cheshire, SK10 2NY Tel: (01625) 610044 Fax: (01625) 511144 E-mail: info@m6papers.co.uk
Pak Wraps Ltd, Unit 16 Sefton Lane Industrial Estate, Liverpool, L31 8BX Tel: 0151-924 0767 Fax: 0151-924 6555
▶ Prima Recycling, 7 D2 Trading Estate, Castle Road, Sittingbourne, Kent, ME10 3RH Tel: (01795) 439307 Fax: (01795) 437344 E-mail: webhouse@primapaper.co.uk
Reelstock Ltd, Old Wharf Industrial Estate, Old Wharf Road, Grantham, Lincolnshire, NG31 7AA Tel: (01476) 567979 Fax: (01476) 565542 E-mail: sales@reelstock.freeserve.co.uk
Roughway Converters Ltd, Roughway Mill, Dunks Green, Tonbridge, Kent, TN11 9SG Tel: (01732) 810811 Fax: (01732) 810838 E-mail: roughway@btconnect.com
▶ Scalderhurst Ltd, Ford Mill, The Street, Little Chart, Ashford, Kent, TN27 0QA Tel: (01233) 840711 Fax: (01233) 840794 E-mail: info@scalderhurst.co.uk
Schades Ltd, Brittain Drive, Ripley, Derbyshire, DE5 3RZ Tel: (01773) 748721 Fax: (01773) 745061 E-mail: schades@schades.co.uk
John Slack Ltd, Bank Vale Mill, Swallow House Lane, Hayfield, High Peak, Derbyshire, SK22 2HA Tel: (01663) 744211 Fax: (01663) 745139
Tullis Russell Coaters Ltd, Brittains Paper Mills, Commercial Road, Hanley, Stoke-on-Trent, ST1 3QS Tel: (01782) 202567 Fax: (01782) 202157 E-mail: enquiries@trcoaters.co.uk
Walki Ltd, Ray Lane, Barnacre, Preston, PR3 1GG Tel: (01995) 604227 Fax: (01995) 605222 E-mail: wawgar@upm-kymmene.com
Welton Bibby & Baron Ltd, Station Road, Midsomer Norton, Radstock, BA3 2BE Tel: (01761) 416523 Fax: (01761) 413862 E-mail: enquiries@welton.co.uk

PAPER CONVERTING ADHESIVES

Stadex Industries Ltd, Coed Aben Road, Wrexham Industrial Estate, Wrexham, Clwyd, LL13 9UH Tel: (01978) 660266 Fax: (01978) 660316 E-mail: sales@stadex.co.uk

PAPER CONVERTING KNIVES

Canaan Carbides Ltd, Unit 13, 13 Briar Close, Evesham, Worcestershire, WR11 4JQ Tel: (01386) 442818 Fax: (01386) 40564 E-mail: canaancarbides@btconnect.com

PAPER CONVERTING MACHINE MANUFRS

Cotec Converting Machinery Ltd, Unit 20 St. Johns Industrial Estate, Lees, Oldham, OL4 3DZ Tel: 0161-626 5350 Fax: 0161-626 5450 E-mail: jackcotten@btconnect.com
Delpro Ltd, Peakdale Road, Glossop, Derbyshire, SK13 6XE Tel: (01457) 862776 Fax: (01457) 862433 E-mail: sales@delpro.co.uk
Dixon, Unit C, 3 Fen End, Astwick Road, Stotfold, Hitchin, Hertfordshire, SG5 4BA Tel: (01462) 834911 Fax: (01462) 834911 E-mail: sales@dixontechnologies.com
International Paper Containers UK Ltd, Haldens Parkway, Thrapston, Kettering, Northamptonshire, NN14 4QS Tel: (01832) 736100 Fax: (01832) 736109
John Lack Equipment, 6 Denington Court, Denington Industrial Estate, Wellingborough, Northamptonshire, NN8 2QR Tel: (01933) 441646 Fax: (01933) 441476 E-mail: johnlackequipment@tiscali.co.uk
Machinery Development Services, Bristol Road, Whitminster, Gloucester, GL2 7NY Tel: (01452) 740112 Fax: (01452) 740511 E-mail: enq@mds-uk.com
Nico Ebergrip Ltd, The Runnings, Cheltenham, Gloucestershire, GL51 9NJ Tel: (01832) 735341 Fax: (01242) 222448
Paper Converting Machine Co. Ltd, Southway Drive, Plymouth, PL6 6EL Tel: (01752) 735881 Fax: (01752) 733290 E-mail: pcmcuk@papcon.co.uk
Pfe Orion Division, Draycott Business Park, Cam, Dursley, Gloucestershire, GL11 5DQ Tel: (01453) 890881 Fax: (01453) 890312 E-mail: mike.comer@orionmachinery.com
Whitminster International Ltd, Dudbridge Road, Stroud, Gloucestershire, GL5 3HF Tel: (01453) 762266 Fax: (01453) 762277 E-mail: mailroom@whitminster.co.uk
Wood Machines Ltd, 1 Galley Hill Industrial Estate, London Road, Swanscombe, Kent, DA10 0AA Tel: (01322) 385566 Fax: (01322) 384449 E-mail: mail@uemcoltd.com
Wood & Stirling, Claughton Industrial Estate, Brockholes Way, Claughton-on-Brock, Preston, PR3 0PZ Tel: (01995) 640664 Fax: (01995) 640065 E-mail: craig@woodandstirling.co.uk

PAPER CUTTING GUILLOTINE BLADES

Norman Haynes Ltd, 900 Thornton Road, Bradford, West Yorkshire, BD8 0JG Tel: (01274) 545115 Fax: (01274) 545113

PAPER CUTTING/GUILLOTINING SERVICES TO THE TRADE

Clifton & Son Ltd, Uplands Business Park, Blackhorse Lane, London, E17 5QJ Tel: (020) 8523 1133 Fax: (020) 8531 1341 E-mail: tim@clifton.org
Elite Cutters Ltd, Oakfield Works, Branksome Hill Road, College Town, Sandhurst, Berkshire, GU47 0QE Tel: (01276) 32991 Fax: (01276) 600146 E-mail: kriswatling@elitecutters.fsnet.co.uk

PAPER ENVELOPES

Ace Envelopes Ltd, Hillside House, 2-6 Friern Park, London, N12 9BT Tel: (020) 8445 0123 Fax: (020) 8446 9423 E-mail: sales@ace-envelopes.co.uk
Antalis, Unit 4 Horizon Wade Road, Kingsland Industrial Estate, Basingstoke, Hampshire, RG24 8LJ Tel: (01256) 776200 Fax: (01256) 724734 E-mail: sales@antalis.co.uk
Bong UK Ltd, Envelope Buildings, Michigan Drive, Tongwell, Milton Keynes, MK15 8HQ Tel: (01908) 216216 Fax: (01908) 216217
Camson Envelopes, Woodlands Mills, Woodlands Road, Tonbridge, Kent, TN9 2NE Tel: (01732) 368949 Fax: (01732) 362429 E-mail: sales@camson.co.uk
Dobson & Crowder Ltd, Berwyn Works, Holyhead Road, Llangollen, Clwyd, LL20 8AE Tel: (01978) 862100 Fax: (01978) 860410
Eagle Envelopes Ltd, Bloxwich Road, Walsall, WS2 7BD Tel: (01922) 613888 Fax: (01922) 613999 E-mail: walsall@eagle-envelopes.com
Gala Marketing Ltd, Farrier House, 221-223 High Street, Henley-In-Arden, West Midlands, B95 5BG Tel: (01564) 794005 Fax: (01564) 793301
Hugh Imlay & Co. Ltd, 3 Duff St, Aberdeen, AB24 5LF Tel: (01224) 640151 Fax: (01224) 647399 E-mail: info@hughimlay.co.uk
Masons Paper, 107 Elkington Street, Birmingham, B6 4SL Tel: 0121-359 5601 Fax: 0121-359 5600
Mekvale Envelopes P.L.C., Grange Mills, Weir Road, London, SW12 0NE Tel: (020) 8673 4367 Fax: (020) 8675 7178 E-mail: mekvale@btclick.com
Post Safe Ltd, 158 Broadway, Knaphill, Woking, Surrey, GU21 2RL Tel: (01483) 486618 Fax: (01483) 489267
Rapid Envelopes, Potters Bar, Herts, EN6 4SP Tel: (01707) 878783
Smith Anderson Envelopes Ltd, Whiteside Industrial Estate, Bathgate, West Lothian, EH48 2RX Tel: (01506) 634463 Fax: (01506) 634366 E-mail: sales@eagle-envelopes.com
Stolk & Reese Kubert BV, D T E House, Hollins Lane, Bury, Lancashire, BL9 8AT Tel: 0161-877 4060 Fax: 0161-877 4090 E-mail: enquires@vsr.nl
Sunderland Paper Mill, Ocean Road, Grangetown, Sunderland, SR2 9RZ Tel: 0191-514 4944 Fax: 0191-510 8012 E-mail: patb@edward-thompson.com

▶ indicates data change since last edition

PAPER ENVELOPES – *continued*

Universal Envelopes Ltd, 5 Bourne Road, Bexley, Kent, DA5 1LG Tel: (01322) 529529 Fax: (01322) 529829

Versapak International, The Versapak Centre, Centurion Way, Erith, Kent, DA18 4AF Tel: (020) 8333 5353 Fax: (020) 8312 2051 E-mail: catsales@versapak.co.uk

Wells Envelopes, 3 Paycocke Close, Basildon, Essex, SS14 3HS Tel: (01268) 284442 Fax: (01268) 271177 E-mail: wellsenv@yahoo.co.uk

PAPER ENVELOPES TO SPECIFICATION

Ace Envelopes Ltd, Hillside House, 2-6 Friern Park, London, N12 9BT Tel: (020) 8445 0123 Fax: (020) 8446 9423 E-mail: sales@ace-envelopes.co.uk

Antalis Ltd, Unit C3 Crossways Boulevard, Greenhithe, Kent, DA9 9BT Tel: (0870) 6073117 Fax: (01322) 226297

Chapman Envelopes Ltd, Grimshaw Bridge, Johnson Road, Eccleshill, Darwen, Lancashire, BB3 3PF Tel: (01254) 682387 Fax: (01254) 775920

Masons Paper, 107 Elkington Street, Birmingham, B6 4SL Tel: 0121-359 5601 Fax: 0121-359 5600

PAPER EXPORT MERCHANTS OR AGENTS

F E Export Ltd, 63-66 Hatton Garden, London, EC1N 8LE Tel: (020) 7242 2606 Fax: (020) 7242 4407 E-mail: john@fexport.demon.co.uk

Firn Overseas Packaging Ltd, Firn House, 61 Church Street, Hungerford, Berkshire, RG17 0JH Tel: (01488) 683193 Fax: (01488) 684701 E-mail: sales@firn.org

Westwind International Ltd, 23 Robjohns Road, Chelmsford, CM1 3AG Tel: (01245) 261201 Fax: (01245) 293615 E-mail: paper@wwi.org

▶ WPT (UK) Ltd., One Canada Square, 28th Floor, Canary Wharf, London, E14 5DY Tel: 020 7956 8697 Fax: 020 7956 8666 E-mail: info@wpt-uk.com

PAPER FOLDING MACHINES

Packaging Craftsman Ltd, Units 1a-1b, Park Mill Way, Clayton West, Huddersfield, HD8 9XJ Tel: (01484) 865680 Fax: (01484) 865681 E-mail: sales@packagingcraftsman.co.uk

PAPER GIFTWARE PACKAGING TO SPECIFICATION

▶ David Hayward Design UK, 29 Suffolk Parade, Cheltenham, Gloucestershire, GL50 2AE Tel: (01242) 570314 Fax: (01242) 263674 E-mail: sales@davidhayward.com

PAPER GUMMING/GUMMED PRODUCTS, *See Gummed Paper/Tape etc*

PAPER HANDLING EQUIPMENT

Avanti Conveyors, Calico Lane, Furness Vale, High Peak, Derbyshire, SK23 7SW Tel: (01663) 740011 Fax: (01663) 745097 E-mail: sales@avanti-conveyors.co.uk

Megtec Systems Ltd, Unit 4, Bell St, Maidenhead, Berkshire, SL6 1BL Tel: 01628 776244

Renaddress Ltd, Target House, Lea Road, Waltham Abbey, Essex, EN9 1AE Tel: (01992) 712592 Fax: (01992) 760902 E-mail: reg@target-sys.co.uk

Rodwell H T B, Bentalls, Basildon, Essex, SS14 3SD Tel: (01268) 286646 Fax: (01268) 287799 E-mail: sales@rodwell-autoclave.com

▶ Rovert Equipment Co. Ltd, Rovert House, Water Tower Road, Clayhill Light Industrial Park, Neston, CH64 3US Tel: 0151-336 2122 Fax: 0151-336 8997 E-mail: david@rovert.co.uk

PAPER HANDLING EQUIPMENT MAINTENANCE/REPAIR SERVICES

▶ Rovert Equipment Co. Ltd, Rovert House, Water Tower Road, Clayhill Light Industrial Park, Neston, CH64 3US Tel: 0151-336 2122 Fax: 0151-336 8997 E-mail: david@rovert.co.uk

PAPER IMPORT MERCHANTS OR AGENTS

The Essential Housewares Co. Ltd, 9 Foster Avenue, Woodside Park, Dunstable, Bedfordshire, LU5 5TA Tel: (01582) 475577 Fax: (01582) 690575 E-mail: sales@essentialhousewares.co.uk

Harver Packaging Co. Ltd, 479 Chester Road, Manchester, M16 9HF Tel: 0161-786 3900 Fax: 0161-848 8656 E-mail: sales@harverpac.co.uk

PAPER INDUSTRY RECRUITMENT

Automation Experts Ltd, Appic Elliot Innovation Centre, Elliot Business Park, 4 Barling Way, Nuneaton, Warwickshire, CV10 7RH Tel: (024) 7679 6666 Fax: (024) 7679 6667 E-mail: info@automationexperts.co.uk

▶ Ecruit UK Ltd, 41 Convent Road, Ashford, Middlesex, TW15 2HJ Tel: (08718) 714605 Fax: (08712) 773138 E-mail: admin@ecruit-direct.co.uk

▶ First Call Contract Services Ltd, 30 Church Street, Enfield, Middlesex, EN2 6BA Tel: (020) 8370 9001 Fax: (020) 8367 1516 E-mail: info@firstcall-enfield.co.uk

▶ Leed Recruitment Ltd, The Manor House, 6-10 St. Margaret's Green, Ipswich, IP4 2BS Tel: (01473) 289000 E-mail: info@leedrecruitment.com

▶ Linx Recruitment, Archway House, Norton Way North, Letchworth Garden City, Hertfordshire, SG6 1BH Tel: (01462) 677669 E-mail: keith@linxrecruitment.co.uk

▶ RecruitEU Ltd, PO Box 43574, London, UK, SW15 1XA Tel: 0207 8708824 Fax: 0870 7051298 E-mail: nigelholmes@recruiteu.com

▶ Tim Cowell, Clayhill Farm, Marden Rd, Cranbrook, Kent, TN17 2LP Tel: (01580) 715111 Fax: (01580) 714718 E-mail: webmaster@manufacturingjobs.co.uk

UJOB - UK Employment Vacancies, PO Box 139, Thornton-Cleveleys, Lancashire, FY5 4WU Tel: (0870) 7668565 E-mail: ujob@ujob.co.uk

PAPER LABEL STOCK

Magnum Materials Ltd, Globe Lane Indust Estate Broadway, Dukinfield, Cheshire, SK16 4UU Tel: 0161-343 1131 Fax: 0161-343 1132 E-mail: sales@magnum-uk.com

Raflatac Ltd, Wareham Road, Eastfield, Scarborough, North Yorkshire, YO11 3DX Tel: (01723) 583661 Fax: (01723) 584896 E-mail: raflatac@raflatac.com

PAPER LABELS

Alpha Print & Design, Unit 12, Sedgemount Industrial Park, Bristol Road, Bridgwater, Somerset, TA6 4AR Tel: (01278) 426958 Fax: (01278) 424001 E-mail: alphaprint@ukonline.co.uk

The Baker Self-Adhesive Label Company Ltd, 37 Sutherland Road, London, E17 6BH Tel: (020) 8523 2174 Fax: (020) 8527 6556

Chiltern Labels, Bassetsbury Lane, High Wycombe, Buckinghamshire, HP11 1HT Tel: (0845) 2239450 Fax: (0845) 2239460

The Classic Label Company Ltd, Unit 9-14 Whitehall Properties, Town Gate, Wyke, Bradford, West Yorkshire, BD12 9JQ Tel: (01274) 690217 Fax: (01274) 690046 E-mail: info@classiclabels.co.uk

Clearprint Labels Ltd, 1-2 Essex Street, Preston, PR1 1QE Tel: (01772) 258185 Fax: (01772) 256622 E-mail: sales@clearprint.co.uk

Icon Labels Ltd, 1 Lower Oakham Way, Oakham Business Park, Mansfield, Nottinghamshire, NG18 5BU Tel: (01623) 421241 Fax: (01623) 421251 E-mail: sales@iconlabels.co.uk

Inkreadible Label Co., 11 Chatto Way, Torquay, TQ1 4UE Tel: (01803) 326818 Fax: (01803) 313102 E-mail: sales@inkreadible.com

Last Bros Ltd, Delamare Road, Cheshunt, Waltham Cross, Hertfordshire, EN8 9TE Tel: (01992) 638283 Fax: (01992) 638286 E-mail: sales@lastbros.co.uk

Lyster & Associates, The Coach House, Ashford Lodge, Sudbury Road, Halstead, Essex, CO9 2RR Tel: (01787) 477777 Fax: (01787) 477377E-mail: postmaster@lyster-assoc.co.uk

Marsh Labels Ltd, 6 Lady Bee Marina Industrial Estate, Albion Street, Southwick, Brighton, BN42 4EP Tel: (01273) 595744 Fax: (01273) 870425 E-mail: sales@marshlabels.co.uk

Piroto Labelling Ltd, 9 Pond Wood Close, Moulton Park Industrial Estate, Northampton, NN3 6RT Tel: (01604) 646600 Fax: (01604) 492090 E-mail: info@piroto-labelling.com

West Yorkshire Printing Co. Ltd, Wyprint House, Smith Way, Wakefield Road, Ossett, West Yorkshire, WF5 9JZ Tel: (01924) 280522 Fax: (01924) 280145 E-mail: sales@westyor.co.uk

PAPER LAMINATING MACHINES

Abbey Design, Unit 4/5, Glen Trading Estate, Wellyhole Street, Oldham, OL4 3BF Tel: 0161-620 8295 Fax: 0161-785 0130 E-mail: sales@abbeydesign.cc

Dayfold Ltd, Unit 4-6 27 Black Moor Road, Ebblake Industrial Estate, Verwood, Dorset, BH31 6BE Tel: 01202 827401 Fax: (01202) 825841 E-mail: enquiries@dayfold.com

John Lack Equipment, 6 Denington Court, Denington Industrial Estate, Wellingborough, Northamptonshire, NN8 2QR Tel: (01933) 441646 Fax: (01933) 441476 E-mail: johnlackequipment@tiscali.co.uk

Press Co., Kiln Lane, Swindon, SN2 2NP Tel: (01793) 716316 Fax: (01793) 511345 E-mail: sales@presco-uk.com

PAPER LINED BOARD

Adlington Paper & Board Supplies Ltd, Unit 1 Adlington Industrial Estate, Adlington, Macclesfield, Cheshire, SK10 4NL Tel: (01625) 850885 Fax: (01625) 850882 E-mail: adlingtonpaper@btconnect.com

PAPER MACHINE BLADES

▶ Jensen Barker Technical Services Ltd, Fowlswick Industrial Estate, Fowlswick Lane, Allington, Chippenham, Wiltshire, SN14 6QE Tel: (01249) 783844 Fax: (01249) 783306 E-mail: info@jensen-barker.com

PAPER MAKERS, *See also other headings under Paper*

Antalis Ltd, Kempson Way, Bury St. Edmunds, Suffolk, IP32 7AR Tel: (0870) 6073103 Fax: (01284) 706116 E-mail: admin@antalis.com

Caledonian Paper plc, Meadowhead Road, Irvine, Ayrshire, KA11 5AT Tel: (01294) 312020 Fax: (01294) 314400 E-mail: sales@upn-kymmene.com

Glatselter UK Ltd, Church Road, Lydney, Gloucestershire, GL15 5EJ Tel: (01594) 842235 Fax: (01594) 844213 E-mail: info@crompton.co.uk

John Hargreaves (Collyhurst & Stalybridge) Ltd, Knowl Street, Stalybridge, Cheshire, SK15 3AJ Tel: 0161-338 6011 Fax: 0161-338 4194 E-mail: jack@john-hargreaves.co.uk

J R Crompton U S A Ltd, 12th Floor, Sunlight House, Manchester, M3 3JZ Tel: 0161-817 6500 Fax: 0161-817 6506 E-mail: info@crompton.co.uk

Manchester Paper Co. Ltd, Victoria Works, Williams Road, Gorton, Manchester, M18 7AY Tel: 0161-223 9363 Fax: 0161-223 9291 E-mail: sales@manchester.com

Mondi Paper UK Ltd, Creams Mill, Mytham Road, Little Lever, Bolton, BL3 1AU Tel: (01204) 573811 Fax: (01204) 862574

▶ Paper Trail Mill Ltd, Frogmore Mill, Fourdrinier Way, Hemel Hempstead, Hertfordshire, HP3 9RY Tel: (01442) 231234 Fax: (01442) 275749 E-mail: frogmoremill@thepapertrial.org.uk

Rigid Paper Ltd, Denison Road, Selby, North Yorkshire, YO8 8DB Tel: (01757) 705151 Fax: (01757) 210009 E-mail: paper@rigid.co.uk

St Regis Paper Co. Ltd, Higher Kings Mill, Cullompton, Devon, EX15 1QJ Tel: (01884) 836300 Fax: (01884) 836333 E-mail: sales@stregis.co.uk

Smurfit Townsend Hook, Paper Mills, Mill Street, Snodland, Kent, ME6 5AX Tel: (01634) 240205 Fax: (01634) 243458 E-mail: sales@smurfit-europe.com

Sonoco Board Mills, Holywell Green, Halifax, West Yorkshire, HX4 9PY Tel: (01422) 374741 Fax: (01422) 371495

Sunderland Paper Mill, Ocean Road, Grangetown, Sunderland, SR2 9RZ Tel: 0191-514 4944 Fax: 0191-510 8012 E-mail: patb@edward-thompson.com

Tullis Russell, Markinch, Markinch, Glenrothes, Fife, KY7 6PB Tel: (01592) 753311 Fax: (01592) 755872 E-mail: papermakers@trg.co.uk

U P M Kymmene Ltd, Weighbridge Road, Deeside Industrial Park, Deeside, Clwyd, CH5 2LL Tel: (01244) 284137 Fax: (01244) 285019 E-mail: info@upm-kymmene.com

Union Papertech Ltd, Simpson Clough Mill, Ashworth Road, Heywood, Lancashire, OL10 4BE Tel: (01706) 364121 Fax: (01706) 624944

Whiteley Ltd, Pool In Wharfedale, Otley, West Yorkshire, LS21 1RP Tel: 0113-284 2121 Fax: 0113-284 2272

PAPER MAKING ACCESSORIES/ ANCILLARY EQUIPMENT

Universal Guards Servicing Ltd, Turnpike Close, Grantham, Lincolnshire, NG31 7XU Tel: (01476) 565858 Fax: (01476) 590296 E-mail: sales@lightguards.com

PAPER MAKING CHEMICALS

Buckman Laboratories Ltd, Millbank House, Bollin Walk, Wilmslow, Cheshire, SK9 1BJ Tel: (01625) 524875 Fax: (01625) 525988

PAPER MAKING CONSULTANTS

Arrow Projects Consultants Ltd, 7 Dorset Road, London, SW19 3EY Tel: (020) 8543 9390 Fax: (020) 8543 8748 E-mail: sales@pmpe.co.uk

Pira International, Cleeve Road, Leatherhead, Surrey, KT22 7RU Tel: (01372) 802000 Fax: (01372) 802238 E-mail: membership@pira-international.co.uk

PAPER MAKING FABRICS

Voith Fabrics Blackburn, Cartmell Road, Blackburn, BB2 2SZ Tel: (01254) 55101 Fax: (01254) 581320 E-mail: info@voith.com

Voith Fabrics Stubbins Ltd, Stubbins Vale Mill, Stubbins Vale Road, Bury, Lancashire, BL0 0NT Tel: (01706) 822951 Fax: (01706) 283401

PAPER MAKING FELT

Albany International Ltd, Pilsworth Road, Bury, Lancashire, BL9 8QE Tel: 0161-767 7531 Fax: 0161-766 2993

PAPER MAKING PLANT/ EQUIPMENT

Elphis Engineering Ltd, 6 St Andrews Park, Princes Road, Wells, Somerset, BA5 1TE Tel: (01749) 676424 Fax: (01749) 675501

Hydraulic & Pneumatic Power Services, Methilhaven Road, Methil, Leven, Fife, KY8 3LA Tel: (01333) 429690 Fax: (01333) 422952 E-mail: info@fcegroup.com

Kadant UK Ltd, PO Box 6, Bury, Lancashire, BL8 1DF Tel: 0161-764 9111 Fax: 0161-797 1496 E-mail: sales@kadant.co.uk

Metso Paper Ltd, Birchwood One, Duehurst Road, Birchwood, Warrington, WA3 7GB Tel: (01925) 286850 Fax: (01925) 286868 E-mail: info@metsopaper.com

Mount Hope, Viewfield Industrial Estate, Glenrothes, Fife, KY6 2RG Tel: (01592) 772612 Fax: (01592) 630016 E-mail: ian.stirling@stowewoodward.com

Pulp & Paper Machinery Ltd, Holman House, Station Road, Staplehurst, Tonbridge, Kent, TN12 0QQ Tel: (01580) 893200 Fax: (01580) 893229 E-mail: sales@pandpmachinery.com

Skillforce Ltd, Eton Hill Road, Radcliffe, Manchester, M26 2ZT Tel: 0161-724 6634 Fax: 0161-723 1661 E-mail: sales@parsonsreiss.com

PAPER MAKING PLANT/ EQUIPMENT IMPORT/EXPORT MERCHANTS OR AGENTS

Cambridge Overseas Trading Ltd, 13 Richmond Walk, St. Albans, Hertfordshire, AL4 9BA Tel: (01727) 833211 Fax: (01727) 810320 E-mail: cambost@aol.com

▶ Kilkie Paper Mill Services, Lovesta, Gowanlea Road, Comrie, Crieff, Perthshire, PH6 2HD Tel: (01764) 670141 Fax: (0870) 1301570 E-mail: sales@kilkie.com

PAPER MAKING PLANT/ EQUIPMENT, RECONDITIONED

B B F Services Ltd, 49 Saxon Road, Whitby, North Yorkshire, YO21 3NU Tel: (01947) 601173 Fax: (0870) 7598439 E-mail: bbfservicesltd@aol.com

Glenaber Engineers Ltd, Denfield House, 5 Smeaton Road, Kirkcaldy, Fife, KY1 2EY Tel: (01592) 651940 Fax: (01592) 651963 E-mail: admin-glenaberengineers@ecosse.net

J J Service, Star Trading Estate, Ponthir, Newport, Gwent, NP18 1PQ Tel: (01633) 420552 Fax: (01633) 430224

PAPER MAKING WIRE

Heimbach, Bradnor Road, Sharston Industrial Area, Manchester, M22 4TS Tel: 0161-998 6911 Fax: 0161-998 8095

PAPER MERCHANTS OR AGENTS

A F Dobbie, A Pitreavie Business Park, Queensferry Road, Dunfermline, Fife, KY11 8PU Tel: (01383) 723111

PAPER MERCHANTS OR AGENTS - *continued*

A1 Paper P.L.C., Roebuck Street, West Bromwich, West Midlands, B70 6RB Tel: 0121-553 7131 Fax: 0121-553 5040 E-mail: sales@a1paper.co.uk

Allied Traders, 28 Seaton Place, Jersey, JE4 5XU Tel: (01534) 722213 Fax: (01534) 870613 E-mail: alliedtraders@jerseymail.co.uk

Allinson's, Allinson House, Lincoln Way, Fairfield Industrial Estate, Louth, Lincolnshire, LN11 0LS Tel: (01507) 600911 Fax: (01507) 600434 E-mail: admin@allinsonwilcox.co.uk

Antalis, Unit 4 Horizon Wade Road, Kingsland Industrial Estate, Basingstoke, Hampshire, RG24 8LJ Tel: (01256) 776200 Fax: (01256) 724734 E-mail: sales@antalis.co.uk

Antalis Ltd, Kempson Way, Bury St. Edmunds, Suffolk, IP32 7AR Tel: (0870) 6073103 Fax: (01284) 706116 E-mail: admin@antalis.com

Antalis Ltd, Gateway House, Pilsworth Road, Bury, Lancashire, BL9 8RD Tel: (0870) 6073112 Fax: 0161-910 8268 E-mail: info@antalis-print.co.uk

Antalis Ltd, Unit C3 Crossways Boulevard, Greenhithe, Kent, DA9 9BT Tel: (0870) 6073117 Fax: (01322) 226297

Antalis, 3 Imperial Park Imperial Way, Watford, WD24 4PP Tel: (01923) 636600 Fax: (0870) 6073168 E-mail: contact@antalis.co.uk

Antalis Ltd, Unit 14, Avenue One, Witney, Oxfordshire, OX29 6XX Tel: (0870) 6073114 Fax: (01993) 779066

Arjo Wiggins Fine Papers Ltd, Chineham, Basingstoke, Hampshire, RG24 8BA Tel: (01256) 728728 Fax: (01256) 728889

Aylesford Paper Sales, Consolidated Paper House, Forstal Road, Aylesford, Kent, ME20 7AE Tel: (01622) 716353 Fax: (01622) 716663 E-mail: sales@aylesfordpaper.co.uk

B Garrad Ltd, Water Lane, Kings Langley, Hertfordshire, WD4 8HW Tel: (01923) 264088 Fax: (01923) 264089 E-mail: artcraft@bgarrad.co.uk

E. Becker Ltd, 2 Hazlemere View, Hazlemere, High Wycombe, Buckinghamshire, HP15 7BY Tel: (01494) 713777 Fax: (01494) 713888 E-mail: e.becker@breathemail.net

H.V. Beever Ltd, Unit 2, Marshgate Trading Estate, Marshgate Lane, London, E15 2NG Tel: (020) 8519 1777 Fax: (020) 8534 5420 E-mail: sales@hvbeeverltd.com

Daniel Boyle & Son, 1 Carruthers Street, Liverpool, L3 6BY Tel: 0151-255 0055 Fax: 0151-255 0011 E-mail: sales@titherleys.co.uk

Brown Brothers Group Ltd, 168/170 South Street, Dorking, Surrey, RH4 2ES Tel: (01306) 742611 Fax: (01306) 742601 E-mail: duncan@brownbros.co.uk

Campsie Paper Co. Ltd, Courtauld Way, Eglinton, Londonderry, BT47 3DN Tel: (028) 7181 1243 Fax: (028) 7181 1626

City Paper Ltd, Xerox House, Maylands Avenue, Hemel Hempstead, Hertfordshire, HP2 7DE Tel: (0870) 2410472 Fax: (0870) 2410473 E-mail: sales@citypaper.com

Contract Paper Ltd, Sovereign House, Rhosili Road, Brackmills, Northampton, NN4 7JE Tel: (0870) 6082374 Fax: (0870) 6082375 E-mail: marketing@hspg.com

Corners Direct Ltd, Hillam Road, Bradford, West Yorkshire, BD2 1QL Tel: (01274) 733213 Fax: (01274) 721128 E-mail: peterwright@cornersdirect.co.uk

Corrugated Paper Sales Ltd, Crown Industrial Estate Canal Road, Timperley, Altrincham, Cheshire, WA14 1TF Tel: 0161-976 3000 Fax: 0161-975 3727

Daniel Paper & Packaging, 133 Old Lane, Manchester, M11 1DD Tel: 0161-301 4710 Fax: 0161-370 9753

Digital & Screen Printing Association (UK) Ltd, Association House, 7A West Street, Reigate, Surrey, RH2 9BL Tel: (01737) 240792 Fax: (01737) 240770 E-mail: info@spauk.co.uk

Direct Paper Agents, Amy Johnson Way, Blackpool, FY4 2RP Tel: (01253) 402502 Fax: (01253) 405872 E-mail: info@direct-paperagentsltd.sagenet.co.uk

Donald Heath Cartons, Unit 22b Calder Trading Estate, Huddersfield, HD5 0RS Tel: (01484) 432900 Fax: (01484) 515800

Donald Murray, 211 Maclellan Street, Glasgow, G41 1RR Tel: 0141-427 1271 Fax: 0141-427 6999 E-mail: sales@donald-murray-paper.co.uk

Downes & Duncan, Unit 2, Ashley Drive, Bothwell, Glasgow, G71 8BS Tel: (01698) 803088 Fax: (01698) 803087 E-mail: sales@downsduncan.co.uk

Elliott Baxter & Company Ltd, Central Way, North Feltham Trading Estate, Feltham, Middlesex, TW14 0RX Tel: (020) 8893 1144 Fax: (020) 8893 2167 E-mail: sales@ebbpaper.co.uk

The Ex Mill Envelope & Paper Company Ltd, 5-9 City Garden Row, London, N1 8DW Tel: (020) 7253 8312 Fax: (020) 7251 5336 E-mail: sales@exmill.co.uk

F J Beswick, 16 Gate Lodge Close, Round Spinney Industrial Estate, Northampton, NN3 8RJ Tel: (01604) 642227 Fax: (01604) 493998 E-mail: salesn@besnorth.co.uk

F J Beswick Ltd, 10 Dudley Road, Oldbury, West Midlands, B69 3DN Tel: 0121-552 5391 Fax: 0121-552 2350 E-mail: salesoldbury@beswick.co.uk

F J Beswick Cotswolds Ltd, Ashville Trading Estate, The Runnings, Cheltenham, Gloucestershire, GL51 9PT Tel: (01242) 514776 Fax: (01242) 580519 E-mail: saleschelt@beswick.co.uk

Fenner Paper Co. Ltd, Unit 15 Orchard Business Centre, Vale Rd, Tonbridge, Kent, TN9 1QF Tel: (01732) 771100 Fax: (01732) 771103 E-mail: info@fennerpaper.co.uk

Georgia Pacific GB Ltd, Mansell Way, Horwich, Bolton, BL6 6JL Tel: (01204) 673300 Fax: (01204) 673301 E-mail:

Allen Glenold Ltd, Glenold House, Crosby Road, Market Harborough, Leicestershire, LE16 9EE Tel: (01858) 467789 Fax: (01858) 432932 E-mail: sales@glenold.co.uk

Samuel Grant Ltd, 146-148 Garnet Road, Leeds, LS11 5LA Tel: 0113-270 7221 Fax: 0113-277 9867 E-mail: sales@samuelgrant.co.uk

Samuel Grant (North East) Ltd, Unit 13-16, Tanfield Lea South Industrial Estate, Tanfield Lea, Stanley, County Durham, DH9 9QX Tel: (01207) 283510 Fax: (01207) 290063 E-mail: nesales@samuelgrant.com

Grosvenor House Papers, Westmorland Business Park, Gilthwaiterigg Lane, Kendal, Cumbria, LA9 6NP Tel: (01539) 726161 Fax: (01539) 733678 E-mail: info@ghpkendal.co.uk

Halcyon Paper Co. Ltd, Unit E, Menin Works, Bond Road, Mitcham, Surrey, CR4 3HG Tel: (020) 8646 4060 Fax: (020) 8648 6197 E-mail: halcyon.paper@cwcom.net

Hale Paper, Premier House, Faringdon Avenue, Romford, RM3 8SP Tel: (01708) 330380 Fax: (01708) 330390 E-mail: information@paper.co.uk

Harris & Co., Farrs Lane, Bristol, BS1 4PZ Tel: 0117-927 7434 Fax: 0117-925 2354

George Harrison Ltd, Selsdon House, 212-220 Addington Road, South Croydon, Surrey, CR2 8LD Tel: (020) 8768 3200 Fax: (020) 8768 3201 E-mail: sales@ghuk.co.uk

Holman Kelly Paper Co. Ltd, Wandle House, Riverside Drive, Mitcham, Surrey, CR4 4BU Tel: (020) 8687 7300 Fax: (020) 8687 7333 E-mail: holmankellypaper@btinternet.com

Robert Horne Ltd, 4A Kingfisher Court, Brambleside, Bellbrook Industrial Estate, Uckfield, East Sussex, TN22 1QQ Tel: (01825) 748494 Fax: (01273) 478546 E-mail: rh.uckkfield@roberthorne.co.uk

Robert Horne Group Ltd, 1 Brooklands Way, Boldon Business Park, Boldon Colliery, Tyne & Wear, NE35 9LZ Tel: 0191-537 7177 Fax: 0191-537 7178 E-mail: rh.newcastle@roberthorne.co.uk

Robert Horne Group P.L.C., Huntsman House, Pontefract Road, Leeds, LS10 1DD Tel: 0113-387 2424 Fax: 0113-271 9408 E-mail: rh.leeds@roberthorne.co.uk

Horne Robert Paper Company Ltd, Huntsman House, 40 Tameside Drive, Birmingham, B35 7BD Tel: 0121-776 7777 Fax: 0121-749 2670 E-mail: rh.birmingham@roberthorne.co.uk

James Mcnaughton Paper Group, Jaymac House, Church Manorway, Erith, Kent, DA8 1DF Tel: (020) 8320 3200 Fax: (020) 8311 4162 E-mail: marketing@mcnaughton-paper.com

John Gray Paper & Twine Ltd, 48 Thomas Street, Manchester, M4 1ER Tel: 0161-832 3313 Fax: 0161-839 7068 E-mail: sales@johngray-packaging.co.uk

David John Papers Ltd, Unit 1A, Middlegreen Trading Estate, Middlegreen Road, Langley, Slough, SL3 6DF Tel: (01753) 570424 Fax: (01753) 512702

Gerald Judd Sales Ltd, 47-51 Gillingham Street, London, SW1V 1HS Tel: (020) 7828 8821 Fax: (020) 7828 0840 E-mail: sales@geraldjudd.co.uk

L & S Middleton Paper Co., Eagle Works, Somerford Place, Willenhall, West Midlands, WV13 3EA Tel: (01902) 635551 Fax: (01902) 636728 E-mail: middletonpaper@compuserve.com

Lewis T Davies, Brewery Road, Carmarthen, Dyfed, SA31 1TF Tel: (01267) 221746 Fax: (01267) 221776 E-mail: info@lewistdavies.co.uk

M6 Paper Group Ltd, Motorway House, Charter Way, Macclesfield, Cheshire, SK10 2NY Tel: (01625) 610044 Fax: (01625) 511144 E-mail: info@m6papers.co.uk

James McNaughton Paper Group Ltd, Unit 3, Maxted Court, Maxted Road, Hemel Hempstead, Hertfordshire, HP2 7BY Tel: (01442) 270104 Fax: (01442) 217390 E-mail: gskelton@mcnaughton-paper.com

Masons Paper, 107 Elkington Street, Birmingham, B6 4SL Tel: 0121-359 5601 Fax: 0121-359 5600

Mason's Paper Ltd, 1 Island House, Bluestem Road, Ipswich, IP3 9RR Tel: (01473) 711123 Fax: (01473) 270109

William Montgomery & Sons, 79 Ladas Drive, Belfast, BT6 9FR Tel: (028) 9040 1593 Fax: (028) 9040 1593

Moorgate Paper Co Ltd, Watercombe Lane, Lynx West Trading Estate, Yeovil, Somerset, BA20 2SU Tel: (01935) 426888 Fax: (01935) 847400

Northwood Paper Sales Ltd, 4 Warner House, Harrovian Business Village, Harrow, Middlesex, HA1 3EX Tel: (020) 8423 0100 Fax: (020) 8423 8880 E-mail: nps@northwoodpaper.com

Nottingham Paper Bag Co. Ltd, Mundella Works, Mundella Road, Nottingham, NG2 2EQ Tel: 0115-986 1376 Fax: 0115-986 2018 E-mail: sales@thepaperman.net

O P B Paper Sales Ltd, 26-28 Sidney Road, Stockwell, London, SW9 0TS Tel: (020) 7737 3131 Fax: (020) 7738 7052 E-mail: opb-paper@freenetname.co.uk

Paperun Group Of Companies, 1 East Barnet Road, Barnet, Hertfordshire, EN4 8RR Tel: (020) 8447 4141 Fax: (020) 8447 4241 E-mail: paper4u@paperun.com

Parkfield Paper, 1-2 Faraday Close, Drayton Fields Industrial Esta, Daventry, Northamptonshire, NN11 8RD Tel: (0870) 8506661 Fax: (08708) 506662 E-mail: info@parkfieldpaper.co.uk

Polar Paper, 1 East Barnet Road, Barnet, Hertfordshire, EN4 8RR Tel: (020) 8447 4240 Fax: (020) 8447 4241 E-mail: paper4u@polarint.com

Premier Paper Ltd, Premier House, Faringdon Avenue, Harold Hill, Romford, RM3 8SP Tel: (01708) 330330 Fax: (01708) 330325

R K Burt & Co. Ltd, 57 Union Street, London, SE1 1SG Tel: (020) 7407 6474 Fax: (020) 7403 3672 E-mail: sales@rkburt.co.uk

Thomas Radcliffe Ltd, Unit 21, White Hoe, Old Castletown Road, Douglas, Isle Of Man, IM2 1QD Tel: (01624) 626767 Fax: (01624) 677337 E-mail: thomasradcliffe@mcb.net

Reelstock Ltd, Old Wharf Industrial Estate, Old Wharf Road, Grantham, Lincolnshire, NG31 7AA Tel: (01476) 567979 Fax: (01476) 565542 E-mail: sales@reelstock.freeserve.co.uk

Reid Printers, 79-109 Glasgow Road, Blantyre, Glasgow, G72 0LY Tel: (01698) 826000 Fax: (01698) 824944 E-mail: sales@reid-print-group.co.uk

Robert Horne, Huntsman House, Woodside Road, Eastleigh, Hampshire, SO50 4ET Tel: (023) 8061 8811 Fax: (023) 8061 0005

Robert Horne Co. Ltd, 3 Nicholson Drive, Newtownabbey, County Antrim, BT36 4FB Tel: (028) 9034 2742 Fax: (028) 9034 2413 E-mail: rh.northern.ireland@roberthorne.co.uk

Robert Horne Group plc, Unit 5a Ty-Nant Court, Morganstown, Cardiff, CF15 8LW Tel: (029) 2081 5555 Fax: (029) 2081 5500 E-mail: sales@roberthorne.co.uk

Robert Horne Group plc, 1 Deerdykes Court South, Cumbernauld, Glasgow, G68 9HW Tel: (01236) 617777 Fax: (01236) 735463 E-mail: rh.scotland@roberthorne.co.uk

Robert Horne Group plc, Orleans House, Edmund Street, Liverpool, L3 9NG Tel: 0151-236 4411 Fax: 0151-255 0359 E-mail: total.support@roberthorne.co.uk

Robert Horne Group plc, Huntsman House, B2 Evelyn Street, London, SE8 5DL Tel: (020) 7231 9634 Fax: (020) 7231 5641

Robert Horne Group plc, Horse Fair House, St Faiths Lane, Norwich, NR1 1NE Tel: (01603) 610386 Fax: (01603) 633381 E-mail: rh.norwich@roberthorne.co.uk

Robert Horne Group plc, Huntsman House, The Midway, Nottingham, NG7 2TS Tel: 0115-986 9161 Fax: 0115-986 1384 E-mail: sales@roberthorne.co.uk

Rothera & Brereton, Fairfield House, 186 Armley Road, Leeds, LS12 2QH Tel: 0113-387 4850 Fax: 0113-387 4820

S C A Graphic Paper UK Ltd, 543 New Hythe Lane, Larkfield, Aylesford, Kent, ME20 7PE Tel: (01622) 883000 Fax: (01622) 883895

▶ Scalderhurst Ltd, Ford Mill, The Street, Little Chart, Ashford, Kent, TN27 0QA Tel: (01233) 840711 Fax: (01233) 840794 E-mail: info@scalderhurst.co.uk

Simpac Ltd, Spiersbridge Business Park, Spiersbridge Avenue, Glasgow, G46 8NL Tel: 0141-571 0220 Fax: 0141-571 0260 E-mail: packaging@simpac.co.uk

Southend Paper Bag Co., 90 Archer Avenue, Southend-on-Sea, SS2 4QT Tel: (01702) 463830

Southern Paper Ltd, 32 Factory Lane, Croydon, CR0 3RL Tel: (020) 8681 7979 Fax: (020) 8681 8235

Southern Paper Group Ltd, 14-16 Admiralty Way, Camberley, Surrey, GU15 3DT Tel: (01276) 36464 Fax: (01276) 600065

Thom & Cook Ltd, Units 1-2 Bricklayers Arms Distribution Centre, Mandela Way, London, SE1 5SP Tel: (020) 7231 1114 Fax: (020) 7237 5139 E-mail: sales@dixonandroe.co.uk

U P M Kymmene Ltd, 2 Victoria Street, Altrincham, Cheshire, WA14 1ET Tel: (0870) 6000876 Fax: (0870) 6060876

United Paper Merchants Ltd, 15 Linfield Industrial Estate, Linfield Road, Belfast, BT12 5LA Tel: (028) 9032 7303 Fax: (028) 9043 8702 E-mail: sales@united-paper.com

W. Ridley & Co. Ltd, 12-16 Bean Street, Hull, HU3 2PQ Tel: (01482) 224691 Fax: (01482) 587098 E-mail: info@wridley.co.uk

Waltham Paper Co. Ltd, County Ho, County Industrial Estate, Boars Tye Road, Silver End, Witham, Essex, CM8 3PW Tel: (01425) 622550 Fax: (01277) 261789

Westward Paper Sales, Cofton Road, Marsh Barton Trading Estate, Exeter, EX2 8QW Tel: (01392) 272096

William Walton & Sons, 152 Stamford Street Central, Ashton-under-Lyne, Lancashire, OL6 6AD Tel: 0161-330 1506

Worsley Paper Ltd, 5 Barshaw Park, Leycroft Road, Beumont Leys, Leicester, LE4 1ET Tel: (0870) 2410474 Fax: (0870) 2402630 E-mail: info@worsleypaper.co.uk

WWF Paper Sales UK, Brunswick House, Regent Park 299 Kingston Road, Leatherhead, Surrey, KT22 7LU Tel: (01372) 385100 Fax: (01372) 386366 E-mail: sales@wwfpapersales.co.uk

PAPER PRODUCTS, *See also heading for particular products*

Dynamic Cassette (International) Ltd, Marsh Lane, Boston, Lincolnshire, PE21 7TX Tel: (01205) 355555 Fax: (01205) 354823 E-mail: sales@dci.co.uk

▶ Forth Valley Packaging, 2a Glasgow Road, Denny, Stirlingshire, FK6 5DW Tel: (01324) 820008 Fax: (01324) 820920

Kimberly-Clark Finance Ltd, Thames House, Crete Hall Road, Gravesend, Kent, DA11 9AD Tel: (01474) 336000 Fax: (01474) 336478 E-mail: sales@kimberley-clark.com

▶ M & N Self Adhesive Labels Ltd, Mossneuk Estate, Gleniffer Braes, Neilston, Glasgow, G78 3AL Tel: (01505) 815892 Fax: (01505) 812740 E-mail: mn.labels@talk21.com

Mamelok Holdings Ltd, Northern Way, Bury St. Edmunds, Suffolk, IP32 6NJ Tel: (01284) 762291 Fax: (01284) 703689 E-mail: sales@mamelok.com

▶ Midco Print & Packaging Ltd, Chantry House Grange Business Park, Enderby Road, Whetstone, Leicester, LE8 6EP Tel: 0116-277 4244 Fax: 0116-277 0167 E-mail: sales@midco-pp.co.uk

N C R Ltd, Bakewell Road, Orton Southgate, Peterborough, PE2 6DP Tel: (01733) 363600 Fax: (01733) 363687

▶ Paper Trading Co. Ltd, 59a Alma Road, Clifton, Bristol, BS8 2DE Tel: (0870) 1662663 E-mail: sales@papertradingcompany.com

▶ Paperwork (UK) Ltd, Victoria Road, Skegness, Lincolnshire, PE25 3SN Tel: (01754) 613120

Premiere Products, Bouncers Lane, Cheltenham, Gloucestershire, GL52 5JD Tel: (01242) 537150 Fax: (01242) 528445 E-mail: premiere@premiereproducts.co.uk

U P M Kymmene Ltd, 2 Victoria Street, Altrincham, Cheshire, WA14 1ET Tel: (0870) 6000876 Fax: (0870) 6060876

PAPER PULP IMPORT MERCHANTS OR AGENTS

Paperun Group Of Companies, 1 East Barnet Road, Barnet, Hertfordshire, EN4 8RR Tel: (020) 8447 4141 Fax: (020) 8447 4241 E-mail: paper4u@paperun.com

PAPER PULP MOULDING MACHINERY

Carbonlite Converting Equipment Ltd, Britannia Foundry, Lomax Street, Rochdale, Lancashire, OL12 0DN Tel: (01706) 359000 Fax: (01706) 654378 E-mail: sales@ccequipment.co.uk

PAPER PULP PROCESSING PLANT

BTG UK, Unit 1 Churchill Court, 58 Station Road, North Harrow, Harrow, Middlesex, HA2 7SA Tel: (020) 8515 6050 Fax: (020) 8515 6099 E-mail: sales@btg-group.com

Soderhamn Errikson, Unit 17 Vauxhall Industrial Estate, Greg Street, Reddish, Stockport, Cheshire, SK5 7BR Tel: 0161-429 9437 Fax: 0161-477 0641 E-mail: info@se-saws.co.uk

PAPER PUNCH TOOLS

Meath Engineering Tools Ltd, Black Bourton Road, Carterton, Oxfordshire, OX18 3EZ Tel: (01993) 841041

PAPER ROLLS

Aylesford Paper Sales, Consolidated Paper House, Forstal Road, Aylesford, Kent, ME20 7AE Tel: (01622) 716353 Fax: (01622) 716663 E-mail: sales@aylesfordpaper.co.uk

E. Becker Ltd, 2 Hazlemere View, Hazlemere, High Wycombe, Buckinghamshire, HP15 7BY Tel: (01494) 713777 Fax: (01494) 713888 E-mail: e.becker@breathemail.net

Canarycliff Co. Ltd, Maple Works, Old Shoreham Road, Hove, East Sussex, BN3 7ED Tel: (01273) 726325 Fax: (01273) 203070 E-mail: sales@ticketmedia.com

Allen Glenold Ltd, Glenold House, Crosby Road, Market Harborough, Leicestershire, LE16 9EE Tel: (01858) 467789 Fax: (01858) 432932 E-mail: sales@glenold.co.uk

Meriden Paper Ltd, 38 Meriden Street, Digbeth, Birmingham, B5 5LS Tel: 0121-643 2168 Fax: 0121-631 3378 E-mail: admin@meridenpaper.co.uk

PAPER SACK IMPORT MERCHANTS OR AGENTS

▶ Tyler Packaging Ltd, Fosse Way, Chesterton, Leamington Spa, Warwickshire, CV33 9JY Tel: (01926) 651451 Fax: (01926) 651691 E-mail: info@tylerpackaging.co.uk

PAPER SACK MANUFRS

Alfred Harrold Containers Ltd, Sandyland, Wisbech, Cambridgeshire, PE13 1TF Tel: (01945) 583776 Fax: (01945) 585577 E-mail: elaine@harrolds.co.uk

C B Packaging Ltd, Ballo Drive, Bangor, County Down, BT19 7QY Tel: (028) 9146 3015 Fax: (028) 9127 0048

D S Smith, Mareham Road, Horncastle, Lincolnshire, LN9 6NG Tel: (01507) 523434 Fax: (01507) 523431

Deetronic Fire Systems Ltd, 41 Hope Street, Chester, CH4 8BU Tel: (01244) 659300 Fax: (01244) 659551 E-mail: info@deetronic.com

East Riding Sacks Ltd, Full Sutton Industrial Estate, Stamford Bridge, Full Sutton, York, YO41 1HS Tel: (01759) 371366 Fax: (01759) 372125 E-mail: sales@eastridingsacks.co.uk

Korsnas Packaging Ltd, Priory Road, Rochester, Kent, ME2 2BD Tel: (01634) 716701 Fax: (01634) 717468

Locpac Suppliers, 2 Queensway Business Centre, Waterloo Road, Widnes, Cheshire, WA8 0FD Tel: 0151-423 2828 Fax: 0151-495 2630 E-mail: enquiries@locpac.co.uk

Peter Marsh & Sons Ltd, Dundee Works, 47 Canal Street, Bootle, Merseyside, L20 8AE Tel: 0151-922 1971 Fax: 0151-922 3804 E-mail: sales@petermarsh.co.uk

Poly Print, 59 High St, London, E17 7AD Tel: (020) 8521 4408 Fax: (020) 8521 4568 E-mail: polyprint@carrierbag.freeserve.co.uk

Premier Sacks & Packaging Ltd, Dean Farm, King St Woodford, Woodford, Stockport, Cheshire, SK7 1RL Tel: (01625) 521971 Fax: (01625) 521972 E-mail: info@premiersacks.co.uk

Simpac Ltd, Spiersbridge Business Park, Spiersbridge Avenue, Glasgow, G46 8NL Tel: 0141-571 0220 Fax: 0141-571 0260 E-mail: packaging@simpac.co.uk

PAPER SHEET COUNTING MACHINES

Vacuumatic, Brunel Way 8, Severalls Industrial Park, Colchester, CO4 9QX Tel: (01206) 841100 Fax: (01206) 841166 E-mail: sales@vacuumatic.com

PAPER SHREDDING MACHINES

C L Shredders, Unit 1, Angeldown Farm, Manor Rd, Wantage, Oxon, OX12 8NQ Tel: (0800) 9757235 Fax: (01235) 765474 E-mail: cluton@clshredders.co.uk

PAPER SLITTING AND REWINDING

Corrugated Paper Sales Ltd, Crown Industrial Estate Canal Road, Timperley, Altrincham, Cheshire, WA14 1TF Tel: 0161-976 3000 Fax: 0161-975 3727

Daniel Paper & Packaging, 133 Old Lane, Manchester, M11 1DD Tel: 0161-301 4710 Fax: 0161-370 9753

Halmatex Converting Ltd, Queens Avenue, Hurdsfield Industrial Estate, Macclesfield, Cheshire, SK10 2BN Tel: (01625) 429315 Fax: (01625) 508288 E-mail: sales@halmatex.com

Listan Paper Converters Ltd, Old Wharf Industrial Estate, Old Wharf Road, Grantham, Lincolnshire, NG31 7AA Tel: (01476) 570052 Fax: (01476) 565542 E-mail: sales@listan.freeserve.co.uk

PAPER SLITTING AND REWINDING MACHINES

Abbey Design, Unit 4/5, Glen Trading Estate, Wellyhole Street, Oldham, OL4 3BF Tel: 0161-620 8295 Fax: 0161-785 0130 E-mail: sales@abbeydesign.cc

Atlas Converting Plc, Wolseley Road, Woburn Road Industrial Estate, Kempston, Bedford, MK42 7XT Tel: (01234) 852584 Fax: (01234) 851151 E-mail: sales.atlas@bobstgroup.com

Double R Consol Ltd, Broadfield Distribution Park, Pilsworth Road, Heywood, Lancashire, OL10 2TA Tel: (01706) 623625 Fax: (01706) 366881 E-mail: sales@drc.co.uk

John Lack Equipment, 6 Denington Court, Denington Industrial Estate, Wellingborough, Northamptonshire, NN8 2QR Tel: (01933) 441646 Fax: (01933) 441476 E-mail: johnlackequipment@tiscali.co.uk

PAPER TAPES, *See headings for particular applications etc*

PAPER TEST EQUIPMENT

▶ Jensen Barker Technical Services Ltd, Fowlswick Industrial Estate, Fowlswick Lane, Allington, Chippenham, Wiltshire, SN14 6QE Tel: (01249) 783844 Fax: (01249) 783306 E-mail: info@jensen-barker.com

Messmer Instruments Ltd, Unit F1 Imperial Business Estate, West Mill, Gravesend, Kent, DA11 0DL Tel: (01474) 566488 Fax: (01474) 560310 E-mail: sales@messmerinstruments.com

PAPER TOWEL SUPPLY SERVICES

Cherwell Packaging Ltd, Southfield Road, Kineton Road Industrial Estate, Southam, Warwickshire, CV47 0FB Tel: (01926) 817585 Fax: (01926) 817806 E-mail: sparkle@cleaningnet.co.uk

Leetex Wipers & Disposables Ltd, Unit 4, Hollis Road, Earlesfield Lane Industrial Estate, Grantham, Lincolnshire, NG31 7QH Tel: (01476) 577777 Fax: (01476) 577774

M & D Cleaning Supplies Ltd, Grove Road, Upholland, Skelmersdale, Lancashire, WN8 0LH Tel: (01695) 632765 Fax: (01695) 632760 E-mail: sales@mandd.co.uk

PAPER TRIMMERS

Rotatrim, 8 Caxton Park, Caxton Road, Elm Farm Industrial Estate, Bedford, MK41 0TY Tel: (01234) 224545 Fax: (01234) 224540 E-mail: sales@rotatrim.co.uk

PAPER TUBES

Caraustar Industrial & Consumer Products Group Ltd, 86 Bison Place, Moss Side, Leyland, PR26 7QR Tel: (01772) 621562 Fax: (01772) 622263 E-mail: david.dredge@caraustar.com

Corenso (UK) Ltd, North Tyne Industrial Estate, Whitley Road, Longbenton, Newcastle Upon Tyne, NE12 9SZ Tel: 0191-266 0222 Fax: 0191-270 1663

Curran Packaging Co. Ltd, Thames Industrial Park, Princess Margaret Road, East Tilbury, Tilbury, Essex, RM18 8RH Tel: (01375) 857131 Fax: (01375) 856884 E-mail: sales@curran.co.uk

Fibrestar Drums Ltd, Redhouse Lane, Disley, Stockport, Cheshire, SK12 2NW Tel: (01663) 764141 Fax: (01633) 762967 E-mail: sales@fibrestar.co.uk

Holmes Mann & Co. Ltd, 17 Harris Street, Bradford, West Yorkshire, BD1 5HZ Tel: (01274) 735881 Fax: (01274) 306324 E-mail: oscar@holman.co.uk

E. Revell & Sons Ltd, Unit 1C Joesph Wilson Industrial Estate, Mill Strood Road, Whitstable, Kent, CT5 3PS Tel: (01227) 277020 Fax: (01227) 770839

Smurfit Composites, Richmond Works, Moresby Road, Hensingham, Whitehaven, Cumbria, CA28 8TS Tel: (01946) 61671 Fax: (01946) 592281

PAPER WIPES

Peter Grant Papers Ltd, Stafford Park 12, Telford, Shropshire, TF3 3BJ Tel: (01952) 292200 Fax: (01952) 291108 E-mail: sales@pgpapers.com

Kitchen Master, Unit 8 Ashurst Drive, Stockport, Cheshire, SK3 0RY Tel: 0161-428 7777 Fax: 0161-428 7755

Whitminster International Ltd, Dudbridge Road, Stroud, Gloucestershire, GL5 3HF Tel: (01453) 762266 Fax: (01453) 762277 E-mail: mailroom@whitminster.co.uk

PAPER, COATED/COATING, *See Coated Paper/Board etc*

PAPER, COMPUTER, *See Computer etc*

PAPER, SILICONE TREATED/ COATED

▶ Ardmair Enterprises Ltd, 82 Brown Edge Road, Buxton, Derbyshire, SK17 7AF Tel: (01298) 78926 Fax: (01298) 25122 E-mail: mail@ardmairenterprises.co.uk

Kalico Products Ltd, Panty Buarth, Gwernaffield, Mold, Clwyd, CH7 5ER Tel: (01352) 742100 Fax: (01352) 742102E-mail: info@kalico.co.uk

PAPER, TECHNICAL/SPECIAL

Arjo Wiggins Fine Papers Ltd, Chineham, Basingstoke, Hampshire, RG24 8BA Tel: (01256) 728728 Fax: (01256) 728889

Portals, Overton Mill, Overton, Basingstoke, Hampshire, RG25 3JG Tel: (01256) 770770 Fax: (01256) 770937 E-mail: sales.portals@delarue.co.uk

PAPERBOARD/CARDBOARD MANUFRS

▶ Able Packaging Designs Ltd, 23 Buckland Road, Penmill Trading Estate, Pen Mill Trading Estate, Yeovil, Somerset, BA21 5HA Tel: (01935) 470070 Fax: (01935) 477706 E-mail: sales@ablebox.com

Antalis Ltd, 2 Blackwater Business Park, Mallusk Way, Newtownabbey, County Antrim, BT36 4AA Tel: (0870) 6073101 Fax: (0870) 6073156

Arctic Paper UK Ltd, Quadrant House, 47 Croydon Road, Caterham, Surrey, CR3 6PB Tel: (01883) 331800 Fax: (01883) 330560 E-mail: info-uk@arcticpaper.com

B P B Paperboard Ltd, B P B UK Service Centre, East Leake, Loughborough, Leicestershire, LE12 6JU Tel: 0115-945 1000 Fax: 0115-945 1199

▶ Caps Cases Ltd, Nurseries Road, Baillieston, Glasgow, G69 6UL Tel: 0141-773 3337 Fax: 0141-773 4443

▶ Chevler Packaging Ltd, Tir Y Berth Industrial Estate, Hengoed, Mid Glamorgan, CF82 8AU Tel: (01443) 865900

▶ Complete Packaging Ltd, Oaklands Business Park, Old Icknield Way, Benson, Wallingford, Oxfordshire, OX10 6PW Tel: (01491) 832222 Fax: (01491) 834222 E-mail: sales@completepackaging.co.uk

▶ D S Smith, Block 13, Vale of Leven Industrial Estate, Dumbarton, G82 3PD Tel: (01389) 721102 Fax: (01389) 721060 E-mail: sales@dumbartondssp.com

Danisco Pack Rhondda Ltd, Ynyshir Road, Ynyshir, Porth, Mid Glamorgan, CF39 0RF Tel: (01443) 683121 Fax: (01443) 685856 E-mail: stephen.ridley@dssp.com

Deva Hawarden Board & Display, Kus Industrial Estate, Manor Lane, Hawarden, Deeside, Clwyd, CH5 3PJ Tel: (01244) 532312 Fax: (01244) 520858 E-mail: enquiries@hawarden.co.uk

▶ Don Greenwood & Partners, Main Road, Nether Broughton, Melton Mowbray, Leicestershire, LE14 3HB Tel: (01664) 823000 Fax: (01664) 823408

▶ Euro Dividers Co. Ltd, Unit 3, Brookfield Industrial Estate, Leacon Road, Ashford, Kent, TN23 4TU Tel: (01233) 649500 Fax: (01233) 649509 E-mail: sales@eurodividers.co.uk

▶ Floryn Ltd, Mid Kent Business Park, Sortmill Road, Snodland, Kent, ME6 5UA Tel: (01634) 240444 Fax: (01634) 241444

Iggesund Paperboard Ltd, Siddick, Workington, Cumbria, CA14 1JX Tel: (01900) 601000 Fax: (01900) 605000

▶ Jewell Pak Ltd, Unit 1, Barton Industrial Estate, Faldo Road, Barton-le-Clay, Bedford, MK45 4RP Tel: (01582) 882543 Fax: (01582) 882548 E-mail: jewellpak@btconnect.com

▶ Kendon Packaging, 37 Wigman Road, Nottingham, NG8 4PA Tel: 0115-916 0055 Fax: 0115-916 0056 E-mail: sales@kendonpackaging.co.uk

▶ Latrave Paper & Cardboard Products, Unit 2 Edison Close, Park Farm Industrial Estate, Wellingborough, Northamptonshire, NN8 6AH Tel: (01933) 678548 Fax: (01933) 678987

Limehouse Boardmills Ltd, 26 Crittall Road, Witham, Essex, CM8 3DR Tel: (01376) 519519 Fax: (01376) 514520 E-mail: sales@limehouse-board.co.uk

▶ Majestic Corrugated Cases Ltd, Unit 30 Parkrose Industrial Estate, Middlemore Road, Smethwick, West Midlands, B66 2DZ Tel: (01902) 733330 Fax: 0121-558 7000

Mason's Paper Ltd, 1 Island House, Bluestem Road, Ipswich, IP3 9RR Tel: (01473) 711123 Fax: (01473) 270109

Mayr Melnhof UK Ltd, Bourne House, Bourne Close, Calcot, Reading, RG31 7BS Tel: 0118-942 5504 Fax: 0118-942 0750

▶ Northern Packaging Distributors Ltd, 1 Angels Close, Aycliffe Industrial Park, Newton Aycliffe, County Durham, DL5 6BG Tel: (01325) 300133

▶ Remploy Ltd, Unit 1, Banbeth Industrial Estate, Leven, Fife, KY8 5HD Tel: (01333) 429607

▶ Sca Packaging Telford, Halesfield 13, Telford, Shropshire, TF7 4PL Tel: (01952) 681950

Slater Harrison & Co. Ltd, Lowerhouse Mills, Bollington, Macclesfield, Cheshire, SK10 5HW Tel: (01625) 578900 Fax: (01625) 578972 E-mail: l.preston@slater-harrison.co.uk

Sonoco Board Mills, Holywell Green, Halifax, West Yorkshire, HX4 9PY Tel: (01422) 374741 Fax: (01422) 371495

Sonoco Consumer Products Ltd, Stokes Street, Manchester, M11 4QX Tel: 0161-230 7000 Fax: 0161-230 1200E-mail: info@sonoco.com

Sonoco Industrial Products, 4 Portadown Road, Lurgan, Craigavon, County Armagh, BT66 8QW Tel: (028) 3832 3501 Fax: (028) 3832 3781 E-mail: info@sonoco.co.uk

Trafalgar Cases Ltd, Stanhope Works, Primrose Hill, Kings Langley, Hertfordshire, WD4 8HS Tel: (01923) 261155 Fax: (01923) 268064 E-mail: sales@trafalgarcases.com

▶ V Pack Sales Ltd, Tollgate Road, Burscough, Ormskirk, Lancashire, L40 8LD Tel: (01704) 895008

Westward Paper Sales, Cofton Road, Marsh Barton Trading Estate, Exeter, EX2 8QW Tel: (01392) 272096

PAPERBOARD/CARDBOARD, RECYCLED

Donald Murray, 211 Maclellan Street, Glasgow, G41 1RR Tel: 0141-427 1271 Fax: 0141-427 6999 E-mail: sales@donald-murray-paper.co.uk

Hollands Recycling Ltd, 1 Holland Park, Bentley Road South, Wednesbury, West Midlands, WS10 8LN Tel: 0121-526 2454 Fax: 0121-568 6148 E-mail: enquiries@hollands-recycling.co.uk

PAPERWEIGHTS

▶ Dora Mouse, 8 Thorley Crescent, Peterborough, PE2 9RF Tel: (01733) 892026

PARACHUTES

G Q Parachutes Ltd, Isfryn Industrial Estate, Blackmill, Bridgend, Mid Glamorgan, CF35 6EQ Tel: (01656) 840300 Fax: (01656) 840396

Thomas Sports Equipment Ltd, Pinfold Lane Industrial Estate, Bridlington, North Humberside, YO16 6XS Tel: (01262) 678299 Fax: (01262) 602063 E-mail: sales@thomas-sports.com

PARAFORMALDEHYDE

Synthite Ltd, Alyn Works, Denbigh Road, Mold, Clwyd, CH7 1BT Tel: (01352) 752521 Fax: (01352) 700182

PARAPET FENCING OR RAILING

Balmer Lindley Group, Dragonby Vale Enterprise Park, Mannaberg Way, Scunthorpe, South Humberside, DN15 8XF Tel: (01724) 289119 Fax: (01724) 281478 E-mail: mail@balmer-group.co.uk

Kilmarnock Engineers, Spittalhill Works, Ayr Road, Kilmarnock, Ayrshire, KA1 5NX Tel: (01563) 830198 Fax: (01563) 830692

P & R Engineering Midlands Ltd, Cable Street, Wolverhampton, WV2 2HX Tel: (01902) 870637 Fax: (01902) 871569

Varley & Gulliver Ltd, Alfred Street, Sparkbrook, Birmingham, B12 8JR Tel: 0121-773 2441 Fax: 0121-766 6875 E-mail: sales@v-and-g.co.uk

PARCEL CONVEYOR SYSTEMS

Caljan Rite Hite Ltd, Moorbridge Road, Bingham, Nottingham, NG13 8GG Tel: (01949) 838850 Fax: (01949) 836953 E-mail: caljanritehite@caljanritehite.co.uk

PARCEL DELIVERY SERVICES

▶ A N C Kent Ltd, Gateway Centre, Castle Road, Sittingbourne, Kent, ME10 3RN Tel: (01795) 413620 Fax: (01795) 413610 E-mail: sales0008@anc.co.uk

▶ A & R Courier & Delivery Service Ltd, CWM Tawel Pontardulais Road, Cross Hands, Llanelli, Dyfed, SA14 6PG Tel: (01269) 845194 Fax: (01269) 845194 E-mail: enqs@swansea-couriers.co.uk

▶ Anc Launceston, Unit 4b, Pennygillam Indust Estate, Pennygillam Industrial Estate, Launceston, Cornwall, PL15 7ED Tel: (01566) 773330 Fax: (01566) 777486 E-mail: sales0072@anc.co.uk

▶ Anywhere Same Day Couriers, Manchester Business Park, 3000 Aviator Way, Manchester, M22 5TG Tel: (0845) 4567722 Fax: (0870) 4323377 E-mail: info@anywhere.ltd.uk

▶ Carousel, Gateway Centre Eurolink Industrial Centre, Castle Road, Sittingbourne, Kent, ME10 3RN Tel: (01795) 413600 Fax: (01795) 413610 E-mail: sales@carousellogistics.co.uk

▶ Crystal Consult, Barton Road, Nuneaton, Warwickshire, CV10 7BN Tel: (024) 7638 5371 Fax: (024) 7638 5371 E-mail: sales@crystal-consult.co.uk

D X L Parcels, Unit 5 Oakfield Trading Estate, Oakfield Road, Altrincham, Cheshire, WA14 5PR Tel: 0161-941 6277 Fax: 0161-941 7383 E-mail: operations@dxlparcels.co.uk

▶ Deca Freelance Couriers Ltd, 240 Burton Road, Lincoln, LN1 3UB Tel: (01522) 851612 Fax: (01522) 851613 E-mail: deca.couriers3@ntlworld.com

▶ Easy Parcel Worldwide, Lawlor House, Cawley Hatch, Harlow, Essex, CM19 5AN Tel: (0800) 1804995 Fax: (01279) 433326 E-mail: sales@easyparcelworldwide.com

▶ Easy Parcel Worldwide, Mercury House, Russell Gardens, Wickford, Essex, SS11 8BH Tel: (0800) 180 4995 Fax: (01268) 570621 E-mail: sales@easyparcel.net

▶ Express Freight Solutions, 15 Leyden Road, Stevenage, Hertfordshire, SG1 2BW Tel: (01707) 333600 Fax: (01438) 725800 E-mail: enfield@xpd.co.uk

PARCEL DELIVERY SERVICES – *continued*

▶ Express Freight Solutions, Marsden Close, Welwyn Garden City, Herts, AL8 6YE Tel: 0870 3505300 Fax: 0870 3505301 E-mail: info@expressfreightsolutions.com
▶ Home Delivery Network Ltd, Abbott House, Abbey Road, London, NW10 7UA Tel: (020) 8961 8774 Fax: (020) 8961 3763
▶ Interparcel, Norman House, 15 Stephenson Way, Crawley, West Sussex, RH10 1TN Tel: 08700 273733 Fax: 01293 785990 E-mail: sales@interparcel.com
▶ iPort (Europe) Ltd, Tudor House, Higham Common Road, Higham, Barnsley, South Yorkshire, S75 1PF Tel: 08701 999 150 Fax: 08701 99 15 15 E-mail: sales@iport.co.uk
▶ Logistical Services Limited, 58 Hellesdon Park Road, Drayton High Road, Norwich, NR6 5DR Tel: 01603 484569 Fax: 01603 427100 E-mail: simon.feilden@comment.uk.net
▶ Mailworkshop, Unit31 Criftin Enterprise Centre, Oxton Road, Epperstone, Nottingham, NG14 6AT Tel: 0115-965 4446 Fax: 0115-965 4033 E-mail: sales@mailworkshop.co.uk
Parcelcarry.co.uk, 1 Lauderdale, Farnborough, Hampshire, GU14 0RR Tel: (01252) 642986 E-mail: info@parcelcarry.co.uk
Parcelflight.Co.Uk, 96 Manchester Road, Worsley, Manchester, M28 3FU Tel: 0161-975 7700 E-mail: parcelflight@ntlworld.com
▶ Rapidline Ltd, Unit 1, 1000 North Circular Road, London, NW2 7JP Tel: 0808 101 6 101 Fax: 020 8830 8379 E-mail: info@doorsteptotheworld.com
▶ Same-day Dispatch Services, International House, 226 Seven Sisters Road, London, N4 3GG Tel: 0845 226 2994 E-mail: admin@samedaydispatch.uk.com
▶ Tuffnells Parcels Express Ltd, Azalea Road, Rogerstone, Newport, Gwent, NP10 9SA Tel: (01633) 891010 Fax: (01633) 891044 E-mail: nick.walters@tuffnells.co.uk

PARCHMENT/VELLUM

William Cowley, 97 Caldecote Street, Newport Pagnell, Buckinghamshire, MK16 0DB Tel: (01908) 610038 Fax: (01908) 611071

PARK OR ROADSIDE OR SHELTER SEATS

A J Bernasconi, 15 Mill Green, Warboys, Huntingdon, Cambridgeshire, PE28 2SA Tel: (01487) 822660 Fax: (0870) 1413038
Earth Anchors Ltd, 15 Campbell Road, Croydon, CR0 2SQ Tel: (020) 8684 9601 Fax: (020) 8684 2230 E-mail: enquiries@earth-anchors.com
Macemain Engineering Ltd, Boyle Road, Willowbrook East Indust, Corby, Northamptonshire, NN17 5XU Tel: (01536) 401331 Fax: (01536) 401298 E-mail: sales@macemainamstad.com
Washbourn & Garrett Ltd, Ashcroft Road, Knowsley Industrial Park North, Liverpool, L33 7TW Tel: 0151-546 2901 Fax: 0151-548 5562 E-mail: enquiries@washbourngarrett.co.uk

PARQUET OR WOOD BLOCK FLOORING

A D Flooring, 23 Ebbisham Road, Worcester Park, Surrey, KT4 8ND Tel: (020) 8330 5419 Fax: (020) 8330 1180 E-mail: adflooring@fsmail.net
Functional Foam Beacons Products, Efi Industrial Estate, Brecon Road, Merthyr Tydfil, Mid Glamorgan, CF47 8RB Tel: (01685) 350011 Fax: (01685) 388396 E-mail: sales@beaconsproducts.co.uk
Kahrs, Unit 2 68 Bognor Road, Chichester, West Sussex, PO19 8NS Tel: (01243) 784417 Fax: (01243) 531237 E-mail: sales@kahrs.se
Mercia Flooring Ltd, 59 The Square, Dunchurch, Rugby, Warwickshire, CV22 6NU Tel: (01788) 522168 Fax: (01788) 811847 E-mail: sales@merciaflooring.co.uk
Victorian Wood Works Contracts Ltd, 54 River Road, Creekmouth, Barking, Essex, IG11 0DW Tel: (020) 8507 5996 Fax: (020) 8507 1149 E-mail: sales@victorianwoodworks.co.uk
Welland Flooring Co Corby Ltd, Weldon Road, Corby, Northamptonshire, NN17 1UZ Tel: (01536) 265195 Fax: (01536) 261323 E-mail: sales@wellandflooring.co.uk
The Worldwide Wood Co., 154 Colney Hatch Lane, London, N10 1ER Tel: (020) 8365 2157 Fax: (020) 8365 3965 E-mail: sales@solidwoodflooring.com

PART P ELECTRICAL TESTING

▶ HMC Electrical Services Ltd, Maidstone Road, Nettlestead, Maidstone, Kent, ME18 5HP Tel: (01622) 870088 Fax: (01622) 870077 E-mail: hmcelectrical@btconnect.com

PART WORN TYRES

Fieldens plc, Star House, Onehouse, Stowmarket, Suffolk, IP14 3EL Tel: (01449) 675071 Fax: (01449) 678282 E-mail: sales@fieldens.co.uk
Vacu Lug Traction Tyres Ltd, Gonerby Hill Foot, Grantham, Lincolnshire, NG31 8HF Tel: (01476) 593095 Fax: (01476) 513809 E-mail: info@vaculug.com

PARTICLE COUNTING INSTRUMENTS

▶ Malvern Instruments Ltd, Enigma Business Park, Grovewood Road, Malvern, Worcestershire, WR14 1XZ Tel: (01684) 892456 Fax: (01684) 892789 E-mail: info@malvern.co.uk
Particle Measuring Systems Europe Ltd, Grovewood Road, Malvern, Worcestershire, WR14 1XZ Tel: (01684) 581000 Fax: (01684) 560337 E-mail: marketing@pmeasuring.co.uk
Turnkey Instruments Ltd, Units 1-2 Dalby Court, Gadbrook Business Centre, Rudheath, Northwich, Cheshire, CW9 7TN Tel: (01606) 44520 Fax: (01606) 331526 E-mail: shop@turnkey-instruments.com

PARTICLE SIZE ANALYSER MANUFRS

Brookhaven Instruments Ltd, Chapel House, Stockwood, Redditch, Worcestershire, B96 6ST Tel: (01386) 792727 Fax: (01386) 792720 E-mail: info@brookhaven.co.uk
Micromeritics Ltd, Chestnut House, 178-182 High Street North, Dunstable, Bedfordshire, LU6 1AT Tel: (01582) 475248 Fax: (01582) 475252 E-mail: ussales@micromeritics.com
▶ Polymer Laboratories Ltd, Essex Road, Church Stretton, Shropshire, SY6 6AX Tel: (01694) 723581 Fax: (01694) 722171 E-mail: sales@polymerlabs.com

PARTITION COMPONENTS

Abbey Storage & Office Systems Ltd, International House, 30 Villa Road, Benfleet, Essex, SS7 5QL Tel: (01268) 794070 Fax: (01268) 566141 E-mail: doug@abbeystorage.freeserve.co.uk
Advanced Industries Ltd, 4 Avocet Trading Estate, Richardson Street, High Wycombe, Buckinghamshire, HP11 2SB Tel: (01494) 450722 Fax: (01494) 448998 E-mail: sales@office-refurbishment.com
Birmingham Partitioning Supplies Ltd, Unit 54 Rovex Business Park, Hay Hall Road, Birmingham, B11 2AQ Tel: 0121-706 0666 Fax: 0121-708 1355 E-mail: sales@bhampartitions.co.uk
C P Supplies Ltd, 1-3 Brixton Road, London, SW9 6DE Tel: (020) 7582 2911 Fax: (020) 7582 0271 E-mail: bmkennington@cpsupplies.co.uk
H E P Rolled Sections, Bayton Road, Exhall, Coventry, CV7 9EJ Tel: (024) 7658 5600 Fax: (024) 7658 5649 E-mail: info@metsec.com
Interior Projects Southern Ltd, 2 Burstow Park Business Centre, Antlands Lane, Shipley Bridge, Horley, Surrey, RH6 9TF Tel: (01293) 823737 Fax: (01293) 823738 E-mail: ip.s@virgin.net
Komfort Office Environments Plc, Units 1-10, Whittle Way, Crawley, West Sussex, RH10 9RW Tel: (01293) 592500 Fax: (01293) 553271 E-mail: general@komfort.com
Lining Systems Ltd, Unit 8 Woodcock Trading Estate, 277 Barton Street, Gloucester, GL1 4JE Tel: (01452) 387771 Fax: (01452) 387771 E-mail: sales@liningsystems.co.uk
Mirage Interiors Ltd, 12 Sand Road, Kewstoke, Weston-super-Mare, Avon, BS22 9UH Tel: (01934) 612439 Fax: (01934) 641900 E-mail: walls@mirage-interiors.com
Nevill Long, Chartwell Drive, Wigston, Leicestershire, LE18 2FL Tel: 0116-257 0670 Fax: 0116-257 0044 E-mail: sales@longnevill.co.uk
Newbyres Engineering, Unit 2, Sherwood Industrial Estate, Bonnyrigg, Midlothian, EH19 3LW Tel: 0131-653 6646 Fax: 0131-663 9046 E-mail: newbyres@aol.com
P & M Fixings, Franchise Street, Wednesbury, West Midlands, WS10 9RG Tel: 0121-526 5775 Fax: 0121-568 6108 E-mail: info@pmfixings.com
Pixie Developments Ltd, 2 New Mills Industrial Estate, Post Office Road, Inkpen, Hungerford, Berkshire, RG17 9PU Tel: (01488) 669184 Fax: (01488) 669185 E-mail: pixiedev.ltd@ukonline.co.uk
Sound Interiots Ltd, 4 Levens Road, Newby Road Industrial Estate, Hazel Grove, Stockport, Cheshire, SK7 5DL Tel: 0161-456 8282 Fax: 0161-456 3030 E-mail: all@sound-interiors.co.uk
Steelcase Strafor plc, Second Floor 2 Carriage Row, 183 Eversholt St, London, NW1 1BU Tel: (020) 7874 0000 Fax: (020) 7380 0153
Top Floor Ltd, 100 Cobham Road, Ferndown Industrial Estate, Wimborne, Dorset, BH21 7PQ Tel: (01202) 876339 Fax: (01202) 891047 E-mail: sales@topfloor.co.uk

PARTITION CONTRACTORS OR SUPPLIERS

A L M Partitioning, 9 East End, Langtoft, Peterborough, PE6 9LP Tel: (01733) 266333 Fax: (01733) 266333
A W R Ceilings & Partitions, Jack O Watton Industrial Estate, Lichfield Road, Water Orton, Birmingham, B46 1NU Tel: 0121-748 2608 Fax: 0121-776 7561 E-mail: triciaharris@eidosnet.co.uk
A30 Interiors, 167 Cannon Workshops, 3 Cannon Drive, London, E14 4AS Tel: (0800) 3161000 Fax: (0207) 719 844 E-mail: enq@a30interiors.com
Aronn Interiors Ltd, 17 West Avenue, Aldwick, Bognor Regis, West Sussex, PO21 3QP Tel: (01243) 823904 Fax: (01243) 841132 E-mail: ceilings@aronn.wanadoo.co.uk
Ata, 37 Smiths Way, Water Orton, Birmingham, B46 1TW Tel: 0121-748 5785 Fax: 0121-748 5785
Axis Intabuild Ltd, PO Box 50, Cranbrook, Kent, TN18 4EL Tel: (01580) 753798 Fax: (01580) 754079 E-mail: richardaxis@btopenworld.com
Axis Scotland Ltd, 12 Auchingramont Road, Hamilton, Lanarkshire, ML3 6JT Tel: (01698) 785000 Fax: (01698) 785111 E-mail: enquiries@axis.gb.com
B & K Ceilings Ltd, Unit B8 Manor Development Centre, 40 Alison Crescent, Sheffield, S2 1AS Tel: 0114-253 1620 Fax: 0114-239 4976
Barnards Ceilings & Partitions Ltd, Mulberry House, Holders Green, Lindsell, Dunmow, Essex, CM6 3QQ Tel: (01371) 870104 Fax: (01371) 870105
Barnes Interiors Ltd, Unit 1 Urban Hive 410, Avenue West Syline 120, Great Notley, Braintree, Essex, CM77 7AA Tel: (01376) 528627 Fax: (01376) 325935 E-mail: info@barnesinteriors.co.uk
Blakiston Ltd, 38 St. Helens Road, Hayling Island, Hampshire, PO11 0BT Tel: (023) 9246 9698 Fax: (023) 9246 9716 E-mail: sales@partitions.net
Bridger & Co Office Interiors, South Ease Cottage, Send Marsh Road, Ripley, Woking, Surrey, GU23 6JQ Tel: (01483) 224920 Fax: (01483) 211599
C A P S Ltd, 80 Pike Helve St, Golds Hill, West Bromwich, West Midlands, B70 0TU Tel: 0121-557 9553 Fax: 0121-522 2795 E-mail: caps.ltd@lineone.net
C F C Group Ltd, Kilnbrook House, Rosekiln Lane, Reading, RG2 0BY Tel: (0845) 0540040 Fax: (0845) 0540041 E-mail: cfc@cfcgroup.co.uk
Carter Ceilings Ltd, 2 Cunningham Road, Stirling, FK7 7SW Tel: (01786) 464914 Fax: (01786) 450012 E-mail: info@carter.co.uk
Castell Ceilings Co, Willow View, 62 Marshfield Road, Castleton, Cardiff, CF3 2UW Tel: (01633) 681411 Fax: (01633) 681700
City Office Services Ltd, Templeworks, Brett Passage, Brett Road, London, E8 1JR Tel: (020) 8510 0555 Fax: (020) 8510 0666
City Partitions, 13 Chesterfield Road, Ashford, Middlesex, TW15 2NB Tel: (01784) 255552
Complete Interior Contracts, Caxton Hall, 88-92 Chapel Street, Salford, M3 5DW Tel: 0161-834 1285 Fax: 0161-834 2170
Construction & Shopfitting Ltd, 117, Piccotts End, Hemel Hempstead, Hertfordshire, HP1 3AU Tel: (01442) 244117 Fax: (01442) 233274 E-mail: cs.co@virgin.net
CPD Distribution, 8 Commerce Way, Trafford Park, Manchester, M17 1HW Tel: 0161-874 5311 Fax: 0161-874 5312 E-mail: mikejennion@cpdplc.co.uk
▶ Davroy Contracts Ltd, 510 Queslett Road, Great Barr, Birmingham, B43 7EJ Tel: 0121-325 0899 Fax: 0121-360 6840 E-mail: post@davroy.co.uk
Dawber Williamson (Lincs) Ltd, Torrington House, Torrington Street, Grimsby, South Humberside, DN32 9QH Tel: (01472) 347532 Fax: (01472) 344223
Decke Newcastle Ltd, 244 Park View, Whitley Bay, Tyne & Wear, NE26 3QX Tel: 0191-251 2606 Fax: 0191-251 4880 E-mail: decke.newcastle@contactbox.co.uk
Divided Space Ltd, Old Station Yard, Cawston, Norwich, NR10 4BB Tel: (01603) 872935 Fax: 01603 872920
Dividers Ltd, Unit 1, Llanelli Gate, Dafen, Llanelli, Dyfed, SA14 8LQ Tel: (01269) 844877 Fax: (01269) 831112 E-mail: sales@esperowalls.com
Duval Products Ltd, Dexion Storage Centre, Armoury Way, London, SW18 1EU Tel: (020) 8870 7541 Fax: (020) 8870 2657 E-mail: sales@duvalproducts.co.uk
Eleco Timber Frame Ltd, Oaksmere Business Park, Eye Airfield Industrial Estate, Yaxley, Eye, Suffolk, IP23 8BW Tel: (01379) 783465 Fax: (01379) 783659 E-mail: stramit@eleco.com
Firsmere Engineering Ltd, Aston Lane, Sharnford, Hinckley, Leicestershire, LE10 3PA Tel: (01455) 273940 Fax: (01455) 273996
Flexiwall Co. Ltd, 15 Iliad Street, Liverpool, L5 3LU Tel: 0151-207 1103 Fax: 0151-207 1588
FOCUS Interiors Ltd, Wellsway Works, Wells Road, Radstock, BA3 3RZ Tel: (01761) 420055 Fax: (01761) 420077 E-mail: enquiries@focusinteriorsltd.co.uk
Global Interiors Ltd, Broadway, Ilminster, Somerset, TA19 7ER Tel: (01460) 57700 Fax: 01460 52736
Groestar Ltd, 1 Morley Business Centre, Tonbridge, Kent, TN9 1RA Tel: (01732) 771121 Fax: (01732) 771124 E-mail: sales@groestar.co.uk
Guildford Partitions, Tylers Croft, Abbotswood Close, Guildford, Surrey, GU1 1XA Tel: (01483) 539068 Fax: (01483) 539068
H E M Group Ltd, H E M House, Kirkstall Road, Leeds, LS4 2BT Tel: 0113-263 2222 Fax: 0113-231 0237 E-mail: info@heminteriors.com
H J S J Ltd, Unit 5 Gorslas Road Industrial Estate, Gorslas, Llanelli, Dyfed, SA14 7NN Tel: (01269) 831181 Fax: (01269) 845648 E-mail: sales@hjsjltd.co.uk
H & R Interiors, 155 High Street, Rhyl, Clwyd, LL18 1UF Tel: (01745) 344443 Fax: (01745) 343303
Hampshire Mezzanine Floors Ltd, Hawkeswood Road, Southampton, SO18 1AB Tel: (023) 8063 1888 Fax: (023) 8023 0033 E-mail: sales@hmf-uk.com
Harrington Associates Ltd, Unit 1 Bright St., Coventry, CV6 5EB Tel: (024) 7666 2731 Fax: (024) 7663 8058 E-mail: sales@harringtonassociates.co.uk
Headway Storage Systems Ltd, 142 Bath Road, Totterdown, Bristol, BS4 3EF Tel: 0117-971 2222 Fax: 0117-972 4912
Hemax Ceilings Ltd, 167 The Grove, Biggin Hill, Kent, TN16 3UJ Tel: (01959) 701554 Fax: (01959) 573006
Hemming & Morris (Shopfitters) Ltd, 60 Lincoln Road, Olton, Birmingham, B27 6NZ Tel: 0121-706 5740 Fax: 0121-706 6192 E-mail: sales@hemmingmorris.co.uk
Interior Contracts Group, Ethos House, 52 Tanners Drive, Blakelands, Milton Keynes, MK14 5BW Tel: (01908) 216766 Fax: (01908) 216744
Ivor Hopkins Suspended Ceilings & Partitions, 10 Kingsmead, Station Road, Kings Cliffe, Peterborough, PE8 6YH Tel: (01780) 470048 Fax: (01780) 470039 E-mail: sales@ivorhopkins.co.uk
G.R. Kinder (Ceilings) Ltd, Unit 1 Rochdale Road Industrial Estate, Church Street, Middleton, Manchester, M24 2PY Tel: (0161) 654 8084 Fax: (0161) 655 3762 E-mail: paul@kinderinteriors.co.uk
Leemo (Partitions) Ltd, Essex House, Kelfall Street, Oldham, OL9 6HR Tel: 0161-665 4666 Fax: 0161-624 4376
Lifetime Interiors Ltd, Unit D2, 86-102 King Street, Farnworth, Bolton, BL4 7AS Tel: (01204) 574166 Fax: (01204) 574263 E-mail: mail@lifetimeinteriors.co.uk
M G K Engineering (Northern) Ltd, Polbeth Industrial Estate, Polbeth, West Calder, West Lothian, EH55 8TJ Tel: (01506) 871757 Fax: (01506) 873400 E-mail: sales@mgkscot.co.uk
M K Contracts Ltd, 50 Buntingbridge Road, Ilford, Essex, IG2 7LR Tel: (020) 8518 2100 Fax: (020) 8518 2984
Mcfeggan Brown Ltd, Unit 1, 38 Midland Road, Staplehill, Bristol, BS16 4NW Tel: 0117-957 3355 Fax: 0117-956 7221
Mcof Ltd, 3 Station Road, Brompton on Swale, Richmond, North Yorkshire, DL10 7SN Tel: (01748) 812612 Fax: (01748) 812618 E-mail: thomaslinckh@btconnect.com
Mainline Ceilings & Partitioners, The Stables Pickerings Farm, Halegate Road, Widnes, Cheshire, WA8 8LY Tel: 0151-425 2412 Fax: 0151-425 4342
Mark II Ltd, Unit S3B Westcott Venture Park, Aylesbury, Buckinghamshire, HP18 0XB Tel: (01296) 653088 Fax: (01296) 653089 E-mail: mail@mark-two.co.uk
Midland Ceilings Ltd, 63 Chartwell Drive, Wigston, Leicestershire, LE18 2FS Tel: 0116-288 7721 Fax: 0116-288 7022
Midland Tool Manufacturing Co. Ltd, Unit 13, Belle Eau Park, Bilsthorpe, Newark, Nottinghamshire, NG22 8TX Tel: (01623) 870411 Fax: (01623) 871857 E-mail: midlandtoolmans@msn.com
Movawall Systems Ltd, 63 Barwell Business Park, Leatherhead Road, Chessington, Surrey, KT9 2NY Tel: (020) 8391 8790 Fax: (020) 8391 8791
Omega Interiors, The Cavendish Centre, Winnall Close, Winchester, Hampshire, SO23 0LB Tel: (01962) 843542 Fax: (01962) 843062 E-mail: tony@omega-online.co.uk
Pba Interiors, 119 Chiltern Drive, Surbiton, Surrey, KT5 8LS Tel: (020) 8390 6855 Fax: (020) 8399 0653
Peveril Interiors Ltd, Peveril House, Alfreton Road, Derby, DE21 4AG Tel: (01332) 344956 Fax: (01332) 380893 E-mail: peverilinteriors@peveril-house.co.uk
Prime Partitioning Systems Ltd, 7 Windmill Business Park, Windmill Road, Kenn, Clevedon, Avon, BS21 6SR Tel: (01275) 343646 Fax: (01275) 343898 E-mail: info@prime-partitioning.co.uk
R & R Ceilings And Partitions, Searchwood, Bishops Down Park Rd, Tunbridge Wells, Kent, TN4 8XU Tel: 01892 544889 Fax: 01892540242
Rae Electrical Services, 116a Blackstock Road, London, N4 2DR Tel: (020) 7226 2962 Fax: (020) 7359 3354 E-mail: raeelectrical@aol.com
Scomar Office Interiors Ltd, 18 Abbey Walk, Grimsby, North East Lincolnshire, DN31 1NB Tel: (01472) 500400 Fax: (01472) 500407 E-mail: scomar@scomar.co.uk
Simply Partitions, 2 Titchfield Park Road, Fareham, Hampshire, PO15 5RW Tel: (01489) 575993 E-mail: norman@simply-partitions.co.uk

PARTITION CONTRACTORS OR SUPPLIERS – *continued*

Sound Interiots Ltd, 4 Levens Road, Newby Road Industrial Estate, Hazel Grove, Stockport, Cheshire, SK7 5DL Tel: 0161-456 8282 Fax: 0161-456 3030 E-mail: all@sound-interiors.co.uk

Southwark & Boon Ltd, 23 Tallon Road, Hutton, Brentwood, Essex, CM13 1TE Tel: (01277) 225661 Fax: (01277) 233620 E-mail: sales@southwarkandboon.com

Storage Concepts Ltd, Pate Road, Melton Mowbray, Leicestershire, LE13 0RG Tel: (01664) 410414 Fax: (01664) 569969 E-mail: sales@storageconcepts.co.uk

▶ Systematic Creative Interiors Ltd, Red Shute Hill Industrial Estate, Red Shute Hill, Hermitage, Thatcham, Berkshire, RG18 9QL Tel: (01635) 201789 Fax: (01635) 200996 E-mail: sale@systematicinteriors.co.uk

Thermofelt (Contracts) Ltd, Kingswood House, 31-39 Miles Road, Mitcham, Surrey, CR4 3DA Tel: (020) 8646 9300 E-mail: thermofeltcontracts@woodcote.com

Thrislington (NI) Ltd, Unit 38 Mallusk Enterprise Park, Mallusk Drive, Newtownabbey, County Antrim, BT36 4GN Tel: (028) 9084 1200 Fax: (028) 9084 4120 E-mail: thrislington@nireland.com

Toveglen Ltd, Unit 1 Drakes Lane, Boreham, Chelmsford, CM3 3BE Tel: (01245) 360435 Fax: (01245) 362322 E-mail: mbladon@toveglen.co.uk

Trills, Enterprise House, 21 Sherwood Road, Bromsgrove, Worcestershire, B60 3DR Tel: (01527) 874920 Fax: (01527) 876857 E-mail: enquiries@trills.co.uk

Tyler Storage Ltd, 2 Compton Drive, Poole, Dorset, BH14 8PW Tel: (01202) 733344 Fax: (01202) 730228

Versatile Kent Ltd, 94 Dover Road, Folkestone, Kent, CT20 1LA Tel: (01303) 850219 Fax: (01303) 220929 E-mail: info@versatile-kent.co.uk

Wakefield Interiors, 7 Monton Ave, Eccles, Manchester, M30 9HS Tel: 0161-788 7126

Westminster Partitions & Joinery Ltd, Unit F, Printing House Lane, Hayes, Middlesex, UB3 1AP Tel: (020) 8848 0126 Fax: (020) 8848 8845 E-mail: info@partition.co.uk

Wiland Wines Ltd, Regent House, Ellis Street, Anstey, Leicester, LE7 7FG Tel: 0116-236 3479 Fax: 0116-234 0262

PARTITIONING SYSTEMS

Ace Systems Ltd, Rose Green Road, Bristol, BS5 7XE Tel: 0117-952 0624 Fax: 0117-935 4255 E-mail: sales@acestorage.co.uk

Amracks Ltd, 2 Cockerell Road, Corby, Northamptonshire, NN17 5DU Tel: (01536) 401361 Fax: (01536) 275909 E-mail: info@amracks.co.uk

B M A Partitioning Group, 3 Ashburn Grove, Wetherby, West Yorkshire, LS22 6WB Tel: (01937) 581421 Fax: (01937) 581421

Broadsword Projects Ltd, Unit 13 Westwood Court, Brunel Road, Totton, Southampton, SO40 3WX Tel: (023) 8067 5888 Fax: (023) 8067 5999

▶ Cicada Interiors Limited, 64 Knightsbridge, London, United Kingdom, SW1X 7JF Tel: (020) 7590 3095 Fax: (020) 7590 9601 E-mail: peter@cicadainteriors.com

Complete Interiors, Ansell Road, Inscape House, Dorking, Surrey, RH4 1QN Tel: (01306) 882198 Fax: (01306) 876427 E-mail: info@completeinteriors.co.uk

Dexion Storage Centre Anglia Ltd, 43 Hurricane Way, Norwich, NR6 6HE Tel: (01603) 418121 Fax: (01603) 418124 E-mail: sales@dexion-anglia.co.uk

Eleco Timber Frame Ltd, Oaksmere Business Park, Eye Airfield Industrial Estate, Yaxley, Eye, Suffolk, IP23 8BW Tel: (01379) 783465 Fax: (01379) 783659 E-mail: stramit@eleco.com

Funasset Ltd, Orchards, 14 Townsend, Ilminster, Somerset, TA19 0AU Tel: (01460) 57065 Fax: (01460) 53538 E-mail: enquiries@funasset.com

Gallagher Partitioning, Springfield Works, Salwick, Preston, PR4 0XJ Tel: (01772) 721091 Fax: (01772) 721091

Hall Partitions Ltd, 113 Church Hill, Loughton, Essex, IG10 1QR Tel: (0845) 6780737 Fax: (0845) 6780747

Hardwood Interiors Ltd, 1 Whitethorn Gardens, Croydon, CR0 7LL Tel: (020) 8656 9520 Fax: (020) 8656 9520

Images Storage & Partitioning Ltd, 68 Iron Mill Lane, Dartford, DA1 4RR Tel: (01322) 525975 Fax: (01322) 558032 E-mail: mrimages@globalnet.co.uk

▶ John Michael Interiors, New Road, Dudley, W. Midlands, DY2 8TA Tel: (01384) 455520 Fax: (01384) 455521

Komfort Office Environments P.L.C., Unit T Gildersome Spur Industrial Estate, Wakefield Road, Morley, Leeds, LS27 7JX Tel: 0113-201 3700 Fax: 0113-238 0447

Lazer Partitions & Ceilings, 119a Tarring Road, Worthing, West Sussex, BN11 4HE Tel: (01903) 205719 Fax: (01903) 204041 E-mail: lazer@mistral.co.uk

Midland Ceilings Ltd, 63 Chartwell Drive, Wigston, Leicestershire, LE18 2FS Tel: 0116-288 7721 Fax: 0116-288 7022

▶ Modular Office & Storage Systems, Unit 321i, Mayoral Way, Team Valley Trading Estate, Gateshead, Tyne & Wear, NE11 0RT Tel: 0191-487 1212 Fax: 0191-487 7979 E-mail: info@modular-systems.co.uk

Montage Design, 3 2 Sycamore House, Vantage Point Business Village, Mitcheldean, Gloucestershire, GL17 0DD Tel: (01594) 546100 Fax: (01594) 546200 E-mail: sales@montagedesigns.co.uk

▶ Moss Bank Styles, 841 Moss Bank Way, Bolton, BL1 5SN Tel: (01204) 844496 Fax: (01204) 460088

▶ Neslo, Port Causeway, Wirral, Merseyside, CH62 4SY Tel: 0151-334 9326 Fax: 0151-334 0668

Niche Operable Systems Ltd, The Studio, Rear Of 18, Bath Street, Bolton, BL1 2DJ Tel: (01204) 381552 Fax: (01204) 381556 E-mail: enquiries@folding-partitions.co.uk

P M C, Cedar House, 100 Station Avenue, Coventry, CV4 9HS Tel: (024) 7642 2777 Fax: (024) 7647 1111

Smileberry Interiors, 18 Church Street, Warnham, Horsham, West Sussex, RH12 3QW Tel: (01403) 242600 Fax: (01403) 264856

Space Plan Interiors Ltd, Henstaff House, Groesfaen, Pontyclun, Mid Glamorgan, CF72 8NG Tel: (029) 2089 2222 Fax: (029) 2089 2233 E-mail: sales@spaceplan.co.uk

Stomet Industries Ltd, Thorpe House, Thorpe Way, Banbury, Oxfordshire, OX16 4SP Tel: (01295) 257565 Fax: (01295) 271762 E-mail: sales@oastdeck.com

Transome Partition Systems, 9 Ducketts Mead, Canewdon, Rochford, Essex, SS4 3QS Tel: (01702) 258720 Fax: (01702) 258582

Troax UK Ltd, Enterprise House, Murdock Road, Dorcan, Swindon, SN3 5HY Tel: (01793) 542000 Fax: (01793) 618784 E-mail: info@troax.co.uk

Ultimate Office Interiors, 307 Mariners House Queens Dock Commercial Centre, Norfolk Street, Liverpool, L1 0BG Tel: 0151-708 7700 Fax: 0151-708 7701 E-mail: liverpool@unilock.co.uk

PARTITIONS

▶ City Walls Ltd, Aztec House, 137a Molesey Avenue, West Molesey, Surrey, KT8 2RY Tel: (01444) 417030 Fax: (020) 8481 7289 E-mail: londonsales@brokhouse.net

Decorfix, Halstow Lane, Upchurch, Sittingbourne, Kent, ME9 7AB Tel: (01795) 843124 Fax: (01795) 842465

▶ J Holdsworth Associates, Alexander House, Robinson Terrace, Washington, Tyne & Wear, NE38 7BD Tel: 0191-417 2543 Fax: 0191-417 1486 E-mail: jhassociates1@aol.com

Lyntons Ceiling & Partitions, 32-34 Albion Road, Sutton, Surrey, SM2 5TF Tel: (020) 8661 7875

T.J, Mee Contracts, 11 Tyler Road, Ratby, Leicester, LE6 0NQ Tel: 0116-238 7628 Fax: 0116-238 7628

▶ Southern Workforce UK Ltd, Ashlands, The Street, Ash, Sevenoaks, Kent, TN15 7HB Tel: (01474) 873517 Fax: (01474) 872335 E-mail: kevin@swf.gb.com

Spazio Folding Door Co., 3 Barnfield, St. Michaels, Tenterden, Kent, TN30 6NH Tel: (01580) 763593 Fax: (01580) 765883 E-mail: susie@spazio.co.uk

▶ Sussex Interior Fixings Ltd, Unit 5b Sewells Farm, Barcombe, Lewes, East Sussex, BN8 5TJ Tel: (01273) 400000 Fax: (01273) 401549

▶ Swift Specialist Interiors Ltd, Bramley House, 91-99 Bradford Road, East Ardsley, Wakefield, West Yorkshire, WF3 2JD Tel: (01924) 828677 Fax: (01924) 828877

PARTY BALLOONS

▶ A Rosy Marriage Balloon & Party Megastore, 14 Barn Way, Hednesford, Cannock, Staffordshire, WS12 0FP Tel: (07795) 102050 E-mail: sales@arosymarriage.co.uk

▶ Abbaballoons, 122 Forester Road, Crawley, West Sussex, RH10 6EF Tel: (01293) 611260 Fax:

Aerial Splendour, St. Giles Farm, Blendworth, Waterlooville, Hampshire, PO8 0AG Tel: (07709) 955294 Fax: (023) 9225 6111 E-mail: aerialsplendour@aol.com

▶ All Wrapped Up, 53 Liverpool Road, Kidsgrove, Stoke-on-Trent, ST7 1EA Tel: (01782) 771007

▶ Balloon Addict, 15 Broom Close, Wath-upon-Dearne, Rotherham, South Yorkshire, S63 7JU Tel: (07800) 906846

▶ Balloon Arcade, 32 Shillito Road, Poole, Dorset, BH12 2BW Tel: (01202) 743465 Fax: (01202) 718488 E-mail: sales@balloon-arcade.co.uk

▶ Balloon Celebration (A), 1 Mill Lane, Broxbourne, Hertfordshire, EN10 7AZ Tel: (01992) 467555 Fax: (01920) 872719 E-mail: sales@aballooncelebration.co.uk

Balloonatics, 21 Mytham Road, Little Lever, Bolton, BL3 1TH Tel: (01204) 792340 E-mail: enquiries@balloonaticsofstockton.co.uk

▶ Balloons Afloat, 90 Freeman Road, Didcot, Oxfordshire, OX11 7DB Tel: (01235) 819904 E-mail: sales@balloonsafloat.co.uk

▶ Balloons For All Occasions, 52 King Street, Ramsgate, Kent, CT11 8NT Tel: (01843) 851087 Fax: (01843) 851087

▶ Balloons By Emma, 62 High Street, Cefn Coed, Merthyr Tydfil, Mid Glamorgan, CF48 2PL Tel: (01685) 721210 Fax: (01685) 721210

Balloons By Post, 1 Audley End, Saffron Walden, Essex, CB11 4JB Tel: (01799) 513335 E-mail: contact@ballonsbypost.com

▶ Balloons & Tunes, Bottom Lock Cottages, Glascote Road, Tamworth, Staffordshire, B77 2AE Tel: (01827) 316600 Fax: (01827) 311066 E-mail: us@balloonsandtunes.co.uk

Balloons Worldwide Ltd, London Road, Brown Street, Alderley Edge, Cheshire, SK9 7EQ Tel: (01625) 583168 Fax: (01625) 586098

▶ Balloonz 'N' Cakes, 94 Delamere Street, Winsford, Cheshire, CW7 2LU Tel: (01606) 860668 E-mail: balloonz@cakes.co.uk

▶ Belle Balloons & Florist, 184 The Chesils, Coventry, CV3 5BH Tel: (024) 7650 6177 Fax: (024) 7650 6177 E-mail: sales@belleballoons.co.uk

▶ Big Bang Balloon, 38 Parkfield Road, Ruskington, Sleaford, Lincolnshire, NG34 9HS Tel: (07906) 951961

▶ Bloomers, 820 Bury Road, Bolton, BL2 6PA Tel: (01204) 531487 E-mail: sales@bloomersballoons.co.uk

▶ Bounce Higher, 32 Ryefield Road, Eastfield, Scarborough, North Yorkshire, YO11 3DW Tel: (01723) 585542 E-mail: info@no1bouncehigher.com

▶ Bouncycastlesforhire.com, 7A High Street, Marlow, Buckinghamshire, SL7 8DW Tel: (01494) 464902 E-mail: info@bouncycastlesforhire.com

▶ Buckingham Balloons Ltd, 113 St Thomas Road, Trowbridge, Wiltshire, BA14 7LT Tel: (01225) 752410 E-mail: sales@buckinghamballoons.co.uk

▶ Buddies, 60 George Street, Hastings, East Sussex, TN34 3EE Tel: (01424) 427290 Fax: (01424) 427290

▶ Bur Boing, 8 Beacon Court, Northampton, NN4 8JU Tel: (01604) 674733 E-mail: bur-boing@tesco.net

▶ Carabou Gifts & Ballons, 105 Market Street, Cannock, Staffordshire, WS12 1AD Tel: (01543) 878201 E-mail: carabou@hotmail.co.uk

▶ Celebration-Balloons, 859 Whittingham Lane, Goosnargh, Preston, PR3 2AU Tel: (01772) 861190 Fax: (01772) 861190 E-mail: info@celebration-balloons.co.uk

Cti Balloons Ltd, 6 Consul Road, Rugby, Warwickshire, CV21 1PB Tel: (01788) 546299 Fax: (01788) 546114 E-mail: ctiballoon@aol.com

▶ Elan, 38 Bloomgate, Lanark, ML11 9ET Tel: (01555) 665777 Fax: (01555) 673888

▶ Every Occasion, 464 Blackburn Road, Bolton, BL1 8PE Tel: (01204) 595100

▶ Floaters, 1A Oxford Street, Guiseley, Leeds, LS20 9AX Tel: (01943) 870467

▶ Gaiety Balloons, 90 Kings Road, Brentwood, Essex, CM14 4DU Tel: (01277) 217997

Great Western Balloons, 6 Redwood Close, Honiton, Devon, EX14 2XS Tel: (01404) 45968 Fax: (01404) 45968

▶ Inflated Ideas By Claire, 76 Clifton Road, Rochford, Essex, SS4 3HJ Tel: (01702) 543757

▶ Lets Party, 35 Saffron Road, Biggleswade, Bedfordshire, SG18 8DJ Tel: (01767) 312252

▶ Norwich Balloon Art, 16 Reepham Road, Norwich, NR6 5LH Tel: (01603) 789100

Occasions, 96 Liverpool Road, Cadishead, Manchester, M44 5AN Tel: 0161-775 7979 Fax: 0161-775 7979

Party Ark Ltd, 4 Winters Bridge Cottages, Portsmouth Road, Thames Ditton, Surrey, KT7 0TB Tel: (020) 8972 9041

The Party People, 41 Croydon Road, Beckenham, Kent, BR3 4AB Tel: (020) 8658 1110 Fax: (020) 8658 1548

▶ Party Poppers Balloons, 26 Church Street, Littleborough, Lancashire, OL15 9AA Tel: (01706) 374951

Party Time Ltd, 37 Cartergate, Newark, Nottinghamshire, NG24 1UA Tel: (01636) 611669 Fax: (01636) 615669 E-mail: enquiries@zillionsofchuckles.com

▶ Puffin Balloons, McGregor's Way, Turnoaks Business Park, Chesterfield, Derbyshire, S40 2WB Tel: 01246 205163 Fax: 01246 270566 E-mail: sales@puffinballoons.com

▶ Pure Genius Events Ltd, 15 Perrymead, Luton, LU2 8UF Tel: (01582) 457263 Fax: 01582 488108 E-mail: info@puregeniusevents.co.uk

▶ Send Me a Balloon, 23 Woodthorpe Road, Ashford, Middlesex, TW15 2RP Tel: (0870) 0117550 Fax: (0870) 0117660 E-mail: sales@staggerin.com

Sonic Party Time, 2a North Street, Heavitree, Exeter, EX1 2RH Tel: (01392) 848785

▶ Talking Balloons, Mcgregors Way, Chesterfield, Derbyshire, S40 2WB Tel: (01246) 270555 Fax: (01246) 270566 E-mail: sales@talkingballoons.com

PARTY CATERING

▶ A J Catering, Concorde House, Concorde Way, Preston Farm Industrial Estate, Stockton-on-Tees, Cleveland, TS18 3RB Tel: (01642) 617948 Fax: (01642) 607906

▶ Badger Bars, The Post Office, Firsby Road, Great Steeping, Spilsby, Lincolnshire, PE23 5PT Tel: 07731 576864

▶ Buffet Car, The, 25 Maplewood Park, Deans, Livingston, West Lothian, EH54 8BB Tel: 01506 415055 Fax: 07931 796940 E-mail: Eileen@TheBuffetCar.com

By Request Ltd, 6 Demmings Road, Demmings Industrial Estate, Cheadle, Cheshire, SK8 2PE Tel: 0161-428 0833 Fax: 0161-491 0411 E-mail: sales@byrequest.co.uk

Creative Canapes, Unit D12, Barwell Business Park, Leatherhead Road, Chessington, Surrey, KT9 2NY Tel: (0845) 3668811 E-mail: enquiries@creativecanapes.co.uk

▶ Great Taste, 5 Garfield Road, Netley Abbey, Southampton, SO31 5DN Tel: (023) 8045 3181 E-mail: enquiries@great-taste.co.uk

▶ Hatters Catering Co., 6 Southgate Parade, Crawley, West Sussex, RH10 6ER Tel: (01293) 550333 Fax: (01293) 552254 E-mail: admin@hatterscatering.co.uk

▶ Hot Chocolates - Chocolate Fountain Hire, 83 Findon Road, Elson, Gosport, Hampshire, PO12 4ER Tel: (023) 9250 1416 E-mail: enquiries@hotchocolates.co.uk

▶ How About Now, 10 Waynflete Lane, Farnham, Surrey, GU9 7BH Tel: (01252) 891790 Fax: E-mail: adam@howaboutnow.co.uk

▶ Minghella Isle Of Wight Ltd, High Street, Wootton Bridge, Ryde, Isle of Wight, PO33 4PL Tel: (01983) 883545 Fax: (01983) 883242 E-mail: sales@minghella.co.uk

▶ MRI Catering, 45 Bishops Way, Andover, Hampshire, SP10 3EH Tel: (01264) 339006 Fax: (01264) 363487 E-mail: kieran@mricatering.co.uk

PARTY EQUIPMENT HIRE

▶ 1st Class Corporate Entertainment, 4 Porchester Court, Bournemouth, BH8 8JE Tel: (01202) 467970 E-mail: funcasino@msn.com

▶ A1 Bouncy Castles, Green Leys, Downley, High Wycombe, Buckinghamshire, HP13 5UH Tel: (01494) 464902

▶ Abbaballoons, 122 Forester Road, Crawley, West Sussex, RH10 6EF Tel: (01293) 611260 Fax:

▶ Animal Bouncers, 122 Forester Road, Crawley, West Sussex, RH10 6EF Tel: (01293) 417346 Fax: E-mail: sales@animalbouncers.co.uk

▶ Bounce Krazee, 14 Green Leys, High Wycombe, Buckinghamshire, HP13 5UH Tel: (01494) 464902 E-mail: info@bouncekrazee.co.uk

▶ Bouncycastlesforhire.com, 7A High Street, Marlow, Buckinghamshire, SL7 8DW Tel: (01494) 464902 E-mail: info@bouncycastlesforhire.com

Carl's Castles, 51 Clydesmuir Road, Tremorfa, Cardiff, CF24 2PX Tel: (029) 2033 1309 Fax: (029) 2033 1309 E-mail: carl@dvsmail.co.uk

▶ Casino-To-Go, Unit 3 Foulswick Business Park, Fowlswick Lane, Allington, Chippenham, Wiltshire, SN14 6QE Tel: (01793) 686402 E-mail: info@casino-to-go.co.uk

▶ Connect Exhibitions Ltd, 73 Lynton Road, Acton, London, W3 9HL Tel: (0845) 0170820 Fax: (020) 8896 2064 E-mail: info@connectexhibitions.com

H X Marquees, 77 Cliffe End Road, Oakes, Huddersfield, HD3 4FG Tel: (01422) 200960 E-mail: mailbox@halifax-marquees.co.uk

▶ Hot Chocolates - Chocolate Fountain Hire, 83 Findon Road, Elson, Gosport, Hampshire, PO12 4ER Tel: (023) 9250 1416 E-mail: enquiries@hotchocolates.co.uk

▶ How About Now, 10 Waynflete Lane, Farnham, Surrey, GU9 7BH Tel: (01252) 891790 Fax: E-mail: adam@howaboutnow.co.uk

▶ Marquee Malarkey, 1 Great Buckmans Farm, Lower Howsell Road, Malvern, Worcestershire, WR14 1UX Tel: (07868) 750480 E-mail: info@marqueemalarkey.com

▶ Moor Leisure, Fingle Cottage, Moretonhampstead Road, Lustleigh, Newton Abbot, Devon, TQ13 9SN Tel: (01647) 277528 Fax: (01647) 277549

▶ Multi Madness, 1 Marsett Way, Whinmoor, Leeds, LS14 2DN Tel: 0113-216 4845

▶ Pure Genius Events Ltd, 15 Perrymead, Luton, LU2 8UF Tel: (01582) 457263 Fax: 01582 488108 E-mail: info@puregeniusevents.co.uk

▶ V Celebrate, 181 Streatfield Road, Harrow, Middlesex, HA3 9DA Tel: (020) 8204 7807 Fax: (020) 8204 7807

PARTY GAMES

▶ Music Bugs, 4 Bowles Road, Abbey Meads, Swindon, SN25 4ZN Tel: (01793) 722072 E-mail: info@musicbugs.co.uk

PartyTimeKids, 2 Apollo Close, Oakhurst, Swindon, SN25 2JB Tel: 07719 570976 E-mail: info@partytimekids.co.uk

PARTY PLANNING

▶ Ann Summers, 97 Allen Road, Irthlingborough, Wellingborough, Northamptonshire, NN9 5QX Tel: (07840) 587700 E-mail: the2honeys2002@yahoo.com

PASSENGER CARRYING BALLOONS

Balloons UK Hot Air Flights, School Farm, School Lane, Stretton, Stafford, ST19 9LJ Tel: (01785) 280450 Fax: (01952) 541856 E-mail: tony@balloonsuk.co.uk

PASSENGER CARRYING BALLOONS
– continued

Cameron Balloons Ltd, St Johns Street, Bedminster, Bristol, BS3 4NH Tel: 0117-963 7216 Fax: 0117-966 1168 E-mail: sales@cameronballoons.co.uk
Champagne Flights, 1 Uppings Farm Cottage, Buckingham Road, Weedon, Aylesbury, Buckinghamshire, HP22 4DR Tel: (01296) 641153 Fax: (01296) 640084
▶ Classic Hot Air Ballooning, Home Farm Cottage, Lenham Heath Road, Sandway, Maidstone, Kent, ME17 2HX Tel: (01622) 858956 Fax: (01622) 853817 E-mail: glen@ballooning.fsnet.co.uk
Floating Sensations Ltd, 1 Fox Cottages, Wellhouse, Hermitage, Thatcham, Berkshire, RG18 9UD Tel: (01635) 201007 Fax: (01635) 202774 E-mail: sales@balloonflights.co.uk
▶ Hot Air Balloons, 1 Home Farm Cottage, Lenham Heath Road, Sandway, Maidstone, Kent, ME17 2HX Tel: (01622) 858956 Fax: (01622) 853817 E-mail: lizmeek@ballooning.fsnet.co.uk
Virgin Balloon Flights, Jesson House, Stafford Park 1, Telford, Shropshire, TF3 3BD Tel: (01952) 212750 Fax: (01952) 292020

PASSENGER CARRYING RAPID TRANSIT SYSTEM CONSTRUCTION CONSULTANCY OR CONSULTING ENGINEERS

Alstom Transport Ltd, PO Box 248, Birmingham, B8 2YF Tel: 0121-328 5455 Fax: 0121-695 3500
Otis Ltd, 187 Twyford Abbey Road, London, NW10 7DG Tel: (020) 8955 3000 Fax: (020) 8955 3001

PASSENGER LIFTS

Artisan Control Equipment, 10 Pinfold Workshops, Pinfold La Industrial Estate, Buckley, Clwyd, CH7 3PL Tel: (01244) 550012 Fax: (01244) 549482
Barson Lift Co. Ltd, Unit 1, Bellgrave Industrial Estate, Honeywell Lane, Oldham, OL8 2JP Tel: 0161-678 9209 Fax: 0161-627 5009
Britton Price Ltd, Unit 14 Hove Business Centre, Fonthill Road, Hove, East Sussex, BN3 6HA Tel: (01273) 235035 Fax: (01273) 235036 E-mail: sales@brittonprice.co.uk
Brooks Stairlifts Ltd, Telecom House Millenium Business Park, Station Road, Steeton, Keighley, West Yorkshire, BD20 6RB Tel: (0800) 834730 Fax: (01535) 290014 E-mail: brooks@stairlifts.co.uk
Caltech Lifts Servicing, Stannergate Road, Dundee, DD1 3NA Tel: (01382) 462810 Fax: (01382) 454134 E-mail: caltechlifts@btinternet.com
Capstan Lift Services, 3 Marlowe Business Centre, Batavia Road, London, SE14 6BQ Tel: (020) 8694 7557 Fax: (020) 8694 6088 E-mail: capstanlifts@aol.com
▶ Gartec Ltd, 6 Midshires Business Park, Smeaton Close, Aylesbury, Buckinghamshire, HP19 8HL Tel: (01296) 397100 Fax: (01296) 397600 E-mail: sales@gartec.com
▶ Genesis Lifts Ltd, 55 Whitemill Road, Chatteris, Cambridgeshire, PE16 6PG Tel: (0870) 7602268 Fax: (07005) 850036 E-mail: trevorsherwood@dsl.pipex.com
Omega City Lifts Ltd, 8 Bridge Gate Centre, Martinfield, Welwyn Garden City, Hertfordshire, AL7 1JG Tel: (01707) 334962 Fax: (01707) 376594 E-mail: sanjay@omegacitylifts.co.uk
Otis Ltd, 187 Twyford Abbey Road, London, NW10 7DG Tel: (020) 8955 3000 Fax: (020) 8955 3001
Pickerings Europe Ltd, 9 Glasgow Road, Baillieston, Glasgow, G69 6JT Tel: 0141-771 7575 Fax: 0141-771 8585 E-mail: info@pickerings.co.uk
Stentorgate, Beech Grove, Eldwick, Bingley, West Yorkshire, BD16 3EG Tel: (01274) 560600

PASSENGER TRANSPORT VEHICLE DOORS

Deans Systems Ltd, Borwick Drive, Grovehill, Beverley, North Humberside, HU17 0HQ Tel: (01482) 868111 Fax: (01482) 881890 E-mail: info@deanssystems.com

PASSIVE ELECTRONIC COMPONENTS

Avnet Time, Avnet House, Rutherford Close, Stevenage, Hertfordshire, SG1 2EF Tel: (01438) 789789 E-mail: timeuk@avnet.com
Sumitomo Electric Europe Ltd, Unit 220 Centennial Park, Elstree, Hertfordshire, WD6 3SL Tel: (020) 8953 4489 Fax: (020) 8207 5950 E-mail: a.bayram@sumielectric.com

PASSIVE FIRE PROTECTION EQUIPMENT OR SYSTEMS

▶ Alderley Materials Ltd, Station Road, Berkeley, Gloucestershire, GL13 9RL Tel: (01453) 511600 Fax: (01453) 810108 E-mail: marketing@alderley.com
M C L Unitex Ltd, Adams Close, Heanor, Derbyshire, DE75 7SW Tel: 01773 535365
Promat U.K Ltd, Wellingborough, Northamptonshire, NN8 6XS Tel: (01933) 271476 Fax: (01933) 276790
Quelfire Ltd, PO Box 35, Altrincham, Cheshire, WA14 5QA Tel: 0161-928 7308 Fax: 0161-924 1340
S P C, Unit 1, Chalford Industrial Estate, Chalford, Stroud, Glos, GL6 8NT Tel: (01453) 885929 Fax: (01453) 731044
Structural Space Ltd, Trident House, Neptune Business Estate, Dolphin Way, Purfleet, Essex, RM19 1NZ Tel: (01708) 683041 Fax: (01708) 683068 E-mail: info@structuralspace.co.uk

PASTEURISATION MONITORS

Redpost Electronic Products Ltd, The Old Pumping Station, Toft Road, Bourn, Cambridge, CB23 2TT Tel: (01954) 718001 Fax: (01954) 718002

PASTRY FOOD PRODUCTS

Apetito, Crackley Way, Peartree Lane Industrial Estate, Dudley, West Midlands, DY2 0UW Tel: (01384) 254389 Fax: (01384) 456334
Fletchers Bakeries Ltd, Claywheels Lane, Sheffield, S6 1LY Tel: 0114-234 8171 Fax: 0114-232 4987 E-mail: enquiries@fletchers.co.uk
Fleur D E Leys Pies Ltd, Baxenden, Accrington, Lancashire, BB5 2SA Tel: (01706) 221993 Fax: (01706) 228044
Ginsters Ltd, Unit 8 New Street, Bridgend Industrial Estate, Bridgend, Mid Glamorgan, CF31 3UD Tel: (01656) 661658 Fax: (01656) 659466
Walter Holland & Sons, Blackburn Road, Accrington, Lancashire, BB5 2SA Tel: (01706) 213591 Fax: (01706) 228044 E-mail: enquiries@hollands-pies.co.uk
Kandys Patisserie, Unit 6-7, Clay Lane, Fishbourne, Chichester, West Sussex, PO18 8AH Tel: (01243) 575166
Pars Foods Ltd, 8-12 Glentanar Road, Glasgow, G22 7XS Tel: 0141-336 7755 Fax: 0141-336 5522
Pastry World, Unit 2. 173-177 Green Lane Road, Leicester, LE5 4PD Tel: 0116-276 9911
Patchi Ltd, Unit 26, Cariocca Business Park Hellidon Close, Ardwick, Manchester, M12 4AH Tel: 0161-272 7207 Fax: 0161-272 7207
Pukka Pies Ltd, The Halfcroft, Syston, Leicester, LE7 1LD Tel: 0116-260 9755 Fax: 0116-264 0092 E-mail: info@pukka-pies.co.uk
R F Brookes, Magna Road, Wigston, Leicestershire, LE18 4ZA Tel: 0116-258 1000 Fax: 0116-258 1001 E-mail: sales@rfbrookes.co.uk
St James Foods Ltd, 67 Milmead Industrial Centre, Mill Mead Road, London, N17 9QU Tel: (020) 8808 3000 Fax: (020) 8808 3355 E-mail: info@theospastry.com
Saxby Brothers Ltd, PO Box 15, Wellingborough, Northamptonshire, NN8 1LH Tel: (01933) 221700 Fax: (01933) 221702 E-mail: info@saxbys.co.uk
T R S International Foods Ltd, Argall Avenue, London, E10 7AS Tel: (020) 8556 2117 Fax: (020) 8556 6151
Winning Blend Ltd (T/U Welsh Pantry), Unit 1 Riverside Industrial Park, Treforest Industrial Estate, Treforest, Pontypridd, Mid Glamorgan, CF37 5TG Tel: (01443) 843587 Fax: (01443) 842304 E-mail: sales@welshpantry.com

PATCH-PANELS

Hellermann Tyton, Ratcliff House, 43-45 Salthouse Road, Brackmills Industrial Estate, Northampton, NN4 7EX Tel: (01604) 706633 Fax: (01604) 705454

PATCHCORDS

Pemberton Engineering, Unit 48 Planetary Industrial Estate, Planetary Road, Willenhall, West Midlands, WV13 3XB Tel: (01902) 863666 Fax: (01902) 863666 E-mail: pembertoneng@btconnect.com

PATENT AGENTS' OR LAWYERS' DRAFTSMEN

▶ Comery Hill & Co., The Poplars, Benthall Lane, Benthall, Broseley, Shropshire, TF12 5RR Tel: 01952 881056 Fax: 01952 881056 E-mail: comeryhillco@btinternet.com
Page White & Farrer, 54 Doughty Street, London, WC1N 2LS Tel: (020) 7831 7929 Fax: (020) 7831 8040 E-mail: sales@pagewhite.com
G.F. Redfern & Co., 7 Staple Inn, Holborn, London, WC1V 7QF Tel: (020) 7242 7680 Fax: (020) 7831 7957
Reed Smith, Park House, Station Square, Coventry, CV1 2FL Tel: (024) 7629 3020 Fax: (024) 7629 3031 E-mail: coventry-email@warner-cranston.com

PATENT AGENTS/ATTORNEYS

A A Thornton & Co., 29 St. Katherines Street, Northampton, NN1 2QZ Tel: (01604) 638242 Fax: (01604) 638164 E-mail: aat@aathornton.com
Abel & Imray, 20 Red Lion Street, London, WC1R 4PQ Tel: (020) 7242 9984 Fax: (020) 7242 9989 E-mail: ai@patentable.co.uk
Anthony Cundy & Co., 39 South Drive, Sutton Coldfield, West Midlands, B75 7TE Tel: 0121-378 4649 Fax: 0121-378 4670 E-mail: cundys@btconnect.com
Appleyard Lees, 15 Clare Road, Halifax, West Yorkshire, HX1 2HY Tel: (01422) 330110 Fax: (01422) 330090 E-mail: ip@appleyardlees.com
Bailey Walsh & Co., 5 York Place, Leeds, LS1 2SD Tel: (0800) 7837623 Fax: 0113-244 5699 E-mail: mail@bailey-walsh.com
Barker Brettell Ltd, 138 Hagley Road, Birmingham, B16 9PW Tel: 0121-456 1364 Fax: 0121-456 1368 E-mail: admin@barkerbrettell.co.uk
Beck Greener, Fulwood House, 12 Fulwood Place, London, WC1V 6HR Tel: (020) 7693 5600 Fax: (020) 7693 5601 E-mail: mail@beckgreener.com
Boult Wade Tennant, Verulam Gardens, 70 Gray's Inn Road, London, WC1X 8BT Tel: (020) 7430 7500 Fax: (020) 7831 1768 E-mail: boult@boult.com
Boult Wade Tennant, 34 Bridge Street, Reading, RG1 2LU Tel: 0118-956 5900 Fax: 0118-950 0442 E-mail: boult@boult.com
Britter & Co., Enterprise House, 14B White Horse Street, Baldock, Hertfordshire, SG7 6QN Tel: (01462) 894200 Fax: (01462) 893636 E-mail: britterco@aol.com
Bromhead & Co., 37 Great James Street, London, WC1N 3HB Tel: (020) 7405 7010 Fax: (020) 7831 5118 E-mail: mail@bromhead-johnson.com
Bromhead Johnson, Kingsbourne House, 19 Buckingham Street, London, WC2N 6EF Tel: (020) 7839 4935 Fax: (020) 7839 6898 E-mail: mail@bromhead-johnson.com
Brookes Batchellor, 102-108 Clerkenwell Road, London, EC1M 5SA Tel: (020) 7253 1563 Fax: (020) 7253 1214
▶ Crossguard Trade Mark Agents, 4 Berkeley Road, Kenilworth, Warwickshire, CV8 1AP Tel: (0845) 0536675 Fax: (0870) 0468361 E-mail: mail@crossguard.info
D Young & Co., 120 Holborn, London, EC1N 2DY Tel: (020) 7269 8550 Fax: (020) 7269 8555 E-mail: mail@dyoung.co.uk
Elkington & Fife, Beacon House, 113 Kingsway, London, WC2B 6PN Tel: (020) 7405 3505 Fax: (020) 7405 1508 E-mail: elkfife@elkfife.co.uk
Elkington & Fife, Prospect House, 8 Pembroke Road, Sevenoaks, Kent, TN13 1XR Tel: (01732) 458881 Fax: (01732) 450346 E-mail: elkfife@elkfife.co.uk
Eric Potter Clarkson LLP, Park View House, 58 The Ropewalk, Nottingham, NG1 5DD Tel: 0115-955 2211 Fax: 0115-955 2201
F J Cleveland & Co., 40-43 Chancery Lane, London, WC2A 1JQ Tel: (020) 7405 5875 Fax: (020) 7831 0749 E-mail: sales@fjcleveland.com
Forrester Ketley & Co., 105 Piccadilly, London, W1J 7NJ Tel: (020) 8889 6622 Fax: (020) 8881 1088 E-mail: fklondon@forresters.co.uk
▶ Frank B Dehn & Co Ltd, 179 Queen Victoria Street, London, EC4V 4EL Tel: (020) 7206 0600 Fax: (020) 7206 0700 E-mail: mail@frankbdehn.com
Gallafent & Co., 9 Staple Inn, London, WC1V 7QH Tel: (020) 7242 3094 Fax: (020) 7539 4999 E-mail: rg@rkallafent.compulink.co.uk
Gill Jennings & Every, 7 Eldon Street, London, EC2M 7LS Tel: (020) 7377 1377 Fax: (020) 7377 1310 E-mail: gje@gje.co.uk
Harrison Goddard Foote, Lincolns Inn Chambers, 40-43 Chancery Lane, London, WC2A 1JA Tel: (020) 7440 8900 Fax: (020) 7440 8901 E-mail: hgf-london@hgfit.com
Haseltine Lake & Co., West Riding House, 67 Albion Street, Leeds, LS1 5AA Tel: 0113-233 9400 Fax: 0113-233 9401 E-mail: sales@haseltinelake.co.uk
▶ Hindle Lowther, 28 Rutland Square, Edinburgh, EH1 2BW Tel: 0131 2216560 E-mail: mail@hindlelowther.com
▶ HLBB Shaw, 303 Science Park, Milton Road, Cambridge, CB4 0WG Tel: (01223) 425891 Fax: 01223 423701 E-mail: mail@hlbb.com
▶ Hlbbshaw, 10th Floor Metropolitan House, 1 Hagley Road, Birmingham, B16 8TG Tel: 0121-454 4962 Fax: 0121-454 4523 E-mail: enquiries@laurenceshaw.co.uk
Hlbbshaw, Shaw House, Pegler Way, Crawley, West Sussex, RH11 7AF Tel: (01293) 528000 Fax: (01293) 528900 E-mail: mail@hlbbshaw.com
I P 21 Ltd, 1 Cornhill, London, EC3V 3ND Tel: (020) 7645 8250 Fax: (020) 7645 8251 E-mail: info@ip21.co.uk
Jenkins, 26 Caxton Street, London, SW1H 0RJ Tel: (020) 7931 7141 Fax: (020) 7222 4660
Jensen & Son, 366-368 Old Street, London, EC1V 9LT Tel: (020) 7613 0280 Fax: (020) 7613 0267 E-mail: mail@jensens.co.uk
Langner Parry, 52-54 High Holborn, London, WC1V 6RR Tel: (020) 7242 5566 Fax: (020) 7405 1908 E-mail: ip@langnerparry.com
Maguire Boss, 24 East Street, St. Ives, Cambridgeshire, PE27 5PD Tel: (01480) 301588 Fax: (01480) 464405 E-mail: tmark@maguires.co.uk
Marks & Clarke, 5 The Quadrant, Coventry, CV1 2EL Tel: (024) 7622 2756 Fax: (024) 7625 6197 E-mail: ip@marks-clarke.com
Marks & Clerk, 27 Imperial Square, Cheltenham, Gloucestershire, GL50 1RQ Tel: (01242) 524520 Fax: (01242) 579383 E-mail: cheltonham@marks-clerk.com
▶ Marks & Clerk, 19 Royal Exchange Square, Glasgow, G1 3AE Tel: 0141-221 5767 Fax: 0141-221 7739 E-mail: glasgow@marks-clerk.com
Marks & Clerk, 90 Long Acre, London, WC2E 9RA Tel: (020) 7420 0000 Fax: (020) 7836 3339
Marks N Clarke, Cliffords Inn, Fetter Lane, London, EC4A 1BX Tel: (020) 7405 4916 Fax: (020) 7831 0343
Mathys & Squire, 120 Holborn, London, EC1N 2SQ Tel: (020) 7830 0000 Fax: (020) 7830 0001 E-mail: sales@mathys-squire.com
Page Hargrave, Manfield House, 1 Southampton Street, London, WC2R 0LR Tel: (020) 7240 6933 Fax: (020) 7379 0268 E-mail: london@pagehargrave.co.uk
Page White & Farrer, 54 Doughty Street, London, WC1N 2LS Tel: (020) 7831 7929 Fax: (020) 7831 8040 E-mail: sales@pagewhite.com
Phillips & Leigh, 5 Pemberton Row, London, EC4A 3BA Tel: (020) 7822 8888 Fax: (020) 7822 8899 E-mail: mail@pandl.com
Raworth Moss & Cook, 36 Sydenham Road, Croydon, CR0 2EF Tel: (020) 8688 8318 Fax: (020) 8760 0055 E-mail: rmc@raworth.co.uk
Reddie & Grose, 16 Theobalds Road, London, WC1X 8PL Tel: (020) 7242 0901 Fax: (020) 7242 3290 E-mail: enquiries@reddie.co.uk
Saunders & Dolleymore, 7-9 Rickmansworth Road, Watford, WD18 0JU Tel: (01923) 238311 Fax: (01923) 246491 E-mail: sales@dolleymores.com
Stevens Hewlett & Perkins, 20-23 Holborn, Halton House, London, EC1N 2JD Tel: (020) 7936 2499 Fax: (020) 7404 1844 E-mail: mail@shplondon.co.uk
Swindell & Pearson, 48 Friargate, Derby, DE1 1GY Tel: (01332) 367051 Fax: (01332) 345200 E-mail: sales@patent.co.uk
Thomson Reuters (Scientific) Ltd, 77 Hatton Gardens, London, EC1N 8JS Tel: (020) 7433 4000 Fax: (020) 7433 4001 E-mail: ts.info.emea@thomson.com
A.A. Thornton & Co., 235 High Holborn, London, WC1V 7LE Tel: (020) 7405 4044 Fax: (020) 7405 3580 E-mail: aat@aathornton.com
Trade Mark Advice & Service Bureau, Fulwood House, 12 Fulwood Place, London, WC1V 6HR Tel: (020) 7242 2535 Fax: (020) 7405 8113 E-mail: info@beckgreener.com
Urquhart Dykes & Lord, 30 Welbeck Street, London, W1G 8ER Tel: (020) 7487 1550 Fax: (020) 7487 1599E-mail: email@udl.co.uk
Urquhart Dykes & Lord, Amen Corner, St Nicholas Chambers, Newcastle upon Tyne, NE1 1PE Tel: 0191-261 8573 Fax: 0191-222 1604 E-mail: newcastle@udl.co.uk
W P Thompson & Co., Eastcheap House, Central Approach, Letchworth Garden City, Hertfordshire, SG6 3DS Tel: (01462) 682139 Fax: (01462) 676775 E-mail: letchworth@wpt.co.uk
W P Thompson & Co., 55 Drury Lane, London, WC2B 5SQ Tel: (020) 7240 2220 Fax: (020) 7240 8505 E-mail: london@wpt.co.uk
Wilson Gunn, Chancery House, 53-64 Chancery Lane, London, WC2A 1QU Tel: (020) 7242 2631 Fax: (020) 7242 0075 E-mail: gee@wilsongunn.com
Wilson Gunn Skerrett, Charles House, 148 Great Charles Street, Birmingham, B3 3HT Tel: 0121-236 1038 Fax: 0121-233 2875 E-mail: skerrett@wilsongunn.com
Withers & Rogers, 75 Colmore Row, Birmingham, B3 2AP Tel: 0121-245 3900 Fax: 0121-245 3930 E-mail: admin@withersrogers.com
Wynne Jones Laine & James, 22 Rodney Road, Cheltenham, Gloucestershire, GL50 1JJ Tel: (01242) 515807 Fax: (01242) 224183 E-mail: patenedagents@wynne-jones.com

PATENT AGENTS/ATTORNEYS, BASED OVERSEAS

G F Redfurn & Co., Lynn House, Ivy Arch Road, Worthing, West Sussex, BN14 8BX Tel: (01903) 820466 Fax: (01903) 820439 E-mail: sueb@gfredfern.com

PATENT AGENTS/ATTORNEYS, EUROPEAN

A A Thornton & Co., 29 St. Katherines Street, Northampton, NN1 2QZ Tel: (01604) 638242 Fax: (01604) 638164 E-mail: aat@aathornton.com
Appleyard Lees, 15 Clare Road, Halifax, West Yorkshire, HX1 2HY Tel: (01422) 330110 Fax: (01422) 330090 E-mail: ip@appleyardlees.com

PATENT AGENTS/ATTORNEYS, EUROPEAN – *continued*

Barker Brettell Ltd, 138 Hagley Road, Birmingham, B16 9PW Tel: 0121-456 1364 Fax: 0121-456 1368 E-mail: admin@barkerbrettell.co.uk

Beck Greener, Fulwood House, 12 Fulwood Place, London, WC1V 6HR Tel: (020) 7693 5600 Fax: (020) 7693 5601 E-mail: mail@beckgreener.com

Boult Wade Tennant, Verulam Gardens, 70 Gray's Inn Road, London, WC1X 8BT Tel: (020) 7430 7500 Fax: (020) 7831 1768 E-mail: boult@boult.com

Boult Wade Tennant, 34 Bridge Street, Reading, RG1 2LU Tel: 0118-956 5900 Fax: 0118-950 0442 E-mail: boult@boult.com

Bromhead & Co., 37 Great James Street, London, WC1N 3HB Tel: (020) 7405 7010 Fax: (020) 7831 5118 E-mail: mail@bromhead-johnson.com

Elkington & Fife, Beacon House, 113 Kingsway, London, WC2B 6PN Tel: (020) 7405 3505 Fax: (020) 7405 1508 E-mail: elkfife@elkfife.co.uk

Forrester & Boehmert, Forrester House, 52 Bounds Green Road, London, N11 2EY Tel: (020) 8889 6625 Fax: (020) 8801 1088 E-mail: fklondon@forresters.co.uk

Franks & Co. Ltd, 15 Jessops Riverside, Brightside Lane, Sheffield, S9 2RX Tel: 0114-256 2677 Fax: 0114-249 9666 E-mail: franksco@franksco.com

Gill Jennings & Every, 7 Eldon Street, London, EC2M 7LS Tel: (020) 7377 1377 Fax: (020) 7377 1310 E-mail: gje@gje.co.uk

Graham Jones & Co 77 Beaconsfield R D, Beaconsfield Road, London, SE3 7LG Tel: (020) 8858 4039 Fax: (020) 8293 5920

▶ Hindle Lowther, 28 Rutland Square, Edinburgh, EH1 2BW Tel: 0131 2216560 E-mail: mail@hindlelowther.com

Hlbbshaw, Shaw House, Pegler Way, Crawley, West Sussex, RH11 7AF Tel: (01293) 528000 Fax: (01293) 528900 E-mail: mail@hlbbshaw.com

Hlbbshaw, Bloxam Court, Corporation Street, Rugby, Warwickshire, CV21 2DU Tel: (01788) 577000 Fax: (01788) 540783 E-mail: mail@hlbbshaw.com

Jensen & Son, 366-368 Old Street, London, EC1V 9LT Tel: (020) 7613 0280 Fax: (020) 7613 0267 E-mail: mail@jensens.co.uk

Kilburn & Strode, 20 Red Lion Street, London, WC1R 4PJ Tel: (020) 7539 4200 Fax: (020) 7539 4299 E-mail: ks@kstrode.co.uk

Maguire Boss, 24 East Street, St. Ives, Cambridgeshire, PE27 5PD Tel: (01480) 301588 Fax: (01480) 464405 E-mail: tmark@maguires.co.uk

Marks & Clarke, 5 The Quadrant, Coventry, CV1 2EL Tel: (024) 7622 2756 Fax: (024) 7625 6197 E-mail: ip@marks-clarke.com

Marks & Clerk, 27 Imperial Square, Cheltenham, Gloucestershire, GL50 1RQ Tel: (01242) 524520 Fax: (01242) 579383 E-mail: cheltonham@marks-clerk.com

▶ Marks & Clerk, 19 Royal Exchange Square, Glasgow, G1 3AE Tel: 0141-221 5767 Fax: 0141-221 7739 E-mail: glasgow@marks-clerk.com

Marks & Clerk, 90 Long Acre, London, WC2E 9RA Tel: (020) 7420 0000 Fax: (020) 7836 3339

Mathys & Squire, 120 Holborn, London, EC1N 2SQ Tel: (020) 7830 0000 Fax: (020) 7830 0001 E-mail: sales@mathys-squire.com

Page Hargrave, Manfield House, 1 Southampton Street, London, WC2R 0LR Tel: (020) 7240 6933 Fax: (020) 7379 0268 E-mail: london@pagehargrave.co.uk

Page White & Farrer, 54 Doughty Street, London, WC1N 2LS Tel: (020) 7831 7929 Fax: (020) 7831 8040 E-mail: sales@pagewhite.com

Raworth Moss & Cook, 36 Sydenham Road, Croydon, CR0 2EF Tel: (020) 8688 8318 Fax: (020) 8760 0055 E-mail: rmc@raworth.co.uk

▶ Sergey Naumkin, 31 Wellington Road, Bollington, Macclesfield, Cheshire, SK10 5JR Tel: (01625) 576077 Fax: 0700 6051662 E-mail: sergey.naumkin@justice.com

Stevens Hewlett & Perkins, 20-23 Holborn, Halton House, London, EC1N 2JD Tel: (020) 7936 2499 Fax: (020) 7404 1844 E-mail: mail@shplondon.co.uk

A.A. Thornton & Co., 235 High Holborn, London, WC1V 7LE Tel: (020) 7405 4044 Fax: (020) 7405 3580 E-mail: aat@aathornton.com

W P Thompson & Co., Eastcheap House, Central Approach, Letchworth Garden City, Hertfordshire, SG6 3DS Tel: (01462) 682139 Fax: (01462) 676775 E-mail: letchworth@wpt.co.uk

Withers & Rogers, 75 Colmore Row, Birmingham, B3 2AP Tel: 0121-245 3900 Fax: 0121-245 3930 E-mail: admin@withersrogers.com

PATENT GLAZING BARS

Lonsdale Metal Industries, Unit 40 Milmead Industrial Centre, Mill Mead Road, London, N17 9QU Tel: (020) 8801 4221 Fax: (020) 8801 1287 E-mail: info@lonsdalemetal.co.uk

Newdawn & Sun Ltd, Springfield Business Park, Alcester, Warwickshire, B49 6EY Tel: (01789) 764444 Fax: (01789) 400164 E-mail: sales@newdawn-sun.co.uk

Safety Glass Replacements Ltd, Garden Street, Newcastle, Staffordshire, ST5 1BW Tel: (01782) 614693 Fax: (01782) 614633

PATENT GLAZING COMPONENTS

Barn Glassworks Ltd, 7 Sandiford Road, Sutton, Surrey, SM3 9RN Tel: (020) 8644 7444 Fax: (020) 8641 5853

PATENT GLAZING SYSTEMS OR UNITS

Barn Glassworks Ltd, 7 Sandiford Road, Sutton, Surrey, SM3 9RN Tel: (020) 8644 7444 Fax: (020) 8641 5853

Howells Glazing, Clock House, Forge Lane, Cradley Heath, West Midlands, B64 5AL Tel: (01384) 820060 Fax: (01384) 820061 E-mail: enquiries@howellsglazing.co.uk

HW Architectural Ltd, Birds Royd Lane, Birds Royd Lane, Brighouse, West Yorkshire, HD6 1NG Tel: (01484) 717677 Fax: (01484) 400148 E-mail: info@hwa.co.uk

Kelsey Roofing Industries Ltd, Kelsey House, Paper Mill Drive, Church Hill South, Redditch, Worcestershire, B98 8QJ Tel: (01527) 594400 Fax: (01527) 594444

Lonsdale Metal Industries, Unit 40 Milmead Industrial Centre, Mill Mead Road, London, N17 9QU Tel: (020) 8801 4221 Fax: (020) 8801 1287 E-mail: info@lonsdalemetal.co.uk

Standard Patent Glazing Co. Ltd, Forge Lane, Dewsbury, West Yorkshire, WF12 9EL Tel: (01924) 461213 Fax: (01924) 458083 E-mail: enquiries@patent-glazing.com

Twide-Paragon Ltd, Glasshouse Fields, London, E1W 9JA Tel: (020) 7790 2333 Fax: (020) 7790 0201 E-mail: paragon@twigroup.co.uk

Universal Glazing Ltd, Unit 12 Silver Court, Intercity Way, Leeds, LS13 4LY Tel: 0113-257 2021 Fax: 0113-239 3317 E-mail: universal@unit12.fsnet.co.uk

PATENT SEARCHERS

Hlbbshaw, Shaw House, Pegler Way, Crawley, West Sussex, RH11 7AF Tel: (01293) 528000 Fax: (01293) 528900 E-mail: mail@hlbbshaw.com

Kingsley & Talboys, 4 Sinclair House, Hastings Street, London, WC1H 9PZ Tel: (020) 7387 8897 Fax: (020) 7387 8714 E-mail: info@kingsleytalboys.com

R W S Group, Tavistock House, Tavistock Square, London, WC1H 9LG Tel: (020) 7554 5400 Fax: (020) 7554 5454 E-mail: sales@rws-group.com

Supertron Ltd, 19-21 Fosse Way, London, W13 0BZ Tel: (020) 8998 4372

▶ Victor Green & Company Ltd, 16-16a Baldwins Gardens, London, EC1N 7RJ Tel: (020) 7269 9200 Fax: 020 7269-9210 E-mail: victor@victorgreen.co.uk

PATHOLOGICAL ANALYSIS LABORATORIES/SERVICES

Charles River Laboratories, Tranent, East Lothian, EH33 2NE Tel: (01875) 614545 Fax: (01875) 614555

PATIO CONSTRUCTION

▶ Avon Valley Landscapes, 10 Ashman Avenue, Long Lawford, Rugby, Warwickshire, CV23 9AG Tel: (01788) 550195 E-mail: mark@avonvalleylandscapes.co.uk

▶ D'arcy Diggers, Hitcham Road, Walthamstow, London, E17 8HL Tel: (020) 8923 6062

▶ Fife Paving, 179 Affric Road, Glenrothes, Fife, KY7 6XA Tel: (01592) 748882 E-mail: info@fifepaving.co.uk

PATIO FURNITURE

▶ GoAfrica, 34 St. Barnabas Street, Wellingborough, Northamptonshire, NN8 3HB Tel: (0845) 6447984 E-mail: gwen@goafrica.co.uk

▶ P J Milligan, 54 Wilson Place, East Kilbride, Glasgow, G74 4QD Tel: (01355) 260990 E-mail: craig.hamilton@pjmilligan.com

▶ Planet Leisure UK, The LnS Building, Unit 4, Crockford Lane, Chineham, Basingstoke, Hampshire, RG24 8NA Tel: (01256) 841950 Fax: (01256) 818255 E-mail: sales@planetleisureuk.co.uk

▶ Treehouse Furniture Ltd, 174 Penarth Road, Cardiff, CF11 6NL Tel: (029) 2023 0796 Fax: (029) 2023 0796 E-mail: ralph@intothewoods.co.uk

PATIO HEATER HIRE

▶ Patioheaters4u.Com, Thor Industrial Estate, Swindon, SN3 5WZ Tel: (01793) 613900 E-mail: sales@patioheaters4u.com

PATIO HEATERS

▶ Clifton Engineering Ltd, Old Road, Clifton-on-Teme, Worcester, WR6 6DR Tel: (01886) 812224 Fax: (01886) 812706

▶ Patioheaters4u.Com, Thor Industrial Estate, Swindon, SN3 5WZ Tel: (01793) 613900 E-mail: sales@patioheaters4u.com

Sierra Leisure Products Ltd, Bridge Works, Mill Lane, Hasketon, Woodbridge, Suffolk, IP13 6HE Tel: (01473) 735773 Fax: (01473) 738316 E-mail: lisa.bean@sierraleisure.co.uk

PATIO LIGHTING

▶ Cristal Lighting, Priory Mill House, Leckhampstead Road, Akeley, Buckingham, MK18 5HG Tel: (01280) 860154 Fax: (01280) 860546 E-mail: sales@crystal-lighting-centre.com

▶ Garden Options Ltd, 3 The Wynd, Melrose, Roxburghshire, TD6 9LD Tel: (01896) 820630 E-mail: enquiries@gardenoptions.co.uk

▶ S A S (Safe and Secure) Ltd, 1 Yale Close, Owlsmoor, Sandhurst, Berkshire, GU47 0UJ Tel: (01276) 31749 Fax: (01276) 31749 E-mail: sasshop@btinternet.com

Solar Illuminations, P.O. Box 19, Rye, East Sussex, TN31 6WZ Tel: (020) 8144 0847 E-mail: sales@solarilluminations.co.uk

PATIO OR PORCH DOORS

▶ A & D Joinery Ltd, Unit 14, Bolton Road Mill, Bolton Road, Bolton, BL5 3JG Tel: (01942) 814501 Fax: (01942) 810468 E-mail: john@aanddjoinery

A W S Group Plc, Systems House, Hoo Farm Industrial Estate, Worcester Road, Kidderminster, Worcestershire, DY11 7RA Tel: (01562) 743700 Fax: (01562) 829775 E-mail: info@awsgroupplc.co.uk

Croxfords Joinery Manufacturers, Meltham Joinery Works, New Street, Meltham, Holmfirth, HD9 5NT Tel: (01484) 850892 Fax: (01484) 850969 E-mail: ralph@croxfords.demon.co.uk

Dorwin Ltd, Unit 1 Forge Works, Mill Lane, Alton, Hampshire, GU34 2QG Tel: (01420) 84217 Fax: (01420) 541648 E-mail: linden.ransley@dorwin.co.uk

East Yorkshire Glazing Co. Ltd, Wiltshire Road, Hull, HU4 6QQ Tel: (01482) 561101 Fax: (01482) 565307 E-mail: eygsales@eygsales.com

▶ Imagine, 28 Buckingham Grove, Scartho Top, Grimsby, North East Lincolnshire, DN33 3RR Tel: (01472) 314266 E-mail: monkey5000@ntlworld.com

S G Aluminium Ltd, Unit B Sett End Road West, Shadsworth Business Park, Blackburn, BB1 2QJ Tel: (01254) 691600 Fax: (01253) 340526 E-mail: info@sg-aluminium.co.uk

Solair Ltd, Pennington Close, West Bromwich, West Midlands, B70 8BG Tel: 0121-525 2722 Fax: 0121-525 6786 E-mail: sales@solair.co.uk

PATISSERIE COUNTERS

La Galinette Ltd, Legacy Centre, Hanworth Trading Estate, Hampton Road West, Hanworth, Feltham, Middlesex, TW13 6DH Tel: (020) 8755 5858 Fax: (020) 8755 5878 E-mail: sales@lagalinette.co.uk

PATROL BOATS

A B S Hovercraft Ltd, Coopers House, The Horsefair, Romsey, Hampshire, SO51 8JZ Tel: (01794) 526300 Fax: (01794) 526301 E-mail: info@abs-hovercraft.com

Offshore Powerboats Ltd, 1 Lymington Yacht Haven, Kings Saltern Road, Lymington, Hampshire, SO41 3QD Tel: (01590) 677955 Fax: (01590) 671890 E-mail: chris@offshorepowerboats.co.uk

VT Halmatic Ltd, Hamilton Road, Cosham, Portsmouth, PO6 4PX Tel: (023) 9253 9600 Fax: (023) 9253 9601 E-mail: info@halmatic.com

PATTERN BOOKS/BUNCHES

Bunchmakers Ltd, Bagley Lane, Farsley, Leeds, LS28 5UH Tel: 0113-255 6933 Fax: 0113-239 3459

C O S Marketing Ltd, Bradford Road, Idle, Bradford, West Yorkshire, BD10 8SQ Tel: (01274) 617373 Fax: (01274) 615129

Fabric Display Ltd, 11 - 12 The Parker Centre, Mansfield Road, Derby, DE21 4SZ Tel: (01332) 382420 Fax: (01332) 290676

Fabric Presentation Ltd, Forman Street, Derby, DE1 1JQ Tel: (01332) 290510 Fax: (01332) 340944 E-mail: fabric.presentations@btinternet.com

L M R Computer Repairs, 2 North Parade, Norris Road, Sale, Cheshire, M33 3JS Tel: 0161-962 8872 Fax: 0161-962 8872

Lee Colourplan Ltd, Crompton Road, Ilkeston, Derbyshire, DE7 4BG Tel: 0115-944 1500 Fax: 0115-944 1481 E-mail: sales@leecolourplan.com

James A. Marshall Ltd, 50 Crownpoint Road, Bridgeton, Glasgow, G40 2QE Tel: 0141-556 1626 Fax: 0141-556 4630 E-mail: enquiries@jamesamarshall.com

Mersey Pattern Ltd, Unit 7-9 & 11, Edwards La Industrial Estate, Liverpool, L24 9HX Tel: 0151-486 9500 Fax: 0151-448 1171

P & J UK Ltd, 1 Kenwood Road, Stockport, Cheshire, SK5 6PH Tel: 0161-443 1557 Fax: 0161-443 1821 E-mail: geoff.walters@pandj.net

Pattern Masters Ltd, 9 Norfolk Street, Peterborough, PE1 2NP Tel: (01733) 555171 Fax: (01733) 555191 E-mail: enquiries@patternmasters.co.uk

Senator Projects Ltd, The Door Centre, Discovery Park, Crossley Road, Stockport, Cheshire, SK4 5BW Tel: 0161-432 5080 Fax: 0161-432 6100

Swatchways Ltd, Unit 13 Ely Industrial Estate, Williamstown, Penygraig, Tonypandy, Mid Glamorgan, CF40 1BY Tel: (01443) 423111 Fax: (01443) 440939

Teckno Developments Ltd, Great Gutter Lane, Willerby, Hull, HU10 6DL Tel: (01482) 657996 Fax: (01482) 651089 E-mail: sales@tecknodev.com

Thomas Brown(Stockport) Ltd, Stanbank Street, Stockport, Cheshire, SK4 1PY Tel: 0161-480 3452 Fax: 0161-480 6207

Unravel Mills Ltd, Broomfield Mill Street, Preston, PR1 1NQ Tel: (01772) 259065 Fax: (01772) 881398 E-mail: sales@unravelmills.co.uk

PATTERN CARDS, COLOUR/ SHADE

Fabric Presentation Ltd, Forman Street, Derby, DE1 1JQ Tel: (01332) 290510 Fax: (01332) 340944 E-mail: fabric.presentations@btinternet.com

Kelly & Barratt Ltd, Scotch Park Trading Estate, Forge Lane, Leeds, LS12 2PS Tel: 0113-231 1322 Fax: 0113-231 1883

Lee Colourplan Ltd, Crompton Road, Ilkeston, Derbyshire, DE7 4BG Tel: 0115-944 1500 Fax: 0115-944 1481 E-mail: sales@leecolourplan.com

Multi Shades Ltd, Sandals Mill, Cliffe Avenue, Baildon, Shipley, West Yorkshire, BD17 6PB Tel: (01274) 580727 Fax: (01274) 531181 E-mail: sales@multishades.co.uk

Multicolor UK Ltd, The Drift, Nacton Road, Ipswich, IP3 9QP Tel: 01473 723443 Fax: (01473) 270671 E-mail: info@multicolor.co.uk

P & J UK Ltd, 1 Kenwood Road, Stockport, Cheshire, SK5 6PH Tel: 0161-443 1557 Fax: 0161-443 1821 E-mail: geoff.walters@pandj.net

Pattern Masters Ltd, 9 Norfolk Street, Peterborough, PE1 2NP Tel: (01733) 555171 Fax: (01733) 555191 E-mail: enquiries@patternmasters.co.uk

Smith Harrison Shade Cards Ltd, Unit 2 Factory Street, Bradford, West Yorkshire, BD4 9NW Tel: (01274) 683579 Fax: (01274) 688936 E-mail: info@smithharrison.co.uk

Wetherby Shade Card Co. Ltd, Grangefield Industrial Estate, Pudsey, West Yorkshire, LS28 6QJ Tel: 0113-257 7381 Fax: 0113-239 3217 E-mail: info@wetherby-shade-card.co.uk

PATTERN CUTTING MACHINES

Cappa Pinking Machinery Ltd, 25 Westgate, Otley, West Yorkshire, LS21 3AT Tel: (01943) 467655 Fax: (01943) 850362 E-mail: sales@emberfern.co.uk

PATTERN IMPRINTED CONCRETE PAVING CONTRACTORS

Pricast-Thermasill Ltd, Otley Road, Charlestown, Shipley, W. Yorkshire, BD17 7HU Tel: (01274) 590522 Fax: (01274) 532264

Stencil Tech, 1 Upland Industrial Estate, Mere Way, Wyton, Huntingdon, Cambridgeshire, PE28 2JZ Tel: (01480) 435919 Fax: (01480) 435922 E-mail: sales@stencil-tech.co.uk

PAVEMENT LIGHTS

Automated Access Ltd, Unit F 59 Sibson Road, Birstall, Leicester, LE4 4DX Tel: 0116-267 1122 Fax: 0116-267 1122 E-mail: enquiries@automated-access-solutions.co.uk

Luxcrete Ltd, Premier House, Disraeli Road, London, NW10 7BT Tel: (020) 8965 7292 Fax: (020) 8961 6337 E-mail: sales@luxcrete.co.uk

▶ UK Pavement Light Construction Luton Ltd, 18 Summers Road, Luton, LU2 9HS Tel: (01582) 724854 Fax: (01582) 455484 E-mail: info@ukpavementlight.co.uk

PAVEMENT RESURFACING

▶ Con Form Ltd, PO Box 4233, Maldon, Essex, CM9 8GX Tel: (01621) 843938 Fax: (01621) 843998 E-mail: sales@con-form.co.uk

PAVEMENT SIGNS

Kremer Signs, 300 New Greenham Park, Greenham, Thatcham, Berkshire, RG19 6HN Tel: (01635) 46125 Fax: (01635) 523170 E-mail: sales@kremersigns.co.uk

PAVING BREAKER ASPHALT CUTTERS

▶ Driveways Stirling, 44 Morningside Road, Morningside, Edinburgh, EH10 4QN Tel: (0800) 0191139 E-mail: info@drivewaysdirectscotland.co.uk

PAVING CONTRACTORS

A P Grieveson, 8 Middlesex Road, Stockport, Cheshire, SK5 8HT Tel: 0161-355 9051 Fax: (07855) 913417 E-mail: p_grieveson@hotmail.com

Apex Asphalt & Paving Co. Ltd, 60 Cato Street, Nechells, Birmingham, B7 4TS Tel: 0121-359 8447 Fax: 0121-359 5418 E-mail: apex@apex-asphalt.co.uk

BDP Surfacing Ltd, Raynesway, Derby, DE24 0DW Tel: (01332) 571806 Fax: (01332) 574278

▶ Border Paving Ltd, Maltkiln Farm, Chapel Lane, Bronington, Whitchurch, Shropshire, SY13 3HR Tel: (01948) 780902 Fax: (01948) 780630

▶ Chafford Landscapes, 14 St. James Avenue East, Stanford-le-Hope, Essex, SS17 7BQ Tel: (01375) 676003 E-mail: ianholloway@btconnect.com

▶ Classic Paving Services, Classic House, Hollands Road, Northwich, Cheshire, CW9 8AU Tel: (01606) 350800 Fax: (01606) 352800

▶ Dart Jerry Ltd, Unit 10 Barton Hill Trading Estate, Maze Street, Bristol, BS5 9TQ Tel: 0117-955 9911 Fax: 0117-955 9922

▶ Gracelands Landscapes Ltd, The Yard, Bramshill Close, Arborfield Cross, Reading, RG2 9PT Tel: 0118-976 0660 Fax: 0118-976 0990 E-mail: info@gracelands-landscapes.co.uk

Granville Steel Contracting plc, Steel Close, Eaton Socon, St. Neots, Cambridgeshire, PE19 8TT Tel: (01480) 213513 Fax: (01480) 405994 E-mail: jane.taylor@aggregate.co.uk

P G Watson Brickwork Contractors, 104 The Causeway, Carshalton, Surrey, SM5 2NB Tel: (020) 8773 3476 Fax: (020) 8401 6340 E-mail: jdw1812@aol.com

Patio Paving Centre, unit 7 Batch Indust Est, Rectory Way, Lympsham, Weston-super-Mare, Avon, BS24 0ES Tel: 01934 750010 Fax: 01934 750010

▶ R & C Landscapes, 82 Groveside Close, Carshalton, Surrey, SM5 2ET Tel: (020) 8773 8296 E-mail: robertgibbs364@hotmail.com

▶ Techniblock Ltd, Kingsway Industrial Park, Kingsway Park Close, Derby, DE22 3FP Tel: (01332) 293977 Fax: (01332) 364488

PAVING EQUIPMENT, ROAD CONSTRUCTION

▶ Bathgate Silica Sand Ltd, Arclid Quarry, Congleton Road, Arclid, Sandbach, Cheshire, CW11 4SN Tel: (01270) 762492 Fax: (01270) 759449 E-mail: sales@bathgatesilica.co.uk

PAVING SLABS OR BRICKS OR BLOCKS

A C Baker & Son Ltd, Wood Cottage, The Green, Sarratt, Rickmansworth, Hertfordshire, WD3 6AT Tel: (01923) 269190 Fax: (01923) 269190

Joseph Barrett & Sons Ltd, 128 Eglish Road, Dungannon, County Tyrone, BT70 1LB Tel: (028) 3754 8646 Fax: (028) 3754 8863 E-mail: info@barrettconcrete.com

Batchelor Concrete Products, Wood End Gardens, Northolt, Middlesex, UB5 4QH Tel: (020) 8422 6892 Fax: (020) 8863 1268

Blanc De Bierges, Eastrea Road, Whittlesey, Peterborough, PE7 2AG Tel: (01733) 202566 Fax: (01733) 205405 E-mail: sales@blancdebierges.com

Bowland Cumbria Ltd, Under Railway Bridge, Dockray Hall Mill, Kendal, Cumbria, LA9 4RU Tel: (01539) 723600 Fax: (01539) 740776 E-mail: sales@boland-stone.com

Bradfords Building Supplies Ltd, 139 Bristol Road, Bridgwater, Somerset, TA6 4AQ Tel: (01278) 422654 Fax: (01278) 450574 E-mail: bbs.bridgwater@bradford.co.uk

Brick Specialists (Midlands) Ltd, 2 Cottage Terrace, The Rope Walk, Nottingham, NG1 5DX Tel: 0115-985 9100 Fax: 0115-947 8960 E-mail: rgb@bricks99.freserve.co.uk

Builders Supply (Wakefield) Ltd, 2 Thornes Lane, Wakefield, West Yorkshire, WF1 5QH Tel: (01924) 376821 Fax: (01924) 362018

Building Supplies (Holme Lane) Ltd, 115 Holme Lane, Sheffield, S6 4JR Tel: 0114-234 2501 Fax: 0114-285 2836

▶ Concrete Fabrications Ltd, Crewshole Road Off, Blackswarth Road, St George, Bristol, BS5 8AU Tel: 0117-955 7530

Concrete Products Kirkcaldy Ltd, Hayfield Place, Hayfield Industrial Estate, Kirkcaldy, Fife, KY2 5DH Tel: (01592) 261326 Fax: (01592) 200498

Concrete Products (Lincoln) 1980 Ltd, Riverside Industrial Estate, Skellingthorpe Road, Saxilby, Lincoln, LN1 2LR Tel: (01522) 704158 Fax: (01522) 704233 E-mail: sales@bowlandlincoln.co.uk

Cooper Clarke Civils & Lintels, Bloomfield Road, Farnworth, Bolton, BL4 9LP Tel: (01204) 862222 Fax: (01204) 795296 E-mail: farnworth@civilsandlintels.co.uk

Days Buildbase, Burrfields Road, Portsmouth, PO3 5NA Tel: (023) 9266 2261 Fax: (023) 9266 6497 E-mail: portsmouth@buildbase.co.uk

▶ Dixon Block Paving, Long Lane, Attenborough, Beeston, Nottingham, NG9 6BG Tel: 0115-925 9511 E-mail: iandixon01@hotmail.com

E. East & Son Ltd, 43-47 Chiltern Avenue, Amersham, Buckinghamshire, HP6 5AF Tel: (01494) 433936 Fax: (01494) 728366

George Farrar (Quarries) Ltd, Bradford Street, Keighley, West Yorkshire, BD21 3EB Tel: (01535) 602344 Fax: (01535) 606247 E-mail: sales@farrar.co.uk

Fencrete Products, Church Lane, Marsworth, Tring, Hertfordshire, HP23 4LZ Tel: (01442) 824174 Fax: (01442) 827856

Ibstock Building Products Ltd, Brickyard Road, Aldridge, Walsall, WS9 8TB Tel: (01922) 741400 Fax: (01922) 743086

Lakeland Concrete Products Ltd, Flusco House, Flusco, Penrith, Cumbria, CA11 0JB Tel: (01768) 483617 Fax: (01768) 483890 E-mail: info@lakelandconcrete.co.uk

Lovie Ltd, Cowbog, New Pitsligo, Fraserburgh, Aberdeenshire, AB43 6PR Tel: (01771) 653777 Fax: (01771) 653527 E-mail: sales@lovie.co.uk

Manchester Brick Services, Haigh Avenue, Whitehill Indust Estate, Reddish, Stockport, Cheshire, SK4 1NU Tel: 0161-480 2621 Fax: 0161-480 0108

Marshalls, Eastern Dry Dock, Corporation Road, Newport, Gwent, NP19 4RE Tel: (01633) 284600 Fax: (01633) 284612 E-mail: suebell@marshalls.co.uk

Pave The Way, Stonebridge Farm, Hundon Road, Kedington, Haverhill, Suffolk, CB9 7QT Tel: (01440) 710315 E-mail: sales@pave-the-way.com

Plasmor Ltd, Womersley Road, Knottingley, West Yorkshire, WF11 0DN Tel: (01977) 673221 Fax: (01977) 607071 E-mail: sales@plasmor.co.uk

R M C Concrete Products Ltd, Dale Road, Dove Holes, Buxton, Derbyshire, SK17 8BG Tel: (01298) 22324 Fax: (01298) 815221

Ridings Construction Co. Ltd, The Ropewalk, Hallfield Road, York, YO31 7XG Tel: (01904) 625269 Fax: (01904) 642280 E-mail: info@ridingsconstruction.co.uk

Scott Bros, 94 Mill Hall, Aylesford, Kent, ME20 7JN Tel: (01622) 717007 Fax: (01622) 717007

Stocks Bros Ltd, Blocks, 5 Ninelands Lane, Garforth, Leeds, LS25 1NT Tel: 0113-232 0022 Fax: 0113-287 0839 E-mail: sales@stocks-blocks.co.uk

Stonemarket Driveway Contractors Ltd, Old Gravel Quarry, Oxford Road, Ryton on Dunsmore, Coventry, CV8 3EJ Tel: (024) 7651 8700 Fax: (024) 7651 8777 E-mail: sales@stonemarket.co.uk

Stowell Concrete, Arnolds Way, Yatton, Bristol, BS49 4QN Tel: (01934) 833340 Fax: (01934) 835474 E-mail: sales@stowellconcrete.co.uk

Tarmac Toppave Ltd, 38 Hatch Pond Road, Nuffield Industrial Estate, Poole, Dorset, BH17 0JZ Tel: (01202) 642400 Fax: (01202) 642405 E-mail: sales@toppave.com

Townscape Products Ltd, Fulwood Road South, Sutton-in-Ashfield, Nottinghamshire, NG17 2JZ Tel: (01623) 513355 Fax: (01623) 440267 E-mail: sales@townscape-products.co.uk

Travis Perkins plc, Chamberlayne Road, London, NW10 3NB Tel: (020) 8964 9000 Fax: (020) 8969 0702 E-mail: enquiries@travisperkins.com

Wyresdale Concrete Products, Bradshaw Lane, Stakepool, Preston, PR3 6AJ Tel: (01253) 790364

PAY AND DISPLAY CAR PARK MACHINES

National Car Parks Ltd (N C P), 21 Bryanston Street, London, W1H 7AB Tel: (0870) 6067050 Fax: (020) 7491 3577 E-mail: marketing@ncp.co.uk

▶ Parking Protection Services Ltd, PO Box 489, Edgware, Middlesex, HA8 9ZR Tel: (0870) 3450310 E-mail: info@parkingprotectionservices.co.uk

Zeag UK Ltd, Zeag House, 17 Deer Park Road, London, SW19 3XJ Tel: (020) 8543 3281 Fax: (020) 8443 5344 E-mail: sales@zeaguk.com

PAYROLL ADMINISTRATING SERVICES

ABCO Computer Services Ltd, Airways House, First Avenue, London Stansted Airport North, Stansted, Essex, CM24 1RY Tel: (01279) 680000 Fax: (01279) 661371 E-mail: abcopay@ndirect.co.uk

▶ B K E Business Services Ltd, 77 Oxford Street, Pontycymmer, Bridgend, Bridgend, Mid Glamorgan, CF32 8DD Tel: 01656 871605 E-mail: louise@bkebusiness.co.uk

Business Tax Centre Ltd, Dte House, Hollins Mount, Bury, Lancashire, BL9 8AT Tel: 0161-796 6090 Fax: 0161 767 1212 E-mail: payroll@dtegroup.com

Capita Printing Services, Unit C Croydon Road Industrial Estate, Tannery Close, Beckenham, Kent, BR3 4BY Tel: (020) 8662 7010 Fax: (020) 8662 7003 E-mail: sales@capita.co.uk

▶ Payman Co UK Ltd, 3 Church Street, Frome, Somerset, BA11 1PW Tel: (01373) 453454 Fax: (01373) 461177 E-mail: info@payman.co.uk

PAYROLL BUREAU SERVICES

▶ 365 Payroll Services Ltd, Kyama House, 5 Ingle Dell, Camberley, Surrey, GU15 2LP Tel: (0845) 0573598 Fax: (01276) 22732 E-mail: jhealy@365payroll.co.uk

ABCO Computer Services Ltd, Airways House, First Avenue, London Stansted Airport North, Stansted, Essex, CM24 1RY Tel: (01279) 680000 Fax: (01279) 661371 E-mail: abcopay@ndirect.co.uk

Business Tax Centre Ltd, Dte House, Hollins Mount, Bury, Lancashire, BL9 8AT Tel: 0161-796 6090 Fax: 0161 767 1212 E-mail: payroll@dtegroup.com

▶ Celerity Payroll Services Ltd, 21 Longhill Road, Brighton, BN2 7BF Tel: (01273) 306836 Fax: (01273) 304604 E-mail: info@payline.co.uk

▶ Greyhound Business Systems Ltd, PO Box 5306, Leicester, LE2 4SS Tel: 0116-271 8808 Fax: 0116-271 8808 E-mail: sales@greyhound-business.co.uk

Hamiltons Accountants & Business Advisors, Meriden House, 6 Great Cornbow, Halesowen, West Midlands, B63 3AB Tel: 0121-585 6655 Fax: 0121-585 6228 E-mail: enquiries@hamiltons-group.co.uk

Ics Computing Ltd, Wessex House, Oxford Road, Newbury, Berkshire, RG14 1PA Tel: (01635) 580802 Fax: (01635) 580803 E-mail: enquiries@icscomputing.co.uk

Northgate Information Solutions, Prolog House, Littlemoor, Eckington, Sheffield, S21 4EF Tel: (01246) 439400 Fax: (01246) 439401 E-mail: enquiries@northgate-is.com

▶ Payman Co UK Ltd, 3 Church Street, Frome, Somerset, BA11 1PW Tel: (01373) 453454 Fax: (01373) 461177 E-mail: info@payman.co.uk

▶ Payroll and Accounting (UK) Ltd, 15a High Street, Tunbridge Wells, Kent, TN1 1UT Tel: 01892 548930 Fax: 01892 542685 E-mail: info@pas-uk.com

▶ Pyranha Solutions Ltd, 4 Monkswell Drive, Bolton le Sands, Carnforth, Lancashire, LA5 8JZ Tel: (07808) 054533 E-mail: andrew@pyranha.co.uk

Systems & Software Ltd, 85 Alvechurch Road, Birmingham, B31 3PG Tel: 0121-604 7001 Fax: 0121-604 7002

▶ UK Payroll, Gilbert Wakefield House, 67 Bewsey Street, Warrington, WA2 7JQ Tel: (01925) 631330 Fax: (01925) 638440 E-mail: info@uk-payroll.net

PAYROLL DOCUMENT PRINTING

▶ B K E Business Services Ltd, 77 Oxford Street, Pontycymmer, Bridgend, Bridgend, Mid Glamorgan, CF32 8DD Tel: 01656 871605 E-mail: louise@bkebusiness.co.uk

PAYROLL OR PENSIONS OR PERSONNEL SOFTWARE

▶ 365 Payroll Services Ltd, Kyama House, 5 Ingle Dell, Camberley, Surrey, GU15 2LP Tel: (0845) 0573598 Fax: (01276) 22732 E-mail: jhealy@365payroll.co.uk

Achiever Business Solutions, Cross Pillory House, Cross & Pillory Lane, Alton, Hampshire, GU34 1HL Tel: (01420) 547507 Fax: (01420) 547501 E-mail: jinny.groome@goachiever.com

Advice By Telephone Ltd, 306 St. Marys Lane, Upminster, Essex, RM14 3HL Tel: (01708) 640110 Fax: (01708) 224802 E-mail: admin@advice.uk.com

Amethyst Associates Ltd, The Old Barn, Oak House, Main Road, Farthinghoe, Brackley, Northamptonshire, NN13 5PB Tel: (01295) 714056 Fax: (0870) 1219961 E-mail: geoff.wenmouth@amethystassociates.co.uk

Bond International, Unit 10 Coped Hall Business Park, Wootton Bassett, Swindon, SN4 8DP Tel: (01793) 856300 Fax: (01793) 856301 E-mail: helpdesk@infosupport.co.uk

CDC Software, 7 Rushmills, Northampton, NN4 7YB Tel: (01604) 630050 Fax: (01604) 630495

Cing Technologies Ltd, 3 Malt House Cottages, 31 Byfield Road, Chipping Warden, Banbury, Oxfordshire, OX17 1LE Tel: (01295) 660682 E-mail: nigel.galletly@cingtech.com

▶ Cirrus Information Technology, 101 Bourges Boulevard, Peterborough, PE1 1NG Tel: (01733) 425930 E-mail: sales@cirrusit.com

Claybrook Computing Holdings Ltd, Sutherland House, Russel Way, Crawley, West Sussex, RH10 1UH Tel: (01293) 604028 Fax: (01293) 604029

▶ Cornwall Bookkeeping Services, 57 Vyvyan Drive, Quintrell Downs, Newquay, Cornwall, TR8 4NF Tel: 01637 851949 Fax: 01637 851949 E-mail: mjd@cornwall-bookkeeping.co.uk

Dealer Systems, 11 Market Hill, Southam, Warwickshire, CV47 0HF Tel: (01926) 815792 Fax: (01926) 813395

Interface D C B Technolgy Ltd, Tyler Close, Normanton Industrial Estate, Normanton, West Yorkshire, WF6 1RL Tel: (01924) 224929 Fax: (01924) 224939 E-mail: general@interf.co.uk

Intex Software Ltd, Diamond Court, Douglas Close, Preston Farm Industrial Estate, Stockton-on-Tees, Cleveland, TS18 3TP Tel: (01642) 672200 Fax: (01642) 671199 E-mail: sales@intex.co.uk

▶ JH Acunting Services, 15 Lunt Place, Bilston, West Midlands, WV14 7AH Tel: (07801) 429827E-mail: enquiries@jh-accounting.co.uk

K C S Management Systems Ltd, Royal Oak Centre, Brighton Road, Purley, Surrey, CR8 2PG Tel: (020) 8660 2444 Fax: (020) 8668 8196 E-mail: sales@kcsconnect.com

▶ Micro-Pension Systems, 12 Burlington Place, Reigate, Surrey, RH2 9HT Tel: (01737) 237859

Plan It Business Systems, 41 Blackburn Street, Radcliffe, Manchester, M26 1NR Tel: 0161-723 0999 Fax: 0161-723 3888 E-mail: info@planitbs.co.uk

Star Seaford, 10 Broad Street, Seaford, East Sussex, BN25 1ND Tel: (01323) 490565 Fax: (01323) 491599

Sysnet Ltd, Avon Court, Cowbridge Road, Bridgend, Mid Glamorgan, CF31 3SR Tel: (01656) 647111 Fax: (01656) 651038 E-mail: enquiries@sysnetltd.co.uk

▶ TT Software Ltd, PO Box 476, Guernsey, GY1 6BB Tel: (01481) 700202 E-mail: sales@ttsoftware.gg

Wisbech Computer Services Ltd, 107 Norwich Road, Wisbech, Cambridgeshire, PE13 2BB Tel: (01945) 464146 Fax: (01945) 464680 E-mail: sales@wisbech.com

PAYROLL SERVICES, *See also Accounting Services; also Computer Services etc*

▶ A C B Office Services, 137-139 St Marychurch Road, Torquay, TQ1 3HW Tel: (01803) 328332 Fax: (01803) 311707 E-mail: acb.officeservices@virgin.net

Adp, 40-48 Pyrcroft Road, Chertsey, Surrey, KT16 9JT Tel: (0845) 2300237 Fax: (0845) 2302371 E-mail: sales@adp-es.co.uk

▶ Aims, 29 Meadowcroft, Higher Kinnerton, Chester, CH4 9AY Tel: (01244) 661859 E-mail: craig.wynne@aims.co.uk

▶ B & C Services, Premier House, 46 Victoria Road, Burgess Hill, West Sussex, RH15 9LR Tel: 01444 248474 Fax: 01444 870146 E-mail: info@redwellassociates.co.uk

Balance Books Ltd, 306 Aberdeen House, 22 Highbury Grove, London, N5 2DQ Tel: (020) 7704 1515 Fax: (020) 7226 0491 E-mail: admin@balance_uk.com

Business Tax Centre Ltd, Dte House, Hollins Mount, Bury, Lancashire, BL9 8AT Tel: 0161-796 6090 Fax: 0161 767 1212 E-mail: payroll@dtegroup.com

▶ Celerity Payroll Services Ltd, 21 Longhill Road, Brighton, BN2 7BF Tel: (01273) 306836 Fax: (01273) 304604 E-mail: info@payline.co.uk

Complete Bookkeeping Payroll Services Ltd, 12 Hatherley Road, Sidcup, Kent, DA14 4BG Tel: (020) 8308 0317 Fax: (020) 8302 7421

▶ Greyhound Business Systems Ltd, PO Box 5306, Leicester, LE2 4SS Tel: 0116-271 8808 Fax: 0116-271 8808 E-mail: sales@greyhound-business.co.uk

Ics Computing Ltd, Wessex House, Oxford Road, Newbury, Berkshire, RG14 1PA Tel: (01635) 580802 Fax: (01635) 580803 E-mail: enquiries@icscomputing.co.uk

▶ Loum Bookkeeping Services, Flat 2, 20 - 21 Richmond Place, Brighton, BN2 9NA Tel: 01273 570453 E-mail: salina.loum@ntlworld.com

M C G Applications Ltd, 150 Hastings Road, Battle, East Sussex, TN33 0TW Tel: (01424) 774748 Fax: (01424) 777190 E-mail: gill@mcg-applications.co.uk

More Paid Ltd, North Wing Burlington House, Crosby Road North, Liverpool, L22 0LG Tel: 0151-949 0082 Fax: 0151-949 1027

Norhgate H R Ltd, Thorpe Park, Peterborough, PE3 6JY Tel: (01733) 555777 Fax: (01733) 312347 E-mail: enquiries@northgatehr.com

Northgate Information Solutions, Prolog House, Littlemoor, Eckington, Sheffield, S21 4EF Tel: (01246) 439400 Fax: (01246) 439401 E-mail: enquiries@northgate-is.com

▶ Payman Co UK Ltd, 3 Church Street, Frome, Somerset, BA11 1PW Tel: (01373) 453454 Fax: (01373) 461177 E-mail: info@payman.co.uk

▶ Payroll and Accounting (UK) Ltd, 15a High Street, Tunbridge Wells, Kent, TN1 1UT Tel: 01892 548930 Fax: 01892 542685 E-mail: info@pas-uk.com

Peter Saxon & Co., 362 Church Road, London, SW19 2QF Tel: (07956) 379622 Fax: (020) 8648 7829 E-mail: peter@petersaxton.co.uk

PAYROLL SERVICES – *continued*

▶ Saffery Champness, 40 Melville Street, Edinburgh, EH3 7TW Tel: 0131-225 2741 Fax: 0131-225 5376

Sidmouth Book Keeping Services, 6 Kings Avenue, Ottery St. Mary, Devon, EX11 1TA Tel: (01404) 813988 Fax: (01404) 813988 E-mail: tony@sbks.freeserve.co.uk

▶ Sterling Financial Ltd, Church Farm, Little Sodbury, Chipping Sodbury, Bristol, BS37 6QA Tel: (01454) 317272 Fax: (07884) 500629 E-mail: mail@sterlingfinancial.ltd.uk

Talent & Production Services, Oakla,, East Grinstead, Salisbury, SP5 3RY Tel: (01722) 712921 Fax: (01722) 712992

▶ UK Payroll, Gilbert Wakefield House, 67 Bewsey Street, Warrington, WA2 7JQ Tel: (01925) 631330 Fax: (01925) 638440 E-mail: info@uk-payroll.net

PEA GRAVEL AGGREGATES

▶ Dalestone Concrete Products & Patio Laying, Whisby Garden Centre, Whisby Road, Whisby Moor, Lincoln, LN6 9BY Tel: (01522) 689530 Fax: (01522) 684040 E-mail: dalestone01@aol.com

PEARL BUTTONS

Charles Singleton Ltd, 1 Church Lane, Hackenthorpe, Sheffield, S12 4AN Tel: 0114-248 7976 Fax: 0114-248 6717

PEARLS, REAL, *See Gemstone Merchants etc*

PEAT PRODUCTS

Border Farm Supplies Ltd, Turfford Park, Earlston, Berwickshire, TD4 6GZ Tel: (01896) 848911 Fax: (01896) 848006

Durston Garden Products, Avalon Farm, Sharpham, Street, Somerset, BA16 9SE Tel: (01458) 442688 Fax: (01458) 448327 E-mail: info@durstongardenproducts.co.uk

Horticultural Ltd, Newferry Road, Bellaghy, Magherafelt, County Londonderry, BT45 8ND Tel: (028) 7938 6555 Fax: (028) 7938 6741 E-mail: info@bulrush.co.uk

Humax Horticulture Ltd, Richardson House, Mill Hill, Gretna, Dumfriesshire, DG16 5HU Tel: (01461) 339260 Fax: (01461) 339269 E-mail: sales@humax.co.uk

PEDESTRIAN CONTROLLED FORKLIFT TRUCKS

Hyster Europe, Flagship House, Reading Road North, Fleet, Hampshire, GU51 4WD Tel: (01252) 810261 Fax: (01252) 770702 E-mail: sales@hyster.co.uk

T A G Forklift Trucks, Barlow Street, Worsley, Manchester, M28 3BQ Tel: 0161-799 6507 Fax: 0161-799 9010

PEDESTRIAN GUARDRAILS

Fabrikat Nottingham Ltd, Hamilton Road, Sutton-in-Ashfield, Nottinghamshire, NG17 5LN Tel: (01623) 442200 Fax: (01623) 442233

P & R Engineering Midlands Ltd, Cable Street, Wolverhampton, WV2 2HX Tel: (01902) 870637 Fax: (01902) 871569

PEDICURE CHAIRS

▶ Manor Beauty, Hove Manor, Hove Street, Hove, East Sussex, BN3 2DF Tel: (01273) 748483 E-mail: admin@blakeneymanor.co.uk

PEEK (POLYETHERETHERKETONE) PRODUCTS/COMPONENTS/ FITTINGS

W J P Engineering Plastics Ltd, Albert Works, Albert Avenue, Bobbers Mill, Nottingham, NG8 5BE Tel: 0115-929 9555 Fax: 0115-929 0422 E-mail: sales@wjpengineeringplastics.co.uk

PELLET BURNING STOVES

▶ Ecoflue Ltd, Copperfields, Beach Road, Kessingland, Lowestoft, Suffolk, NR33 7RW Tel: (01502) 741388 Fax: 07900 606241 E-mail: blojus@aol.com

PELLETING MACHINES

Cumberland Europe Ltd, Daniels Industrial Estate, 104 Bath Road, Stroud, Gloucestershire, GL5 3TJ Tel: (01453) 768980 Fax: (01453) 768990 E-mail: europeansales@cumberland-plastics.com

PEN CASINGS/COMPONENTS, METALLIC

Presspart Manufacturing Ltd, Phillips Road, Blackburn, BB1 5RF Tel: (01254) 582233 Fax: (01254) 584100 E-mail: sales@presspart.com

PENCILS

A T Cross Ltd, Windmill Trading Estate, Thistle Road, Luton, LU1 3XJ Tel: (01582) 422793 Fax: (01582) 456097 E-mail: crossuk@cross.com

Azizoff Co. Ltd, 2 Beechfield Road, London, N4 1PE Tel: (020) 8809 6902 Fax: (020) 8800 5795 E-mail: azizoffltd@tiscali.co.uk

Ryman The Stationer, 175-177 High Street, Guildford, Surrey, GU1 3AW Tel: (01483) 454088 Fax: (01483) 454088

Staedler (UK) Ltd, Cowbridge Road, Pontyclun, Mid Glamorgan, CF72 8YJ Tel: (01443) 235011 Fax: (01443) 237668 E-mail: terry.james@uk.staedler.com

Swan Stabilo Ltd, 75 Buckingham Avenue, Slough, SL1 4PN Tel: (01753) 605656 Fax: (01753) 605657 E-mail: marketing@stabilo.co.uk

PENETRATING OIL

Rapideze Ltd, 2 Barnsdale, Great Easton, Market Harborough, Leicestershire, LE16 8SG Tel: (01536) 770282 Fax: (01327) 830725

Wd-40 Co. Ltd, PO Box 440, Milton Keynes, MK11 3LJ Tel: (01908) 555400 Fax: (01908) 266900 E-mail: sales@wd40.co.uk

PENNANTS

Club Ties, Brook Street Studios, 60 Brook Street, Glasgow, G40 2AB Tel: 0141-554 3066 Fax: 0141-554 4581 E-mail: clubties@hotmail.com

Mccall Promotional Products Ltd, Gorse Farm, Lutterworth Road, Bramcote, Nuneaton, Warwickshire, CV11 6QL Tel: (024) 7637 2835

Up The Pole Ltd, 56 Meadow Road, Catshill, Bromsgrove, Worcestershire, B61 0JL Tel: (01527) 833873 Fax: (01527) 836578

PENS, *See also headings for particular types*

A1 Promotional Pens, 2-4 Mount Pleasant Road, Aldershot, Hampshire, GU12 4NL Tel: (01252) 320571 Fax: (01252) 403635 E-mail: sales@pens.co.uk

The Draughtsmans Centre Ltd, 819 Hagley Road West, Birmingham, B32 1AD Tel: 0121-423 1412 Fax: 0121-423 1812

Senator Pens Ltd, Senator House, Stadium Way, Harlow, Essex, CM19 5GY Tel: (01279) 630700 Fax: (01279) 630750 E-mail: sales@senatorpens.co.uk

PENS, ADVERTISING/ PROMOTIONAL, PRINTERS, DESIGNERS ETC

Actionpoint Packaging Materials, The Old Brickfields, Otterham Quay Lane, Rainham, Gillingham, Kent, ME8 8NA Tel: (01634) 373736

▶ Avant Garde, 28 Tadmarton, Downhead Park, Milton Keynes, MK15 9BD Tel: (01908) 675977 Fax: (01908) 675890 E-mail: page@ag-gifts.co.uk

Azizoff Co. Ltd, 2 Beechfield Road, London, N4 1PE Tel: (020) 8809 6902 Fax: (020) 8800 5795 E-mail: azizoffltd@tiscali.co.uk

Colorphaze, 73 Bunting Road, Northampton, NN2 6EE Tel: (01604) 792001 E-mail: sales@colorphaze.co.uk

▶ Decipher Design, 107, Boundary Rd, London, NW8 0RG Tel: (020) 7328 2545 E-mail: info@decipherdesign.co.uk

G B Promotional Products Ltd, The Old Smoke House Potter Street, Sandwich, Kent, CT13 9DR Tel: (01304) 619390 Fax: (01304) 619391 E-mail: sales@gbpromotionalproducts.co.uk

Pennine Products, Marsh House, Market Place, Honley, Holmfirth, HD9 6NG Tel: (01484) 666303 Fax: (01484) 663260 E-mail: sales@pennineproducts.co.uk

Pens Unlimited, 1 Pottery Units, Forde Road, Newton Abbot, Devon, TQ12 4AD Tel: (01626) 334520 Fax: (01626) 334519 E-mail: pens.unltd@virgin.net

Prestige Enterprises, PO Box 1160, Newtownabbey, County Antrim, BT36 5YP Tel: 0845 230 3818 Fax: 0845 230 3819 E-mail: sales@prestigeenterprises.com

Senator Pens Ltd, Senator House, Stadium Way, Harlow, Essex, CM19 5GY Tel: (01279) 630700 Fax: (01279) 630750 E-mail: sales@senatorpens.co.uk

Swedish Match UK Ltd, Sword House, Totteridge Road, High Wycombe, Buckinghamshire, HP13 6DG Tel: (01494) 533300 Fax: (01494) 437459

PENS, CORPORATE GIFT

▶ Eventous, Unit 26B, 8-10 Glasgow Road, Kirkintilloch, Glasgow, G66 1SH Tel: (0845) 1679565 E-mail: info@eventous.com

▶ Lesmar Ltd, 10 Spencer Street, St. Albans, Hertfordshire, AL3 5EG Tel: (01727) 732631 Fax: (01727) 732632 E-mail: online@lesmar.com

▶ Shout, 24 Sparkford Gardens, London, N11 3GT Tel: (020) 8361 5222 Fax: (020) 8361 6177 E-mail: enquiries@shoutpm.co.uk

PENSION REVIEW FINANCIAL SERVICES

▶ atretirement.co.uk, Tritton House, 14 Bath Road, Swindon, SN1 4BA Tel: (0870) 1904187

PENSTOCK VALVES

Erhard Valves Ltd, Unit 4, Buckingham Close, Bermuda Industrial Estate, Nuneaton, Warwickshire, CV10 7JT Tel: (024) 7635 4470 Fax: (024) 7635 0225 E-mail: sales@erhardvalves.co.uk

PENSTOCKS

▶ Aquatic Control Engineering Ltd, Main Street, Rampton, Retford, Nottinghamshire, DN22 0HR Tel: (01777) 249080 Fax: (01777) 249069 E-mail: info@aquaticcontrol.co.uk

▶ Engineered Piping Products, 36 Southweald Drive, Waltham Abbey, Essex, EN9 1PP Tel: (01992) 719595 Fax: (01992) 787002 E-mail: info@engineered-piping-products.com

PEOPLE COUNTERS

Autoswitch Electronics Ltd, 46 Lammas Way, Letchworth Garden City, Hertfordshire, SG6 4LW Tel: (01462) 677778 Fax: (01462) 480449

Counting Solutions Ltd, 1-3 Bowling Green Road, Kettering, Northamptonshire, NN15 7QW Tel: (01536) 511010 Fax: (01536) 513653 E-mail: sales@counting-solutions.co.uk

▶ Lab Tek Instruments, Star House, The Drive, Hellingly, Hailsham, East Sussex, BN27 4EP Tel: (01323) 840584 Fax: (01323) 840583 E-mail: tom.howe@footfallcounters.com

Solution Product Systems Ltd, Unit 34, Walker Avenue, Wolverton Mill, Milton Keynes, MK12 5TW Tel: (01908) 682700 Fax: (01908) 682739 E-mail: sales@spslretail.com

PEPPERCORNS

▶ Steenbergs Organic, Unit 6-7, Melmerby Green Lane, Barker Business Park, Ripon, North Yorkshire, HG4 5GZ Tel: (01765) 640088 Fax: (01765) 640101 E-mail: sales@steenbergs.co.uk

PERACETIC ACID

Pearl Chemicals Ltd, The White House, Darlaston Park, Stone, Staffordshire, ST15 0ND Tel: (01785) 819747 Fax: (01785) 811567 E-mail: g.dee@pearlchem.co.uk

PERFLUOROELASTOMER PRODUCTS

Precision Polymer Engineering Ltd, Greenbank Road, Blackburn, BB1 3EA Tel: (01254) 295400 Fax: (01254) 680182 E-mail: sales@prepol.com

PERFORATED CABLE TRAYS

Electrix International Ltd, 1a-1b Dovecot Hill, South Church Enterprise Park, Bishop Auckland, County Durham, DL14 6XP Tel: (01388) 774455 Fax: (01388) 777359 E-mail: enquiries@electrix.co.uk

Philip Grahame International Ltd, Dukes Park Industrial Estate, Montrose Road, Chelmsford, CM2 6TE Tel: (01245) 451717 Fax: (01245) 451870 E-mail: sales@pgrahame.com

L P A Niphan Ltd, P O Box 15, Saffron Walden, Essex, CB11 4AN Tel: (01799) 512800 Fax: (01799) 512828 E-mail: sales@lpa-niphan.com

Vantrunk Building Services Ltd, Goddard Road, Astmoor Industrial Estate, Runcorn, Cheshire, WA7 1QF Tel: (01928) 564211 Fax: (01928) 580157 E-mail: sales@vantrunk.co.uk

PERFORATED METAL PRODUCTS

E.E. Ingleton Engineering Ltd, Adelaide Works, 55 Mowbray St, Sheffield, S3 8EZ Tel: 0114-275 7834 Fax: 0114-272 9672 E-mail: sales@eeingleton.co.uk

Nova Metals Ltd, Unit 13 Worsley Business Park, Mosley Common Road, Worsley, Manchester, M28 1NL Tel: 0161-799 4108 Fax: 0161-703 7294 E-mail: ssles@novametals.co.uk

▶ Rmig Ltd, 1-2 Adlington Court, Risley Road, Birchwood, Warrington, WA3 6PL Tel: (01925) 839600 Fax: (01925) 826326 E-mail: info.uk@rmig.com

Robert Bion & Co., 14 Portman Road, Reading, RG30 1LZ Tel: 0118-959 2700 Fax: 0118-959 2701 E-mail: sales@bion.co.uk

PERFORATED METAL PRODUCTS MANUFRS

A & F Supplies, Railway Road, Adlington, Chorley, Lancashire, PR6 9RF Tel: (01257) 480500 Fax: (01257) 483338 E-mail: sales@a-f-supplies.co.uk

A P W Ltd, Unit 12 Deacon Trading Estate, Earle Street, Newton-le-Willows, Merseyside, WA12 9XD Tel: (01925) 295577 Fax: (01925) 295588 E-mail: sales@apw.co.uk

Robert Bion & Co., 14 Portman Road, Reading, RG30 1LZ Tel: 0118-959 2700 Fax: 0118-959 2701 E-mail: sales@bion.co.uk

PERFORATED METAL SHEETS/ STRIPS

Davtex UK Ltd, Link House, Bute Street, Fenton, Stoke-on-Trent, ST4 3PR Tel: (01782) 318000 Fax: (01782) 319000 E-mail: davtexuk@netscapeonline.co.uk

Fratelli, 5 Coundon Industrial Estate, Coundon, Bishop Auckland, County Durham, DL14 8NR Tel: (01740) 629010 Fax: (01740) 629064 E-mail: grahameparnaby@hotmail.com

Reekie Steeltec Ltd, Baden Powell Road, Kirkton Industrial Estate, Arbroath, Angus, DD11 3LS Tel: (01241) 873841 Fax: (01241) 877419 E-mail: colin.cromar@reekiesteeltec.com

▶ Rmig Ltd, 1-2 Adlington Court, Risley Road, Birchwood, Warrington, WA3 6PL Tel: (01925) 839600 Fax: (01925) 826326 E-mail: info.uk@rmig.com

Robert Bion & Co., 14 Portman Road, Reading, RG30 1LZ Tel: 0118-959 2700 Fax: 0118-959 2701 E-mail: sales@bion.co.uk

PERFORATED PLASTIC PRODUCTS

▶ Rmig Ltd, 1-2 Adlington Court, Risley Road, Birchwood, Warrington, WA3 6PL Tel: (01925) 839600 Fax: (01925) 826326 E-mail: info.uk@rmig.com

PERFORATED STEEL BALUSTRADES

▶ Graepel Perforators Ltd, Unit 5 Burtonwood Industrial Centre, Phipps La, Burtonwood, Warrington, WA5 4HX Tel: (01925) 229809 Fax: (01925) 228069 E-mail: sales@graepeluk.com

PERFORATED STEEL PRODUCTS

E.E. Ingleton Engineering Ltd, Adelaide Works, 55 Mowbray St, Sheffield, S3 8EZ Tel: 0114-275 7834 Fax: 0114-272 9672 E-mail: sales@eeingleton.co.uk

PERFORATING MACHINES

BPM Engineering Services Ltd, Unit 18 Failsworth Indust Estate, Morton Street, Failsworth, Manchester, M35 0BN Tel: 0161-682 3377 Fax: 0161-682 7711 E-mail: brian.bpm@btconnect.com

Elmar Services Ltd, Westhill Industrial Estate, Westhill, Aberdeenshire, AB32 6TQ Tel: (01224) 740261 Fax: (01224) 743138 E-mail: sales@elmar.co.uk

Rollem Patent Products Ltd, The Common, Ecclesfield, Sheffield, S35 9WN Tel: 0114-246 8981 Fax: 0114-246 5487 E-mail: sales@rollem.co.uk

PERFORMANCE MANAGEMENT CONSULTANTS, INDUSTRIAL/ PROCESS PLANT

▶ Performance Analytics Ltd, 212 Piccadilly, London, W1J 9HG Tel: (0845) 0574155 Fax: (020) 7439 0262 E-mail: info@performanceanalytics.co.uk

PERFUME BASES/COMPOUNDS

Avon Cosmetics Ltd, Nunn Mills Road, Northampton, NN1 5PA Tel: (01604) 232425 Fax: (01604) 232444 E-mail: info@avon.com

C P L Aromas, Barrington Hall, Dunmow Road, Hatfield Broad Oak, Bishop's Stortford, Hertfordshire, CM22 7LE Tel: (01279) 718573 Fax: (01279) 718527 E-mail: uk.enquiries@cplaromas.com

Cap It All Closures Ltd, 149d Pack Lane, Basingstoke, Hampshire, RG22 5HN Tel: (01256) 466178 Fax: (01256) 816333

Fragrance Oils International Ltd, Eton Hill Road, Radcliffe, Manchester, M26 2FR Tel: 0161-724 9311 Fax: 0161-725 5225 E-mail: uk_sales@fragrance-oils.com

R D Campbell & Co. Ltd, Unit 14 Mill Farm Business Park, Millfield Road, Hounslow, TW4 5PY Tel: (020) 8898 6611 Fax: (020) 8898 6622

Robertet Ltd, Kings Road, Haslemere, Surrey, GU27 2QU Tel: (01428) 644236 Fax: (01428) 656230 E-mail: robertetuk@aol.com

PERFUME OR TOILETRY ATOMISERS AND SPRAYS

Coster Aerosols Ltd, Babbage Rd, Stevenage, Hertfordshire, SG1 2EQ Tel: (01438) 367763 Fax: (01438) 728305 E-mail: sales.uk@coster.com

Cotswold Perfumery Ltd, Victoria Street, Bourton-on-the-Water, Cheltenham, Gloucestershire, GL54 2BU Tel: (01451) 820698 Fax: (01451) 821717 E-mail: sales@cotswold-perfumery.co.uk

▶ Kew Health and Beauty Ltd, Wallace House, New Abbey Court, 51 - 53 Stert Street, Abingdon, Oxfordshire, OX14 3JF Tel: (0870) 7607586 Fax: (0870) 7607598 E-mail: info@kewhb.co.uk

▶ Oriflame Info.biz, 27 Blackthorn Avenue, Lenzie, Glasgow, G66 4DE Tel: (0845) 0090384 E-mail: oriflamebiz@hotmail.co.uk

Titus Pumps Ltd, 3 Chiphouse Road, Bristol, BS15 4TR Tel: 0117-940 6293 Fax: (0870) 7877472 E-mail: sales@tituspumps.co.uk

▶ The Virgin Cosmetics Company, 55 Drovers Way, Bradford, West Yorkshire, BD2 1JZ Tel: 01274 306430 E-mail: nicola@ashton2602.f2s.com

Welby Health Care Ltd, Units 16-17 Evans Business Centre, 53-58 South Avenue, High Blantyre Industrial Estate, Glasgow, G72 0XB Tel: (0845) 2572173 Fax: (0870) 4714144 E-mail: info@welbyhealthcare.co.uk

PERFUMES

Beautimatic International Ltd, Abbey House, Eastways, Witham, Essex, CM8 3YL Tel: (01376) 535535 Fax: (01376) 503503

C P L Aromas, Barrington Hall, Dunmow Road, Hatfield Broad Oak, Bishop's Stortford, Hertfordshire, CM22 7LE Tel: (01279) 718573 Fax: (01279) 718527 E-mail: uk.enquiries@cplaromas.com

F C Ltd, Cromwell Road, Ellesmere Port, CH65 4DP Tel: 0151-355 8234 Fax: 0151-357 1223

▶ Fragrance Online Ltd, 19 High Street, Buxton, Derbyshire, SK17 6ET Tel: (01298) 73955 E-mail: sales@fragranceonline.co.uk

Hampshire Cosmetics Ltd, Brambles House, Waterberry Drive, Waterlooville, Hampshire, PO7 7UW Tel: (023) 9225 7341 Fax: (023) 9226 2003 E-mail: sales@hants-cosmetics.co.uk

International Flavours & Fragrances (I F F) (GB) Ltd, Duddery Hill, Haverhill, Suffolk, CB9 8LG Tel: (01440) 715000 Fax: (01440) 762199 E-mail: iff.uk@iff.com

Michie Charles Pharmaceutical Chemist, 391 Union Street, Aberdeen, AB11 6BX Tel: (01224) 585312 Fax: (01224) 574264 E-mail: info@michies.co.uk

Milton Lloyd Ltd, 42-44 Norwood High Street, London, SE27 9NR Tel: (020) 8670 4433 Fax: (020) 8761 6130 E-mail: worldclass@milton-lloyd.co.uk

The Orange Square Co. Ltd, 45 Vauxhall Bridge Road, London, SW1V 2TA Tel: (020) 7630 9400 Fax: (020) 7630 9500

Robertet Ltd, Kings Road, Haslemere, Surrey, GU27 2QU Tel: (01428) 644236 Fax: (01428) 656230 E-mail: robertetuk@aol.com

PERIOD DESIGN CONSERVATORIES

▶ GR8-conservatories.co.uk, PO BOX 697, Telford, Shropshire, TF7 9AL Tel: 01952 282069 Fax: 0845 2802071 E-mail: info@gr8-services.co.uk

▶ Heritage Hardwood, Star Crossroads, Star, Gaerwen, Gwynedd, LL60 6AL Tel: (01248) 715280 Fax: (01248) 713383 E-mail: sales@heritage-hardwood.co.uk

Oak Valley Fabrications, The Workshop, rear of 91 Chesterfield Road, North Wingfield, Chesterfield, Derbyshire, S42 5LF Tel: 0782 117 9985

▶ Spooner Bros, Hawksworth Trading Estate, Swindon, SN2 1EJ Tel: (01793) 336333 Fax: (01793) 336333 E-mail: Sales@spoonerbrothers.co.uk

PERIOD DESIGN DOORS

Faversham Joinery UK Ltd, Abbey Farm, Abbey Road, Faversham, Kent, ME13 7BL Tel: (01795) 537062 Fax: (01795) 597666 E-mail: enquiries@favershamjoinery.co.uk

PERIOD DESIGN KITCHEN UNITS

▶ Blakes Interior Design, Unit 14, Lakes Farm, Rayne, Braintree, Essex, CM77 6TE Tel: (01371) 850826 Fax: (01371) 850826 E-mail: wayne@blakesinteriordesign.co.uk

UK FITTED KITCHENS, 10 Rosemary Road, Norwich, NR7 8ER Tel: (0800) 075 8100 E-mail: uk.fittedkitchens@fsmail.net

PERIOD DESIGN WINDOWS

Faversham Joinery UK Ltd, Abbey Farm, Abbey Road, Faversham, Kent, ME13 7BL Tel: (01795) 537062 Fax: (01795) 597666 E-mail: enquiries@favershamjoinery.co.uk

PERIPHERAL COMPONENT INTERFACE (PCI) DEVELOPMENT SYSTEM SOFTWARE

Clover Consultancy, 21 The Crescent, Taunton, Somerset, TA1 4EB Tel: (01823) 336220 Fax: (01823) 270105 E-mail: info@cloveruk.net

First Degree Systems, 73-74 Branston Road, Burton-On-Trent, Staffordshire, DE14 3BY Tel: (0870) 4422361 Fax: (0870) 4422362 E-mail: alan-bark@first-degree-systems.com

PERIPHERAL NETWORKING DATA STORAGE SYSTEMS

Select Computers, Suite 2 Rawmec Industrial Park, Plumpton Road, Hoddesdon, Hertfordshire, EN11 0EE Tel: (01992) 448899 Fax: (01992) 471314 E-mail: mailorder@selectcomputers.co.uk

PERISTALTIC PUMPS

Accuramatic Laboratory Equipment, 42 Windsor Road, King's Lynn, Norfolk, PE30 5PL Tel: (01553) 777253 Fax: (01553) 777253 E-mail: info@accuramatic.co.uk

Autoclude, Unit 7, Carnival Park, Carnival Close, Basildon, Essex, SS14 3WN Tel: (01268) 662450 Fax: (01268) 662459 E-mail: info@autocludepumps.com

Automatic Pump Ltd, 36 Lanehead Road, Etruria, Stoke-On-Trent, ST1 5PT Tel: (01782) 279504 Fax: (01782) 279005 E-mail: enquiries@elipse.co.uk

Border Pumps & Transmissions, Station Road, Sandycroft, Deeside, Clwyd, CH5 2PT Tel: (01244) 533065 Fax: (01244) 535635

Electromatic Scientific Instruments Ltd, Orchard House, Jubilee Bank Road, King's Lynn, Norfolk, PE34 4BJ Tel: (01553) 775526 Fax: (01553) 691023

R F Electronics Controls Ltd, 8 Nazeing New Road, Broxbourne, Hertfordshire, EN10 6SU Tel: (01992) 460046 Fax: (01992) 442299 E-mail: sales@rfeltd.com

PERLITE FILTER MEDIA

Harborlite (UK) Ltd, The Westwood, Beverley, North Humberside, HU17 8RQ Tel: (01482) 645265 Fax: (01482) 641176

PERMANENT MAGNET ELECTRIC MOTORS

Intelligent Motion Control Ltd, 4 Brunel Close, Drayton Fields Industrial Estate, Daventry, Northamptonshire, NN11 8RB Tel: (01327) 307600 Fax: (01327) 300319 E-mail: info@inmoco.co.uk

Magnetic Component Engineering (U K) Ltd, 1 Union Street, Luton, LU1 3AN Tel: (01582) 735226 Fax: (01582) 734226 E-mail: eurosales@mceproducts.com

PERMANENT MAGNET GENERATORS

Newton Derby Ltd, Belgrave Works, Town Street, Stanningley, Pudsey, West Yorkshire, LS28 6ES Tel: 0113-218 0717 Fax: 0113-257 2206 E-mail: sales@newtonderby.co.uk

PERMANENT MAGNETS

Aircraft & Commercial Tools (Sheffield) Ltd, Bowling Green Street, Shalesmoor, Sheffield, S3 8SU Tel: 0114-272 8112 Fax: 0114-275 9273 E-mail: aircraft@globalnet.co.uk

F2 Magnetics Ltd, Griffon Road, Quarry Hill Industrial Estate, Ilkeston, Derbyshire, DE7 4RF Tel: 0115-932 9000 Fax: 0115-932 9111 E-mail: sales@f2magnetics.co.uk

Magnet Sales & Service Ltd, Unit 31, Blackworth Industrial Estate, Highworth, SN6 7NA Tel: (01793) 862100 Fax: (01793) 862101 E-mail: sales@magnetsales.co.uk

Tesla Transformers Ltd, Carrington Business Park, Manchester Road, Carrington, Manchester, M31 4ZU Tel: 0161-776 4080 Fax: 0161-776 4446 E-mail: sales@tesla-transformers.com

PERMANENT SPLIT CAPACITOR ELECTRIC MOTORS

Merkle-Korff, Treetops House, Gillotts Lane, Henley-On-Thames, Oxfordshire, RG9 1PT Tel: (01543) 255995 Fax: (01491) 412211 E-mail: sales@acdcsystems.com

PERPETUAL CALENDAR CLOCKS

Tregawne, PO Box 48, Pershore, Worcestershire, WR10 3YE Tel: (01386) 861800 Fax: (01386) 861900 E-mail: sales@tregawne.freeserve.co.uk

PERSONAL COACHING

▶ Creative Mind Skills Therapeutic Training, Holden House, Holden Road, Leigh, Lancashire, WN7 1EX Tel: 08704 323423 E-mail: info@cmst.co.uk

▶ Future You, Lingfield, Walnut Close, Heathfield, East Sussex, TN21 8YL Tel: 0333 4444001 E-mail: coaching@future-you.co.uk

▶ Sheppard Moscow Scotland Ltd, 57 Melville Street, Edinburgh, EH3 7HL Tel: 0131-226 3399 Fax: 0131-226 3344

PERSONAL COMPUTER (PC) LAPTOP HIRE

Hire Intelligence, The Old Farm, Mill Lane, Alhampton, Shepton Mallet, Somerset, BA4 6PX Tel: (01749) 860301 Fax: (01749) 860089 E-mail: sales@hiresouthwest.co.uk

PERSONAL COMPUTER (PC) REPAIR

▶ A1 PC Support, 39 Stirling Road, Bournemouth, BH3 7JQ Tel: (01202) 386292

▶ A1 Repair, Lower Church House, Flyford Flavell, Worcester, WR7 4BX Tel: (07789) 746645 E-mail: sam_munro@hotmail.com

▶ Absolute PC Support, 21 Highbury Road, Hitchin, Hertfordshire, SG4 9SA Tel: (01462) 621658E-mail: tech@absolutepcsupport.co.uk

▶ Absolutely PC Ltd, 11 Bradley Road, Patchway, Bristol, BS34 5LF Tel: 0117-975 9523 E-mail: Sales@AbsolutelyPC.co.uk

▶ A-R-pcrepairs, Mill Close, Elsenham, Bishop's Stortford, Hertfordshire, CM22 6EG Tel: (01279) 810962 E-mail: richard@a-r-pcrepairs.co.uk

▶ Bedford Home Computers, Poplar Avenue, Bedford, MK41 8BL Tel: (07754) 093885

Bisley Computency, 1 The Cottages, Stroud Road, Bisley, Stroud, Gloucestershire, GL6 7BQ Tel: (01452) 770832 Fax: 08717 333315 E-mail: enquiries@bisleydesign.co.uk

▶ Blackdog Services Ltd, 22 Harefield Avenue, Bedford, MK42 9RL Tel: (01234) 294230 Fax: (01234) 295876 E-mail: enquiries@blackdogservices.co.uk

▶ Bluejays PC Services, 76 Davidson Road, Croydon, CR0 6DB Tel: 0208 6561056 E-mail: info@bluejayspc.co.uk

▶ Cando It, 42 Wolfe Road, Norwich, NR1 4HT Tel: (01603) 498999 E-mail: sales@cando-it.co.uk

▶ Chrisalis Ltd, 19 Mount House Close, Formby, Liverpool, L37 3LH Tel: (01704) 870942 E-mail: kellysearch@chrisalis-uk.com

▶ Click4PC Ltd, Station House, 150 New Road, Bromsgrove, Worcestershire, B60 2LG Tel: (0800) 0852143 Fax: (01527) 576611 E-mail: enquiries@click4pc.co.uk

▶ Computek, 21 Harewood Road, Oakworth, Keighley, West Yorkshire, BD22 7NS Tel: (0845) 0094265 Fax: (0871) 5971154 E-mail: help@computek-ltd.co.uk

▶ Computer Geek, 16 Fowey Close, Wellingborough, Northamptonshire, NN8 5WW Tel: (01933) 401010 E-mail: sales@thecomputergeek.co.uk

▶ Computer Home Help, 14 West Park Cr, Inverbervie, Montrose, Angus, DD10 0TX Tel: (01561) 362902 E-mail: lincoln.callander@btinternet.com

▶ Computers Doctor, 19 Bolton Walk, London, N7 7RW Tel: (0845) 3307881 E-mail: info@computersdoctor.com

▶ Computersave.Co.Uk, 45 Windmill Road, Hampton Hill, Hampton, Middlesex, TW12 1QZ Tel: (07950) 412207 Fax: (0795) 0412207 E-mail: info@computersave.co.uk

▶ CP Computers, 21 The Inlands, Daventry, Northants, NN11 4DD Tel: 01327 702182 Fax: 0871 2398138 E-mail: c.palmer@lycos.co.uk

▶ Danoli Solutions Ltd, 116 Yew Tree Road, Ormskirk, Lancashire, L39 1NX Tel: (01695) 579442 E-mail: enquiries@danoli.co.uk

▶ Digit Computers, PO Box 47761, London, NW10 5UN Tel: (08700) 420490 Fax: (070) 92844761 E-mail: info@digitcomputers.co.uk

▶ Dolphin Computer Upgrades Ltd, 30 Arlington Gardens, Brighton, BN2 8QE Tel: (01273) 248871 Fax: (01273) 245717 E-mail: sales@dolphinupgrades.com

▶ Giaicomm Ltd, 76 North Road Avenue, Brentwood, Essex, CM14 4XN Tel: (01277) 230141

▶ Home Computer Services, 6 Lower Road, Breachwood Green, Hitchin, Hertfordshire, SG4 8NS Tel: (0845) 3105645 E-mail: peter@home-computer-services.co.uk

▶ I Fix PC'S, 29 Fuchsia Lane, Ipswich, IP4 1QB Tel: (01473) 422373E-mail: andy@ifixpc.co.uk

▶ K J H, Woodpeckers, Wildcroft Drive, Wokingham, Berkshire, RG40 3HY Tel: (07932) 671564 Fax: 0118-977 5957 E-mail: aardy@btinternet.com

▶ Kabam Computer Services, 248 Broadlands Drive, Lawrence Weston, Bristol, BS11 0PN Tel: (07876) 250434 E-mail: sales@kabam.co.uk

▶ Laptop Support, No. 1 Factory Road, Poole, Dorset, BH16 5SJ Tel: (0800) 1977665 E-mail: repairs@testlink.co.uk

▶ Lyon Computer Solutions, 62, Lyon Road, Crowthorne, Berkshire, RG45 6RT Tel: (01344) 750147

▶ Macuncle.Com, 2a Blakeney Road, Beckenham, Kent, BR3 1HA Tel: (07740) 796183 Fax: E-mail: eamon@macuncle.com

MH CompuTech, 6 Blackwell Close, Higham Ferrers, Northamptonshire, NN10 8PJ Tel: (01933) 315900 E-mail: info@mhcomputech.co.uk

▶ Mr Fixit 4u Surbiton, 12 Perak Court, Elmbridge Avenue, Surbiton, Surrey, KT5 9EU Tel: (020) 8241 9893 Fax: (020) 8241 9893 E-mail: help.surbton@mr-fixit-4u.com

Nettech Solutions, 20 Branch Road, Batley, West Yorkshire, WF17 5RY Tel: (01924) 524873 Fax: (01924) 501183 E-mail: nettech.solutions@ntlworld.com

▶ No Wires Networks, 4 Laxton Close, Luton, LU2 8SJ Tel: (0845) 0093781 Fax: (0870) 1162823 E-mail: info@nowiresnetworks.co.uk

▶ PC Doctor, 26c London Road, Hertford Heath, Hertford, SG13 7PN Tel: (0870) 7771251 E-mail: enquiries@ukpcdoctor.co.uk

▶ PC Media Supplies LTD, Raleigh Road, Newton Abbot, Devon, TQ12 4HH Tel: 0845 4590038 E-mail: info@pcmediasupplies.co.uk

▶ PC Restore Ltd, 56 Glenarm Road, London, E5 0LZ Tel: (020) 8525 9795

▶ PDL Computers, The Barracks, Hillesden, Buckingham, MK18 4DE Tel: (01280) 817743 E-mail: support@pdlcomputers.com

▶ Publicode Ltd, 4 Fulton Court, Boundary Lane, Manchester, M15 6NW Tel: (0800) 1693228 E-mail: info@publicode.com

Rothbury Computers, Townfoot, Rothbury, Morpeth, Northumberland, NE65 7SL Tel: (01669) 620070 E-mail: johnrayner@rothburycomputers.com

▶ S E O Computers, Waterside House, Falmouth Road, Penryn, Cornwall, TR10 8BE Tel: (01326) 378424 Fax: (01326) 376667 E-mail: info@seo-computers.com

▶ Sapient I.T Soultions, 119c High Street, Waltham Cross, Hertfordshire, EN8 7AN Tel: 01992 301550 E-mail: contact@sapientsolutions.co.uk

▶ South Devon Solutions, 6a Prings Court, Market Street, Brixham, Devon, TQ5 8ET Tel: (01803) 850875 E-mail: enquiries@southdevonsolutions.com

▶ Stroud PC (Cinderford), 20 Victoria Street, Cinderford, Gloucestershire, GL14 2HQ Tel: (0870) 804246 Fax: (07092) 812233 E-mail: bryan@stroud-pcs.com

PERSONAL COMPUTER (PC) REPAIR – *continued*

Thecomputerservice.Co.Uk, Unit 2f Carmilles Business Centre, Bradford Road, Birstall, Batley, West Yorkshire, WF17 9JX Tel: (01924) 471949 Fax: (01924) 471949
E-mail: info@thecomputerservice.co.uk

▶ Trilo-Byte, 53 Cayley Promenade, Rhos on Sea, Colwyn Bay, Clwyd, LL28 4EP
Tel: (07780) 713382
E-mail: info@trilo-byte.co.uk

▶ View2IT Ltd, 4, Edge Close, Weybridge, Surrey, KT13 0SZ Tel: 01932 851016
E-mail: info@view2it.co.uk

▶ Voyager Computers, 90a Frankwell, Shrewsbury, SY3 8JR Tel: 01743 341755
E-mail: voyagercomputers@hotmail.com

PERSONAL COMPUTERS (PC)

A C I C International Ltd, Blacknest Road, Blacknest, Alton, Hampshire, GU34 4PX
Tel: (01420) 23930 Fax: (01420) 23921
E-mail: sales@acic.co.uk

A N Audio, 34 Huntingdon Street, St. Neots, Huntingdon, Cambridgeshire, PE19 1BB
Tel: (01480) 472071 Fax: (01480) 386456
E-mail: sales@anaudio.co.uk

Advance Group plc, Ockley Road, Bognor Regis, West Sussex, PO21 2HW Tel: (01243) 829100
Fax: (01243) 866822
E-mail: sales@advancegroup.plc.uk

Alpha Computer Services, Laurel Bank, Chester Road, Kelsall, Tarporley, Cheshire, CW6 0RT
Tel: (01829) 759440 Fax: (01829) 741106
E-mail: admin@alphacomputer.uk.com

Alpha Computer Services UK Ltd, 69 Bransgrove Road, Edgware, Middlesex, HA8 6HZ
Tel: (020) 8905 7245 Fax: (020) 8905 7245

Arena Business Machines, Armitage House, Thorpe Lower Lane, Robin Hood, Wakefield, West Yorkshire, WF3 3BQ Tel: 0113-288 0282
Fax: 0113-288 0671
E-mail: admin@arenagroup.net

Avatar Systems, Davis House, 36 Market Place, Brackley, Northamptonshire, NN13 7DP
Tel: (01280) 700711 Fax: (01280) 700711
E-mail: avatar.systems@virgin.net

Balanced Solutions Ltd, 20 Juniper Road, Southampton, SO18 4EJ Tel: (023) 8063 8393
Fax: (023) 8063 8393
E-mail: info@balancedsolutions.co.uk

Bridgewater Computers, 42 Green End, Whitchurch, Shropshire, SY13 1AA
Tel: (01948) 666630 Fax: (01948) 666630
E-mail: bridgewatermcg@aol.com

Bytecraft Ltd, 5 The Quad, Mercury Court, Chester, CH1 4QP Tel: (01244) 390109
Fax: (01244) 390051
E-mail: sales@bytecraft.co.uk

▶ C M C Mobile Computing Ltd, The Heath Business & Technical Park, Runcorn, Cheshire, WA7 4QX Tel: (0870) 1651465
Fax: (0870) 7623701
E-mail: sales@cmc.org.uk

Cameleon Systems, Cuckoo Lane, Pinchbeck, Spalding, Lincolnshire, PE11 3XT Tel: (01775) 680481
E-mail: martin@chameleon-systems.net

Cantab Millennium Ltd, 95 Mill Road, Cambridge, CB1 2AW Tel: (01223) 322306 Fax: (01223) 322816 E-mail: cantab.millennium@virgin.net

CBC Ltd, 91C-91D Mora Road, London, NW2 6TB Tel: (020) 8450 9185 Fax: (020) 8450 6090

Computer Station Ltd, Station House, Station Road, Rayleigh, Essex, SS6 7HL Tel: (01268) 746746 Fax: (01268) 746747
E-mail: sales@computerstation.co.uk

Computer Wizard, 405 Hatfield Road, St. Albans, Hertfordshire, AL4 0XP Tel: (01727) 861010
E-mail: sales@computerwizard.co.uk

Comtec Computers Ltd, 96-98 Merritt Road, Greatstone, New Romney, Kent, TN28 8SZ
Tel: (01797) 366333 Fax: (01797) 366333
E-mail: stuart.sayer@comteccomputers.co.uk

Continental Ltd, Unit C2 Herrick Way, Staverton Technology Park, Staverton, Cheltenham, Gloucestershire, GL51 6TQ Tel: (01452) 855222 Fax: (01452) 856794
E-mail: sales@continental.co.uk

Crofton Micro Systems Ltd, Forest Hill Industrial Estate, Perry Vale, London, SE23 2LX
Tel: (020) 8699 7575
E-mail: sales@crofton.co.uk

Evesham Technology, 1 Gloucester Court, Gloucester Terrace, Leeds, LS12 2ER
Tel: 0113-203 2000 Fax: 0113-203 2001
E-mail: leeds.showroom@evesham.com

Gardener Computer Systems Ltd, 6 De Montfort Mews, Leicester, LE1 7FW Tel: 0116-223 0233
Fax: 0116-223 0664
E-mail: mark.gcs@ntlworld.com

Goldcrest Computer Services Ltd, 12 Vermont Place, Tongwell, Milton Keynes, MK15 8JQ
Tel: (01908) 211330 Fax: (01908) 211326
E-mail: sales@goldcrest-uk.com

H F Systems, 97 Hill Top, West Bromwich, West Midlands, B70 0RU Tel: 0121-556 5821
Fax: (0845) 8689918
E-mail: info@hfsystems.co.uk

Native Systems Ltd, 22 St. Annes Grove, Knowle, Solihull, West Midlands, B93 9JB
Tel: 0121-743 0875
E-mail: info@nativesystems.co.uk

S & H Computers Ltd, Godfrey Drive, Ilkeston, Derbyshire, DE7 4HU Tel: 0115-875 8164
Fax: 0115-875 8164
E-mail: sales.shcomputers@ntlworld.com

▶ Sharpe Systems, Westthorpe Innovation Centre, Killamarsh, Sheffield, S21 1TZ
Tel: 0114-251 4775 Fax: (0870) 1221505
E-mail: tim.sharpe@sharpe-systems.co.uk

Siemens Business Services Ltd, 62 Boucher CR, Belfast, BT12 6HU Tel: (028) 9066 4331
Fax: (028) 9068 2168
E-mail: owen.mckenna@siemens.ie

Sloan Electronics Ltd, 241 Kells Lane, Gateshead, Tyne & Wear, NE9 5HU
Tel: 0191-491 0191 Fax: 0191-482 6762
E-mail: info@sloanelectronics.co.uk

Thompson Consultants Ltd, The Mow Barton, Northend, Clutton, Bristol, BS39 5QS
Tel: (01761) 453673 Fax: (01761) 452707
E-mail: sales@thompson-consultants.co.uk

U S I Ltd, Unit 1 Steadman Place, Riverside Business Park, Irvine, Ayrshire, KA11 5DN
Tel: (01294) 222444 Fax: (01294) 222456

▶ Xma Ltd, 44 Nottingham South & Wilford Industrial Estate, Nottingham, NG11 7EP
Tel: 0115-846 4000 Fax: 0115-981 0180
E-mail: sales@bsfitness.co.uk

Yellowstone Electronic Solutions Ltd, 17 Lyneham Road, Luton, LU2 9JS Tel: (01582) 722011
Fax: (01582) 654440
E-mail: sales@yellowstone.co.uk

PERSONAL DIGITAL ASSISTANT (PDA) COMPUTER ACCESSORIES

▶ Easy Devices.Company Co .Uk, 14 New Lairdship Yards, Edinburgh, EH11 3UY
Tel: (0871) 7000156 Fax: 0871 7000159
E-mail: sales@easydevices.co.uk

PERSONAL INJURY LITIGATION SUPPORT SERVICES

▶ Ashton Lake Solicitors, Park House, 25 Park Road, Loughborough, Leicestershire, LE11 2ED Tel: (01509) 262621 Fax: (01509) 233550 E-mail: sales@ashtonlake.com

▶ Windsor Bronzite Solicitors, 43 Bargates, Christchurch, Dorset, BH23 1QD Tel: 0870 4020555 Fax: 0870 4020556
E-mail: info@windsorbronzite.co.uk

PERSONAL MONITORING GAS DETECTOR HIRE

A1 Survey Ltd, 1 Cefn Graig, Rhiwbina, Cardiff, CF14 6SW Tel: (029) 2091 5858 Fax: (029) 2091 5858 E-mail: sales@a1survey.net

PERSONAL ORGANISERS

▶ Consider It Done Lifestyle Management Ltd, The Courtyard, 4 Evelyn Road, London, W4 5JL Tel: (020) 8742 8718 Fax: (08712) 428362 E-mail: info@consider-it-done.co.uk

▶ Tempus Lifestyle, 41 High Street, Tarring, Worthing, West Sussex, BN14 7NR Tel: 0845 226 9170
E-mail: enquiries@tempuslifestyle.co.uk

Your Wish Is My Command Limited, 2nd Floor, Westminster House, 188 Stratford Road, Shirley, Solihull, West Midlands, B90 3AQ
Tel: 0845 8380548
E-mail: genie@yourwishismycommand.co.uk

PERSONAL PROTECTION ALARM SYSTEMS

Strathclyde Firemens Personal Alarm Co. Ltd, 234 Allison Street, Glasgow, G42 8RT
Tel: 0141-423 7011
E-mail: ellis.cohen@amserve.net

Tunstall Group Ltd, Whitley Lodge, Whitley Bridge, Goole, North Humberside, DN14 0HR
Tel: (01977) 661234 Fax: (01977) 662570

Walk Easy Ltd, Unit 3, Hadstock Road Industrial Estate, Hadstock Road, Linton, Cambridge, CB21 4XM Tel: (01223) 892623 Fax: (01223) 893880 E-mail: sales@walkeasy.ltd.uk

PERSONAL PROTECTION EQUIPMENT

A & E Russell Ltd, 5 Brown Street, Coatbridge, Lanarkshire, ML5 4AS Tel: (01236) 433511
Fax: (01236) 440070
E-mail: sales@aerussell.co.uk

A & E Russell Ltd, Baird Avenue, Dryburgh Industrial Estate, Dundee, DD2 3TN
Tel: (01382) 811566 Fax: (01382) 833455
E-mail: enquiries@aerussell.com

A & E Russell Ltd, 33 Tennant Street, Edinburgh, EH6 5NA Tel: 0131-555 0577 Fax: 0131-553 4722 E-mail: enquiries@aerussell.co.uk

A & E Russell Ltd, 3 19 Henderson Road, Inverness, IV1 1SN Tel: (01463) 717687
Fax: (01463) 717750
E-mail: enquiries@aerussell.co.uk

A & E Russell Ltd, 7-9 Chetham Court, Winwick Quay, Warrington, WA2 8RF Tel: (01925) 643700 Fax: (01925) 643707
E-mail: warrington@aerussell.co.uk

Avon Welding Supplies, Unit D6 Avondale Works, Woodland Way, Bristol, BS15 1PA
Tel: 0117-947 7532 Fax: 0117-947 7532
E-mail: info@aws-ltd.co.uk

B T S Industrial Supplies, Unit 6, 692 Stratford Road, Sparkhill, Birmingham, B11 4AT
Tel: 0121-702 2404 Fax: 0121-778 6092
E-mail: sales@btssupplies.co.uk

▶ Bodyshop Consumables Ltd, Wilne Road, Long Eaton, Nottingham, NG10 3AN
Tel: 0115-946 1571
E-mail: orders@bodyshopconsumables.co.uk

Enserve Corporation, Parkway House, Worth Way, Keighley, West Yorkshire, BD21 5LD
Tel: (0800) 0377817
E-mail: info@enserve.co.uk

Nigel McLaren, 29 Clifton Court, Northwick Terrace, London, NW8 8HT Tel: (07866) 769268 Fax: (020) 7289 3003
E-mail: nigelmclaren@aol.com

P G S Supplies Ltd, Worthing Road, Sheffield, S9 3JB Tel: 0114-276 5566 Fax: 0114-276 5265 E-mail: sales@pgs-supplies.co.uk

T H P E Ltd, 7 Beighton Street, Sutton-in-Ashfield, Nottinghamshire, NG17 4EG Tel: (01623) 556660 Fax: (01623) 409500 E-mail: thpesales@supanet.com

Talking Headsets Ltd, Woodlands, The Bridle Lane, Hambrook, Chichester, West Sussex, PO18 8UG Tel: (01243) 573226 Fax: (01243) 574318 E-mail: info@talkingheadsets.co.uk

PERSONALISED BIRTHDAY CARDS

▶ Durrants English Wedding Collection, 6 Trevitt Close, Sleaford, Lincolnshire, NG34 8BT
Tel: (01529) 302530 Fax: (01529) 302530
E-mail: info@englishweddingcollection.co.uk

▶ Personal Touch, Unit 1 Moorgate, Ormskirk, Lancashire, L39 4RT Tel: (07966) 711459
Fax: 0151 2932008
E-mail: suedelane@blueyonder.co.uk

▶ Photos On Things, 1 Witney Close, Uxbridge, Middlesex, UB10 8EL Tel: (01895) 635714
Fax: (01895) 635714
E-mail: sheenarosser@photosonthings.co.uk

PERSONALISED CHRISTMAS CARDS

▶ The Promotional Gift Superstore, 79 Villa Road, Stanway, Colchester, CO3 0RN
Tel: (0845) 3701022 Fax: (0845) 3701033
E-mail: sales@promogift-superstore.com

▶ Specialcards4you, 65 Oakfield Road, Benfleet, Essex, SS7 5NS Tel: (01268) 752104
Fax: (01268) 752104
E-mail: specialcards4you@googlemail.com

▶ www.greetingcards-online.co.uk, Barley Sheaf School House, Holland Fen, Lincoln, LN4 4QH
Tel: (01205) 280469 Fax: (01205) 280469
E-mail: enquiries@greetingcards-online.co.uk

PERSONALISED CONFECTIONERY

▶ Candy Designer, The Candy & Chocolate Factory, Hawthorn Road, Skegness, Lincolnshire, PE25 3TD Tel: 01754 896667
E-mail: info@candydesigner.co.uk

Sweet Thoughts, Hawthorn Road, Skegness, Lincolnshire, PE25 3TD Tel: (01754) 896667
E-mail: info@sweetthoughts.co.uk

PERSONALISED GIFT BOXES

Spire-View.Com, 1 Challands Close, Hasland, Chesterfield, Derbyshire, S41 0ET Tel: (01246) 221681

PERSONALISED GIFTWARE

▶ The Design Station Ltd, 9 Turnstone Drive, Featherstone, Wolverhampton, WV10 7TA
Tel: (01902) 722192
E-mail: jackie@thedesignstation.co.uk

▶ Father Christmas Letters Ltd, Old School Lane, Whittlesford, Cambridge, CB22 4YS
Tel: (0870) 7503159 Fax: (0870) 0941215
E-mail: info@fatherchristmasletters.co.uk

▶ Posters4u, Westhill Business Centre, Arnhall Business Park, Westhill, Aberdeenshire, AB32 6UF Tel: (01224) 742598
E-mail: posters4u@yahoo.co.uk

▶ Precious Years, 84 Aylesbury Street, Milton Keynes, MK2 2BA Tel: 01908 644000
Fax: 01908 644000
E-mail: neil@preciousyears.co.uk

PERSONALISED GOLF BALLS

Pegasus Plastics UK Ltd, Unit 24 Eldon Way, Paddock Wood, Tonbridge, Kent, TN12 6BE
Tel: (01892) 832326 Fax: (01892) 832328
E-mail: sales@pegasusplastics.co.uk

▶ Posters4u, Westhill Business Centre, Arnhall Business Park, Westhill, Aberdeenshire, AB32 6UF Tel: (01224) 742598
E-mail: posters4u@yahoo.co.uk

PERSONALISED PRODUCTS

▶ Candy Designer, The Candy & Chocolate Factory, Hawthorn Road, Skegness, Lincolnshire, PE25 3TD Tel: 01754 896667
E-mail: info@candydesigner.co.uk

▶ Captive Calendars, 12 Fairway*, Sawbridgeworth, Hertfordshire, CM21 9NJ
Tel: 01279 319769

▶ David Harber, Valley Farm, Turville, Henley-on-Thames, Oxfordshire, RG9 6QU
Tel: (01491) 576956 Fax: (01491) 413524
E-mail: sales@davidharbersundials.com

heirlooms.uk.com, 11 Fontaine Road, London, SW16 3PB Tel: 02086 792196 Fax: 020 7738 9787 E-mail: info@heirlooms.uk.com

▶ Photos On Things, 1 Witney Close, Uxbridge, Middlesex, UB10 8EL Tel: (01895) 635714
Fax: (01895) 635714
E-mail: sheenarosser@photosonthings.co.uk

▶ Precious Years, 84 Aylesbury Street, Milton Keynes, MK2 2BA Tel: 01908 644000
Fax: 01908 644000
E-mail: neil@preciousyears.co.uk

▶ Your Design, 84 New Court Way, Ormskirk, Lancashire, L39 2YT Tel: (01695) 574264
E-mail: contact@yourdesign.co.uk

PERSONALISED TABLEWARE

▶ Precious Years, 84 Aylesbury Street, Milton Keynes, MK2 2BA Tel: 01908 644000
Fax: 01908 644000
E-mail: neil@preciousyears.co.uk

PERSONALISED WORKWEAR

▶ Brookes (UK) Ltd, Unit 5, Gaw End Lane, Lyme Green, Macclesfield, Cheshire, SK11 0LB Tel: (0800) 0729812 Fax: (0870) 2422995 E-mail: sales@ebrookes.co.uk

Debonair, Anchor House, 4 Bridgeman Street, Walsall, WS2 9NW Tel: (01922) 649399
Fax: (01922) 648091
E-mail: salesdebonair@aol.com

Sandra Thorndyke, 12a Wellesley Road, Tharston, Norwich, NR15 2PD Tel: (01508) 532394 Fax: (01508) 532394

▶ Workwear World, 445 Honeypot Lane, Stanmore, Middlesex, HA7 1JJ Tel: (020) 8206 2004 Fax: (020) 8206 2005
E-mail: sales@workwearworld.co.uk

PERSONNEL MAGAZINES

Personnel Today, Quadrant House The Quadrant, Brighton Road, Sutton, Surrey, SM2 5AS
Tel: (020) 8652 8008 Fax: (020) 8652 3279
E-mail: info@personneltodayjobs.com

PERSONNEL MANAGEMENT (PM) CONSULTANCY

Bridge Associates, 22 Greville Drive, Birmingham, B15 2UU Tel: 0121-440 4503 Fax: 0121-440 4503

Croner Consulting, Croner House, Wheatfield Way, Hinckley, Leicestershire, LE10 1YG
Tel: (01455) 897000 Fax: (01455) 897400
E-mail: info@cronerconsulting.co.uk

Cullen Scholefield Ltd, Maxwelton House, 41 Boltro Road, Haywards Heath, West Sussex, RH16 1BJ Tel: (01444) 455052 Fax: (01444) 459221 E-mail: enquiries@csgconsult.com

Executive Elect Ltd, 17 Brewery Lane, Stansted, Essex, CM24 8LB Tel: (01279) 814971
Fax: (01279) 647259
E-mail: carolineclarke@executive-elect.com

▶ I H R Ltd, 17 Eleanor Grove, Ickenham, Uxbridge, Middlesex, UB10 8BH Tel: (07005) 964088 Fax: (07005) 964099
E-mail: lynn.claydon@tiscali.co.uk

Involvement & Participation Association Ltd, 42 Colebrooke Row, London, N1 8AF Tel: (020) 7354 8040 Fax: (020) 7354 8041
E-mail: involve@ipa-involve.com

Link Project Services Ltd, 12 The Parks, Haydock Park, Newton-Le-Willows, Merseyside, WA12 0JQ Tel: (01942) 408440 Fax: (01942) 408450 E-mail: uk@link-projects.com

Management Advisory Ltd, 5 - 8 Edwards Centre, The Horsefair, Hinckley, Leicestershire, LE10 0AN Tel: (01455) 444222 Fax: (01455) 891251
E-mail: admin@managementadvisory.net

▶ NDF Associates, Chadwick House, Back Grange Avenue, Harrogate, North Yorkshire, HG1 2AN Tel: (01423) 529333 Fax: (01423) 529555E-mail: enquiries@ndfassociates.co.uk

Oilfield Production Support Group Ltd, Old Stoneywood Church, Bankhead Road, Bucksburn, Aberdeen, AB21 9HQ Tel: (01224) 712332 Fax: (01224) 712333
E-mail: sales@opsgrp.com

Rab Personnel Management Services, 18 Dolphin Close, London, SE28 8PY Tel: (020) 8311 1261 Fax: (020) 8311 1261
E-mail: sales@rabpms.co.uk

▶ Selection & Development Ltd, Bronzeoak House, Stafford Road, Caterham, Surrey, CR3 6JG Tel: (01883) 332651 Fax: (01883) 332652
E-mail: info@selectionanddevelopment.co.uk

PERSONNEL MEDIATION SERVICES

▶ Afirm Ltd, 10 Windsor Road, Lindford, Bordon, Hampshire, GU35 0RY Tel: (01420) 473573 Fax: (01420) 473573 E-mail: afirm@freenet.co.uk

PERSPEX ACRYLIC SHEET, *See Acrylic Sheet etc*

PEST CONTROL ELECTRONIC EQUIPMENT

A A Pest Controler, 12 Crossley Crescent, Ashton-under-Lyne, Lancashire, OL6 9EJ Tel: (07835) 423786 Fax: 0161-339 8576 E-mail: info@pestcontroler.co.uk

▶ AAAA Pest Control, 9 Glorat Avenue, Lennoxtown, Glasgow, G66 7DP Tel: (01360) 310977 E-mail: rogie87@fsmail.net

▶ Abate Ltd, Mill House, Browick Road, Wymondham, Norfolk, NR18 0QW Tel: (01953) 603390 Fax: (01603) 852533 E-mail: abatelimited@tiscali.co.uk

Ashman Bros, 43 Swaffham Road, Mundford, Thetford, Norfolk, IP26 5HR Tel: (01842) 879063

MidMos Solutions Limited, 29 Navigation Drive, Hurst Business Park, Brierley Hill, West Midlands, DY5 1UT Tel: (01384) 472930 Fax: (01384) 472911 E-mail: markgroobey@b-one.com

Pro Pest Services, 12 Northumberland Road, Linford, Stanford-le-Hope, Essex, SS17 0PT Tel: (01375) 642619 Fax: (01375) 642619

PEST CONTROL EQUIPMENT, *See also headings for particular types*

▶ Abate Ltd, Mill House, Browick Road, Wymondham, Norfolk, NR18 0QW Tel: (01953) 603390 Fax: (01603) 852533 E-mail: abatelimited@tiscali.co.uk

Agrisense BCS Ltd, Unit 1 3, Taffs Mead Road, Treforest Industrial Estate, Pontypridd, Mid Glamorgan, CF37 5SU Tel: (01443) 841155 Fax: (01443) 841152 E-mail: sales@agrisense.co.uk

Albion Manufacturing Ltd, The Granary, Silfield Road, Wymondham, Norfolk, NR18 9AU Tel: (01953) 605983 Fax: (01953) 606764 E-mail: sales@albionmanufacturing.com

Dazer International, 16 Thorpe Meadows, Peterborough, PE3 6GA Tel: (01733) 315888 E-mail: enquires@dazer.com

▶ Dazer (International), PO Box 456, Altrincham, Cheshire, WA14 5WP Tel: 0161-927 4508 Fax: 0161-927 4502

Russell Fine Chemicals Ltd, Unit 68, Third Avenue, Deeside Industrial Park, Deeside, Clwyd, CH5 2LA Tel: (01244) 281333 Fax: (01244) 281878 E-mail: info@russellipm.com

K9 Euro Ltd, PO Box 133, Wigan, Lancashire, WN1 1AA Tel: 0151-548 4562 Fax: 0151-548 1918 E-mail: martinfarmer@k9euro.co.uk

MidMos Solutions Limited, 29 Navigation Drive, Hurst Business Park, Brierley Hill, West Midlands, DY5 1UT Tel: (01384) 472930 Fax: (01384) 472911 E-mail: markgroobey@b-one.com

Neal Pestforce Ltd, Unit 3, Sutterton Enterprise Park, Sutterton, Boston, Lincolnshire, PE20 2JA Tel: (01205) 460446 Fax: (01205) 460886 E-mail: anninkirton@aol.com

Ratpak Engineering Ltd, Moor Lane, Thorpe-on-the-Hill, Lincoln, LN6 9BW Tel: (01522) 686070 Fax: (01522) 691112 E-mail: sales@ratpak.co.uk

▶ Robop, Peregrine House, Haddington Road, Tranent, East Lothian, EH33 1HW Tel: (01875) 619991 Fax: (01875) 619992

S T V International Ltd, Forge House, Watton Road, Little Cressingham, Thetford, Norfolk, IP25 6ND Tel: (01953) 881580 Fax: (01953) 881452 E-mail: info@stvpestcontrol.com

Terminex Pest & Vermin Control, 53 Gloucester Drive, London, N4 2LJ Tel: (020) 7503 8234 Fax: (020) 7503 8234 E-mail: enquiries@terminex.co.uk

V E S Pest Control, Netherside, Bradwell, Hope Valley, Derbyshire, S33 9JL Tel: (01433) 621199 Fax: (01433) 621714 E-mail: ves@legend.co.uk

PEST CONTROL MATERIALS

▶ Enviropest Control Services, Prince of Wales House Yardley, Wood 62 Prince of Wales Lane, Birmingham, B14 4JY Tel: 0121-693 6616 Fax: 0121-693 6617 E-mail: laurence@enviropest.co.uk

▶ Essex Rodent Control, 3 Fleet Hall Road, Rochford, Essex, SS4 1NF Tel: (01702) 544777 Fax: 01702 54999 E-mail: richlunn@btinternet.com

▶ Pestokill, Graveoak, East Lancs Road, Leigh, Lancashire, WN7 3SE Tel: (0870) 0660999 Fax: (01942) 607570 E-mail: sales@pestokill.co.uk

PEST CONTROL SERVICES

▶ 1st Call Environmental Services Ltd, 61 Derby Road, Melbourne, Derby, DE73 8FE Tel: (01332) 862737 Fax: (01332) 862832

▶ A K A Pest Control, 104a Gorgie Road, Edinburgh, EH11 2NP Tel: (0800) 0737380 Fax: 0131-623 6227

A Quick Kill Pest Control Ltd, 28 Lonsdale Road, Bilston, Bilston, West Midlands, WV14 7AF Tel: (0800) 1957056 Fax: (01902) 403373

A & R Pest Control, Nant Y Cynog, Tywyn, Gwynedd, LL36 9HY Tel: (01654) 710556

A S A P Pest Control, 3 White Cottage, Baldock Road, Royston, Hertfordshire, SG8 9NR Tel: (01763) 853872

A1 Exterminators Pest Control Services, 76 Dormington Road, Birmingham, B44 9LG Tel: 0121-360 1477 Fax: 0121-360 1477

A1 Wasp Control, Hurn Honey Farm, Barrack Road, West Parley, Ferndown, Dorset, BH22 8UB Tel: (01202) 593040

A4 Pest Control, 19 Audley Road, Chippenham, Wiltshire, SN14 0DY Tel: (07966) 527538 Fax: (01249) 447378

Aardvark Pest Control Services, 25 Wheatley Close, Welwyn Garden City, Hertfordshire, AL7 3LJ Tel: (01707) 339183 Fax: (01707) 895886

▶ Abate, Caydon Cottage, Kingsteignton, Newton Abbot, Devon, TQ12 3QD Tel: (0800) 0286689 E-mail: nathanhill@blueyonder.co.uk

▶ Abate Ltd, Mill House, Browick Road, Wymondham, Norfolk, NR18 0QW Tel: (01953) 603390 Fax: (01603) 852533 E-mail: abatelimited@tiscali.co.uk

Able Pest Control, 6 Hemplands, Chedworth, Cheltenham, Gloucestershire, GL54 4NH Tel: (01285) 720651 Fax: (01285) 720651

Abolish Pest & Vermin Control, 11 Cheatham Street, Birmingham, B7 5PS Tel: 0121-326 7904

Absolute Proof, 7 The Hatchingtan, Worplesdon, Guildford, Surrey, GU3 3SB Tel: (0800) 0680409

Academy Pest Control, 46 Star Post Road, Camberley, Surrey, GU15 4DF Tel: (01276) 501911 Fax: (01276) 784493

Acclaim Pest & Environmental Services, 25 Granville Street, Market Harborough, Leicestershire, LE16 9EU Tel: (01858) 432797 Fax: (01858) 445085 E-mail: acclaimpest@hotmail.com

Acorn Environmental, Windsor Terrace, East Herrington, Sunderland, SR3 3SF Tel: 0191-528 2444 Fax: 0191-520 2201

Activ8, 56 Rabans Close, Rabans Lane Industrial Area, Aylesbury, Buckinghamshire, HP19 8RS Tel: (01296) 436378 Fax: (01296) 393401

Active Environmental Services, 12 Cover Green, Home Meadow, Worcester, WR4 0JF Tel: (01905) 723129 Fax: (01905) 330158

Alliance Environmental Pest Control Services, 68 Ellerby Street, London, SW6 6EZ Tel: (020) 7736 1329 Fax: (020) 7610 2071

▶ Ambassador Environmental, 49 Chambers Road, St. Leonards-On-Sea, East Sussex, TN38 9HY Tel: (01424) 201309

Anglian Pest Control, 4 Brick Kiln Barns, Manor Road, North Walsham, Norfolk, NR28 9LH Tel: (01692) 403762 Fax: (01692) 403762

Anglo Scottish Pest Control, 24 Annandale Street, Edinburgh, EH7 4LS Tel: (0800) 0743606 Fax: (01289) 302257

Any Pest Control Services, Apple Trees, Gasden Copse, Witley, Godalming, Surrey, GU8 5QD Tel: (01428) 682359

▶ Anypest, Trelawney Lane, Plymouth, PL3 4JU Tel: (0800) 0960016

Apex Pest Control, Apex House, 15 Stratton Road, Bournemouth, BH9 3PG Tel: (01202) 523838 Fax: (01202) 293954 E-mail: sales@apexpestcontrol.co.uk

Arrestapest Gidding Ltd, Whiteacre 70 Main Street, Great Gidding, Huntingdon, Cambridgeshire, PE28 5NU Tel: (01832) 293463

Associated Pied Pipers, 37 Bowring Close, Exeter, EX1 3TU Tel: (01392) 461991 Fax: (01392) 205153

B A Pest Control, 9 Palmerston Road, Stockport, Cheshire, SK2 7EA Tel: 0161-483 0123 Fax: 0161-483 0123

Balaban Ltd, Sneath Farm, High Green, Great Moulton, Norwich, NR15 2HU Tel: (01379) 677296 Fax: (01379) 677296

Barker, 44 Main Street, Irton, Scarborough, North Yorkshire, YO12 4RH Tel: (01723) 865044

Barpest Pest & Vermin Control, 42 Bittams Lane, Chertsey, Surrey, KT16 9QX Tel: (01932) 872289 Fax: (01932) 872289

Best Pest, 4 Waterloo Place, Duncombe Street, Kingsbridge, Devon, TQ7 1LX Tel: (01548) 854353 Fax: (01548) 857256

Betapest Pest & Vermin Control, 9 Canfield Road, Brighton, BN2 4DN Tel: (0800) 2949332 Fax: (01273) 672270

Bethell Group plc, Dane House Europa Trading Estate, Stoneclough Road, Radcliffe, Manchester, M26 1GE Tel: (01204) 439100 Fax: (01204) 439101 E-mail: mail@bethell.co.uk

▶ Bird Solutions, 26 Sturt Close, Charlbury, Chipping Norton, Oxfordshire, OX7 3SS Tel: (01608) 819000 Fax: (01608) 819000 E-mail: birdsolutions@btconnect.com

Blyth Pest Control Ltd, Worksop Road, Blyth, Worksop, Nottinghamshire, S81 8DX Tel: (01909) 591150 Fax: (01909) 591860

Bounty Pest Control, Unit 108, Ellingham Industrial Estate, Willesborough, Ashford, Kent, TN23 6LZ Tel: (01233) 640191

Bracknell Pest Control Ltd, 2 Talbot Cotts, Forest Road, Wokingham, Berkshire, RG40 5SG Tel: (01344) 482202 Fax: (01344) 482202

Bromley Pest Control, 4-20 Oaklands Road, Bromley, BR1 3SL Tel: (020) 8466 5079 Fax: (020) 8466 5079

Bugbusters Pest Control Ltd, 40 Goodrich Avenue, Bedford, MK41 0DE Tel: (0800) 854757 Fax: (01234) 312426 E-mail: bugbusters.2002@virgin.net

Buzzard Environmental Services, 28 Hillyfields, Dunstable, Bedfordshire, LU6 3NS Tel: (01582) 477597 Fax: (01582) 477597

C T F Ltd, 11 Langley Park Road, Sutton, Surrey, SM1 4TB Tel: (020) 8642 5871 Fax: (020) 8770 1590 E-mail: info@ctfpestcontrol.co.uk

Nick Cann Pest Control, Sturridge Farm, Sandford, Crediton, Devon, EX17 4ED Tel: (01363) 772017 Fax: (01363) 775997

▶ City & Urban, Loubond House, 2 Denham Road, Canvey Island, Essex, SS8 9HB Tel: (01268) 685800 Fax: (01268) 685544

Cleankill Environmental Services Ltd, P O Box 2087, Kenley, Surrey, CR8 5LU Tel: (020) 8668 5477 Fax: (020) 8668 4446

Clearol Pest Control, 29 Nant Y Gaer Road, Llay, Wrexham, Clwyd, LL12 0SH Tel: (01978) 852975 Fax: (01978) 855108

Clearwell Pest Control Services, 26 Chapel Street, Bradford, West Yorkshire, BD1 5DL Tel: (01274) 371577 Fax: (01274) 743173 E-mail: office@clearwell.biz

Clyde Valley Hawks, Glasgow Zoo, Hamilton Rd, Uddingston, Glasgow, G71 7RZ Tel: 0141-781 1712

Command Pest Control Ltd, College Farm Unit 4, The Street, Preston St. Mary, Sudbury, Suffolk, CO10 9NQ Tel: (01787) 248049 Fax: (01787) 247113 E-mail: sales@commandpestcontrol.co.uk

Country Cures Pest Control Ltd, The Boundary, Coxford Down, Micheldever, Winchester, Hampshire, SO21 3BD Tel: (01962) 774342 Fax: (01962) 774342 E-mail: countrycures@aol.com

County Pest Control, 54 Baxter Drive, Sheffield, S6 1GH Tel: 0114-285 3340 Fax: 0114-232 1977

County Pest Control, Greendale, East Allington, Totnes, Devon, TQ9 7RP Tel: (01548) 521388 Fax: (01548) 521326

County Pest Control Contracts, Thickthorn, Lower Shuckburgh, Daventry, Northamptonshire, NN11 6DX Tel: (01327) 705231 Fax: (01327) 878231 E-mail: cpc-contracts@mywebpage.net

Peter Cox Ltd, 53 Cuckoo Road, Birmingham, B7 5SY Tel: 0121-326 6434 Fax: 0121-326 7242 E-mail: petercox.birmingham@ecolab.com

▶ Peter Cox Ltd, Suite 5, Keynes House, Alfreton Road, Derby, DE21 4AS Tel: (01332) 299222 Fax: (01332) 200066

▶ Peter Cox Ltd, Unit 1, Marybank Lane, Dundee, DD2 3DY Tel: (01382) 400242 Fax: (01382) 400262 E-mail: petercox.dundee@ecolab.com

▶ Peter Cox Ltd, John O Gaunts Trading Estate, Leeds Road, Rothwell, Leeds, LS26 0JB Tel: 0113-282 5316 Fax: 0113-393 4927 E-mail: petercox.leeds@ecolab.com

▶ Peter Cox Ltd, Unit M, Orchard Business Centre, St. Barnabas Close, Allington, Maidstone, Kent, ME16 0JZ Tel: (01622) 750081 Fax: (01622) 750083

Peter Cox Ltd, Falcon House, Oakhurst Drive, Stockport, Cheshire, SK3 0XT Tel: 0161-491 3181 Fax: 0161-428 8138

Crown Pest Control & Environmental Services Ltd, Crown House, Thomas Street, Crewe, CW1 2BD Tel: (01270) 256444 Fax: (01270) 587024

▶ Culm Environmental Pest Control, 26 Shortlands Road, Cullompton, Devon, EX15 1HJ Tel: (0800) 0232130

CWT Services Ltd, Bridgend Wigsley Road, Thorney, Newark, Nottinghamshire, NG23 7DF Tel: (01522) 702477 Fax: (01522) 702477

D C H Pest Control, 38 Fish Street, Ripley, Bransgore, Christchurch, Dorset, BH23 8EU Tel: (01425) 672866

D O A Terminators Ltd, 23 Gorof Road, Lower Cwmtwrch, Swansea, SA9 1EH Tel: (01639) 842501 Fax: (01639) 849899

D Sankey, 15 Lewes Road, Haywards Heath, West Sussex, RH17 7SP Tel: (01825) 763159 Fax: (01825) 769736

D Sankey Pest Control Services, 39 Sackville Road, Hove, East Sussex, BN3 3WD Tel: (01273) 203055 Fax: (01825) 769736

D Sankey Pest Control Services, 39 Sackville Road, Hove, East Sussex, BN3 3WD Tel: (01273) 203055 Fax: (01825) 769736

D&R, 36 Dale Street, Chilton, Ferryhill, County Durham, DL17 0HQ Tel: (01388) 721125

Dave Cooper PCT Environmental Services, Imex Business Centre, Shobnall Road, Burton-on-Trent, Staffordshire, DE14 2AU Tel: (01889) 570430 Fax: (01889) 570430

Deer Management & Vermin Control, 2 Browns Farm Cottages, Church St, Belchamp St Paul, Sudbury, Suffolk, CO10 7DQ Tel: 01787 278126 Fax: 01787 278126

Destrodent Pest Control, Mill House, 165 Powder Mill Lane, Twickenham, TW2 6EQ Tel: (020) 8894 3249

Discreet Pest Control, 85 Grinstead Lane, Lancing, West Sussex, BN15 9DT Tel: (01903) 751048 Fax: (01903) 750544

Ecolab Ltd, Caerphilly Business Park, Caerphilly, Mid Glamorgan, CF83 3ED Tel: (029) 2085 2000 Fax: (029) 2086 5969

▶ Ecolab Pest Control Ltd, Falcon House, Lawnhurst Industrial Estate, Stockport, Cheshire, SK3 0XT Tel: 0161-491 3855 Fax: 0161 491 6088

▶ Ecolab Pest Prevention, Unit 47 Clifton Industrial Estate, Cherry Hinton Road, Cambridge, CB1 7ED Tel: (01223) 211303 Fax: (01223) 215151

Ecolab Pest Prevention, John O Gaunts Trading Estate, Leeds Road, Rothwell, Leeds, LS26 0JB Tel: 0113 288 7787 Fax: 0113 282 1298

▶ Ecolab Pest Prevention, Unit 5, Waterside Court, Bone Lane, Newbury, Berkshire, RG14 5SH Tel: (01635) 524780 Fax: (01635) 524761

▶ Ecolab Pest Prevention, 146 Moor Lane, Preston, PR1 1JR Tel: (01772) 563303 Fax: (01772) 561106

▶ Ecolab Services Ltd, Unit 11 Prideaux Close, Tamar View Industrial Estate, Saltash, Cornwall, PL12 6LD Tel: (01752) 841842 Fax: (01752) 840700

Economy Pest Control, 10 Pier Street, Plymouth, PL1 3BS Tel: (01752) 265337 Fax: (01752) 265337 E-mail: sales@pestcontrol4u.com

▶ Ecopro Ltd, Lingwood House, Angel Hill, Earl Stonham, Stowmarket, Suffolk, IP14 5DP Tel: (01449) 710066 Fax: (01449) 710066 E-mail: steve.austen@ecopro.co.uk

Environmental Health Solutions Ltd, 17 Carrongrange Grove, Stenhousemuir, Larbert, Stirlingshire, FK5 3DX Tel: (01324) 562871 Fax: (01324) 562871

Enviroserve, 1 Croft Cottages, Dolgarrog, Conwy, Gwynedd, LL32 8JR Tel: (01492) 660490 Fax: (01492) 660490 E-mail: greg@enviroserve.co.uk

▶ Envirotek Scot Ltd, 102 Millersneuk Crescent, Millerston, Glasgow, G33 6PH Tel: 0141-770 9816 Fax: 0141-770 9386 E-mail: jamie@envirotek-scotland.com

▶ Euro Guard Technical Services, 129-130 Windmill Street, Gravesend, Kent, DA12 1BL Tel: (01474) 334888 Fax: (01474) 364111 E-mail: sales@euro-guard.co.uk

Exact Pest Control Ltd, 18 Becketts Avenue, St. Albans, Hertfordshire, AL3 5RU Tel: (01727) 865922

Falcon Pest Services, 5 Foxglove Road, Newthorpe, Nottingham, NG16 2BG Tel: (01773) 761254 Fax: (01773) 761254 E-mail: enquiries@falconpestservices.com

Fen Pest Control, 1 Langley Park Cottages, Sutton Road, Langley, Maidstone, Kent, ME17 3NQ Tel: (01622) 862210 Fax: (01634) 685068

Food Safety Services Ltd, West View, Longleat Lane, Holcombe, Radstock, BA3 5DX Tel: (01761) 232146 Fax: (01761) 233697

G K Pest Control, Stone Cottage, Ridgeway Road, Dorking, Surrey, RH4 3EY Tel: (01306) 882708 Fax: (01306) 500876

G M Pest Control, 290 Rullion Road, Penicuik, Midlothian, EH26 9JN Tel: (01968) 673904 Fax: (01968) 678769

Galloway Pest Control, 38 Bluebell Close, Kingsnorth, Ashford, Kent, TN23 3NG Tel: (01233) 502811 Fax: (01233) 502811 E-mail: mark@galloway123wanadoo.co.uk

Goldingham Contracts, Crawley Barns, Uley, Dursley, Gloucestershire, GL11 5BH Tel: (01453) 860860 Fax: (01453) 860864 E-mail: admin@goldingham-contracts.co.uk

▶ Good Riddance Pest Control, 34 Bryant Gardens, Clevedon, Avon, BS21 5HE Tel: (01275) 879589 E-mail: info@grpc.co.uk

Graham Environmental Services Ltd, 34 Bellfield Street, Dundee, DD1 5HZ Tel: (01382) 206552 Fax: (01250) 870055

Greenacres Vermin Control, Foulby Lodge, Doncaster Road, Foulby, Wakefield, West Yorkshire, WF4 1PY Tel: (01924) 863562 Fax: (01924) 860418

Greenhunter Ltd, Unit 583B, Perimeter Road South, London Gatwick Airport, Gatwick, West Sussex, RH6 0PQ Tel: (01403) 871440 Fax: (01293) 568768 E-mail: info@greenhunter.co.uk

Guest & Sons Ltd, Cherry Trees, Delmonden Road, Hawkhurst, Cranbrook, Kent, TN18 4XB Tel: (01580) 753357 Fax: (01580) 753357

Gwynedd Environmental Services, 10 St. Georges Drive, Deganwy, Conwy, Gwynedd, LL31 9PP Tel: (01492) 582018 Fax: (01492) 580007

Heath Pest Control, Woodhouse Farm, Woodhouses, Melbourne, Derby, DE73 1DN Tel: (01530) 415577 E-mail: enquiries@heathpest.co.uk

Herefordshire Environmental Services Ltd, Jondori, Moreton-on-Lugg, Hereford, HR4 8DE Tel: (01432) 769232 Fax: (01432) 769232

Hullternative Pest Control Service, 1260 Kingsbury Road, Castle Vale, Birmingham, B35 6AG Tel: 0121-351 5598 Fax: 0121-351 2733

Hygiene Pest Control, 116 Montagu Street, Kettering, Northamptonshire, NN16 8RZ Tel: (01536) 523430 E-mail: info@hygienepestcontrol.co.uk

Hygiene Pest Control, 300 City Road, Sheffield, S2 5HQ Tel: 0114-272 2926 Fax: 0114-275 3776

▶ I C S, 1 Barnfield Wood Rd, Beckenham, Kent, BR3 6SR Tel: 020 86505993

I D M Environmental Services Ltd, Bourn House, Biddisham Lane, Biddisham, Axbridge, Somerset, BS26 2RG Tel: (01934) 751287 Fax: (01934) 751289 E-mail: idmpestcontrol@totalise.co.uk

PEST CONTROL SERVICES – *continued*

Iceni Pest Control Ltd, 65 Brecklands, Mundford, Thetford, Norfolk, IP26 5EG Tel: (01842) 878784 Fax: (01842) 879598

Igrox, A1 Ferrybridge Business Park, Fishergate, Knottingley, West Yorkshire, WF11 8NA Tel: (01977) 678008 Fax: (01977) 607203 E-mail: enquires@idroxomd.co.uk

▶ Impact Environmental, 401 Ash Bank Road, Werrington, Stoke-on-Trent, ST9 0JP Tel: (01782) 251324 E-mail: impactenvironmental@hotmail.co.uk

J A Kent Services East Midlands Ltd, Chestnut Farmhouse, Chestnut Lane, Barton-in-Fabis, Nottingham, NG11 0AE Tel: 0115-983 0691 Fax: 0115-983 1229 E-mail: info@kentservices.fsnet.co.uk

K H S Ltd, 14 Spenlow Drive, Chelmsford, CM1 4UQ Tel: (01245) 440873 Fax: (01245) 422242

Kemkill Pest Control & Hygiene Services, 14 Whilton Close, Sutton-in-Ashfield, Nottinghamshire, NG17 3BF Tel: (01623) 552284 Fax: (01623) 552284

Kent Pest Control, 5 Birling Park Estate, Birling, West Malling, Kent, ME19 5JD Tel: (01732) 845178

Kestrel Pest Control, Rooks Ridge, Up Somborne, Stockbridge, Hampshire, SO20 6RB Tel: (01794) 388346 Fax: (01794) 388608

▶ Knockout, 115 Vale Road, Worcester Park, Surrey, KT4 7EB Tel: (020) 8337 4491 E-mail: knockoutpcs@aol.com

▶ Knockout Pest Control Services, 33 Pennington Road, Chalfont St. Peter, Gerrards Cross, Buckinghamshire, SL9 9PH Tel: (01753) 882182

▶ Laurie Pest Control Ltd, Hunters Moon, The Street, Raydon, Ipswich, IP7 5LW Tel: (01473) 310807 Fax: (01473) 312030

▶ Maclean Environmental, Beeby Road, Scraptoft, Leicester, LE7 9SJ Tel: 0116-276 9592 Fax: 0116-276 9373

Melford Pests, Melford House, Stevenage Road, Little Wymondley, Hitchin, Hertfordshire, SG4 7JA Tel: (01438) 722393 Fax: (01438) 722395

▶ Micro B Pest Control, 3 Dalton House, 60 Windsor Avenue, London, SW19 2RR Tel: (020) 8540 6188 Fax: (020) 8540 7477 E-mail: admin@microbee.co.uk

Midlands Area Rabbit Control, 59 Coventry Road, Bulkington, Bedworth, Warwickshire, CV12 9LZ Tel: (024) 7631 3632

MidMos Solutions Limited, 29 Navigation Drive, Hurst Business Park, Brierley Hill, West Midlands, DY5 1UT Tel: (01384) 472930 Fax: (01384) 472911 E-mail: markgroobey@b-one.com

Mitie Pest Control Ltd, Battledown Works, King Alfred Way, Cheltenham, Gloucestershire, GL52 6QP Tel: (01242) 696969 Fax: (01242) 696970 E-mail: info@eaglepest.co.uk

Mr Wasp, King George V Drive North, Cardiff, CF14 4EJ Tel: (029) 2075 4796

Neal Pestforce Ltd, Unit 3, Sutterton Enterprise Park, Sutterton, Boston, Lincolnshire, PE20 2JA Tel: (01205) 460446 Fax: (01205) 460886 E-mail: anninkirton@aol.com

North & Mid Wales Pest Control, 47 Minera Hall Road, Minera, Wrexham, Clwyd, LL11 3YF Tel: (01978) 753752 Fax: (01978) 753752

Palmer Pest Control Ltd, 33 Ross, Rowley Regis, West Midlands, B65 8DY Tel: 0121-561 5417 Fax: 0121-533 9462 E-mail: ppc.ltd@blueyonder.co.uk

Pennine Pest Control, 54 Mear House, Sheffield Road, New Mill, Holmfirth, HD9 7HA Tel: (01484) 683010

Pest Control Services, Church House, Kimbolton Road, Bolnhurst, Bedford, MK44 2ES Tel: (01234) 376271

Pest Destruction Services Ltd, 32 Colchester Road, West Bergholt, Colchester, CO6 3JG Tel: (01206) 242050 Fax: (01206) 242002

Pest Quest, Back Lane, Chellaston, Derby, DE73 6TP Tel: (01332) 704107 Fax: (01332) 704107

▶ Pest Shield Environmental Services, 17 Unit Factory Estate, Boulevard, Hull, HU3 4AY Tel: (01482) 581505 Fax: (01482) 580678 E-mail: sales@pestshield.co.uk

▶ Pest Solutions Ltd, 38, Colwood Place, Glasgow, G53 7YB Tel: 0141-880 8895

Pestarrest Control Service, 6 Alton Park, Beeford, Driffield, East Yorkshire, YO25 8BZ Tel: (01262) 488306 E-mail: peter.burnel@btopenworld.com

Pestatak Ltd, Pean Hill Park, Whitstable, Kent, CT5 3BJ Tel: (01227) 768189 Fax: (01227) 787298 E-mail: sales@pestatak.co.uk

Pestcall, Spring Close, Eastbourne, East Sussex, BN20 9HD Tel: (01323) 500151 Fax: (01323) 500151

Pestfree D & D Services, 40 Spencer Drive, Llandough, Penarth, Vale of Glamorgan, CF64 2LR Tel: (029) 2031 6860 Fax: (07971) 115024 E-mail: pestfree@pestfreedd.co.uk

Pestline Environmental Services UK Ltd, 12 Sunderland Road, Forest Hill, London, SE23 2PR Tel: (020) 8699 3663 Fax: (020) 8699 1879

Pestokill, Graveoak, East Lancs Road, Leigh, Lancashire, WN7 3SE Tel: (0870) 0660999 Fax: (01942) 607570 E-mail: sales@pestokill.co.uk

Pestproof Ltd, Mitre Street, Failsworth, Manchester, M35 9BY Tel: 0161-684 9451 Fax: 0161-947 0485

▶ Peter Cox Ltd, Unit 10, Avon Riverside Estate, Victoria Road, Avonmouth, Bristol, BS11 9DB Tel: 0117 938 7130 Fax: 0117 938 7137

Peter Cox Ltd, Unit 17, Engineer Park, Sandycroft, Deeside, Clwyd, CH5 2QB Tel: (01244) 538610 Fax: (01244) 534720

▶ Peter Cox, Unit 11d Station Approach, Team Valley Trading Estate, Gateshead, Tyne & Wear, NE11 0ZF Tel: 0191-487 2293 Fax: 0191-487 4804 E-mail: petercox.newcastle@ecolab.com

▶ Peter Cox Ltd, St. Andrews House, 385 Hillington Road, Hillington Industrial Estate, Glasgow, G52 4BL Tel: 0141 810 9100 Fax: 0141 810 9111

▶ Peter Cox Ltd, 103 Sadler Road, Lincoln, LN6 3RS Tel: (01522) 500214 Fax: (01522) 688838

▶ Peter Cox Ltd, 209 Century Buildings, Summers Road, Brunswick Business Park, Liverpool, L3 4BL Tel: 0151 709 1090 Fax: 0151 708 5304

▶ Peter Cox Ltd, 62h Lord Avenue, Thornaby, Stockton-on-Tees, Cleveland, TS17 9JX Tel: (01642) 769983 Fax: (01642) 769421

▶ Pied Piper, 53 Woodstock Gardens, Blackpool, FY4 1JW Tel: (01253) 404445 Fax: (01253) 404445 E-mail: sales@the-piedpiper.com

▶ Pied Piper Enviromental Services, Eastern Avenue, Lichfield, Staffs, WS13 6RL Tel: (01543) 254111 Fax: (01543) 254111

Precision Pest Management Solution Ltd, 267 Iveson Drive, Leeds, LS16 6LP Tel: 0113-226 6800 E-mail: enquiries@precisionpest.co.uk

Premier Pest Control Ltd, 2 Hawksbrook Lane, Beckenham, Kent, BR3 3SR Tel: (020) 8663 1911 Fax: (020) 8658 1711 E-mail: premierpestcontrol@hotmail.com

Premium Pest Control, 56 Oldfield Road, London, NW10 9UE Tel: (020) 8451 7426 Fax: (020) 8451 1044

Pro Kill Environmental Services, 174 Kirkway, Middleton, Manchester, M24 1LN Tel: (0800) 0289715 Fax: 0161-643 5062

▶ Problem Solved, 29 Sheep House, Farnham, Surrey, GU9 8LR Tel: (01252) 727214 Fax: (01252) 727214 E-mail: problemsolved@whsmiths.co.uk

▶ Protect Pest Control, 83 Southern Road, Eastbourne, East Sussex, BN22 9LS Tel: (01323) 500797

Quickil Pest Control Services Ltd, Unit 4 Roebuck Road Trading Estate 15-17 Roebuck Road, Hainault, Ilford, Essex, IG6 3TU Tel: (020) 8500 4999 Fax: (020) 8500 9440 E-mail: jconstantino@quickil.co.uk

R Bickley & Co., 13 Redcar Road, Romford, RM3 9PT Tel: (01708) 348557

Rentokil Ltd, Rentokil House, 4 London Road, Baldock, Hertfordshire, SG7 6ND Tel: (01462) 894422 Fax: (01462) 490174

Rentokil, 4 Singer Road, East Kilbride, Glasgow, G75 0UL Tel: (01355) 239140 Fax: (01355) 264172

Rentokil, Chartists Way, Leeds, LS27 9EG Tel: 0113-252 6633 Fax: 0113-218 9087

Rentokil, Hart Street, Maidstone, Kent, ME16 8RH Tel: (01622) 679821 Fax: (01622) 661206

Rentokil Initial plc, Unit 2-3 Wendle Court, 131-137 Wandsworth Road, London, SW8 2LH Tel: (020) 7498 5978 Fax: (020) 7501 0042

Rentokil Pest Control, 43-45 Duncrue Cresent, Belfast, BT3 9BW Tel: (028) 9037 0631 Fax: (028) 9037 0492 E-mail: fcarville@rentokilpestcontrol.co.uk

Rentokil Pest Control, St. Agnes Gardens, Ryton, Tyne & Wear, NE40 4LH Tel: (0800) 389 2319 Fax: 0191-413 3409

Rightway Environmental Spraying & Pest Control, Noir View, Sexburga Drive, Minster on Sea, Sheerness, Kent, ME12 2LB Tel: (01795) 873119 Fax: (01795) 873119

▶ Ringwood Pest Control, 86 Hightown Gardens, Ringwood, Hampshire, BH24 3EJ Tel: (01425) 474111

Rodent Service East Anglia Ltd, 24 Cooke Road, Lowestoft, Suffolk, NR33 7NA Tel: (01502) 517292 Fax: (01502) 538682 E-mail: enquiries@rodentservice.co.uk

Safeguard Pest Control, 3 Retreat Close, Harrow, Middlesex, HA3 0JQ Tel: (020) 8907 8922

Safeguard Screens, PO Box 2458, Wimborne, Dorset, BH21 5YG Tel: (01725) 551144 Fax: (01202) 892200

Sameday Service, 22 Brynn Street, Widnes, Cheshire, WA8 6BT Tel: (07800) 774224

Scotcare Environmental Services, 670 Duke Street, Glasgow, G31 1JZ Tel: 0141-554 0375 Fax: 0141-554 0013

Scottish Pest Control, Middle Grange, Culross, Dunfermline, Fife, KY12 8EL Tel: (01383) 851944 Fax: (01383) 851944

Serco Ltd, Bar End Road, Winchester, Hampshire, SO23 9NP Tel: (01962) 828400 Fax: (01962) 843017

Shield Pest Control UK Ltd, 10 Ewhurst Road, London, SE4 1AQ Tel: (020) 8690 4481 Fax: (020) 8690 7612

Soham Pest Control, Fordham Road, Soham, Ely, Cambridgeshire, CB7 5AJ Tel: (01353) 720877

Step Pest Control, 92 Meldreth Road, Whaddon, Royston, Hertfordshire, SG8 5RP Tel: (01223) 208349 Fax: (01223) 207373

Strathclyde Pest Services, 53 High Street, Paisley, Renfrewshire, PA1 2AN Tel: 0141-889 1990 Fax: 0141-889 1990

Surekill Pest Control Services, Annerley, Oakfield Road, Edenbridge, Kent, TN8 6JG Tel: (01732) 863206 Fax: (01732) 863206 E-mail: surekill@tinyonline.co.uk

Swiftkill Pest Control, Brookmill Road, London, SE8 4JH Tel: (020) 8694 3666 Fax: (020) 8305 6728

Swiftkill Pest Control Ltd, 50 Friendly Street, London, SE8 4DR Tel: (020) 8692 2935 Fax: (020) 8692 8891 E-mail: swiftkill@yayoo.co.uk

▶ Tamworth Pest Control, 70 Camhouses, Wilnecote, Tamworth, Staffordshire, B77 4HJ Tel: (01827) 898229 E-mail: tamworthpestcontrol@msn.com

Telford Pest Control, 11 Pasteur Drive, Leegomery, Telford, Shropshire, TF1 6PQ Tel: (01952) 223706

Terminex Pest & Vermin Control, 53 Gloucester Drive, London, N4 2LJ Tel: (020) 7503 8234 Fax: (020) 7503 8234 E-mail: enquiries@terminex.co.uk

Town & Country, 53 Bouncers Lane, Prestbury, Cheltenham, Gloucestershire, GL52 5JB Tel: (01242) 239531

Valley Pest Control Ltd, 1f Station Road, Hemyock, Cullompton, Devon, EX15 3SE Tel: (01823) 680932 Fax: (01823) 681247

▶ Vermex Ltd, 16 Low Poppleton Lane, York, YO26 6AZ Tel: (01904) 798676 Fax: (01904) 782365 E-mail: enquiries@vermexpestcontrol.co.uk

Vermicon Pest Control, 3 Middleburn Cottages, Kirkness, Cardenden, Lochgelly, Fife, KY5 0HH Tel: (01592) 868900 Fax: (01592) 868900

▶ Verminator Pest Control, Crossford, Dunfermline, Fife, KY12 8NU Tel: (07774) 034856 E-mail: andymks@fsmail.net

▶ W P M R Ltd, 69 Trinity Street, Leamington Spa, Warwickshire, CV32 5YN Tel: (01926) 338845 Fax: (01926) 336613

Yorkshire Pest Control, Unit 15 Bull Commercial Centre, Stockton Lane, Stockton On The Forest, York, YO32 9LE Tel: (01904) 400082 Fax: (01904) 400082

PESTICIDES

Dow Agro Sciences Ltd, Latchmore Court, Brand Sreet, Hitchin, Hertfordshire, SG5 1NH Tel: (01462) 457272 Fax: (01462) 426605 E-mail: dowagrosciencesuk@dow.com

Fieldcare Ltd, Gamston Airfield, Gamston, Retford, Nottinghamshire, DN22 0QL Tel: (01777) 839000 Fax: (01777) 839111 E-mail: sales@procam.co.uk

Octavius Hunt Ltd, Dove Lane, Redfield, Bristol, BS5 9NQ Tel: 0117-955 5304 Fax: 0117-955 7875 E-mail: info@octavius-hunt.co.uk

Okasan Medical Ltd, 6 Stake Lane, Farnborough, Hampshire, GU14 8NP Tel: (01483) 570052 Fax: (01252) 511911 E-mail: sales@okasanpesticides.co.uk

Rigby Taylor Paints Ltd, Crown Lane, Horwich, Bolton, BL6 5HP Tel: (01204) 677776 Fax: (01204) 677785 E-mail: sales@rigbytaylor.com

Sorex Ltd, Oldgate, Widnes, Cheshire, WA8 8TJ Tel: 0151-424 4328 Fax: 0151-495 1163 E-mail: enquiries@sorex.com

PET FOOD

Clumber Pets, 1 Clumber Street, Warsop, Mansfield, Nottinghamshire, NG20 0LR Tel: (01623) 842652

Killingholme Animal Feeds, Town Street, South Killingholme, Immingham, South Humberside, DN40 3DD Tel: (01469) 540793 Fax: (01469) 540793

▶ Livefoods Direct Ltd, Houghton Road, North Anston Trading Estate, North Anston, Sheffield, S25 4JJ Tel: (01909) 518888 Fax: (01909) 568666 E-mail: sales@livefoodsdirect.co.uk

PET PHOTOGRAPHERS

▶ Exigent, Unit F2 Roden House, Roden Street, Nottingham, NG3 1JH Tel: (07974) 818110 E-mail: contact@by-exigent.co.uk

PET REQUISITES, *See also headings for particular types*

Ancol Pet Products Ltd, Ancol House, 113 Leamore Lane, Walsall, WS2 7DA Tel: (01922) 402428 Fax: (01922) 404983 E-mail: sales@ancol.co.uk

Armitage Pet Care Ltd, Private Road Number 3, Colwick Industrial Estate, Colwick, Nottingham, NG4 2BA Tel: 0115-938 1200 Fax: 0115-961 7496 E-mail: sales@armitages.co.uk

Brookwick Ward, Fearby Road, Masham, Ripon, North Yorkshire, HG4 4ES Tel: (0870) 1118610 Fax: (0870) 1118609 E-mail: sales@brookwickward.com

Burgess Group P.L.C., Woodlands, Priestmans Lane, Thornton Dale, Pickering, North Yorkshire, YO18 7RT Tel: (01751) 476430 Fax: (01751) 477633 E-mail: burgess@dial.pipex.com

Diamond Edge Ltd, 126 Gloucester Road, Brighton, BN1 4BU Tel: (01273) 605922 Fax: (01273) 625074 E-mail: diamondedge@btclick.com

▶ Doggie Solutions, Hazel Edge, Scotts Grove Road, Chobham, Woking, Surrey, GU24 8DX Tel: (01276) 488119 E-mail: info@doggiesolutions.co.uk

Hambry's Angling Equipment, 8 Tamworth Road, Polesworth, Tamworth, Staffordshire, B78 1JH Tel: (01827) 895011

The Hatchwell Co. Ltd, Unit G1 Riverside Industrial Estate, Hermitage Street, Rishton, Blackburn, BB1 4NF Tel: (01254) 888479 Fax: (01254) 883822 E-mail: sales@hatchwell.co.uk

Albert E. James & Son Ltd, Barrow Mill, Barrow Street, Barrow Gurney, Bristol, BS48 3RU Tel: (01275) 463496 Fax: (01275) 463791

Melton Pets Direct Ltd, Unkit 3 Top End Industrial Estate, Thistleton Road, Oakham, Leicestershire, LE15 7PP Tel: (01572) 768444 Fax: (01572) 767123 E-mail: sales@meltonpets.com

Pascoe's Ltd, Kelleythorpe Industrial Estate, Kellythorpe, Driffield, East Yorkshire, YO25 9DJ Tel: (01377) 252571 Fax: (01377) 252576 E-mail: info@pascoes.co.uk

Pets Choice Ltd, Gladstone Street, Blackburn, BB1 3ES Tel: (01254) 54545 Fax: (01254) 681446 E-mail: info@petschoice.co.uk

Reilor Ltd, Astra Business Centre, Roman Way, Preston, PR2 5AP Tel: (01772) 793793 Fax: (01772) 797877E-mail: sales@reilor.com

Shaws Pet Products Ltd, Unit 13 Bordesley Trading Estate, Bordesley Green Road, Birmingham, B8 1BZ Tel: 0121-326 7667 Fax: 0121-328 1734 E-mail: info@shawspet.co.uk

Small Life Supplies, Station Buildings, Station Road, Bottesford, Nottingham, NG13 0EB Tel: (01949) 842446 Fax: (01949) 843036 E-mail: emma@small-life.co.uk

X J F Plastics Ltd, Unit 1 & 2, Southfield Lane Industrial Estate, Whitwell, Worksop, Nottinghamshire, S80 4SB Tel: (01909) 724211 Fax: (01909) 724582 E-mail: enquiries@xjfplastics.co.uk

PETROCHEMICAL ENGINEERING CONSULTANCY

Instrumentation Safety Services Ltd, 173 Hall Road, Lowestoft, Suffolk, NR32 3NR Tel: (01502) 500108 Fax: 01502 500108

PETROCHEMICAL FABRICATORS

B F S Enterprise Fabrications Ltd, 6 Ellough Industrial Estate, Ellough, Beccles, Suffolk, NR34 7TD Tel: (01502) 716383 Fax: (01502) 717416 E-mail: m.spence@bfs-fabs.co.uk

PETROCHEMICAL FLANGES

Flanges Ltd, Portrack Trading Estate, Stockton-on-Tees, Cleveland, TS18 2PL Tel: (01642) 672626 Fax: (01642) 617574 E-mail: sales@flanges-ltd.co.uk

Midsteel Pipeline Ltd, Building 67 Third Avenue, Pensnett Trading Estate, Kingswinford, West Midlands, DY6 7FA Tel: (01384) 400321 Fax: (01384) 400461 E-mail: sales@midsteel.co.uk

PETROCHEMICAL HEAT EXCHANGERS

Heatric, 46 Holton Road, Holton Heath Trading Park, Poole, Dorset, BH16 6LT Tel: (01202) 632299 Fax: (01202) 632299 E-mail: sales@heatric.com

PETROCHEMICAL PLANT AND EQUIPMENT

B F S International, Willowbrook, 20 Bray Road, Bray, Maidenhead, Berkshire, SL6 1UE Tel: (01628) 671458 Fax: (01628) 784337 E-mail: sales@bfs-international.co.uk

PETROCHEMICAL PLANT CONTRACTORS OR DESIGNERS

Bechtel Holdings Ltd, 245 Hammersmith Road, London, W6 8DP Tel: (020) 8846 5111 Fax: (020) 8846 6940

Unit Superheater Engineering Ltd, Unit Works, 2-8 Morfa Road, Swansea, SA1 2ET Tel: (01792) 654091 Fax: (01792) 456198 E-mail: eng@unit.co.uk

Worleyparsons Europe Ltd, Parkview, Great West Road, Brentford, Middlesex, TW8 9AZ Tel: (020) 8758 9477 Fax: (020) 8710 0220 E-mail: info@worleyparsons.com

PETROCHEMICAL PLANT CONTROL COMPUTER SYSTEMS

Aberdeen Computer Services Ltd, 24 Balnagask Road, Aberdeen, AB11 8HR Tel: (01224) 875867 Fax: (01224) 879247 E-mail: sales@acsltd.co.uk

F M A Systems, Unit 37 Monument Business Park, Warpsgrove Lane, Chalgrove, Oxford, OX44 7RW Tel: (01865) 891682 Fax: (01865) 891685 E-mail: sales@fma-systems.com

PETROCHEMICAL PRODUCERS OR SUPPLIERS

Petroleum Experts Ltd, Spectrum House, 2 Powderhall Road, Edinburgh, EH7 4GB Tel: 0131-474 7030 Fax: 0131-474 7031 E-mail: edinburgh@petex.com

S T Services Ltd, Glasgow Road, Clydebank, Dunbartonshire, G81 1TS Tel: 0141-952 0055 Fax: 0141-952 9099

PETROCHEMICAL REFINERY CONTROL SYSTEMS

Aker Kvaerner Subsea Ltd, Unit 59, Clivemont Road, Cordwallis Industrial Estate, Maidenhead, Berkshire, SL6 7BZ Tel: (01628) 506560 Fax: (01628) 506501 E-mail: info@kvaerner.com

PETROL ENGINE MANUFRS

Engine Developments, Leigh Road, Swift Valley Industrial Estate, Rugby, Warwickshire, CV21 1DS Tel: (01788) 541114 Fax: (01788) 546303 E-mail: sales@engdev.com

MAHLE Power Train Ltd, Costin House, St. James Mill Road, Northampton, NN5 5TZ Tel: (0870) 1573000 Fax: (0870) 1573100 E-mail: sales@gb.mahle.com

Maxsym Engine Technology Ltd, 5b Brailes Industrial Estate, Winderton Road, Lower Brailes, Banbury, Oxfordshire, OX15 5JW Tel: (07740) 404574 Fax: (01608) 685156 E-mail: sales@maxsym.com

Mercedes Benz UK Ltd, Quarry Road, Brixworth, Northampton, NN6 9UB Tel: (01604) 880100 Fax: (01604) 882800 E-mail: reception@mercedes-benz-hpe.com

Power Assemblies Ltd, Cooper Street, Wolverhampton, WV2 2JL Tel: (01902) 456767 Fax: (01902) 456761

Power Torque Engineering Ltd, 27 Herald Way, Binley Industrial Estate, Coventry, CV3 2RQ Tel: (024) 7663 5757 Fax: (024) 7663 5878 E-mail: sales@powertorque.co.uk

Ses Engine Services Ltd, 5 Wealdstone Road, Sutton, Surrey, SM3 9QN Tel: (020) 8641 0252 Fax: (020) 8644 3983 E-mail: sales@sesengines.co.uk

Specialised Engines Ltd, 15 Curzon Drive, Grays, Essex, RM17 6BG Tel: (01375) 378606 Fax: (01375) 381249 E-mail: specialisedengines@talk21.com

Tecumseh Power International Ltd, 152-154 Commercial Road, Staines, Middlesex, TW18 2QP Tel: (01784) 460684 Fax: (01784) 453563E-mail: tecumsehukltd@btinternet.com

PETROL PUMP INSTALLATION CONTRACTORS

A.J. Bayliss Petroleum Engineers Ltd, Unit 1, Hodfar Road, Stourport-On-Severn, Worcestershire, DY13 9QB Tel: (01299) 824541 Fax: (01299) 827638 E-mail: simon@ajbayliss.demon.co.uk

Cameron Forecourt, Chambers Road, Platts Common Industrial Estate, Hoyland, Barnsley, South Yorkshire, S74 9SE Tel: (01226) 742441 Fax: (01226) 747441 E-mail: info@cameron-forecourt.co.uk

PETROL PUMP MAINTENANCE/ REPAIR SERVICES

A.J. Bayliss Petroleum Engineers Ltd, Unit 1, Hodfar Road, Stourport-On-Severn, Worcestershire, DY13 9QB Tel: (01299) 824541 Fax: (01299) 827638 E-mail: simon@ajbayliss.demon.co.uk

Gilbarco Veeder Root Ltd, Crompton Close, Basildon, Essex, SS14 3BA Tel: (01268) 533090 Fax: (01268) 524214 E-mail: sales@gilbarco.com

Meldrum Motors Ltd, 3 Market Square, Oldmeldrum, Inverurie, Aberdeenshire, AB51 0AA Tel: (01651) 872247 Fax: (01651) 872247

PETROL PUMP MANUFRS

▶ Hockman, 4 Church Street, Amersham, Buckinghamshire, HP7 0DB Tel: (01494) 726963 Fax: (01494) 431248 E-mail: johnwootton@btconnect.com

Tokheim UK Ltd, 1-3 Baker Road, Broughty Ferry, Dundee, DD5 3RT Tel: (01382) 598000 Fax: (01382) 598001 E-mail: sales@dundee.tokheim.com

PETROL STATION FORECOURT INSTALLATION CONTRACTORS

Forecourt Systems, 1a Downpatrick Street, Saintfield, Ballynahinch, County Down, BT24 7AY Tel: (028) 9751 1644 Fax: (028) 9751 0860

PETROL STATION FORECOURT WATERTIGHT PROTECTION COVERS

▶ CSC Forecourt Services Ltd, 6 Timon View, Heathcote, Warwick, CV34 6ES Tel: (01926) 882377 Fax: (01926) 882377 E-mail: info@cscspec.com

PETROLEUM ADDITIVES

Afton Chemical, London Road, Bracknell, Berkshire, RG12 2UW Tel: (01344) 304141 Fax: (01344) 420666 E-mail: ethyleurope@ethyl.com

Innospec Ltd, Innospec Manufacturing Park, Oil Sites Road, Ellesmere Port, CH65 4EY Tel: 0151 3553611 Fax: 0151 3562349 E-mail: corporatecommunications@innospecinc.com

PETROLEUM COMPANIES OR DISTRIBUTORS OR AGENTS OR TRADERS

▶ Bioroute Ltd, Flint House, 25 Charing Cross, Norwich, NR2 4AX Tel: (01603) 724714 Fax: (01603) 724700 E-mail: biodiesel@bioroute.co.uk

British Benzol, Roentgen Road, Staineshill East, Basingstoke, Hampshire, RG24 8NT Tel: (01256) 811020 Fax: (01256) 355151

C P L Petroleum Ltd, Prince Regent Way, Diss, Norfolk, IP22 4GW Tel: (01379) 652235 Fax: (01379) 643529 E-mail: diss@cplpetroleum.co.uk

Connor's Fuels Ltd, 48 Trench Road, Newtownabbey, County Antrim, BT36 4TY Tel: (028) 9084 8586 Fax: (028) 9084 3909 E-mail: post@maxol.ie

Conocophillips Ltd, 2 Portman Street, London, W1H 6DU Tel: (020) 7408 6000 Fax: (020) 7408 6660

Emo Oils Ni Ltd, Airport Road West, Belfast, BT3 9ED Tel: (028) 9045 4555 Fax: (028) 9046 0921 E-mail: enquiries@emooil.com

Exxon Mobil Group, Exxon Mobil House, Ermyn Way, Leatherhead, Surrey, KT22 8UX Tel: (01372) 222000 Fax: (01372) 222556

George Broughtons & Co Ltd, Whitebirk Road, Whitebirk, Blackburn, BB1 3HZ Tel: (01254) 295509 Fax: (01254) 295501 E-mail: sales@geo-broughton.co.uk

George Hammond plc, Hammond House, Limekiln Street, Dover, Kent, CT17 9EE Tel: (01304) 201201 Fax: (01304) 240374 E-mail: georgehammond@p.plc.uk

Lama Petroleum Ltd, 14 Ensign House, Admirals Way, London, E14 9YR Tel: (020) 7538 2603 Fax: (020) 7515 9780 E-mail: info@ammora.com

Mabanaft Ltd, Malta House, 36-38 Piccadilly, London, W1J 0DP Tel: (020) 7470 7600 Fax: (020) 7447 0077 E-mail: enquiry@mabanaft.co.uk

Manx Petroleums, Battery Pier, Douglas, Isle of Man, IM99 1DE Tel: (01624) 691691 Fax: (01624) 662313 E-mail: info@manx-petroleums.co.im

Mobil Services Co. Ltd, Mobil Court, 3 Clements Inn, London, WC2A 2EB Tel: (020) 7412 4000 Fax: (020) 7412 4084

Petrobrass Europe Ltd, 6th Floor, 35-38 Portman Square, London, W1H 6LR Tel: (020) 7535 1100 Fax: (020) 7467 5800 E-mail: petrobrass.europe@petrobrass.com

Petrostock Control Systems Ltd, 78 Malone Road, Woodley, Reading, RG5 3NJ Tel: 0118-962 6041 Fax: 0118-969 5695 E-mail: sales@petrostock.demon.co.uk

Prince Petroleum Ltd, 139 Abbey Lane, Leicester, LE4 5QZ Tel: 0116-266 1828 Fax: 0116-261 0727 E-mail: lynn@prince-petroleum.co.uk

Sonatrach Petroleum Corporation, 5 Princes Gate, London, SW7 1QJ Tel: (020) 7823 8030 Fax: (020) 7823 7069 E-mail: enquiries@sonatrach.co.uk

Watson Petroleum Ltd, Causeway End, Brinkworth, Chippenham, Wiltshire, SN15 5DN Tel: (01782) 816932

O.J. Williams Ltd, Station Road, St. Clears, Carmarthen, SA33 4BN Tel: (01994) 230355 Fax: (01994) 231585 E-mail: enquiries@ojwilliams.co.uk

Rowland Williams & Co. Ltd, 106 Cherry Lane, Liverpool, L4 8SF Tel: 0151-256 6565 Fax: 0151-256 1616

PETROLEUM CONDITION MONITORING SERVICES

Swansea Tribology Services, Unit 5 Penrice Court, Swansea Enterprise Park, Swansea, SA6 8QW Tel: (01792) 799036 Fax: (01792) 799034 E-mail: swansea_tribology@compuserve.com

PETROLEUM ENGINEERING CONSULTANCY

Petroil Pump & Tank Services, Common Platt, Lydiard Millicent, Purton, Swindon, SN5 5JZ Tel: (01793) 770494 Fax: (01793) 772517 E-mail: petroil.eng@btconnect.com

PETROLEUM HANDLING EQUIPMENT OR FITTINGS

Petro-Man Ltd, Sneyd Street, Stoke-on-Trent, ST6 2NP Tel: (01782) 200750 Fax: (01782) 200755 E-mail: peslenquiries@aol.com

Phoceenne, Birtley House, Claremont Avenue, Woking, Surrey, GU22 7QB Tel: (01483) 742772 Fax: (01483) 742774

PETROLEUM HEAT EXCHANGERS

Heatric, 46 Holton Road, Holton Heath Trading Park, Poole, Dorset, BH16 6LT Tel: (01202) 632299 Fax: (01202) 632299 E-mail: sales@heatric.com

PETROLEUM INDUSTRY VALVES

Phoceenne, Birtley House, Claremont Avenue, Woking, Surrey, GU22 7QB Tel: (01483) 742772 Fax: (01483) 742774

PETROLEUM STORAGE TANK REMOVAL SERVICES

Tanks Direct, Richmond Lodge, Bond Street, Hedon, Hull, HU12 8NY Tel: (07803) 182400 Fax: (01482) 899454 E-mail: john@networkpacific2000.freeserve.co.uk

Yorkshire Demolition Contractors Ltd, 8 Weetworth Ave, Glasshoughton, Castleford, West Yorkshire, WF10 4QA Tel: (01977) 553117 Fax: (01977) 553117

PETROLEUM TANKS

Platinum Engineering & Fabrications Ltd, National Avenue Ind Estate, Hull, HU5 4HF Tel: 01482 446123

PETROLEUM TEST EQUIPMENT MANUFRS

Poulten Selfe & Lee Ltd, Russell House, Burnham Business Park, Burnham-On-Crouch, Essex, CM0 8TE Tel: (01621) 787100 Fax: (01621) 787175 E-mail: info@rheotek.com

SGS UK Ltd, London Road, Purfleet, Essex, RM19 1QS Tel: (01708) 866855 Fax: (01708) 681910

Swansea Tribology Services, Unit 5 Penrice Court, Swansea Enterprise Park, Swansea, SA6 8QW Tel: (01792) 799036 Fax: (01792) 799034 E-mail: swansea_tribology@compuserve.com

PEWTER WARE

A E Williams, 6 Well Lane, Birmingham, B5 5TE Tel: 0121-643 4756 Fax: 0121-643 2977 E-mail: admin@pewtergiftware.com

A R Wentworth Ltd, Monarch Works, Catley Road, Darnall, Sheffield, S9 5JF Tel: 0114-244 7693 Fax: 0114-242 3159 E-mail: sales@wentworth-pewter.com

Art Pewter Silver Ltd, 3B Colvilles Road, Kelvin Industrial Estate, East Kilbride, Glasgow, G75 0RS Tel: (01355) 229446 Fax: (01355) 264762 E-mail: service@artpewter.co.uk

Edwin Blyde & Co. Ltd, Little London Road, Sheffield, S8 0UH Tel: 0114-249 1930 Fax: 0114-249 1950 E-mail: pewter@edwinblyde.co.uk

Pinder Bros Ltd, Sheaf Plate Works, Arundel Street, Sheffield, S1 1DJ Tel: 0114-275 2277 Fax: 0114-272 6718 E-mail: sales@pinder.co.uk

Royal Selangor Pewter UK Ltd, 2 Eastbury Road, London, E6 6LP Tel: (020) 7474 5511 Fax: (020) 7474 5522 E-mail: sales@royalselangor.com

PH METERS

Analytical Measurements Ltd, 14 Selby Road, Ashford, Middlesex, TW15 1JH Tel: (01784) 256236 Fax: (01784) 257938

Professional Test Systems, Summer Court, Manafon, Welshpool, Powys, SY21 8BJ Tel: (01686) 650160 Fax: (01686) 650170 E-mail: sales@proftest.com

Thermor Russell, Station Road, Auchtermuchty, Cupar, Fife, KY14 7DP Tel: (01337) 828871 Fax: (01337) 828972 E-mail: sales.water@thermolfisher.com

PH SENSORS

Professional Test Systems, Summer Court, Manafon, Welshpool, Powys, SY21 8BJ Tel: (01686) 650160 Fax: (01686) 650170 E-mail: sales@proftest.com

Thermor Russell, Station Road, Auchtermuchty, Cupar, Fife, KY14 7DP Tel: (01337) 828871 Fax: (01337) 828972 E-mail: sales.water@thermolfisher.com

Thermosensing Ltd, 30-31 Devonshire Place, Brighton, BN2 1QB Tel: (01903) 214466 Fax: (01903) 214477

PHARMACEUTICAL AUTOMATED DISPENSING SYSTEMS

Swisslog, 707 Stirling Road, Slough, SL1 4SY Tel: (01753) 528545 Fax: (01753) 570407 E-mail: sales@teleliftuk.com

PHARMACEUTICAL BUILDING SERVICES CONSULTANCY

▶ Ndesign Services Ltd, 74 Brighton Road, Newhaven, East Sussex, BN9 9NS Tel: (01273) 515081 Fax: (01273) 515168 E-mail: nathan@ndesignservices.co.uk

PHARMACEUTICAL CHEMICAL RESEARCH AND DEVELOPMENT SERVICES

Catalent Pharma Solutions, Lancaster Way, Wingates Industrial Estate, Westhoughton, Bolton, BL5 3XX Tel: (01942) 790000 Fax: (01942) 799799

▶ High Force Research Ltd, Bowburn North Industrial Estate, Bowburn, Durham, DH6 5PF Tel: 0191-377 9098 Fax: 0191-377 9099

Huntingdon Life Sciences, Occold, Eye, Suffolk, IP23 7PX Tel: (01480) 892000 Fax: (01379) 651165 E-mail: sales@ukorg.huntingdon.com

Synprotec Ltd, 303 Clayton Lane, Clayton, Manchester, M11 4SX Tel: 0161-223 3344 Fax: 0161-220 8778 E-mail: sales@synprotec.com

Xenova, 310 Science Park, Milton Road, Cambridge, CB4 0WG Tel: (01223) 423413 Fax: (01223) 423458 E-mail: sales@xenova.co.uk

PHARMACEUTICAL CHEMICALS

A H Marks & Co. Ltd, Wyke Lane, Wyke, Bradford, West Yorkshire, BD12 9EJ Tel: (01274) 691234 Fax: (01274) 691176 E-mail: info@ahmarks.com

Abbott Laboratories Ltd, North Road, Queenborough, Kent, ME11 5EL Tel: (01795) 580099 Fax: (01795) 593335

Alan Pharmaceuticals, 2 Kingsgate Avenue, London, N3 3BH Tel: (020) 8346 4311 Fax: (020) 8346 5218 E-mail: enquiries@alanpharmaceuticals.com

Baxter Healthcare Ltd, Mount Vernon Hospital, Rickmansworth Road, Northwood, Middlesex, HA6 2RN Tel: (01923) 828230 Fax: (01923) 844764

Bayer UK plc, Bayer House, Strawberry Hill, Newbury, Berkshire, RG14 1JA Tel: (01635) 563000 Fax: (01635) 563393 E-mail: corporate.communications@bayer.co.uk

Bayer UK plc, Bayer House, Strawberry Hill, Newbury, Berkshire, RG14 1JA Tel: (01635) 563000 E-mail: corporate.communications@bayer.co.uk

Boehringer Ingelheim Ltd, Ellesfield Avenue, Bracknell, Berkshire, RG12 8YS Tel: (01344) 746959 Fax: (01344) 741349 E-mail: vetmedica.uk@boehringer-ingelheim.com

Cobra Therapeutics Ltd, The Science Park, University of Keele, Keele, Newcastle, Staffordshire, ST5 5SP Tel: (01782) 714181 Fax: (01782) 714168

Delta Biotechnology Ltd, 59 Castle Boulevard, Nottingham, NG7 1FD Tel: 0115-955 3355 Fax: 0115-955 1299

Glaxo Smith Kline (UK) Ltd, Stockley Park West, Uxbridge, Middlesex, UB11 1BT Tel: (020) 8990 9000 Fax: (020) 8990 4321

Glaxosmithkline, Harmire Road, Barnard Castle, County Durham, DL12 8DT Tel: (01833) 690600 Fax: (01833) 692300

J R B Enterprises Ltd, Dixies Development, High Street, Ashwell, Baldock, Hertfordshire, SG7 5NT Tel: (01462) 742157 Fax: (01462) 742088 E-mail: johnrbonnett@aol.com

Macfarlan Smith Ltd, Wheatfield Road, Edinburgh, EH11 2QA Tel: 0131-337 2434 Fax: 0131-337 9813 E-mail: msl@macsmith.com

PHARMACEUTICAL CHEMICALS – *continued*

Micropharm Ltd, Gernos, Maesllyn, Llandysul, Dyfed, SA44 5LP Tel: (01239) 858972 Fax: (01239) 710529 E-mail: enquiries@micropharm.co.uk

▶ PCC plc, Rivington House, 82 Great Eastern Street, London, EC2A 3JF Tel: 0207 749 7318 Fax: 0870 130 0261 E-mail: sales@pcc.plc.uk

Pfizer Ltd, Walton Oaks, Dorking Road, Tadworth, Surrey, KT20 7NS Tel: (01304) 616161 Fax: (01304) 656221

R Mason Chemicals Ltd, Hare Law Industrial Estate, Stanley, County Durham, DH9 8UL Tel: (01207) 237373 Fax: (01207) 237373 E-mail: masonchem@cs.com

R W Unwin & Co. Ltd, 10 Prospect Place, Welwyn, Hertfordshire, AL6 9EW Tel: (01438) 716441 Fax: (01438) 716067 E-mail: sales@rwunwin.co.uk

Reckitt Benckiser Healthcare, Dansom Lane, Hull, HU8 7DS Tel: (01482) 326151 Fax: (01482) 582532

Sangers N Ireland Ltd, 2 Marshalls Road, Belfast, BT5 6SR Tel: (028) 9040 1111 Fax: (028) 9040 1240 E-mail: peter.surgenor@sangers.co.uk

Selborne Biological Services Ltd, Goleigh Farm, Selborne, Alton, Hampshire, GU34 3SE Tel: (01420) 511535 Fax: (01420) 511537 E-mail: office@sbsuk.net

Stephar UK Ltd, 3 Hewett Road, Harfreys Industrial Estate, Great Yarmouth, Norfolk, NR31 0NN Tel: (01493) 650069 Fax: (01493) 655479 E-mail: stepher@ukpharm.freeserve.co.uk

Thomson & Joseph Ltd, 119 Plumstead Road, Norwich, NR1 4JT Tel: (01603) 439511 Fax: (01603) 700243 E-mail: enquiries@tandj.co.uk

U C B Celltech Ltd, 208 Bath Road, Slough, SL1 3WE Tel: (01753) 534655 Fax: (01753) 536632

Unichem Ltd, 24 Marsh Green Road, Marsh Barton Trading Estate, Exeter, EX2 8LZ Tel: (01392) 434941 Fax: (01392) 425781

PHARMACEUTICAL COLOURS

Colorcon Ltd, Flagship House Victory Way, Crossways, Dartford, DA2 6QD Tel: (01322) 293000 Fax: (01322) 627200 E-mail: info@colorcon.co.uk

PHARMACEUTICAL CONSULTANTS

I B A Associates, Dorford House, Perks Lane, Prestwood, Great Missenden, Buckinghamshire, HP16 0JD Tel: (01494) 865393 Fax: (01494) 865395 E-mail: miranda@ibaassociates.co.uk

Catalent Pharma Solutions, Lancaster Way, Wingates Industrial Estate, Westhoughton, Bolton, BL5 3XX Tel: (01942) 790000 Fax: (01942) 799799

Data Technology Group Ltd, Unit 3-4 The Long Room, Coppermill Lock, Uxbridge, Middlesex, UB9 6JA Tel: (01895) 829300 Fax: (01895) 820555 E-mail: general.information@datatechnology.co.uk

F T Pharmaceuticle Services, 43 Brookland, Tiptree, Colchester, CO5 0BU Tel: (01621) 819317 Fax: (01621) 819418 E-mail: ftpharmser@aol.com

Harmoni Its Ltd, Parklands Business Park, Forest Road, Denmead, Waterlooville, Hampshire, PO7 6XP Tel: (023) 9226 8133 Fax: (023) 9226 8160 E-mail: wci@wcigroup.com

▶ Holmefjord Regulatory Affairs, A 10 Dane Hill Road, Kennett, Newmarket, Suffolk, CB8 7QX Tel: (01638) 604355 Fax: (01638) 604355 E-mail: elizabeth@holmefjord.co.uk

▶ Pharmitas, 38 Hackford Road, Wicklewood, Wymondham, Norfolk, NR18 9QJ Tel: (01953) 423000 Fax: (01953) 423002 E-mail: jon@pharmitas.co.uk

▶ Viatris, Building 2000, Cambridge Research Park, Beach Road, Waterbeach, Cambridge, CB5 9PD Tel: (01223) 205999

PHARMACEUTICAL DISTRIBUTORS OR AGENTS

A A H Pharmaceuticals Ltd, Sapphire Court, Walsgrave Triangle, Coventry, CV2 2TX Tel: (024) 7643 2000 Fax: (024) 7643 2001 E-mail: info@aah.co.uk

A A H Pharmaceuticals Ltd, 120 Lobley Hill Road, Gateshead, Tyne & Wear, NE8 4YR Tel: (024) 7643 2000 Fax: 0191-461 0175

A A H Pharmaceuticals Ltd, 204 Polmadie Road, Glasgow, G42 0PH Tel: 0141-423 5888 Fax: 0141-423 7662

A A H Pharmaceuticals Ltd, Faringdon Avenue, Romford, RM3 8LG Tel: (01708) 349311 Fax: (01708) 370353

A A H Pharmaceuticals Ltd, Stonefield Way, Ruislip, Middlesex, HA4 0JP Tel: (020) 8841 6010 Fax: (020) 8842 1108

Aah Pharmaceuticals Ltd, Woburn Road, Warrington, WA2 8UH Tel: (01925) 240444 Fax: (01925) 230255

Allergan Ltd, Coronation Road, High Wycombe, Buckinghamshire, HP12 3SH Tel: (01494) 444722 Fax: (01494) 473593

Allmi-Care, Biocity Nottingham, Pennyfoot Street, Nottingham, NG1 1GF Tel: 0115-912 4325 Fax: 0115-912 4326 E-mail: admin@allmi-care.co.uk

Ardern Healthcare Ltd, Pipers Brook Farm, Eastham, Tenbury Wells, Worcestershire, WR15 8NP Tel: (01584) 781777 Fax: (01584) 781788 E-mail: info@ardernhealthcare.com

Astellas Pharma, Lovett House, Lovett Road, Staines, Middlesex, TW18 3AZ Tel: (01784) 419400 Fax: (01784) 419401

Boehringer Ingelheim Ltd, Ellesfield Avenue, Bracknell, Berkshire, RG12 8YS Tel: (01344) 746959 Fax: (01344) 741349 E-mail: vetmedica.uk@boehringer-ingelheim.com

C B S Genios Ltd, Garman Road, Tottenham, London, N17 0QN Tel: (020) 8801 6444 Fax: (020) 8808 3650 E-mail: sales@cbsgenios.co.uk

Cameron Graham, Crosland Road Industrial Estate, Netherton, Huddersfield, HD4 7DQ Tel: (01484) 667822 Fax: (01484) 667817 E-mail: info@cameron-graham.co.uk

Ceuta Healthcare Ltd, Hill House, 41 Richmond Hill, Bournemouth, BH2 6HS Tel: (01202) 780558 Fax: (01202) 780559

Chandis Ltd, 5 Great Union Road, St. Helier, Jersey, JE2 3YA Tel: (01534) 736401 Fax: (01534) 768442 E-mail: admin@chandis.com

Chepstow Pharmaceuticals Ltd, Unit 11 Severn Link Distribution Centre, Newhouse Farm Industrial Es, Mathern, Chepstow, Gwent, NP16 6UN Tel: (01291) 624499 Fax: (01291) 624566

Chugai Pharma Europe Ltd, Mulliner House, Flanders Road, London, W4 1NN Tel: (020) 8987 5600 Fax: (020) 8987 5660

Dowelhurst Ltd, 1 Hawkes Drive, Heathcote Industrial Estate, Warwick, CV34 6LX Tel: (01926) 461600 Fax: (01926) 461626

Elan Pharma Ltd, Six Hills Court, Norton Green Road, Stevenage, Hertfordshire, SG1 2BA Tel: (01438) 742700 Fax: (01438) 765000 E-mail: operations@elan.com

Eldon Laboratories Ltd, 4 Pooley Close, Newcastle upon Tyne, NE5 2TF Tel: 0191-286 0446 Fax: 0191-286 0455 E-mail: orders@eldon-specials.co.uk

▶ Farillon Ltd, Ashton Road, Romford, RM3 8UE Tel: (01708) 379000

Ferring Laboratories Ltd, The Courtyard, Waterside Drive, Slough, SL3 6EZ Tel: (01753) 214800 Fax: (020) 8893 1577 E-mail: contact@ferring.co.uk

Gatehouse Pharmacy, Gatehouse 1 & 2, 25 Victoria Promenade, Northampton, NN1 1HB Tel: (01604) 635311 Fax: (01604) 635311

Interchem (Chemist Wholesale) Ltd, 2-26 Anthony Road, Saltley, Birmingham, B8 3AA Tel: 0121-328 3479 Fax: 0121-328 3479 E-mail: dispharma@aol.com

J R B Enterprises Ltd, Dixies Development, High Street, Ashwell, Baldock, Hertfordshire, SG7 5NT Tel: (01462) 742157 Fax: (01462) 742088 E-mail: johnrbonnett@aol.com

Ernest Jackson & Co. Ltd, High Street, Crediton, Devon, EX17 3AP Tel: (01363) 636000 Fax: (01363) 636063 E-mail: crediton.reception@csplc.com

Kuros Ltd, 38-42 Church Street, Ballymena, County Antrim, BT43 6DF Tel: (028) 2565 6732 Fax: (028) 2565 2798

Lloyds Pharmacy Ltd, Sapphire Court, Walsgrave Triangle, Walsgrave, Coventry, CV2 2TX Tel: (024) 7643 2400 Fax: (024) 7643 2301 E-mail: enquiries@lloydspharmacy.com

M & A Pharmachem Ltd, Allenby Laboratories, Wigan Road, Westhoughton, Bolton, BL5 2AL Tel: (01942) 816184 Fax: (01942) 813937 E-mail: info@mapharmachem.co.uk

Mayne Pharma Euro Finance Co. Ltd, Queensway, Leamington Spa, Warwickshire, CV31 3RW Tel: (01926) 820820 Fax: (01926) 821041

Medirex Opticans, 28-29 Wilcox Close, London, SW8 2UD Tel: (020) 7622 1893 Fax: (020) 7652 0033 E-mail:

▶ Mediwin Pharmaceutical Distributors, Unit 12-13 Martello Enterprise Centre, Courtwick Lane, Wick, Littlehampton, West Sussex, BN17 7PA Tel: (01903) 725628 E-mail: contact@mediwin.co.uk

Merck Sharp & Dohme Ltd, Shotton Lane, Cramlington, Northumberland, NE23 3JU Tel: (01670) 716211 Fax: (01670) 593001 E-mail: sales@merck.com

Miller & Miller, Unit 3 15-17 Roebuck Road, Hainault Business Park, Ilford, Essex, IG6 3TU Tel: (020) 8500 6122 Fax: (020) 8500 6124 E-mail: info@millerandmillerchem.co.uk

Novartis Consumer Health UK Ltd, Novartis Horsham Research Centre, Wimblehurst Road, Horsham, West Sussex, RH12 5AB Tel: (01403) 210211 Fax: (01403) 323919

O T C Direct Ltd, Direct House, East Street, Epsom, Surrey, KT17 1BH Tel: (01372) 740004 Fax: (01372) 721175 E-mail: info@otc-direct-ltd.com

Ono Pharma UK Ltd, Marble Arch Tower, 55 Bryanston Street, London, W1H 7AA Tel: (020) 7258 5300 Fax: (020) 7606 5555

Pharmeurope, 4 Rendezvous Street, Folkestone, Kent, CT20 1EX Tel: (01303) 246611 Fax: (01303) 246677 E-mail: pharmeurope@btconnect.com

Phoenix Healthcare Distribution Ltd, Eddison Road, Hamshall Distribution Park, Coleshill, Birmingham, B46 1DA Tel: (01675) 436500 Fax: (01675) 436502

Sangers of Maidstone Ltd, 24 Orsman Road, London, N1 5QJ Tel: (020) 7739 3411 Fax: (020) 7739 2079

Selborne Biological Services Ltd, Goleigh Farm, Selborne, Alton, Hampshire, GU34 3SE Tel: (01420) 511535 Fax: (01420) 511537 E-mail: office@sbsuk.net

Shilchem Ltd, 217 Hinckley Road, Leicester, LE3 0TG Tel: 0116-251 8779 Fax: 0116-251 8779

Solvay Healthcare Ltd, Mansbridge Road, West End, Southampton, SO18 3JD Tel: (023) 8046 7000 Fax: (023) 8046 5350 E-mail: enquiries.shl@solvay.com

Stiefel Laboratories (UK) Ltd, Holtspur Lane, Wooburn Green, High Wycombe, Buckinghamshire, HP10 0AU Tel: (01628) 524966 Fax: (01628) 810021 E-mail: general@stiefel.co.uk

Tanabe Seiyaku, C P House, 97-107 Uxbridge Road, London, W5 5TL Tel: (020) 8566 0356 Fax: (020) 8566 0376 E-mail: sales@tanabe.co.jp

Three Pears Ltd, 6 Station Road Industrial Estate, Station Road, Rowley Regis, West Midlands, B65 0JY Tel: 0121-559 5351 Fax: 0121-559 5353 E-mail: edunn@btconnect.com

Unichem plc, Kingsway, Fforestfach, Swansea, SA5 4HA Tel: (01792) 561561 Fax: (01792) 589493

Unichem (Warehousing) Ltd, Unichem House, Cox Lane, Chessington, Surrey, KT9 1SN Tel: (020) 8391 2323 Fax: (020) 8974 1707

Vitaline Pharmaceuticals (UK) Ltd, Unit 8, Ridgeway, Drakes Drive, Long Crendon, Aylesbury, Buckinghamshire, HP18 9BF Tel: (01844) 202044 Fax: (01844) 202077 E-mail: info@vitaline.co.uk

Waters, 730-740 Centennial Park, Centennial Way, Elstree, Borehamwood, Hertfordshire, WD6 3SZ Tel: (020) 8238 6100 Fax: (020) 8207 7070 E-mail: jobs@corpworld.co.uk

Welbeck Pharmaceuticals & Hospital Supplies Ltd, 37 Marylebone High Street, London, W1U 4QE Tel: (020) 7486 0254 Fax: (020) 7486 1054

Westminster Pharmaceutical Paramedics Supplies, 17 Duncan Road, Gillingham, Kent, ME7 4LA Tel: (01634) 852728 Fax: (01634) 856410

PHARMACEUTICAL ENGINEERING SERVICES

A E Jones, 11 Mortimer Street, Cleckheaton, West Yorkshire, BD19 5AR Tel: (01274) 851126 Fax: (01274) 870155 E-mail: sales@aejones.co.uk

Graham Debling Precision Engineering Ltd, 3A-4 Booth Place, Margate, Kent, CT9 1QN Tel: (01843) 298804 Fax: (01843) 298858 E-mail: gdebling@gdpe.co.uk

Stekko Co Ltd, 4 Avocet Trading Estate, Richardson Street, High Wycombe, Buckinghamshire, HP11 2SB Tel: (01494) 459332 Fax: (01494) 459313 E-mail: sales@stekko.co.uk

PHARMACEUTICAL EXCIPIENTS

Colorcon Ltd, Flagship House Victory Way, Crossways, Dartford, DA2 6QD Tel: (01322) 293000 Fax: (01322) 627200 E-mail: info@colorcon.co.uk

Mandeville Medicines, Mandeville Road, Aylesbury, Buckinghamshire, HP21 8AL Tel: (01296) 394142 Fax: (01296) 397223 E-mail: manmed@bucksnet.co.uk

PHARMACEUTICAL GOODS, SILICONE RUBBER/NATURAL RUBBER (NR)

Icon Polymer Group Ltd, Thrumpton Lane, Retford, Nottinghamshire, DN22 6HH Tel: (01777) 714300 Fax: (01777) 709739 E-mail: info@iconpolymer.com

Rubber Engineering Services, 4 Gorton Cresent, Windmill Lane Industrial Estate, Denton, Manchester, M34 3RB Tel: 0161-320 9900 Fax: 0161-320 9940 E-mail: sales@rubberengineering.co.uk

PHARMACEUTICAL IMPORT/ EXPORT MERCHANTS OR AGENTS

Alphachem Ltd, 55 Nutfield Rd, Merstham, Redhill, RH1 3ER Tel: (01737) 644836 Fax: (01737) 644500

Babylon Health Ltd, 57 Uxbridge Road, Shepherds Bush, London, W12 8NR Tel: (020) 8749 0037 Fax: (020) 8749 5628 E-mail: merrell@globalnet.co.uk

Durbin (U.K.) Ltd, 180 Northolt Road, South Harrow, Harrow, Middlesex, HA2 0LT Tel: (020) 8869 6500 Fax: (020) 8869 6565 E-mail: durbin@durbin.co.uk

Fieldyork International Ltd, The Manor, 306 -308 Leicester Road, Wigston, Leicestershire, LE18 1JX Tel: 0116-257 1572 Fax: 0116-257 8969

Hermes Medical, Kilburn Park Road, London, NW6 5XD Tel: (020) 7625 8014 Fax: (020) 7487 2986 E-mail: marketing@hermesmed.co.uk

Medical Export Co. Ltd, Woolleys Farm, Naseby, Northampton, NN6 6DP Tel: (01858) 575065 Fax: (01858) 575095 E-mail: medexuk@aol.com

Medimpex UK Ltd, 127 Shirland Road, London, W9 2EP Tel: (020) 7266 2669 Fax: (020) 7266 2702 E-mail: enquiries@medimpexuk.com

Monroe Exports (UK) Ltd, 39 Hartland Drive, Edgware, Middlesex, HA8 8RJ Tel: (020) 8958 9673 Fax: (020) 8357 2810 E-mail: jdhruve@btclick.com

P I F Medical Supplies Ltd, Standard House, Prospect Place, Nottingham, NG7 1RX Tel: 0115-947 4531 Fax: 0115-941 7097 E-mail: sales@pif-medical.co.uk

Pacegrove Ltd, Unit 13 Courtyard Workshops, Bath Street, Market Harborough, Leicestershire, LE16 9EW Tel: (01858) 431381 Fax: (01858) 432426 E-mail: winlab@pacegrove.co.uk

R W Unwin & Co. Ltd, 10 Prospect Place, Welwyn, Hertfordshire, AL6 9EW Tel: (01438) 716441 Fax: (01438) 716067 E-mail: sales@rwunwin.co.uk

William Ransom & Son P.L.C., Alexander House, 40a Wilbury Way, Hitchin, Hertfordshire, SG4 0AP Tel: (01462) 437615 Fax: (01462) 420528 E-mail: info@williamransom.com

S & D Chemicals Ltd, Cunningham House, 19-21 Westfield Lane, Harrow, Middlesex, HA3 9ED Tel: (020) 8907 8822 Fax: (020) 8927 0619 E-mail: sales@sdcldn.com

Stephar UK Ltd, 3 Hewett Road, Harfreys Industrial Estate, Great Yarmouth, Norfolk, NR31 0NN Tel: (01493) 650069 Fax: (01493) 655479 E-mail: stepher@ukpharm.freeserve.co.uk

Vital Pharmaceuticals Ltd, 68 Wellington Court, 55-67 Wellington Road, St. Johns Wood, London, NW8 9TA Tel: (020) 7586 7070 Fax: (020) 7586 5757 E-mail: vitalpharm@aol.com

PHARMACEUTICAL INDUSTRY PUMPS

Alfa Laval Ltd, Castle Vale Industrial Estate, Maybrook Road, Minworth, Sutton Coldfield, West Midlands, B76 1AL Tel: 0121-351 3131 Fax: 0121-351 7888 E-mail: admin@alfalaval.com

PHARMACEUTICAL INTERMEDIATES

3M Health Care Ltd, 3M House, Morley Street, Loughborough, Leicestershire, LE11 1EP Tel: (01509) 611611 Fax: (01509) 613061 E-mail: jsmith123@mmm.com

Genzyme Vehicle Leasing Ltd, Hollands Road, Haverhill, Suffolk, CB9 8PU Tel: (01440) 703522 Fax: (01440) 716269

Peboc Division of Eastman Co. (UK) Ltd, Industrial Estate, Llangefni, Gwynedd, LL77 7YQ Tel: (01248) 750724 Fax: (01248) 723890

Phoenix (Wirral) Ltd, Unit 28-34, Thursby Road, Bromborough, Wirral, Merseyside, CH62 3PW Tel: 0151-334 9044 Fax: 0151-334 9045 E-mail: chris@phoenixchem.com

Witton Chemical Co. Ltd, Southgate Avenue, Mildenhall, Bury St. Edmunds, Suffolk, IP28 7AT Tel: (01638) 716001 Fax: (01638) 717658 E-mail: sales@witton.com

PHARMACEUTICAL LABORATORY EQUIPMENT

G. Farley & Sons Ltd, Unit 6 Plaza Business Centre, Stockingswater Lane, Enfield, Middlesex, EN3 7PH Tel: (020) 8804 1367 Fax: (020) 8804 8821 E-mail: sales@g-farleyandsons.co.uk

PHARMACEUTICAL MANUFRS/ CONTRACT MANUFACTURING

Abbott Laboratories Ltd, North Road, Queenborough, Kent, ME11 5EL Tel: (01795) 580099 Fax: (01795) 593335

Aeropak Chemical Products, Viking Road, Great Yarmouth, Norfolk, NR31 0NU Tel: (01493) 660820 Fax: (01493) 660848

Antigen Pharmaceuticals UK, NLA Tower, 12-16 Addiscombe Road, Croydon, CR0 0XT Tel: (020) 8649 8500 Fax: (020) 8686 0807 E-mail: info@gshieldplc.com

Arc Pharmacare (2006) Ltd, PO Box 2146, Bolton, BL6 9AY Tel: (01204) 362236 Fax: (01204) 362239 E-mail: sales@arc-ltd.uk.com

Astellas Pharma, Lovett House, Lovett Road, Staines, Middlesex, TW18 3AZ Tel: (01784) 419400 Fax: (01784) 419401

▶ Astrazeneca, 600 Capability Green, Luton, LU1 3LU Tel: (01582) 836000 Fax: (01582) 835800

Aventis Behring Ltd, Centeon House, Market Place, Haywards Heath, West Sussex, RH16 1DB Tel: (01444) 447400 Fax: (01444) 447401

Bell Sons & Co Druggists Ltd, Slaidburn CR, Southport, Merseyside, PR9 9YF Tel: 0151-422 1200 Fax: 0151-422 1211 E-mail: sales@bells-healthcare.com

PHARMACEUTICAL MANUFRS/ CONTRACT MANUFACTURING –

continued

Bell Sons & Co. (Druggists) Ltd, Tanhouse Lane, Widnes, Cheshire, WA8 0RD Tel: 0151-422 1200 Fax: 0151-422 1211 E-mail: sales@bells-healthcare.com

Biogen Idec, Thames House, Foundation Park, Maidenhead, Berkshire, SL6 3UD Tel: (01628) 823200 Fax: (01628) 501010 E-mail: ukrecpt@biogenidec.com

Biorex Laboratories Ltd, 2 Crossfield Chambers, Gladbeck Way, Enfield, Middlesex, EN2 7HT Tel: (020) 8366 9301 Fax: (020) 8357 4627 E-mail: sales@biorex.co.uk

Boc Edwards Pharmaceutical Systems, P O Box 7, Huntly, Aberdeenshire, AB54 4SY Tel: (01542) 870633 Fax: (01542) 870222 E-mail: paul.vadler1@btinternet.com

Boots Contract Manufacturing, P O Box 429, Nottingham, NG90 2PR Tel: 0115-968 6390

Bristol-Myers Squibb Trustees Ltd, Uxbridge Business Park, Sanderson Road, Uxbridge, Middlesex, UB8 1DH Tel: (01895) 523000 Fax: (01895) 523010

C I Systems Ltd, Brunel Road, Churchfields, Salisbury, SP2 7PX Tel: (01722) 336938 Fax: (01722) 323222 E-mail: sales@cielec.com

Cam, East Carlton Hall, East Carlton Park, East Carlton, Market Harborough, Leicestershire, LE16 8YF Tel: (01536) 771775 Fax: (01536) 771832

Cardinal Health Ltd, Sedge Close, Headway, Great Oakley, Corby, Northamptonshire, NN18 8HS Tel: (01536) 461146 Fax: (01536) 461011

Cardinal Healthcare Ltd, Frankland Road, Blagrove, Swindon, SN5 8RU Tel: (0870) 6011011 Fax: (01793) 613394

Chugai Pharma Europe Ltd, Mulliner House, Flanders Road, London, W4 1NN Tel: (020) 8987 5600 Fax: (020) 8987 5660

Church & Dwight (U K) Ltd, Wear Bay Road, Folkestone, Kent, CT19 6PG Tel: (01303) 850661 Fax: (01303) 858701 E-mail: sales@carterwallace.co.uk

Cobra Therapeutics Ltd, The Science Park, University of Keele, Keele, Newcastle, Staffordshire, ST5 5SP Tel: (01782) 714181 Fax: (01782) 714168

Connected Tote Systems Ltd, 129 Sydenham Rd, Spark Brooke, Birmingham, B11 1DG Tel: 0121-753 3555 Fax: 0121-771 0906 E-mail: mail@toteuk.force9.co.uk

▶ Cosmetica Manufacturing Ltd, Faraday Close, Eastbourne, East Sussex, BN22 9BH Tel: (01323) 506055 Fax: (01323) 520681 E-mail: sales@cosmetica.eu.com

D D D Ltd, 94 Rickmansworth Road, Watford, WD18 7JJ Tel: (01923) 229251 Fax: (01923) 220728

D D S A Pharmuceuticals Ltd, 310 Old Brompton Road, London, SW5 9JQ Tel: (020) 7373 7884 Fax: (020) 7370 4321

Daiichi Sankyo UK Ltd, Sankyo House, Repton Place, Amersham, Buckinghamshire, HP7 9LP Tel: (01494) 766866 Fax: (01494) 766557 E-mail: info@sankyo.co.uk

Dermal Laboratories Ltd, Singer Way, Woburn Road Industrial Estate, Kempston, Bedford, MK42 7AG Tel: (01234) 841555 Fax: (01234) 840498 E-mail: info@dermal.co.uk

Dermal Laboratories Ltd, Tatmore Place, Preston Road, Gosmore, Hitchin, Hertfordshire, SG4 7QR Tel: (01462) 458866 Fax: (01462) 420565

▶ Efamol Ltd, Unit 14, Mole Business Park, Randalls Road, Leatherhead, Surrey, KT22 7BA Tel: (01372) 379828 Fax: (01372) 376599 E-mail: vitamins@wassen.com

Elan Pharma Ltd, Six Hills Court, Norton Green Road, Stevenage, Hertfordshire, SG1 2BA Tel: (01438) 742700 Fax: (01438) 765000 E-mail: operations@elan.com

Eldon Laboratories Ltd, 4 Pooley Close, Newcastle upon Tyne, NE5 2TF Tel: 0191-286 0446 Fax: 0191-286 0455 E-mail: orders@eldon-specials.co.uk

Eli Lilly Holdings Ltd, Kingsclere Road, Basingstoke, Hampshire, RG21 6XA Tel: (01256) 315000 Fax: (01256) 315858

▶ Excel Installations, Little Hyde Farm, Little Hyde Lane, Ingatestone, Essex, CM4 0DU Tel: (01277) 356438 Fax: (01277) 356441

Fenton Pharmaceuticals Ltd, 4J Portman Mansions, Chiltern Street, London, W1U 6NS Tel: (020) 7224 1388 Fax: (020) 7486 7258

▶ Ferndale Pharmaceutical Ltd, Unit 605, Thorp Arch Trading Estate, Thorp Arch, Wetherby, West Yorkshire, LS23 7BJ Tel: (01937) 541122 Fax: (01937) 849682 E-mail: info@ferndalepharma.co.uk

G E Healthcare, Amersham Place, Amersham, Buckinghamshire, HP7 9NA Tel: (01494) 544000 Fax: (01494) 542266

G R Lane Health Products Ltd, Sisson Road, Gloucester, GL2 0GR Tel: (01452) 524012 Fax: (01452) 300105 E-mail: export@laneshealth.com

Galen Herbal Supplies Ltd, Unit 17 St Davids Industrial, Pengam, Blackwood, Gwent, NP12 3SW Tel: (01443) 820024 Fax: (01443) 820037 E-mail: sales@galenherbalsupplies.com

Geistlich Sons Ltd, Long Lane, Chester, CH2 2PF Tel: (01244) 347534 Fax: (01244) 319327 E-mail: sales@geistlich.co.uk

▶ Gilead Sciences Ltd, Granta Park, Abington, Cambridge, CB21 6GT Tel: (01223) 897300 Fax: (01223) 897282

Glaxo Smith Klein Leisure Club, Oldfield Lane North, Greenford, Middlesex, UB6 8QD Tel: (020) 8966 2280 Fax: (020) 8966 4499

Glaxo Smith Kline (UK) Ltd, Stockley Park West, Uxbridge, Middlesex, UB11 1BT Tel: (020) 8990 9000 Fax: (020) 8990 4321

Glaxosmithkline, Park Road, Ware, Hertfordshire, SG12 0DP Tel: (01920) 469469 Fax: (01920) 463172

Halewood Chemicals Group Ltd, Horton Road, Stanwell Moor, Staines, Middlesex, TW19 6BJ Tel: (01753) 682402 Fax: (01753) 685440 E-mail: halewood@lineone.net

Harley Street Supplies Ltd, 29 Westfields Aveue, Barnes, London, SW13 0AT Tel: (020) 8876 2113 E-mail: sales@harveystreetsupplies.com

I P S, 41 Central Avenue, West Molesey, Surrey, KT8 2QZ Tel: (020) 8481 9720 Fax: (020) 8481 9729

I V A X Pharmaceutical UK Ltd, Whitehouse Vale, Aston La North, Runcorn, Cheshire, WA7 3FA Tel: (01928) 707800 Fax: (01928) 707790

Icn Pharmaceuticals Ltd, Cedarwood Crockford Lane, Chineham Business Park, Chineham, Basingstoke, Hampshire, RG24 8WD Tel: (01256) 707744 Fax: (01256) 707334 E-mail: sales@valeant.com

J L Bragg Ipswich Ltd, 34 Boss Hall Road, Ipswich, IP1 5BN Tel: (01473) 748345 Fax: (01473) 749889 E-mail: bragg@charcoal.uk.com

Ernest Jackson & Co. Ltd, High Street, Crediton, Devon, EX17 3AP Tel: (01363) 636000 Fax: (01363) 636063 E-mail: crediton.reception@csplc.com

Janssen Animal Health, PO Box 79, High Wycombe, Buckinghamshire, HP12 4EG Tel: (01494) 567555 Fax: (01494) 567556 E-mail: ahealth@jacgb.jnj.com

Karib Kemi-Pharm Ltd, 63-65 Imperial Way, Croydon, CR0 4RR Tel: (020) 8688 5550 Fax: (020) 8688 6119

▶ Kiel Pharma Ltd, 95b Belfast Road, Carrickfergus, County Antrim, BT38 8BX Tel: (028) 9335 0880 Fax: (028) 9335 0890 E-mail: info@keilpharma.co.uk

▶ Korsch Pharmaceutical Distributors, Stoney Bottom, Grayshott, Hindhead, Surrey, GU26 6HB Tel: (01865) 400424 Fax: (01428) 608728 E-mail: sales@horsch.de

Laboratories For Applied Biology Ltd, 91 Amhurst Park, London, N16 5DR Tel: (020) 8800 2252 Fax: (020) 8809 6884 E-mail: labltd@dircon.co.uk

Laleham Healthcare Ltd, Sycamore Park, Mill Lane, Alton, Hampshire, GU34 2PR Tel: (01420) 566500 Fax: (01420) 566566

Leo Pharma, Longwick Road, Princes Risborough, Buckinghamshire, HP27 9RR Tel: (01844) 347333 Fax: (01844) 342278 E-mail: enquiries@leo-pharma.com

Life Style, 1 Exeter Street, North Tawton, Devon, EX20 2HB Tel: (01837) 82824 Fax: (01837) 82824

Lundbeck Pharmaceuticals Ltd, Seal Sands, Middlesbrough, Cleveland, TS2 1UB Tel: (01642) 546574 Fax: (01642) 546085

Mason's Products, 2 Schofield Street, Littleborough, Lancashire, OL15 0JS Tel: (01706) 379817 Fax: (01706) 379817 E-mail: sales@dogoil.co.uk

Medico-Biological Laboratories Ltd, Kingsend House, 44 Kingsend, Ruislip, Middlesex, HA4 7DA Tel: (01895) 632724 Fax: (01895) 622736

Merc Serono, Bedfont Cross, Bedfont, Feltham, Middlesex, TW14 8NX Tel: (01895) 452200 Fax: (01895) 420605 E-mail: info@merckpharma.co.uk

Merck Sharp & Dohme Ltd, Shotton Lane, Cramlington, Northumberland, NE23 3JU Tel: (01670) 716211 Fax: (01670) 593001 E-mail: sales@merck.com

Owen Mumford Holdings Ltd, Brook Hill, Woodstock, Woodstock, Oxfordshire, OX20 1TU Tel: (01993) 812021 Fax: (01993) 813466 E-mail: info@owenmumford.co.uk

Napp Pharmaceutical Group Ltd, Science Park, Milton Road, Cambridge, CB4 0GW Tel: (01223) 424444 Fax: (01223) 424441 E-mail: vacancies@napp.co.uk

Norgine Ltd, Chaplain House, Widewater Place, Moorhall Road, Uxbridge, Middlesex, UB9 6NS Tel: (01895) 826600 Fax: (01895) 825865 E-mail: enquiries@norgine.com

Novartis Consumer Health UK Ltd, Novartis Horsham Research Centre, Wimblehurst Road, Horsham, West Sussex, RH12 5AB Tel: (01403) 210211 Fax: (01403) 323919

Novartis Pharmaceuticals (UK) Ltd, Frimley Business Park, Frimley, Camberley, Surrey, GU16 7SR Tel: (01276) 691676 Fax: (01276) 692508

Novo Nordisk Holding Ltd, Novo Nordisk House, Broadfield Park, Crawley, West Sussex, RH11 9RT Tel: (01293) 613555 Fax: (01293) 613535 E-mail: sales@novonordisk.co.uk

Npil Pharmaceuticals UK Ltd, Whalton Road, Morpeth, Northumberland, NE61 3YA Tel: (01670) 562400 Fax: (01670) 562401

Organon Laboratories Ltd, 23 Science Park, Milton Road, Cambridge, CB4 0FL Tel: (01223) 432700 Fax: (01223) 424368 E-mail: sales@organon.co.uk

Pacegrove Ltd, Unit 13 Courtyard Workshops, Bath Street, Market Harborough, Leicestershire, LE16 9EW Tel: (01858) 431381 Fax: (01858) 432426 E-mail: winlab@pacegrove.co.uk

Parexel International, The Quays, 101- 125 Oxford Road, Uxbridge, Middlesex, UB8 1LZ Tel: (01895) 238000 Fax: (01895) 238494

Peboc Division of Eastman Co. (UK) Ltd, Industrial Estate, Llangefni, Gwynedd, LL77 7YQ Tel: (01248) 750724 Fax: (01248) 723890

Penn Pharmaceuticals Services Ltd, Unit 23 & 24, Tafarnaubach Industrial Estate, Tafarnaubach, Tredegar, Gwent, NP22 3AA Tel: (01495) 711222 Fax: (01495) 711225 E-mail: penn@pennpharm.co.uk

Pfizer Ltd, Walton Oaks, Dorking Road, Tadworth, Surrey, KT20 7NS Tel: (01304) 616161 Fax: (01304) 656221

▶ Pharmaceutical Development & Manufacturing Services (PDMS) Ltd, 22 Seagoe Industrial Estate, Craigavon, County Armagh, BT63 5QD Tel: (028) 3836 3363 Fax: (028) 3836 3300 E-mail: info@pdms-almac.com

Pharmaserve Ltd, Wynne Avenue, Clifton, Swinton, Manchester, M27 8FF Tel: 0161-794 7423 Fax: 0161-794 0328 E-mail: sales@pharmaserveltd.co.uk

J. Pickles Healthcare, Beech Ho, 62 High St, Knaresborough, N. Yorkshire, HG5 0EA Tel: (01423) 867314 Fax: (01423) 869177 E-mail: enquiries@jpickleshealthcare.com

Pound International Ltd, 109 Baker Street, London, W1U 6RP Tel: (020) 7935 3735 Fax: (020) 7224 3734 E-mail: pound@dial.pipex.com

▶ Protherics plc, 5 Ludgate Hill, London, EC4M 7AA Tel: (020) 7246 9950

Protherics UK Ltd, Blaenwaun, Ffostrasol, Llandysul, Dyfed, SA44 5JT Tel: (01239) 851122 Fax: (01239) 858800

Ranbaxy UK Ltd, 3Rd Floor CP House, 97/107 Uxbridge Road, Ealing, London, W5 5TL Tel: (020) 8280 1600 Fax: (020) 8280 1617

William Ransom & Son P.L.C., Alexander House, 40a Wilbury Way, Hitchin, Hertfordshire, SG4 0AP Tel: (01462) 437615 Fax: (01462) 420528 E-mail: info@williamransom.com

Raught Ltd, 117 The Drive, Ilford, Essex, IG1 3JE Tel: (020) 8554 9921 Fax: (020) 8554 8337 E-mail: raughtltd@aol.com

Dr Reddy's Laboratories UK Ltd, Riverview Road, Beverley, North Humberside, HU17 0LD Tel: (01482) 860228 Fax: (01482) 872042

Charles River UK Ltd, Manston Road, Margate, Kent, CT9 4LT Tel: (01843) 823388 Fax: (01843) 823497 E-mail: enquiries@uk.criver.com

Rosemont Pharmaceuticals Ltd, Braithwaite St, York Dale Industrial Estate, Leeds, LS11 9XE Tel: 0113-244 1400 Fax: 0113-245 3567 E-mail: desk@rosepharma.com

▶ Rxpharma, 17 Bury Lane, Withnell, Chorley, Lancashire, PR6 8RX Tel: (01254) 832321 Fax: (01254) 832322 E-mail: info@rxpharma.co.uk

S T D Pharmaceutical Products Ltd, Plough Lane, Hereford, HR4 0EL Tel: (01432) 373555 Fax: (01432) 371314 E-mail: enquries@stdpharm.co.uk

Sanofi Synthelabo, Edgefield Avenue, Newcastle upon Tyne, NE3 3TT Tel: 0191-285 3931 Fax: 0191-284 9175

Sara Lee Household & Body Care UK Ltd, 225 Bath Road, Slough, SL1 4AU Tel: (01753) 523971 Fax: (01753) 570340 E-mail: info@saralee.co.uk

Shield Medicare Ltd, Hurlands Business Park, 5 Hurlands Close, Farnham, Surrey, GU9 9JE Tel: (01252) 717616 Fax: (01252) 715269 E-mail: info@shieldmedicare.com

Sonet Prebbles Ltd, St. John'S Road, Bootle, Merseyside, L20 8BH Tel: 0151-922 8606 Fax: 0151-944 1048

Tanabe Seiyaku, C P House, 97-107 Uxbridge Road, London, W5 5TL Tel: (020) 8566 0356 Fax: (020) 8566 0376 E-mail: sales@tanabe.co.jp

Teva UK, Unit 3 Leeds Business Park, 18 Bruntcliffe Way, Morley, Leeds, LS27 0JG Tel: 0113-238 0099 Fax: 0113-201 3936 E-mail: morleyreception@tevauk.co.uk

Teva UK Ltd, Albert Basin, Ivax Quays, Albert Basin, London, E16 2QJ Tel: (0870) 5020304 Fax: (0870) 5323334 E-mail: richard.daniel@ivax.co.uk

Thornton & Ross Ltd, Linthwaite, Huddersfield, HD7 5QH Tel: (01484) 842217 Fax: (01484) 847301 E-mail: mail@thorntonross.com

▶ Trinity Sales & Marketing Ltd, Harwell Innovation Centre, 173 Curie Avenue, Harwell Intnl Business Centre, Didcot, Oxfordshire, OX11 0QG Tel: (01235) 838590 Fax: (01235) 838591 E-mail: info@trinitysalesandmarketing.co.uk

Venture Health Care Ltd, Aston Grange, Oaker, Matlock, Derbyshire, DE4 2JJ Tel: (01629) 733860

▶ Walters Houghton, St. Ives Way, Factory Road, Sandycroft, Deeside, Clwyd, CH5 2QS Tel: (01352) 733882 Fax: (01352) 733822 E-mail: info@waltershoughton.com

Waters, 730-740 Centennial Park, Centennial Way, Elstree, Borehamwood, Hertfordshire, WD6 3SZ Tel: (020) 8238 6100 Fax: (020) 8207 7070 E-mail: jobs@corpworld.co.uk

Westminster Pharmaceutical Paramedics Supplies, 17 Duncan Road, Gillingham, Kent, ME7 4LA Tel: (01634) 852728 Fax: (01634) 856410

Workchadt UK Ltd, Ash Road North, Wrexham Industrial Estate, Wrexham, Clwyd, LL13 9UF Tel: (01978) 661261 Fax: (01978) 660130 E-mail: mail@wockhardtuk.co.uk

Wyeth Laboratories, Bath Road, Taplow, Maidenhead, Berkshire, SL6 0AP Tel: (01628) 604377 Fax: (01628) 666368

PHARMACEUTICAL MATERIAL HANDLING SYSTEMS

Harbruc Engineering Co., Charlwoods Road, East Grinstead, West Sussex, RH19 2HU Tel: (01342) 315775 Fax: (01342) 327298 E-mail: sales@harbruc.com

PHARMACEUTICAL METAL DETECTORS

Mettler Toledo Safeline Ltd, Montford Street, Salford, M50 2XD Tel: 0161-848 8636 Fax: 0161-848 8595

PHARMACEUTICAL MOULDINGS

Sovrin Plastics Ltd, Stirling Road, Slough, SL1 4ST Tel: (01753) 825155 Fax: (01753) 654923 E-mail: sales@sovrin.com

PHARMACEUTICAL PACKAGING

▶ Amcor Flexibles Winterbourne, Winterbourne Road, Stoke Gifford, Bristol, BS34 6PT Tel: 0117-987 2000 Fax: 0117-987 2002 E-mail: healthcare_info@amcor-flexibles.com

Britton Gelplas Ltd, Venture House, 5th Avenue, Letchworth Garden City, Herts, SG6 1JT Tel: (01462) 480808 Fax: (01462) 481398 E-mail: roger.young@britton-group.com

E M T Healhcare Ltd, 4 Padge Road, Boulevard Industrial Park, Beeston, Nottingham, NG9 2JR Tel: 0115-849 7700 Fax: 0115-849 7701 E-mail: info@emthealthcare.com

PHARMACEUTICAL PACKAGING CARTON/CONTAINER MANUFRS

Boxes G H Ltd, Palatine Mill, Meadow Street, Great Harwood, Blackburn, BB6 7EJ Tel: (01254) 888151 Fax: (01254) 889569 E-mail: carton@boxesgh.co.uk

Cope Allman Plastic Packaging Ltd, Railway Triangle, Walton Road, Portsmouth, PO6 1TS Tel: (023) 9237 0102 Fax: (023) 9238 0314 E-mail: bridget.lambert@copeallman.com

PHARMACEUTICAL PACKAGING MACHINE TOOLING

Pharmaceutical Machine Sales Ltd, Unit 1, 106 Downs Street, West Molesey, Surrey, KT8 2TA Tel: (020) 8941 2818 Fax: (020) 8941 8625 E-mail: pms@pmsuk.com

PHARMACEUTICAL PACKAGING MACHINERY

Essential Medical, 2 Lynfield Road, Lichfield, Staffordshire, WS13 7BS Tel: (01543) 301726 Fax: (01543) 301725

PHARMACEUTICAL PACKAGING SERVICES

Brecon Pharmaceuticals Ltd, Pharos House Wye Valley Business Park, Brecon Road, Hay-on-Wye, Hereford, HR3 5PG Tel: (01497) 820829 Fax: (01497) 820050 E-mail: admin@brecon-pharm.co.uk

Cardinal Health Ltd, Sedge Close, Headway, Great Oakley, Corby, Northamptonshire, NN18 8HS Tel: (01536) 461146 Fax: (01536) 461011

Pharmaserve Ltd, Wynne Avenue, Clifton, Swinton, Manchester, M27 8FF Tel: 0161-794 7423 Fax: 0161-794 0328 E-mail: sales@pharmaserveltd.co.uk

PHARMACEUTICAL PLANT CONTRACTORS OR DESIGNERS

Atkins Consultants Ltd, Bank Chambers, Faulkner Street, Manchester, M1 4EH Tel: 0161-245 3400 Fax: 0161-245 3500 E-mail: jon.baker@atkinsglobal.com

Maelor Pharmaceuticals Ltd, Riversdale, Cae Gwilym Road, Newbridge, Wrexham, Clwyd, LL14 3JG Tel: (01978) 810153 Fax: (01978) 810169 E-mail: enquiries@maelor.plc.uk

Projen plc, Winnington Avenue, Northwich, Cheshire, CW8 4EE Tel: (01606) 871111 Fax: (01606) 871133 E-mail: mailbox@projen.co.uk

PHARMACEUTICAL PRODUCTION PLANT AND EQUIPMENT MANUFRS

Aeromatic Fielder Ltd, PO Box 15, Eastleigh, Hampshire, SO53 4ZD Tel: (023) 8026 7131 Fax: (023) 8025 3381 E-mail: sales-uk@aeromatic-fielder.com
Astrazeneca After 5pm, Alderley Park, Macclesfield, Cheshire, SK10 4TF Tel: (01625) 582828 Fax: (01625) 585022 E-mail: julia.ainsworth@astrazeneca.com
Ayton Equipment Ltd, Station Yard, Station Road, Stokesley, Middlesbrough, Cleveland, TS9 7AB Tel: (01642) 711455 Fax: (01642) 710100 E-mail: marketing@ayton.com
Bramigk & Co. Ltd, Chelmsford, CM2 7WG Tel: (01245) 477616 Fax: (01245) 477498 E-mail: info@bramigk.co.uk
Buck Systems, 257 Wharfdale Road, Birmingham, B11 2DP Tel: 0121-765 5800 Fax: 0121-765 5802 E-mail: sales@buck-systems.com
Caleva Process Solutions Ltd, Butts Pond Industrial Estate, Sturminster Newton, Dorset, DT10 1AZ Tel: (01258) 471122 Fax: (01258) 471133 E-mail: info@caleva.co.uk
Coates Engineering International Ltd, Millfold, Whitworth, Rochdale, Lancashire, OL12 8DN Tel: (01706) 852122 Fax: (01706) 853629 E-mail: info@bchltd.com
Europrocessing Ltd, Euro Vent Ltd, Govan Road Fenton Industrial, Fenton Industrial Estate, Stoke-on-Trent, ST4 2RS Tel: (01782) 744242 Fax: (01782) 744475 E-mail: sales@eurovent.com
Hickey & Co. Ltd, Slade Green Road, Erith, Kent, DA8 2HX Tel: (01322) 347004 Fax: (01322) 335733 E-mail: sales@hickey.co.uk
Hiley Engineering (Halifax) Co. Ltd, Station Road, Shay Lane, Holmfield, Halifax, West Yorkshire, HX2 9AY Tel: (01422) 248327 Fax: (01422) 240610 E-mail: hileyeng@hileyeng.co.uk
Lonza Biologics plc, Bath Road, Slough, SL1 4DX Tel: (01753) 777000 Fax: (01753) 777001
Perry Process Equipment Ltd, Station Road, Aycliffe Industrial Park, Newton Aycliffe, County Durham, DL5 6EQ Tel: (01325) 315111 Fax: (01325) 301496 E-mail: info@perryprocess.co.uk
R B Plant Construction Ltd, The Square, Lenham, Maidstone, Kent, ME17 2PG Tel: (01622) 858387 Fax: (01622) 858920 E-mail: mail@rb-plant.co.uk
Reliagraphics Engineering, 11 Bilton Road, Erith, Kent, DA8 2AN Tel: (01322) 342375 Fax: (01322) 338916 E-mail: enquires@reliagraphicsengineering.co.uk
Romaco Holdings UK Ltd, Lake View Court, Ermine Business Park, Huntingdon, Cambridgeshire, PE29 6WD Tel: (01480) 435050 Fax: (01480) 414220 E-mail: uk@romaco.com
▶ Saffron Scientific Equipment Ltd, GSPK Technology Park, Manse Lane, Knaresborough, North Yorkshire, HG5 8LF Tel: (01423) 796138 Fax: (01423) 798268 E-mail: sales@saffron-uk.com

PHARMACEUTICAL PRODUCTION PLANT AND EQUIPMENT, USED

Bell Sons & Co. (Druggists) Ltd, Tanhouse Lane, Widnes, Cheshire, WA8 0RD Tel: 0151-422 1200 Fax: 0151-422 1211 E-mail: sales@bells-healthcare.com
▶ Colco Scientific Enterprises Ltd, 6 Peatmore Close, Pyrford, Woking, Surrey, GU22 8TQ Tel: (01932) 349141 E-mail: sales@colco.co.uk

PHARMACEUTICAL RAW MATERIALS

Kent Pharmaceuticals Ltd, Wotton Road, Ashford, Kent, TN23 6LL Tel: (01233) 638614 Fax: (01233) 646899 E-mail: sales@kentpharm.co.uk
Norbrook Exports Ltd, Camlough Road, Newry, County Down, BT35 6JP Tel: (028) 3026 4435 Fax: (028) 3025 1141 E-mail: enquiries@norbrook.co.uk

PHARMACEUTICAL RESEARCH/ TESTING SERVICES

Bodycoat Materials Testing Ltd, Lochend Industrial Estate, Queen Anne Drive, Newbridge, Midlothian, EH28 8PL Tel: 0131-333 4360 Fax: 0131-333 5135 E-mail: sales@bodycote.com
Bodycote Radiography, 1 Blackbrook Valley Industrial Estate, Narrowboat Way, Dudley, West Midlands, DY2 0XQ Tel: (01384) 455880 Fax: (01384) 457250 E-mail: dudley@bodycote-mt.com
Bristol-Myers Squibb Pharmaceuticals, Reeds Lane, Wirral, Merseyside, CH46 1QW Tel: 0151-552 1500 Fax: 0151-552 1615 E-mail: office@bms.com
C S P, Astra House, Christy Close, Southfields Business Park, Basildon, Essex, SS15 6TQ Tel: (01268) 493377 Fax: (01268) 493399 E-mail: sales@cspuk.co.uk
Cambridge Clinical Research, Tunbridge Court, Tunbridge Lane, Bottisham, Cambridge, CB5 9DU Tel: (01223) 811882 Fax: (01223) 813539 E-mail: marrowsmith@cambridge-clinical-research.co.uk
Cardinal Health Ltd, Sedge Close, Headway, Great Oakley, Corby, Northamptonshire, NN18 8HS Tel: (01536) 461146 Fax: (01536) 461011
Catalent Pharma Solutions, Lancaster Way, Wingates Industrial Estate, Westhoughton, Bolton, BL5 3XX Tel: (01942) 790000 Fax: (01942) 799799
F T Pharmaceuticle Services, 43 Brookland, Tiptree, Colchester, CO5 0BU Tel: (01621) 819317 Fax: (01621) 819418 E-mail: ftpharmser@aol.com
G B Caleva Ltd, Butts Pond Industrial Estate, Sturminster Newton, Dorset, DT10 1AZ Tel: (01258) 472742 Fax: (01258) 473569 E-mail: sales@gb-caleva.co.uk
Glaxo Smith Klein Leisure Club, Oldfield Lane North, Greenford, Middlesex, UB6 8QD Tel: (020) 8966 2280 Fax: (020) 8966 4499
Herd Mundy Richardson Ltd, Oak House Bredbury Parkway, Ashton Road, Bredbury Park Industrial Estate, Stockport, Cheshire, SK6 2QN Tel: 0161-406 6767 Fax: 0161-494 8400 E-mail: sue.richardson@hmrlabs.com
L G C Promochem Ltd, Queens Road, Teddington, Middlesex, TW11 0LY Tel: (020) 8943 8480 Fax: (020) 8943 7554 E-mail: uksales@lgcpromochem.com
Medtap International, 20 Bloomsbury Square, London, WC1A 2NS Tel: (020) 7299 4550 Fax: (020) 7299 4555
Simbec Research Ltd, Clinical Research Organisation, Merthyr Tydfil Industrial Park, Merthyr Tydfil, Mid Glamorgan, CF48 4DR Tel: (01443) 690977 Fax: (01443) 692499 E-mail: alan.woodward@simbec.co.uk
Xenova, 310 Science Park, Milton Road, Cambridge, CB4 0WG Tel: (01223) 423413 Fax: (01223) 423458 E-mail: sales@xenova.co.uk

PHARMACEUTICAL SALTS

New Cheshire Salt Works Ltd, Wincham Lane, Wincham, Northwich, Cheshire, CW9 6DD Tel: (01606) 42361 Fax: (01606) 48333 E-mail: general@ncsw.co.uk

PHARMACY DISPENSING LABELS

BP Self Adhesive Labels Ltd, Cypress Drive, St Mellons Business Park, St. Mellons, Cardiff, CF3 0EG Tel: (029) 2077 8500 Fax: (029) 2077 8388 E-mail: hello@bplabels.co.uk

PHENOLIC MATERIALS/ PRODUCTS/COMPONENTS

Glass Bond N W Ltd, Westside Industrial Estate, Jackson Street, St. Helens, Merseyside, WA9 3AT Tel: (01744) 730334 Fax: (01744) 451661 E-mail: sales@glassbond.co.uk
Hepworth Composites, Pollard Moor, Padiham, Burnley, Lancashire, BB12 7JR Tel: (01282) 683444 Fax: (01282) 683445 E-mail: ann.booth@hepworth.co.uk

PHOSPHATING CHEMICAL PRODUCTS

Stowlin Ltd, Radnor Road, Wigston, Leicestershire, LE18 4XY Tel: 0116-278 5373 Fax: 0116-277 2616E-mail: kate@stowlin.com

PHOSPHATING METAL TREATMENT SERVICES TO THE TRADE

Acorn Services, Unit 3 Access Point, Willenhall Industrial Centre, Bloxwich, Walsall, WS3 2XN Tel: (01922) 491676 Fax: (01922) 710305 E-mail: jane@acornservices.wannado.co.uk
Alkemi M F Technologies, Clwyd Close, Manor Lane, Hawarden, Deeside, Clwyd, CH5 3PZ Tel: (01244) 536299 Fax: (01244) 520363 E-mail: simonn@alkemimetalfinishing.co.uk
Clark Electro-Plating (Wrexham) Ltd, The Old Foundry, Hill Street, Rhostyllen, Wrexham, Clwyd, LL14 4AT Tel: (01978) 355803 Fax: (01978) 291321
Foleshill Metal Finishing Ltd, 13 Bayton Road, Exhall, Coventry, CV7 9EJ Tel: (024) 7636 2960 Fax: (024) 7636 5876 E-mail: queries@foleshill.co.uk

PHOSPHOR BRONZE

P & P Non Ferrous (Stockists) Ltd, 47B Premier Trading Estate, The Leys, Brierley Hill, West Midlands, DY5 3UP Tel: (01384) 482888 Fax: (01384) 482088 E-mail: sales@ppnonferrous.co.uk

PHOSPHOR BRONZE BEARINGS

L G Prout & Sons Ltd, Swann Street, Hull, HU2 0PH Tel: (01482) 329600 Fax: (01482) 216296 E-mail: andy@lgprout.co.uk

PHOSPHOR BRONZE CASTINGS MANUFRS

Salmon Consultancy, Littlewood Farm, Cheddleton, Leek, Staffordshire, ST13 7LB Tel: (01538) 361010 Fax: (01538) 361011 E-mail: salmonconsult@btconnect.com
Swinford Engineering Ltd, 191 Hagley Road, Stourbridge, West Midlands, DY8 2JJ Tel: (01384) 397531 Fax: (01384) 440118

PHOSPHOR BRONZE INGOTS

Brookside Metal Co. Ltd, 28 Bilston Lane, Willenhall, West Midlands, WV13 2QE Tel: (01902) 365500 Fax: (01902) 636671 E-mail: richard.payne@brooksidemetal.com

PHOSPHOR BRONZE STRIP MANUFRS

B Mason & Sons Ltd, Wharf Street, Aston, Birmingham, B6 5SA Tel: 0121-327 0181 Fax: 0121-322 8341 E-mail: sales@bmason.co.uk
Diehl Sales UK, 2 West Street, Bradford, West Yorkshire, BD2 3BS Tel: (01274) 632227 Fax: (01274) 632059

PHOSPHOR BRONZE WIRE

Chaplin Bros Birmingham Ltd, Unit 11a Reddicap Trading Estate, Sutton Coldfield, West Midlands, B75 7BU Tel: 0121-378 0565 Fax: 0121-378 0157
Diehl Sales UK, 2 West Street, Bradford, West Yorkshire, BD2 3BS Tel: (01274) 632227 Fax: (01274) 632059

PHOSPHOR COATINGS

Colourmaster, Stock Lane, Peel St, Chadderton, Oldham, OL9 9EY Tel: 0161-624 9479 Fax: 0161-678 8877 E-mail: sales@colour-master.co.uk

PHOSPHOR SCREENS

Applied Scintillation Technologies, Unit 7-8 Roydenbury Industrial Estate, Horsecroft Road, Harlow, Essex, CM19 5BZ Tel: (01279) 641234 Fax: (01279) 413679 E-mail: ast@appscintech.com

PHOTOCHEMICAL ETCHING

A B S Photocopiers, 26 Atherstone Street, Fazeley, Tamworth, Staffordshire, B78 3RF Tel: (01827) 281515 Fax: (01827) 281515
Chempix Ltd, Vantage Way, Erdington, Birmingham, B24 9GZ Tel: 0121 380 0100 Fax: 0121 359 3313 E-mail: sales@precisionmicro.com
Grainge & Hodder Ltd, 26-27 Marshall Street, Birmingham, B1 1LE Tel: 0121-632 6079 Fax: 0121-632 6079 E-mail: grainge@globalnet.co.uk

PHOTOCOMPOSITORS, *See Typesetting Services*

PHOTOCOPIER CONTROL SYSTEMS

Controlled Access Ltd, Treadaway Technical Centre, Treadaway Hill, High Wycombe, Buckinghamshire, HP10 2RS Tel: 0118-977 0667 Fax: (01628) 850251
Copyfast Photocopiers, 57 Cecil Road, Romford, RM6 6LB Tel: (020) 8599 3033 Fax: (020) 8270 9869
Copylogic Ltd, The Palmerston Centre, Oxford Road, Wealdstone, Harrow, Middlesex, HA3 7RG Tel: (020) 8863 4483 Fax: (020) 8861 1620 E-mail: mail@copylogic.co.uk
▶ HI Digital Solutions, 26 Caledonia House, Evanton Way, Glasgow, G46 8JE Tel: 0141-270 9735 Fax: 0141-270 9738 E-mail: admin@hids.co.uk

PHOTOCOPIERS, DIGITAL, COLOUR

▶ A T S Business Machines, Brithdir House, Brithdir Street, Cardiff, CF24 4LE Tel: (029) 2037 7455 Fax: (029) 2037 7455 E-mail: sales@atsbm.co.uk
▶ Arvanti UK Ltd, Unit 6, Morley Business Centre, Morley Road, Tonbridge, Kent, TN9 1RA Tel: (01732) 366063 Fax: (01732) 770890 E-mail: info@arvanti.co.uk
Fox Office Machinery, Rumdoodle, Cotehill, Carlisle, CA4 0EG Tel: (01228) 561669
▶ London Graphic Centre, 16-18 Shelton Street, London, WC2H 9JL Tel: (020) 7759 4500 Fax: (020) 7759 4585 E-mail: matt@londongraphicsystems.co.uk
▶ Lynx Copiers, Unit 10 Lufton Heights Commerce Park Boundary Way, Lufton Tra, Lufton, Yeovil, Somerset, BA22 8UY Tel: (01935) 706914 Fax: (01935) 477110 E-mail: sales@lynxcopiers.co.uk
▶ Peter M Tutty Partnership, 37-39 Princes Avenue, Hull, HU5 3RZ Tel: (01482) 341458 Fax: (01482) 445691E-mail: sales@tutty.co.uk
▶ Sapphire Document Solutions, Unit 4 5 Cae FFWT Business Park, Pendraw'R Llan, Glan Conwy, Colwyn Bay, Clwyd, LL28 5SP Tel: (0845) 8382501 Fax: (01492) 580052 E-mail: sales@sapphire-limited.co.uk
▶ Simon Rowe Copier Sales Aston Leys FM, Haddenham Road, Kingsey, Aylesbury, Buckinghamshire, HP17 8LS Tel: (01844) 290840 Fax: (01844) 292967 E-mail: sales@srcs-copier-resites.co.uk

PHOTOCOPIERS, HIGH VOLUME

▶ London Graphic Centre, 16-18 Shelton Street, London, WC2H 9JL Tel: (020) 7759 4500 Fax: (020) 7759 4585 E-mail: matt@londongraphicsystems.co.uk
▶ Lynx Copiers, Unit 10 Lufton Heights Commerce Park Boundary Way, Lufton Tra, Lufton, Yeovil, Somerset, BA22 8UY Tel: (01935) 706914 Fax: (01935) 477110 E-mail: sales@lynxcopiers.co.uk
▶ Peter M Tutty Partnership, 37-39 Princes Avenue, Hull, HU5 3RZ Tel: (01482) 341458 Fax: (01482) 445691E-mail: sales@tutty.co.uk
▶ Sapphire Document Solutions, Unit 4 5 Cae FFWT Business Park, Pendraw'R Llan, Glan Conwy, Colwyn Bay, Clwyd, LL28 5SP Tel: (0845) 8382501 Fax: (01492) 580052 E-mail: sales@sapphire-limited.co.uk
▶ Sharpline Solutions Ltd, Unit 2, Saturn House, Calleva Park, Aldermaston, RG7 8HA Tel: 0118-982 3930 Fax: 0118-981 2430 E-mail: sales@sharplinesolutions.co.uk

PHOTOCOPYING MACHINE MAINTENANCE/REPAIR SPECIALIST SERVICES

2 R Systems Ltd, Unit 5 Collec Depot, Billington Road, Leighton Buzzard, Bedfordshire, LU7 9HH Tel: (01525) 852151 Fax: (01525) 852149
A C Copiers, Westward House, Bury Road, Hatfield, Hertfordshire, AL10 8BJ Tel: (01707) 259060 Fax: (01707) 259070 E-mail: sales@accopiers.com
Advanced Technology Systems Ltd, 1 Russetts, Basildon, Essex, SS16 6SH Tel: (01268) 491900 E-mail: sales@atsweb.co.uk
Anly Office Services, 1191 Middleton Road, Chadderton, Oldham, OL9 0NN Tel: 0161-627 5870 Fax: 0161-287 3945 E-mail: enquiry@anly.co.uk
Apex Office Solutions Ltd, 147 Bellenden Road, London, SE15 4DH Tel: (020) 7277 5168
B C M Group P.L.C., Unit 1, Wildmere Close, Banbury, Oxfordshire, OX16 3TL Tel: (01295) 267671 Fax: (01295) 269142
Boardman & Co., 8 Clydesdale Street, Oldham, OL8 1BT Tel: 0161-624 2058 Fax: 0161-652 0427 E-mail: boardmanscopiers@btconnect.com
Bradford Business Machines, 155 Bradford Road, Cleckheaton, West Yorkshire, BD19 3SX Tel: (01274) 879608 Fax: (01274) 879608 E-mail: bradfordbusiness@aol.com
Brown's Photocopier Repairs, 57 Leybourne Road, London, E11 3BS Tel: (020) 8530 3569
C C M Sussex Ltd, PO Box 2004, Peacehaven, East Sussex, BN10 7HZ Tel: (01273) 586963 Fax: (01273) 584000 E-mail: sales@ccm.gb.com
Charlwood Copiers, 60 The Street, Charlwood, Horley, Surrey, RH6 0DF Tel: (01293) 862743 Fax: (0870) 8032291 E-mail: info@charlwoodcopiers.co.uk
Chartex Systems, Ashdene House, Langton Road, Langton Green, Tunbridge Wells, Kent, TN3 0HL Tel: (01892) 862024 Fax: (01892) 863437 E-mail: info@chartexsystems.com
City Digital East Midlands Ltd, Samson House, Samson Road, Coalville, Leicestershire, LE67 3FP Tel: (01530) 815581 Fax: (01530) 815262
Clarity Copiers Sheffield, 126 Handsworth Road, Sheffield, S9 4AE Tel: 0114-244 8844 Fax: 0114-244 9944
Concept Group, 66 Carden Place, Aberdeen, AB10 1UL Tel: (01224) 648784 Fax: (01224) 636372 E-mail: enquiries@concept-group.co.uk

PHOTOCOPYING MACHINE MAINTENANCE/REPAIR SPECIALIST SERVICES – *continued*

Contact Copiers, 79 Commercial Street, Risca, Newport, Gwent, NP11 6AW Tel: (01633) 894488 Fax: (01633) 615566

Copiers & Servicing Ltd, 46 Queensway, Wigan, Lancashire, WN1 2HR Tel: (01942) 233505 Fax: (01942) 324877 E-mail: info@copiersandservicing.com

Copydoc Printers, Carlton Hill, Carlton, Nottingham, NG4 1FP Tel: 0115-940 4804 Fax: 0115-847 6941 E-mail: info@copydoc-copyshop.co.uk

Copyfast Photocopiers, 57 Cecil Road, Romford, RM6 6LB Tel: (020) 8599 3033 Fax: (020) 8270 9869

Copymatt Drawing Office Supplies Solihull, 25 Henley Cresent, Solihull, West Midlands, B91 2JD Tel: 0121-711 1112 Fax: 0121-711 4844 E-mail: sales@copymatt.co.uk

Copyserve UK Ltd, 21 Kingswear Parade, Leeds, LS15 8LJ Tel: 0113-260 9026 Fax: 0113-264 0468 E-mail: sales@copyserve.co.uk

CSL Business Machines Ltd, 28/30 Hinckley Road, Leicester, LE3 0RA Tel: 0116-255 1000 Fax: 0116-233 3224

Day Print Photocopiers, 55 Pitt Avenue, Witham, Essex, CM8 1JQ Tel: (01376) 510716 Fax: (01376) 510716

Direct Business Systems, Reema Road, Bellshill, Lanarkshire, ML4 1RY Tel: (01698) 740074 Fax: (01698) 741074

Elmrep Ltd, Elmrep House, Eastern Avenue, Gloucester, GL4 6QS Tel: (01452) 300959 Fax: (01452) 300988

Image Business Machines, 24 Long Croft, Yate, Bristol, BS37 7YW Tel: (01454) 325350 Fax: (01454) 325142

Lanier UK Ltd, Eskdale Road, Winnersh, Wokingham, Berkshire, RG41 5TS Tel: (08702) 202012 Fax: (08702) 202018

London Copier Machine, 244 Blackhorse La, London, E17 6AD Tel: 020 89253019

Monarch Group Systems, 32-33 Monarch Parade, London Road, Mitcham, Surrey, CR4 3HA Tel: (020) 8648 3344 E-mail: sales@mgsonline.co.uk

Photocopier Maintenance Servicing, 3 Church Square, Nottingham, NG7 1SL Tel: 0115-941 4656 Fax: 0115-941 4471

Photostatic Copiers Ltd, Unit 13-14 Village Court, Village Farm Industrial Estate, Pyle, Bridgend, Mid Glamorgan, CF33 6BX Tel: (01656) 743100 Fax: (01656) 744047 E-mail: sales@photostatic.co.uk

Photostatic Copiers & Co., 3 Westmead Drive, Redhill, RH1 5DB Tel: (01293) 775061 Fax: (01293) 824696 E-mail: info@intastatic.co.uk

Protek Services Ltd, Unit 3, Whittall Industrial Estate, Argyle Way, Stevenage, Hertfordshire, SG1 2AD Tel: (01438) 750111 Fax: (01438) 311767

Quilver Business Services Ltd, Unit 13c Riverside Park, Station Road, Wimborne, Dorset, BH21 1QU Tel: (01962) 777631 Fax: (01962) 777565 E-mail: enquiries@quilver.co.uk

Technicopy, Woodford Business Development Centre, London, E18 1AB Tel: (020) 8989 9281

Time Business Systems Ltd, Unit 13 Silver Business Park, Airfield Way, Christchurch, Dorset, BH23 3TA Tel: (01202) 479999 Fax: (01202) 474741 E-mail: sales@time-business.co.uk

VMS UK, 120-126 Holme Lane, Sheffield, S6 4JW Tel: 0114-285 2595 Fax: 0114-231 4145 E-mail: vms@vms.fsbusiness.co.uk

PHOTOCOPYING MACHINE SPARE PARTS/WEARING PARTS

BMP Europe Ltd, Shorten Brook Drive, Altham Business Park, Altham, Accrington, Lancashire, BB5 5YH Tel: (01282) 772000 Fax: (01282) 777700 E-mail: bmp@bmp-europe.co.uk

Milk-Rite, PO Box 2, Melksham, Wiltshire, SN12 6NB Tel: (0870) 7315010 Fax: (01225) 896311 E-mail: sales@milk-rite.com

PHOTOCOPYING MACHINES

▶ 1st Office Equipment, Victoria Orchards, Kennford, Exeter, EX6 7TH Tel: (01392) 833373 Fax: (01934) 713843 E-mail: sales@1st-office.com

A C Copiers, Westward House, Bury Road, Hatfield, Hertfordshire, AL10 8BJ Tel: (01707) 259060 Fax: (01707) 259070 E-mail: sales@accopiers.com

A Kelly Ltd, Mita House, Wester Gourdie Industrial Estate, West Gourdie Industrial Estate, Dundee, DD2 4UH Tel: (01382) 623311 Fax: (01382) 611910 E-mail: admin@kellyscopiers.co.uk

A M F Business Systems Ltd, New Malden, Surrey, KT3 5WN Tel: (020) 8605 1111 Fax: (020) 8605 1105

Abacus Leewell, 30b High Street, Langford, Biggleswade, Bedfordshire, SG18 9RR Tel: (01462) 700229 Fax: (01462) 701291 E-mail: sales@abacus-leewell.co.uk

▶ Access Copiers, 58 Ashton Road, Failsworth, Manchester, M35 9WL Tel: 0161-684 8655 E-mail: access.copiers@virgin.net

Advance Group plc, Ockley Road, Bognor Regis, West Sussex, PO21 2HW Tel: (01243) 829100 Fax: (01243) 866822 E-mail: sales@advancegroup.plc.uk

Alternative Enterprises Ltd, Avocet House Trinity Park, Trinity Way, London, E4 8TD Tel: (020) 8498 4100 Fax: (020) 8498 4200 E-mail: info@alternative.uk.com

Alto Digital, Sommerville House, Leathley Road, Leeds, LS10 1BG Tel: 0113-244 3016 Fax: 0113-242 4765

Altodigital Midlands UK Ltd, Pensnett Trading Estate, Kingswinford, West Midlands, DY6 7FZ Tel: (01384) 404660 Fax: (01384) 404665 E-mail: enquiries@altodigital.com

A-Stat, 15 Hollybush Lane, Wolverhampton, WV4 4JJ Tel: (01902) 342400 Fax: (01902) 342333 E-mail: admin@astat.co.uk

Azzurri Communications Ltd, Elmhirst Lane, Dodworth, Barnsley, South Yorkshire, S75 4LS Tel: (01226) 777111 Fax: (01226) 777100

▶ B B's Copy & Stationery Shop, Hawthorne House, 1 Exeter Road, Ivybridge, Devon, PL21 0BN Tel: (01752) 893959 Fax: (01752) 893959

Bentley Copying Services, 1 Harewood Close, Sandiacre, Nottingham, NG10 5PL Tel: 0115-939 5577 Fax: 0115-939 5512

Blythe Business Equipment Ltd, 161-165 Newcastle Street, Stoke-on-Trent, ST6 3QJ Tel: (01782) 817121 Fax: (01782) 575087 E-mail: sales@blythebusiness.co.uk

Boardman & Co., 8 Clydesdale Street, Oldham, OL8 1BT Tel: 0161-624 2058 Fax: 0161-652 0427 E-mail: boardmanscopiers@btconnect.com

Bradford Business Machines, 155 Bradford Road, Cleckheaton, West Yorkshire, BD19 3SX Tel: (01274) 879608 Fax: (01274) 879608 E-mail: bradfordbusiness@aol.com

Bristol & West Copiers Ltd, 196-198 Cheltenham Road, Bristol, BS6 5QZ Tel: 0117-923 2333 Fax: 0117-923 2031

C S Digital Systems, 63 Seaview Road, Wallasey, Merseyside, CH45 4QW Tel: 0151-691 1783 Fax: 0151-691 1079

C S L Copy Shop, 84 St. Marys Road, Market Harborough, Leicestershire, LE16 7DX Tel: (01858) 465208 Fax: (01858) 465208

Canon Business Solutions, 1 Cromac Quay, Belfast, BT7 2JD Tel: (028) 9072 7500 Fax: (028) 9072 7555

Canon (UK) Ltd, 7TH Floor, 6-16 St. Andrew Street, London, EC4A 3LX Tel: (0870) 6081144 Fax: (0870) 6081145

Carousel Copiers, 148 Westborough Road, Westcliff-on-Sea, Essex, SS0 9JF Tel: (01702) 300886 Fax: (01702) 321083

Central Business Machines Ltd, 112-118 Kingsland Road, London, E2 8DJ Tel: (020) 7729 5588 Fax: (020) 7729 9137

Chartex Systems, Ashdene House, Langton Road, Langton Green, Tunbridge Wells, Kent, TN3 0HL Tel: (01892) 862024 Fax: (01892) 863437 E-mail: info@chartexsystems.com

▶ City Digital Technology, 29 Cressex Enterprise Centre, Lincoln Road, Cressex Business Park, High Wycombe, Buckinghamshire, HP12 3RL Tel: (01494) 532222 Fax: (01494) 538787 E-mail: nigel@cdt-group.com

Clarity Copiers Cornwall & Co, Unit 5d 5d Carminnow Road Industrial Estate, Bodmin, Cornwall, PL31 1EP Tel: (01208) 78201 Fax: (01208) 75916

Clark Business Products Ltd, Old Ferry Road, Lower Bristol Road, Bath, BA2 1ES Tel: (01225) 337600 Fax: (01225) 337206 E-mail: info@clarkbusinessproducts.co.uk

Clear Print Office Equipment, 18-22 Prior Deram Walk, Coventry, CV4 8FT Tel: (024) 7671 6123 Fax: (024) 7671 7427

Club Copying Co. Ltd, 10-18 Sandgate Street, London, SE15 1LE Tel: (020) 7635 5252 Fax: (020) 7635 5714 E-mail: jacquidalton@clubcopying.co.uk

Copier Maintenance Co. Ltd, 642 Warwick Road, Tyseley, Birmingham, B11 2HJ Tel: 0121-624 8484 Fax: 0121-708 2406 E-mail: sales@printersforbusiness.com

Copydoc Printers, Carlton Hill, Carlton, Nottingham, NG4 1FP Tel: 0115-940 4804 Fax: 0115-847 6941 E-mail: info@copydoc-copyshop.co.uk

Copyrite Business Systems Ltd, Copyrite House, Pigot Road, Denbigh, Clwyd, LL16 3DG Tel: (01745) 816473 Fax: (01745) 815516 E-mail: sales@copyrite.com

Copystatic Midlands Ltd, Northern House, Moor Knoll Lane, East Ardsley, Wakefield, West Yorkshire, WF3 2EE Tel: (01924) 823455 Fax: (01924) 820433 E-mail: headoffice@eurocopy.co.uk

▶ Copytec, 104 Newark Road, North Hykeham, Lincoln, LN6 8NA Tel: (01522) 696111 Fax: (01522) 806828

Crailcrest Ltd, Coach House, Birch Grove, Horsted Keynes, Haywards Heath, West Sussex, RH17 7DJ Tel: (01825) 740190 Fax: (01825) 740178 E-mail: sales@crailcrest.com

Crest Reprographics (Northern) Ltd, Crest House, Gibralter Row, Liverpool, L3 7HJ Tel: 0151-236 2642 Fax: 0151-236 2726 E-mail: info@crest-reprographics.co.uk

▶ Dan Wood Group Ltd, 5 The Courtyards, Wyncolls Road, Severalls Industrial Park, Colchester, CO4 9PE Tel: (01206) 754744 Fax: (01206) 754743 E-mail: sales@danwoods.co.uk

Danka UK P.L.C., 1ST Floor, Holvorn Gate, 330 Higher Holvorn, London, WC1B 7QT Tel: (020) 7716 5634 Fax: (020) 7716 5750

▶ Digital Copier Systems, Bristol Courtbetts Avenue Martlesham Heath Business Park, Martlesham Heath, Ipswich, IP5 3RH Tel: (01473) 636000 Fax: (01473) 614400 E-mail: sales@digitalcopyprint.co.uk

Document House, Viscount House Queensway Court Business Park, Arkwright Way, Scunthorpe, South Humberside, DN16 1AD Tel: (01482) 370470 Fax: (01724) 271041 E-mail: sherralee.thompson@documenthouse.co.uk

Dot Copiers Distribution Ltd, Unit 35, Brickyard Road, Aldridge, Walsall, WS9 8XT Tel: (01922) 455359 Fax: (01922) 455316 E-mail: dotcopiers@lineone.net

Eastern Business Systems Ltd, Systems House, Chippenham Hill, Moulton, Newmarket, Suffolk, CB8 7PL Tel: (01638) 552633 Fax: (01638) 552892

▶ Electronic Imaging Solutions, Fulmer House, Ocean Way, Cardiff, CF24 5HF Tel: (029) 2025 0900 Fax: (029) 2025 0901

Equipu, Unit M1, The Maltings, Lodway Business Centre, Pill, Bristol, BS20 0DH Tel: (01275) 813838 Fax: (01275) 813122 E-mail: equipu@eurocopy.co.uk

Eurocopy GB P.L.C., 30 Blacks Road, London, W6 9DT Tel: (020) 8741 7281 Fax: (020) 8741 5068

Excel Office Equipment, 24 Mannamead Road, Plymouth, PL4 7AA Tel: (01752) 660151 Fax: (01752) 225778 E-mail: sales@exeloffice.co.uk

Executive Communications, Hi Tech House, 18 Beresford Avenue, Wembley, Middlesex, HA0 1YP Tel: (020) 8903 3425 Fax: (01784) 431560 E-mail: executivecomm@execs.com

Fengrove Ltd, 4 Mapledale Road, Liverpool, L18 5JE Tel: 0151-733 7628 Fax: 0151-733 0036 E-mail: copiers@fengrove.sagehost.co.uk

▶ First Choice Group, Stileway Business Park, Lower Strode Road, Clevedon, Avon, BS21 6UU Tel: (01275) 871111 Fax: (01275) 871115

▶ G P S, 7 Cardeston Close, Sutton Weaver, Runcorn, Cheshire, WA7 3LH Tel: (01928) 715055 Fax: (01928) 739490 E-mail: gavin@gps1.co.uk

Graphic Office Systems, 64 Pen Y Bryn, Wrexham, Clwyd, LL13 7HY Tel: (01978) 261168 Fax: (01978) 263224 E-mail: sales@graphicofficesystems.com

H A Office Supplies, 25 Pittfield Street, London, N1 6HB Tel: (020) 7608 3670 Fax: (020) 7608 3670

Henley & Burton Business Machines Ltd, 130 South Street, Lancing, West Sussex, BN15 8AU Tel: (01903) 762719 Fax: (0870) 7058679

I O T P.L.C., Crompton Close, Basildon, Essex, SS14 3AZ Tel: (01268) 523366 Fax: (01268) 527135 E-mail: eoe@eurocopy.co.uk

Ikon Office Solutions Ltd, Ikon House, 15 Ullswater Crescent, Coulsdon, Surrey, CR5 2HR Tel: (020) 8763 1010 Fax: (020) 8763 1110

Ikon Office Solutions plc, Ikon Court, 150 Great Cambridge Road, Enfield, Middlesex, EN1 1PW Tel: (020) 8366 9666 Fax: (020) 8367 6729

Ikon Office Solutions Dublin Ltd, Ikon House, 30 Cowcross Street, London, EC1M 6DQ Tel: (020) 7253 4545 Fax: (020) 7250 3690

▶ Independant Document Systems Ltd, Brickyard Road, Roecliffe, York, YO51 9NS Tel: (01423) 326632 Fax: (01423) 326523 E-mail: sales@idslimited.com

▶ Insite Systems, Unit 2, Invicta Business Park, London Road, Wrotham, Sevenoaks, Kent, TN15 7RJ Tel: (01732) 887457 Fax: (01732) 886492

International Copiers Ltd, Westfield Farm House, Henley Road, Medmenham, Marlow, Buckinghamshire, SL7 2HE Tel: (01491) 414345 Fax: (01491) 414346

J M Copiers Ltd, 5 Mansfield Road, Musselburgh, Midlothian, EH21 7DS Tel: 0131-665 3783 Fax: 0131-665 4746 E-mail: jmcopiers@btconnect.com

Kelly's Of Aberdeen, 22-24 South Mount Street, Aberdeen, AB25 2TB Tel: (01224) 638689 Fax: (01224) 649009 E-mail: enquiries@kellyscopiers.co.uk

Konica Minolta Business Solutions (UK) Ltd, 84-86 Bradley Road, Wrexham, Clwyd, LL13 7TP Tel: (01978) 356772 Fax: (01978) 361560 E-mail: info@bs.konicaminolta.co.uk

Kyocera Mica UK Ltd, Beacontree Plaza, Gillette Way, Reading, RG2 0BS Tel: 0118-931 1500 Fax: 0118-931 1108 E-mail: kyocera@kyoceramita.co.uk

London Business Equipment, 529 High Road Leytonstone, London, E11 4PB Tel: (020) 8558 0024 Fax: (020) 8556 4865 E-mail: sales@1ondonbusinessequipment.com

Lyndon Co., Unit 14 Saxon Business Centre, Windsor Avenue, London, SW19 2RR Tel: (020) 8543 9969 Fax: (020) 8543 9765 E-mail: sales@lydongroup.co.uk

M B R Group Ltd, Beezon Road, Kendal, Cumbria, LA9 6EL Tel: (01539) 796400 Fax: (01539) 796499

M & S Reprographics Ltd, 48 Chorley New Road, Bolton, BL1 4AP Tel: (01204) 371188 Fax: (01204) 370737

M2 Digital Ltd, PO Box 2000, Manchester, M16 9EB Tel: 0161-877 0222 Fax: 0161-877 0220 E-mail: sales@m2digital.co.uk

Magenta Technology Ltd, 36 Holme Lacy Road, Hereford, HR2 6BY Tel: (01432) 278296 Fax: (01432) 340388 E-mail: enquiries@magenta-tech.com

Maine Business Systems P.L.C., Hanover Park House, Merebank Lane, Croydon, CR0 4NP Tel: (020) 8688 8855 Fax: (020) 8688 8897 E-mail: post@maine-plc.com

N R G Management Ltd, 66 Chiltern Street, London, W1U 4AG Tel: (020) 7465 1000 Fax: (020) 7224 5740

Photocopier Maintenance Servicing, 3 Church Square, Nottingham, NG7 1SL Tel: 0115-941 4656 Fax: 0115-941 4471

▶ Photocopier Sales, 137 Kings Road, Kingston upon Thames, Surrey, KT2 5JE Tel: (020) 8547 1222 Fax: (020) 8547 3666 E-mail: info@kingsofficesupplies.com

▶ Quick Copy, 334 Woodstock Road, Belfast, BT6 9DP Tel: (028) 9045 4511 Fax: (028) 9073 2180

Regent Reprographics Ltd, Regent House, 38 Hawkes Drive, Heathcote Industrial Estate, Warwick, CV34 6LX Tel: (01926) 450960 Fax: (01926) 450316 E-mail: info@regentdigital.co.uk

Ricoh UK Ltd, 1 Plane Tree Crescent, Feltham, Middlesex, TW13 7HG Tel: (020) 8261 4000 Fax: (020) 8261 4004E-mail: info@ricoh.co.uk

Sharples Group, Tatton Court, Kingsland Grange, Woolston, Warrington, WA1 4RR Tel: (01925) 839599 Fax: (01925) 839580 E-mail: info@sharplesgroup.com

Time Business Systems Ltd, Unit 13 Silver Business Park, Airfield Way, Christchurch, Dorset, BH23 3TA Tel: (01202) 479999 Fax: (01202) 474741 E-mail: sales@time-business.co.uk

Unigraph UK Ltd, 287 Pitsmoor Road, Sheffield, S3 9AS Tel: 0114-275 2801 Fax: 0114-275 9769 E-mail: sales@unigraph.uk

Victoria Communications, Victoria Buildings, Bank Avenue, Morley, Leeds, LS27 9JF Tel: 0113-252 2233 Fax: 0113-252 1846 E-mail: gregg@viccom.co.uk

Westec Office Equipment, 8 Old Town Street, Dawlish, Devon, EX7 9AL Tel: (01626) 888117 Fax: (01626) 888299 E-mail: sales@westec.uk.com

Dan Wood Scotland, Grampian House, Virginia Street, Aberdeen, AB11 5AU Tel: (01224) 211900 Fax: (01224) 212828 E-mail: reception.aberdeen@sctland.co.uk

Xerox Capital Europe plc, Bridge House, Oxford Road, Uxbridge, Middlesex, UB8 1HS Tel: (01895) 251133

Xerox (U K) Ltd, Cheadle Place, Stockport Road, Cheadle, Cheshire, SK8 2JX Tel: 0161-931 3750 Fax: 0161-931 3751

PHOTOCOPYING PAPER

Antalis, Unit 4 Horizon Wade Road, Kingsland Industrial Estate, Basingstoke, Hampshire, RG24 8LJ Tel: (01256) 776200 Fax: (01256) 724734 E-mail: sales@antalis.co.uk

Antalis, 3 Imperial Park Imperial Way, Watford, WD24 4PP Tel: (01923) 636600 Fax: (0870) 6073168 E-mail: contact@antalis.co.uk

Antalis Ltd, Unit 14, Avenue One, Witney, Oxfordshire, OX29 6XX Tel: (0870) 6073114 Fax: (01993) 779066

PHOTOCOPYING SERVICES

▶ Printinc, Sutton Business Centre, Restmor Way, Wallington, Surrey, SM6 7AH Tel: 020 8255 2110 Fax: 020 8255 2115 E-mail: printinc2@btconnect.com

PHOTOCOPYING SERVICES, TRADE/TECHNICAL, *See Reprographic etc*

PHOTOCOPYING SUPPLIES

CCS, Peashill Farm, Peashill Lane, Cotgrave, Nottingham, NG12 3HD Tel: 0115-989 2423 Fax: 0115-989 4951

Complete Imaging plc, 62 Ravenhurst Street, Birmingham, B12 0EL Tel: 0121-766 2000 Fax: 0121-766 5404 E-mail: sales@completeplc.co.uk

Copyfax Ltd, Unit C, Burnham Trading Park, Burnley, Lancashire, BB11 4AA Tel: (01282) 453935 Fax: (01282) 416071 E-mail: sales@copifax.co.uk

Document House, Viscount House Queensway Court Business Park, Arkwright Way, Scunthorpe, South Humberside, DN16 1AD Tel: (01482) 370470 Fax: (01724) 271041 E-mail: sherralee.thompson@documenthouse.co.uk

Equipu, Unit M1, The Maltings, Lodway Business Centre, Pill, Bristol, BS20 0DH Tel: (01275) 813838 Fax: (01275) 813122 E-mail: equipu@eurocopy.co.uk

Logik Copying Systems Ltd, 644 Wimborne Rd, Bournemouth, BH9 2EH Tel: (01202) 518444 Fax: (01202) 516444

P S Office Supplies Ltd, 40 Great Lister Street, Birmingham, B7 4LS Tel: 0121-333 5000 Fax: 0121-333 5001 E-mail: sales@psonline.co.uk

Paper Flow Ltd, Unit 5 & 6, 20 Bugsby Way, London, SE7 7SJ Tel: (020) 8331 2090 Fax: (020) 8331 2001 E-mail: sales@paperflowonline.com

PHOTOCOPYING SUPPLIES – *continued*

Topaz Business Systems Ltd, Pella House, 54-56 Moor Street, Gloucester, GL1 4NJ Tel: (01452) 332211 Fax: (01452) 332212 E-mail: solutions@topazuk.com
Toshiba EIS, Charnwood House, 13 Ocean Way, Cardiff, CF24 5TE Tel: (029) 2025 0900 Fax: (029) 2025 0901
Unigraph UK Ltd, 287 Pitsmoor Road, Sheffield, S3 9AS Tel: 0114-275 2801 Fax: 0114-275 9769 E-mail: sales@unigraph.uk

PHOTODETECTORS

Chromatechnic Ltd, 35 Princes Street, Ulverston, Cumbria, LA12 7NQ Tel: (01229) 581551 E-mail: edavidson@chromatechnic.com

PHOTODIODE OPTODETECTORS

Semelab plc, Coventry Road, Lutterworth, Leicestershire, LE17 4JB Tel: (01455) 556565 Fax: (01455) 558371 E-mail: sales@semelab.co.uk

PHOTOELECTRIC MACHINE GUARDS

Universal Guards Servicing Ltd, Turnpike Close, Grantham, Lincolnshire, NG31 7XU Tel: (01476) 565858 Fax: (01476) 590296 E-mail: sales@lightguards.com

PHOTOELECTRIC OR PHOTOELECTRONIC CONTROLS

Emetco Lighting Ltd, 81 Ellingham Industrial Centre, Ellingham Way, Ashford, Kent, TN23 6JZ Tel: (01233) 663333 Fax: (01233) 663366 E-mail: sales@emetco.co.uk
I M O Electronics Ltd, Unit 15, 1000 North Circular Road, London, NW2 7JP Tel: (020) 8452 6444 Fax: (020) 8450 2274 E-mail: imo@imopc.com
Industrial Controls Ltd, Unit 1 Audley Court, Lodge Way, Thetford, Norfolk, IP24 1HT Tel: (01842) 750800 Fax: (01842) 765900 E-mail: sales@industrialcontrols.co.uk
Longvale Ltd, The Grain Warehouse, Derby Street, Burton-On-Trent, Staffordshire, DE14 2JJ Tel: (01283) 510108 Fax: (01283) 510910 E-mail: rdear@longvale.co.uk
Mercury Instruments Ltd, Station Yard, Station Road, St. Ives, Cambridgeshire, PE27 5BH Tel: (01480) 494471 Fax: (01438) 367711 E-mail: mil@cwcom.net
Nortonics Ltd, Watts Street, Chadderton, Oldham, OL9 9LQ Tel: 0161-626 5316 Fax: 0161-627 0929
Sensopart UK Ltd, Unit G8 The Arch, 48-52 Floodgate Street, Birmingham, B5 5SL Tel: 0121-772 5104 Fax: 0121-772 5126 E-mail: info@sensopart.com
Sick UK Ltd, Waldkirch House, 39 Hedley Road, St. Albans, Hertfordshire, AL1 5BN Tel: (01727) 831121 Fax: (01727) 856767 E-mail: info@sick.co.uk
Synatel Instrumentation Ltd, Walsall Road, Norton Canes, Cannock, Staffordshire, WS11 9TB Tel: (01543) 277003 Fax: (01543) 271217 E-mail: sales@synatel.co.uk
Taylor Dynamic Controls, Unit W4 Blaby Industrial Park, Winchester Avenue, Blaby, Leicester, LE8 4GZ Tel: 0116-278 4100 Fax: 0116-278 4200 E-mail: sales@taylordynamics.com
Telco Sensors Ltd, The Stables, Waen Farm, Nercwys, Mold, Flintshire, CH7 4EW Tel: (0870) 9917058 Fax: (0870) 9917059 E-mail: sales@telco-sensors.co.uk

PHOTOELECTRIC PRESS BRAKE GUARDS

Universal Guards Servicing Ltd, Turnpike Close, Grantham, Lincolnshire, NG31 7XU Tel: (01476) 565858 Fax: (01476) 590296 E-mail: sales@lightguards.com

PHOTOELECTRIC SENSORS

Sensopart UK Ltd, Unit G8 The Arch, 48-52 Floodgate Street, Birmingham, B5 5SL Tel: 0121-772 5104 Fax: 0121-772 5126 E-mail: info@sensopart.com

PHOTOELECTRIC/ELECTRONIC CELLS

Chromatechnic Ltd, 35 Princes Street, Ulverston, Cumbria, LA12 7NQ Tel: (01229) 581551 E-mail: edavidson@chromatechnic.com

Telco Sensors Ltd, The Stables, Waen Farm, Nercwys, Mold, Flintshire, CH7 4EW Tel: (0870) 9917058 Fax: (0870) 9917059 E-mail: sales@telco-sensors.co.uk

PHOTOELECTRIC/ELECTRONIC SAFETY GUARD MANUFRS

Cambrake Ltd, Crescent Mill, Foundry Street, Todmorden, Lancashire, OL14 7NA Tel: (01706) 815711 Fax: (01706) 817967 E-mail: info@cambrake.co.uk
Sick UK Ltd, Waldkirch House, 39 Hedley Road, St. Albans, Hertfordshire, AL1 5BN Tel: (01727) 831121 Fax: (01727) 856767 E-mail: info@sick.co.uk

PHOTOETCHING METAL SERVICES TO THE TRADE

Custom Components Ltd, Unit 3 Boxer Place, Leyland, PR26 7QL Tel: (01772) 455520 Fax: (01772) 436472 E-mail: sales@customcomponents.co.uk
Photofabrication Services Ltd, 14 Cromwell Road, St Neots, St. Neots, Cambridgeshire, PE19 2HP Tel: (01480) 475831 Fax: (01480) 475801 E-mail: sales@photofab.co.uk

PHOTOGRAMMETRY SURVEY SERVICES

Air Views, Old Buckenham Airfield, Abbey Road, Old Buckenham, Attleborough, Norfolk, NR17 1PU Tel: (01953) 861111 Fax: (01953) 861031 E-mail: admin@airviews.co.uk

PHOTOGRAPH ALBUMS

Spicer Hallfield, Banks Road, Haddenham, Aylesbury, Buckinghamshire, HP17 8EG Tel: (01844) 299600 Fax: (01844) 299670 E-mail: sales@spicerhallfield.com

PHOTOGRAPH FRAME STRUTBACKS

Abm Labels & Print, Blaenant Industrial Estate, Blaenavon Road, Brynmawr, Ebbw Vale, Gwent, NP23 4BX Tel: (01495) 312835 Fax: (01495) 312819 E-mail: info@abmlabels.co.uk

PHOTOGRAPH FRAMES

Border Frames Lochmaben Co., Dumfries Road, Lochmaben, Lockerbie, Dumfriesshire, DG11 1RF Tel: (01387) 810455 Fax: (01387) 810693 E-mail: info@borderframes.com
Kitney & Co., Unit 12 Crystal Business Centre, Sandwich, Kent, CT13 9QX Tel: (01304) 611968 Fax: (01304) 614642 E-mail: sales@kitneyandco.com
Spicer Hallfield, Banks Road, Haddenham, Aylesbury, Buckinghamshire, HP17 8EG Tel: (01844) 299600 Fax: (01844) 299670 E-mail: sales@spicerhallfield.com

PHOTOGRAPH FRAMES, WOODEN

▶ Acacia Works, 20 Gayal Croft, Shenley Brook End, Milton Keynes, MK5 7HX Tel: (01908) 501268 E-mail: sales@acaciaworks.co.uk
Framepak Ltd, 21 Robjohns Road, Widford Industrial Estate, Chelmsford, CM1 3AG Tel: (01245) 266633 Fax: (01245) 266933 E-mail: info@framepakltd.com

PHOTOGRAPH RETOUCHING

Creativeretouch, 29 Crossfell Road, Hemel Hempstead, Hertfordshire, HP3 8RG Tel: (07790) 850422 E-mail: simon@creativeretouch.co.uk
▶ The Digital Eye (London) Ltd, Camden Park Studios, Camden Park Road, London, NW1 9AY Tel: (020) 7485 0658
Grasmere (Digital) Imaging Ltd, Bramley Business Centre, Stanningley Road, Leeds, LS13 4EN Tel: 0113-224 8600 Fax: 0113-239 3166 E-mail: admin@grasmeredigital.co.uk
▶ Pixelate Imaging, 8 Flitcroft Street, London, WC2H 8DL Tel: (020) 7240 9808 Fax: (020) 7240 9188 E-mail: studio@pixelate.biz
▶ Taylor James Photographic Services Ltd, 123-125 Curtain Road, London, EC2A 3BX Tel: (020) 7739 4488 Fax: (020) 7739 5958 E-mail: info@taylorjames.com

PHOTOGRAPHERS, AERIAL

▶ Giraffic, Manor Barn, Wilsthorpe, Stamford, Lincolnshire, PE9 4PE Tel: (01778) 560670 Fax: (01778) 560670 E-mail: giraffic@ndirect.co.uk

PHOTOGRAPHIC AND DISPLAY LAMPS

A J S Theatre Lighting & Stage Supplies Ltd, 25-26 Hightown Industrial Estate, Crow Arch Lane, Ringwood, Hampshire, BH24 1ND Tel: (01425) 481100 Fax: (01425) 471398 E-mail: enquiries@ajs.co.uk
C M L Innovative Technologies Ltd, Beetons Way, Bury St. Edmunds, Suffolk, IP32 6RA Tel: (01284) 762411 Fax: (01284) 754406 E-mail: sales@cml-it.com
Primarc Marketing, Unit 8 Wycombe Road, Wembley, Middlesex, HA0 1RH Tel: (020) 8900 8535 Fax: (020) 8900 2232 E-mail: sales@primarc.co.uk

PHOTOGRAPHIC CHEMICAL PRODUCTS/PHOTOCHEMICALS

Champion Photochemistry S.L., 23 Robjohns Road, Chelmsford, CM1 3AG Tel: (01245) 214940 Fax: (01245) 214957 E-mail: sales@championphotochemistry.co.uk
Contract Chemicals Properties Ltd, Penrhyn Road, Knowsley Business Park, Prescot, Merseyside, L34 9HY Tel: 0151-548 8840 Fax: 0151-548 6548 E-mail: info@contract-chemicals.com
I G P (UK) Ltd, Saltcoates Industrial Estate, 1-5 Cutlers Road, South Woodham Ferrers, Chelmsford, CM3 5WD Tel: (01245) 323555 Fax: (01245) 323762 E-mail: sales@igp-ukltd.co.uk
Jay House Ltd, Unit 6/B, Park Lane Trading Estate, Park Lane, Corsham, Wiltshire, SN13 9LG Tel: (01249) 714555 Fax: (01249) 714999 E-mail: sales@fotospeed.com
Process Supplies London Ltd, 13-25 Mount Pleasant, London, WC1X 0AR Tel: (020) 7837 2179 Fax: (020) 7837 8551 E-mail: sales@process-supplies.co.uk
Rayco, 199 King Street, Hoyland, Barnsley, South Yorkshire, S74 9LJ Tel: (01226) 744594 Fax: (01226) 744594 E-mail: info@rayco-chemicals.co.uk
Rockwell Hitec Ltd, 6 Alpha Business Park, Travellers Close, North Mymms, Hatfield, Hertfordshire, AL9 7NT Tel: (01707) 269086 Fax: (01707) 269099 E-mail: rockwell@rockwellhitec.co.uk
Seal Sands Chemicals Ltd, Seal Sands Road, Seal Sands, Middlesbrough, Cleveland, TS2 1UB Tel: (01642) 546546 Fax: (01642) 546068 E-mail: george.christopherson@cambrex.com

PHOTOGRAPHIC CONSULTANTS

A P R Photography Ltd, Robeson Way, Gatley, Manchester, M22 4SX Tel: (01625) 610999 Fax: (01625) 610055 E-mail: tim@aprphoto.co.uk
D M Resources Ltd, 10 Slimbridge Rd, Burgess Hill, W. Sussex, RH15 8QE Tel: (01444) 246391
Hawkeye Aerial Photography, Mansewood, Bellfield Road, Kirkintilloch, Glasgow, G66 1DS Tel: 0141-775 0673 Fax: 0141-775 0673
Lawsons Gibbs & Co. Ltd, 46-47 Dorset Street, London, W1U 7ND Tel: (020) 7580 9000 Fax: (020) 7935 5166 E-mail: sales@lawson-gibbs-co.demon.co.uk
Studio North, 41 Cecil Street, Carlisle, CA1 1NS Tel: (01228) 533344 E-mail: sales@studionorthphotographers.co.uk
Working Images, The Old Stables, Kingston House Estate, Kingston Bagpuize, Abingdon, Oxfordshire, OX13 5AX Tel: (07831) 843338 Fax: (01865) 375855 E-mail: chris@working-images.co.uk

PHOTOGRAPHIC DENSITOMETERS

X-Rite Ltd, The Acumen Centre, First Avenue, Poynton, Stockport, Cheshire, SK12 1FJ Tel: (01625) 871100 Fax: (01625) 871444

PHOTOGRAPHIC EQUIPMENT,

See also headings for particular types

Calumet Ltd, 93-103 Drummond Street, London, NW1 2HJ Tel: (0870) 6030303 E-mail: website@calumetphoto.co.uk
Calumet Photographic Ltd, 4 Downing St Industrial Estate, Charlton Place, Ardwick, Manchester, M12 6HH Tel: 0161-274 4455 Fax: 0161-274 3406 E-mail: michael.collins@calumetphoto.co.uk
Crown Photo Systems, East Portway, Andover, Hampshire, SP10 3LU Tel: (01264) 335334 Fax: (01264) 333349 E-mail: sales@dandfphoto.com
I G P (UK) Ltd, Saltcoates Industrial Estate, 1-5 Cutlers Road, South Woodham Ferrers, Chelmsford, CM3 5WD Tel: (01245) 323555 Fax: (01245) 323762 E-mail: sales@igp-ukltd.co.uk

▶ Kenro Ltd, The Oppenheimer Centre, Greenbridge Road, Swindon, SN3 3LH Tel: (01793) 615836 Fax: (01793) 530108 E-mail: sales@kenro.co.uk
S.W. Kenyon, PO Box 71, Cranbrook, Kent, TN18 5ZR Tel: (01580) 850770 Fax: (01580) 850225 E-mail: swkenyon@btinternet.com
▶ Kongsberg Simrad Ltd, Airport Industrial Estate, Wick Airport, Wick, Caithness, KW1 4QS Tel: (01955) 603606 Fax: (01955) 607520
Litho Supplies (Wessex), Unit 22, Metropolitan Centre, Darby Road, Greenford, Middlesex, UB6 8UJ Tel: (020) 8578 5787 Fax: (020) 8575 6252 E-mail: greenford@litho.co.uk
▶ M P B Photographic, 21-22 Old Steyne, Brighton, BN1 1EL Tel: (01273) 648348 E-mail: sales@mpbphotographic.co.uk
▶ Nova Darkroom Equipment Ltd, Unit 1a, Harris Road, Wedgnock Industrial Estate, Warwick, CV34 5JU Tel: (01926) 403090 E-mail: sales@novadarkroom.com
Photo Optix Ltd, 8 Oak Road, London, W5 3SS Tel: (020) 8840 7028
Photo Optix Ltd, 14 Clivemont Road, Maidenhead, Berkshire, SL6 7BU Tel: (01628) 778787 Fax: (01628) 776145
Polaroid, 800 Capability Green, Luton, LU1 3BA Tel: (01582) 409800 Fax: (01582) 409801
S R Keig Ltd, 51 Strand Street, Douglas, Isle of Man, IM1 2EJ Tel: (01624) 673111 Fax: (01624) 662372 E-mail: sales@keigs.co.uk
▶ Vision Light Plastics Ltd, 2-7 Decoy Road, Worthing, West Sussex, BN14 8ND Tel: (01903) 823339 Fax: (01903) 206868 E-mail: sales@visionlight.co.uk

PHOTOGRAPHIC EQUIPMENT HIRE

Executive Cameras Ltd, 80 York Street, London, W1H 1QW Tel: (020) 7723 4488 Fax: (020) 7723 4488 E-mail: photographers@amserve.co.uk
▶ M P B Photographic, 21-22 Old Steyne, Brighton, BN1 1EL Tel: (01273) 648348 E-mail: sales@mpbphotographic.co.uk
A.J. Purdy & Co. Ltd, 30 Stort Mill, River Way, Harlow, Essex, CM20 2SN Tel: (01279) 414556 Fax: (01279) 450931 E-mail: info@ajpurdy.co.uk

PHOTOGRAPHIC EQUIPMENT MAINTENANCE/REPAIR SPECIALIST SERVICES

Armstrong Hi-Fi & Video Service Ltd, 32a Blackhorse Lane, London, E17 6HJ Tel: (020) 8523 0051 Fax: (020) 8523 4395 E-mail: ahvsltd@aol.com
Cousins & Wright, 5 The Halve, Trowbridge, Wiltshire, BA14 8SB Tel: (01225) 754242
Patterson Photographic, 51 Thorney Road, Emsworth, Hampshire, PO10 8BL Tel: (01243) 377167
Sendean Photographic Equipment Repairs, 9-12 St. Annes Court, London, W1F 0BB Tel: (020) 7734 0895 E-mail: mail@sendeancameras.com

PHOTOGRAPHIC EQUIPMENT, USED

▶ M P B Photographic, 21-22 Old Steyne, Brighton, BN1 1EL Tel: (01273) 648348 E-mail: sales@mpbphotographic.co.uk

PHOTOGRAPHIC FILM

Jefferson Air Photography, Hawarden Airport, Flint Road, Saltney Ferry, Chester, CH4 0GZ Tel: (01244) 520892 Fax: (01244) 520894 E-mail: sales@aerial-photography.net
Process Supplies London Ltd, 13-25 Mount Pleasant, London, WC1X 0AR Tel: (020) 7837 2179 Fax: (020) 7837 8551 E-mail: sales@process-supplies.co.uk

PHOTOGRAPHIC FILM BASES

Harmen Technology Ltd, Ilford Way, Mobberley, Knutsford, Cheshire, WA16 7JL Tel: (01565) 650000 Fax: (01565) 872734

PHOTOGRAPHIC FILM PACKAGING

Crown Photo Systems, East Portway, Andover, Hampshire, SP10 3LU Tel: (01264) 335334 Fax: (01264) 333349 E-mail: sales@dandfphoto.com

PHOTOGRAPHIC GELATIN

PB Gelatins UK, Severn Road, Treforest Industrial Estate, Pontypridd, Mid Glamorgan, CF37 5SQ Tel: (01443) 849300 Fax: (01443) 844209

PHOTOGRAPHIC IMPORT/ EXPORT MERCHANTS OR AGENTS

Capix Ltd, Capix House, Forge Close, Eaton Socon, St. Neots, Cambridgeshire, PE19 8TP Tel: (01480) 470022 Fax: (01480) 215236 E-mail: info@capix.com
Hama Ltd, Unit 4 Cherrywood, Chineham Business Park, Basingstoke, Hampshire, RG24 8WF Tel: (01256) 374700 Fax: (01256) 374749 E-mail: sales@hama.co.uk
Jaytee Biosciences Ltd, Units 171-172, John Wilson Business Park, Chestfield, Whitstable, Kent, CT5 3RB Tel: (01227) 265333 Fax: (01227) 265331 E-mail: sales@jaytee.com
S.W. Kenyon, PO Box 71, Cranbrook, Kent, TN18 5ZR Tel: (01580) 850770 Fax: (01580) 850225 E-mail: swkenyon@btinternet.com

PHOTOGRAPHIC PAPER/BASE PAPER

A1 Paper P.L.C., Roebuck Street, West Bromwich, West Midlands, B70 6RB Tel: 0121-553 7131 Fax: 0121-553 5040 E-mail: sales@a1paper.co.uk
Harmen Technology Ltd, Ilford Way, Mobberley, Knutsford, Cheshire, WA16 7JL Tel: (01565) 650000 Fax: (01565) 872734
Process Supplies London Ltd, 13-25 Mount Pleasant, London, WC1X 0AR Tel: (020) 7837 2179 Fax: (020) 7837 8551 E-mail: sales@process-supplies.co.uk

PHOTOGRAPHIC PROCESSING EQUIPMENT

A P I Foils Ltd, Loughborough University, Ashby Road, Loughborough, Leicester, LE11 3TU Tel: (01509) 265232 Fax: (01509) 232772
Capix Ltd, Capix House, Forge Close, Eaton Socon, St. Neots, Cambridgeshire, PE19 8TP Tel: (01480) 470022 Fax: (01480) 215236 E-mail: info@capix.com
Drurys Engineering Ltd, 21 Knowl Piece, Wilbury Way, Hitchin, Hertfordshire, SG4 0TY Tel: (01462) 420123 Fax: (01462) 420124 E-mail: info@drurys.co.uk
Hewes Products, Wren Park, Cinques Road, Gamlingay, Sandy, Bedfordshire, SG19 3NJ Tel: (01767) 651333 Fax: (01767) 651311 E-mail: info@hewes.co.uk
Jaytee Biosciences Ltd, Units 171-172, John Wilson Business Park, Chestfield, Whitstable, Kent, CT5 3RB Tel: (01227) 265333 Fax: (01227) 265331 E-mail: sales@jaytee.com
Lastolite Ltd, 1 Atlas Road, Coalville, Leicestershire, LE67 3FQ Tel: (01530) 813381 Fax: (01530) 830408 E-mail: sales@lastolite.com
Leopold Professional Services, 57 Lancaster Road, Barnet, Hertfordshire, EN4 8AS Tel: (020) 8441 4310 Fax: (020) 8449 0317 E-mail: paul@leopold.co.uk
Photo Gen Ic Ltd, Unit 4 Parc Industrial Estate, Llanidloes, Powys, SY18 6RB Tel: (01686) 413292 Fax: (01686) 413425 E-mail: sales@photogenic.co.uk
Photomec (London) Ltd, Porters Wood, Valley Road Industrial Estate, St. Albans, Hertfordshire, AL3 6NU Tel: (01727) 850711 Fax: (01727) 843991 E-mail: photomec@photomec.co.uk

PHOTOGRAPHIC SLIDE FILING SYSTEMS

D W Group Ltd, Unit 7 Peverel Drive, Milton Keynes, MK1 1NL Tel: (01908) 642323 Fax: (01908) 640164 E-mail: sales@dw-view.com
Paul Schoeller U K, Unit 2 70 Partridge Way, Cirencester, Gloucestershire, GL7 1BQ Tel: (01285) 657521 Fax: (01285) 657521 E-mail: sales@schoeller.co.uk

PHOTOGRAPHIC STUDIOS/ FACILITIES

A P R Photography Ltd, Robeson Way, Gatley, Manchester, M22 4SX Tel: (01625) 610999 Fax: (01625) 610055 E-mail: tim@aprphoto.co.uk
▶ Colorfoto Lifestyle Portrait Studio, Image House, East Tyndall St, Cardiff Bay, Cardiff, CF24 5EF Tel: 029 20448222 E-mail: info@colorfotolifestyle.co.uk
Paul Cordwell Photography Ltd, Unit 3 Century Park, Garrison Lane, Birmingham, B9 4NZ Tel: (07831) 416477 E-mail: paul@paulcordwell.com
Creative Store Ltd, Studio House, 142 Merton Hall Road, London, SW19 3PZ Tel: (020) 8543 3855 Fax: (020) 8540 7367 E-mail: sales@thecreativestore.co.uk
Knight Andy Ltd, 2-6 Occupation Road, London, SE17 3BE Tel: (020) 7252 5252 Fax: (020) 7252 5111 E-mail: info@andyknight.co.uk
▶ Location25, 25 Clapham Common South Side, London, SW4 7AB Tel: (020) 7720 6514 Fax: (020) 7498 0040 E-mail: info@location25.com
Photoflex Ltd, 36 Spindus Road, Liverpool, L24 1YA Tel: (07860) 836145 Fax: 0151-207 2783 E-mail: mail@photoflex.co.uk
Pixel Visual Communications Ltd, Shieling House, 30 Invincible Road Industrial Estate, Farnborough, Hampshire, GU14 7QU Tel: (01252) 375750 Fax: (01252) 521155 E-mail: info@pixelvisual.com
Rubislaw Studio, 94a Hamilton Place, Aberdeen, AB15 5BA Tel: (01224) 624460
The Studio, 21 Cabul Road, London, SW11 2PR Tel: (020) 7228 5228 Fax: (020) 7228 9975
Working Images, The Old Stables, Kingston House Estate, Kingston Bagpuize, Abingdon, Oxfordshire, OX13 5AX Tel: (07831) 843338 Fax: (01865) 375855 E-mail: chris@working-images.co.uk

PHOTOGRAPHY PORTALS

▶ Photo Models UK, 1 Burford, Brookside, Telford, Shropshire, TF3 1LJ Tel: 01952 279110 E-mail: info@photomodelsuk.co.uk
▶ Red Dog Photography, 31 Cheadle Road, Uttoxeter, Staffordshire, ST14 7BX Tel: (01889) 569232 E-mail: duncan@reddogphoto.co.uk

PHOTOGRAVURE CYLINDERS OR PLATES

Edwards Engineering (Liverpool) Ltd, Lipton Close, St. Johns Road, Brasenose Industrial Estate, Bootle, Merseyside, L20 8PU Tel: 0151-933 5242 Fax: 0151-922 3383 E-mail: edseng@edwardsenglpoolltd.freeserve.co.uk
Rembrandt Engravers, Northgate, White Lund Industrial Estate, Morecambe, Lancashire, LA3 3BE Tel: (01524) 63236 Fax: (01524) 39874

PHOTOGRAVURE PRINTING

Fretwells Ltd, Oslo Road, Hull, HU7 0YN Tel: (01482) 835511 Fax: (01482) 835368 E-mail: info@fretwells.co.uk
Graphicomm Ltd, 17 Willow Court, St. Modwen Road, Plymouth, PL6 8LQ Tel: (01752) 670099 Fax: (01752) 265700 E-mail: sales@graphicomm.co.uk
Polestar Greaves Ltd, Cayton Low Road, Eastfield, Scarborough, North Yorkshire, YO11 3BX Tel: (01723) 588200 Fax: (01723) 581387
Polestar Varnicoat Ltd, Terrace Road, Pinvin, Pershore, Worcestershire, WR10 2DN Tel: (01386) 552181 Fax: (01386) 556554

PHOTOLUMINESCENT MATERIALS, SAFETY ETC

Jalite plc, Wins House, Bentalls, Basildon, Essex, SS14 3BS Tel: (01268) 242300 Fax: (01268) 274148 E-mail: sales@jalite.com

PHOTOLUMINESCENT STAIR NOSINGS

▶ Anti-Slip, 12 Morningside Terrace, Inverurie, Aberdeenshire, AB51 4FE Tel: (01467) 622721

PHOTOMASKS

▶ Microstencil Limited, Starlaw Park, Starlaw Road, Livingston, West Lothian, EH54 8SF Tel: 01506 409190 Fax: 01506 409181 E-mail: n.gorman@microstencil.com

PHOTOMETERS

Megatron Ltd, Unit 24f1, 784-788 High Road, London, N17 0DA Tel: (020) 8365 9797 Fax: (020) 8808 6186 E-mail: sales@megatron.co.uk

PHOTOPLOTTING BUREAU SERVICES

Micro Metallic Ltd, 125 Bridge Street, Birkenhead, Merseyside, CH41 1BD Tel: 0151-647 4641 Fax: 0151-647 5012 E-mail: info@micromet.co.uk
Phillips Digital Services, Unit 16 Jubilee Trade Centre, Jubilee Road, Letchworth Garden City, Hertfordshire, SG6 1SP Tel: (01462) 674733 Fax: (01462) 677223 E-mail: sales@phillipsdigital.co.uk

PHOTORESIST STRIPPERS

E K C Technology Ltd, 19 Law Place, Nerston, East Kilbride, Glasgow, G74 4QL Tel: (01355) 244652 Fax: (01355) 595444 E-mail: sales@ekctech.co.uk
Rockwood Electronic Materials, Amber Business Centre, Greenhill Industrial Estate, Riddings, Alfreton, Derbyshire, DE55 4DA Tel: (01773) 844200 Fax: (01773) 844244

PHOTOVOLTAIC POWER SUPPLIES

Becosolar, 8-10 Speedwell Units, Nelson Road Industrial Estate, Dartmouth, Devon, TQ6 9SZ Tel: (01803) 833636 Fax: (01803) 835379 E-mail: info@becosolar.com

PHYSICAL LABORATORY EQUIPMENT

Hanatek Sevices Ltd, 10 Sunny Close, Goring-By-Sea, Worthing, West Sussex, BN12 4BD Tel: (01903) 246418 Fax: (01903) 506815 E-mail: info@hanatek.co.uk

PHYSICAL OR TOPOGRAPHICAL SURVEY EQUIPMENT

Pentax UK Ltd, Pentax House, Heron Drive, Slough, SL3 8PN Tel: (01753) 792792 Fax: (01753) 792794 E-mail: contactus@.pentax.co.uk
Scientifica, 9 Allied Business Centre, Coldharbour Lane, Harpenden, Hertfordshire, AL5 4UT Tel: (01582) 766888 Fax: (01582) 767888 E-mail: info@scientifica.uk.com

PHYSICAL VAPOUR DEPOSITION (PVD) SERVICES

Bodycote Metallurgical Coatings Ltd, Harrison Way, Brunswick Business Park, Liverpool, L3 4BG Tel: 0151-709 8411 Fax: 0151-709 2622 E-mail: info@aerogistics.com
Ionbond Ltd, Factory 36 Number One Industrial Estate, Medomsley Road, Consett, County Durham, DH8 6TS Tel: (01207) 500823 Fax: (01207) 590254 E-mail: info@ionbond.com

PHYSICAL WATER CONDITIONERS

Hydropath UK Ltd, Acorn Park, Lenton Lane Industrial Estate, Nottingham, NG7 2TR Tel: 0115-986 9966 Fax: 0115-986 9944 E-mail: sales@hydroflow.com
Life Science Products Ltd, 185l Milton Park, Milton, Abingdon, Oxfordshire, OX14 4SR Tel: (01235) 832111 Fax: (01235) 832129 E-mail: sales@lifescience.co.uk

PHYSIOTHERAPY/MASSAGE AIDS

C M E, 6 Ascot Park Estate, Lenton Street, Sandiacre, Nottingham, NG10 5DL Tel: 0115-949 9066 Fax: 0115-939 3102 E-mail: gcb@cme.globalnet.co.uk
Electro-Medical Supplies Greenham, Grove Street, Wantage, Oxfordshire, OX12 7AD Tel: (01235) 772272 Fax: (01235) 763518 E-mail: info@emslimited.co.uk
▶ Equilibrium Complementary Health Centre, 16 Station Street, Lewes, East Sussex, BN7 2DB Tel: (01273) 470955 E-mail: info@equilibrium-clinic.com
Maheono Alternative Therapies, 99 Reading Road, Yateley, Hampshire, GU46 7LR Tel: (01252) 861351 Fax: E-mail: info@maheono.com
Rothband & Co. Ltd, 4-6 Knowsley Road, Haslingden, Rossendale, Lancashire, BB4 4RX Tel: (01706) 830086 Fax: (01706) 830324 E-mail: sales@rothband.co.uk

PIANO RESTORATION

▶ Michael Eeley & Son, Hose Street Works, Hose Street, Stoke-on-Trent, ST6 5AL Tel: (01782) 813383 Fax: (01782) 813383
▶ Plymouth Piano Centre, 77a Upland Drive, Plymouth, PL6 6BE Tel: (01752) 669428 Fax: (01752) 709400 E-mail: enquiries@plymouthpianocentre.co.uk

PIANOS

▶ Plymouth Piano Centre, 77a Upland Drive, Plymouth, PL6 6BE Tel: (01752) 669428 Fax: (01752) 709400 E-mail: enquiries@plymouthpianocentre.co.uk

PICK AND PLACE HANDLING SYSTEM COMPONENTS

▶ E D S Developments Ltd, Unit 20, Saltash Business Park, Forge Lane, Moorlands Trading Estate, Saltash, Cornwall, PL12 6LX Tel: (01752) 847900 Fax: (01752) 837251 E-mail: info@edsdevelopments.com
E M C Component Handling, Priors Mead, Alcester Road, Inkberrow, Worcester, WR7 4HN Tel: (01386) 793471 Fax: (01386) 793471 E-mail: EMCmail@componenthandling.co.uk

PICK AND PLACE HANDLING SYSTEMS

Dugard Logistics Ltd, 2 Sherwood Road, Bromsgrove, Worcestershire, B60 3DU Tel: (01527) 575947 Fax: (01527) 576100 E-mail: richardshowell@msn.com
▶ E D S Developments Ltd, Unit 20, Saltash Business Park, Forge Lane, Moorlands Trading Estate, Saltash, Cornwall, PL12 6LX Tel: (01752) 847900 Fax: (01752) 837251 E-mail: info@edsdevelopments.com
Meco Pak (UK) Ltd, Greenway House, Sugarswell Business Park, Shenington, Banbury, Oxfordshire, OX15 6HW Tel: (01295) 688910 Fax: (01295) 688911 E-mail: info@mecopak.co.uk
Unique Design Systemation, Manor Farm, Pickstock, Shifnal, Shropshire, TF10 8AH Tel: (01952) 550037 Fax: (01952) 551183 E-mail: bob@unique-design.co.uk

PICK AND PLACE ROBOT SYSTEMS

P H D Automation Ltd, Hutchinson Street, Stockton-on-Tees, Cleveland, TS18 1RW Tel: (01642) 677770 Fax: (01642) 676330 E-mail: info@phdautomation.co.uk

PICK UP TRUCK CANOPIES

Ifor Williams Trailers Ltd, The Smithy, Cynwyd, Corwen, Clwyd, LL21 0LB Tel: (01490) 412527 Fax: (01490) 412770 E-mail: sales@iwt.co.uk

PICK-UP ARMS, AUDIO SYSTEMS

S M E Ltd, Mill Road, Steyning, West Sussex, BN44 3GY Tel: (01903) 814321 Fax: (01903) 814269 E-mail: sales@sme.ltd.uk

PICNIC SETS

▶ Buffet Car, The, 25 Maplewood Park, Deans, Livingston, West Lothian, EH54 8BB Tel: 01506 415055 Fax: 07931 796940 E-mail: Eileen@TheBuffetCar.com

PICTURE FRAME MOULDINGS,

See also headings for particular types

▶ Alderglade Picture Framers, The Alderglade, Harefield Road, Uxbridge, Middlesex, UB8 1PN Tel: (01895) 231205 E-mail: john@alderglade.com
Arqadia Ltd, 2 Wolseley Road, Woburn Road Industrial Estate, Bedford, MK42 7AD Tel: (01234) 857488 Fax: (01234) 840190 E-mail: sales@arqadia.co.uk
M G Framing, Unit 8 Islwyn Workshops, Pontymister Industrial Estate, Risca, Newport, Gwent, NP11 6NP Tel: (01633) 612034 Fax: (01633) 612034 E-mail: mgframing@btinternet.com

PICTURE FRAMES

▶ Aesthetic Frames & Pictures, 33 Northfield Crescent, Driffield, East Yorkshire, YO25 5ES Tel: (01377) 256243 E-mail: mick@pictureframing-uk.com
▶ Alderglade Picture Framers, The Alderglade, Harefield Road, Uxbridge, Middlesex, UB8 1PN Tel: (01895) 231205 E-mail: john@alderglade.com
Art Trade Frames, 2 Dagnan Road, London, SW12 9LQ Tel: (020) 8673 8797 Fax: (020) 8265 2221
Fisher & De Domenici, 10 Church Road, Wimbledon Village, London, SW19 5DL Tel: (020) 8946 9781 Fax: (020) 8946 9781
▶ Fletcher Gallery Services, 1 Newbury Street, London, EC1A 7HU Tel: (020) 7726 4811 Fax: (020) 7606 1826 E-mail: fletcher@fletcherframes.co.uk
Frame Craft Minitures Ltd, Litchfield Road, Brownhills, Walsall, WS8 6LH Tel: (01543) 373076 Fax: (01543) 453154 E-mail: sales@framecraft.com

PICTURE FRAMES – *continued*

▶ Frames, 6 Ladbroke Park, Millers Road, Warwick, CV34 5AN Tel: (01926) 419784 Fax: (01926) 419784 E-mail: info@framesuk.co.uk

▶ Framing Workshop, 16-18 Clarendon Place, Glasgow, G20 7PZ Tel: 0141-332 3817 Fax: 0141-331 0163 E-mail: moira@framingscotland.co.uk

Grays Picture Framers, 19 West Tower Street, Carlisle, CA3 8QT Tel: (01228) 531837 Fax: (01228) 531837

▶ N H Picture Frames, 57 Brongwinau, Comins Coch, Aberystwyth, Dyfed, SY23 3BQ Tel: (01970) 615512 E-mail: kyleireland@hotmail.com

Newgate Gallery, 6a The Bank, Barnard Castle, County Durham, DL12 8PQ Tel: (01833) 695201 Fax: (01833) 695201 E-mail: sales@newgategallery.co.uk

Private View, 7 Windham Road, Sudbury, Suffolk, CO10 2XD Tel: (01787) 377199 Fax: (01787) 881979 E-mail: enquiries@privateviewuk.com

Professional Framing Co. Ltd, St. Georges Road, Redditch, Worcestershire, B98 8EF Tel: (01527) 63039 Fax: (01527) 597323

Shirecraft Designs, 159 Victoria Avenue, Borrowash, Derby, DE72 3HF Tel: (01332) 669136 E-mail: sales@shirecraft.co.uk

Spectrum Photos, Belgrave Gate, Leicester, LE1 3GQ Tel: 0116-251 9478 Fax: 0116-251 9478 E-mail: spectrumphoto@virginnet.co.uk

▶ Thou Art In Hampstead Ltd, 106 Mill Lane, London, NW6 1NF Tel: (020) 7431 0701 Fax: (020) 8444 4446 E-mail: info@thouartinhampstead.co.uk

PICTURE FRAMES, ACRYLIC

▶ Acacia Works, 20 Gayal Croft, Shenley Brook End, Milton Keynes, MK5 7HX Tel: (01908) 501268 E-mail: sales@acaciaworks.co.uk

▶ Imagey - photo print and display products, 16 Bull Lane, London, N18 1SX Tel: 0845 833 0783 Fax: 0845 833 0793 E-mail: info@imagey.co.uk

PICTURE FRAMES, ANTIQUE

▶ Thou Art In Hampstead Ltd, 106 Mill Lane, London, NW6 1NF Tel: (020) 7431 0701 Fax: (020) 8444 4446 E-mail: info@thouartinhampstead.co.uk

PICTURE FRAMES, PLASTIC

▶ Acacia Works, 20 Gayal Croft, Shenley Brook End, Milton Keynes, MK5 7HX Tel: (01908) 501268 E-mail: sales@acaciaworks.co.uk

PICTURE FRAMES, TO SPECIFICATION OR CUSTOM BUILT

▶ Fletcher Gallery Services, 1 Newbury Street, London, EC1A 7HU Tel: (020) 7726 4811 Fax: (020) 7606 1826 E-mail: fletcher@fletcherframes.co.uk

▶ Framing Workshop, 16-18 Clarendon Place, Glasgow, G20 7PZ Tel: 0141-332 3817 Fax: 0141-331 0163 E-mail: moira@framingscotland.co.uk

Private View, 7 Windham Road, Sudbury, Suffolk, CO10 2XD Tel: (01787) 377199 Fax: (01787) 881979 E-mail: enquiries@privateviewuk.com

▶ Thou Art In Hampstead Ltd, 106 Mill Lane, London, NW6 1NF Tel: (020) 7431 0701 Fax: (020) 8444 4446 E-mail: info@thouartinhampstead.co.uk

PICTURE FRAMING

A & B Glassworks, 124 Stoke Newington High Street, London, N16 7NY Tel: (020) 7254 4541 Fax: (020) 7254 4541

A Bliss, 5 Bakers Yard, London, EC1R 3HF Tel: (020) 7837 4959 Fax: (020) 7837 8244 E-mail: sales@abliss.co.uk

▶ Aesthetic Frames & Pictures, 33 Northfield Crescent, Driffield, East Yorkshire, YO25 5ES Tel: (01377) 256243 E-mail: mick@pictureframing-uk.com

Aram Picture Framing, 8 Turnham Green Terrace, London, W4 1QP Tel: (020) 8994 8844 Fax: (020) 8994 8844

Art Trade Frames, 2 Dagnan Road, London, SW12 9LQ Tel: (020) 8673 8797 Fax: (020) 8265 2221

Artistuff Framing Ltd, Victoria Road, Swindon, SN1 3BH Tel: (01793) 522152 Fax: (01793) 488379

▶ artstop.biz, 29 Red Lion Street, Aylsham, Norwich, NR11 6ER Tel: (01263) 734571 Fax: (01263) 735804

▶ Blue Goose Gallery, 87 High Street, West End, Southampton, SO30 3DS Tel: (023) 8047 1818 E-mail: kellysearch@bluegoosegallery.co.uk

Border Line Arts Ltd, 17 Macklin Street, Covent Garden, London, WC2B 5NQ Tel: (020) 7691 8938 Fax: (020) 7691 8969 E-mail: info@borderlinearts.co.uk

▶ Canvas Art, 81 East High Street, Forfar, Angus, DD8 2EQ Tel: (01307) 465715 Fax: (0870) 0569440

Carters Glass Company Ltd, 14-16 Crouch End Hill, London, N8 8AA Tel: (020) 8340 2297

Ceejay Photographic, 290 Ashby High Street, Scunthorpe, South Humberside, DN16 2RX Tel: (01724) 280510 Fax: (01724) 289966 E-mail: sales@ceejaysystems.com

Cherry Creek Gallery, 7 Station Road East, Oxted, Surrey, RH8 0BD Tel: (01883) 734755 Fax: (01883) 734755

Chesham Glass Co., 1 Broad Street, Chesham, Buckinghamshire, HP5 3EA Tel: (01494) 792266 Fax: (01494) 782377

David Lee Photography, George Street, Barton-upon-Humber, South Humberside, DN18 5ES Tel: (01652) 632451 Fax: (01652) 637481 E-mail: enquiries@davidleephotography.co.uk

Designer Mirrors, Unit 11, Slingsby Close, Attleborough Fields Industrial Estate, Nuneaton, Warwickshire, CV11 6RP Tel: (024) 7664 1206 Fax: (024) 7664 1260

The Drawing Group Ltd, 3-9 West St, Hull, HU1 3UR Tel: (01482) 324263 Fax: (01482) 325176 E-mail: sales@drawgroup.co.uk

Ingo Fincke & Son, 24 Battersea Rise, London, SW11 1EE Tel: (020) 7228 7966 Fax: (020) 7652 7966 E-mail: ben@ingofincke.com

Fisher & De Domenici, 10 Church Road, Wimbledon Village, London, SW19 5DL Tel: (020) 8946 9781 Fax: (020) 8946 9781

▶ Fletcher Gallery Services, 1 Newbury Street, London, EC1A 7HU Tel: (020) 7726 4811 Fax: (020) 7606 1826 E-mail: fletcher@fletcherframes.co.uk

Frandsen Fine Arts Ltd, 7 Lillie Yard, Lillie Road, London, SW6 1UB Tel: (020) 7385 9930 Fax: (020) 7610 1404

Gale & Co. Ltd, 12 Lee Bank House, Blucher Street, Birmingham, B1 1HP Tel: 0121-643 6639 Fax: 0121-643 6161

▶ Gleeson Framers, 587c Kingston Road, London, SW20 8SA Tel: (020) 8542 5005 Fax: (020) 8542 5005 E-mail: sales@gleesonframers.co.uk

Grove Galleries Ltd, Phoenix House, Ellesmere Street, Manchester, M15 4JY Tel: 0161-834 8051 Fax: 0161-834 8051

Kandaprint Printers, 9 Oakley Hay Lodge, Great Fold Road, Corby, Northamptonshire, NN18 9AS Tel: (01536) 460890 Fax: (01536) 460890 E-mail: kandaprint@aol.com

Memory Lane Prints, 43 Park Road, Hartlepool, Cleveland, TS24 7PW Tel: (01429) 234268 Fax: (01429) 281007

Midland Framing, 988 Tyburn Road, Birmingham, B24 0TL Tel: 0121-384 4831 Fax: 0121-384 4831

▶ N H Picture Frames, 57 Brongwinau, Comins Coch, Aberystwyth, Dyfed, SY23 3BQ Tel: (01970) 615512 E-mail: kyleireland@hotmail.com

Newgate Gallery, 6a The Bank, Barnard Castle, County Durham, DL12 8PQ Tel: (01833) 695201 Fax: (01833) 695201 E-mail: sales@newgategallery.co.uk

Polymaps, 41 Truro Rd, St. Austell, Cornwall, PL25 5JE Tel: (01726) 66666 Fax: (01726) 64797

▶ Retro Spectives, The Minories, Rother Street, Stratford-upon-Avon, Warwickshire, CV37 6NF Tel: (01789) 297706 E-mail: sales@retrospectives.co.uk

Robsons Glass, 101 Church Road, Formby, Liverpool, L37 3ND Tel: (01704) 875855 Fax: (01704) 875855

Rowley Gallery Ltd, 115 Kensington Church Street, London, W8 7LN Tel: (020) 7727 6495 Fax: (020) 7229 5561

Stevens Graham Picture Framers, 5 Middle Row, East Grinstead, West Sussex, RH19 3AX Tel: (01342) 300685 E-mail: grahamstevensgallery@msn.com

Surrounds Picture Framing, 13 Old Woking Road, West Byfleet, Surrey, KT14 6LW Tel: (01932) 400555 Fax: (01932) 400554 E-mail: info@surrounds.co.uk

Suttle, Willis & Co. Ltd, 28 Goodge Street, London, W1T 2QQ Tel: (020) 7636 5391 Fax: (020) 7636 7723 E-mail: info@conserverframe.com

Westmount Picture Framing, 116A Westmount Road, London, SE9 1UT Tel: (020) 8850 5220

Witham Glass Works, 1 Wilton Street, Hull, HU8 7LG Tel: (01482) 329183 Fax: (01482) 211959

PICTURE FRAMING EQUIPMENT

Euro Baguettes (UK) Ltd, 21 Timberlaine Trading Estate, Decoy Road, Worthing, West Sussex, BN14 8JH Tel: (01903) 205825 Fax: (01903) 206666 E-mail: sales@euro-mouldinds.co.uk

W. & M. Joyce Engineers (Taurus Equipment) Ltd, Steele Road, London, NW10 7AR Tel: (020) 8965 2521 Fax: (020) 8961 0242 E-mail: barry@taurus-equipment.co.uk

Lion Picture Framing Supplies Ltd, 148 Garrison Street, Birmingham, B9 4BN Tel: 0121-773 1230 Fax: 0121-771 2540 E-mail: sales@lionpic.co.uk

▶ Peak Rock, Unit 30 Drca Business Centre, Charlotte Despard Avenue, London, SW11 5HD Tel: (020) 7498 8444 Fax: (020) 7498 8333 E-mail: sales@peakrock.com

PICTURE HOOKS

▶ Peak Rock, Unit 30 Drca Business Centre, Charlotte Despard Avenue, London, SW11 5HD Tel: (020) 7498 8444 Fax: (020) 7498 8333 E-mail: sales@peakrock.com

Frank Shaw (Bayonet) Ltd, Merse Road, North Moons Moat, Redditch, Worcestershire, B98 9HL Tel: (01527) 66241 Fax: (01527) 584455 E-mail: sales@frankshaw.co.uk

PICTURE MOUNT BOARDS

Arqadia Ltd, 2 Wolseley Road, Woburn Road Industrial Estate, Bedford, MK42 7AD Tel: (01234) 857488 Fax: (01234) 840190 E-mail: sales@arqadia.co.uk

PICTURE MOUNTS

▶ Britannia Mounts Co. Ltd, Unit E3-E4, Meltham Mills Industrial Estate, Meltham, Holmfirth, HD9 4DS Tel: (01484) 854444 Fax: (01484) 854433 E-mail: sales@britannia-mounts.co.uk

▶ Moonshine Studio, 1 High Street, Penzance, Cornwall, TR18 2SX Tel: (01736) 330887 Fax: (01736) 330887 E-mail: info@frames.uk.com

PICTURE OR WORK OF ART LIGHTING

Classical Lighting, R/O 499 High Rd, Leytonstone, London, E11 4PG Tel: (020) 8556 3056 Fax: (020) 8556 4242 E-mail: sales@classical-lighting.freeserve.co.uk

▶ Peak Rock, Unit 30 Drca Business Centre, Charlotte Despard Avenue, London, SW11 5HD Tel: (020) 7498 8444 Fax: (020) 7498 8333 E-mail: sales@peakrock.com

PIE/TART MAKING MACHINERY

Dexmore Co Ltd, Hartshill Road, Stoke-on-Trent, ST4 7NF Tel: (01782) 846376 Fax: (01782) 414769 E-mail: sales@dexmore.co.uk

Fish In Crewe Engineering Ltd, 14 Gateway, Crewe, CW1 6YY Tel: (01270) 251200 Fax: (01270) 251300 E-mail: sales@fishincrewe.co.uk

Orbiter Food Machinery, Private Road 7, Colwick Industrial Estate, Nottingham, NG4 2JW Tel: 0115-940 0372 Fax: 0115-961 8741 E-mail: enquiries@orbiterfoodmachinery.co.uk

PIECE-END SEWING MACHINES

Merrow Sales UK Ltd, 17 Glebe Road, Groby, Leicester, LE6 0GT Tel: 0116-232 1779 Fax: 0116-287 8099

PIES

▶ Roberts Country Fayre, Bersham Enterprise Centre, Colliery Road, Rhostyllen, Wrexham, Clwyd, LL14 4EG Tel: (01978) 264444 Fax: (01978) 354303 E-mail: robertscountryfayre@virgin.net

Voakes Of Whixley, Whixley Grange, Boroughbridge Road, Whixley, York, YO26 8AY Tel: (01423) 339988 Fax: (01423) 339988

PIEZOELECTRIC CERAMICS

▶ Saint-Gobain Quartz P.L.C, PO Box 6, Wallsend, Tyne & Wear, NE28 6DG Tel: 0191-262 5311 Fax: 0191-263 8040 E-mail: quartz.sales@saint-gobain.com

PIG FEEDING SYSTEMS

E B Equipment Ltd, Barugh Green Road, Redbrook, Barnsley, South Yorkshire, S75 1HR Tel: (01226) 730037 Fax: (01226) 738101 E-mail: info@eb-equipment.com

PIG FOODS

Allen & Page Ltd, Norfolk Mill, Shipdham, Thetford, Norfolk, IP25 7SD Tel: (01362) 822900 Fax: (01362) 822910 E-mail: sales@allenandpage.co.uk

PIG PAPER BEDDING

▶ Paul Garner, 4 Poplar Grove, Ravenfield, Rotherham, South Yorkshire, S65 4LJ Tel: (07737) 036085 E-mail: pj1racing@hotmail.com

PIGGING SYSTEMS

▶ Albion Robotics Ltd, 6 Castletown, Portland, Dorset, DT5 1BD Tel: (01305) 826384 Fax: (01305) 826056 E-mail: shipping@albiongroup.org

G D Engineering, Retford Road, Worksop, Nottinghamshire, S80 2PY Tel: (01909) 482323 Fax: (01909) 477902

Ibex Geo-tech Ltd, Ibex House, Malt Mill Lane, Halesowen, W. Midlands, B62 8JJ Tel: 0121-559 3862 Fax: 0121-559 9404 E-mail: jane.palmer@ibexgeotech.com

Skeltonhall Systems Ltd, 70 Carwood Road, Sheffield, S4 7SD Tel: 0114-243 1332 Fax: 0114-244 9579 E-mail: info@skeltonhall-systems.com

PIGGYBACK CONNECTORS

▶ DogEgg Ltd, Network House, Bolton Road, Pendlebury, Swinton, Manchester, M27 8BB Tel: 0161-728 4666 Fax: (07869) 078013 E-mail: sales@dogegg.net

PIGMENT DISPERSANTS

Anikem Ltd, 18 North Gate, Harborne, Birmingham, B17 9EP Tel: 0121-428 1355 Fax: 0121-428 1366 E-mail: sales@anikem.co.uk

PIGMENT DISPERSIONS

Breamhurst Ltd, Gorsey Lane, Clock Face, St. Helens, Merseyside, WA9 4SE Tel: (01744) 811208 Fax: (01744) 820004 E-mail: info@breamhurstdytran.co.uk

Campbell Plastics Ltd, 6 Robinson Close, Telford Way Industrial Estate, Kettering, Northamptonshire, NN16 8PU Tel: (01536) 516563 Fax: (01536) 310086

D & D Dispersions Ltd, Unit G, St. Marks Road, St. James Industrial Estate, Corby, Northamptonshire, NN18 8AN Tel: (01536) 400488 Fax: (01536) 407365 E-mail: dispersion@dddispersions.co.uk

Dispersion Technology Ltd, Factory Lane, Brantham, Manningtree, Essex, CO11 1NJ Tel: (01206) 395000 Fax: (01206) 392872 E-mail: christine@dispersion-technology.co.uk

Gemini Dispersions Ltd, Holt Mill Road, Rossendale, Lancashire, BB4 7JB Tel: (01706) 214751 Fax: (01706) 218152 E-mail: sales@geminidispersions.com

P J Colours Ltd, Excelsior Works, Castle Park, Flint, Clwyd, CH6 5NT Tel: (01352) 732157 Fax: (01352) 735530 E-mail: info@pjcolours.com

P W Hall Ltd, Woodilee Industrial Estate, Lenzie, Kirkintilloch, Glasgow, G66 3UR Tel: 0141-776 2384 Fax: 0141-776 2382 E-mail: dir@pwhall.co.uk

Prisma Colour Ltd, Hole House Mill, Marple Road, Chisworth, Glossop, Derbyshire, SK13 5DH Tel: (01457) 856505 Fax: (01457) 856505 E-mail: sales@prismacolour.com

Tenants Inks & Coatings Suppliers, Ruspidge Road, Cinderford, Gloucestershire, GL14 3AW Tel: (01594) 822375 Fax: (01594) 826251 E-mail: salessupport@tg-tics.com

Thane Dispersions Ltd, Spedding Road, Fenton Industrial Estate, Stoke-on-Trent, ST4 2ST Tel: (01782) 412217 Fax: (01782) 744769 E-mail: enquiries@thane.uk.com

West & Senior Ltd, Milltown Street, Radcliffe, Manchester, M26 1WE Tel: 0161-724 7131 Fax: 0161-724 9519 E-mail: david.brown@westsenior.co.uk

PIGMENTS, *See also headings for particular types*

Albion Colours Ltd, High Level Way, Halifax, West Yorkshire, HX1 4PN Tel: (01422) 358431 Fax: (01422) 330867 E-mail: colours.sales@albionchemicals.co.uk

Amatar Ltd, Amatar House, Manor Road, Woodley, Stockport, Cheshire, SK6 1RT Tel: 0161-494 6692 Fax: 0161-406 6752 E-mail: djo171135@aol.com

Amps Ltd, Wheatsheaf Buildings, High Street, Rhosymedre, Wrexham, Clwyd, LL14 3YE Tel: (01978) 810808 Fax: (01978) 810700 E-mail: info@amps-ltd.co.uk

Bituchem Group, Laymore Road, Forest Vale Industrial Estate, Cinderford, Gloucestershire, GL14 2YH Tel: (01594) 826768 Fax: (01594) 826948 E-mail: sales@bituchem.com

E.P. Bray & Co. Ltd, Coombes Lane Works, Charlesworth, Glossop, Derbyshire, SK13 5DQ Tel: (01457) 853277 Fax: (01457) 856114 E-mail: epbray@charlesworth81.fsnet.co.uk

BTC Speciality Chemical Distribution Ltd, PO Box 4, Cheadle, Cheshire, SK8 6QG Tel: 0161-488 5223 Fax: 0161-486 6184 E-mail: sales@btc-uk.com

Ciba Specialty Chemicals plc, Charter Road, Macclesfield, Cheshire, SK10 2NX Tel: (01625) 665000 Fax: (01625) 619637

D V M Pigments & Additives, 45 Judeland, Chorley, Lancashire, PR7 1XJ Tel: (01257) 270311 Fax: (01257) 265509 E-mail: sales@dvmpigments.co.uk

PIGMENTS – *continued*

ECL Chemicals Ltd, Impex House, Leestone Road, Sharston, Manchester, M22 4RN Tel: 0161-491 6744 Fax: 0161-491 6774 E-mail: info@eclchem.com
Holliday Pigments Ltd, Morley Street, Hull, HU8 8DN Tel: (01482) 329875 Fax: (01484) 329791 E-mail: sales@holliday-pigments.com
Impalloy Ltd, Alloys House, Willenhall Lane, Bloxwich, Walsall, WS3 2XN Tel: (01922) 714400 Fax: (01922) 714411 E-mail: sales@impalloy.com
James M Brown Ltd, Boving Works, Napier Street, Stoke-on-Trent, ST4 4NX Tel: (01782) 744171 Fax: (01782) 744473 E-mail: sales@jamesmbrown.co.uk
Kronos Ltd, Barons Court, Manchester Road, Wilmslow, Cheshire, SK9 1BQ Tel: (01625) 547200 Fax: (01625) 533123 E-mail: kronos.sales.uk@nli-usa.com
Llewellyn Ryland Ltd, Haden Street, Birmingham, B12 9DB Tel: 0121-440 2284 Fax: 0121-440 0281 E-mail: sales@llewellyn-ryland.co.uk
Magna Colours Ltd, 3 Dodworth Business Park, Upper Cliffe Road, Dodworth, Barnsley, South Yorkshire, S75 3SP Tel: (01226) 731751 Fax: (01226) 731752 E-mail: sales@magnacolours.com
Saville Whittle Ltd, Albion Bridge Works, Vickers Street, Manchester, M40 8EF Tel: 0161-205 1538 Fax: 0161-203 4159 E-mail: sales@savillewhittle.co.uk
Speciality Chemicals, 6 Fairbay Road, Business Park, Little Port, Ely, Cambridgeshire, CB6 1PE Tel: (01353) 863686 Fax: (01353) 863990 E-mail: sales@capricorn.co.uk
Tennants Textile Colours, 31-43 Ravenhill Rd, Belfast, BT6 8DP Tel: (028) 9045 1396 Fax: (028) 9045 8944 E-mail: sales@tennantstextilecolours.com
Unicolour Ltd, Tandem Works, Wakefield Road, Waterloo, Huddersfield, HD5 0AN Tel: (01484) 516974 Fax: (01484) 510667 E-mail: dyes@unicolour.co.uk
Whitchem Ltd, 23 Albert Street, Newcastle, Staffordshire, ST5 1JP Tel: (01782) 711777 Fax: (01782) 717290 E-mail: enquiries@whitchem.co.uk

PIGS, OILFIELD/PIPELINE

▶ Albion Robotics Ltd, 6 Castletown, Portland, Dorset, DT5 1BD Tel: (01305) 826384 Fax: (01305) 826056 E-mail: shipping@albiongroup.org
Girard Industries Europe Ltd, Unit C5, Olympic Business Park, Dundonald, Kilmarnock, Ayrshire, KA2 9BE Tel: (01563) 851062 Fax: (01563) 851411 E-mail: girardindeurope@hotmail.com

PILASTERS

Stevensons Of Norwich Ltd, Roundtree Way, Norwich, NR7 8SQ Tel: (01603) 400824 Fax: (01603) 405113 E-mail: sales@stevensons-of-norwich.co.uk

PILE DRIVING CONTRACTORS

Pennine Projects Ltd, New Line Industrial Estate, Bacup, Lancashire, OL13 9RW Tel: (01706) 877555 Fax: (01706) 879754 E-mail: info@pennine-group.co.uk

PILE DRIVING EQUIPMENT

▶ All Foundations Ltd, PO Box 2146, Watford, WD18 1AS Tel: (0870) 3503050 Fax: (0870) 3503060 E-mail: mail@allfoundations.co.uk
Dawson Construction Plant Ltd, Chesney Wold, Bleak Hall, Milton Keynes, MK6 1NE Tel: (01908) 240300 Fax: (01908) 240222 E-mail: dawson@dcpuk.com

PILE DRIVING EQUIPMENT HIRE

Aldridge Piling Equipment Hire Co. Ltd, Conduit Road, Norton Canes, Cannock, Staffordshire, WS11 9TJ Tel: (01543) 277680 Fax: (01543) 270090 E-mail: info@miniape.com
Dawson Construction Plant Ltd, Chesney Wold, Bleak Hall, Milton Keynes, MK6 1NE Tel: (01908) 240300 Fax: (01908) 240222 E-mail: dawson@dcpuk.com
Watson & Hillhouse Ltd, Whitehouse Road, Ipswich, IP1 5NT Tel: (01473) 748652 Fax: (01473) 240090 E-mail: info@w-h.co.uk

PILE FABRICS, *See also headings for particular types*

J H Walker, Ravensthorpe Mills, Calder Road, Dewsbury, West Yorkshire, WF13 3JS Tel: (01924) 466544 Fax: (01924) 455977
John Holdsworth & Co. Ltd, Shaw Lodge Mills, Halifax, West Yorkshire, HX3 9ET Tel: (01422) 433000 Fax: (01422) 433300 E-mail: sales@holdsworth.co.uk

PILE HOLE BORING EQUIPMENT

Nub Engineering Ltd, Newhouse Industrial Estate, Newhouse, Motherwell, Lanarkshire, ML1 5RX Tel: (01698) 833873 Fax: (01698) 734322 E-mail: sales@nubeng.com

PILING

Green Piling Ltd, Smithy Brook Road, Renishaw, Sheffield, S21 3JS Tel: 08450 511800 Fax: 08450 511811 E-mail: info@greenpiling.co.uk

PILING, CONCRETE

▶ Stent Foundations Ltd, Pavilion C2, Ashwood Park, Ashwood Way, Basingstoke, Hampshire, RG23 8BG Tel: (01256) 400200 Fax: (01256) 400201 E-mail: foundations@stent.co.uk

PILLOW PROTECTORS

Cumulus Mattress Protectors, Selinas Lane, Dagenham, Essex, RM8 1ES Tel: (020) 8592 2233 Fax: (020) 8593 3787 E-mail: enquiries@abbey-quilting.co.uk

PILLOWCASES

▶ Tonder & Tonder, Bryants Farm, Kiln Road, Dunsden, Reading, RG4 9PB Tel: 0118-946 3704 Fax: 0118-946 3801 E-mail: sales@tonderandtonder.com

PIN INSERTION MACHINES, *See also headings for particular types, eg: Spring*

Spirol Industries Ltd, 17 Princewood Road, Earlstrees Industrial Estate, Corby, Northamptonshire, NN17 4ET Tel: (01536) 444800 Fax: (01536) 203415 E-mail: info@spirol.co.uk

PINBALL MACHINE HIRE

▶ Pinball Pleasure, High Road, Chadwell Heath, Romford, RM6 6AU Tel: (020) 8599 6121 E-mail: sales@pinballmachines.co.uk

PINBALL MACHINES

▶ Amusement Caterers Sheffield Ltd, 140 Walkley Lane, Sheffield, S6 2NZ Tel: 0114-234 9808 Fax: 0114-285 2342 E-mail: andy@amusementcaterers.com
▶ Pinball Pleasure, High Road, Chadwell Heath, Romford, RM6 6AU Tel: (020) 8599 6121 E-mail: sales@pinballmachines.co.uk

PINCH VALVES

Bush & Wilton Ltd, 6 Millennium Place, Tiverton Business Park, Tiverton, Devon, EX16 6SB Tel: (01884) 242233 Fax: (01884) 252555 E-mail: sales@bushandwilton.com
Prochem Services Ltd, Mill Street, Congleton, Cheshire, CW12 2AD Tel: (01260) 299770 Fax: (01260) 299880 E-mail: info@prochem-services.com
S & P Spanarc Ltd, Berwick House, 32 Dartford Road, Sevenoaks, Kent, TN13 3TQ Tel: (01732) 743456 Fax: (01732) 742922 E-mail: chris.guinane@spanarc.co.uk

PINE

Chanterlands Pine Centre, 157 Chanterlands Avenue, Hull, HU5 3TJ Tel: (01482) 492682 Fax: (01482) 492682
Retford Pine, Beehive Street, Retford, Nottinghamshire, DN22 6JE Tel: (01777) 869669 Fax: (01777) 700701 E-mail: sales@squeakfree.co.uk

PINE DOORS

▶ Alpha Pine (Harrogate) Ltd, 55 Knaresborough Road, Harrogate, North Yorkshire, HG2 7LT Tel: (01423) 885196 Fax: (01423) 885196 E-mail: info@alphapine.co.uk
Island Pine, 64 Union Place, Dungannon, County Tyrone, BT70 1DL Tel: (028) 8775 3545 Fax: (028) 8775 2747 E-mail: sales@islandpine.co.uk

PINE FURNITURE

▶ A World of Old, The Barns, Wingrave Road, Aston Abbotts, Aylesbury, Buckinghamshire, HP22 4LU Tel: (01296) 680406 Fax: (01296) 680437
A World Of Pine, 2 The Wyndham Centre, Dairy Meadow L, Salisbury, SP1 2TJ Tel: (01722) 413532 Fax: (01722) 413532 E-mail: info@worldofpine.co.uk
Abacus Pine, 34 Rawmarsh Hill, Parkgate, Rotherham, South Yorkshire, S62 6EU Tel: (01709) 719509
All Pine, 97 Dymchurch Road, Hythe, Kent, CT21 6JN Tel: (01303) 262373 Fax: (01303) 262373
Aura Furniture, Unit 1 The Precinct, Cheadle Hulme, Cheadle, Cheshire, SK8 5BB Tel: 0161-486 6566
Avon Pine Ltd, 34 Old Broughton Road, Melksham, Wiltshire, SN12 8BX Tel: (01225) 700878 Fax: (01225) 793540 E-mail: sales@avonpine.co.uk
Barlis Pine Ltd, 5-6 Tentercroft Street Industrial Estate, Lincoln, LN5 7ED Tel: (01522) 567745 Fax: (01522) 544336 E-mail: barlispine@hotmail.com
Bawtry Pine Furniture, Woodhouse, Cooke Street, Bentley, Doncaster, South Yorkshire, DN5 0BH Tel: (01302) 875578
Bracken Wood Craft, The Stanway Centre, Peartree Road, Colchester, CO3 0JX Tel: (01206) 561316 Fax: (01206) 575619
Bracken Woodcraft, Chelmsford Road, Rawreth, Wickford, Essex, SS11 8SJ Tel: (01268) 571800 Fax: (01268) 571870
Broad Oak Woodcraft Ltd, Grange Farm Regis, Hatfield Broad Oak, Bishop's Stortford, Hertfordshire, CM22 7JZ Tel: (01279) 718549 Fax: (01279) 718549
Bumble End Barn Old Pine, Grove Lane, Wishaw, Sutton Coldfield, West Midlands, B76 9PH Tel: 0121-351 3993 Fax: 0121-351 3993 E-mail: bumblepine@aol.com
Burnside Pine Co, Unit 1 Back Grange Avenue, Harrogate, North Yorkshire, HG1 2AN Tel: (01423) 528116
Bury Bank Pine, Bury Bank, Meaford, Stone, Staffordshire, ST15 0QA Tel: (01785) 813928 Fax: (01785) 813928 E-mail: secured@burybankpine.fsnet.co.uk
Butchers Arms Gallery & Coffee Shop, Heol-Y-Sarn, Llantrisant, Pontyclun, Mid Glamorgan, CF72 8DA Tel: (01443) 229285 Fax: (01443) 238436
C & L Pine Bros Ltd, A B Draycott Cross Road, Cheadle, Stoke-on-Trent, ST10 1PN Tel: (01538) 750110 Fax: (01538) 750110
Canadian Pine Co., 159 Victoria Street, Stoke-on-Trent, ST4 6HA Tel: (01782) 710909 Fax: (01782) 710909
Castle Pine Trading Co., Burcroft Hill, Conisbrough, Doncaster, South Yorkshire, DN12 3EF Tel: (01709) 865999 Fax: (01709) 865999
▶ Central Pine, 28-29 Lower Tower Street, Birmingham, B19 3NH Tel: 0121-333 6162 Fax: 0121-333 6162
Chase Pine, Vine Cottage, Winchester Road, Waltham Chase, Southampton, SO32 2LX Tel: (01329) 832366 E-mail: chasepine@yahoo.co.uk
Colne Pine Centre, Colne Lane, Colne, Lancashire, BB8 0EF Tel: (01282) 861978
Copthorne Furniture Co. Ltd, Copthorne Bank, Copthorne, Crawley, West Sussex, RH10 3RE Tel: (01342) 718886 Fax: (01342) 712802
The Cotswold Collection, 1 Babdown Airfield, Beverston, Tetbury, Gloucestershire, GL8 8TT Tel: (01666) 503555 Fax: (01666) 505288
Country Pine, The Tithe Barn, Letheringsett Hill, Holt, Norfolk, NR25 6RY Tel: (01263) 711666 Fax: (01263) 711666 E-mail: sales@holt-country-pine.com
Country Pine Furniture Cowbridge Ltd, Duke of Wellington Mews, Church Street, Cowbridge, South Glamorgan, CF71 7BB Tel: (01446) 775491 Fax: (01446) 775040
Country Theme, 12 South Street, Wareham, Dorset, BH20 4LT Tel: (01929) 553001 Fax: (01929) 553001
Crabtree Cottage Interiors, 24 Shore Road, Enniskillen, County Fermanagh, BT74 7EF Tel: (028) 6632 4333 Fax: (028) 6632 0819
D P Furniture Express, 18-20 Silver Street, Doncaster, South Yorkshire, DN1 1HQ Tel: (01302) 365535 Fax: (01302) 365535
Devonshire Pine Ltd, Caddsdown Industrial Park, Clovelly Road, Bideford, Devon, EX39 3DX Tel: (01237) 421900 Fax: (01237) 470070
Dove Furniture, 1 Nursery Buildings, York Road, Riccall, York, YO19 6QQ Tel: (01757) 249171 Fax: (01757) 249278 E-mail: craigandkim@btinternet.com
Earsham Hall Pine, 6 St Benedicts Street, Norwich, NR2 4AG Tel: (01603) 615710 Fax: (01603) 615710 E-mail: sales@earshamhallpine.co.uk
Ebeniste Pine Ltd, Maunside, Green Line Industrial Estate, Mansfield, Nottinghamshire, NG18 5GU Tel: (01623) 421090 Fax: (01623) 632430 E-mail: info@ebenistepine.co.uk
Emily's Cottage, Unit 21 Hatton Country World, Hatton, Warwick, CV35 7LD Tel: (01926) 843781
Fine Homes, Grove House, 227-233 London Road, Hazel Grove, Stockport, Cheshire, SK7 4HS Tel: 0161-483 0202 Fax: 0161-483 0202 E-mail: info@finehomes.co.uk
▶ First Bed & Pine Centre, 67 London Road, East Grinstead, West Sussex, RH19 1EQ Tel: (01342) 322700 Fax: (01342) 301252
G & A Pine Products, White House Farm, Valley La, Long Bennington, Newark, Notts, NG23 5EE Tel: (01400) 282788 Fax: (01400) 282788
G & B Pine Co., 1 Tanhouse Lane, Widnes, Cheshire, WA8 0RZ Tel: 0151-495 1743 Fax: 0151-495 1743
Hall Pine, 45 Westdale Lane, Carlton, Nottingham, NG4 3JN Tel: 0115-961 2926 Fax: 0115-961 2926
Hanslope Pine & Craft, 16 High Street, Hanslope, Milton Keynes, MK19 7LQ Tel: (01908) 510226 Fax: (01908) 510226
Hardy Antiques, Wisteria Cottage, The Street, Hacheston, Woodbridge, Suffolk, IP13 0DS Tel: (01728) 746568 Fax: (01728) 746568
Harvest Pine, 6 Pepper Street, Nantwich, Cheshire, CW5 5AB Tel: (01270) 627776 Fax: (01270) 627776
▶ Hastings Pine Furniture Warehouse, A 409 Battle Road, St. Leonards-on-Sea, East Sussex, TN37 7BE Tel: (01424) 855120 Fax: (01424) 855120
Highgate Joinery, 18 Wightman Road, London, N4 1SQ Tel: (020) 8341 4823 Fax: (020) 8341 5656
Holders Fine Furniture, 169-173 Malden Road, London, NW5 4HT Tel: (020) 7485 2741 Fax: (020) 7916 9259 E-mail: sales@holders-pine.co.uk
Horncastle Pine, 13 Bull Ring, Horncastle, Lincolnshire, LN9 5HU Tel: (01507) 526666 Fax: (01507) 526666
House Of Pine, 25 St. Martins Precinct, Church Street, Caversham, Reading, RG4 8BA Tel: 0118-947 2333 Fax: 0118-947 2333
Hoverwood Ltd, Alresford Business Centre, Colchester Main Road, Alresford, Colchester, CO7 8DJ Tel: (01206) 826868 Fax: (01206) 826868
Intercasa Ltd, P O Box 92, Manchester, M17 1JQ Tel: 0161-877 3637 Fax: 0161 8773637
J Kruczko, 28 High Street, Benson, Wallingford, Oxfordshire, OX10 6RP Tel: (01865) 340040 Fax: (01865) 340040
J P Pine Ltd, Unit 8 Cci Business Pk, St. Asaph Av, Kinmel Bay, Rhyl, Clwyd, LL18 5HA Tel: 01745 369091
Johnston Pine, 9b Main Street, Guardbridge, St. Andrews, Fife, KY16 0UG Tel: (01334) 838783 Fax: (01334) 838783
Lawrence Joinery Pine Specialists, Unit 15b Greenhill Mills, Grange Road, Batley, West Yorkshire, WF17 6LH Tel: (01924) 422088 Fax: (01924) 422088
Leamington Pine Workshop, Unit 2 Court Street, Milverton House, Leamington Spa, Warwickshire, CV31 2BB Tel: (01926) 312229 Fax: (01926) 312229
Leigh Pine, 73 Leigh Road, Leigh-on-Sea, Essex, SS9 1JN Tel: (01702) 477725 Fax: (01702) 477725 E-mail: enquiries@leighpine.co.uk
Lewis Furniture Ltd, 3A Bridge Street, Halesworth, Suffolk, IP19 8AB Tel: (01986) 874002 Fax: (01986) 874002
M & C Furnishing Pine Centre, 115-117 Albert Road, Colne, Lancashire, BB8 0BT Tel: (01282) 869072 Fax: (01282) 869072
Major Pine Trade Suppliers Ltd, Unit H2 Beckingham Business Park, Beckingham Street, Tolleshunt Major, Maldon, Essex, CM9 8LZ Tel: (01621) 868722 Fax: (01621) 869543
Minehead Pine, E F South Road, Watchet, Somerset, TA23 0HF Tel: (01984) 639044 Fax: (01984) 639396 E-mail: enquiries@pineman.com
Mirage, The Old Bakery, 54 High Street, Methwold, Thetford, Norfolk, IP26 4NX Tel: (01366) 727777 Fax: (01366) 727778
Moorepine, 98 Moore St, Bootle, Merseyside, L20 4PL Tel: 0151-933 7141
Moorside Pine, 3 Keighley Road, Steeton, Keighley, West Yorkshire, BD20 6RJ Tel: (01535) 656925
▶ More Than Pine Ltd, 60-62 Friar Street, Reading, RG1 1DX Tel: 0118-951 0010 Fax: 0118-951 0038 E-mail: morethanpine@fsmail.net
Norcraft Timber Products, Unit B9, Hamar Close, Tyne Tunnel Trading Estate, North Shields, Tyne & Wear, NE29 7XB Tel: 0191-200 8383
Nostalgic Pine & Beds, 1038-1040 Stockport Road, Manchester, M19 3WX Tel: 0161-248 4846 Fax: 0161-248 4846 E-mail: nostalgicpine@aol.com
▶ Off The Wall, Unit 11b Monksbridge Trading Estate, Outgang Lane, Dinnington, Sheffield, S25 3QZ Tel: (01909) 569131 Fax: (01909) 561983
Old Pine Flooring, Park Copse Cottage, Hamptworth, Salisbury, SP5 2DS Tel: (01794) 390434 Fax: (01794) 390434
Old School Pine, The Old School, Kilmuir Easter, Invergordon, Ross-Shire, IV18 0NE Tel: (01862) 842611 Fax: (01862) 842854
Olivers Fine Furniture, 26 Pillory Street, Nantwich, Cheshire, CW5 5BG Tel: (01270) 628830 Fax: (01270) 628830
Oswald Road Pine & Country Furniture, Oswald Road, Oswestry, Shropshire, SY11 1RE Tel: (01691) 670690 Fax: (01691) 670690 E-mail: sales@pinestores.co.uk
Palmer Pine & Design, Unit 6 Alexandra Road, Sudbury, Suffolk, CO10 6XH Tel: (01787) 379819 Fax: (01787) 882425
Past & Present, Faxfleet Hall, Faxfleet, Goole, North Humberside, DN14 7YT Tel: (01430) 449090
Pearce Pine, 3 The Old Dairy, Culverthorpe, Grantham, Lincolnshire, NG32 3NQ Tel: (01529) 455756 Fax: (01529) 455756
▶ Phoenix Pine, Unit 3-4 Ebor Business Park, Ure Bank Top, Ripon, North Yorkshire, HG4 1JD Tel: (01765) 602070 Fax: (01765) 608100
Pine & Bed Centre, 63-65 Pasture Road, Goole, North Humberside, DN14 6BP Tel: (01405) 720444 Fax: (01405) 720444

PINE FURNITURE – *continued*

Pine Direct, 46 John St, Aberdeen, AB25 1LL Tel: (01224) 626404

Pine Factory, 2 Ford Farm, Braintree Road, Dunmow, Essex, CM6 1HU Tel: (01371) 872292 E-mail: sales@pine-factorydunmow.co.uk

The Pine Factory (Truro) Ltd, Unit 2 Visicks Yard, Perranarworthal, Truro, Cornwall, TR3 7NR Tel: (01872) 862696 Fax: (01872) 870394

▶ Pine Nation Ltd, 3 Arrow Industrial Estate, Straight Road, Willenhall, West Midlands, WV12 5AE Tel: (01922) 711177 Fax: (01922) 711177 E-mail: pinenation@btconnect.com

Pine Place, 1 The Old Foundry, Victoria Road, Kington, Herefordshire, HR5 3DA Tel: (01544) 231766

Pine Store, 2 9a Burnett Road, Inverness, IV1 1TF Tel: (01463) 716718 Fax: (01463) 716718

Pine Studio, 11-11a Friars Street, Sudbury, Suffolk, CO10 2AA Tel: (01787) 379624 Fax: (01787) 370982 E-mail: info@pine-studio.co.uk

The Pine Table Co. Ltd, Unit 2, Sleaford Road Industrial Estate, Bracebridge Heath, Lincoln, LN4 2ND Tel: (01522) 511220 Fax: (01522) 511225

Pine Time Trading, 96 London Road, Bexhill-on-Sea, East Sussex, TN39 3LE Tel: (01424) 213002 Fax: (01424) 213002 E-mail: enquiries@pinetimetrading.com

Pine Trading Co., 94-96 The Horsefair, Bristol, BS1 3JS Tel: 0117-929 9186 Fax: 0117-925 4099 E-mail: sales@pinetrading.co.uk

Pine Trading Co., 77 Queens Way, Southampton, SO14 3HJ Tel: (023) 8033 7339 Fax: (023) 8033 7303

▶ Pine Tree, 69 Bruntcliffe Road, Morley, Leeds, LS27 0LQ Tel: 0113-252 0808 Fax: 0113-252 0808 E-mail: sales@thepinetreemorley.co.uk

Pine Workshop, 150 Shore Road, Greenisland, Carrickfergus, County Antrim, BT38 8TT Tel: (028) 9036 4754

Pine Workshop, Manor Barn, Browns Lane, Keyworth, Nottingham, NG12 5BL Tel: 0115-937 7227 Fax: 0115-937 7227

Pine World, 64 Union Road, Camelon, Falkirk, FK1 4PF Tel: (01324) 624467 Fax: (01324) 626217 E-mail: sales@pineworld.co.uk

Pine World, 14 Riverside Walk, Thetford, Norfolk, IP24 2BG Tel: (01842) 766060

The Pine Xchange, Melbourne Airfield, Seaton Ross, York, YO42 4NF Tel: (01759) 318833 Fax: (01759) 318822

Pinetum Ltd, Roman Way Crusader Park, Warminster, Wiltshire, BA12 8SJ Tel: (01985) 224540 Fax: (01985) 211158 E-mail: sales@pinetum.co.uk

Pinewood Furniture, 15 Kilmandil Road, Dunloy, Ballymena, County Antrim, BT44 9BH Tel: (028) 2763 8653 Fax: (028) 2763 8653 E-mail: info@pine-furniture.co.uk

Pinewood Studios Ltd, Godley Road, Halifax, West Yorkshire, HX3 6AH Tel: (01422) 369666 Fax: (01422) 320227

Pineworld, Timworth Green, Timworth, Bury St. Edmunds, Suffolk, IP31 1HS Tel: (01284) 728621 Fax: (01284) 728191 E-mail: sales@pineworlduk.com

Planet Pine, 57 Framfield Road, Uckfield, East Sussex, TN22 5AJ Tel: (01825) 766048

Porky Pine, West Street, Coggeshall, Colchester, CO6 1NT Tel: (01376) 563323 Fax: (01376) 563323 E-mail: info@pinefurnitureessex.com

Principally Pine, 47-49 Ferensway, Hull, HU2 8NA Tel: (01482) 588099 Fax: (01482) 609587

Raynesway Pine Company Ltd, 227 Derby Road, Spondon, Derby, DE21 7LW Tel: (01332) 820211

Reeves Pine, 213 High Street, Chatham, Kent, ME4 4BG Tel: (01634) 401043

Retford Pine, Beehive Street, Retford, Nottinghamshire, DN22 6JE Tel: (01777) 869669 Fax: (01777) 700701 E-mail: sales@squeakfree.co.uk

Riverside Pine, 3 Pingle Farm, Seine Lane, Enderby, Leicester, LE19 4PD Tel: 0116-284 1737

Rural Pine Crafts, Wyevale Garden Centre, 24 Wareham Rd, Galton, Dorchester, Dorset, DT2 8BY Tel: 01305 851541 Fax: 01305 851541

Sabins Pine Furniture, 17 Church Road, Codsall, Wolverhampton, WV8 1EA Tel: (01902) 846027

Scartop Pine Furniture, 191 Station Road, Bamber Bridge, Preston, PR5 6LA Tel: (01772) 697111 Fax: (01772) 312369 E-mail: enquiries@scartop.com

Sizerite Timber, Long Lane, South Hykeham, Lincoln, LN6 9NX Tel: (01522) 685349 Fax: (01522) 682520 E-mail: sizerite@southhykeham.freeserve.co.uk

Special Branch, 5 Brailwood Close, Bilsthorpe, Newark, Nottinghamshire, NG22 8UG Tel: (01623) 871306

Status Pine, 587 Warwick Road, Tyseley, Birmingham, B11 2EX Tel: 0121-707 2077 Fax: 0121-707 4022

Swallow Furniture, Mill Farm, St. Mellons Road, Lisvane, Cardiff, CF14 0SH Tel: (029) 2076 3782

Taylor Made Pine, The Old Workshops, Longbridge Deverill, Warminster, Wiltshire, BA12 7DP Tel: (01985) 840012 Fax: (01985) 840781

Thompson & Robinson, Capel Hall Lane, Trimley St. Martin, Trimley St. Martin, Felixstowe, Suffolk, IP11 0RB Tel: (07791) 167338 Fax: (01394) 448008

Touchwood Carpenters, Covered Yard, 11a King Street, Lancaster, LA1 1JN Tel: (01524) 381048 Fax: (01524) 381048

Town & Country Pine, Photique House, 1 South Road, Erdington, Birmingham, B23 6EA Tel: 0121-382 9002

Trading Hedinghem and Beds, Wash Farm, Queen St, Sible Hedingham, Halstead, Essex, CO9 3RH Tel: (01787) 462228

Vanity Pine, 186 Marsh Lane, Preston, PR1 8RT Tel: (01772) 252187 Fax: (01772) 563253

Vic Smith Ltd, 4-5 Dennis Parade, Winchmore Hill Road, London, N14 6AA Tel: (020) 8882 8292 Fax: (020) 8882 8800 E-mail: sales@vicsmithbeds.co.uk

Warwickshire Pine, 263 Tile Hill Lane, Coventry, CV4 9DW Tel: (024) 7667 5328 Fax: (024) 7667 5328

Windsor Developments, Waddington Street, Oldham, OL9 6QH Tel: 0161-624 6252

Wirral Pine Centre, 315 Chester Road, Little Sutton, Ellesmere Port, CH66 3RF Tel: 0151-339 5520 Fax: 0151-339 5520

Woods & Woods, 311-323 Muswell Hill Broadway, London, N10 1BY Tel: (020) 8444 6055 Fax: (020) 8365 3106

Woodwork, 108 London Road, Southborough, Tunbridge Wells, Kent, TN4 0PS Tel: (01892) 533273 Fax: (01892) 619655 E-mail: simon@wwths.demon.co.uk

▶ www.oldpine.co.uk, Salisbury Road, Breamore, Fordingbridge, Hampshire, SP6 2EA Tel: (01725) 512132 E-mail: info@oldpine.co.uk

Yesterdays Pine Co, 7 Terry Dicken Industrial Estate, Station Road, Stokesley, Middlesbrough, Cleveland, TS9 7AE Tel: (01642) 711101 Fax: (01642) 711101

PINE FURNITURE IMPORT

▶ 1st For Furniture Ltd, Fairclough Hall Farm, Halls Green, Weston, Hitchin, Hertfordshire, SG4 7DP Tel: (01462) 790990 Fax: (01462) 790995 E-mail: info@1st-for-furniture.co.uk

The Furniture Warehouse, The Seed House, Bell Walk, Bell Lane, Uckfield, East Sussex, TN22 1AB Tel: (01825) 769202 E-mail: sales@sofasandfurniture.co.uk

▶ Nortique, 58 Thoroughfare, Halesworth, Suffolk, IP19 8AR Tel: (01986) 875656 E-mail: nortique@nortique.co.uk

▶ www.oldpine.co.uk, Salisbury Road, Breamore, Fordingbridge, Hampshire, SP6 2EA Tel: (01725) 512132 E-mail: info@oldpine.co.uk

PINE KITCHEN FURNITURE

▶ Bingham Pine Furniture, Grantham Road, Radcliffe-on-Trent, Nottingham, NG12 2JP Tel: 0115-933 2555 Fax: 0115-933 2555 E-mail: binghampine@aol.com

▶ The Cabinet Makers, Unit 12 Brighton Road Industrial Estate, Heaton Mersey, Stockport, Cheshire, SK4 2BQ Tel: 0161-432 4455 E-mail: duncan@thecabinetmakers.net

Chanterlands Pine Centre, 157 Chanterlands Avenue, Hull, HU5 3TJ Tel: (01482) 492682 Fax: (01482) 492682

Island Pine, 64 Union Place, Dungannon, County Tyrone, BT70 1DL Tel: (028) 8775 3545 Fax: (028) 8775 2747 E-mail: sales@islandpine.co.uk

▶ Nortique, 58 Thoroughfare, Halesworth, Suffolk, IP19 8AR Tel: (01986) 875656 E-mail: nortique@nortique.co.uk

▶ West Window Interiors, 2 Straw House Cottage, Kirkby Road, Ripon, North Yorkshire, HG4 3JU Tel: (01765) 608609 E-mail: sales@westwindowinteriors.co.uk

▶ www.oldpine.co.uk, Salisbury Road, Breamore, Fordingbridge, Hampshire, SP6 2EA Tel: (01725) 512132 E-mail: info@oldpine.co.uk

PINE OFFICE FURNITURE

The Woodcutter, Receptional 7, Station Square, High Street, Flitwick, Bedford, MK45 1DP Tel: (01525) 715520

PINE OIL

A Touch Of Pine, 150-152 Buckingham Road, Aylesbury, Buckinghamshire, HP19 9QN Tel: (01296) 433883 Fax: (01296) 334822

A Touch Of Pine Shop, Telford Road, Bicester, Oxfordshire, OX26 4LD Tel: (01869) 357100 Fax: (01869) 248867 E-mail: info@atouchofpine.co.uk

Ferguson & Menzies Ltd, 312 Broomloan Road, Glasgow, G51 2JW Tel: 0141-445 3555 Fax: 0141-425 1079 E-mail: sales@fergusonmenzies.co.uk

Lands End Pine Ltd, Lower Leha, St. Buryan, Penzance, Cornwall, TR19 6EJ Tel: (01736) 810211 Fax: (01736) 810211 E-mail: landsendpine@yahoo.co.uk

PINE WALL SKIRTINGS

▶ Alpha Pine (Harrogate) Ltd, 55 Knaresborough Road, Harrogate, North Yorkshire, HG2 7LT Tel: (01423) 885196 Fax: (01423) 885196 E-mail: info@alphapine.co.uk

▶ Ap Floors & Doors, 47 Craigs Crescent, Rumford, Falkirk, FK2 0ET Tel: (01324) 710016 E-mail: donna.peat@btinternet.com

PINS

Fasteners & Engineering Supplies Ltd, 5 Westgate, Cowbridge, South Glamorgan, CF71 7AQ Tel: (01446) 774888 Fax: (01446) 773778 E-mail: sales@f-e-s.co.uk

PIPE ALIGNMENT CLAMPS

H F Northan Ltd, High Street, Haxey, Doncaster, South Yorkshire, DN9 2HH Tel: (01427) 752708 Fax: (01427) 752173

PIPE AND TUBE CLAMPING SYSTEMS

A S D Metal Services, Tunstall Road, Biddulph, Stoke-on-Trent, ST8 6JZ Tel: (01782) 515152 Fax: (01782) 522240 E-mail: asdmetalservices@asdplc.co.uk

Asd, Station Road, Stalbridge, Sturminster Newton, Dorset, DT10 2RW Tel: (01963) 362066 Fax: (01963) 363260 E-mail: yeovil@asdplc.co.uk

Fluid Controls Ltd, 4 Minerva House, Calleva Park, Aldermaston, Reading, RG7 8NA Tel: 0118-981 1004 Fax: 0118-981 0775 E-mail: sales@fluidcontrols.co.uk

PIPE BENDING, *See Tube Manipulation/Bending etc*

PIPE BEVELLING MACHINES

D.L. Ricci Ltd, Station Road, Furness Vale, High Peak, Derbyshire, SK23 7QA Tel: (01663) 746600 Fax: (01663) 746611 E-mail: rpurcell@globalnet.co.uk

PIPE BRACKETS OR HANGERS

Crime Beat Security, 388 High Road, Ilford, Essex, IG1 1TL Tel: (020) 8478 4999 Fax: (020) 8478 7722 E-mail: sales@crimebeatsecurity.co.uk

Longbottom & Co Keighley Ltd, Dalton Mills, Dalton Lane, Keighley, West Yorkshire, BD21 4JH Tel: (01535) 604007 Fax: (01535) 609947

Pipe Supports Ltd, Salwarpe Road, Droitwich, Worcestershire, WR9 9BH Tel: (01905) 795500 Fax: (01905) 794126 E-mail: sales@pipesupports.com

PIPE CLAMPS

Aqua-Gas Avk Ltd, P O Box 143, Northampton, NN4 7ZU Tel: (01604) 601188 Fax: (01604) 604818 E-mail: info@aquagas.co.uk

G S Hydro UK Ltd, Unit 47 Howe Moss Avenue, Kirkhill Industrial Estate, Dyce, Aberdeen, AB21 0GP Tel: (01224) 772111 Fax: (01224) 772054 E-mail: info@gshydro.co.uk

Lisega Ltd, Unit3, Washington Centre, Hales Owen Road, Netherton, West Midlands, DY2 9RE Tel: (01384) 458660 Fax: (01384) 213301 E-mail: sales@lisega.co.uk

P C E S Ltd, 20 Wulfrun Trading Estate, Stafford Road, Wolverhampton, WV10 6HH Tel: (01902) 713402 Fax: (01902) 714216 E-mail: sales@pces.uk.com

S P F Engineering Ltd, 29-30 Harvey Close, Crowther, Washington, Tyne & Wear, NE38 0AB Tel: 0191-419 4400 Fax: 0191-417 4799 E-mail: rgrspf@aol.com

PIPE CLIPS

Bolivar Ltd, Unit 9B Devonshire Works, Riparian Way, Cross Hills, Keighley, West Yorkshire, BD20 7BW Tel: (01535) 631222 Fax: (01535) 637555 E-mail: sales@bolivar-limited.com

Carpenter & Paterson Holdings Ltd, Crown Works, Henfaes Lane, Welshpool, Powys, SY21 7BE Tel: (01938) 552061 Fax: (01938) 555306 E-mail: info@cp-ltd.co.uk

J Preston & Son, Pitt Street, Widnes, Cheshire, WA8 0TG Tel: 0151-424 3718 Fax: 0151-495 2360 E-mail: sales@prestonsofwidnes.co.uk

Longbottom & Co Keighley Ltd, Dalton Mills, Dalton Lane, Keighley, West Yorkshire, BD21 4JH Tel: (01535) 604007 Fax: (01535) 609947

M Greenaway & Son Ltd, Hayward Industrial Park, Vigo Place, Walsall, WS9 8UG Tel: (01922) 743322 Fax: (01922) 743163 E-mail: sales@greenaways.co.uk

▶ Regon Ltd, Unit 21B, Avenue 2, Station Lane Industrial Estate, Witney, Oxfordshire, OX28 4YG Tel: (01993) 771441 Fax: (01993) 774105 E-mail: sales@regon.co.uk

Shawston International Ltd, Great Norbury Street, Hyde, Cheshire, SK14 1BW Tel: 0161-368 4545 Fax: 0161-367 8114

PIPE CUTTERS

▶ Hireman (London) Ltd, Unit 4, Apex Industrial Estate, 22 Hythe Road, London, NW10 6RT Tel: (020) 8964 2464 Fax: (020) 8964 1343

PIPE CUTTING AND BEVELLING COMBINED MACHINES

P C E S Ltd, 20 Wulfrun Trading Estate, Stafford Road, Wolverhampton, WV10 6HH Tel: (01902) 713402 Fax: (01902) 714216 E-mail: sales@pces.uk.com

D.L. Ricci Ltd, Station Road, Furness Vale, High Peak, Derbyshire, SK23 7QA Tel: (01663) 746600 Fax: (01663) 746611 E-mail: rpurcell@globalnet.co.uk

PIPE FABRICATIONS

Fabrication & Installation Ltd, Units 6-9 Enterprise Way, Ladysmith Road, Grimsby, South Humberside, DN32 9TW Tel: (01472) 240409 Fax: (01472) 240408

Midland Tube & Fabrications, 4 Corngreaves Works, Corngreaves Road, Cradley Heath, West Midlands, B64 7DA Tel: (01384) 566364 Fax: (01384) 566365 E-mail: keithcadman@btconnect.com

PIPE FINISHING, *See Tube Finishing etc*

PIPE FITTINGS, STEEL

▶ J K Pipelines Ltd, K121 -123 Pembroke House, Manchester Road, Carrington Business Park, Carrington, Manchester, M31 4DD Tel: 0161-776 4403 Fax: 0161-776 4404 E-mail: jkpipelines@tiscali.co.uk

PIPE FLANGES

Clydesdale Forge Co., Marriott Road, Dudley, West Midlands, DY2 0LA Tel: (01384) 252587 Fax: (01384) 231005 E-mail: sales@clydesdale-forge.co.uk

D & D Stainless, Unit 16 Nettlehill Road, Houstoun Industrial Estate, Livingston, West Lothian, EH54 5DL Tel: (01506) 434325 Fax: (01506) 435345 E-mail: sales@danddstainless.co.uk

Glamal Engineering Ltd, Pegasus House, Wynyard Avenue, Wynyard, Billingham, Cleveland, TS22 5TB Tel: (01740) 645040 Fax: (01642) 565831 E-mail: sales@glamal.co.uk

Van Leeuwen Tubes Ltd, Unit 7 Provincial Park, Nether Lane, Ecclesfield, Sheffield, S35 9ZX Tel: 0114-257 7577 Fax: 0114-257 0639 E-mail: sales@vanleeuwen.nl

PIPE FREEZING MACHINES

Freeze Master, Unit A1, Connaught Business, London, NW9 6JL Tel: (020) 8205 7672 Fax: (020) 8205 7674

PIPE FREEZING SERVICES

Bishop Pipefreezing Ltd, Pipefreezing House, 58A Shirley Road, Croydon, CR0 7EP Tel: (0800) 132750 Fax: (020) 8654 5459 E-mail: bishop@pipefreezingsales.co.uk

Cyril W Bishop, 58a Shirley Road, Croydon, CR0 7EP Tel: (020) 8656 8234 Fax: (020) 8654 5459 E-mail: pipefreezing@bishop.co.uk

Pipefreezing & Hot Tapping Ltd, The Premises, 209 Hackney Road, London, E2 8JL Tel: (020) 7739 0680 Fax: (020) 7739 0690 E-mail: sales@pipefreeze.co.uk

PIPE HANDLING EQUIPMENT

Pipe Equipment Specialists Ltd, 66a Dukesway, Teesside Industrial Estate, Stockton-on-Tees, Cleveland, TS17 9LT Tel: (01642) 769789 Fax: (01642) 769456 E-mail: info@pipe-equipment.co.uk

Schoolhill Hydraulic Engineering Co. Ltd, 3 Greenbank Place, East Tullos Industrial Estate, Aberdeen, AB12 3RJ Tel: (01224) 871086 Fax: (01224) 897135 E-mail: hydraulics@scheng.demon.co.uk

PIPE JACKING OR THRUST BORING CONTRACTORS

Essig Products Ltd, 4 Courtyard 3, Wentworth Road, Mapplewell, Barnsley, South Yorkshire, S75 6DT Tel: (01226) 383384 Fax: (01226) 390880 E-mail: sales@essig.co.uk

PIPE JOINTS OR CONNECTORS OR UNIONS

Anson Ltd, Team Valley Trading Estate, Seventh Avenue, Gateshead, Tyne & Wear, NE11 0JW Tel: 0191-482 0022 Fax: 0191-487 8835 E-mail: anson-gateshead@anson.co.uk

Destec Engineering Ltd, Five Mile Lane, Washingborough, Lincoln, LN4 1AF Tel: (01522) 791721 Fax: (01522) 790033 E-mail: sales@destec.co.uk

Filton Ltd, Caswell Rd, Sydenham Industrial Estate, Leamington Spa, Warwickshire, CV31 1QF Tel: (01926) 423191 Fax: (01926) 450610 E-mail: sales@filtonltd.co.uk

Philmac (U K) Ltd, Diplocks Way, Hailsham, East Sussex, BN27 3JF Tel: (01323) 847323 Fax: (01323) 844775 E-mail: philmacorders@philmac.co.uk

Yorkshire Fittings Ltd, P O Box 166, Leeds, LS10 1NA Tel: 0113-270 6945 Fax: 0113-271 5275 E-mail: info@yorkshirefittings.co.uk

PIPE LAYING CONTRACTORS

Aquatic Engineering & Construction Ltd, Palmerston Centre, 29-31 Palmerston Road, Aberdeen, AB11 5QP Tel: (01224) 573359 Fax: (01224) 577361 E-mail: admin@aquatic.co.uk

Pipeline Services Ltd, 21 Princes Drive Industrial Estate, Coventry Road, Kenilworth, Warwickshire, CV8 2FD Tel: (01926) 511316 Fax: (01926) 512744 E-mail: sales@pipeserve.co.uk

PIPE LINING RESINS

Gadmon Industries Ltd, 57 Glengall Road, London, SE15 6NF Tel: (020) 7277 8878 Fax: (020) 7277 9476

PIPE LININGS

Gadmon Industries Ltd, 57 Glengall Road, London, SE15 6NF Tel: (020) 7277 8878 Fax: (020) 7277 9476

▶ M H 4 Draines, 38 Moss Avenue, Rochdale, Lancashire, OL16 4AA Tel: (01706) 868886 E-mail: mh4drains@btconnect.com

PIPE LOCATING OR DETECTING SERVICES

Ekaw Projects Ltd, Link House, Church Street, Haxey, Doncaster, South Yorkshire, DN9 2HY Tel: (01427) 752006 Fax: (01427) 753581

I E T G plc, Oxford House, 2 Sixth Avenue, Doncaster Finningley Airport, Doncaster, South Yorkshire, DN9 3GG Tel: (01302) 802000 Fax: (01302) 802001E-mail: sales@ietg.co.uk

PIPE LOCATORS OR DETECTING EQUIPMENT

C-Scope International Ltd, Kingsnorth Technology Park, Wotton Road, Ashford, Kent, TN23 6LN Tel: (01233) 629181 Fax: (01233) 645897 E-mail: info@cscope.co.uk

Kerryredd Surveying Equipment Ltd, 1206 London Road, London, SW16 4DN Tel: (020) 8679 7233 Fax: (020) 8679 9147

Palmer Environmental Ltd, Ty Coch House, Llantarnam Industrial Park, Cwmbran, Gwent, NP44 3AW Tel: (01633) 489479 Fax: (01633) 877857 E-mail: information@palmer.co.uk

Pipehawk plc, Systems House, Mill Lane, Alton, Hampshire, GU34 2QG Tel: (01420) 590990 Fax: (01420) 590920 E-mail: sales@pipehawk.com

PIPE OR PIPELINE OR PIPEWORK BRACKETS

Alltube Engineering, 3-9 Siddeley Way, Royal Oak Industrial Estate, Daventry, Northamptonshire, NN11 8PA Tel: (01327) 878250 Fax: (01327) 300478 E-mail: cope@wakefind.co.uk

Boulting Mechanical Services, Unit 11, Warrington Central Trading Estate Bewsey Road, Warrington, WA2 7LP Tel: (01925) 831151 Fax: (01925) 581120 E-mail: mechanical@boulting.co.uk

Debro Engineering & Presswork, Stourvale Trading Estate, Banners Lane, Halesowen, West Midlands, B63 2AX Tel: (01384) 633004 Fax: (01384) 633746

▶ Greenbank Group Inc, Hartshorne Road, Woodville, Swadlincote, Derbyshire, DE11 7GT Tel: (0870) 6078880 Fax: (0870) 6078889 E-mail: info@greenbank.tv

Longbottom & Co Keighley Ltd, Dalton Mills, Dalton Lane, Keighley, West Yorkshire, BD21 4JH Tel: (01535) 604007 Fax: (01535) 609947

M Greenaway & Son Ltd, Hayward Industrial Park, Vigo Place, Walsall, WS9 8UG Tel: (01922) 743322 Fax: (01922) 743163 E-mail: sales@greenaways.co.uk

Nelson Unit Ltd, Victoria Works, Lodge Lane, Dukinfield, Cheshire, SK16 5HY Tel: 0161-330 1007 Fax: 0161-343 1346 E-mail: info@nelsonunit.co.uk

Quality Pipe Supports, 1 Dyffryn Industrial Estate, Pool Road, Newtown, Powys, SY16 3BD Tel: (01686) 629898 Fax: (01686) 629797 E-mail: q.p.s@btinternet.com

Shawston International Ltd, Great Norbury Street, Hyde, Cheshire, SK14 1BW Tel: 0161-368 4545 Fax: 0161-367 8114

Stockton Drilling Ltd, Unit 15 Navigation Court, Calder Park, Wakefield, West Yorkshire, WF2 7BJ Tel: (01924) 242128 Fax: (01924) 253177 E-mail: info@stocktondrilling.com

Support Systems Nottingham Ltd, Nottingham Road, Beeston, Nottingham, NG9 6DP Tel: 0115-922 9067 Fax: 0115-925 5555

PIPE OR PIPELINE OR PIPEWORK HEATERS

Electrothermal Ltd, North Norfolk Ho, Pitmedden Road, Dyce, Aberdeen, AB21 0DP Tel: (01224) 722888 Fax: (01224) 772103 E-mail: eric.florence@rigblast.com

Goldace Industries, Unit 17 Harmill Industrial Estate, Grovebury Road, Leighton Buzzard, Bedfordshire, LU7 4FF Tel: (01525) 851815 Fax: (01525) 852484 E-mail: info@goldaceindustries.com

Lane Mechanical Services Ltd, 5 Tudor Industrial Estate, Wharfdale Road, Birmingham, B11 2DG Tel: 0121-706 8454 Fax: 0121-706 3144 E-mail: lanemech@fsbdial.co.uk

Arthur Pollard Ltd, Unit 38 Churchill Way, Fleckney, Leicester, LE8 8UD Tel: 0116-240 3728 E-mail: arthur.pollard@virgin.net

PIPE REPAIR PRODUCTS

Furmanite Ipsco (UK) Ltd, Sunningdale House, Sunningdale Road, South Park Industrial Estate, Scunthorpe, North Lincolnshire, DN17 2TY Tel: (01724) 849904 Fax: (01724) 861033E-mail: info.ipsco@furmaniteipsco.com

Syddal Engineering Ltd, Palatine Street, Denton, Manchester, M34 3LY Tel: 0161-336 4205 Fax: 0161-320 9525 E-mail: info@syddalengineering.co.uk

Viking Johnson, 46-48 Wilbury Way, Hitchin, Hertfordshire, SG4 0UD Tel: (01462) 443322 Fax: (01462) 443311 E-mail: sales@vikingjohnson.com

PIPE SUPPORT SYSTEMS

Universal Fixings Ltd, Unit 1 2 Balds Lane, Jubilee Business Park, Lye, Stourbridge, West Midlands, DY9 8SH Tel: (01384) 422284

PIPE THREADING MACHINE MAINTENANCE AND REPAIR

▶ Apollo Plant Hire & Sales, 108 St. Francis Way, Chadwell St. Mary, Grays, Essex, RM16 4RH Tel: (01375) 841050 Fax: (01375) 841050 E-mail: apolloplant@blueyonder.co.uk

PIPE THREADING MACHINES

▶ Apollo Plant Hire & Sales, 108 St. Francis Way, Chadwell St. Mary, Grays, Essex, RM16 4RH Tel: (01375) 841050 Fax: (01375) 841050 E-mail: apolloplant@blueyonder.co.uk

PIPE WORKING TOOLS

▶ Silom International Ltd, Unit 6 Abbey Park Industrial Estate, Abbey Road, Barking, Essex, IG11 7BT Tel: (020) 8594 3335

PIPELINE CLEAN IN PLACE (CIP) SYSTEMS

▶ Whirlwind Technologies Ltd, 1 Poplar Street, (Off Buck Street), Leigh, Lancashire, WN7 4HL Tel: (01942) 671300 Fax: (01942) 262042 E-mail: info@whirltech.co.uk

PIPELINE CLEANING OR DESCALING OR PURGING OR INERTING CONTRACTORS OR SERVICES

Metro Rod P.L.C., East Barnet, Barnet, Hertfordshire, EN4 8WR Tel: (020) 8449 8477 Fax: (020) 8449 8466 E-mail: ascriven@sgaservices.co.uk

Ramco Tubular Services Ltd, Badentoy Road Badentoy Park, Badentoy Industrial Estate, Portlethen, Aberdeen, AB12 4YA Tel: (01224) 782278 Fax: (01224) 783001 E-mail: info@ramco-plc.com

PIPELINE CLEANING OR DESCALING OR PURGING OR INERTING EQUIPMENT

Girard Industries Europe Ltd, Unit C5, Olympic Business Park, Dundonald, Kilmarnock, Ayrshire, KA2 9BE Tel: (01563) 851062 Fax: (01563) 851411 E-mail: girardindeurope@hotmail.com

Pipe Equipment Specialists Ltd, 66a Dukesway, Teesside Industrial Estate, Stockton-on-Tees, Cleveland, TS17 9LT Tel: (01642) 769789 Fax: (01642) 769456 E-mail: info@pipe-equipment.co.uk

Pipeline Centre, Helmet Street, Manchester, M1 2NT Tel: 0161-276 0200 Fax: 0161-276 0201

▶ Waterline Equipment Company, Everite Works, Derby Road, Widnes, Cheshire, WA8 9ND Tel: 0151-495 3505 Fax: 0151-495 3522 E-mail: geoff@waterline-uk.com

PIPELINE COATING INSPECTION

▶ DC Voltage Gradient Technology & Supply Ltd, Corbett House, Swan Lane, Hindley Green, Wigan, Lancashire, WN2 4EY Tel: (01942) 522180 Fax: (01942) 522179 E-mail: dcvg@fsbdial.co.uk

PIPELINE COATING OR LINING OR PROTECTION CONTRACTORS

Insituform Technologies Ltd, Roundwood Industrial Estate, Ossett, West Yorkshire, WF5 9SQ Tel: (01924) 277076 Fax: (01924) 265107 E-mail: affholder@insituform.com

Kingfisher Industrial, Rushock Trading Estate, Droitwich, Worcestershire, WR9 0NR Tel: (01299) 251121 Fax: (01299) 251021 E-mail: enquiries@kingfisher-industrial.co.uk

Leyfos Plastics, Unit D1, Rosehill Industrial, Stoke Heath, Market Drayton, Shropshire, TF9 2JU Tel: (01630) 638557 Fax: (01630) 638651 E-mail: sales@leyfos.com

PIPELINE COLD CUTTING SERVICES

Furmanite Ipsco (UK) Ltd, Sunningdale House, Sunningdale Road, South Park Industrial Estate, Scunthorpe, North Lincolnshire, DN17 2TY Tel: (01724) 849904 Fax: (01724) 861033E-mail: info.ipsco@furmaniteipsco.com

R B G, Norfolk House, Pitmedden Road, Dyce, Aberdeen, AB21 0DP Tel: (01224) 215100 Fax: (01224) 723406 E-mail: john.walker@rigblast.com

PIPELINE CONSTRUCTION EQUIPMENT

P C E S Ltd, 20 Wulfrun Trading Estate, Stafford Road, Wolverhampton, WV10 6HH Tel: (01902) 713402 Fax: (01902) 714216 E-mail: sales@pces.uk.com

R S Brookhouse Ltd, Waterloo Industrial Estate, Waterloo Road, Bidford-on-Avon, Alcester, Warwickshire, B50 4JH Tel: (01789) 772485 Fax: (01789) 490129 E-mail: brookhouse.eng@btinternet.com

PIPELINE CONSULTING ENGINEERS OR DESIGNERS

Pegasus International UK Ltd, The Academy, Belmont Street, Aberdeen, AB10 1LB Tel: (01224) 623300 Fax: (01224) 623301 E-mail: aberdeen@pegasus-international.com

PIPELINE CONTRACTORS/ FABRICATORS

A & B Welding Services Ltd, 1a Woodside Road, Bridge of Don Industrial Estate, Aberdeen, AB23 8EF Tel: (01224) 823444 Fax: (01224) 825079 E-mail: sales@abweld.com

A H L Industrial Pipework Specialists Ltd, Unit 22 Royal Industrial Estate, Blackett Street, Jarrow, Tyne & Wear, NE32 3HR Tel: 0191-428 0282 Fax: 0191-483 8893 E-mail: info@ahlpipework.co.uk

Balfour Beatty, Chaddock Lane, Worsley, Manchester, M28 1XW Tel: 0161-790 3000 Fax: 0161-703 5307

Cleanline Engineering Co. Ltd, 27 Acacia Grove, New Malden, Surrey, KT3 3BJ Tel: (07909) 983648 E-mail: c.mence@cleanline-eng.co.uk

D O J Pipe Welding Services, 6 Pear Tree Close, Little Billing, Northampton, NN3 9TH Tel: (01604) 404010 Fax: (01604) 408636 E-mail: welding@pipewelding.co.uk

Fabricon Ltd, Unit 5 Commerce Way, Leighton Buzzard, Bedfordshire, LU7 4RW Tel: (01525) 850244 Fax: (01525) 850245 E-mail: info@fabricon.ltd.uk

▶ Flow Stop Services, 97 Holmsdale Grove, Bexleyheath, Kent, DA7 6PA Tel: (01322) 525616 Fax: (01322) 522227

G S Hydro UK Ltd, Unit 47 Howe Moss Avenue, Kirkhill Industrial Estate, Dyce, Aberdeen, AB21 0GP Tel: (01224) 772111 Fax: (01224) 772054 E-mail: info@gshydro.co.uk

Jordan Engineering Services Ltd, Hardley Industrial Estate, Hardley, Hythe, Southampton, SO45 3NQ Tel: (023) 8084 9988 Fax: (023) 8042 3779 E-mail: enquiries@chb-jordan.co.uk

Lanmar Pipework Engineering Ltd, 35 Lightburn Road, Cambuslang, Glasgow, G72 8UB Tel: 0141-646 2233 Fax: 0141-641 7838

Murphy Pipelines Ltd, Hiview House, Highgate Road, London, NW5 1TN Tel: (020) 7267 4366 Fax: (020) 7482 3107 E-mail: mail@murphygroup.co.uk

Pipeline Induction Heat Ltd, Farrington Road, Burnley, Lancashire, BB11 5SW Tel: (01282) 415323 Fax: (01282) 415326 E-mail: sales@pih.co.uk

Pipeline Services Ltd, 21 Princes Drive Industrial Estate, Coventry Road, Kenilworth, Warwickshire, CV8 2FD Tel: (01926) 511316 Fax: (01926) 512744 E-mail: sales@pipeserve.co.uk

Plant & Automation Ltd, Lord North St, Miles Platting, Manchester, M40 8HT Tel: 0161-205 5756 Fax: 0161-205 0503

Saipem Ltd, Saipem House, Station Road, Motspur Park, New Malden, Surrey, KT3 6JJ Tel: (020) 8296 5000 Fax: (020) 8296 5100

Visser & Smit Hanab UK, Unit 1a Orion Way, Kettering Business Park, Kettering, Northamptonshire, NN15 6NL Tel: (01536) 314700 Fax: (01536) 314709 E-mail: info@vsh-uk.com

Willbros (Overseas) Ltd, The Old Rechtory, Barkston, Grantham, Lincolnshire, NG32 2NB Tel: (020) 8549 4471 Fax: (020) 8974 8536 E-mail: arthur.west@willbros.com

PIPELINE CUSHION PADS

J & H M Dickson Ltd, Seath Road, Rutherglen, Glasgow, G73 1RW Tel: 0141-643 0244 Fax: 0141-643 0219 E-mail: sales@dicksonforsacks.co.uk

PIPELINE EQUIPMENT

R S Brookhouse Ltd, Waterloo Industrial Estate, Waterloo Road, Bidford-on-Avon, Alcester, Warwickshire, B50 4JH Tel: (01789) 772485 Fax: (01789) 490129 E-mail: brookhouse.eng@btinternet.com

PIPELINE FITTING INSTALLATION OR FABRICATION

Enterprise plc, Lancaster House, Lancashire Enterprise Business Park, Leyland, PR26 6TX Tel: (01772) 819000 Fax: (01772) 819001 E-mail: headoffice@enterprise.plc.uk

Maineport Ltd, Rossmore Industrial Estate, Ellesmere Port, CH65 3BS Tel: 0151-355 0111 Fax: 0151-356 1093 E-mail: sales@uecnet.co.uk

Rally Industrial Services Ltd, Beacon Works, Bilston Street, Dudley, West Midlands, DY3 1JE Tel: (01902) 884341 Fax: (01902) 880333

PIPELINE FITTINGS

Accura Pipe Fitting Ltd, Hickman Avenue, Wolverhampton, WV1 2DW Tel: (01902) 453322 Fax: (01902) 453314 E-mail: pipefittings@accura.co.uk

Anvil Alloys Ltd, 1-2 Benwick Road, Whittlesey, Peterborough, PE7 2HD Tel: (01923) 800721 Fax: (01923) 800722

Aqua-Gas Avk Ltd, P O Box 143, Northampton, NN4 7ZU Tel: (01604) 601188 Fax: (01604) 604818 E-mail: info@aquagas.co.uk

Aston Fittings, Springcroft Road, Birmingham, B11 3EL Tel: 0121-778 6001 Fax: 0121-778 6002 E-mail: sales@astonfittings.com

Carbern Pipes & Fittings, Unit 3 Bevan Industrial Estate, Brierley Hill, West Midlands, DY5 3TF Tel: (01384) 76111 Fax: (01384) 262309 E-mail: sales@carbern.co.uk

PIPELINE FITTINGS – *continued*

De Dietrich Process Systems Ltd, Tollgate Drive, Tollgate Industrial Estate, Stafford, ST16 3HS Tel: (01785) 609900 Fax: (01785) 609899 E-mail: reception@qvf.co.uk
Fernco International Ltd, Newlands Way, Valley Park, Wombwell, Barnsley, South Yorkshire, S73 0UW Tel: (01226) 340209 Fax: (01226) 340400 E-mail: enquiries@fernco.co.uk
Hallen Engineering Ltd, PO Box 27, Wednesbury, West Midlands, WS10 7SZ Tel: 0121-556 3324 Fax: 0121-502 0194 E-mail: sales@hallen.co.uk
Ham Baker Hartley, Garner Street, Etruria, Stoke-on-Trent, ST4 7BH Tel: (01782) 202300 Fax: (01782) 203639 E-mail: enquiries@hambaker.co.uk
J Bown & Co Dukinfield Ltd, Wharf Street, Dukinfield, Cheshire, SK16 4PQ Tel: 0161-339 9888 Fax: 0161-343 1052 E-mail: sale@jbown.com
John D Dunlop, 3 Kyle Road, Irvine Industrial Estate, Irvine, Ayrshire, KA12 8JF Tel: (01294) 273475 Fax: (01294) 274297 E-mail: kdylanalexander@btconnect.com
Legris Ltd, Unit 1210, Lansdowne Court, Brockworth, Gloucester, GL3 4AB Tel: (01452) 623500 Fax: (01452) 623501 E-mail: salesuk@legris.com
Leo Fittings Ltd, Lakes Road, Braintree, Essex, CM7 3QS Tel: (01376) 341616 Fax: (01376) 349427 E-mail: info@leofittings.co.uk
MDS Petrochemical Supplies, Unit 48b Premier Partnership Estate, Leys Road, Brierley Hill, West Midlands, DY5 3UP Tel: (01384) 485055 Fax: (01384) 480053 E-mail: sales@mdspetrochemical.co.uk
Petchem Engineering Services Ltd, 61 Ringsfield Road, Beccles, Suffolk, NR34 9PE Tel: (01502) 711330 Fax: (01502) 711081 E-mail: petchemengserv@aol.com
Posiflex, 46-48 Wilbury Way, Hitchin, Hertfordshire, SG4 0UD Tel: (01462) 443131 Fax: (01462) 443128 E-mail: info@posiflex.co.uk
Probe Oil Tools Ltd, Edison Way, Great Yarmouth, Norfolk, NR31 0NG Tel: (01493) 655471 Fax: (01493) 652746 E-mail: sales@probe-oil-tools.co.uk
Vallourec UK Ltd, George House, 121 High Street, Henley-in-Arden, West Midlands, B95 5AU Tel: (01564) 792277 Fax: (01564) 795818 E-mail: sales@vallourec.co.uk
Viking Johnson, 46-48 Wilbury Way, Hitchin, Hertfordshire, SG4 0UD Tel: (01462) 443322 Fax: (01462) 443311 E-mail: sales@vikingjohnson.com

PIPELINE FITTINGS OR FLANGES

▶ Allpipe & Valve, 103a Pontefract Road, Ackworth, Pontefract, West Yorkshire, WF7 7EL Tel: (01977) 600606 Fax: (01977) 704215 E-mail: allpipe@aol.com
B S S Group plc, Fleet House, Lee Circle, Leicester, LE1 3QQ Tel: 0116-262 3232 Fax: 0116-253 1343 E-mail: sales@bssuk.co.uk
Besseges Valves Tubes & Fittings Ltd, Jackson House, Turner Lane, Ashton-under-Lyne, Lancashire, OL6 8LP Tel: 0161-343 2225 Fax: 0161-339 0307 E-mail: enquiries@besseges-vts.co.uk
Boole's Tools & Pipe Fittings Ltd, Haigh Avenue, Whitehill Trading Estate, Stockport, Cheshire, SK4 1NU Tel: 0161-480 7900 Fax: 0161-474 7142 E-mail: enquiries@booles.co.uk
Burnett & Hillman Engineers, Havyatt Road, Coxs Green, Wrington, Bristol, BS40 5NL Tel: (01934) 862980 Fax: (01934) 862616 E-mail: sales@burnettandhillman.co.uk
Canmec Global Ltd, 7 Dawley Brook Road, Kingswinford, West Midlands, DY6 7BD Tel: (01384) 271203 Fax: (01384) 400179 E-mail: sales@canmecglobal.com
Deans Engineering Supplies, E M S House, Rossfield Road, Ellesmere Port, CH65 3BS Tel: 0151-357 1030 Fax: 0151-357 1990
Equipment Supply Co.Ltd, Unit 21, Kirkhill Place, Kirkhill Industrial Estate, Dyce, Aberdeen, AB21 0GU Tel: (01224) 772555 Fax: (01224) 723681
Euro Trading Ltd, Shepperton Marina, Felix Lane, Shepperton, Middlesex, TW17 8NS Tel: (01932) 246153 Fax: (01932) 226711 E-mail: eurotrading.co@virgin.net
F W B Southwest, Threemilestone Industrial Estate, Threemilestone, Truro, Cornwall, TR4 9LD Tel: (01872) 243520 Fax: (01872) 222191 E-mail: enquiries@fwbsw.co.uk
Fithandel (Scotland) Ltd, 1 Woodside Road, Bridge of Don Industrial Estate, Aberdeen, AB23 8EF Tel: (01224) 704964 Fax: (01224) 825421 E-mail: sales@fithandle.com
Forged Flanges & Fittings Ltd, Castle House, Station Road, New Barnet, Hertfordshire, EN5 1PE Tel: (020) 8440 6541 Fax: (020) 8441 6911 E-mail: franklissauer@iraco.co.uk
Frazer, Mid Craigie Road, Dundee, DD4 7RN Tel: (01382) 458989 Fax: (01382) 458998 E-mail: calum.hynes@frazer.eu.com
Full Supply Ltd, Unit 29a Dawley Trading Estate, Stallings Lane, Kingswinford, West Midlands, DY6 7AP Tel: (01384) 402101 Fax: (01384) 402501 E-mail: sales@fullsupply.co.uk
FWB Keithley, C Gresley Road, Keighley, West Yorkshire, BD21 5JG Tel: (01535) 687300 Fax: (01535) 687301 E-mail: sales@fwbkeighley.co.uk
H P F Energy Services, 1 Links Place, Aberdeen, AB11 5DY Tel: (01224) 584588 Fax: (01224) 211938 E-mail: sales@hpf-energy.com
H P F Energy Services, 3 Kinwarton Farm Road, Arden Forest Industrial Estate, Alcester, Warwickshire, B49 6EH Tel: (01789) 761212 Fax: (01789) 761222 E-mail: alcester@hpf-energy.com
H P F Energy Services Ltd, 2-4 Queen Elizabeth Avenue, Hillington Industrial Estate, Glasgow, G52 4NQ Tel: 0141-882 4611 Fax: 0141-883 0826 E-mail: glasgow@hpf-energy.com
H P F Energy Services, 99 Sadler Foster Way, Teeside Industrial Estate, Stockton-on-Tees, Cleveland, TS17 9JY Tel: (01642) 750009 Fax: (01642) 750044 E-mail: thornaby@hpf-energy.com
H Tipton Jones Ltd, 5 Worrall Street, Salford, M5 4TH Tel: 0161-877 1122 Fax: 0161-877 1145 E-mail: sales@tiptonjones.com
Hacketts Connect Ltd, Bell Street, West Bromwich, West Midlands, B70 7BX Tel: 0121-553 0134 Fax: 0121-553 2320 E-mail: info@hackcon.demon.co.uk
HPF Energy Services, 5 Hoyer Industrial Estate, Bridges Road, Ellesmere Port, CH65 4LB Tel: 0151-357 3322 Fax: 0151-357 1334 E-mail: ellesmere@hpf-energy.com
Industrial Pipework Supplies Ltd, Unit 6 Carr Mills Business Centre, Bradford Road, Birstall, West Yorkshire, WF17 9JY Tel: (01924) 470227 Fax: (01924) 470846 E-mail: peteropazs@hotmail.com
International Pipeline Supplies Ltd, 3 Cookson House, River Drive, South Shields, Tyne & Wear, NE33 1TL Tel: 0191-455 9648 Fax: 0191-454 0505 E-mail: office@internationalgroup.fsbusiness.co.uk
Jessops plc, 257 High Street, Cheltenham, Gloucestershire, GL50 3HJ Tel: (0845) 4587074 Fax: (01242) 228054
John Bell Pipeline Caspian, Units 3/4 Camiestone Road, Thainstone Industrial Park, Inverurie, Aberdeenshire, AB51 5GT Tel: (01224) 716079 Fax: (01224) 716079 E-mail: sales@jbpipeline.co.uk
L F F Scotland Ltd, Peregrine Road, Westhill Business Park, Westhill, Aberdeen, AB32 6JL Tel: (01224) 747636 Fax: (01224) 747637 E-mail: a.mitchell@aberdeen.lff.co.uk
Lamberts.Co.Uk Industrial Distributor, Whiffler Road, Norwich, NR3 2AY Tel: (01603) 422100 Fax: (01603) 422130 E-mail: nr.sales@lamberts.co.uk
Leo Fittings Ltd, Lakes Road, Braintree, Essex, CM7 3QS Tel: (01376) 341616 Fax: (01376) 349427 E-mail: info@leofittings.co.uk
Maineport Ltd, Rossmore Industrial Estate, Ellesmere Port, CH65 3BS Tel: 0151-355 0111 Fax: 0151-356 1093 E-mail: sales@uecnet.co.uk
Mardale Pipes Plus Ltd, PO Box 86, Runcorn, Cheshire, WA7 1PX Tel: (01928) 580555 Fax: (01928) 591033 E-mail: sales@mardale-pipes.com
Marla Tube Fittings Ltd, Units 1-2, Kinwarton Farm Road, Kinwarton, Alcester, Warwickshire, B49 6EH Tel: (01789) 761234 Fax: (01789) 761205 E-mail: alcester@hpf-energy.com
Merseyside Pipeline Supplies Ltd, Baltic Road, Bootle, Merseyside, L20 1AW Tel: 0151-933 3835 Fax: 0151-933 4166 E-mail: merseypipes@aol.com
Mid Continent Great Yarmouth Ltd, Gapton Hall Road, Harfreys Industrial Estate, Great Yarmouth, Norfolk, NR31 0HX Tel: (01493) 655269 Fax: (01493) 601512 E-mail: sales@midcontinentgy.com
Newgate Stainless Ltd, Victoria Mills, Cleckheaton, West Yorkshire, BD19 5DR Tel: (01274) 852040 Fax: (01274) 852142 E-mail: newgatesales@btconnect.com
Pipe Centre Plus, Unit 8, Spring Road Industrial Estate, Ettingshall, Wolverhampton, WV4 6JZ Tel: (01902) 409341 Fax: E-mail: p15.wolverhampton@wolsely.com
Pipe Line Centre, 33 Hawkins Lane, Burton-on-Trent, Staffordshire, DE14 1PT Tel: (01283) 567334 Fax: (01283) 510207 E-mail: enquiries@pipelinecenter.co.uk
Pipeline Equipment Supply, Unit 8 Meadow Lane Industrial Park, Ellesmere Port, CH65 4TY Tel: 0151-357 1524 Fax: 0151-357 1958 E-mail: pesnwltd@aol.com
Power Metal Supplies, 2-4 Winton Square, Basingstoke, Hampshire, RG21 8EN Tel: (01256) 811821 Fax: (01256) 811824 E-mail: powermetal@ukonline.co.uk
Premier Pipeline Supplies Ltd, Chatham Street, Halifax, West Yorkshire, HX1 5BU Tel: (01422) 322002 Fax: (01422) 348817 E-mail: info@premierpipeline.co.uk
Scanfit International Ltd, 11-14 Burton Close, Norwich, NR6 6AZ Tel: (01603) 480400 Fax: (01603) 424547 E-mail: mark@scanfit.co.uk
▶ Tyne Tube Ltd, Nile Street, South Shields, Tyne & Wear, NE33 1RH Tel: 0191-455 1144 Fax: 0191-455 4339 E-mail: enquiries@tynetubeservices.co.uk

PIPELINE FLANGES

Mardale Pipes Plus Ltd, PO Box 86, Runcorn, Cheshire, WA7 1PX Tel: (01928) 580555 Fax: (01928) 591033 E-mail: sales@mardale-pipes.com
Petchem Engineering Services Ltd, 61 Ringsfield Road, Beccles, Suffolk, NR34 9PE Tel: (01502) 711330 Fax: (01502) 711081 E-mail: petchemengserv@aol.com
H. Potter Engineering Ltd, Fisher Street, Low Walker, Newcastle Upon Tyne, NE6 4LT Tel: 0191-295 4420 Fax: 0191-295 4482
Priory Woodfield Engineering Ltd, Millbrook Works, Lower Horseley Field, Wolverhampton, WV1 3DZ Tel: (01902) 351530 Fax: (01902) 351290 E-mail: sales@priorywoodfield.com
Probe Oil Tools Ltd, Edison Way, Great Yarmouth, Norfolk, NR31 0NG Tel: (01493) 655471 Fax: (01493) 652746 E-mail: sales@probe-oil-tools.co.uk

PIPELINE HOT TAP LINESTOP SERVICES

Furmanite Ipsco (UK) Ltd, Sunningdale House, Sunningdale Road, South Park Industrial Estate, Scunthorpe, North Lincolnshire, DN17 2TY Tel: (01724) 849904 Fax: (01724) 861033E-mail: info.ipsco@furmaniteipsco.com

PIPELINE HOT TAPPING SERVICES

Bishop Pipefreezing Ltd, Pipefreezing House, 58A Shirley Road, Croydon, CR0 7EP Tel: (0800) 132750 Fax: (020) 8654 5459 E-mail: bishop@pipefreezingsales.co.uk
Cyril W Bishop, 58a Shirley Road, Croydon, CR0 7EP Tel: (020) 8656 8234 Fax: (020) 8654 5459 E-mail: pipefreezing@bishop.co.uk
Pipefreezing & Hot Tapping Ltd, The Premises, 209 Hackney Road, London, E2 8JL Tel: (020) 7739 0680 Fax: (020) 7739 0690 E-mail: sales@pipefreeze.co.uk

PIPELINE IDENTIFICATION WARNING LABELS

B M K Industrial I D Systems, 1 Claremont Street, Aberdeen, AB10 6QP Tel: (01224) 213325 Fax: (01224) 213377 E-mail: bmk.id@talk21.com
Flo-Code (UK) Ltd, Gable End, Holmbury St. Mary, Dorking, Surrey, RH5 6LQ Tel: 01306 731863 Fax: 01306 731864 E-mail: info@flo-code.co.uk
Hibiscus plc, Hudswell Road, Leeds, LS10 1AG Tel: 0113-242 4272 Fax: 0113-242 4230 E-mail: info@hibiscus-plc.com
Premier Tape Converters Ltd, Unit 2, 24-26 Boulton Road, Stevenage, Hertfordshire, SG1 4QX Tel: (01732) 521122 Fax: (01438) 759555

PIPELINE INSPECTION SERVICES

Industrial & Municipal Project Ltd, 1 Wester Burn St, Glasgow, G32 6AT Tel: 0141-763 1234 Fax: 0141-763 0333 E-mail: info@impo.co.uk
UK Systems Inc Ltd, 1a Grantham Road, Bingham, Nottingham, NG13 8BX Tel: (01949) 877770 Fax: (01949) 877771 E-mail: sales@uksl.com

PIPELINE INSTRUMENTATION

Stauff, Unit 30-31, Point Pleasant Industrial Estate, Wallsend, Tyne & Wear, NE28 6HA Tel: 0191-262 6390 Fax: 0191-262 8825 E-mail: enquiries@stauff.com

PIPELINE INSULATION SYSTEMS

Anglitemp Ltd, Unit A3 Third Avenue, Tyne Tunnel Trading Estate, North Shields, Tyne & Wear, NE29 7SW Tel: 0191-258 6646 Fax: 0191-257 8445 E-mail: anglitemp@anglitemp.freeserve.co.uk

PIPELINE LINING EQUIPMENT

J & F Tools (Precision Engineers) Ltd, Thornfield, Spring Bank, New Mills, High Peak, Derbyshire, SK22 4AU Tel: (01663) 743129 Fax: (01663) 747572 E-mail: info@jandftools.com
▶ Waterline Equipment Company, Everite Works, Derby Road, Widnes, Cheshire, WA8 9ND Tel: 0151-495 3505 Fax: 0151-495 3522 E-mail: geoff@waterline-uk.com

PIPELINE MAINTENANCE OR REPAIR OR RENOVATION CONTRACTORS

Murphy Pipelines Ltd, Hiview House, Highgate Road, London, NW5 1TN Tel: (020) 7267 4366 Fax: (020) 7482 3107 E-mail: mail@murphygroup.co.uk

PIPELINE MAINTENANCE OR REPAIR OR RENOVATION EQUIPMENT

Linc Fabrication & Welding, Dawsons Lane Unit 14, The Enterprise Centre, Barwell, Leicester, LE9 8BE Tel: (01455) 840870 Fax: (01455) 840870 E-mail: kevbriggs@btconnect.com
Petropipe International Ltd, Barnsmead, Stockland Bristol, Bridgwater, Somerset, TA5 2PY Tel: (01278) 652545 Fax: (01278) 652565
Pipe Equipment Specialists Ltd, 66a Dukesway, Teesside Industrial Estate, Stockton-on-Tees, Cleveland, TS17 9LT Tel: (01642) 769789 Fax: (01642) 769456 E-mail: info@pipe-equipment.co.uk
▶ Waterline Equipment Company, Everite Works, Derby Road, Widnes, Cheshire, WA8 9ND Tel: 0151-495 3505 Fax: 0151-495 3522 E-mail: geoff@waterline-uk.com

PIPELINE PROTECTIVE COATING SERVICES

Insituform Technologies Ltd, Roundwood Industrial Estate, Ossett, West Yorkshire, WF5 9SQ Tel: (01924) 277076 Fax: (01924) 265107 E-mail: affholder@insituform.com

PIPELINE REHABILITATION MATERIALS

Insituform Technologies Ltd, Roundwood Industrial Estate, Ossett, West Yorkshire, WF5 9SQ Tel: (01924) 277076 Fax: (01924) 265107 E-mail: affholder@insituform.com

PIPELINE STOPPERS

Syddal Engineering Ltd, Palatine Street, Denton, Manchester, M34 3LY Tel: 0161-336 4205 Fax: 0161-320 9525 E-mail: info@syddalengineering.co.uk

PIPELINE SUPPLIES, *See also headings for particular types*

European Pipeline Ltd, Waterton House, Stoneywood, Bucksburn, Aberdeen, AB21 9HX Tel: (01224) 715554 Fax: (01224) 716079 E-mail: sales@europipe.co.uk
Frazer, Mid Craigie Road, Dundee, DD4 7RN Tel: (01382) 458989 Fax: (01382) 458998 E-mail: calum.hynes@frazer.eu.com
J M Hunt & Co. Ltd, 389-391 Castleford Road, Normanton, West Yorkshire, WF6 1RQ Tel: (01924) 890693 Fax: (01924) 893634 E-mail: sales@hunts-pipeline.co.uk
Kennedy & Morrison Ltd, Boucher Road, Belfast, BT12 6QF Tel: (028) 9087 0870 Fax: (028) 9087 0871 E-mail: sales@kandm.co.uk
Kinglea Plant Centre Coffee Shop, Meadgate Road, Nazeing, Waltham Abbey, Essex, EN9 2PB Tel: (01992) 467775 Fax: (01992) 892967 E-mail: sales@kingsboilerhire.com
Kurvers International Supply Services Ltd, Unit 14 Northfields Prospect Business Centre, Northfields, London, SW18 1PE Tel: (020) 8877 1355 Fax: (020) 8874 7266 E-mail: info@ukkurvers.com
Pingly Boris Ltd, 113 Hardwick Road, Streetly, Sutton Coldfield, West Midlands, B74 3DW Tel: 0121-353 3840 Fax: 0121-353 3840 E-mail: sales@pinglyboris.com
Pipe Center, Unit 8B Cosgrove Way, Luton, LU1 1XL Tel: (01582) 404162 Fax: (01582) 459170
Pipe Centre, 18-22 Pages Walk, London, SE1 4SB Tel: (020) 7237 4421 Fax: (020) 7231 3223 E-mail: br.bermondey@wolseley.co.uk
Pipemore, 3 Crompton Road, Glenrothes, Fife, KY6 2SF Tel: (01592) 630633 Fax: (01592) 630623E-mail: sales@pipemorescotland.co.uk
R S Brookhouse Ltd, Waterloo Industrial Estate, Waterloo Road, Bidford-on-Avon, Alcester, Warwickshire, B50 4JH Tel: (01789) 772485 Fax: (01789) 490129 E-mail: brookhouse.eng@btinternet.com
Sabtek International Ltd, Unit 9, 10 Badentoy Place, Portlethen, Aberdeen, AB12 4YF Tel: (01224) 782289 Fax: (01224) 781645 E-mail: info@sabtek.co.uk
Scanfit International Ltd, 11-14 Burton Close, Norwich, NR6 6AZ Tel: (01603) 480400 Fax: (01603) 424547 E-mail: mark@scanfit.co.uk
Stokplas Ltd, Sandall Park, Barnby Dun Road, Doncaster, South Yorkshire, DN2 4QL Tel: (01302) 816040 Fax: (01302) 816050 E-mail: stokplas@crossling.co.uk

PIPELINE SURVEYORS

Fugro Survey Ltd, Morton Peto Road, Great Yarmouth, Norfolk, NR31 0LT Tel: (01493) 440320 Fax: (01493) 440319 E-mail: admin@svitzer.co.uk

▶ indicates data change since last edition

PIPELINE SURVEYORS – *continued*

Subspection Ltd, Shelf House, New Farm Road, Alresford, Hampshire, SO24 9QE Tel: (01962) 734977 Fax: (01962) 735277 E-mail: sales@subspection.com

T.D. Williamson (UK) Ltd, Faraday Road, Dorcan Way, Swindon, SN3 5HF Tel: (01793) 603600 Fax: (01793) 603601 E-mail: pigging@tdw.co.uk

PIPELINE TESTING EQUIPMENT

Horobin Ltd, Willenhall Trading Estate, Midacre, Willenhall, West Midlands, WV13 2JW Tel: (01902) 604060 Fax: (01902) 603366 E-mail: sales@horobin.co.uk

PIPELINE TRENCHING OR BACKFILLING CONTRACTORS

▶ Contradig, Bethania, Capel Garmon, Llanrwst, Conwy, LL26 0RL Tel: (01690) 710309 Fax: (01690) 710154 E-mail: info@contradig.com

PIPELINE UNDER PRESSURE DRILLING OR TAPPING

Pipefreezing & Hot Tapping Ltd, The Premises, 209 Hackney Road, London, E2 8JL Tel: (020) 7739 0680 Fax: (020) 7739 0690 E-mail: sales@pipefreeze.co.uk

PIPELINE UNDER PRESSURE DRILLING OR TAPPING MACHINES

Brewis Engineering, Handlemaker Road, Frome, Somerset, BA11 4RW Tel: (01373) 451387 Fax: (01373) 452714 E-mail: sales@brewisdirect.com

▶ Pipeline Technology Ltd, 6 Albany Business Centre, Wickham Road, Fareham, Hampshire, PO17 5BD Tel: (01329) 234888 Fax: (01329) 231717 E-mail: sales@pipetech.co.uk

PIPELINE VALVES

Stokplas Ltd, Sandall Park, Barnby Dun Road, Doncaster, South Yorkshire, DN2 4QL Tel: (01302) 816040 Fax: (01302) 816050 E-mail: stokplas@crossling.co.uk

PIPEWORK DESIGN SERVICES

Bendall, Brunthill Road, Kingstown Industrial Estate, Carlisle, CA3 0EH Tel: (01228) 526246 Fax: (01228) 525634 E-mail: info@bendalls.co.uk

J K Enterprises Ltd, Unit 2 Hewell Lane, Barnt Green, Birmingham, B45 8NZ Tel: 0121-447 7678 Fax: 0121-447 8333

Robertson Engineering, Chandlers Farm, Bollington Lane, Nether Alderley, Macclesfield, Cheshire, SK10 4TB Tel: (01625) 860007 Fax: (01625) 890007

Snamprogetti Ltd, Snamprogetti House, Basingview, Basingstoke, Hampshire, RG21 4YY Tel: (01256) 461211 Fax: (01256) 482211 E-mail: sales@snampro.co.uk

PIPEWORK ENGINEERING

Earth 1st Hire, 198 Cannock Road, Westcroft, Wolverhampton, WV10 8QP Tel: (01902) 861333 Fax: (01902) 864400

G P Watson Ltd, Unit 5 Lancaster Port, Corintation Road, High Wycombe, Buckinghamshire, HP12 3TD Tel: (01494) 446515 Fax: (01494) 446615 E-mail: sales@gpwatson.co.uk

▶ Lynic Industrial Designs Ltd, 138 Main Street, Billinge, Wigan, Lancashire, WN5 7PD Tel: (01744) 895949 Fax: (01744) 892714 E-mail: info@lynicindes.co.uk

Orbital Specialist Contracting Services, Unit 22 Business Development Centre, Telford, Shropshire, TF3 3BA Tel: (01952) 290777 Fax: (01952) 293277

▶ Pruce Newman Pipework, 5 Riverside House, Lower Southend Road, Wickford, Essex, SS11 8BB Tel: (01268) 739470 Fax: (01268) 764183 E-mail: mail@prucenewman.co.uk

▶ Pruce Newman Pipework Ltd, Ayton Road, Wymondham, Norfolk, NR18 0QJ Tel: (01953) 605123 Fax: (01953) 601115 E-mail: info@prucenewman.co.uk

T B S Engineering, 11 Maylan Road, Earlstrees Industrial Estate, Corby, Northamptonshire, NN17 4DR Tel: (01536) 262697 Fax: (01536) 401053

PIPEWORK ERECTION OR INSTALLATION CONTRACTORS

A B P I Ltd, Waterside House, Waltham Business Park, Brickyard Road, Southampton, SO32 2SA Tel: (01489) 897700 Fax: (01489) 897707

A H L Industrial Pipework Specialists Ltd, Unit 22 Royal Industrial Estate, Blackett Street, Jarrow, Tyne & Wear, NE32 3HR Tel: 0191-428 0282 Fax: 0191-483 8893 E-mail: info@ahlpipework.co.uk

Abbfab Services Ltd, Windley Street, Bolton, BL2 2AH Tel: (01204) 523441 Fax: (01204) 557930 E-mail: admin@abbfab.co.uk

Airchannel, Unit 16, Hurworth Road, Aycliffe Industrial Park, Aycliffe, Newton Aycliffe, County Durham, DL5 6UD Tel: (01325) 321237 Fax: (01325) 318397 E-mail: aycliife@woodsidecompressors.co.uk

Airco Pneumatics Ltd, Malmesbury Road, Kingsditch Trading Estate, Cheltenham, Gloucestershire, GL51 9PL Tel: (01242) 690480 Fax: (01242) 690490 E-mail: info@aircopneumatics.co.uk

Allardyce Engineers, 28 Telford Road, Dryburgh Industrial Estate, Dundee, DD2 3QW Tel: (01382) 832045 Fax: (01382) 832045 E-mail: allardyceengs@ukonline.co.uk

Anglia Pipework Ltd, 27 Manor Farm Close, Drayton, Norwich, NR8 6EE Tel: (01603) 260199 Fax: (01603) 400722 E-mail: angliaparkwork@aol.com

Anglo Standard Pipework, Arisdale Avenue, South Ockendon, Essex, RM15 5DP Tel: (01708) 858800 Fax: (01708) 858811 E-mail: sales@anglostandard.com

Associated Pipework, 35 The Swan Centre, Rosemary Road, London, SW17 0AR Tel: (020) 8879 7042 Fax: (020) 8947 9139 E-mail: assocpipework@ukonline.co.uk

Baron Pipework Services, Unit 2 Baron Business Centre, 75 Cemetery Road, Lye, Stourbridge, West Midlands, DY9 8AD Tel: (01384) 422082 Fax: (01384) 422082

David Bilton Engineering Ltd, 77 Hudson Street, North Shields, Tyne & Wear, NE30 1DL Tel: 0191-296 1249 Fax: 0191-257 8611 E-mail: info@dbeltd.com

Boge Compressors, Units 1-4, Bowen Industrial Estate, Aberbargoed, Bargoed, Mid Glamorgan, CF81 9EP Tel: (01443) 875163 Fax: (01443) 820909

BPS Knowsley Ltd, Haven House, Kirkby Bank Road, Knowsley Industrial Park, Liverpool, L33 7RG Tel: 0151-548 1882 Fax: 0151-548 3884

Carillion, Webb Road, Skippers Lane Industrial Estate, Middlesbrough, Cleveland, TS6 6HD Tel: (01642) 459000 Fax: (01642) 454111

Chemical Services Boulting Group P.L.C., Presentation House, Atkin Street, Walkden, Manchester, M28 3DG Tel: 0161-703 7434 Fax: 0161-703 7426 E-mail: enquiries@chemserv.co.uk

Clydesdale Engineering Services Ltd, Belvoir Way, Fairfield Industrial Estate, Louth, Lincolnshire, LN11 0LQ Tel: (01507) 605991 Fax: (01507) 605991 E-mail: info@clydesdale.fsbusiness.co.uk

Connect Engineering Ltd, Thomas Brown House, Edwin Road, Manchester, M11 3ER Tel: 0161-273 6333 Fax: 0161-273 8351 E-mail: connectengineering@yahoo.co.uk

Constant Air Systems Ltd, Hillbottom Road, Sands Industrial Estate, High Wycombe, Buckinghamshire, HP12 4HJ Tel: (01494) 469529 Fax: (01494) 469549 E-mail: admin@constantair.co.uk

D H L Ltd, Pickerings Road, Halebank Industrial Estate, Widnes, Cheshire, WA8 0NH Tel: 0151-424 5441 Fax: 0151-423 2678 E-mail: d.a.welding9@msn.com

D & T Engineering, Unit 12d Thorn Business Park, Rotherwas, Hereford, HR2 6JT Tel: (01432) 355433 Fax: (01432) 355519 E-mail: d.t.eng@btopenworld.com

Deandi Building Services Ltd, Crown House, Union Street, Willenhall, West Midlands, WV13 1UZ Tel: (01902) 609715 Fax: (01902) 634383

Delta Pipework Services Ltd, 17 Hazel Road, Southampton, SO19 7GA Tel: (023) 8068 5411 Fax: (023) 8042 2435

Edwards Elite Engineering Ltd, 8 Dunkirk Trading Estate, Bypass Road, Dunkirk, Chester, CH1 6LZ Tel: (01244) 851311 Fax: (01244) 851411E-mail: stuartedwards@btconnect.com

Engineering Services (Paisley) Ltd (ESL), 65 Espedair Street, Paisley, Renfrewshire, PA2 6RL Tel: 0141-889 1316 Fax: 0141-887 5344 E-mail: info@eslpaisley.co.uk

Fabricon Ltd, Unit 5 Commerce Way, Leighton Buzzard, Bedfordshire, LU7 4RW Tel: (01525) 850244 Fax: (01525) 850245 E-mail: info@fabricon.ltd.uk

Fabweld New Mills Ltd, 5 Canal Foundry, Albion Road, New Mills, High Peak, Derbyshire, SK22 3EZ Tel: (01663) 746156 Fax: (01663) 747960 E-mail: fabweld@ntlworld.com

Fenweld Engineering Services, Unit 8 Addington Works, Knutsford Way Sealand Indust Estate, Chester, CH1 4LT Tel: (01244) 380880 Fax: (01244) 380294 E-mail: fenweld@compuserve.com

Flowline Engineering (UK) Ltd, Trafford Park Road, Newbridge, Trafford Park, Manchester, M17 1HG Tel: 0161-872 1421 Fax: 0161-872 5247 E-mail: flowline01@aol.com

G R Carr Essex Ltd, Archers Fields, Burnt Mills Industrial Estate, Basildon, Essex, SS13 1DN Tel: (01268) 522226 Fax: (01268) 522126 E-mail: grc@grcarr.com

G R M Engineering & Contract Services Ltd, Ferry Lane, Snaith, Goole, North Humberside, DN14 9LL Tel: (01405) 861720 Fax: (01405) 861991 E-mail: davegrm@btconnect.com

Gage Engineering Ltd, Unit 6 Poole Hall Industrial Estate, Ellesmere Port, CH66 1ST Tel: 0151-357 2070 Fax: 0151-357 3070

George Green (Keighley) Ltd, Parkwood Works, Parkwood Street, Keighley, West Yorkshire, BD21 4PN Tel: (01535) 603728 Fax: (01535) 610340 E-mail: enquiries@georgegreen-uk.com

Heating & Industrial Pipework Ltd, 19-35 Warwick Street, Coventry, CV5 6ET Tel: (024) 7667 2224 Fax: (024) 7671 3391 E-mail: hipcov@aol.com

Heatrite Stockport Ltd, 24 Carnforth Road, Heaton Chapel, Stockport, Cheshire, SK4 5LE Tel: 0161-432 8825 Fax: 0161-432 5057

Hensall Mechanical Services (Holdings) Ltd, Roall, Goole, North Humberside, DN14 0NA Tel: (01977) 661318 Fax: (01977) 662127 E-mail: enquiries@hensall.com

Heventech Mechanical Service Ltd, 3 Redbridge Enterprise Centre, Thompson Close, Ilford, Essex, IG1 1TY Tel: (0845) 1298565 E-mail: sales@heventech.co.uk

Hillend, Ridge Way, Hillend Industrial Park, Hillend, Dunfermline, Fife, KY11 9JH Tel: (01383) 823621 Fax: (01383) 823090 E-mail: nat.hillend@btconnect.com

Industrial Pipe Work Ltd, Unit 5 Heol Ty Gwyn Industrial Estate, Maesteg, Mid Glamorgan, CF34 0BQ Tel: (01656) 738855 Fax: (01656) 738917

Interserve Industrial Services Ltd, PO Box 3, Redditch, Worcestershire, B98 0FH Tel: (01527) 507500 Fax: (01527) 507501

J K Enterprises Ltd, Unit 2 Hewell Lane, Barnt Green, Birmingham, B45 8NZ Tel: 0121-447 7678 Fax: 0121-447 8333

J S A Mechanical Services Ltd, Unit 28 Croft Road Industrial Estate, Croft Road, Newcastle, Staffordshire, ST5 0TW Tel: (01782) 635517 Fax: (01782) 630485

James Ramsey Glasgow Ltd, 85 Dykehead Street, Queenslie Industrial Estate, Glasgow, G33 4AQ Tel: 0141-774 2602 Fax: 0141-774 4321 E-mail: jamesramseyltd@btconnect.com

Jenkins & Davies (Engineering) Ltd, Waterloo Industrial Estate, Pembroke Dock, Dyfed, SA72 6BS Tel: (01646) 685895 Fax: (01646) 621030 E-mail: stephensmedley@jenkinsanddavies.com

Jordan Engineering Services Ltd, Hardley Industrial Estate, Hardley, Hythe, Southampton, SO45 3NQ Tel: (023) 8084 9988 Fax: (023) 8042 3779 E-mail: enquiries@chb-jordan.co.uk

Kelvin Fuel Control Systems Ltd, Fordrough, Birmingham, B25 8DW Tel: 0121-772 0972 Fax: 0121-772 0972

▶ Kington Process Ltd, 38-44 St. Andrews Road, Birmingham, B9 4LN Tel: 0121-772 3000 Fax: 0121-772 7000

Lanmar Pipework Engineering Ltd, 35 Lightburn Road, Cambuslang, Glasgow, G72 8UB Tel: 0141-646 2233 Fax: 0141-641 7838

M R F Fabrications Ltd, Unit 6, Holton Road, Poole, Dorset, BH16 6LT Tel: (01202) 631877 Fax: (01202) 631841 E-mail: larry@mrffabs.fsnet.co.uk

M & W Contractors (Pensnett) Ltd, Morgan House, Folkes Road, Lye, Stourbridge, West Midlands, DY9 8RG Tel: (01384) 424411 Fax: (01384) 892425 E-mail: david@mwcontractors.co.uk

Meldan Fabrications Ltd, St Marys Works, Marsh Lane, Barton-upon-Humber, South Humberside, DN18 5HB Tel: (01652) 632075 Fax: (01652) 660389 E-mail: sales@meldan.co.uk

Merit Process Engineering Ltd, Cumberland House, Cumberland Road, North Balkwell Farm Industrial Estate, North Shields, Tyne & Wear, NE29 8RD Tel: 0191-257 2788 Fax: 0191-257 2784 E-mail: enquiries@meritpe.co.uk

Microgas Systems Ltd, Aztec Ho, Perrywood Business Pk Honeycrock La, Salfords, Redhill, RH1 5DZ Tel: (01737) 378000 Fax: (01737) 378055 E-mail: rsmith@microgas.uk.com

Millside Ltd, Niagra Works, Beeley Wood Road, Sheffield, S6 1NH Tel: 0114-233 3091 Fax: 0114-232 6776

Multi Pneumatics, Motivair House, Crompton Court, Attwood Road, Burntwood, Staffordshire, WS7 3GG Tel: (0845) 0096161 Fax: (0845) 0096162 E-mail: enquiries@multi-pneumatics.co.uk

Nordot Engineering Services Ltd, Rosscliffe Road, Ellesmere Port, CH65 3AS Tel: 0151-355 4678 Fax: 0151-357 2450

North Staffs Pipe Services, 23 High Street, Cheadle, Stoke-on-Trent, ST10 1AA Tel: (01538) 757177 Fax: (01538) 757177

Orbital Specialist Contracting Services, Unit 22 Business Development Centre, Telford, Shropshire, TF3 3BA Tel: (01952) 290777 Fax: (01952) 293277

Perfect Pipework Ltd, 49 Rabans Close, Rabans Lane Industrial Area, Aylesbury, Buckinghamshire, HP19 8RS Tel: (01296) 399330 Fax: (01296) 487029 E-mail: sales@perfectpipework.co.uk

Powerrun Ltd, Prospect Works, South Street, Keighley, West Yorkshire, BD21 1DB Tel: (01535) 667614 Fax: (01535) 667616 E-mail: powerrun@powerrun.co.uk

Process Cooling Solutions, 916 Castle La East, Bournemouth, BH7 6SN Tel: (01202) 434328 Fax: (01202) 434329 E-mail: office@ptcltd.co.uk

▶ Pruce Newman Pipework, 5 Riverside House, Lower Southend Road, Wickford, Essex, SS11 8BB Tel: (01268) 739470 Fax: (01268) 764183 E-mail: mail@prucenewman.co.uk

▶ Pruce Newman Pipework Ltd, Ayton Road, Wymondham, Norfolk, NR18 0QJ Tel: (01953) 605123 Fax: (01953) 601115 E-mail: info@prucenewman.co.uk

R G R Fabrications & Welding Services Ltd, Pensnett Trading Estate, Kingswinford, West Midlands, DY6 7PP Tel: (01384) 401055 Fax: (01384) 400068E-mail: sales@rgrltd.com

R Tindall Fabricators Ltd, Ward Street, Chadderton, Oldham, OL9 9EX Tel: 0161-624 3961 Fax: 0161-627 2978 E-mail: john@tindall-fabricators.co.uk

Relyon Heating Engineering Ltd, Bridge Works, Midland Road, Luton, LU2 0BL Tel: (01582) 730806 Fax: (01582) 481499 E-mail: admin@relyonheating.co.uk

Riverside Engineering Services Ltd, Prince Charles Wharf, Stannergate Road, Dundee, DD1 3NA Tel: (01382) 450099 Fax: (01382) 450088 E-mail: enquiries@resl.co.uk

Robertson Engineering, Chandlers Farm, Bollington Lane, Nether Alderley, Macclesfield, Cheshire, SK10 4TB Tel: (01625) 860007 Fax: (01625) 890007

Rodell Mechanical Services Ltd, Unit 14 Gardener Industrial Estate, Kent House Lane, Beckenham, Kent, BR3 1LF Tel: (020) 8778 2324 Fax: (020) 8676 9901 E-mail: rodellmsldt@hotmail.com

S H J Hospital Pipelines Ltd, 34 Springfield Rd., Chesham, Buckinghamshire, HP5 1PW Tel: (01494) 782168 Fax: (01494) 784478 E-mail: info@shj.co.uk

Shaw Group UK Ltd, Stores Road, Derby, DE21 4BG Tel: (01332) 291122 Fax: (01332) 291123 E-mail: info@shawgrp.com

Statham Engineering Services Ltd, Warrington Lane, Lymm, Cheshire, WA13 0SW Tel: (01925) 754965 Fax: (01925) 754127 E-mail: info@stathameng.co.uk

Studley Engineering Ltd, 17 Vulcan Street, Liverpool, L3 7BG Tel: 0151-236 7825 Fax: 0151-255 0597

Tarvail Ltd, Unit K4, Riverside Industrial Estate, Riverside Way, Dartford, DA1 5BS Tel: (01322) 226064 Fax: (01322) 289959 E-mail: office@tarvail.com

Thames Cryogenics Ltd, Gooch Drive, Southmead Industrial Park, Didcot, Oxfordshire, OX11 7PR Tel: (01235) 815777 Fax: (01235) 815333 E-mail: sales@thamescryogenics.com

Thermax Construction, Unit 3 Dover Court, Dover Road, Latchford, Warrington, WA4 1NW Tel: (01925) 242450 Fax: (01925) 242455 E-mail: malcolmferguson@parflothermax.co.uk

Thomson Ltd, Monk Fryston Park, Betteras Hill Road, Hillam, Leeds, LS25 5PF Tel: (01977) 686100 Fax: (01977) 686149 E-mail: main@thomson-group.co.uk

Tomlander Ltd, Paston Road, Sharston, Manchester, M22 4TF Tel: 0161-902 0226 Fax: 0161-945 5203 E-mail: tomlander@msn.com

Vinci Services Ltd, Ditton Road, Widnes, Cheshire, WA8 0WE Tel: 0151-422 3800 Fax: 0151-423 3934

Woodside Pneumatics Ltd, Stirling Road Industrial Estate, Dykehead Road, Airdrie, Lanarkshire, ML6 7UJ Tel: (01236) 756171 Fax: (01236) 751210 E-mail: sales@woodside-compressors.co.uk

X Tech Stainless Steel Fabrications Ltd, Unit A2 Trecenydd Industrial Estate, Caerphilly, Mid Glamorgan, CF83 2RZ Tel: 029 20886639

Zeataline Projects Ltd, 3 York Close, Washingborough, Lincoln, LN4 1SQ Tel: (01522) 792378 Fax: (01522) 792378

PIPEWORK FABRICATORS

A B C Stainless Ltd, Empson Road, Peterborough, PE1 5UP Tel: (01733) 314515 Fax: (01733) 315273 E-mail: abcstainless@aol.com

A H L Industrial Pipework Specialists Ltd, Unit 22 Royal Industrial Estate, Blackett Street, Jarrow, Tyne & Wear, NE32 3HR Tel: 0191-428 0282 Fax: 0191-483 8893 E-mail: info@ahlpipework.co.uk

A S L R Fabrication Services Ltd, Opal Way, Stone Business Park, Stone, Staffordshire, ST15 0SS Tel: (01785) 286060 Fax: (01785) 818728 E-mail: sales@aslr.co.uk

Abbfab Services Ltd, Windley Street, Bolton, BL2 2AH Tel: (01204) 523441 Fax: (01204) 557930 E-mail: admin@abbfab.co.uk

Allardyce Engineers, 28 Telford Road, Dryburgh Industrial Estate, Dundee, DD2 3QW Tel: (01382) 832045 Fax: (01382) 832045 E-mail: allardyceengs@ukonline.co.uk

▶ Allmec Engineering Ltd, 8 Guardian Street Industrial Estate, Guardian Street, Warrington, WA5 1SJ Tel: (01925) 575820 Fax: (01925) 637796 E-mail: allmec@aol.com

Ansul Fabrication, Downing Street, Smethwick, West Midlands, B66 2JL Tel: 0121-565 3108 Fax: 0121-558 1339 E-mail: ansulfabricationsuk@tyco-bstd.com

Anvil Alloys Ltd, 1-2 Benwick Road, Whittlesey, Peterborough, PE7 2HD Tel: (01923) 800721 Fax: (01923) 800722

PIPEWORK FABRICATORS – *continued*

Anvil Tubesmiths Southern Ltd, Sedlescombe Sawmills, Hawkhurst Road, Staplecross, Robertsbridge, East Sussex, TN32 5SA Tel: (01580) 830770 Fax: (01580) 830220 E-mail: barry.luckham@btopenworld.com

Arco Engineering & Fabrications Ltd, 68-70 Heath Mill Lane, Deritend, Birmingham, B9 4AR Tel: 0121-771 0936 Fax: 0121-766 7396

Balfour Beatty, Chaddock Lane, Worsley, Manchester, M28 1XW Tel: 0161-790 3000 Fax: 0161-703 5307

Banfield Engineering Wisbech Ltd, Unit 8b Tinkers Drove, Wisbech, Cambridgeshire, PE13 3PQ Tel: (01945) 585554 Fax: (01945) 463874 E-mail: sales@banfield-uk.com

Bennett & Skelland Ltd, 306 Liverpool Road, Warrington, WA5 1DP Tel: (01925) 634066 Fax: (01925) 445505 E-mail: bennettandskelland@tiscali.co.uk

David Bilton Engineering Ltd, 77 Hudson Street, North Shields, Tyne & Wear, NE30 1DL Tel: 0191-296 1429 Fax: 0191-257 8611 E-mail: info@dbeltd.com

BPS Knowsley Ltd, Haven House, Kirkby Bank Road, Knowsley Industrial Park, Liverpool, L33 7RG Tel: 0151-548 1882 Fax: 0151-548 3884

C W T Ltd, Hempstalls Lane, Newcastle, Staffordshire, ST5 0SW Tel: (01782) 625222 Fax: (01782) 625333 E-mail: cwtlimited@aol.com

Caletrim Fabrications Ltd, 7a Bowes Road, Middlesbrough, Cleveland, TS2 1LU Tel: (01642) 224121 Fax: (01642) 224121

Carillion, Webb Road, Skippers Lane Industrial Estate, Middlesbrough, Cleveland, TS6 6HD Tel: (01642) 459000 Fax: (01642) 454111

Castle Engineering Resources Ltd, 4 Central Works, Peartree Lane, Dudley, West Midlands, DY2 0QU Tel: (01384) 230233 Fax: (01384) 230757 E-mail: castle.eng@btclick.com

Chemical Services Boulting Group P.L.C., Presentation House, Atkin Street, Walkden, Manchester, M28 3DG Tel: 0161-703 7434 Fax: 0161-703 7426 E-mail: enquiries@chemserv.co.uk

Cronite Scomark Engineering, Church Street, Swadlincote, Derbyshire, DE11 9NR Tel: (01283) 218222 Fax: (01283) 226468 E-mail: tonyknight@scomark.com

D H L Ltd, Pickerings Road, Halebank Industrial Estate, Widnes, Cheshire, WA8 0NH Tel: 0151-424 5441 Fax: 0151-423 2678 E-mail: d.a.welding9@msn.com

D O J Pipe Welding Services, 6 Pear Tree Close, Little Billing, Northampton, NN3 9TH Tel: (01604) 404010 Fax: (01604) 408636 E-mail: welding@pipewelding.co.uk

Deplynn Engineering Ltd, 3 Thornham Grove, London, E15 1DN Tel: (020) 8519 6028 Fax: (020) 8519 6028

Drillfield Engineering Co. Ltd, Scott Works, Unit 1, Mannor Road, Mancetter, Atherstone, Warwickshire, CV9 1RG Tel: (01827) 712468 Fax: (01827) 714252

E & P Engineering Services, 16 St Nicholas Road, Littlestone, New Romney, Kent, TN28 8PT Tel: (01797) 366724

Echo Engineering Southern Ltd, Chapel Land Farm, Ashford Road, New Romney, Kent, TN28 8TH Tel: (01797) 367670 Fax: (01797) 367671 E-mail: sales@echo-eng.com

Edwards Elite Engineering Ltd, 8 Dunkirk Trading Estate, Bypass Road, Dunkirk, Chester, CH1 6LZ Tel: (01244) 851311 Fax: (01244) 851411E-mail: stuartedwards@btconnect.com

Engineering & Maintenance Services Ltd, Unit 12 St. Davids Industrial Estate, St. Davids Road, Swansea Enterprise Park, Swansea, SA6 8RX Tel: (01792) 797579 Fax: (01792) 772490 E-mail: ems@swanseauk.fsworld.co.uk

Enterprise Engineering Services Ltd, Craigshaw Drive, West Tullos Industrial Estate, Aberdeen, AB12 3TH Tel: (01224) 288400 Fax: (01224) 871327 E-mail: sales@eesl.com

Fabricated Products, 4 Foundry House, Sheffield Road, Rotherham, South Yorkshire, S60 1BN Tel: (01709) 720842 Fax: (01709) 720846 E-mail: info@fabricatedproducts.co.uk

Fabweld New Mills Ltd, 5 Canal Foundry, Albion Road, New Mills, High Peak, Derbyshire, SK22 3EZ Tel: (01663) 746156 Fax: (01663) 747960 E-mail: fabweld@ntlworld.com

Flowline Engineering (UK) Ltd, Trafford Park Road, Newbridge, Trafford Park, Manchester, M17 1HG Tel: 0161-872 1421 Fax: 0161-872 5247 E-mail: flowline01@aol.com

Forcecombe Ltd, 23 Havelock Street, Hull, HU3 4JH Tel: (01482) 227722 Fax: (01482) 227722

G R Carr Essex Ltd, Archers Fields, Burnt Mills Industrial Estate, Basildon, Essex, SS13 1DN Tel: (01268) 522226 Fax: (01268) 522126 E-mail: grc@grcarr.com

Gage Engineering Ltd, Unit 6 Poole Hall Industrial Estate, Ellesmere Port, CH66 1ST Tel: 0151-357 2070 Fax: 0151-357 3070

Globe Engineering, Everite Works, Derby Road, Widnes, Cheshire, WA8 9ND Tel: 0151-495 3759

H & I Engineering Ltd, Solway Works, Annan Road, Eastriggs, Annan, Dumfriesshire, DG12 6NJ Tel: (01461) 40500 Fax: (01461) 40801 E-mail: admin@hi-engineering.co.uk

Haycock & Hague, The Vivars Indust Centre, Vivars Way Canal Road, Selby, North Yorkshire, YO8 8BE Tel: (01757) 290011 Fax: (01757) 212112 E-mail: sales@haycockandhague.co.uk

Heatrite Stockport Ltd, 24 Carnforth Road, Heaton Chapel, Stockport, Cheshire, SK4 5LE Tel: 0161-432 8825 Fax: 0161-432 5057

Hedley (Engineering Services) Ltd, West Havelock Street, South Shields, Tyne & Wear, NE33 5DZ Tel: 0191-456 0250 Fax: 0191-455 6040 E-mail: info@hedley.co.uk

Henderson Engineering (N E) Ltd, Vickers Close, Preston Farm Industrial Estate, Stockton-on-Tees, Cleveland, TS18 3TD Tel: (01642) 608008 Fax: (01642) 612636 E-mail: enquiries@hendersonengineering.com

Hes Engineering Services Ltd, Bingswood Trading Estate, Whaley Bridge, High Peak, Derbyshire, SK23 7LY Tel: (01663) 735333 Fax: (01663) 735377

High Pressure Welding Ltd, Sundon Business Park, Dencora Way, Luton, LU3 3HP Tel: (01582) 565400 Fax: (01582) 565500 E-mail: hpweldingltd@aol.com

Howard Cole Developments Ltd, 4 Peterborough Road, Crowland, Peterborough, PE6 0BA Tel: (01733) 211351 Fax: (01733) 211441

J L Engineering Rixton Ltd, Chapel Lane, Warrington, WA3 6HG Tel: 0161-775 0588 Fax: 0161-775 6613 E-mail: info@jleng.co.uk

J.N.J. Fabrications Ltd, Ambrose Street, Gorton, Manchester, M12 5DD Tel: 0161-223 7277 Fax: 0161-223 7277 E-mail: sales@jnjfabs.co.uk

Jenkins & Davies (Engineering) Ltd, Waterloo Industrial Estate, Pembroke Dock, Dyfed, SA72 6BS Tel: (01646) 685895 Fax: (01646) 621030 E-mail: stephensmedley@jenkinsanddavies.com

Jordan Engineering Services Ltd, Hardley Industrial Estate, Hardley, Hythe, Southampton, SO45 3NQ Tel: (023) 8084 9988 Fax: (023) 8042 3779 E-mail: enquiries@chb-jordan.co.uk

K G D Industrial Services, Willow Court, Netherwood Road, Rotherwas Industrial Estate, Hereford, HR2 6JU Tel: (01432) 374374 Fax: (01432) 353419 E-mail: sales@kgdprocess.com

Kesteven Plastics Ltd, Unit 3, Moorland Way, Tritton Road, Lincoln, LN6 7JW Tel: (01522) 695977 Fax: (01522) 695977 E-mail: george@kestevenplasticsltd.co.uk

Lanmar Pipework Engineering Ltd, 35 Lightburn Road, Cambuslang, Glasgow, G72 8UB Tel: 0141-646 2233 Fax: 0141-641 7838

Lenco Engineering (Hull) Ltd, Unit 1D Marfleet Lane Industrial Estate, Burma Drive, Hull, HU9 5SD Tel: (01482) 784988 Fax: (01482) 796661 E-mail: lenco98@hotmail.com

Kevin Lloyd Ltd, 2 Mickleton Road, Middlesbrough, Cleveland, TS2 1RQ Tel: (01642) 226950 Fax: (01642) 226951

M R F Fabrications Ltd, Unit 6, Holton Road, Poole, Dorset, BH16 6LT Tel: (01202) 631877 Fax: (01202) 631841 E-mail: larry@mrffabs.fsnet.co.uk

Mechanical & Pipework Fabrications Ltd, Racecourse Road, Pershore, Worcestershire, WR10 2EY Tel: (01386) 554048 Fax: (01386) 556695 E-mail: sales@mpf-ltd.co.uk

Merit Process Engineering Ltd, Cumberland House, Cumberland Road, North Balkwell Farm Industrial Estate, North Shields, Tyne & Wear, NE29 8RD Tel: 0191-257 2788 Fax: 0191-257 2784 E-mail: enquiries@meritpe.co.uk

Millside Ltd, Niagra Works, Beeley Wood Road, Sheffield, S6 1NH Tel: 0114-233 3091 Fax: 0114-232 6776

Munro & Miller Fittings Ltd, 3 Westerton Road, East Mains Industrial Estate, Broxburn, West Lothian, EH52 5AU Tel: (01506) 853531 Fax: (01506) 856628 E-mail: sales@munro-miller.co.uk

Narvida Ltd, Taxi Way, Hillend Industrial Park, Hillend, Dunfermline, Fife, KY11 9JT Tel: (01383) 823417 Fax: (01383) 823148 E-mail: info@narvida.co.uk

Nordot Engineering Services Ltd, Rosscliffe Road, Ellesmere Port, CH65 3AS Tel: 0151-355 4678 Fax: 0151-357 2450

Penarth Industrial Services Ltd, 8 Gripoly Mills, Sloper Road, Cardiff, CF11 8AA Tel: (029) 2064 1555 Fax: (029) 2064 1899 E-mail: info@pisltd.com

Pipework Engineering Services Ltd, 124 Emily Street, Birmingham, B12 0XJ Tel: 0121-440 5995 Fax: 0121-440 3246 E-mail: thehamoffice@pipeworkengineering.co.uk

Pipework Fabrication Services Ltd, Western Industrial Estate, Caerleon, Newport, NP18 3NN Tel: (01633) 430099 Fax: (01633) 430099

Pipework & Mechanical Contracts Ltd, Ty Verlon Industrial Estate, Cardiff Road, Barry, South Glamorgan, CF63 2BE Tel: (01446) 748611 Fax: (01446) 746906

Pipework Utilities Ltd, Newcastle Road, Smallwood, Sandbach, Cheshire, CW11 2TZ Tel: (01477) 500344 Fax: (01477) 500755 E-mail: sales@pipeworkutilities.co.uk

Pleatward Engineering Ltd, Rawfolds Industrial Estate, Bradford Road, Rawfolds, Cleckheaton, West Yorkshire, BD19 5LT Tel: (01274) 874771 Fax: (01274) 851180 E-mail: sales@pleatward.co.uk

Powerrun Ltd, Prospect Works, South Street, Keighley, West Yorkshire, BD21 1DB Tel: (01535) 667614 Fax: (01535) 667616 E-mail: powerrun@powerrun.co.uk

Prep Tec Systems Ltd, Fern Hill Business Centre, Todd Street, Bury, Lancashire, BL9 5BJ Tel: 0161-761 5214 Fax: 0161-764 1914 E-mail: info@prep-tec.co.uk

Proweld Quality Vessels Ltd, Units 22-23, Lion Court, Daneshill, Basingstoke, Hampshire, RG24 8QU Tel: (01256) 814184 Fax: (01256) 814164 E-mail: simon@proweld.uk.com

Q A Weldtech Ltd, 1a Bowes Road, Middlesbrough, Cleveland, TS2 1LU Tel: (01642) 222831 Fax: (01642) 242003 E-mail: quality@qaweldtech.co.uk

R G R Fabrications & Welding Services Ltd, Pensnett Trading Estate, Kingswinford, West Midlands, DY6 7PP Tel: (01384) 401055 Fax: (01384) 400068E-mail: sales@rgrltd.com

R Kirkland Blyth Ltd, 62-66 Bridge Street, Blyth, Northumberland, NE24 2AP Tel: (01670) 352196 Fax: (01670) 360238

R M F Engineering Ltd, Rotherham Road, Dinnington, Sheffield, S25 3RF Tel: (01909) 567683 Fax: (01909) 562725 E-mail: sales@rmf-engineering.co.uk

R Tindall Fabricators Ltd, Ward Street, Chadderton, Oldham, OL9 9EX Tel: 0161-624 3961 Fax: 0161-627 2978 E-mail: john@tindall-fabricators.co.uk

Robertson Engineering, Chandlers Farm, Bollington Lane, Nether Alderley, Macclesfield, Cheshire, SK10 4TB Tel: (01625) 860007 Fax: (01625) 890007

Rodell Mechanical Services Ltd, Unit 14 Gardener Industrial Estate, Kent House Lane, Beckenham, Kent, BR3 1LF Tel: (020) 8778 2324 Fax: (020) 8676 9901 E-mail: rodellmsldt@hotmail.com

N. Rourke & Son (Engineering) Ltd, 4-6 Barkan Way, Swinton, Manchester, M27 8SF Tel: 0161-793 5171 Fax: 0161-794 4760 E-mail: nrourkeson@hotmail.com

Seafab Consultants Ltd, Wellheads Terrace, Wellheads Industrial Estate, Aberdeen, AB21 7GF Tel: (01224) 770287 Fax: (01224) 723400 E-mail: info@seafab.co.uk

Selwyn Construction Engineering Ltd, Tarran Road, Tarran Industrial Estate, Wirral, Merseyside, CH46 4TU Tel: 0151-678 0236 Fax: 0151-678 8959 E-mail: enquiries@selwyngroup.co.uk

Shaw Group UK Ltd, Stores Road, Derby, DE21 4BG Tel: (01332) 291122 Fax: (01332) 291123 E-mail: info@shawgrp.com

A.L. Starkie Ltd, Wellington Works, Wellington Rd, Ashton-under-Lyne, Lancs, OL6 7EF Tel: 0161-339 4549 Fax: 0161-343 3305 E-mail: sales@superheater.co.uk

Sterling Installations Ltd, 128-129 Leyland Complex, Irthlingborough Road, Wellingborough, Northamptonshire, NN8 1RT Tel: (01933) 226227 Fax: (01933) 226447 E-mail: sterling@computalynx.co.uk

Studley Engineering Ltd, 17 Vulcan Street, Liverpool, L3 7BG Tel: 0151-236 7825 Fax: 0151-255 0597

T B S Engineering, 11 Maylan Road, Earlstrees Industrial Estate, Corby, Northamptonshire, NN17 4DR Tel: (01536) 262697 Fax: (01536) 401053

Tarvail Ltd, Unit K4, Riverside Industrial Estate, Riverside Way, Dartford, DA1 5BS Tel: (01322) 226064 Fax: (01322) 289959 E-mail: office@tarvail.com

Taylor Kerr Couplings Ltd, Disraeli House, 12 Aylesbury End, Beaconsfield, Buckinghamshire, HP9 1LW Tel: (01494) 679500 Fax: (01494) 679505 E-mail: info@teekaycouplings.com

Thomas Lane & Co. Ltd, Hope St Works, Hazel Grove, Stockport, Cheshire, SK7 4EL Tel: 0161-483 9666 Fax: 0161-456 4440 E-mail: fabwork@t-lane.demon.co.uk

Tomlander Ltd, Paston Road, Sharston, Manchester, M22 4TF Tel: 0161-902 0226 Fax: 0161-945 5203 E-mail: tomlander@msn.com

Truarc, 2 Eastgate, Lowfields Business Park, Elland, West Yorkshire, HX5 9DN Tel: (01422) 375191 Fax: (01422) 311685

▶ Tyne Tube Ltd, Nile Street, South Shields, Tyne & Wear, NE33 1RH Tel: 0191-455 1144 Fax: 0191-455 4339 E-mail: enquiries@tynetubeservices.co.uk

Vinci Services Ltd, Ditton Road, Widnes, Cheshire, WA8 0WE Tel: 0151-422 3800 Fax: 0151-423 3934

W Bertram & Sons Ltd, Walpole Street, South Shields, Tyne & Wear, NE33 5EF Tel: 0191-455 6727 Fax: 0191-455 6727

W S Britland & Co. Ltd, Tilmanstone Depot, Pike Road, Eythorne, Dover, Kent, CT15 4DH Tel: (01304) 831583 Fax: (01304) 831983 E-mail: britland.dover@dial.pipex.com

Weldametal Services Ltd, 10-12 Winfield Street, Dunstable, Bedfordshire, LU6 1LS Tel: (01582) 665246 Fax: (01582) 661443 E-mail: weldametal@aol.com

Willas Engineering Ltd, 9-10 Village Farm Road, Village Farm Industrial Estate, Pyle, Bridgend, Mid Glamorgan, CF33 6BL Tel: (01656) 745000 Fax: (01656) 745175 E-mail: ian@willas.co.uk

Winsford Fabrications, Road 5, Winsford Industrial Estate, Winsford, Cheshire, CW7 3SH Tel: (01606) 597305 Fax: (01606) 597308

Woodfield Systems Ltd, Tyler Way, Swalecliffe, Whitstable, Kent, CT5 2RS Tel: (01227) 793351 Fax: (01227) 793625 E-mail: sales@akerkvaerner.com

PIPEWORK FABRICATORS, MILD STEEL

Cookson Bros, Hornby Boulevard, Bootle, Merseyside, L20 5DX Tel: 0151-922 3394 Fax: 0151-922 3014

PIPEWORK MANIFOLDS

Cronite Scomark Engineering, Church Street, Swadlincote, Derbyshire, DE11 9NR Tel: (01283) 218222 Fax: (01283) 226468 E-mail: tonyknight@scomark.com

PIPEWORK SUPPORT SYSTEMS

Atlantic Supports Engineering, 3 Llandough Trading Estate, Penarth Road, Cardiff, CF11 8RR Tel: (029) 2070 8461 Fax: (029) 2035 0437 E-mail: sales@atlantic-supports.co.uk

Carpenter & Paterson Holdings Ltd, Crown Works, Henfaes Lane, Welshpool, Powys, SY21 7BE Tel: (01938) 552061 Fax: (01938) 555306 E-mail: info@cp-ltd.co.uk

Debro Engineering & Presswork, Stourvale Trading Estate, Banners Lane, Halesowen, West Midlands, B63 2AX Tel: (01384) 633004 Fax: (01384) 633746

Richard Edwards Fabrications Ltd, 15 Broadfield Close, Croydon, CR0 4XR Tel: (020) 8686 8616 Fax: (020) 8686 5313

H F Northan Ltd, High Street, Haxey, Doncaster, South Yorkshire, DN9 2HH Tel: (01427) 752708 Fax: (01427) 752173

Lisega Ltd, Unit3, Washington Centre, Hales Owen Road, Netherton, West Midlands, DY2 9RE Tel: (01384) 458660 Fax: (01384) 213301 E-mail: sales@lisega.co.uk

Nelson Unit Ltd, Victoria Works, Lodge Lane, Dukinfield, Cheshire, SK16 5HY Tel: 0161-330 1007 Fax: 0161-343 1346 E-mail: info@nelsonunit.co.uk

Pipe Supports Ltd, Salwarpe Road, Droitwich, Worcestershire, WR9 9BH Tel: (01905) 795500 Fax: (01905) 794126 E-mail: sales@pipesupports.com

Shawston International Ltd, Great Norbury Street, Hyde, Cheshire, SK14 1BW Tel: 0161-368 4545 Fax: 0161-367 8114

PIPEWORK TRUNKING SYSTEMS

Alumasc Interior Building Products Ltd, Unit C1 Halesfield 19, Telford, Shropshire, TF7 4QT Tel: (01952) 580590 Fax: (01952) 587805 E-mail: sales@alumascinteriors.com

Screeduct Ltd, Unit 8, Northcot Business Park, Blockley, Moreton-In-Marsh, Gloucestershire, GL56 9LH Tel: (01386) 701372 Fax: (01386) 701571 E-mail: sales@screeduct.com

PISTON PUMPS

Dawson, Downie, Lamont, 31 Rutherford Road, Glenrothes, Fife, KY6 2RT Tel: (01592) 775577 Fax: (01592) 775517 E-mail: sales@ddl-ltd.com

Denhaolm Oilfield Services, Greenbank Place, East Tullos Industrial Estate, Aberdeen, AB12 3BT Tel: (01224) 249424 Fax: (01224) 249496

PISTON RINGS

Adminglade Ltd, Caxton House, Stoke Street, Sheffield, S9 3QH Tel: 0114-244 1932 Fax: 0114-244 1932

Board Bros, 103 St John's Hill, London, SW11 1SY Tel: (020) 7228 6846 Fax: (020) 7228 8136

Bradford Piston & Piston Ring Co. Ltd, Unit 22, Missouri Avenue, Salford, M50 2NP Tel: 0161-736 5211 Fax: 0161-736 4785 E-mail: bppr@btconnect.com

Cross Manufacturing Co 1938 Ltd, Midford Road, Bath, BA2 5RR Tel: (01225) 837000 Fax: (01225) 834115 E-mail: mail@crossmanufacturing.com

F J Engineering Ltd, 4 Keyhaven Road, Milford on Sea, Lymington, Hampshire, SO41 0QY Tel: (01590) 644644 Fax: (01590) 644644 E-mail: fjengineer@aol.com

Omega Pistons Ltd, Oak Barn Road, Halesowen, West Midlands, B62 9DW Tel: 0121-559 6778 Fax: 0121-559 6779 E-mail: info@omegapistons.com

PISTON VALVES

Blackfive Engineering Ltd, 16 Beeston Court, Stuart Road, Manor Park, Runcorn, Cheshire, WA7 1SS Tel: (01928) 579140 Fax: (01928) 579514 E-mail: blackfive@btconnect.com

PISTONS

Board Bros, 103 St John's Hill, London, SW11 1SY Tel: (020) 7228 6846 Fax: (020) 7228 8136

F W Thornton & Son, 57 Wyle Cop, Shrewsbury, SY1 1XJ Tel: (01743) 357081 Fax: (01743) 367549 E-mail: fwt@nbcgroup.co.uk

Gosnay's Engineering Co. Ltd, Eastern Avenue West, Romford, RM7 7NS Tel: (01708) 740668 Fax: (01708) 733266 E-mail: sales@gosnays.co.uk

PIZZA DELIVERY SYSTEMS

Eawex International Trading Co. Ltd, Rear of 12 Burley Road, Oakham, Leicestershire, LE15 6DH Tel: (01572) 756322 Fax: (01572) 756322 E-mail: kimwahng@hotmail.com

PIZZAS

▶ Pizza Two Four (Manufacturing) Ltd, Radfords Field, Industrial Estate, Maesbury Road, Oswestry, Shropshire, SY10 8HA Tel: (01691) 657664

PLAIN BEARINGS

▶ Coleherne Laser, Newton Moor Industrial Estate, Lodge Street, Hyde, Cheshire, SK14 4LE Tel: 0161-366 6603 Fax: 0161-367 8239 E-mail: brian@coleherneuk.com

K C Engineering Ltd, Hownsgill Drive, Consett, County Durham, DH8 9HU Tel: (01207) 583100 Fax: (01207) 581900 E-mail: sales@kceng.com

J. H. Richards & Co. Ltd, Saltley Road, Birmingham, B7 4TD Tel: 0121-359 2257 Fax: 0121-359 7340 E-mail: andrew@jhrichards.co.uk

PLAN FILING SYSTEMS

E X X Projects, 72 Rivington Street, London, EC2A 3AY Tel: (020) 7684 8200 Fax: 0845-630 1282 E-mail: exx@plax.co.uk

Railex Systems Ltd, Station Road, Lawford, Manningtree, Essex, CO11 1DZ Tel: (08706) 006664 Fax: (01206) 391465 E-mail: info@railex.co.uk

PLAN PRINTING, *See Drawing Office Technical Services/Draughting Services*

PLAN PRINTING MACHINE/ PRINTER MAINTENANCE AND REPAIR

▶ GENUS IT Large Format Systems, Hammond Close, Nuneaton, Warwickshire, CV11 6RY Tel: (024) 7625 4919 Fax: (024) 7638 2319 E-mail: philjones@genusit.com

PLAN PRINTING MACHINE/ PRINTER MANUFRS

▶ GENUS IT Large Format Systems, Hammond Close, Nuneaton, Warwickshire, CV11 6RY Tel: (024) 7625 4919 Fax: (024) 7638 2319 E-mail: philjones@genusit.com

▶ Rush & Warwick Ltd, 1 Acacia Close, Cherrycourt Way, Leighton Buzzard, Bedfordshire, LU7 4QE Tel: (01525) 372205 Fax: (01525) 852566 E-mail: sales@rushandwarwick.co.uk

PLANETARY GEAR HEADS

Mclennan Servo Supplies Ltd, Unit 1, The Royston Centre, Lynchford Road, Ash Vale, Aldershot, Hampshire, GU12 5PQ Tel: (0870) 7700700 Fax: (0870) 7700699 E-mail: sales@mclennan.co.uk

PLANETARY GEARBOXES

Comer Industries (UK) Ltd, Units 2-3, Heath Road, Merrylees Industrial Estate, Desford, Leicester, LE9 9FE Tel: (01530) 231504 Fax: (01530) 231503 E-mail: sales@comer.co.uk

Lancereal Ltd, Springfield Mills, Springfield Lane, Kirkburton, Huddersfield, HD8 0NZ Tel: (01484) 606040 Fax: (01484) 609911 E-mail: sales@lancereal.com

PLANETARY GEARS

▶ A J Transmissions, 4 Stanhope Close, Wilmslow, Cheshire, SK9 2NN Tel: (01625) 533466 Fax: (01625) 533466 E-mail: tomatajt@aol.co.uk

Heynau, Unit 43, Britannia Way, Enterprise Industrial Park, Lichfield, Staffordshire, WS14 9UY Tel: (01543) 255995 Fax: (01543) 250316 E-mail: acdcpowerdrives@aol.com

PLANNED MAINTENANCE SOFTWARE

Anite Mobile Working Solutions, 353 Buckingham Avenue, Slough, Slough, SL1 4PF Tel: (01753) 804000 Fax: (01753) 735735

Chartwell Systems, Malens, Beacon Gardens, Crowborough, East Sussex, TN6 1BG Tel: (01892) 669597 Fax: (01892) 669597 E-mail: chartwell.sys@btconnect.com

PLANNED PREVENTATIVE MAINTENANCE (PPM) CONSULTANCY

Strategic Maintenance Planning Ltd, Stanton Court, Stirling Road South Marston Indust Estate, Swindon, SN1 1PZ Tel: (01793) 823013 Fax: (01793) 823014 E-mail: info@smpltd.co.uk

PLANNING CHARTS

Map Marketing Ltd, 92-104 Carnwath Road, London, SW6 3HW Tel: (020) 7526 2322 Fax: (020) 7371 0473 E-mail: sales@mapmarketing.com

PLANNING CONSULTANCY

Brock Carmichael Architects, 19 Old Hall Street, Liverpool, L3 9JQ Tel: 0151-242 6222 Fax: 0151-236 4467 E-mail: office@brockcarmichael.co.uk

P W Callaghan, Emerys, 2 Bucks Lane, Little Eversden, Cambridge, CB3 7HL Tel: (01223) 262444 Fax: (01223) 263241 E-mail: callaghanpw@aol.com

▶ Chippington Derrick Consultants Ltd, 1 Carlton Close, Camberley, Surrey, GU15 1DS Tel: (01276) 508949

Comprehensive Planning Associates (Overseas), Bromsash House, Bromsash, Ross-On-Wye, Herefordshire, HR9 7PL Tel: (01989) 750243 Fax: (01989) 750243

D T Z Pieda Consulting, 1 Edinburgh Quay, 133 Fountainbridge, Edinburgh, EH3 9QG Tel: 0131-222 4500 Fax: 0131-222 4501

Deka Capital Advisors, 56-58 Clerkenwell Road, London, EC1M 5PX Tel: (020) 7566 0020 Fax: (020) 7566 0050 E-mail: davidcookarch@aol.com

Gibson Consulting Ltd, 3 The Quadrant, Coventry, CV1 2DY Tel: (024) 7624 3607 Fax: (024) 7624 3608 E-mail: mark.gibson@gibsonconsulting.co.uk

▶ Marpal Ltd, Room 34, College Business Centre, The College, Uttoxeter New Road, Derby, DE22 3WZ Tel: (01332) 869290 Fax: (01332) 869291 E-mail: info@marpal.co.uk

Nationwide Machine Services Ltd, Westward House, Regent Road, Salford, M5 8LY Tel: 0161-872 4200 Fax: 0161-877 7610

Pace Group International Ltd, 171 Alcester Road, Birmingham, B13 8JR Tel: 0121-449 4492 Fax: 0121-449 9695 E-mail: ho@pace-gi.com

T J Browne Ltd, 61 Ashford Road, Swindon, SN1 3NS Tel: (01793) 695752 Fax: (01793) 695752 E-mail: tim_browne@talk21.com

PLANNING SUPERVISORS, CONSTRUCTION INDUSTRY

Darnton Elgee Architects, Monk Fryston Hall, Monk Fryston, Leeds, LS25 5DU Tel: (01977) 681001 Fax: (01977) 681006 E-mail: email@darntonelgee.com

▶ Legge Associates Ltd, Annfield House, Eskbank Toll, Dalkeith, Midlothian, EH22 3DY Tel: 0131 654 0101 Fax: 0131 654 9596 E-mail: Symon@leggeassociates.demon.co.uk

▶ Martin Aitken Associates, Aspire Business Centre, 16 Farmeloan Road, Rutherglen, Glasgow, G73 1DL Tel: 0141-647 0101 Fax: 0141-647 0107 E-mail: martinaitkenassociates@btconnect.com

Angus Meek Partnership Ltd, 60 Arley Hill, Bristol, BS6 5PP Tel: 0117-942 8286 Fax: 0117-942 0495 E-mail: admin@angusmeek.co.uk

▶ Stewart Pearl & Associates, 3 Sandy Lane, Prestwich, Manchester, M25 9RU Tel: 0161-798 8811 Fax: 0161-798 8811 E-mail: sales@stewartpearl.co.uk

PLANT AND MACHINERY AUCTION SERVICES

Arrow Auctions, Bartleet Road, Washford, Redditch, Worcestershire, B98 0DQ Tel: (01527) 517707 Fax: (01527) 510924 E-mail: enquiries@arrowauction.co.uk

Empire Auctions, 27 Old Gloucester Street, London, WC1N 3AF Tel: (020) 7419 5059 E-mail: enquiries@empireauctions.co.uk

Go Industry P.L.C., New London Bridge House, 25 London Bridge Street, London, SE1 9BQ Tel: (020) 7098 3700 Fax: (020) 7098 3795 E-mail: lucy.moran@goindustry.com

▶ Marriott & Co., 19 East Street, Farnham, Surrey, GU9 7SD Tel: (01252) 712083 Fax: (01252) 737613 E-mail: mail@marriott.co.uk

O'Neill & Mcbride, 6 Derrynoyd Road, Draperstown, Magherafelt, County Londonderry, BT45 7AH Tel: (028) 7962 8255 Fax: (028) 7962 8878

Thame Farmers Auction Mart Ltd, The Cattle Market, North Street, Thame, Oxfordshire, OX9 3FP Tel: (01844) 217437 Fax: (01844) 261765 E-mail: jonquil@thame-market.co.uk

PLANT AUTOMATION CONTROL SYSTEMS

Datastor Systems Ltd, 74 Manchester Road, Congleton, Cheshire, CW12 2HT Tel: (01260) 277025 Fax: (01260) 270334 E-mail: sales@datastorsystems.com

PLANT DESIGN OR PLANNING CONSULTANCY

Ebene Hall Plant Care Ltd, Widbury Hill Nursery, Widbury Hill, Ware, Hertfordshire, SG12 7QE Tel: (01920) 460368 Fax: (01920) 461488 E-mail: sales@ebanyhall.co.uk

L D H Plant Ltd, South Dock, Alexandra Docks, Newport, Gwent, NP20 2NQ Tel: (01633) 263936 Fax: (01633) 264013 E-mail: sales@ldhplant.co.uk

Plantlife Ltd, The Barn, Old Gardens, Blackhorse Road, Woking, Surrey, GU22 0QT Tel: (01483) 799980 Fax: (01483) 799988 E-mail: info@plantlife-ltd.co.uk

Rentokil Tropical Plants, Middlemore Lane, Walsall, WS9 8SP Tel: (01922) 745970 Fax: (01922) 745972

Rentokil Tropical Plants, Acorn Nursery, Barrow Lane, Cheshunt, Waltham Cross, Hertfordshire, EN7 5LL Tel: (01992) 627333 Fax: (01992) 643568

Veronica Preserved Plants, 131 Ballysnod Road, Larne, County Antrim, BT40 3NP Tel: (028) 2827 4016 Fax: (028) 2827 4016

PLANT DISPLAYS

Cambridge Plant Interiors Ltd, Manor Farm, Royston Road, Harston, Cambridge, CB2 5NJ Tel: (01223) 872828 Fax: (01223) 872886 E-mail: hortus@cambplant.co.uk

PLANT ENGINEERING CONSULTANCY

Arthur Redman Contractors, 9 Moat Farm Lane, Bishampton, Pershore, Worcestershire, WR10 2NJ Tel: (01386) 462426 Fax: (01386) 462426

Arup, 13 Fitzroy Street, London, W1T 4BQ Tel: (020) 7636 1531 Fax: (020) 7755 3716 E-mail: corporate@arup.com

Day Environmental Engineering, 7 Nash Meadows, South Warnborough, Hook, Hampshire, RG29 1RJ Tel: (01256) 862467 Fax: (01256) 862967

Rayner J C B Ltd, 3 Tamdown Way, Braintree, Essex, CM7 2QL Tel: 01376 550246 Fax: 01376 556150

Watts Engineering Services, 22d Orgreave Crescent, Sheffield, S13 9NQ Tel: 0114 2880667

PLANT HIRE, *See also Contractors' Plant Hire or headings for particular types*

▶ 2NITY Machine Operatives, 37 Ripley Road, Canning Town, London, E16 3EA Tel: (020) 7366 4408 Fax: (020) 7366 4408 E-mail: info@2nitypersonnel.co.uk

▶ A M V Construction, Tepna Wharf, Twyford Avenue, Portsmouth, PO2 8QA Tel: (023) 9266 7887 Fax: (023) 9266 7895 E-mail: amvconstrution@btconnect.com

ABBEY PLANT HIRE, Great Frenchstone, South Molton, DEVON, EX36 4JH Tel: (01769) 579460 E-mail: admin@graysplanthire.co.uk

Air Seal Products, Unit 8e, Greenham Business Park, Greenham, Wellington, Somerset, TA21 0LR Tel: (01823) 674411 Fax: (01823) 674486 E-mail: info@air-sealproducts.com

▶ Aj Civil Engineering Ltd, Nantllan, Clarach, Aberystwyth, Dyfed, SY23 3DT Tel: (01970) 828316 Fax: (01970) 820446

▶ A-Plant Ltd, Chaddock Lane Industrial Estate, Kennedy Road, Astley Tyldesley, Manchester, M29 7JY Tel: (01942) 884588

▶ Arla Plant Hire Ltd, 64 Foxcroft Drive, Carterton, Oxon, OX18 3HT Tel: 07717 130983 E-mail: arlaplanthire@aol.com

▶ BJB Lift Trucks Ltd, Armstrong Street, Grimsby, South Humberside, DN31 1XD Tel: (01472) 230244 Fax: (01472) 230245

▶ Brightcast Plant Hire Ltd, 18-22 Hertford Road, London, N1 5SH Tel: (020) 7249 1492 Fax: (020) 7254 6567 E-mail: brightcast@aol.com

▶ Dave Bushby Plant Hire Ltd, Clovelly Road Industrial Estate, Bideford, Devon, EX39 3HN Tel: (01237) 472878

▶ Champion Hire Ltd, Craven House, Craven Street South, Hull, HU9 1AP Tel: (0845) 3456905 Fax: (01482) 214840 E-mail: marknorrie@championshire.com

▶ Clee Hill Plant Ltd, Turner Crescent, Newcastle, Staffordshire, ST5 7JZ Tel: (01782) 566017 Fax: (01782) 565858 E-mail: stoke@cleehill.co.uk

▶ Clive Hurt Ltd, 31 Talbot Road Industrial Centre, Leyland, PR25 2ZF Tel: (01772) 432475 Fax: (01772) 622398 E-mail: clivehurt@btinternet.com

Coates Bros, Manor Farm, Watlington Road, Runcton Holme, King's Lynn, Norfolk, PE33 0EJ Tel: (01553) 810463 Fax: (01553) 811549 E-mail: enquiries@coates-bros.co.uk

▶ Contradig, Bethania, Capel Garmon, Llanrwst, Conwy, LL26 0RL Tel: (01690) 710309 Fax: (01690) 710154 E-mail: info@contradig.com

Cooper M.E, Pantgwyn, Prengwyn, Llandysul, Dyfed, SA44 4LL Tel: (01559) 362399 E-mail: cooperplant@freenetname.co.uk

▶ Corrie Construction Ltd, North Road, Fort William, Inverness-Shire, PH33 6PP Tel: (01397) 700680 Fax: (01397) 703933 E-mail: sales@corrieconstruction.com

▶ D Kerr & Sons, Helenslea, Castlecary Road, Cumbernauld, Glasgow, G68 0HQ Tel: (01324) 840337 Fax: (01324) 840885

Day Plant Hire Co. Ltd, 43-45 Brookhill Road, New Barnet, Barnet, Hertfordshire, EN4 8SE Tel: (020) 8441 4422 Fax: (020) 8447 0193

▶ Deborah Services Ltd, 23, Maple Road, Saddlebow, King's Lynn, Norfolk, PE34 3AH Tel: (01553) 771465 Fax: (01553) 773010 E-mail: kingslynn.hire@deborahservices.co.uk

Electro Services Ltd, 14 Pulloxhill Business Park, Greenfield Road, Pulloxhill, Bedford, MK45 5EU Tel: (01525) 719994 Fax: (01525) 719995 E-mail: electrogbr@aol.com

▶ Fourways Plant Ltd, Second Avenue, London, N18 2PG Tel: (020) 8884 3339 Fax: (020) 8807 8477

Frederick Garrett & Sons, Slittingmill Farm, Staveley Lane, Staveley, Chesterfield, Derbyshire, S43 3YQ Tel: (01246) 432294

▶ Gravelle Plant Hire, Riverside Works, Penybanc Road, Ammanford, Dyfed, SA18 3RB Tel: (01269) 591049 Fax: (01269) 591040

▶ Greenplant Ltd, London Road, Wheatley, Oxford, OX33 1JH Tel: (01865) 876000 Fax: (01865) 876222

▶ H & S Roe & Sons Ltd, Roe House, Boundry Lane, South Hykeham, Lincoln, LN6 9NQ Tel: (01522) 681542 Fax: (01522) 680199

▶ Hewden Hire Centres Ltd, 471 Attercliffe Road, Sheffield, S9 3RA Tel: 0114-244 1887 Fax: 0114-261 8298

▶ Hire Services Southern Ltd, Manor Way, Woking, Surrey, GU22 9JX Tel: (01483) 740960 Fax: (01483) 740135

▶ HSS Hire, 70 Blackstock Road, London, N4 2DR Tel: (020) 7704 8787 Fax: (020) 7704 8717

Ron Hughes, Glanfaes, Llanybydder, Dyfed, SA40 9TZ Tel: (01570) 480376 Fax: (01570) 480376

J A B Hire Services Ltd, J A B House, Delamare Road, Cheshunt, Waltham Cross, Hertfordshire, EN8 9SS Tel: (01992) 634666 Fax: (01992) 634777

▶ J D Hire, Starlings Bridge, Nightingale Road, Hitchin, Hertfordshire, SG5 1RJ Tel: (01462) 442044 Fax: (01462) 442043

▶ J M B Plant Hire Ltd, 3 Trevithick Road, Willowbrook South Industrial Estate, Willowbrook East Industrial Estate, Corby, Northamptonshire, NN17 5XY Tel: (01536) 200262 Fax: (01536) 275929 E-mail: sales@jmbhire.co.uk

▶ James King Plant Ltd, Northampton Road, Blisworth, Northampton, NN7 3DW Tel: (01604) 858558 Fax: (01604) 859204

▶ John Roberts Ffestiniog Ltd, Bont Newydd, Cwm Cynfal, Blaenau Ffestiniog, Gwynedd, LL41 4PT Tel: (01766) 762768 Fax: (01766) 762403

J S Jones, Glenside Bungalow, Blackvein Road, Cross Keys, Newport, Gwent, NP11 7NU Tel: (01633) 263458 Fax: (01633) 263458

▶ K & J Plant Hire, West Park, Yarnscombe, Barnstaple, Devon, EX31 3LZ Tel: (01271) 858540 Fax: (01271) 858574 E-mail: training@ctacentre.co.uk

K J Services Ltd, Capital Valley Industrial Estate, Rhymney, Tredegar, Gwent, NP22 5PT Tel: (01685) 841449 Fax: (01685) 840746 E-mail: sales@kjservices.co.uk

▶ Kane Haulage Ltd, Construction House, Porters Wood, Valley Road Industrial Estate, St. Albans, Hertfordshire, AL3 6NW Tel: (01727) 733600 Fax: (01727) 733607 E-mail: info@kanehaulage.co.uk

▶ L & W Wilson Ltd, Gatebeck Road, Endmoor, Kendal, Cumbria, LA8 0HL Tel: (01539) 567601 Fax: (01539) 567775 E-mail: office@landwwilson.co.uk

▶ Martin Group N W Ltd, Bouthwood Road, Sowerby Woods Industrial Estate, Barrow-in-Furness, Cumbria, LA14 4RD Tel: (01229) 813428 Fax: (01229) 430330

Marwood Group Ltd, Fengate Eastern Industrial Area, Peterborough, PE1 5BN Tel: (01733) 311444 Fax: (01733) 349974 E-mail: enquire@marwoodgroup.co.uk

▶ Morris Leslie South-East Ltd, Greenbays Park, Carthouse Lane, Woking, Surrey, GU21 4YP Tel: (01276) 856642 Fax: (01276) 859014

▶ MTS Nationwide, Ablow Street, Wolverhampton, WV2 4ER Tel: (01902) 422479 Fax: (01902) 422481 E-mail: craig.colley@mtsbobcat.co.uk

▶ Newel Plant Hire, 45 Colwyn Crescent, Rhos on Sea, Colwyn Bay, Clwyd, LL28 4RF Tel: (01492) 533612 Fax: (01492) 533612

▶ North Yorkshire Construction Plant Ltd, P O Box 157, Middlesbrough, Cleveland, TS9 7JB Tel: (01642) 778444

PLANT HIRE – *continued*

NRG PLANT HIRE, North Road Garage, Great North Road, Tuxford, NEWARK, NOTTS, NG22 0NE Tel: (01777) 871199 Fax: (01777) 871199 E-mail: sarahlhoward@fsmail.net

P & D Plant Hire Ltd, 5 Victory Way, Hounslow, TW5 9NN Tel: (020) 8573 5948 Fax: (020) 8573 2725

▶ P & R Materials, Clint Bank, Burnt Yates, Harrogate, North Yorkshire, HG3 3DW Tel: (01423) 770731 Fax: (01423) 771527

▶ Ram Plant, 5 Markham Road, Bournemouth, BH9 1HY Tel: (0800) 1952043 Fax: (01202) 539527

Ready Power Engineering Ltd, Station Road, Kings Langley, Hertfordshire, WD4 8LF Tel: (01923) 264593 Fax: (01923) 269350

▶ Readypower Engineering Ltd, Readypower House, Molly Millars Bridge, Wokingham, Berkshire, RG41 2WY Tel: 01189 774901 Fax: 01189 774902 E-mail: info@readypower.co.uk

▶ Richmack Building Services, 14 Nettlehill Road, Uphall Station, Livingston, West Lothian, EH54 5PP Tel: (01506) 505010 Fax: (01506) 505007

▶ Robinson, Sandy Leas Lane, Elton, Stockton-on-Tees, Cleveland, TS21 1BT Tel: (01642) 588806 Fax: (01642) 588499

Rose Plant Hire (Whittlesey) Ltd, Low Cross House, Padholme Road East, Peterborough, PE1 5XL Tel: (01733) 557575 Fax: (01733) 890005 E-mail: jon@roseplanthire.co.uk

▶ Rosedene Construction Ltd, Tripes Farm Yard Chelsfield Lane, Orpington, Kent, BR6 7RS Tel: (01689) 835807 Fax: (01689) 835807 E-mail: joan.rosedene@btopenworld.com

▶ Selwood Ltd, Derby Road, Langley Mill, Nottingham, NG16 4AA Tel: (01773) 714227 Fax: (01773) 716445 E-mail: nottingham@selwoodgroup.co.uk

▶ Simpsons Excavating Contractors Woolacombe Ltd, Chilworth House, Woolacombe Station Road, Woolacombe, Devon, EX34 7HH Tel: (01271) 870386

▶ Southwest Roofing Services Ltd, 6 Green Street Lane, Ayr, KA8 8BL Tel: (01292) 287936 Fax: (01292) 619719

▶ Southwest Roofing Services Ltd, Commerce Road, Stranraer, Wigtownshire, DG9 7DZ Tel: (01387) 256176 Fax: (01776) 703523

▶ Southwest Roofing Services Ltd, Commerce Road, Stranraer, Wigtownshire, DG9 7DZ Tel: (01387) 256176 Fax: (01776) 703523

Carl Taylor Plant Hire, 10 Garth Grove, Hirwaun, Aberdare, Rhondda Cynon Taff, CF44 9SD Tel: (01685) 813801 Fax: (01685) 813801 E-mail: taylorplant@btconnect.com

▶ Transplant Services, 2 Blacker Road, Mapplewell, Barnsley, South Yorkshire, S75 6BW Tel: (01226) 388878 Fax: (01226) 388450

Vertical Transportation Ltd, Grovebury Road, Leighton Buzzard, Bedfordshire, LU7 4RU Tel: (01525) 850027 Fax: (01525) 851357

▶ West Point Construction, Westpoint House, Securehold Business Centre, Redditch, Worcestershire, B98 7LG Tel: (01527) 528899 Fax: (01527) 529998 E-mail: info@westpoint-construction.co.uk

▶ Whitnell Plant, School Farm Buildings, School Road, Langham, Colchester, CO4 5PB Tel: (01206) 272834 Fax: (01206) 272104 E-mail: sales@whitnell.co.uk

PLANT INSTALLATION/ ERECTION/DISMANTLING ENGINEERS

Allardyce Engineers, 28 Telford Road, Dryburgh Industrial Estate, Dundee, DD2 3QW Tel: (01382) 832045 Fax: (01382) 832045 E-mail: allardyceengs@ukonline.co.uk

Alvent Heating Contractors, Units 5-6 Alexandra Industrial Estate, Locarno Road, Tipton, West Midlands, DY4 9SJ Tel: 0121-557 6727 Fax: 0121-520 8717

▶ C Bradley Engineering, 4-5 Sedgemount Industrial Park, Bristol Road, Bridgwater, Somerset, TA6 4AR Tel: (01278) 426550 Fax: (01278) 446913

Factory Plant Removals UK, European Business Park, Taylors Lane, Oldbury, West Midlands, B69 2BN Tel: 0121-544 4774 Fax: 0121-552 2018 E-mail: barry.jones@factory-plant-removals.co.uk

Finch & Co., Homestead, Eastwick Road, Bookham, Leatherhead, Surrey, KT23 4BA Tel: (01372) 452711 Fax: (01372) 450957 E-mail: info@machinemovers.co.uk

Gatwick Plant Hire, Woodside, The Close, Horley, Surrey, RH6 9EB Tel: (01293) 824777 Fax: (01293) 824077 E-mail: sales@gatwickgroup.com

Gordon Stones Industrial Services, 177 Tettenhall Road, Wolverhampton, WV6 0BZ Tel: (01902) 713972 Fax: (01902) 714134

Hanlon & Wright Ltd, Tudor House, Park Road, Dukinfield, Cheshire, SK16 5LX Tel: 0161-330 7631 Fax: 0161-330 0436 E-mail: sales@hanlonandwright.co.uk

Joy Mining Machinery Ltd, Kirkby La, Pinxton, Nottingham, NG16 6HX Tel: (01773) 515200 Fax: (01773) 515300E-mail: rbailey@joy.co.uk

Howard Kent, 5 Brighton Road, Shoreham-by-Sea, West Sussex, BN43 6RN Tel: (01273) 871871 Fax: (01273) 870970 E-mail: howardkent@ukonline.co.uk

M B Engineering Services Ltd, Lancaster Approach, North Killingholme, Immingham, South Humberside, DN40 3JZ Tel: (01469) 540478 Fax: (01469) 540548

Mechanical Installations International Ltd, Richmond House, 468 Chepstow Road, Newport, Gwent, NP19 8JF Tel: (01633) 282115 Fax: (01633) 290159

Mechanical Services (Luton) Ltd, 158A Beechwood Road, Luton, LU4 9RY Tel: (01582) 494747 Fax: (01582) 494749 E-mail: mechservluton@aol.com

Merit Process Engineering Ltd, Cumberland House, Cumberland Road, North Balkwell Farm Industrial Estate, North Shields, Tyne & Wear, NE29 8RD Tel: 0191-257 2788 Fax: 0191-257 2784 E-mail: enquiries@meritpe.co.uk

Midland Plant Installations Ltd, Curriers Cl, Charter Avenue Industrial Estate, Coventry, CV4 8AW Tel: (024) 7646 1225 Fax: (024) 7669 4261 E-mail: info@mpi-uk.com

N F J Green Ltd, Moor Farm Road West, Airfield Industrial Estate, Ashbourne, Derbyshire, DE6 1HD Tel: (01335) 344801 Fax: (01335) 344801

Savage Cranes Ltd, West Street, Hunton, Maidstone, Kent, ME15 0RR Tel: (01622) 820611 Fax: (01622) 820807

Smethwick Maintenance Co. Ltd, 336 Spon Lane South, West Bromwich, West Midlands, B70 6AZ Tel: 0121-553 3941 Fax: 0121-553 5371 E-mail: sales@sis-group.co.uk

Vinci Services Ltd, Ditton Road, Widnes, Cheshire, WA8 0WE Tel: 0151-422 3800 Fax: 0151-423 3934

PLANT MAINTENANCE/REPAIR SERVICES

A1 Plant Sales Ltd, Stephenson Street, Queensway Meadows Industrial E, Newport, Gwent, NP19 4XB Tel: (01633) 676800 Fax: (01633) 274974 E-mail: reeves.wilfred@ntlworld.com

Avon, Unit 22 Wansdyke Workshops, Unity Road, Keynsham, Bristol, BS31 1NH Tel: 0117-986 6001 Fax: 0117-986 6001 E-mail: sales@avonplantrepairs.co.uk

Crane Hill Engineering Ltd, Harvey Reeves Road, St. James Mill Industrial Estate, Northampton, NN5 5JR Tel: (01604) 587656 Fax: (01604) 588341 E-mail: robinson@cranehill.sagehost.co.uk

E Burke, Dock Road Industrial Estate, Connah's Quay, Deeside, Clwyd, CH5 4DS Tel: (01244) 831952

Enterprise Engineering, Unit 23 Tweedale Court, Tweedale North, Madeley, Telford, Shropshire, TF7 4JR Tel: (01952) 583179

Feorge Plant & Fabrications Ltd, Unit 4 Transport Depot, Thorney, Langport, Somerset, TA10 0DW Tel: (01458) 253140 Fax: (01458) 253309

Finning UK Ltd, Cobbswood Industrial Estate, Brunswick Road, Ashford, Kent, TN23 1EN Tel: (01233) 635466 Fax: (01233) 645046

Forge Engineering, Tarran Way Industrial Estate, Pasture Road, Tarran Industrial Estate, Wirral, Merseyside, CH46 4TP Tel: 0151-678 7777 Fax: 0151-677 0006

Fosters Mobile Plant Services Ltd, Ferndale, Egmanton Road, Tuxford, Newark, Nottinghamshire, NG22 0NR Tel: (01777) 870068

G C Plant, 24 Perry Road, Witham, Essex, CM8 3YZ Tel: (01376) 512122 Fax: (01376) 512122

Gordon Plant, Inglewhite Road, Goosnargh, Preston, PR3 2ED Tel: (01772) 782255 Fax: (01772) 782255 E-mail: gordonplant@hotmail.com

Haig Engineering, Unit 7 Bottings Industrial Estate, Curdridge, Southampton, SO30 2DY Tel: (01489) 790910 Fax: (01489) 790911 E-mail: office@ers1996.freeserve.co.uk

Hewden Hire Plant Ltd, Howard Road, Park Farm, Redditch, Worcestershire, B98 7SE Tel: (01527) 524020 Fax: (01527) 527320

Hewden Plant Hire Ltd, Ellis Road, Mitcham, Surrey, CR4 4HX Tel: (020) 8648 7070 Fax: (020) 8687 0482

Hewden Plant Hire Ltd, Tank Farm Road, Llandarcy, Neath, West Glamorgan, SA10 6EN Tel: (01792) 321111 Fax: (01792) 321346

Holt JCB Ltd, Unit 11, Cooksland Industrial Estate, Bodmin, Cornwall, PL31 2QB Tel: (01208) 78078 Fax: (01208) 78019

▶ Holt JCB Ltd, Third Way, Avonmouth, Bristol, BS11 9ZG Tel: 0117-982 7921 Fax: 0117-982 1028 E-mail: becky.selby@holtjcb.co.uk

J & P Enterprises, West Lodge, West Haddon Road, Crick, Northampton, NN6 7SQ Tel: (01788) 823512 Fax: (01788) 822847

J Wyllie, Towerhill Industrial Estate, Crosshouse Road, Kilmaurs, Kilmarnock, Ayrshire, KA3 2SA Tel: (01563) 539621 Fax: (01563) 539621 E-mail: gimwylieplant@aol.com

K P Engineering Components, Barlow Road, Aldermans Green Industrial Estate, Coventry, CV2 2LD Tel: (024) 7660 3333 Fax: (024) 7660 4444 E-mail: sales@kpecltd.com

▶ London Millwrights, The Forge, Stonehill Green, Dartford, DA2 7HJ Tel: (01322) 667373 Fax: (01322) 662544

M J Farrington Ltd, Locks Farm, Main Road, Dibden, Southampton, SO45 5TD Tel: (023) 8084 0755 Fax: (023) 8084 4588

M & L Crane Plant Services Ltd, 50 Holme Hall Avenue, Scunthorpe, South Humberside, DN16 3PZ Tel: (01724) 281621 Fax: (01724) 281621 E-mail: mlcrane@aol.com

Mac Plant Services Ltd, 1 Mernan Road, Bonnybridge, Stirlingshire, FK4 2BW Tel: (01324) 815330 Fax: (01324) 815305

Marubeni Komatsu Ltd, The Close, Horley, Surrey, RH6 9EB Tel: (01293) 822500 Fax: (01293) 822189

Mechanical Installations International Ltd, Richmond House, 468 Chepstow Road, Newport, Gwent, NP19 8JF Tel: (01633) 282115 Fax: (01633) 290159

Mectech Services, Place Farm, Place Farm Lane, Doddinghurst, Brentwood, Essex, CM15 0JA Tel: (01277) 372848 Fax: (01277) 374942

Midland Steel Traders Ltd, 19 Hogg Street, Airdrie, Lanarkshire, ML6 9JH Tel: (01236) 767288 Fax: (01236) 747116

Mutleys Plant Service, Shepherds Forge, Sutton Road, West Langdon, Dover, Kent, CT15 5HN Tel: (01304) 853938 Fax: (01304) 853937

N F J Green Ltd, Moor Farm Road West, Airfield Industrial Estate, Ashbourne, Derbyshire, DE6 1HD Tel: (01335) 344801 Fax: (01335) 344801

Nasa Plant, Station Road, Four Ashes, Wolverhampton, WV10 7DB Tel: (01902) 791694 Fax: (01902) 790592

Nu Line Engineering Ltd, George Street, Lincoln, LN5 8LG Tel: (01522) 544379 Fax: (01522) 544379 E-mail: nuline.ellis@tiscali.co.uk

Plant Life, 9 Woodland Way, Morden, Surrey, SM4 4DS Tel: (020) 8286 9461 Fax: (020) 8542 4456 E-mail: sales@plantlife.me.uk

R & C Plant Services Ltd, 187 Old Heath Road, Colchester, CO2 8AT Tel: (01206) 793525 Fax: (01206) 792332

R & R Development, Llewellyns Quay, The Docks, Port Talbot, West Glamorgan, SA13 1SD Tel: (01639) 870330 Fax: (01639) 890317

Ram Machining Ltd, Providence Street, Stourbridge, West Midlands, DY9 8HS Tel: (01384) 424144 Fax: (01384) 892396

Ruislip Tractor Hire, 71 Lea Cresent, Ruislip, Middlesex, HA4 6PW Tel: (01895) 673326

Skilton Bros, 13 Thurstons Estate, Binsted, Alton, Hampshire, GU34 4PD Tel: (01420) 22290

Smethwick Maintenance Co. Ltd, 336 Spon Lane South, West Bromwich, West Midlands, B70 6AZ Tel: 0121-553 3941 Fax: 0121-553 5371 E-mail: sales@sis-group.co.uk

Studley Engineering Ltd, 17 Vulcan Street, Liverpool, L3 7BG Tel: 0151-236 7825 Fax: 0151-255 0597

Systematic Servicing Equipment Ltd, Field Works, Broadway Road, Willersey, Broadway, Worcestershire, WR12 7PH Tel: (01386) 852342 Fax: (01386) 858556 E-mail: sales@systematic-servicing.co.uk

T & H Plant Repair Ltd, Oxcroft Bank, Moulton Chapel, Spalding, Lincolnshire, PE12 0XT Tel: (01406) 380029 Fax: (01406) 380336

Trodham Plant Ltd, Liphook Road, Hollywater, Bordon, Hampshire, GU35 9AF Tel: (01428) 751588 Fax: (01428) 751550 E-mail: trodham@aol.com

Vicary Plant Spares, Station Road, North Kilworth, Lutterworth, Leicestershire, LE17 6HY Tel: (01858) 880219 Fax: (01858) 881034

Watts Engineering Services, 22d Orgreave Crescent, Sheffield, S13 9NQ Tel: 0114 2880667

Wooberry Engineering & Marine Co, 21 Parvis Road, West Byfleet, Surrey, KT14 6HD Tel: (01932) 352070 Fax: (01932) 353479

PLANT ROOM PACKAGED DESIGN OR MANUFACTURERS OR INSTALLATION

Basford Plant Ltd, 12 Pinxton Lane, Kirkby-in-Ashfield, Nottingham, NG17 8LT Tel: (01623) 451010 Fax: (01623) 451011

PLANT SHIPPING AND TRANSPORTATION

Abnormal Loads Services International Ltd, 1501 Hedon Road, Hull, HU9 5NX Tel: (01482) 796214 Fax: (01482) 707650 E-mail: info.advertising@abnormal-loads.com

PLANT TUBS/TROUGHS/ PLANTERS, *See also heading for particular material used*

Interior Landscaping Products, The Sussex Barn, New Lodge Farm, Hooe, Battle, East Sussex, TN33 9HJ Tel: (01424) 844444 Fax: (01424) 843666 E-mail: sales@interiorlandscaping.co.uk

Plant Plan, Lyon Close, Wigston, Leicestershire, LE18 2BJ Tel: 0116-281 1933 Fax: 0116-288 6973

▶ Wood For You, Unit 1b, Treburley Industrial Units, Launceston, Cornwall, PL15 9PU Tel: (01579) 370786 E-mail: kevin@wood-4-you.co.uk

PLANT TUBS/TROUGHS/ PLANTERS, GLASS FIBRE OR FIBREGLASS

A B Terratec Ltd, Units 2-2a, Phoebe La Industrial Estate, Halifax, West Yorkshire, HX3 9EX Tel: (01422) 354469 Fax: (01422) 354460 E-mail: sales@plantpots.co.uk

PLANT TUBS/TROUGHS/ PLANTERS, METAL

Brambley Furniture, 108 Westmoor Street, Charlton, London, SE7 8NQ Tel: (020) 8293 6662 Fax: (020) 8305 0907

PLANT TUBS/TROUGHS/ PLANTERS, PLASTIC

Christian Day, 2 Phoenix Building, Rushock Trading Estate, Rushock, Droitwich, Worcestershire, WR9 0NR Tel: (01299) 250385 Fax: (01299) 250335 E-mail: sales@christianday.co.uk

Clarke & Spears International Ltd, Knaphill Nursery, Barrs Lane, Knaphill, Woking, Surrey, GU21 2JW Tel: (01483) 485800 Fax: (01483) 485801 E-mail: sales@clarkandspears.co.uk

Rotational Mouldings Ltd, Knowles Industrial Estate, Buxton Road, Furness Vale, High Peak, Derbyshire, SK23 7PH Tel: (01663) 742897 Fax: (01663) 747584 E-mail: sales@rotationalmouldings.co.uk

PLANT TUBS/TROUGHS/ PLANTERS, WOODEN

Window Box Co., 3 Bridle Road, Woodford, Stockport, Cheshire, SK7 1QH Tel: 0161-439 6585 Fax: 0161-439 6585

▶ Wood For You, Unit 1b, Treburley Industrial Units, Launceston, Cornwall, PL15 9PU Tel: (01579) 370786 E-mail: kevin@wood-4-you.co.uk

PLANT VALUERS, *See also specialist services*

American Appraisal UK Ltd, Aldermary House, 10-15 Queen Street, London, EC4N 1TX Tel: (020) 7329 1776 Fax: (020) 7248 1453 E-mail: sales@american-appraisal.co.uk

Go Industry P.L.C., New London Bridge House, 25 London Bridge Street, London, SE1 9BQ Tel: (020) 7098 3700 Fax: (020) 7098 3795 E-mail: lucy.moran@goindustry.com

Hickman Shearer, 7 Buttermarket, Thame, Oxfordshire, OX9 3EW Tel: (01844) 215755 Fax: (01844) 214549 E-mail: officehs@hickman-shearer.co.uk

Holroyds, 499 Bath Road, Saltford, Bristol, BS31 3HQ Tel: (01225) 873000 Fax: (01225) 873834 E-mail: info@holroyds.org

▶ Marriott & Co., 19 East Street, Farnham, Surrey, GU9 7SD Tel: (01252) 712083 Fax: (01252) 737613 E-mail: mail@marriott.co.uk

Wyles Hardy & Co. Ltd, Ley Hill Road, Bovingdon, Hemel Hempstead, Hertfordshire, HP3 0NW Tel: (01442) 832234 Fax: (01442) 834342 E-mail: enquiries@wyleshardy.com

PLANTER BENCHES

▶ Jakk, Unit 17 Granary Business Centre, North Street, Hellingly, Hailsham, East Sussex, BN27 4DU Tel: (01323) 847115 Fax: (01323) 833040 E-mail: jakkuk@aol.com

PLAQUES, GARDEN, STONE

▶ Recycles Africa, Walnut Cottage, Brockhampton Lane, Swindon Village, Cheltenham, Gloucestershire, GL51 9RS Tel: (01242) 572161 Fax: (01242) 530774 E-mail: tony@recyclesafrica.com

▶ Stone Essentials Ltd, Mount Spring Works, Off Burnley Road East, Waterfoot, Rossendale, Lancashire, BB4 9LA Tel: (01706) 210605 Fax: (01706) 228707 E-mail: stoneessentials@btconnect.com

PLASMA CUTTING CONSUMABLES

P W P Industrial, 84 Pilcroft Street, Bedford, MK42 9BP Tel: (01234) 345111

PLASMA CUTTING EQUIPMENT

Esab Group UK Ltd, Hanover House Britannia Road, Queens Gate, Waltham Cross, Hertfordshire, EN8 7TF Tel: (01992) 768515 Fax: (01992) 715803 E-mail: info@esab.co.uk

PLASMA CUTTING EQUIPMENT – continued

Esprit Automation Ltd, Croft Mills, Church Drive, Sandiacre, Nottingham, NG10 5EE Tel: 0115-939 1888 Fax: 0115-939 1999
Hypertherm UK Ltd, 9 Berkeley Court, Manor Park, Runcorn, Cheshire, WA7 1TQ Tel: (01928) 579074 Fax: (01928) 579604 E-mail: info@hypertherm.co.uk
P W P Industrial, 84 Pilcroft Street, Bedford, MK42 9BP Tel: (01234) 345111
Saf Welding Products Ltd, 2 Low March Industrial Estate, Low March, Daventry, Northamptonshire, NN11 4SD Tel: (01327) 705511 Fax: (01327) 701310 E-mail: sales@saf-wp.co.uk
T & B Welding Products (UK) Ltd, Unit 1B, Ravenstor Road, Wirksworth Industrial Estate, Wirksworth, Matlock, Derbyshire, DE4 4FY Tel: (01629) 823779 Fax: (01629) 824961
Wightman Stewart Ltd, Oldham Road, Sowerby Bridge, West Yorkshire, HX6 4EH Tel: (01422) 823801 Fax: (01422) 824031 E-mail: info@wightmanstewart.co.uk

PLASMA CUTTING SERVICES

Barnshaws Profiles, Anchor Lane, Bilston, West Midlands, WV14 9NE Tel: (01902) 663553 Fax: (01902) 887379 E-mail: enquiries@barnshaws.com
Bretvents Ltd, Bradfords Farm, Little Horsted, Uckfield, East Sussex, TN22 5QP Tel: (01825) 841227 Fax: (01825) 841294
Crew Stainless & Special Alloys, Unit 17 Coneygre Industrial Estate, Tipton, West Midlands, DY4 8XP Tel: 0121-520 1066 Fax: 0121-520 7600 E-mail: sales@crewstainless.co.uk
Leeds Welding Co. Ltd, Westland Square, Leeds, LS11 5SS Tel: 0113-271 1000 Fax: 0113-271 1023 E-mail: sales@leedswelding.co.uk
Newfield Fabrications Co. Ltd, Hall Lane, Elton, Sandbach, Cheshire, CW11 3TU Tel: (01270) 762331 Fax: (01270) 768003 E-mail: sales@newfield.co.uk
Nimgrove Ltd, 8 Anglesey Business Park, Littleworth Road, Cannock, Staffordshire, WS12 1NR Tel: (01543) 426926 Fax: (01543) 426872 E-mail: sales@nimgrove.co.uk
P P Plasma, New Factory, Vere Street, Salford, M50 2GQ Tel: 0161-736 9299 Fax: 0161-745 7915
Plascut Stainless, Coleford Road, Darnall, Sheffield, S9 5PJ Tel: 0114-251 9535 Fax: 0114-251 9536 E-mail: sheffield.zi2@centers.co.uk
Premier Bodies Ltd, Llay Hall Industrial Estate, Mold Road, Cefn Y Bedd, Wrexham, Clwyd, LL12 9YG Tel: (01978) 762224 Fax: (01978) 762693
Springfield Stainless, Springfield Works, Stocks Lane, Batley, West Yorkshire, WF17 8PA Tel: (01924) 420303 Fax: (01924) 423333 E-mail: info@springfield-stainless.co.uk

PLASMA GENERATORS

Advanced Energy Industries UK Ltd, 5 Minton Place, Victoria Road, Bicester, Oxfordshire, OX26 6QB Tel: (01869) 320022 Fax: (01869) 325004

PLASMA SCREEN INSTALLATION

▶ Visual Sounds Ltd, 891 Old Lode Lane, Solihull, West Midlands, B92 8JF Tel: 0121-242 3279 E-mail: enquiries@visualsounds.co.uk

PLASMA SCREENS

GFH SOUND AND VISION LTD, 39 SHERRARDS WAY, BARNET, HERTS, EN5 2BW Tel: 07815 735607 Fax: (020) 8449 6531 E-mail: garretthenderson345@hotmail.com

PLASMA SPRAYING CONTRACTORS OR SERVICES

Celcoat Ltd, 3 Crown Works, Rotherham Road, Beighton, Sheffield, S20 1AH Tel: 0114-269 0771 Fax: 0114-254 0495 E-mail: celcoatltd@tiscali.co.uk
Ceramet Plasma Coatings Ltd, Ryeford Industrial Estate, Ryeford, Stonehouse, Gloucestershire, GL10 2LA Tel: (01453) 828416 Fax: (01453) 823068 E-mail: sales@ceramet.co.uk
Monitor Coatings Ltd, Monitor House 2 Elm Road, West Chirton Industrial Estate, North Shields, Tyne & Wear, NE29 8SE Tel: 0191-293 7040 Fax: 0191-293 7041 E-mail: info@monitorcoatings.co.uk
Plasma Biotal Ltd, 1 Meverill Road, Tideswell, Buxton, Derbyshire, SK17 8PY Tel: (01298) 872348 Fax: (01299) 873708 E-mail: general@plasma-group.co.uk
Plasma Coatings Ltd, 3 Meverill Road, Tideswell, Buxton, Derbyshire, SK17 8PY Tel: (01298) 873700 Fax: (01298) 873708 E-mail: info@plasma-group.co.uk
Plasma & Thermal Coating Ltd, Unit 20 Maesglas Industrial Estate, Newport, Gwent, NP20 2NN Tel: (01633) 245600 Fax: (01633) 245601 E-mail: sales@plasmacoat.co.uk
Rolls Wood Group Repair & Overhauls Ltd, Wellheads CR, Wellheads Industrial Estate, Aberdeen, AB21 7GA Tel: (01224) 797000 Fax: (01224) 771552 E-mail: reception@rwgroup.co.uk

PLASMA WELDING EQUIPMENT

East Midland Welding Supply Co. Ltd, Baker Brook Industrial Estate, Wigwam Lane, Hucknall, Nottingham, NG15 7SZ Tel: 0115-964 2000 Fax: 0115-964 1651 E-mail: sales@eastmidwelding.freeserve.co.uk
Migatronic Welding Equipment Ltd, 21 Jubilee Drive, Loughborough, Leicestershire, LE11 5XS Tel: (01509) 211492 Fax: (01509) 231959 E-mail: sales@migatronic.co.uk
P W P Industrial, 84 Pilcroft Street, Bedford, MK42 9BP Tel: (01234) 345111
Saf Welding Products Ltd, 2 Low March Industrial Estate, Low March, Daventry, Northamptonshire, NN11 4SD Tel: (01327) 705511 Fax: (01327) 701310 E-mail: sales@saf-wp.co.uk

PLASMA WELDING TORCHES

Welding Repairs & Supplies Co. Ltd, Brandon Way, West Bromwich, West Midlands, B70 8JW Tel: 0121-553 6581 Fax: 0121-553 2953 E-mail: weldingrepair@aol.com

PLASTER CONTRACTORS

Andrews Bros Plastering Ltd, Bridge House, Clyst St. Mary, Exeter, EX5 1BR Tel: (01392) 875755 Fax: (01392) 876617
H. & F. Badcock (Fibrous & Solid Plastering) Ltd, Unit 9, 57 Sandgate Street, Old Kent Road, London, SE15 1LE Tel: (020) 7639 0304 Fax: (020) 7358 1239 E-mail: info@hf-badcock.co.uk
Blakemore & Kent Ltd, Cliftonville, Grove Lane, Brenzett, Romney Marsh, Kent, TN29 9RR Tel: (01797) 344577
▶ Border Plastering Services, 33 Elizabeth Road,, Kington, Herefordshire, HR5 3DB Tel: 01544 230099 E-mail: terry@townsend33.fsworld.co.uk
Clarke Contracts, 89 Bann Road, Rasharkin, Ballymena, County Antrim, BT44 8SZ Tel: (028) 2954 0191 Fax: (028) 2954 0401 E-mail: sales@clarkecontracts.com
Cornwall Bros Ltd, 2a Tovil Hill, Maidstone, Kent, ME15 6QS Tel: (01622) 755066 Fax: (01622) 755066
Lloyd Davenport Ltd, Unit 10 Kingfisher Court, Hambridge Road, Newbury, Berkshire, RG14 5SJ Tel: (01635) 529191 Fax: (01635) 524278
Excel Plastering Ilford Ltd, 1 Natal Road, Ilford, Essex, IG1 2HA Tel: (020) 8553 2244 Fax: (020) 8553 4489 E-mail: excelplastering1@btopenworld.com
▶ Fylde Plastering & Dry Wall Contractors, 42 Tyrone Avenue, Blackpool, FY2 0RR Tel: (01253) 593310 Fax: 01253 358202 E-mail: fpdclimited@btinternet.com
Hollywood Plasterers, Woodhouse, Packhorse Lane, Kings Norton, Birmingham, B38 0DN Tel: (01564) 824100 Fax: (01564) 823447
J H Lidstone Ltd, Crozier Road, Plymouth, PL4 7LN Tel: (01752) 664253 Fax: (01752) 600680
▶ J O'Donnell, 17 Barmouth Grove, Biddulph, Stoke-on-Trent, ST8 7QE Tel: (01782) 511042 E-mail: jodonnell.plastering@hotmail.co.uk
▶ JP taping & jointing, 57 Huntington terrace road, Cannock, Staffordshire, WS11 5HB Tel: 07976 284152 Fax: 01543 428578 E-mail: phasey@tiscli.co.uk
▶ L MS Plastering, 21 Hillside Close, Bartley Green, Birmingham, B32 4LT Tel: 0121-585 6773 E-mail: pokernext99126@aol.com
▶ M H Plasterers Ltd, 3 The Pleasance, Swillington, Leeds, LS26 8ED Tel: 0113-287 7144 Fax: 0113-287 7144 E-mail: mhplasterers@fsmail.net
Quadrant Building Services Ltd, 143 Red Lion Road, Surbiton, Surrey, KT6 7RQ Tel: (020) 8397 8811 Fax: (020) 8974 2798
Slough Plastering Co. Ltd, 19 Willoughby Road, Langley, Slough, SL3 8JH Tel: (01753) 543947 Fax: (01753) 594135
Southern Drylining, 32 North Poulner Road, Ringwood, Hampshire, BH24 1SP Tel: (07739) 605060 Fax: (0781) 2245583 E-mail: info@southerndrylining.co.uk
Toveglen Ltd, Unit 1 Drakes Lane, Boreham, Chelmsford, CM3 3BE Tel: (01245) 360435 Fax: (01245) 362322 E-mail: mbladon@toveglen.co.uk
Turney Wylde Construction, Tyne View Terrace, Wallsend, Tyne & Wear, NE28 6SG Tel: 0191-295 8600 Fax: 0191-295 8601
W R R, 5 The Arianne Business Centre Blackburn Road, Townsend Industrial, Houghton Regis, Dunstable, Bedfordshire, LU5 5DZ Tel: (01582) 665718 Fax: (01582) 664490 E-mail: wroberts@wrr-uk.com
Wrights Property Services, Unit 317 Tedco Bus Centre, Viking Industrial Park, Jarrow, Tyne & Wear, NE32 3DT Tel: 0191-428 3362 Fax: 0191-428 3314 E-mail: homeshields@hotmail.co.uk

PLASTER MOULDINGS

Classic Plaster Moulds, 19 Tame Road, Lawson Industrial Estate, Middlesbrough, Cleveland, TS6 6LL Tel: (01642) 246535 Fax: (01642) 246535
▶ Wilton Plaster Mouldings, Wimbledon Avenue, Brandon, Suffolk, IP27 0NZ Tel: (01842) 811117 Fax: (01842) 811991

PLASTER, MODEL/PATTERN MAKING

Ajay Patterns, 236 Berwick Avenue, Slough, SL1 4QT Tel: (01753) 525505 Fax: (01753) 825411
Articole Ltd, 9 Alexander Road, Stotfold, Hitchin, Hertfordshire, SG5 4NA Tel: (01462) 835640 Fax: (01462) 834896 E-mail: steve@articolestudios.co.uk
South Western Industrial Plasters, 63 Netherstreet, Bromham, Chippenham, Wiltshire, SN15 2DP Tel: (01380) 850616
Whitchurch Building Supplies, College Road, Cardiff, CF14 2NZ Tel: (029) 2062 5422 Fax: (029) 2061 6840

PLASTER, SURGICAL/DENTAL

Bellman Carter 2000 Ltd, Rear of, 358-374 Grand Drive, London, SW20 9NG Tel: (020) 8540 1372 Fax: (020) 8544 9424

PLASTERING TRAINING COURSES

Hawk & Trowel Plastering Centre, Office Address:, 3 Overhill Gardens, Brighton, BN1 8ND Tel: (01273) 557932 E-mail: poddie@ntlworld.com
▶ Trade Skills 4 U, 3 Metana House, Priestley Way, Crawley, West Sussex, RH10 9NT Tel: (01293) 529777 E-mail: enquires@tradeskills4u.co.uk

PLASTIC ABRASIVE MATERIALS OR FINISHING MEDIA

Sharmic Engineering Ltd, Baldwin Road, Stourport-on-Severn, Worcestershire, DY13 9AX Tel: (01299) 878123 Fax: (01299) 879409 E-mail: info@sharmic.co.uk
Wheelabrator Group, 43-44 Gravelly Industrial Park, Tyburn Road, Birmingham, B24 8TG Tel: 0121-326 6481 Fax: 0121-328 0256 E-mail: uk-info@wheelabrator.co.uk

PLASTIC ADDITIVES

Areton International Plastics Ltd, Unit 47-48, Clywedog Road North, Wrexham Industrial Estate, Wrexham, Clwyd, LL13 9XN Tel: (01978) 664646 Fax: (01978) 664647 E-mail: sales@areton.co.uk
Chemson Ltd, Hayhole Works, Northumberland Dock Road, Wallsend, Tyne & Wear, NE28 0PB Tel: 0191-259 7000 Fax: 0191-259 7001 E-mail: sales@chemson.co.uk
Ciba Additives, Charter Way, Macclesfield, Cheshire, SK10 2NX Tel: (01625) 421933 Fax: (01625) 619637
Gabriel-Chemie UK Ltd, Transfesa Road, Paddock Wood, Tonbridge, Kent, TN12 6UT Tel: (01892) 836566 Fax: (01892) 836979 E-mail: info@gabriel-chemie.com
Innovo Chemicals Ltd, The Common, Cranleigh, Surrey, GU6 8RY Tel: (01483) 277219 Fax: (01483) 268030 E-mail: sales@innovochem.co.uk

PLASTIC AND RUBBER MACHINERY BLADES

A F Whiteley & Co. Ltd, Bingswood Road, Whaley Bridge, High Peak, Derbyshire, SK23 7NB Tel: (01663) 732288 Fax: (01663) 734180 E-mail: sales@whiteley-knives.com
M G Knife Services, 8 Avon Business Park, Lodge Causeway, Bristol, BS16 3JP Tel: 0117-958 3974 Fax: 0117-958 3997
Rawmec Eec, Rawmec Industrial Park, Plumpton Road, Hoddesdon, Hertfordshire, EN11 0EE Tel: (01992) 471796 Fax: (01992) 471797 E-mail: rawmec@btconnect.com

PLASTIC AND RUBBER TEST EQUIPMENT

Hampden Test Equipment Ltd, Satra House, Rockingham Road, Kettering, Northamptonshire, NN16 9JH Tel: (01536) 518563 Fax: (01536) 519256 E-mail: hampden-test@satra.co.uk
Nortest Scientific Apparatus, Unit 1 The Woodyard, Castle Ashby, Northampton, NN7 1LF Tel: (01604) 696192 Fax: (01604) 696198 E-mail: brian@nortest.co.uk

PLASTIC ASHTRAYS

Melamaster, Bodmin Road, Coventry, CV2 5DB Tel: (024) 7672 4919 Fax: (024) 7672 4920 E-mail: sales@melamaster.co.uk

PLASTIC ASSEMBLERS TO THE TRADE

Cape Warwick Ltd, 47 Britannia Way, Britannia Enterprise Park, Lichfield, Staffordshire, WS14 9UY Tel: (01543) 414544 Fax: (01543) 414599E-mail: enquiries@cape-warwick.co.uk
Inabata UK, Oaktree Place Road 35, Hortonwood Industrial Estate, Telford, Shropshire, TF1 7FR Tel: (01952) 670192 Fax: (01952) 608548 E-mail: enq@ikp.co.uk

PLASTIC AUTOMOTIVE COMPONENT REPAIR

▶ Smartekh, 256 Carmel Road North, Darlington, County Durham, DL3 9TD Tel: (01325) 778161 E-mail: info@smartekh.co.uk

PLASTIC AUXILIARY EQUIPMENT

R P C Container, Plenmeller Works, Haltwhistle, Northumberland, NE49 0HN Tel: (01434) 320526 Fax: (01434) 320136
Summit Systems Ltd, F Tame Park, Vanguard, Wilnecote, Tamworth, Staffordshire, B77 5DY Tel: (01827) 265800 Fax: (01827) 265801 E-mail: info@summitsystems.co.uk

PLASTIC BADGES

Computerised Exhibition Services Badges Ltd, 31 Highbridge Road, Sutton Coldfield, West Midlands, B73 5QB Tel: 0121-354 9595 Fax: 0121-354 6227 E-mail: badgereg@aol.com
D J Morgan Engravers Ltd, 53 Warwick Street, Coventry, CV5 6ET Tel: (024) 7671 1232 Fax: (024) 7671 1232 E-mail: djmorgan@btconnect.com
Diamond Graphics, Norton House, 61a High Street, Wordsley, Stourbridge, West Midlands, DY8 5SD Tel: (01384) 572878 Fax: (01384) 481975
G S M Primographic, Unit 2b Ffrwdgrech Industrial Estate, Ffrwdgrech Road, Brecon, Powys, LD3 8LA Tel: (01874) 624433 Fax: (01874) 624575 E-mail: info@gsmprimographic.co.uk
Kahn Displays Ltd, Unit 5-6 Eleys Estate, Angel Road, London, N18 3BH Tel: (020) 8803 0800 Fax: (020) 8803 0412 E-mail: kahn_displays@btconnect.com
Norman Pendred & Co. Ltd, Unit 4worsley Bridge Rdbroomsleigh Business Park, London, SE26 5BN Tel: (020) 8461 1155 Fax: (020) 8461 1166 E-mail: sales@pendred.com
Plastech Print Ltd, Debdale Lane, Keyworth, Nottingham, NG12 5HN Tel: 0115-937 4041 Fax: 0115-937 3426 E-mail: sales@plastechprint.co.uk
Rand Markings Ltd, 39-40 Brunel Road, St. Leonards-on-Sea, East Sussex, TN38 9RT Tel: (01424) 854646 Fax: (01424) 854645 E-mail: info@randmarkings.co.uk
B. Sanders (Bromsgrove) Ltd, 4 Sherwood Road, Aston Fields Industrial Estate, Bromsgrove, Worcestershire, B60 3DR Tel: (01527) 575757 Fax: (01527) 575539
Spar Plastics, 7 Park Trading Estate, Park Road, Hockley, Birmingham, B18 5HB Tel: 0121-551 6220 Fax: 0121-551 6220
Target Badges, 134 Watnall Road, Hucknall, Nottingham, NG15 7NH Tel: 0115-956 0047 Fax: 0115-956 0047 E-mail: info@targetbadges.co.uk
Total Plastics Ltd, Heming Road, Washford East, Redditch, Worcestershire, B98 0EA Tel: (01527) 500292 Fax: (01527) 501188 E-mail: totalplastics@proweb.co.uk
Universal Button Co. Ltd, 10-12 Witan Street, London, E2 6JX Tel: (020) 7739 5750 Fax: (020) 7739 1961
Wessex Badges Ltd, Unit 1, Silverhills Buildings, Decoy Industrial Estate, Newton Abbot, Devon, TQ12 5LZ Tel: (01626) 363301 Fax: (01626) 363301 E-mail: grahamstephens@tesco.net

PLASTIC BAG MAKING MACHINES

Duplas, Diamond Business Park, 7 Thornes Moor Road, Wakefield, West Yorkshire, WF2 8PT Tel: (01924) 298298 Fax: (01924) 377101 E-mail: sales@duplas.co.uk

PLASTIC BAG TAGS

H M T Plastics Ltd, 31a Framfield Road, Uckfield, East Sussex, TN22 5AH Tel: (01825) 769393 Fax: (01825) 769494 E-mail: hmtp@aol.com

PLASTIC BALL, *See Ball, Plastic etc*

PLASTIC BARRELS

Weltonhurst Ltd, Centurion Way Roman Road Industrial Estate, Roman Road, Blackburn, BB1 2LD Tel: (01254) 671177 Fax: (01254) 671717 E-mail: sales@weltonhurst.co.uk

PLASTIC BASED DAMP PROOF COURSES (DPC)

Cavity Trays Ltd, Boundary Avenue, Lufton Trading Estate, Lufton, Yeovil, Somerset, BA22 8HU Tel: (01935) 474769 Fax: (01935) 428223 E-mail: sales@cavitytrays.co.uk

Plysolene Ltd, Unit 21 Star Road Trading Estate, Star Road, Partridge Green, Horsham, West Sussex, RH13 8RA Tel: (01403) 713555 Fax: (01403) 713666 E-mail: info@wattsgroup.co.uk

PLASTIC BATTERY CONTAINERS

Accuma Plastics Ltd, Princewood Road, Earlstrees Industrial Estate, Corby, Northamptonshire, NN17 4AP Tel: (01536) 263461 Fax: (01536) 263516 E-mail: sales@accuma.co.uk

PLASTIC BEARING BUSHES

Devol Engineering Ltd, 13 Clarence Street, Greenock, Renfrewshire, PA15 1LR Tel: (01475) 720934 Fax: (01475) 787873 E-mail: sales@devol.com

Nylacast Ltd, 200 Hastings Road, Leicester, LE5 0HL Tel: 0116-276 8558 Fax: 0116-274 1954 E-mail: sales@nylacast.com

PLASTIC BEARINGS

ABG Rubber & Plastics Ltd, Galowhill Rd, Brackmills Industrial Estate, Northampton, NN4 7EE Tel: (01604) 700880 Fax: (01604) 766113 E-mail: sales@abgrp.co.uk

Claron Hydraulic Seals Ltd, Station Road, Cradley Heath, West Midlands, B64 6PN Tel: 0121-559 9711 Fax: 0121-559 1036 E-mail: sales@claron-seals.co.uk

Nylacast Ltd, 200 Hastings Road, Leicester, LE5 0HL Tel: 0116-276 8558 Fax: 0116-274 1954 E-mail: sales@nylacast.com

Railko Ltd, Boundary Rd, Loudwater, High Wycombe, Bucks, HP10 9QU Tel: (01628) 524901 Fax: (01628) 810761 E-mail: info@railko.co.uk

Taylor Precision Plastics Ltd, Mile Oak Industrial Estate, Maesbury Road, Oswestry, Shropshire, SY10 8GA Tel: (01691) 679516 Fax: (01691) 670538 E-mail: sales@plasticbearings.co.uk

Westley Plastics Ltd, Gawne Lane, Cradley Heath, West Midlands, B64 5QY Tel: (01384) 414840 Fax: (01384) 414849 E-mail: sales@plastics.co.uk

PLASTIC BEER CASK AND KEG CAPS AND CLOSURES

Morrow Bros Ltd, 433 Walton Summit Centre, Preston, PR5 8AU Tel: 01772 311882

PLASTIC BELLOWS

Cove Ltd, 18 Invincible Road, Invinciblerial Road Industrial Estate, Farnborough, Hampshire, GU14 7QU Tel: (01252) 512919 Fax: (01252) 543384 E-mail: sales@cove-industries.co.uk

PLASTIC BELTING

Habasit Rossi Ltd, Habegger House, Keighley Road, Silsden, Keighley, West Yorkshire, BD20 0EA Tel: (0870) 8359555 Fax: (0870) 8359777 E-mail: info@habasitrossi.com

Intralox Ltd, Building 90, Third Avenue, Pensnett Trading Estate, Kingswinford, West Midlands, DY6 7FW Tel: (0800) 894392 Fax: (01384) 355655

Siegling Ltd, Unit 4, Fifth Avenue, Tameside Park, Dukinfield, Cheshire, SK16 4PP Tel: 0161-331 3412 Fax: 0161-308 4385 E-mail: info@siegling.co.uk

PLASTIC BENDING

Cooper Craft Ltd, 17a Barclay Road, London, E11 3DQ Tel: (020) 8539 3067 E-mail: coopercraft@btopenworld.com

PLASTIC BINDERS

Abbey Plastics Ltd, Unit 4 Orbital Centre, Southend Road, Woodford Green, Essex, IG8 8HD Tel: (020) 8551 8000 Fax: (020) 8551 8453 E-mail: sales@abbeyplastics.com

Ambroplastics Ltd, Chamber House, Halesfield 13, Telford, Shropshire, TF7 4PL Tel: (01952) 684922 Fax: (01952) 581414 E-mail: info@ambro.co.uk

J.P. Charles [Binding Systems] Ltd, Units 11-12, 6 Old Church Road, London, E4 6ST Tel: (020) 8801 4222 Fax: (020) 8529 6464

Elmstok, 4-6 Algores Way, Wisbech, Cambridgeshire, PE13 2TQ Tel: (01945) 463434 Fax: (01945) 582598 E-mail: sales@elmstok.co.uk

Emerald Weld PVC Stationery Manufacturer, 101 Station Road, Reddish, Stockport, Cheshire, SK5 6ND Tel: 0161-432 7200 Fax: 0161-442 1248 E-mail: info@emweld.com

Folders Galore Ltd, 3-4 Advance Road, London, SE27 9LT Tel: (020) 8670 7416 Fax: (020) 8670 9605 E-mail: mail@foldersgalore.com

Gemini Products, Unit 3, Cruso Street, Leek, Staffordshire, ST13 8BJ Tel: (01538) 373600 Fax: (01538) 372600 E-mail: ivan@tesco.net

Imgen Manufrs, New Image Works, 240 Church Road, Layton, London, E10 7JQ Tel: (020) 8887 0709 Fax: (020) 8887 0744

Media Plastics, 8 Merrylees Industrial Estate, Lee Side, Desford, Leicester, LE9 9FS Tel: (01455) 292110 Fax: (01455) 292190 E-mail: sales@mediaplastics.co.uk

G.H. Neville Ltd, Unit 1, Travellers Lane, North Mymms, Hatfield, Hertfordshire, AL9 7HF Tel: (01707) 262 800 Fax: (01707) 263 888 E-mail: sales@emgeeonline.co.uk

Nolene Ltd, Brunel Road, Newton Abbot, Devon, TQ12 4PB Tel: (01626) 333800 Fax: (01626) 368168 E-mail: info@nolene.co.uk

Thames Loose Leaf, 289 Kiln Road, Benfleet, Essex, SS7 1QS Tel: (01702) 551155 Fax: (01702) 559068 E-mail: sales@thameslooseleaf.co.uk

Thanet Plastics, 1 Wilton Road, Haine Industrial Park, Ramsgate, Kent, CT12 5HG Tel: (01843) 590950 Fax: (01843) 590948 E-mail: sales@thanetplastics.co.uk

PLASTIC BLOW MOULD TOOLMAKERS

Alliance Design & Manufacturing, Westbrook Trading Estate, Westbrook Road, Trafford Park, Manchester, M17 1AY Tel: 0161-872 8881 Fax: 0161-872 8883 E-mail: jimkelly@adm.eu.com

Custom Tooling Ltd, Unit 65, Station Road Industrial Estate, Hailsham, East Sussex, BN27 2ED Tel: (01323) 641811 E-mail: custo@btconnect.com

Denny Engineering Ltd, 10 Morgan Way, Bowthorpe Employment Area, Norwich, NR5 9JJ Tel: (01603) 747066 Fax: (01603) 748421 E-mail: dennengltd@aol.com

G T S Moulds, 15 South Lane, New Malden, Surrey, KT3 5HU Tel: (020) 8336 0335 Fax: (020) 8336 0335 E-mail: gtsmoulds@blueyonder.co.uk

Mouldline Ltd, The Old Granary, Station Road, Eccles, Norwich, NR16 2JG Tel: (01953) 887544 Fax: (01953) 887072 E-mail: enquiries@mouldline.com

Solent Mould Tools Ltd, 1 Relay Road, Waterlooville, Hampshire, PO7 7XA Tel: (023) 9223 9950 Fax: (023) 9223 9951 E-mail: solentmd@tcp.co.uk

Synergy Plastics Ltd, 8 Willow Road, Pen-Y-Fan Industrial Estate, Crumlin, Newport, Gwent, NP11 4EG Tel: (01495) 248888 Fax: (01495) 245678 E-mail: sales@synergy-plastics.com

Tolworth Tools Ltd, 46B Fife Rd, Kingston upon Thames, Surrey, KT1 1SU Tel: (020) 8546 2683 Fax: (020) 8546 2683

PLASTIC BLOW MOULDING MACHINE MANUFRS

Hamilton Machinery Sales Ltd, Hamilton House, Broadfields, Bicester Road, Aylesbury, Bucks, HP19 8BU Tel: (01296) 318222 Fax: (01296) 397005 E-mail: john.hat@hamac.co.uk

Henry Lenox Industrial Ltd, 9 Hanworth Road, Hampton, Middlesex, TW12 3DH Tel: (020) 8941 9274 Fax: (020) 8941 9374 E-mail: sales@henrylenox.co.uk

Sidel (UK) Ltd, Lowesden Works, Lambourn Woodlands, Hungerford, Berkshire, RG17 7RU Tel: (01488) 72525 Fax: (01488) 72302

PLASTIC BLOW MOULDINGS

Boxmore Packaging Ltd, Gateway, Crewe, CW1 6YA Tel: (01270) 582137 Fax: (01270) 581615 E-mail: enquiries@boxmoreplastics.com

Chas Tennant & Co., 81 Lochburn Road, Glasgow, G20 9AE Tel: 0141-946 1833 Fax: 0141-946 5752 E-mail: enquiries@tennantsdistribution.com

Dremm Packaging Ltd, Erewash Court, Manners Avenue, Manners Industrial Estate, Ilkeston, Derbyshire, DE7 8EF Tel: 0115-930 7555 Fax: 0115-930 7618 E-mail: sales@dremm.co.uk

Engineering Plastic Products Ltd, Unit 6, Shaw Road, Dudley, West Midlands, DY2 8TS Tel: (01384) 235881 Fax: (01384) 255260

Fellside Plastics Ltd, Wilson Way, Pool, Redruth, Cornwall, TR15 3RX Tel: (01209) 212917 Fax: (01209) 212919 E-mail: fellside@blowit.fsbusiness.co.uk

Inpress Plastics Ltd, 1 Harwood Road, Littlehampton, West Sussex, BN17 7AU Tel: (01903) 724128 Fax: (01903) 730357 E-mail: sales@impressplastics.co.uk

Mouldline Ltd, The Old Granary, Station Road, Eccles, Norwich, NR16 2JG Tel: (01953) 887544 Fax: (01953) 887072 E-mail: enquiries@mouldline.com

Nampak plc, Llantrisant Business Park, Llantrisant, Pontyclun, Mid Glamorgan, CF72 8LF Tel: (01443) 225520 Fax: (01443) 228970 E-mail: info@rpc-llantrisant.co.uk

Nampak Plastics, Unit 15, Number One Industrial Estate, Consett, County Durham, DH8 6SX Tel: (01207) 580402 Fax: (01207) 580265

Neiman Packaging Ltd, Albion Road, New Mills, High Peak, Derbyshire, SK22 3EY Tel: (01663) 743924 Fax: (01663) 741078 E-mail: sales@roymere.co.uk

Northumbria Blow Moulding Ltd, Northumbria House Unit 7 North Tyne Industrial Estate, Whitley Road, Benton, Newcastle upon Tyne, NE12 9SZ Tel: 0191-215 0958 Fax: 0191-266 7790 E-mail: sales@northblowmould.co.uk

Scanbech Ltd, 44 Arkwright Road, Astmoor Industrial Estate, Runcorn, Cheshire, WA7 1NU Tel: (01928) 561747 Fax: (01928) 565672 E-mail: england@scanbech.com

T J Mouldings, Spring Lane South, Malvern, Worcestershire, WR14 1AT Tel: (01684) 562792 Fax: (01684) 560081

Weltonhurst Ltd, Centurion Way Roman Road Industrial Estate, Roman Road, Blackburn, BB1 2LD Tel: (01254) 671177 Fax: (01254) 671717 E-mail: sales@weltonhurst.co.uk

PLASTIC BOTTLE CAPS OR CLOSURES

Berry Plastics UK. Ltd, Stanford Tuck Road, North Walsham, Norfolk, NR28 0TY Tel: (01692) 404488 Fax: (01692) 404373

Cap It All Closures Ltd, 149d Pack Lane, Basingstoke, Hampshire, RG22 5HN Tel: (01256) 466178 Fax: (01256) 816333

Classic Closures Ltd, 12a Eton Grove, London, SE13 5BY Tel: (020) 8852 3874 Fax: (020) 8318 2111

▶ Keith Crafter Agencies, 8 Cause End Road, Wootton, Bedford, MK43 9DA Tel: (01234) 766014 Fax: (01234) 766014 E-mail: jim@kcaclosures.co.uk

Davsons Mouldings Ltd, 20-22 Woodall Road, Redburn Industrial Estate, Enfield, Middlesex, EN3 4LE Tel: (020) 8805 3117 Fax: (020) 8443 4773 E-mail: sales@davsons.co.uk

Howard Plastics Ltd, Unit 16 Alexandra Way, Ashchurch, Tewkesbury, Gloucestershire, GL20 8NB Tel: (01684) 298206 Fax: (01684) 850425 E-mail: sales@howardplastics.com

Massmould Ltd, Cosgrove Way, Luton, LU1 1XL Tel: (01582) 728285 Fax: (01582) 723166

▶ Nampak Plastics Europe Ltd, Jenna Way Interchange Park, Newport Pagnell, Buckinghamshire, MK16 9PQ Tel: (01908) 611554 Fax: (01908) 614994 E-mail: jon.sweet@eu.nampak.com

Neville & More Ltd, Oakhurst Business Park, Wilberforce Way, Southwater, Horsham, West Sussex, RH13 9RT Tel: (01403) 732290 Fax: (01403) 733507 E-mail: info@nevilleandmore.com

R P C Containers Ltd, Fourth Avenue, Colchester Road, Halstead, Essex, CO9 2SY Tel: (01787) 473224 Fax: (01787) 474151 E-mail: sales@rpc-halstead.co.uk

Roma International P.L.C., Lady Lane Industrial Estate, Hadleigh, Ipswich, IP7 6BQ Tel: (01473) 823279 Fax: (01473) 827773 E-mail: sales@roma.co.uk

Scott Closures International Ltd, Balena Close, Creekmoor Trading Estate, Poole, Dorset, BH17 7DZ Tel: (01202) 692428 Fax: (01202) 697944 E-mail: sales@scottclosures.com

United Closures And Plastics Ltd, Salhouse Road, Norwich, NR7 9AL Tel: (01603) 423131 Fax: (01603) 407942

Viscose Closures Ltd, Unit 1 Fleming Way, Crawley, West Sussex, RH10 9JY Tel: (01293) 519251 Fax: (01293) 540005 E-mail: sales@viscose.co.uk

PLASTIC BOTTLE PRINTING

Cannon Plastics, Units 2-3 Barrs Fold Road, Wingates Industrial Estate, Westhoughton, Bolton, BL5 3XP Tel: (01942) 810081 Fax: (01942) 814311 E-mail: sales@cannon-plastics.co.uk

Cockx Sudbury Ltd, Unit A Woodhall House Drury Drive, Woodhall Business Park, Sudbury, Suffolk, CO10 1WH Tel: (01787) 880511 Fax: (01787) 378102E-mail: info@cockx.co.uk

R Foster Screenprint Ltd, 184 Uxbridge Road, London, W7 3TB Tel: (020) 8567 2272 Fax: (020) 8567 2485 E-mail: sales@rfoster.co.uk

PLASTIC BOTTLES

Amcor Pet Packaging Holdings Ltd, Gresford Industrial Park, Gresford, Wrexham, Clwyd, LL12 8LX Tel: (01978) 856111 Fax: (01978) 854168

Audus Noble Ltd, Blyth Industrial Estate, Cowpen Road, Blyth, Northumberland, NE24 5TD Tel: (01670) 543100 Fax: (01670) 364800

Bettix Ltd, Lever Street, Bolton, BL3 6NZ Tel: (01204) 526241 Fax: (01204) 521958 E-mail: sales@bettix.co.uk

Boxmore Packaging Ltd, Gateway, Crewe, CW1 6YA Tel: (01270) 582137 Fax: (01270) 581615 E-mail: enquiries@boxmoreplastics.com

Cambrian Containers, Unit 32 Mochdre Industrial Estate, Mochdre, Newtown, Powys, SY16 4LE Tel: (01686) 611360 Fax: (01686) 611361

Constar International UK Ltd, Moor Lane Trading Estate, Sherburn in Elmet, Leeds, LS25 6ES Tel: (01977) 882000 Fax: (01977) 882092 E-mail: enguiries@constar.net

Davsons Mouldings Ltd, 20-22 Woodall Road, Redburn Industrial Estate, Enfield, Middlesex, EN3 4LE Tel: (020) 8805 3117 Fax: (020) 8443 4773 E-mail: sales@davsons.co.uk

Dremm Packaging Ltd, Erewash Court, Manners Avenue, Manners Industrial Estate, Ilkeston, Derbyshire, DE7 8EF Tel: 0115-930 7555 Fax: 0115-930 7618 E-mail: sales@dremm.co.uk

Esterform Packaging Ltd, Boraston Lane, Tenbury Wells, Worcestershire, WR15 8LE Tel: (01584) 810600 Fax: (01584) 810213 E-mail: paulw@esterform.com

F L Plastics Ltd, 6 Whiffler Road, Norwich, NR3 2AW Tel: (01603) 418989 Fax: (01603) 418990 E-mail: sales@flplastics.net

▶ Fenton Packaging Leeds Ltd, Bridge Street, Morley, Leeds, LS27 0LE Tel: 0113-252 8222 Fax: 0113-253 6394 E-mail: info@pspackaging.co.uk

Involvement Packaging Ltd, Chesterton Estate Yard, Banbury Road, Lighthorne, Warwick, CV35 0AJ Tel: (01926) 651800 Fax: (01926) 651177 E-mail: robert@involvementpkg.co.uk

Johnsen & Jorgensen Group Ltd, Newtons Court, Crossways Business Park, Dartford, DA2 6QL Tel: (01332) 291111 Fax: (01322) 293501 E-mail: info@jjpack.com

M & H Plastics, London Road, Beccles, Suffolk, NR34 8TS Tel: (01502) 715518 Fax: (01502) 712581 E-mail: sales@mhplastics.com

Melzone Plastic Products, 11 Sandgate High Street, Sandgate, Folkestone, Kent, CT20 3BD Tel: (01303) 248545 Fax: (01303) 248545

▶ Nampak Plastics Europe Ltd, Jenna Way Interchange Park, Newport Pagnell, Buckinghamshire, MK16 9PQ Tel: (01908) 611554 Fax: (01908) 614994 E-mail: jon.sweet@eu.nampak.com

Neiman Packaging Ltd, Albion Road, New Mills, High Peak, Derbyshire, SK22 3EY Tel: (01663) 743924 Fax: (01663) 741078 E-mail: sales@roymere.co.uk

Neville & More Ltd, Oakhurst Business Park, Wilberforce Way, Southwater, Horsham, West Sussex, RH13 9RT Tel: (01403) 732290 Fax: (01403) 733507 E-mail: info@nevilleandmore.com

Plastic Bottle Supplies Ltd, 6 Boundary Industrial Estate, Stafford Road, Wolverhampton, WV10 7EL Tel: (01902) 397397 Fax: (01902) 397666 E-mail: sales@plasticbottlesupplies.co.uk

RPC Containers Ltd, 4 Sallow Road, Weldon North Industrial Estate, Corby, Northamptonshire, NN17 5JX Tel: (01536) 263488 Fax: (01536) 272910 E-mail: sales@rpc-corby.co.uk

Roma International P.L.C., Lady Lane Industrial Estate, Hadleigh, Ipswich, IP7 6BQ Tel: (01473) 823279 Fax: (01473) 827773 E-mail: sales@roma.co.uk

RPC Containers Ltd, Gallamore Lane, Market Rasen, Lincolnshire, LN8 3HZ Tel: (01673) 840200 Fax: (01673) 840240 E-mail: sales@rpc-marketrasen.co.uk

RPC Containers Ltd, Grove Street, Raunds, Wellingborough, Northamptonshire, NN9 6ED Tel: (01933) 623311 Fax: (01933) 622126 E-mail: sales@rpc-raunds.co.uk

Scanbech Ltd, 44 Arkwright Road, Astmoor Industrial Estate, Runcorn, Cheshire, WA7 1NU Tel: (01928) 561747 Fax: (01928) 565672 E-mail: england@scanbech.com

Technical Treatments Ltd, Station Works, Rye Lane, Dunton Green, Sevenoaks, Kent, TN14 5HD Tel: (01732) 462656 Fax: (01732) 742602 E-mail: enquiries@technical-treatments.co.uk

Zinsser Analytic (UK) Ltd, Howarth Road, Stafferton Way, Maidenhead, Berkshire, SL6 1AP Tel: (01628) 773202 Fax: (01628) 672199 E-mail: officeuk@zinsser-analytic.com

PLASTIC BOXES

B C L Distribution, Hornbeam Park, Hookstone Road, Harrogate, North Yorkshire, HG2 8QT Tel: (01423) 879787 Fax: (01423) 879030 E-mail: information@bcldistribution.com

Killyleagh Box Co. Ltd, 39 Shrigley Road, Killyleagh, Downpatrick, County Down, BT30 9SR Tel: (028) 4482 8708 Fax: (028) 4482 1222 E-mail: sales@killyleaghbox.co.uk

Lilytone Ltd, 74 Laneside Road, New Mills, High Peak, Derbyshire, SK22 4LX Tel: (01663) 747335 Fax: (01663) 747393 E-mail: sales@plastic-boxes.co.uk

PLASTIC BOXES – *continued*

Solent Plastics, Manor House Avenue, Southampton, SO15 0LF Tel: (023) 8057 2500 Fax: (023) 8057 7775 E-mail: sales@solentplastics.co.uk

PLASTIC BUCKETS AND PAILS

▶ Fenton Packaging Leeds Ltd, Bridge Street, Morley, Leeds, LS27 0LE Tel: 0113-252 8222 Fax: 0113-253 6394 E-mail: info@pspackaging.co.uk

Involvement Packaging Ltd, Chesterton Estate Yard, Banbury Road, Lighthorne, Warwick, CV35 0AJ Tel: (01926) 651800 Fax: (01926) 651177 E-mail: robert@involvementpkg.co.uk

Superfos Runcorn Ltd., Edison Road, Astmoor Industrial Estate, Runcorn, Cheshire, WA7 1PY Tel: (01928) 575051 Fax: (01928) 572038 E-mail: steve.winstanley@superfos.co.uk

PLASTIC BUILDING PRODUCTS

Airflow (Nicoll Ventilators) Ltd, Queensway, New Milton, Hampshire, BH25 5NN Tel: (01425) 611547 Fax: (01425) 638912 E-mail: sales@airflow-vent.co.uk

Boomer Industries Ltd, Vale Works, Stockfield Road, Chadderton, Oldham, OL9 9HD Tel: (028) 9266 2881 Fax: 0161-643 7299 E-mail: enquiries@boomer.co.uk

Brett Martin Roofing Products Ltd, Langley Road, Burscough Industrial Estate, Ormskirk, Lancashire, L40 8JR Tel: (01704) 895345 Fax: (01704) 894229 E-mail: contact@daylightsystems.co.uk

Central Flooring & Tile Co., 51 Mullaghboy Heights, Magherafelt, County Londonderry, BT45 5NU Tel: (028) 7963 3076

Dessian Products Ltd, Boucher Business Centre, Apollo Road, Belfast, BT12 6HP Tel: (028) 9038 1118 Fax: (028) 9066 0741 E-mail: dessian@dessian.co.uk

Frostree Ltd, 31 Station Street, Middlesbrough, Cleveland, TS1 1SR Tel: (01642) 224151 Fax: (01642) 247973 E-mail: sales@frostree.co.uk

Novaseal Plastics Ltd, 4 Blackbrook Business Park, Blackbrook Road, Fareham, Hampshire, PO15 5DR Tel: (01329) 233500 Fax: (01329) 230012 E-mail: info@novaseal.co.uk

▶ Peninsula Plastics Ltd, Coronation Street, Stockport, Cheshire, SK5 7PG Tel: 0161-476 2025 Fax: 0161-476 2068

Reiner Fixing Devices, Church Lane, North Ockendon, Upminster, Essex, RM14 3QH Tel: (01708) 856601 Fax: (01708) 852293 E-mail: sales@reinerfixings.co.uk

Resdev Ni Ltd, 4 22 Duncrue Road, Belfast, BT3 9BP Tel: (028) 9077 6882 Fax: (028) 9077 8492 E-mail: info@resindevelopment.com

Shepherds (UK) Ltd, Eastbourne Road Industrial Estate, Eastbourne Road, Westham, Pevensey, East Sussex, BN24 5NH Tel: (01323) 768232 Fax: (01323) 768257 E-mail: abigail@shepherdsuk.co.uk

Tecseal Ltd, 4 East Chorley Business Centre, East Way, Chorley, Lancashire, PR6 0BJ Tel: (01257) 249933 Fax: (01257) 249944

PLASTIC BUILDING PROTECTION GUARDS

Castle Plastic, Unit 16b Raleigh Hall Industrial Estate, Eccleshall, Stafford, ST21 6JL Tel: (01785) 851842 Fax: (01785) 851370 E-mail: sales@castleplastics.co.uk

▶ V S P Ltd, 4 Malling Walk, Bottesford, Scunthorpe, North Lincolnshire, DN16 3SS Tel: (01724) 335005 Fax: (01724) 338981 E-mail: enquiries@vspuk.com

PLASTIC BULK STORAGE TANK FABRICATORS

Polytek UK Ltd, Water Lane, Exeter, EX2 8BZ Tel: (01392) 204116 Fax: (01392) 204114 E-mail: ghb@polytekuk.com

PLASTIC BUTTONS

Gene Pearl Buttons Ltd, 2 Bridge Rd, London, NW10 9BX Tel: 020 84594460

PLASTIC CABLE COVERS

Boddingtons Ltd, Blackwater Trading Estate, The Causeway, Maldon, Essex, CM9 4GG Tel: (01621) 874200 Fax: (01621) 874299 E-mail: sales@boddingtons-ltd.com

Cove Ltd, 18 Invincible Road, Invinciblerial Road Industrial Estate, Farnborough, Hampshire, GU14 7QU Tel: (01252) 512919 Fax: (01252) 543384 E-mail: sales@cove-industries.co.uk

Osmor Products Ltd, Unit 12 Ditchling Common, Ditchling, Hassocks, West Sussex, BN6 8SG Tel: (01444) 236900 Fax: (01444) 230770 E-mail: sales@osmor.co.uk

PLASTIC CABLE DUCTING

Cove Ltd, 18 Invincible Road, Invinciblerial Road Industrial Estate, Farnborough, Hampshire, GU14 7QU Tel: (01252) 512919 Fax: (01252) 543384 E-mail: sales@cove-industries.co.uk

Floline, Whitehall Industrial Estate, Whitehall Road, Leeds, LS12 5JB Tel: 0113-235 9349 Fax: 0113-235 9348

PLASTIC CABLE GLANDS

Lapp Ltd, 3 Perivale Park, Horsenden La South, Greenford, Middlesex, UB6 7RL Tel: (020) 8758 7800 Fax: (020) 8758 7880 E-mail: sales@lappgroup.com

Protec The Cap Company Ltd, Princes Park Princesway, Team Valley Trading Estate, Gateshead, Tyne & Wear, NE11 0NF Tel: 0191-442 4242 Fax: 0191-442 4222 E-mail: sales@protecplastics.com

Raytech International, Coldnose Road, Rotherwas Industrial Estate, Hereford, HR2 6JL Tel: (01432) 340833 Fax: (01432) 340844 E-mail: sales@raytech.uk.com

PLASTIC CABLE PORTS

▶ Office Electrics Ltd, 1 Calder Point, Monckton Road Industrial Estate, Wakefield, West Yorkshire, WF2 7AL Tel: (01924) 367255 Fax: (01924) 290652 E-mail: sales@office-electrics.co.uk

PLASTIC CABLE SHEATHING SERVICES

A E I Compounds Ltd, Crete Hall Road, Gravesend, Kent, DA11 9AF Tel: (01474) 566736 Fax: (01474) 564386 E-mail: sales@aeicompounds.co.uk

Plasticable Ltd, Unit 3 Riverwey Industrial Park, Newton Lane, Alton, Hants, GU34 2QL Tel: (01420) 80911 Fax: (01420) 80922 E-mail: sales@plasticable.co.uk

PLASTIC CAGE TYPE BALL BEARINGS

Barrell Bearing, Unit G Sawtry Business Park, Sawtry, Huntingdon, Cambridgeshire, PE28 5GQ Tel: (01487) 834053 Fax: (01487) 832887

PLASTIC CAPILLARY TUBES

Drain Center Ltd, Lincoln Road, Cressex Business Park, High Wycombe, Buckinghamshire, HP12 3RB Tel: (01494) 462351 Fax: (01494) 444923

Drain Center, Unit 20, West Churton Industrial Estate, Alder Road, North Shields, Tyne & Wear, NE29 8SD Tel: 0191-257 8125 Fax: 0191-257 8819

Drain Centre, Stenplas Works, Grecian Crescent, Bolton, BL3 6QS Tel: (01204) 388388 Fax: (01204) 389411

Drain Centre, 19 Bank Head Drive, St. Hillindustrial Estate, St.Hill, Edinburgh, EH11 4DW Tel: 0131-552 8181 Fax: 0131-453 2008 E-mail: edinbr@capperplastics.com

Drain Centre, Cinderhill Industrial Estate, Weston Coyney Road, Longton, Stoke-On-Trent, ST3 5JT Tel: (01782) 311311 Fax: (01782) 343400 E-mail: p23.stoke@wolseley.co.uk

Drains Centre, Unit 2B, St. Georges Trading Estate, Avonmouth, Bristol, BS11 9HS Tel: 0117-916 2700 Fax: 0117-982 6820 E-mail: bristol.p11@wolseley.co.uk

Johnstech Interconnect Ltd, 1-2 Usk Street, Newport, Gwent, NP19 7BE Tel: (01633) 674452 Fax: (01633) 674453 E-mail: info@johnstech.com

K C Tooling Ltd, Unit 22, Hayhill Industrial Estate, Sileby Road, Barrow Upon Soar, Loughborough, Leicestershire, LE12 8LD Tel: (01509) 814724 Fax: (01509) 816076

Pipe Centre Plus, Unit 8, Spring Road Industrial Estate, Ettingshall, Wolverhampton, WV4 6JZ Tel: (01902) 409341 Fax: (01902) 353817 E-mail: p15.wolverhampton@wolseley.co.uk

Trueform Engineering Ltd, Unit 4 Pasadena Close, Pump Lane, Hayes, Middlesex, UB3 3NQ Tel: (020) 8561 4959 Fax: (020) 8848 1397 E-mail: sales@trueform.co.uk

PLASTIC CARD PRINTING/ EMBOSSING SYSTEMS, CREDIT/ SECURITY ETC

Communisis Security Products Ltd, Trafford Wharf Road, Trafford Park, Manchester, M17 1HE Tel: 0161-869 1000 Fax: 0161-869 1010

Plastic Data Card Ltd, Unit 1lg Dajen Business Park, Second Avenue, Chatham, Kent, ME4 5AU Tel: (01634) 811455 Fax: (01634) 831080 E-mail: sales@plasticdatacard.co.uk

PLASTIC CARD SYSTEMS

Databac Group, 1 The Ashway Centre, Elm CR, Kingston upon Thames, Surrey, KT2 6HH Tel: (020) 8546 9826 Fax: (020) 8547 1026 E-mail: info@databac.com

Gemplus Ltd, 36 New Lane, Havant, Hampshire, PO9 2NR Tel: (023) 9248 6444 Fax: (023) 9247 0628 E-mail: felicity.best@gemplus.com

Htec Ltd, Unit H George Curl Way, Southampton, SO18 2RX Tel: (023) 8068 9200 Fax: (023) 8068 9201 E-mail: sstocks@htec.co.uk

Plastic Card Design Services Ltd, 15 Bramshill Ave, Kettering, Northamptonshire, NN16 9FL Tel: (01536) 410557 Fax: (01536) 510509 E-mail: info@plasticcardsuk.com

The Plastic Card Shop, Kemps Place, Selborne Road, Greatham, Liss, Hampshire, GU33 6HG Tel: (0845) 6448171 Fax: (0845) 2260814 E-mail: sales@theplasticcardshop.co.uk

Trackcard Ltd, Rassler Wood House, Henley Road, Marlow, Buckinghamshire, SL7 2EN Tel: (01628) 890036 Fax: (01628) 478215 E-mail: sales@trackcard.co.uk

PLASTIC CARDS

Cardex Facilities, Essex Technology & Innovation Centre, The Gables, Ongar, Essex, CM5 0GA Tel: (01277) 364455 Fax: (01277) 366330 E-mail: lillian.hill@cardex.co.uk

Custom Card Services International Ltd, The Lennox, Lennox Road, Basingstoke, Hampshire, RG22 4AP Tel: (01256) 328883 Fax: (01256) 328884 E-mail: mike@ccsi.co.uk

D & M Business Cards, 4 Foxley Court, Oakwood, Derby, DE21 2EU Tel: (01332) 668468 Fax: (01332) 668462 E-mail: sales@dmbusinesscards.co.uk

PLASTIC CARDS, PRINTED/ EMBOSSED

Bristol Business Cards, Cater Road, Bridge House, Bristol, BS13 7TW Tel: 0117-978 4777

Hythe Offset, Telford Way, Severalls Park, Colchester, CO4 9QP Tel: (01206) 848904 Fax: (01206) 852054 E-mail: cards@hythe-uk.com

Plastic Data Card Ltd, Unit 1lg Dajen Business Park, Second Avenue, Chatham, Kent, ME4 5AU Tel: (01634) 811455 Fax: (01634) 831080 E-mail: sales@plasticdatacard.co.uk

Thames Card Technology Ltd, Thames House, Arterial Road, Rayleigh, Essex, SS6 7UQ Tel: (01268) 775555 Fax: (01268) 777660 E-mail: info@thamesgroup.co.uk

PLASTIC CARRY HANDLES

McLaren Plastics Ltd, Pentland Industrial Estate, Loanhead, Midlothian, EH20 9QH Tel: 0131-448 2200 Fax: 0131-448 2221 E-mail: sales@mclaren-plastics.co.uk

PLASTIC CASES

▶ Gard Plasticases Ltd, 2 Arnolds Business Park, Branbridges Road, East Peckham, Tonbridge, Kent, TN12 5LG Tel: (01622) 871887 Fax: (01622) 871895 E-mail: sales@gardplasticases.com

PLASTIC CASH REGISTER ROLL CENTRES

Denroyd Ltd, Lockhill Mills, Holmes Road, Sowerby Bridge, West Yorkshire, HX6 3LD Tel: (01422) 833147 Fax: (01422) 833615 E-mail: sales@denroyd.co.uk

PLASTIC CATALOGUE COVERS

P R Hunter Plastics Ltd, 5 Pembroke Road, Stocklake Indus Estate, Aylesbury, Buckinghamshire, HP20 1DB Tel: (01296) 422423 Fax: (01296) 422423 E-mail: hunter_plastics@hotmail.com

PLASTIC CATERING EQUIPMENT

B B P Marketing Ltd, Lowland Works, Lowland Road, Mirfield, West Yorkshire, WF14 8LY Tel: (01924) 480393 Fax: (01924) 480632 E-mail: sales@bb-plastics.co.uk

Fast Food Essentials Direct, PO Box 1, Halesowen, W. Midlands, B63 2RB Tel: (0845) 6014713 Fax: (0845) 6014201 E-mail: sales@fastfoodessentials.com

Hospitality Equipment Supplies Ltd, Calderwood House, 7 Montpellier Parade, Cheltenham, Gloucestershire, GL50 1UA Tel: (01242) 573227 Fax: (01242) 226121 E-mail: sales@h-e-s.co.uk

Hurst Green Plastics Ltd, 1st Floor, Bowland House, The Sidings Business Park, Whalley, Clitheroe, Lancashire, BB7 9SE Tel: 01254 825588 Fax: 01254 824521 E-mail: info@hurstgreenplastics.com

Llandudno Wholesale Ltd, 98 Trinity Avenue, Llandudno, Gwynedd, LL30 2YQ Tel: (01492) 876579 Fax: (01492) 860080 E-mail: sales@llandudnowholesale.co.uk

PHD, Bromley Road, Congleton, Cheshire, CW12 1PP Tel: (01260) 271243

PLASTIC CD PACKAGING

▶ Clear Packaging Ltd, 215 Torrington Avenue, Coventry, CV4 9AP Tel: (024) 7646 4566 Fax: (024) 7642 2299 E-mail: info@clearpkgltd.co.uk

Media Cards, 108 Davies Road, West Bridgford, Nottingham, NG2 5HY Tel: 0115-914 2369 E-mail: sales@media-cards.co.uk

Piper Media Products, Unit G Bastre Enterprise Park, Newtown, Powys, SY16 1DZ Tel: (01686) 610640 Fax: (01686) 610660

Total Spectrum Ltd, 11 Intec 2, Wade Road, Basingstoke, Hampshire, RG24 8NE Tel: (01256) 814114 Fax: (01256) 814115 E-mail: sales@totalspectrum.co.uk

PLASTIC CHAINS

Ewart Chain Ltd, Colombo Street, Derby, DE23 8LX Tel: (01332) 345451 Fax: (01332) 371753 E-mail: sales@ewartchain.co.uk

PLASTIC CLOSURES

Alcoa C S I (UK) Ltd, Kelvin Way, West Bromwich, West Midlands, B70 7LB Tel: 0121-532 5000 Fax: 0121-553 3710 E-mail: ciaran.martin@alcoa.com

Alexander Industrial Supplies Essex Ltd, Unit D Eastways, Witham, Essex, CM8 3YQ Tel: (01376) 500303 Fax: (01376) 502090 E-mail: sales@alexander-industrial.co.uk

Bericap (U K) Ltd, Oslo Road, Hull, HU7 0YN Tel: (01482) 826666 Fax: (01482) 832839 E-mail: info.uk@bericap.com

Berry Plastics UK. Ltd, Stanford Tuck Road, North Walsham, Norfolk, NR28 0TY Tel: (01692) 404488 Fax: (01692) 404373

Caplugs Ltd, Unit 7, Overfield Industrial Estate, Off Thorpe Way, Banbury, Oxfordshire, OX16 4XR Tel: (01295) 263753 Fax: (01295) 263788 E-mail: support@caplugs.co.uk

Channel Ltd, Fairway, Orpington, Kent, BR5 1EG Tel: (01689) 871522 Fax: (01689) 833428

Constar International UK Ltd, Moor Lane Trading Estate, Sherburn in Elmet, Leeds, LS25 6ES Tel: (01977) 882000 Fax: (01977) 882092 E-mail: enguiries@constar.net

Cope Allman Plastic Packaging Ltd, Railway Triangle, Walton Road, Portsmouth, PO6 1TS Tel: (023) 9237 0102 Fax: (023) 9238 0314 E-mail: bridget.lambert@copeallman.com

▶ Keith Crafter Agencies, 8 Cause End Road, Wootton, Bedford, MK43 9DA Tel: (01234) 766014 Fax: (01234) 766014 E-mail: jim@kcaclosures.co.uk

Davsons Mouldings Ltd, 20-22 Woodall Road, Redburn Industrial Estate, Enfield, Middlesex, EN3 4LE Tel: (020) 8805 3117 Fax: (020) 8443 4773 E-mail: sales@davsons.co.uk

Ever Ready Tools & Plastics Co. Ltd, Unit H, Chesham Close, Romford, RM7 7NA Tel: (01708) 762262 Fax: (01708) 723006 E-mail: everreaytools@btconnect.com

Greif UK Ltd, Merseyside Works, Oil Sites Road, Ellesmere Port, CH65 4EZ Tel: 0151-373 2000 Fax: 0151-373 2072 E-mail: kathy.turton@tri-sure.com

Guala Closures UK Ltd, 6 Whitburn Road, Bathgate, West Lothian, EH48 1HH Tel: (01506) 637501 Fax: (01506) 637502 E-mail: guala@guala.demon.co.uk

Jaycare Ltd, New York Way, New York Industrial Park, Newcastle Upon Tyne, NE27 0QF Tel: 0191-296 0303 Fax: 0191-296 1842

Moss Products Plastics Ltd, Isle of Wight Lane, Kensworth, Dunstable, Bedfordshire, LU6 2PP Tel: (01582) 873366 Fax: (01582) 873399 E-mail: sales@mossproducts.co.uk

Plasticum UK Ltd, 2 Bramble Way, Clover Nook Industrial Park, Somercotes, Alfreton, Derbyshire, DE55 4RH Tel: (01773) 833866 Fax: (01773) 520085

Pound International Ltd, 109 Baker Street, London, W1U 6RP Tel: (020) 7935 3735 Fax: (020) 7224 3734 E-mail: pound@dial.pipex.com

R P C Containers Ltd, Fourth Avenue, Colchester Road, Halstead, Essex, CO9 2SY Tel: (01787) 473224 Fax: (01787) 474151 E-mail: sales@rpc-halstead.co.uk

Robinson Plastic, Lowmoor Road, Kirkby-in-Ashfield, Nottingham, NG17 7JU Tel: (01623) 752869 Fax: (01623) 751726 E-mail: plas@r1pp.co.uk

United Closures And Plastics Ltd, Salhouse Road, Norwich, NR7 9AL Tel: (01603) 423131 Fax: (01603) 407942

Zip Pack Packaging Technology, Unit 17, Shaw Wood Business Park, Doncaster, South Yorkshire, DN2 5TB Tel: (01302) 344119 Fax: (01302) 321703 E-mail: enquiries@zippack.co.uk

PLASTIC COATED FABRICS

Mansam Products Ltd, 49-51 Broughton Lane, Manchester, M8 9UE Tel: 0161-834 1356 Fax: 0161-835 1024 E-mail: sales@mansam.co.uk

PLASTIC COATED STEEL ROOF FLASHING

H B Humphries & Co. Ltd, Telford Way, Telford Way Industrial Estate, Kettering, Northamptonshire, NN16 8UN Tel: (01536) 512588 Fax: (01536) 410140 E-mail: enquiries@hbhumphries.co.uk

J W Entwistle Co. Ltd, 41 Cobden Street, Salford, M6 6WF Tel: 0161-736 2297 Fax: 0161-745 7897 E-mail: adam@jwentwistle.com

Pinfold Fabrications, Pinfold Road, Bourne, Lincolnshire, PE10 9HT Tel: (01778) 421554 Fax: (01778) 393456

PLASTIC COATED TUBES

Pharmatube Ltd, Units 1-2, Shield Drive, Wardley Business Park, Manchester, M28 2QB Tel: 0161-794 7391 Fax: 0161-727 8318 E-mail: sales@pharmatube.com

PLASTIC COATED WIRE

Hampton Steel & Wire, London Road, Wellingborough, Northamptonshire, NN8 2DJ Tel: (01933) 233333 Fax: (01933) 442701 E-mail: sales@hamptonsteel.co.uk

PLASTIC COATED WIRE GOODS

Coltran Products Ltd, 17-31 Church Street, Mexborough, South Yorkshire, S64 0EW Tel: (01709) 584031 Fax: (01709) 584431 E-mail: sales@coltran.com

Hamster Baskets, Aylhill, Aylton, Ledbury, Herefordshire, HR8 2QJ Tel: (01531) 670209 Fax: (01531) 670630 E-mail: richard@hamsterbaskets.co.uk

J W Lister Ltd, Clifton Road, Brighouse, West Yorkshire, HD6 1SL Tel: (01484) 712925 Fax: (01484) 715314 E-mail: sales@jwlister.co.uk

Metalcote Wire Products Mnfrs, Unit 14 Bromyard Road Industrial Estate, Ledbury, Herefordshire, HR8 1NS Tel: (01531) 633704 Fax: (01531) 635085 E-mail: enquiries@metalcote.co.uk

PLASTIC COATING MATERIALS

Parkinson Plastics Ltd, Bankwood Lane, New Rossington, Doncaster, South Yorkshire, DN11 0PS Tel: (01302) 864959 Fax: (01302) 864954

T W Taylor & Co., Whitehouse Enterprise Centre, Whitehouse Road, Newcastle upon Tyne, NE15 6EP Tel: 0191-274 3013 Fax: 0191-274 3013

PLASTIC COATING PROCESSORS OR SERVICES

Ace Townsend Coaters, Two Woods Lane, Brierley Hill, West Midlands, DY5 1TA Tel: (01384) 70331 Fax: (01384) 78981

Asdec Ltd, Unit 7-8 Building 33, Second Avenue, Pensnett Trading Estate, Kingswinford, West Midlands, DY6 7UG Tel: (01384) 402463 Fax: (01384) 402662 E-mail: asdecc@hotmail.com

Dipcoat Plastics, Beoley Mill, Marlfield Lane, Redditch, Worcestershire, B98 8PU Tel: (01527) 60342 Fax: (01527) 60342 E-mail: dipcoat@amserve.com

ESP Coatings Ltd, Units A5-E13, Hastingwood Trading Estate, Harbet Road, Edmonton, London, N18 3HT Tel: (020) 8803 1115 Fax: (020) 8035 567 E-mail: espcoatings@btconnect.com

Industrial Plastic Coatings Ltd, St Helens Way, Thetford, Norfolk, IP24 1HG Tel: (01842) 753529 Fax: (01842) 754060 E-mail: sales@industrialplasticcoatings.co.uk

Kelcoat Engineering Plastics Ltd, Barnfield Road Industrial Estate, Leek, Staffordshire, ST13 5QG Tel: (01538) 383547 Fax: (01538) 387918

Leyfos Plastics, Unit D1, Rosehill Industrial, Stoke Heath, Market Drayton, Shropshire, TF9 2JU Tel: (01630) 638557 Fax: (01630) 638651 E-mail: sales@leyfos.com

Mallatite Ltd, Hardwick View Road, Holmewood, Chesterfield, Derbyshire, S42 5SA Tel: (01246) 593280 Fax: (01246) 593281 E-mail: info@mallatite.co.uk

Omnikote Ltd, Chamberlain Road, Aylesbury, Buckinghamshire, HP19 8DY Tel: (01296) 483266 Fax: (01296) 392285 E-mail: sales@omnikote.co.uk

Plastic Treatments Ltd, Cleggs Lane Mill, Seddon Street, Little Hulton, Manchester, M38 9RN Tel: 0161-799 1039 Fax: 0161-703 8671

Protec Powder Coatings, Unit 3 Winsford Industrial Estate, Winsford Industrial Estate, Winsford, Cheshire, CW7 3PQ Tel: (01606) 593199

S S Central Coating Ltd, Unit 5 Oakhill Trading Estate, Euston Street, Freemens Common, Leicester, LE2 7ST Tel: 0116-255 4748 Fax: 0116-255 4769 E-mail: satu@sscoatings.com

Seal Graphics, Units 2-5, Watkins Close, Burnt Mills Industrial Estate, Basildon, Essex, SS13 1TL Tel: (01268) 722400 Fax: (01268) 725864

South Western Plastics Ltd, The Old Jail, Willway Street, Bristol, BS3 4BG Tel: 0117-953 1811

Southern Plastics Ltd, Unit 3, Unit 3 Holton Heath Industrial Estate, Poole, Dorset, BH16 6LT Tel: (01202) 622311 Fax: (01202) 622102

Toray Europe Ltd, 7 Old Park Lane, London, W1K 1AD Tel: (020) 7663 7700 Fax: (020) 7872 8071

PLASTIC COLOUR COATING SERVICES

▶ Rite Systems, 43 The Stripe, Stokesley, Middlesbrough, Cleveland, TS9 5PX Tel: (01642) 713140 E-mail: jgreen@ritesystems.com

PLASTIC COMBS

G B Kent & Sons plc, London Road, Hemel Hempstead, Hertfordshire, HP3 9SA Tel: (01442) 251531 Fax: (01442) 231672 E-mail: info@kentbrushes.com

John Dobson Milnthorpe Ltd, Bela Mill, Milnthorpe, Cumbria, LA7 7QP Tel: (01539) 563528 Fax: (01539) 562481 E-mail: enquiries@combs.co.uk

PLASTIC COMPONENT DEVELOPMENT AND PROTOTYPE PRODUCTION

East Yorkshire Polymers Ltd, Unit E, Londesborough Business Centre, Hull, HU3 1DR Tel: (01482) 211110 Fax: (01482) 581898 E-mail: pbmcm@eypoly.freeserve.co.uk

Hydrovern Ltd, Unit 21, Wilden Industrial Estate, Wilden Lane, Stourport-On-Severn, Worcestershire, DY13 9JY Tel: (0870) 7706222 Fax: (0870) 7706223 E-mail: info@hydrovern.co.uk

M R D C Ltd, PO Box 5745, Epping, Essex, CM16 4LE Tel: (01992) 577377 Fax: (01992) 577377 E-mail: calvert@mrdcnet.com

Rimparts, 249 Gladstone Road, Barry, Vale of Glamorgan, CF63 1NJ Tel: (01446) 732849 Fax: (01446) 732849

PLASTIC COMPONENT REWORK OR REPAIR

Plastic Rework Solutions Ltd, Unit 9a Castle Mill Works, birmingham New Road, Dudley, West Midlands, DY1 4DA Tel: (01384) 211169 E-mail: prs01384@btconnect.com

PLASTIC COMPONENTS

Minimould Ltd, Units 10A & 10B, Thame Road, Aylesbury, Buckinghamshire, HP17 8LJ Tel: 01844 292880

PLASTIC COMPOUND MANUFRS

A Schulman Inc Ltd, Croespenmaen Industrial Estate, Crumlin, Newport, Gwent, NP11 3AG Tel: (01495) 244090 Fax: (01495) 249277

Asahi Thermofil UK Ltd, 28 New Lane, Havant, Hampshire, PO9 2NQ Tel: (023) 9248 6350 Fax: (023) 9247 2388

Douglas Baker Plastics Ltd, Doubak Works Barton Industrial Estate, Mount Pleasant, Bilston, West Midlands, WV14 7LH Tel: (01902) 353800 Fax: (01902) 353855 E-mail: sales@dbplastics.co.uk

Chemix Ltd, Vauxhall Industrial Estate, Greg Street, Stockport, Cheshire, SK5 7BR Tel: 0161-480 3487 Fax: 0161-480 2394

Distrupol Ltd, Distrupol, Marston Road, Wolverhampton, WV2 4LN Tel: (01902) 426839 Fax: (01902) 426852 E-mail: info@distrupol.com

I C O UK Ltd, 24 Norris Way, Wellingborough Road, Rushden, Northamptonshire, NN10 6BP Tel: (01933) 315500 Fax: (01933) 313300

John Hellyar & Co. Ltd, Tyler Way, Whitstable, Kent, CT5 2RX Tel: (01227) 813200 Fax: (01227) 792203 E-mail: sales@hellyar.co.uk

Matrix Plastics Ltd, 141 Edinburgh Avenue, Slough, SL1 4SS Tel: (01753) 551177 Fax: (01753) 551166 E-mail: sales@matrix-plastics.co.uk

P W Hall Ltd, Woodilee Industrial Estate, Lenzie, Kirkintilloch, Glasgow, G66 3UR Tel: 0141-776 2384 Fax: 0141-776 2382 E-mail: dir@pwhall.co.uk

Perrite Plastic Compounds, 1 Kingsland Grange, Woolston, Warrington, WA1 4RA Tel: (01925) 810608 Fax: (01925) 840001 E-mail: sales@jgp-perrite.co.uk

Prime Polymers & Compounders, Fernbank Mill, Fernbank Avenue, Barnoldswick, Lancashire, BB18 5UX Tel: (0870) 7707617 Fax: (0870) 7707612

Resin Express Ltd, 11 Valley Business Centre, Gordon Road, High Wycombe, Buckinghamshire, HP13 6EQ Tel: (01494) 459881 Fax: (01494) 795334 E-mail: sales@resinexpress.com

Silvergate Plastics, Unit 53 Clywedog Road South, Wrexham Industrial Estate, Wrexham, Clwyd, LL13 9XS Tel: (01978) 661496 Fax: (01978) 660462 E-mail: sales@silvergate-plastics.co.uk

Whitaker Technical Plastics Ltd, Redwood Court, Tytherington Business Park, Macclesfield, Cheshire, SK10 2XH Tel: (01625) 612571 Fax: (01625) 612594 E-mail: g_whitaker@btconnect.com

PLASTIC COMPOUNDING EQUIPMENT

Farrel Ltd, PO Box 27, Rochdale, Lancashire, OL11 2PF Tel: (01706) 647434 Fax: (01706) 638982 E-mail: farreluk@farrel.com

H B Halstead & Sons Ltd, 247 Eldon Street, Ashton-on-Ribble, Preston, PR2 2BB Tel: (01772) 252820 Fax: (01772) 202609 E-mail: sales@hbhalstead.com

PLASTIC COMPRESSION MOULDINGS

British Mica Co. Ltd, 123 Barkers Lane, Bedford, MK41 9RR Tel: (01234) 327977 Fax: (01234) 352016 E-mail: info@britishmica.co.uk

Fairgrieve Mouldings Ltd, 15 Sedling Road, Wear Industrial Estate, Washington, Tyne & Wear, NE38 9BZ Tel: 0191-415 9292 Fax: 0191-415 9696 E-mail: lindabiggins@fairgrieve87.freeserve.co.uk

I C M (Plastic Moulding) Ltd, Enterprise Close, Medway City Estate, Rochester, Kent, ME2 4LY Tel: (01634) 298500 Fax: (01634) 714338 E-mail: info@icm-plasticmoulding.co.uk

Mawson Triton Mouldings Ltd, 4-8 Waterside Industrial Estate, Doulton Road, Rowley Regis, West Midlands, B65 8JG Tel: (01384) 633321 Fax: (01384) 565782 E-mail: sales@mawsontriton.co.uk

Merriott, Tail Mill Lane, Merriott, Somerset, TA16 5PG Tel: (01460) 72457 Fax: (01460) 74481 E-mail: sales@merriott.com

Voestalpine Polynorm Plastics Ltd, PO Box 9, St. Helens, Merseyside, WA10 6FE Tel: (01744) 743333 Fax: (01744) 743300

West Midland Mouldings Ltd, Unit 2 West Coppice Road, Walsall, WS8 7HB Tel: (01543) 378100 Fax: (01543) 378100

PLASTIC CONSULTANTS OR DESIGNERS

Advanced Plastics & Composites Ltd, 31 Bergen Way, Sutton Fields Industrial Estate, Hull, HU7 0YQ Tel: (01482) 823038 Fax: (01482) 822945 E-mail: info@advanced-plastics.co.uk

Alan Griffiths, Fawley Green, Fawley, Henley-on-Thames, Oxfordshire, RG9 6JF Tel: (01491) 414169 Fax: (01491) 414179

Benoil Services Ltd, Norcombe House, Tile Barn, Woolton Hill, Newbury, Berkshire, RG20 9UZ Tel: (01635) 253412 Fax: (01635) 253899 E-mail: sales@benoil.com

British Plastics Federation, 6 Bath Place, Rivington Street, London, EC2A 3JE Tel: (020) 7457 5000 Fax: (020) 7457 5038 E-mail: bpf@bpf.co.uk

Creighton Developments Ltd, Unit 15 Enterprise Centre Two, Chester Street, Stockport, Cheshire, SK3 0BR Tel: 0161-480 0668 Fax: 0161-480 0668

Design 4 Plastics Ltd, Unit 402 Thorp Arch Trading Estate, Thorp Arch, Wetherby, West Yorkshire, LS23 7BJ Tel: (01937) 845176 Fax: (01937) 845419 E-mail: enquiries@design4plastics.com

Detailed Plastic Components Ltd, 8 Rutherford Way, Thetford, Norfolk, IP24 1HA Tel: (01842) 764414 Fax: (01842) 762715 E-mail: sales@dpc.uk.com

Econology Ltd, 4 Norsted Lane, Pratts Bottom, Orpington, Kent, BR6 7PG Tel: (01689) 860686 E-mail: cmaier@btconnect.com

Essex Injection Mouldings Ltd, 15 Temple Farm Industrial Estate, Craftsman Square, Temple Farm Industrial Estate, Southend-on-Sea, SS2 5RH Tel: (01702) 461160 Fax: (01702) 600805 E-mail: ed@essexinjectionmouldings.co.uk

Europlaz Technologies Ltd, The Maltings Industrial Estate, Southminster, Essex, CM0 7EH Tel: (01621) 773471 Fax: (01621) 773792 E-mail: enquiries@europlaz.co.uk

FlowTech Design Ltd, 355 Green Lane, Bolton, BL3 2LU Tel: (01204) 362622 Fax: (01204) 362622 E-mail: clive.fenn@flowtechdesign.com

H D S Design Consultants Ltd, 22 South Street, Rochford, Essex, SS4 1BQ Tel: (01702) 530043 Fax: (01702) 530051 E-mail: projects@hdsdesign.com

H P M Ltd, Unit 9, Ascot Industrial Estate, Lenton St, Nottingham, NG10 5DL Tel: 0115-939 0716 Fax: 0115-949 1106 E-mail: info@hpmltd.com

Harrison Adams Ltd, Victoria Mills, Knowler Hill, Liversedge, West Yorkshire, WF15 6DP Tel: (01924) 402435 Fax: (01924) 404814 E-mail: travor@harrisonadamsmouldings.wannado.co.uk

▶ Howard Consultancy, 26 The Loont, Winsford, Cheshire, CW7 1EU Tel: (01606) 552189 Fax: (01606) 552189 E-mail: roberthoward@onetel.net

M R D C Ltd, PO Box 5745, Epping, Essex, CM16 4LE Tel: (01992) 577377 Fax: (01992) 577377 E-mail: calvert@mrdcnet.com

Maclan Plastics, Unit Ba Keighley Business Centre, South Street, Keighley, West Yorkshire, BD21 1AG Tel: (01535) 680127 Fax: (01535) 680222 E-mail: info@maclanplastics.co.uk

Neppco Ltd, PO Box 88, Manchester, M60 1QD Tel: 0161-200 5706 Fax: 0161-200 5707 E-mail: sales@neppco.co.uk

Plastics Solutions Ltd, 25 St. Martins Road, Upton, Poole, Dorset, BH16 5NQ Tel: (01202) 623598 Fax: (01202) 623598 E-mail: alan@plastics-solutions.com

Playden Tools Ltd, Factory 5-6 The Elms, Church Road, Harold Wood, Romford, RM3 0JR Tel: (01708) 343874 Fax: (01708) 376531

▶ Prime Plastic Mouldings Ltd, 8 Heron Industrial Estate, Basingstoke Road, Spencers Wood, Reading, RG7 1PJ Tel: 0118-988 7525 Fax: 0118-988 7526 E-mail: sales@primeplas.com

Rapra Technology, Shawbury, Shrewsbury, SY4 4NR Tel: (01939) 250383 Fax: (01939) 251118 E-mail: info@rapra.net

Resinfab & Associates, 6 Imex Business Park, Kings Road, Tyseley, Birmingham, B11 2AL Tel: 0121-706 1848 Fax: 0121-706 1848 E-mail: tech@resinfab.co.uk

S G H Moulds Ltd, Hypatia Street, Bolton, BL2 6AA Tel: (01204) 529374 Fax: (01204) 363356 E-mail: sgh@sghmoulds.freeserve.co.uk

Smithers Rapra, Shawbury, Shrewsbury, SY4 4NR Tel: (01939) 250383 Fax: 01939 251118 E-mail: info@rapra.net

Vactec Derby Ltd, Eagle Road, Quarry Hill Industrial Estate, Ilkeston, Derbyshire, DE7 4RB Tel: 0115-930 4806 Fax: 0115-930 4806

PLASTIC CONTAINER LINERS

Linertech Ltd, Wellington Mills, Quebec Street, Elland, West Yorkshire, HX5 9BX Tel: (01422) 377551 Fax: (01422) 311636 E-mail: sales@linertech.co.uk

Philton Polythene Converters Ltd, Charfleets Road, Canvey Island, Essex, SS8 0PQ Tel: (01268) 696331 Fax: (01268) 510517 E-mail: sales@philton.co.uk

PLASTIC CONTAINER RECOVERY/RECYCLING SERVICES

JFC Plastics Ltd, 6 Goldicote Business Park, Banbury Road, Goldicote, Stratford-upon-Avon, Warwickshire, CV37 7NB Tel: (01789) 740102 Fax: (01789) 740037 E-mail: info@delleve.co.uk

Suma Containers, Plot Z Robian Way, Swadlincote, Derbyshire, DE11 9DH Tel: (01283) 224114 Fax: (01283) 218280 E-mail: sales@sumacontainers.co.uk

V10 Polymers Ltd, Rockcliffe Works, Paterson Street, Blackburn, BB2 3SP Tel: (01254) 680384 Fax: (01254) 674933 E-mail: david@holtplastics.co.uk

PLASTIC CONTAINERS

Audus Noble Ltd, Blyth Industrial Estate, Cowpen Road, Blyth, Northumberland, NE24 5TD Tel: (01670) 543100 Fax: (01670) 364800

Beverage Plastics Ltd, 70 Silverwood Road, Craigavon, County Armagh, BT66 6LN Tel: (028) 3832 2221 Fax: (028) 3832 1888 E-mail: enquires@lurgan.plastic.boxmore.com

Boxmore Packaging Ltd, Gateway, Crewe, CW1 6YA Tel: (01270) 582137 Fax: (01270) 581615 E-mail: enquiries@boxmoreplastics.com

Bristol Plastic Containers, Unit 10, Ashley Trading Estate, Ashley Parade, Bristol, BS2 9XS Tel: 0117-955 8500 Fax: 0117-955 8600 E-mail: frwarrencoltd@btconnect.com

Chas Tennant & Co., 81 Lochburn Road, Glasgow, G20 9AE Tel: 0141-946 1833 Fax: 0141-946 5752 E-mail: enquiries@tennantsdistribution.com

Corbett Storage Solutions, Enterprise House, Enterprise Way, Edenbridge, Kent, TN8 6HF Tel: (0800) 3165656 Fax: (01732) 862430 E-mail: customerservice@paulcorbett.co.uk

Fletcher European Containers Ltd, 49-51 Sanders Road, Finedon Road Industrial Estate, Wellingborough, Northamptonshire, NN8 4NL Tel: (01933) 440446 Fax: (01933) 270377 E-mail: sales@fletchereuropean.co.uk

PLASTIC CONTAINERS – *continued*

Floplast Ltd, Eurolink Industrial Centre, Castle Road, Sittingbourne, Kent, ME10 3FP Tel: (01795) 431731 Fax: (01795) 431188 E-mail: sales@floplast.co.uk
Howard Plastics Ltd, Unit 16 Alexandra Way, Ashchurch, Tewkesbury, Gloucestershire, GL20 8NB Tel: (01684) 298206 Fax: (01684) 850425 E-mail: sales@howardplastics.com
James J Carrick & Co. Ltd, 450 Petershill Road, Glasgow, G21 4PB Tel: 0141-558 6008 Fax: 0141-557 0318 E-mail: enquiries@jamesjcarrick.com
Jaycare Ltd, New York Way, New York Industrial Park, Newcastle Upon Tyne, NE27 0QF Tel: 0191-296 0303 Fax: 0191-296 1842
Lee Plastics Ltd, Stapleton House, 6 High Street, Fleckney, Leicester, LE8 8AJ Tel: 0116-240 2798 Fax: 0116-240 2394 E-mail: bob@leeplastics.co.uk
Linpac Materials Handling, Newfield Close, Walsall, WS2 7PB Tel: (01922) 726060 Fax: (01922) 643422 E-mail: lmhsolutions@linpac.com
M & H Plastics, London Road, Beccles, Suffolk, NR34 8TS Tel: (01502) 715518 Fax: (01502) 712581 E-mail: sales@mhplastics.com
Marlin Products Ltd, Boundary Road, Buckingham Road Industrial Estate, Brackley, Northamptonshire, NN13 7ES Tel: (01280) 705484 Fax: (01280) 700242 E-mail: marlinproducts@btconnect.com
Nampak plc, Llantrisant Business Park, Llantrisant, Pontyclun, Mid Glamorgan, CF72 8LF Tel: (01443) 225520 Fax: (01443) 228970 E-mail: info@rpc-llantrisant.co.uk
Otto UK Ltd, Beacon House, Reg's Way, Bardon Hill, Coalville, Leicestershire, LE67 1GH Tel: (01530) 277900 Fax: (01530) 277911 E-mail: sales@otto.co.uk
Polimoon Ltd, Babbage Road, Engineer Park, Sandycroft, Deeside, Clwyd, CH5 2QD Tel: (01244) 537555 Fax: (01244) 526645 E-mail: sales@polimoon.com
Polymer Holdings Ltd, 1 Windmill Lane, Denton, Manchester, M34 3RN Tel: 0161-320 7710 Fax: 0161-320 9940 E-mail: sales@rubberengineering.co.uk
RPC Containers Ltd, Haslingden Road, Blackburn, BB1 2PX Tel: (01254) 682298 Fax: (01254) 583752 E-mail: sales@rpc-blackburn.co.uk
RPC Containers Ltd, St. Vincents Trading Estate, Feeder Road, Bristol, BS2 0UY Tel: 0117-977 9511 Fax: 0117-972 3602
RPC Containers Ltd, Gallamore Lane, Market Rasen, Lincolnshire, LN8 3HZ Tel: (01673) 840200 Fax: (01673) 840240 E-mail: sales@rpc-marketrasen.co.uk
RPC Containers Ltd, Grove Street, Raunds, Wellingborough, Northamptonshire, NN9 6ED Tel: (01933) 623311 Fax: (01933) 622126 E-mail: sales@rpc-raunds.co.uk
Static Scotland Ltd, 16 Cromarty Campus, Rosyth, Dunfermline, Fife, KY11 2WX Tel: (01383) 419833 Fax: (01383) 413028 E-mail: staticscotland@aol.com
Suma Containers, Plot Z Robian Way, Swadlincote, Derbyshire, DE11 9DH Tel: (01283) 224114 Fax: (01283) 218280 E-mail: sales@sumacontainers.co.uk
George Utz Ltd, Grange Close, Clover Nook Industrial Estate, Alfreton, Derbyshire, DE55 4QT Tel: (01773) 541370 Fax: (01773) 543180 E-mail: info@uk.georgutz.com
Wilsanco Plastics Ltd, Killyman Road Industrial Estate, Killyman Road, Dungannon, County Tyrone, BT71 6LN Tel: (028) 8772 3131 Fax: (028) 8772 7318 E-mail: mailbox@wilsanco.com

PLASTIC CONVEYOR ROLLERS

Fastrax Conveyors & Components, Shieling Court, Oakley Hay Industrial Estate, Great Oakley, Corby, Northamptonshire, NN18 9QD Tel: (01536) 747770 Fax: (01536) 747990 E-mail: fastraxcc@aol.com
Moving Methods Ltd, Brooks Lane, Middlewich, Cheshire, CW10 0JH Tel: (01606) 833262 Fax: (01606) 832304
P J Osborne, 16 James Watt Close, Drayton Fields Industrial Estate, Daventry, Northamptonshire, NN11 8RJ Tel: (01327) 312664 Fax: (01327) 342400

PLASTIC CONVEYOR SYSTEMS

Romech Spiral Systems Ltd, Carnaby Industrial Estate, Lancaster Road, Carnaby, Bridlington, North Humberside, YO15 3QY Tel: (01262) 601128 Fax: (01262) 671905 E-mail: sales@romech.co.uk

PLASTIC CORES

A Fax Ltd, Drakes Industrial Estate, Shay Lane, Ovenden, Halifax, West Yorkshire, HX3 6RL Tel: (01422) 331133 Fax: (01422) 323533 E-mail: sales@a-fax.com
bpi.agri, Worcester Road, Leominster, Herefordshire, HR6 0QA Tel: (01568) 617220 Fax: (01568) 611435 E-mail: sales@bpiagri.com

PLASTIC COVERS

D C Plastic Handrails Ltd, Unit 6, Cowen Road, Cowen Road Industrial Estate, Blaydon-On-Tyne, Tyne & Wear, NE21 5TW Tel: 0191-414 0034 Fax: 0191-414 0034 E-mail: davey@dchandrails.freeserve.co.uk

PLASTIC CRATES

Polimoon Ltd, Babbage Road, Engineer Park, Sandycroft, Deeside, Clwyd, CH5 2QD Tel: (01244) 537555 Fax: (01244) 526645 E-mail: sales@polimoon.com

PLASTIC CURTAIN RAIL OR POLE OR FITTINGS

Edward Harpley Ltd, Crownings, Brettenham, Ipswich, IP7 7PA Tel: (01449) 737999 Fax: (01449) 736111 E-mail: edwardharpley@btconnect.com
Hunter & Hyland Ltd, 201-205 Kingston Road, Leatherhead, Surrey, KT22 7PB Tel: (01372) 378511 Fax: (01372) 370038 E-mail: enquiries@hunterandhyland.co.uk

PLASTIC CUTTING MACHINES

Peter Gillard & Co. Ltd, Alexandra Way, Ashchurch Business Centre, Tewkesbury, Gloucestershire, GL20 8NB Tel: (01684) 290243 Fax: (01684) 290330 E-mail: sales@gillard.co.uk

PLASTIC DECKING

▶ Priory Paving (North East) Ltd, 1 Havelock Street, South Shields, Tyne & Wear, NE33 5DZ Tel: 0191-454 3111 Fax: 0191-454 5500 E-mail: sales@priorypaving.com

PLASTIC DIP MOULDINGS

Carn Plastics, Victoria Street, Lurgan, Craigavon, County Armagh, BT67 9DH Tel: (028) 3832 4721 Fax: (028) 3832 4523 E-mail: info@carnplastics.co.uk
Kea Flex Mouldings Ltd, Woolmer Way, Bordon, Hampshire, GU35 9QE Tel: (01420) 473645 Fax: (01420) 487498 E-mail: sales@kea-flex-mouldings.co.uk
▶ Plastic Mouldings Ltd, 4 Ailsa Road, Irvine Industrial Estate, Irvine, Ayrshire, KA12 8LP Tel: (01294) 278091 Fax: (01294) 311655 E-mail: info@plasticmouldings.com
Pyramid Products Ltd, Unit 1 Victoria Street, Mansfield, Nottinghamshire, NG18 5RR Tel: (01623) 421277 Fax: (01623) 421288 E-mail: sales@pyramid-products.co.uk

PLASTIC DISCOUNT CARDS

D & M Business Cards, 4 Foxley Court, Oakwood, Derby, DE21 2EU Tel: (01332) 668468 Fax: (01332) 668462 E-mail: sales@dmbusinesscards.co.uk
PMC Systems, Whitehill Industrial Estate, Whitehill Lane, Wootton Bassett, Swindon, SN4 7DB Tel: (01793) 848817 Fax: (01793) 848846 E-mail: pmccards@aol.com

PLASTIC DRAIN OR SANITARY PIPES

Brett Martin, Brierley Close, Speedwell Industrial Estate Staveley, Staveley, Chesterfield, Derbyshire, S43 3JP Tel: (01246) 280001 Fax: (01246) 280001 E-mail: building@brettmartin.com
Brett Martin Roofing Products Ltd, Langley Road, Burscough Industrial Estate, Ormskirk, Lancashire, L40 8JR Tel: (01704) 895345 Fax: (01704) 894229 E-mail: contact@daylightsystems.co.uk
Geberit Ltd, New Hythe Business Park, Aylesford, Kent, ME20 7PJ Tel: (01622) 717811 Fax: (01622) 716920 E-mail: salesgb@geberit.com
Marley Plumbing & Drainage, Dickley Lane, Lenham, Maidstone, Kent, ME17 2DE Tel: (01622) 858888 Fax: (01622) 858725 E-mail: marketing@marleyext.com
Polypipe Civils Ltd, Bishop Meadow Road, Loughborough, Leicestershire, LE11 5RE Tel: (01509) 615100 Fax: (01609) 610215 E-mail: sales@polypipecivils.co.uk
S V R Plastics Ltd, Units 5-6, Greenhey Place, Skelmersdale, Lancashire, WN8 9SA Tel: (01695) 50717 Fax: (01695) 50052 E-mail: sales@svrplastics.co.uk

PLASTIC DRAINAGE GULLIES

Pipex Ltd, Pipex House Lowman Way, Tiverton Business Park, Tiverton, Devon, EX16 6SR Tel: (01884) 243564 Fax: (01884) 253285

PLASTIC DRAINAGE PRODUCTS

Geberit Ltd, New Hythe Business Park, Aylesford, Kent, ME20 7PJ Tel: (01622) 717811 Fax: (01622) 716920 E-mail: salesgb@geberit.com

PLASTIC DRINKING GLASSES

▶ Cater For You Ltd, Unit 4, Wessex Road, Bourne End, Buckinghamshire, SL8 5DT Tel: (01494) 583743 Fax: (01628) 810093 E-mail: info@cater4you.co.uk

PLASTIC DUCTING

Primaflex Ltd, Arcadia Business Centre, Miller Lane, Clydebank, Dunbartonshire, G81 1UJ Tel: 0141-951 4188 Fax: 0141-952 2001

PLASTIC DUST COVERS

Praybourne Ltd, Unit 11, Dunlop Road, Hunt End Industrial Estate, Redditch, Worcestershire, B97 5XP Tel: (0870) 2420004 Fax: (01527) 543752 E-mail: inquiries@praybourne.co.uk

PLASTIC EDGING STRIPS

Bauschlinnemann UK, Widow Hill Road, Heasandford Industrial Estate, Burnley, Lancashire, BB10 2TB Tel: (01282) 686850 Fax: (01282) 412361 E-mail: armabord@armabord.co.uk
BLP UK Ltd, B L P House, Sandall Stones Road, Kirk Sandall Industrial Estate, Doncaster, South Yorkshire, DN3 1QR Tel: (01302) 890555 Fax: (01302) 886724 E-mail: mail@blpuk.com
David Clouting Ltd, 7B Perry Road, Witham, Essex, CM8 3UD Tel: (01376) 518037 Fax: (01376) 500104 E-mail: sales@davidclouting.co.uk
I T W Angleboard, Crackley Way, Peartree Lane, Dudley, West Midlands, DY2 0UW Tel: (01384) 253290 Fax: (01384) 253321 E-mail: uksales@itwangleboard.net

PLASTIC ELECTRONICS INDUSTRY PRODUCTS/ COMPONENTS/FITTINGS

M G Plastics Ltd, Progress Mill, Marsh House Lane, Darwen, Lancashire, BB3 3JB Tel: (01254) 703930 Fax: (01254) 774472 E-mail: sales@mgplastics.com
Redditch Plastic Products, Pipers Road, Park Farm Industrial Estate, Redditch, Worcestershire, B98 0HU Tel: (01527) 528024 Fax: (01527) 520236 E-mail: sales@rpp.uk.com

PLASTIC ELECTROPLATING

Quality Plated Plastics, Shady Lane, Birmingham, B44 9ER Tel: 0121-366 7500 Fax: 0121-366 6436

PLASTIC EMBOSSING

R W Plastics (UK) Ltd, 16 Manor Park, 35 Willis Way, Fleet Industrial Estate, Poole, Dorset, BH15 3SZ Tel: (01202) 673373 Fax: (01202) 632018

PLASTIC ENCLOSURES

B C L Distribution, Hornbeam Park, Hookstone Road, Harrogate, North Yorkshire, HG2 8QT Tel: (01423) 879787 Fax: (01423) 879030 E-mail: information@bcldistribution.com
Cadlow Enclosures, Bridge House, The Green, Redgrave, Diss, Norfolk, IP22 1RR Tel: (01379) 898810 Fax: (01379) 898812 E-mail: info@cadlow.co.uk
Carmo Ltd, 11-19 Bancrofts Road, Eastern Industrial Area, South Woodham Ferrers, Chelmsford, CM3 5UG Tel: (01245) 322130 Fax: (01245) 328695 E-mail: brian@carmo.co.uk
Customdesigntechnologies Ltd, Greatworth Park, Welsh Lane, Greatworth, Banbury, Oxfordshire, OX17 2HB Tel: (01280) 845530 Fax: (01295) 768888 E-mail: sales@customdesigntechnologies.com
Eldon Electric Ltd, Rother Way, Hellaby, Rotherham, South Yorkshire, S66 8QN Tel: (01709) 701234 Fax: (01709) 701209 E-mail: info.uk@eldon.com
Kenter Plastics, Finches Yard, Eastwick Road, Bookham, Leatherhead, Surrey, KT23 4BA Tel: (01372) 456487 Fax: (01372) 450475
Phoenix Mecano Ltd, 6-7 Faraday Road, Aylesbury, Buckinghamshire, HP19 8TX Tel: (01296) 619100 Fax: (01296) 398866 E-mail: info@phoenix-mecano.ltd.uk

PLASTIC ENGINEERED PRODUCTS/COMPONENT FINISHING SERVICES

Plastics & Engineering Co., Unit 8-9 Merretts Mill, Bath Road, Woodchester, Stroud, Gloucestershire, GL5 5EX Tel: (01453) 836206 Fax: (01453) 836245 E-mail: sales@plastics-machining.com

PLASTIC ENGINEERED PRODUCTS/COMPONENTS

Abaloid Plastics Ltd, 165 Scudamore Road, Leicester, LE3 1UQ Tel: 0116-232 0212 Fax: 0116-232 0569 E-mail: enquiries@abaloidplastics.co.uk
ABG Rubber & Plastics Ltd, Galowhill Rd, Brackmills Industrial Estate, Northampton, NN4 7EE Tel: (01604) 700880 Fax: (01604) 766113 E-mail: sales@abgrp.co.uk
Amberlea Plastics Ltd, 26 Palmerston Business Park, Palmerston Drive, Fareham, Hampshire, PO14 1DJ Tel: (01329) 231031 Fax: (01329) 239995 E-mail: sales@amberlea.co.uk
Asher Andell Ltd, Midway House, Main Road, Upper Broughton, Melton Mowbray, Leicestershire, LE14 3BG Tel: (01664) 822131 Fax: (01664) 823332 E-mail: medical@asher-andell.co.uk
D S W Engineering Co. Ltd, 6 Chester Hall Lane, Basildon, Essex, SS14 3BG Tel: (01268) 523185 Fax: (01268) 534325 E-mail: admin@dsw.biz
Devol Engineering Ltd, 13 Clarence Street, Greenock, Renfrewshire, PA15 1LR Tel: (01475) 720934 Fax: (01475) 787873 E-mail: sales@devol.com
K J K Plastics Ltd, 51 Knowl Piece, Wilbury Way, Hitchin, Hertfordshire, SG4 0TY Tel: (01462) 420422 Fax: (01462) 420242 E-mail: sales@kjkplastics.co.uk
L M C Technik Ltd, Cherry Way, Dubmire Industrial Estate, Houghton le Spring, Tyne & Wear, DH4 5RJ Tel: 0191-385 8500 Fax: 0191-385 7819 E-mail: sales@lmctechnik.com
Luma Plastic Engineering, 4 Baltimore Trading Estate, Baltimore Road, Birmingham, B42 1DD Tel: 0121-344 4414 Fax: 0121-344 4414 E-mail: krysplas@hotmail.com
Nickerson Europe Ltd, 24 Brunel Road, Earlstrees Industrial Estate, Corby, Northamptonshire, NN17 4JW Tel: (01933) 674144 Fax: (01536) 202196 E-mail: info@nickersoneurope.co.uk
Oneida Plastic Fabrications Ltd, 8e Alder Road, North Shields, Tyne & Wear, NE29 8SD Tel: 0191-258 5750 Fax: 0191-259 6969 E-mail: sales@oneidaplastics.com
Q D Plastics Glasgow Ltd, Elm Road, Broadmeadow Industrial Estate, Dumbarton, G82 2RH Tel: (01389) 762377 Fax: (01389) 734438 E-mail: sales@qdplastics.co.uk
▶ R J Lewis Ltd, 90 Cobham Road, Ferndown Industrial Estate, Wimborne, Dorset, BH21 7RE Tel: (01202) 893739 E-mail: info@rjlewis.com
Ryan Plastics, 21A Prince St, Northampton, NN6 0LL Tel: (01604) 811395 Fax: (01604) 812872 E-mail: john@ryanplastics.ssnet.co.uk
S W Plastics, Baldwins Yard, Noahs Ark, Kemsing, Sevenoaks, Kent, TN15 6PF Tel: (01732) 762260 Fax: (01732) 762025 E-mail: sales@swplasticsltd.com
Synthotec Ltd, Sandys Road, Malvern, Worcestershire, WR14 1JJ Tel: (01684) 571900 Fax: (01684) 571909 E-mail: sales@synthotec.com
Theoplastic Ltd, 3 & 45 Barking Industrial Park, Alfreds Way, Barking, Essex, IG11 0TJ Tel: (020) 8591 5534 Fax: (020) 8591 9022 E-mail: theoplastic@aol.com
West Alloy Ltd, Garth Road, Morden, Surrey, SM4 4LN Tel: (020) 8337 2211 Fax: (020) 8330 7640 E-mail: sales@westalloy.com
Westford Plastics & Engineering Ltd, Westford, Wellington, Somerset, TA21 0DU Tel: (01823) 662377 Fax: (01823) 663238 E-mail: l_cross@msn.com
Westley Plastics Ltd, Gawne Lane, Cradley Heath, West Midlands, B64 5QY Tel: (01384) 414840 Fax: (01384) 414849 E-mail: sales@plastics.co.uk

PLASTIC ENGINEERING

▶ 4plas Ltd, 7 Aldin Way, Hinckley, Leicestershire, LE10 0GE Tel: (01455) 612601 Fax: (01455) 613853 E-mail: enquiries@4plas.com
A T A Engineering Processes, Unit 2 Saracen Industrial Estate, Mark Road, Hemel Hempstead, Hertfordshire, HP2 7BJ Tel: (01442) 264411 Fax: (01442) 231383 E-mail: sales@ataeng.com
Alda Plastics, Unit 13 Monks Brook Indust P, School Close, Chandler's Ford, Eastleigh, Hampshire, SO53 4RA Tel: (023) 8027 3396 Fax: (023) 8027 3496
Ashby Engineering Co., 8 Surbiton Hill Road, Surbiton, Surrey, KT6 4TP Tel: (020) 8399 4034 Fax: (020) 8390 4947 E-mail: ashbyeng@aol.com

PLASTIC ENGINEERING – *continued*

C G Plastic Fabrications, Unit 41 New Enterprise Workshops, Mount Street, Nechells, Birmingham, B7 5RD Tel: 0121-327 3895 Fax: 0121-327 3895

Clearex Plastics Ltd, Dubmire Trading Estate, Houghton le Spring, Tyne & Wear, DH4 5RF Tel: 0191-385 2880 Fax: 0191-385 2855

East Kilbride Industrial Plastics, 25-27 Langlands Place, Kelvin South Business Park, East Kilbride, Glasgow, G75 0YF Tel: (01355) 236231 Fax: (01355) 235182 E-mail: ek.plastics@btinternet.com

Flomax Racing, Ruskin Works, Oakridge Road, High Wycombe, Buckinghamshire, HP11 2PE Tel: (01494) 465678 Fax: (01494) 465678

Forest Engineering Designs, 57 West Street, Pontypridd, Mid Glamorgan, CF37 4PS Tel: (01443) 409536 Fax: (01443) 405936

G T Industrial Services Ltd, 16 Enterprise Court, Newton Close, Park Farm Industrial Estate, Wellingborough, Northamptonshire, NN8 6UW Tel: (01933) 405088 Fax: (01933) 405099 E-mail: sales@gtihaxaplas.ukf.net

H L Plastics Ltd, Duffield Road Industrial Estate, Little Eaton, Derby, DE21 5EH Tel: (01332) 832389 Fax: (01332) 830867 E-mail: sales@hlplasticsltd.co.uk

L'hotellier Montrichard (UK) Ltd, Balena Close, Poole, Dorset, BH17 7DU Tel: (01202) 693409 Fax: (01202) 658657 E-mail: sparkesc@lcn.ltd.uk

Plastec Engineering Developments, 14 Bennerley Avenue, Ilkeston, Derbyshire, DE7 8PF Tel: 0115-932 4422 Fax: 0115-932 4422

Plastics & Engineering Co., Unit 8-9 Merretts Mill, Bath Road, Woodchester, Stroud, Gloucestershire, GL5 5EX Tel: (01453) 836206 Fax: (01453) 836245 E-mail: sales@plastics-machining.com

Poly Hi Solidur (U K) Ltd, Halifax Road, Todmorden, Lancashire, OL14 5QQ Tel: (01706) 811000 Fax: (01706) 817571 E-mail: sales@polyhisolidur.co.uk

Premier Plastics Ltd, Unit 43 St. Helens Court, St. Helens Way, Thetford, Norfolk, IP24 1HG Tel: (01842) 750461 Fax: (01842) 754743 E-mail: enquiries@premierplastics.org.uk

▶ R J Lewis Ltd, 90 Cobham Road, Ferndown Industrial Estate, Wimborne, Dorset, BH21 7RE Tel: (01202) 893739 E-mail: info@rjlewis.com

Silwood Plastics Ltd, F Borough Road, Buckingham Road Industrial Estate, Brackley, Northamptonshire, NN13 7BE Tel: (01280) 844800 Fax: (01280) 700122

PLASTIC ENGINEERING INDUSTRY PRODUCTS/ COMPONENTS/FITTINGS

Forest Engineering Designs, 57 West Street, Pontypridd, Mid Glamorgan, CF37 4PS Tel: (01443) 409536 Fax: (01443) 405936

Q D Plastics Glasgow Ltd, Elm Road, Broadmeadow Industrial Estate, Dumbarton, G82 2RH Tel: (01389) 762377 Fax: (01389) 734438 E-mail: sales@qdplastics.co.uk

PLASTIC ENGRAVING SERVICES

I C L Plastics Ltd, Grovepark Mills, Hopehill Road, Glasgow, G20 7NF Tel: 0141-332 1331 Fax: 0141-332 9186

Laser Techniques Ltd, Unit 11 Shaw Crescent, Hutton, Brentwood, Essex, CM13 1JD Tel: (01277) 228194 Fax: (01277) 232840 E-mail: sales@laser-techniques.com

Precision Units Dorset Ltd, 2a Gloucester Road, Poole, Dorset, BH12 2AP Tel: (01202) 741664 Fax: (01202) 716473 E-mail: enquiries@precisionunits.co.uk

PLASTIC ENVELOPES

Bayard Packaging Ltd, Unit 16 Deptford Trading Estate, Blackhorse Road, London, SE8 5HY Tel: (020) 8692 4444 Fax: (020) 8692 3851 E-mail: sales@bayardpackaging.co.uk

Braythorn Ltd, Phillips Street, Birmingham, B6 4PT Tel: 0121-359 8800 Fax: 0121-359 8412 E-mail: sales@braythorn.co.uk

Polyprint Mailing Films Ltd, Mackintosh Road, Rackheath Industrial Estate, Rackheath, Norwich, NR13 6LJ Tel: (01603) 721807 Fax: (01603) 721813 E-mail: jneville@polyprint.co.uk

Wegener Sefton, G 7 Unit Liver Industrial Estate, Long Lane, Walton, Liverpool, L9 7ES Tel: 0151-521 7070 Fax: 0151-525 2458 E-mail: howardpaul@btconnect.com

Wessex Polybags, Unit 1 Ashville Trading Estate, Royston Road, Baldock, Hertfordshire, SG7 6NN Tel: (01462) 490600 Fax: (01462) 490800 E-mail: sales@wessexpolybags.co.uk

PLASTIC EXTRUSION CYLINDERS

Magog Industries Ltd, Swains Mill, Crane Mead, Ware, Hertfordshire, SG12 9PY Tel: (01920) 465201 Fax: (01920) 463345 E-mail: enquiries@magog.co.uk

PLASTIC EXTRUSION DIES

Birkdale Plastics Ltd, Unit 2-4 Fowler Industrial Estate, Chorley New Road, Horwich, Bolton, BL6 5LU Tel: (01204) 698715 Fax: (01204) 698716 E-mail: sales@birkdaleplastics.com

Mapex UK Ltd, Unit 9 Pulloxhill Business Pk, Greenfield Rd, Pulloxhill, Bedford, MK45 5EU Tel: (01525) 719979 Fax: (01525) 719339 E-mail: info@mapex.demon.co.uk

Merlin Extrusion Services, 11 & 12 Walkers Road, Moons Moat North Industrial Estate, Redditch, Worcestershire, B98 9HE Tel: (01527) 64833 Fax: (01527) 66021 E-mail: ron@merlinextrusionservices.freeserve.co.uk

PLASTIC EXTRUSION MANUFRS

Abbey Extrusions Ltd, 2 Ivanhoe Industrial Estate, Tournament Way, Ashby-de-la-Zouch, Leicestershire, LE65 2UU Tel: (01530) 416177 Fax: (01530) 417230 E-mail: sales@abbeyextrusions.co.uk

▶ Apex GB Ltd, Station Approach, Victoria, Roche, St. Austell, Cornwall, PL26 8LG Tel: (0870) 7373771 Fax: (0870) 7373772 E-mail: sales@apexgb.com

Arrow Plastics Ltd, Arrow Works, Hampden Road, Kingston upon Thames, Surrey, KT1 3HQ Tel: (020) 8546 6258 Fax: (020) 8541 4654 E-mail: mail@arrow-plastics.co.uk

B T G Plastics Ltd, Corporation Road, Sparth Bottoms, Rochdale, Lancashire, OL11 4HJ Tel: (01706) 640400 Fax: (01706) 653434 E-mail: btg.plastics@tiscali.co.uk

B W F Kunststoffe GmbH, Unit 4, Orchard Court, Nunn Brook Road, Huthwaite, Sutton-in-Ashfield, Nottinghamshire, NG17 2HZ Tel: (01908) 516177 Fax: (01908) 290468 E-mail: sales@bwfprofiles.co.uk

B & W Lifting, Unit 2e Grangetown Centre, Stapylton Street, Middlesbrough, Cleveland, TS6 7BJ Tel: (01642) 467900 Fax: (01642) 467900 E-mail: bwlifting@hotmail.com

Bardini Plastics, Unit 4 Ellesmere, Manners Industrial Estate, Ilkeston, Derbyshire, DE7 8EF Tel: 0115-944 2733 Fax: 0115-944 2723 E-mail: bardini@bigfoot.com

Be-Plas Marketing Ltd, Unit 2 & 3 Old Hall Industrial Estate, Grisedale Road, Old Hall Industrial Estate, Wirral, Merseyside, CH62 3QA Tel: 0151-334 5133 Fax: 0151-334 9399 E-mail: sales@beplas.com

Birkdale Plastics Ltd, Unit 2-4 Fowler Industrial Estate, Chorley New Road, Horwich, Bolton, BL6 5LU Tel: (01204) 698715 Fax: (01204) 698716 E-mail: sales@birkdaleplastics.com

Boomer Industries Ltd, Vale Works, Stockfield Road, Chadderton, Oldham, OL9 9HD Tel: (028) 9266 2881 Fax: 0161-643 7299 E-mail: enquiries@boomer.co.uk

Buxo Plas, Quarters Farm, Hazle Badge, Bradwell, Hope Valley, Derbyshire, S33 9HX Tel: (01433) 620175 Fax: (01433) 620047 E-mail: sales@buxoplas.co.uk

C & K Extrusions Ltd, 12 Drayton Road, Tonbridge, Kent, TN9 2BE Tel: (01732) 361434 Fax: (01732) 771009 E-mail: admin@ckextrusions.co.uk

Collins Extrusions Ltd, Bidavon Industrial Estate, Waterloo Road, Bidford-on-Avon, Alcester, Warwickshire, B50 4JW Tel: (01789) 773536 Fax: (01789) 490225 E-mail: coltec1@yahoo.com

Custom Extruded Profiles, 35c Lysander Road, Bowerhill, Melksham, Wiltshire, SN12 6SP Tel: (01225) 791818 Fax: (01225) 791818

Flexicare Medical Ltd, CWM Cynon Business Park, Mountain Ash, Mid Glamorgan, CF45 4ER Tel: (01443) 474647 Fax: (01443) 474222 E-mail: sales@flexicare.com

Gap Ltd, 12 Ridge Way, Donibristle Industrial Park, Hillend, Dunfermline, Fife, KY11 9JN Tel: (01383) 824181 Fax: (01383) 824722 E-mail: mark.adams@gap.uk

Gradko International Ltd, St Martins House, 77 Wales Street, Winchester, Hampshire, SO23 0RH Tel: (01962) 860331 Fax: (01962) 841339 E-mail: sales@gradko.co.uk

H L Plastics Ltd, Duffield Road Industrial Estate, Little Eaton, Derby, DE21 5EH Tel: (01332) 832389 Fax: (01332) 830867 E-mail: sales@hlplasticsltd.co.uk

JD Profile Extrusion, 30 Balmer Cut, Buckingham Industrial Estate, Buckingham, MK18 1UL Tel: (01280) 822693 Fax: (01280) 824003 E-mail: sales@jdprofile.co.uk

Leedum Ltd, Stanley Works, Church Street, Eyam, Hope Valley, Derbyshire, S32 5QH Tel: (01433) 630838 Fax: (01433) 631888 E-mail: mail@leedum.co.uk

Marley Plumbing & Drainage, Dickley Lane, Lenham, Maidstone, Kent, ME17 2DE Tel: (01622) 858888 Fax: (01622) 858725 E-mail: marketing@marleyext.com

Marshall Tufflex Ltd, Churchfields Industrial Estate, Sidney Little Road, St. Leonards-on-Sea, East Sussex, TN38 9PU Tel: (0870) 2403200 Fax: (0870) 2403201 E-mail: sales@marshall-tufflex.com

G.H. Maughan Ltd, Bella Street Industrial Estate, Bolton, BL3 4DU Tel: (01204) 653516 Fax: (01204) 657362 E-mail: ghmaughan@lineone.net

Merritt Plastics Ltd, 5 Winster Buildings, Manners Avenue, Manners Industrial Estate, Ilkeston, Derbyshire, DE7 8EF Tel: 0115-944 7661 Fax: 0115-944 1864 E-mail: simon@merrittplastics.fsnet.co.uk

Micrex Profiles Ltd, Stamford Mill, Bayley Street, Stalybridge, Cheshire, SK15 1QQ Tel: 0161-330 6518 Fax: 0161-330 5576 E-mail: enquiry@micrex-profiles.co.uk

Nenplas, Airfield Industrial Estate, Ashbourne, Derbyshire, DE6 1HA Tel: (01335) 347300 Fax: (01335) 340271 E-mail: enquiries@nenplas.com

Novaseal Plastics Ltd, 4 Blackbrook Business Park, Blackbrook Road, Fareham, Hampshire, PO15 5DR Tel: (01329) 233500 Fax: (01329) 230012 E-mail: info@novaseal.co.uk

Park Mill Extrusions Ltd, 2 Campden Street, Mossley, Ashton-under-Lyne, Lancashire, OL5 9BD Tel: (01457) 835339 Fax: (01457) 838591 E-mail: parkmill88@hotmail.com

Permacell Finesse Ltd, Western Road, Silver End, Witham, Essex, CM8 3QB Tel: (01376) 583241 Fax: (01376) 584227 E-mail: sales@pfl.co.uk

Piltec Rubber & Plastic Ltd, Waterloo Park, Bidford-on-Avon, Alcester, Warwickshire, B50 4JG Tel: (01789) 778271 Fax: (01789) 772886 E-mail: sales@piltec.com

Pixie Developments Ltd, 2 New Mills Industrial Estate, Post Office Road, Inkpen, Hungerford, Berkshire, RG17 9PU Tel: (01488) 669184 Fax: (01488) 669185 E-mail: pixiedev.ltd@ukonline.co.uk

Plasticable Ltd, Unit 3 Riverwey Industrial Park, Newton Lane, Alton, Hants, GU34 2QL Tel: (01420) 80911 Fax: (01420) 80922 E-mail: sales@plasticable.co.uk

Polypipe Civils Ltd, Boston Road Industrial Estate, Holmes Way, Horncastle, Lincolnshire, LN9 6JW Tel: (01507) 527373 Fax: (01507) 525099

Polyplas Extrusions Ltd, Unit 1 Wilden Industrial Estate, Wilden Lane, Stourport-on-Severn, Worcestershire, DY13 9JY Tel: (0845) 5314086 Fax: (01299) 827016 E-mail: info@polyplas.co.uk

Pritchard Plastics Ltd, Kings Hill Industrial Estate, Kings Hill, Bude, Cornwall, EX23 8QN Tel: (01288) 353211 Fax: (01288) 355686 E-mail: sales@pritchard-plastics.co.uk

Profile Techniques Ltd, Unit 12-14 Watery La Industrial Estate, Watery Lane, Willenhall, West Midlands, WV13 3SU Tel: (01902) 609545 Fax: (01902) 632319 E-mail: info@profiletechniques.co.uk

Reddiplex Group Logistics, Unit 33 The Furlong, Berry Hill Industrial Estate, Droitwich, Worcestershire, WR9 9BG Tel: (01905) 774400 Fax: (01905) 791866 E-mail: reddiplex@reddiplex.com

Rehau Ltd, Hill Court, Walford, Ross-on-Wye, Herefordshire, HR9 5QN Tel: (01989) 762600 Fax: (01989) 762601 E-mail: enquiries@rehau.com

Rigiflex Extrusions Ltd, Ibex Barn Ferro Fields, Brixworth Indust Estate, Brixworth, Northampton, NN6 9UA Tel: (01604) 880217 Fax: (01604) 880129 E-mail: sales@rigiflexextrusions.co.uk

Russell Plastics, 8a High St, Harpenden, Herts, AL5 2TB Tel: (01582) 762868 Fax: (01582) 461086 E-mail: sales@russellplastics.co.uk

S P P Extrusions, Timothys Bridge Road, Stratford-upon-Avon, Warwickshire, CV37 9NQ Tel: (01789) 298429 Fax: (01789) 414427 E-mail: sales@sp-plastics.co.uk

Sabre Plastics Ltd, Dockfield Road, Shipley, West Yorkshire, BD17 7AD Tel: (01274) 586815 Fax: (01274) 531397 E-mail: info@sabreplastics.co.uk

Shakespeare International Ltd, Enterprise Way, Off Venture Road, Fleetwood, Lancashire, FY7 8RY Tel: (01253) 858787 Fax: (01253) 859595

Shepherds (UK) Ltd, Eastbourne Road Industrial Estate, Eastbourne Road, Westham, Pevensey, East Sussex, BN24 5NH Tel: (01323) 768232 Fax: (01323) 768257 E-mail: abigail@shepherdsuk.co.uk

Slottseal Extrusions Ltd, Tyne Road, Weadon Road Industrial Estate, Northampton, NN5 5AF Tel: (01604) 759535 Fax: (01604) 752780 E-mail: tecplastics@btinternet

Standring Bros Ltd, Wellington Road, Greenfield, Oldham, OL3 7AG Tel: (01457) 877227 Fax: (01457) 877204 E-mail: standring.brothers@btopenworld.com

Tag Plastic Extrusions Ltd, 21 Marsh Green Road North, Marsh Barton Trading Estate, Exeter, EX2 8NY Tel: (01392) 479036 Fax: (01392) 432835

Trimplex Ltd, Darby Way, Narborough, Leicester, LE19 2GP Tel: 0116-286 6611 Fax: 0116-275 0216 E-mail: valplas@freeuk.com

TSL Extrusions, Elton Park Business Centre, Hadleigh Rd, Ipswich, IP2 0HN Tel: 0845 4940747 Fax: (01473) 236044 E-mail: sales@tubeway.co.uk

Vpe, 7 Verwood Industrial Estate, Blackhill, Verwood, Dorset, BH31 6HA Tel: (01202) 827205 Fax: (01202) 827207 E-mail: sales@vpeltd.co.uk

Whitehouse Plastics Ltd, Unit 4 Tiber Way, Glebe Farm Industrial Estate, Rugby, Warwickshire, CV21 1ED Tel: (01788) 541042 Fax: (01788) 552314 E-mail: sales@whitehouseplastics.co.uk

Wilks (Rubber Plastics Manufacturing) Co. Ltd, Woodrolfe Road, Tollesbury, Maldon, Essex, CM9 8RY Tel: (01621) 869609 Fax: (01621) 868863 E-mail: sales@wilks.co.uk

PLASTIC EXTRUSION SCREWS

Magog Industries Ltd, Swains Mill, Crane Mead, Ware, Hertfordshire, SG12 9PY Tel: (01920) 465201 Fax: (01920) 463345 E-mail: enquiries@magog.co.uk

PLASTIC EXTRUSION TOOLMAKERS

Birkdale Plastics Ltd, Unit 2-4 Fowler Industrial Estate, Chorley New Road, Horwich, Bolton, BL6 5LU Tel: (01204) 698715 Fax: (01204) 698716 E-mail: sales@birkdaleplastics.com

Greiner Extrusion Technology UK Ltd, Unit 5 Queens Avenue, Hurdsfield Industrial Estate, Macclesfield, Cheshire, SK10 2BN Tel: (01625) 616061 Fax: (01625) 613689 E-mail: s.wood@greiner-extrusion.co.uk

PLASTIC EXTRUSIONS, FLEXIBLE PROFILE

▶ Altura Extrusions, Horsepool Grange Industrial Estate, Elliotts Lane, Stanton under Bardon, Markfield, Leicestershire, LE67 9TW Tel: (01530) 245500 Fax: (01530) 245599 E-mail: sales@alturaextrusions.com

Polyplas Extrusions Ltd, Unit 1 Wilden Industrial Estate, Wilden Lane, Stourport-on-Severn, Worcestershire, DY13 9JY Tel: (0845) 5314086 Fax: (01299) 827016 E-mail: info@polyplas.co.uk

Vpe, 7 Verwood Industrial Estate, Blackhill, Verwood, Dorset, BH31 6HA Tel: (01202) 827205 Fax: (01202) 827207 E-mail: sales@vpeltd.co.uk

PLASTIC FABRICATING MACHINING SERVICES

JD Plastics, Unit 7 The Match Factory, Speke Road, Garston, Liverpool, L19 2RF Tel: 0151-427 1500 Fax: 0151-427 1539 E-mail: sales@jdplastics.com

PLASTIC FABRICATIONS, *See also headings for particular types*

▶ Fabtech Services, Unit 4b Wilstead Industrial Park, Kenneth Way, Wilstead, Bedford, MK45 3PD Tel: (01234) 741147 Fax: (01234) 741147 E-mail: sales@fabtechservices.co.uk

▶ Plasvent Constructions, 22 Clausen Way, Pennington, Lymington, Hampshire, SO41 8BJ Tel: (01590) 678959 Fax: (01590) 688654

Tanmill Ltd, 8 Meadow Lane, Bilston, West Midlands, WV14 9NQ Tel: (01902) 880991 Fax: (01902) 887477

PLASTIC FABRICATORS

A C C Plastics, Unit A Peacock View, Fenton Industrial Estate, Stoke-on-Trent, ST4 2XJ Tel: (01782) 201601 Fax: (01782) 201782 E-mail: sales@accplastics.co.uk

A & E Plastic Fabrications Ltd, 40 St. Peters Street, Radford, Nottingham, NG7 3FF Tel: 0115-978 0048 Fax: 0115-979 1351 E-mail: info@aaep.co.uk

Adray Plastics Ltd, James Scott Road, Halesowen, West Midlands, B63 2QT Tel: (01384) 569864 Fax: (01384) 411833 E-mail: sales@adrayplastics.co.uk

Alda Plastics, Unit 13 Monks Brook Indust P, School Close, Chandler's Ford, Eastleigh, Hampshire, SO53 4RA Tel: (023) 8027 3396 Fax: (023) 8027 3496

Aluminium & Plastics Ltd, 29a Marlborough Road, Newport, Gwent, NP19 0PZ Tel: (01633) 259188 Fax: (01633) 212217

Aquaflex Ltd, 1 Edison Road, Salisbury, SP2 7NU Tel: (01722) 328873 Fax: (01722) 413068 E-mail: info@aquaflex.co.uk

Arena Plastics Ltd, 5 Lynmouth Avenue, Stockport, Cheshire, SK5 7AL Tel: 0161-442 4000 Fax: 0161-442 4000

Argo Plastics Ltd, Unit 6B, Park Street Industrial Estate, Kidderminster, Worcestershire, DY11 6TN Tel: (01562) 823531 Fax: (01562) 825417

Art Equipment, 3 Craven Street, Northampton, NN1 3EZ Tel: (01604) 632447 Fax: (01604) 632447 E-mail: charlesstradling@aol.com

Ayfab Industrial Plastics, Leaside, Aycliffe Industrial Estate, Aycliffe Industrial Park, Newton Aycliffe, County Durham, DL5 6HX Tel: (01325) 310510 E-mail: ayfab@aycliffe16fsnet.co.uk

B P H Plastics, Woods Farm, Woodham Road, Battlesbridge, Wickford, Essex, SS11 7QU Tel: (01245) 328801 Fax: (01245) 328717 E-mail: bph@btinternet.com

Bay Plastics Ltd, Unit H1, High Flatworth, Tyne Tunnel Trading Estate, North Shields, Tyne & Wear, NE29 7UZ Tel: 0191-258 0777 Fax: 0191-258 1010 E-mail: sales@bayplastics.co.uk

Bec Plastics, 18-20 Lenziemill Road, Cumbernauld, Glasgow, G67 2RL Tel: (01236) 781255 Fax: (01236) 781299 E-mail: enquires@becplastics.co.uk

▶ indicates data change since last edition

PLASTIC FABRICATORS – *continued*

Beckox Plastic Fabrications Ltd, 4-6 Wool Road, Poole, Dorset, BH12 4NG Tel: (01202) 736725 Fax: (01202) 738352 E-mail: reg@beckox.co.uk

Bell Display Ltd, Fernie Road, Market Harborough, Leicestershire, LE16 7PH Tel: (01858) 432652 Fax: (01858) 431621

Betrix Industrial Models Ltd, 18-20 Waterloo Road, Stockport, Cheshire, SK1 3BD Tel: 0161-477 1766 Fax: 0161-474 7052 E-mail: betrixmodels@aol.com

Brisbay Plastics Ltd, Adamsez Industrial Estate, Scotswood Road, Newcastle upon Tyne, NE15 6XA Tel: 0191-274 4774 Fax: 0191-228 0146 E-mail: steve@brisbay.co.uk

C G Plastic Fabrications, Unit 41 New Enterprise Workshops, Mount Street, Nechells, Birmingham, B7 5RD Tel: 0121-327 3895 Fax: 0121-327 3895

C H Reynolds & Sons Ltd, 1358 Stratford Road, Hall Green, Birmingham, B28 9EH Tel: 0121-777 3675 Fax: 0121-777 4883 E-mail: reysigns@aol.com

Cabcare Products, Unit 6 Raleigh Hall Industrial Estate, Eccleshall, Stafford, ST21 6JL Tel: (01785) 851944 Fax: (01785) 851961 E-mail: sales@cabcare.com

Carlon Plastics Leicester Ltd, 128 Fairfax Road, Leicester, LE4 9EL Tel: 0116-276 9562 Fax: 0116-276 1267 E-mail: chris@carlonplastics.co.uk

Champion Plastics Ltd, Bristol Road, Portishead, Bristol, BS20 6QG Tel: (01275) 845105 Fax: (01275) 843081 E-mail: info@albionplastics.co.uk

Colmac Plastic Fabricators, Unit C1 South Way, Bounds Green Industrial Estate, London, N11 2UL Tel: (020) 8361 4807 Fax: (020) 8361 4670

Combined Insulations & Plastics Ltd, 6 Bedford Business Centre, Mile Road, Bedford, MK42 9TW Tel: 01234 211771 Fax: 01234 211771

Crane Plastic Fabrication, 127 Upper Thrift Street, Northampton, NN1 5HR Tel: (01604) 602224 Fax: (01604) 602224 E-mail: craneplastics@tiscali.co.uk

Crown Engineering Co., Unit 9 Hedgend Industrial Estate, Shuart Lane, St. Nicholas at Wade, Birchington, Kent, CT7 0NB Tel: (01843) 845300 Fax: (01843) 848352 E-mail: enquiries@crownengineering.co.uk

Crumpsall Plastics & Engineering Ltd, Pike Fold Works, Frenchbarn Lane, Blackley, Manchester, M9 6PB Tel: 0161-795 5000 Fax: 0161-721 4684

Gilbert Curry Industrial Plastics Co. Ltd, 16 Bayton Road, Exhall, Coventry, CV7 9EJ Tel: (024) 7664 4645 Fax: (024) 7658 8389 E-mail: k-sales@gcip.co.uk

Custom Components Ltd, Unit 3 Boxer Place, Leyland, PR26 7QL Tel: (01772) 455520 Fax: (01772) 436472 E-mail: sales@customcomponents.co.uk

D T R Newnham, Unit C5 Oakendene Industrial Estate, Bolney Road, Cowfold, Horsham, West Sussex, RH13 8AZ Tel: (01403) 864014 Fax: (01403) 864054

Dep Supplies Ltd, Units 2-3 Maressa Building, Icknield Way, Letchworth Garden City, Hertfordshire, SG6 1EX Tel: (01462) 484595 Fax: (01462) 484580 E-mail: sales@depsupplies.co.uk

▶ Ditech Metal Products, 17 Alrewas Road, Kings Bromley, Burton-on-Trent, Staffordshire, DE13 7HW Tel: (01543) 473633 Fax: (01543) 473634 E-mail: info@ditechltd.co.uk

DRM Laminates, Unit B11, Sywell Airport Business Park, Wellingborough Road, Sywell, Northampton, NN6 0BN Tel: (01604) 790377 Fax: (01604) 790266

Dyer Engineering Ltd, Unit 3-5 Morrison Industrial Estate North, Stanley, County Durham, DH9 7RU Tel: (01207) 234355 Fax: (01207) 282834 E-mail: sales@dyer-engineering.ltd.uk

E P L Medical Ltd, 4 Yardley Road, Knowsley Industrial Park, Liverpool, L33 7SS Tel: 0151-548 1494 Fax: 0151-549 2046 E-mail: info@eplmedical.com

East Kilbride Industrial Plastics, 25-27 Langlands Place, Kelvin South Business Park, East Kilbride, Glasgow, G75 0YF Tel: (01355) 236231 Fax: (01355) 235182 E-mail: ek.plastics@btinternet.com

Elgee Plastics Ltd, Wilson Road, Reading, RG30 2RS Tel: 0118-957 5430 Fax: 0118-958 8782

Engineering Plastic Services, 23a Eliot Street, Bootle, Merseyside, L20 4PD Tel: 0151-922 3243 Fax: 0151-922 6306

Enviroplas Services, Unit 2 Shepherd Cross St Industrial Estate, Bolton, BL1 3DE Tel: (01204) 844744 Fax: (01204) 841500 E-mail: sales@enviroplas.co.uk

Eurolux Plastics Ltd, Unit 7 Station Road, Tolleshunt D'Arcy, Maldon, Essex, CM9 8TQ Tel: (01621) 868787 Fax: (01621) 868857 E-mail: euroluxplastic@ukonline.co.uk

Exhall Timber Products, Bayton Road, Exhall, Coventry, CV7 9EL Tel: (024) 7636 6706

Fife Plastics, Fordell, Woodend, Cowdenbeath, Fife, KY4 8EY Tel: (01383) 510256 Fax: (01383) 510256

Fitcast (Plastic Fabrications) Ltd, Unit 12A, Shaw Road Industrial Estate, Speke, Liverpool, L24 9JT Tel: 0151-448 1299 Fax: 0151-448 0716 E-mail: davidfitcast@aol.com

James Fleming Plastics Ltd, 7 Linden Place, Glasgow, G13 1EF Tel: 0141-959 9765 Fax: 0141-954 6693

Fortress Roof Systems Ltd, Grovewood House, Russell Gardens, Wickford, Essex, SS11 8FU Tel: (01268) 571222 Fax: (01268) 570847 E-mail: sales@gts-plastics.com

G F G Plastics Fabrication Ltd, Bridge Works, 101 West Dock Street, Hull, HU3 4HH Tel: (01482) 610110 Fax: (01482) 229044 E-mail: greygfg2003@aol.com

G P Plastics Ltd, 156 Bordesley Middleway, Camp Hill, Birmingham, B11 1BN Tel: 0121-773 1777 Fax: 0121-772 6856 E-mail: admin@gpplastics.co.uk

Gurso Plant & Lining Ltd, Landywood Lane, Cheslyn Hay, Walsall, WS6 7AL Tel: (01922) 418005 Fax: (01922) 412641 E-mail: sales@gurso.demon.co.uk

H L N Supplies, 67 Upper Accommodation Road, Leeds, LS9 8JP Tel: 0113-240 2000 Fax: 0113-240 4000 E-mail: sales@hlnsupplies.co.uk

Heaven Dowsett & Co. Ltd, 197 Shady Lane, Birmingham, B44 9ES Tel: 0121-360 0345 Fax: 0121-360 7328 E-mail: richarddowsett@heavendowsett.com

Henderson Plastics, Lyng Hall Lane, Wood Norton, Dereham, Norfolk, NR20 5BJ Tel: (01362) 683364 Fax: (01362) 683529 E-mail: sales@hendersons.co.uk

Holloway Plastics Ltd, Willenhall La Industrial Estate, Willenhall Lane, Bloxwich, Walsall, WS3 2XN Tel: (01922) 492777 Fax: (01922) 495820 E-mail: sales@holloway-plastics.co.uk

Hurst Green Plastics Ltd, 1st Floor, Bowland House, The Sidings Business Park, Whalley, Clitheroe, Lancashire, BB7 9SE Tel: 01254 825588 Fax: 01254 824521 E-mail: info@hurstgreenplastics.com

▶ Hygrade Industrial Plastics Ltd, Hunters Lane, Rugby, Warwickshire, CV21 1EA Tel: (01788) 571316 Fax: (01788) 541184 E-mail: techsales@hygradeplastics.com

I C L Plastics Ltd, Grovepark Mills, Hopehill Road, Glasgow, G20 7NF Tel: 0141-332 1331 Fax: 0141-332 9186

I D S Plastics, Unit 42 The Acorn Centre, Barry Street, Oldham, OL1 3NE Tel: 0161-627 1054 Fax: 0161-624 4500 E-mail: info@showcasesonline.com

Imageineering Plastic Fabrication, 21 Cater Road, Bristol, BS13 7TW Tel: 0117-978 4114 Fax: 0117-978 4114 E-mail: plasticfabrication@hotmail.com

J D Sign & Display Ltd, Unit 34 Adams Industrial Estate, Dickerage Lane, New Malden, Surrey, KT3 3SF Tel: (020) 8949 4468 Fax: (020) 8949 7758E-mail: john@jdsignanddisplay.com

J M Fabrications, 11 Rochdale Walk, Birmingham, B10 0DF Tel: 0121-685 1310 Fax: 0121-685 1310 E-mail: jmfabs@aol.com

Jilks Plastics Ltd, 31 Trowers Way, Redhill, RH1 2LH Tel: (01737) 779799 Fax: (01737) 779800 E-mail: sales@jilksplasticsltd.co.uk

JTH Patternmakers Ltd, Players Foundry, Clydach, Swansea, SA6 5BQ Tel: (01792) 842363 Fax: (01792) 845275 E-mail: enquiries@jthpatternmakers.co.uk

Just Plastics Ltd, The Maltings, Wayford, Norwich, NR12 9LL Tel: (01692) 581000 Fax: (01692) 581848 E-mail: martin@justplastics.co.uk

K2 Associates Ltd, 6 Haselmere Industrial Estate, Pig Lane, Bishop's Stortford, Hertfordshire, CM23 3HG Tel: (01279) 508305 Fax: (01279) 755530 E-mail: ken.day@k2a.co.uk

Kerton Plastics Ltd, Unit 2 Phoenix Way, Gorseinon, Swansea, SA4 9WF Tel: (01792) 897779 Fax: (01792) 896668 E-mail: enquiries@kerton.co.uk

Kesteven Plastics Ltd, Unit 3, Moorland Way, Tritton Road, Lincoln, LN6 7JW Tel: (01522) 695977 Fax: (01522) 695977 E-mail: george@kestevenplasticsltd.co.uk

L J Constructions (Plastics) Ltd, Ashford Road, Ashford, Middlesex, TW15 1XB Tel: (01784) 421112 Fax: (01784) 427050 E-mail: plastics@ljc.co.uk

L'hotellier Montrichard (UK) Ltd, Balena Close, Poole, Dorset, BH17 7DU Tel: (01202) 693409 Fax: (01202) 658657 E-mail: sparkesc@lcn.ltd.uk

M B Plastics Ltd, Bridge Lane, Woolston, Warrington, WA1 4BA Tel: (01925) 822811 Fax: (01925) 818907 E-mail: sales@mbplastics.co.uk

Marcol Fabrications Ltd, Unit 10 Southfield Road Trading Estate, Nailsea, Bristol, BS48 1JJ Tel: (01275) 810022 Fax: (01275) 810033 E-mail: sales@marcolplastics.co.uk

G.H. Maughan Ltd, Bella Street Industrial Estate, Bolton, BL3 4DU Tel: (01204) 653516 Fax: (01204) 657362 E-mail: ghmaughan@lineone.net

Micro Matic Ltd, Millington House, Stancliffe St Industrial Estate, Blackburn, BB2 2QR Tel: (01254) 671231 Fax: (01254) 682229 E-mail: mmltv@micro-matic.co.uk

Mitchells Millbrook Ltd, Manor Industrial Estate, Millbrook Road, Southampton, SO15 0LD Tel: (023) 8077 1004 Fax: (023) 8070 4736 E-mail: sales@mitchellsworktops.co.uk

Morton Industrial Plastics Ltd, Cook Lane, Heckmondwike, West Yorkshire, WF16 9JG Tel: (01924) 405550 Fax: (01924) 405770 E-mail: info@mipuk.com

N E Plastics Ltd, 1 Ruxley Corner Industrial Estate, Edgington Way, Sidcup, Kent, DA14 5BL Tel: (020) 8308 9990 Fax: (020) 8308 9995 E-mail: sales@neplastics.co.uk

Neptune Plastic Fabrications, 22 Bull Green Road, Longwood, Huddersfield, HD3 4XW Tel: (01484) 656914

Novacrylics Engineering, Shrewley Farm, Hockley Road, Shrewley, Warwick, CV35 7AT Tel: (01926) 400404 Fax: (01926) 400840

Odour Control Systems Ltd, Manor Lane, Hawarden, Deeside, Clwyd, CH5 3PP Tel: (01244) 536700 Fax: (01244) 535184 E-mail: mail@odourcontrolsystems.ltd.co.uk

Oneida Plastic Fabrications Ltd, 8e Alder Road, North Shields, Tyne & Wear, NE29 8SD Tel: 0191-258 5750 Fax: 0191-259 6969 E-mail: sales@oneidaplastics.com

P & G Processors Ltd, 26 Trojan Centre, Finedon Road Industrial Estate, Wellingborough, Northamptonshire, NN8 4ST Tel: (01933) 270967 Fax: (01933) 270967 E-mail: pgprocess@aol.com

P.P.E. Ltd, Horsecroft Rd, The Pinnacles, Harlow, Essex, CM19 5BH Tel: (01279) 412345 Fax: (01279) 419533E-mail: sales@ppe.co.uk

Parkinson Plastics Ltd, Bankwood Lane, New Rossington, Doncaster, South Yorkshire, DN11 0PS Tel: (01302) 864959 Fax: (01302) 864954

Pipeline Centre, Ingram Road, Leeds, LS11 9BB Tel: 0113-242 8280 Fax: 0113-242 8283 E-mail: sales@pipeline.com

Plasbrun Plastics Engineering Ltd, Unit C, Brookfield Drive, Cannock, Staffordshire, WS11 0JR Tel: (01543) 462802 Fax: (01543) 462806 E-mail: plasbrunplastics@yahoo.co.uk

Plastic Facilities, Fen End, Stotfold, Hitchin, Hertfordshire, SG5 4BA Tel: (01462) 832832 Fax: (01462) 832830 E-mail: sales@plasticfacilities.co.uk

Plastic Promotions, Unit 1 Carn Industrial Area, Portadown, Craigavon, County Armagh, BT63 5YY Tel: (028) 3835 6600 Fax: (028) 3835 6601 E-mail: gilbert@plasticpromotion.co.uk

Plastic Sheet Services, Unit 4, 270 Lakey La, Birmingham, B28 8RA Tel: 0121-777 0322 Fax: 0121-777 8987E-mail: hewston@aol.com

▶ Plastic Welded Containers Ltd, The Cottage, Alcester Road, Spernal Ash, Studley, Warwickshire, B80 7PD Tel: (01527) 598848 Fax: (01527) 598848

Plasticraft Ltd, Godiva Place, Coventry, CV1 5PN Tel: (024) 7625 3099 Fax: (024) 7655 1402 E-mail: sales@plasticraft.co.uk

Polytec Plastic Products, Ormrod Street, Bury, Lancashire, BL9 7HF Tel: 0161-705 1901 Fax: 0161-705 1935 E-mail: dmworsley@polytecpf.fsnet.co.uk

Premier Plastics Ltd, Unit 43 St. Helens Court, St. Helens Way, Thetford, Norfolk, IP24 1HG Tel: (01842) 750461 Fax: (01842) 754743 E-mail: enquiries@premierplastics.org.uk

Q D Plastics Glasgow Ltd, Elm Road, Broadmeadow Industrial Estate, Dumbarton, G82 2RH Tel: (01389) 762377 Fax: (01389) 734438 E-mail: sales@qdplastics.co.uk

Quadplas Ltd, Mulberry Trading Estate, Foundry Lane, Horsham, West Sussex, RH13 5PX Tel: (01403) 241533 Fax: (01403) 268234 E-mail: steve.botting@quadplas.co.uk

R J Plastics, 83-84 Buckingham Street, Birmingham, B19 3HU Tel: 0121-233 1077 Fax: 0121-236 6355

Rayburn Plastics Ltd, Whitehouse Street, Walsall, WS2 8HR Tel: (01922) 625572 Fax: (01922) 723333 E-mail: sales@rayburn.co.uk

Raytec Presswork Plastics, Lobro Tools, Premier Business Park, Walsall, WS2 9XP Tel: (01922) 640440 Fax: (01922) 611117 E-mail: sales@raytec-diecastingandplastics.com

▶ Retail Engineering Design Ltd, Unit 2, Pioneer Park, Clough Road, Hull, HU6 7HW Tel: (01482) 333803 Fax: (01482) 333809 E-mail: info@redltd.karoo.co.uk

Ridgeway Plastics (Iver) Ltd, Unit 7B Waldeck House, Waldeck Road, Maidenhead, Berkshire, SL6 8BR Tel: (01628) 636621 Fax: (01628) 636621

Rossendale Plastics, Station Road, Haslingden, Rossendale, Lancashire, BB4 5HX Tel: (01706) 214652 Fax: (01706) 830829 E-mail: info@rossendaleplastics.co.uk

Rotherham Industrial Plastic Co. Ltd, Clifton Terrace, Rotherham, South Yorkshire, S65 2AG Tel: (01709) 372008 Fax: (01709) 820243 E-mail: steve@rip-co.co.uk

Ryan Plastics, 21A Prince St, Northampton, NN6 0LL Tel: (01604) 811395 Fax: (01604) 812872 E-mail: john@ryanplastics.ssnet.co.uk

S M P Plastics Fabrications Ltd, 51 Cyprus Street, Oldbury, West Midlands, B69 4XD Tel: 0121-552 0212 Fax: 0121-544 4863 E-mail: info@smp-plastics.co.uk

Scie-Plas Co. Ltd, Unit 3, Gainsborough Trading Estate, Old Road, Southam, Warwickshire, CV47 1HP Tel: (01926) 814093 Fax: (01926) 813975 E-mail: info@scie-plas.co.uk

Screencraft Publicity Hull, Reservoir Road, Hull, HU6 7QD Tel: (01482) 499999 Fax: (01482) 499994 E-mail: info@screencraft-display.co.uk

Servebrow Ltd, Bay 11 Central Works, Peartree Lane, Dudley, West Midlands, DY2 0XG Tel: (01384) 351453 Fax: (01384) 74948

▶ Shere Lighting, 5 Burrows Lea Farm, Hook Lane, Shere, Guildford, Surrey, GU5 9QQ Tel: (01483) 205333 Fax: (01483) 205334 E-mail: sherelightingltd@aol.com

Spafield Displays Ltd, 404 Bretton Park Way, Dewsbury, West Yorkshire, WF12 9BS Tel: (01924) 452386 Fax: (01924) 465713 E-mail: hazel@sparfield.com

Spectra Plastics Ltd, Southam Road, Long Itchington, Southam, Warwickshire, CV47 9QL Tel: (01926) 812195 Fax: (01926) 817401 E-mail: sales@spectra-plastics.co.uk

Strong's Plastic Products Ltd, 18 Silica Road, Amington Industrial Estate, Tamworth, Staffordshire, B77 4DT Tel: (01827) 302490 Fax: (01827) 54999 E-mail: myles@strongs.co.uk

Superframe Ltd, The Old Electricity Works, Campfield Road, St. Albans, Hertfordshire, AL1 5HJ Tel: (01727) 865555 Fax: (01727) 865566 E-mail: sales@sf2.co.uk

T C Plastic Fabrications Ltd, Hawkmill Industrial Estate, Little Green Lane, Small Heath, Birmingham, B9 5BE Tel: 0121-773 2044 Fax: 0121-766 6623 E-mail: tom@tcplastics.wanadoo.co.uk

Talbot Designs Ltd, 225 Long Lane, Finchley, London, N3 2RL Tel: 0845 8510136 Fax: (020) 8349 0294 E-mail: sales@talbotdesigns.co.uk

Technical Models Ltd, Unit 10 Crosland Industrial Estate, Stockport Road West, Bredbury, Stockport, Cheshire, SK6 2BR Tel: 0161-494 9022 Fax: 0161-430 8406 E-mail: enquiries@technical-models.co.uk

Theoplastic Ltd, 3 & 45 Barking Industrial Park, Alfreds Way, Barking, Essex, IG11 0TJ Tel: (020) 8591 5534 Fax: (020) 8591 9022 E-mail: theoplastic@aol.com

Thor UK Plastics Ltd, Unit B & C Ranalah Estate, New Road, Newhaven, East Sussex, BN9 0EH Tel: (01273) 611444 Fax: (01273) 611113 E-mail: sales@thoruk.co.uk

Unistyle Plastics, Unit 6 Ranton Park, Martindale, Cannock, Staffordshire, WS11 7XL Tel: (01543) 500554 Fax: (01543) 578444 E-mail: unistyleplastics@btconnect.com

York Plastics Engineering Ltd, 70-72 James Street, York, YO10 3WW Tel: (01904) 412852 Fax: (01904) 430202 E-mail: yorkplastics@btinternet.com

PLASTIC FANS

Finna Fans, Unit 2 Hill Street, Kidderminster, Worcestershire, DY11 6TD Tel: (01562) 60035 Fax: (01562) 753188

PLASTIC FAST FOOD CONTAINERS

Autobar Packaging & Veriplast International, Dragonville Industrial Estate, Durham, DH1 2RL Tel: 0191-386 5171 Fax: 0191-386 4429

Christian Salvesen plc, Salvesen Buildings, Ladysmith Road, Grimsby, South Humberside, DN32 9SL Tel: (01472) 327200 Fax: (01472) 327210

Gpi UK Ltd, Unit 6 Merlin Way, North Weald, Epping, Essex, CM16 6HR Tel: (01992) 524439 Fax: (01992) 524522

Sealed Air Ltd, Clifton House, 1 Marston Road, St. Neots, Cambridgeshire, PE19 2HN Tel: (01480) 224000 Fax: (01480) 224063

PLASTIC FILM

Clarifoil, PO Box 5, Derby, DE21 7BP Tel: (01332) 661422 Fax: (01332) 660178 E-mail: info@clarifoil.com

Cornelius Group plc, Woodside, Dunmow Road, Birchanger, Bishop's Stortford, Hertfordshire, CM23 5RG Tel: (01279) 714300 Fax: (01279) 714320 E-mail: sales.dept@cornelius.co.uk

Flexcon Glenrothes Ltd, Whitworth Road, Glenrothes, Fife, KY6 2TF Tel: (01592) 663200 Fax: (01592) 663201 E-mail: enquiries@flexcon-europe.nl

Jones Stroud Insulations, Queen Street, Longridge, Preston, PR3 3BS Tel: (01772) 783011 Fax: (01772) 784200 E-mail: info@krempel-group.com

Stockline Plastics Ltd, Grovepark Mills, Hopehill Road, Glasgow, G20 7NF Tel: 0141-332 9077 Fax: 0141-332 9079 E-mail: sales@stockline-plastics.co.uk

Visqueen Building Products South Wales Ltd, Maerdy Industrial Estate, Rhymney, Tredegar, Gwent, NP22 5PY Tel: (01685) 840672 Fax: (01685) 842580 E-mail: admin@visqueenbuilding.co.uk

PLASTIC FILM CONVERTERS

A A Packaging Ltd, The Light Industrial Estate, Hesketh Bank, Preston, PR4 6SP Tel: (01772) 617481 Fax: (01772) 614856 E-mail: info@aapackaging.co.uk

Aarison Packaging, Townfoot Industrial Estate, Brampton, Cumbria, CA8 1SW Tel: (0845) 1301864 Fax: (0845) 1301864 E-mail: enq@aarison.co.uk

Madico Graphic Films Ltd, 9 Cordwallace Park, Clivemont Road, Maidenhead, Berkshire, SL6 7BU Tel: (01628) 777766 Fax: (01628) 776666 E-mail: info@madico.co.uk

▶ Polyester Converters Ltd, 49-53 Glengall Road, Peckham, London, SE15 6NF Tel: (020) 7740 9740 Fax: (020) 7277 5654 E-mail: sales@psggroup.co.uk

QC Packaging Films Ltd, Technology House, Heage Road Industrial Estate, Ripley, Derbyshire, DE5 3GH Tel: (01773) 740300 Fax: (01773) 740301 E-mail: info@qcpackagingfilms.com

PLASTIC FILM PACKAGING

▶ Alternative Packaging Solutions Ltd, The Studio Prospect Place, Mill Lane, Alton, Hampshire, GU34 2SX Tel: (01420) 544800 Fax: (01420) 544850

PLASTIC FILM PACKAGING – *continued*

Tmec UK Ltd, 6 Sidenhill Close, Shirley, Solihull, West Midlands, B90 2QD Tel: 0121-733 8726 Fax: 0121-733 8726 E-mail: enquiries@tmec.co.uk

PLASTIC FILM PRODUCTION MACHINERY/EQUIPMENT

Kween B Ltd, 29 Dalkeith Road, Sutton Coldfield, West Midlands, B73 6PW Tel: 0121-355 2662 E-mail: info@kweenb.co.uk

PLASTIC FINISHED PRODUCTS

Amco Products, 5 Orchard Road, Royston, Hertfordshire, SG8 5HD Tel: (01763) 242040 Fax: (01763) 245505 E-mail: sales@Amco-products.co.uk

Pure Fabrications Plastics, 16 Bridge Street, Pilsley, Chesterfield, Derbyshire, S45 8HE Tel: (01773) 874206 Fax: (01773) 591699

PLASTIC FINISHING SERVICES

Interplas Coatings Ltd, Lygon Buildings, Peartree Lane, Dudley, West Midlands, DY2 0QU Tel: (01384) 236327 Fax: (01384) 255428 E-mail: sales@interplascoatings.com

Lap Tab Ltd, 205 Tyburn Road, Birmingham, B24 8NB Tel: 0121-328 1697 Fax: 0121-328 9787 E-mail: sales@lap-tab.co.uk

Leabank Coatings Ltd, Wycombe Road, Stokenchurch, High Wycombe, Buckinghamshire, HP14 3RJ Tel: (01494) 483737 Fax: (01494) 484239 E-mail: info@leabank.net

Lemin & Co. Ltd, Unit 4 Albone Way, Biggleswade, Bedfordshire, SG7 5AN Tel: (01767) 600120 Fax: (01767) 600121 E-mail: enquiries@lemin.co.uk

Metal & Plastics Products Fabrication Ltd, 2 Astley Park Estate Chaddock Lane, Astley, Tyldesley, Manchester, M29 7JY Tel: (01942) 894657 Fax: (01942) 897483 E-mail: sales@metalandplastics.co.uk

▶ Oztec, 1 Compass Terrace, Southwell Business Park, Portland, Dorset, DT5 2NP Tel: (01305) 823322 Fax: (01305) 823355 E-mail: enquiries@oztec.co.uk

Prestige Coatings Ltd, 10 Enderby Road Industrial Estate, Whetstone, Leicester, LE8 6HZ Tel: 0116-275 0007 Fax: 0116-275 1692 E-mail: sales@prestigecoatings.com

S S Central Coating Ltd, Unit 5 Oakhill Trading Estate, Euston Street, Freemens Common, Leicester, LE2 7ST Tel: 0116-255 4748 Fax: 0116-255 4769 E-mail: satu@sscoatings.com

Stadium Plastics Midlands Ltd, Unit 4-6 Southways Industrial Estate, Coventry Road, Hinckley, Leicestershire, LE10 0NJ Tel: (01455) 234202 Fax: (01455) 234191 E-mail: chris@spfd.fsbusiness.co.uk

PLASTIC FIRST AID BAGS

▶ Firstaid4sport.co.uk, 6A Exchange Close, North Hykeham, Lincoln, LN6 3TR Tel: (01522) 883344 Fax: (01522) 875253 E-mail: gemma.newlove@firstaid4sport.co.uk

PLASTIC FIRST AID BOXES

Carmo Ltd, 11-19 Bancrofts Road, Eastern Industrial Area, South Woodham Ferrers, Chelmsford, CM3 5UG Tel: (01245) 322130 Fax: (01245) 328695 E-mail: brian@carmo.co.uk

▶ Firstaid4sport.co.uk, 6A Exchange Close, North Hykeham, Lincoln, LN6 3TR Tel: (01522) 883344 Fax: (01522) 875253 E-mail: gemma.newlove@firstaid4sport.co.uk

PLASTIC FLOOR COVERINGS

A. J. B. Floor Coverings Ltd, Unit 1 Bulay Commercial Park, St Thomas Road Longroyd Bridge, Huddersfield, HD1 3LG Tel: (01484) 537255 Fax: (01484) 549328 E-mail: info@ajbflooring.co.uk

The Amtico Co. Ltd, Kingfield Road, Coventry, CV6 5AA Tel: (024) 7686 1400 Fax: (024) 7686 1552 E-mail: info@amtico.com

Roger Fell Ltd, Northside Industrial Park, Whitley Bridge, Goole, North Humberside, DN14 0GH Tel: (01977) 662211 Fax: (01977) 662334 E-mail: fellscarpets@aol.com

Leigh Spinners Ltd, Park Lane, Leigh, Lancashire, WN7 2LB Tel: (01942) 676995 Fax: (01942) 261694 E-mail: carpets@leigh-spinners.demon.co.uk

Tarkett Ltd, Dickley Lane, Lenham, Maidstone, Kent, ME17 2QX Tel: (01622) 854000 Fax: (01622) 854500 E-mail: uksales@tarkett.com

PLASTIC FLUSHING CISTERNS

Thomas Dudley Group Ltd, PO Box 28, Dudley, West Midlands, DY1 4SN Tel: 0121-557 5411 Fax: 0121-557 5345 E-mail: info@thomasdudley.co.uk

PLASTIC FOAM

Acoustafoam Ltd, Unit D, Halesfield 10, Telford, Shropshire, TF7 4QP Tel: (01952) 581340 Fax: (01952) 581455 E-mail: mike@acoustafoam.com

Foam Place, Market Place South, Leicester, LE1 5HB Tel: 0116-251 9538 Fax: 0116-251 1573

Pritex Ltd, Station Mills, Wellington, Somerset, TA21 8NN Tel: (01823) 664271 Fax: (01823) 660023 E-mail: enquiries@pritex.co.uk

Sekisui Alveo, Queens Chambers, Eleanors Cross, Dunstable, Bedfordshire, LU6 1SU Tel: (01582) 600456 Fax: (01582) 600567

Urofoam Ltd, Duddon Road, Askam-in-Furness, Cumbria, LA16 7AN Tel: (01229) 467901 Fax: (01229) 467272

PLASTIC FOAM BUOYANCY MATERIALS

Combass Ltd, Rotherham Close, Norwood Industrial Estate, Sheffield, S21 2JU Tel: 0114-248 0616 Fax: 0114-248 2684 E-mail: irmackie@aol.com

Kayfoam Ltd, Unit 3A Pegasis Business Park, Cameron Street, Hillington, Glasgow, G52 4TY Tel: 0141-810 4333 Fax: 0141-810 1424

PLASTIC FOAM COATING SERVICES

Acoustafoam Ltd, Unit D, Halesfield 10, Telford, Shropshire, TF7 4QP Tel: (01952) 581340 Fax: (01952) 581455 E-mail: mike@acoustafoam.com

Coralfoam Ltd, 12 Petworth Industrial Estate, Petworth, West Sussex, GU28 9NR Tel: (01798) 342441 Fax: (0870) 9223485 E-mail: dave@coralfoam.com

PLASTIC FOAM PRODUCTS

Acoustafoam Ltd, Unit D, Halesfield 10, Telford, Shropshire, TF7 4QP Tel: (01952) 581340 Fax: (01952) 581455 E-mail: mike@acoustafoam.com

Advance Foam Converters Ltd, Maitland Road, London, E15 4EL Tel: (020) 8534 9643 Fax: (020) 8519 0211

Advanced Protective Packaging Ltd, Unit 58 Pioneer Mill, Milltown Street, Radcliffe, Manchester, M26 1WN Tel: 0161-724 8080 Fax: 0161-725 9074 E-mail: brian@advanced-pp.co.uk

Alsamex Products Ltd, 1 Protea Way, Pixmore Avenue, Letchworth Garden City, Hertfordshire, SG6 1JT Tel: (01462) 672951 Fax: (01462) 480660 E-mail: sales@alsamex.co.uk

B I Composites Ltd, Green Lane, Cannock, Staffordshire, WS11 0JW Tel: (01543) 466021 Fax: (01543) 574157 E-mail: firstname.lastname@bi-composites.co.uk

Caligen Foam Ltd, Broad Oak, Accrington, Lancashire, BB5 2BS Tel: (01254) 355000 Fax: (01254) 355111 E-mail: info@caligen.co.uk

Contak components Ltd, Unit A The Anderson Centre, Spitfire Close, Ermine Business Park, Huntingdon, Cambridgeshire, PE29 6XY Tel: (01480) 411022 Fax: (01480) 411082 E-mail: impakgroup@compuserve.com

Cotswold Foam Products, 33 Morelands Trading Estate, Bristol Road, Gloucester, GL1 5RZ Tel: (01452) 521364 Fax: (01452) 310461 E-mail: cotswoldfoam@aol.com

Dee Bee Foams Ltd, 19-20 Pulloxhill Business Park, Greenfield Road, Pulloxhill, Bedford, MK45 5EU Tel: (01525) 718111 Fax: (01525) 718112 E-mail: sales@deebeefoams.co.uk

Foam & Fabric Shop, 23 Broad Street, Seaford, East Sussex, BN25 1LS Tel: (01323) 893716

George Danby & Son Ltd, Bank Terrace, Barwell, Leicester, LE9 8GG Tel: (01455) 845522 Fax: (01455) 846633 E-mail: info@phonefirst.co.uk

Sydney Heath & Son Ltd, P O Box 1 Bycars Road, Stoke-on-Trent, ST6 4SH Tel: (01782) 839121 Fax: (01782) 839124 E-mail: sales@sydney-heath.co.uk

Homeblown, Gilbert Coombe, Redruth, Cornwall, TR16 4HG Tel: (01209) 314446 Fax: (01209) 314446 E-mail: info@homeblown.co.uk

Imagineers Ltd, Abercromby Avenue, High Wycombe, Buckinghamshire, HP12 3BW Tel: (01494) 473861 Fax: (01494) 473863 E-mail: enquiries@imagineersltd.co.uk

Kay Metzeler Ltd, Wellington Road, Bollington, Macclesfield, Cheshire, SK10 5JJ Tel: (01625) 573366 Fax: (01625) 574075 E-mail: info@kay-metzeler.co.uk

P U Components Ltd, Shay Lane, Halifax, West Yorkshire, HX2 9AX Tel: (01422) 380786 Fax: (01422) 380702 E-mail: sales@pucomponents.co.uk

Polyfoam Foam Products, 380c Ringwood Road, Poole, Dorset, BH12 3LT Tel: (01202) 736353 Fax: (01202) 736023 E-mail: peterthompson@polyfoam.sagehost.co.uk

Polyformes Ltd, Cherrycourt Way, Leighton Buzzard, Bedfordshire, LU7 4UH Tel: (01525) 852444 Fax: (01525) 850484 E-mail: sales@polyformes.co.uk

Precision Cut Rubber Co. Ltd, Leafield Industrial Estate, Leafield Way, Corsham, Wiltshire, SN13 9RU Tel: (01225) 816300 Fax: (01225) 816327 E-mail: sales@pcrltd.co.uk

Quality Foam Products, 70-72 Sussex St, Norwich, NR3 3DE Tel: (01603) 622730 Fax: (01603) 622730

Rather Brothers, 26 Knowsley St, Manchester, M8 8HQ Tel: 0161-832 7361 Fax: 0161 8327361

Roe, Salop Street, Bolton, BL2 1DZ Tel: (01204) 523188 Fax: (01204) 523178 E-mail: p_roe@btconnect.com

S J Gaskets Ltd, Tything Park, Tything Road East, Kinwarton, Alcester, Warwickshire, B49 6ES Tel: (01789) 763721 Fax: (01789) 764070 E-mail: sjgaskets@thesjgroup.com

Simply Foam Products Ltd, Harper Street, Willenhall, West Midlands, WV13 1SW Tel: (01902) 632060 Fax: (01902) 683383

Styropack UK Ltd, 1 Stephenson Street, Hillington Industrial Estate, Glasgow, G52 4JD Tel: 0141-882 9166 Fax: 0141-882 7022 E-mail: glasgow@styropack.co.uk

PLASTIC FOOD PACKAGING

A A Packaging Ltd, The Light Industrial Estate, Hesketh Bank, Preston, PR4 6SP Tel: (01772) 617481 Fax: (01772) 614856 E-mail: info@aapackaging.co.uk

Allison Plastics & Paper Ltd, New Pudsey Square, Stanningley, Pudsey, West Yorkshire, LS28 6PX Tel: 0113-256 6435 Fax: 0113-257 5337

Amcor Flexibles, 1 Gass Close, Highbridge, Somerset, TA9 4JT Tel: (01278) 793232 Fax: (01278) 794996 E-mail: sales@amcor.com

Britton Decoflex Ltd, Skerne Road, Oakesway Industrial Estate, Hartlepool, Cleveland, TS24 0RH Tel: (01429) 272102 Fax: (01429) 860388 E-mail: smrsales@britton-group.com

Certiforms Ltd, Lower Heys Mill, Black Lane, Macclesfield, Cheshire, SK10 2AY Tel: (01625) 433390 Fax: (01625) 511333 E-mail: sales@certiforms.co.uk

Convenience Food Systems, Interchange Park, Newport Pagnell, Buckinghamshire, MK16 9PS Tel: (01908) 513500 Fax: (01908) 513555

Gpi UK Ltd, Unit 6 Merlin Way, North Weald, Epping, Essex, CM16 6HR Tel: (01992) 524439 Fax: (01992) 524522

Samuel Grant (North East) Ltd, Unit 13-16, Tanfield Lea South Industrial Estate, Tanfield Lea, Stanley, County Durham, DH9 9QX Tel: (01207) 283510 Fax: (01207) 290063 E-mail: nesales@samuelgrant.com

Ice Cream Container Co. Ltd, 6 Beresford Avenue, Wembley, Middlesex, HA0 1SA Tel: (020) 8903 9021 Fax: (020) 8900 2472 E-mail: sales@icecream-cont.co.uk

Linpac Plastics, Wakefield Road, Featherstone, Pontefract, West Yorkshire, WF7 5DE Tel: (01977) 692111 Fax: (01977) 692450

▶ Plasware, Plasware House, Westmoreland Road, Kingsbury, London, NW9 9RN Tel: (020) 8621 2611 E-mail: info@plaswareuk.com

RPC Containers Ltd, 4 Sallow Road, Weldon North Industrial Estate, Corby, Northamptonshire, NN17 5JX Tel: (01536) 263488 Fax: (01536) 272910 E-mail: sales@rpc-corby.co.uk

▶ R P C Tedeco-Gizeh UK Ltd, Kenfig Industrial Estate, Margam, Port Talbot, West Glamorgan, SA13 2PG Tel: (01656) 746655 Fax: (01656) 743074 E-mail: sales@rpc-tedeco-gizeh.com

Rhinopac Ltd, Tri-Star House, Unit 4, The Arena, Mollison Avenue, Enfield, Middlesex, EN3 7NL Tel: (020) 8443 9100 Fax: (020) 8443 9118 E-mail: sales@rhinopac.com

RPC Containers Ltd, St. Vincents Trading Estate, Feeder Road, Bristol, BS2 0UY Tel: 0117-977 9511 Fax: 0117-972 3602

Sabre Triad Ltd, 42 Roman Way Industrial Estate, Ribbleton, Preston, PR2 5BD Tel: (01772) 655328 Fax: (01772) 655326 E-mail: cmc@sabretriad.co.uk

Sealed Air Ltd, Clifton House, 1 Marston Road, St. Neots, Cambridgeshire, PE19 2HN Tel: (01480) 224000 Fax: (01480) 224063

Sharp Interpack, Colley Lane, Bridgwater, Somerset, TA6 5YS Tel: (01278) 435000 Fax: (01278) 423019 E-mail: info@sharpinterpack.co.uk

Supreme Plastics Group plc, Supreme House, 300 Regents Park Road, London, N3 2JX Tel: (020) 8346 3291 Fax: (020) 8346 1624 E-mail: info@supremeplastics.com

Synpac Ltd, Priory Tec Park Saxon Way, Priory Park, Hessle, North Humberside, HU13 9PB Tel: (01482) 640606 Fax: (01482) 642768 E-mail: sales@synpac.ltd.uk

T Choithram & Sons (London) Ltd, Old Marconi Factory, Lancelot Road, Wembley, Middlesex, HA0 2BG Tel: (020) 8903 8311 Fax: (020) 8900 1426

Weald Ltd, High Street, Buxted, Uckfield, East Sussex, TN22 4LA Tel: (01825) 732000 Fax: (01825) 732722 E-mail: tony@wealdpackaging.freeserve.uk

Wilson Packaging Products, 38 Hatherley Road, Manchester, M20 4RU Tel: 0161-434 0454 Fax: 0161-448 1070 E-mail: wilsonpackaging@btconnect.com

PLASTIC FORME CUTTING/ CREASING SERVICES

Diamond Cutting Formes, 2 Monks Brook Industrial Park, School Close, Chandler's Ford, Eastleigh, Hampshire, SO53 4RA Tel: (023) 8026 7326 Fax: (023) 8027 5187 E-mail: dcformes@izrmail.com

Forme Display 1990 Ltd, 8 Millbrook Road, Birkenhead, Merseyside, CH41 1FL Tel: 0151-691 1592 Fax: 0151-639 0403

PLASTIC FURNITURE COMPONENTS

Micrex Profiles Ltd, Stamford Mill, Bayley Street, Stalybridge, Cheshire, SK15 1QQ Tel: 0161-330 6518 Fax: 0161-330 5576 E-mail: enquiry@micrex-profiles.co.uk

Rustin Allen Ltd, Darlaston Road, Wednesbury, West Midlands, WS10 7TN Tel: 0121-526 4048 Fax: 0121-526 4658 E-mail: sales@palextrusions.co.uk

PLASTIC FURNITURE FITTINGS

Banbury Plastic Fittings Ltd, Unit 13, Overfield, Thorpe Way Industrial Estate, Banbury, Oxfordshire, OX16 4XR Tel: (01295) 264800 Fax: (01295) 264901 E-mail: sales@bpfittings.co.uk

Guy Raymond Engineering Company Ltd, Rollesby Road, King's Lynn, Norfolk, PE30 4LX Tel: (01553) 761401 Fax: (01553) 767459 E-mail: info@guy-raymond.co.uk

Protec The Cap Company Ltd, Princes Park Princesway, Team Valley Trading Estate, Gateshead, Tyne & Wear, NE11 0NF Tel: 0191-442 4242 Fax: 0191-442 4222 E-mail: sales@protecplastics.com

Rustin Allen Ltd, Darlaston Road, Wednesbury, West Midlands, WS10 7TN Tel: 0121-526 4048 Fax: 0121-526 4658 E-mail: sales@palextrusions.co.uk

PLASTIC GARDEN FENCING

▶ Fifield Fencing Services, 898 Fifield, Enford, Upavon, Pewsey, Wiltshire, SN9 6DQ Tel: (01980) 670680 E-mail: mike@mgermany.freeserve.co.uk

Rosedale Aquatics, 81 Home Farm Crescent, Whitnash, Leamington Spa, Warwickshire, CV31 2QY Tel: (01926) 332493 Fax: (01926) 332493 E-mail: info@rosedaleaquatics.co.uk

▶ Sunny Aspects Ltd, 36 Udney Park Road, Teddington, Middlesex, TW11 9BG Tel: (020) 8977 4149 E-mail: info@sunnyaspects.co.uk

PLASTIC GARDEN FURNITURE

Cathedral Garden Furniture, Unit 9 Hetton Lane Industrial Estate, Colliery Lane, Hetton-Le-Holey, Houghton Le Spring, Tyne & Wear, DH5 0BD Tel: 0191-517 1700 Fax: 0191-517 1700 E-mail: sales@cathedralgardenfurniture.co.uk

Cosmo Ltd, PO Box 543, Peterborough, PE1 4FN Tel: (08707) 890110 Fax: (08707) 890110 E-mail: sales@cosmo.uk

Cushendall Ornamental Concrete, 14 Tromra Road, Cushendall, Ballymena, County Antrim, BT44 0SS Tel: (028) 2177 2066 Fax: (028) 2177 2191

▶ Derwentside Cottage, Unit 3 Bradley Workshops, Consett, County Durham, DH8 6HG Tel: (01207) 509895 Fax: (01207) 509895

Garden Centre, 53 High Street, Brecon, Powys, LD3 7AP Tel: (01874) 625913

Keter U.K Ltd, 12-14 Kettles Wood Drive, Birmingham, B32 3DB Tel: 0121-422 6633 Fax: 0121-422 0808 E-mail: sales@outstanding-keter.com

Lytham Garden Funiture, 63 Rossall Rd, Lytham St. Annes, Lancs, FY8 4BY Tel: (01253) 795544 Fax: (01253) 795544

▶ Mrgardenfurniture.Com, 7 Alder Mill, Sheepy Road, Atherstone, Warwickshire, CV9 3AH Tel: (01827) 722320 Fax: (01675) 481572 E-mail: sales@mygardenfurniture.com

Nova Garden Furniture Ltd, Graveney Road, Faversham, Kent, ME13 8UN Tel: (01795) 535511 Fax: (01795) 539215 E-mail: sales@novagardenfurniture.co.uk

Southsea Deck Chairs Ltd, The Old Council Depot, Burrfields Road, Portsmouth, PO3 5LZ Tel: (023) 9265 2865 Fax: (023) 9265 5830 E-mail: info@deckchairs.co.uk

Wentwood Outdoor Timber Products Ltd, Abergavenny Road, Raglan, Usk, Gwent, NP15 2BH Tel: (01291) 691070

Whitefurze Ltd, Burnsall Road Industrial Estate, Burnsall Road, Coventry, CV5 6BT Tel: (024) 7671 7755 Fax: (024) 7671 7474

▶ indicates data change since last edition

PLASTIC GARMENT COVERS

Central Polythene Packaging, Unit 60, Abbey Park Street, Leicester, LE4 5AF Tel: 0116-253 0275 Fax: 0116-253 1832

Concept Covers Ltd, 1 Monarch Works, Balds Lane, Stourbridge, West Midlands, DY9 8TE Tel: (01384) 897101 Fax: (01384) 891171 E-mail: concept-covers@supanet.com

▶ First Source Ltd, Elmdon Grange, Elmdon Park, Solihull, West Midlands, B92 9EL Tel: 0121-722 3900 Fax: 0121-743 4794 E-mail: firstsource@orange.net

Leicester Polythene Packaging Ltd, 93a Gwendolen Road, Leicester, LE5 5FL Tel: 0116-273 4235 Fax: 0116-273 4410 E-mail: sales@lppl.co.uk

PLASTIC GEARS

Unigears Ashford Ltd, Unit 8 Henwood Business Centre, Henwood Industrial Estate, Ashford, Kent, TN24 8DH Tel: (01233) 642798 Fax: (01233) 650725 E-mail: sales@unigears.co.uk

PLASTIC GLASS FIBRE REINFORCED (GFR) CHEMICAL PLANT

A. E. & N. Ashton & Co. Ltd, Sedgeway Farm, Common Road, Wichford, Ely, Cambridgeshire, CB6 2HY Tel: (01353) 662473 Fax: (01353) 667726

G & A Plastics Ltd, Springhill Works, Exchange St, Accrington, Lancashire, BB5 0LE Tel: (01254) 871919 Fax: (01254) 390967 E-mail: david@gaplastics.co.uk

M B Plastics Ltd, Bridge Lane, Woolston, Warrington, WA1 4BA Tel: (01925) 822811 Fax: (01925) 818907 E-mail: sales@mbplastics.co.uk

Polytec Plastic Products, Ormrod Street, Bury, Lancashire, BL9 7HF Tel: 0161-705 1901 Fax: 0161-705 1935 E-mail: dmworsley@polytecpf.fsnet.co.uk

PLASTIC GLAZING MATERIALS OR PRODUCTS

▶ Abacus Agents Ltd, Faraday Street, Dryburgh Industrial Estate, Dundee, DD2 3UG Tel: (01382) 884000 Fax: (01382) 818881 E-mail: enquiries@abacusagents.co.uk

Bridgewater Glass, 44-52 Vicarage Road, Watford, WD18 0EN Tel: (01923) 237533 Fax: (01923) 817118 E-mail: bridgewaterglass@aol.com

Cox Plastics, Kingfisher Way, Sowton Industrial Estate, Exeter, EX2 7LE Tel: (01392) 439701 Fax: (01392) 444017 E-mail: cox.southwest@coxplastics.co.uk

Robert Horne Industrial Plant Ltd, Quantam House, Gee Business Centre, Holborn Hill, Birmingham, B7 5JR Tel: 0121-327 5050 Fax: 0121-327 2818

Robert Horne Group Plc, Huntsman House, Mansion Close, Moulton Park, Northampton, NN3 6LA Tel: (01604) 495333 Fax: (01604) 673495 E-mail: terry.cattle@roberthorne.co.uk

Sign & Display, 2 Tenax Road, Trafford Park, Manchester, M17 1JT Tel: 0161-872 8585 Fax: 0161-876 4056

PLASTIC GRANULATING MACHINES

Cumberland Europe Ltd, Daniels Industrial Estate, 104 Bath Road, Stroud, Gloucestershire, GL5 3TJ Tel: (01453) 768980 Fax: (01453) 768990 E-mail: europeansales@cumberland-plastics.com

PLASTIC GRANULATING SERVICES/REPROCESSING SERVICES

Bromborough Plastics Ltd, Unit 1b Spencer Industrial Estate, Liverpool Road, Buckley, Clwyd, CH7 3LY Tel: (01244) 545202 Fax: (01244) 545202

Royden Granulation, Fishwicks Industrial Estate, Baxters Lane, St. Helens, Merseyside, WA9 3NA Tel: (01744) 851941 Fax: (01744) 820324 E-mail: jd@roydon.com

PLASTIC GRANULE DRYING EQUIPMENT

Summit Systems Ltd, F Tame Park, Vanguard, Wilnecote, Tamworth, Staffordshire, B77 5DY Tel: (01827) 265800 Fax: (01827) 265801 E-mail: info@summitsystems.co.uk

PLASTIC GRANULES

A M F Polymers Ltd, Avondale Way, Avondale Industrial Estate, Pontrhydyrun, Cwmbran, Gwent, NP44 1TS Tel: (01633) 873229 Fax: (01633) 866600

Extrusion & Moulding Compounds Ltd, Cwmavon, Pontypool, Gwent, NP4 8UW Tel: (01495) 772534 Fax: (01495) 772251

PLASTIC GRATINGS

The Grating Co. Ltd, 1 Warner Way, Chilton Business Park, Sudbury, Suffolk, CO10 2GG Tel: (01787) 319922 Fax: (01787) 319963 E-mail: info@gratingco.co.uk

PLASTIC GRP OPEN GRILLE FLOORING

Engineered Composites Ltd, 41 Hope St., Chester, CH4 8BU Tel: (01244) 676000 Fax: (01244) 677267 E-mail: info@engineered-composites.co.uk

PLASTIC GUTTERS

▶ Bedford Building Plastics, 11 Grisedale Court, Woburn Road Industrial Estate, Kempston, Bedford, MK42 7EE Tel: (01234) 855388 Fax: (01234) 855399

PLASTIC HANDLES

Gripworks, Units 11-13 Spectrum West, 20-20 Maidstone Business Estate, St. Laurence Avenue, Allington, Maidstone, Kent, ME16 0LL Tel: (0800) 7311150 Fax: (01622) 693201 E-mail: sales@sinclair-rush.co.uk

Knobs, Leone Works, John Street, New Basford, Nottingham, NG7 7HL Tel: 0115-942 0006 Fax: 0115-970 2106 E-mail: sales@knobs.uk.com

McLaren Plastics Ltd, Pentland Industrial Estate, Loanhead, Midlothian, EH20 9QH Tel: 0131-448 2200 Fax: 0131-448 2221 E-mail: sales@mclaren-plastics.co.uk

Polyan Covers, 5 Bainbridge Wharf, Farnhill, Keighley, West Yorkshire, BD20 9BX Tel: (01535) 631212 Fax: (01535) 631313

PLASTIC HEAT EXCHANGERS

Baxi Heating Ltd, Brook House, Coventry Road, Warwick, CV34 4LL Tel: (01772) 693700 Fax: (01926) 410006 E-mail: service@heatteam.co.uk

E. Braude (London) Ltd, Liberta House, Scotland Hill, Sandhurst, Berkshire, GU47 8JR Tel: (01252) 876123 Fax: (01252) 875281 E-mail: sales@braude.co.uk

PLASTIC HINGES

S P P Extrusions, Timothys Bridge Road, Stratford-upon-Avon, Warwickshire, CV37 9NQ Tel: (01789) 298429 Fax: (01789) 414427 E-mail: sales@sp-plastics.co.uk

PLASTIC HOSES

A R P Co. Ltd, Unit 2 Jubilee Way, Avonmouth, Bristol, BS11 9HU Tel: 0117-982 6301 Fax: 0117-923 5487 E-mail: sales@avonmouth-rubber.co.uk

Abbey Extrusions Ltd, 2 Ivanhoe Industrial Estate, Tournament Way, Ashby-de-la-Zouch, Leicestershire, LE65 2UU Tel: (01530) 416177 Fax: (01530) 417230 E-mail: sales@abbeyextrusions.co.uk

Emplas Ltd, Saddington Road, Fleckney, Leicester, LE8 8AW Tel: 0116-240 3407

Merlett Plastics (UK) Ltd, Unit 2, Waverley Road, Beeches Industrial Estate, Yate, Bristol, BS37 5QT Tel: (01454) 329888 Fax: (01454) 324499

Plastiflex UK Ltd, Ripley Close, Normanton Industrial Estate, Normanton, West Yorkshire, WF6 1TB Tel: (01924) 783600 Fax: (01924) 896715 E-mail: info@plastiflex.co.uk

Primaflex Ltd, Arcadia Business Centre, Miller Lane, Clydebank, Dunbartonshire, G81 1UJ Tel: 0141-951 4188 Fax: 0141-952 2001

Rehau Ltd, Hill Court, Walford, Ross-on-Wye, Herefordshire, HR9 5QN Tel: (01989) 762600 Fax: (01989) 762601 E-mail: enquiries@rehau.com

Steinlock Ltd, Danbury Mews, Wallington, Surrey, SM6 0BY Tel: (020) 8773 4966 Fax: (020) 8773 4968

Test Valley Engineers Ltd, Stoneymarsh, Michelmersh, Romsey, Hampshire, SO51 0LB Tel: (01794) 368308 Fax: (01794) 368693 E-mail: sales@test-valley.co.uk

Trist Draper Hydraulics, Unit 6f Redbrook Business Park, Wilthorpe Road, Barnsley, South Yorkshire, S75 1JN Tel: (01226) 281140 Fax: (01226) 243223 E-mail: sales@tristdraper.co.uk

PLASTIC HOUSEHOLD GOODS

Betterware UK Ltd, Stanley House, Park Lane, Castle Vale, Birmingham, B35 6LJ Tel: (0845) 1294500 Fax: (0845) 1294654 E-mail: info@betterware.co.uk

Crystalware Ltd, Brook Street, Lakeside, Redditch, Worcestershire, B98 8NG Tel: (01527) 63746 Fax: (01527) 584549 E-mail: sales@crystalwareltd.co.uk

Herzbi Ltd, Grosvenor Works, Mount Pleasant Hill, London, E5 9NE Tel: (020) 8806 3232 Fax: (020) 8806 3236

▶ Home Zone, 19 Dalrymple Street, Girvan, Ayrshire, KA26 9EU Tel: (01465) 715961

Robert Scott & Sons, Oakview Mills, Manchester Road, Greenfield, Oldham, OL3 7HG Tel: (01457) 873931 Fax: (01457) 819490 E-mail: admin@robert-scott.co.uk

Strata Products Ltd, Strata Building, Waterloo Road, London, NW2 7UH Tel: (020) 8450 7829 Fax: (020) 8450 3114 E-mail: sales@strataproducts.co.uk

Whitefurze Ltd, Bursnall Road Industrial Estate, Burnsall Road, Coventry, CV5 6BT Tel: (024) 7671 7755 Fax: (024) 7671 7474

PLASTIC INDUSTRIAL DIVIDING CURTAINS

Union Industries, Whitehouse Street, Leeds, LS10 1AD Tel: 0113-244 8393 Fax: 0113-242 1307 E-mail: sales@unionindustries.co.uk

PLASTIC INDUSTRY CONSULTANTS

▶ Howard Consultancy, 26 The Loont, Winsford, Cheshire, CW7 1EU Tel: (01606) 552189 Fax: (01606) 552189 E-mail: roberthoward@onetel.net

PLASTIC INDUSTRY TOOLS

Abbey Tooling Ltd, Longdon Heath, Upton Upon Severn, Worcester, WR8 0RJ Tel: (01684) 592452 Fax: (01684) 592452

Jade Engineering (Coventry) Ltd, 70 Bayton Road Industrial Estate, Exhall, Coventry, CV7 9EJ Tel: (024) 7636 5336 Fax: (024) 7664 4308 E-mail: sales@jade-eng.co.uk

PLASTIC INJECTION MOULDING ASSEMBLY

▶ National Homebuyers, Stirling House, 1 20 Victoria Way, Burgess Hill, West Sussex, RH15 9NF Tel: (01444) 257111 Fax: (01444) 257333 E-mail: info@nationalhomebuyers.co.uk

Precision Engineering Plastics Ltd, Unit 4b Triumph Trading Estate, Tariff Road, London, N17 0EB Tel: (020) 8801 4226 Fax: (020) 8808 7421 E-mail: sales@pep-ltd.co.uk

PLASTIC INJECTION MOULDING MACHINES

Amco Products, 5 Orchard Road, Royston, Hertfordshire, SG8 5HD Tel: (01763) 242040 Fax: (01763) 245505 E-mail: sales@Amco-products.co.uk

Arburg Ltd, Tachbrook Park Drive, Warwick, CV34 6RH Tel: (01926) 457000 Fax: (01926) 457030 E-mail: uk@arburg.com

Billion UK Ltd, 2 Fitzhamon Court, Wolverton Mill, Milton Keynes, MK12 6LB Tel: (01908) 223344 Fax: (01908) 223006 E-mail: sales@billion-uk.co.uk

Boston Matthews Machinery Ltd, Navigation Road, Diglis, Worcester, WR5 3DE Tel: (01905) 763100 Fax: (01905) 763101 E-mail: info@bostonmatthews.co.uk

Cartwright Plastics, 1a Birdcroft Lane, Ilkeston, Derbyshire, DE7 4BE Tel: 0115-932 2744 Fax: 0115-932 9762

Dassett Process Engineering Ltd, Daimler Close, Royal Oak Industrial Estate, Woodford Halse, Daventry, Northants, NN11 8QJ Tel: (01327) 312914 Fax: (01327) 314162 E-mail: info@dassett.com

Eastern Plastics Machinery Ltd, Eastern House, Priors Way, Coggeshall, Colchester, CO6 1TW Tel: (01376) 562288 Fax: (01376) 561385 E-mail: info@easternplastics.co.uk

Ferromatik Milacron Ltd, Klockner House, Carrwood Road, Chesterfield, Derbyshire, S41 9QB Tel: (01246) 260666 Fax: (01246) 260474 E-mail: admin@ferromatik.co.uk

J E T Industrial Services, 13 Rosemary Lane, Liverpool, L37 3HA Tel: (01704) 872972 Fax: (01704) 833986 E-mail: jetind@fsbdial.co.uk

Krauss Maffei U K Ltd, 410 Europa Boulevard, Westbrook, Warrington, WA5 7TR Tel: (01925) 644100 Fax: (01925) 234284 E-mail: sales@kraussmaffei.co.uk

▶ Lynco, 110a Fenlake Road, Bedford, MK42 0EU Tel: (01234) 272425 Fax: (01234) 213141 E-mail: johncuthbert@ntlworld.com

Manumold Ltd, Lawrence Burns Ltd, Griffin Lane, Aylesbury, Buckinghamshire, HP19 8BP Tel: (01296) 435424

MCP, 8 Whitebridge Industrial Estate, Whitebridge Lane, Stone, Staffordshire, ST15 8LQ Tel: (01785) 815651 Fax: (01785) 812115 E-mail: equipment@mcp-group.co.uk

N & P Thermo Plastics Moulders (Whitton) Ltd, Silverdale Road, Hayes, Middlesex, UB3 1AQ Tel: (020) 8569 1300 Fax: (020) 8569 1480

Netstal Ltd, Emerald Way, Stone Business Park, Stone, Staffordshire, ST15 0SR Tel: (01785) 815166 Fax: (01785) 815132 E-mail: email@netstal.co.uk

Northern Products Ltd, Unit 20 Rassau Industrial Estate, Rassau, Ebbw Vale, Gwent, NP23 5SD Tel: (01495) 352577 Fax: (01495) 307545

O F Bell Injection Moulding, Unit 1 Castleside Industrial Estate, Consett, County Durham, DH8 8HG Tel: (01207) 504912 Fax: (01207) 509869 E-mail: sylvia@ofbell.co.uk

Plasplant Ltd, Unit 4 Oakhanger Farm, Oakhanger, Bordon, Hampshire, GU35 9JA Tel: (01420) 473013 Fax: (01420) 475152 E-mail: sales@plasplant.com

S S X Group P.L.C., 319 Vale Enterprise Park, Hayes Road, Sully, Penarth, South Glamorgan, CF64 5SY Tel: (01446) 741133 Fax: (01446) 740841

Sandretto UK Ltd, Leigh Road, Swift Valley Industrial Estate, Rugby, Warwickshire, CV21 1DS Tel: (01788) 544221 Fax: (01788) 542195 E-mail: welcome@sandretto.co.uk

T J H Precision Plastics Ltd, 6 Davy Road, Clacton-on-Sea, Essex, CO15 4XD Tel: (01255) 220736 Fax: (01255) 476446 E-mail: tjh@angliannet.co.uk

Zenith European Ltd, 14-15 Rutherford Way, Drayton Way Industrial Estate, Daventry, Northamptonshire, NN11 5XW Tel: (01327) 311400 Fax: (01327) 311500 E-mail: sales@zenith-european.com

PLASTIC INJECTION MOULDING MATERIALS

Plastohm Technical Parts UK Ltd, Unit 4 Sunrise Enterprise Park, Ferryboat Lane, Sunderland, SR5 3RX Tel: 0191-549 4531 Fax: 0191-549 2891

PLASTIC INJECTION MOULDING PRECISION TOOLS

A V Plastics, Unit 1 Chiddingstone Causeway, Tonbridge, Kent, TN11 8JU Tel: (01892) 870461 Fax: (01892) 871262 E-mail: sales@avplastics.co.uk

Data Plastics, Avenue Three, Witney, Oxfordshire, OX28 4BP Tel: (01993) 700777 Fax: (01993) 700555 E-mail: sales@dataplastics.co.uk

Forteq UK Ltd, Tandem Industrial Estate, Wakefield Road, Tandem, Huddersfield, HD5 0QR Tel: (01484) 424384 Fax: (01484) 535053

▶ Martin Tool Makers, Unit 32 Herons Gate Trading Estate, Paycocke Road, Basildon, Essex, SS14 3EU Tel: (01268) 272240 Fax: (01268) 272097

PLASTIC INJECTION MOULDINGS

▶ Bay Precision, 20 Westgate, Morecambe, Lancashire, LA3 3LN Tel: (01524) 409955

▶ Drya UK Ltd, 33 Goodrich Close, Muxton, Telford, Shropshire, TF2 8SN Tel: (01952) 605932

I V M Ltd, Unit 3-4, Willington, Crook, County Durham, DL15 0UT Tel: (01388) 746538 Fax: (01388) 746538 E-mail: contact.ivm@btconnect.com

▶ Lock Way Plastics, Highfield Mills, Heaton Street, Cleckheaton, West Yorkshire, BD19 3TN Tel: (01274) 869439 Fax: (01274) 869428 E-mail: sales@lockway.co.uk

▶ P C Plastics, Unit A1, Locking Farm Industrial Estate, Locking Moor Road, Weston-Super-Mare, Avon, BS24 8PJ Tel: (01934) 820678 Fax: (01934) 820678

▶ P I M S, Unit 12, Sovereign Way, Downham Market, Norfolk, PE38 9SW Tel: (01366) 385382 Fax: (01366) 387202 E-mail: steve.pims@virgin.net

Plastohm Technical Parts UK Ltd, Unit 4 Sunrise Enterprise Park, Ferryboat Lane, Sunderland, SR5 3RX Tel: 0191-549 4531 Fax: 0191-549 2891

▶ Tariq Plastic, Unit 9B Stag Industrial Estate, Oxford Street, Bilston, West Midlands, WV14 7HZ Tel: (01902) 401263 Fax: (01902) 409364

PLASTIC INJECTION MOULDINGS TO SPECIFICATION

Fastplas Technical Moulding Ltd, 22 Brunel Road, St. Leonards-on-Sea, East Sussex, TN38 9RT Tel: (01424) 851443 Fax: (01424) 851443 E-mail: info@fastplas.co.uk

PLASTIC INJECTION MOULDINGS TO SPECIFICATION – *continued*

Precision Engineering Plastics Ltd, Unit 4b Triumph Trading Estate, Tariff Road, London, N17 0EB Tel: (020) 8801 4226 Fax: (020) 8808 7421 E-mail: sales@pep-ltd.co.uk

PLASTIC INSERT MOULDINGS

Autosplice Brittanic Ltd, Unit 1/6, Crompton Road, Ilkeston, Derbyshire, DE7 4BG Tel: 0115-944 0258 Fax: 0115-944 0587 E-mail: sales@bpte.com
Firstpress Plastic Moulders Ltd, 10 Haden Street, Balsall Heath, Birmingham, B12 9BH Tel: 0121-446 6266 Fax: 0121-446 6269 E-mail: info@firstpress.co.uk
Lennox Foundry Co. Ltd, Bredgar Road, Gillingham, Kent, ME8 6PN Tel: (01634) 386683 Fax: (01634) 386684 E-mail: lennox@kestner-eng.co.uk
Pioneer Associates Ltd, Ibex Barn, Ferro Fields, Brixworth, Northampton, NN6 9UA Tel: (01604) 882362 Fax: (01604) 882362 E-mail: sales@pioneer-associates-ltd.co.uk

PLASTIC INSULATOR COMPONENTS

Deceuninck Ltd, Stanier Road, Porte Marsh Industrial Estate, Calne, Wiltshire, SN11 9PX Tel: (01249) 816969 Fax: (01249) 815234 E-mail: deceuninck.ltd@deceuninck.com
Plastic Shims & Gaskets Co. Ltd, 49-53 Glengall Road, Peckham, London, SE15 6NF Tel: (020) 7740 9705 Fax: (020) 7635 9791 E-mail: sales@psggroup.co.uk

PLASTIC INTEGRATED DESIGN AND MANUFACTURING SERVICES

J D Sign & Display Ltd, Unit 34 Adams Industrial Estate, Dickerage Lane, New Malden, Surrey, KT3 3SF Tel: (020) 8949 4468 Fax: (020) 8949 7758E-mail: john@jdsignanddisplay.com
Neppco Ltd, PO Box 88, Manchester, M60 1QD Tel: 0161-200 5706 Fax: 0161-200 5707 E-mail: sales@neppco.co.uk

PLASTIC JARS

Constar International UK Ltd, Moor Lane Trading Estate, Sherburn in Elmet, Leeds, LS25 6ES Tel: (01977) 882000 Fax: (01977) 882092 E-mail: enquiries@constar.net
M & H Plastics, London Road, Beccles, Suffolk, NR34 8TS Tel: (01502) 715518 Fax: (01502) 712581 E-mail: sales@mhplastics.com
RPC Containers Ltd, 4 Sallow Road, Weldon North Industrial Estate, Corby, Northamptonshire, NN17 5JX Tel: (01536) 263488 Fax: (01536) 272910 E-mail: sales@rpc-corby.co.uk
RPC Containers Ltd, Gallamore Lane, Market Rasen, Lincolnshire, LN8 3HZ Tel: (01673) 840200 Fax: (01673) 840240 E-mail: sales@rpc-marketrasen.co.uk

PLASTIC JERRYCANS

Weltonhurst Ltd, Centurion Way Roman Road Industrial Estate, Roman Road, Blackburn, BB1 2LD Tel: (01254) 671177 Fax: (01254) 671717 E-mail: sales@weltonhurst.co.uk

PLASTIC KNOBS

Knobs, Leone Works, John Street, New Basford, Nottingham, NG7 7HL Tel: 0115-942 0006 Fax: 0115-970 2106 E-mail: sales@knobs.uk.com

PLASTIC LABELS

Diamond Graphics, Norton House, 61a High Street, Wordsley, Stourbridge, West Midlands, DY8 5SD Tel: (01384) 572878 Fax: (01384) 481975
Goldcrest Adhesive Products Ltd, Unit A, Telford Road, Bicester, Oxfordshire, OX26 4LD Tel: (01869) 243201 Fax: (01869) 244734 E-mail: sales@adhesivelabels.co.uk
Intereel Group Ltd, Unit 11, Mountbatten Road, Tiverton, Devon, EX16 6SW Tel: (01884) 256364 Fax: (01884) 257898 E-mail: sales@intereel.co.uk
Label Link, The Old Bakery, High Street, Angmering, Littlehampton, West Sussex, BN16 4AG Tel: (01903) 782588 Fax: (01903) 782588 E-mail: sales@label-link.co.uk
M T M Products Ltd, Dunston Trading Estate, Foxwood Road, Sheepbridge, Chesterfield, Derbyshire, S41 9RF Tel: (01246) 450228 Fax: (01246) 455635 E-mail: sales@mtmlabels.co.uk
Plastic Metal & Profiles Ltd, Unit 99 14 North Tyne Industrial Estate, Whitley Road, Benton, Newcastle upon Tyne, NE12 9SZ Tel: 0191-266 5050 Fax: 0191-266 5724 E-mail: sales@pmpnamesplates.co.uk
Sign & Label Centre Ltd, Dock Road, Connah's Quay, Deeside, Clwyd, CH5 4DS Tel: (01244) 813660 Fax: (01244) 816812 E-mail: sales@signandlabelcentre.com
Ultra Labels, 3 57a Gwendolen Road, Leicester, LE5 5FL Tel: 0116-273 7643 Fax: 0116-273 7643
West Yorkshire Printing Co. Ltd, Wyprint House, Smith Way, Wakefield Road, Ossett, West Yorkshire, WF5 9JZ Tel: (01924) 280522 Fax: (01924) 280145 E-mail: sales@westyor.co.uk

PLASTIC LAMINATING MACHINES

Xcard Printers, 8 Cowley Mill Trading Estate, Longbridge Way, Cowley, Uxbridge, Middlesex, UB8 2YG Tel: (01895) 256332 Fax: (01895) 230902 E-mail: info@xcardtechnology.com

PLASTIC LEATHERCLOTHS

Bhor (Hallbridge Ltd), 28 Brookdene Drive, Northwood, Middlesex, HA6 3NS Tel: (020) 8961 1614 Fax: (020) 8961 1614 E-mail: hallbridge@aol.com

PLASTIC LENSES

Carclo Technical Plastics, 111 Buckingham Avenue, Slough, SL1 4PF Tel: (01753) 575011 Fax: (01753) 811359 E-mail: optics@carclo-optics.com
Crown Leisure Ltd, Gerrish Avenue, Whitehall, Bristol, BS5 9DG Tel: 0117-955 4044 Fax: 0117-955 4045 E-mail: sales@crownleisure.co.uk
Essex Optical Co. Ltd, 172 Enterprise Court, Eastways, Witham, Essex, CM8 3YS Tel: (01376) 512630 Fax: (01376) 515154 E-mail: enquiries@essexoptical.co.uk

PLASTIC LETTERING

Allsigns, 122 Connaught Road, Brookwood, Woking, Surrey, GU24 0AS Tel: (01483) 799100 Fax: (01483) 799188
Barrett Inter Signs Co Ltd, 18 Farlow Road, Northfield, Birmingham, B31 3AE Tel: 0121-477 7396 Fax: 0121-477 7414
Express Signs, 66 Soundwell Road, Bristol, BS16 4QP Tel: 0117-957 1793 Fax: 0117-957 1793 E-mail: andy@expresssigns.fsnet.co.uk
Ultra Labels, 3 57a Gwendolen Road, Leicester, LE5 5FL Tel: 0116-273 7643 Fax: 0116-273 7643

PLASTIC LITTER BINS OR CONTAINERS

▶ Dyfed Industrial Developments, Graig, Burry Port, Dyfed, SA16 0BJ Tel: (01554) 832777 Fax: (01554) 832777 E-mail: did@draenog.freeserve.co.uk
Lones (UK) Ltd, Middlemore Lane West, Aldridge, Walsall, WS9 8BG Tel: (01922) 743833 Fax: (01922) 743760 E-mail: sales@workplace-products.co.uk
Maelor-Trafflex Ltd, Wrexham Industrial Estate, Abbey Road, Wrexham, Clwyd, LL13 9RF Tel: (01978) 661040 Fax: (01978) 661450 E-mail: orders@maelortrafflex.co.uk
MelbaSwintex Ltd, Derby Works, Manchester Road, Bury, Lancashire, BL9 9NX Tel: 0161-761 4933 Fax: 0161-797 1146 E-mail: sales@swintex.co.uk

PLASTIC MACHINE COVERS

Cabcare Products, Unit 6 Raleigh Hall Industrial Estate, Eccleshall, Stafford, ST21 6JL Tel: (01785) 851944 Fax: (01785) 851961 E-mail: sales@cabcare.com
Delmore, Chiswick Avenue, Mildenhall, Bury St. Edmunds, Suffolk, IP28 7AY Tel: (01638) 714805 Fax: (01638) 713043
B. & R. Loughlin, 19 Meadowcourt Road, Oadby, Leicester, LE2 2PD Tel: 0116-271 2373 Fax: 0116-272 0239
Plastic Fabrications Ltd, Unit 12 Newstead Industrial Park, Hazelford Way, Newstead Village, Nottingham, NG15 0DQ Tel: (01623) 720400 Fax: (01623) 720800 E-mail: fabrications@btconnect.com
Wyndham Plastics Ltd, Ogmore Terrace, Bridgend, Mid Glamorgan, CF31 1SU Tel: (01656) 652869 Fax: (01656) 669915 E-mail: steve@wyndham-plastics.co.uk

PLASTIC MACHINE GUARDS

Cabcare Products, Unit 6 Raleigh Hall Industrial Estate, Eccleshall, Stafford, ST21 6JL Tel: (01785) 851944 Fax: (01785) 851961 E-mail: sales@cabcare.com
Camera Bellows, Units 3-5, St. Pauls Road, Birmingham, B12 8NG Tel: 0121-440 1695 Fax: 0121-440 0972 E-mail: sales@camerabellows.com
Plastic Fabrications Ltd, Unit 12 Newstead Industrial Park, Hazelford Way, Newstead Village, Nottingham, NG15 0DQ Tel: (01623) 720400 Fax: (01623) 720800 E-mail: fabrications@btconnect.com
Price Guarding Systems, Waterside Estate, Cradley Road, Dudley, West Midlands, DY2 9RG Tel: 0121-525 4973 Fax: (01384) 241039

PLASTIC MACHINE TOOL SCREWS AND BARRELS

T A V, Thurston Road, Northallerton, North Yorkshire, DL6 2NA Tel: (01609) 760011 Fax: (01609) 783111 E-mail: sales@tavltd.co.uk

PLASTIC MACHINERY ACCESSORIES/ANCILLARY EQUIPMENT/COMPONENTS MANUFRS

A T M Automation Ltd, Winchester Avenue, Blaby Industrial Park, Blaby, Leicester, LE8 4GZ Tel: 0116-277 3607 Fax: 0116-277 9800 E-mail: sales@atmautomation.com
C J Machine Services Ltd, A Commercial Road, Walsall, WS2 7NQ Tel: (01922) 409777 Fax: (01922) 478600 E-mail: cjms@btconnect.com
Cooper Plastics Machinery, Unit 12 Harmill Industrial Estate, Grovebury Road, Leighton Buzzard, Bedfordshire, LU7 4FF Tel: (01525) 850610 Fax: (01525) 218008 E-mail: cooperplastics@btclick.com
Dyn Metal Ltd, 25-29 Chase Road, London, NW10 6TA Tel: (020) 8961 0656 Fax: (020) 8961 8820 E-mail: info@dynmetal.co.uk
▶ Exsup, Malvern View, Callow Farm, Hillside, Martley, Worcester, WR6 6QW Tel: (01886) 888392 Fax: (01886) 888392 E-mail: sales@exsup.co.uk
G T Industrial Services Ltd, 16 Enterprise Court, Newton Close, Park Farm Industrial Estate, Wellingborough, Northamptonshire, NN8 6UW Tel: (01933) 405088 Fax: (01933) 405099 E-mail: sales@gtihaxaplas.ukf.net
GeKu UK Ltd, 35B Pattens Lane, Chatham, Kent, ME4 6JR Tel: (01634) 830122 Fax: (01634) 813523 E-mail: gekujohn@btinternet.com
Tek Machinery Ltd, 9 Stadium Court, Barbot Hall Industrial Estate, Parkgate, Rotherham, South Yorkshire, S62 6EW Tel: (01709) 820820 Fax: (01709) 382504 E-mail: info@tekmachinery.co.uk
White & Street International Ltd, Unit 17-18, Enfield Industrial Estate, Redditch, Worcestershire, B97 6BN Tel: (01527) 67881 Fax: (01527) 69966 E-mail: enquiries@whiteandstreet.com

PLASTIC MACHINERY MAINTENANCE/REPAIR SERVICES

C J Machine Services Ltd, A Commercial Road, Walsall, WS2 7NQ Tel: (01922) 409777 Fax: (01922) 478600 E-mail: cjms@btconnect.com
Cooper Plastics Machinery, Unit 12 Harmill Industrial Estate, Grovebury Road, Leighton Buzzard, Bedfordshire, LU7 4FF Tel: (01525) 850610 Fax: (01525) 218008 E-mail: cooperplastics@btclick.com
Injection Moulding Co., Unit 1b Betton Way, Moretonhampstead, Newton Abbot, Devon, TQ13 8NA Tel: (01647) 440055 Fax: (01647) 441055 E-mail: timco@tiscali.co.uk
Mercia Machinery Sales Ltd, Unit 9 Orchard Industrial Estate, Toddington, Cheltenham, Gloucestershire, GL54 5EB Tel: (01242) 621237 Fax: (01242) 621303 E-mail: mercia@toddingtonglos.fsnet.co.uk

PLASTIC MACHINERY MANUFRS, *See also headings for particular types*

Aeromatic Fielder Ltd, PO Box 15, Eastleigh, Hampshire, SO53 4ZD Tel: (023) 8026 7131 Fax: (023) 8025 3381 E-mail: sales-uk@aeromatic-fielder.com
Akron, Building 107b Aviation Park West, Bournemouth International Air, Hurn, Christchurch, Dorset, BH23 6NW Tel: (01202) 580800 Fax: (01202) 593010 E-mail: office@akron.demon.co.uk
Anchor Plastics Machinery, The Watermill, Royal Quay, Harefield, Uxbridge, Middlesex, UB9 6SA Tel: (01895) 824301 Fax: (01895) 825344 E-mail: info@anchor-pm.co.uk
Ataroth Plastics Machinery Sales Ltd, 5 Maer Lane, Market Drayton, Shropshire, TF9 1QX Tel: (01630) 655148 Fax: (01630) 654055
Battenfeld UK Ltd, 6 Valley Business Centre, Gordon Road, High Wycombe, Buckinghamshire, HP13 6EQ Tel: (01494) 450911 Fax: (01494) 444546 E-mail: abek.r@vuk.battenfeld.com
Blackfriars Ltd, Roman Way, Market Harborough, Leicestershire, LE16 7PQ Tel: (01858) 462249 Fax: (01858) 464755 E-mail: sales@blackfriars.com
C J Machine Services Ltd, A Commercial Road, Walsall, WS2 7NQ Tel: (01922) 409777 Fax: (01922) 478600 E-mail: cjms@btconnect.com
Cooper Plastics Machinery, Unit 12 Harmill Industrial Estate, Grovebury Road, Leighton Buzzard, Bedfordshire, LU7 4FF Tel: (01525) 850610 Fax: (01525) 218008 E-mail: cooperplastics@btclick.com
Cotec Converting Machinery Ltd, Unit 20 St. Johns Industrial Estate, Lees, Oldham, OL4 3DZ Tel: 0161-626 5350 Fax: 0161-626 5450 E-mail: jackcotten@btconnect.com
Euro Rubber Lines, Red Marsh Drive Industrial Estate, Red Marsh Industrial Estate, Thornton-Cleveleys, Lancashire, FY5 4HP Tel: (01253) 850929 Fax: (01253) 850064 E-mail: eurorubberlines@aol.com
▶ Exsup, Malvern View, Callow Farm, Hillside, Martley, Worcester, WR6 6QW Tel: (01886) 888392 Fax: (01886) 888392 E-mail: sales@exsup.co.uk
Ferromatik Milacron Ltd, Klockner House, Carrwood Road, Chesterfield, Derbyshire, S41 9QB Tel: (01246) 260666 Fax: (01246) 260474 E-mail: admin@ferromatik.co.uk
Formech International Ltd, 4 Thrales End Farm, Thrales End Lane, Harpenden, Hertfordshire, AL5 3NS Tel: (01582) 469797 Fax: (01582) 469646 E-mail: sales@formech.com
Global Equipment, 40 George Close, Canvey Island, Essex, SS8 9PU Tel: (01268) 699949 Fax: (01268) 699556 E-mail: info@plasticmachinery.net
John Madeley Machinery Ltd, Firs Industrial Estate, Kidderminster, Worcestershire, DY11 7QN Tel: (01562) 69955 Fax: (01562) 746304 E-mail: madeleyj@aol.com
Kween B Ltd, 29 Dalkeith Road, Sutton Coldfield, West Midlands, B73 6PW Tel: 0121-355 2662 E-mail: info@kweenb.co.uk
B. & R. Loughlin, 19 Meadowcourt Road, Oadby, Leicester, LE2 2PD Tel: 0116-271 2373 Fax: 0116-272 0239
Magnum Venus Products, Stambermill Industrial Estate, Timmis Road, Stourbridge, West Midlands, DY9 7BJ Tel: (01384) 898589 Fax: (01384) 898394 E-mail: sales@mvpeurope.co.uk
Mapex UK Ltd, Unit 9 Pulloxhill Business Pk, Greenfield Rd, Pulloxhill, Bedford, MK45 5EU Tel: (01525) 719979 Fax: (01525) 719339 E-mail: info@mapex.demon.co.uk
Mercia Machinery Sales Ltd, Unit 9 Orchard Industrial Estate, Toddington, Cheltenham, Gloucestershire, GL54 5EB Tel: (01242) 621237 Fax: (01242) 621303 E-mail: mercia@toddingtonglos.fsnet.co.uk
N G C Consultancy Ltd, Unit 1A, The Mayfields, Southcrest, Redditch, Worcestershire, B98 7DU Tel: (01527) 404739 Fax: (01527) 404739
Pixie Developments Ltd, 2 New Mills Industrial Estate, Post Office Road, Inkpen, Hungerford, Berkshire, RG17 9PU Tel: (01488) 669184 Fax: (01488) 669185 E-mail: pixiedev.ltd@ukonline.co.uk
▶ Polymers 1st, D5 West Bridgewater Street, Leigh, Lancashire, WN7 4HB Tel: (01942) 670007 Fax: (01942) 873422
Process Machinery Ltd, 30 Knowl Piece, Wilbury Way, Hitchin, Hertfordshire, SG4 0TY Tel: (01462) 421966 Fax: (01462) 422043 E-mail: sales@processmachinery.co.uk
R S J Process Machinery Ltd, Phoenix House, Tame Street, Stalybridge, Cheshire, SK15 1SY Tel: 0161-338 7288 Fax: 0161-338 3574 E-mail: aquafil@btconnect.com
S S X Group P.L.C., 319 Vale Enterprise Park, Hayes Road, Sully, Penarth, South Glamorgan, CF64 5SY Tel: (01446) 741133 Fax: (01446) 740841
▶ Shelley Thermoformers International Ltd, Stonehill, Stukeley Meadows Industrial Es, Huntingdon, Cambridgeshire, PE29 6DR Tel: (01480) 453651 Fax: (01480) 52113 E-mail: sales@cannon-shelley.co.uk
Sherman Treaters, Dormer Road, Thame Industrial Estate, Thame, Oxfordshire, OX9 3UW Tel: (01844) 213686 Fax: (01844) 217172 E-mail: sales@shermantreaters.co.uk
Tefloturn Ltd, 29 Old Post Road, Briston, Melton Constable, Norfolk, NR24 2NB Tel: (01263) 860001 Fax: (01263) 860055 E-mail: mick@tefloturn.co.uk
Terra Therma Co, Home Farm, Toddington Road, Tebworth, Leighton Buzzard, Bedfordshire, LU7 9QD Tel: (01525) 875166 Fax: (01525) 875166
Trendpam Machinery Ltd, Unit 24, Barwell Business Park, Leatherhead Road, Chessington, Surrey, KT9 2NY Tel: (020) 8391 4411 Fax: (020) 8397 7811

PLASTIC MACHINERY REMOVAL OR RELOCATION

▶ Exsup, Malvern View, Callow Farm, Hillside, Martley, Worcester, WR6 6QW Tel: (01886) 888392 Fax: (01886) 888392 E-mail: sales@exsup.co.uk

PLASTIC MACHINING SERVICES, CNC

A & N Engineering, 2 Emsworth Road, Southampton, SO15 3LX Tel: (023) 8031 5193 Fax: (023) 8070 4033
British Mica Co. Ltd, 123 Barkers Lane, Bedford, MK41 9RR Tel: (01234) 327977 Fax: (01234) 352016 E-mail: info@britishmica.co.uk
Rayburn Plastics Ltd, Whitehouse Street, Walsall, WS2 8HR Tel: (01922) 625572 Fax: (01922) 723333 E-mail: sales@rayburn.co.uk
Reichenbacher-Hamuel, Unit 2 The Moorlands, Lee Lane, Millhouse Green, Sheffield, S36 9NN Tel: (01226) 761799 Fax: (01226) 761589 E-mail: denise@r.co.uk
Wrights Plastics Ltd, Brandon Way, West Bromwich, West Midlands, B70 8JH Tel: 0121-580 3080 Fax: 0121-580 3081 E-mail: sales@wrightsplastics.co.uk

PLASTIC MACHINISTS

Adray Plastics Ltd, James Scott Road, Halesowen, West Midlands, B63 2QT Tel: (01384) 569864 Fax: (01384) 411833 E-mail: sales@adrayplastics.co.uk
Combined Insulations & Plastics Ltd, 6 Bedford Business Centre, Mile Road, Bedford, MK42 9TW Tel: 01234 211771 Fax: 01234 211771
Green Goose Tooling Co., Unit 1-2 Falcons Gate, Dean Road, Yate, Bristol, BS37 5NH Tel: (01454) 312948 Fax: (01454) 313704
Heaven Dowsett & Co. Ltd, 197 Shady Lane, Birmingham, B44 9ES Tel: 0121-360 0345 Fax: 0121-360 7328 E-mail: richarddowsett@heavendowsett.com
Holloway Plastics Ltd, Willenhall La Industrial Estate, Willenhall Lane, Bloxwich, Walsall, WS3 2XN Tel: (01922) 492777 Fax: (01922) 495820 E-mail: sales@holloway-plastics.co.uk
L J Constructions (Plastics) Ltd, Ashford Road, Ashford, Middlesex, TW15 1XB Tel: (01784) 421112 Fax: (01784) 427050 E-mail: plastics@ljc.co.uk
Macgregor Radio Control Ltd, Macgregor House, Cordwallis Street, Maidenhead, Berkshire, SL6 7GF Tel: (01628) 760341 Fax: (01628) 760435
Multi Engineering Components Co., E3 Seedbed Centre, Avenue Road, Nechells, Birmingham, B7 4NT Tel: 0121-359 6022 Fax: 0121-359 0137 E-mail: sales@multiengineering.co.uk
Needs Ltd, 13 Queensway, Enfield, Middlesex, EN3 4SG Tel: (020) 8804 2281 Fax: (020) 8364 7113 E-mail: sales@needsplastics.co.uk
Oadby Plastics Ltd, Elland Road, Leicester, LE3 1TU Tel: 0116-232 1010 Fax: 0116-287 3577 E-mail: sales@oadbyplastics.ltd.uk
Plastic Machining Services, Halesfield 23, Telford, Shropshire, TF7 4NY Tel: (01952) 680369 Fax: (01952) 680371E-mail: info@p-m-s.co.uk
Plastics & Engineering Co., Unit 8-9 Merretts Mill, Bath Road, Woodchester, Stroud, Gloucestershire, GL5 5EX Tel: (01453) 836206 Fax: (01453) 836245 E-mail: sales@plastics-machining.com
Produsit Ltd, Precision Works, 69-70 Moland Street, Birmingham, B4 7EY Tel: 0121-359 5571 Fax: 0121-359 5572 E-mail: produsit@msn.com
▶ Quadrant, 83 Bridge Road East, Welwyn Garden City, Hertfordshire, AL7 1LA Tel: (01707) 361800 Fax: (01707) 361801 E-mail: contact@qplas.com
▶ R J Lewis Ltd, 90 Cobham Road, Ferndown Industrial Estate, Wimborne, Dorset, BH21 7RE Tel: (01202) 893739 E-mail: info@rjlewis.com
Rowley Plastics Co., Lower Road, Ledbury, Herefordshire, HR8 2DH Tel: (01531) 633700 Fax: (01531) 635973
S M P Plastics Fabrications Ltd, 51 Cyprus Street, Oldbury, West Midlands, B69 4XD Tel: 0121-552 0212 Fax: 0121-544 4863 E-mail: info@smp-plastics.co.uk
Sigma Industries Ltd, 19 Dunlop Road, Redditch, Worcestershire, B97 5XP Tel: (01527) 547771 Fax: (01527) 547772 E-mail: sales.sigmaind@btopenworld.com
T K Fabrications, Stone Hall, Down Hall Road, Matching Green, Harlow, Essex, CM17 0RA Tel: (01279) 730093 Fax: (01279) 730135
T M Plastics, 4-6 Fairoak Court, Whitehouse Industrial Estate, Runcorn, Cheshire, WA7 3DX Tel: (01928) 710788 Fax: (01928) 710094 E-mail: tmplastics@tmplastics.co.uk
Waygate Engineering Co Ltd, Stadium Place, Leicester, LE4 0JS Tel: 0116-235 2240 E-mail: rjbwaygate@aol.com

PLASTIC MANHOLES

Pipex Ltd, Pipex House Lowman Way, Tiverton Business Park, Tiverton, Devon, EX16 6SR Tel: (01884) 243564 Fax: (01884) 253285

PLASTIC MASTERBATCH MANUFACTURING

▶ Emsar Polymers UK Ltd, 2 The Court Stanley Green Business Park, Earl Road, Cheadle Hulme, Cheadle, Cheshire, SK8 6GN Tel: 0161-485 7772 Fax: 0161 485 7773 E-mail: info@emsarpolymers.co.uk

PLASTIC MATERIAL PURGING COMPOUNDS

V10 Polymers Ltd, Rockcliffe Works, Paterson Street, Blackburn, BB2 3SP Tel: (01254) 680384 Fax: (01254) 674933 E-mail: david@holtplastics.co.uk

PLASTIC MATERIALS/ PRODUCTS/COMPONENTS/ FITTINGS MANUFRS, *See also other headings under Plastic for particular industry served*

Alpla UK Ltd, Lasborough Road, Kingston, Milton Keynes, MK10 0AB Tel: (01908) 285300 Fax: (01908) 285318
Archmate Ltd, 15 Granby House, Granby Row, Manchester, M1 7AR Tel: 0161-236 2762 Fax: 0161-228 7247
Armstrong Bradley Ltd, 35a Middlewich Road, Sandbach, Cheshire, CW11 1DH Tel: (01270) 758960 Fax: (01270) 764797 E-mail: sales@armstrongbradley.com
Auto Nest Ltd, Stoke Albany Road, Desborough, Kettering, Northamptonshire, NN14 2SP Tel: (01536) 760332 Fax: (01536) 762712
▶ Barkston Plastics Ltd, D5-D7 Unit, Drypool Way, Hull, HU9 1LG Tel: (01482) 323886 Fax: (01482) 214193 E-mail: mailbox@barkstonltd.co.uk
Bay Plastics Ltd, Unit H1, High Flatworth, Tyne Tunnel Trading Estate, North Shields, Tyne & Wear, NE29 7UZ Tel: 0191-258 0777 Fax: 0191-258 1010 E-mail: sales@bayplastics.co.uk
Bec Plastics, 18-20 Lenziemill Road, Cumbernauld, Glasgow, G67 2RL Tel: (01236) 781255 Fax: (01236) 781299 E-mail: enquires@becplastics.co.uk
Bell Display Ltd, Fernie Road, Market Harborough, Leicestershire, LE16 7PH Tel: (01858) 432652 Fax: (01858) 431621
The Bend It Shape It Co Ltd, Elswick Way Industrial Estate, Newcastle Road, South Shields, Tyne & Wear, NE34 0LW Tel: 0191-455 1209 Fax: 0191-456 4671 E-mail: sales@tecform.com
Be-Plas Marketing Ltd, Unit 2 & 3 Old Hall Industrial Estate, Grisedale Road, Old Hall Industrial Estate, Wirral, Merseyside, CH62 3QA Tel: 0151-334 5133 Fax: 0151-334 9399 E-mail: sales@beplas.com
Berleburger, Lumbrook Mills, Westercroft Lynn, Northowram, Halifax, West Yorkshire, HX3 7TY Tel: (01422) 200143 Fax: (01422) 200144 E-mail: maguirejbswuk@aol.com
Bibby Sterlin Ltd, Pengam Road, Aberbargoed, Bargoed, Mid Glamorgan, CF81 9FW Tel: (01443) 830830 Fax: (01443) 821545
Biosil Ltd, Tournament Way, Ashby-de-la-Zouch, Leicestershire, LE65 2UU Tel: (01530) 560204 Fax: (01530) 412715 E-mail: biosil@griffin.co.uk
BKS Plastics Ltd, Unit 2 Station Road Industrial Estate, Great Harwood, Blackburn, BB6 7BB Tel: (01254) 889139 Fax: (01254) 889187 E-mail: bksplastics@btclick.com
Brett Martin, Brierley Close, Speedwell Industrial Estate Staveley, Staveley, Chesterfield, Derbyshire, S43 3JP Tel: (01246) 280001 Fax: (01246) 280001 E-mail: building@brettmartin.com
Brunel Plastics, Unit A1 Hennock Road North, Marsh Barton Trading Estate, Exeter, EX2 8NJ Tel: (01392) 277466 Fax: (01392) 410526
Bryant Plastic Products Ltd, Walk Mills, The Walk, Coney Lane, Keighley, West Yorkshire, BD21 5AR Tel: (01535) 606676 Fax: (01535) 602966 E-mail: sales@bryantplastics.co.uk
Building Products Design Ltd, Brook Hill Industrial Estate, Pinxton, Nottingham, NG16 6NS Tel: (01773) 814123 Fax: (01773) 814101 E-mail: info@buildingproductsdesign.com
Carlton Building Plastics Ltd, 6 Beddington Trading Estate, Bath House Road, Croydon, CR0 4TT Tel: (020) 8665 1221 Fax: (020) 8665 1444
Carter Origin Ltd, Holmes Street, Rochdale, Lancashire, OL12 6AQ Tel: (01706) 656600 Fax: (01706) 524909 E-mail: sales@carterorigin.co.uk
Centriforce Products Ltd, 14/16 Derby Road, Liverpool, L20 8EE Tel: 0151-207 8109 Fax: 0151-298 1319 E-mail: sales@centriforce.co.uk
▶ Cirencester Composites Ltd, Unit 8 Crudwell, Malmesbury, Wiltshire, SN16 9SH Tel: (01666) 577888 Fax: (01666) 577888
Cox Plastics, Kingfisher Way, Sowton Industrial Estate, Exeter, EX2 7LE Tel: (01392) 439701 Fax: (01392) 444017 E-mail: cox.southwest@coxplastics.co.uk
Crumpsall Plastics & Engineering Ltd, Pike Fold Works, Frenchbarn Lane, Blackley, Manchester, M9 6PB Tel: 0161-795 5000 Fax: 0161-721 4684
Gilbert Curry Industrial Plastics Co. Ltd, 16 Bayton Road, Exhall, Coventry, CV7 9EJ Tel: (024) 7664 4645 Fax: (024) 7658 8389 E-mail: k-sales@gcip.co.uk
John Davidson Pipes Ltd, Townfoot, Longtown, Carlisle, CA6 5LY Tel: (01228) 791503 Fax: (01228) 791682 E-mail: jdpcentral@jdpipes.co.uk
Dep Supplies Ltd, Units 2-3 Maressa Building, Icknield Way, Letchworth Garden City, Hertfordshire, SG6 1EX Tel: (01462) 484595 Fax: (01462) 484580 E-mail: sales@depsupplies.co.uk
Dimensional Design Ltd, 3-5 Park Street, Fleckney, Leicester, LE8 8BB Tel: 0116-240 4242 Fax: 0116-240 4488
Direct Plastics Ltd, Unit 12 Portland Business Park, Richmond Park Road, Sheffield, S13 8HS Tel: 0114-256 0889 Fax: 0114-256 0809 E-mail: paul@directplastics.co.uk
Drain Center Ltd, 20 Cosgrove Way, Luton, LU1 1XL Tel: (01582) 414140 Fax: (01582) 451488 E-mail: gary.gillingham@wolseley.co.uk
Engineering & Design Plastics Ltd, 84 High Street, Cherry Hinton, Cambridge, CB1 9HZ Tel: (01223) 249431 Fax: (01223) 411803 E-mail: sales@edplastics.co.uk
Envec Automotive Ltd, Halton Green West, Halton, Lancaster, LA2 6PA Tel: (01524) 811100 Fax: (01524) 811152
Euro Industrial Plastics Ltd, Chamberlain Road, Aylesbury, Buckinghamshire, HP19 8DY Tel: (01296) 482252 Fax: (01296) 425482 E-mail: enquiries@euroindustrialplastics.co.uk
Eurocell Building Plastics Ltd, 1 Valley Buildings, Brunel Road Industrial Eatate, Newton Abbot, Devon, TQ12 4PB Tel: (01626) 335585 Fax: (01626) 336161 E-mail: sales@eurocellbuildingplastics.co.uk
Europlaz Ltd, Hucknall Industrial Park, Daniels Way, Hucknall, Nottingham, NG15 7LL Tel: 0115-968 1888 Fax: 0115-968 0286 E-mail: info@europlaz.co.uk
Ian Flockton Developments Ltd, Estate Road 1, South Humberside Industrial Estate, Grimsby, South Humberside, DN31 2TB Tel: (01472) 359634 Fax: (01472) 241392 E-mail: info@ianflockton.co.uk
H L N Supplies, 67 Upper Accommodation Road, Leeds, LS9 8JP Tel: 0113-240 2000 Fax: 0113-240 4000 E-mail: sales@hlnsupplies.co.uk
Haden Browne, 278 Barton Street, Gloucester, GL1 4JJ Tel: (01452) 525314 Fax: (01452) 300671
Harrold Manufacturing Co. Ltd, Hinstock House, 30 Station Road, Firsby, Spilsby, Lincolnshire, PE23 5PX Tel: (01754) 830679 Fax: (01754) 830477
Heritage Dove Plastics, 3 Watnall Road, Hucknall, Nottingham, NG15 7LD Tel: (01623) 796847 Fax: (01623) 797555 E-mail: kdove@heritagedoveplastics.co.uk
Holscot Plastic Products, 9 Burnmill Industrial Estate, Burnmill Road, Leven, Fife, KY8 4RA Tel: (01333) 427555 Fax: (01333) 422929 E-mail: hnd@holscot.com
Robert Horne Industrial Plant Ltd, Quantam House, Gee Business Centre, Holborn Hill, Birmingham, B7 5JR Tel: 0121-327 5050 Fax: 0121-327 2818
Howgate & Lane Ltd, Stukeley Road, Huntingdon, Cambridgeshire, PE29 6HF Tel: (01480) 413566 Fax: (01480) 433726 E-mail: howgate2000@aol.com
Huhtamaki Van Leer, 180 Gilford Road, Portadown, Craigavon, County Armagh, BT63 5LE Tel: (028) 3836 7200 Fax: (028) 3836 7280 E-mail: portadown@gb.huhtamaki.com
I C L Plastics Ltd, Grovepark Mills, Hopehill Road, Glasgow, G20 7NF Tel: 0141-332 1331 Fax: 0141-332 9186
Imagineering Plastic Fabrication, 21 Cater Road, Bristol, BS13 7TW Tel: 0117-978 4114 Fax: 0117-978 4114 E-mail: plasticfabrication@hotmail.com
Industrial Metal Services Ltd, Metalstock House, Metal Stock House, Vanguard Way, Southend-on-Sea, SS3 9RE Tel: (01702) 296922 Fax: (01702) 296444 E-mail: sales@industrialmetal.co.uk
Inteck Products Ltd, 42 Sheephouse Road, Maidenhead, Berkshire, SL6 8EX Tel: (01628) 771101 Fax: (01628) 637426 E-mail: sales@inteck.co.uk
Involvement Packaging Ltd, Park Road, Stalybridge, Cheshire, SK15 1TA Tel: 0161-338 2807 Fax: 0161-338 2807 E-mail: salesstalybridge@involvementpkg.co.uk
Involvement Packaging Ltd, Chesterton Estate Yard, Banbury Road, Lighthorne, Warwick, CV35 0AJ Tel: (01926) 651800 Fax: (01926) 651177 E-mail: robert@involvementpkg.co.uk
Jaybee Plastic Products, 10 Pywell Court, Willowbrook East Industrial Estate, Corby, Northamptonshire, NN17 5WA Tel: (01536) 266288 Fax: (01536) 266370
Jerome Engineering Ltd, Unit 30 Globe Industrial Estate, Rectory Road, Grays, Essex, RM17 6ST Tel: (01375) 898400 Fax: (01375) 898401 E-mail: tsmith@jeromeuk.com
JFC Plastics Ltd, 6 Goldicote Business Park, Banbury Road, Goldicote, Stratford-upon-Avon, Warwickshire, CV37 7NB Tel: (01789) 740102 Fax: (01789) 740037 E-mail: info@delleve.co.uk
Johnson Polymers Ltd, The Slough, Studley, Warwickshire, B80 7EN Tel: (01527) 850525 Fax: (01527) 850595 E-mail: sales@johnsonpolymers.co.uk
Kirton Kayaks Ltd, Marsh Lane, Lords Meadow Industrial Estate, Crediton, Devon, EX17 1ES Tel: (01363) 773295 Fax: (01363) 775908 E-mail: sales@kirton-kayaks.co.uk
L J Constructions (Plastics) Ltd, Ashford Road, Ashford, Middlesex, TW15 1XB Tel: (01784) 421112 Fax: (01784) 427050 E-mail: plastics@ljc.co.uk
M S Hammond, 38 Manor Bridge Court, Tidworth, Hampshire, SP9 7NH Tel: (01980) 847500 Fax: (01980) 847500
Macgregor Radio Control Ltd, Macgregor House, Cordwallis Street, Maidenhead, Berkshire, SL6 7GF Tel: (01628) 760341 Fax: (01628) 760435
Meridale Plastics Ltd, Meridale Works, Linford Road, Grays, Essex, RM16 4JS Tel: (01375) 850009 Fax: (01375) 851113 E-mail: sales@buildwithplastics.co.uk
Mirus Plastics Ltd, Ridings Business Park, Hopwood Lane, Halifax, West Yorkshire, HX1 3TT Tel: (01422) 345227 Fax: (01422) 347524
Modern Handling Services Ltd, 21 George Street, Milnsbridge, Huddersfield, HD3 4JD Tel: (01484) 461043 Fax: (01484) 461042 E-mail: themhsltd@aol.com
Moyer Manufacturing Co. Ltd, Vansittart Estate, Duke Street, Windsor, Berkshire, SL4 1SG Tel: (01753) 830088 Fax: (01753) 818793 E-mail: moyer@tcom.co.uk
N E Plastics Ltd, 1 Ruxley Corner Industrial Estate, Edgington Way, Sidcup, Kent, DA14 5BL Tel: (020) 8308 9990 Fax: (020) 8308 9995 E-mail: sales@neplastics.co.uk
Neppco Ltd, PO Box 88, Manchester, M60 1QD Tel: 0161-200 5706 Fax: 0161-200 5707 E-mail: sales@neppco.co.uk
Nifco UK Ltd, Yarm Road, Stockton-on-Tees, Cleveland, TS18 3RX Tel: (01642) 672299 Fax: (01642) 611004 E-mail: sales@nifcoeu.com
Northern Ireland Plastics Ltd, 39 Shrigley Road, Killyleagh, Downpatrick, County Down, BT30 9SR Tel: (028) 4482 8753 Fax: (028) 4482 8809 E-mail: sales@nip-ltd.co.uk
Oadby Plastics Ltd, Elland Road, Leicester, LE3 1TU Tel: 0116-232 1010 Fax: 0116-287 3577 E-mail: sales@oadbyplastics.ltd.uk
Ocean Mouldings, Unit 7, Parrett Way, Bridgwater, Somerset, TA6 5LB Tel: (01278) 424447 Fax: (01278) 424447
Omnico Plastics Ltd, Farthing Road, Ipswich, IP1 5AP Tel: (01473) 461461 Fax: (01473) 240518 E-mail: sales@omnico.co.uk
Oxford Scientific Plastics, Varsity Works, Wimblestraw Road, Berinsfield, Wallingford, Oxfordshire, OX10 7QX Tel: (01865) 343555 Fax: (01865) 343123
P J Metals & Plastics, Unit 4 Park Street, Kidderminster, Worcestershire, DY11 6TN Tel: (01562) 824570 Fax: (01562) 865170
Pisces Plastics Ltd, 5-6 Old Racecourse Road, Liverpool, L31 8AW Tel: 0151-531 1175 Fax: 0151-531 1175
Plastic Technology Service Ltd, Flamstone Street, Bishopstone, Salisbury, SP5 4BZ Tel: (01722) 781088 Fax: (01722) 781071 E-mail: info@ptsuk.com
Polybron Plastics Ltd, Unit 4c Loughborough Motorway Trading Estate, Gelders Hall Road, Shepshed, Loughborough, Leicestershire, LE12 9NH Tel: (01509) 507123 Fax: (01509) 507594 E-mail: sales@polybron.co.uk
Pos, 1 Horbury Bridge Mills, Bridge Road, Horbury, Wakefield, West Yorkshire, WF4 5RW Tel: (01924) 276666 Fax: (01924) 276777
Precision Polyurathnne & Rubber, 7-8 East Bank Road, Felnex Industrial Estate, Newport, Gwent, NP19 4PP Tel: (01633) 279704 Fax: (01633) 278653
Preston Industrial Plastics, Aqueduct Street, Preston, PR1 7JQ Tel: (01772) 555224 Fax: (01772) 259473 E-mail: sales@prestonindustrialplastics.co.uk
▶ Quadrant, 83 Bridge Road East, Welwyn Garden City, Hertfordshire, AL7 1LA Tel: (01707) 361800 Fax: (01707) 361801 E-mail: contact@qplas.com
▶ Retail Engineering Design Ltd, Unit 2, Pioneer Park, Clough Road, Hull, HU6 7HW Tel: (01482) 333803 Fax: (01482) 333809 E-mail: info@redltd.karoo.co.uk
Righton Ltd, Unit 7-10 Beeches Trading Estate, Waverley Road, Yate, Bristol, BS37 5FF Tel: (01454) 318601 Fax: (01454) 273392 E-mail: bristol@righton.co.uk
Righton Ltd, Unit 13b Anniesland Industrial Estate, Glasgow, G13 1EU Tel: 0141-954 8962 Fax: 0141-959 3467 E-mail: info@righton.co.uk
Rimparts, 249 Gladstone Road, Barry, Vale of Glamorgan, CF63 1NJ Tel: (01446) 732849 Fax: (01446) 732849
Roomer Products Ltd, Unit 111 Thorp Arch Trading Estate, Thorp Arch, Wetherby, West Yorkshire, LS23 7BJ Tel: (01937) 842002 Fax: (01937) 845174
Ryan Plastics, 21A Prince St, Northampton, NN6 0LL Tel: (01604) 811395 Fax: (01604) 812872 E-mail: john@ryanplastics.ssnet.co.uk
S K Plastics Ltd, Unit 18 Tanfield Lea Industrial Estate South, Tanfield Lea, Stanley, County Durham, DH9 9XB Tel: (01207) 236662 Fax: (01207) 236669 E-mail: sales@skplastics.co.uk
St. Gobain Building Products, Unit 18 Woodford Trading Estate, Southend Road, Woodford Green, Essex, IG8 8HF Tel: (020) 8550 8899 Fax: (020) 8550 3918
Sandpiper Plastics, Unit 4, Heathfield I, Heathfield, Newton Abbot, Devon, TQ12 6UT Tel: (01626) 834342 Fax: (01626) 833724 E-mail: info@sandpiperplastics.co.uk
Sign & Display, 2 Tenax Road, Trafford Park, Manchester, M17 1JT Tel: 0161-872 8585 Fax: 0161-876 4056
Simona (U K) Ltd, Unit 11, Telford Drive, Tollgate Industrial Estate, Stafford, ST16 3ST Tel: (01785) 222444 Fax: (01785) 222080 E-mail: sales@simona.de

PLASTIC MATERIALS/PRODUCTS/ COMPONENTS/FITTINGS MANUFRS

– continued

Skiffy, 5 Wombourne Enterprise Park, Bridgnorth Road, Wombourne, Wolverhampton, WV5 0AL Tel: (01902) 894658 Fax: (01902) 894661 E-mail: skiffyuk@btconnect.com

Smiths Metal Centres Ltd, 42-56 Tottenham Road, London, N1 4BZ Tel: (020) 7241 2430 Fax: (020) 7254 9608

Spa Plastics Ltd, 4 Herald Business Park, Golden Acres Lane, Coventry, CV3 2SY Tel: (024) 7665 0670 Fax: (024) 7665 0680 E-mail: sales@spaplastics.com

Spectra Plastics Ltd, Southam Road, Long Itchington, Southam, Warwickshire, CV47 9QL Tel: (01926) 812195 Fax: (01926) 817401 E-mail: sales@spectra-plastics.co.uk

Stalwart Products, 179 Radstock Road, Southampton, SO19 2HW Tel: (023) 8044 5656 Fax: (023) 8042 2360

Stantons Weybridge Ltd, Canal Bridge, Byfleet Road, New Haw, Addlestone, Surrey, KT15 3JE Tel: (01932) 848131 Fax: (01932) 848447

▶ Stornoway Plastics, Rigs Road, Stornoway, Isle of Lewis, HS1 2RF Tel: (01851) 702122 Fax: (01851) 701287 E-mail: info@stornowayplastics.com

T A Plastics Ltd, Tudhoe Industrial Estate, Spennymoor, County Durham, DL16 6TL Tel: (01388) 814858 Fax: (01388) 819534 E-mail: sales@taplastics.co.uk

Tefloturn Ltd, 29 Old Post Road, Briston, Melton Constable, Norfolk, NR24 2NB Tel: (01263) 860001 Fax: (01263) 860055 E-mail: mick@tefloturn.co.uk

Three Star Plastics, Unit B Spencer Avenue, London, N13 4TR Tel: (020) 8881 4179 Fax: (020) 8881 4179

Titan Environmental Ltd, Seapatrick Road, Seapatrick, Banbridge, County Down, BT32 4PH Tel: (028) 4062 6260 Fax: (028) 4062 6259 E-mail: sales@titanenv.com

Trylon, Bury Close, Higham Ferrers, Rushden, Northamptonshire, NN10 8HQ Tel: (01933) 411724 Fax: (01933) 350357 E-mail: info@trylon.co.uk

Unicorn Metals, 3 Belper Road, Kilburn, Belper, Derbyshire, DE56 0LQ Tel: (01332) 882000 Fax: (01332) 880141

Verifyne Plastic Products Ltd, Lever Mill, Slater Street, Blackburn, BB2 4PA Tel: (01254) 675639 Fax: (01254) 673787 E-mail: enquiries@verifyne-plastics.co.uk

Vivelle (U.K.) Ltd, Victoria House, Croft Street, Widnes, Cheshire, WA8 0NQ Tel: 0151-423 6273 Fax: 0151-495 1438 E-mail: vivelle@globalnet.co.uk

▶ Vulcascot Ltd, Gatwick Gate Industrial Estate, Lowfield Heath, Crawley, West Sussex, RH11 0TG Tel: (01293) 560130 Fax: (01293) 537743 E-mail: sales@vulcascot.co.uk

Vulcascot Ltd, Braintree Road, Ruislip, Middlesex, HA4 0XX Tel: (020) 8841 4211 Fax: (020) 8841 3544

Walker Rubber & Plastics Ltd, Unit 22, Farthing Road, Ipswich, IP1 5AP Tel: (01473) 749131 Fax: (01473) 240917 E-mail: sales@walker-rubber.co.uk

William Beckett Plastics Ltd, Unit 5a, Tinsley Industrial Park, Shepcote Way, Sheffield, S9 1TH Tel: 0114-243 4399 Fax: 0114-256 0196 E-mail: sales@beckettplastics.co.uk

Wolseley UK P.L.C., Furthergate Industrial Park, Hutton Street, Blackburn, BB1 3BY Tel: (01254) 682692 Fax: (01254) 682440 E-mail: blackburn.k87@wolseley.co.uk

PLASTIC MATS

Gradus Carpets Ltd, Chapel Mill, Park Green, Macclesfield, Cheshire, SK11 7LZ Tel: (01625) 859000 Fax: (01625) 850352 E-mail: sales@gradusworld.com

PLASTIC MEDICAL OR SURGICAL GOODS

Apollo Dental Ltd, Tempest House, Lyon Road, Walton-on-Thames, Surrey, KT12 3PU Tel: (01932) 240950 Fax: (01932) 246606

B V Z Marketing Ltd, Unit 34, Meadow Lane, Ellesmere Port, CH65 4EH Tel: 0151-355 3055 Fax: 0151-355 5055

Dubois Ltd, Arkwright Road, Willowbrook North Industrial Estate, Corby, Northamptonshire, NN17 5AE Tel: (01536) 274800 Fax: (01536) 274902 E-mail: huw.lewis@uk.ag.media.com

Flexicare Medical Ltd, CWM Cynon Business Park, Mountain Ash, Mid Glamorgan, CF45 4ER Tel: (01443) 474647 Fax: (01443) 474222 E-mail: sales@flexicare.com

Kimal plc, Sherwood Road, Bromsgrove, Worcestershire, B60 3DR Tel: (01527) 572300 Fax: (01527) 579936 E-mail: sales@kimal.co.uk

Runfold Medical Ltd, Passfield Mill, Mill Lane, Passfield, Liphook, Hampshire, GU30 7QU Tel: (01428) 751999 Fax: (01428) 751990 E-mail: mail@runfoldmedical.com

Viomedex Ltd, Gordon Road, Buxted, Uckfield, East Sussex, TN22 4LH Tel: (01323) 446130 Fax: (01825) 733407 E-mail: vx@viomedex.com

PLASTIC METALLISED FILM

Amcor Flexibles Camvac, Burrell Way, Thetford, Norfolk, IP24 3QY Tel: (01842) 755021 Fax: (0845) 0822426 E-mail: steve.jackson@amcor-flexibles.com

▶ Innovia Films Ltd, Station Rd, Wigton, Cumbria, CA7 9BG Tel: (01697) 342281 Fax: (01697) 341452 E-mail: filmsinfo@innoviafilms.com

Metalised Products Ltd, Pontygwindy Industrial Estate, Caerphilly, Mid Glamorgan, CF83 3HU Tel: (029) 2088 5988 Fax: (029) 2086 3718

PLASTIC MIXING MACHINERY MANUFRS

Coperion Ltd, Victoria House, 19-21 Ack Lane East, Bramhall, Stockport, Cheshire, SK7 2BE Tel: 0161-925 6910 Fax: 0161-925 6911 E-mail: sandra.wyatt@coperion.com

J.E. Elsworth Ltd, 59 Hall Road, Clenchwarton, King's Lynn, Norfolk, PE34 4AS Tel: (01553) 769200 Fax: (01553) 769222

Mitchell Dryers Ltd, Denton Holme, Carlisle, CA2 5DU Tel: (01228) 534433 Fax: (01228) 633555 E-mail: sales@mitchell-dryers.co.uk

PLASTIC MODULAR BELTING

▶ G B Belting Ltd, 55c Perry Avenue, Teesside Industrial Estate, Stockton-on-Tees, Cleveland, TS17 9LN Tel: (01642) 762686 Fax: (01642) 762604 E-mail: sales@gbbelting.com

PLASTIC MOULD BASE PLATES

C G S Brighton Ltd, Unit B4 Modern Moulds Business Centre, Commerce Way, Lancing, West Sussex, BN15 8TA Tel: (01903) 533349 Fax: (01903) 750996 E-mail: admin@cgs-brighton.com

▶ D M E U K, Carrwood Road, Chesterfield Trading Estate, Chesterfield, Derbyshire, S41 9QB Tel: (020) 7133 0037 Fax: (020) 7133 0036 E-mail: dme_uk@dmeeu.com

Mathbirk Ltd, Mansfield Road, Sutton-in-Ashfield, Nottinghamshire, NG17 4HE Tel: (01623) 559333 Fax: (01623) 552109

PLASTIC MOULD CHROME PLATING SERVICES

Polish Craft Ltd, 68g Sapcote Trading Centre, Wyrley Road, Birmingham, B6 7BN Tel: 0121-322 2344 Fax: 0121-322 2344

PLASTIC MOULD CONSULTANTS OR DESIGNERS

Design 4 Plastics Ltd, Unit 402 Thorp Arch Trading Estate, Thorp Arch, Wetherby, West Yorkshire, LS23 7BJ Tel: (01937) 845176 Fax: (01937) 845419 E-mail: enquiries@design4plastics.com

Forest Engineering Designs, 57 West Street, Pontypridd, Mid Glamorgan, CF37 4PS Tel: (01443) 409536 Fax: (01443) 405936

G & A Moulding Technology Ltd, Unit 2, Stonehill, Huntingdon, Cambridgeshire, PE29 6ED Tel: (01480) 414933 Fax: (01480) 414899 E-mail: info@gandamoulding.co.uk

LINPAC Environmental, Leafield Way, Leafield Industrial Estate, Corsham, Wiltshire, SN13 9UD Tel: (01225) 816500 Fax: (01225) 816501 E-mail: paxton@linpac.com

▶ Marlin Design (MD) Ltd, 24 North Street, Chichester, West Sussex, PO19 1LB Tel: (01243) 773552 Fax: (01243) 787227 E-mail: marlindesign@btconnect.com

Plastic Moulds Designs Kingston Ltd, Drake Road, Mitcham, Surrey, CR4 4HQ Tel: (020) 8640 0064 Fax: (020) 8640 0371 E-mail: terry.behing@pmdltd.com

Plastic Products International Ltd, 8-11 Capital Place, Harlow, Essex, CM19 5AS Tel: (01279) 445041 Fax: (08704) 601340 E-mail: sales@plastics-products.net

T J H Precision Plastics Ltd, 6 Davy Road, Clacton-on-Sea, Essex, CO15 4XD Tel: (01255) 220736 Fax: (01255) 476446 E-mail: tjh@angliannet.co.uk

PLASTIC MOULD FINISHING PRODUCTS

Renham & Wade Ltd, Units 1-6 Gas Lane Industrial Estate, Gas La, Middleton In Teesdale, Barnard Castle, County Durham, DL12 0TN Tel: 01833 640050 Fax: 01833 640995 E-mail: enquiries@renhamandwade.co.uk

Zeus Products, Unit E2 Seaden Court, Clacton-on-Sea, Essex, CO15 4XN Tel: (01255) 220996 Fax: (01255) 429991

PLASTIC MOULD HIRE

W R Moulds (UK) Ltd, Aurillac Way, Hallcroft Road, Hallcroft Industrial Estate, Retford, Nottinghamshire, DN22 7SS Tel: (01777) 708432 Fax: (01777) 860383 E-mail: enquries@wrmoulds.co.uk

PLASTIC MOULD MAKING COMPONENTS

Aristocrat Home Improvements, Mowsley End, Wigston, Leicestershire, LE18 3LS Tel: 0116-288 9230 Fax: 0116-288 9230 E-mail: sales@aristocrat-mouldings.co.uk

Sankyo Oilless Industry (U K) Ltd, Huffwood Trading Estate, Billingshurst, West Sussex, RH14 9UR Tel: (01403) 785378 Fax: (01403) 784634 E-mail: sales@sankyo-oilless.co.uk

PLASTIC MOULD POLISHING

Emp Tooling Services Ltd, Brockhampton Lane, Havant, Hampshire, PO9 1LU Tel: (023) 9249 2626 Fax: (023) 9249 2582 E-mail: info@e-m-p.biz

MJK Specialist Mould Polishers & Polishing Consultants, Pickering, North Yorkshire, Tel: (07946) 714777 E-mail: mjk1@sky.com

Pirholite Plastics, 2 Crowhurst Hop Farm, Bullen Lane, East Peckham, Tonbridge, Kent, TN12 5LP Tel: (01622) 872657 Fax: (01622) 872679

Polish Craft Ltd, 68g Sapcote Trading Centre, Wyrley Road, Birmingham, B6 7BN Tel: 0121-322 2344 Fax: 0121-322 2344

PLASTIC MOULD RELEASE AGENTS

Chem-Trend (UK) Ltd, Hough Mills, Bradford Road, Halifax, West Yorkshire, HX3 7BN Tel: (0870) 3504708 Fax: (0870) 3509427 E-mail: uksales@chemtrend.com

Micropol Ltd, Bayley Street, Stalybridge, Cheshire, SK15 1QQ Tel: 0161-330 5570 Fax: 0161-343 7687 E-mail: enquiry@micropol.co.uk

Oiline Ltd, Whitehall Road, Tipton, West Midlands, DY4 7JZ Tel: 0121-557 1475 Fax: 0121-522 2311

P P Composites Ltd, Unit 39c Vale Business Park, Llandow, Cowbridge, South Glamorgan, CF71 7PF Tel: (01446) 775885 Fax: (01446) 775822 E-mail: sales@ppcomposites.ltd.uk

PLASTIC MOULD TOOLING/ TOOLS REFURBISHMENT SERVICES

A 4 Engineering Ltd, 7 Manor Park, 35 Willis Way, Poole, Dorset, BH15 3SZ Tel: (01202) 676047 Fax: (01202) 684675 E-mail: a4eng@a4eng.com

Formula Plastics Ltd, Unit 12 I E S Centre, Horndale Avenue, Aycliffe Industrial Park, Newton Aycliffe, County Durham, DL5 6DS Tel: (01325) 304104 Fax: (01325) 304103 E-mail: john.suggate@formula-plastics.co.uk

PLASTIC MOULD TOOLMAKERS

A J M Engineering Ltd, Park Lane, Park Lane Trading Estate, Corsham, Wiltshire, SN13 9LG Tel: (01249) 712620 Fax: (01249) 714932 E-mail: sales@ajmay.co.uk

A M H Precision Tools Ltd, Unit 4, Thornsett Trading Estate, Birch Vale, High Peak, Derbyshire, SK22 1AH Tel: 01663 745145 Fax: 01663 745252 E-mail: sales@amhtools.co.uk

Adreco Ltd, Bilton Rd, Bletchley, Milton Keynes, MK1 1HW Tel: (01908) 374144 Fax: (01908) 643270 E-mail: sales@adreco.co.uk

Agema Ltd, G4-G6 Little Heath Industrial Estate, Old Church Road, Coventry, CV6 7ND Tel: (024) 7663 7699 Fax: (024) 7663 8014 E-mail: sales@agema-ind.com

Al Tools Ltd, Sidings Road, Lowmoor Road Business Park, Kirkby-in-Ashfield, Nottingham, NG17 7JZ Tel: (01623) 751577 Fax: (01623) 755590 E-mail: alanlockyear@altoolsltd.co.uk

Alltech Moulds, Unit 2, Foxley Court Farm, Ascot Road, Holyport, Maidenhead, Berkshire, SL6 3LA Tel: (01628) 789993 Fax: (01628) 789994 E-mail: andy@alltechmoulds.co.uk

Andel Plastics Ltd, 1 Klaxon Tysley Industrial Estate, 751 Warwick Road, Tyseley, Birmingham, B11 2HA Tel: 0121-765 4042 Fax: 0121-707 3335 E-mail: enquiries@andel-plastics.demon.co.uk

Anderside Tools Ltd, 25 Colvilles Place, Kelvin Industrial Estate, East Kilbride, Glasgow, G75 0PZ Tel: (01355) 245455 Fax: (01355) 230703 E-mail: greg@andersidetools.com

Api Precision Toolmakers, Unit 2 Quell Farm Industrial Estate, Greatham, Pulborough, West Sussex, RH20 2ES Tel: (01798) 875688 Fax: (01798) 872701 E-mail: api@apiprecision.co.uk

Applied Energy Products Ltd, PO Box 220, Peterborough, PE2 9JJ Tel: (01733) 456789 Fax: (01733) 310606 E-mail: joe.barrasso@applied-energy.com

Armada Engineering, Bransford, Worcester, WR6 5JB Tel: (01886) 833672 Fax: (01886) 833906

Armitage Monobond, Ilkley Road, Otley, West Yorkshire, LS21 3JP Tel: (01943) 466222 Fax: (01943) 850265

Arrow Industries Ltd, Unit 13 Tolsons Mill Estate, Lichfield Street, Tamworth, Staffordshire, B78 3QA Tel: (01827) 286959 Fax: (01827) 251952 E-mail: email@arrowindustries.co.uk

Atkinson Engineering, Unit 1 Lancaster Close, Sherburn in Elmet, Leeds, LS25 6NS Tel: (01977) 689665 Fax: (01977) 685624 E-mail: sales@atkinsonprecision.co.uk

Axxicon Moulds Cleveleys Ltd, Dorset Avenue, Thornton-Cleveleys, Lancashire, FY5 2DB Tel: (01253) 823241 Fax: (01253) 869717 E-mail: cleveleys@axxicon.co.uk

Aztec Tooling & Moulding Co. Ltd, Buckholt Drive, Worcester, WR4 9ND Tel: (01905) 754466 Fax: (01905) 754475 E-mail: aztectmltd@aol.com

Aztech Precision Ltd, Church Lane, Barnham, Bognor Regis, West Sussex, PO22 0BP Tel: (01243) 555140 Fax: (01243) 555870 E-mail: mail@aztech-precision.co.uk

B E Ebdon, Leafdale, London Road, Addington, West Malling, Kent, ME19 5PL Tel: (01732) 843351 Fax: (01732) 843351

B F T Engineering Ltd, Hill Street, Kidderminster, Worcestershire, DY11 6TD Tel: (01562) 824225 Fax: (01562) 741692 E-mail: info@bft-eng.com

Bevenden Moulds & Tools Ltd, Unit 5c Triumph Trading Estate, Tariff Road, London, N17 0EB Tel: (020) 8801 2488 Fax: (020) 8808 0982 E-mail: bevendenmandt@btconnect.com

Bournville Engineering, Lifford Trading Estate, Lifford Lane, Birmingham, B30 3DY Tel: 0121-459 9339 Fax: 0121-459 9242

Britestar Plastics Ltd, Unit 7, Broomfield Works, London Road, Swanley, Kent, BR8 8DF Tel: (01322) 669964 Fax: (01322) 660083 E-mail: info@britestar.gb.com

Brooker Mouldings Ltd, 4 Vickers Business Centre, Priestley Road, Basingstoke, Hampshire, RG24 9NP Tel: (01256) 356523 Fax: (01256) 328281

Burnsall Engineering Co. Ltd, Brandon Road, Binley, Coventry, CV3 2AN Tel: (024) 7644 0444 Fax: (024) 7665 2696 E-mail: info@burnsallengineering.com

C G P Engineering Ltd, Cross Street, Oadby, Leicester, LE2 4DD Tel: 0116-271 7715 Fax: 0116-272 0701 E-mail: info@cgp-engineering.com

Cadman Group, The Twitchell, Sutton-In-Ashfield, Nottinghamshire, NG17 5BT Tel: (01623) 553005 Fax: (01623) 440370 E-mail: bcadman@ypm.net

Celect Tools, Ainsworth Street, Rochdale, Lancashire, OL16 5QX Tel: (07814) 349636 Fax: (01706) 648106 E-mail: sales@celect-tools.co.uk

Cellbond Composites Ltd, 4-5 Blackstone Road, Stukeley Meadows Industrial Es, Huntingdon, Cambridgeshire, PE29 6EF Tel: (01480) 435302 Fax: (01480) 450181 E-mail: sales.precision@cellbond.com

Cheswell Engineering Ltd, Waldeck House, Waldeck Road, Maidenhead, Berkshire, SL6 8BR Tel: (01628) 624726 Fax: (01628) 773907

▶ Complexatools Precision Engineers, Railway Stables, Surrey Street, Glossop, Derbyshire, SK13 7AJ Tel: (01457) 864446 Fax: (01457) 861010 E-mail: enquiries@complexatools.co.uk

CPM Moulds Solutions Ltd, Pattison House, Addison Road, Chesham, Buckinghamshire, HP5 2BD Tel: (01494) 782131 Fax: (01494) 778542 E-mail: precision@chesham-moulds.co.uk

Custom Tooling Ltd, Unit 65, Station Road Industrial Estate, Hailsham, East Sussex, BN27 2ED Tel: (01323) 641811 E-mail: custo@btconnect.com

D B C Tools Ltd, Jubilee Trading Estate, Jubilee Road, Letchworth Garden City, Hertfordshire, SG6 1NE Tel: (01462) 679905 Fax: (01462) 480219 E-mail: don.carter@dbctools.co.uk

D & E Plastics Ltd, Ogilvie Road, High Wycombe, Buckinghamshire, HP12 3DS Tel: (01494) 463111 Fax: (01494) 461194 E-mail: enquiries@deplastics.co.uk

D G T Precision Engineering, 9C, Corbin Way, Gore Cross Business Park, Bridpole, Bridport, Dorset, DT6 3UX Tel: (01308) 420024 Fax: (01308) 424007 E-mail: info@dgtpreceng.co.uk

D & G Toolmakers (Frome), Unit 13, Court Farm Trading Estate, Bishops Frome, Worcester, WR6 5AY Tel: (01885) 490714 Fax: (01885) 490380

D H Tools, Unit 9 Newlands End, Basildon, Essex, SS15 6DU Tel: (01268) 540633 Fax: (01268) 540742 E-mail: enquiries@dhtools.co.uk

D Harvey & Co., 4 Mill Park, Cannock, Staffordshire, WS11 7XT Tel: (01543) 573408 Fax: (01543) 462100 E-mail: sales@dharveyandco.co.uk

Den Mark Tools, 4 Queensway Link Industrial Estate, Stafford Park, Telford, Shropshire, TF3 3DN Tel: (01952) 200633 Fax: (01952) 200133 E-mail: mrowlands@den-mark.freeserve.co.uk

Devol Moulding Services Ltd, Edgefield Industrial Estate, Loanhead, Midlothian, EH20 9TB Tel: 0131-440 4367 Fax: 0131-440 3328

PLASTIC MOULD TOOLMAKERS – *continued*

Dimmock Engineering, Unit 6 Westbury Close, Houghton Regis, Dunstable, Bedfordshire, LU5 5BL Tel: (01582) 602588 Fax: (01582) 602588 E-mail: sjdimmock1@aol.com
Elbmar Ltd, 5 Oppenheimer Centre, Greenbridge Road, Greenbridge Industrial Estate, Swindon, SN3 3JD Tel: (01793) 644155 Fax: (01793) 513170 E-mail: elbmar@aol.com
Essex Injection Mouldings Ltd, 15 Temple Farm Industrial Estate, Craftsman Square, Temple Farm Industrial Estate, Southend-on-Sea, SS2 5RH Tel: (01702) 461160 Fax: (01702) 600805
E-mail: ed@essexinjectionmouldings.co.uk
Ever Ready Tools & Plastics Co. Ltd, Unit H, Chesham Close, Romford, RM7 7NA
Tel: (01708) 762262 Fax: (01708) 723006
E-mail: everreaytools@btconnect.com
Excel Precision Wse Ltd, Unit 2 Woodrow Way, Gloucester, GL2 5DX Tel: (01452) 419743
Fax: (01452) 307135
E-mail: sales@excel-precision.co.uk
Express Moulds Ltd, Jubilee Works, 40 Alma Crescent, Vauxhall, Birmingham, B7 4RH
Tel: 0121-359 6378 Fax: 0121-359 3792
E-mail: paul.yeomans@expressmoulds.co.uk
G T Tools Ltd, Coxmoor Road, Sutton-in-Ashfield, Nottinghamshire, NG17 4NE Tel: (01623) 551000 Fax: (01623) 550784
E-mail: sales@gttools.co.uk
G W Lawson Ltd, Units R-U Burnham Trading Estate, Lawson Road, Dartford, DA1 5BH
Tel: (01322) 223363 Fax: (01322) 223234
E-mail: gwlawson@btconnect.com
A.F. Gaskin Ltd, Downley Road, Naphill, High Wycombe, Buckinghamshire, HP14 4QY
Tel: (01494) 563831 Fax: (01494) 562933
E-mail: sales@afgaskin.co.uk
Gaugemaster Co. Ltd, 93 Leopold Street, Birmingham, B12 0UD Tel: 0121-773 6331
Fax: 0121-772 4046
E-mail: enquiries@gaugemaster.net
Gibbs & Rustage Ltd, Albert Works, Victoria Road, Dukinfield, Cheshire, SK16 4UP
Tel: 0161-339 3379 Fax: 0161-343 2207
Glossop Thermoplastics Ltd, Brookfield Industrial Estate, Glossop, Derbyshire, SK13 6JF
Tel: (01457) 866111 Fax: (01457) 861802
E-mail: sales@gt-uk.com
H D M Plastics, Waldeck Road, Maidenhead, Berkshire, SL6 8BR Tel: (01628) 673832
Fax: (01628) 673832
E-mail: hdmplastics68@yahoo.co.uk
Hi Tec Plastics, 1 Sett End Road, Shadsworth Business Park, Blackburn, BB1 2PT
Tel: (01254) 581405 Fax: (01254) 680285
E-mail: dennishi-tech@quista.net
Hilbar Plastics, Windley Works, Wolsey Street, Radcliffe, Manchester, M26 3BB Tel: 0161-724 4325 Fax: 0161-725 9158
Howard 2000 Ltd, Howard Centre, Paper Mill End, Great Barr, Unit 4, Birmingham, B44 8NH
Tel: 0121-356 9833 Fax: 0121-356 0280
Index Plastic Tooling, 31a Newtown Street, Cradley Heath, West Midlands, B64 5LD
Tel: (01384) 569165 Fax: (01384) 569165
Inflite Engineering Services Ltd, Unit A, Broadlink, Manchester, M24 1UB Tel: 0161-653 4222
Fax: 0161-655 3375
E-mail: enquiries@ultratools.co.uk
Injection Plastics Ltd, Winston Avenue, Croft, Leicester, LE9 3GQ Tel: (01455) 283898
Fax: (01455) 285330
E-mail: injectplasleics@aol.com
Investment Tooling International Ltd, 4a Moston Road, Middleton, Manchester, M24 1SL
Tel: 0161-653 8066 Fax: 0161-655 3095
Investment Tooling International Ltd, Sidings Road, Lowmoor Business Park, Kirkby-in-Ashfield, Nottingham, NG17 7JZ
Tel: (01623) 754814 Fax: (01623) 754914
E-mail: sales@iti-kirkby.co.uk
Ironsun Ltd, Lindon Road, Brownhills, Walsall, WS8 7BG Tel: (01543) 454453 Fax: (01543) 454450 E-mail: admin@ironsun-ltd.com
J S G Engineering, Unit 3/4, Wren Centre, Westbourne Road, Emsworth, Hampshire, PO10 7SU Tel: (01243) 379698 Fax: (01243) 379857 E-mail: jim@jsgeng.fsnet.co.uk
Javelin Plastics & Tools, Unit 1M Albany Park Industrial Estate, Frimley Road, Camberley, Surrey, GU16 7PE Tel: (01276) 64446
Fax: (01276) 691174
E-mail: enquries@javelinplastics.co.uk
K J T Plastics Ltd, Unit 4-5 Happy Valley Industrial Estate, Primrose Hill, Kings Langley, Hertfordshire, WD4 8HD Tel: (01923) 267913
Fax: (01923) 261853
K T Moulds, 27 Westbury Close, Townsend Industrial Estate, Houghton Regis, Dunstable, Bedfordshire, LU5 5BL Tel: (01582) 699721
Fax: (01582) 699721
Kavia Mouldings Ltd, Unit 8, Balderstone Close, Heasandford Industrial Estate, Burnley, Lancashire, BB10 2BS Tel: (01282) 423935
Fax: (01282) 426105
E-mail: kavia.mouldingsltd@virgin.net
Kentone Plastics Ltd, Town Farm, Campton Road, Gravenhurst, Bedford, MK45 4JB
Tel: (01462) 711797 Fax: (01462) 711031
E-mail: kentoneplastics@hotmail.com
Langstone Engineering Ltd, Units 1-3 Beaver Industrial Est., Southmoor Lane, Havant, Hampshire, PO9 1JW Tel: (023) 9245 2430
Fax: (023) 9245 2440
E-mail: corporate@langstone-engineering.co.uk
Le Craft Products, Unit 10-11 Ebblake Industrial Estate, Forest Close, Ebblake Industrial Estate, Verwood, Dorset, BH31 6DE
Tel: (01202) 827171 Fax: (01202) 813020
Linton Plastic Moulders Ltd, Unit 3, The Grip, Linton, Cambridge, CB21 4XN Tel: (01223) 892143 Fax: (01223) 894618
E-mail: info@lintonplasticmoulders.co.uk
Lodent Precision, Colliers Close, Coppice Side Industrial Estate, Brownhills, Walsall, WS8 7EU Tel: (01543) 453700 Fax: (01543) 453800 E-mail: info@lodent.flyer.co.uk
Mcausbyrne Tools Ltd, 10 Westbourne Place, Hove, East Sussex, BN3 4GN Tel: (01273) 776318 Fax: (01273) 776318
E-mail: david.austin@btconnect.com
Maclan Plastics, Unit Ba Keighley Business Centre, South Street, Keighley, West Yorkshire, BD21 1AG Tel: (01535) 680127
Fax: (01535) 680222
E-mail: info@maclanplastics.co.uk
Mather Engineering Co. Ltd, 73 River Road, Barking, Essex, IG11 0DR Tel: (020) 8594 1092 Fax: (020) 8594 9247
E-mail: email@mather-engeering.co.uk
Merlin Plastics, Charity Farm, Baxterley, Atherstone, Warwickshire, CV9 2LN
Tel: (01827) 874572 Fax: (01827) 874898
Minimould Ltd, Units 10A & 10B, Thame Road, Aylesbury, Buckinghamshire, HP17 8LJ
Tel: 01844 292880
Modern Moulds Associates Ltd, Lightsfield, Oakley, Basingstoke, Hampshire, RG23 7BY
Tel: (01256) 782333 Fax: (01256) 782915
Modern Moulds & Tools, Commerce Way, Lancing, West Sussex, BN15 8TA Tel: (01903) 851905 Fax: (01903) 851907
E-mail: mail@modernmoulds.co.uk
Moldmet Ltd, Sandall Stones Road, Kirk Sandall Industrial Estate, Doncaster, South Yorkshire, DN3 1QR Tel: (01302) 888810 Fax: (01302) 880333 E-mail: ken@moldmet.com
Moldsytems Plastics, 1 Edwardson Road, Meadowfield Industrial Estate, Durham, DH7 8RL Tel: 0191-378 0747 Fax: 0191-378 9255
D.G. Mortimer & Co. Ltd, Hilton Road, Cobbs Wood Industrial Estate, Ashford, Kent, TN23 1EW Tel: (01233) 621601 Fax: (01233) 622169 E-mail: user@plasticomgroup.com
Mould Import Solutions Ltd, Units A, Crewe Close, Blidworth Industrial Park, Blidworth, Mansfield, Nottinghamshire, NG21 0TA
Tel: (01623) 490070 Fax: (01623) 795687
Mould & Tool Masters, Unit 7 Borough Close, Paignton, Devon, TQ4 7EP Tel: (01803) 527664 Fax: (01803) 663425
Mouldrite Toolmakers, Unit 6 Varney Industrial Estate Spon La Trading Estate, Varney A, West Bromwich, West Midlands, B70 6AE
Tel: 0121-553 2199 Fax: 0121-553 2213
E-mail: mouldritetools@btconnect.com
Mundy & Side, Westwood Farm, Highcross Road, Southfleet, Gravesend, Kent, DA13 9PH
Tel: (01474) 834455 Fax: (01474) 834457
E-mail: anyone@mundy-side.prestel.co.uk
Mycol Engineering, 75 Tenter Road, Moulton Park Industrial Estate, Northampton, NN3 6AX
Tel: (01604) 790389 Fax: (01604) 790389
Naiad Plastics Ltd, 16 Thorgate Road, Wick, Littlehampton, West Sussex, BN17 7LU
Tel: (01903) 724302 Fax: (01903) 730925
E-mail: naiad@naiadplastics.com
Y.M. Newmark, Duchess Street Industrial Estate, Duchess Street, Shaw, Oldham, OL2 7UT
Tel: (01706) 291295 Fax: (01706) 291297
E-mail: info@newmarks.co.uk
Ninefields Holdings Ltd, 1 & 2 Bruce Grove, Heron Trading Estate, Wickford, Essex, SS11 8DB Tel: (01268) 732148 Fax: (01268) 764394 E-mail: info@ninefields.co.uk
Orion Precision, 18 Orion Court, Cranes Farm Road, Basildon, Essex, SS14 3DB
Tel: (01268) 282445 Fax: (01268) 282445
P J Tooling, Hassall Road Industrial Estate, Skegness, Lincolnshire, PE25 3TB
Tel: (01754) 767818 Fax: (01754) 767818
P P Injection Moulds & Moulding Ltd, Beversbrook Industrial Estate, Redman Road, Calne, Wiltshire, SN11 9PL Tel: (01249) 823100 Fax: (01249) 823103
E-mail: sales@ppmoulds.co.uk
Paramount Mould Co. Ltd, Abercromby Avenue, High Wycombe, Buckinghamshire, HP12 3AX
Tel: (01494) 531516 Fax: (01494) 465483
E-mail: tech@paramount-group.net
Patterson & Rothwell Ltd, Mount Pleasant Street, Oldham, OL4 1HH Tel: 0161-621 5000
Fax: 0161-621 5001
E-mail: sales@patterson-rothwell.co.uk
Peak Precision Tools Mansfield Ltd, 9 Anglia Way Industrial Estate, Anglia Way, Mansfield, Nottinghamshire, NG18 4LP Tel: (01623) 623993 Fax: (01623) 623993
Pearton Tooling Ltd, Unit 8 Manor Way, Old Woking, Woking, Surrey, GU22 9JY
Tel: (01483) 773648 Fax: (01483) 756639
E-mail: pearton@pearton.com
Perfectools Plastics, Coombend, Radstock, BA3 3AS Tel: (01761) 432299 Fax: (01761) 435575 E-mail: sales@perfecttools.co.uk
Plaslant Ltd, Unit 154-156 Block 17, Newhouse Industrial Estate, Newhouse, Motherwell, Lanarkshire, ML1 5RX Tel: (01698) 732009
Fax: (01698) 732106
E-mail: plaslant@aol.com
Plasmold Precision, Knightsbridge Gardens, Romford, RM7 9AD Tel: (01371) 876445
Fax: (01708) 732691
E-mail: lee@plasmoldplastics.co.uk
Plastic Moulds Designs Kingston Ltd, Drake Road, Mitcham, Surrey, CR4 4HQ Tel: (020) 8640 0064 Fax: (020) 8640 0371
E-mail: terry.behing@pmdltd.com
Plastic Parts Direct Ltd, Thorpe Way, Banbury, Oxfordshire, OX16 4SP Tel: (01295) 269333
Fax: (01295) 273276
E-mail: info@apmonline.co.uk
Playden Tools Ltd, Factory 5-6 The Elms, Church Road, Harold Wood, Romford, RM3 0JR
Tel: (01708) 343874 Fax: (01708) 376531
Polytech Plastic Products, Bullock Street, West Bromwich, West Midlands, B70 7HE
Tel: 0121-525 7777 Fax: 0121-525 6777
E-mail: riaarnumber2@aol.com
Presspeed Precision Tools Ltd, Hartlepool Workshops, Hartlepool, Cleveland, TS25 1PD
Tel: 01429 269739
Prodec Precision Manufacturing Co. Ltd, Armstrong Buildings, Kilton Terrace, Worksop, Nottinghamshire, S80 2DQ Tel: (01909) 474093 Fax: (01909) 500363
Queensfield Precision Engineering, Unit 4, Beeding Close, Southern Cross Trading Estate, Bognor Regis, West Sussex, PO22 9TS Tel: (01243) 868254 Fax: (01243) 829609 E-mail: post@queensfield.co.uk
R E Knight Ltd, Fishers Way, Belvedere, Kent, DA17 6BS Tel: (020) 8310 8900 Fax: (020) 8311 4530 E-mail: enquiries@reknight.co.uk
R G E Engineering Co. Ltd, Bridge Works, The Avenue, Godmanchester, Huntingdon, Cambridgeshire, PE29 2AF Tel: (01480) 450771 Fax: (01480) 411359
E-mail: sales@rgegroup.com
R Lunn Engineering, 2 Vincent Mill, Vincent Street, Macclesfield, Cheshire, SK11 6UJ
Tel: (01625) 611682 Fax: (01625) 611682
Wylie Redman (Moulds) Ltd, 17 Watt Road, Glasgow, G52 4RZ Tel: 0141 8835284
Rojak Tool & Die Co. Ltd, Falkland Close, Coventry, CV4 8AU Tel: (024) 7646 7969
Fax: (024) 7669 4458 E-mail: rojak@ukf.net
Rugby Plastics Ltd, 11 Lanchester Way, Royal Oak Industrial Estate, Daventry, Northamptonshire, NN11 8PH Tel: (01327) 702668 Fax: (01327) 300468
E-mail: sales@rugbyplastics.com
S Bateman & Sons Ltd, Hart Street, Blackburn, BB1 1HW Tel: (01254) 56153 Fax: (01254) 664416
S G H Moulds Ltd, Hypatia Street, Bolton, BL2 6AA Tel: (01204) 529374 Fax: (01204) 363356
E-mail: sgh@sghmoulds.freeserve.co.uk
S I A Mould Tools Ltd, Russell Street, Sutton-in-Ashfield, Nottinghamshire, NG17 4BE Tel: 01623 553237
Skiller Engineering Ltd, Unit 1, Pig Lane, Bishop'S Stortford, Hertfordshire, CM23 3HG
Tel: 01279 501631
Springfield Tools Ltd, Unit 14B, 54 College Road, Perry Barr, Birmingham, B44 8BS
Tel: 0121-356 3403 Fax: 0121-356 2155
E-mail: andrewregan@btconnect.com
Superite Tools, Unit 3 Hayward Industrial Park, Vigo Place, Walsall, WS9 8UG Tel: (01922) 455769 Fax: (01922) 743176
E-mail: enquiries@superite.co.uk
Surgecrown Ltd, J The Wallows Industrial Estate, Fens Pool Avenue, Brierley Hill, West Midlands, DY5 1QA Tel: (01384) 483712
Fax: (01384) 483712
Sycon Ltd, Underleys, Beer, Seaton, Devon, EX12 3NA Tel: (01297) 21391 Fax: (01297) 625991
T. & J. Plastics Ltd, 23 Cedar Close, Iver Heath, Iver, Buckinghamshire, SL0 0QX Tel: (01753) 652610 Fax: (01753) 652610
E-mail: tandjplast@aol.com
T S D Precision Ltd, Unit 11 Lion Industrial Park, Northgate Way, Walsall, WS9 8RL Tel: (01922) 457620 Fax: 01922 455443
T T Audio Plastics Ltd, Unit 17, St. Margarets Way, Stukeley Meadows Industrial Estate, Huntingdon, Cambridgeshire, PE29 6EB
Tel: (01480) 412345 Fax: (01480) 412533
E-mail: admin@ttap.co.uk
Technical Moulding Projects, Unit 5d Watlington Industrial Estate, Cuxham Road, Watlington, Oxfordshire, OX49 5LU Tel: (01491) 613539
Fax: (01491) 612096
E-mail: tmp@techmouldproj.demon.co.uk
Thurlow Tools, 79a Westbury Avenue, London, N22 6SA Tel: (020) 8889 1217
TMT Toolmakers, Units 1, 3 & 7 Bilton Industrial Estate, Stockmans Close, Birmingham, B38 9TS Tel: 0121-459 0292 Fax: 0121-459 2141
Tolworth Tools Ltd, 46B Fife Rd, Kingston upon Thames, Surrey, KT1 1SU Tel: (020) 8546 2683 Fax: (020) 8546 2683
▶ Total Mould & Insert, Edison Road, St. Ives, Cambridgeshire, PE27 3LF Tel: (01480) 484711 Fax: (01480) 484710
E-mail: sales@totalmould.co.uk
Tower Tool Co. Ltd, Tower Manfactory, Radnor Road, Wigston, Leicestershire, LE18 4XY
Tel: 0116-277 6520 Fax: 0116-277 6388
E-mail: myles@tower-tool.demon.co.uk
Triform Moulds Ltd, Oakridge Road, High Wycombe, Buckinghamshire, HP11 2PF
Tel: (01494) 445354 Fax: (01494) 448200
Triune Precision Engineering Co. Ltd, Spring Lane, Malvern, Worcestershire, WR14 1AJ
Tel: (01684) 573331 Fax: (01684) 893201
Unijig Ltd, Bowling Back Lane, Bradford, West Yorkshire, BD4 8UF Tel: (01274) 656750
Fax: (01274) 668375
E-mail: sales@unijig.co.uk
Universal Moulding Co., 500 Ipswich Rd, Slough, SL1 4EP Tel: (01753) 570023 Fax: (01753) 535005 E-mail: andy@alltechmoulds.co.uk
Verifyne Plastic Products Ltd, Lever Mill, Slater Street, Blackburn, BB2 4PA Tel: (01254) 675639 Fax: (01254) 673787
E-mail: enquiries@verifyne-plastics.co.uk
W H Smith & Sons Tools Ltd, Water Orton Lane, Minworth, Sutton Coldfield, West Midlands, B76 9BG Tel: 0121-748 7777 Fax: 0121-749 6213 E-mail: info@whs-tools.com
Wentworth Tool & Die, Woodbine House, Wold Newton, Driffield, North Humberside, YO25 3YD Tel: (01262) 470270 Fax: (01262) 470270 E-mail: woodbinehouse@aol.com
Wheeler & Clinch Ltd, 75-99 Nathan Way, West Thamesmead Business Park, London, SE28 0BQ Tel: (020) 8854 4261 Fax: (020) 8854 6341 E-mail: whclinch@aol.com
Zeta Plastic Components Ltd, Ravensthorpe Industrial Estate, Dewsbury, West Yorkshire, WF13 3LN Tel: (01924) 491900 Fax: (01924) 491917

PLASTIC MOULDING DECORATING/FINISHING SERVICES

Asdec Ltd, Unit 7-8 Building 33, Second Avenue, Pensnett Trading Estate, Kingswinford, West Midlands, DY6 7UG Tel: (01384) 402463
Fax: (01384) 402662
E-mail: asdecc@hotmail.com
Electroflock Ltd, Unit 7-8 Building 33, Second Avenue, Pensnett Trading Estate, Kingswinford, West Midlands, DY6 7UG
Tel: (01384) 402660 Fax: (01384) 402662
E-mail: electroflock@btinternet.com
Glossop Thermoplastics Ltd, Brookfield Industrial Estate, Glossop, Derbyshire, SK13 6JF
Tel: (01457) 866111 Fax: (01457) 861802
E-mail: sales@gt-uk.com

PLASTIC MOULDING MACHINERY, *See also Plastic Blow Moulding, Injection Moulding etc*

J E T Industrial Services, 13 Rosemary Lane, Liverpool, L37 3HA Tel: (01704) 872972
Fax: (01704) 833986
E-mail: jetind@fsbdial.co.uk

PLASTIC MOULDING MACHINERY COMPONENTS

Eastern Plastics Machinery Ltd, Eastern House, Priors Way, Coggeshall, Colchester, CO6 1TW
Tel: (01376) 562288 Fax: (01376) 561385
E-mail: info@easternplastics.co.uk

PLASTIC MOULDING MATERIALS, POWDERS/ GRANULES

Ampacet UK Ltd, Unit F1, Halesfield 21, Telford, Shropshire, TF7 4NX Tel: (01952) 581814
Fax: (01952) 581815
Glass Bond N W Ltd, Westside Industrial Estate, Jackson Street, St. Helens, Merseyside, WA9 3AT Tel: (01744) 730334 Fax: (01744) 451661 E-mail: sales@glassbond.co.uk
Micropol Ltd, Bayley Street, Stalybridge, Cheshire, SK15 1QQ Tel: 0161-330 5570
Fax: 0161-343 7687
E-mail: enquiry@micropol.co.uk
Raschig UK Ltd, Trafford Road, Salford, M5 4QD
Tel: 0161-877 3933 Fax: 0161-877 3944
E-mail: raschig.uk_ltd@virgin.net

PLASTIC MOULDINGS, *See also headings for particular types*

A J R Precision Plastics Ltd, Unit 13 Calthorpe Industrial Park, Regina Drive, Perry Barr, Birmingham, B42 1BZ Tel: 0121-356 1763
Fax: 0121-356 9680
A & M Plastic Solutions, Wickham Road, Fareham, Hampshire, PO16 7JB Tel: (01329) 225900 Fax: (01329) 823840
E-mail: sales@amplastic.com
A P I C Plastics Ltd, 28 Plantation Road, Amersham, Buckinghamshire, HP6 6HJ
Tel: (01494) 431066 Fax: (01494) 726309
E-mail: apicplastics@lineone.net
A V Engineering Services Ltd, Saxon Way, Melbourn, Royston, Hertfordshire, SG8 6DN
Tel: (01763) 261818 Fax: (01763) 262622
E-mail: sales@aveng.co.uk
A1 Moulders Ltd, Smeckley Wood Close, Chesterfield, Derbyshire, S41 9PZ Tel: (01246) 455705 Fax: (01246) 454895
E-mail: a1moulders@bt.com
Abbey Plastics & Tooling Ltd, Unit 8, 108 Nathan Way, London, SE28 0AQ Tel: (020) 8316 4333
Fax: (020) 8316 4333
Almont Plastics Ltd, Lower Road, Ledbury, Herefordshire, HR8 2DH Tel: (01531) 633640
Fax: (01531) 635925
Amber Plastics Ltd, Broombank Road, Chesterfield, Derbyshire, S41 9QJ Tel: (01246) 453544 Fax: (01246) 450339
E-mail: sales@amberplastics.co.uk
Armitage Monobond, Ilkley Road, Otley, West Yorkshire, LS21 3JP Tel: (01943) 466222
Fax: (01943) 850265
Automotive Applied Technologies Ltd, PO Box 22, Accrington, Lancashire, BB5 0LA Tel: (01254) 357500 Fax: (01254) 357600
E-mail: info@automotive-tech.co.uk

PLASTIC MOULDINGS – *continued*

Autosplice Brittanic Ltd, Unit 1/6, Crompton Road, Ilkeston, Derbyshire, DE7 4BG Tel: 0115-944 0258 Fax: 0115-944 0587 E-mail: sales@bpte.com

Avalon Plastics Ltd, Imco Works, Beckery New Road, Glastonbury, Somerset, BA6 9NR Tel: (01458) 831563 Fax: (01458) 834384 E-mail: enquiries@avalonplastics.co.uk

Aztech Precision Ltd, Church Lane, Barnham, Bognor Regis, West Sussex, PO22 0BP Tel: (01243) 555140 Fax: (01243) 555870 E-mail: mail@aztech-precision.co.uk

B P Y Plastics, J Lincoln Park, Borough Road, Buckingham Road Industrial Estate, Brackley, Northamptonshire, NN13 7BE Tel: (01280) 706335 Fax: (01280) 705675 E-mail: tony@bpy-plastics.com

B & S Injection Moulders Ltd, Units 14-15 Joseph Wilson Industrial Estate, Millstrood Road, Whitstable, Kent, CT5 3PS Tel: (01227) 262599 Fax: (01227) 770767 E-mail: sales@bandsinjection.co.uk

B S R Technical Mouldings Services Ltd, Unit 13/14/18 Lagrange, Lichfield Road Industrial Estate, Tamworth, Staffordshire, B79 7XD Tel: (01827) 63626 Fax: (01827) 63242

B V Z Marketing Ltd, Unit 34, Meadow Lane, Ellesmere Port, CH65 4EH Tel: 0151-355 3055 Fax: 0151-355 5055

B W Manufacturing Plastics Ltd, Rear of, 74 Castle Street, Grimsby, South Humberside, DN32 7TE Tel: (01472) 344444 Fax: (01472) 359523

BC Plastic Mouldings Ltd, Commercial Road, Walsall, WS2 7NQ Tel: (01922) 497888 Fax: (01922) 478600 E-mail: cjms@btconnect.com

Birkbys Plastics Ltd, Headlands Road, Liversedge, West Yorkshire, WF15 6QA Tel: (01924) 414200 Fax: (01924) 400051 E-mail: admin@birkbys.co.uk

BKS Plastics Ltd, Unit 2 Station Road Industrial Estate, Great Harwood, Blackburn, BB6 7BB Tel: (01254) 889139 Fax: (01254) 889187 E-mail: bksplastics@btclick.com

Bonair Plastics Ltd, Old Forge Yard, Swanley Village Road, Swanley, Kent, BR8 7NF Tel: (01322) 664347 Fax: (01322) 664347 E-mail: dave@bonair.freeserve.co.uk

Britestar Plastics Ltd, Unit 7, Broomfield Works, London Road, Swanley, Kent, BR8 8DF Tel: (01322) 669964 Fax: (01322) 660083 E-mail: info@britestar.gb

Cadman Group, The Twitchell, Sutton-In-Ashfield, Nottinghamshire, NG17 5BT Tel: (01623) 553005 Fax: (01623) 440370 E-mail: bcadman@ypm.net

Cameron-Price Medical Division Ltd, Charlotte Road, Stirchley, Birmingham, B30 2BT Tel: 0121-459 2121 Fax: 0121-451 2303 E-mail: info@cameron-price.co.uk

Captive Closures, Burma Road, Blidworth, Mansfield, Nottinghamshire, NG21 0RT Tel: (01623) 491112 Fax: (01623) 491113 E-mail: captive.mick@btconnect.com

Charlesworth & Son Ltd, Wishaw Lane, Curdworth, Sutton Coldfield, West Midlands, B76 9EL Tel: (01675) 470382 E-mail: sales@charlesworth-son.co.uk

Clamcleats Ltd, Watchmead, Welwyn Garden City, Hertfordshire, AL7 1AP Tel: (01707) 330101 Fax: (01707) 321269 E-mail: sales@clamcleat.com

Cobb-Slater Ltd, Cosim Works, Church Road, Darley Dale, Matlock, Derbyshire, DE4 2GG Tel: (01629) 732344 Fax: (01629) 733446 E-mail: technical@cobb-slater.co.uk

Component Moulders, 4-5 Teville Industrials, Dominion Way, Worthing, West Sussex, BN14 8NW Tel: (01903) 235765 Fax: (01903) 212751 E-mail: sales@nordell.co.uk

Copley Decor Ltd, 1 Leyburn Business Park, Harmby Road, Leyburn, North Yorkshire, DL8 5QA Tel: (01969) 623410 Fax: (01969) 624398 E-mail: mouldings@copleydecor.co.uk

Cotech Plastics Ltd, Unit 53 Sapcote Trading Centre, Powke Lane, Cradley Heath, West Midlands, B64 5QX Tel: (01384) 635508 Fax: (01384) 567267

▶ Cox Plastics Technologies Ltd, Weedon Road Industrial Estae, Northampton, NN5 5AX Tel: (01604) 752200 Fax: (01604) 752266 E-mail: info@arkplastics.co.uk

Cox Thermoforming Ltd, Unit 4, Icknield Way Industrial Estate, Tring, Herts, HP23 4JX Tel: (01442) 891055 Fax: (01442) 890967 E-mail: sales@cwpl.net

Creighton Developments Ltd, Unit 15 Enterprise Centre Two, Chester Street, Stockport, Cheshire, SK3 0BR Tel: 0161-480 0668 Fax: 0161-480 0668

Cromwell Plastics Ltd, 53-54 New Street, Quarry Bank, Brierley Hill, West Midlands, DY5 2AZ Tel: (01384) 564146 Fax: (01384) 561645 E-mail: sales@cromwell-plastics.co.uk

D & E Plastics Ltd, Ogilvie Road, High Wycombe, Buckinghamshire, HP12 3DS Tel: (01494) 463111 Fax: (01494) 461194 E-mail: enquiries@deplastics.co.uk

D T Industries Ltd, Unit 10, Coulman Road Industrial Estate, Doncaster, South Yorkshire, DN8 5JU Tel: (01405) 740313 Fax: (01405) 817903 E-mail: sales@dtindustries.co.uk

D W Precision Engineering, 9 Sopwith CR, Hurricane Way, Wickford, Essex, SS11 8YU Tel: (01268) 571616 Fax: (01268) 571626 E-mail: dwp@netcomuk.co.uk

Denroyd Ltd, Lockhill Mills, Holmes Road, Sowerby Bridge, West Yorkshire, HX6 3LD Tel: (01422) 833147 Fax: (01422) 833615 E-mail: sales@denroyd.co.uk

Devol Moulding Services Ltd, Edgefield Industrial Estate, Loanhead, Midlothian, EH20 9TB Tel: 0131-440 4367 Fax: 0131-440 3328

Deyn Plastics Ltd, Netherwood Road, Rotherwas Industrial Estate, Hereford, HR2 6JU Tel: (01432) 359763 Fax: (01432) 351928 E-mail: enquires@deynplastics.co.uk

Dickinson Philips & Co., Snaygill Industrial Estate, Keighley Road, Skipton, North Yorkshire, BD23 2QR Tel: (01756) 700359 Fax: (01756) 700360 E-mail: sales@dickinsonphilips.com

Dorset Technical Mouldings, Unit C20-24, Holton Road, Holton Heath Trading Park, Poole, Dorset, BH16 6LT Tel: (01202) 624790 Fax: (01202) 623761 E-mail: sales@dtm-poole.fsnet.co.uk

E & P Plastics Ltd, Gore Road Industrial Estate, New Milton, Hampshire, BH25 6TB Tel: (01425) 611026 Fax: (01425) 615500

Eaton Automotive Fluid Connectors Operations, P O Box 12, Brierley Hill, West Midlands, DY5 2LB Tel: (01384) 424911 Fax: (01384) 426300

Field Boxmore Healthcare Packaging Belfast Ltd, Enterprise Way, Hightown Indusst Estate, Newtownabbey, County Antrim, BT36 4EW Tel: (028) 9080 4000 Fax: (028) 9080 4300 E-mail: sales@boxmore.com

Firstpress Plastic Moulders Ltd, 10 Haden Street, Balsall Heath, Birmingham, B12 9BH Tel: 0121-446 6266 Fax: 0121-446 6269 E-mail: info@firstpress.co.uk

Fourfold Mouldings, New Close Mills, Howden Road, Silsden, Keighley, West Yorkshire, BD20 0HA Tel: (01535) 654604 Fax: (01535) 654829 E-mail: sales@fourfold.co.uk

William Freeman, Wakefield Road, Staincross, Barnsley, South Yorkshire, S75 6DH Tel: (01226) 284081 Fax: (01226) 731832 E-mail: sales@williamfreeman.com

G M D Mouldings Ltd, Dec House, 143-145 Cardiff Road, Reading, RG1 8JF Tel: 0118-957 2188 Fax: 0118-957 1218 E-mail: martin@mclayton.fsbusiness.co.uk

Glendenning Plastics Ltd, First Avenue, The Pensnett Estate, Kingswinford, West Midlands, DY6 7TZ Tel: (01384) 278256 Fax: (01384) 400091 E-mail: sales@garlandproducts.com

Mick Graham Plastics Ltd, Unit 17 19, Argall Avenue, London, E10 7QP Tel: (020) 8539 7388 Fax: (020) 8539 2355

Grainger Plastics Ltd, Unit 3 Joseph Wilson Industrial Estate, Millstrood Road, Whitstable, Kent, CT5 3PS Tel: (01227) 276806 Fax: (01227) 770731

H P M Ltd, Unit 9, Ascot Industrial Estate, Lenton St, Nottingham, NG10 5DL Tel: 0115-939 0716 Fax: 0115-949 1106 E-mail: info@hpmltd.com

Hampson Composites Ltd, Vale Mill, Vale Street, Bolton, BL2 6QF Tel: (01204) 381626 Fax: (01204) 529457 E-mail: liz@hampson-composites.co.uk

Harrison Adams Ltd, Victoria Mills, Knowler Hill, Liversedge, West Yorkshire, WF15 6DP Tel: (01924) 402435 Fax: (01924) 404814 E-mail: travor@harrisonadamsmouldings. wannado.co.uk

Hi Mark Ltd, Unit A Spectrum Business Park, Wrexham Industrial Estate, Wrexham, Clwyd, LL13 9QA Tel: (01978) 660444 Fax: (01978) 660200 E-mail: sales@hi-mark.co.uk

Hilbar Plastics, Windley Works, Wolsey Street, Radcliffe, Manchester, M26 3BB Tel: 0161-724 4325 Fax: 0161-725 9158

Hillside Plastics Ltd, St. Johns Road, Meadowfield, Durham, DH7 8XQ Tel: 0191-378 0598 Fax: 0191-378 9346 E-mail: enquiries@hillside-plastics.co.uk

Hytec Plastic Mouldings Ltd, Unit 2e & 2g Chase Park Industrial Estate Ring Road, Chasetown Industrial Estate, Burntwood Business Park, Burntwood, Staffordshire, WS7 3JQ Tel: (01543) 687200 Fax: (01543) 673392 E-mail: peterlucas@hytecplastics.com

Inabata UK, Oaktree Place Road 35, Hortonwood Industrial Estate, Telford, Shropshire, TF1 7FR Tel: (01952) 670192 Fax: (01952) 608548 E-mail: enq@ikp.co.uk

Industrial Moulded Products Ltd, Unit 7 Reaymer Close, Walsall, WS2 7QZ Tel: (01922) 497376 Fax: (01922) 491117 E-mail: general@inmodprod.demon.co.uk

Inject Plastics (Devon) Ltd, 1-6 The Stables, Ford Road, Totnes, Devon, TQ9 5LE Tel: (01803) 863704 Fax: (01803) 865991 E-mail: sales@injectplastics.co.uk

Injection Moulding Co., Unit 1b Betton Way, Moretonhampstead, Newton Abbot, Devon, TQ13 8NA Tel: (01647) 440055 Fax: (01647) 441055 E-mail: timco@tiscali.co.uk

J G Coates Burnley Ltd, Trafalgar Street, Burnley, Lancashire, BB11 1TH Tel: (01282) 424376 Fax: (01282) 456166 E-mail: sales@cotel.co.uk

Jonesco (Preston) Ltd, Pittman Way, Fulwood, Preston, PR2 9ZD Tel: (01772) 704488 Fax: (01772) 702209 E-mail: sales@jonesco-plastics.com

JTH Patternmakers Ltd, Players Foundry, Clydach, Swansea, SA6 5BQ Tel: (01792) 842363 Fax: (01792) 845275 E-mail: enquiries@jthpatternmakers.co.uk

K J T Plastics Ltd, Unit 4-5 Happy Valley Industrial Estate, Primrose Hill, Kings Langley, Hertfordshire, WD4 8HD Tel: (01923) 267913 Fax: (01923) 261853

Kavia Mouldings Ltd, Unit 8, Balderstone Close, Heasandford Industrial Estate, Burnley, Lancashire, BB10 2BS Tel: (01282) 423935 Fax: (01282) 426105 E-mail: kavia.mouldingsltd@virgin.net

Kay Dee Engineering Plastics Ltd, 2 Jubilee Court, Thackley Old Road, Shipley, West Yorkshire, BD18 1QF Tel: (01274) 590824 Fax: (01274) 531409 E-mail: info@kaylan.co.uk

Kimlyn Products Ltd, 28 Armstrong Road, Tamworth, Staffordshire, B79 7TA Tel: (01827) 66933 Fax: (01827) 66323

L M C Technik Ltd, Cherry Way, Dubmire Industrial Estate, Houghton le Spring, Tyne & Wear, DH4 5RJ Tel: 0191-385 8500 Fax: 0191-385 7819 E-mail: sales@lmctechnik.com

Ledwell Plastics Ltd, 33 Cannock Street, Leicester, LE4 9HR Tel: 0116-276 6221 Fax: 0116-246 0134 E-mail: sales@ledplasticsgroup.co.uk

Leithen Valley Plastics, Leithen Road, Innerleithen, Peeblesshire, EH44 6HX Tel: (01896) 830345 Fax: (01896) 830345

Lettergold Plastics Ltd, 4 Hammond Close, Newmarket, Suffolk, CB8 0AZ Tel: (01638) 666888 Fax: (01638) 666999 E-mail: info@lettergold.co.uk

▶ Lifecare Hospital Supplies Ltd, Shenstone Drive, Aldridge, Walsall, WS9 8TP Tel: (01922) 455405 Fax: (01922) 749943 E-mail: rhall@hs-lifecare.com

Linpac Automotive Southend, Thornford Gardens, Southend-on-Sea, SS2 6PU Tel: (01702) 349481 Fax: (01702) 343982

LINPAC Environmental, Leafield Way, Leafield Industrial Estate, Corsham, Wiltshire, SN13 9UD Tel: (01225) 816500 Fax: (01225) 816501 E-mail: paxton@linpac.com

Malton Plastics UK Ltd, Enterprise Way, Thornton Road Industrial Estate, Pickering, North Yorkshire, YO18 7NA Tel: (01751) 477760 Fax: (01751) 477760 E-mail: sales@maltonplastics.com

Marlin Products Ltd, Boundary Road, Buckingham Road Industrial Estate, Brackley, Northamptonshire, NN13 7ES Tel: (01280) 705484 Fax: (01280) 700242 E-mail: marlinproducts@btconnect.com

Irvine Martin Ltd, Kenton Road, Debenham, Stowmarket, Suffolk, IP14 6LA Tel: (01728) 860909 Fax: (01728) 861056 E-mail: info@irvine-martin.co.uk

Masona Plastics, Avis Way, Newhaven, East Sussex, BN9 0DH Tel: (01273) 612440 Fax: (01273) 611495 E-mail: ken@masona.co.uk

Massmould Holdings Ltd, Maulden Road, Flitwick, Bedford, MK45 5BZ Tel: (01525) 718718 Fax: (01525) 712111

Merit Plastic Mouldings Ltd, Vinces Road, Diss, Norfolk, IP22 4YE Tel: (01379) 644321 Fax: (01379) 644236 E-mail: mpm@meritplastics.co.uk

Merlin Plastics, Charity Farm, Baxterley, Atherstone, Warwickshire, CV9 2LN Tel: (01827) 874572 Fax: (01827) 874898

Merriott, Tail Mill Lane, Merriott, Somerset, TA16 5PG Tel: (01460) 72457 Fax: (01460) 74481 E-mail: sales@merriott.com

Messider Plastics, 101 Villiers Road, London, NW2 5QB Tel: (020) 8459 3017 Fax: (020) 8830 1787

Milford Mouldings Ltd, Unit 36 38, Station Road Industrial Estate, Hailsham, East Sussex, BN27 2EY Tel: (01323) 440561 Fax: (01323) 449349

Modern Moulds Associates Ltd, Lightsfield, Oakley, Basingstoke, Hampshire, RG23 7BY Tel: (01256) 782333 Fax: (01256) 782915

Moldwell Products Ltd, John Street, Walsall, WS2 8AF Tel: (01922) 631252 Fax: (01922) 631225 E-mail: moldwel@aol.com

Morris Plastics Comallo Ltd, Unit B Spring Bank Industrial Estate, Watson Mill Lane, Sowerby Bridge, West Yorkshire, HX6 3BW Tel: (01422) 831821 Fax: (01422) 834182

MTM Engineering Services, Redfern Indust Estate, Dawson Street, Hyde, Cheshire, SK14 1QZ Tel: 0161-367 7650 Fax: 0161-367 7650 E-mail: carolynoldham@hotmail.co.uk

N P Aerospace Ltd, 473 Foleshill Road, Coventry, CV6 5AQ Tel: (024) 7663 8464 Fax: (024) 7668 7313 E-mail: info@np-aerospace.co.uk

N & P Thermo Plastic Moulders Acton Ltd, 69-73 Stirling Road, London, W3 8DJ Tel: (020) 8992 8258 Fax: (020) 8993 0860

Naiad Plastics Ltd, 16 Thorgate Road, Wick, Littlehampton, West Sussex, BN17 7LU Tel: (01903) 724302 Fax: (01903) 730925 E-mail: naiad@naiadplastics.com

Y.M. Newmark, Duchess Street Industrial Estate, Duchess Street, Shaw, Oldham, OL2 7UT Tel: (01706) 291295 Fax: (01706) 291297 E-mail: info@newmarks.co.uk

Ninefields Holdings Ltd, 1 & 2 Bruce Grove, Heron Trading Estate, Wickford, Essex, SS11 8DB Tel: (01268) 732148 Fax: (01268) 764394 E-mail: info@ninefields.co.uk

Norton Plastics, The Old Gasworks, Belfield Street, Ilkeston, Derbyshire, DE7 8DU Tel: 0115-944 1245 Fax: 0115-932 8975 E-mail: norton.plastics@vigin.net

Norwich Plastics Ltd, Mission Road, Rackheath, Norwich, NR13 6PL Tel: (01603) 720714 Fax: (01603) 721539

Origin Precision Mouldings Ltd, 19 Colvilles Place, Kelvin Industrial Estate, East Kilbride, Glasgow, G75 0PZ Tel: (01355) 244554 Fax: (01355) 245054 E-mail: admin@originprecision.com

Osprey Ltd, 12A Eden Way, Pages Industrial Park, Leighton Buzzard, Bedfordshire, LU7 4TZ Tel: (01525) 851505 Fax: (01525) 851501E-mail: leighton@osprey-plastics.co.uk

Osprey Ltd, Dunslow Road, Scarborough, North Yorkshire, YO11 3GS Tel: (01723) 585333 Fax: (01723) 585226 E-mail: jeff@osprey-plastics.co.uk

P & M Mouldings, 1 Brampton Sidings Industrial Estate, Hempstalls Lane, Newcastle, Staffordshire, ST5 0SR Tel: (01782) 713237 Fax: (01782) 713237

P P Injection Moulds & Moulding Ltd, Beversbrook Industrial Estate, Redman Road, Calne, Wiltshire, SN11 9PL Tel: (01249) 823100 Fax: (01249) 823103 E-mail: sales@ppmoulds.co.uk

Parksville Plastics, Unit 27-29 Crown Trading Centre, Clayton Road, Hayes, Middlesex, UB3 1DU Tel: (020) 8848 4500 Fax: (020) 8573 9596

Partridge Plastics Worthing Ltd, G H Northbrook Trading Estate, Northbrook Road, Worthing, West Sussex, BN14 8PN Tel: (01903) 213178 Fax: (01903) 204684 E-mail: sales@partridgeplastics.com

Peak Plastics Ltd, Derwent Business Park, Heage Road, Ripley, Derbyshire, DE5 3GH Tel: (01773) 743152 Fax: (01773) 513478 E-mail: sales@peakplastics.co.uk

Penatube Ltd, Boomes Trading Estate Dovers Corner, New Road, Rainham, Essex, RM13 8QT Tel: (01708) 555595 Fax: (01708) 526276 E-mail: SAQIB21@GMAIL.COM

Pentech Moulding Co. Ltd, Pump Lane Industrial Estate, Silverdale Road, Hayes, Middlesex, UB3 3BN Tel: (020) 8569 3439 Fax: (020) 8569 1219 E-mail: rapidpartner@gmail.com

Perfectools Plastics, Coombend, Radstock, BA3 3AS Tel: (01761) 432299 Fax: (01761) 435575 E-mail: sales@perfecttools.co.uk

Pioneer Associates Ltd, Ibex Barn, Ferro Fields, Brixworth, Northampton, NN6 9UA Tel: (01604) 882362 Fax: (01604) 882362 E-mail: sales@pioneer-associates-ltd.co.uk

Plasmotec, F Lincoln Park, Ward Road, Buckingham Road Industrial Estate, Brackley, Northamptonshire, NN13 7LE Tel: (01280) 701335 Fax: (01280) 701341 E-mail: sales@plasmotec.co.uk

Plastech Group Ltd, Flemington Road, Glenrothes, Fife, KY7 5PZ Tel: (01592) 752212 Fax: (01592) 610315 E-mail: sales@plastechgroup.com

Plastic Associates Ltd, Unit 1 North Street Trading Estate, Brierley Hill, West Midlands, DY5 3QF Tel: (01384) 480470 Fax: (01384) 480470

Plastic Engineering Ltd, Juno Drive, Leamington Spa, Warwickshire, CV31 3TA Tel: (01926) 334248 Fax: (01926) 461720 E-mail: plastic@pels.co.uk

Plastic Parts Direct Ltd, Thorpe Way, Banbury, Oxfordshire, OX16 4SP Tel: (01295) 269333 Fax: (01295) 273276 E-mail: info@apmonline.co.uk

Plastic Products International Ltd, 8-11 Capital Place, Harlow, Essex, CM19 5AS Tel: (01279) 445041 Fax: (08704) 601340 E-mail: sales@plastics-products.net

Polytech Plastic Products, Bullock Street, West Bromwich, West Midlands, B70 7HE Tel: 0121-525 7777 Fax: 0121-525 6777 E-mail: riaarnumber2@aol.com

Precision Cast Components, Uskway, Newport, Gwent, NP20 2JY Tel: (01633) 214565 Fax: (01633) 216204 E-mail: info@precision-cast.co.uk

▶ Prime Plastic Mouldings Ltd, 8 Heron Industrial Estate, Basingstoke Road, Spencers Wood, Reading, RG7 1PJ Tel: 0118-988 7525 Fax: 0118-988 7526 E-mail: sales@primeplas.com

Protomould Ltd, Unit B2 Springhead Enterprise Park, Springhead Road, Northfleet, Gravesend, Kent, DA11 8HB Tel: (01474) 353525 Fax: (01474) 353526 E-mail: sales@protomould.co.uk

PRP, Unit 7 Tarsmill Court, Rotherwas Industrial Estate, Hereford, HR2 6JZ Tel: (01432) 357686 Fax: (01432) 352702 E-mail: info@prp.co.uk

R & A Components, Thompson Street, Padiham, Burnley, Lancashire, BB12 7BG Tel: (01282) 774397

R B Mouldings Ltd, 3 Kings Haven, Kings Road, Charfleets Industrial Estate, Canvey Island, Essex, SS8 0QW Tel: (01268) 690626 Fax: (01268) 510106 E-mail: roger@rbmouldings.fsbuisness.co.uk

R G E Engineering Co. Ltd, Bridge Works, The Avenue, Godmanchester, Huntingdon, Cambridgeshire, PE29 2AF Tel: (01480) 450771 Fax: (01480) 411359 E-mail: sales@rgegroup.com

Red Rose Mouldings, Unit 9 Fountain Mill, Carluke Street, Blackburn, BB1 3JR Tel: (01254) 693329 Fax: (01254) 278134

Reevite Ltd, 16 Murdock Road, Bicester, Oxfordshire, OX26 4PP Tel: (01869) 252520 Fax: (01869) 241394 E-mail: info@reevite.co.uk

Regency Mouldings Worcester Ltd, Hylton Road, Worcester, WR2 5JS Tel: (01905) 424909 Fax: (01905) 748310 E-mail: timco@btclick.com

Roe, Salop Street, Bolton, BL2 1DZ Tel: (01204) 523188 Fax: (01204) 523178 E-mail: p_roe@btconnect.com

Roland Plastics Ltd, High Street, Wickham Market, Woodbridge, Suffolk, IP13 0RF Tel: (01728) 747777 Fax: (01728) 748222 E-mail: ben@rolandplastics.com

Rolinx Plastics Co. Ltd, Ledson Road, Wythenshawe, Manchester, M23 9WP Tel: 0161-610 6400 Fax: 0161-610 6474 E-mail: enquiries@rolinx.co.uk

PLASTIC MOULDINGS - *continued*

Rubber & Plastic Profiles Co., Unit 1, 35 Boldmere Road, Sutton Coldfield, West Midlands, B73 5UY Tel: 0121-354 6356 Fax: 0121-355 7290 E-mail: info@rubberandplasticprofiles.co.uk

S B Weston Ltd, 5 Cypress Court, Harris Way, Sunbury-on-Thames, Middlesex, TW16 7EL Tel: (01932) 785544 Fax: (01932) 761294 E-mail: sales@sbweston.com

Selsmore (Marketing) Ltd, Unit 23 The Tanneries, Brockhampton Lane, Havant, Hampshire, PO9 1JB Tel: (023) 9249 2907 Fax: (023) 9247 3714 E-mail: selsmore@tiscali.co.uk

Serco Plastic Injection Moulders Ltd, Woden Road, Wolverhampton, WV10 0AU Tel: (01902) 351233 Fax: (01902) 351485

Skiffy, 5 Wombourne Enterprise Park, Bridgnorth Road, Wombourne, Wolverhampton, WV5 0AL Tel: (01902) 894658 Fax: (01902) 894661 E-mail: skiffyuk@btconnect.com

Sovrin Plastics Ltd, Stirling Road, Slough, SL1 4ST Tel: (01753) 825155 Fax: (01753) 654923 E-mail: sales@sovrin.com

Peter Sowter & Co. Ltd, Components House, 5 Holmes Close, Wokingham, Berkshire, RG41 2SG Tel: 0118-978 2691 Fax: 0118-978 2691

Spatz Shop, Unit 9 Brook Street, Redditch, Worcestershire, B98 8NG Tel: (01527) 68168 Fax: (01527) 60026 E-mail: sales@spatz.uk.com

Stadium Plastics South West Ltd, Forde Road, Newton Abbot, Devon, TQ12 4AE Tel: (01626) 333338 Fax: (01626) 331487

Straight Line Products Ltd, Unit 39 Uxbridge Trading Estate, Arundel Road, Uxbridge, Middlesex, UB8 2RP Tel: (01895) 850577 Fax: (01895) 850766 E-mail: george@straightlineproducts.co.uk

Stuma Plastics Ltd, Atlas Works, Mornington Road, Bolton, BL1 4EZ Tel: (01204) 492862 Fax: (01204) 493090 E-mail: enquiries@stuma.co.uk

Styleguard Ltd, 7 Long Acre Trading Estate, Long Acre, Birmingham, B7 5JD Tel: 0121-327 3222 Fax: 0121-328 4312

Sycon Ltd, Underleys, Beer, Seaton, Devon, EX12 3NA Tel: (01297) 21391 Fax: (01297) 625991

T J H Precision Plastics Ltd, 6 Davy Road, Clacton-on-Sea, Essex, CO15 4XD Tel: (01255) 220736 Fax: (01255) 476446 E-mail: tjh@angliannet.co.uk

T.S.G Plastics Caerphilly Ltd, Pontygwindy Industrial Estate, Douglas Works, Caerphilly, Mid Glamorgan, CF83 3HU Tel: (029) 2086 8513 Fax: (029) 2088 8815 E-mail: dave.hunter@tsgplatics.co.uk

Talana Plastics Ltd, 28 Standard Way, Fareham, Hampshire, PO16 8XG Tel: (01329) 822940 Fax: (01329) 231034 E-mail: enquiries@talanaplastics.com

TCB-Arrow Ltd, Watchmoor House, Watchmoor Road, Camberley, Surrey, GU15 3AQ Tel: (01276) 679394 Fax: (01276) 679055 E-mail: sales@tcbarrow.co.uk

Teckno Plastics, 43 Ryecroft Rd, Frampton Cotterell, Bristol, BS36 2HN Tel: 01454 777622

TG Engineering Plastics Ltd, Britannia Mills, Stoney Battery, Huddersfield, HD1 4TL Tel: (01484) 655221 Fax: (01484) 644779 E-mail: tom.tgeng@btconnect.com

Titan Environmental Ltd, 37 Seagoe Industrial Estate, Portadown, Craigavon, County Armagh, BT63 5QD Tel: (028) 3833 0668 Fax: (028) 3835 0171 E-mail: sales@titanenv.com

United Moulders Ltd, Farnham Trading Estate, Farnham, Surrey, GU9 9NY Tel: (01420) 86616 Fax: (01252) 721250 E-mail: sales@uml.co.uk

Vactec Derby Ltd, Eagle Road, Quarry Hill Industrial Estate, Ilkeston, Derbyshire, DE7 4RB Tel: 0115-930 4806 Fax: 0115-930 4806

Wetherells Contracts Ltd, 9 The Crescent, Selby, North Yorkshire, YO8 4PD Tel: (01757) 702161 Fax: (01757) 704026

Wheatley Plastics Ltd, Reynolds Mill, Newbridge Lane, Stockport, Cheshire, SK1 2NR Tel: 0161-477 2800 Fax: 0161-480 6611 E-mail: wheatley.plastics@btconnect.com

Whitmarley Engineering Co. Ltd, Ivy Road, Stirchley, Birmingham, B30 2NX Tel: 0121-458 7491 Fax: 0121-433 4137 E-mail: enquiries@whitmarley.fsnet.co.uk

E. & R. Wild (Plastic Moulders) Ltd, 67 St. Mary's Road, Market Harborough, Leicestershire, LE16 7DS Tel: (01858) 463074 Fax: (01858) 431732

Wyke Plastics Plastic Moulders, Bradford Road, Brighouse, West Yorkshire, HD6 4BW Tel: (01484) 710414 Fax: (01484) 711649

PLASTIC MOULDINGS MATERIAL SELECTION

Resin Express Ltd, 11 Valley Business Centre, Gordon Road, High Wycombe, Buckinghamshire, HP13 6EQ Tel: (01494) 459881 Fax: (01494) 795334 E-mail: sales@resinexpress.com

PLASTIC MOULDINGS TO SPECIFICATION

Arrow Plastics Ltd, Arrow Works, Hampden Road, Kingston upon Thames, Surrey, KT1 3HQ Tel: (020) 8546 6258 Fax: (020) 8541 4654 E-mail: mail@arrow-plastics.co.uk

Dorset Technical Mouldings, Unit C20-24, Holton Road, Holton Heath Trading Park, Poole, Dorset, BH16 6LT Tel: (01202) 624790 Fax: (01202) 623761 E-mail: sales@dtm-poole.fsnet.co.uk

Emp Tooling Services Ltd, Brockhampton Lane, Havant, Hampshire, PO9 1LU Tel: (023) 9249 2626 Fax: (023) 9249 2582 E-mail: info@e-m-p.biz

K J K Plastics Ltd, 51 Knowl Piece, Wilbury Way, Hitchin, Hertfordshire, SG4 0TY Tel: (01462) 420422 Fax: (01462) 420242 E-mail: sales@kjkplastics.co.uk

PLASTIC MOULDINGS, ELECTRICAL/ELECTRONICS INDUSTRY

Lennox Foundry Co. Ltd, Bredgar Road, Gillingham, Kent, ME8 6PN Tel: (01634) 386683 Fax: (01634) 386684 E-mail: lennox@kestner-eng.co.uk

PLASTIC MOULDINGS, INJECTION

Warden Group, 464 Dunstable Road, Luton, LU4 8DR Tel: (01582) 573030 Fax: (01582) 508751 E-mail: admin@wardenplastics.co.uk

PLASTIC MOULDINGS, TECHNICAL/INDUSTRIAL

A P I C Plastics Ltd, 28 Plantation Road, Amersham, Buckinghamshire, HP6 6HJ Tel: (01494) 431066 Fax: (01494) 726309 E-mail: apicplastics@lineone.net

Abaloid Plastics Ltd, 165 Scudamore Road, Leicester, LE3 1UQ Tel: 0116-232 0212 Fax: 0116-232 0569 E-mail: enquiries@abaloidplastics.co.uk

Associated Roto-Plastics Ltd, Green Grove Mill, Dyehouse Lane, Rochdale, Lancashire, OL16 2QN Tel: (0870) 8303900 Fax: (0870) 8303901 E-mail: sales@haywood-rotomoulding.co.uk

Cameron-Price Medical Division Ltd, Charlotte Road, Stirchley, Birmingham, B30 2BT Tel: 0121-459 2121 Fax: 0121-451 2303 E-mail: info@cameron-price.co.uk

Captive Closures, Burma Road, Blidworth, Mansfield, Nottinghamshire, NG21 0RT Tel: (01623) 491112 Fax: (01623) 491113 E-mail: captive.mick@btconnect.com

Chas Tennant & Co., 81 Lochburn Road, Glasgow, G20 9AE Tel: 0141-946 1833 Fax: 0141-946 5752 E-mail: enquiries@tennantsdistribution.com

Component Moulders, 4-5 Teville Industrials, Dominion Way, Worthing, West Sussex, BN14 8NW Tel: (01903) 235765 Fax: (01903) 212751 E-mail: sales@nordell.co.uk

Creighton Developments Ltd, Unit 15 Enterprise Centre Two, Chester Street, Stockport, Cheshire, SK3 0BR Tel: 0161-480 0668 Fax: 0161-480 0668

Cromwell Plastics Ltd, 53-54 New Street, Quarry Bank, Brierley Hill, West Midlands, DY5 2AZ Tel: (01384) 564146 Fax: (01384) 561645 E-mail: sales@cromwell-plastics.co.uk

Crown Plastic Moulding Ltd, Broad Lanes, Bilston, West Midlands, WV14 0RY Tel: (01902) 496151 Fax: (01902) 493102 E-mail: sales@crown-plastic-mouldings.co.uk

C.T.P. Davall Ltd, Durham Lane Industrial Park, Eaglescliffe, Stockton-On-Tees, Cleveland, TS16 0RB Tel: (01554) 749000 Fax: (01642) 790779 E-mail: paul.caldwell@carclo-plc.com

Europlaz Technologies Ltd, The Maltings Industrial Estate, Southminster, Essex, CM0 7EH Tel: (01621) 773471 Fax: (01621) 773792 E-mail: enquiries@europlaz.co.uk

Firma Nicand Plastic Products Ltd, Unit D Woodley Airfield, Headley Road East, Woodley, Reading, RG5 4SA Tel: 0118-969 6939 Fax: 0118-944 1625 E-mail: kiran@firmanicand.com

Glendenning Plastics Ltd, First Avenue, The Pensnett Estate, Kingswinford, West Midlands, DY6 7TZ Tel: (01384) 278256 Fax: (01384) 400091 E-mail: sales@garlandproducts.com

Holloid Plastics Ltd, Stephenson Road, Basingstoke, Hampshire, RG21 6XR Tel: (01256) 334700 Fax: (01256) 473735 E-mail: mail@holloid-plastics.co.uk

I C M (Plastic Moulding) Ltd, Enterprise Close, Medway City Estate, Rochester, Kent, ME2 4LY Tel: (01634) 298500 Fax: (01634) 714338 E-mail: info@icm-plasticmoulding.co.uk

Injection Mouldings Ltd, Cotswold Court Park, Gloucester Road, Staverton, Cheltenham, Gloucestershire, GL51 0TF Tel: (01452) 854077 Fax: (01452) 855077 E-mail: info@injectionmouldingsltd.co.uk

J G Coates Burnley Ltd, Trafalgar Street, Burnley, Lancashire, BB11 1TH Tel: (01282) 424376 Fax: (01282) 456166 E-mail: sales@cotel.co.uk

Jilks Plastics Ltd, 31 Trowers Way, Redhill, RH1 2LH Tel: (01737) 779799 Fax: (01737) 779800 E-mail: sales@jilksplasticsltd.co.uk

L M C Technik Ltd, Cherry Way, Dubmire Industrial Estate, Houghton le Spring, Tyne & Wear, DH4 5RJ Tel: 0191-385 8500 Fax: 0191-385 7819 E-mail: sales@lmctechnik.com

Maclan Plastics, Unit Ba Keighley Business Centre, South Street, Keighley, West Yorkshire, BD21 1AG Tel: (01535) 680127 Fax: (01535) 680222 E-mail: info@maclanplastics.co.uk

Malton Plastics UK Ltd, Enterprise Way, Thornton Road Industrial Estate, Pickering, North Yorkshire, YO18 7NA Tel: (01751) 477760 Fax: (01751) 477760 E-mail: sales@maltonplastics.com

Merlin Plastics, Charity Farm, Baxterley, Atherstone, Warwickshire, CV9 2LN Tel: (01827) 874572 Fax: (01827) 874898

Miles Platts Ltd, 39 Abbey Park Road, Leicester, LE4 5AN Tel: 0116-262 2593 Fax: 0116-253 7889 E-mail: enquiries@milesplatts.co.uk

Minitek Mouldings Ltd, Pennard Close, Brackmills Industrial Estate, Northampton, NN4 7BE Tel: (01604) 767397 Fax: (01604) 706805 E-mail: info@minitekmouldings.co.uk

Moldwell Products Ltd, John Street, Walsall, WS2 8AF Tel: (01922) 631252 Fax: (01922) 631225 E-mail: moldwel@aol.com

Neptune Engineering Co., E Caxton Hill, Extension Road, Hertford, SG13 7LY Tel: (01992) 587889 Fax: (01992) 554478 E-mail: sales@neptune-eng.demon.co.uk

Norton Plastics, The Old Gasworks, Belfield Street, Ilkeston, Derbyshire, DE7 8DU Tel: 0115-944 1245 Fax: 0115-932 8975 E-mail: norton.plastics@vigin.net

Plasmotec, F Lincoln Park, Ward Road, Buckingham Road Industrial Estate, Brackley, Northamptonshire, NN13 7LE Tel: (01280) 701335 Fax: (01280) 701341 E-mail: sales@plasmotec.co.uk

Plastic Development Techniques Ltd, Lyon Way, St. Albans, Hertfordshire, AL4 0LB Tel: (01727) 866317 Fax: (01727) 847060

Plastic Parts Direct Ltd, Thorpe Way, Banbury, Oxfordshire, OX16 4SP Tel: (01295) 269333 Fax: (01295) 273276 E-mail: info@apmonline.co.uk

Rugby Plastics Ltd, 11 Lanchester Way, Royal Oak Industrial Estate, Daventry, Northamptonshire, NN11 8PH Tel: (01327) 702668 Fax: (01327) 300468 E-mail: sales@rugbyplastics.com

Skar Precision Mouldings Ltd, Lady Lane Industrial Estate, Hadleigh, Ipswich, IP7 6AZ Tel: (01473) 828000 Fax: (01473) 828001 E-mail: sales@skar.co.uk

Sky Plastics Ltd, Eastfield Side, Sutton-in-Ashfield, Nottinghamshire, NG17 4JR Tel: (01623) 553527 Fax: (01623) 556737 E-mail: sales@skyplastics.demon.co.uk

Slatebond Ltd, Unit 27 Leafield Industrial Estate, Leafield Way, Neston, Corsham, Wiltshire, SN13 9RS Tel: (01225) 810099 Fax: (01225) 811413 E-mail: sales@slatebond.com

Straight Line Products Ltd, Unit 39 Uxbridge Trading Estate, Arundel Road, Uxbridge, Middlesex, UB8 2RP Tel: (01895) 850577 Fax: (01895) 850766 E-mail: george@straightlineproducts.co.uk

United Moulders Ltd, Farnham Trading Estate, Farnham, Surrey, GU9 9NY Tel: (01420) 86616 Fax: (01252) 721250 E-mail: sales@uml.co.uk

W H Smith & Sons Tools Ltd, Water Orton Lane, Minworth, Sutton Coldfield, West Midlands, B76 9BG Tel: 0121-748 7777 Fax: 0121-749 6213 E-mail: info@whs-tools.com

Wheatley Plastics Ltd, Reynolds Mill, Newbridge Lane, Stockport, Cheshire, SK1 2NR Tel: 0161-477 2800 Fax: 0161-480 6611 E-mail: wheatley.plastics@btconnect.com

Wyke Plastics Plastic Moulders, Bradford Road, Brighouse, West Yorkshire, HD6 4BW Tel: (01484) 710414 Fax: (01484) 711649

Zeta Plastic Components Ltd, Ravensthorpe Industrial Estate, Dewsbury, West Yorkshire, WF13 3LN Tel: (01924) 491900 Fax: (01924) 491917

PLASTIC NAMEPLATES

Abbey Craftsmen, 127 Haslemere Road, Liphook, Hampshire, GU30 7BX Tel: (01428) 727187 Fax: (0800) 0561362 E-mail: terry@abbey.go-plus.net

Alamode Engraving & Sign Co. Ltd, 3 Reform Street, Hull, HU2 8EF Tel: (01482) 323704 Fax: (01482) 216403 E-mail: sales@alamode.freeserve.co.uk

Autosigns Ltd, North Mills, Frog Island, Leicester, LE3 5DH Tel: 0116-262 9526 Fax: 0116-251 2889 E-mail: enquiries@autosigns.co.uk

Barrett Inter Signs Co Ltd, 18 Farlow Road, Northfield, Birmingham, B31 3AE Tel: 0121-477 7396 Fax: 0121-477 7414

Beta Engravers (Northampton) Ltd, Clarence Avenue, Northampton, NN2 6NY Tel: (01604) 715152 Fax: (01604) 717131

Diamond Graphics, Norton House, 61a High Street, Wordsley, Stourbridge, West Midlands, DY8 5SD Tel: (01384) 572878 Fax: (01384) 481975

Gilchrist & Co., 90 Donegall Passage, Belfast, BT7 1BX Tel: (028) 9023 2453 Fax: (028) 9032 6700

GPS Developments Ltd, 14 Darlington Close, Sandy, Bedfordshire, SG19 1RW Tel: (01767) 681560 Fax: (01767) 691685 E-mail: sales@gpsdevelopments.co.uk

Grainword Ltd, 3 Warnford Industrial Estate, Clayton Road, Hayes, Middlesex, UB3 1BQ Tel: (020) 8561 2401 Fax: (020) 8756 0501 E-mail: sales@supapress.com

Hitech Signmakers Ltd, 65-81 Townsend St, Glasgow, G4 0LA Tel: 0141-332 4111 Fax: 0141-331 1906 E-mail: sales@hitechsigns.co.uk

John Mcgavigan Information Technology Ltd, 111 Westerhill Road, Bishopbriggs, Glasgow, G64 2QR Tel: 0141-302 0000 Fax: 0141-302 0290 E-mail: enquiries@mcgavigan.com

Plastic & Metal Engravings, 9 Benson Road, Poole, Dorset, BH17 0GB Tel: (01202) 677393 Fax: (01202) 681455 E-mail: sales@plasticandmetalengraving.co.uk

Rand Markings Ltd, 39-40 Brunel Road, St. Leonards-on-Sea, East Sussex, TN38 9RT Tel: (01424) 854646 Fax: (01424) 854645 E-mail: info@randmarkings.co.uk

F.J. Rogers Engravers, 10 Tacket Street, Ipswich, IP4 1AY Tel: (01473) 251836

Sign & Label Centre Ltd, Dock Road, Connah's Quay, Deeside, Clwyd, CH5 4DS Tel: (01244) 813660 Fax: (01244) 816812 E-mail: sales@signandlabelcentre.com

SJH Engraving, 74 Cecil Street, Birmingham, B19 3SU Tel: 0121-359 1321 Fax: 0121-333 4668

Total Plastics Ltd, Heming Road, Washford East, Redditch, Worcestershire, B98 0EA Tel: (01527) 500292 Fax: (01527) 501188 E-mail: totalplastics@proweb.co.uk

Trade Advertising Services, The Bungalow Manor Lane, Unit 11 K U S Industrial Estate, Hawarden, Deeside, Clwyd, CH5 3DP Tel: (01244) 520351 Fax: (01244) 536363 E-mail: tradeadvertising@aol.com

Vale Nameplates, Winster Grove, Great Barr, Birmingham, B44 9EJ Tel: 0121-360 8785 Fax: 0121-366 6003 E-mail: pat@valenameplates.co.uk

Willprint Screen Process Printers, 7 Pomeroy Drive, Oadby, Leicester, LE2 5NE Tel: 0116-271 0574 Fax: 0116-271 0550 E-mail: sales@willprints.co.uk

PLASTIC NUTS

Allthread Plastics Ltd, Ridley Road, Burnt Mills Industrial Estate, Basildon, Essex, SS13 1EG Tel: (01268) 726559 Fax: (01268) 725287 E-mail: sales@allthread.co.uk

PLASTIC OR ACRYLIC TAP TOPS

Pinmill Products, Units 5H-5K, Baker House, Manor Way Industrial Estate, Curzon Drive, Grays, Essex, RM17 6BG Tel: (01375) 392944 Fax: (01375) 379127 E-mail: pinmill@btinternet.com

PLASTIC OR PVC OR VINYL WALL CLADDING

Be-Plas Marketing Ltd, Unit 2 & 3 Old Hall Industrial Estate, Grisedale Road, Old Hall Industrial Estate, Wirral, Merseyside, CH62 3QA Tel: 0151-334 5133 Fax: 0151-334 9399 E-mail: sales@beplas.com

Specialised Fixing (East Anglia) Ltd, Unit 9, Farthing Road, Ipswich, IP1 5AP Tel: (01473) 461461 Fax: (01473) 240518 E-mail: spencer.priestley@omnico.co.uk

PLASTIC PACKAGED LIQUID TAPS

▶ Worldwide Dispensers, Merton Industrial Park, Lee Road, London, SW19 3WD Tel: (020) 8545 7500 Fax: (020) 8545 7502 E-mail: sales@dsswd.com

PLASTIC PACKAGING THERMOFORMING MACHINES

Henry Lenox Industrial Ltd, 9 Hanworth Road, Hampton, Middlesex, TW12 3DH Tel: (020) 8941 9274 Fax: (020) 8941 9374 E-mail: sales@henrylenox.co.uk

PLASTIC PAINT CONTAINERS

Superfos Runcorn Ltd., Edison Road, Astmoor Industrial Estate, Runcorn, Cheshire, WA7 1PY Tel: (01928) 575051 Fax: (01928) 572038 E-mail: steve.winstanley@superfos.co.uk

PLASTIC PALLET BOXES

▶ Dynawest Plastics Ltd, Jaylyn House, Elton Park Hadleigh Road, Ipswich, IP2 0DG Tel: (01473) 230248 Fax: (01473) 230256 E-mail: sales@dynawest.co.uk

PLASTIC PALLET OR STILLAGES

Clarehill Plastics Ltd, New Building, 21 Clarehill Road, Moira, Craigavon, County Armagh, BT67 0PB Tel: (028) 9261 1077 Fax: (028) 9261 2672 E-mail: info@clarehill.com

Craemer UK Ltd, Craemer House, Hortonwood 1, Telford, Shropshire, TF1 7GN Tel: (01952) 641366 Fax: (01952) 607801 E-mail: sales@craemer.co.uk

Linpac Materials Handling, Newfield Close, Walsall, WS2 7PB Tel: (01922) 726060 Fax: (01922) 643422 E-mail: lmhsolutions@linpac.com

PLASTIC PART DESIGN

Practical Designs, South Road, Harlow, Essex, CM20 2AS Tel: (01279) 432509 Fax: (01279) 431971 E-mail: sales@practical-design.co.uk

PLASTIC PERFORATORS, *See Perforated Plastic etc*

PLASTIC PIPELINE FITTINGS

▶ Glynwed Pipe Systems Ltd, St. Peters Road, Huntingdon, Cambridgeshire, PE29 7DA Tel: (01480 52121 Fax: (01480) 450430 E-mail: enquiries@gpsuk.com

Pipe Center, Unit 8B Cosgrove Way, Luton, LU1 1XL Tel: (01582) 404162 Fax: (01582) 459170

S V R Plastics Ltd, Units 5-6, Greenhey Place, Skelmersdale, Lancashire, WN8 9SA Tel: (01695) 50717 Fax: (01695) 50052 E-mail: sales@svrplastics.co.uk

PLASTIC PIPELINE SYSTEMS

Environ International Ltd, Environ International Ltd, Ernesettle Lane, Plymouth, PL5 2EY Tel: (01752) 360070 Fax: (01752) 360172 E-mail: enquiries@envproduct.com

International Plastic Systems Ltd, Seaham Grange Industrial Estate, Seaham, County Durham, SR7 0PT Tel: 0191-521 3111 Fax: 0191-521 3222 E-mail: info@ips-plastics.com

Jerome Engineering Ltd, Unit 30 Globe Industrial Estate, Rectory Road, Grays, Essex, RM17 6ST Tel: (01375) 898400 Fax: (01375) 898401 E-mail: tsmith@jeromeuk.com

Pipe Center, Unit 8B Cosgrove Way, Luton, LU1 1XL Tel: (01582) 404162 Fax: (01582) 459170

Wavin Plastics Ltd, Parsonage Way, Chippenham, Wiltshire, SN15 5PN Tel: (01249) 766600 Fax: (01249) 443286 E-mail: sales@wavin.co.uk

PLASTIC PIPES, *See Plastic Tubes etc*

PLASTIC PIPEWORK CONTRACTORS

Morton Industrial Plastics Ltd, Cook Lane, Heckmondwike, West Yorkshire, WF16 9JG Tel: (01924) 405550 Fax: (01924) 405770 E-mail: info@mipuk.com

Pipeline Services Ltd, 21 Princes Drive Industrial Estate, Coventry Road, Kenilworth, Warwickshire, CV8 2FD Tel: (01926) 511316 Fax: (01926) 512744 E-mail: sales@pipeserve.co.uk

T C Plastic Fabrications Ltd, Hawkmill Industrial Estate, Little Green Lane, Small Heath, Birmingham, B9 5BE Tel: 0121-773 2044 Fax: 0121-766 6623 E-mail: tom@tcplastics.wanadoo.co.uk

PLASTIC PIPEWORK FABRICATORS

Combined Insulations & Plastics Ltd, 6 Bedford Business Centre, Mile Road, Bedford, MK42 9TW Tel: 01234 211771 Fax: 01234 211771

East Kilbride Industrial Plastics, 25-27 Langlands Place, Kelvin South Business Park, East Kilbride, Glasgow, G75 0YF Tel: (01355) 236231 Fax: (01355) 235182 E-mail: ek.plastics@btinternet.com

Elgee Plastics Ltd, Wilson Road, Reading, RG30 2RS Tel: 0118-957 5430 Fax: 0118-958 8782

Ian Flockton Developments Ltd, Estate Road 1, South Humberside Industrial Estate, Grimsby, South Humberside, DN31 2TB Tel: (01472) 359634 Fax: (01472) 241392 E-mail: info@ianflockton.co.uk

Plasbrun Plastics Engineering Ltd, Unit C, Brookfield Drive, Cannock, Staffordshire, WS11 0JR Tel: (01543) 462802 Fax: (01543) 462806 E-mail: plasbrunplastics@yahoo.co.uk

Rotherham Industrial Plastic Co. Ltd, Clifton Terrace, Rotherham, South Yorkshire, S65 2AG Tel: (01709) 372008 Fax: (01709) 820243 E-mail: steve@rip-co.co.uk

S V R Plastics Ltd, Units 5-6, Greenhey Place, Skelmersdale, Lancashire, WN8 9SA Tel: (01695) 50717 Fax: (01695) 50052 E-mail: sales@svrplastics.co.uk

Wavin Plastics Ltd, Parsonage Way, Chippenham, Wiltshire, SN15 5PN Tel: (01249) 766600 Fax: (01249) 443286 E-mail: sales@wavin.co.uk

PLASTIC PIPEWORK STOCKHOLDERS

Lewis & Mason Plastics, Unit 47 Business Development Centre, Stafford Park 4, Telford, Shropshire, TF3 3BA Tel: (01952) 210322 Fax: (01952) 292647 E-mail: info@lewis-mason-plastics.co.uk

PLASTIC PLUMBING SYSTEMS

Geberit Ltd, New Hythe Business Park, Aylesford, Kent, ME20 7PJ Tel: (01622) 717811 Fax: (01622) 716920 E-mail: salesgb@geberit.com

Hepworth Building Products Holdings Ltd, Hazlehead, Crow Edge, Sheffield, S36 4HG Tel: (01226) 763561 Fax: (01226) 764827 E-mail: info@hepworth.co.uk

Mcalpine & Co. Ltd, 45 Kelvin Avenue, Hillington Industrial Estate, Glasgow, G52 4LF Tel: 0141-882 3213 Fax: 0141-891 5065

PLASTIC POCKET WALLETS

Donside Plastics Welding Ltd, Drill Hall, Upper Platts, Ticehurst, Wadhurst, East Sussex, TN5 7HA Tel: (01580) 200663 Fax: (01580) 200464

Emerald Weld PVC Stationery Manufacturer, 101 Station Road, Reddish, Stockport, Cheshire, SK5 6ND Tel: 0161-432 7200 Fax: 0161-442 1248 E-mail: info@emweld.com

Media Plastics, 8 Merrylees Industrial Estate, Lee Side, Desford, Leicester, LE9 9FS Tel: (01455) 292110 Fax: (01455) 292190 E-mail: sales@mediaplastics.co.uk

Metro Sales, Unit 1 Crathie Road, Off Western Road, Kilmarnock, Ayrshire, KA3 1NG Tel: (01563) 574481 Fax: (01563) 533537 E-mail: sales@metrosales.biz

Transmail Ltd, Unit 21 Concorde Road, Norwich, NR6 6BJ Tel: (01603) 404217 Fax: (01603) 483944 E-mail: sales@transmail.co.uk

PLASTIC POWDER

I C O UK Ltd, 24 Norris Way, Wellingborough Road, Rushden, Northamptonshire, NN10 6BP Tel: (01933) 315500 Fax: (01933) 313300

PLASTIC POWDER COATING SERVICES

Slough Plastic Coatings, 2 David Road, Colnbrook, Slough, SL3 0DG Tel: (01753) 683907 Fax: (01753) 682571 E-mail: sloughplastic@btconnect.com

PLASTIC POWDER GRINDING

Americhem Ltd, Cawdor Street, Eccles, Manchester, M30 0QF Tel: 0161-789 7832 Fax: 0161-787 7832

Extrusion & Moulding Compounds Ltd, Cwmavon, Pontypool, Gwent, NP4 8UW Tel: (01495) 772534 Fax: (01495) 772251

PLASTIC PRESSINGS, *See Plastic Mouldings*

PLASTIC PRESSURE PIPE SYSTEMS

Marley Plumbing & Drainage, Dickley Lane, Lenham, Maidstone, Kent, ME17 2DE Tel: (01622) 858888 Fax: (01622) 858725 E-mail: marketing@marleyext.com

PLASTIC PRICE TICKETS

Norman Pendred & Co. Ltd, Unit 4worsley Bridge Rdbroomsleigh Business Park, London, SE26 5BN Tel: (020) 8461 1155 Fax: (020) 8461 1166 E-mail: sales@pendred.com

PLASTIC PRINTING

Apt Art, PO Box 250, Kidlington, Oxfordshire, OX5 2WA Tel: (01865) 372981 E-mail: sales@aptart.co.uk

Atelier Screen Print Ltd, 130 Pershore Street, Birmingham, B5 6ND Tel: 0121-622 6301 Fax: 0121-666 6487 E-mail: atelier.screenprint@virgin.net

B S P Ltd, 26 Balmer Cut, Buckingham Industrial Estate, Buckingham, MK18 1UL Tel: (01280) 813881 Fax: (01280) 822429 E-mail: sales@buckscreenprint.co.uk

Burall, PO Box 7, Wisbech, Cambs, PE13 2SZ Tel: (0870) 728 7272 Fax: (0870) 728 7273

Cannon Plastics, Units 2-3 Barrs Fold Road, Wingates Industrial Estate, Westhoughton, Bolton, BL5 3XP Tel: (01942) 810081 Fax: (01942) 814311 E-mail: sales@cannon-plastics.co.uk

Cockx Sudbury Ltd, Unit A Woodhall House Drury Drive, Woodhall Business Park, Sudbury, Suffolk, CO10 1WH Tel: (01787) 880511 Fax: (01787) 378102E-mail: info@cockx.co.uk

Concept Card, Marsh Road, Lords Meadow Industrial Estate, Crediton, Devon, EX17 1EU Tel: (01363) 777567 Fax: (01363) 777553 E-mail: sales@conceptcard.co.uk

Corton Bashforth Screenprint Ltd, 78 Catley Road, Sheffield, S9 5JF Tel: 0114-243 0240 Fax: 0114-261 1653

Depicton Ltd, Units 3-5 Maer Lane Industrial Estate, Market Drayton, Shropshire, TF9 1QX Tel: (01630) 655800 Fax: (01630) 653258 E-mail: sales@depicton.com

Fosco Hayes-Hurdley Ltd, Carlton House, 41 Smith Street, Hockley, Birmingham, B19 3EN Tel: 0121-554 7421 Fax: 0121-523 4452 E-mail: enquiries@foscos.co.uk

G K Marketing Services Ltd, Unit 22 Crossfield Industrial Estate, Crossfield Road, Lichfield, Staffordshire, WS13 6RJ Tel: (01543) 414130 Fax: (01543) 250660 E-mail: sales@gkmktg.com

Richard Gardner Ltd, Hadfield Road, Leckwith Industrial Estate, Cardiff, CF11 8AQ Tel: (029) 2022 9764 Fax: (029) 2034 3664 E-mail: yc78@dial.pipex.com

Hills Poly Print Ltd, Alma Park Road, Grantham, Lincolnshire, NG31 9SE Tel: (01476) 577132 Fax: (01476) 590368 E-mail: sales@hillspoly-print.com

Kimco Hot Foil Printers, 1 Waterside Court, Bone Lane, Newbury, Berkshire, RG14 5SH Tel: (01635) 30154 Fax: (01635) 32245 E-mail: petekimco@aol.com

Kingsway Print, The Old Chapel, Peterborough Road, Whittlesey, Peterborough, PE7 1PJ Tel: (01733) 350550

Martindales Polythene Packaging Ltd, Block D, St. Michaels Industrial Estate, Widnes, Cheshire, WA8 8TL Tel: 0151-420 5355 Fax: 0151-420 5356 E-mail: sales@martindalespps.com

Norman Pendred & Co. Ltd, Unit 4worsley Bridge Rdbroomsleigh Business Park, London, SE26 5BN Tel: (020) 8461 1155 Fax: (020) 8461 1166 E-mail: sales@pendred.com

Polyclear (Southampton) Ltd, First Avenue, Millbrook Trading Estate, Southampton, SO15 0LG Tel: (023) 8070 1158 Fax: (023) 8077 1044 E-mail: 20robby@polyclear.co.uk

▶ Print Innovative Technology Ltd, Camilla Court, The Street, Nacton, Ipswich, IP10 0EU Tel: (01473) 655141 Fax: (01473) 655148 E-mail: neil@print-it.tv

Print Permanising Ltd, Graphic House, Telford Way, Severalls Business Park, Colchester, CO4 9QF Tel: (01206) 845655 Fax: (01206) 845246 E-mail: paulc@hythe-uk.com

R W Plastics (UK) Ltd, 16 Manor Park, 35 Willis Way, Fleet Industrial Estate, Poole, Dorset, BH15 3SZ Tel: (01202) 673373 Fax: (01202) 632018

Rapidocolor UK Ltd, Unit 15 Waverley Industrial Estate, Hailsham Drive, Harrow, Middlesex, HA1 4TR Tel: (020) 8863 6404 Fax: (020) 8863 1434 E-mail: sales@rapidocolor.co.uk

Sherwood Plastic Products Ltd, 25 Seavy Road, Goole, North Humberside, DN14 6TA Tel: (01405) 767338 Fax: (01405) 762222 E-mail: sherwoodplastic@btconnect.com

Totalprint Ltd, Station Road, Gedney Hill, Spalding, Lincolnshire, PE12 0NP Tel: (01406) 330122 Fax: (01406) 330123 E-mail: info@totalprintltd.co.uk

PLASTIC PROCESSING HOT RUNNER SYSTEMS

Diemould Service Co. Ltd, 11 Blenheim Road, Cressex Business Park, High Wycombe, Buckinghamshire, HP12 3RS Tel: (01494) 523811 Fax: (01494) 452898 E-mail: sales@dms-diemould.co.uk

Gunther UK Ltd, 52 Lambardes, New Ash Green, Longfield, Kent, DA3 8HU Tel: (01474) 879774 Fax: (01474) 873063 E-mail: info@gunther.co.uk

IMS Hot Runners, Unit 58B, Lincoln Road, Cressex Business Park, High Wycombe, Buckinghamshire, HP12 3RH Tel: (01494) 536900 Fax: (01494) 536999 E-mail: ims-hotrunners@btconnect.com

PLASTIC PROCESSING MACHINERY HEATING ELEMENTS

Chromalox (U K) Ltd, Eltron House, 20-28 Whitehorse Road, Croydon, CR0 2JA Tel: (020) 8665 8900 Fax: (020) 8689 0571 E-mail: uksales@chromalox.com

Soloheat Electrical Heating Equipment, Units 1 & 2 Lightpill Trading Estate, Bath Road, Stroud, Gloucestershire, GL5 3LL Tel: (01453) 752459 Fax: (01453) 752458 E-mail: heatit@aol.com

PLASTIC PRODUCTS

▶ A B Polymers, Ynysboeth Factory Estate, Abercynon, Mountain Ash, Mid Glamorgan, CF45 4SF Tel: (01443) 743930 Fax: (01443) 743939

▶ A1 Glazing Services, Factory Complex, Southchurch Drive, Nottingham, NG11 8AQ Tel: 0115-921 2617 Fax: 0115-914 8777

▶ Absolute Windows Ltd, Unit 7 Priestley Road, Wardley Industrial Estate, Worsley, Manchester, M28 2LY Tel: (01204) 394006

▶ Admiral Signs London, 71 Penenden, New Ash Green, Longfield, Kent, DA3 8LS Tel: 01474 874412 Fax: 01474 874412 E-mail: info@admiralsignslondon.co.uk

▶ Advanced Windows & Conservatories, 5 Law Place, Nerston Industrial Estate, East Kilbride, Glasgow, G74 4QL Tel: (01355) 266889 Fax: (01355) 260888 E-mail: sales@advancedwins.co.uk

Alpla Plastics Ltd, Wood Street, New Ferry, Wirral, Merseyside, CH62 4ZD Tel: 0151-643 5500 Fax: 0151-643 5512

▶ Altex, 58 Tailors Court, Temple Farm Industrial Estate, Southend-on-Sea, SS2 5SX Tel: (01702) 602220 Fax: (01702) 602215 E-mail: sales@altex-uk.com

▶ Amex Holdings, 5 Cherrywood, Stag Oak Lane, Chineham, Basingstoke, Hampshire, RG24 8WF Tel: (01256) 471000 Fax: (01256) 708989

▶ The Ashton Window Company Ltd, Holden Fold Lane, Royton, Oldham, OL2 5BZ Tel: 0161-624 9433 Fax: 0161-652 1326

▶ B B Moulding Ltd, Unit 2 New Street, Bridgtown, Cannock, Staffordshire, WS11 0DD Tel: (01543) 468698

▶ B B S Roof Light Co., Bedes Way, Bede Industrial Estate, Jarrow, Tyne & Wear, NE32 3HG Tel: 0191-489 0960 Fax: 0191-489 2303 E-mail: bbs.factory@keme.co.uk

▶ Chris Benson Signs Ltd, 96-98 Great Howard Street, Liverpool, L3 7AX Tel: 0151-298 1567 Fax: 0151-298 1568 E-mail: info@benson-signs.co.uk

▶ Blair Neill Ltd, 13 Comber Road, Newtownards, County Down, BT23 4QR Tel: (028) 9182 6868 E-mail: peter.blair@blairneill.com

▶ Blenham Window Systems Ltd, 212 Windmill Lane, Cheshunt, Waltham Cross, Hertfordshire, EN8 9AF Tel: (01992) 642300

▶ Brett Martin Ltd, 9 Blairlinn Road, Cumbernauld, Glasgow, G67 2TF Tel: (01236) 725536 Fax: (01236) 725871

▶ Broadland Plastics Ltd, Sutton Road, Catfield, Great Yarmouth, Norfolk, NR29 5BG Tel: 01692 580080 Fax: 01692 580801 E-mail: simon@broadlandplastics.co.uk

▶ C I Products, Lexden Lodge, 7 Crowborough Hill, Crowborough, East Sussex, TN6 2EG Tel: (01892) 654477 Fax: (01892) 653399

Capitol Window Systems Ltd, Unit 58, Third Avenue, Deeside Industrial Park, Deeside, Clwyd, CH5 2LA Tel: (01244) 281777

Central Moulding Services Ltd, Unit 6, Barrington Industrial Estate, Bedlington, Northumberland, NE22 7DQ Tel: (01670) 821166 Fax: (01670) 821500

▶ Charter Commercial Windows & Doors, Hoo Farm Industrial Estate, Worcester Road, Kidderminster, Worcestershire, DY11 7RA Tel: (01562) 745940 Fax: (01562) 66596 E-mail: info@chartercommercial.com

▶ Chater Bros Windows Ltd, 26-38 Jubilee Street, Rugby, Warwickshire, CV21 2JJ Tel: (01788) 540245 Fax: (01788) 547617 E-mail: chaterbrosltd@btconnect.com

▶ Chemi Craft, 112 Newhall Street, Willenhall, West Midlands, WV13 1LQ Tel: (01902) 631531

▶ Clare Window Centre, St. Johns Bridge Road, Plymouth, PL4 0JJ Tel: (01752) 670400 Fax: (01752) 228284

Classic Windows, Construction House, Callywhite Lane, Dronfield, Derbyshire, S18 2XR Tel: (0800) 2980591 Fax: (01246) 413321

▶ Clydesdale Double Glazing Ltd, 18-20 Netherdale Road, Netherton Industrial Estate, Wishaw, Lanarkshire, ML2 0ER Tel: (01698) 355424 Fax: (01698) 355425 E-mail: sales@scottishconservatories.com

▶ Corby Windows Ltd, Pywell Road, Willowbrook East Industrial Estate, Corby, Northamptonshire, NN17 5XJ Tel: (01536) 409100 Fax: (01536) 408757 E-mail: sales@cwg-uk.com

▶ Corio Signs & Printing, Unit 4, Hurlbutt Road, Heathcote Industrial Estate, Warwick, CV34 6TD Tel: (01926) 422262 Fax: (01926) 422262 E-mail: sales@corioprinting.co.uk

▶ Cox Plastics, Unit 1, Brooklands Way, Boldon Business Park, Boldon Colliery, Tyne & Wear, NE35 9LZ Tel: 0191-537 7000

▶ indicates data change since last edition

PLASTIC PRODUCTS – *continued*

▶ Crest Home Improvements Ltd, Crown Trading Estate, Shepton Mallet, Somerset, BA4 5QQ Tel: (01749) 344211 Fax: (01749) 346376

▶ Crest Windows Nottingham Ltd, Park Road East, Calverton, Nottingham, NG14 6LL Tel: 0115-965 5179 Fax: 0115-965 5102

▶ Custom Glass Ltd, Unit 2, Custom Complex, Yardley Road, Liverpool, L33 7SS Tel: 0151-549 1264 E-mail: sales@customglass.co.uk

▶ D Gibson R D & Quarry Services Ltd, Unit 5, 211 Cambuslang Rd, Cambuslang, Glasgow, G72 7TS Tel: 0141-613 1919 Fax: 0141-613 1404 E-mail: sales@gibsonquarry.co.uk

Delyn Packaging Ltd, Delyn House, Acacia Avenue, Hengoed, Mid Glamorgan, CF82 7JR Tel: (01443) 815512 Fax: (01443) 815512 E-mail: mike.knight@delynpackaging.co.uk

▶ Discount Double Glazing Ltd, 844 Romford Road, London, E12 5JP Tel: (020) 8514 0819 E-mail: info@discountdoubleglazing.co.uk

▶ E W L Ltd, 2A Newman Terrace, Gateshead, Tyne & Wear, NE8 3XA Tel: 0191-477 3330

▶ Ecomould Ltd, Park Farm Road, Foxhill Industrial Estate, Scunthorpe, South Humberside, DN15 8QP Tel: (01724) 280495 Fax: (01724) 280496

▶ Economy Windows & Conservatories, Churchgate Way, Terrington St. Clement, King's Lynn, Norfolk, PE34 4PG Tel: (01553) 827318 Fax: (01553) 827369 E-mail: enquiries@economywindows.co.uk

▶ Eddy Hosie, Chapel Road, Cuminestown, Turriff, Aberdeenshire, AB53 5ZA Tel: (01888) 544747 Fax: (01888) 544847

Epwin Group plc, Alders Way, Paignton, Devon, TQ4 7QE Tel: (01803) 697197 Fax: (01803) 697196 E-mail: info@epwin.co.uk

▶ Ertone Plastics Ltd, Unit 3 Telford Close, Aylesbury, Buckinghamshire, HP19 8DS Tel: (01296) 431482 Fax: (01296) 486299

▶ Europalite Ltd, Eastfield Side, Sutton-In-Ashfield, Nottinghamshire, NG17 4JW Tel: (01623) 528760 Fax: (01623) 510955 E-mail: sales@europalite.co.uk

▶ Exxonmobil Chemical Ltd, Unit 1, Harcourt Way, Meridian Business Park, Leicester, LE19 1WP Tel: 0116-289 6122 Fax: 0116-263 1055

▶ Fabrics By Guardian, 5 Cunningham Road, Stirling, FK7 7SW Tel: (01786) 449912 Fax: (01786) 451014

▶ Fabrics By Guardian, 5 Cunningham Road, Stirling, FK7 7SW Tel: (01786) 449912 Fax: (01786) 451014

▶ Fastplas Ltd, Unit 1-2, Block 8, Chapelhall Industrial Estate, Chapelhall, Airdrie, Lanarkshire, ML6 8QH Tel: (01236) 779922 Fax: (01236) 779933 E-mail: sales@fastplas.com

▶ Firth Buildings Scotland Ltd, 125 Auchterderran Road, Lochgelly, Fife, KY5 9BR Tel: (01592) 780405

▶ Fixture Signs South Ltd, 40 Bennett Close, Welling, Kent, DA16 3HU Tel: (020) 8316 7505

▶ Flowtech Precision Mouldings Ltd, Unit 3 Cambrian Industrial Park, Clydach Vale, Tonypandy, Mid Glamorgan, CF40 2XX Tel: (01443) 420130 Fax: (01443) 420140

Forbes Technologies Ltd, Unit 3, Pinnacle Hill Estate, Kelso, Roxburghshire, TD5 8DW Tel: (01573) 224499

▶ Frame Fast UK Ltd, 1 Ascot Drive, Derby, DE24 8ST Tel: (01332) 347544 Fax: (01332) 347544

▶ Frameline PVC U Products, 16-17 Faraday Road, Knowsley Industrial Park, Liverpool, L33 7UT Tel: 0151-546 5577 Fax: 0151-546 5588

▶ Fusion Technology Plastics, 9 Buckland Road, Leicester, LE5 0NT Tel: 0116-274 2038 Fax: 0116-274 2038

▶ G 2 S Ford & Fulford, Unit 5 Woodford Centre Old Sarum Park, Lysander Way, Old Sarum, Salisbury, SP4 6BU Tel: (01722) 334488 Fax: (01722) 414515

▶ G T I Glazing Systems Ltd, The Pavillion Somerton Park, Newport Road, Cowes, Isle of Wight, PO31 8PB Tel: (01983) 280880 Fax: (01983) 290222

▶ Gardenia West Wales Ltd, Spring Gardens, Narberth, Dyfed, SA67 7BT Tel: (01834) 860849 Fax: (01834) 861527 E-mail: sales@gardenia.co.uk

▶ Gardinia Windows Kirklees Ltd, 3 Leeds Road, Huddersfield, HD1 6DD Tel: (01484) 542912 Fax: (01484) 451932 E-mail: info@gardiniawindows.co.uk

▶ Hexis (UK) Ltd, 70 Britannia Way, Britannia Enterprise Park, Lichfield, Staffordshire, WS14 9UY Tel: (01543) 411221

▶ Indigo Products Ltd, Barn Piece Swag, Brickyard Road, Aldridge, Walsall, WS9 8SR Tel: (01922) 743202 Fax: (01922) 743277 E-mail: sales@indigoproducts.com

Inscape Ltd, 23 Elizabeth Avenue, Tattershall Bridge, Lincoln, LN4 4JJ Tel: (01526) 344627 Fax: (01526) 344627 E-mail: sales@inscapeuk.com

▶ J S B Plastics, Unit 2a Knighton Junction Lane, Leicester, LE2 6AR Tel: 0116-244 8049 Fax: 0116-270 2032

▶ Keillor Graphics, 290 High Street, Arbroath, Angus, DD11 1JF Tel: (01241) 876722 Fax: (01241) 871558 E-mail: colin@keilorgraphics.com

▶ Keyframe (UK) Ltd, Unit 32, Lyon Industrial Estate, Moss Lane, Kearsley, Bolton, BL4 8NB Tel: (01204) 705718 Fax: (01204) 705812

▶ L & R Products, 2A Ham Lane, Kingswinford, West Midlands, DY6 7JU Tel: (01384) 293042

▶ Lareine Engineering, Unit 1 Armadale Industrial Estate, Armadale, Bathgate, West Lothian, EH48 2ND Tel: (01501) 731600 Fax: (01501) 733828 E-mail: lareine@btconnect.com

▶ The Lockwood Window Company Ltd, 4 Perseverance Mills, Lockwood Scar, Huddersfield, HD4 6BW Tel: (01484) 519677 Fax: (01484) 519676 E-mail: lockwoodwindow@freeuk.com

▶ Long Life Windows Ltd, Derby Road, Burton-on-Trent, Staffordshire, DE14 1RX Tel: (01283) 545287 Fax: (01283) 566898 E-mail: johnmarson@longlifewindows.co.uk

▶ M1 Plastics, Unit 6, Holly BSNS Park, Belfast, BT11 9DT Tel: (028) 9030 0555 Fax: (028) 9030 0555

▶ Magna Safety Products Ltd, Unit 1, Industrial Estate, London Road, Pampisford, Cambridge, CB22 3EE Tel: (01223) 836643 Fax: (01223) 834648 E-mail: info@magnasafety.co.uk

▶ Man Mat, Matrix House Balthane Industrial Estate, Balthane, Ballasalla, Isle of Man, IM9 2AJ Tel: (01624) 828603 Fax: (01624) 823966 E-mail: sales@manmat.com

▶ Masefield Epson Ltd, Coneygre Road, Tipton, West Midlands, DY4 8XF Tel: 0121-557 3433

▶ Mercury Signs Designs, South Street, Perth, PH2 8PD Tel: (01738) 451450 Fax: (01738) 451412E-mail: ian@mercurysigns-design.com

▶ Merlin Polyurethanes, Camelot House, Claylake, Spalding, Lincolnshire, PE12 6BL Tel: (01775) 722208 Fax: (01775) 722298

▶ Mica Glazing, 113-115 Cable Depot Road, Clydebank, Dunbartonshire, G81 1UY Tel: 0141-952 7069 Fax: 0141-951 1593

▶ Moray Glass & Glazing Co., Chanonry Road, Elgin, Morayshire, IV30 1XH Tel: (01343) 541023 Fax: (01343) 541137

▶ Moss Products Plastics Ltd, Isle of Wight Lane, Kensworth, Dunstable, Bedfordshire, LU6 2PP Tel: (01582) 873366 Fax: (01582) 873399 E-mail: sales@mossproducts.co.uk

▶ Nationwide Frame Services, Brookside Way, Huthwaite, Sutton-in-Ashfield, Nottinghamshire, NG17 2NL Tel: (01623) 551555 Fax: (01623) 552555

Naylor Drainage, Cowley Street, Methil, Leven, Fife, KY8 3QQ Tel: (01592) 717900 Fax: (01592) 717906

▶ Needhams Windows, Unit 1, Great Central Road, Loughborough, Leicestershire, LE11 1RW Tel: (01509) 264066

▶ New Age Systems P V C U Ltd, Units 38-40, Gelli Industrial Estate, Gelli, Pentre, Mid Glamorgan, CF41 7UW Tel: (01443) 431026 Fax: (01443) 422463 E-mail: sales@newagesystems.co.uk

▶ New Look Windows, New Look House Shawclough Trading Estate, Shawclough Road, Rochdale, Lancashire, OL12 6ND Tel: (0800) 888333 Fax: (01706) 524929 E-mail: sales@newlookwindows.com

▶ North Cornwall Glazing, Highfield Industrial Estate, Camelford, Cornwall, PL32 9RA Tel: (01840) 213593 Fax: (01840) 213313

▶ P I M S, Unit 12, Sovereign Way, Downham Market, Norfolk, PE38 9SW Tel: (01366) 385382 Fax: (01366) 387202 E-mail: steve.pims@virgin.net

▶ P M Windows Ltd, Holme Street, Grimsby, South Humberside, DN32 9AD Tel: (01472) 251261 Fax: (01472) 251471 E-mail: sales@pmwindows.co.uk

▶ Pennington Lacey & Sons Ltd, 5-7 Park Road, Southampton, SO15 3AS Tel: (023) 8063 1555 Fax: (023) 8033 4017 E-mail: sales@penningtonlacey.co.uk

▶ Photoscreen, 1378 Ashton Old Road, Manchester, M11 1JU Tel: 0161-301 5348

▶ Plas Tech Windows, Whitegate House, White Lund Industrial Estate, Morecambe, Lancashire, LA3 3BS Tel: (01524) 849170 Fax: (01524) 846929

▶ Plaslyne, Unit D Stafford Park 7, Telford, Shropshire, TF3 3BQ Tel: (01952) 292511 Fax: (01952) 292025

▶ Plastic Village Ltd, Unit A, 126 Rickmansworth Road, Watford, WD18 7AA Tel: (01923) 244577

▶ Points Of Sale, 95-97 Rectory Road, Duckmanton, Chesterfield, Derbyshire, S44 5EE Tel: (01246) 823982 Fax: (01246) 241192

▶ Polycol Ltd, Stephanie Works, Bayley Street, Stalybridge, Cheshire, SK15 1PY Tel: 0161-338 4400 Fax: 0161-338 3377

▶ Prestige Windows Ltd, Vicar Street, Dudley, West Midlands, DY2 8RG Tel: (01384) 456744

▶ Pyramid Windows (Upvc) Ltd, Block 1, Chapelhall Industrial Estate, Chapelhall, Airdrie, Lanarkshire, ML6 8QH Tel: (01236) 765071 Fax: (01236) 747400

▶ R B Precision Moulding, Unit F9 Anchor Brook Industrial Park, Aldridge, Walsall, WS9 8BZ Tel: (01922) 745030 Fax: (01922) 745039 E-mail: rbmoualding@aol.com

▶ R J M Windows, 32-34 Bridge Street, St. Blazey, Par, Cornwall, PL24 2NS Tel: (01726) 816922 Fax: (01726) 816722 E-mail: info@rjmwindows.com

▶ Ramsdale Windows, Maxwell Road, Middlesbrough, Cleveland, TS3 8TE Tel: (01642) 227026 Fax: (01642) 227027

Recognition Express, Grosvenor House First West Business Centre, Linnell Way, Telford Way Industrial Estate, Kettering, Northamptonshire, NN16 8PS Tel: (01536) 527800 Fax: (01536) 412022

▶ Retail Plastics Plus, Unit 2 Cranleigh Gardens Industrial Estate, Southall, Middlesex, UB1 2BZ Tel: (020) 8574 9005 Fax: (020) 8574 9007

▶ Romold Plastic Products, Grangemouth Road, Bo'Ness, West Lothian, EH51 0PU Tel: (01506) 829623 Fax: (01506) 828639

▶ S E H Windows & Doors Ltd, 1 Olimpus Close, Ipswich, IP1 5LJ Tel: (01473) 467171 Fax: (01473) 462240

▶ Sapphire Signs Ltd, Bontoft Avenue, Hull, HU5 4HF Tel: (01482) 474888 Fax: (01482) 474889 E-mail: sales@saphiresigns.co.uk

▶ Scott James Glass Ltd, 12A-14 Armstrong Close, St. Leonards-On-Sea, East Sussex, TN38 9ST Tel: (01424) 854161 Fax: (01424) 853418

▶ Shape Injection Mouldings, Unit 7-8 Thomas Gilchrist Court, Thomas Gilchrist Industrial Estate, Blaenavon, Pontypool, Gwent, NP4 9RJ Tel: (01495) 791369 Fax: (01495) 790582 E-mail: info@shapeplastics.co.uk

▶ Shieldtone Ltd, Holbrook Rise, Holbrook Industrial Estate, Holbrook, Sheffield, S20 3FG Tel: 0114-251 3338 Fax: 0114-251 3341

▶ Sidey, 19 Feus Road, Perth, PH1 2AS Tel: (0800) 234400 Fax: (01738) 631335

▶ Smith Anderson & Co. Ltd, St Johns Works, Falkland, Ladybank, Cupar, Fife, KY15 7AY Tel: (01337) 858201 Fax: (01337) 857172

▶ Spektaglaze Ltd, 137-139 Richmond Row, Liverpool, L3 3BU Tel: 0151-207 4066

▶ Spire Window Systems Ltd, Tattershall Way, Fairfield Industrial Estate, Louth, Lincolnshire, LN11 0YZ Tel: (01507) 607291 Fax: (01507) 600159

▶ Stancombe Stone Ltd, The Camp, Stroud, Gloucestershire, GL6 7EW Tel: (01285) 821839 Fax: (01285) 821841

▶ Staybrite Conservatories, 16 Warwick Row, Coventry, CV1 1EJ Tel: (024) 7622 2956 Fax: (024) 7622 3290

▶ Stornoway Plastics, Rigs Road, Stornoway, Isle of Lewis, HS1 2RF Tel: (01851) 702122 Fax: (01851) 701287 E-mail: info@stornowayplastics.com

▶ Strata Products Ltd, Brookhill Industrial Estate, Pinxton, Nottingham, NG16 6NT Tel: (01773) 510520 Fax: (01773) 510502 E-mail: sales@strata.co.uk

▶ Sunlight Windows, Lloyd House, Gate Lane, Sutton Coldfield, West Midlands, B73 5TT Tel: 0121-355 5509 Fax: 0121-355 5518

▶ Sureframe Windows Ltd, Oxford Works, Oxford Street, Accrington, Lancashire, BB5 1QX Tel: (01254) 235390 Fax: (01354) 388084

▶ T F D (Scotland) Ltd, 2 Rennie Place, College Milton, East Kilbride, Glasgow, G74 5HD Tel: (01355) 268110 E-mail: info@tfdscotland.co.uk

▶ T J Morgan (Barry) Ltd, Ty Verlon Industrial Estate, Cardiff Road, Barry, South Glamorgan, CF63 2BE Tel: (01446) 740376 Fax: (01446) 720164

▶ Tecni-form, Unit 11, Whitebridge Estate, Whitebridge Lane, Stone, Staffordshire, ST15 8LQ Tel: (01785) 286476

▶ TFM, Trafalgar Close, Chandler's Ford, Eastleigh, Hampshire, SO53 4BW Tel: (023) 8026 2288 Fax: (023) 8026 0760

▶ Thermashield Insulation Ltd, 30 Cumbernauld Road, Stepps, Glasgow, G33 6EW Tel: 0141-779 4815 Fax: 0141-779 2044

Thornbury Manufacturing Ltd, Darklake View, Estover, Plymouth, PL6 7TL Tel: (01752) 696697 Fax: (01752) 696698 E-mail: sales@tml-ltd.com

▶ Trade Windows (Bristol), F St Vincents Trading Estate, Feeder Road, Bristol, BS2 0UY Tel: 0117-972 1041 Fax: 0117-977 1133

▶ Trim Tech Trade Ltd, Avenue Industrial Estate, Southend Arterial Road, Harold Wood, Romford, RM3 0BY Tel: (01708) 378269 Fax: (01708) 707751

▶ Truframe Ltd, Unit 3, K L M Hudson Road, Saxby Road Industrial Estate, Melton Mowbray, Leicestershire, LE13 1BP Tel: (01664) 410140

▶ Universal Arches Ltd, 103 Peasley Cross Lane, St. Helens, Merseyside, WA9 3AL Tel: (01744) 612844 Fax: (01744) 694250 E-mail: sales@universalarches.com

▶ Vacplas Mouldings Ltd, 4 Willow Park Business Centre, Lower Barnes Street, Clayton le Moors, Accrington, Lancashire, BB5 5SW Tel: (01254) 875588 Fax: (01254) 875599

▶ Vycon Products Ltd, Western Road, Kilmarnock, Ayrshire, KA3 1NG Tel: (01563) 574481 Fax: (01563) 533537 E-mail: sales@vycon.co.uk

▶ Watershed Plastics Ltd, Unit 7, Bowburn South Industrial Estat, Bowburn, Durham, DH6 5AD Tel: 0191-377 8020

▶ Weatherseal Holdings Ltd, New Business Park, Newhouse Road, Grangemouth, Stirlingshire, FK3 8LL Tel: (01324) 666934 Fax: (01324) 666204

▶ Whitehall Fabrications Ltd, Whitehall House, Bruntcliffe Lane, Morley, Leeds, LS27 0LZ Tel: 0113-222 3000 Fax: 0113-222 3001 E-mail: sales@whitehall-uk.com

▶ Williams Window Fabrication Ltd, Unit 6, South Elgin Place, Clydebank, Dunbartonshire, G81 1XP Tel: 0141-941 3050

▶ Window Warehouse, Bowen Industrial Estate, Aberbargoed, Bargoed, Mid Glamorgan, CF81 9EP Tel: (01443) 879275 Fax: (01443) 839442

▶ Windowblend Double Glazing, 6 Poplar Road, Broadmeadow Industrial Estate, Dumbarton, G82 2RQ Tel: (01389) 761624 Fax: (01389) 761625 E-mail: enquiries@leonardbuilders.co.uk

▶ Xtralite Rooflights Ltd, Unit 9, Spencer Road, Blyth, Northumberland, NE24 5TG Tel: (01670) 354157 Fax: (01670) 364875 E-mail: sales@xtralite.co.uk

▶ York Windows Ltd, Hodson Street, Wigan, Lancashire, WN3 4EN Tel: (01942) 820168 Fax: (01942) 234444 E-mail: yorkwindows@btconnect.com

▶ Zenith Windows, The Marina, Lowestoft, Suffolk, NR32 1HH Tel: (01502) 511555

PLASTIC PRODUCTS REPAIR/ REFURBISHMENT SERVICES

R & R Industries Ltd, Witney Road, Standlake, Witney, Oxfordshire, OX29 7PR Tel: (01865) 300093 Fax: (01865) 300096

PLASTIC PRODUCTS TO SPECIFICATION

▶ C P A Products, 9 Warrior Business Centre, Fitzherbert Road, Portsmouth, PO6 1TX Tel: (023) 9221 0330 Fax: (023) 9220 1594

R P C Container, Plenmeller Works, Haltwhistle, Northumberland, NE49 0HN Tel: (01434) 320526 Fax: (01434) 320136

PLASTIC PRODUCTS, POINT OF SALE (POS)/PURCHASE

Display System Fabrications Ltd, Dunsteads Farm, Trueloves Lane, Ingatestone, Essex, CM4 0NJ Tel: (01277) 352700 Fax: (01277) 352766 E-mail: dsfdisplay@aol.com

Flowerbox designs, Units 5 & 6,, Twyford Business Park, Station Road, Twyford, RG10 9JU Tel: 0118 9340077 Fax: 0118 9343667 E-mail: info@boxinnovations.co.uk

▶ HoloVis, The Brick Barn Bittesby Farm, Mere Lane, Lutterworth, Leicestershire, LE17 4JH Tel: (01455) 553924 Fax: (01455) 557746 E-mail: info@holovis.com

▶ Ino-Plaz Ltd, Unit B2 Chamberlain Business Centre, Chamberlain Road, Hull, HU8 8HL Tel: (01482) 225996 Fax: (01482) 225920 E-mail: sales@ino-plaz.co.uk

PLASTIC RAW/BASIC MATERIALS IMPORT MERCHANTS OR AGENTS

Resin Express Ltd, 11 Valley Business Centre, Gordon Road, High Wycombe, Buckinghamshire, HP13 6EQ Tel: (01494) 459881 Fax: (01494) 795334 E-mail: sales@resinexpress.com

Silwood Plastics Ltd, F Borough Road, Buckingham Road Industrial Estate, Brackley, Northamptonshire, NN13 7BE Tel: (01280) 844800 Fax: (01280) 700122

PLASTIC RAW/BASIC MATERIALS MANUFRS

Abbey Polymers Ltd, Innovation Centre, Staffordshire Technology Park, Stafford, ST18 0AR Tel: (01785) 241343 Fax: (01785) 241340

▶ Acceptus Ingredients & Blends, 109 St. Helens Road, Westcliff-on-Sea, Essex, SS0 7LF Tel: 07979 243025

Alpha Polymers Ltd, Costain Street, Liverpool, L20 8QJ Tel: 0151-933 3020 Fax: 0151-944 1494 E-mail: neil@alpha-polymers.freeserve.co.uk

Arto Chemicals Ltd, Arto House, London Road, Binfield, Bracknell, Berkshire, RG42 4BU Tel: (01344) 860737 Fax: (01344) 860820 E-mail: sales@artochemicals.com

Basell (UK) Ltd, Mount Farm, Bramley Road, Milton Keynes, MK1 1LZ Tel: (01908) 360000 Fax: (01908) 360036

Bayer UK plc, Bayer House, Strawberry Hill, Newbury, Berkshire, RG14 1JA Tel: (01635) 563000 Fax: (01635) 563393 E-mail: corporate.communications@bayer.co.uk

C J P Sales Ltd, The Pavilion, Eastgate, Cowbridge, South Glamorgan, CF71 7AB Tel: (01446) 772015 Fax: (01446) 773755 E-mail: sales@cjpsales.co.uk

C W Polymers Ltd, 10 Felspar Road, Tamworth, Staffordshire, B77 4DP Tel: (01827) 60943 Fax: (01827) 54008 E-mail: sales@cwpollowmas.co.uk

Claymore Plastics, Hegdon, Pencombe, Bromyard, Herefordshire, HR7 4SL Tel: (01885) 400278 Fax: (01885) 400616 E-mail: claymore278@aol.com

Dekura, 19-26 Bracken Hill, South West Industrial Estate, Peterlee, County Durham, SR8 2LS Tel: 0191-586 2379 Fax: 0191-586 1581 E-mail: sales@dekura.co.uk

Distrupol, 119 Guildford Street, Chertsey, Surrey, KT16 9AL Tel: (01932) 566033 Fax: (01932) 560363 E-mail: info@distrupol.com

DSM UK Ltd, D S M House, Paper Mill Drive, Redditch, Worcestershire, B98 8QJ Tel: (01527) 590590 Fax: (01527) 590555 E-mail: sales@dsm.com

PLASTIC RAW/BASIC MATERIALS MANUFRS – *continued*

Elan Polymers Ltd, 176 Leigh Road, Atherton, Manchester, M46 0PJ Tel: (01942) 889525 Fax: (01942) 873422

Eurocell Building Plastics Ltd, 1 Sterling Park, York, YO30 4WU Tel: (01904) 479201 Fax: (01904) 475440

Eurothane Ltd, Warndon Business Park, Prescott Drive, Worcester, WR4 9NE Tel: (01905) 458503 Fax: (01905) 456643 E-mail: sales@eurothane.com

Fablex 2000 Ltd, Unit 1 Tyseley Industrial Estate, Seeleys Road, Birmingham, B11 2LF Tel: 0121-753 0069 Fax: 0121-753 0071 E-mail: elaine@fablex.co.uk

G R P Ltd, Robin Hood Industrial Estate, Alfred St South, Nottingham, NG3 1GE Tel: 0115-924 3244 Fax: 0115-924 3236

G W Webb Plastics Ltd, Brookside Works Tyseley Industrial Estate, Seeleys Road, Birmingham, B11 2LA Tel: 0121-772 5968 Fax: 0121-773 7653 E-mail: sales@webbplastics.uk.com

Greyland Plastics Ltd, Greylands, Laurels Road, Offenham, Evesham, Worcestershire, WR11 8RE Tel: (01386) 421422 Fax: (01386) 421423 E-mail: greylandplastics@btconnect.com

Hardie Polymers Ltd, 53 Stockiemuir Avenue, Bearsden, Glasgow, G61 3JJ Tel: 0141-942 3330 Fax: 0141-942 4001

John Hellyar & Co. Ltd, Tyler Way, Whitstable, Kent, CT5 2RX Tel: (01227) 813200 Fax: (01227) 792203 E-mail: sales@hellyar.co.uk

Lati UK Ltd, West Wing, The Quadrangle, Crewe Hall, Weston Road, Crewe, CW1 6UA Tel: (01270) 501713 Fax: (01270) 509713 E-mail: mfreestone@uk.lati.com

Micropol Ltd, Bayley Street, Stalybridge, Cheshire, SK15 1QQ Tel: 0161-330 5570 Fax: 0161-343 7687 E-mail: enquiry@micropol.co.uk

Offerclass Ltd, 73-75 Shacklewell Lane, London, E8 2EB Tel: (020) 7923 2560 Fax: (020) 7923 2692 E-mail: katrina@offerclass.com

Perrite Plastic Compounds, 1 Kingsland Grange, Woolston, Warrington, WA1 4RA Tel: (01925) 810608 Fax: (01925) 840001 E-mail: sales@jgp-perrite.co.uk

Plascolour Ltd, Unit 1 Sherrington Way, Basingstoke, Hampshire, RG22 4DQ Tel: (01256) 470303 Fax: (01256) 817207 E-mail: plascolour@compuserve.com

Plastribution Ltd, Glenbervie Business Centre, Glenbervie Business Park, Larbert, Stirlingshire, FK5 4RB Tel: (01324) 682105 Fax: (01324) 682106 E-mail: sales@plastribution.co.uk

Polycam, 24 Petersfield Road, Duxford, Cambridge, CB2 4SF Tel: (01223) 835195 Fax: (01223) 510153 E-mail: andrew.huckstep@ntlworld.com

PolyONE Corporation UK Ltd, Langley Road South, Salford, M6 6SN Tel: 0161-737 1717 Fax: 0161-737 3611

▶ Recycling In Action Ltd, Capital Valley Industrial Estate, Rhymney, Tredegar, Gwent, NP22 5PT Tel: (0870) 2404356 Fax: (0870) 2404357 E-mail: info@recycleinginactoin.com

Sabic Plastics, Bo'Ness Road, Grangemouth, Stirlingshire, FK3 9XF Tel: (01324) 483490 Fax: (01324) 667265

Silwood Plastics Ltd, F Borough Road, Buckingham Road Industrial Estate, Brackley, Northamptonshire, NN13 7BE Tel: (01280) 844800 Fax: (01280) 700122

Ticona UK Ltd, Stafford Park 12, Telford, Shropshire, TF3 3BJ Tel: (01952) 292747 Fax: (01952) 292383 E-mail: don.shattuck@ticona.co.uk

Tripenta Ltd, Unit 8, Willersey Industrial Park, Broadway, Worcestershire, WR12 7RR Tel: (01386) 858398 Fax: (01386) 858743 E-mail: tripenta@aol.com

PLASTIC RECYCLING MACHINERY

▶ DJB Recycling Machinery Ltd, 37 Cotswold Road, Sheffield, S6 4QY Tel: 0114-233 3058 Fax: 01142 333058

▶ Oxplas Ltd, 104 Wycombe Road, Princes Risborough, Buckinghamshire, HP27 0EY Tel: (01844) 342184 Fax: (020) 8181 6050 E-mail: info@oxplas.co.uk

P L Plastics Machinery Ltd, Unit 6 Telmere Industrial Estate, Albert Road, Luton, LU1 3QF Tel: (01582) 429224 Fax: (01582) 459133 E-mail: info@pl-plasticsmachinery.co.uk

PLASTIC REELS/SPOOLS

Hearl Heaton Ltd, Halifax Road, Liversedge, West Yorkshire, WF15 6JJ Tel: (01924) 406721 Fax: (01924) 400803 E-mail: info@hearlheaton.co.uk

PLASTIC REINFORCED CONCRETE FORMWORK

Articole Ltd, 9 Alexander Road, Stotfold, Hitchin, Hertfordshire, SG5 4NA Tel: (01462) 835640 Fax: (01462) 834896 E-mail: steve@articolestudios.co.uk

Creteco Sales, 17 St. Martins Street, Wallingford, Oxfordshire, OX10 0EA Tel: (01491) 839488 Fax: (01491) 833879 E-mail: sales@creteco.co.uk

Woodtec, 38 Festival Drive, Loughborough, Leicestershire, LE11 5XJ Tel: (01509) 219246 Fax: (01509) 260117 E-mail: sales@woodtec2.co.uk

PLASTIC ROD MANUFRS

B W F Kunststoffe GmbH, Unit 4, Orchard Court, Nunn Brook Road, Huthwaite, Sutton-in-Ashfield, Nottinghamshire, NG17 2HZ Tel: (01908) 516177 Fax: (01908) 290468 E-mail: sales@bwfprofiles.co.uk

▶ Barkston Plastics Ltd, D5-D7 Unit, Drypool Way, Hull, HU9 1LG Tel: (01482) 323886 Fax: (01482) 214193 E-mail: mailbox@barkstonltd.co.uk

Rimparts, 249 Gladstone Road, Barry, Vale of Glamorgan, CF63 1NJ Tel: (01446) 732849 Fax: (01446) 732849

Simona (U K) Ltd, Unit 11, Telford Drive, Tollgate Industrial Estate, Stafford, ST16 3ST Tel: (01785) 222444 Fax: (01785) 222080 E-mail: sales@simona.de

PLASTIC ROLLER COVERINGS

J Thwaites Ltd, 31 Bretton Street, Dewsbury, West Yorkshire, WF12 9BJ Tel: (01924) 460480 Fax: (01924) 460607 E-mail: info@tufgrip.com

Modern Rollers Ltd, Greengate, Salford, M3 7NS Tel: 0161-834 1539 Fax: 0161-835 3303 E-mail: modernrollers@davidbentley.co.uk

PLASTIC ROLLER SHUTTERS

Defence Group Ltd, 411 Petre Street, Sheffield, S4 8LL Tel: 0114-244 1178 Fax: 0114-244 7710 E-mail: sales@defencegroup.co.uk

Waivis Co. Ltd, 14 Minerva Road, London, NW10 6HJ Tel: (020) 8965 6818 Fax: (020) 8965 6287 E-mail: info@waivis.co.uk

PLASTIC ROOF LIGHTS OR WINDOWS

Astrofade Ltd, Kyle Road, Gateshead, Tyne & Wear, NE8 2YE Tel: 0191-420 0515 Fax: 0191-460 4185 E-mail: sales@astrofade.co.uk

Ubbink (U K) Ltd, Borough Road, Brackley, Northamptonshire, NN13 7TB Tel: (0845) 4563499 Fax: (01280) 705332 E-mail: info@ubbink.co.uk

PLASTIC ROOFING MATERIALS

M B Distribution Cleveland Ltd, Wallis Road, Skippers Lane Industrial Estate, Middlesbrough, Cleveland, TS6 6JB Tel: (01642) 455945 Fax: (01642) 455504 E-mail: sales@mb-distribution.co.uk

Polyroof Products Ltd, Castle Park Industrial Estate, Evans Street, Flint, Clwyd, CH6 5XA Tel: (01352) 735135 Fax: (01352) 735182 E-mail: info@polyroof.co.uk

PLASTIC ROTATIONAL MOULDING MACHINES

Alan Yorke Ltd, 4 Midland Business Centre, Bury Close, Higham Ferrers, Rushden, Northamptonshire, NN10 8BE Tel: (01933) 358219 Fax: (01933) 410546 E-mail: sales@alanyorke.co.uk

PLASTIC ROTATIONAL MOULDING TOOLMAKERS

A C Canoe Products Chester Ltd, Unit 102 Tenth Avenue, Deeside Industrial Park, Deeside, Clwyd, CH5 2UA Tel: (01244) 280416 Fax: (01244) 288190 E-mail: ac.canoe@btinternet.com

RRP Rotational Mould Makers, Unit 5 Sanders Lodge Industrial Estate, Rushden, Northamptonshire, NN10 6BQ Tel: (01933) 413493 Fax: (01933) 413931 E-mail: sales@rrp.uk.com

PLASTIC ROTATIONAL MOULDINGS

A C Canoe Products Chester Ltd, Unit 102 Tenth Avenue, Deeside Industrial Park, Deeside, Clwyd, CH5 2UA Tel: (01244) 280416 Fax: (01244) 288190 E-mail: ac.canoe@btinternet.com

Amber Plastics Ltd, Broombank Road, Chesterfield, Derbyshire, S41 9QJ Tel: (01246) 453544 Fax: (01246) 450339 E-mail: sales@amberplastics.co.uk

Associated Roto-Plastics Ltd, Green Grove Mill, Dyehouse Lane, Rochdale, Lancashire, OL16 2QN Tel: (0870) 8303900 Fax: (0870) 8303901 E-mail: sales@haywood-rotomoulding.co.uk

Mick Graham Plastics Ltd, Unit 17 19, Argall Avenue, London, E10 7QP Tel: (020) 8539 7388 Fax: (020) 8539 2355

Frank Greaves (Moulding) Co. Ltd, Unit 68, Roman Way Industrial Estate, Longridge Road, Grinsargh, Preston, PR2 5BD Tel: (01772) 652902 Fax: (01772) 797748 E-mail: info@eurotransman.co.uk

▶ H P Mouldings Ltd, Units 7-8 Clarkes Meadow, Bromyard Road, Tenbury Wells Business Park, Tenbury Wells, Worcestershire, WR15 8FA Tel: (01584) 819739 Fax: (01584) 811396 E-mail: colin@hpmouldings.com

LINPAC Environmental, Leafield Way, Leafield Industrial Estate, Corsham, Wiltshire, SN13 9UD Tel: (01225) 816500 Fax: (01225) 816501 E-mail: paxton@linpac.com

Perception Kayaks Ltd, Bellbrook Business Park, Uckfield, East Sussex, TN22 1QQ Tel: (01825) 765891 Fax: (01825) 763707 E-mail: info@perception.co.uk

Polymer Holdings Ltd, 1 Windmill Lane, Denton, Manchester, M34 3RN Tel: 0161-320 7710 Fax: 0161-320 9940 E-mail: sales@rubberengineering.co.uk

Pyramid Products Ltd, Unit 1 Victoria Street, Mansfield, Nottinghamshire, NG18 5RR Tel: (01623) 421277 Fax: (01623) 421288 E-mail: sales@pyramid-products.co.uk

Techneat Engineering Ltd, 2a Henry Crabb Road, Littleport, Ely, Cambridgeshire, CB6 1SE Tel: (01353) 862044 Fax: (01353) 862644 E-mail: info@techneat.co.uk

PLASTIC SACKS, *See Polyethylene etc; also Refuse etc*

PLASTIC SADDLE VALVES

Plasson UK Ltd, Plasson House, 27 Albert Drive, Burgess Hill, West Sussex, RH15 9TW Tel: (01444) 244446 Fax: (01444) 258683 E-mail: sales@plasson.co.uk

PLASTIC SANITARY WARE CONNECTORS

Multikwik Ltd, 37 High Street, Totton, Southampton, SO40 9HL Tel: (023) 8066 3777 Fax: (023) 8086 9996 E-mail: sales@multikwik.com

PLASTIC SCRAP/WASTE HANDLING EQUIPMENT

▶ Kongskilde UK Ltd, Hempstead Road, Holt, Norfolk, NR25 6EE Tel: (01263) 713291 Fax: (01263) 712922 E-mail: mail@kuk.kongskilde.com

PLASTIC SCRAP/WASTE IMPORT/EXPORT MERCHANTS OR AGENTS

E Klein & Co., 122-126 Westferry Road, London, E14 3SG Tel: (020) 7987 1171 Fax: (020) 7538 0477

V10 Polymers Ltd, Rockcliffe Works, Paterson Street, Blackburn, BB2 3SP Tel: (01254) 680384 Fax: (01254) 674933 E-mail: david@holtplastics.co.uk

PLASTIC SCRAP/WASTE RECYCLING/DISPOSAL/ MERCHANTS OR PROCESSORS

A M F Polymers Ltd, Avondale Way, Avondale Industrial Estate, Pontrhydyrun, Cwmbran, Gwent, NP44 1TS Tel: (01633) 873229 Fax: (01633) 866600

Bromborough Plastics Ltd, Unit 1b Spencer Industrial Estate, Liverpool Road, Buckley, Clwyd, CH7 3LY Tel: (01244) 545202 Fax: (01244) 545202

Dawnlight Ltd, 56 Lindsay Drive, Harrow, Middlesex, HA3 0TD Tel: (020) 8204 3828 Fax: (020) 8204 3420

Dekura, 19-26 Bracken Hill, South West Industrial Estate, Peterlee, County Durham, SR8 2LS Tel: 0191-586 2379 Fax: 0191-586 1581 E-mail: sales@dekura.co.uk

Extrusion & Moulding Compounds Ltd, Cwmavon, Pontypool, Gwent, NP4 8UW Tel: (01495) 772534 Fax: (01495) 772251

Fablex 2000 Ltd, Unit 1 Tyseley Industrial Estate, Seeleys Road, Birmingham, B11 2LF Tel: 0121-753 0069 Fax: 0121-753 0071 E-mail: elaine@fablex.co.uk

G P Plastic Materials Ltd, 3 Bathville Business Centre, Armadale Industrial Estate, Armadale, Bathgate, West Lothian, EH48 2ND Tel: (01501) 734483 Fax: (01501) 734484

G S W Plastics Ltd, Park Mill Industrial Estate, Manchester Road, Mossley, Ashton-under-Lyne, Lancashire, OL5 9BQ Tel: (01457) 834550 Fax: (01457) 834990

G W Webb Plastics Ltd, Brookside Works Tyseley Industrial Estate, Seeleys Road, Birmingham, B11 2LA Tel: 0121-772 5968 Fax: 0121-773 7653 E-mail: sales@webbplastics.uk.com

Harris & Co., Farrs Lane, Bristol, BS1 4PZ Tel: 0117-927 7434 Fax: 0117-925 2354

JFC Plastics Ltd, 6 Goldicote Business Park, Banbury Road, Goldicote, Stratford-upon-Avon, Warwickshire, CV37 7NB Tel: (01789) 740102 Fax: (01789) 740037 E-mail: info@delleve.co.uk

KLA Plastics (NI) Ltd, Unit 17 Comber Road Industrial Estate, Comber Road, Newtownards, County Down, BT23 4QP Tel: (028) 9181 8187 Fax: (028) 9181 1410 E-mail: info@klaplastics.co.uk

Mainetti (U K) Ltd, Oxnam Road, Jedburgh, Roxburghshire, TD8 6NN Tel: (01835) 865000 Fax: (01835) 863879 E-mail: jwilde@uk.mainetti.com

Precision Polymers & Reclaim Ltd, Bath Road Trading Estate, Lightpill, Stroud, Gloucestershire, GL5 3QF Tel: (01453) 753717 Fax: (01453) 753717

Trident Recycling Ltd, Suite 4, 19 Marine Crescent, Kinning Park, Glasgow, G51 1HD Tel: 0141-420 3131 Fax: 0141-420 3166 E-mail: mail@trident-recycling.co.uk

Philip Tyler Polymers Ltd, Globe House, Love Lane, Cirencester, Gloucestershire, GL7 1YG Tel: (01285) 885330 Fax: (01285) 659774 E-mail: sales@philiptylerpolymers.co.uk

PLASTIC SHEET EXTRUDING MACHINERY, THERMOFORMING

Anchor Plastics Machinery, The Watermill, Royal Quay, Harefield, Uxbridge, Middlesex, UB9 6SA Tel: (01895) 824301 Fax: (01895) 825344 E-mail: info@anchor-pm.co.uk

▶ Ridat Co., Unit E1, Neath Vale Supplier Park, Resolven, Neath, West Glamorgan, SA11 4SR Tel: (0845) 0506525 Fax: (0845) 0506526 E-mail: info@ridat.com

PLASTIC SHEET MANUFRS

Alma Products Ltd, 51-53 Brindley Road, Astmoor Industrial Estate, Runcorn, Cheshire, WA7 1PF Tel: (01928) 580595 Fax: (01928) 581022

Amari Plastics P.L.C., 11-12 Hillman Close, Hornchurch, Essex, RM11 2SJ Tel: (01708) 452525 Fax: (01708) 437030 E-mail: el@amariplastics.com

Amari Plastics plc, Wednesbury One, Blackcountry New Road, Wednesbury, West Midlands, WS10 7NZ Tel: 0121-567 3400 Fax: 0121-567 3401 E-mail: bm@amariplastics.com

Anglia Alloys Ltd, Unit 5 Riverside Industrial Estate, Riverside Road, Gorleston, Great Yarmouth, Norfolk, NR31 6PU Tel: (01493) 651028 Fax: (01493) 655391

Cirrus Plastics, Esky Drive, Carn Industrial Area, Portadown, Craigavon, County Armagh, BT63 5WD Tel: (028) 3835 0001 Fax: (028) 3835 0002 E-mail: sales@cirrusplastics.co.uk

Comco Plastics UK Ltd, 27 Long Wood Road, Trafford Park, Manchester, M17 1PZ Tel: 0161-873 7080 Fax: 0161-873 7079 E-mail: steve.mitchell@vinkplastics.com

Cova Products Ltd, Station Road, Cramlington, Northumberland, NE23 8AQ Tel: (01670) 718222 Fax: (01670) 590096

Cox Plastics, Kingfisher Way, Sowton Industrial Estate, Exeter, EX2 7LE Tel: (01392) 439701 Fax: (01392) 444017 E-mail: cox.southwest@coxplastics.co.uk

Degussa Ltd, Tego House, Chippenham Drive, Kingston, Milton Keynes, MK10 0AF Tel: (0870) 1262250 Fax: (0845) 1289579

Floline, Whitehall Industrial Estate, Whitehall Road, Leeds, LS12 5JB Tel: 0113-235 9349 Fax: 0113-235 9348

Haden Browne, 278 Barton Street, Gloucester, GL1 4JJ Tel: (01452) 525314 Fax: (01452) 300671

Robert Horne Industrial Plant Ltd, Quantam House, Gee Business Centre, Holborn Hill, Birmingham, B7 5JR Tel: 0121-327 5050 Fax: 0121-327 2818

▶ Industrial Textiles & Plastics Ltd, Easingwold Business Park, Oaklands Way, Easingwold, York, YO61 3FA Tel: (01347) 825200 Fax: (01347) 825222 E-mail: sales@indtex.co.uk

K W H Plast UK Ltd, Brunleys, Kiln Farm, Milton Keynes, MK11 3EW Tel: (01908) 566166 Fax: (01908) 568538 E-mail: sales@kwhplast.com

King Plastics, Unit 11 Foxwood Industrial Park, Chesterfield, Derbyshire, S41 9RN Tel: (01246) 260300 Fax: (01246) 260321 E-mail: kingplas@supanet.com

Mabron Plastics Ltd, Unit 28 Mount Street, Accrington, Lancashire, BB5 0PJ Tel: (01254) 385619 Fax: (01254) 231496 E-mail: mabronplastics@aol.com

Brett Martin Ltd, 24 Roughfort Road, Newtownabbey, County Antrim, BT36 4RB Tel: (028) 9084 9999 Fax: (028) 9083 6666 E-mail: sales@brettmartin.com

PLASTIC SHEET MANUFRS – *continued*

Meridale Plastics Ltd, Meridale Works, Linford Road, Grays, Essex, RM16 4JS Tel: (01375) 850009 Fax: (01375) 851113 E-mail: sales@buildwithplastics.co.uk

Monarflex Ltd, Unit 23 North Orbital Commercial Park (Off Natsbury Avenue), St. Albans, Hertfordshire, AL1 1XB Tel: (01727) 830116 Fax: (01727) 868045 E-mail: geos.uk@icopal.com

N E Plastics Ltd, 1 Ruxley Corner Industrial Estate, Edgington Way, Sidcup, Kent, DA14 5BL Tel: (020) 8308 9990 Fax: (020) 8308 9995 E-mail: sales@neplastics.co.uk

Oadby Plastics Ltd, Elland Road, Leicester, LE3 1TU Tel: 0116-232 1010 Fax: 0116-287 3577 E-mail: sales@oadbyplastics.ltd.uk

Plastic Merchant Ltd, 10 Church Street, Brighton, BN1 1US Tel: (01273) 329958 Fax: (01273) 329958

PolyPlus Packaging Ltd, Unit 1 Headley Park Ten, Headley Road East, Woodley, Reading, RG5 4SW Tel: 0845 4941732 Fax: 0118-944 8141 E-mail: sales@polypluspackaging.co.uk

Primex Plastics Ltd, Beaumont Way, Aycliffe Industrial Park, Newton Aycliffe, County Durham, DL5 6SN Tel: (01325) 315768 Fax: (01325) 308875 E-mail: info@primexuk.co.uk

Pureclad, 9 Rake Top Avenue, Higham, Burnley, Lancashire, BB12 9BB Tel: (07710) 934133 Fax: (01282) 773712

Saffron Plastics Ltd, Bakers Court, Paycocke Road, Basildon, Essex, SS14 3EH Tel: (01268) 288874 Fax: (01268) 534592 E-mail: sales@saffronplastics.co.uk

Sign & Display, 2 Tenax Road, Trafford Park, Manchester, M17 1JT Tel: 0161-872 8585 Fax: 0161-876 4056

Southern Sheeting Supplies (Roofing and Cladding), Hill Place Farm, Turners Hill Road (B2110), East Grinstead, West Sussex, RH19 4LX Tel: (01342) 315300 Fax: (01342) 410560E-mail: sales@southernsheeting.co.uk

V T S Doeflex, 3 St. Annes Boulevard, Redhill, RH1 1AX Tel: (01737) 771221 Fax: (01737) 772461 E-mail: sales@vtsdoeflex.co.uk

VTS Royalite, Cliftonhall Road, Newbridge, Midlothian, EH28 8PW Tel: 0131-333 3369 Fax: 0131-333 5161 E-mail: sales@vtsroyalite.co.uk

PLASTIC SHEET THERMOFORMING

▶ Ridat Co., Unit E1, Neath Vale Supplier Park, Resolven, Neath, West Glamorgan, SA11 4SR Tel: (0845) 0506525 Fax: (0845) 0506526 E-mail: info@ridat.com

PLASTIC SHOP FITTINGS

John Anthony Organistation, Greenwood House, Unity Road, Lowmoor Business Park, Kirkby-in-Ashfield, Nottingham, NG17 7LE Tel: (01623) 755090 Fax: (01623) 755110 E-mail: sales@jao.co.uk

Castle Plastic, Unit 16b Raleigh Hall Industrial Estate, Eccleshall, Stafford, ST21 6JL Tel: (01785) 851842 Fax: (01785) 851370 E-mail: sales@castleplastics.co.uk

M M C Ltd, 2ND Floor, Guide Bridge Mill, South Street, Ashton-Under-Lyne, Lancashire, OL7 0HU Tel: 0161-343 1740 Fax: 0161-343 1741 E-mail: pats@mmc93.co.uk

PLASTIC SIGNS

A D Signs & Engraving Ltd, Unit 3 Webner Industrial Estate, Alltingshaw Road, Wolverhampton, WV2 2LD Tel: (01902) 353535 Fax: (01902) 496775 E-mail: sales@ad-signs.co.uk

A & E Plastic Fabrications Ltd, 40 St. Peters Street, Radford, Nottingham, NG7 3FF Tel: 0115-978 0048 Fax: 0115-979 1351 E-mail: info@aaep.co.uk

A S A P Sign Services, 9 Bradley Road, Wrexham, Clwyd, LL13 7TG Tel: (01978) 353265 Fax: (01978) 354689 E-mail: asap.sign-services@dail.pipex.com

Abacus Signs, L4a Unit Colchester Estate, Colchester Avenue, Penylan, Cardiff, CF23 9AP Tel: (029) 2046 5030 Fax: (029) 2048 7376 E-mail: sales@abucussigns.co.uk

Allsteed Signs & Graphics Ltd, Unit 4 & 5 Palmerston Business Park, New Gate Lane, Fareham, Hampshire, PO14 1DJ Tel: (01329) 234224 Fax: 01329 317659 E-mail: sales@allspeedsigns.co.uk

Amberley Signs, 144 Frimley Green Road, Frimley Green, Camberley, Surrey, GU16 6NA Tel: (01252) 836436 Fax: (01252) 836436 E-mail: amberleysigns@discali.co.uk

Aristocrat Signs, Unit 6 Mitchell Close, Fareham, Hampshire, PO15 5SE Tel: (01489) 589292 Fax: (01489) 584909 E-mail: aristocrat@zoom.co.uk

Austin Roberts, Tarran Way South, Tarran Industrial Estate, Wirral, Merseyside, CH46 4UB Tel: 0151-678 6088 Fax: 0151-678 9448 E-mail: austin.roberts@virgin.net

Broadway Signs, Unit 18 Elmbourne Industrial Estate, Crabtree Manorway, Belvedere, Kent, DA17 6AW Tel: (020) 8310 8100 Fax: (020) 8310 1950E-mail: curwood1954@hotmail.com

C Adams, Unit 18 Barton Hill Trading Estate, Maze Street, Bristol, BS5 9TE Tel: 0117-954 2331 Fax: 0117-954 2331

Cambrian Signs, 10 Burnell Road, Sheffield, S6 2AX Tel: 0114-233 0233 Fax: 0114-233 0233

Clarks Signs Ltd, Alchorn Place, Portsmouth, PO3 5QL Tel: (023) 9282 6411 Fax: (023) 9266 9991 E-mail: sales@clarks-signs.co.uk

Coalville Signs, Units 2 3 Stephenson Indust Estate, Stephenson Way, Coalville, Leicestershire, LE67 3HB Tel: (01530) 811398 Fax: (01530) 830958

Colton Signs, Castlegate Mills, Spa Mews, Harrogate, North Yorkshire, HG2 7LF Tel: (01423) 886461 Fax: (01423) 881141 E-mail: coltonsigns@harrogatespa.fsn.co.uk

Concept Signs, 40-42 Albert Road, Braintree, Essex, CM7 3JQ Tel: (01376) 329240 Fax: (01376) 331937 E-mail: signsconcept@aol.com

Creative Signs, 10 Worcester Road Industrial Estate, Chipping Norton, Oxfordshire, OX7 5XW Tel: (01608) 643557 Fax: (01608) 643557 E-mail: sales@creativepubsigns.co.uk

D M A Signs, Unit 5-6 Bridge Works, Kingston Road, Leatherhead, Surrey, KT22 7SU Tel: (01372) 363808 Fax: (01372) 363801 E-mail: sale@dmasigns.co.uk

Decor Signs, Unit 22 Oldbury Business Centre, Oldbury Road, Cwmbran, Gwent, NP44 3JU Tel: (01633) 866349 Fax: (01633) 866349 E-mail: marketing@decorsigns.co.uk

E S P Technologies Group Ltd, 2 Euroway, Wood Close, Quarry Wood, Aylesford, Kent, ME20 7UB Tel: (01622) 715000 Fax: (01622) 797000 E-mail: sales@esptech.co.uk

Embassy Signs Ltd, 83 Bellenden Road, London, SE15 4QJ Tel: (020) 7732 1055 Fax: (020) 7732 4163E-mail: sales@embassysigns.co.uk

Express Signs, 66 Soundwell Road, Bristol, BS16 4QP Tel: 0117-957 1793 Fax: 0117-957 1793 E-mail: andy@expresssigns.fsnet.co.uk

F X Signs, 2 South Street, Isleworth, Middlesex, TW7 7BG Tel: (020) 8560 2124 Fax: (020) 8569 7320

Fastsigns, 11 Colman Parade, Southbury Road, Enfield, Middlesex, EN1 1YY Tel: (020) 8367 3777 Fax: (020) 8367 3863

Fine Signs, Lower Road, Cookham, Maidenhead, Berkshire, SL6 9EH Tel: (01628) 522023 Fax: (01628) 528731 E-mail: signs@finesigns.co.uk

Frome Sign Co. Ltd, Unit 3 Lakeside Park, Mells, Frome, Somerset, BA11 3RH Tel: (01373) 813666 Fax: (01373) 813777 E-mail: fromesigns@aol.com

G P Plastics Ltd, 156 Bordesley Middleway, Camp Hill, Birmingham, B11 1BN Tel: 0121-773 1777 Fax: 0121-772 6856 E-mail: admin@gpplastics.co.uk

Gilchrist & Co., 90 Donegall Passage, Belfast, BT7 1BX Tel: (028) 9023 2453 Fax: (028) 9032 6700

Greens The Signmakers Ltd, Brighton Street, Kingston-upon-Hull, East Riding of Yorkshire, HU3 4UW Tel: (01482) 327371 Fax: (01482) 228050 E-mail: davidragan@greens-signmakers.co.uk

Harper Signs Ltd, 12-20 Diana Street, Newcastle upon Tyne, NE4 6DA Tel: 0191-232 4926 Fax: 0191-261 0676 E-mail: sales@harpersigns.co.uk

Hendon Sign Co., 25-27 The Burroughs, London, NW4 4AR Tel: (020) 8202 8900 Fax: (020) 8202 4071

Imagination Signs, 43 Birdham Road, Chichester, West Sussex, PO19 8TB Tel: (01243) 783569 Fax: (01243) 785011 E-mail: sales@imaginationsigns.co.uk

J G Neon Signs, 639 Walsall Road, Great Barr, Birmingham, B42 1EH Tel: 0121-357 4033 Fax: 0121-357 4033

Jenter Engraving Ltd, Unit 4F, Lansbury Estate, 102 Lower Guildford Road, Knaphill, Woking, Surrey, GU21 2EP Tel: (01483) 289100 Fax: (01483) 289200

L & M Signs, Unit 1 Highlands Close, St Helens Way, Thetford, Norfolk, IP24 1HG Tel: 01842 821990 Fax: 01842 750706 E-mail: trevor@lmsigns.co.uk

Lamb's Signs, Unit B3 Sapphire Way, Rhombus Business Park, Norwich, NR6 6NN Tel: (01603) 410400 Fax: (01603) 410700 E-mail: lambsigns@talk21.com

M G Signs Ltd, Pond Wood Close, Moulton Park Industrial Estate, Northampton, NN3 6RT Tel: (01604) 493226 Fax: (01604) 790288 E-mail: sales@mgsigns.com

M K Marking Systems Ltd, 22 Carters Lane, Kiln Farm Industrial Estate, Kiln Farm, Milton Keynes, MK11 3HL Tel: (01908) 561676 Fax: (01908) 562551 E-mail: sales@mkmarking.co.uk

Maxwell Jones Studios Ltd, 58K Arthur Street, Redditch, Worcestershire, B98 8JY Tel: (01527) 502900 Fax: (01527) 510265 E-mail: sales@maxwelljones.com

N B Sign Services, 72 Winner Street, Paignton, Devon, TQ3 3BH Tel: (01803) 521160 Fax: (01803) 521135

Northern Engraving & Sign Co Ltd, John Spence Sands, Courtney St, Hull, HU8 7QF Tel: (01482) 328110 Fax: (01482) 323077 E-mail: enquiries@northernengraving.co.uk

Nuneaton Signs, 3 Kelsey Close, Attleborough Fields Industrial Estate, Nuneaton, Warwickshire, CV11 6RS Tel: (024) 7634 1922 Fax: (024) 7664 1305 E-mail: sales@nuneatonsigns.co.uk

P & S Promotions Sign & Print, 16 Hodgsons Court, Hodgsons Way, Wickford, Essex, SS11 8XR Tel: (01268) 572616 Fax: (01268) 572122

Paul Spencer Ltd, Consulate House, Sheffield Street, Stockport, Cheshire, SK4 1RU Tel: 0161-477 1688 Fax: 0161-480 4950 E-mail: sales@paulspencersigns.com

PCMI Signs & Badges, Northern Road, Cosham, Portsmouth, PO6 3EP Tel: (023) 9232 2828 Fax: (023) 9232 2831 E-mail: sign.sales@portsmouthcc.gov.uk

Peco Signs, Unit 5, Arrow Road North, Lakeside, Redditch, Worcestershire, B98 8NT Tel: (01527) 595364 Fax: (01527) 595366 E-mail: info@pecostudios.com

Pendle Signs & Plastics Ltd, Kirby Road, Lomeshaye Industrial Estate, Nelson, Lancashire, BB9 6RS Tel: (01282) 601842 Fax: (01282) 617361 E-mail: sales@pendlesigns.co.uk

Peter Tipper Signs & Plates Ltd, 33 Purdeys Industrial Estate, Purdeys Way, Rochford, Essex, SS4 1ND Tel: (01702) 549830 Fax: (01702) 549831 E-mail: info@tipper-signs.co.uk

R & M Signmakers, 2 Whitehill Lane, Gravesend, Kent, DA12 5LY Tel: (01474) 568358 Fax: (01474) 568358

Radar Signs, 143 Beehive Lane, Ilford, Essex, IG4 5DR Tel: (020) 8551 0216 Fax: (020) 8551 1458 E-mail: radarsigns@btclick.com

Rossendale Plastics, Station Road, Haslingden, Rossendale, Lancashire, BB4 5HX Tel: (01706) 214652 Fax: (01706) 830829 E-mail: info@rossendaleplastics.co.uk

Royle & Gemmell, Booth House, Suthers Street, Oldham, OL9 7TQ Tel: 0161-628 9292 Fax: 0161-628 9292

Rye Signs Ltd, 4 11 Fieldings Road, Cheshunt, Waltham Cross, Hertfordshire, EN8 9TL Tel: (01992) 636348 Fax: (01992) 621579 E-mail: dave@ryesigns.demon.co.uk

Sapsford Signs, 4 Mitre Avenue, London, E17 6QG Tel: (020) 8520 3739 Fax: (020) 8520 3739

Shelley Signs Ltd, Eaton-on-Tern, Market Drayton, Shropshire, TF9 2BX Tel: (01952) 541483 Fax: (01952) 541755 E-mail: sales@shelleysigns.co.uk

Sign 7 Ltd, Unit 10 Fox Oak Enterprise Centre, Foxoak Street, Cradley Heath, West Midlands, B64 5DP Tel: (01384) 413704 Fax: (01384) 413705

Sign Designs, 147-149 Hutcheon Street, Aberdeen, AB25 3RY Tel: (01224) 645361 Fax: (01224) 643647 E-mail: dundee@signdesigns.co.uk

Signline, Thistledown Farm, Tivetshall St. Margaret, Norwich, NR15 2DL Tel: (01379) 677699 Fax: (01379) 677879 E-mail: jason.signline@virgin.net

Signs By Morrell Ltd, Tarran Way South, Tarran Industrial Estate, Wirral, Merseyside, CH46 4TP Tel: 0151-678 8989 Fax: 0151-678 8816 E-mail: sales@signs-by-morrell.com

Signs Now, 36a Ashley Road, Bournemouth, BH1 4LH Tel: (01202) 392727 Fax: (01202) 392728 E-mail: signsnowbmth@aol.com

Signwise, Unit 26 Enterprise Way, Newport, Gwent, NP20 2AQ Tel: (01633) 841766 Fax: (01633) 841766 E-mail: info@signwise.net

Stourport Sign Studio, 3 Sandy La Industrial Estate, Stourport-on-Severn, Worcestershire, DY13 9QB Tel: (01299) 826044 Fax: (01299) 826044

Studio Signs, 10-12 High Street, Goldthorpe, Rotherham, South Yorkshire, S63 9LR Tel: (01709) 891160 Fax: (01709) 891160 E-mail: dean@studiosigns.co.uk

Tara Signs Ltd, St. Peters Place, Western Road, Lancing, West Sussex, BN15 8SB Tel: (01903) 750710 Fax: (01903) 754008 E-mail: admin@tarasigns.com

Taylor Electronics Manchester Ltd, 287 Chester Road, Manchester, M15 4EY Tel: 0161-834 5050 Fax: 0161-834 5051

Techniform Graphics Ltd, 172 Bexley Road, London, SE9 2PH Tel: (020) 8850 9191 Fax: (020) 7703 6001 E-mail: sales@techniformgraphics.co.uk

Tubeolight Signcraft C I, 1 Landes Du Marche, La Grande Route De St. Pierre, St. Peter, Jersey, JE3 7AY Tel: (01534) 485591 Fax: (01534) 485592 E-mail: sales@signtechjersey.co.uk

Vista Signs, 267 Nottingham Road, Nottingham, NG7 7DA Tel: 0115-942 1511 Fax: 0115-942 2462 E-mail: sales@vista-signs.co.uk

Walker, 6a Digby Drive, Melton Mowbray, Leicestershire, LE13 0RQ Tel: (01664) 410354 Fax: (01664) 410354

PLASTIC SINKS

Art Equipment, 3 Craven Street, Northampton, NN1 3EZ Tel: (01604) 632447 Fax: (01604) 632447 E-mail: charlesstradling@aol.com

Carron Phoenix, Carron Works, Carron, Falkirk, FK2 8DW Tel: (01324) 638321 Fax: (01324) 620978 E-mail: fgp-sales@carron.com

Rangemaster, Meadow Lane, Long Eaton, Nottingham, NG10 2AT Tel: 0115-946 4000 Fax: 0115-946 0374 E-mail: sales@rangemaster.co.uk

PLASTIC SINTERED FILTERS

Photo Gen Ic Ltd, Unit 4 Parc Industrial Estate, Llanidloes, Powys, SY18 6RB Tel: (01686) 413292 Fax: (01686) 413425 E-mail: sales@photogenic.co.uk

PLASTIC SLITTING/REELING/ REWINDING CONTRACT SERVICES

G.B. Brooks & Co. Ltd, Mackenzie Industrial Park, Bird Hall Lane, Cheadle Heath, Stockport, Cheshire, SK3 0SB Tel: 0161-428 7330 Fax: 0161-428 7294 E-mail: enquiries@gbbrooks.co.uk

PLASTIC SLITTING/REELING/ REWINDING MACHINES

Abbey Design, Unit 4/5, Glen Trading Estate, Wellyhole Street, Oldham, OL4 3BF Tel: 0161-620 8295 Fax: 0161-785 0130 E-mail: sales@abbeydesign.cc

Atlas Converting Plc, Wolseley Road, Woburn Road Industrial Estate, Kempston, Bedford, MK42 7XT Tel: (01234) 852584 Fax: (01234) 851151 E-mail: sales.atlas@bobstgroup.com

Doel Engineering Ltd, 5 Europa Park, Croft Way, Witham, Essex, CM8 2FN Tel: (01376) 515515 Fax: (01376) 500015 E-mail: info@doelengineering.com

Moore Bowman Services Ltd, 2 Glebe Road, Egham, Surrey, TW20 8BT Tel: (01784) 452387 Fax: (01784) 458500

PLASTIC SPRAY PAINTING CONTRACTORS OR SERVICES

Electron Technical Solutions Ltd, 14-15 Arkwright Road, Astmoor Industrial Estate, Runcorn, Cheshire, WA7 1NU Tel: (01928) 567474 Fax: (01928) 580516 E-mail: info@electron-ts.co.uk

Interplas Coatings Ltd, Lygon Buildings, Peartree Lane, Dudley, West Midlands, DY2 0QU Tel: (01384) 236327 Fax: (01384) 255428 E-mail: sales@interplascoatings.com

Stadium Plastics Midlands Ltd, Unit 4-6 Southways Industrial Estate, Coventry Road, Hinckley, Leicestershire, LE10 0NJ Tel: (01455) 234202 Fax: (01455) 234191 E-mail: chris@spfd.fsbusiness.co.uk

PLASTIC STATIONERY SUNDRIES

Flexigate Ltd, Vicarage Lane, Hoo, Rochester, Kent, ME3 9LB Tel: (01634) 251328 Fax: (01634) 250558 E-mail: sales@flexigate.co.uk

Plasart Ltd, Chilton Industrial Estate, Windham Road, Sudbury, Suffolk, CO10 2XD Tel: (01787) 375641 Fax: (01787) 311041

PLASTIC STORAGE VESSELS

Plasticon (U K) Ltd, Grovehill Industrial Estate, Beverley, North Humberside, HU17 0JT Tel: (01482) 862194 Fax: (01482) 871398 E-mail: sales@plasticon.co.uk

PLASTIC STRAPPING

Bandapac Packaging Materials, 9 Fieldings Road, Cheshunt, Waltham Cross, Hertfordshire, EN8 9TL Tel: (01992) 622799 Fax: (01992) 628873

Flip Lock Ltd, 177 Ashby Road, Scunthorpe, South Humberside, DN16 2AQ Tel: (01724) 865692 E-mail: mgdeans@btconnect.com

PLASTIC TANKS

Alda Plastics, Unit 13 Monks Brook Indust P, School Close, Chandler's Ford, Eastleigh, Hampshire, SO53 4RA Tel: (023) 8027 3396 Fax: (023) 8027 3496

Amber Plastics Ltd, Broombank Road, Chesterfield, Derbyshire, S41 9QJ Tel: (01246) 453544 Fax: (01246) 450339 E-mail: sales@amberplastics.co.uk

Boatman Plastics, Newport Road, Market Drayton, Shropshire, TF9 2AA Tel: (01630) 657286 Fax: (01630) 655545

Bryant Plastic Products Ltd, Walk Mills, The Walk, Coney Lane, Keighley, West Yorkshire, BD21 5AR Tel: (01535) 606676 Fax: (01535) 602966 E-mail: sales@bryantplastics.co.uk

Drainage Spares & Pipework Supplies Ltd, Fairy Farm Wethersfield, Wethersfield, Braintree, Essex, CM7 4EP Tel: (01371) 850808 Fax: (01371) 850120 E-mail: adam.dsps@btinternet.com

G F G Plastics Fabrication Ltd, Bridge Works, 101 West Dock Street, Hull, HU3 4HH Tel: (01482) 610110 Fax: (01482) 229044 E-mail: greygfg2003@aol.com

Kel Air Plastics Ltd, Holme Mills, Britannia Road, Huddersfield, HD3 4QF Tel: (01484) 461083 Fax: (01484) 461084 E-mail: tands@fsbdial.co.uk

Mayweld Engineering Co. Ltd, Banners Lane, Halesowen, West Midlands, B63 2SD Tel: (01384) 560285 Fax: (01384) 411456

▶ indicates data change since last edition

PLASTIC TANKS – *continued*

Mottram Industrial Plastics, 99a North Street, Cannock, Staffordshire, WS11 0AZ Tel: (01543) 573735 Fax: (01543) 574925 E-mail: andy@mottramindustrialplastics.co.uk
Niplast Tanks, 187 Higher Hillgate, Stockport, Cheshire, SK1 3JG Tel: 0161-477 6777 Fax: 0161-429 8413 E-mail: contactus@niplast.com
P & G Processors Ltd, 26 Trojan Centre, Finedon Road Industrial Estate, Wellingborough, Northamptonshire, NN8 4ST Tel: (01933) 270967 Fax: (01933) 270967 E-mail: pgprocess@aol.com
Plasbrun Plastics Engineering Ltd, Unit C, Brookfield Drive, Cannock, Staffordshire, WS11 0JR Tel: (01543) 462802 Fax: (01543) 462806 E-mail: plasbrunplastics@yahoo.co.uk
Plastic Fabrications (1991), Unit 10, Bickford Road, Aston, Birmingham, B6 7EE Tel: (0121) 327 1013 Fax: (0121) 326 6139
Plastic Facilities, Fen End, Stotfold, Hitchin, Hertfordshire, SG5 4BA Tel: (01462) 832832 Fax: (01462) 832830 E-mail: sales@plasticfacilities.co.uk
Plasticraft Ltd, Godiva Place, Coventry, CV1 5PN Tel: (024) 7625 3099 Fax: (024) 7655 1402 E-mail: sales@plasticraft.co.uk
T C Plastic Fabrications Ltd, Hawkmill Industrial Estate, Little Green Lane, Small Heath, Birmingham, B9 5BE Tel: 0121-773 2044 Fax: 0121-766 6623 E-mail: tom@tcplastics.wanadoo.co.uk

PLASTIC TAPS

Opella Ltd, Twyford Road, Rotherwas Industrial Estate, Hereford, HR2 6JR Tel: (01432) 357331 Fax: (01432) 264014 E-mail: sales@opella.co.uk
Pinmill Products, Units 5H-5K, Baker House, Manor Way Industrial Estate, Curzon Drive, Grays, Essex, RM17 6BG Tel: (01375) 392944 Fax: (01375) 379127 E-mail: pinmill@btinternet.com
▶ Worldwide Dispensers, Merton Industrial Park, Lee Road, London, SW19 3WD Tel: (020) 8545 7500 Fax: (020) 8545 7502 E-mail: sales@dsswd.com

PLASTIC TEST EQUIPMENT

Martin Instrument Co. Ltd, 160 Darlaston Road, Wednesbury, West Midlands, WS10 7TA Tel: 0121-568 7755 Fax: 0121-568 7744 E-mail: mic.ltd@virgin.net
Ray Ran Test Equipment Ltd, Kelsey Close, Attleborough Fields Ind Estate, Nuneaton, Warwickshire, CV11 6RS Tel: (024) 7634 2002 Fax: (024) 7664 1670 E-mail: polytest@ray-ran.com
▶ Testometric Co. Ltd, Unit 1 Lincoln Business Park, Lincoln Close, Rochdale, Lancashire, OL11 1NR Tel: (01706) 654039 Fax: (01706) 646089 E-mail: info@testometric.co.uk

PLASTIC THERMOFORMING MACHINERY MANUFRS

▶ Shelley Thermoformers International Ltd, Stonehill, Stukeley Meadows Industrial Es, Huntingdon, Cambridgeshire, PE29 6DR Tel: (01480) 453651 Fax: (01480) 52113 E-mail: sales@cannon-shelley.co.uk

PLASTIC THERMOFORMING PROCESSORS OR SERVICES

Adept Vacuum Formers & Patterns Ltd, 141 Waterside Road, Hamilton, Leicester, LE5 1TL Tel: 0116-246 0552 Fax: 0116-246 0987 E-mail: enquiries@adeptvp.freeserve.co.uk
Cox Thermoforming Ltd, Unit 4, Icknield Way Industrial Estate, Tring, Herts, HP23 4JX Tel: (01442) 891055 Fax: (01442) 890967 E-mail: sales@cwpl.net
Desch Plantpak Ltd, Burnham Road, Mundon, Maldon, Essex, CM9 6NT Tel: (01621) 745500 Fax: (01621) 745525 E-mail: sales@desch-plantpak.co.uk
Eyrevac Plastics Ltd, 7-15 Hungerford Road, Bristol, BS4 5HU Tel: 0117-971 5480 Fax: 0117-972 3593 E-mail: mailbox@eyrevac.co.uk
Focal Plastics Ltd, 34-40 Cutlers Road, South Woodham Ferrers, Chelmsford, CM3 5XJ Tel: (01245) 322788 Fax: (01245) 323194 E-mail: sales@focalplastics.co.uk
Graingate, 2 Lockwood Close, Nottingham, NG5 9JN Tel: 0115-967 1888 Fax: 0115-967 1777 E-mail: info@graingate.co.uk
Holloway Plastics Ltd, Willenhall La Industrial Estate, Willenhall Lane, Bloxwich, Walsall, WS3 2XN Tel: (01922) 492777 Fax: (01922) 495820 E-mail: sales@holloway-plastics.co.uk
K & W Fabrications Ltd, Brighton Road, Handcross, Haywards Heath, West Sussex, RH17 6BZ Tel: (01444) 401144 Fax: (01444) 401188 E-mail: user@kw-fabrication.prestel.co.uk
Keyline Associates Ltd, High Meres Road, Leicester, LE4 9LZ Tel: 0116-276 1371 Fax: 0116-274 1570 E-mail: display@keline.co.uk
Linecross Group Ltd, Station Road, South Luffenham, Oakham, Leicestershire, LE15 8NG Tel: (01780) 720720 Fax: (01780) 722333 E-mail: kgday@linex.uk.com
Plastics Manchester Ltd, Plasman Industrial Centre, Peter Moss Way, Manchester, M19 3PX Tel: 0161-257 2929 Fax: 0161-257 3203 E-mail: info@thompson-plastics-group.co.uk
Spatz Shop, Unit 9 Brook Street, Redditch, Worcestershire, B98 8NG Tel: (01527) 68168 Fax: (01527) 60026 E-mail: sales@spatz.uk.com
Styleguard Ltd, 7 Long Acre Trading Estate, Long Acre, Birmingham, B7 5JD Tel: 0121-327 3222 Fax: 0121-328 4312
Thermoform Ltd, The Larches Moor Farm Road, Airfield Industrial Estate, Ashbourne, Derbyshire, DE6 1HD Tel: (01335) 343757 Fax: (01335) 300096 E-mail: enquiries@thermoform-limited.co.uk
Thermovac Plastics Ltd, Unit 1 Low Mill Lane, Ravensthorpe Industrial Estate, Dewsbury, West Yorkshire, WF13 3LN Tel: (01924) 499268 Fax: (01924) 491440 E-mail: sales@thermovacplastics.co.uk
Thompson Plastics Group Ltd, Bridge Works, Hessle, North Humberside, HU13 0TP Tel: (01482) 646464 Fax: (01482) 644446 E-mail: info@thompson-plastics.co.uk

PLASTIC TILES

The Amtico Co. Ltd, Kingfield Road, Coventry, CV6 5AA Tel: (024) 7686 1400 Fax: (024) 7686 1552 E-mail: info@amtico.com
Evertile Ltd, 6 Moresby Road, London, E5 9LF Tel: (020) 8806 3167 Fax: (020) 8806 7434 E-mail: sales@evertile.com
Fabriform Neken Ltd, Station Road, Liphook, Hampshire, GU30 7DR Tel: (01428) 722252 Fax: (01428) 725053 E-mail: sales@neken.co.uk

PLASTIC TOOL BOXES OR CABINETS OR CASES OR CHESTS

Antler Ltd, Pilot Works, Alfred Street, Bury, Lancashire, BL9 9EF Tel: 0161-764 0721 Fax: 0161-764 0723 E-mail: custserv@antler.co.uk
Boydell & Jacks Ltd, Marlborough Street, Burnley, Lancashire, BB11 2HW Tel: (01282) 456411 Fax: (01282) 437496 E-mail: sales@featherwing.com
Raaco GB Ltd, Wenrisc House Meadow Court, High Street, Witney, Oxfordshire, OX28 6ER Tel: (01993) 776333 Fax: (01993) 776444 E-mail: sales@raaco.com

PLASTIC TRAYS

Kesteven Plastics Ltd, Unit 3, Moorland Way, Tritton Road, Lincoln, LN6 7JW Tel: (01522) 695977 Fax: (01522) 695977 E-mail: george@kestevenplasticsltd.co.uk
R H Products & The Sleep Doctor, 87-89 Shaw Street, St. Helens, Merseyside, WA10 1EN Tel: (01744) 733622 Fax: (01744) 733623 E-mail: roger9000h@hotmail.com
RPC Containers Ltd, St. Vincents Trading Estate, Feeder Road, Bristol, BS2 0UY Tel: 0117-977 9511 Fax: 0117-972 3602

PLASTIC TUBE ENDS, *See Plastic Tube etc*

PLASTIC TUBE FITTINGS MANUFRS

A S Plastics, Unit 3, Harvey Court Harvey Lane, Golborne, Warrington, WA3 3QN Tel: (01942) 271271 Fax: (01942) 271271
Anchor Industrial Plastics Ltd, 3 Benjamin Outram Business Centre, Whiteley Road, Ripley, Derbyshire, DE5 3QL Tel: (01773) 513022 Fax: (01773) 570404 E-mail: jkanchorplastics@aol.com
Boole's Tools & Pipe Fittings Ltd, Haigh Avenue, Whitehill Trading Estate, Stockport, Cheshire, SK4 1NU Tel: 0161-480 7900 Fax: 0161-474 7142 E-mail: enquiries@booles.co.uk
Captivair Pneumatics Ltd, Unit B2 Imperial Business Estate, Gravesend, Kent, DA11 0DL Tel: (01474) 334537 Fax: (01474) 333657 E-mail: sales@captivair.co.uk
Collister & Glover (Pipeline Materials) Ltd, Tenth Avenue, Deeside Industrial Park, Deeside, Clwyd, CH5 2UA Tel: (01244) 288000 Fax: (01244) 289000 E-mail: sales@colglo.co.uk
CPV Ltd, Woodington Mill, Woodington Road, East Wellow, Romsey, Hampshire, SO51 6DQ Tel: (01794) 322884 Fax: (01794) 322885 E-mail: sales@cpv.co.uk
Drain Centre, Heron Works, Heron Road, Sowton Industrial Estate, Exeter, EX2 7LL Tel: (01392) 445588 Fax: (01392) 445599
HYDRAQUIP, Unit 7, Oakhurst Business Park, Wilberforce Way, Southwater, Horsham, West Sussex, RH13 9RT Tel: (01403) 731322 Fax: (01403) 730276 E-mail: salmons@hydraquip.co.uk
International Plastic Systems Ltd, Seaham Grange Industrial Estate, Seaham, County Durham, SR7 0PT Tel: 0191-521 3111 Fax: 0191-521 3222 E-mail: info@ips-plastics.com
JD Pipes Ltd, Green Lane, Heywood, Lancashire, OL10 2EU Tel: (01706) 364115 Fax: (01706) 366402 E-mail: heywood@jdpipes.co.uk
Jessops plc, 257 High Street, Cheltenham, Gloucestershire, GL50 3HJ Tel: (0845) 4587074 Fax: (01242) 228054
Mcalpine & Co. Ltd, 45 Kelvin Avenue, Hillington Industrial Estate, Glasgow, G52 4LF Tel: 0141-882 3213 Fax: 0141-891 5065
Pipeline Centre, Millmarsh Lane, Enfield, Middlesex, EN3 7QG Tel: (020) 8805 9588 Fax: (020) 8805 2297
Pipeline Centre, Ingram Road, Leeds, LS11 9BB Tel: 0113-242 8280 Fax: 0113-242 8283 E-mail: sales@pipeline.com
Plasson UK Ltd, Plasson House, 27 Albert Drive, Burgess Hill, West Sussex, RH15 9TW Tel: (01444) 244446 Fax: (01444) 258683 E-mail: sales@plasson.co.uk
Priory Woodfield Engineering Ltd, Millbrook Works, Lower Horseley Field, Wolverhampton, WV1 3DZ Tel: (01902) 351530 Fax: (01902) 351290 E-mail: sales@priorywoodfield.com
Spa Plastics Ltd, 4 Herald Business Park, Golden Acres Lane, Coventry, CV3 2SY Tel: (024) 7665 0670 Fax: (024) 7665 0680 E-mail: sales@spaplastics.com
Uponor Ltd, Berristow Lane, Blackwell, Alfreton, Derbyshire, DE55 5JD Tel: (01773) 811112 Fax: (01773) 812343 E-mail: marketing@uponor.co.uk
Wavin Ni Ltd, Rathdown Close, Lissue Industrial Estate, Lisburn, County Antrim, BT28 2RB Tel: (028) 9262 1577 Fax: (028) 9262 1969 E-mail: sales@wavin.ie

PLASTIC TUBE MANUFRS

Alcan Packaging Corby Ltd, 5 Adderlade House, Corby Gate Business Park, Corby, Northamptonshire, NN17 5JG Tel: (01536) 400500 Fax: (01536) 400333
▶ Apex GB Ltd, Station Approach, Victoria, Roche, St. Austell, Cornwall, PL26 8LG Tel: (0870) 7373771 Fax: (0870) 7373772 E-mail: sales@apexgb.com
B W F Kunststoffe GmbH, Unit 4, Orchard Court, Nunn Brook Road, Huthwaite, Sutton-in-Ashfield, Nottinghamshire, NG17 2HZ Tel: (01908) 516177 Fax: (01908) 290468 E-mail: sales@bwfprofiles.co.uk
B & W Lifting, Unit 2e Grangetown Centre, Stapylton Street, Middlesbrough, Cleveland, TS6 7BJ Tel: (01642) 467900 Fax: (01642) 467900 E-mail: bwlifting@hotmail.com
Bardini Plastics, Unit 4 Ellesmere, Manners Industrial Estate, Ilkeston, Derbyshire, DE7 8EF Tel: 0115-944 2733 Fax: 0115-944 2723 E-mail: bardini@bigfoot.com
Claron Plastics Ltd, Alders Way, Yalberton Industrial Estate, Paignton, Devon, TQ4 7QL Tel: (01803) 528677 Fax: (01803) 525134 E-mail: services@claron.co.uk
Drain Centre, 115 Clyde Place, Cambuslang, Glasgow, G32 8RF Tel: 0141-425 2720 E-mail: glasgow.p28@wolsley.co.uk
Drainage Spares & Pipework Supplies Ltd, Fairy Farm Wethersfield, Wethersfield, Braintree, Essex, CM7 4EP Tel: (01371) 850808 Fax: (01371) 850120 E-mail: adam.dsps@btinternet.com
H L Plastics Ltd, Duffield Road Industrial Estate, Little Eaton, Derby, DE21 5EH Tel: (01332) 832389 Fax: (01332) 830867 E-mail: sales@hlplasticsltd.co.uk
International Plastic Systems Ltd, Seaham Grange Industrial Estate, Seaham, County Durham, SR7 0PT Tel: 0191-521 3111 Fax: 0191-521 3222 E-mail: info@ips-plastics.com
JDP Ltd, 65-69 Ellingham Industrial Centre, Ellingham Way, Ashford, Kent, TN23 6JU Tel: (01233) 618323 Fax: (01233) 618324
Polypipe Civils Ltd, Boston Road Industrial Estate, Holmes Way, Horncastle, Lincolnshire, LN9 6JW Tel: (01507) 527373 Fax: (01507) 525099
Polypipe Civils Ltd, Bishop Meadow Road, Loughborough, Leicestershire, LE11 5RE Tel: (01509) 615100 Fax: (01609) 610215 E-mail: sales@polypipecivils.co.uk
Rigiflex Extrusions Ltd, Ibex Barn Ferro Fields, Brixworth Indust Estate, Brixworth, Northampton, NN6 9UA Tel: (01604) 880217 Fax: (01604) 880129 E-mail: sales@rigiflexextrusions.co.uk
Sabre Plastics Ltd, Dockfield Road, Shipley, West Yorkshire, BD17 7AD Tel: (01274) 586815 Fax: (01274) 531397 E-mail: info@sabreplastics.co.uk
Simona (U K) Ltd, Unit 11, Telford Drive, Tollgate Industrial Estate, Stafford, ST16 3ST Tel: (01785) 222444 Fax: (01785) 222080 E-mail: sales@simona.de
Spa Plastics Ltd, 4 Herald Business Park, Golden Acres Lane, Coventry, CV3 2SY Tel: (024) 7665 0670 Fax: (024) 7665 0680 E-mail: sales@spaplastics.com
Tube Gear Ltd, Unit B1 Springhead Enterprise Park, Springhead Road, Northfleet, Gravesend, Kent, DA11 8HB Tel: (01474) 321954 Fax: (01474) 321988 E-mail: sales@tube-gear.com
Uponor Housing Solutions Ltd, Snapethorpe, Rugby Road, Lutterworth, Leicestershire, LE17 4HN Tel: (01455) 550355 Fax: (01455) 550366 E-mail: hsenquiries@uponor.co.uk

PLASTIC TURNING

Algernon, Unit 1 Algarnon Industrial Estate, Shiremoor, Newcastle upon Tyne, NE27 0NB Tel: 0191-251 4600 Fax: 0191-297 0360 E-mail: algernoneng@aol.com

PLASTIC VACUUM AND PRESSURE FORMING

Fathomtree Ltd, 5 The Midway, Nottingham, NG7 2TS Tel: 0115-986 0096 Fax: 0115-986 0210 E-mail: sales@fathomtreeltd.com
Graingate, 2 Lockwood Close, Nottingham, NG5 9JN Tel: 0115-967 1888 Fax: 0115-967 1777 E-mail: info@graingate.co.uk
J & R Plastics Ltd, 30 Montipilier Rise, Golders Green, London, NW11 9DS Tel: (07957) 627143 E-mail: jrplastics@hotmail.com
Linecross Group Ltd, Station Road, South Luffenham, Oakham, Leicestershire, LE15 8NG Tel: (01780) 720720 Fax: (01780) 722333 E-mail: kgday@linex.uk.com

PLASTIC VACUUM FORMED COMPONENTS

Cox Thermoforming Ltd, Unit 4, Icknield Way Industrial Estate, Tring, Herts, HP23 4JX Tel: (01442) 891055 Fax: (01442) 890967 E-mail: sales@cwpl.net
Daro Products Ltd, Churfield Road, Churchfield Industrial Estate, Sudbury, Suffolk, CO10 2YA Tel: (01787) 881191 Fax: (01787) 374291 E-mail: sales@daroproducts.co.uk

PLASTIC VACUUM FORMING

▶ Vacplas Mouldings Ltd, 4 Willow Park Business Centre, Lower Barnes Street, Clayton le Moors, Accrington, Lancashire, BB5 5SW Tel: (01254) 875588 Fax: (01254) 875599

PLASTIC VACUUM FORMING TOOLMAKERS

A 4 Engineering Ltd, 7 Manor Park, 35 Willis Way, Poole, Dorset, BH15 3SZ Tel: (01202) 676047 Fax: (01202) 684675 E-mail: a4eng@a4eng.com
A P Patterns Ltd, Unit 7-8 Clarendon Industrial Estate, Hyde, Cheshire, SK14 2EW Tel: 0161-368 6389 Fax: 0161-367 9669 E-mail: appatterns@btconnect.com
Abbey Products Toolmakers, 14 Ashville Way, Whetstone, Leicester, LE8 6NU Tel: 0116-286 1862 Fax: 0116-286 1864 E-mail: info@abbey-products.net
Aerovac Ltd, 4 Tetbury Industrial Estate, Cirencester Road, Tetbury, Gloucestershire, GL8 8EZ Tel: (01666) 502546 Fax: (01666) 503009 E-mail: aerovac@saqnet.co.uk
Apex Patterns, Unit 10 Redland Indust Estate, Station Hill St.Georges, Madeley, Telford, Shropshire, TF7 5EF Tel: (01952) 614337 Fax: (01952) 614337 E-mail: apexpatterns1@btclick.com
Balform Patterns Ltd, Unit 28 Soho Mills Industrial Estate, Wooburn Green, High Wycombe, Buckinghamshire, HP10 0PF Tel: (01628) 528021 Fax: (01628) 810213 E-mail: enquiries@balform.co.uk
Crossfield Excalibur Ltd, Unit 21 Woolfold Trading Estate, Mitchell Street, Bury, Lancashire, BL8 1SF Tel: 0161-763 4377 Fax: 0161-763 4926 E-mail: enquiry@excalibur-rm.co.uk
Design Pattern & Tool Co. Ltd, Unit 31A, Central Industrial Estate, Cable Street, Wolverhampton, WV2 2RL Tel: (01902) 872777 Fax: (01902) 872778 E-mail: sales@designpattern.co.uk
Elegant Plaster Mouldings, 1 Talbots La Trading Estate, Talbots Lane, Brierley Hill, West Midlands, DY5 2YX Tel: (01384) 263000 Fax: (01384) 262792 E-mail: die.tech@virgin.net
Fb-Avak, 11 Woolmer Way, Bordon, Hampshire, GU35 9QF Tel: (01420) 477411 Fax: (01420) 488224 E-mail: sales@fb-avak.co.uk
Greenbank Patterns, Southwell Lane, Kirkby-in-Ashfield, Nottingham, NG17 8FN Tel: (01623) 759919 Fax: (01623) 755834 E-mail: sales@greenbankpatterns.com
J H Tool & Pattern Projects Ltd, Unit A, Site 5, Cold Hesledon, Seaham, County Durham, SR7 8ST Tel: 0191-581 5420 Fax: 0191-581 0621 E-mail: johnstand@jh2.co.uk
Narvik Developments Ltd, Clay Lane, Oldbury, West Midlands, B69 4TH Tel: 0121-552 3429 Fax: 0121-552 6162
North West Prototypes, The Little Mill, Palatine Street, Denton, Manchester, M34 3LY Tel: 0161-320 5529 Fax: 0161-335 0928
Progressive Tooling Systems Ltd, Newark Road, Eastern Industry, Peterborough, PE1 5UA Tel: (01733) 313400 Fax: (01733) 348052 E-mail: progt@progtool.co.uk

PLASTIC VACUUM FORMING TOOLMAKERS – *continued*

Renaissance Sales & Distribution Ltd, Pennywell Industrial Estate, Sunderland, SR4 9EN Tel: 0191-534 6061 Fax: 0191-534 3626 E-mail: info@armour-plastics.com
Surrey Pattern & Mould Co., Chiltern House, Drake Avenue, Staines, Middlesex, TW18 2AW Tel: (01784) 457799 Fax: (01784) 458728 E-mail: surreypatternandmould@aol.com
Vacuum Forming Scotland, Newmains Avenue, Inchinnan, Renfrew, PA4 9RR Tel: 0141-812 5075 Fax: 0141-812 5058 E-mail: info@vacfs.co.uk
Zeus Products, Unit E2 Seaden Court, Clacton-on-Sea, Essex, CO15 4XN Tel: (01255) 220996 Fax: (01255) 429991

PLASTIC VALVES

Tomoe Valve Ltd, Estuary Road, Queensway Meadows Industrial Estate, Newport, Gwent, NP19 4SP Tel: (01633) 636800 Fax: (01633) 636801
Valvetech Ltd, Unit 9, Brookside Industrial Estate, Sawtry, Huntingdon, Cambridgeshire, PE28 5SB Tel: (01487) 833080 Fax: (01487) 833081 E-mail: sales@valvetech.co.uk

PLASTIC VETERINARY GOODS

Telsol Ltd, Grove Lodge, 4 West Park Drive East, Leeds, LS8 2EF Tel: 0113-226 0666 Fax: 0113-226 0999 E-mail: enquiries@telsol.co.uk

PLASTIC WATER SEAL TRAPS

Mcalpine & Co. Ltd, 45 Kelvin Avenue, Hillington Industrial Estate, Glasgow, G52 4LF Tel: 0141-882 3213 Fax: 0141-891 5065

PLASTIC WATERING CANS

Haws Watering Cans, 120 Beakes Road, Smethwick, West Midlands, B67 5AB Tel: 0121-420 2494 Fax: 0121-429 1668 E-mail: sales@haws.demon.co.uk
Premier Pure water, Unit 8 Spires Business Centre, Mugiemoss Road, Aberdeen, AB21 9NY Tel: (01224) 680866 Fax: (01224) 680876 E-mail: stacey@premierpure.com

PLASTIC WELDED GOODS

C O S Marketing Ltd, Bradford Road, Idle, Bradford, West Yorkshire, BD10 8SQ Tel: (01274) 617373 Fax: (01274) 615129
Celsur Plastics Ltd, 3 Lovett Road, The Causeway, Staines, Middlesex, TW18 3AZ Tel: (01784) 457175 Fax: (01784) 454605 E-mail: info@celsurplastics.co.uk
J.P. Charles [Binding Systems] Ltd, Units 11-12, 6 Old Church Road, London, E4 6ST Tel: (020) 8801 4222 Fax: (020) 8529 6464
Emerald Weld PVC Stationery Manufacturer, 101 Station Road, Reddish, Stockport, Cheshire, SK5 6ND Tel: 0161-432 7200 Fax: 0161-442 1248 E-mail: info@emweld.com
G F G Plastics Fabrication Ltd, Bridge Works, 101 West Dock Street, Hull, HU3 4HH Tel: (01482) 610110 Fax: (01482) 229044 E-mail: greygfg2003@aol.com
L M R Computer Repairs, 2 North Parade, Norris Road, Sale, Cheshire, M33 3JS Tel: 0161-962 8872 Fax: 0161-962 8872
Tennant PVC, The Midway, Nottingham, NG7 2TS Tel: 0115-988 1300 Fax: 0115-988 5310 E-mail: sales@tennantpvc.co.uk

PLASTIC WELDERS TO THE TRADE

Asbestostrip Innovations, Unit 12 Tufthorn Industrial Estate, Stepbridge Road, Coleford, Gloucestershire, GL16 8PJ Tel: (01594) 837755 Fax: (01594) 836633 E-mail: enquiries@asbestostrip.co.uk
C G Plastic Fabrications, Unit 41 New Enterprise Workshops, Mount Street, Nechells, Birmingham, B7 5RD Tel: 0121-327 3895 Fax: 0121-327 3895
Crane Plastic Fabrication, 127 Upper Thrift Street, Northampton, NN1 5HR Tel: (01604) 602224 Fax: (01604) 602214 E-mail: craneplastics@tiscali.co.uk
Cropper & Jones, New Chester Road, Hooton, Ellesmere Port, CH66 6AQ Tel: 0151-327 2560 E-mail: sales@cjrad.cwc.net
Dapro Ltd, PO Box 194, Hitchin, Hertfordshire, SG4 0TY Tel: (01462) 432021 E-mail: daprosonics@talktalk.net
Elmlead Services Ltd, Unit 1, Riverside Court, Colne Road, Huddersfield, HD1 3ER Tel: (01484) 425565 Fax: (01484) 425418 E-mail: elmlead@yahoo.co.uk
London Binder Manufacturers Ltd, Units 11-12, Bestwood Road, Brookhill Industrial Estate, Pinxton, Nottingham, NG16 6NT Tel: (01773) 813807 Fax: (01773) 580497
Plan Plastics Ltd, 40 The Warren, Chartridge, Chesham, Buckinghamshire, HP5 2RY Tel: (01494) 772577 Fax: (01494) 772577

PLASTIC WELDING, *See Plastic Welding etc*

PLASTIC WELDING EQUIPMENT MANUFRS

Advanced Ultrasonic Technology, Unit C, 127 Parker Drive, Leicester, LE4 0JP Tel: 0116-235 6980 Fax: 0116-236 6066 E-mail: advanced.ultrasonic@virgin.net
ALS Ultrasonic, Unit 24, Uplands Way, Blandford Forum, Dorset, DT11 7UZ Tel: (01258) 459257 Fax: (01258) 459287 E-mail: als.ultrasonics@virgin.net
Barnes Plastic Welding Equiptment Ltd, Unit 4 New Plough Yard, Queen Street, Great Harwood, Blackburn, BB6 7AX Tel: (01254) 882525
▶ Bep Industrial Supplies, Unit 11, Appleby Business Centre, Blackburn, BB1 3BL Tel: (01254) 279841 Fax: (01254) 290129
Machine Techniques Ltd, Unit 3-5 Court Yard Workshops, Bath Street, Market Harborough, Leicestershire, LE16 9EW Tel: (01858) 434059 Fax: (01858) 433638 E-mail: sales@mactec.co.uk
Machine Technology Ltd, 22-23 Arcadia Avenue, London, N3 2JU Tel: (020) 8349 4814 Fax: (020) 8346 6251 E-mail: machinetech@btconnect.com
Phasa Developments, International House, Horsecroft Road, Harlow, Essex, CM19 5SU Tel: (01279) 630200 Fax: (01279) 630222 E-mail: sales@phasa.co.uk
Plastic Promotions, Unit 1 Carn Industrial Area, Portadown, Craigavon, County Armagh, BT63 5YY Tel: (028) 3835 6600 Fax: (028) 3835 6601 E-mail: gilbert@plasticpromotion.co.uk
Stephenson Blake & Co. Ltd, 199 Upper Allen St, Sheffield, S3 7GW Tel: 0114-272 8325 Fax: 0114-272 0065 E-mail: sales@stephensonblake.co.uk
Tempatron Ltd, 5 Darwin Close, Reading, RG2 0TB Tel: 0118-931 4062 Fax: 0118-931 0175 E-mail: info@tempatron.co.uk

PLASTIC WELDING EQUIPMENT, HIGH FREQUENCY/RADIO FREQUENCY (RF)

Machine Techniques Ltd, Unit 3-5 Court Yard Workshops, Bath Street, Market Harborough, Leicestershire, LE16 9EW Tel: (01858) 434059 Fax: (01858) 433638 E-mail: sales@mactec.co.uk
Moore Bowman Services Ltd, 2 Glebe Road, Egham, Surrey, TW20 8BT Tel: (01784) 452387 Fax: (01784) 458500
Stephenson Blake & Co. Ltd, 199 Upper Allen St, Sheffield, S3 7GW Tel: 0114-272 8325 Fax: 0114-272 0065 E-mail: sales@stephensonblake.co.uk

PLASTIC WINDOW FRAMES

▶ D Baff Joinery Ltd, The Rear Workshop, 138 Brookland Road, Bridlington, North Humberside, YO16 4HD Tel: (01262) 676946 Fax: (01262) 676946 E-mail: lorrainbaff@btconnect.com
▶ Express Windows, 7 Tufthorn Industrial Estate, Stepbridge Road, Coleford, Gloucestershire, GL16 8PJ Tel: (01594) 835755 Fax: (01594) 835755

PLASTICISED PVC FILM

A B L Perpack 1985 Ltd, 7 Baron Avenue, Telford Way Industrial Estate, Kettering, Northamptonshire, NN16 8UW Tel: (01536) 412744 Fax: (01536) 412752 E-mail: sales@ablperpack.co.uk
Fuji Seal Europe Ltd, Scimitar Close, Gillingham Business Park, Gillingham, Kent, ME8 0RJ Tel: (01634) 378656 Fax: (01634) 379179 E-mail: sales@uk.fujiseal.com

PLASTICISERS

Cognis Performance Chemicals Ltd, Hardley, Hythe, Southampton, SO45 3ZG Tel: (023) 8089 4666 Fax: (023) 8024 3113 E-mail:
Ideal Plastic Products Ltd, 37a Irlam Road, Bootle, Merseyside, L20 4AE Tel: 0151-922 7221 Fax: 0151-922 3326
J B N Plastics, White Cottage Farm, Lucas Green Road, West End, Woking, Surrey, GU24 9LZ Tel: (01483) 474979 Fax: (01483) 472487

PLASTICS CHEMICALS

Aquaspersions Ltd, Beacon Hill Road, Halifax, West Yorkshire, HX3 6AQ Tel: (01422) 386200 Fax: (01422) 386239 E-mail: info@aquaspersions.co.uk

PLATE BENDING

▶ G W F Engineering Ltd, Woodhouse Road, Scunthorpe, South Humberside, DN16 1BD Tel: (01724) 868646 Fax: (01724) 867747 E-mail: enquiries@gwf.co.uk

PLATE FLANGES

A S Mechanical Engineering Ltd, Unit 16, Depot Road, Middlesbrough, Cleveland, TS2 1LE Tel: (01642) 250180 Fax: (01642) 250180

PLATE HEAT EXCHANGERS

A S A Hydraulik, 22 Brewers Lane, Badsey, Evesham, Worcestershire, WR11 7EU Tel: 01386 833400 Fax: 01386 833555 E-mail: support@asahydraulik.com
Baltairco West Ltd, Ivy House Farm, Wolvershill, Banwell, Avon, BS29 6LB Tel: (01934) 824411 Fax: (01934) 824477
H R S Heat Exchangers Ltd, 10-12 Caxton Way, Watford Business Park, Watford, WD18 8TX Tel: (01923) 232335 Fax: (01923) 230266 E-mail: mail@hrs.co.uk
▶ Tranter Ltd, Unit 50, Monckton Road Industrial Estate, Wakefield, West Yorkshire, WF2 7AL Tel: (01924) 298393 Fax: (01924) 291596 E-mail: sales@tranterphe.com
UK Exchangers Ltd, Unit 13 StileBrook Road, Olney, Buckinghamshire, MK46 5EA Tel: (01234) 244320 Fax: (01234) 714978 E-mail: sales@uk-exchangers.com

PLATED THROUGH HOLE (PTH) PRINTED CIRCUITS

Dial Art (PC) Ltd, 3 Airfield Way, Christchurch, Dorset, BH23 3PE Tel: (01202) 486486 Fax: (01202) 488988 E-mail: sales@dialart.com
G L R Processing Co, 11 Tiber Way, Glebe Farm Industrial Estate, Rugby, Warwickshire, CV21 1ED Tel: (01788) 541390 Fax: (01788) 546103 E-mail: g.l.r@btconnect.com
G S P K Circuits Ltd, Manse Lane, Knaresborough, North Yorkshire, HG5 8LF Tel: (01423) 865641 Fax: (01423) 798246 E-mail: sales@gspkcircuits.ltd.uk
K C E Europe, Ashcombe House, Queen Street, Godalming, Surrey, GU7 1BA Tel: (01483) 528080 Fax: (01483) 528090 E-mail: sales@kce-europe.com
Mho Trak Ltd, Blackhorse Road, Letchworth Garden City, Hertfordshire, SG6 1HB Tel: (01462) 480123 Fax: (01462) 480246 E-mail: data@mhotrak.co.uk
P C B UK, Ramsey Road, Sydenham Industrial Estate, Leamington Spa, Warwickshire, CV31 1PG Tel: (01926) 744414 Fax: (01926) 744411 E-mail: sales@pcbuk.com
Southport Electronics Ltd, 22 Glebe Lane, Banks, Southport, Merseyside, PR9 8EU Tel: (01704) 228510 Fax: (01704) 211057
Systematics Printed Circuits Ltd, Unit 7 R.J. Mitchell Centre, Spitfire Quay, Hazel Road, Woolston, Southampton, SO19 7GB Tel: (023) 8068 5677 Fax: (023) 8068 5625 E-mail: pcbsales@systematicsprintedcircuits.com
Wilson Process Systems Ltd, Waterworks Road, Hastings, East Sussex, TN34 1RT Tel: (01424) 722222 Fax: (01424) 720730 E-mail: sales@wps.co.uk

PLATFORM OR RIG LIGHTING

Davey & Co London Ltd, 1 Commerce Way, Colchester, CO2 8HR Tel: (01206) 500945 Fax: (01206) 500949 E-mail: chandlery@davey.co.uk
Marine Lighting UK Ltd, 80 Dunster Road, Chelmsley Wood, Birmingham, B37 7UU Tel: 0121-770 8522 Fax: 0121-770 0505 E-mail: marlux@btconnect.com

PLATFORM WHEELCHAIR LIFTS

Disability Access Co, 16-18 Chapel Street, Glossop, Derbyshire, SK13 8AT Tel: (01457) 868547 Fax: (08717) 335071 E-mail: sales@disabilityaccessco.com

PLATING ANODES, *See also headings for particular types*

U S Filters Electrocatalytic Products, 9 Norman Way, Severn Bridge Industrial Estate, Portskewett, Caldicot, Gwent, NP26 5YN Tel: (01291) 426500 Fax: (01291) 426501 E-mail: sales@elcat.co.uk

PLATING JIGS

A C Jigs, 10 Porters Way, Birmingham, B9 5RR Tel: 0121-753 0304 Fax: 0121-753 0304
Carrtech Ltd, Crossfield Road, Birmingham, B33 9HP Tel: 0121-683 2600 Fax: 0121-683 2601 E-mail: sales@carrtech.com
Premier Plating Jigs Ltd, 16 New Bartholomew Street, Birmingham, B5 5QS Tel: 0121-643 0727 Fax: 0121-633 3392
Salt & Sadler Ltd, 71 Rea Street, Birmingham, B5 6BB Tel: 0121-622 3887 Fax: 0121-666 6530 E-mail: saltsadler@btconnect.com
WJC Ltd (Plating Jigs), John Street, Brierfield, Nelson, Lancashire, BB9 5NX Tel: (01282) 613985 Fax: (01282) 698677 E-mail: sales@wjc.co.uk

PLATINUM REFINERS

Inco Europe Ltd, 5th Floor Windsor Ho, 50 Victoria St, London, SW1H 0XB Tel: (020) 7931 7733 Fax: (020) 7931 0083
Johnson Matthey plc, Orchard Road, Royston, Hertfordshire, SG8 5HE Tel: (01763) 253000 Fax: (01763) 253492 E-mail: nobleuk@matthey.com

PLAY EQUIPMENT, WOODEN

▶ Playways, Maiden Green, Upottery, Honiton, Devon, EX14 9QT Tel: (01404) 861379 Fax: (01404) 861379 E-mail: enquiries@playways.co.uk

PLAY HOUSES

▶ Anchor Woodworking, 3 Mid Row, Croftouterly, Leslie, Glenrothes, Fife, KY6 3DR Tel: (01592) 748900 Fax: (01592) 748900 E-mail: info@anchorwoodworking.co.uk
▶ Playways, Maiden Green, Upottery, Honiton, Devon, EX14 9QT Tel: (01404) 861379 Fax: (01404) 861379 E-mail: enquiries@playways.co.uk

PLAYGROUND BARK

Longacres Nursery, London Road, Bagshot, Surrey, GU19 5JB Tel: (01276) 476778 Fax: (01276) 452779 E-mail: landscape@longacres.co.uk

PLAYGROUND CONSULTANCY

▶ JC2 (UK) Ltd, 12 Camelot Way, Gillingham, Dorset, SP8 4SY Tel: (01747) 821900 Fax: (01747) 821088 E-mail: justinc@jc2uk.com

PLAYGROUND DESIGN

▶ JC2 (UK) Ltd, 12 Camelot Way, Gillingham, Dorset, SP8 4SY Tel: (01747) 821900 Fax: (01747) 821088 E-mail: justinc@jc2uk.com

PLAYGROUND EQUIPMENT

Adventure Playgrounds Ltd, Old Hall Farm, Hall Road, Carleton Rode, Norwich, NR16 1ND Tel: (01953) 788991 Fax: (01953) 788992
Anglian Playground Services, 6 St.Andrews Court, March, Cambridgeshire, PE15 9GE Tel: (01354) 656174 Fax: (01354) 657182 E-mail: anglian_playgrounds@yahoo.com
B J Leisure Installations Ltd, The Courtyard, Reddicap Trading Estate, Sutton Coldfield, West Midlands, B75 7BU Tel: 0121-311 1166 Fax: 0121-311 1885
John Berry, 187 Meriden Drive, Birmingham, B37 6BT Tel: 0121-770 6226 Fax: 0121-770 6226 E-mail: enquiries@jhberry.co.uk
▶ Bigfoot Play Systems Ltd, Hamilton House, 111 Marlowes, Hemel Hempstead, Hertfordshire, HP1 1BB Tel: (01442) 243355 Fax: (01442) 244330 E-mail: info@bigfootplay.com
▶ The Children's Playground Co. Ltd, 1 George Street, Wolverhampton, WV2 4DG Tel: (01902) 422515 Fax: (028) 9032 7614 E-mail: sales@thechildrensplayground.com
Creative Play (U K) Ltd, P O Box 707, Mold, Clwyd, CH7 1FG Tel: (01244) 375627 Fax: (01244) 374990 E-mail: info@creativeplayuk.com
Duraplay, 3 Craigburn Ct, Dumfries, DG1 4QQ Tel: 01387 248892
Easifall International Ltd, Unit 4 Booth Road, Sale Motorway Estate, Sale, Cheshire, M33 7JS Tel: 0161-969 5009 Fax: 0161-969 5009 E-mail: enquiries@easifall.com
Fearless Ramps, 18 Warren Road, Godalming, Surrey, GU7 3SH Tel: (01483) 420745 Fax: (01483) 416862 E-mail: info@fearlessramps.com
▶ Freestyle Sports & Play Surfaces, 129 Cheshire Street, Market Drayton, Shropshire, TF9 3AH Tel: (01630) 656336 Fax: (01630) 658366 E-mail: lee@freestylesurfaces.com

PLAYGROUND EQUIPMENT – *continued*

G L Jones Playgrounds Ltd, 1 Station Road, Bethesda, Bangor, Gwynedd, LL57 3NE Tel: (01248) 600372 Fax: (01248) 602085 E-mail: info@gljones-playgrounds.co.uk

▶ GBH Engineering Ltd, 11a Haven Road, Poole, Dorset, BH13 7LE Tel: (01202) 706206 Fax: (01202) 706104 E-mail: info@gbhramps.com

Nigel Goddard Ltd, The Barn, Little Blounce, South Warnborough, Hook, Hampshire, RG29 1RX Tel: (01256) 861900 Fax: (01256) 861900 E-mail: nigelgoddardltd@yahoo.co.uk

Greyhound Leisure Ltd, 10 Gores Lane, Market Harborough, Leicestershire, LE16 8AJ Tel: (01858) 432328 Fax: (01858) 469555 E-mail: greyhound.leisure@virgin.net

Hagsplay Ltd, Holwell Road, King Stag, Sturminster Newton, Dorset, DT10 2BA Tel: (01258) 817981 Fax: (01258) 817523 E-mail: info@hags.co.uk

Handmade Places, 14 Old Station Way, Bordon, Hampshire, GU35 9HH Tel: (01420) 474111 Fax: (01420) 474222

House Of Play Ltd, Play House, 91 Abbey Road, Dunscroft, Doncaster, South Yorkshire, DN7 4LE Tel: (01302) 846876 Fax: (01302) 842947

Howth Chains & Chain Assemblies, Unit 6 Brierley Trading Estate, North St, Brierley Hill, W. Midlands, DY5 3SL Tel: (01384) 79458 Fax: (01384) 79458

Image Playgrounds, 4-6 Allen Farmerby Way, York, YO60 6PG Tel: (01347) 868149 Fax: (01347) 667502

▶ Island Leisure Products Ltd, Unit 1a Eurolink Industrial Centre, Castle Road, Sittingbourne, Kent, ME10 3RN Tel: (01795) 436500 Fax: (01795) 436700 E-mail: info@islandleisureproducts.co.uk

▶ Kompan, 21 Roebuck Way, Knowlhill, Milton Keynes, MK5 8HL Tel: (01908) 201002 Fax: (01908) 201007 E-mail: kompan.uk@kompan.com

Lindow Leisure Lines, 15 Windsor Avenue, Wilmslow, Cheshire, SK9 5HE Tel: (01625) 533737

Little Tikes Commercial Playstems, 3 Cross Green, Liverpool, L37 4BH Tel: (01704) 833123 Fax: (01704) 833888

Magical Marking Ltd, Roall, Goole, North Humberside, DN14 0NA Tel: (01977) 662500 Fax: (01977) 663000

Massey & Harris Engineering Ltd, Cook Street Works, King Street West, Stockport, Cheshire, SK3 0AF Tel: 0161-480 5243 Fax: 0161-476 0151 E-mail: masseyharris@btconnect.com

▶ Miracle Design & Play Ltd, 14 Duncan Close, Moulton Park Industrial Estate, Northampton, NN3 6WL Tel: (01604) 591796 Fax: (01604) 591718 E-mail: sales@miracledandp.co.uk

Park Leisure Ltd, Fairview Indust Park, Brisley Lane, Ruckinge, Ashford, Kent, TN26 2PW Tel: (01233) 733782 Fax: (01233) 733578 E-mail: info@parkleisure.com

Play & Leisure Ltd, Unit 6-8 Catheralls Industrial Estate, Brookhill Way, Buckley, Clwyd, CH7 3PS Tel: (01244) 546797 Fax: (01244) 549732 E-mail: sales@playandleisure.org.uk

Play Services, 2 Wright Road, Ipswich, IP3 9JG Tel: (01473) 270820

Playdale Playgrounds Ltd, Haverthwaite, Ulverston, Cumbria, LA12 8AE Tel: (015395) 31561 Fax: (01539) 531539 E-mail: enquiries@playdale.co.uk

Playground Services, Newton Mews, Hungerford, Berkshire, RG17 0HN Tel: (01488) 683797 Fax: (01488) 685053 E-mail: info@playground-services.co.uk

Playgrounds Scotland Ltd, 2 Stewarton Road, Fenwick, Kilmarnock, Ayrshire, KA3 4AA Tel: (01560) 600744 Fax: (01560) 600755

Playline Design Ltd, 72a Gestridge Road, Kingsteignton, Newton Abbot, Devon, TQ12 3HH Tel: (01626) 363262 Fax: (01626) 200302 E-mail: playline.design@lineone.net

Playquest Adventure Ltd, Main Road, Ffynnongroyw, Holywell, Clwyd, CH8 9SW Tel: (01745) 561117 E-mail: sales@playquest.co.uk

Playquip Leisure, Hayfarm Industrial Estate, Cockaynes Lane, Alresford, Colchester, CO7 8BZ Tel: (01206) 825869 Fax: (01206) 827968 E-mail: sales@playquipleisure.co.uk

Playsafe Playgrounds Ltd, The Carthouse, Goldrings Farm, Elsted, Midhurst, West Sussex, GU29 0JS Tel: (01730) 815472 Fax: (01730) 815872 E-mail: sales@playsafeplaygrounds.co.uk

Playscape Playground Equipment, The Street, Surlingham, Norwich, NR14 7AJ Tel: (01508) 538016 Fax: (01508) 538610 E-mail: sales@playscape-playground-equipment.co.uk

R T C Safety Surfaces, Beech House, Smallshaw Lane, Burnley, Lancashire, BB11 5SQ Tel: (01282) 414131 Fax: (01282) 414133 E-mail: sales@rtcsafety.co.uk

▶ Rainbow Playsystems, Ham Lane, Orton Waterville, Peterborough, PE2 5UU Tel: (01733) 391222 Fax: (01733) 391223 E-mail: peterborough@rainbowplaysystems.co.uk

Record Playground Equipment Ltd, Waterfront Complex, Shipyard Industrial Estate, Selby, North Yorkshire, YO8 8AP Tel: (01757) 703620 Fax: (01757) 705158 E-mail: sales@recordplaygrounds.co.uk

Redlynch Leisure Installations Ltd, PO Box 1181, Chippenham, Wiltshire, SN15 3ZD Tel: (01249) 444537 Fax: (01249) 655002

Russell Leisure Ltd, Newbridge Industrial Estate, Newbridge, Midlothian, EH28 8PJ Tel: 0131-335 5400 Fax: 0131-335 5401 E-mail: sales@russell-leisure.co.uk

S M P Playgrounds Ltd, Thorpe Industrial Estate, Ten Acre Lane, Egham, Surrey, TW20 8RJ Tel: (01784) 489100 Fax: (01784) 431079 E-mail: sales@smp.co.uk

Seesaw Design, PO Box 100, Bury, Lancashire, BL8 2FU Tel: (01204) 882222 Fax: (01204) 882200 E-mail: mikeyounge@btconnect.com

Social Climbers Ltd, Parsonage Farm, Childrey, Wantage, Oxfordshire, OX12 9PH Tel: (01235) 751717 Fax: (01235) 751999

Solutions Play By Design, Ninelands La, Garforth, Leeds, LS25 1NX Tel: 0113-287 7565 Fax: 0113-287 7565 E-mail: nev@fsbusiness.co.uk

Stonewood Trading Ltd, Dunmere Road, Bodmin, Cornwall, PL31 2QN Tel: (01208) 73258 Fax: (01208) 74223 E-mail: stonewoodtrading@btconnect.com

Sun Safe Play Systems Ltd, Cedars Coach House, Church Road, Windlesham, Surrey, GU20 6BL Tel: (01276) 489999 Fax: (01276) 489999 E-mail: sales@sunsafe.co.uk

Tree Tops Play Equipment, 78 London Road, Canterbury, Kent, CT2 8LS Tel: (01227) 761899

Universal Play Ltd, 4 Derwent Close, Tangmere, Chichester, West Sussex, PO20 2FQ Tel: (01243) 784722 Fax: (01243) 784742 E-mail: universal.play@primex.co.uk

PLAYGROUND GROUNDWORKS PREPARATION CONSULTANCY

▶ Fosters Construction Ltd, Emmanuel, Trusthorpe Road, Sutton-on-Sea, Mablethorpe, Lincolnshire, LN12 2LL Tel: (01507) 443649 Fax: (01507) 443649 E-mail: neale.bloomfields@homecall.co.uk

▶ JC2 (UK) Ltd, 12 Camelot Way, Gillingham, Dorset, SP8 4SY Tel: (01747) 821900 Fax: (01747) 821088 E-mail: justinc@jc2uk.com

▶ Yates Landscaping Ltd, 6 Hawthorne Business Park, Hawthorne Street, Warrington, WA5 0BT Tel: (01925) 638883 Fax: (01925) 638883 E-mail: yateslandscaping@tiscali.co.uk

PLAYGROUND INSTALLATION

▶ Safeplay Playground Equipment, Kelsey Park Depot, Manor Way, Beckenham, Kent, BR3 3LJ Tel: (020) 8658 5631 Fax: (020) 8658 9060 E-mail: playsafe@safeplay.co.uk

Universal Play Ltd, 4 Derwent Close, Tangmere, Chichester, West Sussex, PO20 2FQ Tel: (01243) 784722 Fax: (01243) 784742 E-mail: universal.play@primex.co.uk

PLAYGROUND MATS

▶ SSP Specialised Sports Products Ltd, Po Box 998, Canterbury, Kent, CT1 9EU Tel: (0870) 7501432 Fax: (0870) 7518935 E-mail: info@ssp-uk.co.uk

Wicksteed Leisure Ltd, Digby St, Kettering, Northamptonshire, NN16 8YJ Tel: (01536) 517028 Fax: (01536) 410633 E-mail: sales@wicksteed.co.uk

PLEATED BLINDS

▶ Apollo Blinds Ltd, 64 Main Street, Rutherglen, Glasgow, G73 2HY Tel: 0141-647 0341 Fax: 0141-647 0341

▶ Apollo Blinds Ltd, 73 South Methven Street, Perth, PH1 5NX Tel: (01738) 622366 Fax: (01738) 622366

▶ Austin Marr, 7 The Nelson Centre, Portfield Road, Portsmouth, PO3 5SF Tel: (023) 9269 0900 Fax: (023) 9269 1300 E-mail: enquiries@austinmarr.co.uk

B J's Blinds, Hillend Bridge, Pudford Lane, Worcester, WR6 6QL Tel: (01886) 888966 Fax: (01886) 888481

Blind Business, Arturi's Garden Centre, Allington Lane, Fair Oak, Eastleigh, Hampshire, SO50 7DE Tel: (023) 8060 2211 Fax: (023) 8060 2211 E-mail: info@theblindbusiness.co.uk

Broadview Blinds Ltd, 57 Hatch Pond Road, Nuffield Industrial Estate, Poole, Dorset, BH17 0JZ Tel: (01202) 679012 Fax: (01202) 671885 E-mail: sales@broadview-blinds.co.uk

Butterfly Blinds, Cambridge Road, Milton, Cambridge, CB24 6AT Tel: (0500) 011363 Fax: (01223) 425355 E-mail: butterflyblinds@tiscali.co.uk

C F M Blindmaker Supplies Ltd, 18 20 James Road, Tyseley, Birmingham, B11 2BA Tel: (0870) 7702965 Fax: (0871) 4332309 E-mail: sales@cfmblinds.co.uk

Highbury Design, 3 Catton Road, Arnold, Nottingham, NG5 7JD Tel: 0115-967 1188 E-mail: info@highburyblinds.co.uk

T.F. Sampson Ltd, Creeting Road, Stowmarket, Suffolk, IP14 5BA Tel: (01449) 613535 Fax: (01449) 678381 E-mail: sales@t-f-sampson.co.uk

Sun Interiors Ltd, Unit 8, Plaxton Park, Cayton Low Road, Eastfield, Scarborough, North Yorkshire, YO11 3BQ Tel: (01723) 585808 Fax: (01723) 585807 E-mail: info@sun-blinds.co.uk

PLEATERS TO THE FASHION TRADE

Arthur Elkin Holdings Ltd, Progress Mill, Parsonage Street, Macclesfield, Cheshire, SK11 7LY Tel: (01625) 423502 Fax: (01625) 612994 E-mail: elkin.sales@arthurelkin.co.uk

Truperm Pleating Co. Ltd, Williams Street, Gorton, Manchester, M18 7AH Tel: 0161-223 3185 Fax: 0161-231 6813

PLIERS

Maun Industries Ltd, Moor Lane, Mansfield, Nottinghamshire, NG18 5SE Tel: (01623) 624525 Fax: (01623) 659969 E-mail: maun.industries@btinternet.com

Stahlwille Tools Ltd, Albany Park, Camberley, Surrey, GU16 7PD Tel: (01276) 24080 Fax: (01276) 24696 E-mail: sales@stahlwille.co.uk

PLOTTER PENS

C.D.S Yorks Ltd, Ledgard Way, Reprographic House, Armley, Leeds, LS12 2ND Tel: 0113-263 0601 Fax: 0113-231 0305 E-mail: sales@cds-yorks.com

PLOUGH GRINDING

Ajs Profiles, Unit 12a Parkrose Industrial Estate, Middlemore Road, Smethwick, West Midlands, B66 2DZ Tel: 0121-565 5379 Fax: 0121-565 5379 E-mail: ajsprofiles.ltd@virgin.net

Belper Tools Ltd, 7 Chapel Street, Levenshulme, Manchester, M19 3QB Tel: 0161-224 7240 Fax: 0161-257 2875

Harbex Profiling & Grinding Ltd, Blackberry Farm, High Oak Hill, Bobbing, Sittingbourne, Kent, ME9 8QD Tel: (01795) 842925 Fax: (01795) 843868 E-mail: sales@harbex.co.uk

Metalpacks Ltd, Old Parsonage Works, High Street, Farningham, Dartford, DA4 0DG Tel: (01322) 862727 Fax: (01322) 865580 E-mail: metalpacks@usa.net

Pegasus Profiles Ltd, Stephenson Way, Thetford, Norfolk, IP24 3RJ Tel: (01842) 755711 Fax: (01842) 755711 E-mail: sales@pegpro.co.uk

Procut Ltd, Unit 51 Youngs Industrial Estate, Paices Hill, Aldermaston, Reading, RG7 4PW Tel: 0118-981 7109 Fax: 0118-981 2832

PLUG AND RING THREAD GAUGES

Threadmaster Gauges Ltd, Princes Dr Industrial Estate, Coventry Road, Kenilworth, Warwickshire, CV8 2FD Tel: (01926) 852428 Fax: (01926) 850047 E-mail: sales@threadmastergauges.co.uk

PLUG VALVES

Flowserve Flow Control UK Ltd, Burrell Road, Haywards Heath, West Sussex, RH16 1TL Tel: (01444) 314400 Fax: (01444) 314401 E-mail: ukfcinfo@flowserve.com

▶ Schuf UK Ltd, 157 Park Road, Teddington, Middlesex, TW11 0BP Tel: (020) 8977 2992 Fax: (020) 8943 3898 E-mail: sales@schuf.co.uk

PLUGS AND SOCKETS, *See also headings for particular types*

Etsgap Electrical Wholesalers, Energy House, Falkland Close, Charter Avenue Industrial Estate, Coventry, CV4 8AU Tel: (024) 7646 8259 Fax: (024) 7669 4090 E-mail: ets.gap@btconnect.com

Northern Connectors Ltd, Abbotsfield Road, Reginald Road Industrial Estate, St. Helens, Merseyside, WA9 4HU Tel: (01744) 815001 Fax: (01744) 814040 E-mail: sales@northern-connectors.co.uk

PLUMBERS MOLESKIN

Brisbane Moss Corduroys Corduroy Manufacturers, Halifax Road, Bridgeroyd Works, Todmorden, Lancashire, OL14 6DF Tel: (01706) 815121 Fax: (01706) 818598 E-mail: brimoss@brisbanemoss.co.uk

Cudworth Of Norden, Baitings Mill, Rochdale, Lancashire, OL12 7TQ Tel: (01706) 641771 Fax: (01706) 641771

PLUMBERS' FITTINGS OR HARDWARE OR BRASS FOUNDRY

Bailey Bros (Engineers) Ltd, 105 Hospital St, Newtown, Birmingham, B19 3XB Tel: 0121-359 8361 Fax: 0121-359 0909 E-mail: sales@cerro-ems.co.uk

Bathstore.com Ltd, Unit 2a Felnex Trading Estate, Wallington, Surrey, SM6 7EL Tel: (01923) 694740 Fax: (020) 8773 5004 E-mail: enquiries@bathstore.com

Bes Ltd, 3 Junction 6 Industrial Park, 66 Electric Avenue, Birmingham, B6 7JA Tel: 0121-322 6400 Fax: 0121-322 6440 E-mail: sales@bes.ltd.uk

Bolivar Ltd, Unit 9B Devonshire Works, Riparian Way, Cross Hills, Keighley, West Yorkshire, BD20 7BW Tel: (01535) 631222 Fax: (01535) 637555 E-mail: sales@bolivar-limited.com

C & S Builders Merchants Stamford Hill Ltd, 278-286 Stamford Hill, London, N16 6TY Tel: (020) 8809 5373 Fax: (020) 8800 3243

Davroc Ltd, Ibroc House, Essex Road, Hoddesdon, Hertfordshire, EN11 0QS Tel: (01992) 441672 Fax: (01992) 708308 E-mail: info@davroc.co.uk

Chas Lowe & Sons (Builders' Merchants) Ltd, 156 London Road, Knebworth, Hertfordshire, SG3 6HA Tel: (01438) 812740 Fax: (01438) 814324 E-mail: peter@chaslowe.co.uk

Marflow Engineering Ltd, Austin Way, Hampstead Industrial Estate, Birmingham, B42 1DU Tel: 0121-358 1555 Fax: 0121-358 1444 E-mail: sales@marflow.co.uk

Marley Plumbing & Drainage Ltd, Rannoch Road, Uddingston, Glasgow, G71 5PA Tel: (01698) 815231 Fax: (01698) 810307

Midland Brass Fittings Ltd, Wynford Industrial Trading Estate, Wynford Road, Birmingham, B27 6JT Tel: 0121-707 6666 Fax: 0121-708 1270 E-mail: sales@midbras.co.uk

Oracstar, Weddell Way, Brackmills, Northampton, NN4 7HS Tel: (01604) 702181 Fax: (01604) 701743 E-mail: orac@oracstar.co.uk

Peglar, Belmont Works, St. Catherines Avenue, Doncaster, South Yorkshire, DN4 8DF Tel: (0870) 1200285 Fax: (01302) 367661 E-mail: export@pegler.com

Pipe Centre, 18-22 Pages Walk, London, SE1 4SB Tel: (020) 7237 4421 Fax: (020) 7231 3223 E-mail: br.bermondey@wolseley.co.uk

Plumb Center, Station Approach, Coulsdon, Surrey, CR5 2YB Tel: (020) 8668 4121 Fax: (020) 8660 8795 E-mail: bk.colcon@woloseley.co.uk

Plumbase Ltd, 542 Millbrook Road West, Southampton, SO15 0LN Tel: (023) 8077 4499 Fax: (023) 8077 3388

Prima Flow, Stargate Business Park, Cuckoo Road, Nechells, Birmingham, B7 5SE Tel: 0121-327 1234 Fax: (0121) 3274046 E-mail: info@muellerprimaflow.com

Rabco Fittings Ltd, Unit 15 Palmers Road, East Moons Moat, Redditch, Worcestershire, B98 0RF Tel: (01527) 510733 Fax: (01527) 510735 E-mail: admin@rabco-fittings.com

Robert Lee, Lea Road, Waltham Abbey, Essex, EN9 1AS Tel: (01992) 703200 Fax: (0800) 3765556

PLUMBERS' MERCHANTS

A B Plumbing Supplies Ltd, Savoy Works, Pershore Road, Kingsnorton, Birmingham, B30 3DR Tel: 0121-433 3099 Fax: 0121-458 5698 E-mail: sales@abplumbing.co.uk

A E Spink Ltd, Kelham Street, Doncaster, South Yorkshire, DN1 3RA Tel: (01302) 321514 Fax: (01302) 327543

A J Paveley & Co., 416 Golden Hillock Road, Sparkbrook, Birmingham, B11 2QH Tel: 0121-772 1739 Fax: 0121-771 1386 E-mail: peterpavely@aol.com

A J Plumbing Supplies Ltd, Greenbank Industrial Estate, Rampart Road, Newry, County Down, BT34 2QU Tel: (028) 3026 3348 Fax: (028) 3026 3263 E-mail: info@ajplumbing.co.uk

A Warren & Sons Ltd, Stamford Works, Constantine Street, Oldham, OL4 3AD Tel: 0161-624 4621 Fax: 0161-627 5163 E-mail: warrens@zen.co.uk

Acrelane Builders Merchants Ltd, 53 Acre Lane, London, SW2 5TN Tel: (020) 7738 3777 Fax: (020) 7738 6842 E-mail: info@diamond-merchants.co.uk

Aerocrete Ltd, 1001 Shore Road, Belfast, BT36 7DE Tel: (028) 9078 2755 Fax: (028) 9078 2766 E-mail: info@jpcorry.co.uk

Aizlewoods Buildbase, Hermitage Mill, Hermitage Lane, Mansfield, Nottinghamshire, NG18 5HA Tel: (01623) 420121 Fax: (01623) 420384 E-mail: mansfield@buildbase.co.uk

▶ Atlas Trading Group Ltd, Oldham Road, Ashton-under-Lyne, Lancashire, OL7 9AZ Tel: 0161-339 2011 Fax: 0161-343 2453 E-mail: info@atlastrading.co.uk

B & B Supplies, 641 Garratt Lane, London, SW18 4SX Tel: (020) 8946 2957 Fax: (020) 8946 2435

B Danby & Company Ltd, English Street, Hull, HU3 2DZ Tel: (01482) 599599 Fax: (01482) 599211 E-mail: enquiries@danbys.co.uk

B Danby & Co., Milners Road, Yeadon, Leeds, LS19 7JE Tel: 0113-250 6511 Fax: 0113-250 0328 E-mail: enquires@danbys.co.uk

B Danby & Co, Albermarle Back Road, Scarborough, North Yorkshire, YO11 1YA Tel: (01723) 360580 Fax: (01723) 352010

B G Romeril Ltd, Dumaresq Street, St. Helier, Jersey, JE2 3WP Tel: (01534) 738806 Fax: (01534) 767016 E-mail: enquiry@romerils.co.je

B M B Ltd, 194 Newbold Road, Chesterfield, Derbyshire, S41 7AF Tel: (01246) 273500 Fax: (01246) 235252 E-mail: chesterfield@buildbase.co.uk

B & S Leicester Ltd, 33 Parker Drive, Leicester, LE4 0JP Tel: 0116-232 3222

PLUMBERS' MERCHANTS – *continued*

B S S Group plc, Fleet House, Lee Circle, Leicester, LE1 3QQ Tel: 0116-262 3232 Fax: 0116-253 1343 E-mail: sales@bssuk.co.uk

▶ Baudains Trade Supplies Ltd, Les Amballes, St. Peter Port, Guernsey, GY1 1WT Tel: (01481) 724642 Fax: (01481) 714399 E-mail: peter@btsgsy.com

Len Beaman Ltd, Eccleston Street, St. Helens, Merseyside, WA10 2PG Tel: (01744) 20717 Fax: (01744) 453012 E-mail: sales@beaman.co.uk

Bearwood Builders Supply Co Smethwick Ltd, Three Shires Oak Road, Smethwick, West Midlands, B67 5BS Tel: 0121-429 2011 Fax: 0121-429 2226

Bes Ltd, 3 Junction 6 Industrial Park, 66 Electric Avenue, Birmingham, B6 7JA Tel: 0121-322 6400 Fax: 0121-322 6440 E-mail: sales@bes.ltd.uk

Bilbeck Ltd, Yorke Street, Mansfield Woodhouse, Mansfield, Nottinghamshire, NG19 9NU Tel: (01623) 651101 Fax: (01623) 653387 E-mail: sales@bilbeck.com

Bradfords Underwood, Tolladine Road, Worcester, WR4 9EG Tel: (01935) 845245 Fax: (01905) 723743

Brittain Adams (Holdings) Ltd, 40 The Boulevard, Stoke-on-Trent, ST6 6DP Tel: (01782) 834175 Fax: (01782) 834176

Brookers Builders Merchants Ltd, 43-53 Norman Road, St. Leonards-on-Sea, East Sussex, TN38 0EQ Tel: (01424) 423107 Fax: (01424) 718341

Buildbase, Crinoline Commercial Area, Rawmarsh Road, Rotherham, South Yorkshire, S60 1SA Tel: (01709) 365686 Fax: (01709) 362365

Builders Centre Sheffield Ltd, Nunnery Drive, Sheffield, S2 1TA Tel: 0114-272 4001 Fax: 0114-241 2840 E-mail: info@builderscentre.co.uk

Builders Supply Co. (Kendal) Ltd, Ann Street, Kendal, Cumbria, LA9 6AA Tel: (01539) 721911 Fax: (01539) 740481 E-mail: info.kendal@builders-supply.co.uk

Burton Bell & Co. Ltd, 3 Kildonan Road, Liverpool, L17 0BU Tel: 0151-727 2231 Fax: 0151-727 2231

C & W Berry Ltd, Golden Hill Lane, Leyland, Leyland, PR25 2YH Tel: (01772) 431216 Fax: (01772) 622314 E-mail: enquiries@cwberry.com

Canvey Supply Co. Ltd, 101 Point Road, Canvey Island, Essex, SS8 7TJ Tel: (01268) 696666 Fax: (01268) 696724 E-mail: canveysupply@btconnect.com

Carver Gases Ltd, Littles Lane, Wolverhampton, WV1 1JY Tel: (01902) 577000 Fax: (01902) 712145 E-mail: mail@carvers.co.uk

Casswells Ltd, 6 High Street, Midsomer Norton, Radstock, BA3 2HR Tel: (01761) 413331 Fax: (01761) 410327

Matthew Charlton Ltd, Station Road, Hexham, Northumberland, NE46 1HB Tel: (01434) 604911 Fax: (01434) 604147

City Plumbing Supplies Ltd, 1 Faraday Street, Dryburgh Industrial Estate, Dundee, DD2 3QQ Tel: (01382) 825625 Fax: (01382) 826926

City Plumbing Supplies Ltd, Unit 1a Roundwood Drive, Sherdley Road Industrial Estate, St. Helens, Merseyside, WA9 5JD Tel: (01744) 453874 Fax: (01744) 27482 E-mail: andrew.ormerod@city-plumbing-supplies.co.uk

City Plumbing Supplies Ltd, 159 Stanley Road, London, Teddington, Middlesex, TW11 8UF Tel: (020) 8943 3933 Fax: (020) 8943 2873

Clower & Son Ltd, 48-52 Nottingham Road, Ripley, Derbyshire, DE5 3AT Tel: (01773) 742351 Fax: (01773) 744610

Connection Aml Ltd, Unit 8-9 Newtown Business Park, Albion Close, Poole, Dorset, BH12 3LL Tel: (01202) 733510 Fax: (01202) 715455 E-mail: info@travisperkins.co.uk

Coopers Great Yarmouth Ltd, New Road, Fritton, Great Yarmouth, Norfolk, NR31 9HR Tel: (01493) 602204 Fax: (01493) 655620 E-mail: enquiries@supercoopers.co.uk

County Heating Centre Ltd, 6-18 Dunstall Street, Scunthorpe, South Humberside, DN15 6LF Tel: (01724) 844872 Fax: (01724) 871197

Crossling Ltd, Coast Road, Heaton, Newcastle upon Tyne, NE6 5TP Tel: 0191-265 4166 Fax: 0191-276 4839 E-mail: marketing@crossling.co.uk

Drakes Plumbing Supplies Ltd, 3 Independent Business Park, Imberhorne Lane, East Grinstead, West Sussex, RH19 1TU Tel: (01342) 319123 Fax: (01342) 319136

E W Moore & Son Ltd, 39-43 Plashet Grove, London, E6 1AD Tel: (020) 8472 0521 Fax: (020) 8472 4702 E-mail: sales@wallposters.org.uk

Edward Foster & Son Bradford Ltd, Benton House, Nelson Street, Bradford, West Yorkshire, BD5 0DP Tel: (01274) 733511 Fax: (01274) 730227

Edwards & Farndon, Lower Dartmouth Street, Birmingham, B9 4LG Tel: 0121-766 6255 Fax: 0121-766 8875

Express, Unit 1b Thorn Business Park, Rotherwas, Hereford, HR2 6JT Tel: (01432) 278138 Fax: (01432) 278138

F K Ellis & Sons Ltd, Unit 2 Lower Sydenham Industrial Estate, Kangley Bridge Road, London, SE26 5BA Tel: (020) 8676 9428 Fax: (020) 8676 9429 E-mail: sales@fkellis.com

F & P Wholesale, Chantry Road, Woburn Road Industrial Estate, Kempston, Bedford, MK42 7SU Tel: (01234) 845600 Fax: (01234) 840379

Farr & Harris Ltd, 3 Dyffryn Industrial Estate, Pool Road, Newtown, Powys, SY16 3BD Tel: (01686) 626261 Fax: (01686) 622630 E-mail: info@farrharris.co.uk

Farr & Harris Ltd, Brassey Road, Old Potts Way, Shrewsbury, SY3 7FA Tel: (01743) 236371 Fax: (01743) 271703 E-mail: sales@farrharris.co.uk

Firwood Timber & Building Supplies, 8 Greengate Lane, Prestwich, Manchester, M25 3HW Tel: 0161-798 8404 Fax: 0161-773 5386 E-mail: firwood@prestwichm25.wanadoo.co.uk

Fraser & Ellis, 80-100 Gwynne Road, London, SW11 3UW Tel: (020) 7228 9999 Fax: (020) 7228 7250

Graham Builders Merchants Ltd, Bridgeman Street, Bolton, BL3 6BS Tel: (01204) 389500 Fax: (01204) 363205

Graham Builders Merchants Ltd, Block 4 Cadzow Industrial Estate, Hamilton, Lanarkshire, ML3 7QU Tel: (01698) 422522 Fax: (01698) 423284 E-mail: sales@grahamgroup.com

Grahams Group plc, 96 Temple Park Cresent, Edinburgh, EH11 1JR Tel: 0131-228 2345 Fax: 0131-228 5405 E-mail: mikedick@graham-group.co.uk

Thomas Griffiths & Son Ltd, 84 Chorlton Road, Manchester, M15 4AL Tel: 0161-226 1834 Fax: 0161-226 3773

Grove Plumbing & Heating Supplies Ltd, Unit 11a National Trading Estate, Bramhall Moor Lane, Hazel Grove, Stockport, Cheshire, SK7 5AA Tel: 0161-456 4495 Fax: 0161-456 2678 E-mail: sales@groveplg.co.uk

Haldane Fisher, Castle Street, Portadown, Craigavon, County Armagh, BT62 1BD Tel: (028) 3833 7321 Fax: (028) 3833 0896 E-mail: sales.portadown@haldane-fisher.com

Haldane Fisher, Carnbane Industrial Estate, Newry, County Down, BT35 6QQ Tel: (028) 3026 3201 Fax: (028) 3026 8101 E-mail: dgrayhaldanefisher@btinternet.com

Harris, Charlotte Road, Stirchley, Birmingham, B30 2BT Tel: 0121-451 1664 Fax: 0121-433 3864 E-mail: sales@harrisofstirchley.co.uk

Haywards Tewksbury Ltd, 126 High Street, Tewksbury, Tewkesbury, Gloucestershire, GL20 5JX Tel: (01684) 292282 Fax: (01684) 850634

Home Heating & Plumbing Supplies Ltd, 17 Middle Hillgate, Stockport, Cheshire, SK1 3AY Tel: 0161-477 2897 Fax: 0161-476 5034

Home Improvement Centre, 229-231 Dunstable Road, Luton, LU4 8BN Tel: (01582) 722189 Fax: (01582) 402789 E-mail: hic10@hotmail.com

Iron Stores Jersey Ltd, 10-12 Commercial Buildings, St. Helier, Jersey, JE1 3UD Tel: (01534) 877755 Fax: (01534) 727449

J C Quirk, 55 Waverley Road, Sale, Cheshire, M33 7AY Tel: 0161-973 6238 Fax: 0161-973 7066

J Clark & Son Kingsbury Ltd, 843-849 Honeypot Lane, Stanmore, Middlesex, HA7 1AR Tel: (020) 8951 1888 Fax: (020) 8951 4882 E-mail: richard.gom1@orange.net

J & G Archibald, Jagal House, Damson Way, Durham, DH1 2YD Tel: 0191-384 8484 Fax: 0191-386 2432 E-mail: sales@archibald.co.uk

J T Dove Ltd, Orchard Street, Newcastle upon Tyne, NE1 3NB Tel: 0191-232 6151 Fax: 0191-222 1870 E-mail: newcastle@jtdove.co.uk

James Payne, 28-29 Vaughan Street, Llandudno, Gwynedd, LL30 1AB Tel: (01492) 876705 Fax: (01492) 860903 E-mail: jamespaynellandudno@hotmail.com.uk

Jewson Ltd, Lyons Lane, Chorley, Lancashire, PR6 0PH Tel: (01257) 276211 Fax: (01257) 260098

Jewson Ltd, 25 Bakewell Road, Loughborough, Leicestershire, LE11 5QY Tel: (01509) 212121 Fax: (01509) 610218

Jewson Ltd, 89-105 High Street, Rowley Regis, West Midlands, B65 0EH Tel: 0121-559 1207 Fax: 0121-561 2461

John Richmond & Co. Ltd, 18-20 Carnoustie Place, Scotland Street, Glasgow, G5 8PA Tel: 0141-429 7441 Fax: 0141-420 1406 E-mail: sales@richmond-phm.co.uk

George Jones & Bros, 1-7 Lower Ashley Road, St. Agnes, Bristol, BS2 9QA Tel: 0117-955 6201 Fax: 0117-955 5503

Jones & Shufflebottom Ltd, Lytton Street, Stoke-on-Trent, ST4 2AG Tel: (01782) 846881 Fax: (01782) 414812 E-mail: stoke@shuffs.co.uk

Keyline Ltd, Bentinck Street, Ashton-under-Lyne, Lancashire, OL7 0PT Tel: 0161-330 2214 Fax: 0161-343 2158

Lakes Buildbase, Parcel Terrace, Derby, DE1 1LQ Tel: (01332) 349083 Fax: (01332) 290178E-mail: derbybuilding@buildbase.co.uk

Leck Curphey Ltd, 6 Gloucester Road, Anfield, Liverpool, L6 4DS Tel: 0151-260 0096

Link Southern Heating Supplies, Bridge House, 283 Kingsland Road, London, E2 8AS Tel: (020) 7729 9328 Fax: (020) 7739 4336

M S Services, 18 Esk Place, Aberdeen, AB16 6SQ Tel: (01224) 691742 Fax: (01224) 691742 E-mail: msservices@fsmai8l.net

Manchester Slate Ltd, 1119 Ashton Old Road, Manchester, M11 1AA Tel: 0161-223 5031 Fax: 0161-220 8925

Manjits Ltd, 304-310 Alcester Road, Birmingham, B13 8LJ Tel: 0121-449 5759 Fax: 0121-449 8925

Mathewson & Rosemond Ltd, Union Mills, 9 Dewsbury Road, Leeds, LS11 5DE Tel: 0113-245 7983 Fax: 0113-242 6986 E-mail: salesmandrleeds@btconnect.com

Mayalls of Wigan, Woodhouse Lane, Wigan, Lancashire, WN6 7TH Tel: (01942) 241711 Fax: (01942) 241271 E-mail: maywigan@travisperkins.co.uk

Naylor Myers Ltd, Wakefield Road, Brighouse, West Yorkshire, HD6 1ZE Tel: (01484) 712531 Fax: (01484) 722365

John Nicholls Trading Ltd, Overthorpe Road, Banbury, Oxfordshire, OX16 4TB Tel: (01295) 262294 Fax: (01295) 270895

Omnico Plastics Ltd, Unit 12 Mace Industrial Estate, Mace Lane, Ashford, Kent, TN24 8PE Tel: (01233) 646749 Fax: (01233) 663101 E-mail: sales@omnico.co.uk

Omnico Plastics Ltd, Farthing Road, Ipswich, IP1 5AP Tel: (01473) 461461 Fax: (01473) 240518 E-mail: sales@omnico.co.uk

T. Patton Ltd, 588 Lea Bridge Road, Leyton, London, E10 7DN Tel: (020) 8539 1599 Fax: (020) 8558 3578 E-mail: sales@tpatton.co.uk

Pemberton Building Supplies Ltd, Richmond Hill, Wigan, Lancashire, WN5 8AA Tel: (01942) 218222 Fax: (01942) 225205

Pipeline Centre, Shails Lane, Trowbridge, Wiltshire, BA14 8LQ Tel: (01225) 762331 Fax: (01225) 771270 E-mail: sales@pipeline.centre.co.uk

Plumb Center Ltd, 2 Dukeminster Estate, Dunstable, Bedfordshire, LU5 4HU Tel: (01582) 666811 Fax: (01582) 664303

Plumbase Ltd, 123-129 Portland Road, Hove, East Sussex, BN3 5QW Tel: (01273) 746161 Fax: (01273) 737677 E-mail: admin.marketing@plumbase.com

Plumbing & Heating Services, 194 Winchester Road, London, E4 9JP Tel: (020) 8523 2222 Fax: (020) 8527 6776 E-mail: phs@chris14.fsnet.co.uk

Robert Pochin Ltd, 11 St Georges Way, Leicester, LE1 1SH Tel: 0116-251 5051 Fax: 0116-253 8829 E-mail: sales.enquiries@robertpochin.co.uk

Price & Oliver Ltd, 254 Lozells Road, Birmingham, B19 1NR Tel: 0121-554 8491 Fax: 0121-554 8989

PTS Plumbing Trade Supplies Ltd, Buccaneer Way, Magna Park, Lutterworth, Leicestershire, LE17 4YZ Tel: (01455) 551210 Fax: (01455) 550772 E-mail: magnareception@bssgroup.com

PTS Plumbing Trade Supplies Ltd, 24 Boleness Road, Wisbech, Cambridgeshire, PE13 2RB Tel: (01945) 589990 Fax: (01945) 474827

Rawle Gammon & Baker Holdings Ltd, Gammon House, Riverside Road, Pottington Business Park, Barnstaple, Devon, EX31 1LX Tel: (01271) 375501 Fax: (01271) 329982 E-mail: barnstable@rgbltd.co.uk

A.F.G. Ray & Sons, The Old Coal Yard, Worcester Road, Kidderminster, Worcestershire, DY11 1HN Tel: (01562) 755585 Fax: (01562) 825218

Robert Lee, Lea Road, Waltham Abbey, Essex, EN9 1AS Tel: (01992) 703200 Fax: (0800) 3765556

Robinson Buildbase Ltd, Green Street, Burton-On-Trent, Staffordshire, DE14 3RX Tel: (01283) 565021 Fax: (01283) 569240 E-mail: burton@buildbase.co.uk

Rodbers Of Richmond Ltd, The Old Cinema, 2 Queens Road, Richmond, North Yorkshire, DL10 4DN Tel: (01748) 822491 Fax: (01748) 826497

S P Brown & Co. Ltd, 31 Lockhart Street, London, E3 4BL Tel: (020) 8981 2747 Fax: (020) 8981 2747

Scobles, Anerley Railway Station, Anerley Station Road, London, SE20 8PY Tel: (020) 8676 7700 Fax: (020) 8676 7711 E-mail: sales@scobles.co.uk

Slocombe Buildbase, Searle Crescent, Winterstoke Commercial Centre, Weston-Super-Mare, Avon, BS23 3YX Tel: (01934) 626503 Fax: (01934) 635334 E-mail: westonsupermare@buildbase.co.uk

Smith Brothers Ltd, Osbaldwick Link Road, York, YO10 3WA Tel: (01904) 415222 Fax: (01904) 413219E-mail: admin@smithbrothersyork.com

Strowger Ltd, 395-397 London Road, Mitcham, Surrey, CR4 4BG Tel: (020) 8648 2401 Fax: (020) 8648 2401

T Crossling & Co. Ltd, Portrack Grange Road, Stockton-on-Tees, Cleveland, TS18 2PF Tel: (01642) 616996 Fax: (01642) 616231 E-mail: sales@crossling.co.uk

T D Ladd & Son, Belle Vue, Clynderwen, Dyfed, SA66 7NQ Tel: (01437) 563217 Fax: (01437) 563217

Tayside Plumbing & Building Supplies Ltd, 1 Dens Road, Dundee, DD3 7SR Tel: (01382) 229401 Fax: (01382) 202447 E-mail: office@tayside-plumbing.co.uk

Thompson Builders Merchants Ltd, Bilton Road, Chelmsford, CM1 2UB Tel: (01245) 266754 Fax: (01245) 359070 E-mail: info@thompson-online.co.uk

Thompson & Leigh Ltd, Unit 1 Bourne Industrial Park, Bourne Road, Crayford, Dartford, DA1 4BZ Tel: (01322) 557729 Fax: (01322) 522455 E-mail: david@t-leigh.sagehost.co.uk

Thompson & Parkes Ltd, Oldington Trading Estate, Kidderminster, Worcestershire, DY11 7QP Tel: (01562) 745881 Fax: (01562) 515578

Travis Perkins plc, The Quay, Fen Lane, Beccles, Suffolk, NR34 9BH Tel: (01502) 712421 Fax: (01502) 711110

Travis Perkins, 1 South Road, Hockley, Birmingham, B18 5LT Tel: 0121-554 3396 Fax: 0121-554 6811

Travis Perkins plc, Fairfield Street, Bradford, West Yorkshire, BD4 9QP Tel: (01274) 681065 Fax: (01274) 688843

Travis Perkins plc, Recreation Lane, Felixstowe, Suffolk, IP11 9DQ Tel: (01394) 278999 Fax: (01394) 273486

Travis Perkins plc, 24-42 Palmerston Road, Harrow, Middlesex, HA3 7RR Tel: (020) 8861 1750 Fax: (020) 8861 3556

Travis Perkins plc, Thurman Street, Ilkeston, Derbyshire, DE7 4BY Tel: 0115-932 4278 Fax: 0115-944 1338

Travis Perkins plc, Long Leys Road, Lincoln, LN1 1DU Tel: (01522) 527113 Fax: (01522) 567905

Travis Perkins, 43 Spindus Road, Speke Hall Industrial Estate, Liverpool, L24 1YB Tel: 0151-486 1660 Fax: 0151-486 3031

Travis Perkins plc, 26 Sangley Road, London, SE6 2JN Tel: (020) 8698 1081 Fax: (020) 8461 1229

Travis Perkins plc, 7 Seph Way, York Road Industrial Park, Malton, North Yorkshire, YO17 6YF Tel: (01653) 692444 Fax: (01653) 600453 E-mail: malton@travisperkins.co.uk

Travis Perkins plc, Manchester Road, Whitehill Industrial Estate, Whitehall Industrial Estate, Stockport, Cheshire, SK4 1NY Tel: 0161-480 0881 Fax: 0161-477 3658

Travis Perkins Trading Co. Ltd, Rowlandson Street, Grimsby, North East Lincolnshire, DN31 3LL Tel: (01472) 345471 Fax: (01472) 242760

Travis Perkins Trading Co. Ltd, Bluebridge Industrial Estate, 11 Second Avenue, Colchester Road, Halstead, Essex, CO9 2HA Tel: (01787) 477882 Fax: (01787) 473761

Unit F, F Liver Industrial Estate, Long Lane, Walton, Liverpool, L9 7ES Tel: 0151-525 3344 Fax: 0151-525 3113 E-mail: liverpool@williamwilson.co.uk

Vickers & Son (Plumbers' Merchants) Ltd, Greenfield Place, Vale Road, Rhyl, Clwyd, LL18 2BP Tel: (01745) 345300 Fax: (01745) 344288 E-mail: sales@vickers-rhyl.co.uk

W H Halmshaw Ltd, Pioneer Works, Goulton St, Hull, HU3 4AS Tel: (01482) 589689 Fax: (01482) 325084 E-mail: info@halmshaws.co.uk

W H Horton, West Street, Tamworth, Staffordshire, B79 7JE Tel: (01827) 52810 Fax: (01827) 66122 E-mail: info@whhorton.co.uk

W Madden Insulation, Swinnow View, Leeds, LS13 4TZ Tel: 0113-257 9818 Fax: 0113-257 7586 E-mail: sales@wmadden.demon.co.uk

Warrington Civils & Lintels, Wilson Patten Street, Warrington, WA1 1HN Tel: (01925) 255700 Fax: (01925) 416520 E-mail: warrington@civilandlintels.co.uk

▶ Wharfebank Contract Associates, The Workshop, Wharfe Bank Terrace, Tadcaster, North Yorkshire, LS24 9AN Tel: (01937) 530048 Fax: (01937) 832676

G.B. Willbond Ltd, Deakins Placed, Radford, Nottingham, NG7 3FT Tel: 0115-841 8888 Fax: 0115-841 8876 E-mail: thogg@willbond.co.uk

Willesden Supplies, Unit 39 Sapcote Trading Estate, 70 Budden Hill Lane Willesden, London, NW10 3EA Tel: (020) 8459 4440 Fax: (020) 8459 8448

Wollens Ltd, Wirrall Park Road, Glastonbury, Somerset, BA6 9XE Tel: (01458) 832244 Fax: (01458) 834926 E-mail: info@wollens.prestel.co.uk

Wolseley Centers Ltd, Boroughbridge Road, Ripon, North Yorkshire, HG4 1SL Tel: (01765) 690690 Fax: (01765) 694516

Uriah Woodhead & Son Ltd, Valley House, Valley Road, Bradford, West Yorkshire, BD1 4RY Tel: (01274) 727528 Fax: (01274) 726574

Woodrows of Salisbury, Stephenson Road, Churchfields Industrial Estate, Salisbury, SP2 7NP Tel: (01722) 328401 Fax: (01722) 412782

PLUMBERS' PUTTY

1st Choice Plumbing Services Nw, 2 Buxton Street, Accrington, Lancashire, BB5 0SF Tel: (07947) 355964 E-mail: john23zx@aol.com

PLUMBERS' THERMAL PROTECTION MATS OR PADS

▶ Rainer Schneider & Ayres, 3 Hereford Close, Buxton, Derbyshire, SK17 9PH Tel: (01298) 79903 Fax: (01298) 72124 E-mail: rsa_bxt@btconnect.com

PLUMBERS' TOOLS

Canvey Supply Co. Ltd, 101 Point Road, Canvey Island, Essex, SS8 7TJ Tel: (01268) 696666 Fax: (01268) 696724 E-mail: canveysupply@btconnect.com

Monument Tools, Restmor Way, Hackbridge Road, Hackbridge, Wallington, Surrey, SM6 7AH Tel: (020) 8288 1100 Fax: (020) 8288 1108 E-mail: info@monument-tools.com

▶ Mtool Ltd, Unit1 & 2 Derker Street, Oldham, OL1 4BE Tel: 0161-626 5556 Fax: 0161-626 3061 E-mail: pr@mtooluk.com

PLUMBERS' TOOLS – *continued*

Skelding's Ltd, 126 Oldbury Road, Smethwick, West Midlands, B66 1JE Tel: 0121-558 0622 Fax: 0121-558 6115

PLUMBING EQUIPMENT

▶ Easy Plumbing, 451 Hinckley Road, Leicester, LE3 0WD Tel: 0116-255 3435 E-mail: easyplumbing@tiscali.co.uk

▶ Plumb Center Ltd, 1 Pennybridge Industrial Estate, Ballymena, County Antrim, BT42 3HB Tel: (028) 2564 1222 Fax: (028) 2564 1777

PLUMBING INFORMATION SERVICES

Falcon Plumbing & Heating Engineers, 3 Lingfield Close, Enfield, Middlesex, EN1 2JL Tel: (020) 8360 0115 Fax: (020) 8360 0115

PLUMBING INSTALLATION

▶ 4 Dimensions, Tall Pines, London Road, Crowborough, East Sussex, TN6 1TA Tel: 01892 663534 E-mail: handy@4dimensions.co.uk

▶ A D S Plumbing Services, 27 Tarrareoch Court, Armadale, Bathgate, West Lothian, EH48 2TF Tel: (01501) 734504 Fax: (01501) 734504 E-mail: adsplumbers@aol.com

▶ Acquatech Plumbing, Heating & Electrical, 301 Amersham Road, Hazlemere, Bucks, HP15 7PX Tel: 01494 717777 E-mail: info@acquatech.co.uk

F. Bentley & Co. (Heating & Plumbing) Ltd, 312 Ware Road, Hertford, SG13 7ER Tel: (01992) 500009 Fax: (01992) 505005

▶ Bentley Mechanical Services Ltd, 140 Barton Road, Comberton, Cambridge, CB23 7BT Tel: (01223) 264240 Fax: (01223) 264240 E-mail: office@bentleymechanicalservices.co.uk

▶ Cleveland Gas Service Engineers, 151 York Road, Hartlepool, Cleveland, TS26 9EQ Tel: (01642) 615232 Fax: (01642) 868336

▶ East Kent Plumbing & Heating Sevices, 5 Pinewood Close, Ramsgate, Kent, CT12 6DH Tel: (01843) 586864 Fax: (01843) 586864 E-mail: Eastkent@msn.com

▶ Evans & Graham Heating Co. Ltd, 108 Westmead Road, Sutton, Surrey, SM1 4JD Tel: (020) 8661 1712 Fax: (020) 8642 3755

▶ G & A Plumbing & Heating Ltd, 1 Primrose Lane, Arlesey, Bedfordshire, SG15 6RD Tel: (01462) 731896 Fax: (01462) 835588 E-mail: carole@gaplumbing.co.uk

▶ General Domestic Appliances, 120 Prime Street, Northwood, Stoke-on-Trent, ST1 6PS Tel: (01782) 204167 E-mail: generaldomestics@aol.com

▶ Hopkins Plumbers Ltd, Unit 10 Oaks Industrial Estate, Festival Drive, Loughborough, Leicestershire, LE11 5XN Tel: (01509) 212332 Fax: (01509) 233704 E-mail: sales@hopkins-plumbers.co.uk

▶ J Hempstock & Co. Ltd, 116-118 South Street, Openshaw, Manchester, M11 2FY Tel: 0161-223 2123 Fax: 0161-220 9259

▶ J N Weatherby Ltd, 133 Frankwell, Shrewsbury, SY3 8JX Tel: (01743) 235392 Fax: (01743) 368619

▶ Lowestoft Electrical Co. Ltd, Service House, Wildes Street, Lowestoft, Suffolk, NR32 1XH Tel: (01502) 565484 Fax: (01502) 588933 E-mail: enquiries@lowestoftelectricalgroup.co.uk

▶ M H Cragg & Sons Ltd, Ingleside, 11 Lee Lane, Horwich, Bolton, BL6 7BP Tel: (01204) 697157 Fax: (01204) 699113

▶ Non Drip Plumbing & Heating, 2 Bosworth Way, March, Cambridgeshire, PE15 9BW Tel: (07952) 669008 E-mail: james@nondrip.co.uk

▶ PlumbSearch UK Ltd, 219 Abbey Road, Basingstoke, Hampshire, RG24 9EG Tel: 0800 6120731 Fax: 01256 471488 E-mail: info@plumbsearch.eu.com

▶ WT Flockhart Ltd, 17c, Water-Ma-Trout, Helston, Cornwall, TR13 0LW Tel: (01326) 561971 E-mail: sales@flockhart-heating.co.uk

PLUMBING SERVICES OR CONTRACTORS

A A Duncan Biggar Ltd, 16a Broughton Road, Biggar, Lanarkshire, ML12 6HA Tel: (01899) 220170 Fax: (01899) 220170

▶ A A Glanville Ltd, 53 Ashford Road, Plymouth, PL4 7BL Tel: (01752) 660906

▶ A C G Installations Ltd, Elisabeth House, Willows Road, Walsall, WS1 2DR Tel: (01922) 648509 Fax: (01922) 648509

▶ A D S Plumbing Services, 27 Tarrareoch Court, Armadale, Bathgate, West Lothian, EH48 2TF Tel: (01501) 734504 Fax: (01501) 734504 E-mail: adsplumbers@aol.com

A & K Services Co., 807 Lea Bridge Road, London, E17 9DS Tel: (020) 8509 2600 Fax: (020) 8520 9678 E-mail: a.kservices@btconnect.com

▶ A M Norris Ltd, Brunel Way, Stephenson Industrial Estate, Coalville, Leicestershire, LE67 3HF Tel: (01530) 831451 Fax: (01530) 813767

Absolutely Splashing Aquatic Consultants, 15 Salkeld Avenue, Ashton-in-Makerfield, Wigan, Lancashire, WN4 9NH Tel: (01942) 511947

Ace Industrial Boiler Cleaners, 10 Rollscourt Avenue, London, SE24 0EA Tel: (020) 7733 1676

Ainsworth, Frenches Works, Chew Valley Road, Greenfield, Oldham, OL3 7AE Tel: (01457) 879000 Fax: (01457) 873279 E-mail: diyshop@ainsworthdiy.co.uk

Air Conditioning (Jersey), 9 New Street, St Helier, Jersey, JE2 3RA Tel: (01534) 870022 Fax: (01534) 870044

▶ Allison Heating Plumbing & Electrical Ltd, Old Station Way, Holt, Norfolk, NR25 6DH Tel: (01263) 713260 Fax: (01263) 713174

▶ Aqualine Services Ltd, 59 Wassand Street, Kingston Upon Hull, Hull, HU3 4AL Tel: (01482) 657709 Fax: (01482) 655777

Avonside Plumbing & Heating Yorkshire Ltd, Dunswell Road, Cottingham, North Humberside, HU16 4JU Tel: (01482) 841146 Fax: (01482) 875137

B A Halston Heating, Stoney Croft, The Lynch, Kensworth, Dunstable, Bedfordshire, LU6 3QZ Tel: (01582) 872445 Fax: (01582) 872445

Baines Herbert Ltd, No 2 Passage Chester Street, Stockport, Cheshire, SK3 0BR Tel: 0161-480 9796

▶ Barkers Plumbing Services, 83 Sketchley Road, Burbage, Hinckley, Leicestershire, LE10 2DU Tel: (01455) 446784 E-mail: barkersplumbingservices@ntlworld.com

Beaumont & Blackburn Ltd, 21 Wellington Road, Dewsbury, West Yorkshire, WF13 1HL Tel: (01924) 461067 Fax: (01924) 430971

Belfast Boiler Services, 574-576 Ballysillan Rd, Belfast, BT14 6RN Tel: (028) 9071 0000 Fax: (028) 9039 1062

▶ Berry's Plumbing & Heating Ltd, 141 Manchester Road East, Little Hulton, Manchester, M38 9AN Tel: 0161-790 9933 Fax: 0161-790 9944

▶ Boiler Healthcare, 16 Kent Road, Folkestone, Kent, CT19 4NT Tel: (01303) 275729 Fax: (01303) 279081 E-mail: sales@boilerhealthcare.co.uk

▶ Boldmere Plumbing, 377 Chester Road, Sutton Coldfield, West Midlands, B73 5BL Tel: 0121-382 7020 E-mail: simonawhite@hotmail.com

Bott Builders Ltd, Birmingham Road, Whitacre Heath Coleshill, Birmingham, B46 2ET Tel: (01675) 462214

▶ Bourne Gas Bournemouth Ltd, Unit 3 Broom Road Business Park, Broom Road, Poole, Dorset, BH12 4PA Tel: (01202) 716665 E-mail: gas@bournebg.ltd.uk

▶ Brenden Fern Heating & Plumbing, 27 Paradise Street, Stoke-on-Trent, ST6 5AG Tel: (01782) 818577 Fax: (01782) 818578 E-mail: info@bfplum.co.uk

Colin Bullot & Sons Ltd, 7 Glendale Walk, Cheshunt, Waltham Cross, Hertfordshire, EN8 9RJ Tel: (01992) 627407 Fax: (01992) 633198 E-mail: colin@bullut.co.uk

C E Bunch, 87 Chapel Street, Dudley, West Midlands, DY2 9PN Tel: (01384) 459241 Fax: (01384) 255166 E-mail: sales@cebunch.co.uk

▶ C & L Plumbing Services, Bridge Works, Wood Lane, Rothwell, Leeds, LS26 0RS Tel: 0113-282 3728 Fax: 0113-282 2105

Cambridge Water plc, 90 Fulbourn Road, Cherry Hinton, Cambridge, CB1 9JN Tel: (01223) 706050 Fax: (01223) 214052 E-mail: info@cambridge-water.co.uk

▶ Centurion Plumbing, 3 Cecil Court, Wall Road, Ashford, Kent, TN24 8NW Tel: 01233 336378 E-mail: mail@centurionplumbing.co.uk

▶ Chiltern Handiman Services, Forest Lodge, Christmas Common, Watlington, Oxfordshire, OX49 5HN Tel: (01491) 613074 E-mail: enquiries@chilternhandiman.co.uk

▶ Chris Hatcher & Son Ltd, 33 High Street, Seaford, East Sussex, BN25 1PL Tel: (01323) 890100 Fax: (01323) 891400

Clipvalve Ltd, 88 Stonefield Road, Hastings, East Sussex, TN34 1QA Tel: (01424) 425682 Fax: (01424) 438789 E-mail: enquiries@clipvalve.co.uk

▶ Colin Laver, Riverside Buildings, Nile Road, Pontypridd, Mid Glamorgan, CF37 1BW Tel: (01443) 404516 Fax: (01443) 486048

Consent Services Ltd, 168 Repps Rd, Martham, Great Yarmouth, Norfolk, NR29 4QZ Tel: (01493) 748647 Fax: (01493) 748647

▶ Cook & Harris Ltd, Unit 36 Barnack Trading Centre, Novers Hill, Bedminster, Bristol, BS3 5QE Tel: 0117-966 4792 Fax: 0117-963 9007

▶ County Plumbimg and Heating, R/O, 33 High Street, Aveley, South Ockendon, Essex, RM15 4BE Tel: (01708) 861878

Craig Wyllie Plumbing & Heating, 20 Scott Court, Alva, Clackmannanshire, FK12 5LZ Tel: (07917) 033271 Fax: (01259) 769027 E-mail: craigwyllie@hotmail.co.uk

Cunninghams, 564-566 Kingston Road, London, SW20 8DR Tel: (020) 8946 3352 Fax: (020) 8540 1626

D A Wright Ltd, 13 Lowman Units Lowman Way, Tiverton Business Park, Tiverton, Devon, EX16 6SR Tel: (01884) 254474 Fax: (01884) 256479 E-mail: info@dawright.co.uk

▶ D Astin & Son, 16 Waddington Road, Clitheroe, Lancashire, BB7 2HJ Tel: (01200) 422315 Fax: (01200) 422315

D Train, 43-45 Fisher Street, Stranraer, Wigtownshire, DG9 7LH Tel: (01776) 702357 Fax: (01776) 702357

Darnells Ltd, Oakfield Industrial Estate, Eynsham, Witney, Oxfordshire, OX29 4TH Tel: (01865) 883996 Fax: (01865) 883986 E-mail: mail@darnells.ltd.uk

Davant Products Ltd, Davant House, Jugs Green Business Park, Staplow, Ledbury, Herefordshire, HR8 1NR Tel: (01531) 630068 Fax: (01531) 640827 E-mail: info@davant.co.uk

David G Alker, The Quern, Chapel Lawn, Bucknell, Shropshire, SY7 0BW Tel: (01547) 530344 Fax: (01547) 530844 E-mail: davequern@aol.com

Day Wellington, 32 Collum End Rise, Leckhampton, Cheltenham, Glos, GL53 0PB Tel: 01242 570584

Drainways Ltd, 108 Summer Road, Erdington, Birmingham, B23 6DY Tel: 0121-377 6583 Fax: 0121-377 7769 E-mail: sales@drainways.com

Driscoll & Crowley Ltd, 496a Barking Road, London, E13 8QB Tel: (020) 7511 9287 Fax: (020) 7473 3019 E-mail: info@driscoll-crowley.co.uk

▶ E Wilkinson Plumbing & Heating Contractors Ltd, 120d Milton Park, Milton, Abingdon, Oxfordshire, OX14 4SA Tel: (01235) 835070 Fax: (01235) 832033

Easiways Bermondsey Ltd, 138 Burnt Ash Road, Lee, London, SE12 8PU Tel: (020) 8852 2984 Fax: (020) 8852 2985

▶ East Goscote Plumbers Ltd, East Goscote Industrial Estate, East Goscote, Leicester, LE7 3SL Tel: 0116-260 7766

Eric C Flower Ltd, 413 Petre Street, Sheffield, S4 8LL Tel: 0114-243 1221 Fax: 0114-243 7196 E-mail: johnwilliams@ericcflowers.co.uk

F W Marsh Electrical & Mechanical Ltd, Ryde Business Park, Nicholson Road, Ryde, Isle of Wight, PO33 1BF Tel: (01983) 562109 Fax: (01983) 615592

Fairley Brown & Co. Ltd, 77a Wilson Road, Reading, RG30 2RT Tel: 0118-958 1641 Fax: 0118-950 3233 E-mail: office@fairleybrown.fsnet.co.uk

Falcon Plumbing & Heating Engineers, 3 Lingfield Close, Enfield, Middlesex, EN1 2JL Tel: (020) 8360 0115 Fax: (020) 8360 0115

▶ Fenhams Contracts, 2-6 Ivy Road, Gosforth, Newcastle Upon Tyne, NE3 1DB Tel: 0191-223 0600

▶ First Call Plumbing, The Old Farmhouse, 9 North Street, Ipplepen, Newton Abbot, Devon, TQ12 5RT Tel: (01803) 814514 Fax: (01803) 814069 E-mail: fcplumbing@btinternet.com

Fisher & Sons Fakenham Ltd, 7 Dereham Road, Hempton, Fakenham, Norfolk, NR21 7LD Tel: (01328) 862781 Fax: (01328) 856229 E-mail: mail@fishers-fakenham.co.uk

▶ Ford, 2 Alexandria Trading Estate, Alexandria Road, Sidmouth, Devon, EX10 9HA Tel: (01395) 571020 Fax: (01395) 571005

Frasc Construction Ltd, Orchard House, Ellenbrook Road, Manchester, M28 1GB Tel: 0161-702 5500 Fax: 0161-702 5502

▶ Fraser Electrical, The Old School, Dewar Street, Dunfermline, Fife, KY12 8AB Tel: (01383) 720569 Fax: (01383) 720722

▶ Fre Flo Plumbing & Heating Services Ltd, Unit 29 800 Brightside Lane, Sheffield, S9 2RX Tel: 0114-242 0004 Fax: 0114-244 5948

William Freer Ltd, 350-360 Melton Road, Leicester, LE4 7SL Tel: 0116-268 9660 Fax: 0116-268 9650

Frise M S & Sons Ltd, 7 Trowbridge Road, Westbury, Wiltshire, BA13 3AY Tel: (01373) 826333 Fax: (01373) 826444 E-mail: sales@frise.co.uk

Fulham Gas & Heating Services, 54 Chesilton Road, London, SW6 5AB Tel: (020) 7736 3254 Fax: (020) 7385 8685

G Abbott & Co. Ltd, Brenda Road, Hartlepool, Cleveland, TS25 2BJ Tel: (01429) 234841 Fax: (01429) 234445

G F Cross & Sons, Unit 10 Kings Meadow, Ferry Hinksey Road, Oxford, OX2 0DP Tel: (01865) 242358 Fax: (01865) 241648 E-mail: info@gfcrossandsons.co.uk

▶ G W Sparrow & Co. Ltd, 5 Cobham Centre, Westmead Industrial Estate, Westlea, Swindon, SN5 7UJ Tel: (01793) 541701 Fax: (01793) 541702

▶ Gas Master, 36 Plover Crescent, Anstey Heights, Leicester, LE4 1EB Tel: 0116-236 7705 E-mail: platform40@hotmail.com

Glenfield Plumbers Ltd, Southfield Industrial Estate, 62 Nasmyth Road, Glenrothes, Fife, KY6 2SD Tel: (01592) 774818 Fax: (01592) 630552

Grail & Preece Ltd, 44 Hamstead Road, Hockley, Birmingham, B19 1DB Tel: 0121-554 6667 Fax: 0121-554 6992 E-mail: info@grailandpreece.co.uk

▶ H Clarke & Sons Ltd, Linton, Skipton, North Yorkshire, BD23 5HH Tel: (01756) 752319 Fax: (01756) 752319

H D Ebbutt & Son, 63 Jarvis Road, South Croydon, Surrey, CR2 6HW Tel: (020) 8688 1157

▶ H F Brown & Son Ltd, Portland Works, Main Street, Hemingbrough, Selby, North Yorkshire, YO8 6QF Tel: (01757) 638262

H Mitton Ltd, 451 Cleckheaton Road, Low Moor, Bradford, West Yorkshire, BD12 0HS Tel: (01274) 691177 Fax: (01274) 691188 E-mail: projects@mittonmechanical.com

▶ H2 Plumbing Ltd, Unit L24 The Old Laboratories, 2 Michael Road, London, SW6 2AD Tel: (020) 7751 3344 E-mail: info@h2plumbing.co.uk

▶ Harry Armistead Ltd, Unit 2 Woodgate Park, Middlegate, White Lund Industrial Estate, Morecambe, Lancashire, LA3 3PS Tel: (01524) 848500 Fax: (01524) 848600

▶ Heating & Plumbing Discounts Co UK Ltd, 14 Willowdown, Worle, Weston-super-Mare, Avon, BS22 9LX Tel: (01934) 514411 Fax: (01934) 514411 E-mail: plumbersunited@aol.com

▶ Hodges & Marten, Unit 6-7 Ringmer Business Centre, Chamberlaines Lane, Lewes, East Sussex, BN8 5NF Tel: (01273) 812771 Fax: (01273) 812746

▶ Hopkins Plumbers Ltd, Unit 10 Oaks Industrial Estate, Festival Drive, Loughborough, Leicestershire, LE11 5XN Tel: (01509) 212332 Fax: (01509) 233704 E-mail: sales@hopkins-plumbers.co.uk

Howard & Buckner Ltd, Unit E1, The Seedbed Centre, Harlow, Essex, CM19 5AF Tel: (01279) 422955 Fax: (01279) 422955

▶ Hutton Premises Solutions, Station Road, Bagshot, Surrey, GU19 5AS Tel: (01276) 472400 Fax: (01276) 470996 E-mail: ben.hutton@virgin.net

▶ I C Rushton, 16 Rostherne Avenue, High Lane, Stockport, Cheshire, SK6 8AR Tel: (01663) 762540 E-mail: IanCRushton@aol.com

J F Heppelthwaite Ltd, Sherwood House 6 Marlborough Parade, Uxbridge Road, Uxbridge, Middlesex, UB10 0LR Tel: (01895) 460002 Fax: (01895) 460004

J H Shouksmith & Sons Ltd, Murton Way, Osbaldwick, York, YO19 5GS Tel: (01904) 411261 Fax: (01904) 412038 E-mail: rps@shouksmiths.co.uk

J R E Dinnage Ltd, 158 Eltham Hill, London, SE9 5EA Tel: (020) 8850 5572 Fax: (020) 8850 2009 E-mail: jredinnage@hotmail.com

J S A Mechanical Services Ltd, Unit 28 Croft Road Industrial Estate, Croft Road, Newcastle, Staffordshire, ST5 0TW Tel: (01782) 635517 Fax: (01782) 630485

▶ J & S Plumbing, 14 Cranmoor Crescent, Halesowen, West Midlands, B63 3TD Tel: 0121 503 0411 E-mail: enquiries@numberoneplumber.co.uk

▶ J W Housden Ltd, 1 Margetts Road, Kempston, Bedford, MK42 8DS Tel: (01234) 852033 Fax: (01234) 841226

Jarvis Heating Ltd, Jarvis House, 212 Station Road, Harpenden, Hertfordshire, AL5 4EH Tel: (01582) 761211 Fax: (01582) 764100 E-mail: info@jarvisheating.co.uk

Jaydee Heating Ltd, Nobel Road, Wester Gourdie Industrial Estate, West Gourdie Industrial Estate, Dundee, DD2 4XE Tel: (01382) 611118 Fax: (01382) 400540

Jennersons Ltd, 17a Highfield Road, Dartford, DA1 2JS Tel: (01322) 275255 Fax: (01322) 225710

John Carter Salt Lane Ltd, 6-10 Salt Lane, Salisbury, SP1 1EE Tel: (01722) 322407 Fax: (01722) 412146 E-mail: enquiry@john-carters.co.uk

K & P Heating & Plumbing, Saxon House, Edward Street, Cambridge, CB1 2LS Tel: (01223) 364129 Fax: (01223) 313886 E-mail: sales@kpheatingplumbing.co.uk

▶ Keda Plumbing Co. Ltd, 912A Bury Road, Bolton, BL2 6NX Tel: (01204) 414545

▶ Kingwood Building Services Ltd, Rainbow Industrial Park, Station Approach, London, SW20 0JY Tel: (020) 8946 1556 Fax: (020) 8946 1585

▶ Kirklees Plumbing & Heating Wigan Ltd, Unit H2 Belle Green Industrial Estate, Belle Green Lane, Ince, Wigan, Lancashire, WN2 2EP Tel: (01942) 324058 Fax: (01942) 491273

Lorne Stewart plc, Barley House, Duncan Road, Park Gate, Southampton, SO31 1ZT Tel: (01489) 885444 Fax: (01489) 885606 E-mail: soton@lornestewart.co.uk

▶ M B Heating Ltd, Unit 1 Darby Lane, Hindley, Wigan, Lancashire, WN2 3DW Tel: (01942) 520100 Fax: (01942) 523173

▶ M B Plumbing & Heating, 189 Ashgate Road, Chesterfield, Derbyshire, S40 4AP Tel: (01246) 555161

M T Buxton Industrial Services Ltd, 237 Station Road, Langley Mill, Nottingham, NG16 4AD Tel: (01773) 714339 Fax: (01773) 535251 E-mail: enquiries@mtbuxton.com

Mcgill, Harrison Road, Dundee, DD2 3SN Tel: (01382) 884488 Fax: (01382) 828777 E-mail: sales@mcgill-electrical.co.uk

▶ Manley Hill Plumbing & Heating Contractors, Unit 7, 8-10 Marlborough Hill, Harrow, Middlesex, HA1 1UX Tel: (020) 8863 0373 Fax: (020) 8424 8500 E-mail: enquiries@manleyhill.co.uk

Mantells, A, 2 Holland Road, London, SE25 5RF Tel: (020) 8654 3163 Fax: (020) 8654 3163

Mechelec Building Services Ltd, Poulton Close, Dover, Kent, CT17 0HL Tel: (01304) 205559 Fax: (01304) 242068

▶ Miller Freeman & Sons Nottingham Ltd, Adco Business Centre, Bobbers Mill, Nottingham, NG8 5AH Tel: 0115-978 9895 Fax: 0115-978 9896

Morfitts Building Services, 16 St Michael's Lane, Leeds, LS6 3AJ Tel: 0113-275 8631 Fax: 0113-261 8701 E-mail: ajm@morfitts.co.uk

C.A. Mulkern, 8 Springfield Road, Chesham, Buckinghamshire, HP5 1PW Tel: (01494) 783802

▶ Newell Plumbing Services Ltd, Lincoln Enterprise Park, Newark Road, Aubourn, Lincoln, LN5 9EJ Tel: (01522) 705522

▶ Non Drip Plumbing & Heating, 2 Bosworth Way, March, Cambridgeshire, PE15 9BW Tel: (07952) 669008 E-mail: james@nondrip.co.uk

▶ P & G Contractors Ltd, 1 Birch Street, Ashton-under-Lyne, Lancashire, OL7 0NX Tel: 0161-339 0831 Fax: 0161-285 3393

PLUMBING SERVICES OR CONTRACTORS - *continued*

▶ P & H Services, 24b Northbrook Industrial Estate, Newmills Road, Coleraine, County Londonderry, BT52 2JB Tel: (028) 7035 2579 Fax: (028) 7035 1182

▶ P R S Plumbing & Heating Services Ltd, Premier House, Popham, Micheldever, Winchester, Hampshire, SO21 3BJ Tel: (01256) 398881 Fax: (01256) 398889

Paine Manwaring Ltd, 7-11 Ardsheal Road, Worthing, West Sussex, BN14 7RW Tel: (01903) 237522 Fax: (01903) 236511 E-mail: enquires@painemanwearing.co.uk

Paterson J Son Plumbers Ltd, 28 East London Street, Edinburgh, EH7 4BQ Tel: 0131-556 7563 Fax: 0131-557 9080 E-mail: sales@ppservices.co.uk

Steve Phillips Plumbing, Cockett Farm, Basford, Leek, Staffordshire, ST13 7ET Tel: (01538) 361110

Pitkerro Ltd, Emmock Road, Tealing, Dundee, DD3 0PZ Tel: (01382) 816272 Fax: (01382) 811512 E-mail: wallace.wiseman@pitkerro.co.uk

Prompt Maintenance Services, 358 Edgware Road, London, W2 1EB Tel: (020) 7724 7234 Fax: (020) 7224 9854 E-mail: contracts@caesarceramics.co.uk

Quickplumb, 13 Rockhall Rd, Cricklewood, London, NW2 6DT Tel: (020) 8438 0214 Fax: (020) 8438 9692

R Baron Ltd, Peel Hall Street Works, Preston, PR1 6PU Tel: (01772) 795115 Fax: (01772) 204562

▶ R Park & Sons Ltd, Unit 1 Aldwych Court, 586A Blackpool Road, Ashton-On-Ribble, Preston, PR2 1JA Tel: (01772) 720007

▶ Redcar Plumbing & Heating, The Innovation Centre, Vienna Court, Kirkleatham Business Park, Redcar, Cleveland, TS10 5SH Tel: (01642) 777800 Fax: (01642) 777850

Renelec Ltd, Brownstone House, New Park Street, Devizes, Wiltshire, SN10 1DS Tel: (01380) 726363 Fax: (01380) 729255 E-mail: postmaster@renelec.co.uk

Robbins & Chapman, 24 Hill Road, Middleton, King's Lynn, Norfolk, PE32 1RN Tel: (01553) 774619 Fax: (01553) 774619

Robert Prettie Co., Colwick Business Park, Private Road 2, Colwick Industrial Estate, Nottingham, NG4 2JR Tel: 0115-940 2222 Fax: 0115-940 2232 E-mail: r.prettie@robert-prettie.co.uk

Gus Robinson Developments Ltd, Stranton House, West View Road, Hartlepool, Cleveland, TS24 0BW Tel: (01429) 234221 Fax: (01429) 869822 E-mail: gus.hartlepool@gusrobinson.com

▶ Roland Amey, Unit B, Copley Hill Farm, Cambridge Road, Babraham, Cambridge, CB2 4AF Tel: (01223) 835725

Rudd Engineering Ltd, 18 Sebergham Grove, London, NW7 2AU Tel: (020) 8959 8181

▶ Seaforth Services, Unit 6 Slader Business Park, Witney Road, Nuffield Industrial Estate, Poole, Dorset, BH17 0GP Tel: (01202) 330630 Fax: (01202) 679100

Sloan Agencies Ltd, Unit 3 Duncrue Industrial Park, Duncrue Road, Belfast, BT3 9BP Tel: (028) 9037 0377 Fax: (028) 9037 0344

T.A. Smith & Co. Ltd, 53-55 Scrutton Street, London, EC2A 4PJ Tel: (020) 7739 1702 Fax: (020) 8500 4634

▶ Status Mechanical Services, Lightning Works Birmingham Road, Hopwood, Alvechurch, Birmingham, B48 7AL Tel: 0121-447 7677 Fax: 0121-447 7432

Fred Stoddart Ltd, 28 Wilson Street North, Sunderland, SR5 1BB Tel: 0191-567 3960 Fax: 0191-564 1624 E-mail: enquiries@fredstoddartltd.co.uk

▶ Stretton Bros Leicester, 27 Lunsford Road, Leicester, LE5 0HW Tel: 0116-274 1166 Fax: 0116-246 0299

▶ Strysen Heating & Plumbing, 4 St James Rd, Sutton Coldfield, West Midlands, B75 5EH Tel: 0121-308 0962 Fax: 0121-323 2838

▶ T Jolly Services Ltd, Unit G Central Industrial Estate, St. Marks Street, Bolton, BL3 6NR Tel: (07738) 486426 Fax: (01204) 365361 E-mail: john.taylor@tjolly.co.uk

▶ Taunton Plumbing & Heating, Unit 6, Venture 11, Priorswood Industrial Estate, Taunton, Somerset, TA2 8DG Tel: (01823) 278887

▶ Tej Heating Plymouth Ltd, 247 Victoria Road, Plymouth, PL5 2DQ Tel: (01752) 351411 Fax: (01752) 351808

Verwin Plumbing & Heating Ltd, Maisonette, 223b London Road, Reading, RG1 3NY Tel: 0118-966 6049 Fax: 0118-935 2686

▶ W H Dunn & Co., 10 William Street, South Shields, Tyne & Wear, NE33 1PQ Tel: 0191-456 7503 Fax: 0191-454 5520

W T Rowley & Sons, 37 Canon Street, Shrewsbury, SY2 5HQ Tel: (01743) 356020

▶ WB Mechanical Services Ltd, 34 Dursley Road, Blackheath, London, SE3 8PD Tel: (020) 8319 4457 E-mail: wbmsltd@aol.com

▶ Wood & Son, 24 Wilton Park Road, Shanklin, Isle of Wight, PO37 7BT Tel: (01983) 866313

▶ Wyre Heating Ltd, Unit 3 Lisle Avenue, Kidderminster, Worcestershire, DY11 7DE Tel: (01562) 751832 Fax: (01562) 748383

Yorkshire Stove & Plumbing Centre, 39 High Street, Boroughbridge, York, YO51 9AW Tel: (01423) 323200 Fax: (01423) 323200

PLUMBING SYSTEMS

▶ A H Hales Ltd, 35 Northampton Road, Scunthorpe, South Humberside, DN16 1UJ Tel: (01724) 843703 Fax: (01724) 271863

Ballcock & Bits Ltd, Broad Lane, Bracknell, Berkshire, RG12 9BJ Tel: (01344) 481212 Fax: (01344) 302512

▶ Better Plumbing Services, 4 Exchange Road, Lincoln, LN6 3JZ Tel: (01522) 688866 Fax: (01522) 688855

Bradfords Building Supplies Ltd, 139 Bristol Road, Bridgwater, Somerset, TA6 4AQ Tel: (01278) 422654 Fax: (01278) 450574 E-mail: bbs.bridgwater@bradford.co.uk

Connection Aml Ltd, Unit 8-9 Newtown Business Park, Albion Close, Poole, Dorset, BH12 3LL Tel: (01202) 733510 Fax: (01202) 715455 E-mail: info@travisperkins.co.uk

▶ Drain Doctor Plumbing, Station House, Macnaghten Road, Southampton, SO18 1GG Tel: (023) 8033 3312 Fax: (023) 8033 2600 E-mail: j-rook@btconnect.com

▶ G B Services, Blackberry Lane, Lingfield, Surrey, RH7 6NG Tel: (01342) 837691 Fax: (01342) 835655

▶ Guilfram Heating Co. Ltd, 1 Wonersh Common, Wonersh, Guildford, Surrey, GU5 0PJ Tel: (01483) 894248 Fax: (01483) 894219 E-mail: ianwarner@guilfram.co.uk

J & G Archibald, Jagal House, Damson Way, Durham, DH1 2YD Tel: 0191-384 8484 Fax: 0191-386 2432 E-mail: sales@archibald.co.uk

▶ Jonathan Mayers Services Ltd, 11 Newman Road, Trevethin, Pontypool, Gwent, NP4 8HQ Tel: (08701) 160821 Fax: (08701) 160821 E-mail: sales@j-m-s.co.uk

Pinmill Products, Units 5H-5K, Baker House, Manor Way Industrial Estate, Curzon Drive, Grays, Essex, RM17 6BG Tel: (01375) 392944 Fax: (01375) 379127 E-mail: pinmill@btinternet.com

Pipe Line Centre, Unit D3 Premier Business Centre, Speedfields Park, Fareham, Hampshire, PO14 1TY Tel: (01329) 237215 Fax: (01329) 823641 E-mail: k73.fareham@wolseley.co.uk

Pipeline Centre, 118a Newmarket Road, Bury St. Edmunds, Suffolk, IP33 3TG Tel: (01284) 753046 Fax: (01284) 750042

▶ Robert J Dutton, 2 Springfield Road, Shepshed, Loughborough, Leicestershire, LE12 7EE Tel: (01509) 502402 Fax: (01509) 600327

▶ Skaino Ltd, West March Industrial Estate, West March, Daventry, Northamptonshire, NN11 4SA Tel: (01327) 871335 Fax: (01327) 706029

W Fayers & Sons, 15 Margaret Road, Barnet, Hertfordshire, EN4 9NR Tel: (020) 8370 6400 Fax: (020) 8370 6415

▶ W S Biggin & Son, 1 Hanger Hill, Creswell, Worksop, Nottinghamshire, S80 4AA Tel: (01909) 720245 Fax: (01909) 723487

Willesden Supplies, Unit 39 Sapcote Trading Estate, 70 Budden Hill Lane Willesden, London, NW10 3EA Tel: (020) 8459 4440 Fax: (020) 8459 8448

PLUMBING TRAINING COURSES

▶ Trade Skills 4 U, 3 Metana House, Priestley Way, Crawley, West Sussex, RH10 9NT Tel: (01293) 529777 E-mail: enquires@tradeskills4u.co.uk

PLYWOOD, *See also other nearby headings for particular types*

Bruynzeel Multipanel, 8 High Street, Southminster, Essex, CM0 7DE Tel: (01621) 774728 Fax: (01621) 773825 E-mail: lbundy@bruynzeelmultipanel.com

C Blumsom Ltd, Maple Wharf, 36-38 River Road, Barking, Essex, IG11 0DN Tel: (020) 8594 5175 Fax: (020) 8507 1334 E-mail: sales@blumson.co.uk

C F Anderson & Son Ltd, 228 Old London Road, Marks Tey, Colchester, CO6 1HD Tel: (020) 7226 1212 Fax: (020) 7359 1112 E-mail: cfanderson@cfanderson.co.uk

Constructional Veneers Ltd, 2 Timberwharf Road, Stamford Hill, London, N16 6DB Tel: (020) 8802 1166 Fax: (020) 8802 4222 E-mail: veneers@talk21.com

H M Lowe & Son Ltd, 476 Garrison Lane, Birmingham, B9 4NT Tel: 0121-772 0330 Fax: 0121-771 3759 E-mail: enquiries@hmlowe.co.uk

Arnold Laver Birmingham Board Timberworld, Dudley Road, Oldbury, West Midlands, B69 3DA Tel: 0121-552 7788 Fax: 0121-544 7186 E-mail: sales@birminghamtimberworld.co.uk

Midland Wallboards Ltd, Severn House, Western Road, Oldbury, West Midlands, B69 4LY Tel: 0121-552 9333 Fax: 0121-552 9330 E-mail: sales@midlandwallboards.co.uk

Norbord Ltd, Hill Village, Nadder Lane, South Molton, Devon, EX36 4HP Tel: (01769) 575350 Fax: (01769) 574848

R P Panels Ltd, Pindar Road, Hoddesdon, Hertfordshire, EN11 0BZ Tel: (01992) 444221 Fax: (01992) 466656

Timber Centre, Hatches Lane, Salisbury, SP1 2NZ Tel: (01722) 414900 Fax: (01722) 414909

Totton Timber Co. Ltd, Maynard Road, Totton, Southampton, SO40 3DB Tel: (023) 8086 0077 Fax: (023) 8087 3168 E-mail: sales@tottontimber.com

Travis Perkins plc, Lodge Way House, Lodge Way, Northampton, NN5 7UG Tel: (01604) 752424 Fax: (01604) 758718 E-mail: careers@contemporary.co.uk

PLYWOOD BOXES/CASES/ CONTAINERS

E Abrahams & Co. Ltd, 1 Crown Close, London, E3 2JH Tel: (020) 8980 1937 Fax: (020) 8980 3762 E-mail: info@abrahamscases.co.uk

Johnson & Akam Ltd, Old Park Court, Harris Street, Bradford, West Yorkshire, BD1 5HW Tel: (01274) 726375 Fax: (01274) 307946 E-mail: general@johnsonandakam.co.uk

PLYWOOD FLUSH DOORS

Acorn Timber & Joinery Ltd, Britannia Works, Upper Cyrus Street, Manchester, M40 7FD Tel: 0161-273 3871 Fax: 0161-274 3203 E-mail: sales@acorntimber.com

▶ Winwood Products, Somerton House, Hazell Drive, Newport, Gwent, NP10 8FY Tel: (0845) 3732733 Fax: (0845) 3732735 E-mail: info@winwood-products.com

PLYWOOD IMPORT MERCHANTS OR AGENTS

Bruynzeel Multipanel, 8 High Street, Southminster, Essex, CM0 7DE Tel: (01621) 774728 Fax: (01621) 773825 E-mail: lbundy@bruynzeelmultipanel.com

C L T Timber & Transport Ltd, Olds Approach, Coalpits Lane, Watford, WD18 9TD Tel: (01923) 711888 Fax: (01923) 711675 E-mail: wood@wattim.co.uk

William T. Eden Ltd, PO Box 3, Barking, Essex, IG11 0DU Tel: (020) 8477 8006 Fax: (020) 8477 8010 E-mail: headoffice@edens.co.uk

Finnforest UK Ltd, 46 Berth Tilbury Docks, Tilbury, Essex, RM18 7HS Tel: (01375) 856855 Fax: (01375) 851555 E-mail: email@finnforest.com

Hanson Plywood Ltd, Unit 15 Drakes Industrial Estate, Shay Lane, Ovenden, Halifax, West Yorkshire, HX3 6RL Tel: (01422) 330444 Fax: (01422) 330706 E-mail: panels@hanson-plywood.co.uk

James Latham, Longlands, Milner Way, Ossett, West Yorkshire, WF5 9JE Tel: (01924) 276111 Fax: (01924) 275156 E-mail: panels.ossett@lathams.co.uk

James Latham, 13 Chartwell Drive, Wigston, Leicestershire, LE18 2FN Tel: 0116-288 9161 Fax: 0116-281 3806 E-mail: panels.wigston@lathams.co.uk

James Latham Sales plc, Unit 2 Swallow Park, Finway Road, Hemel Hempstead Industrial Estate, Hemel Hempstead, Hertfordshire, HP2 7QU Tel: (01442) 849000 Fax: (01442) 239287 E-mail: marketing@lathams.co.uk

Vincent Timber Ltd, 8 Montgomery Street, Birmingham, B11 1DU Tel: 0121-772 5511 Fax: 0121-766 6002 E-mail: gdw@vincenttimber.co.uk

PLYWOOD MOTOR VEHICLE LINING KITS

▶ Demar Ltd, Era House, Weir Lane, Worcester, WR2 4AY Tel: (01905) 422688 Fax: (01905) 422610 E-mail: sales@demarvan.co.uk

▶ The Routing & Packaging Company Ltd, Unit 1 Walk Mill Green Road, Colne, Lancashire, BB8 8AL Tel: (01282) 864629 Fax: (01282) 864661 E-mail: nigel@trppackaging.co.uk

PLYWOOD SHAPES, LAMINATED/PREFORMED

Stonebridge Joinery Works Ltd, 190-206 Acton Lane, London, NW10 7NH Tel: (020) 8965 4349 Fax: (020) 8961 1619 E-mail: info@stonebridge-ltd.com

PNEUMATIC ACTUATORS

A T UK Ltd, Unit A4 Sovereign Park Industrial Estate, Market Harborough, Leicestershire, LE16 9EG Tel: (01858) 468199 Fax: (01858) 468187 E-mail: sales@airtorque.co.uk

Air System Controls, Units 51-52, Business Development Centre, Stafford Park 4, Telford, Shropshire, TF3 3BA Tel: (01952) 290959 Fax: (01952) 292647 E-mail: sales@aircontrol-uk.com

Emmerson Process Management Bettis UK Division, 3 Furz Court, Wickham Road, Fareham, Hampshire, PO16 7SH Tel: (01329) 848900 Fax: (01329) 848901 E-mail: bettisuk_sales@msn.com

Forac, Unit 8 9 Riverbank Business Centre, Old Shoreham Road, Shoreham-by-Sea, West Sussex, BN43 5FL Tel: (01273) 467100 Fax: (01273) 467101 E-mail: sales@forac.co.uk

Inovis Ltd, 1 Bracken Close, Lichfield, Staffordshire, WS14 9RU Tel: (0870) 3504707 Fax: (0870) 3504717 E-mail: info@inovis.uk.com

Kinetrol Ltd, Farnham Trading Estate, Farnham, Surrey, GU9 9NU Tel: (01252) 733838 Fax: (01252) 713042 E-mail: sales@kinetrol.com

Maxam Pneumatics Ltd, Walkmill Lane, Bridgtown, Cannock, Staffordshire, WS11 0LR Tel: (01543) 456000 Fax: (01543) 456001 E-mail: mkemp@parker.com

Paladon Systems Ltd, Ferro Fields, Brixworth Industrial Estate, Brixworth, Northampton, NN6 9UA Tel: (01604) 880700 Fax: (01604) 882424 E-mail: enquiries@paladon.co.uk

▶ Pneumatic Systems Ltd, Unit 32 Poplar Industrial Estate, Witton, Birmingham, B6 7AD Tel: 0121-344 3800 Fax: 0121-344 3866 E-mail: pneumaticsys@aol.com

Severn Glocon Ltd, Olympus Park, Quedgeley, Gloucester, GL2 4NF Tel: (01452) 887900 Fax: (0845) 2232041 E-mail: sales@severnglocon.co.uk

Shelley Autonation Ltd, Block 1 Nortonthorpe Mill, Wakefield Road, Scissett, Huddersfield, HD8 9LA Tel: (01484) 860920 Fax: (01484) 860672 E-mail: shelleyauto@aol.com

Valve Center, 2 Bold Business Centre, Bold Lane, St. Helens, Merseyside, WA9 4TX Tel: (01925) 290660 Fax: (01925) 227463 E-mail: sales@valvecenter.co.uk

Williams Industrial Services Ltd, Unit 5, Hyde Park, Commercial Centre, Newtownabbey, County Antrim, BT36 4PY Tel: (028) 9083 8999 Fax: (028) 9084 2211 E-mail: sales@wis-ni.com

PNEUMATIC ALARM SYSTEMS

H N L Engineering Ltd, Dukesway, Teesside Industrial Estate, Stockton-On-Tees, Cleveland, TS17 9LT Tel: (01642) 765553 Fax: (01642) 762899 E-mail: sales@hnl-uk.com

PNEUMATIC BRAKES

Assured Performance Group Ltd, Kenlis Road, Barnacre, Preston, PR3 1GD Tel: (01995) 604600 Fax: (01995) 606651 E-mail: info@apgroup.uk.com

Knorr Bremse Systems for Commercial Vehicles Ltd, Century House, Follybook Road, Emerald Park East, Emmersons Green, Bristol, BS16 7SE Tel: 0117-984 6100 Fax: 0117-984 6101

Ortlinghaus (UK) Ltd, 19 Sugarbrook Rd, Aston Fields Industrial Estate, Bromsgrove, Worcestershire, B60 3DN Tel: (01527) 579123 Fax: (01527) 579077 E-mail: sales@ortlinghaus.co.uk

S E W Eurodrive Ltd, 5 Sugarbrook Court, Aston Road, Bromsgrove, Worcestershire, B60 3EX Tel: (01527) 877319 Fax: (01527) 575245 E-mail: sales@sew-eurodrive.co.uk

S E W Eurodrive Ltd, 764 Finchley Road, London, NW11 7TH Tel: (020) 8458 8949 Fax: (020) 8458 7417

Walsall Brake Services Ltd, Middlemore Lane West, Aldridge, Walsall, WS9 8BG Tel: (01922) 744625 Fax: (01922) 744626

PNEUMATIC CHUCKS

Pratt Burnerd International, Park Works, Lister Lane, Halifax, West Yorkshire, HX1 5JH Tel: (01422) 366371 Fax: (01422) 359379 E-mail: sales@chucksuk.co.uk

S M W Autoblok, 8 The Metro Centre, Peterborough, PE2 7UH Tel: (01733) 394394 Fax: (01733) 394395 E-mail: sales@smwautoblok.co.uk

PNEUMATIC CLAMPS

Brauer Limited, Dawson Road, Mount Farm, Milton Keynes, MK1 1JP Tel: (01908) 374022 Fax: (01908) 641628 E-mail: sales@brauer.co.uk

Harcross Engineering Barnstaple Ltd, Pilland Way, Pottington Business Park, Barnstaple, Devon, EX31 1LP Tel: (01271) 372235 Fax: (01271) 344642

PNEUMATIC CLUTCHES

Industrial Clutch Parts Ltd, Unit 11 Bingswood Trading Estate, Whaley Bridge, High Peak, Derbyshire, SK23 7LY Tel: (01663) 734627 Fax: (01663) 733023 E-mail: sales@icpltd.co.uk

PNEUMATIC COMPONENTS/ FITTINGS MANUFRS

Leigh Baxter Associates Ltd, 15-17 Robert Leonard Industrial Site, Stock Road, Southend-on-Sea, SS2 5QD Tel: (01702) 460970 Fax: (01702) 600544 E-mail: sales@leighbaxter.co.uk

PNEUMATIC COMPONENTS/ FITTINGS MANUFRS – *continued*

Beeland Controls Ltd, Unit 14 Marcon House, Wyther Lane, Leeds, LS5 3BT Tel: 0113-278 2351 Fax: 0113-278 9663 E-mail: beelandc@aol.com

Spotnails Ltd, Unit 21, Pantglas Industrial Estate, Bedwas, Caerphilly, Mid Glamorgan, CF83 8DR Tel: (029) 2086 0222 Fax: (029) 2086 0999 E-mail: sales@spotnails.co.uk

Three Counties Fluid Power, Unit 26 Albany Trading Estate, Albany Street, Newport, Gwent, NP20 5NQ Tel: (01633) 853956 Fax: (01633) 852832 E-mail: sales@threecounties.homestead.com

PNEUMATIC CONTROL ENGINEERING

H N L Engineering Ltd, Dukesway, Teesside Industrial Estate, Stockton-On-Tees, Cleveland, TS17 9LT Tel: (01642) 765553 Fax: (01642) 762899 E-mail: sales@hnl-uk.com

PNEUMATIC CONTROL PANELS

Engineering Electrics (Wilmslow) Ltd, 67 Oldfield Road, Sale, Cheshire, M33 2AP Tel: 0161-973 8230 Fax: 0161-962 8648

PNEUMATIC CONTROL SYSTEMS MANUFRS

A C A S Pneumatic Controls, D1 Broadway Industrial Estate, King William Street, Salford, M50 3UQ Tel: 0161-876 0096 Fax: 0161-876 0134

Air Power Centre, Unit B4 Anchorage Business Park, Chain Caul Way, Ashton-on-Ribble, Preston, PR2 2YL Tel: (01772) 728513 Fax: (01772) 736506 E-mail: apcpreston@airpowercentre.com

Automated Process & Control Manufacturing Co. Ltd, Unit 11 St. Georges Industrial Estate, Richmond Road, Kingston upon Thames, Surrey, KT2 5BQ Tel: (020) 8549 3331 Fax: (020) 8547 1309 E-mail: info@apcair.co.uk

Baric Systems, 11 Telford Court, Morpeth, Northumberland, NE61 2DB Tel: (01670) 505944 Fax: (01670) 505923 E-mail: sales@baricsale.co.uk

Beeland Controls Ltd, Unit 14 Marcon House, Wyther Lane, Leeds, LS5 3BT Tel: 0113-278 2351 Fax: 0113-278 9663 E-mail: beelandc@aol.com

Control Gear Fluid Power Ltd, Heol Groeswen, Treforest Industrial Estate, Pontypridd, Mid Glamorgan, CF37 5YF Tel: (01443) 843126 Fax: (01443) 842997 E-mail: sales@control-gear.com

Gatley Engineering Pneumatics Ltd, Unit 6d Lowick Close, Hazel Grove, Stockport, Cheshire, SK7 5ED Tel: 0161-483 8615 Fax: 0161-456 5285

H Kuhnke, 21 Abbey Enterprise Centre, Premier Way, Romsey, Hampshire, SO51 9AQ Tel: (01794) 514445 Fax: (01794) 513514 E-mail: sales@kuhnke.co.uk

Honeywell Hymatic Engineering Co. Ltd, Burnt Meadow Road, North Moons Moat, Redditch, Worcestershire, B98 9HJ Tel: (01527) 64931 Fax: (01527) 591117 E-mail: redwich.sales@honeywell.com

International Motion Control, Patrick Gregory Road, Wolverhampton, WV11 3DZ Tel: (01902) 304000 Fax: (01902) 305676 E-mail: sales@imc-uk.com

K V Ltd, Lunar House, Crownhill, Milton Keynes, MK8 0HB Tel: (01908) 561515 Fax: (01908) 561227 E-mail: marketing@kvautomation.co.uk

Legris Ltd, Unit 1210, Lansdowne Court, Brockworth, Gloucester, GL3 4AB Tel: (01452) 623500 Fax: (01452) 623501 E-mail: salesuk@legris.com

Meech Air Technology, 2 Network Point, Range Road, Witney, Oxfordshire, OX29 0YN Tel: (01993) 706700 Fax: (01993) 776977 E-mail: sales@meech.com

Meridian Controls Ltd, 38 Galloway Close, South Ham, Basingstoke, Hampshire, RG22 6SX Tel: 0845 5314080 Fax: (01256) 324209 E-mail: sales@meridian-controls.co.uk

Norgren, Brookside Business Park, Greengate, Middleton, Manchester, M24 1GS Tel: (0800) 0560260 Fax: (0800) 0560261 E-mail: manchester@norgren.com

P & D Pneumatic Supplies, Unit 21 Lichfield Road Industrial Estate, Cavendish, Tamworth, Staffordshire, B79 7XH Tel: (01827) 310849 Fax: (01827) 310849

Pneumatic Components Ltd, Holbrook Rise, Holbrook Industrial Estate, Sheffield, S20 3GE Tel: 0114-248 2712 Fax: 0114-247 8342 E-mail: info@pclairtechnology.com

Pneumatic Engineering & Distribution Ltd, Unit D1 Springhead Enterprise Park, Springhead Road, Northfleet, Gravesend, Kent, DA11 8HH Tel: (01474) 536836 Fax: (01474) 536830 E-mail: SALES@PNEUMATICENGINEERING.COM

Pneumatic Equipment Services, C2 Jubilee Road, Newtownards, County Down, BT23 4YH Tel: (028) 9182 8833 Fax: (028) 9182 8844 E-mail: matik@nireland.com

Production Pneumatics, 10 Townsend Close, Bristol, BS14 8TS Tel: (01275) 835204 Fax: (01275) 835204 E-mail: sales@productionpneumatics.co.uk

R G S Electro Pneumatics Ltd, West End Business Park, Oswaldtwistle, Accrington, Lancashire, BB5 4WZ Tel: (01254) 872277 Fax: (01254) 390133 E-mail: sales@rgs-e-p.co.uk

Roomfoss Ltd, Larch Road, Saddlebow, King's Lynn, Norfolk, PE34 3HP Tel: (01553) 771413 Fax: (01553) 691184 E-mail: sales@roomfoss.co.uk

Ross UK Ltd, Cakemore Road, Rowley Regis, West Midlands, B65 0QW Tel: 0121-559 4900 Fax: 0121-559 5309 E-mail: sales@rossuk.co.uk

Roton Compressors Services Ltd, Roton House, Ellen Street, Oldham, OL9 6QR Tel: 0161-620 5107 Fax: 0161-627 1351 E-mail: roton@btconnect.com

Shelley Autonation Ltd, Block 1 Nortonthorpe Mill, Wakefield Road, Scissett, Huddersfield, HD8 9LA Tel: (01484) 860920 Fax: (01484) 860672 E-mail: shelleyauto@aol.com

Solent Fluid Power, 9 Enterprise Industrial Estate, Enterprise Road, Waterlooville, Hampshire, PO8 0BB Tel: (023) 9259 7437 Fax: (023) 9259 9899 E-mail: sales@solentfluidpower.co.uk

Southern Pneumatics, 496 Ipswich Road, Slough, SL1 4EP Tel: (01753) 511255 Fax: (01753) 511755 E-mail: admin@southern-pneumatics.co.uk

Sunbury Tubing & Pneumatics Ltd, Unit 11 Littleton House, Littleton Road, Ashford, Middlesex, TW15 1UU Tel: (01784) 256309 Fax: (01784) 246470

Target Fluid Services, Millhouse Centre, 118 Commercial Road, Totton, Southampton, SO40 3ZW Tel: (023) 8087 2142 Fax: (023) 8066 6882 E-mail: target.fluid@btinternet.com

TF Automation, Hillam Road, Bradford, West Yorkshire, BD2 1QN Tel: (01274) 308005 Fax: (01274) 394518 E-mail: sales@tfautomation.co.uk

Thorite - Sheffield, Thorite Air Centre, 5 Bamforth Street, Hillsborough, Sheffield, S6 2HD Tel: 0114-233 1128 Fax: 0114-233 1140 E-mail: sheffield@thorite.co.uk

PNEUMATIC CONTROL VALVES

Dresser Valve Ltd, Gillibrands Road, Skelmersdale, Lancashire, WN8 9TU Tel: (01695) 52600 Fax: (01695) 52676 E-mail: dennis_alsancak@dresser.com

Shelley Autonation Ltd, Block 1 Nortonthorpe Mill, Wakefield Road, Scissett, Huddersfield, HD8 9LA Tel: (01484) 860920 Fax: (01484) 860672 E-mail: shelleyauto@aol.com

▶ Smart Valves Ltd, Uxbridge Road, Leicester, LE4 7ST Tel: 0116-268 8120 Fax: 0116-261 0050 E-mail: sales@smartvalves.co.uk

PNEUMATIC CONVEYOR SYSTEMS

Benhar Systems Ltd, Fleming House, 18a Garrell Road,, Burnside Industrial Estate, Kilsyth, Glasgow, G65 9JX Tel: (01236) 827070 Fax: (01236) 827071

Gericke Ltd, Victoria House, Cavendish Street, Ashton-under-Lyne, Lancashire, OL6 7DJ Tel: 0161-344 1140 Fax: 0161-308 3403 E-mail: sales@gericke.co.uk

The Handling Conceps, Unit E, Swallow Court, Bromsgrove, Worcestershire, B60 4FE Tel: (01527) 570900 Fax: (01527) 570947 E-mail: sales@handlingconcepts.co.uk

▶ Kongskilde UK Ltd, Hempstead Road, Holt, Norfolk, NR25 6EE Tel: (01263) 713291 Fax: (01263) 712922 E-mail: mail@kuk.kongskilde.com

Portasilo Ltd, New Lane, Huntington, York, YO32 9PR Tel: (01904) 624872 Fax: (01904) 611760 E-mail: bulk@portasilo.co.uk

Rotolok Bulk Systems Ltd, 38 Woodham Lane, New Haw, Addlestone, Surrey, KT15 3NA Tel: (01932) 854756 Fax: (01932) 859427 E-mail: sales@blotch.co.uk

S T B Engineering Ltd, Toadsmoor Road, Brimscombe, Stroud, Gloucestershire, GL5 2UF Tel: (01453) 885353 Fax: (01453) 886824 E-mail: sales@stbengineering.com

PNEUMATIC CRANES

A P P Lifting Services Ltd, Wrights Business Park, Stevens Road, Doncaster, South Yorkshire, DN4 0LT Tel: (01302) 367755 Fax: (01302) 855222 E-mail: sales@applifting.co.uk

PNEUMATIC CYLINDERS

A M J Pneumatics '99' Ltd, Rossfield Road, Ellesmere Port, CH65 3AW Tel: 0151-355 8978 Fax: 0151-357 1431

Air Systems Controls Ltd, 51-52 The Bus Development Cour, Stafford Park 4, Telford, Shropshire, TF3 3BA Tel: (01952) 290959 Fax: (01952) 292647 E-mail: sales@airsystemcontrols.com

Southern Pneumatics, 496 Ipswich Road, Slough, SL1 4EP Tel: (01753) 511255 Fax: (01753) 511755 E-mail: admin@southern-pneumatics.co.uk

PNEUMATIC ENGINEERS, INSTALLATION OR SERVICE

B C A S Ltd, Unit 8 Thames Park, Lester Way, Wallingford, Oxfordshire, OX10 9TA Tel: (01491) 821737 Fax: (01491) 821730 E-mail: sales@bcaslimited.co.uk

Best Pneumatics Ltd, Units 6-7, Short Way, Thornbury Industrial Estate, Thornbury, Bristol, BS35 3UT Tel: (01454) 415761 Fax: (01454) 414607

Boge Compressors, Units 1-4, Bowen Industrial Estate, Aberbargoed, Bargoed, Mid Glamorgan, CF81 9EP Tel: (01443) 875163 Fax: (01443) 820909

Hydraulic & Pneumatic Cylinders Ltd, 4 Birmingham New Enterprise Workshops, All Saints Road, Birmingham, B18 7RL Tel: 0121-523 8400 Fax: 0121-523 8400 E-mail: sales@hydraulic-pneumatic-cylinders.co.uk

J T Sawyer, 9 Pennine Industrial Estate, Modder Place, Armley, Leeds, LS12 3ES Tel: 0113-231 1255 Fax: 0113-231 1238

Southern Pneumatics, 496 Ipswich Road, Slough, SL1 4EP Tel: (01753) 511255 Fax: (01753) 511755 E-mail: admin@southern-pneumatics.co.uk

PNEUMATIC EQUIPMENT REPAIR

Air System Controls, Units 51-52, Business Development Centre, Stafford Park 4, Telford, Shropshire, TF3 3BA Tel: (01952) 290959 Fax: (01952) 292647 E-mail: sales@aircontrol-uk.com

Economatics Industrial Ltd, Epic House, Darnall Road, Sheffield, S9 5AA Tel: 0114-281 3344 Fax: 0114-243 9306 E-mail: group@economatics.co.uk

PNEUMATIC EQUIPMENT/ SYSTEMS DISTRIBUTORS/ AGENTS/STOCKHOLDERS

A C A S Pneumatic Controls, D1 Broadway Industrial Estate, King William Street, Salford, M50 3UQ Tel: 0161-876 0096 Fax: 0161-876 0134

A M J Pneumatics '99' Ltd, Rossfield Road, Ellesmere Port, CH65 3AW Tel: 0151-355 8978 Fax: 0151-357 1431

A P I, Unit 21-22, Britannia Park Industrial Estate North Road, Stoke-on-Trent, ST6 2PZ Tel: (01782) 206995 Fax: (01782) 206826

Acord Fluid Power Ltd, Unit 21, Llantarnam Industrial Estate, Cwmbran, Gwent, NP44 3AX Tel: (01633) 838181 Fax: (01633) 867711

Air Controls Ltd, Garden Close, Langage Business Park, Plympton, Plymouth, PL7 5EU Tel: (01752) 344443 Fax: (01752) 346789 E-mail: aircontrols@eur-isp.com

Air Controls & Compressors Ltd, 9 Trafalgar Court, Widnes, Cheshire, WA8 0SZ Tel: 0151-423 1750 Fax: 0151-495 2079 E-mail: sales@accltd.com

Air System Controls, Units 51-52, Business Development Centre, Stafford Park 4, Telford, Shropshire, TF3 3BA Tel: (01952) 290959 Fax: (01952) 292647 E-mail: sales@aircontrol-uk.com

Airmark, 6 Becket Road, London, N18 3PN Tel: (020) 8807 7891 Fax: (020) 8884 3898 E-mail: airmarkcom@aol.com

Airomatic Tools Ltd, Coleham Green Farm, Woodchurch, Ashford, Kent, TN26 3PP Tel: (01233) 861400 Fax: (01233) 860040

Anglian Compressors & Equipment Ltd, Storeys Bar Road, Peterborough, PE1 5YS Tel: (01733) 349993 Fax: (01733) 564983 E-mail: business@angliancomp.co.uk

B S H Ltd, 15 Powdrake Road, Grangemouth, Stirlingshire, FK3 9UT Tel: (01324) 474242 Fax: (01324) 665456 E-mail: sales@bshltd.co.uk

Blackwell Hydraulics Ltd, Unit 13 Industrial Estate, Llandudno Junction, Gwynedd, LL31 9SX Tel: (01492) 583821 Fax: (01492) 593591 E-mail: sales@blackwellhydrolics.co.uk

Border Hydraulics & Pneumatics Ltd, 9 Currock Road Trade Centre, Currock Road, Carlisle, CA2 5AD Tel: (01228) 530010 Fax: (01228) 818087

C B S Rotary Power Motion Ltd, Lupin Works, Worcester Road, Kidderminster, Worcestershire, DY10 1JR Tel: (01562) 741808 Fax: (01562) 744312 E-mail: kidderminster@cbs-rpm.co.uk

C & S Equipment Ltd, Unit 9D, Wingbury Courtyard Business Village, Wingrave, Aylesbury, Buckinghamshire, HP22 4LW Tel: (01296) 688500

Castle Hydraulics & Pneumatics Ltd, 3 Amherst Business Centre, Budbrooke Road Industrial Estate, Budbrooke Industrial Estate, Warwick, CV34 5WE Tel: (01926) 419926 Fax: (01926) 497196

City Transair, 58 Loughborough Road, Mountsorrel, Loughborough, Leicestershire, LE12 7AT Tel: 0116-230 0070 Fax: 0116-230 0075

Compressors & Systems Suppliers Ltd, Cane End Lane, Bierton, Aylesbury, Buckinghamshire, HP22 5BH Tel: (01296) 415000 Fax: (01296) 434363 E-mail: graham@cass-air.co.uk

Control Gear (EPS) Ltd, Unit 30 Stroud Business Centre, Oldends Lane, Stonehouse, Gloucestershire, GL10 2DG Tel: (01453) 828559 Fax: (01453) 791048 E-mail: garygriffiths@control-gear.com

Coperion Ltd, Victoria House, 19-21 Ack Lane East, Bramhall, Stockport, Cheshire, SK7 2BE Tel: 0161-925 6910 Fax: 0161-925 6911 E-mail: sandra.wyatt@coperion.com

D M R Engineering Services Ltd, 64 Regent Road, Kirkdale, Liverpool, L5 9SY Tel: 0151-207 4451 Fax: 0151-207 5627 E-mail: dmr1966@hotmail.co.uk

Eastern Compressors Ltd, 1-9 Drapers Road, South Woodham Ferrers, Chelmsford, CM3 5UH Tel: (01245) 320624 Fax: (01245) 328700 E-mail: enquiries@easterns.co.uk

Economatics Industrial Ltd, Epic House, Darnall Road, Sheffield, S9 5AA Tel: 0114-281 3344 Fax: 0114-243 9306 E-mail: group@economatics.co.uk

Economatics (Industrial) Ltd, Unit 6 Alders Court, Watchmead, Welwyn Garden City, Hertfordshire, AL7 1LT Tel: (01707) 322622 Fax: (01707) 330724 E-mail: ailsford@economatics.co.uk

ERIKS UK, Industrial Distribution Service Centre, 5 Perth House, Corby Gate Business Park, Priors Haw Road, Corby, Northamptonshire, NN17 5JG Tel: (01536) 204444 Fax: (01536) 400803 E-mail: corby@eriks.co.uk

ERIKS UK, Industrial Distribution Service Centre, Unit 2-1 Festival Court, Govan, Glasgow, G51 1AR Tel: 0141-419 0112 Fax: 0141-419 0444 E-mail: glasgow@eriks.co.uk

Estuary Engineering Co Ltd, Hamlin Way, King's Lynn, Norfolk, PE30 4NG Tel: (01553) 773678 Fax: (01553) 769121 E-mail: tony@estuary.demon.co.uk

Flangecombe Ltd, 147 Stringes Lane, Willenhall, West Midlands, WV13 1LW Tel: (01902) 602030 Fax: (01902) 604050 E-mail: info@flangecombe-ltd.fsbusiness.co.uk

Fluid Power Components, 14 The Oakwood Centre, Downley Road, Havant, Hampshire, PO9 2NP Tel: (023) 9245 4981 Fax: (023) 9245 4981 E-mail: sales@fluidpowercomponents.com

Gatley Engineering Pneumatics Ltd, Unit 6d Lowick Close, Hazel Grove, Stockport, Cheshire, SK7 5ED Tel: 0161-483 8615 Fax: 0161-456 5285

Harrier Pneumatics Ltd, 5 Belgrave Industrial Estate, Belgrave Road, Southampton, SO17 3EA Tel: (023) 8055 8857 Fax: (023) 8055 6200

Kestrel Equipment Ltd, 21-23, Scott Road, Luton, LU3 3BF Tel: (01582) 563600 Fax: (01582) 563323 E-mail: info@kestrelequipment.co.uk

L L Pneumatic & Engineering Supplies Ltd, Unit 1, Turner Street, Dudley, West Midlands, DY1 1TX Tel: (01384) 230123 Fax: (01384) 456146

Newtown Pneumatic Services Ltd, Newtown Road, Worcester, WR5 1HA Tel: (01905) 29068 Fax: (01905) 24118

Nitto Kohki Europe Co. Ltd, Unit 21, Empire Centre, Imperial Way, Watford, WD24 4TS Tel: (01923) 239005 Fax: (01923) 248815 E-mail: nitto-uk@jais.co.uk

P P S Hydraulics & Pneumatics Ltd, Foxwood Close, Foxwood Industrial Park, Sheepbridge, Chesterfield, Derbyshire, S41 9RN Tel: (01246) 451509 Fax: (01246) 450831 E-mail: ppshydraulics@btconnect.com

Pipemore, 3 Crompton Road, Glenrothes, Fife, KY6 2SF Tel: (01592) 630633 Fax: (01592) 630623E-mail: sales@pipemorescotland.co.uk

Pneu Fix, 255 Kingston Road, Willerby, Hull, HU10 6PG Tel: (01482) 651019 Fax: (01482) 651019

Pneumatic Engineering & Distribution Ltd, Unit D1 Springhead Enterprise Park, Springhead Road, Northfleet, Gravesend, Kent, DA11 8HH Tel: (01474) 536836 Fax: (01474) 536830 E-mail: SALES@PNEUMATICENGINEERING.COM

Pneumatic Tool Services Ltd, Worthing Road, West Grinstead, Horsham, West Sussex, RH13 8LG Tel: (01403) 865609 Fax: (01403) 864198 E-mail: sales@pneumatictoolservices.co.uk

Premier Hydraulics & Pneumatics, Unit 4, Cliffton Business Park, Preston New Road, Clifton, Preston, PR4 0XQ Tel: (01772) 253455 Fax: (01772) 204155

Primary Fluid Power, Caddick Road, Knowsley Business Park, Prescot, Merseyside, L34 9HP Tel: 0151-632 9500 Fax: 0151-548 9896 E-mail:

R A M Ltd, Unit B3 Guy Motors Industrial Park, Park Lane, Wolverhampton, WV10 9QF Tel: (01902) 863506 Fax: (01902) 728402 E-mail: r.a.m.ltd@eur-is.co.uk

Rep Air Services, Unit 23 Monarch Way, Loughborough, Leicestershire, LE11 5XG Tel: (01509) 213452 Fax: (01509) 212102 E-mail: sales@rep-air.co.uk

Robertson & Armitage Ltd, 10 Limekiln Road, Ayr, KA8 8DG Tel: (01292) 282733 Fax: (01292) 287932

Rodcraft UK Ltd, 138 Oyster Lane, Byfleet, West Byfleet, Surrey, KT14 7JQ Tel: (01932) 341020 Fax: (01932) 354954

▶ indicates data change since last edition

PNEUMATIC EQUIPMENT/SYSTEMS DISTRIBUTORS/AGENTS/ STOCKHOLDERS – *continued*

Rogers Duncan Engineering Ltd, 396 Hillington Road, Hillington Industrial Estate, Glasgow, G52 4BL Tel: 0141-882 6211 Fax: 0141-882 5818 E-mail: info@duncanrogers.com

Sapphire Engineering, Atlas Works, Brieryfield Road, Preston, PR1 8SR Tel: (01772) 822133 Fax: (01772) 822144

Simmatic Automation Specialists Ltd, 3 Heathfield Units, Sandy Lane, Titton, Stourport-on-Severn, Worcestershire, DY13 9QA Tel: (01299) 877770 Fax: (01299) 823273 E-mail: sales@simmatic.co.uk

Solent Fluid Power, 9 Enterprise Industrial Estate, Enterprise Road, Waterlooville, Hampshire, PO8 0BB Tel: (023) 9259 7437 Fax: (023) 9259 9899 E-mail: sales@solentfluidpower.co.uk

Southern Fluid Power, E Altbarn Industrial Estate, Revenge Road, Chatham, Kent, ME5 8UD Tel: (01634) 686060 Fax: (01634) 683332 E-mail: info@s-f-p.co.uk

Stoneway Engineering, Unit 2 The Warehouse, Benson Lane, Normanton, West Yorkshire, WF6 2HX Tel: (01924) 895959 Fax: (01924) 890721

Sunbury Tubing & Pneumatics Ltd, Unit 11 Littleton House, Littleton Road, Ashford, Middlesex, TW15 1UU Tel: (01784) 256309 Fax: (01784) 246470

TF Automation, Hillam Road, Bradford, West Yorkshire, BD2 1QN Tel: (01274) 308005 Fax: (01274) 394518 E-mail: sales@tfautomation.co.uk

Thames Valley Pneumatic Ltd, Delta Way, Egham, Surrey, TW20 8RX Tel: (01784) 434999 Fax: (01784) 434499 E-mail: tvpltd@hotmail.com

Thread & Pipe Services Ltd, 26 Elliott Road, Bournemouth, BH11 8JZ Tel: (01202) 576789 Fax: (01202) 579816 E-mail: sales@threadandpipe.com

Three Counties Fluid Power, Unit 26 Albany Trading Estate, Albany Street, Newport, Gwent, NP20 5NQ Tel: (01633) 853956 Fax: (01633) 852832 E-mail: sales@threecounties.homestead.com

Total Air Tool Services Ltd, The Old Sawmill, Harvest Hill Lane, Allesley, Coventry, CV5 9DD Tel: (024) 7640 3624 Fax: (024) 7640 4675 E-mail: total@totalairtools.co.uk

Town & County Engineering Services Ltd, Warden Tree Lane, Pinchbeck, Spalding, Lincolnshire, PE11 3UG Tel: (01775) 725678 Fax: (01775) 767205 E-mail: sales@townandcounty.uk.com

Trecarn Engineering, 1 Ivanhoe Industrial Estate, Tournament Way, Ashby-de-la-Zouch, Leicestershire, LE65 2UU Tel: (01530) 412802 Fax: (01530) 417515

Trent Valley Bearings & Pneumatics Ltd, Transmission House, 1 South Street, Long Eaton, Nottingham, NG10 1ER Tel: 0115-973 2234 Fax: 0115-946 0817 E-mail: sales@trent-valley.co.uk

Universal Air Tool Co. Ltd, Unit 8 Lane End Industrial Park, Lane End, High Wycombe, Buckinghamshire, HP14 3BY Tel: (01494) 883300 Fax: (01494) 883237 E-mail: sales@universal.co.uk

W H Fluidpower Ltd, Unit 9, Rossbank Road, Rossmoor Industrial Estate, Ellesmere Port, CH65 3AN Tel: (0151) 355 2211 Fax: (0151) 355 2277 E-mail: whfluidpower@ukonline.co.uk

Western Automation, Western House, Ipswich Road, Cardiff, CF23 9AQ Tel: (029) 2048 8446 Fax: (029) 2047 1843 E-mail: sales@appliedautomation.co.uk

Wrekin Pneumatics Telford Ltd, Park Road, Dawley Bank, Telford, Shropshire, TF4 2BE Tel: (01952) 505566 Fax: (01952) 504703 E-mail: wrekin@interramp.co.uk

Yorkshire Pneumatic Services, Newhaven Business Park, Lowergate, Milnsbridge, Huddersfield, HD3 4HS Tel: (01484) 642211 Fax: (01484) 461002

PNEUMATIC EQUIPMENT/ SYSTEMS MANUFRS, *See also headings for particular types*

Beaumanor Engineering Ltd, 47 Highmeres Road, Leicester, LE4 9LZ Tel: 0116-276 4728 Fax: 0116-246 0133 E-mail: info@beaumanor.com

Briggs Bros Engineers Ltd, 39 Walkers Road, Moons Moat North Industrial Estate, Redditch, Worcestershire, B98 9HD Tel: (01527) 66779 Fax: (01527) 596130 E-mail: sales@briggsairmotors.com

Davis Pneumatic Systems Ltd, Units C-E Huxley Close, Newnham Industrial Estate, Plympton, Plymouth, PL7 4BQ Tel: (01752) 336421 Fax: (01752) 345828 E-mail: sales@davispneumatic.co.uk

John Gibson Agencies Ltd, Queens Way, Middlesbrough, Cleveland, TS3 8TF Tel: (01642) 221761 Fax: (01642) 242938 E-mail: jga@jgagencies.co.uk

H Kuhnke, 21 Abbey Enterprise Centre, Premier Way, Romsey, Hampshire, SO51 9AQ Tel: (01794) 514445 Fax: (01794) 513514 E-mail: sales@kuhnke.co.uk

Honeywell Hymatic Engineering Co. Ltd, Burnt Meadow Road, North Moons Moat, Redditch, Worcestershire, B98 9HJ Tel: (01527) 64931 Fax: (01527) 591117 E-mail: redwich.sales@honeywell.com

Hydratorc Pneumatic Systems, Unit 11 Bedwas House Industrial Estate, Bedwas, Caerphilly, Mid Glamorgan, CF83 8DW Tel: (029) 2088 8883 Fax: (029) 2086 0004 E-mail: appliedtorque@aol.com

M E C-Air (Pneumatics & Hydraulics) Ltd, Unit 5c, Enterprise Way, Five Lane Ends, Bradford, West Yorkshire, BD10 8EW Tel: (01274) 621037 Fax: (01274) 621230

Maxam Pneumatics Ltd, Walkmill Lane, Bridgtown, Cannock, Staffordshire, WS11 0LR Tel: (01543) 456000 Fax: (01543) 456001 E-mail: mkemp@parker.com

Metal Work Ltd, Blackhill Drive, Wolverton Mill, Milton Keynes, MK12 5TS Tel: (01908) 222288 Fax: (01908) 222824 E-mail: sales@metalwork.co.uk

Micro Pneumatics, 1 Palmer Street, Leicester, LE4 5PT Tel: 0116-261 1055 Fax: 0116-261 1066 E-mail: sales@micropneumatics.co.uk

▶ Pneu Air, 6 Saxon Business Park, Hanbury Road, Stoke Prior, Bromsgrove, Worcestershire, B60 4AD Tel: (01527) 559561 Fax: (01527) 559562

Pneumatic Components Ltd, Holbrook Rise, Holbrook Industrial Estate, Sheffield, S20 3GE Tel: 0114-248 2712 Fax: 0114-247 8342 E-mail: info@pclairtechnology.com

Ram Reman Ltd, Gundrymoor Trading Estate, Collingwood Road, West Moors, Wimborne, Dorset, BH21 6QJ Tel: (01202) 861888 Fax: (01202) 861668

Ross UK Ltd, Cakemore Road, Rowley Regis, West Midlands, B65 0QW Tel: 0121-559 4900 Fax: 0121-559 5309 E-mail: sales@rossuk.co.uk

S M C Pneumatics, Vincent Avenue, Crownhill, Milton Keynes, MK8 0AN Tel: (01908) 563888 Fax: (01908) 561185 E-mail: sales@smcpneumatics.co.uk

Stoneway Engineering, Unit 2 The Warehouse, Benson Lane, Normanton, West Yorkshire, WF6 2HX Tel: (01924) 895959 Fax: (01924) 890721

Thelcastle Ltd, Unit 14, Newhaven Business Park, Barton Lane, Eccles, Manchester, M30 0HH Tel: 0161 7880345

PNEUMATIC FASTENERS

Pneutek (International) Ltd, Unit 1, Sovereign Way, Trafalgar Industrial Estate, Downham Market, Norfolk, PE38 9SW Tel: (01366) 388866 E-mail: airfasteners@thesmallbusinessclinique.com

Trident Group UK Ltd, 14-15 Yeldon Court, Finedon Road Industrial Estate, Wellingborough, Northamptonshire, NN8 4SS Tel: (01933) 228228 Fax: (01933) 229922 E-mail: sales@tridentgroupuk.com

PNEUMATIC FENDERS

▶ Dunlop G R G Holdings Ltd, Unit 62, Touchet, Hall Road, Stakehill Industrial Estate, Middleton, Manchester, M24 2RW Tel: 0161-653 5964 Fax: 0161-643 0184 E-mail: sales@dunlopgrg.co.uk

PNEUMATIC FILTERS

Filtech 2000 Ltd, East Market Street, Newport, Gwent, NP20 2AY Tel: (01633) 253878 Fax: (01633) 267914 E-mail: bc.hydraulics@btinternet.com

PNEUMATIC HOSE COUPLINGS/ FITTINGS MANUFRS

North Devon Hose & Hydraulics Ltd, Unit 20 Castle Park Road, Whiddon Valley Industrial Estate, Barnstaple, Devon, EX32 8PA Tel: (01271) 324443 Fax: (01271) 324568 E-mail: northdevon@hosehyd.fsnet.co.uk

PNEUMATIC INSTRUMENTATION

Fine Controls UK Ltd, Bassendale Road, Bromborough, Wirral, Merseyside, CH62 3QL Tel: 0151-343 9966 Fax: 0151-343 0062 E-mail: sales@finecontrols.com

Protronix Industrial Services, 3-15 Cross Street, Luton, LU2 0DP Tel: (01582) 418490 Fax: (01582) 486588 E-mail: sales@protronix.co.uk

PNEUMATIC MANIFOLDS

Beeland Controls Ltd, Unit 14 Marcon House, Wyther Lane, Leeds, LS5 3BT Tel: 0113-278 2351 Fax: 0113-278 9663 E-mail: beelandc@aol.com

PNEUMATIC MOTORS

Briggs Bros Engineers Ltd, 39 Walkers Road, Moons Moat North Industrial Estate, Redditch, Worcestershire, B98 9HD Tel: (01527) 66779 Fax: (01527) 596130 E-mail: sales@briggsairmotors.com

PNEUMATIC OR AIR OPERATED HOISTS

Castle Pneumatics, Dormston Trading Estate, Burton Road, Dudley, West Midlands, DY1 2UF Tel: (01902) 883727 Fax: (01902) 881208

PNEUMATIC PORTABLE POWER SAWS

Cengar Ltd, 70 Lister Lane, Halifax, West Yorkshire, HX1 5DN Tel: (01422) 354626 Fax: (01422) 349024 E-mail: enquiries@cengar.com

PNEUMATIC PORTABLE POWER TOOLS

Cengar Ltd, 70 Lister Lane, Halifax, West Yorkshire, HX1 5DN Tel: (01422) 354626 Fax: (01422) 349024 E-mail: enquiries@cengar.com

PNEUMATIC PRESSES

Flangecombe Ltd, 147 Stringes Lane, Willenhall, West Midlands, WV13 1LW Tel: (01902) 602030 Fax: (01902) 604050 E-mail: info@flangecombe-ltd.fsbusiness.co.uk

R M T-Gabro Ltd, Hilton Road, Cobbs Wood Industrial Estate, Ashford, Kent, TN23 1EW Tel: (01233) 628976 Fax: (01233) 631888 E-mail: sales@mjallen.co.uk

Tama (UK), P O Box 157, Cannock, Staffordshire, WS11 9WL Tel: (01543) 274100 Fax: (01543) 277112 E-mail: info@tama-uk.fsnet.co.uk

PNEUMATIC PUMPS

▶ Robins Air Team, Unit 22, Llanelli Workshops, Trostre Industrial Park, Llanelli, Dyfed, SA14 9UU Tel: (0800) 0131440 Fax: (01554) 746569 E-mail: robin@robinsairteam.co.uk

PNEUMATIC REGULATORS

Fine Controls UK Ltd, Bassendale Road, Bromborough, Wirral, Merseyside, CH62 3QL Tel: 0151-343 9966 Fax: 0151-343 0062 E-mail: sales@finecontrols.com

PNEUMATIC STAPLING MACHINES

▶ Top Gun Tools & Fixings, Amy Johnson Way, Blackpool, FY4 2RP Tel: (01253) 400900 Fax: (01253) 400900 E-mail: sales@topgun.co.uk

PNEUMATIC TOOL MANUFRS

▶ A T A Grinding Processes Ltd, 37 Dalsetter Avenue, Drumchapel, Glasgow, G15 8TE Tel: 0141-940 4720 Fax: 0141-940 4721 E-mail: ata@atagrinding.co.uk

Arden Power Tools, Albion Works, High Street, Newhall, Swadlincote, Derbyshire, DE11 0EB Tel: (01283) 550347 Fax: (01283) 550720 E-mail: ardenpowertools@btconnect.com

Bostitch, Europa Views, Sheffield Business Park, Sheffield, S9 1XH Tel: (0870) 1630630 Fax: (0870) 1670670 E-mail: bostitchuksales@stanleyworks.com

Castle Pneumatics, Dormston Trading Estate, Burton Road, Dudley, West Midlands, DY1 2UF Tel: (01902) 883727 Fax: (01902) 881208

Desoutter Ltd, Eton Road, Hemel Hempstead, Hertfordshire, HP2 7DR Tel: (01442) 344300 Fax: (01442) 344600

Desoutter Ltd, Eton Road, Hemel Hempstead, Hertfordshire, HP2 7DR Tel: (01442) 344300 Fax: (01442) 344600 E-mail: desoutter.sales@cp.com

Hixons, 45 Denton Road, Audenshaw, Manchester, M34 5BL Tel: 0161-336 3725 Fax: 0161-336 4184 E-mail: sales@hixons.com

K V Ltd, Lunar House, Crownhill, Milton Keynes, MK8 0HB Tel: (01908) 561515 Fax: (01908) 561227 E-mail: marketing@kvautomation.co.uk

Minden Industrial Ltd, Saxham Business Park, Little Saxham, Bury St. Edmunds, Suffolk, IP28 6RX Tel: (01284) 760791 Fax: (01284) 702156 E-mail: sales@minden-ind.co.uk

Thorite - Sheffield, Thorite Air Centre, 5 Bamforth Street, Hillsborough, Sheffield, S6 2HD Tel: 0114-233 1128 Fax: 0114-233 1140 E-mail: sheffield@thorite.co.uk

Trelawny SPT Ltd, 13 Highdown Road, Leamington Spa, Warwickshire, CV31 1XT Tel: (01926) 883781 Fax: (01926) 450352 E-mail: sales@trelawny.co.uk

Yokota UK, Low Common Road, Dinnington, Sheffield, S25 2RJ Tel: (01909) 552471 Fax: (01909) 552472 E-mail: info@yokota.co.uk

PNEUMATIC TOOL REPAIR SERVICES

Castle Pneumatics, Dormston Trading Estate, Burton Road, Dudley, West Midlands, DY1 2UF Tel: (01902) 883727 Fax: (01902) 881208

Drake Pneumatics, 138 Oyster Lane, Byfleet, West Byfleet, Surrey, KT14 7JQ Tel: (01932) 355239 Fax: (01932) 354954 E-mail: info@drakepneumatics.co.uk

Hixons, 45 Denton Road, Audenshaw, Manchester, M34 5BL Tel: 0161-336 3725 Fax: 0161-336 4184 E-mail: sales@hixons.com

Pneumatic Tool Services Ltd, Worthing Road, West Grinstead, Horsham, West Sussex, RH13 8LG Tel: (01403) 865609 Fax: (01403) 864198 E-mail: sales@pneumatictoolservices.co.uk

Thames Valley Pneumatic Ltd, Delta Way, Egham, Surrey, TW20 8RX Tel: (01784) 434999 Fax: (01784) 434499 E-mail: tvpltd@hotmail.com

Tool Repair Services, Unit 51 The Sir Robert Peel Mill, Mill Lane, Fazeley, Tamworth, Staffordshire, B78 3QD Tel: (01827) 286322 Fax: (01827) 259101 E-mail: toolrepairs@hotmail.com

Total Air Tool Services Ltd, The Old Sawmill, Harvest Hill Lane, Allesley, Coventry, CV5 9DD Tel: (024) 7640 3624 Fax: (024) 7640 4675 E-mail: total@totalairtools.co.uk

Yokota UK, Low Common Road, Dinnington, Sheffield, S25 2RJ Tel: (01909) 552471 Fax: (01909) 552472 E-mail: info@yokota.co.uk

PNEUMATIC TUBE CARRIER SYSTEMS

Air Tube Carrier Systems, 79 Turnberry, Bracknell, Berkshire, RG12 8ZH Tel: (01344) 423659 Fax: (01344) 423659

Quirepace Ltd, Cleveland Place, Cleveland Road, Gosport, Hampshire, PO12 2JG Tel: (023) 9251 1008 Fax: (023) 9251 3244 E-mail: info@quirepace.co.uk

PNEUMATIC TUBE/TUBING COUPLINGS/FITTINGS MANUFRS

Three Counties Fluid Power, Unit 26 Albany Trading Estate, Albany Street, Newport, Gwent, NP20 5NQ Tel: (01633) 853956 Fax: (01633) 852832 E-mail: sales@threecounties.homestead.com

PNEUMATIC VALVES

Alpha Controls Ltd, Hindley Industrial Estate, Off Swan Lane, Hindley Green, Wigan, Lancashire, WN2 4HR Tel: (01942) 525833 Fax: (01942) 523413 E-mail: technicalsales@alphacontrols.co.uk

Automated Process & Control Manufacturing Co. Ltd, Unit 11 St. Georges Industrial Estate, Richmond Road, Kingston upon Thames, Surrey, KT2 5BQ Tel: (020) 8549 3331 Fax: (020) 8547 1309 E-mail: info@apcair.co.uk

G C E Fluid Power Ltd, Unit 17 Atlas Estate, Brookvale Road, Witton, Birmingham, B6 7EX Tel: 0121-356 5727 Fax: 0121-344 3629 E-mail: gcefluidpower@btinternet.com

Grange Controls Ltd, Unit 3 Midland Way, Thornbury, Bristol, BS35 2BS Tel: (01454) 418256 Fax: (01454) 415214 E-mail: sales@grangecontrols.co.uk

Maxam Pneumatics Ltd, Walkmill Lane, Bridgtown, Cannock, Staffordshire, WS11 0LR Tel: (01543) 456000 Fax: (01543) 456001 E-mail: mkemp@parker.com

Ross UK Ltd, Cakemore Road, Rowley Regis, West Midlands, B65 0QW Tel: 0121-559 4900 Fax: 0121-559 5309 E-mail: sales@rossuk.co.uk

S M C Pneumatics, Vincent Avenue, Crownhill, Milton Keynes, MK8 0AN Tel: (01908) 563888 Fax: (01908) 561185 E-mail: sales@smcpneumatics.co.uk

Versatile Controls Ltd, Unit R1 Innsworth Technology Park, Innsworth Lane, Gloucester, GL3 1DL Tel: (01452) 731447 Fax: (01452) 731621 E-mail: sales@versatilecontrols.co.uk

PNEUMATIC WINCHES

A P P Lifting Services Ltd, Wrights Business Park, Stevens Road, Doncaster, South Yorkshire, DN4 0LT Tel: (01302) 367755 Fax: (01302) 855222 E-mail: sales@applifting.co.uk

Fisher Offshore, North Meadows, Oldmeldrum, Inverurie, Aberdeenshire, AB51 0GQ Tel: (01651) 873932 Fax: (01651) 873939 E-mail: info@fisheroffshore.com

POCKET DIARIES

Kernow Plusfile, Winship Road, Milton, Cambridge, CB24 6BQ Tel: (01223) 425003 Fax: (01223) 425120

POCKET KNIVES

Egginton Bros Ltd, 25-31 Allen Street, Sheffield, S3 7AW Tel: 0114-276 6123 Fax: 0114-273 8465 E-mail: steve@eggintongroup.co.uk

F E & J R Hopkinson Ltd, 124 Scotland Street, Sheffield, S3 7DE Tel: 0114-272 7486 Fax: 0114-275 0290 E-mail: sales@sheffieldknives.co.uk

Harrison Fisher & Co. Ltd, 78 Milton Street, Sheffield, S3 7WJ Tel: 0114-272 4221 Fax: 0114-275 4187 E-mail: sales@harrison-fisher.co.uk

M G Tools, 158 Charles Street, Sheffield, S1 2NE Tel: 0114-272 2281 Fax: 0114-278 7157 E-mail: info@mgtools.co.uk

Rodgers Wostenholm Ltd, 25-31 Allen Street, Sheffield, S3 7AW Tel: 0114-276 6123 Fax: 0114-273 8465 E-mail: sales@eggintongroup.co.uk

Herbert M. Slater Ltd, 332 Coleford Road, Sheffield, S9 5PH Tel: 0114-261 2308 Fax: 0114-261 2305 E-mail: info@slaterknives.co.uk

Stephenson & Wilson Ltd, Louvic Works, 44 Garden Street, Sheffield, S1 3HL Tel: 0114-249 3889 Fax: 0114-249 3891 E-mail: stephenson@wilsonltd.freeserve.co.uk

POINT OF SALE (POS) DISPLAY PRINT FINISHING

▶ Minford Ltd, Strawberry Lane, Willenhall, West Midlands, WV13 3RS Tel: (01902) 603030 Fax: (01902) 603069 E-mail: sales@minford.co.uk

POINT OF SALE (POS) EQUIPMENT

Farsite Communications Ltd, Tempus Business Centre, 60 Kingsclere Road, Basingstoke, Hampshire, RG21 6XG Tel: (01256) 330461 Fax: (01256) 854931 E-mail: sales@farsite.co.uk

▶ HoloVis, The Brick Barn Bittesby Farm, Mere Lane, Lutterworth, Leicestershire, LE17 4JH Tel: (01455) 553924 Fax: (01455) 557746 E-mail: info@holovis.com

POINT OF SALE (POS)/ PURCHASE ADVERTISING MATERIAL

Bezier Creative Printers, Balne Lane, Wakefield, West Yorkshire, WF2 0DF Tel: (01924) 362921 Fax: (01924) 372615 E-mail: bdw@bezier.co.uk

Bezier P O P, Church Road, Wick, Bristol, BS30 5RF Tel: 0117-937 3989 Fax: 0117-937 2662 E-mail: bdb@bezier.co.uk

Bridgeshire Packaging Ltd, 1 Wimsey Way, Alfreton Trading Estate, Somercotes, Alfreton, Derbyshire, DE55 4LS Tel: (01773) 601000 Fax: (01773) 606075 E-mail: sales@bridgeshire.co.uk

Display Promotions London Ltd, 17 Station Parade, Whitchurch Lane, Edgware, Middlesex, HA8 6RW Tel: (020) 8951 0088 Fax: (020) 8381 3229 E-mail: snb@display.freeserve.co.uk

Formost Packaging Ltd, 10 Dawson Road, Bletchley, Milton Keynes, MK1 1LJ Tel: (01908) 376444 Fax: (01908) 373937 E-mail: sales@formost-packaging.com

Hythe Offset, Telford Way, Severalls Park, Colchester, CO4 9QP Tel: (01206) 848904 Fax: (01206) 852054 E-mail: cards@hythe-uk.com

West Country Cash Registers, 31 Merrivale Road, Beacon Park, Plymouth, PL2 2QG Tel: (01752) 210011 Fax: (01752) 210012

POINT OF SALE (POS)/ PURCHASE DISPLAY UNITS

Advance Display Cabinets Ltd, 29 Sugarbrook Road, Bromsgrove, Worcestershire, B60 3DN Tel: (01527) 579744 Fax: (01527) 579744

Arp Plastics Ltd, Unit M Westminster Industrial Estate, Measham, Swadlincote, Derbyshire, DE12 7DS Tel: (01530) 514280 Fax: (01530) 514281 E-mail: admin@arpplastics.co.uk

Atlas Products, Unit F1 Ash Grove Industrial Park, Heath Place, Bognor Regis, West Sussex, PO22 9SL Tel: (01243) 830324 Fax: (01243) 868404

Avon Business Computers, New Road, High Littleton, Bristol, BS39 6JH Tel: (01761) 470543

Axiom Displays Ltd, Mersey Road North, Failsworth, Manchester, M35 9LT Tel: 0161-681 1371 Fax: 0161-683 4641 E-mail: info@axiom-displays.co.uk

Cardiem Ltd, Station Road, Strines, Stockport, Cheshire, SK6 7GP Tel: (01663) 764861 Fax: (01663) 762377 E-mail: sales@cardiem.co.uk

Creative Display Group, Millersdale Close, Euroway Industrial Estate, Bradford, West Yorkshire, BD4 6RX Tel: (01274) 700690 Fax: (01274) 700699 E-mail: sales@creativedisplaygroup.co.uk

Display System Fabrications Ltd, Dunsteads Farm, Trueloves Lane, Ingatestone, Essex, CM4 0NJ Tel: (01277) 352700 Fax: (01277) 352766 E-mail: dsfdisplay@aol.com

H L, H L House, Riverside Business Park, Dockfield Road, Shipley, West Yorkshire, BD17 7AD Tel: (01274) 531709 Fax: (01274) 594578 E-mail: jackie.perry@hl-rim.co.uk

▶ Rep Engineering & Manufacturing, Unit 11 Rippleside Commercial Estate, Ripple Road, Barking, Essex, IG11 0RJ Tel: (020) 8526 7711 Fax: (020) 8526 7722

Steel Stamping Products Ltd, 15-17 Highmeres Road, Troon Industrial Estate, Leicester, LE4 9LZ Tel: 0116-276 6572 Fax: 0116-276 1624 E-mail: info@steelstampings.co.uk

Stephenson Plastics, The Workshop Pickards Farm, Sandy Lane, Guildford, Surrey, GU3 1HJ Tel: (01483) 565277 Fax: (01483) 505047 E-mail: stephensonplastics@talk21.com

Striking Displays UK Ltd, Display House, North Street, Portslade, Brighton, BN41 1DH Tel: (01273) 423623 Fax: (01273) 420424 E-mail: sales@strikingdisplays.co.uk

POINT OF SALE (POS)/ PURCHASE DISPLAY UNITS, TO SPECIFICATION

C P Arts Ltd, Alphin Brook Road, Marsh Barton Trading Estate, Exeter, EX2 8QF Tel: (01392) 210574 Fax: (01392) 412107 E-mail: cparts@cparts.co.uk

Concept Group, Concept House, Victoria Industrial Park, Victoria Road, Leeds, LS14 2LA Tel: 0113-265 0093 Fax: 0113-265 0132 E-mail: sales@concept-data.com

Indusfoto Ltd, 39-41 Margravine Road, London, W6 8LL Tel: (020) 7385 7618 Fax: (020) 7381 0047 E-mail: mark@indusfoto.co.uk

POINT OF SALE (POS)/ PURCHASE MATERIALS/ PRODUCTS STORAGE AND DISTRIBUTION SERVICES

▶ Comet Home Delivery, Unit 12 Severn Link Distribution Centre, Newhouse Farm Industrial Es, Mathern, Chepstow, Gwent, NP16 6UN Tel: (01291) 628866 Fax: (01291) 630757

▶ Kalas Gemini Ltd, 17a Redstone Industrial Estate, Redstone Road, Boston, Lincolnshire, PE21 8EA Tel: (01205) 311185 Fax: (01205) 366069

Pos Direct Ltd, 99 Boston Road, Leicester, LE4 1AW Tel: 0116-234 4400 Fax: 0116-235 8947 E-mail: sales@pos-direct.co.uk

POINT OF SALE (POS)/ PURCHASE TERMINALS

Avon Business Computers, New Road, High Littleton, Bristol, BS39 6JH Tel: (01761) 470543

Orbital Epos Systems Ltd, Canada House Business Centre, 272 Field End Road, Eastcote, Ruislip, Middlesex, HA4 9NA Tel: (020) 8582 0331 Fax: (020) 8582 0335 E-mail: sales@epossystems.co.uk

Romar Cash Registers, 140 Portway, London, E15 3QW Tel: (020) 8472 4157 Fax: (020) 8552 5748 E-mail: info@romar.co.uk

POINT OF SALE (POS)/ PURCHASE TERMINALS, ELECTRONIC

Alphameric Solutions Ltd, Bishopsgate House, Broadford Park, Guildford, Surrey, GU4 8ED Tel: (01483) 293900 Fax: (01483) 533333 E-mail: enquiries@alphameric.com

B N E Electronics Ltd, 44 Main Street, Toomebridge, Antrim, BT41 3TF Tel: (028) 7965 0502 Fax: (028) 7965 4830 E-mail: edward.duffin@bne.onyxnet.co.uk

Counter Solutions Ltd, Lakeside Business Centre, Shipley, Heanor, Derbyshire, DE75 7JQ Tel: (01773) 530303 Fax: (01773) 530404 E-mail: sales@countersolutions.com

Htec Ltd, Unit H George Curl Way, Southampton, SO18 2RX Tel: (023) 8068 9200 Fax: (023) 8068 9201 E-mail: sstocks@htec.co.uk

Multidata Europe, Hunts Hill, Blunsdon, Swindon, SN26 7BN Tel: (01793) 706161 Fax: (01793) 706150 E-mail: nigel@multidata.co.uk

Taecomm, Penrallt, Cwmbach, Whitland, Dyfed, SA34 0DR Tel: (07770) 555011 Fax: (01994) 448709

Torex Hospitality, Houghton Hall Park, Houghton Regis, Dunstable, Bedfordshire, LU5 5YG Tel: (01582) 869600 Fax: (01582) 869601 E-mail: info@torexretail.com

Toshiba TEC Europe UK Operations, 1 Siskin House, Marlins Meadow, Croxley Business Park, Watford, WD18 8TY Tel: (01923) 233688 Fax: (01923) 233698 E-mail: administrator@toshibatec-eu.co.uk

POINT OF SALE (POS)/ PURCHASE/MARKETING DISPLAYS

3 Dimensional Print Ltd, Unit 37 Acorn Industrial Park, Crayford Road, Dartford, DA1 4AL Tel: (01322) 555942 Fax: (01322) 528973 E-mail: sales@3dp.co.uk

Ace Signs Group, 1 Bentalls, Basildon, Essex, SS14 3BS Tel: (01268) 706800 Fax: (01702) 294325 E-mail: enquiries@asg.co.uk

Ace Signs Group, Oak Tree Road, Binley, Coventry, CV3 2RR Tel: (024) 7660 8200 Fax: (024) 7660 8201 E-mail: info@asg.co.uk

Adept Vacuum Formers & Patterns Ltd, 141 Waterside Road, Hamilton, Leicester, LE5 1TL Tel: 0116-246 0552 Fax: 0116-246 0987 E-mail: enquiries@adeptvp.freeserve.co.uk

Adglow plc, Ledbury House, Alexandra Way, Ashchurch, Tewkesbury, Gloucestershire, GL20 8NB Tel: (01684) 850650 Fax: (01684) 850729 E-mail: mail@adglow.co.uk

Adline Press, 5 Bear Court, Basingstoke, Hampshire, RG24 8QT Tel: (01256) 463779 Fax: (01256) 840591 E-mail: design@adline-group.com

Admiral Display, 18 Seas End Road, Surfleet, Spalding, Lincolnshire, PE11 4DQ Tel: (01775) 680410 Fax: (01775) 680921 E-mail: admiraldisplay@aol.com

Advance Display Cabinets Ltd, 29 Sugarbrook Road, Bromsgrove, Worcestershire, B60 3DN Tel: (01527) 579744 Fax: (01527) 579744

Advance Display Solutions Ltd, 10 Mount Avenue, Bletchley, Milton Keynes, MK1 1LS Tel: (01908) 641008 Fax: (01908) 640579 E-mail: info@advancedisplay.co.uk

Aluminium & Plastics Ltd, 29a Marlborough Road, Newport, Gwent, NP19 0PZ Tel: (01633) 259188 Fax: (01633) 212217

Anglo Fabrications Ltd, Saxon Way, Melbourn, Royston, Hertfordshire, SG8 6DN Tel: (01763) 260872 Fax: (01763) 262615 E-mail: sales@anglofabrication.com

Antone Displays Ltd, Wanstead Road, Leicester, LE3 1TR Tel: 0116-232 4700 Fax: 0116-287 8012 E-mail: lucy.orr@antone.co.uk

Apt Art, PO Box 250, Kidlington, Oxfordshire, OX5 2WA Tel: (01865) 372981 E-mail: sales@aptart.co.uk

Argo Plastics Ltd, Unit 6B, Park Street Industrial Estate, Kidderminster, Worcestershire, DY11 6TN Tel: (01562) 823531 Fax: (01562) 825417

Arrow Screen Print Ltd, 3 Fletcher Way, Weston Road, Norwich, NR3 3ST Tel: (01603) 485942 Fax: (01603) 485385 E-mail: sales@arrowscreenprint.co.uk

Atelier Screen Print Ltd, 130 Pershore Street, Birmingham, B5 6ND Tel: 0121-622 6301 Fax: 0121-666 6487 E-mail: atelier.screenprint@virgin.net

Atlas Products, Unit F1 Ash Grove Industrial Park, Heath Place, Bognor Regis, West Sussex, PO22 9SL Tel: (01243) 830324 Fax: (01243) 868404

Augustus Martin Ltd, 8-20 St. Andrews Way, London, E3 3PB Tel: (020) 7537 4200 Fax: (020) 7537 2184 E-mail: sales@amartin.co.uk

Axiom Displays Ltd, Mersey Road North, Failsworth, Manchester, M35 9LT Tel: 0161-681 1371 Fax: 0161-683 4641 E-mail: info@axiom-displays.co.uk

Balcon Plastics, Unit 6a Challenger Way, Peterborough, PE1 5EX Tel: (01733) 347012 Fax: (01733) 558232 E-mail: wayne.hutton@balconplastics.co.uk

Bell Display Ltd, Fernie Road, Market Harborough, Leicestershire, LE16 7PH Tel: (01858) 432652 Fax: (01858) 431621

Bezier P O P, Church Road, Wick, Bristol, BS30 5RF Tel: 0117-937 3989 Fax: 0117-937 2662 E-mail: bdb@bezier.co.uk

Bray Display Ltd, 23 Woodside Industrial Park, Works Road, Letchworth Garden City, Hertfordshire, SG6 1LA Tel: (01462) 482323 Fax: (01462) 482324 E-mail: jim@braydisplay.co.uk

Brochure Holders International Ltd, Victor Unit, Earls Colne Business Park, Earls Colne, Colchester, CO6 2NS Tel: (01787) 220700 Fax: (01787) 220701 E-mail: sales@brochureholders.co.uk

C B Screenprinting & Display, 87 Foxholes Road, Hyde, Cheshire, SK14 5AP Tel: 0161-367 8072 Fax: 0161-367 8764

C P I UK Ltd, 107 Boston Road, Gorse Hill, Leicester, LE4 1AW Tel: 0116-234 0600 Fax: 0116-235 2592 E-mail: uk.info@cpiglobal.com

Caranco Ltd, Caranco House, Wilford Road, Nottingham, NG2 1EB Tel: 0115-986 2272 Fax: 0115-986 3705 E-mail: sales@caranco.co.uk

Carlon Plastics Leicester Ltd, 128 Fairfax Road, Leicester, LE4 9EL Tel: 0116-276 9562 Fax: 0116-276 1267 E-mail: chris@carlonplastics.co.uk

Centre Point Display Ltd, 91 Parker Drive, Leicester, LE4 0JP Tel: 0116-234 0077 E-mail: center.point.display@orbworld.net

Chaggar Engineering, Murdock Road, Manton Industrial Estate, Bedford, MK41 7PE Tel: (01234) 360557 Fax: (0871) 2422493 E-mail: premchaggar@hotmail.com

Coltran Products Ltd, 17-31 Church Street, Mexborough, South Yorkshire, S64 0EW Tel: (01709) 584031 Fax: (01709) 584431 E-mail: sales@coltran.com

Coutts Retail Communications Ltd, Golden House, Great Pulteney Street, London, W1F 9NN Tel: (020) 7534 8800 Fax: (020) 7534 8805

Crumpsall Plastics & Engineering Ltd, Pike Fold Works, Frenchbarn Lane, Blackley, Manchester, M9 6PB Tel: 0161-795 5000 Fax: 0161-721 4684

Dayman Display Ltd, Sidney House, 262 Aylestone Lane, Wigston, Leicestershire, LE18 1BD Tel: 0116-288 3338 E-mail: sales@daymandisplay.fsnet.co.uk

Dial Marketing Ltd, 68 Dial Hill Road, Clevedon, Avon, BS21 7EW Tel: (01275) 875876 Fax: (01275) 340899 E-mail: dialmarketing@btconnect.com

Display Array Ltd, Unit 4 Britannia Industrial Estate, Cherry Holt Road, Bourne, Lincolnshire, PE10 9LA Tel: (01778) 423400 Fax: (01778) 423444 E-mail: display2u@aol.com

Display System Fabrications Ltd, Dunsteads Farm, Trueloves Lane, Ingatestone, Essex, CM4 0NJ Tel: (01277) 352700 Fax: (01277) 352766 E-mail: dsfdisplay@aol.com

Display-Corr, Unit 3 4 & 6 Elms Yard, Stevenage Road, Little Wymondley, Hitchin, Hertfordshire, SG4 7HY Tel: (01438) 747498 Fax: (01438) 747461 E-mail: sales@displaycor.co.uk

Duram Ltd, Duram House, Cemetery Road, Bradford, West Yorkshire, BD8 9RZ Tel: (01274) 542603 Fax: (01274) 548526 E-mail: sales@duram.co.uk

Durleigh Display Systems, 6 Symons Way, Bridgwater, Somerset, TA6 4DR Tel: (01278) 447447 Fax: (01278) 456376

▶ Elygra Ltd, 6 The Quad, Mercury Court, Chester, CH1 4QP Tel: (01244) 399900 Fax: (01244) 399904 E-mail: mail@elygra.co.uk

Exhibition Services Ltd, 6 271 Merton Road, London, SW18 5JS Tel: (020) 8874 1787 Fax: (020) 8874 1587 E-mail: info@exhibitionservices.com

Eyeline Visual Merchandising Ltd, Amsterdam Road, Hull, HU7 0XF Tel: (01482) 824191 Fax: (01482) 824193 E-mail: enquiries@eyeline.co.uk

Format Screen Printers, Prospect Farm, Thirsk Road, Easingwold, York, YO61 3HL Tel: (01347) 824248 Fax: (01423) 860287 E-mail: studio@screenprint.fsbusiness.co.uk

Futurama Ltd, Island Farm House, Island Farm Road, West Molesey, Surrey, KT8 2TR Tel: (020) 8941 1999 Fax: (020) 8783 1687 E-mail: postbox@futurama.ltd.uk

G P Plastics Ltd, 156 Bordesley Middleway, Camp Hill, Birmingham, B11 1BN Tel: 0121-773 1777 Fax: 0121-772 6856 E-mail: admin@gpplastics.co.uk

G W D Ltd, 12-13 Capital Place, Harlow, Essex, CM19 5AS Tel: (01279) 416093 Fax: (01279) 401104 E-mail: sales@gwd.ltd.uk

Global Vacuum Forming Ltd, Vedonis Works, Leicester Road, Lutterworth, Leicestershire, LE17 4HD Tel: (01455) 556891 Fax: (01455) 556099 E-mail: sales@gvf.co.uk

Gold Bros Ltd, Arches Abc, 408 Ellingfort Road, London, E8 3PA Tel: (020) 8985 7926 Fax: (020) 9898 5729 E-mail: info@goldbros.co.uk

Graphic Forming Ltd, 31a Clerkenwell Green, London, EC1R 0DU Tel: (020) 7251 4041 Fax: (020) 7253 8338 E-mail: sleggatt@btconnect.com

Graphic Impression, C3 Enterprise Point, Melbourne Street, Brighton, BN2 3LH Tel: (01273) 571645 Fax: (01273) 571645 E-mail: amprints@hotmail.com

H L, H L House, Riverside Business Park, Dockfield Road, Shipley, West Yorkshire, BD17 7AD Tel: (01274) 531709 Fax: (01274) 594578 E-mail: jackie.perry@hl-rim.co.uk

▶ H M D Group plc, Olympia House, 4 Garnet Close, Watford, WD24 7JY Tel: (01923) 237012 Fax: (01923) 817421 E-mail: sales@hmdgroup.com

Hancock Corfield & Waller Ltd, 33 High Street, Ewell, Epsom, Surrey, KT17 1SA Tel: (020) 8394 2785 Fax: (020) 8393 7058 E-mail: hcwltd@compuserve.com

Invicta Toys & Games Ltd, PO Box 9, Leicester, LE2 4LB Tel: 0116-272 0555 Fax: 0116-272 0626 E-mail: sales@invictagroup.co.uk

J A M Y Ltd, Unit 17 Roman Way Small Business Park, London Road, Godmanchester, Huntingdon, Cambridgeshire, PE29 2LN Tel: (01480) 456391 Fax: (01480) 414959 E-mail: sales@jamy.co.uk

POINT OF SALE (POS)/PURCHASE/ MARKETING DISPLAYS – *continued*

▶ J D Metalfabs Ltd, 30 Wenlock Way, Leicester, LE4 9HU Tel: 0116-299 8885 Fax: 0116-299 9040 E-mail: sales@jd-m.co.uk

K2 Associates Ltd, 6 Haselmere Industrial Estate, Pig Lane, Bishop's Stortford, Hertfordshire, CM23 3HG Tel: (01279) 508305 Fax: (01279) 755530 E-mail: ken.day@k2a.co.uk

Kesslers International Ltd, 11 Rick Roberts Way, London, E15 2NF Tel: (020) 8522 3000 Fax: (020) 8522 3129 E-mail: kesslers@kesslers.com

Keyline Associates Ltd, High Meres Road, Leicester, LE4 9LZ Tel: 0116-276 1371 Fax: 0116-274 1570 E-mail: display@keline.co.uk

Kingsway Press Ltd, Seventh Avenue, Team Valley Trading Estate, Gateshead, Tyne & Wear, NE11 0SL Tel: 0191-491 0455 Fax: 0191-491 0454 E-mail: sales@kingswaypress.co.uk

Kirk John Design, 18 Hayhill, Barrow upon Soar, Loughborough, Leicestershire, LE12 8LD Tel: (01509) 817100 Fax: (01509) 817101 E-mail: accounts@johnkirkdesign.co.uk

Klemetric Displays Ltd, Old Airfield Industrial Estate, Warboys Airfield, Warboys, Huntingdon, Cambridgeshire, PE28 2SH Tel: (01487) 824015 Fax: (01487) 823746 E-mail: sales@klemetricdisplays.co.uk

KMD Investors Ltd, 140 Queens Road, Leicester, LE2 3FX Tel: 0116-270 9221 Fax: 0116-270 2334 E-mail: steve@kmd-company.co.uk

L M D Associates, Leicester Road, Earl Shilton, Leicester, LE9 7TJ Tel: (01455) 840000 Fax: (01455) 840266 E-mail: sales@lmdassociates.co.uk

Leco Accessories Ltd, London Road, Brandon, Suffolk, IP27 0NG Tel: (01842) 810456 Fax: (01842) 815151

Lock Studios Ltd, 32 Wates Way, Mitcham, Surrey, CR4 4HR Tel: (020) 8648 2381 Fax: (020) 8646 0542

M Latchford, 10 Alstone Lane, Cheltenham, Gloucestershire, GL51 8EG Tel: (01242) 584588 Fax: (01242) 529251 E-mail: sales@marklatchford-screenprint.co.uk

Masson Seeley & Co. Ltd, Rouses Lane, Downham Market, Norfolk, PE38 9AN Tel: (01366) 388000 Fax: (01366) 385222 E-mail: sales@masson-seeley.co.uk

Middlehurst Ltd, 103 Boyn Valley Road, Maidenhead, Berkshire, SL6 4EA Tel: (01628) 628044 Fax: (01628) 773143 E-mail: office@middlehurstlimited.com

Midwest Displays, 22 Oxford Street, Birmingham, B5 5NR Tel: 0121-643 1746 Fax: 0121-616 1014

Millers Retail Design Ltd, Granby House, Greenwood Street, Salford, M6 6PD Tel: 0161-743 1026 Fax: 0161-743 1598

Moorside Marketing, 16 Moorside Drive, Drighlington, Bradford, West Yorkshire, BD11 1HD Tel: 0113-285 3102 Fax: 0113-285 3102

Morris Metal Products Ltd, Unit N6 Troon Way Business Centre, Humberstone Lane, Leicester, LE4 9HA Tel: 0116-246 1787 Fax: 0116-246 0196 E-mail: morrismetals@yahoo.co.uk

Ndi Momentum Ltd, Stanley Court, Stanley Green Business Park, Wilmslow, Cheshire, SK9 3RL Tel: 0161-486 7878 Fax: 0161-486 7999 E-mail: info@momentum-uk.com

News Vendors Equipment, Castle Trading Estate, Portchester, Fareham, Hampshire, PO16 9SF Tel: (023) 9222 1222 Fax: (023) 9222 1234

▶ Opus Fabrication, Unit 3, Phoenix Works, Windsor Road, Enfield, Redditch, Worcestershire, B97 6DJ Tel: (01527) 68533 Fax: (01527) 68534 E-mail: opus-fab@btconnect.com

P 15 Plastics Ltd, 161 Waterside Road, Hamilton, Leicester, LE5 1TL Tel: 0116-276 1495 Fax: 0116-246 0489 E-mail: info@p15plastics.co.uk

Park Wire Display Ltd, 63a Hawks Road, Kingston upon Thames, Surrey, KT1 3EF Tel: (020) 8546 8323

Pentech Moulding Co. Ltd, Pump Lane Industrial Estate, Silverdale Road, Hayes, Middlesex, UB3 3BN Tel: (020) 8569 3439 Fax: (020) 8569 1219 E-mail: rapidpartner@gmail.com

Point Of Purchase Display, Finchley Avenue, Mildenhall, Bury St. Edmunds, Suffolk, IP28 7BG Tel: (01638) 515708 Fax: (01638) 712836

Posit Design, The Granary, Station Road, Sandford, Winscombe, Avon, BS25 5RA Tel: (01934) 823931 Fax: (01934) 823958

Powell Marketing Ltd, P M House Cromer Industrial Estate, Hilton Fold Lane, Middleton, Manchester, M24 2LE Tel: 0161-653 7770 Fax: 0161-655 3795 E-mail: enquiries@powellmarketing.co.uk

Priestleys of Gloucester Ltd, Unit 41 Morlandlands Trading Estate, Bristol Road, Gloucester, GL1 5RZ Tel: (01452) 522281 Fax: (01452) 300702 E-mail: sales@preistgloucs.com

Ripple Group Ltd, Greenacres Road, Oldham, OL4 2AB Tel: 0161-624 8201 Fax: 0161-624 4205 E-mail: info@ripple.co.uk

Roycott Ltd, Royston Road, Byfleet, West Byfleet, Surrey, KT14 7NY Tel: (01932) 343515 Fax: (01932) 351285 E-mail: info@charlesausten.com

S D I Displays Ltd, Ratcliffe Road, Sileby, Loughborough, Leicestershire, LE12 7PZ Tel: (01509) 813166 Fax: (01509) 816369

S P Group, 9 Hedera Road, Redditch, Worcestershire, B98 9EY Tel: (01527) 508014 Fax: (01527) 508015 E-mail: enquiries@spgroup.co.uk

St. Martin's Marketing, 162 Langton Way, London, SE3 7JR Tel: (020) 8858 0577 Fax: (020) 8858 3991

Sanders & Co. (UK) Ltd, 181 Wellingborough Road, Northampton, NN1 4DX Tel: (01604) 630195 Fax: (01604) 633972 E-mail: sandersltd@aol.com

Sanroy Equipment Ltd, 1 Commerce Way, Highbridge, Somerset, TA9 4AG Tel: (01278) 780191 Fax: (01278) 792102 E-mail: mikesanroy@netscapeonline.co.uk

Screenprint Productions Ltd, The Print Mill, Rosebery Street, Elland, West Yorkshire, HX5 0HT Tel: (01422) 371751 Fax: (01422) 371702 E-mail: screenprint@demon.co.uk

Scrutton Engineering Ltd, Duck Lees Lane Industrial Estate, 73 East Duck Lees Lane, Enfield, Middlesex, EN3 7SR Tel: (020) 8443 4010 Fax: (020) 8609 0050 E-mail: info@selfab.com

Seddon Design Ltd, Gelscoe Farm, Diseworth, Derby, DE74 2QQ Tel: (01530) 223777 Fax: (01530) 223666 E-mail: info@seddon-design.co.uk

Serigraphia Digital Ltd, Stonebridge Trading Estate, Sibree Road, Coventry, CV3 4FD Tel: (024) 7663 9425 Fax: (024) 7651 1582 E-mail: sales@serigraphia.co.uk

Show Card, Fontana House, Works Road, Letchworth Garden City, Hertfordshire, SG6 1LD Tel: (01462) 677148 Fax: (01462) 480392 E-mail: sales@showcard.com

Signwise Sign Services Ltd, Unit 7 Bodolph Bridge Trading, Estate Oundle Road, Peterborough, PE2 9QP Tel: (01733) 558554 Fax: (01733) 563384 E-mail: sign.wise@btclick.com

Sloane Group (Holdings) Ltd, 2-20 Booth Drive, Park Farm Estate, Wellingborough, Northamptonshire, NN8 6GR Tel: (01933) 401555 Fax: (01933) 400507 E-mail: info@sloanegroup.co.uk

Spafield Displays Ltd, 404 Bretton Park Way, Dewsbury, West Yorkshire, WF12 9BS Tel: (01924) 452386 Fax: (01924) 465713 E-mail: hazel@sparfield.com

SPG Ltd, Little End Road, Eaton Socon, St. Neots, Cambridgeshire, PE19 8JH Tel: (01480) 403099 Fax: (01480) 406638 E-mail: sales@spgltd.co.uk

Stephenson Plastics, The Workshop Pickards Farm, Sandy Lane, Guildford, Surrey, GU3 1HJ Tel: (01483) 565277 Fax: (01483) 505047 E-mail: stephensonplastics@talk21.com

Stoke On Trent Workshops For The Blind, 211 City Road, Stoke-on-Trent, ST4 2PN Tel: (01782) 233900 Fax: (01782) 234900 E-mail: sales@stokeworkshops.co.uk

Stott O'Connell, 1 Nesfield Street, Bradford, West Yorkshire, BD1 3ET Tel: (01274) 722549 Fax: (01274) 724524

Studio 2, 101 Lockhurst Lane, Coventry, CV6 5SF Tel: (024) 7663 8144 Fax: (024) 7666 1457 E-mail: sales@studio2exhibitions.co.uk

Superframe Ltd, The Old Electricity Works, Campfield Road, St. Albans, Hertfordshire, AL1 5HJ Tel: (01727) 865555 Fax: (01727) 865566 E-mail: sales@sf2.co.uk

Supertube, Darby House, Darby Way, Narborough, Leicester, LE19 2GP Tel: 0116-286 6611 Fax: 0116-275 0216

T K Graphics Screen Printing, 12 Beauchamp Industrial Park, Watling Street, Wilnecote, Tamworth, Staffordshire, B77 5BZ Tel: (01827) 262449 Fax: (01827) 285458 E-mail: tomtkgraphics@aol.com

Thermograve Ltd, 171 Scudamore Road, Leicester, LE3 1UQ Tel: 0116-291 9000 Fax: 0116-291 9001 E-mail: info@thermograve.co.uk

UK Point Of Sale Group Ltd, Emery Court, The Embankment Business Park, Heaton Mersey, Stockport, Cheshire, SK4 3GL Tel: 0161-431 4400 Fax: 0161-431 4411 E-mail: info@ukpos.com

V K F Renzel, 20e Harris Business Park, Hanbury Road, Stoke Prior, Bromsgrove, Worcestershire, B60 4BD Tel: (01527) 878311 Fax: (01527) 878411 E-mail: sales@vkf-renzel.co.uk

W Thompson & Son Ltd, 2 Nobel Road, London, N18 3BH Tel: (020) 8807 7576 Fax: (020) 8807 9517 E-mail: wthompsons@lineone.net

▶ Walkers Manchester, Crabtree Lane, Manchester, M11 4GU Tel: 0161-223 7814 Fax: 0161-231 7212 E-mail: info@walkersmcr.com

Ward Lester Display Co. Ltd, 187 Angel Place, Fore Street, London, N18 2UD Tel: (020) 8803 2425 Fax: (020) 8807 7986 E-mail: sfarthing@wardlester.co.uk

P.J. Wilkes Plastics Ltd, Unit 12A Izons Industrial Estate, Oldbury Road, West Bromwich, West Midlands, B70 9BS Tel: 0121-525 4224 Fax: 0121-525 2242 E-mail: pjw@pjwsigns.freeserve.co.uk

T.C. Wilson Ltd, Unit 3-4, Kelsey Cl, Attleborough Fields Ind Estate, Nuneaton, Warwickshire, CV11 6RS Tel: (024) 7632 9914 Fax: (024) 7634 2486

Wrights Plastics Ltd, Brandon Way, West Bromwich, West Midlands, B70 8JH Tel: 0121-580 3080 Fax: 0121-580 3081 E-mail: sales@wrightsplastics.co.uk

Wyndham Plastics Ltd, Ogmore Terrace, Bridgend, Mid Glamorgan, CF31 1SU Tel: (01656) 652869 Fax: (01656) 669915 E-mail: steve@wyndham-plastics.co.uk

Xavier Press, Unit D6 Barwell Business Park, Leatherhead Road, Chessington, Surrey, KT9 2NY Tel: (020) 8391 4707 Fax: (020) 8397 5202 E-mail: xavierpress@talk21.com

Y C Plastics Ltd, Unit 2, Litchard Industrial Estate, Bridgend, Mid Glamorgan, CF31 2AL Tel: (01656) 647774 Fax: (01656) 647323 E-mail: sales@ycplastics.co.uk

POINTERS/INDICATORS/HAND, DIAL/GAUGE/INSTRUMENT/ METER

C & M Components, 47 East End, Long Clawson, Melton Mowbray, Leics, LE14 4NG Tel: (01664) 822476 Fax: (01664) 822645 E-mail: chris@cmcomponents.com

POLARIMETERS

Index Instruments Ltd, Bury Road Industrial Estate, Ramsey, Huntingdon, Cambridgeshire, PE26 1NF Tel: (01487) 814313 Fax: (01487) 812789 E-mail: sales@indexinstruments.com

Optical Activity Ltd, Industrial Estate, Bury Road, Ramsey, Huntingdon, Cambridgeshire, PE26 1NF Tel: (01487) 813913 Fax: (01487) 812789 E-mail: sales@opticalactivity.com

POLARISERS

Specac Ltd, River House, 97 Cray Avenue, Orpington, Kent, BR5 4HE Tel: (01689) 873134 Fax: (01689) 878527 E-mail: sales@specac.co.uk

POLARISING OR NON POLARISING OPTICAL FILTERS

E M C Plastics UK Ltd, Wychwood Business Centre, Shipton-Under-Wychwobusiness, Chipping Norton, Oxfordshire, OX7 6XU Tel: (01993) 832000 Fax: (01993) 831444 E-mail: sales@emc-uk.com

Image Optics Components, Harvey Road, Basildon, Essex, SS13 1ES Tel: (01268) 728477 Fax: (01268) 590445 E-mail: sales@image-optics.fsnet.co.uk

Optical Filters Ltd, The Business Centre, 14 Bertie Road, Thame, Oxfordshire, OX9 3XA Tel: (01844) 260377 Fax: (01844) 260355 E-mail: information@opticalfilters.co.uk

POLICE EQUIPMENT

M C Products, Unit 1-2 Yardley Centre, Yardley Road, Knowsley Industrial Park, Liverpool, L33 7SS Tel: 0151-548 0144 Fax: 0151-549 2283 E-mail: sales@mcproducts.co.uk

Titheringtons Ltd, 75 Strand Road, Bootle, Merseyside, L20 4BB Tel: 0151-922 4422 Fax: 0151-933 0502 E-mail: sales@sharmaplc.com

POLICE SOFTWARE

Helmdart Ltd, 10a Robin Hood Road, Woking, Surrey, GU21 8SP Tel: (01483) 760338 Fax: (01483) 729158 E-mail: helmdart@btconnect.com

POLISH, MOTOR CAR

Nielson Chemicals Ltd, Rawdon Road, Moira, Swadlincote, Derbyshire, DE12 6DA Tel: (01283) 222277 Fax: (01283) 225731 E-mail: info@nielsenchemicals.com

▶ SmartDent Paintless Dent Removal Training Ltd, Unit 5, Ashwyn Business Centre, Marchants Way, Sheddingdean Industrial Estate, Burgess Hill, West Sussex, RH15 8QY Tel: (01444) 257342 Fax: (01444) 257673 E-mail: colm@smartwise.com

Turtle Wax Ltd, East Gillibrands, Skelmersdale, Lancashire, WN8 9TX Tel: (01695) 722161 Fax: (01695) 716621 E-mail: enquiries@turtlewax.com

POLISHING CLOTHS

D W Begal & Son, Vulcan Works, Malta Street, Manchester, M4 7AP Tel: 0161-273 3296 Fax: 0161-273 3293

Esk Hygeine Supplies Ltd, Saffron Way, Leicester, LE2 6UP Tel: 0116-283 9362 E-mail: sales@eskgroup.co.uk

▶ P C Textiles, 1 Glasgow Road, Denny, Stirlingshire, FK6 5DN Tel: (01324) 826993 Fax: (01324) 826442

Salvatex Holdings Ltd, 1 St. Marks Road, St. James Industrial Estate, Corby, Northamptonshire, NN18 8AN Tel: (01536) 400002 Fax: (01536) 400169

Starchem Ltd, Strawberry Lane, Willenhall, West Midlands, WV13 3RS Tel: (01902) 838880 Fax: (01902) 838881 E-mail: sales@starchem.co.uk

Walter Smith Nelson Ltd, Wenning Street, Nelson, Lancashire, BB9 0LE Tel: (01282) 698142 Fax: (01282) 619109 E-mail: wsmith@provider.co.uk

POLISHING/BUFFING/GRINDING COMPOSITIONS/COMPOUNDS/ MATERIALS

Cal Chem Ltd, Unit A3 Hortonwood 10, Telford, Shropshire, TF1 7ES Tel: (01952) 606220 Fax: (01952) 676278

Central Polishing Supplies, Unit 33 Innage Park, Abeles Way, Holly Lane Industrial Estate, Atherstone, Warwickshire, CV9 2QX Tel: (01827) 714839 Fax: (01827) 714839 E-mail: c.polishing@talk21.com

Finishing Components Co., 1-8 Silverdale, Meadow Road, Worthing, West Sussex, BN11 2RZ Tel: (01903) 205155 Fax: (01903) 205166 E-mail: finishingcomponents@supanet.com

Lea Manufacturing Co., Tongue Lane, Buxton, Derbyshire, SK17 7LN Tel: (01298) 25335 Fax: (01298) 79945 E-mail: sales@lea.co.uk

Merridale Polishing & Plating Co. Ltd, Friar Street, Wednesbury, West Midlands, WS10 0RE Tel: 0121-556 3636 Fax: 0121-556 8886

Metal Finishing Supplies Ltd, 99a North Street, Cannock, Staffordshire, WS11 0AZ Tel: (01543) 505771 Fax: (01543) 466011

POLISHING/BUFFING/GRINDING MACHINE AND EQUIPMENT MANUFRS

Morrisflex Ltd, London Road, Braunston, Daventry, Northamptonshire, NN11 7HX Tel: (01788) 891777 Fax: (01788) 891629 E-mail: sales@morrisflex.co.uk

RJH Morrisflex Holdings Ltd, Artillery Street, Heckmondwike, West Yorkshire, WF16 0NR Tel: (01924) 402490 Fax: (01924) 404635 E-mail: sales@rjheng.co.uk

Shooshyne, 481 Meanwood Road, Leeds, LS6 2BH Tel: 0113-275 2283 Fax: 0113-275 2362 E-mail: shoeshine@compuserve.com

POLISHING/BUFFING/GRINDING MOPS

Merridale Polishing & Plating Co. Ltd, Friar Street, Wednesbury, West Midlands, WS10 0RE Tel: 0121-556 3636 Fax: 0121-556 8886

POLISHING/BUFFING/GRINDING SERVICES

A & K Metal Polishing, Bourne Mills, London Road, Brimscombe, Stroud, Gloucestershire, GL5 2TA Tel: (01453) 883747 Fax: (01453) 883747

Angus Jarvis, 68 Barkby Road, Leicester, LE4 9LF Tel: 0116-246 0258 Fax: 0116-246 0258

C & C Engineering, Unit 3C, Cliffe St, Nelson, Lancashire, BB9 7QR Tel: (01282) 695912 Fax: (01282) 615764 E-mail: sales@candcengineering.co.uk

Clear Polishing, Unit 7 Brandon Way Industrial Estate, Brandon Way, West Bromwich, West Midlands, B70 9PW Tel: 0121-580 4744 Fax: 0121-580 4744

Derwood & Abel Ltd, Imperial Trading Estate, Lambs La North, Rainham, Essex, RM13 9XL Tel: (01708) 554611 Fax: (01708) 559726

Elite Metal Polishing Services, 81 Bunting Road, Northampton, NN2 6EE Tel: (01604) 712191 Fax: (01604) 712191

High Class Metal Polishing, Unit 1-2 Lower Mills, Bridgend, Stonehouse, Gloucestershire, GL10 2BB Tel: (01453) 825464 Fax: (01453) 825464

J D Wyatt, Telford Way, Thetford, Norfolk, IP24 1HU Tel: (01842) 766770 Fax: (01842) 766770

M C M, 26 Donisthorpe Street, Leeds, LS10 1PL Tel: 0113-245 1020 Fax: 0113-243 1971 E-mail: info@mcmpos.co.uk

MJK Specialist Mould Polishers & Polishing Consultants, Pickering, North Yorkshire, Tel: (07946) 714777 E-mail: mjk1@sky.com

S J Polishing, 39 Greville Street, London, EC1N 8PJ Tel: (020) 7404 0382

Ulster Electro Finishes Ltd, 78 Ballyrashane Road, Coleraine, County Londonderry, BT52 2LJ Tel: (028) 7034 3022 Fax: (028) 7035 5985 E-mail: uefltd@aol.com

POLLUTION CONTROL CATALYSTS

Molecular Products Group plc, Mill End, Thaxted, Dunmow, Essex, CM6 2LT Tel: (01371) 830676 Fax: (01371) 830998 E-mail: sales@molprod.com

POLLUTION CONTROL CHEMICALS

H M E Technology, Priory House, Saxon Park, Hanbury Road, Stoke Prior, Bromsgrove, Worcestershire, B60 4AD Tel: (01527) 839000 Fax: (01527) 839001 E-mail: contactus@hme-tech.com
Molecular Products Group plc, Mill End, Thaxted, Dunmow, Essex, CM6 2LT Tel: (01371) 830676 Fax: (01371) 830998 E-mail: sales@molprod.com

POLLUTION CONTROL CONSULTANTS

Alderley plc, Alderley House, Arnolds Field Estate, Wotton-under-Edge, Gloucestershire, GL12 8JD Tel: (01454) 299888 Fax: (01454) 299720 E-mail: marketing@alderley.com
Bellpumps & Pollution Control, La Petite Fosse, St. Ouen, Jersey, JE3 2GN Tel: (01534) 485555 Fax: (01534) 482245 E-mail: enquiries@bellpumps.com
C P A Laboratories Ltd, 318 Worple Road, London, SW20 8QU Tel: (020) 8946 8621 Fax: (020) 8947 1206 E-mail: admincpa@eurofins.com
E P C, PO Box 2229, London, W14 0JA Tel: (020) 7602 2979 Fax: (020) 7371 6431 E-mail: aboi@bmec.org.uk
D.V. Howells Ltd, The MPSC, Milford Haven, Dyfed, SA73 3AQ Tel: (01646) 697041 Fax: (01646) 696345 E-mail: info@dvhowells.com
Midland Environmental Laboratories, Unit D17 Forge Lane, Minworth Industrial Park, Minworth, Sutton Coldfield, West Midlands, B76 1AH Tel: 0121-351 6469 Fax: 0121-351 6469

POLLUTION CONTROL SERVICES

Arundelle Industrial Services Ltd, 250 High Street, Cranleigh, Surrey, GU6 8RL Tel: (01483) 277801 Fax: (01483) 277802 E-mail: sales@arundelle.co.uk
Briggs Environmental Services Ltd, Leading Light Building, 142 Sinclair Road, Aberdeen, AB11 9PR Tel: (01224) 898666 Fax: (01224) 896950 E-mail: marketing@briggsmarine.com
Falmouth Towage Co. Ltd, Falmouth Docks, Falmouth, Cornwall, TR11 4NR Tel: (01326) 319451 Fax: (01326) 319451 E-mail: falmouth@ap-group.co.uk
Fercell Engineering Ltd, Unit 1, Old Mill Lane, Aylesford, Kent, ME20 7DT Tel: (01622) 791414 Fax: (01622) 791515 E-mail: info@fercell.com
D.V. Howells Ltd, The MPSC, Milford Haven, Dyfed, SA73 3AQ Tel: (01646) 697041 Fax: (01646) 696345 E-mail: info@dvhowells.com
Liverpool Water Witch Marine Engineering Co. Ltd, 4 Lightbody Street, Liverpool, L5 9UZ Tel: 0151-207 4874 Fax: 0151-298 1366 E-mail: sales@waterwitch.demon.co.uk
Osprey Corporation, Units 84-85, John Wilson Business Park, Chestfield, Whitstable, Kent, CT5 3QT Tel: (01227) 770979 Fax: (01227) 770949 E-mail: sales@ospreycorporation.com
Redbay Projects Ltd, 15 Dalton Court, Astmoor Industrial Estate, Runcorn, Cheshire, WA7 1PU Tel: (01928) 581782 Fax: (01928) 580619 E-mail: redbayprojects@aol.com

POLLUTION CONTROL SYSTEMS

Environmental Elements (UK) Ltd, Unit 2 Moor Street, Burton-on-Trent, Staffordshire, DE14 3SU Tel: (01283) 740536 Fax: (01283) 563969 E-mail: dcormack@eec1.com
Fosse, 12 Enderby Road Industrial Estate, Whetstone, Leicester, LE8 6HZ Tel: 0116-286 7844 Fax: (0870) 2247842 E-mail: sales@fosse.co.uk
Liverpool Water Witch Marine Engineering Co. Ltd, 4 Lightbody Street, Liverpool, L5 9UZ Tel: 0151-207 4874 Fax: 0151-298 1366 E-mail: sales@waterwitch.demon.co.uk
Megator Ltd, Hendon Street, Sunderland, SR1 2NQ Tel: 0191-567 5488 Fax: 0191-567 8512 E-mail: info@megator.co.uk
Therm Tech Ltd, Unit 4a Kayley Industrial Estate, Richmond Street, Ashton-under-Lyne, Lancashire, OL7 0AU Tel: 0161 339 3049 Fax: 0161 343 3305 E-mail: thermtech@msn.com

POLLUTION CONTROL WORK BOATS

Ro-Clean Desmi Ltd, Unit 24 Shamrock Quay, William Street, Southampton, SO14 5QL Tel: (02380) 829751 Fax: (02380) 339190 E-mail: uk.ro-clean@desmi.com
United Salvage Ltd, 5 Quay Middle, King George Dock,, Hull, HU9 5PR Tel: (01482) 224181 Fax: (01482) 324669 E-mail: svitzersalvage@svitzer.co.uk

POLLUTION CONTROL/ MONITOR SYSTEMS MANUFRS, AIR/ATMOSPHERIC

Codel International Ltd, Station Yard, Station Road, Bakewell, Derbyshire, DE45 1GE Tel: (01629) 814351 Fax: (0870) 0566307 E-mail: sales@codel.co.uk
Emtrol LLC, Davey House, Eaton Ford, St. Neots, Cambridgeshire, PE19 7BA Tel: (01480) 475071 Fax: (01480) 475046 E-mail: technical@emtrolcorp.co.uk
Gresham Engineering, 104 Maybury Road, Woking, Surrey, GU21 5JL Tel: (01483) 765538 Fax: (01483) 765320 E-mail: sales@hacltd.co.uk
Kerton Plastics Ltd, Unit 2 Phoenix Way, Gorseinon, Swansea, SA4 9WF Tel: (01792) 897779 Fax: (01792) 896668 E-mail: enquiries@kerton.co.uk
Pcme, Clearview Building, Edison Road, St. Ives, Cambridgeshire, PE27 3GH Tel: (01480) 468200 Fax: (01480) 463400 E-mail: sales@pcme.co.uk
Radco Services Ltd, Little Limekilns, Middle Lypiatt, Stroud, Gloucestershire, GL6 7LR Tel: (01453) 883746 Fax: (01453) 884211
Signal Group Ltd, Standards House, 12 Doman Road, Camberley, Surrey, GU15 3DF Tel: (01276) 682841 Fax: (01276) 691302 E-mail: instruments@signal-group.com

POLLUTION SERVICES, SPILLAGE, *See Oil Spillage etc*

POLYCARBONATE FILM/SHEET

Plastic Sheet Services, Unit 4, 270 Lakey La, Birmingham, B28 8RA Tel: 0121-777 0322 Fax: 0121-777 8987E-mail: hewston@aol.com
▶ Polyshapes Ltd, Unit 3, Sidings Business Park, Freightliner Road, Hull, HU3 4XA Tel: (01482) 211955 Fax: (01482) 215656 E-mail: sales@polyshapes.co.uk
Sol Systems, Unit 4 Mallorie House, Beaumont Road, Banbury, Oxfordshire, OX16 1RH Tel: (01295) 255536 Fax: (01295) 276492 E-mail: bworsley@btinternet.com
Unipol Plastic Sheeting Supplies, Prospect House, Taylor Business Park, Risley, Warrington, WA3 6HP Tel: (01925) 768001 Fax: (01925) 768008 E-mail: sales@unipoluk.com

POLYCARBONATE INTERIOR AND EXTERIOR LIGHTING FITTINGS

Apex Electrical Distribution Ltd, New York Way, New York Industrial Park, Newcastle upon Tyne, NE27 0QF Tel: 0191-293 0900 Fax: 0191-257 7722
Decorlight, B 68 Pier Avenue, Clacton-on-Sea, Essex, CO15 1NH Tel: (01255) 421818 Fax: (01255) 474147

POLYCARBONATE SHEET (GLAZING) MANUFRS

Lewis & Mason Plastics, Unit 47 Business Development Centre, Stafford Park 4, Telford, Shropshire, TF3 3BA Tel: (01952) 210322 Fax: (01952) 292647 E-mail: info@lewis-mason-plastics.co.uk
P & J Plastics, 7 Lower Cherwell Street, Banbury, Oxfordshire, OX16 5AY Tel: (01295) 269814 Fax: (01295) 275557
Plysolene Ltd, Unit 21 Star Road Trading Estate, Star Road, Partridge Green, Horsham, West Sussex, RH13 8RA Tel: (01403) 713555 Fax: (01403) 713666 E-mail: info@wattsgroup.co.uk
Unipol Plastic Sheeting Supplies, Prospect House, Taylor Business Park, Risley, Warrington, WA3 6HP Tel: (01925) 768001 Fax: (01925) 768008 E-mail: sales@unipoluk.com

POLYCHLOROPRENE (CR) RUBBER PRODUCTS

GUL International Ltd, Callywith Gate Industrial Estate, Bodmin, Cornwall, PL31 2RQ Tel: (01208) 262400 Fax: (01208) 262474 E-mail: gul@gul.com
Sherborne Rubber Co. Ltd, Icknield Square, Ladywood, Birmingham, B16 0AB Tel: 0121-456 1565 Fax: 0121-452 1637 E-mail: sales@sherbourne.co.uk

POLYESTER BUTTONS

Heritage Buttons, 8 Armadale Road, Chichester, West Sussex, PO19 7NR Tel: (01243) 775462 Fax: (01243) 531032 E-mail: info@buttonscompany.co.uk

POLYESTER FABRIC, NET, *See Net Fabrics etc*

POLYESTER FABRICS

Aziz Textiles Ltd, 19-21 Portland St, Aston, Birmingham, B6 5RX Tel: 0121-328 4456 Fax: 0121-328 6941
Broome & Wellington Aviation Ltd, 86 Princess Street, Manchester, M1 6NG Tel: 0161-236 2317 Fax: 0161-228 1326 E-mail: broom@broomwell.com
Kelwood Exports, 70 Blover Road, Lindley, Huddersfield, HD3 3HR Tel: (01484) 653053 Fax: (01484) 658934
Mason's Textiles Ltd, Cricketers Close, Carleton New Road, Skipton, North Yorkshire, BD23 2AZ Tel: (01756) 799333 Fax: (01756) 700182 E-mail: sales@masonsdesign.demon.co.uk

POLYESTER FABRICS, FILAMENT

▶ Philip Whitfield Textiles Ltd, Remoor Mill, Buxton Road, New Mills, High Peak, Derbyshire, SK22 3JT Tel: (01663) 746220 Fax: (01663) 746158 E-mail: paul.butler@philipwhitfield.co.uk

POLYESTER FIBRE CUSHIONS

Recticel Midlands, Unit 3, Azalea Close, Clover Nook Industrial Park, Alfreton, Derbyshire, DE55 4QX Tel: (01773) 520242 Fax: (01773) 520513 E-mail: recticel@midlands.co.uk

POLYESTER FIBRE TERYLENE, *See headings under Polyester*

POLYESTER FILM/SHEET MANUFRS

Hilton Heath Agencies, 67 High Street, Great Missenden, Buckinghamshire, HP16 0AL Tel: (01494) 865120 Fax: (01494) 866152 E-mail: j.hilton@tiscali.co.uk
Jindal Europe, 4 The Street, Wallington, Baldock, Hertfordshire, SG7 6SN Tel: (01763) 288515 Fax: (01763) 288412 E-mail: jindal@dial.pipex.com
Saffron Plastics Ltd, Bakers Court, Paycocke Road, Basildon, Essex, SS14 3EH Tel: (01268) 288874 Fax: (01268) 534592 E-mail: sales@saffronplastics.co.uk

POLYESTER FINISHING SERVICES, WOOD

Bow Finishing, Stansted House, Tilburstow Hill Road, South Godstone, Godstone, Surrey, RH9 8NA Tel: (01342) 892220 Fax: (01342) 892220 E-mail: sales@bowfinishing.co.uk

POLYESTER LASER CUTTING

Laser Cutting Ceramics Ltd, Wide Range Works, Catley Road, Sheffield, S9 5JF Tel: 0114-249 4005 Fax: 0114-242 5194 E-mail: info@lasercutting-ceramics.co.uk

POLYESTER MOULDING COMPOUNDS

Menzolit, Perseverance Works, Halifax Road, Todmorden, Lancashire, OL14 6EG Tel: (01706) 814714 Fax: (01706) 814717 E-mail: sales@menzolit-uk.co.uk

POLYESTER NYLON FABRICS

▶ Philip Whitfield Textiles Ltd, Remoor Mill, Buxton Road, New Mills, High Peak, Derbyshire, SK22 3JT Tel: (01663) 746220 Fax: (01663) 746158 E-mail: paul.butler@philipwhitfield.co.uk

POLYESTER POWDER COATING SERVICES

Birmingham Powder Coatings, Clonmel Road, Birmingham, B30 2BU Tel: 0121-459 4341 Fax: 0121-451 1735 E-mail: sales@b-p-c.co.uk
Circuit Coatings Ltd, Marlow Street, Walsall, WS2 8AQ Tel: (01922) 635589 Fax: (01922) 638444 E-mail: mail@circuit-coating.co.uk
Coatapart Ltd, 58 Arthur Street, Redditch, Worcestershire, B98 8JY Tel: (01527) 528851 Fax: (01527) 517186
Coventry Powder Coating, Unit 5-7 Bilton Industrial Estate, Humber Avenue, Coventry, CV3 1JL Tel: (024) 7645 4694 Fax: (024) 7645 4476 E-mail: info@cpc.co.uk
Ercon Powder Coating Ltd, Unit 16-17, Spring Vale Business Park, Bilston, West Midlands, WV14 0QL Tel: (01902) 491011 Fax: (01902) 492032
Foleshill Metal Finishing Ltd, 13 Bayton Road, Exhall, Coventry, CV7 9EJ Tel: (024) 7636 2960 Fax: (024) 7636 5876 E-mail: queries@foleshill.co.uk
G K Systems, Kilbegs Business Park, Kilbegs Road, Antrim, BT41 4NN Tel: (028) 9446 5360 Fax: (028) 9446 0754 E-mail: sales@gksystems.co.uk
Gwent Powder Coatings Ltd, Unit 37 Springvale Industrial Estate, Cwmbran, Gwent, NP44 5BD Tel: (01633) 860901 Fax: (01633) 872030 E-mail: gpowdercoatings@btconnect.com

POLYESTER POWDER COATINGS

P C S Powders Ltd, Unit 3, Waterloo Industrial Estate, Flanders Road, Hedge End, Southampton, SO30 2QT Tel: (01489) 790400 Fax: (01489) 785295 E-mail: info@pcspowders.co.uk
Thermaset Ltd, Apollo, Lichfield Road Industrial Estate, Tamworth, Staffordshire, B79 7TA Tel: (01827) 55777 Fax: (01827) 53713

POLYESTER RESIN

A P S Ltd, Sea King Road, Lynx Trading Estate, Yeovil, Somerset, BA20 2NZ Tel: (01935) 410710 Fax: (01935) 410888 E-mail: aps@rtv2.co.uk
Llewellyn Ryland Ltd, Haden Street, Birmingham, B12 9DB Tel: 0121-440 2284 Fax: 0121-440 0281 E-mail: sales@llewellyn-ryland.co.uk

POLYESTER SEWING THREAD

American & Efird GB Ltd, Chapelfield, Radcliffe, Manchester, M26 1JF Tel: 0161-766 1333 Fax: 0161-766 9965 E-mail: sales@amefird.co.uk
Donisthorpe, PO Box 137, Leicester, LE4 1BF Tel: 0116-234 7920 Fax: 0116-234 7901 E-mail: sales@amann.com
Somac Threads Manufacturing Ltd, Unit 2-3 Brymau Four Trading Estate, River Lane, Saltney, Chester, CH4 8RF Tel: (01244) 680506 Fax: (01244) 680202 E-mail: sales@somac.co.uk

POLYESTER/COTTON FABRIC IMPORT MERCHANTS OR AGENTS

Indo African Exports Ltd, Failsworth Mill, Ashton Road West, Failsworth, Manchester, M35 0FR Tel: 0161-934 4004 Fax: 0161-683 4280 E-mail: indo@fabric.co.uk

POLYESTER/COTTON FABRICS

Broome & Wellington Aviation Ltd, 86 Princess Street, Manchester, M1 6NG Tel: 0161-236 2317 Fax: 0161-228 1326 E-mail: broom@broomwell.com
Cloverbrook, Peel Mill, Gannow Lane, Burnley, Lancashire, BB12 6JJ Tel: (01282) 712000 Fax: (01282) 457723 E-mail: info@cloverbrook.co.uk
Patchwork Gallery, 17 Mead Close, Knutsford, Cheshire, WA16 0DU Tel: (01565) 632553 E-mail: sales@patchworkgallery.co.uk

POLYETHYLENE (PE) AGRICULTURAL BUILDINGS

National Polytunnels Ltd, 258 Station Road, Bamber Bridge, Preston, PR5 6EA Tel: (01772) 799200 Fax: (01772) 799250 E-mail: sales@nationalalpolytunnels.co.uk

POLYETHYLENE (PE) BAG MAKING MACHINES

Duplas, Diamond Business Park, 7 Thornes Moor Road, Wakefield, West Yorkshire, WF2 8PT Tel: (01924) 298298 Fax: (01924) 377101 E-mail: sales@duplas.co.uk

POLYETHYLENE (PE) BAG/ CARRIER/SACK FILLING MACHINES

Aarison Packaging, Townfoot Industrial Estate, Brampton, Cumbria, CA8 1SW Tel: (0845) 1301864 Fax: (0845) 1301864 E-mail: enq@aarison.co.uk

▶ indicates data change since last edition

POLYETHYLENE (PE) BAG/ CARRIER/SACK FILLING MACHINES

– continued

Brayford Plastics, Horncastle Lane, Dunholme, Lincoln, LN2 3QF Tel: (01522) 530557 Fax: (01522) 730372 E-mail: info@brayfordplastics.com

POLYETHYLENE (PE) BAG/ CARRIER/SACK MANUFRS

A E Taylor & Co. Ltd, 44 Borough Road, Sunderland, SR1 1PW Tel: 0191-567 5078 Fax: 0191-510 2268

A R F Polythene, Unit 5 Building C, Ramsden Road, Rotherwas Industrial Estate, Hereford, HR2 6NP Tel: (01432) 355643 Fax: (01432) 355643

Adams Packaging Ltd, Timberlaine Estate, Quarry Lane, Chichester, West Sussex, PO19 8PP Tel: (01243) 783474 Fax: (01243) 815960 E-mail: adams-adams@cwcom.net

Adept Packaging Co. Ltd, 78-82 Nightingale Grove, Hither Green, London, SE13 6DZ Tel: (020) 8318 7511 Fax: (020) 8852 9120 E-mail: sales@adeptpack.co.uk

Allerton Packaging Service, 7 King Close, Leeds, LS17 7AS Tel: 0113-269 1440 Fax: 0113-294 4330 E-mail: packserve@totalise.co.uk

Allied Packaging Ltd, Brabant House, Portsmouth Road, Thames Ditton, Surrey, KT7 0EY Tel: (020) 8398 8882 Fax: (020) 8398 4485 E-mail: sales@alliedpackaging.co.uk

Alpha Packaging, Gooch, Didcot, Oxfordshire, OX11 7PR Tel: (01235) 511500 Fax: (01235) 510543 E-mail: alpha.packaging@btconnect.com

Amcor Flexibles Ledbury, Lower Road Trading Estate, Ledbury, Herefordshire, HR8 2DJ Tel: (01531) 638638 Fax: (01531) 635716 E-mail: enquiries@rexam.com

Amico Packaging Supplies, 4 Robinson Road, Leicester, LE5 4NS Tel: 0116-276 2786 Fax: 0116-276 9786

Amor Flexibles Europe Ltd, Orleans Close, Four Pools Industrial Estate, Evesham, Worcestershire, WR11 1LA Tel: (01386) 45925 Fax: (01386) 41114

Answerpak Ltd, Unit M, Fircroft Way, Edenbridge, Kent, TN8 6EL Tel: (01732) 869930 Fax: (01732) 869939 E-mail: sales@answerpak.co.uk

Anzeck Plastics (Packaging Division), Battye St, Bradford, West Yorkshire, BD4 8AG Tel: (01274) 669672 Fax: (01274) 663448 E-mail: sales@anzeck.co.uk

Applewade Packaging Ltd, Park House, 15-19 Greenhill CR, Watford, WD18 8PH Tel: (01923) 250202 Fax: (01923) 251101 E-mail: sales@applewade.co.uk

Arrowsacks Packaging, PO Box 234, Dover, Kent, CT15 6GD Tel: (01304) 853604 Fax: (01304) 852540 E-mail: arrowsacks@isleoak.freeserve.co.uk

B P I Consumer V M B, Block C, Blackpole East, Blackpole Road, Worcester, WR3 8ZL Tel: (01905) 755000 Fax: (01905) 456378 E-mail: enquiries@vmb.co.uk

Bailey Packaging Ltd, Unit 26 Garden Estate, Lowtherville Road, Ventnor, Isle of Wight, PO38 1YD Tel: (01983) 855535 Fax: (01983) 853358

Bayard Packaging Ltd, Unit 16 Deptford Trading Estate, Blackhorse Road, London, SE8 5HY Tel: (020) 8692 4444 Fax: (020) 8692 3851 E-mail: sales@bayardpackaging.co.uk

Beck Sack Co., 3 Hermitage Lane, London, SE25 5HH Tel: (0845) 0720750

▶ BPI.Industrial Swansea, Swansea Enterprise Park, Clarion Close, Morriston, Swansea, SA6 8QZ Tel: (01792) 772441 Fax: (01792) 701134 E-mail: salesswansea@bpipoly.com

Brayford Plastics, Horncastle Lane, Dunholme, Lincoln, LN2 3QF Tel: (01522) 530557 Fax: (01522) 730372 E-mail: info@brayfordplastics.com

Bretby Nurseries Ltd, Bretby Lane, Bretby, Burton-on-Trent, Staffordshire, DE15 0QS Tel: (01283) 703355 Fax: (01283) 704035 E-mail: bretby.nurseries@virgin.net

Britton Decoflex Ltd, Skerne Road, Oakesway Industrial Estate, Hartlepool, Cleveland, TS24 0RH Tel: (01429) 272102 Fax: (01429) 860388 E-mail: smrsales@britton-group.com

C & B Co., Wholesale Warehouse, Chappell Drive, Doncaster, South Yorkshire, DN1 2RF Tel: (01302) 361357 Fax: (01302) 361357

C.G.R. Polythene Company Ltd, Unit 72 Powder Mill Lane, Questor Trade Park, Dartford, DA1 1JA Tel: (01322) 292681 Fax: (0845) 6800084 E-mail: gary@cgrpolythene.co.uk

C L P Holding Co. Ltd, Tudor Works, Windmill Lane, Smethwick, West Midlands, B66 3EU Tel: 0121-558 2618 Fax: 0121-558 8825 E-mail: sales@clpzips.co.uk

C L Plastics Ltd, Furnace Road, Oakenshaw, Bradford, West Yorkshire, BD12 7BH Tel: (01274) 603344 Fax: (01274) 691541 E-mail: sales@clplastics.com

Central Polythene Packaging, Unit 60, Abbey Park Street, Leicester, LE4 5AF Tel: 0116-253 0275 Fax: 0116-253 1832

Chiltern Plastics Ltd, Unit 31, Jubilee Trade Centre, Jubilee Road, Letchworth Garden City, Hertfordshire, SG6 1SP Tel: (01462) 676262 Fax: (01462) 481075 E-mail: carrol@chilternplastics.co.uk

Coogan & Watts Ltd, Central Park, Newtownabbey, County Antrim, BT36 4FS Tel: (028) 9084 5800 Fax: (028) 9034 2739 E-mail: info@cooganwatts.co.uk

Copac, 14 Aylesbury Business Centre, Chamberlain Road, Aylesbury, Buckinghamshire, HP19 8DY Tel: (01296) 398844 Fax: (01296) 431153

D U O Plastics Ltd, Vickers Street, Manchester, M40 8PU Tel: 0161-203 5767 Fax: 0161-203 5663 E-mail: duoplastics@btconnect.com

Dale Products Plastics Ltd, Barnsley Road, Hoyland, Barnsley, South Yorkshire, S74 0QW Tel: (01226) 742511 Fax: (01226) 350496 E-mail: dale.products@fsbdial.co.uk

Davis Group, 48 Watersfield Way, Edgware, Middlesex, HA8 6RZ Tel: (020) 8951 4264 Fax: (020) 8951 4342 E-mail: rdavis7054@aol.com

Decomatic, Unit 6, Robins Drive, Bridgwater, Somerset, TA6 4DL Tel: (01278) 444151 Fax: (01278) 422411 E-mail: sales@decomatic.com

▶ Derby Polythene Ltd, Unit 1 Osmaston Park Road, Derby, DE24 8BT Tel: (01332) 331955 Fax: (01332) 361355 E-mail: sales@derbyplastics.co.uk

Derby Polythene Ltd, Unit 1 Osmaston Park Road, Derby, DE24 8BT Tel: (01332) 331955 Fax: (01332) 361355 E-mail: sales@doninggroup.aol.com

Eagle Packaging, Unit 8A Churchfield Business Park, Clensmore Street, Kidderminster, Worcestershire, DY10 2JY Tel: (01562) 862254 Fax: (01562) 862308 E-mail: eaglepackaginguk@aol.com

Express Packaging UK Ltd, Express House, 471 Romford Road, Forest Gate, London, E7 8AB Tel: (020) 8519 9786 Fax: (020) 8519 5880

Ferrari Packaging Ltd, Eastfield Industrial Estate, Penicuik, Midlothian, EH26 8HJ Tel: (01968) 678100 Fax: (01968) 676060 E-mail: jockcwm@aol.com

Fife Plastics, Fordell, Woodend, Cowdenbeath, Fife, KY4 8EY Tel: (01383) 510256 Fax: (01383) 510256

Flexopack Ltd, Mallard Road, Victoria Business Park, Netherfield, Nottingham, NG4 2PE Tel: 0115-940 3939 Fax: 0115-940 3837 E-mail: sales@flexopack.co.uk

Gaffar Packaging Ltd, 65 Cobden Street, Leicester, LE1 2LB Tel: 0116-253 7766 Fax: 0116-229 0290 E-mail: gaffarpackaging@aol.com

Gelpack Excelsior Ltd, Westfields Trading Estate, Hereford, HR4 9NT Tel: (01432) 267391 Fax: (01432) 264809 E-mail: info@gelpack.co.uk

Global Packaging Ltd, 9 Lockwood Way, Black Horse Lane, London, E17 5RB Tel: (020) 8531 3130 Fax: (020) 8503 2319

Glopac, Eddison Road, Hams Hall Distribution Park, Coleshill, Birmingham, B46 1AB Tel: (01675) 431000 Fax: (01675) 431066 E-mail: sales@glopac.co.uk

Goldstar Services Ltd, Unit 1 Spiral Tube Works, Osmaston Park Road, Derby, DE24 8BT Tel: (01332) 363313 Fax: (01332) 361355 E-mail: sales@doningtongroup.co.uk

Goodyer Packaging Ltd, Bunbury Lane, Bunbury, Tarporley, Cheshire, CW6 9QU Tel: (01829) 261052 Fax: (01829) 261129

H & S Polythene Ltd, 36 Redburn Industrial Estate, Woodall Road, Enfield, Middlesex, EN3 4LE Tel: (020) 8050217 Fax: (020) 8050227 E-mail: sales@hspolythene.com

Hado Polythene, Spring Lane, Malvern, Worcestershire, WR14 1AJ Tel: (01684) 574800 Fax: (01684) 892450 E-mail: sales@hadopolythene.co.uk

Halcyon Plastics Ltd, Halcyon House, The Court Yard, Waterloo Farm, Stotfold Road, Arlesey, Bedfordshire, SG15 6XP Tel: (01462) 833000 Fax: (01462) 734414 E-mail: sales@halcyonplastics.co.uk

Hanmere Polythene Ltd, Blackhorse Road, Letchworth Garden City, Hertfordshire, SG6 1HD Tel: (01462) 482222 Fax: (01462) 481096 E-mail: sales@hanmere.co.uk

▶ Harris & Spilsbury Ltd, 131 St Margarets Road, Ward End, Birmingham, B8 2BD Tel: 0121-327 1095 Fax: 0121-326 0818 E-mail: sales@harris-and-spilsbury.co.uk

Harrison Verity Products Ltd, Veritas House, Sett End Road, Shadsworth Business Park, Blackburn, BB1 2PT Tel: (01254) 662979 Fax: (01254) 698580E-mail: sales@hvp.co.uk

Hills Poly Print Ltd, Alma Park Road, Grantham, Lincolnshire, NG31 9SE Tel: (01476) 577132 Fax: (01476) 590368 E-mail: sales@hillspoly-print.com

Imperial Polythene Products Ltd, Unit 3 Lakeside Industrial Estate, Colnbrook, Slough, SL3 0ED Tel: (01753) 686336 Fax: (01753) 682793

Jason Plastics Ltd, Prettywood, Bury New Road, Heap Bridge, Bury, Lancashire, BL9 7HZ Tel: 0161-763 8000 Fax: 0161-763 8052 E-mail: sales@jasonpackaging.co.uk

John C Brow Ltd, Prince Regent Road, Belfast, BT5 6SA Tel: (028) 9079 8171 Fax: (028) 9040 1095 E-mail: sales@browpack.com

John Darvell, 1 Westfield Farm, Henley Road, Medmenham, Marlow, Buckinghamshire, SL7 2TA Tel: (01491) 575286 Fax: (01491) 579617 E-mail: johndarvellpackaging@tiscali.co.uk

Jordan Plastics Ltd, 109 Summerisland Road, Portadown, Craigavon, County Armagh, BT62 1SJ Tel: (028) 3885 3111 Fax: (028) 3885 3112 E-mail: sales@jordanplastics.com

Keenpac Ltd, Centurion Way, Meridian Business Park, Leicester, LE19 1WH Tel: 0116-289 0900 Fax: 0116-289 3757 E-mail: info@keenpac.co.uk

Kingpak Plastic Sheeting Supplies, Unit 11-12, Waterside Business Park, Hadfield, Glossop, Derbyshire, SK13 1BE Tel: (01457) 862521 Fax: (01457) 862138 E-mail: enquiries@kingpak.co.uk

Derek Lambert (Polythene) Ltd, Keighley Road, Bingley, West Yorkshire, BD16 2RD Tel: (01274) 560423 Fax: (01274) 561833 E-mail: sales@dereklambert.co.uk

Leicester Polythene Packaging Ltd, 93a Gwendolen Road, Leicester, LE5 5FL Tel: 0116-273 4235 Fax: 0116-273 4410 E-mail: sales@lppl.co.uk

Lesta Packaging plc, 21 Nedham Street, Leicester, LE2 0HD Tel: (0116) 2624448 Fax: (0116) 2624449 E-mail: enquiries@lestapackaging.co.uk

Liberty Plastics Ltd, Riversleigh Business Centre, 20 Harcourt Road, Dorney Reach, Maidenhead, Berkshire, SL6 0DU Tel: (01628) 773943 Fax: (01628) 788031 E-mail: tony@libertyplastics.freeserve.co.uk

Lo Cost Packaging Ltd, 32 Stephenson Street, London, E16 4SA Tel: (020) 7474 3786 Fax: (020) 7474 5786

Martindales Polythene Packaging Ltd, Block D, St. Michaels Industrial Estate, Widnes, Cheshire, WA8 8TL Tel: 0151-420 5355 Fax: 0151-420 5356 E-mail: sales@martindalespps.com

Medina Packaging, 123 Station Road, Kings Heath, Birmingham, B14 7TA Tel: 0121-444 1425 Fax: 0121-624 3956 E-mail: medinapackaging@blueyonder.co.uk

Melrose Packaging, 6 Lyon Close, Woburn Road Industrial Estate, Kempston, Bedford, MK42 7SB Tel: (01234) 841144 Fax: (01234) 841166 E-mail: info@melrosepackaging.co.uk

N W F Swiftpak, 129 Church Road, Bason Bridge, Highbridge, Somerset, TA9 4RG Tel: (01278) 789200 Fax: (01278) 789100 E-mail: sales@narrowwidthfilms.cwc.net

Nelson Packaging, Waidshouse Mill, Townsley Street, Nelson, Lancashire, BB9 0RY Tel: (01282) 690215 Fax: (01282) 699976

Opalion Plastics, Unit 1 Ashville Trading Estate, Royston Road, Baldock, Hertfordshire, SG7 6NN Tel: (01462) 895600 Fax: (01462) 895800 E-mail: sales@opalion.co.uk

P M C Polythene Ltd, Unit 35 Park Farm Industrial Estate, Ermine Street, Buntingford, Hertfordshire, SG9 9AZ Tel: (01763) 271300 Fax: (01763) 271338

Palagan Ltd, Tavistock Street, Dunstable, Bedfordshire, LU6 1NE Tel: (01582) 600234 Fax: (01582) 601636 E-mail: mail@palagan.co.uk

Parkfield Paper, 1-2 Faraday Close, Drayton Fields Industrial Esta, Daventry, Northamptonshire, NN11 8RD Tel: (0870) 8506661 Fax: (08708) 506662 E-mail: info@parkfieldpaper.co.uk

Peter James Packaging Co., Unit 35 Darbishire Street, Bolton, BL1 2TN Tel: (01204) 381469 Fax: (01204) 386514

Poly Plastics Co., 19 Port Hope Road, Birmingham, B11 1JS Tel: 0121-771 1194 Fax: 0121-753 0244

Poly Print, 59 High St, London, E17 7AD Tel: (020) 8521 4408 Fax: (020) 8521 4568 E-mail: polyprint@carrierbag.freeserve.co.uk

Polypack Polythene Co., 4 Heath St Industrial Estate, Abberley Street, Smethwick, West Midlands, B66 2QZ Tel: 0121-558 9977 Fax: 0121-555 6077 E-mail: info@polypackuk.com

PolyPlus Packaging Ltd, Unit 1 Headley Park Ten, Headley Road East, Woodley, Reading, RG5 4SW Tel: 0845 4941732 Fax: 0118-944 8141 E-mail: sales@polypluspackaging.co.uk

Polystar Plastics Ltd, Peel House, Peel Street, Southampton, SO14 5QT Tel: (023) 8023 2153 Fax: (023) 8023 2157 E-mail: sales@polystar.co.uk

Premier Flexible Packaging Ltd, 14 Aber Road, Flint, Clwyd, CH6 5EX Tel: (01352) 733365 Fax: (01352) 733152 E-mail: info@premierflexible.co.uk

R J H Plastics Ltd, 86 Plume Street, Birmingham, B6 7RT Tel: 0121-327 0297 Fax: 0121-327 2297

R P Whitehead Ltd, Gelderd Road, Leeds, LS12 6NB Tel: 0113-263 0613 Fax: 0113-263 0602

C.S. Robertson (Packaging) Ltd, 4 Young Place, Kelvin Industrial Estate, East Kilbride, Glasgow, G75 0TD Tel: (01355) 244656 Fax: (01355) 265163 E-mail: csrobertsonpkg@btinternet.com

Romar Packaging Ltd, New Market Lane, Leeds, LS9 0SH Tel: 0113-249 4543 Fax: 0113-249 1803 E-mail: info@romar-packaging.co.uk

Ryburn Polythene Ltd, Oldham Road, Ripponden, Sowerby Bridge, West Yorkshire, HX6 4EL Tel: (01422) 823286 Fax: (01422) 823819 E-mail: ryburnpoly@btclick.com

Sai Pac UK Ltd, Poly House, 88 Park Road, Ilford, Essex, IG1 1SF Tel: (020) 8553 4050 Fax: (020) 8553 5151

Seevent Plastics Ltd, Units 2-5, Peter Road, Lancing, West Sussex, BN15 8TH Tel: (01903) 755877 Fax: (01903) 753673 E-mail: admin@seevent.co.uk

Sherwood Packaging Ltd, Amber Drive, Langley Mill, Nottingham, NG16 4BE Tel: (01773) 760101 Fax: (01773) 530527 E-mail: sales@sherwoodpkg.com

▶ Shirlplass Ltd, Unit L Bury Close, Higham Ferrers, Rushden, Northamptonshire, NN10 8HQ Tel: (01933) 411814 Fax: (01933) 411914 E-mail: sales@shirlplass.co.uk

Skymark Packaging Solutions, Manners Avenue, Manners Industrial Estate, Ilkeston, Derbyshire, DE7 8EF Tel: 0115-930 2020 Fax: 0115-907 1525 E-mail: admin@skymark.co.uk

Sterling Packaging Ltd, Unit 3-4 Catherine Street, Warrington, WA5 0LH Tel: (01925) 575520 Fax: (01925) 575521

Supreme Plastics Group plc, Supreme House, 300 Regents Park Road, London, N3 2JX Tel: (020) 8346 3291 Fax: (020) 8346 1624 E-mail: info@supremeplastics.com

Surrey Wholesale, Fleming Way, Crawley, West Sussex, RH10 9JY Tel: (01293) 611111 Fax: (01293) 550555

Symphony Plastic Technologies Plc, Elstree House, Elstree Way, Borehamwood, Hertfordshire, WD6 1LE Tel: (020) 8207 5900 Fax: (020) 8207 5960 E-mail: sales@degradable.net

Talbot Plastics, Talbot House, Ross Road, Reading, RG1 8EL Tel: 0118-957 4211 Fax: 0118-950 2335

Tpi Plastic Sheeting Supplies, Scott Lidgett Road, Stoke-on-Trent, ST6 4NQ Tel: (01782) 837141 Fax: (01782) 575154 E-mail: info@tpi-polythene.co.uk

Tyco Plastics Ltd, Armytage Road, The Industrial Estate, Brighouse, West Yorkshire, HD6 1PT Tel: (01484) 714313 Fax: (01484) 720452 E-mail: info@tycoplastics.com

Visual Packaging Ltd, 100 Albert Road, (Opposite Outram Road), London, N22 7AH Tel: (020) 8888 6622 Fax: (020) 8888 1121

Westside Polythene Ltd, Ribble Works, Wakefield Road, Bispham, Blackpool, FY2 0DL Tel: (01253) 358742 Fax: (01253) 500120 E-mail: info@westsidepolythene.co.uk

Xtex Polythene Ltd, Spring Mills, Main Street, Wilsden, Bradford, West Yorkshire, BD15 0DX Tel: (01535) 272871 Fax: (01535) 275702 E-mail: sales@xtec.co.uk

POLYETHYLENE (PE) BAG/ CARRIER/SACK, GRIP SEAL

Turner & Co., Hamlin Way, Hardwick Narrows Industrial Estate, King's Lynn, Norfolk, PE30 4NG Tel: (01553) 692822

POLYETHYLENE (PE) CONTAINERS

Alexander Trading Co., Oakmere Training Centre, Cherry Lane, Liverpool, L4 6UG Tel: 0151-286 0061 Fax: 0151-284 4380

POLYETHYLENE (PE) CONVERTERS

A R F Polythene, Unit 5 Building C, Ramsden Road, Rotherwas Industrial Estate, Hereford, HR2 6NP Tel: (01432) 355643 Fax: (01432) 355643

B P I Consumer V M B, Block C, Blackpole East, Blackpole Road, Worcester, WR3 8ZL Tel: (01905) 755000 Fax: (01905) 456378 E-mail: enquiries@vmb.co.uk

Bailey Polythene Co. Ltd, Unit 26, Garden Estate, Ventnor, Isle Of Wight, PO38 1YJ Tel: (01983) 855535 Fax: (01983) 853358 E-mail: sales@baileypolythene.co.uk

Certiforms Ltd, Lower Heys Mill, Black Lane, Macclesfield, Cheshire, SK10 2AY Tel: (01625) 433390 Fax: (01625) 511333 E-mail: sales@certiforms.co.uk

E B R Ltd, West Quay Road, Enterprise Park, Sunderland, SR5 2TE Tel: 0191-501 1777 Fax: 0191-501 1700 E-mail: info@ebr.co.uk

Grade Packaging Ltd, 8 Vulcan Court, Vulcan Way, Coalville, Leicestershire, LE67 3FW Tel: (01530) 275755 Fax: (01530) 275766 E-mail: sales@gradepackaging.com

Hado Polythene, Spring Lane, Malvern, Worcestershire, WR14 1AJ Tel: (01684) 574800 Fax: (01684) 892450 E-mail: sales@hadopolythene.co.uk

Harrison Verity Products Ltd, Veritas House, Sett End Road, Shadsworth Business Park, Blackburn, BB1 2PT Tel: (01254) 662979 Fax: (01254) 698580E-mail: sales@hvp.co.uk

Kingpak Plastic Sheeting Supplies, Unit 11-12, Waterside Business Park, Hadfield, Glossop, Derbyshire, SK13 1BE Tel: (01457) 862521 Fax: (01457) 862138 E-mail: enquiries@kingpak.co.uk

Frank Mercer & Sons Ltd, Chequerbent Works Manchester Road, Chequerbent, Westhoughton, Bolton, BL5 3JF Tel: (01942) 841111 Fax: (01942) 842388 E-mail: mercer@toughsheet.co.uk

Polyclear (Southampton) Ltd, First Avenue, Millbrook Trading Estate, Southampton, SO15 0LG Tel: (023) 8070 1158 Fax: (023) 8077 1044 E-mail: 20robby@polyclear.co.uk

Polypack Polythene Co., 4 Heath St Industrial Estate, Abberley Street, Smethwick, West Midlands, B66 2QZ Tel: 0121-558 9977 Fax: 0121-555 6077 E-mail: info@polypackuk.com

Polystar Plastics Ltd, Peel House, Peel Street, Southampton, SO14 5QT Tel: (023) 8023 2153 Fax: (023) 8023 2157 E-mail: sales@polystar.co.uk

POLYETHYLENE (PE) CONVERTERS

– continued

Reynopoly, Polythene Place, Newark Road, Peterborough, PE1 5YD Tel: (01733) 891322 Fax: (01733) 891452 E-mail: sales@reynopoly.freeserve.co.uk
Romar Packaging Ltd, New Market Lane, Leeds, LS9 0SH Tel: 0113-249 4543 Fax: 0113-249 1803 E-mail: info@romar-packaging.co.uk
Seevent Plastics Ltd, Units 2-5, Peter Road, Lancing, West Sussex, BN15 8TH Tel: (01903) 755877 Fax: (01903) 753673 E-mail: admin@seevent.co.uk
Sterling Packaging Ltd, Unit 3-4 Catherine Street, Warrington, WA5 0LH Tel: (01925) 575520 Fax: (01925) 575521
Tyco Plastics Ltd, Unit 2 Westland Square, Leeds, LS11 5SS Tel: 0113-270 3737 Fax: 0113-270 0778
Tyco Plastics Ltd, Unit 2 Westland Square, Leeds, LS11 5SS Tel: 0113-270 3737 Fax: 0113-270 0778

POLYETHYLENE (PE) CONVERTING MACHINE MANUFRS

Clarke Web Ltd, 9 Poplar Industrial Estate, Redditch Road, Studley, Warwickshire, B80 7AY Tel: (01527) 857335 Fax: (01527) 857315 E-mail: clarkeweb@btconnect.com
Delpro Ltd, Peakdale Road, Glossop, Derbyshire, SK13 6XE Tel: (01457) 862776 Fax: (01457) 862433 E-mail: sales@delpro.co.uk
Harnden Plastics, Manchester Road, Hyde, Cheshire, SK14 2BP Tel: 0161-368 1817 Fax: 0161-368 1140 E-mail: harnden@a-m.co.uk
Process Machinery Ltd, 30 Knowl Piece, Wilbury Way, Hitchin, Hertfordshire, SG4 0TY Tel: (01462) 421966 Fax: (01462) 422043 E-mail: sales@processmachinery.co.uk
Radcliffe Machinery Ltd, Radcliffe Machinery Limited, Binn Brow Binns Lane, Holmfirth, HD9 3BJ Tel: (01484) 687811 Fax: (01484) 687769 E-mail: tim@radcliffemachinery.com
Wittey Machinery Ltd, Unit 17 Haddenham Aerodrome Industrial Estate, Dollicott, Haddenham, Aylesbury, Buckinghamshire, HP17 8LJ Tel: (01844) 344723 Fax: (01844) 342004

POLYETHYLENE (PE) ENVELOPES

Antalis Ltd, Unit C3 Crossways Boulevard, Greenhithe, Kent, DA9 9BT Tel: (0870) 6073117 Fax: (01322) 226297
▶ Britton Mailing, Unit 10 B, Temple Farm Industrial Estate, Sutton Road, Southend-on-Sea, SS2 5RD Tel: (01702) 468976 Fax: (01702) 469221 E-mail: enquiries@britton-group.co.uk
Certiforms Ltd, Lower Heys Mill, Black Lane, Macclesfield, Cheshire, SK10 2AY Tel: (01625) 433390 Fax: (01625) 511333 E-mail: sales@certiforms.co.uk
General Packaging Co., Unit 3 Cooksland Industrial Estate, Bodmin, Cornwall, PL31 2QB Tel: (01208) 265870 Fax: (01208) 72457 E-mail: enquiries@generalpackaging.co.uk
Initial Packaging Solutions Ltd, Unit 16 Westgate, Everite Industrial Estate, Widnes, Cheshire, WA8 8RA Tel: 0151-420 4333 Fax: 0151-423 4451 E-mail: sales@initialpackaging.co.uk
Transmail Ltd, Unit 21 Concorde Road, Norwich, NR6 6BJ Tel: (01603) 404217 Fax: (01603) 483944 E-mail: sales@transmail.co.uk
Turner & Co., Hamlin Way, Hardwick Narrows Industrial Estate, King's Lynn, Norfolk, PE30 4NG Tel: (01553) 692822

POLYETHYLENE (PE) EXTRUSIONS

Elite Plastics Ltd, Twyford Road, Rotherwas Industrial Estate, Hereford, HR2 6JR Tel: (01432) 357337 Fax: (01432) 343175 E-mail: sales@eliteplastics.co.uk
Flexfilm, Road One Industrial Estate, Winsford Industrial Estate, Winsford, Cheshire, CW7 3QE Tel: (01606) 550100 Fax: (01606) 551111 E-mail: enquiries@flexfilm.co.uk
Hampshire Polythene Manufacturing Ltd, 2 Queensway, Walworth Industrial Estate, Andover, Hampshire, SP10 5LG Tel: (01264) 332466 Fax: (01264) 356641
Horn UK Ltd, Townfoot Industrial Estate, Brampton, Cumbria, CA8 1SW Tel: (01697) 741080 Fax: (01697) 741022 E-mail: eng@cumbrian.co.uk
▶ Shirlplass Ltd, Unit L Bury Close, Higham Ferrers, Rushden, Northamptonshire, NN10 8HQ Tel: (01933) 411814 Fax: (01933) 411914 E-mail: sales@shirlplass.co.uk

POLYETHYLENE (PE) FILM, *See also Polyethylene (PE) Sheeting etc*

Adept Packaging Co. Ltd, 78-82 Nightingale Grove, Hither Green, London, SE13 6DZ Tel: (020) 8318 7511 Fax: (020) 8852 9120 E-mail: sales@adeptpack.co.uk
Allerton Packaging Service, 7 King Close, Leeds, LS17 7AS Tel: 0113-269 1440 Fax: 0113-294 4330 E-mail: packserve@totalise.co.uk
Alsaplas Ltd, Unit 1, Ramsden Road, Rotherwas Industrial Estate, Hereford, HR2 6LR Tel: (01432) 277747 Fax: (01432) 262600
BPI Films, Warrington Road, Widnes, Cheshire, WA8 0SX Tel: 0151-422 3600 Fax: 0151-422 3620
▶ BPI.Industrial Swansea, Swansea Enterprise Park, Clarion Close, Morriston, Swansea, SA6 8QZ Tel: (01792) 772441 Fax: (01792) 701134 E-mail: salesswansea@bpipoly.com
▶ Britton Taco Ltd, Road One Industrial Estate, Winsford Industrial Estate, Winsford, Cheshire, CW7 3RD Tel: (01606) 593434 Fax: (01606) 866423 E-mail: team@taco.co.uk
Cheshire Polythene Film Co. Ltd, 3 Lawnhurst Trading Estate, Ashurst Drive, Stockport, Cheshire, SK3 0SD Tel: 0161-428 4251 Fax: 0161-428 8329 E-mail: trevor@polythene-films.com
▶ Derby Polythene Ltd, Unit 1 Osmaston Park Road, Derby, DE24 8BT Tel: (01332) 331955 Fax: (01332) 361355 E-mail: sales@derbyplastics.co.uk
Derby Polythene Ltd, Unit 1 Osmaston Park Road, Derby, DE24 8BT Tel: (01332) 331955 Fax: (01332) 361355 E-mail: sales@doningroup.aol.com
Flexfilm, Road One Industrial Estate, Winsford Industrial Estate, Winsford, Cheshire, CW7 3QE Tel: (01606) 550100 Fax: (01606) 551111 E-mail: enquiries@flexfilm.co.uk
Goodyer Packaging Ltd, Bunbury Lane, Bunbury, Tarporley, Cheshire, CW6 9QU Tel: (01829) 261052 Fax: (01829) 261129
Hampshire Polythene Manufacturing Ltd, 2 Queensway, Walworth Industrial Estate, Andover, Hampshire, SP10 5LG Tel: (01264) 332466 Fax: (01264) 356641
I G Industries plc, The Flarepath, Elsham Wolds Industrial Estate, Brigg, South Humberside, DN20 0SP Tel: (01652) 688888 Fax: (01652) 688808 E-mail: sales@igindustries.co.uk
Opalion Plastics, Unit 1 Ashville Trading Estate, Royston Road, Baldock, Hertfordshire, SG7 6NN Tel: (01462) 895600 Fax: (01462) 895800 E-mail: sales@opalion.co.uk
Plasmech Packaging Ltd, Unit 27 Cam Centre, Wilbury Way, Hitchin, Hertfordshire, SG4 0TW Tel: (01462) 432525 Fax: (01462) 432124 E-mail: derek@plasmechpackaging.co.uk
Polyclear (Southampton) Ltd, First Avenue, Millbrook Trading Estate, Southampton, SO15 0LG Tel: (023) 8070 1158 Fax: (023) 8077 1044 E-mail: 20robby@polyclear.co.uk
Romar Packaging Ltd, New Market Lane, Leeds, LS9 0SH Tel: 0113-249 4543 Fax: 0113-249 1803 E-mail: info@romar-packaging.co.uk
▶ Shirlplass Ltd, Unit L Bury Close, Higham Ferrers, Rushden, Northamptonshire, NN10 8HQ Tel: (01933) 411814 Fax: (01933) 411914 E-mail: sales@shirlplass.co.uk
Skymark Packaging International Ltd, Southern Avenue, Leominster, Herefordshire, HR6 0QF Tel: (01568) 611393 Fax: (01568) 611602 E-mail: info@skymark.co.uk
Skymark Packaging Solutions, Manners Avenue, Manners Industrial Estate, Ilkeston, Derbyshire, DE7 8EF Tel: 0115-930 2020 Fax: 0115-907 1525 E-mail: admin@skymark.co.uk
Talbot Plastics, Talbot House, Ross Road, Reading, RG1 8EL Tel: 0118-957 4211 Fax: 0118-950 2335
Xtex Polythene Ltd, Spring Mills, Main Street, Wilsden, Bradford, West Yorkshire, BD15 0DX Tel: (01535) 272871 Fax: (01535) 275702 E-mail: sales@xtec.co.uk

POLYETHYLENE (PE) FILM, AGRICULTURAL/ HORTICULTURAL TRADE

bpi.agri, Worcester Road, Leominster, Herefordshire, HR6 0QA Tel: (01568) 617220 Fax: (01568) 611435 E-mail: sales@bpiagri.com

POLYETHYLENE (PE) FILM, BUILDING TRADE

Alan Roberts Midlands Ltd, Alan Roberts Midlands Ltd, Barton Dock Road, Stretford, Manchester, M32 0YL Tel: (01384) 263266 Fax: (01384) 265830 E-mail: jaspemal@aol.com

POLYETHYLENE (PE) FILM/ CLING WRAPPING FILM (FOOD WRAP) MANUFS

Abpac, Wessex Way, Wincanton Business Park, Wincanton, Somerset, BA9 9RR Tel: (01963) 32913 Fax: (01963) 34358 E-mail: sales@abpac.co.uk
C E D O Ltd, Halesfield 11, Telford, Shropshire, TF7 4LZ Tel: (01952) 272727 Fax: (01952) 274102
Jordan Plastics Ltd, 109 Summerisland Road, Portadown, Craigavon, County Armagh, BT62 1SJ Tel: (028) 3885 3111 Fax: (028) 3885 3112 E-mail: sales@jordanplastics.com
Marshall Wilson, Units 4 a-c Blochairn Industrial Estate, 16-24 Siemens Place, Glasgow, G21 2BN Tel: 0141-552 7577 Fax: 0141-552 5434

POLYETHYLENE (PE) FLAME RETARDANT (FR) SHEETING

Regency International Safety Group Ltd, Allenby Street, Scunthorpe, South Humberside, DN15 6EL Tel: (01724) 277933 Fax: (01724) 277933 E-mail: regencyintgrp@aol.com
▶ Special Fire Systems, Baston Hall, Crews Hill, Alfrick, Worcester, WR6 5HF Tel: (01886) 884747 Fax: (01886) 884125 E-mail: enquiries@special-fire.com

POLYETHYLENE (PE) FOAM

L S P Ltd, 168 Blackfen Road, Hawthorn Terrace, Sidcup, Kent, DA15 8PT Tel: (020) 8859 8877 Fax: (020) 8859 8787 E-mail: sales@lspuk.com
Sekisui Alveo, Queens Chambers, Eleanors Cross, Dunstable, Bedfordshire, LU6 1SU Tel: (01582) 600456 Fax: (01582) 600567

POLYETHYLENE (PE) FOAM PRODUCTS

Advanced Protective Packaging Ltd, Unit 58 Pioneer Mill, Milltown Street, Radcliffe, Manchester, M26 1WN Tel: 0161-724 8080 Fax: 0161-725 9074 E-mail: brian@advanced-pp.co.uk
Carpenters Ltd, Bee Mill, Shaw Road, Royton, Oldham, OL2 6EH Tel: 0161-627 0044 Fax: 0161-627 0951 E-mail: sales.uk@carpenter.com
Functional Foam Beacons Products, Efi Industrial Estate, Brecon Road, Merthyr Tydfil, Mid Glamorgan, CF47 8RB Tel: (01685) 350011 Fax: (01685) 388396 E-mail: sales@beaconsproducts.co.uk
Interactive Packaging Solutions Ltd, Unit 3 Ash Road North, Wrexham Industrial Estate, Wrexham, Clwyd, LL13 9JT Tel: (01978) 661671 Fax: (01978) 661681 E-mail: sales@ips-uk.co.uk
Jit Pak, Unit 14 Pages Industrial Park, Eden Way, Leighton Buzzard, Bedfordshire, LU7 4TZ Tel: (01525) 374412 Fax: (01525) 374416 E-mail: info@jitpak.co.uk
Kayfoam Ltd, Unit 3A Pegasis Business Park, Cameron Street, Hillington, Glasgow, G52 4TY Tel: 0141-810 4333 Fax: 0141-810 1424
Kewell Converters Ltd, 60 Holmethorpe Avenue, Redhill, RH1 2NL Tel: (01737) 771710 Fax: (01737) 769732 E-mail: sales@kewell-converters.co.uk
L S P Ltd, 168 Blackfen Road, Hawthorn Terrace, Sidcup, Kent, DA15 8PT Tel: (020) 8859 8877 Fax: (020) 8859 8787 E-mail: sales@lspuk.com
Livedale Foam & Sundries Ltd, Albert Road, Farnworth, Bolton, BL4 9EL Tel: (01204) 573566 Fax: (01204) 705672 E-mail: sales@1ivedale.co.uk
M B Air Systems Ltd, Unit 13b Enterprise Court, Seaham Grange Industrial Estate, Seaham, County Durham, SR7 0PS Tel: 0191-521 4111 Fax: 0191-521 1616 E-mail: sales@mbairsystems.co.uk
Polyformes Ltd, Cherrycourt Way, Leighton Buzzard, Bedfordshire, LU7 4UH Tel: (01525) 852444 Fax: (01525) 850484 E-mail: sales@polyformes.co.uk
R G H Rubber & Plastics Ltd, Acorn House, Oak Industrial Park, Chelmsford Road, Great Dunmow, Dunmow, Essex, CM6 1XN Tel: (01371) 875941 Fax: (01371) 873804 E-mail: sales@rghrubber.co.uk
S J Gaskets Ltd, Tything Park, Tything Road East, Kinwarton, Alcester, Warwickshire, B49 6ES Tel: (01789) 763721 Fax: (01789) 764070 E-mail: sjgaskets@thesjgroup.com
Sekisui Alveo, Queens Chambers, Eleanors Cross, Dunstable, Bedfordshire, LU6 1SU Tel: (01582) 600456 Fax: (01582) 600567

POLYETHYLENE (PE) FURNITURE COVERS

Tyco Plastics Ltd, Unit 2 Westland Square, Leeds, LS11 5SS Tel: 0113-270 3737 Fax: 0113-270 0778

POLYETHYLENE (PE) HEAT SEALING MACHINES

Coote Vibratory Co. Ltd, 10 The Apex Centre, Speedfields Park, Newgate Lane, Fareham, Hampshire, PO14 1TP Tel: (01329) 287841 Fax: (01329) 827451 E-mail: info@coote-vibratory.co.uk

POLYETHYLENE (PE) HORTICULTURAL GREENHOUSES

Fordingbridge plc, Arundel Road, Fontwell, Arundel, West Sussex, BN18 0SD Tel: (01243) 554455 Fax: (01243) 554433 E-mail: sales@nurserybitz.co.uk
National Polytunnels Ltd, 258 Station Road, Bamber Bridge, Preston, PR5 6EA Tel: (01772) 799200 Fax: (01772) 799250 E-mail: sales@nationalalpolytunnels.co.uk
Polybuild Ltd, Upper Chancton Farm, London Road, Washington, Pulborough, West Sussex, RH20 3DH Tel: (01903) 892333 Fax: (01903) 892777 E-mail: sales@polybuild.com

POLYETHYLENE (PE) LAYFLAT TUBING

Alpha Packaging, Gooch, Didcot, Oxfordshire, OX11 7PR Tel: (01235) 511500 Fax: (01235) 510543 E-mail: alpha.packaging@btconnect.com
Arrow Flexible Packaging Ltd, Millingford Industrial Estate, Golborne, Warrington, WA3 3QE Tel: (01942) 722383 Fax: (01942) 716502 E-mail: sales@polythene.co.uk
▶ Bpi Packaging, Brook Road, Buckhurst Hill, Essex, IG9 5TU Tel: (020) 8504 9151 Fax: (020) 8506 1892 E-mail: salesessex@bpipoly.com
Central Polythene Packaging, Unit 60, Abbey Park Street, Leicester, LE4 5AF Tel: 0116-253 0275 Fax: 0116-253 1832
Dale Products Plastics Ltd, Barnsley Road, Hoyland, Barnsley, South Yorkshire, S74 0QW Tel: (01226) 742511 Fax: (01226) 350496 E-mail: dale.products@fsbdial.co.uk
Derby Polythene Ltd, Unit 1 Osmaston Park Road, Derby, DE24 8BT Tel: (01332) 331955 Fax: (01332) 361355 E-mail: sales@doningroup.aol.com
Gelpack Excelsior Ltd, Westfields Trading Estate, Hereford, HR4 9NT Tel: (01432) 267391 Fax: (01432) 264809 E-mail: info@gelpack.co.uk
N R T Packaging Supplies Ltd, Bampton Packaging Site, Lenton Lane, Nottingham, NG7 2NR Tel: 0115-957 8911 Fax: 0115-986 2984 E-mail: nrtsalesteam@bamptonpackaging.co.uk
R J H Plastics Ltd, 86 Plume Street, Birmingham, B6 7RT Tel: 0121-327 0297 Fax: 0121-327 2297

POLYETHYLENE (PE) LINERS, BAG

Adept Packaging Co. Ltd, 78-82 Nightingale Grove, Hither Green, London, SE13 6DZ Tel: (020) 8318 7511 Fax: (020) 8852 9120 E-mail: sales@adeptpack.co.uk
Cirrus Plastics, Esky Drive, Carn Industrial Area, Portadown, Craigavon, County Armagh, BT63 5WD Tel: (028) 3835 0001 Fax: (028) 3835 0002 E-mail: sales@cirrusplastics.co.uk
Philton Polythene Converters Ltd, Charfleets Road, Canvey Island, Essex, SS8 0PQ Tel: (01268) 696331 Fax: (01268) 510517 E-mail: sales@philton.co.uk
Seevent Plastics Ltd, Units 2-5, Peter Road, Lancing, West Sussex, BN15 8TH Tel: (01903) 755877 Fax: (01903) 753673 E-mail: admin@seevent.co.uk
Talbot Plastics, Talbot House, Ross Road, Reading, RG1 8EL Tel: 0118-957 4211 Fax: 0118-950 2335
Tyco Plastics Ltd, Armytage Road, The Industrial Estate, Brighouse, West Yorkshire, HD6 1PT Tel: (01484) 714313 Fax: (01484) 720452 E-mail: info@tycoplastics.com

POLYETHYLENE (PE) PACKAGING PRODUCTS

A E Taylor & Co. Ltd, 44 Borough Road, Sunderland, SR1 1PW Tel: 0191-567 5078 Fax: 0191-510 2268
Arrowsacks Packaging, PO Box 234, Dover, Kent, CT15 6GD Tel: (01304) 853604 Fax: (01304) 852540 E-mail: arrowsacks@isleoak.freeserve.co.uk
B P I Films, 40 Thursby Road, Croft Business Park, Wirral, Merseyside, CH62 3PZ Tel: 0151-334 8091 Fax: 0151-334 0066 E-mail: enquiries@bpipoly.com
B P I Stretchville, Bath Road, Bridgwater, Somerset, TA6 4BF Tel: (01278) 446262 Fax: (01278) 452252 E-mail: pswexports@brithene.com
Bischof & Klein UK Ltd, Unit C Hortonwood 2, Telford, Shropshire, TF1 7XX Tel: (01952) 606848 Fax: (01952) 606698 E-mail: info@bk-packaging.co.uk
bpi.agri, Worcester Road, Leominster, Herefordshire, HR6 0QA Tel: (01568) 617220 Fax: (01568) 611435 E-mail: sales@bpiagri.com
C E D O Ltd, Halesfield 11, Telford, Shropshire, TF7 4LZ Tel: (01952) 272727 Fax: (01952) 274102

POLYETHYLENE (PE) PACKAGING PRODUCTS – *continued*

Carpenters Ltd, Bee Mill, Shaw Road, Royton, Oldham, OL2 6EH Tel: 0161-627 0044 Fax: 0161-627 0951 E-mail: sales.uk@carpenter.com
D L F Packaging Materials, 56 School Road, Shirley, Solihull, West Midlands, B90 2BB Tel: 0121-744 6101 Fax: 0121-744 9823 E-mail: sales@dlfpackaging.demon.co.uk
▶ Derby Polythene Ltd, Unit 1 Osmaston Park Road, Derby, DE24 8BT Tel: (01332) 331955 Fax: (01332) 361355 E-mail: sales@derbyplastics.co.uk
Flexopack Ltd, Mallard Road, Victoria Business Park, Netherfield, Nottingham, NG4 2PE Tel: 0115-940 3939 Fax: 0115-940 3837 E-mail: sales@flexopack.co.uk
Harrison Verity Products Ltd, Veritas House, Sett End Road, Shadsworth Business Park, Blackburn, BB1 2PT Tel: (01254) 662979 Fax: (01254) 698580E-mail: sales@hvp.co.uk
M I P Ltd, Park Lane, Halesowen, West Midlands, B63 2RE Tel: (01384) 637711 Fax: (01384) 410104
Marshall Wilson, Units 4 a-c Blochairn Industrial Estate, 16-24 Siemens Place, Glasgow, G21 2BN Tel: 0141-552 7577 Fax: 0141-552 5434
Pakex UK plc, 1 Prime Point, Bessemer Road, Welwyn Garden City, Hertfordshire, AL7 1FE Tel: (01707) 384858 Fax: (01707) 332838 E-mail: sales@pakexuk.com
Plasmech Packaging Ltd, Unit 27 Cam Centre, Wilbury Way, Hitchin, Hertfordshire, SG4 0TW Tel: (01462) 432525 Fax: (01462) 432124 E-mail: derek@plasmechpackaging.co.uk
Roughway Converters Ltd, Roughway Mill, Dunks Green, Tonbridge, Kent, TN11 9SG Tel: (01732) 810811 Fax: (01732) 810838 E-mail: roughway@btconnect.com
Transmail Ltd, Unit 21 Concorde Road, Norwich, NR6 6BJ Tel: (01603) 404217 Fax: (01603) 483944 E-mail: sales@transmail.co.uk
W. Ridley & Co. Ltd, 12-16 Bean Street, Hull, HU3 2PQ Tel: (01482) 224691 Fax: (01482) 587098 E-mail: info@wridley.co.uk

POLYETHYLENE (PE) PIPE JOINTING SYSTEMS

Fusion, 9 Fishwicks Industrial Estate, Kilbuck Lane, Haydock, St. Helens, Merseyside, WA11 9SZ Tel: (01942) 271517 Fax: (01942) 716187 E-mail: northwest@fusiongroup.co.uk

POLYETHYLENE (PE) PIPELINE SYSTEMS

Fusion, 9 Fishwicks Industrial Estate, Kilbuck Lane, Haydock, St. Helens, Merseyside, WA11 9SZ Tel: (01942) 271517 Fax: (01942) 716187 E-mail: northwest@fusiongroup.co.uk

POLYETHYLENE (PE) PRODUCTS AND COMPONENTS

Alan Roberts Midlands Ltd, Alan Roberts Midlands Ltd, Barton Dock Road, Stretford, Manchester, M32 0YL Tel: (01384) 263266 Fax: (01384) 265830 E-mail: jaspemal@aol.com
B P I Recycled Products, Unit N Bath Road Trading Estate, Lightpill, Stroud, Gloucestershire, GL5 3QF Tel: (01453) 751471 Fax: (01453) 752843
Beck Sack Co., 3 Hermitage Lane, London, SE25 5HH Tel: (0845) 0720750
Danda UK Packaging Ltd, 8 Drury Way Industrial Estate, Laxcon Close, London, NW10 0TG Tel: (020) 8459 5500 Fax: (020) 8459 2351
Euro Packaging plc, Unit 14 Elderpark Workspace, 100 Elderpark Street, Glasgow, G51 3TR Tel: 0141-445 3003 Fax: 0141-445 5111 E-mail: info@europackaging.co.uk
Gardners, 149 Commercial Street, London, E1 6BJ Tel: (020) 7247 5119
Glopac, Eddison Road, Hams Hall Distribution Park, Coleshill, Birmingham, B46 1AB Tel: (01675) 431000 Fax: (01675) 431066 E-mail: sales@glopac.co.uk
Horn UK Ltd, Townfoot Industrial Estate, Brampton, Cumbria, CA8 1SW Tel: (01697) 741080 Fax: (01697) 741022 E-mail: eng@cumbrian.co.uk
Keymesh Ltd, Premier Business Centre, Attwood Street, Stourbridge, West Midlands, DY9 8RY Tel: (01384) 898899 Fax: (01384) 898775 E-mail: sales@keymesh.com
Lewis T Davies, Brewery Road, Carmarthen, Dyfed, SA31 1TF Tel: (01267) 221746 Fax: (01267) 221776 E-mail: info@lewistdavies.co.uk
M Grovic & Son Ltd, Adelaide Road, Reading, RG6 1PE Tel: 0118-926 2491 Fax: 0118-935 2364 E-mail: mgrovic@ulc.co.uk
M.Laurier & Sons Ltd, Unit 10 Triumph Trading Estate, Tariff Road, London, N17 0EB Tel: (020) 8365 9000 Fax: (020) 8365 9005 E-mail: info@laurier.co.uk
Medina Packaging, 123 Station Road, Kings Heath, Birmingham, B14 7TA Tel: 0121-444 1425 Fax: 0121-624 3956 E-mail: medinapackaging@blueyonder.co.uk
William Montgomery & Sons, 79 Ladas Drive, Belfast, BT6 9FR Tel: (028) 9040 1593 Fax: (028) 9040 1593
N R T Packaging Supplies Ltd, Bampton Packaging Site, Lenton Lane, Nottingham, NG7 2NR Tel: 0115-957 8911 Fax: 0115-986 2984 E-mail: nrtsalesteam@bamptonpackaging.co.uk
Parkfield Paper, 1-2 Faraday Close, Drayton Fields Industrial Esta, Daventry, Northamptonshire, NN11 8RD Tel: (0870) 8506661 Fax: (08708) 506662 E-mail: info@parkfieldpaper.co.uk
Pembroke Packaging & Print Ltd, Victoria Hall, Nelson Street, Pennar, Pembroke Dock, Dyfed, SA72 6RU Tel: (01646) 684664 Fax: (01646) 622226
Poly Hi Solidur (U K) Ltd, Halifax Road, Todmorden, Lancashire, OL14 5QQ Tel: (01706) 811000 Fax: (01706) 817571 E-mail: sales@polyhisolidur.co.uk
Thomas Ford Smithfield, Hereford House, 23 Smithfield Street, London, EC1A 9LF Tel: (020) 7248 5868 Fax: (020) 7248 6330 E-mail: sales@thomasford.biz
Woodway Packaging Ltd, 25-27 Mallard Close, Earls Barton, Northampton, NN6 0JF Tel: (01604) 812678 Fax: (01604) 810678

POLYETHYLENE (PE) PROTECTIVE COVERS OR COVERINGS

Express Polythene Ltd, Barford Street, Birmingham, B5 6AH Tel: 0121-622 2319 Fax: 0121-622 1179 E-mail: sales@expresspolythene.co.uk
N R T Packaging Supplies Ltd, Bampton Packaging Site, Lenton Lane, Nottingham, NG7 2NR Tel: 0115-957 8911 Fax: 0115-986 2984 E-mail: nrtsalesteam@bamptonpackaging.co.uk

POLYETHYLENE (PE) REFUSE SACKS

B P I Recycled Products, Unit N Bath Road Trading Estate, Lightpill, Stroud, Gloucestershire, GL5 3QF Tel: (01453) 751471 Fax: (01453) 752843
Davis Group, 48 Watersfield Way, Edgware, Middlesex, HA8 6RZ Tel: (020) 8951 4264 Fax: (020) 8951 4342 E-mail: rdavis7054@aol.com
Gelpack Excelsior Ltd, Westfields Trading Estate, Hereford, HR4 9NT Tel: (01432) 267391 Fax: (01432) 264809 E-mail: info@gelpack.co.uk
Modern Plastics Moulding Co., Booth Street, Smethwick, West Midlands, B66 2PF Tel: 0121-565 3390 Fax: 0121-565 3390
Plasmech Packaging Ltd, Unit 27 Cam Centre, Wilbury Way, Hitchin, Hertfordshire, SG4 0TW Tel: (01462) 432525 Fax: (01462) 432124 E-mail: derek@plasmechpackaging.co.uk

POLYETHYLENE (PE) SHEETING (HEAVY DUTY) MANUFRS

Copac, 14 Aylesbury Business Centre, Chamberlain Road, Aylesbury, Buckinghamshire, HP19 8DY Tel: (01296) 398844 Fax: (01296) 431153
Flexfilm, Road One Industrial Estate, Winsford Industrial Estate, Winsford, Cheshire, CW7 3QE Tel: (01606) 550100 Fax: (01606) 551111 E-mail: enquiries@flexfilm.co.uk
Liberty Plastics Ltd, Riversleigh Business Centre, 20 Harcourt Road, Dorney Reach, Maidenhead, Berkshire, SL6 0DU Tel: (01628) 773943 Fax: (01628) 788031 E-mail: tony@libertyplastics.freeserve.co.uk
Noble Polythene Ltd, Unit 9-11, Prince Close, Andover, Hampshire, SP10 5LL Tel: (01264) 332459 Fax: (01264) 332874
Regency International Safety Group Ltd, Allenby Street, Scunthorpe, South Humberside, DN15 6EL Tel: (01724) 277933 Fax: (01724) 277933 E-mail: regencyintgrp@aol.com

POLYETHYLENE (PE) TABARDS

M T Developments Lancashire Ltd, Cornfield Cliffe, Industry Street, Darwen, Lancashire, BB3 0HA Tel: (01254) 873837 Fax: (01254) 775268 E-mail: info@aprons.co.uk

POLYETHYLENE (PE) TUBES

Goldstar Services Ltd, Unit 1 Spiral Tube Works, Osmaston Park Road, Derby, DE24 8BT Tel: (01332) 363313 Fax: (01332) 361355 E-mail: sales@doningtongroup.co.uk

POLYETHYLENE (PE) TUNNELLING

Mcgregor Polytunnels Ltd, Winton Farm, Petersfield Road, Monkwood, Alresford, Hampshire, SO24 0HB Tel: (01962) 772368 Fax: (01962) 772471 E-mail: sales@mcgregorpolytunnels.co.uk
Polybuild Ltd, Upper Chancton Farm, London Road, Washington, Pulborough, West Sussex, RH20 3DH Tel: (01903) 892333 Fax: (01903) 892777 E-mail: sales@polybuild.com

POLYETHYLENE TEREPHTHALATE (PET) BOTTLES

Amcor Pet Packaging Holdings Ltd, Gresford Industrial Park, Gresford, Wrexham, Clwyd, LL12 8LX Tel: (01978) 856111 Fax: (01978) 854168
Ball Packaging Europe UK Ltd, Lakeside, Chester Business Park, Chester, CH4 9QT Tel: (01244) 681155 Fax: (01244) 680320 E-mail: chester_reception@ball-europe.com
Johnsen & Jorgensen Group Ltd, Newtons Court, Crossways Business Park, Dartford, DA2 6QL Tel: (01332) 291111 Fax: (01322) 293501 E-mail: info@jjpack.com
Neville & More Ltd, Oakhurst Business Park, Wilberforce Way, Southwater, Horsham, West Sussex, RH13 9RT Tel: (01403) 732290 Fax: (01403) 733507 E-mail: info@nevilleandmore.com
▶ Tekpak (UK), Unit 203, 57 Great George Street, Leeds, LS1 3AJ Tel: (0845) 0537622 Fax: 0113-242 9176 E-mail: andrew.jackson@tekpak.co.uk

POLYETHYLENE TEREPHTHALATE (PET) FILM

Amari Plastics P.L.C., 11-12 Hillman Close, Hornchurch, Essex, RM11 2SJ Tel: (01708) 452525 Fax: (01708) 437030 E-mail: el@amariplastics.com
Amari Plastics plc, Wednesbury One, Blackcountry New Road, Wednesbury, West Midlands, WS10 7NZ Tel: 0121-567 3400 Fax: 0121-567 3401 E-mail: bm@amariplastics.com
Fuji Seal Europe Ltd, Scimitar Close, Gillingham Business Park, Gillingham, Kent, ME8 0RJ Tel: (01634) 378656 Fax: (01634) 379179 E-mail: sales@uk.fujiseal.com

POLYETHYLENE TEREPHTHALATE (PET) MELT VISCOMETERS

Benson Viscometers Ltd, Croft Quarry, West Williamston, Kilgetty, Dyfed, SA68 0TN Tel: (01646) 650065

POLYISOBUTYLENE (PIB) PIPE INSULATION COVERINGS

Kitsons, 139 Scudamore Road, Leicester, LE3 1UQ Tel: 0116-232 5000 Fax: 0116-232 5001

POLYMER DESIGN SOFTWARE

Saros Technology Ltd, 20-21 Market Place, Wallingford, Oxfordshire, OX10 0AD Tel: (01491) 837787 Fax: (01491) 837477 E-mail: info@saros.co.uk

POLYMER ELASTOMERS

Applied Polymer Technology Ltd, Unit 3 Great Western Court, Ashburton Industrial Estate, Ross-on-Wye, Herefordshire, HR9 7XP Tel: (01989) 764270 Fax: (01989) 764269 E-mail: enquiries@appliedpolytech.com
Dowty Engineered Seals Ltd, Ashchurch, Tewkesbury, Gloucestershire, GL20 8JS Tel: (01684) 299111 Fax: (01684) 852210
Inter Euro Polymers, 7/9 The Quadrangle, 57 Ruchill Street, Glasgow, G20 9PX Tel: 0141-946 1221 Fax: 0141-945 4546 E-mail: intereuro@btinternet.com
Plastic Technology Service Ltd, Flamstone Street, Bishopstone, Salisbury, SP5 4BZ Tel: (01722) 781088 Fax: (01722) 781071 E-mail: info@ptsuk.com

POLYMER MODIFICATION STERILISATION SERVICES

Isotron Plc, Moray Road, Elgin Industrial Estate, Swindon, SN2 8XS Tel: (01793) 601000 Fax: (01793) 601010 E-mail: sales@isotron.co.uk
Isotron, Thornhill Industrial Estate, South Marston, Swindon, SN3 4TA Tel: (01793) 823451 Fax: (01793) 827320 E-mail: smarston@isotron.co.uk
Sterigenics (U K) Ltd, Cotes Park Industrial Estate, Somercotes, Alfreton, Derbyshire, DE55 4NJ Tel: (01773) 543200 Fax: (01773) 543210

POLYMER MODIFIED CONCRETE PRODUCTS

Aco Technologies Plc, Hitchin Road, Meppershall, Shefford, Bedfordshire, SG17 5TE Tel: (01462) 816666 Fax: (01462) 815895 E-mail: customersupport@aco.co.uk

POLYMER PRODUCTS

Applied Polymer Technology Ltd, Unit 3 Great Western Court, Ashburton Industrial Estate, Ross-on-Wye, Herefordshire, HR9 7XP Tel: (01989) 764270 Fax: (01989) 764269 E-mail: enquiries@appliedpolytech.com
Asahi Thermofil UK Ltd, 28 New Lane, Havant, Hampshire, PO9 2NQ Tel: (023) 9248 6350 Fax: (023) 9247 2388
J W H Group Ltd, War Industrial Estate, Church Road, Lydney, Gloucestershire, GL15 5EL Tel: (01594) 842406 Fax: (01594) 842232 E-mail: enquire@petlon.co.uk
Milk-Rite, PO Box 2, Melksham, Wiltshire, SN12 6NB Tel: (0870) 7315010 Fax: (01225) 896311 E-mail: sales@milk-rite.com
Powerwall Systems Ltd, 4 Netherton Road, Wishaw, Lanarkshire, ML2 0EQ Tel: (01698) 373305 Fax: (01698) 374503 E-mail: sales@powerwall.co.uk
Precision Polymers & Reclaim Ltd, Bath Road Trading Estate, Lightpill, Stroud, Gloucestershire, GL5 3QF Tel: (01453) 753717 Fax: (01453) 753717
Trelleborg Woodville, Hearthcote Road, Swadlincote, Derbyshire, DE11 9DX Tel: (01283) 222145 Fax: (01283) 222911 E-mail: john.blackham@trelleborg.com

POLYMER TEST EQUIPMENT

Alpha Technologies, Unit 2B Crowood House, Gipsy Lane, Swindon, SN2 8YY Tel: (01793) 601100 Fax: (01793) 615214
Ray Ran Test Equipment Ltd, Kelsey Close, Attleborough Fields Ind Estate, Nuneaton, Warwickshire, CV11 6RS Tel: (024) 7634 2002 Fax: (024) 7664 1670 E-mail: polytest@ray-ran.com

POLYOLEFIN COATED FABRICS

C M I Plastics Ltd, Wood Street Works, Wood Street, Burnley, Lancashire, BB10 1QH Tel: (01282) 420021 Fax: (01282) 831387 E-mail: sales@cmi-ltd.com

POLYOLEFIN SHRINK WRAP FILM

Jordan Plastics Ltd, 109 Summerisland Road, Portadown, Craigavon, County Armagh, BT62 1SJ Tel: (028) 3885 3111 Fax: (028) 3885 3112 E-mail: sales@jordanplastics.com
S Kempner Ltd, 498 Honeypot Lane, Stanmore, Middlesex, HA7 1JZ Tel: (020) 8952 5262 Fax: (020) 8952 8061 E-mail: sales@kempner.co.uk

POLYPROPYLENE (PP) BAGS

Ady, Antrim Road, Warrington, WA2 8JT Tel: (01925) 419933 Fax: (01925) 419944 E-mail: sales@bulkbags.co.uk
Amcor Flexibles Ledbury, Lower Road Trading Estate, Ledbury, Herefordshire, HR8 2DJ Tel: (01531) 638638 Fax: (01531) 635716 E-mail: enquiries@rexam.com
Flexopack Ltd, Mallard Road, Victoria Business Park, Netherfield, Nottingham, NG4 2PE Tel: 0115-940 3939 Fax: 0115-940 3837 E-mail: sales@flexopack.co.uk
Godfreys Technical Textiles, Arrol Road, Wester Gourdie Industrial Estate, Dundee, DD2 4TH Tel: (01382) 618499 Fax: (01382) 618484 E-mail: sales@godfreysofdundee.co.uk
H & S Polythene Ltd, 36 Redburn Industrial Estate, Woodall Road, Enfield, Middlesex, EN3 4LE Tel: (020) 8050217 Fax: (020) 8050227 E-mail: sales@hspolythene.com
Halcyon Plastics Ltd, Halcyon House, The Court Yard, Waterloo Farm, Stotfold Road, Arlesey, Bedfordshire, SG15 6XP Tel: (01462) 833000 Fax: (01462) 734414 E-mail: sales@halcyonplastics.co.uk
I.B.C. Recovery Services Ltd, 28 Brewsdale Road, Middlesbrough, Middlesbrough, Cleveland, TS3 6JZ Tel: 01642 249844 Fax: 01642 220245 E-mail: bagman@ibc-recovery.com
J & H M Dickson Ltd, Seath Road, Rutherglen, Glasgow, G73 1RW Tel: 0141-643 0244 Fax: 0141-643 0219 E-mail: sales@dicksonforsacks.co.uk

▶ indicates data change since last edition

POLYPROPYLENE (PP) BAGS – *continued*

J M J Bulk Packaging Ltd, Earlstrees Road, Earlstrees Industrial Estate, Corby, Northamptonshire, NN17 4AZ Tel: (01536) 274400 Fax: (01536) 261180 E-mail: sales@packaging.uk.com
Norman Knights Ltd, 1 Russell Court, Russell Gardens, Wickford, Essex, SS11 8QU Tel: (01268) 733722 Fax: (01268) 764537 E-mail: sales@normanknights.com
Martins Mill Packaging, Unit 2 Reflecting Roadstuds Induxtrial Estate, Mill Lane, Booth Town, Halifax, West Yorkshire, HX3 6TR Tel: (01422) 363935 Fax: (01422) 300800 E-mail: rmatmmp@aol.com
Tristar (UK) Ltd, 229-231 Dunstable Road, Luton, LU4 8BN Tel: (01582) 652525 Fax: (01582) 402789 E-mail: hic10@hotmail.com

POLYPROPYLENE (PP) BINDERS/BOXES

Ambroplastics Ltd, Chamber House, Halesfield 13, Telford, Shropshire, TF7 4PL Tel: (01952) 684922 Fax: (01952) 581414 E-mail: info@ambro.co.uk
Laleham Products, Unit H Heath Place, Bognor Regis, West Sussex, PO22 9SL Tel: (01243) 826270 Fax: (01243) 829325 E-mail: sales@lalehamproducts.com

POLYPROPYLENE (PP) FABRICS

Don & Low, Glamis Road, Forfar, Angus, DD8 1FR Tel: (01307) 452249 Fax: (01307) 452201 E-mail: sales@donlow.co.uk
Godfreys Technical Textiles, Arrol Road, Wester Gourdie Industrial Estate, Dundee, DD2 4TH Tel: (01382) 618499 Fax: (01382) 618484 E-mail: sales@godfreysofdundee.co.uk

POLYPROPYLENE (PP) FILM

Amcor Flexibles Ledbury, Lower Road Trading Estate, Ledbury, Herefordshire, HR8 2DJ Tel: (01531) 638638 Fax: (01531) 635716 E-mail: enquiries@rexam.com
▶ Innovia Films Ltd, Station Rd, Wigton, Cumbria, CA7 9BG Tel: (01697) 342281 Fax: (01697) 341452 E-mail: filmsinfo@innoviafilms.com
QC Packaging Films Ltd, Technology House, Heage Road Industrial Estate, Ripley, Derbyshire, DE5 3GH Tel: (01773) 740300 Fax: (01773) 740301 E-mail: info@qcpackagingfilms.com
Trespaphan UK Ltd, Unit 608 Delta Business Park, Swindon, SN5 7XL Tel: (01793) 344000 Fax: (01793) 344001

POLYPROPYLENE (PP) FILM CONVERTERS

Primopost Ltd, 1 Staden Park, Staden Lane, Buxton, Derbyshire, SK17 9RZ Tel: (01298) 79113 Fax: (01298) 70435

POLYPROPYLENE (PP) FLOORING

Rimco Services, 20 Orchard Road, Malton, North Yorkshire, YO17 7BH Tel: (01653) 600707 Fax: (01653) 600707 E-mail: sales@rimco.co.uk

POLYPROPYLENE (PP) FOOD PACKAGING

Leroy Packaging Ltd, Heasandford Mill, Netherwood Road, Burnley, Lancashire, BB10 2EJ Tel: (01282) 438016 Fax: (01282) 430289 E-mail: learoyd@learoyd.co.uk
▶ Plasware, Plasware House, West Moreland Road, Kingsbury, London, NW9 9RN Tel: (020) 8621 2611 E-mail: info@plaswareuk.com
Thorpe Packaging Ltd, Ripley Drive, Normanton Industrial Estate, Normanton, West Yorkshire, WF6 1QT Tel: (01924) 898802 Fax: (01924) 898803 E-mail: peter@thorpepackaging.sagehost.co.uk
Trespaphan UK Ltd, Unit 608 Delta Business Park, Swindon, SN5 7XL Tel: (01793) 344000 Fax: (01793) 344001

POLYPROPYLENE (PP) GOODS, MADE-UP

Tri-Pack Plastics Ltd, Estate Road No. 1, South Humberside Industrial Estate, Grimsby, South Humberside, DN31 2TB Tel: (01472) 355038 Fax: (01472) 266930 E-mail: mail@tri-pack.co.uk

POLYPROPYLENE (PP) MATERIALS/PRODUCTS/ COMPONENTS AND FITTINGS

Irvine Martin Ltd, Kenton Road, Debenham, Stowmarket, Suffolk, IP14 6LA Tel: (01728) 860909 Fax: (01728) 861056 E-mail: info@irvine-martin.co.uk

POLYPROPYLENE (PP) MOULDING/EXTRUSION COMPOUNDS

Basell (UK) Ltd, Mount Farm, Bramley Road, Milton Keynes, MK1 1LZ Tel: (01908) 360000 Fax: (01908) 360036
Longfield Chemicals Ltd, Hawthorne Farm, Tarvin Road, Frodsham, WA6 6UZ Tel: (01928) 739977 Fax: (01928) 739553 E-mail: enquiries@longchem.co.uk
Sundolitt, Mirren Court (Three), 123 Renfrew Road, Paisley, Renfrewshire, PA3 4EA Tel: 0141-887 1123 Fax: 0141-889 9878 E-mail: enquiries@sundolitt.co.uk

POLYPROPYLENE (PP) PACKAGING PRODUCTS

Ambroplastics Ltd, Chamber House, Halesfield 13, Telford, Shropshire, TF7 4PL Tel: (01952) 684922 Fax: (01952) 581414 E-mail: info@ambro.co.uk
Laleham Products, Unit H Heath Place, Bognor Regis, West Sussex, PO22 9SL Tel: (01243) 826270 Fax: (01243) 829325 E-mail: sales@lalehamproducts.com
Primopost Ltd, 1 Staden Park, Staden Lane, Buxton, Derbyshire, SK17 9RZ Tel: (01298) 79113 Fax: (01298) 70435

POLYPROPYLENE (PP) SHEET

Primex Plastics Ltd, Beaumont Way, Aycliffe Industrial Park, Newton Aycliffe, County Durham, DL5 6SN Tel: (01325) 315768 Fax: (01325) 308875 E-mail: info@primexuk.co.uk
V T S Doeflex, 3 St. Annes Boulevard, Redhill, RH1 1AX Tel: (01737) 771221 Fax: (01737) 772461 E-mail: sales@vtsdoeflex.co.uk

POLYPROPYLENE (PP) SLITTING

Flexell, Unit 3, Bypass Park Estate, Sherburn in Elmet, Leeds, LS25 6EP Tel: (01977) 685755 Fax: (01977) 685778
Magnum Materials Ltd, Globe Lane Indust Estate Broadway, Dukinfield, Cheshire, SK16 4UU Tel: 0161-343 1131 Fax: 0161-343 1132 E-mail: sales@magnum-uk.com

POLYPROPYLENE (PP) STRAPPING

ConMac, Stoneyhill Industrial Estate, Whitchurch, Ross-On-Wye, Herefordshire, HR9 6BX Tel: (01600) 890401 Fax: (01600) 890934 E-mail: marksnell@conmac.co.uk
Cotswold Industrial Products, Westmead Drive, Westmead Industrial Estate, Swindon, SN5 7YT Tel: (01793) 610880 Fax: (01793) 616941 E-mail: sales@cpkgg.com
Frederick Jones (Belfast) Ltd, 17 Napier Street, Belfast, BT12 5FE Tel: (028) 9032 4467 Fax: (028) 9032 5252 E-mail: sales@fjones.com
Orgapack, 58 Heatherhouse Road, Irvine, Ayrshire, KA12 8HQ Tel: (01294) 311911 Fax: (01294) 311920
▶ Qualitape Ltd, 1 Sarah Court, Piperell Way, Haverhill, Suffolk, CB9 8PA Tel: (01440) 710747 Fax: (01440) 763526 E-mail: sales@qualitape.co.uk
Rajapack, Unit 1, Marston Gate, Bridgemont, Bedford, MK43 0YL Tel: (0800) 5424428 Fax: (0800) 5424429 E-mail: sales@rajapack.co.uk
▶ Signode Machines Group Europe, Queensway, Fforestfach, Swansea, SA5 4ED Tel: (01792) 585758 Fax: (01792) 585078 E-mail: machinesuk@signodeuk.com
Strapex, Unit 50 Empire Industrial Park, Aldridge, Walsall, WS9 8UQ Tel: (01922) 742500 Fax: (01922) 742501 E-mail: info@strapex.co.uk

POLYPROPYLENE (PP) THERMOPLASTIC MATERIALS

Rochling Materials Ltd, Waterwells Drive, Waterwells Business Park, Quedgeley, Gloucester, GL2 2AA Tel: (01452) 727900 Fax: (01452) 728056 E-mail: sales@roechling.co.uk

POLYPROPYLENE (PP) WHEELBARROWS

Maingate Ltd, PO Box 330, Woking, Surrey, GU22 9XS Tel: (0845) 2306585 Fax: (0845) 2307585

POLYPROPYLENE (PP) YARN

Don & Low, Glamis Road, Forfar, Angus, DD8 1FR Tel: (01307) 452249 Fax: (01307) 452201 E-mail: sales@donlow.co.uk
F. Harding (Macclesfield) Ltd, Kershaw Mill, Newton Street, Macclesfield, Cheshire, SK11 6QJ Tel: (01625) 429625 Fax: (01625) 612836 E-mail: sales@f-harding.com
Sillaford Ltd, Martin House, 2 Martin Street, Brighouse, West Yorkshire, HD6 1DA Tel: (01484) 710231 Fax: (01484) 714607 E-mail: sales@sillaford.com

POLYSTYRENE (PS) BALLS

▶ Bean Bag Refill, Beanbag Filling, 11 Belgrave Court, Blackwater, Camberley, Surrey, GU17 9JE Tel: 0 870 285 1593 E-mail: info@bean-bag.co.uk

POLYSTYRENE (PS) CONVERTERS

Adur Packaging Ltd, 1 Brook Farm, Horsham Road, Cowfold, Horsham, West Sussex, RH13 8AH Tel: (01403) 864994 Fax: (01403) 864774 E-mail: adurpackaging@aol.com

POLYSTYRENE (PS) INSULATING MATERIALS

Springvale Eps Ltd (Glossop Division), Dinting Vale Business Park, Glossop, Derbyshire, SK13 6LG Tel: (01457) 863211 Fax: (01457) 869269

POLYSTYRENE (PS) LOOSE FILL PACKAGING

▶ F P International (UK) Ltd, Boundary Road, Brackley, Northamptonshire, NN13 7ES Tel: (01280) 703161 Fax: (01280) 701915 E-mail: sales@fpintl.com
Polyscot Polystyrene, 4 Craigluscar Road, Dunfermline, Fife, KY12 9JA Tel: (01383) 732296 Fax: (01383) 620365 E-mail: eps@polyscot.co.uk
S & B E P S Ltd, Dudley, Cramlington, Northumberland, NE23 7PY Tel: 0191-250 0818 Fax: 0191-250 0548 E-mail: company@sandbeps.com

POLYSTYRENE (PS) MOULDING TOOLS

Mather Engineering Co. Ltd, 73 River Road, Barking, Essex, IG11 0DR Tel: (020) 8594 1092 Fax: (020) 8594 9247 E-mail: email@mather-engeering.co.uk

POLYSTYRENE (PS) MOULDINGS, PACKAGING

Expanded Polystyrene Supplies, Denton Island, Newhaven, East Sussex, BN9 9BA Tel: (01273) 612303 Fax: (01273) 517306 E-mail: sales@pabrico.co.uk
K E B Packaging Ltd, Mills Hill Road, Middleton, Manchester, M24 2FT Tel: 0161-655 3464 Fax: 0161-655 3460 E-mail: sales@keb.co.uk
Linpac Moulded Foams, Unit 4 Dinas Isaf Industrial Estate, Williamstown, Tonypandy, Mid Glamorgan, CF40 1NY Tel: (01443) 441491 Fax: (01443) 441453
Styropack UK Ltd, Unit A Rudford Industrial Estate, Ford Road, Ford, Arundel, West Sussex, BN18 0BD Tel: (01903) 725282 Fax: (01903) 731628 E-mail: ford@styropack.co.uk
Styropack UK Ltd, 1 Stephenson Street, Hillington Industrial Estate, Glasgow, G52 4JD Tel: 0141-882 9166 Fax: 0141-882 7022 E-mail: glasgow@styropack.co.uk
Sundolitt, Mirren Court (Three), 123 Renfrew Road, Paisley, Renfrewshire, PA3 4EA Tel: 0141-887 1123 Fax: 0141-889 9878 E-mail: enquiries@sundolitt.co.uk
Veriplast, Pikelaw Place, West Pimbo, Skelmersdale, Lancashire, WN8 9PX Tel: (01695) 721221 Fax: (01695) 726324

POLYSTYRENE (PS) SHEET

Expanded Polystyrene Supplies, Denton Island, Newhaven, East Sussex, BN9 9BA Tel: (01273) 612303 Fax: (01273) 517306 E-mail: sales@pabrico.co.uk
Saffron Plastics Ltd, Bakers Court, Paycocke Road, Basildon, Essex, SS14 3EH Tel: (01268) 288874 Fax: (01268) 534592 E-mail: sales@saffronplastics.co.uk
V T S Doeflex, 3 St. Annes Boulevard, Redhill, RH1 1AX Tel: (01737) 771221 Fax: (01737) 772461 E-mail: sales@vtsdoeflex.co.uk

POLYTETRAFLUOROETHYLENE (PTFE) BEARINGS

▶ Beldam Crossley Ltd, PO Box 7, Bolton, BL1 6PB Tel: (01204) 494711 Fax: (01204) 493203 E-mail: sales@beldam-crossley.co.uk

POLYTHENE, *See also Polyethylene etc*

Bloomfield Packaging Ltd, Unit 33 Bloomfield Park, Bloomfield Road, Tipton, West Midlands, DY4 9AH Tel: 0121-520 5480 Fax: 0121-520 3580 E-mail: info@bloomfieldpackaging.co.uk
Britton Packbourne Ltd, Unit 11 Ponders End Industrial Estate, 35 East Ducklees Lane, Ponders End, Enfield, Middlesex, EN3 7UP Tel: (020) 8805 8000 Fax: (020) 8805 7727 E-mail: sales@brittongrp-enfield.ffnet.co.uk

POLYURETHANE (PU) ADHESIVES

Chemical Innovations Ltd, 217 Walton Summit Road, Walton Summit Centre, Bamber Bridge, Preston, PR5 8AQ Tel: (01772) 322888 Fax: (01772) 315853 E-mail: sales@polycil.co.uk
Leeson Polyurethanes Ltd, Hermes Close, Tachbrook Park, Warwick, CV34 6NW Tel: (01926) 833367 Fax: (01926) 881469 E-mail: sales@lpultd.com
Lord Corporation Ltd, Stretford Motorway Estate, Barton Dock Road, Stretford, Manchester, M32 0ZH Tel: 0161-865 8048 Fax: 0161-865 0096
Rose Hill Polymers Ltd, Rose Hill Mill, Beech Road, Sowerby Bridge, West Yorkshire, HX6 2JT Tel: (01422) 839456 Fax: (01422) 835786 E-mail: sales@rosehill-polymers.ltd.uk
Rose Hill Polymers Ltd, Rose Hill Mill, Beech Road, Sowerby Bridge, West Yorkshire, HX6 2JT Tel: (01422) 839456 Fax: (01422) 835786 E-mail: sales@rosehill-polymers.ltd.uk

POLYURETHANE (PU) APPLICATION CONSULTANTS

Creative Polymer Developments, 24 Brookfield Drive, Littleborough, Lancashire, OL15 8RH Tel: (01706) 374631 Fax: (01706) 370189 E-mail: michaelgooder@creativepolymer.co.uk
Pinnacle Insulation Ltd, Sandgate Industrial Estate, Hartlepool, Cleveland, TS25 1TZ Tel: (01429) 233828 Fax: (01429) 861047 E-mail: mark@pinnacle-aic.com

POLYURETHANE (PU) BELTING

Ammeraal Beltech Ltd, Parkwood Street, Keighley, West Yorkshire, BD21 4PL Tel: (01535) 667015 Fax: (01535) 610250 E-mail: keighley@ammeraalbeltech.co.uk
Bond-a-Band Transmissions Ltd, Vale Mills, Oakworth, Keighley, West Yorkshire, BD22 0EB Tel: 01535 643123 Fax: 01535 646795 E-mail: sales@bondaband.com
Fenner Drives Ltd, Hudson Road, Leeds, LS9 7DF Tel: (0870) 7577007 Fax: 0113-248 9656 E-mail: sales@fennerdrives.com
HPC Gears Ltd, Unit 14, Foxwood Industrial Park, Foxwood Road, Chesterfield, Derbyshire, S41 9RN Tel: (01246) 268080 Fax: (01246) 260003 E-mail: sales@hpcgears.com
Megadyne U K Ltd, Gildersome Spur, Gildersome, Leeds, LS27 7JZ Tel: 0113-238 2910 Fax: 0113-238 3870 E-mail: sales@megadyne.co.uk
Optibelt UK Ltd, 5 Bishops Court, Winwick Quay, Warrington, WA2 8QY Tel: (0870) 4288800 Fax: (01925) 573751 E-mail: optibelt@optibeltuk.co.uk

POLYURETHANE (PU) CASTINGS

Dataroll Ltd, Knightcott Industrial Estate, Banwell, Avon, BS29 6JN Tel: (01934) 823253 Fax: (01934) 822990 E-mail: mail@dataroll.co.uk

POLYURETHANE (PU) CHEMICAL MANUFRS

A P S Ltd, Sea King Road, Lynx Trading Estate, Yeovil, Somerset, BA20 2NZ Tel: (01935) 410710 Fax: (01935) 410888 E-mail: aps@rtv2.co.uk

POLYURETHANE (PU) CHEMICAL MANUFRS – *continued*

Chemical Innovations Ltd, 217 Walton Summit Road, Walton Summit Centre, Bamber Bridge, Preston, PR5 8AQ Tel: (01772) 322888 Fax: (01772) 315853 E-mail: sales@polycil.co.uk
Elastogran UK Ltd, Wimsey Way, Somercotes, Alfreton, Derbyshire, DE55 4NL Tel: (01773) 607161 Fax: (01773) 602089 E-mail: elastogran-uk@elastogran.co.uk
Huntsman, Hitchen Lane, Shepton Mallet, Somerset, BA4 5TZ Tel: (01749) 335200 Fax: (01749) 344221
I F S Chemicals Ltd, Station Road, Roydon, King's Lynn, Norfolk, PE32 1AW Tel: (01485) 601155 Fax: (01485) 601144 E-mail: sales@ifs-group.com
I M C D UK Ltd, Times House, Throwley Way, Sutton, Surrey, SM1 4AF Tel: (020) 8770 7090 Fax: (020) 8770 7295 E-mail:
Note Dome Ltd, 34 Herald Way, Binley Industrial Estate, Coventry, CV3 2RQ Tel: (024) 7663 5193 Fax: (024) 7663 5509 E-mail: sales@notedome.co.uk
Witton Chemical Co. Ltd, Southgate Avenue, Mildenhall, Bury St. Edmunds, Suffolk, IP28 7AT Tel: (01638) 716001 Fax: (01638) 717658 E-mail: sales@witton.com

POLYURETHANE (PU) COATED FABRICS

The British Millerain Company Ltd, Melloroid Works, Belfield Road, Rochdale, Lancashire, OL16 2XA Tel: (01706) 649242 Fax: (01706) 527611 E-mail: sales@britishmillerain.com
Carrington Novare, Calder Works, Thornhill Road, Dewsbury, West Yorkshire, WF12 9QQ Tel: (01924) 465161 Fax: (01924) 457596 E-mail: enquiries@cpf.co.uk
Coating Applications Group, Newhouse Road, Huncoat Business Park, Accrington, Lancashire, BB5 6NT Tel: (01254) 391769 Fax: (01254) 393519 E-mail: sales@coatingapplications.co.uk
Hammertex Ltd, Nationwide House, 7 Victoria Way, Burgess Hill, West Sussex, RH15 9NF Tel: (01444) 257733 Fax: (01444) 257744 E-mail: sales@hammertex.co.uk
I Q Textiles, Mid Road, Prestonpans, East Lothian, EH32 9ER Tel: (01875) 811200 Fax: (01875) 811452
Proofings Technology Ltd, Hare Hill Road, Littleborough, Lancashire, OL15 9HE Tel: (01706) 372314 Fax: (01706) 370473 E-mail:

POLYURETHANE (PU) DESIGN AND DEVELOPMENT SERVICES

Chase Mouldings Ltd, 5 Swaffield Park, Hyssop Close, Cannock, Staffordshire, WS11 7FU Tel: (01543) 572425 Fax: (01543) 572451 E-mail: chase@chasemouldings.fsnet.co.uk
Hallam Polymer Engineering Ltd, Trasco House, Callywhite Lane, Dronfield, Derbyshire, S18 2XR Tel: (01246) 415511 Fax: (01246) 414818 E-mail: sales@hallampolymer.com

POLYURETHANE (PU) ELASTOMER PRODUCTION MATERIALS

Creative Polymer Developments, 24 Brookfield Drive, Littleborough, Lancashire, OL15 8RH Tel: (01706) 374631 Fax: (01706) 370189 E-mail: michaelgooder@creativepolymer.co.uk
Eurothane Ltd, Warndon Business Park, Prescott Drive, Worcester, WR4 9NE Tel: (01905) 458503 Fax: (01905) 456643 E-mail: sales@eurothane.com
Note Dome Ltd, 34 Herald Way, Binley Industrial Estate, Coventry, CV3 2RQ Tel: (024) 7663 5193 Fax: (024) 7663 5509 E-mail: sales@notedome.co.uk

POLYURETHANE (PU) ELASTOMER PRODUCTS

Clifton Rubber Co. Ltd, 5 Edison Road, St. Ives, Cambridgeshire, PE27 3FF Tel: (01480) 496161 Fax: (01480) 484700 E-mail: sales@cliftonrubber.co.uk
▶ Davies Bros, 5 Holborn Square, Birkenhead, Merseyside, CH41 9HQ Tel: 0151-647 3002 Fax: 0151-647 3002 E-mail: dvsbrn@aol.com
Kay Dee Engineering Plastics Ltd, 2 Jubilee Court, Thackley Old Road, Shipley, West Yorkshire, BD18 1QF Tel: (01274) 590824 Fax: (01274) 531409 E-mail: info@kaylan.co.uk
Texane Ltd, Valley Way, Market Harborough, Leicestershire, LE16 7PS Tel: (01858) 462040 Fax: (01858) 410029 E-mail: sales@taxane.com
Tufthane Ltd, Falkland Close, Charter Avenue Industrial Estate, Coventry, CV4 8AU Tel: (024) 7646 0600 Fax: (024) 7669 4313 E-mail: admin@tufthane.com
Urethane Industrial Products Ltd, Evingar Industrial Estate, Ardglen Road, Whitchurch, Hampshire, RG28 7BB Tel: (01256) 892830 Fax: (01256) 896899 E-mail: urethaneindustrial@hotmail.com

POLYURETHANE (PU) ELASTOMER TYRES

Texane Ltd, Valley Way, Market Harborough, Leicestershire, LE16 7PS Tel: (01858) 462040 Fax: (01858) 410029 E-mail: sales@taxane.com

POLYURETHANE (PU) ENCLOSURES

Orion Industries Ltd, Syma House, Halifax Road, Cressex Business Park, High Wycombe, Buckinghamshire, HP12 3SN Tel: (01494) 453800 Fax: (01494) 442762 E-mail: terry@aquila-innovations.co.uk

POLYURETHANE (PU) FOAM KITS

Recticel Corby, 83-84 Manton Road, Earlstrees Industrial Estate, Corby, Northamptonshire, NN17 4JL Tel: (01536) 402345 Fax: (01536) 400524 E-mail: enquiries@recticel.co.uk
Rooftherm, Dane Mill, Broadhurst Lane, Congleton, Cheshire, CW12 1LA Tel: (01260) 285823 Fax: (01260) 295426 E-mail: info@rooftherm.co.uk

POLYURETHANE (PU) FOAM MOULDINGS

A A C Cyroma Ltd, C P L House, Beaumont Road, Banbury, Oxfordshire, OX16 1RJ Tel: (01295) 759200 Fax: (01295) 270614
Borderfoam Ltd, Lingen Road, Ludlow Business Park, Ludlow, Shropshire, SY8 1XD Tel: (01584) 877107 Fax: (01584) 874073
Interfoam Ltd, 16 Ronald Close, Woburn Road Industrial Estate, Bedford, MK42 7SH Tel: (01234) 855355 Fax: (01234) 855665 E-mail: sales@interfoam.co.uk
M R A Cutting Tools, Unit 29 Lythalls La Industrial Estate, Lythalls Lane, Coventry, CV6 6FL Tel: (024) 7668 5813 Fax: (024) 7668 5813
Woodbridge Foam (UK) Ltd, Caxton Road, Elms Industrial Estate, Bedford, MK41 0EJ Tel: (01234) 211333 Fax: (01234) 272047

POLYURETHANE (PU) FOAM PACKAGING SYSTEMS

A O N Converters Ltd, Unit 2 Holmes Lane, Liverpool, L21 6PL Tel: 0151-920 7329 Fax: 0151-949 0483 E-mail: aonfoam@aol.com
I F S Chemicals Ltd, Station Road, Roydon, King's Lynn, Norfolk, PE32 1AW Tel: (01485) 601155 Fax: (01485) 601144 E-mail: sales@ifs-group.com
Kayfoam Ltd, Unit 3A Pegasis Business Park, Cameron Street, Hillington, Glasgow, G52 4TY Tel: 0141-810 4333 Fax: 0141-810 1424
Recticel Corby, 83-84 Manton Road, Earlstrees Industrial Estate, Corby, Northamptonshire, NN17 4JL Tel: (01536) 402345 Fax: (01536) 400524 E-mail: enquiries@recticel.co.uk

POLYURETHANE (PU) FOAM PRODUCTS

A O N Converters Ltd, Unit 2 Holmes Lane, Liverpool, L21 6PL Tel: 0151-920 7329 Fax: 0151-949 0483 E-mail: aonfoam@aol.com
George Danby & Son Ltd, Bank Terrace, Barwell, Leicester, LE9 8GG Tel: (01455) 845522 Fax: (01455) 846633 E-mail: info@phonefirst.co.uk
Interfoam Ltd, 16 Ronald Close, Woburn Road Industrial Estate, Bedford, MK42 7SH Tel: (01234) 855355 Fax: (01234) 855665 E-mail: sales@interfoam.co.uk
Isothane Ltd, Newhouse Road, Huncoat Industrial Estate, Accrington, Lancashire, BB5 6NT Tel: (01254) 872555 Fax: (01254) 871522 E-mail: enquiries@isothane.com
M R A Cutting Tools, Unit 29 Lythalls La Industrial Estate, Lythalls Lane, Coventry, CV6 6FL Tel: (024) 7668 5813 Fax: (024) 7668 5813
Recticel Carobel, Norman Road, North Shields, Tyne & Wear, NE29 7UX Tel: 0191-296 1010 Fax: 0191-296 3321 E-mail: carobel@compuserve.com
Recticel Manufacturing, 1 Bluebell Close, Clover Nook Industrial Park, Somercotes, Alfreton, Derbyshire, DE55 4RD Tel: (01773) 835721 Fax: (01773) 835563 E-mail: uk@rect.com
Recticel Midlands, Unit 3, Azalea Close, Clover Nook Industrial Park, Alfreton, Derbyshire, DE55 4QX Tel: (01773) 520242 Fax: (01773) 520513 E-mail: recticel@midlands.co.uk
Rocon Foam Products Ltd, 14 Shrub Hill, Worcester, WR4 9EL Tel: (01905) 26616 Fax: (01905) 612319 E-mail: sales@roconfoam.co.uk

POLYURETHANE (PU) FOAM RAW MATERIALS

Edulan Ltd, Unit M North Stage, 92 Broadway, Salford, M50 2UW Tel: 0161-876 8040 Fax: 0161-876 8041 E-mail: sales@edulan.com
I F S Chemicals Ltd, Station Road, Roydon, King's Lynn, Norfolk, PE32 1AW Tel: (01485) 601155 Fax: (01485) 601144 E-mail: sales@ifs-group.com

POLYURETHANE (PU) FOAM STRUCTURAL OR INSULATING SYSTEMS

Kingspan Industrial Insulation Ltd, PO Box 3, Glossop, Derbyshire, SK13 8LE Tel: (0870) 8508555 Fax: (0870) 8508444 E-mail: enquires.uk@insulation.kingspan.com

POLYURETHANE (PU) LACQUERS

Lord Corporation Ltd, Stretford Motorway Estate, Barton Dock Road, Stretford, Manchester, M32 0ZH Tel: 0161-865 8048 Fax: 0161-865 0096

POLYURETHANE (PU) MOULDING SERVICES

Abbey Products Norfolk Ltd, Ayton Road, Wymondham, Norfolk, NR18 0QH Tel: (01953) 602627 Fax: (01953) 601428 E-mail: info@abbey4pu.com
Amcast Ltd, Unit 7, Alliance Close, Attleborough Fields Industrial Estate, Nuneaton, Warwickshire, CV11 6SD Tel: (024) 7635 0575 Fax: (024) 7635 0761 E-mail: enquiries@amcast.co.uk
Anigold Ltd, 5 Woodhill Industries, Nottingham Lane, Old Dalby, Melton Mowbray, Leicestershire, LE14 3LX Tel: (01664) 823359 Fax: (01664) 823359 E-mail: anigold18@hotmail.com
Chase Mouldings Ltd, 5 Swaffield Park, Hyssop Close, Cannock, Staffordshire, WS11 7FU Tel: (01543) 572425 Fax: (01543) 572451 E-mail: chase@chasemouldings.fsnet.co.uk
Elatech Polyurethane Mouldings & Castings Ltd, 34 London Road, Hailsham, East Sussex, BN27 3BW Tel: (01323) 845100 Fax: (01323) 846894
Flemings Seals Ltd, Atlas Mills, Atlas Mill Road, Brighouse, West Yorkshire, HD6 1ES Tel: (01484) 718391 Fax: (01484) 711585 E-mail: sales@flemings-seals.co.uk
Hallam Polymer Engineering Ltd, Trasco House, Callywhite Lane, Dronfield, Derbyshire, S18 2XR Tel: (01246) 415511 Fax: (01246) 414818 E-mail: sales@hallampolymer.com
Marbill Developments Sabden Ltd, Victoria Mill, Watt Street, Clitheroe, Lancashire, BB7 9ED Tel: (01282) 778031 Fax: (01282) 779507 E-mail: sales@marbill.co.uk
Tufthane Ltd, Falkland Close, Charter Avenue Industrial Estate, Coventry, CV4 8AU Tel: (024) 7646 0600 Fax: (024) 7669 4313 E-mail: admin@tufthane.com
Watts Urethane Products Ltd, Church Road, Lydney, Gloucestershire, GL15 5EN Tel: (01594) 847150 Fax: (01594) 843586 E-mail: sales@wattsgroup.co.uk

POLYURETHANE (PU) NOISE CONTROL FOAM PRODUCTS

Pritex Ltd, Station Mills, Wellington, Somerset, TA21 8NN Tel: (01823) 664271 Fax: (01823) 660023 E-mail: enquiries@pritex.co.uk

POLYURETHANE (PU) PRODUCTION MACHINERY MANUFRS

Bright Enterprises Ltd, Enterprise House, London Road, West Kingsdown, Sevenoaks, Kent, TN15 6AP Tel: (01474) 852222 Fax: (01474) 853944 E-mail: sales@rfbright.co.uk

POLYURETHANE (PU) PRODUCTS

A & S Plastics, Unit 138 Harbour Road Trading Estate, Lydney, Gloucestershire, GL15 4EJ Tel: (01594) 843000 Fax: (01594) 843000
Amcast Ltd, Unit 7, Alliance Close, Attleborough Fields Industrial Estate, Nuneaton, Warwickshire, CV11 6SD Tel: (024) 7635 0575 Fax: (024) 7635 0761 E-mail: enquiries@amcast.co.uk
B I Composites Ltd, Green Lane, Cannock, Staffordshire, WS11 0JW Tel: (01543) 466021 Fax: (01543) 574157 E-mail: firstname.lastname@bi-composites.co.uk
B I Composites Halesowen Ltd, 270 Coombs Road, Halesowen, West Midlands, B62 8AA Tel: 0121-550 7577 Fax: 0121-585 5315 E-mail: bi-composites@bi-composites.co.uk
Benoil Services Ltd, Norcombe House, Tile Barn, Woolton Hill, Newbury, Berkshire, RG20 9UZ Tel: (01635) 253412 Fax: (01635) 253899 E-mail: sales@benoil.com
Combass Ltd, Rotherham Close, Norwood Industrial Estate, Sheffield, S21 2JU Tel: 0114-248 0616 Fax: 0114-248 2684 E-mail: irmackie@aol.com
Dataroll Ltd, Knightcott Industrial Estate, Banwell, Avon, BS29 6JN Tel: (01934) 823253 Fax: (01934) 822990 E-mail: mail@dataroll.co.uk
Isothane Ltd, Newhouse Road, Huncoat Industrial Estate, Accrington, Lancashire, BB5 6NT Tel: (01254) 872555 Fax: (01254) 871522 E-mail: enquiries@isothane.com
Marbill Developments Sabden Ltd, Victoria Mill, Watt Street, Clitheroe, Lancashire, BB7 9ED Tel: (01282) 778031 Fax: (01282) 779507 E-mail: sales@marbill.co.uk
Polymer Holdings Ltd, Spurryhillock Industrial Estate, Broomhill Road, Stonehaven, Kincardineshire, AB39 2NH Tel: (01569) 766226 Fax: (01569) 766419 E-mail: sales@tubetec.co.uk
Tufthane Ltd, Falkland Close, Charter Avenue Industrial Estate, Coventry, CV4 8AU Tel: (024) 7646 0600 Fax: (024) 7669 4313 E-mail: admin@tufthane.com

POLYURETHANE (PU) RESINS

Delta Resin Products Ltd, 77 Torkington Road, Hazel Grove, Stockport, Cheshire, SK7 6NR Tel: 0161-483 4513 Fax: 0161-426 0329 E-mail: info@deltaresins.co.uk
M F R Consultancy Services Ltd, Dunelm Ho, 33 Greenfields Rise, Whitchurch, Shropshire, SY13 1EP Tel: (01948) 666778 Fax: (01948) 666775 E-mail: mfrose@mfrcsl.co.uk
Note Dome Ltd, 34 Herald Way, Binley Industrial Estate, Coventry, CV3 2RQ Tel: (024) 7663 5193 Fax: (024) 7663 5509 E-mail: sales@notedome.co.uk
Resdev Ni Ltd, 4 22 Duncrue Road, Belfast, BT3 9BP Tel: (028) 9077 6882 Fax: (028) 9077 8492 E-mail: info@resindevelopment.com
Techsil Ltd, Unit 30 Bidavon Industrial Estate, Waterloo Road, Bidford-on-Avon, Alcester, Warwickshire, B50 4JN Tel: (01789) 773232 Fax: (01789) 774239 E-mail: sales@techsil.co.uk
Whitchem Ltd, 23 Albert Street, Newcastle, Staffordshire, ST5 1JP Tel: (01782) 711777 Fax: (01782) 717290 E-mail: enquiries@whitchem.co.uk

POLYURETHANE (PU) RESINS FOR CERAMICS MANUFACTURE

Watson Group Ltd, Tudor House, Highlands Road, Shirley, Solihull, West Midlands, B90 4ND Tel: 0121-705 4624 Fax: 0121-711 1086 E-mail: jean@wapwatson.com

POLYURETHANE (PU) ROLLER COVERINGS

Dataroll Ltd, Knightcott Industrial Estate, Banwell, Avon, BS29 6JN Tel: (01934) 823253 Fax: (01934) 822990 E-mail: mail@dataroll.co.uk
J R Rubber & Polyurethane Products Ltd, Unit 28, Meadows Road, Queensway Meadows Industrial Estate, Newport, Gwent, NP19 4SS Tel: (01633) 270088 Fax: (01633) 278232 E-mail: info@jr-rubber.com

POLYURETHANE (PU) ROLLERS

Bonaprene Products, Clywedog Road South, Wrexham Industrial Estate, Wrexham, Clwyd, LL13 9XS Tel: (01978) 661478 Fax: (01978) 661190 E-mail: sales@polybush.co.uk
Just Rollers P.L.C., Somerset Industrial Estate, Cwmbran, Gwent, NP44 1QX Tel: (01633) 869436 Fax: (01633) 860046 E-mail: iain.sinclair@justrollers.com
K V Rollers Ltd, Unit 1-3 Claenwern, Avondale Industrial Estate, Pontrhydyrun, Cwmbran, Gwent, NP44 1TY Tel: (01633) 871919 Fax: (01633) 877250 E-mail: kbrollers@tiscali.co.uk
Urethane Industrial Products Ltd, Evingar Industrial Estate, Ardglen Road, Whitchurch, Hampshire, RG28 7BB Tel: (01256) 892830 Fax: (01256) 896899 E-mail: urethaneindustrial@hotmail.com

POLYURETHANE (PU) RUBBER

I T W Devcon, Unit 3 Shipton Way, Express Business Park, Rushden, Northamptonshire, NN10 6GL Tel: (0870) 4587388 Fax: (0870) 4589077 E-mail: sales@itw-devcon.co.uk

POLYURETHANE (PU) SHEET/ FILM MANUFRS

JD Pipes Ltd, Green Lane, Heywood, Lancashire, OL10 2EU Tel: (01706) 364115 Fax: (01706) 366402 E-mail: heywood@jdpipes.co.uk

Lord Corporation Ltd, Stretford Motorway Estate, Barton Dock Road, Stretford, Manchester, M32 0ZH Tel: 0161-865 8048 Fax: 0161-865 0096

Trelleborg Applied Technology, Halfpenny Lane, Knaresborough, North Yorkshire, HG5 0PP Tel: (01423) 862677 Fax: (01423) 868340 E-mail: sales@unitex.co.uk

POLYURETHANE (PU) SOLID WHEELS

▶ Polyphil Ltd, 50 Hurst Lane, Rawtenstall, Rossendale, Lancashire, BB4 7RE Tel: (01706) 229122 Fax: (01706) 211464 E-mail: polyphil@tiscali.co.uk

POLYURETHANE (PU) SPRAY COATING SERVICES

Marbill Developments Sabden Ltd, Victoria Mill, Watt Street, Clitheroe, Lancashire, BB7 9ED Tel: (01282) 778031 Fax: (01282) 779507 E-mail: sales@marbill.co.uk

POLYURETHANE (PU) SYSTEMS

▶ Grade One, Orchansy, Wells Road, Radstock, BA3 3UW Tel: (01761) 420072 Fax: (01761) 420323 E-mail: gdgrade1@aol.com

POLYURETHANE (PU) WHEEL REBONDING SERVICES

M S A Wheels & Casters Ltd, 10 Maclure Road, Rochdale, Lancashire, OL11 1DN Tel: (01706) 516640 Fax: (0870) 7590160 E-mail: sales@msawhhelsandcasters.co.uk

POLYVINYL ACETATE (PVA) ADHESIVES

C B Baggs Ltd, 1 Claremont Industrial Estate, London, NW2 1AL Tel: (020) 8905 5111 Fax: (020) 8905 5222 E-mail: info@cbbaggs.co.uk

Brian Clegg Educational Products Ltd, Regent Mill, Regent Street, Rochdale, Lancashire, OL12 0HQ Tel: (01706) 666620 Fax: (01706) 666621 E-mail: office@brianclegg.co.uk

POLYVINYL ALCOHOL (PVOH) FILM

▶ Clarisol, 1 Holme Lane, Spondon, Derby, DE21 7BP Tel: (01332) 681210 Fax: (01332) 660178 E-mail: info@clarifoil.com

POLYWRAP PACKING SERVICES

▶ John Kettlewell & Son, Warehouse, Newdown Road, Scunthorpe, South Humberside, DN17 2TX Tel: (01724) 281881 Fax: (01724) 270358

POND EQUIPMENT

Dorset Waterlily Co., Dorset Water Lilies, Yeovil Road, Halstock, Yeovil, Somerset, BA22 9RR Tel: (01935) 891668 Fax: (01935) 891946

Fantasea Aquatics, Lenton Street, Sandiacre, Nottingham, NG10 5DX Tel: 0115-939 0704 Fax: 0115-939 0704

Kettering Koi & Ponds Ltd, 63-65 Field Street, Kettering, Northamptonshire, NN16 8EW Tel: (01536) 515304 Fax: (01536) 515304

▶ Owens Aquatics, Roden Lane, Roden, Telford, Shropshire, TF6 6BP Tel: (01952) 770362 Fax: (01952) 770362 E-mail: tim@owensaquatics.co.uk

World Of Water, Mulbrooks, Hailsham, East Sussex, BN27 2RH Tel: (01323) 442400 Fax: (01323) 848400

POND FILTRATION EQUIPMENT

Handcross Aquatics Centre Country Gdn(S), Wyevale Country Gardens, London Road A23, Handcross, Haywards Heath, West Sussex, RH17 6BA Tel: (01444) 401004 Fax: (01444) 401004

POND LINER REPAIR

▶ Flexible Lining Products Ltd, Vantage Point Business Village, Mitcheldean, Gloucestershire, GL17 0DD Tel: (0845) 2262478 Fax: (0845) 2269697 E-mail: info@flexibleliningproducts.co.uk

Kettering Koi & Ponds Ltd, 63-65 Field Street, Kettering, Northamptonshire, NN16 8EW Tel: (01536) 515304 Fax: (01536) 515304

Rosedale Aquatics, 81 Home Farm Crescent, Whitnash, Leamington Spa, Warwickshire, CV31 2QY Tel: (01926) 332493 Fax: (01926) 332493 E-mail: info@rosedaleaquatics.co.uk

POND OR LAKE LINERS

Erdington Aquatic Centre, 97 Church Road, Erdington, Birmingham, B24 9BE Tel: 0121-373 1100 Fax: 0121-373 1100

Pond Liners Direct Ltd, 8 Millbrook Business Park, Hoe Lane, Nazeing, Waltham Abbey, Essex, EN9 2RJ Tel: (01992) 890901 Fax: (01992) 893393 E-mail: info@e-pond.co.uk

Russetts Developments Ltd, 27 Burners Lane, Kiln Farm, Milton Keynes, MK11 3HA Tel: (0870) 7702800 Fax: (0870) 7702801 E-mail: info@russetts.co.uk

Worthing Aquatics, High Street, Angmering, Littlehampton, West Sussex, BN16 4AW Tel: (01903) 778922 Fax: (01903) 778902

PONTOON HIRE

▶ Janson Bridging (UK) Ltd, Charles House, Toutley Rd, Wokingham, Berkshire, RG41 1QN Tel: 0845 5262050 Fax: 0118-979 5472 E-mail: sales@jansonbridging.co.uk

POOL TABLE SUPPLIES

▶ Arcade Clearance Ltd, Unit 4 City Mills, Hull Street, Morley, Leeds, LS27 8QL Tel: 0113 2527602 E-mail: sales@arcadeclearance.com

POOL TABLES

Alpha Pool Table Services, 19 Maple Grove, Tadley, Hampshire, RG26 4ND Tel: 0118-982 0190 Fax: 0118-982 0190

Ambassador Billiard Co., Priesthorpe Lane, Farsley, Pudsey, West Yorkshire, LS28 5RF Tel: 0113-204 7500 Fax: 0113-204 7501 E-mail: sales@snookermarket.co.uk

▶ Arcade Clearance Ltd, Unit 4 City Mills, Hull Street, Morley, Leeds, LS27 8QL Tel: 0113 2527602 E-mail: sales@arcadeclearance.com

▶ Bellmatic Leisure Ltd, 10-12 Boswell Square, Hillington Industrial Estate, Glasgow, G52 4BQ Tel: 0141-882 8320 Fax: 0141-810 4098 E-mail: carrigan@bellmatic.com

Blue Moon Leisure, Unit 9 The Old Retort House Hele Business Park, Witheridge Place, Ilfracombe, Devon, EX34 9RA Tel: (01271) 864922 Fax: (01271) 864922 E-mail: sales@bluemoonleisure.com

C & M Partitioning Ltd, 10-12 Stirling Road, London, E17 6BT Tel: (020) 8531 3834 Fax: (020) 8531 3837

Claremont Automatics Ltd, 40 Oakley Road, Chinnor, Oxfordshire, OX39 4ES Tel: (01844) 353635 Fax: (01844) 352750

Dayboard Ltd, Unit 6 Ravenstone Road Industrial Estate, Coalville, Leicestershire, LE67 3NB Tel: (01530) 813279 Fax: (01530) 510602 E-mail: richard@dayboard.co.uk

Dransfield Novelty Co. Ltd, Dransfield House, Mill Street, Leeds, LS9 8BP Tel: 0113-244 4555 Fax: 0113-234 3948

Kingswood Leisure Ltd, 9 Graiseley Row, Wolverhampton, WV2 4HJ Tel: (01902) 713303 Fax: (01902) 713117 E-mail: info@kwlonline.com

Peradon Ltd, 128 Richmond Row, Liverpool, L3 3BL Tel: 0151-298 1470 Fax: 0151-298 2988 E-mail: peradon@eaclare.co.uk

Pettitt Joinery Co. Ltd, Royce Road, Peterborough, PE1 5YB Tel: (01733) 567742 Fax: (01733) 567742

Thurston, Clare House, 46-48 St. Anne Street, Liverpool, L3 3DW Tel: 0151-482 2700 Fax: 0151-298 1134 E-mail: thurston@eaclare.co.uk

Titan Sports, 10 Ark Royal Way, Lairdside Technology Park, Birkenhead, Merseyside, CH41 9HT Tel: 0151-650 0110 Fax: 0151-647 3438 E-mail: sales@titansports.co.uk

POP UP DISPLAY STAND MAGNETIC TAPES

AMC Exhibitions, 1 Station Road, Foxton, Cambridge, CB22 6SA Tel: (01223) 871360 E-mail: info@amcexhibitions.co.uk

POP UP DISPLAYS

AMC Exhibitions, 1 Station Road, Foxton, Cambridge, CB22 6SA Tel: (01223) 871360 E-mail: info@amcexhibitions.co.uk

▶ Banner & Flag Co., 9 Lubnaig Gardens, Bearsden, Glasgow, G61 4QX Tel: 0141-577 9141 Fax: 0141-563 7147 E-mail: graphics@bf-c.co.uk

Dunns Imaging Group Ltd, Chester Road, Cradley Heath, West Midlands, B64 6AA Tel: (01384) 564770 Fax: (01384) 637165 E-mail: enquiries@dunns.co.uk

POPCORN PROCESSING/ VENDING MACHINES

Cornpoppers Ltd, 40-42 Potters Lane, Wednesbury, West Midlands, WS10 0AT Tel: 0121-505 3311 Fax: 0121-505 3174 E-mail: sales@cornpoppers.co.uk

PORCELAIN TABLEWARE

The Poole Pottery, 48 Wyatts Lane, Corfe Mullen, Wimborne, Dorset, BH21 3SQ Tel: (01202) 600838 E-mail: chris@mrpottery.co.uk

POROUS CERAMIC PRODUCTS

Ceramicos, The Warehouse, Whitehill Cottage, Oxhill, Warwick, CV35 0RH Tel: 01295 680176 Fax: 01295 680174 E-mail: sales@ceramicos.co.uk

Dytech Corporation Ltd, Stubley Lane, Dronfield, Derbyshire, S18 1LS Tel: (01246) 299700 Fax: (01246) 299720 E-mail: sales@hi-por.com

Hofmann Ceramic Ltd, 291 Thompson Hill, High Green, Sheffield, S35 4JT Tel: 0114-284 8161 Fax: 0114-284 6975 E-mail: hofmann.ceramic@btinternet.com

S T C Tiles, 85 Chesterfield Road, Sheffield, S8 0RN Tel: 0114-258 9423 Fax: 0114-258 9423

Valsan Ceramics Ltd, Unit 7c Whitebridge Industrial Estate, Whitebridge Lane, Stone, Staffordshire, ST15 8LQ Tel: (01785) 818626 Fax: (01785) 812114

PORT AND DOCK AUTHORITIES

▶ Great Yarmouth Port Co., 20-21 South Quay, Great Yarmouth, Norfolk, NR30 2RE Tel: (01493) 335500 Fax: (01493) 852480 E-mail: gypa@gypa.co.uk

Port of London Authority, Barkers Hall, 7 Harp Lane, London, EC3R 6LB Tel: (020) 7743 7900 Fax: (020) 7743 7998 E-mail: marketing@portoflondon.co.uk

Port Of Sunderland, Quayside House Wylam Wharf, Low Street, Sunderland, SR1 2BU Tel: 0191-553 2146 Fax: 0191-553 2145 E-mail: sales@portofsunderland.org.uk

PORTABLE AIR COMPRESSORS

▶ Air South West 2000, Unit 20 Bell Park, Bell Close, Plympton, Plymouth, PL7 4TA Tel: (01752) 344010 Fax: (01752) 344011 E-mail: air2000plymouth@eidosnet.co.uk

PORTABLE AIR CONDITIONING (AC) UNITS

Air Supply Systems Ltd, 8 Harmony Square, Glasgow, G51 3LW Tel: 0141-440 2121 Fax: 0141-440 0330

▶ Easy Air Con, Unit A6 Churcham Business Park, Churcham, Gloucester, GL2 8AX Tel: 0845 0751002 Fax: 0845 0751040 E-mail: Sales@easyaircon.co.uk

PORTABLE APPLIANCE TESTERS (PAT)

▶ Ashdale, 61 Manston CR, Leeds, LS15 8BN Tel: 0113-260 0527 Fax: 0113-260 0527 E-mail: ashdalepat@hotmail.co.uk

Halliday Electrical, Unit 31 Lynedoch Industrial Estate, Greenock, Renfrewshire, PA15 4AX Tel: (01475) 888440 Fax: (01475) 888220 E-mail: info@hallidayelectrical.co.uk

Instrotech Ltd, Unit A Penfold Trading Estate, Imperial Way, Watford, WD24 4YY Tel: (01923) 442244 Fax: (01923) 252959 E-mail: sales@instrotech.com

PORTABLE APPLIANCE TESTING (PAT) AND CALIBRATION LABELS

▶ D P H Electrical, 77 Birchtree Avenue, Peterborough, PE1 4HP Tel: (01733) 701254 E-mail: sales@dphpat.co.uk

PORTABLE APPLIANCE TESTING (PAT) SERVICES

▶ A1 Pat Testing, 65 Welldeck Road, Hartlepool, Cleveland, TS26 8JS Tel: 01429 421679 E-mail: info@a1pat-testing.co.uk

▶ ADRS Ltd, 7, Charlton Road, London, N9 8HN Tel: 020 8805 7000 E-mail: info@adrs.ltd.uk

▶ All Test Ltd, 12 Hall Lane, Elsham, Brigg, North Lincolnshire, DN20 0QY Tel: (01652) 680404 Fax: (01652) 680404 E-mail: gerald@alltest.co.uk

Anglia Electrical, Audley Field House, Audley End, Gestingthorpe, Halstead, Essex, CO9 3AU Tel: (01787) 460597 Fax: (01787) 460792 E-mail: mdutch@angliaeletricaltesting.wanado.co.uk

▶ Banbury Pat Testing Services, 157 Delapre Drive, Banbury, Oxfordshire, OX16 3WS Tel: (01295) 271049 E-mail: enquiries@pat-testing-uk.org

▶ BettaPat, Hillcrest, Cooks Cross, Alveley, Bridgnorth, Shropshire, WV15 6LS Tel: 0870 8508667 Fax: 01746 780961 E-mail: adam@bettapat.co.uk

▶ B-SafeUK, 77 Power Street, Newport, NP20 5FS Tel: (01633) 673372 E-mail: clive.blake@ntlworld.com

▶ D P H Electrical, 77 Birchtree Avenue, Peterborough, PE1 4HP Tel: (01733) 701254 E-mail: sales@dphpat.co.uk

E S T Electrical Contractors Ltd, 18 Kenchester Close, Redditch, Worcestershire, B98 0BT Tel: (01527) 529050 Fax: (01527) 510550

Electic, 40 Thorneyfields Lane, Stafford, ST17 9YS Tel: (01785) 229330 Fax: (01785) 229330

Epsilon Test Services Ltd, Epsilon House, The Square, Gloucester Business Park, Gloucester, GL3 4AD Tel: (0845) 2336600 Fax: (0845) 2336633 E-mail: enquiries@epsilontsl.co.uk

▶ G C R, 63 Risbygate Street, Bury St. Edmunds, Suffolk, IP33 3AZ Tel: (01284) 706620 Fax: (0871) 2427521 E-mail: gcrbury@tiscali.co.uk

▶ G & T Electrical Services, 46 Bren Way, Hilton, Derby, DE65 5HP Tel: (01283) 730832 E-mail: imbmbren@aol.com

Genesys I B S Ltd, Singleton Court Business Centre, Wonastow Road, Monmouth, Gwent, NP25 5JA Tel: (01600) 710300 Fax: (01600) 710301 E-mail: nick@genesysibs.com

Hi Spec UK Ltd, 189-191 Willow Lane, Lancaster, LA1 5SG Tel: (01524) 844124 Fax: (01524) 844124

▶ Ideal-Pat, 6 Bishop Street, Alfreton, Derbyshire, DE55 7EF Tel: (07904) 763289 Fax: (01773) 834508 E-mail: david@ideal-handling-derby.co.uk

Kitchner 2000, Gec Business Park, Blackburn Road, Clayton le Moors, Accrington, Lancashire, BB5 5JW Tel: (01254) 239194 Fax: (01254) 232873 E-mail: info@kitchener2000.co.uk

LB Ford Ltd, Park Lane, Nottingham, NG6 0DT Tel: 0115-927 2821 Fax: 0115-976 1041 E-mail: lb@ford.co.uk

▶ Midland Testing Services, 3 Hollis Meadow, East Leake, Loughborough, Leicestershire, LE12 6RU Tel: (01509) 854444 Fax: (01509) 854444 E-mail: kevinspencer@midlandstestingservices.co.uk

▶ MJ Pat Services, 30 Northbank Crescent, Ormesby, Middlesbrough, Cleveland, TS7 9EU Tel: (01642) 326857 E-mail: mike@mjpatservices.co.uk

▶ PAT Testing Services Ltd, 148 Uxbridge Road, Ealing, London, W13 8SB Tel: (0800) 4585041 Fax: (020) 8840 1434 E-mail: sales@pattestingservices.com

Patman Portable Appliance Testing, 33 Fitzgeorge Avenue, London, W14 0SZ Tel: 020 7603 9214 Fax: 020 7603 5366 E-mail: tom@patman.info

Puissance Computer Associates, 1 Bushey Coopers Cottage, Pond Hall Road, Hadleigh, Ipswich, IP7 5PS Tel: (01473) 822002 Fax: (01473) 829665 E-mail: sales@puissance.co.uk

▶ Quickpat, 12 St Bevans Road, Halifax, HX3 0RT Tel: (07050) 259465 Fax: (07050) 259475 E-mail: admin@quickpat.co.uk

▶ R & S Midland, 16 Primrose Meadow, Cannock, Staffordshire, WS11 7FN Tel: (01543) 274383 E-mail: richard.smith077@ntlworld.com

R U Safe Ltd, Aizlewoods Mill, Nursery Street, Sheffield, S3 8GG Tel: 0114-282 3498 Fax: 0114-282 3302 E-mail: rusafe@it-installations.co.uk

▶ Richmond Electronic Services Ltd, 42 Hurricane Way, Norwich Airport Industrial, Estate Norfolk, Norwich, NR6 6JB Tel: (020) 7942 0700 Fax: (020) 7942 0701

▶ SAA ELECTRICAL, 164 Ivyhouse Road, Dagenham, Essex, RM9 5RU Tel: 020 85937880

PORTABLE APPLIANCE TESTING (PAT) SERVICES – *continued*

▶ T2 Technical Services Ltd, PO Box 611, Hull, HU5 3ZW Tel: (0845) 2264661 Fax: (0845) 2264665 E-mail: info@t2technical.co.uk

Test Safe Ltd, Bretby Business Park, Ashby Road, Bretby, Burton-on-Trent, Staffordshire, DE15 0YZ Tel: (01283) 229873 Fax: (01283) 553094 E-mail: sales@test-safe.co.uk

PORTABLE APPLIANCE TESTING (PAT) SOFTWARE

▶ D P H Electrical, 77 Birchtree Avenue, Peterborough, PE1 4HP Tel: (01733) 701254 E-mail: sales@dphpat.co.uk

Ideal Handling Bath, 19 Highfield Gardens, Bitton, Bristol, BS30 6RN Tel: (07717) 294840 Fax: 0117-932 8130 E-mail: les@ideal-handling-bath.co.uk

▶ Ideal Pat Testing (West Midlands), 4 Brooklyn Grove, Coseley, Bilston, West Midlands, WV14 8YH Tel: 0121-557 5254 Fax: 0121-557 5254 E-mail: k-share_13@tiscali.co.uk

▶ Plugtest Ltd, 9 Mill Lane, Alwalton, Peterborough, PE7 3UZ Tel: (0870) 0630200 Fax: (0870) 0630201 E-mail: sales@plugtest.co.uk

▶ Retail Doctor, PO Box 49, Downham Market, Norfolk, PE38 9QP Tel: (0870) 2409905 Fax: (0870) 2409905 E-mail: greg@theretaildoctor.co.uk

▶ RMK Portable Appliance Testing Ltd, 51 Kings Drive, Hassocks, West Sussex, BN6 8DY Tel: (01444) 870885 Fax: (01444) 230999 E-mail: sales@rmk-pat.co.uk

PORTABLE APPLIANCE TESTING (PAT) TEST BAYS

▶ PAT Testing Services Ltd, 148 Uxbridge Road, Ealing, London, W13 8SB Tel: (0800) 4585041 Fax: (020) 8840 1434 E-mail: sales@pattestingservices.com

PORTABLE BLACKSMITHS FORGES

Maurice Gill Blacksmith, 42 Lydia Road, Walmer, Deal, Kent, CT14 9JX Tel: (01304) 362771 Fax: (01304) 362771

Swan Portaforge, Units 1 & 2 Gamma, Orchard Trading Estate, Toddington, Cheltenham, Gloucestershire, GL54 5EB Tel: (01242) 621590 Fax: (01242) 621591 E-mail: swan@swan-portaforge.co.uk

PORTABLE BUILDING HIRE

A G Site Services, Carrington Business Park, Manchester Road, Carrington, Manchester, M31 4QW Tel: 0161-775 8001 Fax: 0161-775 8090 E-mail: sales@agsiteservices.co.uk

Abbas Cabins, 30 Crow Lane, Crow, Ringwood, Hampshire, BH24 3DZ Tel: (01202) 590008 Fax: (01202) 331963 E-mail: enquiries@abbascabins.co.uk

Anglia Accommodation, 118 Lexden Road, West Bergholt, Colchester, CO6 3BP Tel: (01206) 240842 Fax: (01206) 240842

B & A Chamberlain Ltd, Trowell Lane, Sutton Bonington, Loughborough, Leicestershire, LE12 5RW Tel: (01509) 856357 Fax: 0115-985 3221 E-mail: cabins@bachamberlain.fsnet.co.uk

Cabin Centre Ltd, Sandtoft Industrial Estate, Belton Road Road, Sandtoft, Doncaster, South Yorkshire, DN9 1PN Tel: (01427) 873285 Fax: (01427) 874248 E-mail: sales@cabincentreltd.co.uk

CDC Instant Space Ltd, Bissoe, Truro, Cornwall, TR4 8QZ Tel: (08706) 082808 Fax: (01872) 862502

P.H. Clark (Tiers Cross) Ltd, Freshmoor Road, East Moors, Cardiff, CF24 5HS Tel: (029) 2047 3737 Fax: (029) 2048 1132 E-mail: sales@clarkmodualer.co.uk

Classical Toilet Hire Ltd, Unit 19 Shepherds Grove Industrial Estate, Stanton, Bury St. Edmunds, Suffolk, IP31 2AR Tel: (01359) 253556 Fax: (01359) 253557

Concept UK Building Systems, 63 Nevada Road, Canvey Island, Essex, SS8 8EY Tel: (01268) 512121 Fax: (01268) 512121 E-mail: conceptukltd@hotmail.com

Cox Accommodation, Haydock Lane, Haydock Industrial Estate, Haydock, St. Helens, Merseyside, WA11 9UQ Tel: (01942) 727284 Fax: (01942) 271064

Elliott Group Ltd, Littlewell Lane, Stanton-by-Dale, Ilkeston, Derbyshire, DE7 4QW Tel: 0115-944 8380 Fax: 0115-944 3728 E-mail: info@elliotthire.co.uk

Elliott Group Ltd, Chaddock Lane, Worsley, Manchester, M28 1DP Tel: 0161-790 3721 Fax: 0161-703 8294 E-mail: info@elliotthire.co.uk

Elliott Group Ltd, Chesney Wold, Bleak Hall, Milton Keynes, MK6 1LS Tel: (01908) 231361 Fax: (01908) 677262 E-mail: info@elliotthire.co.uk

Elliott Group Ltd, Manor Drive, Peterborough, PE4 7AP Tel: (01733) 298700 Fax: (01733) 573543 E-mail: hirediv@elliott-group.co.uk

Elliott Hire Ltd, Oliver Road, Grays, Essex, RM20 3ED Tel: (01708) 862709 Fax: (01708) 861471 E-mail: sales@workspace.co.uk

Elliotthire, Bowburn South Industrial Estate, Bowburn, Durham, DH6 5AD Tel: 0191-377 8788 Fax: 0191-377 8770 E-mail: info@elliotthire.co.uk

Elliotthire, Scotter Road South, Bottesford, Scunthorpe, South Humberside, DN17 2BW Tel: (01724) 279660 Fax: (01724) 848384 E-mail: info@elliotthire.co.uk

Elliotthire Hire Centres, Shaw Street, West Bromwich, West Midlands, B70 0TX Tel: 0121-506 1060 Fax: 0121-556 5081 E-mail: info@elliotthire.co.uk

F G Portable Buildings, North Barn Farm, Winterborne Stickland, Blandford Forum, Dorset, DT11 0ED Tel: (01258) 881350 Fax: (01258) 880668

Four Jays Site A Loo, Barling Farm, East Sutton, Maidstone, Kent, ME17 3DX Tel: (01622) 843135 Fax: (01622) 844410 E-mail: sales@fourjays.co.uk

Georgian Hire Ltd, Unit 6 Farrington Fields Trading Estate, Farrington Gurney, Bristol, BS39 6UU Tel: (01761) 451457 Fax: (01761) 451458 E-mail: sales@georgianhireltd.co.uk

Greenline Ni Ltd, Mallusk Park, Mallusk Road, Newtownabbey, County Antrim, BT36 4FS Tel: (028) 9083 6000 Fax: (028) 9034 2593 E-mail: info@greenlinebuildings.com

Hewden Plant Hire Ltd, Wallwork Road, Astley, Tyldesley, Manchester, M29 7JX Tel: (01772) 459460 Fax: (01772) 459295

Hewdon Portable Buildings, Norman Road, Belvedere, Kent, DA17 6JY Tel: (020) 8311 9796 Fax: (020) 8310 7265

Hire Station, Manor House Road, Long Eaton, Nottingham, NG10 3GA Tel: 0115-946 1151 Fax: 0115-946 1151

Kabin Hire Ltd, Caerphilly Industrial Park, Van Road, Caerphilly, Mid Glamorgan, CF83 3EL Tel: (029) 2088 3079 Fax: (029) 2088 4518 E-mail: kabinhire@breathemail.net

Keyspace Ltd, Raven Street, Hull, HU9 1PP Tel: (01482) 326565 Fax: (01482) 216337 E-mail: sales@keyspace.co.uk

Kwikspace Portables, Whitesmith, Lewes, East Sussex, BN8 6JG Tel: (01825) 872000 Fax: (01825) 872999

Medway Portable Buildings, 29 Stoke Road, Hoo, Rochester, Kent, ME3 9BE Tel: (01634) 250890 Fax: (01634) 250890

Mobile Storage UK Ltd, Woodham Industrial Park, Creighton Road, Woodham, Aylesbury, Buckinghamshire, HP18 0QE Tel: (01296) 655411 Fax: (01296) 651894 E-mail: info@mobilestorage.com

Pasuda Buildings Ltd, Highfield Lane, Sheffield, S13 9NA Tel: 0114-254 0188 Fax: 0114-254 0705 E-mail: sales@pasuda.co.uk

Pennine Services, Bredbury Park Way, Bredbury Park Industrial Estate, Bredbury, Stockport, Cheshire, SK6 2SN Tel: 0161-406 7555 Fax: 0161-406 7555

Philspace Ltd, 109-111 Bitterne Road West, Southampton, SO18 1AR Tel: (023) 8022 3333 Fax: (023) 8021 5100 E-mail: sales@rigfone.co.uk

▶ Ravenstock MSG Ltd, Albion Parade, Gravesend, Kent, DA12 2RN Tel: (01474) 534665 Fax: (01474) 534668 E-mail: webenquiries@ravenstockmsg.com

Ravenstock MSG Ltd, Philadelphia Complex, Philadelphia, Houghton le Spring, Tyne & Wear, DH4 4TG Tel: 0191-584 1992 Fax: 0191-584 9191 E-mail: webenquiries@ravenstockmsg.com

Raymond Cullen & Sons, 6 Rock Road, Lisburn, County Antrim, BT28 3TF Tel: (028) 9264 8783 Fax: (028) 9264 8331 E-mail: raymondcullensons@btinternet.com

Rollalong Hire, Unit 8 Fordwater Trading Estate, Ford Road, Chertsey, Surrey, KT16 8HG Tel: (0870) 7525929 Fax: (0870) 7525939

Rollalong Hire Ltd, Phoenix Industrial Estate, Inchinnan Road, Paisley, Renfrewshire, PA3 2RP Tel: 0141-887 4124 Fax: 0141-889 0077

▶ S G B plc, 86-88 Gresham Road, London, SW9 7NP Tel: (020) 7924 9000 Fax: (020) 7738 4144

▶ S G B plc, Richmond Walk, Plymouth, PL1 4LT Tel: (01752) 561575 Fax: (01752) 606892

▶ S G B Rovacabin, Green Lane, Felling, Gateshead, Tyne & Wear, NE10 0EZ Tel: (0800) 585383 Fax: 0191-469 5175

▶ S G B Rovacabin, 12 Dunnswood Road, Wardpark South, Cumbernauld, Glasgow, G67 3EN Tel: (01236) 729601 Fax: (01236) 738005

▶ S G B Rovacabin, 609 London Road, Grays, Essex, RM20 3BJ Tel: (0800) 585383 Fax: (01708) 869560

S G B Rovacabin, B Peterley Road, Cowley, Oxford, OX4 2TZ Tel: (01865) 337200 Fax: (01865) 337201 E-mail: rovasales@sgb.co.uk

▶ S G B Rovacabin Haydock, Anglezarke Road, Sankey Valley Industrial Estate, Newton-le-Willows, Merseyside, WA12 8DJ Tel: (0800) 585383 Fax: (01925) 291045

▶ S G B Rovacabin Hire Ltd, Ainleys Industrial Estate, Huddersfield Road, Elland, West Yorkshire, HX5 9BZ Tel: 0161-620 3047 Fax: (01454) 322948

▶ S G B Rovacabin Hire Ltd, Ainleys Industrial Estate, Huddersfield Road, Elland, West Yorkshire, HX5 9BZ Tel: 0161-620 3047 Fax: (01422) 379142

Search Liverpool Ltd, Hammond Road, Knowsley Industrial Park, Liverpool, L33 7UW Tel: 0151-546 3361 Fax: 0151-549 1914 E-mail: info@wgsearch.co.uk

▶ SGB Rovacabin, Unit 54 Hobbs Industrial Estate, Newchapel, Lingfield, Surrey, RH7 6HN Tel: (01342) 833869 Fax: (01342) 835550

Sibcas Ltd, Chanters Indust Estate, Arley Way, Atherton, Manchester, M46 9BP Tel: (01942) 896688 Fax: (01942) 894967

Site Unit Rentals Ltd, Watlington Road, Cowley, Oxford, OX4 6SR Tel: (01865) 747025 Fax: (01865) 774562 E-mail: sales@surhire.com

▶ Speedy Hire plc, Chase House, 16 The Parks, Newton-le-Willows, Merseyside, WA12 0JQ Tel: (01942) 720000 Fax: (01942) 720077 E-mail: customer.services@speedyhire.co.uk

Speedy Space Ltd, The Premier Partnership Estate, Leys Rd, Brockmoore, Brierley Hill, W. Midlands, DY5 3UP Tel: (01384) 572635 Fax: (01384) 480434

Swift Ltd, 150 Walkden Road, Worsley, Manchester, M28 7DP Tel: 0161-790 3428 Fax: 0161-703 8793

Terrapin Ltd, Bomnd Avenue, Bletchley, Milton Keynes, MK1 1JJ Tel: 0115-907 2700 Fax: 0115-972 2203 E-mail: sales@terrapin-ltd.co.uk

Wernick Hire Ltd, Pipe Lane, Banbury, Oxfordshire, OX16 2RP Tel: (01295) 275315 Fax: (01295) 709827

Wernick Hire, Shepherds Grove Industrial Estate, Stanton, Bury St. Edmunds, Suffolk, IP31 2AR Tel: (01359) 250526 Fax: (01359) 252019 E-mail: hire@wernickbury.co.uk

Wernick Hire Ltd, Wellington Road, Gateshead, Tyne & Wear, NE11 9JL Tel: 0191-461 1000 Fax: 0191-461 1001

Wernick Hire Ltd, Cartmore Industrial Estate, Lochgelly, Fife, KY5 8LL Tel: (01592) 783355 Fax: (01592) 783366 E-mail: hire@wenicklockgelly.co.uk

Wernick Hire Ltd, B Fairfax Road, Heathfield Industrial Estate, Newton Abbot, Devon, TQ12 6UD Tel: (01626) 832999 Fax: (01626) 832393

Your Key Ltd, Unit 4, Christie Place, Bognor Regis, West Sussex, PO22 9RT Tel: (01243) 841007 Fax: (01243) 864040 E-mail: portables@your-key.co.uk

PORTABLE BUILDINGS

Ashvale Timber Industries, 62-68 Birling Road, Ashford, Kent, TN24 8BB Tel: (01233) 623592 Fax: (01233) 712611

B & A Chamberlain Ltd, Trowell Lane, Sutton Bonington, Loughborough, Leicestershire, LE12 5RW Tel: (01509) 856357 Fax: 0115-985 3221 E-mail: cabins@bachamberlain.fsnet.co.uk

Barretts Garden Buildings Ltd, Portsmouth Road, Ripley, Woking, Surrey, GU23 6EW Tel: (01483) 224186 E-mail: info@barrettsgardenbuildings.co.uk

Bradley Builders, Talbot Buildings, Newnham Bridge, Tenbury Wells, Worcestershire, WR15 8JF Tel: (01584) 781489 Fax: (01584) 781489

Bullock & Driffill Ltd, Staunton Works, Newark Road, Staunton in the Vale, Nottingham, NG13 9PF Tel: (01400) 280000 Fax: (01400) 280010 E-mail: bullock.driffill@btopenworld.com

Capital Sheds, 12 Western Terrace, Edinburgh, EH12 5QF Tel: 0131-313 3515 Fax: 0131-313 3515 E-mail: info@capitalsheds.com

Chew Valley Hire Ltd, Woodwick Farm, Bristol Road, Compton Martin, Bristol, BS40 6NQ Tel: (01761) 221105 Fax: (01761) 221121 E-mail: hans@cvhire.force9.co.uk

P.H. Clark (Tiers Cross) Ltd, Freshmoor Road, East Moors, Cardiff, CF24 5HS Tel: (029) 2047 3737 Fax: (029) 2048 1132 E-mail: sales@clarkmodualer.co.uk

Classic Portable Buildings Ltd, Gordleton Farm, Silver Street, Sway, Lymington, Hampshire, SO41 6DJ Tel: (01590) 683193 Fax: (01590) 683193 E-mail: mail@classic-pb.co.uk

Crocker Bros, 8-18 Station Road, Chellaston, Derby, DE73 5SU Tel: (01332) 700699 Fax: (01332) 705655 E-mail: sales@crockerbros.co.uk

Elliott Group Ltd, Braemar House, Snelsins Lane, Cleckheaton, West Yorkshire, BD19 3UE Tel: (01274) 863221 Fax: (01274) 861582 E-mail: fastrack@elliott-algeco.com

Elliott Group Ltd, Littlewell Lane, Stanton-by-Dale, Ilkeston, Derbyshire, DE7 4QW Tel: 0115-944 8380 Fax: 0115-944 3728 E-mail: info@elliotthire.co.uk

Elliott Group Ltd, Chesney Wold, Bleak Hall, Milton Keynes, MK6 1LS Tel: (01908) 231361 Fax: (01908) 677262 E-mail: info@elliotthire.co.uk

Elliott Group Ltd, Manor Drive, Peterborough, PE4 7AP Tel: (01733) 298700 Fax: (01733) 573543 E-mail: hirediv@elliott-group.co.uk

Elliott Hire Ltd, Oliver Road, Grays, Essex, RM20 3ED Tel: (01708) 862709 Fax: (01708) 861471 E-mail: sales@workspace.co.uk

Elliott Redispace, Valletta Street, Hull, HU9 5NP Tel: (01482) 781202 Fax: (01482) 712157 E-mail: hirediv@elliott-group.co.uk

Elliotthire, Chittening Industrial Estate, Avonmouth, Bristol, BS11 0YB Tel: 0117 916 3400 Fax: 0117 982 2832 E-mail: info@elliotthire.co.uk

Elliotthire, Bowburn South Industrial Estate, Bowburn, Durham, DH6 5AD Tel: 0191-377 8788 Fax: 0191-377 8770 E-mail: info@elliotthire.co.uk

Elliotthire, Scotter Road South, Bottesford, Scunthorpe, South Humberside, DN17 2BW Tel: (01724) 279660 Fax: (01724) 848384 E-mail: info@elliotthire.co.uk

Elliotthire Hire Centres, Shaw Street, West Bromwich, West Midlands, B70 0TX Tel: 0121-506 1060 Fax: 0121-556 5081 E-mail: info@elliotthire.co.uk

Evans Windows Ltd, Cambrian Place, Pool Road, Newtown, Powys, SY16 1DH Tel: (01686) 626465 Fax: (01686) 627695

Fords Of Blythe Bridge Ltd, 203 Groveindley Lane, Blythe Bridge, Stoke-on-Trent, ST11 9JS Tel: (01782) 392125 Fax: (01782) 396622 E-mail: fords@blythebridge30.fsbusiness.co.uk

G E Capital Modular Space Ltd, Hadnock Rd, Monmouth, Gwent, NP25 3NQ Tel: (01600) 712722 Fax: (01600) 712442

G E Collis & Sons Ltd, Queen St Industrial Estate, Queens Drive, Burntwood, Staffordshire, WS7 4QF Tel: (01543) 686370 Fax: (01543) 675221 E-mail: sales@collissheds.co.uk

Glasdon Manufacturing Ltd, Industrial Estate, Poulton Industrial Estate, Poulton-le-Fylde, Lancashire, FY6 8JW Tel: (01253) 891131 Fax: (01253) 891923 E-mail: sales@glasdon-manufacturing.co.uk

Greenline Ni Ltd, Mallusk Park, Mallusk Road, Newtownabbey, County Antrim, BT36 4FS Tel: (028) 9083 6000 Fax: (028) 9034 2593 E-mail: info@greenlinebuildings.com

Groundhog UK, Ynysygerwn Avenue, Aberdulais, Neath, West Glamorgan, SA10 8HH Tel: (01639) 641166 Fax: (01639) 641188 E-mail: info@groundhog.co.uk

Harveys Garden Buildings, Woodside Garden Centre, Arterial Road, Rayleigh, Essex, SS6 7TZ Tel: (01268) 775770 Fax: (01268) 769155 E-mail: harveysgarden@btconnect.com

Harveys Garden & Leisure Buildings Ltd, Sectional Building Centre, Unit 5, Maltings Road, Battlesbridge, Wickford, Essex, SS11 7RH Tel: (01268) 768616 Fax: (01268) 769155

J M Building Systems, 5 Anglesey Place, Great Barton, Bury St. Edmunds, Suffolk, IP31 2TW Tel: (01284) 787408 Fax: (01284) 787408

J & W Milligan, Galston Road, Hurlford, Kilmarnock, Ayrshire, KA1 5HS Tel: (01563) 527572 Fax: (01563) 536758 E-mail: sales@millicabin.com

Lydney Containers Ltd, Unit 29-30 Vulcan Works, Wargrave Road, Newton-le-Willows, Merseyside, WA12 8RN Tel: 01695 731890 Fax: 01925 229484 E-mail: info@lydneycontainers.co.uk

Medway Portable Buildings, 29 Stoke Road, Hoo, Rochester, Kent, ME3 9BE Tel: (01634) 250890 Fax: (01634) 250890

N G Phillips, Lays Farm, Charlton Road, Keynsham, Bristol, BS31 2SE Tel: 0117-986 6172 Fax: 0117-986 6172

New Line Sheds Ltd, Padworth Saw Mills, Rag Hill, Aldermaston, Reading, RG7 4NU Tel: 0118-971 2245 Fax: 0118-942 6391 E-mail: sales@newlinesheds.co.uk

Passmores Portable Buildings Ltd, Canal Road, Strood, Rochester, Kent, ME2 4DR Tel: (01634) 290033 Fax: (01634) 290084 E-mail: info@passmores.co.uk

Philspace Ltd, 109-111 Bitterne Road West, Southampton, SO18 1AR Tel: (023) 8022 3333 Fax: (023) 8021 5100 E-mail: sales@rigfone.co.uk

Premier Transline Group, Catwick Lane, Brandesburton, Driffield, North Humberside, YO25 8RW Tel: (01964) 542131 Fax: (01964) 543572

Prime Garden Buildings, 1a Vale Drive, Worthing, West Sussex, BN14 0DD Tel: (01903) 873125 Fax: (01903) 873125

R J Wey & Sons, South Street, Crewkerne, Somerset, TA18 8DA Tel: (01460) 72873 Fax: (01460) 72873

R Page Concrete Buildings Ltd, 951-953 High Road, Romford, RM6 4HB Tel: (020) 8590 3701 Fax: (020) 8590 1791

▶ Ravenstock MSG Ltd, 3 Hornock Road, Coatbridge, Lanarkshire, ML5 2QA Tel: (01236) 449060 Fax: (01236) 710593 E-mail: info@mobilestorage.com

Raymond Cullen & Sons, 6 Rock Road, Lisburn, County Antrim, BT28 3TF Tel: (028) 9264 8783 Fax: (028) 9264 8331 E-mail: raymondcullensons@btinternet.com

Rosedale Building Systems Ltd, 234 Shay Lane, Holmfield, Halifax, West Yorkshire, HX2 9AD Tel: (01422) 244303 Fax: (01422) 247877 E-mail: r.b.s.ltd@btconnect.com

Rubb Buildings Ltd, Dukesway, Team Valley Trading Estate, Gateshead, Tyne & Wear, NE11 0QE Tel: 0191-482 2211 Fax: 0191-482 2516 E-mail: info@rubb.co.uk

SGB Rovacabin, 81 North Road, Yate, Bristol, BS37 7PS Tel: (01454) 325010 Fax: (01454) 322948

Bruce Stamp, Station Yard, Pinchbeck, Spalding, Lincolnshire, PE11 3RF Tel: (01775) 723096 Fax: 01755 723096

Tabs Technicom UK P.L.C., Stockholm Road, Suttonfields Industrial Estate, Hull, HU7 0XW Tel: (01482) 825558 Fax: (01482) 825557

Thurston Building Systems, Quarry Hill Industrial Estate, Hawking Croft Road, Horbury, Wakefield, West Yorkshire, WF4 6AJ Tel: (01924) 265461 Fax: (01924) 280246 E-mail: sales@thurstongroup.co.uk

PORTABLE BUILDINGS – *continued*

Tilden Modular Building Systems Ltd, Stable Block, Coombe Lodge, Blagden, Bristol, BS40 7RG Tel: (01454) 413111 Fax: (01761) 462892 E-mail: info@tilden.co.uk

Waker UK Ltd, 99 Bellshill Road, Uddingston, Glasgow, G71 7NT Tel: (01698) 801010 Fax: (01698) 808068

Wernick Hire, Shepherds Grove Industrial Estate, Stanton, Bury St. Edmunds, Suffolk, IP31 2AR Tel: (01359) 250526 Fax: (01359) 252019 E-mail: hire@wernickbury.co.uk

Wernick Hire Ltd, 220 Leads Road, Hull, HU7 0DF Tel: (01482) 791990 Fax: (01482) 791960 E-mail: hire.hull@wernick.co.uk

Wernick Hire Ltd, B Fairfax Road, Heathfield Industrial Estate, Newton Abbot, Devon, TQ12 6UD Tel: (01626) 832999 Fax: (01626) 832393

York Timber Products, Bell Farm, Riccall Road, Escrick, York, YO19 6ED Tel: (01757) 248927 Fax: (01757) 248293 E-mail: sales@yorktimber.co.uk

Your Key Ltd, Unit 4, Christie Place, Bognor Regis, West Sussex, PO22 9RT Tel: (01243) 841007 Fax: (01243) 864040 E-mail: portables@your-key.co.uk

PORTABLE COMPUTER ROOM DATA STORAGE SAFES

Eurotec Distribution Ltd, Church Croft House, Station Road, Rugeley, Staffordshire, WS15 2HE Tel: (01889) 503100 Fax: (01889) 503101 E-mail: sales@media-resources.co.uk

Safe Security, 29 New Hall Lane, Preston, PR1 5NX Tel: (01772) 793792 Fax: (01772) 651886 E-mail: info@thesafeshop.co.uk

PORTABLE COMPUTER SOFTWARE

Beyond 2000 PC Systems Software, 97-103 Upper Parliament Street, Nottingham, NG1 6LA Tel: 0115-924 3000 Fax: (0870) 3304300

PORTABLE COMPUTERS

Toshiba Information Systems (UK) Ltd, Toshiba Court, Weybridge Business Park, Addlestone Road, Weybridge, Surrey, KT15 2UL Tel: (01932) 841600 Fax: (01932) 852455 E-mail: contact@toshiba-tiu.co.uk

PORTABLE DANCE FLOORING

▶ A & M Marquees, 11 Stanley Road, Knutsford, Cheshire, WA16 0DE Tel: (07866) 580529 Fax: (01565) 633977 E-mail: info@ammarquees.com

C P S Seating & Staging, Station Yard, Station Road, Bawtry, Doncaster, South Yorkshire, DN10 6QD Tel: (01302) 711183 Fax: (01302) 711171

Watson Brook, 119a High Street, Tewkesbury, Gloucestershire, GL20 5JY Tel: (01684) 291155 Fax: (01684) 291166 E-mail: sales@watsonbrook.co.uk

PORTABLE DESOLDERING GUNS

▶ Dancap Electronics, 24 Trent Crescent, Thatcham, Berkshire, RG18 3DN Tel: (01635) 866394 Fax: (01635) 869589 E-mail: dancap@btinternet.com

PORTABLE DOMESTIC WATER FILTERS

Aqua Cure P.L.C, Aqua Cure House, Hall Street, Southport, Merseyside, PR9 0SE Tel: (01704) 501616 Fax: (01704) 544916 E-mail: sales@aquacure.plc.uk

Aquapure Water Treatment Equipment, 9 Richmond Mansions, Denton Road, Twickenham, TW1 2HH Tel: (020) 8892 9010 Fax: (020) 8892 9010 E-mail: info@aquapure.co.uk

Silverline UK Ltd, Whitemoor, Iddesleigh, Winkleigh, Devon, EX19 8BN Tel: (01805) 804202 Fax: (01805) 804680 E-mail: enquiries@silverlineuk.co.uk

PORTABLE ELECTRIC HEATERS

BN Thermic Ltd, 34 Woodside Road, London, SE25 5DY Tel: (01293) 547361 Fax: (01293) 531432 E-mail: sales@bnthermic.co.uk

PORTABLE EMBOSSING MACHINES

P R O Marketing Co. Ltd, Unit 10 Jubilee Trade Centre, Jubilee Road, Letchworth Garden City, Hertfordshire, SG6 1SP Tel: (01462) 677188 Fax: (01462) 685275 E-mail: sales@proengraving.com

William Jones Clifton Ltd, 32 Lower Essex Street, Birmingham, B5 6SN Tel: 0121-622 8900 Fax: 0121-622 8909 E-mail: sales@jonesclifton.com

PORTABLE EMERGENCY SHOWER UNITS

Hughes Safety Showers Ltd, Whitefield Road, Bredbury, Stockport, Cheshire, SK6 2SS Tel: 0161-430 6618 Fax: 0161-430 7928 E-mail: sales@hughes-safety-showers.co.uk

Professional Protection Systems Ltd, Protection House, Sherbourne Drive, Tilbrook, Milton Keynes, MK7 8HX Tel: (01908) 272240 Fax: (01908) 371605

PORTABLE EXHIBITION STANDS

▶ Graphic Pavement Signs Ltd, Letchworth Garden City, Hertfordshire, SG6 3XH Tel: (01462) 673831 Fax: (01462) 481703 E-mail: mail@posterholders.fsnet.co.uk

PORTABLE FANS

Astra Distribution Manchester Ltd, Unit 6, Lowercroft Business Park, Lowercroft Road, Bury, Lancashire, BL8 3PA Tel: 0161-797 3222 Fax: 0161-797 3444 E-mail: support@astra247.com

O.N. Beck & Co. Ltd, 104 Fox Lane, Palmers Green, London, N13 4AX Tel: (020) 8886 3444 Fax: (020) 8886 9218 E-mail: sales@onbeck.co.uk

PORTABLE FIRE ESCAPE LADDERS

Cowley Fire, 29 Arkwright Court, Blackpool & Fylde Industrial Estate, Blackpool, FY4 5DR Tel: (01253) 769666 Fax: (01253) 769888 E-mail: info@cowleyfire.co.uk

PORTABLE GAS ANALYSERS

▶ A & R Designs Ltd, Unit 21, Stevenston Industrial Estate, Stevenston, Ayrshire, KA20 3LR Tel: (01294) 601042 Fax: (01294) 601400 E-mail: ardgas@aol.com

PORTABLE GENERATOR SETS

Briggs & Stratton Power Products Group, Road Four, Winsford Industrial Estate, Winsford, Cheshire, CW7 3QN Tel: (01606) 862182 Fax: (01606) 862201

PORTABLE HARDNESS TEST EQUIPMENT

Electro Arc Co. Ltd, The Wallows Industrial Estate, Fens Pool Avenue, Brierley Hill, West Midlands, DY5 1QA Tel: (01384) 263426 Fax: (01384) 79017 E-mail: sales@electroarc.co.uk

PORTABLE HEATERS

Andrews Sykes Hire Ltd, Premier House, Darlington Street, Wolverhampton, WV1 4JJ Tel: (01902) 328700 Fax: (01902) 422466 E-mail: info@andrews-sykes.com

PORTABLE HUTS

Wernick Group Holdings Ltd, Molineux House, Russell Gardens, Wickford, Essex, SS11 8BL Tel: (01268) 735544 E-mail: simon.doran@wernickwickford.co.uk

PORTABLE HYDRAULIC TOOLS

J C B Cab Systems Ltd, Riverside, Rugeley, Staffordshire, WS15 2WA Tel: (01889) 572700 Fax: (01889) 585999 E-mail: enquiries@jcb.com

PORTABLE KIOSKS

Bowden & Dolphin Ltd, 16 Cherrywood Road, Birmingham, B9 4UD Tel: 0121-773 6000 Fax: 0121-773 4070 E-mail: info@bowdenanddolphinsigns.com

Fibaform Products Ltd, 22a Caton Road, Lansil Industrial Estate, Lancaster, LA1 3PQ Tel: (01524) 60182 Fax: (01524) 389829 E-mail: info@fibaform.co.uk

Glasdon Manufacturing Ltd, Industrial Estate, Poulton Industrial Estate, Poulton-le-Fylde, Lancashire, FY6 8JW Tel: (01253) 891131 Fax: (01253) 891923 E-mail: sales@glasdon-manufacturing.co.uk

PORTABLE KITCHEN HIRE

Elliott Gamble Kitchen Rental Ltd, St. Georges House, Gaddesby Lane, Rearsby, Leicester, LE7 4YH Tel: (01664) 424888 Fax: (01664) 424955 E-mail: enquiries@gamble-kr.co.uk

PORTABLE KITCHENS

PKL Group (UK) Ltd, Stella Way, Bishops Cleeve, Cheltenham, Glos, GL52 7DQ Tel: (01242) 663000 Fax: (01242) 677819 E-mail: postbox@pkl.co.uk

PORTABLE LEAK DETECTORS

Girovac Ltd, Units 1 & 2, Douglas Bader Close, North Walsham, Norfolk, NR28 0TZ Tel: (01692) 403008 Fax: (01692) 404611 E-mail: enquiries@girovac.com

Varian Ltd, 28 Manor Road, Walton-On-Thames, Surrey, KT12 2QF Tel: (01932) 898000 Fax: (01932) 228769

PORTABLE LIFTING EQUIPMENT

Reid Lifting Ltd, 3 Bulwark Business Park, Bulwark Road, Bulwark, Chepstow, Gwent, NP16 5JG Tel: (01291) 620796 Fax: (01291) 626490 E-mail: enquiries@reidlifting.com

PORTABLE LIGHTING

Cluson Engineering Ltd, Unit 6, Bedford Road, Petersfield, Hampshire, GU32 3LJ Tel: (01730) 264672 Fax: (01730) 260475 E-mail: sales@clulite.co.uk

PORTABLE MACHINE TOOLS

C & G, 284 North Road, Yate, Bristol, BS37 7LQ Tel: (01454) 228387 Fax: (01454) 228145 E-mail: cgtoolcutter@aol.com

PORTABLE METAL DETECTORS

Elcometer Instruments Ltd, Edge Lane, Droylsden, Manchester, M43 6BU Tel: 0161-371 6000 Fax: 0161-371 6010 E-mail: sale@elcometer.com

PORTABLE MOBILE CONVEYOR SYSTEMS

Conveyor Hire, Unit 15d Nuralite Industrial Centre, Canal Road, Higham, Rochester, Kent, ME3 7JA Tel: (01474) 824747 Fax: (01474) 824747 E-mail: mokempen@blueyonder.co.uk

Newland Engineering Co. Ltd, Captain Clarke Road, Hyde, Cheshire, SK14 4RF Tel: 0161-368 0326 Fax: 0161-367 8004 E-mail: info@newland-conveyors.com

Powerscreen International Distribution Ltd, Coalisland Road, Dungannon, County Tyrone, BT71 4DR Tel: (028) 8774 0701 Fax: (028) 8774 7231 E-mail: sales@powerscreen.co.uk

Rako Products Ltd, Brunel Way, Stonehouse, Gloucestershire, GL10 3SX Tel: (01453) 829900 Fax: (01453) 829928 E-mail: sales@rako-products.co.uk

PORTABLE OIL FIRED HEATERS, *See Heaters, Fuel Oil Fired etc*

PORTABLE OR COLLAPSIBLE SHELTERS

Chaselink UK Ltd, New Street, Chase Terrace, Burntwood, Staffordshire, WS7 1BS Tel: (01543) 459655 Fax: (01543) 459949 E-mail: sales@chaselink.co.uk

J.T. Inglis & Sons Ltd, Riverside Works, Carolina Port, Dundee, DD1 3LU Tel: (01382) 462131 Fax: (01382) 462846

Jordans Sunblinds Ltd, York St, Hull, HU2 0QW Tel: (01482) 326657 Fax: (01482) 212486 E-mail: enquiries@jordansofhull.co.uk

Andrew Mitchell & Co. Ltd, 15 Dunivaig Road, Glasgow, G33 4TT Tel: 0141-773 5454 Fax: 0141-773 5455E-mail: info1@mitco.co.uk

Rubb Buildings Ltd, Dukesway, Team Valley Trading Estate, Gateshead, Tyne & Wear, NE11 0QE Tel: 0191-482 2211 Fax: 0191-482 2516 E-mail: info@rubb.co.uk

PORTABLE OR TEMPORARY SECURITY FENCING

Heras Readyfence Service, Unit B1, Castle Road, Eurolink, Sittingbourne, Kent, ME10 3RL Tel: (01795) 423261 Fax: (01795) 426351 E-mail: readyfence.sales@readyfence.co.uk

PORTABLE OR TEMPORARY SECURITY FENCING HIRE

▶ Advance Supplies Eastern Ltd, Victoria Stables, South Road, Bourne, Lincolnshire, PE10 9JZ Tel: (01778) 426633 Fax: (01778) 426899 E-mail: sales@advancesupplies.co.uk

Elliotthire, Chittening Industrial Estate, Avonmouth, Bristol, BS11 0YB Tel: 0117 916 3400 Fax: 0117 982 2832 E-mail: info@elliotthire.co.uk

Industrial & Agricultural Engineers, Riverside Works, Macclesfield Road, Leek, Staffordshire, ST13 8LB Tel: (01538) 399200 Fax: (01538) 373005 E-mail: sales@iae.co.uk

▶ Site Equipment Ltd, Bowerhurst, Mill Lane, Crondall, Farnham, Surrey, GU10 5RP Tel: (01252) 851988 Fax: (01252) 851989 E-mail: hire@site-equip.co.uk

Wade Building Services Ltd, Groveland Road, Tipton, West Midlands, DY4 7TN Tel: 0121-520 8121 Fax: 0121-557 7061 E-mail: sales@wade-bs.co.uk

PORTABLE OR WARNING ROAD SIGNS

Cougar Developments Glanford Ltd, Sixth Avenue, Flixborough Industrial Estate, Flixborough, Scunthorpe, South Humberside, DN15 8SH Tel: (01724) 841111 Fax: (01724) 841144 E-mail: christine@cougardevelopments.co.uk

PORTABLE POWER TOOL HIRE

A C D Plant, Unit 20 Slingsby Close, Attleborough Fields Ind Estate, Nuneaton, Warwickshire, CV11 6RP Tel: (024) 7638 1503 Fax: (024) 7635 4445

A W V Turner & Co. Ltd, Rex Works, Harvest Lane, Sheffield, S3 8EB Tel: 0114-272 4162 Fax: 0114-276 9284 E-mail: awvturner@awvturner.f9.co.uk

A76 Plant & Tool Hire Ltd, 203-205 Etruria Road, Stoke-on-Trent, ST1 5NS Tel: (01782) 858998 Fax: (01782) 858999

Alpha Tools (Northern) Ltd, Grove Road, Wakefield, West Yorkshire, WF1 1UW Tel: (01924) 384227 Fax: (01924) 363525 E-mail: sales@alphatools.co.uk

Ash Tool Hire & Sales, Unit 2 Walker Street, Oldham, OL8 1SX Tel: 0161-678 8088 Fax: 0161-678 8005

Beaver Tool Hire Ltd, 15-17 Kingston Road, Portsmouth, PO1 5RX Tel: (023) 9282 6632 Fax: (023) 9282 6639

Brandon Hire plc, 63 Lyde Green, Halesowen, West Midlands, B63 2PQ Tel: (01384) 566936 Fax: (01384) 410134 E-mail: info@brandonhire.plc.uk

Brandon Hire plc, 48 Ratcliffe Gate, Mansfield, Nottinghamshire, NG18 2JL Tel: (01623) 635136 Fax: (01623) 624006

▶ Builders Equipment Ltd, City Road, Norwich, NR1 3AN Tel: (01473) 236316 Fax: (01473) 281788E-mail: mail@builders.equipment.co.uk

Carters Tools Ltd, 74-76 Elmers End Road, Anerley, London, SE20 7UX Tel: (020) 8659 7222 Fax: (020) 8659 2727 E-mail: sales@carterstools.co.uk

Chertsey Tool Hire Ltd, 149 Upper Weybourne Lane, Farnham, Surrey, GU9 9DD Tel: (01252) 333122 Fax: (01252) 333155 E-mail: farnhamsales@chertseytoolhire.co.uk

E J Parkinson & Son Ltd, Kirk Lane, Yeadon, Leeds, LS19 7ET Tel: 0113-250 9111 Fax: 0113-250 0223

Engineerstore Ltd, East Street, Prittlewell, Southend-On-Sea, SS2 5EQ Tel: (01702) 611711 Fax: (01702) 600048

Hewden Hire Centres Ltd, 39-40 New Summer Street, Birmingham, B19 3QN Tel: 0121-359 4282 Fax: 0121-333 6866

Lord Hire Centre, Shields Road, Newcastle upon Tyne, NE6 2UD Tel: 0191-224 0044 E-mail: lord@lordhire.co.uk

Power Tool Rentals Ltd, Halifax Road, Hipperholme, Halifax, West Yorkshire, HX3 8ER Tel: (01422) 205616 Fax: (01422) 206282 E-mail: enquiries@powertoolrentals.co.uk

Speedy Hire Centres Ltd, Tollgate House, Tollgate Lane, Bury St. Edmunds, Suffolk, IP32 6DG Tel: (01284) 766254 Fax: (01284) 700542 E-mail: customer.services@speedyhire.co.uk

V H S Hire Store, 1180 Aldridge Road, Great Barr, Birmingham, B44 8PE Tel: 0121-360 8500 Fax: 0121-366 6875

▶ Wolfe Designs Ltd, 125 Clydesdale Place, Moss Side Industrial Estate, Moss Side, Leyland, PR26 7QS Tel: (01772) 456191 Fax: (01772) 622464 E-mail: daviddesouza@btconnect.com

PORTABLE POWER TOOL TRANSFORMERS

A-Belco Property Ltd, Jubilee Industrial Estate, Ashington, Northumberland, NE63 8UG Tel: (01670) 813275 Fax: (01670) 851141 E-mail: sscullion@a-belco.co.uk

PORTABLE POWER TOOLS

Brian Walker & Son, 87 Garraways, Coffee Hall, Milton Keynes, MK6 5DU Tel: (01908) 666690 Fax: (01908) 233211

Dewalt, 210 Bath Road, Slough, SL1 3YD Tel: (01753) 567055 Fax: (01753) 521312 E-mail: sales@dewalt.co.uk

F G Lang Grays Ltd, 44 Clarence Road, Grays, Essex, RM17 6QL Tel: (01375) 374901 Fax: (01375) 374216E-mail: info@langs.co.uk

Goodwins Power Tools, 93 Canterbury Road, Margate, Kent, CT9 5AX Tel: (01843) 220966 Fax: (01843) 220836 E-mail: info@goodwins-tools.demon.co.uk

Makita UK Ltd, Vermont Place, Michigan Drive, Tongwell, Milton Keynes, MK15 8JD Tel: (01908) 211678 Fax: (01908) 211400 E-mail: info@makitauk.com

Power Quip Ltd, Greenbank Road, Liskeard, Cornwall, PL14 3DP Tel: (01579) 345307 Fax: (01579) 345307

Q R Tools Ltd, 251-253 Hanworth Road, Hounslow, TW3 3UF Tel: (020) 8570 5135 Fax: (020) 8572 6833

R & L Superfix, 1 Mead Park Industrial Estate, Mead Road, Cheltenham, Gloucestershire, GL53 7EF Tel: (01242) 224664 Fax: (01242) 222977

PORTABLE PRESSURE WASHERS

▶ The All Clean Group Ltd, 1 Southview Parade, New Road, Rainham, Essex, RM13 8HH Tel: (01708) 554400 Fax: (01708) 554499 E-mail: info@allcleangroup.com

PORTABLE PROJECTION SCREENS

Sahara Presentation Systems P.L.C., Williams House, Hailey Road, Erith, Kent, DA18 4AA Tel: (020) 8319 7777 Fax: (020) 8319 7775 E-mail: jsa@sahara-products.com

PORTABLE RADIO CASES

J & B Leathers, 37 Orford Road, London, E17 9NL Tel: (020) 8923 7720 Fax: (020) 8923 7720 E-mail: sales@jbleathers.co.uk

PORTABLE REMOTELY OPERATED VEHICLES (ROV)

AC-CESS Co. UK Ltd, Tyrebagger Works, Kinellar, Aberdeen, AB21 0TT Tel: (01224) 790100 Fax: (01224) 790111 E-mail: info@ac-cess.com

▶ Sub-Atlantic, Blackburn Business Park, Woodburn Road, Blackburn, Aberdeen, AB21 0PS Tel: (01224) 798660 Fax: (01224) 798661

PORTABLE SCREENING OR CRUSHER PLANT

Extec Screens & Crushers Ltd, Hearthcote Road, Swadlincote, Derbyshire, DE11 9DU Tel: (01283) 212121 Fax: (01283) 217342 E-mail: sales@extecscreens.co.uk

L J H Group Ltd, Leigh Road, Chantry, Frome, Somerset, BA11 3LR Tel: (01373) 836451 Fax: (01373) 836879 E-mail: sales@ljhgroup.co.uk

PORTABLE SECURITY STORAGE UNITS

Cleveland Sitesafe, Dockside Road, Middlesbrough, Cleveland, TS3 8AT Tel: (01642) 244663 Fax: (01642) 244664 E-mail: info@cleveland-sitesafe.ltd.uk

Gateway Fabrications Ltd, Broad Lane, Gilberdyke, Brough, North Humberside, HU15 2TS Tel: (01430) 440185 Fax: (01430) 441850 E-mail: sales@bathroompods.com

Groundhog UK, Ynysygerwn Avenue, Aberdulais, Neath, West Glamorgan, SA10 8HH Tel: (01639) 641166 Fax: (01639) 641188 E-mail: info@groundhog.co.uk

Lydney Containers Ltd, Unit 14 Lydney Industrial Estate, Harbour Road, Lydney, Gloucestershire, GL15 4EJ Tel: (01594) 842378 Fax: (01594) 843213 E-mail: info@lydneycontainers.co.uk

Lydney Containers Ltd, Unit 29-30 Vulcan Works, Wargrave Road, Newton-le-Willows, Merseyside, WA12 8RN Tel: (01695) 731890 Fax: (01925) 229484 E-mail: info@lydneycontainers.co.uk

Polstore Storage Systems Ltd, PO Box 408, Dorking, Surrey, RH5 5YF Tel: (0870) 8504012 Fax: (0870) 8504013 E-mail: info@polstore.co.uk

Twelco Fabrications Ltd, Old Airfield, Belton Road, Sandtoft, Doncaster, South Yorkshire, DN8 5SX Tel: (01724) 710844 Fax: (01724) 710188 E-mail: twelcofabltd@aol.com

Wernick Hire Ltd, Cartmore Industrial Estate, Lochgelly, Fife, KY5 8LL Tel: (01592) 783355 Fax: (01592) 783366 E-mail: hire@wenicklockgelly.co.uk

PORTABLE SELECTIVE ELECTROPLATING

M F S Electro Plating Co., Clifton Road, Huntingdon, Cambridgeshire, PE29 7EJ Tel: (01480) 459966

PORTABLE SELECTIVE ELECTROPLATING EQUIPMENT

R J Faulkes, Unit C3 Guy Motors Industrial Park, Park Lane, Wolverhampton, WV10 9QF Tel: (01902) 306662 Fax: (01902) 306662

PORTABLE TOILET HIRE

Adelphi Plant Hire Centres Ltd, Rear of Service Station 7-9 Tudor Parade, Well Hall Road, London, SE9 6SX Tel: (020) 8850 2430 Fax: (020) 8294 1817

Asles (Tool Hire & Sales) Ltd, 82 Broadway, Shifnal, Shropshire, TF11 8AZ Tel: (01952) 461266 Fax: (01952) 462337

Bunk A Bin Ltd, Tweedale Way, Oldham, OL9 7LD Tel: (0845) 4567899 Fax: (0845) 4566899 E-mail: hires@bunkabin.co.uk

Classical Conveniences, 2 The Pleasance, Harpenden, Hertfordshire, AL5 3NA Tel: (01582) 841143 Fax: (01582) 849354 E-mail: sales@luxuryloos.co.uk

Convenience Co., Harvey Road, Basildon, Essex, SS13 1RP Tel: (0845) 1003330 Fax: (01268) 722313 E-mail: enq@luxurytoilethire.com

▶ Convenience Services Ltd, Unit 1, The Old Dairy, Manor Farm, Fulling Mill Lane, Easton, Winchester, Hampshire, SO21 1DG Tel: (01962) 867808 Fax: (01962) 841784 E-mail: enquiries@justloos.com

Cumbria Loos, Winscales, Workington, Cumbria, CA14 4JZ Tel: (01900) 607272 Fax: (01900) 602323

Elite Mobile Toilets, Owls End Farm, Brook Lane, Himbleton, Droitwich, Worcestershire, WR9 7LF Tel: (01905) 391204

Elliott Group Ltd, Littlewell Lane, Stanton-by-Dale, Ilkeston, Derbyshire, DE7 4QW Tel: 0115-944 8380 Fax: 0115-944 3728 E-mail: info@elliotthire.co.uk

Elliott Group Ltd, Chaddock Lane, Worsley, Manchester, M28 1DP Tel: 0161-790 3721 Fax: 0161-703 8294 E-mail: info@elliotthire.co.uk

Elliott Group Ltd, Chesney Wold, Bleak Hall, Milton Keynes, MK6 1LS Tel: (01908) 231361 Fax: (01908) 677262 E-mail: info@elliotthire.co.uk

Elliott Hire Ltd, Oliver Road, Grays, Essex, RM20 3ED Tel: (01708) 862709 Fax: (01708) 861471 E-mail: sales@workspace.co.uk

Elliotthire, Bowburn South Industrial Estate, Bowburn, Durham, DH6 5AD Tel: 0191-377 8788 Fax: 0191-377 8770 E-mail: info@elliotthire.co.uk

Elliotthire Hire Centres, Shaw Street, West Bromwich, West Midlands, B70 0TX Tel: 0121-506 1060 Fax: 0121-556 5081 E-mail: info@elliotthire.co.uk

Four Jays Site A Loo, Barling Farm, East Sutton, Maidstone, Kent, ME17 3DX Tel: (01622) 843135 Fax: (01622) 844410 E-mail: sales@fourjays.co.uk

▶ M J Brown Ltd, Fallow House, Farm Close, Warnham, Horsham, West Sussex, RH12 3QT Tel: (01403) 252252 Fax: (01403) 252000 E-mail: thomas@therryansweb.co.uk

John Nixon Ltd, 99 Camburn Street, Glasgow, G32 6AX Tel: 0141-763 1213 Fax: 0141-763 2005

Oswestry Cabin Services, 34 Oaklands Road, Chirk Bank, Wrexham, Clwyd, LL14 5DP Tel: (01691) 772904 Fax: (01691) 772904

Rawley Event Toilets, Harvey Road, Basildon, Essex, SS13 1RP Tel: (01268) 722311 Fax: (01268) 722313 E-mail: enq@rawley.co.uk

Regency Marquees Ltd, Bilsington Road, Willow Court, Ruckinge, Ashford, Kent, TN26 2PB Tel: (01233) 732130 Fax: (01233) 733757 E-mail: info@regencymarquees.co.uk

D. & P. Rooke, Coldharbour Cottage, Winchbottom Lane, High Wycombe, Buckinghamshire, HP10 9QG Tel: (01494) 526065 E-mail: info@luxury-toilets.com

▶ Site Equipment Ltd, Bowerhurst, Mill Lane, Crondall, Farnham, Surrey, GU10 5RP Tel: (01252) 851988 Fax: (01252) 851989 E-mail: hire@site-equip.co.uk

William G Search Ltd, Whitehall Road, Leeds, LS12 6EP Tel: 0113-263 9081 Fax: 0113-231 0267 E-mail: info@wgsearch.co.uk

PORTABLE TOILETS

Abba Loos, Brynolwg, Bontgoch, Talybont, Dyfed, SY24 5DP Tel: (01970) 832960 Fax: (01970) 832081

Andiloos Portable Toilets, Crow Trees Farm, Thurvaston Lane, Longford, Ashbourne, Derbyshire, DE6 3DU Tel: (01335) 330053 Fax: (01335) 330053 E-mail: marsh.andrew@btconnect.com

Anglian Siting Services, 3 Mayfield Way, North Walsham, Norfolk, NR28 0DQ Tel: 01692 405885

Borderloos, Alstonby Grange, West Linton, Westlinton, Carlisle, CA6 6AF Tel: (01228) 792792 Fax: (01228) 792791 E-mail: philip.a@borderloos.co.uk

Castle Marquees & Portable Toilets, 22 Georgian Drive, Coxheath, Maidstone, Kent, ME17 4QT Tel: (01622) 745818 Fax: (01622) 745818

▶ Challenger Site Services, 50 Winton Street, Ashton-under-Lyne, Lancashire, OL6 8NL Tel: 0161-344 2581 Fax: 0161-330 8406 E-mail: sales@challenger-site-services.co.uk

▶ Classic Chambers, 6 Penny Lane, Easingwold, York, YO61 3RR Tel: (07767) 776927

Classic Loo's, Litnnets, Ogdens, Fordingbridge, Hampshire, SP6 2PY Tel: (01725) 513130 Fax: (01425) 650634

Convenience Co., Cot Nab Farm, Bishop Wilton, York, YO42 1SY Tel: (01759) 369841 Fax: (01759) 368711

The Convenience Co (Midlands), Canalside Industrial Park, Kinoulton Road, Cropwell Bishop, Nottingham, NG12 3BE Tel: 0115-989 0011 Fax: 0115-989 0022 E-mail: isabel@theconco.co.uk

D A N Toilet Hire, Dillybrook Farm, Poplar Tree Lane, Southwick, Trowbridge, Wiltshire, BA14 9NB Tel: (01373) 830110 Fax: (01373) 830110

D Tox, Bramble Lane, Burntwood, Staffordshire, WS7 9AU Tel: (01543) 670707 Fax: (01543) 673110

Home Counties Toilet Hire, Fairfield Farm, Newton Road, Stoke Hammond, Milton Keynes, MK17 9DE Tel: (01525) 270181 Fax: (01525) 270464 E-mail: sales@hccc.co.uk

Petch Waters, Little Ayton Lane, Great Ayton, Middlesbrough, Cleveland, TS9 6HY Tel: (01642) 724000 Fax: (01642) 723999

Polyportables Ltd, Brickbarns Farm, Evesham Road, Egdon, Worcester, WR7 4QR Tel: (01905) 345840 Fax: (01905) 345849

Portable Conveniences, Weavers Weft, Engine Brow, Tockholes, Darwen, Lancashire, BB3 0ND Tel: (01254) 200181 Fax: (01254) 777787 E-mail: sales@portableconveniences.com

Rawley Event Toilets, Harvey Road, Basildon, Essex, SS13 1RP Tel: (01268) 722311 Fax: (01268) 722313 E-mail: enq@rawley.co.uk

▶ S G B Group, Capper Yard, Bridge Lane, Woolston, Warrington, WA1 4BA Tel: (01925) 846260 Fax: (01925) 846270 E-mail: info@sgb.co.uk

Site Space Ltd, Meresborough Lane, Rainham, Gillingham, Kent, ME8 8PR Tel: (01634) 389440 Fax: (01634) 373151 E-mail: sales@sitespace.co.uk

▶ Toilet Hire, 1 Bottings Industrial Estate, Curdridge, Southampton, SO30 2DY Tel: (01489) 790020 Fax: (01489) 790030

Toilets Plus Ltd, 34 London Road, Wymondham, Norfolk, NR18 9JD Tel: (01953) 601345 Fax: (01953) 601344 E-mail: sales@toilets.co.uk

PORTABLE ULTRASONIC LEAK DETECTORS

Logis-Tech Associates, 140 Boyd Street, Crosshill, Glasgow, G42 8TP Tel: 0141-423 6911 Fax: (0870) 1276102 E-mail: hugo@logis-tech.co.uk

PORTABLE VENTILATORS

Airmed Medical Equipment Mnfrs, Southfield House, 99 Barry Road, London, SE22 0HR Tel: (020) 8693 0594 Fax: (020) 8693 0342 E-mail: info@airmedltd.com

PORTRAIT PHOTOGRAPHERS

▶ GMS Photography, 24 Hannington Road, Bournemouth, BH7 6JT Tel: (01202) 565500 E-mail: info@gmsfoto.com

▶ Picturesque, 1a Asquith Avenue,, Leeds, LS27 9QA Tel: 01132 535588

▶ Suzanne Grala Photography, PO Box 458, Epsom, Surrey, KT17 4WY E-mail: suzi@suzanne.grala.co.uk

POSITION TRANSDUCERS

H T Servo Ltd, 5 Westmarch Business Centre, River Way, Andover, Hants, SP10 1NS Tel: (01264) 355079 Fax: (01264) 337450 E-mail: info@htservo.com

POSITIONING COMPONENTS/ SYSTEMS

Glonav UK Ltd, March House, London Road, Daventry, Northamptonshire, NN11 4NR Tel: (01327) 701270 Fax: (01327) 701299

Measurement Devices Ltd, Silverburn Crescent, Bridge of Don Industrial Estate, Aberdeen, AB23 8EW Tel: (01224) 246700 Fax: (01224) 824987 E-mail: info@mdl.co.uk

Positek Ltd, L6 The Link, Andoversford Industrial Estate, Cheltenham, Gloucestershire, GL54 4LB Tel: 01242 820027 Fax: 01242 820615 E-mail: mark@positek.com

POSITIONING CONTROL SYSTEMS

Positek Ltd, L6 The Link, Andoversford Industrial Estate, Cheltenham, Gloucestershire, GL54 4LB Tel: 01242 820027 Fax: 01242 820615 E-mail: mark@positek.com

POSITIVE DISPLACEMENT PUMPS

Airtex Products Ltd, Hanworth Trading Estate, Hampton Road West, Feltham, Middlesex, TW13 6EH Tel: (020) 8755 4400 Fax: (020) 8894 3026 E-mail: info@airtex.co.uk

Flowrite Ltd, 6 Walnut Tree Close, Cheshunt, Waltham Cross, Hertfordshire, EN8 8NH Tel: (01992) 639205 Fax: (01992) 623993 E-mail: pumps@flowrite.co.uk

J P Pumps Ltd, Meadow Brook Industrial Centre, Maxwell Way, Crawley, West Sussex, RH10 9SA Tel: (01293) 553495 Fax: (01293) 524635 E-mail: mailbox.uk@johnson-pump.com

Johnson Pump UK Ltd, Highfield Industrial Estate, Edison Road, Eastbourne, East Sussex, BN23 6PT Tel: (01323) 509211 Fax: (01323) 507306 E-mail: sales@johnsonpump.com

Netzsch Nemo Pumps Ltd, Unit 3 Middlemore Business Park, Middlemore Lane West, Aldridge, Walsall, WS9 8BG Tel: (01922) 453433 Fax: (01922) 458404 E-mail: npl@netzsch.com

POSITIVE DISPLACEMENT ROOTS BLOWERS

Dresser Roots-Holmes Operations, PO Box B7, Huddersfield, HD1 6RB Tel: (01484) 422222 Fax: (01484) 422668 E-mail: dmd_roots@dresser.co.uk

POST ACCEPTING/HANDLING/ POSTROOM EQUIPMENT, *See also headings for particular types*

Ashby, 33 Ascot Avenue, Kimberley, Nottingham, NG16 2TU Tel: 0115-938 5101 Fax: 0115-938 5102

Hillday Leasing & Supplies Ltd, 1a Haverscroft Industrial Estate, New Road, Attleborough, Norfolk, NR17 1YE Tel: (01953) 454014 Fax: (01953) 454014 E-mail: hillday@btinternet.com

POST PROCESSING SOFTWARE

Advanced Analysis & Integration Ltd, Riverpark Road, Manchester, M40 2XP Tel: 0161-231 1800 Fax: 0161-231 0509 E-mail: sales@aail.co.uk

Intersoft Systems & Programming Ltd, The Mill, Horton Road, Staines, Middlesex, TW19 6BJ Tel: (01753) 687979 Fax: (01753) 687655 E-mail: sales@intersoft.co.uk

Q I S O F T Ltd, 3 Station Brow, Leyland, PR25 3NZ Tel: (01772) 641133 Fax: (01772) 641155 E-mail: admin@qisoft.com

Somat Systems (UK) Ltd, 230 Woodburn Road, Sheffield, S9 3LQ Tel: 0114-275 5292 Fax: 0114-275 8272 E-mail: ajb@somat.com

POST PRODUCTION SERVICES, FILM, TELEVISION ETC

▶ Dynamite Pictures, 8 Wilkinson Terrace, Stutton, Tadcaster, North Yorkshire, LS24 9BP Tel: (07816) 319195 E-mail: richard.ball@lycos.co.uk

▶ Endorfin TV, Lower Green Road, Tunbridge Wells, Kent, TN4 8TE Tel: (01892) 533577 Fax: (01892) 515183E-mail: mark@endorfin.tv

▶ Schtum Ltd, 11 Osram Road, East Lane Business Park, Wembley, Middlesex, HA9 7NG Tel: (020) 8904 4422 Fax: (020) 8904 3777 E-mail: info@schtum.co.uk

▶ Surrey Films Ltd, Valley Farm, Green Lane, Churt, Farnham, Surrey, GU10 2LT Tel: (01428) 609532 E-mail: pete@surreyfilms.co.uk

POSTAGE STAMP VENDING MACHINES

Hilday Leasing & Supplies Ltd, 1a Haverscroft Industrial Estate, New Road, Attleborough, Norfolk, NR17 1YE Tel: (01953) 454014 Fax: (01953) 454014 E-mail: hilday@btinternet.com

POSTAL BOX SYSTEMS

Hayne West, Unit 2 Stoney Hill Industrial Estate, Whitchurch, Ross-on-Wye, Herefordshire, HR9 6BX Tel: (01600) 890119 Fax: (01600) 890133 E-mail: sales@hayne--west.co.uk

POSTAL FRANKING MACHINES

▶ Call Preformance Ltd, 85-87llington Street, Gravesend, Kent, DA12 1JQ Tel: (01474) 574300 Fax: (01474) 574359 E-mail: sales@callperformance.co.uk

Pitney Bowes Office Direct, London Road, London, SE1 6LF Tel: (020) 7200 5408 Fax: (020) 7200 5432 E-mail: hassan.dayem@pb.com

POSTAL SORTING EQUIPMENT

Opex Corporation, Carrington Business Park, Carrington, Manchester, M31 4YR Tel: 0161-776 4033 Fax: 0161-776 2663 E-mail: opexhr@opex.com

POSTCARDS

▶ Lighthouse Printing, 1 Anglesey Street, Cardiff, CF5 1QZ Tel: (029) 2034 4899 Fax: (029) 2034 4899 E-mail: lighthouseprint@ntlworld.com

POSTER DESIGNERS OR PRODUCERS, ADVERTISING/ PROMOTIONAL/INFORMATION

Augustus Martin Ltd, 8-20 St. Andrews Way, London, E3 3PB Tel: (020) 7537 4200 Fax: (020) 7537 2184 E-mail: sales@amartin.co.uk

Buckland Press Ltd, Barwick Road, Dover, Kent, CT17 0LG Tel: (01304) 205900 Fax: (01304) 205619 E-mail: info@buckland.co.uk

Garth Computer Solutions, Blaenpentre, Rhosygarth, Llanilar, Aberystwyth, Dyfed, SY23 4SE Tel: (01974) 241410

Graphic Results, 99 Bridge Street, Belper, Derbyshire, DE56 1BA Tel: (01773) 599159 Fax: (01773) 599259 E-mail: sales@graphic-results.co.uk

Mills Advertising & Publicity, North House, 5 North Road, Stokesley, Middlesbrough, Cleveland, TS9 5DU Tel: (01642) 713156 Fax: (01642) 713174 E-mail: enquiries@millsadvertising.co.uk

Springboard Design, Unit4 Point 2, The Paint Works, Bath Road, Bristol, BS4 3EH Tel: 0117-958 8500 Fax: 0117-958 8501 E-mail: info@springboard-design.co.uk

POSTER FRAMES

▶ arken P-O-P Ltd, Studlands Park Avenue, Newmarket, Suffolk, CB8 7EA Tel: (01638) 565656 Fax: (01638) 662770 E-mail: info@arken-pop.com

Main Event Sales & Hire, Unit 25, Coleshill Industrial Estate, Station Road, Coleshill, Birmingham, B46 1JP Tel: (01675) 464224 Fax: (01675) 466082 E-mail: sales@mainevent.co.uk

POSTER FRAMING

▶ Retro Spectives, The Minories, Rother Street, Stratford-upon-Avon, Warwickshire, CV37 6NF Tel: (01789) 297706 E-mail: sales@retrospectives.co.uk

POSTER INSTALLATION

▶ Mid West Displays, Laundry Lane, Shrewsbury, SY2 6ER Tel: (01743) 248095 Fax: (01743) 248096 E-mail: sales@midwestdisplays.co.uk

POTABLE WATER TREATMENT PLANT AND EQUIPMENT

Ecowater Systems Ltd, 1 Independent Business Park, Mill Road, Stokenchurch, High Wycombe, Buckinghamshire, HP14 3TP Tel: (01494) 484000 Fax: (01494) 484396 E-mail: sales@ecowater.co.uk

POTASSIUM CHLORIDE, MURIATE OF POTASH

Cleveland Potash Ltd, Boulby Mine, Loftus, Saltburn-by-the-Sea, Cleveland, TS13 4UZ Tel: (01287) 640140 Fax: (01287) 640934 E-mail: jan.hunton@clevelandpotash.co.uk

POTATO CRISPS

Glennans Ltd, Dovefields, Dovefields Industrial Estate, Uttoxeter, Staffordshire, ST14 8HU Tel: (01889) 567338 Fax: (01889) 562701 E-mail: richard.thompson@glennans.co.uk

▶ J W Munro, 18 Bogmoor Place, Glasgow, G51 4TQ Tel: 0141-445 4339 Fax: 0141-445 5511

POTATO (PEELED) PRESERVATIVES

Drywite Ltd, PO Box 1, Halesowen, West Midlands, B63 2RB Tel: (01384) 569556 Fax: (01384) 410583 E-mail: enquiries@drywite.co.uk

Humber Quality Foods Ltd, Brigg Road, Scunthorpe, South Humberside, DN15 6TZ Tel: (01724) 270306 Fax: (01724) 270345 E-mail: john@hqf.co.uk

POTATO PLANTERS

Burdens Distribution Ltd, Spalding Road, Sutterton, Boston, Lincolnshire, PE20 2EX Tel: (01205) 460466 Fax: (01205) 460122 E-mail: sales@burdens.com

POTATO PLANTING AND HARVESTING

▶ Organic Potato Growers Scotland Ltd, Dalcross Industrial Estate, Inverness, IV2 7XB Tel: (01667) 462923 Fax: (01667) 461065 E-mail: sales@organicpotatogrowers.co.uk

POTATO SORTING/GRADING MACHINES, COMBINED

Tong Engineering Ltd, Ashby Road, Spilsby, Lincolnshire, PE23 5DW Tel: (01790) 752771 Fax: (01790) 753611 E-mail: sales@tongpeal.com

POTATOES

▶ Adrian Dale Potatoes Ltd, Three Boundries Farm, Coventry Road, Croft, Leicester, LE9 3GP Tel: (01455) 285577 Fax: (01455) 284785

▶ P.J.P Ltd, Paul Jackson Potatoes, Station Road, Firsby, Spilsby, Lincolnshire, PE23 5QS Tel: (01754) 830330 E-mail: sales@pjp.org.uk

POTENTIOMETER MANUFRS,

See also headings under Potentiometers

A B Electronic Ltd, Colbern House, Spring Gardens, Romford, RM7 9LP Tel: (01708) 762222 Fax: (01708) 762981 E-mail: info@abelectronic.com

Murata Electronics Ltd, Oak House, Ancells Road, Fleet, Hampshire, GU51 2QW Tel: (01252) 811666 Fax: (01252) 811777 E-mail: enquiry@murata.co.uk

Pandect Precision Components Ltd, Wellington Road, High Wycombe, Buckinghamshire, HP12 3PX Tel: (01494) 526303 Fax: (01494) 465557 E-mail: enquiries@pandect.demon.co.uk

Precision Varionics Ltd, 307 The Commercial Centre, Picket Piece, Andover, Hampshire, SP11 6RU Tel: (01264) 334522 Fax: (01264) 334422 E-mail: sales@varionics.co.uk

POTENTIOMETERS, PRECISION CONDUCTIVE PLASTIC (LINEAR AND ROTARY)

Young Ecc Electronics, Crown House, Coronation Road, Cressex Business Park, High Wycombe, Buckinghamshire, HP12 3TA Tel: (01494) 753500 Fax: (01494) 753501 E-mail: crown@youngelectronics.com

POTTERY

▶ D & S Pottery Ltd, Unit 14 Chemical Lane, Stoke-on-Trent, ST6 4PB Tel: (01782) 813535 Fax: (01782) 813535 E-mail: sales@dandspottery.co.uk

▶ Gwili Pottery, Alltwalis Road, Carmarthen, Dyfed, SA32 7DU Tel: (01267) 253449 Fax: (01267) 253449

▶ Portmeirion Potteries, 473 King Street, Stoke-on-Trent, ST3 1EU Tel: (01782) 326661 Fax: (01782) 326664

▶ Wold Pottery, 79 High Street, Loftus, Saltburn-By-The-Sea, Cleveland, TS13 4HG Tel: (01287) 640100

POTTERY COLOURS

D N W Ceramics Of Staffordshire, Wood Street, Longton, Stoke-on-Trent, ST3 1EA Tel: (01782) 598949 Fax: (01782) 598949

▶ The Potters Friend, 6 Rawle Close, Cheadle, Stoke-On-Trent, ST10 1UX Tel: (01538) 751200 E-mail: thepottersfriend@aol.com

Sneyd Oxides Ltd, Sneyd Mills, Leonora Street, Stoke-on-Trent, ST6 3BZ Tel: (01782) 577600 Fax: (01782) 835742 E-mail: ceramics@sneydoxides.co.uk

POTTERY EQUIPMENT

Arterial Engineering Works Ltd, Morston Road, Blakeney, Holt, Norfolk, NR25 7BE Tel: (01263) 740444 Fax: (01263) 740444

E J Payne Ltd, 1-3 Belgrave Road, Stoke-on-Trent, ST3 4PR Tel: (01782) 312534 Fax: (01782) 599868 E-mail: sales@ejpayne.com

Firestool, Auckland Street, Stoke-on-Trent, ST6 2AY Tel: (01782) 819164 Fax: (01782) 835642

Hesketh Gallery & Potters Supplies, 4 Lansdown Place, Lewes, East Sussex, BN7 2JT Tel: (01273) 487150 E-mail: enquiries@heskethps.co.uk

J M & R M Heathman, Lewthorn Cottages, Ilsington, Newton Abbot, Devon, TQ13 9RR Tel: (01364) 661303 Fax: (01364) 661257

POTTERY MATERIALS OR POTTERS MILLERS

Arterial Engineering Works Ltd, Morston Road, Blakeney, Holt, Norfolk, NR25 7BE Tel: (01263) 740444 Fax: (01263) 740444

Burnham Pottery, 2-4 Maryland, Wells-Next-The-Sea, Norfolk, NR23 1LY Tel: (01328) 710847 Fax: (01328) 711566 E-mail: oldstation.books@btinternet.com

Celtic Kilncare Ltd, Celtic House, Langland Way, Newport, Gwent, NP19 4PT Tel: (01633) 271455 Fax: (01633) 290663 E-mail: celtic.kilns@btinternet.com

China Millers Ltd, 409 King Street, Stoke-on-Trent, ST4 3EF Tel: (01782) 313291 Fax: (01782) 599494

Cromartie Kilns Ltd, Park Hall Road, Longton, Stoke-On-Trent, ST3 5AY Tel: (01782) 313947 Fax: (01782) 599723 E-mail: enquiries@cromartie.co.uk

Dalehall Mills Ltd, Newport Lane, Stoke-on-Trent, ST6 3PJ Tel: (01782) 837055 Fax: (01782) 577782 E-mail: dalehallmills@tiscali.co.uk

Furlong Mills Ltd, Furlong Lane, Stoke-on-Trent, ST6 3LE Tel: (01782) 838428 Fax: (01782) 834199 E-mail: admin@furlongmills.co.uk

Glynderi Pottery, Sennybridge, Brecon, Powys, LD3 8TS Tel: (01874) 636564

Sydney Heath & Son Ltd, P O Box 1 Bycars Road, Stoke-on-Trent, ST6 4SH Tel: (01782) 839121 Fax: (01782) 839124 E-mail: sales@sydney-heath.co.uk

Hesketh Gallery & Potters Supplies, 4 Lansdown Place, Lewes, East Sussex, BN7 2JT Tel: (01273) 487150 E-mail: enquiries@heskethps.co.uk

Just Mugs Ltd, Unit 5, Hanley Business Park, Cooper Street, Stoke-On-Trent, ST1 4DW Tel: (01782) 274888 Fax: (01782) 202181 E-mail: info@justmugs.com

Mccluskey Pottery, 11 Gortgarn Road, Limavady, County Londonderry, BT49 0QW Tel: (028) 7776 4579 Fax: (028) 7776 4579

Potclays Ltd, Brick Kiln Lane, Stoke-on-Trent, ST4 7BP Tel: (01782) 219816 Fax: (01782) 286506 E-mail: sales@potclays.co.uk

Potterycrafts Ltd, Campbell Road, Stoke-on-Trent, ST4 4ET Tel: (01782) 745000 Fax: (01782) 746000 E-mail: sales@potterycraft.co.uk

Ruardean Garden Pottery, West End, Ruardean, Gloucestershire, GL17 9TP Tel: (01594) 543577 Fax: (01594) 544536

Woodnewton Pottery, 43 Main Street, Woodnewton, Peterborough, PE8 5EB Tel: (01780) 470866 Fax: (01780) 470127 E-mail: sales@studiopottery.co.uk

POTTERY TOOLS

Potterycrafts Ltd, Campbell Road, Stoke-on-Trent, ST4 4ET Tel: (01782) 745000 Fax: (01782) 746000 E-mail: sales@potterycraft.co.uk

POULTRY BATTERY SYSTEMS

O'Kane Hatcheries Ltd, 117 Raceview Road, Ballymena, County Antrim, BT42 4HY Tel: (028) 2586 1445 Fax: (028) 2586 2179 E-mail: okaneh@hotmail.com

POULTRY EQUIPMENT

▶ J A Salisbury, The Smithy, Whitton, Ludlow, Shropshire, SY8 3DB Tel: (01584) 891715 Fax: (01584) 891714

▶ Quill Productions, Manor Farm, Pulham, Dorchester, Dorset, DT2 7EE Tel: (01258) 818239 Fax: (01258) 817261 E-mail: sales@quillprod.co.uk

POULTRY FEEDING SYSTEMS

Danagri - 3 S Ltd, Wenlock Road, Bridgnorth, Shropshire, WV16 4QR Tel: (01746) 762777 Fax: (01746) 764777 E-mail: info@danagri-3s.com

Gridfeed Thornber Ltd, Brearley Mill, Halifax Road, Todmorden, Lancashire, OL14 6EF Tel: (01706) 815131 Fax: (01706) 815455 E-mail: gridthorn@aol.com

Parkland Products, Owley Farm, Acton Lane, Wittersham, Tenterden, Kent, TN30 7HL Tel: (01797) 270399 Fax: (01797) 270899 E-mail: mapipersonfarms@btconnect.com

POULTRY FOODS

Allen & Page Ltd, Norfolk Mill, Shipdham, Thetford, Norfolk, IP25 7SD Tel: (01362) 822900 Fax: (01362) 822910 E-mail: sales@allenandpage.co.uk

G. Bell & Sons Ltd, 11 Kilmore Road, Crossgar, Downpatrick, County Down, BT30 9HJ Tel: (028) 4483 0301 Fax: (028) 4483 2301 E-mail: enquiries@crossgarpoultry.com

▶ Flyte So Fancy, The Cottage, Pulham, Dorchester, Dorset, DT2 7DX Tel: (01300) 345229 Fax: (01300) 345229 E-mail: anne@flytesofancy.freeserve.co.uk

Invek Foods, 18 Birmingham Road, Walsall, WS1 2LT Tel: (01922) 725820 Fax: (01922) 616548

L & M Food Group Ltd, Trelawney House, 454-456 Larkshall Road, Highams Park, London, E4 9HH Tel: (020) 8531 7631 Fax: (020) 8531 8607

M C Kelly Ltd, Elston Farm, Copplestone, Crediton, Devon, EX17 5PB Tel: (01363) 84545 Fax: (01363) 84060 E-mail: sales@mckelly.co.uk

North Antrim Turkeys Ltd, 14 Seneirl Road, Castlecatt, Bushmills, County Antrim, BT57 8TS Tel: (028) 2074 1239 Fax: (028) 2074 1009

POULTRY HOUSE CONTROL/ MONITORING SYSTEMS

Barrow Lane Products, Cherry Tree Farm, Charlton Musgrove, Wincanton, Somerset, BA9 8HW Tel: (01963) 34279 E-mail: info@roosterbooster.co.uk

Electroflora Ltd, The Old Transmitter House, The Baulk, Clapham, Bedford, MK41 6AA Tel: (01234) 262745 Fax: (01234) 262753

Glen-Aaron Services, 31 Gravelhill Road, Lisburn, County Antrim, BT27 5RW Tel: (028) 9262 1732 Fax: (028) 9262 1968

Patrick Pinker Ltd, Latteridge Lane, Iron Acton, Bristol, BS37 9TY Tel: (01454) 228416 Fax: (01454) 228617 E-mail: enquiries@patrickpinker.com

Set To Brood, Turners House, Kingstone, Hereford, HR2 9HU Tel: (01981) 251720 Fax: (01981) 570598 E-mail: addisnicola@aol.com

POULTRY HOUSE HEATING EQUIPMENT

Space-Ray UK, 4-6 Chapel Lane, Claydon, Ipswich, IP6 0JL Tel: (01473) 830551 Fax: (01473) 832055 E-mail: info@spaceray.co.uk

POULTRY HOUSES

A Neaverson & Sons Ltd, St Pegas Road, Peakirk, Peterborough, PE6 7NN Tel: (01733) 252225 Fax: (01733) 252121

▶ Ascott Smallholding Supplies Ltd, Unit 9/10, The Old Creamery, Four Crosses, Llanymynech, Powys, SY22 6LP Tel: (0845) 1306285 Fax: (0870) 7740140 E-mail: phil@ascott.biz

Barrow Lane Products, Cherry Tree Farm, Charlton Musgrove, Wincanton, Somerset, BA9 8HW Tel: (01963) 34279 E-mail: info@roosterbooster.co.uk

C E Davidson Ltd, South View New Street, Fressingfield, Eye, Suffolk, IP21 5PJ Tel: (01379) 586606 Fax: (01379) 586511

Faccenda Group Ltd, High St, Sutton Benger, Chippenham, Wiltshire, SN15 4RF Tel: (01249) 720733 Fax: (01249) 720958

POULTRY INCUBATORS

▶ Ascott Smallholding Supplies Ltd, Unit 9/10, The Old Creamery, Four Crosses, Llanymynech, Powys, SY22 6LP Tel: (0845) 1306285 Fax: (0870) 7740140 E-mail: phil@ascott.biz

Chick Master UK Ltd, Unit 2 Express Park, Bristol Road, Bridgwater, Somerset, TA6 4RN Tel: (01278) 411000 Fax: (01278) 451213 E-mail: sales@chickmaster.com

▶ Ecostat Thermostats, Unit 20 Beehive Workshops, Parkengue, Penryn, Cornwall, TR10 9LX Tel: (01326) 378654 Fax: (01326) 378539 E-mail: ecostat@btconnect.com

POULTRY PAPER BEDDING

▶ Paul Garner, 4 Poplar Grove, Ravenfield, Rotherham, South Yorkshire, S65 4LJ Tel: (07737) 036085 E-mail: pj1racing@hotmail.com

POULTRY PLUCKING EQUIPMENT

Bingham Appliances, Unit 83 Hillgrove Business Park, Nazeing Road, Nazeing, Waltham Abbey, Essex, EN9 2HB Tel: (01992) 899033 Fax: (01992) 899158 E-mail: binghamappliance@aol.com

Whitehead Engineering, Unit 6 Haydon Industrial Estate, Radstock, BA3 3RD Tel: (01761) 432305 Fax: (01761) 435329 E-mail: info@whiteheadengineering.co.uk

POULTRY PROCESSING

Sedgbeer Processing Supplies, Unit 13, Mill Road, Radstock, BA3 5TX Tel: (01373) 812445 Fax: (01373) 812445 E-mail: info@sedgbeer.co.uk

POULTRY PROCESSING EQUIPMENT

Anglia Autoflow Ltd, The Ling, Wortham, Diss, Norfolk, IP22 1SR Tel: (01379) 651031 Fax: (01379) 652832 E-mail: sales@aaflow.com

Bingham Appliances, Unit 83 Hillgrove Business Park, Nazeing Road, Nazeing, Waltham Abbey, Essex, EN9 2HB Tel: (01992) 899033 Fax: (01992) 899158 E-mail: binghamappliance@aol.com

Meyn Poultry Equipment Ltd, 7 Bilton Industrial Estate, Bilton Road, Basingstoke, Hampshire, RG24 8LJ Tel: (01256) 466040 Fax: (01256) 841916 E-mail: peter.meyn@btconnect.com

POWDER BLENDING/MIXING SERVICES

Contract Blending & Packing Ltd, Heys Lane, Great Harwood, Blackburn, BB6 7UA Tel: (01254) 877870 Fax: (01254) 877871

Contract Packers (Midlands) Ltd, Kiln Way, Woodville, Swadlincote, Derbyshire, DE11 8ED Tel: (01283) 224489 Fax: (01283) 224030 E-mail: barrypresscott@vitax.co.uk

Excelsior Packers, Brookside Lane, Oswaldtwistle, Accrington, Lancashire, BB5 3NY Tel: (01254) 356622 Fax: (01254) 356677 E-mail: sales@gemweb.co.uk

Exwold Technology, Tees Bay Business Park, Brenda Road, Hartlepool, Cleveland, TS25 2BU Tel: (01429) 230340 Fax: (01429) 232996 E-mail: sales@exwold.com

Stonehouse Tablet Manufacturing Co. Ltd, Nottingham Road, Beeston, Nottingham, NG9 6DT Tel: 0115-925 4552 Fax: 0115-922 4226 E-mail: info@stonehousetablet.co.uk

Suffolk Stove Enamellers, Bridge Works, Hasketon, Woodbridge, Suffolk, IP13 6HE Tel: (01473) 735585 Fax: (01473) 735585

Teeschem Manufacturing Co. Ltd, Salters Lane, Sedgefield, Stockton-on-Tees, Cleveland, TS21 3EE Tel: (01740) 620853 Fax: (01740) 622898 E-mail: admin@teeschem_mfg.co.uk

Richard Whittaker Ltd, Unit 28 Transpennine Industrial Estate, Gorrels Way, Queensway, Rochdale, Lancashire, OL11 2QR Tel: (01706) 341700 Fax: (01706) 341357 E-mail: sales@richard-whittaker.com

POWDER CLASSIFIERS

British Rema Manufacturing Co. Ltd, Image Works, Foxwood Close, Chesterfield, Derbyshire, S41 9RN Tel: (01246) 269955 Fax: (01246) 269944 E-mail: sales@britishrema.co.uk

Kason Corporation Europe, Unit 12-13 Parkhall Business Village, Parkhall Road, Stoke-on-Trent, ST3 5XA Tel: (01782) 597540 Fax: (01782) 597549 E-mail: sales@kasoneurope.co.uk

POWDER COATING BOOTHS

▶ A G Servicing Ltd, 68 Wychall Drive, Bushbury, Wolverhampton, WV10 8UX Tel: (01902) 787121 Fax: (01902) 787121 E-mail: sales@agservicing.co.uk

Atlas Coating Ltd, Unit 15a Hixon Airfield Estate, New Road, Hixon, Stafford, ST18 0PF Tel: (01889) 271002 Fax: (01889) 271178 E-mail: mail@atlascoating.co.uk

F S L Electrostatic Systems Ltd, 5 A K Business Park, Russell Road, Southport, Merseyside, PR9 7SA Tel: (01704) 506439 Fax: (01704) 505043 E-mail: salesfsl@aol.com

POWDER COATING CURING AGENTS

Trimite Ltd, Albert Road, St. Philips, Bristol, BS2 0YA Tel: 0117-971 6115 Fax: 0117-971 7090

POWDER COATING EQUIPMENT

C J Powder Coatings, Unit 8 Jackson Place, Humberston, Grimsby, South Humberside, DN36 4AS Tel: (01472) 211222 Fax: (01472) 211333

F S L Electrostatic Systems Ltd, 5 A K Business Park, Russell Road, Southport, Merseyside, PR9 7SA Tel: (01704) 506439 Fax: (01704) 505043 E-mail: salesfsl@aol.com

Rayridge Conveyors Ltd, Willenhall Trading Estate, Midacre, Willenhall, West Midlands, WV13 2JW Tel: (01902) 603763 Fax: (01902) 605081 E-mail: mail@ercongroup.com

POWDER COATING JIGS

A C Jigs, 10 Porters Way, Birmingham, B9 5RR Tel: 0121-753 0304 Fax: 0121-753 0304

Premier Plating Jigs Ltd, 16 New Bartholomew Street, Birmingham, B5 5QS Tel: 0121-643 0727 Fax: 0121-633 3392

Wirex Metal Baskets, Marston Road, Hoddesdon, Hertfordshire, EN11 0AD Tel: (01992) 469585 Fax: (01992) 441940

POWDER COATING PLANT

Capital Design Services Ltd, Bridge Buildings, 11A Ladybridge Road, Cheadle Hulme, Cheadle, Cheshire, SK8 5LL Tel: 0161-486 9524 Fax: 0161-485 8605

▶ I & T Projects & Installations Ltd, Unit 2, James W. Properties Business Park, Wood Street, Burton-On-Trent, Staffordshire, DE14 3AB Tel: (01283) 541702 Fax: (01283) 548954 E-mail: sales@iandtprojects.co.uk

P B S Ltd, Unit 13 Lowesmoor Wharf, Lowesmoor, Worcester, WR1 2RS Tel: (01905) 617655 Fax: (01905) 726539 E-mail: gummpowder@aol.com

POWDER COATING PLANT, ENGINEERS, INSTALLATION OR SERVICE

▶ I & T Projects & Installations Ltd, Unit 2, James W. Properties Business Park, Wood Street, Burton-On-Trent, Staffordshire, DE14 3AB Tel: (01283) 541702 Fax: (01283) 548954 E-mail: sales@iandtprojects.co.uk

P B S Ltd, Unit 13 Lowesmoor Wharf, Lowesmoor, Worcester, WR1 2RS Tel: (01905) 617655 Fax: (01905) 726539 E-mail: gummpowder@aol.com

Rayridge Conveyors Ltd, Willenhall Trading Estate, Midacre, Willenhall, West Midlands, WV13 2JW Tel: (01902) 603763 Fax: (01902) 605081 E-mail: mail@ercongroup.com

Systech UK Ltd, Willow House, Kingswood Business Park, Albrighton, Wolverhampton, WV7 3AU Tel: (01902) 373276 Fax: (01902) 373081 E-mail: john@systechuk.com

Thamesdown Coatings Ltd, Unit 33 Whitehill Industrial Estate, Whitehill Lane, Wootton Bassett, Swindon, SN4 7DB Tel: (01793) 729421

POWDER COATING REPAIR AND RESPRAY

Coating Repair Specialists, 2 Somerset Road, Springwell Estate, Sunderland, SR3 4EB Tel: 0191- 522 9577 Fax: 0191- 522 9577 E-mail: j.collier40@ntlworld.com

POWDER COATING SERVICES

A B C Enamelling & Fabrications Ltd, High Street, Nailsea, Bristol, BS48 1BW Tel: (01275) 810454 Fax: (01275) 810535

A J Finishers Ltd, 45 Barton Road, Bletchley, Milton Keynes, MK2 3BA Tel: (01908) 648437 Fax: (01908) 645016

A P Robinson Ltd, 6c Fitzherbert Spur, Farlington, Portsmouth, PO6 1TT Tel: (023) 9238 3427 Fax: (023) 9222 1238 E-mail: aprobinson@btnet.com

A & R Sheet Metal Ltd, 68-70 College Street, Kempston, Bedford, MK42 8LU Tel: (01234) 348841 Fax: (01234) 262784 E-mail: sales@arsheetmetal.co.uk

A1 Powder Coatings Ltd, Unit 5 Beta Buildings Willments Industrial Estate, Hazel Road, Southampton, SO19 7HS Tel: (023) 8044 6874 Fax: (023) 8044 6879 E-mail: enquiries@a1powdercoatings.co.uk

Acorn Services, Unit 3 Access Point, Willenhall Industrial Centre, Bloxwich, Walsall, WS3 2XN Tel: (01922) 491676 Fax: (01922) 710305 E-mail: jane@acornservices.wannado.co.uk

Advanced Finishing Technologies Ltd, 8 Dudley Road, Stourbridge, West Midlands, DY9 8EL Tel: (01384) 898765 Fax: (01384) 898766 E-mail: sales@asp-uk.com

Advanced Sheet Metal Ltd, 6-8 Albany Road, Granby Industrial Estate, Weymouth, Dorset, DT4 9TH Tel: (01305) 771061 Fax: (01305) 752829 E-mail: info@asm-ltd.com

Alpha Bio Systems Ltd, Harlaw Way, Hawlaw Road Industrial Estate, Harlaw Road Industrial Estate, Inverurie, Aberdeenshire, AB51 4SG Tel: (01467) 620266 Fax: (01467) 620265

Alpha Powder Coatings, 6-10 Benedict Square, Peterborough, PE4 6GD Tel: (01733) 320111 Fax: (01733) 320111 E-mail: alphapowder@aol.com

Alw, Tweedale Industrial Estate, Madeley, Telford, Shropshire, TF7 4JR Tel: (01952) 684100 Fax: (01952) 581611 E-mail: bruce@alws.freeserve.co.uk

Amenco (Poole) Ltd, Units 14-18, Willis Way, Fleets Industrial Estate, Poole, Dorset, BH15 3ST Tel: 0845 1306660 Fax: (01202) 671436 E-mail: office@amenco.co.uk

▶ Argonaut Powder Coating Ltd, 13 Nutwood Way, Totton, Southampton, SO40 3SZ Tel: (023) 8087 3455 Fax: (023) 8087 2255 E-mail: info@argonaut-uk.com

Armacoating North West Ltd, Moores Mill, Cathrine Street East, Denton, Manchester, M34 3RQ Tel: 0161-320 9856 Fax: 0161-320 0772

Armadillo Coatings, Unit 3A, Victor Business Centre, Arthur Street, Redditch, Worcestershire, B98 8JY Tel: (01527) 526855 Fax: (01527) 502856E-mail: msalter@aol.com

B C P Industrial Coatings, Unit 14 Hitchin Business Centre, Wilbury Way, Hitchin, Hertfordshire, SG4 0AP Tel: (01462) 440804 Fax: (01462) 440804

B D M, Unit 2 Hudcar Mill, Hudcar Lane, Bury, Lancashire, BL9 6HD Tel: 0161-764 1200 Fax: 0161-764 1235 E-mail: bdmmetal@absonline.net

Barley Chalu Ltd, Ayton Road, Wymondham, Norfolk, NR18 0QH Tel: (01953) 602771 Fax: (01953) 606631 E-mail: sales@barleychalu.co.uk

Batchglow Ltd, Unit 1-2 Bookers Way, Dinnington, Sheffield, S25 3SH Tel: (01909) 563051 Fax: (01909) 564164 E-mail: info@batchglow.co.uk

Beaver Industrial Coatings, Singer Court, Singer Way, Kempston, Bedford, MK42 7AW Tel: (01234) 843614 Fax: (01234) 843309 E-mail: derekjbeaver@aol.com

Benchmark Fabrication Ltd, Jubilee House, Jubilee Road, Letchworth Garden City, Hertfordshire, SG6 1WU Tel: (01462) 633000 Fax: (01462) 481450 E-mail: sales@bench-mark.co.uk

Bernie Richardson, Unit 2 Abbey Manor Industrial Estate, Yeovil, Somerset, BA21 3AR Tel: (01935) 413317

Birmingham Powder Coatings, Clonmel Road, Birmingham, B30 2BU Tel: 0121-459 4341 Fax: 0121-451 1735 E-mail: sales@b-p-c.co.uk

Breakwells Paints Ltd, 1 Harden Road, Walsall, WS3 1EL Tel: (01922) 400444 Fax: (01922) 400555 E-mail: sales@breakwellspaints.co.uk

Breg Products Ltd, Tower Works, Birkhouse Lane, Huddersfield, HD1 4SF Tel: (01484) 469944 Fax: (01484) 469955 E-mail: sales@bregproducts.co.uk

Bristol Product Coating Ltd, The Mill Bath Road, Swineford, Bitton, Bristol, BS30 6LW Tel: 0117-932 3647 Fax: 0117-932 6183

C P K Industrial Finishers Ltd, C P K House, Colndale Road, Colnbrook, Slough, SL3 0HQ Tel: (01753) 684666 Fax: (01753) 685272 E-mail: cpk@technicalwebservices.com

C T C & Co. (Essex) Ltd, Benbridge Indust Estate, The Square, Heybridge, Maldon, Essex, CM9 4LT Tel: (01621) 841100 Fax: (01621) 842233 E-mail: sales@ctcandcompany-essex.co.uk

C T L Components Ltd, Newman Lane, Alton, Hampshire, GU34 2QR Tel: (01420) 86009 Fax: (01420) 87711

C Y Finishes Ltd, 4 Arnhem Road, Newbury, Berkshire, RG14 5RU Tel: (01635) 43860 Fax: (01635) 38547 E-mail: sales@cyfinishes.com

Caliba Spraying, Wallet Street, Nottingham, NG2 3EL Tel: 0115-986 9200 Fax: 0115-986 9204 E-mail: sales@surface-coating.co.uk

Calmac Metal Finishers Ltd, Unit 10 Quay Lane Industrial Estate, Hard Way, Gosport, Hampshire, PO12 4LJ Tel: (023) 9251 1440 Fax: (023) 9252 8814

Cambrian Powder Paints, Site B Unit 200 Rednal Indust Estate, Llanyblodwel, Oswestry, Shropshire, SY10 8NH Tel: (01691) 610596 Fax: (01691) 610596

Cambridge Electro Plating Ltd, 21 25 Union Lane, Cambridge, CB4 1PR Tel: (01223) 352464 Fax: (01223) 361085 E-mail: cep@btinternet.com

Carlton Engineering Products Ltd, Unit 1 Airborne Industrial, Estate Arterial Road, Leigh-on-Sea, Essex, SS9 4EX Tel: (01702) 420300 Fax: (01702) 529542 E-mail: sales@cep.uk.com

Cas Coatings, Old Mill, Victoria Road, Bradford, West Yorkshire, BD2 2BH Tel: (01274) 634493 Fax: (01274) 634493

Chicago Coating Co., Manchester Road, Mossley, Ashton-under-Lyne, Lancashire, OL5 9QA Tel: (01457) 832046 Fax: (01457) 838697

Circuit Coatings Ltd, Marlow Street, Walsall, WS2 8AQ Tel: (01922) 635589 Fax: (01922) 638444 E-mail: mail@circuit-coating.co.uk

Classic Finish, Midseat Cott, Bathgate, West Lothian, EH47 8AA Tel: (01501) 763185 Fax: (01501) 763171

Classic Powder Coating Ltd, Bridge Works, Iver Lane, Uxbridge, Middlesex, UB8 2JG Tel: (01895) 270616 Fax: (020) 8892 4048

Cleftbridge Coatings Ltd, Unit 8a, Lower Road Trading Estate, Ledbury, Herefordshire, HR8 2DH Tel: (01531) 633771 Fax: (01531) 633719 E-mail: enquiries@cleftbridge.co.uk

Coatapart Ltd, 58 Arthur Street, Redditch, Worcestershire, B98 8JY Tel: (01527) 528851 Fax: (01527) 517186

Colour Coatings South East, Unit 19 Warsop Trading Estate, Hever Road, Edenbridge, Kent, TN8 5LD Tel: (01732) 866700 Fax: (01732) 865983 E-mail: info@colour-coatings.co.uk

Colour Powder Coatings Ltd, Westwood House, 10 Westwood Avenue, Colevalley Business Park, Birmingham, B11 3RF Tel: 0121-772 3878 Fax: 0121-772 2697 E-mail: stevemay@colourpodercoatings.co.uk

County Powder Coaters Ltd, Kemp House, Brunel Road, Earlstrees Industrial Estate, Corby, Northamptonshire, NN17 4AU Tel: (01536) 261082 Fax: (01536) 269163

Coventry Powder Coating, Unit 5-7 Bilton Industrial Estate, Humber Avenue, Coventry, CV3 1JL Tel: (024) 7645 4694 Fax: (024) 7645 4476 E-mail: info@cpc.co.uk

Cray Metal Finishers, D1-D2 Unit Riverside Industrial Estate, Riverside Way, Dartford, DA1 5BS Tel: (01322) 220662 Fax: (01322) 288032 E-mail: sales@craymetalfinishers.co.uk

Crewe Stove Enamelling Co. Ltd, Springvale Industrial Estate, Moston Road, Sandbach, Cheshire, CW11 3HL Tel: (01270) 769069 Fax: (01270) 768003

Kate Crown Ltd, Trinity Way, West Bromwich, West Midlands, B70 6NU Tel: 0121-500 6348 Fax: 0121-580 0749 E-mail: katecrown@fsmail.net

Croxgrove Powder Coaters 1987 Ltd, Unit 10 11 The Hayes Trading Estate, Folkes Road, Stourbridge, West Midlands, DY9 8RG Tel: (01384) 423942 Fax: (01384) 423941

Crystal Finishes Ltd, Blackwater Way, Aldershot, Hampshire, GU12 4DP Tel: (01252) 325999 Fax: (01252) 330256

Custom Wytelyne Powder Coating Ltd, 88-90 Hopewell Drive, Chatham, Kent, ME5 7NL Tel: (01634) 819520 Fax: (01634) 819510 E-mail: info@custom-powder.co.uk

D & T Industrial Finishers Ltd, 9 Commerce Way, Stanbridge Road, Leighton Buzzard, Bedfordshire, LU7 4RW Tel: (01525) 376135 Fax: (01525) 217595 E-mail: info@dtindustrialfinishings.co.uk

Davies (Stove Enamellers) Ltd, Unit M Cradock Road Industrial Estate, Cradock Road, Luton, LU4 0JF Tel: (01582) 572582 Fax: (01582) 594703 E-mail: tom@lth.co.uk

Davron Finishing Industries Ltd, 18 Tanners Drive, Blakelands, Milton Keynes, MK14 5BW Tel: (01908) 210799 Fax: (01908) 217211 E-mail: sales@davronfinsihing.co.uk

Dealpage Ltd, Station Road, Uppingham, Rutland, Leicestershire, LE15 9TX Tel: (01572) 823198 Fax: (01572) 823199

Domain Powder Coating, Mayfair Industrial Estate, Maldon Road, Latchingdon, Chelmsford, CM3 6LF Tel: (01621) 742779 Fax: (01621) 742779

R.L. Dumelow & Son, St. Matthews Street, Burton-On-Trent, Staffordshire, DE14 3DE Tel: (01283) 564292 Fax: (01283) 564292

E R A Rodman Bros Ltd, 20 Lower Park Road, London, N11 1QD Tel: (020) 8361 8553 Fax: (020) 8245 6389

East Kent Coatings Ltd, Westwood Industrial Estate, Margate, Kent, CT9 4JG Tel: (01843) 293343 Fax: (01843) 293343

Ede Powder Coatings Ltd, Annie Reed Road, Beverley, North Humberside, HU17 0LF Tel: (01482) 865957 Fax: (01482) 864922 E-mail: info@edepc.com

Edmo, Netherton Road, Overross Industrial Estate, Ross-on-Wye, Herefordshire, HR9 7QQ Tel: (01989) 564215 Fax: (01989) 564644E-mail: sales@edmoengineering.co.uk

Electro Metal Depositors Ltd, 66 Bower Street, Roker Industrial Estate, Oldham, OL1 3LT Tel: 0161-624 8639 Fax: 0161-627 1575 E-mail: tmcpartland@btlink.com

Electronic Metal Work Services Ltd, Hampstead Avenue, Mildenhall, Bury St. Edmunds, Suffolk, IP28 7AS Tel: (01638) 712054 Fax: (01638) 713832E-mail: info@emws.co.uk

Ercon Group Ltd, Midacre Willenhall Trading Estate, Willenhall, West Midlands, WV13 2JW Tel: (01902) 603763 Fax: (01902) 605081 E-mail: mail@ercongroup.com

POWDER COATING SERVICES – *continued*

Ercon Powder Coating Ltd, Unit 16-17, Spring Vale Business Park, Bilston, West Midlands, WV14 0QL Tel: (01902) 491011 Fax: (01902) 492032

ESP Coatings Ltd, Units A5-E13, Hastingwood Trading Estate, Harbet Road, Edmonton, London, N18 3HT Tel: (020) 8803 1115 Fax: (020) 8035 567 E-mail: espcoatings@btconnect.com

Excel Powder Coating Ltd, 15 Chiswick Avenue, Mildenhall, Bury St. Edmunds, Suffolk, IP28 7PU Tel: (01638) 510993 Fax: (01638) 515089 E-mail: excel.sales@btopenworld.com

Felspar Finishings Ltd, C Phoenix Works, Windsor Road, Redditch, Worcestershire, B97 6DJ Tel: (01527) 585878 Fax: (01527) 63167 E-mail: felsparfinish@aol.com

Finishright Powder Coatings, Horsham Trading Estate, Foundry Lane, Horsham, West Sussex, RH13 5PX Tel: (01403) 274374 Fax: (01403) 210057

Foleshill Metal Finishing Ltd, 13 Bayton Road, Exhall, Coventry, CV7 9EJ Tel: (024) 7636 2960 Fax: (024) 7636 5876 E-mail: queries@foleshill.co.uk

Foremost Coatings, Unit 40 Hobbs Industrial Estate, Newchapel, Lingfield, Surrey, RH7 6HN Tel: (01342) 833455 Fax: (01342) 832623E-mail: david@foremostcoatings.co.uk

Fowlers Specialist Treatments Ltd, 126 129 Pritchett Street, Aston, Birmingham, B6 4EH Tel: 0121-359 8571 Fax: 0121-359 4037 E-mail: enquiries@fowlersindustrial.co.uk

G & G Powder Coatings Ltd, 3 Rippleside Commercial Estate, Ripple Road, Barking, Essex, IG11 0RJ Tel: (020) 8592 4555 Fax: (020) 8592 4777 E-mail: info@gg-powdercoating.com

▶ G & L Coatings, 8 Wallace Way, Hitchin, Hertfordshire, SG4 0SE Tel: (01462) 436668 Fax: (01462) 438982 E-mail: george.cooney@talk21.com

Gatehouse Scientific Instruments, 94c Hampstead Avenue, Mildenhall, Bury St. Edmunds, Suffolk, IP28 7AS Tel: (01638) 510555 Fax: (01638) 510555 E-mail: sales@gatehouseindustrial.com

Green Speed Power Coating, Slack Street, Macclesfield, Cheshire, SK11 7JP Tel: (01625) 439993 Fax: (01625) 439993

Griffin Enamellers Ltd, Navigation Road, Worcester, WR5 3DF Tel: (01905) 350511 Fax: (01905) 354500 E-mail: griffin@intrac.co.uk

Gwent Powder Coatings Ltd, Unit 37 Springvale Industrial Estate, Cwmbran, Gwent, NP44 5BD Tel: (01633) 860901 Fax: (01633) 872030 E-mail: gpowdercoatings@btconnect.com

H & S Enamelling (U K) Ltd, Unit 10, Highbridge Industrial Estate, Oxford Rd, Uxbridge, Middlesex, UB8 1LX Tel: (01895) 233251 Fax: (01895) 810800 E-mail: sales@hsenamelling.co.uk

H Snelson Engineers Ltd, Nat Lane, Winsford, Cheshire, CW7 3BS Tel: (01606) 553580 Fax: (01606) 861084 E-mail: sales@snelsons.co.uk

Hane Instruments Ltd, 691 Stirling Road, Slough, SL1 4ST Tel: (01753) 530313 Fax: (01753) 823301 E-mail: info@haneinstruments.co.uk

Hankoe Advanced Surface Treatments Ltd, 823 Yeovil Road, Slough Trading Estate, Slough, SL1 4JA Tel: (01753) 522779 Fax: (01753) 539320 E-mail: hankoe@btconnect.com

Harlow Spraytech, St. James Centre, 7 East Road, Harlow, Essex, CM20 2BJ Tel: (01279) 414665 Fax: (01279) 416828

Henshaw Manufacturing Co. Ltd, Stratford St North, Birmingham, B11 1BP Tel: 0121-772 2232 Fax: 0121-771 1788 E-mail: weekshenshaw@aol.com

High Speed Piercing Ltd, Pindar Road, Hoddesdon, Hertfordshire, EN11 0DE Tel: (01992) 445123 Fax: (01992) 466541 E-mail: admin@highspeedpiercing.co.uk

Hourcover Ltd, 2 Thorgate Road, Wick, Littlehampton, West Sussex, BN17 7LU Tel: (01903) 714234 Fax: (01903) 722877 E-mail: hourcover@aol.com

Hutchcoat Powder Coatings, Manor Farm, Ganthorpe, York, YO60 6QD Tel: (01653) 648436 Fax: (01653) 648436

Industrial Paint & Powder Ltd, 45 Lanark Road, Edinburgh, EH14 1TL Tel: 0131-443 8793 Fax: 0131-455 7806 E-mail: sales@indpaintandpowder.co.uk

Ipf, 37 Whitehill Road, Glenrothes, Fife, KY6 2RW Tel: (01592) 771805 Fax: (01592) 771805

J A Kinnersley & Co. Ltd, Copenhagen Road, Hull. HU7 0XQ Tel: (01482) 826020 Fax: (01482) 878447 E-mail: sales@j-kinnersley.co.uk

J & P Contracts Angus Ltd, 73 Dundee Street, Carnoustie, Angus, DD7 7PN Tel: (01241) 854911 Fax: (01241) 855860 E-mail: sales@jp-coattech.com

J R Bourne Powder Coatings Ltd, Beckingham Road, Great Totham, Maldon, Essex, CM9 8EA Tel: (01621) 892972 Fax: (01621) 893299 E-mail: sales@jrbourne.co.uk

K M H Powder Coating & Shotblasting, 10b Radnor Road, Wigston, Leicestershire, LE18 4XY Tel: 0116-277 0050 Fax: 0116-277 7229 E-mail: hackmower@aol.com

▶ K & N Finishers Southern Ltd, Castle Trading Estate, Fareham, Hampshire, PO16 9SF Tel: (023) 9237 0591 Fax: (023) 9238 0130 E-mail: kandnfinishers@bt.com

K N P Finishing Ltd, Unit 10, Commerce Way, Leighton Buzzard, Bedfordshire, LU7 4RW Tel: (01525) 850478 Fax: (01525) 850479 E-mail: andykendall@btconnect.com

Key Coatings, 288 Aberdeen Avenue, Slough, SL1 4HG Tel: (01753) 537775 Fax: (01753) 570869

L B L Finishers, Gunstore Road, Portsmouth, PO3 5HL Tel: (023) 9269 2020 Fax: (023) 9267 0379 E-mail: sales@tomburn.co.uk

Lap Tab Ltd, 205 Tyburn Road, Birmingham, B24 8NB Tel: 0121-328 1697 Fax: 0121-328 9787 E-mail: sales@lap-tab.co.uk

Leicester Enamellers Ltd, Coventry Road, Narborough, Leicester, LE19 2GG Tel: 0116-275 1231 Fax: 0116-275 1330

Leigh & Letcher, Chequers Lane, Dagenham, Essex, RM9 6QD Tel: (020) 8984 1015 Fax: (020) 8984 1735 E-mail: sales@leighandletcher.co.uk

Lemin & Co. Ltd, Unit 4 Albone Way, Biggleswade, Bedfordshire, SG7 5AN Tel: (01767) 600120 Fax: (01767) 600121 E-mail: enquiries@lemin.co.uk

Liskeard Metal Finishers, 6 Iskeard Enterprise Centre, Station Road, Liskeard, Cornwall, PL14 4BT Tel: (01579) 348251 Fax: (01579) 348258

Lustre Anodising Co. Ltd, Units 22-24, Cannon Business Park, Gough Road, Coseley, Bilston, West Midlands, WV14 8XR Tel: (01902) 494455 Fax: (01902) 494411 E-mail: info@lustre-anodising.co.uk

M K Powder Coaters Ltd, 33 Blundells Road, Bradville, Milton Keynes, MK13 7HD Tel: (01908) 318484 Fax: (01908) 322253

M R K Services, Unit 97 Northwick Business Centre, Northwick Park, Blockley, Moreton-in-Marsh, Gloucestershire, GL56 9RF Tel: (01386) 700912 Fax: (01386) 700922 E-mail: sales@mrkservices.co.uk

Macemain Engineering Ltd, Boyle Road, Willowbrook East Indust, Corby, Northamptonshire, NN17 5XU Tel: (01536) 401331 Fax: (01536) 401298 E-mail: sales@macemainamstad.com

Malcolm Enamellers Midlands Ltd, Lawley Middleway, Birmingham, B4 7XT Tel: 0121-359 7553 Fax: 0121-359 8309 E-mail: sales@malcolms.co.uk

Mastercote Ltd, Wendover Road, Rackheath Industrial Estate, Rackheath, Norwich, NR13 6LH Tel: (01603) 720326 Fax: (01603) 721805

Matann Metal Fabrication Ltd, 5 Blatchford Road, Horsham, West Sussex, RH13 5QR Tel: (01403) 249994 Fax: (01403) 249355

Medway Powder Coatings, 4 Sextant Park, Neptune Close, Medway City Estate, Rochester, Kent, ME2 4LU Tel: (01634) 290992 Fax: (01634) 720073

Metafin Group Holdings Ltd, Green Lane, Walsall, WS2 8JG Tel: (01922) 626073 Fax: (01922) 720673

Metal Coating Services Ltd, Hamburg Road, Off Rotterdam Road, Hull, HU7 0XD Tel: (01482) 820202 Fax: (01482) 820150 E-mail: gareth@metalcoatingservices.com

Metalion Ltd, North Acton Road, London, NW10 6PD Tel: (020) 8965 4677 Fax: (020) 8965 3142

Metreat Ltd t/a Applied Metal Finishers, Units 2-3, Prosper House, Padholme Road East, Peterborough, PE1 5XL Tel: (01733) 703030 Fax: (01733) 704040 E-mail: sales@appliedmetalfinishers.co.uk

Midland Enamellers, 1 Pinfold Road, Thurmaston, Leicester, LE4 8AS Tel: 0116-269 7861 Fax: 0116-264 0739

Miltech Stove Enamellers & Powder Coating, Unit 7 Leyton Avenue, Mildenhall, Bury St. Edmunds, Suffolk, IP28 7BL Tel: (01638) 717880 Fax: (01638) 717880 E-mail: anthonybrooks98@wannado.co.uk

N K Coatings Ltd, 4 Michelin Road, Newtownabbey, County Antrim, BT36 4PT Tel: (028) 9083 3725 Fax: (028) 9083 7433 E-mail: mail@nkcoatings.com

Nationwide Coatings UK Ltd, 5 Canal Estate, Station Road, Langley, Slough, SL3 6EG Tel: (01753) 671612 Fax: (01753) 671613 E-mail: sales@nationwidecoatings.co.uk

Newfold Ltd, Bridgewater Close, Reading, RG30 1NS Tel: 0118-957 3074 E-mail: sales@newfold.com

Northpoint Ltd, Globe Lane, Dukinfield, Cheshire, SK16 4UY Tel: 0161-330 4551 Fax: 0161-339 7169 E-mail: sales@northpoint.ltd.uk

Optimised Power Controls Ltd, Whitelands Road, Ashton-under-Lyne, Lancashire, OL6 6UG Tel: 0161-330 3318 Fax: 0161-285 3737

P & J Powder Coatings, 17 Evanton Place, Thornliebank, Glasgow, G46 8JE Tel: 0141-620 1652 Fax: 0141-620 0928

P & R Finishing, 1 Site 2 North Bridge Road, Berkhamsted, Hertfordshire, HP4 1EH Tel: (01442) 873962 Fax: (01442) 873962

Palace Perma Signs Ltd, Lowmoor Industrial Estate, Prospect Close, Kirkby-in-Ashfield, Nottingham, NG17 7LF Tel: (01623) 754899 Fax: (01623) 752341

Paraid Ltd, Unit 4 Bond Street, West Bromwich, West Midlands, B70 7DQ Tel: 0121-580 0111 Fax: 0121-580 0222

Paramount Powders UK Ltd, 4 Squirrels Trading Estate, Viveash Close, Hayes, Middlesex, UB3 4RZ Tel: (020) 8561 5588 Fax: (020) 8561 5599 E-mail: sales@paramountpowders.co.uk

Phoenix Corporation UK Ltd, Unit 5 North Weylands Industrial Estate, Molesey Road, Walton-on-Thames, Surrey, KT12 3PL Tel: (01932) 246236 Fax: (01932) 246236

Pickersgill Electroplaters Ltd, Pepper Road, Leeds, LS10 2PP Tel: 0113-271 4909 Fax: 0113-276 0546 E-mail: sales@pickersgills.co.uk

Pipeline Induction Heat Ltd, Farrington Road, Burnley, Lancashire, BB11 5SW Tel: (01282) 415323 Fax: (01282) 415326 E-mail: sales@pih.co.uk

Plastic Coatings, Pontymister Industrial Estate, Risca, Newport, Gwent, NP11 6NP Tel: (0845) 6120333 Fax: (01633) 612320 E-mail: enquiries@plastic-coatings.com

Potteries Powder Coating, 9 Hyde Park Trading Estate, City Road, Stoke-on-Trent, ST4 1DS Tel: (01782) 749292 Fax: (01782) 749393

Powdat Enamellers Ltd, Sanders Road, Finedon Road Industrial Estate, Wellingborough, Northamptonshire, NN8 4NL Tel: (01933) 445920 Fax: (01933) 445924

Powder Coatings Ltd, 215 Tyburn Road, Birmingham, B24 8NB Tel: 0121-250 2145 Fax: 0121-250 2154 E-mail: roger@abbeyland.co.uk

Powder Link, 47 Meyrick Drive, Newbury, Berkshire, RG14 6SY Tel: (01635) 30457 Fax: (01635) 31310 E-mail: sales@powderlink.co.uk

Premier Industrial Painting, Unit 10C Newbattle, Abbey College Annexe, Dalkeith, Midlothian, EH22 3LJ Tel: 0131-660 9699 Fax: 0131-660 6841

Priority Technical Services Ltd, Suite 7 Thorn Office Centre, Thorn Business Park, Rotherwas, Hereford, HR2 6JT Tel: (01432) 271080 Fax: (01432) 271137

Pro Tec, 120 Old Coach Road, Templepatrick, Ballyclare, County Antrim, BT39 0HA Tel: (028) 9443 3693 Fax: (028) 9443 3551

Purpose Powder Coatings Ltd, 18 Manor Grove, London, SE15 1SX Tel: (020) 7639 2511 Fax: (020) 7277 5942 E-mail: sales@purposepowdercoatings.com

Quality Coatings Ltd, Russell Street, Chadderton, Oldham, OL9 9LD Tel: 0161-620 0008 Fax: 0161-627 2746

Quality Surface Coatings Ltd, Hackworth Industrial Park, Shildon, County Durham, DL4 1HE Tel: 01388 776197

Quality Tool & Engineering Ltd, Maesyllan, Llanidloes, Powys, SY18 6DF Tel: (01686) 412679 Fax: (01686) 413554 E-mail: qualitytools@btconnect.com

R A Peatey & Sons Ltd, Green Lane, Yeadon, Leeds, LS19 7BY Tel: 0113-250 1046 Fax: 0113-250 7364

R B Industrial Finishers, Unit 4 Kents Avenue, Hemel Hempstead, Hertfordshire, HP3 9XH Tel: (01442) 244343 Fax: (01442) 235127

R P A Motorcycle Powder Coating, 4 Queen Victoria Street, Bristol, BS2 0QR Tel: 0117-954 1002 Fax: 0117-941 2870

Rainbow Spray Services, 5 Berrite Works, Ironbridge Road, West Drayton, Middlesex, UB7 8HY Tel: (01895) 430852 Fax: (01895) 430853

Reeves Engineering Ltd, 15 Swinbourne Drive, Springwood Industrial Estate, Braintree, Essex, CM7 2YP Tel: (01376) 322613 Fax: (01376) 551522

Relion Broma Ltd, Avenue Industrial Estate, Gallows Corner, Romford, RM3 0BY Tel: (01708) 341177 Fax: (01708) 384999

Ripley Engineering Ltd, Rankine Road, Basingstoke, Hampshire, RG24 8PP Tel: (01256) 473940 Fax: (01256) 479991 E-mail: services@ripley-eng.co.uk

Rust Proofing Company (Manchester) Ltd, Vauxhall Works, Greg Street, Reddish, Stockport, Cheshire, SK5 7BR Tel: 0161-480 8341 Fax: 0161-480 8820

Sandwell Stove Enamellers & Powder Coaters Ltd, Unit 12 Blankenhall Industrial Estate, Sunbeam Street, Wolverhampton, WV2 4PF Tel: (01902) 422899 Fax: (01902) 423380

Sandy Powder Coating, 14 Howard Road, Eaton Socon, St. Neots, Cambridgeshire, PE19 8ET Tel: (01480) 470555 Fax: (01480) 477155

Scruse & Crossland Ltd, 2 Wingate Road, Gosport, Hampshire, PO12 4DR Tel: (023) 9250 2403 Fax: (023) 9251 1728 E-mail: sales@scruse.co.uk

Shearfab Ltd, Oldgate, St. Michaels Industrial Estate, Widnes, Cheshire, WA8 8TL Tel: 0151-420 5200 Fax: 0151-420 5190 E-mail: info@shearfab.co.uk

Silver By Coating, Unit 19, Whitworth Industrial Park, Tilton Road, Birmingham, B9 4PP Tel: 0121-772 1536 Fax: 0121-766 5771

Slough Plastic Coatings, 2 David Road, Colnbrook, Slough, SL3 0DG Tel: (01753) 683907 Fax: (01753) 682571 E-mail: sloughplastic@btconnect.com

Smith Engineering GB Ltd, Solway Trading Estate, Maryport, Cumbria, CA15 8NF Tel: (01900) 815831 Fax: (01900) 815553 E-mail: r.smith@moonbuggy.com

Solent, The Sanderson Centre, Lees Lane, Gosport, Hampshire, PO12 3UL Tel: (023) 9251 1924 Fax: (023) 9251 1924 E-mail: peter@solentpowdercoatings.co.uk

▶ Solent Powder Finishers Ltd, 3 Brookwood Industrial Estate, Brookwood Avenue, Eastleigh, Hampshire, SO50 9EY Tel: (023) 8064 2632 Fax: (023) 8064 2631 E-mail: enquiries@s-p-f.co.uk

South Western Plastics Ltd, The Old Jail, Willway Street, Bristol, BS3 4BG Tel: 0117-953 1811

Specialist Coating Ltd, All Saints Industrial Estate, Darlington Road, Shildon, County Durham, DL4 2RD Tel: (01388) 774034 Fax: (01388) 777010 E-mail: sales@specialistcoatings.co.uk

Spray Finishers (Poole), 14 Abingdon Road, Nuffield Industrial Estate, Poole, Dorset, BH17 0UG Tel: (01202) 685488 Fax: (01202) 676260 E-mail: info@sprayfinishes.co.uk

Spraybake JRC, 1 Boarshurst Business Park, Boarshurst Lane, Greenfield, Oldham, OL3 7ER Tel: (01457) 870779 Fax: (01457) 875477 E-mail: info@spraybakejrc.co.uk

Standard & Pochin Ltd, 94 Lyde Road, Yeovil, Somerset, BA21 5DS Tel: (01935) 421481 Fax: (01935) 428030 E-mail: info@ijmcgilltransport.com

Steadhall Finishing, Unit 1, Bay Close, Progress Way, Luton, LU4 9UP Tel: (01582) 561518 Fax: (01582) 493350 E-mail: rainbowfinishers@aol.com

Strathclyde Powder Coatings Scotland Ltd, 40-42 Telford Road, East Lenziemill Industrial Estate, Glasgow, G67 2NH Tel: (01236) 734242 Fax: (01236) 720619 E-mail: douglas.spc@btconnect.com

Sureline Finishing, 1-2 Quarry CR, Pennygillam Industrial Estate, Launceston, Cornwall, PL15 7PF Tel: (01566) 776630 Fax: (01566) 777773

Sussex Blast Cleaning Ltd, 35 Industrial Estate, Station Road, Hailsham, East Sussex, BN27 2ER Tel: (01323) 849229 Fax: (01323) 442442

Swanells & Grylls Ltd, 330-332 Selborne Road, Luton, LU4 8NU Tel: (01582) 573066

Sweeney & Sherlock, Unit 25 Whitworth Industrial Park, Tilton Road, Birmingham, B9 4PP Tel: 0121-753 0960 Fax: 0121-753 0961 E-mail: sales@sweeneysherlock.co.uk

Swift Coatings, Empire Works, Church Street, Darfield, Barnsley, South Yorkshire, S73 9JX Tel: (01226) 752016 Fax: (01226) 752016 E-mail: enquiries@swiftcoatings.co.uk

T M R, Canal Street, Brierley Hill, West Midlands, DY5 1JJ Tel: (01384) 75531 Fax: (01384) 573353 E-mail: sales@tmrracking.com

T M T Powder Coatings Ltd, 62 Hammonds Drive, Eastbourne, East Sussex, BN23 6PW Tel: (01323) 642215 Fax: (01323) 649963 E-mail: tmt.powder@virgin.net

Tanfield Group plc, Vigo Centre, Birtley Road, Washington, Tyne & Wear, NE38 9DA Tel: 0191-417 2170 Fax: (0845) 1557756 E-mail: sales@tanfieldgroup.com

Taurus Engineering, Commerce Way, Lancing, West Sussex, BN15 8TA Tel: (01903) 761188 Fax: (01903) 767268 E-mail: sales@taurusengineering.co.uk

Tecproof Ltd, 266 Dansom Lane North, Hull, HU8 7RS Tel: (01482) 215886 Fax: (01482) 215886

Teversham Engineering Ltd, Hall Farm, Church Road, Teversham, Cambridge, CB1 9AP Tel: 01223 293904

Trestan Finishers Ltd, Unit B, 26 Hazel Road, Southampton, SO19 7GA Tel: (023) 8043 3081 E-mail: info@trestanfinishers.co.uk

Trevon Industrial Finishers, Whitewalls Industrial Estate, Regent Street, Colne, Lancashire, BB8 8LJ Tel: (01282) 861786 Fax: (01282) 863829

Trico Services Ltd, The Old Powder Mill, Powder Mill Lane, Dartford, DA1 1NT Tel: (01322) 276777 Fax: (01322) 276776

Unimet Enamellers Ltd, 183-185 Cardiff Road, Reading, RG1 8HD Tel: 0118-959 5528

Unispray Powder Coatings, Unit 185 Thorp Arch Trading Estate, Thorp Arch, Wetherby, West Yorkshire, LS23 7BJ Tel: (01937) 541267 Fax: (01937) 541267

Up Country Autoproducts UK Ltd, Norwich Road, Halesworth, Suffolk, IP19 8QJ Tel: (01986) 875171 Fax: (01986) 875260 E-mail: sales@upcountry4x4.co.uk

Vanden Powder Coatings Ltd, 79 Manchester Road, Westhoughton, Bolton, BL5 3QD Tel: (01942) 818953 Fax: (01942) 840678

W H Greaves & Son Electroplating Ltd, 2 Lock Street, Sheffield, S6 3BJ Tel: 0114-232 3272 Fax: 0114-232 3273

W L P C Ltd, Unit 19 Manor Complex, Kirkby Bank Road, Knowsley Industrial Park, Liverpool, L33 7SY Tel: 0151-549 1781

Washford Finishings, 9 Washford Industrial Estate, Bartleet Road, Redditch, Worcestershire, B98 0DQ Tel: (01527) 525936 Fax: (01527) 526433

Washington Powder Coatings Ltd, 13 Bridgewater Road, Hertburn Industrial Estate, Washington, Tyne & Wear, NE37 2SG Tel: 0191-416 4085 Fax: 0191-415 7825

Watford Coatings Ltd, Park House, Greenhill CR, Watford, WD18 8QU Tel: (01923) 235640 Fax: (01923) 449229 E-mail: sales@watfordcoatings.co.uk

Webasto Roof Systems Ltd, Unit 7 Kingsbury Business Park, Kingsbury Road, Sutton Coldfield, West Midlands, B76 9DL Tel: 0121-313 5600 Fax: 0121-351 4905 E-mail: customer.service@webasto.co.uk

Welded Presswork (1982) Ltd, Stafford Road, Darlaston, Wednesbury, West Midlands, WS10 8SZ Tel: 0121-526 2022 Fax: 0121-526 4905 E-mail: enquiries@weldedpresswork.co.uk

Westpark Fabrications Ltd, Unit 4 Waterfield Mill, 4 Balmoral Road, Darwen, Lancashire, BB3 2EW Tel: (01254) 760136 Fax: (01254) 762116

Willow Stove Enamellers, Unit 11 Eagle Trading Estate, Willow Lane, Mitcham, Surrey, CR4 4UY Tel: (020) 8646 7169 Fax: (020) 8646 7169

Wyvale Associates Ltd, Wilson Street, Southampton, SO14 5AY Tel: (023) 8063 8066 Fax: (023) 8033 3138

POWDER COATING SERVICES TO SPECIFICATION

▶ Eurospray Ltd, 2 Crompton Road, Glenrothes, Fife, KY6 2SF Tel: (01592) 770055 Fax: (01592) 770066 E-mail: admin@eurospray.sol.co.uk

POWDER COATING, EPOXY POLYESTER

P C S Powders Ltd, Unit 3, Waterloo Industrial Estate, Flanders Road, Hedge End, Southampton, SO30 2QT Tel: (01489) 790400 Fax: (01489) 785295 E-mail: info@pcspowders.co.uk

POWDER COATINGS, *See also headings for particular types*

A Hallworth & Sons, 2 Dale Mill, Roch Street, Rochdale, Lancashire, OL16 2UH Tel: (01706) 648768

Allsops Ltd, Hope Bank Works, New Mil Road, Honley, Holmfirth, HD9 6QG Tel: (01484) 661447 Fax: (01484) 666808 E-mail: info@allsops.co.uk

▶ Aspect Powder Coatings, Coneygre Industrial Estate, Tipton, West Midlands, DY4 8XP Tel: 0121-557 4444

▶ Associated Industrial Paints, Park View Works, Park Street, Stalybridge, Cheshire, SK15 2BT Tel: 0161-303 9008

B G Penny & Co. Ltd, Unit 3, Three Spires Industrial Estate, Ibstock Road, Coventry, CV6 6JR Tel: (024) 7636 7636 Fax: (024) 7636 7636

Beaver Industrial Coatings, Singer Court, Singer Way, Kempston, Bedford, MK42 7AW Tel: (01234) 843614 Fax: (01234) 843309 E-mail: derekjbeaver@aol.com

Becker Powder Coatings Ltd, Goodlass Road, Liverpool, L24 9HJ Tel: 0151-486 0486 Fax: 0151-486 0484

C T C & Co. (Essex) Ltd, Benbridge Indust Estate, The Square, Heybridge, Maldon, Essex, CM9 4LT Tel: (01621) 841100 Fax: (01621) 842233 E-mail: sales@ctcandcompany-essex.co.uk

▶ Casshurst Coatings Ltd, 6 Power Works, Slade Green Road, Erith, Kent, DA8 2HY Tel: (01322) 351820 Fax: (01322) 351816

▶ Circuit Coatings Ltd, Old Walsall Road, Hampstead Industrial Estate, Birmingham, B42 1EA Tel: 0121-357 9365 Fax: 0121-358 7524

Colourtec Powder Coatings, 23a Willow Road, Colnbrook, Slough, SL3 0BS Tel: (01753) 683820 Fax: (01753) 680020

▶ Creative Colour Coatings, Lockhill Mills, Holmes Road, Sowerby Bridge, West Yorkshire, HX6 3LF Tel: (01422) 316066

Dupont Powder Coatings UK Ltd, Whessoe Road, Darlington, County Durham, DL3 0XH Tel: (01325) 355371 Fax: (01325) 380092

▶ Evan Coating Ltd, Unit 31, Garston Industrial Estate, Blackburn Street, Liverpool, L19 8JB Tel: 0151-427 8000 Fax: 0151-427 5000

Excel Powder Coating Ltd, 15 Chiswick Avenue, Mildenhall, Bury St. Edmunds, Suffolk, IP28 7PU Tel: (01638) 510993 Fax: (01638) 515089 E-mail: excel.sales@btopenworld.com

Ferro (G B) Ltd, Westgate, Aldridge, Walsall, WS9 8YH Tel: (01922) 741300 Fax: (01922) 741327

Foremost Coatings, Unit 40 Hobbs Industrial Estate, Newchapel, Lingfield, Surrey, RH7 6HN Tel: (01342) 833455 Fax: (01342) 832623E-mail: david@foremostcoatings.co.uk

▶ G T I Powder Coating, Unit 2, Jenning Street, Hull, HU8 7AN Tel: (01482) 211040 Fax: (01482) 211178

Green Speed Power Coating, Slack Street, Macclesfield, Cheshire, SK11 7JP Tel: (01625) 439993 Fax: (01625) 439993

HMG Coatings South Ltd, Faraday Park, Andover, Hampshire, SP10 3SA Tel: (01264) 337824 Fax: (01264) 338123 E-mail: mail@hmgcoatings.co.uk

▶ Howses Paint & Powder Ltd, Cakemore Road, Rowley Regis, West Midlands, B65 0RD Tel: 0121-559 1451 Fax: 0121-559 2722 E-mail: sales@howsepaints.co.uk

L S N, 1 Wheldon Road, Castleford, West Yorkshire, WF10 2SE Tel: (01977) 604461 Fax: (01977) 604461

▶ MDF Powder Coating Ltd, Bonlea Trading Estate, Thornaby, Stockton-on-Tees, Cleveland, TS17 7AQ Tel: (01642) 603399

▶ Multicoat North East Ltd, 3 Florence Street, Middlesbrough, Cleveland, TS2 1DR Tel: (01642) 213030 Fax: (01642) 213030

New Star, Unit 1 Ucc Indust Estate, 219 Humberstone Lane, Leicester, LE4 9JT Tel: 0116-269 6937 Fax: 0116-269 6566 E-mail: enquiries@powdercoatings.gbr.fm

P C S Powders Ltd, Unit 3, Waterloo Industrial Estate, Flanders Road, Hedge End, Southampton, SO30 2QT Tel: (01489) 790400 Fax: (01489) 785295 E-mail: info@pcspowders.co.uk

Pantex Coatings (Yorkshire) Ltd, Unit 7 Stephenson Road, Inkersall Road Industrial Estate, Staveley, Chesterfield, Derbyshire, S43 3JN Tel: (01246) 475233 Fax: (01246) 475284 E-mail: enquiries@hayford.com

Paramount Powders UK Ltd, 4 Squirrels Trading Estate, Viveash Close, Hayes, Middlesex, UB3 4RZ Tel: (020) 8561 5588 Fax: (020) 8561 5599 E-mail: sales@paramountpowders.co.uk

Pharon Powder Coatings Ltd, 4 Beech Road, Box Hill, Corsham, Wiltshire, SN13 8HF Tel: (01225) 743507 Fax: (01225) 744389

▶ PPC, 39 High Street, Rowhedge, Colchester, CO5 7ET Tel: (01206) 729393

▶ Pro Metal Manufacturing Ltd, 3b Maitland Road, Lion Barn Industrial Estate, Needham Market, Ipswich, IP6 8NZ Tel: (01449) 723082 Fax: (01449) 723080

Quality Industries Ltd, Unit C 18 Stafford Park, Telford, Shropshire, TF3 3BN Tel: (01952) 292166 Fax: (01952) 292167 E-mail: sales@qivansystems.co.uk

▶ Bernie Richardson, Unit 2 Abbey Manor Industrial Estate, Yeovil, Somerset, BA21 3AR Tel: (01935) 413317

Russell-Webb Ltd, Fountain Drive, Hertford, SG13 7UB Tel: (01992) 551774 Fax: (01992) 554178 E-mail: info@russell-webb.com

▶ Spectrum Architectural Coatings, High Street, Princes End, Tipton, West Midlands, DY4 9HG Tel: 0121-522 2244 Fax: 0121-522 2243

▶ Stella Blast, Stella Gill Industrial Estate, Pelton Fell, Chester le Street, County Durham, DH2 2RH Tel: 0191-389 4677 Fax: 0191-389 1999

Superior Plant Sales Services Ltd, Unit 2-3 Cornwall St Industrial Estate, Cornwall Street, Manchester, M11 2WL Tel: 0161-343 3312 Fax: 0161-231 1133

Thermaset Ltd, Apollo, Lichfield Road Industrial Estate, Tamworth, Staffordshire, B79 7TA Tel: (01827 55777 Fax: (01827 53713

▶ Tiger Coatings UK Ltd, 21 Pettyfields Close, Knowle, Solihull, West Midlands, B93 9EG Tel: (01564) 778866 Fax: (01564) 778866

Top Coat Finishers, Station Road, Ecclesfield, Sheffield, S35 9YR Tel: 0114-245 5867

Velspar, 95 Aston Church Road, Birmingham, B7 5RQ Tel: 0121-322 6900 Fax: 0121-322 6901 E-mail: infoeurope@powderstore.com

▶ We Do Powder Coating Ltd, Unit B3 Troon Way Business Centre, Humberstone Lane, Leicester, LE4 9HA Tel: 0116-276 0061

Wraight's Of Dover, Edgar Road, Dover, Kent, CT17 0ES Tel: (01304) 201289 Fax: (01304) 213264

▶ Wrexham Metal Finishing, Unit 250a Redwither Business Park, Redwither Business Park, Wrexham, Clwyd, LL13 9UE Tel: (01978) 664888 Fax: (01978) 664888

POWDER COMPACTION ISOSTATIC PRESSING EQUIPMENT

Isoform Ltd, Maer Lane Industrial Estate, Llewellyn Roberts Way, Market Drayton, Shropshire, TF9 1QS Tel: (01630) 652772 Fax: (01630) 652518 E-mail: isoform@btinternet.com

POWDER CONTAINMENT SYSTEMS

Applied Containment Engineering Ltd, Unit 4, Shaw Cross Business Park, Dewsbury, West Yorkshire, WF12 7RF Tel: (01924) 455339 Fax: (01924) 452295 E-mail: applied.containment@ace-ltd.com

Extract Technology Ltd, Bradley Junction Industrial Estate, Leeds Road, Huddersfield, HD2 1UR Tel: (01484) 432659 Fax: (01484) 432659 E-mail: info@extract-technology.com

Mach Aire Ltd, Bridge Street, Horwich, Bolton, BL6 7BT Tel: (01204) 668905 Fax: (01204) 668906 E-mail: sales@machaire.co.uk

Powder Systems Ltd, Estuary Business Park, Speke, Liverpool, L24 8RG Tel: 0151-448 7700 Fax: 0151-448 7702 E-mail: sales@p-s-l.com

POWDER COUPLINGS

Van Der Graaf UK Ltd, 23 The Metro Centre, Peterborough, PE2 7UH Tel: (01733) 391777 Fax: (01733) 391044 E-mail: paul@vandergraaf.co.uk

POWDER FILLING/PACKAGING EQUIPMENT

All Fill Ltd, 5 Gateshead Close, Sandy, Bedfordshire, SG19 1RS Tel: (01767) 691100 Fax: (01767) 681406 E-mail: info@allfill.co.uk

▶ Qualipack (U K), 50 Kinnersley, Severn Stoke, Worcester, WR8 9JR Tel: (01905) 371226 Fax: (01905) 371529 E-mail: sales@qualipack.co.uk

POWDER HANDLING EQUIPMENT

Dixon-PureFill Ltd, 65 Rainford Road, Billinge, Wigan, Lancashire, WN5 7PG Tel: (01744) 892555 E-mail: sales@dixonpurefill.co.uk

Gericke Ltd, Victoria House, Cavendish Street, Ashton-under-Lyne, Lancashire, OL6 7DJ Tel: 0161-344 1140 Fax: 0161-308 3403 E-mail: sales@gericke.co.uk

Hanteck Ltd, 887 Plymouth Road, Slough Trading Estate, Slough, SL1 4LP Tel: (01753) 811550 Fax: (01753) 811551 E-mail: sales@hanteck.com

Process Link Ltd, Tilemans Lane, Shipston-on-Stour, Warwickshire, CV36 4QZ Tel: (01608) 662878 Fax: (01608) 662968 E-mail: info@processlink.co.uk

Vibrair Materials Handling Equipment, Virginia Mills, 187 Higher Hillgate, Stockport, Cheshire, SK1 3JG Tel: 0161-480 8991 Fax: 0161-474 7737

POWDER MIXERS

Morton Machine Co. Ltd, Atlantic Works, Newhouse Industrial Estate, Motherwell, Lanarkshire, ML1 5SW Tel: (01698) 732021 Fax: (01698) 732546 E-mail: info@morton-machines.co.uk

POWDER PROCESSING CONTRACT SERVICES

Reflec plc, Road One, Winsford Industrial Estate, Winsford, Cheshire, CW7 3QQ Tel: (01606) 593911 Fax: (01606) 559535 E-mail: info@reflec.co.uk

POWDER PROCESSING EQUIPMENT

▶ Kemutec Powder Technologies Ltd, Springwood Way, Macclesfield, Cheshire, SK10 2ND Tel: (01625) 412000 Fax: (01625) 412001 E-mail: sales@kemutec.com

POWDER PUFFS

Gilca Manufacturing Ltd, 853 Wolverhampton Road, Oldbury, West Midlands, B69 4RU Tel: 0121-544 1929 Fax: 0121-544 6301 E-mail: info@gilca.biz

Synlatex Ltd, Unit M2 Innsworth Technology Park, Innsworth Lane, Gloucester, GL3 1DL Tel: (01452) 730068 Fax: (01452) 730048 E-mail: enquiries@slguk.com

POWER CAPACITORS

Adex Technical Ltd, Unit 4 Canal Ironworks, Hope Mill Lane, London Road, Stroud, Gloucestershire, GL5 2SH Tel: (01453) 889202 Fax: (01453) 889203 E-mail: sales@adexltd.co.uk

Phasetech Ltd, Industry Park, Cricketts Lane, Chippenham, Wiltshire, SN15 3EQ Tel: (01249) 651436 Fax: (01249) 462356 E-mail: sales@phasetech.co.uk

Power Products International Ltd, Commerce Way, Edenbridge, Kent, TN8 6ED Tel: (01732) 866424 Fax: (01732) 866399 E-mail: sales@ppi-uk.com

POWER CONDITIONING EQUIPMENT

Advent Communications, Preston Hill House, Preston Hill, Chesham, Buckinghamshire, HP5 3HE Tel: (01494) 774400 Fax: (01494) 791127 E-mail: sales@vislink.com

Eastern Transformer Ltd, Overland Industrial Park, Sudbury Road, Little Whelnetham, Bury St. Edmunds, Suffolk, IP30 0UL Tel: (01284) 388033 Fax: (01284) 386969 E-mail: info@ete.co.uk

POWER CORD CABLES

Apex Cables Ltd, St Johns Road, Meadowfield Industrial Estate, Durham, DH7 8RJ Tel: 0191-378 7900 Fax: 0191-378 7909 E-mail: apex@apexcables.co.uk

POWER CORDS

Sandal P.L.C., Number 5, Harold Close, The Pinnacles, Harlow, Essex, CM19 5TH Tel: (01279) 422022 Fax: (01279) 626304 E-mail: ctaylor@powerconnections.co.uk

POWER DISTRIBUTION CONTRACTORS

▶ Argus Electrical Services Ltd, 150 Avery Hill Road, London, SE9 2EY Tel: (020) 8850 9947 Fax: (020) 8859 8680 E-mail: arguselecservltd@aol.com

▶ Arktech UK Ltd, 11 Tower Road, Washington, Tyne & Wear, NE37 2SH Tel: 0191-419 3996 Fax: 0191-419 3096

Causeway Electricial Services, Catherine Street, Warrington, WA5 0LH Tel: (01925) 633390 Fax: (01925) 243214

Cwmbran Electrical Services Ltd, Unit 34 Court Road Industrial Estate, Cwmbran, Gwent, NP44 3AS Tel: (01633) 483416 Fax: (01633) 874712

D E P E Breaden Electrical Ltd, 396 Finchley Road, London, NW2 2HR Tel: (020) 7435 1304 Fax: (020) 7435 0194

▶ Electrical Site Services, 111 Seaview Road, Wallasey, Merseyside, CH45 4NZ Tel: 0151-638 8444 Fax: 0151-639 5996

Evans & Shea Ltd, 37 Collier Row Lane, Romford, RM5 3BD Tel: (01708) 741055 Fax: (01708) 764289

▶ Event & Electrical Services, 32 Southfields Rise, North Leverton, Retford, Nottinghamshire, DN22 0AY Tel: 01427 880802 E-mail: info@eventelectricalservices.co.uk

Joseph Merritt Group P.L.C., Byron Ave, Lowmoor Business Park, Kirkby-in-Ashfield, Nottingham, NG17 7LA Tel: (01623) 759737 Fax: (01623) 758826 E-mail: enquiries@merrittgroupplc.co.uk

T J Electrical Engineers & Contractors Ltd, Unit 3 Squirrels Lodge, Hards Lane, Peterborough, PE6 8RL Tel: (01778) 349680 Fax: (01778) 349683 E-mail: sales@tjelectrical.co.uk

▶ Walker Macleod Ltd, 8-36 Bulldale Street, Glasgow, G14 0NU Tel: 0141-954 0297 Fax: 0141-950 1351 E-mail: sales@walkermacleod.co.uk

POWER DISTRIBUTION SYSTEMS OR UNITS

Aphel Ltd, Wayside Business Park, Wilsons Lane, Coventry, CV6 6NY Tel: (0870) 7541880 Fax: (0870) 7541881 E-mail: sales@aphel.co.uk

Bryant Broadcast, 70b Stafford Road, Croydon, CR0 4NE Tel: (020) 8404 4050 Fax: (020) 8404 4080 E-mail: sales@bryant-broadcast.co.uk

Colton Electrical Equipment Ltd, Hainge Road, Tividale, Oldbury, West Midlands, B69 2NB Tel: 0121-522 4112 Fax: 0121-522 4174 E-mail: sales@coltonelectricalequipment.co.uk

Mita (U K) Ltd, Manor Farm Industrial Estate, Flint, Clwyd, CH6 5UY Tel: (01352) 792200 Fax: (01252) 792314 E-mail: info@mita.co.uk

POWER DISTURBANCE ANALYSERS

Avpower, C11 Acre Business Park, Acre Road, Reading, RG2 0SA Tel: 0118-975 2555 Fax: 0118-975 3074 E-mail: sales@avpower.com

Qualitrol Hathaway Instruments Division, Brewery Road, Hoddesdon, Hertfordshire, EN11 8HF Tel: (01992) 463502 Fax: (01992) 463507 E-mail: sales@hathaway-systems.com

POWER FACTOR CORRECTION CAPACITORS, *See also Power Factor Correction Equipment etc*

Cambridge Capacitors Ltd, Budds Lane, Romsey, Hampshire, SO51 0ZQ Tel: (01794) 513481 Fax: (01794) 523940 E-mail: sales@camcap.co.uk

Eaton Electric Ltd, Reddings Lane, Tyseley, Birmingham, B11 3EZ Tel: 0121-685 2100 Fax: 0121-706 2012 E-mail: meminfo@eaton.com

Express Electrical, Dunswell Road, Cottingham, North Humberside, HU16 4JG Tel: (01482) 846269 Fax: (01482) 876655 E-mail: sales@express-industrial-exports.co.uk

POWER FACTOR CORRECTION EQUIPMENT, *See also Capacitor, Power Factor Correction etc*

Elcomponent Ltd, Unit 5 Southmill Trading Centre, Southmill Road, Bishop's Stortford, Hertfordshire, CM23 3DY Tel: (01279) 503173 Fax: (01279) 654441 E-mail: sales@elcomponent.co.uk

P S U Designs Ltd, 7 Bloomfield Park, Bloomfield Road, Tipton, West Midlands, DY4 9AP Tel: 0121-557 6499 Fax: 0121-557 6498 E-mail: sales@psudesigns.co.uk

Power Capacitors Ltd, 30 Redfern Road, Birmingham, B11 2BH Tel: 0121-708 2811 Fax: 0121-765 4054 E-mail: sales@powercapacitors.co.uk

SDC Industries Ltd, 18 Colvilles Place, Kelvin Industrial Estate, East Kilbride, Glasgow, G75 0PZ Tel: (01355) 265959 Fax: (01355) 265484 E-mail: sales@sdcindustries.co.uk

POWER FILTER SYSTEMS

Advanced Thinking Systems Ltd, 1 South Lane, Waterlooville, Hampshire, PO8 0RB Tel: (023) 9259 5000 Fax: (023) 9259 5656 E-mail: sales@advanced-thinking.co.uk

POWER FIXED RESISTORS

Tyco Electronics, Head Office, Faraday Road, Swindon, SN3 5HH Tel: (01793) 528171 Fax: (01793) 572516 E-mail: passivesales@tycoelectronics.com

POWER GENERATION FORGINGS

RTR Handelsgesellschaft, 8 Kingsway House, Kingsway, Team Valley Trading Estate, Gateshead, Tyne & Wear, NE11 0HW Tel: 0191-491 1292 Fax: 0191-491 1246 E-mail: sales@rtr.co.uk

POWER GENERATION RECRUITMENT CONSULTANCY

▶ G & T Associates, William Knox House, Britannic Way, Llandarcy, Neath, West Glamorgan, SA10 6EL Tel: (01792) 321202 Fax: (01792) 321295 E-mail: info@gtassociates.co.uk

POWER GENERATION SYSTEMS

▶ Infrastructure Associates Ltd, Weir Bank, Monkey Island Lane, Bray, Maidenhead, Berkshire, SL6 2ED Tel: (01628) 762730 Fax: (01628) 762730 E-mail: scherry@infrastructureassociates.com

POWER LINE INSTALLATION EQUIPMENT

Blackbourne Electrical Co. Ltd, Springfarm Industrial Estate, Antrim, BT41 4NZ Tel: (028) 9446 4231 Fax: (028) 9446 7109 E-mail: bec@karl.co.uk

O Hanlon & Farrell, Springhill Road, Carnbane Industrial Estate, Newry, County Down, BT35 6EF Tel: (028) 3026 9213 Fax: (028) 3026 5513 E-mail: ohanlon_farrell@btinternet.com

POWER MANAGEMENT SYSTEM INTEGRATED CIRCUITS (IC)

▶ Zetex Semiconductors, Zetex Technology Park, Chadderton, Oldham, OL9 9LL Tel: 0161-622 4400 Fax: 0161-622 4446 E-mail: europe.sales@zetex.com

POWER METER MANUFRS

C-Matic Systems Ltd, Warren Court, Park Road, Crowborough, East Sussex, TN6 2QX Tel: (01892) 665688 Fax: (01892) 667515 E-mail: info@cmatic.co.uk

Yokogowa Measurement Technologies Ltd, Solar House, Murcary Park, Wickham Lane, Wooburn Green, Buckinghamshire, HP10 0HH Tel: (01628) 535830 Fax: (01628) 535839 E-mail: info@uk.yokogowa.com

POWER MONITORING EQUIPMENT

C-Matic Systems Ltd, Warren Court, Park Road, Crowborough, East Sussex, TN6 2QX Tel: (01892) 665688 Fax: (01892) 667515 E-mail: info@cmatic.co.uk

POWER OPERATED CHUCKS

P W T, Park Works, Lister Lane, Halifax, West Yorkshire, HX1 5JH Tel: (01422) 358361 Fax: (01422) 359379

Pratt Burnerd International, Park Works, Lister Lane, Halifax, West Yorkshire, HX1 5JH Tel: (01422) 366371 Fax: (01422) 359379 E-mail: sales@chucksuk.co.uk

Universal Engineering Workholding Ltd, New Street, Netherton, Huddersfield, HD4 7EZ Tel: (01484) 663018 Fax: (01484) 663758 E-mail: sales@uew.co.uk

POWER OPERATED ROLLER CONVEYOR SYSTEMS

K F Alliance Engineering Ltd, Units 28-29, Enfield Industrial Estate, Redditch, Worcestershire, B97 6BY Tel: (01527) 63331 Fax: (01527) 591191 E-mail: kfa@btconnect.com

Kimbermatics Ltd, Cheethams Mill, Park Street, Stalybridge, Cheshire, SK15 2BT Tel: 0161-368 4891 Fax: 0161-304 8152 E-mail: kimbermatics@aol.com

Marwel Conveyors Ltd, 108 Dudley Road East, Oldbury, West Midlands, B69 3EB Tel: 0121-552 4418 Fax: 0121-552 4018 E-mail: sales@marwel.com

Rusmail Conveyor Systems Ltd, 33-35 Adams Street, Birmingham, B7 4LT Tel: 0121-359 1549 Fax: 0121-333 3104 E-mail: sales@rusmailconveyors.co.uk

POWER PLANT MAINTENANCE/ REPAIR SERVICES

RWE npower, TS Ferrybridge, Old Great North Road, Knottingley, West Yorkshire, WF11 8PR Tel: (01977) 632201 Fax: (01977) 632311 E-mail: tsg@rwe.com

Veeanco Ltd, 20-22 Dunston Trading Estate, Foxwood Road, Chesterfield, Derbyshire, S41 9RF Tel: (01246) 452152 Fax: (01246) 455940 E-mail: sales@veeanco.com

POWER PRESS GUARDS

Highwood Engineering Ltd, Parkfield Road, Birmingham, B8 3AZ Tel: 0121-327 9212 Fax: 0121-327 4329

POWER PRESS MAINTENANCE/ REPAIR SERVICES

B S & A, Unit 8 Imex Business Centre, Station Lane, Birtley, Co. Durham, DH3 1QT Tel: 0191-411 1411 Fax: 0191-411 1410

Boltdown Power Press Repairs Ltd, Unit 10 Cato Street, Birmingham, B7 4TS Tel: 0121-359 7862 Fax: 0121-359 4645 E-mail: bolstownppr@aol.com

Power Press Repairs Ltd, 69 Kings Road, Tyseley, Birmingham, B11 2AX Tel: 0121-772 1698 Fax: 0121-772 5323 E-mail: sales@powerpressrepairs.co.uk

Sweeney & Blocksidge (Power Presses) Ltd, 126 Parkfield Road, Saltley, Birmingham, B8 3AZ Tel: 0121-327 3231 Fax: 0121-327 4329 E-mail: enquires@sweeneyandblocksidge.co.uk

POWER PRESS MANUFRS

Dan (UK) Ltd, Unit 1, Mucklow Hill 1 Trading Estate, Mucklow Hill, Halesowen, West Midlands, B62 8DF Tel: 0121-585 7171 Fax: 0121-585 7272 E-mail: sales@danlyuk.com

Hulbert Developments Ltd, 6 Grazebrook Industrial Park, Peartree Lane, Dudley, West Midlands, DY2 0XW Tel: (01384) 239019 Fax: (01384) 457280 E-mail: enq@hulbert-group.co.uk

Mid-Bucks Machine Tools Ltd, PO Box 15, Chinnor, Oxfordshire, OX39 4AT Tel: (01844) 352329 Fax: (01844) 352348 E-mail: midbucks@nildram.co.uk

Parkes Machine Tools Ltd, Berkswell, Coventry, CV7 7WF Tel: (01676) 530053 Fax: (01676) 530030 E-mail: sales@parkesmachinetools.co.uk

Stirchley Machine Tool Co. Ltd, 401-407 Tyburn Road, Birmingham, B24 8HJ Tel: 0121-328 2424 Fax: 0121-327 6200

Sweeney & Blocksidge (Power Presses) Ltd, 126 Parkfield Road, Saltley, Birmingham, B8 3AZ Tel: 0121-327 3231 Fax: 0121-327 4329 E-mail: enquires@sweeneyandblocksidge.co.uk

POWER PROTECTION CONSULTANCY

Computer Power Protection, 6 Lynwood Road, Liverpool, L9 3AF Tel: 0151-525 1387 Fax: 0151-525 9044 E-mail: info@cppsales.com

POWER QUALITY CONSULTANTS

Power Factor Systems Ltd, 23 Lyndon Road, North Luffenham, Oakham, Leicestershire, LE15 8JZ Tel: (01780) 721783 Fax: (01780) 721783 E-mail: pfsystems@tiscali.co.uk

Qualitrol Hathaway Instruments Division, Brewery Road, Hoddesdon, Hertfordshire, EN11 8HF Tel: (01992) 463502 Fax: (01992) 463507 E-mail: sales@hathaway-systems.com

POWER RECTIFYING TRANSFORMERS

Jenstar Ltd, Sturmi Way, Village Farm Industrial Estate, Pyle, Bridgend, Mid Glamorgan, CF33 6BZ Tel: (01656) 745818 Fax: (01656) 745818 E-mail: sales@jenstar.co.uk

POWER RESISTORS

Pulse Power & Measurement Ltd, 65 Shrivenham Hundred Business Park, Watchfield, Swindon, SN6 8TY Tel: (01793) 784389 Fax: (01793) 784391 E-mail: sales@ppm.co.uk

POWER SHOWER PUMPS

Damixa Ltd, Edison Courtyard, Brunel Road, Earlstrees Industrial Estate, Corby, Northamptonshire, NN17 4LS Tel: (01536) 409222 Fax: (01536) 400144 E-mail: uksales@damixa.com

POWER STATION CONTRACTORS OR DESIGNERS

Atlantic Project Co., 828 Manchester Road, Rochdale, Lancashire, OL11 3AW Tel: (01706) 345661 Fax: (01706) 648243 E-mail: aslack@apcpower.com

Bechtel Holdings Ltd, 245 Hammersmith Road, London, W6 8DP Tel: (020) 8846 5111 Fax: (020) 8846 6940

▶ Coryton Energy Co. Ltd, Coryton Power Station, The Manorway, Coryton, Stanford-le-Hope, Essex, SS17 9GN Tel: (01375) 645300 Fax: (01375) 645302

Unit Superheater Engineering Ltd, Unit Works, 2-8 Morfa Road, Swansea, SA1 2ET Tel: (01792) 654091 Fax: (01792) 456198 E-mail: eng@unit.co.uk

POWER STEERING PUMPS

Kiley & Clinton, 52-53 Birchall Street, Birmingham, B12 0RP Tel: 0121-772 8000 Fax: 0121-772 3215 E-mail: kileyclinton@btconnect.com

POWER SUPPLIES TO SPECIFICATION

Albacom, George Buckman Drive, Camperdown Industrial Estate, Dundee, DD2 3SP Tel: (01382) 889311 Fax: (01382) 810171 E-mail: sales@albacom.co.uk

B C Electrical Techniques Ltd, Stocklake, Aylesbury, Buckinghamshire, HP20 1DA Tel: (01296) 481995 Fax: (01296) 394158 E-mail: info@bcet.co.uk

Bells Control Equipment Ltd, 49 Scrutton Street, London, EC2A 4XJ Tel: (020) 7729 1979 Fax: (020) 7729 3731 E-mail: bells@mcmh.clara.net

Constant Power Services Ltd (CPS), Units 3, Trust Industrial Estate, Wilbury Way, Hitchin, Hertfordshire, SG4 0UZ Tel: (01462) 422955 Fax: (01462) 422754 E-mail: sales@cps4ups.co.uk

Dynamics (Bristol) Ltd, 1 Evercreech Way, Walrow Industrial Estate, Highbridge, Somerset, TA9 4AN Tel: (01278) 780222 Fax: (01278) 781824 E-mail: info@dynamicsbristol.co.uk

Harrison & Greenwood Transformers Ltd, Mill Lane, Halifax, West Yorkshire, HX3 6TR Tel: (01422) 329003 Fax: (01422) 329009

Riker Ltd, Unit 12 Boat House Meadow, Salisbury, SP2 7LD Tel: (01722) 333153 Fax: (01722) 333139

POWER SUPPLIES, AC/DC, MILITARY APPLICATIONS

Gresham Power Electronics, Gresham House, Telford Road, Salisbury, SP2 7PH Tel: (01722) 413060 Fax: (01722) 413034 E-mail: info@greshampower.com

Wright Electric Company Ltd, 35 Clarendon Avenue, Trowbridge, Wiltshire, BA14 7BW Tel: (01225) 761188 Fax: (01225) 761188 E-mail: sales@wrightelec.demon.co.uk

POWER SUPPLIES, AIRCRAFT/ AVIATION INDUSTRY

▶ Air & Ground Aviation Ltd, Aviation House, London Road, Shirleywich, Stafford, ST18 0PN Tel: (01889) 271777 Fax: (01889) 270756 E-mail: office@airandground.com

POWER SUPPLIES, EMERGENCY/STANDBY

▶ Alpha Technologies, Twyford House, Pig Lane, Thorley, Bishop's Stortford, Hertfordshire, CM22 7PA Tel: (01279) 501110 Fax: (01280) 659870 E-mail: sales@alphaeurope.com

Computerpower Consultants Ltd, 21 Mount Pleasant, Guiseley, Leeds, LS20 9EB Tel: (01943) 870070 Fax: (01943) 879186

Constant Power Services Ltd (CPS), Units 3, Trust Industrial Estate, Wilbury Way, Hitchin, Hertfordshire, SG4 0UZ Tel: (01462) 422955 Fax: (01462) 422754 E-mail: sales@cps4ups.co.uk

Eaton Power Solutions Ltd, Heath Place, Ashgrove Industrial Park, Bognor Regis, West Sussex, PO22 9SJ Tel: (01243) 810500 Fax: (01243) 868613

Emergency Power Systems P.L.C., Carley Drive Business Area, Westfield, Sheffield, S20 8NQ Tel: 0114-247 8369 Fax: 0114-247 8367 E-mail: sales@emergencypowersystems.co.uk

G E Digital Energy, Wheatfield Way, Hinckley, Leicestershire, LE10 1YG Tel: 0116-290 5280 Fax: 0116-290 5281 E-mail: sales@imv.co.uk

Golden Triangle Power Generation, Units 1-2 Weaver Park Industrial Estate, Mill Lane, Frodsham, WA6 7JB Tel: (01928) 722137 Fax: (01928) 722240E-mail: hire@gtgen.co.uk

Linnet Technology Ltd, 3 Darby Gate, West Portway, Andover, Hampshire, SP10 3LF Tel: (01264) 366812 Fax: (01264) 366778 E-mail: sales@linnet-tec.co.uk

Mge Ups Systems Ltd, Orion House, 171-177 High Street, Wealdstone, Harrow, Middlesex, HA3 5EA Tel: (020) 8861 4040 Fax: (020) 8861 2812 E-mail: jason.koffler@mgeups.com

P B Design & Developments Ltd, Unit 9-10, Hither Green, Clevedon, Avon, BS21 6XT Tel: (01275) 874411 Fax: (01275) 874428 E-mail: administrator@pbdesign.co.uk

▶ Rectifier Technologies (UK) Limited, Unit A8, Sturmer End Industrial Estate, Sturmer Road, Haverhill, Suffolk, CB9 7UU Tel: (01440) 706777 Fax: (01440) 762810 E-mail: sales@duvine.co.uk

Woodlands Generators, Crab Apple Way, Vale Park, Evesham, Worcestershire, WR11 1GP Tel: (01386) 760256 Fax: (01386) 442740 E-mail: sales@woodlands-generators.com

POWER SUPPLIES, LINEAR, AC/ AC OR AC/DC

▶ Douglas Electronic Industries Ltd, 55 Eastfield Road, Louth, Lincolnshire, LN11 7AL Tel: (01507) 603643 Fax: (01507) 600502 E-mail: sales@douglas-transformers.co.uk

Mascot UK, PO Box 2090, Salisbury, SP2 2BH Tel: (01722) 504853 Fax: (01264) 396402 E-mail: andrew.parrish@mascot.no

R T E Electronics, 568 Burnley Road, Rossendale, Lancashire, BB4 8AJ Tel: (01706) 227234 Fax: (01706) 227531 E-mail: brain@rtepower.co.uk

Walters OEP Ltd, 15 -17 Wroslyn Road Industrial Estate, Wroslyn Road, Freeland, Witney, Oxfordshire, OX29 8SN Tel: (01993) 886200 Fax: (01993) 886210 E-mail: info@oep.co.uk

POWER SUPPLIES, NOTEBOOK COMPUTER

▶ Cream Computers UK Ltd, The Red House, Kingswood Park, Bonsor Drive, Tadworth, Surrey, KT20 6AY Tel: (01737) 377220 Fax: (01737) 377221 E-mail: ray@creamcomputers.com

POWER SUPPLIES, PLUG-IN, LOW VOLTAGE

Qes Ltd, Niall House, 24-26 Boulton Road, Stevenage, Hertfordshire, SG1 4QX Tel: (01438) 749849 Fax: (01438) 318420 E-mail: sales@qesltd.co.uk

POWER SUPPLIES, UNINTERRUPTIBLE (UPS)

A & R Sheet Metal Ltd, 68-70 College Street, Kempston, Bedford, MK42 8LU Tel: (01234) 348841 Fax: (01234) 262784 E-mail: sales@arsheetmetal.co.uk

Advanced Battery Care Ltd, Whittonditch Works, Whittonditch, Ramsbury, Marlborough, Wiltshire, SN8 2XB Tel: (01672) 520572 Fax: (01672) 520717 E-mail: sales@batterycare.co.uk

Bells Control Equipment Ltd, 49 Scrutton Street, London, EC2A 4XJ Tel: (020) 7729 1979 Fax: (020) 7729 3731 E-mail: bells@mcmh.clara.net

Celab Ltd, 25 Woolmer Way, Bordon, Hampshire, GU35 9QE Tel: (01420) 477011 Fax: (01420) 472034

Chloride Power Ltd, Kempston Court, Manor Road, Kempston Hardwick, Bedford, MK43 9PQ Tel: (01234) 840282 Fax: (01234) 841156

Chloride Power Protection, Unit C George Curl Way, Southampton, SO18 2RY Tel: (023) 8061 0311 Fax: (023) 8061 0852 E-mail: uk.sales@chloridepower.com

Computerpower Consultants Ltd, 21 Mount Pleasant, Guiseley, Leeds, LS20 9EB Tel: (01943) 870070 Fax: (01943) 879186

▶ Douglas Electronic Industries Ltd, 55 Eastfield Road, Louth, Lincolnshire, LN11 7AL Tel: (01507) 603643 Fax: (01507) 600502 E-mail: sales@douglas-transformers.co.uk

E R L Ltd, Iroko House, Bolney Avenue, Peacehaven, East Sussex, BN10 8HF Tel: (01273) 581007 Fax: (01273) 581555 E-mail: erl@fastnet.co.uk

Emergency Power Systems, Suite 16 Enterprise House, Strathkelvin Place, Kirkintilloch, Glasgow, G66 1XQ Tel: 0141-775 1815 Fax: 0141-775 1609 E-mail: sales@emergencypowersystems.co.uk

Emergency Power Systems P.L.C., Carley Drive Business Area, Westfield, Sheffield, S20 8NQ Tel: 0114-247 8369 Fax: 0114-247 8367 E-mail: sales@emergencypowersystems.co.uk

POWER SUPPLIES, UNINTERRUPTIBLE (UPS) – *continued*

Energy Systems, Systems House, Rotherside Road, Eckington, Sheffield, S21 4HL Tel: (01246) 439862 Fax: (01246) 431444 E-mail: websales@aeceuro.co.uk

Erskine Systems Ltd, Salter Road, Eastfield Industrial Estate, Scarborough, North Yorkshire, YO11 3DU Tel: (01723) 583511 Fax: (01723) 581231 E-mail: sales@erskine-systems.co.uk

Gresham Power Electronics, Gresham House, Telford Road, Salisbury, SP2 7PH Tel: (01722) 413060 Fax: (01722) 413034 E-mail: info@greshampower.com

Linnet Technology Ltd, 3 Darby Gate, West Portway, Andover, Hampshire, SP10 3LF Tel: (01264) 366812 Fax: (01264) 366778 E-mail: sales@linnet-tec.co.uk

M J Electronics Services (International) Ltd, Unit 19B, Sedgemount Industrial Park, Bristol Road, Bridgwater, Somerset, TA6 4AR Tel: (01278) 422882 Fax: (01278) 453331 E-mail: sales@mjelectronics.freeserve.co.uk

M S N Network Power Ltd, Fourth Avenue, Globe Park, Marlow, Buckinghamshire, SL7 1YG Tel: (01628) 403200 Fax: (01628) 403203 E-mail: sales@emersonnetworkpower.com

Masterpower Electronics Ltd, Badentoy Cresent, Badentoy Industrial Estate, Portlethen, Aberdeen, AB12 4YD Tel: (01224) 783700 Fax: (01224) 783701 E-mail: sales@masterpower.co.uk

Mge Ups Systems Ltd, Orion House, 171-177 High Street, Wealdstone, Harrow, Middlesex, HA3 5EA Tel: (020) 8861 4040 Fax: (020) 8861 2812 E-mail: jason.koffler@mgeups.com

Piller UK Ltd, 91 Chesterton Lane, Cirencester, Gloucestershire, GL7 1YE Tel: (01285) 657721 Fax: (01285) 654823 E-mail: ukmail@piller.com

Power Systems Warehouse Ltd, Powerguard House, Grimsby Road, Louth, Lincolnshire, LN11 0SX Tel: (01507) 600688 Fax: (01507) 600621 E-mail: sales@powerguard.co.uk

QPQ, Exchange House, Elsthorpe Road, Stainfield, Bourne, Lincolnshire, PE10 0RS Tel: (01778) 570879 E-mail: sales@qpq.co.uk

SDC Industries Ltd, 18 Colvilles Place, Kelvin Industrial Estate, East Kilbride, Glasgow, G75 0PZ Tel: (01355) 265959 Fax: (01355) 265484 E-mail: sales@sdcindustries.co.uk

Secure Power Systems Ltd, 2A Watermoor Road, Cirencester, Gloucestershire, GL7 1JW Tel: (01285) 651768 Fax: (01285) 657053 E-mail: wknight756@aol.com

▶ Siel Ups Systems Ltd, Unit H10 Draycott Business Park, Cam, Dursley, Gloucestershire, GL11 5DQ Tel: (01453) 899212 Fax: (01453) 899215 E-mail: enquiries@sielups.co.uk

Tascom International Ltd, 1 Mars House, Calleva Park, Aldermaston, Reading, RG7 8LA Tel: 0118-982 0400 E-mail: bill.white@tascom.co.uk

▶ Technology Ventures Maritime Ltd, Suite B 29 Harley Street, London, W1G 9QR Tel: (020) 7016 2664 Fax: (07092) 013175 E-mail: info@kinetec.uk.com

Universal Power Systems, Weldon Road, Loughborough, Leicestershire, LE11 5RN Tel: (01509) 261100 Fax: (01509) 261148 E-mail: sales@upsltd.co.uk

POWER SUPPLIES, UNINTERRUPTIBLE (UPS), COMPUTER

B P C EMEA Ltd, B P C House, Romsey Industrial Estate, Greatbridge Road, Romsey, Hampshire, SO51 0HR Tel: (01794) 521200 Fax: (01794) 521400 E-mail: sales@bpc-ups.com

POWER SUPPLIES, UNINTERRUPTIBLE (UPS), DIESEL ROTARY

Euro-Diesel (U K) Ltd, Stato House, Somerford Road, Cirencester, Gloucestershire, GL7 1TW Tel: (01285) 640879 Fax: (01285) 652509 E-mail: info@euro-diesel.co.uk

POWER SUPPLY ADAPTER CASES

Cholcroft Ltd, 7 Dane Drive, Ferndown, Dorset, BH22 8LX Tel: (01202) 874455 Fax: (01202) 874003 E-mail: trevor@cholcroft-ltd.freeserve.co.uk

POWER SUPPLY ADAPTERS

Winslow Adaptics Ltd, Unit 5 Brecon Enterprise Park, Brecon, Powys, LD3 8BT Tel: (01874) 625555 Fax: (01874) 625500 E-mail: sales@winslowadaptics.com

POWER SUPPLY AND DISTRIBUTION

Emerson Embedded Power, Astec House, Waterfront Business Park, Merry Hill, Dudley, West Midlands, DY5 1LX Tel: (01384) 842211 Fax: (01384) 843355 E-mail: sales@astec-europe.com

POWER SUPPLY DISTRIBUTORS OR AGENTS

C A Designs Ltd, The Coach House, 54 The Ridgeway, Rothley, Leicester, LE7 7LE Tel: 0116-237 5248 Fax: (08700) 521513 E-mail: sales@cadesigns.co.uk

Campbell Collins Ltd, 162 High St, Stevenage, Hertfordshire, SG1 3LL Tel: (01438) 369466 Fax: (01438) 316465 E-mail: sales@camcol.co.uk

▶ Haredata Electronics Ltd, 14 Crown House, Hornbeam Square North, Hornbeam Park, Harrogate, North Yorkshire, HG2 8PB Tel: (01423) 853180 Fax: (01423) 853199 E-mail: sales@haredata.co.uk

M J Electronics Services (International) Ltd, Unit 19B, Sedgemount Industrial Park, Bristol Road, Bridgwater, Somerset, TA6 4AR Tel: (01278) 422882 Fax: (01278) 453331 E-mail: sales@mjelectronics.freeserve.co.uk

▶ S J Electronics, Unit 3 Vernon Court, Henson Way, Telford Way Industrial Estate, Kettering, Northamptonshire, NN16 8PX Tel: (01536) 416200 Fax: (01536) 416300 E-mail: sales@sjelectronics.co.uk

Telonic Instruments Ltd, Toutley Industrial Estate, Toutley Road, Wokingham, Berkshire, RG41 1QN Tel: 0118-978 6911 Fax: 0118-979 2338 E-mail: info@telonic.co.uk

Young Ecc Electronics, Crown House, Coronation Road, Cressex Business Park, High Wycombe, Buckinghamshire, HP12 3TA Tel: (01494) 753500 Fax: (01494) 753501 E-mail: sales@youngelectronics.com

POWER SUPPLY MAINS ADAPTERS

Photon Power Technology Ltd, PO BOX 306, Emsworth, Hampshire, PO10 7SU Tel: 01243 373551 Fax: 0845 8338923 E-mail: info@photonpower.co.uk

Walters OEP Ltd, 15 -17 Wroslyn Road Industrial Estate, Wroslyn Road, Freeland, Witney, Oxfordshire, OX29 8SN Tel: (01993) 886200 Fax: (01993) 886210 E-mail: info@oep.co.uk

POWER SUPPLY SYSTEMS OR UNITS, *See also headings for particular types under Power Supplies etc*

▶ Alpha Technologies, Twyford House, Pig Lane, Thorley, Bishop's Stortford, Hertfordshire, CM22 7PA Tel: (01279) 501110 Fax: (01280) 659870 E-mail: sales@alphaeurope.com

Amplicon Liveline Ltd, Unit 11 Centenary Industrial Estate, Hughes Road, Brighton, BN2 4AW Tel: (01273) 570220 Fax: (01273) 570215 E-mail: sales@amplicon.co.uk

Applied Power Techniques Ltd, 7 Maundrell Road, Calne, Wiltshire, SN11 9PU Tel: (01249) 811888 Fax: (01249) 811888

Automation Controls Ltd, Musgrave Park Industrial Estate, Stockmans Way, Belfast, BT9 7JU Tel: (028) 9068 1391 Fax: (028) 9066 3533 E-mail: tom@acl.presstel.co.uk

Bosch Rexroth Ltd, Cromwell Road, St. Neots, Cambridgeshire, PE19 2ES Tel: (01480) 223200 Fax: (01480) 219052 E-mail: info@boschrexroth.co.uk

C A Designs Ltd, The Coach House, 54 The Ridgeway, Rothley, Leicester, LE7 7LE Tel: 0116-237 5248 Fax: (08700) 521513 E-mail: sales@cadesigns.co.uk

Castell Iso Lok, The Castell Building, 217 Kingsbury Road, London, NW9 9PQ Tel: (020) 8511 1858 Fax: (020) 8205 0055 E-mail: sales@castell.com

Eldec Electronics Ltd, Whittle Close, Drayton Fields Industrial Estate, Daventry, Northamptonshire, NN11 8YE Tel: (01327) 307200 Fax: (01327) 307230

▶ Tim Gale Consulting Ltd, Red Shute Mill Business Centre, Red Shute Hill, Hermitage, Thatcham, Berkshire, RG18 9QL Tel: (01635) 202080 Fax: (08700) 940517 E-mail: tim@t-g-c.net

I E C Ltd, 41 Harwell Road, Nuffield Industrial Estate, Poole, Dorset, BH17 0BD Tel: (01202) 680333 Fax: (01202) 680101 E-mail: info@iecltd.co.uk

Mechanelec Ltd, 10 Waterloo Road, Widnes, Cheshire, WA8 0PY Tel: 0151-495 1739 Fax: 0151-495 1227 E-mail: enquiries@mechanelec.co.uk

Murrelektronik Ltd, Albion Street, Pendlebury, Swinton, Manchester, M27 4FG Tel: 0161-728 3133 Fax: 0161-728 3130 E-mail: sales@murrelektronik.co.uk

Optical Test & Calibration Ltd, 21-23 Campus Road, Listerhills Science Park, Bradford, West Yorkshire, BD7 1HR Tel: (01274) 393857 Fax: (01274) 393336 E-mail: sales@otc.co.uk

Rollo UK Ltd, Womersley Road, Grimsby, South Humberside, DN31 3SH Tel: (01472) 358989 Fax: (01472) 241141 E-mail: b.merrison@rollouk.com

▶ Tantronics Ltd, Goyt Mill, Upper Hibbert Lane, Marple, Stockport, Cheshire, SK6 7HX Tel: 0161-427 1100 Fax: 0161-427 5100 E-mail: info@tantronics.co.uk

POWER SUPPLY SYSTEMS/UNIT INSTALLATION SERVICES

Lilleker Bros Ltd, 30 Moorgate Road, Rotherham, South Yorkshire, S60 2AG Tel: (01709) 374073 Fax: (01709) 364517 E-mail: info@lillekerbros.com

POWER SUPPLY SYSTEMS/UNIT MAINTENANCE/REPAIR SERVICES

The Ener G Group, Ener G House, Daniel Adamson Road, Salford, M50 2DT Tel: 0161-745 7450 Fax: 0161-745 7457 E-mail: sales@cpsl.co.uk

Linnet Technology Ltd, 3 Darby Gate, West Portway, Andover, Hampshire, SP10 3LF Tel: (01264) 366812 Fax: (01264) 366778 E-mail: sales@linnet-tec.co.uk

Qes Ltd, Niall House, 24-26 Boulton Road, Stevenage, Hertfordshire, SG1 4QX Tel: (01438) 749849 Fax: (01438) 318420 E-mail: sales@qesltd.co.uk

POWER SUPPLY UNITS, ADJUSTABLE

▶ SwitchMode Ltd, 41 Kidderminster Road, Bewdley, Worcs, DY12 1BU Tel: (0793) 1506665 E-mail: sales@switch-mode.co.uk

POWER SUPPLY UNITS, UNIVERSAL

Industrial Battery & Charger Services Ltd, 46 Catley Road, Sheffield, S9 5JF Tel: 0114-243 3993 Fax: 0114-242 4845 E-mail: peterpgarrat@ibcsltd.demon.co.uk

▶ SwitchMode Ltd, 41 Kidderminster Road, Bewdley, Worcs, DY12 1BU Tel: (0793) 1506665 E-mail: sales@switch-mode.co.uk

POWER TAKE OFF GENERATOR SETS

N J Froment & Co. Ltd, Cliffe Road, Easton on the Hill, Stamford, Lincolnshire, PE9 3NP Tel: (01780) 480033 Fax: (01780) 480044 E-mail: sales@froment.co.uk

POWER TAKE OFF UNITS

Transmission Components Ltd, 2 Jubilee Trading Centre, Jubilee Road, Letchworth Garden City, Hertfordshire, SG6 1NE Tel: (01462) 672222 Fax: (01462) 480001 E-mail: gwhite@transmissioncomponents.com

V H S Hydraulic Components, Unit 1, Block A, Waleswood Road, Wales Bar, Sheffield, S26 5PY Tel: (01909) 772666 Fax: (01909) 773226 E-mail: sales@hydraulic-components.net

W R Winton Ltd, Richmond House, Forsyth Road, Woking, Surrey, GU21 5SB Tel: (01483) 770121 Fax: (01483) 715630 E-mail: info@winton-antlia.com

Webster Drives Ltd, Folds Road, Bolton, BL1 2SE Tel: (01204) 382121 Fax: (01204) 386100

POWER TOOL MAINTENANCE/ REPAIR SERVICES

A J Middleton & Co. Ltd, 45 York Road, Ilford, Essex, IG1 3AD Tel: (020) 8514 1123 Fax: (020) 8478 1501

Aerocom Tools, Green Zone Aviation Park West, Bournemouth International Airpor, Hurn, Christchurch, Dorset, BH23 6NW Tel: (01202) 580333 Fax: (01202) 580333

Alpha Tools (Northern) Ltd, Grove Road, Wakefield, West Yorkshire, WF1 1UW Tel: (01924) 384227 Fax: (01924) 363525 E-mail: sales@alphatools.co.uk

Building & Industrial Tool Supplies, 78 Chester Avenue, Lancing, West Sussex, BN15 8PG Tel: (01903) 766983 Fax: (01903) 764190

C B S Power Tools Ltd, 2 Bramhall Place, Storeys Bar Road, Peterborough, PE1 5YS Tel: (01733) 343031 Fax: (01733) 897151 E-mail: sales@cbspowertools.co.uk

C N S Powertools Sales & Repairs, 111 Neath Road, Briton Ferry, Neath, West Glamorgan, SA11 2BZ Tel: (01639) 824217 Fax: (01639) 824218

Carters Tools Ltd, 74-76 Elmers End Road, Anerley, London, SE20 7UX Tel: (020) 8659 7222 Fax: (020) 8659 2727 E-mail: sales@carterstools.co.uk

E J Parkinson & Son Ltd, Kirk Lane, Yeadon, Leeds, LS19 7ET Tel: 0113-250 9111 Fax: 0113-250 0223

Electric Power & Equipment Co., 619 Stretford Road, Manchester, M16 0QA Tel: 0161-872 1619 Fax: 0161-876 4160

Engineerstore Ltd, East Street, Prittlewell, Southend-On-Sea, SS2 5EQ Tel: (01702) 611711 Fax: (01702) 600048

Farrant Electrical Ltd, 1 Homefield Road, Haverhill, Suffolk, CB9 8QP Tel: (01440) 703497 Fax: (01440) 704332

Fixings & Power Tool Center, Brighton Road, Salfords, Redhill, RH1 5EQ Tel: (01293) 820088 Fax: (01293) 820099

H E S Sales UK Ltd, 14 Bentley Way, Royal Oak Industrial Estate, Daventry, Northamptonshire, NN11 8QH Tel: (01327) 300322 Fax: (01327) 311411 E-mail: daventry@hes-sales.com

Infix Holdings Ltd, 85 87 Stapleton Road, Bristol, BS5 0QF Tel: 0117-955 3987 Fax: 0117-955 9833 E-mail: enquiries@infix.co.uk

J & J Pneumatics Ltd, Hillbottom Road, Sands Industrial Estate, High Wycombe, Buckinghamshire, HP12 4HJ Tel: (01494) 530291 Fax: (01494) 463062 E-mail: sales@jjp.co.uk

Alan Lord (Industrial Tools) Ltd, Unit 21 Bordesley Trading Estate, Bordesley Green Road, Birmingham, B8 1BZ Tel: 0121-328 6033 Fax: 0121-328 1842

Luton Electrical Services, 29 Upper Luton Road, Chatham, Kent, ME5 7BH Tel: (01634) 845413

M P Harvey, 119-123 Middle Watch, Swavesey, Cambridge, CB24 4RP Tel: (01954) 206113 Fax: (01954) 206113

Multequip Power Tools, 61 Willow Road, Bedford, MK42 0QU Tel: (01234) 340461 Fax: (01234) 340461

Murray Power Tools & Abrasives, 14 Primrose Avenue Industrial Estate, Grangemouth, Stirlingshire, FK3 8YD Tel: (01324) 666185 Fax: (01324) 666184 E-mail: sales@murraypowertools.co.uk

Newbury Tools Ltd, 1 Hambridge Road, Newbury, Berkshire, RG14 5SS Tel: (01635) 30804 Fax: (01635) 529068 E-mail: sales@newburytools.com

P S Power Tools, Unit G, Tinhay Industrial Estate, Tinhay, Lifton, Devon, PL16 0AH Tel: (01566) 784385

Power Tool Services, 2 Earl Road, Rackheath, Norwich, NR13 6NT Tel: (01603) 722077 Fax: (01603) 722866

Solent tools, UNIT 009 SOLENT BUSINESS CENTRE, MILLBROOK ROAD WEST, SOUTHAMPTON, SO15 0HW Tel: 023 80578057 Fax: 023 80574470 E-mail: SALES@SOLENTTOOLS.CO.UK

▶ T&T, 199-201 Green Lane, Stoneycroft, Liverpool, L13 6RH Tel: 0151-220 1616 Fax: 0151-220 1616 E-mail: sales@ttpowertools.co.uk

Three Counties Fixings Ltd, 6 Capital Place, Harlow, Essex, CM19 5AS Tel: (01279) 451631 Fax: (01279) 451617 E-mail: tcfltd@msn.com

Wrexham Power Tool Services, Five Fords Gate, Bridge Road, Wrexham Industrial Estate, Wrexham, Clwyd, LL13 9PS Tel: (01978) 660011 Fax: (01978) 664644

POWER TOOLS OR ACCESSORIES

▶ A 1 Hire & Sales Ltd, 76 Old Wareham Road, Poole, Dorset, BH12 4QR Tel: (01202) 736899 Fax: (01202) 732726 E-mail: sales@a1hire.co.uk

A C Supply Ltd, St. Christopher House, 126 Ridge Road, Letchworth Garden City, Hertfordshire, SG6 1PT Tel: (01462) 481808 Fax: (01462) 481806 E-mail: sales@acsupply.co.uk

Ace Fixings, 69 Sydenham Road, Belfast, BT3 9DJ Tel: (028) 9073 8900 Fax: (028) 9073 8903

▶ Akromultihire, Unit 6 Naysmyth Place, Houston Industrial Estate, Livingston, West Lothian, EH54 5EG Tel: (01506) 441991 Fax: (01506) 441856

All Tools Tool Shop, 181 Alder Road, Poole, Dorset, BH12 4AN Tel: (01202) 730376 Fax: (01202) 733145

Alpha Tools (Northern) Ltd, Grove Road, Wakefield, West Yorkshire, WF1 1UW Tel: (01924) 384227 Fax: (01924) 363525 E-mail: sales@alphatools.co.uk

Anglia Fixing Supplies, Anglia House, Grange Avenue, Mayland, Chelmsford, CM3 6BG Tel: (01621) 744490 Fax: (01621) 744821

Apex Industrial Ltd, 26c Orgreave CR, Sheffield, S13 9NQ Tel: 0114-254 0011 Fax: 0114-254 8002 E-mail: sheffield@apexindustrial.co.uk

Arb Sales, 13 School Street, Hazel Grove, Stockport, Cheshire, SK7 4RA Tel: 0161-483 9661 Fax: 0161-483 6160 E-mail: sales.arb@ntlworld.com

▶ AR-EL Workshop Equipment Ltd, PO Box 200, Aberdeen, AB32 6GW Tel: (01224) 749051 Fax: (01244) 749051 E-mail: raymond@workshop-equipment.co.uk

Asset Fixings & Tools Ltd, 40 Wilbury Way, Hitchin, Hertfordshire, SG4 0AP Tel: (01462) 440445 Fax: (01462) 440540 E-mail: sales@assetfixings.co.uk

POWER TOOLS OR ACCESSORIES

– continued

Axminster Power Tool Centre, Chard Street, Axminster, Devon, EX13 5DZ Tel: (01297) 33656 Fax: (01297) 35242

B M J Power Ltd, 25-27 Stokes Croft, Bristol, BS1 3QA Tel: 0117-924 5018 Fax: 0117-942 8902

Beaver Tool Hire Ltd, 15-17 Kingston Road, Portsmouth, PO1 5RX Tel: (023) 9282 6632 Fax: (023) 9282 6639

Bedford Fixings, 1a Dean Street, Bedford, MK40 3EQ Tel: (01234) 360747 Fax: (01234) 217414

Beesley's S S H Ltd, 15 Ashbourne Parade, London, W5 3QS Tel: (020) 8998 1291 Fax: (020) 8998 2112

Bell Donaldson Steele, 17 Westfield Street, Edinburgh, EH11 2QQ Tel: 0131-337 6303 Fax: 0131-313 5328 E-mail: sales@belldonaldsonsteele.fsnet.co.uk

Black & Decker, Unit 25 Clarks Village, Farm Road, Street, Somerset, BA16 0BB Tel: (01458) 840205 Fax: (01458) 840206

▶ Black Market Tools, Unit 19 Faraday Mill Business Park, Faraday Road, Plymouth, PL4 0ST Tel: (01752) 205905 Fax: (01752) 302232E-mail: sales@blackmarket-tools.co.uk

Robert Bosch Ltd, PO Box 98, Uxbridge, Middlesex, UB9 5HJ Tel: (01895) 834466 Fax: (01895) 838388

Brian Walker & Son, 87 Garraways, Coffee Hall, Milton Keynes, MK6 5DU Tel: (01908) 666690 Fax: (01908) 233211

Brighton Tools & Fixings Ltd, 7 Centenary Industrial Estate, Hughes Road, Brighton, BN2 4AW Tel: (01273) 620456 Fax: (01273) 620611 E-mail: info@brightontools.co.uk

Bryant Fixings Ltd, 21 Blatchford Road, Horsham, West Sussex, RH13 5QR Tel: (01403) 265652 Fax: (01403) 218070

Build Centre Ltd, Unit 8 Etna Court, Falkirk, FK2 9ED Tel: (01324) 611787 Fax: (01324) 621375 E-mail: sales@buildcentre.co.uk

Building & Industrial Tool Supplies, 78 Chester Avenue, Lancing, West Sussex, BN15 8PG Tel: (01903) 766983 Fax: (01903) 764190

C B S Power Tools Ltd, 2 Bramhall Place, Storeys Bar Road, Peterborough, PE1 5YS Tel: (01733) 343031 Fax: (01733) 897151 E-mail: sales@cbspowertools.co.uk

Cambrian Power Tools, Glendale, Tregaron, Dyfed, SY25 6QT Tel: (01974) 298244 Fax: (01974) 298288

Campbell Miller (Tools) Ltd, 16-22 Jordanvale Avenue, Clydeside Industrial Estate, Glasgow, G14 0QU Tel: 0141-954 9557 Fax: 0141-954 9979 E-mail: sales@cmtl.co.uk

Carters Tools Ltd, 74-76 Elmers End Road, Anerley, London, SE20 7UX Tel: (020) 8659 7222 Fax: (020) 8659 2727 E-mail: sales@carterstools.co.uk

Castle Hardware Company Ltd The, Park Road, Hockley, Birmingham, B18 5JA Tel: 0121-551 6021 Fax: 0121-554 7507

Cecil W Tyzack, 79-81 Kingsland Road, London, E2 8AH Tel: (020) 7739 2630 Fax: (020) 7729 3373

County Industrial Supplies Ltd, County House, Chapel Street, Pontnewydd, Cwmbran, Gwent, NP44 1DL Tel: (01633) 872226 Fax: (01633) 864922 E-mail: cissales@aol.com

Cromwell Basingstoke, Unit 5, Sherrington Way, Basingstoke, Hampshire, RG22 4DQ Tel: (01256) 355966 Fax: (01256) 477230 E-mail: info@cromwell.co.uk

Cromwell (Birmingham), 217 Chester Street, Aston, Birmingham, B6 4AE Tel: 0121-380 1700 Fax: 0121-380 1710 E-mail: birmingham@cromwell.co.uk

Cromwell Bristol Ltd, Unit E St. Vincents Trading Estate, Bristol, BS2 0UY Tel: 0117-972 1127 Fax: 0117-972 4287 E-mail: bristol@cromwell.co.uk

Cromwell Group Ltd, B Great Fenton Business Park, Grove Road, Stoke-on-Trent, ST4 4LZ Tel: (01782) 746746 Fax: (01782) 414414 E-mail: stoke@cromwell.co.uk

Cromwell Industrial Supplies, Unit 2-3 Anthonys Way, Medway City Estate, Rochester, Kent, ME2 4DN Tel: (01634) 290586 Fax: (01634) 290589 E-mail: rochester@cromwell.co.uk

Cromwell (Portsmouth), Unit 15, Admirals Park, Williams Road, Portsmouth, PO3 5NJ Tel: (023) 9266 8512 Fax: (023) 9269 9179 E-mail: portsmouth@cromwell-tools.co.uk

Cromwell (Smethwick), Middlemore Road, Smethwick, West Midlands, B66 2DR Tel: 0121-558 1133 Fax: 0121-565 3530 E-mail: smethwick@cromwell.co.uk

Cromwell Tools Ltd, 2 Murcar Industrial Estate, Denmore Road, Bridge of Don, Aberdeen, AB23 8JW Tel: (01224) 820851 Fax: (01224) 820877 E-mail: sales@kennedy-tools.co.uk

Cromwell Tools Ltd, 3-4 Tollgate Close, Cardiff, CF11 8TN Tel: (029) 2034 5888 Fax: (029) 2034 5777 E-mail: cardiff@cromwell.co.uk

▶ Cromwell Tools Ltd, Thirsk Place, Derby, DE24 8JJ Tel: (01332) 360660 Fax: (01332) 204239 E-mail: derby@cromwell.co.uk

Cromwell Tools Ltd, Shaw Lane Industrial Estate, Ogden Road, Doncaster, South Yorkshire, DN2 4SQ Tel: (01302) 366600 Fax: (01302) 327556 E-mail: doncaster@cromwell-tools.co.uk

Cromwell Tools Ltd, St. James Street, Hull, HU3 2DH Tel: (01482) 326999 Fax: (01482) 213089 E-mail: hull@cromwell-tools.co.uk

Cromwell Tools Ltd, The Tool Centre, 75 St James Mill Road, Northampton, NN5 5JP Tel: (01604) 752488 Fax: (01604) 753815 E-mail: northampton@cromwell-tools.co.uk

Cromwell Tools Ltd, 131 Queens Road, Beeston, Nottingham, NG9 2FE Tel: 0115-922 3311 Fax: 0115-925 1342 E-mail: nottingham@cromwell-tools.co.uk

Cromwell Tools Ltd, Westcombe Square, Royce Road, Peterborough, PE1 5YB Tel: (01733) 555524 Fax: (01733) 311103 E-mail: peterborough@cromwell-tools.co.uk

Cromwell Tools Ltd, 770 Buckingham Avenue, Slough, SL1 4NL Tel: (01753) 696000 Fax: (01753) 696966 E-mail: slough@cromwell-tools.co.uk

Cromwell Tools Ltd, Ark Grove Industrial Estate, Ross Road, Stockton-on-Tees, Cleveland, TS18 2NH Tel: (01642) 673605 Fax: (01642) 671479 E-mail: stockton@cromwell.co.uk

Cromwells, Waverley House, Effingham Road, Sheffield, S4 7YR Tel: 0114-275 0631 Fax: 0114-275 4447 E-mail: sheffield@cromwell.co.uk

Cromwells Fife, Unit 4 Woodgate Way South, Glenrothes, Fife, KY7 4PF Tel: (01592) 631632 Fax: (01592) 631641 E-mail: fife@cromwell.co.uk

Curtis Holt (East Anglia) Ltd, Harford House, 50 White Lodge Business Estate, Hall Road, Norwich, NR4 6DG Tel: (01603) 671630 Fax: (01603) 671634 E-mail: publications@toolbank.com

Curtis Holt Southampton Ltd, Westwood Business Park, Nutwood Way, Totton, Southampton, SO40 3WW Tel: (023) 8086 1991 Fax: (023) 8066 4505 E-mail: sales@tallbank.com

Curtis Holt Southampton Ltd, Westwood Business Park, Nutwood Way, Totton, Southampton, SO40 3WW Tel: (023) 8086 1991 Fax: (023) 8066 4555 E-mail: sales@tallbank.com

Curtis Holt (St. Albans), Unit 10B Brick Knoll Park, Ashley Road, St. Albans, Hertfordshire, AL1 5UG Tel: (01727) 845095 Fax: (01727) 845082 E-mail: stalbons.sales@torbank.com

Derbyshire Industrial Sales Ltd, Unit 17 Vanguard Trading Estate, Britannia Road, Chesterfield, Derbyshire, S40 2TZ Tel: (01246) 208963 Fax: (01246) 277139

Dewalt, 210 Bath Road, Slough, SL1 3YD Tel: (01753) 567055 Fax: (01753) 521312 E-mail: sales@dewalt.co.uk

Diytools Com Ltd, 20 Market Street, Watford, WD18 0PD Tel: (01923) 250295 Fax: (01923) 818219 E-mail: mur@diytools.com

Eagle Tools & Fixings, The Willows, Eardisland, Leominster, Herefordshire, HR6 9BN Tel: (01544) 388830 Fax: (01544) 388830

Eca Tool Fast, 26 Oswin Road, Leicester, LE3 1HR Tel: 0116-247 0402

Ekp Ltd Discount Tools, 142-143 Parrock Street, Gravesend, Kent, DA12 1EY Tel: (01474) 564829 Fax: (01474) 535266

Electric Power & Equipment Co., 619 Stretford Road, Manchester, M16 0QA Tel: 0161-872 1619 Fax: 0161-876 4160

Elliotts Tool Warehouse, 10 Winchester Trade Park, Easton Lane, Winchester, Hampshire, SO23 7FA Tel: (01962) 827610 Fax: (01962) 827611 E-mail: winchester@elliott-brothers.co.uk

Engineering & Factory Supplies Ltd, Algores Way, Wisbech, Cambridgeshire, PE13 2TQ Tel: (01945) 466644 Fax: (01945) 466232

Engineerstore Ltd, East Street, Prittlewell, Southend-On-Sea, SS2 5EQ Tel: (01702) 611711 Fax: (01702) 600048

▶ Essex Power Tools & Fixings, Unit 1 Bramerton Road, Hockley, Essex, SS5 4AZ Tel: (01702) 207209 Fax: (01702) 203228

Evolution Power Tools Ltd, Venture 1, Long Acre Close, Holbrook Industrial Estate, Sheffield, S20 3FR Tel: 0114-251 1022 Fax: 0114-247 3339 E-mail: bill@evolutionpowertools.com

Fas-Co Engineers Supply Ltd, 1 Caledon Green, Grangemouth, Stirlingshire, FK3 8TR Tel: (01324) 667500 Fax: (01324) 667516 E-mail: sales@fasco.co.uk

Firth Powerfix, 71 Gelderd Road, Leeds, LS12 6HF Tel: 0113-245 1626 Fax: 0113-242 3887 E-mail: sales@powerfixonline.co.uk

Fixfirm Fasteners & Fixing Devices, Pyke Road, Lincoln, LN6 3QS Tel: (01522) 500002 Fax: (0870) 7773828

Fixings Delivery, Unit 6 Catford Road, Roundthorn Industrial Estate, Roundthorn Industrial Estate, Manchester, M23 9LR Tel: 0161-945 0444 Fax: 0161-947 2710

Fixings & Power Tool Center, Brighton Road, Salfords, Redhill, RH1 5EQ Tel: (01293) 820088 Fax: (01293) 820099

Fixmart Services, 80 A The Brent, Dartford, DA1 1YW Tel: (01322) 274226 Fax: (01322) 278178

Foster Industrial, Church Street, Lenton, Lenton, Nottingham, NG7 2FH Tel: 0115-970 0598 Fax: 0115-942 3388 E-mail: richard@fosterindustrial.co.uk

G Hodgson Electrical, 37 Back Bolton Street, Ramsbottom, Bury, Lancashire, BL0 9HU Tel: (01706) 821430

Garrison Dales Ltd, Unit 8, North St Industrial Estate, Droitwich, Worcestershire, WR9 8JB Tel: (01905) 794555 Fax: (01905) 794592 E-mail: sales@garrisondales.co.uk

General Fixings Ltd, Unit 54 Beeches Industrial Estate, Waverley Road, Yate, Bristol, BS37 5QR Tel: (01454) 310015 Fax: (01454) 273164 E-mail: sales@generalfixings.co.uk

Germar, Unit 16, Riland Industrial Centre, Norris Way, Sutton Coldfield, West Midlands, B75 7BB Tel: 0121-378 2600 Fax: 0121-378 1300

Gilbey Electrical Ltd, 55-59 Spear Street, Manchester, M1 1DF Tel: 0161-236 5079 Fax: 0161-228 2155 E-mail: sales@gilbeyelectrical.co.uk

Glowbar Supplies & Power Tools Ltd, 56 Baxters Lane, St. Helens, Merseyside, WA9 3ND Tel: (01744) 816142 Fax: (01744) 816794 E-mail: sales@glowbar.co.uk

Gunn J C B Ltd, Atlantic Street, Broadheath, Altrincham, Cheshire, WA14 5DN Tel: 0161-941 2631 Fax: 0161-942 3399 E-mail: enguireies@gunn-jcb.co.uk

H E S Sales UK Ltd, 14 Bentley Way, Royal Oak Industrial Estate, Daventry, Northamptonshire, NN11 8QH Tel: (01327) 300322 Fax: (01327) 311411 E-mail: daventry@hes-sales.com

H Fisher Distributors & Factors Fareham Ltd, 9-10 Highbury Buildings, Portsmouth Road, Portsmouth, PO6 2SN Tel: (023) 9237 2111 Fax: (023) 9238 0243 E-mail: sales@hfishertools.co.uk

Hayway Tool & Hardware Co. Ltd, Cunliffe Drive, Kettering, Northamptonshire, NN16 8LD Tel: (01536) 481114 Fax: (01536) 483514 E-mail: sales@haywaytools.com

Heward & Dean Ltd, Spurling Works, Pindar Road, Hoddesdon, Hertfordshire, EN11 0DB Tel: (01992) 467557 Fax: (01992) 467477 E-mail: sales@hewardanddean.com

Hewden Hire Centres Ltd, 1640 London Road, Glasgow, G31 4QG Tel: 0141-550 0300 Fax: 0141-556 2239

Hewden Tool Hire, Unit 1 Kingstanding Business Park, Tunbridge Wells, Kent, TN2 3UP Tel: (01892) 616318 Fax: (01892) 616353 E-mail: steve.davies@hewden.co.uk

Highland Industrial Supplies Ltd, 36 Seafield Road, Inverness, IV1 1SG Tel: (01463) 239160 Fax: (01463) 233424 E-mail: sales@hisltd.co.uk

Hitachi Power Tools (UK) Ltd, Precedent Drive, Rooksley, Milton Keynes, MK13 8PJ Tel: (01908) 354700 Fax: (01908) 606642 E-mail: info@hitachi-powertools.co.uk

Curtis Holt Ltd, Longreach, Gallion Boulevard, Crossways Business Park, Dartford, DA2 6QE Tel: (01322) 321300 Fax: (01322) 383641 E-mail: sales@toolbank.com

Curtis Holt (North West), Toolbank House, Appleton Thorn Trading Estate, Lyncastle Way, Appleton, Warrington, WA4 4ST Tel: (01925) 261333 Fax: (01925) 604478

Industrial Tools Supplies (London) Ltd, 607-617 High Road, Leyton, London, E10 6RF Tel: (020) 8539 2231 Fax: (020) 8558 0247 E-mail: sales@itslondon.co.uk

Infix Holdings Ltd, 85 87 Stapleton Road, Bristol, BS5 0QF Tel: 0117-955 3987 Fax: 0117-955 9833 E-mail: enquiries@infix.co.uk

Interhire Power Tool Services Ltd, Park Road, Ilkeston, Derbyshire, DE7 5DA Tel: 0115-930 6382 Fax: 0115-944 0407

Ipc Fixings, 1 National Road, Hunslet Business Park, Leeds, LS10 1TD Tel: 0113-277 9444 Fax: 0113-277 9555

Ipswich Plastics Ltd, Foxtail Road, Ransomes Industrial Estate, Ipswich, IP3 9RX Tel: (01473) 270101 Fax: (01473) 721446

J & B Electric Power Tool Co. Ltd, Dorset House, 65a Manchester Road, Bolton, BL2 1ES Tel: (01204) 531891 Fax: (01204) 364735

Kingtools Power Tools, Norris Way, Rushden, Northamptonshire, NN10 6BP Tel: (01933) 410900 Fax: (01933) 350471 E-mail: sales@kingtools.co.uk

Alan Lord (Industrial Tools) Ltd, Unit 21 Bordesley Trading Estate, Bordesley Green Road, Birmingham, B8 1BZ Tel: 0121-328 6033 Fax: 0121-328 1842

M T S Power Tools, 97 St James Mill Road, Northampton, NN5 5JP Tel: (01604) 751688 Fax: (01604) 759041E-mail: sales@mts.co.uk

Machine Mart Ltd, 17-21 Victoria Road, Swindon, SN1 3AL Tel: (01793) 491717 Fax: (01793) 514787

Machine Sales & Services Ltd, 23 Cowley Road, Nuffield Industrial Estate, Poole, Dorset, BH17 0UJ Tel: (01202) 686238 Fax: (01202) 686661 E-mail: enquiries@machinesalesandservices.co.uk

Marshall, 18 Johnson Street, Sheffield, S3 8GT Tel: 0114-276 7071 Fax: 0114-273 8084 E-mail: sales@geomarshall.co.uk

Marshall & Parsons Ltd, 1111 London Road, Leigh-on-Sea, Essex, SS9 3JL Tel: (01702) 470100 Fax: (01702) 471160 E-mail: marshallandparsons@ancatown.co.uk

Maxim Power Tools (Scotland) Ltd, Couper Street, Glasgow, G4 0DL Tel: 0141-552 5591 Fax: 0141-552 5064 E-mail: info@maxim-power.com

Merton Timber Ltd, 102 Rose Hill, Sutton, Surrey, SM1 3HB Tel: (020) 8644 7884 Fax: (020) 8641 0943 E-mail: sales@merton-timber.co.uk

Merton Timber & Builders Merchants, Unit E 2 Endeavour Way, London, SW19 8UH Tel: (020) 8879 0626 Fax: (020) 8947 6061 E-mail: sales@mertontimber.com

Multi Fix Ltd, Normark House, 48 Mill Lane, Bradford, West Yorkshire, BD5 0HF Tel: (01274) 728065 Fax: (01274) 725213

Newbury Tools Ltd, 1 Hambridge Road, Newbury, Berkshire, RG14 5SS Tel: (01635) 30804 Fax: (01635) 529068 E-mail: sales@newburytools.com

Nortech Services Ltd, Drypool Way, Hull, HU9 1NL Tel: (01482) 327791 Fax: (01482) 320550 E-mail: sales@nortech.co.uk

Northern Tools & Accessories Ltd, PO Box 5, Newcastle upon Tyne, NE6 5XB Tel: 0191-265 2821 Fax: 0191-276 2668 E-mail: marketing@crossling.co.uk

Norton, Works Road, Letchworth Garden City, Hertfordshire, SG6 1LP Tel: (01462) 676944 Fax: (01462) 677192 E-mail: nif-ltd@btconnect.com

P A Bristow & Co., Station Yard Industrial Estate, Station Road, Heckington, Sleaford, Lincolnshire, NG34 9JJ Tel: (01529) 460540 Fax: (01529) 461232 E-mail: carolenpeter@aol.com

P T E Plant Co., Kelham St, Doncaster, South Yorkshire, DN1 3TA Tel: (01302) 321221

P V R Direct Ltd, 8 St. Stephens Business Centre, Poplar Road, Warmley, Bristol, BS30 5HT Tel: 0117-967 5115 Fax: 0117-935 2399 E-mail: vivrooker@aol.com

Paramount Tools & Fasteners Ltd, Unit 7 Paramount Business Park, Nile Street, Burslem, Stoke-on-Trent, ST6 2BG Tel: (01782) 821444 Fax: (01782) 821777 E-mail: paramtoolandfast@aol.com

Parfix Equipment Company Ltd, Locksley House, Unit 4 Locksley Business Park, Belfast, BT6 9JD Tel: (028) 9070 6800 Fax: (028) 9070 6801 E-mail: dflood@parfixwholesaledirect.com

▶ Pen Tools Ltd, Jubilee Building, Westfields Trading Estate, Hereford, HR4 9NS Tel: (01432) 273018

▶ Philpott & Cowlin Ltd, Unit 12 Liberty Industrial Park, South Liberty Lane, Bristol, BS3 2SU Tel: 0117-966 8431 Fax: 0117-966 0129 E-mail: philpottcowlin@pcweldmetals.co.uk

Phoenix Tools, 1 Sandygate Business Park, Strap Lane, Kingsteignton, Newton Abbot, Devon, TQ12 3XF Tel: (01626) 332862 Fax: (01626) 331860

Power Tool Services, 2 Earl Road, Rackheath, Norwich, NR13 6NT Tel: (01603) 722077 Fax: (01603) 722866

Power Tool Supplies Ltd, 379 Kingsway, Hove, East Sussex, BN3 4QD Tel: (01273) 420111 Fax: (01273) 422313

Power Tool Warehouse, 309 Rochdale Road, Royton, Oldham, OL2 5SN Tel: 0161-624 9190

▶ Power Tools Plus Ltd, 360-362 Carlton Hill, Carlton, Nottingham, NG4 1JB Tel: 0115-940 4414 Fax: 0115-940 1114

Power Tools Services (Wolverhampton) Ltd, Holland House, 126 High Street, Princes End, Tipton, West Midlands, DY4 9JA Tel: 0121-557 8690 Fax: 0121-557 5009

R E Thorns & Co., 22 Exchange Street, Norwich, NR2 1AT Tel: (01603) 622891 Fax: (01603) 622952 E-mail: mail@thornsdiy.com

R & J Industrial Supplies, Clay Flatts Trading Estate, Workington, Cumbria, CA14 2TQ Tel: (01900) 605411 Fax: (01900) 605415

R & L Superfix, 1 Mead Park Industrial Estate, Mead Road, Cheltenham, Gloucestershire, GL53 7EF Tel: (01242) 224664 Fax: (01242) 222977

Ranger Fixings Ltd, 8 Central Business Park, Southcote Road, Bournemouth, BH1 3SJ Tel: (01202) 297125 Fax: (01202) 294087 E-mail: ranger.fixings@tiscali.co.uk

Robert Samuel & Co. Ltd, 7 Court Parade, Wembley, Middlesex, HA0 3JA Tel: (020) 8904 1144 Fax: (020) 8904 6349

S A F Power Tools Ltd, 5 Anjou Cresent, Fareham, Hampshire, PO15 5DA Tel: (01329) 844205 Fax: (01329) 844142 E-mail: netsales@safpt.co.uk

S.I.A. (Agencies) Ltd, Unit 2, 96 Beechill Road, Belfast, BT8 7QN Tel: (028) 9049 2744 Fax: (028) 9064 9401 E-mail: alison@siaagencies.com

S K S Welding & Fasteners Supplies Ltd, Unit 33 Parkhouse Road East, Parkhouse Industrial Estate Ea, Newcastle, Staffordshire, ST5 7RB Tel: (01782) 566911 Fax: (01782) 561964 E-mail: sks.enquiries@btconnect.com

Scimitar Engineering Co. Ltd, Power House, 87 Mansel Street, Swansea, SA1 5TZ Tel: (01792) 651781 Fax: (01792) 646229

Solent tools, UNIT 009 SOLENT BUSINESS CENTRE, MILLBROOK ROAD WEST, SOUTHAMPTON, SO15 0HW Tel: 023 80578057 Fax: 023 80574470 E-mail: SALES@SOLENTTOOLS.CO.UK

Southern Power Tools & Abrasives Ltd, Unit A Nickel Close, Winchester, Hampshire, SO23 7RJ Tel: (01962) 856022 Fax: (01962) 842395

Speedy Hire Centres Ltd, Tollgate House, Tollgate Lane, Bury St. Edmunds, Suffolk, IP32 6DG Tel: (01284) 766254 Fax: (01284) 700542 E-mail: customer.services@speedyhire.co.uk

Standard Power Ltd, Unit 13 Riverside, Bolton, BL1 8TU Tel: 01204 527521

Supa Roofing & Power Tools Ltd, Aller Mills, Aller Road, Kingskerswell, Newton Abbot, Devon, TQ12 5AU Tel: (01803) 873288 Fax: (01803) 875277 E-mail: clive@suparoofing.co.uk

Super Stork I P T Ltd, Carlisle Road, London, NW9 0HD Tel: (020) 8200 1144 Fax: (020) 8200 4385 E-mail: sales1@superstork.co.uk

▶ Tameside Tools, Unit 17-18 Alpha Court, Windmill La Industrial Estate, Denton, Manchester, M34 3RB Tel: 0161-337 3400 Fax: 0161-337 3401

Three Counties Fixings Ltd, 6 Capital Place, Harlow, Essex, CM19 5AS Tel: (01279) 451631 Fax: (01279) 451617 E-mail: tcfltd@msn.com

Toga Plant Hire Ltd, 67-71 Kingsland Road, London, E2 8AG Tel: (020) 7729 1471 Fax: (020) 7729 1592

Toolmaster (Oxford) Ltd, 148 Oxford Road, Cowley, Oxford, OX4 2EA Tel: (01865) 712152 Fax: (01865) 747380 E-mail: sales@toolmaster.co.uk

POWER TOOLS OR ACCESSORIES

– continued

Toolpak plc, Rhosddu Industrial Estate, Old Rhosrobin, Rhosrobin, Wrexham, Clwyd, LL11 4YL Tel: (01978) 291771 Fax: (01978) 290068 E-mail: sales@toolpak.co.uk

Trend Machinery & Cutting Tools Ltd, Unit 6, Odhams Trading Estate, Watford, WD24 7TR Tel: (01923) 249911 Fax: (01923) 236879 E-mail: stamperm@trendm.co.uk

Unifix Ltd, Bridge House, Grove Lane, Smethwick, West Midlands, B66 2QT Tel: 0121-609 0099 Fax: 0121-626 0587 E-mail: marketing@unifix.com

▶ Varo (UK), 75 School Lane, Hartford, Northwich, Cheshire, CW8 1PF Tel: (01606) 786860 Fax: (01606) 784566

W W Fixings Ltd, Marston Road, Wolverhampton, WV2 4LA Tel: (01902) 310031 Fax: (01902) 429017 E-mail: sales@wwfix.co.uk

Walton Hire, Knowle Lane, Buckley, Clwyd, CH7 3JA Tel: (01244) 543365 Fax: (01244) 541200

Alan Wasden Ltd, Niloc Works, Penistone Road, Sheffield, S6 2FW Tel: 0114-234 8824 Fax: 0114-232 1246

Wera Tools, Unit 2 McGregors Way, Turnoaks Business Park, Off Storforth Lane, Chesterfield, Derbyshire, S40 2WB Tel: (01246) 277756 Fax: (01246) 273335

Wessex Fixings, Unit 60 South Way, Andover, Hampshire, SP10 5AF Tel: (01264) 332332 Fax: (01264) 332550

Westward Building Services Ltd, Burraton Road, Saltash, Cornwall, PL12 6LU Tel: (01752) 844600 Fax: (01752) 854254 E-mail: sales@westwoodbuildingservices.com

White Milne & Co., Baird Avenue, Dundee, DD2 3XG Tel: (01382) 814822 Fax: (01382) 813751 E-mail: sales@whitemilne.co.uk

Wide Range Engineering Services Ltd, Coventry Road, Acan Way, Narborough, Leicester, LE19 2FT Tel: 0116-275 0100 Fax: 0116-275 0086 E-mail: sales@wres.co.uk

Williams Technical Services Ltd, 36 Station Road, North Harrow, Harrow, Middlesex, HA2 7SE Tel: (020) 8863 2492 Fax: (020) 8863 1524

Winchcombe Power Tools, 299 Wimpson Lane, Southampton, SO16 4PY Tel: (023) 8039 9957 Fax: (023) 8078 1719

Worcester Tools & Fixings Ltd, Unit 10A Shrub Hill Industrial Estate, Shrub Hill Road, Worcester, WR4 9EL Tel: (01905) 723421 Fax: (01905) 25116 E-mail: sales@worcestertool.co.uk

▶ Wrights Tools & Supplies, 98a Creek Road, March, Cambridgeshire, PE15 8RD Tel: (01354) 661778 Fax: (01354) 650646

POWER TOOLS TO SPECIFICATION

Apex Industrial Ltd, 651 Eccles New Road, Salford, M50 1BA Tel: 0161-789 0909 Fax: 0161-787 7113

Poly Fasteners Ltd, 11-12 Rabans Close, Rabans Lane Industrial Area, Aylesbury, Buckinghamshire, HP19 8TP Tel: (01296) 333500 Fax: (01296) 333509 E-mail: sales@polyfasteners.co.uk

POWER TOOLS, HANDHELD

▶ I T W Contstructions Products, Unit R8, Blair Coart, 110 Borain Street, Portdundas Business Park, Glasgow, G4 9XG Tel: 0141-342 1660 Fax: 0141-332 7489 E-mail: sales@itwcp.co.uk

▶ Power Tool Hire Ltd, 504-506 Portswood Road, Southampton, SO17 3SP Tel: (023) 8031 5316 Fax: (023) 8031 5888 E-mail: glen@powertoolhiresales.uk.com

POWER TRANSFORMERS

Admagnetics (Manufaturing Division For Solutions) Ltd, Bolton Avenue, Huncoat Industrial Park, Accrington, Lancashire, BB5 6NJ Tel: (01254) 381869 Fax: (01254) 381674 E-mail:

Bowden Bros Ltd, Brickworks House, Spook Hill, North Holmwood, Dorking, Surrey, RH5 4HR Tel: (01306) 743355 Fax: (01306) 876768 E-mail: info@bowdon-bros.com

Globe Heat Treatment Services Ltd, Unit 4 & 5 Venture Works, Charleywood Road, Knowsley Industrial Park, Liverpool, L33 7SG Tel: 0151-548 5281 Fax: 0151-548 3530 E-mail: sales@globeheat.com

Walsall Transformers Ltd, 246 Green Lane, Walsall, WS2 8HS Tel: (01922) 722933 Fax: (01922) 721222 E-mail: sales@walsall-transformers.co.uk

POWER TRANSMISSION COMPONENTS

Alpha Safety Supplies Ltd, 18 Jeynes Road, Tewkesbury, Gloucestershire, GL20 5NG Tel: (01684) 298083 Fax: (01684) 850420 E-mail: sales@alphasafetysupplies.co.uk

Engineering Services, 5 Gavin Road, Widnes, Cheshire, WA8 8RE Tel: 0151-495 1317 Fax: 0151-495 1559 E-mail: sales@engineering-services.co.uk

POWER TRANSMISSION COUPLINGS

Dynamic Balancing Services, Hughenden Avenue, High Wycombe, Buckinghamshire, HP13 5SQ Tel: (01494) 462977 Fax: (01494) 462916 E-mail: sales@dynamicbalancing.co.uk

NDE Power Transmissions Group, NDE Bldgs, Aldbourne Road, Coventry, CV1 4EQ Tel: (024) 7622 2272 Fax: (024) 7625 8499 E-mail: sales@ndeclarketransmissions.co.uk

Ondrives, Unit 15 Foxwood Industrial Park, Foxwood Road, Chesterfield, Derbyshire, S41 9RN Tel: (01246) 455500 Fax: (01246) 455522

Renold High Tech Couplings, 112 Parkinson Lane, Halifax, West Yorkshire, HX1 3QH Tel: (01422) 255000 Fax: (01422) 320273 E-mail: sales@hitec.renold.com

POWER TRANSMISSION ENGINEERING

Engineering Services, 5 Gavin Road, Widnes, Cheshire, WA8 8RE Tel: 0151-495 1317 Fax: 0151-495 1559 E-mail: sales@engineering-services.co.uk

Hamilton Sundstrand International Corporation, Kingfisher House, 160-162 High Street, Egham, Surrey, TW20 9HP Tel: (01784) 414600 Fax: (01784) 438092 E-mail: alison.doran@hs.utc.com

▶ LDA Chain Specialists, Unit 11, Bamford Business Park, Stockport, Cheshire, SK4 1PL Tel: 0161-477 5252 Fax: 0161-477 9559 E-mail: lda.transmission@btconnect.com

POWER TRANSMISSION EQUIPMENT (INDUSTRIAL/ MECHANICAL) DISTRIBUTORS OR AGENTS

Air America (Rugby) Ltd, Midland Trading Estate, Consul Road, Rugby, Warwickshire, CV21 1PB Tel: (01788) 574555 Fax: (01788) 547997 E-mail: air.america@wyko.co.uk

Aire Bearings, 34 Bradford Road, Stanningley, Pudsey, West Yorkshire, LS28 6DD Tel: 0113-256 5676 Fax: 0113-255 4894 E-mail: sales@airebearings.co.uk

▶ Antifriction Components Ltd, 8-9 Days Road, St. Philips, Bristol, BS2 0QS Tel: 0117-955 2266 Fax: 0117-955 1287 E-mail: bristolsales@afc-uk.com

Apollo Bearings, 8 Priestley Way, Crawley, West Sussex, RH10 9NT Tel: (01293) 539539 Fax: (01293) 538853 E-mail: apollo.bearings@talk21.com

Atlantic Bearings Ltd, Unit 1, Milners Road, Yeadon, Leeds, LS19 7JE Tel: 0113-250 6640 Fax: 0113-250 0031 E-mail: user@atlantic-bearings.fsnet.co.uk

Bearing Supplies Thetford, Unit 1 Brunel Way, Thetford, Norfolk, IP24 1HP Tel: (01842) 765074 Fax: (01842) 754709

Bearing Traders Ltd, 18-20 Desborough Street, High Wycombe, Buckinghamshire, HP11 2LY Tel: (01494) 441301 Fax: (01494) 438085 E-mail: hwsales@bearingtraders.com

Bearing Transmission & Pneumatics Ltd, 6 Chieftain Way, Tritton Road Trading Estate, Lincoln, LN6 7RY Tel: (01522) 560060 Fax: (01522) 560040 E-mail: btplimited@aol.com

Berkshire Bearings & Transmsns Ltd, 27-31 Meadow Road, Newbury, Berkshire, RG14 7AH Tel: (01635) 43449 Fax: (01635) 35447 E-mail: sales@bbt1.sagehost.co.uk

Beta Power Engineering Ltd, Beta House Discovery Park, Crossley Road, Stockport, Cheshire, SK4 5BN Tel: 0161-432 9995 Fax: 0161-431 7800 E-mail: beta_power@btconnect.com

Binson Bearing Co., 335 A Round Hay Road, Leeds, LS8 4HT Tel: 0113-249 0251 Fax: 0113-235 0375 E-mail: sales@binsonbearings.ssnet.co.uk

Brammer Ltd, 8a Blackbrook Valley Industrial Estate, Narrowboat Way, Dudley, West Midlands, DY2 0XQ Tel: (01384) 456783 Fax: (01384) 456795 E-mail: dudley@branner.biz

Brammer Ltd, Claverton Court, Claverton Road, Roundthorn Industrial Estate, Manchester, M23 9NE Tel: 0161-953 8600 Fax: 0161-953 8680 E-mail: enquiries@bslbrammer.co.uk

Brammer Ltd, 16 Javelin Road, Airport Industrial Estate, Norwich, NR6 6HP Tel: (01603) 423756 Fax: (01603) 424693 E-mail: norwich@brammer.biz

Brammer Ltd, Unit 1, Manor Grove Business Centre, Vicarage Farm Road, Peterborough, PE1 5TP Tel: (01733) 565222 Fax: (01733) 896014 E-mail: peterb@bsl.co.uk

Brammer Ltd, 25 Buckingham Avenue, Slough, SL1 4QA Tel: (01753) 537695 Fax: (01753) 572311 E-mail: slough@brammer.biz

Brammer UK Ltd, Headway Road, Wolverhampton, WV10 6PZ Tel: (01902) 395949 Fax: (01902) 395945 E-mail: export@brammer.biz

C B C International Ltd, Coneygre Industrial Estate, Tipton, West Midlands, DY4 8XP Tel: 0121-557 3154 Fax: 0121-557 9570 E-mail: cklowe@cbcint.com

C B S Rotary Power Motion Ltd, Unit 14 Grandstand Business Centre, Westfields Trading Estate, Hereford, HR4 9NS Tel: (01432) 276630 Fax: (01432) 357140 E-mail: hereford@cbs-rpm.co.uk

Camco Engineering Ltd, Malvito House, Dale Street, Bilston, West Midlands, WV14 7JX Tel: (01902) 404090 Fax: (01902) 402070 E-mail: sales@camcoengineering.co.uk

Carrington Bearings & Engineering Ltd, 8 Torridge Close, Telford Way Industrial Estate, Kettering, Northamptonshire, NN16 8PY Tel: (01536) 518666 Fax: (01536) 412131 E-mail: sales@carringtonbearings.co.uk

Citadel Engineering Supplies Ltd, 14 Marlow Street, Rowley Regis, West Midlands, B65 0AY Tel: 0121-561 5557 Fax: 0121-561 5558 E-mail: sales@citadel-eng.co.uk

Custom Power Transmission Ltd, 69 Garamonde Drive, Wymbush, Milton Keynes, MK8 8DD Tel: (01908) 563252 Fax: (01908) 563077 E-mail: custompower@btopenworld.com

D I K Bearings & Transmissions Ltd, J Hawkhill Court, Mid Wynd, Dundee, DD1 4JG Tel: (01382) 228711 Fax: (01382) 202559 E-mail: sales@dik.sol.co.uk

D M R Engineering Services Ltd, 64 Regent Road, Kirkdale, Liverpool, L5 9SY Tel: 0151-207 4451 Fax: 0151-207 5627 E-mail: dmr1966@hotmail.co.uk

E M R Silverthorn Ltd, 4 Abercorn Commercial Centre, Manor Farm Road, Wembley, Middlesex, HA0 1AN Tel: (020) 8903 1390 Fax: (020) 8903 9092 E-mail: emrsilverthorn@ndirect.co.uk

Ebc International Ltd, 7 Grovebury Place Estate, Leighton Buzzard, Bedfordshire, LU7 4SH Tel: (01525) 217217 Fax: (01525) 373772 E-mail: sales@ebcint.co.uk

Europa Bearings (1976) Ltd, Empire Centre, Imperial Way, Watford, WD24 4YH Tel: (01923) 255166 Fax: (01923) 234069 E-mail: sales@europabearings.freeserve.co.uk

Fastener & Machining Supply Ltd, Unit 12 South Staffs Business Park, Hawkins Drive, Cannock, Staffordshire, WS11 0XU Tel: (01922) 419418 Fax: (01922) 411314 E-mail: enquiries@fmsltd.net

Howley Engineering Ltd, 33 Melford Court, Hardwick Grange, Woolston, Warrington, WA1 4RZ Tel: (01925) 810810 Fax: (01925) 813477 E-mail: sales@howley-engineering.co.uk

Leeds Bearings Ltd, Unit 14, Castleton Close, Armley Road, Leeds, LS12 2DS Tel: 0113-234 1919 Fax: 0113-245 0037

London Bearings (Kent) Ltd, Unit 2, Sabre Court, Gillingham Business Park, Gillingham, Kent, ME8 0RW Tel: (01634) 235335 Fax: (01634) 230268 E-mail: lbk.uk@btinternet.com

Newstart Power Transmission, Unit 19 Tamworth Business Centre, Amber Cl, Tamworth, Staffs, B77 4RP Tel: (01827) 313737 Fax: (01827) 313838

P V S Engineers Ltd, 1-2 Murrills Estate, Fareham, Hampshire, PO16 9RD Tel: (023) 9237 9495 Fax: (023) 9238 8801 E-mail: rec@pvsengineers.co.uk

Potteries Specialist Auctions, 271 Waterloo Road, Stoke-on-Trent, ST6 3HR Tel: (01782) 286622 Fax: (01782) 213777 E-mail: potteriesltd@aol.com

Premier Bearings & Transmissions Ltd, Unit 2b Mariner, Lichfield Road Industrial Estate, Tamworth, Staffordshire, B79 7UL Tel: (01827) 60686 Fax: (01827) 60637 E-mail: sales@premierbearings.co.uk

Premier Power Products Ltd, 1 Dampier Mews Edward Close, Hounstone Business Park, Houndstone Business Park, Yeovil, Somerset, BA22 8RU Tel: (01935) 432412 Fax: (01935) 433557

Pti Neepsend Engineering Ltd, Unit 13a Limestone Cottage Lane, Sheffield, S6 1NJ Tel: 0114-233 5580 Fax: 0114-233 5590 E-mail: sales@ptiuk.com

R D R Bearings, 20 Ravenhill Road, Belfast, BT6 8EA Tel: (028) 9073 2321 Fax: (028) 9073 1889 E-mail: rdr@nbcgroup.co.uk

R M B Engineering Services Ltd, Union Street, West Bromwich, West Midlands, B70 6BP Tel: 0121-500 1940 Fax: 0121-500 1941 E-mail: sales@rmbderitend.co.uk

R & M Bearings Ltd, Unit 13 Manhattan Works, Dundonald Street, Dundee, DD3 7PY Tel: (01382) 455400 Fax: (01382) 454645 E-mail: sales@rmbearings.co.uk

Redhill Bearings Ltd, The White House, Brighton Road, Handcross, Haywards Heath, West Sussex, RH17 6BZ Tel: (01444) 400900 Fax: (01444) 400753 E-mail: redhillbearings@aol.com

Replacement & Maintenance Supplies Ltd, Dunsford Road, Meadow La Industrial Estate, Alfreton, Derbyshire, DE55 7RH Tel: (01773) 520181 Fax: (01773) 836370

Rotary Bearing & Transmission Co. Ltd, Unit 11 Forty 8 North 48, Duncrue Street, Belfast, BT3 9BJ Tel: (028) 9074 9377 Fax: (028) 9035 2949 E-mail: sales@rotarybearings-ni.com

S.I.S. Industrial Automation Ltd, 8 Amphion Court Hale Trading Estate, Lower Church Lane, Tipton, West Midlands, DY4 7HN Tel: 0121-520 7211 Fax: 0121-557 8146

Sapphire Engineering, Atlas Works, Brieryfield Road, Preston, PR1 8SR Tel: (01772) 822133 Fax: (01772) 822144

Siemens Automation & Drive Training Centre, Sir William Siemens House, Princess Road, Manchester, M20 2UR Tel: 0161-446 5741 Fax: 0161-446 5742 E-mail: sales@siemens-industry.co.uk

Spire Bearings, 94 Storforth La Trading Estate, Hasland, Chesterfield, Derbyshire, S41 0SN Tel: (01246) 274183 Fax: (01246) 202898 E-mail: sales@spirebearings.co.uk

Sprint Engineering Services Ltd, Unit G3 Imperial Business Estate, West Mill, Gravesend, Kent, DA11 0DL Tel: (01474) 534251 Fax: (01474) 534566 E-mail: info@sprint-uk.com

Sprint Industrial Sales Ltd, 1 Rosehill, Willenhall, West Midlands, WV13 2AR Tel: (01902) 636106 Fax: (01902) 636137 E-mail: sprint@btclick.com

STM Power Transmission Ltd, Unit 10 Hartford Business Centre, Chester Road, Hartford, Northwich, Cheshire, CW8 2AB Tel: (01606) 557200 Fax: (01606) 301260 E-mail: info@stmuk.co.uk

T S J Industrial Supplies Ltd, 44-50 Heaton Street, Cleckheaton, West Yorkshire, BD19 3TN Tel: (01274) 870804 Fax: (01274) 870805 E-mail: andrew@tsji.demon.co.uk

Transdrive Engineering Services Ltd, Units 18-20, Moss Lane Indust Estate, Royton, Oldham, OL2 6HR Tel: (01706) 881940 Fax: (01706) 882436 E-mail: sales@transdrive.co.uk

U K R Transmissions Ltd, 249 Cotmanhay Road, Ilkeston, Derbyshire, DE7 8NE Tel: 0115-932 4572 Fax: 0115-944 0585 E-mail: sales@ukrtrans.co.uk

West Engineering Services Ltd, Unit 1a Abbey Mill Business Centre, Paisley, Renfrewshire, PA1 1TJ Tel: 0141-889 2331 Fax: 0141-887 9564

Whitaker Transmissions, 2 Heys Lane, Oswaldtwistle, Accrington, Lancashire, BB5 3BJ Tel: (01254) 382791 Fax: (01254) 239062

Wyko Group Ltd, Amber Way, Halesowen, West Midlands, B62 8WG Tel: 0121-508 6000 Fax: 0121-508 6464 E-mail: marketing@wyko.co.uk

POWER TRANSMISSION EQUIPMENT (INDUSTRIAL/ MECHANICAL) MAINTENANCE/ REPAIR SERVICES

Clarke Engineering Company Ltd, P.O. Box 76, Bodmin, Cornwall, PL30 5PJ Tel: (01637) 881112 Fax: (01637) 880598

Ets UK Ltd, Northside Industrial Park, Whitley Bridge, Goole, North Humberside, DN14 0GH Tel: (01977) 662910 Fax: (01977) 661797 E-mail: sales@ets-uk.co.uk

R M B Engineering Services Ltd, Union Street, West Bromwich, West Midlands, B70 6BP Tel: 0121-500 1940 Fax: 0121-500 1941 E-mail: sales@rmbderitend.co.uk

T D R Transmissions, 5 Hunsley Street, Sheffield, S4 8DY Tel: 0114-262 6050 Fax: 0114-243 1826 E-mail: sales@tdrtrans.demon.co.uk

POWER TRANSMISSION EQUIPMENT (INDUSTRIAL/ MECHANICAL) MANUFRS

Abec Industrial & Engineering Ltd, Unit 10 Firsland Park Estate, Henfield Road, Albourne, Hassocks, West Sussex, BN6 9JJ Tel: (01273) 494960 Fax: (01273) 494960 E-mail: abeclimited@aol.com

Andantex Ltd, Rowley Drive, Bagington, Coventry, CV3 4LS Tel: (024) 7630 7722 Fax: (024) 7630 4499 E-mail: sales@andantex.com

Berges UK Ltd, 3 Nelson Business Centre, Nelson Street, Denton, Manchester, M34 3ET Tel: (0161) 335 0995 Fax: 0161-335 0935

David Brown Engineering Ltd, Park Works, Park Road, Huddersfield, HD4 5DD Tel: (01484) 465500 Fax: (01484) 465586 E-mail: sales@davidbrown.textron.com

Centa Transmissions Ltd, Thackley Court, Thackley Old Road, Shipley, West Yorkshire, BD18 1BW Tel: (01274) 531034 Fax: (01274) 531159 E-mail: post@centa-uk.co.uk

▶ Drummotors & More, 49 Cyprus Road, Leicester, LE2 8QT Tel: 0116-283 8344 Fax: 0116-283 1544 E-mail: sales@drummotorsandmore.com

Hamilton Sundstrand International Corporation, Kingfisher House, 160-162 High Street, Egham, Surrey, TW20 9HP Tel: (01784) 414600 Fax: (01784) 438092 E-mail: alison.doran@hs.utc.com

I M S International Marketing Services Ltd, Boulton Works, 54 College Road, Perry Barr, Birmingham, B44 8BS Tel: 0121-344 5500 Fax: 0121-344 5504 E-mail: sales@ims-ltd.co.uk

Leyden Transmissions Ltd, Roberttown Lane, Liversedge, West Yorkshire, WF15 7LQ Tel: (01924) 402820 Fax: (01924) 411350 E-mail: info@leyden-ptc.co.uk

J.M. Loveridge P.L.C., Higher Merley Lane, Corfe Mullen, Wimborne, Dorset, BH21 3EQ Tel: (01202) 882306 Fax: (01202) 880059

Maxspeed Engineering Ltd, Foxoak Street, Cradley Heath, West Midlands, B64 5DE Tel: (01384) 564999 Fax: (01384) 564888

Mertech Pumps Ltd, 39 Hastings Street, Luton, LU1 5BE Tel: (01582) 422622 Fax: (01582) 422922 E-mail: mail@mertech.co.uk

Motovario Ltd, Rushock Trading Estate, Rushock, Droitwich, Worcestershire, WR9 0NR Tel: (01299) 250859 Fax: (01299) 251493 E-mail: sales@motovario.co.uk

POWER TRANSMISSION EQUIPMENT (INDUSTRIAL/ MECHANICAL) MANUFRS – *continued*

Nottingham Electrical Transmissions, Northern Court, Nottingham, NG6 0BJ Tel: 0115-975 3655 Fax: 0115-977 0366 E-mail: info@net-eng.co.uk
Power Transmission Equipment Ltd, Unit 12 Spires Business Units, Mugiemoss Road, Bucksburn, Aberdeen, AB21 9NY Tel: (01224) 680022 Fax: (01224) 680033
S E W Eurodrive Ltd, Unit 37 Enterprise House, Springkerse Business Park, Stirling, FK7 7UF Tel: (01786) 478730 Fax: (01786) 450223
Signet Industrial Distribution Doncaster Ltd, Watch House Lane, Doncaster, South Yorkshire, DN5 9LZ Tel: (01302) 390002 Fax: (01302) 390003
South East Power Transmissions Ltd, Network House, Perry Road, Harlow, Essex, CM18 7ND Tel: (01279) 418300 Fax: (01279) 418100 E-mail: stransltd@aol.com
Stieber Brakes, Wichita Building, Ampthill Road, Bedford, MK42 9RD Tel: (01234) 355499 Fax: (01234) 214264 E-mail: diane.lawman@wichita.co.uk
Sumitomo Drive Technologies SM Cyclo (UK) Ltd, Unit 29, Bergen Way, Hull, HU7 0YQ Tel: (01482) 790340 Fax: (01482) 790321 E-mail: marketing@sumitomoeurope.com
WMH Transmissions Ltd, Lichfield Road Industrial Estate, 24 Cavendish, Tamworth, Staffordshire, B79 7XH Tel: (01827) 310311 Fax: (01827) 307118 E-mail: sales@wmh-trans.co.uk
Wraxall Power Transmission Equipment, The Lodge Dunchurch Trading Estate, London Road, Dunchurch, Rugby, Warwickshire, CV23 9LN Tel: (01788) 817522 Fax: (01788) 817852 E-mail: sales@wraxall.com
Wyko Group Ltd, Amber Way, Halesowen, West Midlands, B62 8WG Tel: 0121-508 6000 Fax: 0121-508 6464 E-mail: marketing@wyko.co.uk

POWER TRANSMISSION PULLEYS

Challenge Power Transmission plc, Unit 1 2 Merryhills Enterprise Park, Park Lane, Wolverhampton, WV10 9TJ Tel: (01902) 866116 Fax: (01902) 866117 E-mail: uksales@challengept.com
Rotary Bearing & Transmission Co. Ltd, Unit 11 Forty 8 North 48, Duncrue Street, Belfast, BT3 9BJ Tel: (028) 9074 9377 Fax: (028) 9035 2949 E-mail: sales@rotarybearings-ni.com

POWERED ACCESS EQUIPMENT

Airborne Industrial Access Ltd, Pegasus House 15 Irwin Road, Guildford, Surrey, GU2 7PW Tel: (01483) 451610 Fax: (01483) 533009 E-mail: ringway@btinternet.com
▶ Moore Training Ltd, 17 Canterbury Close, Yate, Bristol, BS37 5TJ Tel: (01454) 321463 Fax: (0871) 6617479 E-mail: info@mooretraining.co.uk
Top Man Access & Handling, 22 Lenside Drive, Bearsted, Maidstone, Kent, ME15 8UE Tel: (01622) 730540 Fax: (01622) 730540 E-mail: sales@topmanaccess.co.uk

POWERED ACCESS PLATFORM HIRE

▶ R Bell, 14 Birch Close, North Walsham, Norfolk, NR28 0UD Tel: (01692) 409080 Fax: (0800) 7832212 E-mail: contact@rbellplatformhire.co.uk

POWERED ACCESS PLATFORM OPERATOR TRAINING

▶ Ainscough Training Services Ltd, Farington Business Park, Golden Hill Lane, Leyland, PR25 3GG Tel: (01772) 623591 Fax: (01772) 622654 E-mail: ianfisher@ainscoughtraining.co.uk
Newlins Access Ltd, Long Close Farm, Wimborne Road, Walford, Wimborne, Dorset, BH21 1NR Tel: (01202) 885300 Fax: (01202) 885400 E-mail: office@newlinaccess.co.uk
▶ UK Operators Ltd, The Pin Mill, New Street, Charfield, Wotton-under-Edge, Gloucestershire, GL12 8ES Tel: (01453) 843121 Fax: (01453) 843079 E-mail: reception@ukoperators.co.uk

POWERED ACCESS PLATFORMS

▶ Claude Fenton (Plant Hire) Ltd, Unit 1 Kennet Weir Business Park, Arrowhead Road, Theale, Reading, RG7 4AE Tel: 0118-930 3066 Fax: 0118-930 3041 E-mail: reading@fentonplant.co.uk
Cradle Access Services Ltd, PO Box 70, Erith, Kent, DA8 3WY Tel: (01322) 345999 Fax: (01322) 345999 E-mail: cradle.access@btconnect.com
G B Access Ltd, 10 Nene Valley Business Park, Oundle, Peterborough, PE8 4HN Tel: (01832) 272408 Fax: (01832) 272484 E-mail: hire@gbaccess.co.uk
▶ Genie UK Ltd, The Maltings, Wharf Road, Grantham, Lincolnshire, NG31 6BH Tel: (01476) 584333 Fax: (01476) 584334 E-mail: infoeurope@genieind.com
Hewden Instant Access Ltd, Unit C1 Fort Wallington Industrial Estate, Military Road, Fareham, Hampshire, PO16 8TT Tel: (01329) 231123 Fax: (01329) 827533
King Highway Products Ltd, Riverside, Market Harborough, Leicestershire, LE16 7PX Tel: (01858) 467361 Fax: (01858) 467161 E-mail: sales@skyking.co.uk
Max Access Ltd, Unit 17 Bankside, Station Approach, Kidlington, Oxfordshire, OX5 1JE Tel: (01865) 373566 Fax: (01865) 378021 E-mail: info@maxaccess.co.uk
▶ Moore Training Ltd, 17 Canterbury Close, Yate, Bristol, BS37 5TJ Tel: (01454) 321463 Fax: (0871) 6617479 E-mail: info@mooretraining.co.uk
Newlins Access Ltd, Long Close Farm, Wimborne Road, Walford, Wimborne, Dorset, BH21 1NR Tel: (01202) 885300 Fax: (01202) 885400 E-mail: office@newlinaccess.co.uk
Niftylift Ltd, Fingle Drive, Stonebridge, Milton Keynes, MK13 0ER Tel: (01908) 223456 Fax: (01908) 312733E-mail: info@niftylift.com
Northern Access Ltd, Unit D Avondale Way, Wakefield, West Yorkshire, WF2 7QU Tel: (01924) 385869 Fax: (01924) 385868 E-mail: sales@northernaccess.co.uk
Northern Platforms Ltd, 8 Hind Heath Road, Wheelock, Sandbach, Cheshire, CW11 3LG Tel: (01270) 761954 Fax: (01270) 761954 E-mail: jc.wood@npl.com
P Hird & Sons Ltd, English Street, Hull, HU3 2BT Tel: (01482) 227333 Fax: (01482) 587710 E-mail: sales@peter-hird.co.uk
Panther Platform Rentals, Derby Dell, Lasham, Alton, Hampshire, GU34 5RX Tel: (01256) 381515 Fax: (01256) 381505 E-mail: basingstoke@panther.uk.com
Safe T Reach Ltd, Crucible Road, Corby, Northamptonshire, NN17 5TS Tel: (01536) 267686 Fax: (01536) 267686
Upright International, Unit F1, Halesfield 4, Telford, Shropshire, TF7 4AP Tel: (01952) 685200 Fax: (01952) 685255 E-mail: mdavey@uprighteuro.com
W Laird, Nethan Street, Motherwell, Lanarkshire, ML1 3TF Tel: (01698) 249249 Fax: (01698) 249385 E-mail: enquiries@williamlaird.co.uk

POWERED GARDEN TOOLS

Bellet Ltd, White House Nurseries, Colchester Main Road, Alresford, Colchester, CO7 8DH Tel: (01206) 827360 Fax: (01206) 823360
▶ CanYouDIY Ltd, 1 Queen Alexandra Road, North Shields, Tyne & Wear, NE29 9AS Tel: 0191 2580070 Fax: 0191 2580075 E-mail: questions@canyoudiy.com
Countax Ltd, Countax House, Great Haseley Trading Estate, Great Haseley, Oxford, OX44 7PF Tel: (01844) 278800 Fax: (01844) 278792 E-mail: sales@countax.com
Dennis Motor Mowers, Howardson Works, Ashbourne Road, Kirk Langley, Ashbourne, Derbyshire, DE6 4NJ Tel: (01332) 824777 Fax: (01332) 824525 E-mail: sales@dennisuk.com
Emak UK Ltd, Unit A1 Chasewater Industrial Estate, Burntwood Business Park, Burntwood, Staffordshire, WS7 3XD Tel: (01543) 687660 Fax: (01543) 670721 E-mail: sales@emak.co.uk
Farm & Forest Equipment, 10-12 Spital Terrace, Gainsborough, Lincolnshire, DN21 2HE Tel: (01427) 612504 Fax: (01427) 678578
Garden Machines (Northampton) Ltd, 66-70 Kingsthorpe Road, Northampton, NN2 6HD Tel: (01604) 716222 Fax: (01604) 722082 E-mail: sales@gardenmachinesltd.co.uk
Power Rewind Ltd, 1 Conder Way, Colchester, CO2 8JN Tel: (01206) 791316 Fax: (01206) 792689
Seddons Plant & Engineers Ltd, Oldfields Business Park, Duke Street, Stoke-on-Trent, ST4 3NX Tel: (01782) 593444 Fax: (01782) 593555

POWERED LAWN MOWERS

Countax Ltd, Countax House, Great Haseley Trading Estate, Great Haseley, Oxford, OX44 7PF Tel: (01844) 278800 Fax: (01844) 278792 E-mail: sales@countax.com
Davies Implements Ltd, Blaenteg, Llwynderi, Trevaughan, Carmarthen, Dyfed, SA31 3QN Tel: (01267) 237726 Fax: (01267) 238696 E-mail: davies@implements.preserve.co.uk
Dennis Motor Mowers, Howardson Works, Ashbourne Road, Kirk Langley, Ashbourne, Derbyshire, DE6 4NJ Tel: (01332) 824777 Fax: (01332) 824525 E-mail: sales@dennisuk.com
Eaton Berry Ltd, Bridge Farm, Reading Road, Arborfield, Reading, RG2 9HT Tel: 0118-976 1076 Fax: 0118-976 0479 E-mail: info@eatonberry.com
Electrolux Outdoor Products, Preston Road, Aycliffe Industrial Park, Newton Aycliffe, County Durham, DL5 6UP Tel: (01325) 300303 Fax: (01325) 310339
Globe Organic Services, Unit S2 Olton Wharf, Richmond Road, Solihull, West Midlands, B92 7RN Tel: 0121-707 4120 Fax: 0121-707 4934 E-mail: globeorganic@btinternet.com
Hallmark Tractors Ltd, Smisby Road, Ashby-de-la-Zouch, Leicestershire, LE65 2UE Tel: (01530) 412811 Fax: (01530) 412512 E-mail: sales@tractors.co.uk
Hayter Ltd, Spellbrook La West, Spellbrook, Bishop's Stortford, Hertfordshire, CM23 4BU Tel: (01279) 723444 Fax: (01279) 723821 E-mail: sales@hayter.co.uk
Henton & Chattell Ltd, London Road, Nottingham, NG2 3HW Tel: 0115-986 6646 Fax: 0115-986 6169 E-mail: info@hentonandchattell.co.uk
Industrial Power Units Ltd, Churchbridge, Oldbury, West Midlands, B69 2AS Tel: 0121-511 0400 Fax: 0121-511 0401 E-mail: ipu@ipu.co.uk
Lloyds & Co. Ltd, Birds Hill, Letchworth Garden City, Hertfordshire, SG6 1JE Tel: (01462) 683031 Fax: (01462) 481964 E-mail: sales@lloydsandco.com

POWERED WORKING PLATFORM HIRE

2 Cousins Access Ltd, Shell House, Watlington Road, Cowley, Oxford, OX4 6NF Tel: (01865) 779778 Fax: (01865) 401041 E-mail: keith@2cousins.co.uk
Traction Equipment (Stafford) Ltd, Glover Street, Stafford, ST16 2NY Tel: (01785) 223355 Fax: (01785) 211074 E-mail: call@tractionequipment.co.uk

POWERED WORKING PLATFORMS

Niftylift Ltd, Fingle Drive, Stonebridge, Milton Keynes, MK13 0ER Tel: (01908) 223456 Fax: (01908) 312733E-mail: info@niftylift.com

PREASSEMBLED MODULE UNITS

Ardeth Engineering Ltd, Dewsbury Road, Elland, West Yorkshire, HX5 9AZ Tel: (01422) 371014 Fax: (01422) 372218E-mail: info@ardeth.com

PRECAST CONCRETE BUILDING FRAMES

Eleco plc, 15 Gentlemens Field, Westmill Road, Ware, Hertfordshire, SG12 0EF Tel: (01920) 443830 Fax: (01920) 469681 E-mail: mail@eleco.com
Trent Concrete Ltd, Private Road 3, Colwick Industrial Estate, Nottingham, NG4 2BG Tel: 0115-987 9747 Fax: 0115-987 9948 E-mail: admin@trentconcrete.co.uk

PRECAST CONCRETE CHIMNEY CONTRACTORS

Portland Chimneys, 4 Portland Avenue, The Industrial Estate, Irvine, Ayrshire, KA12 8JD Tel: (01294) 274813 Fax: (01294) 312008

PRECAST CONCRETE COPING STONES

Albion Architectural Concrete Ltd, Newbrook Works, Pound Lane, Upper Beeding, Steyning, West Sussex, BN44 3JD Tel: (01903) 815262 Fax: (01903) 815619 E-mail: mike@albionart.co.uk

PRECAST CONCRETE FLOORING

Andy's Concrete Grooving, 29 Redlands, Chippenham, Wiltshire, SN14 0JA Tel: (01249) 654683 E-mail: andytuck3@hotmail.com
Bath Patio Slab Centre, Whiteway Road, Bath, BA2 2RG Tel: (01225) 319334 Fax: (01225) 319334 E-mail: info@bathslabs.com
Bison Concrete Products Ltd, Millennium Court, First Avenue, Centrum One Hundred, Burton-On-Trent, Staffordshire, DE14 2WR Tel: (01283) 495000 Fax: (01283) 544900 E-mail: concrete@bison.co.uk
Carter Concrete Ltd, Stone Hill Way, Holt Way Industrial Estate, Cromer, Norfolk, NR27 9JW Tel: (01263) 511009 Fax: (01263) 519053
Cemex Floors, London Road, Wick, Bristol, BS30 5SJ Tel: (01788) 542111 Fax: 0117-937 4695 E-mail: rmc@concreteproducts.co.uk
Collier & Henry Concrete Floors Ltd, Unit 2 Mellors Road, Trafford Park, Manchester, M17 1PB Tel: 0161-872 8410 Fax: 0161-872 9875
Hanson Ltd, Cotes Park Industrial Estate, Birchwood Way, Somercotes, Alfreton, Derbyshire, DE55 4NH Tel: (01773) 602432 Fax: (01773) 603134
Hanson Concrete Products Hoveringham Ltd, Hoveringham Lane, Hoveringham, Nottingham, NG14 7JX Tel: (01636) 832000 Fax: (01636) 832020 E-mail: enquiries@jetfloor.co.uk
New Forest Fencing Ltd, Mill Lane, Nursling, Southampton, SO16 0YE Tel: (023) 8073 3442 Fax: (023) 8074 0181
▶ PCR Systems, 92 Langdale Road, Leyland, PR25 3AS Tel: 01772 457327 Fax: 01772 457280 E-mail: info@winfloor.com
Rackham Housefloors Ltd, Broadmoor Road, Cinderford, Gloucestershire, GL14 2YE Tel: (01594) 826602 Fax: (01594) 826502
Stressline Ltd, Station Road, Stoney Stanton, Leicester, LE9 4LX Tel: (01455) 272457 Fax: (01455) 274564 E-mail: info@stressline.ltd.uk

PRECAST CONCRETE PRODUCTION PLANT OR EQUIPMENT

B S Eaton Ltd, Coppice Lane, Cheslyn Hay, Walsall, WS6 7EY Tel: (01922) 413678 Fax: (01922) 416515 E-mail: enquiries@bseaton.co.uk
Clwyd Concrete Co. Ltd, Varis Works, Bodfari, Denbigh, Clwyd, LL16 4DA Tel: (01745) 710277 Fax: (01745) 710303
Concrete Machinery Systems Ltd, Unit 1A, Farrington Fields, Farrington Gurney, Bristol, BS39 6UU Tel: (01761) 450050 Fax: (01761) 453200 E-mail: sales@concretemachinerysystems.co.uk
S C P Concrete Sealing Technology Ltd, Ver House, London Road, Markyate, St. Albans, Hertfordshire, AL3 8JP Tel: (01582) 842802 Fax: (01582) 842803 E-mail: sales@scp-consealtech.co.uk
Selcrete Of Whitby, Selly Cottage, Guisborough Road, Whitby, North Yorkshire, YO21 1SE Tel: (01947) 603178 Fax: (01947) 821590
Spiroll Precast Services Ltd, 2 Kingsway Industrial Park, Kingsway Park Close, Derby, DE22 3FP Tel: (01332) 365131 Fax: (01332) 291736 E-mail: enquiries@spiroll.co.uk

PRECAST CONCRETE PRODUCTS

Abergwili Concrete Products Ltd, Abergwili, Carmarthen, Dyfed, SA32 7EP Tel: (01267) 236461 Fax: (01267) 237792
Allen Concrete Ltd, 35-37 Rixon Road, Wellingborough, Northamptonshire, NN8 4BA Tel: (01933) 276848 Fax: (01933) 442013 E-mail: info@allenconcrete.co.uk
Anderton Concrete Products Ltd, Anderton Wharf, Soot Hill, Anderton, Northwich, Cheshire, CW9 6AA Tel: (01606) 79436 Fax: (01606) 871590 E-mail: sales@andertonconcrete.co.uk
Thomas Armstrong Construction Ltd, Workington Road, Flimby, Maryport, Cumbria, CA15 8RY Tel: (01900) 68211 Fax: (01900) 602672
B S Eaton Ltd, Coppice Lane, Cheslyn Hay, Walsall, WS6 7EY Tel: (01922) 413678 Fax: (01922) 416515 E-mail: enquiries@bseaton.co.uk
Barr Holdings Ltd, 100 Inchinnan Road, Paisley, Renfrewshire, PA3 2RE Tel: 0141-848 8000 Fax: 0141-848 8001 E-mail: info@barr.co.uk
Bespoke Concrete Products Ltd, Tynedale Works, Princess Way, Prudhoe, Northumberland, NE42 6PL Tel: (01661) 839340 Fax: (01661) 833923 E-mail: info@bespokeconcrete.co.uk
Bison Concrete Products Ltd, Millennium Court, First Avenue, Centrum One Hundred, Burton-On-Trent, Staffordshire, DE14 2WR Tel: (01283) 495000 Fax: (01283) 544900 E-mail: concrete@bison.co.uk
British Estate Services Ltd, 132 Bath Road, Reading, RG30 2EU Tel: 0118-957 2263 Fax: 0118-951 2267
Carter Concrete Ltd, Britons Lane, Beeston Regis, Sheringham, Norfolk, NR26 8TP Tel: (01263) 823434 Fax: (01263) 825678 E-mail: mail@carter-concrete.co.uk
Castle Concrete Ltd, Castle Meadow Road, Nottingham, NG2 1AG Tel: 0115-941 1162 Fax: 0115-948 3362 E-mail: sales@castleconcrete.co.uk
Cemex UK Ltd, St Helens Industrial Estate, Bishop Auckland, County Durham, DL14 9AJ Tel: (01388) 603961 Fax: (01388) 450056 E-mail: john.metcalfe@cemex.co.uk
Charcon Tunnels, Southwell Lane, Kirkby In Ashfield, Nottingham, NG17 8GQ Tel: (01623) 754493 Fax: (01623) 759825 E-mail: sales@tarmacprecast.co.uk
Collier & Henry Concrete Floors Ltd, Unit 2 Mellors Road, Trafford Park, Manchester, M17 1PB Tel: 0161-872 8410 Fax: 0161-872 9875
D D Concrete Ltd, Blaenant Industrial Estate, Brynmawr, Ebbw Vale, Gwent, NP23 4AZ Tel: (01495) 311253 Fax: (01495) 311253
D & H Concrete Products, Fernbank Avenue, Barnoldswick, Lancashire, BB18 5UX Tel: (01282) 812299 Fax: (01282) 812659 E-mail: info@dhconcrete.co.uk
Denby Dale Cast Products Ltd, 230 Cumberworth Lane, Lower Cumberworth, Huddersfield, HD8 8PR Tel: (01484) 863560 Fax: (01484) 865597

PRECAST CONCRETE PRODUCTS – *continued*

Derwent Cast Stone Co. Ltd, Eden Works, Old Malton, Malton, North Yorkshire, YO17 6SD Tel: (01653) 692860 Fax: (01653) 600129 E-mail: dcs@cast-stone.co.uk

Dick Freecast Inverness, Dores Road, Inverness, IV2 4RP Tel: (01463) 237556 Fax: (01463) 222871

Dick Precast Ltd, Taymouth Engineering Works, Anderson Street, Carnoustie, Angus, DD7 7LZ Tel: (01241) 858687 Fax: (01241) 858535

Ebor Concretes Ltd, Ripon, North Yorkshire, HG4 1JE Tel: (01765) 604351 Fax: (01765) 690065 E-mail: sales@eborconcrete.co.uk

Fair City Precast Ltd, Ladeside, St. Catherines Road, Perth, PH1 5RY Tel: (01738) 629501 Fax: (01738) 629501

John Fausset Ltd, 56 Rosslyn Avenue, Preesall, Poulton-le-Fylde, Lancashire, FY6 0HE Tel: (01253) 810358 Fax: (01253) 810358

Fram Concrete Products Ltd, Gilfach Road, Tonyrefail, Porth, Mid Glamorgan, CF39 8YN Tel: (01443) 674624 Fax: (01443) 672433

Glandel Ltd, Wareham Road, Corfe Mullen, Wimborne, Dorset, BH21 3RX Tel: (01202) 697282 Fax: (01202) 692364 E-mail: info@glandel.co.uk

Groutage & Ingram Ltd, Jack O Watton Industrial Estate, Lichfield Road, Water Orton, Birmingham, B46 1NU Tel: 0121-749 1414 Fax: 0121-749 5333 E-mail: sales@grangewoodfencing.com

Gryphonn Concrete Products, Old Mill Works, Lower Gelligroes, Pontllanfraith, Blackwood, Gwent, NP12 2HY Tel: (01495) 232050 Fax: (01495) 222553

Halls Group Ltd, Riverside Road, Gorleston, Great Yarmouth, Norfolk, NR31 6PX Tel: (01493) 663144 Fax: (01493) 440225 E-mail: info@hallsgroup.uk.com

J.R.H. Harvey & Co., 45 Clogher Rd, Hillsborough, Co. Down, BT26 6PJ Tel: (028) 9268 2668 Fax: (028) 9268 2668

J Charles & Son Ltd, Whitbygate, Thornton Dale, Pickering, North Yorkshire, YO18 7RY Tel: (01751) 474303

Jordan Concrete Ltd, 10 Sheepwalk Road, Lisburn, County Antrim, BT28 3RD Tel: (028) 9264 8648 Fax: (028) 9264 8775 E-mail: sales@jordanconcrete.co.uk

Kelcamp Ltd, St. Albans Road Industrial Estate, Stafford, ST16 3DR Tel: (01785) 259415 Fax: (01785) 258022

Ladds Concrete Products, Wilson Way, Pool, Redruth, Cornwall, TR15 3RY Tel: (01209) 213132 Fax: (01209) 314441 E-mail: sales@laddsconcrete.co.uk

Leiths Scotland Ltd, Broomfield Industrial Estate, Broomfield Road, Montrose, Angus, DD10 8SY Tel: (01674) 677037 Fax: (01674) 672809

Malling Products Ltd, Fiddlers Reach, Wouldham Road, Grays, Essex, RM20 4YB Tel: (01375) 486300 Fax: (01375) 372642 E-mail: malling@laingrourke.com

Marshalls Mono Ltd, Landscape House, Premiere Way, Housefield Business Park, Elland, West Yorkshire, HX5 9HT Tel: (01422) 306400 Fax: (01422) 312999

Mexboro Concrete Ltd, Yalberton Tor Industrial Estate, Alders Way, Paignton, Devon, TQ4 7QQ Tel: (01803) 558025 Fax: (01803) 524717 E-mail: adc@mexboroconcrete.com

Millstone Studios Ltd, Works Road, Hollingwood, Chesterfield, Derbyshire, S43 2PE Tel: (01246) 477516 Fax: (01246) 281666 E-mail: millstone@lineone.net

Neaves Paving, School Lane, Smallburgh, Norwich, NR12 9NG Tel: (01692) 536378

▶ Orkney Aggregates Ltd, Garrison Road, Hatston Industrial Estate, Kirkwall, Orkney, KW15 1RE Tel: (01856) 871187 Fax: (01856) 871188 E-mail: sales@orkagg.co.uk

Plean Precast Ltd, President Kennedy Drive, Plean, Stirling, FK7 8AX Tel: (01786) 812221 Fax: (01786) 815369 E-mail: mail@plean-precast.co.uk

R Page Concrete Buildings Ltd, 951-953 High Road, Romford, RM6 4HB Tel: (020) 8590 3701 Fax: (020) 8590 1791

Rhead, Meir Road, Stoke-on-Trent, ST3 7JD Tel: (01782) 599770 Fax: (01782) 599771 E-mail: peter.stephenson@normanrhead.co.uk

Stanton Bonna Concrete Ltd, Littlewell Lane, Stanton-by-Dale, Ilkeston, Derbyshire, DE7 4QW Tel: 0115-944 1448 Fax: 0115-944 1466 E-mail: sbc@stanton-bonna.co.uk

Sterling Precast Ltd, Springkerse Works, Springkerse Industrial Estate, Stirling, FK7 7SX Tel: (01786) 472191 Fax: (01786) 451284 E-mail: general@stirlingprecast.com

▶ Stirling Precast Ltd, Whitehouse Road, Stirling, FK7 7SX Tel: (01786) 472191 Fax: (01786) 451284 E-mail: general@sterlingprecast.com

Stone Products Ltd, Nab Works, Long Lane, Pott Shrigley, Macclesfield, Cheshire, SK10 5SD Tel: (01625) 560757 Fax: (01625) 576494

W H Palmer & Sons, Archers Fields, Burnt Mills Industrial Estate, Basildon, Essex, SS13 1DH Tel: (01268) 520078 Fax: (01268) 521673

Wain Bros Ltd, 774 Leek Road, Stoke-on-Trent, ST1 6AE Tel: (01782) 202180 Fax: (01782) 213127

Western Blocks Ltd, 42 Upton Towans, Hayle, Cornwall, TR27 5BL Tel: (01736) 753128 Fax: (01736) 756857

Whites Concrete Ltd, Ravensthorpe Road, Thornhill Lees, Dewsbury, West Yorkshire, WF12 9EF Tel: (01924) 464283 Fax: (01924) 459183 E-mail: whites@longley.uk.com

William Rainford, Leckwith Road, Bootle, Merseyside, L30 6YF Tel: 0151-525 5991 Fax: 0151-530 1676

Woodside Precast Concrete Ltd, Dawes Lane, Scunthorpe, South Humberside, DN15 6UW Tel: (01724) 281872 Fax: (01724) 280866 E-mail: info@caststone.co.uk

PRECAST CONCRETE SECTIONS

Stoneleigh Concrete Products Ltd, 26 Dalston Close, Camberley, Surrey, GU15 1BT Tel: (01276) 21053 Fax: (01276) 517332

PRECAST CONCRETE STRUCTURES

Stoner Benton Concrete Ltd, Tilley Lane, Boreham Street, Hailsham, East Sussex, BN27 4UU Tel: (01323) 832334 Fax: (01323) 873791 E-mail: info@stonerbenton.co.uk

PRECAST FOUNDATION CONTRACTORS

▶ Berry Bank Bank Farm, Windmill Lane, Hundall, Apperknowle, Dronfield, Derbyshire, S18 4BQ Tel: (01246) 415986 E-mail: mark@berrybankfarm.co.uk

▶ Waycon Precast Ltd, Western Wood Way, Plympton, Plymouth, PL7 5BQ Tel: (01752) 335777 Fax: (01752) 336777

PRECIOUS METAL CASTINGS

Niagara Falls Castings UK Ltd, Budbrooke Road, Warwick, CV34 5XH Tel: (01926) 496258 Fax: (01926) 496250 E-mail: sales@nf-castings.co.uk

PRECIOUS METAL DEALERS

Creative Beadcraft Ltd, 20 Beak Street, London, W1F 9RE Tel: (01494) 778818 Fax: (01494) 718510 E-mail: sales@cb.co.uk

Heraeus Silica & Metals Ltd, Cinderhill Industrial Estate, Stoke-on-Trent, ST3 5LB Tel: (01782) 599423 Fax: (01782) 599802 E-mail: enquiries@4cmd.com

Johnson Matthey plc, Orchard Road, Royston, Hertfordshire, SG8 5HE Tel: (01763) 253000 Fax: (01763) 253492 E-mail: nobleuk@matthey.com

Stephen Betts, 49-63 Spencer Street, Birmingham, B18 6DE Tel: 0121-233 9856 Fax: 0121-236 2265 E-mail: admin@bettsmetals.co.uk

PRECIOUS METAL ELECTRICAL CONTACTS

Ekaton Ltd, Jubilee House, Altcar Road, Formby, Liverpool, L37 8DL Tel: (01704) 870107 Fax: (01704) 831269 E-mail: colinmackay@ekaton.ltd.uk

PRECIOUS METAL ELECTROPLATING

Croydon Electroplaters Ltd, 2 Bridge Parade, Waddon Road, Croydon, CR0 4JH Tel: (020) 8688 4709

East Lancashire Platers Ltd, Oxford Mill, Oxford Road, Burnley, Lancashire, BB11 3BA Tel: (01282) 425621 Fax: (01282) 433618

PRECIOUS METAL RECOVERY, *See also headings for particular types*

O B Metals Co. Ltd, Watery Lane Industrial Estate, Watery Lane, Willenhall, West Midlands, WV13 3SU Tel: (01902) 608691 Fax: (01902) 603312

Phoenix County Metal Ltd, Great Central Way Industrial Estate, Great Central Way, Woodford Halse, Daventry, Northamptonshire, NN11 3PZ Tel: (01327) 260581 Fax: (01327) 260191

Presman Bullion Ltd, 56 Hatton Garden, London, EC1N 8HP Tel: (020) 7404 0903 Fax: (020) 7405 8053

PRECIOUS METAL RECOVERY EQUIPMENT

B E W T Environmental Services Ltd, Warwick, CV35 8PY Tel: (01926) 843233 Fax: (01926) 843233

PRECIOUS METALS, *See also headings for particular types*

A W A Refiners Ltd, 10 Mead Industrial Park, Riverway, Harlow, Essex, CM20 2SE Tel: (01279) 423743 Fax: (01279) 422243 E-mail: sales@awarefiners.com

Birmingham Metal Co. Ltd, Garrison Street, Bordesley, Birmingham, B9 4BN Tel: 0121-766 6022 Fax: 0121-766 7485

▶ Computer Salvage Specialist Ltd, 5 Abex Road, Newbury, Berkshire, RG14 5EY Tel: (01635) 552666 Fax: (01635) 582990 E-mail: enquiries@computersalvagespecialists.com

Cookson Precious Metals Ltd, 49-50 Hatton Garden, Theba House, London, EC1N 8YS Tel: (020) 7400 6500 Fax: (020) 7400 6511 E-mail: sales@cooksongold.com

Johnson Matthey Plc, 40-42 Hatton Garden, London, EC1N 8EE Tel: (020) 7269 8400 Fax: (020) 7269 8433 E-mail: jmpr@matthey.com

Marple Laboratories Birmingham Ltd, 19 Northampton Street, Birmingham, B18 6DU Tel: 0121-233 1504 Fax: 0121-236 3287 E-mail: info@marplelabs.co.uk

Mayhan & Co. Ltd, 24 Tenby Street, Birmingham, B1 3EE Tel: 0121-236 3284 Fax: 0121-236 1981 E-mail: andrew.mayor@btclick.com

Metalor Technologies (UK) Ltd, 74 Warstone Lane, Birmingham, B18 6NG Tel: 0121-236 3241 Fax: 0121-236 3568 E-mail: electrotechnics@metalor.com

Niagara Falls Castings UK Ltd, Budbrooke Road, Warwick, CV34 5XH Tel: (01926) 496258 Fax: (01926) 496250 E-mail: sales@nf-castings.co.uk

Phoenix County Metal Ltd, Great Central Way Industrial Estate, Great Central Way, Woodford Halse, Daventry, Northamptonshire, NN11 3PZ Tel: (01327) 260581 Fax: (01327) 260191

Stephen Betts, 49-63 Spencer Street, Birmingham, B18 6DE Tel: 0121-233 9856 Fax: 0121-236 2265 E-mail: admin@bettsmetals.co.uk

PRECISION ABRASIVE CUTTING SYSTEMS

Birkett Cutmaster Ltd, PO Box 30, Cleckheaton, West Yorkshire, BD19 5LY Tel: (01274) 870311 Fax: (01274) 862754 E-mail: bryn.pritchard@birkett-cutmaster.co.uk

Midland Machine Knives Ltd, Unit 17 Baltic Works, Effingham Road, Sheffield, S9 3QA Tel: 0114-244 8952 Fax: 0114-243 2437

PRECISION BALANCES

A & D Instruments Ltd, 24-26 Blacklands Way, Abingdon, Oxfordshire, OX14 1DY Tel: (01235) 550420 Fax: (01235) 550485 E-mail: sales@aandd-eu.net

Electronic Weighing Services Ltd, Lytton Street, Stoke-On-Trent, ST4 2AG Tel: (01782) 416322 Fax: (01782) 413660 E-mail: sales@electronicweighing.co.uk

Ohaus UK Ltd, 64 Boston Road, Leicester, LE4 1AW Tel: 0116-234 5075 Fax: 0116-235 9256

PRECISION BALL SLIDES

Accuride International Ltd, Liliput Road, Brackmills Industrial Estate, Northampton, NN4 7AS Tel: (01604) 761111 Fax: (01604) 767190 E-mail: saleseurope@accuride-europe.com

Complete It, 3 The Courtyard, Furlong Road, Bourne End, Buckinghamshire, SL8 5AU Tel: (01628) 552850 Fax: (01628) 552851 E-mail: sales@complete-it.co.uk

PRECISION BEARINGS

J & M Belts Veebelts Bearings Oilseals, 72 Bridge Road, Grays, Essex, RM17 6BZ Tel: (01375) 373975 Fax: (01375) 391541 E-mail: sales@jmbelts.com

PRECISION BRAZING

Bodycote Heat Treatment Ltd, 11 Bamfurlong Industrial Park, Staverton, Cheltenham, Gloucestershire, GL51 6SX Tel: (01452) 714440 Fax: (01452) 856097 E-mail: sales@bodycote.co.uk

Bodycote Heat Treatment Ltd, Macclesfield Road, Hazel Grove, Stockport, Cheshire, SK7 5EN Tel: 0161-483 0511 Fax: 0161-483 5450 E-mail: sales@bodycote.co.uk

Bodycote Heat Treatments Ltd, Springwood Court, Springwood Close, Tytherington Business Park, Macclesfield, Cheshire, SK10 2XF Tel: (01625) 505300 Fax: (01625) 505320 E-mail: info@bodycote.co.uk

Bodycote Heating Treatment Ltd, 18 Westgate, Skelmersdale, Lancashire, WN8 8AZ Tel: (01695) 716500 Fax: (01695) 50105 E-mail: sales@bodycote.co.uk

Datasharp 2000, Hoggington Lane, Southwick, Trowbridge, Wiltshire, BA14 9NR Tel: (01225) 756910 Fax: (01225) 756911 E-mail: sales@datasharp2000.co.uk

Lush Heat Treatment Ltd, 128 Great North Road, Hatfield, Hertfordshire, AL9 5JN Tel: (01707) 264104 Fax: (01707) 274850

Quantum Heat Treatment & Brazing Ltd, 43 Barton Road, Bletchley, Milton Keynes, MK2 3DE Tel: (01908) 642242 Fax: (01908) 368629 E-mail: quantumheat@hotmail.com

SPJ Enterprises Ltd, Unit 14-15 Oakleigh Trading Estate, Anchor Road, Bilston, West Midlands, WV14 9NA Tel: (01902) 491818 Fax: (01902) 491818

PRECISION CASTINGS

Caress Precision Products Ltd, Alington Road, Little Barford, St. Neots, Cambridgeshire, PE19 6YH Tel: (01480) 472262 Fax: (01480) 217235 E-mail: caressprescision@btconnect.com

Ceramicast Precision Investment Castings Ltd, Castings House, Boundary Road, Woking, Surrey, GU21 5BX Tel: (01483) 751666 Fax: (01483) 751888 E-mail: sales@ceramicast.com

Cronite Precision Castings Ltd, Blacknell Lane, Crewkerne, Somerset, TA18 7YA Tel: (01460) 270300 Fax: (01460) 72643 E-mail: cpc@cronite.co.uk

Kenwell Precision Die Casting Ltd, 1 Smallbridge Industrial Park, Riverside Drive, Rochdale, Lancashire, OL16 2SH Tel: (01706) 640412 Fax: (01706) 711894 E-mail: sales@kenwellprecisiondiecastings.co.uk

Maybrey Reliance, Worsley Bridge Road, Lower Sydenham, London, SE26 5BE Tel: (01322) 315370 Fax: (01322) 550724 E-mail: sales@maybrey.co.uk

Maycast Nokes Precision Engineering Ltd, Factory La West, Halstead, Essex, CO9 1EX Tel: (01787) 472500 Fax: (01787) 474264 E-mail: enquiries@maycast.co.uk

Medical Technology Ltd, Parkway Close, Parkway Industrial Estate, Sheffield, S9 4WH Tel: 0114-273 8764 Fax: 0114-273 8764

▶ Micro Metalsmiths Ltd, Kirkdale Road, Kirkbymoorside, York, YO62 6PX Tel: 0845 2139030 Fax: (01751) 432061 E-mail: info@micrometalsmiths.co.uk

Terrill Bros (Founders) Ltd, 2 Guildford Road Industrial Estate, Hayle, Cornwall, TR27 4QZ Tel: (01736) 752168 Fax: (01736) 756215 E-mail: sales@terrill-bros.co.uk

V T L Automotors Ltd, Ellen Holme, Luddendenfoot, Halifax, West Yorkshire, HX2 6EL Tel: (01422) 882561 Fax: (01422) 883323

PRECISION COLD FORGINGS

Holzer Ltd, Neachells Lane, Wednesfield, Wolverhampton, WV11 3QG Tel: (01902) 866355 Fax: (01902) 734073 E-mail: admin2@holzerltd-metalldyne.fsnet.co.uk

Howard S Cooke & Co Holdings Ltd, Arrow Road, Redditch, Worcestershire, B98 8PA Tel: (01527) 63231 Fax: (01527) 66770 E-mail: sales@protex.com

Mohling UK Ltd, Dudley Road, Halesowen, West Midlands, B63 3NR Tel: 0121-585 7222 Fax: 0121-501 6817 E-mail: info@mohling.co.uk

PRECISION COMPONENTS

Adaero Precision Components Ltd, Unit 6 Down End, Lords Meadow Industrial Estate, Crediton, Devon, EX17 1HN Tel: (01363) 778660 Fax: (01363) 773977 E-mail: enquiries@adaero.co.uk

Groveley Engineering Ltd, Anchor Works, Groveley Road, Christchurch, Dorset, BH23 3HB Tel: (01202) 483497 Fax: (01202) 486658 E-mail: sales@groveley.co.uk

▶ H K V Engineering, 16 Crawford House, West Avenue, Wigston, Leicestershire, LE18 2FB Tel: 0116-288 7751 Fax: 0116-288 7751 E-mail: carolrobinson@aol.com

PRECISION COMPONENTS TO SPECIFICATION

C M L Group Ltd, Price Street, Birkenhead, Merseyside, CH41 3PT Tel: 0151-647 5531 Fax: 0151-650 0668 E-mail: enquiries@cml-group.com

C M Precision, 3 Brannish Road, Downpatrick, County Down, BT30 6LL Tel: (028) 4461 9920 Fax: (028) 4461 4733 E-mail: dpk@cmprecision.co.uk

D W Precision Engineers, Studio 8 Building 56 Magnet Road, East Lane, Wembley, Middlesex, HA9 7RG Tel: (020) 8904 4038 Fax: (020) 8984 8802 E-mail: sales@dwprecision.freeserve.co.uk

Ipeco Europe, Aviation Way, Southend-on-Sea, SS2 6UN Tel: (01702) 549371 Fax: (01702) 540782 E-mail: sales@ipeco.co.uk

PRECISION COMPONENTS TO SPECIFICATION – *continued*

J S Cantrill Designs & Manufacturing Holdings Ltd, Chosen View Road, Cheltenham, Gloucestershire, GL51 9LT Tel: (01242) 515794 Fax: (01242) 579265 E-mail: sales@cantrillmanufacturing.com

Nofotec Co. Ltd, 72-74 Westdale Lane, Carlton, Nottingham, NG4 3NF Tel: 0115-987 6696 Fax: 0115-940 0070 E-mail: info@nofotec.co.uk

D. Smith Engineering, 90 Nuffield Road, Poole, Dorset, BH17 7SX Tel: (01202) 687123 Fax: (01202) 685042

Chris Taylor Production Engineering, 35 James Carter Road, Mildenhall, Bury St. Edmunds, Suffolk, IP28 7DE Tel: (01638) 510589 Fax: (01638) 515086

PRECISION CUTTING SERVICES

Keenedge Ltd, Unit 7 Summerlands Industrial Estate, Endmoor, Kendal, Cumbria, LA8 0FB Tel: (01539) 561800 Fax: (01539) 561799 E-mail: info@cutting.co.uk

PRECISION DRILLING SERVICES

G & R Pollard Engineering Ltd, Alexandra Way, Ashchurch, Tewkesbury, Gloucestershire, GL20 8NB Tel: (01684) 274847 Fax: (01684) 851960 E-mail: grpoll@globalnet.co.uk

Partridge Microdrilling Services, Priestley Way, Crawley, West Sussex, RH10 9NT Tel: (01293) 526525 Fax: (01293) 526525 E-mail: partridrill@aol.com

PRECISION ENGINEERED FABRICATIONS TO SPECIFICATION

Broughton Mechanical & Civil Engineering Ltd, Ditton Road, Widnes, Cheshire, WA8 0TH Tel: 0151-423 5273 Fax: 0151-495 1390 E-mail: enquiries@jep-engineering.co.uk

C J Welding, Hall Court Farm Cottage, Ripe, Lewes, East Sussex, BN8 6AY Tel: (01323) 811448 Fax: (01323) 811350 E-mail: cj.welding@virgin.net

Eurotech Precision Engineering Ltd, 4-5 Bergen Way, North Lynn Industrial Estate, King's Lynn, Norfolk, PE30 2JG Tel: (01553) 770426 Fax: (01553) 774726 E-mail: epelltd@kingslynn20.fsnet.co.uk

Fife Engineering Co. Ltd, Longrigg, Swalwell, Newcastle upon Tyne, NE16 3AW Tel: 0191-496 1133 Fax: 0191-496 5502 E-mail: admin@fife-engineering.com

Herts & Essex Precision Engineers, Unit 10 Zone B Chelmsford Road Industrial Estate, Chelmsford Road, Dunmow, Essex, CM6 1HD Tel: (01371) 875459 Fax: (01371) 872270 E-mail: hertsessex@aol.com

J E B Engineering Design Ltd, Chiswick Avenue, Mildenhall, Bury St. Edmunds, Suffolk, IP28 7AY Tel: (01638) 718435 Fax: (01638) 717962 E-mail: info@jebeng.com

Micron Engineering Co., Dominion Works, Freshwater Road, Dagenham, Essex, RM8 1RX Tel: (020) 8983 8800 Fax: (020) 8983 8866 E-mail: micronengineering@unit5.freeserve.co.uk

Rodwell Powell Ltd, Chester Hall Lane, Basildon, Essex, SS14 3DQ Tel: (01268) 286641 Fax: (01268) 286644 E-mail: info@rodwell-powell.com

PRECISION ENGINEERED PARTS, *See also headings for particular materials or industry*

Cherox Precision Engineering Co., Unit 1A, Pope Iron Road, Barbourne, Worcester, WR1 3HB Tel: (01905) 21425 Fax: (01905) 25921 E-mail: john@cherox.connectfree.co.uk

Delta Precision Engineering Ltd, 87-89 Sterte Avenue West, Poole, Dorset, BH15 2AW Tel: (01202) 661166 Fax: (01202) 661166 E-mail: sales@deltaprecision.freeserve.co.uk

Rodwell Powell Ltd, Chester Hall Lane, Basildon, Essex, SS14 3DQ Tel: (01268) 286641 Fax: (01268) 286644 E-mail: info@rodwell-powell.com

PRECISION ENGINEERING DESIGN

▶ Armstrong omponents Limited, 57 Groveside, East Rudham, King's Lynn, Norfolk, PE31 8RL Tel: (01485) 529082 Fax: (01485) 529294 E-mail: dave@armstrongsales.f9.co.uk

▶ C G C Technology Ltd, E Grovebell Industrial Estate, Wrecclesham Road, Wrecclesham, Farnham, Surrey, GU10 4PL Tel: (01252) 724274 Fax: (01252) 722624 E-mail: enquiries@cgctech.com

▶ Woodfield Engineering Services Ltd, Unit 2, Woodfield House, Gravel Lane, Banks, Southport, Merseyside, PR9 8BY Tel: (01704) 220729 Fax: (01704) 220515 E-mail: woodfieldservice@btconnect.com

PRECISION ENGINEERS

A B J Precision Engineering, Unit 22 Central City Industrial Estate, Red Lane, Coventry, CV6 5RY Tel: (024) 7658 1877 Fax: (024) 7658 1717

A B M Precisions Nuneaton Ltd, Ansley Common, Nuneaton, Warwickshire, CV10 0QN Tel: (024) 7639 2866 Fax: (024) 7639 7283 E-mail: enquiries@abmprecisions.co.uk

A C D Engineering Ltd, Unit 17 Central City Industrial Estate, Red Lane, Coventry, CV6 5RY Tel: (024) 7666 7555 Fax: (024) 7666 8282

A C W Engineering Services Ltd, The Sanderson Centre, Lees Lane, Gosport, Hampshire, PO12 3UL Tel: (023) 9250 2854 Fax: (023) 9250 2854 E-mail: acwesl@tinyonline.co.uk

A D S Precision Engineering, 53a Jubilee Road, Waterlooville, Hampshire, PO7 7RE Tel: (023) 9226 7643 Fax: (023) 9226 7743 E-mail: admin@adsprecision.co.uk

A D X Precision Engineering, The Sanderson Centre, Lees Lane, Gosport, Hampshire, PO12 3UL Tel: (023) 9252 0027 Fax: (023) 9252 0027 E-mail: dave@adxprecision.freeserve.co.uk

A E M Products Ltd, Unit 141 Leyland Estate, Irthlingborough Road, Wellingborough, Northamptonshire, NN8 1RA Tel: (01933) 442861 Fax: (01933) 225527 E-mail: enquiry@aem-products.co.uk

A F S Engineering Co., 41 Great Lister Street, Birmingham, B7 4LW Tel: 0121-359 5048 Fax: 0121-359 4562

A & G Precision Engineers Ltd, 1 Hythe Works, Diplocks Way, Hailsham, East Sussex, BN27 3JF Tel: (01323) 847718 Fax: (01323) 440138

A H Engineering North East Ltd, Unit 5 Wagonway Road Industrial Estate, Hebburn, Tyne & Wear, NE31 1SP Tel: 0191-483 9807 Fax: 0191-483 8700 E-mail: aheng@lineone.net

A I R Engineering, 4 Tyn Y Bonau Road, Pontarddulais, Swansea, SA4 8SG Tel: (01792) 881112 Fax: (01792) 881113 E-mail: aireng@freenet.com

A J Adams Engineering, Hassall Road, Skegness, Lincolnshire, PE25 3TB Tel: (01754) 765421 Fax: (01754) 765435 E-mail: dave@adamsengineering.ffsnet.co.uk

A J Fabrications, 28A Somerset Street, Northampton, NN1 3LW Tel: (01604) 628070 Fax: (01604) 627929

A J M Engineering Ltd, Park Lane, Park Lane Trading Estate, Corsham, Wiltshire, SN13 9LG Tel: (01249) 712620 Fax: (01249) 714932 E-mail: sales@ajmay.co.uk

A & J Precision Engineering, 3 Fenland Business Centre, Longhill Road, March, Cambridgeshire, PE15 0BL Tel: (01354) 652203 Fax: (01354) 652203 E-mail: anjprecision@tiscali.co.uk

A J Williams & Son Ltd, Wisloe Road, Cambridge, Gloucester, GL2 7AF Tel: (01453) 899099 Fax: (01453) 890642 E-mail: ajwilliamsltd@aol.com

A Kidman Engineering, Atlas Mill Road, Brighouse, West Yorkshire, HD6 1ES Tel: (01484) 720520 Fax: (01484) 401051

A M S Engineering, Units C & D Stratton Park, Biggleswade, Bedfordshire, SG18 8QS Tel: (01767) 600888 Fax: (01767) 600668

A & N Engineering, 2 Emsworth Road, Southampton, SO15 3LX Tel: (023) 8031 5193 Fax: (023) 8070 4033

A N Tools Ltd, Carlyon Road, Atherstone, Warwickshire, CV9 1LQ Tel: (01827) 716878 Fax: (01827) 717859 E-mail: ant@antools.co.uk

A One, Unit 3 Central Park Estate, Staines Road, Hounslow, TW4 5DJ Tel: (020) 8607 4412 Fax: (020) 8607 4413 E-mail: aoneprec@aol.com

▶ A P Precision Engineering, Hopton Industrial Estate, Devizes, Wiltshire, SN10 2EU Tel: (01380) 725710 Fax: (01380) 720565 E-mail: alan-pocock@btconnect.com

A R Craig Engineering Ltd, 6 Vale Lane, Bristol, BS3 5RU Tel: 0117-966 7735 Fax: 0117-966 0604

A T C, Holmethorpe Avenue, Redhill, RH1 2NG Tel: (01737) 765686 Fax: (01737) 764048 E-mail: sales@atcltd.co.uk

A V Engineering Services Ltd, Saxon Way, Melbourn, Royston, Hertfordshire, SG8 6DN Tel: (01763) 261818 Fax: (01763) 262622 E-mail: sales@aveng.co.uk

A & W Precision Tools Ltd, Unit 2 Brookside Industrial Pk, Crankhall La, Wednesbury, W. Midlands, WS10 0QZ Tel: 0121-505 1359 Fax: 0121-505 1359

A1 Turning, 7 Holbrook Lane, Coventry, CV6 4AD Tel: (024) 7668 6333 Fax: (024) 7668 6222 E-mail: salesa1turning@btconnect.com

Aaron Manufacturing Ltd, Unit K-L Waterside, 25-27 Willis Way, Poole, Dorset, BH15 3TD Tel: (01202) 670071 Fax: (01202) 682952 E-mail: enquiries@aaronmanufacturing.co.uk

Abbey Precision Ltd, 72 Alston Drive, Bradwell Abbey, Milton Keynes, MK13 9HG Tel: (01908) 225858 Fax: (01908) 225848 E-mail: sales@abbeyprecision.com

Abtech Precision Ltd, 95 Alston Drive, Bradwell Abbey, Milton Keynes, MK13 9HF Tel: (01908) 318218 Fax: (01908) 318308 E-mail: enquiries@abtech-precision.co.uk

Accurus Ltd, Giles Road, Oldbury, West Midlands, B68 8JG Tel: 0121-544 5335 Fax: 0121-544 5339 E-mail: admin@accurus.co.uk

Ace Precision Engineers, 5 Tait Road, Croydon, CR0 2DT Tel: (020) 8683 0487 Fax: (020) 8684 4583E-mail: l.povada-ace@fsbdial.co.uk

Acsl Precision Engineering, 3 Cartwright Road, Stevenage, Hertfordshire, SG1 4QJ Tel: (01438) 359123 Fax: (01438) 741819 E-mail: acsl@btinternet.com

Adams Engineering, Unit 3c Innsworth Technology Park, Innsworth Lane, Gloucester, GL3 1DL Tel: (01452) 730385 Fax: (01452) 736146

Adnet Precision Engineering Ltd, Nexus Court Unit B1 Gloucester Business Park, Hurricane Road, Brockworth, Gloucester, GL3 4AQ Tel: (01452) 611826 Fax: (01452) 623929 E-mail: info.adnetprecision@virgin.net

Adroit, 1 Townsend Centre Blackburn Road, Townsend Industrial Estate, Houghton Regis, Dunstable, Bedfordshire, LU5 5BQ Tel: (01582) 672141 Fax: (01582) 672140 E-mail: mick.haron@btconnect.com

Advanced Metal Engineering Ltd, 200 Rickmansworth Road, Watford, WD18 7JS Tel: (01923) 211133 Fax: (01923) 241124 E-mail: ameltd@btconnect.com

Aegis Precision Engineering, Bolney Grange Indust Estate, Stairbridge Lane, Bolney, Haywards Heath, West Sussex, RH17 5PA Tel: (01444) 244720 Fax: (01444) 248327 E-mail: info@aegis-rubber-eng.co.uk

▶ Aercomp Precision, 27 Factory Road, Poole, Dorset, BH16 5SL Tel: (01202) 620053 Fax: (01202) 620054

Aeron Automation Ltd, 44-48 Wilson Place, East Kilbride, Glasgow, G74 4QD Tel: (01355) 226022 Fax: (01355) 235077 E-mail: alan@aeron.co.uk

Aerotech Precision Manufacturing Ltd, 1 Stone Lane, Wimborne, Dorset, BH21 1HB Tel: (01202) 848484 Fax: (01202) 848989 E-mail: sales@aero-tech.co.uk

Agra (Precision Engineering) Co. Ltd, 15 Ure Street, Dundee, DD1 5JD Tel: (01382) 229333 Fax: (01382) 226918 E-mail: info@agra-eng.co.uk

▶ Aims Engineering, Unit H, Ditchling Common Industrial Estate, Ditchling, Hassocks, West Sussex, BN6 8SG Tel: (01444) 870221 Fax: (01444) 244860 E-mail: mail@aimsengineering.co.uk

Ajax Minerva Ltd, Edderthorpe Street, Bradford, West Yorkshire, BD3 9JX Tel: (01274) 735910 Fax: (01274) 307706 E-mail: ajax_minerva@hotmail.com

Alan Gordon, George Street, Chorley, Lancashire, PR7 2BE Tel: (01257) 274723 Fax: (01257) 241342 E-mail: sales@alangordoneng.co.uk

Alcina Engineering, Wetherby Road, Ascot Drive, Derby, DE24 8HL Tel: (01332) 343435 Fax: (01332) 385722

Alfa Precision & General Engineering Co. Ltd, Solway Trading Estate, Maryport, Cumbria, CA15 8NF Tel: (01900) 815678 Fax: (01900) 814191 E-mail: alfaprecision@btclick.com

Algernon, Unit 1 Algarnon Industrial Estate, Shiremoor, Newcastle upon Tyne, NE27 0NB Tel: 0191-251 4600 Fax: 0191-297 0360 E-mail: algernoneng@aol.com

Aljon Engineering, Lancaster House, 234-236 Fields New Road, Chadderton, Oldham, OL9 8NZ Tel: 0161-628 7800 Fax: 0161-628 7072 E-mail: atjoneng@zen.co.uk

Allen Engineering, 34 Great Western Industrial Estate, Great Western Close, Birmingham, B18 4QF Tel: 0121-551 5487 Fax: 0121-551 5487

Alman Engineering Services Ltd, 12 Bradfield Close, Finedon Road Industrial Estate, Wellingborough, Northamptonshire, NN8 4RQ Tel: (01933) 275551 Fax: (01933) 275552 E-mail: sales@alman.co.uk

Almik Engineering, Unit 22 Pershore Trading Estate, Pershore, Worcestershire, WR10 2DD Tel: (01386) 553550 Fax: (01386) 556048 E-mail: steve.almik@btconnect.com

Alno Products Services, 17 Brookside Business Centre Northway Lane, Tewkesbury, Gloucestershire, GL20 8JG Tel: (01684) 291050 Fax: (01684) 290887 E-mail: alno@btconnect.com

Alpine Precision Engineering, 27 Telford Road, Wimborne, Dorset, BH21 7RX Tel: (01202) 894478 Fax: (01202) 894441 E-mail: alan.codman@virgin.net

Alpunch Tooling Ltd, 24 Ganton Way, Techno Trading Estate, Swindon, SN2 8EZ Tel: (01793) 613185 Fax: (01793) 642628 E-mail: johntownsend@alpunch.co.uk

Alston Asset Management Services Ltd, Unit 27, 27 Roman Way Industrial Estate, Ribbleton, Preston, PR2 5BD Tel: (01772) 700590 Fax: (01772) 706510 E-mail: info@pre-applied.co.uk

Alton Precision Engineering Ltd, Unit 27a Chemical Lane, Stoke-on-Trent, ST6 4PB Tel: (01782) 813735 Fax: (01782) 813752 E-mail: altonpre@clara.co.uk

Amb Ltd, Brownell Street, Sheffield, S3 7GR Tel: 0114-272 0489 Fax: 0114-272 0489 E-mail: amb@btinternet.com

Amblecote Machine Services, 4 Junction Road, Audnam, Stourbridge, West Midlands, DY8 4YJ Tel: (01384) 374935 Fax: (01384) 373336

Amdale Ltd, 6-7 Culverin Square, Limberline Road, Hilsea, Portsmouth, PO3 5BU Tel: (023) 9266 0726 Fax: (023) 9265 5177 E-mail: sales@amdale.co.uk

Amek Precision Engineers, The Hollies, Campton Road, Meppershall, Shefford, Bedfordshire, SG17 5PB Tel: (01462) 851171 Fax: (01462) 851171

Anderside Tools Ltd, 25 Colvilles Place, Kelvin Industrial Estate, East Kilbride, Glasgow, G75 0PZ Tel: (01355) 245455 Fax: (01355) 230703 E-mail: greg@andersidetools.com

▶ Anderson Engineering, 1 Lochside Industrial Estate, Irongray Road, Dumfries, DG2 0JE Tel: (01387) 721700 Fax: (01387) 721701 E-mail: sales@andeng.uk

Andover Precision Ltd, Marriott Road, Dudley, West Midlands, DY2 0JZ Tel: (01384) 212655 Fax: (01384) 235863 E-mail: dave.andover@btconnect.com

Anglia Precision Engineering, 32 Stapledon Road, Orton Southgate, Peterborough, PE2 6TD Tel: (01733) 703230 Fax: (01733) 703231 E-mail: sales@angliaprecision.com

Anglo Precision Engineering Co. Ltd, Deans Yard, 15 South Road, Baldock, Hertfordshire, SG7 6BZ Tel: (01462) 491105 Fax: (01462) 491106 E-mail: sales@anglo-precision.co.uk

Anlyn Engineering, Taylor Street, Liverpool, L5 5AD Tel: 0151-207 5592 Fax: 0151-207 5594E-mail: anlynsales@agjengineering.co.uk

▶ Apg Precision Engineering & Fabrication, John Street, Warrington, WA2 7UB Tel: (01925) 418790 Fax: (01925) 243403 E-mail: sales@apgprecisionengineeringltd.co.uk

Apollo, 3 Merchant Drive, Mead Lane, Hertford, SG13 7BH Tel: (01992) 558375 Fax: (01992) 501318 E-mail: david@horneandbanks.co.uk

Apsley Engineering, High Post, Salisbury, SP4 6AT Tel: (01722) 782488 Fax: (01722) 782632 E-mail: info@apsleyeng.co.uk

Arba Engineering, 32g Heming Road, Redditch, Worcestershire, B98 0DH Tel: (01527) 520629 Fax: (01527) 520629 E-mail: arba32g@hotmail.com

Arden Precision Ltd, 5 Maidwell Drive, Shirley, Solihull, West Midlands, B90 4QN Tel: 0121-683 5200 Fax: 0121-683 5210

Ariel Machine Products Ltd, Yew Tree Lane, Caerleon, Newport, NP18 1LL Tel: (01633) 420405 Fax: (01633) 430072

Arnold Precision Engineering, 3 46 Holton Road, Holton Heath Trading Park, Poole, Dorset, BH16 6LT Tel: (01202) 621128 Fax: (01202) 621128

Arrow Precision Engineering Ltd, 12 Barley Field, Hinckley Fields Industrial Estate, Hinckley, Leicestershire, LE10 1YE Tel: (01455) 234200 Fax: (01455) 233545 E-mail: sales@arrowprecision.co.uk

Artisan Precision Engineering Co., Snatchwood Road, Abersychan, Pontypool, Gwent, NP4 7BT Tel: (01495) 772644 Fax: (01495) 773844 E-mail: artisan04@supernet.com

Ash Tool Co. Ltd, Lord Street, Ashton-under-Lyne, Lancashire, OL6 6HZ Tel: 0161-330 2325 Fax: 0161-343 2229 E-mail: ash.tool@zen.co.uk

Ashbourne Engineering UK Ltd, Rear of, 71 Westcote Road, London, SW16 6BN Tel: (020) 8664 7170 Fax: (020) 8664 7459

Ashby Engineering Co., 8 Surbiton Hill Road, Surbiton, Surrey, KT6 4TP Tel: (020) 8399 4034 Fax: (020) 8390 4947 E-mail: ashbyeng@aol.com

▶ Ashfield Precision Engineering Ltd, 59 Eastfield Side, Sutton-in-Ashfield, Nottinghamshire, NG17 4JW Tel: (01623) 551954 Fax: (01623) 514109

Ashford Engineering Services, Unit 3 New Street Farm, Great Chart, Ashford, Kent, TN23 3DL Tel: (01233) 668883 Fax: (01233) 668883 E-mail: clive@asheng.freeserve.co.uk

Ashley Precision (Parkstone) Ltd, 12 Broom Road, Parkstone, Poole, Dorset, BH12 4NL Tel: (01202) 744168 Fax: (01202) 744168

Atec Engineering, Albany Park, Cabot Lane, Poole, Dorset, BH17 7BX Tel: (01202) 696260

Atkins Precision, 59 Fairmile Road, Christchurch, Dorset, BH23 2LA Tel: (01202) 478824

Atlantic Auto Engineering, Unit 7b Fernfield Farm, Little Horwood Road, Little Horwood, Milton Keynes, MK17 0PS Tel: (01908) 501904 Fax: (01908) 501904

Atlas Engineering Ltd, Pontefract Street, Derby, DE24 8JD Tel: (01332) 343161 Fax: (01332) 294935 E-mail: tamara@atlaseng.co.uk

Auguste Development Services, Unit 12b Cooksland Industrial Estate, Bodmin, Cornwall, PL31 2QB Tel: (01208) 75593 Fax: (01208) 77499 E-mail: sales@augustedev.fsnet.co.uk

Auto Components Ltd, 11 Coulman Road, Industrial Estate, Thorne, Doncaster, South Yorkshire, DN8 5JS Tel: (01405) 812424 Fax: (01405) 740072 E-mail: info@auto-components.co.uk

Auto Engineering Supplies Ltd, Forties, Wilnecote, Tamworth, Staffordshire, B77 5DG Tel: (01827) 286161 Fax: (01827) 286042 E-mail: jmurphy@autoengsupplies.co.uk

Autofour Precision Engineering Ltd, 5 Alstone Trading Estate, Alstone Lane, Cheltenham, Gloucestershire, GL51 8HF Tel: (01242) 582064 Fax: (01242) 224374 E-mail: info@autofour.co.uk

Automatic Industrial Machines Ltd, Units 9 & 10, Hither Green Industrial Estate, Clevedon, Avon, BS21 6XT Tel: (01275) 877695 Fax: (01275) 878463 E-mail: info@aim-ltd.net

Autoy Ltd, 152 Castleton Road, Deepdale, Preston, PR1 6QH Tel: (01772) 556115 Fax: (01772) 204937 E-mail: autoy@btconnect.com

Avid Tools, 126a Lame Road, Sands, High Wycombe, Buckinghamshire, HP12 4HN Tel: (01494) 465315 Fax: (01494) 465312

Avondale Engineering Ltd, Phoenix Works, Pontnewynydd Industrial Estate, Pontypool, Gwent, NP4 6PD Tel: (01495) 750133 Fax: (01495) 763488 E-mail: sales@avondale-engineering.com

PRECISION ENGINEERS – *continued*

Awr Engineering Services, Unit A11 Abbey Close, Redwither Business Park, Wrexham, Clwyd, LL13 9XG Tel: (01978) 661928 Fax: (01978) 661928

Axxicon Moulds Cleveleys Ltd, Dorset Avenue, Thornton-Cleveleys, Lancashire, FY5 2DB Tel: (01253) 823241 Fax: (01253) 869717 E-mail: cleveleys@axxicon.co.uk

Aztec Precision Engineering, Pixmore Avenue, Letchworth Garden City, Hertfordshire, SG6 1JG Tel: (01462) 677888 Fax: (01462) 677888

Aztech Precision Ltd, Church Lane, Barnham, Bognor Regis, West Sussex, PO22 0BP Tel: (01243) 555140 Fax: (01243) 555870 E-mail: mail@aztech-precision.co.uk

B A W Precision Engineering Ltd, Cwmtawe Business Park, Alloy Industrial Estate, Pontardawe, Swansea, SA8 4EZ Tel: (01792) 862141 Fax: (01792) 865545 E-mail: peter@bawengineering.co.uk

B & B Precision Engineering, 9 Station Court, Park Mill Way, Clayton West, Huddersfield, HD8 9XJ Tel: (01484) 866386 Fax: (01484) 866300

B C T Engineering Ltd, 4 Manor Way, Woking, Surrey, GU22 9JX Tel: (01483) 767756 Fax: (01483) 740548 E-mail: mr.dental@virgin.net

B D H Engineering, Unit 3, Granta Terrace, Great Shelford, Cambridge, CB2 5DJ Tel: (01223) 845088 Fax: (01223) 841973 E-mail: bdheng@aol.com

B D R Micro Instruments Ltd, The Bringey, Church Street, Great Baddow, Chelmsford, CM2 7JW Tel: (01245) 476777 Fax: (01245) 475761 E-mail: info@bdr-micro.co.uk

B H T Engineering Ltd, Unit 8, Hayes Lane Factory Estate, Lye, Stourbridge, West Midlands, DY9 8RH Tel: (01384) 422294 Fax: (01384) 422562 E-mail: bhteng@compuserve.com

B J Ashpole Ltd, Southmill Road, Bishop's Stortford, Hertfordshire, CM23 3DJ Tel: (01279) 653211 Fax: (01279) 651694

B K Engineering Ltd, Kingswood Works, Heath and Reach, Leighton Buzzard, Bedfordshire, LU7 0AZ Tel: (01525) 237411 Fax: (01525) 237827 E-mail: sales@bkengineering.com

B & L Engineering & Castings, Darenth Mill, Darenth Road South, Dartford, DA2 7QT Tel: (01322) 289665 Fax: (01322) 289664 E-mail: blengineering@aol.com

B L Precision Ltd, Unit 6-7 Focal Point, Lacerta Court, Letchworth Garden City, Hertfordshire, SG6 1FJ Tel: (01462) 670800 Fax: (01462) 816865 E-mail: info@blprecision.co.uk

B M B Engineers (Newcastle) Ltd, 96 Millrise Road, Milton, Stoke-on-Trent, ST2 7DN Tel: (01782) 543004 Fax: (01782) 543288 E-mail: steve@bmbengineersltd.co.uk

B O P P Precision Engineers Ltd, A Emms Court, Meeting Lane, Brierley Hill, West Midlands, DY5 3LB Tel: (01384) 78646 Fax: (01384) 78646 E-mail: mail@bopppe.fsnet.co.uk

▶ B S Engineering Ltd, 5 Kings Mill Way, Mansfield, Nottinghamshire, NG18 5ER Tel: (01623) 636899

B S W Engineering UK Ltd, 115a West End Road, Southall, Middlesex, UB1 1JF Tel: (020) 8574 6685 Fax: (020) 8571 5751 E-mail: bswenguk@aol.com

Bailey Marine, 53 Rempstone Road, Wimborne, Dorset, BH21 1TR Tel: (01202) 885052 Fax: (01202) 842817 E-mail: john@bailey-marine.co.uk

Baker Engineering, Devon Road, Bordon, Hampshire, GU35 0BB Tel: (01420) 473953 Fax: (01420) 473953

Balco Prescision Engineering, 24 Benfield Way, Braintree, Essex, CM7 3YS Tel: (01376) 347767 Fax: (01376) 347767

Bar Engineering, 20 West Dock Avenue, Hull, HU3 4JR Tel: (01482) 224966 Fax: (01482) 211443

Bar Knight Precision Engineers Ltd, 588-588a Glasgow Road, Clydebank, Dunbartonshire, G81 1NH Tel: 0141-952 4000 Fax: 0141-952 1157 E-mail: sales@barknight.co.uk

Barenson Engineering Co., Deseronto Estate, St Marys Road, Slough, SL3 7EW Tel: (01753) 543140 Fax: (01753) 540615 E-mail: info@barenson.co.uk

▶ A & D Barrowclough Ltd, Elm Street Works, Elm Street, Burnley, Lancashire, BB10 1NY Tel: (01282) 427048

Barrs Court Engineering Ltd, Netherwood Road, Rotherwas Industrial Estate, Hereford, HR2 6JU Tel: (01432) 353450 Fax: (01432) 353452 E-mail: paul@barrscourt.com

Barton Carbide Tooling Ltd, PO Box 5243, Milton Keynes, MK17 0YL Tel: (0870) 7466390 Fax: (08707) 466391 E-mail: info@barton.uk.com

Barton Precision Engineers Ltd, Dabell Avenue, Blenheim Industrial Estate, Nottingham, NG6 8WA Tel: 0115-927 2368 Fax: 0115-977 0101 E-mail: info@bartonprecision.co.uk

Bayliss Precision Components Ltd, Blenheim Road, Airfield Industrial Estate, Ashbourne, Derbyshire, DE6 1HA Tel: (01335) 342981 Fax: (01335) 343860 E-mail: info@bayliss.uk.com

▶ Baytree Industries Ltd, Resource House, Brunel Road, St. Leonards-on-Sea, East Sussex, TN38 9RT Tel: (01424) 854460 Fax: (01424) 854461 E-mail: sales@bt-ind.com

BDJ Engineering Worcester Ltd, A Carden Close, Worcester, WR1 2AR Tel: (01905) 23616 Fax: (01905) 22242 E-mail: brian@bdjengineering.wanadoo.co.uk

Beard Engineering Co. Ltd, Pye Hill Road, Jacksdale, Nottingham, NG16 5LR Tel: (01773) 602535 Fax: (01773) 540185 E-mail: admin@beardengineering.co.uk

Beavin Engineering Ltd, 33 Haviland Road, Ferndown Industrial Estate, Wimborne, Dorset, BH21 7SA Tel: (01202) 894404 Fax: (01202) 894404 E-mail: beavineng@btconnect.com

Bedestone Ltd, 41 Icknield Street, Hockley, Birmingham, B18 5AY Tel: 0121-554 3283 Fax: 0121-507 0140 E-mail: bedestone@aol.com

Bedford Engineering Co Manchester Ltd, Hollingworth Road, Bredbury, Stockport, Cheshire, SK6 2AU Tel: 0161-430 2650 Fax: 0161-494 6589 E-mail: bedeng@btconnect.com

Bestalinks Engineers Ltd, 2 Wood Street, Dukinfield, Cheshire, SK16 4UT Tel: 0161-330 8515 Fax: 0161-343 2228 E-mail: bestlink@aol.com

Beswick Engineering Co. Ltd, 21 Cowley Road, Blackpool, FY4 4NE Tel: (01253) 761661 Fax: (01253) 761661

Beta Engineering Services Ltd, Unit 3a Goldthorpe Industrial Estate, Commercial Road, Goldthorpe, Rotherham, South Yorkshire, S63 9BL Tel: (01709) 898848 Fax: (01709) 880856 E-mail: enquiries@betaengineeringservices.co.uk

Biddlecombe Engineering Ltd, Unit 18 Landford Common Farm, New Road, Landford, Salisbury, SP5 2AZ Tel: (01794) 322992 Fax: (01794) 323001

Billcar Engineering Ltd, Unit 1a March Way, Battlefield Enterprise Park, Shrewsbury, SY1 3JE Tel: (01743) 469398 Fax: (01743) 450084 E-mail: billcarengine@hotmail.com

Bindon Engineering Co. Ltd, Johns Road, Wareham, Dorset, BH20 4BG Tel: (01929) 553477 Fax: (01929) 554858

Birkdale Engineering Co., 56-62b Cemetery Road, Southport, Merseyside, PR8 5EF Tel: (01704) 538763 Fax: (01704) 544256 E-mail: birkdalejohn@aol.com

Bitton Precision Engineering Ltd, Unit 9f Aldermoor Way, Longwell Green, Bristol, BS30 7DA Tel: 0117-961 2128 Fax: 0117-947 6908 E-mail: john.coggins@bittonprecision.co.uk

BMP, 6 The Half Croft, Syston, Leicester, LE7 1LD Tel: 0116-260 2916 Fax: 0116-260 7296 E-mail: bnpengineers@btconnect.com

Bo Mac Sheffield Ltd, 63 Jenkin Road, Sheffield, S9 1AT Tel: 0114-244 8170 Fax: 0114-243 7104 E-mail: sales@bo-mac.co.uk

Bo Mic Engineering, 1 Brickyard Lane, New Road, Gillingham, Dorset, SP8 4JL Tel: (01747) 824216 Fax: (01747) 821726 E-mail: sale@bomic.co.uk

Bonnell Engineering Ltd, 28-33 Stewart Street, Wolverhampton, WV2 4JW Tel: (01902) 712855 Fax: (01902) 712855

Border Precision Ltd, Pinnaclehill Industrial Estate, Kelso, Roxburghshire, TD5 8DW Tel: (01573) 224941 Fax: (01573) 225220 E-mail: sales@borderprecision.com

Bowman & Sanderson Ltd, Icknield Way, Baldock, Hertfordshire, SG7 5BD Tel: (01462) 892292 Fax: (01462) 490457 E-mail: bowsand@tiscali.co.uk

Bowyer Engineering Ltd, South Way, Walworth Industrial Estate, Andover, Hampshire, SP10 5AF Tel: (01264) 365921 Fax: (01264) 356547 E-mail: sales@bowyerengineering.co.uk

Boxall Engineering, Unit 50 Grace Business Centre, Willow Lane, Mitcham, Surrey, CR4 4TU Tel: (020) 8648 8468 Fax: (020) 8648 4162E-mail: info@boxall-industrial.co.uk

Boxmoor Precision Engineering, 439A London Road, Hemel Hempstead, Hertfordshire, HP3 9BD Tel: (01442) 250147 Fax: (01442) 250147

Bramtool Precision Engineering, 13 109 Sydenham Road, Birmingham, B11 1DG Tel: 0121-773 1345 Fax: 0121-773 1345

▶ Breckland Precision Engineering, Church Road, Watton, Thetford, Norfolk, IP25 6QA Tel: (01953) 885363 Fax: (01953) 885933 E-mail: bpe03@aol.com

Brellant Engineering Co. Ltd, Hole Bottom Mills, Huddersfield, HD5 8HF Tel: (01484) 428892 Fax: (01484) 431712

Brennan Tool & Engineering Co. Ltd, Unit 9-11 Brooke Trading Estate, Lyon Road, Romford, RM1 2AT Tel: (01708) 736600 Fax: (01708) 735500 E-mail: david.brennan@brennan-tools.co.uk

▶ Brightspark Precision Engineering Ltd, 3 Carrside, Lomeshaye Industrial Estate, Nelson, Lancashire, BB9 6RX Tel: (01282) 613444 E-mail: brightsp@globalnet.co.uk

Brimor Engineering Ltd, Blandford Heights, Blandford Forum, Dorset, DT11 7TE Tel: (01258) 452222 Fax: (01258) 480320

Britten Engineering Ltd, 12 Morris Road, Leicester, LE2 6BR Tel: 0116-270 0448 Fax: 0116-270 4998

Britton Engineering, Carlyon Road, Atherstone, Warwickshire, CV9 1LQ Tel: (01827) 712578 Fax: (01827) 713561 E-mail: malcolm.crane@btconnect.com

Broad Oak Gears Ltd, Old Warburton Bakery, Jacob Street, Accrington, Lancashire, BB5 1HU Tel: (01254) 397489 Fax: (01254) 390550 E-mail: bogears@aol.com

Broadbridge Precision Engineering Ltd, 1-5 Marters Avenue, Langley Green, Crawley, West Sussex, RH11 7RX Tel: (01293) 525260 Fax: (01293) 561668 E-mail: broadbridge.eng@pncl.co.uk

Broadleaf Engineering, 1 Craven Street, Leicester, LE1 4BX Tel: 0116-253 9200 Fax: 0116-253 0598

▶ L. & T.I. Brock & Co. Ltd, Unit 1 Falkland House, 19 Falkland Close, Charter Avenue Industrial Estate, Coventry, CV4 8AG Tel: (024) 7642 1200 Fax: (024) 7642 1459 E-mail: enquiries@tangi-flow.com

Bromac Machining Services Ltd, Cradley Heath Factory Centre, Woods Lane, Cradley Heath, West Midlands, B64 7AQ Tel: (01384) 637838 Fax: (01384) 637838

▶ Bronte Precision Engineering, Unit 1, Hanworth Road, Low Moor, Bradford, West Yorkshire, BD12 0SG Tel: (01274) 698900 Fax: (01274) 698909 E-mail: mail@bpel.co.uk

Brookes Engineers Ltd, Hope Street, Rotherham, South Yorkshire, S60 1LH Tel: (01709) 365418 Fax: (01709) 828453 E-mail: sales@brookeseng.co.uk

Brookfield Engineering Co., James Street, Littleborough, Lancashire, OL15 8LT Tel: (01706) 378042 Fax: (01706) 378042

Brooks Precision Engineering Ltd, 6 Chamberlain Road, Aylesbury, Buckinghamshire, HP19 8DY Tel: (01296) 393862 Fax: (01296) 421014

Brookside Engineering, Unit 32j The Washford Industrial Estate, Heming Road, Redditch, Worcestershire, B98 0DH Tel: (01527) 502092 Fax: (01527) 502092

R.W. Brown Precision Engineering, 9 Buchanan Building, Stephenson Road, Clacton-On-Sea, Essex, CO15 4XA Tel: (01255) 220230 Fax: (01255) 220202 E-mail: bob@the-machining-centre.co.uk

Robert Brown Engineering Ltd, Douglas Close, Preston Farm Industrial Estate, Stockton-on-Tees, Cleveland, TS18 3SB Tel: (01642) 675201 Fax: (01642) 615902

Steve Brown Engineering Ltd, 40 Tyne Road, Middlefield Industrial Estate, Sandy, Bedfordshire, SG19 1SA Tel: (01767) 681224 Fax: (01767) 681224

Brownhills Engineering Co, Progress Drive, Cannock, Staffordshire, WS11 0JE Tel: (01543) 502700 Fax: (01543) 520700

Brunshaw Light Engineering Co., 19 Athletic Street, Burnley, Lancashire, BB10 4LP Tel: (01282) 420080 Fax: (01282) 420080 E-mail: brunshaw@btconnect.com

Bude Precision Engineering Ltd, Unit 14a Bude Business Centre, Kings Hill Industrial Estate, Bude, Cornwall, EX23 8QN Tel: (01288) 356656 Fax: (01288) 356657 E-mail: bpneng@tiscalli.co.uk

Bulwell Precision Engineers Ltd, Wharf Road Industrial Estate, Pinxton, Nottingham, NG16 6LE Tel: (01773) 863969 Fax: (01773) 861644 E-mail: bpe@bulwell.com

Bunney & Young Engineering Ltd, Unit V4 Willments Industrial Estate, Hazel Road, Southampton, SO19 7HS Tel: (023) 8042 0993 Fax: (023) 8042 2358

Burbridge 2000 Ltd, Studio's 1 & 2, Channocks Farm, Gilston, Harlow, Essex, CM20 2RL Tel: (01279) 445630 Fax: (01279) 418779 E-mail: enquiries@burbridge2k.co.uk

Burman Tool Co Ltd, Rye Road, Hoddesdon, Hertfordshire, EN11 0DZ Tel: (01992) 466311 Fax: 01992 468900 E-mail: info@burman.co.uk

Burrows & Smith Ltd, Saffron Works, Saffron Lane, Leicester, LE2 6UH Tel: 0116-244 0400 Fax: 0116-244 1100 E-mail: enquiries@burrowsmith.demon.co.uk

Burtech Precision Ltd, First Avenue, Flixborough Industrial Estate, Flixborough, Scunthorpe, South Humberside, DN15 8SE Tel: (01724) 866406 Fax: (01724) 280614

Burton & Smith Ltd, Unit 32p The Washford Industrial Estate, Heming Road, Redditch, Worcestershire, B98 0DH Tel: (01527) 516925 Fax: (01527) 514900 E-mail: burtonandsmith@lycos.co.uk

Bushell & Meadows Ltd, Northway Lane, Tewkesbury, Gloucestershire, GL20 8HG Tel: (01684) 292000 Fax: (01684) 855763 E-mail: info@bushell-meadows.co.uk

BWC Engineering, Unit 11, Westwood Business Park, Dulverton Road, Birmingham, B6 7DS Tel: 0121-326 6920 Fax: 0121-327 7517 E-mail: dalkeydalton@hotmail.com

C A T Engineering Ltd, Glendale Works, 25 Sandhurst Road, Crowthorne, Berkshire, RG45 7HR Tel: (01344) 772934 Fax: (01344) 779283 E-mail: len@cateng.fsnet.co.uk

C A V Aerospace Ltd, Unit 11, Ashville Way, Whetstone, Leicester, LE8 6NU Tel: 0116-284 1520 Fax: 0116-286 7493 E-mail: sales@cav-aerospace.net

C & B Marine Ltd, Chichester Marina, Chichester, West Sussex, PO20 7EJ Tel: (01243) 511273 Fax: (01243) 511273

C D Atkinson Engineering Co. Ltd, Whitacre Road Industrial Estate, Whitacre Road, Nuneaton, Warwickshire, CV11 6BX Tel: (024) 7637 0119 Fax: (024) 7637 0811

C E Edwards Engineers Ltd, Eagle Works, Leek New Road, Stoke-on-Trent, ST6 2LD Tel: (01782) 202400 Fax: (01782) 262781 E-mail: sales@ceedwards.co.uk

C E F Precision Ltd, Beachs Drive, Chelmsford, CM1 2NU Tel: (01245) 353019 Fax: (01245) 491675 E-mail: sales@cef-precision.co.uk

C E Fagg Engineering, 539 Ipswich Road, Slough, SL1 4EP Tel: (01753) 538432

C H E Engineering, Unit 59, Bergen Way, North Lynn Industrial Estate, King's Lynn, Norfolk, PE30 2JL Tel: (01553) 691999 Fax: (01553) 691999

C H Sandall & Son Precision Engineers, Whiteleather Square, Billingborough, Sleaford, Lincolnshire, NG34 0QP Tel: (01529) 240277 Fax: (01529) 241543

C H Young Tools (Cov) Ltd, Oban Road, Coventry, CV6 6HH Tel: (024) 7636 1209 Fax: (024) 7664 4270 E-mail: info@chyoung.ndo.co.uk

C J Cooke, Unit 31 Park Farm Industrial Estate, Ermine Street, Buntingford, Hertfordshire, SG9 9AZ Tel: (01763) 272523 Fax: (01763) 272955

C J Engineering Ltd, 2 Faraday Place, Thetford, Norfolk, IP24 3RG Tel: (01842) 761726 Fax: (01842) 761119 E-mail: kevin@cjeng.co.uk

C J Tools Southern CNC Ltd, Precision House, Northarbour Road, Portsmouth, PO6 3TJ Tel: (023) 9238 9489 Fax: (023) 9237 7119 E-mail: sales@cjtools.com

C K S Precision Ltd, Unit 12, Ptarmigan Place, Attleborough Fields Industrial Estate, Nuneaton, Warwickshire, CV11 6RX Tel: (024) 7664 1693 Fax: (024) 7638 3971 E-mail: sales@cks-precision.co.uk

C M Engineering, 45 College Street, Kempston, Bedford, MK42 8LU Tel: (01234) 214906 Fax: (01234) 217755

C M Precision Components, Killyhelvin Industrial Estate, Killyhevlin, Enniskillen, County Fermanagh, BT74 4EJ Tel: (028) 6632 3361 Fax: (028) 6632 6958 E-mail: martin@cmprecisioncomponents.co.uk

C N F Precision Engineering Ltd, C N F Factory, Southern Road, Aylesbury, Buckinghamshire, HP19 9AY Tel: (01296) 481727 Fax: (01296) 434940 E-mail: sales@cnfengineering.com

C P E Precision Engineering Co. Ltd, Sutherland House, Arlington Way, Sundorne Retail Park, Shrewsbury, SY1 4YA Tel: (01743) 444250 Fax: (01743) 462563

C P Mechanical Designs Ltd, 48 Wellington Road, Portslade, Brighton, BN41 1DT Tel: (01273) 430001 Fax: (01273) 424654 E-mail: enquiries@cpmechanical.co.uk

C T Precision, Hicks Road, Markyate, St. Albans, Hertfordshire, AL3 8LJ Tel: (01582) 840042 Fax: (01582) 840042

C W E Stavely Ltd, Unit 1A Hartington Industrial Estate, Deepdale Close, Staveley, Chesterfield, Derbyshire, S43 3YF Tel: (01246) 280046 Fax: (01246) 474975

Cables Direct Ltd, C Industrial Estate, Heage Road, Ripley, Derbyshire, DE5 3GH Tel: (01773) 514514 Fax: (01773) 514515 E-mail: sales@cablesdirect.co.uk

Caine Precision Ltd, Unit 13 Stocklake Park Industrial Estate, Farmborough Cl, Aylesbury, Bucks, HP20 1DQ Tel: (01296) 434586 Fax: (01296) 432683 E-mail: rcaine@nildron.co.uk

Camale Engineering Ltd, Halas Industrial Estate, Forge Lane, Halesowen, West Midlands, B62 8EB Tel: 0121-550 8089 Fax: 0121-550 8089

Camlit Precision Engineering Ltd, Sand Road Industrial Estate, Sand Road, Great Gransden, Sandy, Bedfordshire, SG19 3AH Tel: (01767) 677263 Fax: (01767) 677720

Camm Precision Engineers Ltd, 45 Winpenny Road, Parkhouse Industrial Estate East, Parkhouse Industrial Estate East, Newcastle, Staffordshire, ST5 7RH Tel: (01782) 565611 Fax: (01782) 562747

Canford Hill Engineering Ltd, 30 Benson Road, Nuffield Industrial Estate, Poole, Dorset, BH17 0GB Tel: (01202) 671119 Fax: (01202) 671119 E-mail: canfordhill@btconnect.com

Canwire Services Ltd, 14 Gospel End Street, Dudley, West Midlands, DY3 3LS Tel: (01902) 881460 Fax: (01902) 881393 E-mail: canwireservices1@aol.com

Carbonlite Converting Equipment Ltd, Britannia Foundry, Lomax Street, Rochdale, Lancashire, OL12 0DN Tel: (01706) 359000 Fax: (01706) 654378 E-mail: sales@ccequipment.co.uk

Carron Tooling, 80 Shelley Road, Bournemouth, BH7 6HB Tel: (01202) 303811 Fax: (01202) 303811

Casey Bros, St Georges Drive, Brinsworth, Rotherham, South Yorkshire, S60 5NG Tel: (01709) 378386 Fax: (01709) 373308

Castle Engineering Lancaster Ltd, River Street, St Georges Quay, Lancaster, LA1 1TA Tel: (01524) 67604 Fax: (01524) 67604

Castle Precision Engineering Glasgow Ltd, 241 Drakemire Drive, Glasgow, G45 9SZ Tel: 0141-634 1377 Fax: 0141-634 3678 E-mail: sales@castleprecision.com

Catherwell Engineering Co. Ltd, Unit 7 & 9 Stanley Lane Industrial Estate, Stanley Lane, Bridgnorth, Shropshire, WV16 4SF Tel: (01746) 766154 Fax: (01746) 766154

Cellbond Composites Ltd, 4-5 Blackstone Road, Stukeley Meadows Industrial Es, Huntingdon, Cambridgeshire, PE29 6EF Tel: (01480) 435302 Fax: (01480) 450181 E-mail: sales.precision@cellbond.com

Ceta Precision Engineering Ltd, Tweedbank Industrial Estate, Tweedbank, Galashiels, Selkirkshire, TD1 3RS Tel: (01896) 757200 Fax: (01896) 758307

Chad Engineering (UK) Ltd, Unit 2, Business Village, Wexham Road, Slough, SL2 5HF Tel: (01753) 537980 Fax: (01753) 553472 E-mail: enquiries@chad-engineering.co.uk

Chadwick Engineering Co. Ltd, 173-179 Tyburn Road, Erdington, Birmingham, B24 8NQ Tel: 0121-327 7997 Fax: 0121-327 7987

Charter Precision Engineering, Unit 25-26, Enfield Industrial Estate, Redditch, Worcestershire, B97 6BY Tel: (01527) 584187 Fax: (01527) 584187

Chartway Industrial Services Ltd, Faraday Drive, Bridgnorth, Shropshire, WV15 5BA Tel: (01746) 764900 Fax: (01746) 768770 E-mail: sales@chartway.co.uk

▶ indicates data change since last edition

PRECISION ENGINEERS – *continued*

Chelburn Precision Ltd, 2 Plot 7-9 Trans Pennine Trading Estate, Gorrells Way, Rochdale, Lancashire, OL11 2PX Tel: (01706) 644538 Fax: (01706) 861733 E-mail: chelburn@zen.co.uk

Cine Engineering Services, 99 Gander Green Lane, Sutton, Surrey, SM1 2ES Tel: (020) 8643 7152 Fax: (020) 7770 7275

CKC Engineering Services, 31 Bowlers Croft, Honeywood Road, Basildon, Essex, SS14 3DZ Tel: (01268) 273188 Fax: (01268) 273199

Classic Precision Engineering Ltd, Unit 2, New Line Road, Kirkby-In-Ashfield, Nottingham, NG17 8JQ Tel: (01623) 720402 Fax: (01623) 720353 E-mail: russ@cpeng.freeserve.co.uk

Clayton (Twickenham) Precision Engineering Co. Ltd, Clock Tower Road, Isleworth, Middlesex, TW7 6DT Tel: (020) 8568 9527 Fax: (020) 8569 9526 E-mail: claytonprecision@aol.com

Clelland Engineering Ltd, 25 Lawmoor Road, Dixons Blazes Industrial Estate, Glasgow, G5 0UG Tel: 0141-429 5585 Fax: 0141-420 1045 E-mail: clelleng@aol.com

Clive Walton Engineering, Rivendell Cottage, Cumrew, Brampton, Cumbria, CA8 9DD Tel: (01768) 896232 Fax: (01768) 896451 E-mail: waltoneng@tiscali.co.uk

CLM Engineering Services Ltd, 711 Banbury Avenue Trading Estate, Slough, SL1 4LR Tel: (01753) 743000 Fax: (01753) 811256 E-mail: lisa.perryman@clm-group.co.uk

Clwyd Precision Engineering, Bridge Road, Wrexham Industrial Estate, Wrexham, Clwyd, LL13 9PS Tel: (01978) 660259 Fax: (01978) 661069 E-mail: cpe@bytecraft.net

Clydeview Precision Engineering & Supplies Ltd, 197a Dumbarton Road, Clydebank, Dunbartonshire, G81 4XJ Tel: 0141-941 1873 Fax: 0141-951 1928

CNC Precision, Unit 15 Enfield Industrial Estate, Redditch, Worcestershire, B97 6BG Tel: (01527) 596727 Fax: (01527) 585049 E-mail: sales@c-n-c.co.uk

Coldon Engineering Co. Ltd, 7 Wates Way, Ongar Road, Brentwood, Essex, CM15 9TB Tel: (01277) 231717 Fax: (01277) 262799 E-mail: sales@coldonengineering.co.uk

Colin Mackenzie Engineering Ltd, 3 Murray Street, Paisley, Renfrewshire, PA3 1QG Tel: 0141-889 3031 Fax: 0141-889 3031

Collingwood Engineering Lincs Ltd, Dam Road, Barton-upon-Humber, South Humberside, DN18 5AS Tel: (01652) 632388 Fax: (01652) 632388

Colonnade UK, Unit 41 Hallmark Trading Estate, Fourth Way, Wembley, Middlesex, HA9 0LB Tel: (020) 8902 7722 Fax: (020) 8795 4187 E-mail: info@colonnadeuk.com

Colpa Precision Engineering Ltd, 100 Cecil Street, Watford, WD24 5AQ Tel: (01923) 237596 Fax: (01923) 213326 E-mail: colpa.ltd@virgin.net

Computerised Engineering Co., Unit 2a High Pastures, Stortford Road, Hatfield Heath, Bishop's Stortford, Hertfordshire, CM22 7DL Tel: (01279) 739455 Fax: (01279) 739454 E-mail: james@computerisedengineering.com

Coote & Hall Engineers Ltd, Spen Vale Street, Heckmondwike, West Yorkshire, WF16 0NQ Tel: (01924) 402854 Fax: (01924) 402854 E-mail: sales@coote-hall.co.uk

Copper Mill Engineering, The Mill, Bath Road, Bitton, Bristol, BS30 6LW Tel: 0117-932 2614 Fax: 0117-932 9388 E-mail: rusell@coppermillengineering.com

Peter Copsey Engineering Ltd, 2 Wheaton Road, Witham, Essex, CM8 3UJ Tel: (01376) 518378 Fax: (01376) 515294 E-mail: sales@pcopseyuk.freeserve.co.uk

Cordelle Precision Engineers, 76 Wharfdale Road, Birmingham, B11 2DE Tel: 0121-706 0525 Fax: 0121-706 3551

▶ Cottenden Ltd, 1 Oakfield Business Corner, Works Road, Letchworth Garden City, Hertfordshire, SG6 1FB Tel: (01462) 672179 E-mail: terry@cottenden.co.uk

Coventry Boring & Metalling Co. Ltd, 3 Coniston Road, Coventry, CV5 6GU Tel: (024) 7667 2372 Fax: (024) 7667 9948

Craftsman Tools Ltd, Side Copse, Otley, West Yorkshire, LS21 1JE Tel: (01943) 466788 Fax: (01943) 850144 E-mail: r.johnson@craftsmantools.com

Crane Hill Engineering Ltd, Harvey Reeves Road, St. James Mill Industrial Estate, Northampton, NN5 5JR Tel: (01604) 587656 Fax: (01604) 588341 E-mail: robinson@cranehill.sagehost.co.uk

Crawford Reid Engineers, Reed Street, North Shields, Tyne & Wear, NE30 1DD Tel: 0191-259 5767 Fax: 0191-259 5767

CRD Tool & Engineering Ltd, Station Road, Manningtree, Essex, CO11 1AA Tel: (01206) 394343 Fax: (01206) 391460 E-mail: merlyncrd@aol.com

Crest Engineering, Malvern View Business Park, Stella Way, Bishops Cleeve, Cheltenham, Gloucestershire, GL52 7DQ Tel: (01242) 674687 Fax: (01242) 679315 E-mail: crest.engineering@virgin.net

Crewe Precision Engineering Ltd, Tricketts Lane, Willaston, Nantwich, Cheshire, CW5 6PY Tel: (01270) 661033 Fax: (01270) 664524 E-mail: chris@cpe-eng.fsnet.co.uk

Croft Engineering Co. Ltd, Unit 7A, Parnall Road, Fishponds, Bristol, BS16 3JH Tel: 0117-958 3286 Fax: 0117-958 4390

Croft Engineering UK Ltd, 4 The Omni Business Centre, Omega Park, Alton, Hampshire, GU34 2QD Tel: (01420) 590009 Fax: (01420) 590009 E-mail: sales@croft-eng.co.uk

Cross Country Ltd, 4 Darby Gate, West Portway, Andover, Hampshire, SP10 3LF Tel: (01264) 351409 Fax: (01264) 333921

Crownfield Engineering Ltd, Crownfield, Wycombe Road, Saunderton, Princes Risborough, Buckinghamshire, HP27 9NR Tel: (01844) 345746 Fax: (01844) 347225 E-mail: crownfield@nildram.co.uk

CTR Engineering Ltd, Whitley Street, Bingley, West Yorkshire, BD16 4JH Tel: (01274) 562550 Fax: (01274) 551218 E-mail: ctrengltd@hotmail.com

Cumbria Extrusion Dies Ltd, Unit 4, Buddle Road, Clay Flatts Industrial Estate, Workington, Cumbria, CA14 3YD Tel: (01900) 66952 Fax: (01900) 66761

Currock Engineering Co. Ltd, Industrial Buildings, Beehive Lane, Chelmsford, CM2 9TE Tel: (01245) 257785 Fax: (01245) 283287 E-mail: currock@compuserve.com

Cutler & Maclean Ltd, Daimler Drive, Cowpen Industrial Estate, Billingham, Cleveland, TS23 4JD Tel: (01642) 564585 Fax: (01642) 371142

Cutter Services Precision Engineers Ltd, 6 Glebe Road, Letchworth Garden City, Hertfordshire, SG6 1DR Tel: (01462) 671861 Fax: (01462) 670532

D B C Tools Ltd, Jubilee Trading Estate, Jubilee Road, Letchworth Garden City, Hertfordshire, SG6 1NE Tel: (01462) 679905 Fax: (01462) 480219 E-mail: don.carter@dbctools.co.uk

D C E Holne Ltd, Mardle Way Industrial Estate, Buckfastleigh, Devon, TQ11 0NS Tel: (01364) 643862 Fax: (01364) 643025 E-mail: enquiries@dce-holne.co.uk

D C Hall Ltd, Woburn Lane, Aspley Guise, Milton Keynes, MK17 8JJ Tel: (01908) 583888 Fax: (01908) 582041E-mail: ray@dchall.co.uk

D & D Engineering Hull Ltd, Stockholm Road, Hull, HU7 0XW Tel: (01482) 879175 Fax: (01482) 838449 E-mail: info@ddeng.co.uk

D E Fabrications, Unit 7e E Plan Estate, New Road, Newhaven, East Sussex, BN9 0EX Tel: (01273) 515876 Fax: (01273) 517963 E-mail: sales@defabrications.freeserve.co.uk

D & G Engineering, Unit 18 Lynx Cresent, Weston-super-Mare, Avon, BS24 9DJ Tel: (01934) 628476 Fax: (01934) 418410

D H Tools, Unit 9 Newlands End, Basildon, Essex, SS15 6DU Tel: (01268) 540633 Fax: (01268) 540742 E-mail: enquiries@dhtools.co.uk

D J J Precision Engineering Ltd, Unit 14 Pontyfelin Avenue Industrial Estate, New Inn, Pontypool, Gwent, NP4 0DQ Tel: (01495) 760561 Fax: (01495) 756256 E-mail: sales@djjengineering.com

D P R Engineering, Unit 11 Prospect Business Park, Longford Road, Cannock, Staffordshire, WS11 0LG Tel: (01543) 577910 Fax: (01543) 572306

D R S Press Tools, Unit 18 Oldfields, Corngreaves Road, Cradley Heath, West Midlands, B64 6BS Tel: (01384) 410711 Fax: (01384) 410711

Dallmac Precision Engineering, Hardley Industrial Estate, Hythe, Southampton, SO45 3NQ Tel: (023) 8084 9211 Fax: (023) 8084 9211

Danatrol Ltd, Canal Bank, Loughborough, Leicestershire, LE11 1QA Tel: (01509) 217516 Fax: (01509) 230886 E-mail: graham@danatrol.com

Daniels Precision Engineering, Queens Road, Southall, Middlesex, UB2 5AY Tel: (020) 8574 3037

Dankroy Ltd, 129 Mayfield Avenue, London, N12 9HY Tel: (020) 8445 2157 Fax: (020) 8445 0538

Dart Precision Engineering, 41 Eton Wick Road, Eton Wick, Windsor, Berkshire, SL4 6LU Tel: (01753) 831110 Fax: (01753) 831110

Data Engineering, Pindar Road, Hoddesdon, Hertfordshire, EN11 0DE Tel: (01992) 462610 Fax: (01992) 450953 E-mail: scherry@dataeng.freeserve.co.uk

Datum Products Ltd, Blatchford Road, Horsham, West Sussex, RH13 5QR Tel: (01403) 253453 Fax: (01403) 272687 E-mail: info@datumporductshorsham.co.uk

Dawn Fire Engineers Ltd, 26 Wooburn Industrial Park, Wooburn Green, High Wycombe, Buckinghamshire, HP10 0PF Tel: (01628) 526531 Fax: (01628) 526634 E-mail: sales@dawnfire.co.uk

Daws Engineering Ltd, Curtis Road, Dorking, Surrey, RH4 1XD Tel: (01306) 881546 Fax: (01306) 740407 E-mail: rob.collinson@dawseng.co.uk

De Montfort Tool Co. Ltd, 4 Mandervell Road, Oadby, Leicester, LE2 5LQ Tel: 0116-271 3223 Fax: 0116-272 0847 E-mail: dmt@btclick.com

Deans Engineering Livingston Ltd, Royston Road, Deans Industrial Estate, Deans, Livingston, West Lothian, EH54 8AH Tel: (01506) 419797 Fax: (01506) 413849 E-mail: enquiries@deansengineering.com

Debanks Engineering, C3-C4 Unit, Grovelands Avenue Workshops, Winnersh, Wokingham, Berkshire, RG41 5LB Tel: 0118-977 3008 Fax: 0118-977 0903

Deeley Precision Engineering Ltd, Unit 1 Aston Fields Industrial Estate, Aston Road, Bromsgrove, Worcestershire, B60 3EX Tel: (01527) 870001 Fax: (01527) 579101

Delfield Precision Engineering Co. Ltd, Apex House, Stonefield Close, Ruislip, Middlesex, HA4 0XT Tel: (020) 8842 0527 Fax: (020) 8845 7796

Deloro Stellite UK (Director) Ltd, Cheney Manor Industrial Estate, Swindon, SN2 2PW Tel: (01793) 498500 Fax: 01793 498501 E-mail: sales@delorostellite.co.uk

Delta Aviation, Newton Hall, Town Street, Newton, Cambridge, CB22 7ZE Tel: (01223) 874343 Fax: (01223) 873702 E-mail: info@newtonhall.co.uk

▶ Delta Precision Engineering, Site 3 Unit 1, Cold Hesledon Industrial Estate, Cold Hesledon, Seaham, County Durham, SR7 8ST Tel: 0191-513 1026 Fax: 0191-513 1027 E-mail: sales@deltaprecision-eng.co.uk

Denner Kelford Grinding Ltd, D3 Seedbed Centre, Avenue Road, Nechells, Birmingham, B7 4NT Tel: 0121-359 7728 Fax: 0121-359 0255

Denny Engineering, Titley Bawk Avenue, Earls Barton, Northampton, NN6 0LA Tel: (01604) 811403 Fax: (01604) 812514

Desman Engineering Ltd, Burma Road, Blidworth, Mansfield, Nottinghamshire, NG21 0RT Tel: (01623) 490086 Fax: (01623) 490087 E-mail: sales@desman-engineering.com

Dial Precision Engineering Ltd, Dial House Dutton Green, Stanney Mill Industrial Park, Little Stanney, Chester, CH2 4SA Tel: 0151-357 2016 Fax: 0151-355 0751 E-mail: warren@dial-eng.co.uk

Diamant Precision Engineering Ltd, Unit 1 Marcus Close, Tilehurst, Reading, RG30 4EA Tel: 0118-945 1222 Fax: 0118-945 1077 E-mail: quality@damantltd.co.uk

Diatest UK Ltd, 18 Avondale Avenue, Hinchley Wood, Esher, Surrey, KT10 0DA Tel: (020) 8398 1100 Fax: (020) 8398 9887 E-mail: sales@diatest.co.uk

Alan Dick Engineering Ltd, Middleton Road, Heysham, Morecambe, Lancashire, LA3 2SE Tel: (01524) 855011 Fax: (01524) 859158 E-mail: adeheysham@btclick.com

Die Max Engineering, 1-2 Mid Wynd, Dundee, DD1 4JG Tel: (01382) 224481 Fax: (01382) 224481

Dimension Engineering, Unit 21 The Business Village, Wexham Road, Slough, SL2 5HF Tel: (01753) 538166 Fax: (01753) 518966

Direct Engineering, Regent Road, Countesthorpe, Leicester, LE8 5RF Tel: 0116-278 0416 Fax: 0116-247 7731

DJS Engineering, 11-12 Benedict Square, Peterborough, PE4 6GD Tel: (01733) 328214 Fax: (01733) 328214

DMS Systems, Ivel Road, Shefford, Bedfordshire, SG17 5JU Tel: (01462) 857955 Fax: (01462) 819168

Donland Engineering Southern Ltd, Foundation House, Stoneylands Road, Egham, Surrey, TW20 9QR Tel: (01784) 436151 Fax: (01784) 436038 E-mail: e@donlandeng.co.uk

Dontaur Engineering Ltd, C1 Wakehurst Road, Ballymena, County Antrim, BT42 3AZ Tel: (028) 2565 9886 Fax: (028) 2564 2487 E-mail: info@dontaur.co.uk

Downhurst Engineering, 15 Aintree Road, Keytec 7 Business Park, Pershore, Worcestershire, WR10 2JN Tel: (01386) 554195 Fax: (01386) 561195 E-mail: downhurst@lineone.net

Dransfields Engineering Services Ltd, Cotswold Avenue, Chadderton, Oldham, OL9 8PJ Tel: 0161-624 4142 Fax: 0161-627 5127 E-mail: sales@dransfields.co.uk

Drey Precision Ltd, 11-12 Priestley Way, Crawley, West Sussex, RH10 9NT Tel: (01293) 542695 Fax: (01293) 553703 E-mail: sales@drey.net

Dun Fab Engineering Company Ltd, Coulman Street, Thorne, Doncaster, South Yorkshire, DN8 5JS Tel: (01405) 812165 Fax: (01405) 740333 E-mail: dunfabengineering@aol.com

Dunblane Light Engineering Ltd, Stirling Road, Fallin, Stirling, FK7 7JB Tel: (01786) 818757 Fax: (01786) 818767 E-mail: john.swan@dle-eng.co.uk

Dunrave Precision Engineers Ltd, Oldbury Road, Cwmbran, Gwent, NP44 3JU Tel: (01633) 873838 Fax: (01633) 871477 E-mail: info@dunrave.co.uk

Dunsmore Products Ltd, 10 Avon Industrial Estate, Rugby, Warwickshire, CV21 3UY Tel: (01788) 571600 Fax: (01788) 541382 E-mail: dunsmoreprodltd@btconnect.com

Dupaul Engineering, Unit 5a Bone Lane, Newbury, Berkshire, RG14 5SH Tel: (01635) 31770 Fax: (01635) 521048 E-mail: dupaul@dupaul-eng.co.uk

Duston Engineering Ltd, 50 Ivy Road, Northampton, NN1 4QT Tel: (01604) 233178 Fax: (01604) 233178

Dyco Engineering, 3 Chancel Place, Boyer Street, Derby, DE22 3SH Tel: (01332) 372266 Fax: (01332) 372266

Dyer Engineering Ltd, Unit 3-5 Morrison Industrial Estate North, Stanley, County Durham, DH9 7RU Tel: (01207) 234355 Fax: (01207) 282834 E-mail: sales@dyer-engineering.ltd.uk

Dyglen Engineering Ltd, 68 Cavendish Way, Glenrothes, Fife, KY6 2SB Tel: (01592) 774881 Fax: (01592) 774871 E-mail: admin@dyglen.co.uk

E B Engineering, 17 All Saints Industrial Estate, All Saints Street, Birmingham, B18 7RJ Tel: 0121-551 3274 Fax: 0121-551 3274

E F Moy Ltd, Elstree Film Studios, Shenley Road, Borehamwood, Hertfordshire, WD6 1JG Tel: (020) 8324 2634 Fax: (020) 8324 2336

E J Mansbridge (Engineering) Ltd, Lancaster Road, High Wycombe, Buckinghamshire, HP12 3NN Tel: (01494) 437325 Fax: (01494) 471736 E-mail: office@ejmansbridge.com

E R Edwards & Sons Ltd, Blatchford Road, Horsham, West Sussex, RH13 5QR Tel: (01403) 224400 Fax: (01403) 224401 E-mail: sales@eredwards.com

Earhtech Engineering Ltd, Unit 1, Grovebury Place Estate, Grovebury Road, Leighton Buzzard, Bedfordshire, LU7 4SH Tel: (01525) 374362 Fax: (01525) 377304

Eaton Socon Engineering, Renhold Road, Ravensden, Bedford, MK44 2RH Tel: (01234) 772145 Fax: (01234) 771881 E-mail: eaton-socon@tiscali.co.uk

Edge Engineering, Unit 8 Mantra Ho, South St, Keighley, W. Yorkshire, BD21 1SX Tel: (01535) 606258

Edgefine Ltd, Unit C1 3 Forum Drive, Rugby, Warwickshire, CV21 1NT Tel: (01788) 537920 Fax: (01788) 537911 E-mail: martin@edgefine.co.uk

Edwards Bros, Unit J1 Dominion Way, Rustington, Littlehampton, West Sussex, BN16 3HQ Tel: (01903) 787184 Fax: (01903) 787184

Edwards Engineering (Liverpool) Ltd, Lipton Close, St. Johns Road, Brasenose Industrial Estate, Bootle, Merseyside, L20 8PU Tel: 0151-933 5242 Fax: 0151-922 3383 E-mail: edseng@edwardsenglpoolltd.freeserve.co.uk

J. & M. Edwards Precision Engineers Ltd, Lefevre Way, Gapton Hall Industrial Estate, Great Yarmouth, Norfolk, NR31 0NW Tel: (01493) 604312 Fax: (01493) 655719 E-mail: sales@jmedwards.co.uk

Ees Engineering Ltd, Sheddingdean Industrial Estate, Marchants Way, Burgess Hill, West Sussex, RH15 8QY Tel: (01444) 244733 Fax: (01444) 236939

Ek Machine Tools Ltd, 14 Singer Road, Kelvin Industrial Estate, East Kilbride, Glasgow, G75 0XS Tel: (01355) 234600 Fax: (01355) 265979 E-mail: info@ekomat.co.uk

Electro-mec (Reading) Ltd, 28 Portman Road, Reading, RG30 1EA Tel: 0118-958 2035 Fax: 0118-950 5049 E-mail: info@electromec.co.uk

Eljays Spark Erosion Services Ltd, 6 Kirby Estate, Trout Road, West Drayton, Middlesex, UB7 7RU Tel: (01895) 448380 Fax: (01895) 420977 E-mail: sales@eljays.co.uk

Elkins Engineering Ltd, Unit 1 Enterprise Park, Ebblake Industrial Estate, Verwood, Dorset, BH31 6YS Tel: (01202) 825322 Fax: (01202) 823971E-mail: sales@elkinsengineering.co.uk

G. Elliot Engineering Services Ltd, Bircotes, Doncaster, East Yorkshire, DN11 8WR Tel: (0844) 8002989 Fax: (01302) 745071 E-mail: sales@elliotteng.co.uk

Elstree Precision Co. Ltd, 26 Theobald Street, Borehamwood, Hertfordshire, WD6 4SF Tel: (020) 8953 3348 Fax: (020) 8207 1636

Engineering Tech Pgp Ltd, Unit 5 Harbour Road Industrial Estate, Lowestoft, Suffolk, NR32 3LZ Tel: (01502) 515768 Fax: (01502) 563211 E-mail: pete@eng-tech.co.uk

Enham Garden Centre, Enham Alamein, Andover, Hampshire, SP11 6JS Tel: (01264) 345800 Fax: (01264) 333638 E-mail: info@enham.co.uk

Enterprise Engineering, Unit 23 Tweedale Court, Tweedale North, Madeley, Telford, Shropshire, TF7 4JR Tel: (01952) 583179

Equinox Precision Engineering, Station Road, Great Harwood, Blackburn, BB6 7BB Tel: (01254) 888009 Fax: (01254) 885550

Erlson Engineering Ltd, 4 Priorswood Place, Skelmersdale, Lancashire, WN8 9QB Tel: (01695) 720149 Fax: (01695) 556426 E-mail: sales@erlson.co.uk

Euroscot Engineering Ltd, 427 Hillington Road, Hillington Industrial Estate, Glasgow, G52 4UJ Tel: 0141-883 2218 Fax: 0141-883 8970 E-mail: office@euroscotengineering.co.uk

Eurotech Precision Engineering Ltd, 4-5 Bergen Way, North Lynn Industrial Estate, King's Lynn, Norfolk, PE30 2JG Tel: (01553) 770426 Fax: (01553) 774726 E-mail: epelltd@kingslynn20.fsnet.co.uk

Evans & White Manufacturing Ltd, Canal Street, Stourbridge, West Midlands, DY8 4LU Tel: (01384) 394731 Fax: (01384) 442603 E-mail: sandra@evansandwhite.co.uk

Exhall Grinding & Engineering Co. Ltd, Bayton Road, Exhall, Coventry, CV7 9DW Tel: (024) 7636 1111 Fax: (024) 7636 1236 E-mail: bhudson319@aol.com

F Askew Engineers Ltd, Thorpe Road, Howden, Goole, North Humberside, DN14 7AY Tel: (01430) 430035 Fax: (01430) 431869 E-mail: enquries@askewengineers.co.uk

F E Robinson Hooton Ltd, Station Works, Hooton Road, Ellesmere Port, CH66 7NF Tel: 0151-327 1315 Fax: 0151-328 1694 E-mail: sales@ferobinson.co.uk

F G Precision Ltd, 10 Arkwright Gate, Andover, Hampshire, SP10 3SB Tel: (01264) 324231 Fax: (01264) 324231 E-mail: fgprecision@lineone.net

F J Dyke & Sons, Rear of 27 Dogfield Street, Cardiff, CF24 4QL Tel: (029) 2022 7074

F M Instruments, 66A High Street, Oakington, Cambridge, CB4 5AG Tel: (01223) 234141 Fax: (01223) 234141

F Mace & Son Ltd, 13a Victoria Avenue, Camberley, Surrey, GU15 3HP Tel: (01276) 65798 Fax: (01276) 686525 E-mail: fmacesons@btconnect.com

F R Mount Ltd, Tempest House, Lyon Road, Walton-on-Thames, Surrey, KT12 3PU Tel: (01932) 230011 Fax: (01932) 230022

F T Engineering, Lane End Works, Skipton Road, Earby, Barnoldswick, Lancashire, BB18 6PX Tel: (01282) 844220 Fax: (01282) 843480

F Worrall, Purdy Road, Batmans Hill Industrial Estate, Bilston, West Midlands, WV14 8UB Tel: (01902) 491366 Fax: (01902) 491366 E-mail: fworreluk@yahoo.com

J. Fairburn Ltd, Waterloo Works, Trafalgar Street, Burnley, Lancashire, BB11 1RF Tel: (01282) 422754 Fax: (01282) 422754 E-mail: pipeprofiling@compuserve.com

PRECISION ENGINEERS - *continued*

Fairfield Tool & Die Co Maesteg Ltd, Cwmdu Institute, Bridgend Road, Maesteg, Mid Glamorgan, CF34 0NW Tel: (01656) 733455 Fax: (01656) 738710 E-mail: ftdtony@btconnect.com

Fairway Engineering (Bristol) Ltd, Station Road Workshops, Station Road, Kingswood, Bristol, BS15 4PJ Tel: 0117-940 9030 Fax: 0117-940 9030E-mail: tony@fairwayeng.freeserve.co.uk

Fairwood Engineering Ltd, Dock Road, The Docks, Port Talbot, West Glamorgan, SA13 1RA Tel: (01639) 892117 Fax: (01639) 899238 E-mail: karen@fairwoodengineering.com

Fastec Engineering Services Ltd, Unit 8 Studlands Park Avenue, Studlands Park Industrial Estate, Newmarket, Suffolk, CB8 7AU Tel: (01638) 660186 Fax: (01638) 667374E-mail: danny@fastecengineeing.co.uk

Felton Engineering, Unit 7, Hoddesdon Industrial Centre, Pindar Road, Hoddesdon, Hertfordshire, EN11 0DD Tel: (01992) 443723 Fax: (01992) 465257 E-mail: feltonengineer@aol.com

Ferrostatics International Ltd, Kings Court, 5 Waterloo Road, Stalybridge, Cheshire, SK15 2AU Tel: 0161-303 2200 Fax: 0161-303 2211 E-mail: sales@ferrostatics-int.com

Field Engineering (Poole) Ltd, 10 Factory Road, Upton Industrial Estate, Poole, Dorset, BH16 5HT Tel: (01202) 622166 Fax: (01202) 632439 E-mail: dave@fieldengineering.co.uk

Field International Ltd, Radfield House, 18-20 Nuffield Road, Nuffield Industrial Estate, Poole, Dorset, BH17 0RB Tel: (01202) 676331 Fax: (01202) 684043 E-mail: sales@fieldinternational.com

Fielde Engineering Ltd, Unit 6-7 The Warren, East Goscote, Leicester, LE7 3XA Tel: 0116-260 8217 Fax: 0116-260 7921 E-mail: field@btconnect.com

Firthstones Ltd, 22-24 Brindley Road, Bayton Road Industrial Estate, Coventry, CV7 9EP Tel: (024) 7636 1010 Fax: (024) 7636 0970 E-mail: sales@firthstones.co.uk

Fisadco Eng (1980) Ltd, Raywell Street, Hull, HU2 8EP Tel: (01482) 324564 Fax: (01482) 222564 E-mail: daren@fisadco.co.uk

Fisher & Co., Units 2-4 Cary Court, Somerton Business Park, Somerton, Somerset, TA11 6SB Tel: (01458) 274017 Fax: (01458) 274145 E-mail: info@fisherandcompany.co.uk

Flavell Precision Engineering Ltd, Moore Street, Wolverhampton, WV1 2HE Tel: (01902) 456583 Fax: (01902) 456583 E-mail: sales@precisionengineering.gbr.fm

Flexible Machining Systems Ltd, 2-3 Blatchford Road, Horsham, West Sussex, RH13 5QR Tel: (01403) 270466 Fax: (01403) 270458 E-mail: sales@fmsltd.co.uk

Flight Refueling, Brook Road, Wimborne, Dorset, BH21 2BJ Tel: (01202) 882121 Fax: (01202) 880096 E-mail: sales@cobham.com

Forest Heath Ltd, 195 Bexhill Road, St. Leonards-on-Sea, East Sussex, TN38 8BG Tel: (01424) 714888 Fax: (01424) 714888 E-mail: forestheath@hotmail.co.uk

▶ Forestmaze Ltd, Anderstaff Industrial Estate, Hawkins Lane, Burton-on-Trent, Staffordshire, DE14 1QH Tel: (01283) 535497 Fax: (01283) 569593

Formark Engineering Ltd, Unit 319, Fauld Industrial Estate, Tutbury, Burton-On-Trent, Staffordshire, DE13 9HS Tel: (01283) 520520 Fax: (01283) 815582

Formet Ltd, Harley Works, Paxton Hill, St. Neots, Cambridgeshire, PE19 6TA Tel: (01480) 475041 Fax: (01480) 472820 E-mail: sales@4met.co.uk

Forrest Precision Engineering Co. Ltd, 538 Edgefauld Road, Glasgow, G21 4NB Tel: 0141-557 3555 Fax: 0141-558 6216

Fort Precision Engineering, Unit 2 3, Golden Hill Park, Freshwater, Isle of Wight, PO40 9UJ Tel: (01983) 753502 Fax: (01983) 755855 E-mail: toolspring@fsbdial.co.uk

Fosse Precision Ltd, East Street, Coventry, CV1 5LS Tel: (024) 7622 5263 Fax: (024) 7652 0919 E-mail: fosse.precision@zen.co.uk

Fossey Engineering, A 2 Venture Court, Ackworth Road, Portsmouth, PO3 5RY Tel: (023) 9269 0246 Fax: (023) 9267 8218

Fox Precision Machine Ltd, 95 Leigh Street, Sheffield, S9 2PR Tel: 0114-244 3969 Fax: 0114-243 9256 E-mail: sales@foxprecision.co.uk

Foxhall Engineering, Delta House, Delta Way, Thorpe Industrial Estate, Egham, Surrey, TW20 8RX Tel: (01784) 472220 Fax: (01784) 472221 E-mail: foxhalleng@hotmail.co.uk

Foxwood Engineering, 8 Park Trading Estate, Park Road, Hockley, Birmingham, B18 5HB Tel: 0121-554 7567 Fax: 0121-554 3834

Frank Dawson Engineering, Rockfield Road, Barrs Court Works, Hereford, HR1 2UA Tel: (01432) 278190 Fax: (01432) 344760

Frisby Extrusion Services Ltd, Unit F Tyson Courtyard, Weldon South Industrial Estate, Corby, Northamptonshire, NN18 8AZ Tel: (01536) 263545 Fax: (01536) 205184 E-mail: welcome@fes-ltd.com

Frome Tool & Gauge Ltd, Manor Road, Marston Trading Estate, Frome, Somerset, BA11 4BL Tel: (01373) 462226 Fax: (01373) 452123 E-mail: frometandg@btconnect.com

F.W. Frost (Engineers) Ltd, Bidewell Close, Drayton High Road, Norwich, NR8 6AP Tel: (01603) 867301 Fax: (01603) 261586 E-mail: sales@fwfrost-engineers.co.uk

FSG, Newtown Industrial Estate, Llantwit Fardre, Pontypridd, Mid Glamorgan, CF38 2EE Tel: (01443) 202281 Fax: (01443) 205747 E-mail: admin@fsgtoolanddie.co.uk

G B M Engineering, Unit 4 Inngae Park, Holly Lane Industrial Estate, Atherstone, Warwickshire, CV9 2NA Tel: (01827) 712213 Fax: (01827) 718503

G C Banks & Son Ltd, 5 Harolds Road, Harlow, Essex, CM19 5BJ Tel: (01279) 424019 Fax: (01279) 452203

G H Tooling Co., Building 107, Prestwick Int Airport, Glasgow Prestwick Intnl Airport, Prestwick, Ayrshire, KA9 2PL Tel: (01292) 474018 Fax: (01292) 671046 E-mail: ghtooling@btinternet.co.uk

G & P Precision Engineers Nottingham Ltd, 38 Hermitage Way, Mansfield, Nottinghamshire, NG18 5ES Tel: (01623) 653576 Fax: (01623) 420526 E-mail: sales@gpprecision.co.uk

G S Brown Precision Engineers Ltd, Beeches, Ladybank, Cupar, Fife, KY15 7LR Tel: (01337) 830264 Fax: (01337) 831269 E-mail: enquiries@gsbrown.com

G & S Precision Engineering Bradford Ltd, 6 Tyersal Works, Tyersal Lane, Bradford, West Yorkshire, BD4 0RB Tel: (01274) 660263 Fax: (01274) 669223

G T G Engineering Co. Ltd, 1 Albert Street, Loughborough, Leicestershire, LE11 2DW Tel: (01509) 215077 Fax: (01509) 234810 E-mail: martingeorge@gtgeng.co.uk

G W Cowler, 16 Merchant Drive, Mead Lane, Hertford, SG13 7AY Tel: (01992) 501494 Fax: (01992) 501495 E-mail: sales@gwcowler.demon.co.uk

G W Lambert Engineers Ltd, 10 Queens Road, High Wycombe, Buckinghamshire, HP13 6AQ Tel: (01494) 525977 Fax: (01494) 528238

G W Martin & Co. Ltd, 7 Bishopstoke Road, Eastleigh, Hampshire, SO50 6AD Tel: (023) 8064 2922 Fax: (023) 8061 1653 E-mail: andyclark@gwmartin.co.uk

Brian Ganman, Fordbrook Industrial Estate, Marlborough Road, Pewsey, Wiltshire, SN9 5NT Tel: (01672) 563759 Fax: (01672) 563759

Gautrey Engineering, 43 Telegraph Street, Cottenham, Cambridge, CB24 8QU Tel: (01954) 251112 Fax: (01954) 206256

Genhart Ltd, 3 Malmesbury Road, Kingsditch Trading Estate, Cheltenham, Gloucestershire, GL51 9PL Tel: (01242) 241734 Fax: (01242) 227500 E-mail: frank@genhart.co.uk

Geomount Ltd, Unit 8 Cranleigh Gardens Industrial Estate, Southall, Middlesex, UB1 2BZ Tel: (020) 8571 7046 Fax: (020) 8571 6992 E-mail: pphillips@geomont.fsnet.co.uk

K.L. Giddings Ltd, Lion Works, Station Road East, Whittlesford, Cambridge, CB22 4WL Tel: (01223) 832638 Fax: (01223) 832189 E-mail: enquires@klgiddings.co.uk

Gill Engineering Ltd, 111 Wickham Road, Fareham, Hampshire, PO16 7HZ Tel: (01329) 221341 Fax: (01329) 221388 E-mail: info@gillengineering.co.uk

Glasgow Precision Ltd, 13 Colquhoun Avenue, Hillington Industrial Estate, Glasgow, G52 4BN Tel: 0141-882 5793 Fax: 0141-810 3061 E-mail: glasp1@netcomuk.co.uk

Glebe Engineering Ltd, Edensor Works, Greendock Street, Stoke-on-Trent, ST3 2NA Tel: (01782) 599161 Fax: (01782) 324410 E-mail: nick.cresswell@glebe.co.uk

Glenborough Engineering Co. Ltd, Station Road, Glenfield, Leicester, LE3 8BT Tel: 0116-231 4444 Fax: 0116-287 5441 E-mail: sales@glenborough.co.uk

Glenhead Engineering Ltd, 60 Beardmore Way, Clydebank, Dunbartonshire, G81 4HT Tel: 0141-952 9945 Fax: 0141-951 1731 E-mail: info@glenheadengineering.co.uk

Glenroy Engineering Services Ltd, Albion Dockside Estate, Hanover Place, Bristol, BS1 6UT Tel: 0117-929 1450 Fax: 0117-925 1938 E-mail: glenroy@nascr.net

Glentworth Precision Engineering Ltd, Molly Millars Bridge, Wokingham, Berkshire, RG41 2WY Tel: 0118-977 1955 Fax: 0118-977 2907 E-mail: john.darcy@glentworth.co.uk

Globel Technologies Racing, Denmans Lane, Fontwell, Arundel, West Sussex, BN18 0SU Tel: (01243) 545000 Fax: (01243) 545050

Goldburn Engineering Co. Ltd, Unit 12, Uddens Trading Estate, Wimborne, Dorset, BH21 7LL Tel: (01202) 893100 Fax: (01202) 861666

Goodchild Precision Engineering Co Ltd, Unit 5 Chiltern Trading Estate, Earl Howe Road, Holmer Green, High Wycombe, Buckinghamshire, HP15 6QT Tel: (01494) 714728 Fax: (01494) 714728

Goodwood Engineering, Enterprise Way, King's Lynn, Norfolk, PE30 4LJ Tel: (01553) 766574 Fax: (01553) 766574 E-mail: andy@goodwoodeng.co.uk

Gould & Williams Engineers, 8-10 The Kerridge Industrial Estate, Station Road, Alton, Hampshire, GU34 2PT Tel: (01420) 87318 Fax: (01420) 84065 E-mail: gouldandwilliams@btinternet.com

GP Precision Engineering Ltd, Unit 19 Nineteen Morses Lane, Industrial Estate, Brightlingsea, Colchester, CO7 0SF Tel: (01206) 303668 Fax: (01206) 303668 E-mail: Enquiries@GPPrecisionEngineering.co.uk

Grangestone Engineering Co., Grangestone Industrial Estate, Ladywell Avenue, Girvan, Ayrshire, KA26 9PL Tel: (01465) 712505 Fax: (01465) 712505

Granton Engineering & Manufacturing Ltd, 1 Davis Way, Fareham, Hampshire, PO14 1JF Tel: (01329) 231144 Fax: (01329) 822759 E-mail: sales@granton-eng.co.uk

Gray Precision Engineering, Units 1-3, Castle Court, Bankside Industrial Estate, Falkirk, FK2 7UU Tel: (01324) 612679 Fax: (01324) 612209 E-mail: stuart.gray@btconnect.com

Grayson Millward Ltd, Wharf Road Industrial Estate, Pinxton, Nottingham, NG16 6LE Tel: (01773) 810144 Fax: (01773) 860321 E-mail:

Greenway Pepper Precision Engineering Ltd, Parkhouse Road East, Parkhouse Industrial Estate East, Newcastle, Staffordshire, ST5 7RB Tel: (01782) 563020 Fax: (01782) 565540 E-mail: office@greenwaypepper.co.uk

Griffiths Devereaux, 334 Bristol Road, Gloucester, GL2 5DN Tel: (01452) 520418 Fax: (01452) 307877

Griffiths Precision Engineering, 5 Hicks Road, Markyate, St. Albans, Hertfordshire, AL3 8LG Tel: (01582) 841192 Fax: (01582) 841395 E-mail: griff@griffithseng.co.uk

Griturn Engineering Ltd, Unit 21d, Icknield Way Farm, Tring Road, Dunstable, Bedfordshire, LU6 2JX Tel: (01582) 661878 Fax: (01582) 472980 E-mail: enquiries@srb-griturn.com

Grosvenor Tooling Services, Unit 12, Ash Road, Wrexham Industrial Estate, Wrexham, Clwyd, LL13 9UF Tel: (01978) 664359 Fax: (01978) 664359

Group 4 Engineering, Pontardawe Industrial Estate, Pontardawe, Swansea, SA8 4EN Tel: (01792) 865000 Fax: (01792) 865099 E-mail: mail@group4engineering.co.uk

Grove Engineering (Bristol) Ltd, Units M1 & M2, Lawrence Drive, Stover Trading Estate, Yate, Bristol, BS37 5PG Tel: (01454) 317766 Fax: (01454) 317334 E-mail: sales@grove-engineering.co.uk

Grove Engineering Services Ltd, Unit C, The Grove, Corby, Northamptonshire, NN18 8EW Tel: (01536) 402732 Fax: (01536) 401133 E-mail: grove_engineering@ic24.net

GWK Engineering, 8 Ham Bridge Trading Estate, Willowbrook Road, Worthing, West Sussex, BN14 8NA Tel: (01903) 232773 Fax: (01903) 211062

H B D Engineering 2000, Unit F4 The Seedbed Centre, Harlow, Essex, CM19 5AF Tel: (01279) 436894 Fax: (01279) 436894 E-mail: sales@hbd2000.co.uk

H Beesley Ltd, Commercial Square, Freemans Common, Leicester, LE2 7SR Tel: 0116-255 4233 Fax: 0116-255 4366 E-mail: enquiries@hbeesley.co.uk

H.C Turk Engineering Services Ltd, 4a The Mews, Bentley Street, Gravesend, Kent, DA12 2DH Tel: (01474) 325331 Fax: (01474) 353140

H J Jennings & Co., St Francis, Silver Street, Shepton Beauchamp, Ilminster, Somerset, TA19 0JZ Tel: (01460) 240499 Fax: (01460) 242179

H M Skenfield Ltd, Laneside Mills, Laneside, Morley, Leeds, LS27 7NR Tel: 0113-253 4120 Fax: 0113-253 4120

H R Adcock Ltd, 17 Gelders Hall Road, Loughborough, Leicestershire, LE12 9NH Tel: (01509) 502493 Fax: (01509) 650442

H T S Precision Engineering Co. Ltd, Unit 3, Shamrock Quay, William Street, Northam, Southampton, SO14 5QL Tel: (023) 8033 3668 Fax: (023) 8063 7216

Hadee Engineering Co. Ltd, New Street, Holbrook Industrial Estate, Holbrook, Sheffield, S20 3GH Tel: 0114-248 3711 Fax: 0114-247 7858 E-mail: peterlowe@hadee.co.uk

Haig Engineering, Unit 7 Bottings Industrial Estate, Curdridge, Southampton, SO30 2DY Tel: (01489) 790910 Fax: (01489) 790911 E-mail: office@ers1996.freeserve.co.uk

Hamilton Precision Engineering, 7 Hamilton Way, Gore Road Industrial Estate, New Milton, Hampshire, BH25 6TQ Tel: (01425) 613181

Hampson Aerospace Machining Ltd, Pegasus House, Bromford Lane, Birmingham, B24 8DW Tel: 0121-683 6200 Fax: 0121-683 6201 E-mail: info@hampsongroup.com

Hampson Composites Ltd, Vale Mill, Vale Street, Bolton, BL2 6QF Tel: (01204) 381626 Fax: (01204) 529457 E-mail: liz@hampson-composites.co.uk

Handmark Engineering, Unit 3c Park Road Industrial Estate, Park Road, Barrow-in-Furness, Cumbria, LA14 4EQ Tel: (01229) 835922 Fax: (01229) 877461 E-mail: enquiries@handmark-engineering.co.uk

Hanley Smith Ltd, 7 South Road, Harlow, Essex, CM20 2AP Tel: (01279) 414446 Fax: (01279) 635101 E-mail: info@hanleysmith.co.uk

Harbour Jig & Tool Ltd, 1a Harwoods Road, Watford, WD18 7RB Tel: (01923) 231112 Fax: (01923) 232330 E-mail: harbourjigtools1@btconnect.com

Harcol Ltd, 5 Croxstalls Road, Walsall, WS3 2XU Tel: (01922) 494951 Fax: (01922) 710370 E-mail: harcol@engs.fslife.co.uk

▶ Hardmetal Engineering Cornwall Ltd, Treleigh Industrial Estate, Jon Davey Drive, Redruth, Cornwall, TR16 4AX Tel: (01209) 202809 Fax: (01209) 202819 E-mail: sales@tungsten-carbide.com

Hargood Engineers Ltd, 134a Virginia Street, Southport, Merseyside, PR8 6SP Tel: (01704) 534668 Fax: (01704) 501862 E-mail: john@hargood-eng.freeserve.co.uk

Harlech Tool & Engineering Co., 5 Ynyscedwyn Industrial Estate, Trawsffordd Road, Ystradgynlais, Swansea, SA9 1DT Tel: (01639) 849044 Fax: (01639) 849045 E-mail: info@harlech-tools.co.uk

Harnam Engineering Works, 7 Adler Industrial Estate, Betam Road, Hayes, Middlesex, UB3 1ST Tel: (020) 8561 4828 Fax: (020) 8573 2960E-mail: harinder@harnameng.co.uk

Harper Reg Engineering, 19 Tallon Road, Hutton, Brentwood, Essex, CM13 1TE Tel: (01277) 223130 Fax: (01277) 212179

Harpham Precision Engineering, Unit 5, Eastwood End, Wimblington, March, Cambridgeshire, PE15 0QQ Tel: (01354) 741336 Fax: (01354) 741517

Harrison & Hutchinson Ltd, Field Road, Heysham, Morecambe, Lancashire, LA3 2XU Tel: (01524) 850200 Fax: (01524) 850605 E-mail: harrison.hutchin@btconnect.com

Hartley Precision Engineering Co. Ltd, Caddick Road, Knowsley Business Park, Prescot, Merseyside, L34 9HP Tel: 0151-548 0777 Fax: 0151-549 1191 E-mail: hartleyprecision@btconnect.com

Hawk Engineering, Bessemer Road, Sheffield, S9 3XN Tel: 0114-281 7111 Fax: 0114-281 7222 E-mail: sales@hawkengineering.co.uk

Hay Engineering, 22-25 Moreland Road, Forton Industrial Estate, Gosport, Hampshire, PO12 4UU Tel: (023) 9258 7453 Fax: (023) 9258 7453 E-mail: robert@hayengineering.com

Hayneswood Engineering UK, Acorn Street, Lees, Oldham, OL4 3DE Tel: 0161-620 5337 Fax: 0161-621 5974 E-mail: engineering@hayneswood.co.uk

Hayward Engineering, Unit 6 11-15 Francis Avenue, Bournemouth, BH11 8NX Tel: (01202) 573235 Fax: (01202) 581903 E-mail: sales@haywardeng.co.uk

Heitz Engineering Ltd, 24 Charles Wood Road, Dereham, Norfolk, NR19 1SX Tel: (01362) 692114 Fax: (01362) 695360 E-mail: sales@heitzeng.com

Helmrick Engineers Ltd, Ossett Lane, Dewsbury, West Yorkshire, WF12 8LS Tel: (01924) 462743 Fax: (01924) 430229 E-mail: helmrickuk@aol.com

Helston Engineering Ltd, Unit 10 Bentley La Industrial Estate, Bentley Lane, Walsall, WS2 8TL Tel: (01922) 641556 Fax: (01922) 746161

Hempstead & Johnson Ltd, Oakridge Road, High Wycombe, Buckinghamshire, HP11 2PF Tel: (01494) 444971 Fax: (01494) 462636

Herts & Essex Precision Engineers, Unit 10 Zone B Chelmsford Road Industrial Estate, Chelmsford Road, Dunmow, Essex, CM6 1HD Tel: (01371) 875459 Fax: (01371) 872270 E-mail: hertsessex@aol.com

Herts Precision Engineering, Unit 1, Riverside Estate, Coldharbour Lane, Harpenden, Hertfordshire, AL5 4UN Tel: (01582) 462728 Fax: (01582) 462805

Hewes Products, Wren Park, Cinques Road, Gamlingay, Sandy, Bedfordshire, SG19 3NJ Tel: (01767) 651333 Fax: (01767) 651311 E-mail: info@hewes.co.uk

Heywood & Palmer Engineering Ltd, The Coach House, William Street, Ashton-under-Lyne, Lancashire, OL7 0BH Tel: 0161-339 0601 Fax: 0161-285 2295 E-mail: sales@heywoodandpalmer.co.uk

Higar Engineering Ltd, Gore Road Industrial Estate, New Milton, Hampshire, BH25 6TH Tel: (01425) 617511 Fax: (01425) 629463 E-mail: sales@higar.com

Higgins Engineering Ltd, 816A Oxford Road, Reading, RG30 1EL Tel: 0118-957 1058 Fax: 0118-957 1058 E-mail: higginsengineering@ntlworld.com

High Tech Engineering Ltd, 3 Mayer Way, Houghton Regis, Dunstable, Bedfordshire, LU5 5BF Tel: (01582) 662277 Fax: (01582) 472235 E-mail: hightech2@compuserve.com

Highline Precision Engineering, Old Mill La Industrial Estate, Mansfield Woodhouse, Mansfield, Nottinghamshire, NG19 9BG Tel: (01623) 654251 Fax: (01623) 621384

Highline Precision Engineering Ltd, Old Mill La Industrial Estate, Mansfield Woodhouse, Mansfield, Nottinghamshire, NG19 9BG Tel: (01623) 654251 Fax: (01623) 621384

Hildred Engineering Co. Ltd, Units 2 4 & 6, Parkway Court, Nottingham, NG8 4GN Tel: 0115-928 2217 Fax: 0115-985 4998 E-mail: hildredengco@aol.com

Hillco Engineering Ltd, Beehive Works Beehive Lane, Chelmsford, CM2 9JY Tel: (01245) 354507 Fax: (01245) 354507 E-mail: hillco@acedial.co.uk

Hillcrest Machinery Engineering Portchester Ltd, 1 Pennant Park, Standard Way, Fareham, Hampshire, PO16 8XU Tel: (01329) 231245 Fax: (01329) 822753 E-mail: office@hillcresteng.co.uk

▶ Hilmax Precision Engineering Ltd, Unit 31, Sedgewick Road, Luton, LU4 9DT Tel: (01582) 573384 Fax: (01582) 508868 E-mail: info@hilmax.co.uk

Hilsea Engineering Ltd, 3 St Georges Indust Estate, Rodney Road, Southsea, Hampshire, PO4 8SS Tel: (023) 9273 1676 Fax: (023) 9282 7801 E-mail: hilseaeng@fsbdial.co.uk

Holford Engineering Ltd, Olivers Lane, Stotfold, Hitchin, Hertfordshire, SG5 4DH Tel: (01462) 730288 Fax: (01462) 733508

Holford Engineering Ltd, 13 Cromwell Road, St. Neots, Cambridgeshire, PE19 2EU Tel: (01480) 217271 Fax: (01480) 219687

Holland & Harrison Ltd, 46 Vale Road, Bushey, WD23 2HQ Tel: (01923) 220752 Fax: (01923) 234011E-mail: cnc@hollandandharrison.co.uk

Bernard Holmes Precision Ltd, The Old Pony Field, Grosvenor Road, Billingborough, Sleaford, Lincolnshire, NG34 0QN Tel: (01529) 240241 Fax: (01529) 240802

▶ indicates data change since last edition

PRECISION ENGINEERS – *continued*

Horne & Banks Group Ltd, 3 Merchant Drive, Mead Lane Industrial Estate, Hertford, SG13 7BH Tel: (01992) 501289 Fax: (01992) 501318 E-mail: david@horneandbanks.co.uk

Humberside Gear Co. Ltd, Thrunscoe House, Thrunscoe Road, Cleethorpes, South Humberside, DN35 8TA Tel: (01472) 601111 Fax: (01472) 602143 E-mail: humberside.gears@virgin.net

Hunprenco Precision Engineering Ltd, Bridlington Road, Hunmanby Industrial Estate, Filey, North Yorkshire, YO14 0PH Tel: (01723) 890105 Fax: (01723) 890018

P. Huntington & Co. Engineering Ltd, 1 Millbrook Road, West Float Industrial Estate, Birkenhead, Merseyside, CH41 1FL Tel: 0151-637 0028 Fax: 0151-639 9919

Hutton Engineering (Precision) Ltd, 31 Wedgwood Road, Bicester, Oxfordshire, OX26 4UL Tel: (01869) 243933 Fax: (01869) 249869 E-mail: sales@hepltd.co.uk

Hyde Aero Products Ltd, Ashton Street, Dukinfield, Cheshire, SK16 4RR Tel: 0161-343 5844 Fax: 0161-343 5833 E-mail: enquiries@hydeaero.co.uk

Hyde Group Ltd, Hadfield Street, Dukinfield, Cheshire, SK16 4QX Tel: 0161-308 2111 Fax: 0161-330 2680 E-mail: sales@hydetool.co.uk

I E C Engineering Ltd, Brookside Avenue, Rustington, Littlehampton, West Sussex, BN16 3LF Tel: (01903) 773337 Fax: (01903) 786619 E-mail: info@ieceng.co.uk

I E C Precision Ltd, 3 Daux Road, Billingshurst, West Sussex, RH14 9SJ Tel: (01403) 783629 Fax: (01403) 784792 E-mail: sales@iecprecision.co.uk

I M I Watson Smith Ltd, Cross Chancellor Street, Leeds, LS6 2RT Tel: 0113-245 7587 Fax: 0113-246 5735 E-mail: enquiries@watsonsmith.com

Ilford Engineering Co. Ltd, Bentalls, Basildon, Essex, SS14 3BY Tel: (01268) 526756 Fax: (01268) 531485 E-mail: mike@ilfordengineering.co.uk

Ilsley & Challis Ltd, Unit 1 ESME House, Coronation Road, Basingstoke, Hampshire, RG21 4ET Tel: 0845 5314149 Fax: (01256) 840204 E-mail: info@ilsley-challis.co.uk

Inchlines Ltd, 11 Hilltop Road, Hamilton Industrial Park, Leicester, LE5 1TT Tel: 0116-276 5111 Fax: 0116-276 6596 E-mail: info@inchlines.com

Industrial Plant Development Ltd, 4 Gloucester Road, Luton, LU1 3HX Tel: (01582) 731925 Fax: (01582) 480448 E-mail: ipdltd@btinternet.com

Ingham (Toolmakers) Ltd, Willow Hall Works, Willowfield Road, Halifax, West Yorkshire, HX2 7NF Tel: (01422) 342189 Fax: (01422) 342497 E-mail: info@inghamtools.co.uk

Insight Ltd, Sandys Road, Malvern, Worcestershire, WR14 1JJ Tel: (01684) 577444 Fax: (01684) 577555 E-mail: sales@insightprecision.co.uk

Intime Engineering Ledbury Ltd, 7c Lower Road, Ledbury, Herefordshire, HR8 2DH Tel: (01531) 633450 Fax: (01531) 635197 E-mail: colin@intime-eng.com

▶ Isosure Ltd, 18 Spring Terrace, Goodshawfold, Rossendale, Lancashire, BB4 8QR Tel: (01706) 225419 Fax: (01706) 230784 E-mail: info@isosure.com

Itasco Precision Ltd, 18 Faraday Road, Glenrothes, Fife, KY6 2RU Tel: (01592) 771285 Fax: (01592) 775164 E-mail: sales@itasco.co.uk

J & A Precision Engineering, 10 Second Avenue, Chatham, Kent, ME4 5AU Tel: (01634) 406727 Fax: (01634) 832115 E-mail: mail@jandaprecisioneng.co.uk

J B S Poyser Mansfield Ltd, Pleasley Vale Works, Pleasley Vale, Mansfield, Nottinghamshire, NG19 8SD Tel: (01623) 810066 Fax: (01623) 812266

J Burrows, 18 Telford Way, Thetford, Norfolk, IP24 1HU Tel: (01842) 752211 Fax: (01842) 753868 E-mail: john@burrowseng.ssnet.co.uk

J C Engineering Ltd, St. Ivel Way, Bristol, BS30 8TY Tel: 0117-961 6535 Fax: 0117-960 5657 E-mail: enquiries@jc-engineering.co.uk

J E A Engineering Components, 18-19 Whitehill Road, Glenrothes, Fife, KY6 2RW Tel: (01592) 771911 Fax: (01592) 771911

J F C, Daleham House, Hillbottom Road, Sands Industrial Estate, High Wycombe, Buckinghamshire, HP12 4HJ Tel: (01494) 447881 Fax: (01494) 436356

J J Churchill Ltd, Station Road, Market Bosworth, Nuneaton, Warwickshire, CV13 0PF Tel: (01455) 299600 Fax: (01455) 292330 E-mail: sales@jjchurchill.com

J & L Precision, 17-18 Ivanhoe Road, Finchampstead, Wokingham, Berkshire, RG40 4QQ Tel: 0118-932 8274 Fax: 0118-932 8084

J M Lane, 121 Harecroft Road, Wisbech, Cambridgeshire, PE13 1RS Tel: (01945) 583292 Fax: (01945) 461435

J P C Engineering, Greenhey Place, Skelmersdale, Lancashire, WN8 9SA Tel: (01695) 729552 Fax: (01695) 725552

J P Precision Engineering, Unit 11a Shrub Hill, Worcester, WR4 9EL Tel: (01905) 20319 Fax: (01905) 20319

J & R Engineering, 29 Willow Lane, Mitcham, Surrey, CR4 4NA Tel: (020) 8640 9028

J S Precision Engineering, Spelthorne Lane, Ashford, Middlesex, TW15 1UX Tel: (01784) 246726 Fax: (01784) 423213 E-mail: info@jsprecisionengineering.co.uk

J & S Precision Engineering, 14a Shuttleworth Road, Elm Farm Industrial Estate, Bedford, MK41 0EP Tel: (01234) 268959 Fax: (01234) 268960 E-mail: jsengltd@btclick.com

J T R Controls Ltd, Bank Street, Walshaw, Bury, Lancashire, BL8 3AZ Tel: 0161-764 3829 Fax: 0161-764 3829

J&B, 7 Cambridge Road, Granby Industrial Estate, Weymouth, Dorset, DT4 9TJ Tel: (01305) 775377 Fax: (01305) 780443

Jable Ltd, Burnley Road, Altham, Accrington, Lancashire, BB5 5TX Tel: (01254) 237035 Fax: (01254) 872343

Jag Precision Engineering, 1 J A S Industrial Park, Titford Lane, Rowley Regis, West Midlands, B65 0PY Tel: 0121-561 4902 Fax: 0121-561 1181 E-mail: jagprecision@btconnect.com

Jason Engineering Ltd, 27-33 High Street, Totton, Southampton, SO40 9HL Tel: (023) 8066 3535 Fax: (023) 8066 3531

Jaybee Engineering Co Brighton Ltd, Avis Way, Newhaven, East Sussex, BN9 0DS Tel: (01273) 514623 Fax: (01273) 513702 E-mail: sales@jaybee-eng.co.uk

Jaylew Engineering Ltd, Unit 12a Autumn Park, Dysart Road, Grantham, Lincolnshire, NG31 7DD Tel: (01476) 565986 Fax: (01476) 562540 E-mail: enquiries@jaylew.com

Jem Sheet Metal & Engineering Ltd, Borron Street, Portwood, Stockport, Cheshire, SK1 2JD Tel: 0161-480 2347 Fax: 0161-480 6210 E-mail: info.jem@btinternet.com

Jencol Engineering Ltd, 1 Somersham Road, St. Ives, Cambridgeshire, PE27 3LN Tel: (01480) 492922 Fax: (01480) 492926 E-mail: sales@jencolengineering.co.uk

Jetwin Precision Engineering Ltd, Enavant House, Reform Road, Maidenhead, Berkshire, SL6 8BT Tel: (01628) 625884 Fax: (01628) 771209

Jigs & Fixtures, Station Yard, Rigg Street, Stewarton, Kilmarnock, Ayrshire, KA3 5AG Tel: (01560) 483512 Fax: (01560) 485160 E-mail: sales@jigsandfixtures.uk.com

John Bold & Co., 1 Willow Street, London, E4 7EG Tel: (020) 8524 9090 Fax: (020) 8524 9191 E-mail: johnboldandco@btconnect.com

John R Oliver Ltd, St James Works, Stourbridge Road, Bridgnorth, Shropshire, WV15 6AQ Tel: (01746) 762337 Fax: 01746 762317 E-mail: jroliver@btinternet.com

▶ John Walker Engineering Co. Ltd, Owens Road, Skippers Lane Industrial Estat, Middlesbrough, Cleveland, TS6 6HE Tel: (01642) 456621 Fax: (01642) 456522

Jones & Shipman Precision Ltd, Murrayfield Road, Braunstone Frith Industrial Estate, Leicester, LE3 1UW Tel: 0116-201 3000 Fax: 0116-201 3002 E-mail: sales@jonesshipman.com

W.G. Jones Ltd, 24 Blackmore Road, Verwood, Dorset, BH31 6BD Tel: 01202 825467

Jude Engineering, Saxon Way East, Corby, Northamptonshire, NN18 9EY Tel: (01536) 460490 Fax: (01536) 460470

K & C Engineering, Unit 7 Three Elms Trading Estate, Hereford, HR4 9PU Tel: (01432) 351612 Fax: (01432) 342290

K C Precision Ltd, Armoury Works, Armoury Road, Birmingham, B11 2PP Tel: 0121-766 6217 Fax: 0121-693 9448

▶ K E Precision, Robey Close, Linby, Nottingham, NG15 8AA Tel: 0115-963 1880 Fax: 0115-963 8789

K F Lever (Precision Engineering) Ltd, 56 Ash Tree Road, Southampton, SO18 1LX Tel: (023) 8055 2351 Fax: (023) 8055 3574 E-mail: klseverltd@yiscalli.co.uk

K M Engineering Ltd, Unit 7b Parnall Road Trading Estate, Parnall Road, Bristol, BS16 3JQ Tel: 0117-965 9336 Fax: 0117-958 3673 E-mail: enquiries@km-engineering.co.uk

K & M Precision Engineering, Knowl Piece, Wilbury Way, Hitchin, Hertfordshire, SG4 0TY Tel: (01462) 422115 Fax: (01462) 436223

K P M Engineering, Premier Partnership Estate, Leys Road, Brierley Hill, West Midlands, DY5 3UP Tel: (01384) 75567 Fax: (01384) 75567

K R G Industries Ltd, Russellcolt Street, Coatbridge, Lanarkshire, ML5 2BN Tel: (01236) 435659 Fax: (01236) 434812 E-mail: sales@krgindustries.com

K W Engineering Poole Ltd, 5 Ency Park, 7 Abingdon Road, Nuffield Industrial Estate, Poole, Dorset, BH17 0UH Tel: (01202) 677990 Fax: (01202) 666355 E-mail: keith.ward@kw-eng.co.uk

Kaby Engineers Ltd, 14-16 Upper Charnwood Street, Leicester, LE2 0AU Tel: 0116-253 6353 Fax: 0116-251 5237E-mail: kb@kb.kaby.co.uk

Kaby Engineers Ltd, 14-16 Upper Charnwood Street, Leicester, LE2 0AU Tel: 0116-253 6353 Fax: 0116-251 5237 E-mail: kaby@kaby.co.uk

Kail & Co. Ltd, 1 Castletown Road, Sunderland, SR5 3HT Tel: 0191-548 7712 Fax: 0191-549 6942 E-mail: sales@kai1.co.uk

Kamway Engineering Ltd, Fircroft Way, Edenbridge, Kent, TN8 6EN Tel: (01732) 862028 Fax: (01732) 866868 E-mail: enquires@kamway.co.uk

Kathglade Ltd, 20 Aston Road, Waterlooville, Hampshire, PO7 7XE Tel: (023) 9226 9777 Fax: (023) 9226 2190

Katron Engineering Precision Ltd, Park Mews Works, Lypiatt Street, Cheltenham, Gloucestershire, GL50 2UB Tel: (01242) 234040 Fax: (01242) 228224 E-mail: denman-groves@tiscali.co.uk

Kayfern Tools, Manchester Road, Mossley, Ashton-under-Lyne, Lancashire, OL5 9AT Tel: (01457) 832747 Fax: (01457) 832747

▶ Kenard Engineering (Tewkesbury) Ltd, Newtown Trading Estate, Green Lane, Tewkesbury, Gloucestershire, GL20 8SJ Tel: (01684) 271400

Kenward Precision & Gear, Unit 1b & 13 Perseverance Mills, Lockwood Scar, Huddersfield, HD4 6BW Tel: (01484) 512355 Fax: (01484) 420793 E-mail: kenward@mywebpage.net

Kerndale Ltd, Pontygwindy Industrial Estate, Caerphilly, Mid Glamorgan, CF83 3HU Tel: (029) 2086 5152 Fax: (029) 2088 7742 E-mail: tonydoel@kerndale.demon.co.uk

Kesson Engineering Co., Manor Drive North, New Malden, Surrey, KT3 5PN Tel: (020) 8337 0800 Fax: (020) 8335 3047

Kestmark Precision Engineering, 3 Winster Grove Industrial Estate, Winster Grove, Birmingham, B44 9EG Tel: 0121-360 8850 Fax: 0121-360 8850 E-mail: eng@kestmark.fsnet.co.uk

Keyford Precision Engineering (Frome) Ltd, Olympic House, Whitworth Road, Marston Trading Estate, Frome, Somerset, BA11 4BY Tel: (01373) 463455 Fax: (01373) 452050 E-mail: sales@keyford.co.uk

King Engineering, Bell Farm, Royston, Hertfordshire, SG8 8ND Tel: (01763) 848899 Fax: (01763) 848899

George. W. King Ltd, Blackhorse Road, Letchworth Garden City, Hertfordshire, SG6 1GE Tel: (01462) 481180 Fax: (01462) 675847 E-mail: george.king@gwkgroup.com

Kings Norton Engineering Co. Ltd, Facet Road, Birmingham, B38 9PT Tel: 0121-458 3538 Fax: 0121-458 3886 E-mail: jharper@kingsnortonengineering.co.uk

KRC, Kings Road, New Haw, Addlestone, Surrey, KT15 3BG Tel: (01932) 353851 Fax: (01932) 353851

Krouse Precision Engineering Ltd, Carterton Industrial Estate, Black Bourton Road, Carterton, Oxfordshire, OX18 3EZ Tel: (01993) 843683 Fax: (01993) 840539 E-mail: sales@jdkrouse.co.uk

L A B Engineering, White City Road, Fforestfach, Swansea, SA5 4EE Tel: (01792) 587363 Fax: (01792) 585370 E-mail: labengineering@btinternet.com

L A Tooling Ltd, Toronto Place, Gosport, Hampshire, PO12 4UZ Tel: (023) 9250 1331 Fax: (023) 9252 0807

L G Prout & Sons Ltd, Swann Street, Hull, HU2 0PH Tel: (01482) 329600 Fax: (01482) 216296 E-mail: andy@lgprout.co.uk

L P E Ltd, Russell St, Johnstone, Renfrewshire, PA5 8BZ Tel: (01505) 331165 Fax: (01505) 328606 E-mail: make@linellengservices.co.uk

L V W Auto Motive Components Ltd, 118 Cleveland Street, Birkenhead, Merseyside, CH41 3QP Tel: 0151-666 2000 Fax: 0151-647 7220 E-mail: precision@senareng.demon.co.uk

Lab Engineering, Bowood Lane, Wendover, Aylesbury, Buckinghamshire, HP22 6PY Tel: (01296) 624222 Fax: (01296) 624222

Lada Engineering Services, Vickers House, Vickers Business Centre Priestley Road, Basingstoke, Hampshire, RG24 9NP Tel: (01256) 333571 Fax: 01256 353130 E-mail: info@ladaengineering.co.uk

Lahoma Engineers Ltd, Manning Road Industrial Estate, Bourne, Lincolnshire, PE10 9HW Tel: (01778) 423942 Fax: (01778) 393136 E-mail: production@lahomaengineers.co.uk

Laig Engineering Ltd, 1 Bunting Road, Bury St. Edmunds, Suffolk, IP32 7BX Tel: (01284) 763852 Fax: (01284) 706866 E-mail: info@laig.uk.com

Lake & Nicholls Engineering, 4 Cornish Way, North Walsham, Norfolk, NR28 0AW Tel: (01692) 404602 Fax: (01692) 406723 E-mail: enquiries@lakeandnicholls.co.uk

Langford Lodge Engineering Co. Ltd, 97 Largy Road, Crumlin, County Antrim, BT29 4RT Tel: (028) 9445 2451 Fax: (028) 9445 2161 E-mail: enquiries@rlc-langford.com

Langton Engineering, Denmark Street, Maidenhead, Berkshire, SL6 7BN Tel: (01628) 632764 Fax: (01628) 776183

Laranca Engineering Ltd, Earlswood Trading Estate, Poolhead Lane, Earlswood, Solihull, West Midlands, B94 5EW Tel: (01564) 702651 Fax: (01564) 702341 E-mail: sales@laranca.com

Larmar Engineering Co. Ltd, Main Road, Margaretting, Ingatestone, Essex, CM4 9JD Tel: (01277) 352058 Fax: (01277) 356447 E-mail: info@larmar.co.uk

Lattimer Engineering Ltd, 79-83 Shakespeare Street, Southport, Merseyside, PR8 5AP Tel: (01704) 535040 Fax: (01704) 541046 E-mail: sales@lattimer.com

Lawrence & Hayward, 148 Abercromby Avenue, High Wycombe, Buckinghamshire, HP12 3BJ Tel: (01494) 520329 Fax: (01494) 520329

Lawton Precision Engineers Ltd, 1 25a Hanworth Road, Sunbury-on-Thames, Middlesex, TW16 5DA Tel: (01932) 789001 Fax: (01932) 789003

Lazgill Ltd, 1 Vicarage Road, Hampton Wick, Kingston Upon Thames, Surrey, KT1 4EB Tel: (020) 8977 2125 Fax: (020) 8943 3248 E-mail: sales@lazgill.co.uk

Le Pla & Co Automation Ltd, Riverside Works, Neepsend Lane, Sheffield, S3 8AU Tel: 0114-273 1020 Fax: 0114-273 9331 E-mail: engineers@le-pla.com

Lenack Engineering Co. Ltd, Thame Road Industrial Estate, Thame Road, Haddenham, Aylesbury, Buckinghamshire, HP17 8BY Tel: (01844) 292923 Fax: (01844) 292925

Leopold Grove Engineering Co. Ltd, Amy Johnson Way, Blackpool, FY4 2RP Tel: (01253) 342144 Fax: (01253) 349667 E-mail: office@leopoldeng.co.uk

Likeprod Engineers Ltd, 37 Furlong Road, Bourne End, Buckinghamshire, SL8 5AF Tel: (01628) 522055 Fax: (01628) 524599

Linton Design & Manufacture Ltd, 6a Bessemer CR, Rabans Lane Industrial Area, Aylesbury, Buckinghamshire, HP19 8TF Tel: (01296) 429179 Fax: (01296) 392290 E-mail: linton.design@btinternet.com

Lipco Engineering Ltd, Hightown Industrial Estate, Crow Arch Lane, Ringwood, Hampshire, BH24 1ND Tel: (01425) 476036 Fax: (01425) 475527

Lister Engineering Ltd, 164 Harris Street, Bradford, West Yorkshire, BD1 5JA Tel: (01274) 721855 Fax: (01274) 721251 E-mail: sales@listerengineering.co.uk

Llanelec Precision Engineering Co. Ltd, Jenkins Road, Skewen, Neath, West Glamorgan, SA10 7GA Tel: (01792) 817676 Fax: (01792) 818187 E-mail: sales@llanelec.co.uk

Locke Engineering Egham, Unit 19, Eversley Way, Thorpe Industrial Estate, Egham, Surrey, TW20 8RG Tel: (01784) 438120 Fax: (01784) 438120

▶ Lodge Engineering Doncaster Ltd, Queens Court, Doncaster, South Yorkshire, DN5 9QH Tel: (01302) 390665 Fax: (01302) 789140

Logica Engineering Ltd, 2 Firbank Court, Firbank Way, Leighton Buzzard, Bedfordshire, LU7 4YJ Tel: (01525) 373377 Fax: (01525) 853377

Long & Marshall Ltd, 2 Downley Road, Havant, Hampshire, PO9 2NJ Tel: (023) 9248 0141 Fax: (023) 9245 3368 E-mail: sales@longmar.com

Longfield Instruments Ltd, East Portway, Andover, Hampshire, SP10 3LU Tel: (01264) 323949 Fax: (01264) 355353 E-mail: eddy@longfield-instruments.co.uk

Loughlin Engineering, 10a Woodham Lane, New Haw, Addlestone, Surrey, KT15 3NA Tel: (01932) 855250 Fax: (01932) 859623

Lymington Precision Engineers, Gosport Street, Lymington, Hampshire, SO41 9EE Tel: (01590) 677944 Fax: (01590) 647000

Lyndhurst Precision Engineering Ltd, Weir Mill, Crosse Hall Street, Chorley, Lancashire, PR6 0UH Tel: (01257) 267876 Fax: (01257) 260724 E-mail: sales@lyndhurst-precision.co.uk

M.A.C.-Rk Precision Engineering Ltd, Unit A1, Bridge Road Industrial Estate, Southall, Middlesex, UB2 4AB Tel: (020) 8843 1999 Fax: (020) 8843 1666 E-mail: office@macfittings.co.uk

M A P Systems, Unit 51, Bergen Way, North Lynn Industrial Estate, King's Lynn, Norfolk, PE30 2JG Tel: (01553) 764314 Fax: (01553) 769388 E-mail: eng@mapsystems.co.uk

M A Taylor Engineering Ltd, Orchard Street, Redditch, Worcestershire, B98 7DP Tel: (01527) 62138 Fax: (01527) 68600 E-mail: micktaylorj@tiscali.co.uk

M C D Engineering Ltd, 4 Smiths Forge, North End Road, Yatton, Bristol, BS49 4AU Tel: (01934) 835450 Fax: (01934) 876427

M H V Products Ltd, 33 Woodthorpe Road, Ashford, Middlesex, TW15 2RP Tel: (01784) 241628 Fax: (01784) 255610 E-mail: sales@mhvproducts.co.uk

M I C Engineering, 1a-B Unit, Dans Castle, Tow Law, Bishop Auckland, County Durham, DL13 4BB Tel: (01388) 731347 Fax: (01388) 731348 E-mail: info@mic-valves-eng.co.uk

M J B Engineering (2000) Ltd, 20 Dodwells Bridge Industrial Estate, Jacknell Road, Hinckley, Leicestershire, LE10 3BS Tel: (01455) 615906 Fax: (01455) 633206 E-mail: m.j.bengltd@btconnect.com

M J Engineering Ltd, Unit E6, Market Harborough, Leicestershire, LE16 7PS Tel: 01858 410620

M & M Precision Engineering, 24-25 Saville Road Industrial Estate, Saville Road, Peterborough, PE3 7PR Tel: (01733) 332117 Fax: (01733) 264424 E-mail: sales@mmpe.co.uk

M N B Precision Ltd, Falkland Close, Charter Avenue Industrial Estate, Coventry, CV4 8AU Tel: (024) 7669 5959 Fax: (024) 7669 5909 E-mail: sales@mnbprecision.com

M P Engineering Stalybridge Ltd, Park View Works, Park Street, Stalybridge, Cheshire, SK15 2BT Tel: 0161-303 9988 Fax: 0161-303 9988

M P S, 45a Claremont Street, Cradley Heath, West Midlands, B64 6HH Tel: (01384) 413933

M S Engineering, Unit 49 Silicon Business Centre, Wadsworth Road, Greenford, Middlesex, UB6 7JZ Tel: (020) 8991 1444 Fax: (020) 8991 1444

M S P Ltd, Roman Way, Coleshill, Birmingham, B46 1HG Tel: (01675) 469100 Fax: (01675) 463699 E-mail: sales@msp.ltd.uk

M & T Engineering, 42b Gloucester Road, Croydon, CR0 2DA Tel: (020) 8683 3696 Fax: (020) 8665 5185

M Wellings Engineering, Unit 38 Premier Partnership Estate, Leys Road, Brierley Hill, West Midlands, DY5 3UP Tel: (01384) 74927 Fax: (01384) 74927 E-mail: mick@mwellings.fsnet.co.uk

Machining Centre Ltd, Pembroke Lane, Milton, Abingdon, Oxfordshire, OX14 4EA Tel: (01235) 831343 Fax: (01235) 834708 E-mail: info@machiningcentre.co.uk

William McKay Ltd, 34 Singer Road, Kelvin Industrial Estate, Glasgow, G75 0XS Tel: (01355) 229756 Fax: (01355) 238106 E-mail: stuart1@s.mckay.free-online.co.uk

PRECISION ENGINEERS – *continued*

▶ Mckenzie Engineering, 32 Cutlers Road, South Woodham Ferrers, Chelmsford, CM3 5XJ Tel: (01245) 425413

Macleod Engineering, North Street Industrial Estate, Droitwich, Worcestershire, WR9 8JB Tel: (01905) 794578 Fax: (01905) 794965

Madeira Engineering, Queens Road, Southall, Middlesex, UB2 5BA Tel: (020) 8571 4627 Fax: (020) 8843 0292

Madeley & Glaze Ltd, 8 The Benyon Centre, Walsall, WS2 7NQ Tel: 01922 407717

Magellan Aerospace Bournemouth, 510 Wallisdown Road, Bournemouth, BH11 8QN Tel: (01202) 517411 Fax: (01202) 530886

Main Tool Co. Ltd, Old Edinburgh Road, Bellshill, Lanarkshire, ML4 3HL Tel: 01698 749473

▶ Manifax Engineering Ltd, 8 Coppen Road, Dagenham, Essex, RM8 1HJ Tel: (020) 8592 8849 Fax: (020) 8592 2553

Manned Precision, Lower Wield, Alresford, Hampshire, SO24 9RX Tel: 01256 389258

Manser Precision Engineering, Unit 2, 216 Barnes Lane, Sarisbury Green, Southampton, SO31 7BG Tel: (01489) 564646 Fax: (01489) 564647 E-mail: jigboremanser@onetel.com

Mantec Engineering Ltd, Unit 1-2 City Course Trading Estate, Whitworth Street, Openshaw, Manchester, M11 2DW Tel: 0161-223 8166 Fax: 0161-223 1084 E-mail: mail@mantec.org.uk

Manton Engineering, 4-5 13 Murdock Road, Manton Industrial Estate, Bedford, MK41 7PE Tel: (01234) 345554 Fax: (01234) 272710

Manufax Engineering Ltd, Cromer Street, Stockport, Cheshire, SK1 2NP Tel: 0161-480 2855 Fax: 0161-474 7159 E-mail: manufax@manufax.co.uk

Manx Engineers Ltd, Wheel Hill, Laxey, Isle of Man, IM4 7NL Tel: (01624) 861362 Fax: (01624) 861914

Marathon Engineering, Unit 15 Chiltern Trading Estate, Earl Howe Road, Holmer Green, High Wycombe, Buckinghamshire, HP15 6QT Tel: (01494) 715528 Fax: (01494) 715528

Marben Engineering Ltd, 3 Cobham Road, Ferndown Industrial Estate, Wimborne, Dorset, BH21 7PE Tel: (01202) 895980 Fax: (01202) 891416 E-mail: marben123@aol.com

Marden Engineering, 1 Priestley Way, Crawley, West Sussex, RH10 9NT Tel: (01293) 530530 Fax: (01293) 530537

Marglen Engineering Co. Ltd, 50a Bunyan Road, Kempston, Bedford, MK42 8HL Tel: (01234) 853270 Fax: (01234) 857179 E-mail: marglen@btconnect.com

Maritime Progress Ltd, 3-5 Holmethorpe Avenue, Redhill, RH1 2LZ Tel: (01737) 763400 Fax: (01737) 782818 E-mail: info@maritimeprogress.com

Markit Precision Engineering, 1 The Oaks Industrial Estate, Ravenstone Road, Coalville, Leicestershire, LE67 3NB Tel: (01530) 834435 Fax: (01530) 834438 E-mail: sales@markitprecisionengineering.sagenet.co.uk

Markwell Ltd, 24-25 Littlewood Lane, Hoveton, Norwich, NR12 8DZ Tel: (01603) 783053 Fax: (01603) 783053

Marlborough Engineering Ltd, 67 Sydenham Road, Belfast, BT3 9DJ Tel: (028) 9073 2181 Fax: (028) 9073 2798 E-mail: marlborough@dnet.co.uk

Marlborough Tools Ltd, 315 Summer Lane, Birmingham, B19 3RH Tel: 0121-359 3491 Fax: 0121-359 3491 E-mail: marlborotools@supanet.com

Marnol Precision Engineering, Unit 9 Bee-Hive Trading Estate, 72-78 Crews Hole Road, St. George, Bristol, BS5 8AY Tel: (01275) 50095

Marquin Engineering Co. Ltd, Alma Street, Wolverhampton, WV10 0EY Tel: (01902) 456904 Fax: (01902) 453089

Martec Engineering, Grange Road, Tipree, Colchester, CO5 0QQ Tel: (01621) 819673 Fax: (01621) 817297 E-mail: marteng@aol.com

Martin Aerospace Ltd, 2 Block 6, Caldwellside Industrial Estate, Lanark, ML11 7SR Tel: (01555) 664751 Fax: (01555) 665860 E-mail: sales@martinaerospace.com

C.S. Martin (Alford) Ltd, 33 West Street, Alford, Lincolnshire, LN13 9DQ Tel: (01507) 463427 Fax: (01507) 466942

Martin Jenkins Engineering Co. Ltd, Nicholls Road, Tipton, West Midlands, DY4 9LG Tel: 0121-557 3663 Fax: 0121-557 9517 E-mail: a7vos@aol.com

Neil Matthews Engineering Ltd, Units 8-9, Newton Close, Park Farm Industrial Estate, Wellingborough, Northamptonshire, NN8 6UW Tel: (01933) 401038 Fax: (01933) 401039 E-mail: sales@neilmatthewsengineering.co.uk

Mayes & Warwick Ltd, 5 Mount Road, Burntwood Industrial Estate, Burntwood, Staffordshire, WS7 0AJ Tel: (01543) 682561 Fax: (01543) 686232E-mail: sales@mayesandwarwick.com

Mayhill Contracts Ltd, 11 Mucklow Hill Trading Estate, Mucklow Hill, Halesowen, West Midlands, B62 8DF Tel: 0121-550 0016 Fax: 0121-550 0017

Maylan Engineering Co., Crucible Road, Corby, Northamptonshire, NN17 5TS Tel: (01536) 261798 Fax: (01536) 200957 E-mail: maylan@maylan.com

▶ Meadow Engineering & Patterns, 53 Kenilworth Drive, Oadby, Leicester, LE2 5LT Tel: 0116-271 1763 Fax: 0116-271 6022

Mec-Lon, 1 Enterprise Park, Etna Road, Bury St. Edmunds, Suffolk, IP33 1JZ Tel: (01284) 706334 Fax: (01284) 706334 E-mail: sales@mec-lon.co.uk

Mectronic Instruments Ltd, West Chirton Trading Estate, North Shields, Tyne & Wear, NE29 7TY Tel: 0191-296 0183 Fax: 0191-296 1163 E-mail: sales@mectronic.co.uk

Meden Vale Engineering Co. Ltd, Meden Square, Pleasley, Mansfield, Nottinghamshire, NG19 7SQ Tel: (01623) 810601 Fax: (01623) 812190

Media Resources, Church Croft House, Station Road, Rugeley, Staffordshire, WS15 2HE Tel: (01889) 503100 Fax: (01889) 503100 E-mail: info@media-resources.co.uk

Meggitt P.L.C., Atlantic House, 3 Aviation Park West, Bournemouth International Airport, Hurn, Christchurch, Dorset, BH23 6EW Tel: (01202) 597597 Fax: (01202) 597555

Mellish (Engineering), Unit 28, Mitchell Close, Segensworth Industrial Estate, Fareham, Hampshire, PO15 5SE Tel: (01489) 582393 Fax: (01489) 885823

Meltham Carbide Precision Co., Bent Ley Mill, Bent Ley Road, Meltham, Holmfirth, HD9 4AP Tel: (01484) 850998 Fax: (01484) 854808 E-mail: mcp.co@btinternet.com

Menrica Engineering Ltd, 17 Paynes Lane, Rugby, Warwickshire, CV21 2UH Tel: (01788) 572434

Mercury Precision, Unit 22 The Hayes Trading Estate, Folkes Road, Stourbridge, West Midlands, DY9 8RG Tel: (01384) 424110 Fax: (01384) 422311

Merlin Engineering, Wallows Road, Brierley Hill, West Midlands, DY5 1HQ Tel: (01384) 571936 Fax: (01384) 793436 E-mail: sales@merlinengineering.co.uk

Metal Technology, 9 Viking Way, Bar Hill, Cambridge, CB23 8EL Tel: (01954) 781729 Fax: (01954) 789901

Metalfold Engineering Ltd, Riverside Works, London Road Terrace, Macclesfield, Cheshire, SK11 7RN Tel: (01625) 511598 Fax: (01625) 618838

Metmachex Engineering Ltd, 9 Monk Road, Alfreton, Derbyshire, DE55 7RL Tel: (01773) 836241 Fax: (01773) 520109 E-mail: sales@metmachex.com

Metric Group Ltd, Metric House, 5 Love Lane, Cirencester, Gloucestershire, GL7 1YG Tel: (01285) 651441 Fax: (01285) 653944 E-mail: postmaster@metricgroup.co.uk

Metsol Engineering, Ridgacre Enterprise Park, Ridgacre Road, West Bromwich, West Midlands, B71 1BW Tel: 0121-553 2189 Fax: 0121-525 3375 E-mail: metsolcnc@aol.com

Mettallicut, Deepdale Lane, Lower Gornal, Dudley, West Midlands, DY3 2AF Tel: (01384) 455115 Fax: (01384) 455015

Metwin Engineering, Unit 16 Charfleets Indust Estate, Charfleets Industrial Estate, Canvey Island, Essex, SS8 0PN Tel: (01268) 685959 Fax: (01268) 696208

Miba Tyzack Ltd, Green Lane Works, Green Lane, Sheffield, S3 8ST Tel: 0114-270 0254 Fax: 0114-276 8547

Micro Precision Ltd, Duxons Turn, Hemel Hempstead, Hertfordshire, HP2 4SB Tel: (01442) 241027 Fax: (01442) 268074 E-mail: enquiries@microprecision.co.uk

Micron Engineering Co., Dominion Works, Freshwater Road, Dagenham, Essex, RM8 1RX Tel: (020) 8983 8800 Fax: (020) 8983 8866 E-mail: micronengineering@unit5.freeserve.co.uk

Micron Engineering Ltd, Unit 5 Earls Way, Earl Way Industrial Estate, Thurmaston, Leicester, LE4 8DL Tel: 0116-264 0040 Fax: 0116-289 1402 E-mail: e.muddimer@btconnect.com

Microtech Precision Ltd, Unit D1 Bersham Enterprise Centre, Colliery Road, Rhostyllen, Wrexham, Clwyd, LL14 4EG Tel: (01978) 362295 Fax: (01978) 352043 E-mail: sales@microtechprecision.co.uk

Midd Engineering Coventry Ltd, Blackhorse Road, Exhall, Coventry, CV7 9FW Tel: (024) 7636 3033 Fax: (024) 7636 3044 E-mail: sales@midd-engineering.co.uk

Middleburn Ltd, 6 Bentley Park, Blacknest Road, Blacknest, Alton, Hampshire, GU34 4PX Tel: (01420) 520227 Fax: (01420) 23796 E-mail: bob@middleburn.co.uk

Midland Precision Equipment Co. Ltd, Haslucks Green Road, Shirley, Solihull, West Midlands, B90 2LY Tel: 0121-744 2719 Fax: 0121-733 1296 E-mail: sales@midland-precision.co.uk

Midland Precision Tool Makers, 3 Cyclo Works, Lifford Lane, Birmingham, B30 3DY Tel: 0121-486 3346 Fax: 0121-486 3346

Midway Precision Ltd, Pontygwindy Industrial Estate, Caerphilly, Mid Glamorgan, CF83 3HU Tel: (029) 2088 3552 Fax: (029) 2086 6410 E-mail: hjh@midwayprecisioneng.co.uk

Milbor Engineering Co. Ltd, Belswains Lane, Hemel Hempstead, Hertfordshire, HP3 9XE Tel: (01442) 242945 Fax: (01442) 257308 E-mail: enquiries@nashmills.herts.sch.uk

Millbrook Engineering, Wesley Road, Cinderford, Gloucestershire, GL14 2JN Tel: (01594) 823822 Fax: (01594) 823222

Millturn Engineering, 17 Burrel Road, St. Ives, Cambridgeshire, PE27 3LE Tel: (01480) 469644 Fax: (01480) 469342

Mintdale Engineering, Unit 8 Devonshire Industrial Hamlet, Station Road, Brimington, Chesterfield, Derbyshire, S43 1JU Tel: (01246) 550316 Fax: (01246) 550236 E-mail: mintdale.eng@virgin.net

Mogul Engineers Ltd, Chesterton Road, Eastwood Trading Estate, Rotherham, South Yorkshire, S65 1SU Tel: (01709) 379293 Fax: (01709) 378869 E-mail: enquires@mogul-engineers.co.uk

Moldsytems Plastics, 1 Edwardson Road, Meadowfield Industrial Estate, Durham, DH7 8RL Tel: 0191-378 0747 Fax: 0191-378 9255

Monad Precision Engineering Ltd, Montague House, 615-621 Kingston Road, London, SW20 8SA Tel: (020) 8543 1701 Fax: (020) 8443 2458 E-mail: admin@monadpe.co.uk

Monard Precision Engineering Ltd, Avon Industrial Estate, Butlers Leap, Rugby, Warwickshire, CV21 3UY Tel: (01788) 569998 Fax: (01788) 568434 E-mail: monard@avonrugby.freeserve.co.uk

Moorgate Precision Engineering, Polymer House, Admin Road, Knowsley Industrial Park, Liverpool, L33 7TZ Tel: 0151-548 7766 Fax: 0151-548 7788 E-mail: ian@moorgate-precison.com

Mortimer & Spake Engineering, Unit 7-8 Spitfire Quay, Hazel Road, Southampton, SO19 7GB Tel: (023) 8043 6643 Fax: (023) 8044 8800

Moughton Engineering Services, Units 12-13, Faraday Road, Great Yarmouth, Norfolk, NR31 0NF Tel: (01493) 650195 Fax: (01493) 650199

Mould Import Solutions Ltd, Units A, Crewe Close, Blidworth Industrial Park, Blidworth, Mansfield, Nottinghamshire, NG21 0TA Tel: (01623) 490070 Fax: (01623) 795687

MTS, Greenside Way, Middleton, Manchester, M24 1SW Tel: 0161-345 4760 Fax: 0161-345 4766 E-mail: sales@mtsprecision.co.uk

Multi Form Machine Tools Ltd, Aviation House, Aviation Way, Southend-on-Sea, SS2 6UN Tel: (0845) 0690290 Fax: (0845) 0690291 E-mail: info@fabricatorsworld.com

Multi Tech Precision Engineering Wantage, 26 Charlton Road, Wantage, Oxfordshire, OX12 8HG Tel: (01235) 768922

Mutad Engineering, Chartwell Road, Lancing, West Sussex, BN15 8TU Tel: (01903) 756006 Fax: (01903) 750423

Mycol Engineering, 75 Tenter Road, Moulton Park Industrial Estate, Northampton, NN3 6AX Tel: (01604) 790389 Fax: (01604) 790389

N F F Precision Ltd, 4 Enterprise Way Aviation Park, Bournemouth Int Airp, Hurn, Christchurch, Dorset, BH23 6EW Tel: (01202) 583000 Fax: (01202) 583058 E-mail: sales@nff.uk.com

N R Engineering, 5 Commercial Road, Reading, RG2 0QZ Tel: 0118-975 0303 Fax: 0118-975 3879

N & R Needham & Co. Ltd, Bridge Street Industrial Estate, Bridge Street, Clay Cross, Chesterfield, Derbyshire, S45 9NU Tel: (01246) 863171 Fax: (01246) 865411

N & S Precision Components Ltd, 63F Milton Park, Abingdon, Oxfordshire, OX14 4RX Tel: (01235) 831563 Fax: (01235) 820253 E-mail: carolnixon@onetel.com

N S R Graphics, 56 Ashton Vale Road, Bristol, BS3 2HQ Tel: 0117-953 2352 Fax: 0117-953 2353 E-mail: nsr@nsr-eng.co.uk

N W H, Downside Farm, Cobham Park Road, Downside, Cobham, Surrey, KT11 3NE Tel: (01932) 864767 Fax: (01932) 864767

Nelson Tool Co Stockport Ltd, Stringer Street, Stockport, Cheshire, SK1 2NZ Tel: 0161-480 6004 Fax: 0161-476 2325 E-mail: info@nelsontool.co.uk

Neptune Engineering Co., E Caxton Hill, Extension Road, Hertford, SG13 7LY Tel: (01992) 587889 Fax: (01992) 554478 E-mail: sales@neptune-eng.demon.co.uk

New Forest Precision Ltd, 3 Parkside, Ringwood, Hampshire, BH24 3SG Tel: (01425) 479007 Fax: (01425) 480231 E-mail: sales@n-f-p.co.uk

Newburgh Engineering Co. Ltd, Newburgh Works, Bradwell, Hope Valley, Derbyshire, S33 9NT Tel: (01709) 724260 E-mail: sales@newburgh.co.uk

Newbyres Engineering, Unit 2, Sherwood Industrial Estate, Bonnyrigg, Midlothian, EH19 3LW Tel: 0131-653 6646 Fax: 0131-663 9046 E-mail: newbyres@aol.com

Newman Precision Engineering Ltd, 11-17 Steeple Street, Macclesfield, Cheshire, SK10 2QR Tel: (01625) 618627 Fax: (01625) 618627 E-mail: newmanprecision@aol.com

Newmont Engineering Co. Ltd, 274 Worton Road, Isleworth, Middlesex, TW7 6EE Tel: (020) 8568 7718 Fax: (020) 8758 9442

Newnham Engineering, 6 Lancing Business Park, Marlborough Road, Lancing, West Sussex, BN15 8UF Tel: (01903) 851120 Fax: (01903) 761253

Newport Spark Erosion Services, 18-19 South Road, Harlow, Essex, CM20 2AR Tel: (01279) 415900 Fax: (01279) 454753 E-mail: sales@newport-eng.co.uk

Norcot Engineering Ltd, Unit 1, Windsor Road, Bedford, MK42 9SU Tel: (01234) 364324 Fax: (01234) 355915 E-mail: jade.operations@btconnect.com

Norris, Halas Industrial Estate, Forge Lane, Halesowen, West Midlands, B62 8EB Tel: 0121-585 6007 Fax: 0121-585 6007

North West Engineering Group Ltd, Mill Lane, Halton, Lancaster, LA2 6NF Tel: (01524) 811224 Fax: (01524) 811288 E-mail: sales@luneside.co.uk

Northants Precision Grinding Ltd, 12 Tenter Road, Moulton Park Industrial Estate, Northampton, NN3 6PZ Tel: (01604) 648772 Fax: (01604) 642851 E-mail: sales@northantsgrinding.co.uk

Norton Precision Ltd, Botley Road, Horton Heath, Eastleigh, Hampshire, SO50 7DN Tel: (023) 8069 3232 Fax: (023) 8060 1551 E-mail: norton.pre@btclick.com

Numac Engineering Ltd, Gerrard Street, Stalybridge, Cheshire, SK15 2JY Tel: 0161-338 2125 Fax: 0161-304 9435

Nuneaton Precisions Ltd, Veasey Close, Attleborough Fields Industrial Estate, Nuneaton, Warwickshire, CV11 6RT Tel: (024) 7634 3116 Fax: (024) 7664 2355 E-mail: sales@nuneaton-precisions.com

Nusell Engineering Co, 484 Penistone Road, Sheffield, S6 2FU Tel: 0114-233 0244 Fax: 0114-232 6998

▶ Oaston Engineering Ltd, 7-8 Ptarmigan Place, Attleborough Fields Industrial Estate, Nuneaton, Warwickshire, CV11 6RX Tel: (024) 7664 2324 Fax: (024) 7635 4597

Obek UK Ltd, Unit C8 Baird Court, Park Farm Industrial Estate, Wellingborough, Northamptonshire, NN8 6QJ Tel: (01933) 675457 Fax: (01933) 675665 E-mail: obekuk@btconnect.com

Olive & Padgett Ltd, Station Lane, Heckmondwike, West Yorkshire, WF16 0NF Tel: (01924) 405661

Olney Precision Ltd, 5 Stilebrook Road, Olney, Buckinghamshire, MK46 5EA Tel: (01234) 712055 Fax: (01234) 241102

Olympic Engineering, Unit F5 Charles House, Bridge Road, Southall, Middlesex, UB2 4BD Tel: (020) 8574 4406 Fax: (020) 8571 1556 E-mail: oloieng@aol.com

Optimum Precision Engineering Ltd, 5b Lancaster Way Business Park, Ely, Cambridgeshire, CB6 3NW Tel: (01353) 666114 Fax: (01353) 666749 E-mail: sales@optimuprecision.co.uk

Orville Engineering, Unit 4 315 Summer Lane, Birmingham, B19 3RH Tel: 0121-359 7560 Fax: 0121-359 7560

Ottaway Engineering Ltd, Renown Close, Chandlers Ford Industrial Estate, Chandler's Ford, Eastleigh, Hampshire, SO53 4HZ Tel: (023) 8026 9977 Fax: (023) 8027 0270 E-mail: info@otteng.co.uk

P B I Precision Engineers, Unit A, Bull Street Trading Estate, Bull Street, Brierley Hill, West Midlands, DY5 3RA Tel: (01384) 79006 Fax: (01384) 79006

▶ P & C Precision Engineers Ltd, Unit 3c Heron Trading Estate, Whitefield Avenue, Luton, LU3 3BB Tel: (01582) 581735 Fax: (01582) 581735

P & D Precision Engineering Ltd, 8 Crondal Road, Exhall, Coventry, CV7 9NH Tel: (024) 7636 8095 Fax: (024) 7664 4903 E-mail: sales@pandd.wireless.pipex.net

▶ P D Precision Grinding, Clarendon Road, Blackburn, BB1 9SS Tel: (01254) 663235 Fax: (01254) 695222E-mail: pdperc@aol..com

P D R Engineering Ltd, 18-20 Uddens Trading Estate, Wimborne, Dorset, BH21 7LE Tel: (01202) 894015 Fax: (01202) 894021

P G Components, 9 Knightsbridge Business Centre, Knightsbridge Green, Knightsbridge, Cheltenham, Gloucestershire, GL51 9TA Tel: (01242) 530930 Fax: (01242) 680260 E-mail: pgc@knightsbridge.fsbusiness.co.uk

P H B Industries Ltd, Fitzherbert Road, Farlington, Portsmouth, PO6 1SB Tel: (023) 9237 9696 Fax: (023) 9237 5822

▶ P J D Engineering Ltd, 4 Henlow Industrial Estate, Henlow, Bedfordshire, SG16 6DS Tel: (01462) 815544 Fax: (01462) 816677

P M H Precision Engineering Ltd, Unit 1, Such Close Works Road, Letchworth Garden City, Hertfordshire, SG6 1JF Tel: (01462) 682616 Fax: (01462) 682616

P M Hill Engineering, 59 Rowsley Street, Leicester, LE5 5JP Tel: 0116-273 7132

P M Precision Engineering, Unit 2A, Bridge Works, Bridge Road, Camberley, Surrey, GU15 2QR Tel: (01276) 691285 Fax: (01276) 27193 E-mail: hillary@pmeng.co.uk

P R Hollowayltd, 34 West Barnes Lane, Raynes Park, London, SW20 0BP Tel: (020) 8946 8872 Fax: (020) 8946 8872

P R Kyte, Unit 2 Hamilton Road, Sutton-in-Ashfield, Nottinghamshire, NG17 5LD Tel: (01623) 556636 Fax: (01623) 556636

▶ P R Smith Engineering, Station Works, Lyndhurst Road, Ascot, Berkshire, SL5 9ED Tel: (01344) 874763 Fax: (01344) 875433 E-mail: topmut@themutznutz.com

P & S Tools, Spring La South, Malvern, Worcestershire, WR14 1AT Tel: (01684) 563632 Fax: (01684) 560825 E-mail: info@pstools.co.uk

P T G Precision Engineers Ltd, Meadow Close, Langage Business Park, Plympton, Plymouth, PL7 5EX Tel: 0845 2130534 Fax: (01752) 345652 E-mail: sales@ptgltd.co.uk

P Valli & Son, 14 Ministry Wharf, Wycombe Road, Saunderton, High Wycombe, Buckinghamshire, HP14 4HW Tel: (01494) 564558 E-mail: enquiries@pvalli.com

P Y C Engineering Co., 2 Eastside Industrial Estate, Jackson Street, St. Helens, Merseyside, WA9 3AS Tel: (01744) 732931 Fax: (01744) 451058 E-mail: sales@pyc-engineering.co.uk

Park Engineering Ltd, Kenwood Road, Stockport, Cheshire, SK5 6PH Tel: 0161-431 8140 Fax: 0161-431 8154 E-mail: sales@parkengineering.co.uk

Parkland Engineering, C Roebuck Road, Ilford, Essex, IG6 3TU Tel: (020) 8501 0211 Fax: (020) 8501 0211

Parland Engineering Ltd, Unit 7, Cobblestone Court, Hoults Estate, Newcastle upon Tyne, NE6 1AB Tel: 0191-276 6660

Parmac Engineering Services Ltd, Cannon Street, Hull, HU2 0AB Tel: (01482) 227200 Fax: (01482) 211849

▶ indicates data change since last edition

PRECISION ENGINEERS – *continued*

Partex Engineering, 7a Hicks Road, Markyate, St. Albans, Hertfordshire, AL3 8LJ Tel: (01582) 840188 Fax: (01582) 840188

Patterns Ltd, Darley Abbey Mills, Darley Abbey, Derby, DE22 1DZ Tel: (01332) 342127 Fax: (01332) 298242 E-mail: enquiries@patternsderby.co.uk

Patterson, Unit 17 Baldock Industrial Estate, London Road, Baldock, Hertfordshire, SG7 6NG Tel: (01462) 893022 Fax: (01462) 490076

Pattison Eurotech Engineering Ltd, Western Industrial Estate, Caerleon, Newport, NP18 3NN Tel: (01633) 420133 Fax: (01633) 430181 E-mail: office@patteuro.com

Paul Engineering Co. Ltd, Victoria Works, North Street, Coventry, CV2 3FW Tel: (024) 7645 8040 Fax: (024) 7644 9494

Paul Rhodes Precission Engineering, Walker Street, Scholes, Cleckheaton, West Yorkshire, BD19 6EQ Tel: (01274) 851225 Fax: (01274) 851270

PDL Engineering Ltd, 5 Whittle Road, Ferndown Industrial Estate, Wimborne, Dorset, BH21 7RJ Tel: (01202) 871188 Fax: (01202) 892499

Peak Precision Engineering Ltd, Alexandra Works, St Annes Road, Manchester, M34 3DY Tel: 0161-303 4800 Fax: 0161-303 4801

Peerdown Engineering Ltd, 24 Dunstall Hill Ind Estate, Gorsebrook Road, Wolverhampton, WV6 0PJ Tel: (01902) 773663 Fax: (01902) 773663

Pekay Tools, Wattville Road, Smethwick, West Midlands, B66 2NU Tel: 0121-558 8028 Fax: 0121-558 8028

Pemberton Engineering, Unit 48 Planetary Industrial Estate, Planetary Road, Willenhall, West Midlands, WV13 3XB Tel: (01902) 863666 Fax: (01902) 863666 E-mail: pembertoneng@btconnect.com

Penshaw Engineering Ltd, 23 Harvey Close, Crowther, Washington, Tyne & Wear, NE38 0AB Tel: 0191-416 5013 Fax: 0191-415 3949

Peterson Engineering Cleveland Ltd, Limerick Road, Redcar, Cleveland, TS10 5JU Tel: (01642) 472361 Fax: (01642) 488816 E-mail: info@peterson-engineering.com

Philip Walker Engineering, 2 Thistleton Road, Market Overton, Oakham, Leicestershire, LE15 7PP Tel: (01572) 767444 Fax: (01572) 767571 E-mail: walkerengineers@aol.com

Phillips Engineering, Bulmer Road Industrial Estate, Bulmer Road, Sudbury, Suffolk, CO10 7HJ Tel: (01787) 373549 Fax: (01787) 880276

Phoenix Precision Ltd, Crompton Road, Southfield Industrial Estate, Glenrothes, Fife, KY6 2SF Tel: (01592) 772077 Fax: (01592) 773535 E-mail: sales@phoenixprecision.com

Phoenix Tooling Ltd, 2 Saracen Close, Gillingham Business Park, Gillingham, Kent, ME8 0QN Tel: (01634) 363168 Fax: (01634) 361103 E-mail: phoenixtooling@btconnect.com

Picross Precision Engineering Co. Ltd, 16-18 Lister Road, Eastbourne, East Sussex, BN23 6PU Tel: (01323) 507322 Fax: (01323) 507581 E-mail: sales@picross-eng.com

Pinnacle Precision Engineers Ltd, 22 Cogan Street, Glasgow, G43 1AP Tel: 0141-649 6638 Fax: 0141-649 6638

Pique Precision Engineering Ltd, Packet Boat Lane, Cowley, Uxbridge, Middlesex, UB8 2JR Tel: (01895) 443373 Fax: (01895) 431137 E-mail: pique_eng@compuserve.com

Plan It, 13 Palacecraig Street, Coatbridge, Lanarkshire, ML5 4SB Tel: (01236) 421082 Fax: (01236) 424311 E-mail: peryslick@gmail.com

Plaslant Ltd, Unit 154-156 Block 17, Newhouse Industrial Estate, Newhouse, Motherwell, Lanarkshire, ML1 5RX Tel: (01698) 732009 Fax: (01698) 732106 E-mail: plaslant@aol.com

Pollards Engineering, Mundy Street, Ilkeston, Derbyshire, DE7 8EU Tel: 0115-932 4787 Fax: 0115-930 3559 E-mail: info@pollardengineering.com

Pope & Meads Ltd, Star Street, Ware, Hertfordshire, SG12 7AN Tel: (01920) 462366 Fax: (01920) 462332

Portchester Engineering, 19 Windmill Grove, Fareham, Hampshire, PO16 9HP Tel: (023) 9237 4771 Fax: (023) 9221 9253 E-mail: sales@portchesterengineering.co.uk

Powell Manufacturing Co. (Coventry) Ltd, Cromwell Street, Coventry, CV6 5EX Tel: (024) 7668 5131 Fax: (024) 7663 7886

Power Precision & Fabrication Ltd, Greenhill Works, Delaware Road, Gunnislake, Cornwall, PL18 9AS Tel: (01822) 832608 Fax: (01822) 834796

Precision 2000 Ltd, Princesway, Team Valley Trading Estate, Gateshead, Tyne & Wear, NE11 0TU Tel: 0191-420 0057 Fax: 0191-423 0100 E-mail: sales@precision2000.co.uk

Precision Component Manufacturing, 8 Holme Mills, West Slaithwaite Road, Huddersfield, HD7 6LS Tel: (01484) 846965 Fax: (01484) 846965 E-mail: precisioncomponent@daisybroadband.co.uk

▶ Precision Engineering Components Ltd, Bentalls, Basildon, Essex, SS14 3BS Tel: (01268) 271144 Fax: (01268) 273222

Precision Engineers Pontefract Ltd, South Baileygate, Pontefract, West Yorkshire, WF8 2JL Tel: (01977) 702439 Fax: (01977) 600284

Preconomy, Orchard Way, Sutton-in-Ashfield, Nottinghamshire, NG17 1JU Tel: (01623) 492100 Fax: (01623) 514057 E-mail: sales@preconomy.com

T. Pretty Engineers, Unit 1 Homestead Farm, Queniborough, Leicester, LE7 3FP Tel: 0116-260 6362 Fax: 0116-260 6362

Price & Weston, Orchard St, Worcester, WR5 3DY Tel: (01905) 360463 Fax: (01905) 763040 E-mail: enquiries@price-weston.co.uk

Prima Engineering, Stonewall Industrial Estate, Stonewall Place, Newcastle, Staffordshire, ST5 6NR Tel: (01782) 711900 Fax: (01782) 711909

Pro Tek Engineering Ltd, Unit 1, Waterloo Park, Alcester, Warwickshire, B50 4JG Tel: (01789) 490490

Production & Tooling Systems Essex, Unit 2 Europa Park, Croft Way, Witham, Essex, CM8 2FN Tel: (01376) 533150 Fax: (01376) 520932

Produmax Ltd, The Tannery, Station Road, Otley, West Yorkshire, LS21 3HX Tel: (01943) 461713 Fax: (01943) 850228 E-mail: mail@produmax.co.uk

Profile Gauge & Tool Co. Ltd, Mangham Way, Rotherham, South Yorkshire, S61 4RL Tel: (01709) 377184 Fax: (01709) 820281

Proto Precision Engineering, Unit 28 Heath Hill Industrial Estate, Dawley, Telford, Shropshire, TF4 2RH Tel: (01952) 506227 Fax: (01952) 506227

Protocon Engineering Ltd, Stock Road, Southend-On-Sea, SS2 5QF Tel: (01702) 612312 Fax: (01702) 461717 E-mail: protocon@btconnect.com

Provincial Engineers Colne Ltd, 2 Waterside Industrial Estate, Mill Green, Colne, Lancashire, BB8 0TA Tel: (01282) 863893 Fax: (01282) 868704

Purpose Engineering Ltd, Manthorpe House, Brittain Drive, Ripley, Derbyshire, DE5 3ND Tel: (01773) 514200 Fax: (01773) 514315 E-mail: dennis.taylor@manthorpe.co.uk

Pyramid Precision Engineering, Unit 25 Lythalls La Industrial Estate, Lythalls Lane, Coventry, CV6 6FL Tel: (024) 7666 3447 Fax: (024) 7666 3447

Qualicut Engineering Ltd, Wharf Street, Chadderton, Oldham, OL9 7PF Tel: 0161-633 1633 Fax: 0161-633 1660 E-mail: info@qualicut.co.uk

Quansboro Plastics Ltd, Melford Road, Acton, Sudbury, Suffolk, CO10 0BB Tel: (01787) 377207 Fax: (01787) 311515 E-mail: quansboro@supanet.com

▶ Quayside Precision Engineering, Unit 14-15 Vancouver Wharf, Hazel Road, Southampton, SO19 7BN Tel: (023) 8043 9700 Fax: (023) 8043 9701

Quick Tools Ltd, Fitzherbert Road, Portsmouth, PO6 1RY Tel: (023) 9237 5718 Fax: (023) 9232 5203 E-mail: sales@quicktoolsltd.co.uk

R A & B A Linfield, Unit 22 Huffwood Trading Estate, Billingshurst, West Sussex, RH14 9UR Tel: (01403) 783486 Fax: (01403) 783486 E-mail: linfield-eng@btconnect.com

R & A Engineering, 15 Stocklake Industrial Estate, Pembroke Road, Aylesbury, Buckinghamshire, HP20 1DB Tel: (01296) 425057 Fax: (01296) 481085 E-mail: sales@randaeng.co.uk

R A Howarth Engineering Ltd, Earl Road, Rackheath Industrial Estate, Rackheath, Norwich, NR13 6NT Tel: (01603) 721155 Fax: (01603) 721648

R A Labone & Co. Ltd, Lower Middleton Street, Ilkeston, Derbyshire, DE7 5TN Tel: 0115-930 1339 Fax: 0115-944 8801 E-mail: reception@ralabone.co.uk

R & C Church Ltd, Anglian House, Sutton Road, Great Yarmouth, Norfolk, NR30 3NB Tel: (01493) 858715 Fax: (01493) 859786 E-mail: ron@church-precision.co.uk

R & D Engineering Ltd, 4 Robin Hood Works, Robin Hood Road, Knaphill, Woking, Surrey, GU21 2LX Tel: (01483) 488545 Fax: (01483) 488058

R D Precision, Unit 1e Pentre Industrial Estate, Chester Road, Pentre, Deeside, Clwyd, CH5 2DQ Tel: (01244) 520559 Fax: (01244) 531992 E-mail: enquiries@rdprecision.co.uk

R D Techniques, 3 Mounts Road, Wednesbury, West Midlands, WS10 0BU Tel: 0121-502 0570 Fax: 0121-505 3238 E-mail: rd.techniques@cableinet.co.uk

R E Cross & Co. Ltd, Joule Road, Basingstoke, Hampshire, RG21 6XH Tel: (01256) 465878 Fax: (01256) 817743 E-mail: sales@recross.co.uk

R F R Precision Engineering Ltd, Unit 16 Lythalls Lane Industrial Estate, Lythalls Lane, Coventry, CV6 6FJ Tel: (024) 7668 9427 Fax: (024) 7668 9427

R G D Engineering Co. Ltd, Stonecross Industrial Estate, Downham Market, Norfolk, PE38 0AD Tel: (01366) 382962 Fax: (01366) 384938 E-mail: rgdengineering@btconnect.com

R & G Precision Engineering Ltd, 106 Washbrook Road, Rushden, Northamptonshire, NN10 6UL Tel: (01933) 411662 Fax: (01933) 411663 E-mail: sales@rgprecisionltd.co.uk

R H G Stone Engineering, 121 Main Street, Walton, Street, Somerset, BA16 9QL Tel: (01458) 442167 Fax: (01458) 447252 E-mail: info@rhgstone.co.uk

R & J Turner Engineering, Purfleet Industrial Park, London Road, Aveley, South Ockendon, Essex, RM15 4YA Tel: (01708) 865043 Fax: (01708) 869403 E-mail: roger@rjturner.com

R J W Ltd, Unit A5, Watery Lane, Sevenoaks, Kent, TN15 6PW Tel: 01732 763122

R J White, Unit F10 Briarsford, Perry Road, Witham, Essex, CM8 3UY Tel: (01376) 500524

R K Davies, 8 Spinnaker Road, Hempsted Lane, Hempsted, Gloucester, GL2 5FD Tel: (01452) 410555 Fax: (01452) 310452

R & K Metal Components, Unit 37 Claro Court Business Centre, Claro Road, Harrogate, North Yorkshire, HG1 4BA Tel: (01423) 523139 Fax: (01423) 523139

R K R Engineering, Northpoint, Enterprise Close, Medway City Estate, Rochester, Kent, ME2 4LY Tel: (01634) 723565 Fax: (01634) 712912

▶ R L R Engineers Ltd, 456 Warrington Road, Rainhill, Prescot, Merseyside, L35 9JE Tel: 0151-426 0245 Fax: 0151-426 8288 E-mail: admin@rlrengineers.co.uk

R M W Witney Ltd, Unit 10br Bromag Industrial Estate, Burford Road, Minster Lovell, Witney, Oxfordshire, OX29 0SR Tel: (01993) 702505 Fax: (01993) 774103 E-mail: sales@rmwwitneyltd.co.uk

R Mcmahon Engineering Ltd, Unit 5 Oldends Industrial Estate, Oldends, Stonehouse, Gloucestershire, GL10 3RQ Tel: (01453) 828666 Fax: (01453) 828360 E-mail: howard@mcmahon-engineering.com

R P A International Ltd, P.O. Box 441, Tonbridge, Kent, TN9 9DZ Tel: (0845) 8803222 E-mail: info@rpainternational.co.uk

R S Precision Engineering, Units 6-7 Parker Industrial Centre, Watling Street, Dartford, DA2 6EP Tel: (01322) 284111 Fax: (01322) 284338 E-mail: sales@rsprec.com

R S T Precision Engineering Ltd, Unit 31 South Hampshire Industrial Park, Totton, Southampton, SO40 3SA Tel: (023) 8066 3663 Fax: (023) 8066 3461 E-mail: rst.prec.eng@virgin.net

R S Tooling Ltd, 368 Brook Lane, Sarisbury Green, Southampton, SO31 7DP Tel: (01489) 584956 Fax: (01489) 584965

Ramp Industries Ltd, 22 Garrett Road, Lynx Trading Estate, Yeovil, Somerset, BA20 2TJ Tel: (01935) 427290 Fax: (01935) 420753 E-mail: mail@ramp.co.uk

Ramsay Precision Engineers Coventry Ltd, Unit 3 Burnsall Road Industrial Estate, Coventry, CV5 6BU Tel: (024) 7667 4220 Fax: (024) 7667 0721 E-mail: info@ramsay-precision.co.uk

Ranelagh Co. Ltd, 8 Kent Close, Granby Industrial Estate, Weymouth, Dorset, DT4 9TF Tel: (01305) 777602 Fax: (0870) 7061481

Rascahan Engineering Ltd, 51 Ballykelly Road, Limavady, County Londonderry, BT49 9DS Tel: (028) 7772 2618 Fax: (028) 7772 2197

C. Rayment (Precision Engineering) Ltd, Addison Road, Chilton Industrial Estate, Sudbury, Suffolk, CO10 2YW Tel: (01787) 372697 Fax: (01787) 881448 E-mail: sales@c-rayment.demon.co.uk

Raywill Engineering Ltd, 87b Whitby Road, Slough, SL1 3DR Tel: (01753) 533552 Fax: (01753) 534464 E-mail: r_welch@btconnect.com

RCJ Precision, Llay Hall Industrial Estate, Mold Road, Cefn-y-Bedd, Wrexham, Clwyd, LL12 9YG Tel: (01978) 761060 Fax: (01978) 762337 E-mail: rcjprec@dialstart.net

RDMG Aerospace, Boardman Road, Swadlincote, Derbyshire, DE11 9EN Tel: (01283) 550960 Fax: (01283) 550961 E-mail: administration@tecalemitaero.co.uk

Redfern Engineering, Unit 7 Durban Road, Bognor Regis, West Sussex, PO22 9QT Tel: (01243) 864191 Fax: (01243) 862514

Redline C N C, Units 4-5, 15 Balcombe Road, Horley, Surrey, RH6 7JR Tel: (01293) 820090 Fax: (01293) 820091 E-mail: sales@redline-cnc.co.uk

Redmayne Engineering Ltd, Romsey Indust Estate, Greatbridge Road, Romsey, Hampshire, SO51 0HR Tel: (01794) 830832 Fax: (01794) 830123

Regal Engineering Co. Ltd, Speedwell House, West Quay Road, Southampton, SO15 1GY Tel: (023) 8036 6407 Fax: (023) 8036 6301 E-mail: engineering@bsa-regal.co.uk

▶ Responsive Engineering Group, Kingsway South, Team Valley, Gateshead, Tyne & Wear, NE11 0SH Tel: 0191-497 3400 Fax: 0191-497 3401 E-mail: sales@responsive-engineering.com

Rhoda Precision Tooling Ltd, Unit 2 Lansdown Industrial Estate, Cheltenham, Gloucestershire, GL51 8PL Tel: (01242) 233791 Fax: (01242) 226236 E-mail: rhodaprecision@btinternet.com

C. Rice Engineering, Units 1,2 & 3 Brookfield Works, Christie Street, Stockport, Cheshire, SK1 4LR Tel: 0161-477 0380 Fax: 0161-480 7387 E-mail: info@criceeng.com

Richard A Fores Ltd, Dagmar Road, Southall, Middlesex, UB2 5NX Tel: (020) 8574 5287 Fax: (020) 8574 3105 E-mail: r.a.fores@btinternet.com

Richmond Electronics & Engineering International Ltd, Armtec Estate, North Lopham, Diss, Norfolk, IP22 2LR Tel: (01379) 686800 Fax: (01379) 688519 E-mail: info@richmondeei.co.uk

Richmond Precision Services, Lancaster Road, Bowerhill, Melksham, Wiltshire, SN12 6SS Tel: (01225) 706840 Fax: (01225) 700841 E-mail: richard.hand@richmondprecision.co.uk

Ridgeway Co Extrusion Technology Ltd, Unit 22 W & G Industrial Estate, Faringdon Road, East Challow, Wantage, Oxfordshire, OX12 9TF Tel: (01235) 760435 Fax: (01235) 763021

Ripley Engineering Ltd, Rankine Road, Basingstoke, Hampshire, RG24 8PP Tel: (01256) 473940 Fax: (01256) 479991 E-mail: services@ripley-eng.co.uk

Rivers Engineering Co Winchester Ltd, Moorside Road, Winchester, Hampshire, SO23 7RX Tel: (01962) 865065 Fax: (01962) 840829 E-mail: riveng1@aol.com

Riverside Precision Products Ltd, Riverside Industrial Estate, Bridge Road, Littlehampton, West Sussex, BN17 5DF Tel: (01903) 732570 Fax: (01903) 732778 E-mail: enquiries@riverside-precision.co.uk

Rockhill Engineering, Eastern Avenue Industrial Estate, Eastern Avenue, Dunstable, Bedfordshire, LU5 4JY Tel: (01582) 690022 Fax: (01582) 608040

Rockwood Engineering, Ty-Rhiw Estate, Taffs Well, Cardiff, CF15 7YP Tel: (029) 2081 0011 Fax: (029) 2081 3361 E-mail: rockwoodeng@lineone.net

Rodwell Engineering Group Ltd, 199-209 Hornchurch Road, Hornchurch, Essex, RM12 4TJ Tel: (01708) 448877 Fax: (01708) 700007

Rofor Precision Engineering, 35 Dorchester Avenue, Bletchley, Milton Keynes, MK3 6PQ Tel: (01908) 375225 Fax: (01908) 648560

Romford Models, 1b Bridge Close, Romford, RM7 0AU Tel: (01708) 743390 Fax: (01708) 743390

Ronco Engineering Ltd, 3a-3b Unit Alderman Wood Road, Tanfield Lea Industrial Estate South, Tanfield Lea, Stanley, County Durham, DH9 9XF Tel: (01207) 284848 Fax: (01207) 290306 E-mail: enquires@ronco-engineering.co.uk

Rotamic Engineering Ltd, Marsh Road, Lords Meadow Industrial Estate, Crediton, Devon, EX17 1EU Tel: (01363) 774473 Fax: (01363) 773371

Roton Precision Engineering Ltd, The Old Ambulance, Stansfield Road, Todmorden, Lancashire, OL14 5DL Tel: (01706) 813399 Fax: (01706) 813399

Rousant Sherwood Ltd, Van Alloys Indust Estate, Busgrove Lane, Stoke Row, Henley-on-Thames, Oxfordshire, RG9 5QW Tel: (01491) 680767 Fax: (01491) 682290 E-mail: rousant@msn.com

Rovic Engineering, 36 Dawkins Road, Poole, Dorset, BH15 4JD Tel: (01202) 683446 Fax: (01202) 684824 E-mail: rovic@roviceng.co.uk

Rush Engineering, 126 Marjorie Street, Leicester, LE4 5GX Tel: 0116-268 2837 Fax: 0116-266 1781

Rushforth & Co. Ltd, Unit 3 Westfield Industrial Estate, Kirk Lane, Leeds, LS19 7LX Tel: 0113-250 9162 Fax: 0113-239 1394

RW Racing, 19a Bridge Industries, Fareham, Hampshire, PO16 8SX Tel: (01329) 236640 Fax: (01329) 236640 E-mail: neil@rwracing.freeserve.co.uk

S A S Engineering Ltd, Fengate, Peterborough, PE1 5XB Tel: (01733) 312522 Fax: (01733) 314221 E-mail: sasfengate@aol.com

S E S Precision Engineers Ltd, 206 Bromley Road, Catford, London, SE6 2XA Tel: (020) 8461 4240 Fax: (020) 8695 6561

S J Clifford & Co. Ltd, B 19 Bayton Road Industrial Estate, Bayton Road, Exhall, Coventry, CV7 9EL Tel: (024) 7636 3961 Fax: (024) 7664 4097 E-mail: sales@sjclifford.co.uk

S & J Engineering Services, 1 Periwinkle Court, Church Street, Milton Regis, Sittingbourne, Kent, ME10 2JZ Tel: (01795) 431111 Fax: (01795) 431111

▶ S J Mcauley, 35 Vow Road, Ballymoney, County Antrim, BT53 7PB Tel: (028) 2766 6646 Fax: (028) 2766 6705 E-mail: info@mcauleyengineering.co.uk

S J Products, Unit 2 Trench Lock 3, Telford, Shropshire, TF1 5ST Tel: (01952) 240656 Fax: (01952) 242281 E-mail: info@sjproductstoolanddie.co.uk

S L S Precision Engineers Ltd, 1 Hermitage Way, Mansfield, Nottinghamshire, NG18 5ES Tel: (01623) 456601 Fax: (01623) 456602 E-mail: slsprec@aol.com

S M E Ltd, Mill Road, Steyning, West Sussex, BN44 3GY Tel: (01903) 814321 Fax: (01903) 814269 E-mail: sales@sme.ltd.uk

S Q A Engineering, 12 Benson Road, Nuffield Industrial Estate, Poole, Dorset, BH17 0GB Tel: (01202) 676520 Fax: (01202) 671234

S R B Engineering 2000 Ltd, Unit 5 Enterprise Court, Newton Close, Park Farm Industrial Estate, Wellingborough, Northamptonshire, NN8 6UW Tel: (01933) 679161 Fax: (01933) 400363 E-mail: sales@srb-engineering.co.uk

S & S Precision Engineers Ltd, 23 Rainhill Close, East Stephenson Industrial Estate, Washington, Tyne & Wear, NE37 3HN Tel: 0191-416 2184 Fax: 0191-419 1586 E-mail: bob@ssprecision.com

S & S Tools Ltd, Units 9-10 Lupin Works, Worcester Road, Kidderminster, Worcestershire, DY10 1JR Tel: (01562) 60765 Fax: (01562) 60765E-mail: sstools@virgin.net

Saint Engineering Ltd, 73 Buckingham Avenue, Slough, SL1 4PN Tel: (01753) 578433 Fax: (01753) 822559 E-mail: sales@saint-eng.co.uk

St John's Engineering Ltd, Station Road, Auchtermuchty, Cupar, Fife, KY14 7DP Tel: (01337) 828980 Fax: (01337) 827032 E-mail: stj-eng@btconnect.com

Salco, 17 Cutlers Road, South Woodham Ferrers, Chelmsford, CM3 5WA Tel: (0560) 0495051 Fax: (01245) 325208 E-mail: salcoengineering@btconnect.com

Samar Precision Engineering, Central Way, Andover, Hampshire, SP10 5AN Tel: (01264) 334410 Fax: (01264) 335315 E-mail: samar_mail@btconnect.com

▶ indicates data change since last edition

PRECISION ENGINEERS – *continued*

Sampson Engineering Co., Stanley Road, Bradford, West Yorkshire, BD2 1AS Tel: (01274) 723299

Sanderson, Wellington Works, Plover Road, Huddersfield, HD3 3HW Tel: (01484) 653665 Fax: (01484) 654254 E-mail: sales@sandersonprecision.com

Sawford Engineering Ltd, B1 Priors Haw Road, Corby, Northamptonshire, NN17 5JG Tel: (01536) 263211 Fax: (01536) 406266 E-mail: sales@sawfordengineering.co.uk

Saxon Engineering, Unit 1, Bredgar Road, Gillingham, Kent, ME8 6PL Tel: (01634) 370023 Fax: (01634) 263250 E-mail: saxoneng@aol.com

Servex Ltd, Bellingdon Road, Chesham, Buckinghamshire, HP5 2NN Tel: (01494) 784501 Fax: (01494) 784086 E-mail: engineering@servexltd.co.uk

Seychell Engineering & Fabrication Ltd, 8 Arkwright Road, Bicester, Oxfordshire, OX26 4SU Tel: (01869) 322035 Fax: (01869) 321174 E-mail: seychellgroup@btconnect.com

Shearline Precision Engineering Ltd, Cambridgeshire Business Park, Angel Drove, Ely, Cambridgeshire, CB7 4EX Tel: (01353) 668668 Fax: (01353) 668203 E-mail: sales@shearline.co.uk

Sherburn Hill Engineering Co. Ltd, Tanfield Lea Industrial Estate South, Tanfield Lea, Stanley, County Durham, DH9 9QT Tel: (01207) 236777 Fax: (01207) 231053 E-mail: sherburnhill@btconnect.com

Shopfittings & Equipment, Waterloo Industrial Estate, Waterloo Road, Bidford-on-Avon, Alcester, Warwickshire, B50 4JH Tel: (01789) 778497 Fax: (01789) 490132 E-mail: sales@shopfittingsandequipment.co.uk

Silverstream Engineering, 60 Bridge Road East, Welwyn Garden City, Hertfordshire, AL7 1JU Tel: (01707) 322552 Fax: (01707) 334124

Silverthorne Engineering Co., Attwood Street, Stourbridge, West Midlands, DY9 8RU Tel: (01384) 897639 Fax: (01384) 423980 E-mail: t.hoskins@virgin.net

Silvey Engineering Ltd, Redstones, Haywicks Lane, Hardwick, Gloucester, GL2 3QE Tel: (01452) 720439

Simaron Engineering, Sunny Hill Road, Barnfields Industrial Estate, Leek, Staffordshire, ST13 5RG Tel: (01538) 386301

Skeens Precision Engineering Ltd, 55-55a Jubilee Road, Waterlooville, Hampshire, PO7 7RE Tel: (023) 9226 2191 Fax: (023) 9225 4219 E-mail: skeens@deans.freeserve.co.uk

▶ Slater & Crabtree Ltd, Thornes Lane, Wakefield, West Yorkshire, WF1 5RW Tel: (01924) 374874 Fax: (01924) 378288 E-mail: precision@slatercrabtree.co.uk

D. Smith Engineering, 90 Nuffield Road, Poole, Dorset, BH17 7SX Tel: (01202) 687123 Fax: (01202) 685042

Smith Jigboring Ltd, Unit 20 Phoenix Industrial Estate, Charles Street, West Bromwich, West Midlands, B70 0AY Tel: 0121-557 0211 Fax: 0121-557 1941

Solstrand Industries Ltd, J J Building, Hillbottom Road, Sands Industrial Estate, High Wycombe, Buckinghamshire, HP12 4HJ Tel: (01494) 522030 Fax: (01494) 472685

South Western Tools Ltd, 26 New Station Road, Bristol, BS16 3RU Tel: 0117-965 9596 Fax: 0117-965 9566

Southern Tools Ltd, 32 Kimpton Road, Sutton, Surrey, SM3 9RB Tel: (020) 8644 1133 Fax: (020) 8641 1914 E-mail: stl@tools64.freeserve.co.uk

Speedgold Ltd, Pierhead, The Docks, Port Talbot, West Glamorgan, SA13 1RH Tel: (01639) 898519 Fax: (01639) 891611

Speedy Sheet Metal Ltd, 5 Teknol House, Victoria Road, Burgess Hill, West Sussex, RH15 9LH Tel: (01444) 248764 Fax: (01444) 247767

Springwood Engineering, Bunces Lane, Burghfield Common, Reading, RG7 3DH Tel: 0118-983 2411 Fax: 0118-983 4731 E-mail: springwood.eng@btopenworld.com

Spur Engineering Services Ltd, River Gardens Business Centre, Spur Road, Feltham, Middlesex, TW14 0SN Tel: (020) 8844 0887 Fax: (020) 8844 0887 E-mail: sales@spurengineering.co.uk

Staffordshire Precision Engineering Ltd, 4 Red Mine Close, Newcastle, Staffordshire, ST5 9HZ Tel: (01782) 630500 Fax: (01782) 638440 E-mail: sales@staffsprecision.co.uk

Standish Engineering Co. Ltd, Mayflower Works, Bradley Lane, Standish, Wigan, Lancashire, WN6 0XF Tel: (01257) 422838 Fax: (01257) 422381 E-mail: enquiries@cnc-machining.co.uk

Stanton Engineering Coventry 1999 Ltd, 9 Lythalls La Industrial Estate, Lythalls Lane, Coventry, CV6 6FL Tel: (024) 7668 8552

Stantree Precision Ltd, Unit F4 Anchor Brook Industrial Park, Aldridge, Walsall, WS9 8BZ Tel: (01922) 455775 Fax: (01922) 455323 E-mail: garymills@stantreeprecision.co.uk

Stega Engineering Ltd, Sendalls Yard, Crawley Road, Horsham, West Sussex, RH12 4HG Tel: (01403) 269271 Fax: (01403) 269364 E-mail: info@stega.co.uk

Steloc Tooling Co, 3 Brunswick Trading Estate, Hertford Street, Sparkbrook, Birmingham, B12 8NP Tel: 0121-440 3467 Fax: 0121-440 5194

Stereomatics Ltd, Seven Stars Industrial Estate, Wheler Road, Coventry, CV3 4LB Tel: (024) 7630 4000 Fax: (024) 7630 4455 E-mail: sales@stereomatic.co.uk

Straight Eight Precision, Unit F2 Phoenix Trading Estate, London Rd, Thrupp, Stroud, Glos, GL5 2BN Tel: (01453) 884762 Fax: (01453) 884763

Streamline Precision Ltd, Spedding Road, Fenton Industrial Estate, Fenton, Stoke-On-Trent, ST4 2ST Tel: (01782) 847408 Fax: (01782) 749261

Sturges Tooling, 9 Priestley Way, Crawley, West Sussex, RH10 9NT Tel: (01293) 527229 Fax: (01293) 553668

Subsea Components, 59 Clivemont Road, Maidenhead, Berkshire, SL6 7BZ Tel: (01628) 506560 Fax: (01628) 506501 E-mail: sales@subsea-components.co.uk

Sulzer Pumps UK Ltd, Manor Mill Lane, Leeds, LS11 8BR Tel: 0113-270 1244 Fax: 0113-272 4404 E-mail: sales@sulzerpumps.com

Summit, Unit 5 Vulcan Road, Solihull, West Midlands, B91 2JY Tel: 0121-709 1898 Fax: 0121-711 1429 E-mail: enquires@summit-precision.co.uk

P.B. Sutton Engineering Co, 3 Hedley Road, St. Albans, Hertfordshire, AL1 5JL Tel: (01727) 858731 Fax: (01727) 847064 E-mail: hazel@pbsuttonsagehost.co.uk

Swansea Precision Engineering Services Ltd, Unit 11 Oxwich Court, Fendrod Business Park, Swansea, SA6 8QW Tel: (01792) 774817 Fax: (01792) 412282

Swift, Unit 13 Glover Centre, Egmont Street, Mossley, Ashton-under-Lyne, Lancashire, OL5 9PY Tel: (01457) 834005 Fax: (01457) 836617 E-mail: enquiries@swiftengineering.co.uk

Swift Engineering Co., 35 River Road, Barking, Essex, IG11 0DA Tel: (020) 8594 7626 Fax: (020) 8594 6207

Swift Precision Engineering, Dogflud Way, Farnham, Surrey, GU9 7UD Tel: (01252) 713695 Fax: (01252) 734754

Swiftool Precision Engineering Ltd, Unit 1, Brierley Indust Park, Stanton Hill, Sutton-in-Ashfield, Nottinghamshire, NG17 3FW Tel: (01623) 515544 Fax: (01623) 442166 E-mail: sales@swiftool.co.uk

D.J.T. Swindon Ltd, Unit 12 Ash Phase, Kembrey Park, Kembrey Street, Swindon, SN2 8UN Tel: (01793) 432543 Fax: (01793) 435397 E-mail: djt@djt-engineering.fsnet.co.uk

T G Sussex, Ivy Arch Road, Worthing, West Sussex, BN14 8BX Tel: (01903) 215515 Fax: (01903) 215211

T Halliday Engineering Ltd, Orchard Road, Hamworth Road Industrial Estate, Sunbury-on-Thames, Middlesex, TW16 5BZ Tel: (01932) 787862 Fax: (01932) 787839 E-mail: keng@btclick.com

T N C Precision Engineering Ltd, 5 Kendall Court, Hurricane Way, Wickford, Essex, SS11 8YB Tel: (01268) 764631 Fax: (01268) 570978 E-mail: tncprecision@aol.com

T O C Ltd, Brandon Road, Binley, Coventry, CV3 2AN Tel: (024) 7645 0020 Fax: (024) 7663 5722 E-mail: sales@toc-ltd.co.uk

T P Cooke, 1 Kym Road, Bicton Industrial Park, Kimbolton, Huntingdon, Cambridgeshire, PE28 0LW Tel: (01480) 860138 Fax: (01480) 860138 E-mail: tpcookeengineering@btinternet.com

T P Precision Engineers Ltd, Unit 9, Betchworth Works, Ifield Road, Charlwood, Horley, Surrey, RH6 0DX Tel: (01293) 862645 Fax: (01293) 863283

T R A Engineering New Mills Ltd, Hague Bar, High Peak, Derbyshire, SK22 3AT Tel: (01663) 743541 Fax: (01663) 743541

T T I Group Ltd, Bamfurlong Industrial Park, Staverton, Cheltenham, Gloucestershire, GL51 6SX Tel: (01452) 712023 Fax: (01452) 714418

T W Engineering Ltd, Angular House, Quarry Hill Road, Ilkeston, Derbyshire, DE7 4DA Tel: 0115-932 3223 Fax: 0115-930 6221 E-mail: tw@tweng.co.uk

Tahanni Ltd, Unit 37 Wessex Trade Centre, Ringwood Road, Poole, Dorset, BH12 3PG Tel: (01202) 746900 Fax: (01202) 723111 E-mail: info@tahanni.com

Tanoga Ltd, Cradock Rd, Luton, LU4 0JF Tel: (01582) 502882 Fax: (01582) 581781 E-mail: info@tanoga.com

Taw Engineering North West Ltd, 194 Price Street, Birkenhead, Merseyside, CH41 3PR Tel: 0151-647 6198 Fax: 0151-666 1347 E-mail: taw.engineering@virgin.net

George Taylor (Engineering) Ltd, Block 5, Burns Road, Chapelhall Industrial Estate, Chapelhall, Airdrie, Lanarkshire, ML6 8QH Tel: (01236) 761114 Fax: (01236) 754327 E-mail: sales@gteng.co.uk

Taylor Kightley Engineering, 1 Pond Wood Close, Moulton Park Industrial Estate, Northampton, NN3 6RT Tel: (01604) 645871 Fax: (01604) 671939 E-mail: sales@tke.co.uk

Taylorfab Precision Engineers, Unit 5 Greenwood Court, Ramridge Road, Luton, LU2 0TN Tel: (01582) 737279 Fax: (01582) 735616

Teescraft Engineering Ltd, Unit Longfield, South Church Enterprise Park, Bishop Auckland, County Durham, DL14 6XB Tel: (01388) 777339 Fax: (01388) 776242 E-mail: info@teescraft.com

Telist Engineering Services, 5 Millside Industrial Estate, Lawson Road, Dartford, DA1 5BW Tel: (01322) 291291 Fax: (01322) 291291

▶ Telmar C N C, Unit 3 Warrier Park, Chandler's Ford, Eastleigh, Hampshire, SO53 4NF Tel: 023 80266366

Tenable Screw Company Ltd, 16 Deer Park Road, London, SW19 3UB Tel: (020) 8542 6225 Fax: (020) 8543 5789 E-mail: sales@tenable.co.uk

Thomas Engineering, Manning Road, Bourne, Lincolnshire, PE10 9HW Tel: (01778) 422720 Fax: (01778) 425530 E-mail: gecrane@totalise.co.uk

Thomas Hamlin & Co., 64 Monmouth Street, Bridgwater, Somerset, TA6 5EJ Tel: (01278) 422452 Fax: (01278) 424036

R.E. Thompson & Co. (Vacuum) Ltd, Evingar Road, Whitchurch, Hampshire, RG28 7EU Tel: 01256 893325 Fax: 01256 893623 E-mail: sales@rethompson.co.uk

Thornpark Ltd, B1-B2 Pegasus Court, Ardglen Road, Whitchurch, Hampshire, RG28 7BP Tel: (01256) 896161 Fax: (01256) 896162 E-mail: sales@thornpark.co.uk

Thunder Engineering Ltd, 1 Garfield Street, Leicester, LE4 5GF Tel: 0116-253 1105 Fax: 0116-253 1105

Timmick Precision Engineering, 17 Arkwright Court, Astmoor, Runcorn, Cheshire, WA7 1NX Tel: (01928) 563009 Fax: (01928) 563009

Tindall Precision Engineers, 11 Peacock Square Blenheim Way, Northfields Industrial Estate, Market Deeping, Peterborough, PE6 8LW Tel: (01778) 344970 Fax: (01778) 344970

Tiptree Precision Engineering, Galliford Road Industrial Estate, Heybridge, Maldon, Essex, CM9 4XD Tel: (01621) 856733 Fax: (01621) 851355 E-mail: tipeng@aol.com

Titan Motorsport & Automotive Engineering, Harley Industrial Park, Paxton Hill, St. Neots, Cambridgeshire, PE19 6TA Tel: (01480) 474402 Fax: (01480) 405668 E-mail: sales@titan.uk.net

Toolmax General Engineering Ltd, St Martins Trade Park, Nickel Close, Winchester, Hampshire, SO23 7RJ Tel: (01962) 855515 Fax: (01962) 827790

Toolturn Engineering Ltd, 8 Brunel Way, Fareham, Hampshire, PO15 5TX Tel: (01489) 578878 Fax: (01489) 578859 E-mail: sales@toolturn.com

Tordoff Engineering Ltd, 118-120 Havelock Street, Kettering, Northamptonshire, NN16 9QA Tel: (01536) 483864 Fax: (01536) 513157

Tower Tool Co. Ltd, Tower Manfactory, Radnor Road, Wigston, Leicestershire, LE18 4XY Tel: 0116-277 6520 Fax: 0116-277 6388 E-mail: myles@tower-tool.demon.co.uk

Tracel Ltd, Sand Road Industrial Site, Great Gransden, Sandy, Bedfordshire, SG19 3AJ Tel: (01767) 677521 Fax: (01767) 677952

Trafalgar Engineering Co., Station Road, Station Mills, Cottingham, North Humberside, HU16 4LL Tel: (01482) 843558

Travelling Wire, Unit 3 Teknol House, Victoria Road, Burgess Hill, West Sussex, RH15 9LH Tel: (01444) 239920 Fax: (01444) 239920 E-mail: twire@btconnect.com

Trelawney Engineering, Old Yard Workshop, Vansittart, Windsor, Berkshire, SL4 1SE Tel: (01753) 850300 E-mail: info@trelawneyengineering.co.uk

Trendrail Ltd, Units 10 & 11, Brindley Road, Reginald Road Industrial Estate, St. Helens, Merseyside, WA9 4HY Tel: (01744) 851100 Fax: (01744) 851122

Trentex Engineering Ltd, Garner Street, Stoke-on-Trent, ST4 7AX Tel: (01782) 207171 Fax: (01782) 207272 E-mail: sales@trentex.co.uk

Treworrick Engineering Ltd, 22b Albert Drive, Burgess Hill, West Sussex, RH15 9TN Tel: (01444) 232513 Fax: (01444) 248565 E-mail: sales@treworrick.co.uk

Triple X Components Machining Ltd, Masons Road, Stratford-upon-Avon, Warwickshire, CV37 9NF Tel: (01789) 200400 Fax: (01789) 414063 E-mail: machining@triplexcm.com

Tripos Tools Ltd, Upper Interfields, Malvern, Worcestershire, WR14 1UT Tel: (01886) 833377 Fax: (01886) 833579

Trucut Technologies UK Ltd, Flavell Works, Garratt Street, Brierley Hill, West Midlands, DY5 1JU Tel: (01746) 764900 Fax: (01384) 481195 E-mail: sales@chartway.co.uk

Tryang Jig & Gauge Co., Unit 3-4 Wynford Industrial Estate, Wynford Road, Birmingham, B27 6JP Tel: 0121-706 8050 Fax: 0121-765 4294 E-mail: mikedavis@tryang.fsbusiness.co.uk

Tunnicliff Engineering Co. Ltd, 30 Derby Road, Hinckley, Leicestershire, LE10 1QF Tel: (01455) 637220 Fax: (01455) 637220

Turncircuit Ltd, 13 Chaucer Bus Park, Watery Lane, Kemsing, Sevenoaks, Kent, TN15 6PW Tel: (01732) 763140 Fax: (01732) 763511

Turnell & Odell Ltd, 61-65 Sanders Road, Finedon Road Industrial Estate, Wellingborough, Northamptonshire, NN8 4NL Tel: (01933) 222061 Fax: (01933) 440073 E-mail: sales@toengineering.co.uk

Turnmil Engineering, Riverside Industrial Estate, Glanamman, Ammanford, Dyfed, SA18 1LQ Tel: (01269) 825684 Fax: (01269) 824650 E-mail: ceri@turnmil.co.uk

Turnwell Engineering, 4 Heritage Way, Corby, Northamptonshire, NN17 5XW Tel: (01536) 260043 Fax: (01536) 260043

Twinbridge Engineering Co., Langley Place, Burscough Industrial Estate, Ormskirk, Lancashire, L40 8JS Tel: (01704) 892959 Fax: (01704) 894892 E-mail: sales@twinbridge.co.uk

Twyman Engineering Ltd, Unit J, Troon Way Business Centre, Leicester, LE4 9HA Tel: 0116-276 5953 Fax: 0116-276 5953

Tyckam Engineering Ltd, 18 Levellers Lane, Eynesbury, St. Neots, Cambridgeshire, PE19 2JL Tel: (01480) 218282 Fax: (01480) 218282

Tyler Bros Sutton In Ashfield Ltd, Hunt Close, Lowmoor Business Park, Kirkby-in-Ashfield, Nottingham, NG17 7ER Tel: (01623) 758286 Fax: (01623) 756144 E-mail: admin@tybro.co.uk

Ufone Precision Engineers Ltd, Unit 21 Thornleigh Trading Estate, Dudley, West Midlands, DY2 8UB Tel: (01384) 233288 Fax: (01384) 252931 E-mail: enquiries@ufone-eng.com

▶ Ultra Precision Engineering, 149 Camford Way, Luton, LU3 3AN Tel: (01582) 595365 Fax: (01582) 597385

Ultra Precision Products Ltd, Homefield Road, Haverhill, Suffolk, CB9 8QP Tel: (01440) 706030 Fax: (01440) 762828 E-mail: info@ultraprecision.co.uk

Unijet Products Ltd, Unit 4 The Ham, Brentford, Middlesex, TW8 8EZ Tel: 020 85608978

Unijig Ltd, Bowling Back Lane, Bradford, West Yorkshire, BD4 8UF Tel: (01274) 656750 Fax: (01274) 668375 E-mail: sales@unijig.co.uk

▶ Unisurf Engineering Ltd, Barnard Road, Bradford, West Yorkshire, BD4 7ED Tel: (0870) 7508833 Fax: (0870) 7508844 E-mail: info@unisurf-eng.co.uk

Universal Grinding Services Ltd, Unit 1/2, Kings Road Works, Kings Road, New Haw, Addlestone, Surrey, KT15 3BG Tel: 01932 346806 Fax: 01932 350978 E-mail: ugsltd@btconnect.com

Universal Tool (Gloucester) Co. Ltd, Unit 16-18, Bamfurlong Industrial Park, Staverton, Cheltenham, Gloucestershire, GL51 6SX Tel: (01452) 712597 Fax: (01452) 857540 E-mail: mike@inona-uk.com

Upfield Engineering, Rutherfords Business Park, Marley Lane, Battle, East Sussex, TN33 0TY Tel: (01424) 775373 Fax: (01424) 777164 E-mail: enquiries@upfieldengineering.co.uk

Upton & Scott, Huntspill Road, Highbridge, Somerset, TA9 3DE Tel: (01278) 783279 Fax: (01278) 783279

▶ V E S Precision Ltd, 10 Cropmead Industrial Estate, Crewkerne, Somerset, TA18 7HQ Tel: (01460) 270600 Fax: (01460) 270601 E-mail: enquiries@vesprecision.com

V L B Products Ltd, 12 Birch Road East Industrial Estate, Birch Road East, Birmingham, B6 7DB Tel: 0121-328 4575

Venda & Sons Engineering Ltd, Unit 31 Kings Grove, Maidenhead, Berkshire, SL6 4DP Tel: (01628) 773315 Fax: (01628) 773315 E-mail: sales@venda-engineering.co.uk

Verdict Aerospace Components Ltd, 3 Chilten Hill, Chalfont St. Peter, Gerrards Cross, Buckinghamshire, SL9 9YZ Tel: (01753) 890922 Fax: (01753) 890933 E-mail: info@verdictaerospace.com

Verwood Precision Services, 3 Holloways Ebblake Industrial Estate, Bessemer Close, Ebblake Industrial Estate, Verwood, Dorset, BH31 6AZ Tel: (01202) 829310 Fax: (01202) 814994 E-mail: verwoodprecision@talktalk.net

Vetraform Ltd, Unit 19-20, Halesfield 18, Telford, Shropshire, TF7 4PP Tel: (01952) 587631 Fax: (01952) 582596 E-mail: alex@vetraform.co.uk

Votex Hereford Ltd, Redhill Depot, Ross Road, Hereford, HR2 8BH Tel: (01432) 274361 Fax: (01432) 352743 E-mail: sales@votex.co.uk

VPM Ltd, Birch House, Fraser Road, Erith, Kent, DA8 1QX Tel: (01322) 430043 Fax: (01322) 430044 E-mail: comptonshaun@aol.com

W A Engineering (Nuneaton) Ltd, Carlyon Road, Carlyon Road Industrial Estate, Atherstone, Warwickshire, CV9 1LQ Tel: (01827) 715188 Fax: (01827) 717168 E-mail: sales@waengineering.co.uk

W E Allard Ltd, 64 Winpenny Road, Parkhouse Industrial Estate E, Parkhouse Industrial Estate Ea, Newcastle, Staffordshire, ST5 7RH Tel: (01782) 563653 Fax: (01782) 273856

W E C S Precision Ltd, Blenheim Road, Longmead Industrial Estate, Epsom, Surrey, KT19 9BE Tel: (01372) 741633 Fax: (01372) 740539 E-mail: npooles@wecsprecision.com

W J Hall & Co., 10a Old Bridge Way, Shefford, Bedfordshire, SG17 5HQ Tel: (01462) 851044 Fax: (01462) 851044 E-mail: info@hallprecision.co.uk

W K W Precision Engineering Co. Ltd, Shaw Royd Works, Shaw Lane, Halifax, West Yorkshire, HX3 9HD Tel: (01422) 351720 Fax: (01422) 330017 E-mail: sales@wkw-eng.co.uk

W Kitchen Galgate Ltd, Mainstone Works, Galgate, Lancaster, LA2 0JJ Tel: (01524) 751210 Fax: (01524) 752532

W Parrot & Sons, Unit 17 Whitegate Industrial Estate, Whitegate Road, Wrexham, Clwyd, LL13 8UG Tel: (01978) 358070 Fax: (01978) 357392

W Taylor & Sons, 2a Warfield Road, Feltham, Middlesex, TW14 8AD Tel: (020) 8890 2153 Fax: (020) 8893 1271 E-mail: w.taylor@aol.com

Wade Precision Engineering, Unit 39 Penley Industrial Estate, Penley, Wrexham, Clwyd, LL13 0LQ Tel: (01948) 830268 Fax: (01948) 830268

Walker Aec Ltd, 16c Dawkins Road, Poole, Dorset, BH15 4JY Tel: (01202) 685135 Fax: (01202) 677415 E-mail: sales@walkeraec.com

Ward Engineering, 15 Acacia Close, Leighton Buzzard, Bedfordshire, LU7 4QE Tel: (01525) 851337 Fax: (01525) 374776 E-mail: wardeng@onetel.com

PRECISION ENGINEERS – *continued*

Warren Engineering Ltd, Birkbeck Road, Sidcup, Kent, DA14 4DB Tel: (020) 8300 5111 Fax: (020) 8308 9977 E-mail: warrenengineering@supanet.com

Warren Precision Engineering, 4 Shield Industrial Estate, Manor House Avenue, Southampton, SO15 0LF Tel: (023) 8032 2618 Fax: (023) 8032 2619

Washford Engineering Ltd, Unit 41, Crossgate Road, Park Farm Industrial Estate, Redditch, Worcestershire, B98 7SN Tel: (01527) 525390 Fax: (01527) 510241 E-mail: enquiries@washfordengineering.co.uk

Washington Components Ltd, Prestex House, Hertburn Industrial Estate, Hertburn, Washington, Tyne & Wear, NE37 2SF Tel: 0191-416 9676 Fax: 0191-417 7087 E-mail: sales@washingtoncomponents.co.uk

Washington Precision Engineering (NSE) Ltd, 6 Tilley Road, Crowther Industrial Estate, Washington, Tyne & Wear, NE38 0AE Tel: 0191-416 1564 Fax: 0191-415 3712 E-mail: info@wp-eng.co.uk

Waymouth Northumbria Ltd, 11 Ennerdale Road, Riverside Business Park, Blyth, Northumberland, NE24 4RT Tel: (01670) 545000 Fax: (01670) 545333 E-mail: enquiries@waymouth.co.uk

Weatherford (UK), Gapton Hall Road, Gapton Hall Industrial Estate, Great Yarmouth, Norfolk, NR31 0NL Tel: (01493) 441155 Fax: (01493) 657403 E-mail: bdk@eu.wetherford.com

Webbro Ltd, Whinfield Drive, Aycliffe Industrial Estate, Aycliffe Industrial Park, Newton Aycliffe, County Durham, DL5 6AU Tel: (01325) 313781 Fax: (01325) 300762

Welburn Precision Engineering Ltd, Barrys Lane, Scarborough, North Yorkshire, YO12 4HA Tel: (01723) 366453 Fax: (01723) 500729

Weller Tools, 815 Warwick Road, Tyseley, Birmingham, B11 2EL Tel: 0121-707 3303 Fax: 0121-707 3303

Wellfield Precision Tooling Co. Ltd, Lower Philips Road, Whitebirk Industrial Estate, Blackburn, BB1 5QN Tel: (01254) 260002 Fax: (01254) 680517 E-mail: sales@wellfieldprecision.co.uk

Wellvil Engineering Company Ltd, Spring Place, New Street, Luton, LU1 5DF Tel: (01582) 727171

West Suffolk Tool & Gauge Ltd, 63d Gorse Industrial Estate, Barnham, Thetford, Norfolk, IP24 2PH Tel: (01842) 890278 Fax: (01842) 890632

West Sussex Engineering Co. Ltd, Wedglen Industrial Estate, Midhurst, West Sussex, GU29 9RE Tel: (01730) 810045 Fax: (01730) 810047

Westfield Precision Engineering, 14 Westfield Industrial Estate, Gosport, Hampshire, PO12 3RX Tel: (023) 9250 1854 Fax: (023) 9252 7423

J. Weston & Partners Ltd, Cudgamoor Farm, East Putford, Holsworthy, Devon, EX22 7XR Tel: (01237) 451838 Fax: (01237) 451553 E-mail: nigel.moulder@hotmail.co.uk

Westrup (UK) Ltd, 30 North Street, Wetherby, West Yorkshire, LS22 6NN Tel: (01937) 581365 Fax: (01937) 586904 E-mail: info@westrup.co.uk

Westwell Developments Ltd, Whitewall Road, Frindsbury, Rochester, Kent, ME2 4DZ Tel: (01634) 726148 Fax: (01634) 727081 E-mail: info@westwelldevelopments.fsnet.com

Westwhite Engineering Services, 32 Boston Road, Gorse Hill Industrial Estate, Leicester, LE4 1AU Tel: 0116-235 7522 Fax: 0116-235 7522

Wetherby Engineering Co. Ltd, Britannia Mills, Portland St, Bradford, West Yorkshire, BD5 0DW Tel: (01274) 827216 Fax: (01274) 390527 E-mail: sales@wetherby-engineering.co.uk

Weyers Bros Ltd, Unit 1 Knight House, Lenthall Road, Loughton, Essex, IG10 3UD Tel: (020) 8508 3886 Fax: (020) 8508 7122 E-mail: john.weyers@weyers.co.uk

Weymouth Precision Engineers Ltd, 4 Kent Close, Granby Industrial Estate, Weymouth, Dorset, DT4 9TF Tel: (01305) 785375 Fax: (01305) 781602 E-mail: enquiries@weymouthprecision.co.uk

WGM Engineering Ltd, 1 Abbey Mill Business Centre, Paisley, Renfrewshire, PA1 1TJ Tel: 0141-889 1009 Fax: 0141-848 6257 E-mail: info@wgmltd.com

Wheeler & Clinch Ltd, 75-99 Nathan Way, West Thamesmead Business Park, London, SE28 0BQ Tel: (020) 8854 4261 Fax: (020) 8854 6341 E-mail: whclinch@aol.com

Whippendell Precision, 477-479 Whippendell Rd, Watford, WD18 7PU Tel: (01923) 221622 Fax: (01923) 816004

Whipple Engineering Co. Ltd, Manor Farm, Caldecott, Wellingborough, Northamptonshire, NN9 6AR Tel: (01933) 461711

Whitton Precision Ltd, Bridge Works, Durnsford Road, London, SW19 8DR Tel: (020) 8946 6431 Fax: (020) 8947 1292 E-mail: whittonprecision@btconnet.com

Wigan Tool & Die Co. Ltd, Unit 1, Great George Street, Wigan, Lancashire, WN3 4DP Tel: (01942) 324866 Fax: (01942) 820618 E-mail: enquiries@wigantoolanddie.co.uk

Wilding Engineering Services Ltd, High Street, Great Cheverell, Devizes, Wiltshire, SN10 5XZ Tel: (01380) 812918 Fax: (01380) 813997

Wildon Engineering Worcester Ltd, White Ladies Close, Worcester, WR1 1QA Tel: (01905) 522014

Williams Engineers Ltd, Unit X Birch House, Birch Walk, Fraser Road, Erith, Kent, DA8 1QX Tel: (01322) 431333 Fax: (01322) 439501 E-mail: williamspes@btconnect.com

Williams & Oakey Engineering Co. Ltd, Radstock Road, Midsomer Norton, Radstock, BA3 2AA Tel: (01761) 412013 Fax: (01761) 417174 E-mail: mail@williams-oakey.co.uk

Willis & Bates, Reservoir Road, Halifax, West Yorkshire, HX2 0ES Tel: (01422) 361228 Fax: (01422) 340480 E-mail: sales@bairstowbrothers.co.uk

Wilson & Sons (Engineering) Ltd, Morley Road, Staple Hill, Bristol, BS16 4QB Tel: 0117-956 9769 Fax: 0117-957 1670 E-mail: admin@wilsons-engineering.co.uk

Wilson Tool & Engineering Co Essex Ltd, 2-4 Parsons Road, Manor Trading Estate, Benfleet, Essex, SS7 4PY Tel: (01268) 752836 Fax: (01268) 565323 E-mail: sales@wilson-tool.co.uk

Winyard Engineering Ltd, 2-3 Cresswell Close, Pinchbeck, Spalding, Lincolnshire, PE11 3TY Tel: (01775) 725285 Fax: (01775) 710620 E-mail: sales@wfpe.co.uk

Woodcroft Engineering Ltd, Rugby Road, Brandon, Coventry, CV8 3GG Tel: (024) 7654 2285 Fax: (024) 7654 2615 E-mail: info@weltd.co.uk

Wright Engineering Co Nottingham Ltd, Colwickwood Works, Colwick Road, Nottingham, NG2 4BG Tel: 0115-950 2284 Fax: 0115-948 4967 E-mail: wright@wright-engineers.co.uk

Wrythe Properties Ltd, 56 St. James Road, Carshalton, Surrey, SM5 2DU Tel: (020) 8647 9100 Fax: (020) 8669 9655

C. Zang Engineering Ltd, Harelaw Industrial Estate, Annfield Plain, Stanley, County Durham, DH9 8UR Tel: (01207) 237793 Fax: (01207) 290100 E-mail: sales@conmecheng.co.uk

PRECISION FIXED RESISTORS

Tyco Electronics, Head Office, Faraday Road, Swindon, SN3 5HH Tel: (01793) 528171 Fax: (01793) 572516 E-mail: passivesales@tycoelectronics.com

PRECISION FORGINGS

Symmetry Medical, Beulah Road, Sheffield, S6 2AN Tel: (0114) 285 5881 Fax: (0114) 233 6978 E-mail: info@tpcl.com

PRECISION GEARS

Biddle & Mumford Gears Ltd, 8-18 Kings Place, Buckhurst Hill, Essex, IG9 5EA Tel: (020) 8505 4615 Fax: (020) 8505 3718 E-mail: sales@biddleandmumford.co.uk

Centa Transmissions Ltd, Thackley Court, Thackley Old Road, Shipley, West Yorkshire, BD18 1BW Tel: (01274) 531034 Fax: (01274) 531159 E-mail: post@centa-uk.co.uk

Colledge & Morley (Gears) Ltd, Curriers Close, Charter Avenue, Canley, Coventry, CV4 8AW Tel: (024) 7646 2328 Fax: (024) 7669 4008

Cornish Engineering Ltd, Popham Street, Nottingham, NG1 7JD Tel: 0115-950 4944 Fax: 0115-950 4215

Gibbs Gears Precision Engineers Ltd, 58 B Western Road, Tring, Hertfordshire, HP23 4BB Tel: (01442) 828898 Fax: (01422) 828020 E-mail: sales@gibbsgears.com

Ground Form Gears Ltd, Unit 4-5 Abeles Way, Holly Lane Industrial Estate, Atherstone, Warwickshire, CV9 2QZ Tel: (01827) 718555 Fax: (01827) 718789 E-mail: gearsground@yahoo.co.uk

Kelston Precisions Gears Ltd, Crews Hole Road, Bristol, BS5 8BB Tel: 0117-955 8671 Fax: 0117-935 0023 E-mail: sales@kelstongears.co.uk

Lamond & Murray Ltd, Burnside, Inverkeithing, Fife, KY11 1HT Tel: (01383) 413541 Fax: (01383) 414548 E-mail: gears@lamondandmurray.co.uk

Pentag Gears & Oilfield Equipment Ltd, 5 John Street, Sheffield, S2 4QR Tel: 0114-258 3473 Fax: 0114-258 4264 E-mail: meril@pentage-gears.com

Precision Technologies International Ltd, 22 Mariner, Tamworth, Staffordshire, B79 7UL Tel: (01827) 54371 Fax: (01827) 310406 E-mail: sales@ptiltd.co.uk

RW Racing, 19a Bridge Industries, Fareham, Hampshire, PO16 8SX Tel: (01329) 236640 Fax: (01329) 236640 E-mail: neil@rwracing.freeserve.co.uk

Sutton Gears Ltd, Unit 2 Lifford Way, Binley Industrial Estate, Binley Industrial Estate, Coventry, CV3 2RN Tel: (024) 7643 1331 Fax: (024) 7665 1000

T K Engineering & Gear Cutting Ltd, Forest Mills, Denman Street East, Nottingham, NG7 3PZ Tel: 0115-970 0978 Fax: 0115-942 2928

PRECISION GRINDING

Asset Engineering Ltd, 16 20 Black Lake Industrial Estate, Black Lake, West Bromwich, West Midlands, B70 9QP Tel: 0121-553 0231 Fax: 0121-525 4856

B W Grinding Services, 15 Bourne End Lane, Hemel Hempstead, Hertfordshire, HP1 2RL Tel: (01442) 872819 Fax: (01442) 872819

Baker Blower Engineering Co. Ltd, 39 Stanley Street, Sheffield, S3 8HH Tel: 0114-272 5527 Fax: 0114-272 7753 E-mail: bakerblower@aol.com

Bradford Grinders UK Ltd, Mount Street, Bradford, West Yorkshire, BD3 9SN Tel: (01274) 733141 Fax: (01274) 734610 E-mail: sales@bradfordgrinders.co.uk

George Burdekin Ltd, 9-11 Holbrook Lane, Coventry, CV6 4AD Tel: (024) 7666 7272 Fax: (024) 7666 8050 E-mail: sales@gburdekin.co.uk

BWC Engineering, Unit 11, Westwood Business Park, Dulverton Road, Birmingham, B6 7DS Tel: 0121-326 6920 Fax: 0121-327 7517 E-mail: dalkeydalton@hotmail.com

C F Smith Precision Grinding, The Station, Station Hill, Overton, Basingstoke, Hampshire, RG25 3JH Tel: (01256) 770457 Fax: (01256) 771701 E-mail: cfsmith@btconnect.com

Camale Engineering Ltd, Halas Industrial Estate, Forge Lane, Halesowen, West Midlands, B62 8EB Tel: 0121-550 8089 Fax: 0121-550 8089

Central Grinding Services, 3a Pomeroy Drive, Oadby, Leicester, LE2 5NE Tel: 0116-271 8188 Fax: 0116-271 8199 E-mail: central@grinding.fsnet.co.uk

Churchill Tool Co. Ltd, Empress Street, Old Trafford, Manchester, M16 9EN Tel: 0161-848 9539 Fax: 0161-872 9234 E-mail: info@churchill-grinders.co.uk

Colstan Profiles Ltd, Unit 4 Central Works, Peartree Lane, Dudley, West Midlands, DY2 0QU Tel: (01384) 861122 Fax: (01384) 861144 E-mail: info@colstanprofiles.co.uk

D C Hall Ltd, Woburn Lane, Aspley Guise, Milton Keynes, MK17 8JJ Tel: (01908) 583888 Fax: (01908) 582041E-mail: ray@dchall.co.uk

Davies Precision Grinding Ltd, 282 Upper Balsall Heath Road, Birmingham, B12 9DR Tel: 0121-440 4400 Fax: 0121-440 1414

Dynasurf, Millbuck Way, Sandbach, Cheshire, CW11 3HT Tel: (01270) 763091 Fax: (01270) 766564 E-mail: dynasurf@btconnect.com

Exhall Grinding & Engineering Co. Ltd, Bayton Road, Exhall, Coventry, CV7 9DW Tel: (024) 7636 1111 Fax: (024) 7636 1236 E-mail: bhudson319@aol.com

Fair Deal Fabrications, Hammond Avenue, Stockport, Cheshire, SK4 1PQ Tel: 0161-474 1316 Fax: 0161-480 0635 E-mail: sales@fairdealfab.co.uk

J. Fairburn Ltd, Waterloo Works, Trafalgar Street, Burnley, Lancashire, BB11 1RF Tel: (01282) 422754 Fax: (01282) 422754 E-mail: pipeprofiling@compuserve.com

Farnworth Grinding Co. Ltd, 20 Gladstone Road, Farnworth, Bolton, BL4 7EH Tel: (01204) 571853 Fax: (01204) 574613

FCJ, 10a Bushey Hall Road, Bushey, WD23 2EA Tel: (01923) 220137 Fax: (01923) 233027 E-mail: sales@fcjprecisiongrinding.co.uk

Flame Kut Profiles, Unit 39 Darlaston Central Trading Estate, Wednesbury, West Midlands, WS10 8XB Tel: 0121-526 6919 Fax: 0121-568 6447E-mail: sales@flamekut.fsbusiness.co.uk

G & R Pollard Engineering Ltd, Alexandra Way, Ashchurch, Tewkesbury, Gloucestershire, GL20 8NB Tel: (01684) 274847 Fax: (01684) 851960 E-mail: grpoll@globalnet.co.uk

Gee Bee Grinding, Gellan House, Carlisle Street, Gateshead, Tyne & Wear, NE10 0LD Tel: 0191-469 2489 Fax: 0191-469 3898 E-mail: sales@geebeegrinding.co.uk

General Utilities Stockport Ltd, Clough Works, Middlewood Road, Poynton, Stockport, Cheshire, SK12 1SJ Tel: (01625) 876321 Fax: (01625) 876284 E-mail: sales@generalutilities.co.uk

Gwent Repetition Engineers Ltd, Factory Road, Newport, Gwent, NP20 5FA Tel: (01633) 251112 Fax: (01633) 246940

H B Bearings Ltd, Riverside Works, Honley, Huddersfield, HD9 6PQ Tel: (01484) 665116 Fax: (01484) 662619 E-mail: sales@hb-bearings.com

Harcol Ltd, 5 Croxstalls Road, Walsall, WS3 2XU Tel: (01922) 494951 Fax: (01922) 710370 E-mail: harcol@engs.fslife.co.uk

Healey & Sprowson Ltd, Stuart Road, Bredbury Park Industrial Estate, Bredbury, Stockport, Cheshire, SK6 2SR Tel: 0161-494 1126 Fax: 0161-406 6162E-mail: hs@absonline.net

Intex Precision Grinders & Engineers, Bumble Bee Gardens, Sharnford, Hinckley, Leicestershire, LE10 3PD Tel: (01455) 274165

Jan Engineering Ltd, Cheethams Mill, Park Street, Stalybridge, Cheshire, SK15 2BT Tel: 0161-338 6024 Fax: 0161-338 6024

K & C Engineering, Unit 7 Three Elms Trading Estate, Hereford, HR4 9PU Tel: (01432) 351612 Fax: (01432) 342290

K M A Grinding, Unit 62 Western Business Park, Great Western Close, Birmingham, B18 4QF Tel: 0121-554 5537 Fax: 0121-554 1933

K & S Engineering, 10 Wadsworth Road, Greenford, Middlesex, UB6 7JX Tel: (020) 8991 0073 Fax: (020) 8997 7786

Kennedy Grinding Ltd, Shrewsbury Road, Craven Arms, Shropshire, SY7 9QH Tel: (01588) 672289 Fax: (01588) 673504 E-mail: kennedygrinding@btconnect.com

Kenward Precision & Gear, Unit 1b & 13 Perseverance Mills, Lockwood Scar, Huddersfield, HD4 6BW Tel: (01484) 512355 Fax: (01484) 420793 E-mail: kenward@mywebpage.net

Kepston Holdings Ltd, Unit 2 Coppice Lane, Walsall, WS9 9AA Tel: (01922) 743133 Fax: (01922) 743130 E-mail: sales@kepston.co.uk

Loks Profiling Services Ltd, Westhoughton Industrial Estate, James Street, Westhoughton, Bolton, BL5 3QR Tel: (01942) 816108 Fax: (01942) 814757

M & D Precision Grinding, Unit 8 North Weylands Industrial Estate, Molesey Road, Walton-on-Thames, Surrey, KT12 3PL Tel: (01932) 246270 Fax: (01932) 246270

Micro Precision Ltd, Duxons Turn, Hemel Hempstead, Hertfordshire, HP2 4SB Tel: (01442) 241027 Fax: (01442) 268074 E-mail: enquiries@microprecision.co.uk

Midland Tool & Design Ltd, Units 19-20, Barnfield Road, Tipton, West Midlands, DY4 9DF Tel: 0121-520 1171 Fax: 0121-557 3410 E-mail: sales@mtdltd.co.uk

O P G Precision Engineering Ltd, Station Road, Rowley Regis, West Midlands, B65 0LD Tel: 0121-559 4121 Fax: 0121-559 3661 E-mail: sales@opg-ltd.co.uk

P B K Micron Ltd, Unit 6 Kingfield Industrial Estate, Coventry, CV1 4DW Tel: (024) 7622 0376 Fax: (024) 7660 7819 E-mail: sales@pbk-micron.co.uk

Pascal Roll Camber Grinding Ltd, 8 Showell Road, Wolverhampton, WV10 9LU Tel: (01902) 424445 Fax: (01902) 423636

Pekay Tools, Wattville Road, Smethwick, West Midlands, B66 2NU Tel: 0121-558 8028 Fax: 0121-558 8028

Peter Randle & Son Grinding, 9 The Washford Industrial Estate, Heming Road, Redditch, Worcestershire, B98 0DH Tel: (01527) 528891 Fax: (01527) 528891

Poole Grinders Ltd, 81 Sterte Avenue West, Poole, Dorset, BH15 2AL Tel: (01202) 675650 Fax: (01202) 666388

R J White, Unit F10 Briarsford, Perry Road, Witham, Essex, CM8 3UY Tel: (01376) 500524

R M Mallen C N C Machinery Ltd, 15 Hainge Road, Tividale, Oldbury, West Midlands, B69 2NR Tel: 0121-557 3141 Fax: 0121-557 3814

R S Precision Engineering, Units 6-7 Parker Industrial Centre, Watling Street, Dartford, DA2 6EP Tel: (01322) 284111 Fax: (01322) 284338 E-mail: sales@rsprec.com

Rockrome, 156 Sandy Road, Liverpool, L21 1AQ Tel: 0151-928 0080 Fax: 0151-928 8388

S & B Tools Ltd, Timmis Road, Stourbridge, West Midlands, DY9 7BQ Tel: (01384) 895555 Fax: (01384) 896675

S J Products, Unit 2 Trench Lock 3, Telford, Shropshire, TF1 5ST Tel: (01952) 240656 Fax: (01952) 242281 E-mail: info@sjproductstoolanddie.co.uk

Scorpion Tooling Services, Unit 7 & 9, Libbys Drive, Stroud, Gloucestershire, GL5 1RN Tel: (01453) 751511 Fax: (01453) 766676

South West Precision, Mill Road, Barnstaple, Devon, EX31 1JQ Tel: (01271) 344221 Fax: (01271) 344355

Speedform Tools (Midlands) Ltd, Windmill Street, Walsall, WS1 3EE Tel: (01922) 635499 Fax: (01922) 722878 E-mail: info@speedform.co.uk

Startrite Designs Ltd, 76 Bissell Street, Birmingham, B5 7HP Tel: 0121 6666865

Sumitomo Electric Hardmetal Ltd, 50 Summerleys Road, Princes Risborough, Buckinghamshire, HP27 9PW Tel: (01844) 342081 Fax: (01844) 342415 E-mail: enquiries@sumitomo-hardmetal.co.uk

Trak Precision Grinders Ltd, St. Georges Way, Bermuda Industrial Estate, Nuneaton, Warwickshire, CV10 7JS Tel: (024) 7634 7117 Fax: (024) 7637 4808 E-mail: enquiries@trakltd.co.uk

Tru Tools, 74 Heming Road, Redditch, Worcestershire, B98 0EA Tel: (01527) 523157 Fax: (01527) 510170

V I Precision Grinders Ltd, Pingemead Farm, Pingewood, Reading, RG30 3UR Tel: 0118 9866546

Wolverhampton Grinding Company Ltd, Rosehill, Willenhall, West Midlands, WV13 2AR Tel: (01902) 606442 Fax: (01902) 636137 E-mail: sprint@btclick.com

PRECISION GRINDING MACHINES

Abwood Machine Tools, 615 Princes Road, Dartford, DA2 6EF Tel: (01322) 225271 Fax: (01322) 291862 E-mail: sales@abwoodcnc.co.uk

Centreless Precision Grinding Ltd, Unit 19b Tyseley Industrial Estate, Seeleys Road, Birmingham, B11 2LQ Tel: 0121-772 1616 Fax: 0121-772 7099

Microtech Precision Ltd, Unit D1 Bersham Enterprise Centre, Colliery Road, Rhostyllen, Wrexham, Clwyd, LL14 4EG Tel: (01978) 362295 Fax: (01978) 352403 E-mail: sales@microtechprecision.co.uk

PRECISION GROUND STEEL BARS

▶ Strongbar, 2 Banningham Road, Aylsham, Norwich, NR11 6PE Tel: (01263) 734034 Fax: (01263) 734790 E-mail: sales@strongbar.co.uk

PRECISION INJECTION MOULDINGS

C.T.P. Davall Ltd, Durham Lane Industrial Park, Eaglescliffe, Stockton-On-Tees, Cleveland, TS16 0RB Tel: (01554) 749000 Fax: (01642) 790779 E-mail: paul.caldwell@carclo-plc.com
Jarzon Plastics Ltd, Golden Cresent, Hayes, Middlesex, UB3 1AQ Tel: (020) 8573 1537 Fax: (020) 8756 0138 E-mail: sales@jarzonplastics.co.uk

PRECISION LINEAR GUIDES

G S F Ltd, Unit 9 Gledrid Industrial Estate, Chirk, Wrexham, LL14 5DG Tel: (01691) 770303 Fax: (01691) 776900 E-mail: enquiries@gsfslides.com
I K O (Nippon Thompson), 2 Vincent Ave, Crownhill, Milton Keynes, MK8 0AB Tel: (01908) 566144 Fax: (01908) 565458 E-mail: sales@iko.co.uk

PRECISION MACHINED ASSEMBLIES

▶ Hi-Spec Precision Engineering, 1 Thistleton Road, Market Overton, Rutland, Oakham, Leicestershire, LE15 7PP Tel: (01572) 768036 Fax: (01780) 481696 E-mail: hi-spec_eng@lycos.co.uk

PRECISION MACHINED COMPONENTS TO SPECIFICATION

Tenable Screw Company Ltd, 16 Deer Park Road, London, SW19 3UB Tel: (020) 8542 6225 Fax: (020) 8543 5789 E-mail: sales@tenable.co.uk

PRECISION MACHINED COMPONENTS, CNC

▶ Hi-Spec Precision Engineering, 1 Thistleton Road, Market Overton, Rutland, Oakham, Leicestershire, LE15 7PP Tel: (01572) 768036 Fax: (01780) 481696 E-mail: hi-spec_eng@lycos.co.uk
Penta Precision Engineering Ltd, Aspen House, Airport Service Road, Portsmouth, PO3 5RA Tel: (023) 9266 8334 Fax: (023) 9266 8335 E-mail: sales@pentaprecision.co.uk

PRECISION MACHINING

A C W Engineering Services Ltd, The Sanderson Centre, Lees Lane, Gosport, Hampshire, PO12 3UL Tel: (023) 9250 2854 Fax: (023) 9250 2854 E-mail: acwesl@tinyonline.co.uk
▶ A D M Precision Engineering Ltd, 31 Chartwell Drive, Wigston, Leicestershire, LE18 2FL Tel: 0116-257 0704 Fax: 0116-257 1647
A E C Engineering, Unit 1a Conway Morfa Indust Estate, Aberconwy, Conwy, Gwynedd, LL32 8HB Tel: (01492) 584139 Fax: (01492) 584139
A M S Engineering, Units C & D Stratton Park, Biggleswade, Bedfordshire, SG18 8QS Tel: (01767) 600888 Fax: (01767) 600668
A & W Jigboring Ltd, 46 Padgets Lane, Redditch, Worcestershire, B98 0RD Tel: (01527) 522196 Fax: (01527) 517389 E-mail: sales@awjigboring.co.uk
Accrofab Ltd, 11 Stoney Gate Road, Station Road, Spondon, Derby, DE21 7RX Tel: (01332) 666878 Fax: (01332) 666245
Acrona Engineering, Unit 1, Woodview Estate, Church Hanborough, Witney, Oxfordshire, OX29 8AA Tel: (01993) 880588 Fax: (01993) 880590 E-mail: sales@acrona-engineering.co.uk
Adnet Precision Engineering Ltd, Nexus Court Unit B1 Gloucester Business Park, Hurricane Road, Brockworth, Gloucester, GL3 4AQ Tel: (01452) 611826 Fax: (01452) 623929 E-mail: info.adnetprecision@virgin.net
Aks Machining Ltd, 5 Wistaston Road Business Centre, Wistaston Road, Crewe, CW2 7RP Tel: (01270) 585554 Fax: (01270) 586606
Allen Engineering, 34 Great Western Industrial Estate, Great Western Close, Birmingham, B18 4QF Tel: 0121-551 5487 Fax: 0121-551 5487
Allstyle Engineering Ltd, Unit 5 60 Arthur Street, Redditch, Worcestershire, B98 8JY Tel: (01527) 527687 Fax: (01527) 500467 E-mail: allstyle@tesco.net
Alstone Engineering, Unit 1 Towers Business Park, Wheelhouse Road, Rugeley, Staffordshire, WS15 1UZ Tel: (01889) 577775 Fax: (01889) 575111
Amech Engineering Ltd, Dudley Road, Yarm Road Industrial Estate, Darlington, County Durham, DL1 4GG Tel: (01325) 488884 Fax: (01325) 382525 E-mail: info@amech.net
Anatric Machine Tools, 3 Sinclair Court, Bletchley, Milton Keynes, MK1 1RB Tel: (01908) 371331 Fax: (01908) 367683
Andrews & Elmes Engineering Ltd, Unit 58b Arthur Street, Redditch, Worcestershire, B98 8JY Tel: (01527) 522771 Fax: (01527) 522771
Apek Design & Developments Ltd, Ferndown Industrial Estate, Wimborne, Dorset, BH21 7RF Tel: (01202) 876149 Fax: (01202) 861210 E-mail: sales@apek.co.uk
APPH Nottingham Ltd, Urban Road, Kirkby-In-Ashfield, Nottingham, NG17 8AP Tel: (01623) 754355 Fax: (01623) 723904 E-mail: sales@beauforteng.co.uk
Arden Precision Ltd, 5 Maidwell Drive, Shirley, Solihull, West Midlands, B90 4QN Tel: 0121-683 5200 Fax: 0121-683 5210
Ariel Machine Products Ltd, Yew Tree Lane, Caerleon, Newport, NP18 1LL Tel: (01633) 420405 Fax: (01633) 430072
Arte Engineering Co., Unit 8 Great Bridge Industrial Estate, Tipton, West Midlands, DY4 0HR Tel: 0121-520 8953 Fax: 0121-520 8953
Aspec Precision Engineers, Unit P1 Dales Manor Business Park, Grove Road, Sawston, Cambridge, CB22 3TJ Tel: (01223) 836710 Fax: (01223) 836294 E-mail: info@aspec.co.uk
▶ Astra Engineering Services, 21 Borough Road, Darlington, County Durham, DL1 1SW Tel: (01325) 389810 Fax: (01325) 355020
Atwell Engineering Holdings Ltd, Unit 1, Dinnington Business Park, Outgang Lane, Sheffield, S25 3QU Tel: (01909) 551133 Fax: (01909) 551123 E-mail: admin@ens-precision.com
B A S Components Ltd, 2 Cramptons Road, Sevenoaks, Kent, TN14 5EF Tel: (01732) 450011 Fax: (01732) 455884 E-mail: info@bas-airospace.co.uk
B A W Precision Engineering Ltd, Cwmtawe Business Park, Alloy Industrial Estate, Pontardawe, Swansea, SA8 4EZ Tel: (01792) 862141 Fax: (01792) 865545 E-mail: peter@bawengineering.co.uk
B & E Engineering Services, First Avenue, Crewe, CW1 6BG Tel: (01270) 586958 Fax: (01270) 585042 E-mail: sales@deengineering.co.uk
B S Ellis, Unit 5 Chillington Fields, Wolverhampton, WV1 2BY Tel: (01902) 459111 Fax: (01902) 459111
B S P Engineering Ltd, Maitland Road, Lion Barn Industrial Estate, Needham Market, Ipswich, IP6 8NZ Tel: (01449) 722222 Fax: (01449) 721989 E-mail: sales@bspengineering.co.uk
Bankside Engineering Ltd, Woodhouse St, Hedon Road, Hull, HU9 1RJ Tel: (01482) 337700 Fax: (01482) 337742 E-mail: users@bie.co.uk
Bar Engineering, 20 West Dock Avenue, Hull, HU3 4JR Tel: (01482) 224966 Fax: (01482) 211443
Barker & Simpkins Ltd, 205 Wincolmlee, Hull, HU2 0PZ Tel: (01482) 320151 Fax: (01482) 320199
Belmar Engineering Services Ltd, Abbotswell Road, Aberdeen, AB12 3AJ Tel: (01224) 875038 Fax: (01224) 879125 E-mail: postmaster@belmar.co.uk
Bico Ltd, Rosemary Lane, Beaumaris, Gwynedd, LL58 8EB Tel: (01248) 810463 Fax: (01248) 810998 E-mail: bicoltd@aol.com
Bramtool Precision Engineering, 13 109 Sydenham Road, Birmingham, B11 1DG Tel: 0121-773 1345 Fax: 0121-773 1345
Brandon Precision, Holmewell Road, Leeds, LS10 4TQ Tel: 0113-277 5671 Fax: 0113-271 2161 E-mail: enquiries@brandon-medical.com
Brass Turned Parts Ltd, 160 Dollman Street, Birmingham, B7 4RS Tel: 0121-359 1234 Fax: 0121-359 4698 E-mail: enquiries@brassturnedparts.co.uk
Briter Components & Manufacturing Ltd, 8 Sandwich Industrial Estate, Ramsgate Road, Sandwich, Kent, CT13 9LN Tel: (01304) 617155 Fax: (01304) 617741 E-mail: brian@britercomponents.com
Bromac Machining Services Ltd, Cradley Heath Factory Centre, Woods Lane, Cradley Heath, West Midlands, B64 7AQ Tel: (01384) 637838 Fax: (01384) 637838
Bunting Engineering Ltd, Unit 14/20, Manor Industrial Estate, Pleck Road, Walsall, WS2 9XX Tel: (01922) 623888 Fax: (01922) 623888
H.E. Butters & Co., Baldwins Gate, Newcastle, Staffordshire, ST5 5DA Tel: (01782) 680253
C E F Precision Ltd, Beachs Drive, Chelmsford, CM1 2NU Tel: (01245) 353019 Fax: (01245) 491675 E-mail: sales@cef-precision.co.uk
Camale Engineering Ltd, Halas Industrial Estate, Forge Lane, Halesowen, West Midlands, B62 8EB Tel: 0121-550 8089 Fax: 0121-550 8089
Cambmac Ltd, 4 Commercial Road, March, Cambridgeshire, PE15 8QP Tel: (01354) 655270 Fax: (01354) 657447 E-mail: info@cambmac.fsnet.co.uk
Chartway Industrial Services Ltd, Faraday Drive, Bridgnorth, Shropshire, WV15 5BA Tel: (01746) 764900 Fax: (01746) 768770 E-mail: sales@chartway.co.uk
Clarkwood Engineering Ltd, 7 Blackenhall Industrial Estate, Sunbeam Street, Wolverhampton, WV2 4PF Tel: (01902) 710868 Fax: (01902) 712840 E-mail: enquiries@clarkwood.co.uk
CMJ Mould Tools, 22 Benfield Way, Braintree, Essex, CM7 3YS Tel: (01376) 347776 Fax: (01376) 347776 E-mail: sales@cmjmouldtools.co.uk
Comcir Radio Communications, 66 Goldstone Villas, Hove, East Sussex, BN3 3RU Tel: (01273) 779828 Fax: (01273) 204900 E-mail: info@comcir.co.uk
Constant Precision, 5 Triumph Way, Woburn Road Industrial Estate, Kempston, Bedford, MK42 7QB Tel: (01234) 851131 Fax: (01234) 841265 E-mail: sales@constant-precision.co.uk
Craft Metal Products, Unit 18 Birksland Industrial Estate, Bradford, West Yorkshire, BD4 8TY Tel: (01274) 731531 Fax: (01274) 731531
Cranford Engineering, 13 Craddocks Parade, Ashtead, Surrey, KT21 1QL Tel: (01372) 272380 Fax: (01372) 273776 E-mail: craneng@aol.com
Craychase Ltd, Alington Road, Eynesbury, St. Neots, Cambridgeshire, PE19 6HY Tel: (01480) 215196 Fax: (01480) 476723
Crompton & Rathbone (Tools) Ltd, 111-117 Sydenham Road, Birmingham, B11 1DG Tel: 0121-773 7140 Fax: 0121-773 7140
Curtis Machine Tools Ltd, Martells Industrial Estate, Ardleigh, Colchester, CO7 7RU Tel: (01206) 230032 Fax: (01206) 231426 E-mail: cnt@douglascurtis.co.uk
Custom Metalcraft Ltd, 36 Bennet Road, Reading, RG2 0QX Tel: 0118-986 8077 Fax: 0118-986 8078
D & D Engineering Hull Ltd, Stockholm Road, Hull, HU7 0XW Tel: (01482) 879175 Fax: (01482) 838449 E-mail: info@ddeng.co.uk
D L I Precision Engineering Ltd, Trimdon Grange Industrial Estate, Trimdon Grange, Trimdon Station, County Durham, TS29 6PA Tel: (01429) 880454 Fax: (01429) 880369 E-mail: info@dlipe.plus.com
D W Engineering, Unit A1 Industrial Estate, Watling Street, Consett, County Durham, DH8 6TA Tel: (01207) 505608 Fax: (01207) 505608
Dartmouth Associates Ltd, 43 Baltimore Road, Great Barr, Birmingham, B42 1DD Tel: 0121-358 0422 Fax: 0121-358 1334 E-mail: dartmouth@dartmouth-associates.co.uk
Dawson Shanahan Ltd, Cranborne Industrial Estate, Cranborne Road, Potters Bar, Hertfordshire, EN6 3JN Tel: (01707) 602000 Fax: (01707) 602049 E-mail: postmaster@dawson-shanahan.co.uk
Stan Dean (Jig-Boring Service) Ltd, Boodle Street, Ashton-Under-Lyne, Lancashire, OL6 8NF Tel: 0161-344 2352 Fax: 0161-339 7165 E-mail: satndeanltd@yahoo.co.uk
Graham Debling Precision Engineering Ltd, 3A-4 Booth Place, Margate, Kent, CT9 1QN Tel: (01843) 298804 Fax: (01843) 298858 E-mail: gdebling@gdpe.co.uk
Denner Kelford Grinding Ltd, D3 Seedbed Centre, Avenue Road, Nechells, Birmingham, B7 4NT Tel: 0121-359 7728 Fax: 0121-359 0255
Dero Fabrication Ltd, Unit 67, Blackpole Trading Estate West, Blackpole Road, Worcester, WR3 8TJ Tel: (01905) 455199 Fax: (01905) 754152 E-mail: sales@dero.co.uk
Die Max Engineering, 1-2 Mid Wynd, Dundee, DD1 4JG Tel: (01382) 224481 Fax: (01382) 224481
Dimill Engineering Ltd, Doric Works, Church Street, Studley, Warwickshire, B80 7LG Tel: (01527) 854672 Fax: (01527) 853683 E-mail: info@dimill.co.uk
Downhurst Engineering, 15 Aintree Road, Keytec 7 Business Park, Pershore, Worcestershire, WR10 2JN Tel: (01386) 554195 Fax: (01386) 561195 E-mail: downhurst@lineone.net
E B Engineering, 17 All Saints Industrial Estate, All Saints Street, Birmingham, B18 7RJ Tel: 0121-551 3274 Fax: 0121-551 3274
E S L Engineers (Basildon) Ltd, Woolaston Way, Basildon, Essex, SS13 1DJ Tel: (01268) 727777 Fax: (01268) 728866 E-mail: sales@eslengineers.co.uk
Eaves Engineering Hyde Ltd, Unit F Adamsons Industrial Estate, Hyde, Cheshire, SK14 1EF Tel: 0161-368 9828 Fax: 0161-367 8143 E-mail: stan-feerick@yahoo.com
Emr Brackley Ltd, County Road, Buckingham Road Industrial Estate, Brackley, Northamptonshire, NN13 7AX Tel: (01280) 701321 Fax: (01280) 701327 E-mail: sales@emreng.co.uk
P.M.J. Engineering Co. Ltd, 5 & 6 Brunswick Road, Birmingham, B12 8NP Tel: 0121 4406760
Excel Precision Engineering Ltd, 32 High St, Drayton, Abingdon, Oxon, OX14 4JW Tel: (01235) 538333 Fax: (01235) 538303 E-mail: neiltyler@btconnect.com
Farnworth & Langan Blackburn Ltd, Unit 6 Stancliffe Street Industrial Estate, Blackburn, BB2 2QR Tel: (01254) 676935 Fax: (01254) 680113 E-mail: farnworth-langan@btconnect.com
Fast Engineering Works Ltd, Unit 1, Area C, 241 Wellington Road Industrial Estate, Perry Barr, Birmingham, B20 2QQ Tel: 0121-344 4345 Fax: 0121-344 4535 E-mail: fastengineering@btconnect.com
Fastec Engineering Services Ltd, Unit 8 Studlands Park Avenue, Studlands Park Industrial Estate, Newmarket, Suffolk, CB8 7AU Tel: (01638) 660186 Fax: (01638) 667374E-mail: danny@fastecengineeing.co.uk
Fisadco Eng (1980) Ltd, Raywell Street, Hull, HU2 8EP Tel: (01482) 324564 Fax: (01482) 222564 E-mail: daren@fisadco.co.uk
Folglade Pipe & Fittings Ltd, Penlake Industrial Estate, Reginald Road, Sutton, St. Helens, Merseyside, WA9 4JA Tel: (01744) 820119 Fax: (01744) 811412 E-mail: sales@folglade.co.uk
Fox Precision Machine Ltd, 95 Leigh Street, Sheffield, S9 2PR Tel: 0114-244 3969 Fax: 0114-243 9256 E-mail: sales@foxprecision.co.uk
Francis W Birkett & Sons Ltd, PO Box 16, Cleckheaton, West Yorkshire, BD19 5JT Tel: (01274) 873366 Fax: (01274) 851615 E-mail: info@swbirkett.com
Freeman & Proctor, PO Box 22, Nuneaton, Warwickshire, CV11 4XY Tel: (024) 7638 2032 Fax: (024) 7637 4353 E-mail: info@freemanandproctor.co.uk
Frisby Extrusion Services Ltd, Unit F Tyson Courtyard, Weldon South Industrial Estate, Corby, Northamptonshire, NN18 8AZ Tel: (01536) 263545 Fax: (01536) 205184 E-mail: welcome@fes-ltd.com
Fulwood Fabrications Ltd, Farndale Road, Staveley, Chesterfield, Derbyshire, S43 3YN Tel: (01246) 477346 Fax: (01246) 280035 E-mail: sales@fulwood.uk.com
G C B Engineering Bilston Ltd, Ash Street, Bilston, West Midlands, WV14 8UP Tel: (01902) 409486 Fax: (01902) 353739 E-mail: gcb@deecon.co.uk
G W Lambert Engineers Ltd, 10 Queens Road, High Wycombe, Buckinghamshire, HP13 6AQ Tel: (01494) 525977 Fax: (01494) 528238
Gauge & Tool Makers Association, 3 Forge House, Summerleys Road, Princes Risborough, Buckinghamshire, HP27 9DT Tel: (01844) 274222 Fax: (01844) 274227 E-mail: gtma@gtma.co.uk
Goodwin Technology Ltd, B2 Prenton Way, North Cheshire Trading Estate, Prenton, Merseyside, CH43 3DU Tel: 0151-608 8666 Fax: 0151-638 2456 E-mail: sales@gtprecision.co.uk
GP Precision Engineering Ltd, Unit 19 Nineteen Morses Lane, Industrial Estate, Brightlingsea, Colchester, CO7 0SF Tel: (01206) 303668 Fax: (01206) 303668 E-mail: Enquiries@GPPrecisionEngineering.co.uk
Griffiths Precision Engineering, 5 Hicks Road, Markyate, St. Albans, Hertfordshire, AL3 8LG Tel: (01582) 841192 Fax: (01582) 841395 E-mail: griff@griffithseng.co.uk
Hampson Aerospace, 129 Scudamore Road, Leicester, LE3 1UQ Tel: 0116-232 2233 Fax: 0116-232 2311E-mail: sales@mibert.com
Harco Engineering Ltd, Canal Street, Harts Hill, Brierley Hill, West Midlands, DY5 1JJ Tel: (01384) 480280 Fax: (01384) 480399 E-mail: info@harcoeng.co.uk
J.A. Harris Ltd, Malinslee, Telford, Shropshire, TF4 2BN Tel: (01952) 505537 Fax: (01952) 504456 E-mail: accounts.harris@virgin.net
Hawk Fasteners Ltd, Brunel Road, Middlesbrough, Cleveland, TS6 6JA Tel: (01642) 468581 Fax: (01642) 440880 E-mail: sales@hawkfast.com
Hay-Tech Engineering, 12 Market Street, Bracknell, Berkshire, RG12 1JG Tel: (01344) 868011 Fax: (01344) 867979 E-mail: wood.c@btconnect.com
Hebble Hydraulic Services Ltd, Spring Grove Mills, Linthwaite, Huddersfield, HD7 5QG Tel: (01484) 846688 Fax: (01484) 847701 E-mail: hebble@btconnect.com
Holmes Engineering, Unit 2 Furtho Court, Towcester Road, Old Stratford, Milton Keynes, MK19 6AN Tel: (01908) 563169 Fax: (01908) 563169
Hyde Precision Components Ltd, Oldham Street, Denton, Manchester, M34 3SA Tel: 0161-337 9242 Fax: 0161-335 0787 E-mail: sales@hyde-precision.co.uk
Insight Ltd, Sandys Road, Malvern, Worcestershire, WR14 1JJ Tel: (01684) 577444 Fax: (01684) 577555 E-mail: sales@insightprecision.co.uk
J & B Limmax, 22 Horsecroft Place, Harlow, Essex, CM19 5BX Tel: (01279) 444243 Fax: (01279) 450571 E-mail: sales@marksmanpaintball.com
J J Hardy & Sons Ltd, Brenda Road, Hartlepool, Cleveland, TS25 2BL Tel: (01429) 279837 Fax: (01429) 860182 E-mail: sales@jjhardy.co.uk
J P Precision Engineering, Unit 11a Shrub Hill, Worcester, WR4 9EL Tel: (01905) 20319 Fax: (01905) 20319
Jarvis Engineering Ltd, Oakridge Road, High Wycombe, Buckinghamshire, HP11 2PA Tel: (01494) 530123 Fax: (01494) 472864 E-mail: jarvis.engineering@virgin.net
Jigs & Fixtures, Station Yard, Rigg Street, Stewarton, Kilmarnock, Ayrshire, KA3 5AG Tel: (01560) 483512 Fax: (01560) 485160 E-mail: sales@jigsandfixtures.uk.com
K H S Engineering Co., 31 Froysell Street, Willenhall, West Midlands, WV13 1QH Tel: (01902) 608784 Fax: (01902) 634466 E-mail: kasengineering@btconnect.com
K M Engineering Ltd, Unit 7b Parnall Road Trading Estate, Parnall Road, Bristol, BS16 3JQ Tel: 0117-965 9336 Fax: 0117-958 3673 E-mail: enquiries@km-engineering.co.uk
K P M Engineering, Premier Partnership Estate, Leys Road, Brierley Hill, West Midlands, DY5 3UP Tel: (01384) 75567 Fax: (01384) 75567
K W Geere Engineering, 4 Lady Bee Marina Industrial Units, Albion Street, Southwick, Brighton, BN42 4EG Tel: (01273) 596211 Fax: (01273) 592196
Kamway Engineering Ltd, Fircroft Way, Edenbridge, Kent, TN8 6EN Tel: (01732) 862028 Fax: (01732) 866868 E-mail: enquires@kamway.co.uk
Kings Norton Engineering Co. Ltd, Facet Road, Birmingham, B38 9PT Tel: 0121-458 3538 Fax: 0121-458 3886 E-mail: jharper@kingsnortonengineering.co.uk

PRECISION MACHINING – *continued*

Kite International Ltd, 4 Low March Industrial Estate, Low March, Daventry, Northamptonshire, NN11 4SD Tel: (01327) 314200 Fax: (01327) 314201

L M S Precision Engineering, 44 Wassage Way, Hampton Lovett, Droitwich, Worcestershire, WR9 0NX Tel: (01905) 779783 Fax: (01905) 779041 E-mail: roger@lmsprecision.co.uk

Langley Components Maidenhead Ltd, Fullers Yard, Sheephouse Road, Maidenhead, Berkshire, SL6 8HA Tel: (01628) 623809 Fax: (01628) 623809

Lesk Engineers Ltd, Carden Street, Worcester, WR1 2AX Tel: (01905) 23187 Fax: (01905) 612536E-mail: company@leskengineers.co.uk

Livingston Precision (Engineering) Ltd, 28 Firth Road, Houstoun Industrial Estate, Livingston, West Lothian, EH54 5DJ Tel: (01506) 435281 Fax: (01506) 433973

M & B Engineering, 62-63 John Wilson Business Park, Thanet Way, Whitstable, Kent, CT5 3QT Tel: (01227) 261917 Fax: (01227) 770809 E-mail: robertacors@tiscali.co.uk

M I C Engineering, 1a-B Unit, Dans Castle, Tow Law, Bishop Auckland, County Durham, DL13 4BB Tel: (01388) 731347 Fax: (01388) 731348 E-mail: info@mic-valves-eng.co.uk

M Tech Engineering, Plot 16 Tufthorn Industrial Estate, Stepbridge Road, Coleford, Gloucestershire, GL16 8PJ Tel: (01594) 837172 Fax: (01594) 832999

Mcbraida plc, Bridgeyate Eng Works, Bath Road, Bridgeyate, Bristol, BS30 5JW Tel: 0117-961 3103 Fax: 0117-960 1417 E-mail: admin@mcbraida.plc.uk

Malcolm Engineering Co. Ltd, Banks Road, McMullen Industrial Estate, Darlington, County Durham, DL1 1YF Tel: (01325) 461549 Fax: (01325) 381196 E-mail: malco@malcolm-eng.co.uk

Malt Mill Engineering Co. Ltd, 4 Kinwarton Workshops, Kinwarton Farm Road, Kinwarton, Alcester, Warwickshire, B49 6EH Tel: (01789) 764497 Fax: (01789) 400161 E-mail: maltmill@aol.com

Manuel Engineering Co. Ltd, Unit 33 Barking Industrial Park, Alfreds Way, Barking, Essex, IG11 0TJ Tel: (020) 8594 9264 Fax: (020) 8594 5507

Martin Jenkins Engineering Co. Ltd, Nicholls Road, Tipton, West Midlands, DY4 9LG Tel: 0121-557 3663 Fax: 0121-557 9517 E-mail: a7vos@aol.com

Matthews Engineering, Whieldon Industrial Estate, Whieldon Road, Stoke-on-Trent, ST4 4JP Tel: (01782) 849534 Fax: (01782) 849534

Merpro Leisure Ltd, Brent Avenue, Forties Road Industrial Estate, Montrose, Angus, DD10 9JA Tel: (01674) 662200 Fax: (01674) 662266 E-mail: sales@merpro.com

Merriefield Engineering Ltd, 7 Willis Way, Poole, Dorset, BH15 3SS Tel: (01202) 680644 Fax: (01202) 684389 E-mail: sales@merriefield.co.uk

Middleburn Ltd, 6 Bentley Park, Blacknest Road, Blacknest, Alton, Hampshire, GU34 4PX Tel: (01420) 520227 Fax: (01420) 23796 E-mail: bob@middleburn.co.uk

Midlands Ltd, Wincanton Close, Ascot Drive Industrial Estate, Derby, DE24 8NB Tel: (01332) 753453 Fax: (01332) 757292

Mounsey Engineering Ltd, Unit 11 North Weylands Industrial Estate, Molesey Road, Walton-on-Thames, Surrey, KT12 3PL Tel: (01932) 888555 Fax: (01932) 225388 E-mail: mounseyengineering@tiscali.co.uk

Mussett Group Ltd, Beccles Industrial Estate, Loddon, Norwich, NR14 6JD Tel: (01508) 522500 Fax: (01508) 528769 E-mail: enquire@mussett.co.uk

Newcom Precision Engineering Ltd, 1 Earith Business Park, Meadow Drove, Earith, Huntingdon, Cambridgeshire, PE28 3QF Tel: (01487) 840870 Fax: (01487) 740046 E-mail: info@newcom-engineering.co.uk

North West Engineering Group Ltd, Mill Lane, Halton, Lancaster, LA2 6NF Tel: (01524) 811224 Fax: (01524) 811288 E-mail: sales@luneside.co.uk

NS Engineering Solutions, Units 23/24, Snibston Drive, Coalville, Leicestershire, LE67 3NQ Tel: (01530) 835400 Fax: (01530) 510947 E-mail: sales@nsengineering.co.uk

Nutter Aircrafts Ltd, New Works, Chadwick Street, Blackburn, BB2 4AA Tel: (01254) 505200 Fax: (01254) 505205

P B K Micron Ltd, Unit 6 Kingfield Industrial Estate, Coventry, CV1 4DW Tel: (024) 7622 0376 Fax: (024) 7660 7819 E-mail: sales@pbk-micron.co.uk

P M P L Telford Ltd, Unit 25 Heath Hill Industrial Estate, Dawley, Telford, Shropshire, TF4 2RH Tel: (01952) 507978 Fax: (01952) 507978 E-mail: daviespmp@aol.com

P V S Engineers Ltd, 1-2 Murrills Estate, Fareham, Hampshire, PO16 9RD Tel: (023) 9237 9495 Fax: (023) 9238 8801 E-mail: rec@pvsengineers.co.uk

Penshaw Engineering Ltd, 23 Harvey Close, Crowther, Washington, Tyne & Wear, NE38 0AB Tel: 0191-416 5013 Fax: 0191-415 3949

Picross Precision Engineering Co. Ltd, 16-18 Lister Road, Eastbourne, East Sussex, BN23 6PU Tel: (01323) 507322 Fax: (01323) 507581 E-mail: sales@picross-eng.com

Portway Tool & Gauge Ltd, 27 Dudley Road, Lye, Stourbridge, West Midlands, DY9 8EX Tel: (01384) 892458 Fax: (01384) 424371 E-mail: info@portwaytoolgauge.co.uk

Precision Mechanical Services, 48 Elliott Road, Love Lane Industrial Estate, Cirencester, Gloucestershire, GL7 1YS Tel: (01285) 655300 Fax: (01285) 641490 E-mail: sales@pms-partners.co.uk

Precision Powertrain UK Ltd, Catto Drive, Peterhead, Aberdeenshire, AB42 1RL Tel: (01779) 473161 Fax: (01779) 477424

Precision Services Of Redditch, 59 Padgets Lane, Redditch, Worcestershire, B98 0RD Tel: (01527) 528000 Fax: (01527) 517174

Precision Supply Co., 5 Block 3, Thornliebank Industrial Estate, Thornliebank, Glasgow, G46 8TU Tel: 0141-638 9060 Fax: 0141-638 9848 E-mail: sales@scottishtools.co.uk

Premax Engineering Ltd, 56 Porchester Street, Birmingham, B19 2LA Tel: 0121-359 5380 Fax: 0121-333 3097 E-mail: info@premax.co.uk

Presto Engineering, Unit 11 Lakeside Industrial Estate, Stanton Harcourt, Witney, Oxfordshire, OX29 5SL Tel: (01865) 883508 Fax: (01865) 881228

Prodec Precision Manufacturing Co. Ltd, Armstrong Buildings, Hilton Terrace, Worksop, Nottinghamshire, S80 2DQ Tel: (01909) 474093 Fax: (01909) 500363

Quick Edge Engineering, Grosvenor Works, Windmill Lane, Denton, Manchester, M34 3LA Tel: 0161-335 0331 Fax: 0161-335 0332 E-mail: keith@quickedge.co.uk

R I N C Engineering, 22 Singer Road, Kelvin Industrial Estate, East Kilbride, Glasgow, G75 0XS Tel: (01355) 248610 Fax: (01355) 248610 E-mail: rinc@wwwmail.co.uk

R K R Engineering, Northpoint, Enterprise Close, Medway City Estate, Rochester, Kent, ME2 4LY Tel: (01634) 723565 Fax: (01634) 712912

R M Engineering, Unit D Colchester Road, Maldon, Essex, CM9 4NL Tel: (01621) 842845 Fax: (01621) 842845

R S T Precision Engineering Ltd, Unit 31 South Hampshire Industrial Park, Totton, Southampton, SO40 3SA Tel: (023) 8066 3663 Fax: (023) 8066 3461 E-mail: rst.prec.eng@virgin.net

Raldon Precision Engineering Ltd, 9 Morcom Road, Birmingham, B11 2JE Tel: 0121-707 5757 Fax: 0121-706 7290 E-mail: sales@raldonengineering.com

RDMG Aerospace, Boardman Road, Swadlincote, Derbyshire, DE11 9EN Tel: (01283) 550960 Fax: (01283) 550961 E-mail: administration@tecalemitaero.co.uk

Ready Roll Ltd, Unit 14, Harris Business Park, Hambury Road, Stoke Piror, Bromsgrove, Worcestershire, B60 4AA Tel: (01527) 881993 Fax: (01527) 881994

C. Rice Engineering, Units 1,2 & 3 Brookfield Works, Christie Street, Stockport, Cheshire, SK1 4LR Tel: 0161-477 0380 Fax: 0161-480 7387 E-mail: info@criceeng.com

Rolled Alloys Ltd, Walker Industrial Park, Guide, Blackburn, BB1 2QE Tel: (01254) 582999 Fax: (01254) 582666 E-mail: sales@rolledalloys.co.uk

Rushforth & Co. Ltd, Unit 3 Westfield Industrial Estate, Kirk Lane, Leeds, LS19 7LX Tel: 0113-250 9162 Fax: 0113-239 1394

RWB Engineering, Corona Works, Heaton Street, Denton, Manchester, M34 3RY Tel: 0161-320 7777 Fax: 0161-336 5255

S B C Precision Engineering, 2 Kings Court Industrial Estate, Sedgley Road East, Tipton, West Midlands, DY4 8XA Tel: 0121-557 0456 Fax: 0121-557 0457

S & J Engineering Services, 1 Periwinkle Court, Church Street, Milton Regis, Sittingbourne, Kent, ME10 2JZ Tel: (01795) 431111 Fax: (01795) 431111

▶ S M I, 7 Gipping Close, Bedford, MK41 7XY Tel: (01234) 266255 Fax: (01234) 266255 E-mail: smiuk@btconnect.com

S S E Precision Engineering, 37a Douglas Road, Poole, Dorset, BH12 2AU Tel: (01202) 463573 Fax: (01202) 463564

S & S Precision Engineering Ltd, 23 Rainhill Close, East Stephenson Industrial Estate, Washington, Tyne & Wear, NE37 3HN Tel: 0191-416 2184 Fax: 0191-419 1586 E-mail: bob@ssprecision.com

Salford Engineering Ltd, Unit 9 Seaford Industrial Estate, Seaford Road, Salford, M6 6AQ Tel: 0161-737 7670 Fax: 0161-745 9224

Samar Precision Engineering, Central Way, Andover, Hampshire, SP10 5AN Tel: (01264) 334410 Fax: (01264) 335315 E-mail: samar_mail@btconnect.com

Sevtek Engineering Services, Unit 3t Innsworth Technology Park, Innsworth Lane, Gloucester, GL3 1DL Tel: (01452) 730457 Fax: (01452) 731706 E-mail: owencooper@sevtek.co.uk

Simaron Engineering, Sunny Hill Road, Barnfields Industrial Estate, Leek, Staffordshire, ST13 5RG Tel: (01538) 386301

▶ Slater & Crabtree Ltd, Thornes Lane, Wakefield, West Yorkshire, WF1 5RW Tel: (01924) 374874 Fax: (01924) 378288 E-mail: precision@slatercrabtree.co.uk

Slater Yendall Ltd, Howard Road, Park Farm North, Redditch, Worcestershire, B98 7SE Tel: (01527) 529069 Fax: (01527) 510359

Sommerwest Technical Services Ltd, 32 Garrett Road, Lynx Trading Estate, Yeovil, Somerset, BA20 2TJ Tel: 01935 412595

South West Precision, Mill Road, Barnstaple, Devon, EX31 1JQ Tel: (01271) 344221 Fax: (01271) 344355

Stanley Vickers Ltd, Snowdon Road, Middlesbrough, Cleveland, TS2 1LG Tel: (01642) 247353 Fax: (01642) 231571 E-mail: info@sv-ltd.co.uk

Startrite Designs Ltd, 76 Bissell Street, Birmingham, B5 7HP Tel: 0121 6666865

Stroma Engineering Ltd, 21 Bickford Road, Birmingham, B6 7EE Tel: 0121-327 5550 Fax: 0121-327 2314

Supercraft Ltd, Canada Road, Byfleet, West Byfleet, Surrey, KT14 7JL Tel: (01932) 351941 Fax: (01932) 340807 E-mail: sales@supercraft.co.uk

Survirn Engineering Ltd, 1581 Bristol Road South, Rednal, Birmingham, B45 9UA Tel: 0121-453 7718 Fax: 0121-453 6915 E-mail: sales@survirn.co.uk

Swindon Engineering Metalworkers, Unit 10 Bramble Close, Swindon, SN2 8DW Tel: (01793) 641808 Fax: (01793) 513029

T B P Tools Ltd, 106-108 Lombard Street, Birmingham, B12 0QR Tel: 0121-622 1762 Fax: 0121-622 1174 E-mail: tbp@btconnect.com

Tees Components Ltd, North Skelton, Skelton-in-Cleveland, Saltburn-by-the-Sea, Cleveland, TS12 2AP Tel: (01287) 650621 Fax: (01287) 652642 E-mail: sales@teescomponents.co.uk

Teescraft Engineering Ltd, Unit Longfield, South Church Enterprise Park, Bishop Auckland, County Durham, DL14 6XB Tel: (01388) 777339 Fax: (01388) 776242 E-mail: info@teescraft.com

Tool & Instruments Engineering Ltd, Archenfield Road, Ross-On-Wye, Herefordshire, HR9 5AZ Tel: (01989) 563002 Fax: (01989) 562068

Triple X Components Machining Ltd, Masons Road, Stratford-upon-Avon, Warwickshire, CV37 9NF Tel: (01789) 200400 Fax: (01789) 414063 E-mail: machining@triplexcm.com

Trucut Technologies UK Ltd, Flavell Works, Garratt Street, Brierley Hill, West Midlands, DY5 1JU Tel: (01746) 764900 Fax: (01384) 481195 E-mail: sales@chartway.co.uk

Turnell & Odell Ltd, 61-65 Sanders Road, Finedon Road Industrial Estate, Wellingborough, Northamptonshire, NN8 4NL Tel: (01933) 222061 Fax: (01933) 440073 E-mail: sales@toengineering.co.uk

Turner Aviation Ltd, Spiersbridge Terrace, Thornliebank, Glasgow, G46 8JQ Tel: 0141-638 2265 Fax: 0141-638 9694 E-mail: enquiries@turner-aviation.co.uk

Ufone Precision Engineers Ltd, Unit 21 Thornleigh Trading Estate, Dudley, West Midlands, DY2 8UB Tel: (01384) 233288 Fax: (01384) 252931 E-mail: enquiries@ufone-eng.com

W P B Machining Services Ltd, 21 Offerton Industrial Estate, Stockport, Cheshire, SK2 5TH Tel: 0161 4778500

Waldham Precision Engineering Ltd, 2 Lennox Road, Bilton Industrial Estate, Basingstoke, Hampshire, RG22 4AP Tel: (01256) 359898 Fax: (01256) 844043 E-mail: sales@waldhamprecision.co.uk

Wardtec Ltd, Unit 92, Heming Road, Washford, Redditch, Worcestershire, B98 0DH Tel: (01527) 520594 Fax: (01527) 502235 E-mail: ward-tec@btconnect.com

Warman CNC, 214 Moseley Street, Birmingham, B5 6LE Tel: 0121-622 4045 Fax: 0121-666 6539 E-mail: warmancnc@aol.com

West Midlands Precision Engineering Ltd, Unit 10/14, Gainsborough Trad Estate, Rufford Road, Stourbridge, West Midlands, DY9 7ND Tel: (01384) 397071 Fax: (01384) 378628 E-mail: info@westmidlandstpreg.co.uk

Westway Precision Engineering Ltd, Henty Road, Southampton, SO16 4GF Tel: (023) 8078 9229 Fax: (023) 8070 2967

Westwell Developments Ltd, Whitewall Road, Frindsbury, Rochester, Kent, ME2 4DZ Tel: (01634) 726148 Fax: (01634) 727081 E-mail: info@westwelldevelopments.fsnet.co.uk

Westwhite Engineering Services, 32 Boston Road, Gorse Hill Industrial Estate, Leicester, LE4 1AU Tel: 0116-235 7522 Fax: 0116-235 7522

Widdowson-Dalebrook Engineers Ltd, Basford Road, Crewe, CW2 6ES Tel: 01270 661111

Woodside Engineers (Cwmbran) Ltd, Forgehammer, 22 Woodside Road, Cwmbran, Gwent, NP44 3AA Tel: (01633) 484448 Fax: (01633) 484448

Wrekin Shell Mouldings Ltd, Unit D1 & D2, Halesfield 21, Telford, Shropshire, TF7 4NX Tel: (01952) 580946 Fax: (01952) 582546 E-mail: wsm@dynafluid.com

PRECISION MANUFACTURING,

See also headings for particular types

A & P Engineering Ltd, 2 Bilston Key Industrial Estate, Oxford Street, Bilston, West Midlands, WV14 7DW Tel: (01902) 408087 Fax: (01902) 408311

Accura Holdings, Hickman Avenue, Wolverhampton, WV1 2DW Tel: (01902) 454460 Fax: (01902) 451840 E-mail: enquiries@accura.co.uk

Aerotech Precision Manufacturing Ltd, 1 Stone Lane, Wimborne, Dorset, BH21 1HB Tel: (01202) 848484 Fax: (01202) 848989 E-mail: sales@aero-tech.co.uk

Alman Engineering Services Ltd, 12 Bradfield Close, Finedon Road Industrial Estate, Wellingborough, Northamptonshire, NN8 4RQ Tel: (01933) 275551 Fax: (01933) 275552 E-mail: sales@alman.co.uk

Cambmac Ltd, 4 Commercial Road, March, Cambridgeshire, PE15 8QP Tel: (01354) 655270 Fax: (01354) 657447 E-mail: info@cambmac.fsnet.co.uk

Canwire Services Ltd, 14 Gospel End Street, Dudley, West Midlands, DY3 3LS Tel: (01902) 881460 Fax: (01902) 881393 E-mail: canwireservices1@aol.com

Pegmount Ltd, Unit 1 Apex Centre, Lovell, Lichfield Road Industrial Estate, Tamworth, Staffordshire, B79 7TA Tel: (01827) 68804 Fax: (01827) 69929 E-mail: sales@phoenixmanufacturing.co.uk

Phoenix Turned Parts, 4-5 Mica Close, Tamworth, Staffordshire, B77 4DR Tel: (01827) 59441 Fax: (01827) 54750 E-mail: mike.pegg@btbusinessconnect.co.uk

PRECISION MEASURING EQUIPMENT

Axis Group, Unit 5 The Lion Centre, Hanworth Trading Estate, Hampton Road West, Feltham, Middlesex, TW13 6DS Tel: (020) 8893 8339 Fax: (020) 8893 8439 E-mail: sales@axis-gb.com

M B Technology, Benfieldside, Milton Road, Wokingham, Berkshire, RG40 1DD Tel: 0118-977 6039 Fax: 0118-978 9386

PRECISION MILLING ENGINEERING SERVICES

A B M Precisions Nuneaton Ltd, Ansley Common, Nuneaton, Warwickshire, CV10 0QN Tel: (024) 7639 2866 Fax: (024) 7639 7283 E-mail: enquiries@abmprecisions.co.uk

A G Precision Huntingdon Ltd, 2 Windover Road, Huntingdon, Cambridgeshire, PE29 7EA Tel: (01480) 52334 Fax: (01480) 456055 E-mail: agprecision@tiscali.co.uk

A & J Precision Engineering, 3 Fenland Business Centre, Longhill Road, March, Cambridgeshire, PE15 0BL Tel: (01354) 652203 Fax: (01354) 652203 E-mail: anjprecision@tiscali.co.uk

A R Craig Engineering Ltd, 6 Vale Lane, Bristol, BS3 5RU Tel: 0117-966 7735 Fax: 0117-966 0604

Bo Mac Sheffield Ltd, 63 Jenkin Road, Sheffield, S9 1AT Tel: 0114-244 8170 Fax: 0114-243 7104 E-mail: sales@bo-mac.co.uk

C E Fagg Engineering, 539 Ipswich Road, Slough, SL1 4EP Tel: (01753) 538432

C J Cooke, Unit 31 Park Farm Industrial Estate, Ermine Street, Buntingford, Hertfordshire, SG9 9AZ Tel: (01763) 272523 Fax: (01763) 272955

Casey Bros, St Georges Drive, Brinsworth, Rotherham, South Yorkshire, S60 5NG Tel: (01709) 378386 Fax: (01709) 373308

Catherwell Engineering Co. Ltd, Unit 7 & 9 Stanley Lane Industrial Estate, Stanley Lane, Bridgnorth, Shropshire, WV16 4SF Tel: (01746) 766154 Fax: (01746) 766154

Charter Precision Engineering, Unit 25-26, Enfield Industrial Estate, Redditch, Worcestershire, B97 6BY Tel: (01527) 584187 Fax: (01527) 584187

Collingwood Engineering Lincs Ltd, Dam Road, Barton-upon-Humber, South Humberside, DN18 5AS Tel: (01652) 632388 Fax: (01652) 632388

Crawford Reid Engineers, Reed Street, North Shields, Tyne & Wear, NE30 1DD Tel: 0191-259 5767 Fax: 0191-259 5767

Dallmac Precision Engineering, Hardley Industrial Estate, Hythe, Southampton, SO45 3NQ Tel: (023) 8084 9211 Fax: (023) 8084 9211

Datum Products Ltd, Blatchford Road, Horsham, West Sussex, RH13 5QR Tel: (01403) 253453 Fax: (01403) 272687 E-mail: info@datumporductshorsham.co.uk

Delta Precision Engineering Ltd, 87-89 Sterte Avenue West, Poole, Dorset, BH15 2AW Tel: (01202) 661166 Fax: (01202) 661166 E-mail: sales@deltaprecision.freeserve.co.uk

Diamond Precision Engineering, 4 Kelvin Park, Dock Road, Birkenhead, Merseyside, CH41 1LT Tel: 0151-647 9050 Fax: 0151-647 9186 E-mail: sales@diamondprecisionengineering.co.uk

Dunblane Light Engineering Ltd, Stirling Road, Fallin, Stirling, FK7 7JB Tel: (01786) 818757 Fax: (01786) 818767 E-mail: john.swan@dle-eng.co.uk

Dunrave Precision Engineers Ltd, Oldbury Road, Cwmbran, Gwent, NP44 3JU Tel: (01633) 873838 Fax: (01633) 871477 E-mail: info@dunrave.co.uk

Duston Engineering Ltd, 50 Ivy Road, Northampton, NN1 4QT Tel: (01604) 233178 Fax: (01604) 233178

Elkins Engineering Ltd, Unit 1 Enterprise Park, Ebblake Industrial Estate, Verwood, Dorset, BH31 6YS Tel: (01202) 825322 Fax: (01202) 823971E-mail: sales@elkinsengineering.co.uk

Eurotech Precision Engineering Ltd, 4-5 Bergen Way, North Lynn Industrial Estate, King's Lynn, Norfolk, PE30 2JG Tel: (01553) 770426 Fax: (01553) 774726 E-mail: epelltd@kingslynn20.fsnet.co.uk

Field Engineering (Poole) Ltd, 10 Factory Road, Upton Industrial Estate, Poole, Dorset, BH16 5HT Tel: (01202) 622166 Fax: (01202) 632439 E-mail: dave@fieldengineering.co.uk

Firthstones Ltd, 22-24 Brindley Road, Bayton Road Industrial Estate, Coventry, CV7 9EP Tel: (024) 7636 1010 Fax: (024) 7636 0970 E-mail: sales@firthstones.co.uk

PRECISION MILLING ENGINEERING SERVICES – *continued*

Formark Engineering Ltd, Unit 319, Fauld Industrial Estate, Tutbury, Burton-On-Trent, Staffordshire, DE13 9HS Tel: (01283) 520520 Fax: (01283) 815582
Fossey Engineering, A 2 Venture Court, Ackworth Road, Portsmouth, PO3 5RY Tel: (023) 9269 0246 Fax: (023) 9267 8218
Frank Dawson Engineering, Rockfield Road, Barrs Court Works, Hereford, HR1 2UA Tel: (01432) 278190 Fax: (01432) 344760
Frome Tool & Gauge Ltd, Manor Road, Marston Trading Estate, Frome, Somerset, BA11 4BL Tel: (01373) 462226 Fax: (01373) 452123 E-mail: frometandg@btconnect.com
G W Cowler, 16 Merchant Drive, Mead Lane, Hertford, SG13 7AY Tel: (01992) 501494 Fax: (01992) 501495 E-mail: sales@gwcowler.demon.co.uk
Helston Engineering Ltd, Unit 10 Bentley La Industrial Estate, Bentley Lane, Walsall, WS2 8TL Tel: (01922) 641556 Fax: (01922) 746161
J&B, 7 Cambridge Road, Granby Industrial Estate, Weymouth, Dorset, DT4 9TJ Tel: (01305) 775377 Fax: (01305) 780443
James Engineering Ltd, Prenton Way, North Cheshire Trading Estate, Prenton, Merseyside, CH43 3DU Tel: 0151-609 1000 Fax: 0151-609 0741 E-mail: sales@jameseng.com
K P Engineering Components, Barlow Road, Aldermans Green Industrial Estate, Coventry, CV2 2LD Tel: (024) 7660 3333 Fax: (024) 7660 4444 E-mail: sales@kpecltd.com
Maydown Precision Engineering Ltd, 11 Carrakeel Drive, Maydown, Londonderry, BT47 6UH Tel: (028) 7186 0531 Fax: (028) 7186 0496 E-mail: info@maydown.com
Monard Precision Engineering Ltd, Avon Industrial Estate, Butlers Leap, Rugby, Warwickshire, CV21 3UY Tel: (01788) 569998 Fax: (01788) 568434 E-mail: monard@avonrugby.freeserve.co.uk
R E Cross & Co. Ltd, Joule Road, Basingstoke, Hampshire, RG21 6XH Tel: (01256) 465878 Fax: (01256) 817743 E-mail: sales@recross.co.uk
Toolturn Engineering Ltd, 8 Brunel Way, Fareham, Hampshire, PO15 5TX Tel: (01489) 578878 Fax: (01489) 578859 E-mail: sales@toolturn.com
Westrup (UK) Ltd, 30 North Street, Wetherby, West Yorkshire, LS22 6NN Tel: (01937) 581365 Fax: (01937) 586904 E-mail: info@westrup.co.uk

PRECISION PRESSINGS

Batten & Allen Ltd, Bridge End, Cirencester, Gloucestershire, GL7 1NQ Tel: (01285) 655220 Fax: (01285) 652650 E-mail: admin@batten-allen.co.uk
DMS Metal Spinning, 6 Grafton Road, Birmingham, B11 1JP Tel: 0121-773 8885 Fax: 0121-773 3141 E-mail: adriandms@aol.com
Fourjay Ltd Presswork, Royal Works, Coleshill Street, Sutton Coldfield, West Midlands, B72 1SJ Tel: 0121-354 1115 Fax: 0121-354 1205 E-mail: enquiries@fourjay.co.uk
Howard S Cooke & Co Holdings Ltd, Arrow Road, Redditch, Worcestershire, B98 8PA Tel: (01527) 63231 Fax: (01527) 66770 E-mail: sales@protex.com
Pressex Engineers, Express Technical Centre, Kingsway, Team Valley Trading Estate, Gateshead, Tyne & Wear, NE11 0JL Tel: 0191-497 3430 Fax: 0191-497 3431 E-mail: pressex@responsive-engioneering.com
Rencol Tolerance Rings, Second Way, Bristol, BS11 8DF Tel: 0117-938 1700 Fax: 0117-915 7982 E-mail: sales@rencol.co.uk
Wild Manufacturing Group Ltd, PO Box 103, Birmingham, B5 5SJ Tel: 0121-643 9611 Fax: 0121-766 5278 E-mail: csd@wild.uk.com

PRECISION REAMERS

Guhring Ltd, Castle Bromwich Business Park, Tameside Drive, Castle Vale, Birmingham, B35 7AG Tel: 0121-749 5544 Fax: 0121-776 7224 E-mail: info@guhring.co.uk
Gun Drill & Reamers Ltd, 37 Southfields Industrial Park, Hornsby Square, Basildon, Essex, SS15 6SD Tel: (01268) 415197 Fax: (01268) 410692
Mapal Ltd, Swift Park, Old Leicester Road, Rugby, Warwickshire, CV21 1DZ Tel: (01788) 574700 Fax: (01788) 569551

PRECISION ROLLED FLAT WIRE

Shaped Wires Ltd, Prospect Mills, Scholes, Cleckheaton, West Yorkshire, BD19 6NJ Tel: (01274) 855635 Fax: (01274) 851116 E-mail: sales@shapedwires.com

PRECISION STEEL CASTINGS

MAHLE Power Train Ltd, Costin House, St. James Mill Road, Northampton, NN5 5TZ Tel: (0870) 1573000 Fax: (0870) 1573100 E-mail: sales@gb.mahle.com

PRECISION SYNTHETIC FILTER CLOTHS

▶ G Bopp & Co. Ltd, Grange Close, Clover Nook Industrial Park, Somercotes, Alfreton, Derbyshire, DE55 4QT Tel: (01773) 521266 Fax: (01773) 521163 E-mail: info@gbopp.com
Plastok Associates Ltd, 79 Market Street, Birkenhead, Merseyside, CH41 6AN Tel: 0151-666 2056 Fax: 0151-650 0073 E-mail: sales@plastok.co.uk
R Cadisch & Sons, Unit 1, 879 High Road, London, N12 8QA Tel: (020) 8492 0444 Fax: (020) 8492 0333 E-mail: info@cadisch.com

PRECISION TOOLMAKERS

A I R Engineering, 4 Tyn Y Bonau Road, Pontardulais, Swansea, SA4 8SG Tel: (01792) 881112 Fax: (01792) 881113 E-mail: aireng@freenet.com
A N Tools Ltd, Carlyon Road, Atherstone, Warwickshire, CV9 1LQ Tel: (01827) 716878 Fax: (01827) 717859 E-mail: ant@antools.co.uk
Allenvale Tools & Productions Ltd, Riverside Works, Thanet Way, Whitstable, Kent, CT5 3JQ Tel: (01227) 277777 Fax: (01227) 277788 E-mail: allenvale@aol.com
Altag Tool & Die, 10 3 Wilton Road, Ramsgate, Kent, CT12 5HG Tel: (01843) 588663 Fax: (01843) 853738 E-mail: info@altag.co.uk
Amery Engineering, Mill Lane, Alton, Hampshire, GU34 2QG Tel: (01420) 80298 Fax: (01420) 549559 E-mail: geoff@ameryeng.swiftserve.net
Api Precision Toolmakers, Unit 2 Quell Farm Industrial Estate, Greatham, Pulborough, West Sussex, RH20 2ES Tel: (01798) 875688 Fax: (01798) 872701 E-mail: api@apiprecision.co.uk
Astra Precision Engineering Ltd, Mnercian Works, Holyhead Road, Ketley, Telford, Shropshire, TF1 5DY Tel: (01952) 616622 Fax: (01952) 616622
B&T, Ironmould Lane, Bristol, BS4 5SA Tel: 0117-971 5295 Fax: 0117-971 5295
Bestalinks Engineers Ltd, 2 Wood Street, Dukinfield, Cheshire, SK16 4UT Tel: 0161-330 8515 Fax: 0161-343 2228 E-mail: bestlink@aol.com
Boundary Precision Engineering Ltd, Limber Road, Lufton, Yeovil, Somerset, BA22 8RR Tel: (01935) 472094 Fax: (01935) 382488
Breton International Ltd, Havelock Buildings, Jubilee Street, Llandudno, Gwynedd, LL30 2NZ Tel: (01492) 875268 Fax: (01492) 860731 E-mail: info@breton-international.com
C & C Engineering, Unit 3C, Cliffe St, Nelson, Lancashire, BB9 7QR Tel: (01282) 695912 Fax: (01282) 615764 E-mail: sales@candcengineering.co.uk
▶ Cromaston Ltd, 17 Swan Street, Sileby, Loughborough, Leicestershire, LE12 7NN Tel: (01509) 812840 Fax: (01509) 813494
Cutter Services Precision Engineers Ltd, 6 Glebe Road, Letchworth Garden City, Hertfordshire, SG6 1DR Tel: (01462) 671861 Fax: (01462) 670532
Data Engineering, Pindar Road, Hoddesdon, Hertfordshire, EN11 0DE Tel: (01992) 462610 Fax: (01992) 450953 E-mail: scherry@dataeng.freeserve.co.uk
Data Tooling & Enginering Services Ltd, Unit 1-2 Paddock Farm, Bethersden Road, Hothfield, Ashford, Kent, TN26 1EP Tel: (01233) 620805 Fax: (01233) 620889 E-mail: info@datatooling.co.uk
DJM Engineering, The Courtyard, Warkworth, Banbury, Oxfordshire, OX17 2AG Tel: (01295) 712424 E-mail: djm.eng@btconnect.com
Donart Engineering Co., Station Street, Bromsgrove, Worcestershire, B60 2BS Tel: (01527) 879722 Fax: (01527) 879722
Duckworth & Kent Reading Ltd, 113 Armour Road, Tilehurst, Reading, RG31 6HB Tel: 0118-942 9828 Fax: 0118-945 1191 E-mail: duckworth.kent@btconnect.com
Duncan Lynch Precision Tools Ltd, Unit E Weller Drive, Finchampstead, Wokingham, Berkshire, RG40 4QZ Tel: 0118-973 4845 Fax: 0118-973 0381 E-mail: sales@duncan-lynch.co.uk
Evridge Precison Engineering Ltd, Holmesdale Works, Holmesdale Road, South Darenth, Dartford, DA4 9JP Tel: (01322) 868961 Fax: (01322) 868962 E-mail: mailbox@evridgeengineering.com
F G Precision Ltd, 10 Arkwright Gate, Andover, Hampshire, SP10 3SB Tel: (01264) 324231 Fax: (01264) 324231 E-mail: fgprecision@lineone.net
Fairway Engineering (Bristol) Ltd, Station Road Workshops, Station Road, Kingswood, Bristol, BS15 4PJ Tel: 0117-940 9030 Fax: 0117-940 9030E-mail: tony@fairwayeng.freeserve.co.uk
Fisher & Co., Units 2-4 Cary Court, Somerton Business Park, Somerton, Somerset, TA11 6SB Tel: (01458) 274017 Fax: (01458) 274145 E-mail: info@fisherandcompany.co.uk
H J Jennings & Co., St Francis, Silver Street, Shepton Beauchamp, Ilminster, Somerset, TA19 0JZ Tel: (01460) 240499 Fax: (01460) 242179
Hanley Precision Tools, 21b Wildmere Road, Banbury, Oxfordshire, OX16 3JU Tel: (01295) 253534 Fax: (01295) 268927 E-mail: sales@glazpart.co.uk
Holford Engineering Ltd, 13 Cromwell Road, St. Neots, Cambridgeshire, PE19 2EU Tel: (01480) 217271 Fax: (01480) 219687
J P Precision Engineering, Unit 11a Shrub Hill, Worcester, WR4 9EL Tel: (01905) 20319 Fax: (01905) 20319
J W Hill Precision Engineers Ltd, 22-26 Bath Road, Worcester, WR5 3EL Tel: (01905) 356712 Fax: (01905) 763155 E-mail: info@jwhill-engineering.co.uk
Langstone Engineering Ltd, Units 1-3 Beaver Industrial Est., Southmoor Lane, Havant, Hampshire, PO9 1JW Tel: (023) 9245 2430 Fax: (023) 9245 2440 E-mail: corporate@langstone-engineering.co.uk
Lobro Tools Ltd, Long Street, Premier Business Park, Walsall, WS2 9XP Tel: (01922) 623140 Fax: (01922) 648297 E-mail: sales@lobrotools.com
M C M, 26 Donisthorpe Street, Leeds, LS10 1PL Tel: 0113-245 1020 Fax: 0113-243 1971 E-mail: info@mcmpos.co.uk
Madeley & Glaze Ltd, 8 The Benyon Centre, Walsall, WS2 7NQ Tel: 01922 407717
Main Tool Co. Ltd, Old Edinburgh Road, Bellshill, Lanarkshire, ML4 3HL Tel: 01698 749473
Manufax Engineering Ltd, Cromer Street, Stockport, Cheshire, SK1 2NP Tel: 0161-480 2855 Fax: 0161-474 7159 E-mail: manufax@manufax.co.uk
▶ Meadow Engineering & Patterns, 53 Kenilworth Drive, Oadby, Leicester, LE2 5LT Tel: 0116-271 1763 Fax: 0116-271 6022
Micromech Precision Tools, Wellfield Street, Rochdale, Lancashire, OL11 1AW Tel: (01706) 646505 Fax: (01706) 646505
Cyril Minns Engineering Ltd, Gladstone Road, Kingswood, Bristol, BS15 1SW Tel: 0117-967 1834 Fax: 0117-961 8638 E-mail: cyrilminns@dial.pipex.com
Multex Ltd, Caputhall Road, Deans Industrial Estate, Deans, Livingston, West Lothian, EH54 8AS Tel: (01506) 460661 Fax: (01506) 460816
N & P Thermo Plastic Moulders Acton Ltd, 69-73 Stirling Road, London, W3 8DJ Tel: (020) 8992 8258 Fax: (020) 8993 0860
Nelson Tool Co Stockport Ltd, Stringer Street, Stockport, Cheshire, SK1 2NZ Tel: 0161-480 6004 Fax: 0161-476 2325 E-mail: info@nelsontool.co.uk
Newcastle Tool & Gauge Ltd, Unit 250 Dukesway, Team Valley Trading Estate, Gateshead, Tyne & Wear, NE11 0PZ Tel: 0191-482 2455 Fax: 0191-491 0559 E-mail: admin@ntg-ltd.co.uk
Nortim Tools Ltd, 5 New Mills Industrial Estate, Libbys Drive, Stroud, Gloucestershire, GL5 1RN Tel: (01453) 759613 Fax: (01453) 753803 E-mail: sue@nortim.co.uk
Parade Products Ltd, 656B Chester Road, Erdington, Birmingham, B23 5TE Tel: 0121-350 8031 Fax: 0121-350 8031
Peak Precision Tools Mansfield Ltd, 9 Anglia Way Industrial Estate, Anglia Way, Mansfield, Nottinghamshire, NG18 4LP Tel: (01623) 623993 Fax: (01623) 623993
Penshaw Engineering Ltd, 23 Harvey Close, Crowther, Washington, Tyne & Wear, NE38 0AB Tel: 0191-416 5013 Fax: 0191-415 3949
Preconomy, Orchard Way, Sutton-in-Ashfield, Nottinghamshire, NG17 1JU Tel: (01623) 492100 Fax: (01623) 514057 E-mail: sales@preconomy.com
Queensfield Precision Engineering, Unit 4, Beeding Close, Southern Cross Trading Estate, Bognor Regis, West Sussex, PO22 9TS Tel: (01243) 868254 Fax: (01243) 829609 E-mail: post@queensfield.co.uk
R S Precision Engineering, Units 6-7 Parker Industrial Centre, Watling Street, Dartford, DA2 6EP Tel: (01322) 284111 Fax: (01322) 284338 E-mail: sales@rsprec.com
Rayleigh Engineering Ltd, 19 Nobel Square, Burnt Mills Industrial Estate, Basildon, Essex, SS13 1LP Tel: (01268) 728380 Fax: (01268) 728205 E-mail: rayleigh.engineer@btconnect.com
Robert P D Frost & Co. Ltd, 45 Burrowfield, Welwyn Garden City, Hertfordshire, AL7 4SS Tel: (01707) 331188 Fax: (01707) 393714 E-mail: sales@rpdfrost.co.uk
S M F, 62 Heming Road, Washford Industrial Estate, Redditch, Worcestershire, B98 0EA Tel: (01527) 514162 Fax: (01527) 514169 E-mail: info@smftools.com
Shesto Ltd, 2 Sapcote Trading Centre, 374 High Road, London, NW10 2DH Tel: (020) 8451 6188 Fax: (020) 8451 5450 E-mail: sales@shesto.co.uk
Speedform Tools (Midlands) Ltd, Windmill Street, Walsall, WS1 3EE Tel: (01922) 635499 Fax: (01922) 722878 E-mail: info@speedform.co.uk
Swansea Precision Engineering Services Ltd, Unit 11 Oxwich Court, Fendrod Business Park, Swansea, SA6 8QW Tel: (01792) 774817 Fax: (01792) 412282
Teescraft Engineering Ltd, Unit Longfield, South Church Enterprise Park, Bishop Auckland, County Durham, DL14 6XB Tel: (01388) 777339 Fax: (01388) 776242 E-mail: info@teescraft.com
TG Carbide Precision Ltd, Unit 3 & 5, Hemmells, Basildon, Essex, SS15 6ED Tel: (01268) 546060 Fax: (01268) 546070 E-mail: carbideprecision@tiscali.co.uk
Tiptree Precision Engineering, Galliford Road Industrial Estate, Heybridge, Maldon, Essex, CM9 4XD Tel: (01621) 856733 Fax: (01621) 851355 E-mail: tipeng@aol.com
Toolmatic Tool Design, 36 Hall Street, Birmingham, B18 6BS Tel: 0121-236 1417 Fax: 0121-233 9240
▶ Topley & Fisher, Station Road, Hatton, Derby, DE65 5DU Tel: (01283) 812350 Fax: (01283) 812080 E-mail: topleyandfisher@btconnect.com
TQ Limited, 22 South Street, Rochford, Essex, SS4 1BQ Tel: (01702) 530051 E-mail: go@toolquotes.com
Tru Tools, 74 Heming Road, Redditch, Worcestershire, B98 0EA Tel: (01527) 523157 Fax: (01527) 510170
Unijig Ltd, Bowling Back Lane, Bradford, West Yorkshire, BD4 8UF Tel: (01274) 656750 Fax: (01274) 668375 E-mail: sales@unijig.co.uk
Versatile Precision Tools Ltd, Victoria Road, Ulverston, Cumbria, LA12 0BZ Tel: (01229) 582366 Fax: (01229) 580871 E-mail: mail@vptools.co.uk
W T H Precision Tooling Ltd, 236 Berwick Avenue, Slough, SL1 4QT Tel: (01753) 521483 Fax: (01753) 694778
Wednesbury Precision Tool Ltd, 7 Conduit Road, Norton Canes, Cannock, Staffordshire, WS11 9TJ Tel: (01543) 274901 Fax: (01543) 277557
Wellfield Precision Tooling Co. Ltd, Lower Philips Road, Whitebirk Industrial Estate, Blackburn, BB1 5QN Tel: (01254) 260002 Fax: (01254) 680517 E-mail: sales@wellfieldprecision.co.uk
Westley Engineering Ltd, 120 Pritchett Street, Birmingham, B6 4EH Tel: 0121-333 1925 Fax: 0121-333 1926 E-mail: engineering@westleyrichards.co.uk

PRECISION TOOLS, *See also headings for particular types*

Abbey Die & Tool Ltd, Bentley Mill Close, Walsall, WS2 0BN Tel: (01922) 626545 Fax: (01922) 721717 E-mail: sales@abbeydieandtool.co.uk
Allenvale Tools & Productions Ltd, Riverside Works, Thanet Way, Whitstable, Kent, CT5 3JQ Tel: (01227) 277777 Fax: (01227) 277788 E-mail: allenvale@aol.com
Allied (Tooling) Ltd, Unit 2, 19 Willis Way, Poole, Dorset, BH15 3SS Tel: (01202) 675767 Fax: (01202) 684422 E-mail: sales@alliedtooling.com
Bico Ltd, Rosemary Lane, Beaumaris, Gwynedd, LL58 8EB Tel: (01248) 810463 Fax: (01248) 810998 E-mail: bicoltd@aol.com
Fastener Tools Birmingham Ltd, Unit 3-4 St. Andrews Street, Birmingham, B9 4JT Tel: 0121-753 2218 Fax: 0121-753 2240 E-mail: fasttools@btconnect.com
Henri Picard & Frere, 8 Pixham Court, Pixham Lane, Dorking, Surrey, RH4 1PG Tel: (020) 8949 3142 Fax: (020) 8949 3142 E-mail: sales@picard.co.uk
John Scott Precision, Unit 4a Star Industrial Estate, Bodmin Road, Coventry, CV2 5DB Tel: (024) 7661 0300 Fax: (024) 7661 7233 E-mail: john@johnscottprecision.co.uk
L S Starrett Co. Ltd, Oxnam Road, Jedburgh, Roxburghshire, TD8 6LR Tel: (01835) 863501 Fax: (01835) 863018 E-mail: sales@starrett.co.uk
Moore & Wright, Unit 15 Bordon Trading Estate, Old Station Way, Bordon, Hampshire, GU35 9HH Tel: 0114-225 0400 Fax: 0114-225 0410 E-mail: sales@moore-and-wright.com
▶ Planning Precision, Planning Precision, Twitten End, North Street, Storrington, West Sussex, RH20 4PB Tel: 01903 742976 E-mail: william@planning-precision.co.uk
R S Tools Ltd, Unit 8, Brunswick Road, Birmingham, B12 8NP Tel: 0121-440 4484 Fax: 0121-440 4484 E-mail: r.s.tools@btconnect.com
Sankey Carbide, Anchor Lane, Bilston, West Midlands, WV14 9NE Tel: (01902) 661144 Fax: (01902) 661100 E-mail: scd@cogent-power.com
G.W.& S. Smith, Lambert St, Greetland, Halifax, W. Yorkshire, HX4 8AA Tel: 01422 370464 Fax: 01422 370464
▶ Starco DML Ltd, Marshfield Bank Employment Park, Middlewich Road, Crewe, CW2 8UY Tel: (01270) 253589 Fax: (01270) 253589 E-mail: paul@dmluk.com

PRECISION TUBES

Kurvers International Supply Services Ltd, Unit 14 Northfields Prospect Business Centre, Northfields, London, SW18 1PE Tel: (020) 8877 1355 Fax: (020) 8874 7266 E-mail: info@ukkurvers.com

PRECISION TUBULAR COMPONENTS

Bristol Bending Sanoh Ltd, Fourth Way, Bristol, BS11 8DL Tel: 0117-982 8260 Fax: 0117-982 2040

▶ indicates data change since last edition

PRECISION TURNED COMPONENTS TO SPECIFICATION

Prima Engineering, Stonewall Industrial Estate, Stonewall Place, Newcastle, Staffordshire, ST5 6NR Tel: (01782) 711900 Fax: (01782) 711909

PRECISION TURNED PARTS

939 Engineering Co., Lodgefield Road, Halesowen, West Midlands, B62 8AX Tel: 0121-559 1133 Fax: 0121-559 0321

A & A Lampkin, Greengate, Silsden, Keighley, West Yorkshire, BD20 9LA Tel: (01535) 652328 Fax: (01535) 657866

A & P Engineering Ltd, 2 Bilston Key Industrial Estate, Oxford Street, Bilston, West Midlands, WV14 7DW Tel: (01902) 408087 Fax: (01902) 408311

A P T (Leicester) Ltd, Rookery Lane, Groby, Leicester, LE6 0GL Tel: 0116-287 0051 Fax: 0116-287 0053 E-mail: sales@aptleicester.co.uk

A T C, Holmethorpe Avenue, Redhill, RH1 2NG Tel: (01737) 765686 Fax: (01737) 764048 E-mail: sales@atcltd.co.uk

Aaron Precision Turned Parts Ltd, 433 Thurmaston Boulevard, Leicester, LE4 9LA Tel: 0116-253 6353 Fax: 0116-251 5237 E-mail: kaby@kaby.co.uk

Anatric Machine Tools, 3 Sinclair Court, Bletchley, Milton Keynes, MK1 1RB Tel: (01908) 371331 Fax: (01908) 367683

Andrews & Elmes Engineering Ltd, Unit 58b Arthur Street, Redditch, Worcestershire, B98 8JY Tel: (01527) 522771 Fax: (01527) 522771

Arduous Manufacturing, The Old Brewery, Norton Fitzwarren, Taunton, Somerset, TA2 6RN Tel: (01823) 339000 Fax: (01823) 339000

Arnold Precision Engineering, 3 46 Holton Road, Holton Heath Trading Park, Poole, Dorset, BH16 6LT Tel: (01202) 621128 Fax: (01202) 621128

Arte Engineering Co., Unit 8 Great Bridge Industrial Estate, Tipton, West Midlands, DY4 0HR Tel: 0121-520 8953 Fax: 0121-520 8953

Auguste Development Services, Unit 12b Cooksland Industrial Estate, Bodmin, Cornwall, PL31 2QB Tel: (01208) 75593 Fax: (01208) 77499 E-mail: sales@augustedev.fsnet.co.uk

Autofour Precision Engineering Ltd, 5 Alstone Trading Estate, Alstone Lane, Cheltenham, Gloucestershire, GL51 8HF Tel: (01242) 582064 Fax: (01242) 224374 E-mail: info@autofour.co.uk

B B W Engineering Co Aston Ltd, 55 Stanhope Street, Birmingham, B12 0UX Tel: 0121-446 5223 Fax: 0121-446 5305 E-mail: m.eaton@btconnect.com

B D H Engineering, Unit 3, Granta Terrace, Great Shelford, Cambridge, CB2 5DJ Tel: (01223) 845088 Fax: (01223) 841973 E-mail: bdheng@aol.com

B G T Automatics Ltd, 2 Paragon Court, Tongham Road, Aldershot, Hampshire, GU12 4AA Tel: (01252) 318111 Fax: (01252) 311831 E-mail: carol@bgtcnc.freeserve.co.uk

B M I Engineering Ltd, Vernon Road, Halesowen, West Midlands, B62 8HN Tel: 0121-559 3406 Fax: 0121-561 2603 E-mail: sales@bmi-engineering.co.uk

B O M Light Engineering Ltd, B O M Engineering Tools, Station Road, Morley, Leeds, LS27 8JT Tel: 0113-253 7544 Fax: 0113-252 7851 E-mail: sales@bomeng.co.uk

B P Engineering Ltd, John Harper Street, Willenhall, West Midlands, WV13 1RE Tel: (01902) 609167 Fax: (01902) 605766

Beta Engineering Services Ltd, Unit 3a Goldthorpe Industrial Estate, Commercial Road, Goldthorpe, Rotherham, South Yorkshire, S63 9BL Tel: (01709) 898848 Fax: (01709) 880856 E-mail: enquiries@betaengineeringservices.co.uk

George Bethell Ltd, Unit 9 Rugby Park, Bletchley Road, Heaton Mersey, Stockport, Cheshire, SK4 3EJ Tel: 0161-442 8805 Fax: 0161-442 8818 E-mail: sales@bethell.com

Bico Ltd, Rosemary Lane, Beaumaris, Gwynedd, LL58 8EB Tel: (01248) 810463 Fax: (01248) 810998 E-mail: bicoltd@aol.com

Biddlecombe Engineering Ltd, Unit 18 Landford Common Farm, New Road, Landford, Salisbury, SP5 2AZ Tel: (01794) 322992 Fax: (01794) 323001

Bilston Engineering Ltd, Spring Road, Wolverhampton, WV4 6LF Tel: (01902) 492004 Fax: (01902) 354510 E-mail: sales@bilston-engineering.co.uk

Bond Engineering Ltd, Harrowbrook Road, Hinckley, Leicestershire, LE10 3DJ Tel: (01455) 632775 Fax: (01455) 632738 E-mail: bondeng31@aol.com

Bonut Engineering Ltd, Universal Works, Hibbert Street, Stockport, Cheshire, SK4 1NS Tel: 0161-480 1068 Fax: 0161-480 6173 E-mail: info@bonutengineering.co.uk

Branberg Machine Tools, Unit 15 Marino Way, Finchampstead, Wokingham, Berkshire, RG40 4RF Tel: 0118-973 4044 Fax: 0118-973 2707

Brass Turned Parts Ltd, 160 Dollman Street, Birmingham, B7 4RS Tel: 0121-359 1234 Fax: 0121-359 4698 E-mail: enquiries@brassturnedparts.co.uk

Bristols & Round Ltd, Longford Road, Cannock, Staffordshire, WS11 0LF Tel: (01543) 503027 Fax: (01543) 505693 E-mail: sales@bristolround.co.uk

Briter Components & Manufacturing Ltd, 8 Sandwich Industrial Estate, Ramsgate Road, Sandwich, Kent, CT13 9LN Tel: (01304) 617155 Fax: (01304) 617741 E-mail: brian@britercomponents.com

Brownhills Engineering Co, Progress Drive, Cannock, Staffordshire, WS11 0JE Tel: (01543) 502700 Fax: (01543) 520700

Bunting Engineering Ltd, Unit 14/20, Manor Industrial Estate, Pleck Road, Walsall, WS2 9XX Tel: (01922) 623888 Fax: (01922) 623888

BWS Security Systems Ltd, BWS Security Systems, Unit18 Church Farm Business Park, Corston, Bath, BA2 9AP Tel: (01225) 872385 Fax: (01225) 874565

C Churchfield, Unit 7 Howsell Road Industrial Estate, Malvern, Worcestershire, WR14 1UJ Tel: (01684) 892150 Fax: (01684) 892150

C & J Industries, Northern House, Station Approach, Hitchin, Hertfordshire, SG4 9UW Tel: (01462) 452414 Fax: (01462) 421105

C N Smart (UK) Ltd, Unit 3, Baltimore Trading Estate, Baltimore Road, Great Barr, Birmingham, B42 1DD Tel: 0121-356 2920 Fax: 0121-356 6129 E-mail: cnsmart@hotmail.com

C O'Connor Engineers Ltd, Halberton Street, Smethwick, West Midlands, B66 2QP Tel: 0121-555 5992 Fax: 0121-555 6007

Chase Precision Engineering Ltd, 10 7 Blackmoor Road, Ebblake Industrial Estate, Verwood, Dorset, BH31 6AX Tel: (01202) 813237 Fax: (01202) 813734

A.J. Clarke (Automatic Machinists) Ltd, Unit 7, Wessex Industrial Estate, Bourne End, Buckinghamshire, SL8 5DT Tel: (01628) 521301 Fax: (01628) 819142 E-mail: sales@ajclarke.info

Clint Hill Engineering, Newton Road, Hinckley, Leicestershire, LE10 3DS Tel: (01455) 239239 Fax: (01455) 238559 E-mail: clinthill@wanadoo.co.uk

Cobra Engineering, 34 Tenby Street, Birmingham, B1 3ES Tel: 0121-233 1724 Fax: 0121-236 3731

D & G Engineering, Unit 18 Lynx Cresent, Weston-super-Mare, Avon, BS24 9DJ Tel: (01934) 628476 Fax: (01934) 418410

D J J Precision Engineering Ltd, Unit 14 Pontyfelin Avenue Industrial Estate, New Inn, Pontypool, Gwent, NP4 0DQ Tel: (01495) 760561 Fax: (01495) 756256 E-mail: sales@djjengineering.com

Daniels Precision Engineering, Queens Road, Southall, Middlesex, UB2 5AY Tel: (020) 8574 3037

Davart Fasteners, Unit 10 Honeybourne Airfield Trading Estate, Honeybourne, Evesham, Worcestershire, WR11 7QF Tel: (01386) 833784 Fax: (01386) 833002 E-mail: sales@davart.co.uk

Denner Kelford Grinding Ltd, D3 Seedbed Centre, Avenue Road, Nechells, Birmingham, B7 4NT Tel: 0121-359 7728 Fax: 0121-359 0255

E B Engineering, 17 All Saints Industrial Estate, All Saints Street, Birmingham, B18 7RJ Tel: 0121-551 3274 Fax: 0121-551 3274

E & E Engineering Ltd, Unit 74 Blackpole Trading Estate West, Worcester, WR3 8TJ Tel: (01905) 453527 Fax: (01905) 457395 E-mail: enquiries@e-and-e.co.uk

E Meyer & Co Mentor Ltd, Unit 15 Abbey Industrial Estate, Mount Pleasant, Wembley, Middlesex, HA0 1QX Tel: (020) 8902 5471 Fax: (020) 8900 1398 E-mail: sales@emeyer.co.uk

E R I Ltd, Bridge Road, Great Bridge, Tipton, West Midlands, DY4 0HR Tel: 0121-520 8171 Fax: 0121-522 2330 E-mail: sales@eritpltd.fsnet.co.uk

Ees Engineering Ltd, Sheddingdean Industrial Estate, Marchants Way, Burgess Hill, West Sussex, RH15 8QY Tel: (01444) 244733 Fax: (01444) 236939

Eram UK Ltd, 110 Malvern Avenue, Nuneaton, Warwickshire, CV10 8NB Tel: (024) 7632 7184 Fax: (024) 7634 2607 E-mail: eramuk@ntlworld.com

F & C Automatic Production Ltd, Quarry Road, Newhaven, East Sussex, BN9 9DG Tel: (01273) 515485 Fax: (01273) 517827

F R Mount Ltd, Tempest House, Lyon Road, Walton-on-Thames, Surrey, KT12 3PU Tel: (01932) 230011 Fax: (01932) 230022

First Components, The Wallows Industrial Estate, Fens Pool Avenue, Brierley Hill, West Midlands, DY5 1QA Tel: (01384) 262068 Fax: (01384) 482383 E-mail: carl@firstcomponents.co.uk

Fosse Precision Ltd, East Street, Coventry, CV1 5LS Tel: (024) 7622 5263 Fax: (024) 7652 0919 E-mail: fosse.precision@zen.co.uk

Foxwood Engineering, 8 Park Trading Estate, Park Road, Hockley, Birmingham, B18 5HB Tel: 0121-554 7567 Fax: 0121-554 3834

Glynnway Engineering & Welding Ltd, Salop Street, Bilston, West Midlands, WV14 0TQ Tel: (01902) 495701 Fax: (01902) 497702 E-mail: sales@glynnway.co.uk

Goldburn Engineering Co. Ltd, Unit 12, Uddens Trading Estate, Wimborne, Dorset, BH21 7LL Tel: (01202) 893100 Fax: (01202) 861666

Goodturn Engineering Ltd, Unit 2 Brook Street, Redditch, Worcestershire, B98 8NG Tel: (01527) 596325 Fax: (01527) 597325 E-mail: mail@goodturn-engineering.co.uk

Gwent Repetition Engineers Ltd, Factory Road, Newport, Gwent, NP20 5FA Tel: (01633) 251112 Fax: (01633) 246940

H G Brunner, Bradbourne House, East Malling, West Malling, Kent, ME19 6DZ Tel: (01732) 873715 Fax: (01732) 875610 E-mail: sales@hgbrunner.com

H P C Services Ltd, Unit 14 Solomon Road, Ilkeston, Derbyshire, DE7 5UA Tel: 0115-932 3773 Fax: 0115-932 2857 E-mail: sales@slidinghead.com

H S Rowe & Partners, Building 80, First Avenue, Pensnett Trading Estate, Kingswinford, West Midlands, DY6 7FQ Tel: (01384) 293862 Fax: (01384) 271805 E-mail: sales@buxtonhayes.co.uk

H T S Precision Engineering Co. Ltd, Unit 3, Shamrock Quay, William Street, Northam, Southampton, SO14 5QL Tel: (023) 8033 3668 Fax: (023) 8063 7216

Halesowen Components Ltd, 126 Coombs Road, Halesowen, West Midlands, B62 8AF Tel: 0121-559 3771 Fax: 0121-561 5323 E-mail: sales@halesowencnc.co.uk

Hamilton Precision Engineering, 7 Hamilton Way, Gore Road Industrial Estate, New Milton, Hampshire, BH25 6TQ Tel: (01425) 613181

Harlech Tool & Engineering Co., 5 Ynyscedwyn Industrial Estate, Trawsffordd Road, Ystradgynlais, Swansea, SA9 1DT Tel: (01639) 849044 Fax: (01639) 849045 E-mail: info@harlech-tools.co.uk

Harris Repair Consultancy Service Ltd, Unit 3, Crondal Road, Exhall, Coventry, CV7 9NH Tel: (024) 7636 4848 Fax: (024) 7664 4411 E-mail: g.harris@harrisrcs.com

Allan Hayes Engineering Ltd, Charlwoods Road, East Grinstead, West Sussex, RH19 2HR Tel: (01342) 324536 Fax: (01342) 312556

Hayfield Engineering Ltd, Sutherland Avenue, Wolverhampton, WV2 2JH Tel: (01902) 352930 Fax: (01902) 351620 E-mail: sales@hayfield.co.uk

Herve Engineering Ltd, 9 Towerfield Road, Shoeburyness, Southend-on-Sea, SS3 9QE Tel: (01702) 293617 Fax: (01702) 297410 E-mail: sales@herveengineering.co.uk

Highbridge Turned Parts Ltd, 23a Highbridge Street, Waltham Abbey, Essex, EN9 1BZ Tel: (01992) 713333 Fax: (01992) 713333 E-mail: highbridgetp@supanet.com

Highfield CNC Engineering Ltd, 39 Knowl Piece, Wilbury Way, Hitchin, Hertfordshire, SG4 0TY Tel: (01462) 442252 Fax: (01462) 442257 E-mail: highfieldcnc@aol.com

Illston & Robson Ltd, Herbert Road, Small Heath, Birmingham, B10 0QQ Tel: 0121-772 5674 Fax: 0121-766 6452 E-mail: illstonandrobson@tiscali.co.uk

J J Hardy & Sons Ltd, Brenda Road, Hartlepool, Cleveland, TS25 2BL Tel: (01429) 279837 Fax: (01429) 860182 E-mail: sales@jjhardy.co.uk

Jaylyn Services (Midlands) Ltd, Unit 5 Shilton Industrial Estate, Coventry, CV7 9QL Tel: (024) 7661 9298 Fax: (024) 7660 2623

K M Engineering Ltd, Unit 7b Parnall Road Trading Estate, Parnall Road, Bristol, BS16 3JQ Tel: 0117-965 9336 Fax: 0117-958 3673 E-mail: enquiries@km-engineering.co.uk

Kamway Engineering Ltd, Fircroft Way, Edenbridge, Kent, TN8 6EN Tel: (01732) 862028 Fax: (01732) 866868 E-mail: enquires@kamway.co.uk

Kershaw & Co. Ltd, Hixon Industrial Estate, Church Lane, Hixon, Stafford, ST18 0PY Tel: (01889) 270556 Fax: (01889) 271295 E-mail: sales@kershaw-engineering.co.uk

Kwik Turn Engineering, Unit 4 The Hayes Trading Estate, Folkes Road, Stourbridge, West Midlands, DY9 8RN Tel: (01384) 898011 Fax: (01384) 896869

L J Dennison, 94 Leopold Street, Birmingham, B12 0UD Tel: 0121-772 8871 Fax: 0121-772 8871

L Person & Son Ltd, 33 Hollands Road, Haverhill, Suffolk, CB9 8PU Tel: (01440) 702811 Fax: (01440) 702711 E-mail: david@personhaverhill.freeserve.co.uk

Leipold (UK) Ltd, Unit D, Stafford Park 2, Telford, Shropshire, TF3 3AR Tel: (01952) 230100 Fax: (01952) 230111 E-mail: info@leipold-uk.com

Leominster Engineering Co., Southern Avenue, Leominster, Herefordshire, HR6 0QF Tel: (01568) 613284 Fax: (01568) 614734

Leonard Bowes Engineering Co. Ltd, 31 Mill Street, Brierley Hill, West Midlands, DY5 2RG Tel: (01384) 573000 Fax: (01384) 573000

M B Techniques Ltd, Douglas Street, Hamilton, Lanarkshire, ML3 0BU Tel: (01698) 457222 Fax: (01698) 891924

M & D Tooling, 12a Carvers Trading Estate, Southampton Road, Ringwood, Hampshire, BH24 1JS Tel: (01425) 489945 Fax: (01425) 489946

M S Engineering, Unit 49 Silicon Business Centre, Wadsworth Road, Greenford, Middlesex, UB6 7JZ Tel: (020) 8991 1444 Fax: (020) 8991 1444

M S P Ltd, Roman Way, Coleshill, Birmingham, B46 1HG Tel: (01675) 469100 Fax: (01675) 463699 E-mail: sales@msp.ltd.uk

Mac Machining Ltd, Unit 26, Hoobrook Enterprise Centre, Worcester Road, Kidderminster, Worcestershire, DY10 1HY Tel: (01562) 67619 Fax: (01562) 861243 E-mail: morris@macmachining.freeserve.co.uk

Machined Component Systems plc, 2-5 Madeley Road, Moons Moat North Industrial Estate, Redditch, Worcestershire, B98 9NB Tel: (01527) 65208 Fax: (01527) 585048 E-mail: sales@machined-components-systems.plc.uk

Manned Precision, Lower Wield, Alresford, Hampshire, SO24 9RX Tel: 01256 389258

Manx Engineers Ltd, Wheel Hill, Laxey, Isle of Man, IM4 7NL Tel: (01624) 861362 Fax: (01624) 861914

Mayhill Contracts Ltd, 11 Mucklow Hill Trading Estate, Mucklow Hill, Halesowen, West Midlands, B62 8DF Tel: 0121-550 0016 Fax: 0121-550 0017

Maytyne Engineering, Gardner Street, Herstmonceux, Hailsham, East Sussex, BN27 4LE Tel: (01323) 833200 Fax: (01323) 833200

Melborha Engineering Co. Ltd, Unit B, Cradock Road, Luton, LU4 0JF Tel: (01582) 494387

Mellorsons Manufacturing Ltd, George Street, West Bromwich, West Midlands, B70 6NH Tel: 0121-580 0520 Fax: 0121-580 0521

Muller Holdings Ltd, Cleobury Mortimer, Kidderminster, Worcestershire, DY14 8DT Tel: (01299) 270271 Fax: (01299) 270877 E-mail: sales@muller-england.co.uk

Muller Redditch Ltd, Bartleet Road, Washford Industrial Estate, Redditch, Worcestershire, B98 0DG Tel: (01527) 526920 Fax: (01527) 502166 E-mail: sales@muller-redditch.co.uk

N C Geary (Precision Engineering), 10 Mill Road, Christchurch, Dorset, BH23 2JY Tel: (01202) 483585 Fax: (01202) 471163 E-mail: nick@geary-engineering.co.uk

N & J Engineering Ltd, Vulcan Road, Solihull, West Midlands, B91 2JY Tel: 0121-704 0440 Fax: 0121-704 0550 E-mail: sales@dohertygroup.co.uk

N R Automatics Ltd, Duckworth Mill, Skipton Road, Colne, Lancashire, BB8 0RH Tel: (01282) 868500 Fax: (01282) 869885

N R Engineering, 5 Commercial Road, Reading, RG2 0QZ Tel: 0118-975 0303 Fax: 0118-975 3879

N S H Turned Parts, Fordwater Trading Estate, Ford Road, Chertsey, Surrey, KT16 8HG Tel: (01932) 561761 Fax: (01932) 563178

Neida Blue 62 Ltd, Golden Hill Works, Coalwell Road, Freshwater, Isle Of Wight, PO40 9TD Tel: (01983) 758800 Fax: (01983) 758822 E-mail: simon.fisher@blue62.co.uk

Newteq Engineering Ltd, 1 Waterside Industrial Estate, Ettingshall Road, Wolverhampton, WV2 2RQ Tel: (01902) 492622 Fax: (01902) 492379 E-mail: sales@newteq.co.uk

Northern Cam Company Ltd, Unit 127 Whitehall Indust Estate, Whitehall Road, Leeds, LS12 5JB Tel: 0113-279 2733 Fax: 0113-279 4547 E-mail: info@northerncam.co.uk

Northwood Engineering Birmingham Co. Ltd, 122 Emily Street, Birmingham, B12 0XJ Tel: 0121-440 6731 Fax: 0121-440 3549 E-mail: northwoodengltd@aol.com

Nova Engineering Co., 5 Stephenson Road, Bayton Road Industrial Estate, Exhall, Coventry, CV7 9EQ Tel: (024) 7636 1408 Fax: (024) 7664 4845 E-mail: enquiries@novaeng.co.uk

Old Oak Engineering, Unit 11, Gilchrist Thomas Industrial Estate, Blaenavon, Pontypool, Gwent, NP4 9RL Tel: (01495) 791615 Fax: (01495) 790866

Paragon Precision Products, 36 Camford Way, Luton, LU3 3AN Tel: (01582) 505005 Fax: (01582) 505010 E-mail: info@paragon-precision.co.uk

Park Engineering Wolverhampton Co. Ltd, Portersfield Industrial Estate, Portersfield Road, Cradley Heath, West Midlands, B64 7BW Tel: (01384) 566263 Fax: (01384) 564700 E-mail: neil_roberts@btconnect.com

Parland Engineering Ltd, Unit 7, Cobblestone Court, Hoults Estate, Newcastle upon Tyne, NE6 1AB Tel: 0191-276 6660

PDL Engineering Ltd, 5 Whittle Road, Ferndown Industrial Estate, Wimborne, Dorset, BH21 7RJ Tel: (01202) 871188 Fax: (01202) 892499

PDQ Engineering Ltd, Industrial Road, Hertburn, Washington, Tyne & Wear, NE37 2SA Tel: 0191-417 2343 Fax: 0191-416 5518 E-mail: john@pdqengineering.com

Peerdown Engineering Ltd, 24 Dunstall Hill Ind Estate, Gorsebrook Road, Wolverhampton, WV6 0PJ Tel: (01902) 773663 Fax: (01902) 773663

Precision 82, 2 Ebley Industrial Park, Westward Road, Ebley, Stroud, Gloucestershire, GL5 4SP Tel: (01453) 752481 Fax: (01453) 767910 E-mail: info@precision82.co.uk

Precision Repetition Ltd, 87 Leamore Lane, Walsall, WS2 7BU Tel: (01922) 473335

Production Engineering Components Ltd, 104 College Street, Kempston, Bedford, MK42 8LU Tel: (01234) 346587 Fax: (01234) 325385 E-mail: jane@pec.uk.com

Qualiturn Products Ltd, 18 Merchant Drive, Mead Lane, Hertford, SG13 7AY Tel: (01992) 584499 Fax: (01992) 551726 E-mail: kssales@qualiturn.co.uk

Quantum Precision Engineering Ltd, 5-11 Tower Street, Birmingham, B19 3UY Tel: 0121-333 4734 Fax: 0121-333 6394 E-mail: info@quantumprecision.co.uk

Quick Tools Ltd, Fitzherbert Road, Portsmouth, PO6 1RY Tel: (023) 9237 5718 Fax: (023) 9232 5203 E-mail: sales@quicktoolsltd.co.uk

R K Components, 5b Eley Estate, Angel Road, London, N18 3BH Tel: (020) 8884 1366 Fax: (020) 8884 3881 E-mail: info@rkcomponents.com

PRECISION TURNED PARTS – *continued*

R K Davies, 8 Spinnaker Road, Hempsted Lane, Hempsted, Gloucester, GL2 5FD Tel: (01452) 410555 Fax: (01452) 310452

▶ R L R Engineers Ltd, 456 Warrington Road, Rainhill, Prescot, Merseyside, L35 9JE Tel: 0151-426 0245 Fax: 0151-426 8288 E-mail: admin@rlrengineers.co.uk

R P L Productions Ltd, Northcote Road, Birmingham, B33 9BE Tel: 0121-624 5000 Fax: 0121-784 5400 E-mail: info@rplproductions.co.uk

R W Cresswell Ltd, Unit 2 79-81 Cheapside, Deritend, Birmingham, B12 0QH Tel: 0121-772 4565

Redfern Stevens Ltd, 40 Brickfield Road, Birmingham, B25 8HE Tel: 0121-766 6464 Fax: 0121-766 6651 E-mail: info@redfernstevens.co.uk

Reed & Seymour Ltd, Cressex Industrial Estate, Lancaster Road, High Wycombe, Buckinghamshire, HP12 3NN Tel: (01494) 474964 Fax: (01494) 474964

Richard A Fores Ltd, Dagmar Road, Southall, Middlesex, UB2 5NX Tel: (020) 8574 5287 Fax: (020) 8574 3105 E-mail: r.a.fores@btinternet.com

Richmond Precision Services, Lancaster Road, Bowerhill, Melksham, Wiltshire, SN12 6SS Tel: (01225) 706840 Fax: (01225) 700841 E-mail: richard.hand@richmondprecision.co.uk

Rodmatic Precision Engineering Co. Ltd, Battle Farm Trading Estate, 30 Portman Road, Reading, RG30 1PD Tel: 0118-959 6969 Fax: 0118-939 3060 E-mail: sales@rodmatic.co.uk

Rosch Engineering, Units 1 2, Calibre Indust Park, Four Ashes, Wolverhampton, WV10 7DZ Tel: (01902) 798100 Fax: (01902) 798844 E-mail: info@rosch.co.uk

Rush Engineering, 126 Marjorie Street, Leicester, LE4 5GX Tel: 0116-268 2837 Fax: 0116-266 1781

F.W. Russell (Gauges) Ltd, 2-3 Avenue Industrial Estate, Gallows Corner, Romford, RM3 0HS Tel: (01708) 376888 Fax: (01708) 374050

S Z N Pendle Automatics Ltd, 1 Stanhope Street, Birmingham, B12 0UZ Tel: 0121-772 2516 Fax: 0121-766 6310

▶ Sassen Engineering Ltd, 19 Aston Road North, Birmingham, B6 4DS Tel: 0121-359 7411 Fax: 0121-359 2404 E-mail: sales@sassenengineering.co.uk

Sensotemp Ltd, Plot 12, Woodford Halse, Daventry, Northamptonshire, NN11 3TZ Tel: 01327 261212

Shanick Engineering Co. Ltd, Byfield Place, Bognor Regis, West Sussex, PO22 9QY Tel: (01243) 863666 Fax: (01243) 827629 E-mail: shannick.eng@surfree.co.uk

SPS Technologies Ltd, Troon Industrial Area, 191 Barkby Road, Leicester, LE4 9HX Tel: 0116-276 8261 Fax: 0116-274 0243

Stereomatics Ltd, Seven Stars Industrial Estate, Wheler Road, Coventry, CV3 4LB Tel: (024) 7630 4000 Fax: (024) 7630 4455 E-mail: sales@stereomatic.co.uk

Sullivan Engineering Co., 9 Doman Road, Camberley, Surrey, GU15 3DF Tel: (01276) 20931 Fax: (01276) 27168 E-mail: sullivaneng42@netscapeonline.co.uk

P.B. Sutton Engineering Co, 3 Hedley Road, St. Albans, Hertfordshire, AL1 5JL Tel: (01727) 858731 Fax: (01727) 847064 E-mail: hazel@pbsuttonsagehost.co.uk

Swift Engineering Co., 35 River Road, Barking, Essex, IG11 0DA Tel: (020) 8594 7626 Fax: (020) 8594 6207

T K M Engineering, 32 Priory Road, Romford, RM3 9AT Tel: (01708) 377723 Fax: (01708) 377022 E-mail: sales@tkmlondon.co.uk

T R Engineering Ltd, Unit 6 Hadrians Way, Glebe Farm Industrial Estate, Rugby, Warwickshire, CV21 1ST Tel: (01788) 552983 Fax: (01788) 552983 E-mail: sales@treng.co.uk

Technoset Ltd, Unit 3A, Roman Way, Rugby, Warwickshire, CV21 1DB Tel: (01788) 560522 Fax: (01788) 541196 E-mail: sales@technoset.com

The Tenable Screw Co. Ltd, Tenable House, Torrington Avenue, Coventry, CV4 9HN Tel: (024) 7669 4422 Fax: (024) 7647 0029 E-mail: sales@tenable.co.uk

The Tenable Screw Co. Ltd, Elcot Lane, Marlborough, Wiltshire, SN8 2AE Tel: (01672) 512900 Fax: (01672) 513915 E-mail: sales@tenable.co.uk

Tercet Precision Ltd, Millarston Industrial Estate, Paisley, Renfrewshire, PA1 2XR Tel: 0141-887 4153 Fax: 0141-887 4586 E-mail: sales@tercet.co.uk

E.H. Thompson & Son (London) Ltd, Hallsford Bridge Industrial Estate, Stondon Road, Ongar, Essex, CM5 9RB Tel: (01277) 365500 Fax: (01277) 365550 E-mail: ehthompsons@btconnects.com

Toolturn Engineering Ltd, 8 Brunel Way, Fareham, Hampshire, PO15 5TX Tel: (01489) 578878 Fax: (01489) 578859 E-mail: sales@toolturn.com

Triumph Precision Engineering, Unit 29 The Acorn Centre, Barry Street, Oldham, OL1 3NE Tel: 0161-626 0550

Trucut Technologies UK Ltd, Flavell Works, Garratt Street, Brierley Hill, West Midlands, DY5 1JU Tel: (01746) 764900 Fax: (01384) 481195 E-mail: sales@chartway.co.uk

Truecut Co, 33 Dulverton Road, Birmingham, B6 7EQ Tel: 0121-327 2815 Fax: 0121-327 2832

Ultra Precision Products Ltd, Homefield Road, Haverhill, Suffolk, CB9 8QP Tel: (01440) 706030 Fax: (01440) 762828 E-mail: info@ultraprecision.co.uk

Unicut, 6 Tewin Court, Welwyn Garden City, Hertfordshire, AL7 1AU Tel: (01707) 331227 Fax: (01707) 390382 E-mail: sales@unicutprecision.com

Unijet Products Ltd, Unit 4 The Ham, Brentford, Middlesex, TW8 8EZ Tel: 020 85608978

V L B Products Ltd, 12 Birch Road East Industrial Estate, Birch Road East, Birmingham, B6 7DB Tel: 0121-328 4575

Vetraform Ltd, Unit 19-20, Halesfield 18, Telford, Shropshire, TF7 4PP Tel: (01952) 587631 Fax: (01952) 582596 E-mail: alex@vetraform.co.uk

W W Grew & Co. Ltd, Stafford Street, Wednesbury, West Midlands, WS10 7JX Tel: 0121-556 3337 Fax: 0121-556 8171 E-mail: info@wwgrew.com

Warren Engineering, 18A Station Close, Potters Bar, Hertfordshire, EN6 1TL Tel: (01707) 642870 Fax: (01707) 642870

Warwick Brassfounders & Engineering Co. Ltd, 14-16 Haden Street, Birmingham, B12 9BH Tel: 0121-440 0901 Fax: 0121-440 6725

Watson Engineering, 12 Upper Gough Street, Birmingham, B1 1JG Tel: 0121-643 1922 Fax: 0121-633 4019

Wealdpark Ltd, Sutton Road, St. Helens, Merseyside, WA9 3DJ Tel: (01744) 22567 Fax: (01744) 451339 E-mail: sales@wealdpark.co.uk

Wedge Engineering Ltd, 16 Darlington Close, Sandy, Bedfordshire, SG19 1RW Tel: (01767) 683527 Fax: (01767) 683529 E-mail: wedgeeng@btconnect.com

Whiteland Engineering Ltd, Torrington Lane, Bideford, Devon, EX39 4BH Tel: (01237) 472203 Fax: (01237) 472205 E-mail: info@whitelandengineering.co.uk

Widdowson-Dalebrook Engineers Ltd, Basford Road, Crewe, CW2 6ES Tel: 01270 661111

Wigpool, 46 Walkers Road, Moons Moat North Industrial Es, Redditch, Worcestershire, B98 9HE Tel: (01527) 64086 Fax: (01527) 62319

Wilco Manufacturing Ltd, Tyseley Industrial Estate, Seeleys Road, Birmingham, B11 2LQ Tel: 0121-772 6212 Fax: 0121-772 2871 E-mail: martinlane@wilcomanufacturing.co.uk

Wrington Precision Automatics, 29 Blue Water Drive, Elborough, Weston-Super-Mare, Avon, BS24 8PF Tel: (01934) 823525 Fax: E-mail: pill@wrington.co.uk

PRECISION WELDING

Comwald Engineering, Unit 8 Bromag Industrial Estate, Minster Lovell, Witney, Oxfordshire, OX29 0SR Tel: (01993) 771478 Fax: (01993) 708220

M J R Fabrications, B Cranborne Industrial Estate, Cranborne Road, Potters Bar, Hertfordshire, EN6 3JN Tel: (01707) 646825 Fax: (01707) 649089

John Ward Welding, Lythalls Lane, Coventry, CV6 6FL Tel: (024) 7666 3200 Fax: (024)7666 3200 E-mail: john@ward-welding.co.uk

PRECISION WOODWORK

Arjay Joinery Co. Ltd, Unit 6, Craufurd Business Park, Silverdale Road, Hayes, Middlesex, UB3 3BN Tel: (020) 8573 3746 Fax: (020) 8569 1807

The Bradshaw Pattern Company Ltd, Rowland House Lion Mill, Fitton Street, Royton, Oldham, OL2 5JX Tel: 0161-624 5043 Fax: 0161-628 3245

H L D Ltd, Old Shipyard, Gainsborough, Lincolnshire, DN21 1NG Tel: (01427) 611800 Fax: (01427) 612867 E-mail: technical@hld.co.uk

J R Spalding, 55 Mill Street, Kingston upon Thames, Surrey, KT1 2RG Tel: (020) 8546 0363 Fax: (020) 8546 0363 E-mail: jrspalding.joinery@amserve.net

Lind Wood Components Ltd, River Mill, Park Road, Dukinfield, Cheshire, SK16 5LR Tel: 0161-330 2624 Fax: 0161-343 1094 E-mail: info@lindwood.co.uk

R E H Kennedy Ltd, Whitehouse Road, Ipswich, IP1 5LT Tel: (01473) 240044 Fax: (01473) 240098 E-mail: sales@rehkennedy.co.uk

Richard Cullinan Joinery Ltd, 8 Ferrier Industrial Estate, Ferrier Street, London, SW18 1SW Tel: (020) 8871 0029 Fax: (020) 8871 0020 E-mail: richard@rcjoinery.co.uk

PRECISION WOVEN MESH

Sefar Ltd, Bury Business Centre, Kay Street, Bury, Lancashire, BL9 6BU Tel: 0161-705 1878 Fax: 0161-763 1382 E-mail: sales@sefar.co.uk

PRECOATED STEEL SHEET

Bondcote Ltd, Unit 15, Lister Road Industrial Estate, Sherrington Way, Basingstoke, Hampshire, RG22 4DQ Tel: (01256) 465983 Fax: (01256) 328818 E-mail: mail@bondcote.co.uk

Capital Coated Steel, East Tyndall Street, Cardiff, CF24 5DA Tel: (029) 2046 0606 Fax: (029) 2048 8687 E-mail: email@capitalcs.com

Organically Coated Steels, Hoo Farm Industrial Estate, Worcester Road, Kidderminster, Worcestershire, DY11 7RA Tel: (01562) 821400 Fax: (01562) 865396 E-mail: ocs@asdmetalservices.co.uk

PREFABRICATED AGRICULTURAL BUILDINGS

J. Waring & Son (Wrea Green) Ltd, Wrea Green, Preston, PR4 2NB Tel: (01772) 682924 Fax: (01772) 671071 E-mail: jwaring@ukonline.co.uk

PREFABRICATED BUILDINGS

A M Warkup Ltd, Aerodrome Works, Lissett, Driffield, North Humberside, YO25 8PT Tel: (01262) 468666 Fax: (01262) 468656 E-mail: amwarkup@amwarkup.co.uk

All In One Leisure Buildings, Rochdale Road, Middleton, Manchester, M24 2RB Tel: (01706) 717427 Fax: (01706) 759759 E-mail: sales@allinone.co.uk

Anglia Accommodation, 118 Lexden Road, West Bergholt, Colchester, CO6 3BP Tel: (01206) 240842 Fax: (01206) 240842

Bailey & Davidson Ltd, The Street, Bishop's Cannings, Devizes, Wiltshire, SN10 2LD Tel: (01380) 860386 Fax: (01380) 860897 E-mail: nbailey@kwikbuild.com

Brad Scott Estates Ltd, 137 Stonnall Road, Walsall, WS9 8JY Tel: (01543) 454098 Fax: (01543) 453352

Britspace Modular Buildings, Unicorn House, Broad Lane, Gilberdyke, Brough, East Yorkshire, HU15 2TS Tel: (01430) 444400 Fax: (01430) 444401 E-mail: info@britspace.com

Caledonian Building Systems Ltd, Carlton Works, Ossington Road, Carlton-on-Trent, Newark, Nottinghamshire, NG23 6NT Tel: (01636) 821645 Fax: (01636) 821261

Cemex Floors, London Road, Wick, Bristol, BS30 5SJ Tel: (01788) 542111 Fax: 0117-937 4695 E-mail: rmc@concreteproducts.co.uk

Conport Structures Ltd, 1 Duke of York Square, London, SW3 4LY Tel: (020) 7730 9105 Fax: (020) 7730 5031 E-mail: sales@conport.com

Edwards Building Services Ltd, Craig Lelo Works, Bryn Saith Marchog, Corwen, Clwyd, LL21 9RY Tel: (01824) 750400 Fax: (01824) 750403 E-mail: info@craiglelo.co.uk

Elliott Group Ltd, Braemar House, Snelsins Lane, Cleckheaton, West Yorkshire, BD19 3UE Tel: (01274) 863221 Fax: (01274) 861582 E-mail: fastrack@elliott-algeco.com

Elliott Redispace, Valletta Street, Hull, HU9 5NP Tel: (01482) 781202 Fax: (01482) 712157 E-mail: hirediv@elliott-group.co.uk

Evans Buildings, Little Acre, Cwmffrwd, Carmarthen, Dyfed, SA31 2LT Tel: (01267) 232478 Fax: (01267) 230588 E-mail: evans.buildings@virgin.net

Frame Homes South West, Jenson House, Cardrew Industrial Estate, Redruth, Cornwall, TR15 1SS Tel: (01209) 310560 Fax: (01209) 310561 E-mail: enquiries@framehomes.co.uk

G E Capital Modular Space Ltd, 2a Pioneer Works, Crabtree Manorway, Belvedere, Kent, DA17 6AH Tel: (020) 8312 4000 Fax: (020) 8311 7643

Guildway Ltd, 194 London Road, Boston, Lincolnshire, PE21 7HJ Tel: (01205) 350555 Fax: (01205) 359261 E-mail: mail@guildway.ltd.uk

Harveys Garden Buildings, Woodside Garden Centre, Arterial Road, Rayleigh, Essex, SS6 7TZ Tel: (01268) 775770 Fax: (01268) 769155 E-mail: harveysgarden@btconnect.com

Harveys Garden & Leisure Buildings Ltd, Sectional Building Centre, Unit 5, Maltings Road, Battlesbridge, Wickford, Essex, SS11 7RH Tel: (01268) 768616 Fax: (01268) 769155

Homestead, Wyndham House, Lupton Road, Wallingford, Oxfordshire, OX10 9BT Tel: (01491) 839421 Fax: (01491) 825973 E-mail: enquiries@homesteadtimberbuildings.co.uk

Ideal Building Systems Ltd, Carnaby Industrial Estate, Lancaster Road, Carnaby, Bridlington, North Humberside, YO15 3QY Tel: (01262) 606750 Fax: (01262) 671960 E-mail: sales@idealbuildingsystems.co.uk

Integrated Piggery Systems Ltd, Showfield Lane, Malton, North Yorkshire, YO17 6BT Tel: (01653) 694994 Fax: (01653) 696685 E-mail: ipsltd@fsmail.net

Lowrie Bros, The Yard, Kenardington, Ashford, Kent, TN26 2LX Tel: (01233) 733833 Fax: (01233) 733899 E-mail: heather@lowriebros.co.uk

Mcavoy Group Ltd, 76 Ballynakilly Road, Dungannon, County Tyrone, BT71 6HD Tel: (028) 8774 0372 Fax: (028) 8774 8175 E-mail: gilliand@mcavoygroup.com

Magna Systems Ltd, Oakridge House, Plane Tree Way, Woodstock, Oxfordshire, OX20 1PG Tel: (01993) 811282 Fax: (01993) 813330 E-mail: pidoux1@aol.com

Northdown Buildings & Supplies Ltd, Shipton Green, Etchenor, Chichester, West Sussex, PO20 7DA Tel: (01243) 513613 Fax: (01243) 671672

Pasuda Buildings Ltd, Highfield Lane, Sheffield, S13 9NA Tel: 0114-254 0188 Fax: 0114-254 0705 E-mail: sales@pasuda.co.uk

Premier Interlink, Catfoss Airfield, Brandesburton, Driffield, North Humberside, YO25 8EJ Tel: (0800) 3160888 Fax: (01964) 545001 E-mail: sales@waco.co.uk

Sibcas Ltd, Brickyard Lane, Studley, Warwickshire, B80 7GA Tel: (01527) 850100 Fax: (01527) 850200

Site Space Ltd, Meresborough Lane, Rainham, Gillingham, Kent, ME8 8PR Tel: (01634) 389440 Fax: (01634) 373151 E-mail: sales@sitespace.co.uk

Springfield Hire (Lancs) Ltd, Collins Industrial Estate, Merton Bank Road, St. Helens, Merseyside, WA9 1HY Tel: (01744) 731215 Fax: (01744) 451842 E-mail: michael@spring-field.co.uk

Thurston Building Systems, Quarry Hill Industrial Estate, Hawking Croft Road, Horbury, Wakefield, West Yorkshire, WF4 6AJ Tel: (01924) 265461 Fax: (01924) 280246 E-mail: sales@thurstongroup.co.uk

Tilden Modular Building Systems Ltd, Stable Block, Coombe Lodge, Blagden, Bristol, BS40 7RG Tel: (01454) 413111 Fax: (01761) 462892 E-mail: info@tilden.co.uk

Welland Timber Products Ltd, Geddington Road, Corby, Northamptonshire, NN18 8ET Tel: (01536) 201992 Fax: (01536) 401178 E-mail: info@wellandtimber.co.uk

PREFABRICATED CHILDREN'S NURSERY BUILDINGS

▶ Step By Step Nursery, Watford College Site, Park Avenue, Bushey, WD23 2DD Tel: (01923) 639333 Fax: (01923) 639334 E-mail: enquiries@sbsnursery.com

PREFABRICATED CHIMNEYS

J R F Chimney Specialists Ltd, 50 Nasmyth Road, Glenrothes, Fife, KY6 2SD Tel: (01592) 771199 Fax: (01592) 771135 E-mail: info@jrf-chimney-spec.co.uk

PREFABRICATED OFFICES

Guildway Ltd, 194 London Road, Boston, Lincolnshire, PE21 7HJ Tel: (01205) 350555 Fax: (01205) 359261 E-mail: mail@guildway.ltd.uk

PREFABRICATED PLUMBING SYSTEMS

Davant Products Ltd, Davant House, Jugs Green Business Park, Staplow, Ledbury, Herefordshire, HR8 1NR Tel: (01531) 630068 Fax: (01531) 640827 E-mail: info@davant.co.uk

Harton Services Ltd, Unit 6 Thistlebrook Industrial Estate, Eynsham Drive, London, SE2 9RB Tel: (020) 8310 0421 Fax: (020) 8310 6785 E-mail: hartons@globalnet.co.uk

Pipe Line Centre, Unit D3 Premier Business Centre, Speedfields Park, Fareham, Hampshire, PO14 1TY Tel: (01329) 237215 Fax: (01329) 823641 E-mail: k73.fareham@wolseley.co.uk

PREFABRICATED SCHOOL BUILDINGS

Guildway Ltd, 194 London Road, Boston, Lincolnshire, PE21 7HJ Tel: (01205) 350555 Fax: (01205) 359261 E-mail: mail@guildway.ltd.uk

PREFABRICATED STEEL FRAME BUILDINGS

A & J Stead Ltd, 31 Derwent Road, York Road Business Park, Malton, North Yorkshire, YO17 6YB Tel: (01653) 693742 Fax: (01653) 691594 E-mail: admin@steadandson.co.uk

Farm & Industrial Buildings Ltd, Ryehill Close, Lodge Farm Industrial Estate, Northampton, NN5 7UA Tel: (01604) 753937 Fax: (01604) 758206 E-mail: nigel@farmindustrial.fsnet.co.uk

G & T Evans, Dulas Mill, Mochdre Lane, Newtown, Powys, SY16 4JD Tel: (01686) 622100 Fax: (01686) 622220 E-mail: sales@gtevans.co.uk

Goddard Engineering Ltd, The Workshop, Rumbolds Farm, Plaistow, Billingshurst, West Sussex, RH14 0PZ Tel: (01403) 871144 Fax: (01403) 871134

Haley Engineering Ltd, Bellcombe, Brent Road, East Brent, Highbridge, Somerset, TA9 4DB Tel: (01278) 760591 Fax: (01278) 760587 E-mail: sales@haleyengineering.co.uk

▶ John Ruck Construction, Longmead, Elms Green, Leominster, Herefordshire, HR6 0NS Tel: (01568) 615807

Kitpac Buildings Ltd, Shares Hill, Great Saredon, Wolverhampton, WV10 7LN Tel: (01922) 415425 Fax: (01922) 414246 E-mail: lisa@kitpac.freeserve.co.uk

PREFABRICATED STEEL FRAME BUILDINGS – *continued*

Mannion Contractors Ltd, High Oak Road, Wicklewood, Wymondham, Norfolk, NR18 9QP Tel: (01953) 601156

Rubb Buildings Ltd, Dukesway, Team Valley Trading Estate, Gateshead, Tyne & Wear, NE11 0QE Tel: 0191-482 2211 Fax: 0191-482 2516 E-mail: info@rubb.co.uk

Shufflebottom Ltd, Heol Parc Mawr, Cross Hands Industrial Estate, Cross Hands, Llanelli, Dyfed, SA14 6RE Tel: (01269) 831831 Fax: (01269) 831031 E-mail: sales@shufflebottom.co.uk

PREFINISHED WOOD FLOORING

▶ Disney Flooring, Albert Avenue, Weston-super-Mare, Avon, BS23 1YJ Tel: (01934) 628320 Fax: (01934) 615006 E-mail: enquiries@disney-flooring.com

▶ G D Floors Ltd, 8 Broomhill Court, Kilwinning, Ayrshire, KA13 6UL Tel: (01294) 559745 E-mail: info@gdfloors.co.uk

▶ Mckay Flooring Ltd, 123 Harmony Row, Glasgow, G51 3NB Tel: 0141-440 1586 Fax: 0141-425 1020 E-mail: enquires@mckay.co.uk

PREFORMED POND LINERS

▶ Flexible Lining Products Ltd, Vantage Point Business Village, Mitcheldean, Gloucestershire, GL17 0DD Tel: (0845) 2262478 Fax: (0845) 2269697 E-mail: info@flexibleliningproducts.co.uk

PREGNANCY TEST KITS

SelfDiagnosis Limited, P O Box 162, Stockport, Cheshire, SK7 3WJ Tel: 07699 392121

▶ Thenewyou Net Ltd, Butterflies 19 Alston Mews, Thatcham, Berkshire, RG19 3XF Tel: (01635) 862239

PREINSULATED PIPES

CPV Ltd, Woodington Mill, Woodington Road, East Wellow, Romsey, Hampshire, SO51 6DQ Tel: (01794) 322884 Fax: (01794) 322885 E-mail: sales@cpv.co.uk

Durotan Ltd, 20 West Street, Buckingham, MK18 1HE Tel: (01280) 814048 Fax: (01280) 817842 E-mail: general@durotan.ltd.uk

PREPACKED SANDWICHES

Barllaeth Bakery & Confectionery Supplies, London House, St Peters Square, Ruthin, Clwyd, LL15 1AA Tel: (01824) 707000

Butties, 657 Ashton New Road, Manchester, M11 4QJ Tel: 0161-220 8000

▶ Dorset Larder, 23a Hambledon Road, Bournemouth, BH6 5PJ Tel: (01202) 467837 Fax: (01202) 467837

PREPACKING SYSTEMS

Haith-Tickhill Group, Cowhouse Lane, Armthorpe, Doncaster, South Yorkshire, DN3 3EE Tel: (01302) 831911 Fax: (01302) 300173 E-mail: sales@haith.co.uk

PREPAINTED ALUMINIUM FABRICATORS

Berry Engineering, 3 Severnside, Brue Avenue, Bridgwater, Somerset, TA6 5LT Tel: (01278) 444861 Fax: (01278) 444865 E-mail: leeberryeng@aol.com

Garwards Engineering, 8 Progress Way, Mid Suffolk Business Park, Eye, Suffolk, IP23 7HU Tel: (01379) 871337 Fax: (01379) 873041 E-mail: gareth@garwards.com

A.C. Yule Son Ltd, Unit 11, Burford Way, Boldon Business Park, Boldon Colliery, Tyne & Wear, NE35 9PZ Tel: 0191-519 6250 Fax: 0191-519 6262 E-mail: boldon@acyule.com

PREPAINTED STEEL STRIPS

Capital Coated Steel, East Tyndall Street, Cardiff, CF24 5DA Tel: (029) 2046 0606 Fax: (029) 2048 8687 E-mail: email@capitalcs.com

Corus, Sengate, The Drove, Brandon, Suffolk, IP27 0JY Tel: (01842) 816200 Fax: (01842) 813019

Corus Service Centre, Garmouth Road, Mosstodloch, Fochabers, Morayshire, IV32 7LH Tel: (01343) 820606 Fax: (01343) 821295

PREPARED FRUIT AND VEGETABLES

▶ Fruit Sallad, 1 Blue Slates Close, Wheldrake, York, YO19 6NB Tel: (01904) 448080 E-mail: fruitsaladcom@btinternet.com

Jackpots, Frith Farm, Frith Lane, Wickham, Fareham, Hampshire, PO17 5AW Tel: (01329) 832902

PREPAYMENT MACHINES, CARD/TOKEN DISPENSER

J W Instruments, 1 Church Lane, Normanton, West Yorkshire, WF6 2DE Tel: (01924) 891049 Fax: (01924) 220846 E-mail: j.wilson@jwinstruments.co.uk

PRESCRIPTION SAFETY SPECTACLES

Ophthalmic Technologies, Dominion Way, Worthing, West Sussex, BN14 8NW Tel: (01903) 212316 Fax: (01903) 212317 E-mail: charmain.otl@btconnect.com

▶ Roope Robert Opticians Ltd, 20 George Street, St. Albans, Hertfordshire, AL3 4ES Tel: (01727) 857798 E-mail: robert@roope.co.uk

PRESENSITISED COPPER CLAD PRINTED CIRCUIT LAMINATES (PCL)

Fotomechanix Ltd, 30 Curzon Street, Birmingham, B4 7XD Tel: 0121-380 0116 Fax: 0121-359 3313

PRESENTATION BOXES/CASES

Arden Box Ltd, Unit, Tything Road East, Kinwarton, Alcester, Warwickshire, B49 6ES Tel: (01527) 545635 Fax: (01527) 540299 E-mail: ardenbox@hotmail.com

M.M. Bell & Sons Ltd, 102 Arundel Street, Sheffield, S1 3BA Tel: 0114-272 4740 Fax: 0114-273 7523 E-mail: packaging@mmbell.co.uk

E.B. Crowhurst & Co. Ltd, Building 50, Pensnett Trading Estate, Kingswinford, West Midlands, DY6 7XD Tel: (01384) 400100 Fax: (01384) 400455 E-mail: sales@crowhurst.cio.uk

M. Fish (Packaging) Ltd, 7 Faraday Close, Oakwood Business Park, Clacton-On-Sea, Essex, CO15 4TR Tel: (01255) 475964 Fax: (01255) 221125 E-mail: sales@m-fish.co.uk

▶ Gard Plasticases Ltd, 2 Arnolds Business Park, Branbridges Road, East Peckham, Tonbridge, Kent, TN12 5LG Tel: (01622) 871887 Fax: (01622) 871895 E-mail: sales@gardplasticases.com

Pollard Boxes, Feldspar Close, Enderby, Leicester, LE19 4SD Tel: 0116-275 2666 Fax: 0116-275 2888 E-mail: info@pollardboxes.co.uk

Presentation Products Ltd, Dundee Road, Arbroath, Angus, DD11 2PT Tel: (01241) 878441 Fax: (01241) 875560 E-mail: ppm@giftpacks.co.uk

Unirose Ltd, Mount Ephraim Farm, Freight Lane, Cranbrook, Kent, TN17 3PG Tel: (01580) 714477 Fax: (01580) 713534

Valleys Woodcraft Ltd, Unit 1-2 Cwmdraw Industrial Estate, Newtown, Ebbw Vale, Gwent, NP23 5AE Tel: (01495) 350758 Fax: (01495) 307054 E-mail: sales@valleyswoodcraft.com

Vincent Rickards, Unit 22 Blackworth Industrial Estate, Highworth, Swindon, SN6 7NA Tel: (01793) 765251 Fax: (01793) 765251 E-mail: vincerickards@onetel.com

PRESENTATION (CONFERENCE) DESIGNERS/PRODUCERS

C L C Presentation Systems, Mill Road Industrial Estate, Linlithgow Bridge, Linlithgow, West Lothian, EH49 7SF Tel: (01506) 848779 Fax: (01506) 202779 E-mail: sales@clc-online.co.uk

Jack Morton Europe Ltd, 16-18 Acton Park Industrial Esta, The Vale, London, W3 7QE Tel: (020) 8735 2000 Fax: (020) 8735 2020

Markland Advertising & Marketing Ltd, The Old Chapel, 13 Victoria Road, Chester, CH2 2AX Tel: (01244) 651951 Fax: (01244) 651952

Parbury Brothers Ltd, The Vicarage, Great Wolford, Shipston-On-Stour, Warwickshire, CV36 5NQ Tel: (07973) 696524 E-mail: sales@parbury.co.uk

▶ Pointblank Media, PO Box 1949, Salisbury, SP4 8ZN Tel: (01980) 594949 E-mail: info@pointblankmedia.net

Slide Show, 24 Middle Street, London, EC1A 7JA Tel: (020) 7796 4664 Fax: (020) 7796 3816 E-mail: info@slideshow.co.uk

▶ Western Eye, Kinley House, 43 The Crescent, Bristol, BS9 4RP Tel: (07803) 593833 E-mail: mail@western-eye.com

PRESENTATION FOLDERS/ PRESENTERS, SALES

Presentation For Business, L1-L2 Unit Kent Kraft Industrial Estate, Lower Road, Northfleet, Gravesend, Kent, DA11 9SR Tel: (01322) 386717 Fax: (01322) 385506 E-mail: info@p4b.co.uk

PRESENTATION PACKAGING

▶ Delux Packaging, 16 Broomknowe Drive, Kincardine, Alloa, Clackmannanshire, FK10 4QL Tel: (01259) 730576 Fax: (01259) 731412

PRESPACED LETTERING VINYL SIGNS

A W S Metal Finishers, 79 Baltimore Road, Birmingham, B42 1DG Tel: 0121-357 3127 Fax: 0121-357 3127 E-mail: airbrush12@aol.com

Curtis Screen Print, 26 Fairfax Road, Colchester, CO2 7EW Tel: (01206) 760666 Fax: (01206) 760666 E-mail: sales@curtisscreenprint.co.uk

Dixon Signs, Stratford Rd, Drayton, Banbury, Oxon, OX15 6EE Tel: (01295) 730707 Fax: (01295) 730026 E-mail: mail@dixonsigns.co.uk

Elite Signs, Albemarle Rd, Taunton, Somerset, TA1 1BE Tel: (01823) 366219 Fax: (01823) 251095 E-mail: signs@elitecameron.com

Express Signs, 66 Soundwell Road, Bristol, BS16 4QP Tel: 0117-957 1793 Fax: 0117-957 1793 E-mail: andy@expresssigns.fsnet.co.uk

Ihkos Digital Ltd, Coventry, CV2 3WB Tel: (024) 7626 7622 Fax: (024) 7672 9855 E-mail: info@ihkos.co.uk

Industrial Signs Ltd, 8 Astor Park, Padholme Road, Peterborough, PE1 5XL Tel: (01733) 555153 Fax: (01733) 555157 E-mail: isignsltd@compuserve.com

J D Signs, PO Box 317, Camberley, Surrey, GU17 0QG Tel: (01276) 600562 Fax: (01273) 600562

Mills Signs Ltd, Unit 55 Queens Court Trading Estate, Greets Green Road, West Bromwich, West Midlands, B70 9EQ Tel: 0121-557 1722 Fax: 0121-557 5394 E-mail: millssigns@btconnect.com

Peel Graphics, 104-106 Bridge Street, Heywood, Lancashire, OL10 1JG Tel: (01706) 621960 Fax: (01706) 625249 E-mail: sales@peelgraphics.co.uk

Phoenix Signs, 1 Paynes Place Farm, Cuckfield Road, Burgess Hill, West Sussex, RH15 8RG Tel: (01444) 254040 Fax: (01444) 258553 E-mail: alan_cooper@btconnect.com

R & M Signmakers, 2 Whitehill Lane, Gravesend, Kent, DA12 5LY Tel: (01474) 568358 Fax: (01474) 568358

Screenprint Studio, The Barns, 9 School Road, Great Massingham, King's Lynn, Norfolk, PE32 2JA Tel: (01485) 520455

Signs & Safety Ltd, Unit 6 Fairlawn Enterprise Park, Bonehurst Road, Redhill, RH2 7QT Tel: (01737) 246969 Fax: (01737) 247979 E-mail: info@signsandsafety.co.uk

Spectrum Signs, 22 Bladon Road, Southampton, SO16 6QD Tel: (023) 8077 2264 Fax: (023) 8032 2264 E-mail: sales@spectrum-signs.co.uk

Tubeolight Signcraft C I, 1 Landes Du Marche, La Grande Route De St. Pierre, St. Peter, Jersey, JE3 7AY Tel: (01534) 485591 Fax: (01534) 485592 E-mail: sales@signtechjersey.co.uk

Ultra Labels, 3 57a Gwendolen Road, Leicester, LE5 5FL Tel: 0116-273 7643 Fax: 0116-273 7643

The Vinyl Cut, Newmill Farm, Stonehaven, Kincardineshire, AB39 3YJ Tel: (0845) 0565589 Fax: (01569) 740102

Walker, 6a Digby Drive, Melton Mowbray, Leicestershire, LE13 0RQ Tel: (01664) 410354 Fax: (01664) 410354

PRESS AUTOMATION EQUIPMENT

Kuka Automation & Robotics Ltd, Hereward Rise, Halesowen, West Midlands, B62 8AN Tel: 0121-585 0800 Fax: 0121-585 0900 E-mail: sales@kuka.co.uk

PRESS BRAKE FACILITIES/ SERVICES

Accurate Section Benders Ltd, Dawley Brook Road, Kingswinford, West Midlands, DY6 7AU Tel: (01384) 402402 Fax: (01384) 402462 E-mail: sales@accuratesectionbenders.co.uk

Barnshaws Plate Bending, Anchor Lane, Bilston, West Midlands, WV14 9NE Tel: (01902) 880250 Fax: (01902) 880505

Comvek Engineering Ltd, Station Drive, Unit 1, Breener Industrial Estate, Brierley Hill, West Midlands, DY5 3JZ Tel: (01384) 571515 Fax: (01384) 262088 E-mail: clbradley@btconnect.com

D Perkins, 3 Maltings Industrial Estate, Derby Road, Burton-on-Trent, Staffordshire, DE14 1RN Tel: (01283) 510451 Fax: (01283) 517977 E-mail: info@cncmetalproducts.co.uk

Daro Engineering Stafford Ltd, Unit 7a & 7b Dewick Depot, Cannock Road, Brocton, Stafford, ST17 0SU Tel: (01785) 660391 Fax: (01785) 665347 E-mail: office@daroengineering.co.uk

Doughty Pressings Ltd, Stewart Street, Wolverhampton, WV2 4JW Tel: (01902) 426264 Fax: (01902) 772245 E-mail: info@doughty.uk.com

Hagley Engineering Ltd, Blackbrook Road, Holly Hall, Dudley, West Midlands, DY2 0QP Tel: (01384) 261858 Fax: (01384) 77394 E-mail: hagleye@btconnect.com

J Harper & Sons Welding Fabrications Ltd, Willenhall La Industrial Estate, Willenhall Lane, Bloxwich, Walsall, WS3 2XN Tel: (01922) 478419 Fax: (01922) 409553

Leeds Welding Co. Ltd, Westland Square, Leeds, LS11 5SS Tel: 0113-271 1000 Fax: 0113-271 1023 E-mail: sales@leedswelding.co.uk

M & B Brakepress Ltd, Bellotts Road, Bath, BA2 3RT Tel: (01225) 317788 Fax: (01225) 448395

M G B Press Break Sections Ltd, Dawley Brook Road, Kingswinford, West Midlands, DY6 7BD Tel: (01384) 400717 Fax: (01384) 400747

Nimgrove Ltd, 8 Anglesey Business Park, Littleworth Road, Cannock, Staffordshire, WS12 1NR Tel: (01543) 426926 Fax: (01543) 426872 E-mail: sales@nimgrove.co.uk

Pressbrake Tools, Breeza Works, Bocking, Cross Roads, Keighley, West Yorkshire, BD22 9AP Tel: (01535) 647169 Fax: (01535) 647013 E-mail: pressbrake@legend.co.uk

R S Micro, 129 Brookfield Place, Walton Summit Centre, Bamber Bridge, Preston, PR5 8BF Tel: (01772) 628000 Fax: (01772) 628888 E-mail: rs_micro@compuserve.com

Scorpio Welding & Fabrications, 1 Old Wharf, Old Birchills, Walsall, WS2 8QD Tel: (01922) 643000 Fax: (01922) 643000

T M R, Canal Street, Brierley Hill, West Midlands, DY5 1JJ Tel: (01384) 75531 Fax: (01384) 573353 E-mail: sales@tmrracking.com

Taylor & Watson Ltd, Wentworth Road, Penistone, Sheffield, S36 6ET Tel: (01226) 762035 Fax: (01226) 370216 E-mail: taylorwatson65@hotmail.com

Thomson Engineering, 66 Whitehill Road, Glenrothes, Fife, KY6 2RP Tel: 01592 774345

PRESS BRAKE (MECHANICAL/ HYDRAULIC) MANUFRS

Bystronic UK Ltd, Chard Junction, Chard, Somerset, TA20 4QR Tel: (01460) 222100 Fax: (01460) 222108 E-mail: sales@bystronic.com

Crescent Machinery Ltd, Unit 1 Moderna Business Park, Moderna Way, Mytholmroyd, Hebden Bridge, West Yorkshire, HX7 5QQ Tel: (01422) 884888 Fax: 01422 881338 E-mail: info@crescentmachinery.co.uk

Multi-Stroke Ltd, King Street, Old Hill, Cradley Heath, West Midlands, B64 6JJ Tel: (01384) 567481 Fax: (01384) 564382

Pearson Production Systems Ltd, Stargate Industrial Estate, Ryton, Tyne & Wear, NE40 3EX Tel: 0191-413 8080 Fax: 0191-413 8822

Press & Shear Machinery Ltd, 12/14 Ninian Park Ninian Way, Wilnecote, Tamworth, Staffordshire, B77 5ES Tel: (01827) 250000 Fax: (01827) 250022 E-mail: sales@pressandshear.com

Pressbrake Tools, Breeza Works, Bocking, Cross Roads, Keighley, West Yorkshire, BD22 9AP Tel: (01535) 647169 Fax: (01535) 647013 E-mail: pressbrake@legend.co.uk

PRESS BRAKE TOOLING MANUFRS

Ashmores Press Brake Tooling Ltd, Lewis Street, Great Bridge, Tipton, West Midlands, DY4 7EF Tel: 0121-557 1064 Fax: 0121-557 1085 E-mail: ashmores@pressbraketool.co.uk

Prom UK, 23 Ash Close, Walters Ash, High Wycombe, Buckinghamshire, HP14 4TR Tel: (01494) 562253

Rolla-V / UKB, Falcon House, Bradley Road, Stourbridge, West Midlands, DY8 1UZ Tel: (01384) 378028 Fax: (01384) 378105

PRESS BRAKES

Multi-Stroke Ltd, King Street, Old Hill, Cradley Heath, West Midlands, B64 6JJ Tel: (01384) 567481 Fax: (01384) 564382

PRESS CUTTING AGENCIES

Durrants Press Cuttings Ltd, Discovery House, 28-42 Banner Street, London, EC1Y 8QE Tel: (020) 7674 0200 Fax: (020) 7674 0222 E-mail: contact@durrants.co.uk

Romeike Ltd, Chess House, 34 Germain St, Chesham, Buckinghamshire, HP5 1SJ Tel: (0800) 289543 Fax: (020) 8882 6716 E-mail: info@romeike.com

PRESS CUTTING AGENCIES – *continued*

T N S Media Intelligence, PA Newcentre, 292 Vauxhall Bridge Road, London, SW1V 1AE Tel: (020) 7963 7600 E-mail: tnsmi_sales@tnsofres.com

PRESS FEED LOADERS/ UNLOADERS, AUTOMATIC

Powair Automation Ltd, Powair House, Nest Road, Gateshead, Tyne & Wear, NE10 0ER Tel: 0191-469 5211 Fax: 0191-469 1858 E-mail: automation@powair.com

PRESS FORGED COMPONENTS

Bifrangi (UK) Ltd, PO Box 22, Lincoln, LN2 5DT Tel: (01522) 585800 Fax: (01522) 529116

Sankey Carbide, Anchor Lane, Bilston, West Midlands, WV14 9NE Tel: (01902) 661144 Fax: (01902) 661100 E-mail: scd@cogent-power.com

Scottish Stampings Ltd, East Park Road, Ayr, KA8 9HR Tel: (01292) 267971 Fax: (01292) 613408

PRESS KNIVES OR CUTTERS

Alpress Hydraulic Engineers, 65 Back Sneddon Street, Paisley, Renfrewshire, PA3 2DD Tel: 0141-848 7175 Fax: 0141-889 5280 E-mail: alpresshs@tiscali.co.uk

Barkby Knives Ltd, 41 Cannock Street, Leicester, LE4 9HR Tel: 0116-276 1101 Fax: 0116-233 2433 E-mail: sales@barkbyknives.co.uk

Rossendale Forme & Knife Co. Ltd, 245 Burnley Road East, Rossendale, Lancashire, BB4 9HU Tel: (01706) 213165 Fax: (01706) 831319 E-mail: info@rossforme.co.uk

Wood Ash Formes Ltd, Kingsfield Ways, Kingsheath, Northampton, NN5 7QN Tel: (01604) 752242 Fax: (01604) 751727

PRESS OR SNAP FASTENERS

Prym Fashion UK, Whitecroft, Lydney, Gloucestershire, GL15 4QG Tel: (01594) 562631 Fax: (01594) 564663 E-mail: sales@prymfashion.co.uk

PRESS PUBLIC RELATION CONSULTANCY OR SERVICES

Arthouse P R, 7a Market Street, Crediton, Devon, EX17 2EE Tel: (01363) 777002 Fax: (01363) 779956 E-mail: sales@arthouse-pr.com

▶ Ballard Communications Management, The Malthouse, Milton Street, Westcott, Dorking, Surrey, RH4 3PX Tel: (01306) 882288 Fax: (01306) 881803 E-mail: info@ballard.co.uk

▶ Bojangle Communications Ltd, 2 Virginia Close, Ashtead, Surrey, KT21 2NW Tel: (01372) 274975 E-mail: lindsey@bojangle.co.uk

▶ Chrome Consulting Ltd, 26 Fitzroy Square, London, W1T 6BT Tel: 020 7323 1610 E-mail: enquiries@chromeconsulting.com

▶ Client Appeal, 13 Crutchley Road, Wokingham, Berkshire, RG40 1XA Tel: 0118-977 6775 E-mail: sales@clientappeal.co.uk

▶ Declaration Ltd, The Bearings, Bowbridge Road, Newark, Nottinghamshire, NG24 4BZ Tel: (01636) 708330 Fax: (01636) 708331 E-mail: rcihard@declaration.co.uk

▶ Editorial Excellence, 29 Ewlyn Road, Cheltenham, Gloucestershire, GL53 7PB Tel: (01242) 576451 Fax: (01242) 576451 E-mail: andrea@editorialexcellence-ad.co.uk

▶ Michelle Figg Freelance Marketing Communications, 9A Orsett Terrace, London, W2 6AJ Tel: (07973) 221331 E-mail: michelle@michellefigg.com

▶ G K A, Unit 1 Bell Business Park, Smeaton Close, Aylesbury, Buckinghamshire, HP19 8JR Tel: (01296) 678300 Fax: (01296) 678301 E-mail: enquiries@gka.co.uk

▶ Headline Promotions, Press and Public Relations, 25 Basingfield Close, Old Basingstoke, Basingstoke, Hampshire, RG24 7BG Tel: 01256 329742 E-mail: info@headlinepromotions.co.uk

▶ The PR Shop, 70 Priory Road, Kenilworth, Warwickshire, CV8 1LQ Tel: 01676 534319 E-mail: kelly@pr-shop.co.uk

▶ Watch PR, 29 Gibbon Road, Kingston upon Thames, Surrey, KT2 6AD Tel: 020 8286 0654 E-mail: enquiries@watchpr.com

▶ Words Worth, Benfleet Water Tower, 335 Benfleet Road, Benfleet, Essex, SS7 1PW Tel: (01268) 756261 Fax: (01268) 750706

PRESS STRIP LUBRICATING SYSTEMS

Engineering & General Equipment Ltd, Eley Estate, Edmonton, London, N18 3BB Tel: (020) 8807 4567 Fax: (020) 8884 2229 E-mail: sales@centralube.com

PRESS TOOL COMPONENT MANUFRS

C O B Engineering, Midland Road, Luton, LU2 0BL Tel: (01582) 736721 Fax: (01582) 402497 E-mail: info@cobengineering.co.uk

Mills & Coombs, 95A Chaplin Road, Easton, Bristol, BS5 3JE Tel: 0117-961 3882 Fax: 0117-961 3887

▶ Rippon Cutting Tools, Hollingworth Road, Bredbury, Stockport, Cheshire, SK6 2AZ Tel: 0161-430 3660 Fax: 0161-430 3661 E-mail: info@rippontools.co.uk

PRESS TOOL DESIGN SERVICES

Columbia Staver Ltd, Russell Gardens Industrial Estate, Wickford, Essex, SS11 8QR Tel: (01268) 733346 Fax: (01268) 735893 E-mail: info@columbia-staver.co.uk

District Tooling Co., 7 Harolds Road, Harlow, Essex, CM19 5BJ Tel: (01279) 424302 Fax: (01279) 451186

Duncan Lynch Precision Tools Ltd, Unit E Weller Drive, Finchampstead, Wokingham, Berkshire, RG40 4QZ Tel: 0118-973 4845 Fax: 0118-973 0381 E-mail: sales@duncan-lynch.co.uk

J E B Engineering Design Ltd, Chiswick Avenue, Mildenhall, Bury St. Edmunds, Suffolk, IP28 7AY Tel: (01638) 718435 Fax: (01638) 717962 E-mail: info@jebeng.com

Meden Vale Engineering Co. Ltd, Meden Square, Pleasley, Mansfield, Nottinghamshire, NG19 7SQ Tel: (01623) 810601 Fax: (01623) 812190

PRESS TOOL DIES

Aluminium Castings Ltd, 3b Celtic Road, Moss Side Industrial Estate, Callington, Cornwall, PL17 7SD Tel: (01579) 383513 Fax: (01579) 384762 E-mail: info@alcast.co.uk

C O B Engineering, Midland Road, Luton, LU2 0BL Tel: (01582) 736721 Fax: (01582) 402497 E-mail: info@cobengineering.co.uk

Sankey Carbide, Anchor Lane, Bilston, West Midlands, WV14 9NE Tel: (01902) 661144 Fax: (01902) 661100 E-mail: scd@cogent-power.com

PRESS TOOL MAINTENANCE/ REPAIR SERVICES

Versatile Precision Tools Ltd, Victoria Road, Ulverston, Cumbria, LA12 0BZ Tel: (01229) 582366 Fax: (01229) 580871 E-mail: mail@vptools.co.uk

PRESS TOOL MONITORING UNITS

Lamba Welding Systems, 31 Racecourse Road, Gallowfields Trading Estate, Richmond, North Yorkshire, DL10 4SU Tel: (01748) 850292 Fax: (01748) 850343

PRESS TOOL PUNCHES

Burrhart Machinery Ltd, Cradock Road, Luton, LU4 0JF Tel: (01582) 563400 Fax: (01582) 493993 E-mail: sales@burrhart.co.uk

Lane Punch Tech Ltd, 1 Apex Business Park, Diplocks Way, Hailsham, East Sussex, BN27 3JU Tel: (01323) 844777 Fax: (01323) 849091 E-mail: michelle.thompson@lanepunch.co.uk

Porter Precision Products Ltd, Masons Road, Stratford-upon-Avon, Warwickshire, CV37 9NF Tel: (01789) 292409 Fax: (01789) 292241

▶ Rippon Cutting Tools, Hollingworth Road, Bredbury, Stockport, Cheshire, SK6 2AZ Tel: 0161-430 3660 Fax: 0161-430 3661 E-mail: info@rippontools.co.uk

Winston & Allan Ltd, Unit 5-6 Nutwood Trading Estate, Limestone Cottage Lane, Sheffield, S6 1NJ Tel: 0114-231 4744 Fax: 0114-232 3967 E-mail: sales@winstonandallan.co.uk

PRESS TOOLS, *See also headings for particular types*

3 D Engineering Midlands Ltd, Unit 15, The Wallows Industrial Estate, Fens Pool Avenue, Brierley Hill, Dudley, West Midlands, DY5 1QA Tel: (01384) 480604 Fax: (01384) 480604 E-mail: 3dengineering@btconnect.com

A B Tools, Marsh Way, Rainham, Essex, RM13 8UP Tel: (01708) 526644 Fax: (01708) 526655

A E Harris & Co Birmingham Ltd, 109-138 Northwood Street, Birmingham, B3 1SZ Tel: 0121-233 2386 Fax: 0121-200 3702 E-mail: sales@aeharris.co.uk

A J Higginson Press Tools Ltd, 19 Industrial Estate, Cornwall Road, Smethwick, West Midlands, B66 2JS Tel: 0121-558 9413 Fax: 0121-558 6489 E-mail: johnking@ajhpresstools.freeserve.co.uk

▶ A P Press Tools, 239 Heneage Street, Birmingham, B7 4LY Tel: 0121-359 2161 Fax: 0121-333 7418

A & W Precision Tools Ltd, Unit 2 Brookside Industrial Pk, Crankhall La, Wednesbury, W. Midlands, WS10 0QZ Tel: 0121-505 1359 Fax: 0121-505 1359

Accurus Ltd, Giles Road, Oldbury, West Midlands, B68 8JG Tel: 0121-544 5335 Fax: 0121-544 5339 E-mail: admin@accurus.co.uk

Acon Equipment Ltd, Constance Road, Leicester, LE5 5DD Tel: 0116-273 9823 Fax: 0116-249 0802 E-mail: cadaconequip@aol.com

Aircraft & Commercial Tools (Sheffield) Ltd, Bowling Green Street, Shalesmoor, Sheffield, S3 8SU Tel: 0114-272 8112 Fax: 0114-275 9273 E-mail: aircraft@globalnet.co.uk

Allenvale Tools & Productions Ltd, Riverside Works, Thanet Way, Whitstable, Kent, CT5 3JQ Tel: (01227) 277777 Fax: (01227) 277788 E-mail: allenvale@aol.com

Aquatools Ltd, 54 Chapel Street, Tipton, West Midlands, DY4 8JB Tel: 0121-520 7978 Fax: 0121-522 2051 E-mail: sales@aquatools.co.uk

Ascot Precision Tooling Ltd, Richington Works, Hall Lane, Walsall Wood, Walsall, WS9 9AS Tel: (01543) 452127 Fax: (01543) 452127

B O P P Precision Engineers Ltd, A Emms Court, Meeting Lane, Brierley Hill, West Midlands, DY5 3LB Tel: (01384) 78646 Fax: (01384) 78646 E-mail: mail@bopppe.fsnet.co.uk

B S Ellis, Unit 5 Chillington Fields, Wolverhampton, WV1 2BY Tel: (01902) 459111 Fax: (01902) 459111

B.W.B Engineering Company Ltd, Baltimore Trading Estate, Baltimore Road, Birmingham, B42 1DD Tel: 0121-356 2879 Fax: 0121-356 2880

Barclay Engineering, Southend Arterial Road, Gallows Corner, Romford, RM3 0BZ Tel: (01708) 345390 Fax: (01708) 370047 E-mail: terry.barclay@lineone.net

Baybridge Press Tools Ltd, 151 Charles Henry Street, Birmingham, B12 0SD Tel: 0121-622 3878 Fax: 0121-622 3743 E-mail: baybridgetools@aol.com

Baylis Automotive, Unit 49g, Pipers Road, Park Farm Industrial Estate, Redditch, Worcestershire, B98 0HU Tel: (01527) 517220 Fax: (01527) 517114 E-mail: tclews@baylisautomotive.com

Bevan, 53a Frederick Street, Birmingham, B1 3HS Tel: 0121-236 9263 Fax: 0121-236 9263

C & D Precision, Bluebird House, Povey Cross Road, Horley, Surrey, RH6 0AG Tel: (01293) 820092 Fax: (01293) 820093 E-mail: dedman@cdprecision.freeserve.co.uk

Caine Precision Ltd, Unit 13 Stocklake Park Industrial Estate, Farmborough Cl, Aylesbury, Bucks, HP20 1DQ Tel: (01296) 434586 Fax: (01296) 432683 E-mail: rcaine@nildron.co.uk

Central Tools & Pressings, Unit D1, Bill House, Birmingham, B19 1AP Tel: 0121-523 7522 Fax: 0121-523 9922

Cheswell Engineering Ltd, Waldeck House, Waldeck Road, Maidenhead, Berkshire, SL6 8BR Tel: (01628) 624726 Fax: (01628) 773907

Chris Jack Toolmaking, Block 6, Upper Mills Trading Estate, Bristol Road, Stonehouse, Gloucestershire, GL10 2BJ Tel: (01453) 826852 Fax: (01453) 826852

Clifton Precision Tools Ltd, Cakemore Road, Rowley Regis, West Midlands, B65 0QW Tel: 0121-559 3096 Fax: 0121-561 5661 E-mail: p.clifton@cliftonprecision.com

Columbia Staver Ltd, Russell Gardens Industrial Estate, Wickford, Essex, SS11 8QR Tel: (01268) 733346 Fax: (01268) 735893 E-mail: info@columbia-staver.co.uk

Comcir Radio Communications, 66 Goldstone Villas, Hove, East Sussex, BN3 3RU Tel: (01273) 779828 Fax: (01273) 204900 E-mail: info@comcir.co.uk

Crompton & Rathbone (Tools) Ltd, 111-117 Sydenham Road, Birmingham, B11 1DG Tel: 0121-773 7140 Fax: 0121-773 7140

▶ CS Press Tools Ltd, Unit 23 Nutwood Trading Estate, Limestone Cottage Lane, Sheffield, S6 1NJ Tel: 0114-234 8563 Fax: 0114-234 6290 E-mail: david@cspresstools.co.uk

D R S Press Tools, Unit 18 Oldfields, Corngreaves Road, Cradley Heath, West Midlands, B64 6BS Tel: (01384) 410711 Fax: (01384) 410711

Danly UK Ltd, 2 Aintree Road, Perivale, Greenford, Middlesex, UB6 7LA Tel: (020) 8998 5381 Fax: (020) 8991 2461 E-mail: sales@danleyuk.com

Data Engineering, Pindar Road, Hoddesdon, Hertfordshire, EN11 0DE Tel: (01992) 462610 Fax: (01992) 450953 E-mail: scherry@dataeng.freeserve.co.uk

Denebank Engineering UK Ltd, 108 Windmill Road, Sunbury-on-Thames, Middlesex, TW16 7HB Tel: (01932) 788180 Fax: (01932) 788150 E-mail: paulgoldthorpe@denebank.co.uk

Denny Engineering Ltd, 10 Morgan Way, Bowthorpe Employment Area, Norwich, NR5 9JJ Tel: (01603) 747066 Fax: (01603) 748421 E-mail: dennengltd@aol.com

District Tooling Co., 7 Harolds Road, Harlow, Essex, CM19 5BJ Tel: (01279) 424302 Fax: (01279) 451186

DMP Group, Unit 5F Canal Estate, Station Road, Langley, Slough, SL3 6EG Tel: (01753) 580101 Fax: (01753) 542685 E-mail: sales@dmpgroup.co.uk

Duncan Lynch Precision Tools Ltd, Unit E Weller Drive, Finchampstead, Wokingham, Berkshire, RG40 4QZ Tel: 0118-973 4845 Fax: 0118-973 0381 E-mail: sales@duncan-lynch.co.uk

E J Tools (Press Toolmakers) Ltd, 112 Middlemore Industrial Estate, Smethwick, Warley, West Midlands, B66 2EP Tel: 0121-558 4154 Fax: 0121-558 4154 E-mail: richard_webb@btconnect.com

E Stubbs Press Tools Ltd, Ann Street, Willenhall, West Midlands, WV13 1EN Tel: (01902) 608589 Fax: (01902) 608589

Erodatools Ltd, Unit 4 Laurence Works, Sheffield Road, Penistone, Sheffield, S36 6HF Tel: (01226) 763725 Fax: (01226) 767139 E-mail: krolfe@aol.com

Excel Precision Engineering Services Ltd, Unit 16, Trostra Industrial Estate, Llanelli, Dyfed, SA14 9UU Tel: (01554) 751935 Fax: (01554) 778804 E-mail: debbie@excel-eng.co.uk

Excel Precision Wse Ltd, Unit 2 Woodrow Way, Gloucester, GL2 5DX Tel: (01452) 419743 Fax: (01452) 307135 E-mail: sales@excel-precision.co.uk

Fairways Engineering, 3 Chiltern House, Waterside, Chesham, Buckinghamshire, HP5 1PS Tel: (01494) 794600 Fax: (01494) 794600

FGH Products, 68 Hunters Vale, Birmingham, B19 2XH Tel: 0121-554 4329 Fax: 0121-554 1857 E-mail: fghsilver@btconnect.com

Friary Metal Products Ltd, 106-110 Bishop Street, Birmingham, B5 6JP Tel: 0121-622 2088 Fax: 0121-666 7277 E-mail: info@thefriarygroup.co.uk

G & D Engineering Vickers Ltd, Poplars Industrial Estate, Moor Lane, Birmingham, B6 7AD Tel: 0121-356 3378

Gauge & Tool Makers Association, 3 Forge House, Summerleys Road, Princes Risborough, Buckinghamshire, HP27 9DT Tel: (01844) 274222 Fax: (01844) 274227 E-mail: gtma@gtma.co.uk

Gibbs & Rustage Ltd, Albert Works, Victoria Road, Dukinfield, Cheshire, SK16 4UP Tel: 0161-339 3379 Fax: 0161-343 2207

Gibtool Engineers, 1 Whitehall Mill, Whitehall Street, Darwen, Lancashire, BB3 2LP Tel: (01254) 705909 Fax: (01254) 705909

Gilbert Tools & Services, Unit 13 Chancel Industrial Estate, Hickman Avenue, Wolverhampton, WV1 2UH Tel: (01902) 455685 Fax: (01902) 455685

Glebe Engineering Ltd, Edensor Works, Greendock Street, Stoke-on-Trent, ST3 2NA Tel: (01782) 599161 Fax: (01782) 324410 E-mail: nick.cresswell@glebe.co.uk

Goss Components Ltd, 43 Fulbourne Road, London, E17 4AF Tel: (020) 8527 5599 Fax: (020) 8527 1142 E-mail: enquiries@gosscomponent.com

Gramton Engineering Ltd, Unit 5 Moilliett Court, Soho Way, Smethwick, West Midlands, B66 2SU Tel: 0121-565 0563 Fax: 0121-565 0563

Green Goose Tooling Co., Unit 1-2 Falcons Gate, Dean Road, Yate, Bristol, BS37 5NH Tel: (01454) 312948 Fax: (01454) 313704

H & H Tool & Engineering Ltd, Unit 4, Harvey Industrial Estate, Shelah Road, Halesowen, West Midlands, B63 3PG Tel: 0121-550 2231 Fax: 0121-585 5789 E-mail: office@hhtools.com

Harper & Simmons Ltd, 19 Howard Road, Park Farm, Redditch, Worcestershire, B98 7SE Tel: (01527) 518121 Fax: (01527) 518123 E-mail: robertsimmons@harperandsimmons.co.uk

Hawkes Metalmex, Holbrook Trading Estate, Old Lane, Halfway, Sheffield, S20 3GZ Tel: 0114-251 0251 Fax: 0114-251 0151 E-mail: sales@pct-automotive.co.uk

Hildred Engineering Co. Ltd, Units 2 4 & 6, Parkway Court, Nottingham, NG8 4GN Tel: 0115-928 2217 Fax: 0115-985 4998 E-mail: hildredengco@aol.com

Hillfax Ltd, Park Road, Willenhall, West Midlands, WV13 1AQ Tel: (01902) 606442 Fax: (01902) 634982 E-mail: sprint@btclick.com

▶ Hunton - R M T - Gabro Machines, Cobbs Wood Industrial Estate, Hilton Road, Ashford, Kent, TN23 1EW Tel: (01233) 628976 Fax: (01233) 664909 E-mail: sales@mjallen.co.uk

J B S Poyser Mansfield Ltd, Pleasley Vale Works, Pleasley Vale, Mansfield, Nottinghamshire, NG19 8SD Tel: (01623) 810066 Fax: (01623) 812266

J S Tool & Gauge Co., Unit 4 Victoria Buildings, Newhall St, Willenhall, West Midlands, WV13 1LQ Tel: (01902) 636028 Fax: (01902) 608187 E-mail: jstool@live1.net

Jubilee Engineering Co., 5 Runnings Road Kingsditch Trading Estate, Cheltenham, Gloucestershire, GL51 9NQ Tel: (01242) 584883 Fax: (01242) 226855

K F C Engineering Ltd, Unit 6 Little Forge Road, Redditch, Worcestershire, B98 7SF Tel: (01527) 520371 Fax: (01527) 520346 E-mail: kevin@kfcengineering.co.uk

K L Precision Engineering Ltd, Athelney Way, Cheltenham, Gloucestershire, GL52 6RT Tel: (01242) 244847 Fax: (01242) 244847

K Pilcher Engineering, Unit D1 Guy Motors Industrial Park, Park Lane, Wolverhampton, WV10 9QF Tel: (01902) 728820 Fax: (01902) 304769 E-mail: kpeng@waverider.co.uk

PRESS TOOLS – *continued*

Kaybee Engineering, Station Street, Bromsgrove, Worcestershire, B60 2BS Tel: (01527) 870845 Fax: (01527) 870845 E-mail: andy.knight@kpe.demon.co.uk
Thomas Keating Ltd, Station Mills, Daux Road, Billingshurst, West Sussex, RH14 9SH Tel: (01403) 782045 Fax: (01403) 785464 E-mail: m.clack@terahertz.co.uk
Kerri Engineering, South March, Long March Industrial Estate, Daventry, Northamptonshire, NN11 4PH Tel: (01327) 876944 Fax: (01327) 300713
Kestmark Precision Engineering, 3 Winster Grove Industrial Estate, Winster Grove, Birmingham, B44 9EG Tel: 0121-360 8850 Fax: 0121-360 8850 E-mail: eng@kestmark.fsnet.co.uk
Kingsbury Engineering Birmingham Ltd, 842 Kingsbury Road, Erdington, Birmingham, B24 9PS Tel: 0121-377 6383 Fax: 0121-377 6694 E-mail: cad@kingsbury-eng.com
Kirkby Jig & Tool Co. Ltd, Bradman Road, Knowsley Industrial Park, Liverpool, L33 7UR Tel: 0151-546 2681 Fax: 0151-546 4937
Kirmell Ltd, Eyre Street, Birmingham, B18 7AA Tel: 0121-456 3141 Fax: 0121-456 3151 E-mail: sales@kirmell.co.uk
L Person & Son Ltd, 33 Hollands Road, Haverhill, Suffolk, CB9 8PU Tel: (01440) 702811 Fax: (01440) 702711 E-mail: david@personhaverhill.freeserve.co.uk
Langdale Bros, Weatherhill Works, Hathersham Close, Smallfield, Horley, Surrey, RH6 9JE Tel: (01342) 843164 Fax: (01342) 843164 E-mail: langdalebros@aol.com
Lobro Tools Ltd, Long Street, Premier Business Park, Walsall, WS2 9XP Tel: (01922) 623140 Fax: (01922) 648297 E-mail: sales@lobrotools.com
London Taxis (International) Plc, Holyhead Road, Coventry, CV5 8JJ Tel: (024) 7657 2000 Fax: (024) 7657 2001 E-mail: exports@lti.co.uk
Ludlow, 6 Prospect View, Rock Lane, Ludlow, Shropshire, SY8 1ST Tel: (01584) 875096
M B Techniques Ltd, Douglas Street, Hamilton, Lanarkshire, ML3 0BU Tel: (01698) 457222 Fax: (01698) 891924
M & D Engineering, 4 Pritchett Street, Birmingham, B6 4EH Tel: 0121-359 1134 Fax: 0121-333 5165
M N B Precision Ltd, Falkland Close, Charter Avenue Industrial Estate, Coventry, CV4 8AU Tel: (024) 7669 5959 Fax: (024) 7669 5909 E-mail: sales@mnbprecision.com
M P M Presstools, 1 Chancel Way Industrial Estate, Chancel Way, Birmingham, B6 7AU Tel: 0121-356 7600 Fax: 0121-356 9766 E-mail: mpm.presstools@btconnect.com
Machtech Press Tool Distributors, Brown Lion Street, Tipton, West Midlands, DY4 9EG Tel: 0121-522 4340 Fax: 0121-522 3860 E-mail: chris.pring@tiscali.co.uk
Maridian Engineers Ltd, Unit 14 Vincent Works, Vincent Lane, Dorking, Surrey, RH4 3HW Tel: (01306) 881250 Fax: (01306) 887415
Marlborough Tools Ltd, 315 Summer Lane, Birmingham, B19 3RH Tel: 0121-359 3491 Fax: 0121-359 3491 E-mail: marlborotools@supanet.com
Meath Engineering Tools Ltd, Black Bourton Road, Carterton, Oxfordshire, OX18 3EZ Tel: (01993) 841041
Meridian Tooling Co. Ltd, Unit 6, Exis Court, Veasey Close, Attleborough Fields Industrial Estate, Nuneaton, Warwickshire, CV11 6RT Tel: (024) 7634 0187 Fax: (024) 7664 1301 E-mail: meridian@netcomuk.co.uk
Midland Tool & Design Ltd, Units 19-20, Barnfield Road, Tipton, West Midlands, DY4 9DF Tel: 0121-520 1171 Fax: 0121-557 3410 E-mail: sales@mtdltd.co.uk
Mills & Coombs, 95A Chaplin Road, Easton, Bristol, BS5 3JE Tel: 0117-961 3882 Fax: 0117-961 3887
Mor Brock Tool & Gauge Co., Maldon Road, Romford, RM7 0JB Tel: (01708) 706606 Fax: (01708) 740906
Ogihara Europe Ltd, Hortonwood Industrial Estate, Queensway, Telford, Shropshire, TF1 7LL Tel: (01952) 222111 Fax: (01952) 222050 E-mail: sales@ogihara.co.uk
Orville Engineering, Unit 4 315 Summer Lane, Birmingham, B19 3RH Tel: 0121-359 7560 Fax: 0121-359 7560
P & B Engineering, Factory Estate College Road, Unit 7, Perry Barr, Birmingham, B44 8BS Tel: 0121-356 5490 Fax: 0121-356 4295
P H B Industries Ltd, Fitzherbert Road, Farlington, Portsmouth, PO6 1SB Tel: (023) 9237 9696 Fax: (023) 9237 5822
Parade Products Ltd, 656B Chester Road, Erdington, Birmingham, B23 5TE Tel: 0121-350 8031 Fax: 0121-350 8031
Paragon Toolmaking & Precision Engineering Co. Ltd, 321 National Avenue, Hull, HU5 4JB Tel: (01482) 343439 Fax: (01482) 448623 E-mail: sales@paragon-tools.co.uk
Patterson Pressings Ltd, Reliance Works, Newpound Common, Wisborough Green, Billingshurst, West Sussex, RH14 0AZ Tel: (01403) 700088 Fax: (01403) 700001 E-mail: r.patterson@patterson.uk.com
Pelsall Tool & Engineering Co.Ltd, Sheffield Mill, Mill Rd, Pelsall, Walsall, WS4 1BU Tel: 01922 682551
Pemberton Engineering, Unit 48 Planetary Industrial Estate, Planetary Road, Willenhall, West Midlands, WV13 3XB Tel: (01902) 863666 Fax: (01902) 863666 E-mail: pembertoneng@btconnect.com
Potteries Die Co. Ltd, 136 Knypersley Road, Stoke-On-Trent, ST6 8JD Tel: (01782) 534348 Fax: (01782) 535297 E-mail: nick@potteriesdie.co.uk
Powell Manufacturing Co. (Coventry) Ltd, Cromwell Street, Coventry, CV6 5EX Tel: (024) 7668 5131 Fax: (024) 7663 7886
Precision Engineers Pontefract Ltd, South Baileygate, Pontefract, West Yorkshire, WF8 2JL Tel: (01977) 702439 Fax: (01977) 600284
Prescient Engineering Ltd, 25 Mereside, Soham, Ely, Cambridgeshire, CB7 5EE Tel: (01353) 720787 Fax: (01353) 723356 E-mail: contact@prescientengineeringltd.co.uk
Prodec Precision Manufacturing Co. Ltd, Armstrong Buildings, Kilton Terrace, Worksop, Nottinghamshire, S80 2DQ Tel: (01909) 474093 Fax: (01909) 500363
Pugh Engineering Co., Unit 20 Poplar Drive, Witton, Birmingham, B6 7AD Tel: 0121-344 3240 Fax: 0121-344 3240
Quality Tool & Engineering Ltd, Station Road, Rowley Regis, West Midlands, B65 0JU Tel: 0121-561 1299 Fax: 0121-561 1299
R G Engineering, 3 Stoney Court, Hotchkiss Way, Binley, Coventry, CV3 2RL Tel: (024) 7644 0508 Fax: (024) 7663 6680 E-mail: r.g.eng@dial.pipex.com
R & M Tools, 105 Frederick Street, Walsall, WS2 9NJ Tel: (01922) 627276 Fax: (01922) 721780
Rayleigh Engineering Ltd, 19 Nobel Square, Burnt Mills Industrial Estate, Basildon, Essex, SS13 1LP Tel: (01268) 728380 Fax: (01268) 728205 E-mail: rayleigh.engineer@btconnect.com
Rayson Engineering, 4 Albion Business Park, Spring Road, Smethwick, West Midlands, B66 1LY Tel: 0121-580 1498 Fax: 0121-580 1498
Reboc Engineering Corp Ltd, 66 Sunbeam Road, Park Royal, London, NW10 6JQ Tel: (020) 8453 0284 Fax: (020) 8453 0288
Rolla-V / UKB, Falcon House, Bradley Road, Stourbridge, West Midlands, DY8 1UZ Tel: (01384) 378028 Fax: (01384) 378105
▶ Romart Tooling Ltd, 3 Tudor Industrial Estate, Wharfdale Road, Birmingham, B11 2DG Tel: 0121-707 7715 Fax: 0121-707 7811
Rushall Tool & Engineering, Darlaston Central Trading Estate, Wednesbury, West Midlands, WS10 8XB Tel: 0121-526 3617 Fax: 0121-568 6015
Rydal Precision Tools Ltd, Unit 5 The Technology Centre, London Road, Swanley, Kent, BR8 7AN Tel: (01322) 614661 Fax: (01322) 614760 E-mail: sales@rydal.co.uk
Ryeland Toolmakers, Units 17-18 Barton Road, Water Eaton Industrial Estate, Milton Keynes, MK2 3JJ Tel: (01908) 647746 Fax: (01908) 270236 E-mail: info@ryelandtoolmakers.co.uk
S P Engineering, M Hawthorns Industrial Estate, Middlemore Road, Handsworth, Birmingham, B21 0BH Tel: 0121-554 1404 Fax: 0121-523 5834
Scanway Engineering Ltd, 123 Vincent Street, Birmingham, B12 9SG Tel: 0121-440 3759 Fax: 0121-440 3759 E-mail: scanway.engineering@virgin.net
Sertrix Tools Ltd, Clayton Road, Hayes, Middlesex, UB3 1BQ Tel: (020) 8848 9545 Fax: (020) 8561 7077
Simmons (Patternmakers) Ltd, Station Street West Business Park, Coventry, CV6 5BP Tel: (024) 7663 7028 Fax: (024) 7663 7030 E-mail: sales@epoxyworktops.com
Sirch Tool & Design Ltd, 1 Park St Industrial Estate, Osier Way, Aylesbury, Buckinghamshire, HP20 1EB Tel: (01296) 330868 Fax: (01296) 330828
Alan Spargo Ltd, Coronation Road, Cressex Business Park, High Wycombe, Buckinghamshire, HP12 3TA Tel: (01494) 529808 Fax: (01494) 464077 E-mail: bobw@alanspargoltd.com
Stour Precision Tools Ltd, George Baylis Road, Berry Hill Industrial Estate, Droitwich, Worcestershire, WR9 9RB Tel: (01905) 773932 Fax: (01905) 776434
Stowfledge Ltd, Mill Works, Mountsorrel Lane, Sileby, Loughborough, Leicestershire, LE12 7NF Tel: (01509) 812915 Fax: (01509) 816648
Sutton Tooling Ltd, Reservoir Road, Hull, HU6 7QD Tel: (01482) 342879 Fax: (01482) 446911 E-mail: suttontool@aol.com
Swift Press Tools, Oldbury Road Industrial Park, 136 Oldbury Road, Smethwick, West Midlands, B66 1JE Tel: 0121-555 5979 Fax: 0121-555 6798
T B P Tools Ltd, 106-108 Lombard Street, Birmingham, B12 0QR Tel: 0121-622 1762 Fax: 0121-622 1174 E-mail: tbp@btconnect.com
▶ T P S Tools, 1 Lea End Cottages Lea End Lane, Hopwood, Alvechurch, Birmingham, B48 7AY Tel: 0121-445 6297 Fax: 0121-445 6297
Tooling 2000 Ltd, 41 Western Road, Birmingham, B18 7QE Tel: 0121 2422000
Toolsharp Engineering Ltd, Westland Square, Westland Road, Leeds, LS11 5SS Tel: 0113-276 0855 Fax: 0113-271 5294 E-mail: toolsharp@btconnect.com
Tritools, 15 Albert Road, Aldershot, Hampshire, GU11 1SZ Tel: (01252) 310429 Fax: (01252) 324428
Turnfield Engineering, Unit D Bowyer Street, Birmingham, B10 0SA Tel: 0121-773 2923 Fax: 0121-766 8773
Turnmil Engineering, Riverside Industrial Estate, Glanamman, Ammanford, Dyfed, SA18 1LQ Tel: (01269) 825684 Fax: (01269) 824650 E-mail: ceri@turnmil.co.uk
V & P Engineering, Wakefield Road, Brighouse, West Yorkshire, HD6 1PE Tel: (01484) 719360 Fax: (01484) 400093
Versatile Precision Tools Ltd, Victoria Road, Ulverston, Cumbria, LA12 0BZ Tel: (01229) 582366 Fax: (01229) 580871 E-mail: mail@vptools.co.uk
Victor Engineering Co., 6d Arndale Road, Wick, Littlehampton, West Sussex, BN17 7HD Tel: 01903 716650
Volkobind Engineering Company Ltd, Unit 1 Tansey Green Trading Estate, Tansey Green Road, Brierley Hill, West Midlands, DY5 4TA Tel: (01384) 79746 Fax: (01384) 75737 E-mail: sales@volkobind.co.uk
W Downing, 79 Spencer Street, Birmingham, B18 6DE Tel: 0121-236 7353 Fax: 0121-200 2429
Wagon Automotive, Tysley Plant, Saville House, Redfern Park Way, Birmingham, B11 2BF Tel: 0121-706 0330 Fax: 0121-706 1929
Walsall Die & Tool Company Ltd, Gatehouse Trading Estate, Lichfield Road, Brownhills, Walsall, WS8 6JZ Tel: (01543) 378887 Fax: (01543) 452246 E-mail: sales@belcot.co.uk
Wednesbury Precision Tool Ltd, 7 Conduit Road, Norton Canes, Cannock, Staffordshire, WS11 9TJ Tel: (01543) 274901 Fax: (01543) 277557
Whiston Industries Ltd, Oak Street, Cradley Heath, West Midlands, B64 5JY Tel: (01384) 560606 Fax: (01384) 638182 E-mail: bob.whiston@whistonindustries.com
Whitton Precision Ltd, Bridge Works, Durnsford Road, London, SW19 8DR Tel: (020) 8946 6431 Fax: (020) 8947 1292 E-mail: whittonprecision@btconnet.com
Winston & Allan Ltd, Unit 5-6 Nutwood Trading Estate, Limestone Cottage Lane, Sheffield, S6 1NJ Tel: 0114-231 4744 Fax: 0114-232 3967 E-mail: sales@winstonandallan.co.uk
Wyken Tools Ltd, Unit 3, Bodmin Road, Coventry, CV2 5DZ Tel: (024) 7662 1515 Fax: (024) 7662 1472 E-mail: jezwykentools@aol.com
X Press Tools Ltd, Station Yard, Thame, Oxfordshire, OX9 3UH Tel: (01844) 214603 Fax: (01844) 214601

PRESS TOOLS TO SPECIFICATION

Fisher & Co., Units 2-4 Cary Court, Somerton Business Park, Somerton, Somerset, TA11 6SB Tel: (01458) 274017 Fax: (01458) 274145 E-mail: info@fisherandcompany.co.uk
Larkshill Engineering Ltd, 8 Bond Street, Hockley, Birmingham, B19 3LB Tel: 0121-236 2617 Fax: 0121-236 6963 E-mail: frankmurphy@larkshilleng.com
Paragon Toolmaking & Precision Engineering Co. Ltd, 321 National Avenue, Hull, HU5 4JB Tel: (01482) 343439 Fax: (01482) 448623 E-mail: sales@paragon-tools.co.uk
Sutton Tooling Ltd, Reservoir Road, Hull, HU6 7QD Tel: (01482) 342879 Fax: (01482) 446911 E-mail: suttontool@aol.com
Victoria Precision (Birmingham) Co., Manchester Street, Aston, Birmingham, B6 4HL Tel: 0121-359 3821 Fax: 0121-359 6704
Walsall Die & Tool Company Ltd, Gatehouse Trading Estate, Lichfield Road, Brownhills, Walsall, WS8 6JZ Tel: (01543) 378887 Fax: (01543) 452246 E-mail: sales@belcot.co.uk

PRESSED FELT

D G Felts, Fox Street, Batley, West Yorkshire, WF17 5QA Tel: (01924) 471462 Fax: (01924) 471462 E-mail: philgibson@fsnet.co.uk
Dolman, 10 Rouse Mill Lane, Batley, West Yorkshire, WF17 5QB Tel: (01924) 445577 Fax: (01924) 443222 E-mail: sales@jamesdolman.co.uk

PRESSED METAL SECTIONS

Folsana Pressed Sections Ltd, Sidney Street, Bolton, BL3 6BF Tel: (01204) 393355 Fax: (01204) 393377 E-mail: dm@folsana.co.uk

PRESSED NUTS

N D Jig & Gauge Co.Ltd, Bush Works, Leabrook Road, Wednesbury, West Midlands, WS10 7NB Tel: 0121-556 0824 Fax: 0121-556 8177 E-mail: sqplatewashers@aol.com

PRESSED PLASTIC COMPONENTS

P S R Industrial Ltd, 72 Snow Hill, Melton Mowbray, Leicestershire, LE13 1PH Tel: (01664) 565401 Fax: (01664) 560030 E-mail: sales@psr-industrial.co.uk

PRESSES, *See also headings for particular types*

OTG Ltd, Maidstone Road, Platt, Sevenoaks, Kent, TN15 8JE Tel: (01732) 780780 Fax: (01732) 780835 E-mail: info@otg-ltd.com

PRESSES, DIE CUTTING

▶ Gerhardt Ltd, Trent La Industrial Estate, Willow Road, Castle Donington, Derby, DE74 2NP Tel: (01332) 853434 Fax: (01332) 810274 E-mail: info@gerhardt.co.uk

PRESSINGS

Baumann Springs & Pressings UK Ltd, East Mill Lane, Sherborne, Dorset, DT9 3DR Tel: (01935) 818100 Fax: (01935) 814141 E-mail: info@baumann-springs.com
Danglo Components Ltd, Unit 9-10, Wedgewood Way, Stevenage, Hertfordshire, SG1 4QB Tel: (01438) 735616 Fax: (01438) 735625 E-mail: sales@danglo.co.uk
Doughty Pressings Ltd, Stewart Street, Wolverhampton, WV2 4JW Tel: (01902) 426264 Fax: (01902) 772245 E-mail: info@doughty.uk.com
Litchfield Bros Ltd, Ripley Road, Ambergate, Belper, Derbyshire, DE56 2EP Tel: (01773) 852435 Fax: (01773) 852661 E-mail: aksimmons@lbplastics.co.uk
William Mitchell Ltd, Tram Way, Oldbury Road, Smethwick, West Midlands, B66 1NY Tel: 0121-558 2694 Fax: 0121-558 4239 E-mail: phil.bytheway@virgin.net
Prestision Engineers, 15-16 St Andrews Industrial Estate, Sydney Road, Birmingham, B9 4QB Tel: 0121-772 4414 Fax: 0121-771 0472 E-mail: geoff@prestision.co.uk
Vernier Springs and Pressings Ltd, Edward Street, Redditch, Worcestershire, B97 6HA Tel: (01527) 582950 E-mail: roger@vernierspring.com

PRESSINGS TO SPECIFICATION

Billington Group, 280 Bawtry Road, Wickersley, Rotherham, South Yorkshire, S66 1JY Tel: (01709) 543837 Fax: (01709) 531215 E-mail: info@billington-group.co.uk
Capital Springs & Pressings Ltd, Commerce Way, Edenbridge, Kent, TN8 6ED Tel: (01732) 867130 Fax: (01732) 867140 E-mail: sales@capitalsprings.com
Cymarc Engineering, 5 Bessemer Way, Sawcliffe Industrial Park, Scunthorpe, South Humberside, DN15 8XE Tel: (01724) 289222 Fax: (01724) 852504 E-mail: cymarcengineering@cwcom.net
H Hipkiss & Co. Ltd, Park House, Clapgate Lane, Birmingham, B32 3BL Tel: 0121-421 5777 Fax: 0121-421 5333 E-mail: info@hipkiss.co.uk

PRESSINGS, ALUMINIUM/ALLOY

Production Presswork & Tooling Ltd, Unit 12 Enterprise Court, Rankin Road, Basingstoke, Hampshire, RG24 8GE Tel: (01256) 816836 Fax: (01256) 812970
Superform Aluminium, Cosgrove Close, Worcester, WR3 8UA Tel: (01905) 874300 Fax: (01905) 874301 E-mail: sales@superform-aluminium.com
Walsall Pressings Co. Ltd, Wednesbury Road, Walsall, WS1 4JW Tel: (01922) 721152 Fax: (01922) 721106 E-mail: post@walpres.co.uk

PRESSINGS, ELECTRICAL/ ELECTRONIC

Cymarc Engineering, 5 Bessemer Way, Sawcliffe Industrial Park, Scunthorpe, South Humberside, DN15 8XE Tel: (01724) 289222 Fax: (01724) 852504 E-mail: cymarcengineering@cwcom.net
David Bowler & Sons Ltd, Hardley Industrial Estate, Hardley, Hythe, Southampton, SO45 3YQ Tel: (023) 8084 3109 Fax: (023) 8084 0034 E-mail: bowler.group@virgin.net
DMP Group, Unit 5F Canal Estate, Station Road, Langley, Slough, SL3 6EG Tel: (01753) 580101 Fax: (01753) 542685 E-mail: sales@dmpgroup.co.uk

PRESSURE DIE CASTINGS

Abbey Die & Tool Ltd, Bentley Mill Close, Walsall, WS2 0BN Tel: (01922) 626545 Fax: (01922) 721717 E-mail: sales@abbeydieandtool.co.uk
Alzin Engineering Ltd, Century Works, Briggate, Elland, West Yorkshire, HX5 9HG Tel: (01422) 373456 Fax: (01422) 373813 E-mail: info@alzin.co.uk
Avon P D C, 40 Holford Way, Witton, Birmingham, B6 7AX Tel: 0121-681 1160 Fax: 0121-344 3902 E-mail: enquiries@avonpdc.co.uk

PRESSURE DIE CASTINGS – *continued*

Bournville Engineering, Lifford Trading Estate, Lifford Lane, Birmingham, B30 3DY Tel: 0121-459 9339 Fax: 0121-459 9242

William Coulthard & Co. Ltd, Stephenson Road, Durranhill Trading Estate, Carlisle, CA1 3NS Tel: (01228) 521418 Fax: (01228) 511310 E-mail: sales@wmcoulthard.com

D R Precision, 8 Shell Corner Industrial Estate, Long Lane, Halesowen, West Midlands, B62 9LD Tel: 0121-561 1874 Fax: 0121-561 1874

Daften Ltd, Trevilling Quay, Wadebridge, Cornwall, PL27 6EB Tel: (01208) 812148 Fax: (01208) 814092 E-mail: diecasting@daften.co.uk

Dynacast (UK) Ltd, Precision House, Arden Road, Alcester, Warwickshire, B49 6HN Tel: (01789) 400100 Fax: (01789) 761058 E-mail: lthomas@dynacast.co.uk

Dyson Diecastings Ltd, Denbigh Industrial Estate, Second Avenue, Bletchley, Milton Keynes, MK1 1EA Tel: (01908) 279200 Fax: (01908) 279219 E-mail: dyson@alumascprecision.co.uk

Etma Engineering Ltd, Victoria Road, Halesowen, West Midlands, B62 8HY Tel: 0121-559 5333 Fax: 0121-559 2236E-mail: sales@etma.co.uk

Farrell Engineering Ltd, Centre House, St. Leonards Road, London, NW10 6ST Tel: (020) 8965 7578 Fax: (020) 8965 7586 E-mail: farrell497@aol.com

H & J Speake Ltd, Strawberry Lane Industrial Estate, Strawberry Lane, Willenhall, West Midlands, WV13 3RS Tel: (01902) 607188 Fax: (01902) 635802 E-mail: hjspeake@freenetname.co.uk

H Mullins Earby Ltd, Western Road, Jarrow, Tyne & Wear, NE32 3DB Tel: 0191-489 1617 Fax: 0191-428 0375 E-mail: h.mullins@mullins.co.uk

Hyde Die Casting & Manufactring Ltd, 1 Providence Mill, Alexandra Street, Hyde, Cheshire, SK14 1DX Tel: 0161-368 0996 Fax: 0161-368 6022 E-mail: hydediecasting@aol.com

Kemlows Diecasting Products Ltd, Charlton Mead Lane, Hoddesdon, Hertfordshire, EN11 0HB Tel: (01992) 460671 Fax: (01992) 446889 E-mail: sales@kemlows.co.uk

L C L Castings Ltd, Showfield Lane, Malton, North Yorkshire, YO17 6BT Tel: (01653) 694436 Fax: (01653) 600224 E-mail: sales@lcl-castings.co.uk

J.H. Lavender & Co. Ltd, Hall Green Works, Crankhall Lane, West Bromwich, West Midlands, B71 3JZ Tel: 0121-588 2273 Fax: 0121-588 7936 E-mail: lavender-diecast@city2000.net

Lesney Industries Ltd, Norwood House, Temple Bank, River way, Harlow, Essex, CM20 2DY Tel: (01279) 260130 Fax: (01279) 413100 E-mail:

McDonald Diecasting Ltd, Unit 21a Coneygre Industrial Estate, Birmingham New Rd, Tipton, West Midlands, DY4 8XP Tel: 0121-520 1177 Fax: 0121-557 0677 E-mail: info@mcdonald-diecasting.co.uk

Metal Castings Ltd, Droitwich Road, Worcester, WR3 7JX Tel: (01905) 754400 Fax: (01905) 754347 E-mail: sales@metalcastingsltd.com

Alexander Pollock Ltd, Hospital Road, Haddington, East Lothian, EH41 3PD Tel: (01620) 823344 Fax: (01620) 824252 E-mail: jstewart@alexander-pollock.co.uk

Polypipe Bathroom & Kitchen Products Ltd, Edlington Lane, Warmsworth, Doncaster, South Yorkshire, DN4 9LS Tel: (01302) 310666 Fax: (01302) 856421

Pressure Cast Products Ltd, Fairacres Industrial Estate, Dedworth Road, Windsor, Berkshire, SL4 4LE Tel: (01753) 868969 Fax: (01753) 840475 E-mail: info@pressurecast.co.uk

R D Castings Ltd, Leyton Avenue, Mildenhall, Bury St. Edmunds, Suffolk, IP28 7BL Tel: (01638) 717944 Fax: (01638) 716590

▶ Regon Ltd, Unit 21B, Avenue 2, Station Lane Industrial Estate, Witney, Oxfordshire, OX28 4YG Tel: (01993) 771441 Fax: (01993) 774105 E-mail: sales@regon.co.uk

Sant Products Ltd, Unit 42 Coneygre Industrial Estate, Tipton, West Midlands, DY4 8XP Tel: 0121-557 7066 Fax: 0121-557 2007

W Hallam Castings Ltd, Coulman Road Industrial Estate, Thorne, Doncaster, South Yorkshire, DN8 5JU Tel: (01405) 813006 Fax: (01405) 813786 E-mail: sales@hallamcastings.co.uk

PRESSURE FILTERS

Howard Filter Systems, East Skirdle, Waterrow, Taunton, Somerset, TA4 2AY Tel: (01984) 623112 Fax: (01984) 624770 E-mail: hfsl@btconnect.co.uk

PRESSURE GAUGES

Abbey Gauge Co. Ltd, 139-141 Becontree Avenue, Dagenham, Essex, RM8 2UL Tel: (020) 8590 3233 Fax: (020) 8590 5082 E-mail: sales@abbeygauge.co.uk

Abbirko UK Ltd, 4 Manor Works, Station Road South, Totton, Southampton, SO40 9HP Tel: (023) 8066 8833 Fax: (023) 8066 7777 E-mail: sales@abbirko.co.uk

B K W Instruments Ltd, Weymouth Road, Winton, Eccles, Manchester, M30 8NN Tel: 0161-707 4838 Fax: 0161-787 7580 E-mail: sales@bkwinstruments.co.uk

Bailey & Mackey Ltd, Baltimore Road, Birmingham, B42 1DE Tel: 0121-357 5351 Fax: 0121-357 8319 E-mail: enquiries@baileymackey.com

Bourdon Haenni Ltd, Unit A Central Estate, Albert Road, Aldershot, Hampshire, GU11 1SZ Tel: (01252) 354000 Fax: (01252) 354009 E-mail: info@bourdon-haenni.co.uk

Checkmate Products Ltd, 64 Lindsell Road, West Timperley, Altrincham, Cheshire, WA14 5NX Tel: 0161-928 0046 Fax: 0161-286 3729 E-mail: checkprod@aol.com

Commercial & Industrial Gauges, Unit 7 Coed Aben Road, Wrexham Industrial Estate, Wrexham Industrial Estate, Wrexham, Clwyd, LL13 9UH Tel: (01978) 661704 Fax: (01978) 660321 E-mail: info@cigltd.co.uk

Dwyer Instruments Ltd, Unit 16 The Wye Estate, London Road, High Wycombe, Buckinghamshire, HP11 1LH Tel: (01494) 461707 Fax: (01494) 465102 E-mail: sales@dwyer-inst.co.uk

E V O Instrumentation Ltd, 31a Coppice Trading Estate, Kidderminster, Worcestershire, DY11 7QY Tel: (01562) 741212 Fax: (01562) 741666 E-mail: sales@evoinstrumentation.co.uk

Industrial & Technical Services Co., Victoria House, 28 Borneo Street, Walsall, WS4 2HY Tel: (01922) 644239 Fax: (01922) 644239

Instrument & Gauges Electronics Ltd, Gravel Lane, Banks, Southport, Merseyside, PR9 8DE Tel: (01704) 505333 Fax: (01704) 505334 E-mail: sales@instruments-gauges.co.uk

LMJ Engineering Services, 379 Verity Cresent, Poole, Dorset, BH17 8TS Tel: (01202) 678688 Fax: (01202) 686457 E-mail: enquiries@lmjengineering.co.uk

Frank W. Murphy Ltd, Swichgage House, Church Road, Laverstock, Salisbury, SP1 1QZ Tel: (01722) 410055 Fax: (01722) 410088 E-mail: sales@fwmurphy.co.uk

Pressure Gauges Ltd, Park Street, Oldbury, West Midlands, B69 4LE Tel: 0121-544 4408 Fax: 0121-544 7332 E-mail: enquiries@pressure-gauges-ltd.com

J.W. Ray & Co. Liverpool Ltd, Unit 87 North Mersey Business Centre, Woodward Road, Knowsley Industrial Park, Liverpool, L33 7UY Tel: 0151-546 2534 Fax: 0151-549 1645

S Brannan & Sons Ltd, Leconfield Industrial Estate, Cleator Moor, Cumbria, CA25 5QE Tel: (01946) 816624 Fax: (01946) 816625 E-mail: sales@brannan.co.uk

Saunders & Weeks Bristol Ltd, 265-267 Church Road, Redfield, Bristol, BS5 9HU Tel: 0117-955 7142 Fax: 0117-955 6064 E-mail: sales@saundersweeks.co.uk

Siemens V D O Automotive Ltd, The Broadlands, 120 Holford Drive, Holford, Birmingham, B6 7UG Tel: 0121-344 2000 Fax: 0121-344 2072 E-mail: admin@vdodayton.com

Star Instruments Ltd, Dunmurry Industrial Estate, Dunmurry, Belfast, BT17 9HU Tel: (028) 9061 8221 Fax: (028) 9060 1803 E-mail: sales@star-instruments.co.uk

Star Instruments Ltd, Barkway, Royston, Hertfordshire, SG8 8EH Tel: (01763) 848886 Fax: (01763) 848881 E-mail: sales@star-instruments.co.uk

Test Plugs Ltd, 12 Falklands Road, Haverhill, Suffolk, CB9 0EA Tel: (01440) 704201 Fax: (01440) 763121 E-mail: sales@test-plugs.com

Vector International Ltd, Unit 31, Wellheads Crescent, Wellheads Industrial Estate, Aberdeen, AB21 7GA Tel: (01224) 775242 Fax: (01224) 772212 E-mail: sales@vector-supplies.ltd.uk

Wood Group Production Technology Ltd, Maersk House, Greenbank Road, East Tullos Industrial Estate, Aberdeen, AB21 3BR Tel: (01224) 840000 Fax: (01224) 216775

Zygal Controls Ltd, 149 Stanwell Road, Ashford, Middlesex, TW15 3QN Tel: (01784) 251134 Fax: (01784) 243688 E-mail: saleszygal@aol.com

PRESSURE INDICATOR/ CONTROLLER MANUFRS

Alert Products, Hollins Lane, Tilstock, Whitchurch, Shropshire, SY13 3NU Tel: (01948) 880627 Fax: (01948) 880339 E-mail: graham.dewson@ukonline.co.uk

British Rototherm Co. Ltd, Kenfig Industrial Estate, Margam, Port Talbot, West Glamorgan, SA13 2PW Tel: (01656) 740551 Fax: (01656) 745915 E-mail: rototherm@rototherm.co.uk

Watts Industries UK Ltd, Grosvenor Business Centre, Enterprise Way, Vale Park, Evesham, Worcestershire, WR11 1GA Tel: (01386) 446997 Fax: (01386) 41923 E-mail: sales@wattsindustries.com

PRESSURE INDICATORS, DIFFERENTIAL

Alert Products, Hollins Lane, Tilstock, Whitchurch, Shropshire, SY13 3NU Tel: (01948) 880627 Fax: (01948) 880339 E-mail: graham.dewson@ukonline.co.uk

PRESSURE INSTRUMENTATION

I M I Watson Smith Ltd, Cross Chancellor Street, Leeds, LS6 2RT Tel: 0113-245 7587 Fax: 0113-246 5735 E-mail: enquiries@watsonsmith.com

LG International, Marsh Road, Lords Meadow Industrial Estate, Crediton, Devon, EX17 1EU Tel: (01363) 777500 Fax: (01363) 777501

▶ Solartron Mobrey Ltd, 158 Edinburgh Avenue, Slough, SL1 4UE Tel: (01753) 756600 Fax: (01753) 823589

PRESSURE REGULATORS, *See also headings for particular types*

Aberdeen Pressure Washer Centre, 22-26 Duff Street, Turriff, Aberdeenshire, AB53 4AX Tel: (01888) 563050 Fax: (01888) 563841 E-mail: info@tapltd.co.uk

Boiswood Ltd, Unit A1 Spinnaker Park, Hempsted, Gloucester, GL2 5JA Tel: (01452) 330011 Fax: (01452) 330088 E-mail: ian.taylor@boiswood.co.uk

Bryan Donkin Ltd, Enterprise Drive, Holmewood, Chesterfield, Derbyshire, S42 5UZ Tel: (01246) 501501 Fax: (01246) 501500 E-mail: sales@bdrmg.co.uk

Dereve Flow Control Ltd, Park Lane, Handsworth, Birmingham, B21 8LE Tel: 0121-553 7021 Fax: 0121-525 5664 E-mail: dc.controls@btinternet.com

I M I Watson Smith Ltd, Cross Chancellor Street, Leeds, LS6 2RT Tel: 0113-245 7587 Fax: 0113-246 5735 E-mail: enquiries@watsonsmith.com

PRESSURE RELIEF DAMPERS

Apreco Ltd, Bruff Works, Suckley, Worcester, WR6 5DR Tel: (01886) 884090 Fax: (01886) 884099 E-mail: info@apreco.co.uk

PRESSURE RELIEF VALVES

Presreg Valve, 18 Bakewell Road, Loughborough, Leicestershire, LE11 5QY Tel: (01509) 264242 Fax: (01509) 263308

PRESSURE SENSITIVE ADHESIVES (PSA)

H B Fuller UK Ltd, Outram Road, Globe Lane Industrial Estate, Dukinfield, Cheshire, SK16 4XE Tel: (01773) 601315 Fax: (0161) 666 0667

PRESSURE SENSITIVE EQUIPMENT, *See headings for particular types*

PRESSURE SENSITIVE LABEL PRINTING MACHINES

Stanley Press Equipment Ltd, Sutton Mill, Byrons Lane, Macclesfield, Cheshire, SK11 7JL Tel: (01625) 619094 Fax: (01625) 619094 E-mail: sales@s-p-e.co.uk

PRESSURE SENSORS

Acam Instrumentation Ltd, 23 Thomas Street, Northampton, NN1 3EN Tel: (01604) 628700 Fax: (01604) 628700 E-mail: tom@acamltd.co.uk

Kavlico Corporation, 11-15 Columbus Walk, Brigantine Place, Cardiff, CF10 4BZ Tel: (029) 2046 3449 Fax: (029) 2045 0852 E-mail: kavlico@btinternet.co.uk

▶ Sensortechnics UK & Ireland, McGowan House, Aspect Business Centre, 66c Somers Road, Rugby, Warwickshire, CV22 7DH Tel: (01788) 560426 Fax: (01788) 561228 E-mail: salesuk@sensortechnics.com

Sensor-Technik UK Ltd, Unit 10 The Granary, Sharnbrook, Bedford, MK44 1NN Tel: 01234 782049

Senstronics Ltd, Unit 2, Angels Close, Aycliffe Industrial Park, Newton Aycliffe, County Durham, DL5 6BG Tel: (01325) 328500 Fax: (01325) 328504 E-mail: sales@senstronics.com

PRESSURE SWITCHES

Able Instruments & Controls Ltd, Danehill, Lower Earley, Reading, RG6 4UT Tel: 0118-931 1188 Fax: 0118-931 2161 E-mail: sales@able.co.uk

Albroco Ltd, Unit C28 Ashmount Enterprise Park, Aber Road, Flint, Clwyd, CH6 5YL Tel: (01352) 734182 Fax: (01352) 734159 E-mail: sales@albrocos.co.uk

Applications Engineering Ltd, 5 Horsted Square, Bellbrook Industrial Estate, Uckfield, East Sussex, TN22 1QG Tel: (01825) 764737 Fax: (01825) 768330 E-mail: info@appeng.co.uk

Bailey & Mackey Ltd, Baltimore Road, Birmingham, B42 1DE Tel: 0121-357 5351 Fax: 0121-357 8319 E-mail: enquiries@baileymackey.com

Bourdon Haenni Ltd, Unit A Central Estate, Albert Road, Aldershot, Hampshire, GU11 1SZ Tel: (01252) 354000 Fax: (01252) 354009 E-mail: info@bourdon-haenni.co.uk

Buckley Elements Ltd, Galveston Grove, Fenton, Stoke-on-Trent, ST3 2JT Tel: (01782) 333071 Fax: (01782) 593485 E-mail: sales@buckleyelements.co.uk

Caerbont Automotive Instruments Ltd, Caerbont, Abercrave, Swansea, SA9 1SH Tel: (01639) 732200 Fax: (01639) 732201

Custom Control Sensors International, 13 Shrivenham Hundred Business Park, Majors Road, Watchfield, Swindon, SN6 8TZ Tel: (01793) 783545 Fax: (01793) 783532 E-mail: pswitch@ccsdualsnap.co.uk

E A C Ltd, PO Box 6023, Solihull, West Midlands, B93 0JN Tel: (01564) 770359 Fax: (01564) 774025 E-mail: eaccomps@aol.com

G S M International, Upper Neatham Mill Farm, Upper Neatham Mill Lane, Holybourne, Alton, Hampshire, GU34 4EP Tel: (01420) 80617 Fax: (01420) 80617 E-mail: gsminternational@ukonline.co.uk

Gems Sensors Pension Trustees Ltd, Lennox Road, Basingstoke, Hampshire, RG22 4AW Tel: (01256) 320244 Fax: (01256) 473680 E-mail: sales@gems-sensors.co.uk

Hydraulic System Products Ltd, Monckton Road, Wakefield, West Yorkshire, WF2 7AL Tel: (01924) 364748 Fax: (01924) 290450 E-mail: sales@h-s-p.co.uk

M & M International UK Ltd, 12 Railton Road, Kempston, Bedford, MK42 7PW Tel: (01234) 855888 Fax: (01234) 856999 E-mail: sales@mmint.co.uk

P V L Ltd, 9 Lexden Lodge Industrial Estate, Crowborough Hill, Crowborough, East Sussex, TN6 2NQ Tel: (01892) 664499 Fax: (01892) 663690 E-mail: info@pd1.co.uk

Pressure & Flow Ltd, Victoria House, 50 Albert Street, Rugby, Warwickshire, CV21 2RH Tel: (01788) 560426 Fax: (01788) 561228 E-mail: uk@sensortechnics.com

Sirco Controls Ltd, Swaines Industrial Estate, Ashingdon Road, Rochford, Essex, SS4 1RQ Tel: (01702) 545125 Fax: (01702) 546873 E-mail: sales@sirco-controls.co.uk

Sor Europe Ltd, Farren Court, The Street, Cowfold, Horsham, West Sussex, RH13 8BP Tel: (01403) 864000 Fax: (01403) 710177 E-mail: sales@soreur.co.uk

Trafag UK Ltd, 12 Josselin Court, Josselin Road, Burnt Mills Industrial Estate, Basildon, Essex, SS13 1QF Tel: (01268) 727172 Fax: (01268) 727572 E-mail: enquiries@trafag.co.uk

Zygal Controls Ltd, 149 Stanwell Road, Ashford, Middlesex, TW15 3QN Tel: (01784) 251134 Fax: (01784) 243688 E-mail: saleszygal@aol.com

PRESSURE TEST EQUIPMENT MANUFRS

▶ Baskerville, 30 Long Wood Road, Trafford Park, Manchester, M17 1PZ Tel: 0161-888 2345 Fax: 0161-888 2345 E-mail: admin@baskervilleautoclaves.co.uk

CMR Controls, 22 Repton Court, Repton Close, Basildon, Essex, SS13 1LN Tel: (01268) 287222 Fax: (01268) 287099 E-mail: sales@cmr.co.uk

Dynisco (UK) Ltd, Unit 2B Crowood House, Gipsy Lane, Swindon, SN2 8YY Tel: (01527) 577077 Fax: (01527) 577070 E-mail: dyniscouk@dynisco.com

Hayes UK Ltd, 7 Eagle Estate, Brookers Road, Billingshurst, West Sussex, RH14 9RZ Tel: (0870) 0711700 Fax: (0870) 0711701 E-mail: sales@hayes-uk.com

Startrite Designs Ltd, Courteney Road, Hoath Way, Gillingham, Kent, ME8 0RZ Tel: (01634) 233216 Fax: (01634) 373516 E-mail: startritedesigns@btinternet.com

Vector International Ltd, Unit 31, Wellheads Crescent, Wellheads Industrial Estate, Aberdeen, AB21 7GA Tel: (01224) 775242 Fax: (01224) 772212 E-mail: sales@vector-supplies.ltd.uk

PRESSURE TEST SERVICES

Cansco Pressure Control Ltd, Badentoy Road, Portlethen, Aberdeen, AB12 4YA Tel: (01224) 782211 Fax: (01224) 782266 E-mail: sales@3plus.co.uk

Industrial Safety Inspections Ltd, Lea Lodge, Ansley, Nuneaton, Warwickshire, CV10 0QU Tel: (01675) 481779 Fax: (01675) 481780 E-mail: sales@isi-uk.net

Jade Air P.L.C., Hanger 1, Shoreham Airport, Shoreham-by-Sea, West Sussex, BN43 5FF Tel: (01273) 464013 Fax: (01273) 465184 E-mail: info@jadeair.co.uk

Oil States MCS Ltd, Bouthwood Road, Sowerby Woods Industrial Estate, Barrow-in-Furness, Cumbria, LA14 4RD Tel: (01229) 825080 Fax: (01229) 839791 E-mail: owen-osmotherly@osmcs-bat.co.uk

PRESSURE TESTING PUMPS

Haskel Energy Systems Ltd, North Hylton Road, Sunderland, SR5 3JD Tel: 0191-549 1212 Fax: 0191-549 0911 E-mail: sales@haskel.co.uk

Hydraulic Pneumatic Services, Unit 3b King Street Trading Estate, Middlewich, Cheshire, CW10 9LF Tel: (01606) 835725 Fax: (01606) 737358 E-mail: kinfo@madan.uk.com

PRESSURE TRANSDUCERS

Ashridge Engineering Ltd, 58 North Road Indust Estate, Okehampton, Devon, EX20 1BQ Tel: (01837) 53381 Fax: (01837) 55022 E-mail: sales@ash-eng.co.uk

Bailey & Mackey Ltd, Baltimore Road, Birmingham, B42 1DE Tel: 0121-357 5351 Fax: 0121-357 8319 E-mail: enquiries@baileymackey.com

CMR Controls, 22 Repton Court, Repton Close, Basildon, Essex, SS13 1LN Tel: (01268) 287222 Fax: (01268) 287099 E-mail: sales@cmr.co.uk

Ellison Sensors International Ltd, Sensor House, Wrexham Technology Park, Wrexham, Clwyd, LL13 7YP Tel: (01978) 262255 Fax: (01978) 262233 E-mail: info@esi-tec.com

G E Sensing, Fir Tree Lane, Groby, Leicester, LE6 0FH Tel: 0116-231 7100 Fax: 0116-231 7101

Gaeltec Ltd, Glendale Road, Dunvegan, Isle of Skye, IV55 8GU Tel: (01470) 521385 Fax: (01470) 521369 E-mail: info@gaeltec.com

Gems Sensors Pension Trustees Ltd, Lennox Road, Basingstoke, Hampshire, RG22 4AW Tel: (01256) 320244 Fax: (01256) 473680 E-mail: sales@gems-sensors.co.uk

Honeywell Process Solutions, Unit 1 Headlands Business Park, Salisbury Road, Blashford, Ringwood, Hampshire, BH24 3PB Tel: (01425) 463950 Fax: (01425) 463953 E-mail: uksales@trendview.com

Kavlico Corporation, 11-15 Columbus Walk, Brigantine Place, Cardiff, CF10 4BZ Tel: (029) 2046 3449 Fax: (029) 2045 0852 E-mail: kavlico@btinternet.co.uk

Pressure & Flow Ltd, Victoria House, 50 Albert Street, Rugby, Warwickshire, CV21 2RH Tel: (01788) 560426 Fax: (01788) 561228 E-mail: uk@sensortechnics.com

▶ Sensortechnics UK & Ireland, McGowan House, Aspect Business Centre, 66c Somers Road, Rugby, Warwickshire, CV22 7DH Tel: (01788) 560426 Fax: (01788) 561228 E-mail: salesuk@sensortechnics.com

T S M Ltd, Sensor House, Wrexham Technology Park, Wrexham, Clwyd, LL13 7YP Tel: (01978) 291800 Fax: (01978) 291888 E-mail: tsm@esi-tec.com

Trafag UK Ltd, 12 Josselin Court, Josselin Road, Burnt Mills Industrial Estate, Basildon, Essex, SS13 1QF Tel: (01268) 727172 Fax: (01268) 727572 E-mail: enquiries@trafag.co.uk

PRESSURE VESSEL DESIGN

Ardeth Engineering Ltd, Dewsbury Road, Elland, West Yorkshire, HX5 9AZ Tel: (01422) 371014 Fax: (01422) 372218E-mail: info@ardeth.com

PRESSURE VESSEL DESIGN CONSULTANTS

Ardeth Engineering Ltd, Dewsbury Road, Elland, West Yorkshire, HX5 9AZ Tel: (01422) 371014 Fax: (01422) 372218E-mail: info@ardeth.com

G F S A Ltd, 4 West Court, Buntsford Park Road, Bromsgrove, Worcestershire, B60 3DX Tel: (01527) 831037 Fax: (01527) 836333 E-mail: enquiries@gfsa.co.uk

Old Park Engineering Services Ltd, Woods Lane, Cradley Heath, West Midlands, B64 7AN Tel: (01384) 412550 Fax: (01384) 410784 E-mail: oldpark@blueyonder.co.uk

Parsons Brinckerhoff Ltd, Amber Court, William Armstrong Drive, Newcastle Business Park, Newcastle upon Tyne, NE4 7YQ Tel: 0191-226 1234 Fax: 0191-226 2104 E-mail: pbpower@pbworld.com

Proserv (North Sea) Ltd, Riverside Business Centre, North Esplanade West, Aberdeen, AB11 5RJ Tel: (01224) 210067 Fax: (01224) 582616 E-mail: info@proservns.co.uk

WBR Design Ltd, 126 High Street West, Glossop, Derbyshire, SK13 8HJ Tel: (01457) 857664 Fax: (01457) 851580 E-mail: wbr@wbrdesign.com

PRESSURE VESSEL LIGHTING

Visilume Ltd, Unit 30 Moor Park Industrial Estate, Tolpits Lane, Watford, WD18 9SP Tel: (01923) 211131 Fax: (01923) 211432 E-mail: sales@visilume.co.uk

PRESSURE VESSEL MANUFRS,

See also headings for particular types

Abbfab Services Ltd, Windley Street, Bolton, BL2 2AH Tel: (01204) 523441 Fax: (01204) 557930 E-mail: admin@abbfab.co.uk

Able Engineering, Cadley Hill Road, Swadlincote, Derbyshire, DE11 9EQ Tel: (01283) 227160 Fax: (01283) 222375 E-mail: dave@able-engineering.co.uk

Allied Filter Systems Ltd, Huntsman Drive, Northbank Industrial Park, Irlam, Manchester, M44 5EG Tel: 0161-777 9505 Fax: 0161-777 9506 E-mail: sales@alliedfilter.com

Allied Tank & Fabrications Ltd, Phoenix Works Industrial Estate, Richards Street, Wednesbury, West Midlands, WS10 8BZ Tel: 0121-568 8166 Fax: 0121-568 8177 E-mail: sales@alliedtanks.co.uk

Armultra Ltd, Armultra House, Hewett Road, Great Yarmouth, Norfolk, NR31 0RB Tel: (01493) 652150 Fax: (01493) 652842 E-mail: sales@armultra.co.uk

Automotive Tanks Ltd, Bilston Lane, Willenhall, West Midlands, WV13 2LH Tel: (01902) 604207 Fax: (01902) 604265 E-mail: sales@automotivetanks.ltd.uk

Basingstoke Pressure Vessels & Pipework Ltd, 11 Brunel Gate, Andover, Hampshire, SP10 3SL Tel: (01264) 351559 Fax: (01264) 332173 E-mail: acole@bpbp.co.uk

Bendall, Brunthill Road, Kingstown Industrial Estate, Carlisle, CA3 0EH Tel: (01228) 526246 Fax: (01228) 525634 E-mail: info@bendalls.co.uk

Francis Brown Ltd, Church Road, Stockton-on-Tees, Cleveland, TS18 2HL Tel: (01642) 806000 Fax: (01642) 806001 E-mail: sales@francisbrown.co.uk

C P E (Pressure Vessels) Ltd, Apollo, Lichfield Road Industrial Estate, Tamworth, Staffordshire, B79 7TA Tel: 01827 68710 Fax: (01827) 54396 E-mail: sales@cpe-ltd.com

C S Struthers, Valletta Street, Hull, HU9 5NU Tel: (01482) 707766 Fax: (01482) 787479 E-mail: sales@csstruthers.co.uk

Conder Products Ltd, Whitehouse Way, South West Industrial Estate, Peterlee, County Durham, SR8 2HZ Tel: 0191-587 8660 Fax: 0191-586 1274 E-mail: sales@conderproducts.co.uk

Cookson & Zinn PTL Ltd, Station Road Works, Station Road, Hadleigh, Ipswich, IP7 5PN Tel: (01473) 825200 Fax: (01473) 828446 E-mail: info@czltd.com

Cronite Scomark Engineering, Church Street, Swadlincote, Derbyshire, DE11 9NR Tel: (01283) 218222 Fax: (01283) 226468 E-mail: tonyknight@scomark.com

Echo Engineering Southern Ltd, Chapel Land Farm, Ashford Road, New Romney, Kent, TN28 8TH Tel: (01797) 367670 Fax: (01797) 367671 E-mail: sales@echo-eng.com

Forster & Hales Ltd, 24 Wadsworth Road, Greenford, Middlesex, UB6 7JD Tel: (020) 8998 9057 Fax: (020) 8998 2922 E-mail: sales@forsterandhales.com

Forsyths, Station Road, Rothes, Aberlour, Banffshire, AB38 7AD Tel: (01340) 831787 Fax: (01340) 831558 E-mail: enquiries@forsyths.com

Gilwood (Fabricators) Co. Ltd, Bradshaw Street, Heywood, Lancashire, OL10 1PL Tel: (01706) 360131 Fax: (01706) 625666 E-mail: sales@gilwood.co.uk

Grant & Livingston Ltd, Kings Road, Canvey Island, Essex, SS8 0RA Tel: (01268) 696855 Fax: (01268) 697018 E-mail: gandl.canvey@btconnect.com

H A Mcewen Boiler Repairs Ltd, Farling Top Boilerworks, Farling Top, Cowling, Keighley, West Yorkshire, BD22 0NW Tel: (01535) 634674 Fax: (01535) 636802 E-mail: maria@mcewen82.fsnet.co.uk

H & I Engineering Ltd, Solway Works, Annan Road, Eastriggs, Annan, Dumfriesshire, DG12 6NJ Tel: (01461) 40500 Fax: (01461) 40801 E-mail: admin@hi-engineering.co.uk

H Pontifex & Sons Ltd, Pepper Road, Leeds, LS10 2NJ Tel: 0113-271 3411 Fax: 0113-277 7985 E-mail: info@pontifex.co.uk

Hallcalm UK, Redworth Street, Hartlepool, Cleveland, TS24 7LG Tel: (01429) 891011 Fax: (01429) 236746 E-mail: engineering@hallcalm.co.uk

John R Boone Ltd, 18 Silk Street, Congleton, Cheshire, CW12 4DH Tel: (01260) 272894 Fax: (01260) 281128 E-mail: sales@jrboone.com

▶ LBBC Ltd, Beechwood Street, Pudsey, West Yorkshire, LS28 6PT Tel: 0113-205 7400 Fax: 0113-256 3509 E-mail: sales@lbbc.co.uk

Mainport Engineering (1990) Ltd, Pembroke Dock, Dyfed, SA72 6WD Tel: (01646) 621563 Fax: (01646) 621305 E-mail: mpe@my-office.co.uk

Merpro Leisure Ltd, Brent Avenue, Forties Road Industrial Estate, Montrose, Angus, DD10 9JA Tel: (01674) 662200 Fax: (01674) 662266 E-mail: sales@merpro.com

Northern Arc Electric Welding Co Leicester Ltd, 161 Scudamore Road, Leicester, LE3 1UQ Tel: 0116-287 4949 Fax: 0116-287 5153

Pressmain (Pressurisation) Co. Ltd, Opal Works, Denhill Road Industrial Estate, Moss Side, Manchester, M15 5NR Tel: 0161-226 4727 Fax: 0161-226 5848 E-mail: sales@pressmain.com

Proserv (North Sea) Ltd, Riverside Business Centre, North Esplanade West, Aberdeen, AB11 5RJ Tel: (01224) 210067 Fax: (01224) 582616 E-mail: info@proservns.co.uk

Proweld Quality Vessels Ltd, Units 22-23, Lion Court, Daneshill, Basingstoke, Hampshire, RG24 8QU Tel: (01256) 814184 Fax: (01256) 814164 E-mail: simon@proweld.uk.com

R G R Fabrications & Welding Services Ltd, Pensnett Trading Estate, Kingswinford, West Midlands, DY6 7PP Tel: (01384) 401055 Fax: (01384) 400068E-mail: sales@rgrltd.com

R M F Engineering Ltd, Rotherham Road, Dinnington, Sheffield, S25 3RF Tel: (01909) 567683 Fax: (01909) 562725 E-mail: sales@rmf-engineering.co.uk

R Sanderson & Sons Ltd, Cannon Street, Hull, HU2 0AB Tel: (01482) 226286 Fax: (01482) 327220 E-mail: info@robert-sanderson.co.uk

Rolls Royce Primary Components HPV Ltd, Sinfin Lane, Derby, DE24 9GJ Tel: (01332) 271111 Fax: (01332) 271234 E-mail: sales@rollsroyce.com

S S T Process Engineering Ltd, Unit 22 Autumn Park, Dysart Road, Grantham, Lincolnshire, NG31 7DD Tel: (01476) 590112 Fax: (01476) 590113 E-mail: sales@sstpe.co.uk

Shand Engineering Ltd, Kiln Lane, Stallingborough, Grimsby, South Humberside, DN41 8DL Tel: (01469) 571586 Fax: (01469) 571073

Site Engineering Services, Reverdane Road, Congleton, Cheshire, CW12 1UN Tel: (01260) 275252 Fax: (01260) 270111 E-mail: sales@phoenixengineering.co.uk

Stanref International Ltd, Northern Way, Bury St. Edmunds, Suffolk, IP32 6NL Tel: 01284 763501

Steel Services Great Yarmouth Ltd, South Denes Road, Great Yarmouth, Norfolk, NR30 3PF Tel: (01493) 856180 Fax: (01493) 852237 E-mail: info@steelservices.co.uk

TMS Services, 7 Brunel Way, Fareham, Hampshire, PO15 5TX Tel: (01489) 564707 Fax: (01489) 575229E-mail: sales@ansti.com

U B H International Ltd, Orrell Lane, Burscough, Ormskirk, Lancashire, L40 0SL Tel: (01704) 898500 Fax: (01704) 898518 E-mail: tanks@ubh.co.uk

▶ Wefco (Gainsborough) Ltd, Brittania Works, Spring Gardens, Gainsborough, Lincolnshire, DN21 2AZ Tel: (01427) 611000 Fax: (01427) 612000 E-mail: glennb@wefco.net

Whiteley Read Engineering Ltd, Gateway Indust Estate, Rotherham, South Yorkshire, S62 6JL Tel: (01709) 710661 Fax: (01709) 710961 E-mail: sales@whitely-read.co.uk

PRESSURE VESSELS TO SPECIFICATION

D & J Fabrications Atherton Ltd, 160 Elizabeth Street, Atherton, Manchester, M46 9JL Tel: (01942) 873393 Fax: (01942) 897967 E-mail: sales@dandjfabrications.co.uk

PRESSURE WASHER DETERGENTS

Farrell Products, 1a Aughrim Road, Magherafelt, County Londonderry, BT45 6AY Tel: (028) 7963 2245 Fax: (028) 7963 1702 E-mail: sales@farrellproducts.com

▶ GP Cleaners, Unit F3, Innsworth Technology Park, Innsworth Lane, Gloucester, GL3 1DL Tel: (01452) 731630 Fax: (01452) 739212 E-mail: sales@gpcleaners.com

▶ Oaklands Pressure Washers, 343 Eakring Road, Mansfield, Notts, NG18 3EL Tel: 01623 651118 Fax: 07875 795050 E-mail: sales@oaklandspressurewashers.co.uk

Ruck Engineering, Kellaw Road, Darlington, County Durham, DL1 4YA Tel: (01325) 286081 Fax: (01325) 480722 E-mail: sales@ruckengineering.com

PRESSURE WASHER SERVICING

Farrell Products, 1a Aughrim Road, Magherafelt, County Londonderry, BT45 6AY Tel: (028) 7963 2245 Fax: (028) 7963 1702 E-mail: sales@farrellproducts.com

▶ GP Cleaners, Unit F3, Innsworth Technology Park, Innsworth Lane, Gloucester, GL3 1DL Tel: (01452) 731630 Fax: (01452) 739212 E-mail: sales@gpcleaners.com

▶ Machine Resources Ltd, 77 Poplars Close, Mardy, Abergavenny, Monmouthshire, NP7 6LQ Tel: (01873) 857093 Fax: (01873) 857093 E-mail: machine-resources@tiscali.co.uk

Ruck Engineering, Kellaw Road, Darlington, County Durham, DL1 4YA Tel: (01325) 286081 Fax: (01325) 480722 E-mail: sales@ruckengineering.com

▶ T&K Summerson, stockgill close, Gamston, Nottingham, NG2 6SA Tel: 0115-981 5153 E-mail: info@tkgardenservices.co.uk

PRESSURE WASHERS

Broadbent & Co. Ltd, Unit 14a Colwick Business Park, Private Road No 2, Colwick Industrial Estate, Nottingham, NG4 2JR Tel: 0115-940 0777 Fax: 0115-987 3744 E-mail: info@industrialcleaningequipment.co.uk

Check Equipment, 2 Spencer Drive, Melbourn, Royston, Hertfordshire, SG8 6HP Tel: (01763) 261971 Fax: (01763) 262995 E-mail:

Demon International Ltd, Abbots Close, Lee Mill Industrial Estate, Ivybridge, Devon, PL21 9GA Tel: (01752) 690690 Fax: (01752) 690919 E-mail: sales@demon-pressure-washers.com

Kleaning Equipment Western Ltd, Park Road, Dawley Bank, Telford, Shropshire, TF4 2BE Tel: (01952) 502600 Fax: (01952) 504703 E-mail: enquiries@cleaning-equipment.co.uk

PRESSURIZATION EQUIPMENT

Ceetak Engineering Ltd, 1 Napier Road, Elm Farm Industrial Estate, Bedford, MK41 0QR Tel: (01234) 343232 Fax: (01234) 341133 E-mail: ceetakengineering@bedford.com

PRESSWORK STEEL BLANKS

Abbey Steel & Shearing Co. Ltd, 5 Cartwright Road, Pin Green Industrial Area, Stevenage, Hertfordshire, SG1 4QJ Tel: (01438) 741888 Fax: (01438) 740980 E-mail: sales@abbeysteel.co.uk

Able Production, 77 Arthur Street, Redditch, Worcestershire, B98 8JY Tel: (01527) 510899 Fax: (01527) 514234

PRESSWORK/PRESSWORKERS

▶ Black Country Pressings Ltd, 2 Alma Works, Darlaston Road, Wednesbury, West Midlands, WS10 7TG Tel: 0121-568 8787 Fax: 0121-568 8788

Samuel Groves & Co. Ltd, Norton Street, Birmingham, B18 5RQ Tel: 0121-554 2001 Fax: 0121-523 2924 E-mail: sales@samuelgroves.co.uk

PRESTRESSED CONCRETE PRODUCTS

Anderton Concrete Products Ltd, Anderton Wharf, Soot Hill, Anderton, Northwich, Cheshire, CW9 6AA Tel: (01606) 79436 Fax: (01606) 871590 E-mail: sales@andertonconcrete.co.uk

Beta, 1 Letts Builder Yard, Dock Road, Worksop, Nottinghamshire, S80 1RX Tel: (01909) 489988

Gee-Co (Precast) Ltd, Upbrooksmill, Taylor Street, Clitheroe, Lancashire, BB7 1NL Tel: (01200) 427960 Fax: (01200) 426719 E-mail: geeco@supernet.com

Hanson Ltd, Cotes Park Industrial Estate, Birchwood Way, Somercotes, Alfreton, Derbyshire, DE55 4NH Tel: (01773) 602432 Fax: (01773) 603134

Macrete Ireland Ltd, 50 Creagh Road, Toomebridge, Antrim, BT41 3SE Tel: (028) 7965 0471 Fax: (028) 7965 0084 E-mail: info@macrete.com

Milbank Industries Ltd, Airfield, Earls Colne, Colchester, CO6 2NS Tel: (01787) 223931 Fax: (01787) 220535 E-mail: estimating@milbank.co.uk

Robeslee Concrete Co. Ltd, 15 Hope Street, Glasgow, G2 6AB Tel: 0141-248 4841 Fax: 0141-248 4659 E-mail: sales@robeslee.co.uk

Stressline Ltd, Lunds Field Quarry, Carnforth, Lancashire, LA5 9NB Tel: (01524) 732204 Fax: (01524) 735831 E-mail: mail@stressline.ltd.uk

Stressline Ltd, Station Road, Stoney Stanton, Leicester, LE9 4LX Tel: (01455) 272457 Fax: (01455) 274564 E-mail: info@stressline.ltd.uk

Supreme Concrete Ltd, Coppingford Hall, Coppingford Road, Sawtry, Huntingdon, Cambridgeshire, PE28 5GP Tel: (01487) 833300 Fax: (01487) 833305 E-mail: sales@supremeconcrete.co.uk

Supreme Concrete Ltd, Crown Quay Lane, Sittingbourne, Kent, ME10 3SL Tel: (01795) 475255 Fax: (01795) 433599 E-mail: enquiries@bourncrete.co.uk

Tarmac Precast Concrete Ltd, Barholm Road, Tallington, Stamford, Lincolnshire, PE9 4RL Tel: (01778) 381000 Fax: (01778) 348041 E-mail: tall@tarmac.co.uk

PRESTRESSING JACKS

Connextions Logistics, Link House, Bute Street, Stoke-on-Trent, ST4 3PR Tel: (01782) 339559 Fax: (01782) 339561

PRICE MARKING LABELS

▶ Bowpak Ltd, 191 Station Road, Shotts, Lanarkshire, ML7 4BA Tel: (01501) 825185 E-mail: bowpak@aol.com

PRICE TICKET HOLDERS

Turton Retail Systems, 18 Hillside Avenue, Bromley Cross, Bolton, BL7 9NG Tel: (01204) 307589 Fax: (01204) 307589 E-mail: sales@turtonretail.co.uk

PRINT DRYING EQUIPMENT

G E W Ec Ltd, Kings Mill Lane, South Nutfield, Redhill, RH1 5NB Tel: (01737) 824500 Fax: (01737) 823822 E-mail: sales@gewuv.com

PRINT FINISHING, LAMINATING PAPER TO BOARD

▶ Minford Ltd, Strawberry Lane, Willenhall, West Midlands, WV13 3RS Tel: (01902) 603030 Fax: (01902) 603069 E-mail: sales@minford.co.uk

PRINT FINISHING, SHRINK WRAPPING

▶ Minford Ltd, Strawberry Lane, Willenhall, West Midlands, WV13 3RS Tel: (01902) 603030 Fax: (01902) 603069 E-mail: sales@minford.co.uk

PRINT FINISHING, VARNISHING

Cellogias Speciality Products, Unit 12C, Exeter Way, Theale Commercial Park, Theale, Reading, RG7 4AW Tel: 0118-930 3656 Fax: 0118-932 3256 E-mail: andy.kirbycelloglas@alcan.co.uk

PRINT MANAGEMENT SERVICES

▶ 3TYUK (uk), 7 The Brent, Dartford, DA1 1YD Tel: (01322) 311899 E-mail: makinfe@yahoo.com

A Pinder Ltd, 16 Moore Street, Sheffield, S3 7US Tel: 0114-272 7574 Fax: 0114-275 1071 E-mail: sales@pindersofsheffield.co.uk

Adare Carwin, Unit B Wellington Gate, Silverthorne Way, Waterlooville, Hampshire, PO7 7XY Tel: (023) 9224 5000 Fax: (023) 9224 5060 E-mail: info@adare.com

▶ B D L Litho Ltd, 3 Bat & Ball Enterprise Centre, Bat & Ball Road, Sevenoaks, Kent, TN14 5LJ Tel: (01732) 464111 Fax: (01732) 462020

Blackburns Of Bolton, Unit H, Lecturers Close, Bolton, BL3 6DG Tel: (01204) 532121 Fax: (01204) 396670 E-mail: sales@blackburns.co.uk

▶ Buzz Connections, Unit 19 Govan Workspace, Harmony Row, Glasgow, G51 3BA Tel: 0141-440 2600 Fax: 0141-445 3217 E-mail: info@buzzconnections.co.uk

Cardiff Trade Print & Design Ltd, 6 Coed Glas Road, Llanishen, Cardiff, CF14 5EN Tel: (029) 2075 0561 Fax: (029) 2076 1448

▶ Cardworks Ltd, 23-25 Great Hollands Square, Bracknell, Berkshire, RG12 8UX Tel: (01344) 450333 Fax: (01344) 483295 E-mail: info@cardworks.co.uk

▶ CBF, Holly Farm Business Park, Honiley, Kenilworth, Warwickshire, CV8 1NP Tel: (01926) 484060 Fax: (01926) 486340

Commercial Facilities & Logistics, 89 Park Road, Didcot, Oxfordshire, OX11 8QT Tel: (01235) 511054 Fax: (01235) 511056 E-mail: mhall@cfl-ltd.co.uk

▶ Dacom (UK) Ltd, 115A Brunswick Park Road, London, N11 1EA Tel: (020) 8361 6560

Fair Business Forms Ltd, 5 Kiln Lane, Horley, Surrey, RH6 8JG Tel: (01293) 432175 Fax: (01293) 432176 E-mail: sales@fbfltd.co.uk

▶ H H Associates Ltd, City House, Sutton Park Road, Sutton, Surrey, SM1 2AE Tel: (020) 8770 7300 Fax: (020) 8770 9970

▶ Mosaic Print Management Ltd, Yealmpton, Plymouth, PL8 2NN Tel: (01752) 881508

Paperhat Imaging Ltd, 44a Curlew Street, London, SE1 2ND Tel: (020) 7089 0360 Fax: (020) 7407 5880 E-mail: tim@paperhat.co.uk

▶ Pavilion Print Management Ltd, Old Run Road, Leeds, LS10 2AA Tel: 0113 201 6300 E-mail: enquiries@paviliongroup.co.uk

PCF Secure Document Systems, Oak House, Langstone Business Park, Langstone Park, Langstone, Newport, Monmouthshire, NP18 2LH Tel: (01633) 415570 Fax: (01633) 415599 E-mail: info@pcf.co.uk

Phoenix Colour plc, 11 Knighton Fields Road West, Leicester, LE2 6LH Tel: 0116-283 5817 Fax: 0116-244 0061 E-mail: admin@phoenix-photo.co.uk

▶ Print Save Ltd, 7 Hawthorn Vale, Chapel Allerton, Leeds, LS7 4PJ Tel: 0113-293 9776

▶ Topform Visual Communication Ltd, 2 The Courtyard, Lamdin Road, Bury St. Edmunds, Suffolk, IP32 6NU Tel: (01284) 747399 Fax: (01284) 747401 E-mail: sales@topformonline.co.uk

Vernon Computer Forms, 5 Spring Mill Business Centre, Avening Road, Nailsworth, Stroud, Gloucestershire, GL6 0BS Tel: (01453) 834466 Fax: (01453) 834554 E-mail: sales@vernoncf.co.uk

Williams Lea UK Ltd, Foxbridge Way, Normanton Industrial Estate, Normanton, West Yorkshire, WF6 1TN Tel: (01924) 890000 Fax: (01924) 245444 E-mail: info@williamslea.com

▶ Willsons Printers (Newark) Ltd, Highlander House, Cross Street, Newark, Nottinghamshire, NG24 1PP Tel: (01636) 702334 Fax: (01636) 701396 E-mail: andy@willsons.com

PRINTED BADGES

Diametric Technical Manufacturing Ltd, 26-28 Manners View, Newport, Isle of Wight, PO30 5FA Tel: (01983) 826611 Fax: (01983) 826622 E-mail: tad.james@diemetric-manufacturing.co.uk

Fabrics Motifs & Prints Ltd, 18 Lancaster Road, Hinckley, Leicestershire, LE10 0AW Tel: (01455) 637710 Fax: (01455) 633503 E-mail: enquiries@fabrics.com

PRINTED BALLOONS

Balloons Galore, 61 Leedham Avenue, Tamworth, Staffordshire, B77 3LZ Tel: (01827) 62995

PRINTED CARTONS, *See Cartons etc*

PRINTED CIRCUIT ACCESSORIES

A G F Circuits, Unit 2, Comet Way, Southend-on-Sea, SS2 6GD Tel: (01702) 420153

PRINTED CIRCUIT ASSEMBLY SERVICES

A C W Technology Ltd, Comines Way, Hedge End, Southampton, SO30 4XX Tel: (023) 8048 6000 Fax: (023) 8048 6001 E-mail: welcome@acw.co.uk

Allgood Technology, Unit 1 Horton Court, Hortonwood 50, Telford, Shropshire, TF1 7GY Tel: (01952) 677145 Fax: (01952) 677145 E-mail: info@allgoodsmt.com

Altros Engineering Ltd, Birch House Commercial Square, Leigh Street, High Wycombe, Buckinghamshire, HP11 2QT Tel: (01494) 443082 Fax: (01494) 436186 E-mail: altros_uk@hotmail.com

Argus Electronics, Frenches, Chew Valley Road, Greenfield, Oldham, OL3 7AE Tel: (01457) 876951 Fax: (01457) 876951

Axis Electronics, Manton Lane, Bedford, MK41 7NY Tel: (01234) 342932 Fax: (01234) 364941 E-mail: sales@axis-electronics.com

B N Precision Assemblies, Unit 10, Portsmouth Enterprise Centre, Quartremaine Road, Portsmouth, PO3 5QT Tel: (023) 9266 6444 Fax: (023) 9266 6444

Beta Electronics, Dukesway, Teesside Industrial Estate, Stockton-on-Tees, Cleveland, TS17 9LT Tel: (01642) 765321 Fax: (01642) 760155 E-mail: jks@betaelectronics.co.uk

Blizard Electronic Assembly Ltd, 8 Greenlea Park, Prince Georges Road, London, SW19 2JD Tel: (020) 8685 9460 Fax: (020) 8840 8688

Geoff Bullen Electronics, Unit 1-2 Woods Way, Goring-by-Sea, Worthing, West Sussex, BN12 4QY Tel: (01903) 244500 Fax: (01903) 700715 E-mail: sales@gbelectronics.com

C D O Electronics Ltd, 17 Bowater Road, Westminster Industrial Estate, London, SE18 5TF Tel: (020) 8855 9508 Fax: (020) 8316 1892 E-mail: jim@cdo-electronics.com

Challenger Solutions Ltd, Unit 85 Haltwhistle Road, South Woodham Ferrers, Chelmsford, CM3 5ZA Tel: (01245) 325252 Fax: (01245) 325301 E-mail: jon@challengersolutions.com

Chemigraphic Ltd, 2 Fleming Centre, Fleming Way, Crawley, West Sussex, RH10 9NF Tel: (01293) 543517 Fax: (01293) 552859 E-mail: sales@chemigraphic.co.uk

▶ Cleveland Circuits Ltd, Skelton Industrial Estate, Skelton-in-Cleveland, Saltburn-by-the-Sea, Cleveland, TS12 2LQ Tel: (01287) 651991 Fax: (01287) 652898 E-mail: sales@pcb.co.uk

Comtrol Europe, Unit 2, Stapleshurst Business Park, Howes Lane, Bicester, Oxfordshire, OX25 3QU Tel: (01869) 352740 Fax: (01869) 323211 E-mail: info@comtrol.co.uk

Cooper Electronics, Tenlons Road, Nuneaton, Warwickshire, CV10 7HT Tel: (024) 7632 0585 Fax: (024) 7632 0564 E-mail: enquiries@cooper-electronics.com

Custom Keyboards Electronics Ltd, Unit 11, Claylands Road, Claylands Park, Bishops Waltham, Southampton, SO32 1BH Tel: (01489) 891851 Fax: (01489) 893708 E-mail: alancoppini@custom-keyboards.co.uk

D & K Wiring Services Ltd, Unit 1 Urban Hive, Sundon Park Road, Luton, LU3 3QU Tel: (01582) 492033 Fax: (01582) 565944 E-mail: sales@dkwiring.co.uk

David Maddox Ltd, 53-55 Gatwick Road, Crawley, West Sussex, RH10 9RD Tel: (01293) 452830 Fax: (01293) 452830 E-mail: david.maddox@virgin.net

E F S Manufacturing, 1 Newmarket Road, Stow-cum-Quy, Cambridge, CB5 9AQ Tel: (01223) 813848 Fax: (01223) 813848

Electro Avionics, D Burnham Road, Dartford, DA1 5BN Tel: (01322) 288698 Fax: (01322) 277520 E-mail: colin@electroavionics.co.uk

G A Assembly Ltd, Alma Works, Coke Hill, Rotherham, South Yorkshire, S60 2HX Tel: (01709) 839911 Fax: (01709) 838373 E-mail: sales@gaa-ltd.co.uk

Hallmark Electronics Ltd, Hallmark House Loomer Road Industrial Estate, Loomer Road, Newcastle, Staffordshire, ST5 7LA Tel: (01782) 562255 Fax: (01782) 565684 E-mail: info@hallmarkelectronics.com

Heart Electronics Ltd, 2 King Edward Road, Nuneaton, Warwickshire, CV11 4BB Tel: (024) 7635 3615 Fax: (024) 7635 3616 E-mail: info@heartelectronics.com

Industrial Electronic Wiring, 10 Birch, Kembrey Park, Swindon, SN2 8UU Tel: (01793) 694033 Fax: (01793) 496295 E-mail: info@iew.co.uk

Intercole Sub-Contract Services Ltd, 3 Avenger Close, Chandlers Ford, Eastleigh, Hampshire, SO53 4YU Tel: (023) 8025 4727 Fax: (023) 8025 1090 E-mail: subcon@intercole.co.uk

J J Electronics Ltd, 3a Telmere Industrial Estate, Albert Road, Luton, LU1 3QF Tel: (01582) 391156 Fax: (01582) 391896 E-mail: sales@jjelectronics.net

Lema Electronics, 1 Talisman Business Centre, Duncan Road, Park Gate, Southampton, SO31 7GA Tel: (01489) 572230 Fax: (01489) 578741 E-mail: sales@lemaelectronics.co.uk

M J P Electronics Ltd, Unit 1, Gore Cross Business Park, Corbin Way, Bradpole, Bridport, Dorset, DT6 3UX Tel: (01308) 425800 Fax: (01308) 455770 E-mail: murry@mjpelectronics.com

Magna Electronics Ltd, 9 Harrow Road, Hereford, HR4 0EH Tel: (01432) 353434 Fax: (01432) 278749 E-mail: mark@magna-electronics.co.uk

Mason & Morton (Electronics) Ltd, 24 Ullswater Crescent, Ullswater Business Park, Coulsdon, Surrey, CR5 2HR Tel: (020) 8410 4610 Fax: (020) 8660 5469

Mode Lighting UK Ltd, Chelsing House, Mead Lane, Hertford, SG13 7AW Tel: (01992) 554566 Fax: (01992) 553644 E-mail: sales@modecontracts.com

Mowden Controls Ltd, Mount View, Standard Way Industrial Estate, Northallerton, North Yorkshire, DL6 2YD Tel: (01609) 779535 Fax: (01609) 779539 E-mail: enquiries@mowden.co.uk

MSR Electronics Ltd, Fernhill Court, Balsall Street, Balsall Common, Coventry, CV7 7FR Tel: (01676) 532468 Fax: (01676) 534247 E-mail: sales@msravionics.com

Nortec Production Ltd, 11 Fourways, Atherstone, Warwickshire, CV9 1LG Tel: (01827) 717896 Fax: (01827) 717842 E-mail: robin.clements@nortec-prod.demon.co.uk

P R S Invistech, The Technology Centre, Easting Close, Worthing, West Sussex, BN14 8HQ Tel: (01903) 217337 Fax: (01903) 217713 E-mail: sales@prsl.co.uk

Parlex Europe Ltd, Taylor Road, Newport, Isle of Wight, PO30 5LG Tel: (01983) 526535 Fax: (01983) 524964 E-mail: sales@uk.parlex.com

Partnertech Poole Ltd, Turnkey House, 31 Benson Road, Nuffield Industrial Estate, Poole, Dorset, BH17 0RY Tel: (01202) 674333 Fax: (01202) 678028 E-mail: info@hansatech.co.uk

Pavecost Manufacturing Ltd, Lilleshall Street, Newport, Gwent, NP19 0FB Tel: (01633) 263986 Fax: (01633) 266939 E-mail: dateelectronicsupp@tiscali.co.uk

Phase One Electronics, Orion Court, 2 Rodney Road, Southsea, Hampshire, PO4 8SZ Tel: (023) 9286 2394 Fax: (023) 9286 2396 E-mail: tonys@t1e.uk.com

Powerlec Products Ltd, Clapgate Farm Woodford Lane, Wombourne, Wolverhampton, WV5 8DS Tel: (01902) 897846 Fax: (01902) 897846

Priheath Ltd, Unit 7 Shire Hill, Saffron Walden, Essex, CB11 3AQ Tel: (01799) 525982 Fax: (01799) 521686 E-mail: priheath@cambridgerapid.co.uk

Quality Precision Electronics Ltd, 15 Faraday Road, Glenrothes, Fife, KY6 2RU Tel: (01592) 771455 Fax: (01592) 772944 E-mail: admin@qpe.co.uk

Quasson Ltd, Quasson House, Rennie Gate, Andover, Hampshire, SP10 3TU Tel: (01264) 332132 Fax: (01264) 334470 E-mail: sales@quasson.co.uk

Quick Circuits Ltd, 1 Loverock Road, Reading, RG30 1DZ Tel: 0118-950 8921 Fax: 0118-956 8237 E-mail: sales@quick-circuits.com

▶ Ramar Electronics Services Ltd, Masons Road, Stratford-upon-Avon, Warwickshire, CV37 9NF Tel: (01789) 204879 Fax: (01789) 299727 E-mail: info@ramarpcb.co.uk

S K Electronics Ltd, Regent Street, Oldham, OL1 3TZ Tel: 0161-620 5414 Fax: 0161-627 3237 E-mail: sales@skelectronics.co.uk

Salford Electronic Systems Ltd, 48 Glastonbury Drive, Poynton, Stockport, Cheshire, SK12 1EN Tel: (01625) 877939 E-mail: roy.lowey@btinternet.com

Santronics Printed Circuit Services, Unit 8e New Yard, Clay Flatts Industrial Estate, Workington, Cumbria, CA14 3YE Tel: (01900) 870961 Fax: (01900) 870961 E-mail: sanmaral@tiscali.co.uk

Satel Electronics, North East Suffolk Business Centre, Pinbush Road, Kessingland, Lowestoft, Suffolk, NR33 7NQ Tel: (01502) 513216 Fax: (01502) 513216 E-mail: satelelectronics@btclick.com

Saturn Engineering Ltd, 68 Wilbury Way, Hitchin, Hertfordshire, SG4 0TP Tel: (01462) 458511 Fax: (01462) 458515 E-mail: saturneng@hotmail.com

Selectron Ltd, 1 Davis Way, Fareham, Hampshire, PO14 1JF Tel: (01329) 230525 Fax: (01329) 822759 E-mail: sales@solectron-ltd.co.uk

Syntech Europe Ltd, 351 Wigan Road, Bolton, BL3 5QU Tel: (01204) 659899 Fax: (01204) 659941 E-mail: andrew@syntech-europe.com

Tabelek (Control Systems) Ltd, Jubilee Road, Waterlooville, Hampshire, PO7 7RE Tel: (023) 9261 0016 Fax: 023 9261 0016

Technic Electric Ltd, Unit 5 Lulworth Business Centre, Nutwood Way, Totton, Southampton, SO40 3WW Tel: (023) 8066 7486 Fax: (023) 8066 3830 E-mail: sales@technic.co.uk

Technology Services, W2 Warrington Business Park, Long Lane, Warrington, WA2 8TX Tel: (01925) 444621 Fax: (01925) 492221

Tenkay Electronics Ltd, Lancing Business Park, Marlborough Road, Lancing, West Sussex, BN15 8TN Tel: (01903) 855455 Fax: (01903) 761942 E-mail: sue.brown@tenkay.co.uk

Trowtronics UK Ltd, Unit 41 South Hampshire Industrial Park, Totton, Southampton, SO40 3SA Tel: (023) 8066 0055 Fax: (023) 8066 0012 E-mail: trowtronics.@aol.conf.au

Walters Group, Walters House, 12 Merlin Centre, Lancaster Road, High Wycombe, Buckinghamshire, HP12 3TB Tel: (01494) 453700 Fax: (01494) 461107 E-mail: sales@waltersmicro.co.uk

Wildtrax Electronics Ltd, Unit 11A Southcourt Road, Worthing, West Sussex, BN14 7DF Tel: 0845 5314279 Fax: (01903) 212003 E-mail: howard@wildtrax.com

Zeta Electronic Systems, Unit 4 Pandy Industrial Estate, Plas Acton Road, Wrexham, Clwyd, LL11 2UD Tel: (01978) 312427 Fax: (01978) 314062E-mail: enquiries@zeta-electronic.com

PRINTED CIRCUIT BACKPANELS

Printec Ltd, 8 Petworth Industrial Estate, Petworth, West Sussex, GU28 9NR Tel: (01798) 343488 Fax: (01798) 344487 E-mail: sales@printec.co.uk

PRINTED CIRCUIT BOARD (PCB) ASSEMBLIES

Alpha Design, 1 Didcot Road, Nuffield Industrial Estate, Poole, Dorset, BH17 0GD Tel: (01202) 684248 Fax: (01202) 666190 E-mail: info@alphadesign-poole.co.uk

Martin Woolman Ltd, Unit 12 Martinfield Business Centre, Martinfield, Welwyn Garden City, Hertfordshire, AL7 1HG Tel: (01707) 373181 Fax: (01707) 373174 E-mail: sales@martinwoolman.co.uk

▶ Printed Wiring Technologies Ltd, 7-8 Alders Court, Watchmead, Welwyn Garden City, Hertfordshire, AL7 1LT Tel: (01707) 338871 Fax: (01707) 372622 E-mail: sales@pwtpcbs.com

PRINTED CIRCUIT BOARD (PCB) ASSEMBLY

Asbury Associates, 40 Croft Holm, Moreton-in-Marsh, Glos, GL56 0JH Tel: (01608) 652214 Fax: (01608) 652214

Danor Circuits, 82 Cannock Street, Leicester, LE4 9HR Tel: 0116-274 0312 Fax: 0116-274 0879 E-mail: sales@danorcircuits.com

DK Assemblies Ltd, Unit 2 Corbin Way, Gorecross Business Park, Bridport, Dorset, DT6 3UX Tel: (01308) 424095 Fax: (01308) 421490 E-mail: info@dkassemblies.com

Electrosembly Co., 35-37 Haviland Road, Ferndown Industrial Estate, Wimborne, Dorset, BH21 7SA Tel: (01202) 893392 Fax: (01202) 893378

Industrial Electronic Wiring, 10 Birch, Kembrey Park, Swindon, SN2 8UU Tel: (01793) 694033 Fax: (01793) 496295 E-mail: info@iew.co.uk

Kays Electronics Ltd, 85 Cavendish Street, Ipswich, IP3 8AX Tel: (01473) 214040 Fax: (01473) 214060 E-mail: enquiries@kayselectronics.com

N E M Co. Ltd, Stevenage Business Park, Wedgewood Way, Stevenage, Hertfordshire, SG1 4SX Tel: (01438) 346600 Fax: (01438) 346632 E-mail: sales@nemco.co.uk

▶ Orchard Electronic, Unit 6 Apex Way, Hailsham, East Sussex, BN27 3WA Tel: (01323) 844422 Fax: (01323) 844422 E-mail: sales@orchardelectronic.co.uk

PRINTED CIRCUIT BOARD (PCB) ASSEMBLY – *continued*

Powerwise Consultant Engineering, Unit 4 Randswood Farm, The Common, West Wratting, Cambridge, CB21 5LR Tel: (01223) 291250 Fax: (01223) 291260 E-mail: powerwise@powerwise.co.uk

Siemens Communications, Technology Drive, Beeston, Nottingham, NG9 1LA Tel: 0115-943 0300 Fax: 0115-925 9610 E-mail: firstname.surname@siemens.com

TRI Technology Ltd, 15 Cowlairs, Southglade Business Park, Hucknall Road, Nottingham, NG5 9RA Tel: 0115-977 0707 Fax: 0115-977 0606 E-mail: enquiries@tritechnology.co.uk

▶ UK Circuits & Electronic Solutions Ltd, Stockfield Road, Chadderton, Oldham, OL9 9LG Tel: 0161-627 4050 Fax: 0161-633 4077 E-mail: sales@ukcircuits.co.uk

PRINTED CIRCUIT BOARD (PCB) ASSEMBLY EQUIPMENT MANUFRS

▶ Active-PCB Solutions Ltd, Unit 4, Acre Road, Reading, RG2 0SU Tel: 0118-931 0292 Fax: 0118-931 2975 E-mail: sales@active-pcb.com

Astro Technologies Ltd, 26 Brunel Way, Segansworth East, Fareham, Hampshire, PO15 5SD Tel: (01489) 555300 Fax: (01489) 555302 E-mail: sales@astrotec.co.uk

Auwell Electronics Ltd, Units 16-19, Oldends Industrial Estate, Oldends, Stonehouse, Gloucestershire, GL10 3RQ Tel: (01453) 791111 Fax: (01453) 791313 E-mail: enquiries@auwell.co.uk

Datum Dynamics, Thistle Business Park South, Craigens Road, Cumnock, Ayrshire, KA18 3AL Tel: (01290) 426200 Fax: (01290) 426212 E-mail: beth@globaldatum.com

Fortex P C Drills Ltd, 17 Fleetwood Road, Leicester, LE2 1YA Tel: 0116-270 8937 Fax: 0116-270 0532

G A Assembly Ltd, Alma Works, Coke Hill, Rotherham, South Yorkshire, S60 2HX Tel: (01709) 839911 Fax: (01709) 838373 E-mail: sales@gaa-ltd.co.uk

Hawk Electronics Ltd, Malt Street, Accrington, Lancashire, BB5 1DR Tel: (01254) 389515 Fax: (01254) 389505 E-mail: sales@hawkelectronics.co.uk

S S U Equipment Ltd, Friars Mount, Friars, Jedburgh, Roxburghshire, TD8 6BN Tel: (01835) 862481 Fax: (01835) 863712 E-mail: davesharman@ssuequipment.co.uk

Walkbury Electronics Ltd, 30 The Metro Centre, Peterborough, PE2 7UH Tel: (01733) 404830 Fax: (01733) 404839 E-mail: sales@walkbury.co.uk

PRINTED CIRCUIT BOARD (PCB) BASED INSTRUMENTATION

G S Designs, Hardwick Close, Stevenage, Hertfordshire, SG2 8UF Tel: (01438) 813332 Fax: (01438) 812215 E-mail: gary@gsdesign.co.uk

PRINTED CIRCUIT BOARD (PCB) COMPUTER AIDED DESIGN (CAD)

Dayford Designs Ltd, The Chaple, Brimscombe Port, Brimscombe, Stroud, Gloucestershire, GL5 2QG Tel: (01453) 732820 Fax: (01453) 732830 E-mail: accounts@dayford.co.uk

▶ Design Analysis Solutions, Bramling Cross Barns, Beauchamp Lane, Worcester, WR2 4UQ Tel: (01905) 830608 Fax: (0870) 7062737 E-mail: info@das4pcbs.co.uk

▶ Orchard Electronic, Unit 6 Apex Way, Hailsham, East Sussex, BN27 3WA Tel: (01323) 844422 Fax: (01323) 844422 E-mail: sales@orchardelectronic.co.uk

Scan & Design, 14 The Warren, Burgess Hill, West Sussex, RH15 0DZ Tel: (01444) 254750 Fax: (01444) 254750 E-mail: scan.design@fsbdial.co.uk

PRINTED CIRCUIT BOARD (PCB) DESIGN SERVICES

▶ A2e Ltd, Adaptive House, Quarrywood Court, Livingston, West Lothian, EH54 6AX Tel: (01506) 463393 Fax: (01506) 461257

▶ Actinic PCB Design, 67 Elm Grove, Brighton, BN2 3ET Tel: (01273) 705525 E-mail: mail@actinicpcb.com

Cadlay Designs Ltd, Sleight House, Sleight Lane, Corfe Mullem, Wimborne, Dorset, BH21 3HL Tel: (01202) 693233 Fax: (01202) 658747 E-mail: sales@cadlay.co.uk

Daletech Electronics Ltd, Regency House, Valley Road, Pudsey, West Yorkshire, LS28 9EN Tel: 0113-239 4220 Fax: 0113-255 3583 E-mail: sales@daletech.co.uk

Designer Systems, 15 Andrew Place, Truro, Cornwall, TR1 3HZ Tel: (01872) 223306 Fax: (01872) 223306 E-mail: sales@designersystems.co.uk

Edicon Ltd, 39 Bucknalls Drive, Bricket Wood, St. Albans, Hertfordshire, AL2 3XJ Tel: (020) 7692 7050 E-mail: info@edicon.co.uk

Gray PCB Designs, 62 Warren Road, St. Ives, Cambridgeshire, PE27 5NW Tel: (01480) 496235 Fax: (01480) 496235 E-mail: graham@gray-pcb-designs.demon.co.uk

▶ High Hill Electronics, 127 High Hill Road, New Mils, High Peak, Derbyshire, SK22 4HQ Tel: 0161 654 9842 E-mail: sales@highhill.co.uk

▶ Independent Circuit Design, 52 North Street, Biddenden, Ashford, Kent, TN27 8AS Tel: (01580) 292239 Fax: (0870) 7059061 E-mail: ian@icdnet.co.uk

▶ Lamerholn Electronics Ltd, Pixmore Centre, Pixmore Avenue, Letchworth Garden City, Hertfordshire, SG6 1JG Tel: (01462) 481396 Fax: (01462) 473942 E-mail: web@lamerholm.com

▶ Orchard Electronic, Unit 6 Apex Way, Hailsham, East Sussex, BN27 3WA Tel: (01323) 844422 Fax: (01323) 844422 E-mail: sales@orchardelectronic.co.uk

PRINTED CIRCUIT BOARD (PCB) DESIGN SOFTWARE

Cadence Design Systems Ltd, Bagshot Road, Bracknell, Berkshire, RG12 0PH Tel: (01344) 360333 Fax: (01344) 869647

▶ Dunne Roberts, Unit 3 Freemantle Business Centre, 152 Millbrook Road East, Southampton, SO15 1JR Tel: (023) 8082 9200 Fax: (023) 8082 9201 E-mail: contactus@dunneroberts.co.uk

G S Designs, Hardwick Close, Stevenage, Hertfordshire, SG2 8UF Tel: (01438) 813332 Fax: (01438) 812215 E-mail: gary@gsdesign.co.uk

Seetrax Ltd, Old Buriton Line Works, Kiln La, Buriton, Petersfield, Hants, GU31 5SJ Tel: (01730) 260062 Fax: (01730) 267273 E-mail: sales@seetrax.com

PRINTED CIRCUIT BOARD (PCB) DEVELOPMENT

▶ Design Analysis Solutions, Bramling Cross Barns, Beauchamp Lane, Worcester, WR2 4UQ Tel: (01905) 830608 Fax: (0870) 7062737 E-mail: info@das4pcbs.co.uk

Scan & Design, 14 The Warren, Burgess Hill, West Sussex, RH15 0DZ Tel: (01444) 254750 Fax: (01444) 254750 E-mail: scan.design@fsbdial.co.uk

PRINTED CIRCUIT BOARD (PCB) DRILL BITS

Cirbo Ltd, 16 Normandy Way, Bodmin, Cornwall, PL31 1EX Tel: (01208) 74174 Fax: (01208) 76801

Fortex P C Drills Ltd, 17 Fleetwood Road, Leicester, LE2 1YA Tel: 0116-270 8937 Fax: 0116-270 0532

PRINTED CIRCUIT BOARD (PCB) DRILL REGRINDING SERVICES

A C S Industries Ltd, Huffwood Trading Estate, Billingshurst, West Sussex, RH14 9UR Tel: (01403) 784225 Fax: (01403) 784046 E-mail: frontend@acsind.co.uk

PRINTED CIRCUIT BOARD (PCB) DRILLING

▶ Cleveland Circuits Ltd, Skelton Industrial Estate, Skelton-in-Cleveland, Saltburn-by-the-Sea, Cleveland, TS12 2LQ Tel: (01287) 651991 Fax: (01287) 652898 E-mail: sales@pcb.co.uk

PRINTED CIRCUIT BOARD (PCB) EQUIPMENT

▶ Peplertech Ltd, The Vicarage, Birtles Lane, Over Alderley, Macclesfield, Cheshire, SK10 4RX Tel: (01625) 861443 Fax: (01625) 861445 E-mail: info@peplertech.co.uk

PRINTED CIRCUIT BOARD (PCB) LAYOUT SERVICES

Gray PCB Designs, 62 Warren Road, St. Ives, Cambridgeshire, PE27 5NW Tel: (01480) 496235 Fax: (01480) 496235 E-mail: graham@gray-pcb-designs.demon.co.uk

PRINTED CIRCUIT BOARD (PCB) MANUFACTURING

Danor Circuits, 82 Cannock Street, Leicester, LE4 9HR Tel: 0116-274 0312 Fax: 0116-274 0879 E-mail: sales@danorcircuits.com

One Way Circuits, Station Road, Lenwade, Norwich, NR9 5LY Tel: (01603) 875100 Fax: (0870) 7517518 E-mail: sales@onewaypcb.com

▶ Printed Wiring Technologies Ltd, 7-8 Alders Court, Watchmead, Welwyn Garden City, Hertfordshire, AL7 1LT Tel: (01707) 338871 Fax: (01707) 372622 E-mail: sales@pwtpcbs.com

Product Support Electronics Ltd, Unit 1/2, Letts Road, Far Cotton, Northampton, NN4 8HQ Tel: (01604) 764520 Fax: (01604) 706834 E-mail: ppse@aol.com

PRINTED CIRCUIT BOARD (PCB) MANUFACTURING CHEMICALS

B L T Circuit Services Ltd, Airfield Industrial Estate, Eye, Suffolk, IP23 7HN Tel: (01379) 870870 Fax: (01379) 870970 E-mail: sales@blt.keme.co.uk

Electra Holdings Ltd, Roughway Mill, Tonbridge, Kent, TN11 9SG Tel: (01732) 811118 Fax: (01732) 811119 E-mail: info@electrapolymers.com

PRINTED CIRCUIT BOARD (PCB) MANUFACTURING EQUIPMENT

▶ Peplertech Ltd, The Vicarage, Birtles Lane, Over Alderley, Macclesfield, Cheshire, SK10 4RX Tel: (01625) 861443 Fax: (01625) 861445 E-mail: info@peplertech.co.uk

PRINTED CIRCUIT BOARD (PCB) PRODUCTION CONVEYOR SYSTEMS

Astro Technologies Ltd, 26 Brunel Way, Segansworth East, Fareham, Hampshire, PO15 5SD Tel: (01489) 555300 Fax: (01489) 555302 E-mail: sales@astrotec.co.uk

Cooper Rason Ltd, 30 Victoria Street, Irthlingborough, Wellingborough, Northamptonshire, NN9 5RG Tel: (01933) 650950 Fax: (01933) 652821 E-mail: sales@cooper-rason.co.uk

PRINTED CIRCUIT BOARD (PCB) PROTOTYPES TO SPECIFICATION

Dayford Designs Ltd, The Chaple, Brimscombe Port, Brimscombe, Stroud, Gloucestershire, GL5 2QG Tel: (01453) 732820 Fax: (01453) 732830 E-mail: accounts@dayford.co.uk

PRINTED CIRCUIT BOARD (PCB) REPAIR/CALIBRATION/ MODIFICATION/ RE-ENGINEERING SERVICES

Bond Instrumentation & Process Control Ltd, Woodrope Building, Woodrolfe Road, Tollesbury, Essex, CM9 8SE Tel: (01621) 862140 Fax: (01621) 862141 E-mail: bond@bond.ipc.com

▶ Calco Instruments, 2 Leonard Street, Beverley Road, Hull, HU3 1SA Tel: (01482) 339300 Fax: (01482) 339301 E-mail: enquiries@calco-instruments.com

Goodies Enterprise Ltd, Mile Road, Bedford, MK42 9TN Tel: (01234) 364104 Fax: (09069) 480201 E-mail: enquiries@goodiesenterprises.com

Industrial Electronic Control By Design, Unit F5 Bersham Enterprise Centre, Colliery Road, Rhostyllen, Wrexham, Clwyd, LL14 4EG Tel: (01978) 368099 Fax: (01978) 354333 E-mail: sales@iecd.co.uk

Jabil Circuit Ltd, Oakbank Park Drive, Mid Calder, Livingston, West Lothian, EH53 0TJ Tel: (01506) 432266 Fax: (01506) 442000

Owen Coyle Anodising, 144 Blyth Road, Hayes, Middlesex, UB3 1BY Tel: (020) 8573 0184 Fax: (020) 8848 1170 E-mail: sales@owencoyle-anodising.co.uk

PRINTED CIRCUIT BOARD (PCB) SCRAP/WASTE RECYCLING/ DISPOSAL/RECOVERY CONTRACTORS/MERCHANTS/ PROCESSORS OR SERVICES

▶ Computer Salvage Specialist Ltd, 5 Abex Road, Newbury, Berkshire, RG14 5EY Tel: (01635) 552666 Fax: (01635) 582990 E-mail: enquiries@computersalvagespecialists.com

J M Circuits Ltd, Unit 4 Kingsley, Bordon, Hampshire, GU35 9LY Tel: (01420) 487339 Fax: (01420) 487339 E-mail: info@jmcircuits.freeserve.co.uk

P R S Invistech, The Technology Centre, Easting Close, Worthing, West Sussex, BN14 8HQ Tel: (01903) 217337 Fax: (01903) 217713 E-mail: sales@prsl.co.uk

PRINTED CIRCUIT BOARD (PCB) SERVICES, *See also headings for particular services*

Alda Production Services Ltd, 14 Deanfield Court, Links 59 Business Park, Clitherhall, Rossendale, Lancashire, BB7 1QS Tel: (01200) 444354 Fax: (01200) 444359 E-mail: alda@alda.co.uk

Chiltern Connections Ltd, 2 Hithercroft Court, Lupton Road, Wallingford, Oxfordshire, OX10 9BT Tel: (01491) 824788 Fax: (01491) 824799 E-mail: sales@chilternconnections.co.uk

PRINTED CIRCUIT BOARD (PCB) SUPPORT PILLARS

Eurotech Group plc, Dinan Way, Exmouth, Devon, EX8 4RZ Tel: (01395) 279393 Fax: (01395) 279902 E-mail: sales@eurotech-group.co.uk

G & B Projects Co., Barnards Green Road, Malvern, Worcestershire, WR14 3LY Tel: (01684) 574367 Fax: (01684) 560225 E-mail: sales@gandbprojects.co.uk

Micro Plastics (International) Ltd, Unit 2, Henley Industrial Park, Henley Road, Coventry, CV2 1SR Tel: (024) 7661 4320 Fax: (024) 7661 4831 E-mail: microplas@aol.com

PRINTED CIRCUIT BOARD (PCB) TEST EQUIPMENT, BARE BOARD

▶ Peplertech Ltd, The Vicarage, Birtles Lane, Over Alderley, Macclesfield, Cheshire, SK10 4RX Tel: (01625) 861443 Fax: (01625) 861445 E-mail: info@peplertech.co.uk

PRINTED CIRCUIT BOARD (PCB) TEST POINTS

Auwell Electronics Ltd, Units 16-19, Oldends Industrial Estate, Oldends, Stonehouse, Gloucestershire, GL10 3RQ Tel: (01453) 791111 Fax: (01453) 791313 E-mail: enquiries@auwell.co.uk

PRINTED CIRCUIT BOARD (PCB) TESTING SERVICES, BARE BOARD, ELECTRICAL

Everrett Charles Technology, Homer House, Sibthorp Street, Lincoln, LN5 7SL Tel: (01522) 548220 Fax: (01522) 568419

Paramount Engineering Ltd, Unit 15 Pontcynon Industrial Estate, Abercynon, Mountain Ash, Mid Glamorgan, CF45 4EP Tel: (01443) 741897 Fax: (01443) 741897 E-mail: paramount@dial.pipex.com

PRINTED CIRCUIT BOARDS (PCB), *See also headings for particular types*

▶ Photronics (UK) Ltd, Trafford Wharf Road, Manchester, M17 1PE Tel: 0161-930 4700 Fax: 0161-930 4801

Product Support Electronics Ltd, Unit 1/2, Letts Road, Far Cotton, Northampton, NN4 8HQ Tel: (01604) 764520 Fax: (01604) 706834 E-mail: ppse@aol.com

PRINTED CIRCUIT CHEMICAL PRODUCTS

Atotech UK Ltd, William Street, West Bromwich, West Midlands, B70 0BE Tel: 0121-606 7777 Fax: 0121-606 7200 E-mail: sales.uk@atotech.com

PRINTED CIRCUIT CHEMICAL PRODUCTS – *continued*

E K C Technology Ltd, 19 Law Place, Nerston, East Kilbride, Glasgow, G74 4QL Tel: (01355) 244652 Fax: (01355) 595444 E-mail: sales@ekctech.co.uk

Electrolube, Midland Road, Swadlincote, Derbyshire, DE11 0AN Tel: (01283) 222111 Fax: (01283) 550177 E-mail: el_sales@hkw.co.uk

P M D UK Ltd, Broad Lane, Coventry, CV5 7AY Tel: (024) 7646 6691 Fax: (024) 7647 3034 E-mail: sales@pmdgroup.co.uk

Schloetter Co. Ltd, Abbey Works, New Road, Pershore, Worcestershire, WR10 1BY Tel: (01386) 552331 Fax: (01386) 556864 E-mail: info@schloetter.co.uk

PRINTED CIRCUIT COMPUTER AIDED DESIGN (CAD)

Blackburn Circuit Design Ltd, Cunliffe Road, Whitebirk Industrial Estate, Blackburn, BB1 5UA Tel: (01254) 680819 Fax: (01254) 682395 E-mail: peter@bc-design.co.uk

Cadalec Control Systems, Three Boundaries Business Park, Coventry Road, Croft, Leicester, LE9 3GP Tel: (01455) 286900 Fax: (01455) 286999 E-mail: sales@cadalec.com

Design Drafting Services, 4 Carr Street, Ramsbottom, Bury, Lancashire, BL0 9AE Tel: (01706) 823331 Fax: (01706) 827910

Diamond Instrumentation Ltd, 46 Swan Road, Swan Industrial Estate, District 9, Washington, Tyne & Wear, NE38 8JJ Tel: 0191-417 8911 Fax: 0191-419 1426

G D S P C B Design, 5 Garton End, Crayspond, Reading, RG8 7QH Tel: (01491) 681235 Fax: (01491) 681380 E-mail: jogilvie@gds.co.uk

Jabil Circuit Ltd, Oakbank Park Drive, Mid Calder, Livingston, West Lothian, EH53 0TJ Tel: (01506) 432266 Fax: (01506) 442000

Lyncolec Ltd, 2 Abingdon Road, Nuffield Industrial Estate, Poole, Dorset, BH17 0UG Tel: (01202) 679797 Fax: (01202) 684530 E-mail: pcb@lyncolec.co.uk

Maidenbury Ltd, 360 Blackfen Road, Sidcup, Kent, DA15 9NY Tel: (020) 8303 4253 Fax: (020) 8303 4253 E-mail: kenhillard@maidenbury.co.uk

Oxford Design Bureau, 2 Fyfield Close, Wantage, Oxfordshire, OX12 8HN Tel: (01235) 770180 Fax: (01235) 770147 E-mail: oxfordpcbdesign@aol.com

P C B UK, Ramsey Road, Sydenham Industrial Estate, Leamington Spa, Warwickshire, CV31 1PG Tel: (01926) 744414 Fax: (01926) 744411 E-mail: sales@pcbuk.com

SMB Design, Coombe Lodge, Bourne Lane, Blagdon, Bristol, BS40 7RG Tel: (01934) 413617 Fax: (01761) 463399 E-mail: sales@smbdesigns.co.uk

PRINTED CIRCUIT CONNECTORS

G T K (U K) Ltd, Unit 1 Maxdata Centre, Downmill Road, Bracknell, Berkshire, RG12 1QS Tel: (01344) 304123 Fax: (01344) 301414 E-mail: sales@gtk.co.uk

Hirose Electric UK Ltd, Crownhill Business Centre, 22 Vincent Avenue, Crownhill, Milton Keynes, MK8 0AB Tel: (01908) 305400 Fax: (01908) 563309 E-mail: sales@hirose.co.uk

Multi-Contact (UK) Ltd, 3 Presley Way, Crownhill, Milton Keynes, MK8 0ES Tel: (01908) 265544 Fax: (01908) 262080 E-mail: uk@multi-contact.com

Takbro Ltd, Unit 5 Albert Drive, Burgess Hill, West Sussex, RH15 9TN Tel: (01444) 245601 Fax: (01444) 872316 E-mail: mail@takbro.co.uk

PRINTED CIRCUIT CONSULTANTS/DESIGNERS/ PRODUCTION SERVICES

A C S Industries Ltd, Huffwood Trading Estate, Billingshurst, West Sussex, RH14 9UR Tel: (01403) 784225 Fax: (01403) 784046 E-mail: frontend@acsind.co.uk

▶ A2e Ltd, Adaptive House, Quarrywood Court, Livingston, West Lothian, EH54 6AX Tel: (01506) 463393 Fax: (01506) 461257

C D O Electronics Ltd, 17 Bowater Road, Westminster Industrial Estate, London, SE18 5TF Tel: (020) 8855 9508 Fax: (020) 8316 1892 E-mail: jim@cdo-electronics.com

Chemigraphic Ltd, 2 Fleming Centre, Fleming Way, Crawley, West Sussex, RH10 9NF Tel: (01293) 543517 Fax: (01293) 552859 E-mail: sales@chemigraphic.co.uk

Danor Circuits, 82 Cannock Street, Leicester, LE4 9HR Tel: 0116-274 0312 Fax: 0116-274 0879 E-mail: sales@danorcircuits.com

▶ Dunne Roberts, Unit 3 Freemantle Business Centre, 152 Millbrook Road East, Southampton, SO15 1JR Tel: (023) 8082 9200 Fax: (023) 8082 9201 E-mail: contactus@dunneroberts.co.uk

Dva Controls, 1 Sunningdale Grove, Colwyn Bay, Clwyd, LL29 6DG Tel: (01492) 534937 E-mail: info@dva-controls.co.uk

Electronic Design Services Ltd, Stewart Street, Bury, Lancashire, BL8 1SP Tel: 0161-705 2117 Fax: 0161-763 6940

▶ Euro Circuitboards Ltd, 6 Diamond Industrial Centre, Works Road, Letchworth Garden City, Hertfordshire, SG6 1LW Tel: (01462) 481010 Fax: (01462) 480978 E-mail: sales@eurocircuitboards.com

The Eurotech Group Plc, Sittingbourne Industrial Park, Crown Quay Lane, Sittingbourne, Kent, ME10 3JH Tel: (01795) 431637 Fax: (01795) 431638 E-mail: eurotech@sittingbourne92.fsnet.co.uk

Fiducial Design Ltd, Chroma House, Shire Hill, Saffron Walden, Essex, CB11 3AQ Tel: (01799) 508039 Fax: (01799) 500379 E-mail: contact@fiducial.co.uk

G & B Electronic Designs Ltd, 54 Woolmer Way, Bordon, Hampshire, GU35 9QF Tel: (01420) 474188 Fax: (01420) 478101 E-mail: sales@gandbelectronics.co.uk

G D S P C B Design, 5 Garton End, Crayspond, Reading, RG8 7QH Tel: (01491) 681235 Fax: (01491) 681380 E-mail: jogilvie@gds.co.uk

G S Designs, Hardwick Close, Stevenage, Hertfordshire, SG2 8UF Tel: (01438) 813332 Fax: (01438) 812215 E-mail: gary@gsdesign.co.uk

▶ Tim Gale Consulting Ltd, Red Shute Mill Business Centre, Red Shute Hill, Hermitage, Thatcham, Berkshire, RG18 9QL Tel: (01635) 202080 Fax: (08700) 940517 E-mail: tim@t-g-c.net

GIGA Systems Ltd, 71 Watercall Avenue, Coventry, CV3 5AX Tel: (0870) 7525515 E-mail: info@gigasystems.co.uk

Industrial Electronics Consultants, 855 Holderness Road, Hull, HU8 9BA Tel: (01482) 374437 Fax: (01482) 796853 E-mail: ray@rayeldred.carouy.co.uk

Jade Design Services, 17 St. James Drive, Brinsley, Nottingham, NG16 5DB Tel: (01773) 780391 E-mail: brian@jadedesign.demon.co.uk

L G K Industries Ltd, Station Approach, Pulborough, West Sussex, RH20 1AY Tel: (01798) 873663 Fax: (01798) 873722 E-mail: sales.logikontrol@btinternet.com

Magna Electronics Ltd, 9 Harrow Road, Hereford, HR4 0EH Tel: (01432) 353434 Fax: (01432) 278749 E-mail: mark@magna-electronics.co.uk

Maidenbury Ltd, 360 Blackfen Road, Sidcup, Kent, DA15 9NY Tel: (020) 8303 4253 Fax: (020) 8303 4253 E-mail: kenhillard@maidenbury.co.uk

Mutech Ltd, Unit 25, Waters Edge Business Park, Modwen Road, Salford, M5 3EZ Tel: 0161-872 0400 E-mail: sales@mutech.co.uk

Option Technology Europe Ltd, Carrs Industrial Estate, Haslingden, Rossendale, Lancashire, BB4 5HR Tel: (01706) 605000 Fax: (01706) 605010 E-mail: sales@option.co.uk

Printed Circuit Design, 5 Holbrook Close, Great Waldingfield, Sudbury, Suffolk, CO10 0XX Tel: (01787) 310990 E-mail: d.holdaway@virgin.net

▶ Printed Wiring Technologies Ltd, 7-8 Alders Court, Watchmead, Welwyn Garden City, Hertfordshire, AL7 1LT Tel: (01707) 338871 Fax: (01707) 372622 E-mail: sales@pwtpcbs.com

Scan & Design, 14 The Warren, Burgess Hill, West Sussex, RH15 0DZ Tel: (01444) 254750 Fax: (01444) 254750 E-mail: scan.design@fsbdial.co.uk

Ticino Desinex Ltd, 69 Fleet Road, Fleet, Hampshire, GU51 3PJ Tel: (01252) 621185 Fax: (01252) 811223

PRINTED CIRCUIT DESIGN SYSTEMS

Active Circuits, 14 North Street, Melton Mowbray, Leicestershire, LE13 1NL Tel: (01664) 562968 Fax: (01664) 562968

▶ Design Analysis Solutions, Bramling Cross Barns, Beauchamp Lane, Worcester, WR2 4UQ Tel: (01905) 830608 Fax: (0870) 7062737 E-mail: info@das4pcbs.co.uk

PRINTED CIRCUIT FLEXIBLE CONDUCTORS

Flex Ability Ltd, Prospect Way, Park View West Industrial Estate, Hartlepool, Cleveland, TS25 1UD Tel: (01429) 860233 Fax: (01429) 869696 E-mail: sales@flex-ability.co.uk

Teknoflex Ltd, Quarry Lane Industrial Estate, Quarry Lane, Chichester, West Sussex, PO19 8PE Tel: (01243) 784516 Fax: (01243) 832832 E-mail: sales@teknoflex.com

Yeovil Circuits Ltd, 1 Armoury Road, Lufton Trading Estate, Lufton, Yeovil, Somerset, BA22 8RL Tel: (01935) 428313 Fax: (01935) 431446 E-mail: yeovil.circuits@eclipse.co.uk

PRINTED CIRCUIT MAINTENANCE/REPAIR SERVICES

Electronic Repair Technology, Signal Works, Talbot Road, Wellingborough, Northants, NN8 1QH Tel: (01933) 228866 Fax: (01933) 443623 E-mail: dave@autocontrol.freeserve.co.uk

L C Kittow Ltd, 34 Spear Road, Southampton, SO14 6UH Tel: (023) 8032 2650 Fax: (023) 8032 2651 E-mail: info@lckittow.com

PRINTED CIRCUIT MANUFRS,

See also headings for particular types under Printed Circuits etc

Anglia Circuits Engineering Ltd, Anglia Works, Burrel Road, St. Ives, Cambridgeshire, PE27 3LB Tel: (01480) 464624 Fax: (01480) 494041 E-mail: sales@angliacircuits.com

Artetch Circuits Ltd, Riverside Industrial Estate, Bridge Road, Littlehampton, West Sussex, BN17 5DF Tel: (01903) 725365 Fax: (01903) 730572 E-mail: sales@artetch.co.uk

Bassett Electronic Systems Ltd, Unit 15 Whitehill Industrial Estate, Whitehill Lane, Wootton Bassett, Swindon, SN4 7DB Tel: (01793) 851013 Fax: (01793) 848765 E-mail: sales@bassettelectronics.com

C P L Electronics Ltd, Unit 8-14 Highcroft Industrial Estate, Enterprise Road, Waterlooville, Hampshire, PO8 0BT Tel: (023) 9259 9333 Fax: (023) 9259 3127 E-mail: cpl@dsl.pipex.com

Chiltern Circuits Ltd, 51 Poppy Road, Princes Risborough, Buckinghamshire, HP27 9DB Tel: (01844) 343437 Fax: (01844) 347102 E-mail: chiltnccts@aol.com

Circuit Dynamics Ltd, 112 Beckenham Road, Beckenham, Kent, BR3 4RH Tel: (020) 8650 0723 Fax: (020) 8650 0921 E-mail: cirtcuitdynamics@businessserve.co.uk

▶ Cleveland Circuits Ltd, Skelton Industrial Estate, Skelton-in-Cleveland, Saltburn-by-the-Sea, Cleveland, TS12 2LQ Tel: (01287) 651991 Fax: (01287) 652898 E-mail: sales@pcb.co.uk

D E B Electronics Ltd, 2 Redbourn Industrial Centre, High St, Redbourn, St. Albans, Hertfordshire, AL3 7LG Tel: (01582) 794466 Fax: (01582) 792559 E-mail: admin@deb-electronics.co.uk

D J Circuits Ltd, Jubilee Works, Anchor Road, Harrogate, North Yorkshire, HG1 4TA Tel: (01423) 889055 Fax: (01423) 884912 E-mail: enquiries@djcircuits.com

Daleba Electronics, 49 Tamworth Road, Hertford, SG13 7DJ Tel: (01992) 582232 Fax: 01992 582222 E-mail: sales@daleba.co.uk

David Maddox Ltd, 53-55 Gatwick Road, Crawley, West Sussex, RH10 9RD Tel: (01293) 452830 Fax: (01293) 452830 E-mail: david.maddox@virgin.net

Design Drafting Services, 4 Carr Street, Ramsbottom, Bury, Lancashire, BL0 9AE Tel: (01706) 823331 Fax: (01706) 827910

Dial Art (PC) Ltd, 3 Airfield Way, Christchurch, Dorset, BH23 3PE Tel: (01202) 486486 Fax: (01202) 488988 E-mail: sales@dialart.com

Diamond Instrumentation Ltd, 46 Swan Road, Swan Industrial Estate, District 9, Washington, Tyne & Wear, NE38 8JJ Tel: 0191-417 8911 Fax: 0191-419 1426

Diamond Point International, Unit 9 North Point Business Estate, Enterprise Close, Medway City Estate, Rochester, Kent, ME2 4LX Tel: (01634) 722390 Fax: (01634) 722398 E-mail: sales@dpie.com

Electroconnect Ltd, Unit 1, Riverside Avenue, Riverside Business Park, Irvine, Ayrshire, KA11 5DL Tel: (01294) 221360 Fax: (01294) 221272 E-mail: sales@electroconnect.co.uk

The Eurotech Group Plc, Sittingbourne Industrial Park, Crown Quay Lane, Sittingbourne, Kent, ME10 3JH Tel: (01795) 431637 Fax: (01795) 431638 E-mail: eurotech@sittingbourne92.fsnet.co.uk

Express Circuits Ltd, 22 Roman Way, Coleshill Industrial Estate, Coleshill, Birmingham, B46 1HQ Tel: (01675) 464884 Fax: (01675) 466759 E-mail: cam@express-circuits.co.uk

Flex Ability Ltd, Prospect Way, Park View West Industrial Estate, Hartlepool, Cleveland, TS25 1UD Tel: (01429) 860233 Fax: (01429) 869696 E-mail: sales@flex-ability.co.uk

▶ Flexible Technology, 23 Wolverstone Drive, Brighton, BN1 7FB Tel: (01273) 566922 Fax: (01273) 566922 E-mail: kb-ftl@netpointproject.net

G B Circuits, Braithwell Way, Hellaby, Rotherham, South Yorkshire, S66 8QY Tel: (01709) 547000 Fax: (01709) 549000 E-mail: gbcircuits@dial.pipex.com

G L R Processing Co, 11 Tiber Way, Glebe Farm Industrial Estate, Rugby, Warwickshire, CV21 1ED Tel: (01788) 541390 Fax: (01788) 546103 E-mail: g.l.r@btconnect.com

G S P K Circuits Ltd, Manse Lane, Knaresborough, North Yorkshire, HG5 8LF Tel: (01423) 865641 Fax: (01423) 798246 E-mail: sales@gspkcircuits.ltd.uk

Graphic plc, Down End, Lords Meadow Industrial Estate, Crediton, Devon, EX17 1HN Tel: (01363) 774874 Fax: (01363) 775753 E-mail: sales@graphic.plc.uk

Huntrose UK Ltd, Jarman Way, Chard Business Park, Chard, Somerset, TA20 1FB Tel: (01460) 61895 Fax: (01460) 67088 E-mail: huntrose@lineone.net

Invotec Circuits Tamworth Ltd, 2-28 Hedging Lane, Wilnecote, Tamworth, Staffordshire, B77 5EP Tel: (01827) 263000 Fax: (01827) 263230 E-mail: firstname.surname@invertechgroup.com

JCD Electronics Ltd, 4a Oakwood Parade, Oakwood Hill, Loughton, Essex, IG10 3EL Tel: (020) 8508 3355 Fax: (020) 8508 3355

Kelan Circuits Ltd, Wetherby Road, Boroughbridge, York, YO51 9UY Tel: (01423) 321100 Fax: (01423) 321107 E-mail: sales@kelan.co.uk

Kibmore Electronics, Bramble Cottage, Axes Lane, Redhill, RH1 5QN Tel: (01737) 765424

Labtech Ltd, Broadaxe Business Park, Presteigne, Powys, LD8 2UH Tel: (01544) 267099 Fax: (01544) 260310 E-mail: ptfe@labtech.ltd.uk

Lormay Ltd, Lormay House, Main Street, Westbury, Brackley, Northamptonshire, NN13 5JR Tel: (01280) 700570 Fax: (01280) 705201

Lyncolec Ltd, 2 Abingdon Road, Nuffield Industrial Estate, Poole, Dorset, BH17 0UG Tel: (01202) 679797 Fax: (01202) 684530 E-mail: pcb@lyncolec.co.uk

▶ M V P UK, Castle Court, Carnegie Campus, Castle Drive, Dunfermline, Fife, KY11 8PB Tel: (01383) 629960 Fax: (01383) 629979

Mho Trak Ltd, Blackhorse Road, Letchworth Garden City, Hertfordshire, SG6 1HB Tel: (01462) 480123 Fax: (01462) 480246 E-mail: data@mhotrak.co.uk

Mode Lighting UK Ltd, Chelsing House, Mead Lane, Hertford, SG13 7AW Tel: (01992) 554566 Fax: (01992) 553644 E-mail: sales@modecontracts.com

O P C UK, Falcon House, 12 Barns Street, Ayr, KA7 1XA Tel: (01292) 272403 Fax: 01292 270123 E-mail: sales@opcuk.co.uk

One Way Circuits, Station Road, Lenwade, Norwich, NR9 5LY Tel: (01603) 875100 Fax: (0870) 7517518 E-mail: sales@onewaypcb.com

P C B UK, Ramsey Road, Sydenham Industrial Estate, Leamington Spa, Warwickshire, CV31 1PG Tel: (01926) 744414 Fax: (01926) 744411 E-mail: sales@pcbuk.com

P & M Services (Rochdale) Ltd, Stoneswood Mill, Bacup Road, Todmorden, Lancashire, OL14 7HG Tel: (01706) 815212 Fax: (01706) 818636 E-mail: sales@p-m-services.co.uk

P&D, 2 Power Industrial Estate, Slade Green Road, Erith, Kent, DA8 2HU Tel: (01322) 346834 Fax: (01322) 336817

Paragon Circuits Ltd, 5 Wainman Road, Peterborough, PE2 7BU Tel: (01733) 234754 Fax: (01733) 238196 E-mail: info@paragoncircuits.co.uk

Photo Mechanical Services Essex Ltd, Co-Ordinated Industrial Estate, Claydons Lane, Rayleigh, Essex, SS6 7UP Tel: (01268) 741486 Fax: (01268) 782538 E-mail: pcbs@photomechanical.co.uk

Precision Engineering Products Ltd, Bellingham Grove, Sneyd Green, Stoke-on-Trent, ST1 6LF Tel: (01782) 202053 Fax: (01782) 285667 E-mail: tsteventon@aol.com

▶ Protetch Printed Circuit Mnfrs, Unit 5 Galalaw Business Park, Hawick, Roxburghshire, TD9 8PZ Tel: (01450) 379728 Fax: (01450) 379728

Quassia Electronics Ltd, Bearwalden Business Park, Wendens Ambo, Saffron Walden, Essex, CB11 4JX Tel: (01799) 541174 Fax: (01799) 541937 E-mail: info@quassiaelectronics.co.uk

Quick Circuits Ltd, 1 Loverock Road, Reading, RG30 1DZ Tel: 0118-950 8921 Fax: 0118-956 8237 E-mail: sales@quick-circuits.com

▶ Ramar Electronics Services Ltd, Masons Road, Stratford-upon-Avon, Warwickshire, CV37 9NF Tel: (01789) 204879 Fax: (01789) 299727 E-mail: info@ramarpcb.co.uk

Screenbond Ltd, 2 Serl Industrial Estate, London Road, Baldock, Hertfordshire, SG7 6NG Tel: (01462) 894600 Fax: (01462) 490463 E-mail: sales@screenbond.co.uk

Silva Ltd, Fleming Road, Kirkton Campus, Livingston, West Lothian, EH54 7BN Tel: (01506) 419555 Fax: (01506) 415906 E-mail: info@silva.ltd.uk

SMB Design, Coombe Lodge, Bourne Lane, Blagdon, Bristol, BS40 7RG Tel: (01934) 413617 Fax: (01761) 463399 E-mail: sales@smbdesigns.co.uk

Southport Electronics Ltd, 22 Glebe Lane, Banks, Southport, Merseyside, PR9 8EU Tel: (01704) 228510 Fax: (01704) 211057

Systematics Printed Circuits Ltd, Unit 7 R.J. Mitchell Centre, Spitfire Quay, Hazel Road, Woolston, Southampton, SO19 7GB Tel: (023) 8068 5677 Fax: (023) 8068 5625 E-mail: pcbsales@systematicsprintedcircuits.com

Teknoflex Ltd, Quarry Lane Industrial Estate, Quarry Lane, Chichester, West Sussex, PO19 8PE Tel: (01243) 784516 Fax: (01243) 832832 E-mail: sales@teknoflex.com

Wasco Circuits, Wasco House, Willow Lane, Lancaster, LA1 5NA Tel: (01524) 69900 Fax: (01524) 67544 E-mail: front.office@nht.co.uk

Wilson Process Systems Ltd, Waterworks Road, Hastings, East Sussex, TN34 1RT Tel: (01424) 722222 Fax: (01424) 720730 E-mail: sales@wps.co.uk

PRINTED CIRCUIT MANUFRS – *continued*

Yeovil Circuits Ltd, 1 Armoury Road, Lufton Trading Estate, Lufton, Yeovil, Somerset, BA22 8RL Tel: (01935) 428313 Fax: (01935) 431446 E-mail: yeovil.circuits@eclipse.co.uk
Zot Engineering Ltd, Inveresk Mills Industrial Park, Musselburgh, Midlothian, EH21 7UQ Tel: 0131-653 6834 Fax: 0131-653 6025 E-mail: data@zot.co.uk

PRINTED CIRCUIT MICROWAVE LAMINATES

Labtech Ltd, Broadaxe Business Park, Presteigne, Powys, LD8 2UH Tel: (01544) 267099 Fax: (01544) 260310 E-mail: ptfe@labtech.ltd.uk

PRINTED CIRCUIT OPTICAL INSPECTION SERVICES

Huntrose UK Ltd, Jarman Way, Chard Business Park, Chard, Somerset, TA20 1FB Tel: (01460) 61895 Fax: (01460) 67088 E-mail: huntrose@lineone.net

PRINTED CIRCUIT PHOTOGRAPHIC SERVICES

Photo Data, Photo Data House 12 Knowl Piece, Wilbury Way, Hitchin, Hertfordshire, SG4 0TY Tel: (01462) 452616 Fax: (01462) 422830 E-mail: sales@photodata.com

PRINTED CIRCUIT PHOTOMECHANICAL SERVICES

Blackwater Photographic Co., 69 Fleet Road, Fleet, Hampshire, GU51 3PJ Tel: (01252) 613243 Fax: (01252) 811223 E-mail: keithe@patrol.i-way.co.uk
Photo Mechanical Services Essex Ltd, Co-Ordinated Industrial Estate, Claydons Lane, Rayleigh, Essex, SS6 7UP Tel: (01268) 741486 Fax: (01268) 782538 E-mail: pcbs@photomechanical.co.uk

PRINTED CIRCUIT PHOTOPLOTTING

Photo Data, Photo Data House 12 Knowl Piece, Wilbury Way, Hitchin, Hertfordshire, SG4 0TY Tel: (01462) 452616 Fax: (01462) 422830 E-mail: sales@photodata.com

PRINTED CIRCUIT PRODUCTION EQUIPMENT

Bohan Engineering, Unit 14a Fiveways Trading Estate, Westwells Road, Hawthorn, Corsham, Wiltshire, SN13 9RG Tel: (01225) 812730 Fax: (01225) 812188 E-mail: sales@bohan.co.uk
Circuit Engineering Marketing Co. Ltd, 1 Silverthorne Way, Waterlooville, Hampshire, PO7 7XB Tel: (023) 9226 2120 Fax: (023) 9226 2089 E-mail: sales@cemco.com
Fortex P C Drills Ltd, 17 Fleetwood Road, Leicester, LE2 1YA Tel: 0116-270 8937 Fax: 0116-270 0532
Fotomechanix Ltd, 30 Curzon Street, Birmingham, B4 7XD Tel: 0121-380 0116 Fax: 0121-359 3313
H.G. Kippax & Sons Ltd, Upper Bankfield Mills, Almondbury Bank, Huddersfield, HD5 8HF Tel: (01484) 426789 Fax: (01484) 541799 E-mail: sales@hgkippax.co.uk
Micromat International, Sanders Lodge Industrial Estate, Rushden, Northamptonshire, NN10 6BQ Tel: (01933) 313093 Fax: (01933) 319293 E-mail: sales@micromat.co.uk
Opsec Marketing Ltd, 27 Little End Road, Eaton Socon, St. Neots, Cambridgeshire, PE19 8JH Tel: (01480) 470400 Fax: (01480) 470401 E-mail: sales@dg2k.co.uk
P & G Processors Ltd, 26 Trojan Centre, Finedon Road Industrial Estate, Wellingborough, Northamptonshire, NN8 4ST Tel: (01933) 270967 Fax: (01933) 270967 E-mail: pgprocess@aol.com
Plastic Fabrications (1991), Unit 10, Bickford Road, Aston, Birmingham, B6 7EE Tel: (0121) 327 1013 Fax: (0121) 326 6139
Seetrax Ltd, Old Buriton Line Works, Kiln La, Buriton, Petersfield, Hants, GU31 5SJ Tel: (01730) 260062 Fax: (01730) 267273 E-mail: sales@seetrax.com
Sensbey, 36 Carters Lane, Kiln Farm, Milton Keynes, MK11 3HL Tel: (01908) 569630 Fax: (01908) 562457 E-mail: sensbeyuk@compuserve.com
Technic Electric Ltd, Unit 5 Lulworth Business Centre, Nutwood Way, Totton, Southampton, SO40 3WW Tel: (023) 8066 7486 Fax: (023) 8066 3830 E-mail: sales@technic.co.uk

PRINTED CIRCUIT PRODUCTION EQUIPMENT/MATERIALS/ ACCESSORIES/SUPPLIES DISTRIBUTORS OR AGENTS

GMF Equipment Ltd, 9A High Street, Kegworth, Derby, DE74 2DA Tel: (01509) 673656 Fax: (01509) 674729 E-mail: sales@gmfequipment.co.uk
HAM Technology UK Ltd, 8 Brookfield, Duncan Close, Moulton Park, Northampton, NN3 6WL Tel: (01604) 494106 Fax: (01604) 499008 E-mail: janet@ham-tech.co.uk
Mega Electronics Ltd, Unit 4, The Grip, Linton, Cambridge, CB21 4XN Tel: (01223) 893900 Fax: (01223) 893894 E-mail: sales@megauk.com
P M D UK Ltd, Broad Lane, Coventry, CV5 7AY Tel: (024) 7646 6691 Fax: (024) 7647 3034 E-mail: sales@pmdgroup.co.uk

PRINTED CIRCUIT PROTOTYPE PRODUCTION EQUIPMENT

Mega Electronics Ltd, Unit 4, The Grip, Linton, Cambridge, CB21 4XN Tel: (01223) 893900 Fax: (01223) 893894 E-mail: sales@megauk.com

PRINTED CIRCUIT SERVICES, MANUFACTURED FROM DATA (MFD), PHOTOPLOTTING

Mecelex & Co, 19a Nottingham Road, Daybrook, Nottingham, NG5 6JW Tel: 0115-967 0665 Fax: 0115-967 0665E-mail: mecelex@aol.com

PRINTED CIRCUIT STORAGE RACKS/SYSTEMS

Bohan Engineering, Unit 14a Fiveways Trading Estate, Westwells Road, Hawthorn, Corsham, Wiltshire, SN13 9RG Tel: (01225) 812730 Fax: (01225) 812188 E-mail: sales@bohan.co.uk
Opsec Marketing Ltd, 27 Little End Road, Eaton Socon, St. Neots, Cambridgeshire, PE19 8JH Tel: (01480) 470400 Fax: (01480) 470401 E-mail: sales@dg2k.co.uk

PRINTED CIRCUIT TEST EQUIPMENT

Cable Check Systems, Unit 18 Quay Lane, Hardway, Gosport, Hampshire, PO12 4LJ Tel: (023) 9252 8396 Fax: (023) 9258 9748 E-mail: info@greenpersonnel.co.uk
Genrad Holdings Ltd, Orion Business Park, Bird Hall Lane, Stockport, Cheshire, SK3 0XG Tel: (01483) 569933 Fax: 0161-491 9501
Peak Test Services, 152a Front Street, Chester le Street, County Durham, DH3 3AY Tel: 0191-387 1923 Fax: 0191-387 1994 E-mail: peak.test@thepeakgroup.com

PRINTED CIRCUIT TESTING SERVICES

Blizard Electronic Assembly Ltd, 8 Greenlea Park, Prince Georges Road, London, SW19 2JD Tel: (020) 8685 9460 Fax: (020) 8840 8688
Photo Data, Photo Data House 12 Knowl Piece, Wilbury Way, Hitchin, Hertfordshire, SG4 0TY Tel: (01462) 452616 Fax: (01462) 422830 E-mail: sales@photodata.com

PRINTED CIRCUITS TO SPECIFICATION

Chiltern Circuits Ltd, 51 Poppy Road, Princes Risborough, Buckinghamshire, HP27 9DB Tel: (01844) 343437 Fax: (01844) 347102 E-mail: chiltnccts@aol.com
M R P Electronics plc, 59 Brunel Road, Bedford, MK41 9TJ Tel: (01234) 216222 Fax: (01234) 219000 E-mail: sales@mrpplc.co.uk

PRINTED CIRCUITS, MICROCIRCUIT, *See Microcircuit etc*

PRINTED CIRCUITS, PTFE

Labtech Ltd, Broadaxe Business Park, Presteigne, Powys, LD8 2UH Tel: (01544) 267099 Fax: (01544) 260310 E-mail: ptfe@labtech.ltd.uk
Stevenage Circuits Ltd, Caxton Way, Stevenage, Hertfordshire, SG1 2DF Tel: (01438) 751800 Fax: (01438) 728103 E-mail: sales@stevenagecircuits.co.uk

Tru-Lon Printed Circuits (Royston) Ltd, Newark Close, York Way Industrial Estate, Royston, Hertfordshire, SG8 5HL Tel: (01763) 248922 Fax: (01763) 249281 E-mail: info@tru-lon.co.uk

PRINTED ENVELOPES

▶ Alternative Packaging Solutions Ltd, The Studio Prospect Place, Mill Lane, Alton, Hampshire, GU34 2SX Tel: (01420) 544800 Fax: (01420) 544850
▶ Business Envelopes, 11 Juniper Grove, Livingston, West Lothian, EH54 5JF Tel: (07790) 439975
G P Print, G P Print Edgerley Business, Challenger Way, Peterborough, PE1 5EX Tel: (01733) 340622 Fax: (08719) 940780 E-mail: info@gpprint.co.uk
Hot Metal Press, Museum Works Elscar Workshops, Wath Road, Elsecar, Barnsley, South Yorkshire, S74 8HJ Tel: (01226) 740498 Fax: (01226) 350201 E-mail: info@hotmetalpress.co.uk
Impress Printers Ltd, 54 Burners Lane, Kiln Farm, Milton Keynes, MK11 3HD Tel: (01908) 262111 Fax: (01908) 262255 E-mail: carol@impress-envelopes.co.uk
T & A Envelopes Ltd, 10 Moray Court, Kimberley, Nottingham, NG16 2TL Tel: 0115-938 4674 Fax: 0115-945 8348 E-mail: t_a.envelopes@mac.com

PRINTED FABRIC LABELS

Arkley Labels, Unit 8, Aslton Works, Alston Road, Barnet, Hertfordshire, EN5 4EL Tel: (020) 8441 2011 Fax: (020) 8441 5909
Bolton Labelling Systems, 53-55 Bridgeman Place, Bolton, BL2 1DE Tel: (01204) 526079 Fax: (01204) 384348 E-mail: sales@boltonlabelling.co.uk
Britannia Labels Ltd, 22b Centurion Way, Meridian Business Park, Leicester, LE19 1WH Tel: 0116-281 5300 Fax: 0116-281 5301 E-mail: sales@britannialabels.com
Byways Ltd, Bramingham Business Park, Enterprise Way, Luton, LU3 4BU Tel: (01582) 524444 Fax: (01582) 491301 E-mail: info@byways.co.uk

PRINTED LABELS

G.H. Neville Ltd, Unit 1, Travellers Lane, North Mymms, Hatfield, Hertfordshire, AL9 7HF Tel: (01707) 262 800 Fax: (01707) 263 888 E-mail: sales@emgeeonline.co.uk
Robrook Press Ltd, Queens Road, Morley, Leeds, LS27 0PF Tel: 0113-253 5753 Fax: 0113-238 0231 E-mail: paul@robrook.com
Sign Wizzard, Griffin Lane, Aylesbury, Buckinghamshire, HP19 0GH Tel: (01296) 398022 Fax: (01296) 398028 E-mail: sign.wizzard@virgin.net

PRINTED LETTERHEADS

Capita Printing Services, Unit C Croydon Road Industrial Estate, Tannery Close, Beckenham, Kent, BR3 4BY Tel: (020) 8662 7010 Fax: (020) 8662 7003 E-mail: sales@capita.co.uk

PRINTED LOTTERY TICKET HOLDERS

▶ D. Collis, 51 Harehill Road, Grangewood, Chesterfield, Derbyshire, S40 2NG Tel: (01246) 540180 Fax: (01246) 540180 E-mail: david@dcollis.wanadoo.co.uk
▶ UK Lottery Online, Unit 142 Roslyn Road, South Tottenham, London, N15 5JJ Tel: (020) 8800 7271 Fax: (020) 8800 7277 E-mail: info@uk-lotteryonline.co.uk

PRINTED NAMEPLATES

Graphic Engineering Northern Ltd, Sheaf Bank Business Park, Prospect Road, Heeley, Sheffield, S2 3EN Tel: 0114-250 0151 Fax: 0114-255 5161 E-mail: sales@graphicengineering.co.uk

PRINTED PAPER LABELS, *See Label Printers etc*

PRINTED POLYPROPYLENE (PP) FILM

▶ Britton Mailing, Unit 10 B, Temple Farm Industrial Estate, Sutton Road, Southend-on-Sea, SS2 5RD Tel: (01702) 468976 Fax: (01702) 469221 E-mail: enquiries@britton-group.co.uk

PRINTED SILK FABRICS

David Evans & Co, Bourne Road, Crayford, Dartford, DA1 4BP Tel: (01322) 557521 Fax: (01322) 550476 E-mail: sales@davidevans.co.uk

PRINTED SPORTS BAGS

M1 Sport Ltd, Phoenix House, Waller Avenue, Luton, LU4 9RS Tel: (01582) 580000 Fax: (01582) 580040

PRINTED STATIONERY TO SPECIFICATION

Compuprint 2000, Centrepoint, North Street, Rotherham, South Yorkshire, S60 1LG Tel: (01709) 373322 Fax: (01709) 373344
H F W Plastics Ltd, Albany Road, Gateshead, Tyne & Wear, NE8 3AT Tel: 0191-477 6519 Fax: 0191-490 1345 E-mail: sales@hfwplastics.co.uk
Infolist Ltd, Valley Business Centre Church Road, Newtownabbey, County Antrim, BT36 7LP Tel: (028) 9085 1133 Fax: (028) 9085 4708 E-mail: info@infolistltd.com
Jim Watts Signs, 27 Abbey Street, Market Harborough, Leicestershire, LE16 9AA Tel: (01858) 467763 Fax: (01858) 434826 E-mail: sales@jwsigns.co.uk
Oyez Straker, 4 City Park Industrial Estate, Gelderd Road, Leeds, LS12 6DR Tel: 0113-203 2100 Fax: 0113-263 9011 E-mail: sales.pudsey@oyezstraker.co.uk
Parbury Brothers Ltd, The Vicarage, Great Wolford, Shipston-On-Stour, Warwickshire, CV36 5NQ Tel: (07973) 696524 E-mail: sales@parbury.co.uk
Systemform Services, 8 Northfield Point, Northfield Avenue, Kettering, Northamptonshire, NN16 9HU Tel: (01536) 411414 Fax: (01536) 411416

PRINTED TICKETS

Aero-Print Securities Ltd, Gatehouse Way, Aylesbury, Buckinghamshire, HP19 8DD Tel: (01296) 485131 Fax: (01296) 485097 E-mail: sales@aero-print.co.uk
▶ Hi Security Ticket Printing, 4th Floor, 7 Collingwood Road, Witham, Essex, CM8 2DY Tel: 0870 4901491 Fax: 0870 4901481 E-mail: office@hisecuritytickets.com
M J Milward Printing Ltd, 21 Nottingham South & Wilford Industrial Estate, Nottingham, NG11 7EP Tel: 0115-981 3378 Fax: 0115-981 2386 E-mail: mgmprint@compuserve.com
Meriden Paper Ltd, 38 Meriden Street, Digbeth, Birmingham, B5 5LS Tel: 0121-643 2168 Fax: 0121-631 3378 E-mail: admin@meridenpaper.co.uk
Scientific Games International Ltd, George Mann Road, Leeds, LS10 1DJ Tel: 0113-385 5000 Fax: 0113-385 5200

PRINTED TINPLATE

Afon Tinplate Co. Ltd, Afon Works, Llangyfelach, Swansea, SA5 7LN Tel: (01792) 312000 Fax: (01792) 312001 E-mail: sales@afontinplate.co.uk
Crown Speciality Packaging, Edgefield Avenue, Fawdon, Newcastle upon Tyne, NE3 3TS Tel: 0191-285 8168 Fax: 0191-284 7570
Cyril Luff Metal Decorators Ltd, 57-58 Springvale Industrial Estate, Cwmbran, Gwent, NP44 5BD Tel: (01633) 869531 Fax: (01633) 865046 E-mail: info@cyrilluff.co.uk
Linpac Packaging Ltd, Caldicot Decorating Works, Caldicot, Monmouthshire, NP26 5XG Tel: (0870) 2426280 Fax: (01291) 307646

PRINTERS, BUSINESS CARD

▶ 3gdesign Studio, 251 Kingsway, Manchester, M19 1AL Tel: (0870) 0638370 Fax: 0161-610 6018 E-mail: sales@3Gdesignstudio.co.uk
▶ Accent Print & Design, 28-29 Maxwell Road, Woodston Industry, Peterborough, PE2 7JE Tel: (01733) 233238 Fax: (01733) 246519 E-mail: sales@accentprint.net
Champion Print & Web Services, 8 Marritt Close, Chatteris, Cambridgeshire, PE16 6PJ Tel: (01354) 692132 Fax: (07092) 144187 E-mail: tony@championprintandwebservices.co.uk
▶ Mercia Instant Print Ltd Trading As Prontaprint, 34 Chapel Ash, Wolverhampton, WV3 0TN Tel: (01902) 771177 Fax: (01902) 422255
▶ Minuteman Press, 3/5 Highfield Road, Hall Green, Birmingham, B28 0EL Tel: 0121-777 0018 Fax: 0121-777 5810 E-mail: karl.mccabe@minutemanpress.com
▶ Premier Print Services UK Ltd, 8 Henshaw Road, Bristol, BS15 1QF Tel: 0117-330 2050 Fax: 0117-330 2051 E-mail: premierprint@blueyonder.co.uk
▶ Pyramid Press Print & Design, 1 Ellesmere Business Park, Nottingham, NG5 1DX Tel: 0115-962 6262 Fax: 0115-969 3394 E-mail: sales@pyramidpress.co.uk

PRINTERS, BUSINESS CARD -

continued

▶ Vision Printers Ltd, Vision House, 1 Silverdale Lane, Tunbridge Wells, Kent, TN4 9LA Tel: (01892) 545006 Fax: (01892) 538069 E-mail: sales@vision-printers.co.uk

PRINTERS, GENERAL OR COMMERCIAL OR JOBBING OR ALL TYPES

21st Century, Security House, 65 Canterbury Street, Blackburn, BB2 2HT Tel: (01254) 661199 Fax: (01254) 699969 E-mail: sales@cctv-uk.com

A D Litho, Unit 3 Wycombe Industrial Mall, West End Street, High Wycombe, Buckinghamshire, HP11 2QY Tel: (01494) 536117 Fax: (01494) 531298 E-mail: adlitho@aol.com

A D M Imaging, 59-61 Summer Lane, Birmingham, B19 3TH Tel: 0121-359 5424 Fax: 0121-359 7038 E-mail: info@abmimaging.co.uk

A D P Marketing Services, Unit 5 Carr Mills, 919 Bradford Road, Birstall, Batley, West Yorkshire, WF17 9JY Tel: (01924) 470990 Fax: (01924) 471644 E-mail: mail@adpservices.net

A.E.Jennings Ltd, 5 Bellingham Trading Estate, Franthorne Way, London, SE6 3BX Tel: (020) 8695 8950 Fax: (020) 8698 0556 E-mail: studio@aejennings

A E Simmons Ltd, Bilton Road, Chelmsford, CM1 2UJ Tel: (01245) 352480 Fax: (01245) 359733 E-mail: sales@simmonsprint.co.uk

A F Litho Ltd, Grenaby Works, Grenaby Road, Croydon, CR0 2EJ Tel: (020) 8689 7849 Fax: (020) 8689 0479 E-mail: sales@aflitho.co.uk

A & J Print Services, 330 London Road, Westcliff-on-Sea, Essex, SS0 7JJ Tel: (01702) 348456 Fax: (01702) 348456

A M Print, Lemsford Road, Hatfield, Hertfordshire, AL10 0DE Tel: (01707) 271512 Fax: (01707) 271512 E-mail: enquiries@amprint.co.uk

▶ A M V Supplies, Laser Quay, Culpeper Close, Medway City Estate, Rochester, Kent, ME2 4HU Tel: (01634) 296900 Fax: (01634) 296990

A R Facer Ltd, Kerry St, Horsforth, Leeds, LS18 4AW Tel: 0113-258 2551 Fax: 0113-259 0868E-mail: sales@facerprinters.demon.co.uk

A Romanes & Son Ltd, Pitreavie Business Park, Dunfermline, Fife, KY11 8QS Tel: (01383) 728201 Fax: (01383) 737040 E-mail: advertising@dunfermlinepress.co.uk

A1 Business Service Centre, 94 University Avenue, Belfast, BT7 1GY Tel: (028) 9032 3334 Fax: (028) 9023 8601 E-mail: a1businessservicecentre@hotmail.com

Aaron Printing Ltd, Aaron House, Island Farm Avenue, West Molesey, Surrey, KT8 2RG Tel: (020) 8224 1122 Fax: (020) 8224 8624 E-mail: gary@aaronprintingltd.com

Abacus Lithographic Printers Ltd, 34-38 Gloucester Way, London, EC1R 0BN Tel: (020) 7278 4637 Fax: (020) 7278 8535 E-mail: sales@abacusprinting.com

Abbotsgate Printers, Lincoln Street, Hull, HU2 0PB Tel: (01482) 225257 Fax: (01482) 225559 E-mail: abbotsgateprint@aol.com

Acorn Print (North Space), 60 Hampton Street, Birmingham, B19 3LU Tel: (01902) 630733 Fax: (01902) 608540 E-mail: sales@acornprint.uk.com

Adams Of Rye Ltd, 8 High Street, Rye, East Sussex, TN31 7JH Tel: (01797) 223136 Fax: (01797) 223380 E-mail: adamsrye@aol.com

Adare Halcyon Ltd, Park Mill, Clayton West, Huddersfield, HD8 9QQ Tel: (01484) 863411 Fax: (01484) 862355 E-mail: info@adare.com

Adline Press, 5 Bear Court, Basingstoke, Hampshire, RG24 8QT Tel: (01256) 463779 Fax: (01256) 840591 E-mail: design@adline-group.com

Aichess Print, Hoo Farm Industrial Estate, Worcester Road, Kidderminster, Worcestershire, DY11 7RA Tel: (01562) 744517 Fax: (01562) 746067

Alanders Hindson Ltd, Merlin Way, New York Business Park, Newcastle upon Tyne, NE27 0YT Tel: 0191-280 0400 Fax: 0191-280 0401 E-mail: info@elandershindson.co.uk

Albanian Press Ltd, 107 Camp Road, St. Albans, Hertfordshire, AL1 5HL Tel: (01727) 853495 Fax: (01727) 846690 E-mail: info@albanian-press.co.uk

Albert Taylor & Sons,Limited, Thames House, Thames Street, Rotherham, South Yorkshire, S60 1LU Tel: (01709) 515131 Fax: (01709) 515135 E-mail: info@taylorsprint.com

Albion Press, 41a Justice Street, Aberdeen, AB11 5HS Tel: (01224) 644242 Fax: (01224) 644060 E-mail: info@albionpress.fsnet.co.uk

Aldebaran Print & Design, 1 Ariane, Tamworth, Staffordshire, B79 7XF Tel: (01827) 50417 Fax: (01827) 63773 E-mail: info@myprinters.co.uk

Aldon Brearley Print, The Engine House, Ashley Lane, Shipley, West Yorkshire, BD17 7DB Tel: (01274) 583192 Fax: (01274) 532862 E-mail: aldon.brearley@btconet.co.uk

Ian Allan Publishing Ltd, Riverdene Business Park, Molesey Road, Walton-On-Thames, Surrey, KT12 4RG Tel: (01780) 484630 Fax: (01932) 266601 E-mail: sales@ianallanpub.co.uk

Allbrook Printers, 12 Fulmar Crescent, Hemel Hempstead, Hertfordshire, HP1 1SG Tel: (01442) 240748 Fax: (01442) 240748 E-mail: steve@allbrookprinters.co.uk

Allinson's, Allinson House, Lincoln Way, Fairfield Industrial Estate, Louth, Lincolnshire, LN11 0LS Tel: (01507) 600911 Fax: (01507) 600434 E-mail: admin@allinsonwilcox.co.uk

Allprint Ltd, Llantrisant Business Park, Llantrisant, Pontyclun, Mid Glamorgan, CF72 8LF Tel: (01443) 228555 Fax: (01443) 237477 E-mail: sales@allprint2000.com

Alpha Printing Services, 227b Withington Road, Manchester, M16 8LU Tel: 0161-862 9922 Fax: 0161-862 9944 E-mail: sales@alphaprint.com

Alphagraphics, 68 Darlington Street, Wolverhampton, WV1 4ND Tel: (01902) 711151 Fax: (01902) 710174 E-mail: wolves016@alphagraphics.co.uk

Alsager Printing Co. Ltd, Excalibur Industrial Estate, Fields Road, Alsager, Stoke-on-Trent, ST7 2LX Tel: (01270) 873897 Fax: (01270) 882804

Andress Printing Co. Ltd, 17 Abercorn Close, South Croydon, Surrey, CR2 8TG Tel: (020) 8651 3005 Fax: (020) 8651 3025

Apollo Press, 8 Decoy Road, Worthing, West Sussex, BN14 8ND Tel: (01903) 232444 Fax: (01903) 230354 E-mail: dyerpress72@aol.com

Aps Printers, 4a West Parade, Lincoln, LN1 1JT Tel: (01522) 525066 Fax: (01522) 525066 E-mail: info@apsprinters.co.uk

Aquarius Press, Aquarius House, Montpelier Business Park, Leacon Road, Ashford, Kent, TN23 4FG Tel: (01233) 662544 Fax: (01233) 662577 E-mail: sales@aquarius.invictornet.co.uk

Area Print & Graphic, Unit 8 Marsland Street, Hazel Grove, Stockport, Cheshire, SK7 4ER Tel: 0161-483 5034 Fax: 0161-483 5034

Argun Printers, 344 Mare Street, London, E8 1HA Tel: (020) 8985 7879 Fax: (020) 8985 3668 E-mail: info@argun.co.uk

Armour Print & Design, 92b Audley Street, Reading, RG30 1BS Tel: 0118-958 8957 Fax: 0118-959 4816 E-mail: dave@armourprint.co.uk

Armstrong Printing Ltd, Unit 4 Carsebridge Court, Alloa, Clackmannanshire, FK10 3LQ Tel: (01259) 722930 Fax: (01259) 721080 E-mail: sales@armstrongprinting.co.uk

Arron Print Ltd, Unit 30 Enfield Industrial Estate, Redditch, Worcestershire, B97 6BY Tel: (01527) 67295 Fax: (01527) 584509 E-mail: info@arron.co.uk

Ashford Press, Bottings Industrial Estate, Curdridge, Southampton, SO30 2DY Tel: (01489) 785311 Fax: (01489) 780716 E-mail: production@asfordpress.co.uk

Ashton Printers, London Street, Fleetwood, Lancashire, FY7 6JE Tel: (01253) 874549 Fax: (01253) 773773 E-mail: ashton@ashtonprinters.fsnet.co.uk

Aspect Design, 89 Newtown Road, Malvern, Worcestershire, WR14 1PD Tel: (01684) 561567 Fax: (01684) 560041 E-mail: help@aspect-design.net

Frank Aspinall & Co., Unit 7, Offerton Industrial Estate, Hempshaw Lane, Stockport, Cheshire, SK2 5TJ Tel: 0161-480 2707 Fax: 0161-480 2707 E-mail: frankaspinall@hotmail.com

Astute, 44-46 Brechin Road, Forfar, Angus, DD8 3JX Tel: (01307) 464467 Fax: (01307) 464561 E-mail: sales@astute.uk.com

Atkinson Print Ltd, 10-11 Lower Church Street, Hartlepool, Cleveland, TS24 7DJ Tel: (01429) 267849 Fax: (01429) 865416 E-mail: enquiries@atkinsonprint.com

Stephen Austin & Sons Ltd, Caxton Hill, Hertford, SG13 7LU Tel: (01992) 584955 Fax: (01992) 500021 E-mail: sales@stephenaustin.co.uk

Automedia Ltd, Prince William Road, Loughborough, Leicestershire, LE11 5GU Tel: (01509) 263411 Fax: (01509) 610062 E-mail: info@automedia.ltd.uk

▶ Axicon Auto Id Ltd, Church Road, Weston-on-the-Green, Bicester, Oxfordshire, OX25 3QP Tel: (01869) 351166 Fax: (01869) 351205 E-mail: info@axicon.com

B A F Printers Ltd, Portland House, Cross Chancellor Street, Leeds, LS6 2TG Tel: 0113-243 9788 Fax: 0113-243 8741 E-mail: office@bafprinters.co.uk

B & D Print Services Ltd, Moss Side Industrial Estatemarathon Place, Leyland, PR26 7QN Tel: (01772) 435050 Fax: (01772) 426601 E-mail: sales@bdprints.co.uk

B J T Print Services Ltd, Common La, Kenilworth, Warwickshire, CV8 2EL Tel: (01926) 852085 Fax: (01926) 859591

B K Screen Print, Queen Street, Carlisle, CA2 5TP Tel: (01228) 542957 Fax: (01228) 514736

B S C Print, B S C House, 48 Weir Road, Wimbledon, London, SW19 8UG Tel: (020) 8947 8571 Fax: (020) 8947 3319 E-mail: sales@bscprint..co.uk

B W P Advertising, 5 Long Meadow Mills Industrial Estate, Dixon Street, Kidderminster, Worcestershire, DY10 1HH Tel: (01562) 744513 Fax: (01562) 820045

Baber Rollaprint Ltd, Coombs Road, Halesowen, West Midlands, B62 8AJ Tel: 0121-559 5111 Fax: 0121-559 6594 E-mail: creativity@baber-rollaprint.co.uk

Albert E. Bailey & Sons Ltd, 25 Holywell Row, London, EC2A 4XE Tel: (020) 7729 1442 E-mail: baileyprintgroup@talk21.com

Barden Print Ltd, Bay Hall Print Works, Common Road, Huddersfield, HD1 5EU Tel: (01484) 422522 Fax: (01484) 435158 E-mail: design@bardenprint.com

Barham & Moore Ltd, 8 Grafton Place, Chelmsford, CM2 6TG Tel: (01245) 450554 Fax: (01245) 450845 E-mail: sales@barham-print.co.uk

Barr Printers Glenrothes Ltd, 4 Faraday Road, Glenrothes, Fife, KY6 2RU Tel: (01592) 776870 Fax: (01592) 770779 E-mail: sales@barrprinters.co.uk

Bartham Press (Watford) Ltd, Unit A, Park Avenue Estate, Sundon Park, Luton, LU3 3BP Tel: (01582) 573471 Fax: (01582) 582024

Bartlett Printing, Swan Yard, Okehampton Street, Exeter, EX4 1HU Tel: (01392) 254086 Fax: (01392) 256224 E-mail: sales@bartlett-printing.co.uk

Beacon Printers Penarth Ltd, Leyshons Buildings, Cornerswell Road, Penarth, South Glamorgan, CF64 2XS Tel: (029) 2070 8415 Fax: (029) 2070 3754 E-mail: sales@beaconprinters.co.uk

G.W. Beamand & Son Ltd, 7-9 Gibraltar Walk, Bethnel Green, London, E2 7LH Tel: (020) 7729 1442 Fax: (020) 7729 0178 E-mail: baileyprintgroup@talk21.com

Beaumanor Press Ltd, 23 Bath Lane, Leicester, LE3 5BF Tel: 0116-233 1337 Fax: 0116-233 5337 E-mail: sales@beaumanor.co.uk

Bendles Print Ltd, Unit 2, Higher Furzeham, Brixham, Devon, TQ5 8QP Tel: (01803) 616161 Fax: (01803) 859446 E-mail: sales@bendles.co.uk

Benwell Cebard Ltd, 24 Crimscott Street, London, SE1 5TE Tel: (020) 7237 5111 Fax: (020) 7252 0683 E-mail: info@benwellsebard.co.uk

Bezier Corporate Print, 145 Sterte Road, Poole, Dorset, BH15 2AF Tel: (01202) 681466 Fax: (01202) 670010 E-mail: sales@bezier.co.uk

Biltmore Printers, 14 Manners View, Newport, Isle of Wight, PO30 5FA Tel: (01983) 529788 Fax: (01983) 825528 E-mail: info@biltmoreprinters.co.uk

Bindmont Print Services Ltd, Heywood Distribution Park, Heywood, Lancashire, OL10 2TT Tel: (01706) 360011 E-mail: bps@btinternet.com

▶ Blackhammer Ltd, 30 Theydon Road, London, E5 9NA Tel: (020) 8442 4040 Fax: (020) 8806 7040 E-mail: mark@blackhammer.net

Blackmore Ltd, Longmead, Shaftesbury, Dorset, SP7 8PX Tel: (01747) 853034 Fax: (01747) 854500 E-mail: sales@.blackmore.co.uk

Blackshaw Sykes & Morris Ltd, PO Box 18, Bolton, BL3 6NH Tel: (01204) 521438 Fax: (01204) 364819

Blairgowrie Printers, 7 Reform Street, Blairgowrie, Perthshire, PH10 6BD Tel: (01250) 872102

Bookham Print & Design, Homestead, Eastwick Road, Bookham, Leatherhead, Surrey, KT23 4BA Tel: (01372) 454506 Fax: (01372) 452087

Border Offset Printers Ltd, Rigg Street, Caldewgate, Carlisle, CA2 5TN Tel: (01228) 526675 Fax: (01228) 515245

George Boyden & Son Ltd, York House, 17 Rother Street, Stratford-Upon-Avon, Warwickshire, CV37 6NB Tel: (01789) 266261 Fax: (01789) 269519 E-mail: news@stratford-herald.co.uk

Brewers Business Solutions Ltd, Water-Ma-Trout, Helston, Cornwall, TR13 0LW Tel: (01326) 563424 Fax: (01326) 563606

Brian Lowndes Print Ltd, Graphichouse, Portland Street, Walsall, WS2 8BE Tel: (01922) 725282 Fax: (01922) 720981 E-mail: mail@blprint.co.uk

Bridgend Printers Edinburgh Ltd, 40 Constitution Street, Edinburgh, EH6 6RS Tel: 0131-554 3883 Fax: 0131-555 0516

Brown & Son, Crow Arch Lane, Ringwood, Hampshire, BH24 1PD Tel: (01425) 476133 Fax: (01425) 477063 E-mail: sales@vanboorn.co.uk

Brunton Business Publications Ltd, Thruxton Down House, Thruxton Down, Andover, Hampshire, SP11 8PR Tel: (01264) 889533 Fax: (01264) 889524 E-mail: publications@brunton.co.uk

Bryning & Wright Printers, Buckley House, Buckley Road Indust Estate, Rochdale, Lancashire, OL12 9EF Tel: (01706) 345897 Fax: (01706) 632767 E-mail: info@atecgroupe.co.uk

Buccleuch Printers Ltd, Carnarvon Street, Hawick, Roxburghshire, TD9 7EB Tel: (01450) 372566 Fax: (01450) 375146 E-mail: info@buccleuchprinters.co.uk

Burgess Printing Ltd, Unit M3 Cody Court, Salford, M50 2GE Tel: 0161-872 7881 Fax: 0161-876 0636

Burrups Ltd, St. Ives House, Lavington Street, London, SE1 0NX Tel: (020) 7928 8844 Fax: (020) 7902 6572 E-mail: london@burrups.com

C P Offset Ltd, Kellaw Road, Darlington, County Durham, DL1 4YA Tel: (01325) 462315 Fax: (01325) 462767 E-mail: administrator@banff-buchan.ac.uk

C & R, Bruce House, Warren Park Way, Enderby, LE19 4ZW Tel: 0116-284 7464 Fax: 0116-284 7440 E-mail: info@candr.co.uk

Calderprint, 80 Manchester Road, Burnley, Lancashire, BB11 1QZ Tel: (01282) 831530 Fax: (01282) 831524 E-mail: enquiries@calderprint.co.uk

Capper Print, Lanelay Road Industrial Estate, Talbot Green, Pontyclun, Mid Glamorgan, CF72 8XX Tel: (01443) 225500 Fax: (01443) 235290 E-mail: sales@capperprint.co.uk

Caprin, Unit 2 Park Industrial Estate, Frogmore, St. Albans, Hertfordshire, AL2 2DR Tel: (01727) 872021 Fax: (01727) 875012 E-mail: office@caprin.co.uk

Cardmaster UK, 2 Christopher Road, Leeds, LS6 2JX Tel: 0113-244 2265 Fax: 0113-244 2265 E-mail: bouncers@inname.com

Carfax Cards Ltd, 76 Glentham Road, London, SW13 9JJ Tel: (020) 8748 1122 Fax: (020) 8748 7110 E-mail: carfax@business-cards.co.uk

Carson Stationery & Print Ltd, 107-109 West Street, Sheffield, S1 4EQ Tel: 0114-272 0342 Fax: 0114-281 2996 E-mail: carson-sp@zoom.co.uk

Cavalry Creative Services, 11 Bury Road, Hatfield, Hertfordshire, AL10 8BJ Tel: (01707) 274584 Fax: (01707) 321043 E-mail: cavalry@ntlworld.com

▶ CDMS, Fallows Way, Whiston, Prescot, Merseyside, L35 1RZ Tel: 0151-290 5500 Fax: 0151-290 5599E-mail: sales@edns.co.uk

Celectron Printing, 18-18a Unit, Vale Business Park, Llandow, Cowbridge, South Glamorgan, CF71 7PF Tel: (01446) 774801 Fax: (01446) 775285 E-mail: info@soprint.co.uk

Centreprint Graphics Ltd, Units 1-2, Lanesfield Drive, Ettingshall, Wolverhampton, WV4 6UA Tel: (01902) 402693 Fax: (01902) 491794 E-mail: sales@centreprint.co.uk

Cestrian, Stanley Green TRDG Estate, Earl Road, Cheadle Hulme, Cheadle, Cheshire, SK8 6QD Tel: 0161-488 3300 Fax: 0161-488 3301 E-mail: reception@cestrian.co.uk

Chapel Press Ltd, Parkgate Close, Bredbury, Stockport, Cheshire, SK6 2SZ Tel: 0161-406 9495 Fax: 0161-292 0200 E-mail: info@chapelpress.com

Chas Hunt & Co. Ltd, Unit 2 Senlan Industrial Estate, Rhymney River Bridge Road, Cardiff, CF23 9AF Tel: (029) 2048 4476 Fax: (029) 2048 9092 E-mail: hunt.chas@virgin.net

Charles Raper, 255 Amhurst Road, London, N16 7UN Tel: (020) 7254 7877 E-mail: charlesraper@btconnect.com

Chase Design & Print, White Cottage Works, Rumer Hill Road, Cannock, Staffordshire, WS11 8EX Tel: (01543) 462334 Fax: (01543) 505707 E-mail: chasedesign2000@hotmail.com

Chase Group Printing & Stationery Ltd, Unit 11 Heston Industrial Mall, Church Rd, Hounslow, TW5 0LD Tel: (020) 8577 1930 Fax: (020) 8572 3065 E-mail: info@chasegrp.co.uk

Chelma Graphics, Unit 17 Brymau 4 Estate, River Lane, Saltney, Chester, CH4 8RF Tel: (01244) 674969 Fax: (01244) 677081 E-mail: sales@chelmagraphics.co.uk

Chrystal & Hill Ltd, 14-30 Woodhead Road, South Nitshill Industrial Estate, Glasgow, G53 7WA Tel: 0141-880 6600 Fax: 0141-880 6611 E-mail: sales@chrystal-hill.co.uk

City Press, The Old Courthouse, 1 The Paddock, Chatham, Kent, ME4 4RE Tel: (01634) 832820 Fax: (01634) 818741

City Print Milton Keynes Ltd, 17 Denbigh Hall Industrial Estate, Denbigh Hall, Bletchley, Milton Keynes, MK3 7QT Tel: (01908) 377085 Fax: (01908) 649335 E-mail: sales@cityprint.net

Clanpress (Kings Lynn) Ltd, 1 Dundee Court, Hamburg Way, King's Lynn, Norfolk, PE30 2ND Tel: (01553) 772737 Fax: (01553) 768403 E-mail: clanpress@aol.com

Clarity, Forge Road, Willenhall, West Midlands, WV12 4HD Tel: (01902) 638340 Fax: (01902) 637594

Clarkeprint Ltd, 45-47 Stour Street, Birmingham, B18 7AJ Tel: 0121-454 7117 Fax: 0121-454 8404 E-mail: sales@clarkeprint.co.uk

Claymore Graphics Ltd, 63 Cotton Street, Aberdeen, AB11 5EG Tel: (01224) 576176 Fax: (01224) 584431 E-mail: mail@claymoregraphics.co.uk

Clifton Packaging Group P.L.C., Maridian Business Park, Centurion Way, Leicester, LE19 1WH Tel: 0116-289 3355 Fax: 0116-289 1113 E-mail: info@cliftonpackaging.co.uk

Clovertone Ltd, 9 Canal Walk, London, N1 5SA Tel: (020) 7923 0300 Fax: (020) 7923 0266 E-mail: sales@clovertone.co.uk

Arthur W. Clowes Ltd, Unit 2 Pepper Road Hazel Grove, Hazel Grove, Stockport, Cheshire, SK7 5BW Tel: 0161-483 1827 Fax: 0161-483 1827 E-mail: sales@clowesprinters.co.uk

▶ Coates & Parker Ltd, 36 Market Place, Warminster, Wiltshire, BA12 9AN Tel: (01985) 213030 Fax: (01985) 217680 E-mail: sales@coatesandparker.co.uk

College Hill Press Ltd, 37 Webber Street, London, SE1 8QW Tel: (020) 7633 0543 Fax: (020) 7633 0181 E-mail: sales@collegehillpress.co.uk

Colophon Press Printers Ltd, 17 Peterfield Road, Carlisle, CA3 0EY Tel: (01228) 524444 Fax: (01228) 590090 E-mail: colophon@btconnect.com

Colourscope Offset Ltd, 6 Beckenham Business Centre, Kent House Lane, Beckenham, Kent, BR3 1LB Tel: (020) 8778 3112 Fax: (020) 8776 8779

Communique Print Services Ltd, 3-11 Little Peter Street, Manchester, M15 4PS Tel: 0161-274 0105 Fax: 0161-236 1251 E-mail: manchester@staniforth.co.uk

Communitis Chorleys Ltd, Manston Lane, Leeds, LS15 8AH Tel: 0113-225 5000 Fax: 0113-225 5400 E-mail: sales@chorleys-communisis.co.uk

Compass Print Ltd, Hareness Road, Altens Industrial Estate, Aberdeen, AB12 3LE Tel: (01224) 875987 Fax: (01224) 896137 E-mail: info@compassprint.co.uk

Connect Colour Ltd, Unit C, Northbridge Road, Berkhamsted, Hertfordshire, HP4 1EH Tel: (01442) 879701 Fax: (01442) 879702 E-mail: sales@connektcolour.com

PRINTERS, GENERAL OR COMMERCIAL OR JOBBING OR ALL TYPES – *continued*

Cooper Printers, 43 Manse Street, Fraserburgh, Aberdeenshire, AB43 9JB Tel: (01346) 518831 Fax: (01346) 511311 E-mail: cooper.printers@virgin.net

Copywise, Unit 6, Block A6, Coombswood Way, Halesowen, West Midlands, B62 8BH Tel: 0121-559 9998

Corners Direct Ltd, Hillam Road, Bradford, West Yorkshire, BD2 1QL Tel: (01274) 733213 Fax: (01274) 721128 E-mail: peterwright@cornersdirect.co.uk

Coubrough & McKeracher (Printers) Ltd, 8 Falfield Street, Glasgow, G5 8HL Tel: 0141-429 0487 Fax: 0141-429 0515 E-mail: enquiries@cmckprinters.com

County Press, County Press Buildings, Station Road, Bala, Gwynedd, LL23 7PG Tel: (01678) 520262 Fax: (01678) 521251 E-mail: budgerigarworld@msn.com

Craneprint Ltd, Marshalls Industrial Estate, Sedgley Street, Wolverhampton, WV2 3AJ Tel: (01902) 450505 Fax: (01902) 450980 E-mail: sales@craneprint.co.uk

▶ Crescent Press Ltd, 9 Wainwright Street, Birmingham, B6 5TH Tel: 0121-326 9223 Fax: 0121-326 9224 E-mail: info@crescentpress.com

Crossprint Ltd, Newport Business Park, 21 Barry Way, Newport, Isle of Wight, PO30 5GY Tel: (01983) 524885 Fax: (01983) 522878 E-mail: info@crossprint.co.uk

F. Crowe & Sons Ltd, 50 Hurricane Way, Norwich, NR6 6JB Tel: (01603) 403349 Fax: (01603) 485164 E-mail: sales@crowes.co.uk

CTD, Unit 2, CTD House, Summit Business Park, Hanworth Road, Sunbury-on-Thames, Middlesex, TW16 5BH Tel: 01932 771300 Fax: 01932 789229 E-mail: sales@ctdprinters.com

Culm Print Ltd, Unit 2 Blundells Road, Tiverton, Devon, EX16 4BZ Tel: (01884) 258904 Fax: (01884) 242466 E-mail: andywestcote@ukonline.co.uk

D R Labelling Systems Ltd, 12 Westgarth Place, College Milton Industrial Estate, East Kilbride, Glasgow, G74 5NT Tel: (01355) 221200 Fax: (01355) 221737 E-mail: sales@drlabelling.co.uk

D W Jones (Printers) Ltd, Beverley St, Port Talbot, West Glamorgan, SA13 1DY Tel: (01639) 883228 Fax: (01639) 882725 E-mail: sales@dwjones.com

Dalton Printers, Dalton House, Thesiger Street, Cardiff, CF24 4BN Tel: (029) 2023 6832 Fax: (029) 2066 6516 E-mail: daltonprinters@dial.pipex.com

Data Print, 11A West Way, Oxford, OX2 0JB Tel: (01865) 243624 Fax: (01865) 243624 E-mail: info@dataprintoxford.co.uk

Dax Printing Co. Ltd, Free Street, Bishops Waltham, Southampton, SO32 1EE Tel: (01489) 891006 Fax: (01489) 891699 E-mail: general@daxprinting.co.uk

Deacon Bros Printers Ltd, Old Mill Park, Kirkintilloch, Glasgow, G66 1SW Tel: 0141-776 5272 Fax: 0141-776 1094 E-mail: sales@deacon-brothers.com

Delta Print, 19 Potters Lane, Kiln Farm, Milton Keynes, MK11 3HF Tel: (01908) 568020 Fax: (01908) 261383 E-mail: sales@deltaprint.fsworld.co.uk

Deltaprint Printers, 5 Warner Industrial Park, Warner Way, Sudbury, Suffolk, CO10 2GG Tel: (01787) 370714 Fax: (01787) 881065 E-mail: info@delta-print.co.uk

Deltor Communications Ltd, Unit C Long Acre, Saltash, Cornwall, PL12 6LZ Tel: (01752) 841717 Fax: (01752) 850450 E-mail: enquiries@deltor.uk

Designs To Print, 15 Devonshire Rd, London, W4 2EU Tel: (020) 8995 5155 Fax: (020) 8995 5156

Documedia, Northern Way, Bury St. Edmunds, Suffolk, IP32 6NR Tel: (01284) 762201 Fax: (01284) 764033 E-mail: sales@documedia.co.uk

R.R. Donnelley UK, Flaxby Moor, Knaresborough, North Yorkshire, HG5 0XJ Tel: (01423) 796500 Fax: (01423) 796501

Down Recorder, 2-4 Church Street, Downpatrick, County Down, BT30 6EJ Tel: (028) 4461 3711 Fax: (028) 4461 4624 E-mail: advertis@downrecorder.uk

Edward Dudfield Ltd, 4 Whilems Works, Forest Road, Ilford, Essex, IG6 3HJ Tel: (020) 8500 4455 Fax: (020) 8500 4488 E-mail: sales@dudfields.co.uk

Dudley Office Products Ltd, 5-6 Empire Way, Wembley, Middlesex, HA9 0XA Tel: (020) 8980 7199 Fax: (0870) 4442883 E-mail: sales@dudley.co.uk

Duffield Printers Ltd, 421 Kirkstall Road, Leeds, LS4 2HA Tel: 0113-279 3011 Fax: 0113-231 0098 E-mail: info@duffieldprinters.co.uk

Dunnsprint Ltd, Clarence Works, Clarence Road, Eastbourne, East Sussex, BN22 8HJ Tel: (01323) 410902 Fax: (01323) 410573 E-mail: sales@dunnsprint.co.uk

J.S. Dutton Ltd, Cale Street, Cale Green, Stockport, Cheshire, SK2 6SW Tel: 0161-480 2346 Fax: 0161-480 0728 E-mail: studio@jsdutton.co.uk

E G Brown Bristol Ltd, 63 Quarrington Road, Bristol, BS7 9PJ Tel: 0117-951 3215 Fax: 0117-935 4250

Econoprint Ltd, Unit 20 Castlebrae Business Centre, Peffer Place, Edinburgh, EH16 4BB Tel: 0131-652 6052 Fax: 0131-652 6026

Eden, 1 Little Dockray, Penrith, Cumbria, CA11 7HL Tel: (01768) 869000 Fax: (01768) 865578 E-mail: david@edengraphics.co.uk

Eden River Press Ltd, Units C-D, Charlwoods Business Centre, East Grinstead, West Sussex, RH19 2HH Tel: (01342) 313577 Fax: (01342) 324125 E-mail: mail@edenriverpress.co.uk

Edward Thompson International Ltd, Richmond Street, Sheepfolds Industrial Estate, Sunderland, SR5 1BQ Tel: 0191-514 4199 Fax: 0191-567 7510 E-mail: info@edward-thompson.com

Efficiency Print Ltd, Engine Lane, Stourbridge, West Midlands, DY9 7AQ Tel: (01384) 891986 Fax: (01384) 893437 E-mail: colin@effprint.u-net.com

▶ Elmar Graphics, Unit 3, 8 Becket Road, Montague Industrial Estate, London, N18 3PN Tel: (020) 8807 2350 Fax: (020) 8803 0370 E-mail: elmarhmg@globalnet.co.uk

Elsam Cross & Co., 5-6 London Road, Spalding, Lincolnshire, PE11 2TA Tel: (01775) 723758 Fax: (01775) 768575 E-mail: geoff.hemsil@virgin.net

Engravings Services Ltd, 21 Radnor Street, Hulme, Manchester, M15 5RD Tel: 0161-226 1197 Fax: 0161-227 9554 E-mail: studio@engraving.pennine.net

Entaprint Ltd, 1 Penfold Road Woodcote, Cranleigh, Surrey, GU6 8NZ Tel: (01483) 273173

F S Moore Ltd, Petersham House, 57a Hatton Garden, London, EC1N 8JG Tel: (020) 7232 4700 Fax: (020) 7232 4750

Falcon Press, St James Mill Road, St James Business Park, Northampton, NN5 5JW Tel: (01604) 759262 Fax: (01604) 581482 E-mail: sales@falconpress.co.uk

Falder Matthews Ltd, 6 Seax Way, Basildon, Essex, SS15 6SW Tel: (01268) 413611 Fax: (01268) 541637 E-mail: enquiries@fmprint.co.uk

Ferguson Print Keswick Ltd, 24 St John Street, Keswick, Cumbria, CA12 5AT Tel: (01768) 772486 Fax: (01768) 771121 E-mail: fergusonbrosltd@btconnect.com

Fericon Press Ltd, 12 Stadium Way, Tilehurst, Reading, RG30 6BX Tel: 0118-945 6100 Fax: 0118-945 4146 E-mail: fericon@dercon.co.uk

Fine Print Stockport Ltd, Unit 6f Lowick Close, Hazel Grove, Stockport, Cheshire, SK7 5ED Tel: 0161-484 2244 Fax: 0161-484 2255 E-mail: info@fineprint-stockport.co.uk

Fisherprint Ltd, Padholme Road, Peterborough, PE1 5UL Tel: (01733) 341444 Fax: (01733) 349416 E-mail: enquiries@fisherprint.co.uk

Flavell Printers, Laurieston Road, Grangemouth, Stirlingshire, FK3 8XX Tel: (01324) 489900 Fax: (01324) 489911E-mail: print@flavell.com

Flayre Press & Printing Services, Unit 1, Thames Industrial Estate, High St South, Dunstable, Bedfordshire, LU6 3HD Tel: (01582) 605085 Fax: (01582) 472249

Foxe Graphics Ltd, Enterprise Road, Golf Road Industrial Estate, Mablethorpe, Lincolnshire, LN12 1NB Tel: (01507) 477748 Fax: (01507) 473128 E-mail: alex@foxe.co.uk

▶ Foxhill Commercial Printers, 80 Sidney Street, Cleethorpes, South Humberside, DN35 7NQ Tel: (01472) 242777 Fax: (01472) 242255 E-mail: spectrumprint@lineone.net

Frewer Brothers Ltd, 3 Wealdstone Road, Sutton, Surrey, SM3 9QN Tel: (020) 8641 7171 Fax: (020) 8644 4779 E-mail: mail@frewerbrothers.co.uk

Friars & Co., Unit 2b Shakespeare Industrial Estate, Shakespeare Street, Watford, WD24 5RU Tel: (01923) 249420 Fax: (01923) 818142 E-mail: friars@ukf.net

G & B Printers, Unit 4 Mount Road Industrial Estate, Feltham, Middlesex, TW13 6AR Tel: (020) 8755 1822 Fax: (020) 8893 3854 E-mail: info@gbprinters.co.uk

G G Stevenson Printers, 2 Lower Pleasance, Dundee, DD1 5QU Tel: (01382) 225768 E-mail: stevensonprinters@lineone.net

G M Business Print & Systems Ltd, Cornhill, Liverpool, L1 8DZ Tel: 0151-709 0676 Fax: 0151-709 0678 E-mail: sales@gmbusinessprint.co.uk

G P S Colour Graphics Ltd, Alexander Road, Belfast, BT6 9HP Tel: (028) 9070 2020 Fax: (028) 9079 8463 E-mail: sales@gpscolour.co.uk

G & S Jones, Unit 1e Bersham Enterprise Centre, Colliery Road, Rhostyllen, Wrexham, Clwyd, LL14 4EG Tel: (01978) 263160 Fax: (01978) 263135 E-mail: graham@gsjonesprint.co.uk

Garden House Press Ltd, G H P House, 23 Aintree Road, Greenford, Middlesex, UB6 7LA Tel: (0870) 7773300 Fax: (0870) 7773301 E-mail: sales@garden-house.co.uk

Garrett & Mcgann, 9 Warren Road, Cheadle Hulme, Cheadle, Cheshire, SK8 5AA Tel: 0161-485 3309 Fax: 0161-485 6327 E-mail: info@garrettmcgann.u-net.com

Gemini Press Ltd, Unit A1 Dolphin Way, Shoreham-by-Sea, West Sussex, BN43 6NZ Tel: (01273) 464884 Fax: (01273) 464744 E-mail: info@gemini-group.co.uk

Ghyll Print Ltd, Ghyll Indust Estate, Heathfield, East Sussex, TN21 8AW Tel: (01435) 866211 Fax: (01435) 861268 E-mail: info@ghyllprint.co.uk

Glendale Print & Finishing Ltd, 8 Orchard Business Centre, North Farm Road, Tunbridge Wells, Kent, TN2 3XF Tel: (01892) 544988 Fax: (01892) 548181 E-mail: info@glendaleprintandfinishing.co.uk

Glenwood Printing, 4 Peter Baines Industrial Estate, Woods Lane, Derby, DE22 3UD Tel: (01332) 368674 Fax: (01332) 381444 E-mail: sales@glenwood-printing.co.uk

Gordon Press Ltd, Caxton House, 2 Bath House Road, Croydon, CR0 4TT Tel: (020) 8684 0313 Fax: (020) 8689 6715 E-mail: sales@thegordonpress.com

Gorman Shorrock & Davies Ltd, 52 Heyrod Street, Manchester, M1 2WW Tel: 0161-273 3909 Fax: 0161-273 6690

Graphic Art Cambridge Ltd, Trinity Hall Farm Industrial Estate, Nuffield Road, Cambridge, CB4 1TG Tel: (01223) 424421 Fax: (01223) 426040 E-mail: mail@graphic-art.co.uk

Graphico Printing Ltd, 69-71 London Road, Croydon, CR0 2RF Tel: (020) 8681 1101 Fax: (020) 8688 8588 E-mail: sales@graphico.com

Greetings UK, South Orbital Trading Park, Hedon Road, Hull, HU9 1NN Tel: (01482) 328383 Fax: (01482) 621298

Grosvenor Northampton Ltd, Unit D Stonecircle Road, Round Spinney, Northampton, NN3 8RF Tel: (01604) 670673 Fax: (01604) 648438

Grosvenor Press, Station Yard, Station Approach, Shanklin, Isle of Wight, PO37 7AS Tel: (01983) 867030 Fax: (01983) 867030

Grosvenor Printing Co., 112-114 Grosvenor Road, Bristol, BS2 8YA Tel: 0117-955 6544 Fax: 0117-955 6544

Guardian Press Boston Ltd, Nelson Way, Boston, Lincolnshire, PE21 8TS Tel: (01205) 363497 Fax: (01205) 310575

Gwasg Helygain Ltd, 70 Kinmel Street, Rhyl, Clwyd, LL18 1AW Tel: (01745) 331411 Fax: (01745) 331310

H B Printing, 175 Bramhall Lane, Stockport, Cheshire, SK2 6JA Tel: 0161-480 5818 Fax: 0161-480 5819

H M Printers Ltd, The Cromwell Centre, 24-30 Minerva Road, London, NW10 6HH Tel: (020) 8965 4621 Fax: (020) 8965 4181 E-mail: print@hmprinters.com

H N Cooper, 353-355 High Street, West Bromwich, West Midlands, B70 9QG Tel: 0121-553 0836 Fax: 0121-553 0836

Halligan Direct Mail Ltd, 66 Addison Road, Bromley, BR2 9HQ Tel: (020) 8290 9000 Fax: (020) 8290 9002 E-mail: info@halligans.co.uk

Halstan & Co. Ltd, 2-10 Plantation Road, Amersham, Buckinghamshire, HP6 6HJ Tel: (01494) 725525 Fax: (01494) 432305 E-mail: sales@halstan.co.uk

Hammond Vivian Ltd, Power House, 27 Market Road, Richmond, Surrey, TW9 4LZ Tel: (020) 8876 6600 Fax: (020) 8392 1946 E-mail: info@hammondvivian.co.uk

Hands On Design & Print Ltd, The Rookery, Flansham Lane, Bognor Regis, West Sussex, PO22 6EP Tel: (01243) 583271

Handsfree Computing Ltd, Enterprise House, Old London Road, Hickstead, Haywards Heath, West Sussex, RH17 5LZ Tel: (01444) 880880 Fax: (01444) 880888 E-mail: info@hands-free.co.uk

Hart & Clough Ltd, Ezra House, Littlewood Drive, West 26 Industrial Estate, Cleckheaton, West Yorkshire, BD19 4TQ Tel: (01274) 863200 Fax: (01274) 863201 E-mail: info@hartandclough.co.uk

Hartington Litho Ltd, Marlborough Road, Lancing Business Park, Lancing, West Sussex, BN15 8UF Tel: (01903) 761401 Fax: (01903) 767301 E-mail: micheal@hartingtonlitho.co.uk

Haven Colourprint UK Ltd, The Print Works, London Road Industrial Estate, Pembroke Dock, Dyfed, SA72 4RZ Tel: (01646) 623700 Fax: (01646) 621121 E-mail: enquiries@havencolourprintuk.com

Marshall Hayward Ltd, Sharston Industrial Estate, Shentonfield Road, Sharston, Manchester, M22 4RW Tel: 0161-428 8062 Fax: 0161-491 4298

Headley Brothers Ltd, The Invicta Press, Queens Road, Ashford, Kent, TN24 8HH Tel: (01233) 623131 Fax: (01233) 612345 E-mail: printing@headley.co.uk

Heathcote Press, Harriott Drive, Heathcote Industrial Estate, Warwick, CV34 6TJ Tel: (01926) 883306 Fax: (01926) 314017 E-mail: heathcotepress@freeuk.com

The Hedgehog Press, Unit B5, Imperial Bus Estate, West Mill, Gravesend, Kent, DA11 0DL Tel: (01474) 322153 Fax: (01474) 535570 E-mail: info@thehedgehogpress.co.uk

Henry Cowan & Son Ltd, 40 Bethnal Green Road, London, E1 6HZ Tel: (020) 7739 8627 Fax: (020) 7739 0729 E-mail: sales@cowansdirect.co.uk

Henry Good, 37 Bowlers Croft, Basildon, Essex, SS14 3DZ Tel: (01268) 272880 Fax: (01268) 272887

The Herald Press Ltd, Burnside Drive, Arbroath, Angus, DD11 1NS Tel: (01241) 872000 Fax: (01241) 870707 E-mail: printing@theheraldpress.fsnet.co.uk

Heron Press, 19-24 White Hays North, Quartermaster Road, West Wilts Trading Estate, Westbury, Wiltshire, BA13 4JT Tel: (01373) 825602 Fax: (01373) 825603 E-mail: sales@heron-press.co.uk

Heronsgate Ltd, Unit 18-20 Herons Gate Trading Estate, Paycocke Road, Basildon, Essex, SS14 3EU Tel: (01268) 288637 Fax: (01268) 272585 E-mail: sales@heronsgateprint.com

Hillbury Press Ltd, Cranborne Industrial Estate, Cranborne Road, Potters Bar, Hertfordshire, EN6 3JN Tel: (01707) 658948 Fax: (01707) 655254 E-mail: printers@hillbury.co.uk

▶ Hine Labels Ltd, Hope Street, Rotherham, South Yorkshire, S60 1LH Tel: (01709) 369222 Fax: (01709) 363660 E-mail: enquiries@hinelabels.com

Hobs Reprographics, 9-11 Grosvenor Gardens, London, SW1W 0BD Tel: (020) 7834 1187 Fax: (020) 7834 0045 E-mail: grosvenor@hobsrepro.ndirect.com

Hodges Print & Design, 12 Hazeldell, Watton At Stone, Hertford, SG14 3SN Tel: (01920) 411288 Fax: (01920) 411288

HSP Milners, Ironworks Road, Barrow-in-Furness, Cumbria, LA14 2PG Tel: (01229) 823392 Fax: (01229) 870274 E-mail: headoffice@hsp-milners.demon.co.uk

Hudson & Pearson Ltd, Bradwood Works, Manchester Road, Dunnockshaw, Burnley, Lancashire, BB11 5PW Tel: (01706) 210582 Fax: (01706) 215692

Huxley Print Ltd, Unit 1 12 John Street, Walsall, WS2 8AF Tel: (01922) 623691 Fax: (01922) 623206 E-mail: info@huxleyprint.co.uk

Hythe Offset, Telford Way, Severalls Park, Colchester, CO4 9QP Tel: (01206) 848904 Fax: (01206) 852054 E-mail: cards@hythe-uk.com

Iles Colour Print Ltd, Chase House, 1-2 Russell Town Avenue, Bristol, BS5 9LT Tel: 0117-954 7460 Fax: 0117-935 1243 E-mail: ilescp@btconnect.com

Image Colourprint Ltd, Grange Park Lane, Willerby, Hull, HU10 6EB Tel: (01482) 652323 Fax: (01482) 651899 E-mail: admin@imagedata.co.uk

Image Ry, 110 Harper Lane, Shenley, Radlett, Hertfordshire, WD7 9HG Tel: (01727) 828000 Fax: (01727) 828222 E-mail: sales@image-ry.co.uk

Impact Printing Of Coleraine Ltd, Unit 8, The Diamond Arcade, Coleraine, County Londonderry, BT52 1DE Tel: (028) 2076 2469 Fax: (028) 7034 4119 E-mail: info@impactpublishers.co.uk

Imprint, Victory House, Dalton Lane, Keighley, West Yorkshire, BD21 4JH Tel: (01535) 667954 Fax: (01535) 600072 E-mail: info@inprintkeighley.co.uk

Inglis Allen Ltd, 40 Townsend Place, Kirkcaldy, Fife, KY1 1HF Tel: (01592) 267201 Fax: (01592) 206049 E-mail: info@scottishcalendars.com

Inter Print, Unit 3 Rivergate, Westlea, Swindon, SN5 7ET Tel: (01793) 613020 Fax: (01793) 436300 E-mail: sales@interprintswindon.co.uk

Inverness Courier, Stadium Drive, Inverness, IV1 1FF Tel: (01463) 233059 Fax: (01463) 238223 E-mail: sales@inverness-courier.co.uk

Ivanhoe Printing Co. Ltd, Station Road, Musselburgh, Midlothian, EH21 7PE Tel: 0131-665 8444 Fax: 0131-653 2691

J B L Printers Ltd, Rabone Lane, Smethwick, West Midlands, B66 3JX Tel: 0121-558 2935 Fax: 0121-558 6591 E-mail: jblprinters@compuserve.com

J F A Printing plc, Wellington CR, New Malden, Surrey, KT3 3NE Tel: (020) 8640 7777 Fax: (020) 8942 7228 E-mail: sales@jfaprint.co.uk

J Greenwood & Sons, 13 North Terrace, Seaham, County Durham, SR7 7EU Tel: 0191-581 2372 Fax: 0191-581 1619

J H Brookes Printers Ltd, Sneyd Green Business Park, Sneyd Street Hanley, Stoke-on-Trent, ST6 2NP Tel: (01782) 219475 Fax: (01782) 202603 E-mail: info@brookesdesignprint.com

J H Greene, Netherton Business Centre, West Netherton Street, Kilmarnock, Ayrshire, KA1 4BT Tel: (01563) 539006 Fax: (01563) 571941

J J Newland Ltd, 10 Brown Avenue, Leeds, LS11 0DX Tel: 0113-271 7340 Fax: 0113-277 9877

J K Printers, The Old Bakery, Tanyards Lane, Bexley, Kent, DA5 1AH Tel: (01322) 555966 Fax: (01322) 555977

J M Tatler & Son Ltd, Abbey Street Works, Derby, DE22 3SW Tel: (01332) 342120 Fax: (01332) 293699 E-mail: willtat@fsbdial.co.uk

J P Prints & Signs, Pantone House, 124 Abertillery Road, Blaina, Gwent, NP13 3DR Tel: (01495) 291795 Fax: (01495) 291716 E-mail: john@jpprint.co.uk

J W B Print & Design, Dixon Court, Dixon Street, Lincoln, LN6 7DA Tel: (01522) 560760 Fax: (01522) 567272 E-mail: sales@jwbprint.co.uk

Jade Press Ltd, Eagle House, Torre Road, Leeds, LS9 7QL Tel: 0113-248 0929 Fax: 0113-248 4609 E-mail: sales@jadepress.co.uk

James A Bruce, 1-5 Cameron Street, Stonehaven, Kincardineshire, AB39 2BL Tel: (01569) 762507 Fax: (01569) 762507

James Hamilton & Co Lurgan Ltd, 1 Moores Lane, Lurgan, Craigavon, County Armagh, BT66 8DW Tel: (028) 3832 3727 Fax: (028) 3831 2312E-mail: sales@jameshamilton.co.uk

Jameson Press, 21 The Fairways, New River Trading Estate, Cheshunt, Waltham Cross, Hertfordshire, EN8 0NL Tel: (01992) 635836 Fax: (01992) 636865 E-mail: info@jamesonpress.co.uk

Jas Print Ltd, 12 Tower Road, Washington, Tyne & Wear, NE37 2SH Tel: 0191-417 6766 Fax: 0191-415 1351 E-mail: john@jasprint.com

Jayprint, 2a Douglas Road, Luton, LU4 8EB Tel: (01582) 490906 Fax: (01582) 490906

Jenkinson Marshall & Co. Ltd, 103 Neepsend Lane, Sheffield, S3 8AT Tel: 0114-272 1311 Fax: 0114-276 6240

Jet Repro Print, 101 Peckham High St, London, SE15 5RS Tel: (020) 7732 4565 Fax: (020) 7635 9098

PRINTERS, GENERAL OR COMMERCIAL OR JOBBING OR ALL TYPES – *continued*

Jevons Brown LLP, 31-41 Worship Street, London, EC2A 2DX Tel: (020) 7065 7100 E-mail: mail@jevonsbrown.co.uk

John Blackburn Supply Ltd, Old Run Road, Leeds, LS10 2AA Tel: 0113-277 7711 Fax: 0113-277 4009 E-mail: sales@jblackburn.co.uk

John Good Ltd Trading As Cantate, Building B Parkfield Industrial Estate, Culvert Place, Battersey, London, SW11 5DZ Tel: (020) 7622 3401 Fax: (020) 7498 1497 E-mail: enquiries@cantate.biz

John L R James & Co. Ltd, Victoria Road Industrial, Estate, Skegness, Lincolnshire, PE25 3SW Tel: (01754) 768521 Fax: (01754) 768936 E-mail: sales@jlrjames.com

John Mckinlay Ltd, 11 King Street, Perth, PH2 8HR Tel: (01738) 625627 Fax: (01738) 628226 E-mail: mckinlayprinters@aol.com

Johnston Printing Ltd, Mill Road, Kilrea, Coleraine, County Londonderry, BT51 5RJ Tel: (028) 2954 0312 Fax: (028) 2954 1070 E-mail: service@johnston-printing.co.uk

Jubilee Press Ltd, 22-24 Abercromby Avenue, High Wycombe, Buckinghamshire, HP12 3AZ Tel: (01494) 533061 Fax: (01494) 462596 E-mail: sales@jubs.co.uk

Jubilee Printers, 430 Edgware Road, London, W2 1EG Tel: (020) 7724 1094 Fax: (020) 7706 0518 E-mail: info@jubileeprinters.co.uk

K L Goddard, 1 Lambton Road, London, SW20 0LW Tel: (020) 8946 9494 Fax: (020) 8947 5675

K & N Press Ltd, Unit 10, 19 Lyon Road, Walton-On-Thames, Surrey, KT12 3PU Tel: (01932) 232307 Fax: (01932) 232350

K & S Commercial Photos Ltd, 90 Commercial Square, Leicester, LE2 7SR Tel: 0116-247 0270 Fax: 0116-247 1026 E-mail: sales@kands.co.uk

Stephen Kay Printers, 236 Park Lane, Poynton, Stockport, Cheshire, SK12 1RQ Tel: (01625) 876229 Fax: (01625) 858399

Bernard Kaymar Ltd, Kaymar Industrial Estate, Trout Street, Preston, PR1 4DL Tel: (01772) 562211 Fax: (01772) 257813 E-mail: sales@bernard-kaymar.co.uk

Keeley & Lowe Ltd, 38 The Oval, London, E2 9DT Tel: (020) 7729 3350 Fax: (020) 7739 5654 E-mail: keeleylowe@btconnect.co.uk

Kestrel Printing Ltd, Journeymans Way, Temple Farm Industrial Estate, Southend-On-Sea, SS2 5TF Tel: (01702) 444888 Fax: (01702) 444880 E-mail: sales@kestrel-printing.co.uk

Kingston Printers Ltd, 52 Kingsgate Road, Kingston upon Thames, Surrey, KT2 5AA Tel: (020) 8549 3311 Fax: (020) 8546 4365

Kite Press Ltd, 3 Central Trading Estate, Signal Way, Swindon, SN3 1PD Tel: (01793) 436452 Fax: (01793) 487192 E-mail: sales@kite-press.co.uk

Kopykat Printing Ltd, 76c Rivington Street, London, EC2A 3AY Tel: (020) 7739 2451 Fax: (020) 7729 5925 E-mail: print@kopykat.co.uk

KRS Ltd, Westfield House, Broad Lane, Leeds, LS13 3HA Tel: 0113-239 3088 Fax: 0113-257 7582

L B Litho, 15 Tait Road, Croydon, CR0 2DT Tel: (020) 8683 4205 Fax: (020) 8683 4193

L J Ruskin & Son, Sibsey Lane, Boston, Lincolnshire, PE21 6HB Tel: (01205) 362380 Fax: (01205) 362380

L T Printing, Alfred Road, Wallasey, Merseyside, CH44 7HY Tel: 0151-647 8006 Fax: 0151-666 1704 E-mail: post@ltprintgroup.co.uk

▶ Labels, 7 City Court Trading Estate, Poland Street, Manchester, M4 6AL Tel: 0161-205 5711 Fax: 0161-205 5722

▶ Lanceni Press Ltd, 1 Garrood Drive, Fakenham, Norfolk, NR21 8NN Tel: (01328) 851578 Fax: (01328) 851298 E-mail: lanceni@clara.net

Last Bros Ltd, Delamare Road, Cheshunt, Waltham Cross, Hertfordshire, EN8 9TE Tel: (01992) 638283 Fax: (01992) 638286 E-mail: sales@lastbros.co.uk

Latimer Trend Printing Group, Estover Road, Plymouth, PL6 7PY Tel: (01752) 201930 Fax: (01752) 201760 E-mail: systems@trends.co.uk

Lazer Printing, 65 Coniston Road, Peterborough, PE4 7UL Tel: (01733) 324404 Fax: (01733) 324404

Lear Seating UK Ltd, Gielgud Way, Cross Point Business Park, Coventry, CV2 2SA Tel: (024) 7686 7200 Fax: (024) 7686 7235

Lear Stationers & Printers, 17 High Street, Bilston, West Midlands, WV14 0EH Tel: (01902) 408660 Fax: (01902) 408660

Leopard Press UK Ltd, Foxoak Street, Cradley Heath, West Midlands, B64 5DP Tel: (01384) 410800 Fax: (01384) 410420 E-mail: enquiries@leopardpress.fsnet.co.uk

Liberty Printers Ltd, Willett Road, Thornton Heath, Surrey, CR7 6AA Tel: (020) 8684 1486 Fax: (020) 8689 3202 E-mail: service@libertyprinters.co.uk

▶ Lion Labels & Packaging, Regent House, Regent Street, Coppull, Chorley, Lancashire, PR7 5AX Tel: (01257) 793335 Fax: (01257) 471530

Lister & Durling Printers, 69 Station Road, Flitwick, Bedford, MK45 1JU Tel: (01525) 713770

Lithograve (Birmingham) Ltd, 8-10 Lawford Close, Birmingham, B7 4HJ Tel: 0121-359 3350 Fax: 0121-359 3119 E-mail: dave@lithograve.com

Lithotech Print Services, Unit 12, The Grove, Parkgate Industrial Estate, Knutsford, Cheshire, WA16 8XP Tel: (01565) 633703 Fax: (01565) 633703 E-mail: bryan@lithotech.freesurf.co.uk

Livesey Ltd, Longden Road, Shrewsbury, SY3 9EB Tel: (01743) 235651 Fax: (01743) 232944 E-mail: info@liveseyltd.co.uk

Lonsdale Print Solutions Ltd, Denington Road, Denington Industrial Estate, Wellingborough, Northamptonshire, NN8 2RA Tel: (01933) 228855 Fax: (01933) 442405 E-mail: info@lonsdaleps.co.uk

Lothian Printers, 109 High Street, Dunbar, East Lothian, EH42 1ES Tel: (01368) 863785 Fax: (01368) 864908 E-mail: lothian.printers@virgin.net

Brian Lowndes Print Ltd, Graphichouse, Portland Street, Walsall, WS2 8BE Tel: (01922) 725282 Fax: (01922) 720981 E-mail: mail@blprint.co.uk

LPC Printing Co. Ltd, Hardley Industrial Estate, Hardley Hythe, Southampton, SO45 3ZX Tel: (023) 8084 6334 Fax: (023) 8084 0389 E-mail: enquiries@lpcprinting.com

Lundie Bros Ltd, 15 Tait Road, Croydon, CR0 2DP Tel: (020) 8683 4451 Fax: (020) 8683 4193 E-mail: print@lundiebros.co.uk

M & A Thomson Litho Ltd, 10 Colvilles Place, East Kilbride, Glasgow, G75 0SN Tel: (01355) 233081 Fax: (01355) 245439

M J Milward Printing Ltd, 21 Nottingham South & Wilford Industrial Estate, Nottingham, NG11 7EP Tel: 0115-981 3378 Fax: 0115-981 2386 E-mail: mgmprint@compuserve.com

M M Palmer Ltd, 3-5 Capital Place, Harlow, Essex, CM19 5AS Tel: (01279) 439023 Fax: (01279) 635940 E-mail: sales@palmersprint.co.uk

M S A In Print, 115 Graingers Lane, Cradley Heath, West Midlands, B64 6AD Tel: (01384) 568790 Fax: (01384) 410320 E-mail: msainprint@fsb.dial.co.uk

Mail Marketing International Ltd, Springfield House, West Street, Bedminster, Bristol, BS3 3NX Tel: 0117-966 6900 Fax: 0117-963 6737 E-mail: sales@formpromm.co.uk

Maldon Printing Co. Ltd, Unit 2-14 Wycke Hill Business Park, Wycke Hill, Maldon, Essex, CM9 6UZ Tel: (01621) 853904 Fax: (01621) 859565

Manor Creative Ltd, 7-8 Edison Road, Eastbourne, East Sussex, BN23 6PT Tel: (01323) 514400 Fax: (01323) 509306

▶ Manor Press Ltd, 36-38 Normanton Spring Road, Sheffield, S13 7BB Tel: 0114-269 5755 Fax: 0114-269 5755 E-mail: manorpress@tiscali.co.uk

Marquee Print, 2 Wharfdale Road, Bournemouth, BH4 9BT Tel: (01202) 769077 Fax: (01202) 752858 E-mail: info@marqueeprint.com

Marshall Cavendish International Ltd, 119 Wardour Street, London, W1F 0UW Tel: (020) 7734 6710 Fax: (020) 7734 6221

James A. Marshall Ltd, 50 Crownpoint Road, Bridgeton, Glasgow, G40 2QE Tel: 0141-556 1626 Fax: 0141-556 4630 E-mail: enquiries@jamesamarshall.com

▶ The Marstan Press Ltd, Princes Street, Bexleyheath, Kent, DA7 4BJ Tel: (020) 8301 5900 Fax: (020) 8298 1612 E-mail: sales@themarstanpress.co.uk

Maslands Ltd, Unit 12 Howden Industrial Estate, Tiverton, Devon, EX16 5HW Tel: (01884) 242767 Fax: (01884) 257103 E-mail: mail@maslands.co.uk

Mason Albums Two Trees Press Ltd, Grey Street, Denton, Manchester, M34 3RU Tel: 0161-336 2002 Fax: 0161-335 0346 E-mail: print@twotreespress.co.uk

Masthead Printers Ltd, 6 Menin Works, Bond Road, Mitcham, Surrey, CR4 3HG Tel: (020) 8640 6559 Fax: (020) 8646 7133 E-mail: peter@mastheadprinters.demon.co.uk

Matain Ltd, 39 Ludgate Hill, London, EC4M 7JN Tel: (020) 7236 0096 Fax: (020) 7236 3957 E-mail: reprocopy@lithoprinting.co.uk

Melton Printers of Lincoln, Unit 3, Sleaford Road, Bracebridge Heath, Lincoln, LN4 2ND Tel: (01522) 541827 Fax: (01522) 528237 E-mail: sales@meltonprinters.co.uk

▶ Menzies Nunn Ltd, The Wallows Industrial Estate, Fens Pool Avenue, Brierley Hill, West Midlands, DY5 1QA Tel: (01384) 262148 Fax: (01384) 265136 E-mail: sales@menzies-nunn.co.uk

Merlin Forms Ltd, Unit 3, 222 London Road Business Park, St. Albans, Hertfordshire, AL1 1PN Tel: (01727) 845077 Fax: (01727) 845013 E-mail: sales@merlinformsltd.co.uk

Midland Regional Printers Ltd, Nottingham Road, Nottingham, NG7 7BT Tel: 0115-955 1000 Fax: 0115-955 1012 E-mail: sales@midlandregionalprinters.co.uk

Millvale Ltd, Briar Close, Evesham, Worcestershire, WR11 4JT Tel: (01386) 446661 Fax: (01386) 442931 E-mail: sales@millvaleltd.co.uk

Molyneux Press, Unit 102 Horton Kirby Trading Estate, Station Road, South Darenth, Dartford, DA4 9BD Tel: (01322) 861582 Fax: (01322) 861584 E-mail: molypress@aol.com

Monument Press Stirling Ltd, 42 Abbey Road, Stirling, FK8 1LP Tel: (01786) 474763 Fax: (01786) 451520 E-mail: gr@monpress.demon.co.uk

Mooncie Printing Services, 62 Evington Valley Road, Leicester, LE5 5LJ Tel: 0116-273 8882 E-mail: mooncieprinting@aol.com

Moore & Tillyer Ltd, Metro House, Northgate, Chichester, West Sussex, PO19 1BE Tel: (01243) 784341 Fax: (01243) 785788 E-mail: enquiries@mooreandtillyer.co.uk

Morris Printing Co. Ltd, 57-61 Pitt Street, Norwich, NR3 1DE Tel: (01603) 629796 Fax: (01603) 626836 E-mail: admin@morrisprint.co.uk

N Long Printers, 8 Buckholt Business Centre, Buckholt Drive, Worcester, WR4 9ND Tel: (01905) 456140 Fax: (01905) 756903

N S Reed Printing Supplies, 9 Dean Court, Great Western Business Park, Yate, Bristol, BS37 5NJ Tel: (01454) 323775 Fax: (01454) 326935 E-mail: nsreed.print@virgin.net

Nayler Group Ltd, Aero Mill, Kershaw Street, Church, Accrington, Lancashire, BB5 4JS Tel: (01254) 234247 Fax: (01254) 383996 E-mail: info@naylorgroup.co.uk

Neil A Robertson Printers & Stationers, 7 Queen Street, Forfar, Angus, DD8 3AJ Tel: (01307) 464078 Fax: (01307) 468523 E-mail: neil.robertson17@btopenworld.com

New Goswell Printing Co., Unit 4 100 The Highway, London, E1W 2BX Tel: (020) 7481 1775 Fax: (020) 7488 9130

Newal Print, Unit 21 Delph Road Industrial Estate, Delph Road, Brierley Hill, West Midlands, DY5 2UA Tel: (01384) 74469 Fax: (01384) 74995

Newton Print, 27a Coleshill Road, Sutton Coldfield, West Midlands, B75 7AX Tel: 0121-378 3711 Fax: 0121-311 1779 E-mail: david.deere@virgin.net

Nicholson & Bass Ltd, 3 Nicholson Drive, Newtownabbey, County Antrim, BT36 4FB Tel: (028) 9034 2433 Fax: (028) 9034 2066 E-mail: sales@nicholsonbass.com

North Account Book Manufacturing Co., 23 Oldfield Lane, Heckmondwike, West Yorkshire, WF16 0JE Tel: (01924) 402309 Fax: (01924) 412070 E-mail: sales@northaccountprinters.co.uk

North Shropshire Conservative & Unionist Association, Sambrook Hall, Noble Street, Wem, Shrewsbury, SY4 5DT Tel: (01939) 235222 Fax: (01939) 232220 E-mail: sales@nsprint.co.uk

Nova Press Printing, 3 The Old Mill, 61 Reading Road, Pangbourne, Reading, RG8 7HY Tel: 0118-984 5370 Fax: 0118-984 5370 E-mail: trevor@novapress.freeserve.co.uk

Nutan Printers, 67-69 Harrison Road, Leicester, LE4 6BT Tel: 0116-266 9405 Fax: 0116-261 0251 E-mail: sales@nutan-printers.co.uk

▶ O M S Ltd, Origination House, 15 Strawberry Street, Hull, HU9 1EN Tel: (01482) 224429

Oldacres & Co. Ltd, 62 Hatton Garden, London, EC1N 8LR Tel: (020) 7242 3242 Fax: (020) 7831 9095 E-mail: services@oldacres.co.uk

Oldham Evening Chronicle, PO Box 47, Oldham, OL1 1EN Tel: 0161-633 2121 Fax: 0161-652 2111 E-mail: cpdadmin@oldham-chronicle.co.uk

▶ Olympus Labels Ltd, Richardshaw Road, Grangefield Industrial Estate, Pudsey, West Yorkshire, LS28 6QW Tel: 0113-236 3283 Fax: 0113-236 3284

Optichrome Group Ltd, Maybury Road, Woking, Surrey, GU21 5HX Tel: (01483) 740290 Fax: (01483) 732609 E-mail: sales@optichrome.com

Oyez Straker, 4 City Park Industrial Estate, Gelderd Road, Leeds, LS12 6DR Tel: 0113-203 2100 Fax: 0113-263 9011 E-mail: sales.pudsey@oyezstraker.co.uk

P B F Press Ltd, 12 Little Ridge, Welwyn Garden City, Hertfordshire, AL7 2BH Tel: (01707) 372185 Fax: (01707) 375580 E-mail: pbf-press@btconnect.com

P D M Office Supplies, 3 Parklands Parade, Bath Road, Hounslow, TW5 9AX Tel: (020) 8570 4488 Fax: (020) 8569 6050

P S Office Supplies Ltd, 40 Great Lister Street, Birmingham, B7 4LS Tel: 0121-333 5000 Fax: 0121-333 5001 E-mail: sales@psonline.co.uk

Page Bros Norwich Ltd, Mile Cross Lane, Norwich, NR6 6SA Tel: (01603) 778800 Fax: (01603) 778801 E-mail: info@pagebros.co.uk

Page Lithoprint Ltd, Enterprise House, Cranes Close, Basildon, Essex, SS14 3JB Tel: (01268) 464464 Fax: (01268) 464465 E-mail: sales@pagemediagroup.com

Pandaprint, 104 Park Road, Rosyth, Dunfermline, Fife, KY11 2JL Tel: (01383) 417847 Fax: (01383) 411863

Paragon Ltd, Park Road, Castleford, West Yorkshire, WF10 4RR Tel: (01977) 669700 Fax: (01977) 603036 E-mail: sales@paragon-castleford.com

Paramount Printers Ltd, 199 Causewayside, Edinburgh, EH9 1PH Tel: 0131-667 4441 Fax: 0131-662 0659 E-mail: sales@ourprinters.com

Pennine Printing Services Ltd, Commercial Mills, Oldham Road, Sowerby Bridge, West Yorkshire, HX6 4EH Tel: (01422) 825333 Fax: (01422) 825444 E-mail: pennineprinting@btconnect.com

Pentagon Press Ltd, Harriot Drive, Heathcote Industrial Estate, Warwick, CV34 6TJ Tel: (01926) 833481 Fax: (01926) 314017

Perfectio Print Finishers Ltd, Wright Street, Manchester, M16 9EW Tel: 0161-877 6238 Fax: 0161-872 0514

Peterborough Printing Services Ltd, Ainsley House, Fengate, Peterborough, PE1 5XG Tel: (01733) 349881 Fax: (01733) 310711 E-mail: info@pps-print.com

Alfred Pettitt Ltd, Unit 6 Hillgate Business Centre, Swallow Street, Stockport, Cheshire, SK1 3AU Tel: 0161-476 4545 Fax: 0161-476 4505

Phoenix Corporation UK Ltd, Unit 5 North Weylands Industrial Estate, Molesey Road, Walton-on-Thames, Surrey, KT12 3PL Tel: (01932) 246236 Fax: (01932) 246236

Phoenix Publicity & Print Ltd, Unit 2, Lister Street, Dudley Hill, Bradford, West Yorkshire, BD4 9PQ Tel: (01274) 681642 Fax: (01274) 681692 E-mail: info@phoenixprinting.com

Pinder P.L.C., Unit 481 Walton Summit Centre, Bamber Bridge, Preston, PR5 8AR Tel: (01772) 620999 Fax: (01772) 620888 E-mail: k.ashley@pinder.com

PLP Commercial Printers, 7 Mowlem Street, London, E2 9HE Tel: (020) 8983 3439 Fax: (020) 8981 3655 E-mail: sales@plpcommercial.co.uk

Polar Print Group Ltd, Venturi House, 9-17 Tuxford Road, Hamilton Industial Park, Leicester, LE4 9WE Tel: 0116-274 4700 Fax: 0116-274 4799

Polypress Ltd, 20 Bridgeland Street, Bideford, Devon, EX39 2QE Tel: (01237) 472272 Fax: (01237) 421414

Portobello Press Ltd, 69-71 Scrubs Lane, London, NW10 6QU Tel: (020) 8960 6796 Fax: (020) 8960 2708 E-mail: sales@portobellopress.co.uk

Postglow Printers, 139 Francis Road, London, E10 6NT Tel: (020) 8539 7559 Fax: (020) 8556 1970 E-mail: sales@frankel.co.uk

Powlson The Printers, Erw Wen Road, Colwyn Bay, Clwyd, LL29 7SD Tel: (01492) 532156 Fax: (01492) 532707 E-mail: sales@powlsons.co.uk

Premier Print & Design Services Ltd, Unit 33 Park Farm Industrial Estate, Ermine Street, Buntingford, Hertfordshire, SG9 9AZ Tel: (01763) 272461 Fax: (01763) 272955

Pressed For Time Ltd, 1 Johnston Road, Woodford Green, Essex, IG8 0XA Tel: (020) 8559 2015 Fax: (020) 8505 9581 E-mail: andrew@pft.uk.com

▶ Prima Print & Design, Henry Close, Battlefield Enterprise Park, Shrewsbury, SY1 3TJ Tel: (01743) 450938 Fax: (01743) 450930 E-mail: mail@primaprint.co.uk

Print Save of Preston, 9 Winckley Street, Preston, PR1 2AA Tel: (01772) 888878 Fax: (01772) 888879 E-mail: office@printsave.co.uk

▶ Print Search Ltd, Westinghouse Road, Trafford Park, Manchester, M17 1PJ Tel: 0161-872 8921 Fax: 0161-848 7323 E-mail: sales@princesearchpromotionalproducts.co.uk

Print & Stationery Management Co. Ltd, 114 Jacob Street, Bristol, BS2 0HU Tel: 0117-926 2459 Fax: 0117-925 1357 E-mail: sales@prism-ltd.co.uk

Printel, 43 Cross Road, Croydon, CR0 6TE Tel: (020) 8681 2262 Fax: (020) 8688 5883 E-mail: printel@btinernet.com

Printline Ltd, Unit 12, Grosvenor Way, London, E5 9ND Tel: (020) 8806 9090 Fax: (020) 8806 9434 E-mail: sales@printline.co.uk

Print-Pac Services, Unit 3 Grampound Road Industrial Estate, Grampound Road, Truro, Cornwall, TR2 4TB Tel: (01726) 883336 Fax: (01726) 883382

Priory Press, Unit 18 Apex Business Centre, Boscombe Road, Dunstable, Bedfordshire, LU5 4SB Tel: (01582) 699851 Fax: (01582) 667493 E-mail: info@priorypress.co.uk

Projects XL Ltd, Glenville House, Spring Gardens, Romford, RM7 9LD Tel: (01708) 751919 Fax: (01708) 725294 E-mail: info@projectsxl.com

Provincial Printing & Publishing Co. Ltd, Sanatorium Road, Cardiff, CF11 8DG Tel: (029) 2022 8729 Fax: (029) 2037 3494 E-mail: sales@printppp.co.uk

Prudential Printers, Unit 71 Birch Road East Industrial Estate, Birch Road East, Birmingham, B6 7DA Tel: 0121-328 1454 Fax: 0121-327 7073 E-mail: prudential_printers@yahoo.co.uk

Purbrook Ltd, 22-26 Stannary Street, London, SE11 4AA Tel: (020) 7735 9142 Fax: (020) 7793 0609 E-mail: info@purbrooks.co.uk

Pureprint Group Ltd, Brambleside, Bellbrook Industrial Estate, Uckfield, East Sussex, TN22 1PL Tel: (01825) 768611 Fax: (01825) 768042 E-mail: print@beaconpress.co.uk

Q R S Stamps, 71 Wordsworth Road, Small Heath, Birmingham, B10 0ED Tel: 0121-772 4165 Fax: 0121-766 6341 E-mail: print.man@virgin.net

Quadgraphics Printers, 22 Hambridge Road, Newbury, Berkshire, RG14 5SE Tel: (01635) 44442 Fax: (01635) 581044 E-mail: zak@quadgraphics.co.uk

Quadraproof Ltd, 12 Orwell Furlong, Cambridge, CB4 0WY Tel: (01223) 420202 Fax: (01223) 424729 E-mail: info@quadraproof.co.uk

Quantum Print & Packaging Ltd, Ashmore Lake Business Park, Spring Lane, Willenhall, West Midlands, WV12 4HN Tel: (01902) 367100 Fax: (01902) 367200 E-mail: sales@quantumppkg.co.uk

Qubic Print Ltd, Sovereign Way, Chester West Employment Park, Chester, CH1 4QU Tel: (01244) 390222 Fax: (01244) 390211

Queensway 2k Ltd, 8 Cumberland Business Park, Cumberland Avenue, London, NW10 7RT Tel: (020) 8965 1676 Fax: (020) 8961 9235 E-mail: m.nelms@btconnect.com

Quickprint, 13 Marsh Parade, Newcastle, Staffordshire, ST5 1BT Tel: (01782) 625512 Fax: (01782) 717302

R A H Advertising Ltd, 320 Palatine Road, Northenden, Manchester, M22 4HF Tel: 0161-902 0555 Fax: 0161-902 0777 E-mail: info@rahadvertising.com

▶ indicates data change since last edition

PRINTERS, GENERAL OR COMMERCIAL OR JOBBING OR ALL TYPES – *continued*

R P Printing Services, 136 High Street, Hanham, Bristol, BS15 3HF Tel: 0117-960 4400 Fax: 0117-960 4400

Radford Press Ltd, Miller House, 30 Wilmot Road, London, E10 5LU Tel: (020) 8558 4814 Fax: (020) 8558 0345 E-mail: sales@radfordpress.co.uk

Raithby Lawrence & Co. Ltd, 18 Slater Street, Leicester, LE3 5AS Tel: 0116-251 0961 Fax: 0116-253 2581E-mail: sales@rlprint.com

Rayment Holland, 1-3 Wealdstone Road, Sutton, Surrey, SM3 9QN Tel: (020) 8641 7272 Fax: (020) 8644 4779 E-mail: mail@frewerbrothers.co.uk

Rediset Business Forms Ltd, Factory Road, Upton Industrial Estate, Poole, Dorset, BH16 5SJ Tel: (01202) 622679 Fax: (01202) 623375

Reedprint, Vale Road, Windsor, Berkshire, SL4 5JL Tel: (01753) 869691 Fax: (01753) 830480 E-mail: sales@reedprint.co.uk

Reflex Print & Design Ltd, Unit 4 Kiln Hill Industrial Estate, Slaithwaite, Huddersfield, HD7 5JS Tel: (01484) 846950 Fax: (01484) 847644

Regency Press, 2a Kent Street, Belfast, BT1 2JA Tel: (028) 9032 1724 Fax: (028) 9033 2280

Regent Print Ltd, 30 Albert Street, Huddersfield, HD1 3PU Tel: (01484) 530789 Fax: (01484) 542533 E-mail: sales@regentprint.co.uk

Reid Printers, 79-109 Glasgow Road, Blantyre, Glasgow, G72 0LY Tel: (01698) 826000 Fax: (01698) 824944 E-mail: sales@reid-print-group.co.uk

Reliant Printers Ltd, Journeymans Way, Temple Farm Industrial Estate, Southend-on-Sea, SS2 5TF Tel: (01702) 618161 Fax: (01702) 444880 E-mail: sales@kestrel-printing.co.uk

Richfield Graphics Ltd, Unit 4b Paddock Road Industrial Estate, Paddock Road, Caversham, Reading, RG4 5BY Tel: 0118-946 2225 Fax: 0118-946 2618 E-mail: sales@richfieldgraphics.co.uk

Ritchie (UK) Ltd, Hurlford Road, Riccarton, Kilmarnock, Ayrshire, KA1 4LA Tel: (01563) 528711 Fax: (01563) 524468 E-mail: sales@ritchie.vir.co.uk

Robert Martins (Printers) Ltd, Pindar Road, Hoddesdon, Hertfordshire, EN11 0DP Tel: (01992) 440676 Fax: (01992) 446840 E-mail: sales@robertmartins.co.uk

Robrook Press Ltd, Queens Road, Morley, Leeds, LS27 0PF Tel: 0113-253 5753 Fax: 0113-238 0231 E-mail: paul@robrook.com

Robson Print Ltd, Haugh La Industrial Estate, Hexham, Northumberland, NE46 3PU Tel: (01434) 602975 Fax: (01434) 608146 E-mail: dave.robsonprint@btinternet.com

Romoprint, 140 Springhill Road, Wednesfield, Wolverhampton, WV11 3AQ Tel: (01902) 730862

Rotadex Systems Ltd, Sytems House, Central Business Park, Mackadown Lane, Birmingham, B33 0JL Tel: 0121-783 7411 Fax: 0121-783 1876 E-mail: cathi.croton@rotadex.co.uk

Rubell Print Ltd, The Hollies, College Lane, Bunbury, Tarporley, Cheshire, CW6 9PQ Tel: (01829) 260420 Fax: (01829) 260426 E-mail: info@rubell.org

Rustin Clark, 45 Waterloo Road, London, NW2 7TX Tel: (020) 8452 1091 Fax: (020) 8452 2008 E-mail: rustinclark@rustinclark.co.uk

S Barber & Co. Ltd, 66-68 Kitchen Street, Liverpool, L1 0AN Tel: 0151-709 7323 Fax: 0151-709 6608 E-mail: sales@barbersprn.co.uk

S F Taylor & Co. Ltd, Whitehill Industrial Estate, Haigh Avenue, Stockport, Cheshire, SK4 1NU Tel: 0161-429 7200 Fax: 0161-429 5720 E-mail: gilltress@sftaylor.com

S G Print Ltd, PO Box 6068, Basildon, Essex, SS14 3WJ Tel: (01621) 773610 Fax: (01621) 773271 E-mail: sales@sgprint.ltd.uk

S L George Printers Ltd, 16 North Street, Leighton Buzzard, Bedfordshire, LU7 1EN Tel: (01525) 373057 Fax: (01525) 852387 E-mail: info@slgeorgeprinters.co.uk

Sackville Oak Ltd, 30 Store Street, London, WC1E 7QD Tel: (020) 7636 8723 Fax: (020) 7636 8726 E-mail: pdfprint@btclick.com

St. Ives Direct (Edenbridge) Ltd, Enterprise Way, Edenbridge, Kent, TN8 6HF Tel: (01732) 862788 Fax: (01732) 868868 E-mail: kevin.johnson@stivesdirect.com

Sale Print & Design, 5 Georges Road, Sale, Cheshire, M33 3NJ Tel: 0161-962 3365

Saltire Graphics, Brook St Studios, 60 Brook Street, Glasgow, G40 2AB Tel: 0141-556 3722 Fax: 0141-554 1621 E-mail: info@saltiregraphics-print.com

Sanders & Co. (UK) Ltd, 181 Wellingborough Road, Northampton, NN1 4DX Tel: (01604) 630195 Fax: (01604) 633972 E-mail: sandersltd@aol.com

Sandy Press Ltd, 2 Handworth Street, Manchester, M12 6LH Tel: 0161-273 7535 Fax: 0161-274 3146

Scanachrome, 49 Glebe Road, Skelmersdale, Lancashire, WN8 9JP Tel: (01695) 725486 Fax: (01695) 722695 E-mail: sales@scanachrome.com

Scottaspress Publishers Ltd, 15 Maberly Street, Aberdeen, AB25 1NA Tel: (01224) 637383 Fax: (01224) 643217 E-mail: info@theprinter.co.uk

Screen Technology, Maerdy Industrial Estate, Maerdy Road, Ferndale, Mid Glamorgan, CF43 4AB Tel: (01443) 730271 Fax: (01443) 730789 E-mail: info@screentec.co.uk

Scrogie Scottaspress, 23 Broad Street, Peterhead, Aberdeenshire, AB42 1HY Tel: (01779) 490869 Fax: (01779) 477853

Seargeant Bros Printers Ltd, Unit 12 Pontyfelin Industrial Estate, New Inn, Pontypool, Gwent, NP4 0DQ Tel: (01495) 752425 Fax: (01495) 763179 E-mail: sales@seargeants.co.uk

Seven Worldwide Ltd, St. Marks House, Shepherdess Walk, London, N1 7LH Tel: (020) 7861 7777 Fax: (020) 7871 7777 E-mail: enquiries@sevenww.com

▶ Severn Signs Ltd, Unit 19 Innsworth Technology Park, Innsworth Lane, Gloucester, GL3 1DL Tel: (01452) 739156 Fax: (01452) 739153

Shaftesbury Engraving/Printing Unit 7, 7 Plaza Business Centre, Stockingswater Lane, Enfield, Middlesex, EN3 7XT Tel: (020) 8443 3970 Fax: (020) 8443 3972 E-mail: sales@shaftesburyengraving.co.uk

Shanks Printers & Finishers Ltd, Unit 6/7 Martello Enterprise Centre, Courtwick Lane, Wick, Littlehampton, West Sussex, BN17 7PA Tel: (01903) 716442 Fax: (01903) 733019 E-mail: terri@shanksprinters.co.uk

Sharpe Media Ltd, 83-87 Cambridge Street, Coventry, CV1 5HU Tel: (024) 7622 4316 Fax: (024) 7652 5622

Shepshed Knight Printing Service Ltd, 91 Charnwood Road, Shepshed, Loughborough, Leicestershire, LE12 9NL Tel: (01509) 502246 Fax: (01509) 503179 E-mail: sales@shepshedknight.com

Sidney Graham Business Supplies Ltd, 236-240 Station Road, Kings Heath, Birmingham, B14 7TE Tel: 0121-443 3377 Fax: 0121-441 1456 E-mail: matt@sidneygraham.plus.com

Sinclair Print, 396 Ashley Road, Poole, Dorset, BH14 0AA Tel: (01202) 730221 Fax: (01202) 380600 E-mail: sales@sinclairprint.co.uk

▶ Skamem and Durham, Unit 7, Park 2000, Millennium Way, Newton Aycliffe, County Durham, DL5 6AR Tel: (01325) 375140 Fax: (01325) 375161

Smith & Ouzman Ltd, 45 Brampton Road, Eastbourne, East Sussex, BN22 9AH Tel: (01323) 524000 Fax: (01323) 524024 E-mail: print@smith-ouzman.com

Soloprint Ltd, 105 Great North Road, Eaton Socon, St. Neots, Cambridgeshire, PE19 8EL Tel: (01480) 213555 Fax: (01480) 218887 E-mail: sales@tsgcf.co.uk

South Eastern Printing & Stationery Co. Ltd, Unit 5H Horndon Industrial Park, Station Road, West Horndon, Brentwood, Essex, CM13 3XL Tel: (01277) 812111 Fax: (01277) 811388

▶ South Yorkshire Printers Ltd, Digital Works, Arvis Lane, Sheffield, S3 8EG Tel: 0114-272 1105 Fax: 0114-276 0633 E-mail: design@southyorkshireprinters.co.uk

▶ Spear Europe Ltd, Christopher Grey Court, Lakeside, Llantarnam Industrial Park, Cwmbran, Gwent, NP44 3SE Tel: (01633) 627600 Fax: (01633) 627601 E-mail: sales@spearsystem.com

Speedprint Services Ltd, Brook Street, Failsworth, Manchester, M35 0BS Tel: 0161-683 4111 Fax: 0161-683 4570

Speedyprint Ltd, 67 Stockport Road, Stockport, Cheshire, SK3 0JG Tel: 0161-480 6038 Fax: 0161-480 5166 E-mail: sales@speedyprint.co.uk

Sprintprint Printers, Aston Road, Waterlooville, Hampshire, PO7 7UD Tel: (023) 9226 7131 Fax: (023) 9224 1448 E-mail: sales@sprintprint.co.uk

Steve Hyde, Unit C Cophall Farm Business Park, Effingham Road, Copthorne, Crawley, West Sussex, RH10 3HZ Tel: (01342) 714230 Fax: (01342) 716760 E-mail: stevehydestudios@btconnect.com

Stewarts of Edinburgh Ltd, Meadowbank Works, 67 Marionville Road, Edinburgh, EH7 6AJ Tel: 0131-659 6010 Fax: 0131-652 1348 E-mail: mail@stewarts.eu.com

Stockport Printing Co. Ltd, 9 Enterprise Centre Two, Chester Street, Stockport, Cheshire, SK3 0BR Tel: 0161-477 2391 Fax: 0161-480 1600 E-mail: sales@stockportprint.co.uk

Stylewrite Press Ltd, 44 Howard Street, Birmingham, B19 3HH Tel: 0121-236 5557 Fax: 0121-236 5717 E-mail: stylewritepress@yahoo.co.uk

Sumfield & Day Ltd, Park View, Alder Close, Eastbourne, East Sussex, BN23 6QE Tel: (01323) 720455 Fax: (01323) 411230 E-mail: sales@sumfieldandday.com

Swift Printers, 7 Stephenson Way, Crawley, West Sussex, RH10 1TN Tel: (01293) 516507

Synergie Ltd, Digital House, The Loddon Centre, Wade Road, Basingstoke, Hampshire, RG24 8QW Tel: (01256) 467771 Fax: (01256) 840383 E-mail: alison@synergie.uk.com

T H Jordan Ltd, 3 Millar Street, Belfast, BT6 8JZ Tel: (028) 9045 0866 Fax: (028) 9073 2587 E-mail: sales@thjordanltd.com

T J Offset Ltd, 6 The Mead Business Centre, Mead Lane, Hertford, SG13 7BJ Tel: (01992) 504438 Fax: (01992) 501891 E-mail: info@tjoffset.co.uk

T & J Printers Ltd, Sturmi Way, Village Farm Industrial Estate, Pyle, Bridgend, Mid Glamorgan, CF33 6BZ Tel: (01656) 744288 Fax: (01656) 741804 E-mail: tandjprinters@btconnect.com

T Stephenson & Son Ltd, 5 Market Place, Prescot, Merseyside, L34 5SB Tel: 0151-426 5161 Fax: 0151-430 7738 E-mail: stephensonprint@btclick.com

Tadberry Evedale Printers Ltd, Unit 2-4 1a Philip Walk, London, SE15 3NH Tel: (020) 7732 2226 Fax: (020) 7358 0006 E-mail: colin@tadberry-evedale.co.uk

Tag Instantprint Ltd, 182 London Road, Kingston Upon Thames, Surrey, KT2 6QW Tel: (020) 8546 6833 Fax: (020) 8547 1441 E-mail: taginstantprint@aol.com

Tannas Office Supplies Ltd, 76 High Road, London, NW10 2PU Tel: (020) 8459 0521 Fax: (020) 8459 8603 E-mail: info@tannas.co.uk

Taws Printers Ltd, 1 Hortonwood, Telford, Shropshire, TF1 7GN Tel: (01952) 281281 Fax: (01952) 281282 E-mail: info@taws.co.uk

Technart Ltd, Unit 45 City Industrial Park, Southern Road, Southampton, SO15 1HG Tel: (023) 8022 2409 Fax: (023) 8021 1403 E-mail: prepress@technart.co.uk

Telprint Ltd, 14 Spring Road Industrial Estate, Lanesfield Drive, Wolverhampton, WV4 6UA Tel: (01902) 403355 Fax: (01902) 353802 E-mail: admin@telprint.co.uk

Thomas Mcgilvray & Son Ltd, Wemyss Road, Dysart, Kirkcaldy, Fife, KY1 2XZ Tel: (01592) 655993 Fax: (01592) 655117 E-mail: sales@mcgilvray-printers.co.uk

Thorne Printing & Publishing Co. Ltd, 272 Friern Barnet Lane, London, N20 0NH Tel: (020) 8446 9910 Fax: (020) 8445 5864 E-mail: thorneprinting@aol.com

Thruxton Press Ltd, Thruxton Down House, Thruxton, Andover, Hampshire, SP11 8PR Tel: (01264) 889552 Fax: (01264) 889622 E-mail: publications@brunton.co.uk

John Till Printers, 32 Woodside Close, Walsall, WS5 3LU Tel: 0121-357 3267 Fax: 0121-357 3267 E-mail: info@johntill.co.uk

Torr Printers, Unit 2 Greg Street, Stockport, Cheshire, SK5 7BS Tel: 0161-480 9821 Fax: 0161-477 0305 E-mail: norman@torrprint.fsnet.co.uk

Tranters Ltd, Markeaton Printing Works, Payne Street, Derby, DE22 3AZ Tel: (01332) 341982 Fax: (01332) 292707 E-mail: trantersales@btconnect.com

Trendell's Print Ltd, Critchmere Lane, Haslemere, Surrey, GU27 1PR Tel: (01428) 643269 Fax: (01428) 656057 E-mail: john@trendells.co.uk

Tresises, Stanley Street, Burton-on-Trent, Staffordshire, DE14 1DY Tel: (01283) 568276 Fax: (01283) 511207

Tressanda Printers, 362 Tamworth Road, Long Eaton, Nottingham, NG10 3AT Tel: 0115-973 2388 Fax: 0115-946 1148 E-mail: sales@tressanda.com

Tuckey Print Ltd, 79 Moseley Road, Birmingham, B12 0HL Tel: 0121-773 7411 Fax: 0121-766 7339 E-mail: sales@tuckeyprint.co.uk

Tudor Press, 209 Oxford Road, Reading, RG1 7PX Tel: 0118-957 4197 Fax: 0118-957 5212

Tyrone Printing Co., Unit 179, Moygashel Mills, Moygashel, Dungannon, County Tyrone, BT71 7HB Tel: (028) 8772 2274 Fax: (028) 8772 6164

Unique Graphics, 136 Lauriston Road, London, E9 7LH Tel: (020) 8986 9686 Fax: (020) 8533 0238 E-mail: mail@justpostcards.co.uk

▶ Universal Showcards, 23 Stonefield Way, Ruislip, Middlesex, HA4 0YF Tel: (020) 8841 4551 Fax: (020) 8845 0737 E-mail: info@universal-sc.co.uk

Vallis Press Ipi Ltd, 1 Thames View, Newtown Road, Henley-on-Thames, Oxfordshire, RG9 1HG Tel: (01491) 576553 Fax: (01491) 410512

Varipart Engineering, Florence Mill Business Park, Whalley New Road, Blackburn, BB1 9SR Tel: (01254) 264394 Fax: (01254) 675555 E-mail: sales@varipartengineering.co.uk

Vision Printers Ltd, 25 Colne Valley Business Park, Huddersfield, HD7 5QG Tel: (01484) 847307 Fax: (01484) 846581 E-mail: sales@visionprint.com

Vyner Litho Plates, 4 Kingside, Ruston Road, London, SE18 5BX Tel: (020) 8854 5544 E-mail: vyners@compuserve.com

W.& A.Ross Ltd, 55 Days Road, St Phillips, St. Philips, Bristol, BS2 0QS Tel: 0117-955 8855 Fax: 0117-935 0518 E-mail: sales@rossofficesupplies.co.uk

W F Arber & Co. Ltd, 459 Roman Road, London, E3 5LX Tel: (020) 8980 2067

W Peters & Son Ltd, 16 High St, Turriff, Aberdeenshire, AB53 4DT Tel: (01888) 563589 Fax: (01888) 563936 E-mail: info@wpeters.co.uk

Walton Press, 7 Adlams Central Park, Wirrall Park Road, Glastonbury, Somerset, BA6 9XE Tel: (01458) 834292 Fax: (01458) 834271 E-mail: sandy@waltonpress.co.uk

Warren Labels, 6 Ullswater Road, Kettering, Northamptonshire, NN16 8UD Tel: (01536) 410842 Fax: (01536) 417070 E-mail: bunnyjsh@warrenlabels.fsnet.co.uk

Waterloo Design & Print Plc, Reliance House, Birmingham St, Halesowen, West Midlands, B63 3HW Tel: 0121-550 1795 Fax: 0121-501 1514 E-mail: admin@waterloo.uk.com

Watermark Business Forms Ltd, 353 Stratford Road, Shirley, Solihull, West Midlands, B90 3BW Tel: 0121-733 1633 Fax: 0121-733 1683 E-mail: sales@watermark.print.com

Watford Printers Ltd, 58 Vicarage Road, Watford, WD18 0EW Tel: (01923) 223885 Fax: (01923) 221757 E-mail: wpl@btconnect.com

Western Printers, 103 Cleveland Street, London, W1T 6PP Tel: (020) 7631 5225 Fax: (020) 7323 6512 E-mail: sales@western-printers.co.uk

William Burrows Printers Ltd, Tansey Green Road, Brierley Hill, West Midlands, DY5 4TL Tel: (01384) 79678 Fax: (01384) 79678

WM Print Ltd, 45-47 Frederick Street, Walsall, WS2 9NE Tel: (01922) 643008 Fax: (01922) 720149 E-mail: cooper@wmprint.co.uk

Williams Lea, Clifton House, 75-77 Worship Street, London, EC2A 2EJ Tel: (020) 7772 4400 Fax: (020) 7772 4468 E-mail: sales@williamslea.com

Williams Weddings, 17 Albany Way, Bristol, BS30 8UA Tel: 0117-949 0297 Fax: 0117-949 0297

Wiltshire Printing Co Croydon Ltd, 131 Love Lane, Mitcham, Surrey, CR4 3YA Tel: (020) 8648 0061 Fax: (020) 8648 6547

Winstanley & Watkins, 104 Duke Street, Liverpool, L1 5AG Tel: 0151-709 0808 Fax: 0151-709 3060 E-mail: info@wwprint.co.uk

Witherby & Co. Ltd, 32-36 Aylesbury Street, London, EC1R 0ET Tel: (020) 7253 5413 Fax: (020) 7336 7493 E-mail: briandoors@witherbys.co.uk

Wolverley Press & Studio Ltd, 39-43 Temple Bar, Willenhall, West Midlands, WV13 1SH Tel: (01902) 604130 Fax: (01902) 637746

Wombourne, Ounsdale Road, Wombourne, Wolverhampton, WV5 8EB Tel: (01902) 324222 Fax: (01902) 894081 E-mail: info@wombourne-printers.co.uk

Wood & Richardson Ltd, Royden House, 156 Haxby Road, York, YO31 8JN Tel: (01904) 622712 Fax: (01904) 620352 E-mail: sales@woodrichardson.co.uk

Woodside Press Ltd, 22a Islington Road, Bristol, BS3 1QB Tel: 0117-985 5500 Fax: 0117-963 9969

William Woolley Ltd, Moseley Press, The Orchard, Bilston, West Midlands, WV14 0EB Tel: (01902) 491601 Fax: (01902) 401257

Wright's Sandbach Ltd, 9 Old Middlewich Road, Sandbach, Cheshire, CW11 1DP Tel: (01270) 762416 Fax: (01270) 760278 E-mail: sales@wrightsprinters.com

Wye Valley Printers, Units 8 & 9, Foley Trading Estate, Hereford, HR1 2SF Tel: (01432) 268286 Fax: (01432) 356322 E-mail: sales@wyevalleyprinters.co.uk

Wyndeham Graphics Ltd, Unit 3-4 Maverton Road, London, E3 2JE Tel: (020) 8983 0022 Fax: (020) 8981 9802

Xavier Press, Unit D6 Barwell Business Park, Leatherhead Road, Chessington, Surrey, KT9 2NY Tel: (020) 8391 4707 Fax: (020) 8397 5202 E-mail: xavierpress@talk21.com

Xyz Printers, 1 Londesborough Road, Market Weighton, York, YO43 3AZ Tel: (01430) 872315 Fax: (01430) 874046

PRINTERS, GRAND FORMAT

▶ Ha'penny Press, Unit 4 Appletree Barns, Folly Lane, Copdock, Ipswich, IP8 3JQ Tel: (01473) 730055 Fax: (01473) 730169 E-mail: tickets@raffle.co.uk

PRINTERS, INSTANT/SAME DAY SERVICES

Prontaprint Ltd, 129 Crawford Street, London, W1U 6BH Tel: (020) 7486 7578 Fax: (020) 7486 0942 E-mail: enquiries@prontaprint-london.com

Prontaprint Ltd, Artemis, Odyssey Business Park West End Road, Ruislip, Middlesex, HA4 6QE Tel: (0800) 343334 Fax: (01895) 872141 E-mail: info@prontaprint.com

Service Point, Unit 3, 8-14 William Road, London, NW1 3EN Tel: (020) 7387 6071 Fax: (020) 7387 1382 E-mail: williamrd@servicepointuk.com

Tag Instantprint Ltd, 182 London Road, Kingston Upon Thames, Surrey, KT2 6QW Tel: (020) 8546 6833 Fax: (020) 8547 1441 E-mail: taginstantprint@aol.com

▶ Vision Printers Ltd, Vision House, 1 Silverdale Lane, Tunbridge Wells, Kent, TN4 9LA Tel: (01892) 545006 Fax: (01892) 538069 E-mail: sales@vision-printers.co.uk

PRINTERS, PARALLEL INKJET

▶ Inkjet-Pruducts4u, 78 Southbridge Road, Croydon, CR0 1AE Tel: 0208 649 7900 Fax: 0208 681 4007 E-mail: sales@injet-products4u.com

PRINTERS, PHOTOCOPIERS, COMBINED UNITS

Photostatic Copiers Anglia & Co., 39-41 West End Street, Norwich, NR2 4NA Tel: (01603) 613969 Fax: (01603) 667373 E-mail: sales@photostatic.com

PRINTING

▶ A S T Print Group Ltd, Ipswich Road, Cardiff, CF23 9AQ Tel: (029) 2049 7901 Fax: (029) 2045 0189

▶ A W Angus & Co. Ltd, 24 Croydon Street, Leeds, LS11 9RT Tel: 0113-245 3246 Fax: 0113-234 1322

▶ indicates data change since last edition

PRINTING – *continued*

▶ Abbey Printers Of Bradford Ltd, Robin Mills, Leeds Road, Idle, Bradford, West Yorkshire, BD10 9TE Tel: (01274) 620238 Fax: (01274) 612964 E-mail: sales@abbeyprinters.co.uk

▶ Allforms Of Print Ltd, 25 Bridges Road, Norton Canes, Cannock, Staffordshire, WS11 9PB Tel: (01543) 276621 Fax: (01543) 450308 E-mail: sales@allforms.co.uk

▶ Axicon Auto Id Ltd, Church Road, Weston-on-the-Green, Bicester, Oxfordshire, OX25 3QP Tel: (01869) 351166 Fax: (01869) 351205 E-mail: info@axicon.com

▶ B D & H Ltd, 37 Europa Way, Martineau Lane, Norwich, NR1 2EN Tel: (01603) 620780 Fax: (01603) 630186

▶ B H F Printers, G 1 Unit Riverside Industrial Estate, Riverside Way, Dartford, DA1 5BS Tel: (01322) 285286 Fax: (01322) 287070

▶ Barclays Print, 6 Dorma Trading Park, Staffa Road, London, E10 7QX Tel: (020) 8556 5955 Fax: (020) 8556 2134 E-mail: admin@barclaysprint.co.uk

▶ The Bertrand Russell Peace Foundation Ltd, Russell House, Bulwell Lane, Nottingham, NG6 0BT Tel: 0115-978 4504 Fax: 0115-942 0433

B-Looney, Buck House, Sunnyside Road, Chesham, Buckinghamshire, HP5 2AR Tel: (01494) 793904 Fax: (01494) 791268 E-mail: balloons@b-loony.co.uk

▶ The Bramwell Label Company Ltd, 33 Long Wood Road, Trafford Park, Manchester, M17 1PZ Tel: 0161-876 7444 Fax: 0161-876 7555

▶ Brynymor Digital, 14 Brynymor Road, Swansea, SA1 4JQ Tel: (01792) 456661 Fax: (01792) 456777 E-mail: info@digipress.co.uk

▶ Burnsides Marketing Aids Ltd, 62 Station Road, Langley Mill, Nottingham, NG16 4BH Tel: (01773) 713687 Fax: (01773) 715801 E-mail: sales@burnsides.co.uk

▶ Carney Print Ltd, 141 New Bedford Road, Luton, LU3 1LF Tel: (01582) 737082 Fax: (01582) 402608

▶ Coates & Parker Ltd, 36 Market Place, Warminster, Wiltshire, BA12 9AN Tel: (01985) 213030 Fax: (01985) 217680 E-mail: sales@coatesandparker.co.uk

▶ Collector Set Printers Ltd, Aylesford Mill, St Michaels Close, Aylesford, Kent, ME20 7BU Tel: (01622) 716636 Fax: (01622) 717515 E-mail: sales@collectorsetprinters.co.uk

▶ D X G Media Ltd, Abc House, Latham Close, Bredbury, Stockport, Cheshire, SK6 2SD Tel: 0161-612 3030 Fax: 0161-612 7001

▶ Dats Print Services Ltd, Victoria House, 30 Victoria Street, Irthlingborough, Wellingborough, Northamptonshire, NN9 5RG Tel: (01933) 650623 Fax: (01933) 650698 E-mail: sales@datsprint.co.uk

Diamond Printed Products Plastic Printers, Maidstone Road, Nettlestead, Maidstone, Kent, ME18 5HP Tel: (01622) 871666 Fax: (01622) 872628 E-mail: info@diamondprinted.com

▶ Ernest Bond Printing, 4 Kingside, Ruston Road, London, SE18 5BX Tel: (020) 8855 7788 Fax: (020) 8855 7799

▶ Hine Labels Ltd, Hope Street, Rotherham, South Yorkshire, S60 1LH Tel: (01709) 369222 Fax: (01709) 363660 E-mail: enquiries@hinelabels.com

▶ Labels, 7 City Court Trading Estate, Poland Street, Manchester, M4 6AL Tel: 0161-205 5711 Fax: 0161-205 5722

▶ Lion Labels & Packaging, Regent House, Regent Street, Coppull, Chorley, Lancashire, PR7 5AX Tel: (01257) 793335 Fax: (01257) 471530

▶ O M S Ltd, Origination House, 15 Strawberry Street, Hull, HU9 1EN Tel: (01482) 224429

▶ Olympus Labels Ltd, Richardshaw Road, Grangefield Industrial Estate, Pudsey, West Yorkshire, LS28 6QW Tel: 0113-236 3283 Fax: 0113-236 3284

▶ Orphans Press Ltd, Arrow Close, Leominster Enterprise Park, Stoke Prior, Leominster, Herefordshire, HR6 0LX Tel: (01568) 612460 Fax: (01568) 613559 E-mail: info@orphanspress.co.uk

▶ Paramount Printing (Hanley) Ltd, Print House, 10 Woodhouse St, Stoke-on-Trent, ST4 1EH Tel: (01782) 413529

Parkes Print & Design, 41 Hitchin Street, Biggleswade, Bedfordshire, SG18 8BE Tel: (01767) 603930 Fax: (01767) 603936

▶ Printing.Com@RasLtd, Lakeland House, 10 Boughton, Chester, CH3 5AG Tel: (01244) 343333 Fax: (01244) 346120 E-mail: sales@rasgroup.co.uk

▶ Prontaprint Ltd, 652-654 Warwick Road, Solihull, West Midlands, B91 3DX Tel: 0121-705 9988 Fax: 0121-711 1309 E-mail: sales@solihull.prontaprint.com

Rainbow Colour, 2 High St, Steventon, Abingdon, Oxfordshire, OX13 6RS Tel: (01235) 200700 Fax: (01235) 200707 E-mail: rainbow.colour@tiscali.co.uk

▶ Recycle Print & Design Ltd, Swains Industrial Estate, Ashingdon Road, Rochford, Essex, SS4 1RG Tel: (01702) 531313 Fax: (01702) 531414

▶ Reel Form Ltd, Riverside Road, Pride Park, Derby, DE24 8HY Tel: (01332) 200222 Fax: (01332) 200805

▶ Rotary Printers Ltd, Mitton Street, Stourport-on-Severn, Worcestershire, DY13 9AA Tel: (01299) 823839 Fax: (01299) 826991 E-mail: sales@rotaryprinters.co.uk

▶ Severn Signs Ltd, Unit 19 Innsworth Technology Park, Innsworth Lane, Gloucester, GL3 1DL Tel: (01452) 739156 Fax: (01452) 739153

▶ Severnprint Ltd, Unit 8-10 Ashville Industrial Estate, Ashville Road, Gloucester, GL2 5EU Tel: (01452) 416391 Fax: (01452) 307001

▶ Skamem and Durham, Unit 7, Park 2000, Millennium Way, Newton Aycliffe, County Durham, DL5 6AR Tel: (01325) 375140 Fax: (01325) 375161

▶ Spear Europe Ltd, Christopher Grey Court, Lakeside, Llantarnam Industrial Park, Cwmbran, Gwent, NP44 3SE Tel: (01633) 627600 Fax: (01633) 627601 E-mail: sales@spearsystem.com

▶ Sphere, 1 Crown Centre, Bond Street, Macclesfield, Cheshire, SK11 6QS Tel: (01625) 425676 Fax: (01625) 511375

▶ Think Print, Cameron Court, Winnington Hall, Winnington, Northwich, Cheshire, CW8 4DU Tel: (01606) 784567 Fax: (01606) 784777

▶ Thomas & Sons Ltd, Harlequin Avenue, Brentford, Middlesex, TW8 9EW Tel: (020) 8568 0231 Fax: (020) 8847 4842

▶ TSC Graphics Ltd, 28 Factory Lane, Croydon, CR0 3RL Tel: (020) 8686 6553

▶ Vision Litho, 70 Wood End Green Road, Hayes, Middlesex, UB3 2SL Tel: (020) 8561 8726 E-mail: visionlitho@mac.com

▶ Vitesse Printing Company Ltd, 18-19 Crimscott Street, London, SE1 5TE Tel: (020) 7274 0120 Fax: (020) 7252 0635 E-mail: sales@vitesseprint.co.uk

▶ Wirral Continuous Ltd, 26 Thursby Rd., Croft Business Park, Wirral, Merseyside, CH62 3PW Tel: 0151-334 0895

PRINTING BLANKETS

Day International Ltd, Balgray Street, Dundee, DD3 8HN Tel: (01382) 422200 Fax: (01382) 832310 E-mail: bill_crowe@day-intel.com

Duco International Ltd, Eastbourne Road, Slough, SL1 4SF Tel: (01753) 522274 Fax: (01753) 691952 E-mail: info@duco.co.uk

Farnbeck Ltd, 32 Swanfield, Edinburgh, EH6 5RX Tel: 0131-553 5353 Fax: 0131-553 3979 E-mail: dm001@post.almac.co.uk

▶ Press Ltd, Cross Road, Annesley, Nottingham, NG15 0AL Tel: (01623) 723444 Fax: (01623) 720784

PRINTING CHEMICALS

A B C Chemical Co, Woodhouse Road, Todmorden, Lancashire, OL14 5TD Tel: (01200) 420180 Fax: (01706) 819554 E-mail: info@abcchem.co.uk

Columbia Ribbon Manufacturing Co. Ltd, Kangley Bridge Road, London, SE26 5AW Tel: (020) 8659 3659 Fax: (020) 8659 6270

Hydro Dynamic Products Ltd, Unit 2-3, Harbour Way, Shoreham-by-Sea, West Sussex, BN43 5HZ Tel: (01273) 464881 Fax: (01273) 464626 E-mail: sales@hdp.co.uk

P J S Chemicals, 8 Station Estate, Station Road, Tadcaster, North Yorkshire, LS24 9SG Tel: (01937) 832928 Fax: (01937) 834852 E-mail: pjschemicals@aol.com

PRINTING DRYING RACKS

Produsit Ltd, Precision Works, 69-70 Moland Street, Birmingham, B4 7EY Tel: 0121-359 5571 Fax: 0121-359 5572 E-mail: produsit@msn.com

PRINTING INDUSTRY LAMINATING SERVICES

Encapsulated Print Services, Unit 3a Prince William Way, Loughborough, Leicestershire, LE11 5DD Tel: (01509) 230892 Fax: (01509) 230877 E-mail: encapprintmids@aol.com

Eurogloss Ltd, Units 3 & 5 Greyhound Commercial Centre, Greyhound Way, Dartford, DA1 4HF Tel: (01322) 557777 Fax: (01322) 555277 E-mail: production@eurogloss.co.uk

G T Laminators, Rear of 60 Great Norbury Street, Hyde, Cheshire, SK14 1HY Tel: (07979) 286187 Fax: 0161-366 0856

Holland & Watts, 1 Paragon Court, Tongham Road, Aldershot, Hampshire, GU12 4AA Tel: (01252) 344200 Fax: (01252) 343466 E-mail: sales@hollandandwatts.com

Kinmel Paper Supplies, 180 Wellington Road, Rhyl, Clwyd, LL18 1LL Tel: (01745) 354589 Fax: (01745) 354589

Laminating East Midlands, 26 Low Farm Place, Moulton Park Industrial Estate, Northampton, NN3 6HY Tel: (01604) 642823 Fax: (01604) 790423 E-mail: postmaster@eml.uk.com

Paragon Cutting Forms, Unit 23 Blaydon Business Centre, Cowen Road, Blaydon-on-Tyne, Tyne & Wear, NE21 5TW Tel: 0191-487 9555 Fax: 0191-487 9666 E-mail: sales@paragoncfl.com

West Midlands Laminating Co. Ltd, 50 Midland Street, Birmingham, B9 4DG Tel: 0121-773 0722 Fax: 0121-773 0741 E-mail: sales@westmidlam.co.uk

PRINTING INDUSTRY SOFTWARE

Redtitan Ltd, 5 Regius Court, Penn, High Wycombe, Buckinghamshire, HP10 8RL Tel: (0870) 8705432 Fax: (0870) 8704560 E-mail: sales@redtitan.com

PRINTING INDUSTRY STAFF RECRUITMENT

D K Associates Ltd, 26-34 Friar Lane, Nottingham, NG1 6DQ Tel: 0115-947 3500 Fax: 0115-985 9007 E-mail: office@dk-recruit.co.uk

▶ Mercury Search & Selection Ltd, Redhill House, Hope Street, Chester, CH4 8BU Tel: (01244) 677219 Fax: (01244) 682710 E-mail: info@mercurysearch.co.uk

PRINTING INDUSTRY VALUERS

▶ Marriott & Co., 19 East Street, Farnham, Surrey, GU9 7SD Tel: (01252) 712083 Fax: (01252) 737613 E-mail: mail@marriott.co.uk

PRINTING INK BASIC/RAW MATERIALS

▶ Union Ink Co. Ltd, 28 Eldon Way, Paddock Wood, Tonbridge, Kent, TN12 6BE Tel: (01892) 834555 Fax: (01892) 834666

PRINTING INK DISPERSION SERVICES

D & D Dispersions Ltd, Unit G, St. Marks Road, St. James Industrial Estate, Corby, Northamptonshire, NN18 8AN Tel: (01536) 400488 Fax: (01536) 407365 E-mail: dispersion@dddispersions.co.uk

Tenants Inks & Coatings Suppliers, Ruspidge Road, Cinderford, Gloucestershire, GL14 3AW Tel: (01594) 822375 Fax: (01594) 826251 E-mail: salessupport@tg-tics.com

PRINTING INK MANUFRS

Antonine Printing Inks Ltd, Block 15, Newhouse Industrial Estate, Motherwell, Lanarkshire, ML1 5RX Tel: (01698) 733768 Fax: (01698) 832861 E-mail: info@antonine-inks.co.uk

Apollo Colours Ltd, 127 Nathan Way, West Thames Mead Business Park, London, SE28 0AB Tel: (020) 8854 0017 Fax: (020) 8316 6956 E-mail: london@apollocolours.co.uk

Coates Lorilleux, Cray Avenue, St. Mary Cray, Orpington, Kent, BR5 3PP Tel: (01689) 894000 Fax: (01689) 894020

Colourspeed Ltd, Stacey House, Bushey Hall Drive, Bushey, WD23 2ER Tel: (01923) 211255 Fax: (01923) 211255 E-mail: colourspeed@aol.com

European Printing Inks Ltd, Precision House, Ring Road, Seacroft, Leeds, LS14 1NH Tel: 0113-273 8333 Fax: 0113-265 0223

European Printing Inks Ltd, Unit 38 Phoenix International Industrial Estate, Charles Street, West Bromwich, West Midlands, B70 0AY Tel: 0121-520 2471

Flint Group UK Ltd, Slinfold, Horsham, West Sussex, RH13 0SH Tel: (01403) 790332 Fax: (01403) 790617

Flint Schmidt, Vauxhall Industrial Estate, Ruabon, Wrexham, Clwyd, LL14 6HU Tel: (01978) 823456 Fax: (01978) 823331

Flint Scmidt Ltd, Qualcast Road Industrial Estate, Wolverhampton, WV1 2QP Tel: (01902) 871028 Fax: (01902) 457461 E-mail: sales@flint-schmidt.com

Hillbrook Printing Inks Ltd, New Street, Slaithwaite, Huddersfield, HD7 5BB Tel: (01484) 843535 Fax: (01484) 840031

Litho Supplies, Flagship Square, Shaw Cross Business Park, Dewsbury, West Yorkshire, WF12 7TH Tel: (01924) 486130 Fax: (01924) 460502 E-mail: dewsbury@litho.co.uk

Luminescence Incorporated, The Fairway, Bush Fair, Harlow, Essex, CM18 6NG Tel: (01279) 453711 Fax: (01279) 421142 E-mail: sales@luminescence.co.uk

Perfectos Printing Inks Co. Ltd, Perfectos Mills, Normanton Lane, Bottesford, Nottingham, NG13 0EL Tel: (01949) 842179 Fax: (01949) 843493 E-mail: info@perfectos.co.uk

Stehlin Hostag Inc UK Ltd, 4 Linkmell Close, Longwall Avenue, Queens Drive Industrial Estate, Nottingham, NG2 1NA Tel: 0115-986 0477 Fax: 0115-986 2681

Sun Chemical Ltd, Head Office, 3 High View Road, South Normanton, Alfreton, Derbyshire, DE55 2DT Tel: (01773) 813704 Fax: (01773) 580045 E-mail: gbsn_info@eu.suncham.com

Sun Chemical, 6 South Crescent, London, E16 4TL Tel: (020) 7712 7121 Fax: (020) 7712 7122

Sun Chemical Gibbon, 151 South Liberty Lane, Bristol, BS3 2TL Tel: 0117-966 9987 Fax: 0117-966 9880

Sun Chemical Swale, Taylor Road, Urmston, Manchester, M41 7SW Tel: 0161-748 7340 Fax: 0161-748 7685

Van Son Ink UK Ltd, 71 Alston Drive, Bradwell Abbey, Milton Keynes, MK13 9HG Tel: (01908) 317717 Fax: (01908) 221005 E-mail: vanson@compuserve.com

PRINTING INKS, METALLIC

Wolstenholme Bidco Ltd, Springfield House, Lower Eccleshill Road, Darwen, Lancashire, BB3 0RP Tel: (01254) 873888 Fax: (01254) 703430 E-mail: sales@wolstenholme-int.com

PRINTING LETTERPRESSES

Cee Gee Agencies, Cee Gee House, College Road, Harrow Weald, Harrow, Middlesex, HA3 6EF Tel: (020) 8863 8596 Fax: (020) 8427 1827

R.R. Donnelley UK, Flaxby Moor, Knaresborough, North Yorkshire, HG5 0XJ Tel: (01423) 796500 Fax: (01423) 796501

E S P Colour, Elgin Drive, Swindon, SN2 8XU Tel: (01793) 438400 Fax: (01793) 530403 E-mail: firstinitial.surname@espcolour.co.uk

Wilfred Edmunds Ltd, 37 Station Road, Chesterfield, Derbyshire, S41 7XD Tel: (01246) 504500 Fax: (01246) 504580 E-mail: editorial@derbyshiretimes.co.uk

Express & Echo Publications Ltd, Heron Road, Sowton Industrial Estate, Exeter, EX2 7NF Tel: (01392) 442211 Fax: (01392) 442294

Hill & Tyler, Glaisedale Drive, Bilbrough, Nottingham, NG8 4LX Tel: 0115-929 9422 Fax: 0115-929 6026 E-mail: sales@hillandtyler.co.uk

L & S Printing Co. Ltd, Unit 10 Hazelwood Trading Estate, Hazelwood Close, Worthing, West Sussex, BN14 8NP Tel: (01903) 821005 Fax: (01903) 821006 E-mail: sue.m@ls-printing.com

Luminescence Incorporated, The Fairway, Bush Fair, Harlow, Essex, CM18 6NG Tel: (01279) 453711 Fax: (01279) 421142 E-mail: sales@luminescence.co.uk

Ralegh Ltd, Aries House, Manby Park, Manby, Louth, Lincolnshire, LN11 8UT Tel: (01507) 327040 Fax: (01507) 327039 E-mail: diesolutions@ralegh.co.uk

Redverse, Unit 3, Benbow Business Park Harlescott Lane, Shrewsbury, SY1 3FA Tel: (01743) 466668 Fax: (01743) 466669 E-mail: info@redverse.com

Simpson's Printers, Transfer Bridge Industrial Estate, County Road, Swindon, SN1 2EL Tel: (01793) 536305 Fax: (01793) 532543 E-mail: sales@simpsonprinters.co.uk

Simpson's Printers, Transfer Bridge Industrial Estate, County Road, Swindon, SN1 2EL Tel: (01793) 536305 Fax: (01793) 532543

Slough & Langley Express, 256 Ipswich Road, Slough, SL1 4EP Tel: (01753) 825111 Fax: (01753) 692254 E-mail: sales@sloughexpress.co.uk

Tyrone Constitution, 25-27 High Street, Omagh, County Tyrone, BT78 1BD Tel: (028) 8224 2721 Fax: (028) 8224 3549

Western Morning News Co. Ltd, 17 Brest Road, Derriford, Plymouth, PL6 5AA Tel: (01752) 765500 Fax: (01752) 765515 E-mail: plymouthfrontcounter@westcountrypublications.co.uk

Wokingham Times, Unit 5 Anville Court, 44 Denmark Street, Wokingham, Berkshire, RG40 2BB Tel: 0118-936 6180 Fax: 0118-936 6190E-mail: editorial@wokingham-times.co.uk

PRINTING MACHINE ACCESSORIES/ANCILLARY EQUIPMENT/COMPONENTS MANUFRS

Ab Graphic International, Carnaby Industrial Estate, Lancaster Road, Carnaby, Bridlington, North Humberside, YO15 3QY Tel: (01262) 671138 Fax: (01262) 606359 E-mail: info@abgint.com

Big Fish, Unit 10 Glenpark Industrial Estate, Glenpark Street, Glasgow, G31 1NU Tel: 0141-550 2001 Fax: 0141-556 1131

Dainippon Screen UK Ltd, Michigan Drive, Tongwell, Milton Keynes, MK15 8HT Tel: (01908) 848500 Fax: (01908) 848501 E-mail: sales@screeneurope.co.uk

General Imaging Technology UK Ltd, Unit 18 Hortonwood 33, Telford, Shropshire, TF1 7YS Tel: (01952) 677510 Fax: (01952) 676332 E-mail: sam@generalimaging.co.uk

Ingham (Toolmakers) Ltd, Willow Hall Works, Willowfield Road, Halifax, West Yorkshire, HX2 7NF Tel: (01422) 342189 Fax: (01422) 342497 E-mail: info@inghamtools.co.uk

M M Digital Ltd, Haig Road, Parkgate Industrial Estate, Knutsford, Cheshire, WA16 8DX Tel: (01565) 755356 Fax: (01565) 755357 E-mail: sales@mmdigital.co.uk

D.R. Markey & Sons, Adcroft Street, Higher Hillgate, Stockport, Cheshire, SK1 3HZ Tel: 0161-480 1440 Fax: 0161-480 6164

Oxy-Dry UK Inc, Unit 2, Whitworth Road, Stevenage, Hertfordshire, SG1 4QS Tel: (01438) 728881 Fax: (01438) 728309

PRINTING MACHINE ACCESSORIES/ ANCILLARY EQUIPMENT/ COMPONENTS MANUFRS – *continued*

Padtec Ltd, 14 Balmercut, Buckingham Industrial Estate, Buckingham, MK18 1SQ Tel: (01280) 822251 Fax: (01280) 822958 E-mail: sales@padtec.co.uk

Parker Graphics Ltd, Progress House, Erskine Road, London, E17 6RT Tel: (020) 8520 7182 Fax: (020) 8521 7846

Precimatic Ltd, 2 Balthane Industrial Estate, Balthane, Ballasalla, Isle of Man, IM9 2AQ Tel: (01624) 823030 Fax: (01624) 824600

Premier Guillotine Systems Ltd, Fairweather Green Works, Rear of 900 Thornton Road, Bradford, West Yorkshire, BD8 0JG Tel: (01274) 499832 Fax: (01274) 547818

Printers Partners Supplies Ltd, Unit 720 Tudor Estate, Abbey Road, London, NW10 7UN Tel: (020) 8951 9500 Fax: (020) 8963 1940 E-mail: sales@rotaprint.com

Quadtech UK Ltd, Maxted Road, Hemel Hempstead, Hertfordshire, HP2 7ED Tel: (01442) 236655 Fax: (01442) 232302

Turner Langdale Ltd, 115 Beddington Lane, Croydon, CR0 4TD Tel: (020) 8689 5122 Fax: (020) 8689 3745 E-mail: sales@turnerlangdale.co.uk

PRINTING MACHINE CLEANING EQUIPMENT

Meech S C T Ltd, 2 Network Point, Range Road, Witney, Oxfordshire, OX29 0YD Tel: (01993) 706700 Fax: (01933) 776977 E-mail: sales@meech.com

PRINTING MACHINE CONSUMABLES

Dynamic Cassette (International) Ltd, Marsh Lane, Boston, Lincolnshire, PE21 7TX Tel: (01205) 355555 Fax: (01205) 354823 E-mail: sales@dci.co.uk

Forms Plus Ltd, The Willows, Church Street, Helston, Cornwall, TR13 8GT Tel: (01326) 564331 Fax: (01326) 564086 E-mail: mail@formsplus.co.uk

Hi Tech Graphics Machinery Ltd, 252 Old Brompton Rd, London, SW5 9HW Tel: 020 72440334 Fax: 020 72440366

PRINTING MACHINE MAINTENANCE/REPAIR SERVICES

▶ Exiserv Ltd, 1 Page Heath Lane, Bromley, BR1 2DR Tel: (07931) 970900 Fax: (01474) 873589 E-mail: sales@exiserv.com

Komori UK Ltd, Kirkstall Industrial Park, Kirkstall Road, Leeds, LS4 2AZ Tel: 0113-279 9944 Fax: 0113-279 9922 E-mail: info@komori-europe.com

Maine Business Systems P.L.C., Hanover Park House, Merebank Lane, Croydon, CR0 4NP Tel: (020) 8688 8855 Fax: (020) 8688 8897 E-mail: post@maine-plc.com

Printing & Graphic Machinery Ltd, Millboard Road, Bourne End, Buckinghamshire, SL8 5XE Tel: (01628) 527372 Fax: (01628) 524466 E-mail: sales@pgm.co.uk

Woodward Services, 14 Eldon Road, Reading, RG1 4DL Tel: 0118-926 6664

PRINTING MACHINE MANUFRS

Ataroth Plastics Machinery Sales Ltd, 5 Maer Lane, Market Drayton, Shropshire, TF9 1QX Tel: (01630) 655148 Fax: (01630) 654055

Britannia Machinery Pontefract Ltd, Stuart Street, Pontefract, West Yorkshire, WF8 4PW Tel: (01977) 790818 Fax: (01977) 600333 E-mail: britannia.machinery@btinternet.com

C R S (London) Ltd, 98A Blackstock Road, London, N4 2DR Tel: (020) 7226 0404 Fax: (020) 7226 1806 E-mail: crslondonltd@hotmail.com

Cooper Printing Machinery Ltd, 42 Coldharbour Lane, Harpenden, Hertfordshire, AL5 4UN Tel: (01582) 764431 Fax: (01582) 768608 E-mail: sales@cooperprint.co.uk

Eurograv Ltd, Sprint Industrial Estate, Chertsey Road, Byfleet, West Byfleet, Surrey, KT14 7BD Tel: (01932) 336262 Fax: (01932) 336271 E-mail: sales@eurograv.co.uk

▶ Forest Systems (FPE), 4 Farriers Field, Upavon, Pewsey, Wiltshire, SN9 6NW Tel: (07973) 921456

Fujifilm Electronics Imaging Ltd, Bretton Way, Bretton, Peterborough, PE3 8YG Tel: (01733) 260490 Fax: (01733) 462222

Graphics Arts Equipment Ltd, 11 Aintree Road, Greenford, Middlesex, UB6 7LE Tel: (020) 8997 8053 Fax: (020) 8997 7706 E-mail: info@gae.co.uk

H W L Engineering Ltd, 99-105 Canterbury Road, Croydon, CR0 3HH Tel: (020) 8689 8300 Fax: (020) 8689 8920

Heidelberg Graphic Equipment Ltd, Intercity Way, Leeds, LS13 4LX Tel: 0113-224 8300 Fax: 0113-239 3118

Hill Brook Printing Inks Ltd, New Hey Rd, Outlane, Huddersfield, HD3 3YJ Tel: 01484 841061 Fax: 01484 377324

H.G. Kippax & Sons Ltd, Upper Bankfield Mills, Almondbury Bank, Huddersfield, HD5 8HF Tel: (01484) 426789 Fax: (01484) 541799 E-mail: sales@hgkippax.co.uk

Komori UK Ltd, Kirkstall Industrial Park, Kirkstall Road, Leeds, LS4 2AZ Tel: 0113-279 9944 Fax: 0113-279 9922 E-mail: info@komori-europe.com

Martek, Unit 12b, Ridings Park, Eastern Way, Cannock, Staffordshire, WS11 7FJ Tel: (01543) 502202 Fax: (01543) 467726 E-mail: info@martekonline.co.uk

Metric Group Ltd, Metric House, 5 Love Lane, Cirencester, Gloucestershire, GL7 1YG Tel: (01285) 651441 Fax: (01285) 653944 E-mail: postmaster@metricgroup.co.uk

▶ Muller Martini Ltd, The Ridgeway, Iver, Buckinghamshire, SL0 9JQ Tel: (01753) 657700 Fax: (01753) 655658 E-mail: enquiries@mullermartini.co.uk

Perfectos Printing Inks Co. Ltd, Perfectos Mills, Normanton Lane, Bottesford, Nottingham, NG13 0EL Tel: (01949) 842179 Fax: (01949) 843493 E-mail: info@perfectos.co.uk

Printing Press Services Ltd, Sellers Street, Preston, PR1 5EU Tel: (01772) 797050 Fax: (01772) 705761E-mail: sales@ppsi.co.uk

▶ Punsh Graphics Ltd, Chestnut House, Northminster Business Park, Northfield Lane, Upper Poppleton, York, YO26 6QR Tel: (01904) 520555 Fax: (01904) 789974 E-mail: infogb@xeikon.com

Purdy Graphic Systems, 37 Kings Road, Berkhamsted, Hertfordshire, HP4 3BJ Tel: (01442) 865112 Fax: (01442) 865113 E-mail: purdygs@globalnet.co.uk

R M Rotary Services Ltd, New Lane, Havant, Hampshire, PO9 2LT Tel: (023) 9249 2360 Fax: (023) 9249 2544 E-mail: info@rmrotary.co.uk

Red Devil, Unit 2e Beehive Lane Works, Beehive Lane, Chelmsford, CM2 9TE Tel: (01255) 553555 Fax: (01255) 553555 E-mail: sales@reddevilmachines.co.uk

Regency Press, 2a Kent Street, Belfast, BT1 2JA Tel: (028) 9032 1724 Fax: (028) 9033 2280

Senior Graphic Machinery Ltd, Thornes La Wharf, Wakefield, West Yorkshire, WF1 5RF Tel: (01924) 386386 Fax: (01924) 386800

Timsons Ltd, Bath Road, Kettering, Northamptonshire, NN16 8NQ Tel: (01536) 411611 Fax: (01536) 411666 E-mail: admin@timsons.com

▶ Total Register Machines, Unit 17 International Business Park, Charfleets Road, Canvey Island, Essex, SS8 0SG Tel: (01268) 680764 Fax: (01268) 680091 E-mail: sales@totalregistermachines.com

W P M Europe, Unit 1-2 Sam Brown Industrial Units, Dog & Gun Lane, Whetstone, Leicester, LE8 6LJ Tel: 0116-275 2393 Fax: 0116-275 3095 E-mail: mharriman@wpm.com

Wantzen Ltd, Anton House, South Park, Sevenoaks, Kent, TN13 1EB Tel: (01732) 458185 Fax: (01732) 458188 E-mail: info@wantzen.co.uk

PRINTING MATERIALS

M & S Mailing & Support Ltd, Unit 17 18, Royce Road, Crawley, West Sussex, RH10 9NX Tel: (01293) 527711 Fax: (01293) 527713

▶ Platinum Print Ltd, Park House, Hookstone Park, Harrogate, North Yorkshire, HG2 7DB Tel: (01423) 881158 Fax: (01423) 886072 E-mail: sales@platinumprint.com

▶ Sil Die Ltd, Fullbridge Quay, Maldon, Essex, CM9 4LE Tel: (01621) 858502 Fax: (01621) 851568

PRINTING NUMBERING MACHINES

Atlantic Zeiser Ltd, 53 Central Way, Andover, Hampshire, SP10 5AN Tel: (01264) 324222 Fax: (01264) 324333 E-mail: sales@atlanticzeiseruk.com

PRINTING PLATE MANUFRS

Granville Reprographics Ltd, Demmings House, Brookfield Road, Demmings Industrial Estate, Cheadle, Cheshire, SK8 2PE Tel: 0161-428 1236 Fax: 0161-428 0418 E-mail: sales@directimaging.co.uk

Kodak Graphic Communications Ltd, Axis 1, Rhodes Way, Watford, WD24 4FD Tel: (01923) 233366 Fax: (01923) 227802

Kodak Polychrome Graphics, Howley Park Estate, Morley, Leeds, LS27 0QT Tel: 0113-253 7711 E-mail: sales@kpgraphics.com

Litho Supplies, Flagship Square, Shaw Cross Business Park, Dewsbury, West Yorkshire, WF12 7TH Tel: (01924) 486130 Fax: (01924) 460502 E-mail: dewsbury@litho.co.uk

Macdermot Autotype Ltd, Grove Road, Wantage, Oxfordshire, OX12 7BZ Tel: (01235) 771111 Fax: (01235) 771196 E-mail: feedback@autotype.com

PRINTING PLATES, PHOTOPOLYMER

Printec (UK) Ltd, Unit 5, Deanfield Court, Link 59 Business Park, Clitheroe, Lancashire, BB7 1QS Tel: (01200) 425500 Fax: (01200) 425511 E-mail: info@printec.uk.com

PRINTING PRESSES, SHEET FED

▶ Graphic Line Machinery Ltd, 45 Prestongate, Hessle, North Humberside, HU13 0RD Tel: (01482) 645645 Fax: (020) 7691 7913 E-mail: info@glm.co.uk

Holmes Mann & Co. Ltd, 17 Harris Street, Bradford, West Yorkshire, BD1 5HZ Tel: (01274) 735881 Fax: (01274) 306324 E-mail: oscar@holman.co.uk

PRINTING PROOF PRESSES

Art Equipment, 3 Craven Street, Northampton, NN1 3EZ Tel: (01604) 632447 Fax: (01604) 632447 E-mail: charlesstradling@aol.com

J.M. Heaford Ltd, Unit 9 Century Park, Pacific Road, Altrincham, Cheshire, WA14 5BJ Tel: 0161-928 5679 Fax: 0161-927 7517 E-mail: sales@jmheaford.co.uk

PRINTING ROLLER COMPOSITION

Grover Clarke Ltd, The Street, Thorndon, Eye, Suffolk, IP23 7JN Tel: (01379) 678149 Fax: (01379) 678691 E-mail: info@groverclarke.com

North West Roller Services Ltd, 1 Tudor Road, Manor Park, Runcorn, Cheshire, WA7 1TY Tel: (01928) 571711 Fax: (01928) 571775 E-mail: enquiries@nwrollers.co.uk

PRINTING ROLLER LASER ENGRAVERS

Laserflex Ltd, J Balthane Industrial Estate, Balthane, Ballasalla, Isle of Man, IM9 2AG Tel: (01624) 822155 Fax: (01624) 824573 E-mail: sales@laserflex.co.uk

Miller Graphic UK Ltd, 2 Hollands Road, Haverhill, Suffolk, CB9 8PP Tel: (01440) 703001 Fax: (01440) 703421 E-mail: sales@millergraphics.com

PRINTING ROLLER MAINTENANCE/REPAIR SERVICES

Tyke Rollers Ltd, 1c Victoria Court, Colliers Way, Clayton West, Huddersfield, HD8 9TR Tel: (01484) 868331 Fax: (01484) 868332 E-mail: sales@tykerollers.com

PRINTING ROLLER MAKERS/ ENGRAVERS

A T Roberts Ltd, 9-13 Aldenham Road, Watford, WD19 4AB Tel: (01923) 223969 Fax: (01923) 244497 E-mail: info@atroberts.fsnet.co.uk

Engraving Tools Ltd, Unit 44 Stakehill Industrial Estate, Touchet Hall Road, Middleton, Manchester, M24 2FL Tel: 0161-653 8103 Fax: 0161-655 4061 E-mail: engrtools@aol.com

Grover Clarke Ltd, The Street, Thorndon, Eye, Suffolk, IP23 7JN Tel: (01379) 678149 Fax: (01379) 678691 E-mail: info@groverclarke.com

Miller Graphic UK Ltd, 2 Hollands Road, Haverhill, Suffolk, CB9 8PP Tel: (01440) 703001 Fax: (01440) 703421 E-mail: sales@millergraphics.com

Park Cross Engineering, 33 Moss Lane, Worsley, Manchester, M28 3WD Tel: 0161-799 0660 Fax: 0161-703 8006 E-mail: mail@park-cross.co.uk

Robant Services Ltd, Unit 24 Mersey Street, Stockport, Cheshire, SK1 2HX Tel: 0161-429 8728 Fax: 0161-474 7630 E-mail: sales@robant.co.uk

Rola Cylinder Manufacturers Ltd, Porritt Street, Bury, Lancashire, BL9 6HJ Tel: 0161-761 3913 Fax: 0161-762 9281

Tecnograv (Angelsea) Ltd, Llangefni Trading Estate, Llangefni, Gwynedd, LL77 7UZ Tel: (01248) 750363 Fax: (01248) 725100

PRINTING SERVICES

▶ Allforms Of Print Ltd, 25 Bridges Road, Norton Canes, Cannock, Staffordshire, WS11 9PB Tel: (01543) 276621 Fax: (01543) 450308 E-mail: sales@allforms.co.uk

▶ Ashprint Web Offset Ltd, 3 Drumhead Road, Chorley North Industrial Park, Chorley, Lancashire, PR6 7BX Tel: (01257) 230988 Fax: (01257) 230977

▶ Axicon Auto Id Ltd, Church Road, Weston-on-the-Green, Bicester, Oxfordshire, OX25 3QP Tel: (01869) 351166 Fax: (01869) 351205 E-mail: info@axicon.com

▶ B W W Printers Ltd, Axe Road, Bridgwater, Somerset, TA6 5LW Tel: (01278) 423637 Fax: (01278) 444032

▶ Brynymor Digital, 14 Brynymor Road, Swansea, SA1 4JQ Tel: (01792) 456661 Fax: (01792) 456777 E-mail: info@digipress.co.uk

▶ Buckstop Print Services, Unit 2, Wisloe Road, Cambridge, Gloucester, GL2 7AF Tel: (01453) 890767 Fax: (01453) 890392

C P I, Concorde House, 56 Station Road, Finchley Central, London, N3 2SA Tel: (020) 8235 3535 Fax: (020) 8235 3555 E-mail: info@cpilondon.com

▶ Caldicot Printing, 2 Newport Road, Caldicot, Gwent, NP26 4HX Tel: (01291) 423294 Fax: (01291) 423294 E-mail: cal.print1@tiscali.co.uk

▶ Digital-Canvas-Print Ltd, 69 Enid Street, London, SE16 3RA Tel: (020) 7237 9333 Fax: (020) 7237 9444 E-mail: angus@superchrome.co.uk

▶ Epic Printing Services, Epic House, Alington Avenue, Dorchester, Dorset, DT1 1EX Tel: (01305) 266055

G P Print, G P Print Edgerley Business, Challenger Way, Peterborough, PE1 5EX Tel: (01733) 340622 Fax: (08719) 940780 E-mail: info@gpprint.co.uk

▶ Hine Labels Ltd, Hope Street, Rotherham, South Yorkshire, S60 1LH Tel: (01709) 369222 Fax: (01709) 363660 E-mail: enquiries@hinelabels.com

I P 3, 83 Guildford Street, Chertsey, Surrey, KT16 9AS Tel: (0870) 3308625 Fax: (0870) 3308615 E-mail: admin@ip3.org.uk

Ivory Graphics Ltd, 2 Halcyon Court, St. Margarets Way, Stukeley Meadows Industrial Estate, Huntingdon, Cambridgeshire, PE29 6DG Tel: (01480) 417511 Fax: (0870) 3001101 E-mail: info@ivorygraphics.plus.com

▶ Keith Day, Unit 51 Van Alloys Industrial Estate, Busgrove Lane, Stoke Row, Henley-on-Thames, Oxfordshire, RG9 5QW Tel: (01491) 680040 Fax: (01491) 682123 E-mail: keithdayprinters@btinternet.com

▶ Label Studio Ltd, 171 Waterside Road, Hamilton, Leicester, LE5 1TL Tel: 0116-276 3569

▶ Labelnet Ltd, Labelnet House Hallsford Bridge Industrial Estate, Stondon Road, Ongar, Essex, CM5 9RB Tel: (01277) 364964 Fax: (01277) 365965

▶ Labels, 7 City Court Trading Estate, Poland Street, Manchester, M4 6AL Tel: 0161-205 5711 Fax: 0161-205 5722

▶ Lion Labels & Packaging, Regent House, Regent Street, Coppull, Chorley, Lancashire, PR7 5AX Tel: (01257) 793335 Fax: (01257) 471530

▶ O M S Ltd, Origination House, 15 Strawberry Street, Hull, HU9 1EN Tel: (01482) 224429

▶ Olympus Labels Ltd, Richardshaw Road, Grangefield Industrial Estate, Pudsey, West Yorkshire, LS28 6QW Tel: 0113-236 3283 Fax: 0113-236 3284

▶ Oyezstraker Professional Print, Unit 4 Stafford Cross Business Park, Croydon, CR0 4TU Tel: (020) 8603 5180 Fax: (020) 8686 4402

▶ Printinc, Sutton Business Centre, Restmor Way, Wallington, Surrey, SM6 7AH Tel: 020 8255 2110 Fax: 020 8255 2115 E-mail: printinc2@btconnect.com

▶ Progressive Print Solutions Ltd, 6 Leodis Court, Leeds, LS11 5JJ Tel: 0113-244 2220 Fax: 0113-244 6011

Quinn's The Printers, 181 Donegall Street, Belfast, BT1 2FJ Tel: (028) 9032 3552 Fax: (028) 9031 9166 E-mail: desgin@quinnstheprinters.com

Rainbow Colour, 2 High St, Steventon, Abingdon, Oxfordshire, OX13 6RS Tel: (01235) 200700 Fax: (01235) 200707 E-mail: rainbow.colour@tiscali.co.uk

▶ Severn Signs Ltd, Unit 19 Innsworth Technology Park, Innsworth Lane, Gloucester, GL3 1DL Tel: (01452) 739156 Fax: (01452) 739153

▶ Skamem and Durham, Unit 7, Park 2000, Millennium Way, Newton Aycliffe, County Durham, DL5 6AR Tel: (01325) 375140 Fax: (01325) 375161

Soabar Marking Systems, 7 Ashville Way, Whetstone, Leicester, LE8 6NU Tel: 0116-284 7000 Fax: 0116-284 7001 E-mail: sales@soabar.co.uk

Sovereign Software Solutions Ltd, 12 Bank Crescent, Burntwood, Staffordshire, WS7 4TL Tel: (01543) 677070 Fax: (01543) 677671 E-mail: info@sovsoft.co.uk

▶ Spear Europe Ltd, Christopher Grey Court, Lakeside, Llantarnam Industrial Park, Cwmbran, Gwent, NP44 3SE Tel: (01633) 627600 Fax: (01633) 627601 E-mail: sales@spearsystem.com

▶ The Square Design & Print Co Ltd, Caxton Court, 43 Garamonde Drive, Wymbush, Milton Keynes, MK8 8DD Tel: (01908) 305018 Fax: (01908) 260901 E-mail: ksthefoodie@thesquareguide.co.uk

Townsend Print Services Ltd, Sterling Court Leyland Business Park, Centurion Way, Farington, Leyland, PR25 3GR Tel: (01772) 622322 Fax: (01772) 624466 E-mail: sales@townsendprint.co.uk

▶ indicates data change since last edition

PRINTING SERVICES - *continued*

▶ Vision Litho, 70 Wood End Green Road, Hayes, Middlesex, UB3 2SL Tel: (020) 8561 8726 E-mail: visionlitho@mac.com

▶ Woods Design & Print, Bumpers Way, Bumpers Farm, Chippenham, Wiltshire, SN14 6NG Tel: (01249) 460630 Fax: (01249) 460631

PRINTING SLEEVES

Day International Ltd, Balgray Street, Dundee, DD3 8HN Tel: (01382) 422200 Fax: (01382) 832310 E-mail: bill_crowe@day-intel.com

PRINTING TRADE CLEANING SOLVENTS/PASTES

A B C Chemical Co, Woodhouse Road, Todmorden, Lancashire, OL14 5TD Tel: (01200) 420180 Fax: (01706) 819554 E-mail: info@abcchem.co.uk

PRINTING TRADE CONSULTANTS, BROKERS, PLANNERS OR REPRESENTATIVES

Salamander Walking Ltd, Langley Drive, Birmingham, B35 7AD Tel: 0121-747 2603 Fax: 0121-748 4205

PRINTING TRADE DIE CUTTING SERVICES

Geoff Emery, Unit 4, 171 Bryants Hill, St. George, Bristol, BS5 8RQ Tel: 0117-975 9111 Fax: 0117-907 7675

Holland & Watts, 1 Paragon Court, Tongham Road, Aldershot, Hampshire, GU12 4AA Tel: (01252) 344200 Fax: (01252) 343466 E-mail: sales@hollandandwatts.com

Joseph H Lines & Sons Ltd, Eagle Road, Moons Moat North Industrial Es, Redditch, Worcestershire, B98 9HF Tel: (01527) 63078 Fax: (01527) 63294 E-mail: j.h.lines@dial.pipex.com

PRINTING TRADE ENGINEERING SERVICES

B B R Graphic Engineers, Kings Yard, Low Mill Road, Ossett, West Yorkshire, WF5 8ND Tel: (01924) 263339 Fax: (01924) 280164 E-mail: service@bbrgraphics.com

Britannia Machinery Pontefract Ltd, Stuart Street, Pontefract, West Yorkshire, WF8 4PW Tel: (01977) 790818 Fax: (01977) 600333 E-mail: britannia.machinery@btinternet.com

H W L Engineering Ltd, 99-105 Canterbury Road, Croydon, CR0 3HH Tel: (020) 8689 8300 Fax: (020) 8689 8920

John Madeley Machinery Ltd, Firs Industrial Estate, Kidderminster, Worcestershire, DY11 7QN Tel: (01562) 69955 Fax: (01562) 746304 E-mail: madeleyj@aol.com

Line Casting Machinery Ltd, Unit 34 John Wilson Business Park, Chestfield, Whitstable, Kent, CT5 3QT Tel: (01227) 770665 Fax: (01227) 277300 E-mail: linecasting@btconnect.com

Premier Guillotine Systems Ltd, Fairweather Green Works, Rear of 900 Thornton Road, Bradford, West Yorkshire, BD8 0JG Tel: (01274) 499832 Fax: (01274) 547818

PRINTING TRADE FINISHING EQUIPMENT MANUFRS

K A S Paper Systems Ltd, Brewers Hill Road, Dunstable, Bedfordshire, LU6 1AD Tel: (01582) 662211 Fax: (01582) 664222 E-mail: mail@kaspapersystems.com

Kolbus UK Ltd, 35 Heathfield, Stacey Bushes, Milton Keynes, MK12 6HR Tel: (01908) 317878 Fax: (01908) 310863 E-mail: sales@kolbus.co.uk

Morgana Systems Ltd, Station Road, Ampthill, Bedford, MK45 2QY Tel: (01525) 403058 Fax: (01525) 404308

▶ Muller Martini Ltd, The Ridgeway, Iver, Buckinghamshire, SL0 9JQ Tel: (01753) 657700 Fax: (01753) 655658 E-mail: enquiries@mullermartini.co.uk

Packaging Craftsman Ltd, Units 1a-1b, Park Mill Way, Clayton West, Huddersfield, HD8 9XJ Tel: (01484) 865680 Fax: (01484) 865681 E-mail: sales@packagingcraftsman.co.uk

Press Co., Kiln Lane, Swindon, SN2 2NP Tel: (01793) 716316 Fax: (01793) 511345 E-mail: sales@presco-uk.com

Printaply Printers' Services, Highfield Lane, Sheffield, S13 9NA Tel: 0114-269 3322 Fax: (0845) 0850077 E-mail: printaply@yahoo.co.uk

Watkiss Automation Sales Ltd, Watkiss House, 1 Blaydon Road, Sandy, Bedfordshire, SG19 1RZ Tel: (01767) 681800 Fax: (01767) 691769 E-mail: sales@watkiss.com

PRINTING TRADE FINISHING SERVICES

A Print Finishing Co Ltd, 26-27 Sittingbourne Industrial Park, Crown Quay Lane, Sittingbourne, Kent, ME10 3JG Tel: (01795) 430050 Fax: (01795) 430495

A & S Print Finishers, Unit 1 Northgate Industrial Pk, Collier Row, Romford, RM5 2BG Tel: (020) 8548 7200 Fax: (020) 8548 7201

Aga Print Finishing Ltd, 76 Cato Street North, Birmingham, B7 5AN Tel: 0121-359 1414 Fax: 0121-333 4388

Cellogias Speciality Products, Unit 12C, Exeter Way, Theale Commercial Park, Theale, Reading, RG7 4AW Tel: 0118-930 3656 Fax: 0118-932 3256 E-mail: andy.kirbycelloglas@alcan.co.uk

Celloglass Ltd, Headley Road East, Woodley, Reading, RG5 4UA Tel: 0118-944 1441 Fax: 0118-944 1913 E-mail: yvonne.parks@celloglas.co.uk

Clifton & Son Ltd, Uplands Business Park, Blackhorse Lane, London, E17 5QJ Tel: (020) 8523 1133 Fax: (020) 8531 1341 E-mail: tim@clifton.org

Cut Above, 7 Langham Road, Leicester, LE4 9WF Tel: 0116-246 1376 Fax: 0116-276 5275 E-mail: sales@cutaboveuk.com

East London Print Finishers, Unit 7 Lockwood Way, London, E17 5RB Tel: (020) 8527 5448 Fax: (020) 8527 0635

Elite Cutters Ltd, Oakfield Works, Branksome Hill Road, College Town, Sandhurst, Berkshire, GU47 0QE Tel: (01276) 32991 Fax: (01276) 600146 E-mail: kriswatling@elitecutters.fsnet.co.uk

Geoff Emery, Unit 4, 171 Bryants Hill, St. George, Bristol, BS5 8RQ Tel: 0117-975 9111 Fax: 0117-907 7675

Encore Encapsulation Ltd, Swallow Mill, Swallow Street, Stockport, Cheshire, SK1 3HJ Tel: 0161-476 2646 Fax: 0161-476 2646 E-mail: sales@encoreencapsulation.co.uk

Eurogloss Ltd, Units 3 & 5 Greyhound Commercial Centre, Greyhound Way, Dartford, DA1 4HF Tel: (01322) 557777 Fax: (01322) 555277 E-mail: production@eurogloss.co.uk

Fisherprint Ltd, Padholme Road, Peterborough, PE1 5UL Tel: (01733) 341444 Fax: (01733) 349416 E-mail: enquiries@fisherprint.co.uk

H & S Partners Ltd, Forstal Road, Aylesford, Kent, ME20 7AD Tel: (01622) 717387 Fax: (01622) 710211 E-mail: hspartners@btconnect.com

Henry Mills Ltd, 30 Chester Street, Aston, Birmingham, B6 4BE Tel: 0121-359 4671 Fax: 0121-333 3153 E-mail: binding@henrymills.co.uk

Holland & Watts, 1 Paragon Court, Tongham Road, Aldershot, Hampshire, GU12 4AA Tel: (01252) 344200 Fax: (01252) 343466 E-mail: sales@hollandandwatts.com

K & H Packaging Ltd, Unit 7 Crayside Industrial Estate, Thames Road, Crayford, Dartford, DA1 4RF Tel: (01322) 521512 Fax: (01322) 553102 E-mail: rmarkrussell2@aol.com

Kenbe Binders, Unit 25, City Industrial Park, Southern Road, Southampton, SO15 1HG Tel: (023) 8022 8976 Fax: (023) 8022 2491 E-mail: binders@kenbe.co.uk

Kensett Ltd, 196 Old Shoreham Road, Hove, East Sussex, BN3 7EX Tel: (01273) 725627 Fax: (01273) 724867

L B Litho, 15 Tait Road, Croydon, CR0 2DT Tel: (020) 8683 4205 Fax: (020) 8683 4193

L T S S Print Finishers Ltd, 329 Stean Street, London, E8 4ED Tel: (020) 7923 3155 Fax: (020) 7923 3562

Laminating East Midlands, 26 Low Farm Place, Moulton Park Industrial Estate, Northampton, NN3 6HY Tel: (01604) 642823 Fax: (01604) 790423 E-mail: postmaster@eml.uk.com

Larkbeare Holdings Ltd, The Talewater Mill, Talaton, Exeter, EX5 2RT Tel: (01404) 850833 Fax: (01404) 850246 E-mail: finishing@larkbeare.com

M & H Print Finishers, Hazel Lane, Walsall, WS6 6AA Tel: (01922) 419323 Fax: (01922) 419323

Medway Cutters, Joseph Wilson Industrial Estate, Millstrood Road, Whitstable, Kent, CT5 3PS Tel: (01227) 273138 Fax: (01227) 770344 E-mail: sales@medwaycutters.co.uk

Midland Trade Stringing & Folding Services, 9-10 The Square, Earls Barton, Northampton, NN6 0NA Tel: (01604) 810420 Fax: (01604) 812509 E-mail: mail@midlandtradestringing.co.uk

Nicom Ltd, Unit 9 Tamebridge Industrial Estate, Aldridge Road, Birmingham, B42 2TX Tel: 0121-356 1667 Fax: 0121-344 3336

Norvall Print Finishing Ltd, 266 York Way, London, N7 9PQ Tel: (020) 7609 8585 Fax: (020) 7700 5644 E-mail: sales@norvall.com

Packaids Ltd, Ruscombe Park, Ruscombe Lane, Ruscombe, Reading, RG10 9LU Tel: 0118-934 3877 Fax: 0118-934 0273 E-mail: sales@packaids.co.uk

Perfectio Print Finishers Ltd, Wright Street, Manchester, M16 9EW Tel: 0161-877 6238 Fax: 0161-872 0514

Plastic Art Co., Unit 6f Hewlett House, 5 Havelock Terrace, London, SW8 4AS Tel: (020) 7627 1976 Fax: (020) 7498 2369 E-mail: london@plastic-art.co.uk

Precision Formes Ltd, 13 Glegg Street, Liverpool, L3 7DX Tel: 0151-207 2446 Fax: 0151-298 1539 E-mail: info@pfl3.co.uk

Print Finishers Ltd, 35 Greenwich Church St, London, SE10 9BJ Tel: (020) 8858 5224 Fax: (020) 8265 6289

Printafoil Ltd, 5 Mitcham Industrial Estate, Streatham Road, Mitcham, Surrey, CR4 2AP Tel: (020) 8640 3074 Fax: (020) 8640 2136 E-mail: info@blockfoil.com

R Howard Ltd, Croft Bank, Skegness, Lincolnshire, PE24 4AW Tel: (01754) 880226 Fax: (01754) 881263

Screen Technology, Maerdy Industrial Estate, Maerdy Road, Ferndale, Mid Glamorgan, CF43 4AB Tel: (01443) 730271 Fax: (01443) 730789 E-mail: info@screentec.co.uk

Sevenoaks Print Finishers Ltd, Enterprise Way, Edenbridge, Kent, TN8 6HF Tel: (01732) 866060 Fax: (01732) 867577

Southbound Print Finishers, 42A Commercial Road, Eastbourne, East Sussex, BN21 3XF Tel: (01323) 647824 Fax: (01323) 647963

Specialised Cutting & Creasing, Unit 16 Hillgate Business Centre, Swallow Street, Stockport, Cheshire, SK1 3AU Tel: 0161-474 7246

Spirax Binding (Scotland) Ltd, Inveralmond Road, Inveralmond Estate, Perth, PH1 3XA Tel: (01738) 626281 Fax: (01738) 630575 E-mail: sales@spirax.co.uk

Stock Associates Print Finishers Ltd, Unit 2-3, Perry Way, Witham, Essex, CM8 3SX Tel: (01376) 500123 Fax: (01376) 501744 E-mail: sales@stock.uk.com

Supreme Die Cutters, Unit 7 Forest Hill Business Centre, Clyde Vale, London, SE23 3JF Tel: (020) 8291 0473 Fax: (020) 8291 0402

Surrey Laminators Ltd, 7 Saxon Way Trading Estate, Harmondsworth, West Drayton, Middlesex, UB7 0LW Tel: (020) 8759 5995 Fax: (020) 8564 7049 E-mail: harmondsworth@surreylaminators.co.uk

Wainwright Print Finishers Ltd, Unit 6 Redfern Industrial Estate, Dawson Street, Market Street, Hyde, Cheshire, SK14 1RD Tel: 0161-368 9797 Fax: 0161-367 8732

West Country Binders Ltd, 35 Buckingham Road, Weston-super-Mare, Avon, BS24 9BG Tel: (01934) 630950 Fax: (01934) 636615 E-mail: alistair@westcountrybinders.co.uk

West Midlands Laminating Co. Ltd, 50 Midland Street, Birmingham, B9 4DG Tel: 0121-773 0722 Fax: 0121-773 0741 E-mail: sales@westmidlam.co.uk

World Wide Direct Mail Ltd, Unit 4, Clipper Close, Medway City Estate, Strood, Rochester, Kent, ME2 4QR Tel: (01634) 723135 Fax: (01634) 713399 E-mail: paul.barford@btconnect.com

Yates Print Finishers, 7 Saffron Way, Leicester, LE2 6UP Tel: 0116-283 9456 E-mail: margaret@yatesltd.fsnet.co.uk

PRINTING TRADE STEREOTYPES

▶ Excel Cutting Formes Ltd, Unit 39, Horndon Industrial Park, West Horndon, Brentwood, Essex, CM13 3XD Tel: (01277) 811116 Fax: (01277) 812778E-mail: info@excelsf.com

Plastotype Ltd, Crustable Close, Mushep Industrial Park, Coleford, Gloucestershire, GL16 8RE Tel: (01594) 837474 Fax: (01594) 837312 E-mail: info@plastotype.com

PRINTING TRADE SUPPLIERS/ DISTRIBUTORS/AGENTS

A B C Chemical Co, Woodhouse Road, Todmorden, Lancashire, OL14 5TD Tel: (01200) 420180 Fax: (01706) 819554 E-mail: info@abcchem.co.uk

A B Parker & Sons, 7 Franklyn Street, Bristol, BS2 9LA Tel: 0117-955 6544 Fax: 0117-955 6544

A M I Supplies Ltd, 2 Centre 2000, St. Michaels Road, Sittingbourne, Kent, ME10 3DZ Tel: (01795) 420430 Fax: (01795) 426817 E-mail: sales@amigroup.co.uk

Alpha Engraving Co. Ltd, Unit F1 Bounds Green Industrial Estate, South Way, London, N11 2UL Tel: (020) 8368 1674 Fax: (020) 8368 1675 E-mail: alphablocks@btconnect.com

Bousfield Ltd, Southway Drive, North Common, Bristol, BS30 5JE Tel: 0117-988 8899 Fax: 0117-988 8866 E-mail: sales@bousfield.net

Channel Matrix plc, 44 Sanders Road, Finedon Road Industrial Estate, Wellingborough, Northamptonshire, NN8 4NL Tel: (01933) 273444 Fax: (01933) 229277 E-mail: info@channel-creasing.com

Chiltern Colour Services, Unit 23 Titan Court, Laporte Way, Luton, LU4 8EF Tel: (01525) 385184 Fax: (01582) 482888

Cooper Printers, 43 Manse Street, Fraserburgh, Aberdeenshire, AB43 9JB Tel: (01346) 518831 Fax: (01346) 511311 E-mail: cooper.printers@virgin.net

Dainippon Screen UK Ltd, Michigan Drive, Tongwell, Milton Keynes, MK15 8HT Tel: (01908) 848500 Fax: (01908) 848501 E-mail: sales@screeneurope.co.uk

European Printing Inks Ltd, Unit 38 Phoenix International Industrial Estate, Charles Street, West Bromwich, West Midlands, B70 0AY Tel: 0121-520 2471

Folex Film Ltd, Unit 19 Monkspath Business Park, Shirley, Solihull, West Midlands, B90 4NY Tel: 0121-733 3833 Fax: 0121-733 3222 E-mail: sales@folex.co.uk

Haynes Graphic Arts Ltd, Policrom House, Station Road, Motspur Park, New Malden, Surrey, KT3 6JJ Tel: (020) 8949 5411 Fax: (020) 8949 4907 E-mail: info@haynes-graphic-art.co.uk

Howarine, Calvert Ltd, Howarine House, 5-6 Empire Way, Wembley, Middlesex, HA9 0XA Tel: (0870) 4420077 Fax: (0870) 4420078 E-mail: graham@howarine.co.uk

Joyce & Co Printing Materials Ltd, 6 Cam Square, Wilbury Way, Hitchin, Hertfordshire, SG4 0TZ Tel: (01462) 420930 Fax: (01462) 421180 E-mail: sales@joyce-pm.com

Kodak Graphic Communications Ltd, Axis 1, Rhodes Way, Watford, WD24 4FD Tel: (01923) 233366 Fax: (01923) 227802

Norman Lane Ltd, 1 Wiggenhall Road, Watford, WD18 0FH Tel: (01923) 235231 Fax: (01923) 222569 E-mail: normanlane@easynet.co.uk

Litho Supplies Ltd, Longmoor Lane, Breaston, Derby, DE72 3BQ Tel: (01332) 873921 Fax: (01332) 875103

Litho Supplies Midlands Region, 1 Tamebridge Industrial Estate, Aldridge Road, Perry Barr, Birmingham, B42 2TX Tel: 0121-344 4222 Fax: 0121-344 4494 E-mail: midlands@litho.co.uk

▶ Mayday Graphic Products, Graphic House, Cratfield Road, Bury St. Edmunds, Suffolk, IP32 7DF Tel: (01284) 701571 Fax: (01284) 750553 E-mail: sales@maydaygraphics.co.uk

Mouldtype Foundry, Leyland Lane, Leyland, PR25 1XB Tel: (01772) 425026 Fax: (01772) 425001 E-mail: mtf@leyprint.co.uk

Ocular Press Ltd, West Avenue, Wigston, Leicestershire, LE18 2FG Tel: 0116-257 1400 Fax: 0116-257 1042

Page Plus, Old School Building, Outclough Road, Brindley Ford, Stoke-on-Trent, ST8 7QD Tel: (01782) 523263 Fax: (01782) 839284 E-mail: pete@pageplus.co.uk

▶ Rathbone Printflo Ltd, Caroline Street, Stoke-on-Trent, ST3 1DB Tel: (01782) 320022 Fax: (01782) 594056 E-mail: sales@tslimited.com

Rayment Holland, 1-3 Wealdstone Road, Sutton, Surrey, SM3 9QN Tel: (020) 8641 7272 Fax: (020) 8644 4779 E-mail: mail@frewerbrothers.co.uk

Service Offset Supplies Ltd, Oakwood Hill Industrial Estate, Oakwood Hill, Loughton, Essex, IG10 3TZ Tel: (020) 8502 4291 Fax: (020) 8502 0200 E-mail: webmaster@sosuk.co.uk

Surebasic Ltd, Units 2 & 3, Castlemeadows Park, Abergavenny, Gwent, NP7 7RZ Tel: (01873) 852663 Fax: (01873) 859128 E-mail: laser@change.co.uk

Tewtrell Ltd, Limekiln Lane, Birmingham, B14 4SP Tel: 0121-430 2161 Fax: 0121-430 2741 E-mail: sales@tewtrell.com

Typecast Machinery, 39 North Howard Street, Belfast, BT13 2AP Tel: (028) 9024 2366 Fax: (028) 9023 7735

Waltham Paper Co. Ltd, County Ho, County Industrial Estate, Boars Tye Road, Silver End, Witham, Essex, CM8 3PW Tel: (01425) 622550 Fax: (01277) 261789

PRINTING, BOOK/MAGAZINE

A Print Finishing Co Ltd, 26-27 Sittingbourne Industrial Park, Crown Quay Lane, Sittingbourne, Kent, ME10 3JG Tel: (01795) 430050 Fax: (01795) 430495

▶ Auto Point, Bank View, First Drove, Fengate, Peterborough, PE1 5BJ Tel: (01733) 566332 Fax: 01733 352933 E-mail: info@fast-print.net

▶ B G P Bicester, Chaucer Business Park, Launton Road, Bicester, Oxfordshire, OX26 4QZ Tel: (01869) 363333 Fax: (01869) 363306 E-mail: marketing@bgprint.co.uk

Benham Goodhead Print Ltd, Newcomen Way, Severalls Industrial Park, Colchester, CO4 9PF Tel: (01206) 752525 Fax: (01206) 752255 E-mail: psimons@bgprint.co.uk

Blackmore Ltd, Longmead, Shaftesbury, Dorset, SP7 8PX Tel: (01747) 853034 Fax: (01747) 854500 E-mail: sales@.blackmore.co.uk

Clays Ltd, St Ives House, Lavington Street, London, SE1 0NX Tel: (020) 7928 8844 Fax: (020) 7902 6436 E-mail: sales@st-ives.co.uk

Commercial Graphics Ltd, 11 Greenway, Conlig, Newtownards, County Down, BT23 7SU Tel: (028) 9127 0431 Fax: (028) 9127 0137 E-mail: sales@commercialgraphics.co.uk

R.R. Donnelley UK, Flaxby Moor, Knaresborough, North Yorkshire, HG5 0XJ Tel: (01423) 796500 Fax: (01423) 796501

William Gibbons & Sons Ltd, PO Box 103, Willenhall, West Midlands, WV13 3XT Tel: (01902) 730011 Fax: (01902) 865835 E-mail: gibbowill@aol.com

Hart & Clough Ltd, Ezra House, Littlewood Drive, West 26 Industrial Estate, Cleckheaton, West Yorkshire, BD19 4TQ Tel: (01274) 863200 Fax: (01274) 863201 E-mail: info@hartandclough.co.uk

M P G Books Ltd, Victoria Square, Bodmin, Cornwall, PL31 1EB Tel: (01208) 73266 Fax: (01208) 73603 E-mail: print@mpg-books.co.uk

Park Communications Ltd, Lea Mill, Eastway, London, E9 5NU Tel: (020) 8525 6200 Fax: (020) 8525 6201 E-mail: heath.mason@btinternet.com

Sarum Colourview Ltd, Unit 7-8 Woodford Centre Old Sarum Park, Lysander Way, Old Sarum, Salisbury, SP4 6BU Tel: (01722) 343600 Fax: (01722) 323604 E-mail: sales@colourview.co.uk

▶ indicates data change since last edition

PRINTING, BOOK/MAGAZINE – *continued*

Styletype Printing Ltd, Glengormley Park, Newtownabbey, County Antrim, BT36 7RJ Tel: (028) 9034 2725 Fax: (028) 9084 8225 E-mail: sales@styletype.co.uk

▶ TJ International Ltd, Trecerus Industrial Estate, Padstow, Cornwall, PL28 8RW Tel: (01841) 532691 Fax: (01841) 532862

PRINTING, POSTER

▶ 999print, 251 Kingsway, Manchester, M19 1AL Tel: 0161-610 8032 Fax: 0161-610 6015 E-mail: sales@999print.com

Allstar Services Ltd, 25 Forward Drive, Harrow, Middlesex, HA3 8NT Tel: (020) 8861 6440 Fax: (020) 8861 3134 E-mail: sales@allstar.co.uk

▶ Disc To Print, Unit 1 Lydd Road Industrial Estate, Lydd Road, New Romney, Kent, TN28 8HD Tel: (01797) 367755 Fax: (01797) 364884 E-mail: sales@disctoprint.co.uk

▶ Jaguar Design & Print, Philpot House, Station Road, Rayleigh, Essex, SS6 7HH Tel: (01268) 776741 Fax: (01268) 776741 E-mail: sales@jaguar-design-print.co.uk

PRINTING, THERMOGRAPHIC,

See Thermographic etc

PRISM LENSES

▶ Stock Optics Ltd, Unit 430, Thorp Arch Estate, Wetherby, West Yorkshire, LS23 7BJ Tel: (01937) 849421 Fax: (01937) 849836 E-mail: optics1@btconnect.com

PRIVATE AUTOMATIC BRANCH EXCHANGE (PABX) INTEGRATED SERVICES DIGITAL NETWORK (ISDN)

P C Utilities, 36 Westbury Lane, Bristol, BS9 2PP Tel: 0117-962 6364 Fax: 0117-962 6365 E-mail: spencer@pcutilities.co.uk

PRIVATE BANKING

Adam & Co. P.L.C., 22 Kings Street, London, SW1Y 6QY Tel: (020) 7839 4615 Fax: (020) 7839 5994 E-mail: london@adambank.com

PRIVATE BRANCH EXCHANGE (PBX) ALARM SYSTEMS

Data Track Technology P.L.C., 153 Somerford Road, Christchurch, Dorset, BH23 3TY Tel: (01425) 270333 Fax: (01425) 270433 E-mail: sales@dtrack.com

PRIVATE CUBICLES

Abacus Building Components, Manor House, Rise Road, Sigglesthorne, Hull, HU11 5QH Tel: (01964) 533720 Fax: (01964) 535958 E-mail: abacuscomp@aol.com

Armitage Venesta Washroom Systems Ltd, Imperial Business Estate, West Mill, Gravesend, Kent, DA11 0DL Tel: (01474) 353333 Fax: (01474) 533558 E-mail: info@armitage-venesta.co.uk

▶ Bushboard Ltd, Rixon Road, Wellingborough, Northamptonshire, NN8 4BA Tel: (01933) 232200 Fax: (01933) 232280 E-mail: washrooms@bushboard.co.uk

Dunhams Of Norwich, Hellesdon Park Road, Drayton High Road, Norwich, NR6 5DR Tel: (01603) 424855 Fax: (01603) 413336

Leicester Bar Fitting Co. Ltd, West Avenue, Wigston, Leicestershire, LE18 2FB Tel: 0116-288 4897 Fax: 0116-281 3122 E-mail: sales@leicesterbarfitting.co.uk

W H Foster & Sons Ltd, Stourdale Road, Cradley, Cradley Heath, West Midlands, B64 7BG Tel: (01384) 415170 Fax: (01384) 415185 E-mail: sales@whfoster.co.uk

Wernick Hire Ltd, Nursteed Road Trading Estate, Mill Road, Devizes, Wiltshire, SN10 3EW Tel: (01380) 727371 Fax: (01380) 721639 E-mail: hire@wernickdevizes.co.uk

PRIVATE MEDICAL INSURANCE

▶ Essential Health Ltd, 2-3 Tabernacle Lane, Yeovil, Somerset, BA20 1QA Tel: (0845) 4085444 Fax: (01935) 476668 E-mail: sales@privatesurgery.info

PRIVATE TELEPHONE EXCHANGES

Avaya UK Ltd, Avaya House, Cathedral Hill, Guildford, Surrey, GU2 7YL Tel: (01483) 308000 Fax: (01483) 308001 E-mail: sales@avaya.co.uk

Synergistic Software Co Ltd, Hughenden House, Main Street, Collingham, Wetherby, West Yorkshire, LS22 5AS Tel: (01937) 573446 Fax: (01937) 574211 E-mail: tony@syn.co.uk

PROBATE LEGAL SERVICES

Classic Legal Services Ltd, Suite 3a & 3b, Britannia House, Cowbridge, South Glamorgan, CF71 7EG Tel: (0800) 389 4137 Fax: (01446) 774000 E-mail: alun@weeks4444.fslife.co.uk

▶ Lee Associates, Denmark House, 3b High Street, Willingham, Cambridge, CB24 5ES Tel: (01954) 262120 Fax: (01954) 262129 E-mail: info@willwriting-services.co.uk

▶ Webster Richard & Co., 30 Leigh Road, Eastleigh, Hampshire, SO50 9DT Tel: (023) 8032 2312 Fax: (023) 8061 1698 E-mail: mail@rwco.co.uk

PROCESS AUTOMATION DESIGN

▶ Controldraw Ltd, 17 Wilberforce Road, Southsea, Hampshire, PO5 3DR Tel: (023) 9279 6719 Fax: (023) 9271 6858 E-mail: fl@controldraw.co.uk

PROCESS CONTROL ALARM SYSTEMS

I C S Triplex, 10-14 Hall Road, Heybridge, Maldon, Essex, CM9 4LA Tel: (01621) 854444 Fax: (01621) 859221 E-mail: sales@icsplc.co.uk

▶ Maag Pumps, PO Box 193, Evesham, Worcestershire, WR11 2WY Tel: (01386) 423756 Fax: (01386) 423862 E-mail: info@suurmond.co.uk

Ronan Engineering Ltd, Factory 1-2 Tilley Road, Crowther, Washington, Tyne & Wear, NE38 0AE Tel: 0191-416 1689 Fax: 0191-416 5856 E-mail: sales@ronan.com

Tunstall Group Ltd, Whitley Lodge, Whitley Bridge, Goole, North Humberside, DN14 0HR Tel: (01977) 661234 Fax: (01977) 662570

PROCESS CONTROL ANALYSERS

Anton Paar Ltd, 13 Harforde Court, John Tate Road, Hertford, SG13 7NW Tel: (01992) 514730 Fax: (01992) 514739 E-mail: info.gb@anton-paar.com

C S P, Astra House, Christy Close, Southfields Business Park, Basildon, Essex, SS15 6TQ Tel: (01268) 493377 Fax: (01268) 493399 E-mail: sales@cspuk.co.uk

Onix Process Analysis, Ion Path, Road Three, Winsford Industrial Estate, Winsford, Cheshire, CW7 3GA Tel: (01606) 548704 Fax: (01606) 548711 E-mail: glewis@onixpa.com

Procal Analytics Ltd, 5 Maxwell Road, Peterborough, PE2 7HU Tel: (01733) 232495 Fax: (01733) 235255 E-mail: post@procalanalytics.com

Thermo Electron, 2a Swift Park, Old Leicester Road, Rugby, Warwickshire, CV21 1DZ Tel: (01788) 820300 Fax: (01788) 820419 E-mail: tewi@thermo.com

PROCESS CONTROL INDICATORS

Automated Process & Control Manufacturing Co. Ltd, Unit 11 St. Georges Industrial Estate, Richmond Road, Kingston upon Thames, Surrey, KT2 5BQ Tel: (020) 8549 3331 Fax: (020) 8547 1309 E-mail: info@apcair.co.uk

Dynisco (UK) Ltd, Unit 2B Crowood House, Gipsy Lane, Swindon, SN2 8YY Tel: (01527) 577077 Fax: (01527) 577070 E-mail: dyniscouk@dynisco.com

▶ Vega Controls Ltd, Kendal House, Victoria Way, Burgess Hill, West Sussex, RH15 9NF Tel: (01444) 870055 Fax: (01444) 870080 E-mail: info@uk.vega.com

PROCESS CONTROLLER INSTRUMENTATION

Capelrig Ltd, Tern Place, Denmore Road, Bridge of Don, Aberdeen, AB23 8JX Tel: (01224) 702211 Fax: (01224) 702219 E-mail: sales@capelrig.co.uk

D P Instrumentation Ltd, 2 Ainslie Street, West Pitkerro Industrial Estate, Broughty Ferry, Dundee, DD5 3RR Tel: (01382) 731200 Fax: (01382) 731201 E-mail: sales@dpil.co.uk

E G S Gauging Ltd, The Atrium, 18-21 Church Gate, Thatcham, Berkshire, RG19 3PN Tel: (01635) 861117 Fax: (01635) 273249 E-mail: info@egsgauging.com

Electroserv International, 30a Townley Street, Macclesfield, Cheshire, SK11 6HZ Tel: (01625) 615626 Fax: (01625) 617559

Electroserv (T C & S) Ltd, PO Box 163, Macclesfield, Cheshire, SK11 6JY Tel: (01625) 618526 Fax: (01625) 500746 E-mail: dh@electroserv.co.uk

G M C Instrumentation (UK) Ltd, Priest House, Priest Street, Cradley Heath, West Midlands, B64 6JN Tel: (01384) 638822 Fax: (01384) 639168 E-mail: sales@gmciuk.com

Honeywell Process Solutions, Unit 1 Headlands Business Park, Salisbury Road, Blashford, Ringwood, Hampshire, BH24 3PB Tel: (01425) 463950 Fax: (01425) 463953 E-mail: uksales@trendview.com

Moore Industries Europe Inc, 1 Lloyds Court, Manor Royal, Crawley, West Sussex, RH10 9QU Tel: (01293) 514488 Fax: (01293) 536852 E-mail: sales@mooreind.com

Octopus Instruments Ltd, 2 Sussex Street, Bedale, North Yorkshire, DL8 2AJ Tel: (01677) 424213 Fax: (01677) 424597 E-mail: peter@octopus-instruments.co.uk

Orange Instruments Ltd, Lower Farm Road, Moulton Park Industrial Estate, Northampton, NN3 6XF Tel: (01604) 790490 Fax: (01604) 790690 E-mail: alan@orangeinst.demon.co.uk

Pneumatic & Electrical Systems, Automation Works, 656 Leeds Road, Deighton, Huddersfield, HD2 1UB Tel: (01484) 533527 Fax: (01484) 512058 E-mail: enquiries@pesystems.co.uk

Process Equipment Parts (UK) Ltd, Kershaw House, 449 Great West Road, Hounslow, TW5 0BU Tel: (020) 8754 3999 Fax: (020) 8754 3990 E-mail: mail@process-equipment.co.uk

▶ Process Plus, Sybrig House, Ridge Way, Hillend, Dunfermline, Fife, KY11 9JN Tel: (01383) 825343 Fax: (01383) 824393 E-mail: sales@processplus.co.uk

Rontec Ltd, 11 Beckbridge Road, Normanton Industrial Estate, Normanton, West Yorkshire, WF6 1TE Tel: (01924) 898209 Fax: (01924) 899854 E-mail: sales@rontec.co.uk

Williams Industrial Services Ltd, Unit 5, Hyde Park, Commercial Centre, Newtownabbey, County Antrim, BT36 4PY Tel: (028) 9083 8999 Fax: (028) 9084 2211 E-mail: sales@wis-ni.com

PROCESS CONTROLLER INSTRUMENTATION ENGINEERS, INSTALLATION OR SERVICE

Bond Instrumentation & Process Control Ltd, Woodrope Building, Woodrolfe Road, Tollesbury, Essex, CM9 8SE Tel: (01621) 862140 Fax: (01621) 862141 E-mail: bond@bond.ipc.com

Control Equipment Ltd, Tyco Park, Grimshaw Lane, Newton Heath, Manchester, M40 2WL Tel: 0161-455 4232 Fax: 0161-455 4441 E-mail: tycocontrolsystems.uk@tycoint.com

Lintott Control System Ltd, Units 3, 5, 7, &9, Jarrold Way, Bowthorpe Industrial Estate, Norwich, NR5 9JD Tel: (01603) 201201 Fax: (01603) 749118

▶ Process Plus, Sybrig House, Ridge Way, Hillend, Dunfermline, Fife, KY11 9JN Tel: (01383) 825343 Fax: (01383) 824393 E-mail: sales@processplus.co.uk

Protuning UK Ltd, 1 Meadow Rise, Lea, Gainsborough, Lincolnshire, DN21 5HE Tel: (01427) 610092 Fax: (01427) 811807 E-mail: enquiries@protune.org

Severn Instruments, 4 Court Street, Upton-upon-Severn, Worcester, WR8 0JT Tel: (01684) 594164 Fax: (01684) 593364

PROCESS CONTROLLER SYSTEMS CONSULTANTS OR DESIGNERS

DSL Systems Holdings Ltd, Adbolton Hall Adbolton Lane, West Bridgford, Nottingham, NG2 5AS Tel: 0115-981 3700 Fax: 0115-813702 E-mail: mail@dsl-systems.com

Electraspec Control Panel Mnfrs, 4 Shell Corner Industrial Estate, Long Lane, Halesowen, West Midlands, B62 9LD Tel: 0121-559 9335 Fax: 0121-559 9362

PROCESS CONTROLLER SYSTEMS ENGINEERS, INSTALLATION OR SERVICE

The Control Shop Ltd, 17 Bilton Industrial Estate, Stockmans Close, Birmingham, B38 9TS Tel: 0121-451 1030 Fax: 0121-459 1511 E-mail: sales@controlshop.co.uk

Eltek Systems Ltd, Eltek House, Nene Valley Business Park, Oundle, Peterborough, PE8 4HN Tel: (01832) 277590 Fax: (01832) 273941 E-mail: info@eltek-systems.com

Norstead, Metnor House, Mylord Crescent, Newcastle upon Tyne, NE12 5YD Tel: 0191-268 4000 Fax: 0191-268 6650 E-mail: engineering@norstead.co.uk

Riverside Automation Ltd, 61 Wostenholm Road, Sheffield, S7 1LE Tel: 0114-255 5500 Fax: 0114-255 5505 E-mail: sales@riverauto.co.uk

PROCESS CONTROLLER SYSTEMS MAINTENANCE/ REPAIR SERVICES

Ritec Automation, 3 Broad Street, Cannock, Staffordshire, WS11 0DA Tel: (01543) 577331 Fax: (01543) 502816 E-mail: ritec@ukonline.co.uk

PROCESS CONTROLLER SYSTEMS MANUFRS

A B B Ltd, Hortonwood 37, Telford, Shropshire, TF1 7XT Tel: (01952) 670477 Fax: (01952) 670455

Adsyst (Automation) Ltd, Unit 1 Ferranti Court, Staffordshire Technology Park, Stafford, ST18 0AR Tel: (01785) 212400 Fax: (01785) 212500 E-mail: info@adsyst.co.uk

Advanced Control Systems Ltd, 140 Aberford Road, Woodlesford, Leeds, LS26 8LG Tel: 0113-282 7123 Fax: 0113-282 5252

Anton Paar Ltd, 13 Harforde Court, John Tate Road, Hertford, SG13 7NW Tel: (01992) 514730 Fax: (01992) 514739 E-mail: info.gb@anton-paar.com

Barton Instrument Systems Ltd, 3 Steyning Way, Southern Cross Trading Estate, Bognor Regis, West Sussex, PO22 9TT Tel: (01243) 826741 Fax: (01243) 860263 E-mail: bartonuk@nuflotech.com

Boiler Management Systems (International) Ltd, 189-191 Rutland Road, Sheffield, S3 9PT Tel: 0114-275 5500 Fax: 0114-275 5533 E-mail: isd@bmsint.com

Brighton Systems Ltd, Unit 24 Euro Business Park, New Road, Newhaven, East Sussex, BN9 0DQ Tel: (01273) 515563 Fax: (01273) 611533 E-mail: sales@brightonsystems.co.uk

Cal Controls Ltd, Bury Mead Road, Hitchin, Hertfordshire, SG5 1RT Tel: (01462) 436161 Fax: (01462) 451801 E-mail: sales@cal-controls.com

Charter Tech Ltd, Leanne Business Centre, Sandford Lane, Wareham, Dorset, BH20 4DY Tel: (01929) 553000 Fax: (01929) 550022 E-mail: paul.burns@charter-tech.com

Data Systems & Solutions, Unit 14 Princes Park Princes Way, Team Valley Trading Estate, Gateshead, Tyne & Wear, NE11 0NF Tel: 0191-499 4000 Fax: 0191-499 4001 E-mail: tomsimpson@ds-s.com

Discovery Electronics, 2 Newark Road South, Glenrothes, Fife, KY7 4NS Tel: (01592) 771755 Fax: (01592) 771758 E-mail: enquiries@discoveryltd.com

Dresser Flow Control, Unit 4 Suite 1.1 Nobel House The Grand Union Office Park, Packe, Uxbridge, Middlesex, UB8 2GH Tel: (01895) 454900 Fax: (01895) 454919 E-mail: sales@dresser-valve.co.uk

Easthill Ltd, 1 Martinfield Business Centre, Martinfield, Welwyn Garden City, Hertfordshire, AL7 1HG Tel: (01707) 377355 Fax: (01707) 377358 E-mail: sales@easthill.co.uk

Electron Systems Ltd, Unit 5b Drum Industrial Estate, Chester le Street, County Durham, DH2 1SS Tel: 0191-492 2007 Fax: 0191-492 2009 E-mail: sales@electronsystems.com

Eltek Systems Ltd, Eltek House, Nene Valley Business Park, Oundle, Peterborough, PE8 4HN Tel: (01832) 277590 Fax: (01832) 273941 E-mail: info@eltek-systems.com

Eproduction Solutions Ltd, Viking Road, Great Yarmouth, Norfolk, NR31 0NU Tel: (01493) 652611 Fax: (01493) 444598 E-mail: andrew.williment@ep-solutions.com

F G H Controls Ltd, Openshaw Way, Letchworth Garden City, Hertfordshire, SG6 3ER Tel: (01462) 686677 Fax: (01462) 480633 E-mail: sales@fgh.co.uk

F W B Southwest, Threemilestone Industrial Estate, Threemilestone, Truro, Cornwall, TR4 9LD Tel: (01872) 243520 Fax: (01872) 222191 E-mail: enquiries@fwbsw.co.uk

Faudler Balfour, P O Box 15, Leven, Fife, KY8 4RW Tel: (01333) 423020 Fax: (01333) 427432 E-mail: mailus@pfaudlerbalfour.co.uk

FWB Keithley, C Gresley Road, Keighley, West Yorkshire, BD21 5JG Tel: (01535) 687300 Fax: (01535) 687301 E-mail: sales@fwbkeighley.co.uk

Golconda, Links House, Southglade Business Park, Hucknall Road, Nottingham, NG5 9RA Tel: 0115-977 1101 Fax: 0115-977 0047 E-mail: golconda@golconda.co.uk

Key Controls Ltd, Unit 6 Spring Street, Keighley, West Yorkshire, BD21 3LE Tel: (01535) 604133 Fax: (01535) 604341

Maybridge Electronics Ltd, 10 Godstone Road, Purley, Surrey, CR8 2DA Tel: (020) 8763 8778 E-mail: purley@aol.com

Measuring & Process Control Ltd, Unit 2, Tabrums Farm, Tabrums Lane, Battlesbridge, Wickford, Essex, SS11 7QX Tel: (01245) 322855 Fax: (01245) 328922

Partech Electronics Ltd, Charlestown Road, St. Austell, Cornwall, PL25 3NN Tel: (01726) 879800 Fax: (01726) 879801 E-mail: sales@partech.co.uk

PROCESS CONTROLLER SYSTEMS MANUFRS – *continued*

Polysius Ltd, The Brackens, London Road, Ascot, Berkshire, SL5 8BE Tel: (01344) 884161 Fax: (01344) 886438 E-mail: sue.caveren@thyssenkrupp.com
Proctor Process Plant Ltd, Taylor Holme House, Baldwin Street, Bacup, Lancashire, OL13 0LT Tel: (01706) 874444 Fax: (01706) 879686 E-mail: info@ppp-ltd.co.uk
Quest Ltd, Victoria House, Accrington Road, Burnley, Lancashire, BB11 5EF Tel: (01282) 838000 Fax: (01282) 452121 E-mail: sales@questelectrical.co.uk
Rebus Control Systems Ltd, 156 Burton Road, Lincoln, LN1 3LS Tel: (01522) 882200 Fax: (01522) 882211 E-mail: sales@rebuscontrol.co.uk
Riverside Automation Ltd, 61 Wostenholm Road, Sheffield, S7 1LE Tel: 0114-255 5500 Fax: 0114-255 5505 E-mail: sales@riverauto.co.uk
Rontec Ltd, 11 Beckbridge Road, Normanton Industrial Estate, Normanton, West Yorkshire, WF6 1TE Tel: (01924) 898209 Fax: (01924) 899854 E-mail: sales@rontec.co.uk
Slater Drive Systems Ltd, 6a Dukesway, Prudhoe, Northumberland, NE42 6PQ Tel: (01661) 835566 Fax: (01661) 833868 E-mail: sales@slater-drives.com
Smartdrive Ltd, 8 Colne Road, Earith, Huntingdon, Cambridgeshire, PE28 3PX Tel: (01487) 843663 Fax: (01487) 843661 E-mail: info@smartdrive.co.uk
Tyco, Jarrold Way, Bowthorpe Employment Area, Norwich, NR5 9JD Tel: (01603) 201201 Fax: (01603) 201333 E-mail: tycocontrolsystems.uk@tycoint.com
Zella Instrumentation & Control Ltd, Brunel Drive, Newark, Nottinghamshire, NG24 2EG Tel: (01636) 704370 Fax: (01636) 640296 E-mail: sales@zella-instrumentation.co.uk

PROCESS COOLING SYSTEM INSTALLATION OR SERVICING

C W D Scotland Ltd, 24 Dundonald Road, Kilmarnock, Ayrshire, KA1 1EG Tel: (01563) 540413 Fax: (01563) 574155
Heat Works Ltd, Unit 2 Moorend Indust Estate, Bradford Road, Cleckheaton, West Yorkshire, BD19 3TT Tel: (01274) 852900 Fax: (01274) 852911 E-mail: info@heatworks.co.uk
Norstead, Metnor House, Mylord Crescent, Newcastle upon Tyne, NE12 5YD Tel: 0191-268 4000 Fax: 0191-268 6650 E-mail: engineering@norstead.co.uk
Process Cooling Solutions, 916 Castle La East, Bournemouth, BH7 6SN Tel: (01202) 434328 Fax: (01202) 434329 E-mail: office@ptcltd.co.uk

PROCESS ENGINEERING AND INSTRUMENTATION SERVICES

Alpha Instrumentation Ltd, 6 Stoke Close, Seaford, East Sussex, BN25 3RN Tel: (01323) 897027 Fax: (01323) 897027
Automation Control & Technology Ltd, 149 Tavistock Road, Fleet, Hampshire, GU51 4EE Tel: (01252) 623316 Fax: (01252) 623316 E-mail: sales@automationcontrol.co.uk
Barrett Europe Ltd, 19 Lenten Street, Alton, Hampshire, GU34 1HG Tel: (01420) 542254 Fax: (01420) 543373 E-mail: sales@barretteurope.co.uk
▶ Brunswick Instrumentation Ltd, Maritime House, Basin Road North, Portslade, Brighton, BN41 1WR Tel: (01273) 704949 Fax: (01273) 248900 E-mail: info@brun-inst.co.uk
Mark Hutchinson Ltd, 105 Elliot Rise, Hedge End, Southampton, SO30 2RW Tel: (01489) 798723 E-mail: m.r.hutchinson@talk21.com
P M G Technical Services Ltd, Unit 9, Walton Industrial Estate, Beacon Road, Stone, Staffordshire, ST15 0NN Tel: (01785) 818857 Fax: (01785) 816587 E-mail: info@pmgtech.co.uk
Semb Corp Simon Carves Ltd, 34 Lowther Street, Whitehaven, Cumbria, CA28 7JS Tel: (01946) 692301 Fax: (01946) 599045 E-mail: info@simoncarves.com

PROCESS ENGINEERING CONSULTANTS/DESIGN SERVICES

A E A Technology plc, Harwell Intnl Business Centre, Didcot, Oxfordshire, OX11 0QJ Tel: (0870) 1901900 Fax: (0870) 1908261 E-mail: enquiry@aeat.co.uk
A M E C Design & Management Ltd, Amec House, Timothy's Bridge Road, Stratford-Upon-Avon, Warwickshire, CV37 9NJ Tel: (01789) 204288 Fax: (01789) 299135
Amec Process & Energy Ltd, 76-78 Old Street, London, EC1V 9RU Tel: (020) 7539 5800 Fax: (020) 7539 5900 E-mail: m.bell@amec.co.uk
Aston Dane P.L.C., Aston Dane House, Waterloo Road, Widnes, Cheshire, WA8 0QR Tel: 0151-423 4494 Fax: 0151-495 1089 E-mail: postbox@astondane.com
Cel International, Cel House Westwood Way, Westwood Business Park, Coventry, CV4 8HS Tel: (024) 7686 2000 Fax: (024) 7686 2200 E-mail: info@cel-international.com
DSL Systems Holdings Ltd, Adbolton Hall Adbolton Lane, West Bridgford, Nottingham, NG2 5AS Tel: 0115-981 3700 Fax: 0115-813702 E-mail: mail@dsl-systems.com
Fichtner Consulting Engineers Ltd, Frederick House, 8 Acorn Business Park, Heaton Lane, Stockport, Cheshire, SK4 1AS Tel: 0161-476 0032 Fax: 0161-474 0618 E-mail: sales@fichtner.co.uk
KBC Process Technology Ltd, 42-50 Hersham Road, Walton-on-Thames, Surrey, KT12 1RZ Tel: (01932) 242424 Fax: (01932) 224214 E-mail: info@kbcat.com
Kvaerner E & C, 68 Hammersmith Road, London, W14 8YW Tel: (020) 7339 1000 Fax: (020) 7339 1100
P & I Design Ltd, 2 Reed Street, Thornaby, Stockton-on-Tees, Cleveland, TS17 7AF Tel: (01642) 617444 Fax: (01642) 616447 E-mail: drr@pidesign.co.uk
Process Line Ltd, Suite 15, Kirkfield Commercial Centre, Leeds, LS19 7LX Tel: 0113-239 7112 Fax: 0113-239 7113 E-mail: enquiries@processline.com
Shepherd Engineering Services Ltd, Mill Mount, York, YO24 1GH Tel: (01904) 629151 Fax: (01904) 610175
Simon-Carves Ltd, PO Box 17, Cheadle, Cheshire, SK8 5BR Tel: 0161-486 4000 Fax: 0161-486 1302 E-mail: simon.carves@simoncarves.com
Tecker Ltd, Kernow House, Tregoniggie Industrial Estate, Falmouth, Cornwall, TR11 4SN Tel: (01326) 378774 Fax: (01326) 378775 E-mail: mail@tecker.co.uk
Vincent Processes Ltd, Turnpike Industrial Estate, Turnpike Road, Newbury, Berkshire, RG14 2NT Tel: (01635) 40295 Fax: (01635) 37680 E-mail: carlsmith@vincentprocesses.co.uk

PROCESS ENGINEERING EQUIPMENT

▶ Robert G Evans & Associates, 17 Crymlyn Parc, Neath, West Glamorgan, SA10 6DG Tel: (01792) 814956 Fax: (01792) 814956 E-mail: rgevans@associates0.demon.co.uk

PROCESS ENGRAVERS/ ENGRAVING SERVICES

Chempix Ltd, Vantage Way, Erdington, Birmingham, B24 9GZ Tel: 0121 380 0100 Fax: 0121 359 3313 E-mail: sales@precisionmicro.com
Classic Engravers, 6 Old Bridge Street, Truro, Cornwall, TR1 2AQ Tel: (01872) 241960 Fax: (01872) 241960
Continental Engravers Precision Ltd, Huxley Close, Newnham Industrial Estate, Plympton, Plymouth, PL7 4JN Tel: (01752) 344474 Fax: (01752) 342938
Elite Engraving, 6 Park Road, Kingswood, Bristol, BS15 1QU Tel: 0117-967 0034 Fax: 0117-967 0043 E-mail: eliteengraving@btconnect.com
Michael Graphics Ltd, 21 Bullivant Street, Nottingham, NG3 4AT Tel: 0115-950 3488 Fax: 0115-950 0447
P L G Yorkshire Ltd, Sherman House, 5 Waterloo Way, Leeds, LS13 2EF Tel: 0113-236 1155 Fax: 0113-236 1156 E-mail: plgoffice@btconnect.com
Regal Engravers, Polsole Bridge Works, Hamlin Lane, Exeter, EX1 2RY Tel: (01392) 278790 Fax: (01392) 278790 E-mail: regalengravers@yahoo.com
Robsons Glass, 101 Church Road, Formby, Liverpool, L37 3ND Tel: (01704) 875855 Fax: (01704) 875855
Trentgate Anglia Ltd, 35 Eastern Way, Bury St. Edmunds, Suffolk, IP32 7AB Tel: (01284) 753500 Fax: (01284) 706389 E-mail: sales@trentgate.co.uk
Trinity Graphic Ltd, Hawthorn Avenue, Hull, HU3 5JD Tel: (01482) 227431 Fax: (01482) 223152 E-mail: trinityg@globalnet.co.uk

PROCESS HEATING PLANT AND EQUIPMENT

Advanced Combustion Engineering Ltd, Carrs Industrial Estate, Commerce Street, Haslingden, Rossendale, Lancashire, BB4 5JT Tel: (01706) 212218 Fax: (01706) 228735 E-mail: enq@aceburners.co.uk
C D R Pumps UK Ltd, 28 Trojan Centre, Finedon Road Industrial Estate, Wellingborough, Northamptonshire, NN8 4ST Tel: (0870) 7561428 Fax: (01933) 226225 E-mail: sales@cdrpumps.com
Kelvin Fuel Control Systems Ltd, Fordrough, Birmingham, B25 8DW Tel: 0121-772 0972 Fax: 0121-772 0972

PROCESS INNOVATION CONSULTANTS

N I S Holdings Ltd, Ackhurst Road, Chorley, Lancashire, PR7 1NH Tel: (01257) 265656 Fax: (01257) 275501 E-mail: info@nisltd.com

PROCESS MEASURING INSTRUMENTS, *See also headings for particular types*

Spectra Sensortech Ltd, Cowley Way, Crewe, CW1 6AG Tel: (01270) 250150 Fax: (01270) 251939

PROCESS MONITORING EQUIPMENT

Brodersen Control Systems, Unit 11 Canbury Business Park, Elm Cresent, Kingston upon Thames, Surrey, KT2 6HJ Tel: (020) 8546 4283 Fax: (020) 8547 3628 E-mail: bcs@brodersen.co.uk
▶ Process Plus, Sybrig House, Ridge Way, Hillend, Dunfermline, Fife, KY11 9JN Tel: (01383) 825343 Fax: (01383) 824393 E-mail: sales@processplus.co.uk
Rotech Ltd, Units 10 11 & 18, Blackworth Industrial Park, Highworth, Swindon, SN6 7NA Tel: (01793) 764700 Fax: (01793) 764554 E-mail: enquiries@rotechkeg.com

PROCESS OPTIMISATION SYSTEMS

▶ Optimorph, Hookstead, Faversham Road, Boughton Aluph, Ashford, Kent, TN25 4PQ Tel: (01233) 334458 E-mail: info@optimorph.co.uk

PROCESS PLANT AND MACHINERY

Clark International Machinery Ltd, PO Box 58, Stratford-upon-Avon, Warwickshire, CV37 7YF Tel: (01789) 263636 Fax: (01789) 263637 E-mail: sales@clarkintmachinery.co.uk
Developlant Ltd, Unit 37, Clocktower Business Centre, Works Road, Hollingwood, Chesterfield, Derbyshire, S43 2PE Tel: (01246) 471982 Fax: (01246) 471886 E-mail: sales@developlant.co.uk
Eiger Torrance Ltd, 253 Europa Boulevard Westbrook, Westbrook, Warrington, WA5 7TN Tel: (01925) 232455 Fax: (01925) 237767 E-mail: sales@eiger-torrance.com
Fillworth (UK) Ltd, Unit 2, Baltic Road, Felling, Gateshead, Tyne & Wear, NE10 0SB Tel: 0191-500 0230 Fax: 0191-500 0231 E-mail: mail@fillworth.com
Fletcher Smith, 33 Brunel Parkway, Pride Park, Derby, DE24 8HR Tel: (01332) 636000 Fax: (01332) 636020 E-mail: info@fletchersmith.com
Foster Wheeler Energy Ltd, Foley House, 5 Seaward Place, Glasgow, G41 1HH Tel: 0141-420 3414 Fax: 0141-420 3416
Foster Wheeler Energy Ltd, High Force Road, Riverside Park Industrial Estate, Middlesbrough, Cleveland, TS2 1RH Tel: (01642) 230600 Fax: (01642) 241097
Hi Line Services Lichfield Ltd, 56 Britannia Way, Britannia Enterprise Park, Lichfield, Staffordshire, WS14 9UY Tel: (01543) 258741 Fax: (01543) 250925 E-mail: info@hilineservices.co.uk
Ken Hope Material Handling Specialists, Unit 38 C WB House, Bingswood Industrial Estate, Whaley Bridge, High Peak, Derbyshire, SK23 7LY Tel: (01663) 734641 Fax: (01663) 734767 E-mail: kenhope@wbhouse.co.uk
▶ Lupus Engineering Services Ltd, Abergeldie Cottage, Ballater, Aberdeenshire, AB35 5SY Tel: (01339) 742073
Netzsch-Mastermix, 23 Lombard Street, Lichfield, Staffordshire, WS13 6DP Tel: (01543) 418938 Fax: (01543) 418926 E-mail: info@nmx.netzsch.com
Orthos Projects Ltd, Fernie Road, Market Harborough, Leicestershire, LE16 7PH Tel: (01858) 462806 Fax: (01858) 464403 E-mail: sales@orthos.uk.com
Perry Process Equipment Ltd, Station Road, Aycliffe Industrial Park, Newton Aycliffe, County Durham, DL5 6EQ Tel: (01325) 315111 Fax: (01325) 301496 E-mail: info@perryprocess.co.uk
Polysius Ltd, The Brackens, London Road, Ascot, Berkshire, SL5 8BE Tel: (01344) 884161 Fax: (01344) 886438 E-mail: sue.caveren@thyssenkrupp.com
Process Equipment International, 2 Como Place, Newcastle, Staffordshire, ST5 2QN Tel: (01782) 618101 Fax: (01782) 612616 E-mail: dougtee@tiscali.co.uk
Rigal Chemical & Process Plant Ltd, Gravelhill Lane, Whitley, Goole, North Humberside, DN14 0JJ Tel: (01977) 661095 Fax: (01977) 662165 E-mail: sales@rigal-luton.co.uk
Sinclair Stainless Fabrications Ltd, Chalk Lane, Snetterton, Norwich, NR16 2JZ Tel: (01953) 887473 Fax: (01953) 888405 E-mail: info@sinclair-stainless.com
R.J. Sparks, Holly Farm, Partridge Lane, Newdigate, Dorking, Surrey, RH5 5BN Tel: (01293) 862608
Thorite, Thorite House, Laisterdyke, Bradford, West Yorkshire, BD4 8BZ Tel: (01274) 663471 Fax: (01274) 668296 E-mail: info@thorite.co.uk
Worleyparsons Europe Ltd, Parkview, Great West Road, Brentford, Middlesex, TW8 9AZ Tel: (020) 8758 9477 Fax: (020) 8710 0220 E-mail: info@worleyparsons.com

PROCESS PLANT AND MACHINERY ENGINEERS, INSTALLATION OR SERVICES

▶ Process Installations Ltd, Riverside Industrial Estate, Bridge Road, Littlehampton, West Sussex, BN17 5DF Tel: (01903) 730900 Fax: (01903) 730234 E-mail: peterb@pumpeng.co.uk

PROCESS PLANT AND MACHINERY, BATCH

▶ Tecstream O M G Ltd, Fernie Road, Market Harborough, Leicestershire, LE16 7PH Tel: (01858) 433624 Fax: (01858) 431042 E-mail: sales@tecstreamomg.com

PROCESS PLANT CONTRACTORS OR DESIGNERS, *See also headings for particular types*

A M E C Design & Management Ltd, Amec House, Timothy's Bridge Road, Stratford-Upon-Avon, Warwickshire, CV37 9NJ Tel: (01789) 204288 Fax: (01789) 299135
Aston Dane P.L.C., Aston Dane House, Waterloo Road, Widnes, Cheshire, WA8 0QR Tel: 0151-423 4494 Fax: 0151-495 1089 E-mail: postbox@astondane.com
Atkins Consultants Ltd, Bank Chambers, Faulkner Street, Manchester, M1 4EH Tel: 0161-245 3400 Fax: 0161-245 3500 E-mail: jon.baker@atkinsglobal.com
Boyd Line, The Orangery Hesslewood Country Office Park, Ferriby Road, Hessle, North Humberside, HU13 0LH Tel: (01482) 324024 Fax: (01482) 323737 E-mail: info@boydline.co.uk
Cel International, Cel House Westwood Way, Westwood Business Park, Coventry, CV4 8HS Tel: (024) 7686 2000 Fax: (024) 7686 2200 E-mail: info@cel-international.com
E P C, PO Box 2229, London, W14 0JA Tel: (020) 7602 2979 Fax: (020) 7371 6431 E-mail: aboi@bmec.org.uk
K J Wykes Ltd, Goosey Lodge, Wymington Lane, Wymington, Rushden, Northamptonshire, NN10 9LU Tel: (01933) 315818 Fax: (01933) 355808
Lentjes UK Ltd, Dukes Court, Duke Street, Woking, Surrey, GU21 5BH Tel: (01483) 730044 Fax: (01483) 729595
M S E Consultants Ltd, North House, 31 North Street, Carshalton, Surrey, SM5 2HW Tel: (020) 8773 4500 Fax: (020) 8773 4600 E-mail: enquiries@mse.co.uk
McMillan Ltd, Prestonpans Industrial Estate, Mid Road, Prestonpans, East Lothian, EH32 9JB Tel: (01875) 811110 Fax: (01875) 814022 E-mail: sales@mcmillanltd.co.uk
▶ Manrochem Ltd, 18 New North Parade, Huddersfield, HD1 5JP Tel: (01484) 453868 Fax: (01484) 453884 E-mail: rih@manrochem.co.uk
Multi Tech Contracts, Unit 6 Bowood Court, Calver Road, Winwick Quay, Warrington, WA2 8QZ Tel: (01925) 418333 Fax: (01925) 418800 E-mail: sales@mtcl.net
Natco Group, C/O Axsia Howmar Ltd, Albany Park Estate, Frimley Road, Camberley, Surrey, GU16 7QQ Tel: (01276) 681101 Fax: (01276) 681107 E-mail: ahl@axsia.com
Projen plc, Winnington Avenue, Northwich, Cheshire, CW8 4EE Tel: (01606) 871111 Fax: (01606) 871133 E-mail: mailbox@projen.co.uk
Surface Engineering Process Equipment Ltd, Bennetts Field Trading Estate, Bennetts Field, Wincanton, Somerset, BA9 9DT Tel: (01963) 31274 Fax: (01963) 31288
Tecnica Europe Ltd, Suite 2 Baxall Business Centre, Adswood, Stockport, Cheshire, SK3 8LF Tel: 0161 480 5700 Fax: 0161 447 4476
Thermax Construction, Unit 3 Dover Court, Dover Road, Latchford, Warrington, WA4 1NW Tel: (01925) 242450 Fax: (01925) 242455 E-mail: malcolmferguson@parflothermax.co.uk
Weir Lge Process, Keith House, 2 Redheughs Rigg, Edinburgh, EH12 9DQ Tel: 0131-317 8787 Fax: 0131-452 3333 E-mail: sales@lgeprocess.com

PROCESS PLANT DRYERS

Atritor Ltd, PO Box 101, Coventry, CV6 5RD Tel: (024) 7666 2266 Fax: (024) 7666 5751 E-mail: sales@atritor.com

PROCESS PLANT TREATMENT EQUIPMENT, CHEMICAL DOSING

▶ Wayvik Ltd, South Road, Ellesmere Port, CH65 4LD Tel: 0151-355 5558 Fax: 0151-356 7022 E-mail: info@wayvik.com

PROCESS PLANT VAPOUR RECOVERY SYSTEMS

Johnson Hall Services Ltd, 93 Gorof Road, Ystradgynlais, Lower Cwmtwrch, Swansea, SA9 1DS Tel: (01639) 849564 Fax: (01639) 845348

PROCESS TEST EQUIPMENT

▶ Setech Solutions Ltd, 53A High Street, Bugbrooke, Northampton, NN7 3PG Tel: (01604) 832623 Fax: (01604) 832623 E-mail: info@setechsolutions.com

PROCESS VESSELS

Allister Welding Co. Ltd, Unit 30, Horndon Industrial Park, Station Road, West Horndon, Brentwood, Essex, CM13 3XL Tel: (01277) 812534 Fax: (01277) 812616 E-mail: enquiry@allister.co.uk

U B H International Ltd, Orrell Lane, Burscough, Ormskirk, Lancashire, L40 0SL Tel: (01704) 898500 Fax: (01704) 898518 E-mail: tanks@ubh.co.uk

PROCESS WATER FILTERS

Amazon Filters Ltd, Albany Park, Frimley Road, Camberley, Surrey, GU15 2RA Tel: (01276) 670600 Fax: (01276) 670101 E-mail: sales@amazonfilters.co.uk

Pall Life Sciences, Walton Road, Farlinton, Portsmouth, PO6 1TD Tel: (023) 9230 2600 Fax: (023) 9230 2601

PROCESSED EGG PRODUCTS

Dean Foods Ltd, Stocks Lane, Duckmanton, Chesterfield, Derbyshire, S44 5HZ Tel: (01246) 822161 Fax: (01246) 826717

Framptons Ltd, 76 Charlton Road, Shepton Mallet, Somerset, BA4 5PD Tel: (01749) 341000 Fax: (01749) 341051 E-mail: enquiries@framptons.ltd.uk

Fridays Ltd, Chequertree Farmhouse, Swattenden Lane, Cranbrook, Kent, TN17 3PN Tel: (01580) 710200 Fax: (01580) 713512 E-mail: fridays@fridays.co.uk

Moy Park Ltd, Screevagh, Lisnaskea, Enniskillen, County Fermanagh, BT92 0FA Tel: (028) 6772 1999 Fax: (028) 6772 2442 E-mail: fernefoods@btinternet.com

PROCESSED GLASS

▶ Breakwells Glass Ltd, 5 Villiers Trading Estate, Marston Road, Wolverhampton, WV2 4LA Tel: (01902) 420457 E-mail: sales@breakwellsglass.com

PROCESSED YARN

Atkinson Dyeing Co. Ltd, Deal Street, Keighley, West Yorkshire, BD21 4LA Tel: (01535) 604288 Fax: (01535) 690710

Dawson International plc, Lochleven Mills, Kinross, KY13 8GL Tel: (01577) 867000 Fax: (01577) 867010 E-mail: enquiries@dawson-international.co.uk

Joseph Horsfall & Sons Ltd, Pellon Lane, Halifax, West Yorkshire, HX1 4AA Tel: (01422) 360213 Fax: (01422) 321579 E-mail: info@jhorsfall.com

Impex Trading Co., 23 Oxford Place, 7 Oxford Road, Manchester, M1 6EY Tel: 0161-273 1908 Fax: 0161-273 7072

Shaw Moor Yarns Ltd, Bryom Mill, Knowl Street, Stalybridge, Cheshire, SK15 3AW Tel: 0161-303 1770 Fax: 0161-303 1069 E-mail: 100436.327@compuserve.com

Thornton Kelley & Co. Ltd, Spring Place Mills, Northorpe, Mirfield, West Yorkshire, WF14 0QT Tel: (01924) 493128 Fax: (01924) 495119 E-mail: david@thorntonkelley.co.uk

PROCUREMENT SERVICES, *See also Sourcing and Procurement Agents etc*

8over8 Ltd, T S I C, University Of Ulster, Northland Road, Londonderry, BT48 7TW Tel: (028) 7137 5655 Fax: (028) 7137 5652 E-mail: jobs@8over8.com

Ardvick Trading & Supply Co., 37-39 Peckham Road, Camberwell, London, SE5 8UH Tel: (020) 7703 9135 Fax: (020) 7708 0844

▶ Berkeley Trade Management Limited, PO Box 25, Darlington, County Durham, DL2 3WX Tel: 01325 710111 Fax: 01325 710108 E-mail: info@trademanagement.co.uk

Compass Oilfield Supply Co. Ltd, James Watt Close, Great Yarmouth, Norfolk, NR31 0NX Tel: (01493) 667037 Fax: (01493) 653603 E-mail: intray@compass-hq.com

Craig International Supplies Ltd, 219 Albert Quay, Aberdeen, AB11 5QA Tel: (01224) 591555 Fax: (01224) 212558 E-mail: cis@craig-group.com

Entec International Ltd, B Belfont Trading Estate, Mucklow Hill, Halesowen, West Midlands, B62 8DR Tel: 0121-585 8800 Fax: 0121-585 8899 E-mail: info@entec-int.com

G T Picton Ltd, Hartham House, Stonely Road, Easton, Huntingdon, Cambridgeshire, PE28 0TT Tel: (01480) 890244 Fax: (01480) 890961 E-mail: sales@finwood.co.uk

Gulf Helicopters Co., 1 Stockwell Works, Stephenson Way, Crawley, West Sussex, RH10 1TN Tel: (01293) 401333 Fax: (01293) 611566 E-mail: mgr_uk@gulfhelicopters.com

Igg Component Technology Ltd, Waterside House, Waterside Gardens, Fareham, Hampshire, PO16 8RR Tel: (01329) 829311 Fax: (01329) 829312 E-mail: enquiries@igg.co.uk

Interim Resolutions Ltd, 4 Crowtrees Park, Rastrick, Brighouse, West Yorkshire, HD6 3XQ Tel: (01484) 710354 E-mail: b.hemingway@ukonline.co.uk

Richard James International Ltd, 48 Davis Street, Bristol, BS11 9JW Tel: 0117-982 8575 Fax: 0117-982 6361 E-mail: mail@richard-james.co.uk

Nessco Services Ltd, Discovery House Arnhall Business, Park, Westhill, Aberdeenshire, AB32 6FG Tel: (01355) 266900 Fax: (01224) 428401 E-mail: sales@nessco.co.uk

Power Equipment Design & Supplies Ltd, Lyndhurst Cottage, Seymour Road, Bath, BA1 6DZ Tel: (01225) 463721 Fax: (0845) 2804920 E-mail: info@pedsltd.co.uk

Supply Control Ltd, Broomlea, Pacemuir Road, Kilmacolm, Renfrewshire, PA13 4JJ Tel: (01505) 873255 E-mail: neilm@supplycontrol.com

T K O Procurement Services Ltd, Unit 18 Hassocks Workshop, Stroudley Rd, Basingstoke, Hants, RG24 8UQ Tel: (01256) 819000 Fax: (01256) 842100 E-mail: tony.osborn@btconnect.com

Trowell Plant Sales Ltd, 111 Station Road, Selston, Nottingham, NG16 6FF Tel: (01773) 580878 Fax: (01773) 580881 E-mail: tpsl@btconnect.com

Vector International Ltd, Unit 31, Wellheads Crescent, Wellheads Industrial Estate, Aberdeen, AB21 7GA Tel: (01224) 775242 Fax: (01224) 772212 E-mail: sales@vector-supplies.ltd.uk

Winchester Procurement Ltd, Unit 7 Winnall Indust Estate, Moorside Road, Winchester, Hampshire, SO23 7FX Tel: (01962) 840008 Fax: (01962) 840009 E-mail: sales@winprop.co.uk

PRODUCT COMPLIANCE LABELLING CONSULTANCY

WEEE Labels.com, Unit 4, City Estate,, Corngreaves Road, Cradley Heath, West Midlands, B64 7EP Tel: 0870 7773645 Fax: 0870 7773644 E-mail: sales@weeelabels.com

PRODUCT CONFIGURATION ELECTRONIC DESIGN

▶ RM Alderton Designs Ltd, 5 Temple Bar Business Park, Strettington, Chichester, West Sussex, PO18 0TU Tel: (0870) 754 2665 Fax: (0870) 622 0445 E-mail: sales@rmalderton.com

▶ Trimerix Ltd, Unit 31 Lincoln Road, Cressex Business Park, High Wycombe, Buckinghamshire, HP12 3RL Tel: (01494) 447712 E-mail: info@trimerix.co.uk

PRODUCT DESIGN SERVICES

A A A www.3d-imaging.co.uk, 4 George Street, Whalley, Clitheroe, Lancashire, BB7 9TH Tel: (0870) 7409016 Fax: (0870) 1315997

Boot Robin Design Associates, 295a Lichfield Road, Sutton Coldfield, West Midlands, B74 4BZ Tel: 0121-308 5913 Fax: 0121-308 5913

▶ Drive Inc Ltd, 1 Rose Lane, Ripley, Woking, Surrey, GU23 6NE Tel: (01483) 211200 E-mail: info@drivein.co.uk

Frazer Designers Ltd, 6 Hampstead West, 224 Iverson Road, London, NW6 2HL Tel: (020) 7624 6011 Fax: (020) 7328 6085 E-mail: info@frazerdesigners.com

▶ Glenelg Product Design, Low Barn, Church View, Menston, Ilkley, West Yorkshire, LS29 6EX Tel: (01943) 871117 Fax: (01943) 871002 E-mail: john@glenelgdesign.com

Killyleagh Box Co. Ltd, 39 Shrigley Road, Killyleagh, Downpatrick, County Down, BT30 9SR Tel: (028) 4482 8708 Fax: (028) 4482 1222 E-mail: sales@killyleaghbox.co.uk

▶ Mishi Ltd, 42 Harvest Way, Witney, Oxfordshire, OX28 1EG Tel: (01993) 708719 Fax: (01993) 708719 E-mail: mishi.ltd@tiscali.co.uk

▶ Nextdesign, The Fence, Ring Fence, Woolaston, Lydney, Gloucestershire, GL15 6NX Tel: (07966) 171478 Fax: (07977) 017247 E-mail: enquiries@nextdesign.co.uk

Pemberton Dear Ltd, Parndon Mill, Parndon Mill Lane, Harlow, Essex, CM20 2HP Tel: (01279) 434868 Fax: (01279) 434875 E-mail: design@pemberton-dear.co.uk

Posit Design, The Granary, Station Road, Sandford, Winscombe, Avon, BS25 5RA Tel: (01934) 823931 Fax: (01934) 823958

Sibert Technology, 2a Merrow Business Centre, Merrow Lane, Guildford, Surrey, GU4 7WA Tel: (01483) 440724 Fax: (01483) 440727 E-mail: NDT@sibtec.com

Sshteel, The Lodge, Cefn Bychan Woods, Pantymwyn, Mold, Clwyd, CH7 5EP Tel: (01352) 742111 Fax: (01352) 742101

▶ Taeno Design Consultants, The Mill, Home Farm, Ardington, Wantage, Oxfordshire, OX12 8PD Tel: (01235) 833785 Fax: (01235) 833860

▶ Technology Ventures Scotland Ltd, Atrium Court, 50 Waterloo Street, Glasgow, G2 6HQ Tel: 0141-572 1600 Fax: 0141-572 1608

PRODUCT DESIGN/ DEVELOPMENT CONSULTANTS OR DESIGNERS

3form Design, Unit 63 Basepoint Business & Innovation Centre, Caxton Close, Andover, Hampshire, SP10 3FG Tel: (01264) 326306 Fax: (01264) 326308 E-mail: info@3formdesign.com

A A A www.3d-imaging.co.uk, 4 George Street, Whalley, Clitheroe, Lancashire, BB7 9TH Tel: (0870) 7409016 Fax: (0870) 1315997

Blackburn With Darwen Borough Council, Town Hall, King William St, Blackburn, BB1 7DY Tel: (01254) 585585 E-mail: regeneration@blackburn.gov.uk

Boot Robin Design Associates, 295a Lichfield Road, Sutton Coldfield, West Midlands, B74 4BZ Tel: 0121-308 5913 Fax: 0121-308 5913

Brent Products Develompent Ltd, Old House Lane, Bisley, Woking, Surrey, GU24 9DB Tel: (01483) 797655 Fax: (01483) 797475 E-mail: sales@brentltd.co.uk

Cambridge Consultants Ltd, Science Park, Milton Road, Cambridge, CB4 0DW Tel: (01223) 420024 Fax: (01223) 423373 E-mail: info@cambridgeconsultants.com

Design 4 Plastics Ltd, Unit 402 Thorp Arch Trading Estate, Thorp Arch, Wetherby, West Yorkshire, LS23 7BJ Tel: (01937) 845176 Fax: (01937) 845419 E-mail: enquiries@design4plastics.com

Destech UK Ltd, 3 Millbrook Business Park, Hoe Lane, Nazeing, Waltham Abbey, Essex, EN9 2RJ Tel: (01992) 899002 Fax: (01992) 899003 E-mail: sales@destech-uk.co.uk

E & P Associates Ltd Ltd, 52 Berwick Street, London, W1F 8SL Tel: (020) 7278 4272 Fax: (020) 7437 8176 E-mail: info@ep-associates.com

▶ Eg Technology, 12 Kings Parade, Cambridge, CB2 1SJ Tel: (01223) 710799 Fax: (08707) 877021 E-mail: info@egtechnology.co.uk

Frazer Designers Ltd, 6 Hampstead West, 224 Iverson Road, London, NW6 2HL Tel: (020) 7624 6011 Fax: (020) 7328 6085 E-mail: info@frazerdesigners.com

▶ Glenelg Product Design, Low Barn, Church View, Menston, Ilkley, West Yorkshire, LS29 6EX Tel: (01943) 871117 Fax: (01943) 871002 E-mail: john@glenelgdesign.com

H D S Design Consultants Ltd, 22 South Street, Rochford, Essex, SS4 1BQ Tel: (01702) 530043 Fax: (01702) 530051 E-mail: projects@hdsdesign.com

Hothouse Product Development Partners, Unit 1 College Fields Business Centre, Prince Georges Road, Merton, London, SW19 2PT Tel: (020) 8687 2093 Fax: (020) 8646 1822 E-mail: studio@hothouse-design.com

IDEO London, White Bear Yard, 144A Clerkenwell Road, London, EC1R 5DF Tel: (020) 7713 2600 Fax: (020) 7713 2601 E-mail: mhoenle@ideo.com

INBIS Ltd, Club Street, Bamber Bridge, Preston, PR5 6FN Tel: (01772) 645000 Fax: (01772) 645001 E-mail: mailbox@assystems.com

Light Matters, 6 Long Street, London, E2 8HQ Tel: (020) 7749 4770 Fax: (020) 7749 4771 E-mail: london@lightmatters.co.uk

P J C, 22 The Drive, Orpington, Kent, BR6 9AP Tel: (07718) 267453 E-mail: studio@pjcdesign.co.uk

P R Designs, 13 Davenport Park Road, Davenport Park, Stockport, Cheshire, SK2 6JU Tel: 0161-483 2655 Fax: 0161-483 2655 E-mail: info@prdesigns.co.uk

Pemberton Dear Ltd, Parndon Mill, Parndon Mill Lane, Harlow, Essex, CM20 2HP Tel: (01279) 434868 Fax: (01279) 434875 E-mail: design@pemberton-dear.co.uk

Pentagram Design Ltd, 11 Needham Road, London, W11 2RP Tel: (020) 7229 3477 Fax: (020) 7727 9932 E-mail: email@pentagram.co.uk

▶ Platform44, Sparkhouse Studios, Rope Walk, Lincoln, LN6 7DQ Tel: (01522) 837241 Fax: (01522) 837201 E-mail: projects@platform44.com

Product Partners Ltd, Church Street, Biggleswade, Bedfordshire, SG18 0JS Tel: (01767) 600456 Fax: (01767) 600155 E-mail: sales@productpartners.co.uk

Product Stream Ltd, 65 Oxford Street, Hull, HU2 0QP Tel: (01482) 327755 Fax: (01482) 327766 E-mail: info@productstream.co.uk

R G Software, Stocktons Courtyard, Overbury, Tewkesbury, Gloucestershire, GL20 7NT Tel: (01242) 233255 Fax: (01386) 725109 E-mail: sales@rgsoftware.co.uk

R W Oliver, 38 Alma Street, Eccles, Manchester, M30 0EX Tel: 0161-789 8474

Renfrew Group, 33 Rutland St, Leicester, LE1 1RE Tel: 0116-253 1961 Fax: 0116-253 9827 E-mail: info@renfrew.com

Springboard Design, Unit4 Point 2, The Paint Works, Bath Road, Bristol, BS4 3EH Tel: 0117-958 8500 Fax: 0117-958 8501 E-mail: info@springboard-design.co.uk

Springetts Brand Design Consultants, 13 Salisbury Place, London, W1H 1FJ Tel: (020) 7486 7527 Fax: (020) 7487 3033 E-mail: all@springetts.co.uk

▶ Taeno Design Consultants, The Mill, Home Farm, Ardington, Wantage, Oxfordshire, OX12 8PD Tel: (01235) 833785 Fax: (01235) 833860

▶ Technology Ventures Scotland Ltd, Atrium Court, 50 Waterloo Street, Glasgow, G2 6HQ Tel: 0141-572 1600 Fax: 0141-572 1608

Vicki Thomas Associates, 195 Tollgate Road, London, E6 5JY Tel: (020) 7511 5767 Fax: (020) 7473 5177

Vincent Processes Ltd, Turnpike Industrial Estate, Turnpike Road, Newbury, Berkshire, RG14 2NT Tel: (01635) 40295 Fax: (01635) 37680 E-mail: carlsmith@vincentprocesses.co.uk

Warwick Design Consultants Ltd, Unit 12, Waterloo Park, Bidford-on-Avon, Alcester, Warwickshire, B50 4JG Tel: (01789) 490591 Fax: (01789) 490592 E-mail: wdc@warwickdesign.com

Whitehead Gardner Tooling Ltd, Unit 2, Spring Gardens Industrial Estate, Romford, RM7 9LD Tel: (01708) 756023 Fax: (01708) 733219 E-mail: enquiries@whiteheads.co.uk

PRODUCT HANDLING EQUIPMENT

▶ Ixia UK, Unit 14 Ridgewood Industrial Estate, New Road, Uckfield, East Sussex, TN22 5SX Tel: (01825) 766800 Fax: (01825) 766500 E-mail: ixiauk@cs.com

PRODUCT IDENTIFICATION BADGES

▶ Badge UK, 58 Crossgate, Cupar, Fife, KY15 5HS Tel: (01334) 656677 Fax: (01334) 656678 E-mail: mail@badgeuk.co.uk

DED Ltd, Mill Road, Lydd, Romney Marsh, Kent, TN29 9EJ Tel: (01797) 320636 Fax: (01797) 320273 E-mail: sales@ded.co.uk

Polycrown Ltd, Unit 3 Smiths Forge, North End Road, Yatton, Bristol, BS49 4AU Tel: (01934) 876349 Fax: (01934) 835406 E-mail: sales@polycrown.com

Recognition Express, Gregory Court, Rothbury, Morpeth, Northumberland, NE65 7PJ Tel: (01669) 621018 Fax: (01669) 620508

PRODUCT INNOVATION CONSULTANTS

▶ Merryfield Associates, Newcott Cottage, Newcott Near Honiton, Honiton, Devon, EX14 9ND Tel: (01404) 861587 E-mail: barriebc@btopenworld.com

Product Stream Ltd, 65 Oxford Street, Hull, HU2 0QP Tel: (01482) 327755 Fax: (01482) 327766 E-mail: info@productstream.co.uk

PRODUCT LAUNCH MANAGEMENT

▶ London Canal Museum, 12-13 New Wharf Road, London, N1 9RT Tel: (020) 7713 0836 Fax: (020) 7689 6679 E-mail: hire@canalmuseum.org.uk

PRODUCT SELECTION AND SPECIFICATION SOFTWARE

▶ Broker Partners Ltd, Studio A Dean Mill, Plumbe Street, Burnley, Lancashire, BB11 3AG Tel: (01282) 453629 Fax: (01282) 453629 E-mail: sales@brokerpartners.co.uk

PRODUCTION CONTROL SYSTEMS, *See Control Systems etc*

PRODUCTION EFFICIENCY MONITORING SYSTEMS

Chroma Visual, 61 Leyland Trading Estate, Wellingborough, Northamptonshire, NN8 1RS Tel: (01933) 443737 Fax: (01933) 271770 E-mail: cvl@globalnet.co.uk
Rhombus Systems Ltd, Sumpter House, 8 Station Road, Histon, Cambridge, CB4 9LQ Tel: (01223) 568240 Fax: (01223) 566909 E-mail: sales@rhombus.co.uk
Sencon (UK) Ltd, Unit P, Blackpole Trading Estate East, Worcester, WR3 8SG Tel: (01905) 755525 Fax: (01905) 456393 E-mail: sales@sencon.co.uk

PRODUCTION ENGINEERING CONSULTANTS

A G C Engineering Co. Ltd, London Road, Apsley, Hemel Hempstead, Hertfordshire, HP3 9ST Tel: (01442) 253694 Fax: (01442) 233332
Amar Engineering Consultants, Unit 70 Station Road Workshops, Station Road, Kingswood, Bristol, BS15 4PJ Tel: 0117-956 5522 Fax: 0117-956 5573 E-mail: webe-amar@demon.co.uk
▶ Multitec Engineering Ltd, Darrion House, 37 Tudor Walk, Watford, WD24 7NY Tel: (01923) 213283 Fax: (01923) 213340 E-mail: Multiteceng@aol.com
Powerwise Consultant Engineering, Unit 4 Randswood Farm, The Common, West Wratting, Cambridge, CB21 5LR Tel: (01223) 291250 Fax: (01223) 291260 E-mail: powerwise@powerwise.co.uk
R P H Engineering, 83 Cobham Road, Ferndown Industrial Estate, Wimborne, Dorset, BH21 7QD Tel: (01202) 870999 Fax: (01202) 870888 E-mail: enquiries@rphmanufacturing.co.uk

PRODUCTION ENGINEERS/ ENGINEERING SERVICES TO THE TRADE

A G C Engineering Co. Ltd, London Road, Apsley, Hemel Hempstead, Hertfordshire, HP3 9ST Tel: (01442) 253694 Fax: (01442) 233332
Aeron Automation Ltd, 44-48 Wilson Place, East Kilbride, Glasgow, G74 4QD Tel: (01355) 226022 Fax: (01355) 235077 E-mail: alan@aeron.co.uk
Apek Design & Developments Ltd, Ferndown Industrial Estate, Wimborne, Dorset, BH21 7RF Tel: (01202) 876149 Fax: (01202) 861210 E-mail: sales@apek.co.uk
Arduous Manufacturing, The Old Brewery, Norton Fitzwarren, Taunton, Somerset, TA2 6RN Tel: (01823) 339000 Fax: (01823) 339000
Arthur A Brown & Co., Fairfield Road, Market Harborough, Leicestershire, LE16 9QH Tel: (01858) 462946 Fax: (01858) 462884 E-mail: partners@aabrown.co.uk
Askey Precision Engineering, Neachells Lane, Willenhall, West Midlands, WV13 3SJ Tel: (01902) 306300 Fax: (01902) 306400
BDJ Engineering Worcester Ltd, A Carden Close, Worcester, WR1 2AR Tel: (01905) 23616 Fax: (01905) 22242 E-mail: brian@bdjengineering.wanadoo.co.uk
C & D Precision, Bluebird House, Povey Cross Road, Horley, Surrey, RH6 0AG Tel: (01293) 820092 Fax: (01293) 820093 E-mail: dedman@cdprecision.freeserve.co.uk
C J Uniques Ltd, Unit 12 Magnus, Tame Valley Industrial Estate, Wilnecote, Tamworth, Staffordshire, B77 5BY Tel: (01827) 261682 Fax: (01827) 261682
Central Engineering Services Ltd, Star Works, Burton St, Leek, Staffordshire, ST13 8BX Tel: (01538) 398127 Fax: (01538) 373774 E-mail: inquire@cepltd.co.uk
Crowle Wharfe Engineers Ltd, Wharf Road, Ealand, Scunthorpe, South Humberside, DN17 4JW Tel: (01724) 710455 Fax: (01724) 711508
Equinox Precision Engineering, Station Road, Great Harwood, Blackburn, BB6 7BB Tel: (01254) 888009 Fax: (01254) 885550
G & R Engineering (Nantwich) Ltd, Tricketts Lane, Willaston, Nantwich, Cheshire, CW5 6PY Tel: (01270) 661033 Fax: (01270) 664524 E-mail: brian@gr-eng.fsnet.co.uk
G S W Haswell, The Workshop, Winchester Street, Botley, Southampton, SO30 2AA Tel: (01489) 785293
G W Atkins & Sons Ltd, 28 Wellington St, Syston, Leicester, LE7 2LG Tel: 0116-269 1240 Fax: 0116-269 3270
Glynnway Engineering & Welding Ltd, Salop Street, Bilston, West Midlands, WV14 0TQ Tel: (01902) 495701 Fax: (01902) 497702 E-mail: sales@glynnway.co.uk
Goodwin Technology Ltd, B2 Prenton Way, North Cheshire Trading Estate, Prenton, Merseyside, CH43 3DU Tel: 0151-608 8666 Fax: 0151-638 2456 E-mail: sales@gtprecision.co.uk
Griffvale Ltd, Alexandra Indust Estate, Alexandra Road, Denton, Manchester, M34 3DX Tel: 0161-335 0175 Fax: 0161-336 0513 E-mail: griffvaleltd@btconnect.com
Kenard Engineering Co. Ltd, Green Street Green Road, Dartford, DA1 1QE Tel: (01322) 421200 Fax: (01322) 421220 E-mail: info@kenard.co.uk
Littler Co. Ltd, 2 Greaves Way Industrial Estate, Stanbridge Road, Leighton Buzzard, Bedfordshire, LU7 4UB Tel: (01525) 373310 Fax: (01525) 381371
Longfield Instruments Ltd, East Portway, Andover, Hampshire, SP10 3LU Tel: (01264) 323949 Fax: (01264) 355353 E-mail: eddy@longfield-instruments.co.uk
Marben Engineering Ltd, 3 Cobham Road, Ferndown Industrial Estate, Wimborne, Dorset, BH21 7PE Tel: (01202) 895980 Fax: (01202) 891416 E-mail: marben123@aol.com
MTM Engineering Services, Redfern Indust Estate, Dawson Street, Hyde, Cheshire, SK14 1QZ Tel: 0161-367 7650 Fax: 0161-367 7650 E-mail: carolynoldham@hotmail.co.uk
▶ Multitec Engineering Ltd, Darrion House, 37 Tudor Walk, Watford, WD24 7NY Tel: (01923) 213283 Fax: (01923) 213340 E-mail: Multiteceng@aol.com
Newteq Engineering Ltd, 1 Waterside Industrial Estate, Ettingshall Road, Wolverhampton, WV2 2RQ Tel: (01902) 492622 Fax: (01902) 492379 E-mail: sales@newteq.co.uk
Numac Engineering Ltd, Gerrard Street, Stalybridge, Cheshire, SK15 2JY Tel: 0161-338 2125 Fax: 0161-304 9435
Produmax Ltd, The Tannery, Station Road, Otley, West Yorkshire, LS21 3HX Tel: (01943) 461713 Fax: (01943) 850228 E-mail: mail@produmax.co.uk
Protolog Sound Ltd, 49 Beech Road, Alresford, Hampshire, SO24 9JS Tel: (01962) 734545 Fax: (01962) 733849
Pyramid Precision Engineering, Unit 25 Lythalls La Industrial Estate, Lythalls Lane, Coventry, CV6 6FL Tel: (024) 7666 3447 Fax: (024) 7666 3447
Q B M Precision, Church Road, Stockton-on-Tees, Cleveland, TS18 2LY Tel: (01642) 673491 Fax: (01642) 677258 E-mail: info@qbmprecision.co.uk
R D Precision, Unit 1e Pentre Industrial Estate, Chester Road, Pentre, Deeside, Clwyd, CH5 2DQ Tel: (01244) 520559 Fax: (01244) 531992 E-mail: enquiries@rdprecision.co.uk
Ramsay Precision Engineers Coventry Ltd, Unit 3 Burnsall Road Industrial Estate, Coventry, CV5 6BU Tel: (024) 7667 4220 Fax: (024) 7667 0721 E-mail: info@ramsay-precision.co.uk
Rank Engineering, Unit 4b Barton Hill Trading Estate, Herapath Street, Bristol, BS5 9RD Tel: 0117-955 1298 Fax: 0117-955 6528
C. Rice Engineering, Units 1,2 & 3 Brookfield Works, Christie Street, Stockport, Cheshire, SK1 4LR Tel: 0161-477 0380 Fax: 0161-480 7387 E-mail: info@criceeng.com
Ricor Ltd, Arrow Works, Birmingham Road, Studley, Warwickshire, B80 7AS Tel: (01527) 857757 Fax: (01527) 857224 E-mail: ricorjrobinson@aol.com
Solstrand Industries Ltd, J J Building, Hillbottom Road, Sands Industrial Estate, High Wycombe, Buckinghamshire, HP12 4HJ Tel: (01494) 522030 Fax: (01494) 472685
Stretton Engineering Co. Ltd, 365 Old Church Road, Coventry, CV6 7DT Tel: (024) 7668 9664 Fax: (024) 7668 9664
Summit, Unit 5 Vulcan Road, Solihull, West Midlands, B91 2JY Tel: 0121-709 1898 Fax: 0121-711 1429 E-mail: enquires@summit-precision.co.uk
Warman CNC, 214 Moseley Street, Birmingham, B5 6LE Tel: 0121-622 4045 Fax: 0121-666 6539 E-mail: warmancnc@aol.com
Williams & Oakey Engineering Co. Ltd, Radstock Road, Midsomer Norton, Radstock, BA3 2AA Tel: (01761) 412013 Fax: (01761) 417174 E-mail: mail@williams-oakey.co.uk
Woolley GMC Engineering Co. Ltd, 18 Crondal Road, Exhall, Coventry, CV7 9NH Tel: (024) 7636 2371 Fax: (024) 7636 8171

PRODUCTION MANAGEMENT SOFTWARE

▶ Auto Flow Ltd, Sirius House, Alderley Road, Chelford, Macclesfield, Cheshire, SK11 9AP Tel: (01625) 860545 Fax: (0870) 4581616 E-mail: sales@autoflow.ltd.uk
▶ Dko Consulting Ltd, Caladh, Rock Road, Storrington, Pulborough, West Sussex, RH20 3AH Tel: (01903) 891528 E-mail: sales@dko-consulting.com
▶ Manusoft UK Ltd, The Groveange, Welford Road, Long Marston, Stratford-upon-Avon, Warwickshire, CV37 8RH Tel: (01789) 721930 Fax: (01789) 721901 E-mail: sales@menusoft.co.uk

PRODUCTION MONITORING AND CONTROL COMPUTER SYSTEMS

Spectra Displays Ltd, 194 Station Road, Willingham, Cambridge, CB4 5HQ Tel: (01954) 261402 Fax: (01954) 261403 E-mail: sales@spectra-displays.co.uk

PRODUCTION SCHEDULING AND CONTROL COMPUTER SYSTEMS

Corbett Engineering Ltd, Unit 1 2 Mercia Villas, Torwood Close Westwood Business Park, Coventry, CV4 8HX Tel: (024) 7646 9930 Fax: (024) 7642 0994E-mail: info@celcat.com

PRODUCTION SCHEDULING/ PLANNING CONSULTANTS

Aspentech Ltd, Unit 1 Century Court, Tolpits La, Watford, WD18 9RS Tel: (01923) 254499 Fax: (01923) 816456

PRODUCTION SERVICES, TELEVISION COMMERCIALS

▶ Endorfin TV, Lower Green Road, Tunbridge Wells, Kent, TN4 8TE Tel: (01892) 533577 Fax: (01892) 515183E-mail: mark@endorfin.tv
Immage Studios Ltd, Margaret Street, Immingham, South Humberside, DN40 1LE Tel: (01469) 515151 Fax: (01469) 515152

PROFILE CUTTING MACHINE MANUFRS

Advanced Cutting Systems, Unit 23 Station Lane Industrial Estate, Old Whittington, Chesterfield, Derbyshire, S41 9QX Tel: (01246) 454536 Fax: (01246) 454536 E-mail: sales@advancedcutting.co.uk

PROFILE CUTTING MACHINES, FLAME

Lynrose Engineering, Unit 12 Shrub Hill Industrial Estate, Worcester, WR4 9EL Tel: (01905) 729795 Fax: (01905) 729798 E-mail: mhlynrosesales@aol.com

PROFILE CUTTING SERVICES

Arthur Stephenson Engineers Ltd, Gibfield Works, Bag Lane, Atherton, Manchester, M46 0RD Tel: (01942) 883046 Fax: (01942) 896025 E-mail: ormerod@enterprise.net
Asset Engineering Ltd, 16 20 Black Lake Industrial Estate, Black Lake, West Bromwich, West Midlands, B70 9QP Tel: 0121-553 0231 Fax: 0121-525 4856
Barnshaws Profiles, Anchor Lane, Bilston, West Midlands, WV14 9NE Tel: (01902) 663553 Fax: (01902) 887379 E-mail: enquiries@barnshaws.com
Belper Tools Ltd, 7 Chapel Street, Levenshulme, Manchester, M19 3QB Tel: 0161-224 7240 Fax: 0161-257 2875
Bolton Profiles Ltd, Brittania Way Industrial Park, Union Road, Bolton, BL2 2HG Tel: (01204) 386441 Fax: (01204) 385705 E-mail: paul@boltonprofiles.co.uk
Bretvents Ltd, Bradfords Farm, Little Horsted, Uckfield, East Sussex, TN22 5QP Tel: (01825) 841227 Fax: (01825) 841294
Byworth Engineering Ltd, Albion Works, Royd Ings Ave, Keighley, W. Yorkshire, BD21 4BZ Tel: (01535) 602780 Fax: (01535) 611319
C A V (Sheffield) Ltd, Meadowbank Works, Meadow Bank Road, Rotherham, South Yorkshire, S61 2NF Tel: (01709) 740744 Fax: (01709) 740755
C.W. (Industrial) Fans Ltd, Unit 25, Thornleigh Trading Estate, Dudley, West Midlands, DY2 8UB Tel: (01384) 211010 Fax: (01384) 238086
Camp Steel, 29 Grafton Road, Sparkbrook, Birmingham, B11 1JP Tel: 0121-772 7821 Fax: 0121-771 0435 E-mail: dave-campsteel@btconnect.com
Chadderton Metal Products Ltd, Unit F2 Westwood Industrial Estate, Arkwright Street, Oldham, OL9 9LZ Tel: 0161-620 7907 Fax: 0161-627 4486 E-mail: sales@cmplimited.wanadoo.co.uk
▶ Charles Day Steels Ltd, Downgate Drive, Sheffield, S4 8BT Tel: 0114-244 5544 Fax: 0114-244 5588 E-mail: sales@daysteel.co.uk
Cladburn Engineering Co., C Block 17 South Avenue, Blantyre Industrial Estate, Blantyre, Glasgow, G72 0XB Tel: (01698) 822550 Fax: (01698) 825130
Colstan Profiles Ltd, Unit 4 Central Works, Peartree Lane, Dudley, West Midlands, DY2 0QU Tel: (01384) 861122 Fax: (01384) 861144 E-mail: info@colstanprofiles.co.uk
D C M Group Ltd, Bayton Road Industrial Estate, 41 Bayton Road, Exhall, Coventry, CV7 9EL Tel: (024) 7636 1601 Fax: (024) 7636 7914 E-mail: sales@dcm.co.uk
D.M.G. Profile, 25 Oak St, Quarry Bank, Brierley Hill, W. Midlands, DY5 2JH Tel: (01384) 561448 Fax: (01384) 561448
Das Fabrications Ltd, Ajax Works, Whitehill Street, Stockport, Cheshire, SK4 1NT Tel: 0161-476 1222 Fax: 0161-476 1333 E-mail: dave@dasfabs.fsbusiness.co.uk
Data Tooling & Enginering Services Ltd, Unit 1-2 Paddock Farm, Bethersden Road, Hothfield, Ashford, Kent, TN26 1EP Tel: (01233) 620805 Fax: (01233) 620889 E-mail: info@datatooling.co.uk
Droitwich Road Aquatics, Droitwich Road, Claines, Worcester, WR3 7SW Tel: (01905) 757376 Fax: (01905) 452242
Ecam Engineering Ltd, Tower Crane Drive, Stoke-on-Trent, ST10 4DB Tel: (01538) 757166 Fax: (01538) 755857 E-mail: nick@ecam.co.uk
Elston Profiles Ltd, Unit G2 Bullock Street, West Bromwich, West Midlands, B70 7HE Tel: 0121-553 6292 Fax: 0121-553 6707
Elston Profiles and Compnents Ltd, St. Annes Road, Cradley Heath, West Midlands, B64 5BH Tel: (01384) 566919 Fax: (01384) 569684
Engineering Tech Pgp Ltd, Unit 5 Harbour Road Industrial Estate, Lowestoft, Suffolk, NR32 3LZ Tel: (01502) 515768 Fax: (01502) 563211 E-mail: pete@eng-tech.co.uk
Essex Laser Job Shop Ltd, Unit D4, Frogmore Industrial Estate, Motherwell Way, Grays, Essex, RM20 3XD Tel: (01708) 689658 Fax: (01708) 865433 E-mail: sales@essexlaser.co.uk
F C Curran Ltd, Duke Street, Nottingham, NG7 7JN Tel: 0115-970 6801 Fax: 0115-942 2221 E-mail: enquiries@fccurran.co.uk
Falcon Grinding, Unit 1 Anne Street, Willenhall, West Midlands, WV13 1EN Tel: (01902) 601478 Fax: (01902) 606055 E-mail: falcongri@aol.com
Flame Kut Profiles, Unit 39 Darlaston Central Trading Estate, Wednesbury, West Midlands, WS10 8XB Tel: 0121-526 6919 Fax: 0121-568 6447E-mail: sales@flamekut.fsbusiness.co.uk
Flanges Ltd, Portrack Trading Estate, Stockton-on-Tees, Cleveland, TS18 2PL Tel: (01642) 672626 Fax: (01642) 617574 E-mail: sales@flanges-ltd.co.uk
Forth Steel Ltd, 28 South Gyle Cresent, Edinburgh, EH12 9EB Tel: 0131-316 4360 Fax: 0131-316 4343 E-mail: forth_steel@mih.co.uk
Franklin Steel Stockholders P.L.C., Franklin Park, Patterson Street, Blaydon-On-Tyne, Tyne & Wear, NE21 5TL Tel: 0191-499 0222 Fax: 0191-499 0223 E-mail: sales@franklinsteel.co.uk
General Utilities Stockport Ltd, Clough Works, Middlewood Road, Poynton, Stockport, Cheshire, SK12 1SJ Tel: (01625) 876321 Fax: (01625) 876284 E-mail: sales@generalutilities.co.uk
Handley Steel Ltd, Phoenix Works Industrial Estate, Richards Street, Wednesbury, West Midlands, WS10 8BZ Tel: 0121-568 6387 Fax: 0121-568 6387
E. Harding & Sons Ltd, Units 10 & 11, Walker Industrial Estate, Walker Road, Guide, Blackburn, BB1 2QE Tel: (01254) 581276 Fax: (01254) 677012 E-mail: sales@ehardings.co.uk
J.A. Harvey (Bassingham) Ltd, The Old Dairy, Navenby Lane, Bassingham, Lincoln, LN5 9JF Tel: (01522) 788111 Fax: (01522) 788195 E-mail: ja.harvey@btconnect.com
Intec Laser Services, Woolaston Road, Park Farm North, Redditch, Worcestershire, B98 7SG Tel: (01527) 518550 Fax: (01527) 518551 E-mail: sales@intec.uk.net
J & M Profile Services Ltd, Vauxhall Iron Works, Beauford Road, Birkenhead, Merseyside, CH41 1HE Tel: 0151-653 6006 Fax: 0151-652 1425 E-mail: jmprofiles@jmprofiles.co.uk
James Engineering Ltd, Prenton Way, North Cheshire Trading Estate, Prenton, Merseyside, CH43 3DU Tel: 0151-609 1000 Fax: 0151-609 0741 E-mail: sales@jameseng.com
Laser Line Engineering Ltd, Unit 14 Avon Business Park, Lodge Causeway, Bristol, BS16 3JP Tel: 0117-965 7002 Fax: 0117-965 7004 E-mail: sales@laser-line.net
Laserweld 2000 Ltd, Walsall Road, Norton Canes, Cannock, Staffordshire, WS11 9TA Tel: (01543) 450099 Fax: (01543) 450098 E-mail: laserweld@aol.com
Laserworld Engineering Co. Ltd, Brownside Mill, Brun Terrace, Burnley, Lancashire, BB10 3JR Tel: (01282) 425999 Fax: (01282) 426739 E-mail: info@laserworldengineering.co.uk
Loks Profiling Services Ltd, Westhoughton Industrial Estate, James Street, Westhoughton, Bolton, BL5 3QR Tel: (01942) 816108 Fax: (01942) 814757
Loks Profiling Services Ltd, Calder Vale Road, Horbury Junction Industrial Estate, Horbury, Wakefield, West Yorkshire, WF4 5ER Tel: (01924) 271978 Fax: (01924) 280006 E-mail: wakesales@locksprofiling.co.uk
Mackays Of Cambridge Ltd, 120 Church End, Cambridge, CB1 3LB Tel: (01223) 508222 Fax: (01223) 510222 E-mail: engineering@mackay.co.uk
Malthouse Engineering Co. Ltd, 3 Hainge Road, Tividale, Oldbury, West Midlands, B69 2NL Tel: 0121-557 8455 Fax: 0121-520 2034
Matrix Lasers North East Ltd, 5 Trafalgar Court, South Nelson Industrial Estate, Cramlington, Northumberland, NE23 1WF Tel: (01670) 739222 Fax: (01670) 739333
Morgan Cooper Ltd, Salmon Road, Great Yarmouth, Norfolk, NR30 3QS Tel: (01493) 843233 Fax: (01493) 844068 E-mail: info@morgan-cooper.co.uk
Morgans UK Ltd, Roma Road, Birmingham, B11 2JH Tel: 0121-706 3216 Fax: 0121-765 4177

PROFILE CUTTING SERVICES - *continued*

Namsbury Engineering Ltd, 56 Penistone Road, Sheffield, S6 3AE Tel: 0114-272 8111 Fax: 0114-270 1859 E-mail: enquiries@namsbury.demon.co.uk

North East Profiling & Engineering Co. Ltd, Bellway Industrial Estate, Whitley Road, Longbenton, Newcastle upon Tyne, NE12 9SW Tel: 0191-266 4521 Fax: 0191-270 0983 E-mail: sales@northeastprofiling.com

P P Plasma, New Factory, Vere Street, Salford, M50 2GQ Tel: 0161-736 9299 Fax: 0161-745 7915

P P Profiles Ltd, Neills Road, Bold, St. Helens, Merseyside, WA9 4SY Tel: (01744) 818992 Fax: (01744) 820179 E-mail: sales@ppprofilesltd.co.uk

Parson & Crosland Ltd, PO Box 10, Middlesbrough, Cleveland, TS2 1HG Tel: (01642) 244161 Fax: (01642) 230487 E-mail: sales@parson-crosland.co.uk

Pearson Profilers, Skippers Lane, Skippers Lane Industrial Estate, Middlesbrough, Cleveland, TS6 6HA Tel: (01642) 466566 Fax: (01642) 466299 E-mail: sales@pearsonprofilers.co.uk

Pegasus Profiles Ltd, Stephenson Way, Thetford, Norfolk, IP24 3RJ Tel: (01842) 755711 Fax: (01842) 755711 E-mail: sales@pegpro.co.uk

Plascut Stainless, Coleford Road, Darnall, Sheffield, S9 5PJ Tel: 0114-251 9535 Fax: 0114-251 9536 E-mail: sheffield.zi2@centers.co.uk

H. Potter Engineering Ltd, Fisher Street, Low Walker, Newcastle Upon Tyne, NE6 4LT Tel: 0191-295 4420 Fax: 0191-295 4482

Precision Profiles, Southway Drive, Bristol, BS30 5LW Tel: 0117-960 9922 Fax: 0117-960 9944 E-mail: info@precisionprofiles.co.uk

Procut Ltd, Unit 51 Youngs Industrial Estate, Paices Hill, Aldermaston, Reading, RG7 4PW Tel: 0118-981 7109 Fax: 0118-981 2832

Profile & Fabrication Services, P O Box 1002, Yateley, Hampshire, GU46 6ZA Tel: (01252) 875739 Fax: (01252) 664124

Abram Pulman & Sons Ltd, Walton Street, Sowerby Bridge, West Yorkshire, HX6 1AN Tel: (01422) 833993 Fax: (01422) 834100 E-mail: sales@pulmans.co.uk

R & S Laser Cutting & Fabrications Ltd, R & S House, Clement Street, Birmingham, B1 2SW Tel: 0121-237 5646 Fax: 0121-236 9339 E-mail: sales@rs-laser-cutting.co.uk

Randalls Profiles Ltd, Cranford Street, Smethwick, West Midlands, B66 2SB Tel: 0121-558 0144 Fax: 0121-558 7426 E-mail: gary.bailey@randals-profiles.co.uk

Robert Smith Steels Ltd, Cathcart Quay, Cathcart Street, Birkenhead, Merseyside, CH41 3HZ Tel: 0151-647 4221 Fax: 0151-647 4839 E-mail: sales@robertsmithsteel.co.uk

S M Thompson Ltd, Marathon Works, Newport Bridge, Middlesbrough, Cleveland, TS1 5TG Tel: (01642) 245161 Fax: (01642) 223392 E-mail: sales@smthompson.co.uk

Sciss Ltd, Unit 9 Larkstore Park, Lodge Road, Staplehurst, Tonbridge, Kent, TN12 0QY Tel: (01580) 890582 Fax: (01580) 890583 E-mail: sales@sciss.co.uk

South Yorkshire Laser Cutting Ltd, Unit 22-23, Bookers Way, Todwick Road Industrial Estate, Dinnington, Sheffield, S25 3SH Tel: (01909) 568682 Fax: (01909) 565648 E-mail: sylc.laser@virgin.net

Southern Flamecuts, 28 Uddens Trading Estate, Wimborne, Dorset, BH21 7NL Tel: 01202 895895

Spectrum Laser Ltd, 2 Aysgarth Road, Waterlooville, Hampshire, PO7 7UG Tel: (023) 9225 2900 Fax: (023) 9223 3766 E-mail: sales@spectrumlaser.co.uk

Steelkit, Abberleri Boatyard, Ynyslas, Borth, Dyfed, SY24 5JU Tel: (01970) 871713 Fax: (01970) 871879E-mail: info@steelkit.com

Strata Flame Cutting & Fabrications, 101 York Road, Hall Green, Birmingham, B28 8LH Tel: 0121-778 5022 Fax: 0121-777 8241

Streamline Waterjet & Laser Cutters Ltd, Kingsway South, Team Valley Trading Estate, Gateshead, Tyne & Wear, NE11 0JL Tel: 0191-491 4422 Fax: 0191-497 3421 E-mail: streamline@responsive-engineering.com

Thomas Lane & Co. Ltd, Hope St Works, Hazel Grove, Stockport, Cheshire, SK7 4EL Tel: 0161-483 9666 Fax: 0161-456 4440 E-mail: fabwork@t-lane.demon.co.uk

Triple T Engineering Ltd, Hackworth Industrial Park, Shildon, County Durham, DL4 1HF Tel: (01388) 774444 Fax: (01388) 774444 E-mail: sales@triple-t-eng.co.uk

Yates, 80 Dollman Street, Birmingham, B7 4RP Tel: 0121-333 7091 Fax: 0121-333 7092 E-mail: akyates@btconnect.com

PROFILE GROUND SPUR GEARS

Jackson Precision Gear Services Ltd, Elmtree Street, Belle Vue, Wakefield, West Yorkshire, WF1 5EQ Tel: (01924) 299866 Fax: (01924) 299338 E-mail: j.s.j@btinternet.com

Planet Gears Ltd, 2 Maguire Industrial Estate, Coventry, CV4 9HN Tel: 024 76474213

PROFILE MILLING

Metalpacks Ltd, Old Parsonage Works, High Street, Farningham, Dartford, DA4 0DG Tel: (01322) 862727 Fax: (01322) 865580 E-mail: metalpacks@usa.net

PROFILED METAL WALL CLADDING

Colamet Manufacturing Ltd, 870 South St, Whiteinch, Glasgow, G14 0SY Tel: 0141-959 1183 Fax: 0141-958 1173 E-mail: info@booth-muirie.co.uk

▶ Coverworld UK Ltd, Mansfield Road, Bramley Vale, Chesterfield, Derbyshire, S44 5GA Tel: (01246) 454711 Fax: (01246) 858223 E-mail: sales@coverworld.co.uk

Euro Clad Ltd, Wentloog Corparate Park, Wentloog Road, Rumney, Cardiff, CF3 2ER Tel: (029) 2079 0722 Fax: (029) 2079 3149 E-mail: sales@euroclad.com

Haironville T A C Ltd, Abbotsfield Road, Abbotsfield Industrial Park, St. Helens, Merseyside, WA9 4HU Tel: (01744) 818181 Fax: (01744) 851555 E-mail: technical@haironvilletac.co.uk

PROFILES, STEEL REINFORCEMENTS

▶ Cook & Hicks Reinforcements, Sunnydene, Gainsborough Road, Scotter, Gainsborough, Lincolnshire, DN21 3UB Tel: (01724) 762523 Fax: (01724) 764645

PROGRAM DOCUMENTATION PROGRAMMABLE LOGIC CONTROLLER (PLC) COMPUTER SOFTWARE

▶ Networks & Data Ltd, 2 Meadow Rise, Wadworth, Doncaster, South Yorkshire, DN11 9AP Tel: (01302) 854969 E-mail: dave@networksanddata.co.uk

PROGRAMMABLE CONTROLLER SUPPORT SOFTWARE

Colter Products Ltd, Unit 7 Zone C Chelmsford Road Industrial Estate, Chelmsford Road, Dunmow, Essex, CM6 1HD Tel: (01371) 876887 Fax: (01371) 875638 E-mail: sales@coltergroup.co.uk

PROGRAMMABLE LOGIC COMPONENTS

Avnet Memec Ltd, 64-65 Rabans Close, Aylesbury, Buckinghamshire, HP19 8TW Tel: (01296) 330061 Fax: (01296) 330065 E-mail: sales@insightuk.memec.com

Iota Device Programming Ltd, Unit A1, Sandy Business Park, Gosforth Close, Sandy, Bedfordshire, SG19 1RB Tel: (01767) 692228 Fax: (01767) 699927 E-mail: sales@iotadpl.co.uk

PROGRAMMABLE LOGIC CONTROL (PLC) PROGRAMMING

Global Engineering Services, Yew Tree Cott, Sampford Moor, Wellington, Somerset, TA21 9QL Tel: (0870) 7651508 Fax: (0870) 7652508 E-mail: mauricepinner@compuserve.com

Maximotive Design Ltd, 70 River Way, Christchurch, Dorset, BH23 2QR Tel: (01202) 565713 Fax: (01202) 565713 E-mail: mylne@maximotive.com

Mitchell & Hewitt Ltd, Ascot Drive, Derby, DE24 8GZ Tel: (01332) 332177 Fax: (01332) 374769 E-mail: admin@mitchellandhewitt.co.uk

PROGRAMMABLE LOGIC CONTROL (PLC) SYSTEMS INTEGRATORS

I C P Projects Ltd, Cwm Cynon Business Park, Mountain Ash, Mid Glamorgan, CF45 4ER Tel: (01443) 477970 Fax: (01443) 476707 E-mail: sales@icpprojects.co.uk

Industrial System Solutions Ltd, 21 Summerhill, East Herrington, Sunderland, SR3 3NJ Tel: (07949) 566186 Fax: 0191-511 0732 E-mail: enquiries@industrialsystemsolutions.co.uk

Soft Control Ltd, Market Chambers, Market Place, Shifnal, Shropshire, TF11 9AZ Tel: (01952) 462976 Fax: (01952) 462797 E-mail: technical@softcontrol.co.uk

▶ Superior Systems, 39 Deerhurst Road, Coventry, CV6 4EJ Tel: (024) 7666 3321 Fax: (024) 7666 3321 E-mail: sales@superior-systems.co.uk

PROGRAMMABLE LOGIC CONTROL (PLC) SYSTEMS MAINTENANCE/REPAIR SERVICES

Maximotive Design Ltd, 70 River Way, Christchurch, Dorset, BH23 2QR Tel: (01202) 565713 Fax: (01202) 565713 E-mail: mylne@maximotive.com

Soft Control Ltd, Market Chambers, Market Place, Shifnal, Shropshire, TF11 9AZ Tel: (01952) 462976 Fax: (01952) 462797 E-mail: technical@softcontrol.co.uk

▶ Superior Systems, 39 Deerhurst Road, Coventry, CV6 4EJ Tel: (024) 7666 3321 Fax: (024) 7666 3321 E-mail: sales@superior-systems.co.uk

PROGRAMMABLE LOGIC CONTROL (PLC) SYSTEMS MANUFRS

Golco Automation Systems, Unit 323-325, Hartlebury Trading Estate, Hartlebury, Kidderminster, Worcestershire, DY10 4JB Tel: (01299) 253009 Fax: (01299) 253013 E-mail: sales@golco.co.uk

Hte Controls, 4 Cala Trading Estate, Ashton Vale Road, Bristol, BS3 2HA Tel: 0117-966 5925 Fax: 0117-966 1940 E-mail: sales@htecontrols.co.uk

J W & E Morris & Son Ltd, South Road, Bridgend Industrial Estate, Bridgend, Mid Glamorgan, CF31 3RB Tel: (01656) 653705 Fax: (01656) 767187 E-mail: sales@jwmorris.co.uk

PROGRAMMABLE LOGIC CONTROLLERS (PLC)

Amtec Automation Ltd, 27 Brooklands Close, Uttoxeter, Staffordshire, ST14 8UH Tel: (07973) 614115 Fax: (01889) 560353 E-mail: info@amt-a.com

▶ Craven Plumbing & Electrical, 75 St. Johns Road, Dartford, DA2 6BE Tel: (01322) 276067 E-mail: julian@squash4.freeserve.co.uk

Dematic Ltd, Sir William Siemens House, Princess Road, Manchester, M20 2UR Tel: 0161-446 5292 Fax: 0161-446 5214 E-mail: sfmpost@plcman.siemens.co.uk

▶ Drawtrend Ltd, 95 Mains Lane, Poulton-le-Fylde, Lancashire, FY6 7LD Tel: (01253) 882158 Fax: (01253) 882158 E-mail: sales@drawtrend.com

Colin Mear Engineering Ltd, Combe Wood, Combe St Nicholas, Chard, Somerset, TA20 3NL Tel: (01460) 67351 Fax: (01460) 65661 E-mail: cme@cme-ltd.com

Parker Hannifin, Unit A30 Arena Business Centre, Holyrood Close, Poole, Dorset, BH17 7BA Tel: (01202) 606300 Fax: (01202) 606301 E-mail: sales.digiplan@parker.com

▶ Wilkie Electronics, 16 Muirhall Terrace, Perth, PH2 7ES Tel: (01738) 621492

PROGRAMMED TEMPERATURE CONTROLLERS

Monika, 10 Brook Park, Gaddesby Lane, Rearsby, Leicester, LE7 4YL Tel: (01664) 423900 Fax: (01664) 420033 E-mail: info@monika.com

PROGRAMMING SERVICES

C A L Software Ltd, Rivington House, Drumhead Road, Chorley North Industrial Estate, Chorley, Lancashire, PR6 7BX Tel: (01257) 231011 Fax: (01257) 230927 E-mail: sales@calsoftware.co.uk

C A M X L Ltd, Avon Court, Cowbridge Road, Bridgend, Mid Glamorgan, CF31 3SR Tel: (01656) 303100 Fax: (01656) 658054 E-mail: andy@camxl.co.uk

Iota Device Programming Ltd, Unit A1, Sandy Business Park, Gosforth Close, Sandy, Bedfordshire, SG19 1RB Tel: (01767) 692228 Fax: (01767) 699927 E-mail: sales@iotadpl.co.uk

Jtag Technologies, Cople Road, Cardington, Bedford, MK44 3SN Tel: (01234) 831212 Fax: (01234) 831616 E-mail: sales@jtag.com

Logical Software Ltd, 143 Clitherow Avenue, London, W7 2BU Tel: (020) 8579 7795 Fax: (020) 8579 7795

M J H Engineering Services, Maycot, Quay Lane, Kirby-le-Soken, Frinton-on-Sea, Essex, CO13 0DP Tel: (01255) 675515 E-mail: info@mjh-engineering.co.uk

▶ Neil Ogden Associates, 63 Franklin Avenue, Tadley, Hampshire, RG26 4EZ Tel: 0118-981 9556 E-mail: neil@neilogdenassociates.co.uk

Powersoft Computer Services, 4 Pelham Court, Pelham Place, Crawley, West Sussex, RH11 9SH Tel: (01293) 562730 Fax: (01293) 522006 E-mail: support@powersoft-services.co.uk

PROGRESSING CAVITY PUMPS

Fluid Equipment International Ltd, 10 Blandford Heights Industrial Estate, Blandford Forum, Dorset, DT11 7TE Tel: (01258) 459401 Fax: (01258) 459068 E-mail: sales.feil@btconnect.com

PROJECT ENGINEERING SPECIALIST SERVICES

A B M Ltd, Pitt Street, Widnes, Cheshire, WA8 0TG Tel: 0151-420 2829 Fax: 0151-495 1689 E-mail: sales@abm-ltd.co.uk

Kvaerner E & C, 68 Hammersmith Road, London, W14 8YW Tel: (020) 7339 1000 Fax: (020) 7339 1100

M B Engineering Solutions Ltd, Logans Road, Motherwell, Lanarkshire, ML1 3NP Tel: (01698) 266111 Fax: (01698) 269774 E-mail: info@mbgroup.com

Project Engineering Services, 26 The Hoskers, Westhoughton, Bolton, BL5 2DW Tel: (01942) 817445 Fax: (01942) 817445 E-mail: project@engservice.freeserve.co.uk

PROJECT MANAGEMENT

▶ ADP, Phoenix House, Phoenix Crescent, Strathclyde Business Park, Bellshill, Lanarkshire, ML4 3NJ Tel: (01488) 662662 Fax: (01698) 501061

▶ Agile Projects, 13 Stourvale Gardens, Chandler's Ford, Eastleigh, Hampshire, SO53 3NE Tel: (023) 8025 1010 Fax: 02380 251010 E-mail: enquiries@agileprojects.co.uk

Andrews & Boyd, 24 Old Burlington Street, Mayfair, London, W1S 3AW Tel: (020) 7494 0399 Fax: (020) 7494 0477 E-mail: info@andrewsboyd.co.uk

W.S. Atkins Ltd, Unit 3 Langstone Business Village, Langstone Park, Langstone, Newport, Gwent, NP18 2LG Tel: (01633) 415500 Fax: (01633) 411211

▶ Babtie Group Ltd, 95 Bothwell Street, Glasgow, G2 7HX Tel: 0141-204 2511 Fax: 0141-226 3109

Cameron Brook & Associates, 1 Royal Oak Passage, High Street, Huntingdon, Cambridgeshire, PE29 3EA Tel: (01480) 436236 Fax: (01480) 436336 E-mail: sales@cameronbrook.co.uk

The Career Centre Ltd, 3 The Courtyard, New North Road, Exeter, EX4 4EP Tel: 01392 277882 E-mail: thecareercentre1@star.co.uk

Cedar Systems Ltd, 2440 The Quadrant, Aztec West, Almondsbury, Bristol, BS32 4AQ Tel: (01454) 878708 Fax: (01454) 878608 E-mail: cedar@cedar.co.uk

Charles Millward Partnership Ltd, Old Angel Cottage, Main Road, Flax Bourton, Bristol, BS48 3QQ Tel: (01275) 464868 Fax: (01275) 464868 E-mail: cmp.ltd@btinternet.com

Construction Leads, Camargue Eagle Tower, Momtpellier Drive, Cheltenham, Gloucestershire, GL50 1TA Tel: (01242) 577277 Fax: (01242) 527277

▶ Corporate Wellbeing, The Office Millworks, 28 Field Road, Glasgow, G76 8SE Tel: 0141-644 8302 Fax: 0141-644 5753

▶ Creation Project Management Ltd, Becks Field House, Becks Field, Stoke-sub-Hamdon, Somerset, TA14 6PB Tel: 0845 3519922 Fax: 01935 829218 E-mail: sales@creationpm.com

Curran Engineering Ltd, Unit 15 Valley Enterprise, Bedwas House Industrial Estate, Bedwas, Caerphilly, CF83 8DW Tel: (029) 2085 0800 Fax: (029) 2085 0800 E-mail: rjh@curranltd.co.uk

Curtins Consulting Engineers plc, 26-29 St. Cross Street, London, EC1N 8UH Tel: (020) 7213 9000 Fax: (020) 7213 9001 E-mail: london@curtins.com

Eurosoft (U K) Ltd, 3 St Stephens Road, Bournemouth, BH2 6JL Tel: (01202) 297315 Fax: (01202) 558280 E-mail: info@eurosoft-uk.com

Executives Online, Dolphin House, St. Peter Street, Winchester, Hampshire, SO23 8BW Tel: (01962) 829705 Fax: (01962) 866116 E-mail: info@executivesonline.co.uk

▶ F I Training Services, 13 Rubislaw Terrace, Aberdeen, AB10 1XE Tel: (01224) 640891 Fax: (01224) 637982 E-mail: sales@fitraining.com

Fletcher Smith, 33 Brunel Parkway, Pride Park, Derby, DE24 8HR Tel: (01332) 636000 Fax: (01332) 636020 E-mail: info@fletchersmith.com

Flex Automation Ltd, 28 Scardale Way, Durham, DH1 2TX Tel: 0191-384 1048

Ford Systems Ltd, Park La, Nottingham, NG6 0EU Tel: 0115-927 2821 Fax: 0115-976 1041 E-mail: arthur.ford@fordgroup.co.uk

Forgetrack Ltd, Thistle House, St Andrews Street, Hertford, SG14 1JA Tel: (01992) 500900 Fax: (01992) 589495 E-mail: info@forgetrack.co.uk

Foster Wheeler Energy Ltd, Foley House, 5 Seaward Place, Glasgow, G41 1HH Tel: 0141-420 3414 Fax: 0141-420 3416

▶ indicates data change since last edition

PROJECT MANAGEMENT – *continued*

Geotech Systems Ltd, 3000 Cathedral Hill Industrial Estate, Guildford, Surrey, GU2 7YB Tel: (01483) 243530 Fax: (01483) 245330

Getronics UK Ltd, Cygnus House, 1 The Southwood Crescent, Apollo Rise, Farnborough, Hampshire, GU14 0NL Tel: (0870) 9068000 Fax: (020) 8874 3014 E-mail: getronics.helpdesk@getronics.com

Hartnell Taylor Cook, 18 Canynge Road, Bristol, BS8 3JX Tel: 0117-923 9234 Fax: 0117-923 9237 E-mail: sales@hartnelltaylorcook.co.uk

Hyperion Systems Ltd, 12 The Mount, Guildford, Surrey, GU2 4HN Tel: (01483) 301793 Fax: (01483) 561657 E-mail: glor.benson@chyp.com

Infosystems, Bridge Farm, Holt Lane, Ashby Magna, Lutterworth, Leicestershire, LE17 5NJ Tel: (01455) 201000 Fax: (01455) 201001 E-mail: sales@infosystems.co.uk

Itec Projects, 30 Severn Road, Aveley, South Ockendon, Essex, RM15 4NR Tel: (01708) 206181 Fax: (0870) 762 8843 E-mail: andrew@i-t-p.com

▶ Jemco Associates, 128 Elderslie Street, Glasgow, G3 7AW Tel: 0141-564 3906

Kappa Lambda Squared Ltd, Erskine House, 53 London Road, Maidstone, Kent, ME16 8JH Tel: (01622) 670095 Fax: (01622) 200119 E-mail: sales@kl2.com

Kramer Lee & Associates Ltd, Vermont House, Chrisy Close, Southfields Business Park, Basildon, Essex, SS15 6EA Tel: (01268) 494500 Fax: (01268) 494555 E-mail: info@kramerlee.com

▶ M G T Ltd, P O Box 200, Kirkcaldy, Fife, KY2 6WD Tel: (0870) 8407000 Fax: (0870) 8407001

▶ Mckeating Ltd, 4 Wykeham Road, Glasgow, G13 3YT Tel: 0141-434 1117 Fax: 0141-954 2987

Marcus Ltd, 39 Outram Street, Darlington, County Durham, DL3 7DP Tel: (01325) 353882 Fax: (01325) 358408 E-mail: sales@newpc.co.uk

Angus Meek Partnership Ltd, 60 Arley Hill, Bristol, BS6 5PP Tel: 0117-942 8286 Fax: 0117-942 0495 E-mail: admin@angusmeek.co.uk

Middlesex Group Ltd, Telford Road, Houndmills Industrial Estate, Basingstoke, Hampshire, RG21 6YU Tel: (01256) 353711 Fax: (01256) 842613 E-mail: sales@middlesex.co.uk

▶ N J Grime, 32 Wentworth Drive, Euxton, Chorley, Lancashire, PR7 6FN Tel: (01257) 232602 Fax: (01257) 232602 E-mail: njgrimepurchaseservices@supanet.com

Nexus Ltd, 32 Carden Place, Aberdeen, AB10 1UP Tel: (01224) 620000 Fax: (01224) 620026

Norec Ltd, Norec House, Fall Bank Industrial Estate, Dodworth, Barnsley, South Yorkshire, S75 3LS Tel: (01226) 730440 Fax: (01226) 730688 E-mail: sales@norec.ltd.uk

Novacroft Ltd, Harvest Barn Spring Hill, Harborough Road, Pitsford, Northampton, NN6 9AA Tel: (01604) 889500 Fax: (01604) 889508 E-mail: clivenotley@novacroft.com

Osprey Mott Macdonald, Welken House, 10-11 Charterhouse Square, London, EC1M 6EH Tel: (020) 7566 7900 Fax: (020) 7566 7911 E-mail: brenda.wiggins@ospreymottmac.com

▶ P P S Food Projects, 11 The Crescent, Plymouth, PL1 3AB Tel: (01752) 510173 Fax: (01752) 512489 E-mail: brianlr@ppsfoodprojects.co.uk

Project Systems Support Ltd, Chatelaine, Gazing Lane, West Wellow, Romsey, Hampshire, SO51 6BS Tel: (01794) 322755 Fax: (01794) 323964 E-mail: robert_toogood@projectsystemssupport.co.uk

▶ Promasol, 63 Harwood Lane, Great Harwood, Blackburn, BB6 7TB Tel: (01254) 885500 Fax: (01254) 885500 E-mail: info@promasol.co.uk

▶ Sacranie.net, Flat1, 40 Woodstock Road, Golders Green, London, NW11 8ER Tel: 0208 9055523 Fax: 0871 2773305 E-mail: raheen@sacranie.net

Sacrosanct Technology Ltd, 3 Sambourn Close, Solihull, West Midlands, B91 2SA Tel: 0121-711 2100 E-mail: robthomas@sacrosanct.co.uk

▶ Solution Management Ltd, Ferryview, Grantown Road, Forres, Morayshire, IV36 2PG Tel: (01309) 672547

▶ Solutions for Management, Upper Leigh View, 195 Coronation Road, Southville, Bristol, BS3 1RQ Tel: 07970 262938 E-mail: jen@solutions4management.co.uk

Startech Engineering Consultancy Ltd, 2 Drayton Ford, Rickmansworth, Hertfordshire, WD3 8FE Tel: (01923) 897903 Fax: (01923) 897904 E-mail: startech@btinternet.com

▶ Stewart & Williamson, 5 Clairmont Gardens, Glasgow, G3 7LW Tel: 0141-332 7475 Fax: 0141-332 6625

▶ TCE Solutions Limited, 25 Dyers Court, Bollington, Macclesfield, Cheshire, SK10 5GG Tel: 0845 2572710 E-mail: Sales@tcesolutions.co.uk

Totaljobs Group Ltd, 57 Rathbone Place, London, W1T 1JU Tel: (020) 7769 9200 Fax: (020) 7769 9201 E-mail: info@totaljobs.com

Transition Computing Ltd, 12 Challenge House, Sherwood Drive, Bletchley, Milton Keynes, MK3 6DP Tel: (0870) 0110999 Fax: (08700) 514550 E-mail: enquiries@transitioncomputing.com

▶ Vanguard Oil & Gas Consultants Ltd, 7 Sunert Road, Milltimber, AB13 0JQ Tel: (01224) 862186 Fax: (01224) 867651

▶ XPT Solutions, One St. Colme Street, Edinburgh, EH3 6AA Tel: 0131-220 8253 Fax: 0131-220 8201

Yarwood Editorial Services, 9 Willow Walk, Needham Market, IP6 8DT Tel: 01449 720558 E-mail: yarwood-editorial-services@phonecoop.coop

▶ Youth Inc, Cannock Chase Technical College, The Green, Cannock, Staffordshire, WS11 7GN Tel: (01543) 438719 Fax: (01543) 574642 E-mail: sandra.gilroy@cannock.ac.uk

PROJECT MANAGEMENT COMPUTER SYSTEMS

E B D Computing Solutions Ltd, 57 Woodside, Ponteland, Newcastle upon Tyne, NE20 9JB Tel: (01661) 820389 Fax: (01661) 820389 E-mail: akoogh@excellencebydesign.co.uk

Project Systems Support Ltd, Chatelaine, Gazing Lane, West Wellow, Romsey, Hampshire, SO51 6BS Tel: (01794) 322755 Fax: (01794) 323964 E-mail: robert_toogood@projectsystemssupport.co.uk

PROJECT MANAGEMENT CONSULTANCY OR CONTRACTORS OR ENGINEERS

▶ All Services Management Ltd, 9 Tennyson Road, High Wycombe, Buckinghamshire, HP11 2XA Tel: (07968) 740788 Fax: (01494) 534279 E-mail: robert@services-management.co.uk

Amec Process & Energy Ltd, 76-78 Old Street, London, EC1V 9RU Tel: (020) 7539 5800 Fax: (020) 7539 5900 E-mail: m.bell@amec.co.uk

Andrews & Boyd, 24 Old Burlington Street, Mayfair, London, W1S 3AW Tel: (020) 7494 0399 Fax: (020) 7494 0477 E-mail: info@andrewsboyd.co.uk

Ayh plc, 1 East Harding Street, London, EC4A 3AH Tel: (020) 7216 1000 Fax: (020) 7216 1001 E-mail: info@ayh.co.uk

Bureau Veritas, The Oast, Newnham Court, Bearsted Road, Maidstone, Kent, ME14 5LH Tel: (01622) 632100 Fax: (01622) 739620 E-mail: oasts@uk.bureauveritas.com

Buro Four Project Services Ltd, 296-300 St. John Street, London, EC1V 4PP Tel: (020) 7833 8663 Fax: (020) 7833 8560 E-mail: rbirchmore@burofour.co.uk

C N Associates, 18 Albemarle Street, London, W1S 4HR Tel: (020) 7491 2521 Fax: (020) 7355 3169

Capon Computer Environmental Services Ltd, 149 Putnoe Street, Bedford, MK41 8JR Tel: (01234) 359791 Fax: (01234) 269995

Chaucer Group, 67 Preston Street, Faversham, Kent, ME13 8PB Tel: (0845) 0724500 Fax: (0845) 0724510 E-mail: sales@chaucer-group.com

Cobweb Computers, 471 Buxton Road, Stockport, Cheshire, SK2 7HE Tel: 0161-484 0100

Conseco International Security Ltd, 5 Manchester Square, London, W1U 3PD Tel: (020) 7486 3661 Fax: (020) 7487 4153 E-mail: marketing@pellfrischmann.com

Cordell Group Ltd, 159-160 High Street, Stockton-on-Tees, Cleveland, TS18 1PL Tel: (01642) 662400 Fax: (01642) 662402 E-mail: enquiries@cordellgroup.com

Currie & Brown, 44 Carden Place, Aberdeen, AB10 1UP Tel: (01224) 624484 Fax: (01224) 628369 E-mail: sales@curriebrown.com

Cursey Technology Ltd, Siddington, Cirencester, Gloucestershire, GL7 6EU Tel: (01285) 650090 Fax: (01285) 650091 E-mail: sales@cursey.co.uk

Darnton Elgee Architects, Monk Fryston Hall, Monk Fryston, Leeds, LS25 5DU Tel: (01977) 681001 Fax: (01977) 681006 E-mail: email@darntonelgee.com

Dashwood Finance Co. Ltd, Georgian House, 63 Coleman Street, London, EC2R 5BB Tel: (020) 7588 3215 Fax: (020) 7588 4818 E-mail: dashwood.group@virgin.net

Davislangdon, Mid City Place, 71 High Holborn, London, WC1V 6QS Tel: (020) 7061 7000 Fax: (020) 7061 7061

Edmond Shipway & Partners, 42 Frederick Rd, Edgbaston, Birmingham, B15 1HN Tel: 0121-454 3515 Fax: 0121-454 3241 E-mail: edmond@shipway.co.uk

Fabermaunsell Ltd, Enterprise House, 160 Croydon Road, Beckenham, Kent, BR3 4DE Tel: (020) 8639 3515 Fax: (020) 8663 6723 E-mail: enquires@fabermaunsell.com

Fichtner Consulting Engineers Ltd, Frederick House, 8 Acorn Business Park, Heaton Lane, Stockport, Cheshire, SK4 1AS Tel: 0161-476 0032 Fax: 0161-474 0618 E-mail: sales@fichtner.co.uk

Foster Wheeler Energy Ltd, Shinfield Park, Shinfield, Reading, RG2 9FW Tel: 0118-913 1234 Fax: 0118-913 2333 E-mail: fw-sales@fwuk.fwc.com

Franklin & Andrews, Sea Containers House, 20 Upper Ground, London, SE1 9LZ Tel: (020) 7633 9966 Fax: (020) 7928 2471 E-mail: michelle.swales@franklinandrews.com

G D E Associates UK, Causeway House, The Causeway, Great Hawksley, Colchester, CO6 4EJ Tel: (01206) 272999 Fax: (01206) 272998 E-mail: consult@gde.co.uk

The G H M Consultancy Group Ltd, Wheathampstead, St. Albans, Hertfordshire, AL4 8BU Tel: (01582) 834233 Fax: (01582) 832176 E-mail: ghm@ghm-group.co.uk

Gardline Information Solutions Ltd, The Design Centre, Hewet Road, Gapton Hall, Great Yarmouth, Norfolk, NR31 0NN Tel: (01493) 440400 Fax: (01493) 442480 E-mail: steve.brown@gardline.co.uk

GSS Projects Ltd, 12 Ambassador Place, Stockport Road, Altrincham, Cheshire, WA15 8EQ Tel: 0161-926 9510 Fax: 0161-926 9536

Guy Property Developments Ltd, Pacioli House 9 Brookfield, Duncan Close, Moulton Park Industrial Estate, Northampton, NN3 6WL Tel: (01604) 496666 Fax: (01604) 499676

Harris & Porter, 49 Whitehall, London, SW1A 2BX Tel: (020) 7839 6064 Fax: (020) 7839 3876 E-mail: handp@nnpland.demon.co.uk

High Point Rendel Ltd, 61 Southwark Street, London, SE1 1SA Tel: (020) 7654 0400 Fax: (020) 7654 0401 E-mail: london@highpointrendel.com

Holbrow Brookes & Partners, Pinewood, Bell Heath Way, Birmingham, B32 3BZ Tel: 0121-423 4000 Fax: 0121-423 4230 E-mail: info@holbrowbrookes.co.uk

Hyder Consulting UK Ltd, 10 Medawar Road, Surrey Research Park, Guildford, Surrey, GU2 7AR Tel: (01483) 535000 Fax: (01483) 535051

I M F Technical Services Ltd, Unit 5 50 Cotton Street, Aberdeen, AB11 5EE Tel: (01224) 210147 Fax: (01224) 572752 E-mail: ian@imftech.freeserve.co.uk

INBIS Group Ltd, St. Johns House, Church Street, Wolverhampton, WV2 4LS Tel: (01902) 427463 Fax: (01902) 714239

Inbis Technology Ltd, 1 The Brooms, Emersons Green, Bristol, BS16 7FD Tel: 0117-987 4000 Fax: 0117-987 4040 E-mail: careers@inbis.com

Isherwood & Ellis, 15 Malone Road, Belfast, BT9 6RT Tel: (028) 9066 3291 Fax: (028) 9068 2727 E-mail: architects@isherwood-ellis.com

Ivan J Cooper Moorside Ltd, Moorside Works, Ellastone Road, Cauldon Low, Stoke-on-Trent, ST10 3ET Tel: (01538) 702738 Fax: (01538) 702662E-mail: brenda-prince@btconnect.com

JCP Consulting, Lomond House, 85 - 87 Holywood Road, Belfast, BT4 3BD Tel: (028) 9065 9299 Fax: (028) 9022 1101 E-mail: consult@jcpconsulting.co.uk

KBR, Hill Park Court, Springfield Drive, Leatherhead, Surrey, KT22 7NL Tel: (01372) 865000 Fax: (01372) 864400

Lewis & Hickey Ltd, 17 Dorset Square, London, NW1 6QB Tel: (020) 7724 1611 Fax: (020) 7724 2282E-mail: all@lewishickeylondon.com

Link Project Services Ltd, 12 The Parks, Haydock Park, Newton-Le-Willows, Merseyside, WA12 0JQ Tel: (01942) 408440 Fax: (01942) 408450 E-mail: uk@link-projects.com

Mclellan & Partners Ltd, 7 Station Approach, West Byfleet, Surrey, KT14 6NL Tel: (01932) 343271 Fax: (01932) 348037 E-mail: mclellan_uk@compuserve.com

Martlet Technological Ltd, 57 Blatchington Road, Hove, East Sussex, BN3 3YJ Tel: (01273) 722305 Fax: (01273) 321915 E-mail: martlettechno@btconnect.com

Angus Meek Partnership Ltd, 60 Arley Hill, Bristol, BS6 5PP Tel: 0117-942 8286 Fax: 0117-942 0495 E-mail: admin@angusmeek.co.uk

Mellersh & Harding, 43 St. James'S Place, London, SW1A 1NS Tel: (020) 7499 0866 Fax: (020) 7522 8501 E-mail: info@mellersh.co.uk

The Millbridge (Group) P.L.C., 43-43 Maddock Street, London, W1S 2PD Tel: (020) 7399 4343 Fax: (020) 7399 4349 E-mail: info@millbridgegroup.co.uk

Mott Macdonald Ltd, St Anne House, 20-26 Wellesley Road, Croydon, CR9 2UL Tel: (020) 8774 2000 Fax: (020) 8681 5706 E-mail: marketing@mottmac.com

Mowlem Engineering Solutions, Bewley Court, Bylands Way, Belasis Hall Technology Park, Billingham, Cleveland, TS23 4EB Tel: (01642) 371313 Fax: (01642) 373101

Mowlem Water Engineering, Port Causeway, Bromborough, Wirral, Merseyside, CH62 4TP Tel: 0151-334 4990 Fax: 0151-334 9403

Multi Tech Contracts, Unit 6 Bowood Court, Calver Road, Winwick Quay, Warrington, WA2 8QZ Tel: (01925) 418333 Fax: (01925) 418800 E-mail: sales@mtcl.net

N I S Holdings Ltd, Ackhurst Road, Chorley, Lancashire, PR7 1NH Tel: (01257) 265656 Fax: (01257) 275501 E-mail: tbromell@nisltd.com

Norec Ltd, Norec House, Fall Bank Industrial Estate, Dodworth, Barnsley, South Yorkshire, S75 3LS Tel: (01226) 730440 Fax: (01226) 730688 E-mail: sales@norec.ltd.uk

Northcroft, 1 Horse Guards Avenue, London, SW1A 2HU Tel: (020) 7839 7858 Fax: (020) 7930 2594 E-mail: surv@northcroft.co.uk

O'Neill Management Ltd, 9 Albany Drive, Bishops Waltham, Southampton, SO32 1GE Tel: (0787) 9463824 E-mail: sales@oneill-management.com

Osprey Mott Macdonald, Welken House, 10-11 Charterhouse Square, London, EC1M 6EH Tel: (020) 7566 7900 Fax: (020) 7566 7911 E-mail: brenda.wiggins@ospreymottmac.com

P M S Morley Ltd, 3 High Mill Business Park, Mill Street, Morley, Leeds, LS27 0WJ Tel: 0113-259 7557 Fax: 0113-259 7251

Paramode Ltd, Harbour Road, Lowestoft, Suffolk, NR32 3LZ Tel: (01502) 574213 Fax: (01502) 501503 E-mail: sales@paramode.co.uk

Pegasus International UK Ltd, The Academy, Belmont Street, Aberdeen, AB10 1LB Tel: (01224) 623300 Fax: (01224) 623301 E-mail: aberdeen@pegasus-international.com

Rider Hunt International, 9 Carden Place, Aberdeen, AB10 1UR Tel: (01224) 650222 Fax: (01224) 631289 E-mail: elizabeth.robertson@rhi-group.com

Rooley Consultants, Greenways, Church Lane, Stoke Poges, Slough, SL2 4PB Tel: (01753) 648040 Fax: (01753) 648048 E-mail: richard@rooley.com

Roplex Engineering Ltd, Roplex House, Church Road, Shedfield, Southampton, SO32 2HW Tel: (01329) 835772 Fax: (01329) 834480

Schal International Management Ltd, Elizabeth House, 39 York Road, London, SE1 7NQ Tel: (020) 7401 4800 Fax: (020) 7401 4900

Serco Integrated Transport Ltd, Cavendish House, Prince's Wharf, Stockton-On-Tees, Cleveland, TS17 6QY Tel: (01642) 636700 Fax: (01642) 636701

Shaw Group, Witan Gate House, 500-600 Witan Gate West, Milton Keynes, MK9 1BA Tel: (01908) 668844 Fax: (01908) 602211 E-mail:

SNC Lavalin UK Ltd, Knollys House, Addiscombe Road, Croydon, CR0 6SR Tel: (020) 8681 4250 Fax: (020) 8681 4299 E-mail: sncl.uk@snclavalin.com

Stace, 273 High Street, Epping, Essex, CM16 4DA Tel: (01992) 565565 Fax: (01992) 560597 E-mail: epping@stace.co.uk

Turner & Coates Ltd, PO Box 91, Salford, M6 6XG Tel: (0845) 8909870 Fax: (0845) 8909871 E-mail: info@turnerandcoates.com

Turner & Townsend, 111 Charles Street, Sheffield, S1 2ND Tel: 0114-272 9025 Fax: 0114-275 3760 E-mail: she@turntown.co.uk

Turner & Townsend, Victoria House, Pearson Way, Thornaby, Stockton-on-Tees, Cleveland, TS17 6PT Tel: (01642) 611116 Fax: (01642) 612414 E-mail: tee@turntown.co.uk

Verdandi Ltd, Verdandi House, Chapel Grove, Addlestone, Surrey, KT15 1UG Tel: (01932) 852888 Fax: (01932) 841954 E-mail: info@verdandi.co.uk

Whessoe Oil & Gas Ltd, Brinkburn Road, Darlington, County Durham, DL3 6DS Tel: (01325) 390000 Fax: (01325) 390001

White Young Green, Wallington House, Starbeck Avenue, Newcastle upon Tyne, NE2 1RH Tel: 0191-232 3043 Fax: 0191-261 0986 E-mail: newcastle@wyg.com

White Young Green Consulting, Family House, 4 Bedford Business Park, Croydon, CR0 2AP Tel: (020) 8649 6600 Fax: (020) 8649 6629

Woodhill Engineering, St Andrews House, West Street, Woking, Surrey, GU21 6EB Tel: (01483) 717600 Fax: (01483) 717630 E-mail: info@woodhill.co.uk

Woolf Ltd, 1 Procter Street, London, WC1V 6DW Tel: (020) 7492 0202 Fax: (020) 7492 0203 E-mail: enquiries@woolfltd.com

PROJECT MANAGEMENT SOFTWARE

Asta Development plc, 5 Goodson Industrial Mews, Wellington Street, Thame, Oxfordshire, OX9 3BX Tel: (01844) 261700 Fax: (01844) 261314 E-mail: sales@astadev.com

Aveva Engineering It Ltd, High Cross, Madingley Road, Cambridge, CB3 0HB Tel: (01223) 556655 Fax: (01223) 556666 E-mail: info@aveva.com

Claremont Controls Ltd, Suite 4 Wansbeck Business Centre, Rotary Parkway, Ashington, Northumberland, NE63 8QZ Tel: (01670) 819000 Fax: (01670) 857886 E-mail: honet@claremont-controls.co.uk

GEDYS-DISKUS, Spencer House, 91 Dewhurst Road, Birchwood, Warrington, WA3 7PG Tel: (01925) 848484 Fax: (01925) 848485 E-mail: info@gedys.co.uk

▶ Innovative Programming Solutions Ltd, Unit 10, Folgate Road, Lyngate Industrial Estate, North Walsham, Norfolk, NR28 0AJ Tel: 01692 406636 E-mail: info@e-ips.co.uk

Sphere IT Ltd, Fernhill House, St. Catherines Hill Lane, Christchurch, Dorset, BH23 2NL Tel: (08707) 373001 Fax: (08707) 373002 E-mail: admin@sphereit.com

PROJECT MANAGEMENT, LOGISTICS

▶ Ashworth Preece Logistics, 7 Memorial Road, Walkden, Manchester, M28 3AQ Tel: (0870) 350 1246 Fax: (0870) 350 1248

▶ Internal Freight Auditing Ltd, 5 Keepers Close, Coleshill, Birmingham, B46 3HB Tel: (01675) 437534 E-mail: Info@IF-Audit.com

PROJECT PLANNING CONSULTANCY

Cabrio Management Services, 6 Ash Meadow, Willesborough, Ashford, Kent, TN24 0LW Tel: (01233) 623230 E-mail: enquiries@cabrio.co.uk
Ferguson Mcilveen LLP, Victoria House, 159 Albert Road, Middlesbrough, Cleveland, TS1 2PX Tel: (01642) 218476 Fax: (01642) 223582 E-mail: postmaster@fermac.com
Informed Solutions Ltd, The Old Bank, Old Market Place, Altrincham, Cheshire, WA14 4PA Tel: 0161-942 2000 Fax: 0161-942 2015
James R Knowles, Suite 1a Cameron Court, Cameron Street, Hillington Industrial Estate, Glasgow, G52 4JH Tel: (0870) 7530820 Fax: 0141-883 9134 E-mail: glasgow@jrknowles.com

PROJECTION SCREENS

Chase AV Ltd, Unit 10, Upper Gamma, West Road, Ransomes Europark, Ipswich, IP3 9SX Tel: (01473) 279992 Fax: (01473) 279993 E-mail: sales2@chaseavdirect.co.uk
D R H Screens Ltd, 3 The High Cross Centre, Fountayne Road, London, N15 4QN Tel: (020) 8885 5504 Fax: (020) 8365 1108 E-mail: sales@drhscreens.co.uk
Harkness Hall Ltd, Norton Road, Stevenage, Hertfordshire, SG1 2BB Tel: (01438) 725200 Fax: (01438) 344400 E-mail: sales@harkness-screens.com
Virtalis, Chester House, 79 Dane Road, Sale, Cheshire, M33 7BP Tel: 0161-969 1155 Fax: 0161-969 1166 E-mail: info@vrweb.com

PROJECTION SYSTEMS

Ivojo Multimedia Ltd, Newton Cross, Hayscastle, Haverfordwest, Dyfed, SA62 5HS Tel: (01348) 840080 Fax: (01348) 841081 E-mail: sales@ivojo.co.uk

PROJECTOR HIRE

Av2hire.com (Manchester) Ltd, 22 Hardwick Street, Buxton, Derbyshire, SK17 6DH Tel: (0845) 0705168 E-mail: manchester@av2hire.com

PROJECTOR LAMPS

A B S (Electrical Engineering & Supplies) Ltd, Unit F, Northbrook Trading Estate, Northbrook Road, Worthing, West Sussex, BN14 8PN Tel: (01903) 235636 Fax: (01903) 232512 E-mail: sales@abs-electrical.co.uk
▶ Audio Visual & Presentation Systems, 34 Curlew Avenue, Chatteris, Cambridgeshire, PE16 6PL Tel: (01354) 696747 Fax: (01354) 695287 E-mail: sales@av-presentation.co.uk
▶ Axis Display LLP, Unit B, Centurion Way, Erith, Kent, DA18 4AF Tel: (020) 8319 7743 Fax: (020) 8319 7776 E-mail: sales@axisdisplay.co.uk

PROJECTOR MANUFRS, *See also headings for particular types under Projectors*

A S K UK, Herschel Street, Slough, SL1 1XS Tel: (01753) 701050 Fax: (01753) 701001
▶ Absolute Audio Visual Solutions, Cheney Lodge, 81 Station Road, Odsey, Baldock, Hertfordshire, SG7 5RP Tel: (01462) 743003 E-mail: enquiry@absoluteavs.co.uk
Fumeo U K, The Old Warehouse, 2 Ashford Road, Brighton, BN1 6LJ Tel: (01273) 508622 Fax: (01273) 564693
Hunt & Co Hinckley Ltd, 4 Turville Close, Burbage, Hinckley, Leicestershire, LE10 2GZ Tel: (01455) 637263 Fax: (01455) 637263
Kingdom Office Supplies Ltd, 150 Means Court, Glenrothes, Fife, KY7 6XP Tel: (01592) 620525 Fax: (08707) 624291 E-mail: sales@kingdomofficesupplies.co.uk

PROMOTIONAL AND ADVERTISING MATERIAL PUBLISHERS

▶ Alliance Publishing Co., 119 Talbot Road, Blackpool, FY1 3QX Tel: (01253) 751614 Fax: (01253) 292915
▶ Richard Atkins, 132 Kingsley Park Terrace, Northampton, NN2 7HJ Tel: (01604) 710050 Fax: (01604) 710170 E-mail: sales@aps-promotions.com
Marcus Ltd, 39 Outram Street, Darlington, County Durham, DL3 7DP Tel: (01325) 353882 Fax: (01325) 358408 E-mail: sales@newpc.co.uk
News & Media Ltd, 233 Seven Sisters Road, London, N4 2DA Tel: (020) 7263 1417 Fax: (020) 7272 8934 E-mail: info@impact-magazines.com

PROMOTIONAL ANIMAL CARTOON CHARACTERS

Moira Munro Illustrations and Cartoons, Glasgow, G76 Tel: 0141-638 9851 E-mail: moira@moiramunro.com

PROMOTIONAL AROMATHERAPY PRODUCTS

▶ Car Air Freshener.Co.Uk, 47 Holmewood Gardens, London, SW2 3NB Tel: (0845) 6066204 E-mail: info@carairfreshener.co.uk
▶ Caroline Hughes, 19, Carlyle Grove, Springbank, Cheltenham, Glos, GL51 0PW Tel: 01242 575670 E-mail: caroline@aromatherapy-makes-scents.co.uk
▶ I D Aromatics Ltd, 12 New Station Street, Leeds, LS1 5DL Tel: 0113-242 4983 Fax: 0113-243 3613 E-mail: info@idaromatics.co.uk
▶ Primavera Aromatherapy Ltd, Manor House, Manor Road, Frome, Somerset, BA11 4BN Tel: (01373) 467103 Fax: (01373) 451532 E-mail: mail@primavera.co.uk

PROMOTIONAL BABY GIFTWARE

▶ Baby Rug, 61 Pepys Road, London, SW20 8NL Tel: (020) 8944 8674 E-mail: info@babyrug.co.uk
▶ First Impressions Castings, 25 High Street, Market Deeping, Peterborough, PE6 8ED Tel: (01778) 344541 Fax: (01778) 344541 E-mail: info@firstimpressionscastings.co.uk
▶ Sharemymemory.com, P.O. Box 3756, Sheffield, S6 9AB Tel: 08707 202 686 Fax: 08707 202 687 E-mail: mail@sharemymemory.com
▶ Special Treasures, 193 Hylton Road, Millfield, Sunderland, SR4 7YE Tel: (07931) 756051 E-mail: emahoward@yahoo.co.uk

PROMOTIONAL BANDANNAS

▶ Teamtogs, 4/Heritage Cottages, Harper Lane, Shenley, Radlett, Hertfordshire, WD7 9HA Tel: (0845) 8385982 Fax: (01727) 826622 E-mail: info@team-togs.com

PROMOTIONAL BELT BUCKLES

Eurobelts.com, 8 Stuart Close, Darwen, Lancashire, BB3 1DP Tel: (01254) 704395 Fax: (01254) 704395 E-mail: roy@eurobelts.com

PROMOTIONAL BEVERAGES

▶ WaterPromotions, PO Box 27, Richmond, Surrey, TW10 6XN Tel: (020) 8948 5551

PROMOTIONAL BODY COSMETICS

Bourjois Ltd, Bourjois House, Queensway, Croydon, CR9 4DL Tel: (020) 8688 7131 Fax: (020) 8688 0012

PROMOTIONAL CANDLES

▶ Gamrie's Candle World, Main Street, Garmond, Turriff, Aberdeenshire, AB53 5TQ Tel: (01888) 544170 Fax: (01888) 544415 E-mail: sales@gamriescandles.co.uk

PROMOTIONAL CARRIER BAGS

Classic Printed Bag Co. Ltd, Unit 5, Silver Business Park, Airfield Way, Christchurch, Dorset, BH23 3TA Tel: (01202) 488144 Fax: (01202) 481341 E-mail: bags@classicbag.co.uk
Donington Plastics Ltd, Unit 1 Spiral Tube Works, Derby, DE24 8BT Tel: (01332) 363313 Fax: (01332) 361355 E-mail: sales@doningtongroup.co.uk
Durasak, Stansfeld Street, Blackburn, BB2 2NG Tel: (01254) 51733 Fax: (01254) 51833 E-mail: sales@durasat.co.uk
Fobbed Off, 3 The Mews, Breadcroft Lane, Harpenden, Hertfordshire, AL5 4TF Tel: (01582) 768295 Fax: (01582) 768295 E-mail: nick@ncooper45.freeserve.co.uk
Keenpac Ltd, Centurion Way, Meridian Business Park, Leicester, LE19 1WH Tel: 0116-289 0900 Fax: 0116-289 3757 E-mail: info@keenpac.co.uk
Packaging Supplies Ltd, Unit 2-3 Thorney Lane North, Iver, Buckinghamshire, SL0 9HF Tel: (01753) 653303 Fax: (01753) 655276 E-mail: sales@pack-supplies.co.uk
Rainbow Bag UK Ltd, 3A Bess Park Road, Trenant Industrial Estate, Wadebridge, Cornwall, PL27 6HB Tel: (01208) 812442 Fax: (01208) 816181 E-mail: sales@rainbowbags.co.uk

PROMOTIONAL CHOPPING BOARDS

▶ Thewoodcarver.Co.Uk, Firthview, Culbo, Culbokie, Dingwall, Ross-Shire, IV7 8JX Tel: (01349) 877546 E-mail: info@thewoodcarver.co.uk

PROMOTIONAL CHRISTMAS HAMPERS

▶ Annie's Hampers, Bar Farm, Market Weighton Road, Holme-on-Spalding-Moor, York, YO43 4ED Tel: (01430) 860339 E-mail: enquires@annieshampers.com
▶ The Gourmet House, Market Place, Durham, DH1 3NJ Tel: 0191-375 7511 E-mail: info@thegourmethouse.co.uk

PROMOTIONAL CIGARETTE LIGHTERS

▶ Savage No.1, 89 Delphi Way, Crookhorn, Waterlooville, Hampshire, PO7 8AY Tel: (07745) 119063 E-mail: savageno1@ntlworld.com

PROMOTIONAL CLEAR VIEW COASTERS

▶ Clearway Sales & Promotional Products, PO Box 2779, Faringdon, Oxfordshire, SN7 7BZ Tel: (01367) 242400 Fax: (01367) 244299 E-mail: enquiry@clearwaykeyrings.co.uk

PROMOTIONAL CLEAR VIEW KEYRINGS

▶ Clearway Sales & Promotional Products, PO Box 2779, Faringdon, Oxfordshire, SN7 7BZ Tel: (01367) 242400 Fax: (01367) 244299 E-mail: enquiry@clearwaykeyrings.co.uk

PROMOTIONAL CLOCKS

▶ A1 Corporate Gifts, 10 Oldhill, Dunstable, Bedfordshire, LU6 3ER Tel: (01582) 660465 Fax: (01582) 601759 E-mail: sales@a1cg.co.uk
▶ Corporate Executive Gifts Ltd, Unit K, Houndswood Gate, Harper Lane, Radlett, Hertfordshire, WD7 7HU Tel: (01923) 852330 Fax: (01923) 859946 E-mail: sales@corporateexecutivegifts.com
▶ Magic Touch, 63 Barnton Street, Stirling, FK8 1HH Tel: (01786) 445992 Fax: (01786) 434922
▶ Myriad, 330 Dereham Road, Norwich, NR2 4DL Tel: (0800) 5875967 E-mail: uk-sales@myriad-uk.net

PROMOTIONAL CLOTHING

A C E Atlas Commission Embroidery, Block 2 Phoenix Works Industrial Estate, Richards Street, Wednesbury, West Midlands, WS10 8BZ Tel: 0121-568 7117 Fax: 0121-526 3909 E-mail: aceembroidery2001@yahoo.co.uk
▶ Ace Embroidery Ltd, 141 Tat Bank Road, Oldbury, West Midlands, B69 4NH Tel: 0121-544 7108 Fax: 0121-544 4965 E-mail: info@ace-embroidery.co.uk
Action Jacket Co., PO Box 1180, Stourbridge, West Midlands, DY9 0ZF Tel: (01562) 887096 Fax: (01562) 882010 E-mail: info@actionjacket.co.uk
Amar Textiles, 105 Grange Street, Derby, DE23 8HD Tel: (01332) 365527 Fax: (01332) 731771
Aythen Fashions Co., 19 Hamstead Road, Hockley, Birmingham, B19 1BX Tel: 0121-523 2815 Fax: 0121-523 2815
Big Screen, 5 Dace Road, London, E3 2NG Tel: (020) 8986 3300 Fax: (020) 8986 3742 E-mail: sales@thebigscreen.co.uk
Blues Clothing Ltd, Brigade House, Parsons Green, London, SW6 4TN Tel: (020) 7371 9900 Fax: (020) 7371 9782 E-mail: marketing@blues-clothing.co.uk
Calver Ltd, 22 The Drive, Orpington, Kent, BR6 9AP Tel: (01689) 898828 Fax: (01689) 898848 E-mail: sales@calver.com
Cotswold Collections, 15 King Street, Ludlow, Shropshire, SY8 1AQ Tel: (01584) 875612 Fax: (01584) 875998
Dexter & Gordon, Priory Farm, Andwell, Hook, Hampshire, RG27 9PA Tel: (01256) 765951 Fax: (01256) 765608 E-mail: sales@printedfootballs.co.uk
Dodd Anderson Ltd, Graphic House, Mylord Cresent, Camperdown Industrial Estate, Newcastle upon Tyne, NE12 5UJ Tel: 0191-268 9993 Fax: 0191-268 6667 E-mail: doddanderson@btconnect.co.uk
Duvatex Mytholmroyd Ltd, 8 Sunderland Street, Halifax, West Yorkshire, HX1 5AF Tel: (01422) 363534 Fax: (01422) 320335
E M J Management Ltd, Aspen House, Airport Service Road, Portsmouth, PO3 5RA Tel: (023) 9243 4650 Fax: (023) 9243 4681 E-mail: info@cjsltd.co.uk
Elite Screen Printing & Embroidery Ltd, 45 Sartoris Road, Rushden, Northamptonshire, NN10 9TL Tel: (01933) 315930 Fax: (01933) 418364 E-mail: elitetex@aol.com
Eurstyle Ltd, Park House, 19-20 Bright Street, Wednesbury, West Midlands, WS10 9HX Tel: 0121-526 2973 Fax: 0121-526 2061 E-mail: sales@vtex.co.uk
▶ Fair Trade Wear, 27, Lauriston Street, Edinburgh, EH3 9DQ Tel: 077 08796447 E-mail: info@ftwear.com
GDB Manufacturing, Leisurewear House, Barnes Road, Bradford, West Yorkshire, BD8 9TG Tel: (01274) 491110 Fax: (01274) 491112
Leonard Hudson, 2 Queen Anne Drive, Edinburgh, EH28 8LH Tel: 0800 0181412 Fax: 0808 1806030 E-mail: sales@leonardhudson.co.uk
I S Enterprises International, Clement House, Commerce Way, Colchester, CO2 8HY Tel: (01206) 798131 Fax: (01206) 791186 E-mail: sales@isenterprisesintl.co.uk
International Insignia, Unit 3 Dunstall Hill Industrial Estate, Gorsebrook Road, Wolverhampton, WV6 0PJ Tel: (01902) 714265 Fax: (01902) 714853 E-mail: sales@internationalinsignia.net
J S M Business Gifts, 9 St. Albans Road, Gloucester, GL2 5FW Tel: (01452) 310030 Fax: (01452) 304454
▶ Klew Gets Wed, Unit 3, Millbrook Business Park Hoe Lane, Nazeing, Waltham Abbey, Essex, EN9 2RJ Tel: (01992) 890378 Fax: 01992 890378 E-mail: info@klew.co.uk
Logo Leisurewear, Unit 22, Caddsdown Industrial Estate, Clovelly Road, Bideford, Devon, EX39 3HN Tel: (01237) 459393 Fax: (01237) 459393 E-mail: sales@logoleisurewear.co.uk
▶ Motif Magic Ltd, 1 Davis Road, Brooklands, Weybridge, Surrey, KT13 0XH Tel: (01932) 830800 Fax: (0870) 7052851 E-mail: linda@motifmagic.co.uk
Offset Marketing, 2 Speedwell Close, Chandler's Ford, Eastleigh, Hampshire, SO53 4BT Tel: (023) 8027 4444 Fax: (023) 8027 0112
P & M Embroidery, Glebe Road, Huntingdon, Cambridgeshire, PE29 7DR Tel: (01480) 411311 Fax: (01480) 412839 E-mail: sales@pmembroidery.co.uk
P & P Clothing, Old Mill La Industrial Estate, Mansfield Woodhouse, Mansfield, Nottinghamshire, NG19 9BG Tel: (01623) 422044 Fax: (01623) 424557 E-mail: sales@pandp.force9.co.uk
▶ Party Pants, 25 Queen Street, Redcar, Cleveland, TS10 1AB Tel: (01642) 515144 Fax: (01642) 805020 E-mail: info@partypants.co.uk
Pelmark Ltd, Barley Road, Flint Cross, Heydon, Royston, Hertfordshire, SG8 7PU Tel: (01763) 208020 Fax: (01763) 208021 E-mail: reception@pelmark.co.uk
▶ Purple Patch Promotions, 3 Gowers Close, Kesgrave, Ipswich, IP5 2XE Tel: (01473) 333388 Fax: (01473) 333388 E-mail: sales@purplepatch.org
R S Farmah & Sons, 111 Hubert Road, Birmingham, B29 6ET Tel: 0121-472 6672 Fax: 0121-472 8017 E-mail: peter@rsfarmah.freeserve.co.uk
S L K Kentex Fashions Ltd, 90-104 Constitution Hill, Hockley, Birmingham, B19 3JT Tel: 0121-236 6653 Fax: 0121-212 3530 E-mail: kentex@btinternet.com
Swantex Ltd, Bromley Ho, Spindle St, Congleton, Cheshire, CW12 1QN Tel: (01260) 291110 Fax: (01260) 291112 E-mail: dave@swantex1.fsnet.co.uk
Taylormade Designs, Unit 14 Silver Business Park, Airfield Way, Christchurch, Dorset, BH23 3TA Tel: (0870) 8015622 Fax: (0870) 8015624 E-mail: james@taylormadedesigns.co.uk
Topaz Blue Ltd, Middlesex Building, Elstree Aerodrome, Elstree, Borehamwood, Hertfordshire, WD6 3AW Tel: (020) 8207 1007 Fax: (020) 8207 0307 E-mail: sales@topazblue.com
Woodstock Neckwear Ltd, Telford Road, Glenrothes, Fife, KY7 4NX Tel: (01592) 771777 Fax: (01592) 631717
Mick Wright Merchandising, 185 Weedon Road, Northampton, NN5 5DA Tel: (07000) 226397 Fax: (01604) 456129 E-mail: tshirts@mickwright.com

PROMOTIONAL CONFECTIONERY

▶ Favouritesweetshop.co.uk, 10 Castle Drive, Kemsing, Sevenoaks, Kent, TN15 6RL Tel: 01732 760480 E-mail: info@favouritesweetshop.co.uk
▶ Fish Promotions Ltd, PO Box 561, Altrincham, Cheshire, WA15 8NY Tel: 0161-980 2805 E-mail: sales@fish-promotions.com
Sweet Thoughts, Hawthorn Road, Skegness, Lincolnshire, PE25 3TD Tel: (01754) 896667 E-mail: info@sweetthoughts.co.uk

PROMOTIONAL DIARIES

Kernow Plusfile, Winship Road, Milton, Cambridge, CB24 6BQ Tel: (01223) 425003 Fax: (01223) 425120

PROMOTIONAL EMBLEMS OR LOGOS

▶ Floor Exposure, Jubilee Park, Hanson Close, Middleton, Manchester, M24 2UH Tel: 0161-655 7019 Fax: 0161-655 7002

Team Colours, The Maltings, Roydon Road, Stanstead Abbotts, Ware, Hertfordshire, SG12 8HG Tel: (01920) 871453 Fax: (01920) 872278 E-mail: sales@teamcolours.co.uk

Versatility Embroiderers, Lullington Hall, Coton Road, Lullington, Swadlincote, Derbyshire, DE12 8EJ Tel: (01827) 373403 Fax: (01827) 373403 E-mail: sales@versatility.freeserve.co.uk

PROMOTIONAL FINE ART PRINTS

▶ A Anthony Art, 4 Stanhope Road, Horncastle, Lincolnshire, LN9 5DG Tel: (01507) 526487 Fax: (01507) 526487 E-mail: tonyfield@btinternet.com

▶ Digital Printing Services, 24 Carre Street, Sleaford, Lincolnshire, NG34 7TR Tel: (01529) 300452 Fax: (01529) 300452 E-mail: matt@dpsfineart.co.uk

▶ Metropolis Modern Art, 29 Compton Street, Chesterfield, Derbyshire, S40 4TA Tel: (01246) 233568

PROMOTIONAL FIRST AID KITS

▶ DetectUpet Ltd, Argyle Suite, Leek New Road, Stoke-on-Trent, ST6 2LB Tel: (01782) 274171 Fax: (01782) 287828 E-mail: martin@detectupet.co.uk

PROMOTIONAL FOAM PRODUCTS

Imagineers Ltd, Abercromby Avenue, High Wycombe, Buckinghamshire, HP12 3BW Tel: (01494) 473861 Fax: (01494) 473863 E-mail: enquiries@imagineersltd.co.uk

PROMOTIONAL FOOTBALLS

▶ Factoryprice, Discounthouse, 3/7 Wyndham Street, Aldershot, Hampshire, GU12 4NY Tel: (01252) 312345 Fax: (01252) 680888 E-mail: m.ltd@ntlworld.com

▶ Sportzone Marketing, PO Box 332, Bushey, WD23 3XZ Tel: 0700 5938868 Fax: 0700 5938869 E-mail: john@sportzone-marketing.co.uk

PROMOTIONAL GARDEN FURNITURE

▶ Kingshall Furniture, 5 Millennium Point, Broadfields, Aylesbury, Buckinghamshire, HP19 8ZU Tel: (01296) 339925 Fax: (01296) 392900 E-mail: info@kingshallfurniture.com

PROMOTIONAL GARMENT BELT BAGS

▶ Teamtogs, 4/Heritage Cottages, Harper Lane, Shenley, Radlett, Hertfordshire, WD7 9HA Tel: (0845) 8385982 Fax: (01727) 826622 E-mail: info@team-togs.com

PROMOTIONAL GARMENT BELTS

▶ Teamtogs, 4/Heritage Cottages, Harper Lane, Shenley, Radlett, Hertfordshire, WD7 9HA Tel: (0845) 8385982 Fax: (01727) 826622 E-mail: info@team-togs.com

PROMOTIONAL GIFTWARE TO SPECIFICATION

▶ D J B Ceramics Ltd, Beaufort Mill, Beaufort Road, Stoke-on-Trent, ST3 1RH Tel: (01782) 312121 Fax: (01782) 312121 E-mail: djb.ceramics@btinternet.com

PROMOTIONAL HANDLING SERVICES/CONSULTANTS

Caburn Hope, Unit D Rusbridge Lane, Lewes, East Sussex, BN7 2XX Tel: (01273) 480404 Fax: (01273) 480505 E-mail: info@caburnhope.co.uk

Dial Marketing Ltd, 68 Dial Hill Road, Clevedon, Avon, BS21 7EW Tel: (01275) 875876 Fax: (01275) 340899 E-mail: dialmarketing@btconnect.com

M & S Mailing & Support Ltd, Unit 17 18, Royce Road, Crawley, West Sussex, RH10 9NX Tel: (01293) 527711 Fax: (01293) 527713

Multi Resource Marketing Ltd, Barberton House, Farndon Road, Market Harborough, Leicestershire, LE16 9NR Tel: (01858) 410510 Fax: (01858) 434190

Pressed For Time Ltd, 1 Johnston Road, Woodford Green, Essex, IG8 0XA Tel: (020) 8559 2015 Fax: (020) 8505 9581 E-mail: andrew@pft.uk.com

Promotional Logistics Ltd, Prolog House, Sudbury, Suffolk, CO10 2XG Tel: (01787) 370272 Fax: (01787) 379935 E-mail: bdm@prolog.uk.com

Selby Marketing Services, Ormonde St Works, Ormonde Street, Ashton-under-Lyne, Lancashire, OL6 8JQ Tel: 0161-339 5132 Fax: 0161-343 1005 E-mail: sales@selby-marketing.co.uk

Teamwork Handling Ltd, Allerthorpe Business Park, Pocklington, York, YO42 1NS Tel: (01759) 322400 Fax: (01759) 303265 E-mail: magnus@teamwork-handling.co.uk

PROMOTIONAL ITEMS

A.P.P.S, 26 Thurnham Street, Lancaster, LA1 1XU Tel: (01524) 841286 Fax: (01524) 842330 E-mail: sales@promotional-goods.org.uk

Actionpoint Packaging Materials, The Old Brickfields, Otterham Quay Lane, Rainham, Gillingham, Kent, ME8 8NA Tel: (01634) 373736

Advanta Marketing Ltd, 190 Cromwell Road, Newport, Gwent, NP19 0HP Tel: (01633) 292939 Fax: (01633) 292938 E-mail: sales@advantamarketing.co.uk

▶ Advantage Business Gifts Ltd, PO Box 35, Mablethorpe, Lincolnshire, LN12 9AA Tel: (01507) 440510 Fax: (01507) 440168 E-mail: info@advantagebg.co.uk

Appletree Press Ltd, 14 Howard St South, Belfast, BT7 1AP Tel: (028) 9024 3074 Fax: (028) 9024 6756 E-mail: info@appletree.ie

▶ Archway Promotions, 7 Kempston Court, Kempston Hardwick, Bedford, MK43 9PQ Tel: (01234) 853500 Fax: (01234) 852826 E-mail: sales@archwaypromotions.co.uk

Bemrose Booth, PO Box 18, Derby, DE21 6XG Tel: (01332) 294242 Fax: (01332) 290366 E-mail: promote@bemrose.co.uk

▶ Creative Images, Garwin House, Romsey Road, East Wellow, Romsey, Hampshire, SO51 6BG Tel: (01794) 322026 Fax: (01794) 322026 E-mail: enquiries@creativeimages.uk.com

Hambleside Business Gift Solutions Ltd, 23 Robjohns Road, Widford Industrial Estate, Chelmsford, CM1 3AG Tel: (01245) 293610 Fax: (01245) 293615 E-mail: gillian@hambleside.co.uk

Lancewich Promotional Items, Unit 14 Wellington Business Park, Dukes Ride, Crowthorne, Berkshire, RG45 6LS Tel: (01344) 753550 Fax: (01344) 753551 E-mail: sales@lancewich.co.uk

▶ Promotional Keyrings, 28 Coulter Close, Cuffley, Hertfordshire, EN6 4RR Tel: (07005) 981697 E-mail: enquiries@promotionalkeyrings.co.uk

▶ Shout Business Promotions, 16 Fords Close, Bledlow Ridge, High Wycombe, Bucks, HP14 4AP Tel: (01494) 481166 Fax: (01494) 481433 E-mail: info@shout-promotions.com

▶ Shout Business Promotions, 94 London Road, Headington, Oxford, OX3 9FN Tel: (0800) 0190967 Fax: (01494) 481433 E-mail: Sales@shout-promotions.com

Sign Wizzard, Griffin Lane, Aylesbury, Buckinghamshire, HP19 0GH Tel: (01296) 398022 Fax: (01296) 398028 E-mail: sign.wizzard@virgin.net

▶ Total Merchandise Ltd, Standen House, Fishponds Lane, Holbrook, Ipswich, IP9 2QZ Tel: (01702) 540043 Fax: (01473) 327537 E-mail: sales@totalmerchandise.co.uk

Westbrook Marketing Ltd, 24 The Dean, Alresford, Hampshire, SO24 9AZ Tel: (01962) 733122 Fax: (01962) 733122 E-mail: sales@westbrookmarketing.co.uk

Wild Thang, 337 Derby Road, Liverpool, Bootle, Merseyside, L20 8LQ Tel: 0151-933 3289 Fax: 0151-922 4865 E-mail: admin@wildthang.co.uk

PROMOTIONAL KITES

▶ Atmosphere Kites, 137 St. Georges Road, Bristol, BS1 5UW Tel: 0117-908 7153 E-mail: sales@atmospherekites.com

PROMOTIONAL KNIVES

Stephenson & Wilson Ltd, Louvic Works, 44 Garden Street, Sheffield, S1 3HL Tel: 0114-249 3889 Fax: 0114-249 3891 E-mail: stephenson@wilsonltd.freeserve.co.uk

PROMOTIONAL MAPPING

▶ Map Marketing Limited, Suite 23,, Hardmans Business Centre, New Hall Hey Road, Rawtenstall, Lancashire, BB4 6HH Tel: 01706 220444 E-mail: glen@mapmarketing.com

PROMOTIONAL MAPS

▶ Falcon (Mapping) Ltd, 35 Couston Drive, Dalgety Bay, Dunfermline, Fife, KY11 9NX Tel: 01383 824886 Fax: 01383 824886 E-mail: webcontact@falmap.com

PROMOTIONAL MARKER PENS

Kolorpik UK, 58 Cowper Crescent, Hertford, SG14 3EA Tel: (01992) 581979 Fax: (01992) 550142 E-mail: kolorpik.uk@ntlworld.com

PROMOTIONAL MEDALLION KEYRINGS

H.B. Sale Ltd, 390 Summer Lane, Birmingham, B19 3PN Tel: 0121-236 5661 Fax: 0121-233 3817

PROMOTIONAL MOBILE TELEPHONE COVERS

▶ Reduce My Bills, 11 New River Green, Exning, Newmarket, Suffolk, CB8 7HS Tel: (0845) 3312673 E-mail: info@reducemybills.co.uk

PROMOTIONAL MODELS

Banjo Inc Ltd, Unit 4d Green End Business Centre, 93a Church Lane, Sarratt, Rickmansworth, Hertfordshire, WD3 6HH Tel: (01923) 266887 Fax: (01923) 266887 E-mail: sales@banjocreative.com

▶ Barrow Models, St. Vincents Primary School, Greenside Street, Manchester, M11 2EX Tel: 0161-231 2272

DJH Engineering Ltd, Consett Business Park, Consett, County Durham, DH8 6BP Tel: (01207) 500050 Fax: (01207) 599757 E-mail: sales@djhpewterworks.co.uk

▶ Donald Smith Model Makers Ltd, Coply Industrial Estate, Old Meldrum, Oldmeldrum, Inverurie, Aberdeenshire, AB51 0NT Tel: (01651) 873043 Fax: (01651) 872008 E-mail: sales@dsmodelmakers.co.uk

Geoffrey Sumpter, Barton End House, Barton End, Horsley, Stroud, Gloucestershire, GL6 0QQ Tel: (01453) 833883 Fax: (01453) 833883

Link Design Development, 17 Brownfields, Welwyn Garden City, Hertfordshire, AL7 1AN Tel: (01707) 331991 Fax: (01707) 327918

Makers, Egerton Street, Nottingham, NG3 4GQ Tel: 0115-941 9290 Fax: 0115-948 1834 E-mail: makers@fsbdial.co.uk

▶ P R Designs, Tong Lane Bus Centre, Tong Lane, Whitworth, Rochdale, Lancashire, OL12 8BE Tel: (01706) 854264 Fax: (01706) 854264 E-mail: prdesignssales@timewarpuk.net

PROMOTIONAL MULTILAYER LABELS

Adare Label Converters Ltd, Falconer Road, Haverhill, Suffolk, CB9 7XU Tel: (01440) 714996 Fax: (01440) 766501 E-mail: sales@labelconverters.co.uk

PROMOTIONAL MUSICAL INSTRUMENTS

▶ Muzikvoice Ltd, 32 Wareham House, Brompton Pool Road, Hall Green, Birmingham, B28 0SL Tel: 0121-474 5228

PROMOTIONAL NAME BADGES

▶ Probadge, The Countyard, 27 High Street, Winslow, Buckingham, MK18 3HE Tel: (01296) 712387 Fax: (01296) 715281 E-mail: sales@probadge.co.uk

PROMOTIONAL NAPKIN RINGS

▶ The Silverware shop, 50a Tenby Street North, Hockley, Birmingham, B1 3EG Tel: 0121-248 7702 Fax: 0121-248 7701 E-mail: silverwareshop@aol.com

PROMOTIONAL PAPER

▶ Shimmee, Plough Road, Great Bentley, Colchester, CO7 8LG Tel: (01206) 250400 Fax: (01206) 250410 E-mail: sales@shimmee.co.uk

PROMOTIONAL PARTY BALLOONS

▶ A Rosy Marriage Balloon & Party Megastore, 14 Barn Way, Hednesford, Cannock, Staffordshire, WS12 0FP Tel: (07795) 102050 E-mail: sales@arosymarriage.co.uk

Aerial Splendour, St. Giles Farm, Blendworth, Waterlooville, Hampshire, PO8 0AG Tel: (07709) 955294 Fax: (023) 9225 6111 E-mail: aerialsplendour@aol.com

▶ Big Bang Balloon, 38 Parkfield Road, Ruskington, Sleaford, Lincolnshire, NG34 9HS Tel: (07906) 951961

▶ Bur Boing, 8 Beacon Court, Northampton, NN4 8JU Tel: (01604) 674733 E-mail: bur-boing@tesco.net

▶ Celebration-Balloons, 859 Whittingham Lane, Goosnargh, Preston, PR3 2AU Tel: (01772) 861190 Fax: (01772) 861190 E-mail: info@celebration-balloons.co.uk

Great Western Balloons, 6 Redwood Close, Honiton, Devon, EX14 2XS Tel: (01404) 45968 Fax: (01404) 45968

PROMOTIONAL PARTY NOVELTIES

▶ A1 Bouncy Castles, Green Leys, Downley, High Wycombe, Buckinghamshire, HP13 5UH Tel: (01494) 464902

PROMOTIONAL PEWTER WARE

▶ English Pewter Co., 1 Blackmore Street, Sheffield, S4 7TZ Tel: 0114-273 0584 Fax: 0114-276 1416 E-mail: sales@englishpewter.co.uk

PROMOTIONAL PRINTING

Alanders Hindson Ltd, Merlin Way, New York Business Park, Newcastle upon Tyne, NE27 0YT Tel: 0191-280 0400 Fax: 0191-280 0401 E-mail: info@elandershindson.co.uk

Baker Print System, Forms House, 20 Lyons Cresent, Tonbridge, Kent, TN9 1EY Tel: (01732) 771188 Fax: (01732) 771999

Biltmore Printers, 14 Manners View, Newport, Isle of Wight, PO30 5FA Tel: (01983) 529788 Fax: (01983) 825528 E-mail: info@biltmoreprinters.co.uk

City Print Milton Keynes Ltd, 17 Denbigh Hall Industrial Estate, Denbigh Hall, Bletchley, Milton Keynes, MK3 7QT Tel: (01908) 377085 Fax: (01908) 649335 E-mail: sales@cityprint.net

Clarity, Forge Road, Willenhall, West Midlands, WV12 4HD Tel: (01902) 638340 Fax: (01902) 637594

Classic Pen Advertising, 23 Cradle Hill Industrial Estate, Seaford, East Sussex, BN25 3JE Tel: (01323) 890873

Crossprint Ltd, Newport Business Park, 21 Barry Way, Newport, Isle of Wight, PO30 5GY Tel: (01983) 524885 Fax: (01983) 522878 E-mail: info@crossprint.co.uk

Epik Incentives, Unit 13 Silver End Business Park, Brettell Lane, Brierley Hill, West Midlands, DY5 3LG Tel: (01384) 77310 Fax: (01384) 481975E-mail: sales@epik.co.uk

William Gibbons & Sons Ltd, PO Box 103, Willenhall, West Midlands, WV13 3XT Tel: (01902) 730011 Fax: (01902) 865835 E-mail: gibbowill@aol.com

Inter Print, Unit 3 Rivergate, Westlea, Swindon, SN5 7ET Tel: (01793) 613020 Fax: (01793) 436300 E-mail: sales@interprintswindon.co.uk

J W B Print & Design, Dixon Court, Dixon Street, Lincoln, LN6 7DA Tel: (01522) 560760 Fax: (01522) 567272 E-mail: sales@jwbprint.co.uk

Jameson Press, 21 The Fairways, New River Trading Estate, Cheshunt, Waltham Cross, Hertfordshire, EN8 0NL Tel: (01992) 635836 Fax: (01992) 636865 E-mail: info@jamesonpress.co.uk

Jordison Ltd, Tralee, Kirkleatham Business Park, Redcar, Cleveland, TS10 5SG Tel: (01642) 495270 Fax: (01642) 495271

Kingsway Print, The Old Chapel, Peterborough Road, Whittlesey, Peterborough, PE7 1PJ Tel: (01733) 350550

M M Palmer Ltd, 3-5 Capital Place, Harlow, Essex, CM19 5AS Tel: (01279) 439023 Fax: (01279) 635940 E-mail: sales@palmersprint.co.uk

PROMOTIONAL PRINTING – *continued*

Maurice Payne Colour Print Ltd, 12 Exeter Way, Theale, Reading, RG7 4PF Tel: 0118-930 3678 Fax: 0118-930 3759

Mills Advertising & Publicity, North House, 5 North Road, Stokesley, Middlesbrough, Cleveland, TS9 5DU Tel: (01642) 713156 Fax: (01642) 713174 E-mail: enquiries@millsadvertising.co.uk

Philip Myers Press Holdings Ltd, 9 Clayton Road, Birchwood, Warrington, WA3 6PH Tel: (01925) 819021 Fax: (01925) 828147 E-mail: print@myerspress.com

▶ Premier Impressions Ltd, Unit 10 & 11 West E Plan Estate, New Road, Newhaven, East Sussex, BN9 0EX Tel: (01273) 512512 Fax: (01273) 517518 E-mail: sales@premierimpressions.co.uk

Regent Print Ltd, 30 Albert Street, Huddersfield, HD1 3PU Tel: (01484) 530789 Fax: (01484) 542533 E-mail: sales@regentprint.co.uk

Sanders & Co. (UK) Ltd, 181 Wellingborough Road, Northampton, NN1 4DX Tel: (01604) 630195 Fax: (01604) 633972 E-mail: sandersltd@aol.com

Service Graphics, 3 Osiers Road, London, SW18 1NL Tel: (020) 8877 6600 Fax: (020) 8871 3521 E-mail: scott.king@servicegraphics.co.uk

Stones The Printers Ltd, 10 Wates Way, Banbury, Oxfordshire, OX16 3ES Tel: (01295) 819300 Fax: (01295) 819390 E-mail: lbrown@stonestheprinters.co.uk

Technart Ltd, Unit 45 City Industrial Park, Southern Road, Southampton, SO15 1HG Tel: (023) 8022 2409 Fax: (023) 8021 1403 E-mail: prepress@technart.co.uk

PROMOTIONAL PRODUCTS, PRINTED

▶ Car Air Freshener.Co.Uk, 47 Holmewood Gardens, London, SW2 3NB Tel: (0845) 6066204 E-mail: info@carairfreshener.co.uk

PROMOTIONAL PUZZLES AND GAMES

▶ The Strawberry Card Co., 8 Clarence Road, Exmouth, Devon, EX8 1LE Tel: (01395) 274923 Fax: (01395) 274923 E-mail: sian@thestrawberrycardcompany.co.uk

PROMOTIONAL REFRIGERATOR MAGNETS

▶ Promotional Keyrings, 28 Coulter Close, Cuffley, Hertfordshire, EN6 4RR Tel: (07005) 981697 E-mail: enquiries@promotionalkeyrings.co.uk

PROMOTIONAL SKATEBOARDS

▶ Bitch Skateboards, 11 Flag Square, Shoreham-by-Sea, West Sussex, BN43 5RZ Tel: (07766) 001121 E-mail: bitchskates@yahoo.co.uk

PROMOTIONAL STAFF RECRUITMENT

▶ 4Leisure Recruitment, PO Box 845, Uxbridge, Middlesex, UB8 9BJ Tel: (0870) 2423339 Fax: (01895) 235581 E-mail: info@4leisurerecruitment.co.uk

Digital Video Interview Services, The City Arc, Curtain Court, 7 Curtain Road, London, EC2A 3LT Tel: 0207 1009270 Fax: 0207 1009310 E-mail: info@digitalvideointerview.co.uk

Elite Promotions Personnel Ltd, 6 Park Lane, Whitefield, Manchester, M45 7PB Tel: 0161-272 1400 Fax: 0161-272 1401 E-mail: sales@elitepromo.co.uk

Instore Merchandising & Demonstrating, 1 Wallace Avenue, Lisburn, County Antrim, BT27 4AA Tel: (028) 9267 4215 Fax: (028) 9267 2015

▶ Spark Promotions Ltd, Building 3.1 Power Road Studio, Power Road, London, W4 5PY Tel: (020) 8742 5920 E-mail: spriestman@blackjack.co.uk

PROMOTIONAL STICKERS

Sign-Maker.Net, Little Knowle Farm, High Bickington, Umberleigh, Devon, EX37 9BJ Tel: (01769) 560675 Fax: (01769) 560819 E-mail: enquiries@sign-maker.net

PROMOTIONAL UMBRELLA PRINTING

▶ SR Designs, 1 Hook Hill Park, Woking, Surrey, GU22 0PX Tel: (01483) 750611 Fax: (01483) 770919 E-mail: golfprizes@aol.com

PROMOTIONAL WATCHES

Harrow Watch & Jewellery Clinic, Unit 4 St. Anns Shopping Centre, St. Anns Road, Harrow, Middlesex, HA1 1AS Tel: (020) 8424 2601 Fax: (020) 8424 2601

PROMOTIONAL WINDOW STICKERS

▶ Lighthouse Printing, 1 Anglesey Street, Cardiff, CF5 1QZ Tel: (029) 2034 4899 Fax: (029) 2034 4899 E-mail: lighthouseprint@ntlworld.com

PROMOTIONAL WINE

▶ Garrigue Wines, Carnoch, Mid Barrwood Road, Kilsyth, Glasgow, G65 0ER Tel: (0845) 8886677 E-mail: themacaloneys@garriguewines.com

PROMOTIONAL WRIST BANDS

▶ Fashion-4U, 87 Woolston Avenue, Congleton, Cheshire, CW12 3ED Tel: (07708) 731770 E-mail: sales@fashion-4u.co.uk

PROMOTIONAL/ADVERTISING BAGS

Conquest Products, 29 Whitley Street, Reading, RG2 0EG Tel: 0118-987 4635 Fax: 0118-987 4638 E-mail: phil@conquestproducts.co.uk

Promotional Fabrics Ltd, The Maltings, School Lane, Amersham, Buckinghamshire, HP7 0ES Tel: (01494) 724172 Fax: (01494) 725283 E-mail: enquiries@amershamfabrics.com

Titheringtons Ltd, 75 Strand Road, Bootle, Merseyside, L20 4BB Tel: 0151-922 4422 Fax: 0151-933 0502 E-mail: sales@sharmaplc.com

PROMOTIONAL/ADVERTISING GIFT

A G Products, 4-5 North Bar Street, Banbury, Oxfordshire, OX16 0TB Tel: (01295) 259608 Fax: (01295) 271787 E-mail: steve@agproducts.co.uk

Accrington Brush Co. Ltd, Lower Grange Mill, Church Street, Accrington, Lancashire, BB5 2ES Tel: (01254) 871414 Fax: (01254) 872064 E-mail: info@a-brush.co.uk

AdGiftsOnline, 17 The Barracks, Barracks Road, Newcastle, Staffordshire, ST5 1LG Tel: (01782) 713177 Fax: (01782) 715431 E-mail: sales@adgiftsonline.com

Advertime Ltd, 752 C Finchley Road, London, NW11 7TH Tel: (020) 8201 9222 Fax: (020) 8201 9111 E-mail: sales@advertime.co.uk

Age Communications, 20 Upper Ground, London, SE1 9PF Tel: (020) 7805 5590 Fax: (020) 7805 5910 E-mail: iln@ilng.co.uk

Atmosphere, 3 Manners Corner, Manners Way, Southend-on-Sea, SS2 6QR Tel: (01702) 335186 Fax: (01702) 337218

Aztec Group, Unit 18 Chiltern Business Village, Arundel Road, Uxbridge, Middlesex, UB8 2SN Tel: (01895) 520600 Fax: (01895) 520650 E-mail: sales@aztecgroup.net

BusinessGift.UK.Com, 92 Langdale Road, Leyland, PR25 3AS Tel: (01772) 435010 Fax: (01772) 457280 E-mail: steve@ad-options.co.uk

The Carole Group Ltd, Oaklands Business Centre, Oaklands Park, Wokingham, Berkshire, RG41 2FD Tel: 0118-977 1424 Fax: 0118-977 2479 E-mail: sales@carolegroup.com

▶ Clipperlight Nautical Books, Albrighton, Wolverhampton, WV7 3WL Tel: (01902) 373217 E-mail: clipperuk@aol.com

G B Promotional Products Ltd, The Old Smoke House Potter Street, Sandwich, Kent, CT13 9DR Tel: (01304) 619390 Fax: (01304) 619391 E-mail: sales@gbpromotionalproducts.co.uk

G K Beaulah & Co. Ltd, 23 Park Street, Hull, HU2 8RU Tel: (01482) 223521 Fax: (01482) 216328 E-mail: info@beaulah.co.uk

G L J Badges, Unit 10 Park Trading Estate, Park Road, Hockley, Birmingham, B18 5HB Tel: 0121-554 9869 Fax: 0121-523 9395 E-mail: sales@gljbadges.co.uk

Galpeg Ltd, 70 Hampden Road, London, N10 2NX Tel: (020) 8444 4455 Fax: (020) 8442 0357 E-mail: sales@galpeg.com

Hambleside Business Gift Solutions Ltd, 23 Robjohns Road, Widford Industrial Estate, Chelmsford, CM1 3AG Tel: (01245) 293610 Fax: (01245) 293615 E-mail: gillian@hambleside.co.uk

Ihkos Digital Ltd, Coventry, CV2 3WB Tel: (024) 7626 7622 Fax: (024) 7672 9855 E-mail: info@ihkos.co.uk

Image Matters, Unit B12, Laser Quay, Rochester, Kent, ME2 4HU Tel: (01634) 296400 Fax: (01634) 296444 E-mail: sales@imagematters.co.uk

Impakt Stationers, Unit 12 Endeavour Way, Croydon, CR0 4TR Tel: (020) 8684 5777 Fax: (020) 8684 5999 E-mail: sales@impakt.co.uk

J D H T Ltd, Jaguar House, 104 Firle Road, Eastbourne, East Sussex, BN22 8EU Tel: (01323) 410403 Fax: (01323) 411481 E-mail: lys@jdhtsales.co.uk

Logo Bugs Plus Ltd, 9 Airfield Way, Christchurch, Dorset, BH23 3PE Tel: (01202) 588500 Fax: (01202) 487177 E-mail: sales@tpd.co.uk

Manhattan Products Ltd, 89 Steward Street, Birmingham, B18 7AF Tel: 0121-454 6404 Fax: 0121-454 1497 E-mail: sales@manhattanproducts.com

MTC Tees, 4 Forest Industrial Park, Forest Road, Ilford, Essex, IG6 3HL Tel: (020) 8501 0922 Fax: (020) 8559 8230

▶ Pebble Promotions, 303a Chester Road, Hartford, Northwich, Cheshire, CW8 1QL Tel: (01606) 75677 Fax: (01606) 75688 E-mail: sales@pebblepromotions.co.uk

Promocan, Plaistow Road, Loxwood, Billingshurst, West Sussex, RH14 0TS Tel: (01403) 753453 Fax: 0845 6120655 E-mail: tmursell@promocan.co.uk

Promotional Ceramics Ltd, Spedding Road, Fenton Industrial Estate, Stoke-on-Trent, ST4 2SU Tel: (01782) 279957 Fax: (01782) 264080 E-mail: accounts@promotionalceramics.co.uk

Rose Colchester Ltd, Clough Road, Severalls Industrial Park, Colchester, CO4 9QT Tel: (01206) 844500 Fax: (01206) 845872 E-mail: sales@rosecalendars.co.uk

Worldwide Ideas Ltd, Ideas House Station Estate, Eastwood Close, London, E18 1RT Tel: (020) 8530 7171 Fax: (020) 8530 7365 E-mail: sales@worldwideideas.co.uk

PROMOTIONAL/ADVERTISING GIFT CASES

Advertime Ltd, 752 C Finchley Road, London, NW11 7TH Tel: (020) 8201 9222 Fax: (020) 8201 9111 E-mail: sales@advertime.co.uk

Angel Multimedia, 32 Blue Street, Carmarthen, Dyfed, SA31 3LE Tel: (01267) 221175 Fax: (01267) 223196 E-mail: sales@angelmm.co.uk

PROMOTIONAL/ADVERTISING MUGS/CERAMICS

▶ Corporate Executive Gifts Ltd, Unit K, Houndswood Gate, Harper Lane, Radlett, Hertfordshire, WD7 7HU Tel: (01923) 852330 Fax: (01923) 859946 E-mail: sales@corporateexecutivegifts.com

K B Design & Promotion Ltd, City Business Centre, Brighton Road, Horsham, West Sussex, RH13 5BA Tel: (01403) 262499 Fax: (01403) 261932 E-mail: sales@kb-design.com

Promotional Ceramics Ltd, Spedding Road, Fenton Industrial Estate, Stoke-on-Trent, ST4 2SU Tel: (01782) 279957 Fax: (01782) 264080 E-mail: accounts@promotionalceramics.co.uk

PROMOTIONAL/ADVERTISING PRODUCTS, *See also headings for particular types*

▶ Advantage Business Gifts Ltd, PO Box 35, Mablethorpe, Lincolnshire, LN12 9AA Tel: (01507) 440510 Fax: (01507) 440168 E-mail: info@advantagebg.co.uk

Big Badge Co., Old School House, Victoria Avenue, London, N3 1GG Tel: (020) 8371 8752 Fax: (020) 8371 8751 E-mail: sales@theknightgroup.com

▶ Car Air Freshener.Co.Uk, 47 Holmewood Gardens, London, SW2 3NB Tel: (0845) 6066204 E-mail: info@carairfreshener.co.uk

PROMOTIONAL/PREMIUM PRODUCT DESIGNERS, PRODUCERS ETC

4 Imprint Group, Broadway House, Trafford Wharf Road, Trafford Park, Manchester, M17 1DD Tel: 0161-872 9527 Fax: (0870) 2413441 E-mail: sales@4imprint.co.uk

A1 Promotional Pens, 2-4 Mount Pleasant Road, Aldershot, Hampshire, GU12 4NL Tel: (01252) 320571 Fax: (01252) 403635 E-mail: sales@pens.co.uk

Abbeygate Diaries & Gifts, 28 Northern Way, Bury St. Edmunds, Suffolk, IP32 6NL Tel: (01284) 760044 Fax: (01284) 750077

Action Jacket Co., PO Box 1180, Stourbridge, West Midlands, DY9 0ZF Tel: (01562) 887096 Fax: (01562) 882010 E-mail: info@actionjacket.co.uk

AdGiftsOnline, 17 The Barracks, Barracks Road, Newcastle, Staffordshire, ST5 1LG Tel: (01782) 713177 Fax: (01782) 715431 E-mail: sales@adgiftsonline.com

Advartex Ltd, Pickforde Lane, Ticehurst, Wadhurst, East Sussex, TN5 7BL Tel: (01580) 200120 Fax: (01580) 201001 E-mail: andy@advartex.co.uk

Alexco Emblems, 94 Guildford Road, Croydon, CR0 2HJ Tel: (020) 8683 0546 Fax: (020) 8689 4749 E-mail: alexco@btconnect.com

Allan & Bertram Ltd, Cuffley Gate, Sopers Road, Cuffley, Hertfordshire, EN6 4RY Tel: (01707) 876677 Fax: (01707) 877960

Allegro Bags, 110 Huttoft Road, Sutton-On-Sea, Mablethorpe, Lincolnshire, LN12 2RU Tel: (01507) 440192 E-mail: allegrobags@btconnect.com

Am Designer Logo Jewellers, Mount Pleasant, Barnet, Hertfordshire, EN4 9HH Tel: (020) 8441 3835 Fax: (020) 8440 7771 E-mail: info@promotionaljewellery.co.uk

Azure Blue Design, 61 Viceroy Court, Wilmslow Road, Didsbury, Manchester, M20 2RH Tel: (07886) 443129 E-mail: sales@azure-blue.co.uk

B I S Trent Rosettes, 7 Railway Enterprise Centre, Shelton New Road, Stoke-on-Trent, ST4 7SH Tel: (01782) 279797 Fax: (01782) 279797

Base 1 Ltd, 41-43 Roebuck Road, Hainault Industrial Estate, Ilford, Essex, IG6 3TU Tel: (020) 8500 5649 Fax: (020) 8559 9456 E-mail: phil@base1.co.uk

Beaumont PPS Ltd, 537 Sauchiehall Street, Glasgow, G3 7PQ Tel: 0141-226 3411 Fax: 0141-221 9249 E-mail: sales@beaumontpps.com

Beaver Business Gifts, 5 Telford Road, Middlesbrough, Cleveland, TS3 8BL Tel: (01642) 252890 Fax: (01642) 773277

Big Stuff, 4 Hall Road Industrial Estate, Southminster, Essex, CM0 7DA Tel: (01621) 774981 Fax: (01621) 774672

Blisters Ltd, Second Avenue, Midsomer Norton, Radstock, BA3 4AR Tel: (01761) 418277 Fax: (01761) 418900 E-mail: enquiries@blisters.ltd.uk

Brenton Handbags Ltd, Darren Mill, Wash Lane, Bury, Lancashire, BL9 7DU Tel: 0161-764 8528 Fax: 0161-763 1503 E-mail: info@brentonbags.com

C B Collections Ltd, 11 Grosvenor Road, Batley, West Yorkshire, WF17 0LX Tel: (01924) 476977 Fax: (01924) 478315 E-mail: silks@dial.pipex.com

C Y Inflatables Ltd, Units 3-3a Queniborough Industrial Estate, Melton Road, Queniborough, Leicester, LE7 3FP Tel: 0116-260 2506 E-mail: steve@inflatables.uk.com

Calver Ltd, 22 The Drive, Orpington, Kent, BR6 9AP Tel: (01689) 898828 Fax: (01689) 898848 E-mail: sales@calver.com

Carter Advertising, 11 Kirkhouse Road, Blanefield, Glasgow, G63 9BX Tel: (01360) 770235 Fax: (01360) 770235 E-mail: sales@carteradvertising.co.uk

Colorphaze, 73 Bunting Road, Northampton, NN2 6EE Tel: (01604) 792001 E-mail: sales@colorphaze.co.uk

Conquest Products, 29 Whitley Street, Reading, RG2 0EG Tel: 0118-987 4635 Fax: 0118-987 4638 E-mail: phil@conquestproducts.co.uk

Contract (H/F) Electrode Supplies Ltd, Newhaven Industrial Estate, Barton Lane, Eccles, Manchester, M30 0HL Tel: 0161-707 4090 Fax: 0161-707 1314 E-mail: enquiries@contractelectrode.co.uk

County Club Ltd, 244 Tolworth Rise South, Surbiton, Surrey, KT5 9NB Tel: (020) 8337 5050 E-mail: sales@countyclub.co.uk

Creative Promotions, 79 West Regent Street, Glasgow, G2 2AW Tel: 0141-332 7471 Fax: 0141-331 2801 E-mail: enquiries@creativepromotions.co.uk

Crescent Silver Repairs & Restoration, 85 Spencer Street, Birmingham, B18 6DE Tel: 0121-236 9006 Fax: 0121-212 1466 E-mail: mail@cresent-silver.co.uk

D & N Design, 2 Weston Road, Thames Ditton, Surrey, KT7 0HN Tel: (020) 8398 9639 Fax: (020) 8398 9639

Darby Rosettes & Trophies, 5 Goulburn Road, Norwich, NR7 9UX Tel: (01603) 440694 Fax: (01603) 440687

Dexter & Gordon, Priory Farm, Andwell, Hook, Hampshire, RG27 9PA Tel: (01256) 765951 Fax: (01256) 765608 E-mail: sales@printedfootballs.co.uk

Dodd Anderson Ltd, Graphic House, Mylord Cresent, Camperdown Industrial Estate, Newcastle upon Tyne, NE12 5UJ Tel: 0191-268 9993 Fax: 0191-268 6667 E-mail: doddanderson@btconnect.co.uk

E H Advertising Ltd, Castlethorpe Court, Castlethorpe, Brigg, North Lincolnshire, DN20 9LG Tel: (01652) 650100 Fax: (01652) 650035 E-mail: eh.advertising@virgin.net

East Lancashire Towel Co. Ltd, Park Mill, Halstead Lane, Barrowford, Nelson, Lancashire, BB9 6HJ Tel: (01282) 612193 Fax: (01282) 697736

Elite Supplies, 19l Solway Trading Estate, Maryport, Cumbria, CA15 8NF Tel: (01900) 810111 Fax: (01900) 810222 E-mail: sales@elite-supplies.com

Elms & Elms, 6-8 Brookfield Road, Cheadle, Cheshire, SK8 2PN Tel: 0161-428 8383 Fax: 0161-428 8855 E-mail: info@elmsandelms.co.uk

Ernex Group, P O Box 53967, London, SW15 3UY Tel: (020) 7731 6707 Fax: (020) 7731 6703 E-mail: ties@ernex.co.uk

Express T-Shirts Ltd, 194 Kingston Road, New Malden, Surrey, KT3 3RJ Tel: (020) 8949 4099 Fax: (020) 8949 3121

▶ Farish Associates, 94 Sutton Court, Chiswick, London, W4 3JF Tel: (020) 8742 3223 Fax: (020) 8742 3226 E-mail: sales@farish.com

PROMOTIONAL/PREMIUM PRODUCT DESIGNERS, PRODUCERS ETC – *continued*

Formula Incentives Ltd, 1 Lockside Office Park, Lockside Road, Preston, PR2 2YS Tel: (01772) 721122 Fax: (01772) 326850 E-mail: sales@incentives.co.uk

Forward Group plc, 57 Buckland Road, London, E10 6QS Tel: (020) 8558 7110 Fax: (020) 8558 5974E-mail: sales@forward-group.co.uk

G H Enterprises, 10 Coope Road, Bollington, Kerridge, Macclesfield, Cheshire, SK10 5AE Tel: (01625) 574336 Fax: (01625) 573727 E-mail: ghe@breathemail.net

Gateacre Press Ltd, Bilail House, 260 Picton Road, Wavertree, Liverpool, L15 4LP Tel: 0151-734 3038 Fax: 0151-734 2860 E-mail: gpl@gatepress.demon.co.uk

The Gift Business, St. Swithins House, Trinity Street, Worcester, WR1 2PW Tel: (01905) 724111 Fax: (01905) 745117 E-mail: sales@giftbusiness.co.uk

Harwell Enterprises Ltd, 43 Platts Eyot, Hampton, Middlesex, TW12 2HF Tel: (020) 8783 0666 Fax: (020) 8941 6977 E-mail: sales@harwell.co.uk

Hedgerow Publishing Ltd, 325 Abbeydale Road, Sheffield, S7 1FS Tel: 0114-255 4873 Fax: 0114-250 9400 E-mail: sales@hedgerow.co.uk

High Profile, 9 Haslemere Way, Banbury, Oxfordshire, OX16 5RW Tel: (01295) 267966 Fax: (01295) 272477 E-mail: sales@high-profile.co.uk

Horton & Newberry (Sales & Marketing) Ltd, 53a High Street Wanstead, London, E11 2AA Tel: (020) 8989 5903 Fax: (020) 8530 4118 E-mail: sales@hortonandnewberry.co.uk

I S Enterprises International, Clement House, Commerce Way, Colchester, CO2 8HY Tel: (01206) 798131 Fax: (01206) 791186 E-mail: sales@isenterprisesintl.co.uk

Icarus Housewares, Unit 1 & 2 Newman Lane, Alton, Hampshire, GU34 2PJ Tel: (01420) 593479 Fax: (01420) 87389 E-mail: lunchboxes@icarus-housewares.com

IMPAMARK, 1Dammerwick Farm, Marsh Road, Burnham-On-Crouch, Essex, CM0 8AG Tel: (01621) 783550 Fax: (01621) 784548 E-mail: info@impamark.co.uk

Initial Incentives, Unit 4, Parr Road, Stanmore, Middlesex, HA7 1NP Tel: (020) 8381 3300 Fax: (020) 8381 3700 E-mail: sales@initialonline.com

Interlogo London Ltd, High Street, Newport, Isle of Wight, PO30 1BQ Tel: (01983) 522470 Fax: (01983) 532891 E-mail: sales@interlogo.co.uk

J S M Business Gifts, 9 St. Albans Road, Gloucester, GL2 5FW Tel: (01452) 310030 Fax: (01452) 304454

Jacee Print & Promotions Ltd, Publicity House, Station Road, Cottingham, East Yorkshire, HU16 4LL Tel: (01482) 842117 Fax: (01482) 875239 E-mail: sales@jaceeprint.co.uk

JC-One, Lomia House, Falmouth Crescent, Normanton, West Yorkshire, WF6 2SW Tel: (01924) 891793 Fax: (01924) 223681 E-mail: sales@jc-one.co.uk

Juniper Trading Ltd, Mayfayre House, London Road, Denington Industrial Estate, Wellingborough, Northamptonshire, NN8 2QH Tel: (01933) 222495 Fax: (01933) 274077 E-mail: sales@juniperproducts.co.uk

K B Design & Promotion Ltd, City Business Centre, Brighton Road, Horsham, West Sussex, RH13 5BA Tel: (01403) 262499 Fax: (01403) 261932 E-mail: sales@kb-design.com

K L M Trophy Centre, 2-3 The Parade, Southfields, Letchworth Garden City, Hertfordshire, SG6 4NB Tel: (01462) 684242 Fax: (01462) 684242 E-mail: klmengravers@aol.com

Keramikos Ltd, Lumsdale Mill, Lower Lumsdale, Matlock, Derbyshire, DE4 5EX Tel: (01629) 580033 Fax: (01629) 582234 E-mail: info@keramikos.co.uk

Logomotif Embroiderers, 2 Eagle Close, Arnold, Nottingham, NG5 7FJ Tel: 0115-920 0777 Fax: 0115-920 0888 E-mail: logomotif@aol.com

LP Marketing Ltd, Millenium House, Junction Road, Sheffield, S11 8XB Tel: 0114-268 2812 Fax: 0114-268 2812

▶ Lucid Innovation Group, PO Box 180, Manchester, M21 9XW Tel: 0161-860 0058 E-mail: ideas@lucidinnovation.com

M T M Promotional, 287 Palatine Road, Northenden, Manchester, M22 4ET Tel: 0161-946 9200 Fax: 0161-946 9209 E-mail: info@mtmpromotional.co.uk

Manchester Umbrella Co. Ltd, Unit 10 Brook St Works, Adcroft Street, Stockport, Cheshire, SK1 3HZ Tel: 0161-480 5328 Fax: 0161-477 7884 E-mail: sales@manchesterumbrellas.co.uk

Marber Promotions & Marketing Ltd, 30b Park Road, Hale, Altrincham, Cheshire, WA15 9NN Tel: 0161-927 9085 Fax: 0161-927 9087 E-mail: enquiries@marber.co.uk

Marketing Solutions, 51 Castleton Road, Ilford, Essex, IG3 9QW Tel: (020) 8590 2703 Fax: (020) 8597 4911 E-mail: mktsolutions@hotmail.com

Mikkimugs Screen Process Printers, Matravers Farm, Uploders, Bridport, Dorset, DT6 4PH Tel: (01308) 485300 Fax: (01308) 485542 E-mail: sales@mikkimugs.demon.co.uk

Mikkis Mouse Mats, Flat 3, 34 Croft Road, Clacton-on-Sea, Essex, CO15 3EF Tel: (01255) 225301 Fax: (01255) 225311 E-mail: sales@mikkis.com

Mister Tee's Rock Stop, 65 Blackwell Street, Kidderminster, Worcestershire, DY10 2EL Tel: (01562) 515291

Moores of London Ltd, Third Floor, Elizabeth House, 54-58 High Street, Edgware, Middlesex, HA8 7EJ Tel: (020) 8731 2120 Fax: (020) 8731 2121 E-mail: sales@mooreslondon.co.uk

Morton & Crowder Ltd, 14 Fortnum Close, Birmingham, B33 0JX Tel: 0121-783 7571 Fax: 0121-783 1327 E-mail: morcro@aol.com

Motiv Business Gifts, 28 Moor Lane, Loughborough, Leicestershire, LE11 1BA Tel: (01509) 262272 Fax: (01509) 267276

The Mug Factory Ltd, 2 Wyndham Court, Clarion Close Enterprise Park, Swansea, SA6 8RB Tel: (01792) 776331 Fax: (01792) 781142

▶ Newline Products, 23 Royal Exchange Square, Glasgow, G1 3AJ Tel: 0141-248 4086 Fax: 0141-847 0530 E-mail: info@newlineproducts.co.uk

Oldeani Ltd, Unit 2a Hoffmanns Way, Chelmsford, CM1 1GU Tel: (01245) 262611 Fax: (01245) 262885 E-mail: sales@oldeani.com

P & M Embroidery, Glebe Road, Huntingdon, Cambridgeshire, PE29 7DR Tel: (01480) 411311 Fax: (01480) 412839 E-mail: sales@pmembroidery.co.uk

Park Packaging Ltd, 2 Ashley Drive, Bothwell, Glasgow, G71 8BS Tel: (01698) 801943 Fax: (01698) 801925 E-mail: info@parkpackaging.co.uk

Pinpoint Badges & Promotions Ltd, Alma Road, Sidcup, Kent, DA14 4EA Tel: (020) 8302 8008 Fax: (020) 8302 4008 E-mail: sales@pinpointbadges.com

Polygonum, 2 Wellington Business Park, Dukes Ride, Crowthorne, Berkshire, RG45 6LS Tel: (01344) 774664 Fax: (01344) 778886 E-mail: sales@polygonum.co.uk

Premier Gifts, Crimple Court, Hornbeam Square North, Harrogate, North Yorkshire, HG2 8PB Tel: (01423) 815611 Fax: (01423) 815612 E-mail: sales@premier-gifts.co.uk

Premier Promotional Services, 38 Bearton Road, Hitchin, Hertfordshire, SG5 1UE Tel: (01462) 442288 Fax: (01462) 458883 E-mail: sales@premierpromotional.co.uk

Pressrite Engineering Ltd, 24 Ogmore Crescent, Bridgend Industrial Estate, Bridgend, Mid Glamorgan, CF31 3TE Tel: (01656) 657067 Fax: (01656) 645857

Prestige Enterprises, PO Box 1160, Newtownabbey, County Antrim, BT36 5YP Tel: 0845 230 3818 Fax: 0845 230 3819 E-mail: sales@prestigeenterprises.com

▶ Product Plus International Ltd, Southbank Business Centre, Ponton Road, London, SW8 5BL Tel: (020) 7393 0033 Fax: (020) 7393 0080 E-mail: sales@product-plus.co.uk

Promark, Beeches, Park Wall Lane, Lower Basildon, Reading, RG8 9PE Tel: (01491) 671539 Fax: (01491) 671832 E-mail: sales@promarkgifts.co.uk

Promo Branding Ltd, New Southgate Industrial Estate, Lower Park Road, London, N11 1QD Tel: (020) 8361 8820 Fax: (020) 8361 8821 E-mail: sales@promobranding.co.uk

Promotional Ceramics Ltd, Spedding Road, Fenton Industrial Estate, Stoke-on-Trent, ST4 2SU Tel: (01782) 279957 Fax: (01782) 264080 E-mail: accounts@promotionalceramics.co.uk

Promotional Products Specialities Scotland Ltd, 537 Sauchiehall Street, Glasgow, G3 7PQ Tel: 0141-221 2420 Fax: 0141-221 9249 E-mail: sales@beaumontpps.com

Queen Elizabeth's Foundation, Bradmere House, Kingston Road, Leatherhead, Surrey, KT22 7NA Tel: (01372) 389940 Fax: (01372) 361386 E-mail: bradhouse@bradhouse.demon.co.uk

R J Smith Ltd, 41-42 Tenby St North, Birmingham, B1 3EG Tel: 0121-233 2160 Fax: 0121-233 9630E-mail: sales@rjs-ltd.com

Regent Publicity Ltd, 8 Milnthorpe Road, Hove, East Sussex, BN3 5HT Tel: (01273) 820300 Fax: (01273) 820144 E-mail: southern.sales@regentpublicity.co.uk

Seppi, 28 High Street, Meldreth, Royston, Hertfordshire, SG8 6JU Tel: (01763) 260326 Fax: (01763) 260035 E-mail: sales@seppities.co.uk

Sherwood Agencies Ltd, Sherwood House Mutual Mills, Aspinall Street, Heywood, Lancashire, OL10 4HW Tel: (01706) 898100 Fax: (01706) 898101 E-mail: admin@sherwoodagencies.com

▶ Shimmee, Plough Road, Great Bentley, Colchester, CO7 8LG Tel: (01206) 250400 Fax: (01206) 250410 E-mail: sales@shimmee.co.uk

Shreds, Station Yard, Station Road, Digby, Lincoln, LN4 3NF Tel: (01526) 320450 Fax: (01526) 320452 E-mail: information@shreds.co.uk

Signet Branded Tags Seals, 3-5 Aintree Road, Perivale, Greenford, Middlesex, UB6 7LA Tel: (020) 8810 7300 Fax: (0844) 9007301

Silver Crane Co., 34a Black Moor Road, Ebblake Industrial Estate, Verwood, Dorset, BH31 6BB Tel: (01202) 825155 Fax: (01202) 823300 E-mail: sales@silvercrane.co.uk

Source Ltd, The Old Stables, 10 Beulah Road, London, SW19 3SB Tel: (020) 8540 4201 Fax: (020) 8540 7380 E-mail: sales@sbsource.co.uk

South Advertising Group, PO Box 118, Congleton, Cheshire, CW12 3RQ Tel: (01260) 273813 Fax: (01260) 273813 E-mail: south@m-i-6.co.uk

Special Efx Ltd, Ettington Park Bus Centre, Stratford-upon-Avon, Warwickshire, CV37 8BT Tel: (01789) 450005

Steel City Marketing Ltd, Allen Street, Sheffield, S3 7AW Tel: 0114-275 4150 Fax: 0114-275 0010 E-mail: sales@steel-city.co.uk

Swedish Match UK Ltd, Sword House, Totteridge Road, High Wycombe, Buckinghamshire, HP13 6DG Tel: (01494) 533300 Fax: (01494) 437459

T O T Shirts, Banksia Road, London, N18 3BF Tel: (020) 8887 7900 Fax: (020) 8345 6095 E-mail: paul@t-o-t-shirts.co.uk

T Shirt Products, Somers Road, Rugby, Warwickshire, CV22 7DG Tel: (0845) 0714405 Fax: (0845) 0714406 E-mail: sales@tsp-tshirts.co.uk

Talbot Designs Ltd, 225 Long Lane, Finchley, London, N3 2RL Tel: 0845 8510136 Fax: (020) 8349 0294 E-mail: sales@talbotdesigns.co.uk

Tie & Scarf Co. Ltd, Warth Park, Radcliffe Road, Bury, Lancashire, BL9 9NB Tel: 0161-761 5151 Fax: 0161-762 0202 E-mail: tieandscarf@chaytow.com

Top TS Kent Ltd, Unit 35 Blenheim Close, Pysons Road Industrial Estate, Broadstairs, Kent, CT10 2YF Tel: (01843) 863737 Fax: (01843) 863684 E-mail: cotts@aol.com

Touchline Promotions Ltd, 17 Rayleas Close, London, SE18 3JN Tel: (020) 8856 1115 Fax: (020) 8319 3035 E-mail: touchproms@aol.com

Toye Kenning & Spencer Ltd, Regalia House, Newtown Road, Bedworth, Warwickshire, CV12 8QR Tel: (024) 7631 5634 Fax: (024) 7664 3018 E-mail: sales@toye.com

Trophyman Supplies Ltd, Olympic Works, 2-4 Kathleen Road, Southampton, SO19 8EX Tel: (023) 8043 8888 Fax: (023) 8068 5604 E-mail: sales@trophyman.co.uk

Uniform Express Ltd, Unit C7 South Way, Bounds Green Industrial Estate, Bounds Green Road, London, N11 2UL Tel: (020) 8368 0114 Fax: (020) 8361 0624 E-mail: mail@uniformexpress.co.uk

Visionstyle Leisure, Houldsworth Mill, Houldsworth Street, Reddish, Stockport, Cheshire, SK5 6DA Tel: 0161-442 7082 Fax: 0161-442 1939 E-mail: sales@visionstyle.co.uk

Vortex T Shirts Ltd, 2 Grange Lane Industrial Estate, Carrwood Road, Barnsley, South Yorkshire, S71 5AS Tel: (01226) 202329 Fax: (01226) 249748 E-mail: sales@vortexuk.com

Westbrook Marketing Ltd, 24 The Dean, Alresford, Hampshire, SO24 9AZ Tel: (01962) 733122 Fax: (01962) 733122 E-mail: sales@westbrookmarketing.co.uk

WH Smith Retail Ltd, Greenbridge Road, Swindon, SN3 3LD Tel: (01793) 616161 Fax: (01793) 426410 E-mail: info@whsmithonline.com

Yorkshire Post, 7-11 Manor Row, Bradford, West Yorkshire, BD1 4PB Tel: (01274) 721571 Fax: (01274) 370165 E-mail: sales@topfile.fsnet.co.uk

PROMPTING SYSTEMS

Autoscript Ltd, Unit 8a Poplar Business Park, Prestons Road, London, E14 9RL Tel: (020) 7538 1427 Fax: (020) 7515 9529 E-mail: sales@autoscript.tv

Portaprompt Ltd, Spearmast Industrial Park, Lane End Road, High Wycombe, Buckinghamshire, HP12 4JQ Tel: (01494) 450414 Fax: (01494) 437591 E-mail: helen@portaprompt.co.uk

PROOF PRINTER (PROOFER) TO THE TRADE

Capital Repro, Tech West House, Warple Way, London, W3 0UE Tel: (020) 8743 0111 Fax: (020) 8743 0112 E-mail: info@caprep.co.uk

Quadraproof Ltd, 12 Orwell Furlong, Cambridge, CB4 0WY Tel: (01223) 420202 Fax: (01223) 424729 E-mail: info@quadraproof.co.uk

Watt Gilchrist Ltd, Ring Road, West Park, Leeds, LS16 6RA Tel: 0113-288 3200 Fax: 0113-275 1690 E-mail: info@gilchrist.co.uk

PROPANE GAS

Budget Gas Ltd, Halesfield 21, Telford, Shropshire, TF7 4NX Tel: (01952) 583908 Fax: (01952) 586692

Flogas UK Ltd, Unit W, Barton Industrial Estate, Faldo Road, Barton-Le-Clay, MK45 4RP Tel: (01582) 600858 Fax: (01582) 882256

Rimco Services, 20 Orchard Road, Malton, North Yorkshire, YO17 7BH Tel: (01653) 600707 Fax: (01653) 600707 E-mail: sales@rimco.co.uk

Spoors Ltd, Railway Street, Bishop Auckland, County Durham, DL14 7LR Tel: (01388) 603865 Fax: (01388) 608029 E-mail: spoors@onyxnet.co.uk

PROPELLER CASTINGS

R K Atkinson Ltd, Main Street, Garton-on-the-Wolds, Driffield, North Humberside, YO25 3EU Tel: (01377) 254090 Fax: (01377) 255700 E-mail: richard@rk-atkinson.co.uk

PROPELLER MAINTENANCE/ REPAIR SPECIALIST SERVICES

Bruntons Propellers Ltd, Oakwood Business Park, Stephenson Road West, Clacton-on-Sea, Essex, CO15 4TL Tel: (01255) 420005 Fax: (01255) 427775 E-mail: info@bruntons-propellers.com

J Crowther Royton Ltd, Eden Works Belgrave Mill, Honeywell Lane, Oldham, OL8 2JP Tel: 0161-652 4234 Fax: 0161-627 4265 E-mail: crowther.marine@tiscali.co.uk

R K Atkinson Ltd, Main Street, Garton-on-the-Wolds, Driffield, North Humberside, YO25 3EU Tel: (01377) 254090 Fax: (01377) 255700 E-mail: richard@rk-atkinson.co.uk

S M M Propeller Services Ltd, Wharf Road, Gravesend, Kent, DA12 2RU Tel: (01474) 320192 Fax: (01474) 335047

Sigma Aerospace Ltd, 12 Imperial Way, Croydon, CR9 4LE Tel: (020) 8688 7777 Fax: (020) 8688 6603 E-mail: info@sigmaaerospace.com

PROPELLER SHAFT MAINTENANCE/REPAIR SERVICES

R K Atkinson Ltd, Main Street, Garton-on-the-Wolds, Driffield, North Humberside, YO25 3EU Tel: (01377) 254090 Fax: (01377) 255700 E-mail: richard@rk-atkinson.co.uk

Rotherham Commercial Hydraulics Ltd, The Chain Works, Masbrough Street, Rotherham, South Yorkshire, S60 1ER Tel: (01709) 375515 Fax: (01709) 376247 E-mail: propshaft@aol.com

Sigma Aerospace Ltd, 12 Imperial Way, Croydon, CR9 4LE Tel: (020) 8688 7777 Fax: (020) 8688 6603 E-mail: info@sigmaaerospace.com

PROPELLER SHAFTS

Bruntons Propellers Ltd, Oakwood Business Park, Stephenson Road West, Clacton-on-Sea, Essex, CO15 4TL Tel: (01255) 420005 Fax: (01255) 427775 E-mail: info@bruntons-propellers.com

Commercial Propshaft Services Ltd, 190 Kingsway South, Team Valley Trading Estate, Gateshead, Tyne & Wear, NE11 0SH Tel: 0191-482 1690 Fax: 0191-482 0582

GKN Driveshafts Ltd, Middlemoor La West, Aldridge, Walsall, WS9 8DT Tel: (01922) 453371 Fax: (01922) 451716 E-mail: martyn.habgood@gkndriveline.com

The Greno Garage & Engineering, Penistone Road, Grenoside, Sheffield, S35 8QG Tel: 0114-246 7409 Fax: 0114-246 7409

I M S International Marketing Services Ltd, Boulton Works, 54 College Road, Perry Barr, Birmingham, B44 8BS Tel: 0121-344 5500 Fax: 0121-344 5504 E-mail: sales@ims-ltd.co.uk

Premier Propshaft Co Ltd, 24-26 Atherstone Road, Hartshill, Nuneaton, Warwickshire, CV10 0SP Tel: (024) 7639 3806 Fax: (024) 7639 3452

Reco-Prop UK Ltd, Unit 4 New Town Trading Estate, Chase Street, Luton, LU1 3QZ Tel: (01582) 412110 Fax: (01582) 480432 E-mail: info@reco-prop.com

PROPELLING PENCILS

Sanford Europe Parker Pen Co., 52 Railway Road, Newhaven, East Sussex, BN9 0AU Tel: (01273) 513233 Fax: (01273) 514773 E-mail: enquiries@parkerpen.co.uk

PROPERTY AGENTS, COMMERCIAL, *See Commercial Property Agents*

PROPERTY AGENTS, INDUSTRIAL, *See Industrial Property Agents*

PROPERTY DEVELOPMENT CONSULTANCY

A C Nicholas Ltd, Nicon House, 45 Silver St, Enfield, Middlesex, EN1 3EF Tel: (020) 8363 8366 Fax: (020) 8367 7841

▶ indicates data change since last edition

PROPERTY DEVELOPMENT CONSULTANCY – *continued*

Amec Developments Ltd, Tolworth Tower, Ewell Road, Surbiton, Surrey, KT6 7EL Tel: (020) 8390 8300 Fax: (020) 8339 4699

B A A Lynton, Medici Court, 67-69 New Bond Street, London, W1S 1DF Tel: (020) 7907 9200 Fax: (020) 7907 9299

Baltic Wharf Boatyard Ltd, Baltic Wharf Business Centre, St. Peters Quay, Totnes, Devon, TQ9 5EW Tel: (01803) 867922 Fax: (01803) 866795 E-mail: sales@balticwharf.co.uk

Barrat Homes Ltd, Barratt House Almondsbury Business Centre, Woodlands, Bradley Stoke, Bristol, BS32 4QH Tel: (01454) 202202 Fax: (01454) 612277

Barwood Developments Ltd, The Grange, Warren Office Village, Wolverton Mill, Milton Keynes, MK12 5NE Tel: (01908) 577600 Fax: (01908) 312017 E-mail: info@barwood.co.uk

Beva Investments Ltd, Chichester Business Centre, Chichester Street, Rochdale, Lancashire, OL16 2AU Tel: (01706) 710740 Fax: (01706) 710536 E-mail: investments@beva.co.uk

Capital & Countys, 40 Broadway, London, SW1H 0BU Tel: (020) 7887 7000 Fax: (020) 7887 0004

Charles Church Developments Ltd, Charles Church House, Knoll Road, Camberley, Surrey, GU15 3TQ Tel: (01276) 808080 Fax: (01276) 808030

▶ Charles James Homes, Chanctonbury Walk, Storrington, Pulborough, West Sussex, RH20 4LT Tel: (01903) 741155 Fax: (01903) 745599

Colliers Cre, 9 Marylebone Lane, London, W1U 1HL Tel: (020) 7935 4499 Fax: (020) 7487 1894 E-mail: property@collierscre.co.uk

Crown Park Consultants Ltd, 343 Union Street, Aberdeen, AB11 6BS Tel: (01224) 588348 Fax: (01224) 584317 E-mail: info@crown-park.fsnet.co.uk

D T Z Debenham Tie Leung, 30 Throgmorton Street, London, EC2N 2BQ Tel: (020) 7710 8000 Fax: (020) 7710 8080

David Lewis & Co., 21 Gloucester Place, London, W1U 8HR Tel: (020) 7486 2277 Fax: (020) 7224 5173

Dencora Property Developers, Dencora Court, Meridian Way, Norwich, NR7 0TA Tel: (01603) 433100 Fax: (01603) 433800 E-mail: admin@dencora.com

Denton & Gibson, Parkside House, 6 Headley Road, Woodley, Reading, RG5 4JB Tel: 0118-944 8558 Fax: 0118-944 8668 E-mail: graham.denton@dentonandgibson.com

Dron & Wright, 80 Cannon Street, London, EC4N 6HL Tel: (020) 7891 2300 Fax: (020) 7891 2300 E-mail: droncity@dronwright.co.uk

E M C O Estates Ltd, Emco House, 5-7 New York Road, Leeds, LS2 7PJ Tel: 0113-244 4236 Fax: 0113-244 0449 E-mail: henry@cityfusion.co.uk

Elliott Property & Leisure Group Ltd, Lee House, 109 Hammersmith Road, London, W14 0QH Tel: (020) 7371 2244 Fax: (020) 7371 2424 E-mail: edl@elliotgroup.co.uk

▶ Ensign Property Management Ltd, Botany Way, Ensign Estate, Arterial Road, Purfleet, Essex, RM19 1TB Tel: (01708) 868844 Fax: (01708) 868278 E-mail: en@mckellargroup.com

The G H M Consultancy Group Ltd, Wheathampstead, St. Albans, Hertfordshire, AL4 8BU Tel: (01582) 834233 Fax: (01582) 832176 E-mail: ghm@ghm-group.co.uk

Greenwood Structures, 67 Trafalgar Road, Moseley, Birmingham, B13 8BL Tel: 0121-449 0278 Fax: 0121-249 2499

Hartnell Taylor Cook, 18 Canynge Road, Bristol, BS8 3JX Tel: 0117-923 9234 Fax: 0117-923 9237 E-mail: sales@hartnelltaylorcook.co.uk

Heron Broadwick Ltd, Heron House, 19 Marylebone Road, London, NW1 5JL Tel: (020) 7486 4477 Fax: (020) 7486 3349

Howard Grove Ltd, 93 Regent Street, Cambridge, CB2 1AW Tel: (01223) 312910 Fax: 01233 312911 E-mail: webmaster@howard-holdings.com

▶ Hugh Bourn Ltd, Louth Road, Wragby, Market Rasen, Lincolnshire, LN8 5PH Tel: (01673) 858831 Fax: (01673) 857006 E-mail: info@hughbourn.co.uk

▶ Huramic Developments Ltd, Manor Mead, Manor Farm Lane, Oldbury, Bridgnorth, Shropshire, WV16 5HG Tel: (01746) 766948

Industrious Ltd, 5th Floor, Radcliffe House, Blenheim Court, Solihull, West Midlands, B91 2AA Tel: 0121-712 6660 Fax: 0121-712 6661 E-mail: info@industrious.co.uk

Jarvis Homes Ltd, No.1 Waterside, Station Road, Harpenden, Hertfordshire, AL5 4US Tel: (01582) 761211 Fax: (01582) 764100

John D Wood, Warnford Court, 29 Throgmorton Street, London, EC2N 2AT Tel: (020) 7588 0557 Fax: (020) 7588 7277 E-mail: paul.kennerley@johndwood.com

John Francis Ltd, 18 Lammas Street, Carmarthen, Dyfed, SA31 3AJ Tel: (01267) 233111 Fax: (01267) 235430 E-mail: carmarthen@johnfrancis.co.uk

Killiney Properties Ltd, 207 Barkby Road, Leicester, LE4 9HZ Tel: 0116-276 7554 Fax: 0116-246 0447

King Sturge, 30 Warwick Street, London, W1B 5NH Tel: (020) 7493 4933 Fax: (020) 7409 0469 E-mail: firstname.surname@kingsturge.com

Mealey Horgan plc, 16 Park Street, London, W1K 2HZ Tel: (020) 7499 4902 Fax: (020) 7499 4903 E-mail: mealyhorgan@btclick.com

Mepc Milton Park Ltd, 6g Milton Park, Milton, Abingdon, Oxfordshire, OX14 4RR Tel: (01235) 865555 Fax: (01235) 865560 E-mail: enquiries@miltonpark.co.uk

Mercian Developments Ltd, Mercian House 9-10 Darwin Court Clayton Way, Oxon Business Park, Bicton Heath, Shrewsbury, SY3 5AL Tel: (01743) 352415 Fax: (01743) 232349 E-mail: mail@merciandev.co.uk

Merriman Mineral Processing, Charnwood Edge, Syston Road, Cossington, Leicester, LE7 4UZ Tel: 0116-269 5137 Fax: 0116-269 2261 E-mail: sales@merrimans.com

O C S Group Ltd, Trafford Bank House, 32 Brindley Road, Manchester, M16 9SA Tel: 0161-876 9151 Fax: 0161-876 2702 E-mail: enquiries@ocs.co.uk

Pavilion Estates Ltd, 7 Somerby Road, Pickwell, Melton Mowbray, Leicestershire, LE14 2RA Tel: (01664) 454869 Fax: (01664) 454869

Persimmon Homes Developments Ltd, Persimmon House, Fulford, York, YO19 4FE Tel: (01904) 642199 Fax: (01904) 610014

Pertwee Holdings Ltd, Lodge Lane, Langham, Colchester, CO4 5NE Tel: (01206) 231000 Fax: (01206) 231132 E-mail: mail@pertwee.co.uk

Rugby Estates plc, 14 Garrick Street, London, WC2E 9SB Tel: (020) 7632 2200 Fax: (020) 7632 2222E-mail: assets@rugbyestates.plc.uk

Try Homes Southern Ltd, Bridge House, 27 Bridge Street, Leatherhead, Surrey, KT22 8HL Tel: (01372) 385170 Fax: (01372) 385199 E-mail: customerservice@tryhomes.co.uk

Tudol International Ltd, Colette Court, 125 Sloane Street, London, SW1X 9AU Tel: (020) 7730 9962 Fax: (020) 7824 8691 E-mail: mail@tudol.co.uk

Peter Ward Homes Ltd, Suite A Annie Reed Court, Annie Reed Road, Beverley, North Humberside, HU17 0LF Tel: (01482) 861484 Fax: (01482) 863227 E-mail: ward@peterwardhomes.co.uk

Westbury Homes, Glanville House, Church Street, Bridgwater, Somerset, TA6 5AT Tel: (01278) 458645 Fax: (01278) 452274

▶ Westbury Homes, Bartley House, Station Road, Hook, Hampshire, RG27 9JF Tel: (01256) 744000 Fax: (01256) 769388

Windlelm Ltd, 130 Western Road, Hove, East Sussex, BN3 1DA Tel: (01273) 770681 Fax: (01273) 321387

PROPERTY DEVELOPMENT HOLDING OR INVESTMENT AUTHORITIES OR COMPANIES

▶ Alston Country Homes, Squirrels Lodge Hards Lane, Frognall, Peterborough, PE6 8RL Tel: (01778) 346773 Fax: (01778) 349131

ASDA Securities Ltd, 58 Queen Anne St, London, W1G 8HW Tel: (020) 7224 1030 Fax: (020) 7224 0574

Bride Hall, 49 Hays Mews, London, W1J 5QQ Tel: (020) 7493 3996 Fax: (020) 7499 4388 E-mail: developments@bride-hall.co.uk

▶ Bryant Homes Southern Counties, Templars House, Lulworth Close, Chandler"s Ford, Eastleigh, Hampshire, SO53 3TJ Tel: (023) 8025 5288 Fax: (023) 8025 1344

Cala Management Ltd, Adobe House, 5 Mid New Cultins, Edinburgh, EH11 4DU Tel: 0131-453 6192 Fax: 0131-535 5201 E-mail: info@cala.co.uk

CB Richard Ellis, 7 Castle Street, Edinburgh, EH3 3AH Tel: 0131-469 7666 Fax: 0131-469 0131 E-mail: info@cbre.com

Charles Church Developments Ltd, Charles Church House, Knoll Road, Camberley, Surrey, GU15 3TQ Tel: (01276) 808080 Fax: (01276) 808030

▶ Clayson Country Homes Ltd, 447 Wellingborough Road, Northampton, NN1 4EZ Tel: (01604) 604033 Fax: (01604) 604762

Clyde Building Group plc, 161-181 Whitefield Road, Glasgow, G51 2SD Tel: 0141-445 1242 Fax: 0141-440 5375

Conder Developments Ltd, 3rd Floor Royal Buildings, Victoria Street, Derby, DE1 1ES Tel: (01332) 299777 Fax: (01332) 299595 E-mail: info@conder.dev.fsnet.co.uk

Dovey Estates Ltd, Suffolk House, Trade Street, Cardiff, CF10 5DQ Tel: (029) 2034 4150 Fax: (029) 2034 4170 E-mail: dovey@estatesltd.fsnet.co.uk

F A Would Ltd, Ladysmith Road, Grimsby, South Humberside, DN32 9SH Tel: (01472) 241303 Fax: (01472) 360262 E-mail: enqiries@wouldgroup.com

First, Corporate Communications Macmillan House, Paddington, London, W2 1FG Tel: (020) 7291 0500 Fax: (020) 7636 1338

Folkes Group Ltd, 7orge House, Dudley Road, Stourbridge, West Midlands, DY9 8EL Tel: (01384) 424242 Fax: (01384) 424425

George Fordy & Son Ltd, Construction House, Northallerton, North Yorkshire, DL7 8ED Tel: (01609) 780700 Fax: (01609) 777236 E-mail: fordy@ftcg.co.uk

George Higginson Ltd, PO Box 7, Chipping Campden, Gloucestershire, GL55 6UL Tel: (01386) 841481 Fax: (01386) 841581

Gerald Eve & Co Services Ltd, 7 Veer Street, London, W1G 0JB Tel: (020) 7493 3338 Fax: (020) 7491 1825 E-mail: evemail@geraldeve.com

Goodman Business Parks UK Ltd, Arlington House, Arlington Business Park, Reading, RG7 4SA Tel: 0118-930 4141 Fax: 0118-930 4383 E-mail: rececption@arlington.com

Grosvenor Securities Ltd, 28 Bolton Street, Mayfair, London, W1J 8BP Tel: (020) 7629 9933 Fax: (020) 7493 5561 E-mail: rogermoss@grosvenorsecurities.com

Helical Bar Chiswell Street Ltd, 11-15 Farm Street, London, W1J 5RS Tel: (020) 7629 0113 Fax: (020) 7408 1666 E-mail: tjm@helical.co.uk

Independent Property Preservation Group, Woodlawn, Sydenham Avenue, Belfast, BT4 2DT Tel: (028) 9065 1750 Fax: (028) 9065 0090

John D Wood & Co., 2 Jewry Street, Winchester, Hampshire, SO23 8RZ Tel: (01962) 863131 Fax: (01962) 841789 E-mail: sales@win.johndwood.co.uk

Robert Jordan & Associates, 10 Alderley Road, Wilmslow, Cheshire, SK9 1JX Tel: (01625) 250000 Fax: (01625) 250005 E-mail: wilmslow@robertjordan.co.uk

Kingstons Homes Ltd, The Estate Office West Hall, Parvis Road, West Byfleet, Surrey, KT14 6EP Tel: (01932) 340111 Fax: (01932) 352602

L C P Developments Ltd, L C P House, The Pensnett Estate, Kingswinford, West Midlands, DY6 7NA Tel: (01384) 400123 Fax: (01384) 400862

Land Securities Finance Ltd, 5 Strand, London, WC2N 5HR Tel: (020) 7413 9000 Fax: (020) 7920202 E-mail: landsecurities@landsecurites.com

Mahler Investments Ltd, Mahler Ho, 130 Worcester Rd, Droitwich, Worcs, WR9 8AN Tel: (01905) 770024 Fax: (01905) 795233

Midas, Trafford Wharf Road, Trafford Park, Manchester, M17 1EX Tel: 0161-877 3000 Fax: 0161-848 8638 E-mail: midas@midas.org.uk

Millhouse Developments, Ravensworth House, 1 Ravensworth Street, Bedlington, Northumberland, NE22 7JP Tel: (01670) 530616 Fax: (01670) 829649

Minns (Oxford) Ltd, Willow Court, 7 West Way, Oxford, OX2 0JB Tel: (01865) 258600 Fax: (01865) 250123 E-mail: kevin.minns@minns.co.uk

P & O Developments Ltd, 4 Carlton Gardens, Pall Mall, London, SW1Y 5AB Tel: (020) 7839 5611 Fax: (020) 7930 2098

Persimmon Homes South East Ltd, Persimmons House, Brooklands Business Park, Weybridge, Surrey, KT13 0YP Tel: (01932) 350555 Fax: (01932) 350022

Richardson Developments Ltd, 100 Dudley Road East, Oldbury, West Midlands, B69 3DY Tel: 0121-544 8000 Fax: 0121-552 9838

Robert Mcalpine Ltd, Eaton Court, Maylands Avenue, Hemel Hempstead Industrial Estate, Hemel Hempstead, Hertfordshire, HP2 7TR Tel: (01442) 233444 Fax: (01442) 230024 E-mail: sales@sir-robert-mcalpine.com

Roce Management, 27 Park Avenue, Wraysbury, Staines, Middlesex, TW19 5EU Tel: (01784) 489090 Fax: (01784) 489099 E-mail: info@roce.co.uk

Safeland (Ground Rents) Ltd, 94/96 Great North Road, London, N2 0NL Tel: (020) 8815 1600

St Martins Group Ltd, Shackleton House, 4 Battlebridge Lane, London, SE1 2HX Tel: (020) 7940 7700 Fax: (020) 7940 7744 E-mail: mail@samaprop.co.uk

Shaftsbury P.L.C., Pegasus House, 37-43 Sackville Street, London, W1S 3DL Tel: (020) 7333 8118 Fax: (020) 7333 0660 E-mail: shaftesbury@shaftesbury.co.uk

Slough Estates P.L.C., 234 Bath Road, Slough, SL1 4EE Tel: (01753) 537171 Fax: (01753) 820585 E-mail: property@sloughestates.co.uk

Tull Properties Ltd, Bath Road, Box, Corsham, Wiltshire, SN13 8AA Tel: (01225) 744321 Fax: (01225) 744333 E-mail: office@tullprop.com

Wereldhave Property Corporation plc, 39 Sloane Street, London, SW1X 9WR Tel: (020) 7235 2080 Fax: (020) 7245 9962

Westhaven Properties Ltd, 1 Sherbourne Road, Acocks Green, Birmingham, B27 6AB Tel: 0121-706 6100 Fax: 0121-707 1890

Wilcon Connooly Ltd, Thomas Wilson House, Tenter Rd, Moulton Park, Northampton, NN3 6QJ Tel: (01604) 790909 Fax: (01604) 790467 E-mail: wilcosconnoolly@wilcon.co.uk

Wilson Connolly Scotland Ltd, 2 Garbett Road, Livingston, West Lothian, EH54 7DL Tel: (01506) 405700 Fax: (01506) 405701 E-mail: scotland@wilsonconnolly.co.uk

Wrexham County Borough Council, The Guildhall, Wrexham, Clwyd, LL11 1AY Tel: (01978) 292000 Fax: (01978) 292106 E-mail: business@wrexham.gov.uk

▶ Zetland Estates Ltd, Estate Office, Aske Hall, Richmond, North Yorkshire, DL10 5HJ Tel: (01748) 822000 Fax: (01748) 826611 E-mail: estate.office@aske.co.uk

PROPERTY FLOOD PROTECTION CONSULTANCY

▶ Affordable Flood Solutions Ltd, 16 Birch Green, Staines, Middlesex, TW18 4HA Tel: (01784) 460874 Fax: (01784) 460894 E-mail: info@a-f-s.biz

PROPERTY HOLDING/OWNING COMPANIES OR ORGANISATIONS

Barratt's International Resorts Ltd, Dalfaber Village, Aviemore, Inverness-Shire, PH22 1ST Tel: (01479) 810810 Fax: (01479) 811510 E-mail: ownerservices@mcdonald-hotel.co.uk

The British Land Corporation Ltd, York House, 45 Seymour Street, London, W1H 7LX Tel: (020) 7486 4466 Fax: (020) 7935 5552 E-mail: info@britishland.com

Greet Steel Properties Ltd, 1 Salters Lane, West Bromwich, West Midlands, B71 4BG Tel: 0121-553 1700 Fax: 0121-553 1700

Howard De Walden Estates Ltd, 23 Queen Anne Street, London, W1G 9DL Tel: (020) 7580 3163 Fax: (020) 7436 8152 E-mail: olwen-seear@howard-de-walden.co.uk

J L G Investments Ltd, 3 Claridge Court, Lower Kings Road, Berkhamsted, Hertfordshire, HP4 2AF Tel: (01442) 877866 Fax: (01442) 877806 E-mail: david@jlginvest.demon.co.uk

James Drewitt & Son Ltd, 865 Ringwood Road, West Howe, Bournemouth, BH11 8IW Tel: (01202) 575757 Fax: (01202) 582500

Kingstons Homes Ltd, The Estate Office West Hall, Parvis Road, West Byfleet, Surrey, KT14 6EP Tel: (01932) 340111 Fax: (01932) 352602

Langpark Ltd, 93 Manthorpe Road, Grantham, Lincolnshire, NG31 8DE Tel: (01476) 574509

Pertwee Holdings Ltd, Lodge Lane, Langham, Colchester, CO4 5NE Tel: (01206) 231000 Fax: (01206) 231132 E-mail: mail@pertwee.co.uk

Pugh Davies & Co. Ltd, 1 Tabley Mews, Stamford Street, Altrincham, Cheshire, WA14 1DA Tel: (0161) 929 1110 Fax: (0161) 228 2520 E-mail: info@pughdavies.co.uk

R & D Aggregates Ltd, 12 Lisle Avenue, Kidderminster, Worcestershire, DY11 7DL Tel: (01562) 745683 Fax: (01562) 820861 E-mail: info@unitstolet.net

▶ Rilmac Scaffolding Ltd, Crofton Drive, Lincoln, LN3 4NJ Tel: (01522) 531711 Fax: (01522) 781444 E-mail: enquiries@rilmac.co.uk

St Martins Group Ltd, Shackleton House, 4 Battlebridge Lane, London, SE1 2HX Tel: (020) 7940 7700 Fax: (020) 7940 7744 E-mail: mail@samaprop.co.uk

Simmons & Hawker Ltd, Falcon House, Central Way, Feltham, Middlesex, TW14 0UQ Tel: (020) 8867 0070 Fax: (020) 8893 1987 E-mail: barryj@hma.co.uk

W D Stirling Ltd, Drummond House, Gainsborough Drive, Sherborne, Dorset, DT9 6DS Tel: (01935) 817399

PROPERTY INVESTMENT AGENTS

Hunting Gate Wilshere Ltd, 2 Hunting Gate, Hitchin, Hertfordshire, SG4 0TJ Tel: (01462) 434444 Fax: (01462) 435905 E-mail: build@hunting-gate.co.uk

Mason Philips, 33 Great Portland Street, London, W1W 8QG Tel: (020) 7436 1212 Fax: (020) 7436 1350 E-mail: property@masonphilips.co.uk

Molyneux Rose Ltd, 143 New Bond Street, London, W1S 2TP Tel: (020) 7409 0130 Fax: (020) 7499 7636 E-mail: retail@molyrose.co.uk

▶ The New Forest Estate Agents, PO Box 5561, Ringwood, Hampshire, BH24 2ZS Tel: 08700 11 45 75 Fax: 08700 11 45 76 E-mail: info@NewForestEstateAgents.com

Peter Taylor & Co., 8 Hanover Street, London, W1S 1PT Tel: (020) 7290 2662 Fax: (020) 7290 2686

United Trade & Services Ltd, 256 Water Road, Wembley, Middlesex, HA0 1HX Tel: (020) 8810 6444 Fax: (020) 8810 6455 E-mail: united.trade@btinternet.com

Warwickshire Investment Partnership, Shire Hall, Warwick, CV34 4SX Tel: (01926) 412830 Fax: (01926) 410268 E-mail: wips@warwickshire.gov.uk

PROPERTY INVESTMENT COMPANIES OR SERVICES

A C Nicholas Ltd, Nicon House, 45 Silver St, Enfield, Middlesex, EN1 3EF Tel: (020) 8363 8366 Fax: (020) 8367 7841

B A A Lynton, Medici Court, 67-69 New Bond Street, London, W1S 1DF Tel: (020) 7907 9200 Fax: (020) 7907 9299

Barlows Securities plc, Chepstow House, Dee Hills Park, Chester, CH3 5AR Tel: (01244) 350202 Fax: (01244) 311522

Barratt Developments plc, Rotterdam House, 116 Quayside, Newcastle upon Tyne, NE1 3DA Tel: 0191-227 2000 Fax: 0191-227 2001

Brixton Plc, 50 Berkeley St, London, W1J 8BX Tel: (020) 7399 4500 Fax: (020) 7399 4550

C L P Structured Finance Ltd, 131 Baker Street, London, W1U 6SE Tel: (020) 7486 0655 Fax: (020) 7935 5489 E-mail: mail@cpl.uk.com

E M C O Estates Ltd, Emco House, 5-7 New York Road, Leeds, LS2 7PJ Tel: 0113-244 4236 Fax: 0113-244 0449 E-mail: henry@cityfusion.co.uk

PROPERTY INVESTMENT COMPANIES OR SERVICES – *continued*

Great Portland Estates P L C, 33 Cavendish Square, London, W1G 0PW Tel: (020) 7647 3000 Fax: (020) 7016 5500 E-mail: firstname.lastname@gpe.co.uk
Ivor Hill Ltd, 413 Durnsford Road, London, SW19 8EE Tel: (020) 8946 8650 Fax: (020) 8946 8650
Industrious Ltd, 5th Floor, Radcliffe House, Blenheim Court, Solihull, West Midlands, B91 2AA Tel: 0121-712 6660 Fax: 0121-712 6661 E-mail: info@industrious.co.uk
Jarvis Homes Ltd, No.1 Waterside, Station Road, Harpenden, Hertfordshire, AL5 4US Tel: (01582) 761211 Fax: (01582) 764100
K B Benfield Group Holdings Ltd, 88 Paynes Lane, Coventry, CV1 5LJ Tel: (024) 7622 7557 Fax: (024) 7622 1217 E-mail: mail@benfieldgroup.co.uk
Land Securities Finance Ltd, 5 Strand, London, WC2N 5HR Tel: (020) 7413 9000 Fax: (020) 7920202 E-mail: landsecurities@landsecurites.com
Lands Improvement Co., 1 Buckingham Place, London, SW1E 6HR Tel: (020) 7222 5331 Fax: (020) 7630 7034 E-mail: enquiries@lih.co.uk
Marmerstein Ltd, 10-14 Hewett Street, London, EC2A 3RL Tel: (020) 7247 1483 Fax: (020) 7539 1111 E-mail: fein@kimpton.co.uk
Mountcity Investments Ltd, Wellington House, Bean Road, Bilston, West Midlands, WV14 9EE Tel: (01902) 887644 Fax: (01902) 887638 E-mail: mountcity@mountcity.com
Norton Newman Investments Ltd, 1-6 Clay Street, London, W1U 6DA Tel: (020) 7486 4889 Fax: (020) 8441 8337 E-mail: mnorton@focusnet.co.uk
Pertwee Holdings Ltd, Lodge Lane, Langham, Colchester, CO4 5NE Tel: (01206) 231000 Fax: (01206) 231132 E-mail: mail@pertwee.co.uk
Properteam Ltd, 15 Boulthurst Way, Oxted, Surrey, RH8 0HT Tel: (01883) 382888 E-mail: sales@properteam.co.uk
R A Hulland Group Ltd, 239 High St, Cymmer, Porth, Mid Glamorgan, CF39 9AD Tel: (01443) 684844 Fax: (01443) 684847 E-mail: ray@rahullandgroup.co.uk
Robert Deards Ltd, Deards Corner, North Circular Road, London, N12 0SH Tel: (020) 8368 5562 Fax: (020) 8368 0002
St Martins Group Ltd, Shackleton House, 4 Battlebridge Lane, London, SE1 2HX Tel: (020) 7940 7700 Fax: (020) 7940 7744 E-mail: mail@samaprop.co.uk
Shelana Fashions Ltd, 31 Eastcastle Street, London, W1N 8NL Tel: (020) 7580 0401 Fax: (020) 7436 5445 E-mail: shelanainvestments@talk21.com
Simmonds Heath Company Estate Agents, 61 Grosvenor Street, London, W1K 3JE Tel: (020) 7491 8845 Fax: (020) 7493 6455 E-mail: robert@simmondsheath.com
▶ Sussex Homesearch Ltd, Fairyhill, Old Broyle Road, Chichester, West Sussex, PO19 3PJ Tel: 01243 771321 Fax: 01243 771321 E-mail: info@sussexhomesearch.co.uk
Tychon Partnership, West Point, 78 Queens Road, Bristol, BS8 1QX Tel: 0117-907 5595 Fax: 0117-925 4556
Wigmore Managements Ltd, 65 Wigmore Street, London, W1U 1BQ Tel: (020) 7935 0192 Fax: (020) 7935 3074

PROPERTY MAGAZINES

Estates Gazette, 147-151 Wardour Street, London, W1F 8BN Tel: (020) 7437 0141 Fax: (020) 7411 2874
EuroProperty, 1 Proctor Street, London, WC1V 6EU Tel: (020) 7911 1700 Fax: (020) 7911 1730 E-mail: customer.services@europroperty.com

PROPERTY MAINTENANCE

A Evans Builders, 7 Langham Green, Sutton Coldfield, West Midlands, B74 3PS Tel: 0121-353 3661 Fax: 0121-353 3661 E-mail: albert.evans@btinternet.com
Abbey Developments Ltd, Abbey House, 2 Southgate Road, Potters Bar, Hertfordshire, EN6 5DU Tel: (01707) 651266 Fax: (01707) 646836
Abbots Mead Builders, Unit 18 Bumpers Lane, Sealand Industrial Estate, Chester, CH1 4LT Tel: (01244) 374987 Fax: (01244) 375544
Advanced Main Drain, 109 High Street, Edenbridge, Kent, TN8 5AX Tel: (01732) 863607 Fax: (01732) 866931
Advanced Property Solutions, 38 Riverside Steps, St. Annes Park, Bristol, BS4 4RH Tel: (07775) 671339 E-mail: anything@advancedpropertysolutions.co.uk
Alpine Preservations, 14 Redpol Avenue, Leigh, Lancashire, WN7 2GA Tel: (01942) 742230 Fax: (01942) 603608 E-mail: p.balickyj@blueyondar.co.uk
▶ Associated Securities, Unit 14 15, Cam Square, Wilbury Way, Hitchin, Hertfordshire, SG4 0TZ Tel: (01462) 421188 Fax: 01462 421188 E-mail: associatedsecurities@btconnect.com
▶ A-Tec Property Services, 9 Redhill Close, Bassett, Southampton, SO16 7BT Tel: (07957) 830615 Fax: (023) 8032 5178 E-mail: paulewilcox@hotmail.com
▶ Blundeston Property Maintenance, 61 Lakeside Rise, Blundeston, Lowestoft, Suffolk, NR32 5BD Tel: (07887) 604133 E-mail: philip.hannant@btinternet.com
▶ Alan Bramwell General Property Maintenance, 7 Holt Drive, Matlock, Derbyshire, DE4 3BB Tel: (07708) 557289 E-mail: handyman@brammy.co.uk
▶ Building & Property Defence Ltd, R A F Beaconside, Stafford, ST18 0AQ Tel: (01785) 250749
C & C Property Consultants, 145-157 St. John Street, London, EC1V 4PY Tel: (0845) 0538867 Fax: (0707) 5209515 E-mail: pmsgwentltd@yahoo.com
▶ C J Worship & Co. (Hull) Ltd, King Edward Road, Thorne, Doncaster, South Yorkshire, DN8 4HU Tel: (01405) 814939
C L C Contractors Anglia, 7 Station Way, Brandon, Suffolk, IP27 0BH Tel: (01842) 813972 Fax: 01842 813113 E-mail: brandon@clcgroup.com
▶ Castle Properties, 7-9 Portland Street, Cheltenham, Gloucestershire, GL52 2NZ Tel: 0870 240 7113 E-mail: info@castleprop.co.uk
▶ City Renovations Ltd, 10 Bond Avenue Bletchley, Bletchley, Milton Keynes, MK1 1SW Tel: (01908) 366936
City Response Ltd, 19 Cross Keys Street, Manchester, M4 5ET Tel: 0161-832 8325 Fax: 0161-834 2260
▶ Cleancut Ltd, 4 Tripps Mews, Manchester, M20 2JT Tel: 0161-448 8090 Fax: 0161-448 8033
Durkan Properties Ltd, Durkan House, 214-224 High Street, Waltham Cross, Hertfordshire, EN8 7DU Tel: (01992) 781400 Fax: (01992) 781500 E-mail: info@durkan.co.uk
Edwards S M Building Contractors, 77 Old Coach Road, Kelsall, Tarporley, Cheshire, CW6 0RA Tel: (01829) 752028 Fax: (01829) 751559
Essex & Anglia Preservation Ltd, 24 Church End Lane, Runwell, Wickford, Essex, SS11 7JQ Tel: (0800) 0851695 Fax: (0800) 0851695 E-mail: info@essexandanglia.co.uk
The Ford Group (Nottingham) Ltd, Park Lane Works, Old Basford, Nottingham, NG6 0EU Tel: 0115-977 0724 Fax: 0115-976 1041 E-mail: ford@fordgroup.co.uk
G I Sykes Ltd, The Hayes, Lye, Stourbridge, West Midlands, DY9 8NX Tel: (01384) 891341 Fax: (01384) 894773
▶ Ga Services, 99 Cumberland Road, London, E13 8LH Tel: (020) 7476 2746 Fax: (020) 7476 5200
GSH Ltd, GSH House, Forge Lane, Stoke-on-Trent, ST1 5PZ Tel: (01782) 200400 Fax: (01782) 285552 E-mail: vacancies@gshgroup.com
H A Window Cleaning, 48 Aberley Avenue, Stourport-On-Severn, Worcestershire, DY13 0LZ Tel: (07801) 369265 E-mail: a.muir1@btinternet.com
Haden Building Management Ltd, Summit House, Glebe Way, West Wickham, Kent, BR4 0RJ Tel: (020) 8918 4200 Fax: (020) 8918 4391
▶ Hollingbourne Property Services Ltd, Eyhorne Green, Musket Lane, Hollingbourne, Maidstone, Kent, ME17 1UU Tel: (01622) 880000 Fax: (01622) 880668
Ian Williams, Station Road, Warmley, Bristol, BS30 8XG Tel: 0117-960 9510 Fax: 0117-935 3772E-mail: lynne.westcott@ianwilliams.co.uk
▶ Inside Out Property Maintenance & Landscaping, 25 Roundhill Way, Guildford, Surrey, GU2 8HJ Tel: 01483 459344 E-mail: insideoutpml@btinternet.com
Integral, Broadoak Business Park, Ashburton Road West, Trafford Park, Manchester, M17 1RW Tel: 0161-872 7925 Fax: 0161-872 9508
▶ J D Property Maintenance, 81 Kingsland Road, Worthing, West Sussex, BN14 9EE Tel: (01903) 527449 E-mail: jd_property_maintenance@hotmail.co.uk
J & R Killick Ltd, 47 Station Approach, Hayes, Bromley, BR2 7EB Tel: (020) 8462 1009 Fax: (020) 8777 2744
Kier Southern, St. Andrews House, West Street, Havant, Hampshire, PO9 1LB Tel: (023) 9248 4343 Fax: (023) 9245 5414 E-mail: lisa.haywood@kier.co.uk
Kilbey Cleaning & Maintenance Services, 104 Mansfield Road, London, NW3 2HX Tel: (020) 7267 8829 Fax: (020) 7284 4525
▶ Kingsmede Ltd, 18 Warbreck Drive Bispham, Blackpool, FY2 9RZ Tel: (01253) 358827 E-mail: handymen@kingsmede.co.uk
KSM Property Maintenance South East Ltd, PO Box 8002, Harlow, Essex, CM20 3XA Tel: (01279) 439777 Fax: (01279) 439750 E-mail: sales@ksm-maintenance.co.uk
The Lord Group Ltd, Oak Mill Mellor Street, Rochdale, Lancashire, OL12 6UY Tel: (01706) 341311 Fax: (01706) 861810 E-mail: info@thelordgroup.co.uk
▶ Main Pro, 51 Waybridge Industrial Estate, Daniel Adamson Road, Salford, M50 1DS Tel: (0870) 7774595 Fax: (0870) 7774596 E-mail: manchester@main-pro.co.uk
Mansell Construction Services Ltd, Roman House, Salisbury Road, Totton, Southampton, SO40 3XF Tel: (023) 8058 0400 Fax: (023) 8058 0401 E-mail: southampton@mansell.plc.uk
Mansell Construction Services Ltd, Wollaston Road, Stourbridge, West Midlands, DY8 4HP Tel: (01384) 440330 Fax: (01384) 440169 E-mail: stourbridge@mansell.plc.uk
Mika Property Building Services, 6 Tern Road, Porthcawl, Mid Glamorgan, CF36 3TS Tel: (01656) 786150 Fax: (01656) 786158 E-mail: mikapbs@aol.com
Mitie Property Services Eastern Ltd, Davey Close, Colchester, CO1 2XL Tel: (01206) 871954 Fax: (01206) 863818 E-mail: property.colchester@mitie.co.uk
Mitie Property Services (Midlands) Ltd, Coppice Side Industrial Estate, Brownhills, Walsall, WS8 7HF Tel: (01543) 375461 Fax: (01543) 378194
▶ Olimax Property Care Ltd, Olimax Property Care Limited,, Olimax House, 17 Donald Aldred Drive, Burley In Wharfedale, Ilkley, West Yorkshire, LS29 7SG Tel: 01943 865721 E-mail: info@olimax.net
▶ P F I Property Maintanence, 1-3 Roland Court, Huntington, York, YO32 9PW Tel: (01904) 750255 Fax: (01904) 750616
Pavilion Estates Ltd, 7 Somerby Road, Pickwell, Melton Mowbray, Leicestershire, LE14 2RA Tel: (01664) 454869 Fax: (01664) 454869
Prestige Building Services (SE), 27 Lennard Road, Dunton Green, Sevenoaks, Kent, TN13 2UX Tel: (01732) 458936 Fax: (07092) 375881 E-mail: sales@prestigebuilding.com
Prodec Contracting, Hallsford Bridge Industrial Estate, Stondon Road, Ongar, Essex, CM5 9RB Tel: (01708) 864774 Fax: (01277) 362225
▶ Proserve UK Ltd, 7 Waterside Trading Estate, Mill Lane, Leigh, Lancashire, WN7 2BG Tel: (01942) 260062 Fax: (01942) 261212 E-mail: sales@mainbuild.co.uk
R Mansell (Developments) Ltd, Roman House, 13/27 Grant Road, Croydon, CR9 6BU Tel: (020) 8654 8191 Fax: (020) 8655 1286 E-mail: mailbox@mansell.plc.uk
R Roberts & Son, 260 Conway Road, Mochdre, Colwyn Bay, Clwyd, LL28 5DS Tel: (01492) 546917 Fax: (01492) 543600
▶ R & S Property Services, Unit 2, 14 Barr's Road, Taplow, Maidenhead, Berkshire, SL6 0LE Tel: (01628) 661666 E-mail: rnsa1@hotmail.com
▶ Reading Maintenance Co., 621 Oxford Road, Reading, RG30 1HP Tel: 0118-950 7450
▶ Reliable Property Maintenance, 43-45 Windsor Drive, Orpington, Kent, BR6 6EY Tel: (01689) 855647 Fax: (01689) 858809
Renlon Holdings Ltd, Richardson House, Boundary Business Court, Mitcham, Surrey, CR4 3TD Tel: (020) 8687 4000 Fax: (020) 8687 4040 E-mail: survey@renlon.com
Rentokil Facilities Maintenance Ltd, Thames House, 27 Elmcroft Road, Orpington, Kent, BR6 0HZ Tel: (01689) 876511 Fax: (01689) 828898 E-mail: rentokfm@netcomuk.co.uk
Ringwood Company Builders, Unit 22 Brookvale Trading Estate, Moor Lane, Birmingham, B6 7AQ Tel: 0121-356 0157 Fax: 0121-344 4867
Rok Property Solutions, 68 Macrae Road, Pill, Bristol, BS20 0DD Tel: (01275) 378800 Fax: (01275) 376369 E-mail: wilkinsonandcoventry@rokgroup.com
Rushforth John Plumbing Heating, 109 King Street, Drighlington, Bradford, West Yorkshire, BD11 1EJ Tel: 0113-285 4539 Fax: 0113-285 3627
S R Industrial Ltd, Unit 42 Longshot Industrial Estate, Longshot Lane, Bracknell, Berkshire, RG12 1RL Tel: (01344) 860145 Fax: (01344) 305313 E-mail: srogers@srindustrial.co.uk
▶ Star Property Maintenance Ltd, Unit 4 Parc-Y-Bont, Millers Avenue, Brynmenyn, Bridgend, CF32 9TD Tel: (01656) 729900 Fax: (01656) 729901 E-mail: star.property.services@virgin.net
Survair Services, Caolils, Glendevon, Dollar, Clackmannanshire, FK14 7JY Tel: (01259) 781282 Fax: (01259) 781291 E-mail: info@survair.co.uk
▶ T&K Summerson, stockgill close, Gamston, Nottingham, NG2 6SA Tel: 0115-981 5153 E-mail: info@tkgardenservices.co.uk
Thames Valley Commercial, 6 Lupton Road, Thame, Oxfordshire, OX9 3SE Tel: (01844) 358200 Fax: (01844) 358201
Thomas Roberts & Co., 13 Chapel Street, Menai Bridge, Gwynedd, LL59 5HW Tel: (01248) 712478
▶ Three Counties Property Maintenance, Aylward Drive, Stevenage, Hertfordshire, SG2 8UR Tel: (01438) 748208 Fax: (01438) 759299 E-mail: info@threecountiespropertymaintenance.co.uk
W.H. Tolley & Son Ltd, Caddywell, Torrington, Devon, EX38 7EL Tel: (01805) 622315 Fax: (01805) 624702 E-mail: wht.hq@virgin.net
▶ Toolbox Buddy, Regus House, George Curl Way, Southampton, SO18 2RZ Tel: 0800 023 4948 E-mail: enquiries@toolboxbuddy.co.uk
▶ W P M R Ltd, 69 Trinity Street, Leamington Spa, Warwickshire, CV32 5YN Tel: (01926) 338845 Fax: (01926) 336613
Waverley Housing Ltd, 27 North Bridge Street, Hawick, Roxburghshire, TD9 9BD Tel: (01450) 364200 Fax: (01450) 375905
▶ WCS, 70 Pendennis Park, Bristol, BS4 4JN Tel: (07966) 504290 E-mail: enq@wcsmaintenance.co.uk
Haden Young Ltd, Suite 7/1 The Skypark 8 Elliot Place, Glasgow, G3 8EP Tel: 0141-248 3701 Fax: 0141-226 4790 E-mail: glasgow@hadenyoung.co.uk

PROPERTY MANAGEMENT AGENTS OR SERVICES

▶ All Property Care, 7 Highfield Close, Danbury, Chelmsford, CM3 4EG Tel: (01245) 222320 E-mail: admin@allpropertycare.co.uk
American Appraisal (UK) Ltd, Portland Buildings, 127-129 Portland Street, Manchester, M1 4PZ Tel: 0161-237 9907 Fax: 0161-237 9908
Arlington Ltd, Gloucester Business Park, Hucclecote, Brockworth, Gloucester, GL3 4AA Tel: (01452) 619281 Fax: (01452) 612943 E-mail: kate.parkin@arlington.co.uk
Armitage Du-Lieu (UK) Ltd, Oakes Mill West, New Hey Road, Lindley, Huddersfield, HD3 4DD Tel: (01484) 648897 Fax: (01484) 648897
Asbestos Surveys & Advice, Suite 7, Cockenzie Business Centre, Edinburgh Road, Cockenzie, Prestonpans, East Lothian, EH32 0HL Tel: 0845 5314268 Fax: (01875) 819111 E-mail: info@asa-asbestos.uk.com
Atco Development, 42 Albemarle Street, London, W1S 4JH Tel: (020) 7491 3664 Fax: (020) 7629 1120 E-mail: liam@atcolondon.com
Bantel Investments Ltd, 45-47 North Bridge Street, Hawick, Roxburghshire, TD9 9PX Tel: (01450) 373352 Fax: (01450) 377531
Bartholomews Chartered Surveyors, 15 Greycoat Place, London, SW1P 1SB Tel: (020) 8546 9441 Fax: (020) 8546 9442 E-mail: enquires@batholomew.com
Bedford Estates, 29a Montague Street, London, WC1B 5BL Tel: (020) 7636 2885 Fax: (020) 7255 1729 E-mail: enquiries@woburnabbey.co.uk
Blaxill Bros Ltd, 122 Stanstead Road, London, SE23 1BX Tel: (020) 8699 3431 Fax: (020) 8699 3431
Bull & Co., 61 La Colomberie, St. Helier, Jersey, JE2 4QA Tel: (01534) 866688 Fax: (01534) 866699 E-mail: enquiries@bullandcompany.com
C I S Communications Ltd, 85 Victoria Road, Netherfield, Nottingham, NG4 2NN Tel: 0115-961 3220 Fax: 0115-911 9449 E-mail: paul.tys@ntlworld.com
▶ Carnochan Brown, 19 Taylor Close, London, N17 0UB Tel: 07770 254470 Fax: 01992 850749 E-mail: will@carnochanbrown.co.uk
Carrington Co. Ltd, Vulcan Way, New Addington, Croydon, CR9 0BN Tel: (01689) 842211
Cartwright Marsdon, 121-123 New Union Street, Coventry, CV1 2NT Tel: (024) 7625 6616 Fax: (024) 7655 1318 E-mail: sales@cartwright-marston.co.uk
Cheltine Ltd, 16 Suffolk Parade, Cheltenham, Gloucestershire, GL50 2AE Tel: (01242) 253243 Fax: (01242) 253243 E-mail: mail@cheltine.co.uk
Cluttons P.L.C., Portman House, 2 Portman Street, London, W1H 6DU Tel: (020) 7408 1010 Fax: (020) 7629 3263 E-mail: ph@cluttons.co.uk
Colliers Cre, 39 George Street, Edinburgh, EH2 2HN Tel: 0131-240 7500 Fax: 0131-240 7599 E-mail: anglia.black@colliersre.co.uk
Co-ordinators Services (Engineering) Ltd, Hazel Lane, Great Wyrley, Walsall, WS6 6AA Tel: (01922) 413712
Dixon Webb, Palmyra Square Chambers, 15 Springfield Street, Warrington, WA1 1BJ Tel: (01925) 577577 Fax: (01925) 579679 E-mail: warrington@dixonwebb.com
Dunster & Morton, 92 London Street, Reading, RG1 4SJ Tel: 0118-955 1700 Fax: 0118-955 1725 E-mail: info@dunsterandmorton.co.uk
Emerson Developments Holdings Ltd, Emerson House, Heyes Lane, Alderley Edge, Cheshire, SK9 7LF Tel: (01625) 588400 Fax: (01625) 585791 E-mail: info@emerson.co.uk
▶ Estate Lettings (Telford & Newport), 119A Trench Road, Trench, EstateLettings.co.uk, Telford, Shropshire, TF2 7DP Tel: 01952 603355 Fax: 08717 312962 E-mail: contact@estatelettings.co.uk
▶ Euro Lab Environmental Ltd, Peartree House, 1 Britannia Road, Warley, Brentwood, Essex, CM14 5LD Tel: (01277) 210022 Fax: (01277) 233049 E-mail: eurolab@btconnect.com
Forsyth J B & G, 79 West Regent St, Glasgow, G2 2AS Tel: 0141-332 8761 Fax: 0141-332 9294
Fresh Wharf Estates Ltd, 1 Fresh Wharf Estate, Highbridge Road, Barking, Essex, IG11 7BP Tel: (020) 8594 2400 Fax: (020) 8594 5105 E-mail: sales@freshwharf.co.uk
Garner & Sons, 15 St Petersgate, Stockport, Cheshire, SK1 1EB Tel: 0161-480 3013 Fax: 0161-477 9125 E-mail: enquiries@garnerandsons.co.uk
George Higginson Ltd, PO Box 7, Chipping Campden, Gloucestershire, GL55 6UL Tel: (01386) 841481 Fax: (01386) 841581
Giordano Ltd, 38-40 Windmill Street, London, W1T 2BE Tel: (020) 7636 7274 Fax: (020) 7636 5845
▶ Global PA Services Ltd, Mayfair House, Heddon Street, London, W1B 4DA Tel: 0207 477 2543 Fax: 0207 477 2543 E-mail: globalpaservices@hotmail.com
Globe Apartments, 36 James Street, London, W1U 1AP Tel: (020) 7935 7531 Fax: (020) 7935 7531 E-mail: lettings@globeapt.com
Greenhaven Letting Agents, 10 Bradford Road, Stanningley, Pudsey, West Yorkshire, LS28 6DD Tel: 0113-255 8333 Fax: 0113-204 0200 E-mail: greenhaven@btinternet.com
Haden Building Management Ltd, Summit House, Glebe Way, West Wickham, Kent, BR4 0RJ Tel: (020) 8918 4200 Fax: (020) 8918 4391

PROPERTY MANAGEMENT AGENTS OR SERVICES – *continued*

▶ Health Management, Scottish Health Service Centre, Crewe Road South, Edinburgh, EH4 2LF Tel: 0131-623 2535 Fax: 0131-315 2369

Heynes Estate Management, 7 Gildredge Road, Eastbourne, East Sussex, BN21 4RB Tel: (01323) 410975 Fax: (01323) 726163

Howard Grove Ltd, 93 Regent Street, Cambridge, CB2 1AW Tel: (01223) 312910 Fax: 01233 312911 E-mail: webmaster@howard-holdings.com

▶ J C M Services Ltd, 44 Burslem Road, Tunbridge Wells, Kent, TN2 3TT Tel: (01892) 526419 E-mail: info@jcmservices.org.uk

J P C Commercial Services Ltd, Elm Tree Farm, Cedar Street, Chesterfield, Derbyshire, S43 2LF Tel: (01246) 280123 Fax: (01246) 477421 E-mail: acom1jpc@aol.com

James Drewitt & Son Ltd, 865 Ringwood Road, West Howe, Bournemouth, BH11 8IW Tel: (01202) 575757 Fax: (01202) 582500

John Brooke & Sons Ltd, Yorkshire Technology & Office Park, Armitage Bridge, Huddersfield, HD4 7NR Tel: (01484) 340000 Fax: (01484) 340001 E-mail: office@yorkspark.com

Kier (Scotland), Buchanan Business Park, Cumbernauld Road, Stepps, Glasgow, G33 6HZ Tel: 0141-779 3020

Killiney Properties Ltd, 207 Barkby Road, Leicester, LE4 9HZ Tel: 0116-276 7554 Fax: 0116-246 0447

Lambert Smith Hampton, 79 Mosley Street, Manchester, M2 3LQ Tel: 0161-228 6411 Fax: 0161-228 7354 E-mail: manchester@lsh.co.uk

Lambert Smith Hampton Group Ltd, Regent Arcade House, 19-25 Argyle Street, London, W1F 7TS Tel: (020) 7494 4000 Fax: (020) 7414 0866 E-mail: westend@lsh.co.uk

Last & Mazin, 21 Welbeck Street, London, W1G 8EE Tel: (020) 7763 7763 Fax: (020) 7763 7764 E-mail: post@lastandmazin.com

Legendary Property Company (Aberdeen) 2002 Ltd, Optimum House, Clippers Quay, Salford, M50 3XP Tel: 0161-872 2622 Fax: 0161-872 2633 E-mail: debbie@lpc1.co.uk

▶ London & Coastal Properties, 37 Bench Manor Crescent, Chalfont St. Peter, Gerrards Cross, Buckinghamshire, SL9 9HL Tel: (01753) 882899 Fax: (01753) 400217

▶ M & R Facilities Management Ltd, Unit 11, 13 Telford Road Thornton, Ellesmere Port, CH65 5EU Tel: 0151-357 1901 Fax: 0151-357 1902 E-mail: sales@mrfm.co.uk

Mellersh & Harding, 43 St. James'S Place, London, SW1A 1NS Tel: (020) 7499 0866 Fax: (020) 7522 8501 E-mail: info@mellersh.co.uk

Michael Anthony & Partners, 54 Kingsbury, Aylesbury, Buckinghamshire, HP20 2JE Tel: (01296) 433666 Fax: (01296) 397686 E-mail: list@michaelanthony.co.uk

Mountcity Investments Ltd, Wellington House, Bean Road, Bilston, West Midlands, WV14 9EE Tel: (01902) 887644 Fax: (01902) 887638 E-mail: mountcity@mountcity.com

Myddelton & Major, The Estate Office, Quartermaster Road, West Wiltshire Trading Estate, Westbury, Wiltshire, BA13 4JT Tel: (01373) 822260 Fax: (01373) 823070 E-mail: wwte@myddeltonmajor.co.uk

Newry & Mourne Enterprise Agency, Win Business Park, Canal Quay, Newry, County Down, BT35 6PH Tel: (028) 3026 7011 Fax: (028) 3026 1316 E-mail: info@nmea.net

Nightingale Chancellors, 132 Sheen Road, Richmond, Surrey, TW9 1UR Tel: (020) 8940 4018 Fax: (020) 8332 1548

O C S Group Ltd, Trafford Bank House, 32 Brindley Road, Manchester, M16 9SA Tel: 0161-876 9151 Fax: 0161-876 2702 E-mail: enquiries@ocs.co.uk

Oakfield Rubber Co., 480 Hawthorne Road, Bootle, Merseyside, L20 9PP Tel: 0151-933 6266 Fax: 0151-922 8743

Ord Carmell & Kritzler, 219 Golders Green Road, London, NW11 9DD Tel: (020) 8455 0057 Fax: (020) 8458 5880

P&O Property Accounts Ltd, 247 Tottenham Court Road, London, W1T 7HH Tel: (020) 7637 1400 Fax: (020) 7631 4280

Parkgate Lettings, 8 Eton Street, Richmond, Surrey, TW9 1EE Tel: (020) 8940 2991 Fax: (020) 8332 2134 E-mail: sales@parkgate-lettings.co.uk

Parsons Son & Basley, 32 Queens Road, Brighton, BN1 3YE Tel: (01273) 326171 Fax: (01273) 821224 E-mail: property@parsons-son-basley.co.uk

Personal Homefinders, 15 London Road, Southampton, SO15 2AE Tel: (023) 8063 5860 Fax: (023) 8063 5877 E-mail: post@personal-homefinders.com

Peter Taylor & Co., 8 Hanover Street, London, W1S 1PT Tel: (020) 7290 2662 Fax: (020) 7290 2686

Priors, 90 Western Road, Hove, East Sussex, BN3 1GG Tel: (01273) 772385 Fax: (01273) 747866 E-mail: management@wmprior.co.uk

Progressive Control Systems, 3 Pear Tree Grove, Shirley, Solihull, West Midlands, B90 1LL Tel: 0121-608 4091 Fax: 0121-604 0426 E-mail: sales@progressivecontrol.com

R M S Commercial, 48A Osborne Road, Newcastle Upon Tyne, NE2 2AL Tel: 0191-212 0000 Fax: 0191-281 9074 E-mail: info@ellisonrms.co.uk

S P S Lamy, 123 Alders Gate Street, London, EC1A 4JQ Tel: (020) 7251 4171 Fax: (020) 7251 3778 E-mail: propertysales@spslamy.com

Simmons & Hawker Ltd, Falcon House, Central Way, Feltham, Middlesex, TW14 0UQ Tel: (020) 8867 0070 Fax: (020) 8893 1987 E-mail: barryj@hma.co.uk

▶ Specialised Investment Property Services Ltd, Suite 5c, Deer Park Business Centre, Eckington, Pershore, Worcestershire, WR10 3DN Tel: (01386) 750990 Fax: 01386 751321 E-mail: admin@sips-ltd.co.uk

▶ Steggles Larner, 25 Charing Cross, Norwich, NR2 4AX Tel: (01603) 724724 Fax: (01603) 724700

Stonedale Property Management Ltd, Romshed Courtyard, Underriver, Sevenoaks, Kent, TN15 0SD Tel: (01732) 746035 Fax: (01732) 454136 E-mail: spm@weald.co.uk

Stuart Edwards Fullermoon, 102-104 High Street, Croydon, CR9 1TN Tel: (020) 8686 4771 Fax: (020) 8688 7121 E-mail: sales@stuart-edwards.com

T S Anderson Ltd, 15 Ashton Road, Glasgow, G12 8SP Tel: 0141-334 1418 Fax: 0141-337 2342

Tony Ling Property Investments, Empire House, Empire Way, Wembley, Middlesex, HA9 0EW Tel: (020) 8970 2130 Fax: (020) 8970 2105

Walker Singleton Commercial Ltd, Property House, Lister Lane, Halifax, West Yorkshire, HX1 5AS Tel: (01422) 430000 Fax: (01422) 430010 E-mail: comm@walkersingleton.co.uk

Waverley Housing Ltd, 27 North Bridge Street, Hawick, Roxburghshire, TD9 9BD Tel: (01450) 364200 Fax: (01450) 375905

Wereldhave Property Corporation plc, 39 Sloane Street, London, SW1X 9WR Tel: (020) 7235 2080 Fax: (020) 7245 9962

Benjamin Whiteley & Sons Ltd, Park Road, Mills, Elland, West Yorkshire, HX5 9HX Tel: (01422) 372272 Fax: (01422) 375651

Yates Estate Ltd, 205 Walworth Road, London, SE17 1RL Tel: (020) 7703 3255 Fax: (020) 7701 6062E-mail: property@yatesestate.co.uk

▶ Young Consultants, The Old Mill, Inverichnie, Banff, AB45 3LL Tel: (01261) 821473

PROPERTY OVERSEAS DEVELOPMENT HOLDING OR INVESTMENT COMPANIES OR AGENTS

▶ Cyprus Ideal, 35 Micklethwaite Grove, Wetherby, West Yorkshire, LS22 5LA Tel: (0870) 4460010 Fax: 01937 583919 E-mail: sales@cyprus-ideal.com

▶ Greenwood Overseas, 25 Regent Street, Rugby, Warwickshire, CV21 2PE Tel: (01788) 552050 Fax: (01788) 579164 E-mail: zlf@greenwoodoverseas.com

▶ Hilton International Properties (UK) Ltd., 1 Bury Old Road, Manchester, M25 0FQ Tel: 0161 7735916 Fax: 0161 7735916 E-mail: info@propertyforsaleinspain.com

▶ Robert Cambell & Associates, Overseas Investment Property Dept, Greenhills, Winsham, Braunton, Devon, EX33 2LX Tel: 0870 241 2139 E-mail: enquires@totalplanet.co.uk

▶ Rosefame Properties, West Cottage, Church Street, Ticehurst, Wadhurst, East Sussex, TN5 7DL Tel: (01580) 201319 Fax: (01580) 201604 E-mail: info@rosefame.co.uk

PROPERTY OWNER INSURANCE

Bradford & Bingley plc, PO Box 88, Bingley, West Yorkshire, BD16 2UA Tel: (01274) 555555 Fax: (01274) 554422 E-mail: enquiries@bbg.co.uk

Cordon Insurance Ltd, Andil House, Court Street, Trowbridge, Wiltshire, BA14 8BR Tel: (01225) 775566 Fax: (01225) 775544 E-mail: info@cordoninsurance.co.uk

Das Legal Expenses Insurance Co. Ltd, D A S House Quay Side, Temple Back, Bristol, BS1 6NH Tel: 0117-934 2000 Fax: 0117-934 2109 E-mail: sales@das.co.uk

Direct Line Group Ltd, 3 Edridge Road, Croydon, CR9 1AG Tel: (020) 8686 3313 Fax: (020) 8681 0512

▶ Letting Solutions, PO Box 3734, Leamington Spa, Warwickshire, CV31 3ZF Tel: (01926) 735754 E-mail: ask@nvh-letting.com

Milne Friend & Partners, Suite 2-5 Renslade House, Bonhay Road, Exeter, EX4 3AY Tel: (01392) 430097 Fax: (01392) 218696 E-mail: rodmilne@milnefriend.co.uk

N I G, Crown House, 145 City Road, London, EC1V 1LP Tel: (020) 7656 6000 Fax: (020) 7251 0345 E-mail: marion.chan@nig-uk.com

Royal & Sun Alliance Insurance P.L.C., Leadenhall Court, 1 Leadenhall St, London, EC3V 1PP Tel: (020) 7283 9000 Fax: (020) 7337 5200 E-mail: piumail@uk.royalsun.com

Steveni Kessler Insurance Services Ltd, Steveni Kessler House Dominion Business Park, Goodwin Road, London, N9 0BG Tel: (020) 8345 5500 Fax: (020) 8482 2000 E-mail: sales@steveni-kessler.co.uk

T H March & Co. Ltd, 10-12 Ely Place, London, EC1N 6RY Tel: (020) 7405 0009 Fax: (020) 7404 4629 E-mail: insurance@thmarch.co.uk

PROPERTY RENTAL SERVICES

▶ Aubs Villa, 26 Masefield Avenue, Orrel, Wigan, Lancs, WN5 8HR Tel: (01942 744587 E-mail: enquires@aubsvilla.co.uk

▶ C&C Property solutions ltd, 72 / 74 Birkendale Road, Sheffield, S6 3NL Tel: 0114 2444008

▶ Clarendon Apartments, Wraysbury Hall, Ferry Lane, Wraysbury, Staines, Middlesex, TW19 6HG Tel: (01784) 489200 Fax: (01784) 489201 E-mail: info@clarendonuk.com

▶ Faulkner Property, 47 Alston Drive, Bradwell Abbey, Milton Keynes, MK13 9HB Tel: (01908) 321200 Fax: (01908) 321600 E-mail: management@faulknerproperty.co.uk

Fred Watson & Co. Ltd, Grove Mills, High Street, Heckmondwike, West Yorkshire, WF16 0AW Tel: (01924) 403386 E-mail: geoff@grovemills.com

▶ Letting Solutions, PO Box 3734, Leamington Spa, Warwickshire, CV31 3ZF Tel: (01926) 735754 E-mail: ask@nvh-letting.com

Maconochies of Kilmarnock Ltd, 22-26 Campbell Street, Riccarton, Kilmarnock, Ayrshire, KA1 4HW Tel: (01563) 522681 Fax: (01563) 541297

▶ Rentinbulgeria.com Ltd, 30 Wood Edge Close, Bolton, BL3 2PD Tel: 01204 709439 E-mail: sales@rentinbulgeria.com

▶ Think Tank Group, 1st Floor, 368 York Road, Leeds, LS9 9EB Tel: (0870) 3609600 E-mail: me@thethinktankgroup.co.uk

▶ Villarebec, 8 Dawlish Drive, Southport, Merseyside, PR9 9RA Tel: (01704) 506697 E-mail: dot@villarebec.com

PROPERTY SERVICES, SALE LEASEBACK

▶ Property Sale By Owner, 2 Windmill Hill Drive, Bletchley, Milton Keynes, MK3 7SD Tel: 01908 371494 Fax: 01908 371494 E-mail: davidf.mills@virgin.net

PROPOSAL WRITING TRAINING

▶ Summers Training, 7 Woodlands, Pickwick, Corsham, Wiltshire, SN13 0DA Tel: (01249) 712037

PROSTHETICS INDUSTRY MATERIALS

New Splint Ltd, Unitech House, Units B1 B2, Bond Close, Kingsland Buisiness Park, Basingstoke, Hampshire, RG24 8PZ Tel: (01256) 365480 Fax: (01256) 365486 E-mail: sales.dept@newsplint.co.uk

▶ Op Care, Hills Road, Cambridge, CB2 2DA Tel: (01223) 243391 Fax: (01225) 416564

PROTECTIVE BELLOWS

Barlow Blinds Ltd, 54 Uppingham Road, Leicester, LE5 0QE Tel: 0116-276 9771 Fax: 0116-246 0490 E-mail: brian@barlow-bellows.co.uk

Beakbane Ltd, Stourport Road, Kidderminster, Worcestershire, DY11 7QT Tel: (01562) 820561 Fax: (01562) 820560 E-mail: sales@beakbane.co.uk

Flexible Connections Ltd, King Street Trading Estate, Middlewich, Cheshire, CW10 9LF Tel: (01606) 836024 Fax: (01606) 836241 E-mail: flexibles@talk21.com

The Flexicon Company, 1 Larch Lea Trading Estate, Whitefield Road, Liverpool, L6 5BN Tel: 0151-260 6141 Fax: 0151-260 4477 E-mail: info@flexicon.org.uk

PROTECTIVE BUILDING COATINGS

Protective Textured Coatings UK Ltd, Unit 16 Haywards Industrial Park, Orton Way, Birmingham, B35 7BT Tel: 0121-749 5088 Fax: 0121-693 7688

Radflex Contract Services Ltd, Unit 35 Wilks Avenue, Questor, Dartford, DA1 1JS Tel: (01322) 276363 Fax: (01322) 270606 E-mail: expjoint@radflex.co.uk

PROTECTIVE CARRYING CASES

Capital Case Co, 55 Lonsdale Road, London, NW6 6RA Tel: (020) 7624 3333 Fax: (020) 7624 2533

Cryo Med Instruments Ltd, Cryomed House, Grove Way, Mansfield Woodhouse, Mansfield, Nottinghamshire, NG19 8BW Tel: (01623) 424200 Fax: (01623) 424777

Glenrothes Industrial Packing Ltd, 75-76 Whitecraigs Road, Glenrothes, Fife, KY6 2RX Tel: (01592) 771052 Fax: (01592) 620158

Gothard Flight Cases, 322 Beverley Road, Hull, HU5 1BA Tel: (07831) 421751 Fax: (01977) 680271 E-mail: info@gothardflightcases.co.uk

Oakleigh Cases Ltd, 10 The Summit Centre, Summit Road, Potters Bar, Hertfordshire, EN6 3JN Tel: (01707) 655011 Fax: (01707) 646447 E-mail: sales@oakleighcases.com

PROTECTIVE CLOTHING

▶ Active Workwear, 56 Bradford Road, Stanningley, Pudsey, West Yorkshire, LS28 6EF Tel: 0113-256 7021 Fax: 0113-256 6600 E-mail: info@workwearshop.co.uk

B T S Industrial Supplies, Unit 6, 692 Stratford Road, Sparkhill, Birmingham, B11 4AT Tel: 0121-702 2404 Fax: 0121-778 6092 E-mail: sales@btssupplies.co.uk

Matric Services & Supplies Ltd, Unit 25-26 Essington Light Industrial Estate, Bognop Road, Essington, Wolverhampton, WV11 2BJ Tel: (01922) 479132 Fax: (01922) 494450 E-mail: matric@amserve.com

Merv Hutchings Workwear, 169 Pinhoe Road, Exeter, EX4 7HZ Tel: (01392) 412376

▶ Ron Smith & Co., 11 Copdale Road, Leicester, LE5 4FG Tel: 0116-273 6880 Fax: 0116-273 5088

▶ Vestguard UK Ltd, Sevenacres, Barnhall Road, Tolleshunt Knights, Maldon, Essex, CM9 8HD Tel: (0845) 6016660 Fax: (01621) 814316 E-mail: info@vestguard.com

PROTECTIVE CLOTHING ACCESSORIES

▶ Normanby Gateway, Lysaghts Way, Scunthorpe, South Humberside, DN15 9YG Tel: (01724) 275000 Fax: (01724) 275285 E-mail: info@climatechsafety.co.uk

PROTECTIVE CLOTHING OR FOOTWEAR

A & E Russell Ltd, 22 Mcgowan Street, Paisley, Renfrewshire, PA3 1QJ Tel: 0141-887 4411 Fax: 0141-889 9431

A R C O Ltd, PO Box 7, Ossett, West Yorkshire, WF5 9JG Tel: (01482) 222522 Fax: (01924) 280262 E-mail: ossett.branch@arco.co.uk

▶ Active Workwear, 56 Bradford Road, Stanningley, Pudsey, West Yorkshire, LS28 6EF Tel: 0113-256 7021 Fax: 0113-256 6600 E-mail: info@workwearshop.co.uk

Air-o-wear, Aydon South Farm, Corbridge, Northumberland, NE45 5PL Tel: (01434) 632816 Fax: (01434) 632849

▶ Allied International Trading Ltd, Unit A1, Hubert Road, Brentwood, Essex, CM14 4JE Tel: (01277) 204355 Fax: (01277) 204377 E-mail: sales@supertouch.co.uk

Allison Gray, Longtown Street, Dundee, DD4 8LF Tel: (01382) 505888 Fax: (01382) 507333 E-mail: allison-gray@dpandl.co.uk

▶ Anti Contamination Equipement Supplies, Carr Mills, Bradford Road, Batley, West Yorkshire, WF17 9JY Tel: (01924) 420750 Fax: (01924) 420530 E-mail: sales@aces.uk.com

Arco East Scotland, Avon Mill Industrial Estate, Mill Road, Linlithgow Bridge, Linlithgow, West Lothian, EH49 7QY Tel: (01506) 844661 Fax: (01506) 847816 E-mail: arco.eastscotland@arco.co.uk

Arco West Scotland, PO Box 6, Irvine, Ayrshire, KA12 8LG Tel: (01294) 315900 Fax: (01294) 271335 E-mail: arco.westscotland@arco.co.uk

Arden Winch & Co. Ltd, 116 Station Road, Beeston, Nottingham, NG9 2AY Tel: 0115-925 8222 Fax: 0115-925 8444 E-mail: roger.graves@ardenwinch.co.uk

Besafe Protective Clothing Ltd, Somerton Works, Prince Avenue, Westcliff-on-Sea, Essex, SS0 0ER Tel: (01702) 333344 Fax: (01702) 433590 E-mail: sales@besafe.co.uk

Bristol Industrial Protection Ltd, Avonmouth Docks Estate, Chittening, Bristol, BS11 0YB Tel: 0117-982 7418 Fax: 0117-923 5961 E-mail: eip@netgates.co.uk

Bromley Brush Co Kent Ltd, 1 Pembroke Road, Bromley, BR1 2TJ Tel: (020) 8464 1707 Fax: (020) 8313 3494

Bunzl Safety & Work Wear, Unit 2b, Adergellay Road, Swansea, SA5 4DY Tel: (01792) 355600 Fax: (01792) 355700 E-mail: sales@bunzlsws.com

Central Safety (Telford) Ltd, Unit 42 Business Development Centre, Stafford Park 4, Telford, Shropshire, TF3 3BA Tel: (01952) 290216 Fax: (01952) 275050 E-mail: info@centralsafetylimited.co.uk

Chain Saw Services, 16 Pinfold Lane, North Luffenham, Oakham, Leicestershire, LE15 8LE Tel: (01780) 721070 Fax: (01780) 729455

Chas E Prossor & Co. Ltd, 14 Dryden Street, Liverpool, L5 5HD Tel: 0151-207 1832 Fax: 0151-298 1101 E-mail: richard.prossor@prossor.com

Cosalt International Ltd, School Road, Lowestoft, Suffolk, NR33 9NB Tel: (01502) 516731 Fax: (01502) 500659 E-mail: lowestoft@cosalt.co.uk

Debaer Incorperating Rimac, 7 Langley Business Centre, Station Road, Langley, Slough, SL3 8DS Tel: (01753) 710071 Fax: (01753) 572772 E-mail: sales@rimac.co.uk

▶ Defence Estates, Building Moss, HMNB Devonport, Plymouth, PL2 2BG Tel: (01752) 554952 Fax: (01752) 554740 E-mail: plymouth@gdpmod.co.uk

PROTECTIVE CLOTHING OR FOOTWEAR – *continued*

Deltawaite Ltd, Old Dairy, Roose Road, Barrow-in-Furness, Cumbria, LA13 0EP Tel: (01229) 821959 Fax: (01229) 820377 E-mail: sales@deltawaite.co.uk

Denby Industrial Supplies Ltd, Chandos Pole Street, Derby, DE22 3BA Tel: (01332) 332831 Fax: (01332) 371206

Energas Ltd, Soho Street, Smethwick, West Midlands, B66 2RH Tel: 0121-555 5050 Fax: 0121-565 3830 E-mail: engweld@smethwick.fslife.co.uk

Enfield Safety Supplies, 40 Queensway, Enfield, Middlesex, EN3 4SP Tel: (020) 8805 1015 Fax: (0870) 3800077

Ernest Draper & Co., 4 Crawford Avenue, Northampton, NN5 5PA Tel: (01604) 752609

Express Welding Suppliers Ltd, Express House, Wilmington Commercial Park, Bedford St, Hull, HU8 8AR Tel: (01482) 223745 Fax: (01482) 210350 E-mail: paul.woodgate@brc.com

Factorsafe Ltd, 2341 Coventry Road, Birmingham, B26 3PN Tel: 0121-722 2200 Fax: 0121-722 2200 E-mail: sales@factorsafe.co.uk

Felford Industrial Clothing & Supplies, Riverside, Market Harborough, Leicestershire, LE16 7PT Tel: (01858) 434218 Fax: (01858) 410706 E-mail: felfordsupplies@btconnect.com

Foxall Industrial Supplies Ltd, Unit 9 Millards Industrial Estate, Izons Lane, West Bromwich, West Midlands, B71 3PX Tel: 0121-553 7937 Fax: 0121-553 7937 E-mail: foxallindsupplies@btopenworld.com

Globus Ltd, 8 Lower Blackhill Industrial Estate, Lerwick, Shetland, ZE1 0DG Tel: (01595) 696222 Fax: (01595) 693771

Gotec Trading Ltd, Boulton Road, Stevenage, Hertfordshire, SG1 4QL Tel: (01438) 740400 Fax: (01438) 740005

Greenham Trading Ltd, Kilmaine Close, Cambridge, CB4 2PH Tel: (01223) 423422 Fax: (01223) 424882 E-mail: cambridge.sale@greenham.co.uk

Greenwoods (Coleshill) Ltd, Unit 28, Roman Way, Coleshill, Birmingham, B46 1HQ Tel: (01675) 464280 Fax: (01675) 467160 E-mail: sales@greenwoodtools.demon.co.uk

Guardsman Ltd, 24 Pasture Lane, Leicester, LE1 4EY Tel: 0116-253 8688 Fax: 0116-251 4202 E-mail: sales@guardsmanltd.co.uk

H T Industrial Supplies, Chapel Street, Goole, North Humberside, DN14 5RJ Tel: (01405) 766428 Fax: (01405) 768053 E-mail: htsupplies@ic24.net

Haxton Safety Ltd, Unit 17 Langlands Avenue, East Kilbride, Glasgow, G75 0YG Tel: (01355) 221818 Fax: (01355) 220333 E-mail: info@haxton.co.uk

Hexagon Safety Products Sales Ltd, Unit 4A Elstree Film Studios, Shenley Road, Borehamwood, Hertfordshire, WD6 1JG Tel: (020) 8207 0003 Fax: (020) 8905 1036 E-mail: borehamwood.hiredesk@hireorbuy.co.uk

Highland Industrial Supplies Ltd, 36 Seafield Road, Inverness, IV1 1SG Tel: (01463) 239160 Fax: (01463) 233424 E-mail: sales@hisltd.co.uk

Highspeed Lubricants Ltd, 1 Newbridge Industrial Estate, Pitt Street, Keighley, West Yorkshire, BD21 4PQ Tel: (01535) 611103 Fax: (01535) 611546 E-mail: info@highspeed.co.uk

Chas Hunter Ltd, Upper Villiers Street, Wolverhampton, WV2 4NR Tel: (01902) 424411 Fax: (01902) 424733 E-mail: chas.hunterltd@virgin.net

Hygiene First Ltd, Melton Road, Queniborough, Leicester, LE7 3FP Tel: 0116-269 4393 Fax: 0116-269 4395 E-mail: sales@hygienefirst.co.uk

I G T C Ltd, 7 Huston Close, Barrow Upon Soar, Loughborough, Leicestershire, LE12 8NB Tel: (0845) 2020235 Fax: (0870) 7202265 E-mail: sales@safetyshopdirect.com

I T S Tools Ltd, Daish Way, Dodnor Lane Industrial Estate, Newport, Isle of Wight, PO30 5XB Tel: (01983) 526344 Fax: (01983) 821547 E-mail: itstools@tiscali.co.uk

Industrial Supplies Wrayson Ltd, 3-4 Brookfield Road, Cheadle, Cheshire, SK8 2PN Tel: 0161-428 0707 Fax: 0161-428 1304 E-mail: sales@wrayson.com

J P Hygiene Supplies, Britannia Estate, Leagrave Road, Luton, LU3 1RJ Tel: (01582) 488851 Fax: (01582) 410005 E-mail: sales@jphygiene.co.uk

James Lister, 2 Miller Street, Birmingham, B6 4NF Tel: 0121-359 3774 Fax: 0121-333 3021 E-mail: birmingham@lister.co.uk

Jay Stores, 130 Lower Road, London, SE16 2UG Tel: (020) 7237 2410 Fax: (020) 7237 2410

Ken Taylor Ltd, Unit 1-2 Crown Business Centre, George Street, Failsworth, Manchester, M35 9BW Tel: 0161-682 9490 Fax: 0161-682 6833 E-mail: sales@kpsupplies.com

Kirklands Ltd, Kirkland House, Main Cross Road, Great Yarmouth, Norfolk, NR30 3NZ Tel: (01493) 843060 Fax: (01493) 853001 E-mail: sales@kirkgroup.co.uk

Langstone Safetywear Ltd, 1 St. Johns Court, Upper Forest Way, Swansea Enterprise Park, Swansea, SA6 8QR Tel: (01792) 535500 Fax: (01792) 535509 E-mail: info@langstone.co.uk

John Liscombe Ltd, Mariner Way, Felnex Industrial Estate, Newport, Gwent, NP19 4PQ Tel: (01633) 284100 Fax: (01633) 284125 E-mail: sales@liscombe.co.uk

▶ M W T International Ltd, Great North Way, York, YO26 6RB Tel: (01904) 789880 Fax: (01904) 693192 E-mail: sales@mwtsafestyle.co.uk

Mcarthur Group Ltd, Economy House Copley Hill Trading Estate, Whitehall Road, Leeds, LS12 1HE Tel: 0113-245 7557 Fax: 0113-242 1150 E-mail: marketing@mcarthur-group.com

Merseyside Industrial Supplies, 241 Rake Lane, Wallasey, Merseyside, CH45 5DJ Tel: 0151-639 7382 Fax: 0151-637 1396 E-mail: sales@misuk.com

Metalpoint Ltd, Factory D, Western Approach, South Shields, Tyne & Wear, NE33 5NN Tel: 0191-455 6086 Fax: 0191-455 2447 E-mail: sales@arndale.co.uk

Joseph Miller & Sons Ltd, 1 Denver Close, Orpington, Kent, BR6 0SB Tel: (01689) 609901 Fax: (01689) 609901 E-mail: hsjmiller@aol.com

Mr Overalls, Silfield Road, Wymondham, Norfolk, NR18 9AU Tel: (01953) 607050 Fax: (01953) 603148 E-mail: sales@mroveralls.uk

Myona Ltd, Watery La Middleway, Bordesley, Birmingham, B9 4HE Tel: 0121-773 4333 Fax: 0121-773 4970 E-mail: sales@myona.co.uk

Northern Ireland Protective Clothing Co., 13 Balmoral Road, Belfast, BT12 6QA Tel: (028) 9068 1107 Fax: (028) 9066 2733 E-mail: sales@nipcco.co.uk

▶ Optical Solutions, 10 William Street, Edinburgh, EH3 7NH Tel: 0131-226 4699

Parker Merchanting, Unit 1 Block E Larkfield Trading Estate, New Hythe Lane, Aylesford, Kent, ME20 6XQ Tel: (01622) 710863 Fax: (01622) 719222

Parker Merchanting Ltd, Chester Street, Aston, Birmingham, B6 4AE Tel: 0121-503 4500 Fax: 0121-503 4501 E-mail: info.parker@hagemeyer.co.uk

Parker Merchanting Ltd, Spitfire Close, Ermine Business Park, Huntingdon, Cambridgeshire, PE29 6YF Tel: (01480) 433335 Fax: (01480) 433409

Parker Merchanting Ltd, John O Gaunts Trading Estate, Leeds Road, Rothwell, Leeds, LS26 0DU Tel: 0113-282 2933 Fax: 0113-282 2620 E-mail: info.parker@hagemeyer.co.uk

Parker Merchanting Ltd, Units 19-20 White Lodge Business Park, Hall Road, Norwich, NR4 6DG Tel: (01603) 763778 Fax: (01603) 763776 E-mail: info.parker@hagemeyer.co.uk

Parker Merchanting Ltd, 3 Cowley Business Centre, Watlington Road, Cowley, Oxford, OX4 6NH Tel: (01865) 785700 Fax: (01865) 785777 E-mail: info.parker@hagemeyer.co.uk

Parker Merchanting Ltd, Unit 38 South Hampshire Industrial Park, Totton, Southampton, SO40 3SA Tel: (023) 8066 1414 Fax: (023) 8066 1415 E-mail: info.parker@hagemeyer.co.uk

Parker Merchanting, Unit 3, 1 Glen Tye Road, Broadleys Industrial Estate, Stirling, FK7 7LH Tel: (01786) 463921 Fax: (01786) 450089 E-mail: stirling.parker@hagemeyer.co.uk

Parker Merchanting Ltd, 4 Horton Industrial Park, Horton Road, West Drayton, Middlesex, UB7 8JD Tel: (01895) 444040 Fax: (01895) 420036 E-mail: info.parker@hagemeyer.co.uk

Parker Merchanting, 2 Page Lane, Widnes, Cheshire, WA8 0AF Tel: 0151-420 7787 Fax: 0151-495 1589 E-mail: info.parker@hagemeyer.co.uk

Pennant Automotive & Industrial Supplies, University Farm, Wasthill Lane, Kings Norton, Birmingham, B38 9EP Tel: 0121-459 4276 Fax: 0121-451 2488

Phoenix Saxton Ltd, Thornton Industrial Trading Estate, Milford Haven, Dyfed, SA73 2RR Tel: (01646) 690588 Fax: (01646) 690570

PJ's Workwear, 42 The Tything, Worcester, WR1 1JT Tel: (01905) 22051 Fax: (01905) 617476

Porta Tool Fixings Ltd, Units 6-8, Brunel Road, Leigh-on-Sea, Essex, SS9 5JL Tel: (01702) 510080 Fax: (01702) 510030 E-mail: portatools@btconnect.com

Progressive Safety Footwear & Clothing Ltd, 101 Worthing Road, Sheffield, S9 3JN Tel: 0114-273 8349 Fax: 0114-275 2452 E-mail: info@psf.co.uk

Protec Manchester Ltd, 2 Rainard Street, Hyde, Cheshire, SK14 2HW Tel: (0870) 3333081 Fax: (0870) 3333061 E-mail: sales@protecdirect.co.uk

Provincial Safety Services Ltd, Portway Road, Oldbury, West Midlands, B69 2BP Tel: 0121-544 5208 Fax: 0121-552 9075 E-mail: provincialsafety@btconnect.com

Quartermasters Protective Equipment, 248 City Road, Cardiff, CF24 3JJ Tel: (029) 2049 1059

R A Young, 582 Clarkston Road, Glasgow, G44 3SQ Tel: 0141-632 5950

R Glover Ascroft Ltd, Ace Works, 157 Ordnance Road, Enfield, Middlesex, EN3 6AW Tel: (01992) 717272 Fax: (01992) 714040 E-mail: enquiries@r-glover-ascroft.com

R JS, 134 High Street, Sheerness, Kent, ME12 1UB Tel: (01795) 660134 Fax: (01795) 427348

Regatta Ltd, Risol House Mercury Park, Mercury Way, Urmston, Manchester, M41 7RR Tel: 0161-749 1313 Fax: 0161-749 1210 E-mail: sales@regatta.com

Rodo Ltd, Lumb Lane, Droylsden, Manchester, M43 7BU Tel: 0161-371 6400 Fax: 0161-371 6401 E-mail: sales@rodo.co.uk

Rushall Protective Clothing Co. Ltd, 501 Bloxwich Road, Walsall, WS3 2XA Tel: (01922) 710055 Fax: (01922) 407885

S R Walsh, Chaddock Lane, Astley, Tyldesley, Manchester, M29 7JT Tel: (01942) 894070 Fax: (01942) 894073 E-mail: sales@srwalsh.co.uk

Safpro Industrial Supply Co., Unit 4-5 Ashville Industrial Estate, Ashville Road, Gloucester, GL2 5EU Tel: (01452) 529050 Fax: (01452) 311221

Samco Products Ltd, Tir Llwyd Enterprise Park, Kinmel Bay, Rhyl, Clwyd, LL18 5JZ Tel: (01745) 362500 Fax: (01745) 362501 E-mail: enquiries@samcoproducts.co.uk

▶ Severnside Safety Supplies Ltd, Malmesbury Road, Kingsditch Trading Estate, Cheltenham, Gloucestershire, GL51 9PL Tel: (01242) 525811 Fax: (01242) 224184 E-mail: sales@sevsafe.co.uk

Silverman's Ltd, Mile End, London, E1 4PS Tel: (020) 7790 0900 Fax: (020) 7791 0008 E-mail: info@silvermans.co.uk

Sorsky Ltd, Yeoward House, Dennis Road, Tanhouse Estate, Widnes, Cheshire, WA8 0SF Tel: 0151-257 2222 Fax: 0151-257 2233 E-mail: sales@sorsky.com

South Staffs Supplies, Langley Heath Business Park, Eastern Avenue, Lichfield, Staffordshire, WS13 6RL Tel: (01543) 258883 Fax: (01543) 417444

Stanton Hope Ltd, 11 Seax Court, Southfields, Laindon, Basildon, Essex, SS15 6LY Tel: (01268) 419141 Fax: (01268) 545992 E-mail: sales@stantonhope.co.uk

Starmaker Welding Services, 16 Pembroke Avenue, Waterbeach, Cambridge, CB25 9QR Tel: (01223) 860662 Fax: (01223) 440009 E-mail: sales@starmake-rwelding.fsnet.co.uk

Steinlock Ltd, Danbury Mews, Wallington, Surrey, SM6 0BY Tel: (020) 8773 4966 Fax: (020) 8773 4968

Sussex Safetywear, East Lodge Farm, Malthouse Lane, Hurstpierpoint, Hassocks, West Sussex, BN6 9LA Tel: (01273) 831800 Fax: (01273) 831880

Swift Industrial Suppliers, Anstey Mill Lane, The Mill House, Alton, Hampshire, GU34 2QQ Tel: (01420) 592500 Fax: (01420) 592501

Taylors, 95 Victoria Rd, Bradmore, Wolverhampton, WV3 7HA Tel: 01902 621882 Fax: 01902 621882 E-mail: taylorsppe@blueyonder.co.uk

Thames Hose & Couplings Ltd, Units 1-2 Canal Industrial Park, Canal Road, Gravesend, Kent, DA12 2PA Tel: (01474) 356485 Fax: (01474) 320392 E-mail: thc.sales@btconnect.com

Tom Taylor & Son, Fish Dock Road, Grimsby, South Humberside, DN31 3PD Tel: (01472) 354604 Fax: (01472) 267071

The Trading Post, Hallmark Farm, Ashford Road, St. Michaels, Tenterden, Kent, TN30 6SP Tel: (01233) 850522 Fax: (01233) 850522

Turton Safety Ltd, 1 Britannia Park, Trident Drive, Wednesbury, West Midlands, WS10 7XB Tel: 0121-567 4100 Fax: 0121-567 4141 E-mail: sales@turton.co.uk

UK Industrial Supplies Ltd, Unit G Motorway Distribution Centre, Avonmouth Way West, Avonmouth, Bristol, BS11 9YT Tel: 0117-923 5653 Fax: 0117-982 0505 E-mail: admin@ukindsup.co.uk

▶ United Safety, Unit 25b Station Lane Industrial Estate, Station Lane, Old Whittington, Chesterfield, Derbyshire, S41 9QX Tel: (01246) 268990 Fax: (01246) 268889 E-mail: unitedsafety@tiscali.co.uk

W G Bingham & Co. Ltd, New Warehouse, Manby Road, Immingham, South Humberside, DN40 2LH Tel: (01469) 573945 Fax: (01469) 576057 E-mail: imminghamsales@sorsky.com

W I S, Kings Castle Business Parke, The Drove, Bridgwater, Somerset, TA6 4AG Tel: (01278) 439128 Fax: (01278) 439129

Warwick Industrial Supplies, Emscote Mill, Wharf Street, Warwick, CV34 5LB Tel: (01926) 497350 Fax: (01926) 403777 E-mail: sales@warwicksupplies.com

▶ Westbury Industrial Supplies, 651 Melton Road, Thurmaston, Leicester, LE4 8EB Tel: 0116-264 0920 Fax: 0116-264 0922

Westguard Safety Ltd, Unit 1 Newporte Business Park, Cardinal Close, Bishops Road, Lincoln, LN2 4SY Tel: (01522) 513512 Fax: (01522) 549658 E-mail: sales@medikit.co.uk

Wise Worksafe, 3 Parr Road, Stanmore, Middlesex, HA7 1PZ Tel: (020) 8381 1811 Fax: (020) 8381 1827

WJJ Supplies Ltd, Unit 2 Greenfield Farm Industrial Estate, Congleton, Cheshire, CW12 4TR Tel: (01260) 218187 Fax: (01260) 218186 E-mail: sales@wjjsupplies.co.uk

Workleen, Rushes Road, Petersfield, Hampshire, GU32 3AR Tel: (0800) 7836484 Fax: (01730) 260633

▶ Workwear World, 445 Honeypot Lane, Stanmore, Middlesex, HA7 1JJ Tel: (020) 8206 2004 Fax: (020) 8206 2005 E-mail: sales@workwearworld.co.uk

PROTECTIVE CLOTHING, CHEMICAL/GAS RESISTANT

Beryl Davis, 1 Primrose Mill, Friday Street, Chorley, Lancashire, PR6 0AA Tel: (01257) 272121 Fax: (01257) 268033 E-mail: sales@beryl-davis.co.uk

Kappler Europe Ltd, Unit 1 Crown Farm Way, Forest Town, Mansfield, Nottinghamshire, NG19 0FT Tel: (01623) 416200 Fax: (01623) 416250 E-mail: sales@kappler.com

O C A S Ltd, PO Box 228, Maidenhead, Berkshire, SL6 6PQ Tel: (01628) 510260 Fax: (01628) 510261 E-mail: ocas@vossnet.co.uk

Professional Protection Systems Ltd, Protection House, Sherbourne Drive, Tilbrook, Milton Keynes, MK7 8HX Tel: (01908) 272240 Fax: (01908) 371605

Respirex, F Kingsfield Business Centre, Philanthropic Road, Redhill, RH1 4DP Tel: (01737) 778600 Fax: (01737) 779441 E-mail: sales@respirex.co.uk

PROTECTIVE CLOTHING/BODY ARMOUR, BALLISTIC/BULLET/ ANTISTAB/SPORTS

Aerospace Bestobell, Ashby Road, Shepshed, Loughborough, Leicestershire, LE12 9EQ Tel: (01509) 500000 Fax: (01509) 500150

C Q C Ltd, Riverside Road, Pottington Business Park, Barnstaple, Devon, EX31 1NB Tel: (01271) 345678 Fax: (01271) 345090 E-mail: pjg@cqc.co.uk

▶ Lba International Ltd, 2 Caxton Close, Drayton Fields Industrial Estate, Daventry, Northamptonshire, NN11 8RT Tel: (01327) 311020 Fax: (01327) 311030 E-mail: sales@lbainternational.com

▶ Security Direct, 1 River Road Business Park, 33 River Road, Barking, Essex, IG11 0DA Tel: (020) 8522 0251 Fax: (020) 8507 9900

▶ Vestguard UK Ltd, Sevenacres, Barnhall Road, Tolleshunt Knights, Maldon, Essex, CM9 8HD Tel: (0845) 6016660 Fax: (01621) 814316 E-mail: info@vestguard.com

PROTECTIVE COATING CONSULTANTS

Archer Technicoat Ltd, E Progress Road, Sands Industrial Estate, High Wycombe, Buckinghamshire, HP12 4JD Tel: (01494) 462101 Fax: (01494) 463049 E-mail: info@cvd.co.uk

PROTECTIVE COATING SERVICES

Aptec Metal Finishing Services, Southbrook Road, Eastern Avenue, Gloucester, GL4 3DN Tel: (01452) 300800 Fax: (01452) 500400 E-mail: admin@poeton.co.uk

Aquablast Blast Cleaning, Crutched Friars, Little Whelnetham, Bury St. Edmunds, Suffolk, IP30 0UH Tel: (01284) 388700 Fax: (01284) 388701 E-mail: sales@aquablast.uk.com

Coastground Ltd, Morton Peto Road, Harfreys Industrial Estate, Great Yarmouth, Norfolk, NR31 0LT Tel: (01493) 650455 Fax: (01493) 655047 E-mail: coastground@rjt.co.uk

Colebrand Ltd, Goodshawfeld Rd, Rossendale, Lancs, BB4 8QF Tel: (01706) 217226 Fax: (01706) 831712

Countrywide Industrial Coatings, Thwaite Lodge, Thwaite Close, Erith, Kent, DA8 1DP Tel: (01322) 338639 Fax: (01322) 359060

Delta G B N Ltd, 115 Lodgefield Road, Halesowen, West Midlands, B62 8AX Tel: 0121-602 1221 Fax: 0121-602 3222 E-mail: rogerw@deltagbn.co.uk

Delta GBM, Unit 4 P D H Industrial Estate, Western Way, Moxley, Wednesbury, West Midlands, WS10 7DQ Tel: 0121-556 6262 Fax: 0121-556 6264

Diffusion Alloys Ltd, 160-162 Great North Road, Hatfield, Hertfordshire, AL9 5JW Tel: (01707) 266111 Fax: (01707) 276669

Gardwell Coatings Ltd, Ellough Airfield, Ellough, Beccles, Suffolk, NR34 7TE Tel: (01502) 712793 Fax: (01502) 711636 E-mail: sales@gardwellcoatings.co.uk

Hesco Bastion Ltd, Unit 41 Knowsthorpe Way, Leeds, LS9 0SW Tel: 0113-248 6633 Fax: 0113-248 3501 E-mail: info@hescobastion.com

Langwith Metal Finishers, Unit 21 Doublegate Lane, Rawreth, Wickford, Essex, SS11 8UD Tel: (01268) 570020 Fax: (01268) 570700 E-mail: enquiries@langwithmetal.com

M & R Coatings, 18a ST. Nicholas Street, Bristol, BS1 1UB Tel: 0117 9257247

Oerlikon Balzers Coatings UK Ltd, Bradbourne Drive, Tilbrook, Milton Keynes, MK7 8AT Tel: (01908) 377277 Fax: (01908) 361361 E-mail: info.balzers.uk@oerlikon.com

▶ T I Protective Coatings, Unit 6, Lodge Bank, Crown Lane, Horwich, Bolton, BL6 5HY Tel: (01204) 468080 Fax: (01204) 695188 E-mail: sales@ticoatings.co.uk

Trevon Industrial Finishers, Whitewalls Industrial Estate, Regent Street, Colne, Lancashire, BB8 8LJ Tel: (01282) 861786 Fax: (01282) 863829

PROTECTIVE COATINGS, *See also headings for particular types*

Chemaide Ltd, Unit 8 Gilmans Industrial Estate, Billingshurst, West Sussex, RH14 9EZ Tel: (01403) 780638 Fax: (01403) 780639 E-mail: info@chemaide.co.uk

Colebrand Ltd, Goodshawfeld Rd, Rossendale, Lancs, BB4 8QF Tel: (01706) 217226 Fax: (01706) 831712

PROTECTIVE COATINGS – *continued*

East Dorset Trading Ltd, Central House, 4 Christchurch Road, Bournemouth, BH1 3LT Tel: (01202) 551212 Fax: (01202) 559090 E-mail: sales@tefcote.co.uk
Indestructible Paint Ltd, 23-25 Pentos Drive, Sparkhill, Birmingham, B11 3TA Tel: 0121-702 2485 Fax: 0121-778 4338 E-mail: sales@indestructible.co.uk
Kirtek Industries Ltd, Thorney Road, Crowland, Peterborough, PE6 0AL Tel: (01733) 211290 Fax: (01733) 212331 E-mail: gkerk01@fsmail.net
Lubrizol Advanced Materials UK Ltd, Carlton Industrial Estate, Albion Road, Carlton, Barnsley, South Yorkshire, S71 3HW Tel: (01226) 723661 Fax: (01226) 728298
Modern Maintenance Products International, Brunel Close, Park Farm Industrial Estate, Wellingborough, Northamptonshire, NN8 6QX Tel: (01933) 670870 Fax: (01933) 670800 E-mail: info@mmp-international.co.uk
Syntema South West, Unit 13 Hither Green, Clevedon, Avon, BS21 6XU Tel: (01275) 342777 Fax: (01275) 340820 E-mail: emma@syntemasouthwest.co.uk
Thorne & Derrick, Units 9-10 Birchills Trading Estate, Emery Road, Bristol, BS4 5PF Tel: 0117-977 4647 Fax: 0117-977 5582 E-mail: southernsales@thorneandderrick.co.uk
Trade Paint Supplies Ltd, Grove Road, Northfleet, Gravesend, Kent, DA11 9AX Tel: (01474) 560382 Fax: (01474) 362926 E-mail: sales@tradepaintsupplies.ltd.uk

PROTECTIVE COATINGS, PEELABLE/STRIPPABLE

▶ Intercontinental Chemical Products Ltd, 56-62 Lincoln Road, Tuxford, Newark, Nottinghamshire, NG22 0HP Tel: (01777) 870756 Fax: (01777) 871766 E-mail: sales@intchems.com
Nitto UK Ltd, Unit2 Berkshire Business Centre, Berkshire Drive, Thatcham, Berkshire, RG19 4EW Tel: (01635) 872172 Fax: (01635) 872332 E-mail: nitto_uk@nittoeur.com

PROTECTIVE COVERING TABLE MATS

Lady Clare Ltd, Oldends Lane Industrial Estate, Oldends, Stonehouse, Gloucestershire, GL10 3RQ Tel: (01453) 824482 Fax: (01453) 827855 E-mail: info@lady-clare.com
Pimpernel (Holdings) Ltd, 26-32 Derwent Street, Consett, County Durham, DH8 8LY Tel: 01207 588402 Fax: (01207) 507873 E-mail: sales@pimpernelinternational.com
Take One Ltd, Unit 1, Moor Barn, Sheldon Lane, Bakewell, Derbyshire, DE45 1QR Tel: (01629) 814610 Fax: (01629) 814610 E-mail: info@takeoneltd.com

PROTECTIVE COVERS TO SPECIFICATION

Bisset & Ross, Riverside Drive, Aberdeen, AB11 7SL Tel: (01224) 580659 Fax: (01224) 583295
Covertech Plastics, Springfield Commerical Centre, Bagley Lane, Farsley, Pudsey, West Yorkshire, LS28 5LY Tel: 0113-255 2288 Fax: 0113-255 2381 E-mail: enquiries@cover-techleeds.co.uk
Thames Valley Textiles, Oddington Grange, Weston-on-the-Green, Bicester, Oxfordshire, OX25 3QW Tel: (01865) 331009 Fax: (01865) 331721 E-mail: info@tvt1.co.uk

PROTECTIVE COVERS/ COVERINGS, HEAVY DUTY, WEATHER PROTECTION

Contarps North West Ltd, Unit D4 Newton Business Park, Talbot Road, Hyde, Cheshire, SK14 4UQ Tel: 0161-367 9341 Fax: 0161-367 9352 E-mail: sales@contarps.co.uk

PROTECTIVE EDGING STRIPS

Celltex Fabrications Ltd, Unit 9a Barnfield Trading Estate, Ramsey Road, Tipton, West Midlands, DY4 9DU Tel: 0121-520 3443 Fax: 0121-520 1772 E-mail: sales@celltex.co.uk

PROTECTIVE FLOOR COVERINGS

A. J. B. Floor Coverings Ltd, Unit 1 Bulay Commercial Park, St Thomas Road Longroyd Bridge, Huddersfield, HD1 3LG Tel: (01484) 537255 Fax: (01484) 549328 E-mail: info@ajbflooring.co.uk
▶ Filmtape Ltd, PO Box 400, Southampton, SO30 3XN Tel: (023) 8047 1922 E-mail: sales@filmtape.co.uk

HCC Protective Coatings Ltd, Bates Business Centre, Church Road, Harold Wood, Romford, RM3 0JF Tel: (01708) 378666 Fax: (01708) 378868 E-mail: hcc.pc@btconnect.com

PROTECTIVE FOOTWEAR

Airwair International Ltd, Cobbs Lane, Wollaston, Wellingborough, Northamptonshire, NN29 7SW Tel: (01933) 663281 Fax: (01933) 663848
Samco Products Ltd, Tir Llwyd Enterprise Park, Kinmel Bay, Rhyl, Clwyd, LL18 5JZ Tel: (01745) 362500 Fax: (01745) 362501 E-mail: enquiries@samcoproducts.co.uk
William Lennon & Co. Ltd, The Bank, Stoney Middleton, Hope Valley, Derbyshire, S32 4TD Tel: (01433) 630451 Fax: (01433) 630954 E-mail: sales@williamlennon.co.uk

PROTECTIVE OR INDUSTRIAL DISPOSABLE CLOTHING

Global Hygiene Ltd, Unit 18, Ladford Fields Industrial Park, Seigford, Stafford, ST18 9QE Tel: (01785) 282900 Fax: (01785) 282222
Kappler Europe Ltd, Unit 1 Crown Farm Way, Forest Town, Mansfield, Nottinghamshire, NG19 0FT Tel: (01623) 416200 Fax: (01623) 416250 E-mail: sales@kappler.com

PROTECTIVE OR NON SLIP FLOOR COATING CONTRACTORS

Aedean Chemical Industrial Ltd, 73A Old Woking Road, West Byfleet, Surrey, KT14 6LF Tel: (01932) 336171 Fax: (01932) 336758 E-mail: info@aedean.co.uk
▶ Layfix Flooring Ltd, PO Box 2764, Calne, Wiltshire, SN11 9QY Tel: (01249) 816713 Fax: (01249) 816713 E-mail: enquiries_layfix@hotmail.com
Specialist Coatings UK Ltd, 5 Tramsheds Industrial Estate, Coomber Way, Croydon, CR0 4TQ Tel: (020) 8665 5888 Fax: (020) 8665 6888 E-mail: info@specialistcoatingsuk.com
Universal Flooring Contractors, 7a George Road, Erdington, Birmingham, B23 7QE Tel: 0121-377 8808 Fax: 0121-377 8184 E-mail: sales@universal-flooring.co.uk

PROTECTIVE OR NON SLIP FLOOR COATINGS

Andura Coatings Ltd, 20 Murdock Road, Bicester, Oxfordshire, OX26 4PP Tel: (01869) 240374 Fax: (01869) 240375 E-mail: admin@andura.com
Anglo Building Products Ltd, Branksome House, Filmer Grove, Godalming, Surrey, GU7 3AB Tel: (01483) 427777 Fax: (01483) 428888 E-mail: sales@anglobuild.co.uk
Industrial Flooring Services Ltd, Sankey Valley Industrial Estate, Newton-le-Willows, Merseyside, WA12 8DN Tel: (01925) 220000 Fax: (01925) 220011 E-mail: info@industrial-flooring.co.uk
J & L Industrial Paint Services Ltd, Unit 21, Knightcott Industrial Estate, Banwell, Avon, BS29 6JN Tel: (01934) 820780 Fax: (01934) 820323 E-mail: jl.paints@virgin.net
Quickset Chemical Flooring Ltd, 30 Runcorn Road, Birmingham, B12 8RQ Tel: 0121-440 0737 Fax: 0121-440 2255 E-mail: sales@uk-quickset.com
Resdev Ltd, Puma Floor House, Ainley Industrial Estate, Elland, West Yorkshire, HX5 9JP Tel: (01422) 379131 Fax: (01422) 370943 E-mail: info@resdev.co.uk

PROTECTIVE OR SAFETY EYE SHIELDS

Harrold Manufacturing Co. Ltd, Hinstock House, 30 Station Road, Firsby, Spilsby, Lincolnshire, PE23 5PX Tel: (01754) 830679 Fax: (01754) 830477
Vectis Optical Laboratories Ltd, 81a High Street, Newport, Isle of Wight, PO30 1BG Tel: (01983) 525272 Fax: (01983) 525272

PROTECTIVE PACKAGING

L F E Material Handling, Units 3-5 Hibberd House, Curriers Close, Charter Avenue Industrial Esta, Coventry, CV4 8AW Tel: (024) 7647 0170 Fax: (024) 7669 4521 E-mail: lfemh@btconnect.com

PROTECTIVE PACKAGING BAGS

Ambassador Packaging, Tundry Way, Chainbridge Road, Blaydon-On-Tyne, Tyne & Wear, NE21 5ST Tel: (0870) 6099888 Fax: 0191-414 6627 E-mail: ambassador.blaydon@pactiv.com

Ambassador Packaging, Unit 2 Venture Park, Stirling Way, Bretton, Peterborough, PE3 8YD Tel: (0870) 6099888 Fax: (01733) 330954 E-mail: ambassador.@pactiv.com
Ambassador Packaging Ltd, Road One, Winsford Industrial Estate, Winsford, Cheshire, CW7 3QB Tel: (01606) 567000 Fax: (01606) 567001 E-mail: ambassador@pregis.com
The Bubble Factory Ltd, Grove Road, Preston, Canterbury, Kent, CT3 1EF Tel: (01227) 722228 Fax: (01227) 722399 E-mail: thebubble.factory@yahoo.co.uk
Jiffy Packaging Co. Ltd, Road Four, Winsford Industrial Estate, Winsford, Cheshire, CW7 3QR Tel: (01606) 551221 Fax: (01606) 592634 E-mail: sales@jiffy.co.uk
Moore & Buckle Ltd, 3 Lancots Lane, St. Helens, Merseyside, WA9 3EX Tel: (01744) 733066 Fax: (01744) 451000 E-mail: info@mooreandbuckle.com
Protective Packaging Ltd, Dane Road Industrial Estate, Sale, Cheshire, M33 7BH Tel: 0161-976 2006 Fax: 0161-976 3330 E-mail: info@protpack.com
Synpac Ltd, Priory Tec Park Saxon Way, Priory Park, Hessle, North Humberside, HU13 9PB Tel: (01482) 640606 Fax: (01482) 642768 E-mail: sales@synpac.ltd.uk

PROTECTIVE PAINTS

▶ Eurochem Automotive Chemicals, Unit1 Bridgeholme Mill, Charley Lane, Chinley, High Peak, Derbyshire, SK23 6DX Tel: (01938) 555754 Fax: (01938) 555754 E-mail: support@eurochem.co.uk

PROTECTIVE PIPELINE COATINGS

Cinque Products Ltd, Harbour Road, Rye, East Sussex, TN31 7TE Tel: (01797) 223561 Fax: (01797) 224530 E-mail: longproducts@aol.com
Practical Compounds Ltd, West Side, Tyne Dock, South Shields, Tyne & Wear, NE34 9PL Tel: 0191-456 9191 Fax: 0191-454 5523 E-mail: practical.comp@btinternet.com

PROTECTIVE PLASTIC CAPS OR PLUGS

Caplugs Ltd, Unit 7, Overfield Industrial Estate, Off Thorpe Way, Banbury, Oxfordshire, OX16 4XR Tel: (01295) 263753 Fax: (01295) 263788 E-mail: support@caplugs.co.uk
Dbi Plastics, Cottage La Industrial Estate, Broughton Astley, Leicester, LE9 6PD Tel: (01455) 283380 Fax: (01455) 283384 E-mail: info@dbiplastics.com
M G Plastics Ltd, Progress Mill, Marsh House Lane, Darwen, Lancashire, BB3 3JB Tel: (01254) 703930 Fax: (01254) 774472 E-mail: sales@mgplastics.com
Plastic Parts Centre, Unit 4, Harelaw Industrial Estate, Annfield Plain, Stanley, County Durham, DH9 8HN Tel: (01207) 290599 Fax: (01207) 299718 E-mail: newcastlesales@plastic-parts.co.uk
Plasticum UK Ltd, 2 Bramble Way, Clover Nook Industrial Park, Somercotes, Alfreton, Derbyshire, DE55 4RH Tel: (01773) 833866 Fax: (01773) 520085
R P C Containers Ltd, Fourth Avenue, Colchester Road, Halstead, Essex, CO9 2SY Tel: (01787) 473224 Fax: (01787) 474151 E-mail: sales@rpc-halstead.co.uk

PROTECTIVE RAINWEAR

A & M Mclellan Ltd, 94-96 Moorside Road, Swinton, Manchester, M27 0HJ Tel: 0161-794 1169 Fax: 0161-794 3733 E-mail: sales@mclellan-sport.co.uk
Norseman (Rainwear) Ltd, Viking Mill, Standish Street, Chorley, Lancs, PR7 3BB Tel: (01257) 262733 Fax: (01257) 261071 E-mail: general@norseman.fsbusiness.co.uk

PROTECTIVE RELAYS

Multitek Ltd, Lancaster Way, Earls Colne, Colchester, CO6 2NS Tel: (01787) 223228 Fax: (01787) 223607 E-mail: chris@multitek-ltd.com
Powernets UK Ltd, 32 Eastlands, Stafford, ST17 9BB Tel: (01785) 242235 Fax: (01785) 612261 E-mail: gbr@powernets.com

PROTECTIVE ROOF COATINGS

Britannia Paints Ltd, Units 7-8, King Street Trading Estate, Middlewich, Cheshire, CW10 9LF Tel: (01606) 834015 Fax: (01606) 837006 E-mail: sales@britanniapaints.co.uk
E A B Associates, 3 Craven Court, Craven Road, Broadheath, Altrincham, Cheshire, WA14 5DY Tel: 0161-926 9077 Fax: 0161-927 7718 E-mail: eaball@eabassoc.co.uk
Remmers UK Ltd, Remmers House, 14 Victoria Way, Burgess Hill, West Sussex, RH15 9NF Tel: (01444) 244144 Fax: (01444) 243500 E-mail: sales@remmers.co.uk

PROTECTIVE SECURITY SCREENS

Bastion Security Ltd, Claremont House, Holly Road, Slough, SL2 3QT Tel: (01753) 646488 Fax: (01753) 646488 E-mail: bastion@tinyworld.co.uk
Stewart Fraser Ltd, Henwood Industrial Estate, Ashford, Kent, TN24 8DR Tel: (01233) 625911 Fax: (01233) 633149 E-mail: sales@stewartfraser.com
▶ Hadrian Security Shopfitters Ltd, 39 Bede Close, Newcastle Upon Tyne, NE12 9SP Tel: 0191-215 1444 Fax: 0191-215 1155 E-mail: sales@hadriansecurity.co.uk
K S Security Ltd, Units 2-6, Warsop Trading Estate, Hever Road, Edenbridge, Kent, TN8 5LD Tel: (01732) 867199 Fax: (01732) 867102 E-mail: info@ks-security.co.uk

PROTECTIVE SPORTS EQUIPMENT

Allied Sports & Leisure Ltd, 2 Westminster House, Thorley Street, Failsworth, Manchester, M35 9PA Tel: 0161-688 7049 Fax: 0161-681 9851 E-mail: sales@asll.co.uk

PROTOTYPE (ENGINEERING) PRODUCTION ENGINEERS/ MACHINISTS/FABRICATORS/ SUPPLIERS

939 Engineering Co., Lodgefield Road, Halesowen, West Midlands, B62 8AX Tel: 0121-559 1133 Fax: 0121-559 0321
A F S Engineering Co., 41 Great Lister Street, Birmingham, B7 4LW Tel: 0121-359 5048 Fax: 0121-359 4562
▶ Aims Engineering, Unit H, Ditchling Common Industrial Estate, Ditchling, Hassocks, West Sussex, BN6 8SG Tel: (01444) 870221 Fax: (01444) 244860 E-mail: mail@aimsengineering.co.uk
Ashbourne Engineering UK Ltd, Rear of, 71 Westcote Road, London, SW16 6BN Tel: (020) 8664 7170 Fax: (020) 8664 7459
Auto Design Ltd, 12 Tallon Road, Hutton, Brentwood, Essex, CM13 1TF Tel: (01277) 225000 Fax: (01277) 225002 E-mail: harvey@autodesign.co.uk
Bowyer Engineering Ltd, South Way, Walworth Industrial Estate, Andover, Hampshire, SP10 5AF Tel: (01264) 365921 Fax: (01264) 356547 E-mail: sales@bowyerengineering.co.uk
▶ Breckland Precision Engineering, Church Road, Watton, Thetford, Norfolk, IP25 6QA Tel: (01953) 885363 Fax: (01953) 885933 E-mail: bpe03@aol.com
Broadbridge Precision Engineering Ltd, 1-5 Marters Avenue, Langley Green, Crawley, West Sussex, RH11 7RX Tel: (01293) 525260 Fax: (01293) 561668 E-mail: broadbridge.eng@pncl.co.uk
C B Powell Ltd, 10 St Josephs Close, Hove, East Sussex, BN3 7ES Tel: (01273) 771144 Fax: (01273) 726966 E-mail: cbpowel@btconnect.com
C J Uniques Ltd, Unit 12 Magnus, Tame Valley Industrial Estate, Wilnecote, Tamworth, Staffordshire, B77 5BY Tel: (01827) 261682 Fax: (01827) 261682
Caress Precision Products Ltd, Alington Road, Little Barford, St. Neots, Cambridgeshire, PE19 6YH Tel: (01480) 472262 Fax: (01480) 217235 E-mail: caressprescision@btconnect.com
▶ Cema Universal Engineering, Bordesley Hall, The Holloway, Alvechurch, Birmingham, B48 7QA Tel: (01527) 596106 Fax: (01527) 69362 E-mail: cema.engineering@tiscali.co.uk
Class 100 Ltd, Units 32-33 London Road Industrial Estate, Baldock, Hertfordshire, SG7 6NG Tel: (01462) 893336 Fax: (01462) 893377 E-mail: cadcam@class100.co.uk
Craintern Ltd, 13-17 Haltwhistle Road, South Woodham Ferrers, Chelmsford, CM3 5ZA Tel: (01245) 322438 Fax: (01245) 328926 E-mail: mailbox@ctlmedical.co.uk
Dave Mac Supplies, 1-3 Northey Road, Coventry, CV6 5NF Tel: (024) 7668 3239 Fax: (024) 7658 1852
Eaton Socon Engineering, Renhold Road, Ravensden, Bedford, MK44 2RH Tel: (01234) 772145 Fax: (01234) 771881 E-mail: eaton-socon@tiscali.co.uk
F I S Loveday Ltd, 16-18 Princip Street, Birmingham, B4 6LE Tel: 0121-359 3176 Fax: 0121-359 1098 E-mail: fisloveday@aol.com
Fabrication & Design Excellence Ltd, Pegasus Buildings, Olympus Business Park, Quedgeley, Gloucester, GL2 4JA Tel: (01452) 722944 Fax: (01452) 722825 E-mail: sales@fdproducts.co.uk
George Lister & Sons Ltd, 505 Coldhams Lane, Cambridge, CB1 3JS Tel: (01223) 518888 Fax: (01223) 504700 E-mail: martin@georgelister.co.uk
Harling Fabrications Ltd, Bunns Bank, Attleborough, Norfolk, NR17 1QD Tel: (01953) 453682 Fax: (01953) 453758 E-mail: harlingfabs@btconnect.com

PROTOTYPE (ENGINEERING) PRODUCTION ENGINEERS/ MACHINISTS/FABRICATORS/ SUPPLIERS – *continued*

Hartoms Engineers, 26-30 Theobald Street, Borehamwood, Hertfordshire, WD6 4SG Tel: (020) 8953 5062 Fax: (020) 8207 1176

Holliday Precision Engineers, Unit 11 Pedmore Industrial Estate, Pedmore Road, Brierley Hill, West Midlands, DY5 1TJ Tel: (01384) 261467

Huxley Bertram Engineering, Brookfield Business Centre, Twentypence Road, Cottenham, Cambridge, CB24 8PS Tel: (01954) 250809 Fax: (01954) 251991 E-mail: info@huxleybertram.com

Index Precision Co., 8a Power Court, Luton, LU1 3JJ Tel: (01582) 728528 Fax: (01582) 728528

Langton Engineering, Denmark Street, Maidenhead, Berkshire, SL6 7BN Tel: (01628) 632764 Fax: (01628) 776183

Lightning Aerospace Ltd, Falkland Close, Charter Avenue Industrial Estate, Coventry, CV4 8AU Tel: (024) 7646 1238 Fax: (024) 7646 4745 E-mail: info@lightningaerospace.co.uk

M H V Products Ltd, 33 Woodthorpe Road, Ashford, Middlesex, TW15 2RP Tel: (01784) 241628 Fax: (01784) 255610 E-mail: sales@mhvproducts.co.uk

Machining Centre Ltd, Pembroke Lane, Milton, Abingdon, Oxfordshire, OX14 4EA Tel: (01235) 831343 Fax: (01235) 834708 E-mail: info@machiningcentre.co.uk

Malordale Engineering Ltd, Unit 10E, Britannia Estate, Leagrave Road, Luton, LU3 1RJ Tel: (01582) 421138 Fax: (01582) 412894 E-mail: tonyfuller@malordale.co.uk

Marnol Precision Engineering, Unit 9 Bee-Hive Trading Estate, 72-78 Crews Hole Road, St. George, Bristol, BS5 8AY Tel: (01275) 50095

Model Making & Graphic Services Ltd, 9 Bath Buildings, Montpelier, Bristol, BS6 5PT Tel: 0117-944 6050 Fax: 0117-944 5973 E-mail: mmgsltd@aol.com

▶ Multitec Engineering Ltd, Darrion House, 37 Tudor Walk, Watford, WD24 7NY Tel: (01923) 213283 Fax: (01923) 213340 E-mail: Multiteceng@aol.com

Norwich Plastics Ltd, Mission Road, Rackheath, Norwich, NR13 6PL Tel: (01603) 720714 Fax: (01603) 721539

P D Models, 2-3 Priory Wharf, Hertford, SG14 1RJ Tel: (01992) 553082 Fax: (01992) 550584 E-mail: jan@pdmodels.demon.co.uk

Proto Precision Engineering, Unit 28 Heath Hill Industrial Estate, Dawley, Telford, Shropshire, TF4 2RH Tel: (01952) 506227 Fax: (01952) 506227

Prototype Pressing Ltd, Unit 12C, Shefford Industrial Park, Shefford, Bedfordshire, SG17 5DZ Tel: (01462) 816978 Fax: (01462) 817242 E-mail: pashby@ashfen.demon.co.uk

Pyramid Precision Engineering, Unit 25 Lythalls La Industrial Estate, Lythalls Lane, Coventry, CV6 6FL Tel: (024) 7666 3447 Fax: (024) 7666 3447

R E Rose, 4 Oakwood Business Park, Stephenson Road West, Clacton-on-Sea, Essex, CO15 4TL Tel: (01255) 428928 Fax: (01255) 434937

R J B Engineering Ltd, Unit 5 Oak Industrial Park, Chelmsford Road, Dunmow, Essex, CM6 1XN Tel: (01371) 876377 Fax: (01371) 876378 E-mail: rbrown7571@aol.com

Raldon Precision Engineering Ltd, 9 Morcom Road, Birmingham, B11 2JE Tel: 0121-707 5757 Fax: 0121-706 7290 E-mail: sales@raldonengineering.com

Reeves Engineering Ltd, 15 Swinbourne Drive, Springwood Industrial Estate, Braintree, Essex, CM7 2YP Tel: (01376) 322613 Fax: (01376) 551522

Repfab Engineering Ltd, Unit 6 Whiteleather Square, Billingborough, Sleaford, Lincolnshire, NG34 0QP Tel: (01529) 240600 Fax: (01529) 240647

Specialist Engineering, Unit 17, Little Ridge, Knella Road Industrial Estate, Welwyn Garden City, Hertfordshire, AL7 2BH Tel: (01707) 336075 Fax: (01707) 330215

Startrite Designs Ltd, 76 Bissell Street, Birmingham, B5 7HP Tel: 0121 6666865

T Halliday Engineering Ltd, Orchard Road, Hamworth Road Industrial Estate, Sunbury-on-Thames, Middlesex, TW16 5BZ Tel: (01932) 787862 Fax: (01932) 787839 E-mail: keng@btclick.com

Tyler Bros Sutton In Ashfield Ltd, Hunt Close, Lowmoor Business Park, Kirkby-in-Ashfield, Nottingham, NG17 7ER Tel: (01623) 758286 Fax: (01623) 756144 E-mail: admin@tybro.co.uk

Warren Engineering Ltd, Birkbeck Road, Sidcup, Kent, DA14 4DB Tel: (020) 8300 5111 Fax: (020) 8308 9977 E-mail: warrenengineering@supanet.com

Wheeler Fabrications Ltd, Orchard House, Sherbourne Road, Balsall Heath, Birmingham, B12 9DJ Tel: 0121-440 2345 Fax: 0121-440 4008 E-mail: wheelerfabs@btconnect.com

Whitehead Gardner Tooling Ltd, Unit 2, Spring Gardens Industrial Estate, Romford, RM7 9LD Tel: (01708) 756023 Fax: (01708) 733219 E-mail: enquiries@whiteheads.co.uk

Woodcrafts, 25 Bayton Road Industrial Estate, Bayton Road, Exhall, Coventry, CV7 9EL Tel: (024) 7636 1022 Fax: (024) 7664 4299 E-mail: pdl@btconnect.com

York Plastics Engineering Ltd, 70-72 James Street, York, YO10 3WW Tel: (01904) 412852 Fax: (01904) 430202 E-mail: yorkplastics@btinternet.com

PROTOTYPE INJECTION MOULDINGS

Norton Precision Mouldings, Unit 11, Crow Arch Lane Industrial Estate, Crow Arch Lane, Ringwood, Hampshire, BH24 1PD Tel: (01425) 461866 Fax: (01425) 471965 E-mail: sales@nortonmouldings.com

PROTOTYPE METAL FABRICATIONS

▶ Fab Tech Automotive Ltd, Unit 5-6 Lichfield Trading Estate, Lagrange, Tamworth, Staffordshire, B79 7XD Tel: (01827) 66602 Fax: (01827) 66168 E-mail: sales@fabtechauto.co.uk

S & S Engineering, Unit 21 Such Close, Letchworth Garden City, Hertfordshire, SG6 1JF Tel: (01462) 675983 Fax: (01462) 675983

PROTOTYPE OR EXPERIMENTAL MACHINE TOOLS

Atc Engineering Services Ltd, C1 Oak Park Estate, Northarbour Road, Portsmouth, PO6 3TJ Tel: (023) 9232 6635 Fax: (023) 9221 0907 E-mail: info@atcengineering.co.uk

Chadwick Engineering Co. Ltd, 173-179 Tyburn Road, Erdington, Birmingham, B24 8NQ Tel: 0121-327 7997 Fax: 0121-327 7987

PROTOTYPE PRINTED CIRCUITS

Dial Art (PC) Ltd, 3 Airfield Way, Christchurch, Dorset, BH23 3PE Tel: (01202) 486486 Fax: (01202) 488988 E-mail: sales@dialart.com

Gilbert Electronics, 35 Lower Road, Malvern, Worcestershire, WR14 4BX Tel: (01684) 576989 Fax: (01684) 576989

PROTOTYPE VACUUM FORMING

Allison Plastics & Paper Ltd, New Pudsey Square, Stanningley, Pudsey, West Yorkshire, LS28 6PX Tel: 0113-256 6435 Fax: 0113-257 5337

PROTOTYPE VACUUM RESIN CASTINGS

MCP, 8 Whitebridge Industrial Estate, Whitebridge Lane, Stone, Staffordshire, ST15 8LQ Tel: (01785) 815651 Fax: (01785) 812115 E-mail: equipment@mcp-group.co.uk

PROTOTYPING SYSTEMS, MECHANICAL STRUCTURES/ MECHANISMS

A P Hollings & Sons Ltd, 14 Brook Road Industrial Estate, Sirdar Road, Rayleigh, Essex, SS6 7XF Tel: (01268) 770681 Fax: (01268) 775144 E-mail: andy@aphollings.co.uk

PROXIMITY CARD READERS

Indala Ltd, 8-10 Clos Menter, Excelsior Business Park, Cardiff, CF14 3AY Tel: (029) 2052 0022 Fax: (029) 2052 8519 E-mail: sales@mraccess.com

Ringdale UK Ltd, 26 Victoria Way, Burgess Hill, West Sussex, RH15 9NF Tel: (01444) 871349 Fax: (01444) 870228 E-mail: sales@ringdale.com

John Wainwright Systems Ltd, Third Avenue, Midsomer Norton, Radstock, BA3 4XD Tel: (01761) 414700 Fax: (01761) 414722 E-mail: post@jwsltd.co.uk

PROXIMITY SENSORS

Bernstein Ltd, Westgate Trading Estate, Westgate, Aldridge, Walsall, WS9 8EX Tel: (01922) 744999 Fax: (01922) 457555 E-mail: sales@bernstein-ltd.co.uk

C W Cole & Co. Ltd, 15 Copthorne, Luton, LU2 8RL Tel: (01582) 726622 Fax: (01582) 731622

Gentech International Ltd, Grangestone Eng Co, Grangestone Indust Estat E Ladywell Avenue, Maidens, Girvan, Ayrshire, KA26 9PL Tel: (01465) 713581 Fax: (01465) 714974 E-mail: enquiries@gentech-international.co.uk

PROXIMITY SWITCHES

C W Cole & Co. Ltd, 15 Copthorne, Luton, LU2 8RL Tel: (01582) 726622 Fax: (01582) 731622

Camis Electronics Ltd, Platts Road, Amblecote, Stourbridge, West Midlands, DY8 4YR Tel: (01384) 441402 Fax: (01384) 370354 E-mail: sales@camis.demon.co.uk

Euchner (U K) Ltd, Unit 2, Petre Drive, Sheffield, S4 7PZ Tel: 0114-256 0123 Fax: 0114-242 5333 E-mail: info@euchner.co.uk

Eukero Controls Ltd, Unit 7 Worton Court, Worton Road, Isleworth, Middlesex, TW7 6ER Tel: (020) 8568 4664 Fax: (020) 8568 4115 E-mail: info@eukero.co.uk

Longvale Ltd, The Grain Warehouse, Derby Street, Burton-On-Trent, Staffordshire, DE14 2JJ Tel: (01283) 510108 Fax: (01283) 510910 E-mail: rdear@longvale.co.uk

Thomas White (Leicester) Ltd, Marlborough Drive, Fleckney, Leicester, LE8 8UR Tel: 0116-240 4005 Fax: 0116-240 4006 E-mail: enquiries@thomaswhitelimited.co.uk

PROXIMITY TRANSDUCERS

IGE Energy Services (UK) Ltd, 2 Kelvin Close, Science Park North, Birchwood, Warrington, WA3 7BL Tel: (01925) 818504 Fax: (01925) 817819

PTFE COATED BANDS

Sig Pack Ltd, 1 Oakham Close, Derby, DE21 4DE Tel: (01332) 626262 Fax: (01332) 626288

PTFE COATED/LINED STEEL TUBES

Edlon, Riverside, Leven, Fife, KY8 4RT Tel: (01333) 426222 Fax: (01333) 426314 E-mail: sales@edlon.co.uk

PTFE COATING PROCESSORS OR SERVICES

Almit Metal Finishing, Whinfield Drive, Aycliffe Industrial Estate, Aycliffe Industrial Park, Newton Aycliffe, County Durham, DL5 6AU Tel: (01325) 311777 Fax: (01325) 316472

East Anglian Fine Weld Ltd, Unit 1, St. Margarets Way, Stukeley Meadows Industrial Estate, Huntingdon, Cambridgeshire, PE29 6EB Tel: (01480) 453412 Fax: (01480) 434952 E-mail: sales@eafw.co.uk

Fluoro Precision Coatings, Units 19-20 Hewitts Industrial Estate, Elmbridge Road, Cranleigh, Surrey, GU6 8LW Tel: (01483) 276887 Fax: (01483) 276130 E-mail: gs@fluoroprecision.co.uk

Fluorocarbon Coatings (Sheffield Division) Ltd, Burlyvale Avenue, Sheffield, S12 2AX Tel: 0114-253 0353 Fax: 0114-253 0355 E-mail: info@fluorocarbon.co.uk

Insoll Components Ltd, 39 Wilbury Way, Hitchin, Hertfordshire, SG4 0TW Tel: (01462) 450741 Fax: (01462) 421162E-mail: sales@insoll.com

K & N Coatings Ltd, 7 Bellingham Close, Bury, Lancashire, BL8 2TU Tel: 0161-797 2909 Fax: 0161-764 2810

Metalcraft Plastic Coatings Ltd, Back Wellington Street, Accrington, Lancashire, BB5 2NW Tel: (01254) 871727 Fax: (01254) 871168 E-mail: claudeen1@btconnect.com

Omnikote Ltd, Chamberlain Road, Aylesbury, Buckinghamshire, HP19 8DY Tel: (01296) 483266 Fax: (01296) 392285 E-mail: sales@omnikote.co.uk

Product Release Europe Ltd, Cusson Road, Knowsley Industrial Park, Liverpool, L33 7BY Tel: 0151-549 1491 Fax: 0151-548 4035

Wildcat Taconic, School Close, Burgess Hill, West Sussex, RH15 9RD Tel: (01444) 247756 Fax: (01444) 248416 E-mail: sales@wildcat-taconic.com

PTFE COMPONENTS, FILLED

Claron Hydraulic Services, Alders Way, Yalberton Industrial Estate, Paignton, Devon, TQ4 7QL Tel: (01803) 528852 Fax: (01803) 525134 E-mail: sales@claron.co.uk

Fluorocarbon Scotland Ltd, 6 Rutherford Square, Brucefield Industrial Estate, Livingston, West Lothian, EH54 9BU Tel: (01506) 411865 Fax: (01506) 412720 E-mail: engineeringplastics@fluorocarbon.co.uk

PTFE FABRICATORS

D & A Plastics, Stubcroft Farm Studios, Stubcroft Lane, East Wittering, Chichester, West Sussex, PO20 8PJ Tel: (01243) 671588 Fax: (01243) 671588

Fluorocarbon Scotland Ltd, 6 Rutherford Square, Brucefield Industrial Estate, Livingston, West Lothian, EH54 9BU Tel: (01506) 411865 Fax: (01506) 412720 E-mail: engineeringplastics@fluorocarbon.co.uk

PTFE HEAT SHRINK TUBING

▶ Analytical Columns, 7 Addington Business Centre, Vulcan Way, New Addington, Croydon, CR0 9UG Tel: (01689) 842736 Fax: (01689) 800199 E-mail: analytical@btconnect.com

PTFE HOSE

Aflex Hose Ltd, Spring Bank Industrial Estate, Watson Mill Lane, Sowerby Bridge, West Yorkshire, HX6 3BW Tel: (01422) 317200 Fax: (01422) 836000 E-mail: sales@aflex-hose.co.uk

Circuit Hydraulics Ltd, Unit 16 Kensington Industrial Park, Kensington Road, Southport, Merseyside, PR9 0RY Tel: (01704) 546288 Fax: (01704) 546313 E-mail: circuit.hyd@btinternet.com

Drain Center Ltd, Lincoln Road, Cressex Business Park, High Wycombe, Buckinghamshire, HP12 3RB Tel: (01494) 462351 Fax: (01494) 444923

Drain Center, Unit 20, West Churton Industrial Estate, Alder Road, North Shields, Tyne & Wear, NE29 8SD Tel: 0191-257 8125 Fax: 0191-257 8819

Drain Centre, 19 Bank Head Drive, St. Hillndustrial Estate, St.Hill, Edinburgh, EH11 4DW Tel: 0131-552 8181 Fax: 0131-453 2008 E-mail: edinbr@capperplastics.com

Drain Centre, Cinderhill Industrial Estate, Weston Coyney Road, Longton, Stoke-On-Trent, ST3 5JT Tel: (01782) 311311 Fax: (01782) 343400 E-mail: p23.stoke@wolseley.co.uk

Drains Centre, Unit 2B, St. Georges Trading Estate, Avonmouth, Bristol, BS11 9HS Tel: 0117-916 2700 Fax: 0117-982 6820 E-mail: bristol.p11@wolseley.co.uk

Goodridge (UK) Ltd, Exeter Airport Business Park, Exeter, EX5 2UP Tel: (01392) 369090 Fax: (01392) 441780

Ideal Hose & Safety Ltd, Spring Lane, Northampton, NN1 2JW Tel: (01604) 621964 Fax: (01604) 232936 E-mail: sales@idealhose.co.uk

Johnstech Interconnect Ltd, 1-2 Usk Street, Newport, Gwent, NP19 7BE Tel: (01633) 674452 Fax: (01633) 674453 E-mail: info@johnstech.com

K C Tooling Ltd, Unit 22, Hayhill Industrial Estate, Sileby Road, Barrow Upon Soar, Loughborough, Leicestershire, LE12 8LD Tel: (01509) 814724 Fax: (01509) 816076

Pipe Centre Plus, Unit 8, Spring Road Industrial Estate, Ettingshall, Wolverhampton, WV4 6JZ Tel: (01902) 409341 Fax: (01902) 353817 E-mail: p15.wolverhampton@wolseley.co.uk

PTFE MACHINISTS

Claron Hydraulic Services, Alders Way, Yalberton Industrial Estate, Paignton, Devon, TQ4 7QL Tel: (01803) 528852 Fax: (01803) 525134 E-mail: sales@claron.co.uk

Claron Plastics Ltd, Alders Way, Yalberton Industrial Estate, Paignton, Devon, TQ4 7QL Tel: (01803) 528677 Fax: (01803) 525134 E-mail: services@claron.co.uk

D & A Plastics, Stubcroft Farm Studios, Stubcroft Lane, East Wittering, Chichester, West Sussex, PO20 8PJ Tel: (01243) 671588 Fax: (01243) 671588

Fluorocarbon Scotland Ltd, 6 Rutherford Square, Brucefield Industrial Estate, Livingston, West Lothian, EH54 9BU Tel: (01506) 411865 Fax: (01506) 412720 E-mail: engineeringplastics@fluorocarbon.co.uk

Insoll Components Ltd, 39 Wilbury Way, Hitchin, Hertfordshire, SG4 0TW Tel: (01462) 450741 Fax: (01462) 421162E-mail: sales@insoll.com

P T F E Components Ltd, Unit 2 Northend Industrial Estate, Bury Mead Rd, Hitchin, Herts, SG5 1RT Tel: (01462) 434502 Fax: (01462) 434503 E-mail: ptfecomp@btconnect.com

S W Plastics, Baldwins Yard, Noahs Ark, Kemsing, Sevenoaks, Kent, TN15 6PF Tel: (01732) 762260 Fax: (01732) 762025 E-mail: sales@swplasticsltd.com

W J P Engineering Plastics Ltd, Albert Works, Albert Avenue, Bobbers Mill, Nottingham, NG8 5BE Tel: 0115-929 9555 Fax: 0115-929 0422 E-mail: sales@wjpengineeringplastics.co.uk

PTFE MATERIALS

P T F E Components Ltd, Unit 2 Northend Industrial Estate, Bury Mead Rd, Hitchin, Herts, SG5 1RT Tel: (01462) 434502 Fax: (01462) 434503 E-mail: ptfecomp@btconnect.com

PTFE PRODUCTS/ COMPONENTS/FITTINGS

Amar Specialised Plastics Ltd, Unit G Alpha Centre, Babbage Road, Totnes, Devon, TQ9 5JA Tel: (01803) 868077 Fax: (01803) 863399 E-mail: amar@specialisedplastics.co.uk

▶ indicates data change since last edition

PTFE PRODUCTS/COMPONENTS/ FITTINGS – *continued*

Bacol Fine Blanking Ltd, Tramway, Oldbury Road, Smethwick, West Midlands, B66 1NY Tel: (01527) 874205 Fax: (01527) 833761 E-mail: info@bacolfineblanking.co.uk

▶ Beldam Crossley Ltd, PO Box 7, Bolton, BL1 6PB Tel: (01204) 494711 Fax: (01204) 493203 E-mail: sales@beldam-crossley.co.uk

Insoll Components Ltd, 39 Wilbury Way, Hitchin, Hertfordshire, SG4 0TW Tel: (01462) 450741 Fax: (01462) 421162E-mail: sales@insoll.com

P T F E Components Ltd, Unit 2 Northend Industrial Estate, Bury Mead Rd, Hitchin, Herts, SG5 1RT Tel: (01462) 434502 Fax: (01462) 434503 E-mail: ptfecomp@btconnect.com

S W Plastics, Baldwins Yard, Noahs Ark, Kemsing, Sevenoaks, Kent, TN15 6PF Tel: (01732) 762260 Fax: (01732) 762025 E-mail: sales@swplasticsltd.com

Trelleborg Sealing Solutions, 1 Cranbrook Way, Shirley, Solihull, West Midlands, B90 4GT Tel: 0121-744 1221 Fax: 0121-733 2442 E-mail: tssuk@trelleborg.com

W J P Engineering Plastics Ltd, Albert Works, Albert Avenue, Bobbers Mill, Nottingham, NG8 5BE Tel: 0115-929 9555 Fax: 0115-929 0422 E-mail: sales@wjpengineeringplastics.co.uk

PTFE RESIN

Lamina Dielectrics Ltd, Daux Road, Billingshurst, West Sussex, RH14 9SJ Tel: (01403) 783131 Fax: (01403) 782237 E-mail: sales@lamina.uk.com

PTFE SHEETS

Fluorocarbon Co. Ltd, Excalibur Way, Irlam, Manchester, M44 5DL Tel: 0161-777 6300 Fax: 0161-776 2503 E-mail: seals@fluorocarbon.co.uk

PTFE TAPE MANUFRS

Abaco Industrial Tapes, Marnic House, 37 Shooters Hill Road, Blackheath, London, SE3 7HS Tel: (020) 8858 8100 Fax: (020) 8305 1401 E-mail: tapes@marnic.com

Biscor Ltd, Kingsmark Freeway, Bradford, West Yorkshire, BD12 7HW Tel: (01274) 694684 Fax: (01274) 694685 E-mail: info@biscor.com

Fluorocarbon Co. Ltd, Excalibur Way, Irlam, Manchester, M44 5DL Tel: 0161-777 6300 Fax: 0161-776 2503 E-mail: seals@fluorocarbon.co.uk

K & N Coatings Ltd, 7 Bellingham Close, Bury, Lancashire, BL8 2TU Tel: 0161-797 2909 Fax: 0161-764 2810

Marnic P.L.C., Armstrong Road, London, SE18 6RS Tel: (020) 8312 7200 Fax: (020) 8312 7250 E-mail: tapes@marnic.com

PUBLIC ADDRESS (PA) SYSTEM HIRE

▶ Avenue Audio, Millbrook Road East, Southampton, SO15 1HS Tel: 07789 695567 E-mail: Info@avenueaudio.co.uk

▶ East Anglian Radio Services, 4 High Beech, Lowestoft, Suffolk, NR32 2RY Tel: (01502) 568021 Fax: (01502) 600176 E-mail: office@eastanglianradio.com

PUBLIC ADDRESS (PA) SYSTEMS

A A Electronique Services Ltd, Unit 5, Gtrove Park Business Estate, Waltham Road, White Waltham, Maidenhead, Berkshire, SL6 3LW Tel: (020) 8893 1907 Fax: (020) 8893 1908

A R B Audio & Visual Hire Ltd, Unit 4, Building G, Tingewick Road Industrial Park, Tingewick Road, Buckingham, MK18 1SU Tel: (01295) 262000 Fax: (01280) 817948 E-mail: info@arb-teamwork.com

Advanced Safety Communications, 26b Brookfield Road, Arnold, Nottingham, NG5 7ER Tel: 0115-967 9067 Fax: 0115-956 1585 E-mail: sales@ascaudio.co.uk

Arc Electronics, 352 Portswood Road, Southampton, SO17 3SB Tel: (023) 8058 4642 Fax: (023) 8055 9199 E-mail: simon@btclick.com

Aston Acoustic Ltd, Unit 7, Bay 1 The Woodsbank Trading Estate, Woden Road West, Wednesbury, West Midlands, WS10 7SU Tel: 0121-505 6500 Fax: 0121-505 6515 E-mail: info@astonacoustic.com

Audix Systems Ltd, Station Road, Wendens Ambo, Saffron Walden, Essex, CB11 4LG Tel: (01799) 540888 Fax: (01799) 541618 E-mail: sales@tepg.com

B L Acoustics Ltd, 152 Enterprise Court, Eastways, Witham, Essex, CM8 3YS Tel: (01376) 521525 Fax: (01376) 521526 E-mail: male@blacoustics.net

Baldwin Boxall Communications Ltd, Wealden Industrial Estate, Farningham Road, Crowborough, East Sussex, TN6 2JR Tel: (01892) 664422 Fax: (01892) 663146 E-mail: mail@baldwinboxall.co.uk

Carlsbro Electronics Ltd, Cross Drive, Kirkby-in-Ashfield, Nottingham, NG17 7LD Tel: 08452 582910 Fax: 01623 755436 E-mail: sales@carlsbro.co.uk

D N H Worldwide Ltd, 31 Clarke Road, Mount Farm, Bletchley, Milton Keynes, MK1 1LG Tel: (01908) 275000 Fax: (01908) 275100 E-mail: dnh@dnh.co.uk

E T S Maintenance, Bridge Works, Hall Green, Little Hallingbury, Bishop's Stortford, Hertfordshire, CM22 7RP Tel: (01279) 730022 Fax: (01279) 731777 E-mail: etsltd@btinternet.com

ES Repairs, Buckhurst Ave, Carshalton, Surrey, SM5 1PF Tel: (020) 8395 1536 E-mail: electrosysrep@blueyonder.co.uk

Folknoll Ltd, 26 Old North Road, Royston, Hertfordshire, SG8 5DT Tel: (01763) 248834 Fax: (01763) 248014 E-mail: general@folknoll.co.uk

French Electrical Services, Chapel House, 25 Chapel Street, Loughborough, Leicestershire, LE12 9AF Tel: (01509) 502533 Fax: (01509) 505773 E-mail: wtfrench@btinternet.com

▶ David Hall Communications, 19 Taylor Avenue, Cringleford, Norwich, NR4 6XY Tel: (01603) 506602 E-mail: david@davidhallcomms.co.uk

Klark Teknik Group UK plc, Coppice Industrial Trading Estate, Walter Nash Road, Kidderminster, Worcestershire, DY11 7HJ Tel: (01562) 741515 Fax: (01562) 745371

Micina Technologies Group, Regent House, 40 Nelson Street, Leicester, LE1 7BA Tel: 0116-233 9944 Fax: 0116-233 9945 E-mail: mike@micina.co.uk

Millbank, Westmorland Business Centre, 41-43 Westmorland Road, Newcastle Upon Tyne, NE1 4EH Tel: 0191-232 1301 Fax: 0191-232 1302 E-mail: enquiries@ampekko.com

Mustang Communications Ltd, Dunslow Road, Eastfield, Scarborough, North Yorkshire, YO11 3UT Tel: (01723) 582555 Fax: (01723) 581673 E-mail: kelly@mustang.co.uk

Next Two, Colliery Road, Pinxton, Nottingham, NG16 6JF Tel: (01773) 864111 Fax: (01773) 582800 E-mail: sales@nexttwo.com

Premier Solutions (Nottingham) Ltd, Ascot Industrial Estate, Sandiacre, Nottingham, NG10 5DL Tel: 0115-939 4122 Fax: 0115-949 0453 E-mail: info@premier-solutions.biz

Protec Fire Detection Export Ltd, Protec House, Churchill Way, Nelson, Lancashire, BB9 6RT Tel: (01282) 717171 Fax: (01282) 717273 E-mail: sales@protec.co.uk

Public Address Systems Ltd, Unit 5 Leestone Road Sharston, Sharston Industrial Area, Manchester, M22 4RN Tel: 0161-611 7171 Fax: 0161-611 7170 E-mail: sales@pad.co.uk

Select Telecom, Colville House, 1 Lynn Road, Littleport, Ely, Cambridgeshire, CB6 1QG Tel: (0800) 0832228 Fax: (01353) 863535 E-mail: nkhokhar@selecttelecom.co.uk

Sitelink Communications, 14 Collingwood Court, Riverside Park Industrial Esta, Middlesbrough, Cleveland, TS2 1RP Tel: (01642) 232468 Fax: (01642) 226155 E-mail: teeside@sitelink.co.uk

Skytronic Ltd, Containerbase, Barton Dock Road, Urmston, Manchester, M41 7BQ Tel: 0161-749 8180 Fax: 0161-749 8181 E-mail: sales@skytronic.co.uk

▶ Sorted Technical Services Ltd, Brafield on the Green, Northampton, NN7 1BT Tel: (01604) 890260 E-mail: enquiries@sortedtech.co.uk

▶ Technical Services, 6-9 Cleveland Road, Gosport, Hampshire, PO12 2JG Tel: (023) 9258 8059 Fax: (023) 9258 9556 E-mail: enquiries@techsoundsystems.co.uk

Technical Services Shropshire Ltd, Unit 8, Bicton Business Park, Isle Lane, Bicton Heath, Shrewsbury, SY3 8DY Tel: (01743) 851313 Fax: (01743) 851211 E-mail: info@tsshropshire.co.uk

Toa Corporation, Unit 2 Hook Rise South Industrial Park, Hook Rise South, Surbiton, Surrey, KT6 7LD Tel: (0870) 7740987 Fax: (0870) 7770839 E-mail: info@toa.co.uk

▶ Total Security Northern, 3 Conyers Avenue, Chester le Street, County Durham, DH2 2HQ Tel: 0191-387 3117 Fax: 0191-387 3117 E-mail: totalnorthern@hotmail.com

Tyco Fire & Integrated Solutions, Molly Avenue, Mapperley, Nottingham, NG3 5FW Tel: 0115-955 1199 Fax: 0115-955 1919 E-mail: spectorlumunex.uk@tycoint.com

Vision Fire & Security, Vision House Focus 31, Mark Road, Hemel Hempstead Industrial Estate, Hemel Hempstead, Hertfordshire, HP2 7BW Tel: (01442) 242330 Fax: (01442) 249327

Whiteley Electronics Ltd, Victoria Street, Mansfield, Nottinghamshire, NG18 5RW Tel: (01623) 415600 Fax: (01623) 420484 E-mail: e-mail@whiteleyelectronics.com

PUBLIC ADDRESS (PA) SYSTEMS BACKGROUND MUSIC SUPPLIERS

Arc Electronics, 352 Portswood Road, Southampton, SO17 3SB Tel: (023) 8058 4642 Fax: (023) 8055 9199 E-mail: simon@btclick.com

Elite, Forest Row, East Sussex, RH18 5ES Tel: (01342) 822292 E-mail: info@elitespage.co.uk

PUBLIC ADDRESS (PA) SYSTEMS CONTRACTORS OR INSTALLATION OR HIRE OR SERVICE OR SUPPLIERS

A R B Audio & Visual Hire Ltd, Unit 4, Building G, Tingewick Road Industrial Park, Tingewick Road, Buckingham, MK18 1SU Tel: (01295) 262000 Fax: (01280) 817948 E-mail: info@arb-teamwork.com

Arc Electronics, 352 Portswood Road, Southampton, SO17 3SB Tel: (023) 8058 4642 Fax: (023) 8055 9199 E-mail: simon@btclick.com

Audio & Acoustics, United House, North Road, London, N7 9DP Tel: (020) 7700 2900 Fax: (020) 7700 6900 E-mail: sales@audioandacoustics.com

Audio Design Services Ltd, St Davids House, Adcroft St, Higher Hillgate, Stockport, Cheshire, SK1 3HW Tel: 0161-476 1010 Fax: 0161-666 6366 E-mail: sales@ads-worldwide.net

▶ Avenue Audio, Millbrook Road East, Southampton, SO15 1HS Tel: 07789 695567 E-mail: Info@avenueaudio.co.uk

C P C Communications, 56 Clive Road, Cardiff, CF5 1HG Tel: (029) 2066 5213 Fax: (01639) 646003

E T S Maintenance, Bridge Works, Hall Green, Little Hallingbury, Bishop's Stortford, Hertfordshire, CM22 7RP Tel: (01279) 730022 Fax: (01279) 731777 E-mail: etsltd@btinternet.com

▶ East Anglian Radio Services, 4 High Beech, Lowestoft, Suffolk, NR32 2RY Tel: (01502) 568021 Fax: (01502) 600176 E-mail: office@eastanglianradio.com

ESW Solutions, Penny Stone Farm, Westerland, Maldon, Paignton, Devon, TQ3 1RU Tel: (01803) 522522 Fax: (0871) 4338777

Fourway Communication Ltd, Delamare Road, Cheshunt, Waltham Cross, Hertfordshire, EN8 9SH Tel: (01992) 629182 Fax: (01992) 639227 E-mail: info@fourway.co.uk

French Electrical Services, Chapel House, 25 Chapel Street, Loughborough, Leicestershire, LE12 9AF Tel: (01509) 502533 Fax: (01509) 505773 E-mail: wtfrench@btinternet.com

Golding Audio, 8 Peartree Business Centre, Peartree Road, Stanway, Colchester, CO3 0JN Tel: (01206) 762462 Fax: (01206) 762633 E-mail: enquiries@goldingaudio.co.uk

Hampshire Sound Services, 39 Fairoak Road, Eastleigh, Hampshire, SO50 6LF Tel: (023) 8061 3339 Fax: (023) 8061 3339 E-mail: hantsound@aol.com

King Communication Services, 19 Coatbank Street, Coatbridge, Lanarkshire, ML5 3SP Tel: (01236) 429445 Fax: (01236) 429445 E-mail: info@kingcoms.com

▶ MAN Audio Services, Catherine Court Farm, Coppershell, Gastard, Corsham, Wiltshire, SN13 9PZ Tel: (01249) 701363 Fax: (01249) 701236 E-mail: matt@manaudio.co.uk

Programmed Communications, Unit 9 Bluebird House, Povey Cross Road, Horley, Surrey, RH6 0AF Tel: (01293) 822033 Fax: (01293) 821958

Shipton Communications Ltd, 1 Frogmore Road, Hemel Hempstead, Hertfordshire, HP3 9TG Tel: (01442) 345600 Fax: (01442) 345663

Telecall Ltd, 1 Stratfield Park, Elettra Avenue, Waterlooville, Hampshire, PO7 7XN Tel: (023) 9225 0525 Fax: (023) 9226 5299 E-mail: sales@telecall.uk.com

Tjaden Ltd, 62a Chatsworth Road, London, E5 0LS Tel: (020) 8533 7234 Fax: (020) 8533 7234

V A Turner & Son, The Chestnuts, High Street, Barcombe, Lewes, East Sussex, BN8 5BA Tel: (01273) 400339 Fax: (01273) 401615

West London Electric Acton Ltd, 9-11 High Street, London, W3 6NQ Tel: (020) 8992 2155 Fax: (020) 8992 4067E-mail: sales@wle.co.uk

Willow Communications Ltd, Kilvey Road, Brackmills Industrial Estate, Northampton, NN4 7BQ Tel: (01604) 877001 Fax: (01604) 877100 E-mail: mail@wcl.biz

PUBLIC ADDRESS (PA) VOICE EVACUATION SYSTEMS

▶ Argus Services, H R S House H R S Industrial Estate, Garretts Green Lane, Birmingham, B33 0UE Tel: 0121-683 1168 Fax: 0121-683 1167 E-mail: admin@argus-services.co.uk

Vision Fire & Security, Vision House Focus 31, Mark Road, Hemel Hempstead Industrial Estate, Hemel Hempstead, Hertfordshire, HP2 7BW Tel: (01442) 242330 Fax: (01442) 249327

PUBLIC RELATION CONSULTANCY OR SERVICES, CORPORATE IDENTITY

Arthouse P R, 7a Market Street, Crediton, Devon, EX17 2EE Tel: (01363) 777002 Fax: (01363) 779956 E-mail: sales@arthouse-pr.com

▶ Bojangle Communications Ltd, 2 Virginia Close, Ashtead, Surrey, KT21 2NW Tel: (01372) 274975 E-mail: lindsey@bojangle.co.uk

▶ Michelle Figg Freelance Marketing Communications, 9A Orsett Terrace, London, W2 6AJ Tel: (07973) 221331 E-mail: michelle@michellefigg.com

▶ Gainsborough Communications, 34-36 High Holborn, London, WC1V 6AE Tel: (020) 7190 1700 Fax: (020) 7190 1701 E-mail: info@gainsboroughcomms.com

▶ Impact Media, The Mm2 Building, 84 Pickford Street, Manchester, M4 5BT Tel: 0161-236 0008 Fax: 0161-236 0204 E-mail: info@impactmediapr.com

▶ M2s Media Consultancy, Twyford Place, Wellington, Somerset, TA21 8BZ Tel: (01823) 663146 Fax: (01823) 663146 E-mail: m2smedia@btconnect.com

Napier Partnership Ltd, Birdham Road, Chichester, West Sussex, PO20 7DU Tel: (01243) 531123 Fax: (01243) 779070 E-mail: napier@napier.co.uk

▶ The PR Shop, 70 Priory Road, Kenilworth, Warwickshire, CV8 1LQ Tel: 01676 534319 E-mail: kelly@pr-shop.co.uk

▶ Prolific Marketing Ltd, 5th Floor, International House, 223 Regent Street, London, W1B 2QD Tel: 020 7544 1010 Fax: 020 7544 1090 E-mail: enquiries@prolificmarketing.co.uk

▶ Watch PR, 29 Gibbon Road, Kingston upon Thames, Surrey, KT2 6AD Tel: 020 8286 0654 E-mail: enquiries@watchpr.com

▶ Words Worth, Benfleet Water Tower, 335 Benfleet Road, Benfleet, Essex, SS7 1PW Tel: (01268) 756261 Fax: (01268) 750706

▶ Zed PR, 182 Fairwater Drive, Woodley, Reading, RG5 3JF Tel: 0118-944 0394 E-mail: claire@zedpr.co.uk

PUBLIC RELATIONS (FINANCIAL) CONSULTANTS OR SERVICES

College Hill Associates Ltd, 78 Cannon Street, London, EC4N 6HH Tel: (020) 7457 2020 Fax: (020) 7248 3295 E-mail: pr@collegehill.co.uk

▶ Gainsborough Communications, 34-36 High Holborn, London, WC1V 6AE Tel: (020) 7190 1700 Fax: (020) 7190 1701 E-mail: info@gainsboroughcomms.com

Incomes Data Services Ltd, 77 Bastwick Street, London, EC1V 3TT Tel: (020) 7250 3434 Fax: (020) 7608 0949 E-mail: sales@incomesdata.co.uk

Manning Selvage & Lee, Pembroke Building, Avonmore Road, London, W14 8DG Tel: (020) 7878 3000 Fax: (020) 7878 3030 E-mail: sales@mslpr.com

Pressential, 222 Godstone Road, Whyteleafe, Surrey, CR3 0EE Tel: (01883) 623329 Fax: (01883) 625506

PUBLIC RELATIONS (OVERSEAS) CONSULTANTS OR SERVICES

Christow Consultants Ltd, 21 Bloomsbury Square, London, WC1A 2NS Tel: (020) 7631 0990 Fax: (020) 7631 0102 E-mail: christow@christow.com

Citigate Public Affairs, 26 Grosvenor Gardens, London, SW1W 0GT Tel: (020) 7838 4800 Fax: (020) 7838 4801

Euro RSCG Biss Lancaster, 6 Briset Street, London, EC1M 5NR Tel: (020) 7022 4000 Fax: (020) 7022 4100

G P C International, 40 Long Acre, London, WC2E 9LG Tel: (020) 7395 7171 Fax: (020) 7395 7181 E-mail: info@gpcinternational.com

Good Relations Ltd, Hobern Gate, 26 South Hampton Buildings, London, WC2A 1PQ Tel: (020) 7861 3030 Fax: (020) 7861 3200 E-mail: info@good-relations.co.uk

Haggie Financial Ltd, Roman House, Wood Street, London, EC2Y 5BA Tel: (020) 7417 8989 Fax: (020) 7417 8247 E-mail: reception@haggie.co.uk

Huntsworth, 15-17 Huntsworth Mews, London, NW1 6DD Tel: (020) 7402 2272 Fax: (020) 7706 4732

Manning Selvage & Lee, Pembroke Building, Avonmore Road, London, W14 8DG Tel: (020) 7878 3000 Fax: (020) 7878 3030 E-mail: sales@mslpr.com

Markmaid Ltd, 55 Beechwood Rd, Swansea, SA2 0JL Tel: (01792) 280610 Fax: (01792) 281414 E-mail: markmaid@btconnect.com

▶ Opera Public Relations, 4 West End, Baslow, Bakewell, Derbyshire, DE45 1RG Tel: (0845) 0600650 Fax: 0870 0113457 E-mail: pr@operapr.com

Persuasion Public Relations, Suite 2 Cheviot House, Beaminster Way East, Newcastle upon Tyne, NE3 2ER Tel: 0191-214 0222 Fax: 0191-214 0240 E-mail: hq@persuasion-pr.com

R P G Associates Ltd, 35 St. Georges Road, Cheltenham, Gloucestershire, GL50 3DU Tel: (01242) 252444 Fax: (01242) 252888

Weber Shandwick, 58 Queens Road, Aberdeen, AB15 4YE Tel: (01224) 806600 Fax: (01224) 208823 E-mail: jrmacdonald@webershandwick.com

PUBLIC RELATIONS/ COMMUNICATIONS CONSULTANTS OR SERVICES

▶ Abucon Ltd, 21a Vincent Square, London, SW1P 2NA Tel: (020) 7834 1066 Fax: (020) 7828 1828 E-mail: info@abucon.co.uk

▶ ACPR, 18 Spencer Mews, Lansdowne Way, London, SW8 1HF Tel: (020) 7820 7768 E-mail: antonia@acpr.co.uk

▶ Activnet Biz, Little Gaddesden, Berkhamsted, Hertfordshire, HP4 1PA Tel: (01442) 843516 Fax: (0870) 7060164 E-mail: marika.woods@activnet.biz

Adams PR & Marketing, 78 Woodside Avenue North, Coventry, CV3 6BD Tel: (024) 7669 0700 Fax: (024) 7669 0700

Alexander Associates, 21 Hillward Close, Orton Longueville, Peterborough, PE2 7AB Tel: (01733) 371770 Fax: (01733) 371770 E-mail: david.thorpe8@ntlworld.com

▶ Antimony Communications, 5 Chestnut Way, Godalming, Surrey, GU7 1TN Tel: (0870) 3214807 Fax: (0870) 7656807 E-mail: kelly@antimony.co.uk

Artizan Communications, Milton Road, Ware, Hertfordshire, SG12 0QD Tel: (01920) 466678 Fax: (01920) 466821 E-mail: jane@artizan-on-line.com

▶ B I Worldwide Ltd, 1 Vantage Court, Tickford Street, Newport Pagnell, Buckinghamshire, MK16 9EZ Tel: (01908) 214700 Fax: (01908) 214777 E-mail: enquires@eu.biworldwide.com

Barneys Advertising Ltd, Royal London Buildings, 42-46 Baldwin Street, Bristol, BS1 1PN Tel: 0117-921 4551 Fax: 0117-926 2529 E-mail: info@barneys.co.uk

Beetlenut, Abbey Barn Farm, Abbey Barn Lane, High Wycombe, Buckinghamshire, HP10 9QQ Tel: (0870) 460 5626 Fax: (0870) 460 5627 E-mail: Debbie@beetlenut.com

Bell Pottinger, 14 Curzon Street, London, W1J 5HN Tel: (020) 7495 4044 Fax: (020) 7861 8506

Bell Pottinger Public Affairs, 330 High Holborn, London, WC1V 7LU Tel: (020) 7861 2400 Fax: (020) 7861 2401 E-mail: enquiries@bpcf.co.uk

Bergmans, Grainger Suite, Dobson House, Regent Centre, Gosforth, Newcastle Upon Tyne, NE3 3PF Tel: 0191-233 6311 Fax: 0191-233 6341 E-mail: bergmans@north-house.com

▶ Binsted Group plc, Attwood House Mansfield Business Park, Lymington Bottom Road, Medstead, Alton, Hampshire, GU34 5PZ Tel: (01420) 568900 Fax: (01420) 565994 E-mail: info@binstedgroup.com

Bird & Moore Ltd, The Vicarage, Church Street, Uttoxeter, Staffordshire, ST14 8AA Tel: (01889) 565111 Fax: (01889) 565700 E-mail: birdandmoore@btinternet.com

Blackwood Communications, 2a New Road, Mytholmroyd, Hebden Bridge, West Yorkshire, HX7 5DZ Tel: (01422) 883688 Fax: (01422) 881376 E-mail: info@blackwood-pr.co.uk

Blue Rocket Group Ltd, 115 Church Road, Hove, East Sussex, BN3 2AF Tel: (01273) 779196 E-mail: daniel@bluerocketgroup.com

Buchanan Communications Ltd, 107 Cheapside, London, EC2V 6DN Tel: (020) 7466 5000 Fax: (020) 7466 5001 E-mail: contact@buchanan.uk.com

Burson Marsteller, 24-28 Bloomsbury Way, London, WC1A 2PX Tel: (020) 7831 2969 Fax: (020) 7340 1033 E-mail: enquiries@bein.com

Butterfield Morris Bushell Ltd, Bute Mills Mill Yard, Guildford Street, Luton, LU1 2NH Tel: (01582) 725454 Fax: (01582) 480024 E-mail: enquiries@bmb.uk.com

C M A Holdings Ltd, Torr Hill, Plymouth, PL8 2HQ Tel: (01752) 881333 Fax: (01752) 882101

C T C, 12 Whiteladies Road, Bristol, BS8 1PD Tel: 0117-311 9009 Fax: 0117-311 9010 E-mail: info@ctcuk.com

Case Alarms Ltd, Unit 5 Taff Workshops, Tresillian Terrace, Cardiff, CF10 5DE Tel: (029) 2038 7006 Fax: (029) 2038 7006 E-mail: cardiff@casesecurity.co.uk

▶ Cerub Limited, 17a Peterborough Avenue, High Wycombe, Buckinghamshire, HP13 6DX Tel: 01494 461784 Fax: 08707 062603 E-mail: ceri@cerubpr.co.uk

Citygate Dewe Rogerson Ltd, 3 London Wall Buildings, London, EC2M 5SY Tel: (020) 7638 9571 Fax: (020) 7628 3444

Clareville Communications, 315-317 New Kings Road, London, SW6 4RF Tel: (020) 7736 4022 Fax: (020) 7736 3504 E-mail: johnstar@clareville.co.uk

Clarke Associates, The Old School House, Chapel Lane, Wythall, Birmingham, B47 6JX Tel: 0121-702 2525 Fax: 0121-702 2085 E-mail: pr@clarke-associates.co.uk

Cohn & Wolfe Ltd, 30 Orange St, London, WC2H 7LZ Tel: (020) 7331 5300 Fax: (020) 7331 9083

Colette Hill Associates, 18-20 Bromells Road, London, SW4 0BG Tel: (020) 7622 8252 Fax: (020) 7622 8253 E-mail: cha@chapr.co.uk

Communique Public Relations Ltd, Waterside, 2 Canal Street, Manchester, M1 3HE Tel: 0161-228 6677 Fax: 0161-228 7391 E-mail: info@communiquepr.co.uk

Countrywide Porter Novelli Ltd, 31 St. Petersburgh Place, London, W2 4LA Tel: (020) 7853 2222 Fax: (020) 7853 2244 E-mail: enquiries@countrywidepn.co.uk

▶ CWP, 37 38 The Old Woodyard, Hall Drive, Hagley, Stourbridge, West Midlands, DY9 9LQ Tel: (01562) 730066 Fax: (01562) 730066 E-mail: chris@cwppr.u-net.com

Davies Associates Ltd, 95 York Street, London, W1H 4QG Tel: (020) 7258 0701 Fax: (020) 7724 0106 E-mail: hq@dapr.com

De Facto Communications Ltd, 1 London Bridge, London, SE1 9BG Tel: (020) 7940 1000 Fax: (020) 7940 1001 E-mail: info@hccdefacto.com

Deeson Group Ltd, Ewell House, Graveney Road, Goodnestone, Faversham, Kent, ME13 8UP Tel: (01795) 535468 Fax: (01795) 535469 E-mail: enquiries@deeson.co.uk

Dunelm Public Relations Ltd, Gun Court, 70 Wapping Lane, London, E1W 2RD Tel: (020) 7480 0600 Fax: (020) 7480 0606 E-mail: info@dunelmpr.co.uk

Dwyers Business Management Services, Belton Ho, 15 Belton Drive, West Bridgford, Nottingham, NG2 7SJ Tel: 0115-984 2642 Fax: 0115-984 2642

Earl & Thompson Marketing Ltd, The Creative Centre, 1 Hucclecote Road, Gloucester, GL3 3TH Tel: (01452) 627100 Fax: (01452) 627101 E-mail: info@earl-thompson.co.uk

Euro RSCG Biss Lancaster, 6 Briset Street, London, EC1M 5NR Tel: (020) 7022 4000 Fax: (020) 7022 4100

F S W Group Ltd, Manor Farm Barns, Fox Road, Framingham Pigot, Norwich, NR14 7PZ Tel: (01508) 491400 Fax: (01508) 494088 E-mail: mail@fsw.co.uk

Fire Imc, Manley House, 10 Dargan Cresent, Belfast, BT3 9JP Tel: (028) 9077 4388 Fax: (028) 9077 6906 E-mail: sales@fireimc.co.uk

▶ Footprint Communications, 24 West Street, Alresford, Hampshire, SO24 9AT Tel: (01962) 738718 E-mail: info@footprint-comms.co.uk

Freshwater UK, Freshwater House, Cardiff Gate Business Park, Pontprennau, Cardiff, CF23 8RS Tel: (029) 2054 5370 Fax: (029) 2054 5380 E-mail: sales@freshwater-uk.com

Future Image Ltd, 26 Church Road, Holywood, County Down, BT18 9BU Tel: (028) 9042 3314 Fax: (028) 9042 4773 E-mail: newsdesk@futureimage.co.uk

G C A S Public Relations, Russell Court, 38-52 Lisburn Road, Belfast, BT9 6AA Tel: (028) 9055 7777 Fax: (028) 9023 0142 E-mail: lawrenced@gcasgroup.com

G P C International, 40 Long Acre, London, WC2E 9LG Tel: (020) 7395 7171 Fax: (020) 7395 7181 E-mail: info@gpcinternational.com

▶ Gainsborough Communications, 34-36 High Holborn, London, WC1V 6AE Tel: (020) 7190 1700 Fax: (020) 7190 1701 E-mail: info@gainsboroughcomms.com

GGH Marketing Communications, 1 West Street, Titchfield, Fareham, Hampshire, PO14 4DH Tel: (01329) 846166 Fax: (01329) 512063 E-mail: geoff@ggh.co.uk

Grayling, 1 Bedford Avenue, London, WC1B 3AU Tel: (020) 7255 5400 Fax: (020) 7255 5454 E-mail: info@uk.grayling.com

Harrison Cowley, Regus House, George Curl Way, Southampton, SO18 2RZ Tel: (023) 8033 7237 Fax: (023) 8023 1665 E-mail: enquiries@harrisoncowley.com

Harvest Marketing Communications, 35 Havant Business Centre, Harts Farm Way, Havant, Hampshire, PO9 1HU Tel: (023) 9244 9655 Fax: (023) 9248 1760 E-mail: info@harvestpr.co.uk

Haslimann Taylor Ltd, 1 Wrens Court, 53 Lower Queen Street, Sutton Coldfield, West Midlands, B72 1RT Tel: 0121-355 3446 Fax: 0121-355 3393 E-mail: info@haslimanntaylor.com

Hill & Knowlton (UK) Ltd, 20 Soho Square, London, W1A 1PR Tel: (020) 7413 3000 Fax: (020) 7413 3111 E-mail: info@hillandknowlton.com

Hopkinson White, 46 Brook Street, Aston Clinton, Aylesbury, Buckinghamshire, HP22 5ES Tel: (01296) 631898 Fax: (01296) 630321 E-mail: info@hopkinson-white.co.uk

▶ Houston Associates, 183-185 Kirkdale, London, SE26 4QH Tel: (020) 8778 1900 Fax: (020) 8659 9191 E-mail: richard@houston-associates.com

Huntsworth, 15-17 Huntsworth Mews, London, NW1 6DD Tel: (020) 7402 2272 Fax: (020) 7706 4732 E-mail: info@huntsworth.com

I A S Smarts, Clarence Mill, Clarence Road, Bollington, Macclesfield, Cheshire, SK10 5JZ Tel: (01625) 578578 Fax: (01625) 578579 E-mail: sue@iasbranding.co.uk

Ias Smarts Ni Ltd, 157 /159 High Street Citigate, Holywood, County Down, BT18 9HU Tel: (028) 9039 5500 Fax: (028) 9039 5600

Imarco Ltd, Herkomer House, 156 High Street, Bushey, WD23 3HF Tel: (020) 8420 4599 Fax: (020) 8420 4273 E-mail: vision@imarco.co.uk

▶ Inside Track Marketing, Beech House, Padgate Business Park, Green Lane, Padgate, Warrington, WA1 4JN Tel: 01925 820600 Fax: 01925 822488 E-mail: info@inside-track.co.uk

Inspirations Design & Communications Ltd, 26 Windermere Drive, Alderley Edge, Cheshire, SK9 7UP Tel: (01625) 599618 E-mail: inspirations@gen.net.uk

Inter Regional Public Relations Ltd, Hill House, 20 Hill House Road, Norwich, NR1 4BE Tel: (01603) 627294 Fax: (01603) 633638 E-mail: pr@interregional.co.uk

Item Ltd, Kingsway House, 103 Kingsway, London, WC2B 6QX Tel: (020) 7405 4767 Fax: (020) 7405 4768 E-mail: coms@item.co.uk

J B A Public Relations, 57 Church Street, Epsom, Surrey, KT17 4PX Tel: (01372) 734200 Fax: (01372) 734201 E-mail: jba@jbapr.com

J P R, Belmont Office Park, 232-240 Belmont Road, Belfast, BT4 2AW Tel: (028) 9076 0066 Fax: (028) 9076 0011 E-mail: mail@jprni.com

▶ Jigsaw public relations, Tower Court, Oakdale Road, Clifton Moor, York, YO30 4XL Tel: 01904 557673 E-mail: sarah@jigsawpr.co.uk

John M Davis & Associates, East Riding Small Business Centre, Annie Reed Road, Beverley, North Humberside, HU17 0LF Tel: (01482) 865766 Fax: (01482) 865766 E-mail: pr@nilspin.com

Kinghorn Davies Advertising Ltd, 35-39 Blandford Street, Newcastle upon Tyne, NE1 4HW Tel: 0191-261 8666 Fax: 0191-232 3635 E-mail: sales@kinghorn-davies.co.uk

Kinross & Render Ltd, 192-198 Vauxhall Bridge Road, London, SW1V 1DX Tel: (020) 7592 3100 Fax: (020) 7931 9640 E-mail: info@kinrossrender.com

Le Baron Marketing, 16 Maddox Street, London, W1S 1PH Tel: (020) 7499 5343 Fax: (020) 7493 7331 E-mail: elena@cxd.co.uk

Main Street Marketing, 1-3 Bachelors Walk, Lisburn, County Antrim, BT28 1XJ Tel: (028) 9268 2059 Fax: (028) 9267 1555

Manning Selvage & Lee, Pembroke Building, Avonmore Road, London, W14 8DG Tel: (020) 7878 3000 Fax: (020) 7878 3030 E-mail: sales@mslpr.com

Mark Williams Associates Ltd, 6 Bute Crescent, Cardiff, CF10 5AN Tel: (029) 2048 8488 Fax: (029) 2049 7776 E-mail: info@thinkmwa.co.uk

▶ Market Link Creative Marketing Ltd, 30 St Georges Square, Worcester, WR1 1HX Tel: (01905) 726575 Fax: (01905) 726090 E-mail: sales@marketlink-uk.com

Mearns & Gill Advertising Ltd, 7 Carden Place, Aberdeen, AB10 1PP Tel: (01224) 646311 Fax: (01224) 631882 E-mail: info@mearns-gill.com

Mills Advertising & Publicity, North House, 5 North Road, Stokesley, Middlesbrough, Cleveland, TS9 5DU Tel: (01642) 713156 Fax: (01642) 713174 E-mail: enquiries@millsadvertising.co.uk

Mistral LPM, Staplehurst Office Centre, Weston On The Green, Bicester, Oxfordshire, OX25 3QU Tel: (01869) 352720 Fax: (01869) 351519

▶ Neesham Public Relations Ltd, The Gallery Ashlyns Hall, Chesham Road, Berkhamsted, Hertfordshire, HP4 2ST Tel: (01442) 879222 Fax: (01442) 879444 E-mail: allane@neesham.co.uk

New Media Group P.L.C., Pinewood Studios, Pinewood Road, Iver, Buckinghamshire, SL0 0NH Tel: (01753) 655866 Fax: (01753) 655118 E-mail: info@newmediagroup.co.uk

New River Industrial Communications Ltd, Nelson Court, Gladstone Road, Ware, Hertfordshire, SG12 0AG Tel: (01920) 468443 Fax: (01920) 460528 E-mail: info@newriver.co.uk

Nomis Ltd, 146a Frimley Road, Camberley, Surrey, GU15 2QN Tel: (01276) 683449 Fax: (01276) 684799 E-mail: sales@nomislimited.com

▶ Opera Public Relations, 4 West End, Baslow, Bakewell, Derbyshire, DE45 1RG Tel: (0845) 0600650 Fax: 0870 0113457 E-mail: pr@operapr.com

Oxygen 8, 10 Mount Ephraim, Tunbridge Wells, Kent, TN4 8AS Tel: (01825) 762444 Fax: (01892) 527652 E-mail: info@oxygenonline.co.uk

▶ P J M C Ltd, 4 Church End, Radford Semele, Leamington Spa, Warwickshire, CV31 1TA Tel: (01926) 312886 Fax: (01926) 435355 E-mail: info@pjmc.com

P R Newswire Europe Ltd, 209-215 Blackfriars Road, London, SE1 8NL Tel: (020) 7490 8111 Fax: (020) 7490 1255 E-mail: info@prnewswire.co.uk

Planned Publicity, 241a Selbourne Road, Luton, LU4 8NP Tel: (01582) 599529 Fax: (01582) 583366 E-mail: briangale@pplgraphics.co.uk

▶ The PR Shop, 70 Priory Road, Kenilworth, Warwickshire, CV8 1LQ Tel: 01676 534319 E-mail: kelly@pr-shop.co.uk

Priority Services Ltd, The Lodge, Castle Bromwich Hall, Birmingham, B36 9DE Tel: (0121) 748 8710 Fax: (0121) 748 8711 E-mail: enquiries@priorityservices.co.uk

Profile Marketing Services, Profile House, 2 Hartfield Close, Kents Hill, Milton Keynes, MK7 6HN Tel: (01908) 605099 Fax: (01908) 672499 E-mail: services@profilemarketing.co.uk

Proscot Public Relations Consultants, Carpet Lane, Edinburgh, EH6 6SP Tel: 0131-468 7067 Fax: 0131-468 7056 E-mail: mail@proscot-pr.co.uk

R D W Advertising Ltd, Urlay Nook Road, Eaglescliffe, Stockton-On-Tees, Cleveland, TS16 0LA Tel: (01642) 790047 Fax: (01642) 781589 E-mail: info@rdw-advertising.co.uk

Raitt Orr & Associates, 16-18 Victoria Chambers, Strutton Ground, London, SW1P 2HP Tel: (020) 7222 5479 Fax: (020) 7222 5480 E-mail: info@raittorr.co.uk

Rapier Public Relations, 33 Brookfield Road, Churchdown, Gloucester, GL3 2PG Tel: (01452) 536810 Fax: (01452) 536810 E-mail: ray@rapier-pr.co.uk

Reeves Green Partners Ltd, Station Road, Lichfield, Staffordshire, WS13 6HX Tel: (01543) 250505 Fax: (01543) 255522 E-mail: marketing@reeves-green.co.uk

Richmond Towers Ltd, 26 Fitzroy Square, London, W1T 6BT Tel: (020) 7388 7421 Fax: (020) 7388 7761 E-mail: mail@richmondtowers.com

Spurgeon Walker Ltd, 67 High Street, Sevenoaks, Kent, TN13 1JY Tel: (01732) 459821 Fax: (01732) 459496 E-mail: info@spurgeonwalker.com

Staffordshire Marketing Ltd, Charrington House, 17 Market Street, Lichfield, Staffordshire, WS13 6JX Tel: (01543) 263942 Fax: (01543) 415249E-mail: info@stratford-marketing.co.uk

Stransky Thompson Public Relations, The Chemistry Lab, 57 Kingsway Place, Sans Walk, London, EC1R OLY Tel: (020) 7689 5159 Fax: (020) 7689 5156 E-mail: enquiries@clear-group.co.uk

T N S Media Intelligence, PA Newcentre, 292 Vauxhall Bridge Road, London, SW1V 1AE Tel: (020) 7963 7600 E-mail: tnsmi_sales@tnsofres.com

▶ Talk Marketing Ltd, Stockton Business Centre, Brunswick Street, Stockton-on-Tees, Cleveland, TS18 1DW Tel: (01642) 345133 Fax: (01642) 345135 E-mail: talkmarketing@fsbdial.co.uk

Tandem Consultancy, Top Executive Suite, 55 West Street, Chichester, West Sussex, PO19 1RU Tel: (01243) 778822 Fax: (01243) 779951 E-mail: creatorbiz@tandemuk.com

Taylor Alden Ltd, 92-94 Toynbee Road, London, SW20 8SL Tel: (020) 8543 3866 Fax: (020) 8543 2841 E-mail: pr@tayloralden.co.uk

Tregartha Dinnie, Chancery House, 199 Silbury Boulevard, Milton Keynes, MK9 1JL Tel: (01908) 306500 Fax: (01908) 306505

Visual Identity, 19 Shenley Pavilions, Chalkdell Drive, Shenley Wood, Milton Keynes, MK5 6LB Tel: (01908) 867171 Fax: (01908) 867170 E-mail: creativity@visualidentity.co.uk

Wakefield Taffarello Associates, 54 Old Street, London, EC1V 9AL Tel: (020) 7250 0500 Fax: (020) 7250 1553 E-mail: wta@wtadspr.demon.co.uk

The Warman Group Ltd, 7 The Wharf, Bridge Street, Birmingham, B1 2JS Tel: 0121-605 1111 Fax: 0121-605 0111 E-mail: enquiries@warmangroup.com

Wordsmith & Co., Farnham Royal, Slough, SL2 3WZ Tel: (01753) 645636 Fax: (01753) 669402 E-mail: dn@wordsmith-and-co.demon.co.uk

Yes Response Ltd, Unit 15 Brookside Business Park, Brookside Road, Uttoxeter, Staffordshire, ST14 8AU Tel: (01889) 561400 Fax: (01889) 568264 E-mail: dhanley@yesresponse.co.uk

PUBLIC SECTOR ELECTRONIC PROCUREMENT (EPROCUREMENT)

Proactis Group Ltd, Holtby Manor, Stamford Bridge Road, Dunnington, York, YO19 5LL Tel: (01904) 481999 Fax: (01904) 481666

PUBLIC SECTOR RECRUITMENT

▶ ARV Solutions, 27 Southmead Road, Westbury-On-Trym, Bristol, BS10 5DL Tel: 0117 9083173 Fax: 0871 661 3669 E-mail: mail@arvsolutions.co.uk

▶ Blue Silicon, 214 Kings Ash Road, Paignton, Devon, TQ3 3XL Tel: (0870) 7070005 E-mail: kellysearch@bluesilicon.co.uk

▶ Community Resourcing Ltd, 5-11 Lavington Street, London, London, SE1 0NZ Tel: (020) 76330007 E-mail: info@resourcinggroup.co.uk

▶ Ecruit UK Ltd, 41 Convent Road, Ashford, Middlesex, TW15 2HJ Tel: (08718) 714605 Fax: (08712) 773138 E-mail: admin@ecruit-direct.co.uk

▶ Linx Recruitment, Archway House, Norton Way North, Letchworth Garden City, Hertfordshire, SG6 1BH Tel: (01462) 677669 E-mail: keith@linxrecruitment.co.uk

▶ Management Consultancy 4 Limited, 7-111 Fleet Street, London, EC4A 2AB Tel: 0 870 770 9116 Fax: 0 870 770 9117 E-mail: info@mc4.co.uk

▶ RecruitEU Ltd, PO Box 43574, London, UK, SW15 1XA Tel: 0207 8708824 Fax: 0870 7051298 E-mail: nigelholmes@recruiteu.com

▶ Helen Sellers, The Dairy, Red House Farm, Priory Road, Fressingfield, Eye, Suffolk, IP21 5PH Tel: (0870) 4215709 E-mail: helen.sellers@crosspoint-resources.co.uk

▶ Tim Cowell, Clayhill Farm, Marden Rd, Cranbrook, Kent, TN17 2LP Tel: (01580) 715111 Fax: (01580) 714718 E-mail: webmaster@manufacturingjobs.co.uk

▶ Top Language Jobs, 770-780 Great Cambridge Road, Enfield, Middlesex, EN1 3RN Tel: (020) 8363 3334

UJOB - UK Employment Vacancies, PO Box 139, Thornton-Cleveleys, Lancashire, FY5 4WU Tel: (0870) 7668565 E-mail: ujob@ujob.co.uk

PUBLICATION BACK ISSUE FULFILMENT SERVICES

▶ 4mags, 30B Grosvenor Road, Caversham, Reading, RG4 5EN Tel: 07939 084481 E-mail: sales@4mags.co.uk

PUBLICATION BACK ISSUE FULFILMENT SERVICES – *continued*

▶ International Marketing & Logistics, 11c Stephenson Road, Clacton-on-Sea, Essex, CO15 4XA Tel: (01255) 479864 Fax: (01255) 474705 E-mail: paul.quenet@iml.uk.com

PUBLICATION WRAPPING SERVICES, POLYETHYLENE (PE)

DHL Global Mail Ltd, Mills Road, Quarry Wood, Aylesford, Kent, ME20 7WZ Tel: (01622) 792111 Fax: (01622) 792333

PUBLICATIONS

A M S Educational, 38 Parkside Road, Leeds, LS6 4QG Tel: 0113-275 9900 Fax: 0113-275 7799 E-mail: admin@amseducational.co.uk

Appletree Press Ltd, 14 Howard St South, Belfast, BT7 1AP Tel: (028) 9024 3074 Fax: (028) 9024 6756 E-mail: info@appletree.ie

▶ Binsted Group plc, Attwood House Mansfield Business Park, Lymington Bottom Road, Medstead, Alton, Hampshire, GU34 5PZ Tel: (01420) 568900 Fax: (01420) 565994 E-mail: info@binstedgroup.com

▶ Chatterbox Magazine, Head Office, 2 Alpine Rise, Styvechale Grange, Coventry, CV3 6NT Tel: (024) 7641 4458 Fax: (024) 76414458 E-mail: enquiries@chatterbox-magazine.co.uk

Cimtech, College Lane, Hatfield, Hertfordshire, AL10 9AB Tel: (01707) 281060 Fax: (01707) 281061 E-mail: c.cimtech@herts.ac.uk

▶ Coleman Taylor Graphic Design, Haven House, 10 Haven Close, Grasscroft, Saddleworth, Oldham, OL4 4DU Tel: (01457) 872666 E-mail: info@colemantaylor.co.uk

D C Thomson & Co. Ltd, Albert Square, Dundee, DD1 9QJ Tel: (01382) 223131 Fax: (01382) 225778 E-mail: amcintosh@dcthomson.co.uk

Darton Longman & Todd Ltd, 140-142 Wandsworth High Street, London, SW18 4JJ Tel: (020) 8875 0155 Fax: (020) 8875 0133 E-mail: tradesales@darton-longman-todd.co.uk

De Agositini, Griffin House, 161 Hammersmith Road, Griffin House, London, W6 8SD Tel: (020) 8600 2000 Fax: (020) 8600 2002

Export Courier, The Flarepath, Elsham Wolds Industrial Estate, Brigg, South Humberside, DN20 0SP Tel: (01652) 680093 Fax: (01652) 688459 E-mail: exporters@exportcourier.co.uk

▶ The Garret (UK) Ltd, 5 Green Dragon Court, London Bridge, London, SE1 9AW Tel: (020) 7159 1485 E-mail: iain@thegarret.co.uk

Gibson Hanson Graphics Ltd, 2nd Floor, Amp House Dingwall Road, Croydon, CR0 2LX Tel: (020) 8260 1200 Fax: (020) 8260 1212 E-mail: clare.stead@gibsonhanson.co.uk

Hamerville Magazines Ltd, Regal House, Regal Way, Watford, WD24 4YF Tel: (01923) 237799 Fax: (01923) 246901 E-mail: office@hamerville.co.uk

Hollis Publishing Ltd, Harlequin House, 7 High Street, Teddington, Middlesex, TW11 8EL Tel: (020) 8973 3400 Fax: (020) 8977 1133 E-mail: hollis@hollis-pr.co.uk

Indexing Specialists UK Ltd, Indexing House, 306a Portland Road, Hove, East Sussex, BN3 5LP Tel: (01273) 424411 E-mail: indexers@indexing.co.uk

Midland Independent Newspaper, 28 Colmore Circus Queensway, Birmingham, B4 6AT Tel: 0121-236 3366 Fax: 0121-236 9638

Mourne Observer Ltd, Castlewellan Road, Newcastle, County Down, BT33 0QU Tel: (028) 4372 2667 Fax: (028) 4372 4566 E-mail: mobserver@btinternet.com

News (International) Ltd, 1 Pennington St, London, E98 1TT Tel: (020) 7481 4100

Pira International, Cleeve Road, Leatherhead, Surrey, KT22 7RU Tel: (01372) 802000 Fax: (01372) 802238 E-mail: membership@pira-international.co.uk

▶ Prolific Marketing Ltd, 5th Floor, International House, 223 Regent Street, London, W1B 2QD Tel: 020 7544 1010 Fax: 020 7544 1090 E-mail: enquiries@prolificmarketing.co.uk

▶ Promarco Ltd, Saltwells Road, Dudley, West Midlands, DY2 9PE Tel: (01384) 565646 Fax: (01384) 351000

Security Specifier, 32 Portland Street, Cheltenham, Gloucestershire, GL52 2PB Tel: (01242) 236336 Fax: (01242) 222331

▶ Sign Update, 1 Allens Orchard, Chipping Warden, Banbury, Oxfordshire, OX17 1LX Tel: (01295) 660666 Fax: (0560) 1162164 E-mail: sb@freerbutler-gds.co.uk

T S O Ltd, Publications Centre, 51 Nine Elms Lane, London, SW8 5DR Tel: (020) 7873 8787 Fax: (0870) 600 5533 E-mail: customer.services@tso.co.uk

Taylor & Francis Group P.L.C., 4 Park Square, Milton Park, Abingdon, Oxfordshire, OX14 4RN Tel: (020) 7583 9855 Fax: (020) 7017 6336 E-mail: enquiries@tandf.co.uk

Telecommunications Users' Association, 7 Sylvan Court, Southfields Business Park, Basildon, Essex, SS15 6TD Tel: (0870) 2202071 Fax: (0870) 2202075 E-mail: tua@dial.pipex.com

Time Life International Ltd, Brettenham House, Lancaster Place, London, WC2E 7TL Tel: (020) 7499 4080 Fax: (020) 7322 1147

Trade Counter Ltd, Unit D Trading Estate Road, London, NW10 7LU Tel: (020) 8385 2753 Fax: (020) 8965 9765 E-mail: ptc@netcomuk.co.uk

Turpin Distribution Services Ltd, Pegasus Drive, Stratton Business Park, Biggleswade, Bedfordshire, SG18 8TQ Tel: (01767) 604800 Fax: (01767) 601640 E-mail: turpin@turpin-distribution.com

PUBLICATIONS, FAMILY HEALTH

▶ Mosaic Shaping Disability Services, Richard Iii Road, Leicester, LE3 5QT Tel: 0116-251 5565 Fax: 0116-251 9969 E-mail: administration@mosaic1898.co.uk

PUBLISHERS' EDITORIAL/TEXT CONSULTANTS/RESEARCHERS/ WRITERS

Bromsgrove Advertiser & Messenger, 5 High Street, Bromsgrove, Worcestershire, B61 8AJ Tel: (01527) 837000 Fax: (01527) 877456 E-mail: carol.hinett@newsquestmidlands.co.uk

The Crier Media Group, 11 Station Road East, Oxted, Surrey, RH8 0BD Tel: (01883) 734582 Fax: (01883) 713640 E-mail: general@crier.co.uk

Cumbrian Newspapers Ltd, Newspaper House, Newspaper House, Dalston Road, Carlisle, CA2 5UA Tel: (01228) 612600 Fax: (01228) 612601 E-mail: news@cumbrian-newspapers.co.uk

First Edition Translations, 22 Newmarket Rd, Cambridge, CB5 8DT Tel: (01223) 356733 Fax: (01223) 321488 E-mail: info@firstedit.co.uk

▶ Claudette Hall Writer & Editor, 40 Devon Close, Perivale, Greenford, Middlesex, UB6 7DP Tel: (020) 8997 2617 E-mail: claudettehall@supanet.com

▶ Market Link Creative Marketing Ltd, 30 St Georges Square, Worcester, WR1 1HX Tel: (01905) 726575 Fax: (01905) 726090 E-mail: sales@marketlink-uk.com

Montrose Review Press Ltd, 59 John Street, Montrose, Angus, DD10 8QU Tel: (01674) 672605 Fax: (01674) 676232 E-mail: reviewnews@montrosereview.com

Neath Guardian, 17 Queen Street, Neath, West Glamorgan, SA11 1DN Tel: (01639) 778888 Fax: (01639) 778884 E-mail: guardian@wme.co.uk

Omega Scientific, Fynamore, Reading Road, Wallingford, Oxfordshire, OX10 9DT Tel: (01491) 837736 Fax: (01491) 825454

Touchstone, 1 Triton Square, London, NW1 3DX Tel: (020) 7121 4700 Fax: (020) 7121 4740

Water Active Ltd, PO Box 627, Watford, WD23 2JW Tel: 01923 235050 Fax: 01923 252220 E-mail: info@wateractive.co.uk

Yarwood Editorial Services, 9 Willow Walk, Needham Market, IP6 8DT Tel: 01449 720558 E-mail: yarwood-editorial-services@phonecoop.coop

PUBLISHERS, BOOK/MAGAZINE

1st Choice Publishing Ltd, 355 Aylsham Road, Norwich, NR3 2RX Tel: (01603) 404001 Fax: (01603) 404410 E-mail: jan@0800service.com

A1 Copying Systems & Supplies Ltd, 36 Church Street, Leighton Buzzard, Bedfordshire, LU7 1BT Tel: (01525) 371333 Fax: (01525) 371339 E-mail: a1copyingsys@btclick.com

Aberdeen Journals Ltd, Lang Stracht, Aberdeen, AB15 6DF Tel: (01224) 690222 Fax: (01224) 699575 E-mail: pj.editor@ajl.co.uk

Age Communications, 20 Upper Ground, London, SE1 9PF Tel: (020) 7805 5590 Fax: (020) 7805 5910 E-mail: iln@ilng.co.uk

Agra Informa Ltd, 80 Calverley Road, Tunbridge Wells, Kent, TN1 2UN Tel: (020) 7017 7500 Fax: (01892) 544895 E-mail: marketing@agra-europe.com

Ian Allan Publishing Ltd, Riverdene Business Park, Molesey Road, Walton-On-Thames, Surrey, KT12 4RG Tel: (01780) 484630 Fax: (01932) 266601 E-mail: sales@ianallanpub.co.uk

Allan Ian Travel, Terminal House, Station Approach, Shepperton, Middlesex, TW17 8AS Tel: (01932) 255676 Fax: (01932) 252748

Appletree Press Ltd, 14 Howard St South, Belfast, BT7 1AP Tel: (028) 9024 3074 Fax: (028) 9024 6756 E-mail: info@appletree.ie

Aspermont UK, Albert House, 1-4 Singer Street, London, EC2A 4BQ Tel: (020) 7216 6060 Fax: (020) 7216 6050 E-mail: info@mining-journal.com

A-Z Group Ltd, Darby House, Bletchingley Road, Merstham, Redhill, RH1 3TT Tel: (01737) 645777 Fax: (01737) 645888 E-mail: sales@a-zgroup.com

B C R Publishing Ltd, 3 Cobden Court, Wimpole Close, Bromley, BR2 9JF Tel: (020) 8466 6987 Fax: (020) 8466 0654 E-mail: bcr@bcrpub.co.uk

Ballymena Guardian, 83-85 Wellington Street, Ballymena, County Antrim, BT43 6AD Tel: (028) 2564 1229 Fax: (028) 2565 3920 E-mail: advertising@ballymenaguardian.co.uk

Michael Barratt, Field House, Ascot Road, Holyport, Maidenhead, Berkshire, SL6 3LD Tel: (01628) 770800 Fax: (01628) 627737 E-mail: michael@mbarrett.co.uk

Bloomfield Books, 26 Meadow Lane, Sudbury, Suffolk, CO10 2TD Tel: (01787) 376374 Fax: (01787) 376967

Bromsgrove Advertiser & Messenger, 5 High Street, Bromsgrove, Worcestershire, B61 8AJ Tel: (01527) 837000 Fax: (01527) 877456 E-mail: carol.hinett@newsquestmidlands.co.uk

Brunton Business Publications Ltd, Thruxton Down House, Thruxton Down, Andover, Hampshire, SP11 8PR Tel: (01264) 889533 Fax: (01264) 889524 E-mail: publications@brunton.co.uk

Brushwork Magazine, 59-61 The Broadway, Haywards Heath, West Sussex, RH16 3AS Tel: (01444) 440188 Fax: (01444) 414813 E-mail: info@airstream.co.uk

Burgess & Bowes, 14 Durham Avenue, Romford, RM2 6JS Tel: (01708) 458990 Fax: (01708) 459885

Burrows Communications Ltd, 106 Stafford Road, Wallington, Surrey, SM6 9AY Tel: (020) 8773 3000 Fax: (020) 8773 8888 E-mail: generalservices@burrows.co.uk

Butterworth Heinemann, Linacre House Jordan Hill Business Park, Banbury Road, Oxford, OX2 8DP Tel: (01865) 888190 Fax: (01865) 314455 E-mail: bhmarketing@repp.co.uk

Cambrian News Ltd, Unit 7, Cefn Llan Science Park, Waunfawr, Aberystwyth, Dyfed, SY23 3AH Tel: (01970) 615000 Fax: (01970) 624699 E-mail: edit@cambrian-news.co.uk

Carlton Books Ltd, 20 Mortimer Street, London, W1T 3JW Tel: (020) 7612 0400 Fax: (020) 7612 0401 E-mail: enquiries@carltonbooks.co.uk

▶ Chrome Molly Publications, 10A Pilot Road, Corby, Northamptonshire, NN17 5YH Tel: (01536) 268968 Fax: (01536) 401489 E-mail: chromemolly@hotmail.com

The Conde Nast Publications, Vogue House, 1 Hanover Square, London, W1S 1JU Tel: (020) 7499 9080 Fax: (020) 7493 1345

Constable & Co. Ltd, 3 Lanchesters, 162-166 Fulham Palace Road, London, W6 9ER Tel: (020) 8741 3663 Fax: (020) 8748 7562 E-mail: enquiries@constablerobinson.com

Contact Public Relations & Management, Unit 11 Hackford Walk, Hackford Road, London, SW9 0QT Tel: (020) 7582 2220 Fax: (020) 7820 0195 E-mail: contactpr@btconnect.com

Inc Council Of Law Reporting For England & Wales, 119 Chancery Lane, London, WC2A 1PP Tel: (020) 7242 6471 Fax: (020) 7831 5247 E-mail: postmaster@iclr.co.uk

D M G World Media, Westgate, 120-130 Station Road, Redhill, RH1 1ET Tel: (01737) 855000 Fax: (01737) 855475 E-mail: pamelatiernan@uk.dmgworldmedia.com

David & Charles Publishers Ltd, Brunel House, Forde Close, Newton Abbot, Devon, TQ12 4PU Tel: (01626) 323200 Fax: (01626) 323291 E-mail: postmaster@dcpublishers.co.uk

Benjamin Dent & Co. Ltd, 33 Bedford Place, London, WC1B 5JU Tel: (020) 7637 2211 Fax: (020) 7637 2248

DMG World Media, Equitable House, Lyon Road, Harrow, Middlesex, HA1 2EW Tel: (020) 8515 2000 Fax: (020) 8515 2080 E-mail: sales@dmgworldmedia.com

Dog World Ltd, Somerfield House, Wotton Road, Ashford, Kent, TN23 6LW Tel: (01233) 621877 Fax: (01233) 645669 E-mail: info@dogworld.co.uk

Dorling Kindersley Holdings P.L.C., 80 The Strand, London, WC2R 0LR Tel: (020) 7010 3000 Fax: (020) 7010 6060

Down Recorder, 2-4 Church Street, Downpatrick, County Down, BT30 6EJ Tel: (028) 4461 3711 Fax: (028) 4461 4624 E-mail: advertis@downrecorder.uk

Eaglemoss Publications Ltd, Beaumont House, Kensington Village, London, W14 8TS Tel: (020) 7590 8300 Fax: (020) 7590 8301 E-mail: sales@eaglemoss.co.uk

▶ Ealing Life Magazine, P O Box 54909, London, W3 9WP Tel: (020) 8932 8302

Economist Newspaper Ltd, 25 St. James's Street, London, SW1A 1HG Tel: (020) 7576 8000 Fax: (020) 7839 2968

Egon Publishers Ltd, Royston Road, Baldock, Hertfordshire, SG7 6NW Tel: (01462) 894498 Fax: (01462) 894660 E-mail: information@egon.co.uk

Elsevier Science, Belway House, 32 Jamestown Road, London, NW1 7BY Tel: (020) 7424 4200 Fax: (020) 7424 4431 E-mail: sales@elsevierscience.com

Emap, Bowling Green Lane, London, EC1R 0DA Tel: (020) 7812 3700 E-mail: claire.jenkinson@ebc.emap.com

EMAP Communications, Greater London House, Hamstead Road, London, NW1 7EJ Tel: (020) 7874 0200 Fax: (020) 7874 0201 E-mail: lgc@lgc.emap.com

Emap Communications, 2ND Floor Scriptor Court, 155 Farringdon Road, London, EC1R 3AD Tel: (020) 7841 6600 Fax: (020) 7841 6605 E-mail: claire.jenkinson@emap.com

Emap Construct Ltd, 151 Roseberry Avenue, London, EC1R 4GB Tel: (020) 7505 6600 Fax: (020) 7505 6889

Euromoney Institional Invester P.L.C., Nestor House, Playhouse Yard, London, EC4V 5EX Tel: (020) 7779 8658 Fax: (020) 7779 8867

Europa Publications Ltd, 11 New Felter La, London, EC4P 4EE Tel: (020) 7589 9855 Fax: (020) 7842 2249 E-mail: sales@europapublications.co.uk

Evans Bros Ltd, 2a Block 2 Portman Mansions, Chiltern Street, London, W1U 6NR Tel: (020) 7935 7160 Fax: (020) 7487 0921 E-mail: sales@evansbooks.co.uk

Faber & Faber Ltd, 3 Queen Square, London, WC1N 3AU Tel: (020) 7465 0045 Fax: (020) 7465 0034 E-mail: mailbox@faber.co.uk

Findlay Publications Ltd, Hawley Mill, Hawley Road, Dartford, DA2 7TJ Tel: (01322) 221144 Fax: (01322) 862644 E-mail: pring@findlay.co.uk

Fish Friers Review Ltd, 4 Greenwood Mount, Meanwood, Leeds, LS6 4LQ Tel: 0113-230 7009 Fax: 0113-230 7010 E-mail: mail@federationoffishfriers.co.uk

W. Foulsham & Co. Ltd, The Publishing House, Bennetts Close, Slough, SL1 5AP Tel: (01753) 526769 Fax: (01753) 535003 E-mail: belasco@foulsham.com

Frame Craft Minitures Ltd, Lichfield Road, Brownhills, Walsall, WS8 6LH Tel: (01543) 373076 Fax: (01543) 453154 E-mail: sales@framecraft.com

Franchise Development Services Ltd, Franchise House, Surrey Street, Norwich, NR1 3FD Tel: (01603) 620301 Fax: (01603) 630174 E-mail: sales@franchise-group.com

Samuel French Ltd, 52 Fitzroy Street, London, W1T 5JR Tel: (020) 7387 9373 Fax: (020) 7387 2161 E-mail: theatre@samuelfrench-london.co.uk

Fresh Produce Journal, 430 438 Market Towers, 1 Nine Elms Lane, London, SW8 5NN Tel: (020) 7501 0300 Fax: (020) 7720 8451 E-mail: sales@freshinfo.com

Gateacre Press Ltd, Bilail House, 260 Picton Road, Wavertree, Liverpool, L15 4LP Tel: 0151-734 3038 Fax: 0151-734 2860 E-mail: gpl@gatepress.demon.co.uk

Gee Publishing Ltd, Customer Service, 100 Avenue Road, London, NW3 3PG Tel: (0845) 6009355 Fax: (020) 7722 4762

Greer Publications, 5B Edgewater Business Park, Belfast Harbour Estate, Belfast, BT3 9JQ Tel: (028) 9078 3200 Fax: (028) 9078 3210 E-mail: mail@greerpublications.com

Guardian Media Group P.L.C., Number 1, Scott Place, Manchester, M3 3GG Tel: 0161-832 7200 Fax: 0161-832 5351

Guardian Newspapers Ltd, 119 Farringdon Road, London, EC1R 3ER Tel: (020) 7278 2332 Fax: (020) 7837 2114

Hachette Livre, 338 Euston Road, London, NW1 3BH Tel: (020) 7873 6000 Fax: (020) 7873 6024

HallidayBooks, Hawthorn Cottage, 32 Rowsham Road, Hulcott, Aylesbury, Buckinghamshire, HP22 5DZ Tel: 01296 426671 E-mail: info@hallidaybooks.com

Hamerville Magazines Ltd, Regal House, Regal Way, Watford, WD24 4YF Tel: (01923) 237799 Fax: (01923) 246901 E-mail: office@hamerville.co.uk

Handsfree Computing Ltd, Enterprise House, Old London Road, Hickstead, Haywards Heath, West Sussex, RH17 5LZ Tel: (01444) 880880 Fax: (01444) 880888 E-mail: info@hands-free.co.uk

Harcourt Education, Linacre House, Jordan Hill, Oxford, OX2 8DP Tel: (01865) 888000 Fax: (01865) 314222

Harpercollins Pubrs Ophelia House, Fulham Palace Road, London, W6 8JA Tel: (020) 8741 7070 Fax: (020) 8307 4813 E-mail: human.resources@harpercollins.co.uk

Harpers Ltd, Media House, Azalea Drive, Swanley, Kent, BR8 8HU Tel: (01322) 611217 Fax: (01322) 616305 E-mail: info@harpers-wine.com

Haymarket Publishing, Teddington Studios, Broom Road, Teddington, Middlesex, TW11 9BE Tel: (020) 8943 5000 Fax: (020) 8267 5872 E-mail: name@haymarketgroup.com

Haynes Publishing, Sparkford, Yeovil, Somerset, BA22 7JJ Tel: (01963) 440635 Fax: (01963) 440001 E-mail: sales@haynes.co.uk

Health & Safety Specifier, 32 Portland St, Cheltenham, Glos, GL52 2PE Tel: (01242) 583222 Fax: (01242) 222331

Hobsons Publishing plc, 42 Adler Street, London, E1 1EE Tel: (020) 7958 5000 Fax: (020) 7958 5001 E-mail: london.recception@hobsons.co.uk

I C Publications Ltd, 7 Coldbath Square, London, EC1R 4LQ Tel: (020) 7713 7711 Fax: (020) 7713 7898 E-mail: icpubs@africasia.com

I P C Media, Focus House, 9 Dingwall Avenue, Croydon, CR9 2TA Tel: (020) 8726 8000 Fax: (020) 8726 8199

I P C Media Ltd, Blue Fin Building, 110 Southwark Street, London, SE1 0SU Tel: (020) 3148 5000 Fax: E-mail: press_office@ipc.media.com

Imray Laurie Norie & Wilson Ltd, Wych House, 20 Broadway, St. Ives, Cambridgeshire, PE27 5BT Tel: (01480) 462114 Fax: (01480) 496109 E-mail: enquiries@imray.com

Incisive Media, 32 & 34 Broadwick Street, London, W1A 2HG Tel: (020) 7316 9000 Fax: (020) 7316 9003

Independent Magazines U K Ltd, 191 Marsh Wall, London, E14 9RS Tel: (020) 7005 5000 Fax: (020) 7005 2999 E-mail: krolfe@img-uk.demon.co.uk

Indexing Specialists UK Ltd, Indexing House, 306a Portland Road, Hove, East Sussex, BN3 5LP Tel: (01273) 424411 E-mail: indexers@indexing.co.uk

PUBLISHERS, BOOK/MAGAZINE – *continued*

Institute of Materials, Minerals & Mining, 1 Carlton House Terrace, London, SW1Y 5DB Tel: (020) 7451 7300 Fax: (020) 7451 7406
Interactive Media Publications Ltd, 26 Rosebery Avenue, London, EC1R 4SX Tel: (020) 7837 3345 Fax: (020) 7837 8901
International Labmate Ltd, Oak Court Business Centre, Sandridge Park Porters Wood, Porters Wood, St. Albans, Hertfordshire, AL3 6PH Tel: (01727) 855574 Fax: (01727) 841694 E-mail: sales@product-search.co.uk
Intras Ltd, Perseus House, Chapel Court Holly Walk, Leamington Spa, Warwickshire, CV32 4YS Tel: (01926) 334137 Fax: (01926) 314755 E-mail: intras@intras.co.uk
Ipc Publishing, Kings Reach Tower, Stamford Street, London, SE1 9LS Tel: (020) 7261 5711 Fax: (020) 7261 6772
Karnac (Books) Ltd, 6 Pembrook Buildings, London, NW10 6RE Tel: (020) 8969 4454 Fax: (020) 8969 5585 E-mail: shop@karnacbooks.com
Kemps Publishing Ltd, 11 Swan Courtyard, Charles Edward Road, Birmingham, B26 1BU Tel: 0121-765 4144 Fax: 0121-706 6210 E-mail: enquiries@kempspublishing.co.uk
L D A, Abbeygate House, East Road, Cambridge, CB1 1DB Tel: (01223) 357744 Fax: (01223) 460557
The Lady Ltd, 39-40 Bedford Street, London, WC2E 9ER Tel: (020) 7379 4717 Fax: (020) 7497 2137 E-mail: info@thelady.co.uk
▶ Laurel Cottage Ltd, 15 Ballyhay Road, Donaghadee, County Down, BT21 0NG Tel: (028) 9188 8033 Fax: (028) 9188 8063 E-mail: info@cottagepublications.com
Laver Publishing, PO Box 7, Liverpool, L19 9EN Tel: 0151-475 7949
Lexisnexis UK, 2 Addiscombe Road, Croydon, CR9 5AF Tel: (020) 8662 2000 Fax: (020) 8662 2012 E-mail: sales@lexisnexis.co.uk
Lion Hudson P.L.C., Mayfield House, 256 Banbury Road, Oxford, OX2 7DH Tel: (01865) 302750 Fax: (01865) 302757 E-mail: enquiries@lionhudson.com
Little Brown Book Group Ltd, Brettenham House, Lancaster Place, London, WC2E 7TL Tel: (020) 7322 1400 Fax: (020) 7911 8100 E-mail: emailuk@twbg.co.uk
Mcgraw-Hill International UK Ltd, Mcgraw-Hill House, Shoppenhangers Road, Maidenhead, Berkshire, SL6 2QL Tel: (01628) 502500 Fax: (01628) 770224 E-mail: info@mcgraw-hill.com
Macmillan Distribution Ltd, Howard Road, St. Neots, Cambridgeshire, PE19 8EZ Tel: (01480) 212666
Macmillan Publishers Ltd, Brunel Road, Houndmills, Basingstoke, Hampshire, RG21 6XS Tel: (01256) 329242 Fax: (01256) 479476
Mcmillan Scott plc, Quay House, Quay Street, Manchester, M3 3JE Tel: 0161-832 6000 Fax: 0161-832 1166
McMillan-Scott Ltd, Trelawney House, Chestergate, Macclesfield, Cheshire, SK11 6DW Tel: (01625) 613000 Fax: (01625) 511446
Macmillian Publishers Ltd, Brunel Road, Houndmills, Basingstoke, Hampshire, RG21 6XS Tel: (01256) 464481 Fax: (01256) 479496
Main Stream Publications, 139 Thomas Street, Portadown, Craigavon, County Armagh, BT62 3BE Tel: (028) 3833 4272 Fax: (028) 3835 1046 E-mail: andrewcrozier@mainstreammagazines.co.uk
Mamelok Holdings Ltd, Northern Way, Bury St. Edmunds, Suffolk, IP32 6NJ Tel: (01284) 762291 Fax: (01284) 703689 E-mail: sales@mamelok.com
Market Intelligence Ltd, Market Towers, 1 Nine Elms Lane, London, SW8 5NQ Tel: (020) 7501 3700 Fax: (020) 7498 6472 E-mail: info@fruitnet.com
Marshall Cavendish International Ltd, 119 Wardour Street, London, W1F 0UW Tel: (020) 7734 6710 Fax: (020) 7734 6221
Mersey Mirror Ltd, The Foundry, 36 Henry Street, Liverpool, L1 5BS Tel: 0151-709 7567 E-mail: post@merseymirror.com
Midland Independent Newspaper, 28 Colmore Circus Queensway, Birmingham, B4 6AT Tel: 0121-236 3366 Fax: 0121-236 9638
Mirror Colour Print Watford Ltd, St. Albans Road, Watford, WD24 7RG Tel: (01923) 230455 Fax: (01923) 249861 E-mail: editor@mirror.co.uk
Mortons of Horncastle Ltd, Morton Way, Boston Road, Horncastle, Lincolnshire, LN9 6JR Tel: (01507) 523456 Fax: (01507) 527840 E-mail: admin@mortons.co.uk
National Magazine Co. Ltd, 72 Broadwick Street, London, W1F 9EP Tel: (020) 7439 5000 Fax: (020) 7437 6886
Nature Publishing Group Ltd, Brunel Road, Houndmills, Basingstoke, Hampshire, RG21 6XS Tel: (01256) 329242 Fax: (01256) 479464
NCJ Media Ltd, Groat Market, Newcastle Upon Tyne, NE1 1ED Tel: 0191-232 7500 Fax: 0191-230 4144
News International P.L.C., Virginia Street, London, E98 1XY Tel: (020) 7782 6000 Fax: (020) 7782 6097
News & Media Ltd, 233 Seven Sisters Road, London, N4 2DA Tel: (020) 7263 1417 Fax: (020) 7272 8934 E-mail: info@impact-magazines.com
Newsquest Blackburn, High Street, Blackburn, BB1 1HT Tel: (01254) 678678 Fax: (01254) 682185 E-mail: let_editorial@lancashire.newsquest.co.uk
Northcliffe Newspapers, 31-32 John Street, London, WC1N 2AT Tel: 0116-222 4060 Fax: (020) 7400 1518
Octopus, Unit 2/4, Heron Quay, London, E14 4JP Tel: (020) 7531 8400 Fax: (020) 7531 8627 E-mail: info@conran-octopus.co.uk
Octupus Publishing Group, Unit 2-4 Heron Quay, London, E14 4JB Tel: (020) 7531 8400 Fax: (020) 7531 8560 E-mail: info@octopus-publishing.co.uk
Pearson Eduction Ltd, Edinburgh Gate, Edinburgh Way, Harlow, Essex, CM20 2JE Tel: (01279) 623623 Fax: (01279) 431059 E-mail: sales@pearson.com
Peco Publications & Publicity Ltd, Beer, Seaton, Devon, EX12 3NA Tel: (01297) 20580 Fax: (01297) 20229 E-mail: sales.peco@btconnect.com
Penguin Books Ltd, 80 Strand, London, WC2R 0RL Tel: (020) 7010 3000 Fax: (020) 7010 6060 E-mail: info@pearson.com
Peter Haddock Ltd, Pinfold Lane Industrial Estate, Bridlington, North Humberside, YO16 6BT Tel: (01262) 678121 Fax: (01262) 400043 E-mail: info@phpublishing.co.uk
Pitkin Unichrome, Dene Road, Healey House, Andover, Hampshire, SP10 2AA Tel: (01264) 409200 Fax: (01264) 334110 E-mail: sales@tempus-publishing.com
Polar Print Group Ltd, Venturi House, 9-17 Tuxford Road, Hamilton Industial Park, Leicester, LE4 9WE Tel: 0116-274 4700 Fax: 0116-274 4799
Police Review Publishing Co. Ltd, 180 Wardour Street, London, W1F 8FY Tel: (020) 8700 3700 Fax: (020) 7287 4765
▶ Port Strategy, The Old Mill, Lower Quay, Fareham, Hampshire, PO16 0RA Tel: 01329 825335 Fax: 01329 825330 E-mail: info@portstrategy.com
Pressdram Ltd, 6 Carlisle Street, London, W1D 3BN Tel: (020) 7437 4017 Fax: (020) 7437 0705 E-mail: strobes@private-eye.co.uk
Proquest Informnation & Learning Ltd, The Quorum, Barnwell Road, Cambridge, CB5 8SW Tel: (01223) 215512 Fax: (01223) 215513 E-mail: mail@proquest.co.uk
Q M J Publishing Ltd, 7 Regent Street, Nottingham, NG1 5BS Tel: 0115-941 1315 Fax: 0115-948 4035 E-mail: sales@qmj.co.uk
Quintet Publishing Ltd, 6 Blundell Street, London, N7 9BH Tel: (020) 7700 6700 Fax: (020) 7700 4191 E-mail: quarto@quarto.com
Random House UK Ltd, 20 Vauxhall Bridge Road, London, SW1V 2SA Tel: (020) 7840 8400 Fax: (020) 7233 8791
Ravette Publishing Ltd, Star Road, Partridge Green, Horsham, West Sussex, RH13 8RA Tel: (01403) 711443 Fax: (01403) 711554 E-mail: ravettepub@aol.com
Reader's Digest Association Ltd, 11 Westferry Circus, London, E14 4HE Tel: (020) 7715 8000 Fax: (020) 7715 8181 E-mail: info@readersdigest.co.uk
Reading Chronicle, 50-56 Portman Road, Reading, RG30 1BA Tel: 0118-950 3030 Fax: 0118-939 1619 E-mail: sales@readingchronicle.co.uk
Recycling World Magazines, Hilltop, Church Rd, Webheath, Redditch, Worcs, B97 5PQ Tel: (01527) 404550 Fax: (01527) 404644 E-mail: recycling@tecweb.com
Reed Business Information Ltd, Quadrant House, The Quadrant, Sutton, Surrey, SM2 5AS Tel: (020) 8652 3674 Fax: (020) 8652 8986
▶ Mike Routledge (Books), 22 Letchworth Crescent, Beeston, Nottingham, NG9 5LL Tel: 0115-922 3726 Fax: (0870) 1221950 E-mail: mikeroutledge@gmail.com
S P G Media Ltd, 57 North Wharf Road, London, W2 1LA Tel: (020) 7915 9660 Fax: (020) 7724 2089 E-mail: info@spgmedia.com
Sage Publications Ltd, 1 Olivers Yard, 55 City Road, London, EC1Y 1SP Tel: (020) 7374 0645 E-mail: info@sagepub.co.uk
Sahara Publications Ltd, 38 Greyhound Road, London, W6 8NX Tel: (020) 7610 1387 Fax: (020) 7610 0078 E-mail: sahara@btconnect.com
Saudi Research & Marketing Ltd, Arab Press House, 182-184 High Holborn, London, WC1V 7AP Tel: (020) 7831 8181 Fax: (020) 7831 2310 E-mail: admin@hhsaudi.com
Send The Light Ltd, PO Box 300, Carlisle, CA3 0QS Tel: (01228) 512512 Fax: (01228) 514949 E-mail: info@stl.org
Setform Ltd, Europa House, 13-17 Ironmonger Row, London, EC1V 3QG Tel: (020) 7253 2545 Fax: (020) 7608 1600 E-mail: sales@setform.com
Sheen Publishing Ltd, 50 Queens Road, Buckhurst Hill, Essex, IG9 5DD Tel: (020) 8504 1661 Fax: (020) 8505 4336
Shipping Guides Ltd, 75 Bell Street, Reigate, Surrey, RH2 7AN Tel: (01737) 242255 Fax: (01737) 222449 E-mail: info@portinfo.co.uk
Slough & Langley Express, 256 Ipswich Road, Slough, SL1 4EP Tel: (01753) 825111 Fax: (01753) 692254 E-mail: sales@sloughexpress.co.uk
Solutions For Business, Royston Business & Design Centre, 8 Priory Lane, Royston, Hertfordshire, SG8 9DU Tel: (01763) 242939 Fax: (01763) 243332 E-mail: sales@solutions-for-business.co.uk
Sparks Ltd, Bullingdon House, 174b Cowley Road, Oxford, OX4 1UE Tel: (01865) 242406 Fax: (01865) 242407 E-mail: sales@sparks.co.uk
Stacey Arts Ltd, 128 Kensington Church Street, London, W8 4BH Tel: (020) 7221 7166 Fax: (020) 7221 9288 E-mail: sales@stacey-international.co.uk
Staffordshire Newsletter Ltd, Publishing Centre, Derby Street, Stafford, ST16 2DT Tel: (01785) 257700 Fax: (01785) 253287 E-mail: admin@staffordshirenewsletter.co.uk
Stanborough Press Ltd, Londonthorpe Road, Grantham, Lincolnshire, NG31 9SL Tel: (01476) 591700 Fax: (01476) 577144 E-mail: stanborg@aol.com
Stanley Gibbons Holdings plc, 399 Strand, London, WC2R 0LX Tel: (020) 7836 8444 Fax: (020) 7836 7342 E-mail: info@stanleygibbons.co.uk
Styletype Printing Ltd, Glengormley Park, Newtownabbey, County Antrim, BT36 7RJ Tel: (028) 9034 2725 Fax: (028) 9084 8225 E-mail: sales@styletype.co.uk
▶ T S I Luckins Ltd, Cherryholt Road, Stamford, Lincolnshire, PE9 2EP Tel: (01780) 750500 Fax: (01780) 750567 E-mail: info@luckins.co.uk
T S O Ltd, Publications Centre, 51 Nine Elms Lane, London, SW8 5DR Tel: (020) 7873 8787 Fax: (0870) 600 5533 E-mail: customer.services@tso.co.uk
T V Times, Kings Reach Tower, Stamford Street, London, SE1 9LS Tel: (020) 7261 7000 Fax: (020) 7261 7888
Tate Publishing Ltd, Millbank, London, SW1P 4RG Tel: (020) 7887 8869 Fax: (020) 7887 8878 E-mail: tgpl@tate.org.uk
Taylor & Francis Group P.L.C., 4 Park Square, Milton Park, Abingdon, Oxfordshire, OX14 4RN Tel: (020) 7583 9855 Fax: (020) 7017 6336 E-mail: enquiries@tandf.co.uk
Thames & Hudson, Esavian House, 181a High Holborn, London, WC1V 7QX Tel: (020) 7845 5000 Fax: (020) 7845 5050 E-mail: sales@thameshudson.co.uk
Transition Support Ltd, Vantage Point Business Village, 7/4, Mitcheldean, Gloucestershire, GL17 0DD Tel: (01594) 546151 Fax: (01594) 546153 E-mail: mail@transition-support.com
Transworld Publishers, 61-63 Uxbridge Road, London, W5 5SA Tel: (020) 8579 2652 Fax: (020) 8579 5479 E-mail: info@transworld-publishers.co.uk
Travel Trade, Ludgate House, 245 Blackfriars Road, London, SE1 9UY Tel: (020) 7921 8005 Fax: (020) 7921 8032 E-mail: enquiries@cmpinformation.com
Trinity Publication Ltd, 1ST Floor Edward House, Edward Street, Birmingham, B1 2RA Tel: 0121-233 8712 Fax: 0121-233 8715 E-mail: techsupport@micromart.co.uk
United Advertising Publications Plc, Link House, 25 West St, Poole, Dorset, BH15 1LL Tel: (01202) 445000 Fax: (01202) 445000 E-mail: enquiries@exchangeandmart.co.uk
United Business Media GP No 3 Ltd, Ludgate House, 245 Blackfriars Road, London, SE1 9UY Tel: (020) 7921 5000 Fax: (020) 7528 2772
United Business Media GP No 3 Ltd, Ludgate House, 245 Blackfriars Road, London, SE1 9UY Tel: (020) 7921 5000 Fax: (020) 7528 2772
Virgin Books Ltd, Thames Wharf Studios, Rainville Road, London, W6 9HA Tel: (020) 7386 3300 Fax: (020) 7386 3360
Wardlock Educational Co. Ltd, 1 Christopher Road, East Grinstead, West Sussex, RH19 3BT Tel: (01342) 318980 Fax: (01342) 410980 E-mail: orders@wleducat.freeserve.co.uk
Western Morning News Co. Ltd, 17 Brest Road, Derriford, Plymouth, PL6 5AA Tel: (01752) 765500 Fax: (01752) 765515 E-mail: plymouthfrontcounter@westcountrypublications.co.uk
The Westmorland Gazette Newspaper, 1 Wainwright Yard, Kendal, Cumbria, LA9 4DP Tel: (01539) 720555 Fax: (01539) 723618 E-mail: gazette@kendal.newsquest.co.uk
Where To Go Ltd, 180 Pentonville Road, London, N1 9LB Tel: (020) 7278 4393 Fax: (020) 7837 5838 E-mail: whatson@whatsoninlondon..co.uk
Which Magazine, 2 Marylebone Road, London, NW1 4DF Tel: (020) 7770 7000 Fax: (020) 7770 7600
Whittles Publishing Services, Roseleigh House, Latheronwheel, Latheron, Caithness, KW5 6DW Tel: (01593) 741240 Fax: (01593) 741360 E-mail: info@whittlespublishing.com
Wholesale Newspaper Services Ltd, Altnagelvin Industrial Estate, Trench Road, Londonderry, BT47 2ED Tel: (028) 7132 0700 Fax: (028) 7132 0701 E-mail: info@wns.co.uk
John Wiley & Sons Ltd, The Atrium Southern Gate, Terminus Road, Chichester, West Sussex, PO19 8SQ Tel: (01243) 779777 Fax: (01243) 775878 E-mail: rlong@wiley.co.uk
Witherby & Co. Ltd, 32-36 Aylesbury Street, London, EC1R 0ET Tel: (020) 7253 5413 Fax: (020) 7336 7493 E-mail: briandoors@witherbys.co.uk
Wolters Kluwer UK Ltd, 145 London Road, Kingston Upon Thames, Surrey, KT2 6SR Tel: (0870) 2415726 Fax: (020) 8547 2638 E-mail: info@wolterkluwer.co.uk
Wordsmith & Co., Farnham Royal, Slough, SL2 3WZ Tel: (01753) 645636 Fax: (01753) 669402 E-mail: dn@wordsmith-and-co.demon.co.uk
World's Fair Ltd, Albert Mill, Albert Street, Oldham, OL8 3QL Tel: 0161-683 8000 Fax: 0161-683 8001 E-mail: wfair@worldsfair.co.uk
▶ WPR Media Limited, 75 Stonegate Road, Meanwood, Leeds, LS6 4HZ Tel: 0113 2788908 E-mail: editorial@wprmedia.co.uk

PUBLISHING COMPOSITION COMPUTER SOFTWARE

Advent Publishing Systems, 3b2 House, 12 Bath Road, Swindon, SN1 4BA Tel: (01793) 511432 Fax: (01793) 536616 E-mail: info@3b2.com
▶ CheapSoftwareOnline, PO BOX 5786, Southend-on-Sea, SS1 9DA Tel: 01702 300801 E-mail: support@cheapsoftwareonline.co.uk
▶ Crox Tech, 48 Crompton Drive, Liverpool, L12 0JX Tel: 0151-222 4691 E-mail: sales@croxtech.com
▶ John Gocher Computing, St Clair, Rouge Huis Avenue, St. Peter Port, Guernsey, GY1 1RX Tel: (01481) 724778 E-mail: john@gocher.co.uk
Oxford Computer Consultants Ltd, 23-38 Hythe Bridge Street, Oxford, OX1 2ET Tel: (01865) 305200 Fax: (01865) 793124 E-mail: oxford@cc.co.uk
▶ www.pembrokedesign.com, 41 Church Street, Pembroke Dock, SA72 6AR Tel: (01646) 687240

PUBLISHING MANUFACTURING COMMUNICATIONS OPERATIONS

Trog Associates Ltd, PO Box 243, South Croydon, Surrey, CR2 6WF Tel: (020) 8786 3614 Fax: (020) 8405 8049 E-mail: gostwrighter@dslpipex.com

PUBLISHING SERVICES

▶ Ask-gutenburg.com Ltd, 2 Frankton Avenue, Haywards Heath, West Sussex, RH16 3QX Tel: (01444) 441444 E-mail: sales@ask-gutenburg.com
Beechwood House Publishing Ltd, Beechwood House 2-3 Commercial Way, Christy Close, Southfields Business Park, Basildon, Essex, SS15 6EF Tel: (01268) 495600 Fax: (01268) 495601 E-mail: info@binleys.co.uk
▶ Bladonmore Ltd, 10-11 Percy Street, London, W1T 1DA Tel: (020) 7631 1155 Fax: (020) 7631 1444 E-mail: info@bladonmore.com
Egon Publishers Ltd, Royston Road, Baldock, Hertfordshire, SG7 6NW Tel: (01462) 894498 Fax: (01462) 894660 E-mail: information@egon.co.uk
Fish Friers Review Ltd, 4 Greenwood Mount, Meanwood, Leeds, LS6 4LQ Tel: 0113-230 7009 Fax: 0113-230 7010 E-mail: mail@federationoffishfriers.co.uk
W. Foulsham & Co. Ltd, The Publishing House, Bennetts Close, Slough, SL1 5AP Tel: (01753) 526769 Fax: (01753) 535003 E-mail: belasco@foulsham.com
Gee Publishing Ltd, Customer Service, 100 Avenue Road, London, NW3 3PG Tel: (0845) 6009355 Fax: (020) 7722 4762
Hollis Publishing Ltd, Harlequin House, 7 High Street, Teddington, Middlesex, TW11 8EL Tel: (020) 8973 3400 Fax: (020) 8977 1133 E-mail: hollis@hollis-pr.co.uk
Mail News & Media Ltd, Blundells Corner, Beverley Road, Hull, HU3 1XS Tel: (01482) 327111 Fax: (01482) 584314
Reed Elsevier Group plc, Second Floor, Grand Buildings, London, WC2N 5JR Tel: (020) 7930 7077 Fax: (020) 7166 5799 E-mail: strand.reception@reedelsevier.com
Roles & Associates Ltd, 3 Pucks Corner, Lower Hampton Road, Sunbury-on-Thames, Middlesex, TW16 5PR Tel: (020) 8783 0777 Fax: (020) 8783 0088 E-mail: roles@easynet.co.uk
Styletype Printing Ltd, Glengormley Park, Newtownabbey, County Antrim, BT36 7RJ Tel: (028) 9034 2725 Fax: (028) 9084 8225 E-mail: sales@styletype.co.uk
Trinity Mirror P.L.C., 6 Heritage Court, Lower Bridge Street, Chester, CH1 1RD Tel: (01244) 861500 Fax: (01244) 861560

PUBLISHING SERVICES TO SPECIFICATION

Business Cartoons, 4 Reyntiens View, Odiham, Hook, Hampshire, RG29 1AF Tel: (01256) 703004 Fax: (01256) 703004 E-mail: flantoons@btinternet.com
The Economist Intelligence Ltd, 15 Regent St, London, SW1Y 4LR Tel: (020) 7930 8763 Fax: (020) 7830 1023 E-mail: info@economist.com
▶ House of Hamilton Publishing, 0 Hamilton Road, Felixstowe, Suffolk, IP11 7BA Tel: 01394 274440 E-mail: enquiries@houseofhamiltonpublishing.co.uk

PUBLISHING SERVICES, PRINT ON DEMAND, SELF PUBLISHING

Business Cartoons, 4 Reyntiens View, Odiham, Hook, Hampshire, RG29 1AF Tel: (01256) 703004 Fax: (01256) 703004 E-mail: flantoons@btinternet.com

PULLEY BLOCKS

Navtec North Europe Ltd, South Moore Lane, Havant, Hampshire, PO9 1JJ Tel: (023) 9248 5777 Fax: (023) 9248 5770 E-mail: navnor@navtec.net

PULLEYS, *See also headings under Pulleys*

Metalite Ltd, 121 Barkby Road, Leicester, LE4 9LU Tel: 0116-276 7874 Fax: 0116-233 0337

R G Wylie & Co. Ltd, Vanguard Way, Shoeburyness, Southend-on-Sea, SS3 9QY Tel: (01702) 296751 Fax: (01702) 297560 E-mail: rg.wylie@dtconect.com

Zerny Engineering Co. Ltd, Unit 13-14, Olds Close, Watford, WD18 9RU Tel: (01923) 774777 Fax: (01923) 774777

PULSATION DAMPENERS

Ceetak Engineering Ltd, 1 Napier Road, Elm Farm Industrial Estate, Bedford, MK41 0QR Tel: (01234) 343232 Fax: (01234) 341133 E-mail: ceetakengineering@bedford.com

▶ Flowguard Ltd, Watford Bridge Road, New Mills, High Peak, Derbyshire, SK22 4HJ Tel: (01663) 745976 Fax: (01663) 742788 E-mail: sales@flowguard.com

Pulsation Dampers At Pulseguard Ltd, Unit 1, Greg Street Industrial Centre, Greg Street, Reddish, Stockport, Cheshire, SK5 7BS Tel: 0161-480 9625 Fax: 0161-480 9627 E-mail: sales@pulsation-dampers.co.uk

PULSE TRANSFORMERS

Custom Transformers Ltd, Unit 23, Whitewalls, Easton Grey, Malmesbury, Wiltshire, SN16 0RD Tel: (01666) 824411 Fax: (01666) 824413 E-mail: sales@custom-transformers.co.uk

PULTRUSION MACHINES

Pultrex Ltd, Century House, North Station Road, Colchester, CO1 1PD Tel: (01206) 369555 Fax: (01206) 576554 E-mail: sales@pultrex.com

PULVERISERS, *See also headings for particular types*

▶ Christie Turner Ltd, Knightsdale Road, Ipswich, IP1 4LE Tel: (01473) 742325 Fax: (01473) 462 773 E-mail: info@christyhunt.co.uk

Falling Leaf, 1 Lodge Bank, Crown Lane, Horwich, Bolton, BL6 5HY Tel: (01204) 696621 Fax: (01204) 667559 E-mail: sales@bigbuckets.com

Sardon International Ltd, 28 Wylde Green Road, Sutton Coldfield, West Midlands, B72 1HD Tel: 0121-354 2165 Fax: 0121-354 2165

PUMICE STONE OR BLOCK PRODUCTS

Bray Group Ltd, Olive House, Regal Way, Faringdon, Oxfordshire, SN7 7BX Tel: (01367) 240736 Fax: (01367) 242625 E-mail: info@bray.co.uk

PUMICE STONE/BLOCK/ POWDER

Maple Aggregates UK Ltd, 50 Preston Road, Brighton, BN1 4QF Tel: (01273) 699001 Fax: (01273) 670977

PUMP DIAPHRAGMS

Kecol Pumps Ltd, Faraday Drive, Bridgnorth, Shropshire, WV15 5BJ Tel: (01746) 764311 Fax: (01746) 764780 E-mail: sales@kecol.co.uk

Totton Pumps, Rushington Business Park, Chaple Lane, Totton, Southampton, SO40 9AH Tel: (023) 8066 6685 Fax: (023) 8066 6880 E-mail: info@totton-pumps.com

PUMP DISTRIBUTORS/AGENTS/ STOCKHOLDERS

A E R Ltd, Wotton Road, Kingsnorth Industrial Estate, Ashford, Kent, TN23 6LN Tel: (01233) 632777 Fax: (01233) 661673 E-mail: sales@aer.co.uk

A J H Pump Supply & Repair, The Warehouse, Church Street, Wakefield, West Yorkshire, WF1 5QY Tel: (01924) 368773 Fax: (01924) 382229 E-mail: john@ajhpumpsupply.co.uk

A M Pumps & Spares Ltd, 429 Jockey Road, Sutton Coldfield, West Midlands, B73 5XH Tel: 0121-321 3488 Fax: 0121-321 3499 E-mail: ampumpsltd@aol.com

Anglian Pumping Services Ltd, APS House, The Drift, Nacton Road, Ipswich, IP3 9QR Tel: (01473) 719950 Fax: (01473) 719951 E-mail: info@anglianpumping.com

Bearings & Drives, Angel Road Works, Advent Way, London, N18 3AH Tel: (020) 8884 2111 Fax: (020) 8884 2112 E-mail: bearings2004@hotmail.co.uk

Birmingham Pump Supplies, 7 Network Park Industrial Estate, Duddeston Mill Road, Saltley, Birmingham, B8 1AU Tel: 0121-503 3000 Fax: 0121-503 3002 E-mail: sales@bhampumps.co.uk

Blagdon Pump Ltd, 2 Lambert Road, Armstrong Estate, Washington, Tyne & Wear, NE37 1QP Tel: 0191-417 7475 Fax: 0191-417 5435 E-mail: sales@blagdonpump.com

CCD Pumps Ltd, 212 Ilderton Road, London, SE15 1NT Tel: (020) 7639 4864 Fax: (020) 7635 0102 E-mail: sales@ccdpumps.co.uk

Ceetak Engineering Ltd, 1 Napier Road, Elm Farm Industrial Estate, Bedford, MK41 0QR Tel: (01234) 343232 Fax: (01234) 341133 E-mail: ceetakengineering@bedford.com

Ceetak Engineering Ltd, Unit 10 Easter Court, Europa Boulevard, Westbrook, Warrington, WA5 7ZB Tel: (01925) 710500 Fax: (01925) 710605

Clyde Associated Engineers Ltd, Block 5, 76 Beardmore Way, Clydebank Industrial Estate, Clydebank, Dunbartonshire, G81 4HT Tel: 0141-951 1331 Fax: 0141-951 3460 E-mail: lac@caeltd.co.uk

Cougar Industries Ltd, 1 Riverpark, Billet Lane, Berkhamsted, Hertfordshire, HP4 1HL Tel: (01442) 860000 Fax: (01442) 864686 E-mail: sales@cougar-industries.co.uk

Cumbria Pumps, Unit 8 Lake District Business Park, Mint Bridge Road, Kendal, Cumbria, LA9 6NH Tel: (01539) 735572 Fax: (01539) 735572

David Bedlington Ltd, Flemingate Works, Flemingate, Beverley, North Humberside, HU17 0NZ Tel: (01482) 867590 Fax: (01482) 866472

Elmbridge Pump Co., 6a Shepherd Road, Gloucester, GL2 5EQ Tel: (01452) 501102 Fax: (01452) 303691 E-mail: sales@elmbridgepump.com

Euro Industrial Engineering, 161 Fog Lane, Manchester, M20 6FJ Tel: 0161-438 0438 Fax: 0161-438 2538 E-mail: info@eieuk.com

Europump Services Ltd, Unit B Stover Trading Estate, Millbrook Road, Yate, Bristol, BS37 5PB Tel: (01454) 323415 Fax: (01454) 273022 E-mail: sales-uk@europump.co.uk

F C E Ltd, Unit 15, St. Davids Square, Fengate, Peterborough, PE1 5QA Tel: (01733) 314387 Fax: (01733) 314487 E-mail: fce.ltd@ukonline.co.uk

Flowrite Ltd, 6 Walnut Tree Close, Cheshunt, Waltham Cross, Hertfordshire, EN8 8NH Tel: (01992) 639205 Fax: (01992) 623993 E-mail: pumps@flowrite.co.uk

Flucon Pumps Ltd, 1 High Street, St. Asaph, Clwyd, LL17 0RG Tel: (01745) 584772 Fax: (01745) 582096 E-mail: info@flucon.co.uk

▶ Fluid UK Ltd, 4 Falcongate Industrial Estate, Old Gorsey Lane, Wallasey, Merseyside, CH44 4HD Tel: 0151-638 0869 Fax: 0151-638 5800 E-mail: sales@fluideng.co.uk

Fordwater Pumping Supplies Ltd, Unit 32 Forest Vale Road, Forest Vale Industrial Estate, Cinderford, Gloucestershire, GL14 2PH Tel: (01594) 826780 Fax: (01594) 826780 E-mail: fordwater@hotmail.com

G M Trebble Ltd, Unit 17 Perkins Way, Mansfield Road, Derby, DE21 4AW Tel: (01332) 294366 Fax: (01332) 295957

John Gaunt Pump Supplies Ltd, Unit 15, Norman Way Industrial Estate, Over, Cambridge, CB24 5QE Tel: (01954) 232323 Fax: (01954) 232322 E-mail: sales@johngauntpumps.co.uk

H & M Compressors & Pumps Ltd, B Enterprise Centre, Paycocke Road, Basildon, Essex, SS14 3DY Tel: (01268) 531288 Fax: (01268) 532013 E-mail: hmcompressos@tiscali.co.uk

Hereford Rewinds Ltd, Unit 12a Thorn Business Park, Rotherwas, Hereford, HR2 6JT Tel: (01432) 275002 Fax: (01432) 353484 E-mail: admin@herefordrewinds.co.uk

Hi-Force Ltd, Royal Oak Industrial Estate, Bentley Way, Daventry, Northamptonshire, NN11 8QH Tel: (01327) 301000 Fax: (01327) 706555 E-mail: sales@hi-force.com

Hortech Systems Ltd, Hallgate, Holbeach, Spalding, Lincolnshire, PE12 7LG Tel: (01406) 426513 Fax: (01406) 426515 E-mail: wayne@hortech.irrigation.co.uk

Hydrostal Ltd, 4-5 The Galloway Centre, Newbury, Berkshire, RG14 5TL Tel: (01635) 550440 Fax: (01635) 550140 E-mail: sales@hidrostal.co.uk

Iwaki Pumps UK Ltd, Monkmoor Road, Shrewsbury, SY2 5SX Tel: (01743) 231363 Fax: (01743) 366507 E-mail: info@iwakipumpsltd.co.uk

J S G Hydraulics, Unit E2 Enterprise Way, Bradford Road, Idle, Bradford, West Yorkshire, BD10 8EW Tel: (01274) 615800 Fax: (01274) 615552

K T Hydraulic Ltd, Hope Hall Mill, Union Street South, Halifax, West Yorkshire, HX1 2LA Tel: (01422) 358885 Fax: (01422) 359512

Kenyon Group Ltd, Regent House, Regent Street, Oldham, OL1 3TZ Tel: 0161-633 6328 Fax: 0161-627 5072 E-mail: sales@gluegunsdirect.com

Kinder Janes Engineers Ltd, Porters Wood, St. Albans, Hertfordshire, AL3 6HU Tel: (01727) 844441 Fax: (01727) 844247 E-mail: info@kinder-janes.co.uk

Koppen & Lethem Ltd, 6 Glenholm Park, Brunel Drive, Newark, Nottinghamshire, NG24 2EG Tel: (01636) 676794 Fax: (01636) 671055 E-mail: sales@koppen-lethem.co.uk

Linden Group Ltd, 1 Leaside North, Aycliffe Industrial Estate, Aycliffe Industrial Park, Newton Aycliffe, County Durham, DL5 6DU Tel: (01325) 311331 Fax: (01325) 300128 E-mail: sales@lindengroup.co.uk

Liquid Metering Instruments Ltd, L M I House, West Dudley Street, Winsford, Cheshire, CW7 3AG Tel: (01606) 550583 Fax: (01606) 550485 E-mail: sales@lmipumps.co.uk

Loader Fluid Engineering, Unit 4 2 Willis Way, Poole, Dorset, BH15 3SS Tel: (01202) 675220 Fax: (01202) 666890 E-mail: sales@loadereng.co.uk

Mack Engineering, Montrose Avenue, Hillington Industrial Estate, Glasgow, G52 4LA Tel: 0141-882 1030 Fax: 0141-882 7330 E-mail: mackengineering@btinternet.com

Marshall Pump Systems Ltd, 4 Rhodes Bank, Oldham, OL1 1UA Tel: 0161-678 6111 Fax: 0161-627 0913 E-mail: info@marshallpumps.co.uk

Northern Pump Suppliers Ltd, Bowling Back Lane, Bradford, West Yorkshire, BD4 8SR Tel: (01274) 721314 Fax: (01274) 730223 E-mail: sales-bradford@northern-pumps.co.uk

P C M Group UK Ltd, Pilot Road, Corby, Northamptonshire, NN17 5YF Tel: (01536) 740200 Fax: (01536) 740201 E-mail: sales@pcmgroupuk.eu

Pollyaim Ltd, 9 Churchill Court, 58 Station Road, North Harrow, Harrow, Middlesex, HA2 7SA Tel: (020) 8863 0457 Fax: (020) 8863 0459 E-mail: sales@pollyaim.com

Precision Pipework Ltd, Horn Hill, Lowestoft, Suffolk, NR33 0PX Tel: (01502) 500646 Fax: (01502) 566957 E-mail: sales@pumps4all.com

Prestige Pumps Ltd, 327 Wakefield Road, Wrenthorpe, Wakefield, West Yorkshire, WF2 0LX Tel: 0845 4940719 Fax: (01924) 379953 E-mail: sales@prestigepumps.co.uk

Pump Action Ltd, 19 Hutchison Road, Edinburgh, EH14 1RA Tel: 0131-444 0888 Fax: 0131-444 2888 E-mail: enquiries@pumpactionltd.co.uk

Pump Technical Sales Ltd, Unit 2b Beco Works, Kent House Lane, Beckenham, Kent, BR3 1LA Tel: (020) 8778 4271 Fax: (020) 8659 3576 E-mail: sales@pts-jung.co.uk

Pumps4U Ltd, Vortex Suite, Bradford, West Yorkshire, BD9 6SJ Tel: (07771) 741416 Fax: (01274) 821958 E-mail: sales@pumps4u.co.uk

Rent A Pump Services, Mold Road, Alltami, Mold, Clwyd, CH7 6LG Tel: (01244) 544962 Fax: (01244) 548557 E-mail: info@rentapump.co.uk

Rogers Industrial Equipment Ltd, 97 Castle Road, Mumbles, Swansea, SA3 5TA Tel: (01792) 361018 Fax: (01792) 361019 E-mail: barry@rogersboilers.fsnet.co.uk

S I Pumps Ltd, Unit 5 Curtis Yard, North Hinksey Lane, Botley, Oxford, OX2 0LX Tel: (01865) 791719 Fax: (01865) 722299 E-mail: sales@sipumps.ltd.uk

Stauff Scotland, Unit 3-4 Altens Trade Centre, Hareness Circle, Altens Industrial Estate, Aberdeen, AB12 3LY Tel: (01224) 238518 Fax: (01224) 238500 E-mail: sales@stauffscotland.co.uk

Tanks & Vessels Industries, Bankwood Lane Industrial Estate, Bankwood Lane, New Rossington, Doncaster, South Yorkshire, DN11 0PS Tel: (01302) 866003 Fax: (01302) 864990 E-mail: sales@tanksandvessels.com

Taylor & Goodman Ltd, 7 Cradock Road, Reading, RG2 0LB Tel: 0118-987 1773 Fax: 0118-931 4945 E-mail: sales@taylorgoodman.co.uk

Walter Hill Plant Ltd, Maze Street, Bristol, BS5 9TQ Tel: 0117-955 5151 Fax: 0117-941 3685

Williams Instruments, 29E Station Road, Desborough, Desborough, Kettering, Northamptonshire, NN14 2RL Tel: (01536) 762674 Fax: (01536) 761973 E-mail: pumppackage@btconnect.com

Wyatt Bros (UK) Ltd, Waymills Industrial Estate, Whitchurch, Shropshire, SY13 1TT Tel: (01948) 662526 Fax: (01948) 667560 E-mail: info@wyattbros.com

PUMP DOWN TOOLS

Black Gold Oil Tools Ltd, Souter Head Road, Altens Industrial Estate, Aberdeen, AB12 3LF Tel: (01224) 894019 Fax: (01224) 879731 E-mail: info@blackgoldoiltools.co.uk

PUMP ELECTRIC MOTORS

Electric Motor Rewinds, 6 Upper Wharf, Fareham, Hampshire, PO16 0LZ Tel: (01329) 233154 Fax: (01329) 280679

Franklin Electric (Henley), Treetops House, Gillotts Lane, Henley-On-Thames, Oxfordshire, RG9 1PT Tel: (01491) 579118 Fax: (01491) 412211 E-mail: fesales@acdcsystems.com

PUMP HIRE

Andrews Sykes Hire Ltd, Unit F17 Ashmount Business Park, Upper Fforest Way, Swansea Enterprise Park, Swansea, SA6 8QR Tel: (01792) 701701 Fax: (01792) 701700

Axflow Ltd, 3 Harlaw Centre Howe Moss Crescent, Kirkhill Industrial Estate, Dyce, Aberdeen, AB21 0GN Tel: (01224) 729367 Fax: (01224) 729368 E-mail: infoscot@axflow.co.uk

Burlington Engineers Ltd, Unit 11 Perival Industrial Park, Horsenden Lane South, Perivale, Greenford, Middlesex, UB6 7RL Tel: (020) 8810 7266 Fax: (020) 8998 3517 E-mail: info@burlington-engineers.co.uk

Contractors Plant Hire Ltd, 3 Green Gables, Tidmarsh Lane, Tidmarsh, Reading, RG8 8HG Tel: 0118-984 3123 Fax: 0118-984 1101

Fordwater Pumping Supplies Ltd, Unit 32 Forest Vale Road, Forest Vale Industrial Estate, Cinderford, Gloucestershire, GL14 2PH Tel: (01594) 826780 Fax: (01594) 826780 E-mail: fordwater@hotmail.com

Longville, 119 Burcott Road, Bristol, BS11 8AD Tel: 0117-982 7657 Fax: 0117-938 4109 E-mail: bristol@sldpumps.com

Longville S L D Ltd, Unit B, Colima Avenue, Sunderland Enter Park, Sunderland, SR5 3XE Tel: 0191-516 5500 Fax: 0191-516 5501

Rent A Pump Services, Mold Road, Alltami, Mold, Clwyd, CH7 6LG Tel: (01244) 544962 Fax: (01244) 548557 E-mail: info@rentapump.co.uk

S L D Specialist Hires, Greenbank Road, East Tullos Industrial Estate, Aberdeen, AB12 4BS Tel: (01224) 248700 Fax: (01224) 890576 E-mail: aberdeen@sldpump.co.uk

▶ Selwood Ltd, Derby Road, Langley Mill, Nottingham, NG16 4AA Tel: (01773) 714227 Fax: (01773) 716445 E-mail: nottingham@selwoodgroup.co.uk

PUMP INSTALLATION/REMOVAL CONTRACTORS

CCD Pumps Ltd, 212 Ilderton Road, London, SE15 1NT Tel: (020) 7639 4864 Fax: (020) 7635 0102 E-mail: sales@ccdpumps.co.uk

Europump Services Ltd, Unit B Stover Trading Estate, Millbrook Road, Yate, Bristol, BS37 5PB Tel: (01454) 323415 Fax: (01454) 273022 E-mail: sales-uk@europump.co.uk

George Green (Keighley) Ltd, Parkwood Works, Parkwood Street, Keighley, West Yorkshire, BD21 4PN Tel: (01535) 603728 Fax: (01535) 610340 E-mail: enquiries@georgegreen-uk.com

Hydro Project Engineering, Sutton Lane, Etwall, Derby, DE65 6LQ Tel: (01283) 730073

Lincs Pumps & Pipeline, Water Gate, Quadring, Spalding, Lincolnshire, PE11 4PY Tel: (01775) 821163 Fax: (01775) 821613

London Fire & Pump Co. Ltd, 11 Bridle Road, Pinner, Middlesex, HA5 2SL Tel: (020) 8866 6342 Fax: (020) 8866 6342

Midland Pumps Ltd, 25 Colemeadow Road, Moons Moat North Industrial Es, Redditch, Worcestershire, B98 9PB Tel: (01527) 598556 Fax: (01527) 598557 E-mail: sales@midlandpumps.co.uk

Simon Moore Water Services, Unit 2, Poundbury West Industrial Estate, Dorchester, Dorset, DT1 2PG Tel: (01305) 251551 Fax: (01305) 257107

Pump Technical Sales Ltd, Unit 2b Beco Works, Kent House Lane, Beckenham, Kent, BR3 1LA Tel: (020) 8778 4271 Fax: (020) 8659 3576 E-mail: sales@pts-jung.co.uk

S I Pumps Ltd, Unit 5 Curtis Yard, North Hinksey Lane, Botley, Oxford, OX2 0LX Tel: (01865) 791719 Fax: (01865) 722299 E-mail: sales@sipumps.ltd.uk

T W Page & Son Ltd, 7 Buxton Road, Frettenham, Norwich, NR12 7NQ Tel: (01603) 898071 Fax: (01603) 898049 E-mail: admin@twpage.co.uk

Walter Hill Plant Ltd, Maze Street, Bristol, BS5 9TQ Tel: 0117-955 5151 Fax: 0117-941 3685

Weir Engineering Services, PO Box 4, Barton-upon-Humber, South Humberside, DN18 5BN Tel: (01652) 632702 Fax: (01652) 633112 E-mail: steemturbines@weir.co.uk

PUMP MAINTENANCE/REPAIR SERVICES

A F S Rotel Ltd, Unit E Central Industrial Estate, St Marks Street, Bolton, BL3 6NR Tel: (01204) 388077 Fax: (01204) 386309 E-mail: info@pump-spares.co.uk

A J H Pump Supply & Repair, The Warehouse, Church Street, Wakefield, West Yorkshire, WF1 5QY Tel: (01924) 368773 Fax: (01924) 382229 E-mail: john@ajhpumpsupply.co.uk

PUMP MAINTENANCE/REPAIR SERVICES – *continued*

Active Pump Service Ltd, Unit G17 Rudford Industrial Estate, Ford Road, Ford, Arundel, West Sussex, BN18 0BD Tel: (01903) 734030 Fax: (01903) 733640 E-mail: nigel@activepumpservices.co.uk

Aish Electro, Unit 2b Cowley Road, Nuffield Industrial Estate, Poole, Dorset, BH17 0UJ Tel: (01202) 677100 Fax: (01202) 677233 E-mail: serbite@aishem.co.uk

Allsebrook Pump Services Ltd, Unit 10 Van Alloys Industrial Estate, Busgrove Lane, Stoke Row, Henley-on-Thames, Oxfordshire, RG9 5QW Tel: (01491) 680628 Fax: (01491) 682318 E-mail: sales-allsebrookservices@btconnect.co.uk

Axflow Ltd, 3 Harlaw Centre Howe Moss Crescent, Kirkhill Industrial Estate, Dyce, Aberdeen, AB21 0GN Tel: (01224) 729367 Fax: (01224) 729368 E-mail: infoscot@axflow.co.uk

B & H Pumps & Engineering Services, Unit 19 Whitemoor Court Industrial Estate, Nottingham, NG8 5BY Tel: 0115-929 9746 Fax: 0115-942 5091

Bearings & Drives, Angel Road Works, Advent Way, London, N18 3AH Tel: (020) 8884 2111 Fax: (020) 8884 2112 E-mail: bearings2004@hotmail.co.uk

Bedford Pump Ltd, Brooklands, Woburn Road Industrial Estate, Kempston, Bedford, MK42 7UH Tel: (01234) 852071 Fax: (01234) 856620 E-mail: sales@bedfordpumps.co.uk

Border Pumps & Transmissions, Station Road, Sandycroft, Deeside, Clwyd, CH5 2PT Tel: (01244) 533065 Fax: (01244) 535635

C & P Services Northern Ltd, 11 Burtonwood Industrial Centre, Phipps Lane, Burtonwood, Warrington, WA5 4HX Tel: (01925) 229118 Fax: (01925) 228022 E-mail: info@candpservices.co.uk

CCD Pumps Ltd, 212 Ilderton Road, London, SE15 1NT Tel: (020) 7639 4864 Fax: (020) 7635 0102 E-mail: sales@ccdpumps.co.uk

Ceetak Engineering Ltd, Unit 10 Easter Court, Europa Boulevard, Westbrook, Warrington, WA5 7ZB Tel: (01925) 710500 Fax: (01925) 710605

Clydesdale Engineering Services Ltd, Belvoir Way, Fairfield Industrial Estate, Louth, Lincolnshire, LN11 0LQ Tel: (01507) 605991 Fax: (01507) 605991 E-mail: info@clydesdale.fsbusiness.co.uk

Cumbria Pumps, Unit 8 Lake District Business Park, Mint Bridge Road, Kendal, Cumbria, LA9 6NH Tel: (01539) 735572 Fax: (01539) 735572

▶ Eastern Counties Pumps, 3 Burrell Road, Ipswich, IP2 8AD Tel: (01473) 400101 Fax: (01473) 400103 E-mail: sales@ecpgroup.com

Europump Services Ltd, Unit B Stover Trading Estate, Millbrook Road, Yate, Bristol, BS37 5PB Tel: (01454) 323415 Fax: (01454) 273022 E-mail: sales-uk@europump.co.uk

F C E Ltd, Unit 15, St. Davids Square, Fengate, Peterborough, PE1 5QA Tel: (01733) 314387 Fax: (01733) 314487 E-mail: fce.ltd@ukonline.co.uk

Ferrier Pumps (Aberdeen) Ltd, Unit 4-5 Barclayhill Place, Portlethen, Aberdeen, AB12 4PF Tel: (01224) 782022 Fax: (01224) 780050 E-mail: aberdeen@ferrierpumps.co.uk

G M Trebble Ltd, Unit 17 Perkins Way, Mansfield Road, Derby, DE21 4AW Tel: (01332) 294366 Fax: (01332) 295957

G M Treble Ltd, New Street, Parkfields, Wolverhampton, WV4 6AN Tel: (01902) 333111 Fax: (01902) 340941 E-mail: sales@gmtreble.co.uk

G O C Engineering Services, Buckingham Cottage, Crow Road, Fintry, Glasgow, G63 0XJ Tel: (01360) 860478 Fax: (01360) 860478 E-mail: jchesney@goceng.co.uk

H S G Pump Services, Unit 13 Riverbank Enterprise Centre, Scout Hill Road, Dewsbury, West Yorkshire, WF13 3RQ Tel: (01924) 453547 Fax: (01924) 452009 E-mail: haj@hsgpumpservices.com

Heasell Electromechanical Services Ltd, 9-11 Baldock Street, Royston, Hertfordshire, SG8 5AY Tel: (0871) 2227896 Fax: (01763) 248108 E-mail: gary@abrams-netlineuk.net

Heavy Parts Hydraulics, 89 Baillie Street East, Rochdale, Lancashire, OL16 2BY Tel: (01706) 356676 Fax: (01706) 646185 E-mail: sales@heavyparts.co.uk

Hereward Engineering Services Ltd, 6 The Sq, Vicarage Farm Rd, Peterborough, PE1 5TS Tel: (01733) 311448 Fax: (01733) 343927

Hortech Systems Ltd, Hallgate, Holbeach, Spalding, Lincolnshire, PE12 7LG Tel: (01406) 426513 Fax: (01406) 426515 E-mail: wayne@hortech.irrigation.co.uk

Hydrostal Ltd, 4-5 The Galloway Centre, Newbury, Berkshire, RG14 5TL Tel: (01635) 550440 Fax: (01635) 550140 E-mail: sales@hidrostal.co.uk

Linden Group Ltd, 1 Leaside North, Aycliffe Industrial Estate, Aycliffe Industrial Park, Newton Aycliffe, County Durham, DL5 6DU Tel: (01325) 311331 Fax: (01325) 300128 E-mail: sales@lindengroup.co.uk

Liquid Metering Instruments Ltd, L M I House, West Dudley Street, Winsford, Cheshire, CW7 3AG Tel: (01606) 550583 Fax: (01606) 550485 E-mail: sales@llmipumps.co.uk

London Fire & Pump Co. Ltd, 11 Bridle Road, Pinner, Middlesex, HA5 2SL Tel: (020) 8866 6342 Fax: (020) 8866 6342

Longville S L D Ltd, Unit B, Colima Avenue, Sunderland Enter Park, Sunderland, SR5 3XE Tel: 0191-516 5500 Fax: 0191-516 5501

M E R Electrical & Mechanical, The Broadway, Mansfield, Nottinghamshire, NG18 2RL Tel: (01623) 621522 Fax: (01623) 627719 E-mail: sales@mer-electrical.co.uk

Ritchie MacKenzie & Co. Ltd, Broomhill Industrial Estate, Kirkintilloch, Glasgow, G66 1TQ Tel: 0141-776 6274 Fax: 0141-776 0285 E-mail: sales@ritmac.co.uk

Mid Kent Electrical Engineering Co., The Street, Detling, Maidstone, Kent, ME14 3JT Tel: (01622) 735702 Fax: (01622) 734844 E-mail: pumpsales@mke.co.uk

Nash Mechanical Seal Services Ltd, Nile Street, Bolton, BL3 6DW Tel: (01204) 388030 Fax: (01204) 361541 E-mail: enquiry@nashseal.com

Pump Service Engineering Ltd, Unit 16 Charlestown Industrial Estate, Robinson Street, Ashton-under-Lyne, Lancashire, OL6 8NS Tel: 0161-330 3875 Fax: 0161-330 5024 E-mail: pumpservice@talk21.com

Rotamec Ltd, 4 Winchester Farm, Draycott Road, Cheddar, Somerset, BS27 3RP Tel: (01934) 743165 Fax: (01934) 743168 E-mail: sales@rotamec.co.uk

Rotary Equipment Services Ltd, Unit 5-6 Castle Way, Severn Bridge Industrial Estate, Portskewett, Caldicot, Gwent, NP26 5YG Tel: (01291) 420670 Fax: (01291) 430165 E-mail: sales@reslimited.com

Rotary Equipment Services Ltd, Unit 2, Expressway Business Park, Station Road, Queensferry, Deeside, Clwyd, CH5 2TF Tel: (01244) 822402 Fax: (01244) 823960 E-mail: jeff.sheen@reslimited.com

S I Pumps Ltd, Unit 5 Curtis Yard, North Hinksey Lane, Botley, Oxford, OX2 0LX Tel: (01865) 791719 Fax: (01865) 722299 E-mail: sales@sipumps.ltd.uk

S P P Pumps Ltd, Unit 1, Stanstead Road, Boyatt Way Estate, Eastleigh, Hampshire, SO50 4RZ Tel: (023) 8061 6004 Fax: (023) 8061 4522 E-mail: sterlingreading@compuserve.com

SLK Engineering & Manufacturing Services Ltd, 4 Castle Road, Ellon, Aberdeenshire, AB41 9EY Tel: (01358) 724002 Fax: (01358) 720166 E-mail: sales@sltengineering.co.uk

Specialist Pumping Services, Walkers Yard, Castle Road, Kidderminster, Worcestershire, DY11 6TH Tel: (01562) 67935 Fax: (01562) 515554

Star Electrical Repairs, 5 Englehard Industrial Estate Valley Road, Bilson, Cinderford, Gloucestershire, GL14 2PB Tel: (01594) 826433 Fax: (01594) 826433

Sulzer Precision Engineers, 7 Twenty Twenty Industrial Estate, St Laurence Avenue, Allington, Maidstone, Kent, ME16 0LL Tel: (01622) 679562 Fax: (01622) 766306

Swift Electrical, Unit 1 Craven Way, Newmarket, Suffolk, CB8 0BW Tel: (01638) 661001 Fax: (01638) 560195 E-mail: swiftsescrubes@hotmail.com

Taylor Fuel Control, Unit 4a New England Estate, Off Pindar Road, Hoddesdon, Hertfordshire, EN11 0BZ Tel: (01992) 451101 Fax: (01992) 444954

Tecker Ltd, Kernow House, Tregoniggie Industrial Estate, Falmouth, Cornwall, TR11 4SN Tel: (01326) 378774 Fax: (01326) 378775 E-mail: mail@tecker.co.uk

Telford Rewinds Ltd, Unit 5, Halesfield 18, Telford, Shropshire, TF7 4PP Tel: (01952) 580703 Fax: (01952) 580703

Torres Engineering & Pumps Ltd, 448 Brightside Lane, Sheffield, S9 2SP Tel: 0114-249 3377 Fax: 0114-242 5885 E-mail: ken_torres@torrespumps.co.uk

Us Marine & Industrial Pump Repair, Site 20 Grangefield Industrial Estate, Richardshaw Lane, Pudsey, West Yorkshire, LS28 6QW Tel: 0113-256 3721 Fax: 0113-255 9820 E-mail: sales@usmarine.co.uk

▶ Vacflow Pumps, Unit 10 Horbury Bridge Mills, Bridge Road, Horbury, Wakefield, West Yorkshire, WF4 5RW Tel: (01924) 274518 Fax: (01924) 279405

Viking Pump Ltd, Viking House, Dannemore Drive, Sheffield, S9 5DF Tel: 0114-244 7701 Fax: 0114-243 2614

W Robinson & Sons Ec Ltd, 35-41 Fowler Road, Hainault Industrial Estate, Ilford, Essex, IG6 3WR Tel: (020) 8559 6000 Fax: (020) 8559 6001 E-mail: info@pump.co.uk

Walter Hill Plant Ltd, Maze Street, Bristol, BS5 9TQ Tel: 0117-955 5151 Fax: 0117-941 3685

Weir Engineering Services, PO Box 4, Barton-upon-Humber, South Humberside, DN18 5BN Tel: (01652) 632702 Fax: (01652) 633112 E-mail: steemturbines@weir.co.uk

Weir Engineering Services, Winnington Avenue, Northwich, Cheshire, CW8 4FT Tel: (01606) 782255 Fax: (01606) 871631 E-mail: sales@upl.weir.co.uk

WGM Engineering Ltd, 1 Abbey Mill Business Centre, Paisley, Renfrewshire, PA1 1TJ Tel: 0141-889 1009 Fax: 0141-848 6257 E-mail: info@wgmltd.com

Wyatt Bros (UK) Ltd, Waymills Industrial Estate, Whitchurch, Shropshire, SY13 1TT Tel: (01948) 662526 Fax: (01948) 667560 E-mail: info@wyattbros.com

PUMP MONITORING EQUIPMENT

Advanced Energy Monitoring Systems Ltd, The Energy Centre, Finnimore Industrial Estate, Ottery St. Mary, Devon, EX11 1NR Tel: (01404) 812294 Fax: (01404) 812603 E-mail: info@yatesmeter.co.uk

PUMP SPARE PARTS/WEARING PARTS

A F S Rotel Ltd, Unit E Central Industrial Estate, St Marks Street, Bolton, BL3 6NR Tel: (01204) 388077 Fax: (01204) 386309 E-mail: info@pump-spares.co.uk

Apex Fluid Engineering Ltd, 4 Morley Road, Staple Hill, Bristol, BS16 4QT Tel: 0117-907 7555 Fax: 0117-907 7556 E-mail: enquiries@apexpumps.com

Cougar Industries Ltd, 1 Riverpark, Billet Lane, Berkhamsted, Hertfordshire, HP4 1HL Tel: (01442) 860000 Fax: (01442) 864686 E-mail: sales@cougar-industries.co.uk

Dawson, Downie, Lamont, 31 Rutherford Road, Glenrothes, Fife, KY6 2RT Tel: (01592) 775577 Fax: (01592) 775517 E-mail: sales@ddl-ltd.com

Electric Motor Rewinds, 114 Islingword Road, Brighton, BN2 9SG Tel: (01273) 685925 Fax: (01273) 685925 E-mail: sales@electricmotorrewinds.co.uk

Gilbeyco Ltd, 32 Edison Road, Rabans Lane Industrial Area, Aylesbury, Buckinghamshire, HP19 8TE Tel: (01296) 414966 Fax: (01296) 414969 E-mail: enquiries@gilbeyco.com

Hereward Engineering Services Ltd, 6 The Sq, Vicarage Farm Rd, Peterborough, PE1 5TS Tel: (01733) 311448 Fax: (01733) 343927

I T T Water & Waste Water, Colwick Indust Estate, Colwick Industrial Estate, Nottingham, NG4 2AN Tel: 0115-940 0111 Fax: (01202) 631008 E-mail: admin@allweiler-pumps.demon.co.uk

Ladenall Ltd, Diesel House 5 Humber Trading Estate, Humber Road, London, NW2 6DW Tel: (020) 8452 1552 Fax: (020) 8452 8471 E-mail: enquiries@ladenall.com

PUMP TEST SERVICES

Advanced Energy Monitoring Systems Ltd, The Energy Centre, Finnimore Industrial Estate, Ottery St. Mary, Devon, EX11 1NR Tel: (01404) 812294 Fax: (01404) 812603 E-mail: info@yatesmeter.co.uk

PUMPING SETS

Allan Aqua-Systems Ltd, Allan Aqua House, Sedgwick Rd, Luton, LU4 9DT Tel: (01582) 574048 Fax: (01582) 574293 E-mail: info@allanaqua.co.uk

Barber Pumps Ltd, Jacksons Yard, Douglas Road North, Fulwood, Preston, PR2 3QH Tel: (01772) 715502 Fax: (01772) 712716 E-mail: barberpumps@aol.com

Wilo Salmson Pumps Ltd, Centrum 100, Burton-on-Trent, Staffordshire, DE14 2WJ Tel: (01283) 523000 Fax: (01283) 523099 E-mail: sales@wilo.co.uk

PUMPS

A B S Pumps Ltd, Astral Towers, 5TH Floor, Betts Way, Crawley, West Sussex, RH10 9UY Tel: (01293) 558140 Fax: (01293) 527972

Airtex Products Ltd, Hanworth Trading Estate, Hampton Road West, Feltham, Middlesex, TW13 6EH Tel: (020) 8755 4400 Fax: (020) 8894 3026 E-mail: info@airtex.co.uk

Alfa Laval Eastbourne Ltd, Birch Road, Eastbourne, East Sussex, BN23 6PQ Tel: (01323) 412555 Fax: (01323) 414515

Alldos Ltd, 82 Gravelly Industrial Park, Birmingham, B24 8TL Tel: 0121-328 3336 Fax: 0121-328 4332 E-mail: alldos.uk@alldos.com

Anglo Pumps Ltd, 4a-B Aston Road, Cambridge Road Industrial Estate, Bedford, MK42 0LJ Tel: (01234) 353525 Fax: (01234) 211655 E-mail: sales@anglo-pumps.co.uk

Apex Fluid Engineering Ltd, 4 Morley Road, Staple Hill, Bristol, BS16 4QT Tel: 0117-907 7555 Fax: 0117-907 7556 E-mail: enquiries@apexpumps.com

Aspen Pumps Ltd, Aspen Building, Apex Way, Hailsham, East Sussex, BN27 3WA Tel: (01323) 848842 Fax: (01323) 848846

▶ Auto Gas Technology Ltd, Unit 2 Sherriff Street, Worcester, WR4 9AB Tel: (01905) 729662 Fax: (01905) 28410

Automatic Pump Ltd, 36 Lanehead Road, Etruria, Stoke-On-Trent, ST1 5PT Tel: (01782) 279504 Fax: (01782) 279005 E-mail: enquiries@elipse.co.uk

Bedford Pump Ltd, Brooklands, Woburn Road Industrial Estate, Kempston, Bedford, MK42 7UH Tel: (01234) 852071 Fax: (01234) 856620 E-mail: sales@bedfordpumps.co.uk

Blagdon Pump Ltd, 2 Lambert Road, Armstrong Estate, Washington, Tyne & Wear, NE37 1QP Tel: 0191-417 7475 Fax: 0191-417 5435 E-mail: sales@blagdonpump.com

C D R Pumps UK Ltd, 28 Trojan Centre, Finedon Road Industrial Estate, Wellingborough, Northamptonshire, NN8 4ST Tel: (0870) 7561428 Fax: (01933) 226225 E-mail: sales@cdrpumps.com

Calpeda Ltd, Wedgwood Road Industrial Estate, Bicester, Oxfordshire, OX26 4UL Tel: (01869) 241441 Fax: (01869) 240681 E-mail: pumps@calpeda.co.uk

Caprari Pumps (UK) Ltd, Caprari House, Bakewell Road, Orton Southgate, Peterborough, PE2 6XU Tel: (01733) 371605 Fax: (01733) 371607 E-mail: info@caprari.co.uk

Centrifugal Pump Services Ltd, Pump House, Bird Hall Lane, Cheadle Heath, Stockport, Cheshire, SK3 0XX Tel: 0161 4280133 Fax: 0161 4280188 E-mail: sales@centrifugalpumps.co.uk

Dab Pumps Ltd, 4 Stortford Hall Industrial Park, Dunmow Road, Bishop's Stortford, Hertfordshire, CM23 5GZ Tel: (01279) 652776 Fax: (01279) 655147 E-mail: info@dabpumps.com

Desmi Ltd, Unit 6A, Rosevale Business Park, Parkhouse Industrial Estate West, Newcastle, Staffordshire, ST5 7UB Tel: (01782) 566900 Fax: (01782) 563666 E-mail: desmi_ltd@desmi.com

Dewatering Service Ltd, The Triangle, Hambridge Lane, Newbury, Berkshire, RG14 5TZ Tel: (01635) 33313

James Dring Power Plant Ltd, 8 Eagle Road, Quarry Hill Industrial Estate, Ilkeston, Derbyshire, DE7 4RB Tel: 0115-944 0072 Fax: 0115-944 0235 E-mail: enquiries@jamesdring.co.uk

Drum International Ltd, Springmill Street, Bradford, West Yorkshire, BD5 7YH Tel: (01274) 718100 Fax: (01274) 718101 E-mail: sales@eu.gardnerdenver.com

▶ Eden Engineering, Tanfield Lea Industrial Estate, Stanley, County Durham, DH9 9QS Tel: (01207) 235811

Egger Turo Pumps (U.K.) Ltd, Fountain House, Cleeve Road, Leatherhead, Surrey, KT22 7NH Tel: (01372) 377688 Fax: (01372) 373587 E-mail: info.uk@eggerpumps.com

▶ Envirotech Pump Systems, Crompton Road, Ilkeston, Derbyshire, DE7 4BG Tel: 0115-932 8300 Fax: 0115-932 8360 E-mail: sales@envirotech-pumpsystems.com

Ferrier Pumps (Aberdeen) Ltd, Unit 4-5 Barclayhill Place, Portlethen, Aberdeen, AB12 4PF Tel: (01224) 782022 Fax: (01224) 780050 E-mail: aberdeen@ferrierpumps.co.uk

Flotronic Pumps Ltd, Ricebridge Works, Brighton Road, Bolney, Haywards Heath, West Sussex, RH17 5NA Tel: (01444) 881871 Fax: (01444) 881860 E-mail: salesdept@flotronicpumps.co.uk

Flowrite Ltd, 6 Walnut Tree Close, Cheshunt, Waltham Cross, Hertfordshire, EN8 8NH Tel: (01992) 639205 Fax: (01992) 623993 E-mail: pumps@flowrite.co.uk

▶ G P Services Ltd, Seafire Works, Henstridge Industrial Estate, Henstridge, Templecombe, Somerset, BA8 0TN Tel: (01963) 363866

Gardner Denver UK Ltd, PO Box 468, Bradford, West Yorkshire, BD5 7HW Tel: (01274) 715240 Fax: (01274) 715241

Gilbert Gilkes & Gordon Ltd, Canal Iron Works, Kendal, Cumbria, LA9 7BZ Tel: (01539) 720028 Fax: (01539) 732110 E-mail: sales@gilkes.com

Goodwin International Ltd, Newstead Industrial Trading Estate, Stoke-on-Trent, ST4 8HU Tel: (01782) 654000 Fax: (01782) 208060 E-mail: goodwinplc@goodwin.co.uk

Grundfos Pumps Ltd, Orford Court, Green Fold Way, Leigh, Lancashire, WN7 3XJ Tel: (0870) 7503888 Fax: (01942) 605970

Grundfos Pumps Ltd, Grovebury Road, Leighton Buzzard, Bedfordshire, LU7 4TL Tel: (01525) 850000 Fax: (01525) 850011 E-mail: ukindustry@grundfos.com

▶ Hayward Tyler Sumo Ltd, Nerston Industrial Estate, East Kilbride, Glasgow, G74 4QZ Tel: (01355) 221301

Hilta TW, Flowplant House, Unit 8A-B Summit Crescent, Summit Estate, Smethwick, West Midlands, B66 1BT Tel: 0121-525 9955 Fax: 0121-525 0748 E-mail: hilta@hiltapumps.com

Hippo Engineering Ltd, 1 Dunelm, Kelverton, Nottingham, NG14 6NN Tel: 0115-965 5138 Fax: 0115-965 5148

Holden & Brooke Ltd, Wenlock Way, Manchester, M12 5JL Tel: 0161-223 2223 Fax: 0161-220 9660 E-mail: marketing@holdenbrooke.com

▶ Howford Hydraulics, Old Howford Road, Catrine, Ayrshire, KA5 5JX Tel: (01290) 551428 Fax: (01290) 550549 E-mail: sales@howford.demon.co.uk

I T T Water & Waste Water, Colwick Indust Estate, Colwick Industrial Estate, Nottingham, NG4 2AN Tel: 0115-940 0111 Fax: (01202) 631008 E-mail: admin@allweiler-pumps.demon.co.uk

Iwaki Pumps UK Ltd, Monkmoor Road, Shrewsbury, SY2 5SX Tel: (01743) 231363 Fax: (01743) 366507 E-mail: info@iwakipumpsltd.co.uk

J L C Pumps & Engineering Co. Ltd, PO Box 225, Bedford, MK45 4PN Tel: (01582) 881946 Fax: (01582) 881951 E-mail: jlcpumps@btconnect.com

Landia UK Ltd, Waymills Indust Estate, Waymills, Whitchurch, Shropshire, SY13 1TT Tel: (01948) 661200 Fax: (01948) 661201 E-mail: info@landia.co.uk

PUMPS – *continued*

Linatex Ltd, Wilkinson House Galway Road, Blackbushe Business Park, Yateley, Hampshire, GU46 6GE Tel: (01252) 743000 Fax: (01252) 743030E-mail: info@linatex.com

Long Reach Irrigation Ltd, Unit 6, Furnham Close, Furnham Road, Chard, Somerset, TA20 1AX Tel: (01460) 261255 Fax: (01460) 261266 E-mail: sales@xlreach.com

Lowara UK Ltd, Weycroft Avenue Millwey Rise Indust Estate, Axminster, Devon, EX13 5HL Tel: (01297) 630200 Fax: (01297) 630270 E-mail: lowara@itt.com

Macro Marine Ltd, Unit 33 Station Road Industrial Estate, Estate, Hailsham, East Sussex, BN27 2ER Tel: (01323) 842331 Fax: 01323 842980

▶ Matchless Ltd, Gilbert Wakefield Lodge, 65 Bewsey Street, Warrington, WA2 7JQ Tel: (01925) 231900 Fax: (01925) 415423

Midland Pump Manufacturing Co. Ltd, Tyseley Industrial Estate, Seeleys Road, Birmingham, B11 2LF Tel: 0121-773 8862 Fax: 0121-771 4363 E-mail: sales@midlandpump.co.uk

Mono Pumps Ltd, Martin St, Audenshaw, Manchester, M34 5JA Tel: 0161-339 9000 Fax: 0161-344 0727 E-mail: info@mono-pumps.com

Netzsch Nemo Pumps Ltd, Unit 3 Middlemore Business Park, Middlemore Lane West, Aldridge, Walsall, WS9 8BG Tel: (01922) 453433 Fax: (01922) 458404 E-mail: npl@netzsch.com

New Haden Pumps Ltd, New Haden Works, Draycott Cross Road, Cheadle, Stoke-on-Trent, ST10 2NW Tel: (01538) 757900 Fax: (01538) 757999 E-mail: info@nhpumps.com

P C M Group UK Ltd, Pilot Road, Corby, Northamptonshire, NN17 5YF Tel: (01536) 740200 Fax: (01536) 740201 E-mail: sales@pcmgroupuk.eu

▶ Penstar Process & Technical Services Ltd, Penstar, Rhoshill, Cardigan, Dyfed, SA43 2TX Tel: (01239) 841458 Fax: (01239) 841307 E-mail: sales@penstar.co.uk

Poolpump Ltd, 2 Beaulieu Road, Christchurch, Dorset, BH23 2EA Tel: (01202) 499392 Fax: (01202) 473662

Pump International Ltd, Trevool, Praze, Camborne, Cornwall, TR14 0PJ Tel: (01209) 831937 Fax: (01209) 831939 E-mail: sales@pumpinternational.com

Pump Technical Sales Ltd, Unit 2b Beco Works, Kent House Lane, Beckenham, Kent, BR3 1LA Tel: (020) 8778 4271 Fax: (020) 8659 3576 E-mail: sales@pts-jung.co.uk

Purolator Products Automotive, Glenco Ho, Drake Ave, Staines, Middx, TW18 2AW Tel: (01784) 493555

Richard Hill Pumps Ltd, Brooke Road, Ridlington, Oakham, Leicestershire, LE15 9AJ Tel: (01572) 823385 Fax: (01572) 821660

S A C Marine International Ltd, 36 Ridleys Cross, Astley, Stourport-on-Severn, Worcestershire, DY13 0RF Tel: (01299) 825908 Fax: (01299) 878699 E-mail: sacmarine.com

S P P Pumps Ltd, Unit 1, Stanstead Road, Boyatt Way Estate, Eastleigh, Hampshire, SO50 4RZ Tel: (023) 8061 6004 Fax: (023) 8061 4522 E-mail: sterlingreading@compuserve.com

▶ Sel Tek, 31 Dellburn Street, Motherwell, Lanarkshire, ML1 1SE Tel: (01698) 262569 Fax: (01698) 259799 E-mail: enquiry@sel-tek.co.uk

Selwood Group, Hixon Industrial Estate, Church Lane, Hixon, Stafford, ST18 0QB Tel: (01889) 270524 Fax: (01889) 270063

Selwood Pump Co. Ltd, 188 Robin Hood Lane, Birmingham, B28 0LG Tel: 0121-777 5631 Fax: 0121-702 2195 E-mail: graham.gallon@selwood-pumps.com

Shurflo Ltd, 5 Sterling Park, Gatwick Road, Crawley, West Sussex, RH10 9QT Tel: (01293) 424000 Fax: (01293) 421880 E-mail: sales@shurflo.com

Sulzer Precision Engineers, 7 Twenty Twenty Industrial Estate, St Laurence Avenue, Allington, Maidstone, Kent, ME16 0LL Tel: (01622) 679562 Fax: (01622) 766306

▶ Sulzer Pumps, 18d Challenge House, Sherwood Drive, Bletchley, Milton Keynes, MK3 6DP Tel: (01908) 632775 Fax: (01908) 274957

Surecast Devizes Ltd, Roundway Mill, London Road, Devizes, Wiltshire, SN10 2EA Tel: (01380) 723402 Fax: (01380) 729063 E-mail: sales@surecast.co.uk

T T Pumps Ltd, Onneley Works, Newcastle Road, Woore, Crewe, CW3 9RU Tel: (01630) 647200 Fax: (01630) 642100 E-mail: response@ttpumps.com

Tapflo UK Ltd, B The Apex Centre, Church Lane, Colden Common, Winchester, Hampshire, SO21 1TN Tel: (01962) 717131 Fax: (01962) 717130 E-mail: mick@tapflo-demon.co.uk

▶ Tokheim UK Ltd, 1-3 Baker Road, Broughty Ferry, Dundee, DD5 3RT Tel: (01382) 598000 Fax: (01382) 598001

Torres Engineering & Pumps Ltd, 448 Brightside Lane, Sheffield, S9 2SP Tel: 0114-249 3377 Fax: 0114-242 5885 E-mail: ken_torres@torrespumps.co.uk

Totton Pumps, Rushington Business Park, Chaple Lane, Totton, Southampton, SO40 9AH Tel: (023) 8066 6685 Fax: (023) 8066 6880 E-mail: info@totton-pumps.com

Stuart Turner Ltd, Market Place, Henley-on-Thames, Oxfordshire, RG9 2AD Tel: (01491) 572655 Fax: (01491) 573704 E-mail: sales@stuart-turner.co.uk

▶ Tytan Jetting Ltd, Unit 1 Broomiesburn Road, Ellon, Aberdeenshire, AB41 9RD Tel: (01358) 729444 Fax: (01358) 729333 E-mail: enquires@tytan.co.uk

Union Pumps Union Pumps, Green Road, Penistone, Sheffield, S36 6BJ Tel: (01226) 763311 Fax: (01226) 766535 E-mail: bkearsley@unionpump.textron.com

W Robinson & Sons Ec Ltd, 35-41 Fowler Road, Hainault Industrial Estate, Ilford, Essex, IG6 3WR Tel: (020) 8559 6000 Fax: (020) 8559 6001 E-mail: info@pump.co.uk

Weir Engineering Services Ltd, 149 Newlands Road, Glasgow, G44 4EX Tel: 0141-637 7141 Fax: 0141-637 7358 E-mail: sales@weir.co.uk

Williamson Pumps, Aviation House, The Street, Poynings, Brighton, BN45 7AQ Tel: (01273) 857752 Fax: (0845) 2263639 E-mail: info@williamsonpumps.co.uk

Wilo Salmson Pumps Ltd, Centrum 100, Burton-on-Trent, Staffordshire, DE14 2WJ Tel: (01283) 523000 Fax: (01283) 523099 E-mail: sales@wilo.co.uk

Wright Rain Irrigation, 4 Christchurch Road, Ringwood, Hampshire, BH24 3SB Tel: (01425) 472251 Fax: (01425) 472258 E-mail: sales@wrightrain.com

PUMPS, DEEP WELL

Sigma Engineering Ltd, 26 Church Street, Altrincham, Cheshire, WA14 4DW Tel: 0161-928 9988 Fax: 0161-926 8726 E-mail: sigmapumps@aol.com

PUMPS, FIRE FIGHTING

▶ Hale Products Europe Ltd, Charles Street, Warwick, CV34 5LR Tel: (01926) 623614 Fax: (01926) 623689 E-mail: sales@haleeurope.com

PUMPS, FISH TANK

▶ Aquatic Systems Ltd, PO Box 330, Blackburn, BB2 3XX Tel: (01254) 278807 Fax: (01254) 278914

Manor Aquatics Centre, 653-657 Romford Road, London, E12 5AD Tel: (020) 8478 4478 Fax: (020) 8514 1400 E-mail: enquiries@manoraquatics.co.uk

▶ Murray Aquatics, 1 Houston Place, Glasgow, G5 8SG Tel: 0141-420 1020 Fax: 0141-420 1040 E-mail: sales@murrayaquatics.co.uk

PUMPS, HYDRAULIC, CYLINDER

▶ Stay Tensioner Services, 3 Tresidder Close, Tregoniggie Industrial Estate, Falmouth, Cornwall, TR11 4SP Tel: (01326) 373310 Fax: (01326) 373124

PUMPS, INSTALLATION SERVICES

▶ Europump Services, 3b Fleming Road, Kirkton Campus, Livingston, West Lothian, EH54 7BN Tel: (01506) 425440 Fax: (01506) 425444 E-mail: dbarrowcliffe@europump.co.uk

▶ North Avon Pumps Ltd, Copp Barn, Westerleigh Road, Westerleigh, Bristol, BS37 8HQ Tel: (01454) 315444 Fax: (01454) 327944 E-mail: sales@northavonpumps.co.uk

PUNCH AND DIE TOOLS

Altag Tool & Die, 10 3 Wilton Road, Ramsgate, Kent, CT12 5HG Tel: (01843) 588663 Fax: (01843) 853738 E-mail: info@altag.co.uk

PUNCH PRESS TOOLS

Burrhart Machinery Ltd, Cradock Road, Luton, LU4 0JF Tel: (01582) 563400 Fax: (01582) 493993 E-mail: sales@burrhart.co.uk

Rydal Precision Tools Ltd, Unit 5 The Technology Centre, London Road, Swanley, Kent, BR8 7AN Tel: (01322) 614661 Fax: (01322) 614760 E-mail: sales@rydal.co.uk

PUNCH PRESSES, TURRET, CNC

▶ Brent Precision, Upcott Avenue, Pottington Business Park, Barnstaple, Devon, EX31 1HN Tel: (01271) 324172 Fax: (01271) 324173 E-mail: karl@brentprecision.co.uk

PUNCHED CARD PUNCHING SERVICES, *See Data Preparation/Processing etc*

PUNCHES, EURO SLOT

Euro Office Supplies Ltd, 11 Bluebell Grove, Up Hatherley, Cheltenham, Gloucestershire, GL51 3BJ Tel: (01242) 227169 E-mail: customers@euro-supplies.com

PUNCHING MACHINES TO SPECIFICATION

▶ Gatfield Systems, Surrey Saw Mills, 70 Wrecclesham Hill, Wrecclesham, Farnham, Surrey, GU10 4JX Tel: (01252) 737357 Fax: (01252) 737358 E-mail: info@gatfield-systems.co.uk

PUNCHING MACHINES, SHEET METAL

Matten Ltd, Market Street, Whitworth, Rochdale, Lancashire, OL12 8PW Tel: (01706) 341197 Fax: (01706) 342580 E-mail: john@mattenltd.co.uk

Tama (UK), P O Box 157, Cannock, Staffordshire, WS11 9WL Tel: (01543) 274100 Fax: (01543) 277112 E-mail: info@tama-uk.fsnet.co.uk

PURCHASING, CONSORTIA

ipa Purchasing Ltd, Oak House, 39-41 The Parade, Claygate, Surrey, KT10 0PD Tel: (01372) 466966 Fax: (01372) 466062 E-mail: enquiries@ipapurchasing.co.uk

PURE NICKEL REFINERS

Inco Europe Ltd, 5th Floor Windsor Ho, 50 Victoria St, London, SW1H 0XB Tel: (020) 7931 7733 Fax: (020) 7931 0083

PURSES

Launer London Ltd, 86 Clarendon Road, Croydon, CR0 3SG Tel: (020) 8681 3573 Fax: (020) 8681 3530 E-mail: sales@launer.com

PUSH BUTTON SWITCHES

Starpoint Electrics Ltd, Units 1-5 King George's Trading Estate, Davis Road, Chessington, Surrey, KT9 1TT Tel: (020) 8391 7700 Fax: (020) 8391 7760 E-mail: sales@starpoint.uk.com

PUSH MOUNTED CABLE TIES

Thornbush Components & Tooling, 156 Woodland Drive, Hove, East Sussex, BN3 6DE Tel: (01273) 383972 Fax: (01273) 881771 E-mail: greenlee@thornbush.co.uk

PUSHCHAIRS

▶ Baby Travel, St. Annes Road, Willenhall, West Midlands, WV13 1DY Tel: (01902) 366333 Fax: (01902) 366333

▶ Bumptastic Maternity Wear, Worthing Road, Lowestoft, Suffolk, NR32 4HD Tel: 01502 583568 E-mail: sarah@bumptastic.co.uk

▶ Snugglytots, 4 Ffordd Derwen, Margam, Port Talbot, West Glamorgan, SA13 2TX Tel: (07709) 656139

PUTTY

Kalon Pension Trustees Ltd, Huddersfield Road, Birstall, Batley, West Yorkshire, WF17 9XA Tel: (01924) 354000 Fax: (01924) 354001 E-mail: sales@kalon.co.uk

Sealocrete PLA Ltd, Greenfield Lane, Rochdale, Lancashire, OL11 2LD Tel: (01706) 352255 Fax: (01706) 860880 E-mail: bestproduct@sealocrete.co.uk

PUZZLES/JIGSAWS

Handley Printers Ltd, 125 Stockport Road West, Bredbury, Stockport, Cheshire, SK6 2AN Tel: 0161-430 8188 Fax: 0161-406 6032 E-mail: puzzhand@aol.com

KMD Investors Ltd, 140 Queens Road, Leicester, LE2 3FX Tel: 0116-270 9221 Fax: 0116-270 2334 E-mail: steve@kmd-company.co.uk

PVC ACCESS RAMPS

▶ The Mayfield Group UK Ltd, Bournemouth, BH1 9GR Tel: (01202) 233959 Fax: (01202) 732853 E-mail: enquiries@themayfieldgroup.co.uk

PVC APRONS

Hanson Textiles Ltd, Surcon House, 11a Copson Street, Manchester, M20 3HE Tel: 0161-718 3888 Fax: 0161-718 3323 E-mail: sales@hansontextiles.co.uk

McCaw Allan & Co. Ltd, Victoria Street, Lurgan, Craigavon, County Armagh, BT67 9DU Tel: (028) 3834 1412 Fax: (028) 3834 3095 E-mail: sales@mccaw-allan.com

PVC BALCONIES

▶ The Mayfield Group UK Ltd, Bournemouth, BH1 9GR Tel: (01202) 233959 Fax: (01202) 732853 E-mail: enquiries@themayfieldgroup.co.uk

PVC BELTING

Habasit Rossi Ltd, Habegger House, Keighley Road, Silsden, Keighley, West Yorkshire, BD20 0EA Tel: (0870) 8359555 Fax: (0870) 8359777 E-mail: info@habasitrossi.com

▶ Marshall Belting Supplies Limited, 11 Cedar Avenue, Spixworth, Norwich, NR10 3PB Tel: 01603 897405 Fax: 01603 897405 E-mail: mbs@tesco.net

Siegling Ltd, Unit 4, Fifth Avenue, Tameside Park, Dukinfield, Cheshire, SK16 4PP Tel: 0161-331 3412 Fax: 0161-308 4385 E-mail: info@siegling.co.uk

PVC BINDERS

Folders Galore Ltd, 3-4 Advance Road, London, SE27 9LT Tel: (020) 8670 7416 Fax: (020) 8670 9605 E-mail: mail@foldersgalore.com

Laleham Products, Unit H Heath Place, Bognor Regis, West Sussex, PO22 9SL Tel: (01243) 826270 Fax: (01243) 829325 E-mail: sales@lalehamproducts.com

PVC CABLE HARNESSES

▶ Eland Cables Ltd, 120 Highgate Studios, 53-79 Highgate Road, London, NW5 1TL Tel: (020) 7241 8787 Fax: (020) 7241 8700 E-mail: sales@eland.co.uk

PVC CARTONS

Transparent Box Co. Ltd, 22 Back Lane, Stonesby, Melton Mowbray, Leicestershire, LE14 4PT Tel: (01664) 464227 Fax: (01664) 464001 E-mail: info@transparentbox.co.uk

PVC COATED FABRICS

Barclay Tarpaulins, New Beke Hall, Beke Hall Chase South, Rayleigh, Essex, SS6 9EX Tel: (01268) 780353 Fax: (01268) 780353 E-mail: enquiries@barcleytarpaulin.co.uk

Bhor (Hallbridge Ltd), 28 Brookdene Drive, Northwood, Middlesex, HA6 3NS Tel: (020) 8961 1614 Fax: (020) 8961 1614 E-mail: hallbridge@aol.com

Carr Reinforcements, Carr House, Brighton Road, Stockport, Cheshire, SK4 2BE Tel: 0161-443 3377 Fax: 0161-443 3388 E-mail: erictaylor@btconnect.com

Coating Applications Group, Newhouse Road, Huncoat Business Park, Accrington, Lancashire, BB5 6NT Tel: (01254) 391769 Fax: (01254) 393519 E-mail: sales@coatingapplications.co.uk

I Q Textiles, Mid Road, Prestonpans, East Lothian, EH32 9ER Tel: (01875) 811200 Fax: (01875) 811452

J B Broadley, Reeds Holme Works, Burnley Road, Rossendale, Lancashire, BB4 8LN Tel: (01706) 213661 Fax: (01706) 227786 E-mail: info@jbbroadley.co.uk

Frank Pine Ltd, Crown Mill, 1 Crown Street, Salford, M3 7DH Tel: 0161-834 0456 Fax: 0161-832 0385E-mail: fpinetex@aol.com

Plasticotta, Union Road, Bolton, BL2 2HL Tel: (01204) 381991 Fax: (01204) 528863

Polyone Acrol, Unit G 3, Newton Business Park, Talbot Road, Hyde, Cheshire, SK14 4UQ Tel: 0161-367 8773 Fax: 0161-367 8281

Shreds, Station Yard, Station Road, Digby, Lincoln, LN4 3NF Tel: (01526) 320450 Fax: (01526) 320452 E-mail: information@shreds.co.uk

Somic plc, PO Box 8, Preston, PR1 5PS Tel: (01772) 790000 Fax: (01772) 795677 E-mail: somic@somic.co.uk

PVC COMPOUND EXPORT MERCHANTS OR AGENTS

Kubach & Sambrook (Metals) Ltd, 57 Manor Park Crescent, Edgware, Middlesex, HA8 7LY Tel: (020) 8951 0688 Fax: (020) 8951 4540 E-mail: info@kubach.co.uk

PVC COMPOUNDS

Michael Ballance Plastics Ltd, Suite 8 Worthington House, 146 High Street, Burton-On-Trent, Staffordshire, DE14 1JE Tel: (01283) 511632 Fax: (01283) 517400 E-mail: mb@ballance-plastics.co.uk

Chemix Ltd, Vauxhall Industrial Estate, Greg Street, Stockport, Cheshire, SK5 7BR Tel: 0161-480 3487 Fax: 0161-480 2394

Distrupol, 119 Guildford Street, Chertsey, Surrey, KT16 9AL Tel: (01932) 566033 Fax: (01932) 560363 E-mail: info@distrupol.com

Distrupol Ltd, Distrupol, Marston Road, Wolverhampton, WV2 4LN Tel: (01902) 426839 Fax: (01902) 426852 E-mail: info@distrupol.com

Doeflex Vitapol, Unit 64 Boswell Way, Stakehill Industrial Estate, Middleton, Manchester, M24 2FL Tel: 0161-655 3265 Fax: 0161-655 3735

Doeflex Vitapol, Hawksworth Trading Estate, Swindon, SN2 1DX Tel: (01793) 442442 Fax: (01793) 442443 E-mail: info@doeflex-vitapol.co.uk

Dugdale plc, Valley Mill, Holmes Road, Sowerby Bridge, West Yorkshire, HX6 2AA Tel: (01422) 832501 Fax: (01422) 833401 E-mail: sales@dugdaleplc.com

Evc Compounds Ltd, Chester Road, Helsby, Frodsham, WA6 0DF Tel: (01928) 762700 Fax: (01928) 725101 E-mail: ken_goodwin@evc-int.com

Hydro Polymers Ltd, Aycliffe Industrial Park, Newton Aycliffe, County Durham, DL5 6EA Tel: (01325) 300555 Fax: (01325) 300215

Longfield Chemicals Ltd, Hawthorne Farm, Tarvin Road, Frodsham, WA6 6UZ Tel: (01928) 739977 Fax: (01928) 739553 E-mail: enquiries@longchem.co.uk

Meda Plastics Ltd, Unit 23 Siddons Factory Estate, Howard Street, West Bromwich, West Midlands, B70 0SU Tel: 0121-502 0463 Fax: 0121-505 3248

PVC CONDUITS

Bardini Plastics, Unit 4 Ellesmere, Manners Industrial Estate, Ilkeston, Derbyshire, DE7 8EF Tel: 0115-944 2733 Fax: 0115-944 2723 E-mail: bardini@bigfoot.com

Plastube Ltd, The Old Foundry, Leech Street, Stalybridge, Cheshire, SK15 1SD Tel: 0161-338 5505 Fax: 0161-338 5502 E-mail: admin@plastube.co.uk

PVC DOOR PROFILE BENDING

Allied Forma, 6 Beacon Road, Poulton Industrial Estate, Poulton-le-Fylde, Lancashire, FY6 8JE Tel: (01253) 884646 Fax: (01253) 899114 E-mail: alangreen1@compuserve.com

PVC DOORS

Chindwell Co. Ltd, Hyde House, The Hyde, London, NW9 6JT Tel: (020) 8208 0808 Fax: (020) 8205 8800 E-mail: chindwell_co_ltd@compuserve.com

▶ Classic Trade Frames Ltd, Unit 7 Priestley Road, Worsley, Manchester, M28 2LY Tel: 0161-793 1166 Fax: 0161-793 1177

CR Smith, Gardeners Street, Dunfermline, Fife, KY12 0RN Tel: (01383) 732181 Fax: (01383) 739095 E-mail: admin@crsmith.co.uk

Colin Dawson Windows Ltd, Chapel Works, John Kennedy Road, King's Lynn, Norfolk, PE30 2AA Tel: (01553) 775191 Fax: (01553) 760639

Dunraven Manufacturing Ltd, Village Farm Industrial Estate, Pyle, Bridgend, Mid Glamorgan, CF33 6BJ Tel: (01656) 745035 Fax: (01656) 745918

Great Northern Windows, 4 Great Northern Road, Eastwood, Nottingham, NG16 3PD Tel: (01773) 533633 Fax: (01773) 533432

Harefield Doors Ltd, 7 Chiltern Trading Estate, Earl Howe Road, Holmer Green, High Wycombe, Buckinghamshire, HP15 6QT Tel: (01494) 716316 Fax: (01494) 718198 E-mail: sales@harefielddoors.co.uk

▶ Sean Timoney & Sons Ltd, 144a Tattygare Road, Mullanaskea, Enniskillen, County Fermanagh, BT74 4JQ Tel: (028) 6632 9252 Fax: (028) 6632 7282 E-mail: seantimoney@yahoo.co.uk

Solent Glass & Glazing Ltd, 1 Hackett Way, Fareham, Hampshire, PO14 1TH Tel: (01329) 828210 Fax: (01329) 828838

Windows & Doors U Fit, Manor Way, Kinmel Bay, Rhyl, Clwyd, LL18 5BE Tel: (01745) 354540 Fax: (01745) 354540 E-mail: sales@conservatories-northwales.co.uk

PVC DOUBLE GLAZED WINDOWS

▶ New Age Systems P V C U Ltd, Units 38-40, Gelli Industrial Estate, Gelli, Pentre, Mid Glamorgan, CF41 7UW Tel: (01443) 431026 Fax: (01443) 422463 E-mail: sales@newagesystems.co.uk

PVC EXTRUSIONS

Abbey Extrusions Ltd, 2 Ivanhoe Industrial Estate, Tournament Way, Ashby-de-la-Zouch, Leicestershire, LE65 2UU Tel: (01530) 416177 Fax: (01530) 417230 E-mail: sales@abbeyextrusions.co.uk

Albion Extrusions Ltd, Penrose Works, Penrose Street, Bolton, BL2 6DX Tel: (01204) 385803 Fax: (01204) 385816 E-mail: info@albionextrusions.co.uk

Birch Valley Plastics Ltd, Darklake View, Estover, Plymouth, PL6 7TL Tel: (01752) 696515 Fax: (01752) 696724 E-mail: admin@birchvalley.co.uk

Boomer Industries Ltd, Vale Works, Stockfield Road, Chadderton, Oldham, OL9 9HD Tel: (028) 9266 2881 Fax: 0161-643 7299 E-mail: enquiries@boomer.co.uk

Merritt Plastics Ltd, 5 Winster Buildings, Manners Avenue, Manners Industrial Estate, Ilkeston, Derbyshire, DE7 8EF Tel: 0115-944 7661 Fax: 0115-944 1864 E-mail: simon@merrittplastics.fsnet.co.uk

▶ Rep Engineering & Manufacturing, Unit 11 Rippleside Commercial Estate, Ripple Road, Barking, Essex, IG11 0RJ Tel: (020) 8526 7711 Fax: (020) 8526 7722

Russell Plastics, 8a High St, Harpenden, Herts, AL5 2TB Tel: (01582) 762868 Fax: (01582) 461086 E-mail: sales@russellplastics.co.uk

Tag Plastic Extrusions Ltd, 21 Marsh Green Road North, Marsh Barton Trading Estate, Exeter, EX2 8NY Tel: (01392) 479036 Fax: (01392) 432835

Trimplex Ltd, Darby Way, Narborough, Leicester, LE19 2GP Tel: 0116-286 6611 Fax: 0116-275 0216 E-mail: valplas@freeuk.com

TSL Extrusions, Elton Park Business Centre, Hadleigh Rd, Ipswich, IP2 0HN Tel: 0845 4940747 Fax: (01473) 236044 E-mail: sales@tubeway.co.uk

PVC FABRICATORS

Aqua Signal & Telegraphic Systems Ltd, Belmont House, Garnett Place, Skelmersdale, Lancashire, WN8 9UB Tel: (01695) 51933 Fax: (01695) 51891

Fife Plastics, Fordell, Woodend, Cowdenbeath, Fife, KY4 8EY Tel: (01383) 510256 Fax: (01383) 510256

Floline, Whitehall Industrial Estate, Whitehall Road, Leeds, LS12 5JB Tel: 0113-235 9349 Fax: 0113-235 9348

Plastic Merchant Ltd, 10 Church Street, Brighton, BN1 1US Tel: (01273) 329958 Fax: (01273) 329958

PVC FILM

Trident Group UK Ltd, 14-15 Yeldon Court, Finedon Road Industrial Estate, Wellingborough, Northamptonshire, NN8 4SS Tel: (01933) 228228 Fax: (01933) 229922 E-mail: sales@tridentgroupuk.com

PVC FILM/CLING WRAPPING FILM, FOOD WRAP

A B L Perpack 1985 Ltd, 7 Baron Avenue, Telford Way Industrial Estate, Kettering, Northamptonshire, NN16 8UW Tel: (01536) 412744 Fax: (01536) 412752 E-mail: sales@ablperpack.co.uk

Wrapex Ltd, Unit 6 Lodge Causeway Trading Estate, Lodge Causeway, Bristol, BS16 3JB Tel: 0117-965 7000 Fax: 0117-958 6886 E-mail: sales@wrapex.co.uk

PVC FIRE EXTINGUISHER COVERS

▶ F P S Fire Protection Ltd, Friemark House, Pioneer Park, Bristol, BS4 3QB Tel: 0117-971 7050 Fax: 0117-935 1605 E-mail: sales@firemarkext.co.uk

Fire Extinguisher Rental, Alfred Works, Woodhill Street, Bury, Lancashire, BL8 1AT Tel: 0161-764 1434 Fax: 0161-764 1434

Fire Safety Express, Tesla Court, Innovation Way, Lynch Wood, Peterborough, PE2 6FL Tel: (01733) 234504 Fax: 01733 234504 E-mail: enquiries@firesafetyexpress.co.uk

Ic International Ltd, Gower Street Trading Estate, St. Georges, Telford, Shropshire, TF2 9HW Tel: (01952) 620206 Fax: (01952) 620456 E-mail: sales@ic-international.com

PVC FLEXIBLE HOSE/TUBING

C M T Flexibles, Unit 14D Two Locks, Hurst Business Park, Brierley Hill, West Midlands, DY5 1UU Tel: (01384) 480197 Fax: (01384) 74840 E-mail: sales@cmtflexibles.com

Merlett Plastics (UK) Ltd, Unit 2, Waverley Road, Beeches Industrial Estate, Yate, Bristol, BS37 5QT Tel: (01454) 329888 Fax: (01454) 324499

Valpar Industrial Ltd, 13 Balloo Drive, Bangor, County Down, BT19 7QY Tel: (028) 9145 4544 Fax: (028) 9145 7512 E-mail: info@valpar.co.uk

PVC FRAME WINDOW INSTALLATION

▶ Wellow Park Developments Ltd T/A Wellow Park Wind, 27 Beresford Street, Mansfield, Nottinghamshire, NG18 2PH Tel: (01623) 422872

PVC FRAMED WINDOWS

A W S Group Plc, Systems House, Hoo Farm Industrial Estate, Worcester Road, Kidderminster, Worcestershire, DY11 7RA Tel: (01562) 743700 Fax: (01562) 829775 E-mail: info@awsgroupplc.co.uk

Albann Mckinney Window Co Ltd, Hyde Park, Mallusk, Newtownabbey, County Antrim, BT36 4PX Tel: (028) 9084 2611 Fax: (028) 9034 2317 E-mail: mailbox@mcneill-mcmanus.com

Anglian Home Improvements Ltd, PO Box 65, Norwich, NR6 6EJ Tel: (01603) 787000 Fax: (01603) 422298 E-mail: matt.carey@angliangroup.com

▶ Asset Manufacturing Ltd, Howletts Way, Thetford, Norfolk, IP24 1HZ Tel: (01842) 763529 Fax: (01842) 752398 E-mail: sales@asset-windows.co.uk

B L W Associates Ltd, 1 Alexandra Drive, Lockerbie, Dumfriesshire, DG11 2PD Tel: (01576) 203595 Fax: (01576) 202276

Black Millwork Co Incorporated, Anderson House, Dallow St, Burton-on-Trent, Staffordshire, DE14 2PQ Tel: (01283) 511122 Fax: (01283) 510863 E-mail: enquiries@andersenwindows.com

▶ Blair Neill Ltd, 13 Comber Road, Newtownards, County Down, BT23 4QR Tel: (028) 9182 6868 E-mail: peter.blair@blairneill.com

▶ Blenham Window Systems Ltd, 212 Windmill Lane, Cheshunt, Waltham Cross, Hertfordshire, EN8 9AF Tel: (01992) 642300

▶ Bradworthy Glass, Units 3d, Langdon Road, Bradworthy, Holsworthy, Devon, EX22 7SF Tel: (01409) 241010 Fax: (01409) 241160

▶ Chatham Windows Ltd, Chatham Mill, Chatham Street, Wigan, Lancashire, WN1 3DB Tel: (01942) 492137 Fax: (01942) 323994

Corinthian Windows, Oak Street, Quarry Bank, Brierley Hill, West Midlands, DY5 2JQ Tel: (01384) 411033

Coulter Windows Ltd, 27 Dunavail Road, Kilkeel, Newry, County Down, BT34 4JT Tel: (028) 4176 3884 Fax: (028) 4176 4665 E-mail: neil@coulterwindows.co.uk

County Windows, 22 Stephenson Road, St. Ives, Cambridgeshire, PE27 3WJ Tel: (01480) 461505 Fax: (01480) 494407 E-mail: enquiries@countywindows.com

Crescent Glass Ltd, Derby Road, Burton-On-Trent, Staffordshire, DE14 1RX Tel: (01283) 563070 Fax: (01283) 566898 E-mail: info@longlifewindows.co.uk

Crown Windows Hull Ltd, New Cleveland Street, Hull, HU8 7HA Tel: (01482) 329043 Fax: (01482) 39043

Colin Dawson Windows Ltd, Chapel Works, John Kennedy Road, King's Lynn, Norfolk, PE30 2AA Tel: (01553) 775191 Fax: (01553) 760639

Diamond Windows, 25 The Fairways, New River Trading Estate, Cheshunt, Waltham Cross, Hertfordshire, EN8 0NL Tel: (01992) 635162 Fax: (01992) 623300

Dorwin Ltd, Unit 1 Forge Works, Mill Lane, Alton, Hampshire, GU34 2QG Tel: (01420) 84217 Fax: (01420) 541648 E-mail: linden.ransley@dorwin.co.uk

Dunraven Manufacturing Ltd, Village Farm Industrial Estate, Pyle, Bridgend, Mid Glamorgan, CF33 6BJ Tel: (01656) 745035 Fax: (01656) 745918

Eas Windows, 25 New Street, Oadby, Leicester, LE2 5EB Tel: 0116-271 0120 Fax: 0116-271 7708 E-mail: enquiries@easwindows.co.uk

East Yorkshire Glazing Co. Ltd, Wiltshire Road, Hull, HU4 6QQ Tel: (01482) 561101 Fax: (01482) 565307 E-mail: eygsales@ukonline.co.uk

Elliott Group Fineline, Commissioners Road, Strood, Rochester, Kent, ME2 4ET Tel: (01634) 719701 Fax: (01634) 716394 E-mail: fineline.windows@virgin.net

Fibrocell Ltd, Willow Street, Oldham, OL1 3QB Tel: 0161-624 1035 Fax: 0161-627 3045 E-mail: john@britanniamill.totalserve.co.uk

Four Seasons Ltd, Unit 14, Papermill End, Aldridge Road, Great Barr, Birmingham, B44 8NH Tel: 0121-356 0909 Fax: 0121-356 0513

▶ Frameforce Conservatories, Claymore, Wilnecote, Tamworth, Staffordshire, B77 5DQ Tel: (01827) 268003

John Fredericks Plastics Ltd, Lindley Moor Road, Huddersfield, HD3 3RW Tel: (01422) 314100 Fax: (01422) 310001 E-mail: sales@johnfredericksplastics.com

Glyngary Joinery Ltd, Unit H2, Risley, Warrington, WA3 6BL Tel: (01925) 763836 Fax: (01925) 762388 E-mail: sales@glyngary.co.uk

Good Openings, Hockley Business Centre, Hooley Lane, Redhill, RH1 6ET Tel: (01737) 772277 Fax: (01737) 772288

Great Northern Windows, 4 Great Northern Road, Eastwood, Nottingham, NG16 3PD Tel: (01773) 533633 Fax: (01773) 533432

Hi Seal Ltd, Bellbanks Corner, Mill Road, Hailsham, East Sussex, BN27 2AH Tel: (01323) 841392 Fax: (01323) 442719

J A G Glazing Ltd, High Street, Cleobury Mortimer, Kidderminster, Worcestershire, DY14 8DP Tel: (01299) 271007 Fax: (01299) 271078 E-mail: sales@jag-glazing.co.uk

Juno Installations, 8 Carlton Park Avenue, London, SW20 8BL Tel: (020) 8543 1697 Fax: (020) 8543 1697 E-mail: harlea0@aol.com

K W Windows, Plumbe Street, Burnley, Lancashire, BB11 3AG Tel: (01282) 448387 Fax: (01282) 416017

M B S Window Systems Ltd, Corringham Road Industrial Estate, Gainsborough, Lincolnshire, DN21 1QB Tel: (01427) 615050 Fax: (01427) 614436

M & L Homestyle Ltd, Lupin Works, Worcester Road, Kidderminster, Worcestershire, DY10 1JR Tel: (01562) 755333 Fax: (01562) 745559

Malbern Windows & Doors Ltd, 3 Malbern Industrial Estate, Holland Street, Denton, Manchester, M34 3WE Tel: 0161-320 5801 Fax: 0161-335 0986 E-mail: sales@malbernwindows.co.uk

Maple Leaf Insulations Conservatories, Maple Leaf House, Canterbury Road, Worthing, West Sussex, BN13 1AW Tel: (01903) 692122 Fax: (01903) 831570

Marsland & Co. Ltd, Commerce Way, Station Road, Edenbridge, Kent, TN8 6EE Tel: (01732) 862501 Fax: (01732) 866737 E-mail: sales@marsland-windows.co.uk

▶ Norfolk Frames Ltd, 26 Old Norwich Road, Marsham, Norwich, NR10 5PR Tel: (01263) 734469 Fax: (01263) 733058 E-mail: enquiries@norfolkframes.co.uk

Nova, 3 Partnership House, Withambrook Park Industrial Estate, Grantham, Lincolnshire, NG31 9ST Tel: (01476) 577635 Fax: (01476) 577635 E-mail: novawindows@hotmail.com

Pearl Window Systems Ltd, 34 Great Bank Road, Westhoughton, Bolton, BL5 3XU Tel: (01942) 843586 Fax: (01942) 843587 E-mail: info@pearlwindows.co.uk

▶ Pioneer Trading Co., Warners Farm, Main Road, Great Waltham, Chelmsford, CM3 1BN Tel: (01245) 362727 Fax: (01245) 362421

Prestige Glazing Services Ltd, Unit 2 Shuttleworth Court, Shuttleworth Road, Elm Farm Industrial Estate, Bedford, MK41 0EN Tel: (01234) 346454 Fax: (01234) 219063 E-mail: prestigeglazing@btconnect.com

Purbeck Glass & Glazing Ltd, Unit 11 Albany Park, Cabot Lane, Poole, Dorset, BH17 7BX Tel: (01202) 659559 Fax: (01202) 659560

▶ Sean Timoney & Sons Ltd, 144a Tattygare Road, Mullanaskea, Enniskillen, County Fermanagh, BT74 4JQ Tel: (028) 6632 9252 Fax: (028) 6632 7282 E-mail: seantimoney@yahoo.co.uk

▶ Seymour Windows Ltd, Unit 13, Wharton Street, Sherdley Road Industrial Estate, St. Helens, Merseyside, WA9 5AA Tel: (01744) 611211 Fax: (01744) 27576 E-mail: seymour.windows@btconnect.com

Spectus Windows Systems Ltd, Pinewood Court, Cycherington Business Park, Macclesfield, Cheshire, SK10 2XR Tel: (01625) 420400 Fax: (01625) 501418

Staybrite Windows, Weston Road, Norwich, NR3 3TP Tel: (0800) 0832656 Fax: (01603) 406185 E-mail: mike.holmes@zsltd.co.uk

Streetly Windows Ltd, 338 Aldridge Road, Streetly, Sutton Coldfield, West Midlands, B74 2DT Tel: 0121-353 5886 Fax: 0121-353 2908

Sunrise, Unit 49g Pipers Road, Park Farm Industrial Estate, Redditch, Worcestershire, B98 0HU Tel: (01527) 522354 Fax: (01527) 517265

Walsall Metropolitan Borough Council, Suffolk Place, Walsall, WS2 7AY Tel: (01922) 653818 Fax: (01922) 722114

Welglaze Ltd, Watermill Industrial Estate, Aspenden Road, Buntingford, Hertfordshire, SG9 9JS Tel: (01763) 271811 Fax: (01763) 273108 E-mail: sales@welgaurd.co.uk

West Midland Glazing Co. Ltd, 123-125 Grove Lane, Birmingham, B17 0QT Tel: 0121-426 1275 Fax: 0121-428 1625

Westmorland Glass Kendal Ltd, Shap Road, Kendal, Cumbria, LA9 6LX Tel: (01539) 730000 Fax: (01539) 740076

Window Craft (Nuneaton) Ltd, Whitacre Road, Nuneaton, Warwickshire, CV11 6BY Tel: (024) 7638 4896 Fax: (024) 7638 4896

The Window Makers Ltd, 1 Larchwood Business Centre, Havant, Hampshire, PO9 3QL Tel: (023) 9265 1700 Fax: (023) 9269 5422 E-mail: sales@leadingwindows.co.uk

Windowmaker, Madleaze Trading Estate, Madleaze Road, Gloucester, GL1 5SG Tel: (01452) 423348 Fax: (01452) 300193 E-mail: mail@swiftsheild.co.uk

PVC FRAMED WINDOWS – *continued*

Younger Homes Ltd, 1 Hall Street, Maghera, County Londonderry, BT46 5DA Tel: (028) 7964 3725 Fax: (028) 7964 4249

PVC GOODS

▶ Uro Frames, 357 Oldham Road, Ashton-under-Lyne, Lancashire, OL7 9NE Tel: 0161-343 7220 E-mail: sales@uroframes.com

PVC PASTES/PLASTISOLS

Speciality Coatings Darwen Ltd, Dewhurst Street, Darwen, Lancashire, BB3 2EN Tel: (01254) 706026 Fax: (01254) 777132 E-mail: sales@sclgroup.com

PVC PIPELINE SYSTEMS

Wavin Plastics Ltd, Parsonage Way, Chippenham, Wiltshire, SN15 5PN Tel: (01249) 766600 Fax: (01249) 443286 E-mail: sales@wavin.co.uk

PVC PRODUCTS/COMPONENTS/ FITTINGS

Ariel Plastics Ltd, Speedwell Industrial Estate, Staveley, Chesterfield, Derbyshire, S43 3JP Tel: (01246) 281111 Fax: (01246) 561115 E-mail: info@arielplastics.com

Brunel Plastics, Unit A1 Hennock Road North, Marsh Barton Trading Estate, Exeter, EX2 8NJ Tel: (01392) 277466 Fax: (01392) 410526

Chemix Ltd, Vauxhall Industrial Estate, Greg Street, Stockport, Cheshire, SK5 7BR Tel: 0161-480 3487 Fax: 0161-480 2394

Circuit Supplies & Engineering Ltd, Unit 4 High Street, Wollaston, Wellingborough, Northamptonshire, NN29 7QF Tel: (01933) 663663 Fax: (01933) 674788

Claymore Plastics, Hegdon, Pencombe, Bromyard, Herefordshire, HR7 4SL Tel: (01885) 400278 Fax: (01885) 400616 E-mail: claymore278@aol.com

Elegant Window Systems Ltd, 1b St Vincent Street, Barrow-in-Furness, Cumbria, LA14 2NT Tel: (01229) 813066 Fax: (01229) 431933

Finesse North West Partnership, 138 Leigh Road, Leigh, Lancashire, WN7 1SJ Tel: (01942) 682000 Fax: (01942) 670030

▶ Genesis Pvcu Ltd, 29 Britannia Way, Britannia Enterprise Park, Lichfield, Staffordshire, WS14 9UY Tel: (01543) 417575 Fax: (01543) 418180

Hastings & Henshaw, Bridgecroft Mills, Tanyard Road, Millsbridge, Huddersfield, HD3 4NF Tel: (01484) 647111 Fax: (01484) 647111

Omega Group UK Ltd, Morley Way, Peterborough, PE2 7BW Tel: (01733) 702000 Fax: (01733) 234114 E-mail: personnel@theomegagroup.co.uk

Renolit UK Ltd, Renolit House, Hamond Road, Bedford, MK41 0UD Tel: (01234) 272999 Fax: (01234) 357313 E-mail: info@renolit.co.uk

Roundbrand TWS, Cow House Lane, Armthorpe, Doncaster, South Yorkshire, DN3 3ED Tel: (01302) 833029 Fax: (01302) 832198 E-mail: enquiries@roundbrand.co.uk

Seal Upvc Products Ltd, Unit 3-4 Heol Stanllyd, Cross Hands Industrial Estate, Cross Hands, Llanelli, Dyfed, SA14 6RB Tel: (01269) 845377 Fax: (01269) 845946

Varipack Ltd, Unit L, Durgates Industrial Estate, Wadhurst, East Sussex, TN5 6DF Tel: (01892) 784567 Fax: (01892) 783477

PVC PROFILE WINDOWS

Archwright Ltd, Unit 29 Maybrook Road, Brownhills, Walsall, WS8 7DG Tel: (01543) 371971 Fax: (01543) 371009

Deceuninck Ltd, Stanier Road, Porte Marsh Industrial Estate, Calne, Wiltshire, SN11 9PX Tel: (01249) 816969 Fax: (01249) 815234 E-mail: deceuninck.ltd@deceuninck.com

Esograt Ltd, Caldervale Works, River Street, Brighouse, West Yorkshire, HD6 1JS Tel: (01484) 716228 Fax: (01484) 400107 E-mail: info@esograt.com

Plastmo Profiles Ltd, Lower Farm Road, Moulton Park Industrial Estate, Northampton, NN3 6XF Tel: (01604) 790780 Fax: (01604) 790110 E-mail: info@plastmo.co.uk

Spectus Windows Systems Ltd, Pinewood Court, Cycherington Business Park, Macclesfield, Cheshire, SK10 2XR Tel: (01625) 420400 Fax: (01625) 501418

PVC PROTECTIVE COVERS OR COVERINGS

D C Plastic Handrails Ltd, Unit 6, Cowen Road, Cowen Road Industrial Estate, Blaydon-On-Tyne, Tyne & Wear, NE21 5TW Tel: 0191-414 0034 Fax: 0191-414 0034 E-mail: davey@dchandrails.freeserve.co.uk

PVC RESINS

Hydro Polymers Ltd, Aycliffe Industrial Park, Newton Aycliffe, County Durham, DL5 6EA Tel: (01325) 300555 Fax: (01325) 300215

PVC RING BINDERS

H F W Plastics Ltd, Albany Road, Gateshead, Tyne & Wear, NE8 3AT Tel: 0191-477 6519 Fax: 0191-490 1345 E-mail: sales@hfwplastics.co.uk

Media Plastics, 8 Merrylees Industrial Estate, Lee Side, Desford, Leicester, LE9 9FS Tel: (01455) 292110 Fax: (01455) 292190 E-mail: sales@mediaplastics.co.uk

Metro Sales, Unit 1 Crathie Road, Off Western Road, Kilmarnock, Ayrshire, KA3 1NG Tel: (01563) 574481 Fax: (01563) 533537 E-mail: sales@metrosales.biz

PVC ROOFING PANELS

Ariel Plastics Ltd, Speedwell Industrial Estate, Staveley, Chesterfield, Derbyshire, S43 3JP Tel: (01246) 281111 Fax: (01246) 561115 E-mail: info@arielplastics.com

PVC SHEETING

Acl Packaging Solutions, Unit F Argent Court, Hook Rise South, Surbiton, Surrey, KT6 7NL Tel: (020) 8391 4660 Fax: (020) 8391 4514 E-mail: sales@aclps.com

▶ Flexible Reinforcements Ltd, Bancroft Road, Burnley, Lancashire, BB10 2TP Tel: (01282) 478222 Fax: (01282) 478210 E-mail: sales@flexr.co.uk

W. J. Leech & Sons Ltd, 275 Derby Road, Bootle, Merseyside, L20 8PL Tel: 0151-933 9334 Fax: 0151-933 5005 E-mail: david@wjleech.com

PVC STRIP DOORS

Kenfield Ltd, 23-25 Prince Road, Kings Norton Business Centre, Norton, Birmingham, B30 3HB Tel: 0121-451 3051 Fax: 0121-433 3247 E-mail: info@pvc-strip-doors.co.uk

Rayflex Rubber Ltd, 11b Palatine Industrial Estate, Causeway Avenue, Warrington, WA4 6QQ Tel: (01925) 638753 Fax: (01925) 416621 E-mail: sales@rayflexrubber.co.uk

Redwood Strip Curtains Ltd, Unit 21 Southfield Road Trading Estate, Southfield Road, Nailsea, Bristol, BS48 1JE Tel: (01275) 810289 Fax: (01275) 810290 E-mail: sales@redwoodstripcurtains.co.uk

Runners, Signal Hill, Lenborough Road, Gawcott, Buckingham, MK18 4BU Tel: (01280) 822288

PVC TUBES

Brett Martin Ltd, 24 Roughfort Road, Newtownabbey, County Antrim, BT36 4RB Tel: (028) 9084 9999 Fax: (028) 9083 6666 E-mail: sales@brettmartin.com

Plymouth Rubber Hose & Hydraulics, Drill Hall, Rocky Hill, Tavistock, Devon, PL19 0DZ Tel: (01822) 616061 Fax: (01822) 617755 E-mail: sales@hoseandhydraulicsgroup.co.uk

Transparent Box Co. Ltd, 22 Back Lane, Stonesby, Melton Mowbray, Leicestershire, LE14 4PT Tel: (01664) 464227 Fax: (01664) 464001 E-mail: info@transparentbox.co.uk

Trimplex Ltd, Darby Way, Narborough, Leicester, LE19 2GP Tel: 0116-286 6611 Fax: 0116-275 0216 E-mail: valplas@freeuk.com

PVC WELDED GOODS

Celsur Plastics Ltd, 3 Lovett Road, The Causeway, Staines, Middlesex, TW18 3AZ Tel: (01784) 457175 Fax: (01784) 454605 E-mail: info@celsurplastics.co.uk

Contract (H/F) Electrode Supplies Ltd, Newhaven Industrial Estate, Barton Lane, Eccles, Manchester, M30 0HL Tel: 0161-707 4090 Fax: 0161-707 1314 E-mail: enquiries@contractelectrode.co.uk

Cougar Designs, 6A Bart Street, Sparkhill, Birmingham, B11 4SA Tel: 0121-773 9491 Fax: 0121-771 0464

Gemini Products, Unit 3, Cruso Street, Leek, Staffordshire, ST13 8BJ Tel: (01538) 373600 Fax: (01538) 372600 E-mail: ivan@tesco.net

Imgen Manufrs, New Image Works, 240 Church Road, Layton, London, E10 7JQ Tel: (020) 8887 0709 Fax: (020) 8887 0744

Kahn Displays Ltd, Unit 5-6 Eleys Estate, Angel Road, London, N18 3BH Tel: (020) 8803 0800 Fax: (020) 8803 0412 E-mail: kahn_displays@btconnect.com

Plasart Ltd, Chilton Industrial Estate, Windham Road, Sudbury, Suffolk, CO10 2XD Tel: (01787) 375641 Fax: (01787) 311041

S M Alexander Plastics Ltd, Little End Road, Eaton Socon, St. Neots, Cambridgeshire, PE19 8JH Tel: (01480) 473140 Fax: (01480) 406968 E-mail: smalexanderplastics@btinternet.com

Synrein Plastics Ltd, Grosvenor Works, Grosvenor Street, Ashton-Under-Lyne, Lancashire, OL7 0RG Tel: 0161-330 8573 Fax: 0161-343 2195 E-mail: sales@synrein.co.uk

Teckno Developments Ltd, Great Gutter Lane, Willerby, Hull, HU10 6DL Tel: (01482) 657996 Fax: (01482) 651089 E-mail: sales@tecknodev.com

Tennant PVC Ltd, Unit A Meadow Grove, Meadow Lane, Nottingham, NG2 3HF Tel: 0115-934 0950 Fax: 0115-934 0955 E-mail: sales@tennantpvc.co.uk

Thanet Plastics, 1 Wilton Road, Haine Industrial Park, Ramsgate, Kent, CT12 5HG Tel: (01843) 590950 Fax: (01843) 590948 E-mail: sales@thanetplastics.co.uk

▶ Vision Light Plastics Ltd, 2-7 Decoy Road, Worthing, West Sussex, BN14 8ND Tel: (01903) 823339 Fax: (01903) 206868 E-mail: sales@visionlight.co.uk

PVC WELDING TO THE TRADE

Contract (H/F) Electrode Supplies Ltd, Newhaven Industrial Estate, Barton Lane, Eccles, Manchester, M30 0HL Tel: 0161-707 4090 Fax: 0161-707 1314 E-mail: enquiries@contractelectrode.co.uk

P R Hunter Plastics Ltd, 5 Pembroke Road, Stocklake Indus Estate, Aylesbury, Buckinghamshire, HP20 1DB Tel: (01296) 422423 Fax: (01296) 422423 E-mail: hunter_plastics@hotmail.com

Tennant PVC Ltd, Unit A Meadow Grove, Meadow Lane, Nottingham, NG2 3HF Tel: 0115-934 0950 Fax: 0115-934 0955 E-mail: sales@tennantpvc.co.uk

Thanet Plastics, 1 Wilton Road, Haine Industrial Park, Ramsgate, Kent, CT12 5HG Tel: (01843) 590950 Fax: (01843) 590948 E-mail: sales@thanetplastics.co.uk

Varipack Ltd, Unit L, Durgates Industrial Estate, Wadhurst, East Sussex, TN5 6DF Tel: (01892) 784567 Fax: (01892) 783477

PVC WINDOW ACCESSORIES

J F Windows Ltd, Blackshaw Mills, Farfield Avenue, Bradford, West Yorkshire, BD6 2DN Tel: (01274) 605894 Fax: (01274) 690520

▶ Lancashire PVC-U Trade Frames Ltd, Unit 7, Meadow Business Park, Meadow Lane, Breightmet, Bolton, BL2 6PT Tel: (01204) 548899 Fax: (01204) 548890 E-mail: info@lancashiretradeframes.co.uk

PVC WINDOW MACHINE OR FABRICATING SYSTEMS

Chris Kilpin Machinery, 20 Bridgwater Court, Oldmixon Cresent, Weston-super-Mare, Avon, BS24 9AY Tel: (01934) 625850 Fax: (01934) 412816 E-mail: sales@ckmachinery.com

Plastmo Profiles Ltd, Lower Farm Road, Moulton Park Industrial Estate, Northampton, NN3 6XF Tel: (01604) 790780 Fax: (01604) 790110 E-mail: info@plastmo.co.uk

Window Machinery Sales Ltd, Unit 3c Hadrians Way, Glebe Farm Industrial Estate, Rugby, Warwickshire, CV21 1ST Tel: (01788) 577577 Fax: (01788) 567938

PVCU BUILDING PRODUCT CLEANING

▶ Stonecraft Weston, Unit 21 Kewstoke Quarry, Kewstoke Road, Worle, Weston-super-Mare, Somerset, BS23 4QA Tel: (07778) 302672 Fax: (01934) 413295 E-mail: nickstonecraft@aol.com

PVCU CONSERVATORIES

Anglian Building Products Ltd, 59 Hurricane Way, Norwich, NR6 6JB Tel: (01603) 422000 Fax: (01603) 422066 E-mail: sales@anglian-building.co.uk

Arrow Window Systems, Warwick Road, Fairfield Industrial Estate, Louth, Lincolnshire, LN11 0YB Tel: (01507) 601861 Fax: (01507) 607642

▶ B B H Ltd, Unit 9-10, 251 Holt Road, Horsford, Norwich, NR10 3EB Tel: (01603) 897350 Fax: (01603) 890080 E-mail: bbh@bbhltd.fx.co.net

B H D Building Products, Unit 5 And 6, Judson Road, Northwest Industrial Estate, Peterlee, County Durham, SR8 2QJ Tel: 0191-415 5220 Fax: (0870) 2421846

B H W Glass, The Gables, Church Road, Partridge Green, Horsham, West Sussex, RH13 8JS Tel: (01403) 713757 Fax: (01403) 864932 E-mail: enquiries@bhwglass.co.uk

Banbury Windows Ltd, Alton Works, Long Bank, Bewdley, Worcestershire, DY12 2UL Tel: (01299) 266332 Fax: (01299) 266676

Barong Windows Ltd, Doves Barn, Copthorne, Felbridge, East Grinstead, West Sussex, RH19 2QQ Tel: (01342) 300903

Bettaprice Systems Ltd, 23k Bridge St Industrial Estate, Lower Mantle Close, Clay Cross, Chesterfield, Derbyshire, S45 9NU Tel: (01246) 865508 Fax: (01246) 865441

C & C Frames Ltd, 3 Hugomont Avenue, Ballymena, County Antrim, BT43 6HW Tel: (028) 2563 0146 Fax: (028) 2563 0146 E-mail: admin@ashgrovecentre.com

C & R Plastics, E4 Unit, Formal Industrial Estate, Treswithian, Camborne, Cornwall, TR14 0PY Tel: (01209) 711878 Fax: (01209) 711895

Carstone Windows Ltd, Unit 7 Mount Industrial Estate, Stone, Staffordshire, ST15 8LL Tel: (01785) 814487 Fax: (01785) 816194

Chapel Windows Ltd, Bevan Industrial Estate, Brierley Hill, West Midlands, DY5 3TF Tel: (01384) 571315 Fax: (01384) 480403

▶ Clearview (Yorkshire) Limited, Unit 4, Sullivan Business Park, West Dock Street, Hull, HU3 4TG Tel: 01482 609310 Fax: 01482 218444 E-mail: sales@conservatoryroofskits.co.uk

Coastal Ltd, D'Oriel House, Holton Heath Trading Park, Poole, Dorset, BH16 6LE Tel: (01202) 624011 Fax: (01202) 622465 E-mail: sales@coastalwindows.co.uk

Conservatory & Window World Ltd, 149-151 Watling Road, Bishop Auckland, County Durham, DL14 9AU Tel: (01388) 458088 Fax: (01388) 810292

Corinthian Windows, Oak Street, Quarry Bank, Brierley Hill, West Midlands, DY5 2JQ Tel: (01384) 411033

Coulter Windows Ltd, 27 Dunavail Road, Kilkeel, Newry, County Down, BT34 4JT Tel: (028) 4176 3884 Fax: (028) 4176 4665 E-mail: neil@coulterwindows.co.uk

CR Smith, Gardeners Street, Dunfermline, Fife, KY12 0RN Tel: (01383) 732181 Fax: (01383) 739095 E-mail: admin@crsmith.co.uk

▶ Crest Home Improvements Ltd, Crown Trading Estate, Shepton Mallet, Somerset, BA4 5QQ Tel: (01749) 344211 Fax: (01749) 346376

▶ Croston Conservatories, Unit 85 Bison Place, Moss Side Industrial Estate, Leyland, PR26 7QR Tel: (01772) 435353 Fax: (01772) 452525 E-mail: sales@crostonconservatories.com

Eas Windows, 25 New Street, Oadby, Leicester, LE2 5EB Tel: 0116-271 0120 Fax: 0116-271 7708 E-mail: enquiries@easwindows.co.uk

Esograt Ltd, Caldervale Works, River Street, Brighouse, West Yorkshire, HD6 1JS Tel: (01484) 716228 Fax: (01484) 400107 E-mail: info@esograt.com

Forestdale Windows Ltd, 4 Lakeside, Neptune Close, Medway City Estate, Rochester, Kent, ME2 4LT Tel: (01634) 717860 Fax: (01634) 719399 E-mail: pjenn59165@aol.com

John Fredericks Plastics Ltd, Lindley Moor Road, Huddersfield, HD3 3RW Tel: (01422) 314100 Fax: (01422) 310001 E-mail: sales@johnfrederickplastics.com

Frostree Ltd, 31 Station Street, Middlesbrough, Cleveland, TS1 1SR Tel: (01642) 224151 Fax: (01642) 247973 E-mail: sales@frostree.co.uk

Future Windows Ltd, 74 West End Road, Morecambe, Lancashire, LA4 4DY Tel: (01524) 410077 Fax: (01524) 410099 E-mail: admin@future-windows.com

Glaze For Trade Ltd, 20 Broom Road, Poole, Dorset, BH12 4NL Tel: (01202) 722220 Fax: (01202) 722002 E-mail: sales@glazefortrade.co.uk

Griffin Windows Ltd, Unit 37 Abergorki Industrial Estate, Treorchy, Mid Glamorgan, CF42 6DL Tel: (01443) 777333 Fax: (01443) 776773 E-mail: suzm@griffinwindows.co.uk

Guernsey Glass & Window, Industrial Estate, Braye Road, St. Sampson, Guernsey, GY2 4WX Tel: (01481) 243535 Fax: (01481) 243390 E-mail: gsyglass@guernsey.net

J & K Glass & Glazing Ltd, Units 4-5, Station Road, Terrington St. Clement, King's Lynn, Norfolk, PE34 4PL Tel: (01553) 828555 Fax: (01553) 827035 E-mail: info@jkwindowsanddoors.com

K L G Glass Ltd, Lenton Lane, Nottingham, NG7 2NR Tel: 0115-942 3000 Fax: 0115-942 3444 E-mail: info@klg-glass.co.uk

Kingston Windows & Conservatories, Melbourne House, Caxton Road, Elm Farm Industrial Estate, Bedford, MK41 0HU Tel: (01234) 271625 Fax: (01234) 327797 E-mail: sales@kingstonwindows.fsnet.co.uk

Lakeland Windows, Holme Mills Industrial Estate, Holme, Carnforth, Lancashire, LA6 1RD Tel: (01524) 781800 Fax: (01524) 781800

▶ Lancashire PVC-U Trade Frames Ltd, Unit 7, Meadow Business Park, Meadow Lane, Breightmet, Bolton, BL2 6PT Tel: (01204) 548899 Fax: (01204) 548890 E-mail: info@lancashiretradeframes.co.uk

M B S Window Systems Ltd, Corringham Road Industrial Estate, Gainsborough, Lincolnshire, DN21 1QB Tel: (01427) 615050 Fax: (01427) 614436

M & L Homestyle Ltd, Lupin Works, Worcester Road, Kidderminster, Worcestershire, DY10 1JR Tel: (01562) 755333 Fax: (01562) 745559

Magnet Ltd, 12 St Machar Road, Aberdeen, AB24 2UU Tel: (01224) 492894 Fax: (01224) 488276

Nuglas Ltd, Euro Business Park, New Road, Newhaven, East Sussex, BN9 0DQ Tel: (01273) 517426 Fax: (01273) 513733 E-mail: sales@nuglas.co.uk

▶ Optimum Conservatory Roof Systems, Halliwell Mill, Raglan Street, Bolton, BL1 8AG Tel: (01204) 555920 Fax: (01204) 385111 E-mail: sales@windowfitplus.co.uk

Penicuik Home Improvements, Eastfield Industrial Estate, Penicuik, Midlothian, EH26 8HA Tel: (0845) 7515000 Fax: (01968) 664023

▶ indicates data change since last edition

PVCU CONSERVATORIES – *continued*

R T E Fabrications Ltd, Lomax Street, Darwen, Lancashire, BB3 0DR Tel: (01254) 873002 Fax: (01254) 704919 E-mail: sales@rtefabs.co.uk
Sash Products UK Ltd, Ferrymoor Way, Grimethorpe, Barnsley, South Yorkshire, S72 7BN Tel: (01226) 715619 Fax: (01226) 780701 E-mail: sales@sashuk.com
Sherwood Windows Ltd, Unit A1, Enterprise Park, Brunel Drive, Newark, Nottinghamshire, NG24 2DZ Tel: (01636) 611611 Fax: (01636) 605976 E-mail: sales@sherwoodwindows.co.uk
▶ Shire Conservatories, Unit 7, Harlescott Barns, Battlefield Enterprise Park, Shrewsbury, SY1 3SY Tel: 01743 463333 Fax: 01743 462200E-mail: info@shireconservatories.co.uk
Simplas, Unit 8 Horcott Industrial Estate, Horcott Road, Fairford, Gloucestershire, GL7 4BX Tel: (01285) 713175 Fax: (01285) 713175
Solent Glass & Glazing Ltd, 1 Hackett Way, Fareham, Hampshire, PO14 1TH Tel: (01329) 828210 Fax: (01329) 828838
▶ Space Solutions Ltd, 23 Ampthill Road, Shefford, Bedfordshire, SG17 5BD Tel: 01462 815206 Fax: 01462 641176 E-mail: space@space-solutions.co.uk
Stag Glass & Windows Ltd, 6 High Street, Chapel-en-le-Frith, High Peak, Derbyshire, SK23 0HE Tel: (01298) 816400 Fax: (01298) 816400 E-mail: info@stagglass.fsnet.co.uk
Sunrise, Unit 49g Pipers Road, Park Farm Industrial Estate, Redditch, Worcestershire, B98 0HU Tel: (01527) 522354 Fax: (01527) 517265
Sunseeker Caravans Ltd, 72-84 Station Road, Burton Latimer, Kettering, Northamptonshire, NN15 5NX Tel: (01536) 722316 Fax: (01536) 725883
▶ Taverham Conservatories, 61 Holt Road, Norwich, NR6 6XS Tel: (01603) 426502 Fax: (01603) 418337
Wendland Roof Solutions, Olympus Park Business Centre, Quedgeley, Gloucester, GL2 4NF Tel: (0870) 420 7900 Fax: (0870) 420 7901
Windmill Windows, 115 Red Bank Road, Blackpool, FY2 9HZ Tel: (01253) 594065 Fax: (01253) 500474 E-mail: sales@windmillwindows.co.uk
Window Craft (Nuneaton) Ltd, Whitacre Road, Nuneaton, Warwickshire, CV11 6BY Tel: (024) 7638 4896 Fax: (024) 7638 4896
Windows & Doors U Fit, Manor Way, Kinmel Bay, Rhyl, Clwyd, LL18 5BE Tel: (01745) 354540 Fax: (01745) 354540 E-mail: sales@conservatories-northwales.co.uk
▶ Zenith Conservatories, Weston Road, Norwich, NR3 3TP Tel: (0800) 0830125 Fax: (01603) 406185 E-mail: mike.holmes@zsltd.co.uk

PVCU DOOR PANELS

▶ Asset Manufacturing Ltd, Howletts Way, Thetford, Norfolk, IP24 1HZ Tel: (01842) 763529 Fax: (01842) 752398 E-mail: sales@asset-windows.co.uk

PVCU DOORS

Abbott Group Ltd, Golden Cross, Hailsham, East Sussex, BN27 4AH Tel: (01825) 872567 Fax: (01825) 872033 E-mail: sales@abbott-group.co.uk
▶ Asociated Agency Co., Factory 1, Pottery Close, Winterstoke Road, Weston-Super-Mare, Avon, BS23 3YH Tel: (01934) 622960 Fax: (01934) 621456
Britannia Windows (UK) Ltd, Britannia Houd, Stroud Road, Clevedon, Avon, BS21 6QH Tel: (01275) 878153 Fax: (01275) 343134 E-mail: info@britanniawindows.co.uk
Carstone Windows Ltd, Unit 7 Mount Industrial Estate, Stone, Staffordshire, ST15 8LL Tel: (01785) 814487 Fax: (01785) 816194
Duraflex Ltd, Severn Drive, Tewkesbury Business Park, Tewkesbury, Gloucestershire, GL20 8TX Tel: (0870) 5351351 Fax: (0870) 0772663 E-mail: sales@duraflex.co.uk
FOCUS Windows Ltd, Unit A Technology Centre, White Oak Square, London Road, Swanley, Kent, BR8 7AG Tel: (01322) 614551 Fax: (01322) 613366
▶ Harper Window Systems Ltd, The Gables, Ash Lane, Alvechurch, Birmingham, B48 7TT Tel: 0121-445 0104 Fax: 0121-445 3138 E-mail: enquiries@harperwindows.co.uk
▶ Jeld-Wen UK Ltd, 169 Watch House Lane, Doncaster, South Yorkshire, DN5 9LR Tel: (01302) 394000 Fax: (01302) 787383 E-mail: customer-services@jeld-wen.co.uk

PVCU DOUBLE GLAZED UNITS

▶ Armour Sealed Units Bristol Ltd, 62 Barrs Court Road, Barrs Court, Bristol, BS30 8DH Tel: 0117-961 3970 Fax: 0117-961 3533
▶ Classique Conservatories, 1-3 Christleton Road, Chester, CH3 5UF Tel: (01244) 345355 Fax: (01244) 345255 E-mail: sales@classique.co.uk
▶ F V Conservatories & Windows, Colchester Road, Elmstead, Colchester, CO7 7EA Tel: (01206) 825374 Fax: (01206) 825405 E-mail: sales@fvconservatories.co.uk
▶ Glassline Ltd, Unit 16 Chaucer Industrial Estate, Dittons Road, Polegate, East Sussex, BN26 6JF Tel: (01323) 482000 Fax: (01323) 482111
Glevum Conservatories, Riverside Lane, Broadoak, Newnham, Gloucestershire, GL14 1JF Tel: (01452) 760000 Fax: (01452) 760001 E-mail: mail@glevum.co.uk
▶ Greenwich Windows & Conservatories, Unit 5 Woodhouse Business Centre, Wakefield Road, Normanton, West Yorkshire, WF6 1BB Tel: (01924) 220770 E-mail: sales@greenwitchwindows.com
▶ Higman Windows, Unit 8, Treloggan Industrial Estate, Newquay, Cornwall, TR7 2SX Tel: (01637) 879343 E-mail: sales@higman-windows.co.uk
▶ Kolorplast Coatings Ltd, Radley House, Hawksworth, Didcot, Oxfordshire, OX11 7PJ Tel: (01235) 511414 Fax: (01235) 516701
▶ Normandy Windows Ltd, 3 Crown Close, Crown Industrial Estate, Taunton, Somerset, TA2 8RX Tel: (01823) 256075 E-mail: info@normandy-windows.co.uk
▶ Smokeson Glass, Dart Mills, Buckfastleigh, Devon, TQ11 0NF Tel: (01364) 644673 Fax: (01364) 642162 E-mail: mail@smokesonglass.co.uk
▶ Stanley J Murphy Ltd, Crompton Road, Stevenage, Hertfordshire, SG1 2EE Tel: (01438) 359923 Fax: (01438) 350651 E-mail: enquiries@sjmgroup.co.uk
Swan Windows, 9 Mandervell Road, Oadby, Leicester, LE2 5LQ Tel: 0116-271 4292 Fax: 0116-271 0611 E-mail: enquiries@swanwindows.co.uk
▶ Westport Manufacturing Ltd, Unit 15 Solway Trading Estate, Maryport, Cumbria, CA15 8NF Tel: (01900) 814225 Fax: (01900) 818581

PVCU DOUBLE GLAZED WINDOWS

5 Star Windows & Conservatories Ltd, The Old Stores, Stanklyn Lane, Summerfield, Kidderminster, Worcestershire, DY11 7RY Tel: (01562) 66955 Fax: (01562) 66955 E-mail: sales@5star-online.co.uk
A.D.S Fasteners, Blackburn Road, Rotherham, South Yorkshire, S61 2DR Tel: (01709) 559856
▶ Classic Trade Frames Ltd, Unit 7 Priestley Road, Worsley, Manchester, M28 2LY Tel: 0161-793 1166 Fax: 0161-793 1177
▶ Cumbrian Windows, 3 Adams Road, Derwent Howe Industrial Estate, Workington, Cumbria, CA14 3YS Tel: (01900) 68337 Fax: (01900) 601592
Davian Designs, 81 Main Road, Waterside, Kilmarnock, Ayrshire, KA3 6JU Tel: (01563) 550091 Fax: (01563) 550091 E-mail: mark@davian79.fsnet.co.uk
▶ Double Plas, 1 Babington Park, Grange Park, Swindon, SN5 6EZ Tel: (01793) 875171 Fax: (01793) 878389
▶ Finesse PVC U Ltd, Arburn House Chapel Place, Dentonholme Trading Estate, Carlisle, CA2 5DF Tel: (01228) 522581 Fax: (01228) 810947 E-mail: info@finessegroup.co.uk
Glevum Conservatories, Riverside Lane, Broadoak, Newnham, Gloucestershire, GL14 1JF Tel: (01452) 760000 Fax: (01452) 760001 E-mail: mail@glevum.co.uk
▶ Higman Windows, Unit 8, Treloggan Industrial Estate, Newquay, Cornwall, TR7 2SX Tel: (01637) 879343 E-mail: sales@higman-windows.co.uk
Liversidge Windows & Double Glazing Ltd, Belgrave Mill, Fitton Hill Road, Oldham, OL8 2LU Tel: 0161-620 4525 Fax: 0161-627 0082 E-mail: liversidge@belgravemill.snet.co.uk
▶ Normandy Windows Ltd, 3 Crown Close, Crown Industrial Estate, Taunton, Somerset, TA2 8RX Tel: (01823) 256075 E-mail: info@normandy-windows.co.uk
▶ Plus Windows & Doors Ltd, Units 16 & 18 Moor Park Industrial Centre, Tolpits Lane, Watford, WD18 9SP Tel: (01923) 225855 Fax: (01923) 256106 E-mail: sales@apluswindows.co.uk
▶ Regency Windows (North East) Ltd, 2-3 Charles Street, Bonners Field Industrial Estate, Sunderland, SR6 0AN Tel: 0191-510 9050 E-mail: enquiries@regencywindows.com
▶ Roseview Windows, Yardley Road Industrial Estate, Olney, Buckinghamshire, MK46 5EA Tel: (01234) 712657 Fax: (01234) 712823 E-mail: info@roseview.co.uk
▶ Smokeson Glass, Dart Mills, Buckfastleigh, Devon, TQ11 0NF Tel: (01364) 644673 Fax: (01364) 642162 E-mail: mail@smokesonglass.co.uk
▶ Stockmill Widows Ltd, Alexa Court, Aston Road, Bedford, MK42 0LW Tel: (01234) 356995 Fax: (01234) 267873
TWC, The Drill Hall, 262 Huddersfield Road, Thongsbridge, Holmfirth, HD9 3JL Tel: (0800) 9171918 Fax: (01484) 685210 E-mail: claire_fisher@btconnect.com
▶ Widnes Windows, 140 Birchfield Road, Widnes, Cheshire, WA8 9ED Tel: 0151-424 3332 Fax: 0151-420 4603 E-mail: info@widneswindows.co.uk
Zenith Staybrite Ltd, Suites 4-6, Joseph King House, Abbey Farm Commercial Park, Horsham St Faith, Norwich, NR10 3JU Tel: (0800) 123 555 Fax: (01603) 892116 E-mail: mike.holmes@zsltd.co.uk

PVCU FABRICATORS

Classic Windows Ne Ltd, Unit 95 Tanfield Lea Industrial Estate North, Tanfield Lea, Stanley, County Durham, DH9 9NX Tel: (01207) 284707 Fax: (01207) 237062 E-mail: classicwindows1@btconnect.com
▶ Crystal Clear Manufacturing Ltd, 1-2 Lacerta Court, Letchworth Garden City, Hertfordshire, SG6 1FD Tel: (01462) 489900 Fax: (01462) 489909
Modern Fabrications (Barnsley) Ltd, Modern House, Summer Lane, Barnsley, South Yorkshire, S70 2NP Tel: (01226) 733337 Fax: (01226) 730004 E-mail: sales@modern-fabrications.co.uk
Walsall Metropolitan Borough Council, Suffolk Place, Walsall, WS2 7AY Tel: (01922) 653818 Fax: (01922) 722114

PVCU FRAME DOORS

Anglian Building Products Ltd, 59 Hurricane Way, Norwich, NR6 6JB Tel: (01603) 422000 Fax: (01603) 422066 E-mail: sales@anglian-building.co.uk
Arrow Window Systems, Warwick Road, Fairfield Industrial Estate, Louth, Lincolnshire, LN11 0YB Tel: (01507) 601861 Fax: (01507) 607642
B A C Ltd, Faringdon Avenue, Romford, RM3 8SP Tel: (01708) 382200 Fax: (01708) 382308 E-mail: sales@bac.ltd.uk
B H D Building Products, Unit 5 And 6, Judson Road, Northwest Industrial Estate, Peterlee, County Durham, SR8 2QJ Tel: 0191-415 5220 Fax: (0870) 2421846
Banbury Windows Ltd, Alton Works, Long Bank, Bewdley, Worcestershire, DY12 2UL Tel: (01299) 266332 Fax: (01299) 266676
Bettaprice Systems Ltd, 23k Bridge St Industrial Estate, Lower Mantle Close, Clay Cross, Chesterfield, Derbyshire, S45 9NU Tel: (01246) 865508 Fax: (01246) 865441
Bridgwater Glass, Unit 2-3 Park View, Gallamore Lane, Market Rasen, Lincolnshire, LN8 3HZ Tel: (01673) 842388 Fax: (01673) 842388
Britannia Windows (UK) Ltd, Britannia Houd, Stroud Road, Clevedon, Avon, BS21 6QH Tel: (01275) 878153 Fax: (01275) 343134 E-mail: info@britanniawindows.co.uk
Coastal Ltd, D'Oriel House, Holton Heath Trading Park, Poole, Dorset, BH16 6LE Tel: (01202) 624011 Fax: (01202) 622465 E-mail: sales@coastalwindows.co.uk
Consort Ltd, 1-4 Export Drive, Huthwaite, Sutton-in-Ashfield, Nottinghamshire, NG17 6AF Tel: (01623) 440880 Fax: (01623) 440396 E-mail: info@consort.ltd.uk
Coulter Windows Ltd, 27 Dunavail Road, Kilkeel, Newry, County Down, BT34 4JT Tel: (028) 4176 3884 Fax: (028) 4176 4665 E-mail: neil@coulterwindows.co.uk
Crocodilla Ltd, East Cottage, Hill View Road, Michelmersh, Romsey, Hampshire, SO51 0NN Tel: (01794) 367286 Fax: (01794) 367286 E-mail: info@crocodilla.co.uk
D Glass, 9 Artillery Road, Lufton Trading Estate, Lufton, Yeovil, Somerset, BA22 8RP Tel: (01935) 471359 Fax: (01935) 420464
Eas Windows, 25 New Street, Oadby, Leicester, LE2 5EB Tel: 0116-271 0120 Fax: 0116-271 7708 E-mail: enquiries@easwindows.co.uk
Excel Glass Ltd, Musgrave Park Industrial Estate, Stockmans Way, Belfast, BT9 7ET Tel: (028) 9038 2121 Fax: (028) 9038 1951 E-mail: bg@excel.dnet.co.uk
Express Windows, 1 Trovers Way, Holmethorpe Industrial Estate, Redhill, RH1 2LH Tel: (01737) 768833 Fax: (01737) 768832 E-mail: mail@expresswindows.co.uk
John Fredericks Plastics Ltd, Lindley Moor Road, Huddersfield, HD3 3RW Tel: (01422) 314100 Fax: (01422) 310001 E-mail: sales@johnfrederickspIastics.com
Glaze For Trade Ltd, 20 Broom Road, Poole, Dorset, BH12 4NL Tel: (01202) 722220 Fax: (01202) 722002 E-mail: sales@glazefortrade.co.uk
Harris Windows & Joinery Ltd, Brighton Road, Tadworth, Surrey, KT20 6UP Tel: (01737) 832328 Fax: (01737) 833964
▶ Hometec UK, 401 Rayleigh Road, Leigh-On-Sea, Essex, SS9 5JG Tel: (01702) 421421 Fax: (01702) 521521 E-mail: sales@hometec.co.uk
Jarvis H Son Joinery Ltd, Longbeck Trading Estate, Redcar, Cleveland, TS11 6HH Tel: (01642) 482366 Fax: (01642) 484015 E-mail: admin@jarvis.co.uk
K E B Fabrications Ltd, 170 Rolfe St, Smethwick, West Midlands, B66 2AU Tel: 0121-555 5533 Fax: 0121-555 5193 E-mail: sales@kebfabrications.co.uk
K L G Glass Ltd, Lenton Lane, Nottingham, NG7 2NR Tel: 0115-942 3000 Fax: 0115-942 3444 E-mail: info@klg-glass.co.uk
Kingston Windows & Conservatories, Melbourne House, Caxton Road, Elm Farm Industrial Estate, Bedford, MK41 0HU Tel: (01234) 271625 Fax: (01234) 327797 E-mail: sales@kingstonwindows.fsnet.co.uk
L B Plastics Ltd, Firs Works, Heage Firs, Nether Heage, Belper, Derbyshire, DE56 2JJ Tel: (01773) 852311 Fax: (01773) 857080 E-mail: sheerframe@lbplastics.co.uk
Lakeland Windows, Holme Mills Industrial Estate, Holme, Carnforth, Lancashire, LA6 1RD Tel: (01524) 781800 Fax: (01524) 781800
Malbern Windows & Doors Ltd, 3 Malbern Industrial Estate, Holland Street, Denton, Manchester, M34 3WE Tel: 0161-320 5801 Fax: 0161-335 0986 E-mail: sales@malbernwindows.co.uk
Permadoor, Upton-Upon-Severn, Worcester, WR8 0RX Tel: (01684) 595200 Fax: (01684) 594283 E-mail: info@permadoor.co.uk
Prestige Glazing Services Ltd, Unit 2 Shuttleworth Court, Shuttleworth Road, Elm Farm Industrial Estate, Bedford, MK41 0EN Tel: (01234) 346454 Fax: (01234) 219063 E-mail: prestigeglazing@btconnect.com
Radway Door & Windows Ltd, Radway House, Oxneasow Road, East Moons Moat, Redditch, Worcestershire, B98 0RE Tel: (01527) 503700 Fax: (01527) 503701 E-mail: info@radways.co.uk
Ramsey Glass & Window Co (Chipwel), A Highlode Industrial Estate, Stocking Fen Road, Ramsey, Huntingdon, Cambridgeshire, PE26 2RB Tel: (01487) 813007 Fax: (01487) 710364 E-mail: salesramseyglass@hotmail.com
Season Master Windows Ltd, 1 Oaks Industrial Estate, Coventry Road, Narborough, Leicester, LE19 2GF Tel: 0116-286 7970 Fax: 0116-284 1693 E-mail: sales@seasonmasterwindows.co.uk
Shelforce, Units 21-23 Erdington Industrial Park, Chester Road, Erdington, Birmingham, B24 0RD Tel: 0121-603 5262 Fax: 0121-603 2771 E-mail: sales@shelforce.co.uk
Sherwood Windows Ltd, Unit A1, Enterprise Park, Brunel Drive, Newark, Nottinghamshire, NG24 2DZ Tel: (01636) 611611 Fax: (01636) 605976 E-mail: sales@sherwoodwindows.co.uk
Spectus Windows Systems Ltd, Pinewood Court, Cycherington Business Park, Macclesfield, Cheshire, SK10 2XR Tel: (01625) 420400 Fax: (01625) 501418
Starglaze Midlands Ltd, Unit 5 Waterside South, Lincoln, LN5 7JD Tel: (01522) 512525 Fax: (01522) 567651 E-mail: sales@sternfenster.co.uk
Sunrise, Unit 49g Pipers Road, Park Farm Industrial Estate, Redditch, Worcestershire, B98 0HU Tel: (01527) 522354 Fax: (01527) 517265
Sunseeker Caravans Ltd, 72-84 Station Road, Burton Latimer, Kettering, Northamptonshire, NN15 5NX Tel: (01536) 722316 Fax: (01536) 725883
T H S Plastics, 5 Claymore, Tame Valley Industrial Estate, Wilnecote, Tamworth, Staffordshire, B77 5DQ Tel: (01827) 282999 Fax: (01827) 262047 E-mail: sales@ths.plastics.co.uk
Thermoshield Window Services Ltd, 11 Purdeys Way, Rochford, Essex, SS4 1ND Tel: (01702) 541841 Fax: (01702) 541729 E-mail: sales@thermoshield.co.uk
Walsall Metropolitan Borough Council, Suffolk Place, Walsall, WS2 7AY Tel: (01922) 653818 Fax: (01922) 722114
Welcome Windows Ltd, Wembley Works, Hemingfield Road, Wombwell, Barnsley, South Yorkshire, S73 0LY Tel: (01226) 340240 Fax: (01226) 340327
Windmill Windows, 115 Red Bank Road, Blackpool, FY2 9HZ Tel: (01253) 594065 Fax: (01253) 500474 E-mail: sales@windmillwindows.co.uk
Window World Of Kent, 24 Juniper Close, Ashford, Kent, TN23 3JY Tel: (01233) 642322 Fax: (0870) 1656459 E-mail: e-breeze@windows-world.fsnet.co.uk
Windowmaker, Madleaze Trading Estate, Madleaze Road, Gloucester, GL1 5SG Tel: (01452) 423348 Fax: (01452) 300193 E-mail: mail@swiftsheild.co.uk

PVCU FRAMED WINDOWS

A C Yule & Son Ltd, 1 Pinefield Parade, Elgin, Morayshire, IV30 6AG Tel: (01343) 545222 Fax: (01343) 542246 E-mail: elgin@acyule.com
Abbott Group Ltd, Golden Cross, Hailsham, East Sussex, BN27 4AH Tel: (01825) 872567 Fax: (01825) 872033 E-mail: sales@abbott-group.co.uk
Academy Windows & Conservatories Ltd, 21 Denmark Street, Wokingham, Berkshire, RG40 2AY Tel: 0118-977 1144 Fax: 0118-989 1268E-mail: academy.gordon@btconnect.com
Alliance Group (Bristol) Ltd, Unit 303 Central Park, Petherton Road, Hengrove, Bristol, BS14 9BZ Tel: (01275) 892882 Fax: (01275) 892766 E-mail: general@alliancegroupbristol.co.uk
Anglian Building Products Ltd, 59 Hurricane Way, Norwich, NR6 6JB Tel: (01603) 422000 Fax: (01603) 422066 E-mail: sales@anglian-building.co.uk
Arrow Window Systems, Warwick Road, Fairfield Industrial Estate, Louth, Lincolnshire, LN11 0YB Tel: (01507) 601861 Fax: (01507) 607642
B A C Ltd, Faringdon Avenue, Romford, RM3 8SP Tel: (01708) 382200 Fax: (01708) 382308 E-mail: sales@bac.ltd.uk
B B Glass Ltd, 7a Buddle Road, Clay Flatts Industrial Estate, Workington, Cumbria, CA14 3YD Tel: (01900) 65445 Fax: (01900) 64789
▶ B B H Ltd, Unit 9-10, 251 Holt Road, Horsford, Norwich, NR10 3EB Tel: (01603) 897350 Fax: (01603) 890080 E-mail: bbh@bbhltd.fx.co.net

PVCU FRAMED WINDOWS – *continued*

B H D Building Products, Unit 5 And 6, Judson Road, Northwest Industrial Estate, Peterlee, County Durham, SR8 2QJ Tel: 0191-415 5220 Fax: (0870) 2421846

B.M.W. Building Products Ltd, Unit 52, Stella Gill Industrial Estate, Pelton Fell, Chester le Street, County Durham, DH2 2RG Tel: 0191-388 9145 Fax: 0191-387 1756 E-mail: johnj@bmwbuilding.co.uk

Banbury Windows Ltd, Alton Works, Long Bank, Bewdley, Worcestershire, DY12 2UL Tel: (01299) 266332 Fax: (01299) 266676

Barong Windows Ltd, Doves Barn, Copthorne, Felbridge, East Grinstead, West Sussex, RH19 2QQ Tel: (01342) 300903

Barretts Glass & Window Centre Ltd, 24a Edward Road, Dorchester, Dorset, DT1 2HL Tel: (01305) 264299 Fax: (01305) 260083 E-mail: sales@barrettsglass.com

Bettaprice Systems Ltd, 23k Bridge St Industrial Estate, Lower Mantle Close, Clay Cross, Chesterfield, Derbyshire, S45 9NU Tel: (01246) 865508 Fax: (01246) 865441

Bridgwater Glass, Unit 2-3 Park View, Gallamore Lane, Market Rasen, Lincolnshire, LN8 3HZ Tel: (01673) 842388 Fax: (01673) 842388

C & R Plastics, E4 Unit, Formal Industrial Estate, Treswithian, Camborne, Cornwall, TR14 0PY Tel: (01209) 711878 Fax: (01209) 711895

Camberley Glass Ltd, 453 London Road, Camberley, Surrey, GU15 3JA Tel: (01276) 684444 Fax: (01276) 28277 E-mail: sales@camberleyglass.co.uk

Carstone Windows Ltd, Unit 7 Mount Industrial Estate, Stone, Staffordshire, ST15 8LL Tel: (01785) 814487 Fax: (01785) 816194

Chapel Windows Ltd, Bevan Industrial Estate, Brierley Hill, West Midlands, DY5 3TF Tel: (01384) 571315 Fax: (01384) 480403

▶ Clearview Pvcu, Hospital Road, Ellon, Aberdeenshire, AB41 9AW Tel: (01358) 722202 E-mail: lawrence.muirhead@btopenworld.com

Clement John Son Glazing, Unit 4 Broadmoor Park, Forest Vale Indust Estate, Dean, Cinderford, Gloucestershire, GL14 2YF Tel: (01594) 822081 Fax: (01594) 825897

Clivnars Ltd, Pindar Road, Hoddesdon, Hertfordshire, EN11 0EA Tel: (01992) 467710 Fax: (01992) 467866 E-mail: sales@clivnars.co.uk

Consort Ltd, 1-4 Export Drive, Huthwaite, Sutton-in-Ashfield, Nottinghamshire, NG17 6AF Tel: (01623) 440880 Fax: (01623) 440396 E-mail: info@consort.ltd.uk

Crown Windows Ltd, Manor Works, Brunel Road, Newton Abbot, Devon, TQ12 4PB Tel: (01626) 332288 Fax: (01626) 333440 E-mail: sales@crown-windows.co.uk

Custom Made (U K) Ltd, Oldends Hall, Oldends Lane, Stonehouse, Gloucestershire, GL10 3RQ Tel: (01453) 826884 Fax: (01453) 791259 E-mail: info@custommade.co.uk

D Glass, 9 Artillery Road, Lufton Trading Estate, Lufton, Yeovil, Somerset, BA22 8RP Tel: (01935) 471359 Fax: (01935) 420464

Devoran Metals, Devoran Joinery Works, Greenbank Road, Devoran, Truro, Cornwall, TR3 6PQ Tel: (01872) 863376 Fax: (01872) 862123 E-mail: richard@devoran-joinery.demon.co.uk

Diamond Seal Ltd, Bowling Back Lane, Bradford, West Yorkshire, BD4 8SX Tel: (01274) 303400 Fax: (01274) 303401

Dick Thompson & Co., Unit 91a Blackdyke Road, Kingstown Industrial Estate, Carlisle, CA3 0PJ Tel: (01228) 549000 Fax: (01228) 521200

Drury Casement Co. Ltd, Blakemore Road, West Bromwich, West Midlands, B70 8JF Tel: 0121-553 2198 Fax: 0121-553 2301 E-mail: garry.jones@btclick.com

▶ Everest Ltd, Cwmsaerbren Street, Treherbert, Treorchy, Mid Glamorgan, CF42 5HY Tel: (01443) 771382 Fax: (01443) 777046

Express Windows, 1 Trovers Way, Holmethorpe Industrial Estate, Redhill, RH1 2LH Tel: (01737) 768833 Fax: (01737) 768832 E-mail: mail@expresswindows.co.uk

Fersina Windows, Unit 3 Dysart Road, Grantham, Lincolnshire, NG31 7EJ Tel: (01476) 593830 Fax: (01476) 590687 E-mail: fersinalincs@aol.com

▶ Fitters Mate Ltd, Unit B8f Broadlands, Heywood Distribution Park, Heywood, Lancashire, OL10 2TS Tel: 0161-761 5055 Fax: 0161-761 2050 E-mail: sales@thefittersmate.com

Four Seasons Ltd, Unit 14, Papermill End, Aldridge Road, Great Barr, Birmingham, B44 8NH Tel: 0121-356 0909 Fax: 0121-356 0513

Future Windows Ltd, 74 West End Road, Morecambe, Lancashire, LA4 4DY Tel: (01524) 410077 Fax: (01524) 410099 E-mail: admin@future-windows.com

G B Windows, New Road Business Park, New Road, Halifax, West Yorkshire, HX1 2LH Tel: (01422) 331141 Fax: (01422) 331145

Glass Northampton Ltd, 25-29 Bailiff Street, Northampton, NN1 3DX Tel: (01604) 233343 Fax: (01604) 233298 E-mail: admin@glassnorthampton.co.uk

Glaze For Trade Ltd, 20 Broom Road, Poole, Dorset, BH12 4NL Tel: (01202) 722220 Fax: (01202) 722002 E-mail: sales@glazefortrade.co.uk

Harris Windows & Joinery Ltd, Brighton Road, Tadworth, Surrey, KT20 6UP Tel: (01737) 832328 Fax: (01737) 833964

▶ Hawthorn Window Services Ltd, Unit 5-6 Vernon Trading Estate, New John Street, Halesowen, West Midlands, B62 8HT Tel: 0121-559 6320 Fax: 0121-559 6106

▶ Hometec UK, 401 Rayleigh Road, Leigh-On-Sea, Essex, SS9 5JG Tel: (01702) 421421 Fax: (01702) 521521 E-mail: sales@hometec.co.uk

J & K Glass & Glazing Ltd, Units 4-5, Station Road, Terrington St. Clement, King's Lynn, Norfolk, PE34 4PL Tel: (01553) 828555 Fax: (01553) 827035 E-mail: info@jkwindowsanddoors.com

Scott James Commercial Ltd, 10-12 Armstrong Close, St. Leonards-on-Sea, East Sussex, TN38 9ST Tel: (0500) 441066 Fax: (01424) 853911 E-mail: sales@scott-james.freeserve.co.uk

Jarvis H Son Joinery Ltd, Longbeck Trading Estate, Redcar, Cleveland, TS11 6HH Tel: (01642) 482366 Fax: (01642) 484015 E-mail: admin@jarvis.co.uk

▶ Jeld-Wen UK Ltd, 169 Watch House Lane, Doncaster, South Yorkshire, DN5 9LR Tel: (01302) 394000 Fax: (01302) 787383 E-mail: customer-services@jeld-wen.co.uk

K E B Fabrications Ltd, 170 Rolfe St, Smethwick, West Midlands, B66 2AU Tel: 0121-555 5533 Fax: 0121-555 5193 E-mail: sales@kebfabrications.co.uk

K L G Glass Ltd, Lenton Lane, Nottingham, NG7 2NR Tel: 0115-942 3000 Fax: 0115-942 3444 E-mail: info@klg-glass.co.uk

Keyline Windows, K Key Industrial Park, Fernside Road, Willenhall, West Midlands, WV13 3YA Tel: (01902) 307685 Fax: (01902) 865800 E-mail: enquiries@keylinewindows.com

Kingston Windows & Conservatories, Melbourne House, Caxton Road, Elm Farm Industrial Estate, Bedford, MK41 0HU Tel: (01234) 271625 Fax: (01234) 327797 E-mail: sales@kingstonwindows.fsnet.co.uk

L B Plastics Ltd, Firs Works, Heage Firs, Nether Heage, Belper, Derbyshire, DE56 2JJ Tel: (01773) 852311 Fax: (01773) 857080 E-mail: sheerframe@lbplastics.co.uk

Lakeland Windows, Holme Mills Industrial Estate, Holme, Carnforth, Lancashire, LA6 1RD Tel: (01524) 781800 Fax: (01524) 781800

Lye Valley Windows & Doors, 4 Stour Vale Road Industrial Estate, Stour Vale Road, Stourbridge, West Midlands, DY9 8PN Tel: (01384) 892952 Fax: (01384) 422626

Main Cabinet Works, 687 Melton Road, Thurmaston, Leicester, LE4 8ED Tel: 0116-269 3078

Malbern Windows & Doors Ltd, 3 Malbern Industrial Estate, Holland Street, Denton, Manchester, M34 3WE Tel: 0161-320 5801 Fax: 0161-335 0986 E-mail: sales@malbernwindows.co.uk

Megaframe, Bridge Inn Yard, League Street, Rochdale, Lancashire, OL16 5RT Tel: (01706) 649111 Fax: (01706) 649111

New Crystal Windows Ltd, 162 Winson Street, Winson Green, Birmingham, B18 4JW Tel: 0121-565 3244 Fax: 0121-565 3500

Nu Homes Manufacturing Ltd, Claymore, Tame Valley Industrial Estate, Wilnecote, Tamworth, Staffordshire, B77 5DQ Tel: (01827) 284061 Fax: (01827) 260632

Nuglas Ltd, Euro Business Park, New Road, Newhaven, East Sussex, BN9 0DQ Tel: (01273) 517426 Fax: (01273) 513733 E-mail: sales@nuglas.co.uk

▶ Omega Windows, Exchange Road, Lincoln, LN6 3JZ Tel: (01522) 685444 Fax: (01522) 521 898

Penicuik Home Improvements, Eastfield Industrial Estate, Penicuik, Midlothian, EH26 8HA Tel: (0845) 7515000 Fax: (01968) 664023

Phoenix Home Improvement Services Ltd, 21 Sandmere Road, Leechmere Industrial Estate, Sunderland, SR2 9TP Tel: 0191-523 7006 Fax: 0191-523 8737

Plastmo Profiles Ltd, Lower Farm Road, Moulton Park Industrial Estate, Northampton, NN3 6XF Tel: (01604) 790780 Fax: (01604) 790110 E-mail: info@plastmo.co.uk

Potton Windows Ltd, Shannon Place, Potton, Sandy, Bedfordshire, SG19 2SP Tel: (01767) 260626 Fax: (01767) 262048 E-mail: sales@pottonwindows.co.uk

Quality Glass Stoke On Trent Ltd, Leek New Road, Stoke-on-Trent, ST6 2JY Tel: (01782) 289700 Fax: (01782) 262656 E-mail: enquiries@qualityglass.co.uk

R B D Builders Norfolk Ltd, 32 Southgates Road, Great Yarmouth, Norfolk, NR30 3LL Tel: (01493) 855891 Fax: (01493) 331615

R T E Fabrications Ltd, Lomax Street, Darwen, Lancashire, BB3 0DR Tel: (01254) 873002 Fax: (01254) 704919 E-mail: sales@rtefabs.co.uk

Ramsey Glass & Window Co (Chipwel), A Highlode Industrial Estate, Stocking Fen Road, Ramsey, Huntingdon, Cambridgeshire, PE26 2RB Tel: (01487) 813007 Fax: (01487) 710364 E-mail: salesramseyglass@hotmail.com

Rion Ltd, Rion House, Lowton Way, Hellaby Business Park, Rotherham, South Yorkshire, S66 8RY Tel: (01709) 703703 Fax: (01709) 700880 E-mail: rionltd1@aol.com

Roman Windows & Doors Ltd, Unit 3 Fir Ralph Trade Centre, Hopton Industrial Estate, London Road, Devizes, Wiltshire, SN10 2FD Tel: (01380) 729000 Fax: (01380) 729038 E-mail: romanwindows@romanglass.co.uk

Sash Products UK Ltd, Ferrymoor Way, Grimethorpe, Barnsley, South Yorkshire, S72 7BN Tel: (01226) 715619 Fax: (01226) 780701 E-mail: sales@sashuk.com

Season Master Windows Ltd, 1 Oaks Industrial Estate, Coventry Road, Narborough, Leicester, LE19 2GF Tel: 0116-286 7970 Fax: 0116-284 1693 E-mail: sales@seasonmasterwindows.co.uk

Sharrow Industries, Parkway Close, Sheffield, S9 4WJ Tel: 0114-203 9446 Fax: 0114-203 9448

Shelforce, Units 21-23 Erdington Industrial Park, Chester Road, Erdington, Birmingham, B24 0RD Tel: 0121-603 5262 Fax: 0121-603 2771 E-mail: sales@shelforce.co.uk

Sherwood Windows Ltd, Unit A1, Enterprise Park, Brunel Drive, Newark, Nottinghamshire, NG24 2DZ Tel: (01636) 611611 Fax: (01636) 605976 E-mail: sales@sherwoodwindows.co.uk

Simplas, Unit 8 Horcott Industrial Estate, Horcott Road, Fairford, Gloucestershire, GL7 4BX Tel: (01285) 713175 Fax: (01285) 713175

South Western Windows Ltd, Panteg Industrial Estate, Station Road, Griffithstown, Pontypool, Gwent, NP4 5LX Tel: (01495) 756868 Fax: (01495) 758274 E-mail: swwindows@aol.com

Stag Glass & Windows Ltd, 6 High Street, Chapel-en-le-Frith, High Peak, Derbyshire, SK23 0HE Tel: (01298) 816400 Fax: (01298) 816400 E-mail: info@stagglass.fsnet.co.uk

Starglaze Midlands Ltd, Unit 5 Waterside South, Lincoln, LN5 7JD Tel: (01522) 512525 Fax: (01522) 567651 E-mail: sales@sternfenster.co.uk

Starseal Window Systems, 37 Hoylake Road, Scunthorpe, South Humberside, DN17 2AZ Tel: (01724) 873500 Fax: (01724) 873600

Streetly Windows Ltd, 338 Aldridge Road, Streetly, Sutton Coldfield, West Midlands, B74 2DT Tel: 0121-353 5886 Fax: 0121-353 2908

Sunseeker Caravans Ltd, 72-84 Station Road, Burton Latimer, Kettering, Northamptonshire, NN15 5NX Tel: (01536) 722316 Fax: (01536) 725883

Thermoshield Window Services Ltd, 11 Purdeys Way, Rochford, Essex, SS4 1ND Tel: (01702) 541841 Fax: (01702) 541729 E-mail: sales@thermoshield.co.uk

Windmill Windows, 115 Red Bank Road, Blackpool, FY2 9HZ Tel: (01253) 594065 Fax: (01253) 500474 E-mail: sales@windmillwindows.co.uk

▶ Window World Services, Unit 3, Crystal Drive, Smethwick, W. Midlands, B66 1QG Tel: 0121-544 1176

Wolverhampton Glass & Windows, Pelham Street, Wolverhampton, WV3 0BJ Tel: (01902) 773831 Fax: (01902) 423294

PVCU SYSTEM WINDOWS

Ambassador Windows Ltd, 8 Heol Gors, Dafen Industrial Estate, Dafen, Llanelli, Dyfed, SA14 8QR Tel: (01554) 752144 Fax: (01554) 753311 E-mail: ambassador@lineone.net

Blaenau Plastics Ltd, Tanygrisiau Trading Estate, Tanygrisiau, Blaenau Ffestiniog, Gwynedd, LL41 3RY Tel: (01766) 833700 Fax: (01766) 833701

Cheadle Glass Co. Ltd, Adswood Road, Cheadle Hulme, Cheadle, Cheshire, SK8 5QA Tel: 0161-486 9333 Fax: 0161-486 9335

Classic Windows Ne Ltd, Unit 95 Tanfield Lea Industrial Estate North, Tanfield Lea, Stanley, County Durham, DH9 9NX Tel: (01207) 284707 Fax: (01207) 237062 E-mail: classicwindows1@btconnect.com

Dartmoor Windows & Conservatories Ltd, 1 Mill Road, Okehampton, Devon, EX20 1PS Tel: (01837) 54543 Fax: (01837) 54192

Diplomat Extrusions Ltd, Dukesway, Gateshead, Tyne & Wear, NE11 0PZ Tel: 0191-482 8800 Fax: 0191-482 0571 E-mail: info@diplomat-extrusions.co.uk

Excalibur Glass & Windows Ltd, 137 Ringwood Road, Poole, Dorset, BH14 0RH Tel: (01202) 743144 Fax: (01202) 716449 E-mail: sales@glassandwindows.co.uk

The London & Local Manufacturing Co. Ltd, 312B Kingston Road, London, SW20 8LX Tel: (020) 8644 5951 Fax: (020) 8641 4119 E-mail: londonandlocal1@aol.co.uk

R & M Enterprise Windows Ltd, Unit 2 Thames House, Middlegreen Trading Estate, Langley, Slough, SL3 6DF Tel: (01753) 526334 Fax: (01753) 517694 E-mail: info@randmwindows.fsnet.co.uk

Radway Door & Windows Ltd, Radway House, Oxneasow Road, East Moons Moat, Redditch, Worcestershire, B98 0RE Tel: (01527) 503700 Fax: (01527) 503701 E-mail: info@radways.co.uk

T H S Plastics, 5 Claymore, Tame Valley Industrial Estate, Wilnecote, Tamworth, Staffordshire, B77 5DQ Tel: (01827) 282999 Fax: (01827) 262047 E-mail: sales@ths.plastics.co.uk

Veka P.L.C., Farrington Road, Rossendale Road Industrial Estate, Burnley, Lancashire, BB11 5DA Tel: (01282) 716611 Fax: (01282) 718490 E-mail: salesenquiry@veka.com

Window World Of Kent, 24 Juniper Close, Ashford, Kent, TN23 3JY Tel: (01233) 642322 Fax: (0870) 1656459 E-mail: e-breeze@windows-world.fsnet.co.uk

PVCU VERTICAL SLIDING SASH WINDOWS

▶ DIY Sash Windows, Unit 2 Whitworth Drive, Aycliffe Industrial Park, Newton Aycliffe, County Durham, DL5 6SZ Tel: (01325) 308888 Fax: (01325) 316002 E-mail: sales@diysashwindows.co.uk

PYJAMAS

▶ Sleepythings, 1 Wood Farm Cottages, Bramdean, Alresford, Hampshire, SO24 0JL Tel: 01962 771784 Fax: 01962 771784 E-mail: info@sleepythings.co.uk

PYROMETER CONTROL ALUMINIUM BRAZING MACHINES

Ipeco Engineering Ltd, Aviation Way, Southend-on-Sea, SS2 6UN Tel: (01702) 544939 Fax: (01702) 546480

PYROMETERS

G M Instrumentation, 102 Sale Lane, Tyldesley, Manchester, M29 8PZ Tel: 0161-703 9100 Fax: 0161-703 9133 E-mail: gmimanchester@aol.com

J.W. Ray & Co. Liverpool Ltd, Unit 87 North Mersey Business Centre, Woodward Road, Knowsley Industrial Park, Liverpool, L33 7UY Tel: 0151-546 2534 Fax: 0151-549 1645

Taylor Tunnicliff Ltd, Normacot Road, Stoke-on-Trent, ST3 1PA Tel: (01782) 501174 Fax: (01782) 328807

PYROTECHNIC DISTRESS SIGNALS

Pains Wessex Ltd, High Post, Salisbury, SP4 6AS Tel: (01722) 411611 Fax: (01722) 428798 E-mail: info@chemringcm.com

PYROTECHNICS, *See also headings under Distress*

Brock's Explosives Ltd, Gateside Factory, Sanquhar, Dumfriesshire, DG4 6JP Tel: (01659) 50531 Fax: (01659) 50526

Kimbolton Fireworks (Displays) Ltd, 7 High Street, Kimbolton, Huntingdon, Cambridgeshire, PE28 0HB Tel: (01480) 860988 Fax: (01480) 861277 E-mail: info@kimboltonfireworks.co.uk

Le Maitre Fireworks Ltd, Unit 6 Forval Close, Mitcham, Surrey, CR4 4NE Tel: (020) 8646 2222 Fax: (020) 8646 1955 E-mail: info@lemaitreltd.com

Leafield Engineering Ltd, Leafield Industrial Estate, Corsham, Wiltshire, SN13 9SS Tel: (01225) 810771 Fax: (01225) 810614 E-mail: lel@leafield.co.uk

P W Defence Ltd, Wilne Mill, Draycott, Derby, DE72 3QJ Tel: (01332) 872475 Fax: (01332) 873046

Theatrical Pyrotechnics Ltd, The Loop, Manston Airport, Manston, Ramsgate, Kent, CT12 5DE Tel: (01843) 823545 Fax: (01843) 822655 E-mail: pyrotec@manstona.fsnet.co.uk

QUAD BIKE ACCESSORIES

▶ Amazon ATV Ltd (Quad Sales & Hire 6-6yrs), Green Street Industrial Estate, 1 Green Street, Eastbourne, East Sussex, BN21 1QN Tel: (01323) 645564 Fax: (01323) 645564 E-mail: elainechild@tiscali.co.uk

▶ Muddy Trax Racing Ltd, The Gate House Cherry Tree Sawmills, Faygate Lane, Faygate, Horsham, West Sussex, RH12 4SJ Tel: (01293) 852600 E-mail: sales@muddytrax.co.uk

QUAD BIKE HIRE

▶ www.a1quads.co.uk, Maesybont, Llanelli, SA14 7SR Tel: (0870) 3215908 Fax: (0870) 3215908 E-mail: oddjob@a1quads.co.uk

QUAD BIKES

Adelphi Coin Ltd, Adelphi House, Freeholdland Road, Pontnewynydd, Pontypool, Gwent, NP4 8LN Tel: (01495) 751933 Fax: (01495) 752872 E-mail: sales@carmarketwales.co.uk

▶ www.a1quads.co.uk, Maesybont, Llanelli, SA14 7SR Tel: (0870) 3215908 Fax: (0870) 3215908 E-mail: oddjob@a1quads.co.uk

QUALITY ASSURANCE CERTIFICATION AND TRAINING

▶ Aegis Verity Yorkshire, 7 Willow Glade, Clifford, Wetherby, West Yorkshire, LS23 6ST Tel: (01937) 541325 Fax: (01937) 841057 E-mail: yorkshire@aegis-verity.com

British Approvals Board Telecommunications Ltd, Claremont House, 34 Molesey Road, Hersham, Walton-on-Thames, Surrey, KT12 4RQ Tel: (01932) 251200 Fax: (01932) 251201 E-mail: m.brain@babt.com

▶ Construction Industry Quality Assurance Ltd, 45 High Street, Walton-on-Thames, Surrey, KT12 1DH Tel: (01932) 231361 Fax: (01932) 222647 E-mail: mail@ciqa.eu.com

Euro Environmental Containers, The Court House, Denmark Street, Wokingham, Berkshire, RG40 2AY Tel: (0845) 0094287 Fax: 0709 231 0266 E-mail: Enquiries@euroenvironmentalcontainers.co.uk

I C S, 178 Reddicap Heath Road, Sutton Coldfield, West Midlands, B75 7ET Tel: 0121-241 2299 Fax: 0121-241 4623 E-mail: wayne@ics-mail.com

▶ Quality Matters Ltd, PO Box 5479, Maldon, Essex, CM9 8GG Tel: (01621) 868767 Fax: (01621) 868728 E-mail: sales@quality-matters.com

▶ Services Ltd, 82 Trent BLVD, West Bridgfore, Nottingham, NG2 5BL Tel: 0115-945 5285 Fax: 0115-981 7137 E-mail: info@servicesltd.co.uk

QUALITY ASSURANCE CONSULTANTS

Aberdeen Quality Associates Ltd, 8 Rubislaw Den North, Aberdeen, AB15 4AN Tel: (01224) 315406 E-mail: bill@aqa.co.uk

Adr International Ltd, 82 High Street, Wallingford, Oxfordshire, OX10 0BT Tel: (01491) 825666 Fax: (01491) 825688 E-mail: info@adr-international.com

Birmingham Chamber Training Ltd, 75 Harbourne Road, Edgbaston, Birmingham, B15 3DH Tel: 0121-454 1999 Fax: 0121-455 8700 E-mail: enquiries@birminghamchamber.org.uk

British Inspecting Engineers Ltd, Chatsworth Technology Park, Dunston Road, Chesterfield, Derbyshire, S41 8XA Tel: (01246) 260260 Fax: (01246) 260919E-mail: info@bieltd.co.uk

British Quality Foundation, 32-34 Great Peter Street, London, SW1P 2QX Tel: (020) 7654 5000 Fax: (020) 7654 5001 E-mail: mail@quality-foundation.co.uk

British Standards Institution, 389 Chiswick High Road, London, W4 4AL Tel: (020) 8996 9000 Fax: (020) 8996 7400 E-mail: info@bsi-global.com

▶ Camm Management Consultants, 63 Ganton Road, Bloxwich, Walsall, WS3 3XQ Tel: 07917 026719 E-mail: marcus@cammconsulting.co.uk

▶ Construction Industry Quality Assurance Ltd, 45 High Street, Walton-on-Thames, Surrey, KT12 1DH Tel: (01932) 231361 Fax: (01932) 222647 E-mail: mail@ciqa.eu.com

D T I (Department of Trade and Industry), 1 Victoria Street, London, SW1H 0ET Tel: (020) 7215 5000 Fax: (020) 7215 3529 E-mail: dti.enquiries@dti.gsi.gov.uk

Edexcel, Stewart House, 32 Russell Square, London, WC1B 5DN Tel: (0870) 2409800 Fax: (020) 7393 4445 E-mail: enquiries@edexcel.org.uk

▶ Guthrie & Craig, Prospect Business Park, Crookhall Lane, Leadgate, Consett, County Durham, DH8 7PW Tel: (01207) 580033 Fax: (01207) 581903 E-mail: guthriecraigrjc@msn.com

H S B Inspection Quality Ltd, Cairo Mill, Greenacres Road, Oldham, OL4 3JA Tel: (01928) 579595 Fax: 0161-621 5680 E-mail: sales@hsbiq.com

Holmes & Mann Associates Ltd, 465 Tachbrook Road, Leamington Spa, Warwickshire, CV31 3DQ Tel: (01926) 426854 Fax: (01926) 426854 E-mail: holmes@holmes-mann.com

I M F Technical Services Ltd, Unit 5 50 Cotton Street, Aberdeen, AB11 5EE Tel: (01224) 210147 Fax: (01224) 572752 E-mail: ian@imftech.freeserve.co.uk

Lloyds Register, 71 Fenchurch Street, London, EC3M 4BS Tel: (020) 7709 9166 Fax: (020) 7488 4796 E-mail: lloydsreg@lr.org

Lombardy Consulting Group, 17 Bedford Sq, London, WC1B 3RA Tel: (020) 8343 0101 Fax: (020) 8343 1666

Polyfield Services Ltd, College Lane, Hatfield, Hertfordshire, AL10 9AB Tel: (01707) 281080 Fax: (01707) 281083 E-mail: sales@polyfield.co.uk

Quality Assurance Advisors Ltd, 68 Ferryhill Road, Aberdeen, AB11 6RR Tel: (01224) 588885 Fax: (01224) 588885 E-mail: qaa@dial.pipex.com

▶ Quality Dun Services, 14 The Wynd, Dalgety Bay, Dunfermline, Fife, KY11 9SH Tel: 01383 823837 E-mail: enquiries@qualitydunservices.co.uk

Quality Management Services, 279 Hagley Road, Pedmore, Stourbridge, West Midlands, DY9 0RJ Tel: (01562) 882677 Fax: (01562) 882677

▶ Quality Management Solutions (UK) Ltd, Iveson, Ampney St Peter, Cirencester, Gloucestershire, GL7 5SH Tel: 01285 850705 E-mail: qms-uk@tiscali.co.uk

▶ Quality Matters Ltd, PO Box 5479, Maldon, Essex, CM9 8GG Tel: (01621) 868767 Fax: (01621) 868728 E-mail: sales@quality-matters.com

Quality System Services, C Sheffield Technology Park, 60 Shirland Lane, Sheffield, S9 3SP Tel: 0114-261 8899 Fax: 0114-261 8878 E-mail: qss@sci-tech.org.uk

Sandberg LLP, 40 Grosvenor Gardens, London, SW1W 0EB Tel: (020) 7730 3461 Fax: (020) 7565 7100 E-mail: ho@sandberg.co.uk

Sigma Consultancy Scotland Ltd, 18 Overton Crescent, Dyce, Aberdeen, AB21 7FW Tel: (01224) 723947 Fax: (01224) 773754

Systems Audits Inspections Ltd, 51 Delph New Road, Delph, Oldham, OL3 5BY Tel: (01457) 870946 Fax: (01457) 870946 E-mail: philiptaylor@sai-online.co.uk

Transition Support Ltd, Vantage Point Business Village, 7/4, Mitcheldean, Gloucestershire, GL17 0DD Tel: (01594) 546151 Fax: (01594) 546153 E-mail: mail@transition-support.com

Turner & Coates Ltd, PO Box 91, Salford, M6 6XG Tel: (0845) 8909870 Fax: (0845) 8909871 E-mail: info@turnerandcoates.com

QUALITY CONTROL SERVICES

The Birmingham Assay Office, P O Box 151, Birmingham, B3 1SB Tel: 0121-236 6951 Fax: (0121) 236 9032

Elcometer Instruments Ltd, Edge Lane, Droylsden, Manchester, M43 6BU Tel: 0161-371 6000 Fax: 0161-371 6010 E-mail: sales@elcometer.com

▶ FURSTENBRUNN LIMITED, 11-15 Coventry Road, Market Harborough, Leicestershire, Market Harborough, Leicestershire, LE16 9BX Tel: 0870 4604226 Fax: 0870 4604228 E-mail: info@furstenbrunn.com

Institute of Quality Assurance, 12 Grosvenor Crescent, London, SW1X 7EE Tel: (020) 7245 6722 Fax: (020) 7245 6788 E-mail: enquiry@iqa.org

John Knox Ltd, 55 Rosebank Street, Leek, Staffordshire, ST13 6AG Tel: (01538) 399733 Fax: (01538) 399985 E-mail: jknox1066@aol.com

Quality & Business Standards Alliance, Ground Floor, 462 Holdenhurst Road, Bournemouth, BH8 9AF Tel: (01202) 386741 Fax: (01202) 392760 E-mail: info@qbsa.org

▶ Services Ltd, 82 Trent BLVD, West Bridgfore, Nottingham, NG2 5BL Tel: 0115-945 5285 Fax: 0115-981 7137 E-mail: info@servicesltd.co.uk

QUALITY CONTROL SOFTWARE

▶ Cambs Quality Ltd, St. Johns Innovation Park, Cowley Road, Cambridge, CB4 0WS Tel: (0800) 0130623 Fax: (0870) 1372532 E-mail: info@cambsquality.com

▶ FURSTENBRUNN LIMITED, 11-15 Coventry Road, Market Harborough, Leicestershire, Market Harborough, Leicestershire, LE16 9BX Tel: 0870 4604226 Fax: 0870 4604228 E-mail: info@furstenbrunn.com

I C C S Ltd, 4 Market Street, Edenfield, Ramsbottom, Bury, Lancashire, BL0 0JN Tel: (01706) 822233 Fax: (01706) 822277 E-mail: info@iccs-ltd.co.uk

QUALITY CONTROL SYSTEMS

C I Systems Ltd, Brunel Road, Churchfields, Salisbury, SP2 7PX Tel: (01722) 336938 Fax: (01722) 323222 E-mail: sales@cielec.com

Faro UK, 9- The Cobalt Centre, Siskin Parkway East, Middlemarch Business Park, Coventry, CV3 4PE Tel: (024) 7621 7690 Fax: (024) 7623 6150 E-mail: uk@faroeurope.com

Harford Cost Control, 35 Harford Street, Flat 2, Trowbridge, Wiltshire, BA14 7HL Tel: (01225) 764461 Fax: (01225) 769733 E-mail: admin@harfordcontrol.com

Scan Systems Ltd, Adswood Industrial Estate, Adswood Road, Stockport, Cheshire, SK3 8LF Tel: 0161-477 7750 Fax: 0161-477 7740 E-mail: sales@scansystems.co.uk

QUALITY MANAGEMENT SERVICES

▶ Total Quality Management Solutions Ltd, 1 Overthwart Crescent, Worcester, WR4 0JW Tel: (01905) 29753 Fax: (01905) 723548 E-mail: tqm.solutions@virgin.net

QUALITY MONITORING SYSTEMS

▶ Activa Solutions Ltd, Activa House, Commerce Way, Edenbridge, Kent, TN8 6ED Tel: (01732) 784300 Fax: (0870) 7544516 E-mail: info@activa.co.uk

QUANTITY SURVEYORS

▶ Brian Pierpoint & Co., Amberley Ridge, Church Road, Woolton, Liverpool, L25 6DD Tel: 0151-428 4019 Fax: 0151 428 4019 E-mail: brian.pierpoint@tiscali.co.uk

Cooke & Arkwright, 7-8 Windsor Place, Cardiff, CF10 3SX Tel: (029) 2034 6346 Fax: (029) 2034 6300 E-mail: sales@coark.com

▶ Ericsson Architects Ltd, Anfield House, Eskbank Toll, Dalkeith, Midlothian, EH22 3DY Tel: 0131-654 0101 Fax: 0131-654 1271

▶ J Holdsworth Associates, Alexander House, Robinson Terrace, Washington, Tyne & Wear, NE38 7BD Tel: 0191-417 2543 Fax: 0191-417 1486 E-mail: jhassociates1@aol.com

Kay Bangham Partnership, Birch House, 3 Myrtle Street, Bolton, BL1 3AH Tel: (01204) 362364 Fax: (01204) 363992

▶ KS Associates, 3c Priory Business Park, Fraser Road, Bedford, MK44 3WH Tel: (01234) 838811 Fax: (01234) 838811 E-mail: admin@ks-associates.co.uk

▶ Legge Associates Ltd, Annfield House, Eskbank Toll, Dalkeith, Midlothian, EH22 3DY Tel: 0131 654 0101 Fax: 0131 654 9596 E-mail: Symon@leggeassociates.demon.co.uk

▶ Luciant Consulting, 72 New Bond Street, London, W1S 1RR Tel: (020) 7514 1789 Fax: (020) 7348 0699 E-mail: info@hbcl.co.uk

▶ Martin Aitken Associates, Aspire Business Centre, 16 Farmeloan Road, Rutherglen, Glasgow, G73 1DL Tel: 0141-647 0101 Fax: 0141-647 0107 E-mail: martinaitkenassociates@btconnect.com

MKA Projects Ltd, 15/20 Churchill Square, Kings Hill, West Malling, Kent, ME19 4YU Tel: (01732) 897917 Fax: (01732) 897927 E-mail: info@mka-projects.co.uk

▶ Quants Ltd, 15 The Oval, Doncaster, South Yorkshire, DN4 5LJ Tel: (01302) 537551 Fax: (01302) 537551 E-mail: quantsltd@btconnect.com

▶ Stewart Pearl & Associates, 3 Sandy Lane, Prestwich, Manchester, M25 9RU Tel: 0161-798 8811 Fax: 0161-798 8811 E-mail: sales@stewartpearl.co.uk

QUARRY DRILLING EQUIPMENT

Boart UK Ltd, Littlemoor, Eckington, Sheffield, S21 4EF Tel: (01246) 435601 Fax: (01246) 435903 E-mail: sales@boartlongyear.com

Colcrete Eurodrill, Tower Business Park, Derby Road, Clay Cross, Chesterfield, Derbyshire, S45 9AG Tel: (01246) 868700 Fax: (01246) 868701 E-mail: info@colcrete-eurodrill.co.uk

Glenco Quarry Services, 19 Meadow Bank Avenue, Sheffield, S7 1PB Tel: 0114-258 3734 Fax: 0114-255 0583

QUARRY FLOORING OR TILES

Tile Supply Solutions Ltd, Thornescroft, West Street, Wiveliscombe, Taunton, Somerset, TA4 2JP Tel: (01984) 624757 Fax: (0845) 2800105 E-mail: simon@tilesupplysolutions.com

QUARRY OPERATORS OR QUARRIED PRODUCTS, *See also headings for individual products*

Aggregates Industries, Whitworth Quarry, Tong Lane, Whitworth, Rochdale, Lancashire, OL12 8BE Tel: (01706) 853296 Fax: (01706) 854286

Alltgoch Quarry, Cwrtnewydd, Llanybydder, Dyfed, SA40 9YL Tel: (01570) 434338 Fax: (01570) 434304

▶ Bardo Midlands, 115 Spalding Road, Deeping St. James, Peterborough, PE6 8SD Tel: (01778) 345609 Fax: (01778) 349258 E-mail: bardo.midlands@btconnect.com

Brauncewell Quarries Ltd, Brauncewell Quarry, Brauncewell, Sleaford, Lincolnshire, NG34 8RL Tel: (01526) 832767 Fax: (01526) 833075

Cemex UK Ltd, Crown House, Evreux Way, Rugby, Warwickshire, CV21 2DT Tel: 0114-242 6050 Fax: (01788) 540166

Chap Quarries (Aberdeen) Ltd, Westhill Industrial Estate, Westhill, Aberdeenshire, AB32 6TQ Tel: (01224) 748500 Fax: (01224) 748501 E-mail: mail@chap.co.uk

M. Wallace Clelland & Co. Ltd, Burnside Industrial Estate, Kilsyth, Glasgow, G65 9JY Tel: (01236) 823015 Fax: (01236) 823256

Collen Brothers Quarries Ltd, Hanover Street, Portadown, Craigavon, County Armagh, BT62 3ET Tel: (028) 3833 4131 Fax: (028) 3884 0313

▶ Dunloy Quarry, 93 Bridge Road, Dunloy, Ballymena, County Antrim, BT44 9EG Tel: (028) 2765 7512

E.W. Creaser (Burnby) Ltd, Partridge Hall Quarry, Burnby, York, YO42 1RD Tel: (01430) 873428 Fax: (01430) 873428

Finlay Hydrascreens, 6 Gillygooly Road, Omagh, County Tyrone, BT78 5PN Tel: (028) 8224 5127 Fax: (028) 8224 4294 E-mail: sales@terexfinlay.com

Frimstone Ltd, Norton Hill, Snettisham, King's Lynn, Norfolk, PE31 7LZ Tel: (01485) 570182 Fax: (01485) 543458

Gibson Bros, Magherally, Banbridge, County Down, BT32 4YN Tel: (028) 4066 2771 Fax: (028) 4062 6704 E-mail: liam@gibbros.freeserve.co.uk

▶ E. & J.W. Glendinning Ltd, Glentor, Ashburton, Newton Abbot, Devon, TQ13 7LF Tel: (01364) 652601 Fax: (01364) 651118 E-mail: sales@ejwglendinning.co.uk

Greaves Welsh Slate Co. Ltd, Llechwedd Slate Mines, Blaenau Ffestiniog, Gwynedd, LL41 3NB Tel: (01766) 830522 Fax: (01766) 830711 E-mail: llechwedd@aol.com

▶ Hanson Aggregates Ltd, Hingston Down Quarry, Gunnislake, Cornwall, PL18 9AU Tel: (01822) 832271 Fax: (01822) 833342

Harris Group, 170 Cardigan Road, Leeds, LS6 1LL Tel: 0113-203 3129 Fax: 0113-203 3128 E-mail: pwcharrisaggs@aol.com

Hillhouse Quarry Group, Hillhouse Quarry, Troon, Ayrshire, KA10 7HX Tel: (01292) 310482 Fax: (01292) 314640

The Hills Group Ltd, Ailesbury Court, High Street, Marlborough, Wiltshire, SN8 1AA Tel: (01672) 516111 Fax: (01672) 516198 E-mail: mhayes@hills-group.co.uk

Hills Westmidlands Ltd, Lickhill Quarry, Bewdley Road North, Stourport-On-Severn, Worcestershire, DY13 8RN Tel: (01299) 827782 Fax: (01299) 827421

Holderness Aggregates Ltd, Mill Hill Quarry, Hull Road, Keyingham, Hull, HU12 9ST Tel: (01964) 622347

Huntsmans Quarries Ltd, The Old School, Naunton, Cheltenham, Gloucestershire, GL54 3AE Tel: (01451) 850555 Fax: (01451) 850670 E-mail: john.milner@huntsmanquarries.co.uk

J Oldham & Co. Ltd, Tearne House, Hollington, Stoke-on-Trent, ST10 4HR Tel: (01889) 507353 Fax: (01889) 507212 E-mail: enquiries@joldham.co.uk

James Stevenson Quarries Ltd, Clinty Quarry, 215 Doury Road, Ballymena, County Antrim, BT43 6SS Tel: (028) 2565 6302 Fax: (028) 2564 6495

▶ Leiths (Scotland) Ltd, Rigifa, Cove, Aberdeen, AB12 3LR Tel: (01224) 876333

Longcliffe Quarries Ltd, Longcliffe, Brassington, Matlock, Derbyshire, DE4 4BZ Tel: (01629) 540284 Fax: (01629) 540569 E-mail: sales@longcliffe.co.uk

Miskelly Bros Ltd, 29 Moss Road, Ballygowan, Newtownards, County Down, BT23 6JE Tel: (028) 9752 8218 Fax: (028) 9752 1792

Morley Bros, Yedingham, Malton, North Yorkshire, YO17 8SS Tel: (07855) 829094 Fax: (01944) 728280

Neil Mullin & Sons Ltd, Mullans Quarry, 203 Altamuskin Road, Sixmilecross, Omagh, County Tyrone, BT79 9HX Tel: (028) 8075 8280

Pickard Group, Fagley Lane, Eccleshill, Bradford, West Yorkshire, BD2 3NT Tel: (01274) 637307 Fax: (01274) 626146 E-mail: sales@pickard.co.uk

C. Porter Ltd, Britannia Road, Waltham Cross, Hertfordshire, EN8 7PE Tel: (01992) 713565 Fax: (01992) 712980

▶ Q M J Publishing Ltd, 7 Regent Street, Nottingham, NG1 5BS Tel: 0115-941 1315 Fax: 0115-948 4035 E-mail: qm@quarrymanagment.com

R M C Materials Ltd, Tannochside Park, Uddingston, Glasgow, G71 5PH Tel: (01698) 811100 Fax: (01698) 816068

Ready Mix (NI) Ltd, RMC House, Upper Dunmurry Lane, Belfast, BT17 0AJ Tel: (028) 9061 6611 Fax: (028) 9061 9969

Riskend Quarry Ltd, 6 Garrell Road, Kilsyth, Glasgow, G65 9JY Tel: (01236) 821486 Fax: (01236) 823256 E-mail: riskendquarry@supanet.com

Ross Hillman Ltd, Station Road, Westbury, Wiltshire, BA13 3JP Tel: (01373) 822447 Fax: (01373) 824492

Shipley Quarries, Rose Cottage, Lartington, Barnard Castle, County Durham, DL12 9BP Tel: (01833) 650529 Fax: (01833) 650529

Singleton Birch Ltd, South Thoresby, Alford, Lincolnshire, LN13 0AR Tel: (01507) 480651 Fax: (01507) 480324 E-mail: sh@singletonbirch.co.uk

Singleton Birch Ltd, Melton Ross Quarries, Barnetby, South Humberside, DN38 6AE Tel: (01652) 688386 Fax: (01652) 686081

Staffordshire Stone Hollington Ltd, Quarry Bank, Hollington, Stoke-on-Trent, ST10 4HQ Tel: (01889) 507435 Fax: (01889) 507365

▶ Tarmac Central Ltd, Hoveringham, Nottingham, NG14 7JY Tel: 0115-966 4292 Fax: 0115-966 5288

Tarmac Western Ltd, PO Box 1, Kington, Herefordshire, HR5 3LQ Tel: (01544) 388959 Fax: (01544) 231406 E-mail: info@tarmac-western.co.uk

Tullyraine Quarries Ltd, 122 Dromore Road, Banbridge, County Down, BT32 4EG Tel: (028) 4066 2481 Fax: (028) 4066 2748 E-mail: enquiries@tullyrainequarries.co.uk

Water Hall Group plc, Paralel House, 32 London Road, Guildford, Surrey, GU1 2AB Tel: (01483) 452333 Fax: (01483) 452322

W. Clifford Watts Ltd, 118-122 Scarborough Road, Bridlington, East Yorkshire, YO16 7NU Tel: (01262) 675383 Fax: (01262) 604629 E-mail: wcliffordwatts@aol.com

Whitemountain Quarries, 26 Ballycarngannon Road, Lisburn, County Antrim, BT27 6YA Tel: (028) 9263 9750 Fax: (028) 9263 9751 E-mail: info@lagan-group.com

Yorkshire Roadstone Lightwater Quarrys Ltd, Potgate Quarry, North Stainley, Ripon, North Yorkshire, HG4 3JN Tel: (01765) 635435 Fax: (01765) 635413

QUARRY PLANT MAINTENANCE OR REPAIR ENGINEERING

CMB International Ltd, Little Alton Farm, Ashby Road, Ravenstone, Coalville, Leicestershire, LE67 2AA Tel: (01530) 563600 Fax: (01530) 563900 E-mail: sales@cmb.uk.com

Folkes Plant & Aggregates Ltd, Welcome Pits, Butt Lane, Burgh Castle, Great Yarmouth, Norfolk, NR31 9PY Tel: (01493) 780274 Fax: (01493) 781118

Heavy Machining Services Ltd, 19 Ashville Way, Cambridge Road, Whetstone, Leicester, LE8 6NU Tel: 0116-275 2225 Fax: 0116-275 2005

Site Engineering Crane Hire, 11 Back Lane, Sileby, Loughborough, Leicestershire, LE12 7RB Tel: (01509) 816655 Fax: (01509) 816060

QUARRY PLANT OR EQUIPMENT

B J D Crushers Ltd, B B I Centre, Innovation Way, Wilthorpe, Barnsley, South Yorkshire, S75 1JL Tel: (01226) 241425 Fax: (01226) 296713 E-mail: sales@bjdcrushers.co.uk

Bell Equipment UK, Unit 6c Graycar Business Park, Barton Turns Barton Under, Barton Under Needwood, Burton-on-Trent, Staffordshire, DE13 8EN Tel: (01283) 712862 Fax: (01283) 712687 E-mail: web@bell.co.za

Benninghoven UK Ltd, Incendium House Centurion Way, Meridian Business Park, Leicester, LE19 1WH Tel: 0116-263 0345 Fax: 0116-282 8741 E-mail: enquiries@benninghoven.co.uk

Canning Conveyor Co. Ltd, Sandy Lane Industrial Estate, Sandy Lane, Worksop, Nottinghamshire, S80 1TN Tel: (01909) 486166 Fax: (01909) 500638 E-mail: andrew.canning@canningconveyor.co.uk

Centristic Ltd, 1 Cavalier Road, Heathfield Industrial Estate, Newton Abbot, Devon, TQ12 6TQ Tel: (01626) 834310 Fax: (01626) 834681 E-mail: centristic@btconnect.com

Esl Engineering, 11a Farrenlester Road, Coleraine, County Londonderry, BT51 3QR Tel: (028) 7035 6145 Fax: (028) 7035 4606 E-mail: eslengineering@btconnect.com

Finlay Hire Ltd, Lakeside House, Ladford Covert Industrial Park, Seighford, Stafford, ST18 9QL Tel: (01785) 282323 Fax: (01785) 282991 E-mail: sales@finlay-group.demon.co.uk

H R International Crushing & Screening Ltd, Huntingdon Court, Huntingdon Way, Measham, Swadlincote, Derbyshire, DE12 7NQ Tel: (01530) 272799 Fax: (01530) 272787 E-mail: hril@lineone.net

▶ Hanson Aggregates Ltd, Caer Glaw Quarry, Gwalchmai, Holyhead, Gwynedd, LL65 4PW Tel: (01407) 720292 Fax: (01407) 720106

Hausherr (U K) Ltd, High St, Clay Cross, Chesterfield, Derbyshire, S45 9PF Tel: (01246) 252000 Fax: (01246) 865077 E-mail: hausherr@btconnect.com

L J H Group Ltd, Leigh Road, Chantry, Frome, Somerset, BA11 3LR Tel: (01373) 836451 Fax: (01373) 836879 E-mail: sales@ljhgroup.co.uk

Linatex Ltd, Wilkinson House Galway Road, Blackbushe Business Park, Yateley, Hampshire, GU46 6GE Tel: (01252) 743000 Fax: (01252) 743030E-mail: info@linatex.com

M E S International Ltd, 11 Copdale Road, Leicester, LE5 4FG Tel: 0116-249 0333 Fax: 0116-249 0142 E-mail: sales@mesinternational.uk.com

Clusky McCloskey International Ltd, 47 Moor Road, Coalisland, Dungannon, County Tyrone, BT71 4QB Tel: (028) 8774 0926 Fax: (028) 8774 7242

▶ Northstone Quarry & Asphalt Division, 50 Craigadoo Road, Ballymena, County Antrim, BT42 4RB Tel: (028) 2589 8151

S P W Group Ltd, Victoria Works, Victoria Road, Stoke-on-Trent, ST4 2QR Tel: (01782) 847911 Fax: (01782) 744420

▶ Tarmac Northern Ltd, 40a Boghill Road, Newtownabbey, County Antrim, BT36 4QS Tel: (028) 9083 3879 Fax: (028) 9083 9494

QUARRYING ELECTRICAL ENGINEERING

R D J, Unit 1 A, Cranmer Road, West Meadows Industrial Estate, Derby, DE21 6JL Tel: (01332) 345472 Fax: (01332) 293509

QUARTZ CRYSTAL UNITS

Fordahl Sa), 225 Hampton Lane, Blackfield, Southampton, SO45 1XA Tel: (023) 8089 8899 Fax: (023) 8089 8899 E-mail: fordahluk@fordahl.com

QUARTZ CRYSTALS

Euroquartz Ltd, Blacknell Lane, Crewkerne, Somerset, TA18 7HE Tel: (01460) 230000 Fax: (01460) 230001 E-mail: sales@euroquartz.co.uk

Fordahl Sa), 225 Hampton Lane, Blackfield, Southampton, SO45 1XA Tel: (023) 8089 8899 Fax: (023) 8089 8899 E-mail: fordahluk@fordahl.com

Magna Frequency Management Ltd, Magna House Dales Manor Business Park, Grove Road, Sawston, Cambridge, CB2 4TJ Tel: (01223) 834800 Fax: (01223) 834600 E-mail: sales@magnafrequency.com

Quartslab Marketing Ltd, PO Box 19, Erith, Kent, DA8 1LH Tel: (01322) 330830 Fax: (01322) 334904 E-mail: sales@quartslab.com

Total Frequency Control Ltd, Units 3-4 Mill Lane, Storrington, West Sussex, RH20 4NF Tel: (01903) 740000 Fax: (01903) 742208 E-mail: sales@tfc.co.uk

QUARTZ ELECTRIC HEATERS

▶ Hyco Manufacturing Ltd, Units 1 & 2, Calder Works, Methley Road, Castleford, West Yorkshire, WF10 1NX Tel: (01977) 517555 Fax: (01977) 517666 E-mail: sales@hycomanufacturing.co.uk

QUERY AND REPORTING SOLUTIONS

▶ ASTRAC Ltd, Innovation Centre, Warwick Technology Park, Warwick, CV34 6UW Tel: (01926) 623060 Fax: (01926) 623061 E-mail: info@astrac.com

QUICHES

▶ Roberts Country Fayre, Bersham Enterprise Centre, Colliery Road, Rhostyllen, Wrexham, Clwyd, LL14 4EG Tel: (01978) 264444 Fax: (01978) 354303 E-mail: robertscountryfayre@virgin.net

QUICK CHANGE TOOL HOLDERS

Coventry Toolholders Ltd, Grovelands Estate, Longford Road, Exhall, Coventry, CV7 9ND Tel: (024) 7664 5999 Fax: (024) 7664 4081 E-mail: info@coventrytoolholders.co.uk

Gewefa UK Ltd, Edinburgh Way, Leafield Industrial Estate, Corsham, Wiltshire, SN13 9XZ Tel: (01453) 872074 Fax: (01225) 811388 E-mail: sales@gewefa.co.uk

QUICK FROZEN FOODS

Sous Vide, 48-50 Edison Road, Rabans Lane Industrial Area, Aylesbury, Buckinghamshire, HP19 8TE Tel: (0845) 1212213 Fax: (01296) 431133 E-mail: lucy@sous-vide.co.uk

QUICK RELEASE COUPLINGS

Euro Fluid Power Ltd, St. Marys Works, Brierley Street, Stoke-on-Trent, ST6 1LB Tel: (01782) 575306 Fax: (01782) 575534 E-mail: eurofluid@aol.com

▶ Maag Pumps, PO Box 193, Evesham, Worcestershire, WR11 2WY Tel: (01386) 423756 Fax: (01386) 423862 E-mail: info@suurmond.co.uk

▶ Macdonald Pneumatique, Peel Park Place, East Kilbride, Glasgow, G74 5LS Tel: (01355) 249507 Fax: (01355) 220091 E-mail: info@macdonaldairtools.co.uk

Tom Parker Ltd, PO Box 36, Preston, PR1 1HY Tel: (01772) 251405 Fax: (01772) 827088 E-mail: sales@tom-parker.co.uk

Rotolok Bulk Systems Ltd, 38 Woodham Lane, New Haw, Addlestone, Surrey, KT15 3NA Tel: (01932) 854756 Fax: (01932) 859427 E-mail: sales@blotch.co.uk

Staubli Unimation Ltd, Lodge Park, Telford, Shropshire, TF1 7ET Tel: (01952) 604827 Fax: (01952) 608579 E-mail: connectors.uk@staubli.com

Subsea Components, 59 Clivemont Road, Maidenhead, Berkshire, SL6 7BZ Tel: (01628) 506560 Fax: (01628) 506501 E-mail: sales@subsea-components.co.uk

Wade, Delta Road, Parr, St. Helens, Merseyside, WA9 2ED Tel: (01744) 451616 Fax: (01744) 26791 E-mail: enquiries@deltafluidproducts.com

Walther Couplings, 29 Akeman Street, Tring, Hertfordshire, HP23 6AN Tel: (01442) 891929 Fax: (01442) 890812 E-mail: sales@walther-couplings.com

Weh (UK) Ltd, 2 Batemans Lane, Wythall, Birmingham, B47 6NG Tel: (01564) 825100 Fax: (01564) 825105 E-mail: instatest@lineone.net

Wilbar Components Ltd, Martindale Industrial Estate, Hawks Green, Cannock, Staffordshire, WS11 7XN Tel: (01543) 578873 Fax: (01543) 570450 E-mail: enquiries@wilbar.co.uk

QUICK RELEASE FASTENERS

Bolhoff Fastenings Ltd, Midacre, Willenhall, West Midlands, WV13 2JW Tel: (01902) 637161 Fax: (01902) 609495 E-mail: enquiries@bollhoff.co.uk

Specialty Fasteners & Components Ltd, Seymour Wharf, Steamer Quay Road, Totnes, Devon, TQ9 5AL Tel: (01803) 868677 Fax: (01803) 868678 E-mail: sales@specialty-fasteners.co.uk

QUICK RELEASE HOSE COUPLINGS

Eaton Fluid Power Group, Thorns Road, Brierley Hill, West Midlands, DY5 2BQ Tel: (01384) 426320 Fax: (01384) 891506 E-mail: mark.ward@aeroquip.com

Flowtech Ltd, Pimbo Road, Skelmersdale, Lancashire, WN8 9RB Tel: (01695) 52770 Fax: (0800) 2987230 E-mail: sales@flowtech.co.uk

Guyson International Ltd, Southview Business Park, Ghyll Royd, Guiseley, Leeds, LS20 9PR Tel: (01943) 870044 Fax: (01943) 870066 E-mail: enquiries@guyson.co.uk

Tom Parker Ltd, PO Box 36, Preston, PR1 1HY Tel: (01772) 251405 Fax: (01772) 827088 E-mail: sales@tom-parker.co.uk

Scully UK, Unit 4 Road One, Winsford Industrial Estate, Winsford, Cheshire, CW7 3QE Tel: (01606) 553805 Fax: (01606) 553824 E-mail: sales@scullyuk.com

Shire Fluid Power Ltd, 6 Racecourse Road, Pershore, Worcestershire, WR10 2EY Tel: (01386) 554744 Fax: (01386) 553743

Walther Couplings, 29 Akeman Street, Tring, Hertfordshire, HP23 6AN Tel: (01442) 891929 Fax: (01442) 890812 E-mail: sales@walther-couplings.com

Wilbar Components Ltd, Martindale Industrial Estate, Hawks Green, Cannock, Staffordshire, WS11 7XN Tel: (01543) 578873 Fax: (01543) 570450 E-mail: enquiries@wilbar.co.uk

Witzenmann UK Ltd, Righead Industrial Estate, Bellshill, Lanarkshire, ML4 3LW Tel: (01698) 749660 Fax: (01698) 740774

Wright Engineering Co. Ltd, Masons Road, Stratford-upon-Avon, Warwickshire, CV37 9JA Tel: (01789) 292939 Fax: (01789) 297458 E-mail: sales@wright-eng.co.uk

QUILT BED-COVERS, *See also Down Quilt Manufrs*

Bedcrest Ltd, Old Hall Street, Middleton, Manchester, M24 1AG Tel: (0870) 7662324

Bolton Hemming Ltd, Halliwell Industrial Estate, Wapping Street, Bolton, BL1 8DP Tel: (01204) 492614 Fax: (01204) 492088 E-mail: enquiries@bolton-hemming.co.uk

Bury Soft Furnishings Ltd, 9 Brantwood Road, Salford, M7 4EN Tel: 0161-792 1492 Fax: 0161-792 1492

Comfy Quilts, Albany Mill, Old Hall Street, Middleton, Manchester, M24 1AG Tel: (0870) 7662324 Fax: (0870) 7662333 E-mail: info@comfyquilts.com

Dorfell Textiles, 50 Cambrian Street, Manchester, M40 7EG Tel: 0161-273 7747 Fax: 0161-274 3862

Dorma Group Ltd, Newtown Mill Lees Street, Pendlebury, Swinton, Manchester, M27 6DB Tel: 0161-251 4400 Fax: 0161-251 4417 E-mail: info@dorma.co.uk

Downland Bedding Co. Ltd, 23 Blackstock Street, Liverpool, L3 6ER Tel: 0151-236 7166 Fax: 0151-236 0062 E-mail: sales@downlandbedding.co.uk

Fogarty Ltd, Havenside, Fishtoft Road, Boston, Lincolnshire, PE21 0AH Tel: (01205) 361122 Fax: (01205) 353202 E-mail: info@fogarty.co.uk

Hamilton Mcbride, Churchill Way, Nelson, Lancashire, BB9 6RT Tel: (01282) 878282 Fax: (01282) 614464 E-mail: enquiries@hamiltonmcbride.co.uk

Snug Company Ltd, Stonegate House, Stoneygate Lane, Gateshead, Tyne & Wear, NE10 0HJ Tel: 0191-495 2322 Fax: 0191-495 2321 E-mail: admin@snug-ltd.com

Trendsetter Home Furnishings Ltd, Brook Mill, Hollins Road, Oldham, OL8 4JY Tel: 0161-627 4458 Fax: 0161-627 0649

William S Graham & Sons Dewsbury Ltd, Ravens Ing Mills, Ravensthorpe, Dewsbury, West Yorkshire, WF13 3JF Tel: (01924) 462456 Fax: (01924) 457985

QUILT COVERS

▶ Flamboyance, 483 Green Lanes, London, N13 4BS Tel: (0845) 8382542 Fax: (0871) 2423304E-mail: sales@FlamboyanceLtd.co.uk

▶ Franklins International Ltd, Scarva Road, Banbridge, County Down, BT32 3AU Tel: (028) 4062 2230 Fax: (028) 4062 3540 E-mail: info@franklinsgroup.net

▶ Goodwill Trade Co. Ltd, 34 Finchley Lane, Hendon, London, NW4 1DL Tel: (020) 8203 8914 E-mail: goodwill-trade@hotmail.com

▶ Onevillage.com, St. Benets, Church Lane, Charlbury, Chipping Norton, Oxfordshire, OX7 3SQ Tel: (01608) 811811

▶ Tonder & Tonder, Bryants Farm, Kiln Road, Dunsden, Reading, RG4 9PB Tel: 0118-946 3704 Fax: 0118-946 3801 E-mail: sales@tonderandtonder.com

QUILTERS TO THE TRADE

B & A Quilting Co. Ltd, Oxford Mill, Oxford Street East, Ashton-under-Lyne, Lancashire, OL7 0LT Tel: 0161-330 5030 Fax: 0161-339 0418 E-mail: info@ba-quilting.co.uk

B.S. Dollamore, Burton Rd, Castle Gresley, Swadlincote, Derbyshire, DE11 9HA Tel: (01283) 217905 Fax: (01283) 550119 E-mail: bsdollamore@aol.com

Harvey Quilting, 11 Robin Hood Industrial Estate, Alfred St South, Nottingham, NG3 1GE Tel: 0115-958 5777 Fax: 0115-950 3339 E-mail: tonyatharveys@hotmail.com

▶ Louis Moreau (The Quilters) Ltd, Unit 9G1 N17 Studios, 784/788 High Road, Tottenham, London, N17 0DA Tel: (020) 8808 1337 Fax: (020) 8365 0547 E-mail: moreau@smeuk.com

P S Gill & Sons, 261-277 Rookery Road, Handsworth, Birmingham, B21 9PT Tel: 0121-554 7521 Fax: 0121-554 9033 E-mail: ssgill@psgill.com

Supreme Quilting Co plc, Brittania Works, Whitehall Road, Tipton, West Midlands, DY4 7JR Tel: 0121-520 7227 Fax: 0121-522 4245

QUILTING MACHINES

Gateway Textiles Ltd, Northgate Terrace, Unit 3 Northern Road, Newark, Nottinghamshire, NG24 2EU Tel: (01636) 676194 Fax: (01636) 611367 E-mail: sales@gatewaysystems.co.uk

QUILTING THREADS

Danfield Ltd, St. Helens Road, Leigh, Lancashire, WN7 3PF Tel: (01942) 675316 Fax: (01942) 670063 E-mail: info@danfield.co.uk

Patchwork Gallery, 17 Mead Close, Knutsford, Cheshire, WA16 0DU Tel: (01565) 632553 E-mail: sales@patchworkgallery.co.uk

Somac Threads Manufacturing Ltd, Unit 2-3 Brymau Four Trading Estate, River Lane, Saltney, Chester, CH4 8RF Tel: (01244) 680506 Fax: (01244) 680202 E-mail: sales@somac.co.uk

QUILTS

Fogarty Ltd, Havenside, Fishtoft Road, Boston, Lincolnshire, PE21 0AH Tel: (01205) 361122 Fax: (01205) 353202 E-mail: info@fogarty.co.uk

▶ Wool Duvets, Jasmine House, Saxlingham Road, Blakeney, Holt, Norfolk, NR25 7PB Tel: (01263) 741799 E-mail: enquiries@woolduvets.co.uk

QUOTA SERVICES, FINANCE

Carlton Corporate Finance Ltd, 38 Berkeley Square, London, W1J 5AE Tel: (020) 7355 2211 Fax: (020) 7355 1633 E-mail: ccf@carltoncf.com

RACING CAR BODIES, ALUMINIUM

Mondiale Car Co. Ltd, 9 Balloo Cresent, Bangor, County Down, BT19 7WP Tel: (028) 9145 2322 Fax: (028) 9145 0932 E-mail: mondiale@lagan.net

Tarcal, Unit 15A, Pershore Trading Estate, Pershore, Worcestershire, WR10 2DD Tel: (01386) 556312 Fax: (01386) 556058

RACING CAR COMPONENTS

A H Fabrication, Thorn Office Centre, Thorn Business Park, Rotherwas, Hereford, HR2 6JT Tel: (01432) 354704 Fax: (01432) 359762 E-mail: alexahfabs@fairadsl.co.uk

Auto Sport (Engineering) Ltd, Brandon Road, Binley, Coventry, CV3 2AH Tel: (024) 7643 7110 Fax: (024) 7645 9757

Leda Suspension Ltd, Unit 1 Park Drive, Braintree, Essex, CM7 1AP Tel: (01376) 326531 Fax: (01376) 326530 E-mail: info@leda.com

Motor Sport (Glass) Ltd, 11 Claymore, Tame Valley Industrial Estate, Wilnecote, Tamworth, Staffordshire, B77 5DQ Tel: (01827) 283688 Fax: (01827) 283689 E-mail: sales@heatedwindscreen.com

▶ Performance Automotive, Unit 5 Bridgeway, St. Leonards-On-Sea, East Sussex, TN38 8AP Tel: 01424 200825 E-mail: performanceautomotive@hotmail.co.uk

Race Engine Components, Kingswood Farm, Kingswood, Albrighton, Wolverhampton, WV7 3AQ Tel: (01902) 373770 Fax: (01902) 373772 E-mail: jivey10194@aol.com

RACING CAR ENGINEERING SERVICES, INCLUDING RALLY VEHICLE/HIGH PERFORMANCE

Ajec Racing, Unit 3 Vernon Court, Meteor Business Park, Cheltenham Road East, Staverton, Gloucester, GL2 9QL Tel: (01452) 615333 Fax: (01452) 615777 E-mail: ajecracing@btconnect.com
Auto Sport (Engineering) Ltd, Brandon Road, Binley, Coventry, CV3 2AH Tel: (024) 7643 7110 Fax: (024) 7645 9757
BTB Exhausts Ltd, 3-5 The Beaver Centre, Great Central Way, Woodford Halse, Daventry, Northamptonshire, NN11 3DP Tel: (01327) 261797 Fax: (01327) 263577
D S A, 4-5 Edison Road, Rabans Lane Industrial Area, Aylesbury, Buckinghamshire, HP19 8TE Tel: (01296) 486911 Fax: (01296) 334335 E-mail: hq@gforcemotorsport.co.uk
J F Engines, Unit 2, The Old Gymnasium, 45 Green Lane, Ewelme, Wallingford, Oxfordshire, OX10 6DA Tel: (01491) 839336 Fax: (01491) 680719
Langford Performance Engineering Ltd, 17 Bradfield Close, Finedon Road Industrial Estate, Wellingborough, Northamptonshire, NN8 4RQ Tel: (01933) 441661 Fax: (01933) 441549 E-mail: sales@lpengines.demon.co.uk
P I Research, The Brookfield Motorsports Centre, Twentypence Road, Cottenham, Cambridge, CB4 8PS Tel: (01954) 253600 Fax: (01954) 253601 E-mail: sales@piresearch.co.uk
Race Engine Components, Kingswood Farm, Kingswood, Albrighton, Wolverhampton, WV7 3AQ Tel: (01902) 373770 Fax: (01902) 373772 E-mail: jivey10194@aol.com
Raceparts (UK) Ltd, Unit 3, Rockfort Industrial Estate, Hithercroft Road, Wallingford, Oxfordshire, OX10 9DA Tel: (01491) 822000 Fax: (01491) 822009 E-mail: sales@raceparts.co.uk
Rock & Tapping Ltd, 10 Wedgwood Road, Bicester, Oxfordshire, OX26 4UL Tel: (01869) 240404 Fax: (01869) 245500 E-mail: sales@stackltd.com
T V R Power Ltd, 339 Bedworth Road, Longford, Coventry, CV6 6BN Tel: (024) 7636 6177 Fax: (024) 7636 5428 E-mail: dom@tvr-power.co.uk
Tarcal, Unit 15A, Pershore Trading Estate, Pershore, Worcestershire, WR10 2DD Tel: (01386) 556312 Fax: (01386) 556058
▶ Wyatt Engineering, Darrow Wood Farm, Shelfanger Road, Diss, Norfolk, IP22 4XY Tel: (01379) 640200 Fax: (01379) 640200

RACING CAR ENGINES

Neil Brown Engineering Ltd, Wardentree Lane Industrial Estate, Benner Road, Pinchbeck, Spalding, Lincolnshire, PE11 3TZ Tel: (01775) 723052 Fax: (01775) 710570 E-mail: admin@nbe.co.uk
(Connaught Competition Engines) Ltd, Wormdale Farm, Wormdale Hill, Newington, Sittingbourne, Kent, ME9 7PX Tel: (01795) 843802 Fax: (01795) 841358 E-mail: info@hillclimb.freeserve.co.uk
Engine Developments, Leigh Road, Swift Valley Industrial Estate, Rugby, Warwickshire, CV21 1DS Tel: (01788) 541114 Fax: (01788) 546303 E-mail: sales@engdev.com
Mercedes Benz UK Ltd, Quarry Road, Brixworth, Northampton, NN6 9UB Tel: (01604) 880100 Fax: (01604) 882800 E-mail: reception@mercedes-benz-hpe.com
Mondiale Car Co. Ltd, 9 Balloo Cresent, Bangor, County Down, BT19 7WP Tel: (028) 9145 2322 Fax: (028) 9145 0932 E-mail: mondiale@lagan.net
Scholar Engines, Blue House, Norwich Road, Mendlesham, Stowmarket, Suffolk, IP14 5NH Tel: (01449) 767711 Fax: (01449) 767772 E-mail: adwsre@aol.com
Swindon Racing Engines Ltd, Crampton Road, Greenbridge Estate, Swindon, SN3 3JJ Tel: (01793) 531321 Fax: (01793) 528484 E-mail: info@swindon-engines.com
Titan Motorsport & Automotive Engineering, Harley Industrial Park, Paxton Hill, St. Neots, Cambridgeshire, PE19 6TA Tel: (01480) 474402 Fax: (01480) 405668 E-mail: sales@titan.uk.net

RACING CAR RESTORATION SERVICES

Leda Suspension Ltd, Unit 1 Park Drive, Braintree, Essex, CM7 1AP Tel: (01376) 326531 Fax: (01376) 326530 E-mail: info@leda.com

RACING CAR SUPPLY SERVICES

Crossle Car Co. Ltd, 217 Old Holywood Road, Holywood, County Down, BT18 9QS Tel: (028) 9076 3332 Fax: (028) 9076 0676 E-mail: arnie@crossle.fsnet.co.uk
Globel Technologies Racing, Denmans Lane, Fontwell, Arundel, West Sussex, BN18 0SU Tel: (01243) 545000 Fax: (01243) 545050
Motor Sport (Glass) Ltd, 11 Claymore, Tame Valley Industrial Estate, Wilnecote, Tamworth, Staffordshire, B77 5DQ Tel: (01827) 283688 Fax: (01827) 283689 E-mail: sales@heatedwindscreen.com

RACING CARS

Crossle Car Co. Ltd, 217 Old Holywood Road, Holywood, County Down, BT18 9QS Tel: (028) 9076 3332 Fax: (028) 9076 0676 E-mail: arnie@crossle.fsnet.co.uk
▶ Ferrari Trackdays, PO Box 169, Wymondham, Norfolk, NR18 0WL Tel: (0870) 9103786 E-mail: info@ferraritrackdays.co.uk
Lola Cars Ltd, 12 Glebe Road, St Peters Hill, Huntingdon, Cambridgeshire, PE29 7DY Tel: (01480) 456722 Fax: (01480) 482970 E-mail: lola@lolacars.com
Pilbeam Racing Designs Ltd, Graham Hill Way, Bourne, Lincolnshire, PE10 9PJ Tel: (01778) 424838 Fax: (01778) 393032 E-mail: info@pilbeamracing.co.uk
RTN, Ironside Way, Hingham, Norwich, NR9 4LF Tel: (01953) 851411 Fax: (01953) 851239 E-mail: g.muff@rtn-racing.co.uk
U2 Sports Cars Ltd, Rowley Wood Lane, Hartwell, Northampton, NN7 2QT Tel: (01604) 863504 Fax: (01604) 863807

RACING QUAD BIKE ACCESSORIES

▶ Muddy Trax Racing Ltd, The Gate House Cherry Tree Sawmills, Faygate Lane, Faygate, Horsham, West Sussex, RH12 4SJ Tel: (01293) 852600 E-mail: sales@muddytrax.co.uk

RACING QUAD BIKES

▶ Muddy Trax Racing Ltd, The Gate House Cherry Tree Sawmills, Faygate Lane, Faygate, Horsham, West Sussex, RH12 4SJ Tel: (01293) 852600 E-mail: sales@muddytrax.co.uk

RACK AND PINION HOISTS

Alimak Hek Ltd, Northampton Road, Rushden, Northamptonshire, NN10 6BW Tel: (01933) 354700 Fax: (01933) 410600 E-mail: ukinfo@alimakhek.com

RACKING SYSTEM REFURBISHMENT

Monarch Shelving Ltd, Unit 7, Moss Lane Industrial Estate, Heyside, Oldham, OL2 6HR Tel: (01706) 880355 Fax: (0870) 7505477 E-mail: sales@monarchdirect.co.uk

RACKING SYSTEMS, WAREHOUSING

I A S Storage Systems, Newtonsyde, Charleston, Nigg, Aberdeen, AB12 3LL Tel: (01224) 897305 Fax: (01224) 897305 E-mail: ias@totalise.co.uk
Randall Storage Systems Ltd, 5 Beaucroft Road, Wimborne, Dorset, BH21 2QW Tel: (01202) 848059 Fax: (01202) 848059

RACKS, *See also headings for particular types*

Abbey Storage & Office Systems Ltd, International House, 30 Villa Road, Benfleet, Essex, SS7 5QL Tel: (01268) 794070 Fax: (01268) 566141 E-mail: doug@abbeystorage.freeserve.co.uk
B & D Shelving, Hadley Park Road Industrial Estate, Leegomery, Telford, Shropshire, TF1 6PY Tel: (01952) 247987 Fax: (01952) 247987
Birchmoor Associates, 16 Norris Way Industrial Estate, Norris Way, Rushden, Northamptonshire, NN10 6BP Tel: (01933) 314499 Fax: (01933) 410495 E-mail: lionel@birchmoorassociates.co.uk
▶ Coker Systems, 7 Fosters Business Park, Old School Road, Hook, Hampshire, RG27 9NY Tel: (01256) 768178 Fax: (01256) 766234 E-mail: sales@cokerexpo.co.uk
Dialrack Ltd, 8 Bilton Industrial Estate, Bilton Road, Basingstoke, Hampshire, RG24 8LJ Tel: (01256) 810907 Fax: (01256) 810942 E-mail: sales@dialrack.co.uk
Independent Storage Installation Services Ltd, 1 Calder Vale Mills, Healey Road, Ossett, West Yorkshire, WF5 8NF Tel: (01924) 281219 Fax: (01924) 281219 E-mail: info@independentstorage.co.uk
Optimum Storage Systems Ltd, Po Box 121, Elland, West Yorkshire, HX5 9AJ Tel: (01422) 379549 Fax: (01422) 377344
Pallett Racking Systems Ltd, Fryer Works, Ann Street, Willenhall, West Midlands, WV13 1EN Tel: (01902) 606205 Fax: (01902) 606681 E-mail: pallettrackingsys@aol.com
Prestige Industrial (Pullman International), India Mill, Clarendon Road, Skew Bridge, Blackburn, BB1 9SY Tel: (01254) 53333 Fax: (01254) 690484 E-mail: sales@prestigeindustrial.co.uk
Rotaglade Ltd, 85 Park Road, Hale, Altrincham, Cheshire, WA15 9LQ Tel: 0161-980 3102 Fax: 0161-980 3102
Springlab Ltd, 2 Whitting Valley Road, Old Whittington, Chesterfield, Derbyshire, S41 9EY Tel: (01246) 455399 Fax: (01246) 452397 E-mail: enquiries@springlab.co.uk
Storage Designs, Station Road, Clive, Shrewsbury, SY4 3LD Tel: (01939) 220269 Fax: (01939) 220484
T J Services Ltd, 38 Briery Acres, Stainburn, Workington, Cumbria, CA14 1XQ Tel: (01900) 65139 Fax: (01900) 607374 E-mail: sales@tjservicessd.co.uk
Thiel Technics UK, 66 Tonacliffe Road, Whitworth, Rochdale, Lancashire, OL12 8SS Tel: (01706) 868822 Fax: (01706) 343402 E-mail: sales@thiel-technics.co.uk
United Storage Systems Ltd, United House, The Street, Takeley, Bishop's Stortford, Hertfordshire, CM22 6QR Tel: (01279) 871787 Fax: (01279) 871636 E-mail: sales@unitedstorage.co.uk

RACKS, WAREHOUSE, USED

▶ EPS Warehousing & Distribution, Euro House, St John Street, Leicester, LE1 3WL Tel: 0116-233 4545 Fax: 0116-233 8028 E-mail: g.hothi@europressing.com

RADAR COMPONENTS

Brasec, Anchorage House, Stoke Street, Rodney Stoke, Cheddar, Somerset, BS27 3UP Tel: (01749) 870888 Fax: (01749) 870999 E-mail: bristec_radar_uk@compuserve.com
Fel Avionics Ltd, 236 North East Road, Southampton, SO19 8BB Tel: (023) 8044 2970 Fax: (023) 8043 1762 E-mail: info@fel-avionics.co.uk

RADAR EQUIPMENT, MARINE

▶ ElecTech Solutions (East) Ltd, The Old Bakery, Keswick Road, Bacton, Norwich, NR12 0HE Tel: (07831) 107578 Fax: (0870) 7065369 E-mail: info@electechsolutions.co.uk

RADAR EQUIPMENT, TRACKING/ SURVEILLANCE

Chemring Ltd, Alchem Works, Rodney Road, Southsea, Hampshire, PO4 8SX Tel: (023) 9273 5457 Fax: (023) 9281 7509
Denbridge Marine Ltd, Cammell Lairds Waterfront Park, Campbell Town Road, Birkenhead, Merseyside, CH41 9HP Tel: 0151-649 4080 Fax: (0870) 0518953 E-mail: info@denbridgemarine.com
Thales UK Ltd, Manor Royal, Crawley, West Sussex, RH10 9PY Tel: (01293) 528787 Fax: (01293) 542818 E-mail: admin@thales-defence.co.uk

RADAR MAINTENANCE AND REPAIR

Fel Avionics Ltd, 236 North East Road, Southampton, SO19 8BB Tel: (023) 8044 2970 Fax: (023) 8043 1762 E-mail: info@fel-avionics.co.uk

RADAR NAVIGATIONAL EQUIPMENT

Brasec, Anchorage House, Stoke Street, Rodney Stoke, Cheddar, Somerset, BS27 3UP Tel: (01749) 870888 Fax: (01749) 870999 E-mail: bristec_radar_uk@compuserve.com
Kelvin Hughes Ltd, New North Road, Hainault, Ilford, Essex, IG6 2UR Tel: (020) 8502 6887 Fax: (020) 8500 0837 E-mail: sales@kelvinhughes.co.uk
Pipehawk plc, Systems House, Mill Lane, Alton, Hampshire, GU34 2QG Tel: (01420) 590990 Fax: (01420) 590920 E-mail: sales@pipehawk.com
Raytheon E-Systems Ltd, The Pinnacles, Elizabeth Way, Harlow, Essex, CM19 5BB Tel: (01279) 426862 Fax: (01279) 410413

RADAR REFLECTORS

Cyclops Technologies Ltd, Durban Road, Bognor Regis, West Sussex, PO22 9QT Tel: (01243) 841123 Fax: (01243) 829321 E-mail: sales@cyclopstech.co.uk

RADIAL TYRES

Continental Tyre Group Ltd, Continental House, 191 High Street, Yiewsley, West Drayton, Middlesex, UB7 7XW Tel: (01895) 425900 Fax: (01895) 425982

RADIANT HEATERS

AmbiRad Ltd, Fens Pool Avenue, Brierley Hill, West Midlands, DY5 1QA Tel: (01384) 489700 Fax: (01384) 489707 E-mail: marketing@ambirad.co.uk
B G Perimeter Systems Ltd, Tomo Industrial Estate, Packet Boat Lane, Uxbridge, Middlesex, UB8 2JP Tel: (01895) 441794 Fax: (01895) 448597 E-mail: sales@bgperimeter.co.uk
Flexel International Ltd, Queensway Industrial Estate, Flemington Road, Glenrothes, Fife, KY7 5QF Tel: (01592) 757313 Fax: (01592) 754535 E-mail: sales@flexel.co.uk

RADIANT HEATING ELEMENTS

Ceramaspeed Ltd, Zortech Avenue, Kidderminster, Worcestershire, DY11 7DY Tel: (01562) 756000 Fax: (01562) 756030

RADIATION DETECTORS

Applied Scintillation Technologies, Unit 7-8 Roydenbury Industrial Estate, Horsecroft Road, Harlow, Essex, CM19 5BZ Tel: (01279) 641234 Fax: (01279) 413679 E-mail: ast@appscintech.com

RADIATION MONITORS

Centronic Ltd, Centronic House, King Henrys Drive, New Addington, Croydon, CR9 0BG Tel: (01689) 808000 Fax: (01689) 841822 E-mail: info@centronic.co.uk
▶ Collingwood Consultancy, 20 Estcourt Road, Great Yarmouth, Norfolk, NR30 4JG Tel: (01493) 842022 Fax: (01493) 331955
J S Engineering, 102 Commercial Road, Skelmanthorpe, Huddersfield, HD8 9DS Tel: (01484) 866254 Fax: (01484) 866255 E-mail: jsengineeringuk@aol.com
Landauer Inc, Unit 12 North Oxford Business Centre, Lakesmere Close, Kidlington, Oxfordshire, OX5 1LG Tel: (01865) 373008 Fax: (01865) 373017
Link Microtek Ltd, Intec 4.1, Wade Road, Basingstoke, Hampshire, RG24 8NE Tel: (01256) 355771 Fax: (01256) 355118 E-mail: sales@linkmicrotek.com
Perkinelmer Ltd, Chalfont Road, Seer Green, Beaconsfield, Buckinghamshire, HP9 2FX Tel: (01494) 874515 Fax: (01494) 679331 E-mail: cc.uk@perkinelmer.com
Perspective Scientific Ltd, 100 Baker Street, London, W1U 6WB Tel: (020) 7486 6837 Fax: (020) 7487 3023 E-mail: nick@perspective.co.uk
Thermo Electron, Grange Lane, Beenham, Reading, RG7 5PR Tel: 0118-971 2121 Fax: 0118-971 2835 E-mail: admin@thermormp.co.uk

RADIATION PROCESSING/TEST SERVICES

Harwell Scientifics, 551 South Becquerel Avenue, Didcot, Oxfordshire, OX11 0TB Tel: (01235) 841970 Fax: (01235) 832287 E-mail: sales@scientifics.com
Isotron Plc, Moray Road, Elgin Industrial Estate, Swindon, SN2 8XS Tel: (01793) 601000 Fax: (01793) 601010 E-mail: sales@isotron.co.uk
Isotron, Thornhill Industrial Estate, South Marston, Swindon, SN3 4TA Tel: (01793) 823451 Fax: (01793) 827320 E-mail: smarston@isotron.co.uk

RADIATION SHIELDING

Booth Industries, PO Box 50, Bolton, BL3 2RW Tel: (01204) 366333 Fax: (01204) 380888 E-mail: sales@booth-industries.co.uk
Leadatom Europe Ltd, 1 Shamrock Enterprise Centre, Wingate Road, Gosport, Hampshire, PO12 4DP Tel: (023) 9252 3973 Fax: (023) 9252 3973 E-mail: sales@leadatom.co.uk
Rothband & Co. Ltd, 4-6 Knowsley Road, Haslingden, Rossendale, Lancashire, BB4 4RX Tel: (01706) 830086 Fax: (01706) 830324 E-mail: sales@rothband.co.uk

RADIATION SHIELDING WINDOWS

British Shielding Windows, Unit 16 Ffordd Richard Davies, St. Asaph Business Park, St. Asaph, Clwyd, LL17 0LJ Tel: (01745) 536730 Fax: (01745) 536735 E-mail: sales@bswin.com

RADIATION STERILISATION

Sterigenics (U K) Ltd, Cotes Park Industrial Estate, Somercotes, Alfreton, Derbyshire, DE55 4NJ Tel: (01773) 543200 Fax: (01773) 543210

RADIATION STERILISATION – *continued*

Swann-Morton Europe Ltd, Owlerton Green, Sheffield, S6 2BJ Tel: 0114-234 4231 Fax: 0114-231 4966 E-mail: services@swann-morton.com

RADIATOR CABINETS

Neil Smith Quality Home Improvements, 24 Hawthorn Hill, Trefechan, Merthyr Tydfil, Mid Glamorgan, CF48 2ES Tel: (01685) 723895 Fax: (01685) 723895

RADIATOR CORES

Hudevad Britain, Bridge House, Bridge Street, Walton-on-Thames, Surrey, KT12 1AL Tel: (01932) 247835 Fax: (01932) 247694 E-mail: sales@hudevad.co.uk

RADIATOR PRODUCTION EQUIPMENT

Emerson & Renwick Ltd, Peel Bank Works, Peel Bank, Church, Accrington, Lancashire, BB5 4EF Tel: (01254) 872727 Fax: (01254) 871109 E-mail: sales@eandr.com

RADIATOR VALVES OR FITTINGS

Herz Valves (UK) Ltd, Progress House, Moorfield Point, Moorfield Road, Guildford, Surrey, GU1 1RU Tel: 01483 502211 Fax: 01483 502025 E-mail: sales@herzvalves.com

RADIATORS, STAINLESS STEEL

▶ Titan-Lite Motorsport, 36 Coleshill Ind Est, Station Rd, Coleshill, Birmingham, B46 1JP Tel: 01675 - 466060 Fax: 01675 - 467675 E-mail: info@titan-lite.com

RADIO ACCESSORIES, *See headings for particular types*

RADIO AERIALS

▶ Gould Electronics, 7 Scorrier House Workshops, Scorrier, Redruth, Cornwall, TR16 5AU Tel: (01209) 821804 Fax: (020) 7691 9587 E-mail: dave@gouldelectronics.co.uk

▶ Silver Television Ltd, 22 Green Street, Saltcoats, Ayrshire, KA21 5HQ Tel: (01294) 461508 Fax: (01294) 464829 E-mail: iain@silvertv.plus.com

RADIO BROADCASTING, *See Broadcasting etc*

RADIO COMMUNICATION TOWERS

Francis & Lewis International, Waterwells Drive, Waterwells Business Park, Quedgeley, Gloucester, GL2 2AA Tel: (01452) 722200 Fax: (01452) 722244 E-mail: sales@fli.co.uk

Saturn Communications Ltd, Park House, 27 Hartswood Road, Warley, Brentwood, Essex, CM14 5AE Tel: (01277) 234131 Fax: (01277) 234156 E-mail: len@saturncomms.co.uk

Swann Engineering Group Ltd, Springwood Drive, Braintree, Essex, CM7 2YN Tel: (01376) 320100 Fax: (01376) 347995

Taylor Bros Oldham Ltd, Lee Street, Oldham, OL8 1EE Tel: 0161-652 3221 Fax: 0161-626 1736 E-mail: karen.taylorbrs@btinternet.com

Tower Structures Marketing Ltd, 44 Westbourne Terrace, London, W2 3UH Tel: (020) 7402 4452 Fax: (020) 7706 8643

RADIO COMMUNICATIONS EQUIPMENT OR SYSTEMS

As Communications UK Ltd, The Green, Agden Green Farm, Great Staughton, St. Neots, Cambridgeshire, PE19 5DQ Tel: (01480) 861824 Fax: (01480) 869453 E-mail: wmumford@ascomms.co.uk

B A E Systems Avionics Ltd, Christopher Martin Road, Basildon, Essex, SS14 3EL Tel: (01268) 522822 Fax: (01268) 883140

Bancom Communications Ltd, P O Box 280, Cambridge, CB2 2DY Tel: (01223) 566577 Fax: (01223) 566588 E-mail: tony@bancom.co.uk

Birtley C B Services, 33 Penshaw View, Birtley, Chester le Street, County Durham, DH3 2JL Tel: 0191-492 0681 Fax: 0191-411 1341 E-mail: bev@phoenixcomms.freeserve.co.uk

▶ Callmonitor, 207 Regent Street, London, W1B 4ND Tel: (020) 7292 9200 Fax: (0800) 0747458 E-mail: sales@satphone.co.uk

Central Communications Group, 54 Glen Road, Castle Bytham, Grantham, Lincolnshire, NG33 4RJ Tel: (01780) 411194 E-mail: cswright@walkietalkie.co.uk

▶ Ceotronics Ltd, The Clocktower, Park Road, Bestwood Village, Nottingham, NG6 8TQ Tel: 0115-977 0100 Fax: 0115-977 0300

Codan UK Ltd, Gostrey House, Union Road, Farnham, Surrey, GU9 7PT Tel: (01252) 717272 Fax: (01252) 717337 E-mail: sales@codanuk.com.au

Commercial Communications, Unit 25 Titan Court, Laporte Way, Luton, LU4 8EF Tel: (01582) 721884 Fax: (01582) 705073 E-mail: sales@commcomms.co.uk

▶ Communications Co., Pickwood Hall, Pickwood Avenue, Leek, Staffordshire, ST13 5BZ Tel: (01538) 372424 Fax: (01538) 388238

Copsey Communication Consultants, Edgcott House, Edgcott, Aylesbury, Buckinghamshire, HP18 0QW Tel: (01296) 770552 Fax: (01296) 770423 E-mail: sales@copesy-coms.com

Cotel, Unit 6 Dudnance Lane, Poole, Redruth, Cornwall, TR15 3QT Tel: (01209) 712376 Fax: (01209) 719331

Data Communication Services Ltd, 447-449 Manchester Road, Stockport, Cheshire, SK4 5DJ Tel: 0161-443 0800 Fax: 0161-443 1336 E-mail: sales@data-comms.com

Data Radio Ltd, 5-7 Falkland Street, Liverpool, L3 8HB Tel: 0151-298 2150 Fax: (0870) 0940005 E-mail: admin@dataradio.co.uk

Dee Communications Ltd, Dutton Green, Stanney Mill, Chester, CH2 4SA Tel: 0151-356 5955 Fax: 0151-356 5944 E-mail: sales@deecommunications.co.uk

Digital Dispatch Ltd, 38-39 Bar Hill Business Park, Saxon Way, Bar Hill, Cambridge, CB23 8SL Tel: (01954) 780888 Fax: (01954) 781612 E-mail: sales@digitaldispatch.com

East Midlands Mobile Communications, 44 High Street, Stanton Hill, Sutton-in-Ashfield, Nottinghamshire, NG17 3GA Tel: (01623) 555276 Fax: (01623) 558197

▶ Field Measurement Services, 32 High Street, Thatcham, Berkshire, RG19 3JD Tel: (01635) 860046 Fax: (01635) 860008 E-mail: sales@fieldmeasurmentservices.co.uk

▶ First Call, 134 Stanley Green Road, Poole, Dorset, BH15 3AH Tel: (01202) 666663 Fax: (01202) 666664 E-mail: sales@allvehicleswanted.co.uk

Fylde Micro Systems Ltd, 8 Avroe Cresent, Blackpool, FY4 2DP Tel: (01253) 407040 Fax: (01253) 407073

Gisco Radio Communication Equipment, 199a Wolverhampton Road West, Walsall, WS2 0DU Tel: (01922) 611384 Fax: (01922) 611384 E-mail: sales@giscouk.com

Good Buddy's C B Radio & Communications Centre, Norland House, Hackworth Industrial Park, Shildon, County Durham, DL4 1HE Tel: (01388) 778368 Fax: (01388) 775832 E-mail: gbcomms102@aol.com

Ian Bannings Car Audio & Security Ltd, 3 The Riverside Business Centre, Walnut Tree Close, Guildford, Surrey, GU1 4UG Tel: (01483) 301500 Fax: (01483) 300813

Jotron (UK) Ltd, Crossland Park, Cramlington, Northumberland, NE23 1LA Tel: (01670) 712000 Fax: (01670) 590265 E-mail: salesair@jotron.com

L M W Electronics Ltd, L M W House Merrylees Industrial Estate, Lee Side, Desford, Leicester, LE9 9FS Tel: (01530) 231141 Fax: (01530) 231143 E-mail: sales@lmw.co.uk

Lowe Electronics Ltd, Bentley Bridge, Chesterfield Road, Matlock, Derbyshire, DE4 5LE Tel: (01629) 580800 Fax: (01629) 580020 E-mail: info@lowe.co.uk

M A L (Meauctore), PO Box 2286, Swindon, SN4 7BA Tel: (01793) 849911 Fax: (01793) 848847 E-mail: info@mal-it.co.uk

M R S Communications Ltd, Viaduct Road, Gwaelod Y Garth, Cardiff, CF10 9JN Tel: (029) 2081 0810 Fax: (029) 2081 3755

Marlborough Radio Services, 9-11 Kildare Terrace, Leeds, LS12 1DB Tel: 0113-243 1626 Fax: 0113-246 1838 E-mail: andy@marlboroughradio.com

Mercia Radio Telephones, Unit 1 Groveandstand Business Centre, Westfields Trading Estate, Hereford, HR4 9NS Tel: (01432) 267864 Fax: (01432) 279953 E-mail: sales@merciaradio.co.uk

Mold CB & Radio, 5 Daniel Owen Precinct, Mold, Clwyd, CH7 1AP Tel: (01352) 757934

Motorola Ltd, Viables Industrial Estate, Jays Close, Basingstoke, Hampshire, RG22 4PD Tel: (01256) 358211 Fax: (01256) 469838 E-mail: sales@mot.com

Nessco Services Ltd, Discovery House Arnhall Business, Park, Westhill, Aberdeenshire, AB32 6FG Tel: (01355) 266900 Fax: (01224) 428401 E-mail: sales@nessco.co.uk

Norcall Ltd, Victoria Chambers, 1 Victoria Road, Northampton, NN1 5EB Tel: (01604) 234333 Fax: (01604) 603866

North West Radio Communications, 6 Low Hill, Liverpool, L6 1BS Tel: 0151-263 9993 Fax: 0151-263 9966 E-mail: sales@northwestradio.co.uk

P R S Communications Ltd, 2 Birch Avenue, Harwich, Essex, CO12 4DB Tel: (01255) 240523 Fax: (01255) 240523 E-mail: sales@prscomms.com

Piper Communications, 4 Severn Road, Chilton, Didcot, Oxfordshire, OX11 0PW Tel: (01235) 834328 Fax: (01235) 834328

Procom Ltd, Unit I3, Springhead Enterprise Park, Springhead Road, Northfleet, Gravesend, Kent, DA11 8HL Tel: (01474) 322244 Fax: (01474) 322135 E-mail: info@procom-pescot.co.uk

Prolink Radio Systems Ltd, Saxon Business Park, Bromsgrove, Worcestershire, B60 4AD Tel: (01527) 577788 Fax: (01527) 577757 E-mail: service@prolink-radio.com

R.F. Technology Ltd, Unit 15d Compton Pl, Surrey Ave, Camberley, Surrey, GU15 1HL Tel: (01276) 686889 Fax: (01276) 686244

Racal Antennas Ltd, First Avenue, Southampton, SO15 0LJ Tel: (023) 8070 5705 Fax: (023) 8070 1122E-mail: sales@raycalantennas.com

▶ Radio Accessories Direct Ltd, Unit 45 Elderpark Workspace, 100 Elderpark Street, Glasgow, G51 3TR Tel: 0141-445 8828 Fax: 0141-445 8814

▶ Radio Products UK Ltd, The Granary, Sutton Lane, Langley, Bucks, Slough, SL3 8AR Tel: (01753) 582030

Radphone Ltd, Unit 1 Caughey Street, Hull, HU2 8TH Tel: (01482) 228725 Fax: (01482) 324717

Rapid Radio Communications, Unit 5 The Acorn Centre, Roebuck Road, Hainault, Ilford, Essex, IG6 3TU Tel: (020) 8500 9999 Fax: (020) 8500 8124 E-mail: mail@rapidradio.com

Sangikyo Corporation, Highbridge Industrial Estate, Oxford Road, Uxbridge, Middlesex, UB8 1HR Tel: (01895) 876101 Fax: (01895) 876257

▶ The Shortwave Shop Ltd, 18 Fairmile Road, Christchurch, Dorset, BH23 2LJ Tel: (01202) 490099 Fax: (01202) 490099 E-mail: sales@shortwave.co.uk

Sinclair Technologies Ltd, William James House, Cowley Road, Cambridge, CB4 0WX Tel: (01223) 420303 Fax: (01223) 420606 E-mail: salesuk@sinctech.com

Skysearchers Radio Communication Equipment, 1 Oak Street, South Bank, Middlesbrough, Cleveland, TS6 6PB Tel: (01642) 453613 Fax: (01642) 453613

T R L Technology Ltd, Shannon Way, Ashchurch, Tewkesbury, Gloucestershire, GL20 8ND Tel: (01684) 278700 Fax: (01684) 850406 E-mail: d_hall@trltech.co.uk

Tardis Communications Ltd, PO Box 446, Aylesbury, Buckinghamshire, HP21 7RJ Tel: (01296) 338747 Fax: (01296) 422014 E-mail: info@tardiscoms.co.uk

Tranex Telecommunications Ltd, 29 High Street, Rothwell, Kettering, Northamptonshire, NN14 6AD Tel: (01536) 711028 Fax: (01536) 713082 E-mail: radiosales@tranex.co.uk

Valkris Communications, Deunant, Capel Curig, Betws-y-Coed, Gwynedd, LL24 0DS Tel: (01690) 720263 Fax: (01690) 720263 E-mail: admin@valkris.co.uk

Les Wallen Manufacturing Ltd, Lambda Works, 45A Whitehall Road, Ramsgate, Kent, CT12 6DE Tel: (01843) 582864 Fax: (01843) 590726 E-mail: lee@wallen-antennae.co.uk

Waters & Stanton plc, 22 Main Road, Hockley, Essex, SS5 4QS Tel: (01702) 206835 Fax: (01702) 205843 E-mail: sales@wsplc.com

Wragby C B & Electrical, Market Place, Wragby, Market Rasen, Lincolnshire, LN8 5QU Tel: (01673) 857064 Fax: (01673) 857064

X L Systems, 1 Leas Road, Warlingham, Surrey, CR6 9LN Tel: (01883) 622778 Fax: (01883) 626991 E-mail: sales@xls.co.uk

Zetron Inc, 27-29 Campbell Court, Bramley, Tadley, Hampshire, RG26 5EG Tel: (01256) 880663 Fax: (01256) 880491 E-mail: uk@zetron.com

RADIO COMMUNICATIONS EQUIPMENT OR SYSTEMS CONSULTANCY

2CL Communications Ltd, Unit 3 The Crosshouse Centre, Crosshouse Road, Southampton, SO14 5GZ Tel: (023) 8033 6411 Fax: (023) 8072 0038 E-mail: sales@2cl.co.uk

D H S Communications, 421 Hertford Road, Enfield, Middlesex, EN3 5PT Tel: (020) 8482 4432 Fax: (020) 8482 4434

▶ Mutek Ltd, Rashieburn, Fintray, Aberdeen, AB21 0YX Tel: (01651) 806455 Fax: (01651) 806696 E-mail: info@mutekrf.com

R F Design Ltd, 27 Weelsby Way, Hessle, North Humberside, HU13 0JN Tel: (01482) 629270 Fax: (01482) 629270 E-mail: martyn@rfdesign.karoo.co.uk

Scancom Radio Communications, Beech House, 6 Banstead Road, Carshalton, Surrey, SM5 3NR Tel: (020) 8669 8212 Fax: (020) 8669 2918

Systems Integration Electronics, 14 Seabeach Lane, Eastbourne, East Sussex, BN22 7NZ Tel: (01323) 647649 E-mail: sales@seacall.org.uk

T E S Ltd, Lancaster House, Bow Lane, Leyland, PR25 4YA Tel: (01772) 901901 Fax: (01772) 901902 E-mail: info@tes.ltd.uk

RADIO COMMUNICATIONS EQUIPMENT OR SYSTEMS HIRE

2CL Communications Ltd, Unit 3 The Crosshouse Centre, Crosshouse Road, Southampton, SO14 5GZ Tel: (023) 8033 6411 Fax: (023) 8072 0038 E-mail: sales@2cl.co.uk

Better Sound Ltd, 31 Cathcart Street, London, NW5 3BJ Tel: (020) 7482 0177 Fax: (020) 7482 2677 E-mail: admin@bettersound.co.uk

Brentwood Communications Ltd, 178 Warley Hill, Warley, Brentwood, Essex, CM14 5HF Tel: (01277) 225254 Fax: (01277) 223089 E-mail: info@bc-ltd.co.uk

C P C Communications, 56 Clive Road, Cardiff, CF5 1HG Tel: (029) 2066 5213 Fax: (01639) 646003

Clive Palmer, 5 Fettiplace Close, Appleton, Oxford, OX2 4HW Tel: (01865) 864662 Fax: (01865) 865436

Consam Communications, 33 Highmeres Road, Leicester, LE4 9LZ Tel: 0116-276 0909 Fax: 0116-276 2141E-mail: info@consam.com

East Midlands Mobile Communications, 44 High Street, Stanton Hill, Sutton-in-Ashfield, Nottinghamshire, NG17 3GA Tel: (01623) 555276 Fax: (01623) 558197

Lothian Communications Ltd, Unit 3 15 Marine Crescent, Glasgow, G51 1HD Tel: 0141-429 2929 Fax: 0141-429 6789 E-mail: mail@mxpower.co.uk

M W Brunsdon, 25 Buckstone Lea, Edinburgh, EH10 6XE Tel: 0131-445 5182

Marlborough Radio Services, 9-11 Kildare Terrace, Leeds, LS12 1DB Tel: 0113-243 1626 Fax: 0113-246 1838 E-mail: andy@marlboroughradio.com

Mercia Radio Telephones, Unit 1 Groveandstand Business Centre, Westfields Trading Estate, Hereford, HR4 9NS Tel: (01432) 267864 Fax: (01432) 279953 E-mail: sales@merciaradio.co.uk

Northern Radio Sytems, 96-98 Constitution Street, Edinburgh, EH6 6AW Tel: 0131-467 7620 Fax: 0131-553 7760

Relcom Communications, Unit 1, Oliver Business Park, Oliver Road, London, NW10 7JB Tel: (020) 8965 2333 Fax: (020) 8965 2323 E-mail: info@relcom.co.uk

Show Hire, Station Lane, Milford, Godalming, Surrey, GU8 5AD Tel: (01483) 414337 Fax: (01483) 426926

South Midlands Communications Ltd, SM House, School Close, Chandler's Ford, Eastleigh, Hampshire, SO53 4RA Tel: (023) 8024 6200 Fax: (023) 8024 6206 E-mail: sales@smc-comms.com

RADIO COMMUNICATIONS EQUIPMENT OR SYSTEMS INSTALLATION CONTRACTORS OR SERVICES

Cartel Communications, Radio House, 15 Sutton Street, Birmingham, B1 1PG Tel: 0121-622 3301 Fax: 0121-622 3328 E-mail: sales@cartel.co.uk

Cumbria Communications 2000 Ltd, Westgate, Milburn, Penrith, Cumbria, CA10 1TW Tel: (01768) 361416 Fax: (01768) 362000

Electrical Power Specialists Reading Ltd, 1 Blenheim Road, Reading, RG1 5NG Tel: 0118-935 1933 Fax: 0118-935 2373 E-mail: info@epsdirect.co.uk

Hames Electronics Ltd, 106A Fair Road, Wibsey, Bradford, West Yorkshire, BD6 1QL Tel: (01274) 606007 Fax: (01274) 607793

J G Electronics, Unit 8 Showfield Lane, Malton, North Yorkshire, YO17 6BT Tel: (01653) 695611 Fax: (01653) 695611

Lincs Radio Engineering, 211-213 Cleethorpe Road, Grimsby, South Humberside, DN31 3BE Tel: (01472) 241418 Fax: (01472) 352099 E-mail: lincsradio@btconnect.com

M R S Communications Ltd, Viaduct Road, Gwaelod Y Garth, Cardiff, CF10 9JN Tel: (029) 2081 0810 Fax: (029) 2081 3755

Pennine Telecom Ltd, Pennine House, Salford Street, Bury, Lancashire, BL9 6YA Tel: 0161-763 3333 Fax: 0161-763 3332 E-mail: info@penninetelecom.com

Radcom Radio Telephone Services Ltd, Belvoir Way, Fairfield Industrial Estate, Louth, Lincolnshire, LN11 0HP Tel: (01507) 604055 Fax: (01507) 600489 E-mail: radcomlimited@louthssbusiness.co.uk

Radio 88, 88 Longbridge Road, Barking, Essex, IG11 8SF Tel: (020) 8594 9979 Fax: (020) 8591 6642

Radio Links Communications Ltd, Eaton House, Great North Road, Eaton Socon, St. Neots, Cambridgeshire, PE19 8EG Tel: (01480) 217220 Fax: (01480) 406667 E-mail: info@radio-links.co.uk

Radio Service, Unit 129 Brookfield Place, Walton Summit Industrial Estate, Bamber Bridge, Preston, PR5 8BF Tel: (01772) 628000 Fax: (01772) 628888 E-mail: ians@rstechnology.co.uk

Rapid Radio Communications, Unit 5 The Acorn Centre, Roebuck Road, Hainault, Ilford, Essex, IG6 3TU Tel: (020) 8500 9999 Fax: (020) 8500 8124 E-mail: mail@rapidradio.com

Resound Ltd, Parkway House, Haddenham Business Park, Thame Road, Haddenham, Aylesbury, Buckinghamshire, HP17 8LJ Tel: (01844) 292346 Fax: (01844) 292860 E-mail: mail@resound.co.uk

Saba Electrical Ltd, 10 1 Maltravers Road, Sheffield, S2 5AA Tel: 0114-278 7956 Fax: 0114-272 2040 E-mail: sales@sabacom.com

Thorcom Network Services Ltd, Unit 4 96b Blackpole Trading Estate We, St, Worcester, WR3 8TJ Tel: (01905) 756700 Fax: (01905) 755777 E-mail: sales@thorcom.co.uk

RADIO COMMUNICATIONS EQUIPMENT OR SYSTEMS INSTALLATION CONTRACTORS OR SERVICES – *continued*

Valkris Communications, Deunant, Capel Curig, Betws-y-Coed, Gwynedd, LL24 0DS Tel: (01690) 720263 Fax: (01690) 720263 E-mail: admin@valkris.co.uk

Zetron Inc, 27-29 Campbell Court, Bramley, Tadley, Hampshire, RG26 5EG Tel: (01256) 880663 Fax: (01256) 880491 E-mail: uk@zetron.com

RADIO COMMUNICATIONS EQUIPMENT, ULTRAHIGH FREQUENCY (UHF)

▶ Radio Europe Ltd, 17-21 Hastings Street, Luton, LU1 5BE Tel: (01582) 481114 Fax: (01582) 481115 E-mail: sales@red-radio.co.uk

RADIO CONTROL UNITS

D C B Electronics, 702 Southchurch Road, Southend-on-Sea, SS1 2PS Tel: (01702) 304030 Fax: (01702) 305030 E-mail: sales@dcb-electronics.co.uk

RADIO DATA TERMINALS (RDT)

Total Control Systems, Upton House, Hartlebury Trading Estate, Hartlebury, Kidderminster, Worcestershire, DY10 4JB Tel: (01299) 250010 Fax: (01299) 254999 E-mail: sales@totalcontrol.co.uk

RADIO EQUIPMENT, VERY HIGH FREQUENCY (VHF)

▶ Cam Com Radio, Gusto Mills, Huntingdon Road, Cambridge, CB3 0DL Tel: (01223) 277274 Fax: (01223) 277207 E-mail: camcom@metronet.co.uk

▶ Radio Europe Ltd, 17-21 Hastings Street, Luton, LU1 5BE Tel: (01582) 481114 Fax: (01582) 481115 E-mail: sales@red-radio.co.uk

RADIO FREQUENCY EQUIPMENT, *See headings for particular applications*

RADIO FREQUENCY IDENTIFICATION (RFID) PRODUCTS

Blackroc Systems Ltd, Drummond Road, Astonfields Industrial Estate, Stafford, ST16 3HJ Tel: (01785) 213777 Fax: (01785) 251546 E-mail: sales@blackroc.com

Codemark Developments Ltd, 8 West Lodge Lane, Sutton, Ely, Cambridgeshire, CB6 2NX Tel: (01353) 775153 Fax: (07932) 231525 E-mail: sales@codemark.co.uk

Opticon Ltd, 960 Capability Green, Luton, LU1 3PE Tel: (01582) 635100 Fax: (01582) 635200 E-mail: sales@opticon.co.uk

Rfid, Wolseley Road, Kempston, Bedford, MK42 7UP Tel: (01234) 840102 Fax: (01234) 840707 E-mail: info@rfid.co.uk

RADIO FREQUENCY IDENTIFICATION (RFID) READERS

Opticon Ltd, 960 Capability Green, Luton, LU1 3PE Tel: (01582) 635100 Fax: (01582) 635200 E-mail: sales@opticon.co.uk

RADIO FREQUENCY IDENTIFICATION (RFID) SOFTWARE

Safetrak Ltd, Wimbourne Road, Barry, Vale of Glamorgan, CF63 3Dh Tel: (01446) 723320 E-mail: info@safetrak.com

RADIO FREQUENCY IDENTIFICATION (RFID) TAG READERS

▶ Bar Code Data Systems Ltd, Ashton House, Margaret Street, Ashton-under-Lyne, Lancashire, OL7 0SH Tel: 0161-330 0077 Fax: 0161 330 0088 E-mail: keith.hardy@bcdata.co.uk

▶ IID Solutions Ltd, Units 9 & 10 Wesley House, Huddersfield Road, Birstall, Batley, West Yorkshire, WF17 9EJ Tel: (01924) 424600 Fax: (01924) 424601 E-mail: sales@iidsolutions.co.uk

▶ Packaging Solutions Provider, 21 Pinewood Drive, Markfield Court, Markfield, Leicestershire, LE67 9RQ Tel: (01530) 243743 E-mail: bob.locke@packaginsolutionsprovider.co.uk

▶ Paxar EMEA HQ, Court 3-4, Awberry Court, Hatters Lane, Watford, WD18 8PD Tel: 0115-989 6705 Fax: 0115-989 6766 E-mail: info@paxar-emea.com

RADIO FREQUENCY IDENTIFICATION (RFID) TAGS

Parlex Europe Ltd, Taylor Road, Newport, Isle of Wight, PO30 5LG Tel: (01983) 526535 Fax: (01983) 524964 E-mail: sales@uk.parlex.com

RADIO FREQUENCY INTERFERENCE (RFI) AND ELECTROMAGNETIC INTERFERENCE (EMI) CONNECTOR ADAPTERS

J M K Ltd, Unit 9 Block 2, Vale of Leven Industrial Estate, Dumbarton, G82 3PW Tel: (01389) 751841 Fax: (01389) 751775 E-mail: jmkfilters@sol.co.uk

Kec Ltd, Orpheus House, Calleva Park, Aldermaston, Reading, RG7 8TA Tel: 0118-981 1571 Fax: 0118-981 1570 E-mail: sales@kec.co.uk

RADIO FREQUENCY INTERFERENCE (RFI) CAPACITORS

Suppression Devices, Unit 8, York Street Business Centre, Clitheroe, Lancashire, BB7 2DL Tel: (01200) 444497 Fax: (01200) 444330 E-mail: sales@suppression-devices.com

RADIO FREQUENCY INTERFERENCE (RFI) SHIELDING ENCLOSURES

European Emc Products Ltd, Unit 8, Saffron Business Centre, Elizabeth Close, Saffron Walden, Essex, CB10 2BL Tel: (01799) 523073 Fax: (01799) 521191 E-mail: info@euro-emc.co.uk

RADIO FREQUENCY (RF) AMPLIFIERS

Antiference, Eastern Avenue, Lichfield, Staffordshire, WS13 7SB Tel: (01889) 272600 Fax: (01296) 84284 E-mail: sales@antiference.co.uk

Carlsbro Electronics Ltd, Cross Drive, Kirkby-in-Ashfield, Nottingham, NG17 7LD Tel: 08452 582910 Fax: 01623 755436 E-mail: sales@carlsbro.co.uk

Com Development Europe Ltd, Unit 10 Triangle Business Park, Quilters Way, Stoke Mandeville, Aylesbury, Buckinghamshire, HP22 5SX Tel: (01296) 616400 Fax: (01296) 616500 E-mail: info@comdev.co.uk

Electrotechnical Engineering Ltd, Unit 3 The Rose Estate, Osbourne Way, Hook, Hampshire, RG27 9UT Tel: (01256) 766914 Fax: (01256) 766915 E-mail: sally-ottaway@eteltd.co.uk

Micina Technologies Group, Regent House, 40 Nelson Street, Leicester, LE1 7BA Tel: 0116-233 9944 Fax: 0116-233 9945 E-mail: mike@micina.co.uk

TMD Technologies Ltd, Intercraft House, Swallowfield Way, Hayes, Middlesex, UB3 1AW Tel: (020) 8573 5555 Fax: (020) 8569 1839 E-mail: wecare@tmd.co.uk

RADIO FREQUENCY (RF) CHOKES

B E C Distribution Ltd, Unit 5, Coronation Grove, Harrogate, North Yorkshire, HG2 8BU Tel: (0845) 4900405 Fax: (0845) 4900406 E-mail: sales@bec.co.uk

Electroustic Ltd, 1 Eaglesfield Industrial Estate, Main Street, Leire, Lutterworth, Leicestershire, LE17 5HF Tel: (01455) 202364 Fax: (01455) 209043 E-mail: sales@electroustic.co.uk

Sycopel International, Viking Industrial Park, Jarrow, Tyne & Wear, NE32 3DT Tel: 0191-428 5004 Fax: 0191-483 5995 E-mail: sycopelint@aol.co.uk

RADIO FREQUENCY (RF) DRYERS

Greenbank Technology Ltd, Unit 420 Glenfield Park Two, Blakewater Road, Blackburn, BB1 5QH Tel: (01254) 690555 Fax: (01254) 690666 E-mail: info@greenbanktechnology.co.uk

RADIO FREQUENCY (RF) EQUIPMENT, IDENTITY (ID) PASSIVE, READ WRITE/READ ONLY

Anaren Microwave Europe Inc, Suites 16-17, Somerset House, Hussar Court, Waterlooville, Hampshire, PO7 7SG Tel: (023) 9223 2392 Fax: (023) 9225 1369 E-mail: anareneurope@anaren.com

▶ Avonwood Developments Ltd, Knoll Technology Centre, Stapehill Road, Wimborne, Dorset, BH21 7ND Tel: (01202) 868000 Fax: (01202) 868001 E-mail: sales@avonwood.co.uk

Intermec Technologies UK Ltd, Reading International Business Park, Reading, RG2 6DD Tel: 0118-923 0800 Fax: 0118-923 0801 E-mail: infoeurope@intermec.com

RADIO FREQUENCY (RF) FILTERS

Powerwave (UK) Ltd, Enterprise Drive, Station Road, Four Ashes, Wolverhampton, WV10 7DF Tel: (01902) 798204 Fax: (01902) 798205

RADIO FREQUENCY (RF) INDUCTORS

Coilcraft (U K), 21 Napier Place, Wardpark North, Cumbernauld, Glasgow, G68 0LL Tel: (01236) 730595 Fax: (01236) 730627 E-mail: sales@coilcraft-europe.com

Sycopel International, Viking Industrial Park, Jarrow, Tyne & Wear, NE32 3DT Tel: 0191-428 5004 Fax: 0191-483 5995 E-mail: sycopelint@aol.co.uk

Wearnes Cambion Ltd, Mill Bridge, Castleton, Hope Valley, Derbyshire, S33 8WR Tel: (01433) 621555 Fax: (01433) 621290 E-mail: sales@cambion.com

RADIO FREQUENCY (RF) INTEGRATED CIRCUITS (IC)

Filtronic, Millennium Way, Heighington Lane Business Park, Newton Aycliffe, County Durham, DL5 6JW Tel: (01325) 301111 Fax: (01325) 306177

RADIO FREQUENCY (RF) POWER SUPPLIES

Tascom International Ltd, 1 Mars House, Calleva Park, Aldermaston, Reading, RG7 8LA Tel: 0118-982 0400 E-mail: bill.white@tascom.co.uk

RADIO FREQUENCY (RF) RELAYS

Signal Management Ltd, Plumpton House, Plumpton Road, Hoddesdon, Hertfordshire, EN11 0LB Tel: (01992) 463603 Fax: (01992) 443824 E-mail: enquiries@signalman.co.uk

RADIO FREQUENCY (RF) SCREENING CANS, *See Shield/Shielding, Radio Frequency (RF) etc*

RADIO FREQUENCY (RF) TAGGING SYSTEMS

▶ Solutions Distributors Ltd, Unit 1 Hixon Industrial Estate, Church Lane, Hixon, Stafford, ST18 0PY Tel: (0871) 4341510 Fax: (0871) 4341514 E-mail: sales@solutions-distributors.co.uk

RADIO FREQUENCY (RF) TECHNOLOGY CONSULTANTS/ SERVICES

Elmac Services, PO Box 111, Chichester, West Sussex, PO19 4ZS Tel: (01243) 533361 Fax: (01243) 790535

RADIO FREQUENCY (RF) TEST EQUIPMENT

A R G Electrodesign Ltd, Querns Business Centre, Whitworth Road, Cirencester, Gloucestershire, GL7 1RT Tel: (01285) 658501 Fax: (01285) 885376 E-mail: info@arg.co.uk

RADIO (MARINE) EQUIPMENT MANUFRS

Alfatronix Ltd, 29 Newtown Business Park, Albion Close, Poole, Dorset, BH12 3LL Tel: (01202) 715517 Fax: (01202) 715122 E-mail: sales@alfatronix.co.uk

Ships Electronic Services Ltd, Chichester House Waterside Court, Neptune Way, Medway City Estate, Rochester, Kent, ME2 4NZ Tel: (01634) 295500 Fax: (01634) 295537 E-mail: sales@ses-marine.com

RADIO MAST CONTRACTORS OR ERECTORS OR SUPPLIERS

Antenna Systems Ltd, Hertford, SG13 8YB Tel: (01707) 878875 Fax: (01707) 876873 E-mail: antenna@euromast.fsbusiness.co.uk

R T M Ltd, 1-4 Morris Close, Park Farm North, Wellingborough, Northamptonshire, NN8 6XF Tel: (01933) 673066 Fax: (01933) 678933 E-mail: sales@rtm-uk.com

Swann Engineering Group Ltd, Springwood Drive, Braintree, Essex, CM7 2YN Tel: (01376) 320100 Fax: (01376) 347995

RADIO MAST EQUIPMENT OR ACCESSORIES

▶ F & L Accessories Ltd, 4 5 Chosen View Road, Cheltenham, Gloucestershire, GL51 9LT Tel: (01242) 571409 Fax: (01242) 574240 E-mail: sales@flacc.co.uk

RADIO MASTS

Clark Masts Teksam Ltd, 18 Ringwood Road, Binstead, Ryde, Isle Of Wight, PO33 3PA Tel: (01983) 563691 Fax: (01983) 566643 E-mail: sales@clarkmasts.com

RADIO MICROPHONES

Audio Ltd, Audio House, Progress Road, Sands Industrial Estate, High Wycombe, Buckinghamshire, HP12 4JD Tel: (01494) 511711 Fax: (01494) 539600 E-mail: info@audioltd.com

Audio Engineering Ltd, New Road, London, N8 8TA Tel: (020) 8341 3500 Fax: (020) 8341 5100 E-mail: sales@micronwireless.co.uk

Derby Electronics, 41 St Thomas Road, Derby, DE23 8RF Tel: (01332) 774825 Fax: (01332) 270127 E-mail: derbyelectronics@btinternet.com

RADIO MODEMS

▶ Mobile Expertise Ltd, Unit B, Wooland Works, Water End Road, Potten End, Berkhamsted, Hertfordshire, HP4 2SJ Tel: (0870) 8508891 Fax: (0870) 0322744 E-mail: sales@mobile-expertise.co.uk

Pacscom Ltd, 6 Majestic Road, Nursling Industrial Estate, Southampton, SO16 0YT Tel: (023) 8073 7557 Fax: (023) 8073 1600 E-mail: sales@pacscom.com

Radio-Tech Ltd, Radio House, The Old Brewery, Lindsey Street, Epping, Essex, CM16 6RD Tel: (01992) 576107 Fax: (01992) 561994 E-mail: sales@radtec.demon.co.uk

Sigtel, Sensor House, Wrexham Technology Park, Wrexham, Clwyd, LL13 7YP Tel: (01978) 312488 Fax: (01978) 312494 E-mail: sigtel@esi-tec.com

Warwick Wireless Ltd, Lychgate Lane, Aston Flamville, Hinckley, Leicestershire, LE10 3AQ Tel: (01455) 233616 Fax: (01455) 233179 E-mail: sales@radiotelemetry.co.uk

RADIO MODULES

Cambridge Silicon Radio, Churchhill House, Cambridge Business Park, Cowley Road, Cambridge, CB4 0WZ Tel: (01223) 692000 Fax: (01223) 692001 E-mail: sales@csr.com

Low Power Radio Solutions Ltd, Two Rivers Industrial Estate, Station Lane, Witney, Oxfordshire, OX28 4BH Tel: (01993) 709418 Fax: (01993) 705415E-mail: sales@lprs.co.uk

Radio-Tech Ltd, Radio House, The Old Brewery, Lindsey Street, Epping, Essex, CM16 6RD Tel: (01992) 576107 Fax: (01992) 561994 E-mail: sales@radtec.demon.co.uk

Warwick Wireless Ltd, Lychgate Lane, Aston Flamville, Hinckley, Leicestershire, LE10 3AQ Tel: (01455) 233616 Fax: (01455) 233179 E-mail: sales@radiotelemetry.co.uk

RADIO (MOTOR CAR/VEHICLE) ACCESSORIES

Clarion G B Ltd, Unit 1-2 & 14, Marshall Road, Hillmead, Swindon, SN5 5YU Tel: (01793) 870400 Fax: (01793) 875747 E-mail: enquiries@clarion.co.uk

RADIO (MOTOR CAR/VEHICLE) SYSTEMS

Audio Images, 187 Westgate, Bradford, West Yorkshire, BD1 3AD Tel: (01274) 733633 Fax: (01274) 776966 E-mail: sales@audioimages.co.uk

Clarion G B Ltd, Unit 1-2 & 14, Marshall Road, Hillmead, Swindon, SN5 5YU Tel: (01793) 870400 Fax: (01793) 875747 E-mail: enquiries@clarion.co.uk

Crescent Audio Ltd, 5 Croydon Road, Penge, London, SE20 7TJ Tel: (020) 8778 3391 Fax: (020) 8778 2574

Ian Bannings Car Audio & Security Ltd, 3 The Riverside Business Centre, Walnut Tree Close, Guildford, Surrey, GU1 4UG Tel: (01483) 301500 Fax: (01483) 300813

John Kleis Car Hi-Fi Communications, 248 Basingstoke Road, Reading, RG2 0HN Tel: 0118-986 6224 Fax: (0870) 7702870 E-mail: sales@johnkleis.com

M A Distributors Ltd, Industrial House, Conway Street, Hove, East Sussex, BN3 3LW Tel: (01273) 720129 Fax: (01273) 820915 E-mail: ash@ma-d.net

Masters Vehicle Security, 57 Anerley Road, London, SE19 2AS Tel: (020) 8289 9835 Fax: (020) 8289 8188

Prestige Audio, 12 High Street, Rickmansworth, Hertfordshire, WD3 1ER Tel: (01923) 711113 Fax: (01923) 776606

Ram Mobile Electronics Ltd, 63a Westgate End, Wakefield, West Yorkshire, WF2 9RL Tel: (01924) 201884 Fax: (01924) 332440

W A S O 2000, 15 Park Avenue, Cheadle Hulme, Cheadle, Cheshire, SK8 6EU Tel: (0870) 9027979 Fax: 0161-428 1790 E-mail: sales@waso.co.uk

RADIO (MOTOR CAR/VEHICLE) SYSTEMS ENGINEERS, INSTALLATION OR SERVICE

Clarion G B Ltd, Unit 1-2 & 14, Marshall Road, Hillmead, Swindon, SN5 5YU Tel: (01793) 870400 Fax: (01793) 875747 E-mail: enquiries@clarion.co.uk

Ian Bannings Car Audio & Security Ltd, 3 The Riverside Business Centre, Walnut Tree Close, Guildford, Surrey, GU1 4UG Tel: (01483) 301500 Fax: (01483) 300813

▶ In Car Discount, Festival House, Jessop Avenue, Cheltenham, Gloucestershire, GL50 3SH Tel: (0870) 7606110 Fax: (01684) 292200 E-mail: sales@incardiscount.co.uk

O E Electronics Ltd, 6 Four Brooks Business Park, Stanier Road, Calne, Wiltshire, SN11 9PP Tel: (01249) 817370 Fax: (01249) 817346 E-mail: sapres@oeelectronics.com

Sextons, 69-71 Milton Road, Portsmouth, PO3 6AL Tel: (023) 9273 8262 Fax: (023) 9282 6110

Unicar Leeds Ltd, 90 Kirkstall Road, Leeds, LS3 1LT Tel: 0113-245 1444 Fax: 0113-243 5532 E-mail: enquiries@unicar.co.uk

RADIO PAGING, *See Paging Systems etc*

RADIO RECEIVER MANUFRS

Robert Bosch Ltd, PO Box 98, Uxbridge, Middlesex, UB9 5HJ Tel: (01895) 834466 Fax: (01895) 838388

Bush Radio P.L.C., Bush House, The Waterfront, Elstree Road, Elstree, Borehamwood, Hertfordshire, WD6 3BS Tel: (020) 8238 7650 Fax: (020) 8953 7117 E-mail: durochers@albaplc.co.uk

Cobweb Solutions Ltd, Delme Place, Cams Hall Estate, Fareham, Hampshire, PO16 8UX Tel: (0845) 2239000 Fax: (0845) 2493310 E-mail: sales@cobweb.co.uk

Fairhaven Electronics Ltd, 378 Boulton Lane, Derby, DE24 9DJ Tel: (01332) 670707 Fax: (0870) 0558899

M & B Radio (Leeds), 86 Bishopgate Street, Leeds, LS1 4BB Tel: 0113-243 5649 Fax: 0113-242 6881

Marine Electronic Supplies, Unit 14 Westwood Court, Brunel Road, Totton, Southampton, SO40 3WX Tel: (023) 8066 3316 Fax: (023) 8066 3241 E-mail: sales@mesuk.com

RADIO REMOTE CONTROL SYSTEMS

Cattron Theimeg UK Ltd, Riverdene Industrial Estate, Molesey Road, Hersham, Walton-On-Thames, Surrey, KT12 4RY Tel: (01932) 247511 Fax: (01932) 220937 E-mail: sales@cattronuk.com

RADIO TELEMETRY EQUIPMENT MANUFRS

Churchill Controls Ltd, Unit 12 Station Industrial Estate, Oxford Road, Wokingham, Berkshire, RG41 2YQ Tel: 0118-989 2200 Fax: 0118-989 2007 E-mail: sales@churchill-controls.co.uk

Sigtel, Sensor House, Wrexham Technology Park, Wrexham, Clwyd, LL13 7YP Tel: (01978) 312488 Fax: (01978) 312494 E-mail: sigtel@esi-tec.com

Warwick Wireless Ltd, Lychgate Lane, Aston Flamville, Hinckley, Leicestershire, LE10 3AQ Tel: (01455) 233616 Fax: (01455) 233179 E-mail: sales@radiotelemetry.co.uk

RADIO TELEMETRY RECEIVERS

Conway Security Products Ltd, Seymour House, Copyground Lane, High Wycombe, Buckinghamshire, HP12 3HE Tel: (01494) 461373 Fax: (01494) 531685 E-mail: sales@conway-cctv.co.uk

RADIO TELEMETRY TRANSMITTERS

Finchdata Ltd, Grove Ho, Lutyens Cl, Lychpit, Basingstoke, Hants, RG24 8AG Tel: (0870) 7460895 Fax: (0870) 1317493 E-mail: sales@finchdata.co.uk

RADIO TELEPHONE CONTRACTORS OR INSTALLATION OR HIRE OR SERVICE

Comhire P.L.C., Communications House, Vauxhall Road, Sheffield, S9 1LD Tel: (0800) 163778 Fax: (020) 8961 9687 E-mail: ccpl.comhire-comhire@btinternet.com

Derby Electronics, 41 St Thomas Road, Derby, DE23 8RF Tel: (01332) 774825 Fax: (01332) 270127 E-mail: derbyelectronics@btinternet.com

Nine Hundred Communications, White Rose Way, Doncaster, South Yorkshire, DN4 5JH Tel: (01302) 368866 Fax: (01302) 340363 E-mail: sales@gbcomms.co.uk

Procom Ltd, Unit I3, Springhead Enterprise Park, Springhead Road, Northfleet, Gravesend, Kent, DA11 8HL Tel: (01474) 322244 Fax: (01474) 322135 E-mail: info@procom-pescot.co.uk

Servicom (High Tech) Ltd, Unit 8 The I.O. Centre, Nash Road, Park Farm North, Redditch, Worcestershire, B98 7AS Tel: (01527) 510800 Fax: (01527) 510975 E-mail: sales@servicom.co.uk

Southern Business Communications, Unit 2 The Broadway, Andover, Hampshire, SP10 2JF Tel: (01264) 336644 Fax: (01264) 332083 E-mail: sbc-ltd@btconnect.com

Surrey Car Telephones Ltd, 3 The Riverside Business Centre, Walnut Tree Close, Guildford, Surrey, GU1 4UG Tel: (01483) 563999 Fax: (01483) 300813 E-mail: info@sctcomms.co.uk

RADIO TELEPHONE SYSTEMS

Commercial Communications, Unit 25 Titan Court, Laporte Way, Luton, LU4 8EF Tel: (01582) 721884 Fax: (01582) 705073 E-mail: sales@commcomms.co.uk

Sam Electronics UK, 18 Dales Industrial Estate, Peterhead, Aberdeenshire, AB42 3JF Tel: (01779) 478233 Fax: (01779) 475060

Southern Business Communications, Unit 2 The Broadway, Andover, Hampshire, SP10 2JF Tel: (01264) 336644 Fax: (01264) 332083 E-mail: sbc-ltd@btconnect.com

RADIO TEST EQUIPMENT

Sinclair Voicenet Ltd, 2 Orbital Court, Peel Park, East Kilbride, Glasgow, G74 5PH Tel: (01355) 900000 Fax: (01355) 900001 E-mail: enquiries@voicerecording.co.uk

RADIO TO COMPUTER BASE ALARM SYSTEMS

Alarm Radio Monitoring Ltd, Southern Avenue, Leominster, Herefordshire, HR6 0QF Tel: (01568) 610016 Fax: (01568) 615511

Tunstall Group Ltd, Whitley Lodge, Whitley Bridge, Goole, North Humberside, DN14 0HR Tel: (01977) 661234 Fax: (01977) 662570

RADIO TRANSMITTING EQUIPMENT

▶ Access Audio Ltd, Unit 32-35,, Hardengreen Business Park, Dalhousie Road, Eskbank, Dalkeith, Midlothian, EH22 3NX Tel: 0131-663 0777 Fax: 0131-660 9777 E-mail: info@accessaudio.co.uk

N R G Kits, 16 Victoria Street, Queensbury, Bradford, West Yorkshire, BD13 1AR Tel: (01274) 816200 Fax: (01274) 816200 E-mail: nrgkitsfm@aol.com

RADIO TYPE APPROVAL TESTING SERVICES

Nuffield Radiographic Inspection, Unit B13-14, 46 Holton Road, Holton Heath Trading Park, Poole, Dorset, BH16 6LT Tel: (01202) 632200 Fax: (01202) 632042 E-mail: sales@nuffieldinspection.co.uk

RADIOACTIVE WASTE WATER SAMPLING, *See Nuclear Waste Water etc*

RADIOCHEMICALS

G E Healthcare, Amersham Place, Amersham, Buckinghamshire, HP7 9NA Tel: (01494) 544000 Fax: (01494) 542266

RADIOGRAPHIC EQUIPMENT

J M E Ltd, Electron House, Old Nelson St, Lowestoft, Suffolk, NR32 1EQ Tel: (01502) 500969 Fax: (01502) 511932 E-mail: sales@jme.co.uk

Radiographic Accessories Ltd, Durham Lane Industrial Park, Guisley Way, Stockton-On-Tees, Cleveland, TS16 0RS Tel: (01642) 790580 Fax: (01642) 790420 E-mail: jack@radac.demon.co.uk

Saferad Ltd, 1 Saferad Ltd Development Off Meadowfi Eld Indust Estate, Durham, DH7 1KK Tel: 0191-378 2130 Fax: 0191-378 2130 E-mail: mwass@saferad.com

Xograph Imaging Systems, Xograph House, Hampton Street, Tetbury, Gloucestershire, GL8 8LD Tel: (01666) 501501 Fax: (01666) 501502 E-mail: enquiry@xograph.com

RADIOGRAPHIC EQUIPMENT MAINTENANCE/REPAIR SERVICES

Saferad Ltd, 1 Saferad Ltd Development Off Meadowfi Eld Indust Estate, Durham, DH7 1KK Tel: 0191-378 2130 Fax: 0191-378 2130 E-mail: mwass@saferad.com

RADIOGRAPHIC TEST SERVICES

A W L Inspection & N D T Services Ltd, Unit 34, Royal Industrial Estate, Jarrow, Tyne & Wear, NE32 3HR Tel: 0191-430 0837 Fax: 0191-430 0837 E-mail: awl_ndt@btconnect.com

Capital Inspection Services, 3 Poyle Technical Centre, Willow Road, Colnbrook, Slough, SL3 0DP Tel: (01753) 684896 Fax: (01753) 681739E-mail: cap.inspection@btconnect.com

JPB Trading Ltd, Martindale, Cannock, Staffordshire, WS11 7XN Tel: (01543) 462676 Fax: (01543) 571368 E-mail: sales@eurospection.co.uk

NDT Services Ltd, 5 Side Ley, Kegworth, Derby, DE74 2FJ Tel: (01509) 680088 Fax: (01509) 680080 E-mail: sales@ndtservices.co.uk

Saferad Ltd, 1 Saferad Ltd Development Off Meadowfi Eld Indust Estate, Durham, DH7 1KK Tel: 0191-378 2130 Fax: 0191-378 2130 E-mail: mwass@saferad.com

RAIL END POSTS

Glass Block Outlet, PO Box 272, Liverpool, L13 7DA Tel: (07940) 895369 Fax: (0845) 2262683 E-mail: info@glassblockoutlet.co.uk

RAIL FREIGHT SERVICES

Creative Logistics Ltd, Duncan Street, Salford, M5 3SQ Tel: 0161-873 7101 Fax: 0161-872 1447 E-mail: enquiries@creative-logistics.co.uk

Jarvis Infrastructure Services, Holbeck Depot, Nineveh Road, Leeds, LS11 9QG Tel: (01904) 712712 Fax: 0113-389 3134

John S Braid & Co. Ltd, Maritime House, 143 Woodville Street, Glasgow, G51 2RQ Tel: 0141-445 2525 Fax: 0141-440 1238 E-mail: ddarroch@braidco.com

Kuehne & Nagel Ltd, Building 317, World Freight Terminal, Manchester Airport, Manchester, M90 5NA Tel: 0161-436 9400 Fax: 0161-436 9429 E-mail: manfa@kuehne-nagel.com

Maina Freight Forwarders plc, 5 Featherstone Industrial Estate, Dominion Road, Southall, Middlesex, UB2 5DP Tel: (020) 8843 1977 Fax: (020) 8571 5628E-mail: info@maina.com

RAILINGS

Ag Con Products Ltd, 45 Newtown Road, Rostrevor, Newry, County Down, BT34 3BZ Tel: (028) 4173 8963 Fax: (028) 4173 8971 E-mail: brian@ag.con.fsnet.co.uk

Araywelds Mobile Services, 6 Flanders Road, London, E6 6DU Tel: (07885) 431727 Fax: (020) 8507 7056

B F Elton, The Bungalow, Bristol Road, Rooksbridge, Axbridge, Somerset, BS26 2TF Tel: (01934) 750433

Bombardier Transportation, West Street, Crewe, CW1 3JB Tel: (01270) 538700 Fax: (01270) 538669 E-mail: info@transportation.bombardier.com

Boston Retail Products, 10a Lower Guildford Road, Knaphill, Woking, Surrey, GU21 2EW Tel: (0870) 7706680 Fax: (0870) 7706681 E-mail: sales@bostonretail.com

Brough & Horner Ltd, Station Road, Loftus, Saltburn-by-the-Sea, Cleveland, TS13 4QB Tel: (01287) 640374

Broxap Dorothea, Rowhurst Industrial Estate, Chesterton, Newcastle, Staffordshire, ST5 6BD Tel: (01782) 564411 Fax: (01782) 565357 E-mail: sales@broxap.co.uk

▶ W. & D. Cole Ltd, Ashford Road, Bethersden, Ashford, Kent, TN26 3AT Tel: (01233) 820240 Fax: (01233) 820805 E-mail: emailus@wdcole.com

D J Installations & Fabrications, The Cottage, Backworth, Newcastle upon Tyne, NE27 0AP Tel: 0191-268 4215 Fax: 0191-268 4215

Decor Iron, Mill Street, Darlaston, Wednesbury, West Midlands, WS10 8TH Tel: 0121-526 7498 Fax: 0121-568 6778

Enterprise Gates & Railings, 2 Herbert Road, Stoke-on-Trent, ST3 4QR Tel: (01782) 593122 Fax: (01782) 593122

Evb Ltd, 48-52 Barking Industrial Park, Alfreds Way, Barking, Essex, IG11 0TJ Tel: (020) 8507 8088 Fax: (020) 8591 2419 E-mail: alanevb@f2s.com

Fabco, 33a Groganstown, Dunmurry, Belfast, BT17 0NR Tel: (028) 9062 6666 Fax: (028) 9062 6666

Fylde Coast Gate, Amy Johnson Way, Blackpool, FY4 2RP Tel: (01253) 347000 Fax: (01253) 407518

G & B Fabrications Services, Unit 20 Newfields Industrial Estate, High Street, Stoke-on-Trent, ST6 5PD Tel: (01782) 824600 Fax: (01782) 824700

Gaytsmaid Wrought Ironwork, Unit 1 St. Johns Lane, Bewdley, Worcestershire, DY12 2QY Tel: (01299) 405153 Fax: (01299) 405153 E-mail: enquiries@gaytsmaid.co.uk

Iron Designs Ltd, 117-119 Victoria Road, Portslade, Brighton, BN41 1XD Tel: (01273) 423685 Fax: (01273) 418927

Leighton Ironcraft Ltd, Unit 4, 39 Willow Lane, Mitcham, Surrey, CR4 4NA Tel: 0845 5314075 Fax: (020) 8971 5098 E-mail: sales@leightonironcraft.co.uk

Madewell Products Ltd, Sandy Way, Tamworth, Staffordshire, B77 4DS Tel: (01827) 67721 Fax: (01827) 67721 E-mail: sales@madewellproducts.co.uk

Norris Adams Fabrications, Unit 6, Upcott Avenue, Pottington Business Park, Barnstaple, Devon, EX31 1HN Tel: (01271) 322969 Fax: (01271) 322969

Northern Machine Guard & Fabrications, Unit 14 Albert Mill, Albert Place, Lower Darwen, Darwen, Lancashire, BB3 0QE Tel: (01254) 662595 Fax: (01254) 662595

Paramount Steel Fence, Florida Close, Hot Lane Industrial Estate, Stoke-on-Trent, ST6 2DJ Tel: (01782) 833333 Fax: (01782) 832222 E-mail: steelfence@btinternet.com

Gary Paul Engineering, 4 Rosewood Park, St. James's Road, Blackburn, BB1 8ET Tel: (01254) 582263 Fax: (01254) 582263

Premier Fabrications, St 1, 54-76 Bissell Street, Birmingham, B5 7HP Tel: 0121-693 9059 Fax: 0121-693 9058

R Ekin, Claylands Avenue, Worksop, Nottinghamshire, S81 7BE Tel: (01909) 472638 Fax: (01909) 472638

Renzland Forge Ltd, 83A London Road, Copford, Colchester, CO6 1LG Tel: (01206) 210212 Fax: (01206) 211290

▶ S W L Engineering, 3 Holmfield Chase, Stanley, Wakefield, West Yorkshire, WF3 4QZ Tel: (07961) 170212 Fax: (01924) 824950 E-mail: swlengineering@msn.com

H. Scrowcroft & Sons, Daisyfield Works, Rosslyn Avenue, Preesall, Poulton-Le-Fylde, Lancashire, FY6 0HE Tel: (01253) 810451

Singer & James Ltd, 33 Roebuck Road, Ilford, Essex, IG6 3TZ Tel: (020) 8500 4115 Fax: (020) 8501 2456 E-mail: info@singerandjames.co.uk

Stansted All-Steel Ltd, Unit 1 Parsonage Farm Industrial Estate, Forest Hall Road, Stansted, Essex, CM24 8TY Tel: (01279) 817801 Fax: (01279) 815704

RAILINGS – *continued*

Steelcraft Ltd, Unit 2-6 Drum Industrial Estate, Chester le Street, County Durham, DH2 1AG Tel: 0191-410 9996 Fax: 0191-410 9228 E-mail: sales@steelcraft.ltd.uk
Steeltech Kinetix Ltd, Dancroft Works, Gauxholme Fold, Todmorden, Lancashire, OL14 7PW Tel: (01706) 817144 Fax: (01706) 817522 E-mail: mail@steeltech-kinetix.co.uk
L.R. Stewart & Sons Ltd, Hampden Road, Hornsey, London, N8 0HG Tel: (020) 8348 5267 Fax: (020) 8340 7774 E-mail: info@lrstewartandsons.co.uk
Supreme Ironcraft Ltd, Unit 26 Brook Road Industrial Estate, Brook Road, Rayleigh, Essex, SS6 7XL Tel: (01268) 747774 Fax: (01268) 770449
T J Blackburn & Son, Victoria, Ableton Lane, Severn Beach, Bristol, BS35 4PR Tel: (01454) 632905 Fax: (01454) 632905

RAILWAY AIR CONDITIONING (AC) EQUIPMENT

Air & Finishing Systems Ltd, 7 Blaenau Enterprise Centre, Rising Sun Industrial Estate, Blaina, Abertillery, Gwent, NP13 3JW Tel: (01495) 292880 Fax: (01495) 292800

RAILWAY BOGIES, ROLLING STOCK

Bombardier, Litchurch Lane, Derby, DE24 8AD Tel: (01332) 344666 Fax: (01332) 266271 E-mail: bombardi@transportation.bombardier.com

RAILWAY BRAKE UNITS

Knorr-Dremse Systems UK Ltd, Westinghouse Way, Hampton Park East, Bowerhill, Melksham, Wiltshire, SN12 6TL Tel: (01249) 442000 Fax: (01225) 898705 E-mail: sales@westbrake.com

RAILWAY BUFFER STOPS

H.J. Skelton & Co. Ltd, 9 The Broadway, Thatcham, Berkshire, RG19 3JA Tel: (01635) 865256 Fax: (01635) 865710 E-mail: info@hjskelton.com

RAILWAY BUFFERS

Oleo International Ltd, Longford Road, Longford Road, Coventry, CV7 9ND Tel: (024) 7664 5555 Fax: (024) 7664 5777 E-mail: roy@oleo.co.uk

RAILWAY CARRIAGE BUILDERS/ REPAIRERS

Alstom Transport Ltd, PO Box 248, Birmingham, B8 2YF Tel: 0121-328 5455 Fax: 0121-695 3500

RAILWAY CARRIAGE FITTINGS

R P L, Brittannic House, 5-7 St Marys Gate, Derby, DE1 3JA Tel: (01332) 349255 Fax: (01332) 294688
Solihull Rail Supplies & Services Ltd, Earlswood Trading Estate, Poolhead Lane, Earlswood, Solihull, West Midlands, B94 5EW Tel: (01564) 700222 Fax: (01564) 702341 E-mail: neil-willets@solrail.fsbusiness.co.uk

RAILWAY CARRIAGE INTERIORS, GLASS FIBRE OR FIBREGLASS

Solihull Rail Supplies & Services Ltd, Earlswood Trading Estate, Poolhead Lane, Earlswood, Solihull, West Midlands, B94 5EW Tel: (01564) 700222 Fax: (01564) 702341 E-mail: neil-willets@solrail.fsbusiness.co.uk

RAILWAY COMMUNICATION EQUIPMENT

Ford Electronics Ltd, Brewood Hall, Sparrows End Lane, Brewood, Stafford, ST19 9DB Tel: (01902) 455555 E-mail: sales@fordelectronics.co.uk
Siemens Transportation Systems, Sopers Lane, Poole, Dorset, BH17 7ER Tel: (01202) 846200 Fax: (01202) 846200 E-mail: internet@sts.siemens.com

RAILWAY CONTRACT STAFF RECRUITMENT AGENCIES/ CONSULTANTS

Bellmaster UK Ltd, 5 Victoria Street, Cinderford, Gloucestershire, GL14 2ET Tel: (01594) 822490 Fax: (01594) 822480
▶ Colega Limited, 5300 Lakeside, Cheadle Royal Business Park, Cheadle, Cheshire, SK8 3GP Tel: 0161 408 0505 E-mail: stephen@colega.co.uk
Strongfield Technologies Ltd, Strongfield House, Unit 2 Inovation Park, 89 Manor Farm Road, Wembley, Middlesex, HA0 1BA Tel: (020) 8813 2684 Fax: (020) 8799 8901 E-mail: anu@strongfield.com

RAILWAY CONTROL SYSTEMS

Bombardier Transportation, West Street, Crewe, CW1 3JB Tel: (01270) 538700 Fax: (01270) 538669 E-mail: info@transportation.bombardier.com
Ditra Systems Ltd, Unit 14 Albury Close, Reading, RG30 1BD Tel: 0118-958 5489 Fax: 0118-959 6343 E-mail: info@ditra-systems.co.uk

RAILWAY ELECTRICAL EQUIPMENT

Alstom Traction International Ltd, Channel Way, Preston, PR1 8XL Tel: (01772) 254777 Fax: (01772) 553554
Balfour Beatty Rail Projects Ltd, Acornfield Road, P O Box 12, Kirby Industrial Estate, Liverpool, L33 7TY Tel: 0151-548 5000 Fax: 0151-548 5320
Signal House Ltd, Cherrycourt Way, Leighton Buzzard, Bedfordshire, LU7 4UH Tel: (01525) 377477 Fax: (01525) 850999 E-mail: admin@collis.co.uk
Trendrail Ltd, Units 10 & 11, Brindley Road, Reginald Road Industrial Estate, St. Helens, Merseyside, WA9 4HY Tel: (01744) 851100 Fax: (01744) 851122

RAILWAY ENGINEERING

Balfour Beatty plc, Fourth Floor, 130 Wilton Road, London, SW1V 1LQ Tel: (020) 7216 6800 Fax: (020) 7216 6950
Bombardier Transportation, West Street, Crewe, CW1 3JB Tel: (01270) 538700 Fax: (01270) 538669 E-mail: info@transportation.bombardier.com
First Engineering Ltd, 137 Euston Road, London, NW1 2AA Tel: (020) 7387 0109 Fax: (020) 7387 0010
Metronet Rew Ltd, 130 Bollo Lane, London, W3 8BZ Tel: (020) 7918 6525 Fax: (020) 7918 6525 E-mail: chris.skuse@metronetrail.com
Sabre Rail Services Ltd, Grindon Way, Heighington Lane Business Park, Newton Aycliffe, County Durham, DL5 6SH Tel: (01325) 300505 Fax: (01325) 300485 E-mail: info@sabre-rail.co.uk

RAILWAY EQUIPMENT

Alstom Traction International Ltd, Channel Way, Preston, PR1 8XL Tel: (01772) 254777 Fax: (01772) 553554
▶ Fast Club, Beacon Lane, Rotherham, South Yorkshire, S66 7SA Tel: 01709 862401
▶ Graybar Electrical Contractors, 10 Fleming Close, Park Farm Industrial Estate, Wellingborough, Northamptonshire, NN8 6UF Tel: (01933) 676700 Fax: (01933) 676800 E-mail: sales@graybar.co.uk
National Railway Supplies Ltd, Leeman Road, York, YO26 4ZD Tel: (01904) 522293 Fax: (01904) 522696 E-mail: commercial@natrail.com

RAILWAY FASTENERS

Fastener Direct Ltd, Unit 5 The Union Centre, Hillbottom Road, Sands Industrial Estate, High Wycombe, Buckinghamshire, HP12 4HJ Tel: (01494) 442743 Fax: (01494) 474726 E-mail: fastenerdirect@aol.com

RAILWAY FOG SIGNALS

Clayton & Co Penistone Ltd, Westhorpe Works, Halifax Road, Sheffield, S36 7EY Tel: (01226) 763130 Fax: (01226) 370145

RAILWAY LIGHTING EQUIPMENT

Track Maintenance Equipment Ltd, Witham Wood, Marley Lane, Haslemere, Surrey, GU27 3PZ Tel: (01428) 651114 Fax: (01428) 644727 E-mail: sales@tmeltd.co.uk

RAILWAY MAGAZINES

Rail Business Intelligence, Quadrant Ho, The Quadrant, Brighton Rd, Sutton, Surrey, SM2 5AS Tel: (020) 8652 3500

RAILWAY MAINTENANCE

▶ Banner Solutions, Banner House, Central Buildings, Parkfield Road, Rugby, Warwickshire, CV21 1QJ Tel: (01788) 559300 Fax: (01788) 559333 E-mail: joanne.lewis@bannerholdings.co.uk
Bombardier, Litchurch Lane, Derby, DE24 8AD Tel: (01332) 344666 Fax: (01332) 266271 E-mail: bombardi@transportation.bombardier.com

RAILWAY MAINTENANCE SAFETY EQUIPMENT

▶ Infra Safety Services Ltd, 6 Cotton Brook Road, Shaftesbury Street, Sir Francis Ley Industrial Park South, Derby, DE23 8YJ Tel: (01332) 542800 Fax: (01332) 542829 E-mail: enquiries@infrasafetyservices.co.uk

RAILWAY MAINTENANCE SUPPORT SYSTEMS

Lloyds British Testing P.L.C., Fabian Way, Swansea, SA1 8PU Tel: (01384) 426900 Fax: (01792) 656998

RAILWAY MATERIAL CONTRACTORS OR SUPPLIERS

▶ Balfour Beatty Ltd, 361-365 Coleford Road, Sheffield, S9 5NF Tel: 0114-256 1656 Fax: 0114-256 2656
Balfour Beatty Rail Projects Ltd, Acornfield Road, P O Box 12, Kirby Industrial Estate, Liverpool, L33 7TY Tel: 0151-548 5000 Fax: 0151-548 5320
Davron, 21 Beechfield Road, Davenport, Stockport, Cheshire, SK3 8SF Tel: 0161-483 5678 Fax: 0161-483 5678 E-mail: sales@davron.co.uk
E G Steele & Co. Ltd, 25 Dalziel Street, Hamilton, Lanarkshire, ML3 9AU Tel: (01698) 283765 Fax: (01698) 891550 E-mail: egsteel@tiscalli.co.uk
K G J Price Railway Contractors Ltd, Penygroes Farm, Llantrisant, Pontyclun, Mid Glamorgan, CF72 8LP Tel: (029) 2088 9220 Fax: (029) 2045 1959
Lucchini UK Ltd, Ashburton Road West, Trafford Park, Manchester, M17 1GU Tel: 0161-872 0492 Fax: 0161-872 2895
Railway Mine & Plantation Equipment Ltd, 4 Grosvenor Place, London, SW1X 7DG Tel: (020) 7201 3399 Fax: (020) 7201 3311
Solihull Rail Supplies & Services Ltd, Earlswood Trading Estate, Poolhead Lane, Earlswood, Solihull, West Midlands, B94 5EW Tel: (01564) 700222 Fax: (01564) 702341 E-mail: neil-willets@solrail.fsbusiness.co.uk

RAILWAY MODELS

Acme Model Products, 48 Highgate Road, Sileby, Loughborough, Leicestershire, LE12 7PP Tel: (01509) 812177 Fax: (01509) 812177 E-mail: sales@acmemodels.co.uk
Model Engineering Supplies (Bexhill), Clifford Mews, Clifford Road, Bexhill-on-Sea, East Sussex, TN40 1QA Tel: (01424) 223702 Fax: (01424) 223702 E-mail: sales@model-engineering.co.uk
Old Barn Model Craftsmen, 9 Monks Avenue, Lancing, West Sussex, BN15 9DJ Tel: (01903) 525077

RAILWAY MONITORING AND TESTING

Siemens Transportation Systems, Sopers Lane, Poole, Dorset, BH17 7ER Tel: (01202) 846200 Fax: (01202) 846200 E-mail: internet@sts.siemens.com

RAILWAY PERSONAL TRACK SAFETY (PTS) MEDICAL TESTING

▶ Infra Safety Services Ltd, 6 Cotton Brook Road, Shaftesbury Street, Sir Francis Ley Industrial Park South, Derby, DE23 8YJ Tel: (01332) 542800 Fax: (01332) 542829 E-mail: enquiries@infrasafetyservices.co.uk

RAILWAY PERSONAL TRACK SAFETY TRAINING

Bellmaster UK Ltd, 5 Victoria Street, Cinderford, Gloucestershire, GL14 2ET Tel: (01594) 822490 Fax: (01594) 822480

RAILWAY POINTS OR SWITCHES

Edgar Allen Ltd, Whitburn Road, Bathgate, West Lothian, EH48 2RB Tel: (01506) 652341 Fax: (01506) 631331
Collis Engineering Ltd, Salcombe Road, Alfreton, Derbyshire, DE55 7RG Tel: (01773) 833255 Fax: (01773) 836525 E-mail: sales@collis.co.uk
Corus Cogifer Switches & Crossings, Hebden Road, Scunthorpe, South Humberside, DN15 8DD Tel: (01724) 862131 Fax: (01724) 295243 E-mail: info@coruscogifer.com
Edgar Allen Ltd, PO Box 42, Sheffield, S9 1QW Tel: 0114-244 6621 Fax: 0114-242 6826
Rowlescourt Engineering Ltd, 15 Clover Nook Road, Cotes Park Industrial Estate, Somercotes, Alfreton, Derbyshire, DE55 4RF Tel: (01773) 831115 Fax: (01773) 835925 E-mail: ruth.berry@rowlescourt.co.uk

RAILWAY ROLLING STOCK

Bombardier, Litchurch Lane, Derby, DE24 8AD Tel: (01332) 344666 Fax: (01332) 266271 E-mail: bombardi@transportation.bombardier.com
▶ Exporteze Export Business Strategy and Sales, 6 Overthwart Crescent, Worcester, WR4 0JW Tel: 01905 619363 Fax: 01905 619363 E-mail: exporteze@btinternet.com
Marcroft Engineering Ltd, Whieldon Road, Stoke-on-Trent, ST4 4HP Tel: (01782) 844075 Fax: (01782) 843579

RAILWAY ROLLING STOCK BOGIE SUSPENSION COMPONENTS

Collis Engineering Ltd, Salcombe Road, Alfreton, Derbyshire, DE55 7RG Tel: (01773) 833255 Fax: (01773) 836525 E-mail: sales@collis.co.uk
Ferrabyrne Ltd, Fort Road Industrial Estate, Wick, Littlehampton, West Sussex, BN17 7QU Tel: (01903) 721317 Fax: (01903) 730452 E-mail: sales@ferrabyrne.co.uk

RAILWAY ROLLING STOCK COMPONENTS

▶ Exporteze Export Business Strategy and Sales, 6 Overthwart Crescent, Worcester, WR4 0JW Tel: 01905 619363 Fax: 01905 619363 E-mail: exporteze@btinternet.com
Marcroft Engineering Ltd, Whieldon Road, Stoke-on-Trent, ST4 4HP Tel: (01782) 844075 Fax: (01782) 843579
Rail Order, Unit 2, Anglia Way, Mansfield, Nottinghamshire, NG18 4LP Tel: 01623 627208 Fax: 01623 633914 E-mail: sales@rail-order.co.uk

RAILWAY ROLLING STOCK CONTRACTORS/SUPPLIERS/ HIRE OR LEASING

E G Steele & Co. Ltd, 25 Dalziel Street, Hamilton, Lanarkshire, ML3 9AU Tel: (01698) 283765 Fax: (01698) 891550 E-mail: egsteel@tiscalli.co.uk
HSBC P.L.C., 12 Calthorpe Road, Edgbaston, Birmingham, B15 1QZ Tel: 0121-455 3255 Fax: 0121-455 3244

RAILWAY ROLLING STOCK LIFTING EQUIPMENT

Lloyds British Testing P.L.C., Fabian Way, Swansea, SA1 8PU Tel: (01384) 426900 Fax: (01792) 656998

RAILWAY ROLLING STOCK WASHING SYSTEMS

Smith Bros & Webb Ltd, 22 Tything Road East, Kinwarton, Alcester, Warwickshire, B49 6EX Tel: (01789) 400096 Fax: (01789) 400231 E-mail: sales@vehicle-washing-systems.co.uk
Wesurail Ltd, 21-22 Auster Road, Clifton Moor, York, YO30 4XA Tel: (01904) 692544 Fax: (01904) 692566 E-mail: admin@wesurail.com

RAILWAY SAFETY EQUIPMENT OR SYSTEMS

▶ Infra Safety Services Ltd, 6 Cotton Brook Road, Shaftesbury Street, Sir Francis Ley Industrial Park South, Derby, DE23 8YJ Tel: (01332) 542800 Fax: (01332) 542829 E-mail: enquiries@infrasafetyservices.co.uk

M C Electronics Ltd, 61 Grimsdyke Road, Pinner, Middlesex, HA5 4PP Tel: (020) 8428 2027 Fax: (020) 8428 2027 E-mail: sales@mcelectronics.co.uk

RAILWAY SIGNAL CONTROL ELECTROMECHANICAL DETECTORS

Ditra Systems Ltd, Unit 14 Albury Close, Reading, RG30 1BD Tel: 0118-958 5489 Fax: 0118-959 6343 E-mail: info@ditra-systems.co.uk

RAILWAY SIGNALLING EQUIPMENT

Bombardier Transportation (Signal Management) U K Ltd, Letcombe Street, Reading, RG1 2HN Tel: 0118-953 8000 Fax: 0118-9538009

Collis Engineering Ltd, Salcombe Road, Alfreton, Derbyshire, DE55 7RG Tel: (01773) 833255 Fax: (01773) 836525 E-mail: sales@collis.co.uk

▶ Global Rail Construction Ltd (GRCL), Unit 20, The I O Centre, Hearle Way, Hatfield, Hertfordshire, AL10 9EW Tel: (0870) 9904074 Fax: (0870) 9904075 E-mail: enquiries@grcl.co.uk

Howells Group plc, Longley Lane, Sharston Industrial Area, Manchester, M22 4SS Tel: 0161-945 5567 Fax: 0161-945 5597 E-mail: j.dolan@howells-railway.co.uk

Rowlescourt Engineering Ltd, 15 Clover Nook Road, Cotes Park Industrial Estate, Somercotes, Alfreton, Derbyshire, DE55 4RF Tel: (01773) 831115 Fax: (01773) 835925 E-mail: ruth.berry@rowlescourt.co.uk

▶ S T S Switchgear Ltd, Doulton Road, Cradley Heath, West Midlands, B64 5QB Tel: (01384) 567755 Fax: (01384) 567710 E-mail: mark.mathews@sts-international.co.uk

Siemens Transportation Systems, Sopers Lane, Poole, Dorset, BH17 7ER Tel: (01202) 846200 Fax: (01202) 846200 E-mail: internet@sts.siemens.com

Signal House Ltd, Cherrycourt Way, Leighton Buzzard, Bedfordshire, LU7 4UH Tel: (01525) 377477 Fax: (01525) 850999 E-mail: admin@collis.co.uk

Sitec International Ltd, Unit 11 Lansdowne Court, Bumpers Way, Bumpers Farm, Chippenham, Wiltshire, SN14 6RZ Tel: (01249) 464150 Fax: (01249) 464160 E-mail: sales@sitec-int.co.uk

Westinghouse Rail Systems Ltd, PO Box 79, Chippenham, Wiltshire, SN15 1JD Tel: (01249) 441441 Fax: (01249) 441442 E-mail: wrsl.marketing@invensys.com

Yardene Engineering Ltd, 3 Daux Road, Billingshurst, West Sussex, RH14 9SJ Tel: (01403) 783558 Fax: (01403) 783104 E-mail: sales@yardene.co.uk

RAILWAY SLEEPERS, *See also headings for particular materials*

Challenge Fencing Contractors Ltd, The Sawyard, Downside Road, Downside, Cobham, Surrey, KT11 3LY Tel: (01932) 860101 Fax: (01932) 866445 E-mail: sales@challengefencing.com

K G J Price Railway Contractors Ltd, Penygroes Farm, Llantrisant, Pontyclun, Mid Glamorgan, CF72 8LP Tel: (029) 2088 9220 Fax: (029) 2045 1959

Railway Sleeper.com, Kilgraney, Owthorpe Road, Cotgrave, Nottingham, NG12 3PU Tel: 0115-989 0445 Fax: 0115-989 3366 E-mail: enquiries@kilgraney.com

RAILWAY SLEEPERS, RECLAIMED

▶ Solid Timber Products, Heathfield Way, Gladstone Industry, Northampton, NN5 7QP Tel: (0845) 1297171 Fax: (0845) 1249499 E-mail: adam@solidonline.co.uk

RAILWAY SYSTEM PLANNING CONSULTANCY

Scott Wilson Railways, The Tri Centre, New Bridge Square, Swindon, SN1 1HN Tel: (01793) 508500 Fax: (01793) 508501 E-mail: rail.marketing@scottwilson.com

RAILWAY TRACK CONTRACTORS, RAIL LIFTING AND PACKING

A L A Rail Ltd, Byass Works, The Docks, Port Talbot, West Glamorgan, SA13 1RS Tel: (01639) 885435 Fax: (01639) 899842 E-mail: sales@ala-rail.com

RAILWAY TRACK DRILLING EQUIPMENT

Rotamag, 41 Capley Road, Darnall, Sheffield, S9 5JF Tel: 0114-291 1020 Fax: 0114-261 8186 E-mail: sales@bryar.co.uk

RAILWAY TRACK EQUIPMENT

Ultra Dynamics Ltd, 2 Upperfield Road, Kingsditch Trading Estate, Cheltenham, Gloucestershire, GL51 9NY Tel: (01242) 707900 Fax: (01242) 707901 E-mail: sales@ultradynamics.demon.co.uk

RAILWAY TRACK FASTENERS OR FITTINGS

John Bradley & Son Ltd, Spring Works, Russell Street, Heywood, Lancashire, OL10 1NU Tel: (01706) 360353 Fax: (01706) 366154 E-mail: jbs@johnbradleygroup.co.uk

Edgar Allen Ltd, PO Box 42, Sheffield, S9 1QW Tel: 0114-244 6621 Fax: 0114-242 6826

Track Maintenance Equipment Ltd, Witham Wood, Marley Lane, Haslemere, Surrey, GU27 3PZ Tel: (01428) 651114 Fax: (01428) 644727 E-mail: sales@tmeltd.co.uk

Vortok International, 6-7 Haxter Close, Roborough, Plymouth, PL6 7DD Tel: (01752) 700601 Fax: (01752) 702353 E-mail: sales@vortok.co.uk

RAILWAY TRACK GAUGES TO SPECIFICATION

Hillside Adr Ltd, 9 Quarry Park Close, Moulton Park Industrial Estate, Northampton, NN3 6QB Tel: (01604) 671251 Fax: (01604) 670868 E-mail: sales@hillsideadr.co.uk

RAILWAY TRACK INSTALLATION OR MAINTENANCE OR RECTIFICATION OR REPAIR

Bellmaster UK Ltd, 5 Victoria Street, Cinderford, Gloucestershire, GL14 2ET Tel: (01594) 822490 Fax: (01594) 822480

Corus Cogifer Switches & Crossings, Hebden Road, Scunthorpe, South Humberside, DN15 8DD Tel: (01724) 862131 Fax: (01724) 295243 E-mail: info@coruscogifer.com

K G J Price Railway Contractors Ltd, Penygroes Farm, Llantrisant, Pontyclun, Mid Glamorgan, CF72 8LP Tel: (029) 2088 9220 Fax: (029) 2045 1959

Rowlescourt Engineering Ltd, 15 Clover Nook Road, Cotes Park Industrial Estate, Somercotes, Alfreton, Derbyshire, DE55 4RF Tel: (01773) 831115 Fax: (01773) 835925 E-mail: ruth.berry@rowlescourt.co.uk

Scott Wilson Pavement Engineering Ltd, 12 Regan Way Faraday Building, Nottingham Science & Technology Park, Chilwell, Nottingham, NG9 6RZ Tel: 0115-907 7000 Fax: 0115 907 7001 E-mail: enquiry@swpe.co.uk

RAILWAY TRACK MAINTENANCE EQUIPMENT

Ballast Tools (UK) Ltd, Unit 4 County Park Business Centre, Shrivenham Road, Swindon, SN1 2NR Tel: (01793) 697800 Fax: (01793) 527020 E-mail: btukltd@aol.com

Geismar UK Ltd, Salthouse Road, Brackmills Industrial Estate, Northampton, NN4 7EX Tel: (01604) 769191 Fax: (01604) 763154 E-mail: admin@geismar.co.uk

Harsco Track Technologies Ltd, Unit 1 Chewton Street, Eastwood, Nottingham, NG16 3HB Tel: (01773) 539480 Fax: (01773) 539481 E-mail: enquiries@harscotrack.com

Portec Rail Products (UK) Ltd, Vauxhall Industrial Estate, Wrexham, Clwyd, LL14 6UY Tel: 01978 820820

RAILWAY TRACK MATERIAL, *See Railway Material etc*

RAILWAY TRACK RAILS

Edgar Allen Ltd, Whitburn Road, Bathgate, West Lothian, EH48 2RB Tel: (01506) 652341 Fax: (01506) 631331

Balfour Beatty Rail Track Systems Ltd, Osmaston Street, Sandiacre, Nottingham, NG10 5AN Tel: 0115-921 8218 Fax: 0115-541 8219 E-mail: phil.bean@bbrail.com

Corus Cogifer Switches & Crossings, Hebden Road, Scunthorpe, South Humberside, DN15 8DD Tel: (01724) 862131 Fax: (01724) 295243 E-mail: info@coruscogifer.com

Corus UK Ltd, Moss Bay Road, Workington, Cumbria, CA14 5AE Tel: (01900) 64321 Fax: (01900) 842237 E-mail: info@britishsteel.co.uk

Pandrol UK Ltd, Bonemill Lane, Worksop, Nottinghamshire, S81 7AX Tel: (01909) 476101 Fax: (01909) 500004

H.J. Skelton & Co. Ltd, 9 The Broadway, Thatcham, Berkshire, RG19 3JA Tel: (01635) 865256 Fax: (01635) 865710 E-mail: info@hjskelton.com

Track Maintenance Equipment Ltd, Witham Wood, Marley Lane, Haslemere, Surrey, GU27 3PZ Tel: (01428) 651114 Fax: (01428) 644727 E-mail: sales@tmeltd.co.uk

RAILWAY TRACK SURVEYING LEVELS

▶ Loy Surveys Ltd, 1 Paisley Road, Renfrew, PA4 8JH Tel: 0141-885 0800 Fax: 0141-885 1202 E-mail: survey@loy.co.uk

RAILWAY TRACTION & CONTROL

▶ Cecube Ltd, 5 Mayfair, Radcliffe On Trent, Radcliffe-on-Trent, Nottingham, NG12 2NP Tel: 0115-933 2673 Fax: 0115-933 2679 E-mail: info@cecube.co.uk

RAILWAY WAGON BUILDERS/ REPAIRERS

E G Steele & Co. Ltd, 25 Dalziel Street, Hamilton, Lanarkshire, ML3 9AU Tel: (01698) 283765 Fax: (01698) 891550 E-mail: egsteel@tiscalli.co.uk

R P L, Brittannic House, 5-7 St Marys Gate, Derby, DE1 3JA Tel: (01332) 349255 Fax: (01332) 294688

W H Davis Ltd, Langwith Road, Langwith Junction, Mansfield, Nottinghamshire, NG20 9SA Tel: (01623) 742621 Fax: (01623) 744474 E-mail: management@whdavis.co.uk

RAINCOATS, *See Rainwear etc*

RAINWATER COLLECTION AND DISTRIBUTION SYSTEMS

▶ Celtic Water Management Ltd, Dolfedwen, Tresaith, Cardigan, Ceredigion, SA43 2JG Tel: (01239) 811465 Fax: (01239) 811918 E-mail: info@celticwater.co.uk

RAINWATER GOODS, *See also headings for particular types*

Aquaduct Systems, Cambridge Street, Ashton-under-Lyne, Lancashire, OL7 0RJ Tel: 0161-339 8828 Fax: 0161-301 5394 E-mail: aquaduct@ukonline.co.uk

C G L Systems, 2 Young Place, East Kilbride, Glasgow, G75 0TD Tel: (01355) 235561 Fax: (01355) 247189 E-mail: sales@cglsystems.co.uk

J.W.D. Rainwater Systems Ltd, Captain Clarke Road, Broadway Industrial Estate, Hyde, Stockport, Cheshire, SK1 4QG Tel: 0161-351 9990 Fax: 0161-351 9992 E-mail: info@rainwatergoods.co.uk

RAINWATER GOODS LINING SERVICES

E. Stephens Gutter Repairs, Little Clanfield Mill, Little Clanfield, Bampton, Oxfordshire, OX18 2RX Tel: (01367) 810380 Fax: (01367) 810390 E-mail: sales@gutter-repairs.co.uk

RALLY COATS/JACKETS

A & S Clothing Manufacturers Ltd, 7 Mott Street, Birmingham, B19 3HD Tel: 0121-233 3625 Fax: 0121-236 2730

Doon Trading Co., 55 Westfield Road, Smethwick, West Midlands, B67 6AW Tel: 0121-555 5398 Fax: 0121-555 5398

Gill & Co., 94 Owen Road, Wolverhampton, WV3 0AL Tel: (01902) 420707 Fax: (01902) 420707

Kewal Brothers Textiles Ltd, Unit 51/52 Bridge Trading Estate, Bridge Street North, Smethwick, West Midlands, B66 2BZ Tel: 0121-555 8080 Fax: 0121-555 8081

M B M Clothing Ltd, 90 Freer Road, Aston, Birmingham, B6 6NB Tel: 0121-554 7522 Fax: 0121-554 7522

Mann Bros Ltd, 142 High Street, West Bromwich, West Midlands, B70 6JJ Tel: 0121-553 7156 Fax: 0121-553 1961 E-mail: info@mannbros.co.uk

Orbit International P.L.C., Orbit House, 5 Dugdale Street, Birmingham, B18 4JA Tel: 0121-558 8444 Fax: 0121-565 0385 E-mail: sales@orbit-int.co.uk

P R Textiles, 31-32 Cliveland Street, Birmingham, B19 3SH Tel: 0121-359 2741 Fax: 0121-333 3600

R S Farmah & Sons, 111 Hubert Road, Birmingham, B29 6ET Tel: 0121-472 6672 Fax: 0121-472 8017 E-mail: peter@rsfarmah.freeserve.co.uk

Saul Trading, 427-431 Moseley Road, Balsall Heath, Birmingham, B12 9BX Tel: 0121-440 3276 Fax: 0121-440 3276

RAM PUMPS

Energy Chemical & Equipment Co, Southwell Business Park, Crew Lane, Southwell, Nottinghamshire, NG25 0TX Tel: (01636) 816600 Fax: (01636) 816602 E-mail: energypumps@aol.com

RAPID GAS FIRED HEATERS

Crawford-Swift, Rosemount Works, Huddersfield Road, Elland, West Yorkshire, HX5 0EE Tel: (01422) 379222 Fax: (01422) 379122 E-mail: mail@crawfordswift.co.uk

Fairbank Brearley International Ltd, Crown Works, Grantham Road, Halifax, West Yorkshire, HX3 6PL Tel: (01422) 360231 Fax: (01422) 355157 E-mail: mail@smarttecgroup.com

RAPID PROTOTYPING ENGINEERING

3d Systems Europe Ltd, Mark House, Mark Road, Hemel Hempstead, Hertfordshire, HP2 7UA Tel: (01442) 282600 Fax: (01442) 282601

A Form Tooling Ltd, 542 Aylestone Road, Leicester, LE2 8JB Tel: 0116-283 5936 Fax: 0116-244 0277 E-mail: aform.tooling@ntlworld.com

A P Hollings & Sons Ltd, 14 Brook Road Industrial Estate, Sirdar Road, Rayleigh, Essex, SS6 7XF Tel: (01268) 770681 Fax: (01268) 775144 E-mail: andy@aphollings.co.uk

Arrk Product Developement Group Ltd, 79 Sadler Foster Way, Teesside Industrial Estate, Stockton-on-Tees, Cleveland, TS17 9JY Tel: (01642) 769930 Fax: (01642) 762352 E-mail: projects@arrkeurope.com

Delcam, Talbot Way, Birmingham, B10 0HJ Tel: 0121-766 5544 Fax: 0121-766 5511 E-mail: marketing@delcam.com

Hothouse Product Development Partners, Unit 1 College Fields Business Centre, Prince Georges Road, Merton, London, SW19 2PT Tel: (020) 8687 2093 Fax: (020) 8646 1822 E-mail: studio@hothouse-design.com

Imirp Rapid Prototyping Ltd, Aston Cross Industrial Estate, 51 Lichfield Road, Birmingham, B6 5RW Tel: 0121-327 3525 Fax: 0121-328 5982E-mail: sales@imirp.co.uk

Martello Ltd, 14 Allens Lane, Hamworthy, Poole, Dorset, BH16 5DA Tel: (01202) 628470 Fax: (01202) 628471 E-mail: sales@martello.co.uk

Malcolm Nicholls Ltd, Waterloo Road, Bidford-on-Avon, Alcester, Warwickshire, B50 4JH Tel: (01789) 490382 Fax: (01789) 490130 E-mail: rp@mnl.co.uk

P D Models, 2-3 Priory Wharf, Hertford, SG14 1RJ Tel: (01992) 553082 Fax: (01992) 550584 E-mail: jan@pdmodels.demon.co.uk

Protechnol Precision Engineers, Unit 4, Christie Place, Bognor Regis, West Sussex, PO22 9RT Tel: (01243) 842233 Fax: (01243) 842233

Rapitypes Ltd, Rockey Studios, Abbey Meadows, Leicester, LE4 5DF Tel: 0116-253 6591 Fax: 0116-253 9827 E-mail: info@rapitypes.com

Third Axis Ltd, Unit N Oldham Central Trading Park, Coulton Close, Oldham, OL1 4EB Tel: (0161) 628 4447 Fax: (0161) 633 0833 E-mail: axiseds@compuserve.com

Tritech Precision Products Ltd, Bridge Road North, Wrexham Industrial Estate, Wrexham, Clwyd, LL13 9PS Tel: (01978) 661111 Fax: (01978) 661392 E-mail: info@tritech-precision-products.co.uk

RAPID PROTOTYPING EQUIPMENT

3d Systems Europe Ltd, Mark House, Mark Road, Hemel Hempstead, Hertfordshire, HP2 7UA Tel: (01442) 282600 Fax: (01442) 282601

L P K F Laser & Electronics Ltd, Coppid Beech Lane, Wokingham, Berkshire, RG40 1PD Tel: (01344) 455046 Fax: (01344) 860547 E-mail: sales@lpkf.co.uk

RASPS AND RIFFLER FILES

Austin Mcgillivray & Co., 124 Scotland Street, Sheffield, S3 7DE Tel: 0114-273 8041 Fax: 0114-275 0290 E-mail: enquiries@sheffieldknives.co.uk

Simonds Industries Ltd, 3 Motorway Industrial Estate, Tyler Street, Sheffield, S9 1DH Tel: 0114-243 3701 Fax: 0114-243 3879

RAW COTTON

Cargill Cotton, 12 Princes Parade, Liverpool, L3 1BG Tel: 0151-242 7500 Fax: (01932) 576256 E-mail: cotton_uk@cargill.com

Plexus Cotton, 2 Ivy Street, Birkenhead, Merseyside, CH41 5EF Tel: 0151-650 8888 Fax: 0151-650 8889 E-mail: mail@plexus-cotton.com

Weil Bros & Stern Raw Cotton, 5 Abbots Quay, Monks Ferry, Birkenhead, Merseyside, CH41 5LH Tel: 0151-650 1000 Fax: 0151-650 0655 E-mail: cotton@weilstern.com

RAW LAMB

▶ The Arran Lamb Co., The Abattoir, Blackwaterfoot, Isle of Arran, KA27 8EZ Tel: (01770) 850264 Fax: (01770) 850264 E-mail: iain@arranlamb.com

RAW VEGETABLE SALADS

▶ Namayasai LLP, Fair Hall, Southover High Street, Lewes, East Sussex, BN7 1HX Tel: (01273) 470667 Fax: (01273) 488816 E-mail: info@namayasai.co.uk

RAW WOOL

C W G Ltd, Priory Depot, Uffington Road, Stamford, Lincolnshire, PE9 2HD Tel: (01780) 762543 Fax: (01780) 755152 E-mail: sales@cwg.co.uk

Devon & Cornwall Wools, Lamellion, Liskeard, Cornwall, PL14 4JT Tel: (01579) 342422 Fax: (01579) 340517

G Modiano, 55 Old Broad Street, London, EC2M 1RX Tel: (020) 7012 0000 Fax: (020) 7374 6468 E-mail: wool@gmodiano.com

D.B. Holdsworth Ltd, 66-69 Pegholme, Ilkley Road, Otley, West Yorkshire, LS21 3JP Tel: (01943) 858358 Fax: (01943) 858359 E-mail: wool@dbholdsworth.demon.co.uk

R E Dickie Ltd, Parkinson Lane, Halifax, West Yorkshire, HX1 3UB Tel: (01422) 341516 Fax: (01422) 357891 E-mail: wool@dickie.co.uk

Scottish Wool Growers, 1 Arkwright Way, North Newmoor Industrial Estate, Irvine, Ayrshire, KA11 4JU Tel: (01294) 203637 Fax: (01294) 203638 E-mail: sales@britishwools.org.com

J. Speak & Co. Ltd, North Dean Mills, West Vale, Greetland, Halifax, West Yorkshire, HX4 8LS Tel: (01422) 378228 Fax: (01422) 370720

Standard Wool UK Ltd, Carlton Bulidings, Bradford, West Yorkshire, BD8 7DB Tel: (01274) 495511 Fax: (01274) 493310 E-mail: woolinfo@standard-wool.co.uk

RAYON FABRICS

James Thornbeer Ltd, Holmes Mill, Greenacre Street, Clitheroe, Lancashire, BB7 1EB Tel: (01200) 423601 Fax: (01200) 429332 E-mail: sales@jamesthornber.com

N Gerstler Ltd, 4 Metro Trading Centre, Second Way, Wembley, Middlesex, HA9 0YJ Tel: (020) 8900 0200 Fax: (020) 8900 8558

W J & H Crozier, 19 Outlack Road, Armagh, BT60 2AN Tel: (028) 3752 2202 Fax: (028) 3752 2283

RAYON YARN

Rex H Perkins Ltd, Hucknall Aerodrome, Watnall Rd, Hucknall, Nottingham, NG15 6EQ Tel: 0115-963 5712 Fax: 0115-963 0129 E-mail: sales@rhperkins.co.uk

RAZOR BARBED FENCING

Siddall & Hilton Mesh Ltd, Birds Royd Lane, Brighouse, West Yorkshire, HD6 1LT Tel: (01484) 401610 Fax: (01484) 721028 E-mail: sales@shmesh.com

RAZOR BLADES

Ever Ready Health Care Ltd, 13 Sentinel Square, Hendon, London, NW4 2EL Tel: (020) 8202 3171 Fax: (020) 8203 9083 E-mail: david@everreadyhealthcare.com

Super-Max Ltd, 5-11 Mono Lane, Feltham, Middlesex, TW13 7LR Tel: (020) 8844 1433 Fax: (020) 8844 1479 E-mail: stirlingfour@aol.com

REACH FORKLIFT TRUCKS

Jungheinrich GB Ltd, Sherbourne House, Sherbourne Drive, Tilbrook, Milton Keynes, MK7 8HX Tel: (01908) 363100 Fax: (01908) 363180 E-mail: info@jungheinrich.co.uk

T A G Forklift Trucks, Barlow Street, Worsley, Manchester, M28 3BQ Tel: 0161-799 6507 Fax: 0161-799 9010

REACTION CALORIMETERS

Thermometric Ltd, 10 Dalby Court, Gadbrook Business Centre, Rudheath, Northwich, Cheshire, CW9 7TN Tel: (01606) 49007 Fax: (01606) 48924

REACTOR VESSELS

Pfaudler Balfour, Riverside Road, Leven, Fife, KY8 4RW Tel: (01333) 423020 Fax: (01333) 427432 E-mail: sales@pfaudlerbalfour.co.uk

Radleys Glassworkers, Shire Hill, Saffron Walden, Essex, CB11 3AZ Tel: (01799) 513320 Fax: (01799) 513283 E-mail: sales@radleys.co.uk

READ WRITE ACTIVE RADIO FREQUENCY IDENTIFICATION (RFID) EQUIPMENT

▶ IID Solutions Ltd, Units 9 & 10 Wesley House, Huddersfield Road, Birstall, Batley, West Yorkshire, WF17 9EJ Tel: (01924) 424600 Fax: (01924) 424601 E-mail: sales@iidsolutions.co.uk

READY MEALS

Meals on the Move, Fearby Road, Masham, Ripon, North Yorkshire, HG4 4ES Tel: (01765) 689595 E-mail: graham.thornton@danbys.biz

READY MIXED CONCRETE

Ablemix Concrete, Gibbet Lane, Shawell, Lutterworth, Leicestershire, LE17 6AA Tel: (01788) 860100 Fax: (01788) 860937

Ace Minimix Ltd, Stancombe Lane, Flax Bourton, Bristol, BS48 3QD Tel: (01275) 465846 Fax: (01275) 465876

Ace Minimix Ltd, Saucepan Industrial Estate, Babraham Road, Sawston, Cambridge, CB22 3LH Tel: (01223) 301436

Ace Minimix, Rover Way, Cardiff, CF24 2RX Tel: (029) 2045 3894 Fax: (029) 2045 3894

Ace Minimix Ltd, Bellhouse Pit, Warren Lane, Stanway, Colchester, CO3 0NN Tel: (01206) 330178 Fax: (020) 8555 2612 E-mail: easten.amix@tarmac.co.uk

Ace Minimix Ltd, Sharpstones Lane, Bayston Hill, Shrewsbury, SY3 0AN Tel: (01743) 874083 Fax: (01544) 232185

▶ Ace Minimix, Warne Road, Weston-super-Mare, Avon, BS23 3UU Tel: (01934) 615470 Fax: (01275) 465876

Admiral Fire Extinguishers, 19 Flude Road, Coventry, CV7 9AQ Tel: (024) 7636 5157 Fax: (024) 7636 2815 E-mail: admiralfire@btopenworld.com

Advanced Concrete Ltd, 154 Beddington Lane, Croydon, CR9 4QD Tel: (020) 8689 3342 Fax: (020) 8684 3012

Allen Newport Ltd, 31 New Path, Walton House, Fordham, Ely, Cambridgeshire, CB7 5JZ Tel: (01638) 720228 Fax: (01638) 721332 E-mail: info@allen-newport.co.uk

Alliance Concrete Ltd, Hargreaves St, Manchester, M4 4EJ Tel: (0800) 7836320 Fax: 0161-819 2624

▶ Anglian Minimix, Dereham Road, New Costessey, Norwich, NR5 0TL Tel: (01603) 745490 Fax: (01603) 741336

▶ Ascus Concrete Pumping Ltd, Burcott Road, Bristol, BS11 8AB Tel: 0117-982 7272 Fax: (029) 2049 9799

Ashbridge Concrete, Pigeon Cote Industrial Estate, Malton Road, York, YO32 9LD Tel: (01904) 425300 Fax: (01904) 427115

B J Kenny, Z Cartwright Business Park, Brue Avenue, Bridgwater, Somerset, TA6 5LT Tel: (01278) 421168 Fax: (01278) 444421

Bardon Concrete Ltd, Lichfield Road, Barton under Needwood, Burton-on-Trent, Staffordshire, DE13 8EF Tel: (01283) 712677 Fax: (01283) 716598 E-mail: general@aggregate.com

Bardon Concrete Ltd, Stephenson Industrial Estate, Willowholme, Carlisle, CA2 5RN Tel: (01228) 599980 Fax: (01228) 599980

Bardon Concrete Ltd, Eskett Quarry, Eskett, Frizington, Cumbria, CA26 3UN Tel: (01946) 862414 Fax: (01946) 862757 E-mail: general@aggregate.com

Bardon Concrete Ltd, Balmore Road, Torrance, Glasgow, G64 4AF Tel: (01360) 622135 Fax: (01360) 620575

Bardon Concrete Ltd, Unit 7, Robert Way, Wickford, Essex, SS11 8DD Tel: (01268) 769696 Fax: (01268) 769097

Joseph Barrett & Sons Ltd, 128 Eglish Road, Dungannon, County Tyrone, BT70 1LB Tel: (028) 3754 8646 Fax: (028) 3754 8863 E-mail: info@barrettconcrete.com

Brett Aggregates, Waldringfield Road, Brightwell, Ipswich, IP10 0BL Tel: (01473) 621007 Fax: (01473) 736721

Brett Concrete Ltd, Oare Road, Faversham, Kent, ME13 7TW Tel: (01795) 533436 Fax: (01795) 536047

Brett Concrete Ltd, Jurys Gap Road, Lydd, Romney Marsh, Kent, TN29 9JW Tel: (01797) 320462 Fax: (01797) 320074 E-mail: sales@fullsupply.co.uk

C & G Concrete Ltd, Uffington Road, Stamford, Lincolnshire, PE9 2HA Tel: (01780) 482000 Fax: (01780) 480066 E-mail: fhgilman@ibm.net

C & H Quickmix Ltd, Woodlands, Dereham Road, New Costessey, Norwich, NR5 0TL Tel: (01603) 740333 Fax: (01603) 741336 E-mail: enquiries@tarmac-southern.co.uk

Caerleon Ready Mixed Concrete Ltd, Western Industrial Estate, Caerleon, Newport, NP18 3NN Tel: (01633) 423549 Fax: (01633) 430413

Cemex, Long Lane, Attenborough, Beeston, Nottingham, NG9 6BL Tel: 0115-943 2260 Fax: 0115-943 1966 E-mail: webmanager.hbm@cemex.co.uk

Cemex Ltd, Haughmond Quarry, Uffington, Shrewsbury, SY4 4RW Tel: (01743) 709256 Fax: (01743) 709462

Cemex Ltd, Leeman Road, York, YO26 4HX Tel: (01904) 621280 Fax: (01904) 619399

Cemex Materials Ltd, Cemex House, Elland Road, Leeds, LS11 8BA Tel: 0113-271 3881 Fax: 0113-271 9793

Cemex RMC Ltd, Lucknow Road South, Bodmin, Cornwall, PL31 1DR Tel: (01208) 74321 Fax: (01208) 74327

Cemex UK Ltd, Town Mead Road, London, SW6 2QL Tel: (020) 7790 3232 Fax: (020) 7371 0339

Cemex UK Ltd, Crown House, Evreux Way, Rugby, Warwickshire, CV21 2DT Tel: 0114-242 6050 Fax: (01788) 517220

Cemx, R M C House, Littleburn Industrial Estate, Langley Moor, Durham, DH7 8HH Tel: 0191-378 7700 Fax: 0191-378 7752

Civil & Marine Slag Cement Ltd, London Road, Grays, Essex, RM20 3NL Tel: (01708) 864813 Fax: (01708) 865907 E-mail: enquiries@civilmarine.co.uk

Con-a-crete Ltd, 52 Haghue Side Way, Rothwell, Leeds, LS26 0UG Tel: 0113-282 7310 Fax: 0113-282 0805

The Concrete Ltd, Station Road, Thorney, Peterborough, PE6 0QE Tel: (01733) 270870 Fax: (01733) 270285

Concrete Developments Great Barr Ltd, Baltimore Road, Great Barr, Birmingham, B42 1DD Tel: 0121-356 5575 Fax: 0121-344 3285 E-mail: james@concrete-developers.freeserve.co.uk

Moreton C. Cullimore Gravels Ltd, 47 London Road, Stroud, Gloucestershire, GL5 2AU Tel: (01453) 765381 Fax: (01453) 766491

Cumbria Minimix, Kendal Lime Works, Underbarrow Road, Kendal, Cumbria, LA9 5RT Tel: (01539) 735784 Fax: (01539) 735784

Cumbrian Mini-mix Concrete, Pittwood Road, Lillyhall Industrial Estate, Lillyhall, Workington, Cumbria, CA14 4JP Tel: (01900) 870601 Fax: (01900) 604426

Cwmna Gro Ltd, Penybryn Farm, Sarnau, Bala, Gwynedd, LL23 7LH Tel: (01678) 530297 Fax: (01678) 530389

D & H Concrete Products, Fernbank Avenue, Barnoldswick, Lancashire, BB18 5UX Tel: (01282) 812299 Fax: (01282) 812659 E-mail: info@dhconcrete.co.uk

▶ Dalzell Precast, 4 Somerset Place, Glasgow, G3 7JT Tel: 0141-332 5345

Dudley Mixed, Peartree Lane, Dudley, West Midlands, DY2 0UU Tel: (01384) 242474 Fax: (01384) 242499

East Antrim Mini Mix, 64 Larne Road, Whitehead, Carrickfergus, County Antrim, BT38 9TF Tel: (028) 9336 7771 Fax: (028) 9336 6949 E-mail: ronnie@eastantrimminimix.co.uk

▶ Eastern Concrete Ltd, Barrells House, Wattisham Road, Hitcham, Ipswich, IP7 7LU Tel: (01449) 744276 Fax: (01449) 722093 E-mail: tom@captonconcrete.fsnet.co.uk

F H Gilman & Co., Bolton Hill Quarry, Tiers Cross, Haverfordwest, Dyfed, SA62 3ER Tel: (01437) 892222 Fax: (01437) 899353

▶ Fahey Concrete Ltd, Penince, Par, Cornwall, PL24 2SX Tel: (01726) 850086 Fax: (01726) 852244

Faheys Concrete Ltd, Knowle Quarry, North Road Industrial Estate, Okehampton, Devon, EX20 1RQ Tel: (01837) 52609 Fax: (01837) 54813

G M C (Concrete) Ltd, Kelston Farm, Gronant Road, Gwespyr, Holywell, Flintshire, CH8 9LU Tel: (01745) 853827

▶ E. & J.W. Glendinning Ltd, Glentor, Ashburton, Newton Abbot, Devon, TQ13 7LF Tel: (01364) 652601 Fax: (01364) 651118 E-mail: sales@ejwglendinning.co.uk

Halton Concrete, Macdermott Road, Widnes, Cheshire, WA8 0PF Tel: (01925) 444397

Hanson Aggregates Ltd, Broad Quay Road, Felnex Industrial Estate, Newport, Gwent, NP19 4PN Tel: (01633) 271728 Fax: (01685) 882005

Hanson Aggregates, Charnley Fold Lane, Bamber Bridge, Preston, PR5 6QJ Tel: (0845) 1205722

▶ Hanson Aggregates Ltd, Ermin Street, Swindon, SN3 4LW Tel: (01793) 822000

Hanson Aggregates Ltd, Clifford House, York Road, Wetherby, West Yorkshire, LS22 7NS Tel: (01937) 581977 Fax: (01937) 545889 E-mail: sales.orderswest@hanson-aggregates.com

Hanson Concrete Products plc, Shepherds Spring Lane, Andover, Hampshire, SP10 1DL Tel: (0845) 6000671

Hanson Premix plc, Pinfold Lane, Bridlington, North Humberside, YO16 6XP Tel: (01262) 674431

▶ Hanson Premix plc, Endeavour Way, London, SW19 8UH Tel: (020) 8946 7694 Fax: (020) 8947 9182 E-mail: sam.whittington@hansonplc.com

Hanson Premix, 231 Tunnel Avenue, London, SE10 0QE Tel: (020) 8423 5333 Fax: (020) 8858 1142

Hanson Premix plc, Castle An Dinas, Ludgvan, Penzance, Cornwall, TR20 8AG Tel: (01736) 364455

Hanson Premix plc, Harvil Road, Ickenham, Uxbridge, Middlesex, UB10 8AJ Tel: (01895) 270011 Fax: (01895) 270458

▶ Hanson Premix (UK) Ltd, Bulls Lodge Quarry, Generals Lane, Boreham, Chelmsford, CM3 3HR Tel: (01245) 451644

Hanson Quarry Products Europe Ltd, The Ridge, Chipping Sodbury, Bristol, BS37 6AY Tel: (01454) 316000 Fax: (01454) 325161

Hartigan Readymix Ltd, 98 High Street, Newport Pagnell, Buckinghamshire, MK16 8EJ Tel: (01908) 611126 Fax: (01908) 210534 E-mail: info@gfxhartiganltd.co.uk

Hibbs W G & Co. Ltd, Solent Industrial Estate Caird Avenue, Lymington Road, New Milton, Hampshire, BH25 5QA Tel: (01425) 611660 Fax: (01425) 619927

Hillhouse Quarry Group, Hillhouse Quarry, Troon, Ayrshire, KA10 7HX Tel: (01292) 310482 Fax: (01292) 314640

Hoddam Contracting Co. Ltd, Hoddom Road, Ecclefechan, Lockerbie, Dumfriesshire, DG11 3BY Tel: (01576) 300634 Fax: (01576) 300798

▶ Island Cement, South Quay, Ramsey, Isle of Man, IM8 1BG Tel: (01624) 814808 Fax: (01624) 620912

J Clubb Ltd, Church Hill, Wilmington, Dartford, DA2 7DZ Tel: (01322) 225431 Fax: (01322) 289932 E-mail: sales@jclubb.co.uk

Ken Abrahams (Concrete) Ltd, Pool Industrial Estate, Pool, Redruth, Cornwall, TR15 3RH Tel: (01209) 218550 Fax: (01209) 314881

Lafarge Aggregates Ltd, Knowsthorpe Gate, Leeds, LS9 0NP Tel: 0113-240 0034

Lafarge Readymix Ltd, Barrington Road Industrial Estat, Bedlington, Northumberland, NE22 7AL Tel: (01670) 823336 Fax: (01670) 823336

Lafarge Readymix Ltd, Dobs Wier Pit, Nazeing New Road, Broxbourne, Hertfordshire, EN10 6TD Tel: (01992) 465865

Lafarge Readymix Ltd, Sandall Stones Road, Kirk Sandall Industrial Estate, Doncaster, South Yorkshire, DN3 1QR Tel: (01302) 883941

Lafarge Readymix Ltd, Jeffreys Road, Enfield, Middlesex, EN3 7XD Tel: (020) 8805 8150

Lafarge Readymix Ltd, Pocklington Industrial Estate, Pocklington, York, YO42 1NP Tel: (01759) 305767

Lincs Mini-mix, R M C House, Long Lane, Attenborough, Nottingham, NG9 6BL Tel: (01205) 353035 Fax: 0115-925 6268

▶ Lovie Ltd, Blackhill Quarry, Tyrie, Fraserburgh, Aberdeenshire, AB43 7DR Tel: (01346) 541212 Fax: (01346) 541424

▶ Mccaffrey Concrete Products, Ummera, Derrylin, Enniskillen, County Fermanagh, BT92 9PZ Tel: (028) 6774 8738 Fax: (028) 6774 8282

Metamix Concrete, Purdy Road, Bilston, West Midlands, WV14 8UB Tel: (01902) 493626 Fax: (01902) 497418

▶ Mix & Lay Concrete Supplies Ltd, Denver Site, Ferry Lane, Rainham, Essex, RM13 9BU Tel: (01708) 521414

Mixamate Concrete, Head Office, Birkenhead Avenue, Kingston upon Thames, Surrey, KT2 6RP Tel: (020) 8547 0300 Fax: (020) 8547 0300

Mixamate Concrete, South Park, Sevenoaks, Kent, TN13 1EA Tel: (0800) 2888047

Mixamate Concrete, Martland Industrial Units, Smarts Heath Lane, Woking, Surrey, GU22 0RQ Tel: (01483) 810101 Fax: (01483) 810101

Mixamate Holdings, 11 West Down, Bookham, Leatherhead, Surrey, KT23 4LJ Tel: (01372) 456714 Fax: (01372) 456714

Modern Mix Concrete Supplies Ltd, Unit 1 Empson Street, London, E3 3LT Tel: (020) 7538 2266 Fax: (020) 7537 3256

New Mix Concrete, Stanningley Industrial Centre, Varley Street, Stanningley, Pudsey, West Yorkshire, LS28 7EL Tel: 0113-257 6738 Fax: 0161-832 0929

Northern Minimix, Haverton Hill, Billingham, Cleveland, TS23 4EY Tel: (01642) 563243 Fax: (01642) 561509

▶ Old Town Paving, Newburgh Building, Warncliffe Industrial Estate, McLintock Way, Barnsley, S. Yorkshire, S70 6BF Tel: (01226) 208005 Fax: (01226) 208005

Peakmix Concrete, Peak Forest, Buxton, Derbyshire, SK17 8EW Tel: (01298) 23013

Pioneer Concrete UK Ltd, Horton Road, Gloucester, GL1 3QA Tel: (01452) 303685 Fax: (01452) 303505

READY MIXED CONCRETE – *continued*

Porthmadog Concrete Ltd, Glan Byl, Criccieth, Gwynedd, LL52 0RD Tel: (01766) 530644 Fax: (01766) 530407 E-mail: robert@porthmadog.co.uk

▶ Premier Concrete, Meadow Drove Farm, Meadow Drove, Bourne, Lincolnshire, PE10 0AL Tel: (0845) 6008113 Fax: (01778) 420374

Proper Mixed Concrete Ltd, Wood Lane, Ellesmere, Shropshire, SY12 0HY Tel: (01691) 626262 Fax: (01691) 626263 E-mail: enquiries@tggroup.co.uk

R Carter, Hale Manor Farm, Hale Common, Newport, Isle of Wight, PO30 3AR Tel: (01983) 867312 Fax: (01983) 868200

R M C Readymix Midlands, Wolverhampton Road, Oldbury, West Midlands, B69 4RJ Tel: (0870) 7762762 Fax: 0121-544 7970

Ready Mixed Concrete Ltd, Quarry, Llanelwedd, Builth Wells, Powys, LD2 3UB Tel: (01982) 553421 Fax: (01982) 552402

Ready Mixed Concrete Ltd, Larne Road, Carrickfergus, County Antrim, BT38 7NN Tel: (028) 9335 1087

Ready Mixed Concrete Ltd, 64 Killough Road, Downpatrick, County Down, BT30 8BL Tel: (028) 4461 2688

Ready Mixed Concrete Midlands Ltd, Slack Lane, Heanor, Derbyshire, DE75 7GX Tel: 0115-922 5225 Fax: 01159-22827

Ready Mixed Concrete Northern Ltd, Charlestown Road, Halifax, West Yorkshire, HX3 9XQ Tel: (01422) 320277

Ready Mixed Concrete Northern Ltd, Black Quarry, Moor Road, Leyburn, North Yorkshire, DL8 5LA Tel: (01969) 623014 Fax: (01969) 624340

Ready Mixed Concrete Northern Ltd, 2 Showfield Lane, Malton, North Yorkshire, YO17 6BT Tel: (01653) 693565 Fax: (01653) 697787

Ready Mixed Concrete Scotland Ltd, Hawbank Road, East Kilbride, Glasgow, G74 5HB Tel: (01355) 236611 Fax: (01355) 264345

Ready Mixed Concrete South West Ltd, Kilmington Quarry, Kilmington, Axminster, Devon, EX13 7RU Tel: (01297) 32684 Fax: (01297) 631235

Ready Mixed Concrete South West Ltd, Venn Quarries, Landkey, Barnstaple, Devon, EX32 0NU Tel: (01271) 830385 Fax: (01271) 830214

Ready Mixed Concrete (Transite) Ltd, The Willows, Barnet Road, London Colney, St. Albans, Hertfordshire, AL2 1BD Tel: (01727) 822331 Fax: (01727) 826606 E-mail: readymix.homecounties@rmc.co.uk

Ready Mixed Concrete Ulster Ltd, 2 Hillview Avenue, Londonderry, BT47 2NU Tel: (028) 7131 1274

▶ Ready Mixed Concrete Western Ltd, Bristol Road, Gloucester, GL2 5DH Tel: (01452) 528463 Fax: (01452) 307862

Ready Mixed Concrete Western Ltd, Cleveland Farm, Ashton Keynes, Swindon, SN6 6QP Tel: (01285) 860301 Fax: 0117-937 2789

Ready Mixed Home Counties, New Building, Hardwick Gravel Pits, Hardwick, Witney, Oxfordshire, OX29 7QF Tel: (01865) 300155 Fax: (01865) 300427

Ready Use Concrete Co. Ltd, 17a Trench Road, Londonderry, BT47 3UB Tel: (028) 7134 1367

▶ Ready Use Concrete Co. Ltd, Ballybarnes Road, Newtownards, County Down, BT23 4UE Tel: (028) 9181 4676

Readymix Huddersfield Ltd, Red Doles Lane, Leeds Road, Huddersfield, HD2 1YD Tel: (01484) 535311 Fax: (01484) 558255 E-mail: sales@readymix-huddersfield.co.uk

Readymix London & South East Ltd, 15 Townmead Road, London, SW6 2QL Tel: (020) 7384 4900 Fax: (020) 7371 0039

Rhondda Ready Mix Concrete, 1 Sunnybank, Williamstown, Tonypandy, Mid Glamorgan, CF40 1PE Tel: (01443) 440044

Riskend Quarry Ltd, 6 Garrell Road, Kilsyth, Glasgow, G65 9JY Tel: (01236) 821486 Fax: (01236) 823256 E-mail: riskendquarry@supanet.com

RMC Readymix East Anglia, R M C House, Whitehall Road, Colchester, CO2 8HD Tel: (01206) 862222 Fax: (01206) 860768 E-mail: enqiries.readymix.eastanglia@rmc.co.uk

RMC Readymix Eastern, Lock Keepers Cottage, Langford Lane, Kidlington, Oxfordshire, OX5 1HT Tel: (01865) 372424 Fax: (01865) 842303

RMC Readymix Western, Hawkesworth Trading Estate, Swindon, SN2 1EF Tel: (01793) 525190 Fax: (01793) 692562

RMC South East Ltd, Aylesford Sand Pit, Rochester Road, Aylesford, Kent, ME20 7DX Tel: (01622) 716904 Fax: (01622) 882462

RMC South East, Gravel Pit, Snails Lane, Blashford, Ringwood, Hampshire, BH24 3PG Tel: (01425) 478396 Fax: (01425) 478396

Roadmix Ltd, Ballyvesey Road, Newtownabbey, County Antrim, BT36 4SY Tel: (028) 9034 2189 Fax: (028) 9084 8198

Roberts Keith Ready Mixed Concrete, 98 Wernoleu Road, Ammanford, Dyfed, SA18 2JL Tel: (01269) 593452

▶ Rouse Concrete, Gilbey Road, Grimsby, South Humberside, DN31 2RL Tel: (01472) 351987 Fax: (01472) 362202

S Morris Ltd, Tout Quarry, Tout Road, Charlton Adam, Somerton, Somerset, TA11 7AN Tel: (01458) 223991 Fax: (01458) 223181 E-mail: sales@smorris.co.uk

St Andrews Fire Equipment, 3 St Williams Way, Norwich, NR7 0AH Tel: (01603) 431122 Fax: (01603) 448640

Sherbourne Stone Co., Cleveland Road, Hartlepool, Cleveland, TS24 0SY Tel: (01429) 223276

Shropshire Mini-Mix, Shawbury Heath, The Oaks, Shawbury, Shrewsbury, SY4 4EA Tel: (01939) 250986 Fax: 01939 251254 E-mail: sales@readymix.com

Small Loads Concrete, Haye Quarry, Stag Lane, Plymouth, PL9 8AX Tel: (01752) 481723 Fax: (01752) 848862

Smiths Concrete Ltd, Southam Road, Banbury, Oxfordshire, OX16 2RR Tel: (01295) 278177 Fax: (01295) 271402 E-mail: info@smithsconcrete.co.uk

▶ Solway Precast, Braehead, Barrhill, Girvan, Ayrshire, KA26 0QR Tel: (01465) 821348 Fax: (01465) 821383

▶ Speedy Mortar, Unit 14, Currock Road Trade Centre, Currock Road, Carlisle, CA2 5AD Tel: (01228) 548001 Fax: (01228) 548001

Spotmix, 99 Carstairs Street, Glasgow, G40 4JQ Tel: 0141-550 1444 Fax: 0141-550 1555 E-mail: sales@spotmix.co.uk

▶ Staffs Concrete Ltd, Litchfield Street, Hanley, Stoke-On-Trent, ST1 3JE Tel: (01782) 849993 Fax: (01782) 398048

Strad Concrete, 125 Straid Road, Bushmills, County Antrim, BT57 8XU Tel: (028) 2073 1751 Fax: 028 20731751

▶ Stroud A & M, 2a The Old Brickworks, Ebley Road, Stonehouse, Gloucestershire, GL10 2LW Tel: (01453) 825111

▶ Supreme Concrete Ltd, Andall Road, Barnwell, Peterborough, PE8 5PD Tel: (01832) 270107

▶ T L Concrete Products, D Station Street Business Park, Station Street, Cinderford, Gloucestershire, GL14 2LG Tel: (01594) 827190

Tarmac Topmix Ltd, Cornelly Quarry, Heol-Y-Splot, South Cornelly, Bridgend, Mid Glamorgan, CF33 4RD Tel: (01656) 740771 Fax: (01656) 748248

Tarmac Topmix Ltd, Unit N Babraham Rd, Sawston, Cambridge, CB2 4LH Tel: 01223 833421

Tarmac Topmix Ltd, Warren Lane, Stanway, Colchester, CO3 0NN Tel: (01473) 210707 Fax: (01206) 330437

Tarmac Topmix Ltd, Tufthorn Business Park, Tufthorn Avenue, Coleford, Gloucestershire, GL16 8PP Tel: (01594) 836621 Fax: (01594) 837450

Tarmac Topmix Ltd, High Craighall Road, Glasgow, G4 9UD Tel: 0141-353 2515 Fax: 0141-353 2515

Tarmac Topmix Ltd, Corporation Road, Newport, Gwent, NP19 0GA Tel: (01633) 280866 Fax: (01633) 290894

Tarmac Topmix Ltd, Private Road 5, Nottingham, NG4 2JU Tel: 0115-961 4931

Tarmac Topmix Ltd, Sharpstones Lane, Bayston Hill, Shrewsbury, SY3 0AN Tel: (01743) 873479 Fax: (01743) 874505

Tarmac Topmix Ltd, Govan Road, Fenton Industrial Estate, Stoke-on-Trent, ST4 2RS Tel: (01782) 263107 Fax: (01782) 413692

Tarmac Western Ltd, PO Box 1, Kington, Herefordshire, HR5 3LQ Tel: (01544) 388959 Fax: (01544) 231406 E-mail: info@tarmac-western.co.uk

Topmix Mortars, Holesmouth, Bristol, BS11 9BN Tel: 0117-938 0111 Fax: 0117-982 8519

▶ Tor Multimix, Unit 10 Thomas Way Industrial Estate, Glastonbury, Somerset, BA6 9LU Tel: (01458) 830630

▶ Turley Bros, 7 Corcreechy Road, Newry, County Down, BT34 1LP Tel: (028) 3026 6421 Fax: (028) 3025 0542

Westcrete Pre-cast Concrete Ltd, Stoney Bridges, Membury Road, Axminster, Devon, EX13 5RL Tel: (01297) 32002 E-mail: sales@westcrete.fsnet.co.uk

Western Blocks Ltd, 42 Upton Towans, Hayle, Cornwall, TR27 5BL Tel: (01736) 753128 Fax: (01736) 756857

READY MIXED MORTAR

Aggregate Industries UK Ltd, Hulland Ward, Ashbourne, Derbyshire, DE6 3ET Tel: (01335) 372222 Fax: (01335) 370074

C P I Euromix Ltd, Unit 27 Fountain Business Centre, Ellis Street, Coatbridge, Lanarkshire, ML5 3AA Tel: (01236) 431700 Fax: (01236) 432090

Cemex RMC Ltd, Lucknow Road South, Bodmin, Cornwall, PL31 1DR Tel: (01208) 74321 Fax: (01208) 74327

Cemex (UK) Ltd, Whitby Street, Hartlepool, Cleveland, TS24 7LP Tel: (01429) 275269 Fax: (01429) 860898

H J Chard & Sons, Albert Rd, St Philips, Bristol, BS2 0XS Tel: 0117-977 7681 Fax: 0117-971 9802

Hanson Aggrigates Ltd, Edge Green Road, Ashton-In-Makerfield, Wigan, Lancashire, WN4 8YA Tel: (0845) 1205725 Fax: (01942) 724650

Ready Use Concrete Co. Ltd, 140 Mallusk Road, Newtownabbey, County Antrim, BT36 4QN Tel: (028) 9034 2291

Roadmix Ltd, Ballyvesey Road, Newtownabbey, County Antrim, BT36 4SY Tel: (028) 9034 2189 Fax: (028) 9084 8198

Smiths Concrete Ltd, Southam Road, Banbury, Oxfordshire, OX16 2RR Tel: (01295) 278177 Fax: (01295) 271402 E-mail: info@smithsconcrete.co.uk

Tilcon South Ltd, Mortar Division, Church Ward House, Kemble Drive, Swindon, SN2 2TA Tel: 0117-941 4973

Topmix Mortars, Holesmouth, Bristol, BS11 9BN Tel: 0117-938 0111 Fax: 0117-982 8519

READY TO EAT BAKERY PRODUCTS

▶ Percy Ingles Bakery Ltd, The Pavilion, High Street, Waltham Cross, Hertfordshire, EN8 7BZ Tel: (01992) 767403

READY TO HANG CURTAINS

▶ Adby Interiors Ltd, 19 Alford Road, High Wycombe, Buckinghamshire, HP12 4PT Tel: (01494) 441507 Fax: (01494) 474330 E-mail: info@adbyinteriors.co.uk

Bury Soft Furnishings Ltd, 9 Brantwood Road, Salford, M7 4EN Tel: 0161-792 1492 Fax: 0161-792 1492

Comfy Quilts, Albany Mill, Old Hall Street, Middleton, Manchester, M24 1AG Tel: (0870) 7662324 Fax: (0870) 7662333 E-mail: info@comfyquilts.com

Dorma Group Ltd, Newtown Mill Lees Street, Pendlebury, Swinton, Manchester, M27 6DB Tel: 0161-251 4400 Fax: 0161-251 4417 E-mail: info@dorma.co.uk

Filigree Ltd, Carter Lane East, South Normanton, Alfreton, Derbyshire, DE55 2EG Tel: (01773) 811619 Fax: (01773) 862777 E-mail: enquiries@filigree.demon.co.uk

Fuda International Trading Co. Ltd, Middle Engine Lane, North Shields, Tyne & Wear, NE29 8HG Tel: 0191-258 2233 Fax: 0191-258 2267

Hamilton Mcbride, Churchill Way, Nelson, Lancashire, BB9 6RT Tel: (01282) 878282 Fax: (01282) 614464 E-mail: enquiries@hamiltonmcbride.co.uk

High Style Furnishings, Saxon Way, Melbourn, Royston, Hertfordshire, SG8 6DN Tel: (01763) 261837 Fax: (01763) 262489 E-mail: enq@highstyle.co.uk

R C Kennedy Ltd, 1 North Street, Manchester, M8 8RE Tel: 0161-832 6182 Fax: 0161-834 3053

REAL TIME COMMUNICATION SYSTEMS

Accutest Ltd, Wren Nest Road, Glossop, Derbyshire, SK13 8HB Tel: (01457) 866613 Fax: (01457) 856789 E-mail: sales@accutest.co.uk

Callscan Ltd, Callscan House Priestley Wharf, 20 Holt Street, Birmingham, B7 4BZ Tel: 0121-359 8941 Fax: 0121-359 1417 E-mail: info@epcuk.com

Cti Data Solutions Ltd, Nordic House, 120 High Street, Purley, Surrey, CR8 2AD Tel: (020) 8763 3888 Fax: (020) 8763 3863 E-mail: info@ctidata.co.uk

Dataflex Design Communications Ltd, 2nd Floor Chancery House, St. Nicholas Way, Sutton, Surrey, SM1 1JB Tel: (020) 8710 1700 Fax: (020) 8710 1705

REAL TIME COMPUTERS

North West Time Recording Co., 197 Bury Old Road, Prestwich, Manchester, M25 1JF Tel: 0161-798 8002 Fax: 0161-773 2441 E-mail: terry@nwtr.co.uk

Ultra Electronics Command & Control Systems, Knaves Beech Business Centre, Loudwater, High Wycombe, Buckinghamshire, HP10 9UT Tel: (01628) 530000 Fax: (01628) 524557 E-mail: info@ueccs.co.uk

REAMERS, ADJUSTABLE/ EXPANDING

C L A Manufacturing Ltd, 10 Binns Close, Coventry, CV4 9TB Tel: (024) 7646 5535 Fax: (024) 7669 4543 E-mail: info@clatools.co.uk

RECEIVERS, GLOBAL POSITIONING SYSTEMS (GPS)

▶ Adventure Electronics, 46 Back Lane, Baxenden, Accrington, Lancashire, BB5 2RE Tel: 01254 399731 Fax: 01254 399731 E-mail: info@adventureelectronics.co.uk

▶ GPS4Less, The Chimneys, Dauntsey Lock, Chippenham, Wiltshire, SN15 4HD Tel: (0845) 4309207 Fax: (0845) 4309208 E-mail: sales@gps4less.co.uk

▶ SuperEtrader, PO Box 4788, Walsall, WS1 9DZ Tel: (0870) 4438446 Fax: (0870) 4438445 E-mail: sales@superetrader.co.uk

RECEPTION DESKS

Clarke Rendall Business Furniture Ltd, 12 Denbigh Hall Industrial Estate, Denbigh Hall, Bletchley, Milton Keynes, MK3 7QT Tel: (01908) 391600 Fax: (01908) 391601 E-mail: salessupport@clarkerendall.com

RECEPTION FURNITURE

Dictacliff Ltd, Burywater Barn, Burywater Lane, Newport, Saffron Walden, Essex, CB11 3TZ Tel: (01799) 542242 Fax: (01799) 542322 E-mail: john@dictacliff.co.uk

▶ Guild Anderson Furniture Ltd, 'Waterways', Watery Lane, Bishopstrow, Warminster, Wiltshire, BA12 9HT Tel: (01985) 216044 Fax: (0870) 0914517 E-mail: info@guildandersonfurniture.co.uk

RECHARGEABLE BATTERY TORCHES

Cluson Engineering Ltd, Unit 6, Bedford Road, Petersfield, Hampshire, GU32 3LJ Tel: (01730) 264672 Fax: (01730) 260475 E-mail: sales@clulite.co.uk

Firstfire Ltd, Howe House, 13 Somers Road, Halesowen, West Midlands, B62 8EN Tel: 0121-585 3870 Fax: 0121-585 3871 E-mail: first.fire@dial.pipex.com

RECIPROCATING COMPRESSOR SEALING COMPONENTS

Hoerbiger, Edderthorpe Street, Bradford, West Yorkshire, BD3 9RB Tel: (01274) 733801 Fax: (01274) 736887 E-mail: sales@hrpu.co.uk

RECIPROCATING JIGSAW BLADES

C 4 Carbides (International) Ltd, 9 Nuffield Road, Cambridge, CB4 1TF Tel: (01223) 506406 Fax: (01223) 225405 E-mail: janice@c4carbides.com

Cengar Ltd, 70 Lister Lane, Halifax, West Yorkshire, HX1 5DN Tel: (01422) 354626 Fax: (01422) 349024 E-mail: enquiries@cengar.com

RECIPROCATING PUMPS

Dawson, Downie, Lamont, 31 Rutherford Road, Glenrothes, Fife, KY6 2RT Tel: (01592) 775577 Fax: (01592) 775517 E-mail: sales@ddl-ltd.com

Holden & Brooke Ltd, Wenlock Way, Manchester, M12 5JL Tel: 0161-223 2223 Fax: 0161-220 9660 E-mail: marketing@holdenbrooke.com

RECLAIMED PUBLIC HOUSE FURNITURE

▶ Cotswold Reclamation Co., 2 Sandy Lane Court, Upper Rissington, Cheltenham, Gloucestershire, GL54 2NF Tel: (01451) 820292 Fax: (01451) 822455 E-mail: info@cotswoldreclamation.com

RECLAIMED TIMBER FLOORING

▶ Cotswold Reclamation Co., 2 Sandy Lane Court, Upper Rissington, Cheltenham, Gloucestershire, GL54 2NF Tel: (01451) 820292 Fax: (01451) 822455 E-mail: info@cotswoldreclamation.com

Floor Coverings Of Doncaster, 2 Richmond Road, Doncaster, South Yorkshire, DN5 8TB Tel: (01302) 812198 E-mail: sales@fcdoncaster.co.uk

▶ Kinv Property Maintenance, 6 High Street, Princes Risborough, Buckinghamshire, HP27 0AX Tel: (01844) 274876 Fax: (01844) 274876 E-mail: info@kinv.co.uk

RECONDITIONED AUTOMOTIVE GEARBOXES

Autotrans Gearbox Centre, Unit 2 Broadhempston, Totnes, Devon, TQ9 6AT Tel: (01803) 762233 Fax: (01803) 762233

Chiltern Transmission, 11 Britannia Industrial Park, Dashwood Avenue, High Wycombe, Buckinghamshire, HP12 3ES Tel: (01494) 534806

Clark Transmissions, Watermill House, 2 Restmor Way, Wallington, Surrey, SM6 7AH Tel: (020) 8647 0570

Gears, 13b Cypress Road, Southport, Merseyside, PR8 6HE Tel: (01704) 535760

RECONDITIONED AUTOMOTIVE GEARBOXES – *continued*

▶ M K Engines Ltd, 6 Clarke Road, Bletchley, Milton Keynes, MK1 1LG Tel: (01908) 366566 Fax: (01908) 366566

John Rawle Automotives, Unit 4, The Millwalk, Birmingham, B31 4HX Tel: 0121-478 2064 Fax: 0121-478 2064

J.R. Transmissions, 35a Queens Road, Farnborough, Hampshire, GU14 6JP Tel: (01252) 548337 Fax: (01252) 370442

RECONDITIONED BAKERY PLANT AND EQUIPMENT

Becketts Bakery Engineers Ltd, Fir Street, Heywood, Lancashire, OL10 1NP Tel: (01706) 364103 Fax: (01706) 625057 E-mail: sales@becketts.co.uk

IBESS Ltd, Birley Hill, Bush Bank, Hereford, HR4 8EN Tel: (01432) 830044 Fax: (01432) 830055 E-mail: sales@ibess.com

Rheon UK, PO Box 25630, London, Greater London, N17 6AZ Tel: 020 83520021

RECONDITIONED BALERS

Lloyds International Ltd, Station Road, Reddish, Stockport, Cheshire, SK5 6ND Tel: 0161-219 0909 Fax: 0161-431 5780 E-mail: vicky@thos-storey.co.uk

Rankinco Ltd, 4 Blades Close, Leatherhead, Surrey, KT22 7JY Tel: (01372) 276390 Fax: (01372) 276390 E-mail: ian_rankin@compuserve.com

RECONDITIONED BOTTLE PRODUCTION PLANT

P C M Group, Folgate Lane, Magdalen, King's Lynn, Norfolk, PE34 3DA Tel: (01553) 811588 Fax: (01553) 810342

Sheppee International Ltd, Airfield Industrial Park, York Road, Elvington, York, YO41 4AU Tel: (01904) 608999 Fax: (01904) 608777 E-mail: sales@sheppee.com

RECONDITIONED BREWERY PLANT AND EQUIPMENT

Central Bottling International Ltd, Plumtree Farm Industrial Estate, Plumtree Road, Bircotes, Doncaster, South Yorkshire, DN11 8EW Tel: (01302) 711056 Fax: (01302) 710802 E-mail: sales@centralbottling.com

RECONDITIONED CHEMICAL PLANT AND EQUIPMENT

Ayton Equipment Ltd, Station Yard, Station Road, Stokesley, Middlesbrough, Cleveland, TS9 7AB Tel: (01642) 711455 Fax: (01642) 710100 E-mail: marketing@ayton.com

Chemical Reactor Services, Unit 5 Lyon Road Industrial Estate, Kearsley, Bolton, BL4 8TG Tel: (01204) 862777 Fax: (01204) 577484

RECONDITIONED CLUTCHES

C I Holdings Ltd, 2 Priory Road, Strood, Rochester, Kent, ME2 2EG Tel: (01634) 717747 Fax: (01634) 731115

Calder Clutch Co. Ltd, Mill Lane, Brighouse, West Yorkshire, HD6 1PN Tel: (01484) 721045 Fax: (01484) 721009 E-mail: sales@calderclutch.co.uk

Clutch Direct, Adrian Avenue, London, NW2 1LX Tel: (020) 8450 5040

Clutch Master, Boundary Road, Buckingham Road Industrial Estate, Brackley, Northamptonshire, NN13 7ES Tel: (01280) 704838 Fax: (01280) 705204 E-mail: admin@clutchmaster.com

Midshires Radiator Services Ltd, 5 Orleton Road, Ludlow Business Park, Ludlow, Shropshire, SY8 1XF Tel: (01584) 874495 Fax: (01584) 874495

RECONDITIONED CONVEYOR SYSTEMS

Bevpak Ltd, 27-28 Arkwright Road, Astmore Industrial Estate, Runcorn, Cheshire, WA7 1NU Tel: (01928) 574815 Fax: (01928) 589487 E-mail: bevpak@hotmail.co.uk

RECONDITIONED CRANES

D B Crane Ltd, Unit 10 Sovereign Works, Deepdale Lane, Dudley, West Midlands, DY3 2AF Tel: (01384) 458763 Fax: (01384) 459766

Delph Electrical Lifting Services Ltd, 3 The Wallows Industrial Estate, Fens Pool Avenue, Brierley Hill, West Midlands, DY5 1QA Tel: (01384) 76222 Fax: (01384) 75524

Severnside Machinery Ltd, Unit 57, Ditton Priors, Bridgnorth, Shropshire, WV16 6SS Tel: 01746 712433

United Crane Services Ltd, Niagara Works, Beeley Wood Rd, Sheffield, S6 1NH Tel: 0114-285 2801 Fax: 0114-232 5626 E-mail: unitedcranes@aol.com

RECONDITIONED DIESEL ENGINE COMPONENTS OR SPARE PARTS

Dartford Rebore Ltd, 15 Overy Street, Dartford, DA1 1UP Tel: (01322) 220634 Fax: (01322) 220634

Industrial & Marine Power Services Ltd, Whisby Way, North Hykeham, Lincoln, LN6 3LQ Tel: (01522) 881000 Fax: (01522) 883555 E-mail: chris@ind-marpower.co.uk

▶ Soni Exports Ltd, PO Box 7923, Leicester, LE4 9LS Tel: 0116-276 4000 Fax: 0116-276 4002 E-mail: sales@soniexports.co.uk

RECONDITIONED DIESEL ENGINES

Bartech Marine Engineers, 11-12 Rushmere Close, West Mersea, Colchester, CO5 8QQ Tel: (01206) 384677 Fax: (01206) 385329 E-mail: sales@bartechmarine.com

Ben Kent Precision Engineers, Riverside Industrial Estate, Marsh Lane, Boston, Lincolnshire, PE21 7PJ Tel: (01205) 362681 Fax: (01205) 362681

Caterpillar Remanufacturing Ltd, Sanders Lodge Industrial Estate, Rushden, Northamptonshire, NN10 6AZ Tel: (01933) 316622 Fax: (01933) 354601 E-mail: sales@wealdstone.co.uk

D.F. Coulam & Sons, Northfields Industrial Estate, 3 Stirling Way, Market Deeping, Peterborough, PE6 8LG Tel: (01778) 346518 Fax: (01778) 380495 E-mail: sales@dfcspares.com

Dalton Power Products Ltd, Unit 19 Autumn Park Industrial Estate, Dysart Road, Grantham, Lincolnshire, NG31 7DD Tel: (01476) 576666 Fax: (01476) 577127 E-mail: dppask@daltonpowerproducts.co.uk

Diesel Industrial Electrical Spares & Equipment (London), Units 19-20 Thurrock Commercial Park, Purfleet Industrial Park, London Road, Aveley, South Ockendon, Essex, RM15 4YA Tel: (01708) 890011 Fax: (01708) 862111 E-mail: dieseluk@aol.com

Diesel Service Centre, Mount Pleasant, Peterborough, PE2 8HW Tel: (01733) 558600

Engine Power, 7 Bryant Road, Bayton Road Industrial Estate, Coventry, CV7 9EN Tel: (024) 7664 4660 Fax: (024) 7664 4634

Eurotex International Ltd, Unit 20 Shipyard Estate, Brightlingsea, Colchester, CO7 0AR Tel: (01206) 304063 Fax: (01206) 304026 E-mail: terry.kershaw@virgin.net

▶ Hindle (Bradford), Nelson Street, Bradford, West Yorkshire, BD5 0EL Tel: (01274) 732284 Fax: (01274) 740237 E-mail: autos@hindle.co.uk

Industrial & Marine Power Services Ltd, Whisby Way, North Hykeham, Lincoln, LN6 3LQ Tel: (01522) 881000 Fax: (01522) 883555 E-mail: chris@ind-marpower.co.uk

Re Trem & Co. Ltd, Old Bawtry Road, Finningley, Doncaster, South Yorkshire, DN9 3BX Tel: (01302) 770203 Fax: (01302) 770868 E-mail: sales@enginesandgenerators.com

RECONDITIONED DIFFERENTIAL UNITS

Auto Europe Parts Ltd, Unit 11 Betchworth Works, Ifield Road, Charlwood, Horley, Surrey, RH6 0DX Tel: (01293) 863777 Fax: (01293) 863888

Geartech Gearboxes, Unit 240 Ikon Industrial Estate, Droitwich Road, Hartlebury, Kidderminster, Worcestershire, DY10 4EU Tel: (01299) 251261

Powertrain Products Ltd, Stringes Close, Willenhall, West Midlands, WV13 1LE Tel: (01902) 366000 Fax: (01902) 366504

RECONDITIONED DUST EXTRACTION PLANT AND EQUIPMENT

J.K. Filters Ltd, Unit 4 Heath Road, Industrial Park, Merrylees Road, Leicester, LE9 9FE Tel: (01455) 828697 Fax: (01455) 828680 E-mail: sales@jkfilters.com

RECONDITIONED ELECTRIC MOTORS

Ace Rewinds Ltd, 25 Ivatt Way, Westwood Industrial Estate, Peterborough, PE3 7PG Tel: (01733) 331464 Fax: (01733) 334075 E-mail: meeksruss@aol.com

Burscough Rewinds, Units 1-10, Red Cat Lane, Burscough, Ormskirk, Lancashire, L40 0RA Tel: (01704) 894501 Fax: (01704) 897787 E-mail: sales@burscough-rewinds.co.uk

Electric Motor Services, Unit C, Lyttleton Road, Northampton, NN5 7ET Tel: (01604) 587700 Fax: (01604) 580073 E-mail: sales@elemoto.com

Electro Power Engineering, Brian Royd Lane, Greetland, Halifax, West Yorkshire, HX4 8PE Tel: (01422) 379570 Fax: (01422) 370612 E-mail: enquiries@electropowerengineering.co.uk

Express Electrical, Dunswell Road, Cottingham, North Humberside, HU16 4JG Tel: (01482) 846269 Fax: (01482) 876655 E-mail: sales@express-industrial-exports.co.uk

Nippon Distribution Ltd, 8c Reddicap Trading Estate, Sutton Coldfield, West Midlands, B75 7BU Tel: 0121-311 0313 Fax: 0121-311 0338 E-mail: nippondis@hotmail.com

Telford Rewinds Ltd, Unit 5, Halesfield 18, Telford, Shropshire, TF7 4PP Tel: (01952) 580703 Fax: (01952) 580703

Webb Elec Ltd, 27 Owen Road Industrial Estate, Willenhall, West Midlands, WV13 2PY Tel: 0121-526 5070 Fax: 0121-568 7208 E-mail: sales@webb-elec.co.uk

RECONDITIONED ENVELOPE MACHINERY

Polygraphica Equipment Ltd, 1 Benton Office Park, Horbury, Wakefield, West Yorkshire, WF4 5RA Tel: (01924) 200444 Fax: (01924) 363714 E-mail: sales@polygraphica.com

RECONDITIONED FIRE EXTINGUISHERS

Berks Extinguisher Services, 48 Ardingly, Bracknell, Berkshire, RG12 8XR Tel: (01344) 425015 Fax: (01344) 304924 E-mail: enquiries@berksext.co.uk

Blacklands Fire, Britannia Enterprise Centre, Waterworks Road, Hastings, East Sussex, TN34 1RT Tel: (01424) 722200 Fax: (01424) 722200

C & C Fire Extinguisher Service Ltd, 39 Pencricket Lane, Oldbury, West Midlands, B68 8LX Tel: 0121-559 6611 Fax: 0121-559 3399

Checkfire, Unit 12, Pontygwindy Industrial Estate, Caerphilly, Mid Glamorgan, CF83 3HU Tel: (029) 2086 8333 Fax: (029) 2085 0627 E-mail: sales@checkfire.co.uk

Extinguishers Direct, 33 Harrington Rd, Worcester, WR2 5HD Tel: 01905 424044

F E S C O, 201 Wylds Lane, Worcester, WR5 1EL Tel: (01905) 351058 Fax: (01905) 351058

Northants Fire Ltd, 58a Ivy Road, Northampton, NN1 4QT Tel: (01604) 460026 Fax: (01604) 601900 E-mail: info@northhantsfire.co.uk

Pacific Scientific, Howarth Road, Maidenhead, Berkshire, SL6 1AP Tel: (01628) 682200 Fax: (01628) 682250 E-mail: custadmin@pacscieurope.com

Pyrotec Fire Detection Ltd, 8 Caburn Enterprise Park, The Broyle, Ringmer, Lewes, East Sussex, BN8 5NP Tel: (01273) 813505 Fax: (01273) 813259 E-mail: sales@pyrotec.co.uk

Romsey Fire Protection Co., 3-4 Eastwood Court, Broadwater Road, Romsey, Hampshire, SO51 8JJ Tel: (01794) 514700 Fax: (01794) 524321 E-mail: enquire@romseyfire.co.uk

Virage, Cambridge Business Park, Cowley Road, Cambridge, CB4 0WZ Tel: (01223) 488540 Fax: (01223) 488541 E-mail: info@virage.com

RECONDITIONED FOOD PROCESSING PLANT AND MACHINERY

Automatic Peeler Co., Premier House, 146 Field Lane, Burton-on-Trent, Staffordshire, DE13 0NN Tel: (01283) 565819 Fax: (01283) 565819 E-mail: sales@autopeel.com

Bradmeres Engineering Ltd, Unit 42 Wilford Industrial Estate, Ruddington Lane, Wilford, Nottingham, NG11 7EP Tel: 0115-981 7814 Fax: 0115-981 9782 E-mail: bradmeres@btconnect.com

Falcon Food Equipment Ltd, Unit 3 The Old Station, Wells Road, Hallatrow, Bristol, BS39 6EN Tel: (01761) 453010 Fax: (01761) 452975 E-mail: sales@falconfoodequipment.com

Handyman, Unit 4 Lower Rectory Farm, Great Brickhill, Milton Keynes, MK17 9AF Tel: (01908) 366228 Fax: (01908) 366661

Humberside Food Machinery Ltd, Spyvee Street, Hull, HU8 7JJ Tel: (01482) 211956 Fax: (01482) 211957 E-mail: user@humbfood.co.uk

Rigal Chemical & Process Plant Ltd, Gravelhill Lane, Whitley, Goole, North Humberside, DN14 0JJ Tel: (01977) 661095 Fax: (01977) 662165 E-mail: sales@rigal-luton.co.uk

World Wide Food Machinery Ltd, Ten Acres, Barton Street, Ashby-cum-Fenby, Grimsby, South Humberside, DN37 0RU Tel: (01472) 827132 Fax: (01472) 220207 E-mail: sales@worldwidefoodmachinery.co.uk

RECONDITIONED FORKLIFT TRUCKS

Capital Lift Trucks, Worting House, Basingstoke, Hampshire, RG23 8PY Tel: (01256) 882047 Fax: (01256) 811876

Multilift Fork Trucks, 4 Burma Road, Blidworth, Mansfield, Nottinghamshire, NG21 0RT Tel: (01623) 794094 Fax: (01623) 795095 E-mail: sales@mlift.co.uk

Used Fork Lifts, 107 Perry Street, Billericay, Essex, CM12 0NH Tel: (01277) 624608 Fax: (01277) 656108

RECONDITIONED GEARBOXES

3d Transmissions, 5 Blackwater Trading Estate, Blackwater Way, Aldershot, Hampshire, GU12 4DJ Tel: (01252) 310413 Fax: (01252) 350572 E-mail: sales@3dtransmissions.com

Abbey Transmission Services Ltd, Unit 15 Sidings Industrial Estate, Hainault Road, London, E11 1HD Tel: (020) 8558 4028 Fax: (020) 8539 0312

Aldenham Gearbox Services, 85-87 Sydney Road, Watford, WD18 7XZ Tel: (01923) 254273 Fax: (01923) 460251 E-mail: iagsgearboxes@btclick.com

Auto Europe Parts Ltd, Unit 11 Betchworth Works, Ifield Road, Charlwood, Horley, Surrey, RH6 0DX Tel: (01293) 863777 Fax: (01293) 863888

Autoglide Garage Services, Birkett House, Wellington Road, Bollington, Macclesfield, Cheshire, SK10 5HT Tel: (01625) 574126 Fax: (01625) 574126

B G Transmission, Unit 1a Brickworks Trading Estate, Buckle Street, Honeybourne, Evesham, Worcestershire, WR11 8QE Tel: (01386) 830870 Fax: (01386) 831611

Beaumont D Gearbox Reconditioners, Lumb Cottage, Wainstalls, Halifax, West Yorkshire, HX2 7UJ Tel: (01422) 244587 Fax: (01422) 243758

Brittons Ltd, Waterlip Works, Cranmore, Shepton Mallet, Somerset, BA4 4RW Tel: (01749) 880371 Fax: (01749) 880347 E-mail: sales@brittons-uk.com

Carford Transmissions Ltd, 68 Rea Street South, Birmingham, B5 6LB Tel: 0121-622 7060 Fax: 0121-622 4060 E-mail: admin@carford.com

Citadel Engineering Supplies Ltd, 14 Marlow Street, Rowley Regis, West Midlands, B65 0AY Tel: 0121-561 5557 Fax: 0121-561 5558 E-mail: sales@citadel-eng.co.uk

E S Engineering, Unit 13, Rowleys Green Lane Industrial Estate, Coventry, CV6 6AN Tel: (024) 7666 2038 Fax: (024) 7663 8946

Geartech Gearboxes, Unit 240 Ikon Industrial Estate, Droitwich Road, Hartlebury, Kidderminster, Worcestershire, DY10 4EU Tel: (01299) 251261

General Transmissions, Wickham Mews, London, SE4 1PQ Tel: (020) 8692 1417 Fax: (020) 8692 3351

Hunter Gears Ltd, Addison Works, Haugh Lane, Blaydon-on-Tyne, Tyne & Wear, NE21 4SB Tel: 0191-414 4545 Fax: 0191-414 0135

K N Transmissions, Slater House Farm, Haighton Green Lane, Preston, PR2 5SQ Tel: (01772) 655550 Fax: (01772) 655520 E-mail: kntransmissions@btopenworld.com

Kennedy Transmission Ltd, Station Road, Facit Whitworth, Rochdale, Lancashire, OL12 8LJ Tel: (01706) 853021 Fax: (01706) 852217 E-mail: kennedytransmissions@hotmail.com

Lancereal Ltd, Springfield Mills, Springfield Lane, Kirkburton, Huddersfield, HD8 0NZ Tel: (01484) 606040 Fax: (01484) 609911 E-mail: sales@lancereal.com

M T M Specialists, Unit 2 Westminster Industrial Estate, Station Road, North Hykeham, Lincoln, LN6 3QY Tel: (07843) 657181 Fax: (01522) 689989 E-mail: mtmspec@fsbdial.co.uk

M T S (Sales) Ltd, Midland House, Hayes Lane, Lye, Stourbridge, West Midlands, DY9 8RD Tel: (01384) 424823 Fax: (01384) 422819 E-mail: sales@gearbox-mts.com

Midland Transmissions Ltd, 87 Melton Road, Thurmaston, Leicester, LE4 8EF Tel: 0116-260 6200 Fax: 0116-260 2548 E-mail: fosse.bearings@btinternet.com

Mike Tucker Autos, Millwood Street, Manselton, Swansea, SA5 9JZ Tel: (01792) 456287

Mitchell Cotts Transmissions, Winterstoke Road, Weston-super-Mare, Avon, BS24 9AT Tel: (01934) 428000 Fax: (01934) 428001 E-mail: andy.cook@gearboxes.com

Nicol Transmission Services, Coppice Trading Estate, Kidderminster, Worcestershire, DY11 7QY Tel: (01562) 752651 Fax: (01562) 823128

P M W Precision Engineering Ltd, 47-55 Alcester Street, Deritend, Birmingham, B12 0PY Tel: 0121-773 9105 Fax: 0121-773 9141

Peartree Engine & Clutch Centre, 1 Peartree Farm, Welwyn Garden City, Hertfordshire, AL7 3UW Tel: (01707) 322026 Fax: (01707) 322026

Power Plant Gears Ltd, Unit 1, Eagle Works, Greets Green Road, West Bromwich, West Midlands, B70 9EJ Tel: (01484) 465500 Fax: 0121-520 0951

Powertrain Products Ltd, Stringes Close, Willenhall, West Midlands, WV13 1LE Tel: (01902) 366000 Fax: (01902) 366504

RECONDITIONED GEARBOXES – continued

R M B Engineering Services Ltd, Union Street, West Bromwich, West Midlands, B70 6BP Tel: 0121-500 1940 Fax: 0121-500 1941 E-mail: sales@rmbgroup.co.uk
R Whitehouse & Son, 16d Halfpenny Green Airport, Bobbington, Stourbridge, West Midlands, DY7 5DY Tel: (01384) 221304 Fax: (01384) 221533 E-mail: colin.whitehouse3@btinternet.com
S B T Engineering Services Ltd, Empress Street, Old Trafford, Manchester, M16 9EN Tel: 0161-877 7755 Fax: 0161-848 9225 E-mail: info@sbtengineering.co.uk
Specialist Bearings & Transmissions Ltd, Lees Road, Knowsley Industrial Park, Liverpool, L33 7SE Tel: 0151-546 9787 Fax: 0151-546 2861
T D R Transmissions, 5 Hunsley Street, Sheffield, S4 8DY Tel: 0114-262 6050 Fax: 0114-243 1826 E-mail: sales@tdrtrans.demon.co.uk
Thornford Transmissions, Unit 4 Station Approach, Yetminster, Sherborne, Dorset, DT9 6LH Tel: (01935) 872500 Fax: (01935) 872779
U K R Transmissions Ltd, 249 Cotmanhay Road, Ilkeston, Derbyshire, DE7 8NE Tel: 0115-932 4572 Fax: 0115-944 0585 E-mail: sales@ukrtrans.co.uk
Universal Transmission Services, Unit 16 Worcester Road, Hoobrook Enterprise Centre, Kidderminster, Worcestershire, DY10 1HB Tel: (01562) 861651

RECONDITIONED GLASS PRODUCTION PLANT

Sheppee International Ltd, Airfield Industrial Park, York Road, Elvington, York, YO41 4AU Tel: (01904) 608999 Fax: (01904) 608777 E-mail: sales@sheppee.com

RECONDITIONED GUTTERS

▶ The Salvage Doctor, Rowhurst Forge, Oxshott Road, Leatherhead, Surrey, KT22 0EN Tel: (01372) 360 191 Fax: (01372) 360 171 E-mail: info@salvagedoctor.com

RECONDITIONED HIGH OR LOW VOLTAGE SWITCHGEARS

Electrical Power Ltd, PO Box 115, Bingley, West Yorkshire, BD16 1WQ Tel: (01274) 510970 Fax: (01274) 511109 E-mail: epsrec@hotmail.com

RECONDITIONED INDUSTRIAL ENGINES

A G B Diesels Ltd, 20 Blaris Industrial Estate, Altona Road, Lisburn, County Antrim, BT27 5QB Tel: (028) 9266 1010 Fax: (028) 9266 7711 E-mail: enquiries@aves.co.uk
Ben Kent Precision Engineers, Riverside Industrial Estate, Marsh Lane, Boston, Lincolnshire, PE21 7PJ Tel: (01205) 362681 Fax: (01205) 362681
Bradbury's Engineering, The Crossways, Loggerheads, Market Drayton, Shropshire, TF9 4BX Tel: (01630) 672900 Fax: (01630) 673858 E-mail: bradburyeng@aol.com
Bradford Grinders UK Ltd, Mount Street, Bradford, West Yorkshire, BD3 9SN Tel: (01274) 733141 Fax: (01274) 734610 E-mail: sales@bradfordgrinders.co.uk
Crane Hill Engineering Ltd, Harvey Reeves Road, St. James Mill Industrial Estate, Northampton, NN5 5JR Tel: (01604) 587656 Fax: (01604) 588341 E-mail: robinson@cranehill.sagehost.co.uk
Dalton Power Products Ltd, Unit 19 Autumn Park Industrial Estate, Dysart Road, Grantham, Lincolnshire, NG31 7DD Tel: (01476) 576666 Fax: (01476) 577127 E-mail: dppask@daltonpowerproducts.co.uk
Gosnay's Engineering Co. Ltd, Eastern Avenue West, Romford, RM7 7NS Tel: (01708) 740668 Fax: (01708) 733266 E-mail: sales@gosnays.co.uk
Bob Harman Performance Ltd, 101-107 Sutton Road, Watford, WD17 2QG Tel: (01923) 224303 Fax: (01923) 226596
Hendy Group Ltd, Southampton Road, Cosham, Portsmouth, PO6 4RW Tel: (023) 9232 2900 Fax: (023) 9232 2960 E-mail: accounts@hendy-group.com
▶ Hindle (Bradford), Nelson Street, Bradford, West Yorkshire, BD5 0EL Tel: (01274) 732284 Fax: (01274) 740237 E-mail: autos@hindle.co.uk
Hurley Engine Services Ltd, 7 The Maltings Industrial Estate, Brassmill Lane, Bath, BA1 3JL Tel: (01225) 336812 Fax: (01225) 442477 E-mail: sales@hurleyengines.co.uk
J D Robertson & Co. Ltd, 26 Magdalen St, Colchester, CO1 2LD Tel: (01206) 572368 Fax: (01206) 549167 E-mail: carhire@jdrobertson.co.uk
K L Engine Centre, Horsleys Fields, King's Lynn, Norfolk, PE30 5DD Tel: (01553) 772422 Fax: (01553) 769372
L C P Automotive Components, Unit 3 Ebbsfleet Industrial Estate, Northfleet, Gravesend, Kent, DA11 9DZ Tel: (01474) 320300 Fax: (01474) 320595
LCP, 3 Mill Road, Portslade, Brighton, BN41 1PD Tel: (01273) 430730 Fax: (01273) 430901 E-mail: sales@lcp-automotive.co.uk
LCP Automotive Components, Bridge Road, Ashford, Kent, TN23 1BB Tel: (01233) 623113 Fax: (01233) 631366
LCP Automotive Components, 15 Acorn Industrial Park, Crayford Road, Dartford, DA1 4AL Tel: (01322) 557825 Fax: (01322) 557829
LCP Automotive Components, 555 Canterbury Street, Gillingham, Kent, ME7 5LF Tel: (01634) 575506 Fax: (01634) 855573
LCP Automotive Components, St. Peter Street, Maidstone, Kent, ME16 0SN Tel: (01622) 672222 Fax: (01622) 672227
LCP Automotive Components, 3 Lamberts Road, Tunbridge Wells, Kent, TN2 3EH Tel: (01892) 544829 Fax: (01892) 548131
Meetens Industrial Engines Ltd, Unit 2, Eclipse Trading Estate, 30 West Hill, Epsom, Surrey, KT19 8JD Tel: (08456) 340295 Fax: (08000) 150707 E-mail: sales@meetens.com
Phoenix Engines Ltd, Phoenix House, Railway Lane, Dimminsdale, Willenhall, West Midlands, WV13 2BE Tel: (01902) 601676 Fax: (01902) 601474 E-mail: david.scriven@phoenixengines.co.uk
Priestley Precision Engineering, 16 Leaside, Aycliffe Industrial Estate, Aycliffe Industrial Park, Newton Aycliffe, County Durham, DL5 6HX Tel: (01325) 316200 Fax: (01325) 310510
Quality Engineered Products, Unit 9/10, Ditchling Common, Ditchling, Hassocks, West Sussex, BN6 8SG Tel: (01444) 247906 Fax: (01444) 243720 E-mail: msaville@qep.uk.com
Redbreast Industrial Equipment Ltd, 1 Stavely Way, Brixworth, Northampton, NN6 9EU Tel: (01604) 882088 Fax: (01604) 882015 E-mail: sales@redbreastrobin.co.uk
Regal Engines, Unit B, 16 Juliet Way, Aveley, South Ockendon, Essex, RM15 4YD Tel: (01708) 868805 Fax: (01708) 868885 E-mail: info@engine-reconditioners.co.uk
Rotherham Reboring & Leisureways, Masbrough Street, Rotherham, South Yorkshire, S60 1HW Tel: (01709) 834103 Fax: (01709) 834136
Shires Vee & Inline Ltd, Royal Oak Way North, Royal Oak Industrial Estate, Daventry, Northamptonshire, NN11 8PQ Tel: (01327) 703235 Fax: (01327) 703281 E-mail: shiresveeinline@ukonline.co.uk
Stanwood Engineering Ltd, 21 Church Street, Bawtry, Doncaster, South Yorkshire, DN10 6HR Tel: (01302) 710661 Fax: (01302) 711663
Thurston Engineering Ltd, Hallsford Bridge Industrial Estate, Stondon Road, Ongar, Essex, CM5 9RB Tel: (01277) 362135 Fax: (01277) 365076 E-mail: sales@thurstonengineering.co.uk
Urbanhurst UK Ltd, Twyford Business Centre, London Road, Bishop's Stortford, Hertfordshire, CM23 3YT Tel: (01279) 755590 Fax: (01279) 652644
Vege, Unit 2 Meltham Lane, Chesterfield, Derbyshire, S41 7LG Tel: (01246) 272227 Fax: (01246) 229991
W Drake Bradford Ltd, Bolling Road, Bradford, West Yorkshire, BD4 7BG Tel: (01274) 733541 Fax: (01274) 740892 E-mail: info@wdrake.co.uk
W E Allard Ltd, 64 Winpenny Road, Parkhouse Industrial Estate E, Parkhouse Industrial Estate Ea, Newcastle, Staffordshire, ST5 7RH Tel: (01782) 563653 Fax: (01782) 273856

RECONDITIONED INTERMEDIATE BULK CONTAINERS (IBC)

J E Jones S & D Ltd, Moor Lane, Birmingham, B6 7HH Tel: 0121-356 9169 Fax: 0121-356 0595 E-mail: jejdrums@aol.com
Liverpool Bulk Bags, 35a Seaforth Vale North, Liverpool, L21 3TR Tel: 0151-920 2280 Fax: 0151-922 4076 E-mail: info@bulkbagsuk.com
R Spivey & Son Ltd, 54 Upper Station Road, Batley, West Yorkshire, WF17 5TA Tel: (01924) 473372 Fax: (01924) 442921 E-mail: david@spiveydrums.co.uk
R. Spivey & Sons Ltd, 30 Pheasant Drive, Birstall, Batley, West Yorkshire, WF17 9LT Tel: (01924) 423200 Fax: (01924) 420006 E-mail: david@spiveydrums.co.uk

RECONDITIONED MACHINE TOOLS

Ada Machining Services Ltd, Kayley Industrial Estate, Richmond Street, Ashton-under-Lyne, Lancashire, OL7 0AU Tel: 0161-339 3221 Fax: 0161-339 3981 E-mail: mail@ada-ms.co.uk
Bell Machinery Ltd, PO Box 56, Tadcaster, North Yorkshire, LS24 9WS Tel: (01937) 830777 Fax: (01937) 830888E-mail: hbellmt@aol.com
C & M Machine Tools Ltd, Station Road, Coleshill, Birmingham, B46 1JN Tel: (01675) 433100 Fax: (01675) 433101 E-mail: info@candmtools.com
D S M Automation Ltd, Eel Street, Oldbury, West Midlands, B69 2BX Tel: 0121-541 1335 Fax: 0121-511 1298
Davmar Machine Tool Services, Unit D1 Whitemoor Business Park, Cliff Common, Selby, North Yorkshire, YO8 7EG Tel: (01757) 289714 Fax: (01757) 704432
Dean Smith & Grace Ltd, PO Box 15, Keighley, West Yorkshire, BD21 4PG Tel: (01535) 605261 Fax: (01535) 680921 E-mail: mail@deansmithandgrace.co.uk
Direct Machine Tools Ltd, Unit 4a Tame Valley Industrial Estate, Wilnecote, Tamworth, Staffordshire, B77 5DQ Tel: (01827) 260272 Fax: (01827) 260838 E-mail: leroy1@easynet.co.uk
Electro Motion, Barkby Road, Leicester, LE4 9LX Tel: 0116-276 6341 Fax: 0116-274 3048 E-mail: sales@electromotion.co.uk
Farrell Engineering Ltd, Centre House, St. Leonards Road, London, NW10 6ST Tel: (020) 8965 7578 Fax: (020) 8965 7586 E-mail: farrell497@aol.com
Flude Machine Tools, 7 Central City Industrial Estate, Red Lane, Coventry, CV6 5RY Tel: (024) 7666 1220 Fax: (024) 7666 1220
G A C Engineering Group Ltd, New Works, Burnley Road, Sowerby Bridge, West Yorkshire, HX6 2TF Tel: (01422) 836091 Fax: (01422) 835396 E-mail: sales@gacgroup.co.uk
G B Engineering, 111 Wilsons Lane, Longford, Coventry, CV6 6AB Tel: (024) 7636 3634 Fax: (024) 7636 3634 E-mail: gb.eng@talk21.com
Herbert & Criddan, 11 Alliance Close, Attleborough Fields Industrial Estate, Nuneaton, Warwickshire, CV11 6SD Tel: (024) 7638 3400 Fax: (024) 7638 5999 E-mail: ken@herbertandcridan.com
Linco Engineering Co. Ltd, 108 Park Street, Motherwell, Lanarkshire, ML1 1PF Tel: (01698) 254541 Fax: (01698) 276178
M F G Machinery, 6 Climax Works, Station Road, Reddish, Stockport, Cheshire, SK5 6YZ Tel: 0161-431 9125 Fax: 0161-432 2440
M I K Engineering, 5 Cannock Street, Leicester, LE4 9HR Tel: 0116-233 3740 Fax: 0116-233 3740
Howard Maden Machine Tools, 23 High Street, Rawcliffe, Goole, East Yorkshire, DN14 8QQ Tel: (01405) 839376 Fax: (01405) 839008
Marrill Engineering Co. Ltd, Waterman Road, Coventry, CV6 5TP Tel: (024) 7668 9221 Fax: (024) 7666 8114 E-mail: sales@marrill.co.uk
Northern Machine Tools (Engineering) Ltd, P O Box Southbank 16, Middlesbrough, Cleveland, TS6 6LP Tel: (01642) 440551 Fax: (01642) 440141 E-mail: sales@nmt.onyxnet.co.uk
Piper Developments Ltd, Townsend House, Townsend Way, Birmingham, B1 2RT Tel: 0121-242 1194 Fax: 0121-242 1194
Preformtools Ltd, First Avenue, Bletchley, Milton Keynes, MK1 1DY Tel: (01908) 370788 Fax: (01908) 362802 E-mail: sales@preformtools.co.uk
W.M. Simpson (Oldham) Ltd, 1-3 St. Chad's High St, Uppermill, Oldham, OL3 6AP Tel: (01457) 870478 Fax: (01457) 871057
Style Machine Tools Ltd, 30a Centurion Industrial Estate, Centurion Way, Farington, Leyland, PR25 4GU Tel: (01772) 624114 Fax: (01722) 624114 E-mail: enquiries@stylemachinetools.co.uk
Synchrodata Ltd, 25 Long Street, Bulkington, Bedworth, Warwickshire, CV12 9JZ Tel: (024) 7631 2218 Fax: (024) 7664 3211 E-mail: sychrodata@rukonline.co.uk
Tribolube Ltd, Unit 4 Woodside, Thornwood, Epping, Essex, CM16 6LH Tel: (01992) 577551 Fax: (01992) 577553

RECONDITIONED MARINE ENGINES

Holderness Ship Repairers Ltd, Wassand Street, Hull, HU3 4AL Tel: (01482) 216055 Fax: (01482) 216056 E-mail: holdernessshiprepairers@compuserve.com

RECONDITIONED OFFICE FURNITURE

Ideal Business Supplies Ltd, Marsh Lanelords Meadow Industrial Estate, Lords Meadow Industrial Estate, Crediton, Devon, EX17 1ES Tel: (01363) 775999 Fax: (01363) 775996 E-mail: info@idealbusinesssupplies.co.uk

RECONDITIONED PACKAGING EQUIPMENT

Galley-Pak, Galley-Pak House, 38 Greenfields, Shillington, Hitchin, Hertfordshire, SG5 3NX Tel: (01462) 711545 Fax: (01462) 712970 E-mail: john@galley-pak.com
P C L Machinery, 5 Elan Court, Norris Way, Rushden, Northants, NN10 6BP Tel: (01933) 410707 Fax: (01933) 410807 E-mail: sales@pclmachinery.co.uk

RECONDITIONED PHOTOCOPIER MACHINE CONSUMABLES

Lanier UK Ltd, Eskdale Road, Winnersh, Wokingham, Berkshire, RG41 5TS Tel: (08702) 202012 Fax: (08702) 202018

RECONDITIONED PHOTOCOPYING MACHINES

A C Copiers, Westward House, Bury Road, Hatfield, Hertfordshire, AL10 8BJ Tel: (01707) 259060 Fax: (01707) 259070 E-mail: sales@accopiers.com
Black & White Systems, 11 Castle Mews, London, N12 9EH Tel: (020) 8446 9999 Fax: (020) 8446 8426 E-mail: blackandwhite@london.com
Copier Maintenance Co. Ltd, 642 Warwick Road, Tyseley, Birmingham, B11 2HJ Tel: 0121-624 8484 Fax: 0121-708 2406 E-mail: sales@printersforbusiness.com
▶ Photocopier Sales, 137 Kings Road, Kingston upon Thames, Surrey, KT2 5JE Tel: (020) 8547 1222 Fax: (020) 8547 3666 E-mail: info@kingsofficesupplies.com
Photomation Copier Services, 25 Kingshill Road, Dursley, Gloucestershire, GL11 4BJ Tel: (01453) 542652 Fax: (01453) 548580 E-mail: sales@photomation.co.uk

RECONDITIONED PLASTIC BLOW MOULDING MACHINES

Hamilton Machinery Sales Ltd, Hamilton House, Broadfields, Bicester Road, Aylesbury, Bucks, HP19 8BU Tel: (01296) 318222 Fax: (01296) 397005 E-mail: john.hat@hamac.co.uk

RECONDITIONED PLASTIC MACHINERY

Akron, Building 107b Aviation Park West, Bournemouth International Air, Hurn, Christchurch, Dorset, BH23 6NW Tel: (01202) 580800 Fax: (01202) 593010 E-mail: office@akron.demon.co.uk
C D K Machine Tool Services, Buckingway Business Park, 2 Rowles Way, Swavesey, Cambridge, CB4 5QX Tel: (01954) 230383 Fax: (01954) 230821 E-mail: info@barwell.com
Castle Labelling, Unit 15A Redwell Court, Harmire Enterprise Park, Harmire Road, Barnard Castle, County Durham, DL12 8BN Tel: (01833) 637647 Fax: (01833) 690942 E-mail: sales@castleautoid.co.uk
G T Industrial Services Ltd, 16 Enterprise Court, Newton Close, Park Farm Industrial Estate, Wellingborough, Northamptonshire, NN8 6UW Tel: (01933) 405088 Fax: (01933) 405099 E-mail: sales@gtihaxaplas.ukf.net

RECONDITIONED POOL TABLES

▶ Arcade Clearance Ltd, Unit 4 City Mills, Hull Street, Morley, Leeds, LS27 8QL Tel: 0113 2527602 E-mail: sales@arcadeclearance.com

RECONDITIONED POWER PRESSES

Boltdown Power Press Repairs Ltd, Unit 10 Cato Street, Birmingham, B7 4TS Tel: 0121-359 7862 Fax: 0121-359 4645 E-mail: boltownppr@aol.com
Hulbert Developments Ltd, 6 Grazebrook Industrial Park, Peartree Lane, Dudley, West Midlands, DY2 0XW Tel: (01384) 239019 Fax: (01384) 457280 E-mail: enq@hulbert-group.co.uk

RECONDITIONED PRINTING MACHINES

C R S (London) Ltd, 98A Blackstock Road, London, N4 2DR Tel: (020) 7226 0404 Fax: (020) 7226 1806 E-mail: crslondonltd@hotmail.com
Ingham (Toolmakers) Ltd, Willow Hall Works, Willowfield Road, Halifax, West Yorkshire, HX2 7NF Tel: (01422) 342189 Fax: (01422) 342497 E-mail: info@inghamtools.co.uk
Woodward Services, 14 Eldon Road, Reading, RG1 4DL Tel: 0118-926 6664

RECONDITIONED PUMPS

Feig Electrical, 98 Clarence Road, London, E5 8HB Tel: (020) 8985 7004 Fax: (020) 8985 0107 E-mail: feigelec@aol.com
Island Scientific Ltd, Old Station Road, Ventnor, Isle of Wight, PO38 1DX Tel: (01983) 855822 Fax: (01983) 852146 E-mail: enquiries@island-scientific.co.uk

RECONDITIONED PUMPS – *continued*

Kennedy Transmission Ltd, Station Road, Facit Whitworth, Rochdale, Lancashire, OL12 8LJ Tel: (01706) 853021 Fax: (01706) 852217 E-mail: kennedytransmissions@hotmail.com
Nash Mechanical Seal Services Ltd, Nile Street, Bolton, BL3 6DW Tel: (01204) 388030 Fax: (01204) 361541 E-mail: enquiry@nashseal.com
SVR, Unit 1 35 Little London, Spalding, Lincolnshire, PE11 2UE Tel: (01775) 760999 Fax: (01775) 724547

RECONDITIONED RADIATORS

County Radiators Ltd, 21 Nobel Square, Burnt Mills Industrial Estate, Basildon, Essex, SS13 1LP Tel: (01268) 728314 Fax: (01268) 728314
Cropper & Jones, New Chester Road, Hooton, Ellesmere Port, CH66 6AQ Tel: 0151-327 2560 E-mail: sales@cjrad.cwc.net
H A Rayson Ltd, Jill House Cornishway North, Galmington Trading Estate, Taunton, Somerset, TA1 5LY Tel: (01823) 275044 Fax: (01823) 338135
Midshires Radiator Services Ltd, 5 Orleton Road, Ludlow Business Park, Ludlow, Shropshire, SY8 1XF Tel: (01584) 874495 Fax: (01584) 874495
Ricketts Radiators Ltd, 4 Viking Way, Winch Wen Industrial Estate, Winch Wen, Swansea, SA1 7DA Tel: (01792) 796504 Fax: (01792) 428338
Scotrad Car Radiator Repairs, 410 Gorgie Road, Edinburgh, EH11 2RN Tel: 0131-337 8887 Fax: 0131-337 9998 E-mail: sales@scotrad.co.uk
Serck Intertruck, Worrall Street, Salford, M5 4TA Tel: 0161-872 5726 Fax: 0161-873 8074 E-mail: si.manchester732@unipart.co.uk
Superior Radiator Co., 86a Victoria Road, London, N4 3SW Tel: (020) 7272 1995 Fax: (020) 7272 7554
Wessex Radiator, Portsmouth Road, Bursledon, Southampton, SO31 8EP Tel: (023) 8040 2848 Fax: (023) 8040 2848

RECONDITIONED REFRIGERATION EQUIPMENT

C R D Refrigeration, Field House, Pudleston, Leominster, Herefordshire, HR6 0RG Tel: (01568) 750620 Fax: (01568) 750386
▶ Carter Retail Equipment, 90 Lea Ford Road, Birmingham, B33 9TX Tel: 0121-250 1111 Fax: 0121-250 1122E-mail: info@cre-ltd.co.uk
Control Centre NRS Ltd, 8 Kestrel Park, Tallon Road, Hutton, Brentwood, Essex, CM13 1TN Tel: (01277) 228060 Fax: (01277) 227970
Hale Refrigeration, Unit 8 Paper Mill End Industrial Estate, Birmingham, B44 8NH Tel: 0121-344 3345 Fax: 0121-344 3346 E-mail: halerefrigeration@compuserve.com
Hall Refrigeration Ltd, Unit 17 Palace Industrial Estate, Bircholt Road, Maidstone, Kent, ME15 9XU Tel: (01622) 663379 Fax: (01622) 663282 E-mail: hallrefrigeration@mistral.co.uk
Humberside Food Machinery Ltd, Spyvee Street, Hull, HU8 7JJ Tel: (01482) 211956 Fax: (01482) 211957 E-mail: user@humbfood.co.uk
Marshall Thermo King Ltd, Cemetery Road, Houghton Regis, Dunstable, Bedfordshire, LU5 5BZ Tel: (01582) 867847 Fax: (01582) 866648 E-mail: houghtonregis@marshallthermoking.co.uk
Preston Refrigeration Ltd, Units 3-4 Chantry Industrial Estate, Kingsbury Road, Curdworth, Sutton Coldfield, West Midlands, B76 9EE Tel: (01675) 470899 Fax: (01675) 470838
W R Refrigeration Ltd, 2 Woolram Wygate, Spalding, Lincolnshire, PE11 1NX Tel: (01775) 768978 Fax: (01775) 768713 E-mail: chriscocks@wrspalding.com

RECONDITIONED SEWING MACHINES

Alan Godrich, 17-20 Charter Street, Leicester, LE1 3UD Tel: 0116-253 2322 Fax: 0116-262 9887 E-mail: sales@alan-godrich.com
Bromley Sewing Machines, 30 Homesdale Road, Bromley, BR2 9LD Tel: (020) 8460 7865 Fax: (020) 8313 9993
Industrial Sewing Services Birmingham Ltd, 225 Lozells Road, Birmingham, B19 1RJ Tel: 0121-554 5073 Fax: 0121-554 5073
Omnistitch Sewing Machines & Accessories, 52b Stapleton Road, Bristol, BS5 0RA Tel: 0117-961 3722 Fax: 0117-961 3790
S B T Machine Co Stockport Ltd, Christie Street Industrial Estate, Christie Street, Stockport, Cheshire, SK1 4LR Tel: 0161-429 6929 Fax: 0161-480 6603 E-mail: sbtworldwide@aol.com
Sewing Machine Shop Ltd, 1 The Broadway, Brighton Road, Worthing, West Sussex, BN11 3EG Tel: (01903) 200771 Fax: (01903) 520036 E-mail: sales@sewingmachineshop.co.uk
Wallington Sewing Machines, 108e Manor Road, Wallington, Surrey, SM6 0DW Tel: (020) 8647 1830

RECONDITIONED TANKS

Boatman Plastics, Newport Road, Market Drayton, Shropshire, TF9 2AA Tel: (01630) 657286 Fax: (01630) 655545
Branchand Ltd, Ashwellthorpe Industrial Estate, Ashwellthorpe, Norwich, NR16 1ER Tel: (01508) 488450 Fax: (01508) 488451 E-mail: info@branchand.co.uk
Northern Radiators Ltd, 3 Dolly Lane, Leeds, LS9 7TU Tel: 0113-243 5051 Fax: 0113-245 7486 E-mail: info@radiatorsonline.co.uk

RECONDITIONED TEXTILE MACHINERY

▶ A M S Manchester, 27 Honey Street, Manchester, M8 8RG Tel: 0161-819 2540 Fax: 0161-819 2541 E-mail: enquiries@ams-steam-eng.co.uk
James Bailey Ltd, Empire Works, Howgate Road, Huddersfield, HD7 5AX Tel: (01484) 842316 Fax: (01484) 846537 E-mail: sales@jamesbailey.co.uk
Hargreaves Hamilton Gears Ltd, PO Box 33, Bolton, BL1 2QE Tel: (01204) 456190 Fax: (01204) 364002 E-mail: info@hargreaveshamilton.co.uk
Macart Textiles Machinery Ltd, Macart House, Farnham Road, Bradford, West Yorkshire, BD7 3JG Tel: (01274) 525900 Fax: (01274) 525901 E-mail: enquiries@macart.com
Karl Mayer Textile Machinery Ltd, Kings Road, Shepshed, Loughborough, Leicestershire, LE12 9HT Tel: (01509) 502056 Fax: (01509) 508065 E-mail: mhyeabsley@karlmayer.co.uk
R G Foster Textile Machinery Ltd, Burnham Way, Queens Bridge Road, Nottingham, NG2 1NB Tel: 0115-988 2222 Fax: 0115-985 1881 E-mail: sales@foster-tm.co.uk
Wilson Knowles & Sons, 6 Chapel Lane, Heckmondwike, West Yorkshire, WF16 9JT Tel: (01924) 402208 Fax: (01924) 406895 E-mail: sales@wilsonknowlesandsons.co.uk

RECONDITIONED VALVES

A-Valvetech Services Ltd, 4 The Courtyard, D'Arcy Business Park, Llandarcy, Neath, West Glamorgan, SA10 6EJ Tel: (01792) 817708 Fax: (01792) 815298 E-mail: valtec3@hotmail.com
Chemtrol Valve Manufacturers, Clerk Green Street, Batley, West Yorkshire, WF17 7SE Tel: (01924) 475481 Fax: (01924) 473579
New Forest Instrument Control Ltd, 84 Cobham Road, Ferndown Industrial Estate, Wimborne, Dorset, BH21 7RW Tel: (01202) 875308 Fax: (01202) 893462 E-mail: info@newforestinstruments.co.uk

RECONDITIONED VIBRATORY SCREENS

Incamesh Filtration Ltd, Dingle Lane, Appleton, Warrington, WA4 3HR Tel: (01925) 261900 Fax: (01925) 860568 E-mail: sales@incamesh.co.uk

RECONDITIONED WELDING EQUIPMENT

Hember Plant Hire Ltd, Lilford Street, Warrington, WA5 0LA Tel: (01925) 656023 Fax: (01925) 653104 E-mail: hire@hemberplant.co.uk
I.T.W Welding Products Group, Horwich Business Park Chorley New Road Unit 102, Rivington House, Horwich, Bolton, BL6 5UE Tel: (01204) 469058 Fax: (01204) 473039 E-mail: sales@itw-welding.co.uk
Meopham Welding Supplies, Railway Sidings, Station Approach, Meopham, Gravesend, Kent, DA13 0LT Tel: (01474) 812050 Fax: (01474) 813714
R W M Wolverhampton Ltd, 34 Commercial Road, Wolverhampton, WV1 3RD Tel: (01902) 871272

RECONDITIONED WOODWORKING MACHINES

Blundell Woodworking Machinery Ltd, Park Drive, Braintree, Essex, CM7 1AP Tel: (01376) 346565 Fax: (01376) 551230 E-mail: blundell@btconnect.com
Maximach Ltd, Gorton Crescent, Windmill Industrial Estate, Denton, Manchester, M34 3RB Tel: 0161-320 3216 Fax: 0161-337 8162 E-mail: helensmax@aol.com

RECONSTITUTED OR ARTIFICIAL OR CAST STONE

Arundel Stone, 62 Aldwick Road, Bognor Regis, West Sussex, PO21 2PE Tel: (01243) 829151 Fax: (01243) 860341 E-mail: info@arundelstone.co.uk
▶ Aspects Of Stone, Broughton Grounds, Broughton, Newport Pagnell, Buckinghamshire, MK16 0HZ Tel: (01908) 830061 Fax: (01908) 830062 E-mail: sales@aspectsofstone.co.uk
Bespoke Concrete Products Ltd, Tynedale Works, Princess Way, Prudhoe, Northumberland, NE42 6PL Tel: (01661) 839340 Fax: (01661) 833923 E-mail: info@bespokeconcrete.co.uk
Chard Stone Co. Ltd, 14 Millfield, Chard, Somerset, TA20 2BB Tel: (01460) 63824 Fax: (01460) 61849
Chilstone, Fordcombe Road, Fordcombe, Tunbridge Wells, Kent, TN3 0RD Tel: (01892) 740866 Fax: (01892) 740249 E-mail: office@chilstone.com
Derwent Cast Stone Co. Ltd, Eden Works, Old Malton, Malton, North Yorkshire, YO17 6SD Tel: (01653) 692860 Fax: (01653) 600129 E-mail: dcs@cast-stone.co.uk
John Fausset Ltd, 56 Rosslyn Avenue, Preesall, Poulton-le-Fylde, Lancashire, FY6 0HE Tel: (01253) 810358 Fax: (01253) 810358
Forti Crete Ltd, Shearstone Factory, Midsomer Norton, Radstock, BA3 4EA Tel: (01761) 413605 Fax: (01761) 413609 E-mail: stone@forticrete.com
Hampton Cast Stone, Unit 7, Merretts Mill, Woodchester, Stroud, Gloucestershire, GL5 5EU Tel: (01453) 836677 Fax: (01453) 835005E-mail: sales@hamptoncaststone.co.uk
Manorhouse Stone, School Lane, Normanton le Heath, Coalville, Leicestershire, LE67 2TH Tel: (01530) 262999 Fax: (01530) 262515
Nasco Ltd, Links Quarry, Newbiggin-by-the-Sea, Northumberland, NE64 6XQ Tel: (01670) 815849 Fax: (01670) 855297
North Yorkshire Artstone Ltd, Unit 12 Showfield Lane, Malton, North Yorkshire, YO17 6BT Tel: (01653) 697714 Fax: (01653) 692427 E-mail: artstone@ukonline.co.uk
Plean Precast Ltd, President Kennedy Drive, Plean, Stirling, FK7 8AX Tel: (01786) 812221 Fax: (01786) 815369 E-mail: mail@plean-precast.co.uk
Rhead, Meir Road, Stoke-on-Trent, ST3 7JD Tel: (01782) 599770 Fax: (01782) 599771 E-mail: peter.stephenson@normanrhead.co.uk
Sedgemoor Stone Products Ltd, Pen Mill, Station Yard, Yeovil, Somerset, BA21 5DD Tel: (01935) 429797 Fax: (01935) 432392 E-mail: info@sedgemoorestone.co.uk
Specialist Precast Products Ltd, Pantglas Industrial Estate, Bedwas, Caerphilly, Mid Glamorgan, CF83 8DR Tel: (029) 2088 0800 Fax: (029) 2088 0700 E-mail: consolidated.specialist@virgin.net
Sterling Precast Ltd, Springkerse Works, Springkerse Industrial Estate, Stirling, FK7 7SX Tel: (01786) 472191 Fax: (01786) 451284 E-mail: general@stirlingprecast.com
Woodside Precast Concrete Ltd, Dawes Lane, Scunthorpe, South Humberside, DN15 6UW Tel: (01724) 281872 Fax: (01724) 280866 E-mail: info@caststone.co.uk

RECORDING INSTRUMENT CHARTS

Chart Right Ltd, Units 34, Aston Fields Trading Estate, Bromsgrove, Worcestershire, B60 3DW Tel: (01527) 571500 Fax: (01527) 571516 E-mail: sales@chartright.com
Richmond Film Services, The Old School, Park Lane, Richmond, Surrey, TW9 2RA Tel: (020) 8940 6077 Fax: (020) 8948 8326
Sensitised Coatings Ltd, Bergen Way, North Lynn Industrial Estate, King's Lynn, Norfolk, PE30 2JL Tel: (01553) 764836 Fax: (01553) 760377 E-mail: sales@senco.co.uk
Turnkey, 114-116 Charing Cross Road, London, WC2H 0JR Tel: (020) 7419 9999 Fax: (020) 7379 0093

RECORDING INSTRUMENT MANUFRS

Alrian Industries Ltd, Unit 2D Lake Enterprise Park, Sandall Stones Road, Kirk Sandall, Doncaster, South Yorkshire, DN3 1QR Tel: (01302) 885851 Fax: (01302) 885851 E-mail: sales@alrian.idps.co.uk
Honeywell Process Solutions, Unit 1 Headlands Business Park, Salisbury Road, Blashford, Ringwood, Hampshire, BH24 3PB Tel: (01425) 463950 Fax: (01425) 463953 E-mail: uksales@trendview.com
Sinclair Voicenet Ltd, 2 Orbital Court, Peel Park, East Kilbride, Glasgow, G74 5PH Tel: (01355) 900000 Fax: (01355) 900001 E-mail: enquiries@voicerecording.co.uk
Sprint Data Systems, Bridge Road, Ashford, Kent, TN23 1JA Tel: (01233) 665822 Fax: (01233) 665821 E-mail: sales@sprint-data.co.uk
Turnkey, 114-116 Charing Cross Road, London, WC2H 0JR Tel: (020) 7419 9999 Fax: (020) 7856 7089

RECORDING INSTRUMENT MULTICHANNEL INSTRUMENTATION

A B B Ltd, Howard Road, St. Neots, Cambridgeshire, PE19 8EU Tel: (01480) 475321 Fax: (01480) 217948 E-mail: automationltd.sales@gb.abb.com
Red Lion 49 Ltd, 25 Springhill Road, Begbroke, Kidlington, Oxfordshire, OX5 1RU Tel: (01865) 842300 Fax: (01865) 842118 E-mail: sales@solid-state-logic.com

RECOVERED SOLVENTS

Chemical Recoveries, Rockingham Works Smoke Lane, Bristol, BS11 0YA Tel: 0117-982 0303 Fax: 0117-982 0301 E-mail: info@chemrec.co.uk
Solvent Resource Management Ltd, Middleton Road, Middleton, Morecambe, Lancashire, LA3 3JW Tel: (01524) 853053 Fax: (01524) 851284 E-mail: sales@srm-ltd.com
Southern Refining Services Ltd, Membury Airfield, Lambourn Woodlands, Hungerford, Berkshire, RG17 7TJ Tel: (01488) 72898 Fax: (01488) 72762 E-mail: richard.srs@btconnect.com

RECREATIONAL PROPERTY ESTATE AGENTS

New Forest Estate Agents, New Forest Estate Agents, PO Box 5561, Ringwood, Hampshire, BH24 2ZS Tel: 08700 11 68 55 E-mail: info@NewForestEstateAgents.com
▶ The New Forest Estate Agents, PO Box 5561, Ringwood, Hampshire, BH24 2ZS Tel: 08700 11 45 75 Fax: 08700 11 45 76 E-mail: info@NewForestEstateAgents.com
▶ Purple Path, 28 Livermore Court, Grove Park, Liverpool, L8 0TL Tel: 0151-734 3530 E-mail: freddy@purplepath.co.uk
▶ The Sandbanks Estate Agents, PO Box 5561, Ringwood, Hampshire, BH24 2ZS Tel: (0870) 0114575 E-mail: info@SandbanksEstateAgents.com
▶ Sands Home Search, PO Box 5561, Ringwood, Hampshire, BH24 1EN Tel: (01425) 462549 Fax: (0871) 6612892 E-mail: info@sandshomesearch.com

RECRUITMENT ADMINISTRATION SOFTWARE

Abraxas plc, 47 Eastcastle Street, London, W1W 8DY Tel: (020) 7255 5555 Fax: (020) 7636 0333 E-mail: corporate@abraxas.com
Cruse Control Ltd, 6 Wolsey Mansions, Main Avenue, Moor Park, Northwood, Middlesex, HA6 2HL Tel: (01923) 842295 Fax: (01923) 842698 E-mail: mail@crusecontrol.com
▶ The Spencer Group Ltd, 308-314 Kings Road, Reading, RG1 4NR Tel: 0118-935 9444 Fax: 0118 935 9445 E-mail: sales@spencergroup.co.uk
▶ Swiftpro, 2 Warner House, Harrovian Business Village, Bessborough Road, Harrow, Middlesex, HA1 3EX Tel: (0870) 8731270 Fax: (0870) 8731271 E-mail: sales@swiftpro.com
TMC, 113 Sandringham Road, Birmingham, B42 1PX Tel: 0121-356 3327
View Point Internet Ltd, Venture House Arlington Square, Downshire Way, Bracknell, Berkshire, RG12 1WA Tel: (01344) 300100 Fax: (01344) 742950 E-mail: sales@viewpoint.net.uk
▶ WinIT Consultancy Ltd, West Mills, Newbury, Berkshire, RG14 5HG Tel: (0870) 2000635 Fax: (0870) 2000755 E-mail: robin@winitconsultancy.co.uk

RECRUITMENT AGENCIES, *See also specialist services, eg Recruitment etc*

A A Apointments, St. Clare House, 30-33 Minories, London, EC3N 1PQ Tel: (01344) 891987 Fax: (020) 7480 5467 E-mail: travel@aaappointments.com
A M S A Ltd, 2 Great Marlborough Street, London, W1F 7HQ Tel: (020) 7734 0532 Fax: (020) 7494 1509 E-mail: recruit@amsa.co.uk
A S A, 12-18 Paul Street, London, EC2A 4JH Tel: (020) 7669 5200 Fax: (020) 7669 5208 E-mail: group@asagroup.co.uk
Abatec Staff Consultants plc, Abatec House, Old Mixon Cresent, Weston-super-Mare, Avon, BS24 9AX Tel: (01934) 635025 Fax: (01934) 419999 E-mail: mail@abatec.co.uk
Accountancy Divisions, 37 George Street, Croydon, CR0 1LB Tel: (020) 8686 5353 Fax: (020) 8686 2666 E-mail: croydon@hays.com
Accountancy & General Ltd, 37 South Molton St, London, W1K 5RJ Tel: (020) 7495 3840 Fax: (020) 7491 0023 E-mail: hr@puddledock.ltd.uk
Accountancy Support Reading Ltd, 8 Hencroft St North, Slough, SL1 1RD Tel: (01753) 533006 Fax: (01753) 533002 E-mail: andy@accountancysupport.co.uk

RECRUITMENT AGENCIES – *continued*

Ace Appointments, 4 Market Square, Northampton, NN1 2DL Tel: (01604) 630781 Fax: (01604) 620495 E-mail: recruit@aceappsnorth.co.uk

Acme Appointments, 122 Middlesex Street, London, E1 7HY Tel: (020) 7377 9923 Fax: (020) 7375 2948

Acme Appointments, 315 Oxford Street, London, W1C 2HH Tel: (020) 7493 4000 Fax: (020) 7493 4383

▶ Action Drive Ltd, 15 Grove Market Place, Court Yard, London, SE9 5PU Tel: (020) 8850 3763 Fax: (020) 8850 4113 E-mail: actiondrive@hotmail.com

Action Staff Bureau Ltd, 47a High St, Tunbridge Wells, Kent, TN1 1XL Tel: (01892) 542822 Fax: (01892) 542827 E-mail: sales@asbrecruitment.com

Adecco UK Ltd, 44 Shenley Road, Borehamwood, Hertfordshire, WD6 1DR Tel: (020) 8953 6700 Fax: (020) 8207 4686 E-mail: info@adecco.co.uk

Adler Recruitment Ltd, 71 Friar Street, Droitwich, Worcestershire, WR9 8EQ Tel: (01905) 795008 Fax: (01905) 795009 E-mail: info@adler-recruitment.co.uk

Adrem Recruitment Ltd, 1-3 Dufferin Street, London, EC1Y 8NA Tel: (020) 7562 8282 Fax: (020) 7562 8283 E-mail: registration@adrum.uk.com

Allied Technical Services Ltd, Aberdeen Studios, 22-24 Highbury Grove, London, N5 2EA Tel: (020) 7226 2220 Fax: (020) 7226 0297

▶ allretailrecruitment, PO Box 551, Chesterfield, Derbyshire, S40 9BX Tel: 01246 551255

▶ Alpha Tutors, No. 6, Russell Flint House, Royal Docks, London, E16 1UT Tel: 0207 4732360

Anchor Employment Agency, 2 The Colonnade, Lind St, Ryde, Isle of Wight, PO33 2NE Tel: (01983) 811244 Fax: (01983) 812866 E-mail: anchoriw@hotmail.com

Angel Catering plc, 65 West Ham Lane, London, E15 4PH Tel: (020) 8555 5533 Fax: (020) 8555 2200 E-mail: east@angelhr.org

Angel Human Resources plc, 54 Uxbridge Rd, Shepherds Bush, London, W12 8LP Tel: (020) 8740 1999 Fax: (020) 8749 4950 E-mail: west@angelhr.org

Angela Mortimer plc, 37-38 Golden Square, London, W1F 9LA Tel: (020) 7287 7788 Fax: (020) 7470 5578 E-mail: name.surname@angelamortimer.com

Applied Executive Selection Ltd, Shales House, 17-19 Mealcheapen St, Worcester, WR1 2DQ Tel: (01905) 23444 Fax: (01905) 23393 E-mail: info@aesco.co.uk

August P A's & Personnel, 8 Gobbitts Yard, Woodbridge, Suffolk, IP12 1DD Tel: (01394) 388828 E-mail: enquiries@august-pas.com

B C P Search & Selection Ltd, Unit 9b Intec 2, Wade Road, Basingstoke, Hampshire, RG24 8NE Tel: (01256) 470704 Fax: (01256) 844054 E-mail: mail@bcprecruitment.co.uk

▶ Backstop Support Ltd, 9 Disraeli Road, London, SW15 2DR Tel: 0870 2247800 Fax: 020 8785 9904

Bailey Employment Services Ltd, Crown House, Market Place, Melksham, Wiltshire, SN12 6ES Tel: (01225) 709494 Fax: (01225) 709044 E-mail: melksham@baileyemploy.co.uk

Barker Ross Contracts, 7 Faraday Court, 36 Conduit Street, Leicester, LE2 0JN Tel: 0116-255 1055 Fax: 0116-255 0811 E-mail: recruitment@barkerross.co.uk

▶ Bennett Secretarial Services Ltd, 51a-52 Market Street, Hyde, Cheshire, SK14 2AB Tel: 0161-368 5511 Fax: 0161-627 1793 E-mail: hyde@bennettstaff.co.uk

▶ Bennett Staff Bureau, 22 St Petersgate, Stockport, Cheshire, SK1 1HD Tel: 0161-480 0411 Fax: 0161-474 7610 E-mail: stockport@bennettstaff.co.uk

Better Engineers, Abatec House, Oldmixon Crescent, Weston-Super-Mare, Avon, BS24 9AX Tel: (01934) 621262 Fax: (01934) 620619 E-mail: mail@betterengineers.co.uk

Bligh Appointments Ltd, 70 North End Road, London, W14 9EP Tel: (020) 7603 6123 Fax: (020) 7371 6898 E-mail: info@bligh.com.uk

Blue Arrow, 5 Colston Centre, Colston Avenue, Bristol, BS1 4UB Tel: 0117-929 8435 Fax: 0117-925 0231 E-mail: info@bluearrow.co.uk

Blue Arrow Ltd, Capability Greenthe Boulevard, Luton, LU1 3BA Tel: (01582) 692692 Fax: (01582) 698698 E-mail: enquiries@bluearrow.co.uk

▶ Bluemonday Recruitment, 18 Soho Square, London, W1D 3QL Tel: (020) 7025 8747 Fax: (020) 7025 8100 E-mail: sales@bluemondayrecruitment.com

Bond Street Personnel Ltd, 22 South Molton Street, London, W1K 5RB Tel: (020) 7629 3692 Fax: (020) 7409 1524 E-mail: enquires@bondstreetpersonnel.co.uk

▶ Bright Eyes Nanny Agency, 11 Gatley Drive, Guildford, Surrey, GU4 7JJ Tel: (01483) 506150 Fax: 01483 506150 E-mail: Brighteyesnannys@aol.com

▶ Burne & Walsh Ltd, Regus House, 268 Bath Road, Slough, SL1 4DX Tel: (01753) 708419 Fax: (01753) 708810 E-mail: info@burnewalsh.co.uk

▶ Business-at.com Ltd, Croft Ford, Watercrook Farm, Natland, Kendal, Cumbria, LA9 7QB Tel: 0845 1200665 E-mail: info@jobs4.com

C E Recruitment, First Floor, 65 Seamoor Road, Bournemouth, BH4 9AE Tel: (01202) 752275 Fax: (01202) 768203 E-mail: info@cer.uk.com

Capital Engineering Personnel Ltd, Broadway House, 112-134 The Broadway, London, SW19 1RL Tel: (020) 8605 2800 Fax: (020) 8946 3899 E-mail: admin@cap-recruit.co.uk

Careers In Design Recruitment Ltd, 28 New Road, Ware, Hertfordshire, SG12 7BU Tel: (01920) 486125 Fax: (01920) 412599 E-mail: recruit@careersindesign.com

Carlisle Staffing plc, 3 Albany Place, Hyde Way, Welwyn Garden City, Hertfordshire, AL7 3BG Tel: (01707) 323000 Fax: (01707) 393398

Central Drivers Ltd, Carlyle Business Centre, Queen Victoria Street, Bristol, BS2 0QR Tel: (0870) 7770544 Fax: 0117-955 9040

Centre Point Associates, 16 St. Helen's Place, London, EC3A 6AU Tel: (020) 7562 1600 Fax: (020) 7562 1651 E-mail: hrservices@centrepointgroup.co.uk

▶ CFR Consulting Group Limited, Sixth Floor, Caxton House, 2 Farringdon Street, London, EC1M 3HN Tel: 0207 729 0929 Fax: 01962 849255 E-mail: cfr@freurope.com

Chambers Communications Ltd, 29-30 High Holborn, London, WC1V 7JZ Tel: (020) 7440 9450 Fax: (020) 7405 5457 E-mail: sales@chamberscomms.com

Church Of Ireland Ace Ventures, The Old Rectory, 217 Holywood Road, Belfast, BT4 2DH Tel: (028) 9065 1135 Fax: (028) 9067 2126 E-mail: aceventures@btconnect.com

Convert Recruitment Solutions Ltd, 127 Hillcroft Crescent, Oxhey, Watford, WD19 4PA Tel: (08700) 333370 Fax: (08700) 333371 E-mail: enquiry@convertrecruitment.co.uk

Cotleigh Engineering Co. Ltd, 586 Green Lanes, London, N8 0RP Tel: (020) 8802 0111 Fax: (020) 8809 5516 E-mail: j.markham@cotleigh.com

▶ D C A Recruitment, 15a High Street, Godalming, Surrey, GU7 1AZ Tel: (01483) 422212 Fax: (01483) 418219 E-mail: vacancy@dcass.co.uk

Direct Computer Training Ltd, Argyle Ho, 29-31 Euston Rd, London, NW1 2SD Tel: (020) 7837 4800 Fax: (020) 7837 1090

Direct Staff & Direct Calculating Ltd, 40 Goodmayes Road, Ilford, Essex, IG3 9UR Tel: (020) 8590 0074 Fax: (020) 8590 8432 E-mail: info@direct-staff.co.uk

Doyen (Cleveland) Ltd, Phonix Centre, Wilton, Redcar, Cleveland, TS10 4RG Tel: (01642) 463344 Fax: (01642) 463355 E-mail: doyen_personnel@btconnect.com

Driver Hire, 4/Maple House, Wykeham Road Northminster Business Park, Upper Poppleton, York, YO26 6QW Tel: (0845) 6023652 Fax: (01904) 557647 E-mail: york@driver-hire.co.uk

E W H Support Services, Edwards House, 327 Whapload Road, Lowestoft, Suffolk, NR32 1QY Tel: (01502) 516971 Fax: (01502) 516970 E-mail: enquire@lecmarine-low.co.uk

▶ East Lancs Recruitment Services, 81 York Street, Heywood, Lancashire, OL10 4NR Tel: (01706) 627662 Fax: (01706) 365912 E-mail: enquiries@elservices.co.uk

Elan Recruitment, Grampian House, Meridian Gate, Marsh Wall, Docklands, London, E14 9XT Tel: (020) 7537 4114 Fax: (020) 7537 3927 E-mail: enquiries@elanrecruitment.com

Ellis Fairbank P.L.C., Ellis Fairbank House, 2 Manor Road, Horsforth, Leeds, LS18 4DX Tel: 0113-259 3000 Fax: (0870) 0110883 E-mail: contactus@ellisfairbank.co.uk

Em-Jay Appointments, 17 Manor Road, Reigate, Surrey, RH2 9LA Tel: (01737) 224411 Fax: (01737) 224410 E-mail: recruitment@tinyonline.co.uk

▶ Encore Personnel, 2 Plough Road, Wellington, Telford, Shropshire, TF1 1ET Tel: (01952) 262970 Fax: (01952) 641880 E-mail: sales@encorepersonnel.co.uk

▶ Encore Personnel Services, Market Chambers, Shelton Square, Coventry, CV1 1DG Tel: (024) 7623 8330 Fax: (024) 7625 6475 E-mail: coventry@encorepersonnel.co.uk

▶ Esprit People Ltd, Unit 18 Pavilion Business Park, Royds Hall Road, Leeds, LS12 6AJ Tel: 0113-220 5530 Fax: 0113-220 5503 E-mail: tom.liptrot@esprit-people.co.uk

Excel Kids' Club & Chilcare Services Ltd, 9 Holliday Square, Battersea, London, SW11 2HR Tel: (020) 8672 3800 Fax: (020) 8767 5139E-mail: admin@excelservices.co.uk

▶ F E S Recruitment & Personnel, 298 Stanley Road, Bootle, Merseyside, L20 3ET Tel: 0151-922 9392 Fax: 0151-922 9592 E-mail: craig@fes-recruitment.co.uk

Falconwood Employment Agency Ltd, 187 High Street, Bromley, BR1 1NN Tel: (020) 8460 1148 Fax: (020) 8313 0984 E-mail: falconwood@ic24.net

Forest Personnel Ltd, Cross Keys House, 11 Bridge Street, Reading, RG1 2LR Tel: 0118-958 7272 Fax: 0118-939 1404 E-mail: mail@forestpersonnel.co.uk

▶ G O S S Consultants Ltd, Square Sail House, Charlestown Road, St. Austell, Cornwall, PL25 3NJ Tel: (01726) 71128 Fax: (01726) 71129 E-mail: info@goss-ltd.co.uk

G S A Tech Source Ltd, Cathedral House, 5 Beacon Street, Lichfield, Staffordshire, WS13 7AA Tel: (0845) 2267200 Fax: (0845) 2267210 E-mail: gsa@gsatechsource.com

Genesis Personnel, 2 Marischal Street, Peterhead, Aberdeenshire, AB42 1HU Tel: (01779) 871980 Fax: (01779) 476312 E-mail: phd@genesis-personnel.co.uk

Guildsrealm Recruitment Agency, 39 Ensign Way, Hamble, Southampton, SO31 4RF Tel: (023) 8074 4440 Fax: (023) 8045 8135 E-mail: office@guildsrealm.com

Hayes Inter-Selection, Roman Wall House, 1-2 Crutched Friars, London, EC3N 2HT Tel: (020) 7680 0077 Fax: (020) 7680 1052

Hays Legal, 37 Sun Street, London, EC2M 2PL Tel: (020) 7523 3700 Fax: (020) 7523 3839 E-mail: info@hayslegal.com

Helix Recruitment Limited, George Street, Hailsham, East Sussex, BN27 1AD Tel: (01323) 445464 Fax: (01323) 440814 E-mail: kelly@helixrecruitment.co.uk

Hillmeglynn Ltd, Ground Floor Marshall Mill, Marshall Street, Leeds, LS11 9YJ Tel: 0113-246 5577 Fax: 0113-244 2926 E-mail: info@hillmeglynn.co.uk

Hodge Recruitment Ltd, 22 Henrietta Street, London, WC2E 8ND Tel: (020) 7420 3950

Horizon Recruitment Ltd, 6 Piccadilly, Bradford, West Yorkshire, BD1 3LW Tel: (01274) 744991 Fax: (01274) 744992

▶ Hudsons Pantry, Hudsons Pantry, Towcester, Northamptonshire, NN12 7HT Tel: (01327) 352443 E-mail: Info@hudsonspantry.co.uk

Elizabeth Hunt Recruitment Consultants Ltd, Coin House, 2 Gees Court, St. Christophers Place, London, W1U 1JA Tel: (020) 7535 5050 Fax: (020) 7535 5053 E-mail: ehwesthunt@elizabethhunt.co.uk

Hunters Employment Services, 65 Commercial Road, Swindon, SN1 5NX Tel: (01793) 433383 Fax: (01793) 422259 E-mail: hunterses@btclick.com

Industrial Engineering Services Southern Ltd, 44 New Borough, Wimborne, Dorset, BH21 1RB Tel: (01202) 888865 Fax: (01202) 841801 E-mail: klia@lineone.net

Infostaff Ltd, 16 North Silver Street, Aberdeen, AB10 1RL Tel: (01224) 336200 Fax: (01224) 428500 E-mail: info@infostaff.co.uk

▶ I-volv Recruitment Solutions, 8 Cilfton Road, High Brooms, Tunbridge Wells, Kent, TN2 3AR Tel: 01892 689301 E-mail: recruitment@i-volv.co.uk

J L Communications Ltd, Ferry Lane, Pembroke, Dyfed, SA71 4RE Tel: (01646) 683123 Fax: (01646) 621111

▶ J N F Employment, 2c The Parade, Edinburgh Drive, Didcot, Oxfordshire, OX11 7LT Tel: (01235) 811600 Fax: (01235) 811601 E-mail: oxfordshire@jnf-employment.co.uk

▶ Jackson Rundle (Rec2Rec), 2 Sheen Road, ., Richmond, Surrey, TW9 1AE Tel: 020 8943 2669 E-mail: kellysearch@jacksonrundle.com

Katie Bard Executive Secretaries Ltd, Neville House, 14 Waterloo Street, Birmingham, B2 5TX Tel: 0121-633 4443 Fax: 0121-633 4746 E-mail: info@katiebardrecruitment.com

▶ Leo Recruitment, 2 The Grand Union Office Park, Packet Boat Lane, Uxbridge, Middlesex, UB8 2GH Tel: (0870) 4214016 E-mail: jobs@leorecruitment.co.uk

LMR Recruitment Agency, 58 Leazes Park Road, Newcastle upon Tyne, NE1 4PG Tel: 0191-232 6622 Fax: (0870) 9901839 E-mail: newcastle@lmr.co.uk

▶ Local Personnel, 26 High Street, Wetherby, Leeds, Leeds, LS22 6LT Tel: 01937 588111 Fax: 01937 588444 E-mail: john@localpersonnel.co.uk

M D A Technical Personnel Ltd, Millbank House, North Way, Runcorn, Cheshire, WA7 2SX Tel: (01928) 734222 Fax: (01928) 739666 E-mail: info@millbank.com

Manley Summers Ltd, 49-50 The Hop Exchange, 24 Southwark St., London, SE1 1TY Tel: (020) 7403 7588 Fax: (020) 7403 0535 E-mail: mjcmanleysummers@aol.com

▶ The Media Agency, 1 Brewery Hill, Arundel, West Sussex, BN18 9DQ Tel: 01903 882836 Fax: 01903 882836 E-mail: themediaagency@hotmail.co.uk

▶ Medics Recruitment Agency, Banchory Business Centre, Burn O' Bennie Road, Banchory, Kincardineshire, AB31 5ZU Tel: (01330) 826700 Fax: (01330) 820670 E-mail: sam@triowise.com

Network Recruitment Partnership, 82 Abington Street, Northampton, NN1 2AP Tel: (01604) 234242 Fax: (01604) 232137 E-mail: northampton.network@pertemps.co.uk

Opus Personnel Ltd, 106 Baker Street, London, W1U 6TW Tel: (020) 7247 6111 Fax: (020) 7486 2111 E-mail: sales@opuscity.co.uk

Orion, 11b Baird House, Newark Road South, Glenrothes, Fife, KY7 4NS Tel: (01592) 775050 Fax: (01592) 772515 E-mail: fife@orioneng.com

Orion Engineering Services Ltd, 21 Albert Street, Aberdeen, AB25 1XX Tel: (01224) 632121 Fax: (01224) 640046 E-mail: abz@orioneng.co.uk

▶ Ortus Professional Search, 5a The Courtyard, 707 Warwick Road, Solihull, West MIdlands, B91 3DA Tel: 0121 7127820

Daniel Owen Associates, Unit 3 The Schoolhouse, Second Avenue, Trafford Park, Manchester, M17 1DZ Tel: 0161-888 2332 Fax: 0161-877 8088 E-mail: info@danielowen.co.uk

Daniel Owen Associates, Hadwyn House, Field Road, Reading, RG1 6AP Tel: 0118-957 1011 Fax: 0118-957 1011 E-mail: paul.wells@danielowen.co.uk

▶ P H D S Engineering Recruitment, 3 Silvan Court, Silvan Way, Southfields Business Park, Laindon, Basildon, Essex, SS15 6TU Tel: (01268) 455520 Fax: (01268) 455521 E-mail: info@phds.co.uk

Part Time Careers Ltd, 10 Golden Square, London, W1F 9JA Tel: (020) 7437 3103 Fax: (020) 7494 1154 E-mail: parttimecareers@btinternet.com

▶ Paterson Healthcare Recruitment, 120 Churchill Road, Bicester, Oxon, OX26 4XD Tel: 01869 244610 Fax: 01869 360024 E-mail: training@paterson-healthcare.co.uk

People Agenda Ltd, 167 Watling St West, Towcester, Northamptonshire, NN12 6BX Tel: (01327) 354871 Fax: (01327) 358799 E-mail: sales@peopleagenda.com

Personnel Selection, 46 West Street, Brighton, BN1 2RA Tel: (01273) 205281 Fax: (01273) 204091 E-mail: brit@persel.co.uk

Pertemps Partnership, 81-82 Darlington St, Wolverhampton, WV1 4JD Tel: (01902) 312345 Fax: (01902) 714357 E-mail: leannesharp@pertemps.co.uk

Pertemps Recruitment Partnership Ltd, 16-18 Temple Street, Birmingham, B2 5BG Tel: 0121-233 2222 Fax: 0121-631 2278 E-mail: birmingham038@pertemps.co.uk

Pertemps Recruitment Partnership Ltd, 22 High Street, Cardiff, CF10 1PY Tel: (029) 2022 0776 Fax: (029) 2023 9345 E-mail: cardiff@pertemps.co.uk

Petrogramme Management Services (UK) Ltd, 32 Alexandra Road, Lowestoft, Suffolk, NR32 1PJ Tel: (01502) 500050 Fax: (01502) 516574 E-mail: vacancies@petrogramme.co.uk

▶ Playtime Nanny Agency, Burley, Bagshot Road, Knaphill, Woking, Surrey, GU21 2SG Tel: (01483) 488511 E-mail: sales@playtimenannies.co.uk

▶ Prestige Recruitment Services Ltd, 39 Deansgate, Manchester, M3 2BA Tel: 0161-835 3999 Fax: 0161 835 3777 E-mail: callcentre@prestigeltd.co.uk

Primat Recruitment, Haughton Road, Darlington, County Durham, DL1 2ED Tel: (01325) 376200 Fax: (01325) 358111

Principal Appointments, 58 Leazes Park Road, Newcastle upon Tyne, NE1 4PG Tel: 0191-232 6660 Fax: 0870-990 1849 E-mail: newcastle@princeappoint.co.uk

▶ Proactive Recruitment Solutions Ltd, Jewellery Business Centre, 95 Spencer Street, Birmingham, B18 6DA Tel: 0121-523 1006 Fax: 0121-523 1016 E-mail: enquiries@proactiverecruitment.co.uk

Project Design Services Ltd, 19 Station Square, Lowestoft, Suffolk, NR32 1BA Tel: (01502) 564892 Fax: (01502) 531658 E-mail: sales@projectdesign.co.uk

▶ PSS Recruitment, Derwent Business Centre, Derby, DE1 2BU Tel: (01332) 363608 Fax: (01332) 363618 E-mail: info@pss-jobs.com

Reed Connections Ltd, 120 Coombe Lane, London, SW20 0BA Tel: (020) 8399 5221 Fax: (020) 8274 4391

▶ Research247.com, 23 Riverford Close, Harpenden, Hertfordshire, AL5 4LX Tel: (01582) 469699 E-mail: info@research247.com

Rigman Offshore (UK) Ltd, Wellheads Centre, 5A Wellheads Crescent, Wellheads Industrial Estate, Aberdeen, AB21 7GA Tel: (01224) 725532 Fax: (01224) 724047 E-mail: admin@rigman.ifb.co.uk

Robert Half International, 1st Floor, 2 Thames Avenue, Windsor, Berkshire, SL4 1QP Tel: (01753) 835900 Fax: (01753) 835901 E-mail: windsor@roberthalf.co.uk

RSD Technology Ltd, Kingsway Business Centre, Kingsway, Fforestfach, Swansea, SA5 4DL Tel: (01792) 585859 Fax: (01792) 580651 E-mail: admin@rsd.uk.com

S G S, Continental House, Oakridge, West End, Woking, Surrey, GU24 9PJ Tel: (01483) 485420 Fax: (01483) 485499 E-mail: gb.wkg@sgs.com

S T S Recruitment Ltd, Radley House, 8 St Cross Road, Winchester, Hampshire, SO23 9HX Tel: (01962) 869478 Fax: (01962) 841982 E-mail: sales@stsrecruit.com

St James Consultancy, 35 Thurloe Street, London, SW7 2LQ Tel: (020) 7589 1866 Fax: (020) 7589 8142 E-mail: recruit@stjc.co.uk

Sales Force GB Ltd, 1 Haven Green, Ealing, London, W5 2UU Tel: (020) 8998 9646 Fax: (020) 8248 7796 E-mail: g.gedge@btconnect.com

Sales Recruitment Services, 59 St. Peters Street, Bedford, MK40 2PR Tel: (01234) 270100 Fax: (01234) 270400 E-mail: salesrecruitmentservices@btinternet.com

Salesvacancies.Com, Charter House, Unit 1 South Bourne Business Park, Eastbourne, East Sussex, BN22 8UY Tel: (01323) 739995 Fax: (01323) 721990 E-mail: sales@salesvacancies.com

Select Appointments plc, Regent Court, Laporte Way, Luton, LU4 8SB Tel: (01582) 811600 Fax: (01582) 811611 E-mail: information@select.co.uk

▶ Helen Sellers, The Dairy, Red House Farm, Priory Road, Fressingfield, Eye, Suffolk, IP21 5PH Tel: (0870) 4215709 E-mail: helen.sellers@crosspoint-resources.co.uk

Skillframe Ltd, 138 Walton Road, East Molesey, Surrey, KT8 0HP Tel: (020) 8941 7733 Fax: (020) 8941 3301 E-mail: info@skillframe.co.uk

Star Executives Ltd, 7 Fitz Roy Mews, London, W1T 6DQ Tel: (020) 7387 6999 Fax: (020) 7387 6999 E-mail: info@starexecutives.com

Stirling Recruitment, 49 Old Steine, Brighton, BN1 1NH Tel: (01273) 324255 Fax: (01273) 325656 E-mail: info@duneofficerecruitment.co.uk

RECRUITMENT AGENCIES – *continued*

Sugarman Medical, 14 Devonshire Square, London, EC2M 4YT Tel: (020) 7456 8777 Fax: (020) 7456 8787 E-mail: info@sugarman.co.uk

▶ Sunshine Au Pair, Wardwick, Derby, DE1 1HA Tel: (0845) 0066245 Fax: (01332) 231320 E-mail: info@sunshineaupairs.co.uk

Technical & Engineering Services Ltd, 2A Saywood Close, Chesham, Buckinghamshire, HP5 3DP Tel: (01494) 771503 Fax: (01494) 771503 E-mail: tesagy@btconnect.com

Tek Personnel Consultants Ltd, Bells Square, Sheffield, S1 2FY Tel: 0114-252 5730 Fax: 0114-252 5731 E-mail: enquiries@tekpersonel.co.uk

Telecoms Personnel Ltd, 2-6 Curtain Road, London, EC2A 3NQ Tel: (020) 7247 0001 Fax: (020) 7247 0003 E-mail: personnel@telecoms.uk.net

▶ Total Quality Staff Ltd, Gorray House, 758-760 Great Cambridge Road, Enfield, Middlesex, EN1 3RN Tel: (020) 8443 7014 Fax: (020) 8443 7044 E-mail: info@tqs.co.uk

Towers Recruitment Services, Chiltern Chambers, St Peters Avenue, Caversham, Reading, RG4 7DH Tel: 0118-946 1200 Fax: 0118-946 3318 E-mail: jobs@towers.co.uk

uk therapist, 9 Kingsmill Industrial Estate, Cullompton, Devon, EX15 1BS Tel: 01884 33489 Fax: 01884 34519 E-mail: jane@uktherapist.co.uk

Westaff UK Ltd, Friary House, 46-50 Southgate Street, Gloucester, GL1 2DR Tel: (01452) 304090 Fax: (01452) 300332 E-mail: chichester@westaff.co.uk

Workforce (Employment) Ltd, Force Group House, 31-33 Albion Street, Stoke-on-Trent, ST1 1QF Tel: (01782) 221900 Fax: (01782) 281047 E-mail: enquiry@workforce-employment.co.uk

Workmates Building Trade, 3 The Schoolhouse, Second Avenue, Trafford Park, Manchester, M17 1DZ Tel: 0161-877 8080 Fax: 0161-877 8088 E-mail: paul.hallsworth@danielowen.co.uk

Workmates (Building Trades) Ltd, Hadwyn House, Field Road, Reading, RG1 6AP Tel: 0118-952 1000 Fax: 0118-950 8181 E-mail: adrian.tigg@workmates.co.uk

Workmates Maintenance Recruitment Ltd, 6 Queen Street, London, EC4N 1SP Tel: (020) 7248 7000 Fax: (020) 7248 6060 E-mail: steve.tombs@workmates.co.uk

Jonathan Wren & Co. Ltd, 34 London Wall, London, EC2M 5RU Tel: (020) 7309 3550 Fax: (020) 7309 3552 E-mail: career@jwren.com

Yvonne Palmer Associates Ltd, Lister Chambers, 25-29 Lister Gate, Nottingham, NG1 7DE Tel: 0115-958 8577 Fax: 0115-948 4205 E-mail: ypa@yvonne-palmer.co.uk

RECRUITMENT AGENCIES, CONSTRUCTION INDUSTRY

A P S Recruitment Ltd, 7 Wellington Court, Wellington Street, Cambridge, CB1 1HZ Tel: (01223) 464040 Fax: (01223) 309002 E-mail: kevin@aps-recruitment.co.uk

Aalpha Solutions (North West) Ltd, 169 Cross Green Lane, Cross Green, Leeds, LS9 0BD Tel: 0113-249 6900 Fax: 0113-249 6906 E-mail: info@aalphasolutions.co.uk

▶ Ably Resources Ltd, 1 Cumbernauld Road, Buchanan Business Park, Stepps, Glasgow, G33 6HZ Tel: 0141-565 1270 Fax: 0141-779 1616 E-mail: enquiries@ablyresource.com

Anders Elite Ltd, Capital House, Houndwell Place, Southampton, SO14 1HU Tel: (023) 8022 3511 Fax: (023) 8022 7911 E-mail: contactus@anderselite.com

▶ Ash Employment Services Ltd, Unit 5a Centre Court, Sir Thomas Longley Road, Medway City Estate, Rochester, Kent, ME2 4BQ Tel: (01634) 710999 Fax: (01634) 712283 E-mail: lesley@ashemploymentservices.com

▶ Ashfield Personnel, Norwich House, 45 Poplar Road, Solihull, West Midlands, B91 3AW Tel: 0121-711 7811 Fax: 0121-711 7801 E-mail: admin@ashfieldpersonnel.co.uk

▶ Best Connection Group Ltd, 10-12 Pall Mall, Liverpool, L3 6AL Tel: 0151-236 0111 Fax: 0151-236 0999 E-mail: liverpool@thebestconnection.co.uk

Best Connection Group Ltd, Hanger Lane Station, Hanger Lane, London, W5 1DL Tel: (020) 8998 9910 Fax: (020) 8997 4928 E-mail: sales@sharestaff.co.uk

Blue Arrow, 32 Friar Lane, Nottingham, NG1 6DQ Tel: 0115-947 2252 Fax: 0115-950 3766 E-mail: nottingham@bluearrow.co.uk

▶ Buzz House Keeping, Trocoll House, Wakering Road, Barking, Essex, IG11 8PD Tel: (020) 8507 9906 Fax: (020) 8507 9066 E-mail: peter@buzzservices.co.uk

C E Recruitment, First Floor, 65 Seamoor Road, Bournemouth, BH4 9AE Tel: (01202) 752275 Fax: (01202) 768203 E-mail: info@cer.uk.com

Capital Group of Companies Ltd, Broadway House, 112-134 The Broadway, London, SW19 1RL Tel: (020) 8542 8131 Fax: (020) 8540 7385 E-mail: admin@cap-recruit.co.uk

▶ Central European Staffing, Thanet Way, Whitstable, Kent, CT5 3JF Tel: (01227) 771888 Fax: (01227) 771666 E-mail: sales@centraleuropeanstaffing.co.uk

▶ Colega Limited, 5300 Lakeside, Cheadle Royal Business Park, Cheadle, Cheshire, SK8 3GP Tel: 0161 408 0505 E-mail: stephen@colega.co.uk

Convert Recruitment Solutions Ltd, 127 Hillcroft Crescent, Oxhey, Watford, WD19 4PA Tel: (08700) 333370 Fax: (08700) 333371 E-mail: enquiry@convertrecruitment.co.uk

▶ Crystal Employment Services Ltd, Gilbert Wakefield House, 67 Bewsey Street, Warrington, WA2 7JQ Tel: 01925 631300 Fax: 01925 638440 E-mail: info@crystalemp.com

Driver Hire, 4/Maple House, Wykeham Road Northminster Business Park, Upper Poppleton, York, YO26 6QW Tel: (0845) 6023652 Fax: (01904) 557647 E-mail: york@driver-hire.co.uk

▶ Exectec Solutions, National Deposit House, 11-13 Goldsmith Street, Nottingham, NG1 5JS Tel: 0115-988 1810 Fax: 0115-950 8900 E-mail: awalker@exectecsolutions.co.uk

▶ F E S Recruitment & Personnel, 298 Stanley Road, Bootle, Merseyside, L20 3ET Tel: 0151-922 9392 Fax: 0151-922 9592 E-mail: craig@fes-recruitment.co.uk

▶ Face - Fit Limited, 1, Farnham Road, Guildford, Surrey, GU2 4RG Tel: 01483 549052 Fax: 01483 549100 E-mail: jobs@face-fit.com

▶ G & T Associates, William Knox House, Britannic Way, Llandarcy, Neath, West Glamorgan, SA10 6EL Tel: (01792) 321202 Fax: (01792) 321295 E-mail: info@gtassociates.co.uk

Craig Hambling Ltd, Hindle Street, Accrington, Lancashire, BB5 1QT Tel: (01254) 301211 Fax: (01254) 393508 E-mail: construction@hambling.co.uk

Hillmeglynn Ltd, Ground Floor Marshall Mill, Marshall Street, Leeds, LS11 9YJ Tel: 0113-246 5577 Fax: 0113-244 2926 E-mail: info@hillmeglynn.co.uk

▶ Jackson Rundle (Rec2Rec), 2 Sheen Road, ., Richmond, Surrey, TW9 1AE Tel: 020 8943 2669 E-mail: kellysearch@jacksonrundle.com

Justengineers.Net, York House, 76 Lancaster Road, Morecambe, Lancashire, LA4 5QN Tel: (0845) 0502000 Fax: (0845) 0502001 E-mail: info@justengineers.net

▶ Mavero Recruitment, 145-157 St John Street, London, EC1V 4PY Tel: 0207 8710727 Fax: 0207 7882992 E-mail: info@mavero.co.uk

MDS Consultants, Tribune Avenue, Broadheath, Altrincham, Cheshire, WA14 5RX Tel: 0161-927 7744 Fax: 0161-927 7612

Meadsway Construction Ltd, 8 Sunbeam Road, Woburn Road Industrial Estate, Kempston, Bedford, MK42 7BY Tel: (01234) 856023 Fax: (01234) 841450

▶ Melsystech, 1 Victoria Street, Portrush, County Antrim, BT56 8DL Tel: (0870) 8504309 Fax: (020) 8708 2490

▶ Network Property Consulting & Construction, Network House, 119 Hagley Road, Birmingham, B16 8LB Tel: 0121-450 5020 Fax: 0121-450 5021E-mail: osb@netrec.co.uk

Daniel Owen Associates, Unit 3 The Schoolhouse, Second Avenue, Trafford Park, Manchester, M17 1DZ Tel: 0161-888 2332 Fax: 0161-877 8088 E-mail: info@danielowen.co.uk

Daniel Owen Associates, Hadwyn House, Field Road, Reading, RG1 6AP Tel: 0118-957 1011 Fax: 0118-957 1011 E-mail: paul.wells@danielowen.co.uk

▶ P H D S Engineering Recruitment, 3 Silvan Court, Silvan Way, Southfields Business Park, Laindon, Basildon, Essex, SS15 6TU Tel: (01268) 455520 Fax: (01268) 455521 E-mail: info@phds.co.uk

▶ Palmer Consulting Ltd, Unit 45 Basepoint Business Centre, Metcalf Way, Crawley, West Sussex, RH11 7XX Tel: (01293) 817730 Fax: (01293) 817731 E-mail: enquiries@palmerconsulting.co.uk

RMJM Scotland Ltd, 10 Bells Brae, Dean Village, Edinburgh, EH4 3BJ Tel: 0131-225 2532 Fax: 0131-226 5117 E-mail: info@rmjm.com

Sales Recruitment Services, 59 St. Peters Street, Bedford, MK40 2PR Tel: (01234) 270100 Fax: (01234) 270400 E-mail: salesrecruitmentservices@btinternet.com

▶ Anna Shaw Associates Ltd, 9 Tramway Drive, Sutton-on-Sea, Mablethorpe, Lincolnshire, LN12 2GS Tel: (01507) 440278 Fax: (01507) 440278 E-mail: info@annashawassociates.co.uk

Staff Smart, Goodacre Son, Church Street, Donington, Spalding, Lincolnshire, PE11 4UA Tel: (01775) 820786 Fax: (01775) 820512 E-mail: info@staffsmartuk.com

▶ theCONSTRUCTIONjob.com, PO Box 2448, Slough, SL1 1ZB Tel: 0870 8701193 Fax: 0870 8701194 E-mail: coz.dauncey@theconstructionjob.com

Troup Bywaters & Anders, 51 Praed Street, London, W2 1NR Tel: (020) 7565 5666 Fax: (020) 7565 5744

Workmates Building Trade, 3 The Schoolhouse, Second Avenue, Trafford Park, Manchester, M17 1DZ Tel: 0161-877 8080 Fax: 0161-877 8088 E-mail: paul.hallsworth@danielowen.co.uk

Workmates (Building Trades) Ltd, Hadwyn House, Field Road, Reading, RG1 6AP Tel: 0118-952 1000 Fax: 0118-950 8181 E-mail: adrian.tigg@workmates.co.uk

Workmates Maintenance Recruitment Ltd, 6 Queen Street, London, EC4N 1SP Tel: (020) 7248 7000 Fax: (020) 7248 6060 E-mail: steve.tombs@workmates.co.uk

▶ www.simply-recruit.com, Baltic Works, Baltic Street, Hartlepool, Cleveland, TS25 1PW Tel: (01833) 638110 Fax: (01833) 630389 E-mail: sarahjane@simply-recruit.com

RECRUITMENT CONSULTANCY

▶ 1st 4 Recruitment, 1 Gurney Lane, Norwich, NR4 7SB Tel: (01603) 456231 E-mail: welcome@1st4jobs.com

▶ 1st Class Drivers, Queen Street, Morley, Leeds, LS27 9BR Tel: 0161-615 1311 Fax: 0113-252 3534

▶ 24 7 Staff Luton, 25 Upper George Street, Luton, LU1 2RD Tel: (01582) 722336 E-mail: luton@247staff.net

▶ 4Leisure Recruitment, PO Box 845, Uxbridge, Middlesex, UB8 9BJ Tel: (0870) 2423339 Fax: (01895) 235581 E-mail: info@4leisurerecruitment.co.uk

Aberdeen Appointments Agency Ltd, 461 Union Street, Aberdeen, AB11 6DB Tel: (01224) 211211 Fax: (01224) 211411 E-mail: info@aaa.uk.com

▶ Adams Franklin, 4 Adelaid Terrace, Northampton, NN2 6AH Tel: (01604) 633000 E-mail: cv@adamsfranklin.com

Adecco UK Ltd, 13-15 Blagrave Street, Reading, RG1 1PJ Tel: 0118-950 0321 Fax: 0118-959 1920 E-mail: first.last@adecco.co.uk

▶ Altmore General Recruitment, Office 15 Townsend Enterprise Park, 28 Townsend Street, Belfast, BT13 2ES Tel: (028) 9032 8411 Fax: (028) 9032 8400 E-mail: cr@altmore.co.uk

▶ Amazon Personnel, 6 Star Street, London, W2 1QD Tel: (020) 7706 9345 Fax: (020) 7706 9456 E-mail: enquiries@amazonpersonnel.co.uk

Amtec Consulting plc, Millennium Centre, 2 Crosby Way, Farnham, Surrey, GU9 7XX Tel: (01252) 737866 Fax: (01252) 737855 E-mail: post@amtec.co.uk

▶ The Angel Services Group Ltd, 61 Bridge Street, Walsall, WS1 1JQ Tel: (01922) 424300 E-mail: charles.trivett@ems-gb.com

▶ Aromask Motor, 24 Chapel Street, Bradford, West Yorkshire, BD1 5DL Tel: (01274) 777662 Fax: (01274) 777665 E-mail: sales@ukmotorjobs.co.uk

▶ Ascend Recruitment, Trym Lodge, 1 Henbury Road, Westbury-on-Trym, Bristol, BS9 3HQ Tel: 0117-310 1270 Fax: 0117-310 1271 E-mail: mail@ascendrecruitment.net

▶ Ash Employment Services Ltd, Unit 5a Centre Court, Sir Thomas Longley Road, Medway City Estate, Rochester, Kent, ME2 4BQ Tel: (01634) 710999 Fax: (01634) 712283 E-mail: lesley@ashemploymentservices.com

Atlan Ltd, Six Acre House, 17 Town Square, Sale, Cheshire, M33 7WZ Tel: 0161-282 1770 Fax: 0161-962 0316 E-mail: cbsnorth@atlanrecruitment.com

August P A's & Personnel, 8 Gobbitts Yard, Woodbridge, Suffolk, IP12 1DD Tel: (01394) 388828 E-mail: enquiries@august-pas.com

▶ August Personnel, Sheraton House, Castle Park, Cambridge, CB3 0AX Tel: (01223) 370162 E-mail: pauline@augustpersonnel.co.uk

▶ Beresford Blake Thomas Ltd, Fifth Floor, 52 Grosvenor Gardens, London, SW1W 0AU Tel: (020) 7881 2700 Fax: (020) 7881 2702 E-mail: administrator@bbt.co.uk

Bligh Appointments Ltd, 70 North End Road, London, W14 9EP Tel: (020) 7603 6123 Fax: (020) 7371 6898 E-mail: info@bligh.com.uk

Blue Arrow, Portland House, Longbrook Street, Exeter, EX4 6AB Tel: (01392) 424733 Fax: (01392) 490486 E-mail: enquiries@bluearrow.co.uk

▶ Blue Enterprises, 130 Shaftesbury Avenue, London, W1D 5EU Tel: (0845) 3702583 Fax: (0845) 3702584 E-mail: info@blue-enterprises.co.uk

Bulldog Engineering Recruitment & Management, 223a-225 South Coast Road, Peacehaven, East Sussex, BN10 8LB Tel: (01273) 580580 E-mail: recruitment@bulldog.co.uk

▶ Bullus & Co., Rumbolds House, Hammonds Road, Sandon, Chelmsford, CM2 7RS Tel: (01245) 474035 Fax: (01245) 477175 E-mail: search@bullus.co.uk

▶ Burne & Walsh Ltd, Regus House, 268 Bath Road, Slough, SL1 4DX Tel: (01753) 708419 Fax: (01753) 708810 E-mail: info@burnewalsh.co.uk

▶ Business & Professional Partners, 1 Gurney Lane, Norwich, NR4 7SB Tel: (0870) 0505144 E-mail: welcome@bppartners.co.uk

▶ Byron Finance, 41 London Road, Reigate, Surrey, RH2 9QE Tel: (01737) 228777 Fax: (01737) 735200 E-mail: recruitment@byronfinance.com

▶ Chameleon Personnel Services Ltd, 1 West Street, Leighton Buzzard, Bedfordshire, LU7 1DA Tel: (01525) 218068 Fax: (01525) 218067 E-mail: info@chameleonpersonnel.co.uk

▶ Chase Consulting, 17 The Chase, Crowthorne, Berkshire, RG45 6HT Tel: (0845) 4501946 Fax: (08454) 501947 E-mail: mail@chaseconsulting.biz

Chevron Technical Services Ltd, Beta Court, 2 Harper Road, Sharston Industrial Area, Manchester, M22 4QE Tel: 0161-902 9029 Fax: 0161-945 0945 E-mail: info@chevrontechnicalservices.com

Choice Technical Recruitment Ltd, 8 West Alley, Hitchin, Hertfordshire, SG5 1EG Tel: (01462) 442929 Fax: (01462) 442828 E-mail: choicetec@ctr.uk.com

▶ City Associates, Centre Gate, Colston Avenue, Bristol, BS1 4TR Tel: 0117-317 8133 Fax: 0117-317 8134 E-mail: sales@city-associates.co.uk

▶ Compass Recruitment Solutions Ltd, Suite 37, Thamesgate House, 37 Victoria Avenue, Southend-on-Sea, SS2 6DF Tel: (01702) 431311 Fax: (01702) 431322

Computer People Midlands Ltd, Alpha Tower, Suffolk St Queensway, Birmingham, B1 1TT Tel: 0121-643 8501 Fax: 0121-632 5996 E-mail: cpbirmingham@computerpeople.co.uk

Connaught Partners Ltd, 111 Hagley Road, Birmingham, B16 8LB Tel: 0121-452 5117 Fax: 0121-452 5118 E-mail: sales@connaughtpartners.com

▶ Contract Design Northern Ltd, 9-11 St James Street, Newcastle upon Tyne, NE1 4NF Tel: 0191-232 2737 Fax: 0191-261 1219 E-mail: sales@contractdesign.co.uk

▶ Corinium Language Associates, Wadham Close, Southrop, Lechlade, Gloucestershire, GL7 3NR Tel: (01367) 851100 E-mail: info@coriniumlanguage.co.uk

▶ Douglas Bates, Suite 8 Phoenix House, 63 Campfield Road, St. Albans, Hertfordshire, AL1 5FL Tel: 01727 736690 E-mail: dougbates@intelligentpeople.co.uk

▶ Ebor Nannies Ltd, No 1 Ebor House, Dike Ray Close, Haxby, York, YO32 3WJ Tel: (01904) 767777 Fax: (01904) 767700 E-mail: jane@ebornannies.co.uk

▶ Edison Consultancy, PO Box 6479, Brackley, Northamptonshire, NN13 5YU Tel: 01280 841500E-mail: work@edison-consultancy.com

▶ EFFICENS RESOURCING LTD, EFFICENS HOUSE, 25 DENBROOK AVENUE, TONG, BRADFORD, WEST YORKSHIRE, BD4 0QJ Tel: 01274 681762 E-mail: career.management@efficens-resourcing.co.uk

Elan I T Computing, St Johns House, Barrington Road, Altrincham, Cheshire, WA14 1JY Tel: 0161-924 3900 Fax: 0161-924 3901 E-mail: info.alt@elanit.co.uk

▶ Emerald Careers, 43 Temple Row, Birmingham, B2 5LS Tel: (0845) 2265857 Fax: (020) 8318 3222 E-mail: muyiwa@emeraldcareers.com

▶ First Choice Recruitment & Training Ltd, 72-73 Bartholomew Street, Newbury, Berkshire, RG14 5DU Tel: (01635) 551111 Fax: (01635) 46000 E-mail: firstchoice@bposs.co.uk

▶ Brian Ford Powell Executive Recruitment, Claybrooke House, Claybrooke Parva, Lutterworth, Leicestershire, LE17 5AE Tel: (01455) 209968 Fax: (01455) 202788 E-mail: contact@bfpexecutiverecruitment.co.uk

▶ Format Recruitment, 44 Rutland Road, Hove, East Sussex, BN3 5FF Tel: (01273) 772200 Fax: (01273) 748735 E-mail: nadina@formatrecruitment.com

▶ Goose Recruit, Walnut Tree Cottage, Main Road, Theberton, Leiston, Suffolk, IP16 4RU Tel: (01728) 833502 Fax: (01728) 833502 E-mail: rlapage@gooserecruit.co.uk

Helix Recruitment Limited, George Street, Hailsham, East Sussex, BN27 1AD Tel: (01323) 445464 Fax: (01323) 440814 E-mail: kelly@helixrecruitment.co.uk

Highfield Human Solutions Ltd, 1 London Road, Newbury, Berkshire, RG14 1JL Tel: (01635) 33923 Fax: (01635) 38837 E-mail: admin@highfielduk.co.uk

▶ Hunter Mabon, 10 Barrow Court, Barrow Gurney, Bristol, BS48 3RP Tel: (0870) 2012495 Fax: (01285) 770003 E-mail: cv@huntermabon.co.uk

I C Resources Ltd, Capital House, 67 - 69 St Johns Road, Isleworth, Middlesex, TW7 6NL Tel: (020) 8400 2444 Fax: (020) 8560 2445 E-mail: enquiry@ic-resources.co.uk

In Parallel Computer Staff Ltd, 3 Church Street, Tewkesbury, Gloucestershire, GL20 5PA Tel: (01684) 291133 Fax: (01684) 291144 E-mail: inparallell@peachs.demon.co.uk

Integrator Software Services Ltd, 15 Stafford Street, Edinburgh, EH3 7BR Tel: 0131-718 2400 Fax: 0131-718 2434

▶ Just I T Training Ltd, The Dragon House, 37 Artillery Lane, London, E1 7LP Tel: (020) 7655 4600 E-mail: recruitment@justit.co.uk

▶ Kingston Partnership, The Prairie, Astwood Lane, Astwood Bank, Redditch, Worcestershire, B96 6HA Tel: (01527) 893793 Fax: (01527) 894029 E-mail: info@kingstonpartnership.com

KMC, 7 Old Park Lane, London, W1K 1QR Tel: (020) 7317 4600 Fax: (020) 7317 4620 E-mail: london@kmcinternational.com

▶ Lechley Recruitment, The Rural Business Centre, Bilsborrow, Preston, PR3 0RY Tel: 01995 642260 Fax: 01995 642258 E-mail: scott@lechley.com

▶ Leed Recruitment Ltd, The Manor House, 6-10 St. Margaret's Green, Ipswich, IP4 2BS Tel: (01473) 289000 E-mail: info@leedrecruitment.com

▶ Lexicon Recruitment Ltd, 7th Floor, 120 Vyse Street, Jewellery Quarter, Birmingham, B18 6NF Tel: 0845 130 6680 Fax: 0709 286 0437 E-mail: info@lexiconrecruitment.com

M D A Technical Personnel Ltd, Millbank House, North Way, Runcorn, Cheshire, WA7 2SX Tel: (01928) 734222 Fax: (01928) 739666 E-mail: info@millbank.com

Maxim Recruitment, 45 Bromley Road, London, E17 4PR Tel: (0870) 2430446 E-mail: contact@maximrecruitment.co.uk

Millennium Au Pairs & Nannies, The Coach House, The CR, Belmont, Sutton, Surrey, SM2 6BP Tel: (020) 8241 9752 Fax: (020) 8643 1268 E-mail: sales@aupairchoice.com

▶ Monterey Recruitment, Suite 8 Merlin House, Mossland Road, Hillington Park, Glasgow, G52 4XZ Tel: (0845) 4332211 Fax: (0845) 4332217

▶ indicates data change since last edition

RECRUITMENT CONSULTANCY – *continued*

▶ NDK Search & Selection Ltd, Chadwick House, Warrington Road, Birchwood Park, Warrington, WA3 6AE Tel: (01925) 813888 Fax: (01925) 813999 E-mail: response@ndksearch.com

Network Design International Ltd, 34 Mortimer Street, London, W1W 7JS Tel: (020) 7580 5151 Fax: (020) 7580 6242 E-mail: get.work@networkdesign.cc

Northern Recruitment Group Ltd, Lloyds Court, 56 Grey Street, Newcastle upon Tyne, NE1 6AH Tel: 0191-232 1222 Fax: 0191-261 8466 E-mail: newcastle@nrgplc.com

P S S Agency, Warrington, WA4 4JU Tel: (01928) 711700 Fax: (01928) 711258

▶ Paterson Healthcare Recruitment, 120 Churchill Road, Bicester, Oxon, OX26 4XD Tel: 01869 244610 Fax: 01869 360024 E-mail: training@paterson-healthcare.co.uk

▶ Personnel Placements Employment Agency, 20 Oatmeal Row, Salisbury, SP1 1TH Tel: (01722) 334433 Fax: (01722) 413208 E-mail: sales@pp-online.co.uk

▶ Polymer Recruitment Services, 71 Warstones Gardens, Wolverhampton, WV4 4PE Tel: (01902) 344631 Fax: (01902) 344631 E-mail: mike_bunce@consultant.com

▶ Prestige Recruitment Services Ltd, 39 Deansgate, Manchester, M3 2BA Tel: 0161-835 3999 Fax: 0161 835 3777 E-mail: callcentre@prestigeltd.co.uk

▶ Prestige Recruitment Services Ltd, Saddlers Court, 650 Warwick Road, Solihull, West Midlands, B91 3DX Tel: 0121-244 4484 Fax: 0121-244 4494

Primary Asset Recruitment, 13 Kingsway House, Kingsway, Gateshd, Gateshead, Tyne & Wear, NE11 0HW Tel: 0191-492 6170 Fax: 0191-206 4001 E-mail: mark.inger@primaryassetrecruitment.co.uk

Prime Recruitment Ltd, 37 Locks Heath Centre, Centre Way, Locks Heath, Southampton, SO31 6DX Tel: (01489) 559090 Fax: (01489) 559995 E-mail: enquiries@prime-recruitment.co.uk

▶ Proactive Recruitment Solutions Ltd, Jewellery Business Centre, 95 Spencer Street, Birmingham, B18 6DA Tel: 0121-523 1006 Fax: 0121-523 1016 E-mail: enquiries@proactiverecruitment.co.uk

▶ Proem It Recruitment, Mere House, 61a King Street, Knutsford, Cheshire, WA16 6DX Tel: (01565) 624010 Fax: (01565) 624011 E-mail: cv@proem-it.com

▶ Professional Management Resources Ltd, P O Box 23, Wadhurst, East Sussex, TN5 6XL Tel: (01892) 784226 Fax: 01892 784228 E-mail: info@pmr-worldjobs.co.uk

Project People Ltd, Whitefriars, Lewins Mead, Bristol, BS1 2NT Tel: 0117-908 7000 Fax: 0117-925 4676 E-mail: sales@handsets.com

Quay Education, Lutomer House Business Centre, 100 Prestons Road, London, E14 9SB Tel: (020) 7537 3399 Fax: (020) 7531 6793 E-mail: education@tslgroup.uk.com

▶ Redline Group P.L.C., Brandon House 30, 23-25 Brandon Street, Hamilton, Lanarkshire, ML3 6DA Tel: (01698) 527120 Fax: (01698) 527105 E-mail: info@redlineplc.com

Reflex Computer Recruitment Ltd, Regent House 1-3 Queensway, Redhill, RH1 1QT Tel: (01737) 778282 Fax: (01737) 778950 E-mail: reflexgroup@reflexgroup.co.uk

▶ S D W Recruitment, 33 Currie House, Herbert Walker Avenue, Southampton, SO15 1HJ Tel: (023) 8033 6633 Fax: (023) 8033 6633 E-mail: info@sdwrecruitment.co.uk

▶ S R S Pensions, Broad Quay House, Broad Quay, Bristol, BS1 4DJ Tel: 0117-905 8734 Fax: 0117-963 7949 E-mail: sales@srs-pensions.co.uk

Sanderson Recruitment P.L.C., Somerset House, 18 Canynge Road, Clifton, Bristol, BS8 3JX Tel: 0117-970 6666 Fax: 0117-970 6665 E-mail: mail@sandersonplc.com

▶ Search & Supply Recruitment, The Sanctuary, Shelley Close, Armitage, Staffordshire, WS15 4UW Tel: 01543 304583 Fax: 01543 304583 E-mail: enquiry@searchandsupply.co.uk

Skillframe Ltd, 138 Walton Road, East Molesey, Surrey, KT8 0HP Tel: (020) 8941 7733 Fax: (020) 8941 3301 E-mail: info@skillframe.co.uk

Staffhunt, 30 Birch Grove, Menstrie, Clackmannanshire, FK11 7DW Tel: (01786) 834776 E-mail: info@staffhunt.org

▶ Stephen Ward & Company, Warwick Corner, 42 Warwick Road, Kenilworth, Warwickshire, CV8 1HE Tel: 01926 866610 Fax: 01926 851534 E-mail: mail@stephen-ward.com

Time, Moulton Park Business Centre, Redhouse Road, Moulton Park, Northampton, NN3 6AQ Tel: (01604) 670555 Fax: (01604) 497501 E-mail: info@recruitingtime.co.uk

▶ Try Temps Ltd, Unit A2 Imex Business Park, Kings Road, Tyseley, Birmingham, B11 2AL Tel: 0121-693 3311 Fax: 0121-693 3355 E-mail: sales@trytemps.co.uk

Whitehall Recruitment Ltd, 37-41 High Street, Edenbridge, Kent, TN8 5AD Tel: (01732) 864777 Fax: (01732) 865777 E-mail: info@whitehall.uk.com

▶ Will Recruit, Kingswood House, The Avenue, Cliftonville, Northampton, NN1 5BT Tel: (0870) 0468686 E-mail: info@willrecruit.com

The Work Shop, 7 High Street, Ringwood, Hampshire, BH24 1AB Tel: (01425) 489393 Fax: (01425) 489402 E-mail: sales@thework-shop.net

RECRUITMENT CONSULTANCY, HOSPITALITY

Minto Recruitment, 1 North Pallant, Chichester, West Sussex, PO19 1TL Tel: (01243) 787003 Fax: (01243) 787694 E-mail: info@mintorecruit.com

RECRUITMENT MANAGEMENT CONSULTANCY, ON LINE

▶ The Angel Services Group Ltd, 61 Bridge Street, Walsall, WS1 1JQ Tel: (01922) 424300 E-mail: charles.trivett@ems-gb.com

RECRUITMENT MANAGEMENT SOLUTIONS

▶ Jobtrain Solutions, Sandpiper House, No.1 Modwen Road, Salford Quays, Salford, M5 3EZ Tel: 0161-875 1406 E-mail: jason.tye@jobtrain.co.uk

RECRUITMENT TO RECRUITMENT CONSULTANCY

▶ Appointments Direct Ltd, 62 Eden Road, Beckenham, Kent, BR3 4AT Tel: (020) 8402 2776 E-mail: rec@appointmentsdirect.co.uk

RECRUITMENT, INTERNET BASED

▶ ARV Solutions, 27 Southmead Road, Westbury-On-Trym, Bristol, BS10 5DL Tel: 0117 9083173 Fax: 0871 661 3669 E-mail: mail@arvsolutions.co.uk

▶ Ash Associates, PO Box 5374, Ferndown, Dorset, BH22 0ZX Tel: (0845) 1232701 E-mail: recruit@ash-associates.com

▶ Blooming Good Jobs, BGJ House, Ashford, Kent, TN21 0LT Tel: (0871) 24225232 E-mail: info@bloominggoodjobs.com

▶ The CV People, 46 Woodhead Grove, Armadale, Bathgate, West Lothian, EH48 3HU Tel: (07981) 347380

▶ Douglas Bates, Suite 8 Phoenix House, 63 Campfield Road, St. Albans, Hertfordshire, AL1 5FL Tel: 01727 736690 E-mail: dougbates@intelligentpeople.co.uk

E M P Chefs, 12 Hidings Court Lane, Morecambe, Lancashire, LA4 4QJ Tel: (07834) 364732 E-mail: info@emp-chefs.com

▶ FinanceCVs.co.uk, 18 Bedfordshire Down, Warfield, Bracknell, Berkshire, RG42 3UA Tel: (07006) 300980 E-mail: info@financecvs.co.uk

▶ Hunter Mabon, 10 Barrow Court, Barrow Gurney, Bristol, BS48 3RP Tel: (0870) 2012495 Fax: (01285) 770003 E-mail: cv@huntermabon.co.uk

▶ Job-Recruit, PO Box 139, Thornton-Cleveleys, Lancashire, FY5 4WU Tel: (07834) 986958 E-mail: admin@job-recruit.co.uk

▶ Lexicon Recruitment Ltd, 7th Floor, 120 Vyse Street, Jewellery Quarter, Birmingham, B18 6NF Tel: 0845 130 6680 Fax: 0709 286 0437 E-mail: info@lexiconrecruitment.com

Millennium Au Pairs & Nannies, The Coach House, The CR, Belmont, Sutton, Surrey, SM2 6BP Tel: (020) 8241 9752 Fax: (020) 8643 1268 E-mail: sales@aupairchoice.com

▶ O J M Recruitment, Gresham House, 7 Veryan, Fareham, Hampshire, PO14 1NN Tel: (0845) 8330875 Fax: (0845) 8330873 E-mail: info@ojmrecruitment.com

▶ Salestarget.co.uk, Holden House, 57 Rathbone Place, London, W1T 1LD Tel: 020 7769 9200 Fax: 020 7769 9008 E-mail: info@salestarget.co.uk

▶ Salestarget.co.uk, Holden House, 57 Rathbone Place, London, W1T 1JU Tel: (020) 7769 9147 Fax: (020) 7769 9205 E-mail: sales@salestarget.co.uk

▶ Sunshine Au Pair, Wardwick, Derby, DE1 1HA Tel: (0845) 0066245 Fax: (01332) 231320 E-mail: info@sunshineaupairs.co.uk

▶ - Swayo - Internet Solutions, PO Box 37491, London, United Kingdom, N3 2XR Tel: 0845 257 0392 Fax: 0871 242 5970 E-mail: sales@swayo.co.uk

▶ Top Language Jobs, 770-780 Great Cambridge Road, Enfield, Middlesex, EN1 3RN Tel: (020) 8363 3334

Totaljobs Group Ltd, 57 Rathbone Place, London, W1T 1JU Tel: (020) 7769 9200 Fax: (020) 7769 9201 E-mail: info@totaljobs.com

▶ Helen Watson, PO Box 565, East Grinstead, West Sussex, RH19 1WQ Tel: (07799) 645907 E-mail: jobs@networking4you.net

RECTANGULAR CONNECTORS

I Q C International Ltd, PO Box 1024, Arundel, West Sussex, BN18 0LT Tel: (0870) 0130999 Fax: (0870) 0130888 E-mail: sales@iqc.co.uk

RECTIFIER (ELECTRICAL) MANUFRS

D P Energy Services, Unit 5 & 6, Heron Avenue, Wickford, Essex, SS11 8DL Tel: (01268) 560040 Fax: (01268) 560261 E-mail: sales@drakepower.com

Dynamics (Bristol) Ltd, 1 Evercreech Way, Walrow Industrial Estate, Highbridge, Somerset, TA9 4AN Tel: (01278) 780222 Fax: (01278) 781824 E-mail: info@dynamicsbristol.co.uk

Electrical Power Ltd, PO Box 115, Bingley, West Yorkshire, BD16 1WQ Tel: (01274) 510970 Fax: (01274) 511109 E-mail: epsrec@hotmail.com

Gilbeyco Ltd, 32 Edison Road, Rabans Lane Industrial Area, Aylesbury, Buckinghamshire, HP19 8TE Tel: (01296) 414966 Fax: (01296) 414969 E-mail: enquiries@gilbeyco.com

Hivolt Capacitors Ltd, Maydown, Londonderry, BT47 6UQ Tel: (028) 7186 0265 Fax: (028) 7186 0479 E-mail: hivoltcapacitors@easynet.co.uk

Riker Ltd, Unit 12 Boat House Meadow, Salisbury, SP2 7LD Tel: (01722) 333153 Fax: (01722) 333139

Wright Electric Company Ltd, 35 Clarendon Avenue, Trowbridge, Wiltshire, BA14 7BW Tel: (01225) 761188 Fax: (01225) 761188 E-mail: sales@wrightelec.demon.co.uk

RECTIFIERS, SEMICONDUCTOR,

See Semiconductor etc

RECYCLED BULK CONTAINERS

Liverpool Bulk Bags, 35a Seaforth Vale North, Liverpool, L21 3TR Tel: 0151-920 2280 Fax: 0151-922 4076 E-mail: info@bulkbagsuk.com

S C A Industrial, Dodwells Road, Hinckley, Leicestershire, LE10 3BX Tel: (01455) 251400 Fax: (01455) 251404 E-mail: info.industrial@sca.com

RECYCLED LAMPS

W F Ltd, Upper Gallery, Station Approach Industrial Estate, Pulborough, West Sussex, RH20 1AQ Tel: (01798) 875312 Fax: (01798) 875570 E-mail: wf@wf-online.com

W F O L C Ltd, Unit 6 Woking Business Park, Albert Drive, Woking, Surrey, GU21 5JY Tel: (01483) 727571 Fax: (01483) 725066

RECYCLED PAPER

James Mcnaughton Paper Group, Jaymac House, Church Manorway, Erith, Kent, DA8 1DF Tel: (020) 8320 3200 Fax: (020) 8311 4162 E-mail: marketing@mcnaughton-paper.com

Kappa SSK Ltd, Mount Street, Birmingham, B7 5RE Tel: 0121-327 1381 Fax: 0121-322 6300 E-mail: sales@sskpaper.co.uk

Pearce Recycling Co. Ltd, 4 Acrewood Way, St. Albans, Hertfordshire, AL4 0JY Tel: (01727) 861522 Fax: (01727) 846428 E-mail: sales@pearce-recycling.co.uk

▶ Recyclo, Prince William Avenue, Sandycroft, Deeside, Clwyd, CH5 2QZ Tel: (01244) 521800 Fax: (0845) 4515332 E-mail: enquiries@recyclowastemanagement.co.uk

Sca Recycling UK, Daneshill Industrial Estate, Armstrong Road, Basingstoke, Hampshire, RG24 8NU Tel: (01256) 351456 Fax: (01256) 842147

Sunderland Paper Mill, Ocean Road, Grangetown, Sunderland, SR2 9RZ Tel: 0191-514 4944 Fax: 0191-510 8012 E-mail: patb@edward-thompson.com

RECYCLED PRODUCT CONTAINERS

B P I Recycled Products, Heanor Gate Industrial Estate, Heanor, Derbyshire, DE75 7RG Tel: (01773) 530530 Fax: (01773) 533347

Faulks & Co. Ltd, 21 Moat Way, Barwell, Leicester, LE9 8EY Tel: (01455) 848184 Fax: (01455) 844134 E-mail: sales@faulks.co.uk

Randalls Fabrications Ltd, Randall Fabrication, Hoyle Mill Road, Kinsley, Pontefract, West Yorkshire, WF9 5JB Tel: (01977) 615132 Fax: (01977) 610059 E-mail: sales@randallsfabrications.co.uk

Terbergmatec UK Ltd, Highgrounds Way, Rhodesia, Worksop, Nottinghamshire, S80 3AF Tel: (01909) 484000 Fax: (01909) 489000

RECYCLED THERMOFORMED PLASTIC

B P I Recycled Products, Heanor Gate Industrial Estate, Heanor, Derbyshire, DE75 7RG Tel: (01773) 530530 Fax: (01773) 533347

RECYCLING WASTE COLLECTION VEHICLES

▶ Motor Vehicle Dismantlers Association Of Great Britain, 33 Market Street, Lichfield, Staffordshire, WS13 6LA Tel: (01543) 254254 Fax: (01543) 254274 E-mail: enquires@mvda.org.uk

RED WINE

▶ Aldanca Wine, 19 Mountbatten Court, Raleigh Close, New Milton, Hampshire, BH25 5LB Tel: 01425 621733 Fax: 01425 618440 E-mail: marketing@aldanca-wine.co.uk

Chateau Papillon Estates, C7 Boston Trade Park, Norfolk Street, Boston, Lincolnshire, PE21 9HG Tel: (0845) 8381790 Fax: (0870) 1313172 E-mail: info@chateau-papillon.com

Donatel Freres Ltd, The Vintage House, 42 Old Compton Street, London, W1D 4LR Tel: (020) 7437 2592 Fax: (020) 7734 1174 E-mail: vintagehouse.co@virgin.net

▶ Genesis Wines Ltd, 78Tachbrook Street, London, SW1V 2NE Tel: (020) 7963 9060 Fax: (0870) 8502038 E-mail: sales@genesiswines.com

▶ Splash Winery Ltd, 16 Briar Avenue, Meltham, Holmfirth, HD9 5LQ Tel: (01484) 323814 Fax: (01484) 323814

REDUCING VALVES

Auld Valves Ltd, Finlas Street, Cowlairs Industrial Estate, Glasgow, G22 5DQ Tel: 0141-557 0515 Fax: 0141-558 1059 E-mail: bob@auldvalves.com

Dereve Flow Control Ltd, Park Lane, Handsworth, Birmingham, B21 8LE Tel: 0121-553 7021 Fax: 0121-525 5664 E-mail: dc.controls@btinternet.com

Safety Systems UK Ltd, Sharp Street, Worsley, Manchester, M28 3NA Tel: (01925) 820281 Fax: 0161-799 4335 E-mail: support@safetysystemsuk.com

REDUNDANT ARRAY OF INDEPENDENT DISK (RAID) STORAGE SYSTEMS

Delf Technology, Carrington Business Park, Manchester Road, Carrington, Manchester, M31 4QQ Tel: 0161-776 4802 Fax: 0161-776 4803 E-mail: info@delftechnology.com

Workstation Technologies Ltd, 21 Sovereign Road, Kings Norton Business Centre, Birmingham, B30 3HN Tel: 0121-486 1234 Fax: (0870) 9901918 E-mail: info@wtluk.com

REDUNDANT STOCK DEALERS,

See Surplus etc

REED RELAYS

Hamlin Electronics Europe Ltd, Saw Mills Road, Diss, Norfolk, IP22 4NX Tel: (01379) 649700 Fax: (01379) 649702 E-mail: simon.pitkin@hamlin.com

Pickering Electronics Ltd, Stephenson Road, Clacton-on-Sea, Essex, CO15 4NL Tel: (01255) 428141 Fax: (01255) 475058 E-mail: sales@pickeringrelay.com

Standex Electronics (U.K.) Ltd, 40 Morley Road, Tonbridge, Kent, TN9 1RA Tel: (01732) 771023 Fax: (01732) 770122 E-mail: sales@standex.co.uk

REED SWITCHES

Gentech International Ltd, Grangestone Eng Co, Grangestone Indust Estat E Ladywell Avenue, Maidens, Girvan, Ayrshire, KA26 9PL Tel: (01465) 713581 Fax: (01465) 714974 E-mail: enquiries@gentech-international.co.uk

Standex Electronics (U.K.) Ltd, 40 Morley Road, Tonbridge, Kent, TN9 1RA Tel: (01732) 771023 Fax: (01732) 770122 E-mail: sales@standex.co.uk

REEDS/HEALDS, TEXTILE WEAVING

H Cocker & Sons Ltd, Reed Heald Works, Jubilee Street, Halifax, West Yorkshire, HX3 9HY Tel: (01422) 353358 Fax: (01422) 353358

REEDS/HEALDS, TEXTILE WEAVING

– continued

Lund Precision Reeds Ltd, St. Andrews House, Russell Street, Keighley, West Yorkshire, BD21 2JU Tel: (01535) 662580 Fax: (01535) 608428

REEL HANDLING EQUIPMENT

Mechandling Ltd, 11b Greenfield Farm Industrial Estate, Congleton, Cheshire, CW12 4TR Tel: (01260) 299411 Fax: (01260) 299032 E-mail: sales@mechandling.co.uk

Wilmat Handling Company Ltd, 43 Steward Street, Birmingham, B18 7AE Tel: 0121-454 7514 Fax: 0121-456 1792 E-mail: info@wilmat-handling.co.uk

REFINED TAR

Liver Grease Oil & Chemical Company Ltd, 11 Norfolk Street, Liverpool, L1 0BE Tel: 0151-709 7494 Fax: 0151-709 3774 E-mail: sales@livergrease.co.uk

REFLECTING ROAD STUDS

Highway & Industrial Equipment Ltd, East Moors Road, Cardiff, CF24 5EE Tel: (029) 2049 4623 Fax: (029) 2048 3611

Reflecting Roadstuds Ltd, 1 Mill Lane, Halifax, West Yorkshire, HX3 6TR Tel: (01422) 360208 Fax: (01422) 349075

REFLECTIVE ARMBANDS

▶ Kemco Technology, Acorn House, Tonbridge Road, Bough Beech, Edenbridge, Kent, TN8 7AU Tel: (01892) 870077 Fax: (01892) 870777 E-mail: info@kemcotech.com

REFLECTIVE CORPORATE BADGES

Dalman & Narborough Ltd, 38-40 Lombard Street, Birmingham, B12 0QN Tel: 0121-772 2008 Fax: 0121-771 4182 E-mail: sales@dalman-narborough.co.uk

High Profile, 9 Haslemere Way, Banbury, Oxfordshire, OX16 5RW Tel: (01295) 267966 Fax: (01295) 272477 E-mail: sales@high-profile.co.uk

J & A International Ltd, Vale Road, Spilsby, Lincolnshire, PE23 5HE Tel: (01790) 752757 Fax: (01790) 754132 E-mail: ja-int@ja-int.co.uk

Master Badge, 306 Gloucester Road, Cheltenham, Gloucestershire, GL51 7AG Tel: (01242) 580430 Fax: (01242) 580430 E-mail: info@masterbadge.co.uk

Quazar International, Unit 1c Deacon Trading Estate, Forstal Road, Aylesford, Kent, ME20 7SP Tel: (01622) 792222 Fax: (01622) 790099 E-mail: sales@quazarinternational.co.uk

REFLECTIVE INSULATION

▶ Roofing Solutions, 1 The Shipyard, Upper Brents, Faversham, Kent, ME13 7DZ Tel: (01795) 597998 Fax: (01795) 591811 E-mail: roofsolutions@btinternet.com

REFLECTIVE MATERIALS

Celloglas Speciality Products, Unit 12C, Exeter Way, Theale Commercial Park, Theale, Reading, RG7 4AW Tel: 0118-930 3656 Fax: 0118-932 3256 E-mail: andy.kirbycelloglas@alcan.co.uk

Dawk Trimmers, Crown Mill, 1 Crown Street, Salford, M3 7DH Tel: 0161-832 3262 Fax: 0161-834 4704E-mail: fpinetex@aol.com

REFLECTIVE PRODUCTS

Quazar International, Unit 1c Deacon Trading Estate, Forstal Road, Aylesford, Kent, ME20 7SP Tel: (01622) 792222 Fax: (01622) 790099 E-mail: sales@quazarinternational.co.uk

REFLECTIVE PROMOTIONAL SIGNS

Marneon Signs Ltd, 11 Pontygladwr Street, Swansea, SA1 2BH Tel: (01792) 646949 Fax: (01792) 652227 E-mail: andrew-cotford@marneonsigns.com

Quazar International, Unit 1c Deacon Trading Estate, Forstal Road, Aylesford, Kent, ME20 7SP Tel: (01622) 792222 Fax: (01622) 790099 E-mail: sales@quazarinternational.co.uk

REFLECTIVE WALL INSULATION

▶ Roofing Solutions, 1 The Shipyard, Upper Brents, Faversham, Kent, ME13 7DZ Tel: (01795) 597998 Fax: (01795) 591811 E-mail: roofsolutions@btinternet.com

REFRACTOMETER MANUFRS

Bellingham & Stanley Ltd, Longfield Road, Tunbridge Wells, Kent, TN2 3EY Tel: (01892) 500400 Fax: (01892) 543115 E-mail: sales@bellinghamandstanley.co.uk

Index Instruments Ltd, Bury Road Industrial Estate, Ramsey, Huntingdon, Cambridgeshire, PE26 1NF Tel: (01487) 814313 Fax: (01487) 812789 E-mail: sales@indexinstruments.com

K P M Moisture Meters Aqua Boy, Manndalin, Harrogate View, Leeds, LS17 8AZ Tel: 0113-268 5054 Fax: 0113-268 5054 E-mail: kpmmeters@aol.com

Optical Activity Ltd, Industrial Estate, Bury Road, Ramsey, Huntingdon, Cambridgeshire, PE26 1NF Tel: (01487) 813913 Fax: (01487) 812789 E-mail: sales@opticalactivity.com

REFRACTORIES MANUFACTURERS OR PRODUCERS

Calderys UK Ltd, 5-8 Ashfieldway, Leeds, LS12 5JB Tel: 0113-263 6268 Fax: 0113-279 0539 E-mail: uksales@calderys.com

Capital Refractories Ltd, 2 Station Road, Clowne, Chesterfield, Derbyshire, S43 4AB Tel: (01246) 811163 Fax: (01246) 819573 E-mail: info@capital-refractories.com

Castle Monolithics Europe Ltd, Sheaf Bank Works, Prospect Road, Heeley, Sheffield, S2 3EN Tel: 0114-273 0588 Fax: 0114-276 2045

Causeway Steel Products Ltd, Five Ash Road, Gravesend, Kent, DA11 0RF Tel: (01474) 567871 Fax: (01474) 328993 E-mail: causewaysteel@causeway-steel.co.uk

D S F Refractories & Minerals Ltd, Friden, Newhaven, Buxton, Derbyshire, SK17 0DX Tel: (01629) 636271 Fax: (01629) 636892 E-mail: dsf@dsf.co.uk

▶ Dyson Industries Ltd, Griffs Works, Stopes Road, Stannington, Sheffield, S6 6BW Tel: 0114-234 8663 Fax: 0114-232 2519 E-mail: enq@dyson-holloware.com

Electro Furnace Products Ltd, Hull Road, Saltend, Hull, HU12 8ED Tel: (01482) 899141 Fax: (01482) 890196 E-mail: sales@efp-hull.co.uk

Foseco FS Ltd, Coleshill Road, Tamworth, Staffordshire, B78 3TL Tel: (01827) 289999 Fax: (01827) 250806 E-mail: enquiries@foseco.com

Furnace Services, 42 Ellison Avenue, Scunthorpe, Lincolnshire, DN16 3TD Tel: (01724) 868578

G H S Refractories Ltd, Tingley Bar Industrial Estate, Bridge Street, Morley, Leeds, LS27 0HE Tel: 0113-252 7144 Fax: 0113-253 1527 E-mail: info@ghsrefractories.co.uk

Grange Aggregates, Waterloo Road, Stoke-on-Trent, ST6 3HX Tel: (01782) 212765 Fax: (01782) 537900

Harbison-Walker Refractories Ltd, Dock Road South, Bromborough, Wirral, Merseyside, CH62 4SP Tel: 0151-641 5900 Fax: 0151-641 5910 E-mail: sales@hwr.co.uk

Monocon International Refractories Ltd, Denaby Lane, Old Denaby, Doncaster, South Yorkshire, DN12 4LQ Tel: (01709) 864848 Fax: (01709) 860481 E-mail: sales@monocon.com

Parkinson-Spencer Refractories Ltd, Holmfield, Halifax, West Yorkshire, HX3 6SX Tel: (01422) 254472 Fax: (01422) 254473 E-mail: admin@parkinson-spencer.co.uk

Penn Refractories Ltd, Dudley Road, Stourbridge, West Midlands, DY9 8EL Tel: (01384) 422192 Fax: (01384) 422195

Penny Hydraulics Ltd, Station Road, Clowne, Chesterfield, Derbyshire, S43 4AB Tel: (01246) 811475 Fax: (01246) 810403 E-mail: sales@pennyhydraulics.com

R H I Refractories UK Ltd, PO Box 3, Clydebank, Dunbartonshire, G81 1RW Tel: 0141-952 1990 Fax: 0141-435 7445

Robert Lickley Ltd, Dudley, West Midlands, DY1 2RL Tel: (01902) 880123 Fax: (01902) 880019 E-mail: admin@robertlickley.co.uk

Saint Gobain Industrial Ceramics Ltd, Mill Lane, Rainford, St. Helens, Merseyside, WA11 8LP Tel: (01744) 882941 Fax: (01744) 883514 E-mail: andrew.smith.rainford@saint-gobain.com

Specialist Induction Refractories Ltd, Wednesbury Trading Estate, Wednesbury, West Midlands, WS10 7JW Tel: 0121-556 6288 Fax: 0121-556 5326

Studweldpro UK Ltd, Ollerton Road, Tuxford, Newark, Nottinghamshire, NG22 0PQ Tel: (01777) 874500 Fax: (01777) 874555 E-mail: sales@swpuk.com

REFRACTORIES MERCHANTS OR AGENTS OR SUPPLIERS

Adament Refractory Settings Ltd, 54 Bolton Road, Kearsley, Bolton, BL4 9BT Tel: (01204) 573197 Fax: (01204) 571517

Artisan Refractories Ltd, Hanley Road, Stoke-on-Trent, ST1 6BG Tel: (01782) 266563 Fax: (01782) 266563 E-mail: artisanref@aol.com

B J Construction, Units 29-30, Manor Industrial Estate, Flint, CH6 5UY Tel: (01352) 730111 Fax: (01352) 730444

Capital Refractories Ltd, 2 Station Road, Clowne, Chesterfield, Derbyshire, S43 4AB Tel: (01246) 811163 Fax: (01246) 819573 E-mail: info@capital-refractories.com

Central Refractories (Scotland) Ltd, PO Box 14871, Falkirk, FK1 1RP Tel: (01324) 624412 Fax: (01324) 626923

Dramicom, 14 Moorside Lane, Neston, Parkgate, Neston, CH64 6QP Tel: 0151-336 5107 Fax: 0151-336 5107

F G F Continental Ltd, Shadwell House, Shadwell Street, Birmingham, B4 6LJ Tel: 0121-233 1144 Fax: 0121-212 2539 E-mail: sales.fgf@ukonline.co.uk

Flouch Engineering Co. Ltd, Hazlehead, Crow Edge, Sheffield, S36 4HH Tel: (01226) 763239 Fax: (01226) 370205 E-mail: sales@flouch-engineering.co.uk

G H S Refractories Ltd, Tingley Bar Industrial Estate, Bridge Street, Morley, Leeds, LS27 0HE Tel: 0113-252 7144 Fax: 0113-253 1527 E-mail: info@ghsrefractories.co.uk

Hines Milling & Processing Ltd, Scott Lidgett Industrial Estate, Scott Lidgett Road, Longport, Stoke-On-Trent, ST6 4NQ Tel: (01782) 819616 Fax: (01782) 837174 E-mail: hines@iclwebkite.co.uk

Jay's Refractory Specialists Ltd, Callywhite Lane, Dronfield, Derbyshire, S18 2XR Tel: (01246) 410241 Fax: (01246) 290221 E-mail: info@jrsuk.com

Kitson Insulation Products Ltd, Cwmdu Industrial Estate, Carmarthen Road, Gendros, Swansea, SA5 8JF Tel: (01792) 588461 Fax: (01792) 583849 E-mail: swansea@kitsonsthermal.co.uk

MacGregor & Moir, Unit 4, 95 Westburn Drive, Cambuslang, Glasgow, G72 7NA Tel: 0141-643 3636 Fax: 0141-641 8505 E-mail: info@macgregorandmoir.com

R H I Refractories UK Ltd, PO Box 3, Clydebank, Dunbartonshire, G81 1RW Tel: 0141-952 1990 Fax: 0141-435 7445

R H I Refractories UK Ltd, International House, Brunel Drive, Newark, Nottinghamshire, NG24 2EG Tel: (01636) 704494 Fax: (01636) 704495 E-mail: rhi.uk@rhi-ag.com

Vesuvius UK Ltd, Unit 10 Wednesbury Trading Estate, Wednesbury, West Midlands, WS10 7JN Tel: 0121-502 6000 Fax: 0121-556 7401

REFRACTORY ANCHORS

A Bush Engineering Services Ltd, 16-18 Manor Road, Leeds, LS11 9AH Tel: 0113-246 0581 Fax: 0113-246 0043E-mail: info@abush.co.uk

Causeway Steel Products Ltd, Five Ash Road, Gravesend, Kent, DA11 0RF Tel: (01474) 567871 Fax: (01474) 328993 E-mail: causewaysteel@causeway-steel.co.uk

▶ Mach One (Holdings) Ltd, Unit 8 Norfolk Business Park, Foley Street, Sheffield, S4 7YW Tel: 0114-270 0545 Fax: 0114-276 7438 E-mail: sales@mach-int.com

▶ V H I UK Ltd, Raines House, Denby Dale Road, Wakefield, West Yorkshire, WF1 1HR Tel: (0870) 1206170 Fax: (0870) 1206171 E-mail: office@vhi-UK.com

REFRACTORY BLOCKS OR BRICKS

D S F Refractories & Minerals Ltd, Friden, Newhaven, Buxton, Derbyshire, SK17 0DX Tel: (01629) 636271 Fax: (01629) 636892 E-mail: dsf@dsf.co.uk

G H S Refractories Ltd, Tingley Bar Industrial Estate, Bridge Street, Morley, Leeds, LS27 0HE Tel: 0113-252 7144 Fax: 0113-253 1527 E-mail: info@ghsrefractories.co.uk

Parkinson-Spencer Refractories Ltd, Holmfield, Halifax, West Yorkshire, HX3 6SX Tel: (01422) 254472 Fax: (01422) 254473 E-mail: admin@parkinson-spencer.co.uk

R E Knowles Ltd, Buxton Road, Furness Vale, High Peak, Derbyshire, SK23 7PJ Tel: (01663) 744127 Fax: (01663) 741562

Saint Gobain Industrial Ceramics Ltd, Mill Lane, Rainford, St. Helens, Merseyside, WA11 8LP Tel: (01744) 882941 Fax: (01744) 883514 E-mail: andrew.smith.rainford@saint-gobain.com

REFRACTORY CEMENT

Lafarge Aluminates Ltd, Dolphin Way, Purfleet, Essex, RM19 1NZ Tel: (01708) 863333 Fax: (01708) 861033

REFRACTORY COATINGS

Polybond Ltd, Unit 6 William Street, Northam, Southampton, SO14 5QH Tel: (023) 8022 3266 Fax: (0870) 0527587 E-mail: tom@polybond.co.uk

REFRACTORY CONSULTANTS OR DESIGNERS

Combustion Lining Ltd, Jacaidam Works, Walley Street, Stoke-on-Trent, ST6 2AH Tel: (01782) 822712 Fax: (01782) 823920 E-mail: info@combustionlinings.com

Kiln Refractory Services Ltd, 221 Birches Head Road, Stoke-on-Trent, ST1 6NB Tel: (01782) 851685 Fax: (01782) 768949 E-mail: krs@cwcom.net

Refractory Installation Services, 27 Park Lane, Rothwell, Leeds, LS10 3BA Tel: 0113-282 2258 E-mail: paul.harvey@ris-leeds.co.uk

▶ V H I UK Ltd, Raines House, Denby Dale Road, Wakefield, West Yorkshire, WF1 1HR Tel: (0870) 1206170 Fax: (0870) 1206171 E-mail: office@vhi-UK.com

York Linings International Ltd, Millfield Industrial Estate, Wheldrake, York, YO19 6NA Tel: (01904) 449777 Fax: (01904) 449888 E-mail: yorkhq@yli-ltd.demon.co.uk

REFRACTORY INSTALLATION OR LINING OR REPAIR OR SETTING OR TEST CONTRACTORS

A T Refractories, Ryandel Business Park, Brookhouse Way, Cheadle, Stoke-on-Trent, ST10 1SR Tel: (01538) 750461 Fax: (01538) 750461

Adament Refractory Settings Ltd, 54 Bolton Road, Kearsley, Bolton, BL4 9BT Tel: (01204) 573197 Fax: (01204) 571517

Artisan Refractories Ltd, Hanley Road, Stoke-on-Trent, ST1 6BG Tel: (01782) 266563 Fax: (01782) 266563 E-mail: artisanref@aol.com

B J Construction, Units 29-30, Manor Industrial Estate, Flint, CH6 5UY Tel: (01352) 730111 Fax: (01352) 730444

Bowden-Jackson (Construction) Ltd, PO Box Hk7, Leeds, LS11 7DY Tel: 0113-277 9539 Fax: 0113-277 9539

Calderys UK Ltd, 5-8 Ashfieldway, Leeds, LS12 5JB Tel: 0113-263 6268 Fax: 0113-279 0539 E-mail: uksales@calderys.com

Cameron Furnace Co. Ltd, 7a Alleysbank Road,, Fameloan Industrial Estate, Rutherglen, Glasgow, G73 1LX Tel: (0141) 643 2244 Fax: (0141) 643 0088 E-mail: cameron.furnace@dial.pipex.com

Cermeteq, Treswell, Retford, Notts, DN22 0EQ Tel: 01777 248822 Fax: 01777 248666

Combustion Lining Ltd, Jacaidam Works, Walley Street, Stoke-on-Trent, ST6 2AH Tel: (01782) 822712 Fax: (01782) 823920 E-mail: info@combustionlinings.com

Nub Engineering Ltd, Newhouse Industrial Estate, Newhouse, Motherwell, Lanarkshire, ML1 5RX Tel: (01698) 833873 Fax: (01698) 734322 E-mail: sales@nubeng.com

Penny Hydraulics Ltd, Station Road, Clowne, Chesterfield, Derbyshire, S43 4AB Tel: (01246) 811475 Fax: (01246) 810403 E-mail: sales@pennyhydraulics.com

▶ Phoenix Site Services, Unit 4b Gateway Close, Parkgate, Rotherham, South Yorkshire, S62 6LJ Tel: (01709) 529951 Fax: (01709) 529549 E-mail: paul.phoenixservices@btopenworld.com

R B B Refractory Engineers Ltd, 291 Watling Street, Dartford, DA2 6EP Tel: (01322) 394850 Fax: (01322) 394860 E-mail: enquiries@rbbrefractory.co.uk

Refractory Installation Services, 27 Park Lane, Rothwell, Leeds, LS10 3BA Tel: 0113-282 2258 E-mail: paul.harvey@ris-leeds.co.uk

Robert Lickley Ltd, Dudley, West Midlands, DY1 2RL Tel: (01902) 880123 Fax: (01902) 880019 E-mail: admin@robertlickley.co.uk

S G Blair & Co. Ltd, Davy Road, Astmoor Industrial Estate, Runcorn, Cheshire, WA7 1SL Tel: (01928) 503200 Fax: (01928) 715200 E-mail: sales@sgblair.com

SHL Refractories UK Limited, Celcius House, Lawn Road, Carlton-In-Lindrick, Worksop, Nottinghamshire, S81 9LB Tel: (01909) 731959 Fax: (01909) 731579 E-mail: sales@shl-refractories.co.uk

Simpson Refractories, Wood Croft, The Hills, Bradwell, Hope Valley, Derbyshire, S33 9HZ Tel: (01433) 621171 Fax: (01433) 623292

Specialist Induction Refractories Ltd, Wednesbury Trading Estate, Wednesbury, West Midlands, WS10 7JW Tel: 0121-556 6288 Fax: 0121-556 5326

Tab Refractory Construction & Maintenance Co. Ltd, Unit 7 Parkdale Industrial Estate, Wharf Street, Warrington, WA1 2HT Tel: (01925) 230222 Fax: (01925) 230430 E-mail: tabrcm@aol.com

Vesuvius Flogates, British Steel Complex, Lackenby Works, Middlesbrough, Cleveland, TS6 7RW Tel: 01642 440054 Fax: 01642 465966

REFRACTORY INSTALLATION OR LINING OR REPAIR OR SETTING OR TEST CONTRACTORS – *continued*

York Linings International Ltd, Millfield Industrial Estate, Wheldrake, York, YO19 6NA Tel: (01904) 449777 Fax: (01904) 449888 E-mail: yorkhq@yli-ltd.demon.co.uk

REFRACTORY LINING FASTENERS

Castle Monolithics Europe Ltd, Sheaf Bank Works, Prospect Road, Heeley, Sheffield, S2 3EN Tel: 0114-273 0588 Fax: 0114-276 2045

Penny Hydraulics Ltd, Station Road, Clowne, Chesterfield, Derbyshire, S43 4AB Tel: (01246) 811475 Fax: (01246) 810403 E-mail: sales@pennyhydraulics.com

REFRACTORY METALS

Designcode Ltd, 5 Merseyton Road, Ellesmere Port, CH65 2JE Tel: 0151-355 9172 Fax: 0151-357 2868 E-mail: designcode@tinyworld.co.uk

H C Starck Ltd, Unit 1 Harris Road, Calne, Wiltshire, SN11 9PT Tel: (01249) 822122 Fax: (01249) 823800 E-mail: sally.field@hcstarck.co.uk

REFRACTORY RAW MATERIALS

James Durrans & Sons Ltd, Phoenix Works, Thurlstone, Sheffield, S36 9QU Tel: (01226) 370000 Fax: (01226) 370336 E-mail: enquiries@durrans.co.uk

Electro Furnace Products Ltd, Hull Road, Saltend, Hull, HU12 8ED Tel: (01482) 899141 Fax: (01482) 890196 E-mail: sales@efp-hull.co.uk

Keith Ceramic Materials Ltd, Fishers Way, Belvedere, Kent, DA17 6BS Tel: (020) 8311 8299 Fax: (020) 8311 8238

Monocon International Refractories Ltd, Denaby Lane, Old Denaby, Doncaster, South Yorkshire, DN12 4LQ Tel: (01709) 864848 Fax: (01709) 860481 E-mail: sales@monocon.com

R H I Refractories UK Ltd, PO Box 3, Clydebank, Dunbartonshire, G81 1RW Tel: 0141-952 1990 Fax: 0141-435 7445

R H I Refractories UK Ltd, International House, Brunel Drive, Newark, Nottinghamshire, NG24 2EG Tel: (01636) 704494 Fax: (01636) 704495 E-mail: rhi.uk@rhi-ag.com

Resco Products UK Ltd, Newbold Works, Worthington Lane, Newbold Coleorton, Coalville, Leicestershire, LE67 8PJ Tel: (01530) 222694 Fax: (01530) 223086 E-mail: rescoukltd@aol.com

REFRIGERANT HANDLING EQUIPMENT

Polar Pumps Ltd, Brunel Industrial Estate, Harworth, Doncaster, South Yorkshire, DN11 8QA Tel: (01302) 751253 Fax: (01302) 751254

Rda, Unit 1 Plot 7 River Way Industrial Estate, Newport, Isle of Wight, PO30 5UX Tel: (01983) 821189 Fax: (01983) 821149 E-mail: sales@rda-eng.com

REFRIGERANT RECLAIM/ RECOVERY EQUIPMENT

Javac UK Ltd, 6 Drake Court, Middlesbrough, Cleveland, TS2 1RS Tel: (01642) 232880 Fax: (01642) 232870E-mail: info@javac.co.uk

REFRIGERANT RECLAIM/ RECOVERY SERVICES

A C Environmental Refrigeration Ltd, Evergreen Venture Park, Barton Road, Wisbech, Cambridgeshire, PE13 4TP Tel: (01945) 419081 Fax: (01945) 419082

A & R Refrigeration & Fabrication, 102 Soho Street, Liverpool, L3 8AS Tel: 0151-207 0344 Fax: 0151-207 0344

Dyson Group plc, 381 Fulwood Road, Sheffield, S10 3GB Tel: 0114-230 3921 Fax: 0114-230 8583

Harp International Ltd, Gelli-Hirion Industrial Estate, Pontypridd, Mid Glamorgan, CF37 5SX Tel: (01443) 842255 Fax: (01443) 841805 E-mail: sales@harpintl.com

REFRIGERANT VALVES

Environmental Process Systems Ltd, 32 Mere View Industrial Estate, Yaxley, Peterborough, PE7 3HS Tel: (01733) 243400 Fax: (01733) 243344 E-mail: sales@epsltd.co.uk

REFRIGERANTS

Climate Centre, Unit 428, Oak Shop Place, Walton Summit Centre, Bamberbridge, Preston, PR5 8AT Tel: (01772) 628608 Fax: (01772) 628599 E-mail: preston.gl@wolseley.co.uk

Climate Services, Unit 1 Bold Street, Sheffield, S9 2LQ Tel: 0114-261 0111 Fax: 0114-261 8949

Cold Temp Refrigeration Service, Vicarage Lane, Skirlaugh, Hull, HU11 5HE Tel: (01964) 562773 Fax: (01964) 563350 E-mail: sales@coldtemp.co.uk

Driffield Refrigeration, Acorns, Ruston Parva, Driffield, North Humberside, YO25 4DG Tel: (01377) 254527 Fax: (01377) 254527

Environmental Process Systems Ltd, 32 Mere View Industrial Estate, Yaxley, Peterborough, PE7 3HS Tel: (01733) 243400 Fax: (01733) 243344 E-mail: sales@epsltd.co.uk

H R Refridgeration Ltd, 43 Morpeth Road, London, E9 7LD Tel: (020) 8525 1151 Fax: (020) 8525 1420

Isceon Distribution Services, P O Box 46, Bristol, BS11 9YF Tel: 0117-948 4170 Fax: 0117-948 4254 E-mail: andy.cook@eu.rhodia.com

Lec Refrigeration, Unit Dundonald Enterprise Park, Carrowreagh Road, Dundonald, Belfast, BT16 1QT Tel: (028) 9041 9400 Fax: (028) 9041 9229

Michael John Edwin Vernon, The Park, Edstaston, Wem, Shrewsbury, SY4 5RF Tel: (01939) 232070 Fax: (01939) 234897

Rabtherm International Ltd, Unit 11, Empire Close, Aldridge, Walsall, WS9 8XZ Tel: (01922) 743273 Fax: (01922) 743119 E-mail: bgas@rabtherm.co.uk

Refrigerated Storage Systems Ltd, Avon Valley Busines Park, Pixash Lane, Keynsham, Bristol, BS31 1TS Tel: 0117-986 9333 Fax: 0117-986 8978 E-mail: enquiries@refrigerationdesign.co.uk

Thornbury Refrigeration Co., 34 Mill Lane, Witham, Essex, CM8 1BP Tel: (01376) 520391 Fax: (01376) 515095

REFRIGERATED DISPLAY CABINETS OR CASES

Autonumis Ltd, Cirencester Road, Tetbury, Gloucestershire, GL8 8SA Tel: (01666) 502641 Fax: (01666) 505100 E-mail: info@autonumis.co.uk

Bailey & Smith Ltd, Hammerstone Road, Gorton, Manchester, M18 8EF Tel: 0161-223 5000 Fax: 0161-223 2989 E-mail: info@baileysmith.co.uk

▶ Carter Retail Equipment, 90 Lea Ford Road, Birmingham, B33 9TX Tel: 0121-250 1111 Fax: 0121-250 1122E-mail: info@cre-ltd.co.uk

Challenge Maintenance, 3 Daniels Way, Hucknall, Nottingham, NG15 7LL Tel: (0870) 9502221 Fax: (0870) 9503222 E-mail: sales@challengemaintenance.com

Enodis (UK) Food Service Ltd, Unit 5E, Langley Business Centre, Station Road, Langley, Slough, SL3 8DS Tel: (01753) 485900 E-mail: enodis.uk.sales@enodis.com

Gram (UK) Ltd, 2 The Technology Centre, London Road, Swanley, Kent, BR8 7AG Tel: (01322) 616900 Fax: (01322) 616901 E-mail: info@gramuk.co.uk

Hussmann Refrigeration Ltd, Clydeway Skypark, 8 Elliot Place, Glasgow, G3 8EP Tel: 0141-285 8500 Fax: 0141-227 2734

Linde Refrigeration & Retail Systems Ltd, Meridian House, Peter's Way, Oxford, OX4 6HQ Tel: (01865) 337700 Fax: (01865) 337799

The Nuttall Group Ltd, Orchard House, Dodwells Road, Hinckley, Leicestershire, LE10 3BZ Tel: (01455) 638300 Fax: (01455) 638302 E-mail: fsc@nuttalls.co.uk

▶ Phoenix Retail Service Ltd, Fryers Farm Office, Fryers Farm Lane, Lane End, High Wycombe, Buckinghamshire, HP14 3NP Tel: (01494) 880200 Fax: (01494) 881204 E-mail: sales@phoenixretail.com

REFRIGERATED ROOMS, *See Cold Rooms, Freezer Rooms etc*

REFRIGERATED TRAILER ROAD TRANSPORT AND HAULAGE

Alfreton Transport, Wimsey Way, Somercotes, Alfreton, Derbyshire, DE55 4LS Tel: (01773) 604347 Fax: (01773) 603834

▶ C & D Transport Ltd, 9 New Line Industrial Estate, The Sidings, Bacup, Lancashire, OL13 9RW Tel: (01706) 870333

▶ MMK Solutions, 8 De Mandeville Road, Elsenham, Bishop's Stortford, Hertfordshire, CM22 6LR Tel: (01279) 816230 Fax: (01279) 816030 E-mail: sales@mmksolutions.co.uk

REFRIGERATED TRAILERS

David Payne & Son Coachbuilders Ltd, Beddow Way, Aylesford, Kent, ME20 7BT Tel: (01622) 718645 Fax: (01622) 716365

Eldapoint Ltd, Sub-Station Road, Felixstowe, Suffolk, IP11 3JB Tel: (01394) 613110 Fax: (01394) 613218 E-mail: sales@eldapoint.co.uk

Gray & Adams (Ireland) Ltd, Houstons Corner, Ballyearl, Newtownabbey, County Antrim, BT36 4TP Tel: (028) 9034 2160 Fax: (028) 9084 8933 E-mail: b.dougan@grayadamsireland.com

REFRIGERATED TRANSPORT

A J Lockwood, Lynn Road, West Winch, King's Lynn, Norfolk, PE33 0PD Tel: (01553) 842188 Fax: (01553) 842170

Andrew Johnson Knudtzon, Boulevard, Hull, HU3 4DY Tel: (01482) 326873 Fax: (01482) 327934 E-mail: info@ajkltd.co.uk

Associated Cold Stores & Transport Ltd, South Humberside Industrial Estate, Grimsby, South Humberside, DN31 2WR Tel: (01472) 240269 Fax: (01472) 240269 E-mail: acoldnsn@acst.co.uk

B T Refrigeration, 20 Nelson Street, Bradford, West Yorkshire, BD5 0HD Tel: (01274) 727777 Fax: (01274) 739797 E-mail: btrefrigeration@btconnect.com

George Barker (Transport) Ltd, Gallions Close, Thames Road, Barking, Essex, IG11 0JD Tel: (020) 8594 7911 Fax: (020) 8591 8828

Bruce's Shellfish, 9 Balconie Street, Evanton, Dingwall, Ross-Shire, IV16 9UN Tel: (01349) 830187 Fax: (01349) 830187

Celsius First Ltd, Scania House, Annwell St, Hoddesdon, Hertfordshire, EN11 8TT Tel: 01992 449600 Fax: (01992) 467148 E-mail: information@celsiusfirst.com

Cold Chain Instruments Ltd, 1 Martlets Way, Goring-by-Sea, Worthing, West Sussex, BN12 4HF Tel: (01903) 249000 Fax: (01903) 248740 E-mail: sales@transcan.co.uk

Cold Start Ltd, Little Tennis St South, Nottingham, NG2 4EU Tel: 0115-950 5095 Fax: 0115-950 5096 E-mail: sue@coldstart.freeserve.co.uk

Cool Running Rental, Blueberry Business Park, Wallhead Road, Off Kingsway, Rochdale, Lancashire, OL16 5AF Tel: (01706) 640055 Fax: (01706) 640067 E-mail: richard@rentruck.co.uk

Cooperative Retail Logistics Ltd, Unit 24, Raleigh Hall Industrial Estate, Eccleshall, Stafford, ST21 6JL Tel: (01785) 850831 Fax: (01785) 851850

Country Kitchen, 84 Northern Rd, Portsmouth, PO6 3ER Tel: 023 92321148

▶ Courier Express, Unit 4, Blowick Business Park, Crowland Street, Southport, Merseyside, PR9 7RU Tel: (0870) 4644422 Fax: 0161-799 5940 E-mail: enquiries@refigeratedtransportuk.com

David Payne & Son Coachbuilders Ltd, Beddow Way, Aylesford, Kent, ME20 7BT Tel: (01622) 718645 Fax: (01622) 716365

Eldapoint Ltd, Sub-Station Road, Felixstowe, Suffolk, IP11 3JB Tel: (01394) 613110 Fax: (01394) 613218 E-mail: sales@eldapoint.co.uk

Eskimo Express, Unit 8, Penton Hook Marina, Staines Road, Chertsey, Surrey, KT16 8PQ Tel: (01932) 560222 Fax: (01932) 569723 E-mail: sales@eskimoexpress.co.uk

Herbert Fletcher Transport Ltd, M62 Trading Estate, Rawcliffe Road, Goole, North Humberside, DN14 8JW Tel: (01405) 769968 Fax: (01405) 762513 E-mail: enquiries@herbertfletcher.co.uk

Fransen Transport Ltd, 6 Lisle Avenue, Foley Park, Kidderminster, Worcestershire, DY11 7DE Tel: (01562) 820261 Fax: (01562) 754977 E-mail: info@fransentransport.fsnet.co.uk

Gist, Wardentree Lane, Pinchbeck, Spalding, Lincolnshire, PE11 3UG Tel: (01775) 764000 Fax: (01775) 764101

Iqbal Bros & Co., IBCO Ltd, Lord North Street, Hulme Hall Lane, Miles Platting, Manchester, M4 8AD Tel: 0161-230 7280 Fax: 0161-202 8201

Jim Brackenridge Transport Ltd, Unit 1 Dalcross Industrial Estate, Inverness, IV2 7XB Tel: (01667) 462999 Fax: (01667) 462788 E-mail: robert@jbt.co.uk

Michael Ward Refrigerated Transport, 5 Rookes Enterprise Park, Little Catterton Lane, Islington, Tadcaster, North Yorkshire, LS24 8EA Tel: (01937) 834808 Fax: (01937) 835025 E-mail: service@michealward.co.uk

▶ MMK Solutions, 8 De Mandeville Road, Elsenham, Bishop's Stortford, Hertfordshire, CM22 6LR Tel: (01279) 816230 Fax: (01279) 816030 E-mail: sales@mmksolutions.co.uk

Norfolk Line, Transit 3, Westbank Road, Belfast, BT3 9JL Tel: (028) 9077 1122 Fax: (028) 9077 2645 E-mail: belfast@norfolkline.com

Norfolk Line Ltd, The Dock, Felixstowe, Suffolk, IP11 3UY Tel: (01394) 603614 Fax: (01394) 603608 E-mail: felixstowe@norfolkline.com

Potato Man Ltd, Mellor Street, Rochdale, Lancashire, OL11 1PF Tel: (01706) 644384 Fax: (01706) 639926 E-mail: enquiries@ronchalker.co.uk

Road Cool Refrigeration Ltd, Unit 17-18 Sandybridge Lane Industrial Estate, Shafton, Barnsley, South Yorkshire, S72 8PH Tel: (01226) 781999 Fax: (01226) 781888 E-mail: sales@roadcoolrefrigeration.co.uk

Ship To Shore, Carnaby Industrial Estate, Lancaster Road, Carnaby, Bridlington, North Humberside, YO15 3QY Tel: (01262) 605896 Fax: (01262) 605896 E-mail: craig.davies8@btopenworld.com

Springs Smoked Salmon, Edburton Road, Edburton, Henfield, West Sussex, BN5 9LN Tel: (01273) 857338 Fax: (01273) 857228

T D G UK Storage, Stock Office, Portland Road, Retford, Nottinghamshire, DN22 7NR Tel: (01777) 702616 Fax: (01777) 860521 E-mail: wayt@tdg.co.uk

Turners Soham Ltd, Fordham Road, Newmarket, Suffolk, CB8 7NR Tel: (01638) 720335 Fax: (01638) 720940 E-mail: carol.chapman@turners-distribution.com

George Walker & Sons F R Ltd, Station Road, Mallaig, Inverness-Shire, PH41 4PY Tel: (01687) 462305 Fax: (01687) 462178

REFRIGERATED TRANSPORT UNITS

Cronos Containers Ltd, The Ice House, Dean Street, Marlow, Buckinghamshire, SL7 3AB Tel: (01628) 405580 Fax: (01628) 405650 E-mail: bjp@cronos.com

R V L (Northern) Ltd, Victoria Works, Raglan Street, Bradford, West Yorkshire, BD3 8NL Tel: (01274) 668223 Fax: (01274) 668021

Refrigerated Transport Information Society, 140 Newmarket Road, Cambridge, CB5 8HE Tel: (01223) 461352 Fax: (01223) 461522 E-mail: crt@crtech.demon.co.uk

▶ Refrigeration Support Ltd, Burtonhead Road, St. Helens, Merseyside, WA9 5DS Tel: (01744) 736002 Fax: (01744) 736164

Southern Sales & Services Ltd, Sterling House, Mayflower Close, Chandler's Ford, Eastleigh, Hampshire, SO53 4AR Tel: (023) 8026 1188 Fax: (023) 8025 4054 E-mail: jules@southernsales.co.uk

REFRIGERATED VEHICLE/ TRAILER HIRE

Cool Running Rental, Blueberry Business Park, Wallhead Road, Off Kingsway, Rochdale, Lancashire, OL16 5AF Tel: (01706) 640055 Fax: (01706) 640067 E-mail: richard@rentruck.co.uk

Cool-Move, Nautilus Works, 2 Goldcroft, Yeovil, Somerset, BA21 4DQ Tel: (01935) 700777 Fax: (01935) 700723 E-mail: sales@cool-move.com

▶ Glenthorpe Contracts Ltd, Flat 2, 49 West Cliff Road, Bournemouth, BH4 8BA Tel: (01202) 767926 Fax: (01202) 767948 E-mail: glenthorpecontracts@f2s.com

Mobile Freezer Rentals Ltd, Greensbury Farm, Thurleigh Road, Bolnhurst, Bedford, MK44 2ET Tel: (01234) 376999 Fax: (01234) 376060 E-mail: julie@mfrltd.co.uk

REFRIGERATED VEHICLES

Batley Body Builders Ltd, Thomas St, Bradford Road, Batley, West Yorkshire, WF17 8PR Tel: (01924) 473602 Fax: (01924) 471161

Carrier Transicold UK Ltd, 260 Cygnet Court, Centre Park, Warrington, WA1 1RR Tel: (01925) 401200 Fax: (01925) 401222

Cool Running Rental, Blueberry Business Park, Wallhead Road, Off Kingsway, Rochdale, Lancashire, OL16 5AF Tel: (01706) 640055 Fax: (01706) 640067 E-mail: richard@rentruck.co.uk

▶ Glenthorpe Contracts Ltd, Flat 2, 49 West Cliff Road, Bournemouth, BH4 8BA Tel: (01202) 767926 Fax: (01202) 767948 E-mail: glenthorpecontracts@f2s.com

Jiffy Trucks Ltd, Unit 26 Jubilee Way, Shipley, West Yorkshire, BD18 1QG Tel: (01274) 596000 Fax: (01274) 596444 E-mail: jiffy@jiffytrucks.co.uk

Paneltex Ltd, Kingston International Park, Somerden Road, Hull, HU9 5PE Tel: (01482) 787236 Fax: (01482) 787238 E-mail: sales@paneltex.co.uk

Solomon Holdings Ltd, Knowlsey Road Industrial Estate, Haslingden, Rossendale, Lancashire, BB4 4RX Tel: (01706) 211211 Fax: (01706) 831518 E-mail: sales@solocom.co.uk

Vehicle Build, 4 George Baylis Road, Berry Hill Industrial Estate, Droitwich, Worcestershire, WR9 9RB Tel: (01905) 826083 Fax: (01905) 826093

REFRIGERATING COMPRESSOR MAINTENANCE OR RECONDITIONING OR REMANUFACTURE OR REPAIR

Aces Ltd, Unit 10 Manor Farm, Peppard Common, Henley-on-Thames, Oxfordshire, RG9 5LA Tel: (01491) 629671 Fax: (01491) 629621 E-mail: sales@acescomp.co.uk

Preston Refrigeration Ltd, Units 3-4 Chantry Industrial Estate, Kingsbury Road, Curdworth, Sutton Coldfield, West Midlands, B76 9EE Tel: (01675) 470899 Fax: (01675) 470838

REFRIGERATION COMPONENTS

Gray & Adams Ltd, Lyneburn Industrial Estate, Halbeath Place, Dunfermline, Fife, KY11 4JT Tel: (01383) 731707 Fax: (01383) 730519

Gray & Adams Doncaster Ltd, Pipering Lane, Doncaster, South Yorkshire, DN5 9EL Tel: (01302) 787755 Fax: (01302) 783675 E-mail: sales@gray-adams-donc.co.uk

Henry Technologies Ltd, Mossland Road, Hillington Industrial Estate, Glasgow, G52 4XZ Tel: 0141-882 4621 Fax: 0141-882 4624 E-mail: sales@henrytech.co.uk

▶ I M A Cooling Systems, Hamburg Way, North Lynn Industrial Estate, King's Lynn, Norfolk, PE30 2ND Tel: (01553) 767446 Fax: (01553) 767457

Refrigeration Spares Ltd, 31 Harrow Road, London, E11 3PT Tel: (020) 8555 1321 Fax: (020) 8519 8219

Technical Transport Equipment Ltd, 87 Styal Road, Gatley, Cheadle, Cheshire, SK8 4JQ Tel: 0161-491 3150 Fax: 0161-491 3150

REFRIGERATION COMPRESSORS

Aces Ltd, Unit 10 Manor Farm, Peppard Common, Henley-on-Thames, Oxfordshire, RG9 5LA Tel: (01491) 629671 Fax: (01491) 629621 E-mail: sales@acescomp.co.uk

Linde Refrigeration & Retail Systems Ltd, Meridian House, Peter's Way, Oxford, OX4 6HQ Tel: (01865) 337700 Fax: (01865) 337799

Thermacom Ltd, Green Lane, Burghfield Bridge, Reading, RG30 3XN Tel: 0118-950 0606 Fax: 0118-956 0039 E-mail: sales@thermagroup.com

REFRIGERATION CONSULTANCY OR DESIGN

Air Conditioning & Refrigeration Industry Board, Kelvin House, 76 Mill Lane, Carshalton, Surrey, SM5 2JR Tel: (020) 8647 7033 Fax: (020) 8773 0165 E-mail: ior@ior.org.uk

Bry-Kol Group of Companies, 10 Newcastle Street, Burslem, Stoke-On-Trent, ST6 3QF Tel: (01782) 577991 Fax: (01782) 577511 E-mail: info@bry-Kol.co.uk

Daventry Refrigeration, 4 Cross Lane, Braunston, Daventry, Northamptonshire, NN11 7HH Tel: (01788) 890469 Fax: (01788) 891453

▶ Electro-Freeze Ltd, Summerhill Quarry, Douglas, Isle of Man, IM2 4PF Tel: (01624) 673921 Fax: (01624) 662312 E-mail: sales@electrofreeze.4mg.com

Frimatec UK Ltd, 5 Townsend Centre Blackburn Road, Townsend Industrial Estate, Houghton Regis, Dunstable, Bedfordshire, LU5 5BQ Tel: (01582) 471600 Fax: (01582) 472050 E-mail: frimatec@nildram.co.uk

Ice Refrigeration Ltd, Spring Court House, High Street, Stapleford, Nottingham, NG9 8AG Tel: 0114-230 6555 Fax: 0115-949 9275 E-mail: john@agrice.co.uk

▶ KDH Construction, KDH House, Millfield Road, Donington, Spalding, Lincolnshire, PE11 4UR Tel: 01775 822888 Fax: 01775 822891 E-mail: sales@kdhconstruction.co.uk

McAlpine Grant Ilco, Osney Mead Industrial Estate, Oxford, OX2 0ER Tel: (01865) 251225 Fax: (01865) 791877 E-mail: info@mglitd.co.uk

Shivers Installation Ltd, 2 The Old School House, Southdown Road, Seaford, East Sussex, BN25 4JS Tel: (01323) 899888 Fax: (01323) 896810

Syncro Ltd, 6th Floor Furness House, Furness Quay, Salford, M50 3XZ Tel: 0161-786 4400 Fax: 0161-877 5233

Tameside Refrigeration & Air Conditioning Ltd, 2 Gate Centre Bredbury Park Way, Bredbury Park Industrial Estate, Bredbury, Stockport, Cheshire, SK6 2SN Tel: 0161-406 8995 Fax: 0161-406 8997

REFRIGERATION CONTROL/ MONITOR SYSTEMS MANUFRS

Ace, Farleigh Cottage, Ricketts Hill Road, Tatsfield, Westerham, Kent, TN16 2NA Tel: (01959) 577139 Fax: (01959) 577283 E-mail: aceukaircon@btinternet.com

Fridge Controls Ltd, 4-5 Plantagaenet Estate, Kineton, Warwick, CV35 0HU Tel: (01926) 640171 Fax: (01926) 641707 E-mail: sales@fridgecontrols.co.uk

J T L Systems Ltd, Unit 41, Kingfisher Court, Hambridge Road, Newbury, Berkshire, RG14 5SJ Tel: (01635) 263646 Fax: (01635) 263647 E-mail: sales@jtl.co.uk

Key Controls Ltd, Unit 6 Spring Street, Keighley, West Yorkshire, BD21 3LE Tel: (01535) 604133 Fax: (01535) 604341

Mitchell & Hewitt Ltd, Ascot Drive, Derby, DE24 8GZ Tel: (01332) 332177 Fax: (01332) 374769 E-mail: admin@mitchellandhewitt.co.uk

Sandycott Pump Mnfrs, Manor House, Church Street, Eckington, Sheffield, S21 4BH Tel: (01246) 436632 Fax: (01246) 433372 E-mail: sales@hydron-pumps.com

REFRIGERATION DESIGN OR INSTALLATION OR COMMISSIONING OR SERVICING

3CL, Stafford Park 16, Telford, Shropshire, TF3 3BS Tel: (01952) 290941 Fax: (01952) 290943 E-mail: info@3cl.com

A C Environmental Refrigeration Ltd, Evergreen Venture Park, Barton Road, Wisbech, Cambridgeshire, PE13 4TP Tel: (01945) 419081 Fax: (01945) 419082

A E R Cooling Ltd, 21 Woburn St, Ampthill, Bedford, MK45 2HP Tel: (01525) 403221 Fax: (01525) 406060

A F Goose Services Ltd, 41 Southwold Drive, Nottingham, NG8 1PA Tel: 0115-928 2999 Fax: 0115-928 8831

Aairecool Technical Services Ltd, 3 Eastfield Farm Road, Penicuik, Midlothian, EH26 8EZ Tel: (01968) 679365 Fax: (01968) 679316 E-mail: aairecool@btconnect.com

Acme Refrigeration Ltd, Cunliffe Road, Whitebirk Industrial Estate, Blackburn, BB1 5ST Tel: (01254) 277999 Fax: (01254) 277988 E-mail: email@acmerefrigeration.co.uk

Acrokool Ltd, 1 Veerman Park, Thaxted Road, Saffron Walden, Essex, CB10 2UP Tel: (01799) 513631 Fax: (01799) 513635 E-mail: sales@acrokool.co.uk

Acrol Air Conditioning Services Ltd, Unit 49b, Leechmare East Industrial Estate, Sunderland, SR2 9TE Tel: 0191-523 6441 Fax: 0191-523 6425 E-mail: mail@aacs.demon.co.uk

Action Refrigeration, 18-22 North Street, Jarrow, Tyne & Wear, NE32 3PG Tel: 0191-483 3579 Fax: 0191-428 5615

Adcock Refrigeration & Air Conditioning Ltd, 5 Industrial Estate, London Road, Pampisford, Cambridge, CB22 3XX Tel: (01223) 834189 Fax: (01223) 837116 E-mail: enquiries@adcock.co.uk

Adcock Refrigeration & Air Conditioning Ltd, 152 London Road, Copford, Colchester, CO6 1BQ Tel: (01206) 212502 Fax: (01206) 212080 E-mail: mail20@adcock.co.uk

▶ Adcock Refrigeration & Air Conditioning Ltd, Unit E5 Premier Business Centre, Speedfields Park, Fareham, Hampshire, PO14 1TY Tel: (01329) 235800 Fax: (01329) 233216

Advance Cryo Refrigeration Services, 37 St Catherines Avenue, Luton, LU3 1QG Tel: (01582) 416036 Fax: (01582) 454782 E-mail: ade@advanecryo1945.fsnet.co.uk

Air Conditioning Refrigeration and Environmental, 56 Moathouse Lane East, Wednesfield, Wolverhampton, WV11 3DD Tel: (01902) 733503 Fax: (01902) 307899

Aircon Refrigeration Ltd, 35e Dukesway, Teesside Industrial Estate, Stockton-on-Tees, Cleveland, TS17 9LT Tel: (01642) 760565 Fax: (01642) 764011 E-mail: aircon.refrigeration@btinternet.com

Airedale Cooling Services Ltd, Airedale Building, East Parade, Keighley, West Yorkshire, BD21 5HZ Tel: (01535) 602202 Fax: (01535) 610772 E-mail: info@airedalecooling.com

Airkool Projects Ltd, 10 Rotterdam Road, Hull, HU7 0XD Tel: (01482) 371888 Fax: (01482) 371889 E-mail: info@airkool.co.uk

Albany Appliances, 16 Albany Road, Cardiff, CF24 3RP Tel: (029) 2048 3168

▶ Albion Electrical & Mechanical Engineering, 15, Parkfield Avenue, Warrington, WA4 1NY Tel: (01925) 636010 Fax: (01925) 575777 E-mail: albioneng@btconnect.com

Alpha Refrigeration, 25 Langdale Road, Blackburn, BB2 5DP Tel: (01254) 209577 Fax: (01254) 209577

Ambient Control Ltd, Unit 3b Glevum Works, Upton Street, Gloucester, GL1 4LA Tel: (01452) 303311 Fax: (01452) 330682 E-mail: info@ambientcontrol.co.uk

Anderson Refrigeration, 30 Gartclush Gardens, Bannockburn, Stirling, FK7 8QA Tel: (01786) 817677 Fax: (01786) 817677 E-mail: enquiries@andersonrefrigeration.co.uk

Ankold Refrigeration Equipment, The Old Shippon, Lily Lane, Byley, Middlewich, Cheshire, CW10 9NH Tel: (01606) 836312 Fax: (01606) 836883

Arctic Refrigeration Ltd, 36 Bath Street, Bolton, BL1 2DJ Tel: (01204) 524655 Fax: (01204) 526557

Argus Refrigeration Ltd, 21 King Street, Port Glasgow, Renfrewshire, PA14 5JA Tel: (01475) 741053 Fax: (01475) 741038 E-mail: smithargus@yahoo.co.uk

Arrow Refrigeration & Air Conditioning, 54 Chesterton Close, Redditch, Worcestershire, B97 5XS Tel: (01527) 541420 Fax: (01527) 543843 E-mail: arrowcooling@tiscali.com

Artic Air Refrigeration & Air Conditioning, 14 Bell Mead, Studley, Warwickshire, B80 7SH Tel: (01527) 857578 Fax: (01527) 857578

Ashton Refrigeration Co., 106 Minto Street, Ashton-under-Lyne, Lancashire, OL7 9DA Tel: 0161-343 1446 Fax: 0161-339 0152 E-mail: ashtonrefrigeration@tiscali.co.uk

Asquith & Co Refrigeration Ltd, Searches Lane, Bedmond, Abbots Langley, Hertfordshire, WD5 0SB Tel: (01727) 852488 Fax: (01727) 859226 E-mail: info@asquiths.co.uk

Atlantic Ltd, K Chadwell Heath Industrial Park, Kemp Road, Dagenham, Essex, RM8 1SL Tel: (020) 8599 0600 Fax: (0870) 7774412 E-mail: atlantic@eidosnet.co.uk

Automatic Cooling Engineers Ltd, 96 Milnbank Street, Glasgow, G31 3AL Tel: 0141-556 7691 Fax: 0141-554 2928

B B Mathias Ltd, 102 St Davids Road, Letterston, Haverfordwest, Dyfed, SA62 5SJ Tel: (01348) 840318 Fax: (01348) 840900

B G Slattery & Son, Unit 3 Martlets Way, Goring-by-Sea, Worthing, West Sussex, BN12 4HF Tel: (01903) 506128

B L D Refrigeration, 104 Castle Lea, Caldicot, Gwent, NP26 4PL Tel: (01291) 420854 Fax: (01291) 420894 E-mail: bldref@btconnect.com

B&D, Church Lane, Tydd St. Giles, Wisbech, Cambridgeshire, PE13 5LG Tel: (01945) 870204 Fax: (01945) 870820

Barber Refrigeration, Hazelwood Row, Cwmavon, Port Talbot, West Glamorgan, SA12 9DP Tel: (01639) 871675 Fax: (01639) 871675 E-mail: barber.refridge@btconnect.com

Bartlett Refrigeration Ltd, Marsh Green Road West, Marsh Barton Trading Estate, Exeter, EX2 8PT Tel: (01392) 203000 Fax: (01392) 203001 E-mail: sales@bartlett.uk.com

Beaven & Sons Ltd, 183 Westgate Street, Gloucester, GL1 2RN Tel: (01452) 314384 Fax: (01452) 300195

Benson Refrigeration Ltd, Kings Cottage, Starlings Green, Clavering, Saffron Walden, Essex, CB11 4PP Tel: (01279) 777963 Fax: (01279) 777869

Birdsall Services Ltd, 6 Frogmore Road, Apsley, Hemel Hempstead, Hertfordshire, HP3 9RW Tel: (01442) 212501 Fax: (01442) 248989 E-mail: lynne.culliton@birdsall.co.uk

Bradley Refrigeration Ltd, 929 Abbeydale Road, Sheffield, S7 2QD Tel: 0114-236 9971 Fax: 0114-236 8681 E-mail: ecroft@bradley-refrigeration.com

Braywhite & Co. Ltd, Halligan Buildings, Johnstone Street, Birmingham, B19 1SZ Tel: 0121-551 6001 Fax: 0121-511 7120 E-mail: info@braywhite.co.uk

Brifrost Engineering, 9 The Drive, Wheathampstead, St. Albans, Hertfordshire, AL4 8LE Tel: (01438) 832402 Fax: (01438) 833526

Bristolfridge Air Conditioning, 343 Southmead Road, Westbury-on-Trym, Bristol, BS10 5LW Tel: 0117-950 6800 Fax: 0117-950 0483 E-mail: bristolfridge@tiscali.co.uk

C & M Environmental Ltd, 52 Strathmore Road, Glasgow, G22 7DW Tel: 0141-336 7774 Fax: 0141-336 5559 E-mail: enfor@cmenvironmental.co.uk

Harry Carr Ltd, Armstrong Street, Grimsby, North East Lincolnshire, DN31 1LG Tel: (01472) 246600 Fax: (01472) 240466 E-mail: engineers@harrycarr.co.uk

Carter Refrigeration, 111-115 Marsh Lane, Bootle, Merseyside, L20 4JD Tel: 0151-922 2342 Fax: 0151-922 4004 E-mail: liverpool.contracts@crrs.co.uk

▶ Cemac Building Services, 514, Filton Avenue, Horfield, Bristol, BS7 0QE Tel: 0117-979 3053

Centigrade Ltd, 9 Beverley Road, Tilehurst, Reading, RG31 5PT Tel: 0118-942 4939 Fax: 0118-942 4939

Centigrade Refrigeration Ltd, Unit 17 South Quay Industrial Estate, Douglas, Isle of Man, IM1 5AT Tel: (01624) 622114 Fax: (01624) 624450

Cevac & Co., 4 Marechal Niel Parade, Main Road, Sidcup, Kent, DA14 6QF Tel: (020) 8308 0808 Fax: (020) 8308 0181

Challenge Maintenance, 3 Daniels Way, Hucknall, Nottingham, NG15 7LL Tel: (0870) 9502221 Fax: (0870) 9503222 E-mail: sales@challengemaintenance.com

Cheshire Refrigeration Ltd, Unit E6, Ford Street, Chestergate, Stockport, Cheshire, SK3 0BT Tel: 0161-480 4084 Fax: 0161-480 7355 E-mail: cheshire.refrig@cwcom.net

Chill Factor, 71 Ellenborough Cl, Bishop's Stortford, Herts, CM23 4HT Tel: (01279) 506543 Fax: (01279) 506543

City Air Conditioning Ltd, 6 Palace Industrial Estate, Bircholt Road, Maidstone, Kent, ME15 9XU Tel: (01622) 692338 Fax: (01622) 672377 E-mail: cityair@cityairltd.co.uk

City Technical Services UK Ltd, 38 Southcroft Road, Rutherglen, Glasgow, G73 1UG Tel: 0141-643 2248 Fax: 0141-613 4432

▶ Climate Cooling, East Malling Enterprise Centre, New Road, West Malling, Kent, ME19 6SJ Tel: (0783) 6385567 Fax: (01732) 874598

Clover Technical Services, 4 Valiant Way, Lairdside Technology Park, Birkenhead, Merseyside, CH41 9HS Tel: 0151-650 1551 Fax: 0151-650 1213 E-mail: sales@cloveruk.com

▶ Clwyd Refrigeration Ltd, Conwy Morfa Enterprise Park, Parc Caer Seion, Conwy, Gwynedd, LL32 8FA Tel: (01492) 572323 Fax: (01492) 582626 E-mail: sevice@clwydrefrigeration.com

Cold Service Ltd, Avonside House, Kingfisher Park, Blashford, Ringwood, Hampshire, BH24 3NX Tel: (01425) 485700 Fax: (01425) 485701 E-mail: enquiries@coldservice.co.uk

▶ Collin Burrows Air Conditioning Ltd, 9 Josselin Court, Josselin Road, Burnt Mills Industrial Estate, Basildon, Essex, SS13 1QF Tel: (01268) 590369 Fax: (01268) 590370

Commercial Cooling Equipment Ltd, 57-59 Cross Street, Nelson, Lancashire, BB9 7NQ Tel: (01282) 604003 Fax: (01282) 720829

Commercial & Domestic Refrigeration, 1 Stansty Drive, Wrexham, Clwyd, LL11 2DG Tel: (01978) 352563 Fax: (01978) 352563

Commercial Trade Services Group Ltd, Lea Park Trading Estate, Warley Close, London, E10 7LF Tel: (020) 8558 9988 Fax: (020) 8558 1155 E-mail: services@comtrad.co.uk

Connolly Refrigeration Ltd, 13 Howlett Way, Thetford, Norfolk, IP24 1HZ Tel: (01842) 766655 Fax: (01842) 763497 E-mail: sales@connollyrefrigeration.co.uk

Constant Cooling Services, 2 London Road Industrial Estate, London Road, Pampisford, Cambridge, CB2 4EE Tel: (01223) 834711 Fax: (01223) 837818 E-mail: constantcooling@hotmail.com

Cool Cair, 34 Benview, Bannockburn, Stirling, FK7 0HY Tel: (01786) 815335 Fax: (01786) 815335

Coolco Refrigeration Ltd, Unit 18 Green Lane Industrial Estate, Second Avenue, Small Heath, Birmingham, B9 5QP Tel: 0121-771 3373 Fax: 0121-771 3687 E-mail: coolcoltd@btconnect.com

▶ Co-Ordinated Services, 24, Ullswater Crescent, Coulsdon, Surrey, CR5 2HR Tel: (020) 8763 8874

Coutts Refrigeration, Blackhills, Peterhead, Aberdeenshire, AB42 3LJ Tel: (01779) 478074 Fax: (01779) 478074

Crystal Refrigeration, 4 Dolman Road, London, W4 5UY Tel: (020) 8994 9398 Fax: (020) 8994 1445

Cutts Refrigeration Ltd, Rowbrook Farm, Ryton, Dorrington, Shrewsbury, SY5 7NR Tel: (01743) 718871 Fax: (01743) 718040

D E Jenkins, Brynawelon, Llanddarog Road, Carmarthen, Dyfed, SA32 8AP Tel: (01267) 275381 Fax: (01267) 275443

Daw Refrigeration Equipment, Lake Barton, Newton St. Cyres, Exeter, EX5 5AU Tel: (01392) 851613 Fax: (01392) 851909 E-mail: info@dawref.com

Delta Environmental Ltd, Delta House Stanney Mill Industrial Park, Dutton Green, Little Stanney, Chester, CH2 4SA Tel: 0151-357 1121 Fax: 0151-357 2480 E-mail: sales@deltaenvironmental.net

Dobbin Refrigeration Services Ltd, 93 Creevy Road, Boardmills, Lisburn, County Antrim, BT27 6UL Tel: (028) 9263 8814 Fax: (028) 9263 9233

E F R Refrigeration, 695 High Road, Ilford, Essex, IG3 8RH Tel: (020) 8590 0022 Fax: (020) 8599 2870 E-mail: danney535@fsmail.net

E J M Engineered Systems Ltd, Unit 1 Thornley Station Industrial Estate, Shotton Colliery, Durham, DH6 2QA Tel: (01429) 836161 Fax: (01429) 838034 E-mail: sales@ejmrefrigeration.co.uk

Eastleigh Domestic Appliance Services, 53 Twyford Road, Eastleigh, Hampshire, SO50 4HH Tel: (023) 8064 4984 Fax: (023) 8061 2799 E-mail: sales@eastleigh-services.co.uk

Eastwood Air Conditioning Ltd, Eastwood House, Hubert Street, Aston, Birmingham, B6 4BA Tel: 0121-380 0555 Fax: 0121-359 8152 E-mail: sales@eastwoodgroup.co.uk

▶ Ecs Air Conditioning, 17 Station Road, London, SE20 7BE Tel: (020) 8778 9661 Fax: (020) 8778 9514

John Edwards Refrigeration, 4 Portland Grange, Hucknall, Nottingham, NG15 6RS Tel: 0115-963 5257

Electricold Refrigeration, 13 Hillbury Road, Whyteleafe, Surrey, CR3 0ER Tel: (020) 8660 4641 Fax: (020) 8668 2358

Electro Refrigeration Services, Unit 5, Ashfield Close, Whitehall Industrial Estate, Leeds, LS12 5JB Tel: 0113-279 7000 Fax: 0113-279 4100

Express Refrigeration, Stoneleigh, 12 High Street, Bugbrooke, Northampton, NN7 3QF Tel: (01604) 832788 Fax: (01604) 832788

Express Refrigeration Contractors Ltd, 2 Princess Street, Immingham, South Humberside, DN40 1LN Tel: (01469) 574561 Fax: (01469) 574628

F & T Refrigeration Ltd, D C Griffiths Way, Neath, West Glamorgan, SA11 1BT Tel: (01639) 634171 Fax: (01639) 644422 E-mail: tony@ftrefrigeration.co.uk

Forbes Refrigeration Ltd, Ythanview, Station Road, Ellon, Aberdeenshire, AB41 9AY Tel: (01358) 720853 Fax: (01358) 721898 E-mail: nncg@dialstart.net

Formost Air Conditioning Ltd, Unit 9 Wilford Lane Industrial Estate, Ruddington Lane, Wilford, Nottingham, NG11 7EP Tel: 0115-945 5033 Fax: 0115-974 5527 E-mail: smurphy@formost.co.uk

Fox Refrigeration Services Ltd, 369 London Road, Grays, Essex, RM20 4AA Tel: (01375) 392545 Fax: (01375) 382156

G B A Electrical Ltd, 3 Williams Way, West Row, Bury St. Edmunds, Suffolk, IP28 8QB Tel: (01638) 718289 Fax: (01638) 718289

G B R Refrigeration, 8 Crossmount Court, Carluke, Lanarkshire, ML8 5ST Tel: (01555) 759371 Fax: (01555) 759371 E-mail: gbr_refrigeration@msn.com

G B Refrigeration, 58-60 Brown Street West, Colne, Lancashire, BB8 9ND Tel: (01282) 862646 Fax: (01282) 867631

G.L.A.Refrigeration Services Ltd, No 1 Partridge Court, 61 Price Street, Birmingham, B4 6JZ Tel: 0121-359 6731 Fax: 0121-333 4213

G R P Leeds Ltd, Bagley Lane, Farsley, Pudsey, West Yorkshire, LS28 5LL Tel: 0113-255 4664 Fax: 0113-239 3215 E-mail: sales@grp-leeds.co.uk

Gibson Refrigeration, 88 Sullington Mead, Broadbridge Heath, Horsham, West Sussex, RH12 3NW Tel: (01403) 265328 Fax: (01403) 269642

REFRIGERATION DESIGN OR INSTALLATION OR COMMISSIONING OR SERVICING – *continued*

Global Refrigeration & Air Conditioning Co. Ltd, Unit 41, 3 Halifax Road, Metropolitan Centre, Greenford, Middlesex, UB6 8XU Tel: (020) 8575 7557 Fax: (020) 8566 6342 E-mail: enquiries@globalrefrigeration.co.uk

Gray & Adams Doncaster Ltd, Pipering Lane, Doncaster, South Yorkshire, DN5 9EL Tel: (01302) 787755 Fax: (01302) 783675 E-mail: sales@gray-adams-donc.co.uk

Grenco Reefer Services Ltd, Hauliers Road, Felixstowe, Suffolk, IP11 3SF Tel: (01394) 613116 Fax: (01394) 613133

H A Davie Ltd, Market Place Industrial Estate, Houghton le Spring, Tyne & Wear, DH5 8AN Tel: 0191-584 2652 Fax: 0191-584 2752 E-mail: mail@hadavie.co.uk

H G Compressors, Unit 3, 3 Tyersal Lane, Bradford, West Yorkshire, BD4 0RB Tel: (01274) 669733 Fax: (01274) 669797 E-mail: ahmad@hgcompressors.co.uk

H T W Thanet Refrigeration, Stanley Place, Ramsgate, Kent, CT11 7NT Tel: (01843) 592905 Fax: (01843) 850256

Hale Refrigeration, Unit 8 Paper Mill End Industrial Estate, Birmingham, B44 8NH Tel: 0121-344 3345 Fax: 0121-344 3346 E-mail: halerefrigeration@compuserve.com

▶ J. & E. Hall, Questor House, 191 Hawley Road, Dartford, DA1 1PU Tel: (01322) 394420 Fax: (01322) 394421 E-mail: helpline@jehall.co.uk

Hall Refrigeration Ltd, Unit 17 Palace Industrial Estate, Bircholt Road, Maidstone, Kent, ME15 9XU Tel: (01622) 663379 Fax: (01622) 663282 E-mail: hallrefrigeration@mistral.co.uk

Halton Refrigeration, 83 Lynton Crescent, Widnes, Cheshire, WA8 7NT Tel: 0151-424 5293 Fax: 0151-424 5293

J.L. Harrison & Son (Air Conditioning) Ltd, Unit 17, Olympic Business Centre, Paycocke Road, Basildon, Essex, SS14 3EX Tel: (01268) 532414 Fax: (01268) 532415 E-mail: info@chillerservices.co.uk

Hawkes Refrigeration Engineers, 2 Gibcracks, Basildon, Essex, SS14 1PE Tel: (01268) 556663 Fax: (01268) 584525 E-mail: sales@refrigeration-uk.com

Henson Refrigeration Service, 6 Olympus Square, London, E5 8PL Tel: (020) 8533 5322 Fax: (020) 7686 0851

Hesketh Refrigeration, 190 Preston Road, Standish, Wigan, Lancashire, WN6 0NP Tel: (01257) 423571 Fax: (01257) 423571

Colin Holmes Refrigeration Ltd, 79 Crossways, Romford, RM2 6AS Tel: (01708) 741143 Fax: (01708) 741143

Huntley Refrigeration & Air-Conditioning, 80 Broad Street, Coventry, CV6 5AZ Tel: (024) 7666 5252 Fax: (024) 7627 7102 E-mail: sales@huntleyrefrigeration.co.uk

Hussmann (Europe) Ltd, 4-5 Bonville Road, Brislington, Bristol, BS4 5NF Tel: 0117-971 2121 Fax: 0117-971 9098

Hutt Refrigeration, 11-13 Station Parade, Station Hill, Cookham, Maidenhead, Berkshire, SL6 9BR Tel: (01628) 530605 Fax: (01628) 530505

Hymas Refrigeration & Catering Ltd, 178 Grove Green Road, London, E11 4EL Tel: (020) 8539 4222 E-mail: hymas_ref@fsmail.net

I C Refrigeration & Air Conditioning, 12 Broad Meadow, Ipswich, IP8 3SP Tel: (01473) 680629 Fax: (01473) 680629

I C S Group, Gore Road Industrial Estate, New Milton, Hampshire, BH25 6SA Tel: (01425) 625900 Fax: (01425) 639041 E-mail: info@industrialcooling.co.uk

Ice Cold Refrigeration, The Laurels, Main Road, East Boldre, Brockenhurst, Hampshire, SO42 7WU Tel: (01590) 626253 Fax: (01590) 626225

Industrial Refrigeration Services Ltd, 2 West Court, Buntsford Park Road, Bromsgrove, Worcestershire, B60 3DX Tel: (01527) 577999 Fax: (01527) 578300 E-mail: refrigeration@irs.co.uk

Innovate Logistics, 1 Willow Drive, Annesley, Nottingham, NG15 0DP Tel: (01623) 727300

J & E Hall Ltd, 2 Fairbrother Street, Salford, M5 3EN Tel: 0161-872 7022 Fax: 0161-371 0555

J & E Hall Ltd, 3 28 Botley Road, Hedge End, Southampton, SO30 2HE Tel: (01489) 890200 Fax: (01489) 788292 E-mail: g.warn@jehall.co.uk

John Rudkin Refrigeration Ltd, 91, Catherine Street East, Horwich, Bolton, BL6 7JZ Tel: (01204) 697662 Fax: (01204) 669762

Johnson Controls, 14-16 St. Martins Avenue, Fieldhead Business Centre, Bradford, West Yorkshire, BD7 1LG Tel: (01274) 737070 Fax: (01274) 765301 E-mail: mike.metcalfe@jci.com

K M Services Ltd, 16 Bourne Industrial Estate, Wrotham Road, Borough Green, Sevenoaks, Kent, TN15 8DG Tel: (01732) 882280 Fax: (01732) 886011

Kroyair Ltd, 262 Moseley Road, Birmingham, B12 0BX Tel: 0121-440 5383 Fax: 0121-446 4236 E-mail: info@kroyair.fsnet.co.uk

Larchfield Services, 30 Spruce Road, Woodley, Reading, RG5 4BB Tel: 0118-944 1239 Fax: 0118-944 2495 E-mail: larchfield@ntlworld.com

Lightfoot Refrigeration Co. Ltd, Unit D2, Premier Business Centre, Newgate Lane, Fareham, Hampshire, PO14 1TY Tel: (01329) 237272 Fax: (01329) 237276 E-mail: office@lightfootrefrigeration.com

Lloyds Refrigeration & Air Conditioning Ltd, 1 Wylds Road, Bridgwater, Somerset, TA6 4LF Tel: (01278) 422074 Fax: (01278) 429369 E-mail: lloydssales@lloydsrac.co.uk

Low Temp Refrigeration, Unit 13 Robert Davies Court, Nuffield Road, Cambridge, CB4 1TP Tel: (01223) 426067 Fax: (01223) 426067

M J Pawsey Refrigeration, 129 Parkway, Dorking, Surrey, RH4 1ET Tel: (01306) 884121

McAlpine Grant Ilco, Osney Mead Industrial Estate, Oxford, OX2 0ER Tel: (01865) 251225 Fax: (01865) 791877 E-mail: info@mglitd.co.uk

Maco Refrigeration Ltd, 106 Havelock Street, Kettering, Northamptonshire, NN16 9QA Tel: (01536) 514105 Fax: (01536) 415645 E-mail: mail@maco-ltd.demon.co.uk

Major Refrigeration & Air Conditioning Services Ltd, 6 Broadway Road, Evesham, Worcestershire, WR11 1BH Tel: (01386) 49342 Fax: (01386) 45232 E-mail: info@majorcooling.co.uk

Mansfield Refrigeration & Air Conditioning Co. Ltd, Dallas Street, Mansfield, Nottinghamshire, NG18 5SZ Tel: (01623) 626168 Fax: (01623) 420915

Marshall Thermo King Ltd, Teversham House, Newmarket Road, Teversham, Cambridge, CB5 8AA Tel: (01223) 377800 Fax: (01223) 377819 E-mail: sales@marshall-thermoking.co.uk

Marshall Thermo King Ltd, Cemetery Road, Houghton Regis, Dunstable, Bedfordshire, LU5 5BZ Tel: (01582) 867847 Fax: (01582) 866648 E-mail: houghtonregis@marshallthermoking.co.uk

Maskold Ltd, Unit 70 Wimbledon Stadium Business Centre, Riverside Road, London, SW17 0BA Tel: (020) 8946 0483 Fax: (020) 8947 8782 E-mail: service@maskold.co.uk

Mastercool Southern Ltd, 7a Baker Street, Ampthill, Bedford, MK45 2QE Tel: (01525) 840689 Fax: (01525) 840699 E-mail: mastercool15@btopenworld.com

Met Anglia Ltd, Unit 2 Garrod Drive Industrial Estate, Fakenham, Norfolk, NR21 8NN Tel: (01328) 862026 Fax: (01328) 855961

Nene Refrigeration, 12 Rotton Row, Raunds, Wellingborough, Northamptonshire, NN9 6HU Tel: (01933) 623441 Fax: (01933) 623441

Newsome Holdings Ltd, Calderbank, Saddleworth Road, Elland, West Yorkshire, HX5 0RY Tel: (01422) 371711 Fax: (01422) 377372 E-mail: enquiries@newsome.ltd.uk

Noblet Refrigeration, Unit 10 Kenyons Farm, Gough Lane, Bamber Bridge, Preston, PR5 6AQ Tel: (01772) 628828 Fax: (01772) 628417 E-mail: nobletref@btconnect.com

Oxford Refrigeration & Air Conditioning Ltd, 78-81 Magdalen Road, Oxford, OX4 1RF Tel: (01865) 424424 Fax: (01865) 424425 E-mail: ian.law@oracoxford.co.uk

P W Adamson Ltd, Howe Moss Drive, Kirkhill Industrial Estate, Dyce, Aberdeen, AB21 0GL Tel: (01224) 724976 Fax: (01224) 724851 E-mail: support@pwadamson.co.uk

Peachman Refrigeration Ltd, 2 Jupiter Road, Norwich, NR6 6SU Tel: (01603) 789574 Fax: (01603) 789574 E-mail: mail@peachman.co.uk

Peak Refrigeration, Unit 3 Cedar Avenue, Talke, Stoke-on-Trent, ST7 1JZ Tel: (01782) 782829 Fax: (01782) 774244

Pennine Environmental Services Ltd, Sherwood House, Thornhill Drive, Calverley, Pudsey, West Yorkshire, LS28 5QW Tel: 0113-239 3999 Fax: 0113-256 9175 E-mail: pennine@pennine-env.co.uk

Pitkin & Ruddock Ltd, Unit 6 Moorpark Indust Estate, Bury St. Edmunds, Suffolk, IP32 7AJ Tel: (01284) 767579 Fax: (01284) 760784

▶ Polacap, Unit 4, Shaw Lane Industrial Estate, Shaw Lane, Stoke Prior, Bromsgrove, Worcestershire, B60 4DT Tel: (01527) 874410 Fax: (01527) 874411

Polarcold Refrigeration Ltd, 2 The Parade, Tattenham Way, Burgh Heath, Tadworth, Surrey, KT20 5NG Tel: 01737 373367 Fax: 01737 373387 E-mail: info@polarcold.co.uk

Polarcool Refrigeration Ltd, Unit K1 Beckingham Business Park, Tolleshunt Major, Maldon, Essex, CM9 8LZ Tel: (01621) 868584 Fax: (01621) 868989 E-mail: sales@polarcool.co.uk

▶ Prima Air Conditioning & Refrigeration Ltd, 44 London Road, Cowplain, Waterlooville, Hampshire, PO8 8EN Tel: (023) 9226 8882

▶ Priory, 38 Old Priory Road, Bournemouth, BH6 3AQ Tel: (07766) 900820 E-mail: davidquinn@prioryrefrigeration.com

▶ Quantum Cooling Technology, Botany Way, Purfleet, Essex, RM19 1TB Tel: (01708) 890081 Fax: (01708) 863850

▶ R C L Air Conditioning, Unit 10 Birch Business Park, Progress Drive, Cannock, Staffordshire, WS11 0BF Tel: (01543) 462422 Fax: (01543) 468777

R M S, Unit 6 Hopton Court, Hopton Industrial Estate, Devizes, Wiltshire, SN10 2EU Tel: (01380) 729292 Fax: (01380) 729140

R T Refrigeration & Air Conditioning, 1a Rowan Trade Park, Neville Road, Bradford, West Yorkshire, BD4 8TQ Tel: (01274) 737248 Fax: (01274) 309767

Radius Refrigeration Ltd, 19 Wilshaw Street, London, SE14 6TN Tel: (020) 8694 2786 Fax: (020) 8694 2786

Raine's Refrigeration Equipment, Stewner Park Farm, Marton, Ulverston, Cumbria, LA12 0NR Tel: (01229) 463871 Fax: (01229) 465056

Ransome Group Services Ltd, Unit 5-6 Clopton Commercial Park, Clopton, Woodbridge, Suffolk, IP13 6QT Tel: (01473) 737731 Fax: (01473) 737398 E-mail: info@ransomeengineering.co.uk

Rayvac Refrigeration Services, East Thurrock Road, Grays, Essex, RM17 6SP Tel: (01375) 390113 Fax: (01375) 381381 E-mail: keithneall@btopenworld.com

Refrigeration Aberdeen Ltd, Hillview Road, East Tullos Industrial Estate, Aberdeen, AB12 3HB Tel: (01224) 873115 Fax: (01224) 899919

Refrigeration Engineering Ltd, 120 Victoria Road, Scarborough, North Yorkshire, YO11 1SW Tel: (01723) 375711 Fax: (01723) 375712

Refrigeration & Engineering Services Ltd, Humber Street, Grimsby, South Humberside, DN31 3HL Tel: (01472) 352201 Fax: (01472) 250842

Refrigeration On The Wolds, Albion Street, Driffield, North Humberside, YO25 6PZ Tel: (01377) 252518

Refrigeration Sales & Rentals Ltd, 129 Dorchester Road, Upton, Poole, Dorset, BH16 5NW Tel: (01202) 624007 Fax: (01202) 249186 E-mail: j.forsyth@virgin.net

Refrigeration Service (Ruislip) Ltd, 288 West End Road, Ruislip, Middlesex, HA4 6LS Tel: (01895) 622286 Fax: (01895) 622259

Refrigeration Services, 6 Fort Street, Ayr, KA7 1HU Tel: (01292) 264098 Fax: (01292) 261191 E-mail: refridgerationservices@lycos.co.uk

Refrigeration Services, 9 Wynford Road, Bournemouth, BH9 3ND Tel: (01202) 512188

Refrigeration Yorkshire Ltd, Woodhouse Street, Hull, HU9 1RJ Tel: (01482) 587333 Fax: (01482) 589593E-mail: ryorks1@aol.com

Robins Refrigeration Ltd, Units 18A & B, Chapman Way, Tunbridge Wells, Kent, TN2 3EF Tel: (01892) 537291 Fax: (01892) 549794 E-mail: sue@robinsrefrigeration.co.uk

Rolls Refrigeration Ltd, 37 Hylton Drive, Cheadle Hulme, Cheadle, Cheshire, SK8 7DH Tel: 0161-486 0828 Fax: 0161-488 4033

S O S Refrigeration, 15 Thurston Avenue, Southend-on-Sea, SS2 4UJ Tel: (01702) 465061 Fax: (01702) 614000

Scotford & Teasdale, Unit 8 Thames Park, Lester Way, Wallingford, Oxfordshire, OX10 9TA Tel: 01491 821737 Fax: 01491 821730

▶ Scotia Energy Saving Systems, 60 Mollinsburn Street, Glasgow, G21 4SF Tel: 0141-772 4621 Fax: 0141-557 3848

Scottish Electric (Services) Ltd, Locarno Works, Brown Street, Dundee, DD1 5EE Tel: (01382) 228071 Fax: (01382) 322898 E-mail: scot.elec.grp@btconnect.com

Secker & Sons (Norwich) Ltd, St. Johns Close, Norwich, NR1 2PR Tel: (01603) 616419 Fax: (01603) 622247 E-mail: servise@seckers.com

Selectricks Ltd, 98 Reginald Rd, Southsea, Hants, PO4 9HW Tel: 023 92738214

Shoreline UK Ltd, Unit 6-7 Martello Enterprise Centre, Courtwick Lane, Wick, Littlehampton, West Sussex, BN17 7PA Tel: (01903) 733877 Fax: (01903) 733891 E-mail: info@shoreline-uk.com

Sidney Cubbage Heating & Ventilating Ltd, 37-43 Green Street, High Wycombe, Buckinghamshire, HP11 2RF Tel: (01494) 523661 Fax: (01494) 462707 E-mail: scl@sidneycubbage.com

South Durham Refrigeration, Unit 2b Trimdon Grange Industrial Estate, Trimdon Grange, Trimdon Station, County Durham, TS29 6PA Tel: (01429) 880544 Fax: (01429) 880544

Sparks Mechanical Services Ltd, Broadfold Road, Bridge of Don, Aberdeen, AB23 8EE Tel: (01224) 704448 Fax: (01224) 703864 E-mail: info@sparksms.co.uk

SRS Cooling, Archard House, Waverley Road, Weymouth, Dorset, DT3 5HL Tel: (01305) 750020 Fax: (01305) 750021 E-mail: sales@southernrefrigeration.freeserve.co.uk

Star Refrigeration Ltd, Thornliebank Industrial Estate, Nitshill Road, Glasgow, G46 8JW Tel: 0141-638 7916 Fax: 0141-638 8111 E-mail: star@star-ref.co.uk

Stay Cool Refrigeration, Manchester Road, Preston, PR1 4HL Tel: (01772) 827722 Fax: (01772) 827720

Staycool Refrigeration, 320 Spring Lane, Mapperley, Nottingham, NG3 5RQ Tel: 0115-920 0166 Fax: 0115-920 0166

Sterling Environmental Engineering Ltd, Sterling House, 12 Gate Lane, Sutton Coldfield, West Midlands, B73 5TT Tel: 0121-321 2244 Fax: 0121-321 3151 E-mail: enquiries@sterling.uk.com

Sterlings D F C Ltd, Ynys Bridge, Hoel-Yr-Ynys, Tongwynlais, Cardiff, CF15 7NT Tel: (029) 2081 3131 Fax: (029) 2081 3598 E-mail: rvs@easynet.co.uk

Stoneman Refrigeration, 10 Fore Street, Witheridge, Tiverton, Devon, EX16 8AH Tel: (01884) 860595 Fax: (01884) 860676

Strand Refrigeration, 82 Marlborough Rd, Hyde, Cheshire, SK14 5HX Tel: 0161-366 0037

Peter Swan & Sons Ltd, 3 Dryden Loan, Loanhead, Midlothian, EH20 9HR Tel: 0131-448 0880 Fax: 0131-448 0881

Syncro Ltd, 6th Floor Furness House, Furness Quay, Salford, M50 3XZ Tel: 0161-786 4400 Fax: 0161-877 5233

T S Refrigeration, 21 Whitwick Way, Leicester, LE3 9TG Tel: 0116-251 9907 Fax: 0116-251 9907

Tate Refrigeration Ltd, Unit 7 Glan Llwyd, Tyn Y Bonau Road Industrial Estate, Pontardduiais, Swansea, SA4 8SF Tel: (01792) 885585 Fax: (01792) 883351

Tempest Refrigeration & Air Conditioning Services Ltd, 4-4a Rabone Lane, Smethwick, West Midlands, B66 3JH Tel: 0121-558 3531 Fax: 0121-558 3531

▶ Thames Valley Refrigeration, 24 Victoria Road, Tilehurst, Reading, RG31 5AD Tel: 0118-942 8505 Fax: 0118-376 9110 E-mail: j@thamesvalleyrefrigeration.com

Thermacom Ltd, Green Lane, Burghfield Bridge, Reading, RG30 3XN Tel: 0118-950 0606 Fax: 0118-956 0039 E-mail: sales@thermagroup.com

Thermocold Mechanical Services Ltd, Unit 11 Albion Business Park, Spring Road, Smethwick, Warley, West Midlands, B66 1LY Tel: 0121-525 5887

Total Refrigeration Ltd, Unit 2A, East Tame Business Park, Talisot Road, Hyde, Cheshire, SK14 4EJ Tel: 0161-366 2504 Fax: 0161-366 2517 E-mail: sales@totalrefrigeration.co.uk

Universal Cooling Ltd, Unit 1a West End Business Park, Oswaldtwistle, Accrington, Lancashire, BB5 4WE Tel: (01254) 396005 Fax: (01254) 396055 E-mail: sales@universalcooling.co.uk

George Varcas & Partners, Windshield, Brimpton Common, Reading, RG7 4RU Tel: 0118-981 4983 Fax: 0118-981 7138 E-mail: paul@varcas.co.uk

W R Refrigeration Ltd, 8 Buckingham Court, Springfield, Chelmsford, CM2 6XW Tel: (01245) 463405 Fax: (01245) 463411

W R Refrigeration Ltd, 1 Calow Lane, Hasland, Chesterfield, Derbyshire, S41 0AL Tel: (01246) 272281 Fax: (01246) 550153

W R Refrigeration Ltd, Shor Street, Evesham, Worcestershire, WR11 3AU Tel: (01386) 40359 Fax: (01386) 40359

W R Refrigeration Ltd, 47 Colvilles Place, Kelvin Industrial Estate, East Kilbride, Glasgow, G75 0PZ Tel: (01355) 237237 Fax: (01355) 241888

W R Refrigeration Ltd, Frog Island, Leicester, LE3 5BG Tel: 0116-251 1060 Fax: 0116-242 5766

W R Refrigeration Ltd, 2 Woolram Wygate, Spalding, Lincolnshire, PE11 1NX Tel: (01775) 768978 Fax: (01775) 766713 E-mail: chriscocks@wrspalding.com

Watford Refrigeration & Air Conditioning Ltd, Wiggenhall Industrial Estate, Watford, WD18 0FT Tel: (01923) 227726 Fax: (01923) 233525 E-mail: sales@watref.co.uk

Wednesfield Refrigeration Services Ltd, 262 Penn Road, Wolverhampton, WV4 4AD Tel: (01902) 345111 Fax: (01902) 620346 E-mail: sales@wednesfieldrefrigeration.co.uk

Wescott Refrigeration Ltd, 188 Fenside Avenue, Coventry, CV3 5NJ Tel: (024) 7641 6677 Fax: (024) 7641 6647

Western Refrigeration Services Ltd, 46 Aldercombe Road, Bristol, BS9 2QL Tel: 0117-968 3964 Fax: 0117-968 3964

Western Refrigeration Co. (Taunton), 53 Hamilton Road, Taunton, Somerset, TA1 2EL Tel: (01823) 272347 Fax: (01823) 272368 E-mail: sales@westfridge.sagehost.co.uk

World of Catering, 684-692 Lea Bridge Road, London, E10 6AW Tel: (020) 8556 5038 Fax: (020) 8558 9410 E-mail:

York Refrigeration Ltd, Eaves Court Bonham Drive, Eurolink Commercial Park, Sittingbourne, Kent, ME10 3RY Tel: (01795) 472361 Fax: (01795) 427602

Zedra Solutions Ltd, Estate Office, Bishop's Sutton, Alresford, Hampshire, SO24 0AA Tel: (01962) 738884 Fax: (01962) 738885 E-mail: contact@zedra.co.uk

REFRIGERATION EQUIPMENT HIRE

A C Environmental Refrigeration Ltd, Evergreen Venture Park, Barton Road, Wisbech, Cambridgeshire, PE13 4TP Tel: (01945) 419081 Fax: (01945) 419082

Boldon Drilling Ltd, Private Road 3, Colwick Industrial Estate, Nottingham, NG4 2BB Tel: 0115-961 1250 Fax: 0115-961 7338 E-mail: drill@bds.co.uk

Border Holdings Coldstore (UK) Ltd, Avonmouth Way, Avonmouth, Bristol, BS11 9LX Tel: 0117-982 8589 Fax: 0117-982 4565

Cold Temp Refrigeration Service, Vicarage Lane, Skirlaugh, Hull, HU11 5HE Tel: (01964) 562773 Fax: (01964) 563350 E-mail: sales@coldtemp.co.uk

Coldstore Hire UK, Unit 6 Morley Street, Daybrook, Nottingham, NG5 6JX Tel: 0115-926 5965 Fax: 0115-926 5963 E-mail: sales@coldstorehire.co.uk

Sam Coulbeck (Refrigeration Rentals) Ltd, North Quay Fish Docks, Grimsby, South Humberside, DN31 3SY Tel: (01472) 345827 Fax: (01472) 358083

Foster Environmental Ltd, Scotter Road South, Bottesford, Scunthorpe, South Humberside, DN17 2BW Tel: (01724) 270717 Fax: (01724) 271410 E-mail: darren@forsterac.co.uk

Hymas Refrigeration & Catering Ltd, 178 Grove Green Road, London, E11 4EL Tel: (020) 8539 4222 E-mail: hymas_ref@fsmail.net

Ice House Hire & Kool Trailers Hire Limited, PO Box 7366, Hook, Hampshire, RG27 7EZ Tel: (01256) 703687 Fax: (07718) 161141 E-mail: info@icehousehire.co.uk

REFRIGERATION EQUIPMENT HIRE

– continued

Lowe Refrigeration Ltd, 101 Ballynahinch Road, Carryduff, Belfast, BT8 8DP Tel: (028) 9081 2248 Fax: (028) 9081 2608 E-mail: mail@loweref.co.uk

P W Adamson Ltd, Howe Moss Drive, Kirkhill Industrial Estate, Dyce, Aberdeen, AB21 0GL Tel: (01224) 724976 Fax: (01224) 724851 E-mail: support@pwadamson.co.uk

Portable Refrigeration Co. Ltd, St Georges House, Gaddesby Lane, Rearsby, Leicester, LE7 4YH Tel: (01483) 233133 Fax: (01483) 233135 E-mail: admin@portablerefrigeration.co.uk

Thornton International, Unit 1-3 Denver Industrial Estate, 44 Ferry Lane, Rainham, Essex, RM13 9YH Tel: (01233) 740009 Fax: (01708) 557353 E-mail: thornton.international@btinternet.com

REFRIGERATION EQUIPMENT HIRE, EMERGENCY

Ice House Hire & Kool Trailers Hire Limited, PO Box 7366, Hook, Hampshire, RG27 7EZ Tel: (01256) 703687 Fax: (07718) 161141 E-mail: info@icehousehire.co.uk

REFRIGERATION EQUIPMENT MANUFRS, *See also headings for particular types*

A R C, Silver Springs, Church Lane, Tydd St Giles, Wisbech, Cambridgeshire, PE13 5LG Tel: (01945) 871081 Fax: (01945) 871081

Ace Refrigeration, 21 Mayhall Rd, Portsmouth, PO3 5AU Tel: 023 92696322

Adcock Refrigeration & Air Conditioning Ltd, 35 Key Street, Ipswich, IP4 1BZ Tel: (01473) 258090 Fax: (01473) 232160

Adcock Refrigeration & Air Conditioning Ltd, 22 Mason Road, Norwich, NR6 6RF Tel: (01603) 786900 Fax: (01603) 418147

▶ Advanced Coldstore Technology Ltd, Unit 25C, Anniesland Industrial Estate, Glasgow, G13 1EU Tel: 0141-959 9200 Fax: 0141-959 9400E-mail: sales@advancedcoldstores.co.uk

Ambience Air Conditioning & Refrigeration Services Ltd, 1 Foxlease Terrace, Shrubbs Hill Road, Lyndhurst, Hampshire, SO43 7DJ Tel: (07074) 284837

Arctic Circle Ltd, Coldnose Court, Coldnose Road, Rotherwas Industrial Estate, Hereford, HR2 6JL Tel: (01432) 273333 Fax: (01432) 264616 E-mail: enquiries@acl-online.com

Arctic Refrigeration Ltd, 36 Bath Street, Bolton, BL1 2DJ Tel: (01204) 524655 Fax: (01204) 526557

Beehive Coils Ltd, Studlands Park Industrial Estate, Newmarket, Suffolk, CB8 7AU Tel: (01638) 664134 Fax: (01638) 661623 E-mail: info@beehivecoils.co.uk

Boyd Food Machinery, Ramas, Buckie, Banffshire, AB56 4BA Tel: (01542) 835885 Fax: (01542) 835080 E-mail: boyd@boydfood.com

Caterform Works, Victoria Road, Eccleshill, Bradford, West Yorkshire, BD2 2BN Tel: (01274) 626751 Fax: (01274) 626752 E-mail: aireseal@airedale-group.co.uk

Tom Chandley Ltd, Windmill La Industrial Estate, Denton, Manchester, M34 3RB Tel: 0161-337 3700 Fax: 0161-335 0972 E-mail: info@chandleyovens.co.uk

Ciat Ozonair Ltd, 5 Byfleet Technical Centre, Canada Road, Byfleet, Surrey, KT14 7JX Tel: (01932) 354955 Fax: (01932) 342998 E-mail: sales@ciat.co.uk

City Technical Services UK Ltd, 38 Southcroft Road, Rutherglen, Glasgow, G73 1UG Tel: 0141-643 2248 Fax: 0141-613 4432

Climate Centre, Unit 17, Durham Street, Kenning Park Way Estate, Glasgow, G41 1BS Tel: 0141-427 6899 Fax: 0141-427 4680

Climate Parts Ltd, Unit 3 Jack Lane Industrial Estate, Jack Lane, Leeds, LS11 9NP Tel: 0113-243 1339 Fax: 0113-234 0262

▶ Coldstream, 21 Wingate Road, Gosport, Hampshire, PO12 4DR Tel: (0870) 8501568 Fax: (023) 9252 9272

▶ Coolspan, 23 Botwell Lane, Hayes, Middlesex, UB3 2AB Tel: (020) 8842 3344 Fax: (020) 8842 3311

Copeland Corporation Ltd, Unit 17, Theale Lakes Business Park, Moulden Way, Sulhamsted, Reading, RG7 4GB Tel: 0118-983 8000 Fax: 0118-983 8001 E-mail: uksales@ecopeland.com

Creative Retail Solutions Ltd, 33 - 35 Chapel Road, Parkstone, Poole, Dorset, BH14 0JU Tel: (01202) 710842 Fax: (01202) 710845 E-mail: mary@creativeretailsolutiuons.co.uk

▶ D J Refrigeration & Air Conditioning, Woodland Works, Station Road, Pontnewydd, Cwmbran, Gwent, NP44 1NY Tel: (01633) 486260 Fax: (01633) 486292

▶ Diamond Compresser Services, 23 Mayfield Road, Chaddesden, Derby, DE21 6FX Tel: (01332) 677835 Fax: (01332) 677835 E-mail: ap@diamondcompressor.fsnet.co.uk

Eadie Refrigeration Ltd, 4 Old Perth Road, Cowdenbeath, Fife, KY4 9DR Tel: (01383) 513657 Fax: (01383) 611480

Easy Cool Refrigeration Ltd, 30 Eleanor Crescent, Newcastle, Staffordshire, ST5 3SA Tel: (01782) 628750 Fax: (01782) 628750 E-mail: info@rsm-reallycool.co.uk

Electrolux Ltd, Cornwall House, 55-57 High Street, Slough, SL1 1DZ Tel: (01753) 872500 Fax: (01753) 872501

Elgin Refrigeration Services Ltd, Unit 1, Linkwood Industrial Estate, Elgin, Morayshire, IV30 1HY Tel: (01343) 543116 Fax: (01343) 549910

Elstar Manufacturing Ltd, Unit A & B, Newbold Drive, Castle Donington, Derby, DE74 2NP Tel: (01332) 850090 Fax: (01332) 853173 E-mail: matthew.trotter@elstar.co.uk

Enodis Ltd, Provincial Park, Nether Lane, Ecclesfield, Sheffield, S35 9ZX Tel: 0114-257 0100 Fax: 0114-257 0251 E-mail: geremy.hobbs@enodis.co.uk

Eurogel Ltd, PO Box 45, Swadlincote, Derbyshire, DE11 0ZX Tel: (01283) 210055 Fax: (01283) 215130E-mail: eurogel@ic24.net

Forest (UK) Ltd, 7 Hurstwood Court, Mercer Way, Shadsworth Business Park, Blackburn, BB1 2QU Tel: (0870) 850 0301 Fax: (0870) 850 0302 E-mail: contactus@forest-uk.com

▶ G H England, Vincients Road, Bumpers Farm, Chippenham, Wiltshire, SN14 6NQ Tel: (01249) 449300 Fax: (01249) 447799 E-mail: sales@englandrefrigeration.co.uk

H & D Air Conditioning Ltd, 133 Royal George Road, Burgess Hill, West Sussex, RH15 9TD Tel: (01444) 232552 Fax: (01444) 246568 E-mail: brighton@mail.aireserv.com

H R P Ltd, 140 St. Andrews Road, Glasgow, G41 1PP Tel: 0141-420 1606 Fax: 0141-420 1755 E-mail: glasgow@hrpltd.co.uk

H R P Ltd, National Road, Hunslet Business Park, Leeds, LS10 1TD Tel: 0113-277 5000 Fax: 0113-270 6800

H T G Trading Ltd, Hillview, Church Road, Otley, Ipswich, IP6 9NP Tel: (01473) 890522 Fax: (01473) 890758 E-mail: info@hubbard.co.uk

Hall Refrigeration Ltd, Unit 17 Palace Industrial Estate, Bircholt Road, Maidstone, Kent, ME15 9XU Tel: (01622) 663379 Fax: (01622) 663282 E-mail: hallrefrigeration@mistral.co.uk

Harris & Russell Ltd, Eagle Way, Sowton Industrial Estate, Exeter, EX2 7HY Tel: (01392) 257666 Fax: (01392) 256880

Henry Technologies Ltd, Mossland Road, Hillington Industrial Estate, Glasgow, G52 4XZ Tel: 0141-882 4621 Fax: 0141-882 4624 E-mail: sales@henrytech.co.uk

Hesketh Refrigeration, 190 Preston Road, Standish, Wigan, Lancashire, WN6 0NP Tel: (01257) 423571 Fax: (01257) 423571

HT Cooling services, 65 Park View, Moulton, Northampton, NN3 7UZ Tel: (01604) 645135 Fax: (01604) 645135 E-mail: colin.htcooling@btopenworld.com

J & E Hall Ltd, 22 Lorn Street, Birkenhead, Merseyside, CH41 6AR Tel: 0151-647 6974 Fax: 0151-666 1873

Kent Refrigeration Ltd, 6 Yew Tree Industrial Estate, Mill Hall, Aylesford, Kent, ME20 7ET Tel: (01622) 792228 Fax: (01622) 790530 E-mail: sales@kentrefrigeration.com

Kooltech Ltd, 433 Hillington Road, Hillington Industrial Estate, Glasgow, G52 4BL Tel: 0141-883 0447 Fax: 0141-883 5642 E-mail: sales@kooltech.co.uk

Kooltech Refrigeration Equipment, 53 Wharton St Industrial Estate, Wharton Street, Birmingham, B7 5TR Tel: 0121-327 6565 Fax: 0121-327 6868

Lunar Refrigeration Ltd, Unit 5 Forestgate, White Lund Industrial Estate, Morecambe, Lancashire, LA3 3PD Tel: (01524) 64273 Fax: (01524) 846357 E-mail: lunar.refrig@virgin.net

M2 Refrigeration Services Ltd, Ivy Farm, Lidsing, Gillingham, Kent, ME7 3NL Tel: (01634) 263636 Fax: (01634) 263636

Mac Marney Refrigeration & Air Conditioning Ltd, The Old Forge, Stone Street, Crowfield, Ipswich, IP6 9SZ Tel: (01449) 760560 Fax: (01449) 760590 E-mail: sales@macmarney.co.uk

MBS, 24 Hanson Close, Middleton, Manchester, M24 2HD Tel: 0161-643 6151 Fax: 0161-643 6151

Mueller Cooling Systems Ltd, Unit B Manor Farm, Main Street, Pinvin, Pershore, Worcestershire, WR10 2ES Tel: (01386) 561757 Fax: (01386) 561750 E-mail: phil.valentine@mueller-cooling.co.uk

NGF, Unit 11, Allerton Bywater, Castleford, West Yorkshire, WF10 2DB Tel: (0845) 6444566 Fax: (0845) 6445123 E-mail: sales@ngfindustrialdoors.co.uk

Parts Center, Unit C Tamar Road, Bristol, BS2 0TX Tel: 0117-972 1376 Fax: 0117-977 6399 E-mail: nrs-bristol@climatecentre.co.uk

Pendle Refrigeration Services Ltd, Whithams Mill, Plumbe Street, Burnley, Lancashire, BB11 3AW Tel: (01282) 412352 Fax: (01282) 451807 E-mail: sales@pendle-refrig.co.uk

Penmann Climatic Systems Ltd, Highfield, Pool Road, Pool in Wharfedale, Otley, West Yorkshire, LS21 1EG Tel: 0113-202 7300 Fax: 0113-202 7301 E-mail: office@penmann.co.uk

▶ Pontardawe Referigation, Unit A, Lon Hir, Alltwen, Pontardawe, Swansea, SA8 3DE Tel: (01792) 869515 Fax: (01792) 869522

▶ R D S, 5 Rigby Close, Heathcote Industrial Estate, Warwick, CV34 6TH Tel: (01926) 435255 Fax: (01926) 336594 E-mail: sales@rdstransport.co.uk

R J Coleman Plumbing & Heating, Glebe Road, Scunthorpe, South Humberside, DN15 6AF Tel: (01724) 851111 Fax: (01724) 852111 E-mail: sales@rjc.co.uk

R K Refrigeration Ltd, 2-4 South Croston Street, Manchester, M16 7WP Tel: 0161-232 9163 Fax: 0161-232 7277 E-mail: rkrefrigeration@talk21.com

R S C Spares Ltd, B 4 CWM Road, Swansea, SA1 2AY Tel: (01792) 654639 Fax: (01792) 654658 E-mail: sales@rsc-spares.co.uk

Rabtherm International Ltd, Unit 11, Empire Close, Aldridge, Walsall, WS9 8XZ Tel: (01922) 743273 Fax: (01922) 743119 E-mail: bgas@rabtherm.co.uk

Radius Services, Unit 23-24, Resolution Way, London, SE8 4NT Tel: (020) 8692 0257 Fax: (020) 8694 2786

▶ Refrigerated Transport, 57, Wellington Street, Aberdeen, AB11 5BX Tel: (01224) 210549 Fax: (01224) 210325

Refrigeration & Air Conditioning Services, 25 Highfield Road, London, N21 3HD Tel: (020) 8360 0701 Fax: (020) 8360 4345

Refrigeration Mitton Ltd, Polar House, East Norfolk Street, Carlisle, CA2 5JL Tel: (01228) 522481 Fax: (01228) 514897

▶ Refrigeration Parts Wholesale Ltd, Unit 2 Vine Street, Aston, Birmingham, B6 5TS Tel: 0121-328 8388 Fax: 0121-327 7266

Refrigeration Parts Wholesale Ltd, Delta House, Fairway, Cannock, Staffordshire, WS11 0DJ Tel: (01543) 437010 Fax: (01543) 437029 E-mail: sales@rpw.co.uk

Regency Refrigeration, 5 Medina Way, Kidsgrove, Stoke-on-Trent, ST7 4TJ Tel: (01782) 773103

▶ Roy Dixon Associates, Unit 4, Westerham Trade Centre, The Flyers Way, Westerham, Kent, TN16 1DE Tel: (01959) 561010 Fax: (01959) 563777

Russell Ltd, 125 Business Park, Llanthony Road, Gloucester, GL2 5JQ Tel: (01452) 312851 Fax: (01452) 306388 E-mail: info@russell.co.uk

Starfrost UK Ltd, Starfrost House, Newcombe Road, Lowestoft, Suffolk, NR32 1XA Tel: (01502) 562206 Fax: (01502) 584104 E-mail: info@starfrost.co.uk

Sussex Refrigeration Wholesale Ltd, The Glen, Halwill, Beaworthy, Devon, EX21 5TJ Tel: 01409 221195

Technical Transport Equipment Ltd, 87 Styal Road, Gatley, Cheadle, Cheshire, SK8 4JQ Tel: 0161-491 3150 Fax: 0161-491 3150

Thermal Exchange Ltd, 15 Chiswick Road, Leicester, LE2 7SX Tel: 0116-254 6652 Fax: 0116-255 9176 E-mail: sales@thermalexchange.co.uk

Thermofrost Cryo P.L.C., Robert Fawkes Ho, Rea Street South, Birmingham, B5 6LB Tel: 0121-666 4700 Fax: 0121-622 7268 E-mail: admin@thermofrostcryo.co.uk

▶ Toshiba Carrier UK Ltd, United Technologies House, Guildford Road, Fetcham, Leatherhead, Surrey, KT22 9UT Tel: (01372) 220220 Fax: (01372) 220221

Trend Refrigeration Ltd, Holt Lane, Liverpool, L27 2YB Tel: 0151-487 9278 Fax: 0151-487 9254

▶ United Refrigeration Ltd, Lindberg Road, Ferndown Industrial Estate, Wimborne, Dorset, BH21 7SP Tel: (01202) 855855 Fax: (01202) 855995 E-mail: ukbranch04@uri.com

▶ Unitor Refrigeration Equipment, Sovereign Way, Dock Road, Birkenhead, Merseyside, CH41 1DL Tel: 0151-670 5150 Fax: 0151-670 5159

Unitor UK Ltd, Kelvin House, 40 Kelvin Road, Wallasey, Merseyside, CH44 7JW Tel: 0151-630 3869 Fax: 0151-637 0151 E-mail: sales@unitor.com

Vertical Cabinet Co. Ltd, Hithercroft Road, Wallingford, Oxfordshire, OX10 9DG Tel: (01491) 839966 Fax: (01491) 835656 E-mail: sales@ver.co.uk

Vulkan Industries Ltd, Archer Road, Armytage Road Industrial Estate, Brighouse, West Yorkshire, HD6 1XF Tel: (01484) 712273 Fax: (01484) 721376 E-mail: sales@vulkan.co.uk

W R Refrigeration Ltd, Frog Island, Leicester, LE3 5BG Tel: 0116-251 1060 Fax: 0116-242 5766

▶ W W Installations, 19 Gregorys Mill Street, Worcester, WR3 8BA Tel: (01905) 723113

Ware Sheet Metal Ltd, Units 3-6, Charlton Mead Lane, Hoddesdon, Hertfordshire, EN11 0DJ Tel: (01992) 466483 Fax: (01992) 469604 E-mail: sales@waresheetmetal.co.uk

Welvent Ltd, Whisby Way, Whisby Road, Lincoln, LN6 3LQ Tel: (01522) 693008 Fax: (01522) 500429 E-mail: enquiries@welvent.com

Western Air Ltd, Bencroft View House, Studley Hill, Studley, Calne, Wiltshire, SN11 9NL Tel: (01249) 817579 Fax: (01249) 819006

Wintergreen Trading Co. Ltd, PO Box 415, Southampton, SO31 9ZQ Tel: (01489) 607300 Fax: (01489) 607600

World of Catering, 684-692 Lea Bridge Road, London, E10 6AW Tel: (020) 8556 5038 Fax: (020) 8558 9410 E-mail:

York International Ltd, Gardiners La South, Basildon, Essex, SS14 3HE Tel: (01268) 246000 Fax: (01268) 246001 E-mail: sales@york.co.uk

REFRIGERATION EQUIPMENT, COMMERCIAL

▶ Catex Catering Equipment (2002) Ltd, Unit 2 La Rue Le Gros, La Rue Des Pres Trading Estate, St. Saviour, Jersey, JE2 7QP Tel: (01534) 725582 Fax: (01534) 734314 E-mail: catex@jerseymail.co.uk

Chelmer Food Machinery, Stone Cottage Farm, Ipswich Road, Dedham, Colchester, CO7 6HS Tel: (01206) 321221 Fax: (01206) 321221 E-mail: sales@cfmsupplies.com

▶ Isotek, Unit 3, Bode Business Park, Ball Haye Green, Leek, Staffordshire, ST13 6BW Tel: (01538) 384008 Fax: (01538) 384016 E-mail: info@cooltrailers.co.uk

▶ Polestar Cooling Ltd, Ford Airfield, Ford Airfield Industrial Estate, Ford, Arundel, West Sussex, BN18 0HY Tel: (01903) 724400 Fax: (01903) 725169 E-mail: info@polestarcooling.com

REFRIGERATION PLANT, FREEZING/CHILLING, FOOD INDUSTRY

Farm Electronics Ltd, Alma Park Industrial Estate, Grantham, Lincolnshire, NG31 9SR Tel: (01476) 591592 Fax: (01476) 591188 E-mail: info@farmelec.co.uk

Parkin International Engineering Services Ltd, Trinity Business Park, Wakefield, West Yorkshire, WF2 8EF Tel: (01924) 331700 Fax: (01924) 331733 E-mail: info@parkingroup.co.uk

REFRIGERATION SYSTEMS, TRUCK

▶ Marshall Thermo King Ltd, Units 7-8, Willment Way, Bristol, BS11 8DJ Tel: 0117-982 1455 Fax: 0117-982 2899

REFRIGERATION UNIT COMPRESSORS

Thermacom Ltd, Green Lane, Burghfield Bridge, Reading, RG30 3XN Tel: 0118-950 0606 Fax: 0118-956 0039 E-mail: sales@thermagroup.com

REFRIGERATION UNITS

Atlantic Refrigeration Ltd, Peel Street, Northam, Southampton, SO14 5QT Tel: (023) 8033 9141 Fax: (023) 8022 9840 E-mail: grantwest@atlantic-refrig.co.uk

Carrier Refrigeration, United Technologies House, Guildford Road, Fetcham, Leatherhead, Surrey, KT22 9UT Tel: (01865) 337700 Fax: (01372) 230190

Centigrade Ltd, 9 Beverley Road, Tilehurst, Reading, RG31 5PT Tel: 0118-942 4939 Fax: 0118-942 4939

Cool Rite Air Conditioning Ltd, 65 High Street, Winterbourne, Bristol, BS36 1RA Tel: (01454) 772011 Fax: (01454) 250687 E-mail: sales@coolrite.com

Copeland Corporation Ltd, Unit 17, Theale Lakes Business Park, Moulden Way, Sulhamsted, Reading, RG7 4GB Tel: 0118-983 8000 Fax: 0118-983 8001 E-mail: uksales@ecopeland.com

County Hospital & Mortuary Equipment, 13 Westfield Crescent, Brighton, BN1 8JB Tel: (01273) 885441 Fax: (01273) 240954 E-mail: county@pavilion.co.uk

Dean & Wood Ltd, Mole Business Park, Randalls Road, Leatherhead, Surrey, KT22 2BA Tel: (01372) 378788 Fax: (01372) 386239 E-mail: dw@dean-wood.co.uk

Elstar Manufacturing Ltd, Unit A & B, Newbold Drive, Castle Donington, Derby, DE74 2NP Tel: (01332) 850090 Fax: (01332) 853173 E-mail: matthew.trotter@elstar.co.uk

H T G Trading Ltd, Hillview, Church Road, Otley, Ipswich, IP6 9NP Tel: (01473) 890522 Fax: (01473) 890758 E-mail: info@hubbard.co.uk

Harrison & Cross Ltd, Unit 6 The Sidings Industrial Estate, Settle, North Yorkshire, BD24 9RP Tel: (01729) 823423 Fax: (01729) 823423

Kool It Services Ltd, 85-87 Wellington Road, Eccles, Manchester, M30 9GW Tel: 0161-707 2580 Fax: 0161-288 0135

▶ Perkins R & Sons, 201 London Central Markets, London, EC1A 9LH Tel: (020) 7329 4612 Fax: (020) 7329 4192 E-mail: info@rperkins.co.uk

Robertson Refrigeration, Upper Gartally, Drumnadrochit, Inverness, IV63 6XS Tel: (01456) 450536 Fax: (01456) 450680 E-mail: rob.refrig@btopenworld.com

REFRIGERATION UNITS, MOBILE

Accessible Hire & Refrigeration Ltd, Masters House, 46 Bridgnorth Road, Wollaston, Stourbridge, West Midlands, DY8 3QG Tel: (01384) 446000 Fax: (01384) 375242 E-mail: hire@ahrltd.co.uk

REFRIGERATOR CABINETS

Hoshizaki UK, Unit 2 Marquis Business Centre, Royston Road, Baldock, Hertfordshire, SG7 6XL Tel: (0845) 4560585 Fax: (01462) 499080 E-mail: sales@hoshizakiuk.co.uk

REFRIGERATOR COMPONENTS AND SPARE PARTS

A C R Heat Transfer Ltd, Rollesby Road, King's Lynn, Norfolk, PE30 4LN Tel: (01553) 763371 Fax: (01553) 771322 E-mail: acrheat@msn.com

A F R Refrigeration Ltd, Units 5-6 Delta Business Park, 10 Smugglers Way, London, SW18 1EG Tel: (020) 8875 1999 Fax: (020) 8875 0125 E-mail: sales@afr.co.uk

Blue Ice Refrigeration, 8 Harpham Road, Marshchapel, Grimsby, South Humberside, DN36 5TR Tel: (01472) 388491 Fax: (01472) 388491

Climate Center, 63 Pritchett Street, Birmingham, B6 4EX Tel: 0121-333 3636 Fax: 0121-359 8497 E-mail: gk.aston@wolseley.co.uk

Costan UK Ltd, Unit 8 Haslemere Industrial Estate, The Pinnacles, Harlow, Essex, CM19 5SZ Fax: (01279) 415266

Dean & Wood Ltd, Unit 1, Camwal Road, St. Philips, Bristol, BS2 0UZ Tel: 0117-971 7413 Fax: 0117-972 1561

Dean & Wood Ltd, Mole Business Park, Randalls Road, Leatherhead, Surrey, KT22 2BA Tel: (01372) 378788 Fax: (01372) 386239 E-mail: dw@dean-wood.co.uk

H R P Ltd, Rougham Industrial Estate, Rougham, Bury St. Edmunds, Suffolk, IP30 9XA Tel: (01359) 271131 Fax: (01359) 272225 E-mail: sales@hrpltd.co.uk

Hotfrost, 72-76 Brighton Road, Surbiton, Surrey, KT6 5PP Tel: (020) 8399 7151 Fax: (020) 8399 9549

HRP Sales Ltd, The Teardrop, London Road, Swanley, Kent, BR8 8TJ Tel: (01322) 614811 Fax: (01322) 614733

Kason Hardware (UK) Ltd, Unit 3, Monmore Park Industrial Estate, Ettingshall Road, Wolverhampton, WV2 2LQ Tel: (01902) 409431 Fax: (01902) 353939 E-mail: kasonukltd@tiscali.co.uk

Kooltech Ltd, 433 Hillington Road, Hillington Industrial Estate, Glasgow, G52 4BL Tel: 0141-883 0447 Fax: 0141-883 5642 E-mail: sales@kooltech.co.uk

REFRIGERATOR FITTINGS OR ACCESSORIES

Brace, Main Road, Milfield, Wooler, Northumberland, NE71 6JD Tel: (01668) 216306 Fax: (01668) 216348 E-mail: david@braceltd.co.uk

Coolrite Refrigeration Ltd, Unit 382H Jedburgh Court, 11th Avenue, Team Valley Trading Park, Gateshead, Tyne & Wear, NE11 0BQ Tel: 0191-491 0096 Fax: 0191-482 0514

Hamster Baskets, Aylhill, Aylton, Ledbury, Herefordshire, HR8 2QJ Tel: (01531) 670209 Fax: (01531) 670630 E-mail: richard@hamsterbaskets.co.uk

Alan Nuttall Ltd, Hall Street, Dudley, West Midlands, DY2 7DQ Tel: (01384) 245100 Fax: (01384) 245102

Tomkins Buckle, Brockhurst CR, Walsall, WS5 4QG Tel: (01922) 723003 Fax: (01922) 723149 E-mail: sales@fhtomkins.com

REFRIGERATOR LATCHES

Kason Hardware (UK) Ltd, Unit 3, Monmore Park Industrial Estate, Ettingshall Road, Wolverhampton, WV2 2LQ Tel: (01902) 409431 Fax: (01902) 353939 E-mail: kasonukltd@tiscali.co.uk

REFRIGERATOR MAINTENANCE AND SERVICING EQUIPMENT

Anderson & Brooks, 85 New Road, Kidderminster, Worcestershire, DY10 1AE Tel: (01562) 864500 Fax: (01562) 864600

Beeline, 9 London Road, Pakefield, Lowestoft, Suffolk, NR33 7AA Tel: (01502) 514756 Fax: (01502) 516043 E-mail: sales@beeline-refrigeration.co.uk

David Payne & Son Coachbuilders Ltd, Beddow Way, Aylesford, Kent, ME20 7BT Tel: (01622) 718645 Fax: (01622) 716365

F T Refrigeration Ltd, 166 Old Road, Stockport, Cheshire, SK4 1TD Tel: 0161-480 4825 Fax: 0161-480 4825

Martins Ltd, 11b Roderick Road, London, NW3 2NN Tel: (020) 7485 5922

REFRIGERATOR REPAIR

Topaz Refrigeration & Air Conditioning, 113 Main Road, Marchwood, Southampton, SO40 4UZ Tel: (023) 8086 5202 Fax: (023) 8066 7562

REFRIGERATORS, *See also headings for particular types*

C & M Refrigeration, Unit C, The Loddon Centre, Wade Road, Basingstoke, Hampshire, RG24 8FL Tel: (01256) 811400 Fax: (01256) 801200 E-mail: coldkit@btconnect.com

Cleveland Refrigeration Co. Ltd, Unit 5, Leven Road, Lawson Industrial Estate, Middlesbrough, Cleveland, TS3 6LG Tel: (01642) 242592 Fax: (01642) 226020 E-mail: agcrl@cdnscustomers.com

Climate Centers Ltd, Unit 8 Brickyard Business Park, Excelsior Road, Off Western Avenue, Cardiff, CF14 3AT Tel: (029) 2062 0033 Fax: (029) 2069 1155

Costan UK Ltd, Unit 8 Haslemere Industrial Estate, The Pinnacles, Harlow, Essex, CM19 5SZ Fax: (01279) 415266

D & S Air Conditioning Ltd, 5-6 Millbrook Close, Northampton, NN5 5JF Tel: (01604) 586482 Fax: (01604) 586477 E-mail: admin@dandsairconditioning.co.uk

Deal Rentals Ltd, 46 Gillender Street, London, E14 6RN Tel: (020) 7537 1257 Fax: (020) 7537 1257 E-mail: info@dealref.co.uk

▶ Glebe Radio & Television Ltd, 33 Glebe Farm Road, Birmingham, B33 9LY Tel: 0121-783 3352 Fax: 0121-783 1498 E-mail: glebetv@freedomnames.co.uk

Global Refrigeration & Air Conditioning Co. Ltd, Unit 41, 3 Halifax Road, Metropolitan Centre, Greenford, Middlesex, UB6 8XU Tel: (020) 8575 7557 Fax: (020) 8566 6342 E-mail: enquiries@globalrefrigeration.co.uk

Hoover Candy Group, New Chester Road, Bromborough, Wirral, Merseyside, CH62 3PE Tel: 0151-334 2781 Fax: 0151-334 0185

Hussmann Refrigeration Ltd, Clydeway Skypark, 8 Elliot Place, Glasgow, G3 8EP Tel: 0141-285 8500 Fax: 0141-227 2734

J W Lovitt, Station Road, Tempsford, Sandy, Bedfordshire, SG19 2BA Tel: (01767) 640934 Fax: (01767) 640839 E-mail: jwlrefrigeration@aol.com

▶ Koolatron International, Unit C3 Knights Park, Knight Road Strood, Rochester, Kent, ME2 2LS Tel: (01634) 297383 Fax: (01634) 297374

Kroyair Ltd, 262 Moseley Road, Birmingham, B12 0BX Tel: 0121-440 5383 Fax: 0121-446 4236 E-mail: info@kroyair.fsnet.co.uk

M Williams & Sons Ltd, Llys, Clawddnewydd, Ruthin, Clwyd, LL15 2NB Tel: (01824) 750750 Fax: (01824) 750357

Mcbain Refrigeration, Fremington, Barnstaple, Devon, EX31 2NT Tel: (01271) 371774 Fax: (01271) 321199

Montgomery Refrigeration Ltd, 5 Falcon Road, Adelaide Industrial Estate, Belfast, BT12 6RD Tel: (028) 9066 2111 Fax: (028) 9068 1130 E-mail: service@montgomery-ltd.co.uk

Osbourne Refrigerators Ltd, Rose Green Road, Bognor Regis, West Sussex, PO21 3EG Tel: (01243) 267711 Fax: (01243) 265853 E-mail: sales@osborne-ref.co.uk

Refrigeration Norwest (Llandudno) Ltd, Tremarl Industrial Estate, Llandudno Junction, Gwynedd, LL31 9PN Tel: (01492) 581358 Fax: (01492) 593171

▶ Refrigeration Parts Wholesale Ltd, Delta House, Fairway, Cannock, Staffordshire, WS11 0DJ Tel: (01543) 437010

Refrigeration Spares (Manchester) Ltd, Milltown Street, Radcliffe, Manchester, M26 1WN Tel: 0161-723 4426 Fax: 0161-725 9169

S R W (Sussex Refrigeration Wholesale) Ltd, Unit 4, Harbour Way, Shoreham-By-Sea, West Sussex, BN43 5HG Tel: (01273) 455530 Fax: (01273) 455575 E-mail: info@srw.co.uk

Sussex Refrigeration Wholesale Ltd, The Glen, Halwill, Beaworthy, Devon, EX21 5TJ Tel: 01409 221195

W R Refrigeration Ltd, 8 Buckingham Court, Springfield, Chelmsford, CM2 6XW Tel: (01245) 463405 Fax: (01245) 463411

Weald Refrigeration, 5 Vestry Industrial Estate, Vestry Road, Sevenoaks, Kent, TN14 5EL Tel: (01732) 452050 Fax: (01732) 452122 E-mail: sales@wealdrefrigeration.com

Whattam Refrigeration, The Warehouse, George Court, York, YO31 7PG Tel: (01904) 630795 Fax: (01904) 634859

REFUSE COLLECTING VEHICLE CONTAINER LIFTING EQUIPMENT

Otto UK Ltd, Beacon House, Reg's Way, Bardon Hill, Coalville, Leicestershire, LE67 1GH Tel: (01530) 277900 Fax: (01530) 277911 E-mail: sales@otto.co.uk

REFUSE COLLECTING VEHICLES

Asset Co Group Ltd, Ruislip Workshop, 800 Field End Road, Ruislip, Middlesex, HA4 0QH Tel: (020) 8515 3999 Fax: (020) 8515 3999 E-mail: sales@assetco.com

Dennis Eagle Ltd, Heathcote Way, Heathcote Industrial Estate, Warwick, CV34 6TE Tel: (01926) 316000 Fax: (01926) 316550

Faun Municipal Vehicles Ltd, Unit 4 Bryn Cefni Industrial Park, Llangefni, Gwynedd, LL77 7XA Tel: (01248) 722777 Fax: (01248) 750220 E-mail: sales@faun.demon.co.uk

Geesink Norba Ltd, Llantrisant Business Park, Llantrisant, Pontyclun, Mid Glamorgan, CF72 8XZ Tel: (01443) 222301 Fax: (01443) 237192 E-mail: sales@pdegeesink.co.uk

Heil Europe Ltd, Taxi Way, Hillend Industrial Park, Hillend, Dunfermline, Fife, KY11 9ES Tel: (01383) 823625 Fax: (01383) 824062 E-mail: sales@heileuro.com

Hemmings Waste Management Ltd, St. Gabriels Road, Easton, Bristol, BS5 0RU Tel: (0117) 951 2000 Fax: (0117) 935 4524

Johnston Sweepers Ltd, Curtis Road, Dorking, Surrey, RH4 1XF Tel: (01306) 884722 Fax: (01306) 884151 E-mail: enquiries@johnstonsweepers.com

Londonderry Garage Ltd, New Garage, Londonderry, Northallerton, North Yorkshire, DL7 9NB Tel: (01677) 422185 Fax: (01677) 428311

Trio Skips & Hooks Ltd, Ashville Road, Gloucester, GL2 5DA Tel: (01452) 331022 Fax: (01452) 331566 E-mail: info@trio-waste.co.uk

V H F Engineering Ltd, Point West Virage Park, Green Lane, Cannock, Staffordshire, WS11 0NH Tel: (01543) 571631 Fax: (01543) 462303 E-mail: sales@vhfengineering.co.uk

REFUSE CONTAINER (WHEELED) MANUFRS

Kliko Environmental Systems, 23 Gladstone House, High Street, Hadley, Telford, Shropshire, TF1 5NF Tel: (01952) 641366 Fax: (01952) 641766 E-mail: info@kliko.co.uk

REFUSE DISPOSAL CONTRACTORS

Biffa Holdings Ltd, Coronation Road, Cressex, High Wycombe, Buckinghamshire, HP12 3TZ Tel: (0800) 307307 E-mail: marketing@biffa.co.uk

Cory Environmental Municipal Services, Riverside, London, SE7 7SU Tel: (020) 8858 2008 Fax: (020) 8858 2107

Hales Waste Control Ltd, Coronation Road, Cressex Business Park, High Wycombe, Buckinghamshire, HP12 3TZ Tel: (01494) 521221 Fax: (01992) 640212 E-mail: marketing@biffa.co.uk

Premier Waste Management Ltd, Prospect House, Aykley Heads, Durham, DH1 5TS Tel: 0191-384 4000 Fax: 0191-384 5869

S I T A, Packington House, Packington Lane, Meriden, Coventry, CV7 7HN Tel: (01675) 434700 Fax: (01675) 465740

Sita South Gloucestershire Ltd, Grenfell Road, Maidenhead, Berkshire, SL6 1ES Tel: (01628) 513100 Fax: (01628) 513101

Veolia Enviromental Services, Brookside Depot, Buxton Road, Frettenham, Norwich, NR12 7NQ Tel: (01603) 890960 Fax: (01603) 890061 E-mail: broodland@veolia.co.uk

REFUSE DISPOSAL SYSTEMS

Dartford Metalcrafts Ltd, Priory Road, Rochester, Kent, ME2 2EG Tel: (01634) 296123 Fax: (01634) 296129 E-mail: dmc@dartfordmetalcrafts.co.uk

REFUSE DISPOSAL SYSTEMS INSTALLATION CONTRACTORS

Dartford Metalcrafts Ltd, Priory Road, Rochester, Kent, ME2 2EG Tel: (01634) 296123 Fax: (01634) 296129 E-mail: dmc@dartfordmetalcrafts.co.uk

REFUSE SACKS

Beck Sack Co., 3 Hermitage Lane, London, SE25 5HH Tel: (0845) 0720750

REFUSE SORTING/SHREDDING/ BALING EQUIPMENT

Lyndex Recycling Systems Ltd, Stafford Park 10, Telford, Shropshire, TF3 3BP Tel: (01952) 290333 Fax: (01952) 290229 E-mail: info@lindexrecycling.com

REGALIA, CIVIC

Rebus Badges & Regalia Ltd, Clayfields, Bodenham, Hereford, HR1 3LG Tel: (01568) 797401 Fax: (01568) 797402 E-mail: sales@e-badges.co.uk

Shaw & Sons Ltd, Shaway House, 21 Bourne Park, Bourne Road, Crayford, Dartford, DA1 4BZ Tel: (01322) 621100 Fax: (01322) 550553 E-mail: sales@shaws.co.uk

REGISTERED EXCISE DEALERS, SHIPPING

Mitsui O S K Bulk Shipping Europe Ltd, Dexter House, Royal Mint Court, London, EC3N 4JR Tel: (020) 7265 7500 Fax: (020) 7265 7560

REGISTRATION SYSTEMS, SCHOOLS

Radun Controls Ltd, Unit 42 Aberaman Industrial Estate, Aberaman, Aberdare, Mid Glamorgan, CF44 6UZ Tel: (01685) 887600 Fax: (01685) 887601 E-mail: general@radun.com

REGRIND PLASTIC SCRAP MIXERS

▶ Comtech Enterpises Ltd, 41 Leigh Road, Cobham, Surrey, KT11 2LF Tel: (01932) 589667 Fax: (01932) 862181 E-mail: office@comtech.eu.com

REGRINDING SERVICES, KNIVES/CUTTERS

Easicut Grinding Co. Ltd, Leestone Road, Sharston Industrial Area, Manchester, M22 4RN Tel: 0161-428 3265 Fax: 0161-428 3267 E-mail: w.kilbride@virgin.net

Kennedy Grinding Ltd, Shrewsbury Road, Craven Arms, Shropshire, SY7 9QH Tel: (01588) 672289 Fax: (01588) 673504 E-mail: kennedygrinding@btconnect.com

S P C Tools, Unit B, Lyttleton Road, Northampton, NN5 7ET Tel: (01604) 583411 Fax: (01604) 758567 E-mail: spc001@hotmail.co.uk

REGULATION PUBLISHING SERVICES

I P 3, 83 Guildford Street, Chertsey, Surrey, KT16 9AS Tel: (0870) 3308625 Fax: (0870) 3308615 E-mail: admin@ip3.org.uk

REGULATIONS, MEDICAL DEVICES INDUSTRY

Atlantic Bridge Ltd, Zenith House, 11 The Street, Chirton, Devizes, Wiltshire, SN10 3QS Tel: (01380) 848170 Fax: (01380) 840152 E-mail: sales@atlanticbridge.co.uk

REGULATOR VALVES

Boiswood Ltd, Unit A1 Spinnaker Park, Hempsted, Gloucester, GL2 5JA Tel: (01452) 330011 Fax: (01452) 330088 E-mail: ian.taylor@boiswood.co.uk

Majorsell International Ltd, Unit G Springhill Business Park, 111 Steward Street, Birmingham, B18 7AF Tel: 0121-455 0200 Fax: 0121-455 0272 E-mail: sales@majorsell.co.uk

REGULATORY COMPLIANCE CONSULTANCY

▶ Stibbards Consultancy Ltd, 26 Downs Court Road, Purley, Surrey, CR8 1BB Tel: (020) 8660 3440 E-mail: stibbardsconsultancy@yahoo.co.uk

REHABILITATION EQUIPMENT MANUFRS

Cit Realisations Ltd, 6 Wedgwood Road, Bicester, Oxfordshire, OX26 4UL Tel: (01869) 327173 Fax: (01869) 247214 E-mail: sales@chilterninvadex.co.uk

East Anglian Motor & Sheet Metal Co. Ltd, 10 Garden Street, Norwich, NR1 1QX Tel: (01603) 625664 Fax: (01603) 760545 E-mail: sales@ea-arc.co.uk

Hoskins Medical Equipment, Woodsbank Trading Estate, Woden Road West, Wednesbury, West Midlands, WS10 7BL Tel: 0121-707 6600 Fax: 0121-502 2092 E-mail: sales@hoskinsme.co.uk

REINFORCED CONCRETE, *See Concrete, Reinforced etc*

REINFORCED CONCRETE CONTRACTORS OR ENGINEERS

Beighton Construction Ltd, 58 Dunston Road, Whittington Moor, Chesterfield, Derbyshire, S41 8XA Tel: (01246) 451098 Fax: (01246) 455421
E-mail: beightonconstruction@hotmail.com
Bierrum Structural Services Ltd, 105 High Street, Houghton Regis, Dunstable, Bedfordshire, LU5 5BJ Tel: (01582) 845745 Fax: (01582) 845746 E-mail: admin@bierrum.co.uk
Ferrosteel (Structures) Ltd, 60 Lichfield St, Walsall, WS4 2BX Tel: (01922) 637467 Fax: (01922) 720364
Re Bar Engineering Design Ltd, 68a Reddicap Hill, Sutton Coldfield, West Midlands, B75 7BG Tel: 0121-378 3777 Fax: 0121-378 0214
E-mail: rebardesignltdsc@aol.com
Technaseal Concrete Repairing Services, 11 Marriott Close, Heigham Street, Norwich, NR2 4UX Tel: (01603) 667106 Fax: (01603) 612636 E-mail: info@technasel.co.uk
▶ Versotech Ltd, 81D Main Street, Calderbank, Airdrie, Lanarkshire, ML6 9SG Tel: (01236) 753875 Fax: (01236) 754497
E-mail: info@versotech.co.uk
▶ W B Formwork Co 1990, Atlas Works, Robinson Street, Stalybridge, Cheshire, SK15 1TH Tel: 0161-338 4543 Fax: 0161-338 8269

REINFORCED CONCRETE DRILLING

D Drill Master Drillers Ltd, 84 Clun Street, Sheffield, S4 7JS Tel: 0114-273 9199 Fax: 0114-276 5884
E-mail: sheffield@d-drill.co.uk
Geotex Ground Services Ltd, PO Box 5071, Market Harborough, Leicestershire, LE16 7WJ Tel: (01858) 545111 Fax: (01858) 545914
E-mail: sales@geotex.co.uk

REINFORCED CONCRETE PRODUCTS

Albion Architectural Concrete Ltd, Newbrook Works, Pound Lane, Upper Beeding, Steyning, West Sussex, BN44 3JD Tel: (01903) 815262 Fax: (01903) 815619
E-mail: mike@albionart.co.uk
▶ E P Rothwell & Sons Ltd, Farnham Common Nurseries, Crown Lane, Farnham Royal, Slough, SL2 3SF Tel: (01753) 646012 Fax: (01753) 644087
Edenhall Concrete Ltd, Evergreen, Hale Purlieu, Fordingbridge, Hampshire, SP6 2NN Tel: (01725) 510174 Fax: (01725) 512824

REINFORCED PLASTIC RAINWATER GOODS

M S P (Scotland) Ltd, 1 Telford Road, Cumbernauld, Glasgow, G67 2AX Tel: (01236) 729591 Fax: (01236) 721859
E-mail: helenshaw@mspscot.co.uk
N R S Ltd, 14 Lysander Road, Bowerhill, Melksham, Wiltshire, SN12 6SP Tel: (01225) 709408 Fax: (01225) 708719
E-mail: info@n-rs.co.uk
Polyroof Products Ltd, Castle Park Industrial Estate, Evans Street, Flint, Clwyd, CH6 5XA Tel: (01352) 735135 Fax: (01352) 735182
E-mail: info@polyroof.co.uk
Salty Yacht Productions Ltd, Victoria Wharf, River Bank, Old Town Dock, Newport, Gwent, NP20 2BS Tel: (01633) 250652 Fax: (01633) 842267 E-mail: sales@saltyyachts.com
Shepherds (UK) Ltd, Eastbourne Road Industrial Estate, Eastbourne Road, Westham, Pevensey, East Sussex, BN24 5NH Tel: (01323) 768232 Fax: (01323) 768257
E-mail: abigail@shepherdsuk.co.uk
Specialised Fixing (East Anglia) Ltd, Unit 9, Farthing Road, Ipswich, IP1 5AP Tel: (01473) 461461 Fax: (01473) 240518
E-mail: spencer.priestley@omnico.co.uk

REINFORCED RUBBER SHEET

John Heathcoat & Co Holdings Ltd, Westexe, Tiverton, Devon, EX16 5LL Tel: (01884) 254949 Fax: (01884) 252897
E-mail: email@heathcoat.co.uk

REINFORCING BLACK STEEL BARS

Metal Enterprises & Co. Ltd, 150 Buckingham Palace Road, London, SW1W 9TR Tel: (020) 7730 6134 Fax: (020) 7730 0740
Rom Group Ltd, Eastern Avenue, Trent Valley, Lichfield, Staffordshire, WS13 6RN Tel: (01543) 414111 Fax: (01543) 421605

REINFORCING FABRICS

Express Reinforcements Ltd, High Street, Newburn, Newcastle upon Tyne, NE15 8LN Tel: 0191-264 3311 Fax: 0191-264 7842
Saint Gobain Bti UK Ltd, Unit 4-5 Walworth Industrial Estate, Crown Way, Andover, Hampshire, SP10 5LU Tel: (01264) 333400 Fax: (01264) 359610
E-mail: sales.uk.sgtfc@saint-gobain.com

REINFORCING RINGS, FOR RUBBER HOSES

A.K. Orme & Son, 114-122 Arundel Street, Sheffield, S1 4RE Tel: 0114-272 2409 Fax: 0114-272 2409
E-mail: ormerings@aol.com

REINFORCING WIRE MESH OR FABRICS

Speedwell Reinforcement Ltd, White Lane, Chapeltown, Sheffield, S35 2YG Tel: 0114-246 7551 Fax: 0114-240 2519
E-mail: enquiries@speedwellreinforcement.co.uk

REINSURANCE AGENTS

Compre Group, 110 Fenchurch Street, London, EC3M 5JT Tel: (020) 7816 4400 Fax: (020) 7816 4401
E-mail: consult@compre-group.com

RELATIVE HUMIDITY SENSORS

Enviro Technology Services plc, Unit B1 Kingfisher Business Park, London Road, Thrupp, Stroud, Gloucestershire, GL5 2BY Tel: (01453) 733200 Fax: (01453) 733201
E-mail: sales@et.co.uk

RELAYS, *See also headings for particular types*

B C H Relays Ltd, Unit 15, Phoenix Business Park, Brindley Road, Dodwells Bridge Industrial Estate, Hinckley, Leicestershire, LE10 3BY Tel: (01455) 239675 Fax: (01455) 238795 E-mail: billpower@btconnect.com
Easby Electronics Ltd, Mercury Road, Gallowfields Trading Estate, Richmond, North Yorkshire, DL10 4TQ Tel: (01748) 850555 Fax: (01748) 850556
E-mail: sales@easby.co.uk
Globe Electronics (UK) Ltd, 19 Westmorland Drive, Warfield, Bracknell, Berkshire, RG42 3QJ Tel: (01344) 420775 Fax: (01344) 421194 E-mail: globeuk@btinternet.com
Lohmeier-Comat UK Ltd, 1 Dunston Pl, Dunston Rd, Chesterfield, Derbyshire, S41 8XA Tel: (01246) 264300 Fax: (01246) 264301
E-mail: sales@edlcomat.co.uk
More Control (UK) Ltd, Control House, Mount Farm Industrial Estate, Clarke Road, Bletchley, Milton Keynes, MK1 1LG Tel: (01908) 364555 Fax: (01908) 364511
E-mail: more@more-control.com
Pennine Components Ltd, PO Box 1, Todmorden, Lancashire, OL14 5BB Tel: (01706) 815737 Fax: (01706) 817628
E-mail: sales@penninecomponents.co.uk
Siemens Protection Devices Ltd, PO Box 7, Hebburn, Tyne & Wear, NE31 1TZ Tel: 0191-401 5555 Fax: 0191-401 5575
Telerelay Sales Ltd, Park Drive Industrial Estate, Braintree, Essex, CM7 1AW Tel: (01376) 321216 Fax: (01376) 347910
E-mail: sales@telerelay.sagehost.co.uk
V T M U K Ltd, 8 Corinium Centre, Raans Road, Amersham, Buckinghamshire, HP6 6JQ Tel: (01494) 738600 Fax: (01494) 738610
E-mail: admin@vtm.co.uk

RELAYS, ELECTRICAL/ ELECTROMAGNETIC, *See also headings under Relays*

B C H Relays Ltd, Unit 15, Phoenix Business Park, Brindley Road, Dodwells Bridge Industrial Estate, Hinckley, Leicestershire, LE10 3BY Tel: (01455) 239675 Fax: (01455) 238795 E-mail: billpower@btconnect.com
I M O Electronics Ltd, Unit 15, 1000 North Circular Road, London, NW2 7JP Tel: (020) 8452 6444 Fax: (020) 8450 2274
E-mail: imo@imopc.com
Nortonics Ltd, The Old Bakery, 265 Yorktown Road, Sandhurst, Berkshire, GU47 9BN Tel: (01276) 32777 Fax: (01276) 31977
P & B Weir, Unit 10 Leafield Industrial Estate, Leafield Way, Corsham, Wiltshire, SN13 9SW Tel: (01225) 811449 Fax: (01225) 810909
E-mail: sales@pbweir.com

RELEASE AGENT MANUFRS, *See also headings for particular types*

ECL Chemicals Ltd, Impex House, Leestone Road, Sharston, Manchester, M22 4RN Tel: 0161-491 6744 Fax: 0161-491 6774
E-mail: info@eclchem.com
Macphie of Glenbervie Ltd, Glenbervie, Stonehaven, Kincardineshire, AB39 3YG Tel: (01569) 740641 Fax: (01569) 740677
E-mail: cservice@macphie.com
Pick Quick Service, 380 Meanwood Road, Leeds, LS7 2JF Tel: 0113-216 8811 Fax: 0113-216 8833 E-mail: sales@pickquick.co.uk
Regent Kemicals Ltd, 20 Jubilee Drive, Glenfield, Leicester, LE3 8LJ Tel: 0116-233 6430 Fax: 0116-233 6429

RELEASE COATINGS

Metalcraft Plastic Coatings Ltd, Back Wellington Street, Accrington, Lancashire, BB5 2NW Tel: (01254) 871727 Fax: (01254) 871168
E-mail: claudeen1@btconnect.com

RELEASE FILMS

A P I Coated Products Ltd, The Vineyards, Gloucester Road, Cheltenham, Gloucestershire, GL51 8NH Tel: (01242) 512345 Fax: (01242) 576633
E-mail: enquiries@adcoat.co.uk
Kalico Products Ltd, Panty Buarth, Gwernaffield, Mold, Clwyd, CH7 5ER Tel: (01352) 742100 Fax: (01352) 742102E-mail: info@kalico.co.uk

RELEASE PAPERS

A P I Coated Products Ltd, The Vineyards, Gloucester Road, Cheltenham, Gloucestershire, GL51 8NH Tel: (01242) 512345 Fax: (01242) 576633
E-mail: enquiries@adcoat.co.uk

RELIABILITY TESTING, ELECTRONIC COMPONENT, ENVIRONMENTAL

▶ Reliability Plus, 5 High Street, South Woodchester, Stroud, Gloucestershire, GL5 5EL Tel: 01453 878540 Fax: 01453 878595
E-mail: bob.page@environmental.org.uk

RELIEF VALVES

Prochem Services Ltd, Mill Street, Congleton, Cheshire, CW12 2AD Tel: (01260) 299770 Fax: (01260) 299880
E-mail: info@prochem-services.com
Taylor Valves Ltd, Dowker Works, Dowker Street, Milnsbridge, Huddersfield, HD3 4JX Tel: (01484) 651177 Fax: (01484) 645854

RELIGIOUS BANNERS

▶ Adoremus Contemporary Church Textiles, 14 Beamont Drive, Preston, PR1 8UN Tel: 01772 889111 E-mail: information@adoremus.co.uk

RELIGIOUS CLOAKS

▶ Adoremus Contemporary Church Textiles, 14 Beamont Drive, Preston, PR1 8UN Tel: 01772 889111 E-mail: information@adoremus.co.uk

RELOCATABLE BUILDINGS

▶ Burtenshaw Garden Buildings, Maidstone Road, Paddock Wood, Tonbridge, Kent, TN12 6QJ Tel: (01892) 838027 Fax: (01892) 838027
E-mail: enquiries@burtenshawgardenbuildings.co.uk

RELOCATION CONSULTANTS

▶ Albion Homefinders Yorkshire Ltd, 31 Moor Lane, Addingham, Ilkley, West Yorkshire, LS29 0PS Tel: (01943) 831807
E-mail: info@albionhomefinders.co.uk
Ascott Clark, 42 Western Lane, Buxworth, High Peak, Derbyshire, SK23 7NS Tel: (01663) 734221 Fax: (01663) 734318
E-mail: info@ascottclark.com
▶ Cendant Mobility Ltd, Frankland Road, Swindon, SN5 8RS Tel: (01793) 756000 Fax: (01793) 756400
E-mail: salesemea@cartus.com
Compass Relocation Ltd, 5a Oxenturn Rd, Wye, Ashford, Kent, TN25 5BH Tel: (01233) 813305 Fax: (01233) 812730
Country Wide Mobility Partners, Copenhagen Court, 32 New Street, Basingstoke, Hampshire, RG21 7DT Tel: (01256) 812700 Fax: (01256) 333420
E-mail: info@countrywidemobility.co.uk
Crown Worldwide Movers Ltd, 1 Ninian Park, Ninian Way, Wilnecote, Tamworth, Staffordshire, B77 5ES Tel: (01827) 264100 Fax: (01827) 264101
E-mail: general@crownrelo.com
D A P International Removals Ltd, 209 Manor Road, Erith, Kent, DA8 2AD Tel: (01322) 335621 Fax: (01322) 332518
E-mail: dapinternational@btinternet.com
Charles Dean Partnership Ltd, Brasted Lodge, Westerham Road, Westerham, Kent, TN16 1QH Tel: (01959) 565909 Fax: (01959) 565606 E-mail: sales@charlesdean.co.uk
▶ Morrell Homefinders, 97 Birchwood Way, Park Street, St. Albans, Hertfordshire, AL2 2SF Tel: (01727) 874622 Fax: (01727) 874611
E-mail: info@morrellhomefinders.co.uk
▶ Relocate Cambridge, Manor Farm House, 68 Town Street, Newton, Cambridge, CB2 5PE Tel: (01223) 871394 Fax: (01223) 871394
E-mail: info@relocatecambridge.co.uk
▶ Relocate South West, 12 Aish Park, Shebbear, Beaworthy, Devon, EX21 5QL Tel: (01409) 281546 Fax: (01409) 281991
E-mail: enquiries@relocatesouthwest.co.uk
Relocation Information Services, 4 Oxted Chambers, 185 Station Road East, Oxted, Surrey, RH8 0QE Tel: (01883) 732000 Fax: (01883) 732222
E-mail: info@ris-move.co.uk
▶ Relocation Relocation, 35A Ludgate, Alloa, Clackmannanshire, FK10 1DS Tel: (01259) 212478 Fax: (01259) 212478
E-mail: lisa@relocationrelocation.net
Team Relocations, 20 Thistle St La North West, Edinburgh, EH2 1EA Tel: 0131-260 3360 Fax: 0131-260 3361
Your Wish Is My Command Limited, 2nd Floor, Westminster House, 188 Stratford Road, Shirley, Solihull, West Midlands, B90 3AQ Tel: 0845 8380548
E-mail: genie@yourwishismycommand.co.uk

REMOTE BACKUP SOFTWARE

▶ Project Desk2Web, 5 Ashburn Avenue, Waterside, Londonderry, BT47 5QE Tel: (020) 8123 6355
E-mail: allannospam@desk2web.co.uk

REMOTE CONTROL SYSTEMS, CABLE/ELECTRICAL

Remote Control Ltd, Unit 40 Trent Valley Trading Estate, Station Road, Rugeley, Staffordshire, WS15 2HQ Tel: (01889) 577676 Fax: (01889) 577676
E-mail: lesgarbett@remotecontrol.co.uk

REMOTE CONTROL SYSTEMS, RADIO, MODEL CAR

▶ LYLLOY Co.,LTD, Unit 60, 3-9 Hyde Road, Ardwick Green, Manchester, M12 6BQ Tel: 0773 0383126
Seaton Hobby Shop, Goulden Lion House, 23 Fore Street, Seaton, Devon, EX12 2LE Tel: (01297) 22025 Fax: (01297) 22025
E-mail: email@seatonhobbyshop.com

REMOTE DATA ACQUISITION SYSTEMS

A Ii D Solutions Ltd, 2 Wyvern Avenue, Stockport, Cheshire, SK5 7DD Tel: 0161-480 3163 Fax: 0161-480 3043 E-mail: info@aiid.co.uk
Data Track Technology P.L.C., 153 Somerford Road, Christchurch, Dorset, BH23 3TY Tel: (01425) 270333 Fax: (01425) 270433
E-mail: sales@dtrack.com
Field Electronics Ltd, 23 Star Road, Star Trading Estate, Partridge Green, Horsham, West Sussex, RH13 8RA Tel: (01403) 713772 Fax: (0870) 0271033
E-mail: sales@fieldelectronics.com
Radio Data Logger Co. Ltd, 75 Silver Street, Newport Pagnell, Buckinghamshire, MK16 0EQ Tel: (01908) 618932 Fax: (01908) 618932 E-mail: enq@radiolog.co.uk

REMOTE HANDLING TOOLS

Cee Vee Engineering Ltd, Shepherds Close, Cooden Sea Road, Bexhill-on-Sea, East Sussex, TN39 4SL Tel: (01424) 845566 Fax: (01424) 842144
E-mail: sales@ceevee.co.uk

REMOTE MONITORING CLOSED CIRCUIT TELEVISION (CCTV) SYSTEMS

▶ P & R Security Systems Ltd, 119 Lees Road, Oldham, OL4 1JW Tel: 0161-652 9984 Fax: 0161-620 8111
E-mail: sales@pandrsecurities.co.uk

▶ indicates data change since last edition

REMOTE OPERATIONS TECHNOLOGY CONSULTANTS OR DESIGNERS

Insite Ltd, PO Box 77, Tunbridge Wells, Kent, TN2 5ZL Tel: (01892) 686000 Fax: (01892) 676002 E-mail: sales@insite-europe.co.uk

REMOVABLE SECURITY POST SYSTEMS

Aremco Products, Foxoak Street, Cradley Heath, West Midlands, B64 5DQ Tel: (01384) 568566 Fax: (01384) 634601 E-mail: sales@aremco-products.co.uk

Centinel Security Services, 2 Corn Kiln Close, Cogenhoe, Northampton, NN7 1NX Tel: (01604) 890686 Fax: (01604) 890686 E-mail: sales@centinel.fsnet.co.uk

REMOVAL CONTRACTORS, *See also specialist services*

1st Class Transport, 60 Birchen Grove, London, NW9 8SA Tel: (020) 8205 2244 Fax: (020) 8838 1515

▶ A B C Removals & Storage, High Peaks, Church Lane, Bledlow Ridge, High Wycombe, Buckinghamshire, HP14 4AX Tel: (01494) 481277 E-mail: info@abcremovalsandstorage.com

A E Corkill Removals Ltd, Removal House, Finch Road, Douglas, Isle of Man, IM1 2PW Tel: (01624) 675495 Fax: (01624) 661095

A Wilkins & Sons, Unit 1 3 The Elms Centre, Glaziers Lane, Normandy, Guildford, Surrey, GU3 2DF Tel: (01483) 575919 Fax: (01483) 570140

AA Removals, 64 Ridge Road, Crouch End, London, N8 9LH Tel: (07845) 783589 E-mail: rachel_taylor_007@hotmail.com

Abbey Self Storage, Abbey Business Centre, Ingate Place, London, SW8 3NS Tel: (020) 7627 8000 Fax: (020) 7720 6633

Abels Moving Services Ltd, Wimbledon Avenue, Brandon, Suffolk, IP27 0NZ Tel: (01842) 816600 Fax: (01842) 813613 E-mail: enquiries@abels.co.uk

▶ Able Removal Services, 6 K9 Industrial Estate, Ferry Lane, Rainham, Essex, RM13 9YH Tel: (01708) 555665 Fax: (01708) 555778

Albatross, 63 Orchard Way, Croydon, CR0 7NQ Tel: (020) 8777 2665 E-mail: albatrossremoval@aol.com

▶ All-Around Handyman Services, Benedicts, Bosham Lane, Bosham, West Sussex, PO18 8HG Tel: 01243 572127 E-mail: office@all-around.co.uk

Armstrongs, Hawthorne Road, Bootle, Merseyside, L20 2DG Tel: 0151-922 1910 Fax: (01704) 896890

▶ Arrowpak Removals & Storage, Westwood Farm, Westwood, Peterborough, PE3 9UW Tel: (01733) 333445 Fax: (01733) 333665

B Vaughan & Partners, 14 Northbourne Avenue, Shanklin, Isle of Wight, PO37 7LT Tel: (01983) 864175 E-mail: mark.harrison@tiscali.co.uk

Badgers Removals, Unit 11 Nathan Way, London, SE28 0BQ Tel: (020) 8317 4500 Fax: (020) 8317 3539

Barnes Of Lincoln Ltd, Fort Barnes, Freeman Road, North Hykeham, Lincoln, LN6 9AP Tel: (01522) 686404 Fax: (01522) 681000

Benn & Sons (Halifax) Ltd, Essex Street Industrial Park, Essex Street, Bradford, West Yorkshire, BD4 7PG Tel: (01422) 365308 Fax: (01274) 393537

Bishop's Blatchpack, Kestrel Way, Sowton Industrial Estate, Exeter, EX2 7PA Tel: (01392) 202040 Fax: (01392) 201251 E-mail: blatchpack@bishops-move.co.uk

Bishops Move, 1-5 Kelvin Way, Crawley, West Sussex, RH10 9SP Tel: (01293) 512646 Fax: (01293) 550105 E-mail: crawley@bishopsmove.com

▶ Bishops Move, Unit 11, South Hampshire Industrial Park, Totton, Southampton, SO40 3SA Tel: (023) 8023 7100 Fax: (023) 8086 7888 E-mail: southampton@bishopsmove.com

Bishop's Move, Bishops House, Lodge Road, Long Hanborough, Witney, Oxfordshire, OX29 8LQ Tel: (01993) 883377 Fax: (01993) 883646 E-mail: oxford@bishops-move.co.uk

▶ Bishops Move Birmingham, Unit 10 The I O Centre, Nash Road, Redditch, Worcestershire, B98 7AS Tel: (01527) 522925 Fax: (01527) 528252 E-mail: liverpool@bishopsmove.com

Bishops Move Chichester Ltd, 3 The Nelson Centre, Portfield Road, Portsmouth, PO3 5SF Tel: (023) 9266 9350 Fax: (023) 9266 9399 E-mail: portsmouth@bishopsmove.co.uk

Bishops Move (Guildford) Ltd, Unit 3 Riverway Industrial Estate, Portsmouth Road, Peasmarsh, Guildford, Surrey, GU3 1LZ Tel: (01483) 722207 Fax: (01483) 302454 E-mail: gillford@bishopsmove.com

Bishop's Move Industrial & Household, South Road, Brighton, BN1 6SB Tel: (01273) 557423 Fax: (01273) 501295 E-mail: brighton@bishops-move.co.uk

Bishops Move Maidstone, 14 Spa Industrial Park, Longfield Road, Tunbridge Wells, Kent, TN2 3EN Tel: (01892) 530191 Fax: (01892) 540201 E-mail: tunbridgewells@bishopsmove.com

Bishop'S Move Overseas, Bishops House, 102-104 Stewarts Road, London, SW8 4UG Tel: (020) 8391 8222 Fax: (020) 7498 0749 E-mail: commercial@bishops-move.co.uk

Bishops Move Wokingham Ltd, Oaklands Business Centre, Oaklands Park, Wokingham, Berkshire, RG41 2FD Tel: (01276) 685515 Fax: 0118-977 3183 E-mail: wokingham@bishopsmove.co.uk

Bonner International, 19 Kennet Road, Dartford, DA1 4QN Tel: (020) 8303 6261 Fax: (01322) 556882 E-mail: moving@dbonner.co.uk

Britania Leatherbarrows, Building, 105 Aviation Park West, Hurn, Christchurch, Dorset, BH23 6NW Tel: (01202) 495600 Fax: (01202) 581639 E-mail: admin@1eatherbarrows.co.uk

▶ Brittains Removals, Alington Road, Eynesbury St Neots, St. Neots, Cambridgeshire, PE19 6YH Tel: (01480) 405161 E-mail: admin@brittainsremovals.co.uk

Burke Bros, Foxs Lane, Wolverhampton, WV1 1PA Tel: (01902) 714555 Fax: (01902) 427837 E-mail: sales@burkebros.co.uk

Burton & Smith Moving Ltd, Movement House Soho Mills, London Road, Wallington, Surrey, SM6 7HN Tel: (020) 8773 1122 Fax: (020) 8773 0590 E-mail: sales@burton-smith.co.uk

Business Moves Ltd, 4 Acre Road, Reading, RG2 0SX Tel: 0118-933 6600 Fax: 0118-975 3586 E-mail: info@businessmove.com

C Bain Of Upminster, 164 Upminster Road, Upminster, Essex, RM14 2RB Tel: (01708) 440113 Fax: (01708) 454321

C G Removal, 184-186 Oakleigh Road North, London, N20 0UA Tel: (020) 8361 7273 Fax: (020) 8368 9590

▶ Carters Removals Ltd, Penlan Works, Llandegai, Llandygai, Bangor, Gwynedd, LL57 4AA Tel: (01248) 370109 Fax: (0870) 7059127 E-mail: mail@cartersremovals.plus.com

Casserly's Removals & Storage Ltd, Unit 10, Gledrid Industrial Park, Gledrid, Chirk, Wrexham, LL14 5DG Tel: (0800) 3581822 Fax: (01691) 778580

City Moving & Storage Ltd, Canada House Business Centre, 272 Field End Road, Ruislip, Middlesex, HA4 9NA Tel: (020) 8582 0420 Fax: (020) 8582 0421 E-mail: info@citymoving.co.uk

▶ Clockwork Removals Ltd, 2 Armoury Way, London, SW18 1SH Tel: (020) 8870 6176 Fax: (020) 8870 6054

Colemans Removals & Storage, Unit 16, Garston Industrial Estate, Blackburne Street, Liverpool, L19 8JA Tel: 0151-494 3251 Fax: 0151-494 0034

Commercial & Personal Relocations Ltd, Space Centre, Legg Brothers Industrial Estate, Spring Road, Wolverhampton, WV4 6JT Tel: (01902) 491001 Fax: (01902) 491002 E-mail: liz@cpr-uk.com

▶ Cranbury's Removals & Storage, 25 Leigh Road, Eastleigh, Hampshire, SO50 9FF Tel: (023) 8065 2630 Fax: (023) 8061 7164

▶ Crispins Services Ltd, 35-37 Pearson Street, London, E2 8JD Tel: (020) 7739 0303 Fax: (020) 7739 7757 E-mail: e-mail@crispins-removals.co.uk

Crofton Park Removals Ltd, Unit 8 Thurston Industrial Estate, Jerrard Street, London, SE13 7SH Tel: (020) 8318 5731 Fax: (020) 8318 5787

▶ Crown Worlwide Movers Ltd, 7 Lockwood Court, Middleton Grove Road, Leeds, LS11 5TY Tel: 0113-277 1000

D J Mills, 23 Mead Road, Cheltenham, Gloucestershire, GL53 7DY Tel: (01242) 528633 Fax: (01242) 528633

Delivery Service Ltd, Stoke Hall Road, Ipswich, IP2 8EJ Tel: (01473) 601564 Fax: (01473) 602789 E-mail: sales@ipswichdeliveryservice.co.uk

Deltamove Ltd, Clare Terrace, Carterton, Oxfordshire, OX18 3ES Tel: (01993) 845020 Fax: (01993) 843023 E-mail: andy@deltamove.co.uk

Denmans Of Whitchurch, Highgate, Whitchurch, Shropshire, SY13 1SD Tel: (01948) 666611 Fax: (01948) 667723 E-mail: denmanmovers@aol.com

Dibbin's Removals & Storage, Nicholson Road, Ryde, Isle of Wight, PO33 1BQ Tel: (01983) 566425 Fax: (01983) 566211 E-mail: sales@dibbensremovals.com

Drury Smart, 148 Brierley Road, Walton Summit Centre, Bamber Bridge, Preston, PR5 8AH Tel: (01704) 533243 Fax: (01772) 318400

E & A Wates Ltd, 82-84 Mitcham Lane, London, SW16 6NR Tel: (020) 8769 2205 Fax: (020) 8677 4766 E-mail: sales@eandawates.co.uk

▶ Easymove (Bristol) Ltd, Albert Crescent, Bristol, BS2 0SU Tel: 0117-977 1460

Edwards, Strathmore Avenue, Luton, LU1 3NZ Tel: (01582) 730256 Fax: (01582) 730256

▶ Elite Removals, Dane Road, Margate, Kent, CT9 2AF Tel: (01843) 226736 E-mail: bernie@eliteremovalsmargate.co.uk

Enterprise Storage & Removals, 118-120 Garratt Lane, London, SW18 4DJ Tel: (020) 8874 6673

Eric Delo Ltd, Padstow Road, Coventry, CV4 9XB Tel: (024) 7669 5011 Fax: (024) 7669 4303 E-mail: eric.delo@virgin.net

▶ European Van Lines International Ltd, Unit 3 100 Church Street, Staines, Middlesex, TW18 4YA Tel: (01784) 466117 Fax: (01784) 464484 E-mail: info@evl.co.uk

Exclusive Move Solutions, 1 Cooks Road, London, E15 2PW Tel: (020) 8555 5179 Fax: (020) 8555 5172 E-mail: info@move-ems.com

▶ F Chapman & Sons Ltd, International House, 19 Kennet Road, Dartford, DA1 4QN Tel: (01892) 833313 Fax: (01322) 556882

F R Hackworthy & Sons, Depository, Elliott Road, Plymouth, PL4 0SB Tel: (01752) 228815 Fax: (01752) 600615

▶ Falconer Removals, Foundry Road, Ammanford, Dyfed, SA18 2LS Tel: (01792) 465353 Fax: (01269) 597697

Fergusons (Blyth) Ltd, Ennerdale Road, Kitty Brewster Estate, Blyth, Northumberland, NE24 4RD Tel: (01670) 353761 Fax: (01670) 357401 E-mail: sales@fergusonsremovals.co.uk

Finch & Co., Homestead, Eastwick Road, Bookham, Leatherhead, Surrey, KT23 4BA Tel: (01372) 452711 Fax: (01372) 450957 E-mail: info@machinemovers.co.uk

▶ Five Valleys Removals, 22 Quedgeley Trading Estate East, Haresfield, Stonehouse, Gloucestershire, GL10 3EX Tel: (01452) 729056 Fax: (01452) 729494

Fleet Removals Of Liverpool, Fleet House, Stretton Way, Liverpool, L36 6JF Tel: 0151-489 7990 Fax: 0151-480 6277 E-mail: malf@fleetremovals.co.uk

Fletchers Removals, Racecourse Industrial Park, Mansfield Road, Derby, DE21 4SX Tel: (01332) 371470 Fax: (01332) 294397 E-mail: sales@webbesremovals.net

▶ Fox Group Ltd, 10 Somerset Road, Cwmbran, Gwent, NP44 1QX Tel: (0800) 3893863 E-mail: sales@fox-moving.com

Fox Moving & Storage, Block C, Stourbridge Industrial Estate, Mill Race Lane, Stourbridge, West Midlands, DY8 1YL Tel: (01384) 395072 Fax: (01384) 440520 E-mail: stourbridge@fox-moving.com

G B Liners Ltd, 8 Haslemere Industrial Estate, Third Way, Avonmouth, Bristol, BS11 9TP Tel: 0117-982 8141 E-mail: bristol@gbliners.com

G B Liners Ltd, Blaisdon Way, Cheltenham, Gloucestershire, GL51 0WH Tel: (01242) 523785 Fax: (01242) 221189 E-mail: cheltenham@gbliners.com

G B N Removal Co. Ltd, Estate Way, London, E10 7JN Tel: (020) 8556 2211 Fax: (020) 8532 8519 E-mail: Gbnremoval@aol.com

G C Parish & Sons, 92 High Street, Bovingdon, Hemel Hempstead, Hertfordshire, HP3 0HJ Tel: (01442) 832341 Fax: (01442) 409313 E-mail: sales@parishremovals.co.uk

George Pickersgill & Sons Ltd, Unit 11 Hirstwood Works, Hirst Wood Road, Shipley, West Yorkshire, BD18 4BU Tel: (01274) 594333 Fax: (01274) 594888 E-mail: sales@georgepickersgill.co.uk

▶ Gibson Taylor Tranzol Ltd, Bent Ley Farm, Bent Ley Road, Meltham, Holmfirth, HD9 4AP Tel: (01484) 859293 Fax: (01484) 859339 E-mail: zoltan.gibsontaylor@btconnect.com

Gilbert Norris Removals, Wakefield Road, Netherton, Bootle, Merseyside, L30 6TZ Tel: 0151-530 1196 Fax: 0151-524 1808

Hadley & Ottaway Ltd, The Depository, Muspole Street, Norwich, NR3 1DJ Tel: (01603) 622538 E-mail: info@hadleyandottaway.co.uk

Hardakers Removal & Storage Ltd, 87-89 Gillett Street, Hull, HU3 4JF Tel: (01482) 323069 Fax: (01482) 580652 E-mail: enqures@hardakers.co.uk

Harold Jones Removals & Storage, 15 Westfield Road, Rhyl, Clwyd, LL18 4PN Tel: (01745) 855145 Fax: (01745) 855145

Harrow Green Removals Ltd, Unit Q1, Queen Elizabeth Distribution Park, Purfleet, Essex, RM19 1TT Tel: (020) 8551 3555 Fax: (020) 8551 9199 E-mail: sales@harrowgreen.com

Hartgrove Bros, Station Road, Redcar, Cleveland, TS10 1RD Tel: (01642) 489937 Fax: (01642) 489937

Higgs Removals Great Barr Ltd, 31 Rippingille Road, Birmingham, B43 7DJ Tel: 0121-360 9366 Fax: 0121-325 0921

Holbrook Removals, 24 Abingdon Road, Ryde, Isle of Wight, PO33 2RR Tel: (01983) 566616 Fax: (01983) 566616

Hoults Removals Ltd, Crown House, Earlsway, Team Valley Trading Estate, Gateshead, Tyne & Wear, NE11 0RQ Tel: 0191-265 3696 Fax: 0191-482 4259 E-mail: houltsremovals@hoults.co.uk

House Removals, Fosse Way, Thrussington, Leicester, LE7 4TF Tel: (0800) 9805866 Fax: (01664) 424919 E-mail: sales@houseremovals.com

Hunt S Removals Ltd, 11-13 Market Close, Crewe, CW1 2NA Tel: (01606) 44655 Fax: (01270) 255884 E-mail: enquiries@huntsremovals.co.uk

The International Moving Co., Unit B1, Stewart Road, Altrincham, Cheshire, WA14 5GR Tel: 0161-876 8844 Fax: 0161-929 8765 E-mail: sthelens@int-moving.com

Island Removals, Manners View, Newport, Isle of Wight, PO30 5FA Tel: (01983) 526374 Fax: (01983) 526374 E-mail: info@islandremovals.co.uk

J Kool, Acre Holdings, Little Weighton Road, Skidby, Cottingham, North Humberside, HU16 5TP Tel: (01482) 875747 Fax: (01482) 845024 E-mail: sales@jkoo1-engineers.co.uk

J Newby & Sons, Mintsfeet Road South, Kendal, Cumbria, LA9 6ND Tel: (01539) 720819 Fax: (01539) 734607 E-mail: pickfords.preston@pickfords.com

Jarretts Transport Ltd, 115-121 Waterworks Road, Norwich, NR2 4DE Tel: (01603) 621862 Fax: (01603) 629087 E-mail: info@jarrettsremovals.co.uk

Jeakins Removals Ltd, Charles House, Denbigh Road, Basildon, Essex, SS15 6PY Tel: (01268) 417320 Fax: (01268) 414443 E-mail: enquiries@jeakins-removals.co.uk

Jet Removal Services, Plantation Road, Burscough Industrial Estate, Burscough, Lancashire, L40 8JT Tel: (01704) 895206 Fax: (01704) 896890 E-mail: sales@jetremovals.co.uk

▶ Jex Engineering Co. Ltd, Adam Smith Street, Grimsby, South Humberside, DN31 1SJ Tel: (01472) 361311 Fax: (01472) 240218 E-mail: phill.bodsworth@jexengineering.com

John Mason London Ltd, 35 Wilson Road, Huyton, Liverpool, L36 6AE Tel: 0151-449 3938 Fax: 0151-449 2690 E-mail: sales@johnmason.com

F.A. Jones & Son, 57 West Road, Shoeburyness, Southend-On-Sea, SS3 9DR Tel: (01702) 292320 Fax: (01702) 294501

Jordan & Cook, Ivy Arch Road, Worthing, West Sussex, BN14 8BX Tel: (01903) 235701 Fax: (01903) 824245 E-mail: phremovals@aol.com

K C Office Services Ltd, The Relocation Centre, Blenheim Road, Lancing, West Sussex, BN15 8UQ Tel: (01903) 600400 Fax: (01903) 607082 E-mail: ops@kcos.co.uk

▶ Kellylink Ltd, Unit 2, Arrow Road North, Lakeside, Redditch, Worcestershire, B98 8NT Tel: (01527) 62222 Fax: (01527) 62222 E-mail: info@kellylink.co.uk

Kidd Services (Yorkshire), International House, Cliff Road, Hornsea, North Humberside, HU18 1JB Tel: (01964) 537000 Fax: (01964) 537111 E-mail: user@kidds.co.uk

Laceys I O W Ltd, 42 High Street, Bembridge, Isle of Wight, PO35 5SF Tel: (01983) 872663 Fax: (01983) 872575 E-mail: sales@laceysremovals.co.uk

▶ Lakehaven, Unit K2, Eagle Road, Langage Business Park, Plymouth, PL7 5JY Tel: (01752) 231881 Fax: (01752) 231882

▶ Lanes Storage & Removals, Greenbottom, Chacewater, Truro, Cornwall, TR4 8QW Tel: (01872) 560147 Fax: (01872) 561051

Larchbond Facilities Ltd, Ongar Hall Farm, Brentwood Road, Orsett, Grays, Essex, RM16 3HU Tel: (01375) 892929 Fax: (01375) 892624 E-mail: sales@larchbond.co.uk

Lewis & Sons, 8 Silver Street, Barnstaple, Devon, EX32 8HR Tel: (01271) 342336 Fax: (01271) 323330

▶ Lund-Conlon Removers & Storers, Remstore House, Wolseley Road, Kempston, Bedford, MK42 7EF Tel: (01234) 404411 Fax: (01234) 404422

▶ Mac Pac, Units 1 & 2, Baillieston Distribution Centre, Baillieston, Glasgow, G69 6UL Tel: 0141-781 4888 Fax: 0141-781 4788

Magpie Services, Derwent Howe Indust Estate, Adams Road, Derwent Howe Industrial Estate, Workington, Cumbria, CA14 3YS Tel: (01900) 872892 Fax: (01900) 67765 E-mail: magpie@thismove.com

Martells Of Sutton Ltd, Unit 3, 4, Charlwoods Road, East Grinstead, West Sussex, RH19 2HG Tel: (01342) 321303 Fax: (01342) 302145 E-mail: removals@martells.co.uk

Masons Moving Group Ltd, Storage House, Priority Business Park, Barry, South Glamorgan, CF63 2BG Tel: (01446) 733330 Fax: (01446) 733827 E-mail: enquiries@masonsmovinggroup.co.uk

▶ Matthew James Ltd, 6 Poyntell Cresent, Chislehurst, Kent, BR7 6PJ Tel: (020) 8467 6292 Fax: (01322) 437508

Mendz Industrial Move Ltd, Abbey Meadows, Back Lane, Cotes, Loughborough, Leicestershire, LE12 5TA Tel: (01509) 212711 Fax: (01509) 212722

A.J. & R.J. Mew, 20 Mayfield Road, Ryde, Isle Of Wight, PO33 3TR Tel: (01983) 852835 Fax: (01983) 568758

Michael Gerson Finance plc, Downland Close, Whetstone, London, N20 9LB Tel: (020) 8446 1300 Fax: (020) 8446 5088 E-mail: moving@michaelgerson.com

F.C. Morgan (Removals) Ltd, 30 Crosby Road North, Liverpool, L22 4QF Tel: 0151-928 3154 Fax: 0151-928 2848

Morleys, 2 Waterworks Road, Eastbourne, East Sussex, BN22 8LR Tel: (01323) 725793 Fax: (01323) 734193

▶ Company Moves, 39 Invinsible Road, Farnborough, Hampshire, GU14 7QU Tel: (01252) 549381 Fax: (01252) 376413 E-mail: comoves7@aol.com

Moving Home Co. Ltd, Serin House, Hindsley Place, London, SE23 2NF Tel: (020) 8699 6766 Fax: (020) 8699 5067 E-mail: services@movinghomecompany.com

▶ Nationwide Self Storage Ltd, 620 Western Avenue, London, W3 0TE Tel: (020) 8992 1700

▶ Needhams Removals, 302 Old Shoreham Road, Southwick, Brighton, BN42 4LN Tel: (01273) 889403 E-mail: info@needhams.co.uk

New Move, Tenmore House, Kennford Road, Marsh Barton Trading Estate, Exeter, EX2 8LY Tel: (01392) 491000 Fax: (01392) 491911

Northover & Gilbert Removals, Gundry Lane, Bridport, Dorset, DT6 3RJ Tel: (01308) 423939 Fax: (01308) 423939

▶ Osbornes Removals & Storage Ltd, Remco House, Wharf Road, Sale, Cheshire, M33 2AF Tel: 0161-236 0358 Fax: 0161-969 9879

Overs Of Camberley Ltd, Springlakes Estate, Deadbrook Lane, Aldershot, Hampshire, GU12 4UH Tel: (01252) 714233 Fax: (01252) 345861 E-mail: internationalrelocation@overs.co.uk

REMOVAL CONTRACTORS – *continued*

P Fahey & Sons Holdings Ltd, 92 Chorlton Road, Stretford, Manchester, M15 4AL Tel: 0161-226 5959 Fax: 0161-227 9747 E-mail: removals@faheygroup.co.uk

Page The Packers, Old Station Road, Ventnor, Isle of Wight, PO38 1DX Tel: (01983) 852951 Fax: (01983) 855956 E-mail: info@page-packers.fsnet.co.uk

Peters Removals, 14 Alun Cresent, Chester, CH4 8HN Tel: (01244) 682084

PHS Teacrate The Crate Rental Specialists, 151 Scrubs Lane, London, NW10 6RH Tel: (020) 8282 0000 Fax: (020) 8282 0022 E-mail: info@teacrate.com

Pickfords Ltd, 2a Brunel Way, Fareham, Hampshire, PO15 5TX Tel: (023) 9282 1325 Fax: (01489) 573128

Pickfords Ltd, 37C Munster Rd, London, SW6 4ES Tel: (020) 7736 2381 Fax: (020) 7731 6459

Pink & Jones, Britannia House, Riley Road, Telford Way Industrial Estate, Kettering, Northamptonshire, NN16 8NN Tel: (01604) 714448 Fax: (01604) 410584 E-mail: removals@pinkandjones.co.uk

▶ Andrew Porter Ltd, Huyton Road, Adlington, Chorley, Lancashire, PR7 4EZ Tel: (01257) 482398 Fax: (01257) 484324

Porters Of Woking, 5 North Road, Woking, Surrey, GU21 5DS Tel: (01483) 765432 Fax: (01483) 756432 E-mail: sales@portersremovals.co.uk

Potbury & Sons Ltd, 17-31 High Street, Sidmouth, Devon, EX10 8LN Tel: (01395) 515555 Fax: (01395) 512608 E-mail: potbury@aol.com

Prentice Logistics Ltd, 14 Clifton Road, Cambridge, CB1 7EA Tel: (01223) 213131 Fax: (01223) 240021 E-mail: mail@prenticeofcambridge.com

Purvers International Ltd, Gateway House, Fareham Road, Gosport, Hampshire, PO13 0FW Tel: (01329) 238111 Fax: (01329) 825888 E-mail: mail@purvers.co.uk

Quickmove Of Whiltshire Ltd, Harris Road, Portemarsh Trading Estate, Calne, Wiltshire, SN11 9PT Tel: (01249) 813430

Reads Removal, Westwood Farm, Westwood, Peterborough, PE3 9UW Tel: (01733) 334411 Fax: (01733) 334320 E-mail: sales@readsremovals.co.uk

Revells Warehousing & Transport, Eastlands Industrial Estate, Leiston, Suffolk, IP16 4LL Tel: (01728) 830849 Fax: (01728) 830849 E-mail: revellsremovals@aol.com

Keith Rhodes Machinery Installations Ltd, Ashmore House, Lower Tuffley Lane, Gloucester, GL2 5DP Tel: (01452) 303037 Fax: (01452) 311166 E-mail: keithrhodes@lineone.net

Richman Ring Ltd, Eurolink Way, Sittingbourne, Kent, ME10 3HH Tel: (01795) 427365 Fax: (01795) 428804 E-mail: info@richman-rwg.com

▶ RJ Haulage, 15 Kingscote Road, Croydon, CR0 7DP Tel: 079 32156627 E-mail: roger@rjhaulage.co.uk

A. Robins & Sons Ltd, Unit 9 Spring Lakes Industrial Estate, Deadbrooke Lane, Aldershot, Hampshire, GU12 4UH Tel: (0800) 243433 Fax: (01252) 345861 E-mail: sales@overs.co.uk

Robinsons International Removals Ltd, Nuffield Way, Abingdon, Oxfordshire, OX14 1TN Tel: (01235) 552266 Fax: (01235) 553573 E-mail: oxford@robinsons-intl.com

Robinsons International Removals Ltd, Bartleet Road, Redditch, Worcestershire, B98 0DG Tel: (01527) 830850 Fax: (01527) 526812 E-mail: redditch@robinsons-intl.com

▶ Robinsons International Removals Ltd, Oakley Road, Southampton, SO16 4LL Tel: (023) 8051 5111

Rumsey & Sons, Market House, Market Road, Richmond, Surrey, TW9 4LZ Tel: (020) 8892 1896 Fax: (020) 8876 9969 E-mail: removals@rumseyandson.com

Ryans Move International Ltd, Unit 14 Gateway Industrial Estate, Hythe Road, London, NW10 6RJ Tel: (020) 8969 7047 Fax: (020) 8969 1326E-mail: britannia@ryansmove.co.uk

S Dell & Sons Ltd, Unit 1 Canalside, North Bridge Road, Berkhamsted, Hertfordshire, HP4 1EG Tel: (01442) 863959 Fax: (01442) 862163

S J Sharp (Nuneaton) Ltd, Weddington Road, Nuneaton, Warwickshire, CV10 0AE Tel: (024) 7638 3232 Fax: (024) 7638 2362

Saunders of Harpenden, 31 Frogmore, Park Street, St. Albans, Hertfordshire, AL2 2NH Tel: (01727) 875348 Fax: (01727) 875068

Security Escorts Services, 6 Standard Road, London, NW10 6EU Tel: (020) 8965 3215 Fax: (020) 8961 5298 E-mail: sales@securityescorts.com

Selles Removals & Storage, Dairycoates Industrial Estate, Wiltshire Road, Hull, HU4 6PA Tel: (01482) 562822 Fax: (01482) 562832

Selles Removals & Storage, Dairycoates Industrial Estate, Wiltshire Road, Hull, HU4 6PA Tel: (01482) 562822 Fax: (01482) 562832 E-mail: nicola.mason@selles-removals.co.uk

F.W. Shaw & Sons (Worthing) Ltd, 3 Tudor Buildings, Aldwick Street, Bognor Regis, West Sussex, PO21 3AW Tel: (01903) 237174 Fax: (01243) 860267 E-mail: move@sussex-moving-services.com

Small Removal Co., 2 Southdown Industrial Estate, Southdown Road, Harpenden, Hertfordshire, AL5 1PW Tel: (01582) 760783 Fax: (01582) 760783

Smarts Of Northolt, Unit 15 The Metropolitan Centre, Derby Road, Greenford, Middlesex, UB6 8UJ Tel: (0500) 030609 Fax: (020) 8575 8804 E-mail: sales@smartsremovals.co.uk

Stewart Harvey & Woodbridge Ltd, Eldenwall Industrial Estate, Whalebone La South, Dagenham, Essex, RM8 1AU Tel: (020) 8517 0011 Fax: (020) 8592 0827 E-mail: shw@shwlondon.co.uk

Strank's Removals, Unit 5 Wotton Trading Estate, Ashford, Kent, TN23 6LL Tel: (01233) 646478 Fax: (01233) 645653 E-mail: admin@stranks-removals.co.uk

D. Sully & Son Ltd, Unit 4 Coldharbour Lane Industrial Estate, 129 Coldharbour Lane, London, SE5 9NY Tel: (020) 7733 3559 E-mail: sales@sully.co.uk

▶ Sutton's Removals, 12 Sandiford Road, Sutton, Surrey, SM3 9RD Tel: (020) 8641 6767 Fax: (020) 8644 4018 E-mail: sales@sutton-removals.com

Taylors Removals Ltd, The Potters, 13 Central Way, Cwmbran, Gwent, NP44 5HT Tel: (01633) 276555 Fax: (01633) 290888

Thomas Removals, 50 Salop Road, Wrexham, Clwyd, LL13 7AF Tel: (0800) 7834581 Fax: (01978) 366478 E-mail: info@thomas-removals.co.uk

Thompsons, Boxwood Street, Blackburn, BB1 9TW Tel: (01254) 691348 Fax: (01254) 695122

▶ Town & Country, Water Eaton Lane, Penkridge, Stafford, ST19 5QE Tel: (01785) 714600 Fax: (01785) 711221 E-mail: andycoombs@townandcountry.uk.com

▶ Town & Country, Water Eaton Lane, Penkridge, Stafford, ST19 5QE Tel: (01785) 714600 Fax: (01785) 711221 E-mail: andycoombs@townandcountry.uk.com

Transpeed Removals, Unit 2B, Gatwick Business Park, Kennel Lane Kennel Lane Kennel Lane, Hookwood, Horley, Surrey, RH6 0AY Tel: (01293) 774672 Fax: (01293) 822564 E-mail: sales@transpeed-removals.co.uk

Turner Removal Services, Huyton Road, Adlington, Chorley, Lancashire, PR7 4JR Tel: (01254) 56182 Fax: (01257) 484324

Turners Removals, 7 The Courtyard, Crawley Road, Faygate, Horsham, West Sussex, RH12 4SE Tel: (01293) 852030 Fax: (01293) 852031 E-mail: turnersremovals@aol.com

U T S Johnsons Removals Storage, Unit 1 Parker Industrial Estate, Mansfield Road, Derby, DE21 4SZ Tel: (01332) 371452 Fax: (01332) 298803 E-mail: moves@johnsons-rs.co.uk

W H Humphreys & Son Ltd, 1 Sydney Road, Watford, WD18 7XX Tel: (01923) 226206 Fax: (01923) 210355 E-mail: sales@humphreys-moving.com

W Mcmullin & Sons, 27 Desborough Lane, Plymouth, PL4 9PJ Tel: (01752) 660874 Fax: (01752) 660874 E-mail: wmcmullinandsons@btconnect.com

Walker Holding Ltd, 33-34 Liliput Road, Brackmills Industrial Estate, Northampton, NN4 7DT Tel: (01604) 760529 Fax: (01604) 675641 E-mail: sales@walkerpack.co.uk

Walmley Removals & Transport, 270 Great Lister Street, Birmingham, B7 4DB Tel: 0121-359 8558 Fax: 0121-359 6889 E-mail: sales@whitesremovals.co.uk

Wardle & Keach, Mill Lane, Kislingbury, Northampton, NN7 4BD Tel: (01604) 891133 Fax: (01604) 891155 E-mail: sales@wardleandkeach.co.uk

Warren Ltd, Ackender Road, Alton, Hampshire, GU34 1JT Tel: (01420) 85401 Fax: (01420) 89808

W. Wellington & Son Ltd, Old Station Yard, Industrial Estate, Kingsbridge, Devon, TQ7 1EF Tel: (01548) 852166 Fax: (01548) 852066

C. Oliver Whitby & Sons Ltd, Hospital Fields, Fulford Road, York, YO10 4FS Tel: (01904) 655106 Fax: (01904) 627663 E-mail: wcoliver@aol.com

White's Removals & Transport Ltd, 257 Great Lister Street, Birmingham, B7 4DB Tel: 0121-359 3571 Fax: 0121-359 6889 E-mail: enquiries@whitesremovals.co.uk

Whittle Movers Ltd, Charnley Fold Lane, Bamber Bridge, Preston, PR5 6AA Tel: (01772) 626565 Fax: (01772) 627770 E-mail: mail@whittle.co.uk

Witcombs Removals, 45 Wentworth Way, Birmingham, B32 2UZ Tel: 0121-426 6703 Fax: 0121-426 5294 E-mail: sales@witcombs-removals.co.uk

Woods Dorchester, 34-35 High East Street, Dorchester, Dorset, DT1 1HN Tel: (01305) 262666 Fax: (01305) 250073 E-mail: woodsdor@globalnet.co.uk

Worthing Removals & Storage Co P & H Ltd, Ivy Arch Road, Worthing, West Sussex, BN14 8BX Tel: (01903) 204280 Fax: (01903) 824245E-mail: sales@worthingremovals.co.uk

▶ WSG Packaging Ltd, 7 Smiths Forge, North End Road, Yatton, Bristol, BS49 4AU Tel: (01934) 877272 Fax: (01934) 877287

Wyards Removals, Knightsdale Road, Ipswich, IP1 4HE Tel: (01473) 463708 Fax: (01473) 744447 E-mail: sales@wyardsremovals.co.uk

▶ Xpress Relocation Ltd, Dane Road, Bletchley, Milton Keynes, MK1 1JQ Tel: (01908) 374999

REMOVAL CONTRACTORS OPERATING OVERSEAS

▶ A B C Removals & Storage, High Peaks, Church Lane, Bledlow Ridge, High Wycombe, Buckinghamshire, HP14 4AX Tel: (01494) 481277 E-mail: info@abcremovalsandstorage.com

Armstrongs, Hawthorne Road, Bootle, Merseyside, L20 2DG Tel: 0151-922 1910 Fax: (01704) 896890

Arrowpak Transport & Warehousing Ltd, Norwood Road, Brandon, Suffolk, IP27 0PB Tel: (01842) 812165 Fax: (01842) 813051 E-mail: sales@arrowpak.co.uk

Bishops Move, 1-5 Kelvin Way, Crawley, West Sussex, RH10 9SP Tel: (01293) 512646 Fax: (01293) 550105 E-mail: crawley@bishopsmove.com

Bishops Move Chichester Ltd, 3 The Nelson Centre, Portfield Road, Portsmouth, PO3 5SF Tel: (023) 9266 9350 Fax: (023) 9266 9399 E-mail: portsmouth@bishopsmove.co.uk

Bishops Move (Guildford) Ltd, Unit 3 Riverway Industrial Estate, Portsmouth Road, Peasmarsh, Guildford, Surrey, GU3 1LZ Tel: (01483) 722207 Fax: (01483) 302454 E-mail: gillford@bishopsmove.com

Bishop's Move Industrial & Household, South Road, Brighton, BN1 6SB Tel: (01273) 557423 Fax: (01273) 501295 E-mail: brighton@bishops-move.co.uk

Bishops Move Wokingham Ltd, Oaklands Business Centre, Oaklands Park, Wokingham, Berkshire, RG41 2FD Tel: (01276) 685515 Fax: 0118-977 3183 E-mail: wokingham@bishopsmove.co.uk

Bonner International, 19 Kennet Road, Dartford, DA1 4QN Tel: (020) 8303 6261 Fax: (01322) 556882 E-mail: moving@dbonner.co.uk

Britania Leatherbarrows, Building, 105 Aviation Park West, Hurn, Christchurch, Dorset, BH23 6NW Tel: (01202) 495600 Fax: (01202) 581639 E-mail: admin@1eatherbarrows.co.uk

Crown Worldwide Ltd, Cullen Square, Deans Road, Deans Industrial Estate, Livingston, West Lothian, EH54 8SJ Tel: (01506) 468150 Fax: (01506) 468151 E-mail: general.gblob@crownworldwide.com

Crown Worldwide Movers Ltd, 1 Ninian Park, Ninian Way, Wilnecote, Tamworth, Staffordshire, B77 5ES Tel: (01827) 264100 Fax: (01827) 264101 E-mail: general@crownrelo.com

D A P International Removals Ltd, 209 Manor Road, Erith, Kent, DA8 2AD Tel: (01322) 335621 Fax: (01322) 332518 E-mail: dapinternational@btinternet.com

Davies Turner Worldwide Movers Ltd, 49 Wates Way, Mitcham, Surrey, CR4 4HR Tel: (020) 7622 4393 Fax: (020) 7720 3897 E-mail: removals@daviesturner.co.uk

Drury Smart, 148 Brierley Road, Walton Summit Centre, Bamber Bridge, Preston, PR5 8AH Tel: (01704) 533243 Fax: (01772) 318400

Fletchers Removals, Racecourse Industrial Park, Mansfield Road, Derby, DE21 4SX Tel: (01332) 371470 Fax: (01332) 294397 E-mail: sales@webbesremovals.net

Galleon International Shipping Co. Ltd, Galleon House Thurrock Commercial Centre, Purfleet Industrial Park, Aveley, South Ockendon, Essex, RM15 4YA Tel: (01708) 868068 Fax: (01708) 864321 E-mail: galleon.international@virgin.net

Harrow Green Ltd, Cooks Road, London, E15 2PW Tel: (020) 8522 0101 Fax: (020) 8522 0252 E-mail: info@harrowgreen.com

Interdean Interconex Ltd, Interdean House, 15 Central Way, London, NW10 7XW Tel: (020) 8961 4141 Fax: (020) 8965 4484 E-mail: interdean@interconex.com

Jet Removal Services, Plantation Road, Burscough Industrial Estate, Burscough, Lancashire, L40 8JT Tel: (01704) 895206 Fax: (01704) 896890 E-mail: sales@jetremovals.co.uk

John Mason London Ltd, 35 Wilson Road, Huyton, Liverpool, L36 6AE Tel: 0151-449 3938 Fax: 0151-449 2690 E-mail: sales@johnmason.com

▶ Koyanagi Worlwide Ltd, Units 8 & 9, Crystal Way, Harrow, Middlesex, HA1 2HP Tel: (020) 8427 6355

Masons Moving Group Ltd, Storage House, Priority Business Park, Barry, South Glamorgan, CF63 2BG Tel: (01446) 733330 Fax: (01446) 733827 E-mail: enquiries@masonsmovinggroup.co.uk

Michael Gerson Finance plc, Downland Close, Whetstone, London, N20 9LB Tel: (020) 8446 1300 Fax: (020) 8446 5088 E-mail: moving@michaelgerson.com

▶ Needhams Removals, 302 Old Shoreham Road, Southwick, Brighton, BN42 4LN Tel: (01273) 889403 E-mail: info@needhams.co.uk

James Nicholas International Removals, Units 12-13, Whitehill Industrial Park, Whitehill Lane, Wootton Bassett, Swindon, SN4 7DB Tel: (01793) 849315 Fax: (01793) 849317

Overs Of Camberley Ltd, Springlakes Estate, Deadbrook Lane, Aldershot, Hampshire, GU12 4UH Tel: (01252) 714233 Fax: (01252) 345861 E-mail: internationalrelocation@overs.co.uk

▶ Robinson International Removals, Unit 1 Hamilton Close, Basingstoke, Hampshire, RG21 6YT Tel: (01256) 859410 E-mail: oxford@robinsons-intl.com

Robinsons International Removals Ltd, Nuffield Way, Abingdon, Oxfordshire, OX14 1TN Tel: (01235) 552266 Fax: (01235) 553573 E-mail: oxford@robinsons-intl.com

Robinsons International Removals Ltd, Bartleet Road, Redditch, Worcestershire, B98 0DG Tel: (01527) 830850 Fax: (01527) 526812 E-mail: redditch@robinsons-intl.com

Ryans Move International Ltd, Unit 14 Gateway Industrial Estate, Hythe Road, London, NW10 6RJ Tel: (020) 8969 7047 Fax: (020) 8969 1326E-mail: britannia@ryansmove.co.uk

Stewart Harvey & Woodbridge Ltd, Eldenwall Industrial Estate, Whalebone La South, Dagenham, Essex, RM8 1AU Tel: (020) 8517 0011 Fax: (020) 8592 0827 E-mail: shw@shwlondon.co.uk

Team Relocations plc, Drury Way, Brentpark, Neasden, London, NW10 0JN Tel: (020) 8784 0100 Fax: (020) 8451 0061

W H Humphreys & Son Ltd, 1 Sydney Road, Watford, WD18 7XX Tel: (01923) 226206 Fax: (01923) 210355 E-mail: sales@humphreys-moving.com

Wardle & Keach, Mill Lane, Kislingbury, Northampton, NN7 4BD Tel: (01604) 891133 Fax: (01604) 891155 E-mail: sales@wardleandkeach.co.uk

White's Removals & Transport Ltd, 257 Great Lister Street, Birmingham, B7 4DB Tel: 0121-359 3571 Fax: 0121-359 6889 E-mail: enquiries@whitesremovals.co.uk

Whittle Movers Ltd, Charnley Fold Lane, Bamber Bridge, Preston, PR5 6AA Tel: (01772) 626565 Fax: (01772) 627770 E-mail: mail@whittle.co.uk

RENDERING MACHINES OR EQUIPMENT

W Forrest & Son Paisley Ltd, 241 Biggar Road, Newarthill, Motherwell, Lanarkshire, ML1 5LY Tel: (01698) 860149 Fax: (01698) 860920

RENEWABLE ENERGY CONSULTANCY

▶ Green Energy Centre, Ambassador House, Brigstock Road, Thornton Heath, Surrey, CR7 7JG Tel: (020) 8683 6683 Fax: (020) 8683 6601

RENEWABLE ENERGY POWER GENERATION SYSTEMS

▶ Dabbrook Power Systems, Unit 23, Bells Marsh Rd, Gorleston, Great Yarmouth, Norfolk, NR31 6PT Tel: (01493) 441711 Fax: (01493) 440322 E-mail: info@dabbrook.com

Deutz AG - UK, Willow Park, Burdock Close, Cannock, Staffordshire, WS11 7FQ Tel: (01543) 438900 Fax: (01543) 438932

REPETITION ENGINEERING

C K S Precision Ltd, Unit 12, Ptarmigan Place, Attleborough Fields Industrial Estate, Nuneaton, Warwickshire, CV11 6RX Tel: (024) 7664 1693 Fax: (024) 7638 3971 E-mail: sales@cks-precision.co.uk

REPETITION WOODWORK

Bloxwich Co., Park Road, Bloxwich, Walsall, WS3 3SS Tel: (01922) 710588 Fax: (01922) 710588

D W General Wood Machinists Ltd, 855 High Road, Tottenham, London, N17 8EY Tel: (020) 8801 1127 Fax: (020) 8808 1215 E-mail: sales@dw-group.co.uk

M A P Woodcraft (Caerphilly) Ltd, The Rhos, Bedwas Road, Caerphilly, Mid Glamorgan, CF83 3AU Tel: (029) 2088 2339 Fax: (029) 2086 8315

Shaw Timber Ltd, Bridge Street, Slaithwaite, Huddersfield, HD7 5JN Tel: (01484) 848484 Fax: (01484) 848494 E-mail: sales@shawtimber.com

REPETITION WORK MACHINISTS, AUTOMATIC

Alfred Wood & Sons Ltd, 32 Eveline Road, Mitcham, Surrey, CR4 3LE Tel: (020) 8648 3528 Fax: (020) 8640 8707 E-mail: roger.felstead@virgin.net

Autoy Ltd, 152 Castleton Road, Deepdale, Preston, PR1 6QH Tel: (01772) 556115 Fax: (01772) 204937 E-mail: autoy@btconnect.com

B G T Automatics Ltd, 2 Paragon Court, Tongham Road, Aldershot, Hampshire, GU12 4AA Tel: (01252) 318111 Fax: (01252) 311831 E-mail: carol@bgtcnc.freeserve.co.uk

B M I Engineering Ltd, Vernon Road, Halesowen, West Midlands, B62 8HN Tel: 0121-559 3406 Fax: 0121-561 2603 E-mail: sales@bmi-engineering.co.uk

Barnes & Gannon Ltd, Charles House, Royle Barn Road, Rochdale, Lancashire, OL11 3DT Tel: (01706) 344997 Fax: (01706) 641653 E-mail: sales@aqua-check.co.uk

REPETITION WORK MACHINISTS, AUTOMATIC – *continued*

Bunting Engineering Ltd, Unit 14/20, Manor Industrial Estate, Pleck Road, Walsall, WS2 9XX Tel: (01922) 623888 Fax: (01922) 623888

BWS Security Systems Ltd, BWS Security Systems, Unit18 Church Farm Business Park, Corston, Bath, BA2 9AP Tel: (01225) 872385 Fax: (01225) 874565

C N Smart (UK) Ltd, Unit 3, Baltimore Trading Estate, Baltimore Road, Great Barr, Birmingham, B42 1DD Tel: 0121-356 2920 Fax: 0121-356 6129 E-mail: cnsmart@hotmail.com

Carnation Engineering Co, 19 Highmeres Road, Leicester, LE4 9LZ Tel: 0116-276 0124 Fax: 0116-276 0124

Clayton Engineering Co., Church Street, Belper, Derbyshire, DE56 1EY Tel: (01773) 828955 Fax: (01773) 828243 E-mail: claytonenguk@aol.com

Cobra Engineering, 34 Tenby Street, Birmingham, B1 3ES Tel: 0121-233 1724 Fax: 0121-236 3731

Denray Machine Tools & Automation Ltd, Westwood House, Westwood Road, Earlsdon, Coventry, CV5 6GF Tel: (024) 7667 8916 Fax: (024) 7669 1478

Duright Engineering Co., Portway Road, Wednesbury, West Midlands, WS10 7DZ Tel: 0121-556 7718 Fax: 0121-556 7745 E-mail: sales@duright.co.uk

E G L Vaughan Ltd, Brook St, Glossop, Derbyshire, SK13 8BG Tel: (01457) 866614 Fax: (01457) 869364 E-mail: egl.vaughan@virgin.net

E J M Engineering Ltd, Regent Road, Countesthorpe, Leicester, LE8 5RF Tel: 0116-278 7020 Fax: 0116-278 7020 E-mail: eric@ejm-engineering.co.uk

E Meyer & Co Mentor Ltd, Unit 15 Abbey Industrial Estate, Mount Pleasant, Wembley, Middlesex, HA0 1QX Tel: (020) 8902 5471 Fax: (020) 8900 1398 E-mail: sales@emeyer.co.uk

Feltonquest Turned Parts Ltd, Unit 16 Britannia Estate, Leagrave Road, Luton, LU3 1RJ Tel: (01582) 738892 Fax: (01582) 721634 E-mail: tony.abbott@feltonquest.co.uk

Forgeway Engineering Co. Ltd, 2-3 Forgehammer Industrial Estate, Cwmbran, Gwent, NP44 3AA Tel: (01633) 485468 Fax: (01633) 875439

Fosse Precision Ltd, East Street, Coventry, CV1 5LS Tel: (024) 7622 5263 Fax: (024) 7652 0919 E-mail: fosse.precision@zen.co.uk

Gwent Repetition Engineers Ltd, Factory Road, Newport, Gwent, NP20 5FA Tel: (01633) 251112 Fax: (01633) 246940

H Mullins Earby Ltd, Western Road, Jarrow, Tyne & Wear, NE32 3DB Tel: 0191-489 1617 Fax: 0191-428 0375 E-mail: h.mullins@mullins.co.uk

H S Rowe & Partners, Building 80, First Avenue, Pensnett Trading Estate, Kingswinford, West Midlands, DY6 7FQ Tel: (01384) 293862 Fax: (01384) 271805 E-mail: sales@buxtonhayes.co.uk

Highbridge Turned Parts Ltd, 23a Highbridge Street, Waltham Abbey, Essex, EN9 1BZ Tel: (01992) 713333 Fax: (01992) 713333 E-mail: highbridgetp@supanet.com

A. & D. Hughes Ltd, Pope's Lane, Nelson Street, Oldbury, West Midlands, B69 4PA Tel: 0121-552 4500 Fax: 0121-511 1072

Hullmatic Engineering Ltd, 1 Lancaster Way Earls Colne Business Park, Airfield, Earls Colne, Colchester, CO6 2NS Tel: (01787) 222099 Fax: (01787) 224317 E-mail: hullmatic@aol.com

Kershaw & Co. Ltd, Hixon Industrial Estate, Church Lane, Hixon, Stafford, ST18 0PY Tel: (01889) 270556 Fax: (01889) 271295 E-mail: sales@kershaw-engineering.co.uk

M J C Technical Ltd, 12 York Street, Stourport-on-Severn, Worcestershire, DY13 9EF Tel: (01299) 827272 Fax: (01299) 827273

Malcolm Engineering Co. Ltd, Banks Road, McMullen Industrial Estate, Darlington, County Durham, DL1 1YF Tel: (01325) 461549 Fax: (01325) 381196 E-mail: malco@malcolm-eng.co.uk

Mellorsons Manufacturing Ltd, George Street, West Bromwich, West Midlands, B70 6NH Tel: 0121-580 0520 Fax: 0121-580 0521

Muller Holdings Ltd, Cleobury Mortimer, Kidderminster, Worcestershire, DY14 8DT Tel: (01299) 270271 Fax: (01299) 270877 E-mail: sales@muller-england.co.uk

Northwood Engineering Birmingham Co. Ltd, 122 Emily Street, Birmingham, B12 0XJ Tel: 0121-440 6731 Fax: 0121-440 3549 E-mail: northwoodengltd@aol.com

Park Engineering Wolverhampton Co. Ltd, Portersfield Industrial Estate, Portersfield Road, Cradley Heath, West Midlands, B64 7BW Tel: (01384) 566263 Fax: (01384) 564700 E-mail: neil_roberts@btconnect.com

Precision Repetition Ltd, 87 Leamore Lane, Walsall, WS2 7BU Tel: (01922) 473335

R K Components, 5b Eley Estate, Angel Road, London, N18 3BH Tel: (020) 8884 1366 Fax: (020) 8884 3881 E-mail: info@rkcomponents.com

▶ R L R Engineers Ltd, 456 Warrington Road, Rainhill, Prescot, Merseyside, L35 9JE Tel: 0151-426 0245 Fax: 0151-426 8288 E-mail: admin@rlrengineers.co.uk

R P L Productions Ltd, Northcote Road, Birmingham, B33 9BE Tel: 0121-624 5000 Fax: 0121-784 5400 E-mail: info@rplproductions.co.uk

R W Cresswell Ltd, Unit 2 79-81 Cheapside, Deritend, Birmingham, B12 0QH Tel: 0121-772 4565

S Z N Pendle Automatics Ltd, 1 Stanhope Street, Birmingham, B12 0UZ Tel: 0121-772 2516 Fax: 0121-766 6310

Sabre Repetitions Ltd, Golf Road, Hale, Altrincham, Cheshire, WA15 8AH Tel: 0161-925 4020 Fax: 0161-925 4021 E-mail: rep@sabreuk.com

▶ Sassen Engineering Ltd, 19 Aston Road North, Birmingham, B6 4DS Tel: 0121-359 7411 Fax: 0121-359 2404 E-mail: sales@sassenengineering.co.uk

Stanbridge Precision Turned Parts Ltd, 20 Bilton Way, Luton, LU1 1UU Tel: (01582) 617000 Fax: (01582) 401630 E-mail: info@stanbridge-precision.co.uk

Swan Engineering, 70 Scarborough Street, Hull, HU3 4TG Tel: (01482) 890140 Fax: (01482) 323077E-mail: sales@swan-engineering.co.uk

T K M Engineering, 32 Priory Road, Romford, RM3 9AT Tel: (01708) 377723 Fax: (01708) 377022 E-mail: sales@tkmlondon.co.uk

Taylorfab Precision Engineers, Unit 5 Greenwood Court, Ramridge Road, Luton, LU2 0TN Tel: (01582) 737279 Fax: (01582) 735616

Warwick Brassfounders & Engineering Co. Ltd, 14-16 Haden Street, Birmingham, B12 9BH Tel: 0121-440 0901 Fax: 0121-440 6725

West Midlands Precision Engineering Ltd, Unit 10/14, Gainsborough Trad Estate, Rufford Road, Stourbridge, West Midlands, DY9 7ND Tel: (01384) 397071 Fax: (01384) 378628 E-mail: info@westmidlandstpreg.co.uk

Wigpool, 46 Walkers Road, Moons Moat North Industrial Es, Redditch, Worcestershire, B98 9HE Tel: (01527) 64086 Fax: (01527) 62319

Wilco Manufacturing Ltd, Tyseley Industrial Estate, Seeleys Road, Birmingham, B11 2LQ Tel: 0121-772 6212 Fax: 0121-772 2871 E-mail: martinlane@wilcomanufacturing.co.uk

Wrington Precision Automatics, 29 Blue Water Drive, Elborough, Weston-Super-Mare, Avon, BS24 8PF Tel: (01934) 823525 Fax: E-mail: pill@wrington.co.uk

REPLACEABLE ELEMENT FILTERS

Vee Bee Ltd, Old Wharf Road, Stourbridge, West Midlands, DY8 4LS Tel: (01384) 378884 Fax: (01384) 374179 E-mail: veebee-filtration@veebee.co.uk

REPLACEMENT BRUSHES

P M R Industrial Services, 13-21 Liverpool Road, Kidsgrove, Stoke-on-Trent, ST7 1EA Tel: (01782) 776325 Fax: (01782) 771912

REPLACEMENT KITCHEN UNIT DOORS

▶ 1st Choice Kitchens, 6 The Dell, Yateley, Hampshire, GU46 6EL Tel: 01252 860661 Fax: 01252 665237

▶ David Edgar Kitchen Designs, 228 Spearing Road, High Wycombe, Buckinghamshire, HP12 3LA Tel: (01494) 472247 E-mail: daveedgar@rock.com

▶ Gates D I Y, 6 Vesey Path, London, E14 6BT Tel: (020) 7987 4045 Fax: (020) 7987 4015 E-mail: info@gatesdiy.com

REPORT PUBLISHING SERVICES

▶ Bladonmore Ltd, 10-11 Percy Street, London, W1T 1DA Tel: (020) 7631 1155 Fax: (020) 7631 1444 E-mail: info@bladonmore.com

Noroil Publications, PO Box 487, Kingston Upon Thames, Surrey, KT2 5WF Tel: (020) 8547 2411 Fax: (020) 8547 2157 E-mail: noroilcontacts@enterprise.net

REPROCESSED THERMOPLASTIC MATERIALS

Johnson Polymers Ltd, The Slough, Studley, Warwickshire, B80 7EN Tel: (01527) 850525 Fax: (01527) 850595 E-mail: sales@johnsonpolymers.co.uk

REPRODUCTION CHAIRS

All Pine, 97 Dymchurch Road, Hythe, Kent, CT21 6JN Tel: (01303) 262373 Fax: (01303) 262373

E F M A, 4 Northgate Close, Rottingdean, Brighton, BN2 7DZ Tel: (01273) 495002 Fax: (01273) 495022 E-mail: sales@efma.co.uk

REPRODUCTION FURNITURE

Andrena Direct Furniture, Auction House, Geddings Road, Hoddesdon, Hertfordshire, EN11 0NT Tel: (01992) 451722 Fax: (01992) 466024 E-mail: enquiries@anrenda.co.uk

Baldock Reproduction Furniture, Mansfield Road, Baldock, Hertfordshire, SG7 6EB Tel: (01462) 892134 Fax: (01462) 892134

Barley Reproduction, Arch 3 Pedley Street, London, E1 5EW Tel: (020) 7377 2081 Fax: (020) 7247 9241

Bed Workshop, Braunton Road, Bristol, BS3 3AA Tel: 0117-963 6659 E-mail: info@thebedworkshop.co.uk

Benardout John & Robert Reproduction Furnisher Dealers, 168 Upper Richmond Road West, London, SW14 8AW Tel: (020) 8878 7775 Fax: (020) 8876 4620 E-mail: sales@benardoutfurniture.com

Bevan Funnell Ltd, Reprodux House, Norton Road, Newhaven, East Sussex, BN9 0BZ Tel: (01273) 513762 Fax: (01273) 516735 E-mail: enquiries@bevan-funnell.co.uk

Boswell & Davis, 1 Sunbury Workshops, Swanfield Street, London, E2 7LF Tel: (020) 7739 5738

Bradley Furniture Kent Ltd, Bradley House, Park Farm Close, Park Farm Industrial Estate, Folkestone, Kent, CT19 5ED Tel: (01303) 850011 Fax: (01303) 244028 E-mail: info@bradleyfurniture.co.uk

Brights Of Nettlebed, 61-63 Leigh Road, Wimborne, Dorset, BH21 1AE Tel: (01202) 884613 Fax: (01202) 885679 E-mail: enquiries@brightsofnettlebed.com

Castle Reproduction Furniture, 461 Hackney Road, London, E2 9DY Tel: (020) 7739 2074 Fax: (020) 7256 1218 E-mail: enquiries@castlefurniture.demon.co.uk

▶ Cathedral City Furniture Ltd, Millennia Park, Thornes Road, Wakefield, West Yorkshire, WF2 8PW Tel: (01924) 379100 Fax: (01924) 376136

Charles Barr Furniture, 72 Sunderland Road, Sandy, Bedfordshire, SG19 1QY Tel: (01767) 681444 Fax: (01767) 681397 E-mail: enquiries@charlesbarr.com

The Corner Shop, 47 Portland Street, Lincoln, LN5 7JZ Tel: (01522) 512600 Fax: (01522) 512600

Elva Wholesale Ltd, 406 Long St, London, E2 8HG Tel: (020) 7739 5622 Fax: (020) 7739 8128 E-mail: elvawholesale@ukbusiness.com

Farthingale Furniture, 90 High Street, Odiham, Hook, Hampshire, RG29 1LP Tel: (01256) 704080 Fax: (01256) 704080 E-mail: info@farthingalefurniture.co.uk

Febland Group Ltd, Ashworth Road, Marton, Blackpool, FY4 4UN Tel: (01253) 600600 Fax: (01253) 792211 E-mail: info@febland.co.uk

Felix Campania Ltd, 42 Ditton Hill Road, Surbiton, Surrey, KT6 5JD Tel: (020) 8339 0011 Fax: (020) 8398 5495 E-mail: felix.campania@btinternet.com

Fleur De Lys, 230 Gloucester Road, Bishopston, Bristol, BS7 8NZ Tel: 0117-957 1229 Fax: 0117-957 1229

Fredrick Smith & Sons Furniture Ltd, 10 Rigg Approach, London, E10 7QN Tel: (020) 8539 0158 Fax: (020) 8556 3030 E-mail: sales@smithandsons.co.uk

Furniture Fusion, Bedford Road, Apsley Guise, Milton Keynes, MK17 8DJ Tel: (01908) 586334 Fax: (01908) 586332 E-mail: info@furniturefusion.co.uk

Furniture Maker Furniture Maker, Unit 19, Hoobrook Enterprise Centre, Worcester Road, Kidderminster, Worcestershire, DY10 1HB Tel: (01562) 825995

Garven Antique Reproductions, Gorphwysfa, Defynnog, Brecon, Powys, LD3 8SB Tel: (01874) 638028 Fax: (01874) 638028

Thomas Goode & Co. Ltd, 19 South Audley Street, London, W1K 2BN Tel: (020) 7499 2823 Fax: (020) 7629 4230 E-mail: info@thomasgoode.com

Handcraft Artistic Furniture, Sterling Industrial Estate, Rainham Road South, Dagenham, Essex, RM10 8TX Tel: (020) 8593 0184 Fax: (020) 8984 8384

James Harden, 85 Falls Road, Belfast, BT12 4PE Tel: (028) 9029 0700

Harris Fine Furniture Ltd, 1 Bulmer Road Industrial Estate, Sudbury, Suffolk, CO10 7HJ Tel: (01787) 375527 Fax: (01787) 377036 E-mail: hsf.co@easynet.co.uk

Holland Of Rye, 145 South Undercliff, Rye, East Sussex, TN31 7HW Tel: (01797) 222648 Fax: (01797) 224909

Hove Park Reproductions, 93 Old Shoreham Road, Hove, East Sussex, BN3 7AQ Tel: (01273) 737305 Fax: (01273) 737305

In N Out Trading, 946 North Circular Rd, Staples Corner, London, NW2 7JR Tel: (020) 8452 0300 Fax: (020) 8452 0077 E-mail: ash@innout.co.uk

Larkswood Ltd, Bedford Road, Aspley Guise, Milton Keynes, MK17 8DJ Tel: (01908) 583897 Fax: (01908) 583317 E-mail: sales@larkswood.f2s.com

Littleline Ltd, 41 West Road, Tottenham, London, N17 0RE Tel: (020) 8880 3790 Fax: (020) 8880 3830

M & R Joinery Ltd, The Barn, Nine Yews, Cranborne, Wimborne, Dorset, BH21 5PW Tel: (01725) 517220

Mccarthy's, 1 Dundonald Road, Broadstairs, Kent, CT10 1PE Tel: (01843) 600053 Fax: (01843) 600048 E-mail: mccarthysreproductions@virgin.net

Marshbeck Reproduction Furniture, 60e High Street, Lavenham, Sudbury, Suffolk, CO10 9PY Tel: (01787) 247548 Fax: (01787) 249498 E-mail: enquiries@marshbeck.co.uk

Newtons Of Bury, 151 The Rock, Bury, Lancashire, BL9 0ND Tel: 0161-764 1863 Fax: 0161-761 7129 E-mail: enquiries@tablecare.co.uk

H.F. Noakes (Ceilings) Ltd, 355 Railway Arches, Laburnum St, London, E2 8BB Tel: (020) 7739 9304 Fax: (020) 7739 3424

Packman Furniture Ltd, 256-261 Paradise Row, London, E2 9LE Tel: (020) 7729 4268 Fax: (020) 7729 0169

Period Oak Reproduction Ltd, Stonham Road, Mickfield, Stowmarket, Suffolk, IP14 5LS Tel: (01449) 711782 Fax: (01449) 711569

Sabins Pine Furniture, 17 Church Road, Codsall, Wolverhampton, WV8 1EA Tel: (01902) 846027

Scarthingwell Replicas, Scarthingwell Centre Scarthingwell, Barkston Ash, Tadcaster, North Yorkshire, LS24 9Pf Tel: (01937) 557877 Fax: (01937) 558084 E-mail: sales@scarthingwell.co.uk

Andrew Sharpe Reproductions Ltd, The Old Carpenters Shop, The Cliff, Matlock, Derbyshire, DE4 5EW Tel: (01629) 55560

Simbeck Furniture Ltd, Spring Gardens Road, High Wycombe, Buckinghamshire, HP13 7AG Tel: (01494) 528617 Fax: (01494) 471737 E-mail: info@simbeck.com

Paul Smith Furniture, C4 Newton Road, Peacehaven, East Sussex, BN10 8JQ Tel: (01273) 580454 Fax: (01273) 586994 E-mail: sales@paulsmithfurn.com

▶ Southern Court Furniture Co. Ltd, 14 Newport Industrial Estate, Launceston, Cornwall, PL15 8EX Tel: (01566) 779880 Fax: (01566) 779880 E-mail: sales@southerncourtfurniture.co.uk

T & T Furnishings, Coldharbour Lane House, 108 Coldharbour Lane, Hayes, Middlesex, UB3 3HD Tel: (020) 8569 0162 Fax: (020) 8848 0294

Table Place Ltd, 1 Thistleton Road, Market Overton, Oakham, Leicestershire, LE15 7PP Tel: (01572) 767636 Fax: (01572) 767932

Tasha Sleigh Beds, Forstal Farm, Goudhurst Road, Lamberhurst, Tunbridge Wells, Kent, TN3 8AG Tel: (01892) 890769 Fax: (01892) 890769

Treasures Of Woodchurch, 1-3 The Green, Woodchurch, Ashford, Kent, TN26 3PE Tel: (01233) 860249

Victoriana, Station Road, Petersfield, Hampshire, GU31 4AH Tel: (01730) 264009 Fax: (01730) 264009

Webber & Harrison, Unit 270 Ricardo Way, Lymington, Hampshire, SO41 8JU Tel: (01590) 689009 Fax: (01590) 689006 E-mail: allanwebber@btconnect.com

Wilcox Reproductions Ltd, D Lea Road, Waltham Abbey, Essex, EN9 1AS Tel: (01992) 760707 Fax: (01992) 788021

Wimborne Leather Co., Unit 2b, Sunrise Business Park, Blandford Forum, Dorset, DT11 8ST Tel: (01258) 455397 Fax: (01258) 480610

Wood & Mott Ltd, 29 Morses Lane, Brightlingsea, Colchester, CO7 0SD Tel: (01206) 303929 Fax: (01206) 304925 E-mail: ernie@wood-and-mott.co.uk

Woodcraft Of Burston Ltd, Station Buildings, Station Road, Burston, Diss, Norfolk, IP22 5UB Tel: (01379) 741090 Fax: (01379) 741095 E-mail: apires6939@aol.com

Yesterdays Of Wolston, 2 Warwick Road, Wolston, Coventry, CV8 3HB Tel: (024) 7654 4818 Fax: (024) 7654 5510 E-mail: yesterdaysemail@aol.com

REPRODUCTION MIRRORS

Gray & Mcdonnell, Unit 3 4 City Cross Business Park, Salutation Road, London, SE10 0AT Tel: (020) 8858 8050 Fax: (020) 8269 1513 E-mail: mirrors@graymcdonnell.co.uk

REPROGRAPHIC EQUIPMENT

Crest Reprographics (Northern) Ltd, Crest House, Gibralter Row, Liverpool, L3 7HJ Tel: 0151-236 2642 Fax: 0151-236 2726 E-mail: info@crest-reprographics.co.uk

Service Point, Enfield House, Enfield Road, Birmingham, B15 1QA Tel: 0121-456 4554 Fax: 0121-454 9908 E-mail: birmingham@servicepointuk.com

REPROGRAPHIC PREPRESS SERVICES

Digital Repro, Cambridge Road Industrial Estate, Milton, Cambridge, CB4 6AZ Tel: (01223) 420444 Fax: (01223) 420783

▶ Itarus Ltd, Unit 6-8 Kingsthorpe Business Centre, Studland Road, Northampton, NN2 6NE Tel: (01604) 468100 Fax: (01604) 711736 E-mail: northaampton@itarus.com

Polestar Jowetts, Evanston Avenue, Kirkstall Road, Leeds, LS4 2HR Tel: (0113) 279 5041 Fax: (0113) 231 0193

Taylowe Ltd, Malvern Road, Furze Platt, Maidenhead, Berkshire, SL6 7RF Tel: (01628) 413333 Fax: (01628) 413397 E-mail: taylowereception@taylowe.com

▶ indicates data change since last edition

REPROGRAPHIC PRINTING

A D M Imaging, 59-61 Summer Lane, Birmingham, B19 3TH Tel: 0121-359 5424 Fax: 0121-359 7038 E-mail: info@abmimaging.co.uk
A Pinder Ltd, 16 Moore Street, Sheffield, S3 7US Tel: 0114-272 7574 Fax: 0114-275 1071 E-mail: sales@pindersofsheffield.co.uk
▶ Advance Reprographic Printers Ltd, Olympic House, 317 Latimer Road, London, W10 6RA Tel: (020) 8969 6055
Alpha, 2-6 Spottiswoode Road, Edinburgh, EH9 1BQ Tel: 0131-447 9111 Fax: 0131-452 8259 E-mail: alphabm@btconnect.com
Alpha Printing Services, 227b Withington Road, Manchester, M16 8LU Tel: 0161-862 9922 Fax: 0161-862 9944 E-mail: sales@alphaprint.com
Anton Graphics Ltd, Unit 3b Duke Close, West Way, Andover, Hampshire, SP10 5AS Tel: (01264) 358544 Fax: (01264) 358242 E-mail: brian@antongraphics.co.uk
Ashford Overload Services, Bottings Industrial Estate, Curdridge, Southampton, SO30 2DY Tel: (01489) 787071 Fax: (01489) 787621 E-mail: ashford.overload@dial.pipex.com
Bezier Corporate Print, 145 Sterte Road, Poole, Dorset, BH15 2AF Tel: (01202) 681466 Fax: (01202) 670010 E-mail: sales@bezier.co.uk
Border Reprographics, Tuppenny Lane, Emsworth, Hampshire, PO10 8HG Tel: (01243) 377721 Fax: (01243) 379200 E-mail: info@border-repro.co.uk
James Byrne Printing Ltd, Unit 10 Sandleheath Industrial Estate, Old Brickyard Road, Sandleheath, Fordingbridge, Hampshire, SP6 1PA Tel: (01425) 655090 Fax: (01425) 656844 E-mail: studio@jamesbyrne.co.uk
Call Print 16 Ltd, 201 Shenley Road, Borehamwood, Hertfordshire, WD6 1AT Tel: (020) 8207 1188 Fax: (020) 8207 0193 E-mail: bwood@callprint.co.uk
Claygate Digital Services Ltd, Airport House, Purley Way, Croydon, CR0 0XZ Tel: (020) 8288 3588 Fax: (020) 8288 3599 E-mail: sales@claygate.com
Color Co. Ltd, C7 The Chambers, Chelsea Harbour, London, SW10 0XF Tel: (020) 7351 4310 Fax: (020) 7795 1419
▶ Colourspec Ltd, 11 Cricketers Way, Chatteris, Cambridgeshire, PE16 6UR Tel: (01354) 696496 E-mail: sales@colourspec.co.uk
Copyprint UK Ltd, Ground Floor West Block Westminster Business Square, Durham Street, London, SE11 5JH Tel: (020) 7735 0956 Fax: (020) 7793 0519 E-mail: sales@copyprint.co.uk
Danka (UK) P.L.C., Parkfield House, Moss Lane, Altrincham, Cheshire, WA15 8FH Tel: 0161-927 8500 Fax: 0161-927 8519
Designex Ltd, Caxton House, Hopewell Drive, Chatham, Kent, ME5 7NP Tel: (01634) 844644 Fax: (01634) 831519 E-mail: info@designex.co.uk
The Digital Printed Word Ltd, 19 Briset Street, London, EC1M 5NR Tel: (020) 7250 1404 Fax: (020) 7253 4675 E-mail: printedword@btconnect.com
Direct Copiers plc, Former Royal Mail Building, Horseley Road, Tipton, West Midlands, DY4 7DB Tel: 0121-521 0200 Fax: 0121-521 0220
E S P Colour, Elgin Drive, Swindon, SN2 8XU Tel: (01793) 438400 Fax: (01793) 530403 E-mail: firstinitial.surname@espcolour.co.uk
Falcon Press (Stockton-on-Tees) Ltd, Task Industrial Estate, Portrack Lane, Stockton-On-Tees, Cleveland, TS18 2ES Tel: (01642) 674298 Fax: (01642) 612382 E-mail: enquiries@falconpress-printing.co.uk
Gemini Press Ltd, Unit A1 Dolphin Way, Shoreham-by-Sea, West Sussex, BN43 6NZ Tel: (01273) 464884 Fax: (01273) 464744 E-mail: info@gemini-group.co.uk
Hobs Reprographics, 56d Milton Park, Milton, Abingdon, Oxfordshire, OX14 4RX Tel: (01235) 833044 Fax: (01235) 831666 E-mail: abington@hobsrepro.com
Hobs Reprographics, 178 Old Christchurch Road, Bournemouth, BH1 1NU Tel: (01202) 553233 Fax: (01202) 557616 E-mail: bournemouth@hobsrepro.com
Hobs Reprographics, 18a Slater Street, Liverpool, L1 4BS Tel: 0151-709 0261 Fax: 0151-709 4769 E-mail: liverpool@hobsrepro.com
Hobs Reprographics, 9-11 Grosvenor Gardens, London, SW1W 0BD Tel: (020) 7834 1187 Fax: (020) 7834 0045 E-mail: grosvenor@hobsrepro.ndirect.com
J W L Ltd, 1 Mundells, Welwyn Garden City, Hertfordshire, AL7 1EU Tel: (01707) 338410 Fax: (01707) 338731 E-mail: info@jwl.co.uk
Jas Print Ltd, 12 Tower Road, Washington, Tyne & Wear, NE37 2SH Tel: 0191-417 6766 Fax: 0191-415 1351 E-mail: john@jasprint.com
John E Wright & Co Ltd, 9-11 Marble Street, Leicester, LE1 5XB Tel: 0116-255 6030 E-mail: leicester@johnewright.com
Knockout Colour Ltd, Unit 6 Shore Business Centre, 14-16 Shore Rd, London, E9 7TA Tel: (020) 8533 1177 Fax: (020) 8533 5895
Leemicks Business Equipment, Image House, Lancashire Hill, Stockport, Cheshire, SK4 1UB Tel: 0161-480 4001 Fax: 0161-480 2428
Litho Supplies Midlands Region, 1 Tamebridge Industrial Estate, Aldridge Road, Perry Barr, Birmingham, B42 2TX Tel: 0121-344 4222 Fax: 0121-344 4494 E-mail: midlands@litho.co.uk
M F S Reprographics, 15 Blackmoor Gate, Furzton, Milton Keynes, MK4 1DS Tel: (01908) 504550 Fax: (01908) 504550 E-mail: mfsrepro@btinternet.com
M R M Graphics Ltd, 61 Station Road, Winslow, Buckingham, MK18 3DZ Tel: (01296) 712364 Fax: (01296) 713733 E-mail: keith@mrmgraphics.co.uk
Mirren Drawing Office Services Ltd, 13 Old Sneddon Street, Paisley, Renfrewshire, PA3 2AG Tel: 0141-561 7213 Fax: 0141-561 7213
Oldacres & Co. Ltd, 62 Hatton Garden, London, EC1N 8LR Tel: (020) 7242 3242 Fax: (020) 7831 9095 E-mail: services@oldacres.co.uk
Output Ltd, 1 Amptronic Industrial Estate, Heath Mill Road, Wombourne, Wolverhampton, WV5 8AP Tel: (01902) 895107 Fax: (01902) 895113 E-mail: sales@outputdigital.com
Pinnacle Images Ltd, 69-85 Tabernacle Street, London, EC2A 4BD Tel: (020) 7253 0383 Fax: (020) 7253 2159 E-mail: studio@pinnacleimages.co.uk
▶ Printinc, Sutton Business Centre, Restmor Way, Wallington, Surrey, SM6 7AH Tel: 020 8255 2110 Fax: 020 8255 2115 E-mail: printinc2@btconnect.com
Qualitech Print Ltd, Bramhall Moor Industrial Park, Pepper Road, Stockport, Cheshire, SK7 5BW Tel: 0161-456 6866 Fax: 0161-487 1588 E-mail: sales@qualitech.co.uk
Service Point, 68 Whiteladies Road, Bristol, BS8 2NH Tel: 0117-970 6500 Fax: 0117-970 6182 E-mail: Bristol@servicepointuk.com
Service Point, 11-12 Enterprise Way, Cheltenham Trade Park, Cheltenham, Gloucestershire, GL51 8LZ Tel: (01242) 514813 Fax: (01242) 581752 E-mail: cheltenham@servicepointuk.com
Service Point, 3 Hursley Road, Chandler's Ford, Eastleigh, Hampshire, SO53 2FW Tel: (023) 8026 2000 Fax: (023) 8025 1195 E-mail: southampton@servicepointuk.com
Service Point, Unit 3, 8-14 William Road, London, NW1 3EN Tel: (020) 7387 6071 Fax: (020) 7387 1382 E-mail: williamrd@servicepointuk.com
Service Point, 161-165 Farringdon Road, London, EC1R 3AL Tel: (020) 7520 0200 Fax: (020) 7833 9781 E-mail: infouk@servicepointuk.com
Service Point UK, 49 Charles Street, Cardiff, CF10 2GD Tel: (029) 2022 4316 Fax: (029) 2034 2712 E-mail: info@servicepointuk.com
Service Point UK Ltd, 95 Fore Street, Exeter, EX4 3QY Tel: (01392) 250431 Fax: (01392) 410250 E-mail: exeter@servicepointuk.com
Service Point UK, 40-42 Mayflower Street, Plymouth, PL1 1QX Tel: (01752) 669701 Fax: (01752) 222117 E-mail: plymouth@servicepointuk.com
Servicepoint, 81 Endell Street, London, WC2H 9AJ Tel: (020) 7836 9422 Fax: (020) 7836 4248 E-mail: coventgarden@servicepointuk.com
Servicepoint (U K) Ltd, 539-543 Sauchiehall St, Glasgow, G3 7PQ Tel: 0141-275 2424 Fax: 0141-204 3801 E-mail: glasgow@servicepointuk.com
Sharp Printing, 8 The Green, Richmond, Surrey, TW9 1PL Tel: (020) 8940 7129 Fax: (020) 8940 8647 E-mail: sharppaint@london.com
Soloprint Ltd, 105 Great North Road, Eaton Socon, St. Neots, Cambridgeshire, PE19 8EL Tel: (01480) 213555 Fax: (01480) 218887 E-mail: sales@tsgcf.co.uk
South Wales Photocopiers, 32 Elgin St, Swansea, SA5 8QF Tel: (01792) 476065 Fax: (01792) 456849 E-mail: enquiries@southwalesphotocopiers.co.uk
Stanford Marsh Ltd, Buckholt Drive, Worcester, WR4 9ND Tel: (01905) 458000 Fax: (01905) 754057 E-mail: sales@stanfordmarsh.co.uk
Tag, 29 Clerkenwell Road, London, EC1M 5TA Tel: (020) 7251 4571 Fax: (020) 7253 5355 E-mail: info@tagmedia.co.uk
Tdo, 15 Maddox Street, London, W1S 2QQ Tel: (020) 7629 5661 Fax: (020) 7629 7500 E-mail: post@timesdrawingoffice.co.uk
Unique Technical Services, 62 Willesden Lane, London, NW6 7SX Tel: (020) 8232 8889 Fax: (020) 8568 6777
V M R Publicity, 241 Redcatch Road, Knowle, Bristol, BS4 2HQ Tel: 0117-972 0505 Fax: 0117-972 0606 E-mail: vmrviv@aol.com
Ward Philipson Group Ltd, Dunston Industrial Estate, Halifax Road, Gateshead, Tyne & Wear, NE11 9HW Tel: 0191-460 5915 Fax: 0191-460 8540 E-mail: info@wardphilipson.co.uk
Watt Gilchrist Ltd, Ring Road, West Park, Leeds, LS16 6RA Tel: 0113-288 3200 Fax: 0113-275 1690 E-mail: info@gilchrist.co.uk
Zeta Image to Print Ltd, Octavia House, 54 Ayres Street, London, SE1 1EU Tel: (020) 7787 3993 Fax: (020) 7787 3995 E-mail: sales@zeta-print.co.uk

REPROGRAPHIC PRINTING EQUIPMENT, *See Plan Printing etc*

REPROGRAPHIC PRINTING TRADE SUPPLIERS/ DISTRIBUTORS/AGENTS

A M I Supplies Ltd, 2 Centre 2000, St. Michaels Road, Sittingbourne, Kent, ME10 3DZ Tel: (01795) 420430 Fax: (01795) 426817 E-mail: sales@amigroup.co.uk
A & R Printing, The Gables, 160A London Road, Brandon, Suffolk, IP27 0LP Tel: (01842) 811331 Fax: (01842) 811375 E-mail: ray.boreham@btinternet.com
Bousfield Ltd, Southway Drive, North Common, Bristol, BS30 5JE Tel: 0117-988 8899 Fax: 0117-988 8866 E-mail: sales@bousfield.net
Britannia Machinery Pontefract Ltd, Stuart Street, Pontefract, West Yorkshire, WF8 4PW Tel: (01977) 790818 Fax: (01977) 600333 E-mail: britannia.machinery@btinternet.com
Copy Prints Ltd, 1 Talbot Yard, London, SE1 1YP Tel: (020) 7407 2079 Fax: (020) 7403 5411 E-mail: sales@copyprintsltd.co.uk
Cosmographics, 1 Mowat Industrial Estate, Sandown Road, Watford, WD24 7UY Tel: (01923) 210909 Fax: (01923) 211657 E-mail: enquiries@cosmographics.co.uk
E C S (Nottingham) Ltd, Unit 17 Hazelford Way, Newstead Village, Nottingham, NG15 0DQ Tel: (01623) 720444 Fax: (01623) 720445 E-mail: sales@ecsnotts.co.uk
Elmstok, 4-6 Algores Way, Wisbech, Cambridgeshire, PE13 2TQ Tel: (01945) 463434 Fax: (01945) 582598 E-mail: sales@elmstok.co.uk
Entwistle Thorpe & Co. Ltd, 18 St Nicholas Street, Bristol, BS1 1UB Tel: 0117-927 3467 Fax: 0117-925 1579
Haynes Graphic Arts Ltd, Policrom House, Station Road, Motspur Park, New Malden, Surrey, KT3 6JJ Tel: (020) 8949 5411 Fax: (020) 8949 4907 E-mail: info@haynes-graphic-art.co.uk
Heatherbank Drawing Office Supplies, 4 Milethorn Lane, Doncaster, South Yorkshire, DN1 2SU Tel: (01302) 325146
Hobs Reprographics, 56d Milton Park, Milton, Abingdon, Oxfordshire, OX14 4RX Tel: (01235) 833044 Fax: (01235) 831666 E-mail: abington@hobsrepro.com
Hussey & Greaves Ltd, 94 Hutton Road, Shenfield, Brentwood, Essex, CM15 8ND Tel: (01277) 226262 Fax: (01277) 261287 E-mail: sales@husseyandgreaves.co.uk
Hussey & Knights Ltd, 60 Bethel Street, Norwich, NR2 1NR Tel: (01603) 428110 Fax: (01603) 761032 E-mail: sales@hussey-knights.co.uk
Infotec UK Ltd, 1230 Arlington Business Park, Theale, Reading, RG7 4TX Tel: 0118-928 4900 Fax: 0118-928 4901
Letraset Ltd, Kingsnorth Industrial Estate, Wotton Road, Ashford, Kent, TN23 6FL Tel: (01233) 624421 Fax: (01233) 658877 E-mail: info@letraset.com
Lomas & Thorpe Ltd, Bentley Avenue, Stakehill, Middleton, Manchester, M24 2RW Tel: 0161-653 9310 Fax: (0161) 655 3648 E-mail: enquiries@lomas-thorpe.co.uk
London Graphic Centre, 16-18 Shelton Street, London, WC2H 9JL Tel: (020) 7759 4500 Fax: (020) 7759 4585 E-mail: mailorder@londongraphics.co.uk
Lynbrook Reprographic Ltd, Unit 15A, Boxer Place, Leyland, PR26 7QL Tel: (01772) 452125 Fax: (01772) 622304 E-mail: sales@lynbrookreprographic.co.uk
M R M Graphics Ltd, 61 Station Road, Winslow, Buckingham, MK18 3DZ Tel: (01296) 712364 Fax: (01296) 713733 E-mail: keith@mrmgraphics.co.uk
▶ Mayday Graphic Products, Graphic House, Cratfield Road, Bury St. Edmunds, Suffolk, IP32 7DF Tel: (01284) 701571 Fax: (01284) 750553 E-mail: sales@maydaygraphics.co.uk
Parker Graphics Ltd, Progress House, Erskine Road, London, E17 6RT Tel: (020) 8520 7182 Fax: (020) 8521 7846
Parsia International Ltd, Unit 4 Powergate Business Park, Volt Avenue, London, NW10 6PW Tel: (020) 8453 6580 Fax: (020) 8453 6590 E-mail: sales@parsia.co.uk
Polydraft Ltd, The Tracings, 3-5 Dunston Road, London, E8 4EH Tel: (020) 7923 1130 Fax: (020) 7249 6818 E-mail: info@polydraft.co.uk
Service Point, 68 Whiteladies Road, Bristol, BS8 2NH Tel: 0117-970 6500 Fax: 0117-970 6182 E-mail: Bristol@servicepointuk.com
Sharp Printing, 8 The Green, Richmond, Surrey, TW9 1PL Tel: (020) 8940 7129 Fax: (020) 8940 8647 E-mail: sharppaint@london.com
Unigraph UK Ltd, 287 Pitsmoor Road, Sheffield, S3 9AS Tel: 0114-275 2801 Fax: 0114-275 9769 E-mail: sales@unigraph.uk
West Design Products Ltd, West House, Shearway Business Park, Pent Road, Folkestone, Kent, CT19 4RJ Tel: (01303) 297888 Fax: (01303) 297877 E-mail: sales@westdesignproducts.co.uk
Wimbledon Copy Bureau, 257-261 Haydons Road, London, SW19 8TY Tel: (020) 8542 8342 Fax: (020) 8715 8959 E-mail: colour@wcb.co.uk

REPROGRAPHIC SUPPLY SERVICES

D C T Services, Summer Trees, Hawley Drive, Hale Barns, Altrincham, Cheshire, WA15 0DP Tel: 0161-621 0730 Fax: 0161-904 7392
Fife Shutter Services, Unit 11 Coal Wynd, Kirkcaldy, Fife, KY1 2RA Tel: (01592) 266868 Fax: (01592) 642868 E-mail: info@fifeshutterservices.co.uk
Litho Supplies, Flagship Square, Shaw Cross Business Park, Dewsbury, West Yorkshire, WF12 7TH Tel: (01924) 486130 Fax: (01924) 460502 E-mail: dewsbury@litho.co.uk
Rapidos Ltd, Unit 11 Steyning Way, Hounslow, TW4 6DL Tel: (020) 8570 9393 Fax: (020) 8577 3450 E-mail: printroom@repropoint.com
Repropoint Ltd, 332 London Road, Portsmouth, PO2 9JY Tel: (023) 9266 9941 Fax: (023) 9269 6514 E-mail: info@repropoint.com

REPROGRAPHIC TONERS

Ballpoint Office Supplies, Unit 21 The Bell Centre, Newton Road, Crawley, West Sussex, RH10 9FZ Tel: (01293) 433330 Fax: (01293) 434484 E-mail: sales@ballpoint.co.uk

REQUIREMENT ENGINEERING TRAINING

▶ Summers Training, 7 Woodlands, Pickwick, Corsham, Wiltshire, SN13 0DA Tel: (01249) 712037

RESCUE CRAFT

Maritime Rescue Institute Lifeboat Station, Old Pier, Stonehaven, Kincardineshire, AB39 2JU Tel: (01569) 765768 Fax: (01569) 764066

RESCUE EQUIPMENT, INFLATABLE, *See Inflatable etc*

RESEARCH ANALYSTS, *See Research, Materials etc*

RESEARCH AND DEVELOPMENT ENGINEERING SERVICES, INDUSTRIAL/ CONTRACT

Beta Research & Development Ltd, 50 Goodsmoor Road, Sinfin, Derby, DE24 9GN Tel: (01332) 770500 Fax: (01332) 771591 E-mail: project@betard.co.uk
BMT Cordah Ltd, Grove House, 7 Ocean Way, Southampton, SO14 3TJ Tel: (023) 8023 2222 Fax: (023) 8023 2891 E-mail: jenny.bell@bmtcordah.com
Construction Elliz Ltd, Chart House Farm, Bullen Road, Ryde, Isle of Wight, PO33 1QB Tel: (01983) 612317 Fax: (01983) 615600 E-mail: iow@mansell.plc.uk
Davison Chemographics Ltd, 28 Woolmer Way, Bordon, Hampshire, GU35 9QF Tel: (01420) 487275 Fax: (01420) 488041 E-mail: sales@davchemo.demon.co.uk
E A Technology Ltd, Capenhurst Lane, Capenhurst, Chester, CH1 6ES Tel: 0151-339 4181 Fax: 0151-347 2404 E-mail: john.hutchinson@eatechnology.com
Huxley Bertram Engineering, Brookfield Business Centre, Twentypence Road, Cottenham, Cambridge, CB24 8PS Tel: (01954) 250809 Fax: (01954) 251991 E-mail: info@huxleybertram.com
Imperial Innovations Ltd, Imperial College, London, SW7 2AZ Tel: (020) 7581 4949 Fax: (020) 7589 3553 E-mail: sales@imperial.ac.uk
Insight Ltd, Sandys Road, Malvern, Worcestershire, WR14 1JJ Tel: (01684) 577444 Fax: (01684) 577555 E-mail: sales@insightprecision.co.uk
M E L Research, 8 Holt Court North, Heneage St West, Birmingham, B7 4AX Tel: 0121-604 4664 Fax: 0121-604 6776 E-mail: info@m-e-l.co.uk
Mecon Ltd, 5a Pound Hill, Cambridge, CB3 0AE Tel: (01223) 355990 Fax: (01223) 354297 E-mail: enquiries@mecon.ltd.uk
Protherics P.L.C., The Heath Business & Technical Park, Runcorn, Cheshire, WA7 4QX Tel: (01928) 518000 Fax: (01928) 518002 E-mail: information@protherics.com
Research & Enterprise Office, University of Hull, Cottingham Road, Hull, HU6 7RX Tel: (01482) 465139 Fax: (01482) 466852 E-mail: k.j.butler@admin.hull.ac.uk
T R W Automotive, Technical Centre, Stratford Road, Shirley, Solihull, West Midlands, B90 4GW Tel: 0121-627 4141 Fax: 0121-627 3584 E-mail: rob.miller@trw.com

RESEARCH AND DEVELOPMENT ENGINEERING SERVICES, INDUSTRIAL/CONTRACT – *continued*

T S L Technology Ltd, The Station Mill, Station Road, Alresford, Hampshire, SO24 9DE Tel: (01962) 735707 Fax: (01962) 735502 E-mail: enquiries@tsltechnology.com

U F C Ltd, Synergy House, Guildhall Close, Manchester Science Park, Manchester, M15 6SY Tel: 0161-232 5500 Fax: 0161-232 5501 E-mail: info@ultrafine.co.uk

University Of Wales Institute Cardiff, Western Avenue, Cardiff, CF5 2SG Tel: (029) 2041 6070 Fax: (029) 2041 6286 E-mail: info@uwic.ac.uk

Wooberry Engineering & Marine Co, 21 Parvis Road, West Byfleet, Surrey, KT14 6HD Tel: (01932) 352070 Fax: (01932) 353479

Zeta Dynamics Ltd, Zeta House, Daish Way, Newport, Isle of Wight, PO30 5XJ Tel: (01983) 527725 Fax: (01983) 821024 E-mail: info@zeta-dynamics.com

RESEARCH AND DEVELOPMENT, AGRICULTURAL

Family Farm Development Ltd, Milestone Centre Termon Business Park Quarry Road, Sixmilecross, Omagh, County Tyrone, BT79 9AL Tel: (028) 8076 1719 Fax: (028) 8076 1779 E-mail: familyfarm@btconnect.com

RESEARCH LABORATORIES OR ORGANISATIONS OR SERVICES,

See also headings for particular industries or products

Abertec Ltd, Cledwyn Building, Penglais, Aberystwyth, Dyfed, SY23 3DD Tel: (01970) 622385 Fax: (01970) 622959 E-mail: dkc@aber.ac.uk

B & W Group, Elm Grove Lane, Steyning, West Sussex, BN44 3SA Tel: (01903) 817200 Fax: (01903) 815801

Biozyme Holdings Ltd, Tnit 6 Gilchrist Thomas Estate, Bleanavon, Pontypool, Gwent, NP4 9RL Tel: (01495) 790678 Fax: (01495) 791780 E-mail: sales@biozyme.co.uk

BMTGroup Ltd, Goodrich House, 1 Waldegrave Road, Teddington, Middlesex, TW11 8LZ Tel: (020) 8943 5544 Fax: (020) 8943 5347 E-mail: enquiries@bmtmail.com

BP International Ltd, Research & Engineering Centre, Chertsey Rd, Sunbury-on-Thames, Middx, TW16 7LN Tel: (01932) 762000 Fax: (01932) 762999

Brewing Research International Ltd, Lyttel Hall, Coopers Hill Road, Redhill, RH1 4HY Tel: (01737) 822272 Fax: (01737) 822747 E-mail: bri@brewingresearch.co.uk

British Antarctic Survey, High Cross, Madingley Road, Cambridge, CB3 0ET Tel: (01223) 221400 Fax: (01223) 362616 E-mail: information@bas.ac.uk

Building Research Establishment Ltd, Bucknalls Lane, Garston, Watford, WD25 9XX Tel: (01923) 664000 Fax: (01923) 664010 E-mail: enquiries@bre.co.uk

Ceramic Research Ltd, Queens Road, Stoke-on-Trent, ST4 7LQ Tel: (01782) 764444 Fax: (01782) 412331 E-mail: sales@ceram.co.uk

Doctor's Laboratory plc, 60 Whitfield Street, London, W1T 4EU Tel: (020) 7460 4800 Fax: (020) 7460 4848

Edwards' Analytical, Rose Cottage, Walker Hall, Winston, Darlington, County Durham, DL2 3PN Tel: (01325) 730766 Fax: (01325) 730911 E-mail: davidjhe@aol.com

Flow Science Ltd, Goldstein Laboratory, Liverpool Road, Eccles, Manchester, M30 7RU Tel: 0161-787 8749 Fax: 0161-787 8749 E-mail: flowsci@fs1.ae.man.ac.uk

I H Laboratories Ltd, Station Approach, Meopham, Gravesend, Kent, DA13 0LT Tel: (01474) 814917 Fax: (01474) 813117

Institute for Animal Health, Pirbright Laboratory, Ash Road, Pirbright, Woking, Surrey, GU24 0NF Tel: (01483) 232441 Fax: (01483) 232448

Intracel Ltd, 4 Station Road, Shepreth, Royston, Hertfordshire, SG8 6PZ Tel: (01763) 262680 Fax: (01763) 262676 E-mail: intracel@intracel.co.uk

Itf Oil & Gas Exploration, Exploration House, Exploration Drive, Bridge of Don, Aberdeen, AB23 8GX Tel: (01224) 853400 Fax: (01224) 853480 E-mail: itf@oil-itf.com

J R H Bio Sciences Ltd, West Portway, Andover, Hampshire, SP10 3LF Tel: (01264) 333311 Fax: (01264) 332412 E-mail: info@jrheurope.com

M S Laboratories Ltd, 33 Sanders Road, Finedon Road Industrial Estate, Wellingborough, Northamptonshire, NN8 4NL Tel: (01933) 276668 Fax: (01933) 273841 E-mail: enquiries@mslabs.co.uk

Marchwood Scientific Services, Unit 4G, Marchwood Industrial Pk, Marchwood, Southampton, SO40 4PB Tel: (023) 8066 9126 Fax: (023) 8066 9127 E-mail: enquiries@marchwood-scientific.co.uk

Minton Treharne & Davies Ltd, Merton House The Avenue Industrial Park, Croescadarn Close, Cardiff, CF23 8HF Tel: (029) 2054 0000 Fax: (029) 2054 0111 E-mail: mtd@minton.co.uk

Morgan Materials Technology Ltd, Bewdley Road, Stourport-on-Severn, Worcestershire, DY13 8QR Tel: 01299 827557 Fax: 01299 827187 E-mail: mormetalloys@mormet.co.uk

▶ Mylnefield Research Services Ltd, Invergowrie, Dundee, DD2 5DA Tel: (01382) 568568 Fax: (01382) 568501

National Physical Laboratory, Hampton Road, Teddington, Middlesex, TW11 0LW Tel: (020) 8977 3222 Fax: (020) 8943 6458 E-mail: enquiry@npl.co.uk

Paint Research Association, 14 Castle Mews, High Street, Hampton, Middlesex, TW12 2NP Tel: (020) 8487 0800 Fax: (020) 8487 0801 E-mail: coatings@pra.org.uk

Charles River Laboratories, Tranent, East Lothian, EH33 2NE Tel: (01875) 614545 Fax: (01875) 614555

Rodette International Ltd, 19 Sturges Road, Ashford, Kent, TN24 8NE Tel: (01233) 611660 Fax: (01233) 011722 E-mail: sales@orbaorginals.com

Royal Institution Of Great Britain, 21 Albemarle Street, London, W1S 4BS Tel: (020) 7409 2992 Fax: (020) 7629 3569 E-mail: info@ri.ac.uk

Satra Technology Centre Ltd, Satra House, Rockingham Road, Kettering, Northamptonshire, NN16 9JH Tel: (01536) 410000 Fax: (01536) 410626 E-mail: info@satra.co.uk

Sci Tech Laboratories, The Grove, Craven Arms, Shropshire, SY7 8DA Tel: (01588) 672600 Fax: (01588) 672880 E-mail: enquiries@scitech-labs.com

Sequani Ltd, Bromyard Road, Ledbury, Herefordshire, HR8 1LH Tel: (01531) 634121 Fax: (01531) 634753 E-mail: sales@sequani.com

Serotec Ltd, Unit 22 Bankside, Station Approach, Kidlington, Oxfordshire, OX5 1JE Tel: (01865) 852700 Fax: (01865) 373899 E-mail: sales@serotec.co.uk

Servier Laboratories Ltd, Wexham Springs, Framewood Road, Wexham, Slough, SL3 6RJ Tel: (01753) 662647 Fax: (01753) 663456

Simbec Research Ltd, Clinical Research Organisation, Merthyr Tydfil Industrial Park, Merthyr Tydfil, Mid Glamorgan, CF48 4DR Tel: (01443) 690977 Fax: (01443) 692499 E-mail: alan.woodward@simbec.co.uk

Spectral Fusion Technologies Ltd, Unit 45 Coleshill Industrial Estate, Station Road, Coleshill, Birmingham, B46 1JT Tel: (01675) 466111 Fax: (01675) 467111

UK Analytical Ltd, Lower Ground Floor, Dison Building, Buslingthorpe Lane, Leeds, LS7 2DG Tel: (0113) 2392 572 Fax: (0113) 2392 575 E-mail: uka@kirkstall.fsbusiness.co.uk

University Of Plymouth, Drake Circus, Plymouth, PL4 8AA Tel: (01752) 600600

Waterlife Aquatic Exotic Plant & Pet Centre, 476 Bath Road, Longford Near Heathrow, West Drayton, Middlesex, UB7 0ED Tel: (01753) 685696 Fax: (01753) 685437 E-mail: sales@waterlife.co.uk

Wit Press, Ashurst Lodge, Lyndhurst Road, Ashurst, Southampton, SO40 7AA Tel: (023) 8029 3223 Fax: (023) 8029 2853 E-mail: witpress@witpress.com

Wood Mackenzie Global Consultants, 74-77 Queen Street, Edinburgh, EH2 4NF Tel: 0131-243 4400 Fax: 0131-243 4653 E-mail: sales@woodmac.com

Zeta Dynamics Ltd, Zeta House, Daish Way, Newport, Isle of Wight, PO30 5XJ Tel: (01983) 527725 Fax: (01983) 821024 E-mail: info@zeta-dynamics.com

RESEARCH ORGANISATIONS, FORECASTING/INFORMATION GATHERING/PLANNING, *See also specialist services*

Deven Anderson Ltd, George House, 121 High Street, Henley-in-Arden, West Midlands, B95 5AU Tel: (01564) 795565 Fax: (01564) 795122 E-mail: headhunt@devenanderson.co.uk

Brewing Research International Ltd, Lyttel Hall, Coopers Hill Road, Redhill, RH1 4HY Tel: (01737) 822272 Fax: (01737) 822747 E-mail: bri@brewingresearch.co.uk

Building Services Research & Information Associati Ltd, Old Bracknell Lane West, Bracknell, Berkshire, RG12 7AH Tel: (0845) 1309030 Fax: (01344) 465626 E-mail: bsria@bsria.co.uk

Canadean Ltd, Unit 9-12 Faraday Court, Rankine Road, Basingstoke, Hampshire, RG24 8PF Tel: (01256) 394200 Fax: (01256) 394201 E-mail: sales@canadean.com

Commodities Research Unit Ltd, 31 Mount Pleasant, London, WC1X 0AD Tel: (020) 7278 0414 Fax: (020) 7837 0976

The Gallup Organisation Ltd, Drapers Court, Kingston Hall Road, Kingston upon Thames, Surrey, KT1 2BG Tel: (020) 8939 7000 Fax: (020) 8939 7039

The Institute Of Economic Affairs, 2 Lord North Street, London, SW1P 3LB Tel: (020) 7799 3745 Fax: (020) 7799 2137 E-mail: iea@iea.org.uk

Stuart James Systems Ltd, 69 Trent Valley Road, Lichfield, Staffordshire, WS13 6EZ Tel: (01543) 256979 Fax: (01543) 251516

Knight Chapman Psychological Ltd, 1 The Friars, High Street, Lewes, East Sussex, BN7 2AD Tel: (01273) 487333 Fax: (01273) 471475 E-mail: service@kcpltd.com

Eli Lilly & Co. Ltd, Erl Wood Manor, Sunninghill Road, Windlesham, Surrey, GU20 6PH Tel: (01276) 483000

Medtap International, 20 Bloomsbury Square, London, WC1A 2NS Tel: (020) 7299 4550 Fax: (020) 7299 4555

Milar Ltd, Minereva House, 1 Bilton Road, Rugby, Warwickshire, CV22 7NZ Tel: (01788) 551288 Fax: (01788) 552142

Mintel Group Ltd, 18-19 Long Lane, London, EC1A 9PL Tel: (020) 7606 4533 Fax: (020) 7606 5932 E-mail: info@mintel.com

Russell Reynolds Associates Inc, 24 St James's Square, London, SW1Y 4HZ Tel: (020) 7839 7788 Fax: (020) 7839 9295

Spring Technology Staffing Services, First Floor, Bishops Weald House, Albion Way, Horsham, West Sussex, RH12 1AH Tel: (01403) 262345 E-mail: itpersonnel-birmingham@spring.com

The Tokyo Electric Power Company, Incorporated, Masaki Chiba, Berkeley Square House, London, W1J 6BR Tel: (020) 7629 5271 Fax: (020) 7629 5282

Trada Technology Ltd, Stocking Lane, Hughenden Valley, High Wycombe, Buckinghamshire, HP14 4ND Tel: (01494) 569600 Fax: (01494) 565487 E-mail: information@trada.co.uk

RESERVOIR ENGINEERING

Bowsprit Contracting Ltd, J The Henfield Business Park, Shoreham Road, Henfield, West Sussex, BN5 9SL Tel: (01273) 491499 Fax: (01273) 491982 E-mail: enquiries@bowspritltd.co.uk

Geosynthetic Technology Ltd, Little Bulmer Farm, Wiston Road, Nayland, Colchester, CO6 4LT Tel: (01206) 262676 Fax: (01206) 262998 E-mail: sales@geosynthetic.co.uk

Veritas DGC Ltd, Crompton Way, Crawley, West Sussex, RH10 9QN Tel: (01293) 443000 Fax: (01293) 443010 E-mail: info@veritasdgc.com

RESERVOIR LINERS

Aquaflex Ltd, 1 Edison Road, Salisbury, SP2 7NU Tel: (01722) 328873 Fax: (01722) 413068 E-mail: info@aquaflex.co.uk

▶ Industrial Textiles & Plastics Ltd, Easingwold Business Park, Oaklands Way, Easingwold, York, YO61 3FA Tel: (01347) 825200 Fax: (01347) 825222 E-mail: sales@indtex.co.uk

Monarflex Ltd, Unit 23 North Orbital Commercial Park (Off Natsbury Avenue), St. Albans, Hertfordshire, AL1 1XB Tel: (01727) 830116 Fax: (01727) 868045 E-mail: geos.uk@icopal.com

RESERVOIR OR TANK HEATERS

Hasco-Thermic Ltd, 134 Birchfield Lane, Oldbury, West Midlands, B69 2AY Tel: 0121-552 4911 Fax: 0121-544 8143E-mail: mail@hasco.co.uk

RESIDENTIAL BUILDING SURVEY SERVICES

▶ Building Surveying Solutions, 376 City Road, London, EC1V 2QA Tel: (020) 7278 4060 Fax: (020) 7287 4717

▶ HCL Developments Limited, 26, Cornwall Road, Ruislip, Middlesex, HA4 6AN Tel: (07961) 111245 E-mail: sc@hcld.co.uk

▶ Ndesign Services Ltd, 74 Brighton Road, Newhaven, East Sussex, BN9 9NS Tel: (01273) 515081 Fax: (01273) 515168 E-mail: nathan@ndesignservices.co.uk

RESIDENTIAL INTERIOR DESIGN

▶ 1:50, 15 Silver Birch Close, Sholing, Southampton, SO19 8FY Tel: (0845) 2262817 E-mail: info@1-50.co.uk

▶ A P Lane, 257 Lampits, Hoddesdon, Hertfordshire, EN11 8EE Tel: 01992 445886 E-mail: antpatlane@yahoo.co.uk

▶ Abode Interior Design, Oxbow Farm, Avon Dassett, Southam, Warwickshire, CV47 2AQ Tel: (01295) 690196 Fax: (01295) 690194 E-mail: info@uk-designer.com

▶ Cheshire Interiors, 75 Shepperton Close, Appleton, Warrington, WA4 5JZ Tel: 01925 213339 E-mail: tamara@cheshireinteriors.com

▶ Design 5, 17 Crimp Hill Road, Old Windsor, Windsor, Berkshire, SL4 2QY Tel: (01753) 620000 Fax: (01753) 622522 E-mail: mail@design5.co.uk

▶ Emma Pettifer Richardson, Cavenagh House, The Square, Sheriff Hutton, York, YO60 6QX Tel: (01347) 878173 Fax: (01347) 878176 E-mail: info@abouthouse.co.uk

▶ Fun Art Design, Suite 205, The Citadel Business Centre, Bath Road, Chippenham, Wiltshire, SN15 2AB Tel: (0794) 0716747 E-mail: info@funartdesign.co.uk

Hollis Design LLP, 30 St Catherines Road, Winchester, Hampshire, SO23 0PS Tel: (0845) 8382034 E-mail: architect@hollisdesign.co.uk

▶ Imagey - photo print and display products, 16 Bull Lane, London, N18 1SX Tel: 0845 833 0783 Fax: 0845 833 0793 E-mail: info@imagey.co.uk

▶ in2style Ltd, 143 Richmond Road, London, E8 3NJ Tel: (020) 7249 4286 E-mail: info@in2style.org

▶ Inspirit Interiors, Repton Road, Nottingham, NG6 9GE Tel: 0115-877 6959 Fax: 0115-877 6959 E-mail: enquiries@inspirit-interiors.co.uk

▶ Interior Love, 15 Bridle Lane, Streetly, Sutton Coldfield, Birmingham, B74 3PT Tel: (0797) 1425195 E-mail: design@interiorlove.co.uk

▶ Interior Solutions, 57 Comiston View, Edinburgh, EH10 6LT Tel: 0131-445 2200 Fax: 0131-466 1516 E-mail: mail@interiorsolutionsedinburgh.com

▶ Ladesigns.Co.Uk, 20 Hartfield Road, Eastbourne, East Sussex, BN21 2AR Tel: (07801) 421368 E-mail: info@ladesigns.co.uk

Photography & Philosophy Ltd, 20 Camden Crescent, Bath, BA1 5HY Tel: (01225) 484446 Fax: (01225) 484446 E-mail: jacquimustard@photographyphilosophy.com

▶ The Property Coach, 33 Sandwich House, Sandwich Street, London, London, WC1H 9PR Tel: 020 7388 0242 E-mail: brian@property-coach.co.uk

▶ Time 4 U, 10 Market Street, Woodstock, Oxfordshire, OX20 1SX Tel: (01993) 810450 Fax: (01993) 810450 E-mail: sales@time4u.co.uk

▶ WonderFalls, Manderley, Auldgirth, Dumfries, DG2 0SA Tel: 01387 740685 Fax: 01387 740697 E-mail: ian@wonderfalls.co.uk

RESIDENTIAL VENUE FINDING

▶ St. Andrews House Rental, 10 Pipeland Farm, St. Andrews, Fife, KY16 8NL Tel: (01334) 473360 E-mail: webmaster@sKooF.co.uk

RESIDUAL CURRENT DEVICE (RCD) CIRCUIT BREAKERS (CB)

Electrium Sales Ltd, Walkmill Business Park, Walkmill Way, Cannock, Staffordshire, WS11 0XE Tel: (01543) 455000 Fax: (01543) 455001 E-mail: darren.garbett@electrium.co.uk

Protek Ltd, Phoenix House, Phoenix Road, Hawks Green, Cannock, Staffordshire, WS11 7LR Tel: (01543) 467575 Fax: (01543) 462370 E-mail: sales@protekuk.co.uk

RESIDUAL CURRENT DEVICE (RCD) TESTER CALIBRATING

▶ Richmond Electronic Services Ltd, 42 Hurricane Way, Norwich Airport Industrial, Estate Norfolk, Norwich, NR6 6JB Tel: (020) 7942 0700 Fax: (020) 7942 0701

RESILIENT METAL SEALS

Nicholsons Sealing Technologies Ltd, Hamsterley, Newcastle upon Tyne, NE17 7SX Tel: (01207) 560505 Fax: (01207) 561004 E-mail: info@nicholsons.co.uk

RESIN BADGES

Dectek Ltd, Unit 29 Business Development Centre, Main Ave, Treforest Industrial Estate, Pontypridd, M. Glam, CF37 5UR Tel: (01443) 841840 Fax: (01443) 842815 E-mail: sales@dectek.co.uk

Graphicraft Ltd, 6-8 Singer Way, Woburn Road Industrial Estate, Kempston, Bedford, MK42 7AN Tel: (01234) 846000 Fax: (01234) 843601 E-mail: sales@cgi-visual.com

RESIN BASED FLOOR COATINGS

▶ Acrylicon Installations North East Ltd, North Speed House, Moor View, Leeds, LS11 9NF Tel: 0113-245 2707 Fax: 0113-245 2649 E-mail: acrylicon@hotmail.co.uk

Optus Resin Technology Ltd, 22 Tarran Way North, Tarran Industrial Estate, Wirral, Merseyside, CH46 4UA Tel: 0151-604 0001 Fax: 0151-522 0733 E-mail: information@optus.co.uk

Smith & Rodger Ltd, 34 Elliott Street, Glasgow, G3 8EA Tel: 0141-248 6341 Fax: 0141-248 6475 E-mail: info@smithandrodger.co.uk

RESIN FIGURINES

Country Artists Ltd, Country Artists House, Loxley Road, Wellesbourne, Warwick, CV35 9JY Tel: (01789) 473000 Fax: (01789) 473001 E-mail: reception1@country-artists.co.uk

North Light, Royal Victiora Pottery, West POrt Road, Birslum, Stoke-On-Trent, ST8 4AG Tel: (01782) 259403 Fax: (01782) 575195

▶ www.321Deco.co.uk, 14 Bridgeway Centre, Wrexham Industrial Estate, Wrexham, LL13 9QS Tel: (01978) 661572 Fax: (01978) 661572 E-mail: sd@ukmemory.com

RESIN INJECTION CONTRACTORS OR SERVICES

Balvac Whitley Moran Ltd, 24 Woodside Business Park, Birkenhead, Merseyside, CH41 1EL Tel: 0151-650 0184 Fax: 0151-650 0358 E-mail: info@balvac.co.uk

Barcol Ltd, Oak Lodge, Studland Avenue, Wickford, Essex, SS12 0JF Tel: (01268) 764642 Fax: (01268) 764644

Kent Grouting Services Ltd, 10 Gun Lane, Rochester, Kent, ME2 4UB Tel: (01634) 717554 Fax: (01634) 711396 E-mail: martinstromsoy@freenetname.co.uk

Markham (Sheffield) Ltd, Marspal House, Lawn Road Industrial Estate, Carlton-In-Lindrick, Worksop, Nottinghamshire, S81 9LB Tel: (01909) 730861 Fax: (01909) 733584 E-mail: sales@markham-sheffield.co.uk

RESIN INJECTION UNDERPINNING CONTRACTORS

▶ Uretek UK Ltd, Peel House, Peel Rd, Skelmersdale, Lancs, WN8 9PT Tel: (01695) 50525 Fax: (01695) 555212 E-mail: sales@uretek.co.uk

RESIN MOULDINGS/CUSTOM MOULDERS

Copratec Mouldings Ltd, Unit 1-4 Cats Lane, King George Road, Minehead, Somerset, TA24 5JE Tel: (01643) 705843 Fax: (01643) 707979

Jonesco (Preston) Ltd, Pittman Way, Fulwood, Preston, PR2 9ZD Tel: (01772) 704488 Fax: (01772) 702209 E-mail: sales@jonesco-plastics.com

RESIN REPAIR SYSTEMS, TIMBER

▶ Valley Builders Ltd, 214 London Road, East Grinstead, West Sussex, RH19 1HE Tel: (01342) 311377 Fax: (01342) 300251 E-mail: sales@valleybuildersltd.co.uk

RESISTANCE TEMPERATURE DETECTOR/SENSOR/ THERMOMETER MANUFRS

Carel Components, 24 Endeavour Way, London, SW19 8UH Tel: (020) 8946 9882 Fax: (020) 8946 6259 E-mail: ccs@carel.co.uk

Crossland Components Ltd, Unit L Tanfield Lea Industrial Estate South, Tanfield Lea, Stanley, County Durham, DH9 9XA Tel: (01207) 230269 Fax: (01207) 283849 E-mail: info@crossland.co.uk

Electro Mechanical Installations Ltd, 7 Mackenzie Industrial Estate, Bird Hall Lane, Stockport, Cheshire, SK3 0SB Tel: 0161-428 7800 Fax: 0161-428 8999 E-mail: office@emiltd.co.uk

Minta Instrumentation Ltd, Caddick Road, Knowsley Business Park, Prescot, Merseyside, L34 9HP Tel: 0151-548 6818 Fax: 0151-548 5578 E-mail: sales@mintasensors.co.uk

R T D Products, Unit 10-11 A K Business Park, Russell Road, Southport, Merseyside, PR9 7SA Tel: (01704) 507696 Fax: (01704) 507055 E-mail: rnice@rtd-products.co.uk

Sensing Devices Ltd, 97 Tithebarn Road, Southport, Merseyside, PR8 6AG Tel: (01704) 546161 Fax: (01704) 546231 E-mail: sales@sensing-devices.co.uk

Sterling Sensors Ltd, Fitmec Works Hawksley Street, Oldham, OL8 4PQ Tel: 0161-627 0507 Fax: 0161-627 0507 E-mail: sales@sterlingsensors.co.uk

Thermal Detection Ltd, Unit 6 Orde Wingate Way, Stockton-on-Tees, Cleveland, TS19 0GA Tel: (01642) 602878 Fax: (01642) 618307 E-mail: tdl@thermal-detection.com

Thermo Devices Ltd, Floats Road, Roundthorn Industrial Estate, Manchester, M23 9NF Tel: 0161-286 5100 Fax: 0161-286 5093 E-mail: sales@tdl.endress.com

Universal Thermosensors Ltd, Units 10-11 Castle Road Technical Centre, Castle Road, Murston, Sittingbourne, Kent, ME10 3RG Tel: (01795) 470924 Fax: (01795) 476733 E-mail: sales@universal-thermosensors.co.uk

▶ Vydas International Marketing, Swan House, Passfield Business Centre, Lynchborough Road, Passfield, Liphook, Hampshire, GU30 7SB Tel: (01428) 751822 Fax: (01428) 751833 E-mail: info@vydas.co.uk

West Midlands Thermocouples, Unit 203 Telsen Industrial Centre, Thomas Street, Birmingham, B6 4TN Tel: 0121-359 0535 Fax: 0121-359 4005

RESISTANCE WELDING ELECTRODES

E Partridge & Sons Ltd, Maypole Fields, Halesowen, West Midlands, B63 2QH Tel: (01384) 566667 Fax: (01384) 410211

M H Spencer Co Ltd, Charter Avenue, Coventry, CV4 8AF Tel: (024) 7646 4044 Fax: (024) 7669 4011 E-mail: james.evans@mhspencer.co.uk

Sciaky Electric Welding Machines Ltd, 212 Bedford Avenue, Slough, SL1 4RH Tel: (01753) 525551 Fax: (01753) 821416 E-mail: sales@sciaky.co.uk

Vacuum Impregnated Products Ltd, Hew Cut Lane, Woolston, Warrington, WA1 4AG Tel: (01925) 817213 Fax: (01925) 823862 E-mail: sales@viproducts.co.uk

RESISTANCE WELDING EQUIPMENT

Adlington Welding Supplies Ltd, Highfield Industrial Estate, North Street, Chorley, Lancashire, PR7 1QD Tel: (01257) 279364 Fax: (01257) 241352 E-mail: adweld@easynet.co.uk

RESISTOR LOAD BANKS

Hillstone Products Ltd, Unit 2, Portland Industrial Estate, Portland Street, Bury, Lancashire, BL9 6EY Tel: 0161-763 3100 Fax: 0161-763 3158 E-mail: sales@hillstone.co.uk

RESISTORS, ELECTRICAL/ ELECTRONIC, *See also headings under Resistors*

Dubilier Electronic Component Distributors, Station House Station Yard Industrial Park, Station Road, Dunmow, Essex, CM6 1XD Tel: (01371) 875758 Fax: (01371) 875075 E-mail: sales@dubilier.co.uk

HVR International Ltd, Bede Trading Estate, Jarrow, Tyne & Wear, NE32 3EN Tel: 0191-489 7771 Fax: 0191-483 9501 E-mail: info@hvrint.com

Lock Engineering Co Ltd, Western Trading Estate, 22 Trading Estate Road, London, NW10 7LY Tel: (020) 8961 6649 Fax: (020) 8961 1036 E-mail: ss@lockeng.co.uk

LPC Holdings Ltd, Coundon Industrial Estate, Coundon, Bishop Auckland, County Durham, DL14 8NR Tel: (01388) 608270 Fax: (01388) 450048 E-mail: enquiries@lpcholdings.co.uk

T T Electronics Welwyn Components Ltd, Welwyn Electronics Park, Bedlington, Northumberland, NE22 7AA Tel: (01670) 822181 Fax: (01670) 829465 E-mail: info@welwyn-tt.com

RESOLVERS, *See also headings for particular types*

Precision Varionics Ltd, 307 The Commercial Centre, Picket Piece, Andover, Hampshire, SP11 6RU Tel: (01264) 334522 Fax: (01264) 334422 E-mail: sales@varionics.co.uk

RESPIRATORY MEASURING SYSTEMS

TMS Services, 7 Brunel Way, Fareham, Hampshire, PO15 5TX Tel: (01489) 564707 Fax: (01489) 575229E-mail: sales@ansti.com

Vitalograph Ltd, Maids Moreton House, Vitalograph Business Park, Maids Moreton, Buckingham, MK18 1SW Tel: (01280) 827100 Fax: (01280) 823302 E-mail: sales@vitalograph.co.uk

RESTAURANT FITTER AND FURNISHERS

Ital Catering Equipment Ltd, 91 Old Oak Common Lane, London, W3 7DD Tel: (020) 8749 4832 Fax: (020) 8743 7885 E-mail: ray@frozen.co.uk

RESTAURANT FURNITURE

Imperial Finishers Ltd, 8 Windmill Close, Stansted, Essex, CM24 8GH Tel: (01279) 817500 Fax: (01279) 817517

RESTAURANTS, BUSINESS LUNCHES AND DINNERS

▶ City Restaurants Guide, 4 Oak Close, Measham, Swadlincote, Derbyshire, DE12 7JY Tel: (01530) 274830 Fax: 01530 274823 E-mail: info@cityrestaurantsguide.com

RESTRICTED ACCESS PILING

▶ Sonic Drilling Supplies Ltd, 141 St Johns Road, Congleton, Cheshire, CW12 2EH Tel: (01260) 273956 Fax: (01260) 276923 E-mail: info@sonicdrill.co.uk

RESUSCITATION EQUIPMENT

Laerdal Medical Ltd, Laerdal House, Goodmead Road, Orpington, Kent, BR6 0HX Tel: (01689) 876634 Fax: (01689) 873800 E-mail: customer.service@laerdal.co.uk

Vitalograph Ltd, Maids Moreton House, Vitalograph Business Park, Maids Moreton, Buckingham, MK18 1SW Tel: (01280) 827100 Fax: (01280) 823302 E-mail: sales@vitalograph.co.uk

RETAIL BRAND DESIGN MARKETING CONSULTANCY

▶ Prodo Ltd, Littleton Old Hall, Little Heath Road, Littleton, Chester, CH3 &DW Tel: 0870 7562828 Fax: 0870 7562838 E-mail: sales@prodo.com

RETAIL CUSTOMER SERVICES

▶ GSL Consulting, 40 Avebury, Slough, SL1 5SY Tel: (07764) 751762 Fax: (01753) 533226 E-mail: giles@gslconsulting.co.uk

▶ Roys Wroxham Ltd, B9 Pinetrees Road, Norwich, NR7 9BB Tel: (01603) 700954 Fax: (01603) 702670

RETAIL DISPLAY CLIPS

▶ Instore Field Marketing, Blockhouse Close, Worcester, WR1 2BT Tel: (01905) 726079 Fax: (01905) 611063

RETAIL MANAGEMENT SYSTEMS

Retail Business Solutions Ltd, 24-26 Vincent Avenue, Crownhill, Milton Keynes, MK8 0AB Tel: (01908) 226226 Fax: (01908) 225533

RETAIL SECURITY SERVICES

▶ Censor Security, Unit 342 Camberwell Business Centre, 99-103 Lomond Grove, London, SE5 7HN Tel: (0845) 2309816 Fax: (020) 7703 7243 E-mail: admin@censorgroup.co.uk

▶ Duel, Unit 1 Parkers Yard, Marlborough Road, Ilfracombe, Devon, EX34 8JP Tel: (01271) 863397 Fax: (01271) 863024 E-mail: enquiries@duel-investigations.com

RETAIL STORE SECURITY SYSTEMS OR EQUIPMENT

Checkpoint Meto, 43 Western Road, Bracknell, Berkshire, RG12 1RF Tel: (01344) 701200 Fax: (01344) 701333 E-mail: lfardell@eur.checkpt.com

▶ Innovation 2 Market Ltd, Kings Rd, The Docks, Swansea, SA1 8PH Tel: (01792) 295520 Fax: (01792) 295588 E-mail: sales@i2m-uk.com

RETAIL TICKETING SOFTWARE

Retail Assist Ltd, 3 Westleigh Park, Scirroco Close, Northampton, NN3 6AP Tel: (01604) 647002 Fax: (01604) 644625

RETAINING RING MANUFRS

UK Spring Supplies, 7 Elmwood, Sawbridgeworth, Hertfordshire, CM21 9NL Tel: (01279) 723666 Fax: (01279) 723729 E-mail: larryelmwood@aol.com

RETAINING WALLS

R A D Products Ltd, 19 Dodwells Bridge Industrial Estate, Jacknell Road, Hinckley, Leicestershire, LE10 3BS Tel: (01455) 891122 Fax: (01455) 891133 E-mail: sales@radproducts.co.uk

RETIREMENT PLANNING FINANCIAL SERVICES

▶ atretirement.co.uk, Tritton House, 14 Bath Road, Swindon, SN1 4BA Tel: (0870) 1904187

▶ Grace Consulting Care Advisory Service, The Street, Orchard House, Albury, Guildford, Surrey, GU5 9AG Tel: (01483) 203066 Fax: (01483) 202535 E-mail: info@graceconsulting.co.uk

RETRACTABLE BOLLARDS

▶ R A M Perimeter Protection Ltd, 179 Higher Hillgate, Stockport, Cheshire, SK1 3JG Tel: 0161-477 4001 Fax: 0161-477 1007 E-mail: ramperimeterprotection@btconnect.com

REUSABLE SELF ADHESIVE PLASTIC LABELS

Amberley Adhesive Labels Ltd, Team House, Higher Shaftesbury Road, Blandford Forum, Dorset, DT11 7FG Tel: (01258) 455772 Fax: (01258) 453215 E-mail: sales@amberley.net

REVERSE MORTGAGES

▶ Mortgage Simplicity, Inglewood House, Inglewood, Alloa, Clackmannanshire, FK10 2HU Tel: (0845) 8381502 E-mail: info@mortgagesimplicity.co.uk

REVERSE OSMOSIS EQUIPMENT

A W E Anderson Water Equipment Ltd, R04-R05 Unit Cardiff Bay Business Centre, Titan Road, Cardiff, CF24 5EL Tel: (029) 2049 2848 Fax: (029) 2049 1369 E-mail: sales@aweltd.co.uk

▶ Fresh Water Filter Company, Carlton House, Aylmer Road, London, E11 3AD Tel: (020) 8558 7495 Fax: (0870) 4423639 E-mail: info@freshwaterfilter.com

▶ Micro-Membrane Systems Ltd, 9 Cork Terrace, Bath, BA1 3BE Tel: (01225) 444290 Fax: (01225) 461060 E-mail: info@micromembrane.co.uk

REVERSE OSMOSIS SYSTEM WATER TREATMENT PLANT AND EQUIPMENT

Aqua Spring Ltd, 177 Kingston Road, Leatherhead, Surrey, KT22 7NX Tel: (01372) 373023 Fax: (01372) 360003 E-mail: sales@aquaspring.co.uk

▶ Bridgemary Library, 74 Brewers Lane, Gosport, Hampshire, PO13 0LA Tel: (0845) 6035631 Fax: (01329) 511390 E-mail: bridgemaryaquatics@ntlworld.com

G E Water, Hydro House, Newcombe Way, Orton Southgate, Peterborough, PE2 6SE Tel: (01733) 394555 Fax: (01733) 390179

Purite Ltd, Bandet Way, Thame Industrial Estate, Thame, Oxfordshire, OX9 3SJ Tel: (01844) 217141

Salt Separation Services, Grosvenor House, Gorrell Street, Rochdale, Lancashire, OL11 1AP Tel: (01706) 655522 Fax: (01706) 654475 E-mail: sss@saltsep.co.uk

REVERSIBLE ELECTRIC MOTORS

Merkle-Korff, Treetops House, Gillotts Lane, Henley-On-Thames, Oxfordshire, RG9 1PT Tel: (01543) 255995 Fax: (01491) 412211 E-mail: sales@acdcsystems.com

REVOLVING DOORS

Boon Edam Ltd, Holldan House, Crowbridge Road, Orbital Park, Ashford, Kent, TN24 0GR Tel: 0113-287 6300 Fax: (01233) 505909 E-mail: sales@boonedam.co.uk

Boon Edam, Moss Dean Lodge, Nelson Road, Bristol, BS16 5HX Tel: 0117-956 6910 Fax: 0117-956 6911 E-mail: sales@boonedam.co.uk

Gunnebo Entrance Control Ltd, Optimus, Bell Lane, Bellbrook Industrial Estate, Uckfield, East Sussex, TN22 1QL Tel: (01825) 761022 Fax: (01825) 763835 E-mail: info@gunneboe.co.uk

Horton Automatics Ltd, Hortonwood 31, Telford, Shropshire, TF1 7YZ Tel: (01952) 670169 Fax: (01952) 670181 E-mail: sales@horton-automatics.ltd.uk

Marrutt Ltd, Unit 9 Bellbrook Industrial Estate, Uckfield, East Sussex, TN22 1QL Tel: (01825) 764057 Fax: (01825) 768841 E-mail: digital@marrutt.com

REVOLVING HEAD HAND VICES

Swindens Revolving Head Vices Ltd, Suite 401 Langham Ho, 302 Regent St, London, W1B 3AT Tel: (020) 7580 6491 Fax: (020) 7580 4729 E-mail: am@swindens-vices.co.uk

REWORK SYSTEMS

Plastic Rework Solutions Ltd, Unit 9a Castle Mill Works, birmingham New Road, Dudley, West Midlands, DY1 4DA Tel: (01384) 211169 E-mail: prs01384@btconnect.com

RHEOLOGICAL EQUIPMENT

Ravenfield Designs Ltd, Russell Street, Heywood, Lancashire, OL10 1NX Tel: (01706) 369307 Fax: (01706) 360472 E-mail: post@ravenfield.com

RIBBON CABLES

Alex Everett Ltd, 34 Victoria Road, Writtle, Chelmsford, CM1 3PA Tel: (01245) 421198 Fax: (01245) 422433 E-mail: aelconnectors@btclick.com

J N R Electronics Assemblies, 158 Wheatfield Road, Luton, LU4 0TD Tel: (01582) 471278 Fax: (01582) 600703E-mail: admin@jnr.org.uk

Samms Electronics, Unit C 7 Sandy Business Park, Gosforth Close, Sandy, Bedfordshire, SG19 1RB Tel: (01767) 680049 Fax: (01767) 680073 E-mail: sales@samms-electronics.co.uk

Wessex Belden CDT, Unit 8 Crow Arch Lane Industrial Estate, Crow Arch Lane, Ringwood, Hampshire, BH24 1PE Tel: (01425) 480804 Fax: (01425) 480805 E-mail: sales@wessexcdt.co.uk

RIBBON PRINTING SERVICES, CLOTHING LABEL

Four Seasons Village, Kirkpatrick Hill, Closeburn, Thornhill, Dumfriesshire, DG3 5JY Tel: 01848 330273 Fax: 01848 330848 E-mail: info@fourseasonsvillage.co.uk

RIBBON PRODUCTS TO CUSTOMER DESIGN

Berisfords Ltd, Thomas Street, Congleton, Cheshire, CW12 1EF Tel: (01260) 274011 Fax: (01260) 274014 E-mail: office@berisfords-ribbons.co.uk

Gift Design Co. Ltd, Old Griffin Field, Windsor Street, Pentre, Mid Glamorgan, CF41 7JJ Tel: (01443) 441616 Fax: (01443) 440419 E-mail: mail@gift-design.co.uk

RIBBONS, HABERDASHERY

Barnett Lawson Trimmings Ltd, 16-17 Little Portland Street, London, W1W 8NE Tel: (020) 7636 8591 Fax: (020) 7580 0669 E-mail: info@bltrimmings.com

Baxter Hart & Abraham Ltd, 141 New Bedford Road, Luton, LU3 1LF Tel: (01582) 721381 Fax: (01582) 451033 E-mail: hornbha@aol.com

Brooklyn Bow & Ribbon Co. Ltd, Herald Business Park, Golden Acres Lane, Coventry, CV3 2RT Tel: (024) 7663 5599 Fax: (024) 7663 5525 E-mail: sales@brooklynbow.co.uk

Franklins Sewing Centre, 48 Fisherton Street, Salisbury, SP2 7RB Tel: (01722) 554466 Fax: (01722) 554466

Randall Ribbons, 12 Frederick Street, Luton, LU2 7QS Tel: (01582) 721301 Fax: (01582) 720060 E-mail: sales@randallribbons.com

Super Finish Elastics Ltd, 42 London Street, Leicester, LE5 3RU Tel: 0116-276 1007 Fax: 0116-276 1005 E-mail: sales@superfinishelastics.co.uk

RIDING JACKETS

▶ Hackers Tack, Shute Barn, Lerryn, Lostwithiel, Cornwall, PL22 0QE Tel: (01208) 871220

RIG CONSTRUCTION CONTRACTORS OR DESIGNERS/MAINTENANCE/ REPAIR/SERVICING/TEST SERVICES

Aberdeen Fabrication Ltd, Links Place, Aberdeen, AB11 5DY Tel: (01224) 588321 Fax: (01224) 583898 E-mail: sales@afab.co.uk

Aker Kvaerner, Wellesley Road, Methil, Leven, Fife, KY8 3RA Tel: (01592) 268181 Fax: (01592) 715574 E-mail: peter.holt@akerkvaerner.com

Heerema Hartlepool Ltd, Greenland Road, Hartlepool, Cleveland, TS24 0RQ Tel: (01642) 340200 Fax: (01642) 340208 E-mail: info@heerema.co.uk

Seaweld Engineering Ltd, The Limes, The Street, Acle, Norwich, NR13 3QJ Tel: (01493) 751421 Fax: (01493) 750064 E-mail: admin@seaweld.co.uk

RIG CONSTRUCTION ENGINEERS

Aker Kvaerner, Wellesley Road, Methil, Leven, Fife, KY8 3RA Tel: (01592) 268181 Fax: (01592) 715574 E-mail: peter.holt@akerkvaerner.com

Heerema Hartlepool Ltd, Greenland Road, Hartlepool, Cleveland, TS24 0RQ Tel: (01642) 340200 Fax: (01642) 340208 E-mail: info@heerema.co.uk

▶ R J Watkinson & Partners, 12 High Street, Lyndhurst, Hampshire, SO43 7BD Tel: (023) 8028 3794 Fax: (023) 8028 3655 E-mail: rjwptrs@rjwatkinsons.co.uk

RIG ENGINEERING EQUIPMENT ENGINEERS OR FABRICATORS OR MANUFACTURERS

C P S Engineering, Wentworth Road, Mapplewell, Barnsley, South Yorkshire, S75 6DU Tel: (01226) 386515 Fax: (01226) 380165 E-mail: cpsengineering@aol.com

Haki Ltd, Magnus, Tame Valley Industrial Estate, Wilnecote, Tamworth, Staffordshire, B77 5BY Tel: (01827) 282525 Fax: (01827) 250329 E-mail: info@haki.co.uk

RIG OR PLATFORM FABRICATION ENGINEERING

Almal Engineering Ltd, Derrington Lane, Derrington, Stafford, ST18 9NH Tel: (01785) 255108 Fax: (01785) 248108 E-mail: almalengineering@supanet.com

Burntisland Fabrications, Seaforth Place, West Shore, Burntisland, Fife, KY3 9AU Tel: (01592) 222000 Fax: (01592) 874688 E-mail: enquiries@bifab.co.uk

C P S Engineering, Wentworth Road, Mapplewell, Barnsley, South Yorkshire, S75 6DU Tel: (01226) 386515 Fax: (01226) 380165 E-mail: cpsengineering@aol.com

Calder Engineering Ltd, Unit 15 Ormlie Industrial Estate, Thurso, Caithness, KW14 7QU Tel: (01847) 892122 Fax: (01847) 892345 E-mail: admin@calderengineering.co.uk

Cort Engineering, 27 Waidshouse Road, Nelson, Lancashire, BB9 0RZ Tel: (01282) 612938 Fax: (01282) 612938

D & T Engineering, Unit 12d Thorn Business Park, Rotherwas, Hereford, HR2 6JT Tel: (01432) 355433 Fax: (01432) 355519 E-mail: d.t.eng@btopenworld.com

Dales Engineering Ltd, Dales Industrial Estate, Peterhead, Aberdeenshire, AB42 3JF Tel: (01779) 478778 Fax: (01779) 471846 E-mail: sales@dalesgroup.co.uk

Doublescale, Beili Glas Uchaf, Gwaun Cae Gurwen, Ammanford, Dyfed, SA18 1PR Tel: (01269) 822440 Fax: (01269) 822440 E-mail: sales@doublescale.ltd.uk

Molesey Metal Works, 22 Island Farm Avenue, West Molesey, Surrey, KT8 2UA Tel: (020) 8979 1772 Fax: (020) 8979 7337

N Gosling, Occupation Lane, New Bolingbroke, Boston, Lincolnshire, PE22 7JZ Tel: (01205) 480691 Fax: (01205) 480691

Regal Engineering, Church Lane, Kelbrook, Barnoldswick, Lancashire, BB18 6UJ Tel: (01282) 844224 Fax: (01282) 841030 E-mail: regal.eng@btconnect.com

SMS Ltd, 1 Lytham Road, Warton, Preston, PR4 1AH Tel: (01772) 634042 Fax: (01772) 635942

Stelex Construction Equipment Ltd, Prees Industrial Estate, Shrewsbury Rd, Prees, Whitchurch, Shropshire, SY13 2DJ Tel: (01948) 840840 Fax: (01948) 841147 E-mail: info@stelex.co.uk

RIG OR PLATFORM SITE SURVEY SERVICES

Fugro Survey Ltd, Morton Peto Road, Great Yarmouth, Norfolk, NR31 0LT Tel: (01493) 440320 Fax: (01493) 440319 E-mail: admin@svitzer.co.uk

Moduspec Engineering UK Ltd, 2 Craigshaw Road, West Tullos Industrial Estate, Aberdeen, AB12 3AQ Tel: (01224) 248144 Fax: (01224) 284125 E-mail: sales@moduspec.com

RIG POSITIONING SERVICES

Marine & Offshore Consultants Ltd, Magellan House, James Watt Close, Great Yarmouth, Norfolk, NR31 0NX Tel: (01493) 440166 Fax: (01493) 658490 E-mail: support@modgy.co.uk

Offshore Marine Contractors Ltd, Magellan House, James Watt Close, Gapton Hall Industrial Estate, Great Yarmouth, Norfolk, NR31 0NX Tel: (01493) 658489 Fax: (01493) 658490 E-mail: yarmouth@omcon.com

RIG SUPPLY/SERVICE VESSEL OR BASE OPERATORS

Instock Disposables Ltd, Howe Moss Drive, Kirkhill Industrial Estate, Dyce, Aberdeen, AB21 0GL Tel: (01224) 723823 Fax: (01224) 725586

RIGGING CONTRACTORS

Crusader Sails, The Sail Loft, Cobbs Quay, Poole, Dorset, BH15 4EU Tel: (01202) 670580 Fax: (01202) 675578 E-mail: info@cruisadersails.com

GRM Rigging Services, 7 Tarbet Street, Gourock, Renfrewshire, PA19 1UF Tel: (01475) 638811 Fax: (01475) 638811

Solent Rigging Services Ltd, 21 Shamrock Quay, William Street, Southampton, SO14 5QL Tel: (023) 8055 0444 Fax: (023) 8023 0608

Spencer Rigging Ltd, Empire Buildings, St. Mary's Road, Cowes, Isle Of Wight, PO31 7SX Tel: (01983) 292022 Fax: (01983) 291589 E-mail: info@spencerrigging.co.uk

RIGGING SCREWS

Solid Stampings Ltd, Porters Field Road, Cradley Heath, West Midlands, B64 7BL Tel: (01384) 636421 Fax: (01384) 639163 E-mail: info@solidswivel.co.uk

RIGHT ANGLE GEARBOXES

Robert Cupitt Ltd, 4 Joplin Court, Sovereign Business Park, Crownhill, Milton Keynes, MK8 0JP Tel: (01908) 563063 Fax: (01908) 562910 E-mail: sales@robertcupitt.co.uk

RIGID HULL INFLATABLE BOATS

Delta Power Services, Newby Road Industrial Estate, Newby Road, Hazel Grove, Stockport, Cheshire, SK7 5DR Tel: 0161-456 6588 Fax: 0161-456 6686 E-mail: cdyas@deltarib.u-net.com

Scorpion Ribs Ltd, Haven Quay, Mill Lane, Lymington, Hampshire, SO41 9AZ Tel: (01590) 677080 Fax: (01590) 671911 E-mail: sales@scorpionribs.com

Tornado Boats International Ltd, Dairycoates Industrial Estate, Wiltshire Road, Hull, HU4 6PA Tel: (01482) 353972 Fax: (01482) 572475 E-mail: sales@tornado-boats.com

RIGID INTERMEDIATE BULK CONTAINERS (IBC)

Mailbox Mouldings International Ltd, Bayley Street, Stalybridge, Cheshire, SK15 1QQ Tel: 0161-330 5577 Fax: 0161-330 5576 E-mail: ch@mailboxmouldings.co.uk

Pensteel Ltd, Unit 1, Horndon Industrial Park, West Horndon, Essex, CM13 3XL Tel: (01277) 810211 Fax: (01277) 811971 E-mail: sales@pensteel.co.uk

Warwick Container Systems (UK) ltd, Stoneleigh Visual Centre, Queensway, Leamington Spa, Warwickshire, CV31 3JT Tel: (01926) 314120 Fax: (01926) 885719 E-mail: post@warwickcontainer.demon.co.uk

RIGID PLASTIC PACKAGING

Storeys Industrial Products Ltd, Brantham, Manningtree, Essex, CO11 1NJ Tel: (01206) 392401 Fax: (01206) 395288 E-mail: info@wardlestoreys.com

RING BINDERS

▶ Capital Binder Services, 287 Green Lanes, The Triangle, London, N13 4XS Tel: (020) 8882 4612 Fax: (020) 8882 8949

RING ROLL PRODUCTS

W.A. Patterson, Unit 34 Muckamore Industrial Estate, Muckamore, Antrim, BT41 4QE Tel: 028 94429090

Roballo Engineering Co. Ltd, 2 Mill Hill, North West Industrial Estate, Peterlee, County Durham, SR8 2HR Tel: 0191-518 5600 Fax: 0191-586 9096 E-mail: info@roballo.co.uk

RING ROLLING

J J Haslam Ltd, Park Works, Clegg Street, Bolton, BL2 6DU Tel: (01204) 527342 Fax: (01204) 388259 E-mail: malcolm.green@jjhaslam.com

Phoenix Fabrications Ltd, Unit 11 Meadow Drove, Earith, Huntingdon, Cambridgeshire, PE28 3QF Tel: (01487) 843888 Fax: (01487) 843905

RINGS, NICKEL TITANIUM

▶ A I Materials, Otter Street, Sheffield, S9 3WL Tel: 0114-243 1206 Fax: 0114-261 1419 E-mail: sales@ai-materials.co.uk

RISING SECURITY SCREENS

Safetell International Ltd, Unit 46, Fawkes Avenue, Dartford, DA1 1JQ Tel: (01322) 223233 Fax: (01322) 277751

RISK ASSESSMENT CONSULTANCY

▶ 4 Sight Consulting, 20 Watt Road, Bridge of Weir, Renfrewshire, PA11 3DL Tel: (01505) 615119 Fax: (01505) 615119 E-mail: enquiries@4-sightconsulting.co.uk

Asher Consulting Ltd, Asher House, Barsbank Lane, Lymm, Cheshire, WA13 0ED Tel: (01925) 751444 Fax: (01925) 751555 E-mail: info@asherconsulting.co.uk

Atlantic Bridge Ltd, Zenith House, 11 The Street, Chirton, Devizes, Wiltshire, SN10 3QS Tel: (01380) 848170 Fax: (01380) 840152 E-mail: sales@atlanticbridge.co.uk

▶ Icon Health & Safety, 34 Aylward Drive, Stevenage, Hertfordshire, SG2 8UR Tel: (01438) 748208 Fax: (01438) 759299 E-mail: info@iconhealthandsafety.co.uk

▶ Massie Consulting Ltd, 20 Upper Olland Street, Bungay, Suffolk, NR35 1BH Tel: 01986 895030 E-mail: harold@massieconsulting.co.uk

▶ P J G Creative Design Ltd, 11 Mayer Gardens, Shenley Lodge, Milton Keynes, MK5 7EN Tel: (01908) 231175 E-mail: info@pjgcreative.com

RISK ASSESSMENT SERVICES, DISPLAY SCREEN EQUIPMENT (DSE)

Asher Consulting Ltd, Asher House, Barsbank Lane, Lymm, Cheshire, WA13 0ED Tel: (01925) 751444 Fax: (01925) 751555 E-mail: info@asherconsulting.co.uk

COPE Ergonomics, Unit 1, The Business Park, Technology Drive, Nottingham, NG9 2ND Tel: 0115-925 9222 Fax: 0115-925 2111 E-mail: nick.aubrey@copeohs.com

▶ Enricosmog Ergonomics, 21 Tisbury Row, Tisbury, Salisbury, SP3 6RZ Tel: (01747) 871868 Fax: (01747) 871868 E-mail: info@enricosmog.com

▶ Peak Health Promotions, 39 Shurnhold, Melksham, Wiltshire, SN12 8DF Tel: (01225) 700997 E-mail: trainenq@peakhealth.firm.org.uk

RISK ASSESSMENT SERVICES, TECHNICAL

▶ 4 Sight Consulting, 20 Watt Road, Bridge of Weir, Renfrewshire, PA11 3DL Tel: (01505) 615119 Fax: (01505) 615119 E-mail: enquiries@4-sightconsulting.co.uk

RISK ASSESSMENT TRAINING

▶ Sovrin First Aid Training, Carreg Cwrnach, Pentrefelin, Amlwch, Gwynedd, LL68 9PF Tel: (01407) 830165 E-mail: office@sovrintraining.co.uk

RISK MANAGEMENT CONSULTANCY OR SERVICES

B S C Management Ltd, 150 Minories, London, EC3N 1LS Tel: (0870) 2406117 Fax: (0870) 2406118 E-mail: bsc@bscconsulting.com

British Approvals Board Telecommunications Ltd, Claremont House, 34 Molesey Road, Hersham, Walton-on-Thames, Surrey, KT12 4RQ Tel: (01932) 251200 Fax: (01932) 251201 E-mail: m.brain@babt.com

▶ Chiene & Taite CA, 61 Dublin Street, Edinburgh, EH3 6NL Tel: 0131-558 5800 Fax: 0131-558 5899

Edn Insurance Services Ltd, Standeven House, 27 Union Street, Oldham, OL1 1XS Tel: 0161-624 3801 Fax: 0161-627 4045 E-mail: enquiries@edaviesnorthern.freeserve.co.uk

Egerton Consulting Ltd, The Green, Minety, Malmesbury, Wiltshire, SN16 9PL Tel: (01666) 860993 Fax: (0870) 7622911 E-mail: enquiries@egertonconsulting.co.uk

Encore International Limited, 26 York Street, London, W1U 6PZ Tel: 020 7788 7772 Fax: 020 7788 7773 E-mail: enquiries@encore-international.net

Enviros Consulting Group, Waterfront Quay, Salford, M50 3XW Tel: 0161-874 3600 Fax: 0161-848 0181 E-mail: paul.bromley@enviros.com

RISK MANAGEMENT CONSULTANCY OR SERVICES – *continued*

Frazer Nash Consultancy Ltd, Stonebridge The Dorking Business Park, Station Road, Dorking, Surrey, RH4 1HJ Tel: (01306) 885050 Fax: (01306) 886464 E-mail: info@fnc.co.uk

Insight Consulting, Churchfield House, 3 & 5 The Quintet, Churchfield Road, Walton-On-Thames, Surrey, KT12 2TZ Tel: (01932) 241000 Fax: (01932) 244590 E-mail: insight@insight.co.uk

▶ Intelligent Risk Management Ltd, PO Box 148, Kendal, Cumbria, LA9 7WY Tel: (01539) 736126 Fax: (01539) 736286 E-mail: david.arnold@i-rm.com

O'Neill Management Ltd, 9 Albany Drive, Bishops Waltham, Southampton, SO32 1GE Tel: (0787) 9463824 E-mail: sales@oneill-management.com

R L S Associates, 68 Crabtree Lane, Bromsgrove, Worcestershire, B61 8NZ Tel: (01527) 875144 Fax: (01527) 575912

▶ Services Ltd, 82 Trent BLVD, West Bridgford, Nottingham, NG2 5BL Tel: 0115-945 5285 Fax: 0115-981 7137 E-mail: info@servicesltd.co.uk

Servo, Oakwell Way, Birstall, Batley, West Yorkshire, WF17 9LU Tel: (01924) 422111 Fax: (0870) 1218302 E-mail: info@icm-computer.co.uk

RISK MANAGEMENT, FINANCIAL

▶ McCormack & Kent Consulting Ltd, PO Box 49, Ashford, Kent, TN24 9WF Tel: (0845) 0573257 Fax: (01622) 338900 E-mail: team@mccormack-kent.co.uk

RISK MANAGEMENT, INFORMATION TECHNOLOGY (IT)

▶ Dexter-IT, 11 Babylon Lane, Bishampton, Pershore, Worcestershire, WR10 2NN Tel: 0845 6442414 Fax: 0870 1328311 E-mail: enquiries@Dexter-IT.co.uk

RIVER FLOOD PROTECTION CONSULTANCY

▶ Affordable Flood Solutions Ltd, 16 Birch Green, Staines, Middlesex, TW18 4HA Tel: (01784) 460874 Fax: (01784) 460894 E-mail: info@a-f-s.biz

▶ Bauer Inner City, The Dallam Court, Dallam Lane, Warrington, WA2 7LT Tel: (01925) 428940 Fax: (01925) 244133 E-mail: info@bauerinnercity.co.uk

▶ Water Out UK, PO Box 139, Upminster, Essex, RM14 2YD Tel: (0500) 510052 Fax: (01708) 507212 E-mail: floodlines@aol.com

RIVET BUSHES

Feltonquest Turned Parts Ltd, Unit 16 Britannia Estate, Leagrave Road, Luton, LU3 1RJ Tel: (01582) 738892 Fax: (01582) 721634 E-mail: tony.abbott@feltonquest.co.uk

Fit-Lock Systems Ltd, Unit 3/A, Aspect Court, Cannel Row, Silverdale Enterprise Park, Silverdale, Newcastle, Staffordshire, ST5 6SS Tel: (01782) 626450 Fax: (01782) 614197 E-mail: sales@fitlocksystems.com

John Walsh & Co Inserts Ltd, 183 High Street, Wealdstone, Harrow, Middlesex, HA3 5EA Tel: (020) 8863 9133 Fax: (020) 8427 3307 E-mail: thinsheetfastner@btinternet.com

RIVET DISTRIBUTORS OR AGENTS OR STOCKHOLDERS

A J S Fasteners Ltd, 9 Maple Business Park, Walter Street, Birmingham, B7 5ET Tel: 0121-327 0660 Fax: 0121-327 3553 E-mail: sales@ajsfasteners.co.uk

Bright Screw Co. Ltd, Bagley Lane, Rodley, Leeds, LS13 1JB Tel: 0113-256 4166 Fax: 0113-239 3480 E-mail: sales@brightscrew.co.uk

W.J. Cons & Co., 20 Queensway, Enfield, Middlesex, EN3 4SA Tel: (020) 8443 4001 Fax: (020) 8804 0805E-mail: info@berbo.com

Dave Vickers, Thame Station Industrial Estate, Thame, Oxon, OX9 3UH Tel: (01844) 260100 Fax: (01844) 260900

▶ Doidge Fastenings, George Baylis Road, Berry Hill Industrial Estate, Droitwich, Worcestershire, WR9 9RB Tel: (01905) 779448 Fax: (0845) 0780334 E-mail: sales@doidge.com

Fit-Lock Systems Ltd, Unit 3/A, Aspect Court, Cannel Row, Silverdale Enterprise Park, Silverdale, Newcastle, Staffordshire, ST5 6SS Tel: (01782) 626450 Fax: (01782) 614197 E-mail: sales@fitlocksystems.com

Logistic Fasteners (UK) Ltd, Unit 2A Odell House, Summerleys Road, Princes Risborough, Buckinghamshire, HP27 9DT Tel: (01844) 275816 Fax: (01844) 342880 E-mail: logfast@aol.com

Valley Fastners, 65 Hay Hall Road, Birmingham, B11 2AU Tel: 0121-693 0031 Fax: 0121-693 0032 E-mail: sales@siemensvdo.com

RIVET NUTS

Bralo UK Ltd, Leabrook Road, Wednesbury, West Midlands, WS10 9NB Tel: 0121-567 3230 Fax: 0121-505 1378E-mail: bralouk@bralo.net

Fit-Lock Systems Ltd, Unit 3/A, Aspect Court, Cannel Row, Silverdale Enterprise Park, Silverdale, Newcastle, Staffordshire, ST5 6SS Tel: (01782) 626450 Fax: (01782) 614197 E-mail: sales@fitlocksystems.com

Roy Hopwood Ltd, Hibbert Street, Whitehill Industrial Estate, Stockport, Cheshire, SK4 1NS Tel: 0161-429 6066 Fax: 0161-429 6166 E-mail: info@rhf.co.uk

Rivetnut Technology Systems Ltd, 5 Bridgegate Business Park, Gatehouse Way, Gatehouse Industrial Area, Aylesbury, Buckinghamshire, HP19 8XN Tel: (01296) 330331 Fax: (01296) 331018 E-mail: sales@rivetnut.com

Rocfast, Unit 20, Worton Hall Industrial Estate, Worton Road, Isleworth, Middlesex, TW7 6ER Tel: (020) 8568 1616 Fax: (020) 8568 5656 E-mail: Info@rocfast.co.uk

Trifast P.L.C., Trifast House, Bellbrook Park, Uckfield, East Sussex, TN22 1QW Tel: (01825) 769696 Fax: (01825) 767882

RIVETING (BLIND) SYSTEMS TOOLING

Bralo UK Ltd, Leabrook Road, Wednesbury, West Midlands, WS10 9NB Tel: 0121-567 3230 Fax: 0121-505 1378E-mail: bralouk@bralo.net

Roy Hopwood Ltd, Hibbert Street, Whitehill Industrial Estate, Stockport, Cheshire, SK4 1NS Tel: 0161-429 6066 Fax: 0161-429 6166 E-mail: info@rhf.co.uk

RIVETING MACHINES

Brandone Machine Tool Ltd, Unit 1, 57 Bushey Grove Road, Bushey, WD23 2JW Tel: (01923) 637893 Fax: (01923) 248055 E-mail: brandone@btconnect.com

▶ Doidge Fastenings, George Baylis Road, Berry Hill Industrial Estate, Droitwich, Worcestershire, WR9 9RB Tel: (01905) 779448 Fax: (0845) 0780334 E-mail: sales@doidge.com

Rivfast Ltd, Unit 23 Bordesley Trading Estate, Bordesley Green Road, Birmingham, B8 1BZ Tel: 0121-359 4500 Fax: 0121-359 4501 E-mail: mark@rivfast.co.uk

Turner Machine Tools, 23 Waterloo Park, Bidford-on-Avon, Alcester, Warwickshire, B50 4JG Tel: (01789) 772921 Fax: (01789) 778614 E-mail: info@turner-riveters.co.uk

Weber Automatic Assembly Systems Ltd, 3 Landscape Close, Weston Business Park, Weston-On-The-Green, Oxfordshire, OX25 3SX Tel: (01869) 343688 Fax: (01869) 343699 E-mail: sales@weberautomation.com

RIVETS, *See also headings under Rivets*

Ariel Fastners Ltd, Ariel Works, Temple Road, Leicester, LE5 4JG Tel: 0116-273 6541 Fax: 0116-249 0024 E-mail: enquiries@arielfasteners.com

Bradleys Rivets Ltd, Unit 8b Reddicap Trading Estate, Sutton Coldfield, West Midlands, B75 7BU Tel: 0121-326 7468 Fax: 0121-327 1092 E-mail: enquiries@bradleyrivets.com

Bralo UK Ltd, Leabrook Road, Wednesbury, West Midlands, WS10 9NB Tel: 0121-567 3230 Fax: 0121-505 1378E-mail: bralouk@bralo.net

Clevedon Fasteners Ltd, Reddicap Trading Estate, Sutton Coldfield, West Midlands, B75 7BU Tel: 0121-378 0619 Fax: 0121-378 3186 E-mail: sales@clevedon-fasteners.co.uk

Danglo Components Ltd, Unit 9-10, Wedgewood Way, Stevenage, Hertfordshire, SG1 4QB Tel: (01438) 735616 Fax: (01438) 735625 E-mail: sales@danglo.co.uk

▶ Doidge Fastenings, George Baylis Road, Berry Hill Industrial Estate, Droitwich, Worcestershire, WR9 9RB Tel: (01905) 779448 Fax: (0845) 0780334 E-mail: sales@doidge.com

Henrob, Second Avenue, Deeside Industrial Park, Deeside, Clwyd, CH5 2NX Tel: (01244) 837220 Fax: (01244) 837222 E-mail: sales@henrob.co.uk

Bruce Pickles Engineering Ltd, 6 Maple Works, Maple Road, Redhill, RH1 5HE Tel: (01737) 770123 Fax: (01737) 770804 E-mail: paul@brucepickles.freeserve.co.uk

Rivfast Ltd, Unit 23 Bordesley Trading Estate, Bordesley Green Road, Birmingham, B8 1BZ Tel: 0121-359 4500 Fax: 0121-359 4501 E-mail: mark@rivfast.co.uk

Sapphire Products Ltd, 4 Dunton Trading Estate, Mount Street, Birmingham, B7 5QL Tel: 0121-326 6000 Fax: 0121-328 5518 E-mail: sapphireproducts@boltblue.com

Stone Fasteners Ltd, Woolwich Road, London, SE7 8SL Tel: (020) 8293 5080 Fax: (020) 8293 4935 E-mail: sales@stonefasteners.com

ROAD AND RAIL PLANT HIRE

▶ Gordon Bow Plant Hire, 82-86 East Main St, Broxburn, West Lothian, EH52 5EG Tel: (01506) 855913 Fax: (01506) 856393 E-mail: info@gordonbow.co.uk

Carl Taylor Plant Hire, 10 Garth Grove, Hirwaun, Aberdare, Rhondda Cynon Taff, CF44 9SD Tel: (01685) 813801 Fax: (01685) 813801 E-mail: taylorplant@btconnect.com

ROAD CONSTRUCTION CONTRACTORS

▶ A Coupland Surfacing Ltd, Pudding Lane, Off Warden Tree Lane, Pinchbeck, Spalding, Lincolnshire, PE11 3TJ Tel: (01775) 767110 Fax: (01775) 711246

▶ A D Bly, Unit 4d Nup End Business Centre, Old Knebworth, Knebworth, Hertfordshire, SG3 6QJ Tel: (01438) 821779 Fax: (01438) 821870

▶ A H Lewis Contractors, 50 Cradge Bank, Spalding, Lincolnshire, PE11 3AB Tel: (01775) 411570

▶ A T Knott & Sons, Cornelian Cottages, 76a Manor Road, Wallington, Surrey, SM6 0AB Tel: (020) 8669 5208 Fax: (020) 8669 5150

▶ Adana Construction Ltd, Europa Business Park, Bird Hall Lane, Stockport, Cheshire, SK3 0XA Tel: 0161-428 1613

▶ All Way Surfacing & Construction Ltd, 1 Fermoy, Frome, Somerset, BA11 2EP Tel: (01373) 473641 Fax: (01373) 452532

▶ Alltgoch Construction, Cwrtnewydd, Llanybydder, Dyfed, SA40 9YJ Tel: (01570) 434337 Fax: (01437) 899353

▶ Amey Infer- Structure Services Ltd, Second Floor, 1 Redcliff Street, Bristol, BS1 6QZ Tel: 0117-934 8836

▶ Ashworth Norman Ltd, Mellor Street, Rochdale, Lancashire, OL11 5BT Tel: (01706) 648501 Fax: (01706) 345721

▶ Barr Ltd, Killoch Depot, Ochiltree, Cumnock, Ayrshire, KA18 2RL Tel: (01290) 700681

▶ Bedrock Crushing & Recycled Materials Ltd, Bow Depot, Marshgate Sidings, London, E15 2PB Tel: (020) 8503 0006

▶ Bellstan Ltd, Old Post House, Wood Lane, Beech Hill, Reading, RG7 2BE Tel: 0118-988 3413 Fax: 0118-988 2820

▶ Brookside Construction, 19a Church Street, Oadby, Leicester, LE2 5DB Tel: 0116-271 0680 Fax: 0116-271 0991 E-mail: caroline@brooksideconstruction.co.uk

▶ C & D Facilities & Ground Maintenance, 38 Wendover Way, Tilehurst, Reading, RG30 4RU Tel: 0118-942 3999 Fax: 0118-942 6682

▶ Carlier Asphalt, Factory Lane, Croydon, CR0 3RL Tel: (020) 8688 4351

▶ Cemex UK Construction Services Ltd, Smithfold Lane, Little Hulton, Worsley, Manchester, M28 0GP Tel: 0161-702 6366 Fax: 0161-702 6422

▶ Charles Lawrence Surfaces plc, Newbridge Industrial Estate, Newbridge, Midlothian, EH28 8PJ Tel: 0131-333 3030 Fax: 0131-333 4154

▶ Classic Paving Services, Classic House, Hollands Road, Northwich, Cheshire, CW9 8AU Tel: (01606) 350800 Fax: (01606) 352800

▶ Clehonger Plant Hire Ltd, Unit 4-5 Beech Business Park, Tillington Road, Hereford, HR4 9QJ Tel: (01432) 277366 Fax: (01432) 277366

▶ Coslin Construction Ltd, 120 London Road, Gloucester, GL1 3PL Tel: (01452) 305055 Fax: (01452) 308735

▶ Coulson Construction Ltd, Woodbine Cottage Birtley, Birtley, Hexham, Northumberland, NE48 3HL Tel: (01434) 230612

▶ Crummock Scotland Ltd, Butlerfield Industrial Estate, Bonnyrigg, Midlothian, EH19 3JQ Tel: (01875) 823222 Fax: (01875) 823444

▶ Cuchulain Construction, 124 Kings Park Avenue, Glasgow, G44 4HS Tel: 0141-632 3020

▶ Cumbrian Industrials Ltd, 150 Preston Road, Lytham St. Annes, Lancashire, FY8 5AT Tel: (01253) 741730 Fax: (01253) 796532

▶ D & E Mackay Contractors Ltd, Craigearn Business Park, Midmills, Kintore, Inverurie, Aberdeenshire, AB51 0TH Tel: (01467) 633388 Fax: (01467) 633454

▶ D G Pool & Leisure, Bines Green, Partridge Green, Horsham, West Sussex, RH13 8EH Tel: (01403) 711581 Fax: (01403) 713581

▶ Dales Sports Surfaces Ltd, Sharpes Lane, Sheepgate, Leverton, Boston, Lincolnshire, PE22 0AR Tel: (01205) 761066 Fax: (01205) 760856

▶ Dart Jerry Ltd, Unit 10 Barton Hill Trading Estate, Maze Street, Bristol, BS5 9TQ Tel: 0117-955 9911 Fax: 0117-955 9922

▶ Driveway Design, 2 Randolph Court, Randolph Industrial Estate, Kirkcaldy, Fife, KY1 2YY Tel: (01592) 654300 Fax: (01592) 654390

▶ Driveway Co Scotland Ltd, 69 Buchanan Street, Glasgow, G1 3HL Tel: 0141-314 3839 Fax: 0141-314 3738

▶ Duncan Pryde, Cartmore Industrial Estate, Lochgelly, Fife, KY5 8LL Tel: (01592) 783130

▶ Earthworks & Contracting Ltd, The Walfe, Main Street, Hickling, Melton Mowbray, Leicestershire, LE14 3AH Tel: (01664) 823789 Fax: (01664) 823382

▶ F & T Goodwin Ltd, Maple Tree Farm, Chawston Lane, Chawston, Bedford, MK44 3BH Tel: (01480) 407500 Fax: (01480) 407870

▶ First Engineering Ltd, Station Road, Crianlarich, Perthshire, FK20 8QN Tel: (01838) 300255

▶ Flynn Surfacing Ltd, Sandfold Lane, Manchester, M19 3BJ Tel: 0161-248 8842 Fax: 0161-248 8805

▶ Fullwood Holdings Ltd, 10 Jerviston Street, New Stevenston, Motherwell, Lanarkshire, ML1 4LY Tel: (01698) 733351

▶ G & B Roadmarkings, Cairnhill Trading Estate, Unit 9, Cairnhill Rd, Airdrie, Lanarkshire, ML6 9HA Tel: (01236) 764867 Fax: (01236) 767336

▶ G B Site Services, 21 Bonnyside Road, Bonnybridge, Stirlingshire, FK4 2AD Tel: (01324) 882503 Fax: (01324) 882504

▶ G D M Surfacing Contractors Ltd, Bottings Industrial Estate, Curdridge, Southampton, SO30 2DY Tel: (01489) 796373 Fax: (01489) 796374

▶ G Thornton (Contracts) Ltd, Metcalf Drive, Altham Industrial Estate, Accrington, Lancashire, BB5 5TU Tel: (01282) 777345

▶ Gilvar Lining Ltd, Old Station Yard, Walton Lane, Barton under Needwood, Burton-on-Trent, Staffordshire, DE13 8EJ Tel: (01283) 712450 Fax: (01283) 716525

▶ Glendale Grounds Management Ltd, 401 Walsall Road, Perry Barr, Birmingham, B42 1BT Tel: 0121-356 4226 Fax: 0121-331 1871

▶ Gordon Graham, The Garage, Gilsland, Brampton, Cumbria, CA8 7BT Tel: (01697) 747501 Fax: (01697) 747690

▶ Govin & Clarke Ltd, 11 Greendale Crescent, Leigh, Lancashire, WN7 2LQ Tel: (01942) 604018

▶ H M S Highway Maintenance Specialists Ltd, Bruntingthorpe Industrial Estate, Lutterworth, Leicestershire, LE17 5QZ Tel: 0116-279 9099 E-mail: sales@hmslimited.co.uk

▶ Hanson Quarry Products Europe Ltd, The Ridge, Chipping Sodbury, Bristol, BS37 6AY Tel: (01454) 316000 Fax: (01454) 325161

▶ Harlequin Swimming Pools Ltd, Innersdown Farm, Micheldever, Winchester, Hampshire, SO21 3BW Tel: (01962) 774004 Fax: (01962) 774008

▶ Hecket Multiserve Steelphalt Ltd, Sheffield Road, Rotherham, South Yorkshire, S60 1DR Tel: (01709) 300500 Fax: (01709) 300599

▶ Henry Kemp (Road Maintenance) Ltd, Century House, Century Road, Retford, Nottinghamshire, DN22 7TD Tel: (01777) 703643

▶ Howatson, Cae Bricks Brickfield Lane, Denbigh Road, Ruthin, Clwyd, LL15 1PE Tel: (01824) 703638 Fax: (01824) 707210 E-mail: dave.burke@tarmac.co.uk

▶ Inbowles & Leisure, Sportsman Farm, Hollywood Road, Mellor, Stockport, Cheshire, SK6 5LR Tel: 0161-484 5488 Fax: 0161-484 5486

▶ Inverness Caledonian Thistle Football Club, Caledonian Stadium, Stadium Road, Inverness, IV1 1FF Tel: (01463) 222880

▶ J A Block Paving Ltd, Railstone Terminal, Marlborough Road, Wootton Bassett, Swindon, SN4 7EH Tel: (01793) 852129 Fax: (01793) 850162

▶ J Chaplow & Sons Ltd, Helsington Mills, Helsington, Kendal, Cumbria, LA9 5RL Tel: (01539) 720358 Fax: (01539) 735593 E-mail: enquiries@jchaplow.co.uk

▶ J H Connon Ltd, Harlaw Road, Inverurie, Aberdeenshire, AB51 4FH Tel: (01467) 621406 Fax: (01467) 620806 E-mail: sales@jhconnon.co.uk

▶ J Hendry Ashphalt Contractors, Clippens Yard, Loanhead, Midlothian, EH20 9NS Tel: 0131-440 1109 Fax: 0131-440 4231

▶ J P C S Ltd, The Sidings, Hampton Heath Industrial Estate, Hampton, Malpas, Cheshire, SY14 8LU Tel: (01948) 820696 Fax: (01948) 820252

▶ John A Bates Contractors Ltd, Chance House, Crystal Drive, Smethwick, West Midlands, B66 1RD Tel: 0121-558 3823 Fax: 0121-555 5942

▶ Kearns & Co. Ltd, 8 Hamilton Road, St. Albans, Hertfordshire, AL1 4PZ Tel: (01727) 865981

Kelly Bros Road Markings Ltd, 15 Station Road, Yate, Bristol, BS37 5HT Tel: (01454) 312675 Fax: (01454) 320425

▶ KG Contractors Ltd, 184 Avenue Farm, Sutton Bridge, Spalding, Lincolnshire, PE12 9QF Tel: (01406) 359115 Fax: (01406) 359114

▶ Kyle Tarmacadam Ltd, 2 Murdoch Place, Oldhall West Industrial Estate, Irvine, Ayrshire, KA11 5DG Tel: (01294) 279206

▶ L & R Roadlines Ltd, 24-32 Forth Street, Liverpool, L20 8JW Tel: 0151-933 6293

▶ Lewis Buxton Groundworks, Unit 2, Thurnscoe Business Park, Phoenix Lane, Rotherham, South Yorkshire, S63 0BH Tel: (01709) 890600

▶ Line Markings Ltd, Brownsburn Industrial Estate, Airdrie, Lanarkshire, ML6 9SE Tel: (01236) 755114 Fax: (01236) 751880

▶ M D Clarke (Contractors) Ltd, Midland House, Brent, Ninian Way, Tame Valley Industrial Estate, Tamworth, Staffordshire, B77 5DF Tel: (01827) 282323

ROAD CONSTRUCTION CONTRACTORS – *continued*

▶ M & E Civil Engineering & Groundwork Ltd, Unit 2 Evegate Park Barn, Ashford, Kent, TN25 6SX Tel: (01303) 814444 E-mail: sales@mecivilengineering.co.uk

▶ M & M Road Surfacing, 9A Bankhead Medway, Edinburgh, EH11 4BY Tel: (07860) 388272

▶ Mabey Hire Ltd, Oakwood Grange, Robbinetts Lane, Cossall, Nottingham, NG16 2RX Tel: 0115-930 1154 Fax: 0115-944 0195

▶ McCarthy Surfacing Ltd, Beckton Works, Jenkins Lane, Barking, Essex, IG11 0AD Tel: (020) 8594 1966 Fax: (020) 8594 7244

▶ Markon Ltd, Marcon, Inchneuk Road, Glenboig, Coatbridge, Lanarkshire, ML5 2QX Tel: (01236) 875134 Fax: (01236) 875525 E-mail: enquiries@markon.co.uk

▶ Marshall Surfacing Contracts Ltd, 249 Godstone Road, Whyteleafe, Surrey, CR3 0EN Tel: (01883) 622241 Fax: (01883) 627265

▶ MCB Roads, 54 Ronaldstone Road, Sidcup, Kent, DA15 8QU Tel: (020) 8850 6428

▶ Mead Construction (Cambridge) Ltd, Liberty Barns, Heath Road, Swaffham Prior, Cambridge, CB5 0LA Tel: (01638) 742463

▶ Moorhead Excavations, Westfield Court, Lower Wortley Road, Leeds, LS12 4PX Tel: 0113-279 6556 Fax: 0113-231 0096

▶ N R A Roofing & Flooring Services Ltd, Rock House, Belfield Street, Ilkeston, Derbyshire, DE7 8DU Tel: 0115-930 4019 Fax: 0115-944 1728

▶ National Road Planning, School Road, Bulkington, Bedworth, Warwickshire, CV12 9JB Tel: (024) 7664 0664 Fax: (024) 7664 0663

▶ New County Road Surfacing Ltd, Penshaw Way, Birtley, Chester Le Street, County Durham, DH3 2SA Tel: 0191-410 9061

▶ Newmac Asphalt Services Ltd, Hunter Street, Paisley, Renfrewshire, PA1 1DN Tel: 0141-889 3174 Fax: 0141-889 3175

▶ North Yorkshire County Contractors Ltd, Grimbald Park, Wetherby Road, Knaresborough, North Yorkshire, HG5 8LJ Tel: (01423) 865584 Fax: (01423) 861162

▶ Northern Highways Ltd, Charnock Road, Liverpool, L9 7ET Tel: 0151-521 8400 Fax: 0151-521 8500

▶ O'Rourke Construction Ltd, 154-158 Sydenham Road, London, SE26 5JZ Tel: (020) 8659 6559 Fax: (020) 8778 7224 E-mail: info@orouke-uk.com

▶ Ottley & Sons, Downham Road, Ramsden Heath, Billericay, Essex, CM11 1PZ Tel: (01268) 711347 Fax: (01268) 711867

▶ P S M Builders, Orchard, Birdham Road, Chichester, West Sussex, PO20 7EQ Tel: (01243) 774605

▶ P T Saunders, Southleigh Farm, Southleigh Road, Havant, Hampshire, PO9 2NX Tel: (023) 9248 0878

▶ Pave Aways Ltd, Avenue Mill, Knockin, Oswestry, Shropshire, SY10 8HQ Tel: (01691) 682111 Fax: (01691) 682123

▶ Pike W L & Son Ltd, Tarvonga, Hill Brow Road, Liss, Hampshire, GU33 7LH Tel: (01730) 892884 Fax: (01730) 895647

▶ PP Construction, Deepwater Yard, Part Lane, Swallowfield, Reading, RG7 1TB Tel: 0118-988 7211 Fax: 0118-988 7266

▶ Prestigue Civil Engineering Westbury Ltd, Duncote, Towcester, Northamptonshire, NN12 8AL Tel: (01327) 358653 Fax: (01327) 358753 E-mail: info@prestigecivil.co.uk

▶ Q E Paving, Unit 45, Tumulus Way, Llandow Trading Estate, Cowbridge, South Glamorgan, CF71 7PB Tel: (01446) 794793

▶ R Elliott & Sons Ltd, Sandford Farm, Newhouse, Motherwell, Lanarkshire, ML1 5SX Tel: (01698) 870222

▶ R L Davies, 25 Raven Road, Walsall, WS5 3PZ Tel: (01922) 645443 Fax: (01922) 645443

▶ R Lindsay & Co. Ltd, Hayfield Place, Hayfield Industrial Estate, Kirkcaldy, Fife, KY2 5DH Tel: (01592) 260154 Fax: (01592) 641813 E-mail: sales@rlindsay.com

▶ Rail Ability Ltd, Unit B Tilcon Avenue, Stafford, ST18 0YJ Tel: (01785) 214747 Fax: (01785) 214717 E-mail: mail@railability.co.uk

▶ Raynesway Construction (Southern) Ltd, 260 Aztec West, Almondsbury, Bristol, BS32 4SY Tel: (01454) 617620

▶ Riggott & Co. Ltd, Station Lodge, Lodge Lane, Tuxford, Newark, Nottinghamshire, NG22 0NL Tel: (01777) 872525 Fax: (01777) 872626 E-mail: info@riggott.co.uk

▶ Ringway Highway Services, St. Michaels Close, Aylesford, Kent, ME20 7TZ Tel: (01622) 882274 Fax: (01622) 790987

▶ Ringway Highway Services, Stanton House, Stanton Way, Huntingdon, Cambridgeshire, PE29 6PY Tel: (01480) 434365 Fax: (01480) 433282

▶ Ringway Signs Ltd, Twenty Twenty Industrial Estate, St. Laurence Avenue, Allington, Maidstone, Kent, ME16 0LL Tel: (01622) 693476 Fax: (01622) 685992

▶ Roberts (C G T) Ltd, Lunn Lane, Beal, Goole, North Humberside, DN14 0SE Tel: (01977) 670082

▶ Sac Heartland Environmental, Ferguson Building, Craibstone Estate, Bucksburn, Aberdeen, AB21 9YA Tel: (01224) 711095 Fax: (01224) 711268 E-mail: info@sac.ac.uk

▶ Seymour, 6 Mousebank Lane, Lanark, ML11 7PP Tel: (01555) 666123 Fax: (01555) 661302

▶ Smith Construction Heckington Ltd, Station Road, Heckington, Sleaford, Lincolnshire, NG34 9NF Tel: (01529) 461500 Fax: (01529) 461463 E-mail: info@smithsportscivils.co.uk

▶ Souters Sports Ltd, Unit 80, Bandeath Industrial Estate, Stirling, FK7 7NP Tel: (01786) 480720

▶ South Yorks Tarmacadam Contractors Ltd, Wentworth Industrial Estate, Wentworth Way, Tankersley, Barnsley, South Yorkshire, S75 3DH Tel: (01226) 748748

▶ Sports Turf Services, Bellfield Park, Kinross, KY13 0NL Tel: (01577) 863864

▶ Suffolk Fleet Maintenance, Blyth Road, Halesworth, Suffolk, IP19 8EN Tel: (01986) 874427 Fax: (01986) 873279

▶ T K P Surfacing Ltd, Unit 5, Argyle Commercial Centre, Argyle Street, Swindon, SN2 8AR Tel: (01793) 430014

▶ T McKie, Deans Park, Irongray Road, Dumfries, DG2 0HS Tel: (01387) 720826

▶ Tayside Contracts, Brioch Road, Crieff, Perthshire, PH7 3SG Tel: (01764) 652115 Fax: (01764) 655418

▶ Tayside Contracts, Feus Road, Perth, PH1 2UQ Tel: (01738) 630044 Fax: (01738) 630515

▶ Terracarbon Ltd, The Garage, Hingham Road, Hackford, Wymondham, Norfolk, NR18 9HF Tel: (01953) 851535 Fax: (01953) 851328

▶ Tidey & Webb Ltd, Broomers Corner, Shipley, Horsham, West Sussex, RH13 8PX Tel: (01403) 741673 Fax: (01403) 741674

▶ Tonic Construction Ltd, The Coach House, Queen Court, West Tockenham, Swindon, SN4 7PJ Tel: (01793) 741234

▶ W I & A Gilbert Road Contractors, Easter Kersland, Dalry, Ayrshire, KA24 4JA Tel: (01294) 834433 Fax: (01294) 833343

▶ W M Donald Ltd, Marlaine, Netherley, Stonehaven, Kincardineshire, AB39 3QN Tel: (01569) 730590 Fax: (01569) 731315

▶ W T Construction Poole Ltd, Selbys Yard, Huntick Road, Lytchett Matravers, Poole, Dorset, BH16 6BB Tel: (01202) 620541 Fax: (01202) 620543

ROAD CONSTRUCTION EQUIPMENT

▶ A R Plant Hire Ltd, Tanglewood Derritt Lane, Bransgore, Christchurch, Dorset, BH23 8AR Tel: (01425) 673388 Fax: (01425) 674485 E-mail: mail@ar-planthire.co.uk

Benninghoven UK Ltd, Incendium House Centurion Way, Meridian Business Park, Leicester, LE19 1WH Tel: 0116-263 0345 Fax: 0116-282 8741 E-mail: enquiries@benninghoven.co.uk

Dominion (England) Ltd, 6 Strathmore Court, 143 Park Rd, London, NW8 7HY Tel: (020) 7483 2117 Fax: (020) 7586 6974 E-mail: dominionengland@cs.com

Highway & Industrial Equipment Ltd, East Moors Road, Cardiff, CF24 5EE Tel: (029) 2049 4623 Fax: (029) 2048 3611

Jetpatcher UK Ltd, Unit 10a Woodbine Street Hendon, Sunderland, SR1 2NL Tel: 0191-565 4400 Fax: 0191-564 1096 E-mail: info@jetpatcher.co.uk

ROAD FREIGHT FORWARDERS

▶ A G International Freight Ltd, Claybrook Drive, Washford Industrial Estate, Redditch, Worcestershire, B98 0DT Tel: (01527) 838520 Fax: (01527) 838529 E-mail: stevec@avon-groupage.co.uk

A P S Freight Ltd, Lord Warden House, Lord Warden Square, Dover, Kent, CT17 9EQ Tel: (01304) 225600 Fax: (01304) 225601 E-mail: office@apsfreight.com

▶ Audit Logistics UK, Apex House, 72 Peghouse Rise, Uplands, Stroud, Gloucestershire, GL5 1UR Tel: (01453) 750740 Fax: (01453) 750786 E-mail: contact@auditlogistics.co.uk

Felixstowe Freight Ltd, 23 Schneider Close, Felixstowe, Suffolk, IP11 3SS Tel: (01394) 677248 Fax: (01394) 677249 E-mail: graeme@felixstowefreight.co.uk

▶ S D W Recruitment, 33 Currie House, Herbert Walker Avenue, Southampton, SO15 1HJ Tel: (023) 8033 6633 Fax: (023) 8033 6633 E-mail: info@sdwrecruitment.co.uk

Smith's Solutions, 27 Kiln Lane, Hope, Wrexham, Clwyd, LL12 9PH Tel: (01978) 769090 Fax: 01978 769173 E-mail: sales@smiths-solutions.co.uk

▶ Uneek Freight Services Ltd, Amberley Way, Hounslow, TW4 6BH Tel: (020) 8569 4949 Fax: (020) 8569 5101 E-mail: info@uneekfreight.com

▶ Viamaster International Ltd, Valley Farm Way, Leeds, LS10 1SE Tel: 0113-270 0033 Fax: 0113 270 0065 E-mail: mail@viamaster-intl.com

ROAD GRITTERS

Econ Engineering Ltd, Boroughbridge Road, Ripon, North Yorkshire, HG4 1UE Tel: (01765) 605321

ROAD GRITTING MATERIALS

Broste Ltd, Unit 8 North Lynn Business Village, Bergen Way, North Lynn Industrial Estate, King's Lynn, Norfolk, PE30 2JG Tel: (01553) 776066 Fax: (01553) 767319 E-mail: broste.uk@broste.com

Peacock Salt Ltd, North Harbour, North Harbour Street, Ayr, KA8 8AE Tel: (01292) 292000 Fax: (01292) 292001 E-mail: info@peacocksalt.co.uk

ROAD HAULAGE MAGAZINES

Motor Transport, Quadrant House, The Quadrant, Sutton, Surrey, SM2 5AS Tel: (020) 8652 3500

ROAD MARKING

Stretford Industrial Services Ltd, 8 Radnor Street, Stretford, Manchester, M32 8LE Tel: 0161-865 4235 Fax: 0161-865 0139 E-mail: sales@sisgroup.co.uk

ROAD MARKING CRAYONS

Rowland Sandwith Ltd, 32 Canford Bottom, Wimborne, Dorset, BH21 2HD Tel: (01202) 882323 Fax: (01202) 842815 E-mail: hancocks@rowland-sandwith.co.uk

ROAD MARKING EQUIPMENT

Moon's Plant Hire, 3 Laureate Industrial Estate, Newmarket, Suffolk, CB8 0AP Tel: (01638) 662622 Fax: (01638) 660961

Ridgedeck Road Markings Ltd, Station Road, East Preston, Littlehampton, West Sussex, BN16 3AA Tel: (01903) 782465 Fax: (01903) 859671

Springwood Engineering, Bunces Lane, Burghfield Common, Reading, RG7 3DH Tel: 0118-983 2411 Fax: 0118-983 4731 E-mail: springwood.eng@btopenworld.com

ROAD MARKING MATERIALS

Adbruf Ltd, Gibbs Marsh Trading Estate, Stalbridge, Sturminster Newton, Dorset, DT10 2RX Tel: (01963) 362640 Fax: (01963) 363762 E-mail: sales@adbruf.com

Coupe Line Ltd, Hackworth Industrial Park, Shildon, County Durham, DL4 1HG Tel: (01388) 774040 Fax: (01388) 776010

▶ Kestrel Thermoplastics Ltd, 3 High Street, Prescot, Merseyside, L34 3LD Tel: 0151-426 9969 Fax: 0151-430 6633 E-mail: sales@kestrelplastics.com

▶ Potters Europe, Ask House, 2 Northgate Avenue, Bury St. Edmunds, Suffolk, IP32 6BB Tel: (01284) 715400 Fax: (01284) 715401 E-mail: info.potters@dial.pipex.com

R S Clare & Co. Ltd, 8 Stanhope Street, Liverpool, L8 5RQ Tel: 0151-709 2902 Fax: 0151-709 0518 E-mail: sales@rsclare.com

Rommco (UK) Ltd, Road Care House, New Works Road, Lowmoor, Bradford, West Yorkshire, BD12 0RU Tel: (01274) 606770 Fax: (01274) 602802

ROAD ROLLERS

Bomag Great Britain Ltd, Sheldon Way, Larkfield, Aylesford, Kent, ME20 6SE Tel: (01622) 715252 Fax: (01622) 710233 E-mail: sales@bomag.com

▶ Clee Hill Plant Ltd, 41 Downiebrae Road, Rutherglen, Glasgow, G73 1PW Tel: 0141-647 0067 Fax: 0141-647 7600 E-mail: glasgow@cleehill.co.uk

Clee Hill Plants, Mansfield Road, Corbriggs, Chesterfield, Derbyshire, S41 0JW Tel: (01246) 551637 Fax: (01246) 551639 E-mail: sales@cleehill.co.uk

H M Plant Ltd, Monkton Business Park North, Hebburn, Tyne & Wear, NE31 2JZ Tel: 0191-430 8400 Fax: 0191-430 8500 E-mail: info@hmplant.ltd.uk

ROAD SAFETY OR DANGER EQUIPMENT

Brookes & Sons Ltd, Bangor Road, Penmaenmawr, Gwynedd, LL34 6LF Tel: (01492) 622685 Fax: (01492) 622943 E-mail: gavin@brookestarpaulins.co.uk

Delta Scientific Corporation UK Ltd, Delta House, 70 South View Avenue, Caversham, Reading, RG4 5BB Tel: 0118-948 1133 Fax: 0118-948 1122 E-mail: deltascuk@aol.com

Hazard Safety Products, 55-57 Bristol Road, Birmingham, B5 7TU Tel: 0121-446 4433 Fax: 0121-446 4230 E-mail: sales@hazard.co.uk

Highway Safety Systems Ltd, Units 4A-B, Manor Lane Business Park, Manor Lane, Holmes Chapel, Crewe, CW4 8AF Tel: (01477) 536000 Fax: (01477) 536006

M C Electronics Ltd, 61 Grimsdyke Road, Pinner, Middlesex, HA5 4PP Tel: (020) 8428 2027 Fax: (020) 8428 2027 E-mail: sales@mcelectronics.co.uk

MelbaSwintex Ltd, Derby Works, Manchester Road, Bury, Lancashire, BL9 9NX Tel: 0161-761 4933 Fax: 0161-797 1146 E-mail: sales@swintex.co.uk

ROAD SIGNS

Alpha Sign Systems, Oakwood Bussiness Park, Oldmixon Crescent, Weston-Super-Mare, Avon, BS24 9AY Tel: (01934) 625444 Fax: (01934) 625358 E-mail: sales@alphasignsystems.com

Altaroute Ltd, 10 North Road, Yate, Bristol, BS37 7PA Tel: (01454) 311475 Fax: (01454) 273065 E-mail: sales@altaroute.com

Centurion Components Ltd, 38 Carron Place, East Kilbride, Glasgow, G75 0TS Tel: (01355) 265222 Fax: (01355) 230331 E-mail: sales@centurionsigns.co.uk

Dee-Organ, Signature House, 4 Newmains Avenue, Inchinnan, Paisley, Renfrewshire, PA4 9RR Tel: 0141-812 5121 Fax: 0141-812 5125 E-mail: signs@dee-organ.co.uk

H & H Alloy Sales Ltd, J A S House, Titford Lane, Rowley Regis, West Midlands, B65 0PY Tel: 0121-559 6466 Fax: 0121-559 8723 E-mail: signs@warleyholdings.co.uk

Highway & Industrial Equipment Ltd, East Moors Road, Cardiff, CF24 5EE Tel: (029) 2049 4623 Fax: (029) 2048 3611

I R S Ltd, Lion Works, Castle Acre Road, Swaffham, Norfolk, PE37 7HS Tel: (01760) 721399 Fax: (01760) 723726 E-mail: sales@irs-ltd.co.uk

Instyle Leather Goods Ltd, Publicity House, Tweedy Lane, Newport, Gwent, NP19 8DZ Tel: (01633) 282412 Fax: (01633) 282413 E-mail: m-freeman@btinternet.com

Lancashire County Engineering Services, Dewhurst Row, Bamber Bridge, Preston, PR5 6BB Tel: (01772) 628323 Fax: (01772) 532343 E-mail: hq@lces.lancscc.gov.uk

Manchester Safety Services Ltd, Fir Street, Heywood, Lancashire, OL10 1NW Tel: (01706) 364943 Fax: (01706) 360026 E-mail: sales@manchestersafety.co.uk

MelbaSwintex Ltd, Derby Works, Manchester Road, Bury, Lancashire, BL9 9NX Tel: 0161-761 4933 Fax: 0161-797 1146 E-mail: sales@swintex.co.uk

Midland Signs Leicester Ltd, 15 Foxholes Road, Golfcourse Lane, Leicester, LE3 1TH Tel: 0116-254 4445 Fax: 0116-254 2020 E-mail: info@ggstreetnameplates.com

Morelock Signs Ltd, Morelock House, Strawberry Lane, Willenhall, West Midlands, WV13 3RS Tel: (01902) 605040 Fax: (01902) 637576 E-mail: mail@morelock.co.uk

Nibra Sign Ltd, Ivy House Farm, Wolvershill Road, Banwell, Somerset, BS29 6LB Tel: (01934) 822772 Fax: (01934) 822517 E-mail: nibra.signs@btopenworld.com

Nordis Industries, Cornhill Close, Lodge Farm Industrial Estate, Northampton, NN5 7UB Tel: (01604) 596910 Fax: 01604 758470

Ringway Signs Ltd, Winterstoke Road, Weston-super-Mare, Avon, BS24 9BQ Tel: (01934) 421400 Fax: (01934) 421401 E-mail: signs@ringway.co.uk

Royal British Legion Industries, Royal British Legion Village, Hall Road, Aylesford, Kent, ME20 7NL Tel: (01622) 795900 Fax: (01622) 882195 E-mail: enquries@rbli.co.uk

S P Frames, Savile Street, Batley, West Yorkshire, WF17 6JS Tel: (01924) 502050 Fax: (01924) 503050

The Sign Factory, Burnbank Road, Bainsford, Falkirk, FK2 7PE Tel: (01324) 501950 Fax: (01324) 501951 E-mail: info@falkirk.gov.uk

Signpost Signs, 137 Upper Wickham Lane, Welling, Kent, DA16 3AL Tel: (020) 8854 8777 Fax: (020) 8855 0577 E-mail: enquiries@signpostsigns.co.uk

Signs & Labels Ltd, Willow Business Park, 21 Willow Lane, Mitcham, Surrey, CR4 4NA Tel: (020) 8274 3700 Fax: (020) 8274 3702 E-mail: sales@signsandlabels.co.uk

Traffic & Commercial Signs Ltd, Unit 14 Merryhills Enterprise Park, Park Lane, Wolverhampton, WV10 9QF Tel: (01902) 307879 Fax: (01902) 728976

Traffic Safety Supplies (U K) Ltd, Tait Road Industrial Estate, Croydon, CR0 2DP Tel: (020) 8684 6643 Fax: (020) 8684 6532

Vista Signs, 267 Nottingham Road, Nottingham, NG7 7DA Tel: 0115-942 1511 Fax: 0115-942 2462 E-mail: sales@vista-signs.co.uk

ROAD SIMULATION TEST EQUIPMENT

Data Physics (UK) Ltd, South Rd, Hailsham, East Sussex, BN27 3JJ Tel: (01323) 846464 Fax: (01323) 847550 E-mail: sales@dataphysics.com

ROAD SURFACING BITUMINOUS MATERIALS

Bituchem Group, Laymore Road, Forest Vale Industrial Estate, Cinderford, Gloucestershire, GL14 2YH Tel: (01594) 826768 Fax: (01594) 826948 E-mail: sales@bituchem.com

ROAD SURFACING BITUMINOUS MATERIALS – *continued*

Prismo Road Surfacing Material Mnfrs, 5 Drumhead Road, Chorley North Industrial Park, Chorley, Lancashire, PR6 7BX Tel: (01257) 225100 Fax: (01257) 224605

Tenants Tar Distillers, 9 Airport Road West, Belfast, BT3 9ED Tel: (028) 9045 5135 Fax: (028) 9046 0077 E-mail: ttd@ctni.co.uk

ROAD SURFACING EQUIPMENT

▶ Clee Hill Plant Ltd, Turner Crescent, Newcastle, Staffordshire, ST5 7JZ Tel: (01782) 566017 Fax: (01782) 565858 E-mail: stoke@cleehill.co.uk

Econ Engineering Ltd, Boroughbridge Road, Ripon, North Yorkshire, HG4 1UE Tel: (01765) 605321

Jetpatcher UK Ltd, Unit 10a Woodbine Street Hendon, Sunderland, SR1 2NL Tel: 0191-565 4400 Fax: 0191-564 1096 E-mail: info@jetpatcher.co.uk

ROAD SURFACING EQUIPMENT HIRE

Jetpatcher UK Ltd, Unit 10a Woodbine Street Hendon, Sunderland, SR1 2NL Tel: 0191-565 4400 Fax: 0191-564 1096 E-mail: info@jetpatcher.co.uk

Proteus Equipment Ltd, P O Box 33, Bury St. Edmunds, Suffolk, IP33 2RS Tel: (01284) 753954 Fax: (01284) 701369 E-mail: enquiries@proteusequipment.com

ROAD SURFACING MATERIALS,

See also headings for particular types

Adbruf Ltd, Gibbs Marsh Trading Estate, Stalbridge, Sturminster Newton, Dorset, DT10 2RX Tel: (01963) 362640 Fax: (01963) 363762 E-mail: sales@adbruf.com

Colas Ltd, Wallage Lane, Rowfant, Crawley, West Sussex, RH10 4NF Tel: (01342) 711000 Fax: (01342) 711198 E-mail: info@colas.co.uk

G R S Roadstone Ltd, Leicester Road, Wolvey, Hinckley, Leicestershire, LE10 3HL Tel: (01455) 222700 Fax: (01455) 222737 E-mail: west@grsroadstone.co.uk

Hanson Projects, The Ridge, Chipping Sodbury, Bristol, BS37 6AY Tel: (01454) 338650 Fax: (01454) 338660 E-mail: info@hanson.co.uk

R M C Roadstone Ltd, Roadstone, Huggate, York, YO42 1YR Tel: (01377) 288117 Fax: (01377) 288461

Salop Sand & Gravel Supply Co. Ltd, Station Road, Admaston, Telford, Shropshire, TF5 0AN Tel: (01952) 254101 Fax: (01952) 223932 E-mail: info@gravel.co.uk

Tarmac Topmix Ltd, PO Box 5, Chester Le Street, County Durham, DH3 2ST Tel: (01539) 727932

Tarmac Western, Morfe Bank, Corus Works, Port Talbot, West Glamorgan, SA13 2NG Tel: (01639) 883052 Fax: (01639) 884435

W. Clifford Watts Ltd, 118-122 Scarborough Road, Bridlington, East Yorkshire, YO16 7NU Tel: (01262) 675383 Fax: (01262) 604629 E-mail: wcliffordwatts@aol.com

ROAD SWEEPER OR COLLECTOR VEHICLE HIRE

Arbscapes, Rawreth Lodge, Church Road, Rawreth, Wickford, Essex, SS11 8SG Tel: (01268) 560006 Fax: (01268) 733251 E-mail: info@arbscapes.co.uk

Earl Road Sweepers Ltd, Shardlowes Farm, Hedingham Road, Gosfield, Halstead, Essex, CO9 1PL Tel: (01787) 273777 Fax: (01787) 273777 E-mail: office@ersweepers.wanadoo.co.uk

Economy Hire (Dorset) Ltd, 10 Parkside Industrial Estate, Ringwood, Hampshire, BH24 3SQ Tel: (01425) 474593 Fax: (01425) 479964 E-mail: jclark@economyhire.co.uk

MHS Highway Hire, Highway House, Station Road, Shirehampton, Bristol, BS11 9XA Tel: 0117-916 2400 Fax: 0117-916 2427 E-mail: info@mhs-hire.co.uk

ROAD SWEEPER OR COLLECTOR VEHICLES

Asset Co Group Ltd, Ruislip Workshop, 800 Field End Road, Ruislip, Middlesex, HA4 0QH Tel: (020) 8515 3999 Fax: (020) 8515 3999 E-mail: sales@assetco.com

▶ Bicester Sweepers Ltd, Glebe Court, Fringford, Bicester, Oxfordshire, OX27 8RJ Tel: (01869) 277410 Fax: (01869) 277704

Dennis Eagle Ltd, Heathcote Way, Heathcote Industrial Estate, Warwick, CV34 6TE Tel: (01926) 316000 Fax: (01926) 316550

Faun Municipal Vehicles Ltd, Unit 4 Bryn Cefni Industrial Park, Llangefni, Gwynedd, LL77 7XA Tel: (01248) 722777 Fax: (01248) 750220 E-mail: sales@faun.demon.co.uk

J & J Services, 29 Dunville Road, Bedford, MK40 4DY Tel: (01234) 378289 Fax: (01234) 325479 E-mail: lindopjj@aol.com'

Johnston Sweepers Ltd, Curtis Road, Dorking, Surrey, RH4 1XF Tel: (01306) 884722 Fax: (01306) 884151 E-mail: enquiries@johnstonsweepers.com

Londonderry Garage Ltd, New Garage, Londonderry, Northallerton, North Yorkshire, DL7 9NB Tel: (01677) 422185 Fax: (01677) 428311

ROAD SWEEPERS, MAGNETIC

Zenith Industrial Products Ltd, Tilemans Lane, Shipston-on-Stour, Warwickshire, CV36 4PR Tel: (01608) 664366 Fax: (01608) 663951

ROAD SWEEPING BRUSHES

Cottam Bros Ltd, Wilson Street North, Sheepfolds Industrial Estate, Sunderland, SR5 1BB Tel: 0191-567 1091 Fax: 0191-510 8187 E-mail: cottam.bros@dial.pipex.com

Danline International Ltd, Nebo Road, Llanrwst, Gwynedd, LL26 0SE Tel: (01492) 640651 Fax: (01492) 641601 E-mail: sales@danline.co.uk

Dawson & Son Ltd, Clayton Wood Rise, West Park Ring Road, Leeds, LS16 6RH Tel: 0113-275 9321 Fax: 0113-275 2761 E-mail: sales@dawsonbrush.co.uk

Hilton's Brush Mnfrs, 84 Uxbridge Street, Ashton-under-Lyne, Lancashire, OL6 7EH Tel: 0161-339 2390 Fax: 0161-343 2627

P D C Brush UK Ltd, Marshfield Bank Employment Park, Marshfield Bank, Crewe, CW2 8UY Tel: (01270) 259777 Fax: (01270) 259770

Robert Cresser, 40 Victoria Street, Edinburgh, EH1 2JW Tel: 0131-225 2181 Fax: 0131-225 2181

Widdop De Courcy Ltd, Prospect Works, Allerton Road, Allerton, Bradford, West Yorkshire, BD15 7AF Tel: (01274) 495709 Fax: (01274) 547396 E-mail: sales@widdops.com

ROAD TANKERS

Clayton Commercials Ltd, Langley Road, Burscough Industrial Estate, Ormskirk, Lancashire, L40 8JR Tel: (01704) 894244 Fax: (01704) 894226 E-mail: sales@claytoncommercials.com

G C A Transport Ltd, Romy House, 163-167 Kings Road, Brentwood, Essex, CM14 4EG Tel: (01277) 235230 Fax: (01277) 235240

▶ M F Compton & Son, Grovebury Road, Leighton Buzzard, Bedfordshire, LU7 4TS Tel: (01525) 371707 Fax: (01525) 851891 E-mail: enquiries@tankers-r-us.com

Purfleet Commercials Ltd, 520 London Road, Grays, Essex, RM20 3BE Tel: (01708) 863931 Fax: (01708) 868226 E-mail: tmason@harris-group.co.uk

Trailer Engineering, Central Avenue, Cradley Heath, West Midlands, B64 7BY Tel: (01384) 564765 Fax: (01384) 410782 E-mail: info@trailerengineering.co.uk

Whale Tankers Ltd, Ravenshaw, Solihull, West Midlands, B91 2SU Tel: 0121-704 5700 Fax: 0121-704 5701 E-mail: whalemail@whale.co.uk

ROAD TRAILERS

A H P Trailers Ltd, Heath Mill Road, Wombourne, Wolverhampton, WV5 8AP Tel: (01902) 895281 Fax: (01902) 894577

A Lloyd & Son, Urban Road, Kirkby-in-Ashfield, Nottingham, NG17 8AP Tel: (01623) 752965 Fax: (01623) 752965

Artic Trailers, Holton Road, Nettleton, Market Rasen, Lincolnshire, LN7 6AW Tel: (01472) 851314 Fax: (01472) 851314

Aviation Enterprises Ltd, Membury Airfield, Lambourn, Hungerford, Berkshire, RG17 7TJ Tel: (01488) 72224 Fax: (01488) 72224 E-mail: sales@aviationenterprises.co.uk

Bank Farm Trailers, The Garage, Llangunnor, Carmarthen, Dyfed, SA31 2PG Tel: (01267) 231565 Fax: (01267) 222154 E-mail: sales@bankfarm-trailers.co.uk

Bank Farm Trailers, Bank Farm, Spytty Road, Newport, Gwent, NP19 4QW Tel: (01633) 290291 Fax: (01633) 270400

Bank Farm Trailers Ltd, Unit 1 Mill Brook Yard, Landore, Swansea, SA1 2JG Tel: (01792) 795834 Fax: (01792) 799251 E-mail: sales@bankfarm-trailers.co.uk

Bateson Trailers Ltd, Doodfield Works, Windlehurst Road, Marple, Stockport, Cheshire, SK6 7EN Tel: 0161-426 0500 Fax: 0161-426 0245 E-mail: sales@bateson-trailers.co.uk

Blue Line Trailers, New Office, Main Road, Algarkirk, Boston, Lincolnshire, PE20 2BE Tel: (01205) 460777 Fax: (01205) 460014

The Boughton Group, Graycar Business Park, Barton Turn, Barton under Needwood, Burton-on-Trent, Staffordshire, DE13 8EN Tel: (01283) 711771 Fax: (01283) 711669 E-mail: enquiries@reynoldsboughton.com

Crusely Trailer Engineering Ltd, Beacon Hill Industrial Estate, Botany Way, Purfleet, Essex, RM19 1SR Tel: (01708) 861144 Fax: (01708) 863308

Eagle Trailers, 241A Blandford Road, Hamworthy, Poole, Dorset, BH15 4AZ Tel: (01202) 671057 Fax: (01202) 671057

East Cheshire Trailers, Sandy Lane Garage, Sandy Lane, Macclesfield, Cheshire, SK10 4RJ Tel: (01625) 611550 Fax: (01625) 611550

Fieldfare Trailer Centre, Fieldfare House, Old Malthouse Lane, Ford, Salisbury, SP4 6DR Tel: (01980) 611853 Fax: (01980) 611130 E-mail: info@fieldfairtrailers.co.uk

Hanford Trailer Spares, 152 Stone Road, Stoke-on-Trent, ST4 8NS Tel: (01782) 658594

Harrogate Trailer & Towbar Centre, 6 Provincial Works, The Avenue, Harrogate, North Yorkshire, HG1 4QE Tel: (01423) 884962 Fax: (01423) 888953

Hazlewood Trailers, Bishampton Road, Rous Lench, Evesham, Worcestershire, WR11 4UN Tel: (01386) 792916 Fax: (01386) 793320 E-mail: admin@hazelwoodtrailers.co.uk

Houghton Trailers, Colliery Lane, Hetton-le-Hole, Houghton le Spring, Tyne & Wear, DH5 0BG Tel: 0191-517 0154 Fax: 0191-517 0154

Indespension Ltd, 38a Nimmings Road, Halesowen, West Midlands, B62 9JE Tel: 0121-561 5467 Fax: 0121-561 2180 E-mail: westmids@indespention.com

Kaygee Engineering, 55 Great Union Street, Hull, HU9 1AG Tel: (01482) 326281 Fax: (01482) 219240 E-mail: info@kaygee.co.uk

Lynton Trailers UK Ltd, Constable Street, Manchester, M18 8GJ Tel: 0161-223 8211 Fax: 0161-223 0933 E-mail: lyntonmail@aol.com

M & G Trailers Ltd, Hayes Lane, Stourbridge, West Midlands, DY9 8PA Tel: (01384) 424200 Fax: (01384) 424452 E-mail: mandgtrailers@lyeone.net

Montracon Ltd, Carr Hill, Doncaster, S. Yorkshire, DN4 8DE Tel: (01302) 739292 Fax: (01302) 730660 E-mail: enquiries@montracon.com

Oldbury UK Ltd, Bulliol Business Park, Wobaston Road, Wolverhampton, WV9 5EU Tel: (01902) 397216 Fax: (01902) 878265 E-mail: sales@oldburyuk.co.uk

S M Trailers, Bevis Lane, Wisbech St Mary, Wisbech, Cambridgeshire, PE13 4RR Tel: (01945) 410200 Fax: (01945) 410651 E-mail: sales@smtrailersltd.co.uk

Scott Trailers, 33 West End, Walcott, Lincoln, LN4 3ST Tel: (01526) 860741 Fax: (01526) 861357 E-mail: sales@scott-trailers.co.uk

Tow B Fabs, Unit 5-6 Kents Avenue, Hemel Hempstead, Hertfordshire, HP3 9XH Tel: (01442) 256764 Fax: (01442) 256764

Towone Trailers, 40 Havelock Street, Hessle Road, Hull, HU3 4JH Tel: (01482) 225645 Fax: (01482) 585979

Towrite Fabrications Ltd, Albert Road, Market Harborough, Leicestershire, LE16 7LU Tel: (01858) 467805 Fax: (01858) 434209 E-mail: sales@towrite.co.uk

Waggonworks Trailers & Towing Equipment, 1 White Cottage, Marshside, Canterbury, Kent, CT3 4EJ Tel: (01227) 860650 Fax: (01227) 860650

Warwick Bros Alresford Ltd, The Dean, Alresford, Hampshire, SO24 9BN Tel: (01962) 732681 Fax: (01962) 735385 E-mail: info@warwicktrailers.co.uk

Weightlifter Bodies Ltd, Grange Lane North, Scunthorpe, South Humberside, DN16 1BN Tel: (01724) 872444 Fax: (01724) 853647

ROAD TRANSPORT AND HAULAGE

▶ 21st Century Transport Ltd, Unit G2-G3 G6 H5-H6 Hastingwood Trading Estate, 35 Harbet Road, London, N18 3HT Tel: (020) 8887 0796 Fax: (020) 8807 7624

▶ 4ja Transport Ltd, Welton Industrial Estate, Railway Road, Blairgowrie, Perthshire, PH10 6EP Tel: (01250) 872233 Fax: (01250) 872299

▶ 7 Valley Transport Ltd, Unit 29 Shifnal Industrial Estate, Lamledge Lane, Shifnal, Shropshire, TF11 8SD Tel: (01952) 461991 Fax: (01952) 461950 E-mail: sales@7valleytransport.com

▶ A 2 B Removals, 64 Longtown Road, Dundee, DD4 8JS Tel: (01382) 860830

▶ A A Carriers Ltd, Oaks Lane, Barnsley, South Yorkshire, S71 1HT Tel: (01226) 285222 Fax: (01226) 285222

▶ A B C Grimsby Ltd, Lancaster Approach, North Killingholme, Immingham, South Humberside, DN40 3JZ Tel: (01469) 540966 Fax: (01469) 540908

A B C Transport Ltd, Plot U Unswood Industrial Estate, Theaklen Drive, St. Leonards-on-Sea, East Sussex, TN38 9AZ Tel: (01424) 755059 Fax: (01424) 722234

A B E (Ledbury) Ltd, Bromyard Road, Ledbury, Herefordshire, HR8 1LG Tel: (01531) 633195 Fax: (01531) 633192

A B Powles, Porters Lodge, Coughton, Ross-on-Wye, Herefordshire, HR9 5ST Tel: (01989) 565137 Fax: (01989) 565139

▶ A B T International Ltd, Westwood Farm, Westwood, Peterborough, PE3 9UW Tel: (01733) 333322

A Beasley, Lanesfield Drive Industrial Estate, Wolverhampton, WV4 6UB Tel: (01902) 353820 Fax: (01902) 354264

▶ A Black, Hangar 3, Drem Airfield, North Berwick, East Lothian, EH39 5AW Tel: (01620) 850263 Fax: (01620) 850517

▶ A C C Distribution Ltd, Distribution Depot, Mossburn Avenue, Harthill, Shotts, Lanarkshire, ML7 5NF Tel: (01501) 753333

A Cars Express Despatch Ltd, Unit 14 Langley Terrace Industrial Park, Latimer Road, Luton, LU1 3XQ Tel: (01582) 731900 Fax: (0870) 2330612 E-mail: acars@acars.co.uk

A Clarke & Co Smethwick Ltd, Union Road, Oldbury, West Midlands, B69 3ER Tel: 0121-552 2854 Fax: 0121-552 6385 E-mail: barry@clarketransport.co.uk

▶ A Clarke & Co Smethwick Ltd, Unit 6 Kenfig Industrial Estate, Margam, Port Talbot, West Glamorgan, SA13 2PE Tel: (01656) 745767 Fax: (01656) 741518

▶ A Clarke & Co Smethwick Ltd, Pickering Works, Netherton Road, Wishaw, Lanarkshire, ML2 0EQ Tel: (01698) 350088 Fax: (01698) 358400

▶ A & D Haulage (Telford) Ltd, Unit B3, Court Works Industrial Estate, Bridgnorth Road, Telford, Shropshire, TF7 4JB Tel: (01952) 582800 Fax: (01952) 585467 E-mail: andhaulage@tiscali.co.uk

▶ A & D Logistics, Gas Street, Johnstone, Renfrewshire, PA5 8BJ Tel: (01505) 329539 Fax: (01505) 327486

A D V Transport, 42 Mill Hill, Shoreham-by-Sea, West Sussex, BN43 5TH Tel: (01273) 462696 Fax: (01273) 462697 E-mail: advtransport@btinternet.net

▶ A Davie, East Happas Farm, Forfar, Angus, DD8 2JW Tel: (01307) 820264 Fax: (01307) 463353

▶ A E Costin Ltd, Unit 3 Morgan Close, Willenhall, West Midlands, WV12 4LH Tel: (01902) 635939 Fax: (01902) 608556

A E Hawkins, Oak Lane, Kingswinford, West Midlands, DY6 7JS Tel: (01384) 294949 Fax: (01384) 400069

A E Parker Ltd, Terminus Road, Chichester, West Sussex, PO19 8TX Tel: (01243) 783319 Fax: (01243) 532617 E-mail: transport@parkerltd.co.uk

▶ A E Partridge & Sons, The Laurels, Morchard Bishop, Crediton, Devon, EX17 6PL Tel: (01363) 877266

▶ A E Rumens, Upper Crowbourne, Blind Lane, Goudhurst, Cranbrook, Kent, TN17 1JD Tel: (01580) 211413

▶ A E Wilson Commercials Ltd, Belton Road, Sandtoft, Doncaster, South Yorkshire, DN8 5SX Tel: (01724) 710373 Fax: (01724) 711178

▶ A & F Grant, Georgetown Farm, Ballindalloch, Banffshire, AB37 9BA Tel: (01807) 500211 Fax: (01807) 500364

A G Beech, Purdy Road, Batmans Hill Trading Estate, Bilston, West Midlands, WV14 8UB Tel: (01902) 491728 Fax: (01902) 491728

A Hingley Transport Ltd, Talbots La Trading Estate, Talbots Lane, Brierley Hill, West Midlands, DY5 2YX Tel: (01384) 262221 Fax: (01384) 573286

▶ A Hoggarth & Sons, Selly Hill, Guisborough Road, Whitby, North Yorkshire, YO21 1SG Tel: (01947) 604777 Fax: (01947) 829829

▶ A & J Butterworth Ltd, Road End Garage, Off Chew Valley Road, Greenfield, Oldham, OL3 7JL Tel: (01457) 872098 Fax: (01457) 870760

A J Carlier & Sons Ltd, Mansfield Road, Derby, DE21 4AW Tel: (01332) 380615

▶ A J F Transport, Trinidad Works, Wanstrow, Shepton Mallet, Somerset, BA4 4SL Tel: (01749) 880554 Fax: (01749) 880288

▶ A J Maiden & Son Ltd, Cross Green, Allscott, Telford, Shropshire, TF6 5EG Tel: (01952) 255877 Fax: (01952) 222289 E-mail: info@maidensoftelford.co.uk

▶ A & J Nelson Ltd, Great North Road, Kelty, Fife, KY4 0HE Tel: (01383) 830359 Fax: (01383) 831685

A Jardine & Sons, Northgate, White Lund Industrial Estate, Morecambe, Lancashire, LA3 3PA Tel: (01524) 33113 Fax: (01524) 843262

▶ A K Transport Ltd, Blenheim Road, Airfield Industrial Estate, Ashbourne, Derbyshire, DE6 1HA Tel: (01335) 342958 Fax: (01335) 345103

▶ A M P M Transport, 35 Underwood Road, Paisley, Renfrewshire, PA3 1TH Tel: 0141-889 7754

A M Transport (Liverpool) Ltd, Unit 12 B, Candy Park, Plantation Road, Bromborough, Wirral, Merseyside, CH62 3QS Tel: 0151-346 1780 Fax: 0151-346 1781

▶ A Melville Ltd, Beechwood Garage, Glamis Road, Kirriemuir, Angus, DD8 5DF Tel: (01575) 572635 Fax: (01575) 572912

▶ A N C Aylesbury, 1-4 Smeaton Close, Rabans Lane Industrial Area, Aylesbury, Buckinghamshire, HP19 8SU Tel: (01296) 427484 Fax: (01296) 489130

▶ A N C Ayrshire, Block 5, Moorfield Industrial Estate, Kilmarnock, Ayrshire, KA2 0AG Tel: (01563) 571363 Fax: (01563) 522700

▶ A N C Holdings, 7-9 Finch Drive, Braintree, Essex, CM7 2SF Tel: (01376) 341708 Fax: (01376) 341708

▶ A N C London West, 9 Central Way, London, NW10 7XQ Tel: (020) 8453 3500 Fax: (020) 8453 3501

A N C Nottingham Ltd, Unit 2 Finch Close, Nottingham, NG7 2NN Tel: 0115-985 0800 Fax: 0115-985 0900 E-mail: customerservices0139@anc.co.uk

▶ A N C Parcels, 2 Babbage Road, Engineer Park, Sandycroft, Deeside, Clwyd, CH5 2QD Tel: (01244) 530562 Fax: (01244) 530563

▶ A P C Glasgow Ltd, 1 239 Blairtummock Road, Glasgow, G33 4ED Tel: 0141-771 6888 Fax: 0141-771 7888

ROAD TRANSPORT AND HAULAGE

– continued

▶ A P Distribution, 8 Block 6, Myregormie Place, Mitchelston Industrial Estate, Kirkcaldy, Fife, KY1 3NA Tel: (01592) 650222 Fax: (01592) 650222

▶ A P Hollingworth Ltd, 71 Barnsley Road, Upper Cumberworth, Huddersfield, HD8 8NS Tel: (01484) 606282 Fax: (01484) 607762

▶ A P W Transport Ltd, Hownsgill Drive, Consett, County Durham, DH8 9HU Tel: (01207) 581019 Fax: (01207) 503920

▶ A Purchase Ltd, Level Street, Brierley Hill, West Midlands, DY5 1UA Tel: (01384) 78725 Fax: (01384) 78386

A R Gurteen Ltd, Kingsley House, Freezemoor Road, Houghton le Spring, Tyne & Wear, DH4 7BH Tel: 0191-584 4555 Fax: 0191-512 0222

▶ A S T Express, Preston Street, Manchester, M18 8DB Tel: 0161-223 7878 Fax: 0161-230 7745

A S Transport, 359a Staines Road, Hounslow, TW4 5AP Tel: (020) 8577 5888 Fax: (020) 8577 1588 E-mail: clairecooley@hotmail.com

▶ A T Goodyear & Son Ltd, Weston Hills, Spalding, Lincolnshire, PE12 6BX Tel: (01775) 722281

▶ A To Z Logistics, 9 Law Place, Nerston Industrial Estate, East Kilbride, Glasgow, G74 4QL Tel: (01355) 224480 Fax: (01355) 265230

▶ A V Dawson Ltd, Riverside Park Road, Middlesbrough, Cleveland, TS2 1QW Tel: (01642) 219271 Fax: (01642) 256828

▶ A Watson (Hauliers) Ltd, Thorpe Lane Garage, Thorpe Lane, Leeds, LS10 4EP Tel: 0113-270 1871

A Wilkins & Sons, Unit 1 3 The Elms Centre, Glaziers Lane, Normandy, Guildford, Surrey, GU3 2DF Tel: (01483) 575919 Fax: (01483) 570140

Aad Logistics Ltd, Unit 49b Atcham Industrial Estate, Upton Magna, Shrewsbury, SY4 4UG Tel: (01743) 761992 Fax: (01743) 761993

▶ Abbey Roadtanks Ltd, 2 Littlefair Road, Hull, HU9 5LP Tel: (01482) 798177 Fax: (01482) 797713 E-mail: sales@abbeyroadtanks.com

Abnormal Loads Services International Ltd, 1501 Hedon Road, Hull, HU9 5NX Tel: (01482) 796214 Fax: (01482) 707650 E-mail: info.advertising@abnormal-loads.com

Access Shipping Ltd, Rainham House Rainham Trading Estate, New Road, Rainham, Essex, RM13 8RA Tel: (01708) 521113 Fax: (01708) 521151 E-mail: access-shipping@cnsmail.co.uk

Ace Freight, Penshaw Way, Portobello Industrial Estate, Birtley, Chester Le Street, County Durham, DH3 2SA Tel: 0191-410 5511 Fax: 0191-410 6344

J.R. Adams (Newcastle) Ltd, Hannington Works, Longrigg, Swalwell, Newcastle Upon Tyne, NE16 3AS Tel: 0191-488 7911 Fax: 0191-488 3101

Advance Despatch Ltd, Station Road Business Park, 1 Station Road, Auchtermuchty, Cupar, Fife, KY14 7DP Tel: (01337) 827333 Fax: (01337) 828080

▶ Advance Removals Ltd, 1 Station Road, Auchtermuchty, Cupar, Fife, KY14 7DP Tel: (0800) 7819397 E-mail: sales@advancedremovals.co.uk

▶ Agribulk Ltd, Milner Road, Chilton Road Industrial Estate, Sudbury, Suffolk, CO10 2XG Tel: (01787) 375533 Fax: (01787) 374004

▶ Ainsworth & Martin Preston Ltd, Crossley House, Leyland Road, Penwortham, Preston, PR1 9QP Tel: (01772) 744396 Fax: (01772) 744461

Air Cargo Transport Ltd, 4 Ladygate, Diseworth, Derby, DE74 2QF Tel: (01332) 811464 Fax: (01332) 812223 E-mail: admin@air-cargo.uk.com

▶ Alan Price & Sons (Bargoed) Ltd, End-Y-Deri, Deri, Bargoed, Mid Glamorgan, CF81 9JA Tel: (01443) 831639

▶ Alberti Ltd, Allenbrook Road, Rosehill Industrial Estate, Carlisle, CA1 2UT Tel: (01228) 533965 Fax: (01228) 514983

▶ Alexander Removals Ltd, 7 Nobel Road, West Gourdie Industrial Estate, Dundee, DD2 4UH Tel: (01382) 401403 Fax: (01382) 401402

Alf Arrowsmith & Son Ltd, Church View, Cheswardine, Market Drayton, Shropshire, TF9 2RW Tel: (01630) 661208 Fax: (01630) 661334

Alfreton Transport, Wimsey Way, Somercotes, Alfreton, Derbyshire, DE55 4LS Tel: (01773) 604347 Fax: (01773) 603834

▶ Allegro Transport Ltd, Birchwood Way, Somercotes, Alfreton, Derbyshire, DE55 4QQ Tel: (01773) 541771 Fax: (01773) 541774

▶ Allelys Heavy Haulage Ltd, The Slough, Studley, Warwickshire, B80 7EN Tel: (01527) 852408 Fax: (01527) 857623 E-mail: enquiries@allelys.co.uk

▶ Allelys Heavy Haulage Ltd, The Slough, Studley, Warwickshire, B80 7EN Tel: (01527) 852408 Fax: (01527) 857623

▶ Allens Stourbridge Transport Ltd, 4 Old Wharf Road, Stourbridge, West Midlands, DY8 4LS Tel: (01384) 370721 Fax: (01384) 371741

▶ Allied Transport Scotland Ltd, 120 Springhill Parkway, Glasgow Business Park, Baillieston, Glasgow, G69 6GA Tel: 0141-781 9414

▶ Allport Ltd, 7-8 Nurseries Road, Baillieston, Glasgow, G69 6UL Tel: 0141-773 2266 Fax: 0141-773 3044

▶ Amtrak Express Parcels, Craigshaw Road, West Tullos Industrial Estate, Aberdeen, AB12 3AR Tel: (01224) 894927 Fax: (01224) 879864

▶ Amtrak Express Parcels, 1 Barrs Fold Road, Wingates Industrial Estate, Westhoughton, Bolton, BL5 3XW Tel: (01942) 811542 Fax: (01942) 842036

▶ Amtrak Express Parcels, Unit A3 Mid Craigie Trading Estate, Mid Craigie Road, Dundee, DD4 7RH Tel: (0870) 8110619 Fax: (01382) 458855

▶ Amtrak Express Parcels, Waleswood House Aldred Close, Norwood Industrial Estate, Killamarsh, Sheffield, S21 2JH Tel: 0114-247 2049 Fax: 0114-247 2831

▶ Anc Birmingham, 99 Amington Road, Birmingham, B25 8EP Tel: 0121-708 4444 Fax: 0121-708 4433

Anderson Haulage Ltd, 85 Channing Street, Belfast, BT5 5GP Tel: (028) 9045 1771 Fax: (028) 9073 9047 E-mail: andersonhaulage@btconnect.com

▶ Anderson Moves, 45 Maclellan Street, Glasgow, G41 1RR Tel: 0141-419 7070 Fax: 0141-427 9994

▶ Anglo Overseas Ltd, 1 Ennis Close, Roundthorn Industrial Estate, Manchester, M23 9LE Tel: 0161-945 3333 Fax: 0161-998 2181 E-mail: admin@anglooverseas.com

▶ Anglotan Ltd, 47 Cricket Inn Crescent, Sheffield, S2 5AQ Tel: 0114-272 9220 Fax: 0114-272 9220 E-mail: transport@anglotan.com

▶ Angus Removals, Peasie Hill, Elliot Industrial Estate, Arbroath, Angus, DD11 2NJ Tel: (01241) 871711

▶ Anstey Transport Services, London Warehouse, Chittening Industrial Estate, Chittening, Bristol, BS11 0YB Tel: 0117-982 3111 Fax: 0117-982 5111

▶ Answer Transport Express Ltd, Strothers Road, High Spen, Rowlands Gill, Tyne & Wear, NE39 2EX Tel: (01207) 544111

▶ Ants Removals & Storage, 60a Milmead Industrial Centre, Mill Mead Road, London, N17 9QU Tel: (020) 8880 9190 Fax: (020) 8880 3131

▶ Aodh Hannon, 21 Brankinstown Road, Aghalee, Craigavon, County Armagh, BT67 0DF Tel: (028) 9265 1441 Fax: (028) 9265 1995 E-mail: sales@hannon.transport.co.uk

Arbuckle Smith & Co., 106 Abercorn Street, Paisley, Renfrewshire, PA3 4AY Tel: (0141) 887 5252 Fax: (0141) 887 4461 E-mail: craig_hodgson@zieglergroup.com

Arch Services, Bodymoor Green Farm, Coventry Road, Kingsbury, Tamworth, Staffordshire, B78 2DZ Tel: (01827) 875558 Fax: (01827) 875539

Archbold Logistics Ltd, Albert Road, Morley, Leeds, LS27 8TT Tel: 0113-252 2333 Fax: 0113-252 7915 E-mail: enq@archbold.co.uk

Arr Craibs, Howe Moss Drive, Dyce, Aberdeen, AB21 0GL Tel: (01224) 771122 Fax: (01224) 724461 E-mail: info@arr-craib.co.uk

▶ Arran Deliveries, Dock Road, Ardrossan, Ayrshire, KA22 8DA Tel: (01294) 469492

▶ Arran Haulage Services Ltd, The Home Farm, Brodick, Isle of Arran, KA27 8DD Tel: (01770) 302777 Fax: (01770) 302500

▶ Arrowpak International, 11 Crompton Road, Hadleigh Road Industrial Estat, Ipswich, IP2 0UQ Tel: (01473) 210459 Fax: (01473) 210458

▶ Art Logistics Ltd, 1 Victoria Industrial Estate, Victoria Road, London, W3 6UU Tel: (020) 8993 8811 Fax: (020) 8993 8833

▶ Asda Distribution Centre, Westmains Industrial Estate, Grangemouth, Stirlingshire, FK3 8YE Tel: (01324) 492102 Fax: (01324) 492025

▶ Ashworth Preece Logistics, 7 Memorial Road, Walkden, Manchester, M28 3AQ Tel: (0870) 350 1246 Fax: (0870) 350 1248

Astons Of Dudley Ltd, Shaw Road, Dudley, West Midlands, DY2 8TP Tel: (01384) 456836 Fax: (01384) 211953

▶ Austin Wilkinson Ltd, Coal Pit Lane, Atherton, Manchester, M46 0RY Tel: (01942) 887000 Fax: (01942) 888222

▶ Auto Carriers, Oxford Road, Ryton on Dunsmore, Coventry, CV8 3EF Tel: (024) 7651 1167 Fax: (024) 7663 9661

▶ Autocare Distribution Ltd, Carrington Power Station, Manchester Road, Carrington, Manchester, M31 4AX Tel: 0161-775 7576 Fax: 0161-775 7556

▶ Autopoint, Bramshall Industrial Estate, Bramshall, Uttoxeter, Staffordshire, ST14 8TD Tel: (01889) 566605 Fax: (01889) 566684

Avery's Garage & Transport Services Ltd, Grovebury Road, Leighton Buzzard, Bedfordshire, LU7 4SQ Tel: (01525) 373385 Fax: (01525) 371900

B B Christorfersen, Crimond Airfield, Crimond, Fraserburgh, Aberdeenshire, AB43 8QQ Tel: (01346) 532686 Fax: (01346) 532294

▶ B B S Transport Ltd, 26 Bayton Road, Exhall, Coventry, CV7 9EJ Tel: (024) 7664 5666

▶ B Harper, North Road, Insch, Aberdeenshire, AB52 6XP Tel: (01464) 820011 Fax: (01464) 821145

▶ B J Express Ltd, 106 Abercorn Street, Paisley, Renfrewshire, PA3 4AY Tel: 0141-887 1429 Fax: 0141-887 3467

▶ B L Penwarden Haulage, Chalk Pit, College Road, Epsom, Surrey, KT17 4JA Tel: (01372) 749977 Fax: (01372) 739284

▶ B Mullen & Sons Ltd, Crookston, Musselburgh, Midlothian, EH21 8QF Tel: 0131-665 2335

▶ B Proudfoot, 151 Balmoral Street, Glasgow, G14 0HB Tel: 0141-959 4555

▶ B T S Haulage Ltd, Manchester Road, Carrington, Manchester, M31 4BD Tel: 0161-775 5277 Fax: 0161-777 9267 E-mail: admin@btshaulage.co.uk

▶ B Thompson & Sons Ltd, Station Road, Moretonhampstead, Newton Abbot, Devon, TQ13 8NQ Tel: (01647) 440505 Fax: (01647) 440507

B Vaughan & Partners, 14 Northbourne Avenue, Shanklin, Isle of Wight, PO37 7LT Tel: (01983) 864175 E-mail: mark.harrison@tiscali.co.uk

▶ Bacton Transport Services Ltd, Tomo Industrial Estate, Creeting Road, Stowmarket, Suffolk, IP14 5AY Tel: (01449) 618210 Fax: (01449) 676406 E-mail: haulage@bacton.co.uk

Allan Badman Transport Ltd, Bamfield House, Bristol, BS14 0XD Tel: (01275) 839417 Fax: (01275) 839375 E-mail: enquiries@badmantransport.co.uk

▶ Bailey Taylor Haulage Ltd, Winter Closes, Underwood, Nottingham, NG16 5GR Tel: (01773) 530339 Fax: (01773) 530528

N. & J. Bailey Transport, Canal Lane, Tunstall, Stoke-on-Trent, ST6 4PA Tel: (01782) 575740 Fax: (01782) 837096

Baird Lends A Hand Ltd, 75 Beardmore Way, Clydebank, Dunbartonshire, G81 4HT Tel: 0141-952 0962 Fax: 0141-941 2205 E-mail: jb@baird-uk.com

H. Baker (Haulage) Ltd, Florence Street, Leeds Road, Bradford, West Yorkshire, BD3 8EX Tel: (01274) 664249 Fax: (01274) 668224 E-mail: julie.todd@btconnect.com

▶ Barbour European Ltd, Craig Leith Road, Springkerse Industrial Estate, Stirling, FK7 7BA Tel: (07764) 162640

▶ Barclay Bros Ltd, Station Road, Methil, Leven, Fife, KY8 3HA Tel: (01333) 422955 Fax: (01333) 422966

▶ Barnstaple Removals, 14-15 Tree Beech Rural Estate, Goodleigh, Barnstaple, Devon, EX32 7NZ Tel: (01271) 831164 Fax: (01271) 831165

▶ Barr Ltd, Brayhead, Barrhill, Girvan, Ayrshire, KA26 0QR Tel: (01465) 821300

▶ Barry Ives Haulage Ltd, Rippers Court, Sible Hedingham, Halstead, Essex, CO9 3PY Tel: (01787) 462111 Fax: (01787) 462178

Bartrums Haulage & Storage Ltd, Langton Green, Eye, Suffolk, IP23 7HN Tel: (01379) 870693 Fax: (01379) 870942 E-mail: info@bartrums.com

▶ Bartrum's Road Services Ltd, 57 Victoria Road, Diss, Norfolk, IP22 4JD Tel: (01379) 642384

▶ Baylis Distribution Ltd, Dealain House 72 Napier Road, Wardpark North, Cumbernauld, Glasgow, G68 0DF Tel: (01236) 736510 Fax: (01236) 736525 E-mail: admin@bayliss.co.uk

Baylis Distribution Ltd, New Potter Grange Road, Goole, North Humberside, DN14 6BZ Tel: (01405) 766174 Fax: (01405) 766270

Baylis Distribution Ltd, Billington Road, Leighton Buzzard, Bedfordshire, LU7 9HH Tel: (01525) 375550 Fax: (01525) 850149 E-mail: email@baylislogistics.com

Baylis Distribution Ltd, Hamilton House, Birchwood Lane, Moore, Warrington, WA4 6XJ Tel: (01925) 656770 Fax: (01925) 571049

Baylis Logistics Ltd, Unit 11, Pucklechurch Trading Estate, Pucklechurch, Bristol, BS16 9QH Tel: 0117-937 2580 Fax: 0117-937 4161

▶ Baynes & Son Ltd, Unit 16 Llandygai Industrial Estate, Llandygai, Bangor, Gwynedd, LL57 4YH Tel: (01248) 353533 Fax: (01248) 361144

▶ Beanacre Enterprises Ltd, Juliet Way, Aveley, South Ockendon, Essex, RM15 4YD Tel: (01708) 864231 Fax: (01708) 862327

Belcher Cammack Transport Ltd, Norton Way, Moss Lane Industrial Estate, Sandbach, Cheshire, CW11 3YT Tel: (01270) 750992 Fax: (01270) 762882

S.A. Bell Ltd, The Old Spital Beck, Barton Hill, York, YO60 7JX Tel: (01653) 618578 Fax: (01653) 618824

▶ Ben Mundell, Bardaravine, Tarbert, Argyll, PA29 6YF Tel: (01880) 820223 Fax: (01880) 820491

▶ Ben Transport Services, Centurion House, Leyland Business Park, Farington, Leyland, PR25 3GR Tel: (01772) 459909 Fax: (01772) 459899

▶ Bergen Transport Ltd, Mellors Road, New Bridge, Trafford Park, Manchester, M17 1PB Tel: 0161-873 0300 Fax: 0161-872 4379 E-mail: sales@bergen.co.uk

▶ Bestway Nottingham Ltd, 5 Chestnut Drive, Broadmeadows, South Normanton, Alfreton, Derbyshire, DE55 3AH Tel: (01773) 860844

Betchworth International Heavy Transport, Old Reigate Road, Betchworth, Surrey, RH3 7LW Tel: (0870) 1671671 Fax: (0870) 1671672

▶ BFS Transport Ltd, Dove Court, West Lane, Sykehouse, Goole, North Humberside, DN14 9BD Tel: (01405) 785373 Fax: (01405) 785249

Bibby Distribution Ltd, 3 West Bank Road, Belfast, BT3 9JL Tel: (028) 9077 3997 Fax: (028) 9077 3117

Bibby Distributions Ltd, 105 Duke St, Liverpool, L1 5JQ Tel: 0151-708 8000 Fax: 0151-794 1001 E-mail: iain.speak@bibbydist.co.uk

▶ Bibby Logistics Ltd, P9 Parklands, Heywood Distribution Park, Heywood, Lancashire, OL10 2TT Tel: (01706) 620222 Fax: (01706) 367107

▶ Billy Walker, Shandonan, The Belts, Turriff, Aberdeenshire, AB53 5PN Tel: (01888) 562738

▶ Bingham Transport Ltd, Woodkirk International Freight, Terminal, Quarry Lane, Dewsbury, West Yorkshire, WF12 7JJ Tel: (01924) 423655

Birds Groupage Services Ltd, Tat Bank Road, Oldbury, West Midlands, B69 4NQ Tel: 0121-543 6400 Fax: 0121-544 4928 E-mail: ken@birds.co.uk

▶ Bishops Move Ltd, Unit 12 Moor La Trading Estate, Sherburn in Elmet, Leeds, LS25 6ES Tel: (01977) 680061 Fax: (01977) 680063

▶ Bishops Move Aberdeen, Howe Moss Terrace, Kirkhill Industrial Estate, Dyce, Aberdeen, AB21 0GR Tel: (0800) 1696126 Fax: (01224) 729722

▶ Bishops Waltham Removals, 33 Claylands Road, Bishops Waltham, Bishops Waltham, Southampton, SO32 1BH Tel: (07802) 824547 Fax: (01489) 895387

▶ Black Lion, Unit 14 Mayfield Avenue Industrial Park, Fyfield Road, Weyhill, Andover, Hampshire, SP11 8HU Tel: (01264) 771199 Fax: (01264) 773993

▶ Black Van Removals, Unit 5a-5b Ribbleton La Trading Estate, Crook Street, Preston, PR1 5LS Tel: (01772) 794160 Fax: (01772) 702540

W. Bloy & Son, King Edward Street, Grimsby, North East Lincolnshire, DN31 3JP Tel: (01472) 354069 Fax: (01472) 354069

▶ Blue Team, 6 Eton Garages, Lambolle Place, London, NW3 4PE Tel: (020) 7794 3777 Fax: (020) 7794 4651

▶ Blueline Hire, Sellwood Court Enterprise Park, Sleaford, Lincolnshire, NG34 8GJ Tel: (01529) 300233

▶ Bodelwyddan Cold Stores Ltd, Royal Welsh Avenue, Kinmel Park, Bodelwyddan, Rhyl, Clwyd, LL18 5TY Tel: (01745) 582966

▶ Bogyoch Transport Co. Ltd, Fortrie Cottage, Fortrie, Turriff, Aberdeenshire, AB53 4HG Tel: (01466) 730310 Fax: (01466) 730347

▶ Bond Trucking Co, The Old Brickyard, Ashton Keynes, Swindon, SN6 6QR Tel: (01285) 861875 Fax: (01285) 861875

▶ Bondelivery, Dundrod Road, Nutts Corner, Crumlin, County Antrim, BT29 4SR Tel: (028) 9082 5151 Fax: (028) 9082 5296

▶ Bookspeed, 16 Salamander Yards, Edinburgh, EH6 7DD Tel: 0131-467 8100 Fax: 0131-467 8008

▶ Bootham Removals & Storage, Compass House, Common Road, Dunnington, York, YO19 5PD Tel: (0500) 011355 Fax: (01904) 488519

▶ Border Traffic Service Ltd, Border View, Norham, Berwick-upon-Tweed, TD15 2JZ Tel: (01289) 382400 Fax: (01289) 382312

▶ Boston Freight Services Ltd, St. Johns Road, Boston, Lincolnshire, PE21 6HG Tel: (01205) 311666 Fax: (01205) 310471 E-mail: judybarnes@rsboston.com

Boswell Bros (Salisbury) Ltd, Ford, Salisbury, SP4 6DJ Tel: (01722) 333781 Fax: (01722) 327858 E-mail: boswell.broth@virgin.net

▶ Boughey Distribution Ltd, Wardle Industrial Estate, Wardle, Nantwich, Cheshire, CW5 6RS Tel: (01829) 260704

▶ The Bow Group, 2274 Dunbeath Road, Elgin, Swindon, SN2 6EA Tel: (01793) 651000

Bower Green Ltd, Dryden Street, Bradford, West Yorkshire, BD1 5ND Tel: (01274) 733537 Fax: (01274) 393511 E-mail: info@bowergreen.co.uk

▶ Boyle Transport Ltd, Block F, Porterfield Road, Renfrew, PA4 8DJ Tel: 0141-886 6000

▶ Bramwells, 14 Nelson Avenue, St. Albans, Hertfordshire, AL1 5RY Tel: (01727) 860703 Fax: (01727) 860703 E-mail: bramwells@hotmail.com

David Bratt & Sons (Haulage) Ltd, 102 Grove Lane, Cheadle Hulme, Cheadle, Cheshire, SK8 7ND Tel: 0161-439 8124 Fax: 0161-439 9002

▶ Breeze Mount Transport, Topcliffe Lane, Tingley, Wakefield, West Yorkshire, WF3 1SP Tel: 0113-218 9541 Fax: 0113-218 9541

Bretts Transport Ltd, Thorney Road, Guyhirn, Wisbech, Cambridgeshire, PE13 4AG Tel: (01733) 849245 Fax: (01733) 849363

▶ Brewer & Turnbull Ltd, The Royal Hall, 40 Arthurstone Terrace, Dundee, DD4 6QT Tel: (01382) 226437

▶ Brian Burgess, 18 Fairway Drive, Greenford, Middlesex, UB6 8PW Tel: (020) 8578 7233 Fax: (020) 8578 7180

Brian Harris Ltd, Pottery Road, Bovey Tracey, Newton Abbot, Devon, TQ13 9DS Tel: (01626) 833371 Fax: (01626) 834680

▶ Bridgnorth Transport Co. Ltd, Stourbridge Road, Bridgnorth, Shropshire, WV15 6AN Tel: (01746) 762681 Fax: (01746) 765152

Malcolm Bright Haulage, 18 Castlefields Industrial Estate, Bingley, West Yorkshire, BD16 2AG Tel: (01274) 561994 Fax: (01274) 566665

▶ Brighton & Hove Removals, 190 Portland Road, Hove, East Sussex, BN3 5QN Tel: (01273) 735111

Britannia Greer's of Elgin Ltd, The Depository, Edgar Road, Elgin, Morayshire, IV30 6YQ Tel: (01343) 542229

▶ Britannia Movers Of Edinburgh, 26 Bath Road, Edinburgh, EH6 7JU Tel: 0131-553 4374 Fax: 0131-554 9357

▶ Britannia Tusons (Waltham Cross) Ltd, Marsh Lane, Ware, Hertfordshire, SG12 9QN Tel: (01920) 461616

British Airways Cargo, Cargo Centre, Belfast Int Airport, Belfast, BT29 4AA Tel: (028) 9442 2731 Fax: (028) 9445 2570 E-mail: belfast@baregionalcargo.com

▶ indicates data change since last edition

ROAD TRANSPORT AND HAULAGE
– continued

▶ Brittains Removals, Alington Road, Eynesbury St Neots, St. Neots, Cambridgeshire, PE19 6YH Tel: (01480) 405161 E-mail: admin@brittainsremovals.co.uk
▶ Broadleaze Transport, Noahs Cottage, Cricklade, Swindon, SN6 6HU Tel: (01793) 751129 Fax: (01793) 750022
▶ Brocks Haulage Ltd, Beacon Hill Industrial Estate, Botany Way, Purfleet, Essex, RM19 1SR Tel: (01708) 861021 Fax: (01708) 864224
▶ Brodie Group Of Companies, Bathville Business Park, Armadale, Bathgate, West Lothian, EH48 2JS Tel: (01501) 733667
Brogan Fuels, Nethan Street, Motherwell, Lanarkshire, ML1 3TF Tel: (01698) 265132 Fax: (01698) 262547
▶ Brooks Haulage Ltd, Apy Hills Lane, Tickhill, Doncaster, South Yorkshire, DN11 9PD Tel: (01302) 742999
▶ Brora Transport Ltd, West End Garage, Brora, Sutherland, KW9 6NY Tel: (01408) 621223
▶ Brown & Illingworth, Ford 5 5 Hoults Estate, Walker Road, Newcastle upon Tyne, NE6 1AB Tel: 0191-265 3860 Fax: 0191-265 3860
T.H. Brown Ltd, Estate Road No. 1, South Humberside Industal Estate, Grimsby, North East Lincolnshire, DN31 2TA Tel: (01472) 362603 Fax: (01472) 360112 E-mail: admin@thbrown.co.uk
▶ Brunels Removal Services Ltd, 4 Crown Industrial Estate, Crown Road, Warmley, Bristol, BS30 8JB Tel: 0117-907 7855 Fax: 0117-907 7856E-mail: info@brunel.co.uk
▶ Bryan's Ltd, Gorhuish, Northlew, Okehampton, Devon, EX20 3BU Tel: (01837) 810501 Fax: (01837) 810705
▶ Bulk Food Transport Ltd, Crossway Farm, Thurlton, Norwich, NR14 6NZ Tel: (01508) 548338
▶ Bullet Express, 5 Ashley Drive, Bothwell, Glasgow, G71 8BS Tel: (01698) 811777 Fax: (01698) 811222 E-mail: info@bulletexpress.co.uk
Bulmers Logistics (Malton) Ltd, Eston Road, Lazenby, Middlesbrough, Cleveland, TS6 8DR Tel: (01642) 462608 Fax: (01642) 462932
Burgoynes Lyonshall Ltd, Lyonshall, Kington, Herefordshire, HR5 3JR Tel: (01544) 340283 Fax: (01544) 340228 E-mail: enquiries@burgoynes-lyonshall.co.uk
▶ Burke Bros, Foxs Lane, Wolverhampton, WV1 1PA Tel: (01902) 714555 Fax: (01902) 427837
▶ Burns Express Freight Ltd, 4 Fulbar Road, Paisley, Renfrewshire, PA2 9AP Tel: 0141-848 0555
▶ Burrpark Ltd, Imperial Dock, Edinburgh, EH6 7DT Tel: 0131-553 1188 Fax: 0131-554 5111
▶ Business Express, Unit 2, Hareness Park, Hareness Circle, Altens Industrial Estate, Aberdeen, AB12 3QY Tel: (01224) 879038
▶ Business Moves Ltd, Offco House, Town Street, Stanningley, Pudsey, West Yorkshire, LS28 6HQ Tel: 0113-236 0136 Fax: 0113-236 0185
▶ Business Moves, Unit 5 The Three Sisters Enterprise Park, Antler Court, Ashton-In-Makerfield, Wigan, Lancashire, WN4 8DU Tel: (01942) 724167 Fax: (01942) 724440
▶ Business Post Ltd, 6 Block 1, Hareness Road, Altens Industrial Estate, Aberdeen, AB12 3LE Tel: (01224) 248336 Fax: (01224) 248311
▶ Business Post Ltd, Unit B-C Ronald Close, Woburn Road Industrial Estate, Kempston, Bedford, MK42 7SH Tel: (01234) 840088 Fax: (01234) 853918
▶ Business Post Ltd, Unit 23 Nelson Way, Camberley, Surrey, GU15 3DH Tel: (01276) 686757 Fax: (01276) 686558
▶ Business Post Ltd, 11 Crystal Way, Harrow, Middlesex, HA1 2BJ Tel: (020) 8861 1599 Fax: (020) 8424 0708
▶ Business Post Ltd, Arden Grange, London Road, Albourne, Hassocks, West Sussex, BN6 9BJ Tel: (01273) 831832 Fax: (01273) 835301
▶ Business Post Ltd, Gillsleigh Villas, Gills Green, Cranbrook Road, Hawkhurst, Kent, TN18 5ES Tel: (01580) 754499 Fax: (01580) 754400
▶ Business Post Ltd, Access Point, Eastman Way, Hemel Hempstead Industrial Estate, Hemel Hempstead, Hertfordshire, HP2 7DU Tel: (01442) 439700 Fax: (01442) 261167
▶ Business Post Ltd, 73 St James Mill Road, St James Business Park, Northampton, NN5 5JP Tel: (01604) 592929 Fax: (01604) 592930
Business Post Ltd, 14 The Midway, Nottingham, NG7 2TS Tel: 0115-986 1086 Fax: 0115-986 1102
John Butlin Ltd, Arthur Road, Yardley, Birmingham, B25 8HA Tel: 0121-772 0313 Fax: 0121-773 4383 E-mail: john.butlin@virgin.net
▶ C B Morgan Farmers King's Somborne Ltd, Shaftesbury, Shaftesbury, Dorset, SP7 9HD Tel: (01747) 851003
▶ C & C James, Stowford Barton, Halwill, Beaworthy, Devon, EX21 5UN Tel: (01409) 221632 Fax: (01409) 221993
▶ C C Jessop Haulage Co. Ltd, North Side, King George Dock, Hull, HU9 5PR Tel: (01482) 796135
▶ C D S Transport Ltd, Craigshaw Drive, West Tullos Industrial Estate, Aberdeen, AB12 3BE Tel: (01224) 872828
▶ C & D Transport Ltd, 9 New Line Industrial Estate, The Sidings, Bacup, Lancashire, OL13 9RW Tel: (01706) 870333
▶ C Fare Products, 7e Glengallan Road, Oban, Argyll, PA34 4HG Tel: (01631) 565569 Fax: (01631) 566558
▶ C & G Brewster, Lanark House, Kirriemuir, Angus, DD8 5QF Tel: (01307) 466166 Fax: (01307) 468800
C H Bennett & Son, Plasheulwen, Llanfair Road, Newtown, Powys, SY16 3JY Tel: (01686) 626872 Fax: (01686) 621479 E-mail: chbennett@virgin.net
C & H Hauliers, Broker House, Tilbury, Essex, RM18 7EH Tel: (01375) 842683 Fax: (01375) 847095 E-mail: cnh.hauliers@btinternet.com
C Herring & Son Ltd, Windermere Road, Hartlepool, Cleveland, TS25 1NX Tel: (01429) 221104 Fax: (01429) 861989 E-mail: gareth@cherring.co.uk
▶ C I S Industrial Storage Ltd, Owler Lane, Birstall, Batley, West Yorkshire, WF17 9BW Tel: (01924) 443290
▶ C J Burgess & Son Ltd, The Old Mutton House, Bodiam, Robertsbridge, East Sussex, TN32 5UP Tel: (01580) 830888 Fax: (01580) 830284
▶ C J Express, Unit 6, Spedition House, Holme Industrial Estate, York, YO43 4BB Tel: (01430) 861450
▶ C K T Express, Sandybank Garage, Bacup Road, Rossendale, Lancashire, BB4 7JE Tel: (01706) 230666
▶ C L Transport, Unit 22 Wireworks Estate, Bristol Road, Bridgwater, Somerset, TA6 4AP Tel: (01278) 439062 Fax: (01278) 447194
▶ C M Lane Distribution Services Ltd, Unit A, Monarch Courtyard 11 Salthouse Road, Brackmills Industrial Estate, Northampton, NN4 7BD Tel: (01604) 587781 Fax: (01604) 826030 E-mail: sales@cmlane.co.uk
C M Shaw Ltd, Clarence Row, Stockton-on-Tees, Cleveland, TS18 2HD Tel: (01642) 606668 Fax: (01642) 617845 E-mail: cmshaw@stkn.freeserve.co.uk
▶ C Mccullam & Son Transport Ltd, Chapel Street, Stalybridge, Cheshire, SK15 2AW Tel: 0161-338 4616 Fax: 0161-338 4616
C & N Transport Services Ltd, Coundon Industrial Estate, Coundon, Bishop Auckland, County Durham, DL14 8NR Tel: (01388) 664500 Fax: (01388) 664550 E-mail: cntransport@btconnect.com
C S Ellis Group Ltd, Wireless Hill Ind Estate, South Luffenham, Oakham, Leicestershire, LE15 8NF Tel: (01780) 720133 Fax: (01780) 721801 E-mail: mail@csellis.co.uk
▶ C Shearer, Kilmaurs Road, Fenwick, Kilmarnock, Ayrshire, KA3 6AX Tel: (01560) 600552 Fax: (01560) 600670
C Sparks & Sons Ltd, Wells Road, Glastonbury, Somerset, BA6 9AG Tel: (01458) 831742 Fax: (01458) 835078 E-mail: info@sparkstransport.co.uk
▶ C T Transport Castleford Ltd, Carr Wood Industrial Estate, Carr Wood Road, Castleford, West Yorkshire, WF10 4SB Tel: (01977) 557817 Fax: (01977) 557817
▶ C W Bolton, Uplands Farm, Highstreet Road, Hernhill, Faversham, Kent, ME13 9EJ Tel: (01227) 752207 Fax: (01227) 751281
▶ C W & M A Evans Ltd, Everite Road, Widnes, Cheshire, WA8 8PT Tel: 0151-423 2771
▶ C Winfield, Smestow Bridge Industrial Estate, Bridgnorth Road, Wombourne, Wolverhampton, WV5 8AY Tel: (01902) 896666 Fax: (01902) 326611
▶ C & Y Transport, Lockerbie Road, Dumfries, DG1 3PG Tel: (01387) 259800 Fax: (01387) 259800
▶ Calderdale Distribution Ltd, Unit 3A Royds Mill, Royd Business Park, Dye House Lane, Brighouse, West Yorkshire, HD6 1LL Tel: (01484) 722011
▶ Caledonian Logistics Ltd, Weatherford House, Lawson Drive, Dyce, Aberdeen, AB21 0DR Tel: (01224) 723905 Fax: (01224) 725253
Canute Haulage Company Ltd, Gamston Airfield, Retford, Nottinghamshire, DN22 0QL Tel: (01777) 833300 Fax: (01777) 838880 E-mail: traffic@canutegroup.com
Capper Fuels, 124 Tamnamore Road, Dungannon, County Tyrone, BT71 6HW Tel: (028) 8772 6888 Fax: (028) 8772 7276 E-mail: info@cappertrading.com
▶ Carberry Haulage, Colesleigh House, Bury Road, Stanton, Bury St. Edmunds, Suffolk, IP31 2BZ Tel: (01359) 252212 Fax: (01359) 252220
▶ Careful Co., Burnfield House, 4 Burnfield Avenue, Thornliebank, Glasgow, G46 7TL Tel: 0141-637 1010 Fax: 0141-637 1010
▶ Carl J Brogan, Martindale, Cannock, Staffordshire, WS11 7XN Tel: (01543) 505001 Fax: (01543) 579406
▶ Carlson Vehicle Transfer, Bradfield Road, Wix, Manningtree, Essex, CO11 2SP Tel: (01255) 871600 Fax: (01255) 871606
▶ Carntyne Transport Co. Ltd, 440 Petershill Road, Glasgow, G21 4AA Tel: 0141-557 1199 Fax: 0141-557 2272
▶ Carry Gently Ltd, 7 The Brook Trading Estate, Deadbrook Lane, Aldershot, Hampshire, GU12 4XB Tel: (01252) 318841 Fax: (01252) 311066 E-mail: ops@carry-gently.co.uk
▶ Cassels Transport Ltd, Rollestone Crossroads, Shrewton, Salisbury, SP3 4DS Tel: (01980) 621701
▶ Castledene Motor Co. Ltd, Mill Hall, Aylesford, Kent, ME20 7JN Tel: (01622) 710717 Fax: (01622) 792828 E-mail: sales@castledenetransport.co.uk
▶ Ceva Automotive Logistics UK Ltd, Hawleys Lane, Warrington, WA2 8JR Tel: (01925) 652277 Fax: (01925) 231215
▶ Ceva News Fast, Earn Avenue, Righead Industrial Estate, Bellshill, Lanarkshire, ML4 3LW Tel: (01698) 844737 Fax: (01698) 740862 E-mail: sales@newsfast.co.uk
Chamberlain Transport Ltd, Duchy Road, Crewe, CW1 6NB Tel: (01270) 502800 Fax: (01270) 502809 E-mail: sales@palletforce.com
▶ Charles Footman, Alltwalis Road, Pontarsais, Carmarthen, Dyfed, SA32 7DU Tel: (01267) 253443 Fax: (01267) 253545
▶ Charles Hewitt Ltd, Merton Farm, Merton Lane, Canterbury, Kent, CT4 7BA Tel: (01227) 464386
▶ Charles Russell International Ltd, Walton Hill Farm, Tewkesbury Road, Gloucester, GL19 4BN Tel: (01242) 680678 Fax: (01242) 680078
Charles W Michie Ltd, 54 Park Road, Aberdeen, AB24 5PA Tel: (01224) 632281 Fax: (01224) 649012E-mail: carolyn@michietransport.co.uk
▶ Charlwood Ltd, Old Park, Whitfield, Dover, Kent, CT16 2HQ Tel: (01304) 822411 Fax: (01304) 822401
▶ Cherwell Logistics Ltd, The Freight Terminal, Bicester Road, Enstone, Chipping Norton, Oxfordshire, OX7 4NP Tel: (01608) 677112 Fax: (01608) 677162 E-mail: info@cherwell-logistics.com
▶ Chestminster Ltd, Bridgefields, Welwyn Garden City, Hertfordshire, AL7 1RX Tel: (01707) 391390 Fax: (01707) 391394
Frank Chivers & Son, 1 Estcourt Street, Devizes, Wiltshire, SN10 1LQ Tel: (01380) 723411 Fax: (01380) 728078
Chris Bennett Heavy Haulage Ltd, Arden Hall, Castle Hill, Bredbury, Stockport, Cheshire, SK6 2RY Tel: 0161-406 8466 Fax: 0161-406 8335 E-mail: sales@chrisbennett.co.uk
▶ Chris Hayter Transport Ltd, Northwood Road, Witney, Oxfordshire, OX29 7HB Tel: (01993) 771551 Fax: (01993) 773139
▶ Chris Precious Ltd, Fox Lane, Wakefield, West Yorkshire, WF1 2AJ Tel: (01924) 382500 Fax: (01924) 382037
▶ Chris Wright Road Planning Ltd, Hollins Hill, Baildon, Shipley, West Yorkshire, BD17 7QB Tel: (01274) 533905 Fax: (01274) 530045
▶ Christian Salvesen plc, Regional Distribution Centre, Melford Road, Righead Industrial Estate, Bellshill, Lanarkshire, ML4 3QD Tel: (01698) 844050 Fax: (01698) 842845
▶ Christian Salvesen plc, Flex Meadow, Harlow, Essex, CM19 5TX Tel: (01279) 626444 Fax: (01279) 441291
▶ Christian Salvesen plc, 2 Roundhead Road, Heathfield Industrial Estate, Newton Abbot, Devon, TQ12 6UE Tel: (01626) 835560 Fax: (01626) 835540 E-mail: info@salversan.co.uk
▶ Christian Salvesen plc, Beaufort House Beaufort Court, Sir Thomas Longley Road, Medway City Estate, Rochester, Kent, ME2 4FB Tel: (01634) 731700 Fax: (01634) 731748
▶ Christian Salvessen Industrial Division, Swift House, Lodge Way Industrial Estate, Duston, Northampton, NN5 7TU Tel: (01604) 759900 Fax: (01604) 590323
Christian Salvessen Industrial Division, Swift House, Lodge Way Industrial Estate, Duston, Northampton, NN5 7TU Tel: (01604) 759900 Fax: (01604) 584101 E-mail: sales@salvesen.com
▶ Clan Distribution, Seabegs Road, Bonnybridge, Stirlingshire, FK4 2BT Tel: (01324) 812914
▶ Clarendon Haulage Ltd, New Trees Garage, Myerscough Road, Mellor Brook, Blackburn, BB2 7LB Tel: (01254) 814997 Fax: (01254) 814049 E-mail: info@aaisecurity.co.uk
Clark Contracting, Brentford Grange Farm, Beaconsfield Road, Coleshill, Amersham, Buckinghamshire, HP7 0JU Tel: (01494) 431871 Fax: (01494) 431872 E-mail: sales@clark-contracting.co.uk
▶ Clark & Rose, Barclayhill Place, Portlethen, Aberdeen, AB12 4LH Tel: (0845) 2301906 Fax: (01224) 782822
▶ Clayton Transport D A Ltd, Granville Way, Bicester, Oxfordshire, OX26 4JT Tel: (01869) 253897 Fax: (01869) 245666
Clearway Distribution, Triumph Road, Nottingham, NG7 2GA Tel: 0115-924 8484 Fax: 0115-942 3148
▶ Clockwork Removals & Storage, 38-40 West Harbour Road, Edinburgh, EH5 1PU Tel: 0131-551 5800 Fax: 0131-657 2624
Colin E J Bennett, Bridgend Works, Bridgend, Stonehouse, Gloucestershire, GL10 2BA Tel: (01453) 825090 Fax: (01453) 825868
Connexions Logistics, Link House, Bute Street, Stoke-on-Trent, ST4 3PR Tel: (01782) 339559 Fax: (01782) 339561
▶ Consolidated Carriers Ltd, 27 Burnside Place, Troon, Ayrshire, KA10 6LZ Tel: (01292) 310510 Fax: (01292) 310810 E-mail: sales@ccl-logistics.com
▶ Convoys Ltd, Wardley Industrial Estate, Holloway Drive, Worsley, Manchester, M28 2LA Tel: 0161-727 8323 Fax: 0161-794 4435
▶ Conway Bailey Transport, Goonearl, Scorrier, Redruth, Cornwall, TR16 5EB Tel: (01209) 820283 Fax: (01209) 820284
▶ Peter Cook Ltd, Wholeflats Road, Grangemouth, Stirlingshire, FK3 9UY Tel: (01324) 666089
Cool Chalis Ltd, 4 Tyne Road, Sandy, Bedfordshire, SG19 1SA Tel: (01767) 680930 Fax: (01767) 692053 E-mail: coolchalis@cs.com
Coombe Valley Transport Ltd, 16a Primrose Road, Dover, Kent, CT17 0JA Tel: (01304) 206498 Fax: (01304) 240059 E-mail: info@coombevalley.net
Cooper Buckley Ltd, Third Avenue, Crewe, CW1 6XU Tel: (01270) 251458 Fax: (01270) 251460
Paul Cooper Transport Ltd, Top House Farm, High Street, West Cowick, Goole, North Humberside, DN14 9EB Tel: (01405) 860330 Fax: (01405) 862604
▶ Co-Operative Retail Logistics, 5 Wardpark Road, Cumbernauld, Glasgow, G67 3HW Tel: (01236) 458568 Fax: (01236) 731609
▶ Corby Chilled Northern Ltd, Strutherhill Industrial Estate, Larkhall, Lanarkshire, ML9 2PD Tel: (01698) 889542
▶ Cosco, Unit C2 Zenith, Paycocke Road, Basildon, Essex, SS14 3DW Tel: (01268) 643000 Fax: (01268) 643019
▶ Coscom (U K) Ltd, Unit 1, Dooley Road, Felixstowe, Suffolk, IP11 3HG Tel: (01394) 675404 Fax: (01394) 675424
▶ Cotton Transport & Sons Ltd, Church Street, Church Gresley, Swadlincote, Derbyshire, DE11 9NR Tel: (01283) 213777 Fax: (01283) 550408
Coulling Brothers Ltd, Sandway Road, Sandway, Maidstone, Kent, ME17 2LX Tel: (01622) 858448 Fax: (01622) 850609 E-mail: mail@coullingbrothers.co.uk
▶ Cowern Transport, Unit 1-2 Building 13, Stanmore Industrial Estate, Bridgnorth, Shropshire, WV15 5HP Tel: (01746) 763848 Fax: (01746) 769760 E-mail: sales@clivecowerntransport.co.uk
Craft Engineering, Unit 21 Huffwood Trading Estate, Billingshurst, West Sussex, RH14 9UR Tel: (01403) 784603 Fax: (01403) 784603
▶ Craig Chalmers & Son, 6 Drumgelloch Street, Airdrie, Lanarkshire, ML6 7EW Tel: (01236) 756655 Fax: (01236) 749390
Cranleigh Freight Services Ltd, Building 68 Dunsfold Park, Stovolds Hill, Cranleigh, Surrey, GU6 8TB Tel: (01483) 201330 Fax: (01483) 272124 E-mail: info@cranleigh.co.uk
▶ Crawford Transport Services, Industrial Road, Hertburn, Washington, Tyne & Wear, NE37 2SD Tel: 0191-415 1771 Fax: 0191-419 0396
Creative Logistics Ltd, Duncan Street, Salford, M5 3SQ Tel: 0161-873 7101 Fax: 0161-872 1447 E-mail: enquiries@creative-logistics.co.uk
▶ Crewkerne Carriers Ltd, 18 Buckland Road, Pen Mill Trading Estate, Yeovil, Somerset, BA21 5EA Tel: (01935) 477003 Fax: (01935) 477001
▶ Crowfoot Carriers Ltd, Gosforth Rd, Ascot Drive, Derby, DE24 8HU Tel: (01332) 372621 Fax: (01332) 346171
▶ Crowfoots Carriers (Manchester) Ltd, Park Street, Stalybridge, Cheshire, SK15 2BT Tel: 0161-303 7133 Fax: 0161-304 8226
▶ Crown Worlwide Movers Ltd, 7 Lockwood Court, Middleton Grove Road, Leeds, LS11 5TY Tel: 0113-277 1000
Currie European Transport Ltd, Heathhall, Dumfries, DG1 3NX Tel: (01387) 267333 Fax: (01387) 267339 E-mail: info@currie-european.com
▶ Currys Home Delivery Service, Unit 5, Walworth Road, Aycliffe Industrial Park, Newton Aycliffe, County Durham, DL5 6XF Tel: (01325) 320082 Fax: (01325) 300481
▶ Curvin Transport Ltd, 21 Cowley Road, Nuffield Industrial Estate, Poole, Dorset, BH17 0UJ Tel: (01202) 679369 Fax: (01202) 681228
▶ D A Bird Ltd, Camp Hill, Bugbrooke, Northampton, NN7 3PH Tel: (01604) 830455 Fax: (01604) 832369
D Blowers Ltd, High Croft, London Road, Halesworth, Suffolk, IP19 8LR Tel: (01986) 872861 Fax: (01986) 873048
▶ D & D Snack Foods Ltd, Orchard Works, Badsell Road, Five Oak Green, Tonbridge, Kent, TN12 6QU Tel: (01892) 838418 Fax: (01892) 838450
▶ D D Thomson, Northraw, East Calder, Livingston, West Lothian, EH53 0ET Tel: (01506) 881588
▶ D F D S Transport Ltd, Block 3, Bothwell Park Industrial Estate, Uddingston, Glasgow, G71 6NZ Tel: (01698) 811522 Fax: (01698) 810199
▶ D J Dunabie Ltd, Drummurran Garage, 51 Kirkoswald Road, Maybole, Ayrshire, KA19 8BW Tel: (01655) 883668 Fax: (01655) 883668
▶ D & J Sibbald, Hardhill Garage, Bathgate, West Lothian, EH48 2HL Tel: (01506) 655711 Fax: (01506) 632449
▶ D J Thomas & Sons, Aurora, Llanarth, Dyfed, SA47 0NF Tel: (01545) 580213 Fax: (01545) 580053 E-mail: djtandsons@aol.com
D L Turner & Son Ltd, Underedge Farm, Rowland, Bakewell, Derbyshire, DE45 1NR Tel: (01629) 640305 Fax: (01629) 640684
▶ D M Clarkson, Borderline Garage, Biggar, Lanarkshire, ML12 6JJ Tel: (01899) 220346 Fax: (01899) 221279
▶ D Malloch & Co., Walk Mill, Coupar Angus, Blairgowrie, Perthshire, PH13 9DG Tel: (01828) 627452
D N D Ltd, Billington Road, Leighton Buzzard, Bedfordshire, LU7 9HH Tel: (01525) 370888 Fax: (01525) 851619E-mail: traffic@dnd.co.uk
D & N Transport, Unit 4b Arrow Trading Estate, Corporation Road, Audenshaw, Manchester, M34 5LR Tel: 0161-336 3024 Fax: 0161-320 3124 E-mail: dntransport@nippinet.co.uk

ROAD TRANSPORT AND HAULAGE

– continued

▶ D R Macleod, 9 Henderson Road, Inverness, IV1 1SN Tel: (01463) 715217 Fax: (01463) 715232

▶ D S Carriers, Lyon Road, Linwood Industrial Estate, Linwood, Paisley, Renfrewshire, PA3 3BQ Tel: (01505) 337520 Fax: (01505) 331418 E-mail: info@dscarriersandsons.co.uk

▶ D & T Campbell (Meigle) Ltd, Forfar Road Garage, Meigle, Blairgowrie, Perthshire, PH12 8RS Tel: (01828) 640261

▶ D W Weaver Ltd, Blenheim Road, Airfield Industrial Estate, Ashbourne, Derbyshire, DE6 1HA Tel: (01335) 344182

D W Weaver Ltd, Park Farm, Park Lane, Endon, Stoke-on-Trent, ST9 9JB Tel: (01782) 503186 Fax: (01782) 504998

Dachser Transport UK Ltd, Oxwich Close, Brackmills Industrial Estate, Northampton, NN4 7BH Tel: (01604) 666222 Fax: (01604) 666239 E-mail: dachser.northampton@dachser.com

▶ Dalkeith Transport & Storage Ltd, Westerton Road, East Mains Industrial Estate, Broxburn, West Lothian, EH52 5AU Tel: (01506) 858544 Fax: (01506) 855862

▶ Dalkeith Transport & Storage Co Ltd, Lady Victoria Business Centre, Newtongrange, Dalkeith, Midlothian, EH22 4QN Tel: 0131-663 2451 Fax: 0131-654 0284

▶ Dalton Transport, Eling Terminal, 26 High Street, Totton, Southampton, SO40 9HN Tel: (023) 8086 0844 Fax: (023) 8086 0901

▶ Dalton Transport, Eling Terminal, 26 High Street, Totton, Southampton, SO40 9HN Tel: (023) 8086 0844 Fax: (023) 8086 0901

▶ Damac Transporters Ltd, Mariners Street, Goole, North Humberside, DN14 5BW Tel: (01405) 766979 Fax: (01405) 782612

▶ Dane Valley Haulage, Wood Flour Mills, Tunstall Road, Bosley, Macclesfield, Cheshire, SK11 0PE Tel: (01260) 223284 Fax: (01260) 223746

▶ Darlington Group plc, Bankfields Drive, Wirral, Merseyside, CH62 0AZ Tel: 0151-328 5600 Fax: 0151-328 5605

▶ Darlington Group plc, Bankfields Drive, Wirral, Merseyside, CH62 0AZ Tel: 0151-328 5600 Fax: 0151-328 5605 E-mail: martin@darlingtons-group.co.uk

▶ Dart Distribution Ltd, Plot 5, Sub-Station Road, Felixstowe, Suffolk, IP11 3JB Tel: (01394) 600420 Fax: (01394) 676062

▶ Data Run, 2 Quebec Way, London, SE16 7LF Tel: (020) 7232 1616 Fax: (020) 7252 0315

▶ Datec Electronic Holdings, Cromwell House, 142 High Street, Stevenage, Hertfordshire, SG1 3HN Tel: (01438) 360300

▶ Davella Transport Ltd, 21 Bradfield Close, Finedon Road Industrial Estate, Wellingborough, Northamptonshire, NN8 4RQ Tel: (01933) 273946 Fax: (01933) 225896

A. & H. Davey (Roadways) Ltd, Shelton New Road, Cliffe Vale, Stoke-on-Trent, ST4 7DL Tel: (01782) 847691 Fax: (01782) 747181 E-mail: ahdavey@btclick.com

▶ David Fox (Transport) Ltd, Stora Terminal, Immingham Dock, Immingham, South Humberside, DN40 2NT Tel: (01469) 577380 Fax: (01469) 577014 E-mail: traffic@davidfox.co.uk

▶ David Heeps (Haulage) Ltd, 5 Hugh Place, Lochgelly, Fife, KY5 9DN Tel: (01592) 780393

▶ David Mellor Ltd, Sandybrook Garage, Buxton Road, Ashbourne, Derbyshire, DE6 1EX Tel: (01335) 343840 Fax: (01335) 343816

▶ David Stanley, Vulcan Court, Vulcan Way, Coalville, Leicestershire, LE67 3FW Tel: (01530) 831200 Fax: (01430) 814143

▶ Davidson & Wilson Ltd, Sclattie Quarry Industrial Estate, Bankhead, Bucksburn, Aberdeen, AB21 9EG Tel: (01224) 716588 Fax: (01224) 716170

Davies, Sunningdale, Great North Road, Bawtry, Doncaster, South Yorkshire, DN10 6DF Tel: (01302) 719341 Fax: (01302) 711181

▶ Davies International Transport Ltd, 21 Brunel Way, Fareham, Hampshire, PO15 5SD Tel: (01489) 579957 Fax: (01489) 575728

Dawson Bros, Gauntlet Road, Bicker, Boston, Lincolnshire, PE20 3AU Tel: (01775) 820273 Fax: (01775) 821691

De Rijke Intermodal UK Ltd, 1 Aston Lane N Preston Brook, Preston Brook, Runcorn, Cheshire, WA7 3GE Tel: (01928) 755400 Fax: (01928) 759816

▶ Deans Telford Ltd, Unit 1 & 24 Shifnal Industrial Estate, Lamledge Lane, Shifnal, Shropshire, TF11 8SD Tel: (01952) 462877 Fax: (01952) 463047

▶ Debach Enterprises Ltd, Blue Stem Road, Ransomes Industrial Estate, Ipswich, IP3 9RR Tel: (01473) 270207 Fax: (01473) 719939 E-mail: sales@debach.co.uk

▶ Deben Transport Southampton Ltd, Oyster House, Andes Road, Nursling, Southampton, SO16 0YZ Tel: (023) 8073 5566 Fax: (023) 8073 5567

▶ Del Monte Fresh Produce, Kingsway North, Team Valley Trading Estate, Gateshead, Tyne & Wear, NE11 0JH Tel: 0191-487 2700 Fax: 0191-487 6787

▶ Delta Galil, 6 Gambrel Road, Westgate Industrial Estate, Northampton, NN5 5BB Tel: (01604) 594600 Fax: (01604) 594610

Denby Transport Ltd, 73 Sadler Road, Lincoln, LN6 3JR Tel: (01522) 503900 Fax: (01522) 686372 E-mail: sales@denbytransport.co.uk

Derek Cooper, Turnpike Road, Red Lodge, Bury St. Edmunds, Suffolk, IP28 8LB Tel: (01638) 751974 Fax: (01638) 751665

▶ Derek Cooper Transport Ltd, Yarmouth Road, Blofield, Norwich, NR13 4DS Tel: (01603) 715888 Fax: (01603) 715424

Derek Horton, Rollingmill Street, Walsall, WS2 9EG Tel: (01922) 621909 Fax: (01922) 634829

Dews, Yew Green Road, Huddersfield, HD4 5EN Tel: (01484) 304060 Fax: (01484) 304477 E-mail: traffic@dews-haulage.co.uk

▶ DHL P.L.C., West Bay Road, Western Docks, Southampton, SO15 1AW Tel: (023) 8022 1835

▶ Direct Distribution, Unit 7 Forties Commercial Campus, Rosyth, Dunfermline, Fife, KY11 2XB Tel: (01383) 420867 Fax: (01383) 420869

Direct Fuel Services Ltd, Sandy Lane, Titton, Stourport-on-Severn, Worcestershire, DY13 9PN Tel: (01299) 828449 Fax: (01299) 828435E-mail: sales@directfuelservices.co.uk

▶ Direct Parcel Services, 1 Purley Chase Estate, Pipers Lane, Nuneaton, Warwickshire, CV10 0RH Tel: (024) 7639 5750 Fax: (024) 7639 5756

▶ Direct Transportation Ltd, Swan Street, Chappel, Colchester, CO6 2EE Tel: (01787) 223301

▶ Direct Vehicles Logistics Ltd, Standhill, Inchcross, Bathgate, West Lothian, EH48 2HS Tel: (01506) 655800

▶ DMG Freight Services, Mead Park Industrial Estate, Harlow, Essex, CM20 2SE Tel: (01279) 452468 Fax: (01279) 415810 E-mail: info@dmg-freight.com

Dobbs Logistics Ltd, 23 Hawthorn Road, Eastbourne, East Sussex, BN23 6QA Tel: (08708) 518770 Fax: (01323) 641539 E-mail: services@dobbslogistics.co.uk

▶ Donnell & Ellis, 24 Beltany Road, Omagh, County Tyrone, BT78 5NA Tel: (028) 8224 7015 Fax: (028) 8225 0545

▶ Doonin Plant Ltd, New Road, Cambuslang, Glasgow, G72 7PU Tel: 0141-641 3731 Fax: 0141-641 3761

▶ Doree Bonner International, Unit 21 Leafield Industrial Estate, Leafield Way, Corsham, Wiltshire, SN13 9SW Tel: (01225) 811992 Fax: (01225) 812536

▶ Double Jay Furniture Transport Ltd, Unit 3C, Garston Industrial Estate, Blackburn Street, Liverpool, L19 8JB Tel: 0151-427 6686

Double M Transport Ltd, The Courtyard, Warkworth, Banbury, Oxfordshire, OX17 2AG Tel: (01295) 712828 Fax: (01295) 711886 E-mail: stuartdoublem@aol.com

▶ Douglas F Mitchell Ltd, Archgrove, Station Road, Laurencekirk, Kincardineshire, AB30 1BE Tel: (01561) 377741 Fax: (01561) 378035

Douglas Transport Ltd, Baker House, The Hayes, Lye, Stourbridge, West Midlands, DY9 8RS Tel: (01384) 424489 Fax: (01384) 893754

▶ Dovedale Fleet Deliveries, 34 Woodmans Croft, Hatton, Derby, DE65 5QQ Tel: (01283) 520445 Fax: (01283) 520445

▶ Draycote Continental Transport Ltd, Glebe Farm Road, Rugby, Warwickshire, CV21 1GF Tel: (01788) 579060

Drennan Transport Ltd, 103 Main Street, Tobermore, Magherafelt, County Londonderry, BT45 5PP Tel: (028) 7964 2116 Fax: (028) 7964 3570 E-mail: sales@drennan-transport.co.uk

▶ Dronfield Storage Centre, Rosemarie House, Wreakes Lane, Dronfield, Derbyshire, S18 1PN Tel: (01246) 290590 Fax: (01246) 290348

▶ Drummond Distribution, Eastmains Freight Centre, 1 Bathgate Road, Armadale, Bathgate, West Lothian, EH48 2PE Tel: (01501) 730221 Fax: (01501) 732981 E-mail: sales@drummond-distribution.co.uk

▶ Drysdale Freight, The Courtyard Tower Farm, Cockburnspath, Berwickshire, TD13 5YU Tel: (01368) 830640 Fax: (01368) 830730

Duggan Transport Ltd, Church Road, Shilton, Coventry, CV7 9HX Tel: (024) 7661 2871 Fax: (024) 7661 2871

▶ Duncan, Glenfield Industrial Estate, Perth Road, Cowdenbeath, Fife, KY4 9HT Tel: (01383) 610956

▶ Duncan Collier Haulage, Block 1, Woodend Industrial Estate, Cowdenbeath, Fife, KY4 8HW Tel: (01383) 510329

Dyce Carrier, Kirkton Avenue, Dyce, Aberdeen, AB21 0BF Tel: (01224) 723571 Fax: (01224) 770328E-mail: info@dycecar.fsbuisiness.co.uk

▶ E C Farrell (Transport) Ltd, Ashton Lane, Chester, CH3 8AA Tel: (01829) 751558

▶ E C M Vehicle Delivery Service Ltd, Carlisle Airport, Carlisle, CA6 4NW Tel: (01228) 573491 Fax: (01228) 573390

▶ E F F, Haw Road, Londonderry, BT47 6XT Tel: (028) 7186 5050

▶ E Francis & Son, Highgate, Leverton, Boston, Lincolnshire, PE22 0AW Tel: (01205) 870341 Fax: (01205) 871447

E H Lee Ltd, Sleaford Road, Bracebridge Heath, Lincoln, LN4 2NL Tel: (01522) 520251 Fax: (01522) 512239 E-mail: enquiries@ehleeatpeterborough.co.uk

▶ E Nixon & Son Ltd, Morley Bridge Works, Chester Road, Bridge Trafford, Chester, CH2 4JS Tel: (01244) 300641 Fax: (01244) 300489

▶ E Pawson & Son Ltd, Field Houses, Ashton Lane, Braithwell, Rotherham, South Yorkshire, S66 7RL Tel: (01709) 813901 Fax: (01709) 814330

▶ E Rankin, 178 Highmoor Road, Cross, Londonderry, BT47 3HS Tel: (028) 7130 1875 Fax: (028) 7130 1961

▶ E Robson & Son, Crowle Street, Hull, HU9 1RH Tel: (01482) 226038 Fax: (01482) 325467

▶ E & S J Walpole Ltd, Greens Road, Dereham, Norfolk, NR20 3TG Tel: (01362) 655410 Fax: (01362) 655419

▶ E T Morris & Sons Ltd, King George Dock, Hull, HU9 5PR Tel: (01482) 786818 Fax: (01482) 782284

E W Taylor & Co Forwarding Ltd, Dunbar House Eurolink Industrial Centre, Castle Road, Sittingbourne, Kent, ME10 3RN Tel: (01795) 410110 Fax: (01795) 410111 E-mail: sharonlambert@ewtaylorgroup.com

▶ Eardley International, Ecclefechan, Lockerbie, Dumfriesshire, DG11 3JD Tel: (01576) 300500 Fax: (01576) 300555

▶ Easymove (Bristol) Ltd, Albert Crescent, Bristol, BS2 0SU Tel: 0117-977 1460

Eclipse Motor Transport Co. Ltd, Clay Street, Hull, HU8 8HD Tel: (01482) 320066 Fax: (01482) 586617

Edge Hill Transport, Wilkinsons Yard, Ardleigh Road, Liverpool, L13 2BD Tel: 0151-228 7029 Fax: 0151-228 9477

▶ Edgley Distribution Express Ltd, 11 Acer Road, Saddlebow Industrial Estate, King's Lynn, Norfolk, PE34 3HN Tel: (01553) 761513

Edwards Logisitcs, PO Box 107, Hull, HU5 4JJ Tel: (01482) 492194 Fax: (01482) 473620 E-mail: info@edwards-logistics.com

▶ Edwards Logistics Ltd, Unit 5, James Street, Righead Industrial Estate, Bellshill, Lanarkshire, ML4 3LU Tel: (01698) 849977

Eggbeers Transport Ltd, Greenhill Way, Kingsteignton, Newton Abbot, Devon, TQ12 3SB Tel: (01626) 352562 Fax: (01626) 333119

Elliott Nationwide Transport Ltd, Elliott House, Greg Street, Stockport, Cheshire, SK5 7BS Tel: 0161-429 9485 Fax: 0161-429 9094

▶ Ernest Cooper Ltd, Unit 43 Lidgate CR, South Kirkby, Pontefract, West Yorkshire, WF9 3NR Tel: (01977) 642191 Fax: (01977) 649994

Eurgent Ecspress, Unit 1b, Charnwood Park, Bridgend, Mid Glamorgan, CF31 3PL Tel: (01656) 645555 Fax: (01656) 656534 E-mail: enq@eurgent.co.uk

Eurocontinental Logistics Ltd, Unit 7, Everitt Close, Denington Industrial Estate, Wellingborough, Northamptonshire, NN8 2QE Tel: (01933) 223851 Fax: (01933) 272630 E-mail: info@eurocontinental-logistics.co.uk

▶ Euroline Time Critical Freight Ltd, 30 Inkerman Street, Birmingham, B7 4SB Tel: 0121-333 3900 Fax: 0121-333 3868

Evans Transport, Braunton Road, Barnstaple, Devon, EX31 1LE Tel: (01271) 326632 Fax: (01271) 326616 E-mail: evanstransport@btconnect.com

Evans Transport Ltd, Peamore Truck Centre, Alphington, Exeter, EX2 9SL Tel: (01392) 833030 Fax: (01392) 833540 E-mail: sales@palletforce.com

▶ Excess Baggage, 4 Hannah Close, Great Central Way, London, NW10 0UX Tel: (020) 8324 2000 Fax: (020) 8324 2089

▶ Exel, Brownsburn Industrial Estate, Airdrie, Lanarkshire, ML6 9SE Tel: (01236) 748181 Fax: (01236) 755656

▶ Exel, Bell Road, Basingstoke, Hampshire, RG24 8PU Tel: (01256) 463392

▶ Exel, Unit 1 Westfield Industrial Estate, Cumbernauld, Glasgow, G68 9HD Tel: (01236) 730030 Fax: (01236) 738061

▶ Exel PLC, 2 Hannah Close, London, NW10 0UX Tel: (020) 8903 3533 Fax: (020) 8903 7278

▶ Exel, Sandy La West, Littlemore, Oxford, OX4 6JU Tel: (01865) 774544 Fax: (01865) 775099

▶ Exel Haulage, PO Box 1, Scunthorpe, South Humberside, DN16 1BP Tel: (01724) 865316 Fax: (01724) 847027

▶ Exel Logisitics Ltd, Haydock Lane Trading Estate, Bahama Close, St. Helens, Merseyside, WA11 9XN Tel: (01942) 271111

▶ Exel Logistics Ltd, Riversdale Road, Carlyon Road Industrial Estate, Atherstone, Warwickshire, CV9 1LP Tel: (01827) 715333

▶ Exel For Somerfield, Bishopdyke Road, Sherburn In Elmet, Leeds, LS25 6JH Tel: (01977) 696000

▶ Exel Tankfreight Ltd, Smeaton Road, West Gourdie Industrial Estate, Dundee, DD2 4UT Tel: (01382) 621199

▶ Expert Logistics, Bury Road, Radcliffe, Manchester, M26 2XH Tel: 0161-777 1130

Export Centre, Unit 72 Wimbledon Stadium Business Centre, Rosemary Road, London, SW17 0BA Tel: (020) 8947 6767 Fax: (020) 8944 1414 E-mail: info@london-frieght.co.uk

▶ Express Dairies Ltd, Smisby Road, Ashby-de-la-Zouch, Leicestershire, LE65 2UF Tel: (01530) 412858 Fax: (01530) 411237

▶ Express Despatch, Unit 10 Horton Road, West Drayton, Middlesex, UB7 8JL Tel: (01895) 437792 Fax: (01895) 437782

▶ Express Freight Services (UK) Ltd, St Andrews House, Tilbury Docks, Tilbury, Essex, RM18 7EB Tel: (01375) 844384

▶ Express Parcel Services, Unit 2 Gateside Industrial Estate, Lesmahagow, Lanark, ML11 0JR Tel: (01555) 894300 Fax: (01555) 895117

▶ Express Parcels, Unit 5, Monklands Industrial Estate, Kirkshaws Road, Coatbridge, Lanarkshire, ML5 4RP Tel: (01236) 449922

▶ Express Removals, 48 Clyde Street, Clydebank, Dunbartonshire, G81 1NW Tel: 0141-952 6000 Fax: 0141-951 4527

▶ Express Removals, 48 Clyde Street, Clydebank, Dunbartonshire, G81 1NW Tel: 0141-952 6000 Fax: 0141-951 4527

▶ F D T Transport Ltd, 1 Crane Street, Manchester, M12 6EF Tel: 0161-274 4017

F Dickson Transport Ltd, 51 Imperial Way, Croydon, CR0 4RR Tel: (020) 8686 6707 Fax: (020) 8686 9297 E-mail: higher@dicksons.co.uk

▶ F Lloyd Penley Ltd, Bridge Road, Wrexham Industrial Estate, Wrexham, Clwyd, LL13 9SQ Tel: (01978) 661751 Fax: (01978) 664408

F M Caine & Sons Ltd, Broad Eaves, Penybont Road, Knighton, Powys, LD7 1HB Tel: (01547) 528654 Fax: (01547) 529006

▶ F Robbins (Transport) Ltd, Wholesmouth, St Andrews Road, Bristol, BS11 9BP Tel: 0117-982 7804

▶ F & S Gibbs Transport Services Ltd, 40 Boreham Road, Warminster, Wiltshire, BA12 9JR Tel: (01985) 213084

F Short Ltd, Green Lane, Felling, Gateshead, Tyne & Wear, NE10 0EZ Tel: 0191-469 4627 Fax: 0191-438 4680

▶ Failsworth Haulage, 9-12A Limekilns Road, Cumbernauld, Glasgow, G67 2RN Tel: (01236) 733307

Fairway P S D, Unit 3, Langley Business Centre, Station Road, Langley, Slough, SL3 8DS Tel: (0870) 389 1701 Fax: (0870) 3891751

▶ Falkirk Car Carriers, Dalgrain Industrial Estate, Grangemouth, Stirlingshire, FK3 8EB Tel: (01324) 482382 Fax: (01324) 482484

▶ Famac Network Ltd, Unit 5, 200 Swan Lane, Hindley Green, Wigan, Lancashire, WN2 4HD Tel: (01942) 525191

▶ Farrens Freight, Unit 1a Garrion Business Park, Wishaw, Lanarkshire, ML2 0RY Tel: (01698) 352266 Fax: (01698) 352255

▶ Fastsource Ltd, Pepper Road, Leeds, LS10 2EU Tel: 0113-270 1637 Fax: 0113-270 4366

Fedex UK, 41 Rosevale Road, Parkhouse Industrial Estate West, Newcastle, Staffordshire, ST5 7EF Tel: (01782) 564544 Fax: (01782) 561553E-mail: sales@anc.co.uk

▶ Fenton Transport Ltd, Mains of Duncrub, Dunning, Perth, PH2 0QN Tel: (01764) 684244

▶ Fenwick Haulage Ltd, Church Lane, Adwick-le-Street, Doncaster, South Yorkshire, DN6 7AY Tel: (01302) 728496 Fax: (01302) 726489

▶ Ferguson Transport (Spean Bridge) Ltd, Tigharan, Spean Bridge, Inverness-Shire, PH34 4EP Tel: (01397) 712396 Fax: (01397) 712462

▶ Ferguson Transport (Spean Bridge) Ltd, Tigharan, Spean Bridge, Inverness-Shire, PH34 4EP Tel: (01397) 712396 Fax: (01397) 712462

Fergusons (Blyth) Ltd, Ennerdale Road, Kitty Brewster Estate, Blyth, Northumberland, NE24 4RD Tel: (01670) 353761 Fax: (01670) 357401 E-mail: sales@fergusonsremovals.co.uk

▶ Ferriday & Alder, 4 Acre Road, Reading, RG2 0SX Tel: 0118-986 2510 Fax: 0118-975 1358 E-mail: info@movers.co.uk

▶ Ferryfast Produce Ltd, Ascot Road, Pershore, Worcestershire, WR10 2JJ Tel: (01386) 552131 Fax: (01386) 562407 E-mail: sales@ferryfast.co.uk

▶ Ferryman Ltd, Unit 2, Newbridge Road Industrial Estate, Pontllanfraith, Blackwood, Gwent, NP12 2XF Tel: (01495) 222300 Fax: (01495) 222302 E-mail: sales@ferryman.org.uk

▶ Fielding Transport, 21 Askew Farm Lane, Grays, Essex, RM17 5XR Tel: (01375) 399496 Fax: (01375) 399493

▶ Fillinghams Transport, Unit B1 Abbey La Industrial Estate, Abbey Lane, Burscough, Ormskirk, Lancashire, L40 7SR Tel: (01704) 897917 Fax: (01704) 897918

Fine Wine Shipping Agency, Golf Road, Deal, Kent, CT14 6QQ Tel: (01304) 368877 Fax: (01304) 363101 E-mail: info@bmexpressfreight.co.uk

Alan Firmin Ltd, Mid Kent Business Park, Sortmill Road, Snodland, Kent, ME6 5GP Tel: (01634) 241200 Fax: (01622) 820823 E-mail: transport@alanfirmin.co.uk

Firmin Coates Ltd, Wares Farm, Redwall Lane, Linton, Maidstone, Kent, ME17 4BB Tel: (01622) 820273 Fax: (01622) 820823 E-mail: afl@alanfirmin.co.uk

▶ First Line Contracts Ltd, 5 Delaware Drive, Tongwell, Milton Keynes, MK15 8HG Tel: (01908) 611229

James Fisher Tankships Ltd, 4th Floor, 7 Birchen Lane, London, EC3V 9BW Tel: (020) 7338 5800 Fax: (020) 7338 5850 E-mail: info@james-fisher.co.uk

Fishleighs Of Galsworthy, Galsworthy, Buckland Brewer, Bideford, Devon, EX39 5NP Tel: (01409) 261231 Fax: (01409) 261231

▶ Fleet Removals, Bolesworth Road, Tattenhall, Chester, CH3 9HL Tel: (01829) 770169

Herbert Fletcher Transport Ltd, M62 Trading Estate, Rawcliffe Road, Goole, North Humberside, DN14 8JW Tel: (01405) 769968 Fax: (01405) 762513 E-mail: enquiries@herbertfletcher.co.uk

▶ Floboth (London) Ltd, Unit 1 C, Middlegreen Trading Estate, Langley, Slough, SL3 6DF Tel: (01753) 521878

▶ Floyd Schofield Haulage, Unit 11 Sowarth Industrial Estate, Settle, North Yorkshire, BD24 9AF Tel: (01729) 825396 Fax: (01729) 825396

▶ Foley & Miles, 732 London Road, Grays, Essex, RM20 3NL Tel: (01708) 869986 Fax: (01708) 869987

ROAD TRANSPORT AND HAULAGE

– continued

▶ Food Services, Ruthvenfield Road, Inveralmond Industrial Estate, Perth, PH1 3EE Tel: (01738) 646666 Fax: (01738) 646667 E-mail: enquiries@callumwalker.com

▶ Forem Universal Products Ltd, Canal Wharf, Wyther Lane, Leeds, LS5 3BT Tel: 0113-224 2000 Fax: 0113-224 2200 E-mail: sales@forceproducts.co.uk

Forest Freight Ltd, Fairview Indust Park, Barlow Way, Rainham, Essex, RM13 8BT Tel: (01708) 552222 Fax: (01708) 553330 E-mail: sales@forestfreight.co.uk

▶ Four Speed Express Ltd, 6 27-29 Station Road, Kings Norton, Birmingham, B38 8SN Tel: 0121-433 3359 Fax: 0121-433 3449

▶ Fowler Welch & Coolchain, Deptford Road, Gateshead, Tyne & Wear, NE8 3AZ Tel: 0191-490 0083

Fox Moving & Storage Groups Ltd, Pentland Close, Llanishen, Cardiff, CF14 5DJ Tel: (029) 2075 0967 Fax: (029) 2074 7383

▶ Francis Transport, 15 Dell Avenue, Grimethorpe, Barnsley, South Yorkshire, S72 7HN Tel: (01226) 710032

▶ Frank Burton Transport Ltd, Gomer Street West, Willenhall, West Midlands, WV13 2NR Tel: (01902) 605311 Fax: (01902) 606719

▶ Frank Hoyle Ltd, 2 Broadway, Hyde, Cheshire, SK14 4QQ Tel: 0161-368 8444 Fax: 0161-368 8555

▶ Frank Hudson Transport Ltd, Etherley Bank, High Etherley, Bishop Auckland, County Durham, DL14 0LG Tel: (01388) 832247 Fax: (01388) 835645

Frankie Wainman, Foster Cliffe Farm South, Low Lane, Silsden, Keighley, West Yorkshire, BD20 9JH Tel: (01535) 652487 Fax: (01535) 658286

Fransen Transport Ltd, 6 Lisle Avenue, Foley Park, Kidderminster, Worcestershire, DY11 7DE Tel: (01562) 820261 Fax: (01562) 754977 E-mail: info@fransentransport.fsnet.co.uk

▶ Fred Sweeting & Sons, Orchardlea, Station Road, Sandford, Winscombe, Avon, BS25 5RQ Tel: (01934) 822341 Fax: (01934) 820445

▶ Frederick R Miller Ltd, Home Farm, By-Pass Road, Hurtmore, Godalming, Surrey, GU8 6AD Tel: (01483) 811297 Fax: (01483) 810073 E-mail: sales@frederickmiller.co.uk

Freeland Freight Services Ltd, Blackness Road, Altens Industrial Estate, Aberdeen, AB12 3LH Tel: (01224) 873601 Fax: (01224) 879863 E-mail: enquiries@freelandfreight.co.uk

Freemans, Salvesen Way, Brighton Street Industrial Estate, Hull, HU3 4UQ Tel: (01482) 221366 Fax: (01482) 221343 E-mail: hull@isotank.co.uk

▶ Freight Control Services Ltd, Unit 10 Cambrian Industrial Estate East Side, Coedcae Lane, Pontyclun, Mid Glamorgan, CF72 9EW Tel: (01443) 222796 Fax: (01443) 223006

▶ Freight Express Ltd, Pomathorn Store, Penicuik, Midlothian, EH26 8PJ Tel: (01968) 670066 Fax: (01968) 676010 E-mail: sales@freightexpress.co.uk

▶ Freight Solutions, Honywood Road, Basildon, Essex, SS14 3DS Tel: (01268) 287979 Fax: (01268) 287978 E-mail: sales@freightsolutionsuk.com

▶ Freight Speed Commercial, Highland House, The Heath, Tendring, Clacton-on-Sea, Essex, CO16 0DA Tel: (01255) 870622

Freight Transport Ltd, C3-C5 Unit, Railway Triangle, Walton Road, Portsmouth, PO6 1TW Tel: (023) 9232 4213 Fax: (023) 9221 0324 E-mail: sales@freighttransport.co.uk

▶ Freight-Mate, 463 Stourport Road, Kidderminster, Worcestershire, DY11 7BD Tel: (01562) 638508

▶ Frenni Transport Ltd, Station Road, Crymych, Dyfed, SA41 3RL Tel: (01239) 831557

Fresh Freight Ltd, North East Fruit & Vegetable Market, Team Valley Trading Estate, Gateshead, Tyne & Wear, NE11 0QY Tel: 0191-491 0505 Fax: 0191-491 0090

Fuller & Sons Warehouse Ltd, Kelvin Way, West Bromwich, West Midlands, B70 7LH Tel: 0121-553 6211 Fax: 0121-525 9085 E-mail: fullerandsonsltd@aol.com

▶ Fullers Logistics Group Holdings Ltd, 126 Fairlie Road, Slough, SL1 4PY Tel: (01753) 519000 Fax: (01753) 519001

Future Forwarding Co. Ltd, Building 305, World Freight Terminal, Manchester Airport, Manchester, M90 5PY Tel: 0161-436 8181 Fax: 0161-499 0654 E-mail: andreadelves@futureforwarding.com

▶ G B Liners Ltd, 28 Armstrong Way, Southall, Middlesex, UB2 4SD Tel: (020) 8574 1285 Fax: (020) 8574 5992

▶ G Brocklehurst Ltd, Goods Lane, Off Railway Street, Dewsbury, West Yorkshire, WF12 8DZ Tel: (01924) 468811 Fax: (01924) 451161

G & C Johnson Claxby Ltd, Crosby Grange, Crosby Grange Road, Scunthorpe, South Humberside, DN15 8UH Tel: (01724) 856262 Fax: (01724) 854626 E-mail: gc.johnson@btconnect.com

▶ G C N (Scotland) Ltd, Garrion Business Park, Wishaw, Lanarkshire, ML2 0RY Tel: (01698) 351343

▶ G & D Cunningham Ltd, Cemetery Road, Galston, Ayrshire, KA4 8HZ Tel: (01563) 820409 Fax: (01563) 822004

▶ G Donald (Warehouseman) Ltd, 7 St Andrew St, Peterhead, Aberdeenshire, AB42 1DS Tel: (01779) 474737

▶ G Easton & Son Ltd, South Street, Alford, Lincolnshire, LN13 9AQ Tel: (01507) 463400

▶ G Easton & Son Ltd, South Street, Alford, Lincolnshire, LN13 9AQ Tel: (01507) 463400

▶ G Force Express Parcels Ltd, Halesfield 2, Telford, Shropshire, TF7 4QH Tel: (01952) 582888 Fax: (01952) 582801

▶ G H Martin & Son, Lindleys, Corsham, Wiltshire, SN13 9PG Tel: (01249) 712200

▶ G I S T Ltd, 22 Lenziemill Road, West Lenziemill Industrial Estate, Cumbernauld, Glasgow, G67 2XN Tel: (01236) 727981

G & J Ping Ltd, 63 Coates Road, Eastrea, Whittlesey, Peterborough, PE7 2BA Tel: (01733) 203383 Fax: (01733) 351204

▶ G & M Distribution, 2 Block 9, Chapelhall Industrial Estate, Chapelhall, Airdrie, Lanarkshire, ML6 8QH Tel: (01236) 755447 Fax: (01236) 766306

▶ G & M Distribution, Dalcross Industrial Estate, Inverness, IV2 7XB Tel: (01667) 462466 Fax: (01667) 461161

▶ G Revill (Haulage) Ltd, Kiln Lane, Stallingborough, Grimsby, South Humberside, DN41 8DW Tel: (01469) 575468

G Reyner Ltd, Dowry Street, Oldham, OL8 2LP Tel: 0161-622 2400 Fax: 0161-622 2444

G Reyner Ltd, Dowry Street, Oldham, OL8 2LP Tel: 0161-622 2400 Fax: 0161-622 2444

G T S Ltd, 85 Templepatrick Road, Ballyclare, County Antrim, BT39 9RQ Tel: (028) 9334 0510 Fax: (028) 9334 9339 E-mail: gts61242@aol.com

G T Stone & Son, Dudnance Lane, Pool, Redruth, Cornwall, TR15 3QZ Tel: (01736) 763777 Fax: (01209) 710285

▶ G & T Transport, Unit 6 Llwyn Y Graig, Gorseinon, Swansea, SA4 9WG Tel: (01792) 899499 Fax: (01792) 899898 E-mail: info@gandttransport.co.uk

▶ G W Twilley & Son Ltd, 71 Coburg Road, London, N22 6UB Tel: (020) 8888 1660 Fax: (020) 8888 1660 E-mail: twilly@aol.com

▶ Gallacher Bros Haulage Ltd, Morrison Industrial Estate North, Stanley, County Durham, DH9 7RU Tel: (01207) 233334 Fax: (01207) 283552

▶ Galt Transport, Bankend Road, Broadmeadow Industrial Estate, Dumbarton, G82 2RB Tel: (01389) 765454 Fax: (01389) 730460

Gardner Freight International Ltd, Mersey Chambers, Covent Garden, Liverpool, L2 8XT Tel: 0151-236 7366 Fax: 0151-243 3463 E-mail: harrisons@liverpool.co.uk

Gaylee Ltd, Pope Street, Smethwick, West Midlands, B66 2JP Tel: 0121-558 2027 Fax: 0121-558 2029

▶ Gee's Haulage Ltd, Unit 2 Monckton Road Industria, Wakefield, West Yorkshire, WF2 7AL Tel: (01924) 372269

Gefco UK Ltd, Fields End Business Park, Thurnscoe, Rotherham, South Yorkshire, S63 0JF Tel: (01709) 886000 Fax: (01709) 886006 E-mail: sales.uk@gefco.co.uk

Gent Transport, Unit 5, Badminton Road, Yate, Bristol, BS37 5NS Tel: (01454) 881000 Fax: (01454) 881122

Geodis UK Ltd, Linwood Industrial Estate, Lyon Road, Linwood, Paisley, Renfrewshire, PA3 3BQ Tel: (01505) 321111 Fax: (01505) 325555

George H Kime & Co. Ltd, Main Road, Wrangle, Boston, Lincolnshire, PE22 9AW Tel: (01205) 870282 Fax: (01205) 871024 E-mail: accounts@kimes.co.uk

George Mackay, 3 March Road East, Buckie, Banffshire, AB56 4BY Tel: (01542) 833948 Fax: (01542) 833953

▶ George P McLaughlan Ltd, Inchcape Place, North Muirton Industrial Estat, Perth, PH1 3DU Tel: (01738) 634321

▶ George Varney (Bulk Services) Ltd, Varneys Yard, Watford, Northampton, NN6 7UF Tel: (01327) 872288

Georgia Pacific GB Ltd, Llandow Trading Estate, Llandow, Cowbridge, South Glamorgan, CF71 7PB Tel: (01446) 794011 Fax: (01446) 795208

▶ Gerald D Harris & Sons, Rowlands View, Cold Blow, Narberth, Dyfed, SA67 8RG Tel: (01834) 860464 Fax: (01834) 896156

▶ Gerard Removers Ltd, 32 Burnfield Road, Giffnock, Glasgow, G46 7PZ Tel: 0141-954 3939 Fax: 0141-954 5290 E-mail: sales@gerardremovers.co.uk

▶ Gibbs Transport Ltd, 6 Coln Industrial Estate, Old Bath Road, Colnbrook, Slough, SL3 0NJ Tel: (01753) 685566 Fax: (01753) 681700

Geoff Gilbert International Ltd, Station Road, Swineshead, Boston, Lincolnshire, PE20 3PN Tel: (01205) 721000 Fax: (01205) 721004 E-mail: transport@geoffgilbert.co.uk

Gilbraith Tankers Ltd, Atlas Garage, Atlas Street, Clayton Le Moors, Accrington, Lancashire, BB5 5JX Tel: (01254) 231111 Fax: (01254) 390505 E-mail: chris@gilbraithtankers.co.uk

▶ Giles Haulage Ltd, Adderson Way, Ipswich, IP6 0RL Tel: (01473) 830644

▶ Gillott Transport, Steel Street, Rotherham, South Yorkshire, S61 1DF Tel: (01709) 553325 Fax: (01709) 558586

▶ Gills Transport Ltd, Ever Ready Site Station Road, Four Ashes Industrial Estate, Four Ashes, Wolverhampton, WV10 7DB Tel: (01902) 791366 Fax: (01902) 791538

▶ Gist, Three Cherry Trees Lane, Hemel Hempstead Industrial Estate, Hemel Hempstead, Hertfordshire, HP2 7PZ Tel: (01442) 241442 Fax: (01442) 235717

Gist, Wardentree Lane, Pinchbeck, Spalding, Lincolnshire, PE11 3UG Tel: (01775) 764000 Fax: (01775) 764101

▶ Gist Ltd, Lichfield Road Industrial Estate, Apollo, Tamworth, Staffordshire, B79 7TA Tel: (01827) 310044 Fax: (01827) 310055

▶ Gist, Pickerings Road, Halebank, Widnes, Cheshire, WA8 8XW Tel: 0151-420 8240 Fax: 0151-424 6556

▶ Glasgow Building Preservation Trust, Wellpark Enterprise Centre, 120 Sydney Street, Glasgow, G31 1JF Tel: 0141-550 7500 Fax: 0141-550 4443

▶ Global Moving Solutions, Unit O2 Clyde Workshops, Fullarton Road, Glasgow East Investment Park, Glasgow, G32 8YL Tel: 0141-646 2700 Fax: 0141-646 2704

▶ Global Transport Services Ltd, 2 Horton Industrial Park, Horton Road, West Drayton, Middlesex, UB7 8JD Tel: (01895) 447888 Fax: (01895) 420258

▶ GMC Transport Ltd, 12 Lansdowne Road, Tilbury, Essex, RM18 7QB Tel: (01375) 851607 Fax: (01375) 851607

Goddard Warehousing Ltd, Compton House, Furnace Lane, Finedon, Wellingborough, Northamptonshire, NN9 5NY Tel: (01536) 726060 Fax: (01536) 726006 E-mail: admin@goddardwarehousing.com

▶ Godwin Transport, Central Way, Feltham, Middlesex, TW14 0UQ Tel: (020) 8844 2121

▶ Gold Star Transport Ltd, Fenn Corner, St. Mary Hoo, Rochester, Kent, ME3 8RF Tel: (01634) 270061 Fax: (01634) 270075

Goman Couriers Ltd, 58c Arthur Street, Redditch, Worcestershire, B98 8JY Tel: (01527) 515055 Fax: (01527) 510779

Gondrand U.K., Gondrand House, 2 Oriental Road, London, E16 2BZ Tel: (020) 7540 2000 Fax: (020) 7540 2001 E-mail: info@gondrand.co.uk

▶ Peter Graeme Ltd, Unit 14 Flemington Industrial Park, Craigneuk Street, Motherwell, Lanarkshire, ML1 2NT Tel: (01698) 269111 Fax: (01698) 269666

▶ Grampian Maclennan Distribution Services, Industrial Estate, Cornhill Road, Aberchirder, Huntly, Aberdeenshire, AB54 7ST Tel: (01466) 780345 Fax: (01466) 780644

▶ Grampian Maclennan's Distribution Services Ltd, Station Road, Fordoun, Laurencekirk, Kincardineshire, AB30 1NN Tel: (01561) 320641 Fax: (01561) 320643

Tom Granby Liverpool, Caddick Road, Knowsley Business Park, Prescot, Merseyside, L34 9HP Tel: 0151-548 8768 Fax: 0151-549 1979 E-mail: a.smith@dbcfoodservice.co.uk

▶ Grange Storage & Distribution, Grange Road, Batley, West Yorkshire, WF17 6LW Tel: (01924) 420777

▶ Grayston Automotive Ltd, Station Yard, Station Lane, Nateby, Preston, PR3 0LT Tel: (01995) 602116 Fax: (01995) 600188 E-mail: sales@grayston.co.uk

▶ Great Bear Distribution Ltd, N Industrial Estate, Sinfin Lane, Derby, DE24 9GL Tel: (01332) 770099 Fax: (01332) 770061

▶ Gregory Distribution, St Erth Industrial Estate, Rose-An-Grouse, Canonstown, Hayle, Cornwall, TR27 6LP Tel: (01736) 754291

▶ GTS Transport Ltd, Thornton Yard, Strathore Road, Thornton, Kirkcaldy, Fife, KY1 4DF Tel: (01592) 631880 Fax: (01592) 770101

▶ Guardian Moving & Storage, Clifton View, East Mains Industrial Estate, Broxburn, West Lothian, EH52 5NE Tel: 0131-551 6780 Fax: 0131-552 1269 E-mail: sales@guardianremovals.co.uk

▶ Gunns International Transport & Shipping Ltd, Bronze Age Way, Erith, Kent, DA8 1AX Tel: (01322) 441188 Fax: (01322) 441199

▶ Gwyn Davies Transport, Unit 3, Llandow Industrial Estate, Cowbridge, South Glamorgan, CF71 7PB Tel: (01446) 774862

▶ H & B Logistics, Unit 3, Elizabeths Park, Denton, Manchester, M34 3RU Tel: 0161-335 9009 Fax: 0161-335 9747

▶ H C Herbert & Son Maesteg Ltd, 3 Brynmawr Place, Maesteg, Mid Glamorgan, CF34 9PB Tel: (01656) 733264 Fax: (01656) 736800

H Curtis & Sons, Stanton Wick Farm, Stanton Wick, Pensford, Bristol, BS39 4DB Tel: (01761) 490372 Fax: (01761) 490004 E-mail: andrew@hcurtis.co.uk

▶ H D Fraser & Sons, Balblair Cottage, Balblair, Dingwall, Ross-Shire, IV7 8LG Tel: (01381) 610268 Fax: (01381) 610292

H E Payne, 66 The Lane, Wyboston, Bedford, MK44 3AP Tel: (01480) 212798 Fax: (01480) 212070 E-mail: admin@hepayne.co.uk

▶ H F Owen Transport Ltd, Ddol Farm Bethel, Bethel, Caernarfon, Gwynedd, LL55 1UN Tel: (01248) 670487 Fax: (01248) 671201 E-mail: enquiries@hfowentransport.co.uk

▶ H Gittins, 27 Aston Road, Bromsgrove, Worcestershire, B60 3EX Tel: (01527) 870400 Fax: (01527) 870403 E-mail: haulage@gittinstransport.co.uk

▶ H L Friel & Son Ltd, 47-49 Mearns Street, Greenock, Renfrewshire, PA15 4BN Tel: (01475) 722056

▶ H & P Freightways Ltd, 1203 Hedon Road, Hull, HU9 5LY Tel: (01482) 702185 Fax: (01482) 701722 E-mail: enquiries@hpfreightways.com

▶ H & R Gray Haulage Ltd, 1a Bandeath Industrial Estate, Throsk, Stirling, FK7 7NP Tel: (01786) 489111 Fax: (01786) 489222

▶ H & S Roe & Sons Ltd, Roe House, Boundry Lane, South Hykeham, Lincoln, LN6 9NQ Tel: (01522) 681542 Fax: (01522) 680199

▶ H Sladen & Son Ltd, Daniels Way, Hucknall, Nottingham, NG15 7LL Tel: 0115-840 2203 Fax: 0115-840 2204

▶ H Tideswell & Sons Ltd, The Glebe Garage, Hazles Cross Road, Kingsley, Stoke-on-Trent, ST10 2AX Tel: (01538) 753887 Fax: (01538) 750385

H Whittaker & Son Ltd, Heapy Street, Macclesfield, Cheshire, SK11 7JD Tel: (01625) 424637 Fax: (01625) 613470

▶ H Williams Haulage, 115 Hampstead Hill, Birmingham, B20 1BX Tel: 0121-358 5755 Fax: 0121-358 4020

▶ H Young Ltd, Main Street, Glengarnock, Beith, Ayrshire, KA14 3BD Tel: (01505) 682101 Fax: (01505) 682333

Halcion Logistics Ltd, Unit 1 Parkhouse Road East, Parkhouse Industrial Estate East, Parkhouse Industrial Estate Ea, Newcastle, Staffordshire, ST5 7RB Tel: (01782) 566665 Fax: (01782) 565667 E-mail: info@halcion.co.uk

▶ Halls Removals, Phoenix Works, Tram Street, Platt Bridge, Wigan, Lancashire, WN2 5JE Tel: (01942) 867448 Fax: (01942) 864814

Hamilton Shipping Ltd, 14 Clarendon Road, Belfast, BT1 3BG Tel: (028) 9053 3200 Fax: (028) 9053 3222 E-mail: containers@hamiltonshipping.com

Tom Hamilton Transport, Burnside, Kinglassie, Lochgelly, Fife, KY5 0UP Tel: (01592) 882307 E-mail: tom@tht.co.uk

Hamnett Machinery Removals, Gibbet Street, Halifax, West Yorkshire, HX2 0AR Tel: (01422) 345571 Fax: (01422) 346766 E-mail: hamnett@btinternet.com

▶ Hampson Haulage Ltd, 49 Grove Lane, Smethwick, West Midlands, B66 2SZ Tel: 0121-558 3235 Fax: 0121-555 5774

▶ Hanbury Davies Containers Ltd, 1 Walton Avenue, Felixstowe, Suffolk, IP11 3AG Tel: (01394) 675356 Fax: (01394) 673538

▶ Hanson Logistics Ltd, 303 Brownsburn Industrial Esta, Airdrie, Lanarkshire, ML6 9SE Tel: (01236) 768822

Hanson Recycling & Demolition, Sheffield Bottom, Off Station Road, Theale, Reading, RG7 4AJ Tel: 0118-957 6243

▶ Harbour Haulage Ltd, Damhead Way, Peterhead, Aberdeenshire, AB42 3GY Tel: (01779) 481410 Fax: (01779) 490727

▶ Hargreaves Bulk Liquid Transport, Fryers Road, Walsall, WS3 2XJ Tel: (01922) 470799 Fax: (01922) 470790

Harradines Removals, 25-27 Gordon Road, London, SE15 2AF Tel: (020) 7639 1791 Fax: (020) 7639 9408 E-mail: enquiries@harradines.co.uk

▶ Harrow Green, 5 Centrus, Arenson Way, Houghton Regis, Dunstable, Bedfordshire, LU5 5BN Tel: (01582) 500890 Fax: (01582) 665777

▶ Hartley Haulage, 150 Stevenson Road, Sheffield, S9 3XG Tel: 0114-243 4569 Fax: 0114-243 4621

N.S. Harvey, Station Farm, Sleaford Road, Tattershall, Lincoln, LN4 4JG Tel: (01526) 343719 Fax: (01526) 343729

▶ Hatfield Rob Haulage, Beechcroft, Main Street, Kilnwick, Driffield, North Humberside, YO25 9JD Tel: (01377) 270005 Fax: (01377) 270006

Hatton Logistics Ltd, Station Road, Blaxton, Doncaster, South Yorkshire, DN9 3AG Tel: (01302) 770284 Fax: (01302) 771663 E-mail: msmith@hattonlogistics.fsbusiness.co.uk

Haul Small Ltd, Unit 2 Knightwood Court, Edison Way, Gapton Hall Industrial Estate, Great Yarmouth, Norfolk, NR31 0NG Tel: (01493) 604691 Fax: (01493) 604692

▶ Haulways Road Haulage Services, Pleasant Street, Lyng, West Bromwich, West Midlands, B70 7DP Tel: 0121-553 1975 Fax: 0121-500 5845

▶ Hauser Ltd, Heighington Lane, Aycliffe Industrial Park, Newton Aycliffe, County Durham, DL5 6UE Tel: (01325) 300855 Fax: (01325) 300844 E-mail: northeast@hauser.co.uk

▶ Hauser Sheffield Ltd, Alliance House, Roman Ridge Road, Sheffield, S9 1GB Tel: 0114-244 9977 Fax: 0114-242 3481 E-mail: sheffield@hauser.co.uk

▶ Hay's Distribution, Penilee Road, Hillington Industrial Estate, Glasgow, G52 4UW Tel: 0141-883 4555

▶ Hays Logistics, Unit 7 Clydesmill Place, Clydesmill Industrial Estate, Glasgow, G32 8RF Tel: 0141-643 3800 Fax: 0141-643 3801

▶ Hayton Coulthard Ltd, The Garage, Kirk Brae, Twynholm, Kirkcudbright, DG6 4NX Tel: (01557) 860661 Fax: (01557) 860293

Hayward, Portland Street, Walsall, WS2 8AD Tel: (01922) 621417 Fax: (01922) 642943 E-mail: supertruckin@haytrans.co.uk

Hayward, Portland Street, Walsall, WS2 8AD Tel: (01922) 621417 Fax: (01922) 642943 E-mail: supertruckin@haytrans.co.uk

Haywood Transport Services, Chelmsford Road, Rawreth, Wickford, Essex, SS11 8SY Tel: (01268) 561305 Fax: (01268) 561304

▶ Healey Transport Ltd, Herring Lane, Pinchbeck, Spalding, Lincolnshire, PE11 3ST Tel: (01775) 722946 Fax: (01775) 722549

▶ Heanor Haulage Ltd, Wesley Street, Langley Mill, Nottingham, NG16 4AL Tel: (01773) 715265 Fax: (01773) 530829 E-mail: sales@heanorhaulage.co.uk

H.F. Heard Ltd, Lloyd Maunder Road, Willand, Cullompton, Devon, EX15 2PJ Tel: (01884) 821768 Fax: (01884) 821866

▶ Hebrides Haulage Ltd, Rigs Road, Stornoway, Isle of Lewis, HS1 2RF Tel: (01851) 703255 Fax: (01851) 706001

▶ indicates data change since last edition

ROAD TRANSPORT AND HAULAGE

– continued

Claude Hellowell Ltd, Thorpe Garage, Triangle, Sowerby Bridge, West Yorkshire, HX6 3DL Tel: (01422) 823248 Fax: (01422) 824234

▶ Henry Gillies, Roman Camp Blaes Bing, Drumshoreland Road, Pumpherston, Livingston, West Lothian, EH53 0LH Tel: (01506) 431622 Fax: (01506) 439954

▶ Henry Gillies Haulage Contractors, 62 Pumpherston Road, Uphall Station, Livingston, West Lothian, EH54 5PT Tel: (01506) 431321 Fax: (01506) 439954

▶ Henry Gray, 4 Randolph Place, Randolph Industrial Estate, Kirkcaldy, Fife, KY1 2YX Tel: (01592) 652684

▶ Heritage Refurbishment, Cherry Holt Road, Bourne, Lincolnshire, PE10 9LA Tel: (01778) 425543 Fax: (01778) 423998

▶ Hexagon International Transport Ltd, Cheetwood Road, Manchester, M8 8AQ Tel: 0161-792 1912

▶ Hick Logisticks, Unit 57 Symondscliffe Way, Severn Bridge Industrial Estate, Portskewett, Caldicot, Gwent, NP26 5PW Tel: (01291) 421954 Fax: (01291) 430504

▶ Highland Haulage Ltd, 11 Walker Place, Inverness, IV1 1TY Tel: (01463) 714444 Fax: (01463) 714445

▶ Hills Delivery Ltd, Feeder Road, Bristol, BS2 0TW Tel: 0117-971 1717

▶ Leonard Hind, 4 Abbots Road, Grangemouth, Stirlingshire, FK3 8HX Tel: (01324) 483652

▶ Leonard Hind & Son, Mandal House, South Shore Road, Grangemouth, Stirlingshire, FK3 8AE Tel: (01324) 474719 Fax: (01324) 473211 E-mail: sales@lenhind.com

Joseph Holloway Ltd, Valencia Wharf, Churchbridge, Oldbury, West Midlands, B69 2AP Tel: 0121-552 2146 Fax: 0121-552 2991

▶ Home Delivery Network, Arkwright Way, North Newmoor Industrial Estate, Irvine, Ayrshire, KA11 4JU Tel: (01294) 213458 Fax: (01294) 217244

▶ Home Delivery Network Ltd, Heathcote Way, Heathcote Industrial Estate, Warwick, CV34 6QP Tel: (01926) 311430 Fax: (01926) 450605

Horley Services Ltd, Salfords Industrial Estate, Salfords, Redhill, RH1 5ES Tel: (01293) 771481 Fax: (01293) 786701 E-mail: sales@horleysg.demon.co.uk

▶ Horsleys Of Stafford, Unit 2, Tollgate Drive, Tollgate Industrial Estate, Stafford, ST16 3HS Tel: (01785) 253723 Fax: (01785) 257662 E-mail: sales@horsleysofstafford.co.uk

Hottot Transport, Blue Waters Industrial Estate, Bovey Tracey, Newton Abbot, Devon, TQ13 9YF Tel: (01626) 833147 Fax: (01626) 834200

Howard Tenens Andover Ltd, Unit 2c Macadam Way, West Portway, Andover, Hampshire, SP10 3LF Tel: (01264) 324449 Fax: (01264) 332253 E-mail: boston@tenens.com

Howard Tenens Associates Ltd, Kingfisher Business Park, London Road, Thrupp, Stroud, Gloucestershire, GL5 2BY Tel: (01453) 885087 Fax: (01453) 886145 E-mail: enquiries@tenens.com

Howard Tenens Boston Ltd, Riverside Industrial Estate, Marsh Lane, Boston, Lincolnshire, PE21 7SZ Tel: (01205) 311808 Fax: (01205) 354086 E-mail: sales@tenens.com

Howarth Bros Haulage Ltd, Unit 3 Moss Lane, Royton, Oldham, OL2 6HR Tel: (01706) 847514 Fax: (01706) 882607 E-mail: howarth.bros@btinternet.com

▶ Howland Haulage Co., Fernside, London Road, Dunkirk, Faversham, Kent, ME13 9LL Tel: (01227) 751465 Fax: (01227) 752586

▶ Hoyle & Dean Ltd, Hillcrest Garage, Argyle Street, Accrington, Lancashire, BB5 1DJ Tel: (01254) 232467 Fax: (01254) 872821

▶ Hudson Haulage, Unit 8 Grove Lane, Elmswell, Bury St. Edmunds, Suffolk, IP30 9HN Tel: (01359) 242777 Fax: (01359) 242567 E-mail: info@hudsonhaulage.com

Hudsons Of Dudley Ltd, Canal St/Brickkiln Street, Brierley Hill, West Midlands, DY5 3LQ Tel: (01384) 262126 Fax: (01384) 481170 E-mail: hudsonsofdudley@aol.com

Joseph Hughes & Sons Ltd, Black Flag Works, Pottery Street, Castleford, West Yorkshire, WF10 1NJ Tel: (01977) 552424 Fax: (01977) 551105 E-mail: juilebresnan@josephughes.co.uk

▶ Hunt Bros Ltd, Sankey Valley Industrial Estate, Junction Lane, Newton-le-Willows, Merseyside, WA12 8DN Tel: (01925) 222068 Fax: (01925) 220407

Hunt S Removals Ltd, 11-13 Market Close, Crewe, CW1 2NA Tel: (01606) 44655 Fax: (01270) 255884 E-mail: enquiries@huntsremovals.co.uk

▶ Huntdene Ltd, Thames Europort Clipper Boulevard, Crossways, Dartford, DA2 6QB Tel: (01322) 278855 Fax: (01322) 278866

▶ Hurst (Transport) Ltd, Osborne Road, Stallingborough, Grimsby, South Humberside, DN41 8DG Tel: (01469) 577077

Hyde Transport, Pretoria Road, Chertsey, Surrey, KT16 9LW Tel: (01932) 567964 Fax: (01932) 567964

▶ Hyway Logistics, Lincoln Court, Washington Street, Bolton, BL3 5EZ Tel: (01204) 365403 Fax: (01204) 365418 E-mail: delivery@hywaylogistics.co.uk

▶ I A & C Maciver Ltd, Unit 4 & 5, Parkend Industrial Estate, Sandwick, Isle Of Lewis, HS2 0AN Tel: (01851) 705050

▶ I C D Ltd, 1 Paxton Place, Skelmersdale, Lancashire, WN8 9QH Tel: (01695) 722031 Fax: (01695) 51803

▶ I Craig (Haulage) Ltd, Eilanda, Drove Loan, Head of Muir, Denny, Stirlingshire, FK6 5LE Tel: (01324) 812250

▶ I D S Transport, Unit 1, Honeybourne Airfield Trading Estate, Honeybourne, Evesham, Worcestershire, WR11 7QF Tel: (01386) 841363 Fax: (01386) 835574

▶ Ian Craig (Haulage) Ltd, 44-46 Broomhill Road, Bonnybridge, Stirlingshire, FK4 2AN Tel: (01324) 812250

▶ Ian Reid Removals, Hagdale Industrial Estate, Baltasound, Unst, Shetland, ZE2 9DS Tel: (01957) 711410

▶ Ict Express, Coleshill Freight Terminal, Station Road, Coleshill, Birmingham, B46 1JJ Tel: (01675) 463000 Fax: (01675) 465999

Imorex, Dooley Road, Felixstowe, Suffolk, IP11 3HG Tel: (01394) 607743 Fax: (01394) 607767 E-mail: info@imorex.co.uk

▶ Imp Freight Services Ltd, The Chapel House, Kings Road, Immingham, South Humberside, DN40 1QS Tel: (01469) 577566 Fax: (01469) 572998

▶ Imp Transport, Unit 4, George Street, Lincoln, LN5 8LG Tel: (01522) 560414 Fax: (01522) 535510

▶ Imr Transport, Unit 10 Ballon Wood Industrial Estate, Coventry Lane, Bramcote, Nottingham, NG9 3GJ Tel: 0115-928 8683 Fax: 0115-928 1197

▶ Inchcape Automotive (Scotland) Ltd, Arrol Square, Deans Industrial Estate, Deans, Livingston, West Lothian, EH54 8QZ Tel: (01506) 465000 Fax: (01506) 463322

▶ Initial City Link, 8 Logman Centre, Greenbank CR, East Tullos Industrial Estate, Aberdeen, AB12 3BG Tel: (01224) 249966 Fax: (01224) 249624

▶ Initial City Link, 12-13 Blenheim Road, Cressex Business Park, High Wycombe, Buckinghamshire, HP12 3RS Tel: (01494) 769030 Fax: (01494) 512635

▶ Interdean Relocation, Blackburn Industrial Estate, Kinellar, Aberdeen, AB21 0RX Tel: (01224) 790000 Fax: (01224) 791900

▶ Interlink Express Parcels Ltd, 10 Blackburn Road, Bathgate, West Lothian, EH48 2EY Tel: (01506) 630459 Fax: (01506) 634013

▶ Interlink Express Parcels Ltd, Borderline Garage, Biggar, Lanarkshire, ML12 6JJ Tel: (01899) 221226 Fax: (01899) 221279

▶ Interlink Express Parcels Ltd, Unit 2a Meadowbrook Park, Halfway, Sheffield, S20 3PJ Tel: 0114-251 1110 Fax: 0114-251 0888 E-mail: depot444@interlinkexpress.com

▶ Interlink Express Parcels Ltd, 1 Junction Industrial Estate, Dartmouth Road, Smethwick, West Midlands, B66 1AX Tel: 0121-525 2020 Fax: 0121-525 2090

▶ Interlink Express Parcels Ltd, 10 Queens Way, Southampton, SO14 3AZ Tel: (023) 8039 3666

▶ Interlink Express Parcels Ltd, 49d Sadler Forster Way, Teesside Industrial Estate, Stockton-on-Tees, Cleveland, TS17 9JY Tel: (01642) 751122 Fax: (01642) 750055

▶ Interlink Express Parcels Ltd, Units 4-5, Coppice Lane, Walsall Wood, Walsall, WS9 9AA Tel: (01922) 745422 Fax: (01922) 745433

▶ Interlink Express Parcels Ltd, 12 & 13 Shipston Close, Worcester, WR4 9XN Tel: (01905) 754055 Fax: (01905) 754234

▶ Internal Transport Garage, Unit 1d, West Byrehill Ind Estate, Kilwinning, Ayrshire, KA13 6HR Tel: (01294) 552129

▶ International Parcel Express, 1 Quayside Lodge, William Morris Way, London, SW6 2UZ Tel: (020) 7731 6888 Fax: (020) 7384 2384

▶ Ipg Imports, Whiteley House, 84 Miller Street, Glasgow, G1 1DT Tel: 0141-204 5288

▶ Isbister Bros, Quoyloo, Stromness, Orkney, KW16 3LT Tel: (01856) 841525 Fax: (01856) 841525

▶ J A F Carriers Ltd, 14 Fairfield Street, Dundee, DD3 8HX Tel: (01382) 833366

▶ J A Hutchinson & Sons Haulage Ltd, Station Road, Ailsworth, Peterborough, PE5 7AH Tel: (01733) 380955

J A Renton & Sons, Ashby Road, Thringstone, Coalville, Leicestershire, LE67 8UH Tel: (01530) 222224 Fax: (01530) 224069 E-mail: renton.lorries@btinternet.com

▶ J B Rawcliffe & Sons Ltd, Stanley Way, Stanley Industrial Estate, Skelmersdale, Lancashire, WN8 8EA Tel: (01695) 737880 Fax: (01695) 737881

▶ J B Transport, Leyland House, Old Stone Bridge, Ironville, Nottingham, NG16 5NE Tel: (01773) 602762 Fax: (01773) 540635

J B Wheaton & Sons Ltd, Chard Junction, Chard, Somerset, TA20 4QN Tel: (01460) 220531 Fax: (01460) 221456 E-mail: mark.wheaton@jbwheaton.co.uk

▶ J Bairner & Sons, 69 Main Street, Douglas, Lanark, ML11 0QG Tel: (01555) 851409 Fax: (01555) 851520

▶ J Barrett Haulage Ltd, Wellyhole Street, Oldham, OL4 3BB Tel: 0161-633 0224 Fax: 0161-628 7472

J Bradshaw & Sons Ltd, High Street, Sturton-By-Stow, Lincoln, LN1 2BX Tel: (01427) 788223 Fax: (01427) 788498

▶ J C S Express, Bellshill Road, Uddingston, Glasgow, G71 7NT Tel: (01698) 818555 Fax: (01698) 811728

▶ J F Peden (Edinburgh) Ltd, 71 Polton Street, Bonnyrigg, Midlothian, EH19 3DQ Tel: 0131-663 7009

▶ J G B Logistics Ltd, Altens Lorry Park, Hareness Road, Aberdeen, AB12 3LE Tel: (01224) 876455

J G B Transport Ltd, Units 1-2 Altens Lorry Park, Hareness Road, Aberdeen, AB12 3LE Tel: (01224) 876674 Fax: (01224) 874222 E-mail: alan.simpson@jgbtransport.com

▶ J G B Transport, Building 789, Murray Road, Europark, Dunfermline, Fife, KY11 2EB Tel: (01383) 416009 Fax: (01383) 414176

J G Stamper, The Cottage Brooklands, Carleton Road, Penrith, Cumbria, CA11 8LT Tel: (01768) 863032 Fax: (01768) 863976

▶ J G Winterbottom Charlsworth Ltd, Raglan Street, Hyde, Cheshire, SK14 2DX Tel: 0161-368 9090 Fax: 0161-368 0005

▶ J H Cunningham, 13 Glasgow Road, Kilmarnock, Ayrshire, KA3 1TJ Tel: (01563) 522640

J H Davies Haulage Ltd, Foundry Lane, Ditton, Widnes, Cheshire, WA8 8TZ Tel: 0151-420 8877 Fax: 0151-495 1994 E-mail: admin@jhdavies.com

▶ J I N Transport Service, Drum Industrial Estate, Drum Industrial Estate, Chester le Street, County Durham, DH2 1AG Tel: 0191-410 0525 Fax: 0191-411 1552

▶ J Innes & Son, Banff, Banff, AB45 2YX Tel: (07896) 999900 Fax: (01261) 843033

▶ J J Bartlett Haulage Ltd, Hotchkiss Way, Binley Industrial Estate, Coventry, CV3 2RL Tel: (024) 7644 5111 Fax: (024) 7644 5303

▶ J & J Murdoch, Station Garage Station Yard Industrial Estate, Oakwell Road, Castle Douglas, Kirkcudbrightshire, DG7 1LA Tel: (01556) 502062 Fax: (01556) 503282

▶ J L Young, 4 Skye Road, Shawfarm Industrial Estate, Prestwick, Ayrshire, KA9 2TA Tel: (01292) 671716 Fax: (01292) 671716

▶ J Long & Sons (Haulage) Ltd, Sandleas Way, Leeds, LS15 8AW Tel: 0113-264 0106

▶ J M C Logistics UK Ltd, St Francis House, Old Bath Road, Colnbrook, Slough, SL3 0NP Tel: (01753) 689745 Fax: (01753) 684479

▶ J M Gorry & Son Ltd, Middlegate, White Lund Industrial Estate, Morecambe, Lancashire, LA3 3BN Tel: (01524) 67530 Fax: (01524) 33446 E-mail: info@jmgorry.co.uk

▶ J & M Taylor Haulage Ltd, 9 Wallace Street, Paisley, Renfrewshire, PA3 2BU Tel: 0141-889 3513

▶ J Mchugh, 20 Carmoney Road, Eglinton, Londonderry, BT47 3JJ Tel: (028) 7186 0162

▶ J & P Vehicle Deliveries Ltd, 1 Green Acre Park, Howard Street, Bolton, BL1 8HN Tel: (01204) 366464 Fax: (01204) 373465

▶ J R Elliott, Rigg Farm, Auchinleck, Cumnock, Ayrshire, KA18 1RT Tel: (01290) 420000 Fax: (01290) 422113

▶ J R Harding & Sons Frome Ltd, Manor Furlong, Frome, Somerset, BA11 4RJ Tel: (01373) 465581 Fax: (01373) 467352 E-mail: enquiries@jrhardings.co.uk

▶ J R Holland Food Services Ltd, 245 Dukesway, Team Valley Trading Estate, Gateshead, Tyne & Wear, NE11 0PZ Tel: 0191-491 0856 Fax: 0191-487 9021

J R Hood Ltd, Chesney Farm, Wansford Road, Driffield, North Humberside, YO25 5NW Tel: (01377) 252135 Fax: (01377) 252958

J R Marriott Collingham Ltd, Brunel Drive, Newark, Nottinghamshire, NG24 2EG Tel: (01636) 703800 Fax: (01636) 605254

▶ J R Smith Transport Ltd, Langdon Street, Tring, Hertfordshire, HP23 6DJ Tel: (0844) 3578282 Fax: (0870) 0664380 E-mail: info@jrsmith.co.uk

▶ J Revis & Sons, Southfield Lane, Tockwith, York, YO26 7QP Tel: (01423) 358181 Fax: (01423) 358051

▶ J S T International Transport, Room 101-102, Building 309, World Freight Terminal, Manchester Airport, Manchester, M90 5PH Tel: 0161-498 8882

▶ J Sinclair, 1 Eglinton, Kelliebank, Alloa, Clackmannanshire, FK10 1NT Tel: (01259) 212657 Fax: (01259) 213277

J W J Car & Commercial Repairs, 113-115 Codicote Road, Welwyn, Hertfordshire, AL6 9TY Tel: (01438) 820351

▶ J W Suckling Transport Ltd, Manor Road, West Thurrock, Grays, Essex, RM20 4BA Tel: (01708) 861234 Fax: (01708) 861483

J White & Co Tde Ltd, Meadow Bank Road, Rotherham, South Yorkshire, S61 2NF Tel: (01709) 740099 Fax: (01709) 740438 E-mail: jwhite-tde@jwhite-tde.co.uk

J. Jackson (Transport) Ltd, 31-33 Midland Road, Scunthorpe, North Lincolnshire, DN16 1DQ Tel: (01724) 856925 Fax: (01724) 859835

Jade 2000 Ltd, 38 Dukewood Road, Clayton West, Huddersfield, HD8 9HF Tel: (01484) 863752 Fax: (01484) 862573

▶ Jaguar Freight Services Ltd, The Linen House, 253 Kilburn Lane, London, W10 4BQ Tel: (020) 8964 2621 Fax: (020) 8964 1055 E-mail: sales@jaguarfreight.com

▶ James Booth Bolton Ltd, Manchester Road, Westhoughton, Bolton, BL5 3QH Tel: (01942) 818800 Fax: (01942) 818484 E-mail: sales@jamesbooth.co.uk

James Jack Listing Services Ltd, Oilfield Support Base, Shore Road, Invergordon, Ross-Shire, IV18 0EX Tel: (01349) 853000 Fax: (01349) 853416E-mail: invergordon@james-jack.co.uk

▶ James Kemball Ltd, 1 Hodgkinson Road, Felixstowe, Suffolk, IP11 3QT Tel: (01394) 601500 Fax: (01394) 673006

James Kinnear Thornton Ltd, 91 Main Street, Thornton, Kirkcaldy, Fife, KY1 4AQ Tel: (01592) 774352 Fax: (01592) 771411

▶ James Meffan Ltd, Parkend Farm, Kirriemuir, Angus, DD8 4PD Tel: (01575) 572152 Fax: (01575) 572130

▶ James Moffat & Sons Cardenden Ltd, Fulmar Way, Donibristle Industrial Park, Hillend, Dunfermline, Fife, KY11 9YY Tel: (01383) 821888 Fax: (01383) 821880

▶ James Nuttall Transport Ltd, Royle Barn Road, Rochdale, Lancashire, OL11 3DT Tel: (01706) 356255 Fax: (01706) 354806 E-mail: sales@jamesnuttall.co.uk

▶ James Smith Denny Ltd, Boghead Garage, Broad Street, Denny, Stirlingshire, FK6 6EA Tel: (01324) 823823 Fax: (01324) 825476

▶ James Smith Denny Ltd, Boghead Garage, Broad Street, Denny, Stirlingshire, FK6 6EA Tel: (01324) 823823 Fax: (01324) 825476

James Stevenson Quarries Ltd, Clinty Quarry, 215 Doury Road, Ballymena, County Antrim, BT43 6SS Tel: (028) 2565 6302 Fax: (028) 2564 6495

▶ James Timms Transport Ltd, 5 Quedgeley Trading Estate West, Bristol Road, Hardwicke, Gloucester, GL2 4PA Tel: (01452) 722880 Fax: (01452) 722992

▶ JBP Transport Ltd, Oakmills, Lower Mill Street, Tillicoultry, Clackmannanshire, FK13 6BP Tel: (01259) 750459 Fax: (01259) 750459

Jensa Distribution Ltd, Unit 3-5 Manton Centre, Manton Lane, Manton Industrial Estate, Bedford, MK41 7PX Tel: (01234) 782679 Fax: (01234) 349918

▶ Jesscam Transport, Gannow Lane, Burnley, Lancashire, BB12 6HY Tel: (01282) 423366

▶ Jim Brackenridge Transport Ltd, Unit 10 Hareness Park, Hareness Circle, Altens Industrial Estate, Aberdeen, AB12 3QY Tel: (01224) 899677 Fax: (01224) 899692

▶ Jim Brackenridge Transport Ltd, Old Inns, Wardpark Industrial Estate, Cumbernauld, Glasgow, G68 0DA Tel: (01236) 458908 Fax: (01236) 735205

▶ John B Mcbean (Haulage) Ltd, Mid Camp Industrial Estate, Kirknewton, Midlothian, EH27 8DF Tel: (01506) 881325

▶ John Catlow & Son Leeds Ltd, Scotch Park Trading Estate, Forge Lane, Leeds, LS12 2PT Tel: 0113-263 0526 Fax: 0113-263 0526

John Cotton, 111 Pallance Road, Cowes, Isle of Wight, PO31 8LS Tel: (01983) 299722 Fax: (01983) 299722

▶ John Duncan Removals, Polton House, Polton Road, Lasswade, Midlothian, EH18 1BW Tel: 0131-654 1200 Fax: 0131-654 1006

▶ John Langley, Sedgway Industrial Estate, Common Road, Witchford, Ely, Cambridgeshire, CB6 2HY Tel: (01353) 667777 Fax: (01353) 666866

▶ John M Allen Transport Ltd, Cuckoo Bridge Farm, Cuckoo Bridge, Spalding, Lincolnshire, PE11 3JY Tel: (01775) 722428

▶ John Mcdonald Airfreight Forwarding, Units 1 & 2 Cargo Terminal, Glasgow Airport, Abbotsinch, Paisley, Renfrewshire, PA3 2SG Tel: 0141-887 7722 Fax: 0141-889 3761

▶ John Mack (Haulage) Ltd, Greens Road, Yaxham Road Industrial Estate, Dereham, Norfolk, NR20 3TG Tel: (01362) 691150

▶ John Mitchell Grangemouth Ltd, Earls Road, Grangemouth, Stirlingshire, FK3 8XA Tel: (01324) 486511 Fax: (01324) 665116

John Owen Aggregates Ltd, Unit 11 Monksbridge Trading Estate, Outgang Lane, Dinnington, Sheffield, S25 3QZ Tel: (01909) 564191 Fax: (01909) 564234

▶ John Phillips & Sons Haulage Ltd, Borland, Cumnock, Ayrshire, KA18 4PQ Tel: (01290) 420831

John Raymond Transport Ltd, South Road, Bridgend Industrial Estate, Bridgend, Mid Glamorgan, CF31 3PU Tel: (01656) 666800 Fax: (01656) 666801 E-mail: customers@jrt.co.uk

▶ John Roberts Ffestiniog Ltd, Bont Newydd, Cwm Cynfal, Blaenau Ffestiniog, Gwynedd, LL41 4PT Tel: (01766) 762768 Fax: (01766) 762403

John S Braid & Co. Ltd, Maritime House, 143 Woodville Street, Glasgow, G51 2RQ Tel: 0141-445 2525 Fax: 0141-440 1238 E-mail: ddarroch@braidco.com

▶ John T Evans Haulage Contractors, Atlantic Way, Barry, South Glamorgan, CF63 3RA Tel: (01446) 420800 Fax: (01446) 421015

▶ John Truswell & Sons Garages Ltd, Fall Bank Industrial Estate, Dodworth, Barnsley, South Yorkshire, S75 3LS Tel: (01226) 289471 Fax: (01226) 249402

John Truswell & Sons Garages Ltd, Fall Bank Industrial Estate, Dodworth, Barnsley, South Yorkshire, S75 3LS Tel: (01226) 289471 Fax: (01226) 249402 E-mail: traffic@truswell.co.uk

▶ John Weaver Transport, Unit 3 15-17 Willis Way, Poole, Dorset, BH15 3SS Tel: (01202) 673089 Fax: (01202) 678256

Johnsons (Burscough) Ltd, 3 Red Cat Lane, Burscough, Ormskirk, Lancashire, L40 0RD Tel: (01704) 893103

▶ Jones & Jones, Goole Road, Moorends, Doncaster, South Yorkshire, DN8 4JX Tel: (01405) 812413 Fax: (01405) 816363

▶ Joss Aberdeen Ltd, Rigifa, Cove, Aberdeen, AB12 3LR Tel: (01224) 774422 Fax: (01224) 772444

▶ JRS Logistics, Unit D Mid Cragie Trading Estate, Mid Craigie Road, Dundee, DD4 7RH Tel: (01382) 450404 Fax: (01382) 450506

▶ Judds Transport Ltd, Allers Back Lane, Kingston, Hazelbury Bryan, Sturminster Newton, Dorset, DT10 2DT Tel: (01258) 817394

ROAD TRANSPORT AND HAULAGE

– *continued*

▶ K Carriers, Continental House, Avis Way, Newhaven, East Sussex, BN9 0DH Tel: (01273) 514599 Fax: (01273) 515939

▶ K & D Haulage, Unit 9 Star Trading Estate, Ponthir, Newport, Gwent, NP18 1PQ Tel: (01633) 422896

▶ K & E Co. Ltd, 40 Strathmore Road, Glasgow, G22 7DW Tel: 0141-336 6111

▶ K Hayton, Units 2-3 Dumfries Enterprise Park, Tinwald Downs Road, Heathhall, Dumfries, DG1 3SJ Tel: (01387) 263435 Fax: (01387) 279523

K M B Shipping Ltd, Lower Church Lane, Tipton, West Midlands, DY4 7PH Tel: 0121-557 3352 Fax: 0121-520 0936 E-mail: info@onestopshipping.co.uk

K & M Hauliers Ltd, The Aerodrome, Watnall Road, Hucknall, Nottingham, NG15 6EN Tel: 0115-963 0630 Fax: 0115-968 0126 E-mail: traffic@kmhauliers.co.uk

▶ K P I Transport Ltd, Unit 4, Mckay Trading Estate, Blackthorne Road, Slough, SL3 0AH Tel: (01753) 682362 Fax: (01753) 682535 E-mail: sales@kpitransport.co.uk

▶ K S Distribution, Kearsley Mill, Crompton Road, Radcliffe, Manchester, M26 1RH Tel: (01204) 702338 Fax: (01204) 573394

▶ K & S J Harvey & Sons, Old Hall St, Farnworth, Bolton, BL4 8HJ Tel: (01204) 791563

▶ K & W Brick Haulage Ltd, 21 Commerce Way, Highbridge, Somerset, TA9 4AG Tel: (01278) 792623 Fax: (01278) 785950

Kammac plc, Gladden Place, Skelmersdale, Lancashire, WN8 9SY Tel: (01695) 727272 Fax: (01695) 720854 E-mail: info@kammac.com

Kelly Freight, C Cedars Transport Depot, Church Manorway, Erith, Kent, DA8 1DE Tel: (01322) 430231 Fax: (01322) 463446 E-mail: upn55scott@aol.com

Kelly Freight, C Cedars Transport Depot, Church Manorway, Erith, Kent, DA8 1DE Tel: (01322) 430231 Fax: (01322) 463446 E-mail: upn55scott@aol.com

▶ Ken Abram Ltd, Stanley Way, Skelmersdale, Lancashire, WN8 8EA Tel: (01695) 50177

▶ Ken Mallinson & Sons Ltd, Clough Green, Lane Head Road, Cawthorne, Barnsley, South Yorkshire, S75 4AD Tel: (01226) 792250 Fax: (01226) 792235

▶ Kenmac Haulage Ltd, Building 76 Greenfield Business Park, Bagillt Road, Greenfield, Holywell, Clwyd, CH8 7HJ Tel: (01352) 715425 Fax: (01352) 712704

▶ Kent Connection Ltd, Factory Road, Blaydon-on-Tyne, Tyne & Wear, NE21 5RU Tel: 0191-414 0055

▶ Kent Transport, Archers Fields, Burnt Mills Industrial Estate, Basildon, Essex, SS13 1DN Tel: (01268) 530805 Fax: (01268) 530811

▶ Kentvale Transport Ltd, Beacon Hill Industrial Estate, Botany Way, Purfleet, Essex, RM19 1SR Tel: (01708) 868833 Fax: (01708) 860901

Kenyon Road Haulage Ltd, Thornley Avenue, Blackburn, BB1 3HJ Tel: (01254) 503600 Fax: (01254) 503601 E-mail: sales@kenyon-haulage.com

▶ Kilmarnock Removals International, 9-15 West Netherton Street, Kilmarnock, Ayrshire, KA1 4BU Tel: (01563) 520001 Fax: (01563) 536939

Ernest F. Kime & Son Ltd, Commonside, Old Leake, Boston, Lincolnshire, PE22 9PP Tel: (01205) 870482

▶ Kingford Transport Ltd, 7 Silverwood, Snow Hill, Crawley Down, Crawley, West Sussex, RH10 3EN Tel: (01342) 714113 Fax: (01342) 715195

▶ Kings Transport Devon Ltd, Durham Way, Heathpark Industrial Estate, Honiton, Devon, EX14 1SQ Tel: (01404) 44555 Fax: (01404) 47555 E-mail: kingoffice@cs.com

Kirkpatrick Holdings Ltd, 88 Arthur Street, Redditch, Worcestershire, B98 8JY Tel: (01527) 522384 Fax: (01527) 517065 E-mail: sales@kirkpatrickcarriers.com

▶ Knighton Haulage, Station Yard, Station Road, Knighton, Powys, LD7 1DT Tel: (01547) 529500 Fax: (01547) 529236

Knowles Transport Ltd, New Road, Wimblington, March, Cambridgeshire, PE15 0RG Tel: (01354) 740233 Fax: (01354) 741333 E-mail: sales@knowles-transport.co.uk

L A Reed & Son Haulage Ltd, 47 Low Street, Swinefleet, Goole, North Humberside, DN14 8DF Tel: (01405) 704351 Fax: (01405) 766654

L V Transport Ltd, Norfolk Road, Gravesend, Kent, DA12 2PS Tel: (01474) 567361 Fax: (01474) 564455 E-mail: lv.transport@btopenworld.com

▶ L & W Wilson Ltd, Gatebeck Road, Endmoor, Kendal, Cumbria, LA8 0HL Tel: (01539) 567601 Fax: (01539) 567775 E-mail: office@landwwilson.co.uk

▶ La Deliveries, 3 Beacon Farm, Moor Road, Great Staughton, St. Neots, Cambridgeshire, PE19 5BW Tel: (01234) 378861

▶ Lakehaven Ltd, 179 Milton Park, Abingdon, Oxfordshire, OX14 4SD Tel: (01235) 832281 E-mail: sales@lakehaven-removals.co.uk

▶ Langside Storage & Distribution, Unit 5 70 Strathclyde Street, Glasgow, G40 4JR Tel: 0141-550 3200

Lanz Transport Ltd, Galleymead House, Old Bath Road, Colnbrook, Slough, SL3 0NT Tel: (01753) 682005 Fax: (01753) 682040

Laser Transport International Ltd, Lympne Industrial Estate, Lympne, Hythe, Kent, CT21 4LR Tel: (01303) 260471 Fax: (01303) 264851 E-mail: sales@laserint.co.uk

Lavers Transport Ltd, North Downs Business Park, Limepit Lane, Dunton Green, Sevenoaks, Kent, TN13 2TL Tel: (01732) 462320 Fax: (01732) 740133

▶ Lavery Transport, 14 Derryvore Lane, Portadown, Craigavon, County Armagh, BT63 5RS Tel: (028) 3835 0231 Fax: (028) 3836 8258 E-mail: info@laverytransport.co.uk

▶ Harry Lawson Ltd, Balunie Drive, Dundee, DD4 8UU Tel: (01382) 738100 Fax: (01382) 480275

▶ Lawson Richard Motor Co., Rossfield Road, Ellesmere Port, CH65 3BS Tel: 0151-355 2155 Fax: 0151-357 1229

E.H. Lee Ltd, Holly House, New Road, Woodston, Peterborough, PE2 9HB Tel: (01733) 554853 Fax: (01733) 897024 E-mail: info@ehlee.co.uk

Harry Leeks Freight Ltd, St. Leonard's Street, Bedford, MK42 9BS Tel: (01234) 359402 Fax: (01234) 348891

▶ Leicester Machine Movers Ltd, 40 Great Central Street, Leicester, LE1 4JT Tel: 0116-253 6662 Fax: 0116-251 0631

▶ Lektron Services Ltd, Middleton Avenue, Strutherhill Industrial Estate, Larkhall, Lanarkshire, ML9 2TL Tel: (01698) 885333

Lenham Storage Ltd, Ham Lane, Lenham, Maidstone, Kent, ME17 2LH Tel: (01622) 858441 Fax: (01622) 850469 E-mail: info@lenhamstorage.co.uk

Lenham Storage Southern Ltd, Fyfield Road, Weyhill, Andover, Hampshire, SP11 8DL Tel: (01264) 772166 Fax: (01264) 773431 E-mail: administration@lenhamstoragesouthern.co.uk

▶ Lentrol Ltd, Unit 22 Weaver Park Industrial Estate, Mill Lane, Frodsham, WA6 7JB Tel: (01928) 735345 Fax: (01928) 735300

Lewis J C Maidenhead Ltd, 117 Blackamoor Lane, Maidenhead, Berkshire, SL6 8RQ Tel: (01628) 621013 Fax: (01628) 781009

▶ Lightning Transport Group, P Acorn Industrial Estate, Strawberry Street, Hull, HU9 1EN Tel: (01482) 327070 Fax: (01482) 586712

Link Logistics Scotland Ltd, 9 Limekilns Road, Cumbernauld, Glasgow, G67 2RN Tel: (01236) 457789 Fax: (01236) 457944

▶ Lloyd Fraser Ltd, Furnace Lane, Nether Heyford, Northampton, NN7 3LB Tel: (01327) 349111 Fax: (01327) 349288

▶ Loc, 100 Mildenhall Road, Fordham, Ely, Cambridgeshire, CB7 5NR Tel: (01638) 720653 Fax: (01638) 721376 E-mail: mmusridd@btconnect.com

Lochmaben Coal Co., Crofts Vennel, Queen Street, Lochmaben, Lockerbie, Dumfriesshire, DG11 1PP Tel: (01387) 810466 Fax: (01387) 810497

▶ Lock Bros Plant Hire Ltd, Union Yard, Manor Road, Erith, Kent, DA8 2AD Tel: (01322) 350679 Fax: (01322) 351160

▶ Longcrofts Transport Services Ltd, Cutlers House, Lumen Road, Royston, Hertfordshire, SG8 7AG Tel: (01763) 247386 Fax: (01763) 249352

Sam Longson (Buckston) Ltd, Town End Garage, Chapel-En-Le-Frith, High Peak, Derbyshire, SK23 0PF Tel: (01298) 812301 Fax: (01298) 815013

▶ Low Fell Removals, Ropery Works, Sunderland, SR6 0DN Tel: 0191-514 0282 Fax: 0191-565 6769

▶ Lund-Conlon Removers & Storers, Remstore House, Wolseley Road, Kempston, Bedford, MK42 7EF Tel: (01234) 404411 Fax: (01234) 404422

▶ Lynx Express Ltd, Stephenson Road, Durranhill Industrial Estate, Carlisle, CA1 3NX Tel: (01228) 529483 Fax: (01228) 592368

▶ Lynx Express Ltd, Unit 60, Dalcross Industrial Estate, Inverness, IV2 7XB Tel: (01667) 461303 Fax: (01667) 460185

▶ Lynx Express Ltd, Scotia Road, Stoke-on-Trent, ST6 4HG Tel: (01782) 814403 Fax: (01782) 814343

▶ M A C Transport, Albion Parade, Gravesend, Kent, DA12 2RN Tel: (01474) 320999

M A Jordan (Transportation), Jordans Compound, Merrylees Road, Leicester, LE9 9FE Tel: (01455) 828333

M & D Russell Haulage Ltd, Myothill Mains, Denny, Stirlingshire, FK6 5HH Tel: (01324) 822734 Fax: (01324) 829301

▶ M & D Transport, Burtonhead Road, St. Helens, Merseyside, WA9 5EA Tel: (01744) 25900 Fax: (01744) 453574

M & G Express, M & G House, Head Road, Douglas, Isle Of Man, IM1 5BF Tel: (01624) 623841 Fax: (01624) 623004 E-mail: postmaster@mcb.net

▶ M & G Haulage Container Service Ltd, 9 Arcade Workshops, Atlantic Trading Estate, Barry, South Glamorgan, CF63 3RF Tel: (01446) 738212 Fax: (01446) 735294

▶ M Glover, Dalbeattie Road, Castle Douglas, Kirkcudbrightshire, DG7 1HZ Tel: (01556) 503303 Fax: (01556) 502028

▶ M J D & Sons Ltd, White Cliff Park, Manor Way, Swanscombe, Kent, DA10 0LL Tel: (01322) 370700 Fax: (01322) 427424

M J Nelmes, Cornworthy, Coombe Road, Salisbury, SP2 8BT Tel: (01722) 324351

▶ M J Refrigeration Transport Ltd, Treetops, Holyhead Road, Nesscliffe, Shrewsbury, SY4 1AY Tel: (01743) 741658 Fax: (01743) 741766

▶ M N Stewart, Ashlea Cottage, Dunecht, Westhill, Aberdeenshire, AB32 7EQ Tel: (01330) 860363 Fax: (01330) 860939

▶ M R C T Ltd, Potash Lane, Mid Suffolk Business Park, Eye, Suffolk, IP23 7HE Tel: (01379) 871500 Fax: (01379) 872985

▶ M & S Carriers, Unit 24, Charnley Fold Industrial Estat, School Lane, Bamber Bridge, Preston, PR5 6PS Tel: (01772) 696555

▶ M & S Carriers, 60 Causewayhead Road, Stirling, FK9 5EZ Tel: (01786) 470072 Fax: (01786) 470072

▶ M S Wayman & Sons, Chalk Lane, Sutton Bridge, Spalding, Lincolnshire, PE12 9YF Tel: (01406) 350216 Fax: (01406) 351622

▶ M Williams, Hortonwood 8, Telford, Shropshire, TF1 7GR Tel: (01952) 606023 Fax: (01952) 603334

▶ Maal Transport Ltd, Crossley Park, Crossley Road, Heaton Chapel, Stockport, Cheshire, SK4 5BF Tel: 0161-431 1030

▶ Mcadie & Reeve Ltd, Crowness Road, Hatston, Kirkwall, Orkney, KW15 1RG Tel: (01856) 872101 Fax: (01856) 876087

▶ Macaskill Fuels, 14 Inaclete Road, Stornoway, Isle of Lewis, HS1 2RB Tel: (01851) 702569 Fax: (01851) 702639

▶ Macaulay Askernish Ltd, Hillside Office, Lochboisdale, Isle of South Uist, HS8 5TH Tel: (01878) 700278 Fax: (01878) 700310

▶ Mcburney Transport, East Lakes Business Park, Gilwilly Industrial Estate, Penrith, Cumbria, CA11 9BB Tel: (01768) 895636 Fax: (01768) 895637

▶ Macburnie International Transport Ltd, Supergas Industrial Estate, Downs Road, Witney, Oxfordshire, OX29 0SZ Tel: (01993) 708882 Fax: (01993) 708884

▶ McCulloch European Transport, Unit 1, Loch Park Industrial Estate, Stonehouse, Larkhall, Lanarkshire, ML9 3LS Tel: (01698) 791367

▶ McFadyen's Contractors (Campbeltown) Ltd, Glebe Street, Campbeltown, Argyll, PA28 6JJ Tel: (01586) 552961

▶ Mcfadyens Transport Ltd, Glebe Street, Campbeltown, Argyll, PA28 6LR Tel: (01586) 551111 Fax: (01586) 552000

▶ Mcgarrie's Ltd, Latherford Close, Four Ashes, Wolverhampton, WV10 7DY Tel: (01902) 791661 Fax: (01902) 791644

▶ Mcgawn Bros, Thistle House, Alloway Road, Maybole, Ayrshire, KA19 8AA Tel: (01655) 882119

▶ Mcgeown's Transport International, 67a Rathfriland Road, Newry, County Down, BT34 1LD Tel: (028) 3025 1616 Fax: (028) 3025 1617 E-mail: info@mcgeowninternational.com

▶ Mckay's Transport, 9 Broomfield Industrial Estate, Broomfield Road, Montrose, Angus, DD10 8SY Tel: (01674) 673020 Fax: (01674) 673409

▶ Mackenzie & Son Transport, 86 Cloglands, Forth, Lanark, ML11 8DY Tel: (01555) 811635 Fax: (01555) 812071

▶ Mclanachan Transport Ltd, 12a Garrell Road, Kilsyth, Glasgow, G65 9JX Tel: (01236) 823539 Fax: (01236) 826347 E-mail: sales@mtltransport.com

▶ McLaughlan Transport, 10 Almswall Road, Kilwinning, Ayrshire, KA13 6BN Tel: (01294) 559224

▶ McLellans Transport, 6 Wellington Road, Bishopbriggs, Glasgow, G64 2SA Tel: 0141-772 7757

▶ Mcpherson Ltd, Fisherton Garage, Aberlour, Banffshire, AB38 9LB Tel: (01340) 871401 Fax: (01340) 871721

▶ Mac's Removals (Dorset) Ltd, Suite 7, Space Maker House, 518 Wallisdown Road, Bournemouth, BH11 8PT Tel: (01202) 535044

▶ Mactaggart Bros, Oakwell Road, Castle Douglas, Kirkcudbrightshire, DG7 1LE Tel: (01556) 503791 Fax: (01556) 504003

H.R. Maiden & Sons, Overley, Telford, Shropshire, TF6 5HD Tel: (01952) 740281 Fax: (01952) 740496

▶ Mainline Haulage Ltd, Neachells Park Distribution C, Neachells Lane, Willenhall, West Midlands, WV13 3RR Tel: (01902) 631127

▶ Manton Transport Ltd, Springfield Farm Cold Cotes Road, Kettlesing Head, Felliscliffe, Harrogate, North Yorkshire, HG3 2LW Tel: (01423) 770520

▶ Marcus (Bradford) Ltd, Low Fold Farm, Back Heights Road, Thornton, Bradford, West Yorkshire, BD13 3RP Tel: (01274) 835232

▶ Marcus (Bradford) Ltd, Unit 10, Northside Industrial Estate, Northside Road, Bradford, West Yorkshire, BD7 2QT Tel: (01274) 573488

▶ Maritime Transport Ltd, C/O Freight Liners, Millbrook Road East, Southampton, SO15 1JS Tel: (023) 8077 6851

▶ Mark Two Distributors, Basai Dai, Prestleigh Road, Evercreech, Shepton Mallet, Somerset, BA4 6LN Tel: 0117-982 2531 Fax: 0117-982 2531

Marshall Barry (Lincoln) Ltd, Camp Road, Witham St. Hughes, Lincoln, LN6 9TW Tel: (01522) 868844 Fax: (01522) 868855 E-mail: marshall.barry@dial.pipex.com

▶ Marshall Thermo King Ltd, Units 7-8, Willment Way, Bristol, BS11 8DJ Tel: 0117-982 1455 Fax: 0117-982 2899

▶ Marshalls Transport Services Ltd, Glenfoot Farm, Tillicoultry, Clackmannanshire, FK13 6BT Tel: (01259) 750631

▶ Martin Jolly Ltd, Calgow Farm, Newton Stewart, Wigtownshire, DG8 7AN Tel: (01671) 402161 Fax: (01671) 402161

▶ Mason Bros Transport Ltd, Fairfield Farm, Blackjack Road, Swineshead, Boston, Lincolnshire, PE20 3HG Tel: (01205) 820236 Fax: (01205) 821085

▶ Matlock Trading & Supply Co., Northwood Lane, Darley Dale, Matlock, Derbyshire, DE4 2HQ Tel: (01629) 732231 Fax: (01629) 732176

▶ Matlock Transport Ltd, Northwood Lane, Darley Dale, Matlock, Derbyshire, DE4 2HQ Tel: (01629) 733357 Fax: (01629) 732176

▶ Matt Purdie & Sons Ltd, 48-54 East Main Street, Blackburn, Bathgate, West Lothian, EH47 7QS Tel: (01506) 652792 Fax: (01506) 632370

▶ Matthew Cornish Transport Ltd, Sub Station Road, Felixstowe, Suffolk, IP11 8JB Tel: (01394) 676134

▶ Matthew James Ltd, 6 Poyntell Cresent, Chislehurst, Kent, BR7 6PJ Tel: (020) 8467 6292 Fax: (01322) 437508

▶ Matthews Haulage Ltd, Mead Lane, Hertford, SG13 7BB Tel: (01992) 553737 Fax: (01992) 551360

Matthews Transport, Greengate, Middleton, Manchester, M24 1RU Tel: 0161-653 5441 Fax: 0161-655 3956 E-mail: sales@matthewstransport.com

Maxi Haulage Ltd, Macadam Way, West Portway Industrial Estate, Andover, Hampshire, SP10 3LF Tel: (01264) 361888 Fax: (01264) 332206

▶ Maxi Haulage Ltd, 3 Belgrave Street, Bellshill Industrial Estate, Bellshill, Lanarkshire, ML4 3NP Tel: (01698) 748444 Fax: (01698) 745364

Maxi Haulage Ltd, Maxi Haulage Ltd, Oldham Road, Manchester, M40 5AF Tel: 0161-205 9000 Fax: 0161-205 9191

Maxi Haulage Ltd, Hawkes Drive, Heathcote Industrial Estate, Warwick, CV34 6LX Tel: (01926) 881192 Fax: (01926) 881937 E-mail: action@maxihaulage.co.uk

▶ Mayling Transport Ltd, Broadwater Lane, Harefield, Uxbridge, Middlesex, UB9 6AH Tel: (01895) 822541 Fax: (01895) 823184

▶ MDB Group, Cavendish House, Cavendish Rd, Stevenage, Hertfordshire, SG1 2EQ Tel: 01438 365451 E-mail: sales@mdbgroup.co.uk

▶ Meachers Transport, East Side Park East Service Road, Raynesway, Spondon, Derby, DE21 7BF Tel: (01332) 666670 Fax: (01332) 666690

Meakins Transport Ltd, The Garage, Back Lane, Spencers Wood, Reading, RG7 1JB Tel: 0118-988 2134 Fax: 0118-988 4150

▶ Mercury Express, 8 Ashley Park, Uddingston, Glasgow, G71 6LU Tel: (01698) 811010

▶ Merthe Logistics, 62-82 Greystone Road, Antrim, BT41 1NU Tel: (028) 9446 8300 Fax: (028) 9446 8338

▶ Mifflin Motors, Barrs Court Road, Hereford, HR1 1EG Tel: (01432) 356268 Fax: (01432) 357052

Mightyhire Ltd, Unit 40, Foster Street Industrial Estate, Hull, HU8 8BT Tel: (01482) 325954 Fax: (01482) 325490 E-mail: ppwmightyhire@hotmail.com

▶ Mike Beer Ltd, Port Zone, Old Park, Whitfield, Dover, Kent, CT16 2HQ Tel: (01304) 828600 Fax: (01304) 829255 E-mail: info@mikebeer.co.uk

▶ Milbank Trucks Ltd, Denton Wharf, Mark Lane, Gravesend, Kent, DA12 2QD Tel: (01474) 364326

▶ Milbank Trucks Ltd, 15 The Old Depot, Bridge Street, Weedon, Northampton, NN7 4PS Tel: (01327) 342678 Fax: (01327) 342623

▶ Millar International Freight Transport Ltd, Springkerse Road, Stirling, FK7 7SN Tel: (01786) 451409

▶ Milne Trucking, 501 Blackbyres Road, Barrhead, Glasgow, G78 1TN Tel: 0141-876 4188

Mini Clipper Ltd, 7 Chartmoor Road, Leighton Buzzard, Bedfordshire, LU7 4WG Tel: (01525) 244700 Fax: (01525) 851445 E-mail: sales@miniclipper.co.uk

Mmapp Haulage Contractors Ltd, Railway Arch 501, Silwood Street, London, SE16 2TD Tel: (020) 7394 0099 Fax: (020) 7394 9997

Montgomery Refrigerated Ltd, 111 Vicarage Road, Portadown, Craigavon, County Armagh, BT62 4HF Tel: (028) 3833 5544 Fax: (028) 3835 0777

▶ Montgomery Transport Ltd, 607 Antrim Road, Glengormley, Newtownabbey, County Antrim, BT36 4RF Tel: (028) 9084 9321

▶ Montgomery Transport Ltd, Unit 502 Green Place, Walton Summit Centre, Bamber Bridge, Preston, PR5 8AY Tel: (01772) 339818 Fax: (01772) 620517

▶ Andrew Moran & Son Ltd, Unit 6, Stuart Industrial Estate, Napier, Paisley, Renfrewshire, PA3 3AJ Tel: (01505) 382345 E-mail: sales@movewithmoran.com

Moreton C Cullimore & Son Ltd, Fromebridge Lane, Whitminster, Gloucester, GL2 7PD Tel: (01452) 740436 Fax: (01452) 740866

Allan Morris Transport Ltd, Factory Road, Sandycroft, Deeside, Flintshire, CH5 2QJ Tel: (01244) 533320 Fax: (01244) 533766 E-mail: enq@allanmorris.co.uk

▶ Morris Young Group, Hillyland Farm, 57-61 Crieff Road, Perth, PH1 2NU Tel: (01738) 625246 Fax: (01738) 629327

Morrow Transport, 7 Sanda Road, Newtownabbey, County Antrim, BT37 9UB Tel: (028) 9085 1867 Fax: (028) 9036 5061

▶ Mortimers Transport, Unit A Chiltern Park Industrial Estate, Boscombe Road, Dunstable, Bedfordshire, LU5 4LT Tel: (01582) 471155 Fax: (01582) 471511

ROAD TRANSPORT AND HAULAGE

– continued

▶ Mrs Distribution Ltd, 41 Inchmuir Road, Whitehill Industrial Estate, Bathgate, West Lothian, EH48 2EP Tel: (01506) 634634 Fax: (01506) 631159 E-mail: mail@mrsdistribution.co.uk

J. & M. Murdoch & Son Ltd, Crofthead Industrial Estate, Lochlibo Road, Neilston, Glasgow, G78 3NE Tel: 0141-580 6322 Fax: 0141-580 6323 E-mail: info@jmmurdoch.com

▶ N F T Distribution Ltd, 51 Eldon Way, Crick, Northampton, NN6 7SL Tel: (01788) 823921

▶ N K Pollock International, 5 Prospect 3, Gemini CR, Dundee Technology Park, Dundee, DD2 1SW Tel: (01382) 568468 Fax: (01382) 561666

▶ N R Evans & Son Ltd, Care Dawn Cardington, Meadow Lane, Cardington, Bedford, MK44 3SB Tel: (01234) 838153 Fax: (01234) 831674

N Y K Logistics, Common Road, Huthwaite, Sutton-in-Ashfield, Nottinghamshire, NG17 2JY Tel: (01623) 510510 Fax: (01623) 518612 E-mail:

▶ National Courier Network, Unit 1 2, Block 12, Nobel Road, West Gourdie Industrial Estate, Dundee, DD2 4UH Tel: (01382) 400900

National Milk Records, Meaford Power Station, Meaford, Stone, Staffordshire, ST15 0UG Tel: (01782) 374057 Fax: (01782) 374059

▶ Naylors Transport (Leyland) Ltd, Comet Road, Moss Side Industrial Estate, Leyland, PR26 7PF Tel: (01772) 424731 Fax: (01772) 621065

R.K. Neil Ltd, The Old Sawmills, The Street, Kilmington, Warminster, Wiltshire, BA12 6RG Tel: (01985) 844112 Fax: (01985) 844113 E-mail: info@martinbrosltd.com

▶ Neil Williams Haulage, Unit 13, Mayfield Industrial Estate, Dalkeith, Midlothian, EH22 4AD Tel: 0131-663 0048

Nelsons Transport Keighley Ltd, Bocking Farm, Keighley, West Yorkshire, BD22 9BG Tel: (01535) 642097 Fax: (01535) 647015 E-mail: nelsonstransport@btinternet.com

▶ Newton Transport & Storage, Wareing Road, Liverpool, L9 7AU Tel: 0151-524 0060

▶ NFT Distribution Ltd, 4 Riverside Industrial Estate, London Colney By Passage, London Colney, St. Albans, Hertfordshire, AL2 1AY Tel: (01727) 822771 Fax: (01727) 823309

Nichol Transport Ltd, Brickyard Road, Aldridge, Walsall, WS9 8SR Tel: (01922) 458279 Fax: (01922) 458279

▶ Nicholas Rowell Haulage, Torr Quarry Industrial Estate, East Allington, Totnes, Devon, TQ9 7QQ Tel: (01548) 521333 Fax: (01548) 521292

H. Nickolls & Son (Milford) Ltd, The Green, Milford, Stafford, ST17 0UR Tel: (01785) 661221 Fax: (01785) 660122 E-mail: info@nickolls.co.uk

Nigel Rice Ltd, Barmston Close, Swinemoor Lane, Beverley, North Humberside, HU17 0LS Tel: (01482) 862123 Fax: (01482) 872006 E-mail: info@nrice.co.uk

▶ Nightfreight (GB) Ltd, Tower House, Unitcc Capel Hendre Industrial Estate, Ammanford, Dyfed, SA18 3SJ Tel: (01269) 841241 Fax: (01269) 841251

Nightfreight GB Ltd, Europa House, 122 Conway Street, Birkenhead, Merseyside, CH41 6RY Tel: 0151-649 0123 Fax: 0151-649 0101 E-mail: itdepartment@nightfreight.co.uk

Nightfreight (GB) Ltd, Imberhorne Way, East Grinstead, West Sussex, RH19 1RL Tel: (01342) 316221 Fax: (01342) 316134 E-mail: info@nightfreight.co.uk

▶ Nightfreight (GB) Ltd, Unit 5 3 Stars Industrial Estate, Ten Acre Lane, Egham, Surrey, TW20 8SJ Tel: (01784) 434435 Fax: (01784) 437157

Nightfreight GB Ltd., Doddington Road, Earls Barton, Northampton, NN6 0NW Tel: (01604) 812123 Fax: (01604) 812101

▶ Nightingale Removal & Storage Ltd, Aisecome Way, Weston-super-Mare, Avon, BS22 8NA Tel: (01934) 625134 Fax: (01934) 629833

Nightspeed Ltd, 18 Stadium Way, Tilehurst, Reading, RG30 6BX Tel: 0118-942 2477

▶ Nimrod Transport, Kirktonlees, Castleton Road, Auchterarder, Perthshire, PH3 1JS Tel: (01764) 664400 Fax: (01764) 663371

▶ Niven Milk Haulage, Lockerbie Creamery, Lockerbie, Dumfriesshire, DG11 1LW Tel: (01387) 811694 Fax: (01387) 811400

Norbert Dentressangle, Billington Road, Leighton Buzzard, Bedfordshire, LU7 9HH Tel: (01525) 243900 Fax: (01525) 382066

Norfolk Line, Transit 3, Westbank Road, Belfast, BT3 9JL Tel: (028) 9077 1122 Fax: (028) 9077 2645 E-mail: belfast@norfolkline.com

▶ Norfolk Line, Middleton Avenue, Strutherhill Industrial Estate, Strutherhill Industrial Estate, Larkhall, Lanarkshire, ML9 2TL Tel: (01698) 552500 Fax: (01698) 552506

▶ Norfrost Ltd, Unit 23 Industrial Estate, Evanton, Dingwall, Ross-Shire, IV16 9XJ Tel: (01349) 830037

▶ Norman Offer (Transport) Ltd, Southern Road, Southampton, SO15 1HB Tel: (023) 8033 1515

▶ North American (UK) Ltd, Unit 1 Ashurst Drive, Lawnhurst Trading Estate, Cheadle Heath, Stockport, Cheshire, SK3 0SD Tel: 0161-491 5141

▶ North West Express, Mersey View Road, Widnes, Cheshire, WA8 8LL Tel: 0151-425 5555 Fax: 0151-425 4444

▶ Northern Istallations Ltd, Lumbrook Mills, Westercroft Lane, Halifax, West Yorkshire, HX3 7TY Tel: (01422) 202777 Fax: (01422) 202888 E-mail: info@northerninstallations.co.uk

▶ Northwards Ltd, Garson, Stromness, Orkney, KW16 3JU Tel: (01856) 851083 Fax: (01856) 851081 E-mail: sales@northwardsltd.co.uk

Norton Transport Ltd, Norton Street, Miles Platting, Manchester, M40 8HD Tel: 0161-205 4455 Fax: 0161-205 3208

▶ Ochil Carriers, Hill Street, Tillicoultry, Clackmannanshire, FK13 6HF Tel: (01259) 750080

▶ Olivers Transport Ltd, Hassington Road, Eccles, Kelso, Roxburghshire, TD5 7QS Tel: (01890) 840547

▶ Osem North UK Ltd, Unit 18 Lyon Road Industrial Estate, Kearsley, Bolton, BL4 8NB Tel: (01204) 574371 Fax: (01204) 862847

▶ Osmonds Transport & Planning Ltd, Greenacres Farm, Old Hay, Brenchley, Tonbridge, Kent, TN12 7DG Tel: (01892) 834193 Fax: (01892) 837141 E-mail: sales@osmonds-transport.com

▶ Owen (Road Services) Ltd, Dafen Industrial Estate, Dafen, Llanelli, Dyfed, SA14 8QE Tel: (01554) 754465 Fax: (01554) 770725

▶ Oxcart Ltd, Unit 5a Power Park, Station Approach, Banbury, Oxfordshire, OX16 5AB Tel: (01295) 709607 Fax: (01295) 709807

▶ P A Laing, Windyridge, Bonchester Bridge, Hawick, Roxburghshire, TD9 8QY Tel: (01450) 860200 Fax: (01450) 860362

▶ P & C Hamilton, 16 Grangestone Industrial Estate, Ladywell Avenue, Girvan, Ayrshire, KA26 9PF Tel: (01465) 714742 Fax: (01465) 714842

P D S Direct, Units 7 & 8, Church Lane Industrial Estate, West Bromwich, West Midlands, B71 1AR Tel: 0121-553 7555 Fax: 0121-553 5990

▶ P D Tattersall, Beevers Bridge, Sykehouse, Goole, North Humberside, DN14 9AB Tel: (01405) 862791 Fax: (01405) 862793

P F Couriers Ltd, Unit 2, Lowfield Heath Industrial Estate, Crawley, West Sussex, RH11 0PQ Tel: (01293) 515661 Fax: (01293) 547045 E-mail: reception@pfcouriers.co.uk

▶ P F Whitehead Storage Ltd, 120 Beddington Lane, Croydon, CR9 4ND Tel: (020) 8665 0110 Fax: (020) 8665 0110 E-mail: info@pfwhitehead.com

P J Butler & Son Ltd, Parsonage St, Oldbury, West Midlands, B69 4PH Tel: 0121-552 1052 Fax: 0121-544 8618

▶ P J Grant & Sons Haulage Contractors, Forres Road, Nairn, IV12 5QD Tel: (01667) 452243 Fax: (01667) 454168

▶ P M Clarke Ltd, Seven Brethren Bank, Sticklepath, Barnstaple, Devon, EX31 2AS Tel: (01271) 345151 Fax: (01271) 323103

▶ P Maddison Haulage Ltd, Coldham Road, Coningsby, Lincoln, LN4 4SD Tel: (01526) 342597 Fax: (01526) 343064 E-mail: info@maddisonhaulage.demon.co.uk

P Monkhouse, Durham Road, Wolsingham, Bishop Auckland, County Durham, DL13 3JB Tel: (01388) 528814 Fax: (01388) 527213 E-mail: sales@monkhousehaulage.co.uk

▶ P & O Ferrymasters Ltd, Dock Street, Fleetwood, Lancashire, FY7 6HR Tel: (01253) 615800 Fax: (01253) 615801

▶ P R Stockinger (Transport) Ltd, 5 Furlong Road, Stoke Ferry, King's Lynn, Norfolk, PE33 9SU Tel: (01366) 500971

▶ P S Ridgway Ltd, 5 Smeaton Road, West Gourdie Industrial Estate, Dundee, DD2 4UT Tel: (01382) 614500 Fax: (01382) 614522

▶ P S Transport, 1 Enterprise Way, Ladysmith Road, Grimsby, South Humberside, DN32 9TW Tel: (01472) 359426 Fax: (01472) 347745 E-mail: sales@pstransport.co.uk

▶ P W Archer & Son Ltd, Springwell Lane, Northallerton, North Yorkshire, DL7 8QP Tel: (01609) 772466 Fax: (01609) 770111 E-mail: cranes@archers-removals.co.uk

▶ P W Transport, Hercules Way, Bowerhill, Melksham, Wiltshire, SN12 6TS Tel: (01225) 704865 Fax: (01225) 702661

▶ Pallas Forwarding Ltd, Unit 1 Bewicke Main Birtley, Chester Le Street, Chester le Street, County Durham, DH3 1ST Tel: 0191-410 5620 Fax: 0191-492 1314

▶ Pallet Express Systems Ltd, Dalewood Road, Lymedale Business Park, Newcastle, Staffordshire, ST5 9QH Tel: (01782) 566628 Fax: (01782) 566390

▶ Pallett Force, Quickbury Farm, Hatfield Heath Road, Sawbridgeworth, Hertfordshire, CM21 9HY Tel: (01279) 600377

▶ Panic Transport (Contracts) Ltd, Dunchurch Trading Estate, London Road, Dunchurch, Rugby, Warwickshire, CV23 9LN Tel: (01788) 815501

▶ Panther Express Ltd, Unit 9-10 The Three Sisters En, Antler Court, Ashton-in-Makerfield, Wigan, Lancashire, WN4 8DU Tel: (01942) 728400

▶ Paperpact Ltd, Gordon House, 6 Lissenden Gardens, London, NW5 1LX Tel: (020) 8838 9780 Fax: (020) 8838 9782

▶ Papi Transport (UK) Ltd, 69 Southend Road, Hockley, Essex, SS5 4PZ Tel: (01702) 205545

▶ Parcelnet Logistics, Anchor House, Ingleby Road, Bradford, West Yorkshire, BD99 2XG Tel: (01274) 625625

▶ Park Logistics, Private Road No 4, Colwick Industrial Estate, Nottingham, NG4 2JT Tel: 0115-940 3332 Fax: 0115-940 2728 E-mail: sales@parklogistics.co.uk

Parkside Warehousing & Transport Co. Ltd, Parkside House, Tomo Industrial Estate, Creeting Road, Stowmarket, Suffolk, IP14 5AY Tel: (01449) 676551 Fax: (01449) 672954

▶ Parkstone Removals, Unit 23 Newtown Business Park, Albion Close, Poole, Dorset, BH12 3LL Tel: (01202) 733803 Fax: (01202) 732559

Colin Parsons & Sons Ltd, Heywood Bridge, Mucklow Hill, Halesowen, West Midlands, B62 8DL Tel: 0121-550 7531 Fax: 0121-585 5341

▶ Patrick Gillooly Ltd, Old Northfield Brickworks, Gray Street, Shotts, Lanarkshire, ML7 5EX Tel: (01501) 820150

▶ Pattemores Transport Crewkerne Ltd, Mosterton Road, Misterton, Crewkerne, Somerset, TA18 8NT Tel: (01460) 72046 Fax: (01460) 76435

▶ Pattersons Tankers, Woodend House, Woodend Road, Lower Hopton, Mirfield, West Yorkshire, WF14 8QD Tel: (01924) 481850

▶ Penn Transport, Purbrook Road, Wolverhampton, WV1 2EJ Tel: (01902) 455601 Fax: (01902) 454381

Perfect Engineering, Harfreys Road, Great Yarmouth, Norfolk, NR31 0JL Tel: (01493) 657131 Fax: (01493) 441526 E-mail: info@lgperfect.com

▶ Perfect Logistics Ltd, Churchill Road, Doncaster, South Yorkshire, DN1 2TH Tel: (01302) 363733 Fax: (01302) 730797

▶ Perrys, Unit 4 Mitchells Enterprise Centre, Bradberry Balk Lane, Wombwell, Barnsley, South Yorkshire, S73 8HR Tel: (01226) 755655 Fax: (01226) 751172

▶ Perth Removals & Transport, The Warehouse, Inveralmond Road, Inveralmond Industrial Estate, Perth, PH1 3TW Tel: (01738) 633080 Fax: (01738) 643766 E-mail: sales@perthremovals.sagenet.co.uk

▶ Perthdown Ltd, Bootham Lane Industrial Estate, Bootham Lane, Dunscroft, Doncaster, South Yorkshire, DN7 4JU Tel: (01302) 351378 Fax: (01302) 849337

Peter D Stirling Ltd, Reema Road, Bellshill, Lanarkshire, ML4 1RR Tel: (01698) 749555 Fax: (01698) 740569

▶ Peter Field Transport Ltd, Unit 8, Heron Business Estate, Whitefield Avenue, Luton, LU3 3BB Tel: (01582) 595377

▶ Peter Mckerral & Co., Darlochan Yard, Campbeltown, Argyll, PA28 6NT Tel: (01586) 820258 Fax: (01586) 820488

▶ Peter Simpson & Sons, Long Chimney, 83 Thorpe Lane, Leeds, LS10 4EP Tel: 0113-277 8780 Fax: 0113-271 8997

▶ Peterhead Transport, Suite 1 Alexandra House, Port Henry Pier, Peterhead, Aberdeenshire, AB42 1ZY Tel: (01779) 477282 Fax: (01779) 475656

▶ Peters Food Service, Lincoln Road, Cressex Business Park, High Wycombe, Buckinghamshire, HP12 3RD Tel: (01494) 463925 Fax: (01494) 464278

Phillips Haulage, 236 Queens Road, Sheffield, S2 4DL Tel: 0114-276 0281 Fax: 0114-270 1510

▶ Pickfords Ltd, Minto Avenue, Altens Industrial Estate, Aberdeen, AB12 3JZ Tel: (01224) 871609 Fax: (01224) 899791 E-mail: sales@pickfords.co.uk

▶ Pickfords Ltd, 15 Banks Road, Darlington, County Durham, DL1 1YF Tel: 0191-497 3800 Fax: 0191-487 1350

▶ Pickfords Ltd, 62 West Harbour Road, Edinburgh, EH5 1PW Tel: 0131-552 4242 Fax: 0131-552 0362

▶ Pickfords Ltd, Great Western Road, Gloucester, GL1 3NJ Tel: (01242) 517393 Fax: (01452) 422420

▶ Pickfords Ltd, Olympic Business Park, Drybridge Road, Dundonald, Kilmarnock, Ayrshire, KA2 9BE Tel: (01292) 611613 Fax: 0141-336 5335

▶ Pickfords Ltd, Olympic Business Park, Drybridge Road, Dundonald, Kilmarnock, Ayrshire, KA2 9BE Tel: (01292) 611613 Fax: 0141-336 5335

▶ Pickfords Ltd, Trafford Park Road, Trafford Park, Manchester, M17 1NJ Tel: 0161-873 2460 Fax: 0161-877 7483

▶ Pickfords Ltd, Pickfords House, Foxbridge Way, Normanton Industrial Estate, Normanton, West Yorkshire, WF6 1TN Tel: (01482) 878866 Fax: (01924) 899387

▶ Pickfords Ltd, Pickfords House, Foxbridge Way, Normanton Industrial Estate, Normanton, West Yorkshire, WF6 1TN Tel: (01482) 878866 Fax: (01924) 899387

▶ Pickfords Ltd, Hucknall Industrial Park, Watnall Road, Hucknall, Nottingham, NG15 7LN Tel: 0115-968 1321 Fax: 0115-968 1477

▶ Pickfords Ltd, 12 Canal CR, Perth, PH2 8HT Tel: (01738) 627201

▶ Pickfords Ltd, Boscombe Down Business Park, Mills Way, Amesbury, Salisbury, SP4 7RX Tel: (01202) 548355 Fax: (01202) 548366

▶ Pickfords Ltd, Phoenix Industrial Estate, Kerse Road, Stirling, FK7 7SG Tel: (01786) 475867 Fax: 0141-336 8891

▶ Pickfords Business Moving, 2 Hurricane Park, Heartlands Parkway, Birmingham, B7 5PP Tel: (0845) 6121008

▶ Pickfords Business Moving, 3-9 Willow Lane, Mitcham, Surrey, CR4 4NA Tel: (0845) 6121008 Fax: (020) 8646 1973

▶ Pickfords Vanguard, 14-16 Lomond Street, Glasgow, G22 6JZ Tel: 0141-347 0177 Fax: 0141-336 7968

Pitter Bros Ltd, Botley Road Garage, Botley Road, West End, Southampton, SO30 3HA Tel: (023) 8047 2385 Fax: (023) 8046 4291 E-mail: traffic@pitterbrothers.idps.co.uk

Pollock Express Ltd, 42-52 Nelson Street, London, E1 2DQ Tel: (020) 7790 3266 Fax: (020) 7265 8498 E-mail: express@pollock.co.uk

▶ Pollock Scotrans Ltd, Olivebank, Newhailes Road, Musselburgh, Midlothian, EH21 6SW Tel: 0131-665 2375 Fax: 0131-653 6200

George Poole Metal Processors, Clough Street, Hanley, Stoke-On-Trent, ST1 4AS Tel: (01782) 265377 Fax: (01782) 263226 E-mail: georgepoolescrap@aol.com

Steve Porter Transport Ltd, Dallimore House Somerton Industrial Park, Newport Road, Cowes, Isle of Wight, PO31 8PB Tel: (01983) 291732 Fax: (01983) 299746 E-mail: freight@steveportertransport.com

Potteries Demolition Co. Ltd, Brocksford Street, Stoke-on-Trent, ST4 3EZ Tel: (01782) 313234 Fax: (01782) 598371

▶ Premier Moving Services, 4f Morses Lane, Brightlingsea, Colchester, CO7 0SF Tel: (01206) 306644 Fax: (01206) 306688

Richard Preston & Son Ltd, Potto, Northallerton, North Yorkshire, DL6 3HX Tel: (01642) 700243 Fax: (01642) 700081 E-mail: pofpotto@aol.com

▶ Prima Distribution Services Ltd, Strudwick House, 92-94 Church Road, Mitcham, Surrey, CR4 3TD Tel: (020) 8640 8486

A.J. Purkiss Ltd, Horseshoe Farm, London Road, Latton, Harlow, Essex, CM17 9LH Tel: (01279) 422632

▶ Quattro, Victoria Road, London, NW10 6NG Tel: (020) 8838 5959 Fax: (020) 8838 2741

Quick Tripper Transport, 63 Wyrley Road, Birmingham, B6 7BT Tel: 0121-327 0925 Fax: 0121-327 1136

▶ Quickfreight Services Ltd, Rednal Industrial Estate, Rednal, West Felton, Oswestry, Shropshire, SY11 4HS Tel: (01691) 610431 Fax: (01691) 610664

▶ R A Haulage Co. Ltd, 5 Princes Road, London, N18 3PR Tel: (020) 8803 7374 Fax: (020) 8807 7031

▶ R A Rousell & Son, The Poplars, Latcham, Wedmore, Somerset, BS28 4SA Tel: (01934) 712518 Fax: (01934) 713755

R Barker & Sons Transport Ltd, School House Farm, Tollgate Road, Burscough, Ormskirk, Lancashire, L40 8LD Tel: (01704) 893303 Fax: (01704) 893878 E-mail: barkertransport@btconnect.com

▶ R C Tucker Ltd, 2 Kimberley, Stathern Lane, Harby, Melton Mowbray, Leicestershire, LE14 4DA Tel: (01949) 860203 Fax: (01949) 861094

R Collett & Sons Transport Ltd, Albert Road, Halifax, West Yorkshire, HX2 0DF Tel: (01422) 255233 Fax: (01422) 255244 E-mail: sales@collett.co.uk

▶ R Cox Haulage Ltd, Trent Street, Sheffield, S9 3XU Tel: 0114-244 2115 Fax: 0114-244 8275

▶ R D Anderson Haulage Ltd, 64 Longstone Road, Edinburgh, EH14 2BA Tel: 0131-443 5981 Fax: 0131-443 9438 E-mail: sales@rdanderson.co.uk

R D M Distribution, Santareen Road, Unit 3, Tharston, Norwich, NR15 2NZ Tel: (01508) 530115

▶ R D Williams & Sons (Haulage) Ltd, Wayside, Thrapston Road, Easton, Huntingdon, Cambridgeshire, PE28 0UA Tel: (01480) 891494 Fax: (01480) 890181

R E Fielding Trucking Ltd, Iconfield Park, Freshfields Road, Parkeston, Harwich, Essex, CO12 4EN Tel: (01255) 504848 Fax: (01255) 508754

▶ R & F Campbell (Inverness) Ltd, 3 Walker Road, Inverness, IV1 1TD Tel: (01463) 231726

R F Martin Haulage Ltd, 26 Mark Avenue, Horncastle, Lincolnshire, LN9 5BD Tel: (01507) 523212 Fax: (01507) 522623

R H Stevens Tankers Ltd, Gunco Lane, Off Byrons Lane, Macclesfield, Cheshire, SK11 7JL Tel: (01625) 613939 Fax: (01625) 616829 E-mail: enquiries@rhstevens.co.uk

▶ R J Aynsley, Unit 10 Sawmills Industrial Estate, South Road, Alnwick, Northumberland, NE66 2QW Tel: (01665) 602803 Fax: (01665) 510990

▶ R J C Projects Engineering Ltd, Unit 1 & 2 Federal Estate, Newton Road, Higham Ferrers, Rushden, Northamptonshire, NN10 8HW Tel: (01933) 418999 Fax: (01933) 418998

▶ R & J Milne Ltd, Norwood Ardmiddle, Turriff, Aberdeenshire, AB53 4HJ Tel: (01888) 562945 Fax: (01888) 563670

▶ R J Priestley & Son, Station Road, Langworth, Langworth, Lincoln, LN3 5BD Tel: (01522) 752519 Fax: (01522) 750850 E-mail: rjp@vodavp.com

▶ R K Eggleton, Curridge, Thatcham, Berkshire, RG18 9DR Tel: (01635) 202604

▶ R K Plant & Transport Ltd, Moorclose, Trewithey Farm, North Hill, Launceston, Cornwall, PL15 7NH Tel: (01566) 782995 Fax: (01566) 782765

▶ R & N Cessford, Whanland Farm, Farnell, Brechin, Angus, DD9 6UF Tel: (01674) 674253 Fax: (01674) 820225

R R Transport Ltd, Stanley Way, Cardrew, Redruth, Cornwall, TR15 1SP Tel: (01209) 310816 Fax: (01209) 210141 E-mail: contact@rrtransport.com

R Steel & Co., 28 Sinclair Street, Helensburgh, Dunbartonshire, G84 8SU Tel: (01436) 675444 Fax: (01436) 675004 E-mail: info@rbsteel.co.uk

▶ indicates data change since last edition

ROAD TRANSPORT AND HAULAGE

– continued

▶ R Swain, Priory Road, Rochester, Kent, ME2 2BD Tel: (01634) 733333 Fax: (01634) 733344

▶ R Swain & Sons, 41 Wynne Avenue, Swinton, Manchester, M27 8FT Tel: 0161-794 4226 Fax: 0161-794 9582

▶ R T McEwan Ltd, Myreside Farm, Arbroath, Angus, DD11 5RL Tel: (01241) 830261

▶ R T Stamp & Son Ltd, Skellingthorpe Road, Saxilby, Lincoln, LN1 2LR Tel: (01522) 702111 Fax: (01522) 704089

▶ R Taylor & Sons, Tieglum Road, Milton Industrial Estate, Lesmahagow, Lanark, ML11 0JN Tel: (01555) 890155 Fax: (01555) 890166

R W Boyles Transport Ltd, Shires Road, Buckingham Road Industrial Estate, Brackley, Northamptonshire, NN13 7EZ Tel: (01280) 702690 Fax: (01280) 701619 E-mail: ron@boyles.fslife.co.uk

▶ R W Simpson Transport Ltd, 263 Oilmills Road, Ramsey Mereside, Ramsey, Huntingdon, Cambridgeshire, PE26 2TT Tel: (01733) 844235 Fax: (01733) 844651

▶ R W Simpson Transport Ltd, Hydra Park, Nether Lane, Ecclesfield, Sheffield, S35 9ZX Tel: 0114-232 9100 Fax: 0114-232 9111

Raeburn Brick Ltd, East Avenue, Blantyre, Glasgow, G72 0JB Tel: (01698) 828888 Fax: (01698) 824039

▶ Rai Group, 298 Soho Road, Handsworth, Birmingham, B21 9LX Tel: 0121-554 4100 Fax: 0121-551 4100

▶ Rainbow Wholesale, 141 West Nile Street, Glasgow, G1 2RN Tel: 0141-333 6599

▶ Rais A Cabin Transport Ltd, 112 Beddington Lane, Croydon, CR0 4TD Tel: (020) 8665 0051 Fax: (020) 8665 0054

▶ RB Transport Co. Ltd, Unit 14 Oldbury Road, West Bromwich, West Midlands, B70 9DE Tel: 0121-553 3674 Fax: 0121-553 7743

RDL Distribution Ltd, Shireoaks, Worksop, Nottinghamshire, S81 8NW Tel: (01909) 537700 Fax: (01909) 537753

▶ Rea Distribution Ltd, 30 Main Street, Ballyclare, County Antrim, BT39 9AA Tel: (028) 9334 2320 Fax: (028) 9335 2699

▶ React Transport Services Ltd, 24 West Shore Road, Edinburgh, EH5 1QD Tel: 0131-551 5531 Fax: 0131-551 5528

George Read, Wilderness Quarry, Mitcheldean, Gloucestershire, GL17 0DF Tel: (01452) 830530 Fax: (01452) 830530

▶ Real Mckay Ltd, March Road East, Buckie, Banffshire, AB56 4BY Tel: (01542) 833949 Fax: (01542) 833953

▶ Ree Distribution Ltd, Unit 1, Summerlands Industrial Estate, Endmoor, Kendal, Cumbria, LA8 0ED Tel: (01539) 561222

▶ Reid Freight Services Ltd, Cinderhill Industrial Estate, Stoke-on-Trent, ST3 5LB Tel: (01782) 599581 Fax: (01782) 593323

▶ Ian Reid Removals, Hagdale Industrial Estate, Baltasound, Unst, Shetland, ZE2 9DS Tel: (01957) 711410

▶ Reid Transport Co. Ltd, Cassillis Garage, Cassillis, Maybole, Ayrshire, KA19 8DN Tel: (01292) 442324

▶ Reids Food Service, 38 James Street, Dalry, Ayrshire, KA24 5ET Tel: (01294) 833001 Fax: (01294) 833032

▶ Reliable Removals, Unit 14 Globe Industrial Estate, Rectory Road, Grays, Essex, RM17 6ST Tel: (0800) 0931660 Fax: (01375) 399994

▶ Removal Services Scotland, 11 Granton Square, Edinburgh, EH5 1HX Tel: 0131-551 4272 Fax: 0131-551 5949

Rendrive Haulage Ltd, Church Manor Way, Erith, Kent, DA8 1DE Tel: (01322) 442206 Fax: (01322) 463232

Revells Warehousing & Transport, Eastlands Industrial Estate, Leiston, Suffolk, IP16 4LL Tel: (01728) 830849 Fax: (01728) 830849 E-mail: revellsremovals@aol.com

▶ Reynolds Transport Hereford Ltd, 26 Romney Huts, Chapel Road, Rotherwas Industrial Estate, Hereford, HR2 6LD Tel: (01432) 279289

RH Freight Services Ltd, The Atlantic Terminal, Liverpool Intermodal Freeport Terminal, Bootle, Merseyside, L20 1HA Tel: 0151-944 4455 Fax: 0151-944 4433

▶ RH Stevens Tankers Ltd, Bentley Moor Lane, Adwick-Le-St, Doncaster, South Yorkshire, DN6 7BD Tel: (01302) 337337

Rhenus Hauser Ltd, Bowden House, Luckyn Lane, Basildon, Essex, SS14 3AX Tel: (01268) 592180 Fax: (01268) 592181 E-mail: london@uk.rhenus.com

▶ Rhys Davies Freight Logistics Scotland Ltd, Murraysgate Industrial Estate, Whitburn, Bathgate, West Lothian, EH47 0LE Tel: (01501) 743772 Fax: (01501) 742232

▶ Rhys Davies & Sons Ltd, Old Parkbury Lane, Colney Street, St. Albans, Hertfordshire, AL2 2EB Tel: (01923) 853666 Fax: (01923) 853611

Joseph Rice & Son Ltd, 26 Hempsted Lane, Gloucester, GL2 5JF Tel: (01452) 527473 Fax: (01452) 300456 E-mail: info@joseph-rice.co.uk

▶ Richard Preston & Son Ltd, Howard Road, Eaton Socon, St. Neots, Cambridgeshire, PE19 8ET Tel: (01480) 213200 Fax: (01480) 405671

Richard Read Ltd, Monmouth Road, Longhope, Gloucestershire, GL17 0QG Tel: (01452) 830456 Fax: (01452) 831422 E-mail: sales@richardreadtransport.co.uk

Richard T Porter Transport Services Ltd, Hylton Road, Worcester, WR2 5JS Tel: (01905) 748384 Fax: (01905) 748385

Richard & Osborne Ltd, Goss Moor, Fraddon, St. Columb, Cornwall, TR9 6EU Tel: (01726) 860308 Fax: (01726) 861135

Risewood Ltd, 68 Birchwood Road, Lichfield, Staffordshire, WS14 9UW Tel: (01543) 417550 Fax: (01543) 264212

Road & Sea Express Ltd, Unit 9 Holmes Chapel Business Park, Manor Lane, Holmes Chapel, Crewe, CW4 8AF Tel: (01477) 536536 Fax: (01477) 536537 E-mail: sales@roadseaexpress.co.uk

Roadferry Ltd, 65 Dargan Road, Belfast, BT3 9JU Tel: (028) 9051 3513 Fax: (028) 9051 3514 E-mail: customer.services@roadferry.co.uk

Roadferry Ltd, Carr Lane, Leyland, Leyland, PR25 3RD Tel: (01772) 455338 Fax: (01772) 422311

Roadliner International Ltd, Unit 7, Graham Industrial Estate, Belfast, BT3 9LP Tel: (028) 9037 1701 Fax: (028) 9037 1901 E-mail: sales@roadliner.com

Roadways Container Logistics Ltd, Gartsherrie Road, Coatbridge, Lanarkshire, ML5 2DS Tel: (01236) 504700 Fax: (01236) 504730

Rob Rowe Livestock Haulage, St. Teath, Bodmin, Cornwall, PL30 3LJ Tel: (01208) 850730

▶ Robert Darvall Ltd, 4 Acre Road, Reading, RG2 0SX Tel: 0118-986 4422 Fax: 0118-975 1358

▶ Robert Dunlop Bros, Hillhead Farm, Auchengray, Carnwath, Lanark, ML11 8LN Tel: (01501) 785200

Robert Walker Haulage Ltd, Hall Lane, Woodley, Stockport, Cheshire, SK6 1PR Tel: 0161-430 2618 Fax: 0161-430 3154 E-mail: john@rwalkers.co.uk

▶ Robinson Haulage, 1 The Ridgeway Business Park, The Ridgeway, Blunham, Bedford, MK44 3DE Tel: (01767) 641244 Fax: (01767) 641255

▶ Robinsons International Removals, 5 Aquarius Business Park, Priestley Way, London, NW2 7AJ Tel: (020) 8208 8480 Fax: (020) 8208 8488

▶ Rock & Go, Unit 16 Millbuck Way, Sandbach, Cheshire, CW11 3HT Tel: (01270) 759949 Fax: (01270) 759939 E-mail: info@rockandgo.co.uk

E.M. Rogers (Transport) Ltd, Rye Hill Close, Lodge Farm Industrial Estate, Northampton, NN5 7UA Tel: (01604) 755511 Fax: (01604) 756417

▶ Roland Young Ltd, Hadleigh Buildings, Bangor Road, Conwy, Gwynedd, LL32 8DN Tel: (01492) 582666

▶ Romford Chilled Transportation Ltd, Botany Way, Purfleet, Essex, RM19 1SR Tel: (01708) 864223 E-mail: sales@ytgroup.com

Rooneys Scrap Merchants Ltd, South Shore Road, Gateshead, Tyne & Wear, NE8 3AE Tel: 0191-478 7833 Fax: 0191-478 7833 E-mail: rooneys@btconnect.com

A. Rose (Newark) Ltd, 17 Cross Street, Newark, Nottinghamshire, NG24 1PP Tel: (01636) 703581 Fax: (01636) 640363

▶ Rosewood Warehousing & Distribution, Unit /12 Seddon Place, Stanley Industrial Estate, Skelmersdale, Lancashire, WN8 8EB Tel: 01695 555580 Fax: 01695 724253 E-mail: parratt_andy@Btconnect.Com

Rother Cartage South East Ltd, Unit 1 The Woodlands Centre, A22 Whitesmith, Lewes, East Sussex, BN8 6JB Tel: (01825) 873308 Fax: (01825) 873291

▶ Rotherham Logistics, Goods Station West, Russell Road, Kilnhurst, Mexborough, South Yorkshire, S64 5SH Tel: (01709) 571430 Fax: (01709) 571339

▶ Roy Broad & Sons, High Lanes, High Lane, Manaccan, Helston, Cornwall, TR12 6HT Tel: (01326) 231403 Fax: (01326) 231101

▶ Roy Elliott Haulage Contractors, Green Lane, Chickerell, Weymouth, Dorset, DT3 4AL Tel: (01305) 785838

▶ Royal Mail, Bridge of Don Delivery Office, Cloverhill Road, Bridge of Don, Aberdeen, AB23 8AA Tel: (01224) 704168

▶ Royal Mail, Arbroath Delivery Office, 10 Hill Street, Arbroath, Angus, DD11 1AA Tel: (01241) 871060

▶ Royal Mail, Eyemouth Delivery Office, Upper Houndlaw, Eyemouth, Berwickshire, TD14 5BP Tel: (01890) 750267

▶ Royal Mail, 4 Ogilvys Close, Kirriemuir, Forfar, Angus, DD8 4AA Tel: (01575) 573950

▶ Royal Mail, Delivery Office, 21 Muirend Avenue, Glasgow, G44 3DZ Tel: 0141-637 1346

▶ Royal Mail, Aldholm, Lochmaddy, Isle Of North Uist, HS6 5AA Tel: (01876) 500330

▶ Royal Mail, Leven Delivery Office, Banbeath Industrial Estate, Kennoway Road, Leven, Fife, KY8 5XY Tel: (01333) 423764

▶ Royal Mail, Motherwell Sorting & Delivery, 214-218 Muir Street, Motherwell, Lanarkshire, ML1 1AA Tel: (01698) 264397

▶ Royal Mail, Portree Delivery Office, Dunvegan Road, Portree, Isle of Skye, IV51 9AA Tel: (01478) 612799

▶ Royal Mail Group Ltd, Annan Post Office, Station Road, Annan, Dumfriesshire, DG12 6TS Tel: (01461) 202758

▶ Royal Mail Group Ltd, 22 Clerk Street, Brechin, Angus, DD9 6AA Tel: (01356) 625465

▶ Royal Mail Group Ltd, Letter Delivery Offices, Russell Road, Edinburgh, EH11 2DJ Tel: 0131-470 6801

▶ Royal Mail Group Ltd, 26 Queen Elizabeth Avenue, Hillington Industrial Estate, Glasgow, G52 4TT Tel: 0141-882 1307

▶ Royal Mail Group Ltd, Uddingston Delivery Office, 7 Church Street, Uddingston, Glasgow, G71 7LP Tel: (01698) 816542

▶ Royal Mail Group Ltd, Clarkston Delivery Office, Rowallan Lane, Clarkston, Glasgow, G76 7BE Tel: 0141-638 1527

▶ Royal Mail Group Ltd, Brodick Delivery Office, Mayish Road, Brodick, Isle of Arran, KA27 8AA Tel: (01770) 302507

▶ Royal Mail Group Ltd, Main Street, Lairg, Sutherland, IV27 4DB Tel: (01549) 402025

▶ Royal Mail Group Ltd, Nairn Delivery Office, Cawdor Street, Nairn, IV12 4QU Tel: (01667) 452154

▶ Royal Mail Group Ltd, Selkirk Sorting Office, 30 Market Place, Selkirk, TD7 4BP Tel: (01750) 21266

▶ Royal Mail Group Ltd, Stornoway Delivery Office, Sandwick Road, Stornoway, Isle of Lewis, HS1 2AA Tel: (01851) 702166 Fax: (01851) 706583

Royal Mail Group Ltd, 12 Church Street, Troon, Ayrshire, KA10 6AU Tel: (01292) 314437

▶ S C A Transport UK Ltd, 1-3 Branch Road, Lower Darwen, Darwen, Lancashire, BB3 0PR Tel: (01254) 680325 Fax: (01254) 680326

S C A Transport UK Ltd, Bath Road, Colthrop, Thatcham, Berkshire, RG19 4NQ Tel: (01635) 862244 Fax: (01635) 874165

▶ S C D Express, Whittle Road, Stoke-on-Trent, ST3 7QA Tel: (01782) 599967 Fax: (01782) 594445

▶ S & C Haulage, Enderby Road, Whetstone, Leicester, LE8 6JL Tel: 0116-286 3886

▶ S C S Haulage Ltd, 178 Avenue Road, Rushden, Northamptonshire, NN10 0SW Tel: (01933) 417920 Fax: (01933) 417921

▶ S D Cooper Transport Ltd, Little London Lane, West Cowick, Goole, North Humberside, DN14 9EG Tel: (01405) 860506 Fax: (01405) 860061

S H S Freight Services Ltd, Unit 20 Riverside Development, Chesterton Road, Eastwood Trading Estate, Rotherham, South Yorkshire, S65 1SU Tel: (01709) 377071 Fax: (01709) 820959 E-mail: davidmaw@aol.com

▶ S & H Storage & Haulage Ltd, 189 Dumbarton Road, Clydebank, Dunbartonshire, G81 4XJ Tel: 0141-952 1816 Fax: 0141-952 2102

▶ S J S Cannock Ltd, Unit 13, Cinder Road, Zone 3 Burntwood Business Park, Burntwood, Staffordshire, WS7 3FS Tel: (01543) 670066

S Jones Transport Ltd, Anglian Road, Walsall, WS9 8ET Tel: (01922) 450000 Fax: (01922) 455920 E-mail: info@sjonestransport.com

▶ S Lyon & Son Haulage Ltd, Lincoln Road, Skellingthorpe, Lincoln, LN6 5SA Tel: (01522) 682519 Fax: (01522) 500041

▶ S M Davies, Acrefield Yard, Henfaes Lane, Welshpool, Powys, SY21 7BE Tel: (01938) 553446 Fax: (01938) 556842

▶ S M H Fleet Solutions Ltd, Building 140 Thurleigh Airfield, Business Park, Thurleigh, Bedford, MK44 2YP Tel: (01234) 353172 Fax: (01234) 357511 E-mail: thurleigh.logistics@smhfleet.com

S P D S Ltd, Unit 4 Minto Drive, Altens Industrial Estate, Aberdeen, AB12 3LW Tel: (01224) 896106 Fax: (01224) 896112 E-mail: admin@spds.co.uk

S Patterson, 58 Rathkeel Road, Broughshane, Ballymena, County Antrim, BT42 4QD Tel: (028) 2586 1254 Fax: (028) 2586 1574

S & S Distribution, 400 Vale Road, Tonbridge, Kent, TN9 1SW Tel: (01732) 358800 Fax: (01732) 770772 E-mail: traffic@ssdistribution.co.uk

▶ S Smith & Co. Ltd, Dowgate Wharf, 26 Orsman Road, London, N1 5QJ Tel: (020) 7739 1591

sale echo, Unit 30 Wolverton Mill East, Mill Park, High Park Drive Wolverton, Milton Keynes, MK12 5TT Tel: (0845) 124 1700 Fax: (01908) 441750 E-mail: enquires@echoltd.com

▶ Salop Haulage Ltd, Brixton Way, Shrewsbury, SY1 3LB Tel: (01743) 466518 Fax: (01743) 440904

▶ Saltire International Ltd, Lower Bathville, Armadale, Bathgate, West Lothian, EH48 2JS Tel: (01501) 735222

▶ Sandy Bruce Trucking Ltd, Blackdog Centre, Bridge of Don, Aberdeen, AB23 8BT Tel: (01224) 824936 Fax: (01224) 820945

▶ Sandy Bruce Trucking, T2 Rudford Industrial Estate, Ford Road, Ford, Arundel, West Sussex, BN18 0BD Tel: (01903) 731303 Fax: (01903) 722049

▶ Sandy Mccracken & Son Ltd, Ayr Road, Rigside, Lanark, ML11 9NP Tel: (01555) 880890 Fax: (01555) 880891

▶ Sandy McCracken & Son Ltd, Canderside Toll, Larkhall, Lanarkshire, ML9 3PJ Tel: (01698) 791722

Elliott Sargeant Ltd, 4 Rushington Business Park, Rushington Lane, Totton, Southampton, SO40 9AH Tel: (023) 8066 1666 Fax: (023) 8066 1567

▶ Sas Logistics Ltd, Poyle 14, Newlands Drive, Colnbrook, Slough, SL3 0DX Tel: (01753) 687317 Fax: (01753) 684165 E-mail: sales@saslogistics.co.uk

Schenker B T L Ltd, Kelsey Close, Attleborough Fields Industrial Estate, Nuneaton, Warwickshire, CV11 6XN Tel: (024) 7635 7000 Fax: (024) 7635 4546 E-mail: enquiries@schenker.com

Scorpion Bath Distributors Ltd, B Brookfield Park, Manvers Way, Wath-upon-Dearne, Rotherham, South Yorkshire, S63 7JY Tel: (01709) 878878 Fax: (01709) 879879

▶ Scot Pak Ltd, Unit 4 Hanson Street, Glasgow, G31 2JW Tel: 0141-550 4452 Fax: 0141-550 8836

▶ Scotlee Transport, Portland Place, Heatherhouse Industrial Estate, Irvine, Ayrshire, KA12 8LW Tel: (01294) 311427 Fax: (01294) 271483

▶ Scott Bros Ltd, Annie House, Master Road, Thornaby, Stockton-on-Tees, Cleveland, TS17 0BE Tel: (01642) 750444 Fax: (01642) 766544

▶ Scottish Book Source, 32 Finlas Street, Cowlairs Industrial Estate, Glasgow, G22 5DU Tel: 0141-558 1366

▶ Scotts Heavy Haulage Ireland Ltd, Whites Close, Alfreton, Derbyshire, DE55 7RB Tel: (01773) 606700 Fax: (01773) 608088

▶ Seabrook Warehousing Ltd, Unit 2-5 Heath Park Industrial Estate, Freshwater Road, Dagenham, Essex, RM8 1RX Tel: (020) 8548 3540 Fax: (0870) 9901921

Seaham Harbour Dock Co., Cargo Durham Distribution Centre, Seaham, County Durham, SR7 7NZ Tel: 0191-516 1700 Fax: 0191-516 1701 E-mail: info@seahamharbour.com

▶ Seaway Transport, Station Brae, Macduff, Banffshire, AB44 1UL Tel: (01261) 832877 Fax: (01261) 833377 E-mail: sales@seawaygroup.co.uk

▶ Securicor Omega Logistics Ltd, Irongray Road, Dumfries, DG2 0HS Tel: (01387) 721212

▶ Security Air Express Ltd, Coppermill Court, Coppermill Lane, Rickmansworth, Hertfordshire, WD3 9XS Tel: (01895) 825258 Fax: (01895) 825259

Security Escorts Services, 6 Standard Road, London, NW10 6EU Tel: (020) 8965 3215 Fax: (020) 8961 5298 E-mail: sales@securityescorts.com

▶ Selby Transport, 32 Midland Road, Scunthorpe, South Humberside, DN16 1DQ Tel: (01724) 277577 Fax: (01724) 277720

Seymour Transport Ltd, New Hythe Lane, Larkfield, Aylesford, Kent, ME20 6SB Tel: (01622) 716441 Fax: (01622) 715146 E-mail: mr@seymourtransport.co.uk

▶ Seymour Transport, Whaley Road, South Yorkshire Industrial Estate, Barnsley, South Yorkshire, S75 1HT Tel: (01226) 731100 Fax: (01226) 731344

Shaws Metals Ltd, Hartland Works, Haydock Park Road, Derby, DE24 8HW Tel: (01332) 383341 Fax: (01332) 294085 E-mail: sales@shawsmetalsltd.sagenet.co.uk

▶ Sheehan Haulage, Woodstock Road, Yarnton, Kidlington, Oxfordshire, OX5 1PH Tel: (01865) 379931

▶ Sheldon & Clayton Ltd, Black Country Road, West Bromwich, West Midlands, B70 0BD Tel: 0121-520 7070

Shepherd Distribution Services, Birley Vale Avenue, Birley Vale Industrial Estate, Intake, Sheffield, S12 2AW Tel: 0114-264 3638 Fax: 0114-253 1326 E-mail: trafffic@shepherd-distribution.co.uk

▶ Shetland Transport Ltd, Greenhead, Lerwick, Shetland, ZE1 0PY Tel: (01595) 695792 Fax: (01595) 693722

Shipley Transport Ltd, Castlefield Yard, Station Road, Hibaldstow, Brigg, South Humberside, DN20 9DU Tel: (01652) 651720 Fax: (01652) 651787 E-mail: jshiptransport@aol.com

▶ Shott Transport & Removals, The Lingfield Estate, Mcmullen Road, Darlington, County Durham, DL1 1RW Tel: (01642) 677780 Fax: (01325) 380346

▶ Sibley Haulage Ltd, Crabtree Lane, Lower End, Wavendon, Milton Keynes, MK17 8AP Tel: (01908) 583154 Fax: (01908) 587631

Sibley Material Movements Ltd, Andes Road, Nursling, Southampton, SO16 0YZ Tel: (023) 8073 7773 Fax: (023) 8074 0193 E-mail: sales@materialmovements.com

▶ Silver Machines Scotland, Deanston House Lodge, Doune, Perthshire, FK16 6AD Tel: (0845) 0661662 Fax: (01786) 843009

▶ Simon Transport Services Ltd, 43 Ember Road, Slough, SL3 8ED Tel: (01753) 547818 Fax: (01753) 545992

▶ Simpson, 27 Sinclair Road, Aberdeen, AB11 9PL Tel: (01224) 890221 Fax: (01224) 871516

W.J. Sims Ltd, 10 Endeavour Way, Croydon, CR0 4TR Tel: (020) 8689 2198 Fax: (020) 8689 4027

▶ Sissons & French Transport Services Ltd, Lows Lane, Stanton-by-Dale, Ilkeston, Derbyshire, DE7 4QU Tel: 0115-932 3535 Fax: 0115-932 3535

▶ The Skelton Group, Cooting Road, Aylesham, Canterbury, Kent, CT3 3EP Tel: (01303) 249561 Fax: (01303) 245007

▶ Skye Transport, Crossal, Drynoch, Carbost, Isle of Skye, IV47 8SP Tel: (01478) 640243 Fax: (01478) 640473

Skyline Relocation Services Ltd, Unit 2, Inchinnan Road, Paisley, Renfrewshire, PA3 2RE Tel: 0141-887 5444 Fax: 0141-887 3730

Slough International Freight & Packing Ltd, 820 Yeovil Road, Slough, SL1 4JA Tel: (01753) 691011 Fax: (01753) 825669 E-mail: sloughinter@btconnect.com

John Smillie Ltd, 40 Carmichael Street, Glasgow, G51 2QT Tel: 0141-445 2574 Fax: 0141-425 1315

▶ Smith & Rhodes, Kirk Syke Farm, Lothersdale, Keighley, West Yorkshire, BD20 8HX Tel: (01535) 633636 Fax: (01535) 633784

▶ Smith of Whiteinch Ltd, 85 Clydeholm Road, Glasgow, G14 0SE Tel: 0141-954 8071

▶ Smooth Move Ltd, Unit 2, 9 Paul Street, Liverpool, L3 6DX Tel: 0151-236 7666

▶ indicates data change since last edition

ROAD TRANSPORT AND HAULAGE

– continued

▶ Sneddon Transport, Unit 1, Block 1, Brownsburn Industrial Estate, Airdrie, Lanarkshire, ML6 9SE Tel: (01236) 759036

▶ Solihull Transport Ltd, 337 Tanworth Lane, Solihull, West Midlands, B90 4DU Tel: 0121-733 8248

South Eastern Carriage Co. Ltd, Unit 11, 71-73 Nathan Way, London, SE28 0BQ Tel: (020) 8854 4655 Fax: (020) 8854 0614

▶ South Link Distribution, Units 11-12 Winston Business Centre, Chartwell Road, Lancing, West Sussex, BN15 8TU Tel: (01903) 851852 Fax: (01903) 851444

South West Crane Hire Ltd, Tan Lane, Exeter, EX2 8EG Tel: (01392) 256148 Fax: (01392) 270603 E-mail: info@sw-crane-hire.co.uk

Stamford Plant Hire Ltd, Uffington Road, Stamford, Lincolnshire, PE9 2HA Tel: (01780) 482888 Fax: (01780) 480066 E-mail: shgilmer@atglobal.net

▶ Stan Robinson Stafford Ltd, Tiverton Junction, Cullompton, Devon, EX15 2QD Tel: (01884) 821777 Fax: (01884) 821787

▶ Stan Robinson Stafford Ltd, Drumhead Road, Glasgow East Investment Park, Glasgow, G32 8EX Tel: 0141-641 6141 Fax: 0141-641 8641

Standard Motor Transport, 15 Lisle Avenue, Kidderminster, Worcestershire, DY11 7DJ Tel: (01562) 745308 Fax: (01562) 754546 E-mail: rob@standardmotortransport.co.uk

Star Transport & Warehousing Ltd, Brunel Way, Thetford, Norfolk, IP24 1HP Tel: (01842) 752603 Fax: (01842) 765085 E-mail: traffic@star-transport.co.uk

Stardes Ltd, Ashes Building, Old Lane, Sheffield, S20 3GZ Tel: 0114-251 0051 Fax: 0114-251 0555 E-mail: info@stardes.co.uk

▶ Steadman Transport, 732 London Road, Grays, Essex, RM20 3NL Tel: (01708) 869600

Stephen Dalton Scrap Metal Merchants, Station Road, Gogarbank, Edinburgh, EH12 9BU Tel: 0131-339 5355 Fax: 0131-317 7168 E-mail: dalton@daltondemo.co.uk

▶ Stevenson Bros, Blackston Road, Avonbridge, Falkirk, FK1 2NB Tel: (01324) 861331 Fax: (01324) 861666 E-mail: sales@stevensonbros.co.uk

▶ Steves Transport Services (Wraysbury) Ltd, John Taylor House, Blackthorne Road, Colnbrook, Slough, SL3 0AH Tel: (01753) 685544

Stiller Group Ltd, Vulcan Road, Bilston, West Midlands, WV14 7LB Tel: (01902) 491151 Fax: (01902) 402613

Stiller Group, Boeing Way, Preston Farm Industrial Estate, Stockton-on-Tees, Cleveland, TS18 3TE Tel: (01642) 607777 Fax: (01642) 607711 E-mail: enquiries@stiller.co.uk

▶ Stocade, Unit 3, Heron Industrial Estate, Basingstoke Road, Spencers Wood, Reading, RG7 1PJ Tel: 0118-988 1490

Stoddards Ltd, Greenhill Garage, Leek Road, Cheadle, Stoke-on-Trent, ST10 1JF Tel: (01538) 754420 Fax: (01538) 750375 E-mail: sales@stoddards.co.uk

▶ Stva UK Ltd, 26 1 Whitburn Road, Bathgate, West Lothian, EH48 1HH Tel: (01506) 650505 Fax: (01506) 650905

▶ Stva UK Ltd, Cva House, 2 Cooper Road, Thornbury, Bristol, BS35 3UP Tel: (01454) 410200 Fax: (01454) 410230 E-mail: sales@stva.com

Sudlows Carriers Ltd, Stamford Mill, Bayley Street, Stalybridge, Cheshire, SK15 1QQ Tel: 0161-344 2600 Fax: 0161-330 5407

Super Trucks Ltd, Beaufort Street, St. Helens, Merseyside, WA9 3BQ Tel: (01744) 25348 Fax: (01744) 27772 E-mail: supertrucks@btinternet.com

Surefast Freight Ltd, 2 Abercorn Avenue, Hillington Industrial Estate, Glasgow, G52 4XZ Tel: 0141-883 4660

Sussex Port Forwarding Ltd, Shoreham Port, Harbour Office, 84-86 Albion Street, Southwick, Brighton, BN42 4ED Tel: (01273) 598100 Fax: (01273) 592492 E-mail: info@shoreham-port.co.uk

▶ Suttle Stone Quarries, Swanworth Quarry, Worth Matravers, Swanage, Dorset, BH19 3LE Tel: (01929) 439444 Fax: (01929) 439446

Sutton & Son Ltd, Sutton Heath, St. Helens, Merseyside, WA9 5BW Tel: (01744) 811611 Fax: (01744) 813324

▶ Sutton & Son St Helens Ltd, Wilson Street, Thornaby, Stockton-on-Tees, Cleveland, TS17 7AR Tel: (01642) 606160

R. Swain & Sons Ltd, Medway Freight Terminal, Corys Road, Rochester, Kent, ME1 1PZ Tel: (01634) 830531 Fax: (01634) 829318 E-mail: davidmorton@rswain.com

▶ R. Swain & Sons Ltd, Occupation Lane, Woodville, Swadlincote, Derbyshire, DE11 8EU Tel: 0121-505 3894

R. Swains & Son, The Pool Works, Occupation Lane, Woodville, Swadlincote, Derbyshire, DE11 8EU Tel: (01283) 214776 Fax: (01283) 222112 E-mail: ensor@rswains.com

▶ Swales Haulage Ltd, Unit 53 Youngs Industrial Estate, Paices Hill, Aldermaston, Reading, RG7 4PW Tel: 0118-970 8000 Fax: 0118-982 0829 E-mail: admin@swaleshaulage.com

▶ Swift & French, 23a Church Road, Kingston upon Thames, Surrey, KT1 3DJ Tel: (020) 8549 2536 Fax: (020) 8547 1585

▶ Systems Transport Services Ltd, Unit 1a, Court Lane, Iver, Buckinghamshire, SL0 9HL Tel: (01753) 653023 Fax: (01753) 655305 E-mail: transportsts@aol.com

▶ T A Jervis & Co. Ltd, Holywell Lane, Lightmoor, Telford, Shropshire, TF4 3QJ Tel: (01952) 505778 Fax: (01952) 504520

▶ T A Walker Ltd, 168a Loughborough Road, Mountsorrel, Loughborough, Leicestershire, LE12 7AX Tel: (01509) 416602 Fax: (01509) 620064

▶ T A Wells Co Ltd, 268 Hamworth Road, Hounslow, TW3 3UB Tel: (020) 8569 5577

T B S Haulage, Mercia Way, Foxhills Industrial Estate, Scunthorpe, South Humberside, DN15 8RE Tel: (01724) 858999

▶ T Baden Hardstaff Ltd, Hillside, Gotham Road, Kingston-on-Soar, Nottingham, NG11 0DF Tel: 0115-983 1234 Fax: 0115-983 1225

▶ T Barry Haulage, Broadway Trading Estate, Broadway Lane, South Cerney, Cirencester, Gloucestershire, GL7 5UH Tel: (01285) 860665 Fax: (01285) 862137

▶ T Bourne & Son Ltd, Draper Street, Tunbridge Wells, Kent, TN4 0PG Tel: (01892) 528271

▶ T D G, PO Box 1, Kirkcaldy, Fife, KY1 2SB Tel: (01592) 647405

▶ T D G, Caton Road, Lancaster, LA1 3PE Tel: (01524) 35024 Fax: (01524) 36758 E-mail: france@tdg.co.uk

T D G European Chemical Division, Picow Farm Road, Runcorn, Cheshire, WA7 4UW Tel: (01928) 580588 Fax: (01928) 565968

T D G European Chemicals, Euro Terminal, Westinghouse Road, Trafford Park, Manchester, M17 1PY Tel: 0161-932 6900 Fax: 0161-932 6990 E-mail: businessenquiries@tdg.co.uk

▶ T J French, Stonebriggs, Cronberry, Cumnock, Ayrshire, KA18 3LP Tel: (01290) 425164 Fax: (01290) 420900

▶ T J French, Stonebriggs, Cronberry, Cumnock, Ayrshire, KA18 3LP Tel: (01290) 425164 Fax: (01290) 420900

▶ T J & W M Cardy Ltd, Lodge Farm House, The Green, Fornham All Saints, Bury St. Edmunds, Suffolk, IP28 6JX Tel: (01284) 728432

▶ T Mcmillan Ltd, Lyon Road, Linwood, Paisley, Renfrewshire, PA3 3BD Tel: (01505) 337410 Fax: (01505) 337411

▶ T N T Express, Wimblebury Road, Littleworth, Cannock, Staffordshire, WS12 2HW Tel: (01543) 426333 Fax: (01543) 877655

▶ T N T Fashion Group, Earn Avenue, Righead Industrial Estate, Bellshill, Lanarkshire, ML4 3LW Tel: (01698) 844602 Fax: (01698) 845087

▶ T N T Logistics, Pilsley Road, Danesmoor, Chesterfield, Derbyshire, S45 9BX Tel: (01246) 862452 Fax: (01246) 865578

▶ T N T Transport Systems, G E C Business Park, Blackburn Road, Clayton Le Moors, Accrington, Lancashire, BB5 5YG Tel: (01254) 382171 E-mail: admin@tntlaw.co.uk

▶ T Naughton Ltd, New Bank Street, Manchester, M12 4TN Tel: 0161-273 7115

T O Tomlins Ltd, Halfway House, Station Lane, Halfway House, Shrewsbury, SY5 9DB Tel: (01743) 884235 Fax: (01743) 884424

T P Niven, Woodhead, Palnackie, Castle Douglas, Kirkcudbrightshire, DG7 1PG Tel: (01556) 600276 Fax: (01556) 600330

▶ T R Handley Ltd, Lilac House, Crosby Garrett, Kirkby Stephen, Cumbria, CA17 4PR Tel: (01768) 371929 Fax: (01768) 371929

▶ T T S Shipping Ltd, Charter House, 14 Park Road, Melton Mowbray, Leicestershire, LE13 1TT Tel: (01664) 410441 Fax: (01664) 410208 E-mail: admin@tts.co.uk

T W Bowler Ltd, Shadyoak, Marple Road, Stockport, Cheshire, SK2 5HF Tel: 0161-487 3363 Fax: 0161-487 3527 E-mail: sales@bowlers-stockport.co.uk

▶ T W E Haulage, Thorpe Mead, Banbury, Oxfordshire, OX16 4RZ Tel: (01295) 262299 Fax: (01295) 262255

T W Logistics Ltd, The Old Ship Yard, Gainsborough, Lincolnshire, DN21 1NQ Tel: (01427) 614551 Fax: (01427) 613770

Tab Logix Ltd, 200 Milton Park, Abingdon, Oxfordshire, OX14 4TF Tel: (01235) 864818 Fax: (01235) 861275

Tackwood Transport, Foundry Way, Little End Road Industrial Estate, Eaton Socon, St. Neots, Cambridgeshire, PE19 8TR Tel: (01480) 214340 Fax: (01480) 406468 E-mail: ts@tackwoodservices.co.uk

▶ Taft International Transport, Weatherfield Lodge, Each End, Ash, Canterbury, Kent, CT3 2BZ Tel: (01304) 813406 Fax: (01304) 813404 E-mail: sales@roadhaulageuk.com

▶ Tal Freeway Ltd, Wellington Road, Gateshead, Tyne & Wear, NE11 9JL Tel: 0191-460 5037 Fax: 0191-460 9477

▶ Tankfreight Ltd, South Shore Road, Grangemouth, Stirlingshire, FK3 8TT Tel: (01324) 665340 Fax: (01324) 483436

▶ Tappin Storage & Removals, 209 Askew Road, London, W12 9AZ Tel: (020) 8749 4434 Fax: (020) 8749 4434

▶ Taurus Logistics, New Portreath Road, Redruth, Cornwall, TR16 4HN Tel: (01209) 314772 Fax: (01209) 314773

Taylor Barnard Container Services Ltd, Eling Wharf, Totton, Southampton, SO40 9LH Tel: 023 80871444

▶ Taylors Transport, 123 Nutty Lane, Shepperton, Middlesex, TW17 0RQ Tel: (01932) 788597 Fax: (01932) 785116

▶ TDG, Condor Glen, Holytown, Motherwell, Lanarkshire, ML1 4UY Tel: (01698) 505800 Fax: (01698) 505220

▶ TDG UK Ltd, Bromford Gate, Bromford Lane, Erdington, Birmingham, B24 8DW Tel: 0121-327 2883 Fax: 0121-327 2551

TDG UK Ltd, High Street, Coleshill, Birmingham, B46 3BP Tel: (01675) 467447 Fax: (01675) 467585

▶ Temperature Controlled Express, Bryn Y Plentyn Farm, Middleton, Oswestry, Shropshire, SY11 4LP Tel: (01691) 657229

▶ Tesco Distribution, Kilbegs Road, Antrim, BT41 4NN Tel: (028) 9444 7100 Fax: (028) 9444 7153

▶ Tesco Distribution, Caputhall Road, Deans, Livingston, West Lothian, EH54 8AS Tel: (01506) 771100 Fax: (01506) 771143

▶ Tesco Distribution, Deer Park Road, Moulton Park Industrial Estate, Northampton, NN3 6RX Tel: (01604) 447900 Fax: (01604) 447934

▶ Tescos, Tesco Warehouse, Collett, Didcot, Oxfordshire, OX11 7PN Tel: (01235) 707100 Fax: (01235) 707157

▶ Thameside Freight Services Ltd, Unit A, 124 New Road, Rainham, Essex, RM13 8RS Tel: (01708) 559871

Thomas Graham, 19 Kinneil Road, Bo'Ness, West Lothian, EH51 0AY Tel: (01506) 829090 Fax: (01506) 829075

▶ Thomas Guy Ltd, Tollgate Road, Burscough, Ormskirk, Lancashire, L40 8LD Tel: (01704) 893304 Fax: (01704) 893603

Thomas Harwood & Son Ltd, 131 Church Street, Little Lever, Bolton, BL3 1BW Tel: (01204) 708888 Fax: (01204) 701700 E-mail: traffic@thomasharwood.co.uk

▶ Thomas Kelly & Sons, 5 Picton Road, Wavertree, Liverpool, L15 4LD Tel: 0151-733 9966 Fax: 0151-733 9966

Thomas Long & Sons Ltd, Park House, Mile End Road, Colwick, Nottingham, NG4 2DW Tel: 0115-961 8888 Fax: 0115-940 0118 E-mail: enquiries@thomaslonggroup.co.uk

▶ Thomas R Callan, 22 Smith Street, Ayr, KA7 1TF Tel: (01292) 267681 E-mail: info@trcallan.com

Thomas Removals, 50 Salop Road, Wrexham, Clwyd, LL13 7AF Tel: (0800) 7834581 Fax: (01978) 366478 E-mail: info@thomas-removals.co.uk

▶ Thomson Henry J Haulage Contractor, Kirkwood, Inverurie, Aberdeenshire, AB51 7LQ Tel: (01330) 833570 Fax: (01330) 833650

▶ Tibe & Britten P.L.C., Camerons Wood, Nettlehill Road, Houstoun Industrial Estate, Livingston, West Lothian, EH54 5DL Tel: (01506) 474000

Tipton Transport Ltd, Eagle Industrial Estate, Bagnall Street, Great Bridge, Tipton, West Midlands, DY4 7BS Tel: 0121-557 3201 Fax: 0121-520 1092 E-mail: sals@palletforce.com

▶ TK Direct (Light Haulage) Coventry, 20 Springfield Crescent, Bedworth, Warwickshire, CV12 8NX Tel: (07970) 151944 Fax: (024) 7673 1422 E-mail: info@tkdirect.co.uk

TNT, Telford Road, Durranhill Industrial Estate, Carlisle, CA1 3NW Tel: (01228) 525645 Fax: (01228) 547991 E-mail: paul.beatie@tntlogistics.co.uk

▶ TNT Newsfast Ltd, Olivers Place, Fulwood, Preston, PR2 9WT Tel: (01772) 561259 Fax: (01772) 791995

Tomsetts Distribution Ltd, North Quay Road, Newhaven, East Sussex, BN9 0AB Tel: (01273) 513347 Fax: (01273) 516042 E-mail: enquiries@tomsetts.com

▶ Torridge Transport Ltd, School Lane, Torrington, Devon, EX38 7AJ Tel: (01805) 623477 Fax: (01805) 622727

▶ Tortank Ltd, Marlin House, Kings Road, Immingham, South Humberside, DN40 1AW Tel: (01469) 510777

▶ Total Haulage Ni Ltd, 1 Bay View Industrial Park, Dargan CR, Belfast, BT3 9JP Tel: (028) 9077 1121 Fax: (028) 9077 9274

▶ Tradeteam Ltd, Eddison Road, Hams Hall Distribution Park, Coleshill, Birmingham, B46 1TT Tel: (01675) 468500 Fax: (01675) 467541 E-mail: phil.storer@tradeteam.com

▶ Tradeteam Ltd, Stockingswater Lane, Enfield, Middlesex, EN3 7PZ Tel: (020) 8216 6900 Fax: (020) 8216 6929

▶ Tradeteam Ltd, Scottish Distribution Centre, Dale Avenue, Cambuslang, Glasgow, G72 7DX Tel: 0141-646 3500 Fax: 0141-646 3530

▶ Trans Bridge Freight Services Ltd, 384 Heywood Old Road, Middleton, Manchester, M24 4SB Tel: 0161-655 0100 Fax: 0161-655 0111

Transam Distributors Ltd, 13 Furnace Road, Muirkirk, Cumnock, Ayrshire, KA18 3RE Tel: (01290) 661515

▶ Transland International, Ocean Park, Birkenhead, Merseyside, CH41 1NE Tel: 0151-653 4540 Fax: 0151-653 4547 E-mail: sales@translandgroup.ie

Translift Freight Ltd, Womersley Road, Knottingley, West Yorkshire, WF11 0DN Tel: (01977) 672301 Fax: (01977) 607071

▶ Transpan Scotland Ltd, 53 Cornfield Road, Turriff, Aberdeenshire, AB53 4BP Tel: (01888) 563059

Transportomatic, Tollgate Drive, Tollgate Industrial Estate, Stafford, ST16 3HS Tel: (01785) 258500

▶ Transtech Removals, Westinghouse Industrial Estate, Trafford Park, Manchester, M17 1DF Tel: 0161-877 5622 Fax: 0161-877 5623

▶ Transworld Transport Ltd, Pitt Street, Widnes, Cheshire, WA8 0TG Tel: 0151-423 6168 Fax: 0151-420 0902

▶ Trevor Ward, 19 Tandragee Road, Newry, County Down, BT35 6QE Tel: (028) 3026 5613 Fax: (028) 3026 6610

▶ Trialout Ltd, Unit 7 Cornwall Street, Parr Industrial Estate, St. Helens, Merseyside, WA9 1QT Tel: (01744) 616222 Fax: (01744) 616333

▶ Trucks Ltd, Carleton House, Ashley Crescent, Southampton, SO19 9NA Tel: (023) 8044 4434

▶ Truswell Haulage Ltd, Cairn Lodge, Douglas, Lanark, ML11 0RJ Tel: (01555) 851844 Fax: (01555) 851392

▶ Truswell Haulage, Surbiton Street, Sheffield, S9 2DN Tel: 0114-244 9568 Fax: 0114-242 6630

Tryus Transport Ltd, 1 Delph Industrial Estate, Delph Road, Brierley Hill, West Midlands, DY5 2UA Tel: (01384) 265237 Fax: (01384) 262474

▶ TSL Vanguard Ltd, Psalters Lane, Steel Street, Holmes, Rotherham, South Yorkshire, S61 1DF Tel: (0870) 6096009 Fax: (0870) 6096010E-mail: ian.liversidge@btconnect.com

Tuffnells Parcel Express, Caswell Road, Brackmills Industrial Estate, Northampton, NN4 7PW Tel: (01604) 768765 Fax: (01604) 766116

Turner Removal Services, Huyton Road, Adlington, Chorley, Lancashire, PR7 4JR Tel: (01254) 56182 Fax: (01257) 484324

▶ Turners Hoole Ltd, 53 Liverpool Old Road, Much Hoole, Preston, PR4 4GA Tel: (01772) 613434 Fax: (01772) 617666

▶ Turners Soham Ltd, 1 Allerton Bywater Business Park, Newton Lane, Allerton Bywater, Castleford, West Yorkshire, WF10 2AL Tel: (01977) 603395 Fax: (01977) 603679

Turners Soham Ltd, Fordham Road, Newmarket, Suffolk, CB8 7NR Tel: (01638) 720335 Fax: (01638) 720940 E-mail: carol.chapman@turners-distribution.com

Tyson H Burridge Ltd, Old Coach Works, Distington, Workington, Cumbria, CA14 5XJ Tel: (01946) 830333 Fax: (01946) 830777 E-mail: sales@haulagecumbria.co.uk

▶ U C I Logistics Ltd, Unit 131, Heathhall Industrial Estate, Heathhall, Dumfries, DG1 3PH Tel: (01387) 265268

▶ UK Deliveries (Birmingham) Ltd, Duddeston Mill Trading Estate, Duddeston Mill Road, Saltley, Birmingham, B8 1AP Tel: 0121-333 3640 Fax: 0121-333 3640 E-mail: ukdels@btconnect.com

▶ UK Direct Couriers, Unit 10B, Gatehouse Trading Estate, Lichfield Road, Brownhills, Walsall, WS8 6JZ Tel: (01543) 372225

▶ United Freight Distributuion Ltd, 2 Ashley Drive, Bothwell, Glasgow, G71 8BS Tel: (01698) 802802 Fax: (01698) 802800

United Parcels Service (UPS) Ltd, Gresham Road, Nuneaton, Warwickshire, CV10 7QR Tel: (0845) 7877877 Fax: (024) 7664 2188 E-mail: callcentre@europe.ups.com

▶ Uts Scotland Ltd, Anniesland Industrial Estate, Glasgow, G13 1EU Tel: 0141-959 4477

V G Mathers Ltd, Cottown Garage, Kintore, Inverurie, Aberdeenshire, AB51 0XQ Tel: (01467) 642742 Fax: (01467) 642842 E-mail: vic.mathers@tesco.net

▶ Van Ellis Ltd, F Lambs Farm Business Park, Basingstoke Road, Swallowfield, Reading, RG7 1PQ Tel: 0118-988 9290 Fax: 0118-988 9294

▶ Vaughan Logistics Ltd, Dukeries Industrial Estate, Claylands Avenue, Worksop, Nottinghamshire, S81 7BQ Tel: (01909) 486371

Vectis Transport Ltd, Riverway Industrial Estate, Newport, Isle Of Wight, PO30 5UX Tel: (01983) 523515 Fax: (01983) 526225 E-mail: vectis@redfunnel.co.uk

▶ Venture Logistics & Distribution, Venture House, Bilton Way, Lutterworth, Leicestershire, LE17 4JA Tel: (01455) 555400

Vic Haines, Racecourse Road, Pershore, Worcestershire, WR10 2EY Tel: (01386) 553288 Fax: (01386) 554615

▶ Victoria Transport, Commercial St, Macduff, Banffshire, AB44 1SB Tel: (01261) 833157

Visual Impact Signs, Breach Road, West Thurrock, Grays, Essex, RM20 3NR Tel: (01708) 865566 Fax: (01708) 865566

▶ Vos Logistics Cargo, Oxnam Road, Jedburgh, Roxburghshire, TD8 6NN Tel: (01835) 864972 Fax: (01835) 863953 E-mail: cmercer@voslogistics.com

▶ W A Humphreys International Transport Ltd, Unit 8 Ely Valley Industrial Estate, Pontyclun, Mid Glamorgan, CF72 9DZ Tel: (01443) 226582 Fax: (01443) 237647

▶ W A Jaines & Son Ltd, Warwick Road, Fairfield Industrial Estate, Louth, Lincolnshire, LN11 0YB Tel: (01507) 606497 Fax: (01507) 600505

▶ W Allen Bolton Ltd, James Street, Westhoughton, Bolton, BL5 3QR Tel: (01942) 818888 Fax: (01942) 818886

W Baybutt Ltd, Plantation Road, Burscough Industrial Estate, Ormskirk, Lancashire, L40 8JT Tel: (01704) 892905 Fax: (01704) 892262

▶ W Carter, Alconbury Airfield, Alconbury, Huntingdon, Cambridgeshire, PE28 4WX Tel: (01480) 453355 Fax: (01480) 454265

W Carters (Haulage) Ltd, Sub Station Road, The Dock, Felixstowe, Suffolk, IP11 3JB Tel: (01394) 676623 Fax: (01394) 673560

▶ W Coy & Son Ltd, Unit 5, Langar Industrial Estate, South Harby Road, Nottingham, NG13 9HY Tel: (01949) 860216

▶ W D Cooper, Progress Drive, Cannock, Staffordshire, WS11 0JE Tel: (01543) 503192 Fax: (01543) 572719

▶ indicates data change since last edition

ROAD TRANSPORT AND HAULAGE

– continued

▶ W E & I Wright Ltd, Garage, High Stoop, Tow Law, Bishop Auckland, County Durham, DL13 4HJ Tel: (01388) 730297 Fax: (01388) 730130

▶ W F Hall & Son Ltd, Wern Road, Goodwick, Dyfed, SA64 0AA Tel: (01348) 872272 Fax: (01348) 872991 E-mail: sales@wfhalltransport.co.uk

▶ W Freeman & Son Ltd, Dunton Wharf, Lichfield Road, Curdworth, Sutton Coldfield, West Midlands, B76 9EN Tel: (01675) 470777 Fax: (01675) 470743

W G & H Horsley, Ashville, Main Street, Newton on Derwent, York, YO41 4DA Tel: (01904) 608742 Fax: (01904) 608755

W H Bowker Ltd, Holme Road, Bamber Bridge, Preston, PR5 6BP Tel: (01772) 628800 Fax: (01772) 628801 E-mail: enquiries@bowker.co.uk

▶ W H Bowker International Ltd, Littlefair Road, Hull, HU9 5LP Tel: (01482) 706557 Fax: (01482) 706533 E-mail: info@bowkertransport.co.uk

▶ W & H Leslie Ltd, Enterprise Drive, Westhill Industrial Estate, Westhill, Aberdeenshire, AB32 6TQ Tel: (01224) 740203 Fax: (01224) 742041

▶ W H Malcolm Ltd, 201 Castlebank Street, Glasgow, G11 6DZ Tel: 0141-334 9841

W H Malcolm Ltd, 865 South Street, Glasgow, G14 0BX Tel: 0141-435 5299 Fax: 0141-435 5298 E-mail: contact@whm.co.uk

▶ W H Malcolm Ltd, Nethermains Road, Kilwinning, Ayrshire, KA13 6PY Tel: (01294) 551321 Fax: (01294) 552803 E-mail: admin@malcolmgroup.co.uk

▶ W H Malcolm Ltd, Newton Picot Depot, Gatenby, Northallerton, North Yorkshire, DL7 9NG Tel: (01677) 424096 Fax: (01677) 423124

▶ W J Jenkins & Sons Tipton Ltd, Pound Garage, Bridge Road, Tipton, West Midlands, DY4 0JW Tel: 0121-557 6085 Fax: 0121-520 6815 E-mail: wjjenkinsandsons@tiscali.co.uk

W J Law Plant & Transport Ltd, 171 Moira Road, Lisburn, County Antrim, BT28 1RW Tel: (028) 9266 6602 Fax: (028) 9260 3663

▶ W J Simms Ltd, 14-16 Beddington Farm Road, Croydon, CR0 4XB Tel: (020) 8684 4288

▶ W K Edwards, Ketley Road, Kingswinford, West Midlands, DY6 8DA Tel: (01384) 270936 Fax: (01384) 291488

▶ W Kirk Ltd, London Road, Adlington, Macclesfield, Cheshire, SK10 4NL Tel: (01625) 879990

W M Young Transport Ltd, School House Farm, Beamhurst, Uttoxeter, Staffordshire, ST14 5EA Tel: (01889) 507279 Fax: (01889) 563266

▶ W Martin Oliver, Carrsgate, Bardon Mill, Hexham, Northumberland, NE47 7EX Tel: (01434) 344555

▶ W Pringle & Sons, The Garage Hamburg Cottages, Lawhill Road, Carluke, Lanarkshire, ML8 5HF Tel: (01555) 770550 Fax: (01555) 770556

▶ W.R Woolgar Furnisher Removels, 12 Heathfield Road, Handsworth, Birmingham, B19 1HB Tel: 0121-554 4963

▶ W Sharples & Sons Ltd, Unit 38a Lune Industrial Estate, Lancaster, LA1 5QP Tel: (01524) 849836 Fax: (01524) 388299 E-mail: info@wrightandco-nw.co.uk

▶ W Smith, Murrayfield Road, Leicester, LE3 1UW Tel: 0116-231 3007 Fax: 0116-231 3005

▶ W Sweeting & Sons Ltd, Washbrook, Hill Road, Sandford, Winscombe, Avon, BS25 5RJ Tel: (01934) 822588 Fax: (01934) 820564

W Tabern & Sons Ltd, Duncan Street, St. Helens, Merseyside, WA10 3TF Tel: (01744) 24763 Fax: (01744) 24764

▶ Wainwright Transport, 19 Wood Street, Ashby-de-la-Zouch, Leicestershire, LE65 1EL Tel: (01530) 412057 Fax: (01530) 415824

▶ W. Walker Transport, Granitehill Road, Aberdeen, AB16 7AX Tel: (01224) 698844 Fax: (01224) 685967 E-mail: steve@williamwalkertransport.co.uk

▶ Walkers International Movers Ltd, 33-34 Liliput Road, Brackmills Industrial Estate, Northampton, NN4 7DT Tel: (01604) 704030

Waller Transport Services Ltd, Brewery Yard, 6 Landseer Road, Ipswich, IP3 0AZ Tel: (01473) 254717 Fax: (01473) 250582 E-mail: ipswichtraffic@wallertransport.co.uk

▶ Roger Warnes Transport Ltd, Station Road, Leziate, King's Lynn, Norfolk, PE32 1EJ Tel: (01553) 841087

Watford Express Ltd, Unit 20 Peerglow Industrial Est, Olds Approach, Tolpits La, Watford, WD18 9SR Tel: (01923) 771383 Fax: (01923) 771383

▶ Watkins & Sole, Unit 5 Garonor Way, Portbury, Bristol, BS20 7XE Tel: (01275) 376370 Fax: (01275) 376371

Watkinson Lifting & Transportation Ltd, Invincible Works, Marriner Road, Keighley, West Yorkshire, BD21 5LW Tel: (01535) 600151 Fax: (01535) 692249 E-mail: sales@watkinsons.com

▶ Watson & Co., Kiln Lane, Stallingborough, Grimsby, South Humberside, DN41 8DS Tel: (01469) 572728 Fax: (01469) 578410

▶ Watts Transport, The Moat, Buckland, Buntingford, Hertfordshire, SG9 0QB Tel: (01763) 271653 Fax: (01763) 273319

Waugh Road Services Ltd, Wesley Way, Benton Square Industrial Estate, Newcastle Upon Tyne, NE12 9TA Tel: 0191-266 1046 Fax: 0191-215 0754

G. Webb Haulage Ltd, Station Road, Longstanton, Cambridge, CB4 5DS Tel: (01954) 260691 Fax: (01954) 261211 E-mail: sales@gwebb.uk.com

Gerry Webb Transport Services Ltd, 4 Shelson Parade, Ashford Road, Feltham, Middlesex, TW13 4QZ Tel: (020) 8867 0000 Fax: (020) 8867 0088 E-mail: gerrywebbtpt@talk21.com

▶ Welburn Transport, Hackett Street, Tipton, West Midlands, DY4 0JJ Tel: 0121-557 1776 Fax: 0121-520 6783

Welch Transport Ltd, Granta Terrace, Stapleford, Cambridge, CB2 5DL Tel: (01223) 843011 Fax: (01223) 843979 E-mail: ianlawton@welchgroup.co.uk

▶ Welchs Transport Ltd, High Street, Henlow, Bedfordshire, SG16 6BS Tel: (01462) 812888 Fax: (01462) 817217

▶ Welch's Transport Ltd, 6 Industrial Estate, Crittall Road, Witham, Essex, CM8 3DE Tel: (01376) 512295 Fax: (01376) 511772 E-mail: sales@welchgroup.co.uk

▶ Wensley Transport, Green Lane, Castleford, West Yorkshire, WF10 2RY Tel: (01977) 550259 Fax: (01977) 514239 E-mail: wensley@transport76.fsnet.co.uk

▶ West Pennine Trucks Ltd, Cardronna, Station Road, Knighton, Powys, LD7 1DT Tel: (01547) 528600 Fax: (01547) 520597

▶ Westerman Road Haulage Services, Station Road, Sutton-in-Ashfield, Nottinghamshire, NG17 5FH Tel: (01623) 441111 Fax: (01623) 440301

▶ Westfield International Transport, Hortham Lane, Gaunts Earthcott, Almondsbury, Bristol, BS32 4JP Tel: (01454) 775566 Fax: (01454) 776817

Westfield Truro Cornwall Ltd, Kerley Paddock, Chacewater, Truro, Cornwall, TR4 8JY Tel: (01872) 560860 Fax: (01872) 561056 E-mail: info@westfieldtransport.com

▶ Westlink Transport, Unit 6-7 Euro Way, Blagrove, Swindon, SN5 8YW Tel: (01793) 421611 Fax: (01793) 541542 E-mail: sales@westlinkuk.co.uk

▶ Weston Transport Ltd, Units 1-2, 50 Woodhead Road, Chryston, Glasgow, G69 9HY Tel: 0141-779 4177

▶ WH Smith Retail Ltd, Holford Way, Holford, Birmingham, B6 7AX Tel: 0121-344 4455 Fax: 0121-356 7186

▶ White & Co plc, Pitreavie Business Park, Pitreavie Business Park, Dunfermline, Fife, KY11 8UT Tel: (01383) 739933 Fax: (01383) 621577

▶ White & Co plc, 2 St. Peters Technical Park, St. Peter, Jersey, JE3 7ZN Tel: (01534) 484002 Fax: (01534) 485448

▶ White & Co. plc, Dundas Spur, Portsmouth, PO3 5NL Tel: (023) 9266 3221 Fax: (023) 9265 0114

▶ Whitefield Distribution Ltd, F Birch Industrial Estate, Whittle Lane, Heywood, Lancashire, OL10 2SX Tel: (01706) 361970 Fax: (01706) 361997

Whitehead, Unit 4 Coomber Way, Croydon, CR0 4TQ Tel: (020) 8684 4507 Fax: (020) 8683 3100 E-mail: info@pfwhitehead.com

▶ Widdowson Group, The Mill Lane, Glenfield, Leicester, LE3 8DX Tel: 0116-231 1188 Fax: 0116-287 9898

Wildman Transport (Bedford) Ltd, Postley Road, Kempston, Bedford, MK42 7BU Tel: (01234) 854244 Fax: (01234) 841362 E-mail: roy@wildmantransport.com

▶ William Clegg, 105 Main Road, Fenwick, Kilmarnock, Ayrshire, KA3 6DY Tel: (01560) 600673

William Coutts, Howemuir, Blackhills, Peterhead, Aberdeenshire, AB42 3LJ Tel: (01779) 476086 Fax: (01779) 476947

▶ William Hamilton & Sons Contractors Ltd, Dovesdale Farm, Stonehouse, Larkhall, Lanarkshire, ML9 3PR Tel: (01698) 792211 Fax: (01698) 792212

▶ William Kirk Ltd, Adlington Industrial Estate, London Road, Adlington, Macclesfield, Cheshire, SK10 4NL Tel: (01625) 879990 Fax: (01625) 879807

▶ William Nicol Aberdeen Ltd, 27-29 Barclayhill Place, Portlethen, Aberdeen, AB12 4PF Tel: (01224) 782100 Fax: (01224) 782681

▶ William Thompson & Son (Dumbarton) Ltd, Birch Road, Dumbarton, G82 2RN Tel: (01389) 762271 Fax: (01389) 742217

▶ Williams Shipping Transport Ltd, Manor House Avenue, Southampton, SO15 0LF Tel: (023) 8052 9555 Fax: (023) 8052 9444

Williams Shipping Transport Ltd, Manor House Avenue, Southampton, SO15 0LF Tel: (023) 8070 1314 Fax: (023) 8077 2422 E-mail: enquires@willams-shipping.co.uk

▶ Williams Tanker Service Ltd, Howley Park Road East, Morley, Leeds, LS27 0BS Tel: 0113-289 7990 Fax: 0113-289 7574

▶ James Wilson (Transport) Ltd, Springfield Garage, Muirkirk, Cumnock, Ayrshire, KA18 3QU Tel: (01290) 661244

▶ Wilsons Deliveries, Hallam Fields Road, Ilkeston, Derbyshire, DE7 4AZ Tel: 0115-944 7007 Fax: 0115-944 7013

▶ Wincanton Group Ltd, Faraday Avenue, Hams Hall Distribution Park, Coleshill, Birmingham, B46 1AL Tel: (01675) 433333 Fax: (01675) 433366

▶ Wincanton Group Ltd, Caledonian Mill, Leith Docks, Edinburgh, EH6 6NZ Tel: 0131-554 0803

▶ Wincanton Logistics Ltd, Newbridge Road, Little Stanney, Chester, CH2 4RA Tel: 0151-356 6323

▶ Wincanton Logistics Ltd, Northway Trading Estate, Northway Lane, Tewkesbury, Gloucestershire, GL20 8JH Tel: (01684) 278500 Fax: (01684) 278501

▶ Witherley Services Ltd, Witherley House, Hazelway, Nuneaton, Warwickshire, CV10 7QG Tel: (024) 7635 1188

Woodall Services Ltd, Station Road, Coleshill, Birmingham, B46 1HT Tel: (01675) 466020 Fax: (01675) 465745 E-mail: enquiries@woodalltransport.co.uk

▶ Woodland International Transport, 2 Woodland House, Hall Dene Way, Seaham Grange Industrial Estate, Seaham, County Durham, SR7 0PU Tel: 0191-521 9780 Fax: 0191-521 9797

Woodrush Distribution, Unit 6 Greenfield Road, Pulloxhill, Bedford, MK45 5EY Tel: (01525) 717199 Fax: (01525) 717606 E-mail: sales@woodrush.co.uk

Woods Transport Ltd, 6 Climax Works, Garnet Road, Leeds, LS11 5JY Tel: 0113-276 1116 Fax: 0113-276 1116

Woodside Haulage Ltd, 61 Carrickfergus Road, Ballynure, Ballyclare, County Antrim, BT39 9QJ Tel: (028) 9335 2255 Fax: (028) 9334 0427 E-mail: info@woodsides.com

▶ Woodside Haulage (G B) Ltd, Unit 280 Carnfield Place, Walton Summit Industrial Estate, Bamber Bridge, Preston, PR5 8AN Tel: (01772) 323381 Fax: (01772) 627020 E-mail: info@woodside-haulage.co.uk

▶ Woodview Light Transport Ltd, Ransome Road, Northampton, NN4 8AD Tel: (01604) 766201 Fax: (01604) 701210

Wrefords Transport, Ransome Road, Northampton, NN4 8AD Tel: (01604) 761429 Fax: (01604) 768764 E-mail: sales@swwreford.co.uk

▶ Wymondham Recovery Services, Valleyside Industrial Estate, Station Road, Wymondham, Norfolk, NR18 0NN Tel: (01953) 602376

▶ Yorkie Removals & Storage Ltd, Quedgeley Enterprise Centre, Naas Lane, Quedgeley, Gloucester, GL2 4SA Tel: (01452) 725554

Yorkshire Plant (Humber) Ltd, Clay Street, Chamberlain Road, Hull, HU8 8HF Tel: (01482) 329441 Fax: (01482) 225027 E-mail: jez@yorkshireplant.co.uk

▶ Yorwaste Ltd, The Rawcliffe Depot, Shipton Road, York, YO30 5YA Tel: (01904) 423626 Fax: (01904) 639666

Yuill & Dodds Ltd, Unit 6 Whistleberry Industrial Park Estate, Hamilton, Lanarkshire, ML3 0ED Tel: (01698) 720700 Fax: (01698) 720709

▶ Zooom Express Deliveries, Unit 1, Greenbank Business Centre, Greenbank Road, East Tullos Industrial Estate, Aberdeen, AB12 3BN Tel: (01224) 878783

ROAD TRANSPORT AND HAULAGE FOR CHILLED FOOD

▶ CRS 24: 7, 6 Whitburn Road, Bathgate, West Lothian, EH48 1HH Tel: (0870) 7665 206 Fax: (01506) 637562 E-mail: gary@crs247.com

▶ Manton Transport Ltd, Springfield Farm Cold Cotes Road, Kettlesing Head, Fellscliffe, Harrogate, North Yorkshire, HG3 2LW Tel: (01423) 770520

▶ Violet Farm Foods Ltd, Units 10-11, Uddens Trading Estate, Wimborne, Dorset, BH21 7LQ Tel: (01202) 891006 Fax: (01202) 896281 E-mail: sales@vff.co.uk

ROAD TRANSPORT AND HAULAGE SERVICES, EUROPE

▶ Anglotan Ltd, 47 Cricket Inn Crescent, Sheffield, S2 5AQ Tel: 0114-272 9220 Fax: 0114-272 9220 E-mail: transport@anglotan.com

▶ Clive's Light Removals, 4 Coastguard Cottages, Isle of Grain, Rochester, Kent, ME3 0DS Tel: 0777 8872492 E-mail: clive@fsmail.net

▶ Hauser Ltd, Heighington Lane, Aycliffe Industrial Park, Newton Aycliffe, County Durham, DL5 6UE Tel: (01325) 300855 Fax: (01325) 300844 E-mail: northeast@hauser.co.uk

▶ Hauser Sheffield Ltd, Alliance House, Roman Ridge Road, Sheffield, S9 1GB Tel: 0114-244 9977 Fax: 0114-242 3481 E-mail: sheffield@hauser.co.uk

Rhenus Hauser Ltd, Bowden House, Luckyn Lane, Basildon, Essex, SS14 3AX Tel: (01268) 592180 Fax: (01268) 592181 E-mail: london@uk.rhenus.com

ROAD TRANSPORT AND HAULAGE, HORSE

▶ Boothroyden Boarding Cattery, Boothroyden Cottage, Boothroyden Terrace, Manchester, M9 0SB Tel: 0161-653 6483 Fax: 0161-653 7191 E-mail: peter.gramm7@btinternet.com

Hollis Horse & Hollis Farriers, Kentisbeare, Cullompton, Devon, EX15 2BT Tel: (01884) 266398

Horse Power Self Drive Equine Transport, 7 Riverside, Storrington, Pulborough, West Sussex, RH20 4NN Tel: (01903) 746800 Fax: (0845) 1275210 E-mail: sales@horsebox-selfdrive.com

▶ LOC LIMITED INTERNATIONAL HORSE TRANSPORT, 5 KETTLES COTTAGES, TRIG STREET, BEARE GREEN, DORKING, SURREY, RH5 4QF Tel: 01306 710100 E-mail: LIZ@LOCLTD.COM

John Parker International Ltd, Little Owl Barn, Pedlinge, Hythe, Kent, CT21 4JJ Tel: (01303) 266621 Fax: (01303) 269400

ROAD TRANSPORT AND HAULAGE, TRANSPORT INTERNATIONAL ROUTIER (TIR)

Air Cargo Transport Ltd, 4 Ladygate, Diseworth, Derby, DE74 2QF Tel: (01332) 811464 Fax: (01332) 812223 E-mail: admin@air-cargo.uk.com

Apple Freight Ltd, Trafford House, Chester Road, Stretford, Manchester, M32 0RS Tel: 0161-872 0718 Fax: 0161-872 9751

Arends International Ltd, Sankey Valley Industrial Estate, Anglezarke Road, Newton-le-Willows, Merseyside, WA12 8DJ Tel: (01925) 223323 Fax: (01925) 229800 E-mail: sales@arends.co.uk

Betchworth International Heavy Transport, Old Reigate Road, Betchworth, Surrey, RH3 7LW Tel: (0870) 1671671 Fax: (0870) 1671672

Bidcorp P.L.C., 6 Stratton Street, London, W1J 8LD Tel: (020) 7408 0123 Fax: (020) 7495 8284

Bower Green Ltd, Station Road, Norwood Green, Halifax, West Yorkshire, HX3 8QD Tel: (01274) 672450 Fax: (01274) 693136 E-mail: norwood@bowergreen.co.uk

Chambers & Cook Ltd, European House, Perrywell Road, Witton, Birmingham, B6 7AT Tel: 0121-356 1441 Fax: 0121-356 7880 E-mail: admin@chambers-and-cook.co.uk

Cotrans International Ltd, Strathallen House, 197 Winchester Road, Chandlers Ford, Eastleigh, Hampshire, SO53 2DU Tel: (023) 8027 3222 Fax: (023) 8027 3244 E-mail: gary_m_turner@hotmail.co.uk

Creative Logistics Ltd, Duncan Street, Salford, M5 3SQ Tel: 0161-873 7101 Fax: 0161-872 1447 E-mail: enquiries@creative-logistics.co.uk

Dachser Transport UK Ltd, Oxwich Close, Brackmills Industrial Estate, Northampton, NN4 7BH Tel: (01604) 666222 Fax: (01604) 666239 E-mail: dachser.northampton@dachser.com

Dodds Ltd, Mansfield Road, Aston, Sheffield, S26 2BS Tel: 0114-287 4187 Fax: 0114-287 2251 E-mail: traffic@dodds.co.uk

Eurocontinental Logistics Ltd, Unit 7, Everitt Close, Denington Industrial Estate, Wellingborough, Northamptonshire, NN8 2QE Tel: (01933) 223851 Fax: (01933) 272630 E-mail: info@eurocontinental-logistics.co.uk

▶ F Edmondson & Sons, Southgate, White Lund Industrial Estate, Morecambe, Lancashire, LA3 3DA Tel: (01524) 382211 Fax: (01524) 60729

F F G Hillebrand, Dissigna House, Weston Avenue, West Thurrock, Grays, Essex, RM20 3ZP Tel: (01708) 689000 Fax: (01708) 689001 E-mail: sales@ffg-hil.com

Frans Maas (U K) Ltd, 36 North Quay, Great Yarmouth, Norfolk, NR30 1JE Tel: (01493) 336600 Fax: (01493) 858730 E-mail: sales@fmaas.co.uk

Freeland Freight Services Ltd, Blackness Road, Altens Industrial Estate, Aberdeen, AB12 3LH Tel: (01224) 873601 Fax: (01224) 879863 E-mail: enquiries@freelandfreight.co.uk

G S I Pallet Force, Seymour House, Dunhams Lane, Letchworth Garden City, Hertfordshire, SG6 1LL Tel: (01462) 485726 Fax: (01462) 678381 E-mail: sales@palletforce.com

Geodis Overseas (U K) Ltd, PO Box 92, High Wycombe, Buckinghamshire, HP12 3TW Tel: (01494) 446541 Fax: (01494) 446329 E-mail: hwcustomerservies@geodisuk.com

Geoff Gilbert International Ltd, Station Road, Swineshead, Boston, Lincolnshire, PE20 3PN Tel: (01205) 721000 Fax: (01205) 721004 E-mail: transport@geoffgilbert.co.uk

Gist, Wardentree Lane, Pinchbeck, Spalding, Lincolnshire, PE11 3UG Tel: (01775) 764000 Fax: (01775) 764101

Howard Shipping Services Ltd, Showell Road, Wolverhampton, WV10 9JY Tel: (01902) 738838 Fax: (01902) 862962 E-mail: peterhoward@hoship.com

Hoyer UK Ltd, 517 Leeds Road, Huddersfield, HD2 1YJ Tel: (01484) 548221 Fax: (01484) 518933 E-mail: enquires@hoyer-group.com

Intersped Logistics UK Ltd, Unit 9 Gatesway Business Centre, Tom Cribb Road, London, SE28 0EZ Tel: (020) 8316 4300 Fax: (020) 8316 1210 E-mail: logistics@intersped.co.uk

Kenyon Road Haulage Ltd, Thornley Avenue, Blackburn, BB1 3HJ Tel: (01254) 503600 Fax: (01254) 503601 E-mail: sales@kenyon-haulage.com

Kuehne & Nagel Ltd, Worton Drive Industrial Estate, Imperial Way, Reading, RG2 0TH Tel: 0118-986 5865 Fax: 0118-986 5801 E-mail: knrdg.dx@kuehne-nagel.com

Laser Transport International Ltd, Lympne Industrial Estate, Lympne, Hythe, Kent, CT21 4LR Tel: (01303) 260471 Fax: (01303) 264851 E-mail: sales@laserint.co.uk

ROAD TRANSPORT AND HAULAGE, TRANSPORT INTERNATIONAL ROUTIER (TIR) – *continued*

Lichfield International Freight Terminal Ltd, Units 1,2 & 4, Wellington Road, Burton-on-Trent, Staffordshire, DE14 2TG Tel: (01283) 511888 Fax: (01283) 511900 E-mail: ops@lichfieldinternational.co.uk
Murray Hogg Ltd, Sandy Lane, North Gosforth, North Gosforth, Newcastle Upon Tyne, NE3 5HE Tel: 0191-236 4211 Fax: 0191-236 3189 E-mail: sales@murrayhogg.co.uk
R.K. Neil Ltd, The Old Sawmills, The Street, Kilmington, Warminster, Wiltshire, BA12 6RG Tel: (01985) 844112 Fax: (01985) 844113 E-mail: info@martinbrosltd.com
Norbert Dentressangle, Billington Road, Leighton Buzzard, Bedfordshire, LU7 9HH Tel: (01525) 243900 Fax: (01525) 382066
P T S UK Ltd, 10 Cliff Road, Ipswich, IP3 0AY Tel: (01473) 282600 Fax: (01473) 287521 E-mail: sales@ptsukltd.co.uk
R H Group, Lenton Lane, Nottingham, NG7 2NR Tel: 0115-943 8000 Fax: 0115-943 8045
R & T Shipping Ltd, 2nd Floor, Holegate House, Holegate Court, Western Road, Romford, RM1 3JS Tel: (0870) 7745612 Fax: (0870) 7745602
Rhys Davies & Sons Ltd, Moy Road Industrial Estate, Taffs Well, Cardiff, CF15 7QR Tel: (029) 2081 0587 Fax: (029) 2081 0717 E-mail: sales@rhysdavies.co.uk
Rycon Shipping & Forwarding Ltd, Rycon Warehouse, Rye Harbour Road, Rye, East Sussex, TN31 7TE Tel: (01797) 222747 Fax: (01797) 224535 E-mail: ryecon@btconnect.com
Sealandair Transport Co., 101 Stephenson Street, London, E16 4SA Tel: (020) 7511 2288 Fax: (020) 7511 1466 E-mail: frt@sealandair.com
Standard Freight Forwarders Ltd, 73 Maltings Place, London, SW6 2BY Tel: (020) 7384 1212 Fax: (020) 7384 1030 E-mail: exports@standardfreight.com
T M Logistics, Edgar House, Berrow Green Road, Martley, Worcester, WR6 6PQ Tel: (01886) 888241 Fax: (01886) 888196
Teamsped Ltd, Unit 4 Waterfall La Trading Estate, Cradley Heath, West Midlands, B64 6PU Tel: 0121-561 3886 Fax: 0121-561 3959 E-mail: john@teamsped.co.uk
Tibbett & Britten Group P.L.C., Centennial Park, Centennial Avenue, Elstree, Borehamwood, Hertfordshire, WD6 3TL Tel: (020) 8327 2000 Fax: (020) 8327 2199 E-mail: info@tandb.co.uk
Transalliance UK Ltd, Stonehouse Lane, Purfleet, Essex, RM19 1NX Tel: (01708) 869111 Fax: (01708) 867386 E-mail: hnpurfleet@btconnect.com
Union Transport Group plc, Imperial House, 21-25 North Street, Bromley, BR1 1SJ Tel: (020) 8290 1234 Fax: (020) 8402 7770 E-mail: utg.plc@uniontransport.co.uk
Unitrans International Ltd, Woodfield House, Hatmill Lane, Brenchley, Tonbridge, Kent, TN12 7AE Tel: (01892) 723270 Fax: (01892) 724188 E-mail: robert-fogg@unitrans.fsnet.co.uk
Universal Express Ltd, 139-141 Hamilton Road, Felixstowe, Suffolk, IP11 7BL Tel: (01394) 282867 Fax: (01394) 286767 E-mail: info@universalexpress.co.uk
World Transport Agency Ltd, 19-21 Schneider Close, Felixstowe, Suffolk, IP11 3BQ Tel: (01394) 673247 Fax: (01394) 673721 E-mail: arb@wta.co.uk
Wrefords Transport, Ransome Road, Northampton, NN4 8AD Tel: (01604) 761429 Fax: (01604) 768764 E-mail: sales@swwreford.co.uk

ROAD TRANSPORT TANKS

▶ Hargreaves Bulk Liquid Transport, Fryers Road, Walsall, WS3 2XJ Tel: (01922) 470799 Fax: (01922) 470790
▶ M F Compton & Son, Grovebury Road, Leighton Buzzard, Bedfordshire, LU7 4TS Tel: (01525) 371707 Fax: (01525) 851891 E-mail: enquiries@tankers-r-us.com

ROAST BEEF

▶ Encore Catering, Blair Court, Port Dundas Business Park, 100 Borron Street, Glasgow, G4 9XE Tel: 0141-353 9148 Fax: 0141-353 9145

ROASTED COFFEE BEANS

▶ Coffee Merchants, Rathdown Road, Lissue Industrial Estate, Lisburn, County Antrim, BT28 2RE Tel: (028) 9262 2733 Fax: (028) 9262 2734 E-mail: stuart@coffeemerchantsltd.com
Roberts & Co., Art Cedar Farm Galleries, Mawdesley, Ormskirk, Lancashire, L40 3SY Tel: (01704) 822433 Fax: (01704) 822005 E-mail: sales@e-coffee.co.uk
▶ TAZZA D'ORO, UNIT 20, PARK ROYAL BUSINESS CENTRE, 9-21 PARK ROYAL ROAD, LONDON, NW10 7LQ Tel: 0208 9654505 Fax: 0208 9654121 E-mail: tazzadoro@btconnect.com

ROASTED PEANUTS

Trigon Snacks Ltd, Atherton Road, Liverpool, L9 7AQ Tel: 0151-523 8700 Fax: 0151-521 5370 E-mail: sales@trigon-snacks.com

ROBOT ATTACHMENTS OR TOOLING

B T M Automation Products (UK) Ltd, Unit 6, Stephenson Road, St. Ives, Cambridgeshire, PE27 3WJ Tel: 0845 5314209 Fax: (01480) 497479 E-mail: btmautomation@btconnect.com
GeKu UK Ltd, 35B Pattens Lane, Chatham, Kent, ME4 6JR Tel: (01634) 830122 Fax: (01634) 813523 E-mail: gekujohn@btinternet.com
Hartford Engineering Ltd, Bradford Road, Winsford, Cheshire, CW7 2PE Tel: (01606) 860888 Fax: (01606) 860889 E-mail: he@hartford-eng.co.uk
T I A Robotic Tooling Solutions, Unit 4C Derby Business Park, Canal Street, Derby, DE1 2RJ Tel: (01332) 204850 Fax: (01332) 204851 E-mail: info@tatem.co.uk

ROBOT AUTOMATION, *See also headings under Robot*

▶ Robotic Gripping Solutions, 6 Clyde Road, Manchester, M20 2WH Tel: 0161-446 2079 E-mail: sales@roboticgrippingsolutions.co.uk

ROBOT BASED SYSTEMS MANUFRS

Global Robots, Unit 5 Beancroft Farm, Beancroft Road, Marston Moretaine, Bedford, MK43 0QE Tel: (01234) 766450 Fax: (01234) 766623 E-mail: tom@robotsltd.co.uk

ROBOT CONTROLLED TELEVISION CAMERAS

▶ Oliver Control Systems Ltd, Units 4 - 6 Sun Valley Business Park, Winall Close, Winchester, Hants, SO23 0LB Tel: (01962) 859306 Fax: (01962) 859304 E-mail: sales@oliver-control.com

ROBOT MAINTENANCE/REPAIR SERVICES

Bereton Electronics Ltd, Unit 49 Kettley Business Park, Ketley, Telford, Shropshire, TF1 5JD Tel: (01952) 253222 Fax: (01952) 244445 E-mail: mail@bereton.co.uk
Clarke Designs Ltd, Imberhorne Lane, East Grinstead, West Sussex, RH19 1RJ Tel: (01342) 321021 Fax: (01342) 321021

ROBOT SYSTEMS CONSULTANTS OR DESIGNERS

Clarke Designs Ltd, Imberhorne Lane, East Grinstead, West Sussex, RH19 1RJ Tel: (01342) 321021 Fax: (01342) 321021
Labman Automation Ltd, Stokesley Industrial Park, Middlesbrough, Cleveland, TS9 5JZ Tel: 0845 4941644 Fax: (01642) 710667 E-mail: mailroom@labman.co.uk
Motoman Robotics UK Ltd, Unit 2 Johnson Park, Wildmere Road, Banbury, Oxfordshire, OX16 3JU Tel: (01295) 272755 Fax: (01295) 267127 E-mail: derekpasquire@motoman.co.uk
Senior Design Associates Ltd, Unit 4 Dukes Street, Windsor, Berkshire, SL4 1SE Tel: (01753) 833382 Fax: (01753) 833709 E-mail: contactus@sda.uk.com

ROBOT TRAINING/TEACHING SYSTEMS

L J Technical Systems Ltd, 5-6 Francis Way, Bowthorpe Employment Area, Norwich, NR5 9JA Tel: (01603) 740421 Fax: (01603) 746340 E-mail: uksales@ljgroup.com

ROBOT WELDING

C H K Engineering Ltd, Pyms Lane, Crewe, CW1 3PJ Tel: (01270) 255520 Fax: (01270) 211263 E-mail: sales@chk-engineering.co.uk

ROBOTIC ASSEMBLY MACHINES

Brillopak, 29 Victory Park, Trident Close, Rochester, Kent, ME2 4ER Tel: (01634) 295050 Fax: 01825 840882 E-mail: info@brillopak.co.uk

ROBOTIC AUTOMATED ASSEMBLY MACHINES

Kuka Automation & Robotics, Hereward Rise, Halesowen, West Midlands, B62 8AN Tel: 0121-585 0800 Fax: 0121-585 0900 E-mail: sales@kuka.co.uk
▶ P R Automation Ltd, Quality House, Fisher Street, Dudley Port, Tipton, West Midlands, DY4 8XE Tel: 0121-557 4311 Fax: 0121-557 4314

ROBOTIC AUTOMATED DISPENSING SYSTEMS

Intertronics Electronic Equipment Component, 17a Station Field Industrial Estate, Kidlington, Oxfordshire, OX5 1JD Tel: (01865) 842842 Fax: (01865) 842172 E-mail: enquiries@intertronics.co.uk

ROBOTIC AUTOMATION SOLUTIONS

▶ Form Automation, 42 Harwell Road, Nuffield Industrial Estate, Poole, Dorset, BH17 0GE Tel: (01202) 660400 Fax: (01202) 660470 E-mail: sales@formautomation.co.uk
▶ P W Butler Ltd, 7 Grafton Place, Bilston, West Midlands, WV14 6LH Tel: (01902) 568623 Fax: (01902) 568623 E-mail: pb004l7138@blueyonder.co.uk

ROBOTIC COMPONENTS (PICK AND PLACE) MANUFRS

Robotica Ltd, 17-19 Park Terrace Lane, Glasgow, G3 6BQ Tel: 0141-353 2261 Fax: 0141-353 2614

ROBOTIC CONSULTANTS

Sixaxis Ltd, 3 Hinton Way, Houghton Regis, Dunstable, Bedfordshire, LU5 5RB Tel: (07801) 719853 Fax: (07808) 769198 E-mail: sales@sixaxis.ltd.uk

ROBOTS, *See also headings for particular types*

Robotica Ltd, 17-19 Park Terrace Lane, Glasgow, G3 6BQ Tel: 0141-353 2261 Fax: 0141-353 2614
Robotics-technology.com, 54 Haymarket, London, SW1Y 4RP Tel: (020) 7590 9933 Fax: (020) 7590 9944 E-mail: info@robotics-technology.com

ROCK BOLTS OR ANCHORS

Dywidag Systems International Ltd, Northfield Road, Kineton Road Industrial Estate, Southam, Warwickshire, CV47 0FG Tel: (01926) 813980 Fax: (01926) 813817 E-mail: sales@dywidag.co.uk

ROCK CORE ANALYSIS CONSULTANCY

Baker Hughes Ltd, Campus 1, Aberdeen Science And Technology Centre, Bridge Of Don, Aberdeen, AB22 8GT Tel: (01224) 226000 Fax: (01224) 226006
Blackbourn Geological Services, Carriden House, Bo'Ness, West Lothian, EH51 9SN Tel: (01506) 826777 Fax: (01506) 826888 E-mail: carriden_house@compuserve.com
Corex (UK) Ltd, Units B1-B3 Airport Industrial Park, Howe Moss Drive, Dyce, Aberdeen, AB21 0GL Tel: (01224) 770434 Fax: (01224) 771716 E-mail: mail@corex.co.uk
Oil Plus Ltd, Unit E Dominion House, Kennet Side, Newbury, Berkshire, RG14 5PX Tel: (01635) 30226 Fax: (01635) 49618 E-mail: m.bowyer@oilplus.co.uk

ROCK DRILLING CONTRACTORS

Bulroc (UK) Ltd, Station Lane, Old Whittington, Chesterfield, Derbyshire, S41 9QX Tel: (01246) 450608 Fax: (01246) 454621 E-mail: info@bulroc.com
▶ Drillcut Ltd, Unit 4b Cadleigh Close, Lee Mill Industrial Estate, Ivybridge, Devon, PL21 9GB Tel: (01752) 691992 Fax: (01752) 691993
Geotechnical Engineering Ltd, Centurion House, Olympus Park, Quedgeley, Gloucester, GL2 4NF Tel: (01452) 527743 Fax: (01452) 507435 E-mail: sales@geoeng.co.uk
▶ Van Elle Ltd, Windsor Terrace, Springwell, Gateshead, Tyne & Wear, NE9 7QN Tel: 0191-417 8332 Fax: 0191-417 8334 E-mail: info@van-elle.co.uk

ROCK DRILLING EQUIPMENT

Boart UK Ltd, Littlemoor, Eckington, Sheffield, S21 4EF Tel: (01246) 435601 Fax: (01246) 435903 E-mail: sales@boartlongyear.com
Bulroc (UK) Ltd, Station Lane, Old Whittington, Chesterfield, Derbyshire, S41 9QX Tel: (01246) 450608 Fax: (01246) 454621 E-mail: info@bulroc.com
Terex Halco, PO Box 25, Halifax, West Yorkshire, HX3 9TW Tel: (01422) 399900 Fax: (01422) 330186 E-mail: halco@halcodrilling.com

ROCK DRILLS

Archway Engineering (UK) Ltd, Ainleys Industrial Estate, Elland, West Yorkshire, HX5 9JP Tel: (01422) 373101 Fax: (01422) 374847 E-mail: sales@archway-engineering.com
Boart UK Ltd, Littlemoor, Eckington, Sheffield, S21 4EF Tel: (01246) 435601 Fax: (01246) 435903 E-mail: sales@boartlongyear.com
Bulroc (UK) Ltd, Station Lane, Old Whittington, Chesterfield, Derbyshire, S41 9QX Tel: (01246) 450608 Fax: (01246) 454621 E-mail: info@bulroc.com
Weldgrip, 2d Redbrook Business Park, Wilthorpe Road, Barnsley, South Yorkshire, S75 1JN Tel: (01226) 785553 Fax: (01226) 731563 E-mail: info@weldgrip.com

ROCKWELL METHOD HARDNESS TEST EQUIPMENT

Brooks Inspection Equipment Ltd, 1 Parsons Lane, Colchester, CO1 2NN Tel: (01206) 799170 Fax: (01206) 798238 E-mail: sales@brooksinspection.com

ROD END BEARINGS

N M B Minebea UK Ltd, Doddington Road, Lincoln, LN6 3RA Tel: (01522) 500933 Fax: (01522) 500975
Tuthill Linkage Ltd, Unit 41 Suttons Industrial Park, Reading, RG6 1AZ Tel: 0118-929 9900 Fax: 0118-966 5978 E-mail: dneave@tuthill.com

ROD ENDS, *See also headings for particular types*

L J Bearing & Engineering Services, Unit A5 Imex Business Park, Kings Rd, Tyseley, Birmingham, B11 2AL Tel: 0121-604 7131 Fax: 0121-604 7122 E-mail: enquiries@bearings-uk.com

ROLE PLAY GAMES

▶ Role'N'Play Model Shops, 174 Stafford Street, Wolverhampton, WV1 1NA Tel: (01902) 310027 E-mail: info@role-n-play.co.uk
▶ Wooden Choice Ltd, 127 Manchester Road, Worsley, Manchester, M28 3JT Tel: 0161-703 7919 E-mail: info@woodenchoice.co.uk

ROLL CALIPER GAUGES, MEASURING

Metrology Systems Wales, 21 Bessant Close, Cowbridge, Vale of Glamorgan, CF71 7HP Tel: (01446) 772926 Fax: (01446) 772926

ROLL CONTAINERS

▶ Euroquipment Ltd, Mallard House, Avon Way, Newbury Business Park, Newbury, Berkshire, RG14 2RF Tel: (0870) 1630077 Fax: (0870) 1630099 E-mail: sales@euroquipment.co.uk
K. Hartwall Ltd, Green Lane Industrial Estate, Spennymoor, County Durham, DL16 6BP Tel: (01388) 824700 Fax: (01388) 824724
Korva Ltd, 2 Maxwelltown Industrial Estate, Glasgow Road, Dumfries, DG2 0NW Tel: (01387) 268572 Fax: (01387) 268657 E-mail: cdoyle@korva.co.uk

ROLL GRINDING ENGINEERS/ SERVICES

Bender Machine Services Ltd, Manchester Road, Haslingden, Rossendale, Lancashire, BB4 5SL Tel: (01706) 225521 Fax: (01706) 218844 E-mail: info@bendermachine.com
John D Hotchkiss Ltd, Main Road, West Kingsdown, Sevenoaks, Kent, TN15 6ER Tel: (01474) 853131 Fax: (01474) 853288 E-mail: sales@hotchkiss-engineers.co.uk
Metrology Systems Wales, 21 Bessant Close, Cowbridge, Vale of Glamorgan, CF71 7HP Tel: (01446) 772926 Fax: (01446) 772926
Pascal Roll Camber Grinding Ltd, 8 Showell Road, Wolverhampton, WV10 9LU Tel: (01902) 424445 Fax: (01902) 423636

ROLL GRINDING ENGINEERS/ SERVICES – *continued*

S B C Precision Engineering, 2 Kings Court Industrial Estate, Sedgley Road East, Tipton, West Midlands, DY4 8XA Tel: 0121-557 0456 Fax: 0121-557 0457

ROLL GRINDING MACHINES

D B Grinders Ltd, Primrose Works, Primrose Bank, Oldham, OL8 1HQ Tel: 0161-626 4202 Fax: 0161-626 4210 E-mail: dbgrinders@btconnect.com

ROLL HANDLING SYSTEMS

Rolpex Ltd, Marple, Stockport, Cheshire, SK6 6EF Tel: 0161-449 7707 Fax: 0161-449 7707 E-mail: rolpexuk@aol.com

ROLL ON ROLL OFF (RORO) RAMP CONSTRUCTORS

▶ Janson Bridging (UK) Ltd, Charles House, Toutley Rd, Wokingham, Berkshire, RG41 1QN Tel: 0845 5262050 Fax: 0118-979 5472 E-mail: sales@jansonbridging.co.uk

ROLLED GLASS

Pilkington UK Ltd, 10-12 Alder Hills, Poole, Dorset, BH12 4AL Tel: (01202) 742700 Fax: (01202) 736155

ROLLED STEEL ANGLES

Frank Hughes & Son Ltd, Lunts Heath Road, Widnes, Cheshire, WA8 5SG Tel: 0151-424 5731 Fax: 0151-495 2063 E-mail: sales@frankhughes.co.uk

ROLLED STEEL PRODUCTS

A W S, Nelsons Wharf, Sandy Lane Industrial Estate, Stourport-on-Severn, Worcestershire, DY13 9QB Tel: (01299) 829202 Fax: (01299) 829203 E-mail: sales@aws-services.co.uk

Albion Section Ltd, Albion Road, West Bromwich, West Midlands, B70 8BD Tel: 0121-553 1877 Fax: 0121-553 5507 E-mail: albionsections@enterprise.net

Compound Sections Ltd, Bond Avenue, Bletchley, Milton Keynes, MK1 1JS Tel: (01908) 622400 Fax: (01908) 622421

Ductile Stourbridge Cold Mills Ltd, PO Box 13, Willenhall, West Midlands, WV13 1HQ Tel: (01902) 365400 Fax: (01902) 365444 E-mail: info@dscm.co.uk

Legg Brothers Holdings Ltd, Spring Road, Ettingshall, Wolverhampton, WV4 6JT Tel: (01902) 408188 Fax: (01902) 408228 E-mail: mail@leggbrothers.co.uk

ROLLED STEEL RINGS/ FLANGES

Forged Products, Venture House, Cross Street, Macclesfield, Cheshire, SK11 7PG Tel: (01625) 428399 Fax: (01625) 508200 E-mail: forgedproducts@dial.pipex.com

ROLLED STEEL SECTIONS

Ayrshire Metal Products plc, Pocket Nook Street, St. Helens, Merseyside, WA9 1LT Tel: (01744) 29145 Fax: (01744) 451257 E-mail: ampsth@compuserve.com

Superior Sections Ltd, 32 Regal Drive, Walsall Enterprise Park, Walsall, WS2 9HQ Tel: (01922) 620333 Fax: (01922) 610555 E-mail: sales@superiorsections.co.uk

ROLLER BANNER EXHIBITION STANDS

▶ Banner & Flag Co., 9 Lubnaig Gardens, Bearsden, Glasgow, G61 4QX Tel: 0141-577 9141 Fax: 0141-563 7147 E-mail: graphics@bf-c.co.uk

▶ Excalibur Exhibitions Ltd, 4 Stowe Close, Buckingham, MK18 1HY Tel: (01280) 815093 Fax: (01280) 822022 E-mail: info@excaliburexhibitions.com

▶ Knew Image Ltd, 33 Hampton Road, Twickenham, TW2 5QE Tel: (020) 8893 9661 Fax: (020) 8893 9662 E-mail: sales@knewimage.co.uk

Redcliffe Imaging Ltd, 21 Dragon Court, Crofts End Road, Bristol, BS5 7XX Tel: 0117-952 0105 Fax: 0117-951 8911 E-mail: info@redcliffe.co.uk

ROLLER BEARING MANUFRS, *See also headings under Roller Bearings*

B M C Security Systems N I Ltd, 2 Orchard Road, Strabane, County Tyrone, BT82 9QR Tel: (028) 7138 2936 Fax: (028) 7138 2937 E-mail: bmcsecsys@hotmail.com

Ball Bearing Centre Ltd, Unit 1-55, 57 Park Royal Road, London, NW10 7JJ Tel: (020) 8965 8833 Fax: (020) 8965 7080 E-mail: ballbrgctr@btconnect.com

Central Bearings & Transmissions Ltd, 43 Padgets Lane, Redditch, Worcestershire, B98 0RD Tel: (01527) 500803 Fax: (01527) 510462 E-mail: sales@centralbearings.com

Cooper Roller Bearings Co. Ltd, Wisbech Road, King's Lynn, Norfolk, PE30 5JX Tel: (01553) 767677 Fax: (01553) 761113 E-mail: sales@cooperbearings.com

Kent Bearings, John Wilson Business Park Harvey Drive, Unit 128a, Chestfield, Whitstable, Kent, CT5 3QY Tel: (01227) 772111 Fax: (01227) 771444

Mike Davies Bearings Ltd, Leamore Lane, Walsall, WS2 7DE Tel: (01922) 494940 Fax: (01922) 407760 E-mail: sales@mikedaviesbearings.com

R T Bearings Ltd., Units 19 & 20, Bevan Industrial Estate, Brockmoor, Brierley Hill, West Midlands, DY5 3TF Tel: (01384) 868458 Fax: (01384) 865458 E-mail: sales@rtbearings.com

Timken Aerospace Uk Ltd, PO Box 667, Wolverhampton, WV2 4UH Tel: (01902) 719300 Fax: (01902) 719301 E-mail: talkbox@timken.com

Timken (Coventry) Ltd, Progress Close, Leofric Business Park, Binley, Coventry, CV3 2TF Tel: (024) 7623 3233 Fax: (024) 7629 6991

ROLLER BLINDS

Aaron Blinds, B 8 Chester Road, Whitby, Ellesmere Port, CH65 6RU Tel: 0151-355 2704 Fax: 0151-355 2704

Albany Blind Co., The Albany Boat House, Lower Ham Road, Kingston upon Thames, Surrey, KT2 5BB Tel: (020) 8549 5436 Fax: (020) 8549 5332 E-mail: peter@albany-blind.co.uk

Apollo Blinds Ltd, 102 BMK Industrial Estate, Wakefield Road, Liversedge, West Yorkshire, WF15 6BS Tel: (01924) 413010 Fax: (01924) 410170 E-mail: sales@apollo-blinds.co.uk

Appeal Conservatory Blinds Ltd, Unit 6 Vale Lane, Bristol, BS3 5SD Tel: 0117-963 7734 Fax: 0117-966 6216 E-mail: sales@appealblinds.com

Baileys Blinds Ltd, Unit 15 Bellway Industrial Estate, Whitley Road, Newcastle Upon Tyne, NE12 9SW Tel: 0191-270 0501 Fax: 0191-266 8993 E-mail: info@baileys-blinds.co.uk

Bath Blind Co., Lower Bristol Road, Bath, BA2 7DL Tel: (01225) 837517 Fax: (01225) 837517E-mail: stewart.davies@ukonline.co.uk

Blind Business, Arturi's Garden Centre, Allington Lane, Fair Oak, Eastleigh, Hampshire, SO50 7DE Tel: (023) 8060 2211 Fax: (023) 8060 2211 E-mail: info@theblindbusiness.co.uk

Hillary's Blinds (Northern) Ltd, Glover Industrial Estate, Spire Road, Washington, Tyne & Wear, NE37 3ES Tel: 0191-416 2354 Fax: 0191-416 2369

Bradrail Blinds & Awnings, 7-15 Main Street, Bulwell, Nottingham, NG6 8QH Tel: 0115-927 5251 Fax: 0115-977 0274 E-mail: enquiries@bradrail.co.uk

Brightview Blinds, 91 Charlock Way, Watford, WD18 6JT Tel: (01923) 243392 Fax: (01923) 231092

Broadview Blinds Ltd, 57 Hatch Pond Road, Nuffield Industrial Estate, Poole, Dorset, BH17 0JZ Tel: (01202) 679012 Fax: (01202) 671885 E-mail: sales@broadview-blinds.co.uk

Charles Bell 1963 Ltd, 344 Oldpark Road, Belfast, BT14 6QE Tel: (028) 9074 7244 Fax: (028) 9074 7248

Cheshire Drapes Ltd, Chichister Road, Romley, Stockport, Cheshire, SK6 4BL Tel: 0161-430 4110 Fax: 0161-406 6327

Coverlite Blinds & Awnings, 9-11 Hanover Street, Bolton, BL1 4TG Tel: (01204) 364444 Fax: (01204) 397232

W. Dickson (Blinds & Shutters) Ltd, 25 Sunnyside, Easter Road, Edinburgh, EH7 5RA Tel: 0131-661 8877 Fax: 0131-661 5922

Discount Blind Centre, 11 Centurion Street, Belfast, BT13 3AS Tel: (028) 9033 3606 Fax: (028) 9024 5724

Dixons Blinds Manufacturers Ltd, Customes House, Ridley Street, Blyth, Northumberland, NE24 3AG Tel: (01670) 355011 Fax: (01670) 355011

Faber Blinds UK Ltd, Kilvey Road, Brackmills Industrial Estate, Northampton, NN4 7BQ Tel: (01604) 766251 Fax: (01604) 768802 E-mail: sales@faberblinds.co.uk

Hannan Blinds & Window Fashions, 72-74 Plungington Road, Preston, PR1 7RA Tel: (01772) 254140 Fax: (01772) 202198

Harley Blinds Ltd, 13 Ryton Street, Worksop, Nottinghamshire, S80 2AY Tel: (01909) 482320 Fax: (01909) 482639

Hillarys Blinds Ltd, Private Road 2, Colwick Industrial Estate, Nottingham, NG4 2JR Tel: 0115-961 7420 Fax: 0115-852 2525 E-mail: enquiries@hillarys.co.uk

Hunter Douglas Ltd, Unit 8a Swanscombe Business Centre, London Road, Swanscombe, Kent, DA10 0LH Tel: (01322) 624580 Fax: (01322) 624558 E-mail: info.contract@luxaflex-sunway.co.uk

L & S Sun Blinds Ltd, 2 Holme Street, Grimsby, South Humberside, DN32 9AD Tel: (01472) 351855 Fax: (01472) 251011 E-mail: enquiries@blinds4sale.co.uk

Levolux Ltd, 1 Forward Drive, Harrow, Middlesex, HA3 8NT Tel: (020) 8863 9111 Fax: (020) 8863 8760 E-mail: info@levolux.com

Levolux A T Ltd, Levolux House 24 Eastville Close, Eastern Avenue, Gloucester, GL4 3SJ Tel: (01452) 500007 Fax: (01452) 527496 E-mail: info@levolux.com

Malvern Blinds, The Old Fire Station, Howsell Road, Malvern, Worcestershire, WR14 1TF Tel: (01684) 574047 Fax: (01684) 892729 E-mail: info@malvernblinds.co.uk

Marquees Ltd, Keens Lane, Guildford, Surrey, GU3 3JS Tel: (01483) 232394 Fax: (01483) 236420 E-mail: sales@guildfordshades.co.uk

Milton Keynes Blind Co. Ltd, 12 Wolseley Road Woburn Industrial Estate, Woburn Road Industrial Estate, Kempston, Bedford, MK42 7TN Tel: (01234) 841515 Fax: (01234) 840682 E-mail: sales@concordeblinds.com

North West Sunblinds, 19 Kilburn Close, Heald Green, Cheadle, Cheshire, SK8 3LP Tel: 0161-437 6808 Fax: 0161-437 6808 E-mail: nwblinds@aol.com

Olympic Blinds Ltd, Olympic House Bilton Court, Bilton Way, Luton, LU1 1LX Tel: (01582) 737878 Fax: (01582) 402182 E-mail: sales@olympicblindsltd.co.uk

P & K Services Ltd, Albert Street, Horwich, Bolton, BL6 7AP Tel: (01204) 667703 Fax: (01204) 667702

Phoenox Home Furnishings Ltd, Spring Grove Mills, Clayton West, Huddersfield, HD8 9HH Tel: (01484) 863227 Fax: (01484) 865352 E-mail: info@phoenox.co.uk

Radiant Blinds Ltd, 101 Ewell Road, Surbiton, Surrey, KT6 6AH Tel: (020) 8390 8755 Fax: (020) 8390 2005 E-mail: info@radiantblinds.co.uk

Rol Lite Blinds Ltd, St Pauls Trading Estate, Demesne Drive, Stalybridge, Cheshire, SK15 2QF Tel: 0161-338 2681 Fax: 0161-338 4193 E-mail: rol-lite@ben.co.uk

Saxon Blinds Ltd, 7 Magee Street, Northampton, NN1 4JT Tel: (01604) 601888 Fax: (01604) 631212 E-mail: saxonblinds@hotmail.com

Sheraton Blinds Ltd, Unit 3 High Cross Centre, Fountayne Road, London, N15 4QN Tel: (020) 8885 5518 Fax: (020) 8365 1108 E-mail: barry@sheraton-blinds.co.uk

Solihull Blinds Ltd, A 85, Skelcher Road, Shirley, Solihull, West Midlands, B90 2EY Tel: 0121-733 1001 Fax: 0121-733 3062 E-mail: solihullblinds@blueyonder.co.uk

Sunrite Blinds Ltd, 4 Newhailes Industrial Estate, Musselburgh, Edinburgh, EH21 6SY Tel: 0131-669 2345 Fax: 0131-665 7711 E-mail: info@sunrite.co.uk

SW Blinds & Interiors Ltd, Unit 60-61 Faraday Mill Business Park, Faraday Road, Plymouth, PL4 0ST Tel: (01752) 663517 Fax: (01752) 226150 E-mail: info@swblinds.com

Turner Sunblinds, Forrest Street, Blackburn, BB1 3BB Tel: (01254) 57763 Fax: (01254) 272101

W & P Blinds, Unit M2 The Paddocks, 347 Cherry Hinton Road, Cambridge, CB1 8DH Tel: (01223) 243030 Fax: (01223) 243030 E-mail: info@wandpblinds.co.uk

Window World Wholesale, Marl Road, Knowsley Industrial Park, Liverpool, L33 7UH Tel: 0151-546 0333 Fax: 0151-546 0333

ROLLER BURNISHING

A H Garner Ltd, Harrimans Lane, Lenton Lane Industrial Estate, Nottingham, NG7 2SD Tel: 0115-978 5161 Fax: 0115-924 4704 E-mail: sales@ahgarner.co.uk

ROLLER CHAINS

Albion Transmission, Unit 5 Industry Road, Carlton, Barnsley, South Yorkshire, S71 3PQ Tel: (01226) 726200 Fax: (01226) 726979

Challenge Power Transmission plc, Unit 1 2 Merryhills Enterprise Park, Park Lane, Wolverhampton, WV10 9TJ Tel: (01902) 866116 Fax: (01902) 866117 E-mail: uksales@challengept.com

Diamond Chain Co., Unit 7-9 Blaydon Industrial Park, Chainbridge Road, Blaydon-on-Tyne, Tyne & Wear, NE21 5AB Tel: 0191-414 8822 Fax: 0191-414 8877 E-mail: sales@diamondchain.co.uk

F B Chain Ltd, Jubilee Road, Letchworth Garden City, Hertfordshire, SG6 1NE Tel: (01462) 670844 Fax: (01462) 480745 E-mail: phil.taylor@fbchain.com

Flexon plc, Upper Church Lane, Tipton, West Midlands, DY4 9PA Tel: 0121-521 3600 Fax: 0121-520 0822 E-mail: sales@flexon.co.uk

ROLLER COVERING SERVICES OR PROCESSORS

Boettcher U K Ltd, Cwmdraw Industrial Estate, Newtown, Ebbw Vale, Gwent, NP23 5AE Tel: (01495) 350300 Fax: (01495) 350064 E-mail: admin@boettcher.co.uk

Jason Industrial Ltd, Unit 29 Normanby Park Workshops, Normanby Road, Scunthorpe, North Lincolnshire, DN15 8QZ Tel: (01724) 861006 Fax: (01724) 869846

Just Rollers P.L.C., Somerset Industrial Estate, Cwmbran, Gwent, NP44 1QX Tel: (01633) 869436 Fax: (01633) 860046 E-mail: iain.sinclair@justrollers.com

K V Rollers Ltd, Unit 1-3 Claenwern, Avondale Industrial Estate, Pontrhydyrun, Cwmbran, Gwent, NP44 1TY Tel: (01633) 871919 Fax: (01633) 877250 E-mail: kbrollers@tiscali.co.uk

Longs Ltd, Hanworth Lane Business Park, Chertsey, Surrey, KT16 9LZ Tel: (01932) 561241 Fax: (01932) 567391 E-mail: sales@longs.co.uk

Robant Services Ltd, Unit 24 Mersey Street, Stockport, Cheshire, SK1 2HX Tel: 0161-429 8728 Fax: 0161-474 7630 E-mail: sales@robant.co.uk

Rotadyne UK Ltd, Saxon House, Henson Way, Telford Way Industrial Estate, Kettering, Northamptonshire, NN16 8PX Tel: (01536) 414421 Fax: (01536) 411091 E-mail: pevans@rotadyne.com

S M Goodchild Ltd, East Common Lane, Scunthorpe, South Humberside, DN16 1DE Tel: (01724) 848200 Fax: (01724) 280274

ROLLER CROWBARS

Dorvic Engineering Co. Ltd, New Street, Holbrook Industrial Estate, Holbrook, Sheffield, S20 3GH Tel: 0114-248 5633 Fax: 0114-251 0654 E-mail: sales@dorvic.com

ROLLER CUTTING PRESSES

Moore Bowman Services Ltd, 2 Glebe Road, Egham, Surrey, TW20 8BT Tel: (01784) 452387 Fax: (01784) 458500

ROLLER PRESS MACHINES

Kee Engineering, Unit 14a Miller Business Park, Station Road, Liskeard, Cornwall, PL14 4DA Tel: (01579) 344285 Fax: (01579) 348635 E-mail: chris@kee.co.uk

Rossendale Forme & Knife Co. Ltd, 245 Burnley Road East, Rossendale, Lancashire, BB4 9HU Tel: (01706) 213165 Fax: (01706) 831319 E-mail: info@rossforme.co.uk

ROLLER SHUTTER DOORS

Alliance Industrial Doors Ltd, Unit 4a Sovereign Works, Deepdale Lane, Dudley, West Midlands, DY3 2AF Tel: (01384) 251951 Fax: (01384) 255888

▶ P & K Shutter Services Ltd, Canada House, Canada Street, Horwich, Bolton, BL6 7PB Tel: (01204) 667703 Fax: (01204) 667702 E-mail: pk_shutters@hotmail.com

Ro Dor Ltd, Stevens Drove, Houghton, Stockbridge, Hampshire, SO20 6LP Tel: (01794) 388080 Fax: (01794) 388090 E-mail: info@ro-dor.co.uk

Security Shutters Ltd, Unit 2 Brooklands Approach, Romford, RM1 1DX Tel: (01708) 722334 Fax: (01708) 750900 E-mail: sales@securityshuttersltd.co.uk

Stanair Industrial Door Services Ltd, Unit 2 Henson Way, Telford Way Industrial Estate, Kettering, Northamptonshire, NN16 8PX Tel: (01536) 482187 Fax: (01536) 411799 E-mail: admin@shiresecurity.co.uk

Stanair Industrial Door Services Ltd, 5 Fairweather Court, Peterborough, PE1 5UN Tel: (01733) 314097 Fax: (01733) 314097 E-mail: info@stanair.co.uk

▶ Swift Shutters, Unit 3-4 Harp Industrial Estate, Queensway, Rochdale, Lancashire, OL11 2QQ Tel: (01706) 653777 Fax: (01706) 653666

Wellgate Door Systems, Ladyship Centre, Old Lane, Halifax, West Yorkshire, HX3 5QN Tel: (01422) 320520 Fax: (01422) 320499 E-mail: sales@wellgate-doors.co.uk

ROLLER SHUTTER FITTINGS OR ACCESSORIES

Astra Commerical Doors, 2a Window Lane, Liverpool, L19 8EJ Tel: 0151-494 2880 Fax: 0151-494 9648

Dave Cox, 43 Ingrave Road, Brentwood, Essex, CM15 8AZ Tel: (01277) 228240 Fax: (01277) 228240

Fife Shutter Services, Unit 11 Coal Wynd, Kirkcaldy, Fife, KY1 2RA Tel: (01592) 266868 Fax: (01592) 642868 E-mail: info@fifeshutterservices.co.uk

Guardian Shutter Co. Ltd, 23 Sefton Street, Toxteth, Liverpool, L8 5SL Tel: 0151-708 0819 Fax: 0151-709 1279 E-mail: sales@guardian-shutter.co.uk

Homeshield, 21townley Street, Middleton, Manchester, M24 1AT Tel: 0161-643 4433 Fax: 0161-643 4466 E-mail: sales@homesheildshutters.co.uk

Hopkins, Prospect House, Jameson Road, Birmingham, B6 7SJ Tel: (0845) 4563018 Fax: (0845) 4563019 E-mail: enquires@hopkinsfittings.co.uk

▶ indicates data change since last edition

ROLLER SHUTTER FITTINGS OR ACCESSORIES – *continued*

Luton Glass, 2b Miller Road, Bedford, MK42 9NY Tel: (01582) 726000 Fax: (01582) 480980 E-mail: info@allregionsglazing.co.uk

Portico Products, Lath Lane, Smethwick, West Midlands, B66 1EA Tel: 0121-553 7222 Fax: 0121-553 3577 E-mail: sales@porticoproducts.com

Property Protection Services, Unit 5E Caldeshaw Centre, Ings Lane, Rochdale, Lancashire, OL12 7LQ Tel: (01706) 718000 Fax: (01706) 718888

Securicorp Shutters Ltd, 43 Beacon Road, Romiley, Stockport, Cheshire, SK6 3ET Tel: 0161-494 2900 Fax: 0161-494 8300

ROLLER SHUTTER MAINTENANCE OR REPAIR

Amy Shutters, 8 Slader Business Park, Witney Roe, Nuffield Industrial Estate, Poole, Dorset, BH17 0GP Tel: (01202) 666702 Fax: (01202) 666705 E-mail: info@amyshutters.co.uk

Cambridge Door Services, 127 Mereside, Soham, Ely, Cambridgeshire, CB7 5EG Tel: (01353) 725000 Fax: (01353) 725001 E-mail: alan@camdoor.fsnet.co.uk

Cherry Security Co., 53 Cherry Garden Rd, Eastbourne, E. Sussex, BN20 8HG Tel: (01323) 641759 Fax: (01323) 641759 E-mail: andy@cherrysecurity.co.uk

D M S 2000 Ltd, 4 Doynton Mill, Mill Lane, Doynton, Bristol, BS30 5TQ Tel: 0117-937 2136 Fax: 0117-937 4756 E-mail: dms2k@fsmail.net

Farrell Fabrications Ltd, Wallis Road, Skippers Lane Industrial Estate, Middlesbrough, Cleveland, TS6 6JB Tel: (01642) 453800 Fax: (01642) 453800

Fife Shutter Services, Unit 11 Coal Wynd, Kirkcaldy, Fife, KY1 2RA Tel: (01592) 266868 Fax: (01592) 642868 E-mail: info@fifeshutterservices.co.uk

Industrial Doors Ltd, 8 Alexandra Industrial Estate, Locarno Road, Tipton, West Midlands, DY4 9SJ Tel: 0121-557 8757 Fax: 0121-520 9011 E-mail: mac@mandsshutterservicesltd.co.uk

Keldrigg Shutters & Grilles Ltd, Keldrigg House, Woodhouse, Milnthorpe, Cumbria, LA7 7NQ Tel: (01539) 564550 Fax: (01539) 564681

Lambourne's Ltd, White Post Hill, Farningham, Dartford, DA4 0LB Tel: (08700) 362436 Fax: (01322) 865491 E-mail: sales@lambournes.co.uk

M & S Shutter Services Ltd, 8 Alexandra Industrial Estate, Locarno Road, Tipton, West Midlands, DY4 9SJ Tel: 0121-520 6505 Fax: 0121-520 9011 E-mail: mandsshutters@hotmail.com

Middleton Maintenance Services Ltd, The London Centre, 99 Queensland, London, N7 7AJ Tel: (020) 7700 7070 Fax: (020) 7609 3223 E-mail: sales@middleton-maintenance.co.uk

Neway Doors Ltd, Lionel Works, 89/91 Rolfe Street, Smethwick, West Midlands, B66 2AY Tel: 0121-558 6406 Fax: 0121-555 7140 E-mail: sales@priory-group.co.uk

The Priory Group Ltd, Lionel Works, 89-91 Rolfe Street, Smethwick, West Midlands, B66 2AY Tel: 0121-558 6406 Fax: 0121-555 7140

Ratcliff Care Ltd, Unit 19, Saddleback Road, Westgate Industrial Estate, Northampton, NN5 5HL Tel: (01604) 591359

Security Shutters Ltd, Unit 2 Brooklands Approach, Romford, RM1 1DX Tel: (01708) 722334 Fax: (01708) 750900 E-mail: sales@securityshuttersltd.co.uk

Shutter Door Repair & Maintenance Ltd, Lionel Works, 89-91 Rolfe Street, Smethwick, West Midlands, B66 2AY Tel: 0121-558 6406 Fax: 0121-555 7140 E-mail: sales@priory-group.com

Shutter Door Services, Unit 15 Pant Industrial Estate, Dowlais, Merthyr Tydfil, CF48 2SR Tel: (01685) 375777 Fax: (01685) 373344

System 2000 Group Ltd, 39-41 Wood End Lane, Erdington, Birmingham, B24 8AN Tel: 0121-350 2000 Fax: 0121-377 6300

Watties Welders & Fabricators, New Cottage Rosemill, Bridgefoot, Dundee, DD3 0PW Tel: (01382) 812794 Fax: (01382) 884114 E-mail: info@wattieswelders.com

ROLLER SHUTTERS

Aar Dee Locks & Shutters Ltd, 16 Boswell Square, Hillington, Hillington Industrial Estate, Glasgow, G52 4BQ Tel: 0141-810 3444 Fax: 0141-810 3777 E-mail: sales@aaree.co.uk

Aaron Roller Shutters, Unit 3 Northburn Road Industrial Estate, Coatbridge, Lanarkshire, ML5 2HY Tel: (01236) 423445 Fax: (01236) 606673 E-mail: info@aaronrollershutters.co.uk

Abbey Roller Shutters & Doors, Unit A-B Caxton St North, London, E16 1JL Tel: (020) 7476 4422 Fax: (020) 7476 4433

Able Shutter Services Ltd, Unit 3, 46 Chalgrove Road, London, N17 0JB Tel: (020) 8885 5332 Fax: (020) 8885 6786 E-mail: admin@able-shutters.co.uk

Access Door Services, Unit 6-7 Trent South Industrial Park, Nottingham, NG2 4EQ Tel: 0115-958 0768 Fax: 0115-985 9240

Access Gates & Shutters, Suite 2-3 Banters La Ecf Complex, Main Road, Great Leighs, Chelmsford, CM3 1QX Tel: (01245) 360366 Fax: (01245) 361401

Action Shutters Midlands Ltd, 2 Garretts Green Trading Estate, Valepits Road, Birmingham, B33 0TD Tel: 0121-605 6005 Fax: 0121-605 7050

Adlor Garage Door Services, 8 Brittania Business Park, Mills Road, Quarry Wood, Aylesford, Kent, ME20 7NT Tel: (01622) 882370 Fax: (01622) 882313

Airedale Blinds & Shutters, 10 Wellington Street, Laisterdyke, Bradford, West Yorkshire, BD4 8BW Tel: (01274) 661266 Fax: (01274) 661222 E-mail: abs@fallers.co.uk

All Secure Roller Shutters, The Office, 103 Rockbank Road, Liverpool, L13 7BG Tel: 0151-220 6000 Fax: 0151-228 1609 E-mail: info@shuttersandgrilles.co.uk

▶ Alliance Door Engineering, Unit E3 1 Moss Industrial Estate, St. Helens Road, Leigh, Lancashire, WN7 3PT Tel: (01942) 683601 Fax: (01942) 683607 E-mail: mikelabrey@alliancedoors.co.uk

Allsecure, Unit 4a Arun Buildings, Arundel Road, Uxbridge, Middlesex, UB8 2RP Tel: (01895) 255950

Allswell Security Ltd, 3 Saville Road, Peterborough, PE3 7PR Tel: (01733) 333560 Fax: (01733) 332601 E-mail: martintaylor@ukdoor.co.uk

▶ Amo Security Roller Systems Ltd, Unit 6 Sycamore Industrial Estate, Walkley Lane, Heckmondwike, West Yorkshire, WF16 0NL Tel: (01924) 412666 Fax: (01924) 412233 E-mail: sales@amosecurity.co.uk

Armadillo Window Protection, 1 The Avenue, Burwell, Cambridge, CB25 0DE Tel: (01638) 610490 Fax: (01638) 742167

Armour Blinds, Whitehouse Enterprise Centre, Whitehouse Road, Newcastle upon Tyne, NE15 6EP Tel: 0191-228 0912 Fax: 0191-228 0912 E-mail: armoursecurity@cwcom.net

▶ Artisan Security Doors, Unit 5 Usher St Business Park, Bradford, West Yorkshire, BD4 7DS Tel: (01274) 723123 Fax: (01274) 727477 E-mail: sales@artisan-doors.co.uk

Attenborough Industrial Doors Ltd, Merlin Way, Quarry Hill Industrial Estate, Ilkeston, Derbyshire, DE7 4RA Tel: 0115-930 0815 Fax: 0115-944 8930 E-mail: information@attenboroughdoor.co.uk

▶ Autoroll U K, Wilden Road, Pattinson Industrial Estate, Washington, Tyne & Wear, NE38 8QB Tel: 0191-415 5888 Fax: 0191-419 4800

Barlass Shutters Ltd, 59 Shaw Street, Liverpool, L6 1HL Tel: 0151-427 1340 Fax: 0151-207 2801

Beacon Associates, The Pines, Templewood Lane, Farnham Common, Slough, SL2 3HQ Tel: (01753) 648234 Fax: (01753) 648234

Britannia Security Group UK Ltd, Britannia House, Lake Street, Stockport, Cheshire, SK2 7NU Tel: 0161-456 2103 Fax: 0161-487 4174

Budget Steel Fabrications, 48 English Street, Hull, HU3 2DT Tel: (01482) 320346 Fax: (01482) 215799 E-mail: business@budgetsteel.co.uk

Cambridge Door Services, 127 Mereside, Soham, Ely, Cambridgeshire, CB7 5EG Tel: (01353) 725000 Fax: (01353) 725001 E-mail: alan@camdoor.fsnet.co.uk

Central Shutters & Doors, Unit 39 Phoenix International Industrial Estate, Charles Street, West Bromwich, West Midlands, B70 0AY Tel: 0121-557 3434 Fax: 0121-557 3403

Cherry Security Co., 53 Cherry Garden Rd, Eastbourne, E. Sussex, BN20 8HG Tel: (01323) 641759 Fax: (01323) 641759 E-mail: andy@cherrysecurity.co.uk

▶ Cordula Ltd, Unit 6, Vale Lane, Bristol, BS3 5SD Tel: 0117-902 0259 Fax: 0117-966 6216 E-mail: sales@cordula.co.uk

D M S 2000 Ltd, 4 Doynton Mill, Mill Lane, Doynton, Bristol, BS30 5TQ Tel: 0117-937 2136 Fax: 0117-937 4756 E-mail: dms2k@fsmail.net

Defence Group Ltd, 411 Petre Street, Sheffield, S4 8LL Tel: 0114-244 1178 Fax: 0114-244 7710 E-mail: sales@defencegroup.co.uk

W. Dickson (Blinds & Shutters) Ltd, 25 Sunnyside, Easter Road, Edinburgh, EH7 5RA Tel: 0131-661 8877 Fax: 0131-661 5922

DLT Shop Front & Shutter Systems Ltd, Shaw Road, Dudley, West Midlands, DY2 8TS Tel: (01384) 455277 Fax: (01384) 458847 E-mail: sales@weatherite-group.co.uk

Dominion Shutters, 8 Argall Avenue, London, E10 7QD Tel: (020) 8558 6572 Fax: (020) 8556 6956 E-mail: dominionshutters@btconnect.com

Door Maintenance Co. Ltd, Unit 8, Curran Industrial Estate, Curran Road, Cardiff, CF10 5DF Tel: (029) 2066 5539 Fax: (029) 2066 8207E-mail: rpickford@harlechdoors.net

Doorco Ltd, Phoenix Works, Whitefield Road, Bredbury, Stockport, Cheshire, SK6 2QR Tel: 0161-406 8660 Fax: 0161-406 8433 E-mail: info@doorco.co.uk

Dudley Factory Doors Ltd, Unit G6, Grice Street, West Bromwich, West Midlands, B70 7EZ Tel: 0121-555 8989 Fax: 0121-558 4616

Elero UK Ltd, Foundry Lane, Halebank, Widnes, Cheshire, WA8 8TZ Tel: (0870) 2404219 Fax: (0870) 2404086 E-mail: sales@elerouk.co.uk

Emmerson Industrial Doors Ltd, Enterprise Way, Sherburn in Elmet, Leeds, LS25 6NA Tel: (01977) 685566 Fax: (01977) 681981 E-mail: sales@emmerson-doors.co.uk

Enfield Roller Shutter Co., Unit 10 Kimberley Road Works, Billet Road, London, E17 5DT Tel: (020) 8527 2406 Fax: (01708) 750900 E-mail: ersco@lineone.net

Essex Blinds & Shutters, Brook Farm, Murthering Lane, Navestock, Romford, RM4 1HL Tel: (01277) 374100 Fax: (01277) 374100 E-mail: essexblinds@talk21.com

Euro Shutter Engineers Ltd, Woodside, Thornwood, Epping, Essex, CM16 6LJ Tel: (01992) 570044 Fax: (01992) 561176 E-mail: office@euroshutters.co.uk

Fix A Door Ltd, 1 Library Road, Ferndown, Dorset, BH22 9JP Tel: (01202) 855999 Fax: (01202) 855888 E-mail: fixadoor@aol.com

The Garage Door Centre, 6-8 Meadow Close, Wellingborough, Northamptonshire, NN8 4BH Tel: (01933) 229135 Fax: (01933) 442676

Global Security Shutters Ltd, 114 Liverpool Road, Kidsgrove, Stoke-On-Trent, ST7 4EH Tel: (07985) 307343 Fax: (01782) 783104

Griffin Grilles & Shutters, Maryfields, Bangors Road North, Iver, Buckinghamshire, SL0 0BH Tel: (01753) 652129 Fax: (01753) 717686 E-mail: griffingp@tiscali.co.uk

H & C Fabrications Ltd, Corporation Road, Birkenhead, Merseyside, CH41 8FA Tel: 0151-653 7677 Fax: 0151-652 0626

H V P Security Shutters Ltd, 4 Grace Road West, Marsh Barton, Exeter, EX2 8PU Tel: (01392) 270218 Fax: (01392) 278548 E-mail: info@hvpshutters.co.uk

Henry Lewis & Son Ltd, 7 Bolling Road, Bradford, West Yorkshire, BD4 7HN Tel: (01274) 307359 Fax: (01274) 370784

High Wood Security, 2-4 Slaters Road, Stanningley, Pudsey, West Yorkshire, LS28 6EY Tel: 0113-257 7707 Fax: 0113-257 4051

Holgate Roller Shutters, 3 Wicket Grove, Clifton, Swinton, Manchester, M27 6ST Tel: 0161-728 4767 Fax: 0161-728 4767

J R S Roller Shutter Doors, Unit B8 Valleys Enterprise Centre, Merthyr Tydfil Industrial Park, Pentrebach, Merthyr Tydfil, Mid Glamorgan, CF48 4DR Tel: (01443) 692962 Fax: (01443) 692912

Lakeside Security Shutters, Bruce Road, Fforestfach, Swansea, SA5 4HS Tel: (01792) 561117 Fax: (01792) 587046 E-mail: sails@lakesidesecurity.co.uk

Leyton Engineering Services Ltd, Unit 8 Horndon Industrial Park, Station Road, West Horndon, Brentwood, Essex, CM13 3XL Tel: (01277) 812404 Fax: (01277) 810853 E-mail: sales@leytongroup.com

Lowland Ensor Doors Ltd, 9 Pickering Works, Netherton Road, Wishaw, Lanarkshire, ML2 0EQ Tel: (01698) 376444 Fax: (01698) 376888 E-mail: sales@lowlandensor.co.uk

M & S Shutter Services Ltd, 8 Alexandra Industrial Estate, Locarno Road, Tipton, West Midlands, DY4 9SJ Tel: 0121-520 6505 Fax: 0121-520 9011 E-mail: mandsshutters@hotmail.com

Marian Engineering Ltd, First Avenue, Team Valley Trading Estate, Gateshead, Tyne & Wear, NE11 0NU Tel: 0191-482 2891 Fax: 0191-491 0891 E-mail: admin@mariandoors.co.uk

Marquees Ltd, Keens Lane, Guildford, Surrey, GU3 3JS Tel: (01483) 232394 Fax: (01483) 236420 E-mail: sales@guildfordshades.co.uk

Northern Doors (UK) Ltd, Kingsforth Road, Thurcroft, Rotherham, South Yorkshire, S66 9HU Tel: (01709) 545999 Fax: (01709) 545341 E-mail: mail@northerndoors.co.uk

P & K Services Ltd, Albert Street, Horwich, Bolton, BL6 7AP Tel: (01204) 667703 Fax: (01204) 667702

Peter Tomas & Co., 50 Lancaster Street, Higham Ferrers, Rushden, Northamptonshire, NN10 8HY Tel: (01933) 359688

Portman Doors Ltd, Unit 3 Bradshaw Works, Printers Lane, Bolton, BL2 3DW Tel: (01204) 699521 Fax: (01204) 669094 E-mail: info@portmandoors.co.uk

Ranyard Signs Ltd, Brigg Road, Caistor, Market Rasen, Lincolnshire, LN7 6RX Tel: (01472) 852528 Fax: (01472) 851516 E-mail: sales@ranyard-signs.co.uk

Romford Blinds & Shutters Ltd, Danes Road, Romford, RM7 0HL Tel: (01708) 754754 Fax: (01708) 733128

Ross & Bonnyman Ltd, Roberts Street, Forfar, Angus, DD8 3DG Tel: (01307) 469366 Fax: (01307) 461567

Sandwell Doors 2000, 79 Grafton Road, West Bromwich, West Midlands, B71 4EG Tel: 0121-553 7470 Fax: 0121-525 9684

Secuirdoor North East Ltd, Commercial Road, South Shields, Tyne & Wear, NE33 1RP Tel: 0191-425 0000 Fax: 0191-425 0037

Secure Shutters, 105 Richmond Road, Grays, Essex, RM17 6DN Tel: (01375) 397100 Fax: (01375) 397101 E-mail: sales@secureshutters.co.uk

Shackleton Mortimer & Sons Ltd, 25 Pitcliffe Way, Bradford, West Yorkshire, BD5 7SG Tel: (01274) 726890 Fax: (01274) 390384

Shutter Door Services, Unit 15 Pant Industrial Estate, Dowlais, Merthyr Tydfil, CF48 2SR Tel: (01685) 375777 Fax: (01685) 373344

Sterling Security Shutters, 42 Huddersfield Road, Barnsley, South Yorkshire, S75 1DW Tel: (01226) 207030 Fax: (01226) 770088

Stratford Wire Works, Rowse Close, London, E15 2HX Tel: (020) 8534 1950 Fax: (020) 8534 8280

▶ Swift Shutters, Unit 3-4 Harp Industrial Estate, Queensway, Rochdale, Lancashire, OL11 2QQ Tel: (01706) 653777 Fax: (01706) 653666

▶ Taymore, Block 4A Unit 8, Larkhall Industrial Estate, Larkhall, Lanarkshire, ML9 2PA Tel: (01698) 884000 Fax: (01698) 886888

Vanguard Shutters Ltd, Vanguard Works, Coldhurst Street, Oldham, OL1 2DN Tel: 0161-652 3498 Fax: 0161-627 2697 E-mail: sfyfe@dovervanguard.co.uk

W M Shutters Ltd, Springhill Trading Estate, Aston Street, Shifnal, Shropshire, TF11 8DR Tel: (01952) 272265 Fax: (01952) 272331 E-mail: sales@wmshutters.com

Waivis Co. Ltd, 14 Minerva Road, London, NW10 6HJ Tel: (020) 8965 6818 Fax: (020) 8965 6287 E-mail: info@waivis.co.uk

Walker Wade, Security House, Cleckheaton, West Yorkshire, BD19 3TT Tel: 01274 852261

Watson Bros Ltd, 30-34 Wilson Place, East Kilbride, Glasgow, G74 4QD Tel: (01355) 233144 Fax: (01355) 233850 E-mail: colin@turnersrollerdoors.com

Wilmshurst Bros Ltd, North Wing New England House, New England Street, Brighton, BN1 4GH Tel: (01273) 683255 Fax: (01273) 683255 E-mail: wilmshurstbros@yahoo.co.uk

The Window Glass Company Bristol Ltd, 11 Emery Road, Bristol, BS4 5PF Tel: 0117-977 9292 Fax: 0117-977 9299 E-mail: mail@windowglass.co.uk

Window World Of Kent, 24 Juniper Close, Ashford, Kent, TN23 3JY Tel: (01233) 642322 Fax: (0870) 1656459 E-mail: e-breeze@windows-world.fsnet.co.uk

ROLLER SKATES

Shiner Ltd, 22 Church Road, Lawrence Hill, Bristol, BS5 9JB Tel: 0117-955 7432 Fax: 0117-955 4686 E-mail: admin@shiner.co.uk

Ventronic Imports Co., Unit 9 Derby Road Industrial Estate, Hounslow, TW3 3UH Tel: (020) 8572 1201 Fax: (020) 8572 1195 E-mail: sales@californiapro.com

ROLLER TOOLS

▶ L. & T.I. Brock & Co. Ltd, Unit 1 Falkland House, 19 Falkland Close, Charter Avenue Industrial Estate, Coventry, CV4 8AG Tel: (024) 7642 1200 Fax: (024) 7642 1459 E-mail: enquiries@tangi-flow.com

ROLLERS, PRE-INKED, CASH REGISTER/CALCULATOR ETC

Gold (UK) Scanning Systems Ltd, 12a Pimlico Road, Runcorn, Cheshire, WA7 4US Tel: (01928) 500505 Fax: (01928) 500242 E-mail: golduk@btconnect.com

ROLLERS, PRINTING, *See Printing Roller etc*

ROLLERS, TO SPECIFICATION/ CUSTOM BUILT

Bonaprene Products, Clywedog Road South, Wrexham Industrial Estate, Wrexham Industrial Estate, Wrexham, Clwyd, LL13 9XS Tel: (01978) 661478 Fax: (01978) 661190 E-mail: sales@polybush.co.uk

ROLLING GRILLES

Armadillo Window Protection, 1 The Avenue, Burwell, Cambridge, CB25 0DE Tel: (01638) 610490 Fax: (01638) 742167

D K O Designs, 66 Georges Road, London, N7 8HX Tel: (020) 7607 2653 Fax: (020) 7607 0515

D M S 2000 Ltd, 4 Doynton Mill, Mill Lane, Doynton, Bristol, BS30 5TQ Tel: 0117-937 2136 Fax: 0117-937 4756 E-mail: dms2k@fsmail.net

Dominion Shutters, 8 Argall Avenue, London, E10 7QD Tel: (020) 8558 6572 Fax: (020) 8556 6956 E-mail: dominionshutters@btconnect.com

Enfield Roller Shutter Co., Unit 10 Kimberley Road Works, Billet Road, London, E17 5DT Tel: (020) 8527 2406 Fax: (01708) 750900 E-mail: ersco@lineone.net

Euro Shutter Engineers Ltd, Woodside, Thornwood, Epping, Essex, CM16 6LJ Tel: (01992) 570044 Fax: (01992) 561176 E-mail: office@euroshutters.co.uk

Trellidor Ltd, Unit 20 Bloomfield Park, Bloomfield Road, Tipton, West Midlands, DY4 9AH Tel: 0121-557 0303 Fax: 0121-557 0353 E-mail: sales@trellidor.co.uk

ROLLING MILL PLANT AND EQUIPMENT MANUFRS

The Davy Roll Co. Ltd, P O Box 21, Gateshead, Tyne & Wear, NE8 3DX Tel: 0191-477 1261 Fax: 0191-477 8096 E-mail: enquiries@davyroll.co.uk

ROLLING MILL PLANT AND EQUIPMENT MANUFRS – *continued*

Fast Engineering Works Ltd, Unit 1, Area C, 241 Wellington Road Industrial Estate, Perry Barr, Birmingham, B20 2QQ Tel: 0121-344 4345 Fax: 0121-344 4535 E-mail: fastengineering@btconnect.com

Jbi Technology Ltd, Unit 2-3 Bond Street, West Bromwich, West Midlands, B70 7DQ Tel: 0121-553 0500 Fax: 0121-553 5333 E-mail: info@jbitech.co.uk

Morgan Europe Ltd, Morgan House, Brompton Road, Sheffield, S9 2PA Tel: 0114-261 7177 Fax: 0114-261 7178 E-mail: lidgates@morganco.com

Sarclad Ltd, Broombank Park, Chesterfield, Derbyshire, S41 9RT Tel: (01246) 457000 Fax: (01246) 457010 E-mail: sarclad@sarclad.com

W Durston Ltd, Progress House, Hospital Hill, Chesham, Buckinghamshire, HP5 1PJ Tel: (01494) 793244 Fax: (01494) 792966

ROLLING MILL PRODUCTS, *See Rolled Metal etc*

ROLLING MILL ROLLMAKERS

Ready Roll Ltd, Unit 14, Harris Business Park, Hambury Road, Stoke Piror, Bromsgrove, Worcestershire, B60 4AA Tel: (01527) 881993 Fax: (01527) 881994

ROOF BEAMS

▶ Philip Hadfield, 10 Queens Drive, Stockport, Cheshire, SK4 3JW Tel: 0161-442 0907

ROOF CLADDING

▶ B S L Hire Ltd, 11 Churchill Road, Wimborne, Dorset, BH21 2AT Tel: (01202) 882126 Fax: (01202) 882126 E-mail: billy@bslhire.wanadoo.co.uk

ROOF CLADDING CONTRACTORS OR FIXING SERVICES

▶ Able, 10 Moretons Close, Whittlesey, Peterborough, PE7 1XP Tel: (01733) 208992 Fax: (01733) 208992 E-mail: ableroofing44@tiscali.co.uk

▶ B S L Hire Ltd, 11 Churchill Road, Wimborne, Dorset, BH21 2AT Tel: (01202) 882126 Fax: (01202) 882126 E-mail: billy@bslhire.wanadoo.co.uk

▶ Cheshire Rooffix, 6 St. Augustines Road, Stockport, Cheshire, SK3 0JN Tel: (01614) 771449 Fax: (01614) 771449 E-mail: john.h.carroll@btinternet.com

Cobsen-Davies Roofing Leicester Ltd, 20 Sompting Road, Worthing, West Sussex, BN14 9EP Tel: (01903) 821616 Fax: (01903) 208044 E-mail: info@cobsen-davies.co.uk

Dagenham Construction Ltd, 3 Ardmore Road, South Ockendon, Essex, RM15 5TH Tel: (01708) 851631 Fax: (01708) 852247 E-mail: dagenhamcon@btconnect.com

Grainger Building Services Ltd, 163 Church Road, Holywood, County Down, BT18 9BZ Tel: (028) 9042 2555 Fax: (028) 9042 5428 E-mail: info@grainger-uk.com

High Edge (UK) Ltd, 70 Maes Hyfryd, Beaumaris, Anglesey, LL58 8HN Tel: (01248) 810112 E-mail: info@highedge-uk.com

Kelsey Roofing Industries Ltd, Kelsey House, Paper Mill Drive, Church Hill South, Redditch, Worcestershire, B98 8QJ Tel: (01527) 594400 Fax: (01527) 594444

KGM Roofing, Glenside South, Glenside, Pinchbeck, Spalding, Lincolnshire, PE11 3SA Tel: (01775) 717800 Fax: (01775) 717829

▶ Lane Roofing, Walsall House, 167 Walsall Road, Perry Barr, Birmingham, B42 1TX Tel: 0121-331 4407 Fax: 0121-344 3782 E-mail: info@laneroofing.co.uk

▶ Lingfield Roofing, 52 Saxbys Lane, Lingfield, Surrey, RH7 6DR Tel: (01342) 833018

▶ M D G Property Services, 60 Sandholme Drive, Bradford, West Yorkshire, BD10 8EY Tel: (01274) 200078 E-mail: mikegreasley@blueyonder.co.uk

▶ M S L Ltd, 81 Highmarsh Crescent, Newton-Le-Willows, Merseyside, WA12 9WE Tel: (01925) 223666 Fax: (01925) 223666 E-mail: contracts@managementservicesnw.co.uk

▶ MSL Roofing & Cladding, 26 Wargrave Road, Newton-Le-Willows, Merseyside, WA12 9QZ Tel: (01925) 223666 Fax: (01925) 226662 E-mail: info@msl-nw.co.uk

▶ Prentice Roofing, 2 Front Road, Lisburn, County Antrim, BT27 5JZ Tel: (028) 9082 7187 Fax: (028) 9082 7167 E-mail: info@prenticeroofing.co.uk

ROOF FALL ARREST SYSTEMS

▶ Highwire Ltd, 4 Fairfield Avenue, Fairfield Wells, Droylsden, Manchester, M43 6ED Tel: 0161-612 7633 Fax: 0161-612 2105 E-mail: sales@highwire.info

▶ Nationwide Safety Nets Ltd, Longdene House, Longdene Road, Haslemere, Surrey, GU27 2PH Tel: (0870) 345 0650 E-mail: info@nwsafetynets.com

ROOF FLASHING CONTRACTORS

▶ Elevations Roofing Specialists (UK) Ltd, The Ridings, Biggin Hill, Westerham, Kent, TN16 3LE Tel: (0800) 5877765 Fax: (01959) 572462 E-mail: info@elevationsroofing.co.uk

ROOF LIGHTS OR WINDOWS

Architectural Aluminium Systems Ltd, Sandleheath Industrial Estate, 6 Old Brickyard Road, Sandleheath, Fordingbridge, Hampshire, SP6 1PA Tel: (01425) 654080 Fax: (01425) 652038

Astrofade Ltd, Kyle Road, Gateshead, Tyne & Wear, NE8 2YE Tel: 0191-420 0515 Fax: 0191-460 4185 E-mail: sales@astrofade.co.uk

B B S Building Components, Spon Lane, West Bromwich, West Midlands, B70 6AP Tel: 0121-553 5509 Fax: 0121-500 5425 E-mail: mail@bbsrooflights.co.uk

Brett Martin Daylight Systems Ltd, Sandford Close, Aldermans Green Industrial Estate, Coventry, CV2 2QU Tel: (024) 7660 2022 Fax: (024) 7660 2745

Cox Building Products Ltd, Shaw Road, Bushbury, Wolverhampton, WV10 9LA Tel: (01902) 371800 Fax: (01902) 371810 E-mail: sales@coxbp.com

Duplus Architectural Systems Ltd, 370 Melton Road, Leicester, LE4 7SL Tel: 0116-261 0710 Fax: 0116-261 0539 E-mail: sales@duplus.co.uk

Fife Joinery Manufacturing Ltd, Telford Road, Glenrothes, Fife, KY7 4NX Tel: (01592) 773181 Fax: (01592) 773253

Lightpipe Co. Ltd, 116B High Street, Cranfield, Bedford, MK43 0DG Tel: (0870) 2416680 Fax: (01234) 751144

▶ Loft Shop Ltd, 37 Westley Road, Birmingham, B27 7UQ Tel: 0121-707 7900 Fax: 0121-707 7933

Luxcrete Ltd, Premier House, Disraeli Road, London, NW10 7BT Tel: (020) 8965 7292 Fax: (020) 8961 6337 E-mail: sales@luxcrete.co.uk

Mckenzie Martin Ltd, Eton Hill Works, Eton Hill Road, Radcliffe, Manchester, M26 2US Tel: 0161-723 2234 Fax: 0161-725 9531 E-mail: general@mckenziemartin.co.uk

Stoakes Systems Ltd, 1 Banstead Road, Purley, Surrey, CR8 3EB Tel: (020) 8660 7667 Fax: (020) 8660 5707 E-mail: admin@stoakes.co.uk

Ubbink (U K) Ltd, Borough Road, Brackley, Northamptonshire, NN13 7TB Tel: (0845) 4563499 Fax: (01280) 705332 E-mail: info@ubbink.co.uk

Velux Company Ltd, Woodside Way, Glenrothes East, Glenrothes, Fife, KY7 4ND Tel: (01592) 772211 Fax: (01592) 771839 E-mail: enquiries@velux.co.uk

Vulcan Plastics Ltd, Hosey Hill, Westerham, Kent, TN16 1TZ Tel: (01959) 562304

Wenmore Rooflights, Unit 1A Parnall Industrial Estate, Parnall Road, Fishponds, Bristol, BS16 3JF Tel: 0117-958 5865 Fax: 0117-958 5865

ROOF MOUNTED FANS

Pacet Manufacturing Ltd, Wyebridge, Cores End Road, Bourne End, Buckinghamshire, SL8 5HH Tel: (01628) 526754 Fax: (01628) 810080 E-mail: enquiries@pacet.co.uk

ROOF RACKS/BARS, MOTOR CAR

Mac Farr Engineering Co. Ltd, Garn Road, Blaenavon, Pontypool, Gwent, NP4 9RT Tel: (01495) 790648 Fax: (01495) 790648

Mountney Ltd, Vandyke Road, Leighton Buzzard, Beds, LU7 3HH Tel: (01525) 383131 Fax: (01525) 370443

Tow B Fabs, Unit 5-6 Kents Avenue, Hemel Hempstead, Hertfordshire, HP3 9XH Tel: (01442) 256764 Fax: (01442) 256764

V C Saunders Engineering Ltd, 20 Weir Road, London, SW19 8UG Tel: (020) 8947 5262 Fax: (020) 8944 1812

ROOF SAFETY TRAINING

▶ Trade Skills 4 U, 3 Metana House, Priestley Way, Crawley, West Sussex, RH10 9NT Tel: (01293) 529777 E-mail: enquires@tradeskills4u.co.uk

ROOF SHEETING CONTRACTORS OR FIXING SERVICES

Cobsen-Davies Roofing Leicester Ltd, 20 Sompting Road, Worthing, West Sussex, BN14 9EP Tel: (01903) 821616 Fax: (01903) 208044 E-mail: info@cobsen-davies.co.uk

Hardy Sherwood Special Projects Ltd, 32 Hemmells, Basildon, Essex, SS15 6ED Tel: (01268) 417733 Fax: (01268) 541135 E-mail: specialproducts@hardysherwood.fsnet.co.uk

▶ Lingfield Roofing, 52 Saxbys Lane, Lingfield, Surrey, RH7 6DR Tel: (01342) 833018

ROOF SOLAR PANELS

Solstice Energy Ltd, 14 Gladwyn Road, Putney, London, SW15 1JY Tel: 020 8789 4717 Fax: 020 8789 4717 E-mail: info@solsticeenergy.co.uk

▶ Sun Save, 37 The Meadway, Shoreham-by-Sea, West Sussex, BN43 5RN Tel: (01273) 455500 Fax: (01273) 441631 E-mail: sales@sun-save.co.uk

ROOF TILES

William Blyth, Pasture Road North, Barton-upon-Humber, South Humberside, DN18 5RB Tel: (01652) 632175 Fax: (01652) 660966 E-mail: sales@williamblyth.co.uk

C W Property Services Ltd, 126 Ashleigh Road, London, SW14 8PX Tel: (020) 8876 9941 Fax: (020) 8878 3942 E-mail: cwps126@hotmail.com

▶ Fairford Roof Tile Manufacturers, The Rhymes Yard, Rhymes Lane, Fairford, Gloucestershire, GL7 4RD Tel: (01285) 713653 Fax: (01285) 712169 E-mail: fairfordrooftile@aol.com

Forticrete Ltd, Bridle Way, Bootle, Merseyside, L30 4UA Tel: 0151-521 3545 Fax: 0151-521 5696 E-mail: sswift@forticrete.com

Hinton, Perry & Davenhill Ltd, Pensnett, Brierley Hill, West Midlands, DY5 4TH Tel: (01384) 77405 Fax: (01384) 74553 E-mail: office@drednort.tiles.co.uk

Keymer Tiles Ltd, Nye Road, Burgess Hill, West Sussex, RH15 0LZ Tel: (01444) 232931 Fax: (01444) 871852 E-mail: info@keymer.co.uk

Michelmersh Brick & Tile Co. Ltd, Hill View Road, Michelmersh, Romsey, Hampshire, SO51 0NN Tel: (01794) 368506 Fax: (01794) 368845 E-mail: sales@michelmersh.co.uk

Monier Ltd, 61 Largy Road, Crumlin, County Antrim, BT29 4RR Tel: (0870) 5601000 Fax: (028) 9442 2165

Russell Roof Tiles Ltd, Halleaths, Lockerbie, Dumfriesshire, DG11 1LR Tel: (01387) 810567 Fax: (01387) 811385 E-mail: christine.donaldson@rmc.co.uk

Sandtoft Holdings Ltd, Sandtoft, Doncaster, South Yorkshire, DN8 5SY Tel: (01427) 872696 Fax: (01427) 871222 E-mail: info@sandtoft.co.uk

Sussex Terracotta, Aldershaw Farm, Kent St, Sedlescombe, Battle, E. Sussex, TN33 0SD Tel: (01424) 756777 Fax: (01424) 756888

Swallows Tiles Cranleigh Ltd, Bookhurst Hill, Bookhurst Road, Cranleigh, Surrey, GU6 7DP Tel: (01483) 274100 Fax: (01483) 267593 E-mail: sales@swallowsrooftiles.co.uk

ROOF TRUSS SYSTEMS

Mitek Industries Ltd, Grazebrook Industrial Park, Peartree Lane, Dudley, West Midlands, DY2 0XW Tel: (01384) 451400 Fax: (01384) 451411 E-mail: sales@mitek.co.uk

Pinewood Structures Ltd, 3 Station Road, Gamlingay, Sandy, Bedfordshire, SG19 3HB Tel: (01767) 651218 Fax: (01767) 651928 E-mail: enquiries@pinewood-structures.co.uk

Wolf Systems Ltd, Shilton Industrial Estate, Shilton, Coventry, CV7 9QL Tel: (0870) 7339933 Fax: (0870) 7339944 E-mail: mail@wolfsystem.co.uk

Wyckham Blackwell Group Ltd, Old Station Road, Hampton-In-Arden, Solihull, West Midlands, B92 0HB Tel: (01675) 442233 Fax: (01675) 442227E-mail: info@wyckham-blackwell.co.uk

ROOF VENTILATORS

C K Supplies (UK) Ltd, 128 Grange Road, Wigston, Leicestershire, LE18 1JJ Tel: 0116-288 4252 Fax: 0116-288 8072 E-mail: sales@airtrac.co.uk

Hambleside Danelaw Ltd, 2-8 Bentley Way, Royal Oak Industrial Estate, Daventry, Northamptonshire, NN11 8QH Tel: (01327) 701900 Fax: (01327) 701909 E-mail: marketing@hambleside-danelaw.co.uk

Rytons Building Products Ltd, Design House, Orion Way, Kettering Business Park, Kettering, Northamptonshire, NN15 6NL Tel: (01536) 511874 Fax: (01536) 310455 E-mail: vents@rytons.com

Ubbink (U K) Ltd, Borough Road, Brackley, Northamptonshire, NN13 7TB Tel: (0845) 4563499 Fax: (01280) 705332 E-mail: info@ubbink.co.uk

ROOFING ALUMINIUM PRODUCTS

Areco Roofing Supplies, Coppice Lane, Walsall Wood, Walsall, WS9 9AA Tel: (01922) 743553 Fax: (01922) 743554 E-mail: sales@areco.co.uk

R T E Fabrications Ltd, Lomax Street, Darwen, Lancashire, BB3 0DR Tel: (01254) 873002 Fax: (01254) 704919 E-mail: sales@rtefabs.co.uk

ROOFING AND CLADDING CONTRACTORS ASSOCIATION

High Edge (UK) Ltd, 70 Maes Hyfryd, Beaumaris, Anglesey, LL58 8HN Tel: (01248) 810112 E-mail: info@highedge-uk.com

▶ Sharkey & Co Ltd, Vincent Court, Hubert St, Aston Locks, Birmingham, B6 4BA Tel: 0121-380 3700

ROOFING COMPONENTS

Foregale Ltd, Union Road, Liversedge, West Yorkshire, WF15 7JS Tel: (01924) 401020 Fax: (01924) 405872

Lancastria Roofing Distributors, Fairhills Industrial Estate, Woodrow Way, Irlam, Manchester, M44 6ZQ Tel: 0161-777 9009 Fax: 0161-777 7557

Marley Building Materials Ltd, Station Road, Coleshill, Birmingham, B46 1HP Tel: (01675) 468400 Fax: (01675) 468485

Ward Roofing, Cleatham Road, Kirton Lindsey, Gainsborough, Lincolnshire, DN21 4JR Tel: (01652) 641950 Fax: (01652) 648161 E-mail: reception@wardroofing.co.uk

ROOFING COMPOUNDS

W.H. Keys Ltd, Hall End Works, Church Lane, West Bromwich, West Midlands, B71 1BN Tel: 0121-553 0206 Fax: 0121-500 5820 E-mail: sales@wh-keys.fsnet.com

Plaspertex Paint Co. Ltd, 71 Mereside, Soham, Ely, Cambridgeshire, CB7 5EE Tel: (01353) 720796 Fax: (01353) 624327 E-mail: mail@plaspertex.co.uk

ROOFING CONSULTANCY

▶ Abel Building & Roofing Services, Station Road, Rowlands Gill, Tyne & Wear, NE39 1QD Tel: (01207) 544633

ROOFING FELT

Calderbrook Jute Co., Stansfield Mill, Calderbrook Road, Littleborough, Lancashire, OL15 9NP Tel: (01706) 378711 Fax: (01706) 371345

IKO Ltd, Appley Lane North, Appley Bridge, Wigan, Lancashire, WN6 9AB Tel: (01257) 255771 Fax: (01257) 252514

Monarflex Ltd, Unit 23 North Orbital Commercial Park (Off Natsbury Avenue), St. Albans, Hertfordshire, AL1 1XB Tel: (01727) 830116 Fax: (01727) 868045 E-mail: geos.uk@icopal.com

ROOFING INSULATED COMPOSITE PANELS

Corus Panels Profiles, Llandeilo Road Industrial Estate, Llandybie, Ammanford, Carmarthenshire, SA18 3JG Tel: (01269) 850691 Fax: (01269) 851272

▶ Enviropanel, Albright Road, Widnes, Cheshire, WA8 8FY Tel: 0151 423 0023 Fax: 0151 423 0043 E-mail: info@enviropanel.com

Gilmour Ecometal, 245 Govan Road, Glasgow, G51 2SQ Tel: 0141-427 1264 Fax: 0141-427 2205 E-mail: info@gilmour-ecometal.co.uk

Rigidal Systems Ltd, Unit 62 Blackpole Trading Estate West, Worcester, WR3 8ZJ Tel: (01905) 750500 Fax: (01905) 750555 E-mail: info@rigidal.co.uk

Sheffield Insulations Ltd, Hillsborough Works, Langsett Road, Sheffield, S6 2LW Tel: 0114-285 6300 Fax: 0114-285 6375 E-mail: info@sigplc.co.uk

ROOFING INSULATION CONTRACTORS, *See Roofing Contractors etc*

ROOFING LINING FRAME GALVANISED STEEL SECTIONS

Euro Clad Ltd, Wentloog Corparate Park, Wentloog Road, Rumney, Cardiff, CF3 2ER Tel: (029) 2079 0722 Fax: (029) 2079 3149 E-mail: sales@euroclad.com

ROOFING MATERIALS, *See also headings for particular materials*

Ariel Plastics Ltd, Speedwell Industrial Estate, Staveley, Chesterfield, Derbyshire, S43 3JP Tel: (01246) 281111 Fax: (01246) 561115 E-mail: info@arielplastics.com

Asphaltic Roofing Supplies Ltd, Page Green Road, London, N15 4PG Tel: (020) 8808 0459 Fax: (020) 8801 3259 E-mail: tottenham@asphaltic.co.uk

▶ Barrass Hull Ltd, 16 Alfred Street, Hull, HU3 2DD Tel: (01482) 324954 Fax: (01482) 213598 E-mail: user@barrasshull.co.uk

Building Product Design Ltd, 6 Tonbridge Chambers, Pembury Road, Tonbridge, Kent, TN9 2HZ Tel: (01732) 355519 Fax: (01732) 355536 E-mail: info@bpd.com

E D S Roofing Supplies (Midlands) Ltd, Unit 3, Bilton Way, Lutterworth, Leicestershire, LE17 4JA Tel: (01455) 558877 Fax: (01455) 550116 E-mail: sales@eds-midlands.co.uk

Formerton Ltd, Forton Works, First Avenue, Millbrook Trading Estate, Southampton, SO15 0LG Tel: (023) 8036 5555 Fax: (023) 8070 1197 E-mail: southampton@formertonroofing.co.uk

Keyline Builders Merchants Ltd, Moulton Park Industrial Estate, Northampton, NN3 6TE Tel: (01604) 643622 Fax: (01604) 790353 E-mail: welcome@keylineco.uk

L A Hall (Hull) Ltd, 19-27 Lime Street, Hull, HU8 7AB Tel: (01482) 320367 Fax: (01482) 320367

Lakes Buildbase, Parcel Terrace, Derby, DE1 1LQ Tel: (01332) 349083 Fax: (01332) 290178E-mail: derbybuilding@buildbase.co.uk

Lancastria Roofing Distributors, Fairhills Industrial Estate, Woodrow Way, Irlam, Manchester, M44 6ZQ Tel: 0161-777 9009 Fax: 0161-777 7557

Letchworth Roofing Co. Ltd, Roof Centre, Works Road, Letchworth Garden City, Hertfordshire, SG6 1JY Tel: (01462) 755766 Fax: (01462) 755750 E-mail: sales@letchworthroofing.co.uk

M S P (Scotland) Ltd, 1 Telford Road, Cumbernauld, Glasgow, G67 2AX Tel: (01236) 729591 Fax: (01236) 721859 E-mail: helenshaw@mspscot.co.uk

Mcarthur Group Ltd, 27 Perimeter Road, Pinefield Industrial Estate, Elgin, Morayshire, IV30 6AF Tel: (01343) 548694 Fax: (01343) 541688 E-mail: marketing@mcarthur-group.com

Marley Building Materials Ltd, Station Road, Coleshill, Birmingham, B46 1HP Tel: (01675) 468400 Fax: (01675) 468485

Marley Eternit Ltd, Lichfield Road, Branston, Burton-on-Trent, Staffordshire, DE14 3HD Tel: (01283) 722588 Fax: (01283) 722219 E-mail: profile@marleyeternit.co.uk

Matthews Of Keynsham Ltd, Keynsham Road, Keynsham, Bristol, BS31 2DE Tel: 0117-986 4356 Fax: 0117-986 7491 E-mail: sales@matthewsofkeynsham.com

▶ Millers Roofing & Roofline, Bourne House, Milbourne Street, Carlisle, CA2 5XF Tel: (0800) 0837641 E-mail: millers@roofing111.wanadoo.co.uk

Nu-Style Products Ltd, 25 Silverburn Crescent, Bridge Of Don Industrial Estate, Aberdeen, AB23 8EW Tel: (01224) 823000 Fax: (01224) 823111 E-mail: info@nu-styles.co.uk

Parry Bowen, Unit S Chasewater Industrial Estate, Burntwood Business Park, Burntwood, Staffordshire, WS7 3GQ Tel: (01543) 678000 Fax: (01543) 677237

▶ Pasquill Roof Trusses Ltd, Grays Road, Uddingston, Glasgow, G71 6ET Tel: (01698) 801560 Fax: (01698) 801570 E-mail: uddingston@pasquill.co.uk

▶ Pasquill Roof Trusses Ltd, 3 Dalcross Industrial Estate, Inverness, IV2 7XB Tel: (01667) 462102 Fax: (01667) 462131 E-mail: inv@pasquill.co.uk

A.M. Proos & Sons Ltd, Spring Vale Road, Darwen, Lancashire, BB3 2ES Tel: (01254) 777777 Fax: (01254) 706666 E-mail: info@proos.co.uk

▶ Richmond Building Products, The Barn, White Horse Lane, Witham, Essex, CM8 2BU Tel: (01376) 510002

Roberts & Burling Roofing Supplies Ltd, 120 Beddington Lane, Croydon, CR0 4YZ Tel: (020) 8689 0481 Fax: (020) 8689 3063 E-mail: bmcroydon@robertsandburling.co.uk

Robseal Kits Ltd, 3 Nimrod Industrial Estate, Nimrod Way, Reading, RG2 0EB Tel: 0118-975 4888 Fax: 0118-975 4854

Roofing Construction Services Ltd, 122 High Street, Lye, Stourbridge, West Midlands, DY9 8NF Tel: (01384) 423586 Fax: (01384) 894079

Roofrite (East Anglia) Ltd, The Street, Sheering, Bishop's Stortford, Hertfordshire, CM22 7LY Tel: (01279) 734515 Fax: (01279) 734568

Rooftech, RoofTech House, Four Seasons Crescent, Kimpton Road, Sutton, Surrey, SM3 9QR Tel: (020) 8641 7077 Fax: (020) 8641 7006 E-mail: mail@rooftech.info

Sexton Sales Ltd, D Wiggenhall Road Goods Yard, Wiggenhall Road, Watford, WD18 0EZ Tel: (01923) 240434 Fax: (01923) 818454 E-mail: enquiries@sextonsales.com

South Coast Roofing Supplies Ltd, Daveys Lane, Lewes, East Sussex, BN7 2BQ Tel: (01273) 488888 Fax: (01273) 489999

Southern Sheeting Supplies (Roofing and Cladding), Hill Place Farm, Turners Hill Road (B2110), East Grinstead, West Sussex, RH19 4LX Tel: (01342) 315300 Fax: (01342) 410560E-mail: sales@southernsheeting.co.uk

Swift Roofing Contracts Ltd, Kent House, Ware Street, Bearsted, Maidstone, Kent, ME14 4PA Tel: (01622) 632420 Fax: (01622) 632510

T Blackshaw, Conway St Depot, Conway Street, Stockport, Cheshire, SK5 7PS Tel: 0161-480 6040 Fax: 0161-474 7225 E-mail: sales@tomblackshaw.com

Travis Perkins plc, Lissadel Street, Salford, M6 6BR Tel: 0161-736 8751 Fax: 0161-737 9744

Wedge Roofing Centres, Belfont Trading Estate, Mucklow Hill, Halesowen, West Midlands, B62 8DR Tel: 0121-550 2729 Fax: 0121-585 5258

Wedge Roofing Centres Ltd, Unit 16, Salamons Way, Rainham, Essex, RM13 9UL Tel: (01708) 555213 Fax: (01708) 550255

Uriah Woodhead & Son Ltd, Valley House, Valley Road, Bradford, West Yorkshire, BD1 4RY Tel: (01274) 727528 Fax: (01274) 726574

Wormells Roofing Centre, Regent Street, Coventry, CV1 3EL Tel: (024) 7622 0755 Fax: (024) 7652 5463 E-mail: coventry@wedge-roofing-centres.com

ROOFING SCAFFOLDING

▶ Adis Scaffolding Ltd, M1 Commerce Park, Markham Lane, Duckmanton, Chesterfield, Derbyshire, S44 5HS Tel: (01246) 827997 Fax: (01246) 827998 E-mail: adisscaffolding@tiscali.co.uk

ROOFING SLATE

▶ Delabole Slate Co. Ltd, Pengelly Road, Delabole, Cornwall, PL33 9AZ Tel: (01840) 212242 Fax: (01840) 212948 E-mail: sales@delaboleslate.com

M Camilleri & Sons Roofing Ltd, Sully Moors Road, Sully, Penarth, South Glamorgan, CF64 5RP Tel: (01446) 721450 Fax: (01446) 749710 E-mail: general@camilleri.co.uk

Alfred McAlpine Slate Ltd, Penrhyn Quarry, Bethesda, Bangor, Gwynedd, LL57 4YG Tel: (01248) 600656 Fax: (01248) 601171 E-mail: slate@mcalpineplc.co.uk

ROOFING TOOLING OR EQUIPMENT

C M S Tools Ltd, Don Pedro Close, Normanton Industrial Estate, Normanton, West Yorkshire, WF6 1TD Tel: (01924) 895999 Fax: (01924) 896999 E-mail: info@cmstools.co.uk

Imtech Services, 33 The Warren, Worcester Park, Surrey, KT4 7DH Tel: (020) 8337 6254 Fax: (020) 8337 6254 E-mail: ian.male@btopenworld.com

Lancastria Roofing Distributors, Fairhills Industrial Estate, Woodrow Way, Irlam, Manchester, M44 6ZQ Tel: 0161-777 9009 Fax: 0161-777 7557

ROOFING WATERPROOF MEMBRANES

Bauder Ltd, Broughton House, 26 Broughton Road, Ipswich, IP1 3QR Tel: (01473) 257671 Fax: (01473) 230761 E-mail: marketing@bauder.co.uk

D R C Polymer Products Ltd, 1 Regal Lane, Soham, Ely, Cambridgeshire, CB7 5BA Tel: (01353) 720989 Fax: (01353) 624668 E-mail: info@drc-polymers.com

E A B Associates, 3 Craven Court, Craven Road, Broadheath, Altrincham, Cheshire, WA14 5DY Tel: 0161-926 9077 Fax: 0161-927 7718 E-mail: eaball@eabassoc.co.uk

Pallard Contracts Ltd, 84 Court Lane, Cosham, Portsmouth, PO6 2LR Tel: (023) 9221 0075 Fax: (023) 9232 5716 E-mail: enquiries@pallard.co.uk

ROOM AIR CONDITIONING (AC) EQUIPMENT

Acm Air Conditioning, Unit 10 Armley Workshops, Pickering Street, Leeds, LS12 2QG Tel: 0113-203 8240 Fax: 0113-279 7088

Fresh Air Ventilation Systems, 35a Salhouse Road, Rackheath, Norwich, NR13 6PD Tel: (01603) 720330 Fax: (01603) 720331 E-mail: sales@thefreshaircompany.co.uk

ROOM TEMPERATURE VULCANISING (RTV) SILICONE RUBBER

Gap Ltd, 12 Ridge Way, Donibristle Industrial Park, Hillend, Dunfermline, Fife, KY11 9JN Tel: (01383) 824181 Fax: (01383) 824722 E-mail: mark.adams@gap.uk

W P Notcutt Ltd, Homewood Farm, Newark Lane, Ripley, Woking, Surrey, GU23 6DJ Tel: (01483) 223311 Fax: (01483) 479594 E-mail: sales@notcutt.com

ROPE ACCESS SERVICES

▶ Cumbria Access Services Ltd, Stonegarth, Crosthwaite, Kendal, Cumbria, LA8 8HT Tel: (01539) 568001 Fax: 015395 68002 E-mail: info@casaccess.co.uk

▶ I R A T A, 99 West Street, Farnham, Surrey, GU9 7EN Tel: (01252) 739150 Fax: (01252) 739140 E-mail: info@irata.org

Ropetech International Ltd, The Old School, Brynrefail, Caernarfon, Gwynedd, LL55 3NB Tel: 01286 685471 Fax: 01286 685473 E-mail: info@ropetech.com

ROPE BARRIERS

Main Event Sales & Hire, Unit 25, Coleshill Industrial Estate, Station Road, Coleshill, Birmingham, B46 1JP Tel: (01675) 464224 Fax: (01675) 466082 E-mail: sales@mainevent.co.uk

ROPE CLEATS

Clamcleats Ltd, Watchmead, Welwyn Garden City, Hertfordshire, AL7 1AP Tel: (01707) 330101 Fax: (01707) 321269 E-mail: sales@clamcleat.com

ROPE SLINGS

John Hemsley Ropes & Lifting Equipment Ltd, Unit 19 Sapcote Industrial Estate, 20 James Road, Tyseley, Birmingham, B11 2BA Tel: 0121-706 5748 Fax: 0121-706 6703

RSS Group, Unit 32A/32B Village Farm Industrial Estate, Pyle, Bridgend, Mid Glamorgan, CF33 6BL Tel: (01656) 740074 Fax: (01656) 747057 E-mail: steve@rssgroup.co.uk

ROPES, *See also headings for particular types*

▶ Can London Ltd, Unit A Springhead Enterprise Park, Springhead Road, Northfleet, Gravesend, Kent, DA11 8HB Tel: (01474) 538100 Fax: (01474) 538101 E-mail: info@canlondon.co.uk

▶ Certex UK Ltd, Unit 4 Third Avenue, Southampton, SO15 0LD Tel: (023) 8070 3894 Fax: (023) 8070 3901 E-mail: admin@certex.co.uk

Cotesi Ltd, 5-7 Mill Fold, Sowerby Bridge, West Yorkshire, HX6 4DJ Tel: (01422) 821000 Fax: (01422) 821007 E-mail: enquiries@cotesi.co.uk

DSM, Riverside Works, Huddersfield Road, Mirfield, West Yorkshire, WF14 9DL Tel: (01924) 490781 Fax: (01924) 491128 E-mail: sales@dsm-group.co.uk

Emlyn Canvas & Cordage Co. Ltd, George Street Conservatory Centre, Granville Square, Newport, Gwent, NP20 2AB Tel: (01633) 262262 Fax: (01633) 222420

Fleming's Ropes & Twines Woolston Ltd, Bridge Road, Woolston, Warrington, WA1 4AT Tel: (01925) 499955 Fax: (01925) 492208

▶ Graham Tiso, 41 Commercial St, Edinburgh, EH6 6JD Tel: 0131-554 0804 Fax: 0131-554 9682 E-mail: mail@tiso.co.uk

Hamble Ropes & Rigging Ltd, 65-69 Bernard Street, Southampton, SO14 3BA Tel: (023) 8033 8286 Fax: (023) 8033 8288 E-mail: info@hrrlcovercraft.fsnet.co.uk

J. Harper Ltd, 32A Temple Street, Wolverhampton, WV2 4AN Tel: (01902) 422865 Fax: (01902) 422865

Henry Winning & Co. Ltd, 16-18 Caroline Street, Glasgow, G31 5DD Tel: 0141-554 2767 Fax: 0141-554 8496 E-mail: sales@twines.co.uk

Independent Twine Manufacturing Co. Ltd, Westbank Road, Llay Industrial Estate, Llay, Wrexham, Clwyd, LL12 0PZ Tel: (01978) 854812 Fax: (01978) 854229 E-mail: keithmacguire@indtwineco.com

Kent & Co Twines Ltd, Long Lane, Walton, Liverpool, L9 7DE Tel: 0151-525 1601 Fax: 0151-523 1410 E-mail: kenttwines@aol.com

Linear Composites Ltd, Vale Mills, Oakworth, Keighley, West Yorkshire, BD22 0EB Tel: (01535) 643363 Fax: (01535) 643605 E-mail: mail@linearcomposites.com

Marlow Ropes Ltd, Rope Maker Park, Dipilocks Way, Hailsham, East Sussex, BN27 3GU Tel: (01323) 444444 Fax: (01323) 444455 E-mail: sales@marlowropes.com

Master Rope Makers Ltd, The Historic Dockyard, Chatham, Kent, ME4 4TG Tel: (01634) 827812 Fax: (01634) 827217 E-mail: sales@master-ropemakers.co.uk

Mayor & Son Ltd, 1 Brierley Street, Ashton-on-Ribble, Preston, PR2 2AU Tel: (01772) 254488 Fax: (01772) 259897

Metcalf Leenside Ltd, 139-143 Canal Street, Nottingham, NG1 7HD Tel: 0115-958 0865 Fax: 0115-959 8934 E-mail: sales@metcalf.co.uk

Montrose Rope & Sail Co., 13 Bents Road, Montrose, Angus, DD10 8QA Tel: (01674) 672657 Fax: (01674) 675785 E-mail: neilpaton@montroseropeandsail.co.uk

▶ Mudfords Sheffield Ltd, 400 Petre Street, Sheffield, S4 8LU Tel: 0114-243 3033 Fax: 0114-244 4536 E-mail: sales@mudfords.co.uk

Nu Ropes, Coker Ropery, West Coker, Yeovil, Somerset, BA22 9BN Tel: (01935) 862327 Fax: (01935) 862274 E-mail: evanstherope1@supanet.co.uk

Pfeifer Drako Ltd, Marshfield Bank, Crewe, CW2 8UY Tel: (01270) 587728 Fax: (01270) 587913 E-mail: admin@pfeiferdrako.co.uk

Pritchard Ropes & Canvas Solutions Ltd, Freehold Street, Loughborough, Leicestershire, LE11 1AN Tel: (01509) 212400 Fax: (01509) 219375

R. Billson & Sons Ltd, 431 Thurmaston Boulevard, Off Claymill Road, Leicester, LE4 9LA Tel: 0116-276 2555 Fax: 0116-276 9234

Rope & Tackle Solent Ltd, Marchwood Industrial Estate, Normandy Way, Marchwood, Southampton, SO40 4PB Tel: (023) 8066 5470 Fax: (023) 8066 5471

Securit Ropes & Packaging Ltd, Unit 6 Phoenix Court, Dominion Way, Rustington, West Sussex, BN16 3HQ Tel: 0845 5261818 Fax: (0845) 634 0262 E-mail: sales@securit-ropes-packaging.co.uk

▶ Simpers Ltd, 17 Mercers Row, Cambridge, CB5 8HY Tel: (01223) 351729 Fax: (01223) 311818 E-mail: info@simpers.co.uk

W Coates & Sons Nottingham Ltd, Montpelier Road, Nottingham, NG7 2JW Tel: 0115-978 5103 Fax: 0115-978 5103

W R Outhwaite & Son Ropemakers, Burtersett Road, Hawes, North Yorkshire, DL8 3NT Tel: (01969) 667487 Fax: (01969) 667576 E-mail: sales@ropemakers.com

ROSARY BEADS, STONE

▶ Le Rule Originals, 2 Selsey Close, Hayling Island, Hampshire, PO11 9SX Tel: 02392 463845 Fax: 02392 463845 E-mail: louise@leruleoriginals.co.uk

ROSE WINE

▶ Aldanca Wine, 19 Mountbatten Court, Raleigh Close, New Milton, Hampshire, BH25 5LB Tel: 01425 621733 Fax: 01425 618440 E-mail: marketing@aldanca-wine.co.uk

Chateau Papillon Estates, C7 Boston Trade Park, Norfolk Street, Boston, Lincolnshire, PE21 9HG Tel: (0845) 8381790 Fax: (0870) 1313172 E-mail: info@chateau-papillon.com

▶ Genesis Wines Ltd, 78Tachbrook Street, London, SW1V 2NE Tel: (020) 7963 9060 Fax: (0870) 8502038 E-mail: sales@genesiswines.com

▶ Splash Winery Ltd, 16 Briar Avenue, Meltham, Holmfirth, HD9 5LQ Tel: (01484) 323814 Fax: (01484) 323814

ROSETTES

B I S Trent Rosettes, 7 Railway Enterprise Centre, Shelton New Road, Stoke-on-Trent, ST4 7SH Tel: (01782) 279797 Fax: (01782) 279797

Beck Farm Cottatges, Beck Farm, Trunch Hill, Denton, Harleston, Norfolk, IP20 0AE Tel: (01986) 788454 Fax: (01986) 788454 E-mail: pearlcharnick@tesco.net

Cornish Rosette Co., Higher Bofarnel, Lostwithiel, Cornwall, PL22 0LP Tel: (01208) 871001 Fax: (01208) 871001 E-mail: conishrosette@ukonline.co.uk

Darby Rosettes & Trophies, 5 Goulburn Road, Norwich, NR7 9UX Tel: (01603) 440694 Fax: (01603) 440687

Dave's Trophies, Unit 29 Lewisham Centre, Riverdale, London, SE13 7EP Tel: (020) 8852 7013 Fax: (020) 8852 7013

Fastsigns, 12 Boar Lane, Leeds, LS1 6EN Tel: 0113-246 9300 Fax: 0113-246 9393

Jaytrix Rosettes, Bryncam Farm, Argoed Road, Ammanford, Dyfed, SA18 2PR Tel: (01269) 593195 Fax: (01269) 593195

Laurel Signs, Bankfield Works, Chapel Street, Stanningley, Pudsey, West Yorkshire, LS28 6BW Tel: 0113-236 1219 Fax: 0113-236 3697 E-mail: bwaller@btconnect.com

M K Trophies, 21 Scott Drive, Newport Pagnell, Buckinghamshire, MK16 8PW Tel: (01908) 615326 Fax: (01908) 615326

Moran's, Retail Market, Bank Street, Warrington, WA1 2EN Tel: (01925) 576299

Southend Sports Trophies, 536 Sutton Road, Southend-on-Sea, SS2 5PW Tel: (01702) 616046 Fax: (01702) 616046

ROSIN

Langley-Smith & Co. Ltd, 36 Spital Square, London, E1 6DY Tel: (020) 7247 7473 Fax: (020) 7375 1470 E-mail: sales@langley-smith.co.uk

ROTARY ACTUATORS

Belimo Automation UK Ltd, Unit 10 Shepperton Business Park, Govett Avenue, Shepperton, Middlesex, TW17 8BA Tel: (01932) 260460 Fax: (01932) 269222 E-mail: welcome@belimo.co.uk

ROTARY ACTUATORS – *continued*

Masterflo Valve Co (U K) Ltd, Blackness Road, Altens Industrial Estate, Altens, Aberdeen, AB12 3LH Tel: (01224) 878999 Fax: (01224) 878989 E-mail: info@masterflo.co.uk

▶ Ringwood Hydraulics Ltd, 78 Cobham Road, Ferndown Industrial Estate, Wimborne, Dorset, BH21 7RW Tel: (01202) 890401 Fax: (01202) 897713

Rota Engineering Ltd, Wellington Street, Bury, Lancashire, BL8 2BD Tel: 0161-764 0424 Fax: 0161-762 9729 E-mail: sales@rota-eng.com

Titan Fluid Power Ltd, Titan Works, Claremount Road, Halifax, West Yorkshire, HX3 6NT Tel: (01422) 398288 Fax: (01422) 398287

ROTARY ATOMISERS AND SPRAYS

Micron Sprayers Ltd, Bromyard Industrial Estate, Bromyard, Herefordshire, HR7 4HS Tel: (01885) 482397 Fax: (01885) 483043 E-mail: micron@micron.co.uk

Newland Design Ltd, Lodge Quarry, Lancaster Road, Carnforth, Lancashire, LA5 9DW Tel: (01524) 733424

ROTARY BRUSHES

Stoddard Manufacturing Co. Ltd, Denturax Works, Icknield Way, Letchworth Garden City, Hertfordshire, SG6 4AH Tel: (01462) 686221 Fax: (01462) 480711 E-mail: admin@stoddard.co.uk

ROTARY BURRS

Kayson Green Ltd, 9 Commerce Park, Commerce Way, Colchester, CO2 8HX Tel: (01206) 751500 Fax: (01206) 791916 E-mail: abrasives@kaysongreen.co.uk

ROTARY CUTTER DIES

A & M Rotary, Wheatear, Perry Road, Witham, Essex, CM8 3YY Tel: (01376) 515600 Fax: (01376) 513502

Arden Dies Ltd, Shepley Lane Industrial Estate, Hawk Green, Marple, Stockport, Cheshire, SK6 7JW Tel: 0161-449 6000 Fax: 0161-449 0497 E-mail: orderdies@ardendies.com

ROTARY CUTTERS

Blade & Cutter Ltd, Unit 5 Hattersley Industrial Estate, Stockport Road, Hyde, Cheshire, SK14 3QT Tel: 0161-367 8240 Fax: 0161-367 8785

FCE Engineering Ltd, Methilhaven Road, Methil, Leven, Fife, KY8 3LA Tel: (01333) 423557 Fax: (01333) 423582

Ident Machines Ltd, Stapleton Lane, Barwell, Leicester, LE9 8HE Tel: (01455) 840056 Fax: (01455) 848070 E-mail: ident.machines@talk21.com

Prym Whitecroft (UK) Ltd, Whitecroft, Lydney, Gloucestershire, GL15 4QG Tel: (01594) 562631 Fax: (01594) 563662 E-mail: sales@whitecroft.co.uk

Rotatrim, 8 Caxton Park, Caxton Road, Elm Farm Industrial Estate, Bedford, MK41 0TY Tel: (01234) 224545 Fax: (01234) 224540 E-mail: sales@rotatrim.co.uk

ROTARY DRILLING SITE INVESTIGATION

▶ Castle Rock Geotech, 22 Morley Road, Colwick, Nottingham, NG3 6LL Tel: 0115-979 9228 Fax: 0115-982 7060 E-mail: enquiry@crgeo.co.uk

Geotechnical Services, 28 Rusper Close, Stanmore, Middlesex, HA7 4QD Tel: (020) 8954 4190 Fax: (020) 8954 4190 E-mail: geotservices@aol.com

ROTARY DRYERS

Abru Ltd, Derwentside Industrial Park, Derby Road, Belper, Derbyshire, DE56 1WE Tel: (01773) 525700 Fax: (01773) 828059 E-mail: sales@abru.co.uk

JND Technologies Ltd, Thrumpton Lane, Retford, Nottinghamshire, DN22 7AN Tel: (01777) 706777 Fax: (01777) 713192 E-mail: info@jnd.co.uk

R Simon Dryers Ltd, Private Road No 3 Colwick Industrial Estate, Colwick Industrial Estate, Nottingham, NG4 2BD Tel: 0115-961 6276 Fax: 0115-961 6351 E-mail: sales@simon-dryers.co.uk

ROTARY ENCODERS

Hubner Elektromaschinen A.G., PO Box 4022, Reading, RG8 8UD Tel: 0118-984 5351 Fax: 0118-984 3979 E-mail: sales@powertronic.co.uk

Innovative Measurement Technology, 49 Christchurch Crescent, Bognor Regis, West Sussex, PO21 5SL Tel: (01243) 824506 Fax: (01243) 826340 E-mail: sales@imeasure.co.uk

Renishaw Plc, New Mills, Wotton-under-Edge, Gloucestershire, GL12 8JR Tel: (01453) 524126 Fax: (01453) 524201 E-mail: uk@renishaw.com

ROTARY ENGINEERS TABLES

RÖHM (Great Britain) Ltd, 12 Ashway Centre, Elm Crescent, Kingston Upon Thames, Surrey, KT2 6HH Tel: (020) 8549 6647 Fax: (020) 8541 1783 E-mail: sales@rohmgb.co.uk

Weber Automatic Assembly Systems Ltd, 3 Landscape Close, Weston Business Park, Weston-On-The-Green, Oxfordshire, OX25 3SX Tel: (01869) 343688 Fax: (01869) 343699 E-mail: sales@weberautomation.com

Weiss UK Ltd, 27 Manchester Drive, Leegomery, Telford, Shropshire, TF1 6XY Tel: (01952) 240953 Fax: (01952) 244442 E-mail: info@weiss.uk.com

ROTARY HEAT SEALING MACHINE CONSUMABLES

Global Enterprises, The Old Stores, Penny Royal Road, Danbury, Chelmsford, CM3 4ED Tel: (01245) 226004 Fax: (01245) 225995 E-mail: enquiries@globalheatseal.com

ROTARY HEAT SEALING MACHINES

Proseal UK Ltd, Adlington Road Business Park, Bollington, Macclesfield, Cheshire, SK10 5HG Tel: (01625) 856600 Fax: (01625) 856611 E-mail: info@prosealuk.com

ROTARY INDEXING TABLES

▶ Seymour Engineering Ltd, Phoebe Lane, Halifax, West Yorkshire, HX3 9AS Tel: (01422) 362135 Fax: (01422) 322511 E-mail: info@seymourengineering.co.uk

ROTARY JOINTS

Deublin Ltd, Royce Close, Andover, Hampshire, SP10 3TS Tel: (01264) 333355 Fax: (01264) 333304 E-mail: deublin@deublin.co.uk

Johnson Systems International Ltd, Little Lane, Ilkley, West Yorkshire, LS29 8HY Tel: (01943) 607550 Fax: (01943) 609463

Kempster Engineering Ltd, 1 Astra Centre, Royle Barn Road, Rochdale, Lancashire, OL11 3DT Tel: (01706) 345599 Fax: (01706) 657396 E-mail: sales@kempsteruk.com

MOOG Components Group Ltd, 30 Suttons Park Avenue, Suttons Business Park, Reading, RG6 1AW Tel: 0118-966 6044 Fax: 0118-966 6524 E-mail: mcg@moog.com

Rotaflow F V Ltd, Rotec House, Bingswood Trading Estate, Whaley Bridge, High Peak, Derbyshire, SK23 7LY Tel: (01663) 735003 Fax: (01663) 735006 E-mail: sales@rotaflow.com

ROTARY PRESSURE GLAND JOINTS

Filton Ltd, Caswell Rd, Sydenham Industrial Estate, Leamington Spa, Warwickshire, CV31 1QF Tel: (01926) 423191 Fax: (01926) 450610 E-mail: sales@filtonltd.co.uk

ROTARY PRISM FIXED TEXT VARIABLE MESSAGE ROAD SIGNS (FTVMS)

Altaroute Ltd, 10 North Road, Yate, Bristol, BS37 7PA Tel: (01454) 311475 Fax: (01454) 273065 E-mail: sales@altaroute.com

Thermotor Ltd, Beacon House, Station Road, East Preston, Littlehampton, West Sussex, BN16 3AA Tel: (01903) 850650 Fax: (01903) 850428 E-mail: sales@thermotor.co.uk

ROTARY PUMPS

Alfa Laval Eastbourne Ltd, Birch Road, Eastbourne, East Sussex, BN23 6PQ Tel: (01323) 412555 Fax: (01323) 414515

N B Services Olney Ltd, 8 Leyside, Bromham, Bedford, MK43 8NF Tel: (01234) 828900 Fax: (01234) 308972

▶ Vogelsang, Unit 10/12, Quakers Coppice, Crewe, CW1 6EW Tel: (01270) 216600 Fax: (01270) 216699 E-mail: sales@vogelsang.co.uk

ROTARY SCREW AIR COMPRESSORS

Associated Compressor Engineers, Sheffield Street, Stockport, Cheshire, SK4 1RU Tel: 0161-476 3800 Fax: 0161-476 6300 E-mail: sales@acecompressors.com

Compair UK Ltd, Reavell House, 53-56 White House Road, Ipswich, IP1 5PB Tel: (01473) 242000 Fax: (01473) 745451 E-mail: sales.ipswich@compair.com

Economatics Industrial Ltd, 145 Leycroft Road, Leicester, LE4 1ET Tel: 0116-234 0555 Fax: 0116-234 0467 E-mail: leicester@economatics.co.uk

Fini (UK) Ltd, Unit A5 & A6, Greenwood Court, Veasey Close, Attleborough Fields Industrial Estate, Nuneaton, Warwickshire, CV11 6RT Tel: (024) 7632 2850 Fax: (024) 7634 9607 E-mail: finicompressors@yahoo.co.uk

Ingersoll Rand Co. Ltd, Swan Lane, Hindley Green, Wigan, Lancashire, WN2 4EZ Tel: (01942) 257171 Fax: (01942) 522747

Tailored Panels, Unit 4 Minster Park, Grundymore Estate West Moors, Wimborne, Dorset, BH21 6QW Tel: (01202) 871998 Fax: (01202) 861215 E-mail: tailored-panel@hotmail.com

Thorite Ltd, 55 Lowfields Road, Leeds, LS12 6BS Tel: 0113-244 4554 Fax: 0113-242 4700 E-mail: leeds@thorite.co.uk

ROTARY SCREW COMPRESSORS

Howden Compressors Ltd, 133 Barfillan Drive, Glasgow, G52 1BE Tel: 0141-882 3346 Fax: 0141-882 8648 E-mail: sales@howdencompressors.co.uk

Howden Industrial, Braehead Industrial Estate, Old Govan Road, Renfrew, PA4 8XJ Tel: 0141-885 7500 Fax: 0141-886 1963 E-mail: hpc.sales@howden.com

ROTARY SENSORS

Active Sensors Ltd, Unit 12 Sea Vixen Industrial Estate, 3 Wilverley Road, Christchurch, Dorset, BH23 3RU Tel: (01202) 480620 Fax: (01202) 480664 E-mail: sales@activesensors.com

Penny & Giles Controls Ltd, Unit 36 Nine Mile Point Industrial Estate, Cwmfelinfach, Ynysddu, Newport, Gwent, NP11 7HZ Tel: (01495) 202000 Fax: (01495) 202006 E-mail: sales@pennyandgiles.com

ROTARY SWITCHES

C & K Systems Ltd, Cunliffe Drive, Northfield Ave., Kettering, Northamptonshire, NN16 8LF Tel: (01536) 410595 Fax: (01536) 416602

Davron, 21 Beechfield Road, Davenport, Stockport, Cheshire, SK3 8SF Tel: 0161-483 5678 Fax: 0161-483 5678 E-mail: sales@davron.co.uk

Elma Electronic UK Ltd, Premier Business Centre, Speedfields Park, Fareham, Hampshire, PO14 1TY Tel: (01329) 289100 Fax: (01329) 289101 E-mail: info@elma-electronic.co.uk

ROTARY TRANSDUCERS

Hubner, Tree Tops House, Gillotts Lane, Henley-on-Thames, Oxfordshire, RG9 1PT Tel: (01491) 412055 Fax: (01491) 413006 E-mail: sales@sensortronic.co.uk

Millstream Services, Horn Street, Hythe, Kent, CT21 5SL Tel: (01303) 770777 Fax: (01303) 770888 E-mail: sales@millstreamtaximeters.com

Sailes Marketing Ltd, 15 Aintree Road, Keytec 7 Business Park, Pershore, Worcestershire, WR10 2JN Tel: (01386) 554210 Fax: (01386) 552461 E-mail: sales@sailesmarketing.com

ROTARY TRANSFER MACHINE MANUFRS

Denray Machine Tools & Automation Ltd, Westwood House, Westwood Road, Earlsdon, Coventry, CV5 6GF Tel: (024) 7667 8916 Fax: (024) 7669 1478

Haesler Machine Tools, 14 Leyden Road, Stevenage, Hertfordshire, SG1 2BW Tel: (01438) 350835 Fax: (01438) 229482 E-mail: ben.haesler@ntlworld.com

P S G Precision Tooling, 158 Hearsall Lane, Coventry, CV5 6HH Tel: (024) 7671 1388 Fax: (024) 7667 8617

Parkes Machine Tools Ltd, Berkswell, Coventry, CV7 7WF Tel: (01676) 530053 Fax: (01676) 530030 E-mail: sales@parkesmachinetools.co.uk

Pfiffner UK Ltd, 9 Manor Courtyard, Hughenden Avenue, High Wycombe, Buckinghamshire, HP13 5RE Tel: (01494) 510166 Fax: (01494) 510211

Vordale Ltd, Irthlingborough Road, Little Addington, Kettering, Northamptonshire, NN14 4AS Tel: (01933) 652330 Fax: (01933) 651592

ROTARY VACUUM PUMPS

N B Services Olney Ltd, 8 Leyside, Bromham, Bedford, MK43 8NF Tel: (01234) 828900 Fax: (01234) 308972

ROTARY VALVES

Bush & Wilton Ltd, 6 Millennium Place, Tiverton Business Park, Tiverton, Devon, EX16 6SB Tel: (01884) 242233 Fax: (01884) 252555 E-mail: sales@bushandwilton.com

Midland Industrial Designers Ltd, Common Lane, Watnall, Nottingham, NG16 1HD Tel: 0115-938 2154 Fax: 0115-938 6315 E-mail: sales@mid.uk.com

ROTARY VANE COMPRESSORS

Kompressors Ltd, Southgate Avenue, Mildenhall, Bury St. Edmunds, Suffolk, IP28 7AT Tel: (01638) 715361 Fax: (01638) 510762

ROTATING MACHINERY CONDITION MONITORING

Ramac Engineering, 142 Old Shoreham Road, Hove, East Sussex, BN3 7BD Tel: (01273) 622394 Fax: (01273) 202009 E-mail: nfo@whippendell-marine.co.uk

ROTOGRAVURE PRESS MANUFRS

J.M. Heaford Ltd, Unit 9 Century Park, Pacific Road, Altrincham, Cheshire, WA14 5BJ Tel: 0161-928 5679 Fax: 0161-927 7517 E-mail: sales@jmheaford.co.uk

ROUGH TERRAIN FORKLIFT TRUCKS

Truck Masters Handling, Norwich Livestock, Hall Road, Norwich, NR4 6EQ Tel: (01603) 458817 Fax: (01603) 452789 E-mail: mail@truckmasters.co.uk

▶ UK Forks, Central House, Beckwith Knowle, Otley Road, Beckwithshaw, Harrogate, North Yorkshire, HG3 1UD Tel: (0800) 123101 Fax: (01423) 565657 E-mail: info@ukforks.com

ROUND BELTING

Bond-a-Band Transmissions Ltd, Vale Mills, Oakworth, Keighley, West Yorkshire, BD22 0EB Tel: 01535 643123 Fax: 01535 646795 E-mail: sales@bondaband.com

ROUND SLINGS

Damar Webbing Products Ltd, Unit 3 Cobnar Wood Close, Chesterfield, Derbyshire, S41 9RQ Tel: (01246) 269969 Fax: (01246) 269946 E-mail: sales@damarwebbingproducts.com

ROUTER CUTTERS, *See also headings for particular types*

Clico Sheffield Tooling Ltd, 7 Fell Road, Sheffield, S9 2AL Tel: 0114-243 3007 Fax: 0114-243 4158 E-mail: info@clico.co.uk

CNC Support Ltd, Advance Factory Site, Skipton Road, Trawden Colne, Colne, Lancashire, BB8 8BJ Tel: (01282) 859122 Fax: (01282) 859144 E-mail: sales@cncsupport.co.uk

K W O Tools (UK) Ltd, 4 Strawberry Vale, Vale Road, Tonbridge, Kent, TN9 1SJ Tel: (01732) 364444 Fax: (01732) 351144 E-mail: sales@kwo.co.uk

Prime Time Innovations, 22 Austin Way, Royal Oak Industrial Estate, Daventry, Northamptonshire, NN11 8QY Tel: (01327) 300761 Fax: (01327) 878743

Titman Tip Tools Ltd, Valley Road, Clacton-on-Sea, Essex, CO15 6PP Tel: (01255) 220123 Fax: (01255) 221422 E-mail: sales@titman.co.uk

Trend Machinery & Cutting Tools Ltd, Unit 6, Odhams Trading Estate, Watford, WD24 7TR Tel: (01923) 249911 Fax: (01923) 236879 E-mail: stamperm@trendm.co.uk

ROUTER WASTE DUST EXTRACTION SYSTEMS

Unicorn Mucksuckers, 41 High Street, Clophill, Bedford, MK45 4AA Tel: (01525) 860255 Fax: (01525) 861635 E-mail: info@uti.co.uk

ROUTING MACHINES

Avontech Machines, Park Yard, Old Down, Tockington, Bristol, BS32 4PB Tel: (0845) 070 4343 Fax: (0845) 070 4346 E-mail: avontech@blueyonder.co.uk
Pacer Systems Ltd, Gauntley Street, Nottingham, NG7 5HF Tel: 0115-988 7777 Fax: 0115-988 7788 E-mail: sales@pacersys.co.uk
Technic Electric Ltd, Unit 5 Lulworth Business Centre, Nutwood Way, Totton, Southampton, SO40 3WW Tel: (023) 8066 7486 Fax: (023) 8066 3830 E-mail: sales@technic.co.uk

ROV (REMOTELY OPERATED VEHICLE) DISTRIBUTORS OR AGENTS

Gate Place, 140 Poulton Road, Southport, Merseyside, PR9 7DB Tel: (01704) 224365 Fax: (01704) 507500

ROV (REMOTELY OPERATED VEHICLE) OPERATORS/ BUILDERS

Eaton Aerospace Ltd, Abbey Park, Southampton Road, Titchfield, Fareham, Hampshire, PO14 4QA Tel: (01329) 853000 Fax: (01329) 853797
Fugro Survey Ltd, Morton Peto Road, Great Yarmouth, Norfolk, NR31 0LT Tel: (01493) 440320 Fax: (01493) 440319 E-mail: admin@svitzer.co.uk
▶ Izax Offshore Marine Services, 2 Littlemoor Lane, Newton, Alfreton, Derbyshire, DE55 5TY Tel: (01773) 875986 Fax: (01773) 875986 E-mail: matt_izax@hotmail.com
Perry Slingsby Systems Ltd, Ings Lane, Kirkbymoorside, York, YO62 6EZ Tel: (01751) 431751 Fax: (01751) 431388 E-mail: pssl@uk.perrymail.com
Selex Centre At Airbourne Systems, Ferry Road, Edinburgh, EH5 2XS Tel: 0131-332 2411 Fax: 0131-343 4011
SMD Hydrovision Ltd, Davy Banks, Wallsend, Tyne & Wear, NE28 6UZ Tel: +44 (0) 1224 772150 Fax: +44 (0) 1224 772166 E-mail: smd@smdhydrovision.com
Submersible Television Surveys Ltd, 4 Barratt Trading Estate, Denmore Road, Bridge of Don, Aberdeen, AB23 8JW Tel: (01224) 823333 Fax: (01224) 824639 E-mail: admin@stsrov.com
Tritech International Ltd, Peregrine Road, Westhill Business Park, Westhill, Aberdeenshire, AB32 6JL Tel: (01224) 744111 Fax: (01224) 741771 E-mail: sales@tritech.co.uk

ROWING BOAT HIRE

▶ Atlantic Focus, 17 Leachkin Avenue, Inverness, IV3 8LH Tel: 01463 712638 E-mail: info@atlanticfocus.co.uk
▶ Chichester Canal Trading Ltd, Canal Society HQ, Canal Basin Canal Wharf, Chichester, West Sussex, PO19 8DT Tel: (01243) 576701 Fax: (01243) 671051E-mail: jco37ja@aol.com

RUBBER ADDRESS STAMPS

Long Neck Enterprises Ltd, 4 Leacroft Close, Kenley, Surrey, CR8 5EX Tel: 07092 887252 Fax: 07092 887252 E-mail: kwalexander@longneck.co.uk
▶ Long Neck Stamps, 4 Leacroft Close, Kenley, Surrey, CR8 5EX Tel: 0709 288 7252 Fax: 0709 288 7252 E-mail: kwalexander@longneck.co.uk

RUBBER ADHESIVES

Bondex Adhesives & Coatings Ltd, C.P Farms, Woburn Road, Wootton, Bedford, MK43 9EL Tel: (01234) 757763 Fax: (01234) 765550
Industrial Latex Compounds Ltd, Burns Mill, Manchester Street, Heywood, Lancashire, OL10 1DN Tel: (01706) 366161 Fax: (01706) 625664 E-mail: enquiries@indlatex.co.uk

RUBBER APRONS

M G Rubber Co. Ltd, Moorbridge Road, Bingham Industrial Estate, Nottingham, NG13 8GG Tel: (01949) 839112 Fax: (01949) 831357 E-mail: sales@mgrubber.com

RUBBER BADGES

▶ Delta Labelling, Unit A Apollo Park Apollo, Litchfield Road Industrial, Lichfield Road Industrial Estate, Tamworth, Staffordshire, B79 7TA Tel: (01827) 302862 Fax: (01827) 300891E-mail: enquiries@delta-labelling.co.uk

RUBBER BAND MANUFRS

Atson Ltd, 3 Marsh Lane, Bootle, Merseyside, L20 4LZ Tel: 0151-922 7486 Fax: 0151-922 1907 E-mail: enquiries@atson.co.uk
FOCUS Marketing Rubber Band Specialist, 62 Broadoak Avenue, Maidstone, Kent, ME15 6DH Tel: (01622) 755517 E-mail: sales@bandit.co.uk
Lee-Healey, Manchester, M24 2XH Tel: 0161-655 0303 Fax: 0161-655 0304 E-mail: info@lee-healey.com

RUBBER BASED ANTIVIBRATION PRODUCTS

▶ Island Leisure Products Ltd, Unit 1a Eurolink Industrial Centre, Castle Road, Sittingbourne, Kent, ME10 3RN Tel: (01795) 436500 Fax: (01795) 436700 E-mail: info@islandleisureproducts.co.uk
▶ Polymax, School of Electrical & Mechanical Engineers, Budds Lane, Bordon, Hampshire, GU35 0JE Tel: (01420) 474123 Fax: (01420) 487816 E-mail: contactus@polymax.co.uk

RUBBER BELLOWS

Beakbane Ltd, Stourport Road, Kidderminster, Worcestershire, DY11 7QT Tel: (01562) 820561 Fax: (01562) 820560 E-mail: sales@beakbane.co.uk
Engineering Appliances Ltd, 11 Brooklands Close, Sunbury-on-Thames, Middlesex, TW16 7DX Tel: (01932) 788888 Fax: (01932) 761263 E-mail: info@engineering-appliances.com
▶ Plastic Mouldings Ltd, 4 Ailsa Road, Irvine Industrial Estate, Irvine, Ayrshire, KA12 8LP Tel: (01294) 278091 Fax: (01294) 311655 E-mail: info@plasticmouldings.com

RUBBER BELTING

Arntz Belting Co. Ltd, Pennyburn Passage, Londonderry, BT48 0AE Tel: (028) 7126 1221 Fax: (028) 7126 3386 E-mail: abcderry@globalnet.co.uk
Optibelt UK Ltd, 5 Bishops Court, Winwick Quay, Warrington, WA2 8QY Tel: (0870) 4288800 Fax: (01925) 573751 E-mail: optibelt@optibeltuk.co.uk
R A P Conveyors Ltd, Conveyors House, Newcastle, Staffordshire, ST5 7LU Tel: (01782) 566440 Fax: (01782) 566385 E-mail: suegater@btconnect.com
Specialised Belting Supplies (Doncaster), Wheatcroft Farm, Hayfield Lane, Auckley, Doncaster, South Yorkshire, DN9 3NP Tel: (01302) 869090 Fax: (01302) 867373 E-mail: sales@sbsbelting.com

RUBBER BONDED ENGINEERING PRODUCTS

Ashwood, Stanshope Hall, Stanshope, Ashbourne, Derbyshire, DE6 2AD Tel: (01335) 310278 Fax: (01335) 310470 E-mail: jvelas@ashwood.biz

RUBBER BONDED PRODUCTS

Aegis Rubber Engineering Ltd, 15 Stairbridge Lane, Bolney, Haywards Heath, West Sussex, RH17 5PA Tel: (01444) 871116 Fax: (01444) 248327 E-mail: are-ape.sales@netmail.co.uk
Edgware Motor Accessories, 33 Albany Close, Bushey, WD23 4SG Tel: (020) 8950 4694 Fax: (020) 8950 6557 E-mail: enquiries@rubbertrim.co.uk
R B Associates, 65 Sea Mills Lane, Stoke Bishop, Bristol, BS9 1DR Tel: 0117-968 1374 Fax: 0117-968 1374 E-mail: rbass@avnet.co.uk
SRC Ltd, Buckingham Road, Stockport, Cheshire, SK4 4QZ Tel: 0161-432 3222 Fax: 0161-443 2025 E-mail: sales@src.ltd.uk

RUBBER BUSHES

Grommets Ltd, Unit 2 Hollands La Industrial Estate, Henfield, West Sussex, BN5 9QY Tel: (01273) 493355 Fax: (01273) 493388 E-mail: sales@grommets.co.uk

RUBBER CARPET UNDERLAY

Ball & Young Division Of Vitafoan Ltd, 53 Causeway Road, Earlstrees Industrial Estate, Corby, Northamptonshire, NN17 4DU Tel: (01536) 200502 Fax: (01536) 269554 E-mail: sales@underlay.com
Lee Floorstok Ltd, Unit B1 The Dresser Centre, Whitworth Street, Openshaw, Manchester, M11 2NE Tel: 0161-231 8080 Fax: 0161-231 8787 E-mail: leefloor@aol.com
Underlay Direct, 1 Woodlea Gardens, Sauchie, Alloa, Clackmannanshire, FK10 3BD Tel: (07768) 588714 Fax: (01259) 218097 E-mail: sales@underlaydirectscotland.co.uk

RUBBER CASH REGISTER PRINTING STEREOS

Mid Glam Cash Registers, Croftmore, Gelliwion Woods, Maesycoed, Pontypridd, Mid Glamorgan, CF37 1QB Tel: 07957 566120 Fax: 01443 407738 E-mail: Paul.Suminski@midglamcashregisters.co.uk

RUBBER COATED BELLOW FABRICS

John Heathcoat & Co Holdings Ltd, Westexe, Tiverton, Devon, EX16 5LL Tel: (01884) 254949 Fax: (01884) 252897 E-mail: email@heathcoat.co.uk

RUBBER COATING/LINING SERVICES

I Q L Ltd, Stirling Road, Cressex Business Park, High Wycombe, Buckinghamshire, HP12 3ST Tel: (01494) 463636 Fax: (01494) 439639 E-mail: sales@iqllimited.co.uk

RUBBER COMPOUNDS

Avon Ruber P.L.C., Hampton Park West, Melksham, Wiltshire, SN12 6NB Tel: (01225) 896300 Fax: (01225) 896302 E-mail: enquieries@avon-rubber.com
B D Technical Polymers Ltd, 202b Cooks Road, Weldon North Industrial Estate, Corby, Northamptonshire, NN17 5JT Tel: (01536) 200913 Fax: (01536) 400836 E-mail: sales@bdtechnicalpolymer.co.uk
Clwyd Compounders Ltd, Gardden Industrial Estate, Ruabon, Wrexham, Clwyd, LL14 6RG Tel: (01978) 810551 Fax: (01978) 810740 E-mail: sales@clwydcompounders.com
Devon Rubber Co. Ltd, Central Avenue, Lee Mill Industrial Estate, Ivybridge, Devon, PL21 9PE Tel: (01752) 894695 Fax: (01752) 690794 E-mail: drubber@bandvulc.co.uk
Eastland Compounding Ltd, Bank Street, Manchester, M11 4AS Tel: 0161-223 3241 Fax: 0161-223 3240
Icon Polymer Group Ltd, Thrumpton Lane, Retford, Nottinghamshire, DN22 6HH Tel: (01777) 714300 Fax: (01777) 709739 E-mail: info@iconpolymer.com
Marple Polymer Processors Ltd, Primrose Mill, Mill Brow, Marple Bridge, Stockport, Cheshire, SK6 5AS Tel: 0161-427 2534 Fax: 0161-427 7872
Milliken Walk Off Mats, Hilton Fold Lane, Middleton, Manchester, M24 2HZ Tel: 0161-655 1380 Fax: 0161-655 1379 E-mail: mcse@milliken.com
Nelson Roller & Rubber Co., Bankgate Mills, Bankgate, Slaithwaite, Huddersfield, HD7 5DL Tel: (01484) 845015 Fax: (01484) 842900 E-mail: info@nelco.co.uk
Protective Rubber Coatings Ltd, Paynes Shipyard, Coronation Road, Ashton Gate, Bristol, BS3 1RP Tel: 0117-966 1155 Fax: 0117-966 1158 E-mail: sales@bmspc.co.uk

RUBBER CONSULTANTS OR DESIGNERS

Rapra Technology, Shawbury, Shrewsbury, SY4 4NR Tel: (01939) 250383 Fax: (01939) 251118 E-mail: info@rapra.net
Rubber Consultants, Brickendonbury, Brickendon, Hertford, SG13 8NL Tel: (01992) 554657 Fax: (01992) 504248 E-mail: info@tarrc.co.uk
Smithers Rapra, Shawbury, Shrewsbury, SY4 4NR Tel: (01939) 250383 Fax: 01939 251118 E-mail: info@rapra.net

RUBBER CONVERTERS

Kirkfield Ltd, Unit 1/2 Schofield Business Park, Sugarbrook Road, Bromsgrove, Worcestershire, B60 3DN Tel: (01527) 559345 Fax: (01527) 835690 E-mail: sales@kirkfield.co.uk

RUBBER COVERED ROLLERS

Bottcher UK, Jubilee Way, Shipley, West Yorkshire, BD18 1QG Tel: (01274) 530531 Fax: (01274) 530532

RUBBER CRUMB MIXERS

▶ Tyre Crumb Limited, Long Acre, Long Lane, Bovingdon, Hertfordshire, HP3 0NE Tel: 07747 633338 Fax: 01442 833130 E-mail: Sales@TyreCrumb.com

RUBBER CUTTING MACHINES

Peter Gillard & Co. Ltd, Alexandra Way, Ashchurch Business Centre, Tewkesbury, Gloucestershire, GL20 8NB Tel: (01684) 290243 Fax: (01684) 290330 E-mail: sales@gillard.co.uk

RUBBER DIAPHRAGMS

C D I Polytek Ltd, 130 Oldfield Road, Hampton, Middlesex, TW12 2HT Tel: (020) 8481 8300 Fax: (020) 8941 3107 E-mail: sales@cdipolytek.co.uk
Metflex, Queen Street, Great Harwood, Blackburn, BB6 7AU Tel: (01254) 884171 Fax: (01254) 887753 E-mail: sales@metlex.co.uk
Synthotech Elastomers Ltd, Mangham Road, Barbot Hall Industrial Estate, Rotherham, South Yorkshire, S61 4RJ Tel: (01709) 363705 Fax: (01709) 369165 E-mail: info@synthotech-rubber.co.uk

RUBBER DIPPED PRODUCTS

Chainbond Ltd, Rose Mill, Union Street, Middleton, Manchester, M24 6DD Tel: 0161-653 2931 Fax: 0161-653 2931
Denber Trading Co., Unit H3 Rudford Industrial Estate, Ford Road, Ford, Arundel, West Sussex, BN18 0BD Tel: (01903) 723155 Fax: (01903) 733160 E-mail: denberint.rubber@virgin.net
M A Consultant, 87 Cobham Road, Ilford, Essex, IG3 9JL Tel: (020) 8599 1421 Fax: (020) 8599 1421 E-mail: ma_afzal@btinternet.com
Precision Dipping Marketing Ltd, Stover Trading Estate, Millbrook Road, Yate, Bristol, BS37 5PB Tel: (01454) 318004 Fax: (01454) 319961E-mail: sales@precisiondippings.co.uk
Specialised Latex Services Ltd, Lupton Road, Thame Industrial Estate, Thame, Oxfordshire, OX9 3SE Tel: (01844) 212489 Fax: (01844) 212489 E-mail: sales@specialisedlatex.co.uk

RUBBER DOCK OR LOADING BAY BUMPERS

Easilift Loading Systems Ltd, Spring Grove, Penistone Road, Kirkburton, Huddersfield, HD8 0PL Tel: (01484) 601400 Fax: (01484) 601401 E-mail: sales@easilift-loading-systems.co.uk
Thorworld Industries Ltd, Unit 37, Station Lane Industrial Estate, Old Whittington, Chesterfield, Derbyshire, S41 9QX Tel: (01246) 260981 Fax: (01246) 260493 E-mail: info@thorworld.co.uk
Warehouse Direct Industrial Ltd, PO Box 928, Woking, Surrey, GU23 7ZN Tel: 08707 700709 Fax: 08707 700659 E-mail: sales@wdil.co.uk

RUBBER DOORS

Harefield Doors Ltd, 7 Chiltern Trading Estate, Earl Howe Road, Holmer Green, High Wycombe, Buckinghamshire, HP15 6QT Tel: (01494) 716316 Fax: (01494) 718198 E-mail: sales@harefielddoors.co.uk
Rayflex Rubber Ltd, 11b Palatine Industrial Estate, Causeway Avenue, Warrington, WA4 6QQ Tel: (01925) 638753 Fax: (01925) 416621 E-mail: sales@rayflexrubber.co.uk
Syston Rolling Shutters Ltd, 33 Albert Street, Syston, Leicester, LE7 2JB Tel: 0116-260 8841 Fax: 0116-264 0846 E-mail: sales@syston.com

RUBBER EXTRUSION DIES

▶ Dunlop Extrusions, Nufox Rubber Ltd, Bentley Avenue, Middleton, Manchester, M24 2GP Tel: 0161-655 0170 Fax: 0161-655 0171 E-mail: sales@dunlopextrusions.com

RUBBER EXTRUSIONS

Advanced Seals & Gaskets, Polymer Works, Hope Street, Dudley, West Midlands, DY2 8RS Tel: (01384) 252555 Fax: (01384) 252373 E-mail: kate@advancedseals.co.uk
Allied Rubber Products, 15 Cornwall Road Industrial Estate, Smethwick, West Midlands, B66 2JT Tel: 0121-565 0961 Fax: 0121-565 0976
Arms Technical Engineering, Arms House, 29 Glen Road, Oldham, OL4 1LP Tel: 0161-626 5293 Fax: 0161-626 5293 E-mail: sales@armstechnicalengineering.co.uk
Brentwood, 2 Whitehouse Road, Dordon, Tamworth, Staffordshire, B78 1QF Tel: (01827) 705450 Fax: (01827) 705450 E-mail: bob.kind@ntlworld.com
British Gaskets Ltd, Bulmer Road Industrial Estate, Bulmer Road, Sudbury, Suffolk, CO10 7HJ Tel: (01787) 881188 Fax: (01787) 880595
C D I Polytek Ltd, 130 Oldfield Road, Hampton, Middlesex, TW12 2HT Tel: (020) 8481 8300 Fax: (020) 8941 3107 E-mail: sales@cdipolytek.co.uk

RUBBER EXTRUSIONS - *continued*

P.J. Donnelly Rubber, 15 Cornwall Road Industrial Park, Smethwick, West Midlands, B66 2JT Tel: 0121-565 0988 Fax: 0121-565 0976

Fabprene Ltd, Broadway, Globe Lane Industrial Estate, Dukinfield, Cheshire, SK16 4UU Tel: 0161-342 6902 Fax: 0161-342 6903 E-mail: sales@fabprene.co.uk

Harltex Ltd, 12 Norman-D-Gate Industrial Estate, Norman-D-Gate, Northampton, NN1 5NT Tel: (01604) 632343 Fax: (01604) 632344 E-mail: harltex@btconnect.com

Inglecliff Ltd, Unit 2 Barsbank Lane, Lymm, Cheshire, WA13 0ER Tel: (01925) 752471 Fax: (01925) 755784 E-mail: sales@inglecliff.co.uk

Newnham Rubber Mills Ltd, Bullo Pill, Newnham, Gloucestershire, GL14 1ED Tel: (01594) 516233 Fax: (01594) 516608 E-mail: sales@lee-healey.fssnet.co.uk

Portmere Rubber Ltd, Victoria Street, Northam, Southampton, SO14 5QZ Tel: (023) 8022 3628 Fax: (023) 8022 3250

Reddiplex Group Logistics, Unit 33 The Furlong, Berry Hill Industrial Estate, Droitwich, Worcestershire, WR9 9BG Tel: (01905) 774400 Fax: (01905) 791866 E-mail: reddiplex@reddiplex.com

Rubberlast (Britain) Ltd, Unit 2 Gelderd Trading Estate, Brown Lane West, Leeds, LS12 6BD Tel: 0113-245 5234 Fax: 0113-244 8293 E-mail: sales@rubberlast.com

Sherborne Rubber Co. Ltd, Icknield Square, Ladywood, Birmingham, B16 0AB Tel: 0121-456 1565 Fax: 0121-452 1637 E-mail: sales@sherbourne.co.uk

T R P Sealing Systems Ltd, 24 Netherwood Road, Rotherwas Industrial Estate, Hereford, HR2 6JU Tel: (01432) 279366 Fax: (01432) 273017 E-mail: admin@trpsealing.com

TCB-Arrow Ltd, Watchmoor House, Watchmoor Road, Camberley, Surrey, GU15 3AQ Tel: (01276) 679394 Fax: (01276) 679055 E-mail: sales@tcbarrow.co.uk

V I P-polymers, 15 Windover Road, Huntingdon, Cambridgeshire, PE29 7EB Tel: (01480) 411333 Fax: (01480) 450430 E-mail: sales@vip-polymers.com

Veker Extrusions Ltd, Shaftmoor Lane, Hall Green, Birmingham, B28 8SP Tel: 0121-777 5000 Fax: 0121-777 5015 E-mail: paul@vekex.com

Walker Rubber & Plastics Ltd, Last House, 21-23 Burnet Road, Sweetbriar Industrial Estate, Norwich, NR3 2BS Tel: (01603) 487371 Fax: (01603) 406502 E-mail: sales@walker-rubber.co.uk

Wilks (Rubber Plastics Manufacturing) Co. Ltd, Woodrolfe Road, Tollesbury, Maldon, Essex, CM9 8RY Tel: (01621) 869609 Fax: (01621) 868863 E-mail: sales@wilks.co.uk

RUBBER FABRICATORS

Atlantic Rubber Company Ltd, Castleton Works, Atlantic Street, Altrincham, Cheshire, WA14 5BX Tel: 0161-928 3727 Fax: 0161-926 9755 E-mail: info@atlanticgb.co.uk

▶ Avon Rubber, Cory Way, West Wilts Trading Estate, Westbury, Wiltshire, BA13 4QT Tel: (01373) 863106 Fax: (01373) 863107

▶ Berwin Group Ltd, 39 A & B Broadway, Globe Lane Industrial Estate, Dukinfield, Cheshire, SK16 4UJ Tel: 0161-330 2504

British Seals & Rubber Mouldings Ltd, Unit 7 Childerditch Indust Park, Childerditch Hall Drive, Brentwood, Essex, CM13 3HD Tel: (01277) 815300 Fax: (01277) 815350 E-mail: seals@british-gaskets.co.uk

▶ Challis Rubber & Plastic Product, 8 Thorne Farm House, Thorne Hill, Ramsgate, Kent, CT12 5DS Tel: (01843) 826006 Fax: (01843) 826005 E-mail: jwchallisco@aol.com

▶ Happich Profiles Ltd, Unit 31 Fort Industrial Park, Chester Road, Castle Vale, Birmingham, B35 7AR Tel: 0121-748 1005 Fax: 0121-748 1006 E-mail: sales@happich.com

Ilga U K Ltd, 175 Cocklaw Street, Kelty, Fife, KY4 0DH Tel: (01383) 831626 Fax: (01383) 831499 E-mail: info@taybuildscotia.co.uk

▶ Interfloor Ltd, Edinburgh Road, Heathhall, Dumfries, DG1 1QA Tel: (01387) 253111 Fax: (01387) 268937

L J A Miers & Co. Ltd, Hawkesden Road, St. Neots, Cambridgeshire, PE19 1QS Tel: (01480) 211177 Fax: (01480) 211190 E-mail: sales@ljamiers.co.uk

▶ M F Sealing Systems Ltd, 2C Brighouse Business Village, Brighouse Road, Middlesbrough, Cleveland, TS2 1RT Tel: (01642) 253253 Fax: (01642) 257980

▶ Martland Ltd, Unit 1D, Cricket Street Business Centre, Cricket Street, Wigan, Lancashire, WN6 7TP Tel: (01942) 497064 Fax: (01942) 497075 E-mail: martland-ltd@tiscali.co.uk

Multifabs Survival Ltd, Units 4-5, Balmoor Industrial Estate, Peterhead, Aberdeenshire, AB42 1QG Tel: (01779) 470848 Fax: (01779) 478099

Orchid Plastics Ltd, The Lime Store, Florence Road, Kelly Bray, Callington, Cornwall, PL17 8EQ Tel: (01579) 384239 Fax: (01579) 383934

▶ Polineri Europa UK Ltd, Bo'Ness Road, Grangemouth, Stirlingshire, FK3 9XE Tel: (01324) 692200 Fax: (01324) 473915

▶ Ryburn Rubber Ltd, Watson Mill Lane, Sowerby Bridge, West Yorkshire, HX6 3BW Tel: (01422) 316323 Fax: (01422) 835898 E-mail: sales@ryburnrubber.co.uk

▶ TBS, 2 Harlaw Centre Howe Moss CR, Kirkhill Industrial Estate, Dyce, Aberdeen, AB21 0GN Tel: (01224) 729580 Fax: (01224) 729581 E-mail: tbsoring@aol.com

▶ Tennant Group Ltd, The Midway, Nottingham, NG7 2TS Tel: 0115-985 2222 Fax: 0115-988 5330 E-mail: info@tennantgroup.co.uk

▶ Trellevorg Celing Solutions, Ashchurch, Tewkesbury, Gloucestershire, GL20 8JS Tel: (01684) 852211 Fax: (01684) 852210

Walker Rubber & Plastics Ltd, Last House, 21-23 Burnet Road, Sweetbriar Industrial Estate, Norwich, NR3 2BS Tel: (01603) 487371 Fax: (01603) 406502 E-mail: sales@walker-rubber.co.uk

RUBBER FENDERS

Portmere Rubber Ltd, Victoria Street, Northam, Southampton, SO14 5QZ Tel: (023) 8022 3628 Fax: (023) 8022 3250

RUBBER FLOORING

Freudenberg Building Systems, Gilmorton Road, Lutterworth, Leicestershire, LE17 4DU Tel: (01455) 261200 Fax: (01455) 556529 E-mail: noraük@freudenberg.com

Geo Brady Flooring Ltd, Brunswick Industrial Estate, Brunswick Village, Newcastle upon Tyne, NE13 7BA Tel: 0191-217 0202 Fax: 0191-217 0202

J P Polymer Sheetings Ltd, Coneygre Industrial Estate, Tipton, West Midlands, DY4 8XP Tel: 0121-520 5020 Fax: 0121-522 4610 E-mail: sales@jppolymer.co.uk

Linatex Ltd, Wilkinson House Galway Road, Blackbushe Business Park, Yateley, Hampshire, GU46 6GE Tel: (01252) 743000 Fax: (01252) 743030E-mail: info@linatex.com

▶ The Rubber Flooring Co., Unit 12-13, Phoenix Way, Smallshaw Industrial Estate, Burnley, Lancashire, BB11 5SX Tel: (01282) 411014 Fax: (01282) 411015 E-mail: mail@therubberflooringcompany.co.uk

▶ Rubber Flooring Online, Chy Rudden, Mill Lane, Grampound, Truro, Cornwall, TR2 4RU Tel: (01726) 883783

RUBBER GASKETS

▶ Challis Rubber & Plastic Product, 8 Thorne Farm House, Thorne Hill, Ramsgate, Kent, CT12 5DS Tel: (01843) 826006 Fax: (01843) 826005 E-mail: jwchallisco@aol.com

Rayflex Rubber Ltd, 11b Palatine Industrial Estate, Causeway Avenue, Warrington, WA4 6QQ Tel: (01925) 638753 Fax: (01925) 416621 E-mail: sales@rayflexrubber.co.uk

RUBBER GLOVES

Specialised Latex Services Ltd, Lupton Road, Thame Industrial Estate, Thame, Oxfordshire, OX9 3SE Tel: (01844) 212489 Fax: (01844) 212489 E-mail: sales@specialisedlatex.co.uk

RUBBER HANDICRAFT STAMPS

Kershaw's Rubber Stamps, Cotton Hall Street, Darwen, Lancashire, BB3 0DW Tel: (01254) 703040 Fax: (01254) 703373 E-mail: info@planetree.co.uk

RUBBER HOSE MANUFRS

Arco Ltd, Tenax Circle, Trafford Park, Manchester, M17 1EZ Tel: 0161-869 5800 Fax: 0161-869 5858 E-mail: traffordpark.branch@arco.co.uk

Arco East Scotland, Avon Mill Industrial Estate, Mill Road, Linlithgow Bridge, Linlithgow, West Lothian, EH49 7QY Tel: (01506) 844661 Fax: (01506) 847816 E-mail: arco.eastscotland@arco.co.uk

Arco Glasgow, 210 Edmiston Drive, Glasgow, G51 2YY Tel: 0141-419 3200 Fax: 0141-419 3232 E-mail: arco-glasgow@arco.com

Arco South East, Cray Avenue, Orpington, Kent, BR5 3QB Tel: (01689) 875411 Fax: (01689) 876538 E-mail: orpington.branch@arco.co.uk

Arco Tyne & Wear Ltd, PO Box 8, Blaydon-on-Tyne, Tyne & Wear, NE21 5TP Tel: 0191-414 7721 Fax: 0191-414 0258 E-mail: arco.tynewear@arco.co.uk

Arcode UK Ltd, 41 Ebrington Road, Kenton, Harrow, Middlesex, HA3 0LS Tel: (020) 8907 1309 Fax: (020) 8907 9132 E-mail: sales@arcode.co.uk

Artel Rubber Co., The Studio Unit 3/A, Waterloo Industrial Estate, Waterloo Road, Bidford-on-Avon, Alcester, Warwickshire, B50 4JH Tel: (01789) 774099 Fax: (01789) 774599 E-mail: sales@artelrubber.co.uk

Atlantic Rubber Company Ltd, Castleton Works, Atlantic Street, Altrincham, Cheshire, WA14 5BX Tel: 0161-928 3727 Fax: 0161-926 9755 E-mail: info@atlanticgb.co.uk

Bradford Rubber Services Ltd, 25 Annison Street, Garnet Street, Bradford, West Yorkshire, BD3 9HJ Tel: (01274) 307030 Fax: (01274) 305699 E-mail: sales@bradfordrubber.co.uk

James Dawson & Son Ltd, Unit 7, 2ND Avenue, Poynton Industrial Estate, Poynton, Cheshire, SK12 1ND Tel: (01625) 879494 Fax: (01625) 879555 E-mail: indico@indico-europe.co.uk

Designation Ltd, Newark Road, Peterborough, PE1 5YD Tel: (01733) 893333 Fax: (01733) 314889 E-mail: sales@desihose.com

Dura Hose & Fittings Ltd, Unit 8, Mountheath Industrial Park, Prestwich, Manchester, M25 9WB Tel: 0161-798 8665 Fax: 0161-773 3048 E-mail: sales@dura-hose.com

Harltex Ltd, 12 Norman-D-Gate Industrial Estate, Norman-D-Gate, Northampton, NN1 5NT Tel: (01604) 632343 Fax: (01604) 632344 E-mail: harltex@btconnect.com

Hose & General Supplies Ltd, Daux Road, Billingshurst, West Sussex, RH14 9SJ Tel: (01403) 783221 Fax: (01403) 783221

Hoselines & Industrial Supplies (North West) Ltd, Units 8 & 9 Knoll Street Industrial Estate, Bury New Rd, Salford, M7 2BL Tel: 0161-792 0481 Fax: 0161-792 5328 E-mail: sales@hoselines.com

Lee-Healey, Manchester, M24 2XH Tel: 0161-655 0303 Fax: 0161-655 0304 E-mail: info@lee-healey.com

North Devon Hose & Hydraulics Ltd, Unit 20 Castle Park Road, Whiddon Valley Industrial Estate, Barnstaple, Devon, EX32 8PA Tel: (01271) 324443 Fax: (01271) 324568 E-mail: northdevon@hosehyd.fsnet.co.uk

Oldham Seals Ltd, Jetpac Works Gravel Lane, Quarry Lane Industrial Estate, Chichester, West Sussex, PO19 8PG Tel: (01243) 782296 Fax: (01243) 781933 E-mail: sales@oldhamseals.co.uk

Power Pipes Pendle, Maud Street Works, Maud Street, Barrowford, Nelson, Lancashire, BB9 8NX Tel: (01282) 601896 Fax: (01282) 697034 E-mail: sales@powerpipes.co.uk

Semperit Industrial Products Ltd, Cottesbrooke Park, Heartlands Business Park, Daventry, Northamptonshire, NN11 8YL Tel: (01327) 313140 Fax: (01327) 313149 E-mail: paul.phillips@semperit.co.uk

Silflex Ltd, Coedcae Lane, Pontyclun, Mid Glamorgan, CF72 9HJ Tel: (01443) 238464 Fax: 01443 238464 E-mail: silflex@silflex.com

Steinlock Ltd, Danbury Mews, Wallington, Surrey, SM6 0BY Tel: (020) 8773 4966 Fax: (020) 8773 4968

Vitamol Ltd, Rycroft St, Ashton-under-Lyne, Lancashire, OL7 0BN Tel: 0161-342 1400 Fax: 0161-343 1872 E-mail: r.winter@vitamol.co.uk

RUBBER HOSE, WIRE BRAID REINFORCED

Hydraquip Hose, Head Office, 2 Raleigh Court, Crawley, West Sussex, RH10 9PD Tel: (01293) 615166 Fax: (01293) 614965 E-mail: sales@hydraquip.co.uk

RUBBER INDUSTRY MOULDS

Alchemie Ltd, Warwick Road, Kineton, Warwick, CV35 0HU Tel: (01926) 640600 Fax: (01926) 641698 E-mail: sales@alchemie.com

Europix Designs Ltd, Westgate Mill, Wiseman Street, Burnley, Lancashire, BB11 1RU Tel: (01282) 459031 Fax: (01282) 459031 E-mail: europix@shoemolds.com

R & D Tool & Engineering Ltd, Hamilton Road, Sutton-in-Ashfield, Nottinghamshire, NG17 5LD Tel: (01623) 556287 Fax: (01623) 552240 E-mail: sales@rdtool.co.uk

T & P Tooling Co., Mardyke Works, St Marys Lane, North Ockendon, Upminster, Essex, RM14 3PA Tel: (01708) 224220 Fax: (01708) 224220

Technicast Moulds, Unit 1 Garnett Close, Watford, WD24 7GN Tel: (01923) 246530 Fax: (01923) 255983 E-mail: isoo4e2893@blueyonder.co.uk

Tower Tool Co. Ltd, Tower Manfactory, Radnor Road, Wigston, Leicestershire, LE18 4XY Tel: 0116-277 6520 Fax: 0116-277 6388 E-mail: myles@tower-tool.demon.co.uk

Wigan Tool & Die Co. Ltd, Unit 1, Great George Street, Wigan, Lancashire, WN3 4DP Tel: (01942) 324866 Fax: (01942) 820618 E-mail: enquiries@wigantoolanddie.co.uk

RUBBER INJECTION MOULDING MACHINES

Brooker Mouldings Ltd, 4 Vickers Business Centre, Priestley Road, Basingstoke, Hampshire, RG24 9NP Tel: (01256) 356523 Fax: (01256) 328281

RUBBER INJECTION MOULDINGS

Boverton Precision, Unit 2 Oxbutts Industrial Etate, Woodmancote, Cheltenham, Gloucestershire, GL52 9HW Tel: (01242) 675405 Fax: (01242) 677411 E-mail: bovertonprecision@wwmail.co.uk

L V S Rubber Mouldings Ltd, Robins Rd, Chasetown Industrial Estate, Burntwood, Staffordshire, WS7 3FX Tel: (01543) 673989 Fax: (01543) 683823 E-mail: sales@lvsrubber.com

Metflex, Queen Street, Great Harwood, Blackburn, BB6 7AU Tel: (01254) 884171 Fax: (01254) 887753 E-mail: sales@metlex.co.uk

Slatebond Ltd, Unit 27 Leafield Industrial Estate, Leafield Way, Neston, Corsham, Wiltshire, SN13 9RS Tel: (01225) 810099 Fax: (01225) 811413 E-mail: sales@slatebond.com

Vitamol Ltd, Rycroft St, Ashton-under-Lyne, Lancashire, OL7 0BN Tel: 0161-342 1400 Fax: 0161-343 1872 E-mail: r.winter@vitamol.co.uk

Wye Valley Precision Engineering (Holdings) Ltd, Station Approach, Ross-On-Wye, Herefordshire, HR9 7AQ Tel: (01989) 763519 Fax: (01989) 766662 E-mail: sales@wye-valley.co.uk

RUBBER LABELS/BRANDING TAPES

Polymeric Labels Ltd, 12 Greenacres Road, Oldham, OL4 1HA Tel: 0161-678 9005 Fax: 0161-627 1378 E-mail: sales@polymeric.co.uk

RUBBER LATEX

Bellman Carter 2000 Ltd, Rear of, 358-374 Grand Drive, London, SW20 9NG Tel: (020) 8540 1372 Fax: (020) 8544 9424

Formulated Polymer Products Ltd, 8 Garden Street, Ramsbottom, Bury, Lancashire, BL0 9BQ Tel: (01706) 828208 Fax: (01706) 828820 E-mail: neil@polymers.co.uk

RUBBER LINERS OR LINING SYSTEMS

D R C Polymer Products Ltd, 1 Regal Lane, Soham, Ely, Cambridgeshire, CB7 5BA Tel: (01353) 720989 Fax: (01353) 624668 E-mail: info@drc-polymers.com

I Q L Ltd, Stirling Road, Cressex Business Park, High Wycombe, Buckinghamshire, HP12 3ST Tel: (01494) 463636 Fax: (01494) 439639 E-mail: sales@iqllimited.co.uk

Kemtile Ltd, Unit C3, Taylor Business Park, Risley, Warrington, WA3 6BL Tel: (01925) 763045 Fax: (01925) 763381 E-mail: all@kemtile.co.uk

Linertech Ltd, Wellington Mills, Quebec Street, Elland, West Yorkshire, HX5 9BX Tel: (01422) 377551 Fax: (01422) 311636 E-mail: sales@linertech.co.uk

P V H Rubber & Plastic Linings & Manufacturing Ltd, Unit 16, Webnor Industrial Estate, Ettingshall Road, Wolverhampton, WV2 2LD Tel: (01902) 409186 Fax: (01902) 497265 E-mail: kdelveir@aol.com

Protective Rubber Coatings Ltd, Paynes Shipyard, Coronation Road, Ashton Gate, Bristol, BS3 1RP Tel: 0117-966 1155 Fax: 0117-966 1158 E-mail: sales@bmspc.co.uk

Rema Tip Top UK, Mill Lane, Coppull, Chorley, Lancashire, PR7 5AW Tel: (01257) 793487 Fax: (01257) 793930 E-mail: kath.greenhalgh@tip-top.co.uk

H.D. Sharman Ltd, High Peak Works, Chapel-en-le-Frith, High Peak, Derbyshire, SK23 0HW Tel: (01298) 812371 Fax: (01298) 812237 E-mail: info@hdsharman.co.uk

T K H Rubber Linings, 81 Musgrave Road, Birmingham, B18 5HH Tel: 0121-515 1800 Fax: 0121-554 3900 E-mail: tkh@btconnect.com

RUBBER MACHINERY

Arburg Ltd, Tachbrook Park Drive, Warwick, CV34 6RH Tel: (01926) 457000 Fax: (01926) 457030 E-mail: uk@arburg.com

Blackfriars Ltd, Roman Way, Market Harborough, Leicestershire, LE16 7PQ Tel: (01858) 462249 Fax: (01858) 464755 E-mail: sales@blackfriars.com

Euro Rubber Lines, Red Marsh Drive Industrial Estate, Red Marsh Industrial Estate, Thornton-Cleveleys, Lancashire, FY5 4HP Tel: (01253) 850929 Fax: (01253) 850064 E-mail: eurorubberlines@aol.com

Lewis & Raby (Engineers) Ltd, Birchill Road, Knowsley Industrial Park, Liverpool, L33 7TG Tel: 0151-546 2882 Fax: 0151-549 1585

Machinery Products UK Ltd, Four Trees, Main Road, South Elkington, Louth, Lincolnshire, LN11 0RU Tel: (01507) 610108 Fax: (01507) 610044 E-mail: johnny.walker@btconnect.com

R S J Process Machinery Ltd, Phoenix House, Tame Street, Stalybridge, Cheshire, SK15 1SY Tel: 0161-338 7288 Fax: 0161-338 3574 E-mail: aquafil@btconnect.com

S G M Mapelli, 2 Como Place, Newcastle, Staffordshire, ST5 2QN Tel: (01782) 618101 Fax: (01782) 612616 E-mail: dougtee@mapelli.co.uk

RUBBER MATS

Arcode UK Ltd, 41 Ebrington Road, Kenton, Harrow, Middlesex, HA3 0LS Tel: (020) 8907 1309 Fax: (020) 8907 9132 E-mail: sales@arcode.co.uk

RUBBER MATS – *continued*

Bonar Floors Ltd, High Holborne Road, Ripley, Derbyshire, DE5 3XD Tel: (01773) 744121 Fax: (01773) 744142 E-mail: enquires@bonarfloors.com
Bradford Rubber Services Ltd, 25 Annison Street, Garnet Street, Bradford, West Yorkshire, BD3 9HJ Tel: (01274) 307030 Fax: (01274) 305699 E-mail: sales@bradfordrubber.co.uk
Cosmos Motor Products Ltd, Unit 3A Neptune Industrial Estate, Neptune Road, Harrow, Middlesex, HA1 4HX Tel: (020) 8863 8666 Fax: (020) 8427 3689 E-mail: salescomopro@cs.com
William Freeman, Wakefield Road, Staincross, Barnsley, South Yorkshire, S75 6DH Tel: (01226) 284081 Fax: (01226) 731832 E-mail: sales@williamfreeman.com
Langdean Manufacturing Ltd, 3 Thames Industrial Estate, High St South, Dunstable, Bedfordshire, LU6 3HD Tel: (01582) 696369 Fax: (01582) 666658 E-mail: langdean@btconnect.com
P H S Mat Services Ltd, Unit 5 Transport Avenue, Brentford, Middlesex, TW8 9HF Tel: (020) 8568 1005 Fax: (020) 8568 7425
Soverign Rubber, Hillgate Industrial Estate, Carrington Field St, Stockport, Cheshire, SK1 3JN Tel: 0161-429 8787 Fax: 0161-480 3573E-mail: salessov@sovereign-rubber.co.uk
Threshold Floorings Ltd, Marston Gate, South Marston Park, Swindon, SN3 4TQ Tel: (01793) 764301 Fax: (01793) 765319 E-mail: sales@thresholdflr.co.uk

RUBBER MOULD RELEASE AGENTS

Newgate Simms Ltd, PO Box 32, Chester, CH4 0BY Tel: (01244) 660771 Fax: (01244) 661220 E-mail: info@newgatesimms.co.uk

RUBBER MOULD TOOLMAKERS

A J M Engineering Ltd, Park Lane, Park Lane Trading Estate, Corsham, Wiltshire, SN13 9LG Tel: (01249) 712620 Fax: (01249) 714932 E-mail: sales@ajmay.co.uk
Burnsall Engineering Co. Ltd, Brandon Road, Binley, Coventry, CV3 2AN Tel: (024) 7644 0444 Fax: (024) 7665 2696 E-mail: info@burnsallengineering.com
D C I Precision Engineering, 5b1 Ramsden Road, Rotherwas Industrial Estate, Hereford, HR2 6LR Tel: (01432) 279555 Fax: (01432) 279777
Griffin & Fudge Ltd, Whiteheads Lane, Bradford-on-Avon, Wiltshire, BA15 1JU Tel: (01225) 863391 Fax: (01225) 864060 E-mail: jon@griffin-fudgeltd.demon.co.uk
J S G Engineering, Unit 3/4, Wren Centre, Westbourne Road, Emsworth, Hampshire, PO10 7SU Tel: (01243) 379698 Fax: (01243) 379857 E-mail: jim@jsgeng.fsnet.co.uk
Mouldrite Toolmakers, Unit 6 Varney Industrial Estate Spon La Trading Estate, Varney A, West Bromwich, West Midlands, B70 6AE Tel: 0121-553 2199 Fax: 0121-553 2213 E-mail: mouldritetools@btconnect.com
Pyramid Tool & Die Co., Unit A, Leopold Street, Pemberton, Wigan, Lancashire, WN5 8DH Tel: (01942) 227938 Fax: (01942) 211179 E-mail: enquiries@pyramid-tool.co.uk
▶ Total Mould & Insert, Edison Road, St. Ives, Cambridgeshire, PE27 3LF Tel: (01480) 484711 Fax: (01480) 484710 E-mail: sales@totalmould.co.uk

RUBBER MOULDED PRODUCTS

Allied Rubber Products, 15 Cornwall Road Industrial Estate, Smethwick, West Midlands, B66 2JT Tel: 0121-565 0961 Fax: 0121-565 0976
L V S Rubber Mouldings Ltd, Robins Rd, Chasetown Industrial Estate, Burntwood, Staffordshire, WS7 3FX Tel: (01543) 673989 Fax: (01543) 683823 E-mail: sales@lvsrubber.com

RUBBER MOULDINGS MANUFRS

Amery Engineering, Mill Lane, Alton, Hampshire, GU34 2QG Tel: (01420) 80298 Fax: (01420) 549559 E-mail: geoff@ameryeng.swiftserve.net
Arms Technical Engineering, Arms House, 29 Glen Road, Oldham, OL4 1LP Tel: 0161-626 5293 Fax: 0161-626 5293 E-mail: sales@armstechnicalengineering.co.uk
Brentwood, 2 Whitehouse Road, Dordon, Tamworth, Staffordshire, B78 1QF Tel: (01827) 705450 Fax: (01827) 705450 E-mail: bob.kind@ntlworld.com
Broadoak Manufacturing Ltd, The Forge, Cricket Hill Lane, Yateley, Hampshire, GU46 6BB Tel: (01252) 890707 Fax: (01252) 890808
Butser Rubber Ltd, Mint Road, Liss, Hampshire, GU33 7BQ Tel: (01730) 894034 Fax: (01730) 894344 E-mail: butserrubber@btinternet.com
C D I Polytek Ltd, 130 Oldfield Road, Hampton, Middlesex, TW12 2HT Tel: (020) 8481 8300 Fax: (020) 8941 3107 E-mail: sales@cdipolytek.co.uk
Camberley Rubber Mouldings Ltd, Unit 10, Springlake Industrial Estate, Aldershot, Hampshire, GU12 4UH Tel: (01252) 330200 Fax: (01252) 330218 E-mail: sales@camberleyrubber.com
Cellular Mouldings Ltd, 2 Pytchley Lodge Industrial Estate, Pytchley Lodge Road, Kettering, Northamptonshire, NN15 6JQ Tel: (01536) 513452 Fax: (01536) 411206 E-mail: sales@cellularmouldings.co.uk
Clingbrook Ltd, Unit 10 Lakes Industrial Park, Lower Chapel Hill, Braintree, Essex, CM7 3RU Tel: (01376) 327206 Fax: (01376) 330755
D E C Rubber Co. Ltd, Unit 20, Fordhouse Road Industrial Estate, Fordhouses, Wolverhampton, WV10 9XD Tel: (01902) 780046 Fax: (01902) 780076
Darac, 37 The Meadway, Shoreham-by-Sea, West Sussex, BN43 5RN Tel: (01273) 455607 Fax: (01273) 441631 E-mail: sales@darac.com
Deerness Rubber Co. Ltd, Coulson Street, Spennymoor, County Durham, DL16 7RS Tel: (01388) 420301 Fax: (01388) 420284 E-mail: sales@deerness-rubber.co.uk
Denber Trading Co., Unit H3 Rudford Industrial Estate, Ford Road, Ford, Arundel, West Sussex, BN18 0BD Tel: (01903) 723155 Fax: (01903) 733160 E-mail: denberint.rubber@virgin.net
P.J. Donnelly Rubber, 15 Cornwall Road Industrial Park, Smethwick, West Midlands, B66 2JT Tel: 0121-565 0988 Fax: 0121-565 0976
William Freeman, Wakefield Road, Staincross, Barnsley, South Yorkshire, S75 6DH Tel: (01226) 284081 Fax: (01226) 731832 E-mail: sales@williamfreeman.com
Fussell's Rubber Co. Ltd, 2 Brimbleworth Lane, St. Georges, Weston-Super-Mare, Avon, BS22 7XS Tel: (01934) 513473 Fax: (01934) 521019
GMS, 175 Booth Street, Birmingham, B21 0NU Tel: 0121-551 5440 Fax: 0121-554 5344 E-mail: enquiries@gmspolymer.co.uk
The Harborough Rubber Co. Ltd, Riverside, Market Harborough, Leicestershire, LE16 7PT Tel: (01858) 410610 Fax: (01858) 410006 E-mail: admin@harboro.co.uk
Harltex Ltd, 12 Norman-D-Gate Industrial Estate, Norman-D-Gate, Northampton, NN1 5NT Tel: (01604) 632343 Fax: (01604) 632344 E-mail: harltex@btconnect.com
Industrial Marine Rubber, 3 Spurryhillock Industrial Estate, Broomhill Road, Stonehaven, Kincardineshire, AB39 2NH Tel: (01569) 766344 Fax: (01569) 766419
Industrial Moulded Products Ltd, Unit 7 Reaymer Close, Walsall, WS2 7QZ Tel: (01922) 497376 Fax: (01922) 491117 E-mail: general@inmodprod.demon.co.uk
J M E Rubber Co., Unit 4, Hattersley Industrial Estate, Stockport Road, Hattersley, Hyde, Cheshire, SK14 3QT Tel: 0161-368 9755 Fax: 0161-368 9767
J R Rubber & Polyurethane Products Ltd, Unit 28, Meadows Road, Queensway Meadows Industrial Estate, Newport, Gwent, NP19 4SS Tel: (01633) 270088 Fax: (01633) 278232 E-mail: info@jr-rubber.com
Kea Flex Mouldings Ltd, Woolmer Way, Bordon, Hampshire, GU35 9QE Tel: (01420) 473645 Fax: (01420) 487498 E-mail: sales@kea-flex-mouldings.co.uk
L V S Rubber Mouldings Ltd, Robins Rd, Chasetown Industrial Estate, Burntwood, Staffordshire, WS7 3FX Tel: (01543) 673989 Fax: (01543) 683823 E-mail: sales@lvsrubber.com
Meadex Mouldings Ltd, Units 1-2, Tanyard Lane, Ross-On-Wye, Herefordshire, HR9 7BH Tel: (01989) 567999 Fax: (01989) 768022 E-mail: sales@meadex.co.uk
Midhope Products, Unit 26-27 Albion Mills, Miry Lane, Thongsbridge, Holmfirth, HD9 7HP Tel: (01484) 688646 Fax: (01484) 688648 E-mail: midprod@btinternet.com
T.P. Millen Co. Ltd, 4 Stuart Way, East Grinstead, West Sussex, RH19 4RS Tel: (0787) 6658207 Fax: (01342) 335747 E-mail: tmillen@vodafone.net
Moseley Rubber Co. Ltd, Hoyle Street, Mancunian Way, Manchester, M12 6HL Tel: 0161-273 3341 Fax: 0161-274 3743 E-mail: info@moseleysrubber.com
Mowtec Elastomeric Components Ltd, Units 28 & 29, Sketchley Lane Industrial Estate, Burbage, Hinckley, Leicestershire, LE10 3EF Tel: (01455) 251324 Fax: (01455) 610760 E-mail: terry.eyre1@btinternet.com
Oldham Seals Ltd, Jetpac Works Gravel Lane, Quarry Lane Industrial Estate, Chichester, West Sussex, PO19 8PG Tel: (01243) 782296 Fax: (01243) 781933 E-mail: sales@oldhamseals.co.uk
P T M UK Ltd, Haigh Avenue, Stockport, Cheshire, SK4 1NZ Tel: 0161-477 6486 Fax: 0161-480 4624 E-mail: sales@ptmuk.co.uk
Polymer Holdings Ltd, Spurryhillock Industrial Estate, Broomhill Road, Stonehaven, Kincardineshire, AB39 2NH Tel: (01569) 766226 Fax: (01569) 766419 E-mail: sales@tubetec.co.uk
Precision Cut Rubber Co. Ltd, Leafield Industrial Estate, Leafield Way, Corsham, Wiltshire, SN13 9RU Tel: (01225) 816300 Fax: (01225) 816327 E-mail: sales@pcrltd.co.uk
J. Price (Bath) Ltd, Quarry Hill, Box, Corsham, Wiltshire, SN13 8LH Tel: (01225) 742141 Fax: (01225) 743237 E-mail: derek@price30.fsbusiness.co.uk
PRP, Unit 7 Tarsmill Court, Rotherwas Industrial Estate, Hereford, HR2 6JZ Tel: (01432) 357686 Fax: (01432) 352702 E-mail: info@prp.co.uk
Reevite Ltd, 16 Murdock Road, Bicester, Oxfordshire, OX26 4PP Tel: (01869) 252520 Fax: (01869) 241394 E-mail: info@reevite.co.uk
Rubber Components Stalybridge Ltd, Millwood Mill, Wakefield Road, Stalybridge, Cheshire, SK15 1AB Tel: 0161-338 2435 Fax: 0161-338 2435
Rubber & Plastic Profiles Co., Unit 1, 35 Boldmere Road, Sutton Coldfield, West Midlands, B73 5UY Tel: 0121-354 6356 Fax: 0121-355 7290 E-mail: info@rubberandplasticprofiles.co.uk
Rubberatkins Ltd, Hareness Road, Altens Industrial Estate, Aberdeen, AB12 3LE Tel: (01224) 248341 Fax: (01224) 248342 E-mail: sales@rubberatkins.com
Rubbertec International Ltd, Maydown Industrial Estate, Londonderry, BT47 6UQ Tel: (028) 7186 0005 Fax: (028) 7186 1411 E-mail: info@rubbertecinternational.com
S R M Peakland Ltd, Vulcan Way, Coalville, Leicestershire, LE67 3AP Tel: (01530) 838317 Fax: (01530) 835122 E-mail: sales@srmpeakland.co.uk
Specialised Engineering Products, Unit C3-7 The Premier Centre, Premier Way, Romsey, Hampshire, SO51 9DG Tel: (01794) 830757 Fax: (01794) 830736 E-mail: sales@specialisedengineering.co.uk
Stockwell Mouldings, 4 Oughton Road, Birmingham, B12 0DF Tel: 0121-440 6555 Fax: 0121-440 6555 E-mail: info@stockwell-mouldings.co.uk
Superior Seals, 7 Nimrod Way, East Dorset Trade Park, Wimborne, Dorset, BH21 7SH Tel: (01202) 854300 Fax: (01202) 854313 E-mail: sales.seals@superiorltd.com
T R P Sealing Systems Ltd, 24 Netherwood Road, Rotherwas Industrial Estate, Hereford, HR2 6JU Tel: (01432) 279366 Fax: (01432) 273017 E-mail: admin@trpsealing.com
Thistle Special Beltings, Bridge of Mondynes, Fordoun, Laurencekirk, Kincardineshire, AB30 1LD Tel: (01569) 740204 Fax: (01569) 740322 E-mail: mail@thistle.uk.com
V I P-polymers, 15 Windover Road, Huntingdon, Cambridgeshire, PE29 7EB Tel: (01480) 411333 Fax: (01480) 450430 E-mail: sales@vip-polymers.com
Vale Brothers Ltd, Long Street, Walsall, WS2 9QG Tel: (01922) 624363 Fax: (01922) 720994 E-mail: sales@valebrothersvalebrothers.co.uk
Vitamol Ltd, Rycroft St, Ashton-under-Lyne, Lancashire, OL7 0BN Tel: 0161-342 1400 Fax: 0161-343 1872 E-mail: r.winter@vitamol.co.uk
W J Webb & Co. Ltd, 35 Broadgate, Whaplode Drove, Spalding, Lincolnshire, PE12 0TN Tel: (01406) 330467 Fax: (01406) 330887 E-mail: webb1@which.net
Wilmurten Manufacturing Co. Ltd, Manorway Industrial Estate, Bridge Road, Grays, Essex, RM17 6BJ Tel: (01375) 373984 Fax: (01375) 391867 E-mail: wilmurten@aol.com
Wye Valley Precision Engineering (Holdings) Ltd, Station Approach, Ross-On-Wye, Herefordshire, HR9 7AQ Tel: (01989) 763519 Fax: (01989) 766662 E-mail: sales@wye-valley.co.uk

RUBBER MOULDINGS TO SPECIFICATION

Butser Rubber Ltd, Mint Road, Liss, Hampshire, GU33 7BQ Tel: (01730) 894034 Fax: (01730) 894344 E-mail: butserrubber@btinternet.com
Envec Automotive Ltd, Halton Green West, Halton, Lancaster, LA2 6PA Tel: (01524) 811100 Fax: (01524) 811152
Escadean, Baltimore Road, Birmingham, B42 1DP Tel: 0121-356 1001 Fax: 0121-356 7411

RUBBER OR SUBSTITUTE GROMMETS

British Gaskets Ltd, Bulmer Road Industrial Estate, Bulmer Road, Sudbury, Suffolk, CO10 7HJ Tel: (01787) 881188 Fax: (01787) 880595
Grommets Ltd, Unit 2 Hollands La Industrial Estate, Henfield, West Sussex, BN5 9QY Tel: (01273) 493355 Fax: (01273) 493388 E-mail: sales@grommets.co.uk
Medasil (Surgical) Ltd, Medasil House, Hunslet Road, Leeds, LS10 1AU Tel: 0113-243 3491 Fax: 0113-242 9276 E-mail: medasil@dial.pipex.com
Plastic Parts Centre, New Road, Ridgewood, Uckfield, East Sussex, TN22 5SX Tel: (0845) 7585070 Fax: (01825) 762621 E-mail: sales@plastic-parts.co.uk

RUBBER PACKINGS AND JOINTINGS

Clingbrook Ltd, Unit 10 Lakes Industrial Park, Lower Chapel Hill, Braintree, Essex, CM7 3RU Tel: (01376) 327206 Fax: (01376) 330755
Langdean Manufacturing Ltd, 3 Thames Industrial Estate, High St South, Dunstable, Bedfordshire, LU6 3HD Tel: (01582) 696369 Fax: (01582) 666658 E-mail: langdean@btconnect.com

RUBBER PIPE SEALS

M W Polymer Products Ltd, The Old Brewery, Duffield Road, Little Eaton, Derby, DE21 5DS Tel: (01332) 835001 Fax: (01332) 835051
Trellborg Forsheda Pipe Seals, 4 Station Yard, Station Road, Bakewell, Derbyshire, DE45 1GE Tel: (01629) 813835 Fax: (01629) 814658 E-mail: jwest@forsheda.com
Trelleborg Sealing Solutions, 1 Cranbrook Way, Shirley, Solihull, West Midlands, B90 4GT Tel: 0121-744 1221 Fax: 0121-733 2442 E-mail: tssuk@trelleborg.com

RUBBER PRODUCTS, *See also headings for particular types*

All Hose & Hydraulics Norwich Ltd, 2 Javelin Road, Norwich, NR6 6HX Tel: (01603) 788686 Fax: (01603) 483081 E-mail: allhosesales@btinternet.com
Allison Gray, Longtown Street, Dundee, DD4 8LF Tel: (01382) 505888 Fax: (01382) 507333 E-mail: allison-gray@dpandl.co.uk
Arcode UK Ltd, 41 Ebrington Road, Kenton, Harrow, Middlesex, HA3 0LS Tel: (020) 8907 1309 Fax: (020) 8907 9132 E-mail: sales@arcode.co.uk
▶ Avon Rubber, Cory Way, West Wilts Trading Estate, Westbury, Wiltshire, BA13 4QT Tel: (01373) 863106 Fax: (01373) 863107
▶ Berwin Group Ltd, 39 A & B Broadway, Globe Lane Industrial Estate, Dukinfield, Cheshire, SK16 4UJ Tel: 0161-330 2504
Butser Rubber Ltd, Mint Road, Liss, Hampshire, GU33 7BQ Tel: (01730) 894034 Fax: (01730) 894344 E-mail: butserrubber@btinternet.com
▶ Challis Rubber & Plastic Product, 8 Thorne Farm House, Thorne Hill, Ramsgate, Kent, CT12 5DS Tel: (01843) 826006 Fax: (01843) 826005 E-mail: jwchallis@aol.com
Denby Industrial Supplies Ltd, Chandos Pole Street, Derby, DE22 3BA Tel: (01332) 332831 Fax: (01332) 371206
Hill's Rubber Co. Ltd, 85 Bedford Road, Reading, RG1 7EZ Tel: 0845 4940717 Fax: 0118-950 3083 E-mail: hillsrubber@hotmail.com
▶ Interfloor Ltd, Edinburgh Road, Heathhall, Dumfries, DG1 1QA Tel: (01387) 253111 Fax: (01387) 268937
J M C Washers & Gaskets, Unit 3 Hartlebury Trading Estate, Hartlebury, Kidderminster, Worcestershire, DY10 4JB Tel: (01299) 251339 Fax: (01299) 251008
Kirkfield Ltd, Unit 1/2 Schofield Business Park, Sugarbrook Road, Bromsgrove, Worcestershire, B60 3DN Tel: (01527) 559345 Fax: (01527) 835690 E-mail: sales@kirkfield.co.uk
L J A Miers & Co. Ltd, Hawkesden Road, St. Neots, Cambridgeshire, PE19 1QS Tel: (01480) 211177 Fax: (01480) 211190 E-mail: sales@ljamiers.co.uk
▶ Lucite International UK Ltd, P O Box 34, Darwen, Lancashire, BB3 3GB Tel: (01254) 874444 Fax: (01254) 874202
▶ M F Sealing Systems Ltd, 2C Brighouse Business Village, Brighouse Road, Middlesbrough, Cleveland, TS2 1RT Tel: (01642) 253253 Fax: (01642) 257980
▶ Martland Ltd, Unit 1D, Cricket Street Business Centre, Cricket Street, Wigan, Lancashire, WN6 7TP Tel: (01942) 497064 Fax: (01942) 497075 E-mail: martland-ltd@tiscali.co.uk
Midland Rubber Co. Ltd, Unit 8, Commerce Court, Challenge Way, Bradford, West Yorkshire, BD4 8NW Tel: (01274) 820268
▶ John Miles, 7 Halliwell Industrial Estate, Rossini Street, Bolton, BL1 8DL Tel: (01204) 844538 Fax: (01204) 848592
Multifabs Survival Ltd, Units 4-5, Balmoor Industrial Estate, Peterhead, Aberdeenshire, AB42 1QG Tel: (01779) 470848 Fax: (01779) 478099
Namron Aqua Products Ltd, Canklow Meadows Industrial Estate, West Bawtry Road, Rotherham, South Yorkshire, S60 2XL Tel: (01709) 371006 Fax: (01709) 367295 E-mail: namron@scubauk.com
Pentonville Rubber Products Ltd, 104-106 Pentonville Road, London, N1 9JB Tel: (020) 7837 4582 Fax: (020) 7278 7392 E-mail: enquiries@pentonvillerubber.co.uk
▶ Polineri Europa UK Ltd, Bo'Ness Road, Grangemouth, Stirlingshire, FK3 9XE Tel: (01324) 692200 Fax: (01324) 473915
▶ RSH, Unit 2a Chipchase Court, Seaham Grange Industrial Estate, Seaham, County Durham, SR7 0PP Tel: 0191-523 8989 Fax: 0191-523 8890 E-mail: rshseaham@aol.com
▶ Ryburn Rubber Ltd, Watson Mill Lane, Sowerby Bridge, West Yorkshire, HX6 3BW Tel: (01422) 316323 Fax: (01422) 835898 E-mail: sales@ryburnrubber.co.uk
Stafford Rubber Co. Ltd, Belsize Close, Norton Canes, Cannock, Staffordshire, WS11 9TQ Tel: (01543) 270002 Fax: (01543) 278046 E-mail: sales@stafford-rubber.co.uk
▶ Tennant Group Ltd, The Midway, Nottingham, NG7 2TS Tel: 0115-985 2222 Fax: 0115-988 5330 E-mail: info@tennantgroup.co.uk

RUBBER PRODUCTS – *continued*

▶ Trellevorg Celing Solutions, Ashchurch, Tewkesbury, Gloucestershire, GL20 8JS Tel: (01684) 852211 Fax: (01684) 852210

W C Munsch & Co., Unit Ag2 3 Clarence Business Park, Clarence Road, Bollington, Macclesfield, Cheshire, SK10 5JZ Tel: (01625) 573971 Fax: (01625) 573250 E-mail: sales@wcmunsch.co.uk

W J Nelson & Son Ltd, Fashoda Street, Belfast, BT5 5EX Tel: (028) 9045 6020 Fax: (028) 9073 8312 E-mail: wjnsafe@aol.com

RUBBER PRODUCTS, AIRCRAFT INDUSTRY

F P T Industries Ltd, Airport Service Road, Portsmouth, PO3 5PE Tel: (023) 9266 2391 Fax: (023) 9267 0899 E-mail: info@fptind.co.uk

RUBBER PRODUCTS, MEDICAL/ SURGICAL/HOSPITAL

D B T Medical Ltd, 14 The Crofts, Witney, Oxfordshire, OX28 4DJ Tel: (01993) 773673 Fax: (01993) 778267 E-mail: office@dbtmedical.co.uk

Icon Polymer Group Ltd, Thrumpton Lane, Retford, Nottinghamshire, DN22 6HH Tel: (01777) 714300 Fax: (01777) 709739 E-mail: info@iconpolymer.com

W J Rendell Ltd, Ickleford Manor, Ickleford, Hitchin, Hertfordshire, SG5 3XE Tel: (01462) 432596 Fax: (01462) 420423

RUBBER ROLLER COVERINGS

Boettcher U K Ltd, Cwmdraw Industrial Estate, Newtown, Ebbw Vale, Gwent, NP23 5AE Tel: (01495) 350300 Fax: (01495) 350064 E-mail: admin@boettcher.co.uk

Bonaprene Products, Clywedog Road South, Wrexham Industrial Estate, Wrexham Industrial Estate, Wrexham, Clwyd, LL13 9XS Tel: (01978) 661478 Fax: (01978) 661190 E-mail: sales@polybush.co.uk

Broadoak Manufacturing Ltd, The Forge, Cricket Hill Lane, Yateley, Hampshire, GU46 6BB Tel: (01252) 890707 Fax: (01252) 890808

Grover Clarke Ltd, The Street, Thorndon, Eye, Suffolk, IP23 7JN Tel: (01379) 678149 Fax: (01379) 678691 E-mail: info@groverclarke.com

J M E Rubber Co., Unit 4, Hattersley Industrial Estate, Stockport Road, Hattersley, Hyde, Cheshire, SK14 3QT Tel: 0161-368 9755 Fax: 0161-368 9767

J R Rubber & Polyurethane Products Ltd, Unit 28, Meadows Road, Queensway Meadows Industrial Estate, Newport, Gwent, NP19 4SS Tel: (01633) 270088 Fax: (01633) 278232 E-mail: info@jr-rubber.com

Just Rollers P.L.C., Somerset Industrial Estate, Cwmbran, Gwent, NP44 1QX Tel: (01633) 869436 Fax: (01633) 860046 E-mail: iain.sinclair@justrollers.com

K V Rollers Ltd, Unit 1-3 Claenwern, Avondale Industrial Estate, Pontrhydyrun, Cwmbran, Gwent, NP44 1TY Tel: (01633) 871919 Fax: (01633) 877250 E-mail: kbrollers@tiscali.co.uk

Longs Ltd, Hanworth Lane Business Park, Chertsey, Surrey, KT16 9LZ Tel: (01932) 561241 Fax: (01932) 567391 E-mail: sales@longs.co.uk

Miller Graphic UK Ltd, 2 Hollands Road, Haverhill, Suffolk, CB9 8PP Tel: (01440) 703001 Fax: (01440) 703421 E-mail: sales@millergraphics.com

Modern Rollers Ltd, Greengate, Salford, M3 7NS Tel: 0161-834 1539 Fax: 0161-835 3303 E-mail: modernrollers@davidbentley.co.uk

Moseley Rubber Co. Ltd, Hoyle Street, Mancunian Way, Manchester, M12 6HL Tel: 0161-273 3341 Fax: 0161-274 3743 E-mail: info@moseleysrubber.com

Nelson Roller & Rubber Co., Bankgate Mills, Bankgate, Slaithwaite, Huddersfield, HD7 5DL Tel: (01484) 845015 Fax: (01484) 842900 E-mail: info@nelco.co.uk

Spraybake JRC, 1 Boarshurst Business Park, Boarshurst Lane, Greenfield, Oldham, OL3 7ER Tel: (01457) 870779 Fax: (01457) 875477 E-mail: info@spraybakejrc.co.uk

Tyke Rollers Ltd, 1c Victoria Court, Colliers Way, Clayton West, Huddersfield, HD8 9TR Tel: (01484) 868331 Fax: (01484) 868332 E-mail: sales@tykerollers.com

RUBBER ROLLERS

Boettcher U K Ltd, Cwmdraw Industrial Estate, Newtown, Ebbw Vale, Gwent, NP23 5AE Tel: (01495) 350300 Fax: (01495) 350064 E-mail: admin@boettcher.co.uk

Bottcher UK, Jubilee Way, Shipley, West Yorkshire, BD18 1QG Tel: (01274) 530531 Fax: (01274) 530532

Exactaform Cutting Tools Ltd, G2 Little Heath Industrial Estate, Old Church Road, Coventry, CV6 7ND Tel: (024) 7666 5823 Fax: (024) 7663 8251 E-mail: sales@exactaform.co.uk

Hill's Rubber Co. Ltd, 85 Bedford Road, Reading, RG1 7EZ Tel: 0845 4940717 Fax: 0118-950 3083 E-mail: hillsrubber@hotmail.com

Modern Rollers Ltd, Greengate, Salford, M3 7NS Tel: 0161-834 1539 Fax: 0161-835 3303 E-mail: modernrollers@davidbentley.co.uk

Nelson Roller & Rubber Co., Bankgate Mills, Bankgate, Slaithwaite, Huddersfield, HD7 5DL Tel: (01484) 845015 Fax: (01484) 842900 E-mail: info@nelco.co.uk

Robant Services Ltd, Unit 24 Mersey Street, Stockport, Cheshire, SK1 2HX Tel: 0161-429 8728 Fax: 0161-474 7630 E-mail: sales@robant.co.uk

Rotadyne UK Ltd, Saxon House, Henson Way, Telford Way Industrial Estate, Kettering, Northamptonshire, NN16 8PX Tel: (01536) 414421 Fax: (01536) 411091 E-mail: pevans@rotadyne.com

RUBBER ROOFING

National Roofing, Imperial Buildings, Bridge Street, West End, Newport, Abercarn, Gwent, NP11 4SB Tel: (0800) 7834890 Fax: (01495) 248448 E-mail: sales@diyroofing.co.uk

RUBBER SADDLERY PRODUCTS

Choice Saddlery, 1 Broad Street, Knighton, Powys, LD7 1BL Tel: (01547) 528385 Fax: (01547) 528385

Kiln Saddlery, Park House, Layer Road, Kingsford, Colchester, CO2 0HT Tel: (01206) 734695 Fax: (01206) 734688 E-mail: kiln.saddlery@tiscali.co.uk

Oakfield Direct, Oakfield Riding Stables, Stanifield Lane, Farington, Leyland, PR25 4UA Tel: (01772) 421999 Fax: (01772) 619694 E-mail: info@oakfield-direct.co.uk

P & A Newcombe, 1 Canal Terrace, Worksop, Nottinghamshire, S80 2DF Tel: (01909) 475664

Shires Equestrian, 15 Southern Avenue, Leominster, Herefordshire, HR6 0QF Tel: (01568) 613600 Fax: (01568) 613599 E-mail: sales@shires-equestrian.co.uk

Sydney Free (Saddlers) Ltd, 54 Querns Lane, Cirencester, Gloucestershire, GL7 1RH Tel: (01285) 655384 Fax: (01285) 650213 E-mail: enquiries@sydneyfree.co.uk

Vale Brothers Ltd, Long Street, Walsall, WS2 9QG Tel: (01922) 624363 Fax: (01922) 720994 E-mail: sales@valebrothersvalebrothers.co.uk

Young & Co., Unit 4b Charles Holland Street, Willenhall, West Midlands, WV13 1NQ Tel: (01902) 602338 Fax: (01902) 631745

RUBBER SAFETY SURFACING

▶ Bigfoot Play Systems Ltd, Hamilton House, 111 Marlowes, Hemel Hempstead, Hertfordshire, HP1 1BB Tel: (01442) 243355 Fax: (01442) 244330 E-mail: info@bigfootplay.com

▶ Playtop Ltd, Brunel House, Jessop Way, Newark, Nottinghamshire, NG24 2ER Tel: (01636) 614180 Fax: (01636) 610222 E-mail: sales@playtop.com

▶ SSP Specialised Sports Products Ltd, Po Box 998, Canterbury, Kent, CT1 9EU Tel: (0870) 7501432 Fax: (0870) 7518935 E-mail: info@ssp-uk.co.uk

Universal Play Ltd, 4 Derwent Close, Tangmere, Chichester, West Sussex, PO20 2FQ Tel: (01243) 784722 Fax: (01243) 784742 E-mail: universal.play@primex.co.uk

RUBBER SEAL (INDUSTRIAL) MANUFRS

Blue Diamond Bearings Ltd, Rolwey House, School Close, Chandler's Ford, Eastleigh, Hampshire, SO53 4BY Tel: (023) 8025 8966 Fax: (023) 8025 8925 E-mail: bdsales@rolwey.com

Deerness Rubber Co. Ltd, Coulson Street, Spennymoor, County Durham, DL16 7RS Tel: (01388) 420301 Fax: (01388) 420284 E-mail: sales@deerness-rubber.co.uk

Dichtomatik Ltd, Donington House, Riverside Road, Pride Park, Derby, DE24 8HY Tel: (01332) 202121 Fax: (01332) 524404 E-mail: mail@dichtomatik.co.uk

Honeycrown Ltd, Miners Road, Llay Industrial Estate, Llay, Wrexham, Clwyd, LL12 0PJ Tel: (01978) 853730 Fax: (01978) 856320 E-mail: sales@honeycrown.co.uk

Inglecliff Ltd, Unit 2 Barsbank Lane, Lymm, Cheshire, WA13 0ER Tel: (01925) 752471 Fax: (01925) 755784 E-mail: sales@inglecliff.co.uk

Northern Engineering Sheffield Ltd, Haigh Moor Drive, Dinnington, Sheffield, S25 2JY Tel: (01909) 560203 Fax: (01909) 560184 E-mail: sales@northerneng.co.uk

Oldham Seals Ltd, Jetpac Works Gravel Lane, Quarry Lane Industrial Estate, Chichester, West Sussex, PO19 8PG Tel: (01243) 782296 Fax: (01243) 781933 E-mail: sales@oldhamseals.co.uk

Rubbertec International Ltd, Maydown Industrial Estate, Londonderry, BT47 6UQ Tel: (028) 7186 0005 Fax: (028) 7186 1411 E-mail: info@rubbertecinternational.com

Stevron Marine, 38 Farriers Way, Bootle, Merseyside, L30 4XL Tel: 0151-525 9555 Fax: 0151-521 7190 E-mail: sales@stevron.co.uk

Veker Extrusions Ltd, Shaftmoor Lane, Hall Green, Birmingham, B28 8SP Tel: 0121-777 5000 Fax: 0121-777 5015 E-mail: enquiries@vekex.com

RUBBER SEALS, *See Rubber Seal etc*

RUBBER SHEET

British Seals & Rubber Mouldings Ltd, Unit 7 Childerditch Indust Park, Childerditch Hall Drive, Brentwood, Essex, CM13 3HD Tel: (01277) 815300 Fax: (01277) 815350 E-mail: seals@british-gaskets.co.uk

Ferguson Polycom Ltd, Windsor Mill, Hollinwood, Oldham, OL8 3RA Tel: 0161-681 2206 Fax: 0161-947 1326 E-mail: info@fergusonpolycom.co.uk

Icon Polymer Group Ltd, Thrumpton Lane, Retford, Nottinghamshire, DN22 6HH Tel: (01777) 714300 Fax: (01777) 709739 E-mail: info@iconpolymer.com

Maclellan Rubber, Neachells Lane, Wolverhampton, WV11 3QG Tel: (01902) 725515 Fax: (01902) 305201 E-mail: sales@maclellanrubber.com

Sampson Gaskets Ltd, Unit 22, Leigh Road, Ramsgate, Kent, CT12 5EU Tel: (01843) 854800 Fax: (01843) 854801 E-mail: uksales@sampsons.co.uk

▶ Trafford Rubber Products Ltd, Greengate Works, Broadoak Business Park, Ashburton Road West, Trafford Park, Manchester, M17 1RW Tel: 0161-873 7172 Fax: 0161-848 9762 E-mail: traffordrubber@beeb.net

RUBBER SHEET, INDUSTRIAL/ MECHANICAL

D R C Polymer Products Ltd, 1 Regal Lane, Soham, Ely, Cambridgeshire, CB7 5BA Tel: (01353) 720989 Fax: (01353) 624668 E-mail: info@drc-polymers.com

RUBBER SPORTS SURFACES

B R G International Ltd, Carrington Field Street, Stockport, Cheshire, SK1 3JN Tel: 0161-477 4487 Fax: 0161-480 3573 E-mail: sales@brginternational.co.uk

▶ Playtop Ltd, Brunel House, Jessop Way, Newark, Nottinghamshire, NG24 2ER Tel: (01636) 614180 Fax: (01636) 610222 E-mail: sales@playtop.com

RUBBER STAMP COMPONENTS

Dormy Ltd, Battersea Road, Heaton Mersey, Stockport, Cheshire, SK4 3EN Tel: 0161-432 9451 Fax: 0161-431 8442 E-mail: sales@dormy.co.uk

RUBBER STAMP MANUFRS

A & J Print Services, 330 London Road, Westcliff-on-Sea, Essex, SS0 7JJ Tel: (01702) 348456 Fax: (01702) 348456

▶ Andover Rubber Stamp Service, Unit 1, Balksbury Estate, Upper Clatford, Andover, Hampshire, SP11 7LW Tel: (01264) 362925 Fax: (01264) 333079 E-mail: service@andover-rubberstamp.com

Ash Rubber Stamp Co Ltd, 149 Barford Street, Birmingham, B5 6AS Tel: 0121-622 4040 Fax: 0121-622 6600 E-mail: sales@ashstamp.co.uk

Astute, 44-46 Brechin Road, Forfar, Angus, DD8 3JX Tel: (01307) 464467 Fax: (01307) 464561 E-mail: sales@astute.uk.com

▶ Bay Area Sign Solutions, Unit 1, Farfield Business Park, Main Road, Wykeham, Scarborough, North Yorkshire, YO13 9QB Tel: (01723) 866680 Fax: (01723) 865509 E-mail: info@bay-area.co.uk

Birmingham Rubber Stamp Co Ltd, 209 Streetly Road, Erdington, Birmingham, B23 7AH Tel: 0121-377 7757 Fax: 0121-377 7718 E-mail: sales@britishstamp.com

Blade Rubber Stamps Ltd, 12 Bury Place, London, WC1A 2JL Tel: (020) 7831 4123 Fax: (020) 7831 4242 E-mail: sales@bladerubber.co.uk

C R S Stamps, Cheltenham, Gloucestershire, GL52 2YS Tel: (01242) 241141 Fax: (01242) 690032 E-mail: sales@crsstamps.com

Cambridge Rubber Stamps Direct, 58 Victoria Road, Cambridge, CB4 3DU Tel: (01223) 361600 Fax: (01223) 461391 E-mail: admin@stampsdirect.co.uk

B.R. Chambers Ltd, 15 Southcroft Road, Rutherglen, Glasgow, G73 1SP Tel: 0141-647 9777 Fax: 0141-613 2068 E-mail: artwork@brchambers.co.uk

▶ CraftingCards.com, 75 Walsall Road, Darlaston, West Midlands, WS10 9JU Tel: 0121 531-8082 E-mail: chris@craftingcards.com

Dormy Ltd, Battersea Road, Heaton Mersey, Stockport, Cheshire, SK4 3EN Tel: 0161-432 9451 Fax: 0161-431 8442 E-mail: sales@dormy.co.uk

Dormy Custom Products, 144 Neilston Road, Paisley, Renfrewshire, PA2 6QH Tel: 0141-884 6441 Fax: 0141-884 7819

E M Richford Ltd, Curzon Road, Sudbury, Suffolk, CO10 2XW Tel: (01787) 375241 Fax: (01787) 310179 E-mail: sales@richstamp.co.uk

English Stamp Co., French Grass Quarry, Kingston Road, Worth Matravers, Swanage, Dorset, BH19 3JP Tel: (01929) 439117 Fax: (01929) 439150 E-mail: sales@englishstamp.com

Europa Rubber Stamps, 8 Mill Lane, Horsford, Norwich, NR10 3ET Tel: (01603) 898225 Fax: (01603) 893276

Dennis D. Evans & Co. Ltd, 391 Holywood Road, Belfast, BT4 2LS Tel: (028) 9065 2220 E-mail: materials@devans.co.uk

Express Services, Henson Way, Telford Way Industrial Estate, Kettering, Northamptonshire, NN16 8PX Tel: (01536) 481778 Fax: (01536) 521412 E-mail: sales@express-services.uk.com

Tom Gutherless Ltd, 34 & 34a St James Street, Hull, HU3 2DH Tel: (01482) 214184 Fax: (01482) 215211 E-mail: print@tom-guther.co.uk

Hayling Rubber Stamps, 17 Sea Front Estate, Hayling Island, Hampshire, PO11 9JJ Tel: (023) 9246 1962 Fax: (023) 9246 1962 E-mail: sales@haylingrubberstamps.com

Kershaw's Rubber Stamps, Cotton Hall Street, Darwen, Lancashire, BB3 0DW Tel: (01254) 703040 Fax: (01254) 703373 E-mail: info@planetree.co.uk

KRS Ltd, Westfield House, Broad Lane, Leeds, LS13 3HA Tel: 0113-239 3088 Fax: 0113-257 7582

Long Neck Enterprises Ltd, 4 Leacroft Close, Kenley, Surrey, CR8 5EX Tel: 07092 887252 Fax: 07092 887252 E-mail: kwalexander@longneck.co.uk

▶ Long Neck Stamps, 4 Leacroft Close, Kenley, Surrey, CR8 5EX Tel: 0709 288 7252 Fax: 0709 288 7252 E-mail: kwalexander@longneck.co.uk

M K Marking Systems Ltd, 22 Carters Lane, Kiln Farm Industrial Estate, Kiln Farm, Milton Keynes, MK11 3HL Tel: (01908) 561676 Fax: (01908) 562551 E-mail: sales@mkmarking.co.uk

▶ Mark C Brown Ltd, PO Box 69, Hull, HU2 8HS Tel: (01482) 218172 Fax: (01482) 214999 E-mail: info@markcbrown.co.uk

Moat Bros, 391 Holywood Road, Belfast, BT4 2LS Tel: (028) 9065 5328 Fax: (028) 9065 7225 E-mail: rubberstamps@devans.co.uk

Roger Needham & Sons Ltd, Units 15-16 Salford Enterprise Centre, Guide Street, Salford, M50 1EW Tel: 0161-745 7277 Fax: 0161-745 7826 E-mail: frankrnsl@aol.com

November Express, 25 Portswood Road, Southampton, SO17 2ES Tel: (023) 8058 5050 Fax: (023) 8067 1137 E-mail: novemberexpress@btinternet.com

Par Printing Press & Rubber Stamps, 9 Garton Street, Peterborough, PE1 4EL Tel: (01733) 562666 Fax: (01733) 567883 E-mail: parprinting@onetel.net

PDM Products, 104 Rushlake Road, Brighton, BN1 9AF Tel: (01273) 604691 Fax: (01273) 673238 E-mail: sales@pdmproducts.co.uk

Pioneer Marking Devices, Amy House, Askew Road West, Gateshead, Tyne & Wear, NE8 2PD Tel: 0191-477 8444 Fax: (08451) 668197 E-mail: pioneer@marking.wonadoo.co.uk

Polydiam Instant Rubber Stamp Co., 70-72 Markfield Road, London, N15 4QF Tel: (020) 8493 1060 Fax: (020) 8885 5711 E-mail: sales@rubberstamp.co.uk

Q R S Stamps, 71 Wordsworth Road, Small Heath, Birmingham, B10 0ED Tel: 0121-772 4165 Fax: 0121-766 6341 E-mail: print.man@virgin.net

Rubber Stamp Of Northampton, 10 Freehold Street, Northampton, NN2 6EW Tel: (01604) 720663 Fax: (01604) 720663 E-mail: sales@rubberstamp.uk.com

Stampreo Rubber Ltd, Plexus House, Stockholm Road, Hull, HU7 0XW Tel: (01482) 348134 Fax: (01482) 446453 E-mail: stamps@plexus-net.co.uk

Stamps Direct Ltd, 125 Carholme Road, Lincoln, LN1 1RT Tel: (01522) 534729 Fax: (01522) 521038 E-mail: linc@rubber-stamps.co.uk

Stamps Direct, 24 Halls Road, Stapleford, Nottingham, NG9 7FQ Tel: 0115-939 0333 Fax: 0115-949 0415 E-mail: nott@rubber-stamps.co.uk

Stat Shop, 3-9 Station Street, Sittingbourne, Kent, ME10 3DU Tel: (01795) 425424 Fax: (0870) 7777827 E-mail: admin@statshop.co.uk

Supreme Rubber Stamp Co., 1 Valley End Business Centre, Nunn Brook Road, Huthwaite, Sutton-in-Ashfield, Nottinghamshire, NG17 2HU Tel: (01623) 514942 Fax: (01623) 559849 E-mail: faststampsuk@yahoo.co.uk

Thow Blockmakers, 13 Old Glamis Road, Dundee, DD3 8JB Tel: (01382) 823824 Fax: (01382) 823825

G.H. Tomlin & Co. Ltd, 11 Sandon Industrial Estate, Sandon Way, Liverpool, L5 9YN Tel: 0151-207 7216 Fax: 0151-298 2347 E-mail: mark@tomlinsighns.com

RUBBER STAMP MANUFRS – *continued*

W Goddard, Baths Road, Bromley, BR2 9RB Tel: (020) 8460 9600 Fax: (020) 8460 9601 E-mail: goddardstamps@btinternet.com
West Riding Engravers Ltd, 60 Wellington Street, Leeds, LS1 2EE Tel: 0113-243 9156 Fax: 0113-246 0787 E-mail: sales@wre-ltd.com
William Jones Clifton Ltd, 32 Lower Essex Street, Birmingham, B5 6SN Tel: 0121-622 8900 Fax: 0121-622 8909 E-mail: sales@jonesclifton.com
XL Marking Systems, Unit 405 Thorp Arch Trading Estate, Thorp Arch, Wetherby, West Yorkshire, LS23 7BJ Tel: (01937) 844014 Fax: (01937) 842137
Y Ryte Ltd, 5 Runnings Road, Kingsditch Trading Estate, Cheltenham, Gloucestershire, GL51 9NQ Tel: (01242) 515826 Fax: (01242) 584877 E-mail: sales@y-ryte.co.uk

RUBBER STAMP PADS

Cambridge Rubber Stamps Direct, 58 Victoria Road, Cambridge, CB4 3DU Tel: (01223) 361600 Fax: (01223) 461391 E-mail: admin@stampsdirect.co.uk
English Stamp Co., French Grass Quarry, Kingston Road, Worth Matravers, Swanage, Dorset, BH19 3JP Tel: (01929) 439117 Fax: (01929) 439150 E-mail: sales@englishstamp.com

RUBBER STAMP PRODUCTION EQUIPMENT MANUFRS

Unicorn Office Products Ltd, Unit 25 Station Road Workshops, Station Road, Bristol, BS15 4PJ Tel: 0117-907 6662 Fax: 0117-907 6663 E-mail: sales@unicornonline.net

RUBBER STAMPS, BAND

▶ Cardehar Rubber Stamps, PO Box 159, Consett, County Durham, DH8 7WT Tel: (01207) 508003 Fax: (01207) 508826 E-mail: seals@crown-stamps.co.uk
▶ Southampton Rubber Stamp Co., 23a Rumbridge Street, Totton, Southampton, SO40 9DQ Tel: (023) 8086 2993 Fax: (023) 8086 9998 E-mail: sales@southamptonrubberstamp.com
Stamp It UK, Davyhulme Road East, Stretford, Manchester, M32 0DN Tel: 0161-610 9405 Fax: 0161 610 9406 E-mail: sales@stampituk.co.uk

RUBBER STAMPS, PRE-INKED

▶ Andover Rubber Stamp Service, Unit 1, Balksbury Estate, Upper Clatford, Andover, Hampshire, SP11 7LW Tel: (01264) 362925 Fax: (01264) 333079 E-mail: service@andover-rubberstamp.com
B.R. Chambers Ltd, 15 Southcroft Road, Rutherglen, Glasgow, G73 1SP Tel: 0141-647 9777 Fax: 0141-613 2068 E-mail: artwork@brchambers.co.uk
Dormy Custom Products, 144 Neilston Road, Paisley, Renfrewshire, PA2 6QH Tel: 0141-884 6441 Fax: 0141-884 7819
E M Richford Ltd, Curzon Road, Sudbury, Suffolk, CO10 2XW Tel: (01787) 375241 Fax: (01787) 310179 E-mail: sales@richstamp.co.uk
Kershaw's Rubber Stamps, Cotton Hall Street, Darwen, Lancashire, BB3 0DW Tel: (01254) 703040 Fax: (01254) 703373 E-mail: info@planetree.co.uk
November Express, 25 Portswood Road, Southampton, SO17 2ES Tel: (023) 8058 5050 Fax: (023) 8067 1137 E-mail: novemberexpress@btinternet.com
Par Printing Press & Rubber Stamps, 9 Garton Street, Peterborough, PE1 4EL Tel: (01733) 562666 Fax: (01733) 567883 E-mail: parprinting@onetel.net
Polydiam Instant Rubber Stamp Co., 70-72 Markfield Road, London, N15 4QF Tel: (020) 8493 1060 Fax: (020) 8885 5711 E-mail: sales@rubberstamp.co.uk

RUBBER STEREOTYPES, *See Stereotype etc*

RUBBER STRIPS

▶ Challis Rubber & Plastic Product, 8 Thorne Farm House, Thorne Hill, Ramsgate, Kent, CT12 5DS Tel: (01843) 826006 Fax: (01843) 826005 E-mail: jwchallisco@aol.com
W C Munsch & Co., Unit Ag2 3 Clarence Business Park, Clarence Road, Bollington, Macclesfield, Cheshire, SK10 5JZ Tel: (01625) 573971 Fax: (01625) 573250 E-mail: sales@wcmunsch.co.uk

RUBBER (SYNTHETIC) SHEETING

East Anglian Sealing Co. Ltd, Units 4 & 5, Goldingham Hall, Bulmer, Sudbury, Suffolk, CO10 7ER Tel: (01787) 880433 Fax: (0871) 4338858 E-mail: sales@easeals.co.uk

RUBBER TEST EQUIPMENT

▶ Hartest Precision Instruments Ltd, 4 St Georges Industrial Estate, Richmond Road, Kingston upon Thames, Surrey, KT2 5BQ Tel: (020) 8541 4333 Fax: (020) 8549 3374 E-mail: sales@sheeninstruments.com

RUBBER TOURNIQUET CUFFS

Hawksley & Sons Ltd, Marlborough Road, Lancing, West Sussex, BN15 8TN Tel: (01903) 752815 Fax: (01903) 766050 E-mail: enquiries@hawksley.co.uk

RUBBER WASHERS

Honeycrown Ltd, Miners Road, Llay Industrial Estate, Llay, Wrexham, Clwyd, LL12 0PJ Tel: (01978) 853730 Fax: (01978) 856320 E-mail: sales@honeycrown.co.uk
J M C Washers & Gaskets, Unit 3 Hartlebury Trading Estate, Hartlebury, Kidderminster, Worcestershire, DY10 4JB Tel: (01299) 251339 Fax: (01299) 251008

RUBBER WASTE/SCRAP CONTRACTORS/PROCESSORS

J. Allcock & Sons Ltd, Textile Street, West Gorton, Manchester, M12 5DL Tel: 0161-223 7181 Fax: 0161-223 0173 E-mail: ja@allcocks.co.uk
▶ Tyre Crumb Limited, Long Acre, Long Lane, Bovingdon, Hertfordshire, HP3 0NE Tel: 07747 633338 Fax: 01442 833130 E-mail: Sales@TyreCrumb.com

RUBBER, GRANULATED/ POWDERED

Charles Lawrence International Ltd, Jessop Way, Newark, Nottinghamshire, NG24 2ER Tel: (01636) 610680 Fax: (01636) 610222 E-mail: sales@clgplc.co.uk
▶ Qualipack (U K), 50 Kinnersley, Severn Stoke, Worcester, WR8 9JR Tel: (01905) 371226 Fax: (01905) 371529 E-mail: sales@qualipack.co.uk

RUBBER, SYNTHETIC

Arto Chemicals Ltd, Arto House, London Road, Binfield, Bracknell, Berkshire, RG42 4BU Tel: (01344) 860737 Fax: (01344) 860820 E-mail: sales@artochemicals.com

RUBBER/METAL BONDED PRODUCTS

A T C, Holmethorpe Avenue, Redhill, RH1 2NG Tel: (01737) 765686 Fax: (01737) 764048 E-mail: sales@atcltd.co.uk
Aldona Seals, 1 Brindley Road, South West Industrial Estate, Peterlee, County Durham, SR8 2LT Tel: 0191-518 1555 Fax: 0191-518 0555 E-mail: gtsm@gtgroup.co.uk
Anti Vibration Methods Rubber Co. Ltd, 3 Woodcock Industrial Estate, Woodcock Road, Warminster, Wiltshire, BA12 9DX Tel: (01985) 219032 Fax: (01985) 219849 E-mail: sales@antivibrationmethodsrubber.co.uk
Bloxwich Engineering Ltd, Fryers Road, Walsall, WS2 7LZ Tel: (01922) 710510 Fax: (01922) 713510 E-mail: bloxwich@bloxwich.u-net.com
Bonded Motor Spares Ltd, 95 Cooperative Street, Stafford, ST16 3DA Tel: (01785) 250850 Fax: (01785) 250852
Bromley Enterprises UK Ltd, Unit 7 Bruntingthorpe Industrial Estate, Upper Bruntingthorpe, Lutterworth, Leicestershire, LE17 5QZ Tel: 0116-247 8912 Fax: 0116-247 8969 E-mail: bromleyenterprises@googlemail.com
C M T Dynamics, PO Box 36, Cradley Heath, West Midlands, B64 7DQ Tel: (01384) 563220 Fax: (01384) 563225 E-mail: sales@cmt-dynamics.co.uk
Camberley Rubber Mouldings Ltd, Unit 10, Springlake Industrial Estate, Aldershot, Hampshire, GU12 4UH Tel: (01252) 330200 Fax: (01252) 330218 E-mail: sales@camberleyrubber.com
D E C Rubber Co. Ltd, Unit 20, Fordhouse Road Industrial Estate, Fordhouses, Wolverhampton, WV10 9XD Tel: (01902) 780046 Fax: (01902) 780076
Darac, 37 The Meadway, Shoreham-by-Sea, West Sussex, BN43 5RN Tel: (01273) 455607 Fax: (01273) 441631 E-mail: sales@darac.com
P.J. Donnelly Rubber, 15 Cornwall Road Industrial Park, Smethwick, West Midlands, B66 2JT Tel: 0121-565 0988 Fax: 0121-565 0976
Essential Equipment Ltd, Unit 24 Planetary Industrial Estate, Planetary Road, Willenhall, West Midlands, WV13 3XA Tel: (01902) 725055 Fax: (01902) 862684 E-mail: enquiries@essentialequipment.co.uk
Industrial Marine Rubber, 3 Spurryhillock Industrial Estate, Broomhill Road, Stonehaven, Kincardineshire, AB39 2NH Tel: (01569) 766344 Fax: (01569) 766419
J M E Rubber Co., Unit 4, Hattersley Industrial Estate, Stockport Road, Hattersley, Hyde, Cheshire, SK14 3QT Tel: 0161-368 9755 Fax: 0161-368 9767
Midhope Products, Unit 26-27 Albion Mills, Miry Lane, Thongsbridge, Holmfirth, HD9 7HP Tel: (01484) 688646 Fax: (01484) 688648 E-mail: midprod@btinternet.com
Polymer Holdings Ltd, Spurryhillock Industrial Estate, Broomhill Road, Stonehaven, Kincardineshire, AB39 2NH Tel: (01569) 766226 Fax: (01569) 766419 E-mail: sales@tubetec.co.uk
PRP, Unit 7 Tarsmill Court, Rotherwas Industrial Estate, Hereford, HR2 6JZ Tel: (01432) 357686 Fax: (01432) 352702 E-mail: info@prp.co.uk
Rubberatkins Ltd, Hareness Road, Altens Industrial Estate, Aberdeen, AB12 3LE Tel: (01224) 248341 Fax: (01224) 248342 E-mail: sales@rubberatkins.com
S R M Peakland Ltd, Vulcan Way, Coalville, Leicestershire, LE67 3AP Tel: (01530) 838317 Fax: (01530) 835122 E-mail: sales@srmpeakland.co.uk
Stockwell Mouldings, 4 Oughton Road, Birmingham, B12 0DF Tel: 0121-440 6555 Fax: 0121-440 6555 E-mail: info@stockwell-mouldings.co.uk
T R P Sealing Systems Ltd, 24 Netherwood Road, Rotherwas Industrial Estate, Hereford, HR2 6JU Tel: (01432) 279366 Fax: (01432) 273017 E-mail: admin@trpsealing.com
Trelleborg Automotive (U K) Ltd, Holbrook Lane, Coventry, CV6 4QX Tel: (024) 7629 3300 Fax: (024) 7629 3390 E-mail: diane.whitworth@trelleborg.com
Trelleborg Industrial Avs, 1 Hoods Close, Leicester, LE4 2BN Tel: 0116-267 0300 Fax: 0116-267 0301 E-mail: auto@trelleborg.com

RUBBER/METAL BONDING AGENTS

V I P-polymers, 15 Windover Road, Huntingdon, Cambridgeshire, PE29 7EB Tel: (01480) 411333 Fax: (01480) 450430 E-mail: sales@vip-polymers.com

RUBBERISED FABRICS

Farnbeck Ltd, 32 Swanfield, Edinburgh, EH6 5RX Tel: 0131-553 5353 Fax: 0131-553 3979 E-mail: dm001@post.almac.co.uk

RUBBERISED ROTARY WIRE BRUSHES

Austen Brush Co., Station Street West Business Park, Station Street West, Foleshill, Coventry, CV6 5BP Tel: (024) 7666 1326 Fax: (024) 7668 8603 E-mail: sales@scaleaway-tools.co.uk

RUCKSACKS

Penrith Survival Equipment, Sandale, Coupland Beck, Appleby-in-Westmorland, Cumbria, CA16 6LN Tel: (01768) 351666 Fax: (01768) 353666 E-mail: hg@survival.u-net.com
Stewardsons, Main Street, Hawkshead, Ambleside, Cumbria, LA22 0NT Tel: (01539) 436741 Fax: (01539) 436675 E-mail: sales@stewardsons.co.uk

RUG FABRICS

Mendit Rug & Tack, Unit 2 Enterprise Park, Piddlehinton, Dorchester, Dorset, DT2 7UA Tel: (01305) 849070 Fax: (01305) 849070 E-mail: info@menditsaddery.co.uk
▶ Rugs @ Rugs UK, 93 Highgate, Kendal, Cumbria, LA9 4EN Tel: (0808) 1089657 E-mail: mark_battista@hotmail.com

RUG NEEDLES

The Needle Co. Ltd, 27a Lubenham Hill, Market Harborough, Leicestershire, LE16 9DG Tel: (01858) 555500 Fax: (01858) 555588 E-mail: needles@btconnect.com

RUG TUFTING MACHINES

David Almond Ltd, Union Works, Bacup Road, Rossendale, Lancashire, BB4 7LN Tel: (01706) 214817 Fax: (01706) 214819 E-mail: venor@davidalmond.freeserve.uk

RUGGEDISED PORTABLE COMPUTERS

D R S Rugged Systems (Europe) Ltd, Lynwood House, The Trading Estate, Farnham, Surrey, GU9 9NN Tel: (01252) 734488 Fax: (01252) 730530
Kontron UK Ltd, 9 Ben Turner Industrial Estate, Oving Road, Chichester, West Sussex, PO19 7ET Tel: (01243) 523500 Fax: (01243) 532949 E-mail: uksales@kontron.com

RUGS, *See also headings for particular types*

Coraff Ltd, 51 Market Place, London, NW11 6JT Tel: (020) 8731 7766 Fax: (020) 8209 0098 E-mail: sales@coraffcarpets.co.uk
Easirider Co. Ltd, S2 Nene Centre, Freehold Street, Northampton, NN2 6EF Tel: (01604) 714103 Fax: (01604) 714106 E-mail: info@easirider.com
▶ Fringes, Strode Road, Newnham Industrial Estate, Plympton, Plymouth, PL7 4AY Tel: (01752) 345464 Fax: (01752) 345464
Joseph Lavian, Oriental Carpet Centre, 105 Eade Road, London, N4 1TJ Tel: (020) 8800 0707 Fax: (020) 8800 0404 E-mail: lavian@lavian.com
Morlands Glastonbury, 3 Creeches Lane, Walton, Street, Somerset, BA16 9RR Tel: (01458) 446969 Fax: (01458) 840108 E-mail: morlands@btinternet.com
▶ Oriental Rugs, 4 Upper Richmond Road, London, SW15 2SD Tel: (020) 8874 1000 E-mail: Info@Al-Nasir.com
Phoenox Home Furnishings Ltd, Spring Grove Mills, Clayton West, Huddersfield, HD8 9HH Tel: (01484) 863227 Fax: (01484) 865352 E-mail: info@phoenox.co.uk
Plantation Rug Co. Ltd, Steanard Lane, Mirfield, West Yorkshire, WF14 8EZ Tel: (01924) 493200 Fax: (01924) 493600 E-mail: sales@plantationrug.co.uk
▶ The Rug Seller Ltd, Unit 19 The Bridgewater Centre, Off Robson Ave, Trafford Park, Manchester, M41 7TE Tel: 0161 7469535 E-mail: sales@therugseller.co.uk
▶ Rugs @ Rugs UK, 93 Highgate, Kendal, Cumbria, LA9 4EN Tel: (0808) 1089657 E-mail: mark_battista@hotmail.com
Sykes & Tunnicliffe Rugs Ltd, Chapel House, Chapel Street, Taylor Hill, Huddersfield, HD4 6HL Tel: (01484) 428433 Fax: (01484) 435280
T W Bowler Ltd, Shadyoak, Marple Road, Stockport, Cheshire, SK2 5HF Tel: 0161-487 3363 Fax: 0161-487 3527 E-mail: sales@bowlers-stockport.co.uk
Vigo Carpet Gallery Ltd, 6A Vigo Street, London, W1S 3HF Tel: (020) 7439 6971 Fax: (020) 7439 2353 E-mail: vigo@btinternet.com
Wilding Partnership, The Malt House, Eardisley, Hereford, HR3 6NH Tel: (01544) 327405 Fax: (01544) 327902 E-mail: allen@wildingpartnership.co.uk
Woodward Grosvenor & Co. Ltd, Green Street, Kidderminster, Worcestershire, DY10 1HR Tel: (01562) 820020 Fax: (01562) 820042 E-mail: sales@woodward.com

RULERS

Fisco Ltd, 21 Brook Road, Rayleigh, Essex, SS6 7XD Tel: (01268) 747074 Fax: (01268) 782801 E-mail: sales@fisco.co.uk

RULES, PLASTIC

Geometrix Ltd, Chase Road, Brownhills, Walsall, WS8 6JU Tel: (01543) 452424 Fax: (01543) 453012 E-mail: enquiries@geometrix.co.uk

RUM

▶ Black Seal UK, Smallfield Road, Horne, Horley, Surrey, RH6 9JP Tel: (07932) 782435 E-mail: bermuda@blackseal.co.uk
▶ Wine and Spirit International Ltd, 9th Floor Hyde House, Edgware Road, Hendon, London, NW9 6LH Tel: (020) 8975 1023 Fax: (020) 8975 1025 E-mail: sales@wineandspirit.com

RUSKS

Ripon Select Foods Ltd, Dallamires Way North, Ripon, North Yorkshire, HG4 1TL Tel: (01765) 601711 Fax: (01765) 607481 E-mail: ingredients@rsf.co.uk

▶ indicates data change since last edition

RUSSIAN GOODS IMPORT OR EXPORT

▶ Dimensionize Ltd, 145-157 St. John Street, London, EC1V 4PY Tel: (0870) 7538485 Fax: (0870) 7538483 E-mail: contact@dimensionize.com

RUST INHIBITORS OR PREVENTATIVES

Ferro-Betol (UK), Southgreen Farm, Southgreen, Sittingbourne, Kent, ME9 7RR Tel: (01622) 884454 Fax: (01622) 884433

Neutra Rust International Ltd, 24-31 London Road, Newbury, Berkshire, RG14 1JX Tel: (01784) 455454 Fax: (01784) 450752

Valvoline Oil Co., Dock Road, Birkenhead, Merseyside, CH41 1DR Tel: 0151-652 1551 Fax: 0151-653 8900 E-mail: sales@valvolineuk.com

Wymark Ltd, Runnings Road Ind Estate, Cheltenham, Gloucestershire, GL51 9NQ Tel: 01242 520966

RUST PROOFING SERVICES

Joseph Ash, North Road, Bridgend Industrial Estate, Bridgend, Mid Glamorgan, CF31 3TP Tel: (01656) 668735 Fax: (01656) 767139 E-mail: bend@josephash.co.uk

Merseyside Rustproofing Co., 84 Seel Street, Liverpool, L1 4BH Tel: 0151-709 2409

RUST REMOVERS

Ferro-Betol (UK), Southgreen Farm, Southgreen, Sittingbourne, Kent, ME9 7RR Tel: (01622) 884454 Fax: (01622) 884433

SACHET FILLING SERVICES

A.P. Sachets Ltd, Stafford Park 6, Telford, Shropshire, TF3 3AT Tel: (01952) 234100 Fax: (01952) 234111 E-mail: sales@sachets.co.uk

Custom Packaging Ltd, Unit 1, Hortonwood 33, Telford, Shropshire, TF1 7EX Tel: (01952) 608270 Fax: (01952) 608041 E-mail: alantown@custom-pkg.co.uk

▶ Flexible Packing Services Ltd, Unit 4, Cedab Road, Ellesmere Port, CH65 4FE Tel: 0151-355 2333 Fax: 0151-355 3332 E-mail: enquiries@flexpackservices.co.uk

SACHET PACKAGING MACHINES

Soudal Ltd, Telford Way, Stephenson Industrial Estate, Coalville, Leicestershire, LE67 3HE Tel: (01530) 510502 Fax: (01530) 510970 E-mail: sales@soudal.co.uk

SACK FILLING MACHINES

A T Sack Fillers, Unit 26 Highlode Industrial Estate, Stocking Fen Road, Ramsey, Huntingdon, Cambridgeshire, PE26 2RB Tel: (01487) 814002 Fax: (01487) 814002 E-mail: sales@simplafillsystems.co.uk

Accrapak Systems Ltd, Burtonwood Industrial Centre, Burtonwood, Warrington, WA5 4HX Tel: (01925) 222926 Fax: (01925) 220137 E-mail: enquiries@accrapak.co.uk

Darenth Weighing Services Ltd, 75 Campbell Road, Maidstone, Kent, ME15 6PS Tel: (0870) 4436670 Fax: (0870) 4436671

SACK MANUFRS, *See also headings for under Sacks and for particular materials*

M Grovic & Son Ltd, Adelaide Road, Reading, RG6 1PE Tel: 0118-926 2491 Fax: 0118-935 2364 E-mail: mgrovic@ulc.co.uk

South Wales Sack & Bag, 4 Rhymney River Bridge Road, Cardiff, CF23 9AF Tel: (029) 2049 5060 Fax: (029) 2049 5055 E-mail: andrew_manuel@amserve.net

SACK OPENING/EMPTYING MACHINES

Entecon UK Ltd, Stanhope Road, Yorktown Industrial Estate, Camberley, Surrey, GU15 3BW Tel: (01276) 414540 Fax: (01276) 414544 E-mail: enquiries@entecon.co.uk

SACK PRINTING BLOCKS

Thow Blockmakers, 13 Old Glamis Road, Dundee, DD3 8JB Tel: (01382) 823824 Fax: (01382) 823825

SACK SEWING MACHINES

▶ Dunlap Sunbrand International, Unit 9 Taber Place, Crittall Road, Witham, Essex, CM8 3YP Tel: (01376) 516333 Fax: (01376) 516332 E-mail: denisekemp@dsinternational.co.uk

Intersack Systems Ltd, 10 Foster La, Bolton, BL2 5HW Tel: 01204 532663 Fax: 01204 532663

SACRIFICIAL ANODES

▶ Aberdeen Foundries, 23-41 Willowdale Place, Aberdeen, AB24 5AQ Tel: (01224) 635435 Fax: (01224) 633919 E-mail: sales@aberdeenfoundries.co.uk

Impalloy Ltd, Alloys House, Willenhall Lane, Bloxwich, Walsall, WS3 2XN Tel: (01922) 714400 Fax: (01922) 714411 E-mail: sales@impalloy.com

A.H. Latham Marine, Highfield Business Centre, 1 Simmonds Road, Wincheap Industrial Estate, Canterbury, Kent, CT1 3RA Tel: (01227) 472822 Fax: (01227) 768597 E-mail: sales@zincsmart.com

▶ MCPS Ltd, Tedco BSNS Works, Tedco Business Works, Henry Robson Way, South Shields, Tyne & Wear, NE33 1RF Tel: 0191-454 4444 Fax: 0191-427 4607 E-mail: sales@mcpsltd.com

SADDLE TREES

Aulton & Butler Ltd, Ashtree Works Bentley Lane Industrial Park, Bentley Lane, Walsall, WS2 8TL Tel: (01922) 623297 Fax: (01922) 613586 E-mail: aulton-butler@tiscali.co.uk

Beebee & Beebee Ltd, 48 Lower Forster Street, Walsall, WS1 1XB Tel: (01922) 623407 Fax: (01922) 722575

▶ KingswoodSaddlery.co.uk, Barleycorn Cottage, Babylon Lane, Lower Kingswood, Tadworth, Surrey, KT20 6XD Tel: (01737) 249121 Fax: (01737) 249121 E-mail: sales@kingswoodsaddlery.co.uk

Vale Brothers Ltd, Long Street, Walsall, WS2 9QG Tel: (01922) 624363 Fax: (01922) 720994 E-mail: sales@valebrothersvalebrothers.co.uk

Walsall Riding Saddle Co. Ltd, Crosby House, Garden Street, Walsall, WS2 8EF Tel: (01922) 624768 Fax: (01922) 641438 E-mail: sales@exsell.com

SADDLERY WEBBING PRODUCTS

Garretts Saddlers, South View, The Street, Draycott, Cheddar, Somerset, BS27 3TH Tel: (01934) 742367

Penfold & Sons, Old Talbot House, High Street, Cuckfield, Haywards Heath, West Sussex, RH17 5JX Tel: (01444) 454164 Fax: (01444) 451120

SADDLERY/HARNESS IRONMONGERY

Alsager & Sandbach Saddlery, Day Green Farm, Hassall Road, Sandbach, Cheshire, CW11 4XU Tel: (01270) 872095

Grant Barnes & Son, Horsefair, Malmesbury, Wiltshire, SN16 0AP Tel: (01666) 822316 Fax: (01666) 822316

Castle Saddlery, Hendra Farm, Liskeard, Cornwall, PL14 3LJ Tel: (01579) 344998 Fax: (01579) 344998

D Lycett & Sons Ltd, Long Street, Premier Business Park, Walsall, WS2 9DY Tel: (01922) 625393 Fax: (01922) 616761 E-mail: donshir@tiscali.co.uk

Equestrian World UK Ltd, Peppard Common, Henley-on-Thames, Oxfordshire, RG9 5LA Tel: (01491) 628548 Fax: (01491) 628968

F Martin & Son Ltd, Bridgeman Street, Walsall, WS2 9NR Tel: (01922) 624666 Fax: (01922) 724198 E-mail: info@fmartinandsonltd.co.uk

Frank Baines Saddlery Ltd, Northcote Street, Walsall, WS2 8BQ Tel: (01922) 640847 Fax: (01922) 616475 E-mail: enquiries@frankbaines-saddlery.com

Gibson Saddlers Ltd, Queensbury Road, Newmarket, Suffolk, CB8 9AX Tel: (01638) 662330 Fax: (01638) 666467 E-mail: gibsonsaddlers@btconnect.com

Ideal Saddle Co., The Old School, Hollyhedge Lane, Walsall, WS2 8PZ Tel: (01922) 620233 Fax: (01922) 623853

Llwynon Saddlery, Llwynon, Llywel, Brecon, Powys, LD3 8RG Tel: (01874) 638091 Fax: (01874) 638091 E-mail: enquiries@llwynonsaddlery.co.uk

M A Hadfield, 57 Commercial Street, Norton, Malton, North Yorkshire, YO17 9HX Tel: (01653) 694095 E-mail: mhadfield@lineone.net

Mccoy Saddlery & Leathercraft, High Street, Porlock, Minehead, Somerset, TA24 8QD Tel: (01643) 862518 Fax: (01643) 863088 E-mail: sales@mccoysaddlery.co.uk

Stanley Bros, Long Street, Premier Business Park, Walsall, WS2 9DX Tel: (01922) 621788 Fax: (01922) 723560 E-mail: info@stanley-brothers.com

Swift Signs Ltd, Vere Court, Grantham, Lincolnshire, NG31 8FB Tel: (01476) 563981 Fax: (01476) 590655

W Thacker & Sons Ltd, Field Gate, Walsall, WS1 3DJ Tel: (01922) 622302 Fax: (01922) 647790

SADDLERY/HARNESS TOOLS

E Jeffries & Sons, Unit 32 New Firms Centre, Fairground Way, Walsall, WS1 4NU Tel: (01922) 642222 Fax: (01922) 615043 E-mail: sales@ejeffries.co.uk

Hucklesby's Tack Shop, Pear Tree Farm Long Road, Saham Waite, Shipdham, Thetford, Norfolk, IP25 7RH Tel: (01362) 820235 Fax: (01362) 821033

J A & F Bullock Saddlery, North Moor, Easingwold, York, YO61 3NB Tel: (01347) 823430 Fax: (01347) 823430

Shires Equestrian, 15 Southern Avenue, Leominster, Herefordshire, HR6 0QF Tel: (01568) 613600 Fax: (01568) 613599 E-mail: sales@shires-equestrian.co.uk

Sian Saddlery, Coopers Green, Uckfield, East Sussex, TN22 4AT Tel: (01825) 732636 Fax: (01825) 732636

SADDLERY/HARNESSES

A B C Saddlery Ltd, 31 Hasse Road, Soham, Ely, Cambridgeshire, CB7 5UW Tel: (01353) 721673 Fax: (01353) 721673

A French & Sons, Huntingdon Road, Cambridge, CB3 0DL Tel: (01223) 276638

Albion Saddlemakers, 17-21 Bridgeman Street, Walsall, WS2 9PG Tel: (01922) 646210 Fax: (01922) 643777 E-mail: sales@albionsaddlemakers.co.uk

B Jenkinson & Sons, 5 Wellington Road East, Dewsbury, West Yorkshire, WF13 1HF Tel: (01924) 454681 Fax: (01924) 458696 E-mail: sales@elico.co.uk

Bellingdon End Farm Supplies, Bellingdon End Farm, Bellingdon, Chesham, Buckinghamshire, HP5 2UR Tel: (01494) 758239 Fax: (01494) 758051 E-mail: enquires@bel.co.uk

Biggleswade Saddlery, South View, Biggleswade, Bedfordshire, SG18 8BZ Tel: (01767) 316089 E-mail: sales@biggleswadesaddlery.co.uk

▶ Bookham Saddlery Ltd, 10 Grove Corner, Lower Shot, Bookham, Leatherhead, Surrey, KT23 4LP Tel: (01372) 450555 Fax: (01372) 450555

Butler Saddlery Ltd, 4 Fieldgate Works, New Street, Walsall, WS1 3DJ Tel: (01922) 627192 Fax: (01922) 627192

Buttons Saddlery, 44 Guildford Road, West End, Woking, Surrey, GU24 9PW Tel: (01276) 857771 Fax: (01276) 857771 E-mail: sales@buttonssaddlery.com

Central Saddlery, Drumbroider Farm, Avonbridge, Falkirk, FK1 2HN Tel: (01324) 861229 Fax: (01324) 861462

Chase Saddlery, 76 Chase Side, Enfield, Middlesex, EN2 6NX Tel: (020) 8363 7238 Fax: (020) 8367 8190 E-mail: sales@chase-saddlery.co.uk

Colne Saddlery, The Barn, Tewkesbury Road, Norton, Gloucester, GL2 9LH Tel: (01452) 731456 Fax: (01452) 731456 E-mail: sales@colnesaddlery.co.uk

Country Ways, 115 Holburn Street, Aberdeen, AB10 6BQ Tel: (01224) 585150 Fax: (01224) 581023 E-mail: sales@countryways.com

County Saddlery, New Street, Walsall, WS1 3DF Tel: (01922) 659080 Fax: (01922) 659089 E-mail: countysaddlery@btconnect.com

P.J. Coyne Ltd, Unit 4A Huckers Buildings, Long Acre Street, Walsall, WS2 8HP Tel: (01922) 646511 Fax: (01922) 639544

D B Sign & Engraving Co., Unit 4, Windmill Lane Industrial Estate, Denton, Manchester, M34 3RB Tel: 0161-320 0068 Fax: 0161-320 6829

Dragonfly Saddlery, Ditchling, Hassocks, West Sussex, BN6 8UQ Tel: (01273) 844606

E J Wicks, Newbury Street, Lambourn, Hungerford, Berkshire, RG17 8PB Tel: (01488) 71766 Fax: (01488) 71707 E-mail: sales@ejwicks.co.uk

E Jeffries & Sons, Unit 32 New Firms Centre, Fairground Way, Walsall, WS1 4NU Tel: (01922) 642222 Fax: (01922) 615043 E-mail: sales@ejeffries.co.uk

▶ Edgemere Saddlery & Riding Wear, Clifford House, Hampton Heath Industrial Estate, Hampton, Malpas, Cheshire, SY14 8LU Tel: (01948) 820720 Fax: (01948) 820720

Edward Robert Saddlery Ltd, 10 Berkeley Close, Moor Lane, Staines, Middlesex, TW19 6ED Tel: (01784) 460248

Ellerby & Webster Saddlers, Northfield Lane, Upper Poppleton, York, YO26 6QF Tel: (01904) 798532 Fax: (01904) 798532 E-mail: ewsaddlers@yahoo.co.uk

Equicraft, 42 Rodney Road, Backwell, Bristol, BS48 3HW Tel: (01275) 463933 Fax: (01275) 794414

Equimix Feeds & Saddlery, Sandy Lane, Titton, Stourport-on-Severn, Worcestershire, DY13 9QA Tel: (01299) 827744 Fax: (01299) 879470 E-mail: info@equimix.co.uk

▶ The Equine Shop, CWRT Y Draenog, Porthyrhyd, Carmarthen, Dyfed, SA32 8PG Tel: (01267) 275586 Fax: (01267) 275911 E-mail: sales@equineshopwales.co.uk

▶ Equine Wear, Unit 7 Lower Rectory Farm, Great Brickhill, Milton Keynes, MK17 9AF Tel: (01908) 271615

Equisport Saddlery & Riding Wear, 54 Walsall Street, Willenhall, West Midlands, WV13 2DU Tel: (01902) 603083 Fax: (01902) 609389 E-mail: pjequest@aol.com

Eskdale Harness, Craigshaws, Eaglesfield, Lockerbie, Dumfriesshire, DG11 3AH Tel: (01461) 600224 Fax: (01461) 600224

Eskdale Saddlery, 4 High Street, Longtown, Carlisle, CA6 5UE Tel: (01228) 792040

Everything Equestrian, Westerton Avenue, Clarkston, Glasgow, G76 8JU Tel: 0141-644 2698 Fax: 0141-423 5733

▶ Falmouth Horsewise, 9 West End Industrial Estate, West End, Penryn, Cornwall, TR10 8RT Tel: (01326) 378828 Fax: (01326) 378828 E-mail: info@falmouthhorsewise.co.uk

Farthing Saddlery, Southwest View, Punnetts Town, Heathfield, East Sussex, TN21 9DE Tel: (01435) 830440 Fax: (01435) 830440 E-mail: farthings_42@msn.com

Field Sports, 99 Hartforde Road, Borehamwood, Hertfordshire, WD6 5HY Tel: (020) 8207 1300

Fieldhouse Riding Equipment Ltd, Green Lane, Birchills, Walsall, WS2 8LE Tel: (01922) 638094 Fax: (01922) 622921 E-mail: sales@fieldhouse.co.uk

Hac Tac Ltd, The S M D Group Ltd, Faringdon, Oxfordshire, SN7 8LA Tel: (01367) 242818 Fax: (01367) 242819 E-mail: info@hac-tac.co.uk

M . Hancock & Son Ltd, Hanover Mills, Mersham, Ashford, Kent, TN25 6NU Tel: (01233) 720871 Fax: (01233) 721200 E-mail: mhancockson@btinternet.com

Handsome Horses, 195a High Street, Cottenham, Cambridge, CB24 8RX Tel: (01954) 206061 Fax: 01954 206061 E-mail: enquiries@handsomehorses.8k.com

▶ Haskayne Country Pets & Equine, Moor Farm, School Lane, Downholland, Ormskirk, Lancashire, L39 7JG Tel: (01704) 840234

Horse Bits Dorset Ltd, 1a Froud Way, Corfe Mullen, Wimborne, Dorset, BH21 3UU Tel: (01202) 600550 Fax: (01202) 386841 E-mail: trish@horsebitsdorset.co.uk

Horse Requisites Newmarket Ltd, Black Bear Lane, Newmarket, Suffolk, CB8 0WB Tel: (01638) 664619 Fax: (01638) 661562

Horse & Rider, 7 Exeter Street, Launceston, Cornwall, PL15 9EQ Tel: (01566) 774253 Fax: (01566) 774253

▶ Horse World Suppliers, Unit 5-7 Brook Farm, Stoneleigh Road, Coventry, CV4 7AB Tel: (024) 7669 6997 Fax: (024) 7669 7145

▶ Horse-Aholics, Bankside Industrial Estate, Falkirk, FK2 7UY Tel: (01324) 637722 Fax: (01324) 637722

Hulland Saddlery, Hulland Ward, Ashbourne, Derbyshire, DE6 3EA Tel: (01335) 370858 Fax: (01335) 370858

Hunter Saddlery, Redhills Business Park, Redhills Lane, Redhills, Penrith, Cumbria, CA11 0DT Tel: (01768) 899919 Fax: (01768) 899919

Hurn Bridge Saddlery, Hurn Bridge Equestrian Centre, Hurn, Christchurch, Dorset, BH23 6AD Tel: (01202) 483931

Huw R Thomas, 35 Commercial Street, Kenfig Hill, Bridgend, Mid Glamorgan, CF33 6DH Tel: (01656) 740391 Fax: (01656) 740391

Hyde Park Riding Ltd, 63 Bathurst Mews, London, W2 2SB Tel: (020) 7706 8968 Fax: (020) 7823 4512 E-mail: info@hydeparkstables.com

Ingram Salisbury Ltd, 44 Catherine Street, Salisbury, SP1 2DD Tel: (01722) 333802 Fax: (01722) 333802

Jabez Cliff & Co. Ltd, Globe Works, Lower Forster Street, Walsall, WS1 1XG Tel: (01922) 621676 Fax: (01922) 722575 E-mail: saddlery@barnsby.com

Jerusalem Farm Riding School, Skipton Old Road, Colne, Lancashire, BB8 7EW Tel: (01282) 865888 Fax: (01282) 869900

Kate Negus, Maidstone Road, Sidcup, Kent, DA14 5BG Tel: (020) 8302 3597 Fax: (020) 8309 5188 E-mail: sales@katenegus.com

Keith Bryan, 13a Lime Street, Walsall, WS1 2JL Tel: (01922) 628325 Fax: (01922) 628325

Ken Langford Saddlers, Eaton Road, Appleton, Abingdon, Oxfordshire, OX13 5JH Tel: (01865) 863774 Fax: (01865) 863774

Killingholme Animal Feeds, Town Street, South Killingholme, Immingham, South Humberside, DN40 3DD Tel: (01469) 540793 Fax: (01469) 540793

John Kington, The Larches, Four Oaks, Newent, Gloucestershire, GL18 1LU Tel: (01531) 890445 Fax: (01531) 890770

L & R Saddles Ltd, Clifford House, 10-14 Butts Road, Walsall, WS4 2AR Tel: (01922) 630740 Fax: (01922) 721149 E-mail: landrsaddles@btconnect.com

▶ Lindsay Saddlery & Riding Wear, Solway Trading Estate, Maryport, Cumbria, CA15 8NF Tel: (01900) 819955

M Thornley, 12a High Street, Waltham, Grimsby, South Humberside, DN37 0LL Tel: (01472) 827019

Matchmakers International Ltd, Park View Mills, Wibsey Park Avenue, Wibsey, Bradford, West Yorkshire, BD6 3SR Tel: (01274) 711011 Fax: (01274) 711030 E-mail: reception@matchmakers.co.uk

Mendit Rug & Tack, Unit 2 Enterprise Park, Piddlehinton, Dorchester, Dorset, DT2 7UA Tel: (01305) 849070 Fax: (01305) 849070 E-mail: info@menditsaddery.co.uk

Michael Longland, 2 Church Way, Alconbury Weston, Huntingdon, Cambridgeshire, PE28 4JB Tel: (01480) 891034 Fax: (01480) 891034

▶ Milford Saddlery Ltd, Parknook Farm, Ranton, Stafford, ST18 9JU Tel: (01785) 282034

SADDLERY/HARNESSES – *continued*

Millview Saddlery, 1 Haxey Road, Misterton, Doncaster, South Yorkshire, DN10 4AA Tel: (01427) 890509 Fax: (01427) 890509 E-mail: sales@millviewsaddlery.com
Modern Saddlery Ltd, Leamore Lane, Walsall, WS2 7NT Tel: (01922) 476166 Fax: (01922) 497958 E-mail: enquiries@modernsaddlery.co.uk
Morris & Nolan, 115-120 Stafford Street, Walsall, WS2 8DX Tel: (01922) 637673 Fax: (01922) 637345 E-mail: info@morrisandnolan.co.uk
Murphys Saddlery, The Tack Shop, Hewish, Weston-super-Mare, Avon, BS24 6SG Tel: (01934) 833138 Fax: (01934) 832304
▶ New Equine Wear, Unit 3 Priory Industrial Estate, Tetbury, Gloucestershire, GL8 8HZ Tel: (01666) 501960 Fax: (01666) 501969 E-mail: sales@newequinewear.co.uk
Old Basing Saddlery, 69 The Street, Old Basing, Basingstoke, Hampshire, RG24 0BY Tel: (01256) 323510 Fax: (01256) 323510
Ollard Westcombe, Bridge Street, Downpatrick, County Down, BT30 6HD Tel: (028) 4461 7557 Fax: (028) 4461 3580 E-mail: office@dthomason.freeserve.com
Plympton Tack, 11 Underwood Rd, Plymouth, PL7 1SY Tel: 01752 343384
Pointing Saddlery, Blathwayt Stables, Lansdown, Bath, BA1 9BT Tel: (01225) 462136 Fax: (01225) 483983 E-mail: info@pointings-saddlery.co.uk
Pritchards Saddlery, Newbridge Road, Llantrisant, Pontyclun, Mid Glamorgan, CF72 8EX Tel: (01443) 224370 Fax: (01443) 224370
Purbeck Pets & Equestrian, 8 West Street, Wareham, Dorset, BH20 4JU Tel: (01929) 552568 Fax: (01929) 554904
Quick Stitch, Bromson Hill Court, Ashorne, Warwick, CV35 9AD Tel: (01926) 651286 Fax: (01926) 651286 E-mail: stuwartjys@aol.com
Retford Saddlery Services, Bramble House, London Road, Retford, Nottinghamshire, DN22 7JG Tel: (01777) 701707 Fax: (01777) 701707
Gerry Reynolds Saddlery, Unit 3,, Victoria Way, Studlands Industrial Estate, Newmarket, Suffolk, CB8 7SH Tel: (01638) 668837 Fax: (01638) 665890 E-mail: gr.saddlery@btconnect.com
Robinson & Co., Norton Road, Norton, Malton, North Yorkshire, YO17 9RU Tel: (01653) 697442 Fax: (01653) 696555 E-mail: robinsonsequestrian@hotmail.co.uk
F. Robinson & Co., 26 Hopgrove Lane South, York, YO32 9TG Tel: (01904) 426496 Fax: (01904) 431748
Robinsons Country Leisure Ltd, 71-77 Warrington Road, Ashton-In-Makerfield, Wigan, Lancashire, WN4 9PJ Tel: (01942) 712555 Fax: (0870) 1123644
Ryland Saddlers Ltd, 5 Ashley Road, Cheveley, Newmarket, Suffolk, CB8 9DP Tel: (01638) 730113 Fax: (01638) 730113
▶ S O S Saddlery, Little Pengelly Farm, Lower Sticker, St. Austell, Cornwall, PL26 7JJ Tel: (01726) 65022 Fax: (01726) 72727
Sabre Leather Co. Ltd, 19-21 Sandwell Street, Walsall, WS1 3DR Tel: (01922) 629925 Fax: (01922) 723463 E-mail: sales@sabreleather.co.uk
Saddle Rack, 93 Canterbury Road, Hawkinge, Folkestone, Kent, CT18 7BS Tel: (01303) 893659 Fax: (01303) 893659
▶ Saddle Up, Unit 18 Hill Street, Ardrossan, Ayrshire, KA22 8HE Tel: (01294) 469999 Fax: (01294) 469999 E-mail: sales@saddlery-online.co.uk
Saddlers Apprentice, Frankby Stiles, Wirral, Merseyside, CH48 1PL Tel: 0151-625 2551 Fax: 0151 625 6477
Saferide Saddlery Products, 2 Newfield Close, Walsall, WS2 7PB Tel: (01922) 646512 Fax: (01922) 646554
Cecil Sale, The Mill, Roe Green, Sandon, Buntingford, Hertfordshire, SG9 0QQ Tel: (01763) 288206 Fax: (01763) 288422 E-mail: info@salesofsandon.co.uk
Sandons The Saddlery, Powleys Yard, Bintree Road, Foulsham, Dereham, Norfolk, NR20 5RL Tel: (01362) 683383 Fax: (01362) 683383
Seaforth Saddlers, 23 Harbour Road, Inverness, IV1 1SY Tel: (01463) 223803 Fax: (01463) 223803
Shamley Saddlery, Fifield House Farm, Oakley Green Road, Oakley Green, Windsor, Berkshire, SL4 4QF Tel: (01628) 777664 Fax: (01628) 777664 E-mail: info@shamleysaddlery.co.uk
Shelton House Saddlery, Starnhill Farm, Granby Lane, off Grantham Road, Bingham, NG13 8DH Tel: (01949) 838886 Fax: (01949) 838887 E-mail: sheltonsaddlery@bhtinternet.com
Shires Equestrian, 15 Southern Avenue, Leominster, Herefordshire, HR6 0QF Tel: (01568) 613600 Fax: (01568) 613599 E-mail: sales@shires-equestrian.co.uk
Sian Saddlery, Coopers Green, Uckfield, East Sussex, TN22 4AT Tel: (01825) 732636 Fax: (01825) 732636
Sierra Saddle Co., 602 High Road, Benfleet, Essex, SS7 5RW Tel: (01268) 792769 Fax: (01268) 566775
▶ Simply Rugs, Unit 7 Skein Enterprise Park, Hodsoll Street, Sevenoaks, Kent, TN15 7LB Tel: (01732) 820304
Sterling Saddlery, Court Lodge Farm, Bodiam, Robertsbridge, East Sussex, TN32 5UJ Tel: (01580) 830891 Fax: (01580) 830186
Leonard Stevens, 16 Crown Street, Eastbourne, East Sussex, BN21 1NX Tel: (01323) 734496
▶ Sussex Saddlery, Cowfold Road, West Grinstead, Horsham, West Sussex, RH13 8LP Tel: (01403) 865961 E-mail: info@sussexsaddlery.com
T & C Robinson, Tattershall Road, Billinghay, Lincoln, LN4 4BN Tel: (01526) 860436 Fax: (01526) 861352 E-mail: sales@saddleforce9.co.uk
T Craine, 2 Barn Court, Thicketford Road, Bolton, BL2 2LN Tel: (01204) 525830
T Jones & Son, 27 Leg Street, Oswestry, Shropshire, SY11 2NN Tel: (01691) 652822
Tack A Round Saddlery Ltd, 41A High Street, Billingshurst, West Sussex, RH14 9PP Tel: (01403) 783862 Fax: (01403) 786069 E-mail: sales@tackaround.co.uk
▶ Tack Shack, 44 Calder Road, Mirfield, West Yorkshire, WF14 8NR Tel: (01924) 491119 Fax: (01924) 503777
Thorowgood Ltd, The Saddlery, Fryers Road, Bloxwich, Walsall, WS3 2XJ Tel: (01922) 711676 Fax: (01922) 711654 E-mail: enquiries@thorowgood.co.uk
Tidenhan Saddlery & Horse Feed, Stroat Farm, Stroat, Chepstow, Gwent, NP16 7LR Tel: (01594) 529226
▶ Total Equine (UK), 46 Bridge Street, Heywood, Lancashire, OL10 1JF Tel: (01706) 620003
Track Right, Bridge Farm, Cuckfield Road, Burgess Hill, West Sussex, RH15 8RE Tel: (01444) 246370 Fax: (01444) 246370
Urad Saddlery & Leathercare Products, Unit 4 Cavans Way, Binley Industrial Estate, Coventry, CV3 2SF Tel: (024) 7645 4244 Fax: (024) 7645 4245
Victorian Saddles, 117 Halifax Road, Rochdale, Lancashire, OL12 9BA Tel: (01706) 644490 Fax: (01706) 644490 E-mail: sales@victoriansaddles.co.uk
Viking Saddlery, Dean Court Farm, Lower Dean, Buckfastleigh, Devon, TQ11 0LT Tel: (01364) 644064 E-mail: info@vikingsaddlery.force9.co.uk
Village Saddlery, 182 Chester Road, Warrington, WA4 6AR Tel: (01925) 629629 Fax: (01925) 629628
W Todd & Sons, Mintsfeet Road North, Kendal, Cumbria, LA9 6LZ Tel: (01539) 724311 Fax: (01539) 720277
Walsall Riding Saddle Co. Ltd, Crosby House, Garden Street, Walsall, WS2 8EF Tel: (01922) 624768 Fax: (01922) 641438 E-mail: sales@exsell.com
Warren Farm, Southport Old Road, Liverpool, L37 0AN Tel: (01704) 833630 Fax: (01704) 873820
Wealden Saddlery, Buckhurst Farm, Merriments Lane, Hurst Green, Etchingham, East Sussex, TN19 7RG Tel: (01580) 860860 Fax: (01580) 860860 E-mail: wealdensaddlery@btconnect.com
White Lodge Saddlery, White Lodge, Middle Road, Tiptoe, Lymington, Hampshire, SO41 6FX Tel: (01590) 682396 Fax: (01590) 681717 E-mail: sales@whitelodgesaddlery.co.uk
White Rose Saddlery, Wiger Mews, Langton Road, Norton, Malton, North Yorkshire, YO17 9QG Tel: (01653) 697440 Fax: (01653) 697440 E-mail: enquiries@whiteroseseddlery.com
Patrick Wilkinson Saddlers Ltd, 108 Walkergate, Beverley, North Humberside, HU17 9BT Tel: (01482) 870800 Fax: (01482) 883376
Witham Saddlery, 63b Newland Street, Witham, Essex, CM8 1AA Tel: (01376) 512366 Fax: (01376) 512366
World Beta Standard Equestrian Products, Unit 12, Ennerdale Road, Kitty Brewster Industrial Estate, Blyth, Northumberland, NE24 4RT Tel: (01670) 357300 Fax: (01670) 357301 E-mail: sales@falpro.com

SAFE DEPOSIT FACILITIES/ SERVICES

Hatton Garden Safe Deposit Ltd, 88-90 Hatton Garden, London, EC1N 8PN Tel: (020) 7405 9600 Fax: (020) 7242 5682
The London Safe Deposit Co. Ltd, 20 Regent Street, London, SW1Y 4PH Tel: (020) 7930 8846 Fax: (020) 7976 1250
London Silver Vaults, Chancery House, 53-64 Chancery Lane, London, WC2A 1QT Tel: (020) 7242 3844 Fax: (020) 7405 5648

SAFE MAINTENANCE/REPAIR SERVICES

Associated Security Ltd, 59 London Road, Wallington, Surrey, SM6 7HW Tel: (020) 8669 7811 Fax: (020) 8669 9890 E-mail: sales@associatedsecuritygroup.co.uk
Capital Lock & Safe Company Ltd, 91 Lancaster Road, Enfield, Middlesex, EN2 0DN Tel: (020) 8367 2775 Fax: (020) 8366 5091
Cheshire Lock & Safe Co., Unit 3 Fence Avenue Industrial Estate, Macclesfield, Cheshire, SK10 1LT Tel: (01625) 614178 Fax: (01625) 617898 E-mail: sales@cheshirelock.co.uk
Thomas Fox & Co. Ltd, 3 Rhodes Way, Watford, WD24 4YA Tel: (01923) 811700 Fax: (01923) 811710 E-mail: enquiries@thomasfox.co.uk
Independent Safes, 5 Hatton Garden, London, EC1N 8AA Tel: (020) 7405 1540 Fax: (020) 7405 1640E-mail: independentsafes@aol.com
London Lock & Safe Co., 10 Great Eastern Street, London, EC2A 3NT Tel: (020) 7241 3535 Fax: (020) 7650 8999 E-mail: londonlocksafe7@btconnect.com
Midland Safe, Halesfield 2, Telford, Shropshire, TF7 4QH Tel: (01952) 682000 Fax: (01952) 682009 E-mail: sales@midland-safe.co.uk

SAFE REMOVAL OR INSTALLATION CONTRACTORS

Associated Security Group Ltd, 277 Wandsworth Bridge Road, London, SW6 2TX Tel: (020) 7736 7092 Fax: (020) 8669 9890 E-mail: info@associatedsecuritygroup.co.uk
Business Moves Ltd, 4 Acre Road, Reading, RG2 0SX Tel: 0118-933 6600 Fax: 0118-975 3586 E-mail: info@businessmove.com
C & M Apostolides Ltd, 257 Wood Street, Walthamstow, London, E17 3NG Tel: (020) 8923 5050 Fax: (020) 8923 6060 E-mail: mail@cama.co.uk
Commercial Trading Co. Ltd, Unit D6 Sandown Industrial Park, Mill Road, Esher, Surrey, KT10 8BL Tel: (01372) 468383 Fax: (01372) 468576 E-mail: admin@ctc.co.uk
Furneaux Industrial Supplies Ltd, 5 Sinclair House, Hastings Street, London, WC1H 9PZ Tel: (020) 7387 8450 Fax: (020) 7388 0197 E-mail: furnlocks@fsbdial.co.uk
Insafe International Ltd, Westcombe House 4th Floor, 2-4 Mount Ephraim, Tunbridge Wells, Kent, TN4 8AS Tel: (01892) 533000 Fax: (01892) 525100 E-mail: sales@insafe.co.uk
▶ Lock Services Ltd, Unit 2e Queensway Enterprise Centre, Queensway, New Milton, Hampshire, BH25 5NN Tel: (01425) 623093 Fax: (01425) 638501 E-mail: sales@lock-services.co.uk
London Lock & Safe Co., 10 Great Eastern Street, London, EC2A 3NT Tel: (020) 7241 3535 Fax: (020) 7650 8999 E-mail: londonlocksafe7@btconnect.com
Midland Safe, Halesfield 2, Telford, Shropshire, TF7 4QH Tel: (01952) 682000 Fax: (01952) 682009 E-mail: sales@midland-safe.co.uk
Reeder Lock & Safe Co. Ltd, 587 Barking Road, London, E13 9EZ Tel: (020) 7476 5450 Fax: (020) 8503 4145
▶ T Oconnor, D 795 London Road, Grays, Essex, RM20 3LH Tel: (01708) 890885 Fax: (01708) 890815 E-mail: sales@toconnor.co.uk
Wedberry Safe Co. Ltd, Premier House, Tennyson Drive, Pitsea, Basildon, Essex, SS13 3BT Tel: (01268) 556724 Fax: (01268) 558755

SAFES, *See also headings for particular types*

A & D Lock & Key Co. Ltd, 6-7 Hockley Hill, Birmingham, B18 5AA Tel: 0121-554 7894 Fax: 0121-554 8220 E-mail: reconditionedsafes@btconnect.com
▶ Access 24, 3 Stadhampton Road, Drayton St. Leonard, Wallingford, Oxfordshire, OX10 7AR Tel: (01865) 400928 E-mail: admin@access24.co.uk
Ace Safe Co. Ltd, Forest Corner Farm, Hangersley Hill, Hangersley, Ringwood, Hampshire, BH24 3JW Tel: (01425) 489860 Fax: (01425) 478780 E-mail: sales@acesafes.co.uk
Associated Security Ltd, 59 London Road, Wallington, Surrey, SM6 7HW Tel: (020) 8669 7811 Fax: (020) 8669 9890 E-mail: sales@associatedsecuritygroup.co.uk
Banham Security Ltd, 10 Pascal Street, London, SW8 4SH Tel: (020) 7622 5151 Fax: (020) 7498 2461 E-mail: security@banham.com
Brattonsound Engineering Ltd, Unit 4 Kimpton Trade & Business Centre, Minden Road, Sutton, Surrey, SM3 9PF Tel: (020) 8254 6800 Fax: (020) 8641 9991
Capital Lock & Safe Company Ltd, 91 Lancaster Road, Enfield, Middlesex, EN2 0DN Tel: (020) 8367 2775 Fax: (020) 8366 5091
Cummings Bros, 5-7 Merridale Road, Wolverhampton, WV3 9RX Tel: (01902) 427000 Fax: (01902) 712247
Dudley Safes Ltd, Unit 17 Deepdale Works, Deepdale Lane, Upper Gornal, Dudley, West Midlands, DY3 2AF Tel: (01384) 239991 Fax: (01384) 455129 E-mail: sales@dudleysafes.com
Elite Safe & Security Services, Stanmore Industrial Estate, Bridgnorth, Shropshire, WV15 5HP Tel: (01952 684855 E-mail: epicsafes@lineone.net
Fbh-Fichet Ltd, 7/8 Amor Way, Letchworth Garden City, Hertfordshire, SG6 1UG Tel: (01462) 472900 Fax: (01462) 472901 E-mail: sales@fbh-fichet.com
Thomas Fox & Co. Ltd, 3 Rhodes Way, Watford, WD24 4YA Tel: (01923) 811700 Fax: (01923) 811710 E-mail: enquiries@thomasfox.co.uk
Gunnebo UK Ltd, Wolverhampton, WV10 0BY Tel: 01902 455111 E-mail: marketing@gunnebo.com
Hamber Safes, Radford Way, Billericay, Essex, CM12 0EG Tel: (01277) 624450 Fax: (01277) 657533
Independent Safes, 5 Hatton Garden, London, EC1N 8AA Tel: (020) 7405 1540 Fax: (020) 7405 1640E-mail: independentsafes@aol.com
Insafe International Ltd, Westcombe House 4th Floor, 2-4 Mount Ephraim, Tunbridge Wells, Kent, TN4 8AS Tel: (01892) 533000 Fax: (01892) 525100 E-mail: sales@insafe.co.uk
Lumsden Security, 128-130 John Street, Aberdeen, AB25 1LE Tel: (01224) 632428 Fax: (01224) 645656 E-mail: sales@lumsdensecurity.co.uk
Phoenix Safe Co. Ltd, Apex House, No. 1 Orrell Mount, Liverpool, L20 6NS Tel: 0151-944 6444 Fax: 0151-944 6445 E-mail: sales@phoenixsafe.co.uk
S M P Security Ltd, Halesfield 24, Telford, Shropshire, TF7 4NZ Tel: (01952) 585673 Fax: (01952) 582816
Wedberry Safe Co. Ltd, Premier House, Tennyson Drive, Pitsea, Basildon, Essex, SS13 3BT Tel: (01268) 556724 Fax: (01268) 558755
Withy Grove Stores Ltd, 35-39 Withy Grove, Manchester, M4 2BJ Tel: 0161-834 0044

SAFES, SECURITY CABINET

Checkmate Devices Ltd, Gore Cross Business Park, Corbin Way, Bradpole, Bridport, Dorset, DT6 3UX Tel: (01308) 423871 Fax: (01308) 458276 E-mail: checkmate@ackerman-eng.com
Dynamica Ltd, Enterprise Road, Mablethorpe, Lincolnshire, LN12 1NB Tel: (01507) 473052 Fax: (01507) 478832
Gunnebo UK Ltd, Wolverhampton, WV10 0BY Tel: 01902 455111 E-mail: marketing@gunnebo.com

SAFETY ARMBANDS

▶ Kemco Technology, Acorn House, Tonbridge Road, Bough Beech, Edenbridge, Kent, TN8 7AU Tel: (01892) 870077 Fax: (01892) 870777 E-mail: info@kemcotech.com

SAFETY BELTS

Mindex Ltd, Melita House, Yattendon Road, Horley, Surrey, RH6 7BS Tel: (01293) 408123 Fax: (01293) 408125 E-mail: sales@mindex-ltd.co.uk
Securon Amersham Ltd, Winchmore Hill, Amersham, Buckinghamshire, HP7 0NZ Tel: (01494) 434455 Fax: (01494) 726499 E-mail: sales@securon.co.uk

SAFETY CLOTHING

A R C O Ltd, PO Box 7, Ossett, West Yorkshire, WF5 9JG Tel: (01482) 222522 Fax: (01924) 280262 E-mail: ossett.branch@arco.co.uk
Apex Industrial Ltd, 651 Eccles New Road, Salford, M50 1BA Tel: 0161-789 0909 Fax: 0161-787 7113
Arco, Blackburn Interchange Trade Park, Commercial Road, Darwen, Lancashire, BB3 0DB Tel: (01254) 778680 Fax: (01482) 388029 E-mail: darwen.branch@arco.co.uk
▶ Arco Group Ltd, Parkway Avenue, Sheffield, S9 4YX Tel: 0114-272 3333 E-mail: admin@arco.co.uk
Carrington Career & Workwear Ltd, Market Street, Adlington, Chorley, Lancashire, PR7 4HE Tel: (01257) 476850 Fax: (01257) 476852 E-mail: info@carrington.uk.com
Chain Saw Services, 16 Pinfold Lane, North Luffenham, Oakham, Leicestershire, LE15 8LE Tel: (01780) 721070 Fax: (01780) 729455
Chelmsford Safety Supplies, 10 Marlborough Road, Chelmsford, CM2 0JR Tel: (01245) 355243 Fax: (01245) 290660
Clwyd Welding Services Ltd, Clwyd Close, Hawarden Industrial Park, Hawarden, Deeside, Clwyd, CH5 3PZ Tel: (01244) 531667 Fax: (01244) 531842 E-mail: clwydweld@aol.com
Concorde Hydraulics Ltd, Unit 10 Vastre Industrial Estate, Newtown, Powys, SY16 1DZ Tel: (01686) 624945 Fax: (01686) 624595 E-mail: sales@concord-hydraulics.co.uk
Cromwell Tools Ltd, 19 Concorde Road, Norwich, NR6 6BJ Tel: (01603) 410939 Fax: (01603) 410939 E-mail: norwich@cromwell-tools.co.uk
D D Health & Safety Supplies Ltd, Unit 2, Kingsway, City Trading Estate, Norwich, NR2 4UE Tel: (01603) 628891 Fax: (01603) 764882 E-mail: bpuplett@dd-healthandsafetysupplies.co.uk
East Anglia Cleaning & Safety Supplies, Langton Green, Eye, Suffolk, IP23 7HL Tel: (01379) 871110 Fax: (01379) 871160 E-mail: workwearunderstoreeastanglia@hotmail.com
Euro Safety & Abrasives, Unit 3, 13 Cobham Road, Ferndown Industrial Estate, Wimborne, Dorset, BH21 7TE Tel: (01202) 870661 Fax: (01202) 870095
Factorsafe Ltd, 2341 Coventry Road, Birmingham, B26 3PN Tel: 0121-722 2200 Fax: 0121-722 2200 E-mail: sales@factorsafe.co.uk
Gas & Welding Equipment Ltd, 239 Ilkeston Road, Nottingham, NG7 3FX Tel: 0115-942 0519 Fax: 0115-942 3743 E-mail: info@gwe-ltd.com

SAFETY CLOTHING – *continued*

Chas Hunter Ltd, Upper Villiers Street, Wolverhampton, WV2 4NR Tel: (01902) 424411 Fax: (01902) 424733 E-mail: chas.hunterltd@virgin.net
Hy Protec Health & Safety Ltd, Withambrook Park Industrial Estate, Grantham, Lincolnshire, NG31 9ST Tel: (01476) 573460 Fax: (01476) 563635 E-mail: paul@hy-protec.com
London Tools Ltd, 1 Gatton Road, London, SW17 0EX Tel: (020) 8672 1086 Fax: (020) 8672 0248 E-mail: londontools@hotmail.com
M & A Environmental Northern Ltd, 2 Royd Business Park, Dye House Lane, Brighouse, West Yorkshire, HD6 1LL Tel: (01484) 475100 Fax: (01484) 475103 E-mail: sales@brook-industrial.fsnet.co.uk
Maco Manufacturing Co. Ltd, 6d The St Industrial Estate, Heybridge Street, Maldon, Essex, CM9 4XT Tel: (01621) 856789 Fax: (01621) 851358 E-mail: info@maco.uk.com
Murray, Castle Court, Bodmin Road, Coventry, CV2 5DB Tel: (024) 7658 7980 Fax: (024) 7658 7981 E-mail: jheadley@jheadley.co.uk
Parker Merchanting Ltd, Cofton Road, Marsh Barton Trading Estate, Exeter, EX2 8QW Tel: (01392) 288900 Fax: (01392) 288901 E-mail: info.parker@hagemeyer.co.uk
Parker Merchanting Ltd, 730 South Street, Glasgow, G14 0TR Tel: 0141-342 5600 Fax: 0141-342 5601 E-mail: info.parker@hagemeyer.co.uk
Parker Merchanting Ltd, 1-2 Longwall Avenue, Queens Drive Industrial Estate, Nottingham, NG2 1NA Tel: 0115-986 2121 Fax: 0115-986 2509 E-mail: info.parker@hagemeyer.co.uk
Parker Merchanting Ltd, Unit 8-9 Seaway Parade Industrial Estate, Port Talbot, West Glamorgan, SA12 7BR Tel: (01639) 813878 Fax: (01639) 823079 E-mail: info.parker@hagemeyer.co.uk
Parker Merchanting Ltd, J Guild Trading Estate, Ribbleton Lane, Preston, PR1 5DP Tel: (01772) 796939 Fax: (01772) 793138 E-mail: info.parker@hagemeyer.co.uk
Parker Merchanting, Unit 2 3, Orbital Centre Southend Road, Woodford Green, Essex, IG8 8HH Tel: (020) 8709 7600 Fax: (020) 8709 7636 E-mail: info.parker@hagemeyer.co.uk
Rodo Ltd, Lumb Lane, Droylsden, Manchester, M43 7BU Tel: 0161-371 6400 Fax: 0161-371 6401 E-mail: sales@rodo.co.uk
Safe Guy, Simon Scotland Road, King's Lynn, Norfolk, PE30 4JF Tel: (01553) 774449 Fax: (01553) 761670
Southern Safety Centres Ltd, 3 South Parade, Stafford Road, Wallington, Surrey, SM6 9AJ Tel: (020) 8395 8913 Fax: (020) 8773 2937 E-mail: safety@sscltd.fsnet.co.uk
Stalwart Signs & Industrial Supplies Ltd, Anglian House Admiralty Road, Great Yarmouth, Norfolk, NR30 3DY Tel: (01493) 857410 Fax: (01493) 852383 E-mail: stalwartsafety@dsl.pipex.com
Stanton Hope Ltd, 11 Seax Court, Southfields, Laindon, Basildon, Essex, SS15 6LY Tel: (01268) 419141 Fax: (01268) 545992 E-mail: sales@stantonhope.co.uk
Stronghold Safety Workwear, Cocklebury Road, Chippenham, Wiltshire, SN15 3NT Tel: (01249) 655976 Fax: (01249) 460623
Swift Industiral Suppliers, Anstey Mill Lane, The Mill House, Alton, Hampshire, GU34 2QQ Tel: (01420) 592500 Fax: (01420) 592501
Tuf Work & Safety Wear, 26 North Road, Yate, Bristol, BS37 7PA Tel: (01454) 335500 Fax: (01454) 335001 E-mail: sales@tuf.com
UK Industrial Supplies Ltd, Unit G Motorway Distribution Centre, Avonmouth Way West, Avonmouth, Bristol, BS11 9YT Tel: 0117-923 5653 Fax: 0117-982 0505 E-mail: admin@ukindsup.co.uk
Wilsons Safety Supplies Ltd, Gibson Street, Amble, Morpeth, Northumberland, NE65 0LR Tel: (01665) 712572 Fax: (01665) 713096 E-mail: dennis@wilson-safety.co.uk

SAFETY COUPLINGS

Staubli Unimation Ltd, Lodge Park, Telford, Shropshire, TF1 7ET Tel: (01952) 604827 Fax: (01952) 608579 E-mail: connectors.uk@staubli.com

SAFETY CUTTERS

Martor Direct UK Ltd, Ahed House, Sandbeds Trading Estate, Ossett, West Yorkshire, WF5 9ND Tel: (01924) 281333 Fax: (01924) 281444 E-mail: dennis@martor-uk-demon.co.uk

SAFETY EQUIPMENT

1ccormick, 8 John Street, Stratford-upon-Avon, Warwickshire, CV37 6UB Tel: (01789) 264098 Fax: (01789) 264101
▶ Active Workwear, 56 Bradford Road, Stanningley, Pudsey, West Yorkshire, LS28 6EF Tel: 0113-256 7021 Fax: 0113-256 6600 E-mail: info@workwearshop.co.uk
▶ Arco Plymouth, Unit A Estover Road, Plymouth, PL6 7PY Tel: (01752) 751650
Avon Welding Supplies, Unit D6 Avondale Works, Woodland Way, Bristol, BS15 1PA Tel: 0117-947 7532 Fax: 0117-947 7532 E-mail: info@aws-ltd.co.uk
▶ Beacon Lights, Capel Grange, Bedford Road, Holwell, Hitchin, Hertfordshire, SG5 3RT Tel: (01462) 711919
Binneys Coventry, Unit 1 Challenge Business Park, Challenge Close, Coventry, CV1 5JG Tel: (024) 7622 0228 Fax: (024) 7652 5342 E-mail: info@binneys.co.uk
▶ Dee Safety & Embroidery, Unit B1 Evans Easyspace, Deeside Industrial Park, Deeside, Clwyd, CH5 2JZ Tel: (01244) 280090
Enserve Corporation, Parkway House, Worth Way, Keighley, West Yorkshire, BD21 5LD Tel: (0800) 0377817 E-mail: info@enserve.co.uk
Firecare Ltd, 72 Tartnakilly Road, Limavady, County Londonderry, BT49 9NA Tel: (028) 7776 4002 E-mail: sales@fire-care.co.uk
▶ Fraser Brown Engineering Ltd, Unit 11, Evanton Indust Estate, Evanton, Dingwall, Ross-Shire, IV16 9XJ Tel: (01349) 831144 Fax: (01349) 831012 E-mail: info@eyelevels.co.uk
H C L Safety Ltd, Unit 1 Ball Street, Walsall, WS1 2HG Tel: (01922) 619470 Fax: (01922) 619471 E-mail: birmingham@hclgroup.co.uk
I T S Tools Ltd, Daish Way, Dodnor Lane Industrial Estate, Newport, Isle of Wight, PO30 5XB Tel: (01983) 526344 Fax: (01983) 821547 E-mail: itstools@tiscali.co.uk
▶ J S P Ltd, Cotswold Innovation Centre, Rissington Business Park, Upper Rissington, Cheltenham, Gloucestershire, GL54 2QB Tel: (01451) 822534 Fax: (01451) 822304
L H R Marine Ltd, Unit 3a Deemouth Business Centre, South Esplanade East, Aberdeen, AB11 9PB Tel: (01224) 248821 Fax: (01224) 248831 E-mail: info@lhrmarine.com
▶ Millwood Servicing Ltd, 102 Stafford Road, Wallington, Surrey, SM6 9AY Tel: (020) 8669 0080 Fax: (020) 8669 2727 E-mail: tracey@millwood.co.uk
▶ Phoenix Safety Services, Unit 23 Prestwood Court, Leacroft Road, Birchwood, Warrington, WA3 6SB Tel: (01925) 880008 Fax: (01925) 880008 E-mail: enquiries@phoenixsafetyhire.co.uk
▶ Precision Safety Footware, St. Ivel Way, Bristol, BS30 8TY Tel: 0117-961 2400 Fax: 0117-961 2470 E-mail: sales@precisionsafety.co.uk
▶ Pro-Tech Offshore, 10 Howe Moss Drive, Kirkhill Industrial Estate, Dyce, Aberdeen, AB21 0GL Tel: (01224) 729888 Fax: (0870) 1313377
Sling & Tackle, Unit 57, Third Avenue, Bletchley, Milton Keynes, MK1 1DR Tel: (01908) 449300 Fax: (01908) 449301 E-mail: sales@slingandtackle.co.uk
Southern Safety Centres Ltd, 3 South Parade, Stafford Road, Wallington, Surrey, SM6 9AJ Tel: (020) 8395 8913 Fax: (020) 8773 2937 E-mail: safety@sscltd.fsnet.co.uk
Talking Headsets Ltd, Woodlands, The Bridle Lane, Hambrook, Chichester, West Sussex, PO18 8UG Tel: (01243) 573226 Fax: (01243) 574318 E-mail: info@talkingheadsets.co.uk
▶ Thistle Scientific Ltd, Goldie Road, Bothwell Park Industrial Estate, Uddingston, Glasgow, G71 6PB Tel: (01698) 338844
▶ Tyco Electronic Product Group, 160 Billet Road, London, E17 5DR Tel: (020) 8919 4000 Fax: (020) 8919 4040
▶ X5 Ltd, Unit 6, 77 London Road, Newbury, Berkshire, RG14 1JN Tel: (0870) 2863666 Fax: (0870) 2863866 E-mail: sales@x5.ltd.uk

SAFETY EYEWASH/FACE WASH UNITS/FOUNTAINS

▶ B S P Method Ltd, 3 Millbrook Business Centre, Floats Road, Roundthorn Industrial Estate, Manchester, M23 9YJ Tel: 0161-998 1999 Fax: 0161-946 1697 E-mail: info@bspmethod.com
Hughes Safety Showers Ltd, Whitefield Road, Bredbury, Stockport, Cheshire, SK6 2SS Tel: 0161-430 6618 Fax: 0161-430 7928 E-mail: sales@hughes-safety-showers.co.uk
Hughes Safety Showers Ltd, Whitefield Road, Bredbury, Stockport, Cheshire, SK6 2SS Tel: 0161-430 6618 Fax: 0161-430 7928 E-mail: sales@hughes-safety-showers.co.uk
Kays Medical, 3-7 Shaw Street, Liverpool, L6 1HH Tel: 0151-482 2830 Fax: 0151-207 3384 E-mail: kays@kaysmedical.com

SAFETY FIRE COLLARS

▶ Blocker Products Ltd, Pals Haven, Hook Lane, Aldingbourne, Chichester, West Sussex, PO20 3TE Tel: (01243) 545465 Fax: (01243) 545475 E-mail: millerbrian@btconnect.com

SAFETY FOOTWEAR

Coast To Coast Boot Co. Ltd, Lower Fold, Marple Bridge, Stockport, Cheshire, SK6 5DU Tel: (01663) 745461 Fax: (01663) 741433
D D Health & Safety Supplies Ltd, Unit 2, Kingsway, City Trading Estate, Norwich, NR2 4UE Tel: (01603) 628891 Fax: (01603) 764882 E-mail: bpuplett@dd-healthandsafetysupplies.co.uk
Davmar Workwear, 1 Centenary Court, Earlsway, Team Valley Trading Estate, Gateshead, Tyne & Wear, NE11 0RQ Tel: 0191-487 2249 Fax: 0191-491 4237 E-mail: contact@davmarworkwear.com
Factorsafe Ltd, 2341 Coventry Road, Birmingham, B26 3PN Tel: 0121-722 2200 Fax: 0121-722 2200 E-mail: sales@factorsafe.co.uk
Footsure Western Ltd, 1 Alvin Street, Gloucester, GL1 3EJ Tel: (01452) 422002 Fax: (01452) 307220 E-mail: david.bush@footsure.net
▶ Footwear-Safety, 117 South Quay, Great Yarmouth, Norfolk, NR30 3LD Tel: (01493) 842289 Fax: (01493) 853416 E-mail: sales@footwear-safety.co.uk
Goliath Footwear Ltd, Goliath House, Chain Bar Road, Cleckheaton, West Yorkshire, BD19 3QF Tel: (0845) 3306430 Fax: (0845) 3306431 E-mail: enquiries@goliath.co.uk
I G T C Ltd, 7 Huston Close, Barrow Upon Soar, Loughborough, Leicestershire, LE12 8NB Tel: (0845) 2020235 Fax: (0870) 7202265 E-mail: sales@safetyshopdirect.com
Jallatte SAS Ltd, Unit C, Riverside Industrial Estate, Atherstone Street, Fazeley, Tamworth, Staffordshire, B78 3RW Tel: (01827) 831260 Fax: (01827) 831261
Main Man Supplies, Station Approach, Adisham, Canterbury, Kent, CT3 3JE Tel: (01304) 842030 Fax: (01304) 841312 E-mail: mnshydra@hotmail.com
PH Industrial Ltd, 8 Wheldon Road, Widnes, Cheshire, WA8 8FW Tel: 0151-257 9696 Fax: 0151-257 8585
Progressive Safety Footwear & Clothing Ltd, 101 Worthing Road, Sheffield, S9 3JN Tel: 0114-273 8349 Fax: 0114-275 2452 E-mail: info@psf.co.uk
Provincial Safety Services Ltd, Portway Road, Oldbury, West Midlands, B69 2BP Tel: 0121-544 5208 Fax: 0121-552 9075 E-mail: provincialsafety@btconnect.com
Stronghold Safety Workwear, Cocklebury Road, Chippenham, Wiltshire, SN15 3NT Tel: (01249) 655976 Fax: (01249) 460623
Wilsons Safety Supplies Ltd, Gibson Street, Amble, Morpeth, Northumberland, NE65 0LR Tel: (01665) 712572 Fax: (01665) 713096 E-mail: dennis@wilson-safety.co.uk

SAFETY GATES, BABY

Clippa Safe Ltd, Lanthwaite Road, Nottingham, NG11 8LD Tel: 0115-921 1899 Fax: 0115-984 5554 E-mail: sales@clippasafe.co.uk

SAFETY GLASS

▶ Advanced Glass Products, Site 7, Kidderminster Road, Rushock, Droitwich, Worcestershire, WR9 0NS Tel: (01299) 851525 Fax: (01299) 851544
Darby Glass Ltd, Darby House, Sunningdale Road, Scunthorpe, South Humberside, DN17 2SS Tel: (01724) 280044 Fax: (01724) 868295
Dunstable Glass Co. Ltd, 87-91 High St North, Dunstable, Bedfordshire, LU6 1JJ Tel: (01582) 663277 Fax: (01582) 699907
G K N Aerospace Transparancy Systems Ltd, Eckersall Road, Birmingham, B38 8SR Tel: 0121-606 4100 Fax: 0121-458 6880
Glas Seal Ni Ltd, 80 Belfast Road, Ballynahinch, County Down, BT24 8EB Tel: (028) 9756 2932 Fax: (028) 9756 1096 E-mail: post@glas-seal.co.uk
Ledlite Glass Ltd, 168 London Road, Southend-on-Sea, SS1 1PH Tel: (01702) 345893 Fax: (01702) 435099 E-mail: sales@ledlite-glass.co.uk
Merrick & Heath, Rolfe Street, Smethwick, West Midlands, B66 2AW Tel: 0121-558 1291 Fax: 0121-558 1291
Nicholls & Clarke Glass Ltd, Units 27 Gemini Business Park, Hornet Way, Beckton, London, E6 7FF Tel: (020) 7473 0999 Fax: (020) 7476 1017
Pilkington Birmingham, Nechells Park Road, Birmingham, B7 5NQ Tel: 0121-326 5300 Fax: 0121-328 4277 E-mail: john.hawkins@pilkington.com
Pilkington Sealed Units, Churchbridge Indust Estate, Oldbury, West Midlands, B69 4FH Tel: 0121-541 1601 Fax: 0121-552 3748 E-mail: sealed.units@pilkington.com
Pilkington UK Ltd, Unit 26 Bermondsey Trading Estate, Rotherhithe New Road, London, SE16 3LE Tel: (020) 7252 0004 Fax: (020) 7237 1428 E-mail: glazing@pilkington.com
Solaglas Ltd, Trinity Trading Estate, Mill Way, Sittingbourne, Kent, ME10 2PD Tel: (01795) 421534 Fax: (01795) 473651
Tough Glass Ltd, 158 Harbour Road, Kilkeel, Newry, County Down, BT34 4AU Tel: (028) 4176 3444 Fax: (028) 4176 3252 E-mail: johna@toughglass.com
Tyneside Safety Glass, Kingsway North, Team Valley Trading Estate, Gateshead, Tyne & Wear, NE11 0JX Tel: 0191-487 5064 Fax: 0191-487 0358 E-mail: sales@safetyglass.co.uk
Walford E A Chelmsford, Navigation Road, Chelmsford, CM2 6HD Tel: (01245) 262426 Fax: (01245) 352301

SAFETY GLASS PRODUCTION PLANT

Glasstech Ltd, PO Box 62, Worcester, WR4 9RQ Tel: (01905) 723663 Fax: (01905) 20400 E-mail: sales@glasstech.com
▶ Glassworks Ltd, Runcorn Road, Birmingham, B12 8QP Tel: 0121-442 2073 Fax: 0121-442 2079

SAFETY GLASS REPLACEMENT SERVICES

All Regions, B 2 Miller Road, Bedford, MK42 9NY Tel: (01234) 355388 Fax: (01234) 355504 E-mail: all.regions@ntlworld.com
Greenberg Glass Ltd, 10 Bard St, Birmingham, B11 4SA Tel: 0121-753 1900 Fax: 0121-772 3683 E-mail: website@greenbergglass.co.uk
Pilkington UK Ltd, Unit 26 Bermondsey Trading Estate, Rotherhithe New Road, London, SE16 3LE Tel: (020) 7252 0004 Fax: (020) 7237 1428 E-mail: glazing@pilkington.com
Warner Glass Croydon Ltd, 431 Brighton Road, South Croydon, Surrey, CR2 6YG Tel: (020) 8660 9271 Fax: (020) 8668 0374

SAFETY GUARDS

Baker Thompson Ltd, 371 Selsdon Road, South Croydon, Surrey, CR2 6PT Tel: (020) 8681 1952 Fax: (020) 8760 9935 E-mail: sales@thompsonplastics.com

SAFETY HARNESS FITTINGS AND HOOKS

Chapman & Smith Ltd, Safir Works, South Street, East Hoathly, Lewes, East Sussex, BN8 6EW Tel: (01825) 840323 Fax: 01825 840827 E-mail: sales@chapman-smith.co.uk
I S C Ltd, Deiniolen, Caernarfon, Gwynedd, LL55 3DE Tel: (01286) 871999 Fax: (01286) 870127 E-mail: sales@iscwales.com
Make Fast Ltd, 31 Mochdre Industrial Estate, Mochdre, Newtown, Powys, SY16 4LE Tel: (01686) 629010 Fax: (01686) 626700 E-mail: sales@makefast.com

SAFETY HARNESS TAGGING SYSTEMS

▶ Safetytags.co.uk, 1 Beverley Drive, Kimberley, Nottingham, NG16 2TW Tel: 0115-938 2810 Fax: 0115-938 2810 E-mail: sales@safetytags.co.uk

SAFETY HARNESSES, *See also headings for particular types*

Capital Safety Group Ltd, 7 Christleton Court, Manor Park, Runcorn, Cheshire, WA7 1ST Tel: (01928) 571324 Fax: (01928) 571325 E-mail: csgne@csgne.co.uk
Clippa Safe Ltd, Lanthwaite Road, Nottingham, NG11 8LD Tel: 0115-921 1899 Fax: 0115-984 5554 E-mail: sales@clippasafe.co.uk
Gecko Safety Systems Ltd, Unit M5 Cherrycourt Way, Leighton Buzzard, Bedfordshire, LU7 4UH Tel: (01525) 382040 Fax: (01525) 378956 E-mail: info@geckosafety.co.uk
Honey Bros, New Pond Road, Peasmarsh, Guildford, Surrey, GU3 1JR Tel: (01483) 575098 Fax: (01483) 535608 E-mail: sales@honeybros.co.uk
Spanset Ltd, Telford Way, Middlewich Bus Industrial, Park, Middlewich, Cheshire, CW10 0HX Tel: (01606) 737494 Fax: (01606) 737502 E-mail: sales@spanset.com
Total Restraint Systems Ltd, Unit 4 Hurricane Close, Old Sarum, Salisbury, SP4 6LG Tel: (01722) 326080 Fax: (01722) 334437 E-mail: post@totalrestarint.com

SAFETY HELMETS, FIREFIGHTER/PARAMEDIC

Helmet Integrated Systems, 3 Focus 4, Fourth Avenue, Letchworth Garden City, Hertfordshire, SG6 2TU Tel: (01462) 478000 Fax: (01462) 478010 E-mail: sales@helmets.co.uk
O C A S Ltd, PO Box 228, Maidenhead, Berkshire, SL6 6PQ Tel: (01628) 510260 Fax: (01628) 510261 E-mail: ocas@vossnet.co.uk

SAFETY INTERLOCKS

Fortress Interlocks Ltd, Birmingham New Road, Wolverhampton, WV4 6NT Tel: (01902) 499600 Fax: (01902) 499610 E-mail: sales@fortress-interlocks.co.uk
Lockwise Lock Smiths, Border Road, Wallsend, Tyne & Wear, NE28 6RX Tel: 0191-263 0003 Fax: 0191-263 0075 E-mail: enquiries@lockwise.co.uk

SAFETY LAMPS

The Wolf Safety Lamp Co. Ltd, Saxon Road Works, Heeley, Sheffield, S8 0YA Tel: 0114-255 1051 Fax: 0114-255 7988 E-mail: info@wolf-safety.co.uk

SAFETY LIGHT CURTAINS

Cambrake Ltd, Crescent Mill, Foundry Street, Todmorden, Lancashire, OL14 7NA Tel: (01706) 815711 Fax: (01706) 817967 E-mail: info@cambrake.co.uk

SAFETY LIGHTING

Drum Closures Ltd, Borwick Rails, Millom, Cumbria, LA18 4JT Tel: (01229) 772101 Fax: (01229) 774972 E-mail: sales@drum-closures.co.uk

SAFETY MANAGEMENT TRAINING

▶ Employee Development Forum, Unit 11a Lyons Farm Estate, Lyons Road, Slinfold, Horsham, West Sussex, RH13 0QP Tel: (01403) 791292 Fax: (01403) 791293 E-mail: sales@theedf.com

Key Consultancy Ltd, 277 Birmingham Road, Bromsgrove, Worcestershire, B61 0EP Tel: (01527) 575182 Fax: (01527) 576288 E-mail: sales@thekeyconsultancy.co.uk

Petans Ltd, Bullocks Hill, Horsham St. Faith, Norwich, NR10 3HT Tel: (01603) 891255 Fax: (01603) 890827 E-mail: michael@petans.co.uk

Teesside Training Enterprise Ltd, Middlesbrough Road East, South Bank, Middlesbrough, Cleveland, TS6 6TZ Tel: (01642) 462266 Fax: (01642) 460873 E-mail: info@tte.co.uk

SAFETY (MARINE) EQUIPMENT/ SYSTEMS MANUFRS

Cosalt International Ltd, School Road, Lowestoft, Suffolk, NR33 9NB Tel: (01502) 516731 Fax: (01502) 500659 E-mail: lowestoft@cosalt.co.uk

I Y E England Ltd, 1 Towerfield Road, Shoeburyness, Southend-on-Sea, SS3 9QE Tel: (01702) 291291 Fax: (01702) 291391 E-mail: info@iye-england.co.uk

Jotron (UK) Ltd, Crossland Park, Cramlington, Northumberland, NE23 1LA Tel: (01670) 712000 Fax: (01670) 590265 E-mail: salesair@jotron.com

Land & Marine Products Ltd, 32 Woolmer Way, Bordon, Hampshire, GU35 9QF Tel: (01420) 474484 Fax: (01420) 489002 E-mail: sales@landandmarine.co.uk

P G Products Ltd, Folgate Road, North Walsham, Norfolk, NR28 0AJ Tel: (01692) 500390 Fax: (01692) 402863 E-mail: sales@pgproducts.com

Piplers Chandlers, The Quay, Poole, Dorset, BH15 1HF Tel: (01202) 673056 Fax: (01202) 683065 E-mail: sales@piplers.co.uk

Raymarine Ltd, Quaypoint, North Harper Road, Portsmouth, PO6 3TD Tel: (023) 9269 3611 Fax: (023) 9269 4642 E-mail: info@raymarine.com

Resmar Ltd, Adec House, Fitzherbert Road, Portsmouth, PO6 1RU Tel: (023) 9221 5700 Fax: (023) 9237 6744 E-mail: sales@resmar.co.uk

Umoe Schat Harding Ltd, Mumby Road, Gosport, Hampshire, PO12 1AE Tel: (023) 9258 1331 Fax: (023) 9258 2565 E-mail: sales@schat-harding.co.uk

SAFETY NET TRAINING

Pro Net Uk Ltd, Bloomhill Road, Moorends, Doncaster, South Yorkshire, DN8 4SP Tel: (01405) 817557 Fax: (01405) 741277

SAFETY NETS

Fastnets UK Ltd, 20l Hall End Business Park, A5 Watling Street Dordon, Dordon, Tamworth, Staffordshire, B78 1SZ Tel: (01827) 899101 Fax: (0870) 6091707 E-mail: sales@fastnetsuk.com

Safehire Safety Netting Ltd, 96 Cobham Road, Ferndown Industrial Estate, Wimborne, Dorset, BH21 7RE Tel: (01202) 855330 Fax: (01202) 855331

Sicor International Ltd, 3 Murcar Industrial Estate, Denmore Road, Bridge of Don, Aberdeen, AB23 8JW Tel: (01224) 707560 Fax: (01224) 707561 E-mail: sales.sicorabdn@virgin.net

SAFETY NETTING

Enserve Corporation, Parkway House, Worth Way, Keighley, West Yorkshire, BD21 5LD Tel: (0800) 0377817 E-mail: info@enserve.co.uk

Pro Net Uk Ltd, Bloomhill Road, Moorends, Doncaster, South Yorkshire, DN8 4SP Tel: (01405) 817557 Fax: (01405) 741277

SAFETY NETTING SUPPORT SYSTEMS

Fastnets UK Ltd, 20l Hall End Business Park, A5 Watling Street Dordon, Dordon, Tamworth, Staffordshire, B78 1SZ Tel: (01827) 899101 Fax: (0870) 6091707 E-mail: sales@fastnetsuk.com

Pro Net Uk Ltd, Bloomhill Road, Moorends, Doncaster, South Yorkshire, DN8 4SP Tel: (01405) 817557 Fax: (01405) 741277

SAFETY OR FIRST AID SIMULATION EXERCISE TRAINING

Aberdeen Drilling Consultants Ltd, 58 Queens Road, Aberdeen, AB15 4YE Tel: (01224) 209123 Fax: (01224) 209579 E-mail: adcltd@msn.com

Corporate Health Ltd, 30 Bradford Road, Slough, SL1 4PG Tel: (01753) 781600 Fax: (01753) 517889 E-mail: enquiries@corporatehealth.co.uk

First Aid Supplies & Training Wales, 305 Gladstone Road, Barry, South Glamorgan, CF63 1NL Tel: (01446) 735680 Fax: (01446) 735680

First For Aid Training, 30 Cennon Group, Ingleby Barwick, Stockton-On-Tees, Cleveland, TS17 5DB Tel: (01642) 769014 E-mail: firstforaid@talk21.com

▶ First Response, Unit 1, 48 Beacon Lane, Exeter, EX4 8LJ Tel: (01392) 499951 Fax: (01392) 499696

Intek Europe, 24 Thomas Drive, Newport Pagnell, Buckinghamshire, MK16 8TH Tel: (01908) 610093 E-mail: sales@intek.co.uk

Nutec Centre For Safety, Nutec Centre For Safety, Haverton Hill Industrial Estate, Billingham, Cleveland, TS23 1PZ Tel: (01642) 566656 Fax: (01642) 563224 E-mail: enquiries@nutecuk.com

Stockport Engineering Training Association Ltd, Hammond Avenue, Stockport, Cheshire, SK4 1PQ Tel: 0161-480 9822 Fax: 0161-477 4720 E-mail: julie-burns@lineone.net

Wallace, Cameron & Co. Ltd, 26 Netherhall Road, Netherton Industrial Estate, Wishaw, Lanarkshire, ML2 0JG Tel: (01698) 354600 Fax: (01698) 354700 E-mail: sales@wallacecameron.com

SAFETY PROCESS CONTROLLER SYSTEMS

Chilworth Technology Ltd, Beta House Enterprise Road, Chilworth Science Park, Chilworth, Southampton, SO16 7NS Tel: (023) 8076 0722 Fax: (023) 8076 7866 E-mail: info@chilworth.co.uk

Emerson Process Management, Meridian East, Leicester, LE19 1UX Tel: 0116-282 2822 Fax: 0116-289 2896

SAFETY RELAYS

Dold Industries, 11 Hamberts Road, Blackall Industrial Estate, South Woodham Ferrers, Chelmsford, CM3 5UW Tel: (01245) 324432 Fax: (01245) 325570 E-mail: admin@dold.co.uk

Pilz Automation Technology, Willow House, Medlicott Close, Oakley Hay Business Park, Corby, Northamptonshire, NN18 9NF Tel: (01536) 460766 Fax: (01536) 460866 E-mail: sales@pilz.co.uk

▶ Rayleigh Instruments Ltd, Raytel House, 19 Brook Road, Rayleigh, Essex, SS6 7XH Tel: (01268) 749300 Fax: (01268) 749309 E-mail: sales@rayleigh.co.uk

SAFETY RELIEF VALVES

Auld Valves Ltd, Finlas Street, Cowlairs Industrial Estate, Glasgow, G22 5DQ Tel: 0141-557 0515 Fax: 0141-558 1059 E-mail: bob@auldvalves.com

B I S Valves Ltd, Unit 17 Kingfisher Park, Three Cross Road, West Moors, Wimborne, Dorset, BH21 6US Tel: (01202) 896322 Fax: (01202) 896718 E-mail: info@bisvalves.co.uk

Fort Vale Engineering Ltd, Parkfield Works, Brunswick Street, Nelson, Lancashire, BB9 0SG Tel: (01282) 440000 Fax: (01282) 440046 E-mail: sales@fortvale.com

G J Johnson & Sons Ltd, 7 Trinity Court, Brunel Road, Totton, Southampton, SO40 3WX Tel: (023) 8066 9666 Fax: (023) 8066 9606 E-mail: sales@johnsonvalves.com

NABIC, Delta Road, Parr, St. Helens, Merseyside, WA9 2ED Tel: (01744) 451616 Fax: (01744) 26791 E-mail: enquiries@deltafluidproducts.com

Safety Systems UK Ltd, Sharp Street, Worsley, Manchester, M28 3NA Tel: (01925) 820281 Fax: 0161-799 4335 E-mail: support@safetysystemsuk.com

Taylor Valves Ltd, Dowker Works, Dowker Street, Milnsbridge, Huddersfield, HD3 4JX Tel: (01484) 651177 Fax: (01484) 645854

SAFETY SEATS, CHILD IN MOTOR CAR

Airbags International Ltd, Viking Way, Congleton, Cheshire, CW12 1TT Tel: (01260) 294300 Fax: (01260) 294301

Britax Excelsior Ltd, 1 Churchill Way West, Andover, Hampshire, SP10 3UW Tel: (01264) 333343 Fax: (01264) 334146

S C S London Ltd, Success House, Works Road, Letchworth Garden City, Hertfordshire, SG6 1LP Tel: (01462) 484858 Fax: (01462) 485029 E-mail: bma@scs.co.uk

SAFETY SHUT OFF VALVES

James Southerton Ltd, Unit 24A, Reddicap Trading Estate, Sutton Coldfield, West Midlands, B75 7BU Tel: 0121-378 0194 Fax: 0121-378 3438 E-mail: rjsd@southertons.com

SAFETY SHUTDOWN SYSTEMS

Arden Control Systems Ltd, Arden Street, New Mills, High Peak, Derbyshire, SK22 4NS Tel: (01663) 746060 Fax: (01663) 746189 E-mail: sales@ardencontrolsystems.co.uk

Invensys Systems (UK) TLtd, 2 City Place, Beehive Ring Road, London Gatwick Airport, Gatwick, West Sussex, RH6 0PA Tel: (01293) 527777 Fax: (01293) 552640

Yokogawa UK Ltd, Solar House, Mercury Park, Wycombe Lane, Wooburn Green, High Wycombe, Buckinghamshire, HP10 0HH Tel: (01628) 535640 Fax: (0870) 2384342 E-mail: christine.amos@uk.yokogawa.co.uk

SAFETY SIGNS

Acorn Signs, 203 London Road, Stoke-on-Trent, ST4 5RW Tel: (01782) 412020 Fax: (01782) 412259

Allsteed Signs & Graphics Ltd, Unit 4 & 5 Palmerston Business Park, New Gate Lane, Fareham, Hampshire, PO14 1DJ Tel: (01329) 234224 Fax: 01329 317659 E-mail: sales@allspeedsigns.co.uk

Centurion Components Ltd, 38 Carron Place, East Kilbride, Glasgow, G75 0TS Tel: (01355) 265222 Fax: (01355) 230331 E-mail: sales@centurionsigns.co.uk

A.J. Darling & Sons Ltd, Unit 1, Mereway Road, Twickenham, TW2 6RF Tel: (020) 8898 5555 Fax: (020) 8898 9874 E-mail: darlingsigns@aol.com

Deltaband Ltd, 2280 Coventry Road, Sheldon, Birmingham, B26 3JR Tel: 0121-742 9922 Fax: 0121-742 9933 E-mail: enquiries@deltaband.co.uk

Denmark Signs, 150 London Road, Bedford, MK42 0PS Tel: (01234) 269025 Fax: (01234) 269025 E-mail: sales@denmarksigns.co.uk

Doric Productions Ltd, 6-8 Kellner Road, London, SE28 0AX Tel: (020) 8316 0222 Fax: (020) 8316 0316 E-mail: sales@doricsigns.co.uk

Essex Graphic Signs, Cobwebs, 26 Scarletts, Basildon, Essex, SS14 2HZ Tel: (01268) 293293 Fax: (01268) 452525 E-mail: sign.sales@virgin.net

Eureka Direct, Unit 5, Sterte Road Industrial Estate, Sterte Road, Poole, Dorset, BH15 2AF Tel: (0800) 3580085 Fax: (0800) 3580095 E-mail: sales@eurekadirect.co.uk

Euro Signs UK Ltd, 92 Cato Street, Hartlands, Birmingham, B7 4TS Tel: 0121-359 5566 Fax: 0121-359 5354 E-mail: sales@europlate.com

G S Fire Protection, 46 Gotham Road, Birmingham, B26 1LB Tel: 0121-244 4747 Fax: 0121-693 3883 E-mail: info@gsfireprotection.co.uk

Gemini Group, Unit 21 Derryloran Industrial Estate, Sandholes Road, Cookstown, County Tyrone, BT80 9LU Tel: (028) 8676 1292 Fax: (028) 8676 5566 E-mail: sales@thegeminigroup.co.uk

Gpa Signs & Graphics, 51 Rowms Lane, Swinton, Mexborough, South Yorkshire, S64 8AA Tel: (01709) 588856 Fax: (01405) 815503 E-mail: gpa.signs@virgin.net

The Harris Sign Group Ltd, Springfield Road, Coventry, CV1 4GN Tel: (024) 7622 9950 Fax: (024) 7638 1320

Hollywood Signs Ltd, Coal Valley Business Park, Westwood Avenue, Birmingham, B11 3RF Tel: 0121-773 3123 Fax: 0121-773 3324 E-mail: sales@hollywoodsigns.co.uk

I R S Ltd, Lion Works, Castle Acre Road, Swaffham, Norfolk, PE37 7HS Tel: (01760) 721399 Fax: (01760) 723726 E-mail: sales@irs-ltd.co.uk

Infosigns Signs & Nameplates, Unit 1 Howsell Road Industrial Estate, Malvern, Worcestershire, WR14 1UJ Tel: (01684) 577744 Fax: (01684) 566862 E-mail: info@infosigns.uk.com

J A M Design Screen Print, 143a Croydon Road, Caterham, Surrey, CR3 6PF Tel: (01883) 343444 Fax: (01883) 343444 E-mail: jim.rimmington@btinternet.com

Jemco, The Street, Manor Farm, Calthorpe, Norwich, NR11 7QR Tel: (01263) 761798 Fax: (01263) 768142 E-mail: jim@jemco.fsnet.co.uk

Kingfisher Facilities Group, Kingfisher House, Rowan Way, New Balderton, Newark, Nottinghamshire, NG24 3AU Tel: (01636) 610776 Fax: (01636) 610150 E-mail: kingfisher.graphics@ntlworld.com

Lancashire County Engineering Services, Dewhurst Row, Bamber Bridge, Preston, PR5 6BB Tel: (01772) 628323 Fax: (01772) 532343 E-mail: hq@lces.lancscc.gov.uk

Leda-Lite International Ltd, The Briars, Mayes Lane, Sandon, Chelmsford, CM2 7RP Tel: (01245) 227500 Fax: (01245) 221673 E-mail: leda-lite-international@aol.com

Magna Display Systems Ltd, Unit 13 Alliance Close, Attleborough Fields Industrial Estate, Nuneaton, Warwickshire, CV11 6SD Tel: (024) 7632 0032 Fax: (024) 7635 0213 E-mail: info@magnadisplaysystems.co.uk

Omnisigns Ltd, Devereux Way, Boston Road Industrial Estate, Horncastle, Lincolnshire, LN9 6AU Tel: (01507) 522000 Fax: (01507) 523710 E-mail: sales@omnisigns.co.uk

Paragon Signs & Labels Ltd, Paragon House, Homefield Road, Haverhill, Suffolk, CB9 8QP Tel: (01440) 761405 Fax: (01440) 712147 E-mail: sales@paragon-signs.co.uk

Phillips Payne Products Ltd, Crabtree Farm, Church Street, Newnham, Daventry, Northamptonshire, NN11 3ET Tel: (01327) 879100 Fax: (01327) 871633 E-mail: mh@icm-cambs.co.uk

Plastics W Graham Ltd, 114 Cowgate, Dundee, DD1 2JU Tel: (01382) 223734 Fax: (01382) 201799 E-mail: sales@pwgsigns.com

S K Signs & Labels Ltd, The Brookside Centre, Sumpters Way, Southend-on-Sea, SS2 5RR Tel: (01702) 462401 Fax: (01702) 662404 E-mail: info@sksigns.co.uk

Seaward Safety Ltd, 24 Harvest Drive, Lowestoft, Suffolk, NR33 7NJ Tel: (01502) 512834 Fax: (01502) 512837 E-mail: mail@seawardsafety.co.uk

The Sign Shop (Horsham) Ltd, 55a Park Terrace East, Horsham, West Sussex, RH13 5DJ Tel: (01403) 268988 Fax: (01403) 253085 E-mail: enquiries@thesignshop.co.uk

Signs & Labels Ltd, Willow Business Park, 21 Willow Lane, Mitcham, Surrey, CR4 4NA Tel: (020) 8274 3700 Fax: (020) 8274 3702 E-mail: sales@signsandlabels.co.uk

Signs & Safety Ltd, Unit 6 Fairlawn Enterprise Park, Bonehurst Road, Redhill, RH2 7QT Tel: (01737) 246969 Fax: (01737) 247979 E-mail: info@signsandsafety.co.uk

Signwise Sign Services Ltd, 4 Challenger Way, Peterborough, PE1 5EX Tel: (01733) 565770 Fax: (01733) 563384 E-mail: info@signwisesignservices.co.uk

Simply Read, Stanley Road, Hartlepool, Cleveland, TS25 1QP Tel: (01429) 868866 Fax: (01429) 868866 E-mail: sales@simply-read.com

Slater Signs, Unit 32 Crayford Industrial Estate, Swaisland Drive, Crayford, Dartford, DA1 4HS Tel: (01322) 558409 Fax: (01322) 554474 E-mail: sales@slatersigns.co.uk

Snell Signs & Supplies Ltd, 243-245 Cleethorpe Road, Grimsby, South Humberside, DN31 3BE Tel: (01472) 342000 Fax: (01472) 240027

Stalwart Signs & Industrial Supplies Ltd, Anglian House Admiralty Road, Great Yarmouth, Norfolk, NR30 3DY Tel: (01493) 857410 Fax: (01493) 852383 E-mail: stalwartsafety@dsl.pipex.com

Symbol Signs, 3 Rennie Road, Skippers Lane Industrial Estate, Middlesbrough, Cleveland, TS6 6PX Tel: (01642) 467533 Fax: (01642) 463393 E-mail: symbolsigns@btconnect.com

Symbol Signs, 21 St. Peters Street, Nottingham, NG7 3EN Tel: 0115-979 1456 Fax: 0115-979 0987 E-mail: info@symbol-signs.freeserve.co.uk

SAFETY SPECTACLES

The Manor Optical Co. Ltd, Manor House, Dudley Road, Halesowen, West Midlands, B63 4LS Tel: 0121-550 2609 Fax: 0121-550 5915 E-mail: sales@manor-optical.co.uk

Ophthalmic Technologies, Dominion Way, Worthing, West Sussex, BN14 8NW Tel: (01903) 212316 Fax: (01903) 212317 E-mail: charmain.otl@btconnect.com

▶ Retrospecs.co.uk, 20 George Street, St. Albans, Hertfordshire, AL3 4ES Tel: (01727) 761048 E-mail: admin@retrospecs.co.uk

▶ Roope Robert Opticians Ltd, 20 George Street, St. Albans, Hertfordshire, AL3 4ES Tel: (01727) 857798 E-mail: robert@roope.co.uk

SAFETY STAFF ATTACK SYSTEMS

Dove Technology UK Ltd, 8 London Road, Worcester, WR5 2DL Tel: (01905) 353153 Fax: (01905) 352863 E-mail: sales@dovetech.co.uk

Lismore Instruments Ltd, 2 Tristar Business Centre, Star Road, Partridge Green, Horsham, West Sussex, RH13 8RA Tel: (01403) 713121 Fax: (01403) 713141 E-mail: sales@intercall.com

▶ Sensorium Ltd, 9 Nethertown Broad Street, Dunfermline, Fife, KY12 7DS Tel: (01383) 720600 Fax: (01383) 739793 E-mail: info@sensorium.co.uk

SAFETY STEPS

Coningsby Metals Ltd, 47-49 Silver Street, Coningsby, Lincoln, LN4 4SG Tel: (01526) 342141 Fax: (01526) 343382 E-mail: sales@cml-gt.co.uk

G P C Industries Ltd, Market St, Spilsby, Lincolnshire, PE23 5JT Tel: (01790) 753835 Fax: (01790) 752109 E-mail: sales@gpcind.co.uk

Hyprosteps Ltd, Unit 6-7 Brandon Business Centre, Putney Close, Brandon, Suffolk, IP27 0PA Tel: (01842) 815972 Fax: (01842) 815347 E-mail: hyprosteps@aol.com

Redhill Manufacturing Ltd, Unit 6, Padgets Lane, South Moons Moat Industrial Estate, Redditch, Worcestershire, B98 0RA Tel: (01527) 529002 Fax: (01527) 523950 E-mail: sales@redhillmanufacturing.co.uk

Wilman Equipment Ltd, Baker Street, Bradford, West Yorkshire, BD2 4NX Tel: (01274) 636977 Fax: (01274) 636714

SAFETY STORAGE EQUIPMENT/ SYSTEMS

Denios Ltd, Unit 1 - 3, Audley Avenue Enterprise Park, Newport, Shropshire, TF10 7DW Tel: (01952) 811991 Fax: (01952) 825687 E-mail: sales@denios.co.uk

SAFETY SURFACING, PLAYGROUND

▶ Playtop Ltd, Brunel House, Jessop Way, Newark, Nottinghamshire, NG24 2ER Tel: (01636) 614180 Fax: (01636) 610222 E-mail: sales@playtop.com

SAFETY SWITCHES

Kay Electrical Swansea Ltd, 345 Llangyfelach Road, Brynhyfryd, Swansea, SA5 9LQ Tel: (01792) 461753 Fax: (01792) 460470 E-mail: kay.electrical@virgin.net

Mechan Controls Ltd, 14 Seddon Place, Stanley Industrial Estate, Skelmersdale, Lancashire, WN8 8EB Tel: (01695) 722264 Fax: (01695) 729664 E-mail: info@mechancontrols.co.uk

Otter Controls Ltd, Hardwick Square South, Buxton, Derbyshire, SK17 6LA Tel: (01298) 762300 Fax: (01298) 72664 E-mail: sales@ottercontrols.com

SAFETY SYSTEM DESIGN

▶ Safetywise Solutions Limited, Corner House, Main Road, South Reston, Louth, Lincolnshire, LN11 8JJ Tel: (01507) 4 50865 E-mail: info@safetywise.co.uk

SAFETY VALVES

▶ Smart Valves Ltd, Uxbridge Road, Leicester, LE4 7ST Tel: 0116-268 8120 Fax: 0116-261 0050 E-mail: sales@smartvalves.co.uk

SAIL CUTTERS

Lyteze Products Ltd, 8 Colne Road, Brightlingsea, Colchester, CO7 0DL Tel: (01206) 302699 Fax: (01206) 302699 E-mail: annecook@lyteze.com

SAIL MAKING ACCESSORIES OR HARDWARE

▶ Blue Sails, Garage Street, Llandudno, Conwy, LL30 1DW Tel: (01492) 879914

SAILING CLOTHING

C & L Products, Tall Trees, Lazenbys Estate, Walliswood, Dorking, Surrey, RH5 5RE Tel: (01306) 627721 Fax: (01306) 627721 E-mail: sales@c-lproducts.co.uk

Henri Lloyd International Ltd, Smithfold Lane, Worsley, Manchester, M28 0GP Tel: 0161-799 1212 Fax: 0161-975 2500 E-mail: information@henrilloyd.co.uk

Musto Ltd, Christy Way, Laindon, Basildon, Essex, SS15 6TR Tel: (01268) 491555 Fax: (01268) 491440 E-mail: marketing@musto.co.uk

▶ Ocean Leisure, 11-14 Northumberland Avenue, London, WC2N 5AQ Tel: (020) 7930 5050 Fax: (020) 7930 3032 E-mail: info@oceanleisure.co.uk

▶ Tack N Jibe, Flat 1, 2 Linden Road, Bexhill-on-Sea, East Sussex, TN40 1DN Tel: (07917) 341778

SAILS

Arun Sails Ltd, The Sail Centre Southfields Industrial Estate, Delling Lane, Bosham, Chichester, West Sussex, PO18 8NW Tel: (01243) 573185 Fax: (01243) 573032 E-mail: arun@sailmakers.com

Banks Sails Ltd, 372 Brook Lane, Sarisbury Green, Southampton, SO31 7ZA Tel: (01489) 582444 Fax: (01489) 589789 E-mail: enquiries@banks.co.uk

▶ Barford Sails, 11 Nothe Parade, Weymouth, Dorset, DT4 8TX Tel: (01305) 768282

▶ Batt Sails, 10 Broadbridge Business Centre, Delling Lane, Bosham, Chichester, West Sussex, PO18 8NF Tel: (01243) 575505 Fax: (01243) 574404 E-mail: info@battsails.com

C & J Marine Textiles, Clay Lane, Chichester, West Sussex, PO19 3JG Tel: (01243) 785485 Fax: (01243) 785487 E-mail: sales@cjmarine.co.uk

▶ Concept Sails, Unit B1, Romany Centre Business Park, Wareham Road, Holton Heath, Poole, Dorset, BH16 6JL Tel: (01202) 623355

Crusader Sails, The Sail Loft, Cobbs Quay, Poole, Dorset, BH15 4EU Tel: (01202) 670580 Fax: (01202) 675578 E-mail: info@cruisadersails.com

East Coast Sales Limited, Woolverstone Marina, Woolverstone, Ipswich, IP9 1AS Tel: (01473) 780007 Fax: (01473) 780007

G Stanley, 5 Wyke Street, Hull, HU9 1PA Tel: (01482) 225590 Fax: (01482) 588764 E-mail: sales@gstanleys.co.uk

Garland Sails, 246a Soundwell Road, Bristol, BS15 1PN Tel: 0117-935 3233 Fax: 0117-935 3233 E-mail: garlandsails@ukonline.co.uk

Gowen Ocean Sailmakers Ltd, 130 Coast Road, West Mersea, Colchester, CO5 8PG Tel: (01206) 384412 Fax: (01206) 382834 E-mail: sales@gosails.com

Hood Sailmakers Ltd, Bath Road, Lymington, Hampshire, SO41 3RW Tel: (01590) 675011 Fax: (01590) 673797 E-mail: sales@hoodsails.com

J Mccready & Co. Ltd, 123 Corporation Street, Belfast, BT1 3EJ Tel: (028) 9023 2842 Fax: (028) 9023 6187

James Lawrence, 22-28 Tower Street, Brightlingsea, Colchester, CO7 0AL Tel: (01206) 302863 Fax: (01206) 305858

Jeckells Of Wroxham Ltd, Station Road, Hoveton, Norwich, NR12 8UT Tel: (01603) 782223 Fax: (01603) 784023 E-mail: sails@jeckells.co.uk

Lonton & Gray Sailmakers, 61c High Street, Burnham-on-Crouch, Essex, CM0 8AH Tel: (01621) 786200 Fax: (01621) 786201 E-mail: dicklonton@clara.net

Mcwilliam Sailmakers Ltd, Cowes Yacht Haven, Vectis Yard, Cowes, Isle of Wight, PO31 7AY Tel: (01983) 281100 Fax: (01983) 281101 E-mail: keith@mcwsales.co.uk

Maxiroach Ltd, Unit 2 Crowarch Lane Industrial Estate, Ringwood, Hampshire, BH24 1PG Tel: (01425) 480408 Fax: (01425) 480996 E-mail: sales@easyreef.com

Mitchell Sails, 28 North Street, Fowey, Cornwall, PL23 1DD Tel: (01726) 833731 Fax: (01726) 833731 E-mail: info@sailmakers.uk.com

Mouse Sails, Porthdafarch, Holyhead, Gwynedd, LL65 2LP Tel: (01407) 763636 Fax: (01407) 763049

M. Nicol & Co. Ltd, Unit 5, Slaidburn Crescent, Southport, Merseyside, PR9 9YF Tel: (01704) 509667 Fax: (01704) 509669

Nicolson Hughes Sails (Sailmakers), Silverhills, Rosneath, Helensburgh, Dunbartonshire, G84 0RW Tel: (01436) 831356 Fax: (01436) 831356 E-mail: sailmaker@nh-sails.co.uk

Number One Sails, New Road, Middlestown, Wakefield, West Yorkshire, WF4 4NS Tel: (01924) 274073 Fax: (01924) 274073

Penrose, 50 Church Street, Falmouth, Cornwall, TR11 3DS Tel: (01326) 312705 Fax: (01326) 312033 E-mail: robbie@penrosesales.freeserve.co.uk

Performance Sails, Victoria Loft, Hill Furze, Pershore, Worcestershire, WR10 2NB Tel: (01386) 861161 Fax: (01386) 861253 E-mail: performancesails@hotmail.com

Quay Sails Poole Ltd, 20 Lagland Street, Poole, Dorset, BH15 1QG Tel: (01202) 681128 Fax: (01202) 668270 E-mail: info@quaysails.com

Ratsey & Lapthorn Ltd, 37 Medina Road, Cowes, Isle of Wight, PO31 7BX Tel: (01983) 294051 Fax: (01983) 294053 E-mail: ratseysails@ratsey.com

Rochester Sails, 1 Old Cottages, Backfields, Rochester, Kent, ME1 1UH Tel: (01634) 407557 Fax: (01634) 407557

S K B Sails, The Sail Loft, Commercial Road, Penryn, Cornwall, TR10 8AG Tel: (01326) 372107 Fax: (01326) 373792

Sail Register, 4 Yarborough Court, Ulceby, South Humberside, DN39 6RZ Tel: (01469) 589444

Sail Style, 2 St. Marys Road, Unit 6, Hayling Island, Hampshire, PO11 9BY Tel: (023) 9246 3720 Fax: (023) 9246 6451 E-mail: info@sailstyle.co.uk

Sails & Canvas, 10 The Quay, The Strand, Topsham, Exeter, EX3 0JB Tel: (01392) 877527 Fax: (01392) 876258

▶ Saltern Sail Co., Gasworks Lane, Norton, Yarmouth, Isle of Wight, PO41 0SE Tel: (01983) 760120 Fax: (01983) 760120

Tedford Rigging & Rafts, Unit 24 Ormeau Business Park, 8 Gromac Avenue, Belfast, BT7 2JA Tel: (028) 9032 6763 Fax: (028) 9023 4566 E-mail: info@tedfords.co.uk

Valiant Sails, 7 Fullbridge, Maldon, Essex, CM9 4LE Tel: (01621) 853558 Fax: (01621) 853566 E-mail: osc@chandler.eu.com

W Sails, 51 Southsea Avenue, Leigh-on-Sea, Essex, SS9 2AX Tel: (01702) 714550 Fax: (01702) 714550

Wilkinson Sails, Swale Marina, Conyer, Teynham, Sittingbourne, Kent, ME9 9HN Tel: (01795) 521503 Fax: (01795) 521503 E-mail: wilkinsonsails@yahoo.co.uk

SALADS

▶ Gowrie Growers, Longforgan, Dundee, DD2 5HJ Tel: (01382) 360620

Hillhampton Salads, Hillhampton, Great Witley, Worcester, WR6 6JU Tel: (01299) 896717 Fax: (01299) 896717 E-mail: laura@hillhamptonsalads.co.uk

SALES AND MARKETING SERVICES

▶ Mailboosters, The Gables, Holt Hill, Beoley, Redditch, Worcestershire, B98 9AT Tel: (0870) 4421862 Fax: (0870) 0664267 E-mail: enquiries@responsegeneration.co.uk

▶ SalesFirst Limited, Regency House, 6-7 Elwick Road, Ashford, Kent, TN23 1PD Tel: 01233 638888 E-mail: enquiries@salesfirst.co.uk

SALES FORCE PERSONNEL RECRUITMENT AGENCIES/ CONSULTANTS/SERVICES

▶ Adams Franklin, 4 Adelaid Terrace, Northampton, NN2 6AH Tel: (01604) 633000 E-mail: cv@adamsfranklin.com

▶ allretailrecruitment, PO Box 551, Chesterfield, Derbyshire, S40 9BX Tel: 01246 551255

▶ Ascend Recruitment, Trym Lodge, 1 Henbury Road, Westbury-on-Trym, Bristol, BS9 3HQ Tel: 0117-310 1270 Fax: 0117-310 1271 E-mail: mail@ascendrecruitment.net

BMS, Mead House, 49 High Street, Egham, Surrey, TW20 9EW Tel: (01784) 434334 Fax: (01784) 435584 E-mail: jobs@bms-uk.com

▶ Burne & Walsh Ltd, Regus House, 268 Bath Road, Slough, SL1 4DX Tel: (01753) 708419 Fax: (01753) 708810 E-mail: info@burnewalsh.co.uk

C V Screen, 12 Octagon Court, High Wycombe, Buckinghamshire, HP11 2HS Tel: (01494) 769191 Fax: (01494) 447621 E-mail: matt@cvscreen.co.uk

Executive Facilities Ltd, 43 High Street, Marlow, Buckinghamshire, SL7 1BA Tel: (01628) 898556 Fax: (01628) 898139 E-mail: eft@efrecruitment.co.uk

Garrett Lloyd Ltd, Unit 39-40 Derwent Business Centre, Clarke Street, Derby, DE1 2BU Tel: (01332) 206219 Fax: (01332) 206225 E-mail: recruitment@garrett-lloyd.com

▶ HighVeld Select, P O Box 196, Morpeth, Northumberland, NE61 6WQ Tel: (01670) 789965

L A International, International House, Festival Way, Stoke-on-Trent, ST1 5UB Tel: (01782) 203000 Fax: (01782) 203050 E-mail: mail@lainternational.co.uk

Park Recruitment Partnership, Webster House, Dudley Road, Tunbridge Wells, Kent, TN1 1LE Tel: (01892) 535351 Fax: (01892) 543020 E-mail: sales@partjobs.com

▶ Pitch Perfect (UK) Ltd., Communications House, 26 York Street, London, W1U 6PZ Tel: 0845 351 0615 E-mail: info@pitchperfect.biz

Salesvacancies.Com, Charter House, Unit 1 South Bourne Business Park, Eastbourne, East Sussex, BN22 8UY Tel: (01323) 739995 Fax: (01323) 721990 E-mail: sales@salesvacancies.com

▶ UK Sales Jobfinders Ltd, Saffron Walden, Essex, CB11 4JL Fax: (01799) 541117 E-mail: info@salesjobsfinder.co.uk

Whitehall Recruitment Ltd, 37-41 High Street, Edenbridge, Kent, TN8 5AD Tel: (01732) 864777 Fax: (01732) 865777 E-mail: info@whitehall.uk.com

Ken Wilson Associates, 25 Collingwood Street, Newcastle upon Tyne, NE1 1JE Tel: 0191-261 7171 Fax: 0191-232 0146 E-mail: debra@kwa.co.uk

SALES LEAD GENERATION SERVICES

▶ Business Calls Direct, Pentland House, Pentland Park, Glenrothes, Fife, KY6 2AH Tel: (01592) 777800 Fax: (01592) 772860

▶ Lead-In Research, Walton Road, 13-14 Wellesbourne House, Wellesbourne, Warwick, CV35 9JB Tel: (01789) 471555 Fax: (01789) 471550 E-mail: info@leadinresearch.co.uk

SALES LEAD INFORMATION SERVICES

▶ China Company Research Services Ltd, Catherinefield House, Catherinefield Business Park, Dumfries, DG1 3PQ Tel: (01387) 247588 Fax: (01387) 257143 E-mail: info@ccrs.info

Emap Glenigan, 41-47 Seabourne Road, Bournemouth, BH5 2HU Tel: (0800) 373771 Fax: (01202) 431204 E-mail: info@glenigan.emap.com

SALES PROMOTION CONSULTANTS OR SERVICES

Applied Management Techniques, 33 Harts Leap Road, Sandhurst, Berkshire, GU47 8EW Tel: (01344) 773153 Fax: (01344) 776216

The Brightstart Company Services Ltd, Kersal, Woodlands Lane, Windlesham, Surrey, GU20 6AH Tel: (01276) 850644 Fax: (0870) 1384969 E-mail: promotions@brightstart.plus.com

Case Alarms Ltd, Unit 5 Taff Workshops, Tresillian Terrace, Cardiff, CF10 5DE Tel: (029) 2038 7006 Fax: (029) 2038 7006 E-mail: cardiff@casesecurity.co.uk

Chartered Institute Of Marketing, Moor Hall, The Moor, Cookham, Maidenhead, Berkshire, SL6 9QH Tel: (01628) 427500 Fax: (01628) 427499 E-mail: marketing@cim.co.uk

Copyright Promotions, 6th Floor, 3 Shortlands, London, W6 8PP Tel: (020) 8563 6400 Fax: (020) 8563 6465E-mail: sales@cprg.com

D A Marketing & Communications Ltd, Prince Consort House, 109-111 Farringdon Road, London, EC1R 3BW Tel: (020) 7841 0088 E-mail: enquiries@damarketing.co.uk

Direct Know How, 17 St. Annes Court, London, W1F 0BQ Tel: (020) 7734 3532 Fax: (020) 7734 1779 E-mail: postmaster@tsm-direct.co.uk

Euro RSDG Riley, Hanover House, Queen Charlotte Street, Bristol, BS1 4LG Tel: 0117-925 7777 Fax: 0117-925 7001 E-mail: nick.brian@eurorscg-riley.co.uk

▶ The Farmyard, 5 Samuel Court, Templecombe, Somerset, BA8 0JN Tel: (01963) 370841 E-mail: info@the-farmyard.com

Impress Solutions Ltd, 268-272 North Street, Romford, RM1 4QN Tel: (01708) 759760 Fax: (01708) 759761 E-mail: accounts@impress-solutions.com

Innovative Marketing International Ltd, 21 Dorset Square, London, NW1 6QE Tel: (020) 7723 7228 Fax: (020) 7723 1192 E-mail: enquiries@innovativemarketing.co.uk

KLP, 109 Wardour Street, London, W1F 0UH Tel: (020) 7478 3400 Fax: (020) 7478 3578 E-mail: sales@klpeuroscd.co.uk

Lambert Smith Hampton, 79 Mosley Street, Manchester, M2 3LQ Tel: 0161-228 6411 Fax: 0161-228 7354 E-mail: manchester@lsh.co.uk

Mando Brand Assurance Ltd, 27-28 Faraday Road, Rabans La Industrial Area, Aylesbury, Buckinghamshire, HP19 8TY Tel: (01296) 717900 Fax: (01296) 394273

▶ Market Synergies Ltd, 65 Cannon Court Road, Maidenhead, Berkshire, SL6 7QP Tel: (0790) 9993682 E-mail: enquiries@marketsynergies.co.uk

Mithril Racing Ltd, Goodwood Airfield, Goodwood, Chichester, West Sussex, PO18 0PH Tel: (01243) 528815 Fax: (01243) 771522 E-mail: chris@mithril.co.uk

N C H Marketing Services Ltd, Earls Tree Industrial Estate, Corby, Northamptonshire, NN17 4DU Tel: (01536) 400123 Fax: (01536) 443319 E-mail: shagan@nchmarketing.co.uk

One For One Ltd, 121-141 Westbourne Terrace, London, W2 6JR Tel: (020) 7706 2306 Fax: (020) 7258 3757

O'Sullivan Promotions, 18 Bankes Avenue, Orrell, Wigan, Lancashire, WN5 8HU Tel: (01942) 707071 Fax: (01942) 515000

Procurement International Ltd, Falcon House, 30 Ivanhoe Road, Hogwood Industrial Estate, Finchampstead, Wokingham, Berkshire, RG40 4QQ Tel: 0118-973 4422 Fax: 0118-973 0808 E-mail: info@procurement.ltd.uk

Promotional Fabrics Ltd, The Maltings, School Lane, Amersham, Buckinghamshire, HP7 0ES Tel: (01494) 724172 Fax: (01494) 725283 E-mail: enquiries@amershamfabrics.com

Roche Diagnostics Ltd, Charles Avenue, Burgess Hill, West Sussex, RH15 9RY Tel: (01273) 480444 Fax: (0808) 1008060 E-mail: lewes.info-uk@roche.com

Selby Marketing Services, Ormonde St Works, Ormonde Street, Ashton-under-Lyne, Lancashire, OL6 8JQ Tel: 0161-339 5132 Fax: 0161-343 1005 E-mail: sales@selby-marketing.co.uk

Stopford Graham & Co. Ltd, Chapel House, 1 Borough Road, Altrincham, Cheshire, WA15 9RA Tel: 0161-941 1024 Fax: 0161-926 9773

Western Industries Co. Ltd, 5 Garage Road, Queens Drive, London, W3 0HE Tel: (020) 8992 1360 Fax: (020) 8993 7780 E-mail: w.industries@talk21.com

Yes Response Ltd, Unit 15 Brookside Business Park, Brookside Road, Uttoxeter, Staffordshire, ST14 8AU Tel: (01889) 561400 Fax: (01889) 568264 E-mail: dhanley@yesresponse.co.uk

SALES RECRUITMENT AGENCIES, CONSTRUCTION INDUSTRY

allretailrecruitment, PO Box 551, Chesterfield, Derbyshire, S40 9BX Tel: 01246 551255
Misura Recruitment Services Ltd, PO BOX 625, Rotherham, South Yorkshire, S60 9BB Tel: (01709) 739278 Fax: (01709) 739278 E-mail: info@misurajobs.co.uk
Network Property Consulting & Construction, Network House, 119 Hagley Road, Birmingham, B16 8LB Tel: 0121-450 5020 Fax: 0121-450 5021E-mail: osb@netrec.co.uk
theCONSTRUCTIONjob.com, PO Box 2448, Slough, SL1 1ZB Tel: 0870 8701193 Fax: 0870 8701194 E-mail: coz.dauncey@theconstructionjob.com

SALES RECRUITMENT AGENCIES, MEDIA INDUSTRY

Misura Recruitment Services Ltd, PO BOX 625, Rotherham, South Yorkshire, S60 9BB Tel: (01709) 739278 Fax: (01709) 739278 E-mail: info@misurajobs.co.uk
Target Talent, 23 Castalia Square, London, E14 3NG Tel: (0845) 0097030 Fax: (0871) 7143355 E-mail: info@ttrec.co.uk

SALES TRAINING SPECIALISTS/ SALESMANSHIP SCHOOLS

Alison Hodge Associates, 12 Heathfield Gardens, London, W4 4JY Tel: (020) 8995 5485 Fax: (020) 8995 4341 E-mail: alisonhodge@dial.pipex.com
Answers Training International Ltd, Rose Lodge, Old Potbridge Road, Winchfield, Hook, Hampshire, RG27 8BT Tel: (01252) 845500 Fax: (01252) 845585 E-mail: info@answers-group.com
Michael Barratt, Field House, Ascot Road, Holyport, Maidenhead, Berkshire, SL6 3LD Tel: (01628) 770800 Fax: (01628) 627737 E-mail: michael@mbarrett.co.uk
Marcus Bohn Associates Ltd, Studio House, Delamare Road, Cheshunt, Waltham Cross, Hertfordshire, EN8 9SH Tel: (01992) 633882 Fax: (01992) 627831 E-mail: sales@marcusbohn.co.uk
Business & Employment Skills Training Ltd, 20 Eglinton Street, Irvine, Ayrshire, KA12 8AS Tel: (01294) 313144 Fax: (01294) 313177
Huthwaite International, Hoober House, Hoober, Rotherham, South Yorkshire, S62 7SA Tel: (01709) 710081 Fax: (01709) 710065 E-mail: sales@huthwaite.co.uk
Influence International, Cedar Crt, London, SE1 3GA Tel: (07802) 944593 E-mail: csykes@influenceinternational.com
Ridgemond Training, Caxton Way, Stevenage, Hertfordshire, SG1 2DF Tel: (01438) 842200 Fax: (01438) 842250 E-mail: c.collins@ridgemond.freeserve.co.uk
S T T Associates, PO Box 18, Ledbury, Herefordshire, HR8 2YR Tel: (01531) 633604 Fax: (01531) 632790
Sales Training UK, Davies Avenue, Leeds, LS8 1JZ Tel: (0870) 1998962 Fax: (0709) 2037133 E-mail: john.pykett@ntlworld.com
Spearhead Training, 19 Cheriton House Cromwell Park Banbury Road, Chipping Norton, Oxfordshire, OX7 5SR Tel: (01608) 644144 Fax: (01608) 649680 E-mail: info@spearhead-training.co.uk
Spence Associates, 41 Francis Gardens, Winchester, Hampshire, SO23 7HD Tel: (01962) 867425 Fax: (01962) 841425 E-mail: sales@spencea.com
Thomson Net G Ltd, 1 Hogarth Business Park, Burlington Lane, London, W4 2TJ Tel: (020) 8994 4404 Fax: (020) 8994 5611

SALMON

Orkney Herring Co. Ltd, Garson Industrial Estate, Stromness, Orkney, KW16 3JU Tel: (01856) 850514 Fax: (01856) 850568 E-mail: sales@orkneyherring.com
West Coast Smoked Foods Ltd, Stonebarn, Gilgarran, Workington, Cumbria, CA14 4RF Tel: (01946) 834475 Fax: (01946) 833996 E-mail: info@westcoastseafoods.co.uk

SALMON POACHERS

West Coast Smoked Foods Ltd, Stonebarn, Gilgarran, Workington, Cumbria, CA14 4RF Tel: (01946) 834475 Fax: (01946) 833996 E-mail: info@westcoastseafoods.co.uk

SALT, *See also headings for particular types*

Cleveland Potash Ltd, Boulby Mine, Loftus, Saltburn-by-the-Sea, Cleveland, TS13 4UZ Tel: (01287) 640140 Fax: (01287) 640934 E-mail: jan.hunton@clevelandpotash.co.uk
Direct Salt Supplies Ltd, Runcorn, Cheshire, WA7 4JE Tel: (0845) 6030444 Fax: (0845) 6030333 E-mail: direct.salt@ineofenterprises.com
Dri Pak Ltd, Furnace Road, Ilkeston, Derbyshire, DE7 5EP Tel: 0115-932 5165 Fax: 0115-944 0297 E-mail: sales@dripak.co.uk
Firenzi Asphalte Drayton Park Ltd, Triumph Trading Estate, Tariff Road, London, N17 0EB Tel: (020) 8801 8016 Fax: (020) 8801 8015
Holme, Dodsworth (Rock Salt) Ltd, 59-69 Heaton Park Road, Newcastle upon Tyne, NE6 1SQ Tel: 0191-265 9077 Fax: 0191-276 5125
Maldon Crystal Salt Co. Ltd, Wycke Hill Business Park, Wycke Hill, Maldon, Essex, CM9 6UZ Tel: (01621) 853315 Fax: (01621) 858191 E-mail: sales@maldonsalt.co.uk
F.W.P. Matthews Ltd, Station Road, Shipton-Under-Wychwood, Chipping Norton, Oxfordshire, OX7 6BH Tel: (01993) 830342 Fax: (01993) 831615
New Cheshire Salt Works Ltd, Wincham Lane, Wincham, Northwich, Cheshire, CW9 6DD Tel: (01606) 42361 Fax: (01606) 48333 E-mail: general@ncsw.co.uk
O S O Products Ltd, 5-7 Hanbury Street, Droitwich, Worcestershire, WR9 8PL Tel: (01905) 795300 Fax: (01905) 797707
Peacock Salt Ltd, North Harbour, North Harbour Street, Ayr, KA8 8AE Tel: (01292) 292000 Fax: (01292) 292001 E-mail: info@peacocksalt.co.uk
RHM Ltd, Prospect Works, Spa Street, Cobridge, Stoke-On-Trent, ST6 2LN Tel: (01782) 286711 Fax: (01782) 264352 E-mail: jphillips@centura.co.uk
Stratton Sales Ltd, 1 Station Road, Shepton Mallet, Somerset, BA4 5DD Tel: (01749) 344071 Fax: (01749) 346134 E-mail: info@strattonsales.co.uk
Walker Eurosalt Ltd, 6 Northern Road, Belfast, BT3 9AL Tel: (028) 9074 8551 Fax: (028) 9075 4937 E-mail: info@chem-vite.co.uk

SALT BATH BRAZING

Electrobase RP Ltd, 7 Maxim Road, Dartford, DA1 4BG Tel: (01322) 555938 Fax: (01322) 555099 E-mail: sales@electrobaserp.co.uk
Expert Heat Treatments Kent, 12 Tribune Drive, Trinity Trading Estate, Sittingbourne, Kent, ME10 2PT Tel: (01795) 426545 Fax: (01795) 424449 E-mail: southsales@eht.co.uk

SALT IMPORT/EXPORT MERCHANTS OR AGENTS

Broste Ltd, Unit 8 North Lynn Business Village, Bergen Way, North Lynn Industrial Estate, King's Lynn, Norfolk, PE30 2JG Tel: (01553) 776066 Fax: (01553) 767319 E-mail: broste.uk@broste.com
Darlington Group plc, Bankfields Drive, Wirral, Merseyside, CH62 0AZ Tel: 0151-328 5600 Fax: 0151-328 5605 E-mail: martin@darlingtons-group.co.uk
INEOS Enterprises Ltd, Salt Business, Mersey View Road, Weston Point, Runcorn, Cheshire, WA7 4HB Tel: (0800) 590810 Fax: (01928) 572261 E-mail: salt-enquiries@ineosenterprises.com
Peacock Salt Ltd, North Harbour, North Harbour Street, Ayr, KA8 8AE Tel: (01292) 292000 Fax: (01292) 292001 E-mail: info@peacocksalt.co.uk

SALTED PEANUTS

Trigon Snacks Ltd, Atherton Road, Liverpool, L9 7AQ Tel: 0151-523 8700 Fax: 0151-521 5370 E-mail: sales@trigon-snacks.com

SAME DAY COURIER SERVICES

1Coast-2-Coast, 54 Foads Lane, Cliffsend, Ramsgate, Kent, CT12 5JJ Tel: (07921) 355318 Fax: (01843) 581045 E-mail: c2ccouriers@aol.com
2nd 2 None Ltd, 235 Beehive Lane, Chelmsford, CM2 9SH Tel: (07815) 290214 Fax: (01245) 602046 E-mail: info@2nd2noneltd.com
3d Courier Services, 71 Furnace Lane, Sheffield, S13 9XD Tel: (07817) 708363 E-mail: info@3dcourier.com
3-Towns Courier Services, 1 New England Road, Saltcoats, Ayrshire, KA21 6JT Tel: (07890) 981 974 Fax: (01294) 471 294 E-mail: sean.docherty@3-townscourierservices.co.uk
A N C Kent Ltd, Gateway Centre, Castle Road, Sittingbourne, Kent, ME10 3RN Tel: (01795) 413620 Fax: (01795) 413610 E-mail: sales0008@anc.co.uk
A N Logistics, 18 Canal Side, Beeston, Nottingham, NG9 1NG Tel: (0800) 8818167 Fax: 0845 4660167 E-mail: alan@anlogistics.co.uk
A S A P Same Day Delivery Service, 30 Clarendon Court, Winwick Quay, Warrington, WA2 8QP Tel: (01925) 637453 E-mail: pete@asapsameday.com
A Spriggs Courier Services, 46 Garth Avenue, Normanton, West Yorkshire, WF6 1DJ Tel: (01924) 782005 E-mail: andy@aspriggs.com
A3 Light Haulage, Suite 8 Enterprise Centre, Bowen Industrial Estate, Aberbargoed, Bargoed, Mid Glamorgan, CF81 9EP Tel: (01443) 839622 Fax: (01443) 839622 E-mail: info@a3lighthaulage.co.uk
Ace Courier Services, 13 Ullswater Road, Tyldesley, Manchester, M29 7AQ Tel: (01942) 873990 Fax: (01942) 709137 E-mail: al63@blueyonder.co.uk
ADR Qwik-Trak Couriers, Park Road, Hagley, Stourbridge, West Midlands, DY9 0NS Tel: (07812) 126717 Fax: (01562) 884234 E-mail: despatch@qwik-trak.co.uk
AG Transport Services, 26 Mill Acre Close, Ilkeston, Derbyshire, DE7 9JQ Tel: 0115-876 9368 E-mail: t.garbett@ntlworld.com
Alders of Corsham, 61 Northleaze, Bradford Road, Corsham, Wiltshire, SN13 0QP Tel: (01249) 713939 Fax: (01249) 701845 E-mail: bookings@aldersofcorsham.co.uk
All-Ways Couriers, Unit 6 Owen O' Cork Mills, Beersbridge Road, Belfast, BT5 5DX Tel: (028) 9073 2468 Fax: (028) 9045 7010 E-mail: info@allwayscouriers.com
Anywhere Same Day Couriers, Manchester Business Park, 3000 Aviator Way, Manchester, M22 5TG Tel: (0845) 4567722 Fax: (0870) 4323377 E-mail: info@anywhere.ltd.uk
Arrow Light Haulage, 18 Fletcher Drive, Wickford, Essex, SS12 9FA Tel: 01375 643897 E-mail: kevinscorpion@aol.com
Barry Ward, 10 Vowell Close, Bristol, BS13 9HS Tel: (07831) 447764 Fax: 0117-904 4859 E-mail: barry@barrywardcourierservices.co.uk
Black Cat Cars Ltd, 312 Channelsea Business Centre, Canning Road, London, E15 3ND Tel: (020) 8555 4545 Fax: (020) 8519 2333 E-mail: office@BlackCatCouriers.co.uk
Bromley Sameday Couriers, 16 Amesbury Road, Bromley, BR1 2QJ Tel: 07783 238436 E-mail: jamesmaycock@bromleysamedaycouriers.co.uk
The Bullit Courier Company Ltd, 12 Charlotte Street, Brighton, BN2 1AG Tel: (0845) 2268556 E-mail: info@bullitcouriers.com
C & R Transport Ltd, 24-26 High Street, Snodland, Kent, ME6 5DF Tel: 08703 121247
Carousel, Gateway Centre Eurolink Industrial Centre, Castle Road, Sittingbourne, Kent, ME10 3RN Tel: (01795) 413600 Fax: (01795) 413610 E-mail: sales@carousellogistics.co.uk
CDL Couriers, 32 Raymond Drive, Bradford, West Yorkshire, BD5 8HS Tel: (01274) 206329 E-mail: cdlcouriers@yahoo.co.uk
Confidential Couriers, The Willows, The Cadney, Bettisfield, Whitchurch, Shropshire, SY13 2LP Tel: (0800) 2983485 Fax: (01948) 710730 E-mail: confcouriers@aol.com
Corby Courier Services, 4 Lovap Way, Great Oakley, Corby, Northamptonshire, NN18 8JL Tel: (01536) 742412 Fax: (01536) 742412 E-mail: sales@corbycouriers.co.uk
Courier Connect, McKean Road, Birmingham, B69 4BA Tel: (07813) 519 954 Fax: 0121-544 6231 E-mail: info@courierconnect.co.uk
Courier Network Systems, K 301 Tower Bridge Business Complex, 100 Clements Road, London, SE16 4DG Tel: (020) 7231 9030 Fax: (020) 7231 9102 E-mail: yes@couriernetworks.co.uk
Creative Air Express, Unit 8c Rainbow Industrial Estate, Trout Road, West Drayton, Middlesex, UB7 7XT Tel: (01895) 448072 Fax: (0870) 7777881 E-mail: operations@creativeair.co.uk
Crystal Consult, Barton Road, Nuneaton, Warwickshire, CV10 7BN Tel: (024) 7638 5371 Fax: (024) 7638 5371 E-mail: sales@crystal-consult.co.uk
D L M Distribution, 54 Birch Avenue, Quarry Bank, Brierley Hill, West Midlands, DY5 1BG Tel: (01384) 820511 Fax: E-mail: davem65@hotmail.com
Dagmar Courier Services, 18 St. Rumbold Street, Lincoln, LN2 5AP Tel: (01522) 567588 Fax: (01522) 567588 E-mail: dagmarcouriers@fsmail.net
Deca Freelance Couriers Ltd, 240 Burton Road, Lincoln, LN1 3UB Tel: (01522) 851612 Fax: (01522) 851613 E-mail: deca.couriers3@ntlworld.com
Dispatchit Bath Ltd, 58 Claude Avenue, Bath, BA2 1AG Tel: (01225) 444443 Fax: (01225) 461123 E-mail: dispatchit@btconnect.com
Dna Logistics, Unit 5 Chariot Way, Glebe Farm Industrial Estate, Rugby, Warwickshire, CV21 1DA Tel: (01788) 535111 Fax: (01788) 567117 E-mail: dnalogistics@btconnect.com
Dove Despatch Ltd, 83 Essington Road, Willenhall, West Midlands, WV12 5DT Tel: (01922) 404857 Fax: (01922) 408803 E-mail: sales@dovedespatch.co.uk
Dumfries Carriers, 12 Mosspark Road, Dumfries, DG1 4EE Tel: (01387) 266100 Fax: (01387) 266100 E-mail: samedaycourier@tiscali.co.uk
Easy Parcel Worldwide, Lawlor House, Cawley Hatch, Harlow, Essex, CM19 5AN Tel: (0800) 1804995 Fax: (01279) 433326 E-mail: sales@easyparcelworldwide.com
Ecourier.Co.Uk, Cityside House, 40 Adler Street, London, E1 1EE Fax: (020) 7877 6501 E-mail: mybigquestion@ecourier.co.uk
Essential Deliveries Ltd, 12 Seymour Court, Runcorn, Cheshire, WA7 1SY Tel: (01928) 579001 Fax: (0871) 2215400 E-mail: peter@essentialdeliveries.co.uk
Example Courier Services, 4 Hayfield Close, Baildon, Shipley, West Yorkshire, BD17 6TY Tel: (01274) 585321 Fax: (01274) 583609 E-mail: office@exsamplecourierservices.com
Excel Couriers UK, 11 St. Johns Road, Peterborough, PE2 8BL Tel: (07786) 128197 Fax: (0870) 7625282 E-mail: pete@excel-couriers.co.uk
Express Freight Solutions, 15 Leyden Road, Stevenage, Hertfordshire, SG1 2BW Tel: (01707) 333600 Fax: (01438) 725800 E-mail: enfield@xpd.co.uk
Express Freight Solutions, Marsden Close, Welwyn Garden City, Herts, AL8 6YE Tel: 0870 3505300 Fax: 0870 3505301 E-mail: info@expressfreightsolutions.com
Fleetlink, Rose Cottage, Churchway, Curry Rivel, Langport, Somerset, TA10 0EF Tel: (01458) 259581 Fax: (01458) 259582 E-mail: jeff@fleetlink.org.uk
G S G Cargo Ltd, Unit 14 Northbrook Business Park, Northbrook Road, Worthing, West Sussex, BN14 8PQ Tel: (01903) 204666 Fax: (01903) 212966 E-mail: sales@gsgcargo.com
Gazelle Logistics, 42 Robert Cort Industrial Estate, Britten Road, Reading, RG2 0AU Tel: 0118-975 6777 Fax: 0118-975 6778 E-mail: info@getgazelle.com
Grease Lightning, 22 Windrush Road, Berinsfield, Wallingford, Oxfordshire, OX10 7PF Tel: (01865) 341166 Fax: (01865) 341176 E-mail: greaselightningcouriers@yahoo.co.uk
The Great British Courier Co., 33 Harris Crescent, Needingworth, St. Ives, Cambridgeshire, PE27 4TE Tel: (01480) 465450 E-mail: gbcc@btinternet.com
A.J. Griffiths Transport, 193 Birmingham Road, Walsall, WS1 2NX Tel: (07976) 372316 Fax: (07789) 909005
GT Express Logistics, 283 Henwick Road, Worcester, WR2 5PG Tel: 07976 835328 E-mail: gillypep79@hotmail.com
Handy Vans, 23 West Street, Enderby, Leicester, LE19 4LT Tel: 0116-286 9249 E-mail: sales@handyvans.co.uk
Alan Harvey, 76 Curbar Road, Great Barr, Birmingham, B42 2AU Tel: (0786) 3555365 Fax: E-mail: aharvey76@hotmail.com
Steve Hobbs Logistics, 8 Harrowden Road, Luton, LU2 0SP Tel: (01582) 457040 Fax:
Interparcel, Norman House, 15 Stephenson Way, Crawley, West Sussex, RH10 1TN Tel: 08700 273733 Fax: 01293 785990 E-mail: sales@interparcel.com
J 4 Deliveries Ltd, Cromer House, Caxton Way, Stevenage, Hertfordshire, SG1 2DF Tel: (01438) 236022 Fax: (01438) 236023 E-mail: j4deliveries@aol.com
J D Haulage, 1 Wayside Crescent, Eccleshill, Bradford, West Yorkshire, BD2 2JY Tel: (01274) 626999 Fax: (01274) 402381 E-mail: denise@jd-haulage.co.uk
J G S Couriers, 13 Crown Meadow, Lower Broadheath, Worcester, WR2 6QJ Tel: (01905) 640518 Fax: (01905) 640518 E-mail: info@jgscouriers.co.uk
J W Services, 31 Woodview Avenue, Baildon, Shipley, West Yorkshire, BD17 7LG Tel: (01274) 530928 Fax: (01274) 530928 E-mail: jwservices999@hotmail.com
Jarvis Couriers, 109 Oakridge Road, Basingstoke, Hampshire, RG21 5RW Tel: (01256) 884103 Fax: (01256) 361753
JMC PARCELS T/A FASTWAY COURIERS, 37 SOUTHFIELD RD, CUMBERNAULD, G68 9DZ Tel: 01236 732018 E-mail: paul@paul474.wanadoo.co.uk
Kage Express Delivery, 24 Japonica Gardens, St. Helens, Merseyside, WA9 4WP Tel: (07841) 112210 E-mail: info@samedaynationwide.co.uk
KCR Transport & Removals, 447 Burton Road, Midway, Swadlincote, Derbyshire, DE11 7NB Tel: (0800) 4488839 Fax: 01283 211934 E-mail: kevin@kcrtransport.co.uk
Kimberley Couriers, 35 Cotswold Road, Stourbridge, West Midlands, DY8 4UW Tel: (0800) 7833681 Fax: (01384) 443396 E-mail: info@kimberleycouriers.com
Logistical Services Limited, 58 Hellesdon Park Road, Drayton High Road, Norwich, NR6 5DR Tel: 01603 484569 Fax: 01603 427100 E-mail: simon.feilden@comment.uk.net
LTG Couriers, Unit B12, Parkside Commercial Centre, Terry Avenue, York, YO23 1JP Tel: 08000 191211 Fax: 0871 8710028 E-mail: info@ltg-ltd.com
Lucas Express Couriers, 11 Benbow Close, Hinckley, Leicestershire, LE10 1RQ Tel: (01455) 634705 E-mail: rich@lucasexpress.co.uk
M & A Couriers, 6 Stanley Close, Sherburn, Durham, DH6 1JS Tel: 0191-372 1210 Fax: 0191-372 1210 E-mail: info@maac.co.uk
MDBXPRESS, 9 Flax Gardens, Kings Norton, Birmingham, B38 9QY Tel: (07917) 784210 Fax: 0121-451 3272 E-mail: enquiries@mdbxpress.co.uk
Mitchell Storage & Distribution Ltd, Unit 12 The Warren, East Goscote, Leicester, LE7 3XA Tel: 0116-260 4080 Fax: 0116-260 4081 E-mail: sales@ncexpress.com
Monarkle Couriers, 154 Cannock Road, Wednesfield, Wolverhampton, WV10 8PX Tel: (01902) 563354 E-mail: courier@monarkle.com
Mr D's Couriers Ltd, Gothic House, Barker Gate, Nottingham, NG1 1JU Tel: (0870) 7506396 Fax: (0870) 7506397 E-mail: mrdscouriers@hotmail.com
MVP Couriers, 64 Toms Town Lane, Studley, Warwickshire, B80 7QP Tel: (01527) 458716 E-mail: mickpegg@supanet.com

SAME DAY COURIER SERVICES – *continued*

▶ N S T Direct Ltd, Premium House, Hambridge Road, Newbury, Berkshire, RG14 5SS Tel: (01635) 31177 Fax: (01635) 31184 E-mail: info@nstdirect.co.uk

Neill Transport, 3 Walker Road, Irlam, Manchester, M44 6ZL Tel: 0161-288 3864 Fax: 0161-288 3864 E-mail: adrian@neill6562.fsbusiness.co.uk

▶ Nightspeed Services Ltd, Delta Wharf Trading Estate, Tunnel Avenue, London, SE10 0QH Tel: (020) 8858 5282 Fax: (020) 8858 1861 E-mail: acceptabell@yahoo.co.uk

▶ Northwest Couriers, 30 Whitfield Cross, Glossop, Derbyshire, SK13 8NW Tel: (07939) 540345 E-mail: gleatherbarrow@hotmail.com

▶ NTS International Express Ltd, 3 Capel Close, Leacon Road, Ashford, Kent, TN23 4GY Tel: (01233) 637722 Fax: (01233) 637733 E-mail: ashford@nts-express.co.uk

▶ OneDay Couriers, Unit 629, Great Northern House, 275 Deansgate, Manchester, M3 4EL Tel: 0800 8818178

▶ The Online Courier, 17 Armada Drive, Teignmouth, Devon, TQ14 9NF Tel: (0845) 6447069 E-mail: info@theonlinecourier.co.uk

▶ Orbital Express, 2 Falcon Road, Dewsbury, West Yorkshire, WF12 9NH Tel: (01924) 439977 E-mail: svali@orbital-express.co.uk

▶ P.D.Q.Logistics, 11 The Lizard, Wymondham, Norfolk, NR18 9BH Tel: (07944) 087289 E-mail: pdqlogistics@hotmail.co.uk

▶ P H D Couriers, 158 Coneygree Road, Stanground, Peterborough, PE2 8LQ Tel: (01733) 560270 E-mail: phday68@yahoo.co.uk

P Harcombe Couriers, Bretby Business Park, Ashby Road, Bretby, Burton-on-Trent, Staffordshire, DE15 0YZ Tel: (01283) 219903 Fax: (01283) 219903 E-mail: paulhark@madasafish.com

▶ P&S Couriers (Croydon), 112 Hartscroft, Croydon, CR0 9LE Tel: 0800 5118348 E-mail: pscouriers@hotmail.com

▶ Patni Express, 127 Milton Avenue, London, E6 1BN Tel: (0870) 9504837 Fax: (0870) 9503897 E-mail: info@patniexpress.com

▶ Paul Harrison Deliveries, 31 Pool Street, Southport, Merseyside, PR9 8HZ Tel: 07770 727490 Fax: 01704 505151 E-mail: Info@phdeliveries.co.uk

▶ PDQ Couriers (York), Netherwindings, Haxby, York, YO32 3FB Tel: (01904) 760180 Fax: (01904) 760180 E-mail: pdqcouriers@fsmail.net

▶ Pend Logistics, 62 St. Marys Road, Edmonton, London, N9 8NJ Tel: (07957) 728769 E-mail: sales@pendlog.com

▶ PSL Couriers, Briarfield Gardens, Bradford, West Yorkshire, BD18 2BE Tel: (07890) 194132 E-mail: pslcouriers@yahoo.co.uk

▶ Rapidline Ltd, Unit 1, 1000 North Circular Road, London, NW2 7JP Tel: 0808 101 6 101 Fax: 020 8830 8379 E-mail: info@doorsteptotheworld.com

Rapidvan Distribution, 15 Murrayfield Terrace, Bannockburn, Stirling, FK7 8NG Tel: (07795) 621490

▶ Reads light haulage & courier service 24/7, 92 Church Lane, Brinsley, Nottingham, NG16 5AB Tel: (07925) 17653 E-mail: david.read67@virgin.net

RTL Couriers Ltd, 2. Astlethorpe Two Mile Ash, Two Mile Ash, Milton Keynes, MK8 8EN Tel: (01908) 568016 Fax: (08707) 620334

▶ Runcorn Express Deliveries, 17 Victoria Road, Runcorn, Cheshire, WA7 5BN Tel: 01928 830280 E-mail: enquiries@runcornexpresscourires.co.uk

▶ Rush Courier Services, 7 Oakleigh Court, Bond Road, Surbiton, Surrey, KT6 7SH Tel: (020) 8241 1341 Fax: (020) 8241 1638 E-mail: info@rushcouriers.co.uk

S I S Stafford, 1 North Avenue, Stafford, ST16 1NP Tel: (01785) 600113 Fax: (01785) 600113E-mail: stafford.couriers@ntlworld.com

▶ S & J Couriers (North Devon), 63 East Ridge View, Bideford, Devon, EX39 4RS Tel: (07815) 814616 Fax: (01237) 420307 E-mail: jamie246@btinternet.com

▶ Sameday Co., Unit 16, Focus 303 Business Centre, Focus Way, Andover, Hampshire, SP10 5NY Tel: (01264) 352352 Fax: (01264) 369001

▶ Same-day Dispatch Services, International House, 226 Seven Sisters Road, London, N4 3GG Tel: 0845 226 2994 E-mail: admin@samedaydispatch.uk.com

▶ Sameday UK, 8 Elstow Close, Eastcote, Ruislip, Middlesex, HA4 9RA Tel: (0800) 435740 Fax: (01925) 292447 E-mail: info@samedayuk.com

▶ Silverbirch Sameday Couriers, Silverbirch Estate, Middleton, Manchester, M24 5JU Tel: 0161-654 7439 E-mail: contact@sscouriers.co.uk

▶ Speedwell Couriers, 23 Plough Lane, Whitstable, Kent, CT5 2NZ Tel: (01227) 792790 E-mail: speedwellcouriers@yahoo.co.uk

▶ Steadfast Courier Services, 34 Caerhendy Street, Merthyr Tydfil, Mid Glamorgan, CF47 9NJ Tel: (07782) 162061 E-mail: steadfastcourier@aol.com

SW Courier Services, 1 Willowbank, Favordale Road, Colne, Lancashire, BB8 7AG Tel: (01282) 861147 Fax: (01282) 861147

▶ T & A Logistics Newcastle Ltd, 8 Holystone Grange, Stonelea, Holystone, Newcastle upon Tyne, NE27 0UX Tel: (07968) 725110 Fax: 0191-215 1300 E-mail: sales@talogistics.co.uk

▶ Tailored Transport Solutions Ltd, 12 Amos Crescent, Scunthorpe, South Humberside, DN16 1RA Tel: (01724) 339169 E-mail: bobby76_373@hotmail.com

▶ Andy Theaker Ltd, 49 Wordsworth Road, Stockport, Cheshire, SK5 6JH Tel: 0161-221 1296 Fax: 0161-221 1178

▶ TM Courier, 52 Chester Road, Stevenage, Hertfordshire, SG1 4LE Tel: (01438) 237667 E-mail: info@tmcourier.co.uk

▶ Topaz Courier Services, 8 Wolverham Road, Ellesmere Port, CH65 5BU Tel: 0151-201 3629 Fax: 0151-201 3629

▶ Transporter, Bexhill Road, Eastbourne, East Sussex, BN22 7JH Tel: (0781) 7332392 Fax:

▶ Tranzlink Storage District, 13 Canyon Road, Netherton Industrial Estate, Wishaw, Lanarkshire, ML2 0EG Tel: (01698) 377000 Fax: 08456 343223 E-mail: sales1@somethingsensible.com

▶ U K Logistic Solutions, Unit 23 Parsonage Ind Est, Forest Hall Road, Stansted, Essex, CM24 8TY Tel: (01279) 817001 Fax: (01279) 817004 E-mail: uklogistics@btconnect.com

▶ Van & Deliver, 3 Warkton Close, Chilwell, Nottingham, NG9 5FR Tel: 0845 1214484 E-mail: enquiries@van-and-deliver.co.uk

▶ Wallace Couriers Ltd, 286 Muswell Hill Broadway, London, N10 2QR Tel: (020) 8352 3634 Fax: (07785) 789024 E-mail: paulwallace@blueyonder.co.uk

▶ Steve Wicks Transport, 19 Crescent Grove, Hartshill, Stoke-On-Trent, ST4 6EN Tel: (01782) 768871 Fax: (01782) 768871 E-mail: stevewickstransport@hotmail.com

▶ Wiltshire Couriers.co.uk, Abercarn, Newtown, Heytesbury, Warminster, Warminster, Wiltshire, BA12 0HN Tel: 01985 840321 Fax: 01985 840321 E-mail: info@wiltshirecouriers.co.uk

SAME DAY DELIVERY SERVICES

▶ A & R Courier & Delivery Service Ltd, CWM Tawel Pontardulais Road, Cross Hands, Llanelli, Dyfed, SA14 6PG Tel: (01269) 845194 Fax: (01269) 845194 E-mail: enqs@swansea-couriers.co.uk

▶ P & H Delivery Services Ltd, Unit 40 Goodwins Yard, Rougham Industrial Estate, Rougham, Bury St. Edmunds, Suffolk, IP30 9ND Tel: (01359) 272797 Fax: (01359) 271700 E-mail: sales@wedeliverit.net

▶ Paul Harrison Deliveries, 31 Pool Street, Southport, Merseyside, PR9 8HZ Tel: 07770 727490 Fax: 01704 505151 E-mail: Info@phdeliveries.co.uk

SAMPLE CASES

Antler Ltd, Pilot Works, Alfred Street, Bury, Lancashire, BL9 9EF Tel: 0161-764 0721 Fax: 0161-764 0723 E-mail: custserv@antler.co.uk

SAMPLE COOLING EQUIPMENT

Fabricated Products, 4 Foundry House, Sheffield Road, Rotherham, South Yorkshire, S60 1BN Tel: (01709) 720842 Fax: (01709) 720846 E-mail: info@fabricatedproducts.co.uk

SAMPLE PREPARATION EQUIPMENT

Cem Microwave Technology Ltd, 2 Middle Slade, Buckingham Industrial Estate, Buckingham, MK18 1WA Tel: (01280) 822873 Fax: (01280) 822342 E-mail: info.uk@cem.com

Datech Scientific Ltd, Unit 13 Step Business Centre, Wortley Road, Deepcar, Sheffield, S36 2UH Tel: (0870) 7469810 Fax: (0870) 7469811E-mail: sales@datech-scientific.co.uk

SAMPLING EQUIPMENT, BOTTOM HOLE, OILWELL

Proserv (North Sea) Ltd, Riverside Business Centre, North Esplanade West, Aberdeen, AB11 5RJ Tel: (01224) 210067 Fax: (01224) 582616 E-mail: info@proservns.co.uk

SAMPLING EQUIPMENT, GAS/ AIR

Gresham Engineering, 104 Maybury Road, Woking, Surrey, GU21 5JL Tel: (01483) 765538 Fax: (01483) 765320 E-mail: sales@hacltd.co.uk

Luxfer Gas Cylinders, Colwick Industrial Estate, Nottingham, NG4 2BH Tel: 0115-980 3800 Fax: 0115-980 3899 E-mail: info@luxfercylinders.com

Mr Plant Hire plc, 120 Hertford Road, Enfield, Middlesex, EN3 5AX Tel: (020) 8351 3434 Fax: (020) 8351 3636 E-mail: info@mrplanthire.co.uk

S K C Ltd, Unit 11, Sunrise Park, Higher Shaftesbury Road, Blandford Forum, Dorset, DT11 8ST Tel: (01258) 480188 Fax: (01258) 480184 E-mail: info@skcltd.com

SAMPLING VALVES

Blackfive Engineering Ltd, 16 Beeston Court, Stuart Road, Manor Park, Runcorn, Cheshire, WA7 1SS Tel: (01928) 579140 Fax: (01928) 579514 E-mail: blackfive@btconnect.com

Tecnica Europe Ltd, Suite 2 Baxall Business Centre, Adswood, Stockport, Cheshire, SK3 8LF Tel: 0161 480 5700 Fax: 0161 447 4476

SAND

Aggregate Industries P.L.C., Garside Sands, Eastern Way, Heath & Reach, Leighton Buzzard, Bedfordshire, LU7 9LF Tel: (01525) 237911 Fax: (01525) 237991 E-mail: emma.george@aggregate.com

Allen Newport Ltd, 31 New Path, Walton House, Fordham, Ely, Cambridgeshire, CB7 5JZ Tel: (01638) 720228 Fax: (01638) 721332 E-mail: info@allen-newport.co.uk

Anglesey Sand Pits, Ogley Hay Road, Newtown, Brownhills, Walsall, WS8 7PR Tel: (01543) 372344

Borough Green Sand Pits Ltd, Commercial Road, Strood, Rochester, Kent, ME2 2AD Tel: (01634) 717515 Fax: (01634) 717153

Boswell Bros (Salisbury) Ltd, Ford, Salisbury, SP4 6DJ Tel: (01722) 333781 Fax: (01722) 327858 E-mail: boswell.broth@virgin.net

Brett Aggregates Ltd, Brett House, Bysing Wood Road, Faversham, Kent, ME13 7UD Tel: (01795) 594051 Fax: (01795) 594027

Brett Aggregates, Waldringfield Road, Brightwell, Ipswich, IP10 0BL Tel: (01473) 621007 Fax: (01473) 736721

Brett Aggregates, North Sea Terminal, Cliffe, Rochester, Kent, ME3 7SX Tel: (01634) 220631 Fax: (01634) 220067

Bucbricks Ardleigh Sands, Martells Industrial Estate, Slough Lane, Ardleigh, Colchester, CO7 7RU Tel: (01206) 230310 Fax: (01206) 231057 E-mail: sands@bucbricks.co.uk

Buckingham Aggregates Ltd, Unit 6 Ballmoor, Buckingham Industrial Estate, Buckingham, MK18 1RT Tel: (01280) 817611 Fax: (01280) 817749

C & G Concrete Ltd, Mansgate Hill, Caistor, Market Rasen, Lincolnshire, LN7 6NT Tel: (01472) 851281 Fax: (01472) 851117

Cemex (NI) Ltd, 30 Creagh Road, Toomebridge, Antrim, BT41 3SE Tel: (028) 7965 0626 Fax: (028) 7965 0204

Moreton C. Cullimore Gravels Ltd, 47 London Road, Stroud, Gloucestershire, GL5 2AU Tel: (01453) 765381 Fax: (01453) 766491

▶ D H Loveday & Son Ltd, 96 Cotterells, Hemel Hempstead, Hertfordshire, HP1 1JG Tel: (01442) 256254

David Ball Group plc, Huntingdon Road, Cambridge, CB23 8HN Tel: (01954) 780687 Fax: (01954) 782912 E-mail: sales@davidballgroup.com

M. Dickerson Ltd, Ely Road, Waterbeach, Cambridge, CB5 9PG Tel: (01223) 860000 Fax: (01223) 440378 E-mail: reception@m-dickerson.co.uk

F G Davis & Sons Contractors Ltd, Smestow Bridge Industrial Estate, Bridgnorth Road, Wombourne, Wolverhampton, WV5 8AY Tel: (01902) 892364 Fax: (01902) 895283

Folkes Plant & Aggregates Ltd, Welcome Pits, Butt Lane, Burgh Castle, Great Yarmouth, Norfolk, NR31 9PY Tel: (01493) 780274 Fax: (01493) 781118

Grant & Stone Ltd, 54 Montem Lane, Slough, SL1 2QJ Tel: (01753) 520462 Fax: (01753) 511582 E-mail: sales@grant-stone.co.uk

J. Handford & Son Ltd, Milford House, 431 Buxton Road, Stockport, Cheshire, SK2 7HE Tel: 0161-487 3888 Fax: 0161-487 4555

Harrison Jewitt Ltd, Flat, The Brickyard, Scotter Road South, Scunthorpe, South Humberside, DN17 2BT Tel: (01724) 281453 Fax: (01724) 281453 E-mail: sales@jewittonline.co.uk

Holderness Aggregates Ltd, Mill Hill Quarry, Hull Road, Keyingham, Hull, HU12 9ST Tel: (01964) 622347

Humber Sand & Gravel Ltd, West Quay, Alexandra Dock, Hedon Road, Hull, HU9 1TA Tel: (01482) 328144 Fax: (01482) 585163

J C Phillips & Son Ltd, 162a South Street, Bridport, Dorset, DT6 3NP Tel: (01308) 422179 Fax: (01308) 421956

J Clubb Ltd, Church Hill, Wilmington, Dartford, DA2 7DZ Tel: (01322) 225431 Fax: (01322) 289932 E-mail: sales@jclubb.co.uk

J Curtis & Sons Ltd, Thrupp Lane, Radley, Abingdon, Oxfordshire, OX14 3NG Tel: (01235) 524545 Fax: (01235) 524545

K T Ivory plc, Harper Lodge Farm, Harper Lane, Radlett, Hertfordshire, WD7 7HU Tel: (01923) 856081 Fax: (01923) 852470 E-mail: ivorys1@btconnect.com

Phillip W. Keen Ltd, 284 High Road, Northweld, Epping, Essex, CM16 6EG Tel: (01992) 524824 Fax: (01992) 524239

Lafarge Aggregates Ltd, Whisby Quarry, Thorpe Road, Whisby, Lincoln, LN6 9BT Tel: (01522) 694342 Fax: (01522) 694226

Longwater Gravel, Longwater Industrial Estate, Dereham Road, New Costessey, Norwich, NR5 0TX Tel: (01603) 743767 Fax: (01603) 747302

Lovie Ltd, Cowbog, New Pitsligo, Fraserburgh, Aberdeenshire, AB43 6PR Tel: (01771) 653777 Fax: (01771) 653527 E-mail: sales@lovie.co.uk

Mid-Essex Gravel Ltd, Essex Regiment Way, Broomfield, Chelmsford, CM3 3PZ Tel: (01245) 440621 Fax: (01245) 442212 E-mail: info@midessexgravel.co.uk

R J Donaghy & Sons, 71b Lissan Road, Cookstown, County Tyrone, BT80 8QX Tel: (028) 8676 3202 Fax: (028) 8676 2835

Ross Hillman Ltd, Station Road, Westbury, Wiltshire, BA13 3JP Tel: (01373) 822447 Fax: (01373) 824492

Rotherham Sand & Gravel Co. Ltd, Scrooby Top Quarry, Scrooby Top, Doncaster, South Yorkshire, DN10 6AY Tel: (01777) 818203 Fax: (01777) 816040

Salisbury & Wood Ltd, Old Coach Road, Tansley, Matlock, Derbyshire, DE4 5FY Tel: (01629) 582272 Fax: (01629) 583989

Scott Toomebridge Ltd, 7 Creagh Road, Toomebridge, Antrim, BT41 3SD Tel: (028) 7965 0461 Fax: (028) 7965 0238 E-mail: sales@scottrooftiles.com

Supermix Concrete, 76 Strabane Road, Newtownstewart, Omagh, County Tyrone, BT78 4JZ Tel: (028) 8166 1391 Fax: (028) 8166 1391

United Marine Aggregates Ltd, Uma House, Shopwhyke Road, Chichester, West Sussex, PO20 2AD Tel: (01243) 817200 Fax: (01243) 817216 E-mail: info@umag.co.uk

William Rainford, Leckwith Road, Bootle, Merseyside, L30 6YF Tel: 0151-525 5991 Fax: 0151-530 1676

Thomas Williams (Euxton) Ltd, Springfield, Wigan Road, Euxton, Chorley, Lancashire, PR7 6LB Tel: (01257) 262642

SAND BAG FILLING HOPPERS

Peel Weld, Rosebank, Church Bank, Llandovery, Dyfed, SA20 0BA Tel: (01550) 720854 Fax: (01550) 720945 E-mail: info@peelweld.co.uk

SAND BAGS

▶ Cliffe Industrial Packaging Ltd, Marshfield Bank Employment Park, Marshfield Bank, Crewe, CW2 8UY Tel: (01270) 212136 Fax: (01270) 212145

M.Laurier & Sons Ltd, Unit 10 Triumph Trading Estate, Tariff Road, London, N17 0EB Tel: (020) 8365 9000 Fax: (020) 8365 9005 E-mail: info@laurier.co.uk

SAND BAGS, POLYPROPYLENE (PP)

▶ Cliffe Industrial Packaging Ltd, Marshfield Bank Employment Park, Marshfield Bank, Crewe, CW2 8UY Tel: (01270) 212136 Fax: (01270) 212145

SAND BLASTING CONTRACTORS

Cameo Glass, Old Saw Mills Road, Faringdon, Oxfordshire, SN7 7DS Tel: (01367) 242421 Fax: (01367) 242978 E-mail: sales@camio-glass.com

Glass Design & Decorating, 7a Queens Road, Sunninghill, Ascot, Berkshire, SL5 9AF Tel: (01344) 623017 Fax: (01344) 623017 E-mail: info@gdd-glassdesign.co.uk

SAND TREATMENT OR WASHING OR PREPARATION PLANT AND EQUIPMENT

C D E Ireland Ltd, Ballyreagh Industrial Estate, Sandholes Road, Cookstown, County Tyrone, BT80 9DG Tel: (028) 8676 7900 Fax: (028) 8676 1414 E-mail: info@cdeireland.com

Howie Minerals Ltd, Dornie Quarry, Torlundy, Fort William, Inverness-Shire, PH33 6SW Tel: (01397) 702227 Fax: (01397) 702308 E-mail: blaurie@howie-forest.co.uk

Quarry Plant & Roadsprays (Q P R), Ivy Mill, Longton Road, Stone, Staffordshire, ST15 8TB Tel: (01785) 812706 Fax: (01785) 811747 E-mail: nsirrigation@aol.com

SANDBLASTING EQUIPMENT

Power Blast International, 9 Colhook Industrial Park, Petworth, West Sussex, GU28 9LP Tel: (01428) 707895 Fax: (01428) 707894 E-mail: sales@powerblast.co.uk

SANDING MACHINES, *See also headings for particular types*

Hire Technicians Group, Chalk Hill House, 8 Chalk Hill, Watford, WD19 4BH Tel: (0845) 2303340 Fax: (0845) 2303345 E-mail: sales@hiretech.biz

SANDWICH BREAD

▶ A J Catering, Concorde House, Concorde Way, Preston Farm Industrial Estate, Stockton-on-Tees, Cleveland, TS18 3RB Tel: (01642) 617948 Fax: (01642) 607906
Aberdeen Catering, 38 Upperkirkgate, Aberdeen, AB10 1BA Tel: (01224) 658588 Fax: (01224) 658588
Barllaeth Bakery & Confectionery Supplies, London House, St Peters Square, Ruthin, Clwyd, LL15 1AA Tel: (01824) 707000
▶ Dorset Cake Co. Ltd, 50 Dorchester Road, Weymouth, Dorset, DT4 7JZ Tel: (01305) 786252 Fax: (01305) 777487 E-mail: office@dorsetcakeco.sagehost.co.uk
Executive Catering Services, 107a High Street, Carrville, Durham, DH1 1BQ Tel: 0191-386 3682 Fax: 0191-383 0280 E-mail: eccs107a@aol.com

SANDWICH FILLINGS

Barllaeth Bakery & Confectionery Supplies, London House, St Peters Square, Ruthin, Clwyd, LL15 1AA Tel: (01824) 707000
Capital Catering Co. Ltd, 4 Bear Court, Daneshill East Industrial Estate, Basingstoke, Hampshire, RG24 8QT Tel: (01256) 470044 Fax: (01256) 818485 E-mail: admin@capitalsandwiches.co.uk

SANITARY INSTALLATION OR SERVICING

Tantofex Ltd, The Bathroom Works, National Avenue, Hull, HU5 4HS Tel: (01482) 346461 Fax: (01482) 445886

SANITARY TOWEL VENDING MACHINES

Lympsham Concrete Supplies, Wharfside, Lympsham, Weston-super-Mare, Avon, BS24 0EZ Tel: (01934) 750257 Fax: (01934) 750257
Unicorn Containers Ltd, 5 Ferguson Drive, Lisburn, County Antrim, BT28 2EX Tel: (028) 9266 7264 Fax: (028) 9262 5616 E-mail: sales@unicorn-containers.com

SANITARY TOWELS

Dambi UK Ltd, Units 24-25, Rassau Industrial Estate, Rassau, Ebbw Vale, Gwent, NP23 5SD Tel: (01495) 350855 Fax: (01495) 350074 E-mail: enquiries@dambi.co.uk
Sabre Supply Co., 35-37 Brent Street, London, NW4 2EF Tel: (020) 8457 1510 Fax: (020) 8201 7368 E-mail: sabre@sabresupply.co.uk

SANITARY WARE

A.G.M. (Distributors) Ltd, 40b Ravenhill Road, Belfast, BT6 8EB Tel: (028) 9045 2613 Fax: (028) 9045 0023 E-mail: sales@agmbuckley.demon.co.uk
A J Plumbing Supplies Ltd, Greenbank Industrial Estate, Rampart Road, Newry, County Down, BT34 2QU Tel: (028) 3026 3348 Fax: (028) 3026 3263 E-mail: info@ajplumbing.co.uk
Aston Matthews Ltd, 141-147a Essex Road, London, N1 2SN Tel: (020) 7226 7220 Fax: (020) 7354 5951 E-mail: sales@astonmatthews.co.uk
B & B Supplies, 641 Garratt Lane, London, SW18 4SX Tel: (020) 8946 2957 Fax: (020) 8946 2435
Cooper Callas Ltd, 3c Gatwick Gate Industrial Estate, Lowfield Heath, Crawley, West Sussex, RH11 0TG Tel: (01293) 551921 Fax: (01293) 526106
Dambi UK Ltd, Units 24-25, Rassau Industrial Estate, Rassau, Ebbw Vale, Gwent, NP23 5SD Tel: (01495) 350855 Fax: (01495) 350074 E-mail: enquiries@dambi.co.uk
Drakes Plumbing Supplies Ltd, 3 Independent Business Park, Imberhorne Lane, East Grinstead, West Sussex, RH19 1TU Tel: (01342) 319123 Fax: (01342) 319136
F B S Engineering & Sanitary Supplies Ltd, Cockburn Works, Gowan Avenue, Falkirk, FK2 7HJ Tel: (01324) 628431 Fax: (01324) 611175E-mail: fsb.distribution@btconnect.com
F & P Wholesale, Chantry Road, Woburn Road Industrial Estate, Kempston, Bedford, MK42 7SU Tel: (01234) 845600 Fax: (01234) 840379
Farmiloe & Farmiloe (WBS) Ltd, 28 Willow Lane, Mitcham, Surrey, CR4 4UH Tel: (020) 8685 6800 Fax: (020) 8685 6850 E-mail: sales@farmilos.com
Folkard Bolding, 27 The Vale, London, W3 7RR Tel: (020) 8749 1021 Fax: (020) 8740 1466
G L M & I S I International Ltd, 143 Woburn Tower, Broomcroft Avenue, Northolt, Middlesex, UB5 6HU Tel: (07956) 877690 Fax: (020) 8845 1010 E-mail: hawigeorge@hotmail.com
H M James & Sons Ltd, 736 Romford Road, London, E12 6BT Tel: (020) 8477 1000 Fax: (020) 8478 4091 E-mail: mail@hmjames.co.uk
Jewson Ltd, Orchard Road, Royston, Hertfordshire, SG8 5HA Tel: (01763) 241561 Fax: (01763) 247759
Jobec UK Ltd, Stonnall House Farm, Mill Lane Lower Stonnall, Stonnall, Walsall, WS9 9HN Tel: (01543) 483172 Fax: (01543) 483173 E-mail: jobec@tinyworld.co.uk
Scobles, Anerley Railway Station, Anerley Station Road, London, SE20 8PY Tel: (020) 8676 7700 Fax: (020) 8676 7711 E-mail: sales@scobles.co.uk
Stainless Design Services Ltd, C The Old Bakery, Kiln Lane, Swindon, SN2 2NP Tel: (01793) 692666 Fax: (01793) 487242 E-mail: sds@stainlessdesign.co.uk
Twyford Bathrooms Ltd, Lawton Road, Alsager, Stoke-on-Trent, ST7 2DF Tel: (01270) 879777 Fax: (01270) 873864

SANITARY WARE MOULDS

▶ Bathrooms Etc, 102-104 Hammersmith Road, London, W6 7JP Tel: (020) 8563 2255 Fax: (020) 8563 0333

SAPPHIRE BALLS

A Blundell Jewel Bearings Ltd, 203 Torrington Avenue, Coventry, CV4 9UT Tel: (024) 7647 3625 Fax: (024) 7646 6399

SATELLITE ANTENNAS

▶ Paradigm Communications Systems Ltd, Station Road, Alton, Hampshire, GU34 2PZ Tel: (01420) 88199 Fax: (08709) 024001

SATELLITE BROADBAND INTERNET ACCESS EQUIPMENT

Farsite Communications Ltd, Tempus Business Centre, 60 Kingsclere Road, Basingstoke, Hampshire, RG21 6XG Tel: (01256) 330461 Fax: (01256) 854931 E-mail: sales@farsite.co.uk
▶ Pipemedia Ltd, Unit 1 Warren Park Way, Enderby, Leicester, LE19 4SA Tel: (0871) 5757575 Fax: (0871) 4250008 E-mail: sales@pipemedia.com

SATELLITE BROADCASTING CONSULTANTS

▶ Paradigm Communications Systems Ltd, Station Road, Alton, Hampshire, GU34 2PZ Tel: (01420) 88199 Fax: (08709) 024001

SATELLITE BROADCASTING FACILITIES

Atrium Ltd, Yateley Lodge, Reading Road, Yateley, Hampshire, GU46 7AA Tel: (01252) 862423 Fax: (01252) 890596 E-mail: info@atriumcom.com
Digital Sales, Chip House, Byron CR, Coppull, Chorley, Lancashire, PR7 5BE Tel: (01257) 471204 Fax: (01257) 793525 E-mail: sales@digitalsales.co.uk

SATELLITE COMMUNICATION EQUIPMENT

Advantech, Edison Road, St. Ives, Cambridgeshire, PE27 3LF Tel: (01480) 357600 Fax: (01480) 357601 E-mail: sales.europe@advantechamt.com
Alphameric Solutions Ltd, Bishopsgate House, Broadford Park, Guildford, Surrey, GU4 8ED Tel: (01483) 293900 Fax: (01483) 533333 E-mail: enquiries@alphameric.com
Caprock UK Ltd, Caprock Building, Denmore Road, Bridge Of Don, Aberdeen, AB23 8JW Tel: (01224) 707377 Fax: (01224) 707254 E-mail: info@caprock.co.uk
Digital Sales, Chip House, Byron CR, Coppull, Chorley, Lancashire, PR7 5BE Tel: (01257) 471204 Fax: (01257) 793525 E-mail: sales@digitalsales.co.uk
Double D Electronics Ltd, 6 Robins Wharf, Grove Road, Northfleet, Gravesend, Kent, DA11 9AX Tel: (01474) 333456 Fax: (01474) 333414 E-mail: sales@ddelec.co.uk
Global Communications (UK) Ltd, Winterdale Manor, Southminster Road, Athorne, Chelmsford, CM3 6BX Tel: (01621) 743440 Fax: (01621) 743676 E-mail: info@globalcom.co.uk
Livewire Digital Ltd, 14-15 First Quarter, Blenheim Road, Epsom, Surrey, KT19 9QN Tel: (01372) 731400 Fax: (01372) 731420 E-mail: enquirie@livewire.co.uk
Peak Communications, Kirklees House, 22 West Park Street, Brighouse, West Yorkshire, HD6 1DU Tel: (01484) 714200 Fax: (01484) 723666 E-mail: sales@peakcom.co.uk
Satcom Distribution, 3 The Woodford Centre Old Sarum Park, Lysander Way, Old Sarum, Salisbury, SP4 6BU Tel: (01722) 410800 Fax: (01722) 410777 E-mail: sales@satcomdistribution.com
Scientific Atlanta Western Europe Ltd, 49 Suttons Park Avenue, Reading, RG6 1AZ Tel: (0870) 8325400 Fax: (0870) 8325444
Timestep Electronics, PO Box 2001, Dartmouth, Devon, TQ6 9HN Tel: (01803) 833366 E-mail: sales@time-step.com

SATELLITE COMMUNICATION EQUIPMENT ENGINEERS, INSTALLATION OR SERVICE

Bullock Bros Electronics, 132 Cheltenham Road, Gloucester, GL2 0LY Tel: (01452) 529806 Fax: (01452) 529806 E-mail: sales@bullock-bros.com
Heuston Technologies, 39 Princetown Road, Bangor, County Down, BT20 3TA Tel: (028) 9147 8054 Fax: (028) 9147 8054 E-mail: richardheuston@utvinternet.co.uk
▶ Metro Digital Television, Unit D20-21 Fieldhouse Industrial Estate, Fieldhouse Road, Rochdale, Lancashire, OL12 0AA Tel: (01706) 358222 Fax: (01706) 350211 E-mail: sales@mdtv.co.uk
▶ Paradigm Communications Systems Ltd, Station Road, Alton, Hampshire, GU34 2PZ Tel: (01420) 88199 Fax: (08709) 024001
Sangikyo Corporation, Highbridge Industrial Estate, Oxford Road, Uxbridge, Middlesex, UB8 1HR Tel: (01895) 876101 Fax: (01895) 876257

SATELLITE COMMUNICATIONS EQUIPMENT SERVICE PROVIDER

A N D & Group, Tanners Bank, North Shields, Tyne & Wear, NE30 1JH Tel: (01233) 635278 Fax: (0870) 4449680 E-mail: info@and-group.net

SATELLITE DISHES

▶ Maxview Ltd, Common Lane, Setch, King's Lynn, Norfolk, PE33 0AT Tel: (01553) 813300 Fax: (01553) 813301 E-mail: sales@maxview.ltd.uk
Pace P.L.C., Victoria Road, Saltaire, Shipley, West Yorkshire, BD18 3LF Tel: (01274) 532000 Fax: (01274) 532010

SATELLITE NAVIGATION INSTALLATION

▶ Fleet Optimise Ltd, 47 Hundred Acre Road, Streetly, Sutton Coldfield, West Midlands, B74 2LA Tel: (0871) 2106686 Fax: (0871) 2106687E-mail: enquiries@fleetoptimise.co.uk

SATELLITE POSITIONING SYSTEMS

Glonav UK Ltd, March House, London Road, Daventry, Northamptonshire, NN11 4NR Tel: (01327) 701270 Fax: (01327) 701299

SATELLITE TELEVISION RECEIVING EQUIPMENT AND ACCESSORIES

Amstrad plc, Brentwood House, 169 Kings Road, Brentwood, Essex, CM14 4EF Tel: (01277) 228888 Fax: (01277) 211350 E-mail: admin@amstrad.com
Hi-Way Hi-Fi Ltd, 318-324 Edgware Road, London, W2 1DY Tel: (020) 7723 5251 Fax: (020) 7535 3280
MVS, 1 The Croft, Flitwick, Bedford, MK45 1DL Tel: (01525) 718079 E-mail: mvs@ntlworld.com
Pace P.L.C., Victoria Road, Saltaire, Shipley, West Yorkshire, BD18 3LF Tel: (01274) 532000 Fax: (01274) 532010

SATELLITE TELEVISION RECEIVING EQUIPMENT INSTALLATION CONTRACTORS/ RENTAL/SERVICE/SUPPLIERS

A1 Aerials Ltd, 14 Arden Oak Road, Sheldon, Birmingham, B26 3LX Tel: 0121-742 0026 Fax: 0121-742 7360 E-mail: a1aerials@btconnect.com
Eagle Aerials, Mount Pleasant, Chapel Lane, Cannock Wood, Rugeley, Staffordshire, WS15 4SE Tel: (01543) 684558 Fax: (01543) 684558
G P Aerials (1955) Ltd, 7 Maida Vale Business Centre, Maida Vale Road, Cheltenham, Gloucestershire, GL53 7ER Tel: (01242) 515216 Fax: (01242) 519125 E-mail: gp.aerials@virgin.net
M F T Co Ltd, 22 Bedford Road, Lower Stondon, Henlow, Bedfordshire, SG16 6EA Tel: (01462) 850536 Fax: (01462) 851522 E-mail: sales@mftsat.co.uk
▶ Metro Digital Television, Unit D20-21 Fieldhouse Industrial Estate, Fieldhouse Road, Rochdale, Lancashire, OL12 0AA Tel: (01706) 358222 Fax: (01706) 350211 E-mail: sales@mdtv.co.uk
T V A Installations Stockport Ltd, Waterloo House, Hopes Carr, Stockport, Cheshire, SK1 3BL Tel: 0161-480 2265 Fax: 0161-480 6720 E-mail: tva@btconnect.com
Videotron Ltd, 441-443 Cranbrook Road, Ilford, Essex, IG2 6EW Tel: (020) 8554 7617 Fax: (020) 8554 0110 E-mail: phobbs@videotronltd.freeserve.co.uk
Wilsecure Installations, 292 Dewsbury Road, Leeds, LS11 6JT Tel: 0113-271 6097 Fax: 0113-270 4259 E-mail: sales@tindsdaletv.co.uk

SATELLITE TELEVISION SYSTEMS

▶ Matthew Aerial & Satellite Systems, 57a Glencoe Road, Bushey, WD23 3DP Tel: (020) 8950 2213 Fax: (020) 8950 4262

SAUCE PORTION PACKS

Ravendell Foods, Blowick Business Park, Crowland Street, Southport, Merseyside, PR9 7SJ Tel: (01704) 539181 Fax: (01704) 539247 E-mail: sales@ravendellfoods.co.uk

SAUCES, CATERING

Tilda Ltd, Coldharbour Lane, Rainham, Essex, RM13 9YQ Tel: (01708) 717777 Fax: (01708) 717700 E-mail: sales@tilda.com

SAUNA EQUIPMENT

Alan Bettin Holdings Ltd, Seale Lane, Seale, Farnham, Surrey, GU10 1LD Tel: (01252) 782022 Fax: (01252) 782283 E-mail: sales@abpools.co.uk
▶ Caernarfon Sun Studio, 25 Bangor Street, Caernarfon, Gwynedd, LL55 1AT Tel: (01286) 672754
▶ Drom UK Ltd, Trackside Business Centre, Abbot Close, Byfleet, West Byfleet, Surrey, KT14 7JN Tel: (01932) 355655 Fax: (01932) 250351 E-mail: info@dromuk.com
Eclipse Tanning, 5 St. Johns Way, Corringham, Stanford-le-Hope, Essex, SS17 7NA Tel: (01375) 673397
Golden Promotions Ltd, Chartwell, Hundred End Lane, Hundred End, Preston, PR4 6XL Tel: (01772) 815931 Fax: (01772) 815097 E-mail: george@goldenpromotions.co.uk
Leisure Repair, PO Box 613, Croydon, CR0 2XQ Tel: (020) 8665 4271 Fax: (020) 8665 4234 E-mail: leisurerepair@btconnect.com
Leisurequip Ltd, Longwood, The Mount, Headley, Bordon, Hampshire, GU35 8AG Tel: (01428) 713185 Fax: (01428) 713185
Mcintyre Leisure, Whitehouse Farm, Britwell Road, Watlington, Oxfordshire, OX49 5JY Tel: (01491) 613284 Fax: (01491) 614778
Nordic Saunas Ltd, Unit 5, Fairview Industrial Estate, Holland Road, Oxted, Surrey, RH8 9BD Tel: (01883) 732400 Fax: (01883) 716970 E-mail: info@nordic.co.uk
▶ S & S Tan Seakers, Wheatley House, Laughton, Gainsborough, Lincolnshire, DN21 3QF Tel: (01427) 628571
Sauna Finn, 44 Napier Road, Poole, Dorset, BH15 4NA Tel: (01202) 675702 Fax: (01202) 675702
▶ Sunscan Ltd, Unit 9D, Brindley Road, Reginald Road Industrial Estate, St. Helens, Merseyside, WA9 4HY Tel: (01744) 811788 Fax: (0870) 3212406
▶ Sunspar Services, Elswick Road, Fenton Industrial Estate, Stoke-on-Trent, ST4 2PZ Tel: (01782) 415733 Fax: (01782) 417042
Super Tan, Unit 17b Asquith Bottom, Sowerby Bridge, West Yorkshire, HX6 3BT Tel: (01422) 831122 Fax: (01422) 831122
▶ Tantastic Tanning, 63 Chingford Mount Road, London, E4 8LU Tel: (020) 8527 3727

SAUSAGE CASINGS

By Products Keighley Ltd, Deal Street, Keighley, West Yorkshire, BD21 4LA Tel: (01535) 607008 Fax: (01535) 691480
Devro plc, Gartferry Road, Chryston, Glasgow, G69 0JE Tel: (01236) 872261 Fax: (01236) 811005 E-mail: mail.plc@devro-casing.com
Devro-teepak Ltd, 5 Belgrave Street, Bellshill Industrial Estate, Bellshill, Lanarkshire, ML4 3LD Tel: (01236) 878699 Fax: (01698) 746273 E-mail: male.plc@devro-casings.com
Harder Bros, Valley Road, Morley, Leeds, LS27 8EX Tel: 0113-253 5325 Fax: 0113-252 4522 E-mail: harderbros@aol.com
F. Heinemann Ltd, PO Box 76, Northwood, Middlesex, HA6 3AJ Tel: (01923) 829993 Fax: (01923) 825519 E-mail: heinecas@btinternet.com

SAUSAGE CASINGS – *continued*

Jaeger Casings, Irthlingborough Road, Wellingborough, Northamptonshire, NN8 1RA Tel: (01933) 222466

Kalle UK Ltd, Perry Road, Industrial Estate East, Witham, Essex, CM8 3YY Tel: (01376) 531800 Fax: (01376) 518522 E-mail: sales@kalle.co.uk

Logue Casings Ltd, Flying Horse Industrial Estate, Brannish Road, Downpatrick, County Down, BT30 6LL Tel: (028) 4461 4700

Smithfield Casings & Sundries, Unit 6 West Burrowfield, Welwyn Garden City, Hertfordshire, AL7 4TW Tel: (01707) 328557 Fax: (01707) 335801

W. Weschenfelder & Sons Ltd, 2 North Road, Middlesbrough, Cleveland, TS2 1DD Tel: (01642) 247524 Fax: (01642) 249336 E-mail: weschies@compuserve.com

SAUSAGE CASINGS, NATURAL

▶ Designasausage, 12 Hibel Road, Macclesfield, Cheshire, SK10 2AB Tel: (01625) 611888 Fax: (01625) 611956 E-mail: sausages@sausagemaking.co.uk

SAUSAGE MACHINES

Handtmann Ltd, 23-24 North Luton Industrial Estate, Sedgewick Road, Luton, LU4 9DT Tel: (01582) 576116 Fax: (01582) 597164 E-mail: enquiries@handtmann.co.uk

Handyman, Unit 4 Lower Rectory Farm, Great Brickhill, Milton Keynes, MK17 9AF Tel: (01908) 366228 Fax: (01908) 366661

SAUSAGES

Adams Pork Products Ltd, Sleaford Road, Ruskington, Sleaford, Lincolnshire, NG34 9BL Tel: (01526) 832216 Fax: (01526) 833439

Adams Pork Products Ltd, Crescent House, Fulney Lane, Spalding, Lincolnshire, PE12 6EZ Tel: (01775) 766161 Fax: (01775) 710717 E-mail: sales@geo-adams.co.uk

Church's Pork Butchers Ltd, 224 High Street, Epping, Essex, CM16 4AQ Tel: (01992) 573231 Fax: (01992) 561525

D & E Wilson & Sons Ltd, 60 Bold Street, Preston, PR1 7NX Tel: (01772) 254648 Fax: (01772) 203667

Delenco Foods Ltd, Unit 6 Heybridge Way Lea Bridge Road, London, E10 7NQ Tel: (020) 8558 3278 Fax: (020) 8558 6585

F A Gill Ltd, Parkfield Road, Wolverhampton, WV4 6EH Tel: (01902) 331141 Fax: (01902) 340772 E-mail: fagill@btconnect.com

▶ Frostbite, 98 Eastbourne Avenue, Gateshead, Tyne & Wear, NE8 4NH Tel: 0191-478 4159

Korker Sausages Ltd, High Street, Rolvenden, Cranbrook, Kent, TN17 4LN Tel: (01580) 241307 Fax: (01580) 240092 E-mail: enquiries@korker-sausages.co.uk

KWTJ Products Ltd, 155A Hampton Road, Southport, Merseyside, PR8 5DJ Tel: (01704) 534798 Fax: (01704) 534798

Lane Farm Country Foods, Lane Farm, Brundish, Woodbridge, Suffolk, IP13 8BW Tel: (01379) 384593 Fax: (01379) 384934

McLay Ltd, Glentanar Road, The Balmore Industrial Estate, Glasgow, G22 7XS Tel: 0141-336 6543 Fax: 0141-336 4857 E-mail: meat@mclay.co.uk

New Forset Pond Services, Station Road, Sway, Lymington, Hampshire, SO41 6AA Tel: (01590) 681339 Fax: (01590) 682302

O'Hagans's Sausages, 71 Fishbourne Road West, Chichester, West Sussex, PO19 3JJ Tel: (01243) 532833 Fax: (01243) 576733 E-mail: ohagans@topsausages.com

Bryan Pickering, 30 The Street, Costessey, Norwich, NR8 5DB Tel: (01603) 742002 Fax: (01603) 743352

Procters Sausage Mnfrs, 12 The Walk, Ipswich, IP1 1EE Tel: (01473) 281191 E-mail: sales@procters-sausages.co.uk

Procter's Speciality Sausages, 17 Maidenhall Green, Ipswich, IP2 8PJ Tel: (01473) 683158 Fax: (01473) 683158 E-mail: sales@proctersspecialitysausages.co.uk

R A Robinson & Son, Unit 7 Turnpike Industrial Estate, Newbury, Berkshire, RG14 2LR Tel: (01635) 41045 Fax: (01635) 41045

Robertson, Unit 5 Hardengreen Industrial Estate, Dalkeith, Midlothian, EH22 3NX Tel: 0131-663 6666 Fax: 0131-663 6664

Tulip Ltd, Mantle Lane, Coalville, Leicestershire, LE67 3DU Tel: (01530) 836501 Fax: (01530) 510708

W.A. Turner Ltd, Broadwater Lane, Tunbridge Wells, Kent, TN2 5RD Tel: (01892) 515215 Fax: (01892) 510028 E-mail: sales@waturner.co.uk

Vale Of Mowbray Ltd, 5-6 Mowbray Terrace, Leeming Bar, Northallerton, North Yorkshire, DL7 9BL Tel: (01677) 422661 Fax: (01677) 424986 E-mail: sales@valeofmowbray.com

W F Chinn Ltd, Marsh Lane, Crediton, Devon, EX17 1ES Tel: (01363) 772639 Fax: (01363) 772639 E-mail: wfchinn@lineone.net

K.D. Winkle, 46-47 Retreat Street, Wolverhampton, WV3 0JT Tel: (01902) 428738

Yetman Sausages, 52-54 Hazelwick Road, Crawley, West Sussex, RH10 1LZ Tel: (01293) 525235

SAVOURY EGGS

Sensine Flavors Ltd, Felinfach, Lampeter, Dyfed, SA48 8AG Tel: (01570) 470277 Fax: (01570) 470958

SAVOURY SNACKS

▶ Corn Dolly, Unit 4 Ballinacraig Way, Greenbank Industrial Estate, Newry, County Down, BT34 2QX Tel: (028) 3026 0525 Fax: (028) 3083 2818 E-mail: corndolly@btconnect.com

SAW BENCHES

D B Keighley Machinery Ltd, Vickers Place, Stanningley, Pudsey, West Yorkshire, LS28 6LZ Tel: 0113-257 4736 Fax: 0113-257 4293 E-mail: sales@dbkeighley.co.uk

SAW BLADES

Allied (Tooling) Ltd, Unit 2, 19 Willis Way, Poole, Dorset, BH15 3SS Tel: (01202) 675767 Fax: (01202) 684422 E-mail: sales@alliedtooling.com

Birmingham Saw Blades Ltd, 117 Station Road, Cradley Heath, West Midlands, B64 6PL Tel: 0121-559 5931 Fax: 0121-561 5121 E-mail: sales@dynashape.co.uk

Burton Saw International Ltd, Trading Estate, Valmar Road, London, SE5 9NW Tel: (020) 7737 3577 Fax: (020) 7733 2368 E-mail: blades@burtonsaw.co.uk

Columbia Saw Works Ltd, 120 Hackney Road, London, E2 7QL Tel: (01708) 550601 Fax: (020) 8281 1260 E-mail: kevin@columbia37.freeserve.co.uk

Gelmic Machine Tools Ltd, 28 Old Bedford Road, Luton, LU2 7NZ Tel: (01582) 731371 Fax: (01582) 453189

Gomex Tools Ltd, Orchard Road, Finedon, Wellingborough, Northamptonshire, NN9 5JF Tel: (01933) 680492 Fax: (01933) 680693 E-mail: sales@gomex.co.uk

Lancashire Saw Co. Ltd, Imperial Mill, Gorse Street, Blackburn, BB1 3EU Tel: (01254) 51116 Fax: (01254) 672046 E-mail: info@lancashiresaw.co.uk

Leicester Saw Blades Ltd, 6 Morris Road, Leicester, LE2 6BR Tel: 0116-270 9293

N L S Tools, Station Approach, Waltham Cross, Hertfordshire, EN8 7LZ Tel: (01992) 710888 Fax: (01992) 713938 E-mail: sales@nlstools.co.uk

Sawmatic Tool Sharpening, Commercial Way, Oakengates, Telford, Shropshire, TF2 6SG Tel: (01952) 615489 Fax: (01952) 613469 E-mail: info@sawmatic.com

Supreme Saws Ltd, Detection House, Brooklands Approach, Romford, RM1 1DX Tel: (01708) 736220 Fax: (01708) 745726 E-mail: sales@supremesaws.co.uk

Yorkshire Diamond Products, 66 Effingham Road, Sheffield, S4 7YS Tel: 0114-275 5252 Fax: 0114-273 9385

SAW SHARPENING OR MAINTENANCE OR REPAIR

A A Smith Ltd, Pontefract, West Yorkshire, WF7 6WZ Tel: (0845) 3303805 Fax: (0845) 3303806 E-mail: sales@aasmith.co.uk

Apollo Multiform Ltd, 14 Gorst Road, London, NW10 6LE Tel: (020) 8965 8571 Fax: (020) 8838 2588 E-mail: info@apolloltd.co.uk

Atkins Saws, 53 Richmond Road, Solihull, West Midlands, B92 7RR Tel: 0121-707 1600

Bandsaw Service Ltd, Fairacres Industrial Estate, Dedworth Road, Windsor, Berkshire, SL4 4LE Tel: (01753) 862029 Fax: (01753) 830051 E-mail: saws@eclipse.co.uk

C & G Cutters & Grinding Ltd, Clarendon Road, Blackburn, BB1 9SS Tel: (01254) 663193 Fax: (01254) 665139 E-mail: sales@cg-grind-eng-serv.co.uk

Columbia Saw Works Ltd, 120 Hackney Road, London, E2 7QL Tel: (01708) 550601 Fax: (020) 8281 1260 E-mail: kevin@columbia37.freeserve.co.uk

Davenport Western Ltd, Oxford Road, Pen Mill Trading Estate, Yeovil, Somerset, BA21 5HR Tel: (01935) 425311 Fax: (01935) 432816

E Crowley & Son Ltd, Bentalls, Pipps Hill Industrial Estate, Basildon, Essex, SS14 3BY Tel: (01268) 293605 Fax: (01268) 285452 E-mail: sales@crowleysaws.com

E Witten & Son, 7 Riverbank Business Centre, Old Shoreham Road, Shoreham-by-Sea, West Sussex, BN43 5FL Tel: (01273) 441255 Fax: (01273) 441264

Five Star Saw Service Ltd, 3 All Saints Industrial Estate, All Saints Street, Birmingham, B18 7RJ Tel: 0121-551 5341

Fourways Bandsaw Service, 5b Cannock Wood Industrial Estate, Cannock Wood Street, Cannock, Staffordshire, WS12 0PL Tel: (01543) 879711 Fax: (01543) 423654

Gelmic Machine Tools Ltd, 28 Old Bedford Road, Luton, LU2 7NZ Tel: (01582) 731371 Fax: (01582) 453189

Haydens Saw & Cutter Service, 1 The Mazes, East Street, Braintree, Essex, CM7 3JJ Tel: (01376) 325380 Fax: (01376) 552286

Heath Saws, Leeside Works, Lawrence Avenue, Stanstead Abbotts, Ware, Hertfordshire, SG12 8DL Tel: (01920) 870230 Fax: (01920) 871996

Huddersfield Saw & Tool Co., Vine Street, Huddersfield, HD1 6NT Tel: (01484) 424055 Fax: (01484) 421244

Leicester Saw Blades Ltd, 6 Morris Road, Leicester, LE2 6BR Tel: 0116-270 9293

M & E James, Unit 2 Hare Street, Bilston, West Midlands, WV14 7DX Tel: (01902) 408030 Fax: (01902) 490166 E-mail: saws@supanet.com

North Shields Grinding, The Old Maltings, Tanners Bank, North Shields, Tyne & Wear, NE30 1JH Tel: 0191-257 2342 Fax: 0191-258 5310 E-mail: nsgrinding@aol.com

▶ Sawtech North West, 9 Brown Street, Oldham, OL1 3QE Tel: 0161-624 1440 Fax: 0161-624 1440 E-mail: sales@sawtech.co.uk

South Eastern Saws (Industrial) Ltd, Unit 6 Spectrum, Parkwood Industrial Estate, Maidstone, Kent, ME15 9XZ Tel: (01622) 750177 Fax: (01622) 688112

South Midland Saws Ltd, Lincoln Road, Cressex Business Park, High Wycombe, Buckinghamshire, HP12 3RQ Tel: (01494) 520612 Fax: (01494) 465373 E-mail: sales@scsaws.co.uk

Stevens Saw & Tool Services, 1 Pope Iron Road, Worcester, WR1 3HB Tel: (01905) 26413

Super Sharp Saw Service, 174 London Road, Mitcham, Surrey, CR4 3LD Tel: (020) 8648 2154 Fax: (020) 8648 2154

Western Saw Service, Unit 37 Willan Industrial Estate, Vere Street, Salford, M50 2GR Tel: 0161-736 9608 Fax: 0161-736 9608

SAWDUST CONTRACTORS

Snowflake Animal Bedding Ltd, Riverside Industrial Estate, Marsh Lane, Boston, Lincolnshire, PE21 7ST Tel: (0870) 3003355 Fax: (01205) 310298 E-mail: snowflakesales@plevin.co.uk

Snowflake Animal Bedding Ltd, Slimbridge Crossroads, Bristol Road, Slimbridge, Gloucester, GL2 7DW Tel: (0870) 3003355 Fax: (01453) 890047 E-mail: snowflakesales@plevin.co.uk

Whitfire Shavings & Sawdust Supplies Ltd, Heatherfield Works, Church Lane, Farington Moss, Leyland, PR26 6RD Tel: (01772) 335178 Fax: (01772) 629843

SAWING MACHINES

Gelmic Machine Tools Ltd, 28 Old Bedford Road, Luton, LU2 7NZ Tel: (01582) 731371 Fax: (01582) 453189

Meba Saw Co Ltd, 27 Palmer Road, Retford, Nottinghamshire, DN22 6SS Tel: (01777) 860102 Fax: (01777) 860306 E-mail: mebasaw@btconnect.com

S M Tech Ltd, 1 Ritchie Avenue, Monifieth, Dundee, DD5 4DJ Tel: (01382) 530999 Fax: (01382) 530752 E-mail: sales@findlers.co.uk

Soderhamn Errikson, Unit 17 Vauxhall Industrial Estate, Greg Street, Reddish, Stockport, Cheshire, SK5 7BR Tel: 0161-429 9437 Fax: 0161-477 0641 E-mail: info@se-saws.co.uk

SAWING SERVICES

▶ D Drill Master Drillers Ltd, Unit 7 Wood Street, Poulton Industrial Estate, Poulton-le-Fylde, Lancashire, FY6 8JY Tel: (01253) 894554 Fax: (01253) 893848

D Drill Master Drillers Ltd, 84 Clun Street, Sheffield, S4 7JS Tel: 0114-273 9199 Fax: 0114-276 5884 E-mail: sheffield@d-drill.co.uk

SAWING/SAW MILL MACHINES, TIMBER

Downey Engineering, Pontrilas, Hereford, HR2 0BB Tel: (01981) 240427 Fax: (01981) 240953

Mackintosh & Partners (Properties) Ltd, The Sawmills, Small Dole, Henfield, West Sussex, BN5 9XG Tel: (01273) 497100 Fax: (01273) 497139 E-mail: sales@mackintosh.co.uk

Penrose Wood Industries Ltd, Whitesmith, Lewes, East Sussex, BN8 6JB Tel: (01825) 872828 Fax: (01825) 873059

Stenner Ltd, Lowman Works, Tiverton, Devon, EX16 4JX Tel: (01884) 255700 Fax: (01884) 257794 E-mail: stenner@stenner.co.uk

SAWN AND PLANED WOOD SERVICES

▶ A & G King Timber Ltd, Terregles Sawmill, Terregles, Dumfries, DG2 9RU Tel: (01387) 720210 Fax: (01387) 720165

▶ A Gordon & Co. Ltd, Bridgend Sawmill, Longside, Peterhead, Aberdeenshire, AB42 4XE Tel: (01779) 821295

A J R Elsworth Ltd, Firwood Works, Firwood Industrial Estate, Thicketford Road, Firwood Fold, Bolton, BL2 3TR Tel: (01204) 595710 Fax: (01204) 302096

A J Smith & Son Benfleet Ltd, 242 High Road, Benfleet, Essex, SS7 5LA Tel: (01268) 792771 Fax: (01268) 750780 E-mail: info@ajsmith.uk.com

Allen & Orr Ltd, The Albion Sawmills, Union Walk, Chesterfield, Derbyshire, S40 4SA Tel: (01246) 232426 Fax: (01246) 559099

▶ Arden Wood Shavings Ltd, Kenilworth Road, Hampton-in-Arden, Solihull, West Midlands, B92 0LP Tel: (01675) 443888 Fax: (01675) 443873

▶ Argyll Sawmills Ltd, Strachur, Cairndow, Argyll, PA27 8DW Tel: (01369) 860701 Fax: (01369) 860709

▶ Atkinsons Fencing Ltd, Green Lane, Cutsyke, Castleford, West Yorkshire, WF10 5JL Tel: (01977) 550441 Fax: (01977) 515321 E-mail: sales@atkinsonfencing.co.uk

B S W Timber plc, East End, Earlston, Berwickshire, TD4 6JA Tel: (01896) 849255 Fax: (01896) 848080E-mail: sales@bsw.co.uk

Beecroft & Wightman Bradford Ltd, 94 Garnett Street, Bradford, West Yorkshire, BD3 9HB Tel: (01274) 725276 Fax: (01274) 725276

Bendrey Bros, Bath Road, Bridgeyate, Bristol, BS30 5JW Tel: 0117-967 4382 Fax: 0117-967 4383

Bennetts & Co (Grimsby) Ltd, 101 Charlton St, Grimsby, South Humberside, DN31 1SW Tel: (01472) 350151 Fax: (01472) 250053 E-mail: bennettstimber@aol.com

C M Nicholls Timber Products, The Sawmill, Ketsby, Louth, Lincolnshire, LN11 8QW Tel: (01507) 480672

▶ Cally Sawmill Ltd, Cally Sawmill, Dunkeld, Perthshire, PH8 0HU Tel: (01350) 727305

Carronbridge Sawmill Ltd, Carronbridge, Thornhill, Dumfriesshire, DG3 5AY Tel: (01848) 331661 Fax: (01848) 331121

▶ Chirnside Sawmills Ltd, Chirnside, Duns, Berwickshire, TD11 3XJ Tel: (01890) 818213 Fax: (01890) 818698

Constructional Veneers Ltd, 2 Timberwharf Road, Stamford Hill, London, N16 6DB Tel: (020) 8802 1166 Fax: (020) 8802 4222 E-mail: veneers@talk21.com

▶ James Cordiner & Son Ltd, Silverbank Sawmill, Banchory, Kincardineshire, AB31 5PY Tel: (01330) 823366

▶ Creca Sawmills, Crece Camp, Creca, Annan, Dumfriesshire, DG12 6RP Tel: (01461) 500523 Fax: (01461) 500645

D A Security Systems Ltd, 5 Cornfield Road, Lee-On-The-Solent, Hampshire, PO13 8HZ Tel: (023) 9255 0627

D W General Wood Machinists Ltd, 855 High Road, Tottenham, London, N17 8EY Tel: (020) 8801 1127 Fax: (020) 8808 1215 E-mail: sales@dw-group.co.uk

Dinefwr Gates, Cwmcib Ganol, Ffairfach, Llandeilo, Dyfed, SA19 6TE Tel: (01558) 822833 Fax: (01558) 824612

Drenagh Sawmills Ltd, 89 Dowland Road, Limavady, County Londonderry, BT49 0HR Tel: (028) 7776 5611 Fax: (028) 7776 5984 E-mail: mark@drenagh.co.uk

E Preston & Sons Ladybank Sawmills Ltd, Cupar Road, Ladybank, Cupar, Fife, KY15 7LS Tel: (01337) 830307 Fax: (01337) 830307

E T C Sawmills Ltd, Elson, Ellesmere, Shropshire, SY12 9EU Tel: (01691) 622441 Fax: (01691) 623468 E-mail: info@etcsawmills.co.uk

East Bros Holdings Ltd, The Sawmills, West Dean, Salisbury, SP5 1JA Tel: (01794) 340270 Fax: (01794) 341317 E-mail: mail@eastbros.co.uk

Edmund Robson & Co Ltd, West Side, Tyne Dock, South Shields, Tyne & Wear, NE34 9PJ Tel: 0191-489 8134 Fax: 0191-489 0696 E-mail: timber@edmundrobson.co.uk

Empress Fencing Ltd, Empress Sawmills, Clitheroe Road, Chatburn, Clitheroe, Lancashire, BB7 4JY Tel: (01200) 441215 Fax: (01200) 449931 E-mail: sales@empressfencing.co.uk

Forest Products Ltd, Workshop Forestry Commission Lightmoor Dept, Speech House Road, Cinderford, Gloucestershire, GL14 3HU Tel: (01594) 822223 Fax: (01594) 826901 E-mail: enquiries@forest-products.com

▶ George Laing Fencing Ltd, Railway Place, Cupar, Fife, KY15 5HZ Tel: (01334) 655744 Fax: (01334) 656133 E-mail: sales@forestcraft.co.uk

John Gordon & Son Ltd, Balblair Road, Nairn, IV12 5LY Tel: (01667) 453223 Fax: (01667) 452168 E-mail: enquiries@gordontimber.co.uk

▶ Hamilton & Kinneil (1987) Ltd, Lennoxlove Estate Office, Haddington, East Lothian, EH41 4NZ Tel: (01620) 823720

Roger Haydock & Co. Ltd, Mersey View Road, Widnes, Cheshire, WA8 8LN Tel: 0151-425 2525 Fax: 0151-425 4141 E-mail: rdh@haydockwidnes.demon.co.uk

▶ Holmsley Mill Ltd, Holmsley, Burley, Ringwood, Hampshire, BH24 4HY Tel: (01425) 402507 Fax: (01425) 403516 E-mail: sales@holmsleymill.co.uk

▶ Howie Forest Products Ltd, Kenmuir Sawmill, Dalbeattie, Kirkcudbrightshire, DG5 4PL Tel: (01556) 610876 Fax: (01556) 611488

International Timber, Timber Division, Earls Road, Grangemouth, Stirlingshire, FK3 8UU Tel: (01324) 666000 Fax: (01324) 666111

P. Irving & Sons Ltd, Hutton Roof Sawmills, Kirkby Lonsdale, Carnforth, Lancashire, LA6 2PE Tel: (01524) 271510 Fax: (01524) 272410

SAWN AND PLANED WOOD SERVICES – *continued*

J Callander & Son Ltd, Abbotshaugh Sawmill, Abbots Road, Falkirk, FK2 7XU Tel: (01324) 621563 Fax: (01324) 634386 E-mail: info@jcallander.co.uk

▶ J K F Ltd, Scoonie Road, Leven, Fife, KY8 4SE Tel: (01333) 424457 Fax: (01333) 424340

▶ James Jones & Sons, Kinnoir, Huntly, Aberdeenshire, AB54 7XY Tel: (01466) 792372 Fax: (01466) 794393

John Mcmurtry & Co. Ltd, 42 Douglas Terrace, Ballymena, County Antrim, BT42 3AP Tel: (028) 2564 8116 Fax: (028) 2564 2519

James Jones & Sons Ltd, Garmouth Road, Mosstodloch, Fochabers, Morayshire, IV32 7LH Tel: (01343) 821421 Fax: (01343) 821299 E-mail: mosstodloch@jamesjones.co.uk

▶ Kerr Timber Products Ltd, Hecklegirth Works, Annan, Dumfriesshire, DG12 6SN Tel: (01461) 201622 Fax: (01461) 201633

Keyline Builders Merchants Ltd, 130 Salkeld Street, Glasgow, G5 8HD Tel: 0141-429 5141 Fax: 0141-429 4992

L E Haslett & Co., 21 Ballagh Road, Clogher, County Tyrone, BT76 0JY Tel: (028) 8554 8285 Fax: (028) 8554 8683 E-mail: lehasslet@hotmail.com

Lawson Timber Ltd, White Hart Road, London, SE18 1DH Tel: (020) 8855 7621 Fax: (020) 8854 6552

M H Southern & Co. Ltd, Church Bank Sawmills, Jarrow, Tyne & Wear, NE32 3EB Tel: 0191-489 8231 Fax: 0191-428 0146 E-mail: sales@mhsouthern.co.uk

M & J Timber Ltd, 32 Union Street, Greenock, Renfrewshire, PA16 8DJ Tel: (01475) 723737 Fax: (01475) 722537

Nicks & Co Timber Ltd, Canada Wharf, Bristol Road, Gloucester, GL1 5TE Tel: (01452) 300159 Fax: (01452) 307682

Nidd Valley Saw Mills Ltd, Dacre Banks, Harrogate, North Yorkshire, HG3 4EA Tel: (01423) 780220 Fax: (01423) 780220

▶ Penkiln, Baldoon Stores, Wigtown, Newton Stewart, Wigtownshire, DG8 9AF Tel: (01988) 402414 Fax: (01988) 840300

Pontrilas Timber & Builders Merchants Ltd, The Saw Mills, Pontrilas, Hereford, HR2 0BE Tel: (01981) 240444 Fax: (01981) 240748 E-mail: sales@pontrilastimber.co.uk

▶ Richard Baty & Sons, Gibbhill Sawmill, Kirkcudbright, DG6 4TJ Tel: (01557) 330568

Russwood Ltd, Station Yard, Newtonmore, Inverness-Shire, PH20 1AR Tel: (01540) 673648 Fax: (01540) 673661 E-mail: sales@russwood.co.uk

S C Soffe & Sons, Sundew, Pollards Moor Road, Copythorne, Southampton, SO40 2NZ Tel: (023) 8081 2278

▶ S H Somerscales Ltd, Roxton Lane, Keelby, Grimsby, South Humberside, DN41 8JB Tel: (01469) 560704 Fax: (01469) 561354

Sawmill UK Ltd, Ward Lane, Stanley, Wakefield, West Yorkshire, WF3 4LU Tel: (01924) 374953 Fax: (01924) 378294

Stansted Sawmill Ltd, Stansted Park, Rowland's Castle, Hampshire, PO9 6DU Tel: (023) 9241 2445 Fax: (023) 9241 3434

Ternex Ltd, Ayot Green Sawmill, 27 Ayot Green, Ayot St. Peter, Welwyn, Hertfordshire, AL6 9BA Tel: (01707) 324606 Fax: (01707) 334371 E-mail: sales@ternex.co.uk

Thornbridge Sawmills Ltd, Laurieston Road, Grangemouth, Stirlingshire, FK3 8XX Tel: (01324) 612121 Fax: (01324) 612100

Thorogood Timber plc, Colchester Road, Ardleigh, Colchester, CO7 7PQ Tel: (01206) 233100 Fax: (01206) 233115 E-mail: sales@thorogood.co.uk

Tonge Bridge Timber Sales UK Ltd, Turner Bridge Works, Windley Street, Bolton, BL2 2DF Tel: (01204) 417676 Fax: (01204) 417583 E-mail: sales@tongebridgetimber.co.uk

▶ Treeway Fencing Ltd, 9 Cannock Wood Industrial Estate, Cannock Wood Street, Cannock, Staffordshire, WS12 0PL Tel: (01543) 425893 Fax: (01543) 423654 E-mail: sales@treeway.co.uk

W L West & Sons Ltd, Selham, Petworth, West Sussex, GU28 0PJ Tel: (01798) 861611 Fax: (01798) 861633

Whitmores Timber Co. Ltd, Main Road, Claybrooke Magna, Lutterworth, Leicestershire, LE17 5AQ Tel: (01455) 209121 Fax: (01455) 209041 E-mail: info@whitmores.co.uk

Hunter Wilson & Partners Ltd, The Sawmill, Rigg, Gretna, Dumfriesshire, DG16 5JL Tel: (01461) 338454 Fax: (01461) 338468 E-mail: sales@hunterwilson.co.uk

▶ Windymains Farm Ltd, Windymains Farm, Humbie, East Lothian, EH36 5PA Tel: (01875) 833602

SAWN TIMBER

▶ Cordiner, 5 Crombie Place, Aberdeen, AB11 9PJ Tel: (01224) 877611 Fax: (01224) 875510

SAWS, *See also headings for particular types*

Allied Machinery Ltd, Star Works, Tong Road, Leeds, LS12 3BH Tel: 0113-279 2792 Fax: 0113-279 9799

Bedford Saw & Tool Co., Ampthill Road, Bedford, MK42 9JP Tel: (01234) 217417 Fax: (01234) 270663 E-mail: info@bedfordsaw.co.uk

Davenport Western Ltd, Oxford Road, Pen Mill Trading Estate, Yeovil, Somerset, BA21 5HR Tel: (01935) 425311 Fax: (01935) 432816

E Witten & Son, 7 Riverbank Business Centre, Old Shoreham Road, Shoreham-by-Sea, West Sussex, BN43 5FL Tel: (01273) 441255 Fax: (01273) 441264

Floyd Automatic Tooling Ltd, 17 Bondor Business Centre, London Road, Baldock, Hertfordshire, SG7 6HP Tel: (01462) 491919 Fax: (01462) 490835 E-mail: info@floydautomatic.co.uk

Haydens Saw & Cutter Service, 1 The Mazes, East Street, Braintree, Essex, CM7 3JJ Tel: (01376) 325380 Fax: (01376) 552286

Hegner, 8 North Cresent, Diplocks Way, Hailsham, East Sussex, BN27 3JF Tel: (01323) 442440 Fax: (01323) 840696 E-mail: sales@hegner.co.uk

Quicksharp Services, Signal Hill Farm, Lenborough Road, Gawcott, Buckingham, MK18 4JG Tel: (01280) 822062 Fax: (08707) 778463

Saw Centre Ltd, 650 Eglinton Street, Glasgow, G5 9RP Tel: (0870) 7280222 Fax: 0141-429 5609 E-mail: sales@thesawcentre.co.uk

Sawcraft UK Ltd, Penncricket Lane, Rowley Regis, West Midlands, B65 0RE Tel: 0121-561 5616 Fax: 0121-561 5691 E-mail: sales@sawcraftukltd.co.uk

Sawmatic Tool Sharpening, Commercial Way, Oakengates, Telford, Shropshire, TF2 6SG Tel: (01952) 615489 Fax: (01952) 613469 E-mail: info@sawmatic.com

South Eastern Saws (Industrial) Ltd, Unit 6 Spectrum, Parkwood Industrial Estate, Maidstone, Kent, ME15 9XZ Tel: (01622) 750177 Fax: (01622) 688112

Supreme Saws Ltd, Detection House, Brooklands Approach, Romford, RM1 1DX Tel: (01708) 736220 Fax: (01708) 745726 E-mail: sales@supremesaws.co.uk

SAWS, TIMBER

Anglo Norden Forest Products Ltd, Orwell Terminal Eagle Wharf, Helena Road, Ipswich, IP3 0BT Tel: (01473) 233244 Fax: (01473) 230805 E-mail: sales@anglonorden.co.uk

Atkinson Walker Saws Ltd, Bower Street, Sheffield, S3 8RU Tel: 0114-272 4748 Fax: 0114-272 5065 E-mail: sales@atkinson-walker-saws.co.uk

E P S Services, Ford Road, Wiveliscombe, Taunton, Somerset, TA4 2RE Tel: (01984) 624273 Fax: (01984) 623204 E-mail: info@eps-services.co.uk

E T & Lee Roberts, 1b Graeme Road, Enfield, Middlesex, EN1 3UU Tel: (020) 8363 6452 Fax: (020) 8804 1102

Thomas Flinn & Co., 114 Harvest Lane, Sheffield, S3 8EG Tel: 0114-272 5387 Fax: 0114-272 5389 E-mail: info@flinn-garlick-saws.co.uk

SCAFFOLD BOLTS

Apollo Construction Products, Unit 4 Weights Lane, Redditch, Worcestershire, B97 6RG Tel: (01527) 63999 Fax: (01527) 64999 E-mail: sales@apollofix.co.uk

Layher Ltd, Works Road, Letchworth Garden City, Hertfordshire, SG6 1WL Tel: (01462) 475100 Fax: (01462) 475101 E-mail: info@layher.com

SCAFFOLD TOWER HIRE

A & A Scaffolding Plus 8 2003 Ltd, Garner Street, Stoke-on-Trent, ST4 7AX Tel: (01782) 202474 Fax: (01782) 201354 E-mail: info@scaffoldingstaffordshire.co.uk

A M P Scaffold Co. Ltd, 39A Deakin Road, Erdington, Birmingham, B24 9AJ Tel: 0121-373 3863 Fax: 0121-377 8588 E-mail: sales@ampscaffold.co.uk

Archway Services plc, Bound Oak, Eversley Road, Arborfield Cross, Reading, RG2 9PN Tel: 0118-976 1610 Fax: 0118-976 1510 E-mail: archway.service@virgin.net

Bells Tool Hire, Unit 337 Rushock Trading Estate, Rushock, Droitwich, Worcestershire, WR9 0NR Tel: (01299) 250578 Fax: (01299) 250578

Go Hire Access Ltd, 6 Droicon Industrial Estate, Portway Road, Rowley Regis, West Midlands, B65 9BY Tel: 0121-559 0660 Fax: 0121-559 0770 E-mail: dudley@gohireaccess.co.uk

▶ Hadley Southern Ltd, Rollins St Scaffold Yard, London, SE15 1EP Tel: (020) 7635 5141 Fax: (020) 7635 7297

▶ Kimberley Scaffolding Ltd, Park Road, Bestwood Village, Nottingham, NG6 8TQ Tel: 0115-927 8222 Fax: 0115-927 8333

▶ L A T Access Ltd, Creech Mills Industrial Estate, Taunton, Somerset, TA3 5PX Tel: (01823) 413327 Fax: (01823) 413383 E-mail: lataccess@btopenworld.com

Modular Scaffolding & Building Equipment Ltd, 950 Grimesthorpe Road, Sheffield, S4 8EL Tel: 0114-243 6090 Fax: 0114-243 6046 E-mail: andy@modular.org.uk

▶ Ram Scaffolding, 2 Grays Terrace, Taunton, Somerset, TA1 3HE Tel: (01823) 283692 Fax: (01823) 333395

Towers & Sanders, Unit 1 Bellingham Trading Estate, Franthorne Way, London, SE6 3BX Tel: (020) 8695 6400 Fax: (0845) 2575992 E-mail: info@scaffold-tower.co.uk

SCAFFOLD TOWERS

Deborah Services Ltd, 137 Gelderd Road, Leeds, LS12 6BZ Tel: 0113-244 4629 Fax: 0113-242 0475

Potteries Towers, Unit 10 Norton Industrial Estate, Bellerton Lane, Stoke-on-Trent, ST6 8ED Tel: (01782) 537263 Fax: (01782) 537213

▶ Scaffold-towers.com, Unit 9 Haysbridge Farm, Brickhouse Lane, South Godstone, Godstone, Surrey, RH9 8JW Tel: (01342) 844218 Fax: (01342) 844588 E-mail: dan@scaffoldtowershop.co.uk

Toptower Ltd, Access House, Bromsgrove Road, Halesowen, West Midlands, B63 3HJ Tel: 0800 197 3662 Fax: 0121-585 7989 E-mail: neil@toptower.co.uk

SCAFFOLDING COMPONENTS, *See also headings for particular materials*

Blueridge, 10 Chillingham Way, Camberley, Surrey, GU15 2NS Tel: (07773) 334000 Fax: (07092) 862302 E-mail: info@blueridge.org.uk

▶ Maxcess Scaffolding Erectors, 2 Albert Road, Edinburgh, EH6 7DP Tel: 0131-555 5645 Fax: 0131-555 5997

SCAFFOLDING CONTRACTORS OR ERECTORS

A & A Scaffolding Plus 8 2003 Ltd, Garner Street, Stoke-on-Trent, ST4 7AX Tel: (01782) 202474 Fax: (01782) 201354 E-mail: info@scaffoldingstaffordshire.co.uk

A M P Scaffold Co. Ltd, 39A Deakin Road, Erdington, Birmingham, B24 9AJ Tel: 0121-373 3863 Fax: 0121-377 8588 E-mail: sales@ampscaffold.co.uk

▶ Access Scaffolding Contractors, Marston Hall Depot, Marston Jabbett, Bedworth, Warwickshire, CV12 9SD Tel: (024) 7649 4433 Fax: (024) 7649 4477

Access Company Services Ltd, 103-106 Chadwick Road, Astmoor Industrial Estate, Runcorn, Cheshire, WA7 1PW Tel: (01928) 590880 Fax: (01928) 590877

Ake Scaffolding, Unit 1, Hereford Way, King's Lynn, Norfolk, PE30 4JD Tel: (01553) 775326 Fax: (01553) 773262 E-mail: akescaff@aol.com

▶ Alp Scaffolding, 58-60 High Street, Sandy, Bedfordshire, SG19 1AJ Tel: (01767) 692811 Fax: (01767) 699233 E-mail: alpscaffolding@supanet.com

▶ Altitude Alloy Towers Ltd, 3 The Aerodrome, Stoke Road, Stoke Orchard, Cheltenham, Gloucestershire, GL52 7RS Tel: (01242) 676662 Fax: (01242) 676662

Anglesey Scaffolding (Ynys Mon) Co. Ltd, Amlwch Industrial Estate, Amlwch, Gwynedd, LL68 9BQ Tel: (01407) 831331 Fax: (01407) 831788 E-mail: sales@angleseyscaffolding.co.uk

▶ Another Sampson Scaffold, Samson House, 78 Napier Road, South Croydon, Surrey, CR2 6HG Tel: (020) 8688 2714 Fax: (020) 8667 1327

▶ Apex Scaffolding Northampton Ltd, 165 St. Andrews Road, Northampton, NN2 6HL Tel: (01604) 719422

Archway Services plc, Bound Oak, Eversley Road, Arborfield Cross, Reading, RG2 9PN Tel: 0118-976 1610 Fax: 0118-976 1510 E-mail: archway.service@virgin.net

Aura Q, 33 Grayham Road, Malvern, Worcestershire, WR14 2HU Tel: (01684) 577990 E-mail: sales@ntl-uk.com

▶ Austins Cradles Ltd, Unit 7 Sussex Park Indust Estate 270/272 Old Shoreham Road, Hove, East Sussex, BN3 7DX Tel: (01273) 734744 Fax: (01273) 220810

▶ B & A Scaffolding Ltd, Unit D, Therm Road, Hull, HU8 7BF Tel: (01482) 325952

▶ Beaver 84 Ltd, Bunny Lane, Sherfield English, Romsey, Hampshire, SO51 6FT Tel: (01794) 884876 Fax: (01794) 884277

▶ Benchmark Scaffolding Ltd, Unit 32 The Waterside Trading Centre, Trumpers Way, London, W7 2QD Tel: (020) 8867 9977 Fax: (020) 8867 9900 E-mail: info@benchmarkscaffolding.com

Bishops Stortford Scaffolding Ltd, 64 Garnetts, Takeley, Bishop's Stortford, Hertfordshire, CM22 6RN Tel: (01279) 870680 Fax: (01279) 870680 E-mail: arthouseint@btconnect.com

Blueridge, 10 Chillingham Way, Camberley, Surrey, GU15 2NS Tel: (07773) 334000 Fax: (07092) 862302 E-mail: info@blueridge.org.uk

▶ BMH, 37 Crow Lane, Little Billing, Northampton, NN3 9BZ Tel: (01604) 403322 Fax: (01604) 403329

Bolton Scaffolding, Unit 4b-C Horwich Loco Estate, Chorley New Road, Horwich, Bolton, BL6 5UE Tel: (01204) 478910 Fax: (01204) 478919 E-mail: hardmana@biltonscaffolding.co.uk

Bond Scaffolding Ltd, 31 Lamb Lane, London, E8 3PL Tel: (020) 7254 4444 Fax: (020) 7254 9046

▶ Border Scaffold Services LLP, Unit 2-3 Holmer Trading Estate, Hereford, HR1 1JS Tel: (01432) 352530 Fax: (01432) 352533

▶ Boss Scaffolding Ltd, Repton Street, London, E14 7RW Tel: (020) 7702 7805

Bowller Roofing Supplies, Station Road, Harston, Cambridge, CB22 7QP Tel: (01223) 872260 Fax: (01223) 871143 E-mail: admin@bowller.co.uk

▶ Brecon Scaffolding Ltd, Box Bush Farm, Three Cocks, Brecon, Powys, LD3 0SH Tel: (01874) 754262 Fax: (01874) 754862

▶ Brighton Scaffolding, 98a Pelham Rise, Peacehaven, East Sussex, BN10 8BD Tel: (01273) 691454 E-mail: brightonscaffolding@fsmail.net

▶ Brunel Scaffolding Ltd, 5 James Watt Close, Hawkesworth Trading Estate, Swindon, SN2 1EL Tel: (01793) 531539 Fax: (01793) 542510

▶ C C Scaffolding Surrey, 1 Croft End Close, Chessington, Surrey, KT9 1RD Tel: (020) 8391 5618 Fax: (020) 8397 7927 E-mail: sales@ccscaffolding.co.uk

▶ C & D Industrial Services Ltd, 63 Portland Street, Mansfield Woodhouse, Mansfield, Nottinghamshire, NG19 8BE Tel: (01623) 781200 Fax: (01623) 420496

C & E Scaffolding, M Waterside, 25-27 Willis Way, Poole, Dorset, BH15 3TD Tel: (01202) 661714 Fax: (01202) 661760 E-mail: lynn@cescaffolding.sagehost.co.uk

Cambridge Scaffolding Ltd, 56 Cowley Road, Cambridge, CB4 0DN Tel: (01223) 504422 Fax: (01223) 570888

Cape Industrial Services Ltd, Kirkton Drive, Dyce, Aberdeen, AB21 0BG Tel: (01224) 215800 Fax: (01224) 722879 E-mail: sales@capeindustrialservices.co.uk

Cape Industrial Services Ltd, Cape House, No 3 Redhall Avenue, Paragon Business Village, Wakefield, West Yorkshire, WF1 2UL Tel: (01924) 871000 Fax: (01924) 876291

Cheshire Scaffolds Ltd, Haigh Avenue, Whitehall Trading Estate, Stockport, Cheshire, SK4 1NU Tel: 0161-476 2223 Fax: 0161-476 2227

▶ City Scaffolding Ltd, City House, 124a Chesterfield Road, Barlborough, Chesterfield, Derbyshire, S43 4TT Tel: (01246) 819125 Fax: (01246) 819060 E-mail: city@scaffoldingm1.fsnet.co.uk

Claw Scaffold Ltd, Arrowhead Road, Theale, Reading, RG7 4AE Tel: 0118-930 6688 Fax: 0118-930 6713 E-mail: royclarke@clawscaffold.co.uk

Clocktower Scaffolding, 17 Parkway, Romford, RM2 5NT Tel: (01708) 731781 Fax: (01708) 742112

Colmil Plant & Equipment Co. Ltd, Abbotsford Road, Gateshead, Tyne & Wear, NE10 0LF Tel: 0191-469 4926 Fax: 0191-469 6084 E-mail: sales@colmil.fsnet.co.uk

▶ Contract Scaffolding Services Ltd, Carleton Depot, Carleton, Carlisle, CA1 3DS Tel: (01228) 549411 Fax: (01228) 810867

▶ Crest Scaffolding Ltd, 654 Liverpool Road, Irlam, Manchester, M44 5AD Tel: 0161-776 1055 Fax: 0161-775 9990

Crowe Plant Fabrication Ltd, 11-29 Groton Road, Earlsfield, London, SW18 4HT Tel: (020) 8870 5121 Fax: (020) 8877 9239

▶ Cumbria Design Scaffold Ltd, Unit 3 North Lonsdale Road, Olverston, Ulverston, Cumbria, LA12 9DL Tel: (01229) 587804

Cumbria Kendal Scaffold Co., Mintsfeet Road North, Kendal, Cumbria, LA9 6LZ Tel: (01539) 722674 Fax: (01539) 730640

D H Keys & Sons Ltd, 45 Belvedere Road, Ipswich, IP4 4AB Tel: (01473) 728117 Fax: (01473) 729729

D & R Scaffold Eastern, Archers Fields, Burnt Mills Industrial Estate, Basildon, Essex, SS13 1DH Tel: (01268) 525678 Fax: (01268) 284478

▶ Darlington Scaffolding Ltd, Lingfield Way, Darlington, County Durham, DL1 4GD Tel: (01325) 480450 Fax: (01325) 354565

▶ Deborah Services Ltd, 23, Maple Road, Saddlebow, King's Lynn, Norfolk, PE34 3AH Tel: (01553) 771465 Fax: (01553) 773010 E-mail: kingslynn.hire@deborahservices.co.uk

Deborah Services Ltd, 137 Gelderd Road, Leeds, LS12 6BZ Tel: 0113-244 4629 Fax: 0113-242 0475

Deborah Services Ltd, Thornes Moor Road, Wakefield, West Yorkshire, WF2 8PT Tel: (01924) 378222 Fax: (01924) 366250 E-mail: enquiries@deborahservices.co.uk

▶ Denholm Industrial Services Ltd, Hoe Gate Farm, Hoe Street, Hambledon, Waterlooville, Hampshire, PO7 4RD Tel: (023) 9263 2828 E-mail: paulfoskett@denholmindustrial.co.uk

Denholm Industrial Services Ltd, Boundary Way, Lufton Trading Estate, Yeovil, Somerset, BA22 8HZ Tel: (01935) 420081 Fax: (01935) 472383

Dundee Plant Co. Ltd, Longtown Street, Dundee, DD4 8LF Tel: (01382) 507506 Fax: (01382) 507550

▶ Ea Scaffolding & Systems, Unit 16 North Luton Industrial Estate, Sedgewick Road, Luton, LU4 9DT Tel: (01582) 575200 Fax: (01582) 599254

SCAFFOLDING CONTRACTORS OR ERECTORS – *continued*

Erect A Scaffold Ltd, Crewe Bank Yard, Castle Foregate, Shrewsbury, SY1 2EB Tel: (01743) 360314 Fax: (01743) 272565 E-mail: info@erectascaffold.co.uk

Euro Scaffolding, Unit 1 Heathfield Way, Kings Heath Industrial Estate, Northampton, NN5 7QP Tel: (01604) 583334 Fax: (01604) 583336

▶ Flooks, Crown Industrial Estate, Crown Road, Warmley, Bristol, BS30 8JJ Tel: 0117-960 6069 Fax: 0117-960 6009

Foremost Scaffolding (Supplies) Ltd, Green Acres Trading Estate, Aveley Road, Upminster, Essex, RM14 2TN Tel: (01708) 225549 Fax: (01708) 225607 E-mail: foremostscaffold@btconnect.com

▶ Fourways Plant Ltd, Second Avenue, London, N18 2PG Tel: (020) 8884 3339 Fax: (020) 8807 8477

▶ Framework Specialist Works, North Bridge Road, Berkhamsted, Hertfordshire, HP4 1EH Tel: (01442) 877566 Fax: (01442) 874999

▶ G & D Scaffolding Services Ltd, Leadside Depot, Wellwood, Dunfermline, Fife, KY12 0RS Tel: (01383) 738783 Fax: (01383) 732353

▶ Gesta UK Ltd, 8 Centre Park, Slutchers Lane, Warrington, WA1 1QL Tel: (01925) 241424 Fax: (01925) 241416

▶ Grandstand Hire & Services, 6 Maltings Way, Grimsby, South Humberside, DN31 1QS Tel: (01472) 813271 Fax: (01472) 813271

▶ Grenrose Scaffolding, Crompton Road, Stevenage, Hertfordshire, SG1 2EE Tel: (01438) 813948 Fax: (01438) 742917

Grosvenor Scaffolding Co. Ltd, Station Road, Bagillt, Clwyd, CH6 6AF Tel: (01352) 732148 Fax: (01352) 763628

▶ GTS Scaffolding, 90 Albert Drive, Deganwy, Conwy, Gwynedd, LL31 9RL Tel: (01492) 585343

H & E Scaffolding, Unit 16 Trench Lock 2, Telford, Shropshire, TF1 5SW Tel: (01952) 254248 Fax: (01952) 222084 E-mail: john@hescaffolding.co.uk

▶ H & S Scaffolding Ltd, 1-3 Comet Street, London, SE8 4AN Tel: (020) 8692 4818

Hertel Services UK Ltd, Bromfield Road, Ludlow, Shropshire, SY8 1DN Tel: (01584) 875658 Fax: (01584) 879921

Hewden Tool Hire, Unit 1 Kingstanding Business Park, Tunbridge Wells, Kent, TN2 3UP Tel: (01892) 616318 Fax: (01892) 616353 E-mail: steve.davies@hewden.co.uk

▶ Heywood Scaffolding Services, Unit 4 Green Lane, Heywood, Lancashire, OL10 2EU Tel: (01706) 365742 Fax: (01706) 627377 E-mail: enquiries@heywoodscaffolding.co.uk

▶ Highbridge Scaffolding Ltd, 1 Roscow Road, Fishbrook Industrial Estate, Kearsley, Bolton, BL4 8NX Tel: (01204) 794073 Fax: (01204) 794073

▶ Interserve Industrial Services Ltd, Burcott Road, Bristol, BS11 8AD Tel: (01446) 753674 Fax: 0117-923 5299

▶ Interserve Industrial Services Ltd, Rough Hey Road, Grimsargh, Preston, PR2 5AR Tel: (01772) 792268 Fax: (01772) 703122 E-mail: info@interservices.co.uk

▶ K O Scaffolding Services Ltd, 25 Derwent Road, Whitmore Park, Coventry, CV6 2HB Tel: (024) 7633 7803 Fax: (024) 76366727 E-mail: info@koscaffolding.co.uk

▶ Kingdom Scaffolding Ltd, Building 11, Forties Commercial Campus, Rosyth, Dunfermline, Fife, KY11 2XB Tel: (01383) 420212 Fax: (01383) 420304

Landfall Scaffolding Ltd, 77 Whitecraigs Road, Glenrothes, Fife, KY6 2RX Tel: (01592) 771345 Fax: (01592) 630349 E-mail: sales@landfallscaffolding.co.uk

Leguard Scaffolding Co. Ltd, 53 Gunnersbury Lane, London, W3 8ED Tel: (020) 8993 6306 Fax: (020) 8992 9617

▶ Linear Scaffolding Solutions, 71 Denmark Street, Bedford, MK40 3TH Tel: (01234) 295164 Fax: 01234 295164 E-mail: linearscaff@hotmail.com

▶ Linmark Scaffolding Ltd, Compass Road, Rose Dock, Cardiff, CF10 4LT Tel: (029) 2046 0999 Fax: (029) 2046 1999

▶ M A G Scaffolding Services Ltd, 170 Bitterne Road West, Southampton, SO18 1BG Tel: (023) 8021 1393

M.Laurier & Sons Ltd, Unit 10 Triumph Trading Estate, Tariff Road, London, N17 0EB Tel: (020) 8365 9000 Fax: (020) 8365 9005 E-mail: info@laurier.co.uk

Marah Timms & Sons Scaffolding Ltd, 6 High Street, New Whittington, Chesterfield, Derbyshire, S43 2DX Tel: (01246) 450673 Fax: (01246) 452262

Modular Scaffolding & Building Equipment Ltd, 950 Grimesthorpe Road, Sheffield, S4 8EL Tel: 0114-243 6090 Fax: 0114-243 6046 E-mail: andy@modular.org.uk

▶ Murray Mcgowan Ltd, Clock Mill Road, Gateshead, Tyne & Wear, NE8 2QX Tel: 0191-460 9696 Fax: 0191-460 9686

MW Scaffolding Ltd, Glan Yr Afon Industrial Estate, Llanbadarn Fawr, Aberystwyth, Dyfed, SY23 3JQ Tel: (01970) 624927 Fax: (01970) 624247 E-mail: sales@mwscaffolding.demon.co.uk

▶ Nevron Eurotherm Insulation Services Ltd, Unit 16, Valley Road Business Park, Birkenhead, Merseyside, CH41 7EL Tel: 0151-652 6213 Fax: 0151-652 6213 E-mail: info@nevroninsulation.co.uk

▶ Niall Scaffolders Ltd, Hartwell Depot, Oxford Road, Hartwell, Aylesbury, Buckinghamshire, HP17 8QG Tel: (01296) 427171 Fax: (01296) 434427 E-mail: sales@niallscaffolders.com

▶ No 1 Scaffolding Services Ltd, Swinbourne Road, Burnt Mills Industrial Estate, Basildon, Essex, SS13 1EF Tel: (01268) 724793 Fax: (01268) 725606 E-mail: enquiries@no1scaffolding.co.uk

▶ Norfolk Scaffolding Service, Woodside, Fakenham Road, Morton on the Hill, Norwich, NR9 5SP Tel: (01603) 872183 Fax: (01603) 872293

▶ Northern Scaffold Co. Ltd, Derbyshire Yard, 21 Chesterfield Road, Sheffield, S8 0RL Tel: 0114-255 3100

▶ P J Scaffolding, Fort Bridgewood, Maidstone Road, Rochester, Kent, ME1 3DQ Tel: (01634) 828829 Fax: (01634) 828971

Palmer & Harvey Ltd, 11 Barnes Wallis Road, Fareham, Hampshire, PO15 5TT Tel: (01489) 555800 Fax: (01489) 555883 E-mail: enquiries@palmersgroup.co.uk

▶ Palmers Ltd, North Lane, Aldershot, Hampshire, GU12 4QN Tel: (0870) 0465188 Fax: (0870) 0465189 E-mail: aldershotenq@palmersgroup.co.uk

▶ Par Scaffolding Ltd, 74 Albion Road, Edinburgh, EH7 5QZ Tel: 0131- 656 9333 Fax: 0131- 656 9444 E-mail: par.scaffolding@virgin.net

▶ Pheonix Scaffolding, Unit H Smarden Business Estate, Smarden, Ashford, Kent, TN27 8QL Tel: (01233) 770373 Fax: (01233) 770776

▶ Powertherm Access Services Ltd, Lunn Lane, Beal, Goole, North Humberside, DN14 0SE Tel: (01977) 670111 Fax: (01977) 670444

▶ Premier Scaffolding, Coalpit Lane, Rugeley, Staffordshire, WS15 1EW Tel: (01889) 586152 Fax: (01889) 570274

▶ Prendy Scaffolding Ltd, Daventry Works, 17 Daventry Avenue, London, E17 9AQ Tel: (020) 8520 8556 Fax: (020) 8521 6330

▶ Project Scaffolding, 36 Grange Road, Houstoun Industrial Estate, Livingston, West Lothian, EH54 5DE Tel: (01506) 441144 Fax: (01506) 440044

▶ R B S Scaffolding Ltd, The Grove, Upper Northam Drive, Hedge End, Southampton, SO30 4BG Tel: (023) 8047 1119 Fax: (023) 8047 2828

R J & R J Scaffolding, 22 Chambers Drive, Apse Heath, Sandown, Isle Of Wight, PO36 0LR Tel: (01983) 864674 Fax: (01983) 401092 E-mail: anne-kevin@hotmail.com

▶ R & R Scaffolding Services Ltd, Podder Lane, Nottingham, NG3 5RL Tel: 0115-967 0047 Fax: 0115-967 3130

Ramport Scaffolding Co. Ltd, Martins Yard, 82a Endwell Road, London, SE4 2PD Tel: (020) 7732 4646 Fax: (020) 7732 0321 E-mail: scaffolding@ramport.co.uk

▶ Renvac Scaffolding Ltd, Front Street, Bebside, Blyth, Northumberland, NE24 4HP Tel: (01670) 821385 Fax: (01670) 825640

▶ Rilmac Scaffold Scunthorpe Ltd, Brigg Road, Scunthorpe, South Humberside, DN16 1AX Tel: (01724) 845888 Fax: (01724) 876005 E-mail: enquiries@rilmac.co.uk

▶ Rilmac Scaffolding Ltd, Crofton Drive, Allenby Road Industrial Estate, Lincoln, LN3 4NJ Tel: 01522 531711 Fax: 01522 510291 E-mail: enquiries@rilmac.co.uk

▶ Rilmac Scaffolding Ltd, Brigg Road, Scunthorpe, North Lincolnshire, DN16 1AX Tel: (01724) 845888 Fax: (01724) 876005 E-mail: enquiries@rilmac.co.uk

Ryan Scaffolding Co. Ltd, 132 St. Pauls Way, London, E3 4AL Tel: (020) 7987 2254

S G B plc, Unit 5 Pucklechurch Trading Estate, Pucklechurch, Bristol, BS16 9QH Tel: 0117-937 3218 Fax: 0117-937 2247

▶ S G B plc, Park Lane, Stoke-on-Trent, ST4 3JP Tel: (01782) 313104 Fax: (01782) 335164 E-mail: lpattyson@sgb.co.uk

▶ S G B Group Transport, 31 Hobbs Industrial Estate, Newchapel, Lingfield, Surrey, RH7 6HN Tel: (01342) 835555 Fax: (01342) 835003

S G B Hire Plus, High Street, West End, Southampton, SO30 3JF Tel: (023) 8047 0333 Fax: (023) 8047 3030

▶ Safe Access Scaffolding Midlands Ltd, Belfield Street, Ilkeston, Derbyshire, DE7 8DU Tel: 0115-932 7878 Fax: 0115-944 7812

▶ Safeguard D & J Scaffolding Ltd, Station Goods Yard, Ham Road, Shoreham-by-Sea, West Sussex, BN43 6PA Tel: (01273) 465337 Fax: (01273) 453212

Sandwell Scaffold Co. Ltd, Unit 2B, Charles Street, West Bromwich, West Midlands, B70 0AZ Tel: 0121-557 9464 Fax: 0121-522 3466 E-mail: westbromwich@sandwellscaffold.co.uk

Scaffold Design Ltd, 409 Maltravers Road, Sheffield, S2 5AB Tel: 0114-281 3100 Fax: 0114-281 3104 E-mail: allen@scaffolddesignsltd.co.uk

Scaffold Erection Services Ltd, 225 Tyburn Road, Birmingham, B24 8NB Tel: 0121-322 2088 Fax: 0121-327 2592 E-mail: sales@scaffolder.co.uk

Scaffold Services Ltd, Hawarden Avenue, Leicester, LE5 4NN Tel: 0116-276 8125 Fax: 0116-274 2338 E-mail: sales@scaffoldservicesltd.co.uk

▶ Severnside Scaffolding Ltd, Morley House, Llanthony Road, Hempsted, Gloucester, GL2 5HL Tel: (01452) 529601 Fax: (01452) 305616

SGB plc, Crabtree Lane, Manchester, M11 4GU Tel: 0161-223 3151 Fax: 0161-231 7575 E-mail: sturner@sgb.co.uk

SGB Island Scaffolding, Peel Road Industrial Estate, Douglas, Isle of Man, IM4 4LE Tel: (01624) 674528 Fax: (01624) 663815

▶ Shore Scaffolding Ltd, 9 Harvey Road, Basildon, Essex, SS13 1DG Tel: (01268) 727633 Fax: (01268) 590958 E-mail: shorescaffold@talk21.com

▶ Skill Scaffolding Ltd, Third Avenue, Southampton, SO15 0JX Tel: (023) 8077 7750 Fax: (023) 8070 4535

Skyline, Unit 16 First Avenue, Drum Industrial Estate, Chester le Street, County Durham, DH2 1AG Tel: 0191-410 7917 Fax: 0191-492 0620

▶ Skyway Scaffold Ltd, Unit 1 Sams Lane, West Bromwich, West Midlands, B70 7EG Tel: 0121-525 2666 Fax: 0121-580 4666

Somerset Scaffolding Ltd, Southwood, Evercreech, Shepton Mallet, Somerset, BA4 6LX Tel: (01749) 830159 Fax: (01749) 831159 E-mail: somersetscaff@btinternet.com

▶ Speedier Scaffolding Ltd, Manchester Road, Westhoughton, Bolton, BL5 3QH Tel: (01942) 841919

▶ Startright Scaffold Hire Ltd, Unit 7 Lyon Road Industrial Estate, Kearsley, Bolton, BL4 8NB Tel: (01204) 604441 Fax: (01204) 604442

▶ Stourton Grange Scaffolding Ltd, Unit 3 Long Close Ind Estate, Dolly Lane, Leeds, LS10 4SF Tel: 0113- 277 9045 Fax: 0113-277 9993 E-mail: john@sgsltd.co.uk

Sureway Scaffold Co., Vale Lane, Hartcliffe Way, Bristol, BS3 5RU Tel: 0117-966 8393 Fax: 0117-963 7043 E-mail: sales@surewayscaffolding.co.uk

Swift Brickwork Contractors Ltd, Hampton House, Chelmsford, CM2 9RX Tel: (01245) 255000 Fax: (01245) 255001 E-mail: construction@swiftgroup.co.uk

▶ T A G Scaffolding, Stanley Street, Glasgow, G41 1JA Tel: 0141-429 2204 Fax: 0141-429 6703

Telford Tower & Scaffolding Co. Ltd, Unit F7 Castle Trading Estate, Snedshill, Telford, Shropshire, TF2 9NP Tel: (01952) 612814 Fax: (01952) 613006

▶ Tone Scaffolding Services, 87-91 Beddington Lane, Croydon, CR0 4TD Tel: (020) 8684 3771 Fax: (020) 8684 3772 E-mail: chris.burch@tonescaffolding.co.uk

Tower Scaffolding South West, Unit 7 Milber Trading Estate, Newton Abbot, Devon, TQ12 4SG Tel: (01626) 331446 Fax: (01626) 335515 E-mail: tower.info@btopenworld.com

▶ Town & Country, Home Farm Works, Clifton Road, Deddington, Banbury, Oxfordshire, OX15 0TP Tel: (01869) 337070

Trad Group Ltd, Pelican Wharf, Imperial Street, London, E3 3ED Tel: (020) 8980 1155 Fax: (020) 8981 3019 E-mail: enquiries@trad.co.uk

▶ Trio Scaffoldings, 400 Edgware Road, London, NW2 6ND Tel: (020) 8452 3337 Fax: (020) 8208 0621

Tubular Scaffolding Ltd, 1081 Duke St, Glasgow, G31 5NX Tel: 0141-554 3801 Fax: 0141-554 3801

Turner Hire Drive Ltd, 65 Craigton Road, Glasgow, G51 3EQ Tel: 0141-440 1900 Fax: 0141-307 1213

▶ V & S Scaffolding Services Ltd, Unit 10A Warehams Lane, Hertford, SG14 1LA Tel: (01992) 558464

Vange Scaffolding & Engineering Co. Ltd, 14 Brunel Road, Benfleet, Essex, SS7 4PS Tel: (01268) 792701 Fax: (01268) 795542 E-mail: vangenicky@aol.com

W & J Scaffolding Ltd, Construction House, Toll End Road, Tipton, West Midlands, DY4 0HW Tel: 0121-522 4454 Fax: 0121-522 4457 E-mail: tipton@wjscaffolding.co.uk

▶ Worth Scaffolding Co., Rookfield, Crawley Road, Faygate, Horsham, West Sussex, RH12 4SA Tel: (01293) 852619 Fax: (01293) 852620

▶ WW Scaffolding, Unit 9-10 Capital Industrial Centre, Willow Lane, Mitcham, Surrey, CR4 4NA Tel: (020) 8648 1444 Fax: (020) 8640 3440

Xpress Scaffold Systems, Batham Gate Road, Fairfield, Buxton, Derbyshire, SK17 7HS Tel: (01298) 73136 Fax: (01298) 23630

SCAFFOLDING FITTINGS

▶ Metric Scaffolding Co. Ltd, Stanley Works, Ampthill Road, Kempston Hardwick, Bedford, MK45 3JE Tel: (01234) 325005 Fax: (01234) 210933

▶ ScaffCap, 12 Greenholm Road, Eltham, London, SE9 1UH Tel: (020) 8123 0505 E-mail: pcheek@scaffcap.co.uk

SCAFFOLDING HIRE OR SUPPLY SERVICES

A & A Scaffolding Plus 8 2003 Ltd, Garner Street, Stoke-on-Trent, ST4 7AX Tel: (01782) 202474 Fax: (01782) 201354 E-mail: info@scaffoldingstaffordshire.co.uk

A M P Scaffold Co. Ltd, 39A Deakin Road, Erdington, Birmingham, B24 9AJ Tel: 0121-373 3863 Fax: 0121-377 8588 E-mail: sales@ampscaffold.co.uk

Access Scaffold Systems Ltd, Unit 5, Duchess Industrial Estate, Sievewright Street, Rutherglen, Glasgow, G73 1LL Tel: 0141-613 0000 Fax: 0141-613 0011

▶ Ace Scaffolding Manchester Ltd, Weymouth Road, Eccles, Manchester, M30 8BT Tel: 0161-787 7872 Fax: 0161-787 7565

Albion Tower Properties Ltd, 177 Greets Green Road, West Bromwich, West Midlands, B70 9ET Tel: 0121-557 4000 Fax: 0121-522 2703

Archway Services plc, Bound Oak, Eversley Road, Arborfield Cross, Reading, RG2 9PN Tel: 0118-976 1610 Fax: 0118-976 1510 E-mail: archway.service@virgin.net

Banson Tool Hire Ltd, 125 Pellon Lane, Halifax, West Yorkshire, HX1 5QN Tel: (01422) 254999 Fax: (01422) 254778

▶ Beaver 84 Ltd, Watson Close, Grays, Essex, RM20 3EF Tel: (01708) 861821 Fax: (01708) 869537

Boulton Ltd, Cannon Business Park, Darkhouse Lane, Bilston, West Midlands, WV14 8XQ Tel: (01902) 385300 Fax: (01902) 385330 E-mail: info@boultonlimited.com

Brandon Hire plc, Llangunnor Road, Carmarthen, Dyfed, SA31 2PB Tel: (01267) 237405 Fax: (01267) 238299 E-mail: carmarthen@brandonhire.plc.uk

Clocktower Scaffolding, 17 Parkway, Romford, RM2 5NT Tel: (01708) 731781 Fax: (01708) 742112

Colmil Plant & Equipment Co. Ltd, Abbotsford Road, Gateshead, Tyne & Wear, NE10 0LF Tel: 0191-469 4926 Fax: 0191-469 6084 E-mail: sales@colmil.fsnet.co.uk

▶ Cumbria Design Scaffold Ltd, Unit 3 North Lonsdale Road, Olverston, Ulverston, Cumbria, LA12 9DL Tel: (01229) 587804

D & R Scaffold Eastern, Archers Fields, Burnt Mills Industrial Estate, Basildon, Essex, SS13 1DH Tel: (01268) 525678 Fax: (01268) 284478

Deborah Services Ltd, Souter Head Industrial Centre, Souter Head Road, Altens Industrial Estate, Aberdeen, AB12 3LF Tel: (01224) 878529 Fax: (01224) 897927 E-mail: aberdeen.hire@deborahservices.co.uk

▶ Deborah Services Ltd, Quarry Lane, Chichester, West Sussex, PO19 8NY Tel: (01243) 782345 Fax: (01243) 527581

Deborah Services Ltd, 731-761 Harrow Road, London, NW10 5NY Tel: (020) 8969 1191 Fax: (020) 8968 1301 E-mail: harrow.contracts@deborahservices.co.uk

Deborah Services Ltd, 227-231 Selbourne Road, Luton, LU4 8NR Tel: (01582) 491000 Fax: (01582) 493384 E-mail: luton.hire@deborahservices.co.uk

Equiphire Northern, Bradford Road, Cleckheaton, West Yorkshire, BD19 5YR Tel: (01274) 871817 Fax: (01274) 851224

Equiphire Northern Ltd, Morley Hire Centre, West Street, Morley, Leeds, LS27 9EU Tel: 0113-252 5320 Fax: (01274) 851224

▶ Framework Specialist Works, North Bridge Road, Berkhamsted, Hertfordshire, HP4 1EH Tel: (01442) 877566 Fax: (01442) 874999

Haki Ltd, Magnus, Tame Valley Industrial Estate, Wilnecote, Tamworth, Staffordshire, B77 5BY Tel: (01827) 282525 Fax: (01827) 250329 E-mail: info@haki.co.uk

H.C. Hill Ltd, PO Box 137, Beckenham, Kent, BR3 4WY Tel: (020) 8650 7890 Fax: (020) 8650 0535 E-mail: enquiries@hchill.co.uk

▶ Kirk Scaffolding Ltd, Greenbank Works, Gorse Street, Blackburn, BB1 3EU Tel: (01254) 672337 Fax: (01254) 667711

Langridge Scaffolding Sussex Ltd, Unit M1 Rudford Industrial Estate, Ford Road, Ford, Arundel, West Sussex, BN18 0BF Tel: (01903) 725873 Fax: (01903) 723468 E-mail: enquiries@langridgescaffolding.co.uk

▶ Lansford Access Ltd, 10 Chancel Close, Gloucester, GL4 3SN Tel: (01452) 520144 Fax: (01452) 308369 E-mail: sales@lansfordaccess.co.uk

Layher Ltd, Works Road, Letchworth Garden City, Hertfordshire, SG6 1WL Tel: (01462) 475100 Fax: (01462) 475101 E-mail: info@layher.com

▶ Lodge Scaffold Ltd, Crows Nest, Ashton Road, Billinge, Wigan, Lancashire, WN5 7XY Tel: (01744) 891717 Fax: (01744) 891718

▶ M R Scaffolding Anglia Ltd, Harfreys Road, Great Yarmouth, Norfolk, NR31 0LS Tel: (01493) 665066 Fax: (01493) 664050

Midland Plant & Scaffolding Ltd, 171 Gloucester Crescent, Wigston, Leicestershire, LE18 4YH Tel: 0116-278 6677

▶ Midshires Scaffolding Co. Ltd, Unit 22 Bilton Industrial Estate, Humber Avenue, Coventry, CV3 1JL Tel: (024) 7665 2901 Fax: (024) 7665 2902

Mitie Generation Ltd, Meriton Street, Bristol, BS2 0SZ Tel: 0117-972 4550 Fax: 0117-972 4502 E-mail: bristol@generationuk.co.uk

▶ Mitie Generation Ltd, Kingsfield Way, Kings Heath Industrial Estate, Northampton, NN5 7QN Tel: (01604) 580444 Fax: (01604) 580487

▶ P & T Scaffolding Ltd, Bells Yew Green Business Centre, Bells Yew Green, Tunbridge Wells, Kent, TN3 9BL Tel: (01892) 750715 Fax: (01892) 750967

R J & R J Scaffolding, 22 Chambers Drive, Apse Heath, Sandown, Isle Of Wight, PO36 0LR Tel: (01983) 864674 Fax: (01983) 401092 E-mail: anne-kevin@hotmail.com

S G B plc, Unit 5 Pucklechurch Trading Estate, Pucklechurch, Bristol, BS16 9QH Tel: 0117-937 3218 Fax: 0117-937 2247

S G B plc, Pontefract Road, Leeds, LS10 1SP Tel: 0113-271 2951 Fax: 0113-270 7726 E-mail: rentalandsales@sgb.co.uk

SCAFFOLDING HIRE OR SUPPLY SERVICES – *continued*

▶ S G B plc, Park Lane, Stoke-on-Trent, ST4 3JP Tel: (01782) 313104 Fax: (01782) 335164 E-mail: lpattyson@sgb.co.uk

S G B Rental & Sales, 104 Scrubs Lane, Willesden, London, NW10 6SF Tel: (020) 8969 3661 Fax: (020) 8960 6033

▶ S K Scaffolding Dorset Ltd, 47 Enterprise Park, Piddlehinton, Dorchester, Dorset, DT2 7UA Tel: (01305) 849400 E-mail: sales@sk-scaffolding.co.uk

Sandwell Scaffold Co. Ltd, Unit 2B, Charles Street, West Bromwich, West Midlands, B70 0AZ Tel: 0121-557 9464 Fax: 0121-522 3466 E-mail: westbromwich@sandwellscaffold.co.uk

Scaffold Services Ltd, Hawarden Avenue, Leicester, LE5 4NN Tel: 0116-276 8125 Fax: 0116-274 2338 E-mail: sales@scaffoldservicesltd.co.uk

SGB plc, Crabtree Lane, Manchester, M11 4GU Tel: 0161-223 3151 Fax: 0161-231 7575 E-mail: sturner@sgb.co.uk

▶ Skill Scaffolding Ltd, Third Avenue, Southampton, SO15 0JX Tel: (023) 8077 7750 Fax: (023) 8070 4535 E-mail: skill.foton@btconnect.com

Somerset Scaffolding Ltd, Southwood, Evercreech, Shepton Mallet, Somerset, BA4 6LX Tel: (01749) 830159 Fax: (01749) 831159 E-mail: somersetscaff@btinternet.com

Speedy Hire Centres Northern Ltd, Lakeside Buildings, St. Helens, Merseyside, WA10 3TT Tel: (01744) 697000 Fax: (01744) 739975

▶ Standard Scaffolding Specialists Ltd, 131 Church Street, Little Lever, Bolton, BL3 1BW Tel: (01204) 574064 Fax: (01204) 862612

Telford Tower & Scaffolding Ltd, Unit F7 Castle Trading Estate, Snedshill, Telford, Shropshire, TF2 9NP Tel: (01952) 612814 Fax: (01952) 613006

▶ Tone Scaffolding Services, 87-91 Beddington Lane, Croydon, CR0 4TD Tel: (020) 8684 3771 Fax: (020) 8684 3772 E-mail: chris.burch@tonescaffolding.co.uk

▶ UK Access Solution Ltd, Kelvin Way, West Bromwich, West Midlands, B70 7JY Tel: 0121-500 5055

Unique Scaffolding Ltd, Kangley Bridge Road, London, SE26 5AU Tel: (020) 8778 8483 Fax: (020) 8676 8439

Universal Access & Power Plants Ltd, 14 Pony Road, Cowley, Oxford, OX4 2RD Tel: (01865) 450000 Fax: (01865) 451111 E-mail: sales@universalhire.co.uk

▶ W G K London Ltd, Old Bovingdon Airfield, Whelpley Hill, Chesham, Buckinghamshire, HP5 3RR Tel: (01442) 831856 Fax: (01442) 831857

▶ W & J Scaffolding Ltd, Ennerdale Road, Shrewsbury, SY1 3LD Tel: (01743) 442204

SCAFFOLDING PROTECTION COVERS

Hy-Tops Ltd, Budden Road, Coseley, Bilston, West Midlands, WV14 8JZ Tel: 0121-557 2191 Fax: 0121-520 3020 E-mail: sales@hickmanandlove.co.uk

Terapin Curtain Systems, 2 Glenavy Road, Upper Ballinderry, Lisburn, County Antrim, BT28 2EU Tel: (028) 9265 1007 Fax: (028) 9265 2019 E-mail: info@terapin.com

SCAFFOLDING REFURBISHMENT SPECIALIST SERVICES

Blemkleen NW Ltd, PO Box 688, Lancaster, LA2 6WY Tel: (01524) 812832 Fax: (01524) 811747 E-mail: tony@blemkleen.freeserve.co.uk

▶ Rilmac Scaffolding Ltd, Brigg Road, Scunthorpe, North Lincolnshire, DN16 1AX Tel: (01724) 845888 Fax: (01724) 876005 E-mail: enquiries@rilmac.co.uk

SCAFFOLDING SAFETY EQUIPMENT

Blueridge, 10 Chillingham Way, Camberley, Surrey, GU15 2NS Tel: (07773) 334000 Fax: (07092) 862302 E-mail: info@blueridge.org.uk

▶ ScaffCap, 12 Greenholm Road, Eltham, London, SE9 1UH Tel: (020) 8123 0505 E-mail: pcheek@scaffcap.co.uk

▶ Scaffold Alarms.Com, 168 Church Lane, London, NW9 8SP Tel: (0845) 1304591 Fax: (0845) 1304592 E-mail: sales@scaffoldalarms.co.uk

SCAFFOLDING SAFETY NETS

▶ PMC Safety Netting Ltd, Unit 3, Appian Way, Europa Business Park, Grimsby, Lincolnshire, DN31 2UT Tel: (01472) 267733 Fax: (01472) 350921 E-mail: pmc.safetynetting@ntlworld.com

▶ R W P Scaffolding & Safety Netting Services, 1 Pelton Walk, Monsall, Manchester, M40 8QY Tel: 0161-277 9704 Fax: 0161-205 5981 E-mail: rwpscaffolding@aol.com

SCALE HIRE

Autoweigh Scales UK Ltd, James Street, Elland, West Yorkshire, HX5 0HB Tel: (01422) 376965 Fax: (01422) 378109 E-mail: autoweigh.sales@virgin.net

Avery Weigh-Tronix, Unit D4, Capital Point, Capital Business Park, Wentloog, Cardiff, CF3 2PY Tel: (029) 2083 9510 Fax: (0870) 9018166

County Scales Ltd, Langley Business Park, Station Road, Langley Mill, NG16 4DG Tel: (0800) 7311774 Fax: (01773) 763222

D Brash & Sons Ltd, 840 Chester Road, Stretford, Manchester, M32 0QJ Tel: 0161-865 0333 Fax: 0161-865 0444 E-mail: sales@dbrash.co.uk

Select Scales Ltd, 36 Skinner Street, Creswell, Worksop, Nottinghamshire, S80 4JH Tel: (01909) 725043 Fax: (01909) 724057

SCALE MAINTENANCE/REPAIR SERVICES

Metropolitan Weighing Machine Co. Ltd, Metro Weighing Machines, Foxton Road, Grays, Essex, RM20 4XX Tel: (01375) 390140 Fax: (01375) 390140 E-mail: enquiries@metroweigh.com

Shropshire Scale Co., 27 Kestrel Drive, Shrewsbury, SY1 4TT Tel: (01743) 468928

Tanita International Ltd, The Barn Philpots Close, West Drayton, Middlesex, UB7 7RY Tel: (01895) 438577 Fax: (01895) 438511

SCALE MODELS

▶ A Models, 56 Shoreditch High Street, London, E1 6JJ Tel: (020) 7613 0424 Fax: (020) 7613 2955

▶ Aircraft Replicas Ltd, Unit 4E, Industrial Estate, Sinfin Lane, Derby, DE24 9GL Tel: (01332) 271600 Fax: (01332) 271600

▶ Albatross Models, The Coach House, St. Pauls Walden, Hitchin, Hertfordshire, SG4 8BP Tel: (01438) 871688 Fax: (01438) 871874 E-mail: enquiries@albatrossmodels.co.uk

Amerang Ltd, 15b Commerce Way, Lancing, West Sussex, BN15 8TA Tel: (01903) 765496 Fax: (01903) 765178 E-mail: sales@amerang-group.com

▶ Baccus Model Makers, Bardwell Road, Sheffield, S3 8AS Tel: 0114-272 4491 Fax: 0114-272 4491

Cod Steaks, 2 Cole Road, St Philips, Bristol, BS2 0UG Tel: 0117-980 3910 Fax: 0117-972 8999 E-mail: mail@codsteaks.com

▶ Comber Model Makers, 6 Viewpoint, Boxley Road, Penenden Heath, Maidstone, Kent, ME14 2DZ Tel: (01622) 355850 Fax: (01622) 355860

Concept Creative Services Ltd, Unit 1, Baird House, Dudley Innovation Centre, Pensnett Trading Estate, Kingswinford, West Midlands, DY6 7YA Tel: (01384) 400161 Fax: (01384) 400190 E-mail: sales@concept-models.com

▶ Cruiseline Models, 16 Winston Road, Barry, South Glamorgan, CF62 9SW Tel: (01446) 420901

En Aid Design Workshop, Wassage Way, Hampton Lovett, Droitwich, Worcestershire, WR9 0NX Tel: (01905) 451501 Fax: (01905) 771771 E-mail: enaid@btclick.com

▶ Gateway Global UK Ltd, Unit 2 Amor Way, Letchworth Garden City, Hertfordshire, SG6 1UG Tel: (01462) 670888 Fax: (01462) 670886

Geoffrey Sumpter, Barton End House, Barton End, Horsley, Stroud, Gloucestershire, GL6 0QQ Tel: (01453) 833883 Fax: (01453) 833883

Hart Models Ltd, The Cricket Grn, Hartley Wintney, Hook, Hants, RG27 8QB Tel: 01252 842637 Fax: 01252 842637

John Glossop Model Makers, The Corner House, Coles Lane, Cambridge, CB21 4JS Tel: (01223) 892444 Fax: (01223) 894211

Kellforms Woodmasters Ltd, Derehams Lane, Loudwater, High Wycombe, Buckinghamshire, HP10 9RH Tel: (01494) 472233 Fax: (01494) 462269 E-mail: kevin@kellforms.com

Knight Andy Ltd, 2-6 Occupation Road, London, SE17 3BE Tel: (020) 7252 5252 Fax: (020) 7252 5111 E-mail: info@andyknight.co.uk

Mackinnon & Saunders Ltd, 146-148 Seamons Road, Altrincham, Cheshire, WA14 4LJ Tel: 0161-929 4441 Fax: 0161-929 1441

▶ Maldon Rail Centre Ltd, 8 Silver Street, Maldon, Essex, CM9 4QE Tel: (01621) 858188 Fax: (01621) 855527

Mallard Models & Effects, 133 Dorset Road, London, SW19 3EQ Tel: (020) 8540 4430 Fax: (020) 8715 7301

Metropolis, Grange Business Centre, Belasis Avenue, Billingham, Cleveland, TS23 1LG Tel: (01642) 361255 Fax: (01642) 365700 E-mail: sales@metropolisdevelopments.co.uk

Milestone Minitures Ltd, 25 West End, Redruth, Cornwall, TR15 2SA Tel: (01209) 218356 Fax: (01209) 217983

Mirage R C Enterprises Ltd, 19 William Nadin Way, Swadlincote, Derbyshire, DE11 0BB Tel: (01283) 226570 Fax: (01283) 229401

▶ Model Enthusiasts, Lower Station Road, Henfield, West Sussex, BN5 9UG Tel: (0870) 7552241

Model Making & Graphic Services Ltd, 9 Bath Buildings, Montpelier, Bristol, BS6 5PT Tel: 0117-944 6050 Fax: 0117-944 5973 E-mail: mmgsltd@aol.com

Pritchard Patent Product Co. Ltd, Underleys, Beer, Seaton, Devon, EX12 3NA Tel: (01297) 21542 Fax: (01297) 20229

R A E Models, Unit 15, 113 Fordwater Road, Chertsey, Surrey, KT16 8HB Tel: (01932) 563600 Fax: (01932) 564778 E-mail: raemodels@supernet.com

R P M Model Making, 3 Station Approach, Wendover, Aylesbury, Buckinghamshire, HP22 6BN Tel: (01296) 622625 Fax: (01296) 625755 E-mail: enquiries@rpm.modelmakers.co.uk

▶ Rocket Creative Solutions, 70 Stanley Gardens, London, W3 7SZ Tel: (020) 8740 5225 Fax: (020) 8740 7450

Sarik Vacform, Unit 8-9 Pixash Business Centre, Pixash Lane, Keynsham, Bristol, BS31 1TP Tel: 0117-986 0404 Fax: 0117-986 0424 E-mail: info@sarik-vacform.com

Space Models Ltd, Pier Road, North Feltham Trading Estate, Feltham, Middlesex, TW14 0TW Tel: (020) 8890 5542 Fax: (020) 8751 1731 E-mail: enq@spacemodels.co.uk

Technical Models Ltd, Unit 10 Crosland Industrial Estate, Stockport Road West, Bredbury, Stockport, Cheshire, SK6 2BR Tel: 0161-494 9022 Fax: 0161-430 8406 E-mail: enquiries@technical-models.co.uk

Thorp Modelmakers Ltd, Whitmore Lane, Sunningdale Village, Ascot, Berkshire, SL5 0NS Tel: (01344) 876776 Fax: (01344) 876583 E-mail: thorp@atomltd.com

Weird Dimensions, 33a Lowman Road, London, N7 6DE Tel: (020) 7607 2176 Fax: (020) 7609 6848

Willow Models, 4 Willow Grove, Golcar, Huddersfield, HD7 4RX Tel: (01484) 658832 Fax: (01484) 658832 E-mail: sales@willowmodels.com

▶ www.farmmodels.co.uk, The Old Manor Farmhouse, Lower Road, Edington, Westbury, Wiltshire, BA13 4QW Tel: (01380) 831459 Fax: (01380) 830659 E-mail: office@farmmodels.co.uk

York Plastics Engineering Ltd, 70-72 James Street, York, YO10 3WW Tel: (01904) 412852 Fax: (01904) 430202 E-mail: yorkplastics@btinternet.com

SCALE SCOOPS

Poole & Son Scoops Ltd, Unit 15 Delta House, Adderley Street, Birmingham, B9 4ED Tel: 0121-753 0912 Fax: 0121-753 0912

SCALE TREE MODELS

4 D Model Shop Ltd, 120 Leman Street, London, E1 8EU Tel: (020) 7264 1288 Fax: (020) 7264 1299 E-mail: info@modelshop.co.uk

SCALES, *See also headings for particular types*

▶ 24-7 Weighing Solutions Ltd, 63 Blenheim Place, Stenhousemuir, Larbert, Stirlingshire, FK5 4PW Tel: (01324) 878569 Fax: (01324) 878816E-mail: sales@weighingsolutions.co.uk

A Ring-A-Till Ltd, 129 Stanningley Road, Armley, Leeds, LS12 3PJ Tel: (0800) 0189713 Fax: 0113-203 8282

Accuweigh, Unit 14, East Riding Business Centre, Annie Reed Road, Beverley, North Humberside, HU17 0LS Tel: (01482) 475650

Ace Business Machines, 1 Lacre Way, Letchworth Garden City, Hertfordshire, SG6 1NR Tel: (01462) 676002 Fax: (01462) 484315 E-mail: sales@acetills.co.uk

B & M Business Machines Ltd, 30 Military Road, Colchester, CO1 2AJ Tel: (01206) 576872 Fax: (01206) 576873

Barnsley Cash Registers, 2the Parade, Clough Fields Road, Hoyland, Barnsley, South Yorkshire, S74 0HR Tel: (01226) 744003 Fax: (01226) 744003 E-mail: barnsleytills@aol.com

Birmingham Cash Registers Ltd, 135 Quinton Road West, Birmingham, B32 2RE Tel: 0121-565 3131 Fax: 0121-565 3213 E-mail: lesley@birminghamcash.co.uk

Cas Corporation UK Ltd, 29A Junction Street South, Oldbury, West Midlands, B69 4TA Tel: 0121-552 0009 Fax: 0121-511 1317 E-mail: sales@casuk.co.uk

Channel Weighing, Unit 16 Chislet Close, Lakesview International Business Park, Hersden, Canterbury, Kent, CT3 4LB Tel: (01227) 711020 Fax: (01227) 711040 E-mail: sales@channel-weighing.co.uk

Crane Scales Ltd, 21-23 Bagnall Street, Ocker Hill, Tipton, West Midlands, DY4 0EF Tel: 0121-556 4062 Fax: 0121-556 8217 E-mail: info@cranescales.co.uk

D Brash & Sons Ltd, 840 Chester Road, Stretford, Manchester, M32 0QJ Tel: 0161-865 0333 Fax: 0161-865 0444 E-mail: sales@dbrash.co.uk

Euroscales Holdings Ltd, Queens Court, Queens Avenue, Macclesfield, Cheshire, SK10 2BN Tel: (01625) 619554 Fax: (01625) 613295 E-mail: sales@euroscales.com

▶ Excell Precision Europe, Stanton Upon Hine Heath, Shrewsbury, SY4 4LW Tel: (01939) 250699

Exeter Scale & Equipment Co., Grace Road Central, Marsh Barton Trading Estate, Exeter, EX2 8QA Tel: (01392) 275324

Fisher Scales, 11-11a Unit, Station Road Industrial Estate, Attleborough, Norfolk, NR17 2NP Tel: (01953) 450310 Fax: (01953) 456391 E-mail: fisher.scales@virgin.net

Gardners, 149 Commercial Street, London, E1 6BJ Tel: (020) 7247 5119

Hereford Scale Co., 1 Vaga Street, Hereford, HR2 7AT Tel: (01432) 356472 Fax: (01432) 352646

Howard Scale Co. Ltd, 14 Oughton Road, Birmingham, B12 0DF Tel: 0121-446 5190 Fax: 0121-446 5191 E-mail: sale@howardscale.com

▶ Kent & Sussex Scales Ltd, Wilderwick Road, East Grinstead, West Sussex, RH19 3NT Tel: (01342) 870221 Fax: (01342) 870104 E-mail: sales@kentandsussexscales.co.uk

Langley Business Systems Ltd, 29 Junction Street South, Oldbury, West Midlands, B69 4TA Tel: 0121-552 2570 Fax: 0121-511 1317E-mail: sales@lbswholesale.demon.co.uk

Northern Data Machines, 35 The Square, Grantown-on-Spey, Morayshire, PH26 3HF Tel: (01479) 873777 Fax: (01479) 87377 E-mail: enquiries@northerndata.co.uk

Ohaus UK Ltd, 64 Boston Road, Leicester, LE4 1AW Tel: 0116-234 5075 Fax: 0116-235 9256

Salter Weigh-Tronix Ltd, Unit 1 Tilson Road, Roundthorn Industrial Estate, Manchester, M23 9GF Tel: (0870) 4420000 Fax: 0161-946 0228

Scalesmart Ltd, Unit 37, The Warren, East Goscote, Leicester, LE7 3XA Tel: (0800) 9154201 Fax: (0800) 9154202 E-mail: scales@scalesmart.com

Select Scales Ltd, 36 Skinner Street, Creswell, Worksop, Nottinghamshire, S80 4JH Tel: (01909) 725043 Fax: (01909) 724057

Southern Scales & Equipment Co., 15 Chorley Avenue, Saltdean, Brighton, BN2 8AQ Tel: (01273) 303692 Fax: (01273) 279578

Surrey Scales Co, 2 The Parade, Philanthropic Road, Redhill, RH1 4DN Tel: (01737) 769745 Fax: (01737) 760390

XL Scales Ltd, Units 7-8 Trafalgar Industrial Estate, Sovereign Way, Downham Market, Norfolk, PE38 9SW Tel: (01366) 384554 Fax: (01366) 385300 E-mail: contact@xlscales.com

SCALES, BATHROOM, ELECTRONIC

▶ 1 Stop Scale Shop, 47 Market Place, Henley-on-Thames, Oxfordshire, RG9 2AN Tel: (0845) 1307330 Fax: (0845) 1307440 E-mail: sales@1stopscaleshop.co.uk

▶ Bathroom Deals, 102 Finlay Road, Gloucester, GL4 6TP Tel: (01452) 336250 Fax: (01452) 332338 E-mail: sales@bathroomdeals.com

▶ E & G Websales Ltd, Delfryn, Lixwm, Holywell, Flintshire, CH8 8NQ Tel: (01352) 781944 E-mail: enquiries@digital-scales-company.co.uk

SCALES, ELECTRONIC/ MECHANICAL

Abbey Signs, 6-8 Glentanar Place, Glasgow, G22 7XT Tel: 0141-336 3610 Fax: 0141-336 4629 E-mail: sales@abbeysigns.fsnet.co.uk

D Brash & Sons Ltd, 840 Chester Road, Stretford, Manchester, M32 0QJ Tel: 0161-865 0333 Fax: 0161-865 0444 E-mail: sales@dbrash.co.uk

Design Initiative Ltd, The Old Granary, The Street, Glynde, Lewes, East Sussex, BN8 6SX Tel: (01273) 858525 Fax: (01273) 858531 E-mail: info@designit.eu.com

Fairweigh International, 5 Kimpton Enterprise Park, Kimpton, Hitchin, Hertfordshire, SG4 8HP Tel: (01438) 833613 Fax: (01438) 833614

Hanson (UK) Ltd, 81A Marlowes, Hemel Hempstead, Hertfordshire, HP1 1LF Tel: (01442) 270444 Fax: (01442) 270666 E-mail: sales@hansonuk.com

Healthcheck Services Ltd, Unit 49 Riverside Estate, Sir Thomas Longley Road, Medway City Estate, Rochester, Kent, ME2 4DP Tel: (01634) 296234 Fax: (01634) 712607 E-mail: info@healthcheckservices.co.uk

Metropolitan Weighing Machine Co. Ltd, Metro Weighing Machines, Foxton Road, Grays, Essex, RM20 4XX Tel: (01375) 390140 Fax: (01375) 390140 E-mail: enquiries@metroweigh.com

MK Scales Ltd, Cherrycourt Way, Leighton Buzzard, Bedfordshire, LU7 4UH Tel: (01525) 375519 Fax: (01525) 377290 E-mail: sales@mkscales.co.uk

Oh Yeah, 100 Southchurch Road, Southend-on-Sea, SS1 2LX Tel: (01702) 469785 Fax: (01702) 469785

St Turier, Unit 7 Block 5 Shenstone Trading Estate, Bromsgrove Road, Halesowen, West Midlands, B63 3XB Tel: 0121-501 6880 Fax: 0121-501 6881 E-mail: sales@turierscales.co.uk

SCALES, ELECTRONIC/ MECHANICAL – *continued*

Scalesmart Ltd, Unit 37, The Warren, East Goscote, Leicester, LE7 3XA Tel: (0800) 9154201 Fax: (0800) 9154202 E-mail: scales@scalesmart.com

Talent Weighing S & S Ltd, 3j Anchor Bridge Way, Dewsbury, West Yorkshire, WF12 9QS Tel: (01924) 438127 Fax: (01924) 438129 E-mail: info@talentweighing.co.uk

Weightron (U K) Ltd, Weightron House, Brimington Road North, Chesterfield, Derbyshire, S41 9AN Tel: (01246) 260062 Fax: (01246) 260844 E-mail: info@weightroncb.co.uk

SCALES, MECHANICAL/ AUTOMATIC

Chasmors Weighing Equipment, 18 Camden High Street, London, NW1 0JH Tel: (020) 7387 2060 Fax: (020) 7387 2060

D & L Cash Registers, 67 North Street, London, E13 9HL Tel: (020) 8552 5294 Fax: (020) 8472 1654

▶ Top Weigh Ltd, Scale House, Jeffrey Estate, Rockcliffe, Carlisle, CA6 4BH Tel: (01228) 672400 Fax: (01228) 672402

Turrier Scales Ltd, Units 3-4, Vernon Trading Estate, New John Street, Halesowen, West Midlands, B62 8HT Tel: 0121-559 1127 Fax: 0121-561 1046

SCAN CONVERTING EQUIPMENT

TV One, V Continental Approach, Westwood Industrial Estate, Margate, Kent, CT9 4JG Tel: (01843) 873311 Fax: (01843) 873301 E-mail: web@vinemicros.com

SCANNERS

A4 Computers, 2nd Floor, 32 B Church Road, Ashford, Middlesex, TW15 2UY Tel: (0870) 0634283 Fax: (0870) 0632106 E-mail: info@a4it.co.uk

▶ Bolton P C, 57 Bramhall Avenue, Harwood, Bolton, BL2 4ES Tel: (0870) 0174010 Fax: (0870) 0174011 E-mail: sales.kellysearch@boltonpc.co.uk

S D I Displays Ltd, Ratcliffe Road, Sileby, Loughborough, Leicestershire, LE12 7PZ Tel: (01509) 813166 Fax: (01509) 816369

SCARF MANUFRS

Beckford Silk Ltd, Ashton Road, Beckford, Tewkesbury, Gloucestershire, GL20 7AU Tel: (01386) 881507 Fax: (01386) 882019 E-mail: sales@beckfordsilk.co.uk

Boardman Bros Ltd, 50 Red Bank, Manchester, M4 4HF Tel: 0161-832 2381 Fax: 0161-833 2456 E-mail: reception@boardmanbros.co.uk

C B Collections Ltd, 11 Grosvenor Road, Batley, West Yorkshire, WF17 0LX Tel: (01924) 476977 Fax: (01924) 478315 E-mail: silks@dial.pipex.com

Capemist Gloves Ltd, 158 Fenaghy Road, Cullybackey, Ballymena, County Antrim, BT42 1DZ Tel: (028) 2588 1190 Fax: (028) 2588 1682E-mail: capemist.gloves@virgin.net

Creative Club Ties, The Whitehouse, 84 Cromley Road, High Lane, Stockport, Cheshire, SK6 8BU Tel: (01663) 762173 Fax: (01663) 810243 E-mail: karen9702@hotmail.co.uk

Criag Mill Of Scotland, 17 Station Road, Biggar, Lanarkshire, ML12 6BS Tel: (01899) 220289 Fax: (01899) 221182E-mail: calzeat@aol.com

F & A Hill Ltd, 80 Brewer Street, London, W1F 9TZ Tel: (020) 7734 0652 Fax: (020) 7434 3698

Hucknall Manufacturing Co Ltd, Titchfield Street, Hucknall, Nottingham, NG15 7BH Tel: 0115-963 3034 Fax: 0115-963 5947

Johnstons Of Elgin Ltd, Newmill, Elgin, Morayshire, IV30 4AF Tel: (01343) 554000 Fax: (01343) 554055 E-mail: elgin@johnstoncashmere.com

Loch Carron, Waverley Mill, Huddersfield Street, Galashiels, Selkirkshire, TD1 3AY Tel: (01896) 752091 Fax: (01896) 758833 E-mail: sales@1ochcarron.com

Maccravats Ltd, Byrons Lodge, Byrons Lane, Macclesfield, Cheshire, SK11 7JW Tel: (01625) 422079 Fax: (01625) 614641 E-mail: maccravats@yahoo.com

McDade Neckware Ltd, Unit 20, Imex Bussiness Centre, 198 Swanston Street, Glasgow, G40 3HH Tel: 0141-554 0448 Fax: 0141-556 2403 E-mail: mcdadeties@cwcom.net

Mallalieu's Of Delph Ltd, Valley Mill, Millgate, Delph, Oldham, OL3 5DG Tel: (01457) 874811 Fax: (01457) 870231 E-mail: sales@mallalieus.com

Rees Productions Ltd, Unit 14 Cygnus Business Centre, Dalmeyer Road, London, NW10 2XA Tel: (020) 8459 1886 Fax: (020) 8459 8126 E-mail: info@reesproductions.co.uk

Robert Mackie & Co. Ltd, Holm Mill, Stewarton, Kilmarnock, Ayrshire, KA3 5HT Tel: (01560) 482124 Fax: (01560) 485213 E-mail: mackies@dial.pipex.com

▶ Sam's Brother Co., 18 Cannon Hill Road, Birmingham, B12 9NN Tel: (07786) 476273 Fax: 0121-078 0987 E-mail: sam888uk@yahoo.co.uk

Tie & Scarf Co. Ltd, Warth Park, Radcliffe Road, Bury, Lancashire, BL9 9NB Tel: 0161-761 5151 Fax: 0161-762 0202 E-mail: tieandscarf@chaytow.com

Totes Isotoner UK Ltd, Eastman House, Radford Cresent, Billericay, Essex, CM12 0DN Tel: (01277) 630277 Fax: (01277) 630276

D.H.J. Weisters Ltd, Anchor Mill, Darwen, Lancashire, BB3 0AH Tel: (01254) 873333 Fax: (01254) 873659 E-mail: customer-services@weisters.co.uk

SCARVES, LADIES'

▶ Sam's Brother Co., 18 Cannon Hill Road, Birmingham, B12 9NN Tel: (07786) 476273 Fax: 0121-078 0987 E-mail: sam888uk@yahoo.co.uk

SCHOOL BLAZERS

Togged-Up, 2 Wellgate, Clitheroe, Lancashire, BB7 2DP Tel: (01200) 427630 Fax: (01200) 424873 E-mail: linda@tusport.co.uk

SCHOOL CHALK

Binney & Smith Europe Ltd, Ampthill Road, Bedford, MK42 9RS Tel: (01234) 266702 Fax: (01234) 342110

SCHOOL FLOORING CONTRACTORS

▶ B U Interiors Ltd, Unit 15 Nonsuch Industrial Estate, Kiln Lane, Epsom, Surrey, KT17 1DH Tel: (01372) 747677 Fax: (01372) 747706 E-mail: sales@buinteriors.co.uk

▶ Iona Flooring Services Ltd, 109 Langside Drive, Glasgow, G43 2SX Tel: 0141-637 7444 Fax: 0141 6375026 E-mail: ionaflooring@aol.com

▶ Layfix Flooring Ltd, PO Box 2764, Calne, Wiltshire, SN11 9QY Tel: (01249) 816713 Fax: (01249) 816713 E-mail: enquiries_layfix@hotmail.com

Parkett Borse Ltd, 81 Bolton Street, Chorley, Lancashire, PR7 3AG Tel: (01257) 270148 Fax: (01257) 270147 E-mail: info@parkettborse.com

SCHOOL FURNITURE

Ambic Ltd, 41-44 Stella Gill Industrial, Estate Pelton Fell, Pelton Fell, Chester le Street, County Durham, DH2 2RH Tel: 0191-389 1888 Fax: 0191-389 1999 E-mail: enquiries@ambic.ltd.uk

▶ The Education Furniture Co. Ltd, Education House, 22A Cobbet Road, Burntwood, Staffordshire, WS7 3GL Tel: (01543) 495086 Fax: (01543) 495089

▶ Primary Plus UK Ltd, PO Box 11232, Birmingham, B32 2XP Tel: 0121-241 9818 Fax: 0121-241 9818 E-mail: johncave@blueyonder.co.uk

▶ Simply Direct, Adelphi Mill, Grimshaw Lane, Bollington, Macclesfield, Cheshire, SK10 5JB Tel: (01625) 576527 Fax: (01625) 576545 E-mail: sales@simplydirect.net

SCHOOL HOMEWORK DIARIES

▶ Lords College Ltd, 53 Manchester Road, Bolton, BL2 1ES Tel: (01204) 523731 Fax: (0870) 4299706 E-mail: principal@lordscollege.co.uk

SCHOOL STATIONERY

C O S, Unit 9, Hastingwood Business Centre, Hastingwood, Harlow, Essex, CM17 9GD Tel: (0845) 3893030 Fax: (0845) 3893031 E-mail: sales@colouroffset.co.uk

Philip & Tacey Ltd, North Way, Andover, Hampshire, SP10 5BA Tel: (01264) 332171 Fax: (01264) 384808 E-mail: export@philipandtacey.co.uk

▶ UK Business Print Ltd, 15 Hendersyde Park, Kelso, Roxburghshire, TD5 7TU Tel: (01573) 224889 Fax: (01573) 223854 E-mail: sales@ukbrand.com

SCHOOL TEACHER PLANNERS

▶ Coaching With Soul - Modern VOCAL COACH, Trentham, Stoke-on-Trent, ST4 8TU Tel: (07957) 127348 E-mail: thesessionsinger@tiscai.co.uk

▶ Teachernet, Sanctuary Buildings, Great Smith Street, London, SW1P 3BT Tel: (0870) 0002288 Fax: (01928) 794248

SCHOOL WEAR

A & K Clothing (Derby) Ltd, 110A Porter Road, Derby, DE23 6RA Tel: (01332) 772795 Fax: (01332) 772794 E-mail: info@akclothing.com

Arodix Ltd, Unit 4, 36 Greenford Road, Harrow, Middlesex, HA1 3QH Tel: (020) 8864 2272 Fax: (020) 8423 8870

Arthur Elkin Holdings Ltd, Progress Mill, Parsonage Street, Macclesfield, Cheshire, SK11 7LY Tel: (01625) 423502 Fax: (01625) 612994 E-mail: elkin.sales@arthurelkin.co.uk

Billings & Edmonds Ltd, Shop, 132 High Street, Eton, Windsor, Berkshire, SL4 6AR Tel: (01753) 818290 Fax: (01753) 831145 E-mail: sales@billingsandedmonds.co.uk

▶ Brennand Clothing Ltd, Halliwell Industrial Estate, Rossini Street, Bolton, BL1 8DL Tel: (01204) 493160 Fax: (01204) 493190

Charles Kirk & Co. Ltd, Horton Buildings, Goring Street, Goring-by-Sea, Worthing, West Sussex, BN12 5AD Tel: (01903) 244863 Fax: (01903) 700577 E-mail: sales@charleskirk.co.uk

William Christy & Son Ltd, 1 Mopack Business Complex, Ballycolman Avenue, Strabane, County Tyrone, BT82 9AF Tel: (028) 7188 5566 Fax: (028) 7188 6746

Gee, 138 Richmond Road, Kingston upon Thames, Surrey, KT2 5EZ Tel: (020) 8546 4453 Fax: (020) 8546 2057 E-mail: drewgoater@hotmail.co.uk

H M Fashions, 10 Sycamore Road, Handsworth, Birmingham, B21 0QL Tel: 0121-554 1068 Fax: 0121-523 4891 E-mail: mandeepranu84@hotmail.com

Leonard Hudson, 2 Queen Anne Drive, Edinburgh, EH28 8LH Tel: 0800 0181412 Fax: 0808 1806030 E-mail: sales@leonardhudson.co.uk

Kiddies World, Roseville House, Grant Avenue, Leeds, LS7 1QB Tel: 0113-243 5003 Fax: 0113-243 5004

▶ M S Furnishings, 14 Canning Road, London, E15 3NW Tel: (020) 8555 3928 Fax: (020) 8519 7672 E-mail: msfurnishingsuk@yahoo.co.uk

Malro Ltd, Malro House, 245 Wood Street, London, E17 3NT Tel: (020) 8521 5137 Fax: (020) 8521 6862

John Matthews Clothing Ltd, Building 62, Third Avenue, Pensnett Trading Estate, Kingswinford, West Midlands, DY6 7PP Tel: (01384) 401071 Fax: (01384) 401840

Milano Sports Ltd, 2-4 Winifred Street, Hucknall, Nottingham, NG15 7RX Tel: 0115-963 8945 Fax: 0115-963 8420

Naxos Schoolwear, 369 High Road, London, N22 8JA Tel: (020) 8889 7950 Fax: (020) 8889 7950

Perry Clothes Ltd, 43 Carr Crofts, Leeds, LS12 3HB Tel: 0113-263 7841 Fax: 0113-231 1490 E-mail: lisa@perryclothes.co.uk

Phull Knitwear Manufacturing Co., 146 Soho Road, Birmingham, B21 9LN Tel: 0121-554 1559 Fax: 0121-554 1559

Samraj Fashions, 5 Ireton Road, Leicester, LE4 9ER Tel: 0116-220 7576 E-mail: samrajfashion@hotmail.com

School Shop, Prospect Hill, Kidderminster, Worcestershire, DY10 1PA Tel: (01562) 823763 Fax: (01562) 864637

Swift Ltd, Mistral House, Parsons Lane, Hinckley, Leicestershire, LE10 1XT Tel: (01455) 238398 Fax: (01455) 238866

T S S Technology Ltd, 214 Moss Lane, Bramhall, Stockport, Cheshire, SK7 1BD Tel: 0161-439 0005 Fax: 0161-439 0006 E-mail: sales@colorconsultancy.com

Team Colours, The Maltings, Roydon Road, Stanstead Abbotts, Ware, Hertfordshire, SG12 8HG Tel: (01920) 871453 Fax: (01920) 872278 E-mail: sales@teamcolours.co.uk

Togged-Up, 2 Wellgate, Clitheroe, Lancashire, BB7 2DP Tel: (01200) 427630 Fax: (01200) 424873 E-mail: linda@tusport.co.uk

Wilsport, 5 Fleming Close, Wellingborough, Northamptonshire, NN8 6UF Tel: (01933) 403404 Fax: (01933) 405070 E-mail: edw@wilsport.freeserve.co.uk

Winterton Leisurewear Ltd, Regent Road, Countesthorpe, Leicester, LE8 5RF Tel: 0116-277 9789 Fax: 0116-278 4395 E-mail: info@magicfit.co.uk

SCHOOLS OR COLLEGES, TRADE OR VOCATIONAL TRAINING, *See Training, Trade/Vocational etc*

SCIENCE MAGAZINES

New Scientist, 147-151 Wardour St, London, W1F 8BN Tel: (020) 7611 1200 Fax: (020) 7331 2772

SCIENTIFIC AND LABORATORY MARKETING RECRUITMENT

▶ Access Job Boards Ltd, BioCity, Pennyfoot Street, Nottingham, NG1 1GF Tel: 0845 644 5481 Fax: 0845 644 5482 E-mail: info@access-sciencejobs.co.uk

SCIENTIFIC AND LABORATORY SALES RECRUITMENT

▶ Access Job Boards Ltd, BioCity, Pennyfoot Street, Nottingham, NG1 1GF Tel: 0845 644 5481 Fax: 0845 644 5482 E-mail: info@access-sciencejobs.co.uk

▶ Ascend Recruitment, Trym Lodge, 1 Henbury Road, Westbury-on-Trym, Bristol, BS9 3HQ Tel: 0117-310 1270 Fax: 0117-310 1271 E-mail: mail@ascendrecruitment.net

▶ Futurefind Sales Recruitment, Wira House, Ring Road, West Park, Leeds, LS16 6EB Tel: 0113-275 5656 Fax: 0113-278 2181 E-mail: recruitment@futurefind.co.uk

▶ New Line Sales Recruitment Ltd, Clay House, 5 Horninglow Street, Burton-on-Trent, Staffordshire, DE14 1NG Tel: (01283) 500077 Fax: (08701) 163370 E-mail: sales@newlinesales.co.uk

▶ Salestarget.co.uk, Holden House, 57 Rathbone Place, London, W1T 1JU Tel: (020) 7769 9147 Fax: (020) 7769 9205 E-mail: sales@salestarget.co.uk

SCIENTIFIC COMPUTER SYSTEMS

Cognitech Ltd, City Cloisters, 188-194 Old St, London, EC1V 9FR Tel: (020) 7251 9316 Fax: (020) 7251 9317

SCIENTIFIC CONSULTANTS

Chemspeed Ltd, Unit 20, Helix Business Park, Camberley, Surrey, GU15 2QT Tel: (01276) 670668 Fax: (01276) 709907 E-mail: chemspeed@chemspeed.com

▶ Edotek Ltd, Silver Birches Water Lane, Fewcott, Bicester, Oxfordshire, OX27 7NX Tel: (01869) 345386 Fax: 0871 243 9813 E-mail: info@edotek.co.uk

Ergotech Scientific Apparatus, 8 Cae FFWT Business Park, Pendraw'R Llan, Glan Conwy, Colwyn Bay, Clwyd, LL28 5SP Tel: (01492) 592684 Fax: (01492) 592685 E-mail: sales@ergotech.co.uk

Opus Scientific Ltd, The Old Bakery, Church Street, Litlington, Royston, Hertfordshire, SG8 0RD Tel: (01763) 853948 Fax: (01763) 853949

Sci Tek Instruments Ltd, N B House, 24 Stilebrook Road, Olney, Buckinghamshire, MK46 5EA Tel: (01234) 240765 Fax: (01234) 240965

Seltek Consultants, 25a Hockerill Street, Bishop's Stortford, Hertfordshire, CM23 2DH Tel: (01279) 657716 Fax: (01279) 651119 E-mail: sales@seltekconsultants.co.uk

SCIENTIFIC GLASSWARE MANUFRS

A J Cope & Son Ltd, 11-12 The Oval, London, E2 9DU Tel: (020) 7729 2405 Fax: (020) 7729 2657 E-mail: marketing@ajcope.co.uk

Dalon International Ltd, 12 The Spire Green Centre, Harlow, Essex, CM19 5TR Tel: (01279) 453823 Fax: (01279) 453824 E-mail: longdalon@aol.com

Enterprise Q Ltd, 1 Tallow Way, Fairhills Industrial Park, Irlam, Manchester, M44 6RJ Tel: 0161-777 4888 Fax: 0161-777 4899 E-mail: info@enterprise-q.co.uk

Euro Lab Supplies Ltd, 43-44 Fourways, Carlyon Road Industrial Estate, Atherstone, Warwickshire, CV9 1LH Tel: (01827) 721781 Fax: (01827) 721781 E-mail: kay.cauldwell@eurolabsupplies.co.uk

Glass Blowing Scientific, 5 Union Bridge Works, Roker Lane, Pudsey, West Yorkshire, LS28 9LE Tel: 0113-236 3322 Fax: 0113-236 3616E-mail: glassblowingscientific@fsmail.net

Jaytec Glass Ltd, Jaytec House, 1 Burgess Road, Hastings, East Sussex, TN35 4NR Tel: (01424) 424181 Fax: (01424) 721224 E-mail: enquiries@jaytecglass.co.uk

Lichfield Studio Glass Ltd, Boston Industrial Estate, Power Station Road, Rugeley, Staffordshire, WS15 2HS Tel: (01889) 575551 Fax: (01889) 575551 E-mail: lich@globalnet.co.uk

Moores Evic Glassworks Ltd, Evic Works, 143 Hersham Road, Walton-on-Thames, Surrey, KT12 1RR Tel: (01932) 222314 Fax: (01932) 243330 E-mail: sales@moores-glass.co.uk

Poulten & Graf Ltd, 1 Alfreds Way Industrial Estate, Alfreds Way, Barking, Essex, IG11 0AS Tel: (020) 8594 4256 Fax: (020) 8594 8419 E-mail: volacjpl@aol.com

R.B. Radley & Co. Ltd, Shirehill, Saffron Walden, Essex, CB11 3AZ Tel: (01799) 513320 Fax: (01799) 513283 E-mail: sales@radleys.co.uk

▶ Saint-Gobain Quartz P.L.C, PO Box 6, Wallsend, Tyne & Wear, NE28 6DG Tel: 0191-262 5311 Fax: 0191-263 8040 E-mail: quartz.sales@saint-gobain.com

Sci Lab Supplies, 14a Fifth Avenue, Bluebridge Industrial Estate, Halstead, Essex, CO9 2SZ Tel: (01787) 472068 Fax: (01787) 473970 E-mail: sci-labsupplies@btconnect.com

SCIENTIFIC GLASSWARE MANUFRS

– continued

Tuffnell Glass, Unit 2b, 35 Eastgate North, Driffield, North Humberside, YO25 6DG Tel: (01377) 240745 Fax: (01377) 240746 E-mail: sales@tuffnellglass.co.uk

York Glassware Services Ltd, 9 The Crescent, York, YO24 1AW Tel: (01904) 651493 Fax: (01904) 611932 E-mail: mail@ygs.net

SCIENTIFIC INSTRUMENT ENGINEERING/DEVELOPMENT CONSULTANTS

Crownfield Engineering Ltd, Crownfield, Wycombe Road, Saunderton, Princes Risborough, Buckinghamshire, HP27 9NR Tel: (01844) 345746 Fax: (01844) 347225 E-mail: crownfield@nildram.co.uk

▶ Scilutions, Trinafour, Abingdon Road, Marcham, Abingdon, Oxfordshire, OX13 6NU Tel: (01865) 391460 Fax: (01865) 391385 E-mail: kellysweb@scilutions.co.uk

Sycopel Scientific Ltd, 15 Sedling Road, Wear Industrial Estate, Washington, Tyne & Wear, NE38 9BZ Tel: 0191-417 8788 Fax: 0191-417 6627 E-mail: sales@sycopel.com

SCIENTIFIC INSTRUMENT MAINTENANCE/REPAIR SERVICES

I S S Group Ltd, Pellowe House, Francis Road, Withington, Manchester, M20 4XP Tel: 0161-445 5446 Fax: 0161-445 4914 E-mail: sales@iss-group.co.uk

Inserv Ltd, Willow House, Buckley Hill Lane, Milnrow, Rochdale, Lancashire, OL16 4BU Tel: (0870) 0112030 Fax: (0870) 0112040 E-mail: service@inserv.co.uk

W. & A. Jarvie, Wester Auchenrivoch, Banton, Kilsyth, Glasgow, G65 0QZ Tel: (01236) 823297 Fax: (01236) 823297 E-mail: walter@wajarvie.freeserve.co.uk

Mass Spectrometry Solutions, 19 Lawrence Close, Cranage, Crewe, CW4 8FA Tel: (01477) 532540 Fax: (01477) 532541 E-mail: jim.speakman@mass-spectrometry-solutions.co.uk

Metrology Instrument Solutions, 94 Repton Road, Hartshorne, Swadlincote, Derbyshire, DE11 7AE Tel: (01283) 223800 E-mail: metrology@mcmail.com

NLG Analytical Ltd, Grimshaw Lane, Bollington, Macclesfield, Cheshire, SK10 5JB Tel: (01625) 574633 Fax: (01625) 574699 E-mail: sales@nlg_analytical.co.uk

Scancad Services Ltd, Sussex House, Ewhurst Road, Cranleigh, Surrey, GU6 7AE Tel: (01483) 273770 Fax: (01483) 275931 E-mail: rbennet@btconnect.com

Semtron Services Ltd, Carlton House, 8 Gwash Way, Stamford, Lincolnshire, PE9 1XR Tel: (01780) 766736 Fax: (01780) 766736 E-mail: ken.swanson@semtron.co.uk

Spectronic Analytical Insruments, Tudor House, Barley Hill Road, Garforth, Leeds, LS25 1DX Tel: 0113-286 4536 Fax: 0113-232 0424 E-mail: spectrouk@aol.com

SCIENTIFIC INSTRUMENT MANUFRS

Alda Production Services Ltd, 14 Deanfield Court, Links 59 Business Park, Clitherhall, Rossendale, Lancashire, BB7 1QS Tel: (01200) 444354 Fax: (01200) 444359 E-mail: alda@alda.co.uk

Analox Instruments Ltd, 8 Goldhawk Industrial Estate, 2a Brackenbury Road, London, W6 0BA Tel: (020) 8749 7644 Fax: (020) 8740 6608 E-mail: info@analox.com

Analytical Technology International Ltd, 5 Heather Close, Lyme Green Business Park, Macclesfield, Cheshire, SK11 0LR Tel: (01625) 616431 Fax: (01625) 612494 E-mail: sales@ati-ltd.co.uk

Apek Design & Developments Ltd, Ferndown Industrial Estate, Wimborne, Dorset, BH21 7RF Tel: (01202) 876149 Fax: (01202) 861210 E-mail: sales@apek.co.uk

Applied Biosystems, Lingley House, 120 Birchwood Boulevard, Birchwood, Warrington, WA3 7QH Tel: (01925) 825650 Fax: (01925) 282502 E-mail: abdirect@eur.apliedbiosystems.com

Biacore International, 2 Meadway Court, Rutherford Close, Stevenage, Hertfordshire, SG1 2EF Tel: (01438) 846200 Fax: (01438) 846201 E-mail: enquiries@biacore.com

Bright Instrument Co. Ltd, St. Margarets Way, Stukeley Meadows Industrial Estate, Huntingdon, Cambridgeshire, PE29 6EU Tel: (01480) 454528 Fax: (01480) 456031 E-mail: sales@brightinstruments.com

Brunner Scientific, Unit 4c Hunmanby Industrial Estate, Hunmanby, Filey, North Yorkshire, YO14 0PH Tel: (01723) 891611 Fax: (01723) 890872 E-mail: sales@brunnerscientific.com

Burkard Scientific (Sales) Ltd, PO Box 55, Uxbridge, Middlesex, UB8 2RT Tel: (01895) 230056 Fax: (01895) 230058 E-mail: sales@burkardscientific.co.uk

Cairn Research Ltd, Graveny Road, Faversham, Kent, ME13 8UP Tel: (01795) 590140 Fax: (01795) 594510 E-mail: sales@cairnweb.com

▶ Cambridge Magnetic Refrigeration, Britannia House, 19-21 Godesdone Road, Cambridge, CB5 8HR Tel: (01223) 473631 Fax: (01223) 474164

Cecil Instruments Ltd, Cambridge Road Industrial Estate, Milton, Cambridge, CB24 6AZ Tel: (01223) 420821 Fax: (01223) 420475 E-mail: info@cecilinstruments.com

Chandos Intercontinental, 6 St Anns Close, Chapel-en-le-Frith, High Peak, Derbyshire, SK23 9SG Tel: (01298) 814949 Fax: (01298) 814949 E-mail: chandos6@highpeak14.freeserve.co.uk

Copley Scientific Ltd, Colwick Quays Business Park, Private Road Number 2, Colwick, Nottingham, NG4 2JY Tel: 0115-961 6229 Fax: 0115-961 7637 E-mail: sales@copleyscientific.co.uk

Crawford Scientific Ltd, Holm Street, Strathaven, Lanarkshire, ML10 6NB Tel: (01357) 522961 Fax: (01357) 522168 E-mail: enquiries@crawfordscientific.com

Discovery Workshops, 516A Burnley Road, Accrington, Lancashire, BB5 6JZ Tel: (01254) 237649 Fax: (01254) 237649 E-mail: mail@dicoveryworkshops.co.uk

Duncan & Associates, Jeeves Bank, Fernleigh Road, Grange-over-Sands, Cumbria, LA11 7HT Tel: (01539) 533857 Fax: (01539) 534963 E-mail: info@duncanandassociates.co.uk

Eagle Scientific Ltd, Regent House, Lenton Street, Sandiacre, Nottingham, NG10 5DJ Tel: 0115-949 1111 Fax: 0115-939 1144 E-mail: equip@eagle-scientific.co.uk

Edinburgh Designs Ltd, 27 Ratcliffe Terrace, Edinburgh, EH9 1SX Tel: 0131-662 4748 Fax: 0131-662 9156 E-mail: enquiries@edesign.co.uk

Envirochem Technologists Ltd, Holt Lodge Farm, Hugmore La, Llan Y Pwll, Wrexham, Clwyd, LL13 9YE Tel: 01978 661933 Fax: 01978 661611

Ergotech Scientific Apparatus, 8 Cae FFWT Business Park, Pendraw'R Llan, Glan Conwy, Colwyn Bay, Clwyd, LL28 5SP Tel: (01492) 592684 Fax: (01492) 592685 E-mail: sales@ergotech.co.uk

Euro DPC Ltd, Glyn Rhonwy, Llanberis, Caernarfon, Gwynedd, LL55 4EL Tel: (01286) 871871 Fax: (01286) 871802 E-mail: euro@dpconline.com

F W Parrett Ltd, 65 Ridefield Road, London, SE9 2RA Tel: (020) 8859 3254 Fax: (020) 7504 3536 E-mail: fparrett@aol.com

Fisher Scientific Holding UK Ltd, Bishop Meadow Road, Loughborough, Leicestershire, LE11 5RG Tel: (01509) 231166 Fax: (01509) 231893 E-mail: info@fisher.co.uk

Freeman Technology, Boulters Farm Centre, Castlemorton Common, Welland, Malvern, Worcestershire, WR13 6LE Tel: (01684) 310860 Fax: (01684) 310236

G R I Ltd, Gene House, Queenborough Lane, Rayne, Braintree, Essex, CM77 6TZ Tel: (01376) 332900 Fax: (01376) 344724 E-mail: gri@gri.co.uk

▶ Geneflow Scientific Apparatus, Wood End Lane, Fradley, Lichfield, Staffordshire, WS13 8NF Tel: (01543) 414704 Fax: (01543) 255666 E-mail: sales@geneflow.co.uk

GR Scientific Ltd, Hiam Business Centre, New Road, Maulden, Bedford, MK45 2BG Tel: (01525) 404747 Fax: (01525) 404848

Gradko International Ltd, St Martins House, 77 Wales Street, Winchester, Hampshire, SO23 0RH Tel: (01962) 860331 Fax: (01962) 841339 E-mail: sales@gradko.co.uk

▶ Gresham Scientific Instruments, Sirius House, Watery Lane, Wooburn Green, High Wycombe, Buckinghamshire, HP10 0AP Tel: (01628) 533060 Fax: (01628) 533034 E-mail: e2vsi.admin@e2v.com

▶ GT Vision Ltd, Hazelsub Depo Unit Camps Road, Haverhill, Suffolk, CB9 9AS Tel: (01440) 714737 Fax: (01440) 714737 E-mail: sales@gt-vision.com

Hach Ultra Analytics, Unit 4 Chesterfield Road, Holmewood, Chesterfield, Derbyshire, S42 5US Tel: (01246) 599760 Fax: (01246) 599778 E-mail: uksales@hachultra.com

Heath Scientific Co Ltd, 1 North House, Bond Avenue, Bletchley, Milton Keynes, MK1 1SW Tel: (01908) 646700 Fax: (01908) 645209 E-mail: info@heathsien.com

Hilton Instruments Ltd, 32 Holland Street, Aberdeen, AB25 3UL Tel: (01224) 620121 Fax: (01224) 620125 E-mail: info@hilton-instruments.co.uk

Hitachi Hi-Technology Corporation, 7 Ivanhoe Road, Hogwood Industrial Estate, Finchampstead, Wokingham, Berkshire, RG40 4QQ Tel: 0118-932 8632 Fax: 0118-932 8779 E-mail: sales@hitachi-hitec-uk.com

Hook & Tucker Zenyx Ltd, Vulcan Way, New Addington, Croydon, CR0 9UG Tel: (01689) 843345 Fax: (01689) 841792 E-mail: sales@htz.biz

I S S Group Ltd, Pellowe House, Francis Road, Withington, Manchester, M20 4XP Tel: 0161-445 5446 Fax: 0161-445 4914 E-mail: sales@iss-group.co.uk

▶ Ice Cryogenic Engineering Ltd, Unit 3, Ferrymills, Osney Mead, Oxford, OX2 0ES Tel: (01865) 202300 Fax: (01865) 727759 E-mail: sales@iceoxford.com

Intek Services Ltd, Smalls Hill Road, Norwood Hill, Horley, Surrey, RH6 0HR Tel: (01293) 863434 Fax: (01293) 863252 E-mail: trevor@intekservices.co.uk

▶ Isopharm Systems, Unit 2, Umborne Bridge, Dolphin Street, Colyton, Devon, EX24 6LU Tel: (01297) 553775 Fax: (01297) 553775

▶ J J Quartz, 4 Normans Hall Farm, Shrigley Road, Pott Shrigley, Macclesfield, Cheshire, SK10 5SE Tel: (01625) 571077 Fax: (01625) 571077 E-mail: jjquartz@ntlworld.com

Jeol UK Ltd, Silver Court, Watchmead, Welwyn Garden City, Hertfordshire, AL7 1LT Tel: (01707) 377117 Fax: (01707) 373254 E-mail: uk.sales@jeoleuro.com

Kratos Analytical Ltd, Trafford Wharf Road, Trafford Park, Manchester, M17 1GP Tel: 0161-888 4400 Fax: 0161-888 4401 E-mail: sales@kratos.co.uk

L O T-Oriel Ltd, 1 Mole Business Park, Randalls Road, Leatherhead, Surrey, KT22 7BA Tel: (01372) 378822 Fax: (01372) 375353 E-mail: sales@lotoriel.co.uk

▶ Lascells Scientific Apparatus, Walkmill Business Park, Market Drayton, Shropshire, TF9 2HT Tel: (01630) 657801 Fax: (01630) 656726 E-mail: sales@lascells.co.uk

Linkam Scientific Instruments Ltd, 8 Epsom Downs Metro Centre, Waterfield, Tadworth, Surrey, KT20 5HT Tel: (01737) 363476 Fax: (01737) 363480 E-mail: info@linkam.co.uk

▶ Longshore Systems Engineering Ltd, Pentire Workshops, High Street, Delabole, Cornwall, PL33 9AH Tel: (01840) 212122 Fax: (01840) 212173 E-mail: info@longshores.co.uk

Mass Sectrometry International Ltd, Unit C, Tudor Road, Broadheath, Altrincham, Cheshire, WA14 5RZ Tel: 0161-929 7583 Fax: 0161-941 5540

Materials Science, Victoria House, 15 Craven Terrace, Kirkgate, Settle, North Yorkshire, BD24 9DB Tel: (01729) 822327 Fax: (01729) 824500 E-mail: edward.hindle@btinternet.com

Mediworld Ltd, 444 - 446 Streatham High Road, London, SW16 3PX Tel: (020) 8764 1806 Fax: (020) 8679 2489 E-mail: sales@mediworld.co.uk

Microscal Ltd, 79 Southern Row, London, W10 5AL Tel: (020) 8969 3935 Fax: (020) 8968 7302 E-mail: info@microscal.com

Microscopy Supplies & Consultants Ltd, Park House, 6a Carneil Road, Carnock, Dunfermline, Fife, KY12 9JH Tel: (01383) 851434 Fax: (01383) 851434

Millbrook Instruments Ltd, Greenbank Business Park, Challenge Way, Blackburn, BB1 5QB Tel: (01254) 699606 Fax: (01254) 699610 E-mail: info@millbrook-instruments.com

Navrish Ltd, Navrish Nivas, 17 Bishops Close, Mays Lane, Arkley, Barnet, Hertfordshire, EN5 2QH Tel: (020) 8440 0803 Fax: (020) 8441 6813 E-mail: sales@navrish.co.uk

New Brunswick Scientific UK Ltd, 17 Alban Park, Hatfield Road, St. Albans, Hertfordshire, AL4 0JJ Tel: (01727) 853855 Fax: (01727) 835666 E-mail: sales@nbsuk.co.uk

Norwood Instruments Ltd, New Mill Road, Honley, Holmfirth, HD9 6QD Tel: (01484) 661318 Fax: (01484) 661319 E-mail: gpc@norwood.cc

Nu Instruments Ltd, Unit 74 Clywedog Road South, Wrexham Industrial Estate, Wrexham, Clwyd, LL13 9XS Tel: (01978) 661304 Fax: (01978) 664301 E-mail: sales@nu-ins.com

Optical Instruments Balham Ltd, Unit 39 Neville Court, 23 Neville Road, Croydon, CR0 2DS Tel: (020) 8664 9799 Fax: (020) 8664 9771 E-mail: info@optil.co.uk

Oxford Applied Research Ltd, Unit 31 Crawley Mill Industrial Estate, Dry Lane, Crawley, Witney, Oxfordshire, OX29 9SP Tel: (01993) 773575 Fax: (01993) 702326 E-mail: sales@oaresearch.co.uk

Oxford Cryosystems, 3 Blenheim Office Park, Lower Road, Long Hanborough, Witney, Oxfordshire, OX29 8LN Tel: (01993) 883488 Fax: (01993) 883988 E-mail: info@oxfordcryosystems.co.uk

Oxford Instruments Superconductivity, Tubney Woods, Abingdon, Oxfordshire, OX13 5QX Tel: (01865) 393200 Fax: (01865) 393333 E-mail: nanoscience@oxinst.co.uk

Peak Scientific Instruments Ltd, Fountain Crescent, Inchinnan Business Park, Inchinnan, Renfrew, PA4 9RE Tel: 0141-812 8100 Fax: 0141-812 8200 E-mail: info@peakscientific.com

Perkinelmer Ltd, Chalfont Road, Seer Green, Beaconsfield, Buckinghamshire, HP9 2FX Tel: (01494) 874515 Fax: (01494) 679331 E-mail: cc.uk@perkinelmer.com

Phenomenex Ltd, Melville House, Queens Avenue, Hurdsfield Industrial Estate, Macclesfield, Cheshire, SK10 2YF Tel: (01625) 501367 Fax: (01625) 501796 E-mail: info@phenomenex.com

Qstar Precision Ltd, 2 Shortsands Yard, Cambridge Street, St. Neots, Cambridgeshire, PE19 1PQ Tel: (01480) 210915 Fax: (01480) 210927 E-mail: info@qstarprecision.co.uk

Ravencourt Ltd, Drift Road, Stamford, Lincolnshire, PE9 1UZ Tel: (01780) 489100 Fax: (01780) 489099 E-mail: sales@ravencourt.com

Ravenfield Designs Ltd, Russell Street, Heywood, Lancashire, OL10 1NX Tel: (01706) 369307 Fax: (01706) 360472 E-mail: post@ravenfield.com

Research Equipment London Ltd, 72 Wellington Road, Twickenham, TW2 5NX Tel: (020) 8977 5529 Fax: (020) 8943 2219 E-mail: info@research-equipment.com

S S Scientific, 6 Granary Business Centre, North Street, Hellingly, Hailsham, East Sussex, BN27 4DU Tel: (01323) 441920 Fax: (01323) 441968 E-mail: sales@ss-sci.com

Schuco International London Ltd, Lyndhurst Avenue, London, N12 0NE Tel: (020) 8368 1642 Fax: (020) 8361 3761 E-mail: sales@schuco.co.uk

Science Exchange Service, Rutherford House, 43 Terrace Road, Walton-on-Thames, Surrey, KT12 2SP Tel: (01932) 246688 Fax: (01932) 246680

Scientifica, 9 Allied Business Centre, Coldharbour Lane, Harpenden, Hertfordshire, AL5 4UT Tel: (01582) 766888 Fax: (01582) 767888 E-mail: info@scientifica.uk.com

Scitec Instruments, Bartles Industrial Estate, North Street, Redruth, Cornwall, TR15 1HR Tel: (01209) 314608 Fax: (01209) 314609 E-mail: info@scitec.uk.com

Sherwood Scientific Ltd, Unit J1 The Paddocks, 347 Cherry Hinton Road, Cambridge, CB1 8DH Tel: (01223) 243444 Fax: (01223) 243300 E-mail: info@sherwood-scientific.com

Shimadzu UK, Mill Court, Featherstone Road, Wolverton Mill, Milton Keynes, MK12 5RD Tel: (01908) 552200 Fax: (01908) 552211 E-mail: sales@shimadzu.co.uk

Signal Ambitech Division, Ambitech Division, 9A Regal Way, Faringdon, Oxfordshire, SN7 7BX Tel: (01367) 242660 Fax: (01367) 242700 E-mail: ambitech@signal-group.com

Singer Instrument Co. Ltd, Roadwater, Watchet, Somerset, TA23 0RE Tel: (01984) 640226 Fax: (01984) 641166 E-mail: yeast@singerinst.co.uk

Solent Scientific Ltd, 14 Matrix Park, Talbot Road, Segensworth, Fareham, Hampshire, PO15 5AP Tel: (0870) 7747140 Fax: (0870) 7747150 E-mail: sales@solentsci.com

Synoptics Ltd, Beacon House, Nuffield Road, Cambridge, CB4 1TF Tel: (01223) 727100 Fax: (01223) 727101 E-mail: sales@synoptics.co.uk

Chris Taylor Production Engineering, 35 James Carter Road, Mildenhall, Bury St. Edmunds, Suffolk, IP28 7DE Tel: (01638) 510589 Fax: (01638) 515086

Techmate Ltd, 10 Bridgeturn Avenue, Old Wolverton, Milton Keynes, MK12 5QL Tel: (01908) 322222 Fax: (01908) 319941

Teltron Ltd, Unit 14, 98 Victoria Road, London, NW10 6NB Tel: (020) 8453 1224 Fax: (020) 8963 0310

Thermo Electron Co Operation, Unit 24 Birches Industrial Estate, East Grinstead, West Sussex, RH19 1UB Tel: (01342) 327211 Fax: (01342) 315074 E-mail: john.wolstenholme@thermo.com

Thermometric Ltd, 10 Dalby Court, Gadbrook Business Centre, Rudheath, Northwich, Cheshire, CW9 7TN Tel: (01606) 49007 Fax: (01606) 48924

Uvitec Ltd, 36a Union Lane, Cambridge, CB4 1QB Tel: (01223) 568060 Fax: (01223) 306198 E-mail: uvi@uvitec.co.uk

V S W Atomtech Ltd, Unit 4 Heather Close, Lyme Green Business Park, Macclesfield, Cheshire, SK11 0LR Tel: (01625) 500108 Fax: (01625) 500801

Vaseco Ltd, Bromley House, Barlow Drive, Woodford Park Industrial Park, Winsford, Cheshire, CW7 2JZ Tel: (01606) 590000 Fax: (01606) 590100 E-mail: sales@vaseco.com

Vitech Scientific Ltd, Unit 14 Huffwood Trading Estate, Partridge Green, Horsham, West Sussex, RH13 8AU Tel: (01403) 710479 Fax: (01403) 710382 E-mail: sales@vitech.co.uk

SCIENTIFIC INSTRUMENT SUBCONTRACT SERVICES

Mass Spectrometry Solutions, 19 Lawrence Close, Cranage, Crewe, CW4 8FA Tel: (01477) 532540 Fax: (01477) 532541 E-mail: jim.speakman@mass-spectrometry-solutions.co.uk

Semtron Services Ltd, Carlton House, 8 Gwash Way, Stamford, Lincolnshire, PE9 1XR Tel: (01780) 766736 Fax: (01780) 766736 E-mail: ken.swanson@semtron.co.uk

SCIENTIFIC PHOTOGRAPHERS

▶ Clouds Hill Imaging Ltd., Rock House, Curland, Taunton, Somerset, TA3 5SB Tel: 01823 481894 E-mail: david@cloudshillimaging.co.uk

SCIENTIFIC SOFTWARE

4c Electronics Ltd, Diamond Court Douglas Close, Preston Farm Business Park, Preston Farm Industrial Estate, Stockton-on-Tees, Cleveland, TS18 3SB Tel: (01642) 616449 Fax: (01642) 605772 E-mail: sales@4celectronics.co.uk

Acropolis Computers Ltd, 2D Dolphin Way, Stapleford, Cambridge, CB2 5DW Tel: (01223) 841700 Fax: (01223) 841802 E-mail: info@biosoft.com

SCIENTIFIC SUPPLY SERVICES

Aston Scientific Ltd, 111 Wendover Road, Stoke Mandeville, Aylesbury, Buckinghamshire, HP22 5TD Tel: (01296) 614144 Fax: (01296) 614228

▶ indicates data change since last edition

SCIENTIFIC SUPPLY SERVICES – *continued*

Chemspeed Ltd, Unit 20, Helix Business Park, Camberley, Surrey, GU15 2QT Tel: (01276) 670668 Fax: (01276) 709907 E-mail: chemspeed@chemspeed.com
Dalon International Ltd, 12 The Spire Green Centre, Harlow, Essex, CM19 5TR Tel: (01279) 453823 Fax: (01279) 453824 E-mail: longdalon@aol.com
F E I, Philips House Cambridge Business Park, Cowley Road, Cambridge, CB4 0HF Tel: (01223) 468555 Fax: (01223) 468599
G R I Ltd, Gene House, Queenborough Lane, Rayne, Braintree, Essex, CM77 6TZ Tel: (01376) 332900 Fax: (01376) 344724 E-mail: gri@gri.co.uk
L O T-Oriel Ltd, 1 Mole Business Park, Randalls Road, Leatherhead, Surrey, KT22 7BA Tel: (01372) 378822 Fax: (01372) 375353 E-mail: sales@lotoriel.co.uk
Lab 3 Ltd, 1 Dragon Court, Crofts End Road, Bristol, BS5 7XX Tel: (0870) 1260333 Fax: (0870) 1260349
Lab 3 Ltd, 1 The Business Centre, Ross Road, Weedon Road Industrial Estate, Northampton, NN5 5AX Tel: (0870) 4445553 Fax: (0870) 1260350 E-mail: sales@lab3.co.uk
Owens Polyscience Ltd, 34 Chester Road, Macclesfield, Cheshire, SK11 8DG Tel: (01625) 610118 Fax: (01625) 423850
Perkinelmer Ltd, Chalfont Road, Seer Green, Beaconsfield, Buckinghamshire, HP9 2FX Tel: (01494) 874515 Fax: (01494) 679331
Spectronic Analytical Insruments, Tudor House, Barley Hill Road, Garforth, Leeds, LS25 1DX Tel: 0113-286 4536 Fax: 0113-232 0424 E-mail: spectrouk@aol.com
Swann Technology Ltd, 3 The Quadrant, Newark Close, Royston, Hertfordshire, SG8 5HL Tel: (01763) 249967 Fax: (01763) 249626 E-mail: swancygnet@cs.com
Vitech Scientific Ltd, Unit 14 Huffwood Trading Estate, Partridge Green, Horsham, West Sussex, RH13 8AU Tel: (01403) 710479 Fax: (01403) 710382 E-mail: sales@vitech.co.uk

SCINTILLATION PRODUCTS

Applied Scintillation Technologies, Unit 7-8 Roydenbury Industrial Estate, Horsecroft Road, Harlow, Essex, CM19 5BZ Tel: (01279) 641234 Fax: (01279) 413679 E-mail: ast@appscintech.com

SCISSOR LIFT HIRE

Harman Plant Hire Ltd, The Hyde, Brighton, BN2 4JE Tel: (01273) 603021 Fax: (01273) 690647 E-mail: info@harmanhire.co.uk
HSS Lift & Shift, 8 Oakwood Industrial Park, Gatwick Road, Crawley, West Sussex, RH10 9AZ Tel: (01293) 611010 Fax: (01293) 618041
Universal Aerial Platforms, Swinbourne Road, Burnt Mills Industrial Estate, Basildon, Essex, SS13 1GZ Tel: (01268) 722700 Fax: (01268) 722706 E-mail: basildon@universalplatforms.com

SCISSOR LIFTS

▶ Austin Design & Manufacture Ltd, Unit 2 Warish Hall, Warish Hall Road, Takeley, Bishop's Stortford, Hertfordshire, CM22 6NZ Tel: (01279) 871527 Fax: (01279) 871544 E-mail: keith@admfloors.com
George Lane & Sons Ltd, Bannerley Road, Birmingham, B33 0SL Tel: 0121-784 5525 Fax: 0121-783 6988 E-mail: info@georgelane.co.uk
Logitrans UK Ltd, Unit 5 Ascot Industrial Estate, Icknield Way, Letchworth Garden City, Hertfordshire, SG6 1TD Tel: (01462) 678444 Fax: (01462) 678555
Mr Plant Hire plc, 120 Hertford Road, Enfield, Middlesex, EN3 5AX Tel: (020) 8351 3434 Fax: (020) 8351 3636 E-mail: info@mrplanthire.co.uk
Polymathic Trucks Ltd, Coolie House, Unit 2 Anders, Lichfield Road Industrial Estate, Tamworth, Staffordshire, B79 7TA Tel: (01827) 63441 Fax: (01827) 310765 E-mail: sales@coolie.co.uk
Tecmach Ltd, PO Box 29, St. Albans, Hertfordshire, AL1 5NU Tel: (01727) 860355 Fax: (01727) 844062 E-mail: sales@tecmach.co.uk

SCISSORS, *See also headings for particular types*

Acme United Europe, Estate Office Thorncliffe Park Estate, Newton Chambers Road, Chapeltown, Sheffield, S35 2PH Tel: 0114-220 3709 Fax: 0114-220 3706 E-mail: sales@acmeunited.co.uk
F E & J R Hopkinson Ltd, 124 Scotland Street, Sheffield, S3 7DE Tel: 0114-272 7486 Fax: 0114-275 0290 E-mail: sales@sheffieldknives.co.uk
H Webber & Sons Ltd, Bridge House, Station Road Gomshall, Guildford, Surrey, GU5 9NP Tel: (01483) 202963 Fax: (01306) 740811 E-mail: info@hwebber.co.uk
Harrison Fisher & Co. Ltd, 78 Milton Street, Sheffield, S3 7WJ Tel: 0114-272 4221 Fax: 0114-275 4187 E-mail: sales@harrison-fisher.co.uk
Janome Group UK Ltd, Southside, Bredbury, Stockport, Cheshire, SK6 2SP Tel: 0161-430 6011 Fax: 0161-494 0179
L Bingham Ltd, 36 Malinda Street, Sheffield, S3 7EJ Tel: 0114-272 1525 Fax: 0114-249 3397 E-mail: lbinghamltd@aol.com
▶ PHFS, Chance Hall Lane, Scholar Green, Stoke-on-Trent, ST7 3ST Tel: 01270 873072 E-mail: phfsbask2000@yahoo.co.uk
Saloneasy.Com, 3 Pye Road, Wirral, Merseyside, CH60 0DB Tel: 0151-342 6271 Fax: 0151-342 1130 E-mail: sales@saloneasy.com
Sheffield Shears Co. Ltd, 28 Trinity Street, Sheffield, S3 7AJ Tel: 0114-272 2644 Fax: 0114-272 2644
Herbert M. Slater Ltd, 332 Coleford Road, Sheffield, S9 5PH Tel: 0114-261 2308 Fax: 0114-261 2305 E-mail: info@slaterknives.co.uk
William Whiteley & Sons (Sheffield) Ltd, Unit 1 Lakeside Rother Valley Wa, Holbrook Industrial Estate, Holbrook, Sheffield, S20 3RW Tel: 0114-251 4999 Fax: 0114-251 2919 E-mail: sales@whiteley.co.uk

SCOURERS/SCOURING PADS

Trollull Ltd, 17-18 Brunel Gate, West Portway Industrial Estate, Andover, Hampshire, SP10 3SL Tel: (01264) 333443 Fax: (01264) 334428 E-mail: trollull@trollull.co.uk

SCRAP METAL CUTTING EQUIPMENT

C F Gill & Son Ltd, The Yard, Bedford Street, Peterborough, PE1 4DN Tel: (01733) 566403

SCRAP METAL EXPORT MERCHANTS OR AGENTS

Clearway Disposals Ltd, 41 Dobbin Road, Portadown, Craigavon, County Armagh, BT62 4EY Tel: (028) 3833 7333 Fax: (028) 3833 6716 E-mail: info@clearwaypordesign.ffs.uk
▶ Nextel Metals, 20 Woodlea Grove, Yeadon, Leeds, LS19 7YT Tel: (07946) 842491 Fax: 0113-250 4700 E-mail: nextelmetals@aol.com
S Norton & Co., Bankfield Site, Regent Road, Bootle, Merseyside, L20 8RQ Tel: 0151-955 3300 Fax: 0151-955 3399 E-mail: s.norton@s-norton.co.uk

SCRAP METAL MERCHANTS/ PROCESSORS, *See also headings for individual metal*

A E Burgess & Sons Ltd, Ulverscroft Road, Leicester, LE4 6BY Tel: 0116-262 0065 Fax: 0116-251 0501
A W A Refiners Ltd, 10 Mead Industrial Park, Riverway, Harlow, Essex, CM20 2SE Tel: (01279) 423743 Fax: (01279) 422243 E-mail: sales@awarefiners.com
Abbotsfield Metals, Abbotsfield Road, Reginald Road Industrial Estate, St. Helens, Merseyside, WA9 4HU Tel: (01744) 817474 Fax: (01744) 817474
Accrington Non Ferrous Metals, Argyle Street, Accrington, Lancashire, BB5 1DQ Tel: (01254) 234550 Fax: (01254) 234550
Acre Metals Ltd, Unit 6 Claremont Way Industrial Estate, Cricklewood, London, NW2 1BG Tel: (020) 8458 0581 Fax: (020) 8201 9807
Albert Looms Ltd, Megaloughton Lane, Spondon, Derby, DE21 7ND Tel: (01332) 673663 Fax: (01332) 660430
Albert Alderton, Town Cross Avenue, Bognor Regis, West Sussex, PO21 2DP Tel: (01243) 824700 Fax: (01243) 821482
Ampthill Metal Co. Ltd, Station Road Industrial Estate, Ampthill, Bedford, MK45 2QY Tel: (01525) 403388 Fax: (01525) 404908 E-mail: mick@ampthillmetal.co.uk
Apm Metals Ltd, Plantation Works, Eurolink Way, Sittingbourne, Kent, ME10 3HH Tel: (01795) 426021 Fax: (01795) 421858 E-mail: apmmetalsltd@btconnect.com
Arkoss Metals Ltd, 112 Latimer Road, Chesham, Buckinghamshire, HP5 1QQ Tel: (01494) 776163 Fax: (01494) 771511
ASM Metal Recycling Ltd, Griffin Lane, Aylesbury, Buckinghamshire, HP19 8BB Tel: (01296) 337711 Fax: (01296) 337751 E-mail: asm@asm-recycling.co.uk
Atlas Metals Ltd, Cranford Street, Smethwick, West Midlands, B66 2RX Tel: 0121-555 5000 Fax: 0121-558 8600
George Ausden Ltd, 253 High Street, Watford, WD17 2HW Tel: (01923) 223530 Fax: (01923) 223530 E-mail: info@geo-ausden.com
Bainbridge Liversidge Group, Pepper Road, Hunslet, Leeds, LS10 2NL Tel: 0113-270 5431 Fax: 0113-276 0379
Barnes E A & Sons Ltd, Unit 5, Vulcan Road, Lichfield, Staffordshire, WS13 6RW Tel: (01543) 250480 Fax: (01543) 250480 E-mail: sales@eabarnes.co.uk
Bates & Davis 1998, 82 Pikehelve Street, West Bromwich, West Midlands, B70 0TU Tel: 0121-557 3346 Fax: 0121-557 4162 E-mail: sales@wpmgroupltd.co.uk
Bidwell Metals Ltd, Tiger Works, Clandown, Radstock, BA3 3BR Tel: (01761) 432391 Fax: (01761) 432522
Bruce Bishop & Sons Ltd, Lake Avenue, Slough, SL1 3BZ Tel: (01753) 525206 Fax: (01753) 532801
Bow Metals, 49 Moody Street, London, E1 4BZ Tel: (020) 8981 0903
Bowater S J, Sidney Street, Wolverhampton, WV2 4HH Tel: (01902) 425677 Fax: (01902) 771540
Harry Bowser & Son, Providence Place, Driffield, North Humberside, YO25 6QQ Tel: (01377) 252134
Bradford Moor Iron & Steel Co. Ltd, Cow Lane, Newark, Nottinghamshire, NG24 1HQ Tel: (01636) 703645 Fax: (01636) 672167
W.M. Briers & Son (Tamworth) Ltd, Anchor Siding, Glascote Road, Tamworth, Staffordshire, B77 2AN Tel: (01827) 62668 Fax: (01827) 53721 E-mail: equiries@wmbriers.co.uk
John Brocklesby & Sons Ltd, Courtney Street, Hull, HU8 7QF Tel: (01482) 320120 Fax: (01482) 587005
Arthur Brook Ltd, Low Mill Lane, Ravensthorpe Industrial Estate, Dewsbury, West Yorkshire, WF13 3LN Tel: (01924) 492457 Fax: (01924) 480466
Brook Street Metal Co. Ltd, Bridge Street, Bury, Lancashire, BL9 6HH Tel: 0161-764 4950 Fax: 0161-764 4619
Burdett Metals, Railway Arch 214-216, Witan Street, London, E2 6JX Tel: (020) 7739 3951 Fax: (020) 7739 3951
Burke Bros Cheltenham Ltd, Hayricks Wharf, Tewkesbury Road, Cheltenham, Gloucestershire, GL51 9AH Tel: (01242) 519227 Fax: (01242) 231293
C F Gill & Son Ltd, The Yard, Bedford Street, Peterborough, PE1 4DN Tel: (01733) 566403
C Gearing & Son, 28-30 Seabeach Lane, Eastbourne, East Sussex, BN22 7NZ Tel: (01323) 726029 Fax: (01323) 726029
C Herring & Son Ltd, Windermere Road, Hartlepool, Cleveland, TS25 1NX Tel: (01429) 221104 Fax: (01429) 861989 E-mail: gareth@cherring.co.uk
C & R Grieveson, Station Road, Walker, Newcastle upon Tyne, NE6 3PN Tel: 0191-262 8470 Fax: 0191-295 4469
C & W Scott, 23 West Street, St. Ives, Cambridgeshire, PE27 5PL Tel: (01480) 469999
▶ Chris Allsop Ltd, Covert Farm, Langar Road, Colston Bassett, Nottingham, NG12 3FT Tel: (01949) 81945 Fax: (01949) 81785 E-mail: allsopcranes@aol.com
Coleshill Metals, 234 Station Road, Nether Whitacre, Coleshill, Birmingham, B46 2BY Tel: (01675) 464533
E.R. Coley (Steel) Ltd, James Scott Road, Off Park Lane, Halesowen, West Midlands, B63 2QT Tel: (01384) 567121 Fax: (01384) 411259
T. Collins, 20 Sugar House Lane, Stratford, London, E15 2QS Tel: (020) 8519 8476 Fax: (020) 8555 4076
Constructional Steel & Alloy, Unit 7 Salamons Way, Rainham, Essex, RM13 9UL Tel: (01708) 551967 Fax: (01708) 555453
Corus Engineering Steels, Station Works, 680 Warwick Rd, Tyseley, Birmingham, B11 2HL Tel: 0121-706 1110 Fax: 0121-706 8459 E-mail: enquiries.ces@corusgroup.com
Cramlington & District Metals Ltd, Appleby Street, North Shields, Tyne & Wear, NE29 6TE Tel: 0191-257 2049 Fax: 0191-257 9907
D J Howe (Weston) Ltd, The Yard, Winterstoke Road, Weston-super-Mare, Avon, BS23 3YE Tel: (01934) 623228 Fax: (01934) 620074
Darncrest Recycling & Commodities, Unit 11 Lyon Industrial Estate, River Road, Barking, Essex, IG11 0JS Tel: (020) 8594 4779 Fax: (020) 8591 3998
David Band Metals Ltd, Friarton Road, Perth, PH2 8BB Tel: (01738) 634991 Fax: (01738) 628439
F. Davis & Co., 64 London Road, Bexhill-On-Sea, East Sussex, TN39 3LE Tel: (01424) 211248 Fax: (01424) 730568
Derek Cooper, Turnpike Road, Red Lodge, Bury St. Edmunds, Suffolk, IP28 8LB Tel: (01638) 751974 Fax: (01638) 751665
Dietiker Metals (UK) Ltd, 89-91 Freckleton Rd, Eccleston Hill, St. Helens, Merseyside, WA10 3AS Tel: (01744) 454141 Fax: (01744) 453535 E-mail: dietikermetals@ic24.net
J. Doyle Ltd, Manchester Road, Chequerbent, Westhoughton, Bolton, BL5 3JA Tel: (01942) 813231 Fax: (01942) 840505 E-mail: louise@holtgordon.co.uk
Albert Draper & Son Ltd, Black 5 Works, Ravenstreet, Hull, HU9 1PP Tel: (01482) 320712 Fax: (01482) 585312 E-mail: info@adraper.co.uk
▶ Drapers Developments Ltd, Black Five Works, Raven Street, Hull, HU9 1PP Tel: (01482) 323223 Fax: (01482) 585312
Drayton Recycling Ltd, Old Mill Sidings, Thorney Mill Road, West Drayton, Middlesex, UB7 7EZ Tel: (01895) 442612 Fax: (01895) 422174
E Cook Iron & Steel Ltd, 11 Monmore Road, Wolverhampton, WV1 2TZ Tel: (01902) 404740
E L G Haniel Metals Ltd, Heath Road, Darlaston, Wednesbury, West Midlands, WS10 8LU Tel: 0121-526 2444 Fax: 0121-526 4831 E-mail: info@elgdarlaston.co.uk
E M R Ltd, Tynedale Works, Factory Road, Blaydon-On-Tyne, Tyne & Wear, NE21 5RZ Tel: 0191-414 3618 Fax: 0191-414 0751 E-mail: info@amrltd.com
E & S B Davis Ltd, West View, Brighton Road, Tadworth, Surrey, KT20 6SU Tel: (01737) 833286 Fax: (01737) 832770
E & S Metals, Cadwell Lane, Hitchin, Hertfordshire, SG4 0SA Tel: (01462) 455171 Fax: (01462) 453037
Econ Construction Ltd, Old Maidstone Road, Sidcup, Kent, DA14 5AZ Tel: (020) 8302 4691 Fax: (020) 8308 0483 E-mail: econconstruction@aol.com
Elg Haniel Metals Ltd, Templeborough Works, Sheffield Road, Sheffield, S9 1RT Tel: 0114-244 3333 Fax: 0114-256 1742 E-mail: enquiries@elg.co.uk
Emr, Manor Road, Erith, Kent, DA8 2AD Tel: (01322) 336970 Fax: (01322) 331581
European Metal Recycling Ltd, Harvey Reeves Road, Northampton, NN5 5JR Tel: (01604) 752257 Fax: (01604) 754885
European Metal Recycling Ltd, Kingston Wharf, Brighton Road, Shoreham-by-Sea, West Sussex, BN43 6RN Tel: (01273) 462064 Fax: (01273) 440666 E-mail: info@emrltd.com
European Metal Recycling Ltd, Sirius House, Delta CR, Westbrook, Warrington, WA5 7NS Tel: (01925) 715400 Fax: (01925) 713480
Europian Metal Recycling Ltd, Longbeck Trading Estate, Marske-By-The-Sea, Redcar, Cleveland, TS11 6HB Tel: (01642) 482386 Fax: (01642) 243566
Evans & Mondon Ltd, Bassett Road, Halesowen, West Midlands, B63 2RE Tel: (01384) 564224 Fax: (01384) 637305 E-mail: evansmillshaw@compuserve.com
F D O'Dell & Sons Ltd, Cow Close Langford Road, Langford Road, Biggleswade, Bedfordshire, SG18 9JT Tel: (01767) 313113 Fax: (01767) 313113
F J Church Holdings Ltd, Centenary Works, Manor Way, Rainham, Essex, RM13 8RH Tel: (01708) 522651 Fax: (01708) 522786 E-mail: dave@fjchurch.co.uk
F Murphy Metals Ltd, 29-35 Brougham Street, Leicester, LE1 2BA Tel: 0116-262 1468 Fax: 0116-253 2129
F & W Hetherington Ltd, Garter Street, Sheffield, S4 7QX Tel: 0114-256 1177 Fax: 0114-256 1177 E-mail: fwhetherington@supernet.com
F W Singleton Scrap Metal Merchants Ltd, Score Street, Manchester, M11 2SN Tel: 0161-220 8058 Fax: 0161-220 8059 E-mail: scrap@fwsingleton.freeserve.co.uk
William Firth & Son Ltd, Wombwell Lane, Barnsley, South Yorkshire, S70 3NT Tel: (01226) 287717 Fax: (01226) 730348
John Ford & Sons Ltd, Longships Road, Cardiff, CF10 4RP Tel: (029) 2046 1579 Fax: (029) 2046 1579 E-mail: rwford@supanet.com
William Fry & Co. Ltd, Mitre Works, Neasden Goods Depot, Neasden Lane, London, NW10 2UG Tel: (020) 8459 5141 Fax: (020) 8459 2290 E-mail: md@metalandwaste.com
James Fuller & Son, 51 Huntingdon Road, Chatteris, Cambridgeshire, PE16 6ED Tel: (01354) 692740 Fax: (01354) 692740
G D Metal Recycling Ltd, Powke Lane, Cradley Heath, West Midlands, B64 5PT Tel: 0121-559 1156 Fax: 0121-561 5371
G E Richardson & Sons Ltd, 53 New England Street, Brighton, BN1 4GQ Tel: (01273) 570246 Fax: (01273) 570246 E-mail: metcycle@yahoo.co.uk
G H Newbery & Son Ltd, 4 Ashton Road, Marsh Barton Industrial Estate, Exeter, EX2 8LN Tel: (01392) 275377 Fax: (01392) 435249 E-mail: ghnewbery@btconnect.com
G H Towers & Son, 528 Aylestone Road, Leicester, LE2 8JB Tel: 0116-283 2033 Fax: 0116-283 2033
G & R Metals Skip Hire, 64 London Rd, Bexhill-on-Sea, E. Sussex, TN39 3LE Tel: (01424) 730568
G Sait Ltd, 9 Cobham Road, Ferndown Industrial Estate, Wimborne, Dorset, BH21 7PE Tel: (01202) 875612 Fax: (01202) 874412
GD Metal Recycling Ltd, Reclamation House, Albion Row, Byker, Newcastle upon Tyne, NE6 1LQ Tel: 0191-224 3113 Fax: 0191-276 0221 E-mail: gd.metals@virgin.net
Gormans Metals Ltd, Harlington Works, Kingsteignton Road, Newton Abbot, Devon, TQ12 2QA Tel: (01626) 352266 Fax: (01626) 352266
Gravesend Metal Recycling Denton Wharf Ltd, 7 Wharf Road, Gravesend, Kent, DA12 2RU Tel: (01474) 361244 Fax: (01474) 568172
▶ Griffin Stringer Ltd, Allenway, Sunningdale Road, Leicester, LE3 1UX Tel: 0116-231 2840 Fax: 0116-231 2840
H F Bates & Sons, 94 Fairfield Road, London, E3 2QP Tel: (020) 8980 1133 Fax: (020) 8980 1797
H G Trading Northern Ltd, Unit 3a Rainford Industrial Estate, Mill Lane, Rainford, St. Helens, Merseyside, WA11 8LS Tel: (01744) 886444 Fax: (01744) 886355
H Ripley & Co., Apex Way, Hailsham, East Sussex, BN27 3WA Tel: (01323) 440672 Fax: (01323) 841282 E-mail: jason@hripleys.co.uk
H Williams & Sons Ltd, Wallace Way, Stevenage, Hertfordshire, SG1 1XX Tel: (01462) 454872 Fax: (01462) 421805
Habgood & Co., Gas Lane, Bristol, BS2 0QL Tel: 0117-955 6423 Fax: 0117-955 6423
Peter Hanratty, Albion Street, Whitehaven, Cumbria, CA28 9AA Tel: (01946) 693954 Fax: (01946) 693954 E-mail: phanratty2003@yahoo.co.uk

SCRAP METAL MERCHANTS/ PROCESSORS – *continued*

Hayward & Cook Ltd, 125 Cheston Road, Birmingham, B7 5EA Tel: 0121-327 5699 Fax: 0121-327 5899

Henderson Kerr Ltd, Kirklee Road, Bellshill, Lanarkshire, ML4 2QW Tel: (01563) 541325 Fax: (01563) 541325 E-mail: info@hendersonkerr.com

Hereford Metal Recycling, Units 109-110 Holmer Trading Estate, College Road, Hereford, HR1 1JS Tel: (01432) 269154

Walter Heselwood Ltd, Stevenson Road, Sheffield, S9 2SG Tel: 0114-244 2042 Fax: 0114-243 2806 E-mail: aiden@heselwood.com

Hodsons Bloxwich Ltd, Bloxwich Road, Walsall, WS2 7BD Tel: (01922) 649649 Fax: (01922) 631823

Holden Environmental Ltd, Shore Road, Perth, PH2 8BH Tel: (01738) 634747 Fax: (01738) 637150 E-mail: sales@holden-enviro.com

George Howard Ltd, 94 Folly Lane, Warrington, WA5 0NG Tel: (01925) 444455 Fax: (01925) 444466 E-mail: georgehowardltd@btconnect.com

Hudsons Of Dudley Ltd, Canal St/Brickkiln Street, Brierley Hill, West Midlands, DY5 3LQ Tel: (01384) 262126 Fax: (01384) 481170 E-mail: hudsonsofdudley@aol.com

Ireland Alloys Ltd, PO Box 18, Glasgow, G72 0TQ Tel: (01698) 822461 Fax: (01698) 825166E-mail: a.addison@ireland-alloys.co.uk

J & A Metals, 12 Skidmore Road, Bilston, West Midlands, WV14 8SE Tel: (01902) 497382 Fax: (01902) 497382

J A Williams & Sons Ltd, 30 Birmingham Road, West Bromwich, West Midlands, B71 4JZ Tel: 0121-553 7305 Fax: 0121-553 0503

J Doyle Ltd, PO Box 33, Bolton, BL1 2QS Tel: (01204) 527008 Fax: (01204) 364002 E-mail: j.doyle@hargreaveshamilton.co.uk

J F Lloyd & Son, Nottingham Road, Ashby-de-la-Zouch, Leicestershire, LE65 1DR Tel: (01530) 413347 Fax: (01530) 560264

J Hudson Metals, Hudson Industrial Estate, Dixon Street, Wolverhampton, WV2 2DB Tel: (01902) 457177 Fax: (01902) 457177

J Lawrence, 1 Alma Street, Walsall, WS2 8JQ Tel: (01922) 628759 Fax: (01922) 639969

J S B (Metals) Ltd, Factory Road, Blaydon-on-Tyne, Tyne & Wear, NE21 5RZ Tel: 0191-414 8989 Fax: 0191-414 1191

J S Bamforth & Co. Ltd, Top Vale Works, Colne Vale Road, Huddersfield, HD3 4NY Tel: (01484) 652777 Fax: (01484) 461460

J W Burford Metals, Russell Gardens, Wickford, Essex, SS11 8BH Tel: (01268) 732112 Fax: (01268) 573080

J & W Robinson Glasgow Ltd, 719 South Street, Glasgow, G14 0BX Tel: 0141-950 1812 Fax: 0141-950 1944

J W Thompson & Sons, 5 Mile Hill, Mansfield Road, Hasland, Chesterfield, Derbyshire, S41 0JN Tel: (01246) 234940 Fax: (01246) 557425

Jebb Metals Newcastle Ltd, Station Road, Walker, Newcastle upon Tyne, NE6 3PN Tel: 0191-262 7099 Fax: 0191-262 5458 E-mail: jebbmetals@btconnect.com

John R Adam & Sons Ltd, Riverside Berth, King George V Dock, Renfrew Road, Glasgow, G51 4SD Tel: 0141-440 0424 Fax: 0141-440 0874 E-mail: sales@jradam.co.uk

W. Harold John & Co. Ltd, Adelaide Street, Crindau, Newport, Gwent, NP20 5RR Tel: (01633) 855273 Fax: (01633) 854778 E-mail: scrap@haroldjohn.com

C.D. Jordans & Sons Ltd, Dundas Spur, Dundas Lane, Copnor, Portsmouth, PO3 5NX Tel: (023) 9266 1391 Fax: (023) 9267 9503 E-mail: michelle@cdjordan.co.uk

L Clancey & Sons, Murton Lane, Murton, York, YO19 5UF Tel: (01904) 489169 Fax: (01904) 489508 E-mail: clancey.l@btconnect.com

L & D Mortimer, Birch Street, Bury, Lancashire, BL9 5AL Tel: 0161-764 1362 Fax: 0161-761 6836

L K Metals, 37 Hollinhall Street, Oldham, OL4 3EH Tel: 0161-633 3536 Fax: 0161-633 3536

L Rifkin (Liverpool) Ltd, Marsh Street, Kirkdale, Liverpool, L20 2BL Tel: 0151-922 3004 Fax: 0151-922 0780 E-mail: dhale.rifkin@cybase.co.uk

Laindon Metals, Roberts Works, Wrexham Road, Laindon, Basildon, Essex, SS15 6PX Tel: (01268) 543741 Fax: (01268) 491766

Lord & Midgley, Harrow Street, Hull, HU3 4LB Tel: (01482) 320324 Fax: (01482) 328211

Lord & Midgley, Reservoir Road, Hull, HU6 7QH Tel: (01482) 342394 Fax: (01482) 441301

William McCormac & Henderson & Co. Ltd, 9 Broomhead Drive, Dunfermline, Fife, KY12 9DR Tel: (01383) 721882

Mccoy Bros Ltd, 1 Ebenezer Street, Birkenhead, Merseyside, CH42 1NH Tel: 0151-645 7720 Fax: 0151-643 8964

H. McDermott & Sons, 49 Rivulet Road, Wrexham, Clwyd, LL13 8DU Tel: (01978) 262489

Mark Metals Ltd, Seven Stars Road, Oldbury, West Midlands, B69 4JR Tel: 0121-552 7479 Fax: 0121-552 9088

Mason Metals Ltd, Two Woods Lane, Mill Street, Brierley Hill, West Midlands, DY5 1TA Tel: (01384) 79841 Fax: (01384) 76414 E-mail: info@masonmetals.co.uk

Meadow Lane Scrap Co. Ltd, Grainger Street, Nottingham, NG2 3HA Tel: 0115-986 3884 Fax: 0115-986 4050

Metal & Waste Recycling, Powke Lane, Cradley Heath, West Midlands, B64 5PT Tel: 0121-559 1156 Fax: 0121-561 5371 E-mail: enquires@nbrookes.co.uk

Morecambe Metals Ltd, Northgate, White Lund Industrial Estate, Morecambe, Lancashire, LA3 3AZ Tel: (01524) 69191 Fax: (01524) 843987 E-mail: sales@morecambemetals.co.uk

Morley Waste Traders Ltd, Treefield Industrial Estate, Gelderd Road, Gildersome, Morley, Leeds, LS27 7JU Tel: 0113-252 6699 Fax: 0113-253 1091 E-mail: kay@morleywastetraders.fsnet.co.uk

Mountelm Ltd, 8 Junction Street, Carlisle, CA2 5XH Tel: (01228) 523136 Fax: (01228) 530550 E-mail: m.liddle@btconnect.com

Thomas Muir (Metals) Ltd, Den Road, Kirkcaldy, Fife, KY1 2ER Tel: (01592) 202222 Fax: (01592) 642177 E-mail: muirmetals@aol.com

Nelson Stanley Ltd, 217 Alder Road, Poole, Dorset, BH12 4AP Tel: (01202) 241020 Fax: (01202) 735204

▶ Nextel Metals, 20 Woodlea Grove, Yeadon, Leeds, LS19 7YT Tel: (07946) 842491 Fax: 0113-250 4700 E-mail: nextelmetals@aol.com

North Staffs Aluminium Ltd, 530 Hartshill Road, Stoke-On-Trent, ST4 6AF Tel: (01782) 616578 Fax: (01782) 712904

Oakley Arnold Ltd, Cockshot Lane, Broseley, Shropshire, TF12 5NE Tel: (01952) 882322 Fax: (01952) 882707

P Dobbins Chester Ltd, British Railway Building, Saltney Ferry Road, Saltney Ferry, Chester, CH4 0BN Tel: (01244) 680095 Fax: (01244) 680095

Par Metals Ltd, Unit 68 Birch Road East Industrial Estate, Birch Road East, Birmingham, B6 7DB Tel: 0121-327 2891 Fax: 0121-327 2765

Phelps Bros, Sudmeadow Road, Gloucester, GL2 5HG Tel: (01452) 527133 Fax: (01452) 418513 E-mail: nick@phelpsbros.co.uk

George Poole Metal Processors, Clough Street, Hanley, Stoke-On-Trent, ST1 4AS Tel: (01782) 265377 Fax: (01782) 263226 E-mail: georgepoolescrap@aol.com

Jonathan Potts Ltd, Estate Road 1, South Humberside Industrial Estate, Grimsby, South Humberside, DN31 2TB Tel: (01472) 355946 Fax: (01472) 268258

C.L. Prosser & Co. Ltd, 7 Parkfield Road, Stockton-On-Tees, Cleveland, TS18 3DJ Tel: (01642) 676043 Fax: (01642) 617418 E-mail: lenabain@freeserve.co.uk

Chas B. Pugh (Walsall) Ltd, Heath Road, Darlaston, Wednesbury, West Midlands, WS10 8LU Tel: 0121-568 7568 Fax: 0121-568 8666 E-mail: pughmail@supanet.com

R & H Tomlinson Ltd, The Recycling Centre, Hackworth Industrial Park, Shildon, County Durham, DL4 1HF Tel: (01388) 778222 Fax: (01388) 778333 E-mail: nicktomlinson007@aol.com

R M Recycling, 9 Twyford Business Centre, London Road, Bishop's Stortford, Hertfordshire, CM23 3YT Tel: (01279) 654366 Fax: (01279) 654366

R M Supplies Inverkeithing Ltd, Cruickness Road, Ferryhills Road, Inverkeithing, Fife, KY11 1HL Tel: (01383) 418901 Fax: (01383) 418198

Ray Pillinger, Aldred Close, Norwood Industrial Estate, Killamarsh, Sheffield, S21 2JH Tel: 0114-248 3739 Fax: 0114-248 8081

Reliance Scrap Metal Merchants Ltd, 78-86 Nuffield Road, Nuffield Industrial Estate, Poole, Dorset, BH17 0RS Tel: (01202) 673539 Fax: (01202) 669509

Robert Gibbs Contracting Co. Ltd, Bridge Works, Rye Park Industrial Estate, Hoddesdon, Hertfordshire, EN11 0EW Tel: (01992) 441585 Fax: (01992) 463932 E-mail: sales@gibbsscrap.co.uk

Robinson & Birdsell, Audby House, Audby Lane, Wetherby, West Yorkshire, LS22 7FD Tel: (01937) 548800 Fax: (01937) 548801 E-mail: r-b@robinson-birdsell.co.uk

James Rollason, 63 High Street, Wellington, Telford, Shropshire, TF1 1JT Tel: (01952) 244934 Fax: (01952) 257531

Rooneys Scrap Merchants Ltd, South Shore Road, Gateshead, Tyne & Wear, NE8 3AE Tel: 0191-478 7833 Fax: 0191-478 7833 E-mail: rooneys@btconnect.com

D. & W. Round Scrap Metal Merchants Ltd, Triton Works, Woods Lane, Cradley Heath, West Midlands, B64 7AE Tel: (01384) 562720 Fax: (01384) 565922

S Norton & Co., Bankfield Site, Regent Road, Bootle, Merseyside, L20 8RQ Tel: 0151-955 3300 Fax: 0151-955 3399 E-mail: s.norton@s-norton.co.uk

S R Payne Non Ferrous Metals, Unit 8-10, Sibthorpe Street, Mansfield, Nottinghamshire, NG18 5DE Tel: (01623) 623354 Fax: (01623) 623354

S. Sacker (Claydon) Ltd, Railway Sidings, Gipping Road, Ipswich, IP6 0JB Tel: (01473) 830373 Fax: (01473) 832535 E-mail: recycle@sackers.co.uk

Shakespeares, Oak Lane, Kingswinford, West Midlands, DY6 7JS Tel: (01384) 296757 Fax: (01384) 401059

Shearer Mormet Ltd, 349 Shettleston Road, Glasgow, G31 5JL Tel: 0141-554 2401 Fax: 0141-556 3448 E-mail: shearermormet@btclick.com

Simms Group UK Ltd, Foundry Road, Camborne, Cornwall, TR14 7XB Tel: (01209) 712333 Fax: (01209) 612512

Sims Metal Management, Long Marston, Stratford-upon-Avon, Warwickshire, CV37 8AQ Tel: (01789) 720431 Fax: (01789) 720940 E-mail: info.uk@simsmm.com

Sims Metal UK Ltd, Gatton Road, Bristol, BS2 9SH Tel: 0117-955 7767 Fax: 0117-955 8098 E-mail: info@simsmetal.com.au

Sims Metal UK Ltd, 7 Christow Road, Marsh Barton Trading Estate, Exeter, EX2 8QT Tel: (01392) 276292 Fax: (01392) 422420 E-mail: sales@sims-group.com

Sims Metal UK Ltd, Alexandra Docks, Newport, Gwent, NP20 2WE Tel: (01633) 250650 Fax: (01633) 250850

Sims Metal UK Ltd, Blackbushe House, Vigo Lane, Yateley, Hampshire, GU46 6ED Tel: (01252) 873222 Fax: (01252) 876072

Sims Metals UK Ltd, Paget Street, Burton-On-Trent, Staffordshire, DE14 3TQ Tel: (01283) 568549 Fax: (01283) 511989

Sinclair & Hay Ltd, Poynernook Road, Aberdeen, AB11 5QX Tel: (01224) 580940 Fax: (01224) 584453

Slater Bros, 20 Highgate Place, Birmingham, B12 0DD Tel: 0121-440 5665 Fax: 0121-440 5005

Andrew & Mark Smith Metals Ltd, Darbishire Street, Bolton, BL1 2TN Tel: (01204) 533662 Fax: (01204) 392480 E-mail: mark@smithmetals.co.uk

Smith & Co. (Holdings) Ltd, Cauldwell Walk, Bedford, MK42 9DT Tel: (01234) 272572 Fax: (01234) 271891 E-mail: info@emrltd.com

C.F. Sparrowhawk Ltd, 24 Epsom Lane North, Tadworth, Surrey, KT20 5EH Tel: (01737) 352889 Fax: (01737) 371088

Special Alloys Northern Ltd, Greasbrough Road, Rotherham, South Yorkshire, S60 1RW Tel: (01709) 828333 Fax: (01709) 829915 E-mail: nickeightyatspecialalloys@fsmail.net

Stephen Dalton Scrap Metal Merchants, Station Road, Gogarbank, Edinburgh, EH12 9BU Tel: 0131-339 5355 Fax: 0131-317 7168 E-mail: dalton@daltondemo.co.uk

Stone Bros, Unit 9 Withy Road Trading Estate, Bilston, West Midlands, WV14 0RX Tel: (01902) 496651 Fax: (01902) 496651

Swiftread Metals Ltd, 87 High View Road, London, E18 2HL Tel: (020) 8989 1113 Fax: (020) 8989 0875

Symsmetal, Candys Lane, Corfe Mullen, Wimborne, Dorset, BH21 3EF Tel: (01202) 885019 Fax: (01202) 889400

T J Thomson & Son Ltd, Millfield Works, Grangefield Road, Stockton-on-Tees, Cleveland, TS18 4AE Tel: (01642) 672551 Fax: (01642) 672556 E-mail: postbox@tjthomson.co.uk

T J Turner & Son, Withy Road Industrial Estate, Withy Road, Bilston, West Midlands, WV14 0RX Tel: (01902) 404851 Fax: (01902) 662924

T Pearson & Son, 153-157 Eardley Road, London, SW16 6BB Tel: (020) 8769 2325

Thompson (Metals) Ltd, Winterton Road, Scunthorpe, South Humberside, DN15 0BA Tel: (01724) 843831 Fax: (01724) 847786 E-mail: thompsonmetals@fsnet.co.uk

Simon Urquhart Ltd, Orchardbank Industrial Estate, Forfar, Angus, DD8 1TD Tel: (01307) 462584 Fax: (01307) 465229

W Collins, Cupola Works, Masbrough Street, Rotherham, South Yorkshire, S60 1EX Tel: (01709) 382556

W F Foster & Son, 62a Fordwater Road, Chertsey, Surrey, KT16 8HL Tel: (01932) 563019 Fax: (01932) 567010

W H Marren Ltd, Temple Bar, Willenhall, West Midlands, WV13 1SD Tel: (01902) 605208 Fax: (01902) 601014

W & J Smith Metal Stockists Ltd, Ashmore Lake Way, Willenhall, West Midlands, WV12 4LF Tel: (01902) 607336 Fax: (01902) 634905

W N Thomas & Sons Ltd, Stoke Gardens, Slough, SL1 3QA Tel: (01753) 524575 Fax: (01753) 694765 E-mail: info@thomasmetalrecycling.co.uk

W R Roberts & Sons, 60-64 Chapel Street, Wincham, Northwich, Cheshire, CW9 6DA Tel: (01606) 45849 Fax: (01606) 41281 E-mail: robertsscrap@talk21.com

Wades of Wednesbury Ltd, Webb Street, Coseley, Bilston, West Midlands, WV14 8XL Tel: (01902) 496491 Fax: (01902) 491982

Wallhurst Metals Ltd, 97 Holborn Hill, Birmingham, B6 7QX Tel: 0121-327 3597 Fax: 0121-327 3597

Donald Ward Ltd, Moira Road, Woodville, Swadlincote, Derbyshire, DE11 8DG Tel: (01283) 217192 Fax: (01283) 212515

Warwick Street Metal Works Ltd, 77 Warwick Street, Birmingham, B12 0NH Tel: 0121-773 5181 Fax: 0121-766 7104

William Waugh Edinburgh Ltd, Custom House, 11 West Harbour Road, Edinburgh, EH5 1PH Tel: 0131-552 7758 Fax: 0131-552 7758 E-mail: recycle@williamwaugh.co.uk

Weymouth Scrap Co., 20 Cambridge Road, Granby Industrial Estate, Weymouth, Dorset, DT4 9TJ Tel: (01305) 785538 Fax: (01305) 777595

White Reclamation Ltd, New Hall Farm, Liverpool Road, Eccles, Manchester, M30 7LJ Tel: 0161-789 3268 Fax: 0161-707 5909 E-mail: mail@thewhitegroup.co.uk

Wilson Metals Ltd, Ifton Colliery, St. Martins, Oswestry, Shropshire, SY11 3DA Tel: (01691) 778363 Fax: (01691) 778363 E-mail: wilson@pedigreecomputers.co.uk

A. Winchester & Sons, 9 Great Queen Street, Dartford, DA1 1TJ Tel: (01322) 221388 Fax: (01322) 227659 E-mail: dartfordskips@aol.com

SCRAP METAL PROCESSING PLANT AND EQUIPMENT, *See also headings under Waste Compaction*

C F Gill & Son Ltd, The Yard, Bedford Street, Peterborough, PE1 4DN Tel: (01733) 566403

Integrated Recycling Systems Ltd, Burnt Meadow Road, North Moons Moat, Redditch, Worcestershire, B98 9PA Tel: (01527) 65432 Fax: (01527) 65868 E-mail: info@mastermagnets.co.uk

SCRAPBOOK ACCESSORIES

▶ Crafting Mad, 14 Fulmar Brae, Livingston, West Lothian, EH54 6UY Tel: (01506) 414398 E-mail: angela@crafting-mad.co.uk

▶ The Mulberry Bush, Limberlost Farm, Swife Lane, nr. Broad Oak, Heathfield, East Sussex, TN21 8YA Tel: (01435) 882014

SCREEN DOOR LOCKS

▶ Abbey Locksmiths, 54 Halsey Park, London Colney, St. Albans, Hertfordshire, AL2 1BH Tel: (01727) 828048 Fax: (07092) 003147 E-mail: service@abbeylocks.co.uk

SCREEN PRINTERS/PRINTING SERVICES

A P D Screen Process Ltd, 39A Albert Street, Syston, Leicester, LE7 2JA Tel: 0116-260 2606 Fax: 0116-264 0105

A P G Screenprint Ltd, Unit 2 Fullwood Close, Aldermans Green Industrial Estate, Coventry, CV2 2SS Tel: (024) 7660 2060 Fax: (024) 7660 2003 E-mail: apg.screenprint@btinternet.com

A R Dixon Display Ltd, 7a Waterloo Industrial Estate, Waterloo Road, Bidford-on-Avon, Alcester, Warwickshire, B50 4JH Tel: (01789) 772233 Fax: (01789) 490928

Abacus Signs, L4a Unit Colchester Estate, Colchester Avenue, Penylan, Cardiff, CF23 9AP Tel: (029) 2046 5030 Fax: (029) 2048 7376 E-mail: sales@abucussigns.co.uk

Abbott Signs, 29 Victoria Road, Northampton, NN1 5ED Tel: (01604) 636793 Fax: (01604) 632302 E-mail: info@abbottsigns.co.uk

Abee Signs London Ltd, 435 Lordship Lane, London, N22 5DH Tel: (020) 8889 6126 Fax: (020) 8888 9009 E-mail: sales@abeesigns.co.uk

Alfabet Screenprint Ltd, 9 Sargeant Turner Trading Estate, Bromley Street, Stourbridge, West Midlands, DY9 8HZ Tel: (01384) 897355 Fax: (01384) 893414E-mail: info@alfabet.com

Alston Studio, Unit 4A, Great Northern Works, Hartham Lane, Hertford, SG14 1QN Tel: (01992) 534200 Fax: (01992) 534201 E-mail: gmtech@btconnect.com

Amacord Screenprint, Unit 14-16 Arden Business Centre, Arden Road, Alcester, Warwickshire, B49 6HW Tel: (01789) 764926 Fax: (01789) 764797 E-mail: sales@amacord.co.uk

Animm Textiles Ltd, Mangochi House, 107-115 Gwendolen Road, Leicester, LE5 5FL Tel: 0116-212 1234 Fax: 0116-273 3396 E-mail: info@animm.com

Anotek (Nameplates) Ltd, 22 Simpson Place, Nethermains Industrial Estate, Kilwinning, Ayrshire, KA13 6PT Tel: (01294) 557932 Fax: (01294) 557809 E-mail: anotek@btconnect.com

Apt Art, PO Box 250, Kidlington, Oxfordshire, OX5 2WA Tel: (01865) 372981 E-mail: sales@aptart.co.uk

Arro Signs, Unit 4 Three Springs Industrial Estate, Vincent Road, Worcester, WR5 1BW Tel: (01905) 356333 Fax: (01905) 764406

Ashprint London Ltd, 46 South Building 56 Magnet Road, East Lane, Wembley, Middlesex, HA9 7RG Tel: (020) 8904 6479 Fax: (020) 8908 0315 E-mail: sales@ashprint-international.co.uk

Atelier Screen Print Ltd, 130 Pershore Street, Birmingham, B5 6ND Tel: 0121-622 6301 Fax: 0121-666 6487 E-mail: atelier.screenprint@virgin.net

Augustus Martin Ltd, 8-20 St. Andrews Way, London, E3 3PB Tel: (020) 7537 4200 Fax: (020) 7537 2184 E-mail: sales@amartin.co.uk

▶ Aurora Colors P.L.C., Crossways Park, Caerphilly, Mid Glamorgan, CF83 3NL Tel: (029) 2088 0888

B E P Signs Ltd, 8a South Street, Greenock, Renfrewshire, PA16 8TX Tel: (01475) 784423 Fax: (01475) 729213 E-mail: enquiries@bepsigns.co.uk

Banbury Nameplates Ltd, Dashwood Road, Banbury, Oxfordshire, OX16 5HD Tel: (01295) 267638 Fax: (01295) 271745 E-mail: sales@banburynameplates.co.uk

Beekay Products, 152-154 Ilderton Road, London, SE15 1NT Tel: (020) 7732 8608 Fax: (020) 7277 6996

Bex Design Services Ltd, Stainer Road, Porte Marsh Industrial Estate, Calne, Wiltshire, SN11 9PX Tel: (01249) 821127 Fax: (01249) 817072 E-mail: sales@bexdesign.co.uk

Bezier Creative Printers, Balne Lane, Wakefield, West Yorkshire, WF2 0DF Tel: (01924) 362921 Fax: (01924) 372615 E-mail: bdw@bezier.co.uk

SCREEN PRINTERS/PRINTING SERVICES – *continued*

▶ Blue Print, 7 Barton House, Barton Industrial Estate, Upper Wield, Alresford, Hampshire, SO24 9RN Tel: (01420) 560600 Fax: (01420) 560600
Booth Signs, 45 Stafford Road, Wallington, Surrey, SM6 9AP Tel: (020) 8669 1625 Fax: (020) 8773 3429 E-mail: boothsigns@lineone.net
Alexander Boyd Displays Ltd, Lambeg Mills, Ballyskeagh Road, Lisburn, County Antrim, BT27 5SX Tel: (028) 9030 1115 Fax: (028) 9030 1305E-mail: sboyd@alexanderboyd.com
Brentwood Marketing, Lockhill Mills, Holmes Road, Sowerby Bridge, West Yorkshire, HX6 3LD Tel: (01422) 831185 Fax: (01422) 831186 E-mail: info@brentwoodmarketing.co.uk
▶ Bretby Services, Ashby Road East, Bretby, Burton-on-Trent, Staffordshire, DE15 0PS Tel: (01283) 550491
Briggs Priestley Ltd, 1-3 Lord Street, Halifax, West Yorkshire, HX1 5AE Tel: (01422) 354565 Fax: (01422) 356687 E-mail: dan@briggspriestley.ndo.co.uk
Briggs William & Co., Unit 52 Halliwell Industrial Estate, Rossini Street, Bolton, BL1 8DL Tel: (01204) 599100 Fax: (01204) 599149
Butchers Printed Products Ltd, 498-506 Moseley Road, Birmingham, B12 9AL Tel: 0121-440 2612 Fax: 0121-440 3239 E-mail: md@bppscreengraphics.co.uk
Buzzard Screen Print Ltd, 17 Wing Road, Leighton Buzzard, Bedfordshire, LU7 2NG Tel: (01525) 373527 Fax: (01525) 851260 E-mail: sales@buzzardscreenprint.co.uk
C B Screenprinting & Display, 87 Foxholes Road, Hyde, Cheshire, SK14 5AP Tel: 0161-367 8072 Fax: 0161-367 8764
C O S Marketing Ltd, Bradford Road, Idle, Bradford, West Yorkshire, BD10 8SQ Tel: (01274) 617373 Fax: (01274) 615129
C O S Print, Blakehill Works, Bradford Road, Idle, Bradford, West Yorkshire, BD10 8SQ Tel: (01274) 615142 Fax: (01274) 615129 E-mail: cospresentation@ndirect.co.uk
C P Arts Ltd, Alphin Brook Road, Marsh Barton Trading Estate, Exeter, EX2 8QF Tel: (01392) 210574 Fax: (01392) 412107 E-mail: cparts@cparts.co.uk
C Y Finishes Ltd, 4 Arnhem Road, Newbury, Berkshire, RG14 5RU Tel: (01635) 43860 Fax: (01635) 38547 E-mail: sales@cyfinishes.com
Cardiem Ltd, Station Road, Strines, Stockport, Cheshire, SK6 7GP Tel: (01663) 764861 Fax: (01663) 762377 E-mail: sales@cardiem.co.uk
▶ Carnell L & J, Delamare Road, Cheshunt, Waltham Cross, Hertfordshire, EN8 9SH Tel: (01992) 642261 E-mail: enquiries@ljcarnell.co.uk
Cestrian, Stanley Green TRDG Estate, Earl Road, Cheadle Hulme, Cheadle, Cheshire, SK8 6QD Tel: 0161-488 3300 Fax: 0161-488 3301 E-mail: reception@cestrian.co.uk
City County Screen Print, 7 Adco Business Centre, Bobbers Mill, Nottingham, NG8 5AH Tel: 0115-970 1130 Fax: 0115-970 4557 E-mail: paul@ccsigns.co.uk
City Screen Print Ltd, Unit 2 Sextant Park Neptune Close, Medway City Estate, Rochester, Kent, ME2 4LU Tel: (01634) 297779 Fax: (01634) 294264 E-mail: info@cityscreenprint.co.uk
Cockx Sudbury Ltd, Unit A Woodhall House Drury Drive, Woodhall Business Park, Sudbury, Suffolk, CO10 1WH Tel: (01787) 880511 Fax: (01787) 378102E-mail: info@cockx.co.uk
Colourprint Screen Printers, Moor Lane, North Hykeham, Lincoln, LN6 9BD Tel: (01522) 680254 Fax: (01522) 501052
▶ Colourspec Ltd, 11 Cricketers Way, Chatteris, Cambridgeshire, PE16 6UR Tel: (01354) 696496 E-mail: sales@colourspec.co.uk
Concorde Graphics Ltd, Units 21-23, Chiltonian Industrial Estate, Manor Lane, London, SE12 0TX Tel: (020) 8297 1115 Fax: (020) 8297 9755 E-mail: david.b@concordegraphics.co.uk
Contrax Industrial Services, B11 46 Holton Road, Holton Heath Trading Park, Poole, Dorset, BH16 6LT Tel: (01202) 621681 Fax: (01202) 621618
Corton Bashforth Screenprint Ltd, 78 Catley Road, Sheffield, S9 5JF Tel: 0114-243 0240 Fax: 0114-261 1653
Creative Display Group, Millersdale Close, Euroway Industrial Estate, Bradford, West Yorkshire, BD4 6RX Tel: (01274) 700690 Fax: (01274) 700699 E-mail: sales@creativedisplaygroup.co.uk
Crown Plastic Moulding Ltd, Broad Lanes, Bilston, West Midlands, WV14 0RY Tel: (01902) 496151 Fax: (01902) 493102 E-mail: sales@crown-plastic-mouldings.co.uk
Crown Products International Ltd, Innovation House, Cobnar Wood Close, Chesterfield, Derbyshire, S41 9RQ Tel: (01246) 451451 Fax: (01246) 260122 E-mail: sales@crownproducts.demon.co.uk
Crystal Finishes Ltd, Blackwater Way, Aldershot, Hampshire, GU12 4DP Tel: (01252) 325999 Fax: (01252) 330256
Curtis Screen Print, 26 Fairfax Road, Colchester, CO2 7EW Tel: (01206) 760666 Fax: (01206) 760666 E-mail: sales@curtisscreenprint.co.uk
Custom Print, 2 Ashvale Road, Tooting, London, SW17 8PW Tel: (020) 8672 3511 Fax: (020) 8682 2904 E-mail: sales@customprint.com
D3 Display, 1 Cyril Road, Small Heath, Birmingham, B10 0SS Tel: 0121-772 1815 Fax: 0121-766 6052 E-mail: info@d3display.co.uk
Damar Advertising Ltd, 32 Cogan Street, Barrhead, Glasgow, G78 1EJ Tel: 0141-881 3733 Fax: 0141-881 0430 E-mail: enquiries@damar-printing.co.uk
Danielson Ltd, Commercial House, 52 Perrymount Road, Haywards Heath, West Sussex, RH16 3DT Tel: (01444) 883430 Fax: (01444) 440469
Dartford Engraving Ltd, 4 Power Works Estate, Slade Green Road, Erith, Kent, DA8 2HY Tel: (01322) 340194 Fax: (01322) 347819 E-mail: mail@desp.co.uk
Daytona Visual Marketing Ltd, Amber Close, Tamworth, Staffordshire, B77 4RP Tel: (01827) 54551 Fax: (01827) 63159 E-mail: info@daytonavisual.com
▶ Deben Print Co., 1 Bailey Close, Hadleigh Road Industrial Estat, Ipswich, IP2 0UD Tel: (01473) 210244 Fax: (01473) 217299 E-mail: sales@debenprint.co.uk
Digital & Screen Printing Association (UK) Ltd, Association House, 7A West Street, Reigate, Surrey, RH2 9BL Tel: (01737) 240792 Fax: (01737) 240770 E-mail: info@spauk.co.uk
Dixon & Stell Ltd, 21-25 Main Street, Cross Hills, Keighley, West Yorkshire, BD20 8TX Tel: (01535) 632138 Fax: (01535) 635983 E-mail: sales@dixontarget.com
Dry Transfers Ltd, 1 Jubilee Street, Melton Mowbray, Leicestershire, LE13 1ND Tel: (01664) 565785 Fax: (01664) 410344 E-mail: sales@dry-transfers.co.uk
E S P Technologies Group Ltd, 2 Euroway, Wood Close, Quarry Wood, Aylesford, Kent, ME20 7UB Tel: (01622) 715000 Fax: (01622) 797000 E-mail: sales@esptech.co.uk
Effective Screen & Photographic, 11 Malborough Way, Yardley Gobion, Towcester, Northamptonshire, NN12 7TU Tel: (01908) 543547 E-mail: 40quatro@tesco.net
Elite Engraving, 6 Park Road, Kingswood, Bristol, BS15 1QU Tel: 0117-967 0034 Fax: 0117-967 0043 E-mail: eliteengraving@btconnect.com
Elliott Marshall Signs, Morven Road, Morven Studio, St. Austell, Cornwall, PL25 4PP Tel: (01726) 72863 Fax: (01726) 72863 E-mail: sales@elliottmarshall.com
Enterprise Graphics Ltd, 1 Earls Close, Earls Close Industrial Estate, Thurmaston, Leicester, LE4 8FZ Tel: 0116-260 0879 Fax: 0116-269 7729 E-mail: fiona@enterprisegraphics.wannado.co.uk
Express Moulds Ltd, Jubilee Works, 40 Alma Crescent, Vauxhall, Birmingham, B7 4RH Tel: 0121-359 6378 Fax: 0121-359 3792 E-mail: paul.yeomans@expressmoulds.co.uk
F & M Displays Ltd, Tower Hamlets Road, Dover, Kent, CT17 0BJ Tel: (01304) 208889 Fax: (01304) 205807
Falcon Signs Ltd, 109 Grove Technology Park, Wantage, Oxfordshire, OX12 9FA Tel: (01235) 768872 Fax: (01235) 768822 E-mail: sales@falconsigns.co.uk
Fifth Column Design & Print, 276 Kentish Town Road, London, NW5 2AA Tel: (020) 7485 8599 Fax: (020) 7267 3718 E-mail: sales@fifthcolumn.co.uk
Fitt Signs Ltd, 60-62 Pitt Street, Norwich, NR3 1DF Tel: (01603) 619128 Fax: (01603) 760524 E-mail: info@fitt-signs.co.uk
Format Screen Printers, Prospect Farm, Thirsk Road, Easingwold, York, YO61 3HL Tel: (01347) 824248 Fax: (01423) 860287 E-mail: studio@screenprint.fsbusiness.co.uk
Frank Layton (Display), 9 Broadway Place, London, SW19 3TP Tel: (020) 8946 5041 Fax: (020) 8944 7324
Frome Sign Co. Ltd, Unit 3 Lakeside Park, Mells, Frome, Somerset, BA11 3RH Tel: (01373) 813666 Fax: (01373) 813777 E-mail: fromesigns@aol.com
G M K Graphics, 57 Cromwell Road, Belfast, BT7 1JY Tel: (028) 9032 7905 Fax: (028) 9043 8893 E-mail: gmk.graphics@dnet.co.uk
G S M Industrial Graphics, Avenue One, Witney, Oxfordshire, OX28 4BZ Tel: (01993) 776511 Fax: (01993) 778238 E-mail: gsmindustrialgraphics@gsmgroup.co.uk
Richard Gardner Ltd, Hadfield Road, Leckwith Industrial Estate, Cardiff, CF11 8AQ Tel: (029) 2022 9764 Fax: (029) 2034 3664 E-mail: yc78@dial.pipex.com
Genesis Display Ltd, Unit 14 Lee Bank Business Centre, Holloway Head, Birmingham, B1 1HP Tel: 0121-643 4237 Fax: 0121-633 3977 E-mail: rob@genesisltd.wanadoo.co.uk
Girdwood Display, 44 St. Marys Street, Edinburgh, EH1 1SZ Tel: 0131-556 7024 Fax: 0131-557 8288 E-mail: girdwooddisplay@aol.com
Goodlands Displays, Unit 16 College Fields Business Centre, Prince Georges Road, London, SW19 2PT Tel: (020) 8687 8254 Fax: (020) 8687 8257 E-mail: printing@goodlands.co.uk
Graphic Art Cambridge Ltd, Trinity Hall Farm Industrial Estate, Nuffield Road, Cambridge, CB4 1TG Tel: (01223) 424421 Fax: (01223) 426040 E-mail: mail@graphic-art.co.uk
Graphic Displays Ltd, Selhurst 13 Coates Hill Road, Bickley, Bromley, BR1 2BJ Tel: (020) 8467 5700 Fax: (020) 8467 5277 E-mail: steve@graphicdisplays.co.uk
Graphic Impression, C3 Enterprise Point, Melbourne Street, Brighton, BN2 3LH Tel: (01273) 571645 Fax: (01273) 571645 E-mail: amprints@hotmail.com
Gremida Screen Print Ltd, Sunnybank Works, Sunnybank Street, Ossett, West Yorkshire, WF5 8PE Tel: (01924) 265957 Fax: (01924) 265957E-mail: gremida.screenprint@virgin.net
Griffin Design & Print Services Ltd, 713 High Road, Leyton, London, E10 5AB Tel: (020) 8558 4721 Fax: (020) 8558 4415 E-mail: mail@griffindp.freeserve.co.uk
Halligan & Raby, 55 The Avenue, Rubery, Rednal, Birmingham, B45 9AL Tel: 0121-453 1741 Fax: 0121-453 7657 E-mail: sales@halliganraby.co.uk
Harlow Spraytech, St. James Centre, 7 East Road, Harlow, Essex, CM20 2BJ Tel: (01279) 414665 Fax: (01279) 416828
Horsham Engraving Ltd, Foundry Lane, Horsham, West Sussex, RH13 5PX Tel: (01403) 260729 Fax: (01403) 210057 E-mail: horshamengraving@aol.com
Hyspec Screen Process Printers, Brunel Road, Bedford, MK41 9TG Tel: (01234) 217972 Fax: (01234) 328182 E-mail: info@hyspec.co.uk
I D C Signs & Engraving, 26 Harwood Street, Blackburn, BB1 3BS Tel: (01254) 263679 Fax: (01254) 263699 E-mail: sales@idcsigns.co.uk
▶ Image Data Ltd, Burley Hill Trading Estate, Leeds, LS4 2PU Tel: 0113-389 4050 Fax: 0113-278 4826
Inprints (Screenprinters) Ltd, 32-36 Garden St, Sheffield, S1 4BJ Tel: 0114-272 7733 Fax: 0114-272 1976 E-mail: sales@inprints.co.uk
J A M Design Screen Print, 143a Croydon Road, Caterham, Surrey, CR3 6PF Tel: (01883) 343444 Fax: (01883) 343444 E-mail: jim.rimmington@btinternet.com
J & J Screen Printing, 16 High Street, Stanstead Abbotts, Ware, Hertfordshire, SG12 8AE Tel: (01920) 872284
J Sperry & Son Ltd, 204 Prestbury Road, Cheltenham, Gloucestershire, GL52 3ER Tel: (01242) 244677 Fax: (01242) 244677
Jacee Print & Promotions Ltd, Publicity House, Station Road, Cottingham, East Yorkshire, HU16 4LL Tel: (01482) 842117 Fax: (01482) 875239 E-mail: sales@jaceeprint.co.uk
Harold Jackson Screenprint Ltd, 986 Pollokshaws Road, Glasgow, G41 2HE Tel: 0141-649 1783 Fax: 0141-649 6087 E-mail: enquiries@jacksonscreenprint.co.uk
Jaro Screens Ltd, Unit 20 Shaftmoor Industrial Estate, 226 Shaftmoor Lane, Hall Green, Birmingham, B28 8SP Tel: 0121-702 2157 Fax: 0121-778 6995 E-mail: sales@jaroscreensltd.co.uk
Jarvis Print Ltd, Unit 2-19 Lakeside Business Park, Pinfold Road, Thurmaston, Leicester, LE4 8AT Tel: 0116-260 3026 Fax: 0116-264 0222 E-mail: jarvis.print@btinternet.com
Joe Public Screen Print, Gables House, Bristol Road, Falfield, Wotton-under-Edge, Gloucestershire, GL12 8DL Tel: (01454) 260304 Fax: (01454) 261682
John S Burns Ltd, 107 Coltness Lane, Queenslie Industrial Estate, Glasgow, G33 4DR Tel: 0141-766 3355 Fax: 0141-766 1991 E-mail: sales@johnsburn.co.uk
K N P Finishing Ltd, Unit 10, Commerce Way, Leighton Buzzard, Bedfordshire, LU7 4RW Tel: (01525) 850478 Fax: (01525) 850479 E-mail: andykendall@btconnect.com
Kaylee Transfers Ltd, New Tythe Street, Long Eaton, Nottingham, NG10 2DP Tel: 0115-973 5247 Fax: 0115-946 0801 E-mail: sales@kayleetransfers.uk
Bernard Kaymar Ltd, Kaymar Industrial Estate, Trout Street, Preston, PR1 4DL Tel: (01772) 562211 Fax: (01772) 257813 E-mail: sales@bernard-kaymar.co.uk
Kennedy Print, 11a Wilson Road, Liverpool, L36 6AN Tel: 0151-449 2984 Fax: 0151-449 3270
Kolorcraft Ltd, Concept House, Mortimer Rise Milner Way, Ossett, West Yorkshire, WF5 9JE Tel: (01924) 780780 Fax: (01924) 262586
Kremer Signs Ltd, Units 18, East Road Industrial Estate, Sleaford, Lincolnshire, NG34 7EQ Tel: (01529) 415511 Fax: (01529) 415444 E-mail: sales@kremersigns.co.uk
Kullasigns Sign Writers, 1 Benham Water Farm, Ashford Road, Newingreen, Hythe, Kent, CT21 4JD Tel: (01303) 261279 Fax: (01303) 261280 E-mail: sales@legendsigns.co.uk
Kwikfill Ltd, Bullock Street, West Bromwich, West Midlands, B70 7HE Tel: 0121-553 0433 Fax: (0121) 553 0433 E-mail: sales@quickfill.co.uk
L M R Computer Repairs, 2 North Parade, Norris Road, Sale, Cheshire, M33 3JS Tel: 0161-962 8872 Fax: 0161-962 8872
L & M Signs, Unit 1 Highlands Close, St Helens Way, Thetford, Norfolk, IP24 1HG Tel: 01842 821990 Fax: 01842 750706 E-mail: trevor@lmsigns.co.uk
Lansdowne Cartmel Ltd, 3e West Way, Andover, Hampshire, SP10 5AS Tel: (01264) 353234 Fax: (01264) 359025 E-mail: lansdownecartmel@aol.com
Legend Signs Ltd, 1 Benham Business Park, Ashford Road, Newingreen, Hythe, Kent, CT21 4JD Tel: (01303) 261278 Fax: (01303) 261280 E-mail: info@kullasigns.co.uk
Lineprint Screen Process Printers, 6 Woodside Industrial Park, Works Road, Letchworth Garden City, Hertfordshire, SG6 1LA Tel: (01462) 672914 Fax: (01462) 681124 E-mail: lineprint@hotmail.com
Livingston Precision (Engineering) Ltd, 28 Firth Road, Houstoun Industrial Estate, Livingston, West Lothian, EH54 5DJ Tel: (01506) 435281 Fax: (01506) 433973
Lock Studios Ltd, 32 Wates Way, Mitcham, Surrey, CR4 4HR Tel: (020) 8648 2381 Fax: (020) 8646 0542
London Screen Printing, St. Clare Business Park, Holly Road, Hampton, Middlesex, TW12 1PZ Tel: (020) 8941 8285 Fax: (020) 8941 8806
LP Marketing Ltd, Millenium House, Junction Road, Sheffield, S11 8XB Tel: 0114-268 2812 Fax: 0114-268 2812
M Latchford, 10 Alstone Lane, Cheltenham, Gloucestershire, GL51 8EG Tel: (01242) 584588 Fax: (01242) 529251 E-mail: sales@marklatchford-screenprint.co.uk
Mcrobb Display, 70 Montgomery Street, Edinburgh, EH7 5JA Tel: 0131-556 9633 Fax: 0131-556 7657 E-mail: info@mcrobb.co.uk
Mason Pearce Ltd, Canterbury Road, Worthing, West Sussex, BN13 1AW Tel: (01903) 264231 Fax: (01903) 830175 E-mail: masonpearce@hotmail.com
Matform Ltd, Matform Business Centre, Terminus Road, Chichester, West Sussex, PO19 8UL Tel: (01243) 780157 Fax: (01243) 789029 E-mail: pdown@matform.net
Micro Matic Ltd, Millington House, Stancliffe St Industrial Estate, Blackburn, BB2 2QR Tel: (01254) 671231 Fax: (01254) 682229 E-mail: mmltv@micro-matic.co.uk
Midway Metalcraft, Ridgeway Court, Grovebury Rd, Leighton Buzzard, Bedfordshire, LU7 4SW Tel: (01525) 374861 Fax: (01525) 374082 E-mail: enquiries@midwaymetalcraft.com
Midwest Displays, 22 Oxford Street, Birmingham, B5 5NR Tel: 0121-643 1746 Fax: 0121-616 1014
Multi Sign Makers, 30 New John Street West, Birmingham, B19 3NB Tel: 0121-359 0707 Fax: 0121-359 6066 E-mail: sales@multisignmakers.co.uk
▶ N P M Ltd, Riverside Road, Pride Park, Derby, DE24 8HA Tel: (01332) 600020 Fax: (01332) 600313
Newdev UK, 52-54 Snow Hill, Melton Mowbray, Leicestershire, LE13 1PH Tel: (01664) 569805 Fax: (01664) 481581 E-mail: newdevuk@aol.com
Nicol & Moon Ltd, 7 Wimbledon Stadium Business Centre, Riverside Road, London, SW17 0BA Tel: (020) 8879 6000 Fax: (020) 8879 6111 E-mail: info@nicolandmoon.ltd.uk
Opus Publicity Ltd, Electron Works, Willow Avenue, Denham, Uxbridge, Middlesex, UB9 4BG Tel: (01895) 234441 Fax: (01895) 271520 E-mail: stacey@opus-publicity.freeserve.co.uk
Opus Screen Print Ltd, Unit 11-12, 865 Ringwood Road, Bournemouth, BH11 8LW Tel: (01202) 590202 Fax: (01202) 580280 E-mail: enq@opus99.co.uk
P & O Aerosols, 2 Hale Industrial Estate, Lower Church Lane, Tipton, West Midlands, DY4 7PQ Tel: 0121-520 8883 Fax: 0121-520 8080 E-mail: sales@pxoaerosols.co.uk
P&D, 2 Power Industrial Estate, Slade Green Road, Erith, Kent, DA8 2HU Tel: (01322) 346834 Fax: (01322) 336817
Pemberton Technologies Ltd, 47 Knowl Piece, Wilbury Way, Hitchin, Hertfordshire, SG4 0TY Tel: (01462) 440003 Fax: (01462) 440550 E-mail: pemtech@clara.co.uk
Peplicity Ltd, 20a Meadow Lane, Loughborough, Leicestershire, LE11 1JY Tel: (01509) 217397 Fax: (01509) 217397
Photo Mechanical Services Essex Ltd, Co-Ordinated Industrial Estate, Claydons Lane, Rayleigh, Essex, SS6 7UP Tel: (01268) 741486 Fax: (01268) 782538 E-mail: pcbs@photomechanical.co.uk
Plastisigns, Oak Tre Farm, Escrick Road, Wheldrake, York, YO19 6BQ Tel: (01904) 449970 Fax: (01904) 449970 E-mail: plastisigns@supanet.com
Plumridge & Peters Ltd, Unit 5, Gillmans Industrial Estate, Natts Lane, Billingshurst, West Sussex, RH14 9EY Tel: (01403) 783762 Fax: (01403) 784288 E-mail: plumridge@ndirect.co.uk
Polyprint Plastics (Nottingham) Ltd, Nicholas House, 385 Nottingham Road, New Basford, Nottingham, NG7 7FE Tel: 0115-970 4475 Fax: 0115-942 2531 E-mail: info@poly-print.com
Practivewear, 47-49 Park Royal Road, London, NW10 7LQ Tel: (020) 8963 0888 Fax: (020) 8963 0343
Presletta Graphics, 66 Kitchener Road, High Wycombe, Buckinghamshire, HP11 2SN Tel: (01494) 526285 E-mail: roy@presletta.com
Priestleys of Gloucester Ltd, Unit 41 Morlandlands Trading Estate, Bristol Road, Gloucester, GL1 5RZ Tel: (01452) 522281 Fax: (01452) 300702 E-mail: sales@preistgloucs.com
▶ Print Innovative Technology Ltd, Camilla Court, The Street, Nacton, Ipswich, IP10 0EU Tel: (01473) 655141 Fax: (01473) 655148 E-mail: neil@print-it.tv
Print One Ltd, Mayfield House, Tockholes Road, Darwen, Lancashire, BB3 1LL Tel: (01254) 776735 Fax: (01254) 775802 E-mail: mail@print1uk.com
▶ Printon Plastics & Assemblies Ltd, Unit 4 Attwood Business Centre, Attwood Street, Lye, Stourbridge, West Midlands, DY9 8RY Tel: (01384) 77007 Fax: (01384) 77747 E-mail: info@printonplastics.co.uk
Projects XL Ltd, Glenville House, Spring Gardens, Romford, RM7 9LD Tel: (01708) 751919 Fax: (01708) 725294 E-mail: info@projectsxl.com

▶ indicates data change since last edition

SCREEN PRINTERS/PRINTING SERVICES – *continued*

Publicity & Display Ltd, Corium House, Douglas Drive, Godalming, Surrey, GU7 1HJ Tel: (01483) 428326 Fax: (01483) 424566 E-mail: print@p-and-d.com

Q B Print Ltd, 7 Parham Drive, Eastleigh, Hampshire, SO50 4NU Tel: (023) 8061 1833 Fax: (023) 8061 0828 E-mail: john@qbprint.co.uk

Quicksign Signs & Nameplates, 7 Hightown Industrial Estate, Crow Arch Lane, Ringwood, Hampshire, BH24 1ND Tel: (01425) 470445 Fax: (01425) 476289 E-mail: steve@quicksign.co.uk

▶ R Elliott & Co. Ltd, Alchorne Place, Portsmouth, PO3 5QL Tel: (023) 9262 7700 Fax: (023) 9266 9991

R & T Industrial Engravers, 26 The Tanneries, Brockhampton Lane, Havant, Hampshire, PO9 1JB Tel: (023) 9245 4751 Fax: (023) 9247 2709 E-mail: rt.engraving@tinyworld.co.uk

Rapid Engraving Horley Ltd, Bayhorne Lane, Balcombe Road, Horley, Surrey, RH6 9ES Tel: (01293) 820688 Fax: (01293) 820655 E-mail: rapidengraving@hotmail.com

Reflex Studio Ltd, Reflex House, Bells Yew Green, Tunbridge Wells, Kent, TN3 9BQ Tel: (01892) 752888 Fax: (01892) 752889 E-mail: sales@reflex-print.co.uk

RGS Signs & Screenprinting, Reval Green, Oathlaw, Forfar, Angus, DD8 3PT Tel: (01307) 850260 Fax: (01307) 850260 E-mail: sales@revalgreen.com

Riverside Screen Print Ltd, 59-61 Blundell Street, Liverpool, L1 0AJ Tel: 0151-709 0421 Fax: 0151-708 7257

S P Group, 9 Hedera Road, Redditch, Worcestershire, B98 9EY Tel: (01527) 508014 Fax: (01527) 508015 E-mail: enquiries@spgroup.co.uk

Sagittarian Embroidery, 27 Durham Road, Sacriston, Durham, DH7 6LN Tel: 0191-371 9371 Fax: 0191-371 2288 E-mail: sagittarianemb@clara.co.uk

Screen Art Enterprises, Industrial Estate, St. Ives, Cambridgeshire, PE27 3LE Tel: (01480) 464649 Fax: (01480) 496426

Screen Print 2000, Northbridge Road, Berkhamsted, Hertfordshire, HP4 1EH Tel: (01442) 875879 Fax: (0845) 4567706 E-mail: fp2000@phillipsplastics.co.uk

Screen Pro Ltd, Unit 14 Shaftmoor Industrial Estate, Shaftmoor Lane, Hall Green, Birmingham, B28 8SP Tel: 0121-778 6808 Fax: 0121-778 5676 E-mail: sales@screenprouk.com

Screencraft Publicity Hull, Reservoir Road, Hull, HU6 7QD Tel: (01482) 499999 Fax: (01482) 499994 E-mail: info@screencraft-display.co.uk

Screenmaster Ltd, 23 Hurlbutt Road, Heathcote Industrial Estate, Warwick, CV34 6TD Tel: (01926) 425325 Fax: (01926) 888792 E-mail: info@screenmaster.co.uk

Screenprint Printers, Unit 14 Hall Barn Road Industrial Estate, Hall Barn Road, Isleham, Ely, Cambridgeshire, CB7 5RJ Tel: (01638) 780200 Fax: (01638) 780 300 E-mail: screenprint@mail.islehamnet.co.uk

Screenprint Productions Ltd, The Print Mill, Rosebery Street, Elland, West Yorkshire, HX5 0HT Tel: (01422) 371751 Fax: (01422) 371702 E-mail: screenprint@demon.co.uk

Selway Signs Ltd, Leonard House, Queen Street, Belper, Derbyshire, DE56 1NR Tel: (01773) 825445 Fax: (01773) 821619 E-mail: sales@selway-group.com

Seppi, 28 High Street, Meldreth, Royston, Hertfordshire, SG8 6JU Tel: (01763) 260326 Fax: (01763) 260035 E-mail: sales@seppities.co.uk

Serigraphia Digital Ltd, Stonebridge Trading Estate, Sibree Road, Coventry, CV3 4FD Tel: (024) 7663 9425 Fax: (024) 7651 1582 E-mail: sales@serigraphia.co.uk

Shades Screenprint Ltd, Stur Mill, Broadstone Hall Road, Stockport, Cheshire, SK5 7BY Tel: 0161-477 4688 Fax: 0161-474 7629 E-mail: admin@shadesscreenprint.co.uk

Shawcross Ltd, Priory Street, Priory Industrial Estate, Birkenhead, Merseyside, CH41 5JH Tel: 0151-647 6692 Fax: 0151-666 1569 E-mail: info@shawcrosssigns.co.uk

Shires Art Printing Ltd, Brinksway Trading Estate, Stockport, Cheshire, SK3 0BZ Tel: 0161-480 8316 Fax: 0161-480 2357 E-mail: sales@shiresart.fsnet.co.uk

Sign A Rama, 328-330 Hobs Moat Road, Solihull, West Midlands, B92 8JT Tel: 0121-742 5888 Fax: 0121-742 5656 E-mail: birminghamsouth@sign-a-rama.co.uk

▶ Sign Directory, 38 Sandport Street, Edinburgh, EH6 6EP Tel: 0131-553 4224 Fax: 0131-554 5797 E-mail: signdirectory@btclick.com

Sign & Label Centre Ltd, Dock Road, Connah's Quay, Deeside, Clwyd, CH5 4DS Tel: (01244) 813660 Fax: (01244) 816812 E-mail: sales@signandlabelcentre.com

Sign Studios Ltd, 16 Broomhills Industrial Estate, Rayne Road, Braintree, Essex, CM7 2RG Tel: (01376) 349529 Fax: (01376) 552635 E-mail: sign.studios@btinternet.com

Sign Work Of Cambridge Sign Manufacturers, 303 St.Neots Road Hardwick, Hardwick, Cambridge, CB23 7QL Tel: (01954) 211611 Fax: (01954) 211010 E-mail: admin@signwork.co.uk

Signgrave Signs & Nameplates, Tudor Court, Harold Court Road, Romford, RM3 0AE Tel: (01708) 373827 Fax: (01708) 381069 E-mail: sign.grave@virgin.net

Signline, Unit 5a Ridge Hill Farm, Nash, Milton Keynes, MK17 0EH Tel: (01908) 379600 Fax: (01296) 715113

Signwork, Crosshouse Road, Southampton, SO14 5GZ Tel: (023) 8063 8243 Fax: (023) 8023 4512 E-mail: info@signwork.net

Signworld Screen Printers Ltd, Henson Way, Telford Way Industrial Estate, Kettering, Northamptonshire, NN16 8PX Tel: (01536) 527940 Fax: (01536) 527944 E-mail: sales@signworld.co.uk

Simpson's Printers, Transfer Bridge Industrial Estate, County Road, Swindon, SN1 2EL Tel: (01793) 536305 Fax: (01793) 532543 E-mail: sales@simpsonprinters.co.uk

Simpson's Printers, Transfer Bridge Industrial Estate, County Road, Swindon, SN1 2EL Tel: (01793) 536305 Fax: (01793) 532543

Slater Signs, Unit 32 Crayford Industrial Estate, Swaisland Drive, Crayford, Dartford, DA1 4HS Tel: (01322) 558409 Fax: (01322) 554474 E-mail: sales@slatersigns.co.uk

Solar Signs, Normanby Road, Nettleton, Market Rasen, Lincolnshire, LN7 6TB Tel: (01472) 851914 Fax: (01472) 851037 E-mail: enquires@solarsigns.co.uk

Staffordshire Signs & Graphics Ltd, 154 Lime Lane, Pelsall, Walsall, WS3 5AP Tel: (01543) 373006 Fax: (01543) 374550 E-mail: richard@signs-and-graphics.co.uk

Streamline Graphics, Banhaw Wood Lodge, Lower Benefield, Peterborough, PE8 5AG Tel: (01832) 205363 Fax: (01733) 205216 E-mail: streamline-graphics@tiscali.co.uk

Studio One Screen, 13 Paramount Industrial Estate, Sandown Road, Watford, WD24 7XA Tel: (01923) 494944 Fax: (01923) 494940

Supersine Duramark Ltd, Freemantle Road, Lowestoft, Suffolk, NR33 0EA Tel: (01502) 501234 Fax: (01502) 560620 E-mail: info@ssdm.co.uk

Swatchways Ltd, Unit 13 Ely Industrial Estate, Williamstown, Penygraig, Tonypandy, Mid Glamorgan, CF40 1BY Tel: (01443) 423111 Fax: (01443) 440939

Swift Creative Print Ltd, 2 Albright Road Off Newstead, Road Speke Approach Ditton, Widnes, Cheshire, WA8 8FY Tel: 0151-423 8300 Fax: 0151-423 8329

Symbol Signs, 21 St. Peters Street, Nottingham, NG7 3EN Tel: 0115-979 1456 Fax: 0115-979 0987 E-mail: info@symbol-signs.freeserve.co.uk

T K Graphics Screen Printing, 12 Beauchamp Industrial Park, Watling Street, Wilnecote, Tamworth, Staffordshire, B77 5BZ Tel: (01827) 262449 Fax: (01827) 285458 E-mail: tomtkgraphics@aol.com

T & R Prints, Unit 3, 55 St. Peters Road, Dunstable, Bedfordshire, LU5 4HY Tel: (01582) 660768 Fax: (01582) 660768 E-mail: tandrprints@yahoo.co.uk

Taylors Print, 12 Gildart Street, Liverpool, L3 8ET Tel: 0151-207 2096 Fax: 0151-298 1198

Tealwood Company, 1 Seagull Lane, Emsworth, Hampshire, PO10 7QH Tel: (01243) 371524 Fax: (01243) 378123 E-mail: sales@tealwood.co.uk

Terrane Promotions, Terrane House, Whisby Way Industrial Estate, Lincoln, LN6 3LQ Tel: (01522) 697000 Fax: (01522) 697154 E-mail: sales@terrane.co.uk

Thermograve Ltd, 171 Scudamore Road, Leicester, LE3 1UQ Tel: 0116-291 9000 Fax: 0116-291 9001 E-mail: info@thermograve.co.uk

▶ Thumbprint (Cirencester) Ltd, Wilkinson Road, Love Lane, Cirencester, Gloucestershire, GL7 1YT Tel: (01285) 656927 Fax: (01285) 659134 E-mail: frank@thumbprint.uk.net

Tiviot Prints Ltd, Lymefield Mill, Broadbottom, Hyde, Cheshire, SK14 6AG Tel: (01457) 763297 Fax: (01457) 765499 E-mail: info@tiviotprintsltd.demon.co.uk

Top TS Kent Ltd, Unit 35 Blenheim Close, Pysons Road Industrial Estate, Broadstairs, Kent, CT10 2YF Tel: (01843) 863737 Fax: (01843) 863684 E-mail: cotts@aol.com

Torbay Posters, 93 Union Street, Torquay, TQ1 3DW Tel: (01803) 294777 Fax: (01803) 294777

Treble Nine Signs, 8 Whittingham Road, Halesowen, West Midlands, B63 3TE Tel: 0121-550 1581 Fax: 0121-550 1581 E-mail: russ@treble-nine-signs.freeserve.co.uk

V M R Publicity, 241 Redcatch Road, Knowle, Bristol, BS4 2HQ Tel: 0117-972 0505 Fax: 0117-972 0606 E-mail: vmrviv@aol.com

Valley Signs, 2 Farnworth Park Industrial Estate, Queen Street, Farnworth, Bolton, BL4 7BY Tel: (01204) 795444 Fax: (01204) 792033

Vendredi Screen Print, 23 Airfield Road, Christchurch, Dorset, BH23 3TG Tel: (01202) 470570 Fax: (01202) 470570 E-mail: vendredi@btconnect.com

Viva Imaging Ltd, Photographic House, Northgate, Nottingham, NG7 7BE Tel: 0115-978 4527 Fax: 0115-978 3791 E-mail: sales@vivaimaging.co.uk

▶ Walkers Manchester, Crabtree Lane, Manchester, M11 4GU Tel: 0161-223 7814 Fax: 0161-231 7212 E-mail: info@walkersmcr.com

▶ Wallace Screen Print Ltd, 7 Ballard Business Park, Cuxton Road, Rochester, Kent, ME2 2NY Tel: (01634) 724772 Fax: (01634) 727490 E-mail: sales@wprintgroup.co.uk

Wellan Studios Printers)Ltd, Unit 1, Grange Valley Road, Batley, West Yorkshire, WF17 6GG Tel: (01924) 473481 Fax: (01924) 477353 E-mail: sales@wellanstudios.com

Wellington Signs Ltd, 66 Winchester Road, Southampton, SO16 6UL Tel: (023) 8078 0780 Fax: (023) 8036 0361

Yateley Industries For The Disabled Ltd, Mill Lane, Yateley, Hampshire, GU46 7TF Tel: (01252) 872337 Fax: (01252) 860620

SCREEN PRINTING CHEMICALS

John T. Keep & Sons Ltd, PO Box 78, Beckenham, Kent, BR3 4BL Tel: (020) 8658 2299 Fax: (020) 8658 8672 E-mail: sales@bollom.com

A.J. Purdy & Co. Ltd, 30 Stort Mill, River Way, Harlow, Essex, CM20 2SN Tel: (01279) 414556 Fax: (01279) 450931 E-mail: info@ajpurdy.co.uk

Screen Pro Ltd, Unit 14 Shaftmoor Industrial Estate, Shaftmoor Lane, Hall Green, Birmingham, B28 8SP Tel: 0121-778 6808 Fax: 0121-778 5676 E-mail: sales@screenprouk.com

SCREEN PRINTING ENGRAVERS

▶ Bay Area Sign Solutions, Unit 1, Farfield Business Park, Main Road, Wykeham, Scarborough, North Yorkshire, YO13 9QB Tel: (01723) 866680 Fax: (01723) 865509 E-mail: info@bay-area.co.uk

Medway Engraving Products, 62 High Street, Newington, Sittingbourne, Kent, ME9 7JL Tel: (01795) 842617 Fax: (01795) 843782

P M E Engraving & Screen Printing Ltd, 11 Robert Cort Industrial Estate, Britten Road, Reading, RG2 0AU Tel: 0118-986 4858 Fax: 0118-975 3415 E-mail: pms-sales@compuserve.com

SCREEN PRINTING FABRIC/GAUZE/MESH

Colenso Screen Services Ltd, Unit 2-3, Fairoak Court, Runcorn, Cheshire, WA7 3DX Tel: (01928) 701356 Fax: (01928) 713047 E-mail: sales@colenso.co.uk

Joe Public Screen Print, Gables House, Bristol Road, Falfield, Wotton-under-Edge, Gloucestershire, GL12 8DL Tel: (01454) 260304 Fax: (01454) 261682

SCREEN PRINTING FABRIC/GAUZE/MESH STRETCHING SERVICES

Joe Public Screen Print, Gables House, Bristol Road, Falfield, Wotton-under-Edge, Gloucestershire, GL12 8DL Tel: (01454) 260304 Fax: (01454) 261682

SCREEN PRINTING INKS

Acorn Screen Products Ltd, Meadow Lane, Loughborough, Leicestershire, LE11 1JX Tel: (01509) 610665 Fax: (01509) 212972 E-mail: enquiries@acornscreenproducts.co.uk

Fuji Films Sericol UK Ltd, Pysons Road, Broadstairs, Kent, CT10 2LE Tel: (01843) 866668 Fax: (01843) 872184 E-mail: uksales@sericol.com

John T. Keep & Sons Ltd, PO Box 78, Beckenham, Kent, BR3 4BL Tel: (020) 8658 2299 Fax: (020) 8658 8672 E-mail: sales@bollom.com

Kromex Ltd, Shepherds Grove Industrial Estate, Stanton, Bury St. Edmunds, Suffolk, IP31 2AR Tel: (01359) 250565 Fax: (01359) 250561 E-mail: sales@kromex.co.uk

Nor Cote International Ltd, 7 Warrior Park, Eagle Close, Chandler's Ford, Eastleigh, Hampshire, SO53 4NF Tel: (023) 8027 0542 Fax: (023) 8027 0543 E-mail: sales@norcote.com

Polyone Formulators UK Ltd, Everite Road, Ditton, Widnes, Cheshire, WA8 8PT Tel: 0151-424 1341 Fax: 0151-495 1853

Rondec Screen Process, Lisle Lane, Ely, Cambridgeshire, CB7 4AS Tel: (01353) 645631 Fax: (01353) 667998 E-mail: sales@rondec.com

Sun Chemical Screen, Cray Valley Road, St. Mary Cray, Orpington, Kent, BR5 3TT Tel: (01689) 899666 Fax: (01689) 878262 E-mail: orpington@coates.com

SCREEN PRINTING MACHINE/EQUIPMENT MANUFRS

Adelco Screen Process Ltd, 16 18 Highview, High Street, Bordon, Hampshire, GU35 0AX Tel: (01420) 488388 Fax: (01420) 476445 E-mail: sales@adelco.co.uk

Dek Printing Machines Ltd, 11 Albany Road, Granby Industrial Estate, Weymouth, Dorset, DT4 9TH Tel: (01305) 760760 Fax: (01305) 760123 E-mail: marketing@dek.com

H.G. Kippax & Sons Ltd, Upper Bankfield Mills, Almondbury Bank, Huddersfield, HD5 8HF Tel: (01484) 426789 Fax: (01484) 541799 E-mail: sales@hgkippax.co.uk

Parker Graphics Ltd, Progress House, Erskine Road, London, E17 6RT Tel: (020) 8520 7182 Fax: (020) 8521 7846

Petter Potter Ltd, Water Lane, Storrington, Pulborough, West Sussex, RH20 3EA Tel: (01903) 743397 Fax: (01903) 746248

Screen Art Enterprises, Industrial Estate, St. Ives, Cambridgeshire, PE27 3LE Tel: (01480) 464649 Fax: (01480) 496426

SCREEN PRINTING PHOTOSTENCILS

Adelco Screen Process Ltd, 16 18 Highview, High Street, Bordon, Hampshire, GU35 0AX Tel: (01420) 488388 Fax: (01420) 476445 E-mail: sales@adelco.co.uk

Coated Screens Ltd, Unit 4 218 Purley Way, Croydon, CR0 4XG Tel: (020) 8256 1500 Fax: (020) 8256 1515 E-mail: enquiries@coated-screens.co.uk

Colenso Screen Services Ltd, Unit 2-3, Fairoak Court, Runcorn, Cheshire, WA7 3DX Tel: (01928) 701356 Fax: (01928) 713047 E-mail: sales@colenso.co.uk

SCREEN PRINTING SCREENS

Abee Signs London Ltd, 435 Lordship Lane, London, N22 5DH Tel: (020) 8889 6126 Fax: (020) 8888 9009 E-mail: sales@abeesigns.co.uk

SCREEN PRINTING SERVICES, LARGE FORMAT

▶ G5 Graphics Ltd, St Luke's Place, Unit 6, Glasgow, G5 0TS Tel: 0141-429 4240 Fax: 0141-429 4241 E-mail: info@g5graphics.com

Maximus Operandi Ltd, Unit 3b Sanders Lodge Industrial Estate, Rushden, Northamptonshire, NN10 6BQ Tel: (01933) 413113 Fax: (01933) 413114 E-mail: info@maximusuk.com

SCREEN PRINTING STENCILS

Contrax Industrial Services, B11 46 Holton Road, Holton Heath Trading Park, Poole, Dorset, BH16 6LT Tel: (01202) 621681 Fax: (01202) 621618

SCREEN PRINTING TRADE ENGINEERING SERVICES

Taurus Engineering, Commerce Way, Lancing, West Sussex, BN15 8TA Tel: (01903) 761188 Fax: (01903) 767268 E-mail: sales@taurusengineering.co.uk

SCREEN PRINTING TRADE SUPPLIERS

Coated Screens Ltd, Unit 4 218 Purley Way, Croydon, CR0 4XG Tel: (020) 8256 1500 Fax: (020) 8256 1515 E-mail: enquiries@coated-screens.co.uk

Colenso Screen Services Ltd, Unit 2-3, Fairoak Court, Runcorn, Cheshire, WA7 3DX Tel: (01928) 701356 Fax: (01928) 713047 E-mail: sales@colenso.co.uk

Contra Vision Ltd, Victoria House, 19-21 Ack Lane East, Bramhall, Stockport, Cheshire, SK7 2BE Tel: 0161-439 9307 Fax: 0161-440 7934 E-mail: sales@contravision.com

Digital & Screen Printing Association (UK) Ltd, Association House, 7A West Street, Reigate, Surrey, RH2 9BL Tel: (01737) 240792 Fax: (01737) 240770 E-mail: info@spauk.co.uk

Jade Screen Supplies Ltd, 153 Upper Aughton Road, Southport, Merseyside, PR8 5EX Tel: (01704) 563186 Fax: (01704) 563186

Ritrama UK Ltd, Lynwell Road, Lyntown Trading Estate, Eccles, Manchester, M30 9QG Tel: 0161-786 1700 Fax: 0161-786 1701 E-mail: info@ritrama.co.uk

Screen Machine Supply Co., 6 Lyon Road, Bletchley, Milton Keynes, MK1 1EX Tel: (01908) 270600 Fax: (01908) 270601 E-mail: sales@screenmachinesupply.com

SCREEN PRINTING, PRECISION

▶ Advanced Screen Technology Ltd, 5 Enterprise Close, Croydon, CR0 3RZ Tel: (020) 8665 9887 E-mail: info@astluk.com

SCREEN PRINTING, TEXTILE,

See Textile Printing etc

SCREENED CONDUITS

Kopex International Ltd, 3rd Floor Crossbow House, 40 Liverpool Road, Slough, SL1 4QZ Tel: (01753) 502502 Fax: (01753) 693521 E-mail: jaustin@kopex.co.uk

SCREENS, SEWAGE/ INDUSTRIAL EFFLUENT

▶ Longwood Engineering Co. Ltd, Silver Street, Huddersfield, HD5 9BS Tel: (01484) 424545 Fax: (01484) 437379 E-mail: email@longwoodengineering.co.uk

Screen Systems Ltd, PO Box 237, Warrington, WA5 0JZ Tel: (01925) 659906 Fax: (01925) 571060 E-mail: info@screensystems.com

SCREW AND WASHER ASSEMBLIES

Burntwood Fasteners Ltd, Hawks Green Business Park, Cannock, Staffordshire, WS11 7XN Tel: (01543) 572731 Fax: (01543) 572735 E-mail: sales@burntwoodfasteners.co.uk

Europa Fastenings, Unit 5D, Leaton Industrial Estate, Bomere Heath, Shrewsbury, SY4 3AP Tel: (01939) 291199 Fax: (01939) 291299 E-mail: stephen@europafastenings.co.uk

Trifast P.L.C., Trifast House, Bellbrook Park, Uckfield, East Sussex, TN22 1QW Tel: (01825) 769696 Fax: (01825) 767882

SCREW CONVEYOR SYSTEMS

Astwell Augers Ltd, A14 Huntingdon Road, Thrapston, Kettering, Northamptonshire, NN14 4PT Tel: (01832) 735300 Fax: (01832) 735533 E-mail: sales@astwell.co.uk

C T M Systems Ltd, Unit 8, Arkwright Road Industrial Estate, Cambridge Road, Bedford, MK42 0LE Tel: (01234) 355700 Fax: (01234) 351155 E-mail: sales@ctm-systems.demon.co.uk

Conveyor & Elevator Co., Grange Works, Wellington Street, Accrington, Lancashire, BB5 2NT Tel: (01254) 390727 Fax: (01254) 390521

Handling Techniques Ltd, Units 30-31, Upper Mills Estate, Stonehouse, Gloucestershire, GL10 2BJ Tel: (01453) 826016 Fax: (01453) 823994 E-mail: david@handlingtechniques.co.uk

The Nicholson Group of Companies, Meridian Centre, King Street, Oldham, OL8 1EZ Tel: (08450) 540526 Fax: (08450) 540527 E-mail: enquiries@nicholson-group.co.uk

Pressed Flights Ltd, 6 Ferrand Lodge, Todmorden Road, Littleborough, Lancashire, OL15 9EG Tel: (01706) 372551 Fax: (01706) 377598 E-mail: sales@pressedflights.co.uk

WAM Engineering Ltd, Unit 14, Alexandra Way, Ashchurch Business Centre, Tewkesbury, Gloucestershire, GL20 8NB Tel: (01684) 299100 Fax: (01684) 299104 E-mail: shev@wameng.com

SCREW THREAD CUTTING DIES

Berger Tools Ltd, Units B 1-2 Chaucer Business Park, Watery Lane, Kemsing, Sevenoaks, Kent, TN15 6QY Tel: (01732) 763377 Fax: (01732) 763335 E-mail: sales@berger-tools.co.uk

Nonpareil Taps & Dies Ltd, 15 Rookwood Way, Haverhill, Suffolk, CB9 8PB Tel: (01440) 703625 Fax: (01440) 712101 E-mail: info@nonpareiltapsanddies.co.uk

T-Tech Tooling Ltd, 70 Prince Of Wales Lane, Yardley Wood, Birmingham, B14 4JZ Tel: 0121-474 2255 Fax: 0121-474 2066 E-mail: sales@t-tech.co.uk

SCREWDRIVER BITS

Wera Tools, Unit 2 McGregors Way, Turnoaks Business Park, Off Storforth Lane, Chesterfield, Derbyshire, S40 2WB Tel: (01246) 277756 Fax: (01246) 273335

SCREWED WIRE COMPONENTS

▶ D F Smith & Co. Ltd, Unit 15 The Wallows Industrial Estate, Wallows Road, Brierley Hill, West Midlands, DY5 1QB Tel: (01384) 482958 Fax: (01384) 482958

SCREWS, *See also headings under Screws*

A C T (Fasteners & Components) Ltd, Units 13 & 16, Four Ashes Industrial Estate, Station Road, Four Ashes, Wolverhampton, WV10 7DB Tel: (01902) 791880 Fax: (01902) 791884 E-mail: info@actfasteners.co.uk

▶ A D A Fastfix Ltd, 5 Parkhouse Business Centre, Desborough Park Road, Parkhouse Business Centre, High Wycombe, Buckinghamshire, HP12 3DJ Tel: (0870) 7207100 Fax: (0870) 7207120 E-mail: alan@adafastfix.co.uk

Abec Fixings Ltd, Unit 22 Small Heath Trading Estate, Armoury Road, Birmingham, B11 2RJ Tel: 0121-683 0061 Fax: 0121-683 0064 E-mail: sales@abecfixings.co.uk

Acorn Fasteners Ltd, Unit W4 Lambs Business Park, Tilburstow Hill Road, South Godstone, Godstone, Surrey, RH9 8LJ Tel: (01342) 893500 Fax: (01342) 892820 E-mail: sales@acornfastenersltd.co.uk

Alfast Engineering Supplies Ltd, 2 Gloucester Road, Luton, LU1 3HX Tel: (01582) 418498 Fax: (01582) 418833 E-mail: sales@alfast.co.uk

Allfix Ltd, 2 Leyland Road, Poole, Dorset, BH12 5HB Tel: (01202) 519066 Fax: (01202) 518353 E-mail: sales@allfix.co.uk

▶ Anixter Industrial - Barrow, Unit 2D Ashburner Way, Walney Road Industrial Estate, Barrow-In-Furness, Cumbria, LA14 5UZ Tel: (01229) 825871 Fax: (01229) 827442

Anixter Industrial - Chesterfield, Brimington Road North, Chesterfield, Derbyshire, S41 9BE Tel: (01246) 452188 Fax: (01246) 455778 E-mail: chesterfield.sales@alistairindustrial.com

Armstrong Fastenings Ltd, PO Box 6, Wednesbury, West Midlands, WS10 8UL Tel: 0121-224 2000 Fax: 0121-224 2007 E-mail: info@armfast.com

Asco Fixings Ltd, Colliery Road, West Bromwich, West Midlands, B71 4JT Tel: 0121-553 1177 Fax: 0121-553 1199 E-mail: info@ascofixings.co.uk

Ashby Engineering Co., 8 Surbiton Hill Road, Surbiton, Surrey, KT6 4TP Tel: (020) 8399 4034 Fax: (020) 8390 4947 E-mail: ashbyeng@aol.com

Bapp Industrial Supplies Lancs Ltd, Trafalgar Centre, Belfield Road, Rochdale, Lancashire, OL16 2UX Tel: (01706) 359500 Fax: (01706) 640270

Bapp Industrial Supplies Preston Ltd, 57 Roman Way Industrial Estate, Ribbleton, Preston, PR2 5BE Tel: (01772) 704700 Fax: (01772) 704701

Barnket Ltd, 128 Milton Road, Gravesend, Kent, DA12 2PG Tel: (01474) 327576 Fax: (01474) 567318

Belmey Industrial Supplies, Unit 12 & 17 Oldbury Business Centre, Oldbury Road, Cwmbran, Gwent, NP44 3JU Tel: (01633) 872474 Fax: (01633) 875557 E-mail: sales@belmey.co.uk

Bonner-Regis Manufacturing Ltd, High Street, Princes End, Tipton, West Midlands, DY4 9HR Tel: 0121-522 2616 Fax: 0121-557 6864 E-mail: sales@regis-bolt.co.uk

Bradleys Rivets Ltd, Unit 8b Reddicap Trading Estate, Sutton Coldfield, West Midlands, B75 7BU Tel: 0121-326 7468 Fax: 0121-327 1092 E-mail: enquiries@bradleysrivets.com

Carn Fasteners Ltd, 29 Garvagh Road, Swatragh, Maghera, County Londonderry, BT46 5QE Tel: (028) 7940 1248 Fax: (028) 7940 1533 E-mail: info@carnfasteners.com

Challenge Europe Ltd, Shuttleworth Road, Elm Farm Industrial Estate, Bedford, MK41 0EP Tel: (01234) 346242 Fax: (01234) 327349 E-mail: sales@challenge-indfast.co.uk

Charnwood Fasteners Ltd, F27-30 Trading Estate, Cumberland Road, Loughborough, Leicestershire, LE11 5DF Tel: (01509) 237280 Fax: (01509) 262428

Clerkenwell Screws Ltd, 107-109 Clerkenwell Road, London, EC1R 5BY Tel: (020) 7405 1215 Fax: (020) 7831 3057

Commando Fasteners Co. Ltd, 3 Canal Street, Stourbridge, West Midlands, DY8 4LU Tel: (01384) 393949 Fax: (01384) 393933 E-mail: info@comfast.co.uk

Danfast, English Street, Hull, HU3 2DZ Tel: (01482) 599333 Fax: (01482) 599321 E-mail: enquiries@danfast.co.uk

Elite Engineering, 9 Neptune Works, Upper Trinity Street, Birmingham, B9 4EG Tel: 0121-772 8070 Fax: 0121-772 2230

Elmor Supplies Ltd, 104 Branbridges Road, East Peckham, Tonbridge, Kent, TN12 5HH Tel: (01622) 871870 Fax: (01622) 872024

F K Moore & Son Ltd, 5 Wilton Road, Haine Industrial Park, Ramsgate, Kent, CT12 5HD Tel: (01843) 593440 Fax: (01843) 585883 E-mail: sales@fkmoore.co.uk

Fastener Warehouse Ltd, 5 Ambassador Industrial Estate, 9 Airfield Road, Christchurch, Dorset, BH23 3TG Tel: (01202) 479621 Fax: (01202) 477222 E-mail: sales@fastenerwarehouse.co.uk

Fincham Fasteners, 18 Industrial Estate, Sanders Road, Bromsgrove, Worcestershire, B61 7DG Tel: (01527) 875413 Fax: (01527) 875413 E-mail: sales@finchamfasteners.com

G I Fasteners Ltd, 8 Windmill Road Industrial Estate, Windmill Road, Loughborough, Leicestershire, LE11 1RA Tel: (01509) 260747 Fax: (01509) 217945

Glenwood Bolts, 2 Lintech Court, The Grip, Linton, Cambridge, CB21 4XN Tel: (01223) 893931 Fax: (01223) 894122 E-mail: glenwoodbolts@talk21.com

Henry Halstead Ltd, 492 Holly Place, Walton Summit, Bamber Bridge, Preston, PR5 8AX Tel: (01772) 339521 Fax: (01772) 332233 E-mail: sales@henry-halstead.co.uk

Haroby Ltd, Unit 139 Bradley Hall Trading Estate, Bradley Lane, Standish, Wigan, Lancashire, WN6 0XQ Tel: (01257) 478100 Fax: (01257) 478109 E-mail: fasteners@haroby.co.uk

I L S Ltd, Third Avenue, Pensnett Trading Estate, Kingswinford, West Midlands, DY6 7XX Tel: (01384) 402200 Fax: (01384) 402201 E-mail: marketing@ilsonline.com

Industrial Fasteners Ltd, Chilcott Avenue, Brynmenyn Industrial Estate, Brynmenyn, Bridgend, CF32 9RQ Tel: (01656) 724775 Fax: (01656) 729612

▶ Industrial Fasteners Ltd, Unit 10 Sundon Business Park, Dencora Way, Luton, LU3 3HP Tel: (01582) 563100 Fax: (01582) 563040 E-mail: sales@anixterfasteners.com

▶ Industrial Fasteners Ltd, 7 Bell Park Bell Close, Newnham Industrial Estate, Plympton, Plymouth, PL7 4TA Tel: (01752) 341100 Fax: (01752) 346012

▶ Industrial Fasteners Ltd, 6 Station Road, Thatcham, Berkshire, RG19 4RB Tel: (01635) 865885 Fax: (01635) 871511

Gilbert Laurence Ltd, 1 Union Buildings, Wallingford Road, Uxbridge, Middlesex, UB8 2FR Tel: (01895) 455980 Fax: (01895) 455999 E-mail: sales@gilbertlaurence.co.uk

Lazer Vix Ltd, Turner Buildings, Russell Road, Birkenhead, Merseyside, CH42 1LU Tel: 0151-644 8860 Fax: 0151-643 1204

Leyton Fasteners Ltd, 9-15 Cook Street, Ellesmere Port, CH65 4AU Tel: 0151-355 8045 Fax: 0151-356 1885 E-mail: sales@leytonfasteners.co.uk

London Screw Co. Ltd, Park Lane, Halesowen, West Midlands, B63 2QY Tel: (01384) 569832 Fax: (01384) 410296 E-mail: sales@londonscrew.com

M D Fasteners Ltd, 129 Smiths Lane, Windsor, Berkshire, SL4 5PF Tel: (01753) 855773 Fax: (05600) 759015 E-mail: mdkfateners@yahoo.co.uk

M G H Industries Ltd, Lancaster House, Old Wellington Road, Eccles, Manchester, M30 9QG Tel: 0161-707 7690 Fax: 0161-707 7701 E-mail: sales@nultz-boltz.co.uk

Masons Fasteners Ltd, 3-4 Doris Road, Bordesley Green, Birmingham, B9 4SJ Tel: 0121-766 7500 Fax: 0121-766 8551

Mid Essex Fasteners Ltd, Beehive Lane Works, Beehive Lane, Chelmsford, CM2 9TE Tel: (01245) 257323 Fax: (01245) 252460 E-mail: midessexfasteners@btinternet.com

Modern Screws Ltd, 5 Dartford Road, Bexley, Kent, DA5 2BH Tel: (01322) 553224 Fax: (01322) 555093 E-mail: sales@modern-screws.co.uk

Nu Screw & Nut, 311 Neasden La North, London, NW10 0AG Tel: (020) 8452 8633 Fax: (020) 8452 2987 E-mail: sales@nu-screw.co.uk

Nufast Ltd, 17 Hayward Industrial Estate, Vigo Place Aldridge, Walsall, WS9 8UG Tel: (01922) 740360 Fax: (01922) 453610 E-mail: sales@nufast.co.uk

Olympus Distribution Ltd, Olympus Drive, Great Bridge, Tipton, West Midlands, DY4 7HY Tel: 0121-522 5600 Fax: 0121-522 5601 E-mail: sales@olympusdistribution.com

P A Hill Fasteners Ltd, 25 Sherwood Road, Bromsgrove, Worcestershire, B60 3DR Tel: (01527) 575838 Fax: (01527) 870419 E-mail: sales@pahillfasteners.co.uk

P & M Fixings, Franchise Street, Wednesbury, West Midlands, WS10 9RG Tel: 0121-526 5775 Fax: 0121-568 6108 E-mail: info@pmfixings.com

Paget Ltd, 115 Penarth Road, Cardiff, CF11 6JU Tel: (029) 2022 2552 Fax: (029) 2037 8439

Rapid Industrial Fasteners Ltd, 9 Gun Barrel Industrial Centre, Hayseech, Cradley Heath, West Midlands, B64 7JZ Tel: 0121-501 3903 Fax: 0121-585 5163 E-mail: sales@rapidfast.co.uk

RSR Fasteners Ltd, 2 Pasadena Close, Hayes, Middlesex, UB3 3NQ Tel: (020) 8756 1818 Fax: (020) 8756 1819 E-mail: sales@rsrfasteners.co.uk

S De Saulles & Son Ltd, St Johns Road, Stourbridge, West Midlands, DY8 1YS Tel: (01384) 393151 Fax: (01384) 393152

Smart Screw Ltd, Portland House, Floodgate Street, Digbeth, Birmingham, B5 5SL Tel: 0121-772 2115 Fax: 0121-766 5828 E-mail: sales@smartscrew.co.uk

Staytite Ltd, Unit B Coronation Road, Cressex BSNS Park, High Wycombe, Buckinghamshire, HP12 4PR Tel: (01494) 462322 Fax: (01494) 464747 E-mail: fasteners@staytite.com

Stones Bros, Garratt Street, Brierley Hill, West Midlands, DY5 1JU Tel: (01384) 79888 Fax: (01384) 77966

Supa Roofing & Power Tools Ltd, Aller Mills, Aller Road, Kingskerswell, Newton Abbot, Devon, TQ12 5AU Tel: (01803) 873288 Fax: (01803) 875277 E-mail: clive@suparoofing.co.uk

Swift Screw Products, Dunmore, Alexandra Park Avenue, Belfast, BT15 3GD Tel: (028) 9077 0721 Fax: (028) 9037 0914 E-mail: sales@swiftscrewproducts.co.uk

The Tenable Screw Co. Ltd, Tenable House, Torrington Avenue, Coventry, CV4 9HN Tel: (024) 7669 4422 Fax: (024) 7647 0029 E-mail: sales@tenable.co.uk

The Tenable Screw Co. Ltd, Elcot Lane, Marlborough, Wiltshire, SN8 2AE Tel: (01672) 512900 Fax: (01672) 513915 E-mail: sales@tenable.co.uk

Tigges UK Ltd, Unit 13, Road 32, Telford, Shropshire, TF1 7EU Tel: (01952) 670173 Fax: (01952) 670190 E-mail: tigges@icom-web.com

Universal Manufacturing Supplies, 25 Whitehorse Street, Baldock, Hertfordshire, SG7 6QB Tel: (01462) 892277 Fax: (01462) 892277

Westgate Fastenings, Gapton Hall Industrial Estate, Viking Road, Great Yarmouth, Norfolk, NR31 0NU Tel: (01493) 603207 Fax: (01493) 656284 E-mail: westgatefastenings@connectfree.co.uk

Westwood Bolt & Nut Co. Ltd, Claypit Lane, West Bromwich, West Midlands, B70 9UP Tel: 0121 5532405

Wurth (UK) Ltd, 1 Centurion Way, Erith, Kent, DA18 4AE Tel: (0870) 5987841 Fax: (0870) 5987842 E-mail: info@wurth.co.uk

SCREWS TO SPECIFICATION

Burntwood Fasteners Ltd, Hawks Green Business Park, Cannock, Staffordshire, WS11 7XN Tel: (01543) 572731 Fax: (01543) 572735 E-mail: sales@burntwoodfasteners.co.uk

SCREWS, HEX-SOCKET

Brocol Engineers Supplies Ltd, 58 Hotchkiss Way, Binley Industrial Estate, Binley Industrial Estate, Coventry, CV3 2RL Tel: (024) 7644 1303 Fax: (024) 7644 1353 E-mail: sales@gtssltd.co.uk

SCREWS, NUMBER PLATE

▶ G T Grafix, PO Box 154, Ashton-Under-Lyne, Lancashire, OL6 6WB Tel: (0845) 8385167 E-mail: info@gtgrafix.com

▶ The Private Plate Co., PO Box 77, Swansea, SA7 9YR Tel: (01639) 888833 Fax: (01639) 888844 E-mail: sales@myownplate.co.uk

SCRUBBING COLUMNS

▶ Eta Process Plant, King Street, Fenton, Stoke-on-Trent, ST4 2LT Tel: (01782) 744561 Fax: (01782) 602293 E-mail: tracey.bagley@etapp.com

SCSI COMPONENTS

Star Computer Services (U K) Ltd, Unit 21 Woodside Park, Rugby, Warwickshire, CV21 2NP Tel: (01788) 551522 Fax: (01788) 551523

SCUBA DIVING EQUIPMENT

▶ Canary Divers, 188 Burnley Road, Blackburn, BB1 3HW Tel: (01254) 696690 Fax: (01254) 696690 E-mail: info@canarydivers.com

▶ Divebitz, The Shop, High Street, Brasted, Westerham, Kent, TN16 1JA Tel: (01959) 569960 Fax: (01959) 562353 E-mail: info@divebitz.com

▶ DiveLife, 151 Bury New Road, Whitefield, Manchester, M45 6AA Tel: 0161 7960300 E-mail: info@divelife.co.uk

▶ The Outdoor Pursuits Co-operative, 22-24 Radford Street, Stone, Staffordshire, ST15 8DA Tel: (01785) 818500

▶ Worcester Urban Scuba, The Stables, Upper Battenhall, Worcester, WR7 4RU Tel: (07971) 032679 E-mail: info@urbanscuba.com

SCULPTOR'S TOOLS

Alec Tiranti Ltd, 3 Pipers Court, Berkshire Drive, Thatcham, Berkshire, RG19 4ER Tel: 0118-930 2775 Fax: (0845) 1232101 E-mail: enquiries@tiranti.co.uk

SCULPTURES

Lakeland Mouldings, Soulby, Penrith, Cumbria, CA11 0JE Tel: (01768) 486989 Fax: (01768) 486989 E-mail: ann@lakelandmouldings.co.uk

Reflection Art Furniture, Tresparrett, Camelford, Cornwall, PL32 9ST Tel: (01840) 261212 Fax: (01840) 261212 E-mail: cornishfunky@aol.com

Stef's Models, Reeth Dale Centre, Silver Street, Reeth, Richmond, North Yorkshire, DL11 6SP Tel: (01748) 884498 Fax: (01748) 884334 E-mail: sales@stefsmodels.co.uk

SEA FREIGHT FORWARDERS

▶ A G International Freight Ltd, Claybrook Drive, Washford Industrial Estate, Redditch, Worcestershire, B98 0DT Tel: (01527) 838520 Fax: (01527) 838529 E-mail: stevec@avon-groupage.co.uk

▶ Cargo Overseas Ltd, Room 110 Building 308, World Freight Terminal, Manchester Airport, Manchester, M90 5PZ Tel: 0161-498 6111 Fax: 0161-498 6222 E-mail: groche@cargo-overseas.co.uk

Cromac Smith Ltd, 34-40 Warwick Road, Kenilworth, Warwickshire, CV8 1HE Tel: (01926) 865800 Fax: (01926) 865808 E-mail: albatros@cromacsmith.com

Global Logistics Systems Ltd, 448 Oakshot Place, Bamber Bridge, Preston, PR5 8AT Tel: (01772) 626400 Fax: (01772) 627251

Porter & Laker, Dissegna House, Weston Avenue, West Thurrock, Grays, Essex, RM20 3ZP Tel: (01708) 689400 Fax: (01708) 689401

▶ Premier, 24 Brunel Way, Fareham, Hampshire, PO15 5SD Tel: (01489) 565577 Fax: (01489) 565588 E-mail: sales@psap.co.uk

▶ Uneek Freight Services Ltd, Amberley Way, Hounslow, TW4 6BH Tel: (020) 8569 4949 Fax: (020) 8569 5101 E-mail: info@uneekfreight.com

SEA FREIGHT FORWARDERS – *continued*

▶ Viamaster International Ltd, Valley Farm Way, Leeds, LS10 1SE Tel: 0113-270 0033 Fax: 0113 270 0065 E-mail: mail@viamaster-intl.com

SEAFOOD

Anchor Seafoods Ltd, Devonshire House, High Street, Handcross, Haywards Heath, West Sussex, RH17 6BJ Tel: (01444) 400363 Fax: (01444) 400949 E-mail: sales@anchorseafoods.com

SEAL DISTRIBUTORS OR AGENTS (HYDRAULIC/OIL/FLUID)

A B Seals, Unit 15 Canal Industrial Park, Canal Road, Gravesend, Kent, DA12 2PA Tel: (01474) 350777 Fax: (01474) 533314 E-mail: sales@abseals.com

A N Hydraulics, Sandlow Green Farm, Marsh Lane, Holmes Chapel, Crewe, CW4 8AS Tel: (01477) 533522 Fax: (01477) 533522

▶ Action Seals Ltd, Westfield Road, Wallasey, Merseyside, CH44 7JA Tel: 0151-652 6661 Fax: 0151-653 4994 E-mail: sales@actionseals.co.uk

Aire Bearings, 34 Bradford Road, Stanningley, Pudsey, West Yorkshire, LS28 6DD Tel: 0113-256 5676 Fax: 0113-255 4894 E-mail: sales@airebearings.co.uk

M. Barnwell Services Ltd, 5 Bessemer Crescent, Rabans Lane Industrial Estate, Aylesbury, Buckinghamshire, HP19 8TF Tel: (01296) 431429 Fax: (01296) 435716 E-mail: aylesbury@barnwell.co.uk

Bearing Factors, Progress Road, Whitewalls Industrial Estate, Nelson, Lancashire, BB9 8TE Tel: (01282) 693540 Fax: (01282) 691881 E-mail: sales@bearingfactors.co.uk

C B S Rotary Power Motion Ltd, Unit 14 Grandstand Business Centre, Westfields Trading Estate, Hereford, HR4 9NS Tel: (01432) 276630 Fax: (01432) 357140 E-mail: hereford@cbs-rpm.co.uk

City Seals & Bearings Ltd, Stevenson Road, Sheffield, S9 3XG Tel: 0114-244 3030 Fax: 0114-244 0044 E-mail: info@cityseals.co.uk

Clarendon Engineering Ltd, 30 High Street, Earl Shilton, Leicester, LE9 7DG Tel: (01455) 841200 Fax: (01455) 841110 E-mail: sales@clarendoneng.co.uk

F T L Seals Technology, Leeds Twenty-Seven Business Park, Bruntcliffe Avenue, Morley, Leeds, LS27 0TG Tel: 0113-252 1061 Fax: 0113-252 2627 E-mail: tonys@ftlseals.co.uk

Gulf Coast Seal (UK) Ltd, 2 Seaforth Road South, Hillington, Glasgow, G52 4PB Tel: 0141-302 5000 Fax: 0141-302 5100

Manchester Seals, Hilmar House, 5 Girton Street, Salford, M7 1UR Tel: 0161-832 7922 Fax: 0161-833 1637 E-mail: sally@manchesterseals.co.uk

M-Tec, 3 Craven Court, Canada Road, Byfleet, West Byfleet, Surrey, KT14 7JL Tel: (01932) 354100 Fax: (01932) 340200 E-mail: m.tec@lineone.net

O S L Group Ltd, Imperial Works, Sheffield Road, Tinsley, Sheffield, S9 2YL Tel: 0114-221 2500 Fax: 0114-221 2560 E-mail: sales@oslgroup.com

S C H Bearings & Power Transmission, Unit 1 Great Bridge Business Park, Unit 1 Greatbridge Busn Park, Budds Lane, Romsey, Hampshire, SO51 0HA Tel: (01794) 830377 Fax: (01794) 830366 E-mail: sales@schgroup.com

Seals & Components Ltd, Village Road, Norton, Shifnal, Shropshire, TF11 9ED Tel: (01952) 730685 Fax: (01952) 730665

Sealtight Gaskets Ltd, Unit 15 Calow Brook Drive, Hasland, Chesterfield, Derbyshire, S41 0DR Tel: (01246) 222400 Fax: (01246) 222401 E-mail: harveyslack@supernet.com

Supaseal (U K) Ltd, PO Box 5329, Market Harborough, Leicestershire, LE16 7PT Tel: (01858) 434141 Fax: (01858) 434717 E-mail: admin@supaseal.co.uk

Derek Timms Seals Ltd, 90 Evelyn Road, Birmingham, B11 3JJ Tel: 0121-773 7666 Fax: 0121-766 5590 E-mail:

Universal Seals & Bearings Ltd, Waterloo Indust Park, Upper Brook Street, Stockport, Cheshire, SK1 3BP Tel: 0161-429 0287 Fax: 0161-477 2940

Vulcan Engineering Ltd, Troutbeck Road, Sheffield, S7 2QA Tel: 0114-249 3333 Fax: 0114-249 3322 E-mail: service@vulcan-eng.com

Wyko Seals Ltd, Hereward Rise, Halesowen Industrial Park, Halesowen, West Midlands, B62 8AN Tel: 0121-501 2021 Fax: 0121-501 3014 E-mail: sales@dichta.com

SEAL (MECHANICAL) DISTRIBUTORS OR AGENTS

Euroseals (Wirral), 26 Carrock Road, Bromborough, Wirral, Merseyside, CH62 3RA Tel: 0151-343 1020 Fax: 0151-343 1020 E-mail: euroseals@btconnect.com

F T L Seals Technology, Leeds Twenty-Seven Business Park, Bruntcliffe Avenue, Morley, Leeds, LS27 0TG Tel: 0113-252 1061 Fax: 0113-252 2627 E-mail: tonys@ftlseals.co.uk

▶ Fluid UK Ltd, 4 Falcongate Industrial Estate, Old Gorsey Lane, Wallasey, Merseyside, CH44 4HD Tel: 0151-638 0869 Fax: 0151-638 5800 E-mail: sales@fluideng.co.uk

▶ North West Seals & Profiles, 67 Stour Road, Tyldesley, Manchester, M29 7WB Tel: (01942) 731046 Fax: (01942) 745968 E-mail: sales@seals-profiles.co.uk

Norton Wells, 69 Bolton Road, Windsor, Berkshire, SL4 3JX Tel: (01753) 855336 Fax: (01753) 856727 E-mail: brett@nortonwells.com

South Coast Seals Services Ltd, 16 Fareham Enterprise Centre, Hackett Way, Fareham, Hampshire, PO14 1TH Tel: (01329) 230916 Fax: (01329) 823783

WGM Engineering Ltd, 1 Abbey Mill Business Centre, Paisley, Renfrewshire, PA1 1TJ Tel: 0141-889 1009 Fax: 0141-848 6257 E-mail: info@wgmltd.com

SEAL (MECHANICAL) MAINTENANCE/REPAIR/RECONDITIONING/REFURBISHMENT SERVICES

Euroseals (Wirral), 26 Carrock Road, Bromborough, Wirral, Merseyside, CH62 3RA Tel: 0151-343 1020 Fax: 0151-343 1020 E-mail: euroseals@btconnect.com

▶ Fluid UK Ltd, 4 Falcongate Industrial Estate, Old Gorsey Lane, Wallasey, Merseyside, CH44 4HD Tel: 0151-638 0869 Fax: 0151-638 5800 E-mail: sales@fluideng.co.uk

John Crane, Nash Road, Trafford Park, Manchester, M17 1SS Tel: 0161-872 2484 Fax: 0161-872 1654

Nash Mechanical Seal Services Ltd, Nile Street, Bolton, BL3 6DW Tel: (01204) 388030 Fax: (01204) 361541 E-mail: enquiry@nashseal.com

Norton Wells, 69 Bolton Road, Windsor, Berkshire, SL4 3JX Tel: (01753) 855336 Fax: (01753) 856727 E-mail: brett@nortonwells.com

RB Maintenance Services Ltd, Unit 28 Penley Industrial Estate, Penley, Wrexham, Clwyd, LL13 0LQ Tel: (01948) 830595 Fax: (01948) 830672 E-mail: rbms@ic24.net

Tekhniseal Ltd, Unit 1 Priestley Road, Worsley, Manchester, M28 2LY Tel: 0161-794 6063 Fax: 0161-794 4773 E-mail: tekhniseal@btconnect.com

SEAL (MECHANICAL) MANUFRS, *See also headings for particular types under Seals, Mechanical etc*

Acumen Seales, Wharton House, Wharton Lane, Little Hulton, Manchester, M38 9XF Tel: 0161-703 9999 Fax: 0161-703 9988 E-mail: office@acumenseals.co.uk

John Crane UK Ltd, Buckingham House, 361-366 Buckingham Avenue, Slough, SL1 4LU Tel: (01753) 224000 Fax: (01753) 224224

Cross Manufacturing Co 1938 Ltd, Midford Road, Bath, BA2 5RR Tel: (01225) 837000 Fax: (01225) 834115 E-mail: mail@crossmanufacturing.com

▶ Eagleburgmann Industries UK, Welton Road, Warwick, CV34 5PZ Tel: (01926) 417600 Fax: (01926) 417617 E-mail: sales@burgmann.co.uk

First4seals P.L.C., Mount Street, Bradford, West Yorkshire, BD3 9SN Tel: (01274) 720775 Fax: (01274) 729022 E-mail: seals@first4seals.com

Flowserve Ltd, Dakota Avenue, Salford, M50 2PU Tel: 0161-869 1200 Fax: 0161-869 1235

John Crane, Nash Road, Trafford Park, Manchester, M17 1SS Tel: 0161-872 2484 Fax: 0161-872 1654

Mechanical Seals, Swinton, Manchester, M27 8UJ Tel: 0161-3 516666

Norton Wells, 69 Bolton Road, Windsor, Berkshire, SL4 3JX Tel: (01753) 855336 Fax: (01753) 856727 E-mail: brett@nortonwells.com

Pamargan Products Ltd, Unit 47 Mochdre Industrial Estate, Mochdre, Newtown, Powys, SY16 4LE Tel: (01686) 625181 Fax: (01686) 627849 E-mail: info@pamargan.co.uk

Pioneer Weston, Smithfold Lane, Worsley, Manchester, M28 0GP Tel: 0161-703 2000 Fax: 0161-703 2025 E-mail: info@pwi-ltd.com

RB Maintenance Services Ltd, Unit 28 Penley Industrial Estate, Penley, Wrexham, Clwyd, LL13 0LQ Tel: (01948) 830595 Fax: (01948) 830672 E-mail: rbms@ic24.net

Roplan Ltd, 2 Enterprise Court, Rarking Rd, Daneshill West, Newbury, Berkshire, RG20 4SW Tel: (01635) 299091 Fax: (01635) 298505 E-mail: enquiries@roplan.com

Tekhniseal Ltd, Unit 1 Priestley Road, Worsley, Manchester, M28 2LY Tel: 0161-794 6063 Fax: 0161-794 4773 E-mail: tekhniseal@btconnect.com

Trelleborg Cealing Solutions UK, Unit 6 Dyffryn Industrial Estate, Pool Road, Newtown, Powys, SY16 3RD Tel: (01686) 617000 Fax: (01686) 624875

Vulcan Engineering Ltd, Troutbeck Road, Sheffield, S7 2QA Tel: 0114-249 3333 Fax: 0114-249 3322 E-mail: service@vulcan-eng.com

SEAL (PTFE) MANUFRS

Advanced Products (Seals & Gaskets) Ltd, Unit 25C, Number One Industrial Estate, Consett, Co. Durham, DH8 6SR Tel: (01207) 500317 Fax: (01207) 501210 E-mail: gc@advancedproducts.co.uk

Amar Specialised Plastics Ltd, Unit G Alpha Centre, Babbage Road, Totnes, Devon, TQ9 5JA Tel: (01803) 868077 Fax: (01803) 863399 E-mail: amar@specialisedplastics.co.uk

▶ Beldam Crossley Ltd, PO Box 7, Bolton, BL1 6PB Tel: (01204) 494711 Fax: (01204) 493203 E-mail: sales@beldam-crossley.co.uk

Claron Hydraulic Services, Alders Way, Yalberton Industrial Estate, Paignton, Devon, TQ4 7QL Tel: (01803) 528852 Fax: (01803) 525134 E-mail: sales@claron.co.uk

Hoerbiger, Edderthorpe Street, Bradford, West Yorkshire, BD3 9RB Tel: (01274) 733801 Fax: (01274) 736887 E-mail: sales@hrpu.co.uk

Pioneer Weston, Smithfold Lane, Worsley, Manchester, M28 0GP Tel: 0161-703 2000 Fax: 0161-703 2025 E-mail: info@pwi-ltd.com

▶ SKF Economos UK Ltd, 83 Buckingham Avenue, Trading Estate, Slough, SL1 4PN Tel: (01753) 696565 Fax: (01753) 696181 E-mail: uk.sales@economos.com

SEALANT APPLICATION EQUIPMENT

Flexible Heating Hoses Ltd, Unit Z Sapcote Trading Centre, 68 Wyrley Road, Aston, Birmingham, B6 7BN Tel: 0121-250 2525 Fax: 0121-250 2526 E-mail: sales@flexible-heated-hoses.co.uk

Liquid Control Ltd, Stewarts Road, Finedon Road Industrial Estate, Wellingborough, Northamptonshire, NN8 4RJ Tel: (01933) 277571 Fax: (01933) 440273 E-mail: sales@liquidcontrol.co.uk

P C Cox Ltd, Turnpike Industrial Estate, Newbury, Berkshire, RG14 2LR Tel: (01635) 264500 Fax: (01635) 264555 E-mail: sales@pccox.co.uk

Sealant Techniques Ltd, Harvey Road, Basildon, Essex, SS13 1EP Tel: (01268) 726500 Fax: (01268) 590226

Wilson UK Ltd, Unit 3 Bloxwich Lane Industrial Estate, Bloxwich Lane, Walsall, WS2 8TF Tel: (01922) 725800 Fax: (01922) 649888 E-mail: uksales@wilsononline.com

SEALANT TEST/RESEARCH SERVICES/LABORATORIES

E E F, Broadway House, Cothill Street, London, SW1H 9NQ Tel: (020) 7222 7777 Fax: (020) 7343 3190 E-mail: enquires@eef-fed.org.uk

SEALANTS, *See also headings for particular types*

Adshead Ratcliffe & Co. Ltd, 4 Woodford Trading Estate, Southend Road, Woodford Green, Essex, IG8 8HG Tel: (020) 8551 0031 Fax: (020) 8550 2142

▶ Anixper Luton, Unit 10, Sundon Business Park, Dencora Way, Luton, LU3 3HP Tel: (01582) 491748 Fax: (01582) 491280 E-mail: luton.adesco@infast.com

Construction Sealants Ltd, 59 Warwick Road, Rainham, Essex, RM13 9XU Tel: (01708) 631421 Fax: (01708) 631407

▶ Gluemart Ltd, Robins Farm, Matson Lane, Matson, Gloucester, GL4 6DZ Tel: (01452) 423883 Fax: (01452) 308229 E-mail: sales@gluemart.co.uk

Hookings Mastics Ltd, Unit B11 Suttons Business Park, New Road, Rainham, Essex, RM13 8DE Tel: (01708) 522090 Fax: (01708) 526147 E-mail: ken@hookingsmastics.com

Seal Service Ltd, 1 & 2 Kingfisher Court, Kestrel Close, Quarry Hill Industrial Estate, Ilkeston, Derbyshire, DE7 4RD Tel: 0115-932 4308 Fax: 0115-944 0279

Sealant Techniques Ltd, Harvey Road, Basildon, Essex, SS13 1EP Tel: (01268) 726500 Fax: (01268) 590226

Tecseal Ltd, 4 East Chorley Business Centre, East Way, Chorley, Lancashire, PR6 0BJ Tel: (01257) 249933 Fax: (01257) 249944

Thermocrete, Mortimer Street, Bradford, West Yorkshire, BD8 9RL Tel: (01274) 544442 Fax: (01274) 484448 E-mail: thermocretehq@aol.com

Unibond, Apollo Court, 2 Bishops Square Business Park, Hatfield, Hertfordshire, AL10 9EY Tel: (01707) 289041 Fax: (01707) 289099

SEALED LEAD ACID BATTERY CHARGERS

Dartpoint Ltd, Unit 1b Kitewell Lane, Lydd, Romney Marsh, Kent, TN29 9LP Tel: (01797) 320910 Fax: (01797) 320571 E-mail: sales@dartpoint.co.uk

SEALING CABLE GLANDS

Plastube Ltd, The Old Foundry, Leech Street, Stalybridge, Cheshire, SK15 1SD Tel: 0161-338 5505 Fax: 0161-338 5502 E-mail: admin@plastube.co.uk

SEALING RINGS

Adminglade Ltd, Caxton House, Stoke Street, Sheffield, S9 3QH Tel: 0114-244 1932 Fax: 0114-244 1932

Cross Manufacturing Co 1938 Ltd, Midford Road, Bath, BA2 5RR Tel: (01225) 837000 Fax: (01225) 834115 E-mail: mail@crossmanufacturing.com

Helical Technology Ltd, Dock Road, Lytham, Lancashire, FY8 5AQ Tel: (01253) 733122 Fax: (01253) 794880 E-mail: sales@helical-technology.co.uk

Hoerbiger, Edderthorpe Street, Bradford, West Yorkshire, BD3 9RB Tel: (01274) 733801 Fax: (01274) 736887 E-mail: sales@hrpu.co.uk

Wills Engineered Polymers Ltd, Dunball Park, Dunball, Bridgwater, Somerset, TA6 4TP Tel: (01278) 686800 Fax: (01278) 686848 E-mail:

SEALS, *See also headings for particular types under Seals*

Dantec Ltd, Tarran Way, Tarran Industrial Estate, Wirral, Merseyside, CH46 4TL Tel: 0151-678 2222 Fax: 0151-606 0188 E-mail: sales@dantec.ltd.uk

Dichtomatik Ltd, Donington House, Riverside Road, Pride Park, Derby, DE24 8HY Tel: (01332) 202121 Fax: (01332) 524404 E-mail: mail@dichtomatik.co.uk

East Anglian Sealing Co. Ltd, Units 4 & 5, Goldingham Hall, Bulmer, Sudbury, Suffolk, CO10 7ER Tel: (01787) 880433 Fax: (0871) 4338858 E-mail: sales@easeals.co.uk

First4seals P.L.C., Mount Street, Bradford, West Yorkshire, BD3 9SN Tel: (01274) 720775 Fax: (01274) 729022 E-mail: seals@first4seals.com

Flexitallic Ltd, PO Box 3, Cleckheaton, West Yorkshire, BD19 5BT Tel: (01274) 851273 Fax: (01274) 851386 E-mail: ukmarketing@flexitallic.com

Gulf Coast Seal (UK) Ltd, 2 Seaforth Road South, Hillington, Glasgow, G52 4PB Tel: 0141-302 5000 Fax: 0141-302 5100

Linear Ltd, Coatham Avenue, Aycliffe Industrial Park, Newton Aycliffe, County Durham, DL5 6DB Tel: (01325) 310151 Fax: (01325) 307200 E-mail: enquiries@linear-ltd.com

Rafseal Ltd, Millers Avenue, Brynmenyn Industrial Estate, Brynmenyn, Bridgend, Mid Glamorgan, CF32 9TD Tel: (01656) 725118 Fax: (01656) 724520 E-mail: rafseal@btclick.com

Ram Gasket Solutions Ltd, Unit 14, Cardrew Indust Estate, Redruth, Cornwall, TR15 1SS Tel: (01209) 314700 Fax: (01209) 314900 E-mail: mailbox@ramgasket.co.uk

▶ SKF Economos U.K. Ltd, Unit 20 Avonbank Industrial Estate, West Town Rd, Bristol, BS11 9DE Tel: 0117-982 5729 Fax: 0117-982 5730 E-mail: bristol@economos.com

▶ SKF Economos U.K. Ltd, Unit B2, Connaught Business Centre, 22 Willow Lane, Mitcham, Surrey, CR4 4NA Tel: (020) 8648 0252 Fax: (020) 8648 0248 E-mail: mitcham@economos.com

▶ SKF Economos U.K. Ltd, Unit 32, Stirling Close, Pattinson South Industrial Estate, Washington, Tyne & Wear, NE38 3QD Tel: 0191-417 1094 Fax: 0191-417 1118 E-mail: washington@economos.com

▶ SKF Economos UK Ltd, 83 Buckingham Avenue, Trading Estate, Slough, SL1 4PN Tel: (01753) 696565 Fax: (01753) 696181 E-mail: uk.sales@economos.com

Wyko Seals Ltd, Hereward Rise, Halesowen Industrial Park, Halesowen, West Midlands, B62 8AN Tel: 0121-501 2021 Fax: 0121-501 3014 E-mail: sales@dichta.com

SEALS TO SPECIFICATION

A B Seals, Unit 15 Canal Industrial Park, Canal Road, Gravesend, Kent, DA12 2PA Tel: (01474) 350777 Fax: (01474) 533314 E-mail: sales@abseals.com

SEALS, BOTTLING/CANNING PLANT

▶ SKF Economos U.K. Ltd, Unit 20 Avonbank Industrial Estate, West Town Rd, Bristol, BS11 9DE Tel: 0117-982 5729 Fax: 0117-982 5730 E-mail: bristol@economos.com

SEALS, BOTTLING/CANNING PLANT

– *continued*

▶ SKF Economos U.K. Ltd, Unit 32, Stirling Close, Pattinson South Industrial Estate, Washington, Tyne & Wear, NE38 3QD Tel: 0191-417 1094 Fax: 0191-417 1118 E-mail: washington@economos.com

SEALS, HYDRAULIC/FLUID

Aldona Seals, 1 Brindley Road, South West Industrial Estate, Peterlee, County Durham, SR8 2LT Tel: 0191-518 1555 Fax: 0191-518 0555 E-mail: gtsm@gtgroup.co.uk

Blue Diamond Bearings Ltd, Rolwey House, School Close, Chandler's Ford, Eastleigh, Hampshire, SO53 4BY Tel: (023) 8025 8966 Fax: (023) 8025 8925 E-mail: bdsales@rolwey.com

Dli Seals Ltd, Unit A-D Trimdon Court, Trimdon Grange Industrial Estate, Trimdon Grange, Trimdon Station, County Durham, TS29 6PE Tel: (01429) 881660 Fax: (01429) 882299 E-mail: sales@dliseals.co.uk

Flemings Seals Ltd, Atlas Mills, Atlas Mill Road, Brighouse, West Yorkshire, HD6 1ES Tel: (01484) 718391 Fax: (01484) 711585 E-mail: sales@flemings-seals.co.uk

Hallite France Ltd, 130 Oldfield Road, Hampton, Middlesex, TW12 2HT Tel: (020) 8941 2244 Fax: (020) 8783 1669 E-mail: seals@hallite.com

Kea Flex Mouldings Ltd, Woolmer Way, Bordon, Hampshire, GU35 9QE Tel: (01420) 473645 Fax: (01420) 487498 E-mail: sales@kea-flex-mouldings.co.uk

▶ North West Seals & Profiles, 67 Stour Road, Tyldesley, Manchester, M29 7WB Tel: (01942) 731046 Fax: (01942) 745968 E-mail: sales@seals-profiles.co.uk

Polyurethane Progress Ltd, Church Street, Wakefield, West Yorkshire, WF1 5QY Tel: (01924) 387310 Fax: (01924) 382951 E-mail: enquiries@polyurethane-progress.co.uk

Ramsay Services Ltd, Unit C Bamburgh Court, Team Valley Trading Estate, Gateshead, Tyne & Wear, NE11 0TX Tel: 0191-422 4200 Fax: 0191-422 4222

Sealing Solutions Ltd, 1 Wheatear, Perry Road, Witham, Essex, CM8 3YY Tel: (01376) 503633 Fax: (01376) 503733

Seals & Components Ltd, Village Road, Norton, Shifnal, Shropshire, TF11 9ED Tel: (01952) 730685 Fax: (01952) 730665

▶ SKF Economos UK Ltd, Unit 2 Airport Commerce Park, Howmoss Drive, Kirkhill Industrial Estate, Dyce, Aberdeen, AB21 0GL Tel: (01224) 725400 Fax: (01224) 725686 E-mail: aberdeen@economos.com

▶ SKF Economos UK Ltd, Unit 5-6, Armley Link, Armley Road, Leeds, LS12 2QN Tel: 0113-231 0303 Fax: 0113-231 0395 E-mail: leeds@economos.com

SEALS, PNEUMATIC/AIR

Polyurethane Progress Ltd, Church Street, Wakefield, West Yorkshire, WF1 5QY Tel: (01924) 387310 Fax: (01924) 382951 E-mail: enquiries@polyurethane-progress.co.uk

Sealing Solutions Ltd, 1 Wheatear, Perry Road, Witham, Essex, CM8 3YY Tel: (01376) 503633 Fax: (01376) 503733

▶ SKF Economos U.K. Ltd, Unit 17, Block D Wednesbury Trading Estate, Darlaston Rd, Wednesbury, W. Midlands, WS10 7JN Tel: 0121-505 2112 Fax: 0121-505 2045 E-mail: wednesbury@economos.com

SEAM WELDING MACHINES

Specialized & General Welding, Unit 35 The Wallows Industrial Estate, Brierley Hill, West Midlands, DY5 1QA Tel: (01384) 480408 Fax: (01384) 480828

SEAMLESS CASINGS

Carrack Ltd, Badentoy Crescent, Badentoy Industrial Estate, Portlethen, Aberdeen, AB12 4YD Tel: (01224) 783100 Fax: (01224) 783400 E-mail: sandym@carrackltd.com

Vallourec Mannesmann Oil & Gas UK Ltd, 4 Prospect Place, Westhill, Aberdeenshire, AB32 6SY Tel: (01224) 279340 Fax: (01224) 279341 E-mail: info@vmog.co.uk

SEARCH ENGINE PLACEMENT SERVICES

▶ Breathing Space Advertising Directory & Search Shop, Breathing Space Head OfficeHarbertonford, Two Stepps Cottage Studios, Old Road, Harbertonford, Totnes, Devon, TQ9 7TE Tel: (01803) 732171 E-mail: directory@breathingspacedevon.com

▶ Upthejunction.Com, 3 Saxon Road, Hoylake, Wirral, Merseyside, CH47 3AE Tel: 0151-632 2451 E-mail: info@upthejunction.com

SEASHELL JEWELLERY

Aetee Ltd, Unit 11 Spring Mill Industrial Estate, Avening Road, Nailsworth, Stroud, Gloucestershire, GL6 0BS Tel: (01453) 835857 Fax: (01453) 836009 E-mail: admin@aetee.com

SEAT CONTRACTORS, TIERED/ TIP-UP/STADIUM

Arena Seating Ltd, Membury, Lambourn Woodlands, Hungerford, Berkshire, RG17 7TQ Tel: (01488) 674800 Fax: (01488) 674822 E-mail: info@arenaseating.com

SEAT STICKS

Boyco Co., Europa Way, Stockport, Cheshire, SK3 0XE Tel: 0161-428 7077

Noirit Ltd, 17-18 Hatherton Street, Walsall, WS4 2LE Tel: (01922) 625471 Fax: (01922) 722339 E-mail: sales@noirit.com

Stroud Metal Co. Ltd, Dudbridge, Stroud, Gloucestershire, GL5 3EZ Tel: (01453) 763331 Fax: (01453) 753804 E-mail: enquiries@stroudmetal.co.uk

SEATING, HOME THEATRE

▶ Reality Logic Ltd, 28 Harsfold Road, Rustington, Littlehampton, West Sussex, BN16 2QE Tel: (01903) 775352 Fax: (0870) 4589021 E-mail: jeremy.aston@realitylogic.com

SEATS

A C F Office Seating Collection, Wellington Street, Bury, Lancashire, BL8 2BD Tel: 0161-761 6889 Fax: 0161-761 6853

▶ Active Seating, 1 35 Brook Road, Rayleigh, Essex, SS6 7XJ Tel: (01268) 779991 Fax: (01268) 773289 E-mail: info@arrowoffice.co.uk

Arena Seating Ltd, Membury, Lambourn Woodlands, Hungerford, Berkshire, RG17 7TQ Tel: (01488) 674800 Fax: (01488) 674822 E-mail: info@arenaseating.com

Chapman Drivers Seating, 68 Burners Lane, Kiln Farm, Milton Keynes, MK11 3HD Tel: (01908) 265030 Fax: (01908) 265499

Edge Performance, 231 Shawfield Road, Ash, Aldershot, Hampshire, GU12 5DL Tel: (01252) 331888 Fax: (01252) 331888 E-mail: sales@edge-performance.co.uk

I E P Gardening Products, Unit 3 Budds Lane, Romsey, Hampshire, SO51 0HA Tel: (01794) 830899 Fax: (01794) 830923 E-mail: iepgp@btinternet.com

Isringhausen GB Ltd, Second Avenue, Redwither Industrial Complex, Redwither Business Park, Wrexham, Clwyd, LL13 9XQ Tel: (01978) 666300 Fax: (01978) 660192 E-mail: isrigb@isrigb.co.uk

▶ J & R Seating, 31 Heol Tir Coed, Penllergaer, Swansea, SA4 9QZ Tel: (01792) 899726

Komac, Unit 17-18, Narrowboat Way, Blackbrook Valley Indusrial Estate, Dudley, West Midlands, DY2 0XQ Tel: (01384) 481396 Fax: (01384) 481397

▶ Phoenix Seating, Second Avenue, Pensnett Trading Estate, Kingswinford, West Midlands, DY6 7UZ Tel: (01384) 296622 Fax: (01384) 287831

Profile Seating Ltd, Unit 11A, Fills Road, Willow Farm BusinessPark, Castle Donington, Derby, DE74 2US Tel: (01332) 817888 Fax: (01332) 817899 E-mail: mail@profileuk.com

T E K Seating Ltd, 7 Spa Industrial Park, Longfield Road, Tunbridge Wells, Kent, TN2 3EN Tel: (01892) 515028 Fax: (01892) 529751 E-mail: sales@tekseating.co.uk

▶ Tony Walker Interiors, Whitehall Court, 14 Telford Road, Edinburgh, EH4 2BA Tel: 0131-343 6151 Fax: 0131-332 4366 E-mail: enquiries@tonywalker.co.uk

SEATS, BUS/COACH

Cogent Passenger Seating Ltd, 12 Prydwen Road, Fforestfach, Swansea, SA5 4HN Tel: (01792) 585444 Fax: (01792) 588191 E-mail: enquiries@cogentseating.co.uk

The Comfy Seat Co., George Baylis Road, Berry Hill Industrial Estate, Droitwich, Worcestershire, WR9 9RB Tel: (01905) 795955 Fax: (01905) 794683 E-mail: sales@comfyseating.co.uk

Isringhausen GB Ltd, Second Avenue, Redwither Industrial Complex, Redwither Business Park, Wrexham, Clwyd, LL13 9XQ Tel: (01978) 666300 Fax: (01978) 660192 E-mail: isrigb@isrigb.co.uk

North West Seating Ltd, 5 Tower Enterprise Park, Great George Street, Wigan, Lancashire, WN3 4DP Tel: (01942) 244074 Fax: (01942) 244074 E-mail: northwestseating@lineone.net

R G Ergonomics Ltd, 7 Princewood Road, Earlstrees Industrial Estate, Corby, Northamptonshire, NN17 4AP Tel: (01536) 263691 Fax: (01536) 274988 E-mail: enquires@rgergonomics.co.uk

Rescroft Ltd, 20 Oxleasow Road, Redditch, Worcestershire, B98 0RE Tel: (01527) 521300 Fax: (01527) 521301 E-mail: enquiries@rescroft.com

Richards & Shaw (Trim) Ltd, 57 Cradley Road, Cradley Heath, West Midlands, B64 7BP Tel: (01384) 633800 Fax: (01384) 410791 E-mail: slynch@richards-shaw.co.uk

Scot Seats Direct, Gainford Business Centre, Fenwick, Kilmarnock, Ayrshire, KA3 6AR Tel: (01560) 600100 Fax: (01560) 600100 E-mail: gainford@lineone.net

SEATS, GENERAL/INDUSTRIAL, OFFICE/FACTORY ETC

A C F Office Seating Collection, Wellington Street, Bury, Lancashire, BL8 2BD Tel: 0161-761 6889 Fax: 0161-761 6853

B I Composites Halesowen Ltd, 270 Coombs Road, Halesowen, West Midlands, B62 8AA Tel: 0121-550 7577 Fax: 0121-585 5315 E-mail: bi-composites@bi-composites.co.uk

Entertainment Seating UK Ltd, 562-564 Lawmoor Street, Dixon Blazes Industrial Estate, Glasgow, G5 0TY Tel: 0141-420 1016 Fax: 0141-429 4661 E-mail: sales@entertainmentseating.co.uk

Inspire2Design Limited, 17C Mill Road, Stourport-on-Severn, Worcestershire, DY13 9BG Tel: (01299) 827646 E-mail: info@inspire2design.co.uk

Just Seating International Ltd, Croxdale, Durham, DH6 5HT Tel: (01325) 300123 Fax: (01388) 812416 E-mail: sales@justseating.co.uk

Pentos Office Furniture Ltd, Asher Lane, Pentrich, Ripley, Derbyshire, DE5 3RE Tel: (01773) 570700 Fax: (01773) 570160 E-mail: email@pentos-plc.co.uk

Stenochair Ltd, 30 Stilebrook Road, Industrial Estate, Olney, Buckinghamshire, MK46 5EA Tel: (01234) 711354 Fax: (01234) 713652 E-mail: sales@stenochair.co.uk

Timack NW Ltd, Premier Mill, Begonia Street, Darwen, Lancashire, BB3 2DP Tel: (01254) 775401 Fax: (01254) 703318 E-mail: sales@timack.co.uk

Tubular Furniture Ltd, Unit F1-F3, Coedcae Industrial Estate, Pontyclun, Mid Glamorgan, CF72 9HG Tel: (01443) 229326 Fax: (01443) 230493 E-mail: sales@tubular-furniture.co.uk

SEATS, TIERED/TIP-UP/STADIUM

Alto Tower Systems, 24 Walkers Road, North Moons, Moons Moat North Industrial Estate, Redditch, Worcestershire, B98 9HE Tel: (01527) 62946 Fax: (01527) 597444 E-mail: sales@alto-towers.co.uk

C P S Seating & Staging, Station Yard, Station Road, Bawtry, Doncaster, South Yorkshire, DN10 6QD Tel: (01302) 711183 Fax: (01302) 711171

Tubestyle Products Ltd, New John Street, Halesowen, West Midlands, B62 8HT Tel: 0121-561 5522 Fax: 0121-561 5834

Uni Seat Northern Contracts Ltd, Firlands Mills, South Parade, Pudsey, West Yorkshire, LS28 8AD Tel: 0113-255 9606 Fax: 0113-256 5088

SECONDARY WINDOWS

Selectaglaze Ltd, 1 Campfield Road, St. Albans, Hertfordshire, AL1 5HT Tel: (01727) 837271 Fax: (01727) 844053 E-mail: enquiries@selectaglaze.co.uk

SECONDHAND MACHINERY MERCHANTS OR AGENTS, *See Machinery Merchants or Agents*

SECRETARIAL SERVICES OR AGENCIES

A T Office Services, 15 Spence Avenue, Byfleet, West Byfleet, Surrey, KT14 7TG Tel: (01932) 344833 Fax: (01932) 344833 E-mail: enquiries@atofficeservices.co.uk

▶ A Virtual Solution, 11 Langley Close, Louth, Lincolnshire, LN11 8YP Tel: (01507) 609043 Fax: (01507) 609043 E-mail: sales@avirtualsolution.co.uk

▶ Abela Secretarial Services, 26 Campbell Road, Maidstone, Kent, ME15 6QA Tel: 01622 210552 Fax: 01622 210552 E-mail: info@abelasecretarial.com

▶ AP Office Services, 44 Christchurch Road, Tring, Hertfordshire, HP23 4EH Tel: 01442 890597 Fax: 0871 661 3480 E-mail: alison@aptyping.f9.co.uk

Blue Arrow, 5 Colston Centre, Colston Avenue, Bristol, BS1 4UB Tel: 0117-929 8435 Fax: 0117-925 0231 E-mail: info@bluearrow.co.uk

Bond Street Business Base, 3 Bond Street, St. Helier, Jersey, JE2 3NP Tel: (01534) 724100 Fax: (01534) 759662 E-mail: info@bondbase.info

▶ Business Friend Ltd, 5 Mayland Quay, Maylandsea, Chelmsford, CM3 6GJ Tel: (07931) 759611 Fax: (01621) 744292 E-mail: telmemore@businessfriend.net

▶ CMP Support, 46 Freshwater Drive, Poole, Dorset, BH15 4JE Tel: (01202) 245318 Fax: 01202 245318 E-mail: enquiries@cmpsupport.co.uk

Complus Teltronic Ltd, Sibleys Green, Thaxted, Dunmow, Essex, CM6 2NU Tel: (01371) 830326 Fax: (01371) 831096 E-mail: enquires@complusteltronic.co.uk

Concorde Agency, 28a High Street, Harpenden, Hertfordshire, AL5 2SX Tel: (01582) 715000 Fax: (01582) 461306 E-mail: sue.churchhouse@concord-agency.com

Credo Business Group, 146 Welling Way, Welling, Kent, DA16 2RS Tel: (020) 8856 1700 Fax: (020) 8856 9394

▶ Digital Secretary, Feldwicke Cottage, Ardingly Road, West Hoathly, East Grinstead, West Sussex, RH19 4RA Tel: (01342) 716137 Fax: (01342) 716137 E-mail: info@digital-secretary.co.uk

Elliott Services, Seven Oaks, School Lane, Moffat, Dumfriesshire, DG10 9AX Tel: (01683) 220584 Fax: (01683) 221984 E-mail: mfelliott@aol.com

▶ Girl Friday Solutions, 13 Lower Icknield Way, Marsworth, Tring, Hertfordshire, HP23 4LW Tel: (07921) 770516 E-mail: girlfridaysolutions@hotmail.co.uk

Hampton Leasing Ltd, 7 Mount Mews, High Street, Hampton, Middlesex, TW12 2SH Tel: (020) 8979 2262 Fax: (020) 8941 2645 E-mail: info@messagebase.com

▶ Havelock Secretarial Services, Havelock Secretarial Services, Enterprise 5, Five Lane Ends, Idle, Bradford, West Yorkshire, BD10 8EW Tel: 01274 618821 Fax: 01274 612604 E-mail: ltaylor@tayloredwebs.co.uk

▶ Infinite Distance Secretarial Services, 35 Nursery Road, Edgbaston, Birmingham, B15 3JX Tel: 0121-244 3633 E-mail: infinitedistance@blueyonder.co.uk

▶ K3 Secretarial Services, Blenheim Court, 17 Beulah Hill, London, SE19 3LJ Tel: (07786) 923079 Fax: (020) 8771 3651 E-mail: info@kzvirtualassistant.com

▶ London Law Agency Ltd, 67-69 Southampton Row, London, WC1B 4ET Tel: (020) 7436 5880 Fax: (020) 7583 1531 E-mail: info@londonlaw.co.uk

M & N Group Ltd, 118 London Road, Kingston upon Thames, Surrey, KT2 6QJ Tel: (020) 8974 5252 Fax: (020) 8974 5588 E-mail: sales@mn-group.com

Manpower UK Ltd, 12 Hall Quay, Great Yarmouth, Norfolk, NR30 1HP Tel: (01493) 853222 Fax: (01493) 330366 E-mail: great.yarmouth@manpower.co.uk

▶ MF Home Typists, 34 Devon Avenue, Twickenham, Twickenham, TW2 6PW Tel: (020) 8755 4450 E-mail: farrm001@rgfl.org.uk

▶ NG Office Solutions, 19 Regency Green, Colchester, CO3 4TD Tel: 01206 369 530 Fax: 01206 369 530 E-mail: enquiries@ngofficesolutions.com

▶ Nichols Secretarial Services, 18 St. Johns Road, Belton, Great Yarmouth, Norfolk, NR31 9NS Tel: (01493) 781899 E-mail: elizabeth@nicholssecretarialservices.co.uk

▶ Office Assist, 2a Cowper Road, Bedford, MK40 2AS Tel: (07771) 995545 E-mail: mail@office-assist.co.uk

▶ OnLine Office Services, 15 Knocklands Court, Ballymoney, County Antrim, BT53 6LN Tel: (028) 2766 9566 Fax: (028) 2766 9566 E-mail: info@onlineofficeservices.co.uk

▶ Online Secretarial Services, 31 Derwent Drive, Ferry Fryston, Castleford, West Yorkshire, WF10 3SX Tel: 0771 8320166 E-mail: onlinesecretarialservices@hotmail.co.uk

Orion, 11b Baird House, Newark Road South, Glenrothes, Fife, KY7 4NS Tel: (01592) 775050 Fax: (01592) 772515 E-mail: fife@orioneng.com

▶ Purple Creature, 6 Rosemount Square, Aberdeen, AB25 2UB Tel: (01224) 643673 E-mail: info@purplecreature.co.uk

Qualitext Business Services Ltd, 1 Howard Road, Reigate, Surrey, RH2 7JE Tel: (01737) 242999 Fax: (01737) 248117 E-mail: hialje@qualitext.freeserve.co.uk

▶ Secretarial Solutions, 6 Stonebridge Court, Blackbridge Lane, Horsham, West Sussex, RH12 1TX Tel: (01403) 253021 Fax: (01403) 253021 E-mail: tlnhome@hotmail.com

Select Appointments plc, Regent Court, Laporte Way, Luton, LU4 8SB Tel: (01582) 811600 Fax: (01582) 811611 E-mail: information@select.co.uk

Select Office Services, Forum House Business Centre, Stirling Road, Chichester, West Sussex, PO19 7DN Tel: (01243) 787932 Fax: (01243) 786930 E-mail: 100622.3205@compuserve.com

▶ Shepperton Clerical Services, 7 Hawthorn Way, Upper Halliford, Shepperton, Middlesex, TW17 8QE Tel: 01932 429210 Fax: 01932 429210 E-mail: helen@sheppertonclerical.co.uk

▶ SJM Secretarial Services, Nelson Street, Burton-on-Trent, Staffordshire, DE15 0DE Tel: (01283) 509854

▶ Stop Gap, 18 Hillcrest Drive, Little Sutton, Ellesmere Port, CH66 4QD Tel: 0151-347 1974 Fax: 0151-347 1974

Tmwsecretarial Services, Tesla House, 37 Hartland Road, Reading, RG2 8AB Tel: (0845) 2011635 Fax: (0845) 2011925 E-mail: info@tmwsecretarial.com

SECRETARIAL SERVICES OR AGENCIES – *continued*

▶ Typing For Business, Ridge Mount, Middlewich Road, Wistaston, Nantwich, Cheshire, CW5 6PB Tel: (01270) 252065
E-mail: info@typingforbusiness.co.uk

Typing Workshop, 60 Shirley Road, Croydon, CR0 7EP Tel: (020) 8655 3503 Fax: (020) 8655 3588

▶ Virtual Assistant, 11 Farquhar Road, Port Glasgow, Renfrewshire, PA14 5AS
Tel: (07732) 213368
E-mail: info@thevirtualassistant.me.uk

▶ Virtual Office Bureau Limited, 4 Twyfords, Crowborough, East Sussex, TN6 1YE
Tel: 01892 653325 Fax: 01892 665861
E-mail: virtualofficebureau@yahoo.co.uk

▶ Virtual Secretarial Services, 235 The Broadway, Sunderland, SR4 9HB Tel: (07986) 854995 Fax: 0191-534 3657
E-mail: info@virtual-secretarialservices.com

Virtusec.Com, 5 Abbotsford Court, Kelso, Roxburghshire, TD5 7SQ Tel: (07765) 246124
Fax: (01573) 224731
E-mail: info@virtusec.com

Woodrow Business Centre, 65-66 Woodrow, London, SE18 5DH Tel: (020) 8854 1194
Fax: (020) 8317 0394
E-mail: info@woodrowbusinesscentre.com

Gordon Yates Ltd, Palladium House, 1-4 Argyll Street, London, W1F 7TA Tel: (020) 7494 4466
Fax: (020) 7494 4499

SECTION BENDING SERVICES TO THE TRADE

Anvil Tubesmiths Southern Ltd, Sedlescombe Sawmills, Hawkhurst Road, Staplecross, Robertsbridge, East Sussex, TN32 5SA
Tel: (01580) 830770 Fax: (01580) 830220
E-mail: barry.luckham@btopenworld.com

Atlas Tube Bending Ltd, Albert Street, Oldham, OL8 3QP Tel: 0161-683 5556 Fax: 0161-683 5557 E-mail: admin@atlastubebending.co.uk

B Saxton & Co. Ltd, Unit 6a Arrow Trading Estate, Corporation Road, Audenshaw, Manchester, M34 5LR Tel: 0161-320 1444
Fax: 0161-320 1555
E-mail: sales@banshaws.com

Barnshaw Steel Benders, 89 Bothwell Road, Hamilton, Lanarkshire, ML3 0DW Tel: (01698) 421010 Fax: (01698) 421177
E-mail: hamilton@barnshaws.com

W.A. Patterson, Unit 34 Muckamore Industrial Estate, Muckamore, Antrim, BT41 4QE
Tel: 028 94429090

T H E Section Bending Co. Ltd, Houghton Road, North Anston Trading Estate, North Anston, Sheffield, S25 4JJ Tel: (01909) 550080
Fax: (01909) 550114
E-mail: sales@thebending.co.uk

Taylor & Watson Ltd, Wentworth Road, Penistone, Sheffield, S36 6ET Tel: (01226) 762035 Fax: (01226) 370216
E-mail: taylorwatson65@hotmail.com

White Cross Ring Co. Ltd, Battye Street, Bradford, West Yorkshire, BD4 8AG
Tel: (01274) 669933 Fax: (01274) 660137
E-mail: jason@whitecrossring.co.uk

SECTION PRODUCTION, METAL,

See headings for particular types

SECTION ROLLING MACHINES

Bulldog Industrial Holdings Ltd, Carrington Road, Stockport, Cheshire, SK1 2JT Tel: 0161-477 0775 Fax: 0161-480 0133
E-mail: sales@bulldogprocess.com

SECTIONAL BUILDINGS

A B Creasy & Sons, Scotter Common, Gainsborough, Lincolnshire, DN21 3JF
Tel: (01724) 762664 Fax: (01724) 762664

A & B Fencing & Roofing Ltd, Love Lane Industrial Estate, Love Lane, Cirencester, Gloucestershire, GL7 1YG Tel: (01285) 651330 Fax: (01285) 651330

Beaver Timber Co., Barcaldine Sawmills, Barcaldine, Oban, Argyll, PA37 1SG
Tel: (01631) 720353 Fax: (01631) 720430
E-mail: info@beavertimber.co.uk

T.A. Brooks, 1 Staffa Drive, Tibshelf, Alfreton, Derbyshire, DE55 5PJ Tel: (01773) 872361
Fax: (01773) 872361

Fords Of Blythe Bridge Ltd, 203 Groveindley Lane, Blythe Bridge, Stoke-on-Trent, ST11 9JS
Tel: (01782) 392125 Fax: (01782) 396622
E-mail: fords@blythebridge30.fsbusiness.co.uk

L E Haslett & Co., 21 Ballagh Road, Clogher, County Tyrone, BT76 0JY Tel: (028) 8554 8285 Fax: (028) 8554 8683
E-mail: lehasslet@hotmail.com

Lucas Sectional Buildings, The Row, West Dereham, King's Lynn, Norfolk, PE33 9RH
Tel: (01366) 500502 Fax: (01366) 501005
E-mail: info@fjlucas.com

Newstar Sectional Buildings, Ash Grove Beverley Road, Beverley Road, Hull, HU5 1LT
Tel: (01482) 444256 Fax: (01482) 449885

Prisma Products, 37 Parkside, Nottingham, NG8 2NQ Tel: 0115-925 4506 Fax: 0115-925 9327

Riddle & Simmons, 4 Sanders Close, Finedon Road Industrial Estate, Wellingborough, Northamptonshire, NN8 4HQ Tel: (01933) 276567 Fax: (01604) 406545

Sparkford Sawmills Ltd, Sparkford, Yeovil, Somerset, BA22 7LH Tel: (01963) 440414
Fax: (01963) 440982
E-mail: enquiries@sparkford.com

Stable Co., Outgang Lane, Osbaldwick, York, YO19 5UP Tel: (01904) 430630 Fax: (01904) 430363
E-mail: enquire@thestablecompany.com

Taylor's Garden Buildings, Ashwellthorpe Industrial Estate, Ashwellthorpe, Norwich, NR16 1ER Tel: (01508) 489260 Fax: (01508) 481622

Timberkraft, Scrambledfields Yard, Higher Halstock Leigh, Higher Halstock Leigh, Yeovil, Somerset, BA22 9QX Tel: (07970) 688297
Fax: (01935) 891007

Wadland Bros, Lower Hampt, Luckett, Callington, Cornwall, PL17 8NT Tel: (01579) 370234
Fax: (01579) 370234

SECTIONAL GARAGES

Castle Portable Buildings Ltd, Wharf Street, Dukinfield, Cheshire, SK16 4PG Tel: 0161-339 3911 Fax: 0161-339 3911
E-mail: info@castleportable.co.uk

Cheshire Portable Buildings, 214c Manchester Road, Altrincham, Cheshire, WA14 5LU
Tel: 0161-941 6631 Fax: 0161-927 7693
E-mail: sales@cheshireportablebuildings.co.uk

Concrete Garage Co Pudsey Ltd, Premier House, Vickers Place, Stanningley, Pudsey, West Yorkshire, LS28 6HN Tel: 0113-256 0011
Fax: 0113-256 9971

County Pre Cast Ltd, Sectional Building Centre, Maltings Industrial Estate, Maltings Road, Battlesbridge, Wickford, Essex, SS11 7RH
Tel: (01268) 735261 Fax: (01268) 571575
E-mail: enquiries@countyprecast.co.uk

Evans Windows Ltd, Cambrian Place, Pool Road, Newtown, Powys, SY16 1DH Tel: (01686) 626465 Fax: (01686) 627695

Houghton Concrete Ltd, 8 Firsdale Industrial Estate, Nangreaves Street, Leigh, Lancashire, WN7 4TN Tel: (01942) 676446 Fax: (01942) 608018

Wain Bros Ltd, 774 Leek Road, Stoke-on-Trent, ST1 6AE Tel: (01782) 202180 Fax: (01782) 213127

SECTIONAL STEEL TANKS

Braithwaite Engineers Ltd, Neptune Works Cork Wharf, Mill Parade, Newport, Gwent, NP20 2UY Tel: (01633) 262141 Fax: (01633) 250631 E-mail: tanks@braithwaite.co.uk

SECTIONAL TANKS

A C Plastic Industries Ltd, Armstrong Road, Basingstoke, Hampshire, RG24 8NU
Tel: (01256) 329334 Fax: (01256) 817862
E-mail: sales@ac-plastics.com

Galglass Ltd, 321 Hough Lane, Wombwell, Barnsley, South Yorkshire, S73 0LR
Tel: (01226) 340370 Fax: (01226) 344200
E-mail: sscott@galglass.co.uk

Goodwin Tanks Ltd, Pontefract Street, Derby, DE24 8JD Tel: (01332) 363112 Fax: (01332) 294683 E-mail: sales@goodwintanks.co.uk

▶ Vulcan Tanks Ltd, Cotes Park Lane, Cotes Park Industrial Estate, Somercotes, Alfreton, Derbyshire, DE55 4NJ Tel: (01773) 835321
Fax: (01773) 836578
E-mail: sales@vulcantanks.co.uk

SECTIONAL TIMBER BUILDINGS

Skinners Sheds Ltd, 161 Bexhill Road, St. Leonards-On-Sea, East Sussex, TN38 8BG
Tel: (01424) 716716 Fax: (01424) 716716
E-mail: info@skinners-sheds.com

▶ Weatherstrong Timber Framed Buildings, Henfield Road, Cowfold, Horsham, West Sussex, RH13 8DU Tel: (01403) 865666
E-mail: andrwpar9@aol.com

SECTIONAL WATER CISTERNS

Brimar Plastic Ltd, North Road, Yate, Bristol, BS37 7PR Tel: (01454) 322111 Fax: (01454) 316955 E-mail: brimar@brimarplastics.co.uk

SECURE ACCOMMODATION MODULES

Caledonian Building Systems Ltd, Carlton Works, Ossington Road, Carlton-on-Trent, Newark, Nottinghamshire, NG23 6NT Tel: (01636) 821645 Fax: (01636) 821261

Wide Range Services Ltd, Alexandra Dock, Hull, HU9 1TA Tel: (01482) 898261 Fax: (01482) 587271 E-mail: sales@wrshull.co.uk

SECURE COMMUNICATION SYSTEMS

Global Communications, 9 Belfast Road, Bangor, County Down, BT20 3PN Tel: (028) 9145 7900
Fax: (028) 9145 7900
E-mail: info@global-mob.com

SECURE STORAGE

Access Self Storage Ltd, 93 Park Lane, London, W1K 7TB Tel: (020) 7297 4100
E-mail: enquiries@accessstorage.com

▶ Bondelivery, Dundrod Road, Nutts Corner, Crumlin, County Antrim, BT29 4SR Tel: (028) 9082 5151 Fax: (028) 9082 5296

▶ City Storage Vault, The Pentagon Centre, 30 Washington Street, Glasgow, G3 8AZ
Tel: (0845) 8500400 Fax: 0141-226 3944
E-mail: info@citystoragevault.com

▶ Mac Pac, Units 1 & 2, Baillieston Distribution Centre, Baillieston, Glasgow, G69 6UL
Tel: 0141-781 4888 Fax: 0141-781 4788

▶ Nelson The Removal Co., Irongrey Park, Irongray Road, Dumfries, DG2 0JE
Tel: (01387) 722320 Fax: (01387) 722321
E-mail: info@nelsonremovals.co.uk

SECURE STORAGE EQUIPMENT OR SYSTEMS

▶ Finspa Storage Handling Ltd, 3 Dewing Road, Rackheath Industrial Estate, Rackheath, Norwich, NR13 6PS Tel: (01603) 722002
Fax: (01603) 720322 E-mail: info@finspa.com

Sortimo International Ltd, Old Sarum Park, Old Sarum, Salisbury, SP4 6EB Tel: (01722) 411585 Fax: (01722) 320831
E-mail: sales@sortimo.co.uk

SECURITY ACCESS CONTROL INSTALLATION OR SERVICING

A M Security Group Ltd, Unit 7 English Business Park, Hove, East Sussex, BN3 7ET
Tel: (01273) 740400 Fax: (01273) 740401

Aar Dee Locks & Shutters Ltd, 16 Boswell Square, Hillington, Hillington Industrial Estate, Glasgow, G52 4BQ Tel: 0141-810 3444
Fax: 0141-810 3777
E-mail: sales@aaree.co.uk

Access Control Services, 20-26 High Street, Greenhithe, Kent, DA9 9NN Tel: (01322) 370777 Fax: (01322) 370076
E-mail: admin@xplan.com

Access Controls UK Ltd, 62 Ocean Close, Fareham, Hampshire, PO15 6QP Tel: (01329) 513222 Fax: (01329) 513221
E-mail: enquiries@accesscontrols.co.uk

Access Fire & Security Ltd, Henley House, 1293-1295 Warick Road, Acocks Green, Birmingham, B27 6PU Tel: 0121-765 4900
Fax: 0121-765 4901
E-mail: michael@accessfire.co.uk

▶ Ace Security Systems Ltd, 12 Triumph Way, Kempston, Bedford, MK42 7QB Tel: (01234) 854455 Fax: (01234) 855345
E-mail: sales@acesecurity.co.uk

▶ Alarmstrong Security Systems Ltd, 16 Adelaide Road, St. Leonards-on-Sea, East Sussex, TN38 9DA Tel: (01424) 442366
E-mail: info@alarmstrongsecurity.co.uk

Avon Armour Holdings Ltd, Unit 12, 1-2 Portview Road, Bristol, BS11 9LD Tel: 0117-982 6288
Fax: 0117-982 8322
E-mail: sales@avonarmour.co.uk

B & E Services, Greenhill Mills, Grange Road, Batley, West Yorkshire, WF17 6LH
Tel: (01924) 420800 Fax: (01924) 420800

B J C Communication Contracts Ltd, 198 Hydean Way, Stevenage, Hertfordshire, SG2 9YD
Tel: (07879) 605543 Fax: (0844) 5875728
E-mail: mail@bjccommunications.co.uk

Ble Ltd, Church Street, Eckington, Sheffield, S21 4BH Tel: (01246) 436361 Fax: (01246) 436726 E-mail: sales@blegroup.co.uk

C J Security Systems Ltd, Unit 3 Fence Avenue, Macclesfield, Cheshire, SK10 1LT Tel: (01625) 613707 Fax: (01625) 617898
E-mail: sales@cheshirelock.co.uk

▶ C S I, 36 Luzley Brook Road, Royton, Oldham, OL2 6SQ Tel: (01706) 843249
E-mail: spencer.marsden1@btinternet.com

Carter Voce Access Control Ltd, 111 Chiltern Drive, Surbiton, Surrey, KT5 8LS Tel: (020) 8339 9111 Fax: (020) 8390 1727

Cobra Security Systems Ltd, 155 Station Road, London, E4 6AG Tel: (020) 8529 0179
Fax: (020) 8529 0091
E-mail: keith@cobra-security.fsnet.co.uk

▶ D M G Security Systems, Knowler Hill, Liversedge, West Yorkshire, WF15 6DY
Tel: (01924) 400927
E-mail: sales@dmgsecuritysystems.co.uk

Eastern Hydraulics, Unit 7 Wennington Hall Farm, Wennington Road, Rainham, Essex, RM13 9EF Tel: (01708) 558144 Fax: (01708) 555919 E-mail: janetgiles@onetel.com

▶ Essex Security Services Ltd, 154 Church Hill, Loughton, Essex, IG10 1LJ Tel: (020) 8502 1360 Fax: (020) 8502 2700
E-mail: all@essexsecurity.co.uk

Eurotime Systems Ltd, 101 Blandford Avenue, Birmingham, B36 9JB Tel: 0121-776 6860
Fax: (0871) 9942954
E-mail: sales@eurotime.co.uk

▶ Executive Security Solutions, Unit 6, Kings Ride Park, Ascot, Berkshire, SL5 8BL
Tel: (01344) 319403 Fax: (01344) 319404
E-mail: mail@essukltd.co.uk

▶ Home Security Services UK Ltd, 3 Campbell Street, Roe Lee, Blackburn, BB1 9AF
Tel: (0800) 6520642 Fax: (01254) 698064
E-mail: sales@homesecurityservicesuk.co.uk

I R Security & Safety, 1 Berrington Road, Leamington Spa, Warwickshire, CV31 1NB
Tel: (01926) 437000 Fax: (01926) 437005
E-mail: ir_customerservice@eu.irco.com

Ids Security Systems Ltd, Unit 11 Field Way, Cardiff, CF14 4HY Tel: (029) 2052 2885
Fax: (029) 2052 2747

Initial Electronic Security, Maxwelltown Industrial Estate, Glasgow Road, Dumfries, DG2 0NW
Tel: (01387) 261060 Fax: (01387) 250708
E-mail: dumfries@ies.uk.com

Initial Electronic Security Systems Ltd, 1 Orbit Centre, Ashworth Road, Bridgemead, Swindon, SN5 7YG Tel: (01793) 531955
Fax: (01793) 488850
E-mail: swindon@ies.uk.com

Magnetic Solutions, Unit B7, Crabtree Road, Thorpe Industrial Estate, Egham, Surrey, TW20 8RN Tel: (01784) 438666 Fax: (01784) 438777 E-mail: trushton@magsol.co.uk

▶ Maximeyes Security Ltd, Unit 2, Dalewood Road, Lymedale Business Park, Newcastle, Staffordshire, ST5 9QH Tel: (01782) 566611
Fax: (01782) 566616
E-mail: maximeyes2003@yahoo.co.uk

Metro Security, 5 Ashton Road, Harold Hill, Romford, RM3 8UJ Tel: (0870) 6090095
Fax: (0870) 6090096
E-mail: info@metrosecurity.co.uk

N T Security Ltd, Unit A Cambridge House, Waterside Court, Neptune Close, Medway City Estate, Rochester, Kent, ME2 4NZ
Tel: (01634) 296869 Fax: (01634) 296992
E-mail: sales@ntsecurity.co.uk

New Parking Solutions, Unit 81, Pembroke Centre, Cheney Manor Industrial Estate, Swindon, SN2 2PQ Tel: (01793) 700608
Fax: (01793) 700608
E-mail: sales@newparkingsolutions.co.uk

Ontime Systems Ltd, Unit 3 Bessemer Crescent, Aylesbury, Buckinghamshire, HP19 8TF
Tel: 0800 975 0960 Fax: (01296) 395787
E-mail: ontime-sales@btconnect.com

Orbis Property Protection, 106 Oxford Road, Uxbridge, Middlesex, UB8 1NA Tel: (01895) 465500 Fax: (01895) 465499
E-mail: pat.sullivan@ux.orbis-opp.com

Sentinel Security Systems, 7 Southern Avenue, Leominster, Herefordshire, HR6 0QF
Tel: (01568) 615500 Fax: (01568) 610555
E-mail: sentinelss@btinternet.com

Severn Valley Lock & Safe, 9-10 Comberton Road, Kidderminster, Worcestershire, DY10 1UA Tel: (01562) 829406 Fax: (01562) 864089 E-mail: sales@severnlocks.co.uk

Simplex Security Systems, PO Box 33903, London, NW9 6ER Tel: (020) 8200 9991
Fax: (020) 8200 6598
E-mail: sales@simplex.org.uk

South Coast Alarms Ltd, 54 Overcombe Drive, Weymouth, Dorset, DT3 6QF Tel: (01305) 832614
E-mail: admin@southcoastalarms.co.uk

Teccom Ltd, Howbury Centre, Crayford, Dartford, DA1 4RQ Tel: (0845) 8900844
E-mail: info@teccom.ltd.uk

Telco Security Locks Ltd, Connaught Road, Bournemouth, BH7 6NA Tel: (01202) 420444
Fax: (01202) 432073
E-mail: sales@telcolocks.fsnet.co.uk

Valley Systems Ltd, 26 Moorfields Close, Staines, Middlesex, TW18 3LU Tel: (01784) 457645
Fax: (01784) 438777
E-mail: trushton@magsol.co.uk

SECURITY ACCESS CONTROL SYSTEMS

▶ 1st Call Lockouts Ltd, 9 Beaumont Road, Bournville Birmingham, Birmingham, B30 2EA
Tel: 0121-459 8772 Fax: 0121-451 1315
E-mail: enquiries@1stcalllockouts.co.uk

A M Security Group Ltd, Unit 7 English Business Park, Hove, East Sussex, BN3 7ET
Tel: (01273) 740400 Fax: (01273) 740401

Access Control Automation Ltd, Arun Business Park, Bognor Regis, West Sussex, PO22 9SX
Tel: (01243) 830641 Fax: (01243) 830738
E-mail: sales@accesscontrolautomation.com

Access Control Services, 20-26 High Street, Greenhithe, Kent, DA9 9NN Tel: (01322) 370777 Fax: (01322) 370076
E-mail: admin@xplan.com

Access Controls UK Ltd, 62 Ocean Close, Fareham, Hampshire, PO15 6QP Tel: (01329) 513222 Fax: (01329) 513221
E-mail: enquiries@accesscontrols.co.uk

Alarm Communication Ltd, 1 Westfield Road, Woking, Surrey, GU22 9LZ Tel: (01483) 771186 Fax: (01483) 771861
E-mail: office@alarmcommunication.co.uk

Alert Alarms, 16 Church Parade, Canvey Island, Essex, SS8 9RQ Tel: (01268) 696534
Fax: (01268) 680785
E-mail: alertalarms@blueyonder.co.uk

Amberley Security, 185-187 Copnor Road, Portsmouth, PO3 5BT Tel: 0800 0217066
Fax: (023) 9265 0349
E-mail: scottandrews@amberley-security.co.uk

SECURITY ACCESS CONTROL SYSTEMS – *continued*

B C Technology Ltd, 3 Wallis Close, Park Farm Industrial Estate, Wellingborough, Northamptonshire, NN8 6AG Tel: (01933) 405050 Fax: (01933) 405454 E-mail: info@bctechnologyltd.co.uk
Bell System Telephones Ltd, Presley Way, Crownhill, Milton Keynes, MK8 0ET Tel: (01908) 261106 Fax: (01908) 261116 E-mail: sales@bellsystem.co.uk
Borer Data Systems Ltd, Gotelee House, Market Place, Wokingham, Berkshire, RG40 1AN Tel: 0118-979 1137 Fax: 0118-977 3526 E-mail: borer@borer.co.uk
BSB Electronics Ltd, Cambridge Street, Great Harwood, Blackburn, BB6 7BU Tel: (01254) 883348 Fax: (01254) 889113 E-mail: sales@progeny.co.uk
▶ C D I Services, 8 Oak Road, Epping, Essex, CM16 5DJ Tel: (0845) 8382390 Fax: (0845) 8382391 E-mail: sales@cdiservices.co.uk
C X Access Systems Ltd, Unit 5, Cricketts Lane Industrial Park, Chippenham, Wiltshire, SN15 3EQ Tel: (01249) 443898 Fax: (01249) 443336 E-mail: cxaccess@aol.com
Castle Care Tech Ltd, North Street, Winkfield, Windsor, Berkshire, SL4 4SY Tel: (01344) 890582 Fax: (01344) 890024 E-mail: sales@castle-caretech.com
Clarke Instruments Ltd, Distloc House, Old Sarum Airfield, Old Sarum, Salisbury, SP4 6DZ Tel: (01722) 323451 Fax: (01722) 335154 E-mail: sales@clarke-inst.com
Clover Systems, 7 Endsleigh Gardens, Long Ditton, Surbiton, Surrey, KT6 5JL Tel: (020) 8399 1822 Fax: (020) 8770 0556 E-mail: cloversystems@btconnect.com
▶ Computerguard Ltd, Hazlewell House, Graffham, Petworth, West Sussex, GU28 0QA Tel: (01798) 867133 Fax: (01798) 867135
Deister Electronic UK, Camel Gate, Spalding, Lincolnshire, PE12 6ET Tel: (01775) 717100 Fax: (01775) 717101 E-mail: info@deister.co.uk
Edmundson Electrical Ltd, 6 Springlakes Estate, Deadbrook Lane, Aldershot, Hampshire, GU12 4UH Tel: (01252) 343443 Fax: (01252) 328104
▶ Electrogate Ltd, Unit 4, Ahed Trading Estate, Dewsbury Road, Ossett, West Yorkshire, WF5 9ND Tel: (01924) 283322 Fax: (01924) 283344 E-mail: info@electrogate.co.uk
Engineered Solutions, Unit 2, North Court, Armstrong Road, Maidstone, Kent, ME15 6JZ Tel: (01622) 750650 Fax: (01622) 355199 E-mail: sales@engsolutions.co.uk
Eurotime Systems Ltd, 101 Blandford Avenue, Birmingham, B36 9JB Tel: 0121-776 6860 Fax: (0871) 9942954 E-mail: sales@eurotime.co.uk
Faac Security Equipment, Unit 6 Hamilton Close, Basingstoke, Hampshire, RG21 6YT Tel: (01256) 318100 Fax: (01256) 318101 E-mail: sales@faac.co.uk
Feedback Data Ltd, Park Road, Crowborough, East Sussex, TN6 2QR Tel: (01892) 601400 Fax: (01892) 601429 E-mail: info@feedback-data.com
Fermax UK Ltd, Fermax House, Bebington Close, Billericay, Essex, CM12 0DT Tel: (01277) 634777 Fax: (01277) 634666 E-mail: sales@fermaxuk.com
Greenlight Locksmith, 42 Preston Parade, Whitstable, Kent, CT5 4AJ Tel: (01227) 274738 E-mail: greenlightlocks@btinternet.com
Group 4 Security Systems Ltd, Challenge House, Northway LaneInternational Drive, Tewkesbury, Gloucestershire, GL20 8UQ Tel: (01684) 274874 Fax: (01684) 294845
▶ Hillside Electrical (Southern) Ltd, Unit 7 Kingdom Close, Fareham, Hampshire, PO15 5TJ Tel: (01489) 577465 Fax: (01489) 481816 E-mail: info@hillside-electrical.co.uk
▶ Home Security Services UK Ltd, 51 Highbank, Blackburn, BB1 9SX Tel: (0800) 6520642 Fax: (01254) 698064 E-mail: Info@hssukltd.co.uk
Houseguard Security Systems Ltd, 35 Peabody Road, Farnborough, Hampshire, GU14 6HA Tel: (01252) 377688 Fax: (01252) 375387
Initial Electronic Security, Maxwelltown Industrial Estate, Glasgow Road, Dumfries, DG2 0NW Tel: (01387) 261060 Fax: (01387) 250708 E-mail: dumfries@ies.uk.com
Integrated Building Management Systems Ltd, Brunel Drive, Newark, Nottinghamshire, NG24 1SF Tel: (01636) 674875 Fax: (01636) 612228 E-mail: controls@integratedbms.co.uk
Isgus International Ltd, Unit 10 Springfield Business Centre, Brunel Way, Stroudwater Business Park, Stonehouse, Gloucestershire, GL10 3SX Tel: (01453) 827373 Fax: (01453) 827360 E-mail: admin@isgus.co.uk
Isoscan UK Ltd, Unit 1 Portelant Barns, Cowdown Farm, Micheldever, Winchester, Hampshire, SO21 3DN Tel: (01962) 774411 Fax: (01962) 774477 E-mail: sales@isoscan.co.uk
N A C D Ltd, 10 Avebury Court, Hemel Hempstead, Hertfordshire, HP2 7TA Tel: (01442) 211848 Fax: (01442) 212776 E-mail: sales@nacd.co.uk
New Parking Solutions, Unit 81, Pembroke Centre, Cheney Manor Industrial Estate, Swindon, SN2 2PQ Tel: (01793) 700608 Fax: (01793) 700608 E-mail: sales@newparkingsolutions.co.uk
Optex Europe Ltd, 32a Clivemont Road, Maidenhead, Berkshire, SL6 7BZ Tel: (01628) 631000 Fax: (01628) 636311 E-mail: sales@optex-europe.com
P A C International Ltd, 1 Park Gate Close, Bredbury Park Way, Bredbury, Stockport, Cheshire, SK6 2SZ Tel: 0161-494 1331 Fax: 0161-430 8658 E-mail: info@pac.co.uk
▶ Raytel Security Systems Ltd, 3 Block 5 Oakbank Industrial Estate, Garscube Road, Glasgow, G20 7LU Tel: 0141-332 4232 Fax: 0141-332 6952 E-mail: sales@raytelsecurity.co.uk
▶ Raytel Security Systems Ltd, 19 Brook Road, Rayleigh, Essex, SS6 7XH Tel: (01268) 749311 Fax: (01268) 745001 E-mail: info@raytelsecurity.co.uk
Ringdale UK Ltd, 26 Victoria Way, Burgess Hill, West Sussex, RH15 9NF Tel: (01444) 871349 Fax: (01444) 870228 E-mail: sales@ringdale.com
S G S Systems Ltd, Oakley Corner, 16 Kingswear Avenue, Perton, Wolverhampton, WV6 7RJ Tel: (01902) 745565 Fax: (01902) 757786 E-mail: simon@sgssystems.com
▶ Secure-Axcess Ltd, 8 Westerman Close Sawtry, Huntingdon, Cambridgeshire, PE28 5PJ Tel: (01487) 830324 Fax: 01487 832906 E-mail: secure-axcess@dsl.pipex.com
Severn Valley Lock & Safe, 9-10 Comberton Road, Kidderminster, Worcestershire, DY10 1UA Tel: (01562) 829406 Fax: (01562) 864089 E-mail: sales@severnlocks.co.uk
▶ SGW Security Consulting, The Innovation Centre, 217 Portobello, Sheffield, S1 4DP Tel: 0114-224 2421 Fax: (0845) 0097220
Teccom Ltd, Howbury Centre, Crayford, Dartford, DA1 4RQ Tel: (0845) 8900844 E-mail: info@teccom.ltd.uk
Time & Data Systems International Ltd, Sentinel House, Nuffield Road, Nuffield Industrial Estate, Poole, Dorset, BH17 0RE Tel: (01202) 666222 Fax: (01202) 679730 E-mail: info@tdsi.co.uk
Tynetec Ltd, Cowley Road, Blyth Industrial Estate, Blyth, Northumberland, NE24 5TF Tel: (01670) 352371 Fax: (01670) 362807 E-mail: sales@tynetec.co.uk
▶ Universal Security UK Ltd, Unit 120 City Business Park, Somerset Place, Plymouth, PL3 4BB Tel: (01752) 511222 Fax: (01752) 202426 E-mail: sales@uniseclltd.co.uk
▶ Webnet Ltd, 41 Tintern Avenue, Tyldesley, Manchester, M29 7WL Tel: (01942) 516162 Fax: (01942) 730484 E-mail: sales@yourhomedirect.co.uk
▶ Zeag UK Ltd, 17 Deer Park Road, London, SW19 3XJ Tel: 0208 543 3281 Fax: 0208 543 5344 E-mail: info@zeaguk.com

SECURITY ALARM CABLES

A & A Services, 22 Laycock Avenue, Aston, Sheffield, S26 2FU Tel: 0114-287 2787
Justice Security Systems Ltd, Prestige House, Kingsbury Close, Minworth, Sutton Coldfield, West Midlands, B76 9DH Tel: 0121-313 1330 Fax: 0121-313 0909 E-mail: sales@justicesecurity.co.uk
Sentinel Security Europe Ltd, 9 Oxhill Road, Shirley, Solihull, West Midlands, B90 1LR Tel: 0121-436 5999 Fax: 0121-436 5444 E-mail: info@sentinelgroup.co.uk

SECURITY ALARM SYSTEMS

A B C Fire Ltd, Unit 14 Heath Hill Industrial Estate, Dawley, Telford, Shropshire, TF4 2RH Tel: (01952) 505098 Fax: (01952) 505098
A K Security, 12 Hailsham Close, Mickleover, Derby, DE3 0PE Tel: (01332) 518070
▶ Ace Security Systems Ltd, 12 Triumph Way, Kempston, Bedford, MK42 7QB Tel: (01234) 854455 Fax: (01234) 855345 E-mail: sales@acesecurity.co.uk
Active Security Systems, 25 Engaine Drive, Shenley Church End, Milton Keynes, MK5 6BA Tel: (01908) 508998
Alarm Communication Ltd, 1 Westfield Road, Woking, Surrey, GU22 9LZ Tel: (01483) 771186 Fax: (01483) 771861 E-mail: office@alarmcommunication.co.uk
▶ Alarm it, 26 Kennett Dr, Leyland, PR25 3QX Tel: 07734 822279E-mail: Sales@leylec.co.uk
▶ B C Connections Ltd, 27a Erewash Square, Ilkeston, Derbyshire, DE7 5SP Tel: 0115-977 0586 Fax: (0870) 1319548 E-mail: bcconnection@emailaccount.com
Blanchards Home Hardware, 51 Mill Street, Bideford, Devon, EX39 2JS Tel: (01237) 472084 E-mail: kellysearch@blanchardsecurity.co.uk
▶ C D I Services, 8 Oak Road, Epping, Essex, CM16 5DJ Tel: (0845) 8382390 Fax: (0845) 8382391 E-mail: sales@cdiservices.co.uk
Caretech Systems Ltd, 114 Cateran Way, Cramlington, Northumberland, NE23 6HG Tel: (01670) 739987 Fax: (0845) 2827347 E-mail: sales@caretechsystems.co.uk
▶ Cassini, 141 Shirley Road, Southampton, SO15 3FH Tel: (023) 8022 1740 Fax: (023) 8033 9220 E-mail: enquiry@cassinigroup.co.uk
Cobra Security Systems Ltd, 155 Station Road, London, E4 6AG Tel: (020) 8529 0179 Fax: (020) 8529 0091 E-mail: keith@cobra-security.fsnet.co.uk
▶ Covert Surveillance & Investigations, 107 Brookdale Road, Liverpool, L15 3JF Tel: 0151-222 1188 Fax: 0151-222 1188 E-mail: enqurities@csilimited.co.uk
Dent Ltd, 191-195 Sturton St., Cambridge, CB1 2QH Tel: (01223) 350038 Fax: (01223) 300996 E-mail: dentsecur@aol.com
Destec Systems, 21 Grovelands Avenue, Swindon, SN1 4ET Tel: (01793) 496217 Fax: (01793) 610739 E-mail: info@destecsystems.co.uk
Eagle Security Solutions Ltd, 162 Trafalgar Road, London, SE10 9TZ Tel: (0845) 9002950 E-mail: info@eaglesecuritysolutions.co.uk
Emexco Ltd, Unit 1, 46B Bulkington, Devizes, Wiltshire, SN10 1SL Tel: (01380) 828900 Fax: (01380) 828999 E-mail: sales@emexco.co.uk
▶ Fire Break Fire Securities, Tweedside Trading Estate, Tweedmouth, Berwick-upon-Tweed, TD15 2XF Tel: (01289) 307691
Fosse Security Systems, South View, Sawbridge Road, Grandborough, Rugby, Warwickshire, CV23 8DN Tel: (01788) 812662 Fax: (01788) 812662
▶ Garrison Vehicle Locks, 3 Rolleston Close, Market Harborough, Leicestershire, LE16 8BZ Tel: (07891) 340168 E-mail: info@garrisonlocks.co.uk
▶ Harrisons Electrical Mechanical & Property Services Ltd, Harrison House, Sheep Walk, Langford Road, Biggleswade, Bedfordshire, SG18 9RB Tel: (01767) 600259 Fax: (01767) 600269 E-mail: info@harrisonselec.co.uk
Household Automation Ltd, Fox Way, Pinkhurst Lane, Slinfold, Horsham, West Sussex, RH13 0QR Tel: (0870) 3300071 E-mail: afe@globalnet.co.uk
▶ Oracle Security Systems Ltd, 19 Godric Square, Woodston Industrial Estate, peterborough, PE2 7JL Tel: 08700 801716 Fax: 01733 233323 E-mail: info@oraclesecurity.co.uk
S G S Systems Ltd, Oakley Corner, 16 Kingswear Avenue, Perton, Wolverhampton, WV6 7RJ Tel: (01902) 745565 Fax: (01902) 757786 E-mail: simon@sgssystems.com
Scope Communications (UK) Ltd, Quantum House, Steamer Quay Road, Totnes, Devon, TQ9 5AL Tel: (01803) 860700 Fax: (01803) 863716 E-mail: sales@scope-uk.com
▶ Secure-Axcess Ltd, 8 Westerman Close Sawtry, Huntingdon, Cambridgeshire, PE28 5PJ Tel: (01487) 830324 Fax: 01487 832906 E-mail: secure-axcess@dsl.pipex.com
Southern Antennae Ltd, 15 Grosvenor Road, Broadstairs, Kent, CT10 2BT Tel: (01843) 865673 Fax: (01843) 864542 E-mail: sales@southern-antenna.demon.co.uk
▶ Spa Security Solutions, 8 Spa Road, Ballynahinch, County Down, BT24 8LU Tel: (028) 9756 1065 Fax: (028) 9756 1065 E-mail: sales@spacctv.com
▶ Sparc Systems Ltd, 430 Allesley Old Road, Coventry, CV5 8GF Tel: (07930) 854033 E-mail: wilson@sparcsys.co.uk
Standfast Security Systems Ltd, 120 Coldharbour Road, Redland, Bristol, BS6 7SL Tel: 0117-942 3366 Fax: 0117-944 6241 E-mail: sales@standfast.co.uk
Star Security (UK) Ltd, Somerset House, School Lane, East Harling, Norwich, NR16 2LU Tel: (01953) 718600 Fax: (01953) 718662 E-mail: steve@starsecurity.co.uk
Tritech Security & Electrical Services, 22 Muriel Street, Barrhead, Glasgow, G78 1QB Tel: 0141-881 1100 Fax: 0141-881 4449
Van Gadgets, 137 Heston Road, Hounslow, TW5 0RD Tel: (0870) 3833388 Fax: (020) 8572 8510 E-mail: sales@vangadgets.co.uk
▶ Vanilla Heaven, 4 Northfield Avenue, Lincoln, LN2 2FB Tel: (01522) 753781 E-mail: sales@global-gadgets.com

SECURITY ANTIHOLD UP DEVICES OR SYSTEMS

B H P Alarms, Unit B3, Balliniska Business Park, Springtime Industrial Estate, Londonderry, BT48 0LY Tel: (028) 7126 2757 Fax: (028) 7137 2225 E-mail: info@bhpalarms.com
Conway Security Services Ltd, 18 Bridgegate, Retford, Nottinghamshire, DN22 6AA Tel: (01777) 706478 Fax: (01777) 706478
Globe Alarms Ltd, 10 Orient Road, Salford, M6 8LD Tel: 0161-787 7470
Guardian Security Group (UK) Ltd, 5 Axis, Hawkfield Business Park, Hawkfield Way, Bristol, BS14 0BY Tel: 0117-946 5505 Fax: 0117-946 5506 E-mail: sales@guardiansecurity.co.uk
Hartburn Security Alarms, 8 Spalding Rd, Hartlepool, Cleveland, TS25 2LD Tel: (01429) 871111
Pro Tec Alarms Ltd, 91 Swansea Road, Pontlliw, Swansea, SA4 9EF Tel: (01792) 894995 Fax: (01792) 894995
Protect Security Systems, Merrills Head Farm, Long Causeway, Cliviger, Burnley, Lancashire, BB10 4RR Tel: (01282) 425544 Fax: (01282) 420938
R G L Security, 21 Denbigh Grove, Burnley, Lancashire, BB12 6AX Tel: (01282) 416051 E-mail: sales@rglsecurity.co.uk
R & I Security, 48a Westwood Park, Deans, Livingston, West Lothian, EH54 8QW Tel: (01506) 414793 Fax: (01506) 460007

SECURITY ANTITHEFT DEVICES/ SYSTEMS, INDIVIDUAL ITEMS

1 2 1 Security, 17 Henley Fields, St. Michaels, Tenterden, Kent, TN30 6EL Tel: (01580) 762588 Fax: (0704) 4066150
Calder Security Services Ltd, 219 King Cross Road, King Cross, Halifax, West Yorkshire, HX1 3JL Tel: (01422) 347313 Fax: (01422) 321106E-mail: mickyb@promapropertys.co.uk
Car Radio Alarms, Clarence Road, Sutton, Surrey, SM1 1RJ Tel: (020) 8661 1122 Fax: (020) 8770 7114 E-mail: admin@carradioalarms.co.uk
Hawk Ltd, Suite 2, Concourse House, 432 Dewsbury Road, Leeds, LS11 7DF Tel: 0113-270 4415 Fax: (01274) 305551 E-mail: leeds@ies.com
Jet Security Ltd, 28 Horsenden La North, Greenford, Middlesex, UB6 0PA Tel: (020) 8422 5552 Fax: (020) 8422 5552
ProTag Retail Security, Units 2-3, Short Way, The Industrial Estate, Thornbury, Bristol, BS35 3UT Tel: (01454) 418500 Fax: (01454) 413708 E-mail: martin@touchpanels.co.uk
Road Radio Ltd, 41 Station Road, Burgess Hill, West Sussex, RH15 9DE Tel: (01444) 242107 Fax: (01444) 871040

SECURITY BAGS

Ampack Security Products Ltd, Saxon Way, Melbourn, Royston, Hertfordshire, SG8 6DN Tel: (01763) 261900 Fax: (01763) 261234

SECURITY BARBED TAPES

Siddall & Hilton Mesh Ltd, Birds Royd Lane, Brighouse, West Yorkshire, HD6 1LT Tel: (01484) 401610 Fax: (01484) 721028 E-mail: sales@shmesh.com

SECURITY BARRIERS

Arkas Ltd, Nubal House, Headcorn Road, Sutton Valence, Maidstone, Kent, ME17 3EH Tel: 0845 5314195 Fax: (01622) 843488 E-mail: danny@arkas.co.uk
Automatic Systems Equipment UK Ltd, Unit G4, Middlesex Business Centre, Bridge Road, Southall, Middlesex, UB2 4AB Tel: (020) 8744 7669 Fax: (020) 8744 7670 E-mail: sales@automaticsystems.co.uk
D Morris, 5 The Laurels, Bedworth, Warwickshire, CV12 0PW Tel: (024) 7631 0762 Fax: (024) 7631 0385 E-mail: d.g.morris@talk21.com
Primac, 6 New Mills, Post Office Road, Inkpen, Hungerford, Berkshire, RG17 9PU Tel: (01488) 668008 Fax: (01488) 668883 E-mail: primac@flowdatasystems.co.uk
Zeag UK Ltd, Zeag House, 17 Deer Park Road, London, SW19 3XJ Tel: (020) 8543 3281 Fax: (020) 8443 5344 E-mail: sales@zeaguk.com

SECURITY CABINET MANUFRS

ArmorGard Security Products, Castle Trading Estate, Portchester, FAREHAM, Hants, PO16 9SF Tel: 02392 380280 Fax: 02392 200715 E-mail: sales@armorgardsecurity.com
Locktec Ltd, Unit 7-11, Pentlandfield Business Park, Roslin, Midlothian, EH25 9RE Tel: 0131-445 7788 Fax: 0131-445 7527 E-mail: sales@locktec.net
Scooter Store Ltd, Unit 11 Italstyle Buildings, Cambridge Road, Harlow, Essex, CM20 2HE Tel: (01279) 453565 Fax: (01279) 454030 E-mail: albertwass@site-safe.co.uk

SECURITY CAGES/COMPOUNDS

Athag Ltd, Well Spring Close, Carlyon Road Industrial Estate, Atherstone, Warwickshire, CV9 1HU Tel: (01827) 713040 Fax: (01827) 717307 E-mail: info@dogcages.uk.com
B & M Wireworks, Prescot Trade Centre, Oliver Lyme Road, Prescot, Merseyside, L34 2SH Tel: 0151-431 0101 Fax: 0151-431 0101 E-mail: rickymartin@supanet.co.uk
Storplan Racking Ltd, The Airfield, Full Sutton, York, YO41 1HS Tel: (01759) 371553 Fax: (01759) 372451 E-mail: storplan@ic24.net

SECURITY CAMERA SYSTEMS

▶ Secure-Axcess Ltd, 8 Westerman Close Sawtry, Huntingdon, Cambridgeshire, PE28 5PJ Tel: (01487) 830324 Fax: 01487 832906 E-mail: secure-axcess@dsl.pipex.com

SECURITY CASES

Alarmguard Security, 9 Cromwell Centre, Roebuck Road, Ilford, Essex, IG6 3UG Tel: (020) 8559 8989 Fax: (020) 8559 8425 E-mail: srb1625@aol.co.uk
Dynamica Ltd, Enterprise Road, Mablethorpe, Lincolnshire, LN12 1NB Tel: (01507) 473052 Fax: (01507) 478832

SECURITY CHAINS

Alarms For All Premises, Little Adelaide, Lower Road, East Farleigh, Maidstone, Kent, ME15 0JN Tel: (01622) 729439 Fax: (01622) 729439

Fast Signs Scotland Ltd, Unit 1, Millstreet Industrial Estate, Airdrie, Lanarkshire, ML6 6JJ Tel: (01236) 766050 Fax: (01236) 751647 E-mail: fastsigns@btconnect.com

Lock Assist, 139 Royal George Road, Burgess Hill, West Sussex, RH15 9TD Tel: (01444) 244344 Fax: (01444) 241324 E-mail: info@lockassist.co.uk

SECURITY CONSULTANCY

▶ Advanced Security, Chevron House, 346 Long Lane, Hillingdon, Uxbridge, Middlesex, UB10 9PF Tel: (01895) 201800 Fax: (01895) 201801 E-mail: info@securiplan.co.uk

Alliance Security Ltd, Alliance House, 180 Kingston Road, Leatherhead, Surrey, KT22 7PZ Tel: (01372) 362213 Fax: (01372) 386249

Beaver International, Station Road, Plumtree, Plumtree, Nottingham, NG12 5NA Tel: 0115-937 5900 Fax: 0115-937 4074

Bowman & Porter Security Ltd, 678 High Road, North Finchley, London, N12 9PT Tel: (020) 8446 2541 Fax: (020) 8445 6016

Bulldog Intruder Detection Systems, 29 Arthur Street, Derby, DE1 3EF Tel: (01332) 360220 Fax: (01332) 384854 E-mail: sales@bulldog-security.co.uk

Control Risks, Cottons Centre, Cottons Lane, London, SE1 2QG Tel: (020) 7970 2100 Fax: (020) 7970 2222 E-mail: enquiries@control.risks.com

▶ E J C, PO Box 103, Aylesbury, Buckinghamshire, HP17 8WL Tel: (0845) 3510603 E-mail: enquiries@essenjay.com

Electrical & Alarm Services, Colebrook Road, Plympton, Plymouth, PL7 4AA Tel: (01752) 337271 Fax: (01752) 337271 E-mail: easdale@eurobell.co.uk

▶ Excubo, Tudor House, Harrogate, North Yorkshire, HG1 8JE Tel: (07710) 470825

First Security Ltd, European Business Centre, The Hyde, Belgrave Road, London, NW9 5AE Tel: (020) 8374 4007 Fax: (020) 8952 4535

Gamma Secure Systems, Diamond House, 149 Frimley Road, Camberley, Surrey, GU15 2PS Tel: (01276) 702500 Fax: (01276) 692903 E-mail: dbrewer@gammassl.co.uk

Global, PO Box 101, Northampton, NN1 4BS Tel: (01604) 636531 Fax: (01604) 760656 E-mail: info@globalintelligence.ltd.uk

Kirby Security (UK) Ltd, Southbank House, Black Prince Road, London, SE1 7SJ Tel: (020) 7834 6714

Lodge Service International Ltd, Imperial Life House, 400 High Road, Wembley, Middlesex, HA9 6UD Tel: (020) 8903 3033 Fax: (020) 8902 6655 E-mail: info@lodgeservice.com

Mallusk Security Services Ltd, 495 Upper Newtownards Road, Belfast, BT4 3LL Tel: (028) 9047 1394 Fax: (028) 9047 2227 E-mail: mallusksecurity@hotmail.com

Mercia Security, 4 Redhill, Telford, Shropshire, TF2 9PA Tel: (01952) 610894 Fax: (01952) 610894

John Moore Security Ltd, Glencoe House, 559 Anlaby Road, Hull, HU3 6HP Tel: (01482) 507507 Fax: (01482) 509109 E-mail: sallymoore@johnmooresecurity.co.uk

Multiplex Security Communications Ltd, 32-34 Constitution Hill, Birmingham, B19 3JT Tel: 0121-236 6977

Mustard Research, Hop Studios, 2 Jamaica Road, London, SE1 2BX Tel: (020) 7231 4700 Fax: (020) 7231 1640

Northern Protection, Unit 38 The Brampton Centre, Brampton Road, Wath-upon-Dearne, Rotherham, South Yorkshire, S63 6BB Tel: (01709) 879333 Fax: (01709) 879443 E-mail: cm@nightforce.co.uk

Phillipa Enterprises Ltd, 33 West Drive, Ferring, Worthing, West Sussex, BN12 5QY Tel: (0781) 4548428 Fax: (01903) 242789 E-mail: bryanlp@totalise.co.uk

Reliance Security Group plc, Boundary House, Cricketfield Road, Uxbridge, Middlesex, UB8 1QG Tel: (01895) 205000 Fax: (01895) 205100 E-mail: info@reliancesecurity.co.uk

Reliance Security Services Ltd, London Street, 2-4 Old Pye Street, London, SW1P 2LE Tel: (020) 7222 6044 Fax: (020) 7222 9415 E-mail: info@reliancesecurity.co.uk

▶ Saracen International Ltd, Adamson House, Towers Business Park, Wilmslow Road, Didsbury, Manchester, M20 2YY Tel: 0161-955 4217 Fax: 0161-955 4201 E-mail: vigilant@saracen-int.com

SDS Group Ltd, 3 Courtlands Farm, Turnden Road, Cranbrook, Kent, TN17 2QL Tel: (01580) 715038 Fax: (01580) 712056 E-mail: sales@sdsgroupltd.co.uk

Secon Solutions Ltd, River House, 85 Esher Road, Walton-on-Thames, Surrey, KT12 4LN Tel: (020) 8255 0777 Fax: (020) 8255 7511 E-mail: sales@secon.co.uk

Securitas Group, 203-205 Lower Richmond Road, Richmond, Surrey, TW9 4LN Tel: 0845 5314061 Fax: (020) 8876 4650 E-mail: jenny.campbell@securitas.uk.com

Sterling Security Systems Ltd, PO Box 999, Tamworth, Staffordshire, B79 8EY Tel: (01827) 310059 Fax: (0870) 0558852 E-mail: info@sterling-security.co.uk

Systems Technology Consultants Ltd, Bedford Street, Stoke-on-Trent, ST1 4PZ Tel: (01782) 286300 Fax: (01782) 280036 E-mail: sytech@ebstar.co.uk

▶ Xtp international, Adamson House, Towers Business Park, Wilmslow Road, Didsbury, Manchester, M20 2YY Tel: 0161-955 4227 Fax: 0161-445 8225 E-mail: stevew34@hotmail.com

SECURITY CONTROL OR MONITORING SYSTEMS

B C Security Ltd, 8 Sandbach Rd South, Alsager, Stoke-on-Trent, ST7 2LU Tel: 01270 884646

Checkpoint Meto, 43 Western Road, Bracknell, Berkshire, RG12 1RF Tel: (01344) 701200 Fax: (01344) 701333 E-mail: lfardell@eur.checkpt.com

First Security Ltd, European Business Centre, The Hyde, Belgrave Road, London, NW9 5AE Tel: (020) 8374 4007 Fax: (020) 8952 4535

Identec Ltd, Mercantile Road, Rainton Bridge Industrial Estate, Houghton le Spring, Tyne & Wear, DH4 5PH Tel: 0191-584 4084 Fax: 0191-584 9077E-mail: info@identic.co.uk

Joyce-Loebl Ltd, 390 Princesway, Team Valley Trading Estate, Gateshead, Tyne & Wear, NE11 0TU Tel: 0191-420 3000 Fax: 0191-420 3030 E-mail: andy.kevins@joyce-loebel.com

Len Lothian U Store, 11 Bankhead Broadway, Edinburgh, EH11 4DB Tel: 0131-538 8200 Fax: 0131-538 8210 E-mail: info@lenlothain.com

Multiplex Security Communications Ltd, 32-34 Constitution Hill, Birmingham, B19 3JT Tel: 0121-236 6977

Southon Engineering Ltd, Aveley Indust Estate, Ardmore Road, Sth Ockendon, South Ockendon, Essex, RM15 5TH Tel: (01708) 858757 Fax: (01708) 858757 E-mail: john@southonengineering.co.uk

Synnex Information Technology Ltd, Synnex House, Nedge Hill, Telford, Shropshire, TF3 3AH Tel: (01952) 207200 E-mail: enquiries@smartwater.com

Thames Manufacturing Co. Ltd, 29 Mansfields, Writtle, Chelmsford, CM1 3NH Tel: (01245) 422062 Fax: (01245) 422062

Time & Data Systems International Ltd, Sentinel House, Nuffield Road, Nuffield Industrial Estate, Poole, Dorset, BH17 0RE Tel: (01202) 666222 Fax: (01202) 679730 E-mail: info@tdsi.co.uk

SECURITY DOOR INSTALLATION

Avon Armour Holdings Ltd, Unit 12, 1-2 Portview Road, Bristol, BS11 9LD Tel: 0117-982 6288 Fax: 0117-982 8322 E-mail: sales@avonarmour.co.uk

Cherry Security Co., 53 Cherry Garden Rd, Eastbourne, E. Sussex, BN20 8HG Tel: (01323) 641759 Fax: (01323) 641759 E-mail: andy@cherrysecurity.co.uk

Costello Security, 77 Nork Way, Banstead, Surrey, SM7 1HN Tel: (0845) 2608830 Fax: 01737 353742 E-mail: info@costellosecurity.co.uk

▶ Pensher-Skytech, Felling Works, William Street, Gateshead, Tyne & Wear, NE10 0JP Tel: 0191-438 0455 Fax: 0191-438 2328 E-mail: sales@pensher.co.uk

QRS Ltd, Malthouse Road, Tipton, West Midlands, DY4 9AE Tel: 0121-557 3601 Fax: 0121-520 1233

▶ Security Link Services Ltd, 124 Lea Vale Road, Norton, Stourbridge, West Midlands, DY8 2AU Tel: (0870) 2415883 E-mail: sales@securitylink.org.uk

▶ Stafford Bridge Doors Ltd, Bedford Road, Pavenham, Bedford, MK43 7PS Tel: (01234) 826316 Fax: (01234) 826319 E-mail: sales@sbdoors.com

Technocover Ltd, Henfaes Lane, Welshpool, Powys, SY21 7BE Tel: (01938) 555511 Fax: (01938) 555527 E-mail: terry.batten@technocover.co.uk

SECURITY DOORS

1st Choice Security Services Ltd, Unit 4 Hall Court, Bridge Street, Polesworth, Tamworth, Staffordshire, B78 1DT Tel: (01827) 899972 Fax: (01827) 899953 E-mail: pgrace@1stcss.co.uk

Amy Shutters, 8 Slader Business Park, Witney Road, Nuffield Industrial Estate, Poole, Dorset, BH17 0GP Tel: (01202) 666702 Fax: (01202) 666705 E-mail: info@amyshutters.co.uk

Attenborough Industrial Doors Ltd, Merlin Way, Quarry Hill Industrial Estate, Ilkeston, Derbyshire, DE7 4RA Tel: 0115-930 0815 Fax: 0115-944 8930 E-mail: information@attenboroughdoor.co.uk

Bastion Security Ltd, Claremont House, Holly Road, Slough, SL2 3QT Tel: (01753) 646488 Fax: (01753) 646488 E-mail: bastion@tinyworld.co.uk

Beck Engineering Co (Bridlington) Ltd, Camlock Works, 13 & 15 Bridlington Road, Hunmanby, Filey, North Yorkshire, YO14 0LR Tel: (01723) 890631 Fax: (01723) 891554 E-mail: shane@becktransglobal.co.uk

BenweldSecure, Unit 14a Hartlebury Trading Estate, Hartlebury, Kidderminster, Worcestershire, DY10 4JB Tel: (01299) 251750 Fax: (01299) 253576 E-mail: info@benweld.co.uk

Britannia Security Group UK Ltd, Britannia House, Lake Street, Stockport, Cheshire, SK2 7NU Tel: 0161-456 2103 Fax: 0161-487 4174

Cirrus Communication Systems Ltd, Hampton Lovett Industrial Estate, Lovett Road, Hampton Lovett, Droitwich, Worcestershire, WR9 0QG Tel: (01905) 827252 Fax: (01905) 827253 E-mail: info@coltronic.co.uk

CNC Doors, Premier Partnership Estate, Leys Road, Brierley Hill, West Midlands, DY5 3UP Tel: (01384) 78833 Fax: (01384) 78867 E-mail: cncdoors@btconnect.com

▶ Complete Technical Services Ltd, Hope Street, Rotherham, South Yorkshire, S60 1LH Tel: (01709) 821757 Fax: (01709) 385068 E-mail: gary.collinson@complete-tech.co.uk

Data Spectrum, Sycamore House, Wendlebury, Bicester, Oxfordshire, OX25 2PB Tel: (01869) 325266E-mail: enquiries@dataspectrum.co.uk

Doors & Hardware Ltd, Taskmaster Works, Maybrook Road, Minworth, Sutton Coldfield, West Midlands, B76 1AL Tel: 0121-351 5276 Fax: 0121-313 1228 E-mail: sales@doors-and-hardware.com

Elite Safe & Security Services, Stanmore Industrial Estate, Bridgnorth, Shropshire, WV15 5HP Tel: (01952 684855 E-mail: epicsafes@lineone.net

Evb Ltd, 48-52 Barking Industrial Park, Alfreds Way, Barking, Essex, IG11 0TJ Tel: (020) 8507 8088 Fax: (020) 8591 2419 E-mail: alanevb@f2s.com

Fix A Door Ltd, 1 Library Road, Ferndown, Dorset, BH22 9JP Tel: (01202) 855999 Fax: (01202) 855888 E-mail: fixadoor@aol.com

Stewart Fraser Ltd, Henwood Industrial Estate, Ashford, Kent, TN24 8DR Tel: (01233) 625911 Fax: (01233) 633149 E-mail: sales@stewartfraser.com

Guardian Security Group (UK) Ltd, 5 Axis, Hawkfield Business Park, Hawkfield Way, Bristol, BS14 0BY Tel: 0117-946 5505 Fax: 0117-946 5506 E-mail: sales@guardiansecurity.co.uk

Liddle Doors, Wagonway Industrial Estate, Wagonway Road, Hebburn, Tyne & Wear, NE31 1SP Tel: 0191-483 5449 Fax: 0191-489 0698 E-mail: liddle@liddledoors.co.uk

Newton Fabrications Ltd, 9 York Street, Ayr, KA8 8AN Tel: (01292) 269135 Fax: (01292) 610258 E-mail: davidcorson@newtonholdings.com

Rol Trac Automatic Doors Ltd, Unit 1 Brookfield Works, Quebec Street, Elland, West Yorkshire, HX5 9AP Tel: (01422) 375000 Fax: (01422) 379076 E-mail: sales@roltrac.com

▶ Rose UK, Unit 13 Vision Business Park, Firth Way, Nottingham, NG6 8GF Tel: 0115-927 9542 Fax: 0115-976 1986 E-mail: rose@roseuksecurityservices.co.uk

Sunray Engineering Ltd, Wotton Road, Ashford, Kent, TN23 6LL Tel: (01233) 639039 Fax: (01233) 625137 E-mail: sales@sunraydoors.co.uk

T G S Doors Ltd, Unit 4 Manor Complex, Kirkby Bank Road, Knowsley Industrial Park, Liverpool, L33 7SY Tel: 0151-548 9890 Fax: 0151-549 2119

Thornavon Ltd, Unit 4 Brook Street Business Centre, Brook Street, Colchester, CO1 2UZ Tel: (01206) 796888 Fax: (01206) 796889 E-mail: thornavon@tiscali.co.uk

Tyco Fire & Integrated Solutions, Tyco Park, Grimshaw Lane, Manchester, M40 2WL Tel: 0161-455 4475 Fax: 0161-455 4532 E-mail: wfs.doors.uk@tycoint.com

SECURITY DRUG DETECTORS

▶ Detect International Ltd, Hulmes Bridge House, North Moor Lane, Halsall, Ormskirk, Lancashire, L39 8RF Tel: (0870) 3007201 Fax: (0870) 3007202 E-mail: info@dik9.com

SDS Group Ltd, 3 Courtlands Farm, Turnden Road, Cranbrook, Kent, TN17 2QL Tel: (01580) 715038 Fax: (01580) 712056 E-mail: sales@sdsgroupltd.co.uk

SECURITY FASTENINGS OR FIXINGS

C A T Engineering Ltd, Glendale Works, 25 Sandhurst Road, Crowthorne, Berkshire, RG45 7HR Tel: (01344) 772934 Fax: (01344) 779283 E-mail: len@categ.fsnet.co.uk

Mechfast Ltd, Unit 3 & 4 Dalehouse La Industrial Estate, Cotton Drive, Kenilworth, Warwickshire, CV8 2UE Tel: (01926) 858698 Fax: (01926) 858051 E-mail:

Nuts & Bolts (Cannock) Ltd, Unit 40 Rumer Hill Business Estate, Rumer Hill Rd, Cannock, Staffordshire, WS11 0ET Tel: (01543) 466100 Fax: (01543) 466699 E-mail: sales@nutsandbolts-staffs.co.uk

SECURITY FENCING

Albion Fencing Ltd, 2239 London Road, Glasgow, G32 8XL Tel: 0141-778 1672 Fax: 0141-778 6688 E-mail: info@albionfencing.co.uk

Arkrite Fencing Manufacturers Ltd, Progress Drive, Cannock, Staffordshire, WS11 0JE Tel: (01543) 577677 Fax: (01543) 574446 E-mail: arkrite@btconnect.com

Hercules Security Fabrications Ltd, 1 Agl Business Park, Coundon Industrial Estate, Coundon, Bishop Auckland, County Durham, DL14 8NR Tel: (01388) 458794 Fax: (01388) 458806 E-mail: info@hercules-security.co.uk

▶ Mcarthur, 198-202 Broomhill Road, Bristol, BS4 5SF Tel: 0117-977 3311 Fax: 0117-977 6164

Myatt & Degville Fabrications Ltd, Selborne Street, Walsall, WS1 2JN Tel: (01922) 648222 Fax: (01922) 613565

Paramount Steel Fence, Florida Close, Hot Lane Industrial Estate, Stoke-on-Trent, ST6 2DJ Tel: (01782) 833333 Fax: (01782) 832222 E-mail: steelfence@btinternet.com

Procter Bros Ltd, Ninelands Lane, Leeds, LS25 2BY Tel: 0113-287 6282 Fax: 0113-242 2649 E-mail: info@procter-brothers.co.uk

Rennyco Ltd, West Tree Building, Whessoe Road, Darlington, County Durham, DL3 0QT Tel: (01325) 480502 Fax: (01325) 384278 E-mail: sales@rennycoltd.com

Rutland Electric Fencing Co Ltd, Fencing House, 8 Landsend Way, Oakham, Rutland, LE15 6RF Tel: (01572) 722455 Fax: (01572) 757614 E-mail: enquiries@rutland-electric-fencing.co.uk

Sampson & Partners Fencing, Aubrey Works, 15 Aubrey Ave, London Colney, St. Albans, Herts, AL2 1NE Tel: (01727) 822222 Fax: (01727) 826307 E-mail: primasampson@compuserve.com

Standard Fencing (Glasgow) Ltd, Downiebrae Road, Rutherglen, Glasgow, G73 1PW Tel: 0141-613 1555 Fax: 0141-613 1811 E-mail: standardfencing@btconnect.com

Thames Steel & Equipment Ltd, Turkey Cottage, Curload, Stoke St. Gregory, Taunton, Somerset, TA3 6JE Tel: (01823) 698881 Fax: (01823) 698988 E-mail: douglas.billington@lineone.net

Vandgard Anti Climb Guards, PO Box 51, Edenbridge, Kent, TN8 6WY Tel: (01797) 229872

SECURITY FENCING CONTRACTORS

▶ Advance Supplies Eastern Ltd, Victoria Stables, South Road, Bourne, Lincolnshire, PE10 9JZ Tel: (01778) 426633 Fax: (01778) 426899 E-mail: sales@advancesupplies.co.uk

Albion Fencing Ltd, 2239 London Road, Glasgow, G32 8XL Tel: 0141-778 1672 Fax: 0141-778 6688 E-mail: info@albionfencing.co.uk

Alltype Fencing Co. Ltd, Howgare Road, Broad Chalke, Salisbury, SP5 5DR Tel: (01722) 780563 Fax: (01722) 780138 E-mail: sales@alltypefencing.fsnet.co.uk

Brads Fencing Co. Ltd, 22 Hare Lane, Godalming, Surrey, GU7 3EE Tel: (01483) 414745 Fax: (01483) 419394

Coates Fencing Ltd, Unit 3 Barham Close, Bridgwater, Somerset, TA6 4DS Tel: (01278) 423577 Fax: (01278) 427760 E-mail: info@coatesfencing.co.uk

D E Fencing Ltd, Forthill Avenue, Jedburgh, Roxburghshire, TD8 6HJ Tel: (01835) 863623 Fax: (01835) 862113

Dale Fencing Ltd, 834 London Road, North Cheam, Sutton, Surrey, SM3 9BJ Tel: (020) 8641 2367 Fax: (020) 8641 1838 E-mail: dale@fences.fsbusiness.co.uk

Fernden Construction Winchester Ltd, Barfield Close, Winchester, Hampshire, SO23 9SQ Tel: (01962) 866400 Fax: (01962) 864139 E-mail: sales@ferndenwin.co.uk

Havering Fencing Co, 237 Chase Cross Road, Romford, RM5 3XS Tel: (01708) 747855 Fax: (01708) 721010 E-mail: enquiries@haveringfencing.com

Hercules Security Fabrications Ltd, 1 Agl Business Park, Coundon Industrial Estate, Coundon, Bishop Auckland, County Durham, DL14 8NR Tel: (01388) 458794 Fax: (01388) 458806 E-mail: info@hercules-security.co.uk

Howell-Blys Engineering Co. Ltd, Unit 23 Parkfield Mills, Queens Road, Morley, Leeds, LS27 0PF Tel: 0113-238 1444 Fax: 0113-238 1356 E-mail: howellblys@aol.com

Kingsforth Landscape & Construction Ltd, Mangham Way, Rotherham, South Yorkshire, S61 4RL Tel: (01709) 378977 Fax: (01709) 838992 E-mail: enquiries@kingsforthfencing.co.uk

Lewbuild Fence Products, Ashton Rd, Bardsley, Oldham, OL8 3HT Tel: 0161-633 2301 Fax: 0161-624 7525

N K Fencing, 40 Trailcock Road, Carrickfergus, County Antrim, BT38 7NU Tel: (028) 9335 1172 Fax: (028) 9333 6433 E-mail: sales@nkfencing.com

Roche Engineering, Spodden Mill, Station Road, Whitworth, Rochdale, Lancashire, OL12 8LJ Tel: (01706) 853385 Fax: (01706) 853385 E-mail: alan@rocheengineering.fsnet.co.uk

Warefence Ltd, Clare Terrace, Carterton, Oxfordshire, OX18 3ES Tel: (01993) 847227 Fax: (01993) 840551 E-mail: info@warefence.co.uk

SECURITY FILING KEY CABINETS

Securikey Ltd, PO Box 18, Aldershot, Hampshire, GU12 4SL Tel: (01252) 311888 Fax: (01252) 343950 E-mail: sales@securikey.co.uk

SECURITY FILING KEY CABINETS – *continued*

▶ Shurlok (UK), Unit 5 Oak Tree Park, Burns Medow Road, Moons Moat Industrial Estate, Redditch, Worcestershire, B98 9NW Tel: (01527) 592999 Fax: (01527) 592666 E-mail: sales@shurlok-keystorage.co.uk

▶ Tagster, Unit 30, 63 Jeddo Road, London, W12 9EE Tel: (0870) 0605528 Fax: (020) 8735 0150 E-mail: sales@tagster.co.uk

SECURITY GATE OR BARRIER INSTALLATION OR SERVICING

Automate UK, 9 Hill La Industrial Estate, Markfield, Leicestershire, LE67 9PN Tel: (01530) 249444 Fax: (01530) 249444 E-mail: sales@automateuk.co.uk

B F T Automation, Unit 8e Newby Road Industrial Estate, Newby Road, Hazel Grove, Stockport, Cheshire, SK7 5DA Tel: 0161-456 0456 Fax: 0161-456 9090 E-mail: info@bftautomation.co.uk

J A Smith, Harrowgate Road, London, E9 5ED Tel: (020) 8525 9842 Fax: (020) 8525 9842

▶ Maximeyes Security Ltd, Unit 2, Dalewood Road, Lymedale Business Park, Newcastle, Staffordshire, ST5 9QH Tel: (01782) 566611 Fax: (01782) 566616 E-mail: maximeyes2003@yahoo.co.uk

▶ Securit Security Systems Ltd, Unit 1, Sleaford Industrial Estate, Sleaford Road, Bracebridge Heath, Lincoln, LN4 2ND Tel: (01522) 569960

Window & Door Security Systems Ltd, Building 63, Third Avenue, Pensnett Trading Estate, Kingswinford, West Midlands, DY6 7XU Tel: (01384) 288321 Fax: (01384) 288212 E-mail: sales@windowanddoorsecurity.co.uk

SECURITY GATEHOUSES

1st Choice Security Services Ltd, Unit 4 Hall Court, Bridge Street, Polesworth, Tamworth, Staffordshire, B78 1DT Tel: (01827) 899972 Fax: (01827) 899953 E-mail: pgrace@1stcss.co.uk

C B Fabrications, Units 4-4a The Old Co-Op Bakery, Kellet Road, Carnforth, Lancashire, LA5 9LR Tel: (01524) 736577 Fax: (01524) 736577 E-mail: sales@cbfabrications.co.uk

SECURITY GATES OR BARRIERS

Beacon Associates, The Pines, Templewood Lane, Farnham Common, Slough, SL2 3HQ Tel: (01753) 648234 Fax: (01753) 648234

BID Group Ltd, Elland Close, Wingates Industrial Estate, Westhoughton, Bolton, BL5 3XE Tel: 0870 607 5050 Fax: 0870 6081271 E-mail: sales@bidgroup.co.uk

▶ Bradbury Security Grilles, Dunlop Way, Queensway Enterprise Estate, Scunthorpe, South Humberside, DN16 3RN Tel: (01724) 271999 Fax: (01724) 271888 E-mail: sales@bradburyuk.com

E J Collins & Son, 57 Addington Village Road, Croydon, CR0 5AS Tel: (01689) 843059

Easeserve Ltd, 3 The Mill, Durham Street, Droylsden, Manchester, M43 6DT Tel: 0161-370 9580 Fax: 0161-370 6746

Forge Fabrications, 8 South Street, Crowland, Peterborough, PE6 0AJ Tel: (01733) 211441 Fax: (01733) 211258 E-mail: justin@forgefabrications.co.uk

Fort Knox Security, Tollhurst Farm, Blackham, Tunbridge Wells, Kent, TN3 9UB Tel: (01892) 740839 Fax: (01892) 740839 E-mail: sales@fortknoxsecurity.ltd.uk

Gate A Mation Ltd, 8 Boundary Business Centre, Boundary Way, Woking, Surrey, GU21 5DH Tel: (01483) 747373 Fax: (01483) 776688 E-mail: sales@gate-a-mation.com

Gosport Engineering Co. Ltd, Lordship Lane, London, N17 8NS Tel: (020) 8808 2326 Fax: (020) 8885 2867 E-mail: gosporteng@btconnect.com

Ironcraft, 92 High Street, Earl Shilton, Leicester, LE9 7DG Tel: (01455) 847548 Fax: (01455) 842422 E-mail: office@ironcraft.co.uk

▶ Mcarthur, 198-202 Broomhill Road, Bristol, BS4 5SF Tel: 0117-977 3311 Fax: 0117-977 6164

▶ Taymore, Block 4A Unit 8, Larkhall Industrial Estate, Larkhall, Lanarkshire, ML9 2PA Tel: (01698) 884000 Fax: (01698) 886888

SECURITY GLASS

Solaglas Ltd, Trinity Trading Estate, Mill Way, Sittingbourne, Kent, ME10 2PD Tel: (01795) 421534 Fax: (01795) 473651

SECURITY GRILLES

Adlor Garage Door Services, 8 Brittania Business Park, Mills Road, Quarry Wood, Aylesford, Kent, ME20 7NT Tel: (01622) 882370 Fax: (01622) 882313

Airedale Blinds & Shutters, 10 Wellington Street, Laisterdyke, Bradford, West Yorkshire, BD4 8BW Tel: (01274) 661266 Fax: (01274) 661222 E-mail: abs@fallers.co.uk

Araywelds Mobile Services, 6 Flanders Road, London, E6 6DU Tel: (07885) 431727 Fax: (020) 8507 7056

B & M Wireworks, Prescot Trade Centre, Oliver Lyme Road, Prescot, Merseyside, L34 2SH Tel: 0151-431 0101 Fax: 0151-431 0101 E-mail: rickymartin@supanet.co.uk

B Rourke & Co. Ltd, Accrington Road, Burnley, Lancashire, BB11 5QD Tel: (01282) 422841 Fax: (01282) 458901 E-mail: info@rourkes.co.uk

BCP Fabrication Ltd, Dormston Trading Estate, Burton Road, Dudley, West Midlands, DY1 2UF Tel: (01902) 885777 Fax: (01902) 883344

C.P. Belcher (Welding) Ltd, 115B Blythswood Road, Tyseley, Birmingham, B11 2BX Tel: 0121-706 9689 Fax: 0121-706 8477 E-mail: steve@cpbsteel.fsnet.co.uk

Bluntray Ltd, 55 Lonsdale Road, London, NW6 6RA Tel: (020) 7624 8151 Fax: (020) 7624 2533

Burbage Gates Ltd, Sapcote Road, Burbage, Hinckley, Leicestershire, LE10 2AU Tel: (01455) 613844 Fax: (01455) 611333 E-mail: sales@burbagegates.co.uk

Central Iron Craft, Bissell Street, Birmingham, B5 7HP Tel: 0121-622 3123 Fax: 0121-622 3123

Cruddas Security Services Ltd, 1 Oak Street Industrial Park, Oak Street, Cradley Heath, West Midlands, B64 5JY Tel: (01384) 569307 Fax: (01384) 569307

D K O Designs, 66 Georges Road, London, N7 8HX Tel: (020) 7607 2653 Fax: (020) 7607 0515

D P Security, Ryecroft House, Green St Green Road, Dartford, DA2 8DX Tel: (01474) 707030 Fax: (01474) 707313 E-mail: info@dpsecurity.co.uk

▶ Drummond Security Ltd, 44 The Broadway, Darkes Lane, Potters Bar, Hertfordshire, EN6 2HW Tel: (01707) 644454 Fax: (01707) 651314 E-mail: enquiries@drummondsecurity.com

▶ Flairmet, Unit 1 2, Ladfordfields Industrial Park, Seighford, Stafford, ST18 9QE Tel: (01785) 282301 Fax: (01785) 282626 E-mail: flairmet@weathervane.uk.com

Grange Welding Services, Earl Street, Sheffield, S1 4PY Tel: 0114-272 7606 Fax: 0114-272 7606

H V P Security Shutters Ltd, 4 Grace Road West, Marsh Barton, Exeter, EX2 8PU Tel: (01392) 270218 Fax: (01392) 278548 E-mail: info@hvpshutters.co.uk

Hercules Security Fabrications Ltd, 1 Agl Business Park, Coundon Industrial Estate, Coundon, Bishop Auckland, County Durham, DL14 8NR Tel: (01388) 458794 Fax: (01388) 458806 E-mail: info@hercules-security.co.uk

Home Protection Security Grilles Ltd, 11a Bedford Road, London, SW4 7SH Tel: (020) 7737 2228 Fax: (020) 7737 2228

Industrial Doors Ltd, 8 Alexandra Industrial Estate, Locarno Road, Tipton, West Midlands, DY4 9SJ Tel: 0121-557 8757 Fax: 0121-520 9011 E-mail: mac@mandsshutterservicesltd.co.uk

Mirlyn Ltd, 57 Coleridge Street, Hove, East Sussex, BN3 5AB Tel: (01273) 733404 Fax: (01273) 703330

Myatt & Degville Fabrications Ltd, Selborne Street, Walsall, WS1 2JN Tel: (01922) 648222 Fax: (01922) 613565

Neway Doors Ltd, Lionel Works, 89/91 Rolfe Street, Smethwick, West Midlands, B66 2AY Tel: 0121-558 6406 Fax: 0121-555 7140 E-mail: sales@priory-group.co.uk

The Priory Group Ltd, Lionel Works, 89-91 Rolfe Street, Smethwick, West Midlands, B66 2AY Tel: 0121-558 6406 Fax: 0121-555 7140

R K R Security Ltd, 6 Bilton Road, Erith, Kent, DA8 2AN Tel: (01322) 334881

S Buck, 36 Stanley Road, Warmley, Bristol, BS15 4NX Tel: 0117-967 4740 Fax: 0117-961 8050

Scorpio Welding & Fabrications, 1 Old Wharf, Old Birchills, Walsall, WS2 8QD Tel: (01922) 643000 Fax: (01922) 643000

H. Scrowcroft & Sons, Daisyfield Works, Rosslyn Avenue, Preesall, Poulton-Le-Fylde, Lancashire, FY6 0HE Tel: (01253) 810451

Secure Shutters, 105 Richmond Road, Grays, Essex, RM17 6DN Tel: (01375) 397100 Fax: (01375) 397101 E-mail: sales@secureshutters.co.uk

Shading Systems Ltd, Unit F5 Innsworth Technology Park, Innsworth Lane, Gloucester, GL3 1DL Tel: (01452) 536000 Fax: (01452) 731901 E-mail: sales@shadings.co.uk

Shutter Door Repair & Maintenance Ltd, Lionel Works, 89-91 Rolfe Street, Smethwick, West Midlands, B66 2AY Tel: 0121-558 6406 Fax: 0121-555 7140 E-mail: sales@priory-group.com

Stratford Wire Works, Rowse Close, London, E15 2HX Tel: (020) 8534 1950 Fax: (020) 8534 8280

Tambour Doors Ltd, 21 Marston Lane, Marston, Northwich, Cheshire, CW9 6DL Tel: (01606) 42423 Fax: (01606) 48118

Trellidor Ltd, Unit 20 Bloomfield Park, Bloomfield Road, Tipton, West Midlands, DY4 9AH Tel: 0121-557 0303 Fax: 0121-557 0353 E-mail: sales@trellidor.co.uk

Welding Engineers (Glasgow) Ltd, 38 Dalness Street, Glasgow, G32 7RF Tel: 0141-778 8461 Fax: 0141-763 0152 E-mail: sales@weldingengineers.co.uk

SECURITY GUARD PATROL MONITORING SYSTEM CLOCKS

Addtime Recording Co. Ltd, 2 Eastwell Road, Ashton-in-Makerfield, Wigan, Lancashire, WN4 9QQ Tel: (01942) 272061 Fax: (01942) 274601 E-mail: sales@addtimerecording.co.uk

▶ All Year Security, 1 Peall Road, Croydon, CR0 3EX Tel: (0845) 9000707 Fax: (0845) 9000808 E-mail: info@allyearsecurity.co.uk

Autoclock Systems Ltd, 93-97 Second Avenue, Newcastle upon Tyne, NE6 5XT Tel: 0191-276 1611 Fax: 0191-265 0586 E-mail: sales@autoclocksystems.co.uk

Thames Manufacturing Co. Ltd, 29 Mansfields, Writtle, Chelmsford, CM1 3NH Tel: (01245) 422062 Fax: (01245) 422062

SECURITY GUARD PATROL SERVICES

Academy Guards Limited, 36a Church Hill, Loughton, Essex, IG10 1LA Tel: 0870 0847010 Fax: 0870 0847011 E-mail: info@academyguards.co.uk

Alliance Security Ltd, Alliance House, 180 Kingston Road, Leatherhead, Surrey, KT22 7PZ Tel: (01372) 362213 Fax: (01372) 386249

▶ Anglo Security, 33 Morecambe Road, Brighton, BN1 8TL Tel: (01273) 702500 Fax: (01273) 562479 E-mail: kenneth.mees@ntlworld.com

▶ Anubis Protection (UK), 46 Yewlands Avenue, Higher Blackley, Manchester, M9 6QR Tel: 0845 456 8717 Fax: 08712 365 328 E-mail: enquiries@anubis-protection.co.uk

▶ Diamond Event Security Ltd, 60 Heol Collen, Cardiff, CF5 5TX Tel: (029) 2059 1340 Fax: (029) 2059 6091 E-mail: info@diamondeventsecurity.co.uk

First National Security, 58 Castle Boulevard, Nottingham, NG7 1FN Tel: 0115-979 9299 Fax: 0115-979 9799 E-mail: info@firstnationalsecurity.co.uk

▶ Maximum Security, 60 Skylark Rise, Plymouth, PL6 7SN Tel: (01752) 695569 Fax: (01752) 548020 E-mail: safeandsecure@maximum-security.co.uk

▶ Protek security, 89 Circular Road, Denton, Manchester, M34 6NQ Tel: 0161-292 0662 E-mail: steventurnbull@msn.com

▶ Scion Electronics, 161 Hospital Street, Birmingham, B19 3XA Tel: 0121-359 6366 Fax: 0121-359 6448 E-mail: lee.davis@scionelectronics.co.uk

SECURITY GUARD SERVICES

Academy Guards Limited, 36a Church Hill, Loughton, Essex, IG10 1LA Tel: 0870 0847010 Fax: 0870 0847011 E-mail: info@academyguards.co.uk

▶ Alamo Security Services, Channelsea House, Canning Road, Stratford, London, E15 3ND Tel: (020) 8519 8866 Fax: (020) 8519 1191 E-mail: info@alamosecurity.co.uk

▶ Anglo Security, 33 Morecambe Road, Brighton, BN1 8TL Tel: (01273) 702500 Fax: (01273) 562479 E-mail: kenneth.mees@ntlworld.com

Grenadier Guards Security Services, Grenadier House, Condover, Shrewsbury, SY5 7BG Tel: 08450 539198 E-mail: info@grenadiersecurity.co.uk

▶ Maximum Security, 60 Skylark Rise, Plymouth, PL6 7SN Tel: (01752) 695569 Fax: (01752) 548020 E-mail: safeandsecure@maximum-security.co.uk

▶ Protek security, 89 Circular Road, Denton, Manchester, M34 6NQ Tel: 0161-292 0662 E-mail: steventurnbull@msn.com

SECURITY GUARD TRAINING

Myton Systems Ltd, 3 West End, Lund, Driffield, North Humberside, YO25 9TN Tel: (01377) 217364 Fax: (01377) 217364 E-mail: sales@mytonsystems.co.uk

▶ Panad Ltd, Unit 27, Brierley Business Centre, Mirion St, Crewe, CW1 2AZ Tel: (01270) 253533 Fax: (01270) 253544 E-mail: panad.limited@ntlworld.com

▶ PANAD Limited, Panad House, Alvaston Business Park, Middlewich Road, Nantwich, Cheshire, CW5 6PF Tel: (01270) 618520 Fax: (01270) 626613 E-mail: info@panadgroup.org

▶ Pyramid Training (UK) Ltd, Beechwood House, 34 Beechwood Avenue, Bradford, West Yorkshire, BD6 3AF Tel: (01274) 677776 E-mail: info@pyramid2000.fsnet.co.uk

SECURITY IDENTIFICATION SYSTEMS

Identicar, Rushland Farm, Knowle Lane, Wookey, Wells, Somerset, BA5 1LD Tel: (01749) 677381

Identify UK Ltd, Prestongate, Hessle, North Humberside, HU13 0RD Tel: (01482) 222070 Fax: (01482) 327214 E-mail: info@rfidsystems.co.uk

Identilam plc, Faygate Business Centre, Faygate Lane, Faygate, Horsham, West Sussex, RH12 4DN Tel: (01293) 851711 Fax: (01293) 851742 E-mail: sales@indentilam.co.uk

Oxley Developments Co. Ltd, Priory Park, Ulverston, Cumbria, LA12 9QG Tel: (01229) 582621 Fax: (01229) 483263 E-mail: sales@oxleygroup.com

Raytheon Systems Ltd, Fullerton Road, Queensway Industrial Estate, Glenrothes, Fife, KY7 5PY Tel: (01592) 754311 Fax: (01592) 759775 E-mail: carol.fleming@raytheon.co.uk

SECURITY INDUSTRY TRAINING ORGANISATION (SITO) APPROVED TRAINING

▶ Nemesis Security & Training Ltd, Unit 15, Belmont Business Centre, East Hoathly, Lewes, East Sussex, BN8 6QL Tel: (0845) 3653768 E-mail: nemesissecurityltd@hotmail.com

SECURITY INSTALLATION CONTRACTORS

3D Security Systems Ltd, 66A Market Street, Watford, WD18 0PX Tel: (01923) 219141 Fax: (01923) 219142

Abacus Crime Prevention, 17 Staverton Close, Bracknell, Berkshire, RG42 2HH Tel: (01344) 303606 Fax: (01344) 648765

Abode Security, 155 Moor Lane, Salford, M7 3QE Tel: 0161-792 4223

Ace Security & Electrical Ltd, 150-152 Loughton Way, Buckhurst Hill, Essex, IG9 6AR Tel: (020) 8506 1421 Fax: (020) 8506 6666

Armaplate UK Ltd, Central Workshops, Back Longworth Road, Horwich, Bolton, BL6 7DB Tel: (01204) 468295 Fax: (01204) 468356 E-mail: info@armaplate.com

Atlas Fire & Security Ltd, Unit 8A Lansil Industrial Estate, Caton Road, Lancaster, LA1 3PQ Tel: (01524) 69488 Fax: (01524) 842972

Blanchard Security, 51 Mill Street, Bideford, Devon, EX39 2JS Tel: (01237) 472084 Fax: (01237) 423703 E-mail: Kellysearch@blanchards.f9.co.uk

Britannic Security Systems Ltd, The Exchange, Haslucks Green Road, Shirley, Solihull, West Midlands, B90 2EL Tel: 0121-744 0770 Fax: (0870) 2000772 E-mail: information@britannic-security.com

▶ C D S Security Ltd, 8-9 Dragonville Industrial Park, Dragon Lane, Durham, DH1 2XH Tel: 0191-384 0079 Fax: 0191-384 0071

Clayman Electronics Ltd, 91 Stour View Gardens, Corfe Mullen, Wimborne, Dorset, BH21 3TL Tel: (01202) 849777

Connelly Security Systems, 100 Glentanar Road, Glasgow, G22 7XS Tel: 0141-336 3336 Fax: 0141-336 1456

Cooper Security Systems Ltd, 11 Tenby Grove, Worksop, Nottinghamshire, S80 2PP Tel: (01909) 487411

Cowper Shaw Locksmiths Ltd, 33-34 Blandford Street, Sunderland, SR1 3JJ Tel: 0191-567 2882 Fax: 0191-564 0383

Crown Securities UK Ltd, Security House, Bunsley Bank, Audlem, Crewe, CW3 0HS Tel: (01270) 812286 Fax: (01270) 812322 E-mail: mail@crownsecurities.co.uk

D R Security Systems, 96 Osborne Road, London, E7 0PL Tel: (020) 8534 7130 Fax: (020) 8519 5147 E-mail: info@drsecurity.co.uk

Door Entry Systems Ltd, Belgrave Business Centre, 45 Frederick Street, Edinburgh, EH2 1EP Tel: (01905) 799110 Fax: 0131-220 3550

Elite Security Services Ltd, Suite 1 2 Bateman Business Centre, Bateman Street, Derby, DE23 8JQ Tel: (01332) 383630 Fax: (01332) 299981 E-mail: sales@elite-derby.co.uk

Fairfield Security Systems Ltd, 10 Wyndham Cresent, Cardiff, CF11 9EH Tel: (029) 2022 5003 Fax: (029) 2021 5335

G M C Fire & Security-Protection, Service, 14 Railway St, Malton, North Yorkshire, YO17 7NR Tel: (01653) 697917 Fax: (01653) 697836

Gem Alarms & Security Services, 24 West Bay, Bridport, Dorset, DT6 4HD Tel: (01308) 423470 Fax: (01308) 423470

Hereford Security Services Ltd, Unit 5 50 Catherine Street, Hereford, HR1 2DU Tel: (01432) 264544 Fax: (01432) 264544 E-mail: mail@herefordsecurityservices.co.uk

Hi-Tech Alarms, 5 Tingley Crescent, Tingley, Wakefield, West Yorkshire, WF3 1JF Tel: 0113-252 9917

In Car Connection Ltd, 3 Stirling Road, Dunblane, Perthshire, FK15 9EP Tel: (01786) 825581 Fax: (01786) 825581

Intek Electronics, 248 Ashley Road, Poole, Dorset, BH14 9BZ Tel: (01202) 716091 Fax: (01202) 716092 E-mail: info@intek-electronics.co.uk

J D Groves Ltd, 7 Lenham Road East, Rottingdean, Brighton, BN2 7GP Tel: (01273) 306394 Fax: (01273) 300658

Kings Security Systems Ltd, Security House, Bob Hardisty Drive, Bishop Auckland, County Durham, DL14 7AL Tel: (01388) 451433 Fax: (01388) 451269

Kwick Key & Lock Service, Sherman Road, Bromley, BR1 3JN Tel: (020) 8464 3249 Fax: (020) 8464 5332

SECURITY INSTALLATION CONTRACTORS – *continued*

Lynx Security, The Old Pump Station, Furnace Lane, Finedon, Wellingborough, Northamptonshire, NN9 5NZ Tel: (01604) 621727 Fax: (01536) 724666 E-mail: enquiries@lynxsecurity.net

M & S Security Systems, 11 Houlson Street, Penywern, Dowlais, Merthyr Tydfil, CF48 3NW Tel: (01685) 389143 Fax: (01685) 389143

Mcgill, Harrison Road, Dundee, DD2 3SN Tel: (01382) 884488 Fax: (01382) 828777 E-mail: sales@mcgill-electrical.co.uk

Rayitson Communications, 17 Balfour Business Centre, Balfour Road, Southall, Middlesex, UB2 5BD Tel: (020) 8574 4340 Fax: (020) 8574 4289

Romec, 3 Gorgie Park Road, Edinburgh, EH14 1UA Tel: 0131-452 7900 Fax: 0131-452 7955

Romec Security Services, 3 Gorgie Park Road, Edinburgh, EH14 1UA Tel: 0131-452 7974 Fax: 0131-452 7922

S G D Security Ltd, 26-28 Dalcross Street, Cardiff, CF24 4SD Tel: (029) 2046 4120 Fax: (029) 2047 0843 E-mail: info@sgdsecurity.com

S P S, 63 Magna Road, Bournemouth, BH11 9ND Tel: (01202) 570142 Fax: (01202) 570142 E-mail: dave.robinson@spssecurity.org.uk

Safegard Security, 1a Old Torquay Road, Paignton, Devon, TQ3 2QY Tel: (01803) 523455 Fax: (01803) 556686 E-mail: info@safegardsecurity.co.uk

Safeway Security Services Ltd, 17 Hook Road, Goole, North Humberside, DN14 5JB Tel: (01405) 760664 Fax: (01405) 768727 E-mail: sales@safewaysecurityservices.com

Scantec Systems, Nicker Hill, Keyworth, Nottingham, NG12 5GD Tel: 0115-937 2023

Scotshield Burglar Alarm Systems, 1 Dryden Vale, Bilston Glen, Loanhead, Midlothian, EH20 9HN Tel: 0131-448 0583 Fax: 0131-448 0584 E-mail: admin@scotshield.com

Sign Shop, 93 West Main Street, Broxburn, West Lothian, EH52 5LE Tel: (01506) 853601 Fax: (01506) 853601

Siteguard UK Ltd, Unit 30 Canal Bridge Enterprise Centre, Meadow Lane, Ellesmere Port, CH65 4EH Tel: 0151-355 3456 Fax: 0151-355 7809 E-mail: info@siteguarduk.com

Swift Security Systems (Midlands) Ltd, 6-10 Rising Lea, Derby Road, Risley, Derby, DE72 3SS Tel: 0115-949 9449 Fax: 0115-939 7620

Swindon Security Systems, 2 Kitefield, Cricklade, Swindon, SN6 6NF Tel: (01793) 752820 Fax: (01793) 752820

Technical Services Shropshire Ltd, Unit 8, Bicton Business Park, Isle Lane, Bicton Heath, Shrewsbury, SY3 8DY Tel: (01743) 851313 Fax: (01743) 851211 E-mail: info@tsshropshire.co.uk

Telesat Communications, 84 Sleaford Road, Boston, Lincolnshire, PE21 8EU Tel: (01205) 369934 Fax: (01205) 369934 E-mail: telesat@totalise.co.uk

Top Security Alarm Systems, 1 Hall Lane, Prescot, Merseyside, L34 5UN Tel: (0800) 378226 Fax: 0151-289 5532

▶ Unique Integrated Systems, 3c Selby Place, Stanley Industrial Estate, Skelmersdale, Lancashire, WN8 8EF Tel: (01695) 50332 Fax: (01695) 50644

W R S Alarms, 103 High Street, Yatton, Bristol, BS49 4DR Tel: (01934) 834013 Fax: (01934) 876142 E-mail: admin@wrsalarms.com

Westronics Ltd, 11-12 Marcus Close, Tilehurst, Reading, RG30 4EA Tel: 0118-942 6726 Fax: 0118-945 1481 E-mail: sales@westronics.co.uk

SECURITY INVESTIGATION

▶ Angel Investigations - Privacy Consultants, The 401 Centre, Regent Street, London, W1 Tel: (020) 7692 0000 E-mail: ahunter149@hotmail.com

Public Service Investigations Ltd, 5 Hunsterson Road, Hatherton, Nantwich, Cheshire, CW5 7RA Tel: 01270 842655 Fax: 01270 842427 E-mail: info@psi-ltd.com

Research Associates, 282 Latimer Road, London, W10 6QW Tel: (020) 7854 9000 Fax: (020) 7854 9090 E-mail: private@investigationservices.co.uk

Securitas Group, 203-205 Lower Richmond Road, Richmond, Surrey, TW9 4LN Tel: 0845 5314061 Fax: (020) 8876 4650 E-mail: jenny.campbell@securitas.uk.com

Williams Associates, 9 Carlton Cresent, Southampton, SO15 2EZ Tel: (023) 8033 9959 Fax: (023) 8033 3582 E-mail: wilassoc@hants09.freeserve.co.uk

SECURITY LABELS

▶ Maxtag (UK) Ltd, 8 Suttons Bussiness Park, Reading, RG6 1AZ Tel: 0118-935 6180 Fax: 0118-935 6181 E-mail: sales@maxtag.com

▶ Security Label, 76 High Street, Dunbar, East Lothian, EH42 1JH Tel: (01368) 869921 E-mail: enquiry@security-label.co.uk

SECURITY LIGHTING

All Electrical Services Ltd, North Mace House, Viaduct Road, Cardiff, CF15 9XF Tel: (029) 2081 0274 Fax: (029) 2081 0282 E-mail: info@allelectricalserviceswales.com

Voltek Automation, Churchill Way, Nelson, Lancashire, BB9 6RT Tel: (0870) 7454971 Fax: (0870) 7454972 E-mail: sales@voltek.co.uk

SECURITY LIGHTING SYSTEM INSTALLATION OR SERVICING

▶ Axxess 28 Ltd, 18 Rosemary Lane, Blackwater, Camberley, Surrey, GU17 0LS Tel: (01276) 36915 Fax: (01276) 36917 E-mail: sales@axxess28.com

Millers Alarms Ltd, Moorley House, 539 Woodborough Road, Mapperly, Nottingham, NG3 5FR Tel: 0115-960 4232 Fax: 0115-955 2552 E-mail: millersalarms@ntlworld.com

▶ David Webster Ltd, Field House, Station Approach, Harlow, Essex, CM20 2FB Tel: (01279) 645100 Fax: (01279) 645101 E-mail: info@dwltd.co.uk

SECURITY LIGHTING SYSTEMS

Airkool Projects Ltd, 10 Rotterdam Road, Hull, HU7 0XD Tel: (01482) 371888 Fax: (01482) 371889 E-mail: info@airkool.co.uk

Kinetic Products Ltd, Unit B1, Brookside Business Park, Greengate Middleton, Manchester, M24 1GS Tel: 0161-654 9595 Fax: 0161-654 9596 E-mail: sales@kinetic-security.co.uk

Luminite Security Equipment, 2a Bellevue Road, London, N11 3ER Tel: (020) 8368 7887 Fax: (020) 8368 3952 E-mail: sales@luminite.co.uk

Peca Electronics, 1 Parnell Court, Andover, Hampshire, SP10 3LX Tel: (01264) 355975 Fax: (01264) 366536 E-mail: sales@peca-electronics.co.uk

Timeguard Ltd, Victory Park, 400 Edgware Road, London, NW2 6ND Tel: (020) 8450 8944 Fax: (020) 8452 5143 E-mail: csc@timeguard.com

Unicom Group, Enterprise Way, Edenbridge, Kent, TN8 6EW Tel: (01732) 865238 Fax: (01732) 866820 E-mail: info@uni-com.uk.com

SECURITY LOCKS

Barnet Lock & Security, 123-125 Baker Street, Enfield, Middlesex, EN1 3HA Tel: (020) 8342 0040 Fax: (020) 8342 0230 E-mail: barnetlock@btconnect.com

Guardian Lock & Engineering Co. Ltd, Imperial Works, Wednesfield Road, Willenhall, West Midlands, WV13 1AL Tel: (01902) 633396 Fax: (01902) 630675

Irm Bristol Ltd, Unit 1 2 Armstrong Court, Armstrong Way, Yate, Bristol, BS37 5NG Tel: (01454) 321311 Fax: (01454) 273411 E-mail: sales@irm-bristol.co.uk

Ison Ltd, Victoria St, High Wycombe, Buckinghamshire, HP11 2LT Tel: (01494) 437020 Fax: (01494) 526615 E-mail: fred@isonuk.net

J. Newsome (Tools) Ltd, Unit 1, Harleston Street, Sheffield, S4 7QB Tel: 0114-275 7002 Fax: 0114-279 7070 E-mail: newsome@syol.com

Ronis-Dom Ltd, Moor Street South, Blakenhall, Wolverhampton, WV2 3JJ Tel: (01902) 715440 Fax: (01902) 715145

Securefast plc, Meadow Dale Works, Dimminsdale, Willenhall, West Midlands, WV13 2BE Tel: (01902) 607503 Fax: (01902) 609327 E-mail: sales@securefast.co.uk

Sharp Maintenance Services, 57 Ballens Road, Chatham, Kent, ME5 8NX Tel: (01634) 683232 Fax: (01634) 200025

Special Security Products, 37 Warren Hill Road, Birmingham, B44 8HA Tel: 0121-344 4593 Fax: 0121-356 0867 E-mail: enquiries@special-locks.com

Specialized Security Products Ltd, Unit 18, Park Farm Industrial Estate, Ermine Street, Buntingford, Hertfordshire, SG9 9AZ Tel: (01763) 274223 Fax: (01763) 273515 E-mail: sales@specialized-security.co.uk

Wadsworth Security Products, Unit 1 Epsom Downs Metro Centre, Waterfield, Tadworth, Surrey, KT20 5EZ Tel: (01737) 360512 Fax: (01737) 370475

Worrall Locks Ltd, Erebus Works, Albion Road, Willenhall, West Midlands, WV13 1NH Tel: (01902) 605038 Fax: (01902) 633558 E-mail: sales@worrall-locks.co.uk

SECURITY LOCKS AND KEYS

▶ Fast Key Services Ltd, 5c Russell Court, Russell Gardens, Wickford, Essex, SS11 8QU Tel: (01268) 562562 Fax: (01268) 570121 E-mail: marc@fastkeys.co.uk

▶ Locksmiths I/C Supplies Division, Unit B6, Rudford Industrial Estate, Ford, Arundel, West Sussex, BN18 0BF Tel: (01903) 735321 Fax: (01903) 732777 E-mail: sales@icsupplies.co.uk

SECURITY LOCKS, GATE

Atlantic Security, Unit 462 Robeson Street, Bow Common Lane, London, E3 4JA Tel: (020) 8981 5559 Fax: (020) 8981 5559 E-mail: atlansecur@yahoo.co.uk

▶ Security & Control Scotland, Block 15, West Avenue, Blantyre Industrial Estate, Glasgow, G72 0UZ Tel: 01698 713100 Fax: 01698 713111 E-mail: sales@security-control.co.uk

SECURITY MARKING LABELS

Cash's, Torrington Avenue, Coventry, CV4 9UZ Tel: (024) 7646 6466 Fax: (024) 7646 2525 E-mail: sales@jjcash.co.uk

SECURITY MARKING SERVICES, POSSESSION/OFFICE EQUIPMENT/VEHICLE ETC

Farmkey Ltd, Alpha Building, London Road, Nantwich, Cheshire, CW5 7JW Tel: (08708) 707107 Fax: (01270) 616702 E-mail: info@farmkey.co.uk

Retainagroup Ltd., 134-136 Buckingham Palace Road, London, SW1W 9SA Tel: (020) 7823 6868 Fax: (020) 7823 6864 E-mail: general.sales@retainagroup.co.uk

Selectamark Security Systems Ltd, 1 Locks Court, 429 Crofton Road, Orpington, Kent, BR6 8NL Tel: (01689) 860757 Fax: (01689) 860693 E-mail: sales@selectamark.co.uk

SECURITY METAL DETECTORS

L3 Comunnications Ltd, Astro House, Brants Bridge, Bracknell, Berkshire, RG12 9HW Tel: (01344) 477900 Fax: (01344) 477901 E-mail: matthew.woodman@l-3.com

SECURITY NIGHT VISION EQUIPMENT

Qinetiq, Cody Technology Park, Ively Road, Farnborough, Hampshire, GU14 0LX Tel: 08700 100942 Fax: (01252) 393399 E-mail: contactus@qinetiq.com

SECURITY PAPER

Communisis Security Products Ltd, Trafford Wharf Road, Trafford Park, Manchester, M17 1HE Tel: 0161-869 1000 Fax: 0161-869 1010

Portals, Overton Mill, Overton, Basingstoke, Hampshire, RG25 3JG Tel: (01256) 770770 Fax: (01256) 770937 E-mail: sales.portals@delarue.co.uk

SECURITY POST BOXES

GlenCall International, 4 Balgedie Court, Glenlomond, Kinross, KY13 9HF Tel: 01592 840 853 E-mail: enquiries@glencall.co.uk

SECURITY PRINTERS/PRINTING SERVICES

Aero-Print Securities Ltd, Gatehouse Way, Aylesbury, Buckinghamshire, HP19 8DD Tel: (01296) 485131 Fax: (01296) 485097 E-mail: sales@aero-print.co.uk

Stephen Austin & Sons Ltd, Caxton Hill, Hertford, SG13 7LU Tel: (01992) 584955 Fax: (01992) 500021 E-mail: sales@stephenaustin.co.uk

Brown Knight & Truscott Holdings Ltd, North Farm Road, High Brooms, Tunbridge Wells, Kent, TN2 3BW Tel: (01892) 511678 Fax: (01892) 511343

Capita Printing Services, Unit C Croydon Road Industrial Estate, Tannery Close, Beckenham, Kent, BR3 4BY Tel: (020) 8662 7010 Fax: (020) 8662 7003 E-mail: sales@capita.co.uk

Communisis Security Products Ltd, Trafford Wharf Road, Trafford Park, Manchester, M17 1HE Tel: 0161-869 1000 Fax: 0161-869 1010

Communitis Chorleys Ltd, Manston Lane, Leeds, LS15 8AH Tel: 0113-225 5000 Fax: 0113-225 5400 E-mail: sales@chorleys-communisis.co.uk

Community Security Products Ltd, Frances Street, Crewe, CW2 6HG Tel: (01270) 502600 Fax: (01270) 502601

CTD, Unit 2, CTD House, Summit Business Park, Hanworth Road, Sunbury-on-Thames, Middlesex, TW16 5BH Tel: 01932 771300 Fax: 01932 789229 E-mail: sales@ctdprinters.com

De La Rue Holdings plc, De Lane Rue House, Jays Close, Basingstoke, Hampshire, RG22 4BS Tel: (01256) 329122 Fax: (01256) 351323 E-mail: sales@delarue.com

Gordon Press Ltd, Caxton House, 2 Bath House Road, Croydon, CR0 4TT Tel: (020) 8684 0313 Fax: (020) 8689 6715 E-mail: sales@thegordonpress.com

Intrusion Security Services, 1 Ancells Court, Rye Close, Fleet, Hampshire, GU51 2UY Tel: (01252) 812030 Fax: (01252) 812040 E-mail: sales@intrusion.com

Kalamazoo Secure Solutions Ltd, Northfield, Birmingham, B31 2NY Tel: 0121-256 2222 Fax: 0121-256 2249 E-mail: kalamazoo@ksp.co.uk

▶ Menzies Nunn Ltd, The Wallows Industrial Estate, Fens Pool Avenue, Brierley Hill, West Midlands, DY5 1QA Tel: (01384) 262148 Fax: (01384) 265136 E-mail: sales@menzies-nunn.co.uk

▶ Micro Computer Forms Ltd, 9 Blackbrook Valley Industrial Estate, Narrowboat Way, Dudley, West Midlands, DY2 0XQ Tel: (01384) 455221 Fax: (01384) 455223 E-mail: lsm@mcforms.co.uk

R W Pierce & Co. Ltd, 17 Dargan CR, Belfast, BT3 9HJ Tel: (028) 9037 1010 Fax: (028) 9037 2501

Seareach Ltd, Seareach House, 34a, The Broadway, Leigh-on-Sea, Essex, SS9 1AJ Tel: 01702 476286 Fax: 01702 476385 E-mail: info@seareach.plc.uk

Smith & Ouzman Ltd, 45 Brampton Road, Eastbourne, East Sussex, BN22 9AH Tel: (01323) 524000 Fax: (01323) 524024 E-mail: print@smith-ouzman.com

▶ T A L L Security Print Ltd, Unit 2 Pembroke Court, Manor Park, Runcorn, Cheshire, WA7 1TJ Tel: (01928) 579200 Fax: (01928) 579294

Tresises, Stanley Street, Burton-on-Trent, Staffordshire, DE14 1DY Tel: (01283) 568276 Fax: (01283) 511207

SECURITY SAFES

Associated Security Group Ltd, 277 Wandsworth Bridge Road, London, SW6 2TX Tel: (020) 7736 7092 Fax: (020) 8669 9890 E-mail: info@associatedsecuritygroup.co.uk

▶ Bradbury Security Grilles, Dunlop Way, Queensway Enterprise Estate, Scunthorpe, South Humberside, DN16 3RN Tel: (01724) 271999 Fax: (01724) 271888 E-mail: sales@bradburyuk.com

Fbh-Fichet Ltd, 7/8 Amor Way, Letchworth Garden City, Hertfordshire, SG6 1UG Tel: (01462) 472900 Fax: (01462) 472901 E-mail: sales@fbh-fichet.com

Gunnebo UK Ltd, Wolverhampton, WV10 0BY Tel: 01902 455111 E-mail: marketing@gunnebo.com

▶ JB Locksmith, 33 Park Road, Conisbrough, Doncaster, South Yorkshire, DN12 2EQ Tel: (01709) 867361 Fax: (01709) 867361 E-mail: john@jblocksmithdoncaster.co.uk

SECURITY SCREEN INSTALLATION SERVICES

K S Security Ltd, Units 2-6, Warsop Trading Estate, Hever Road, Edenbridge, Kent, TN8 5LD Tel: (01732) 867199 Fax: (01732) 867102 E-mail: info@ks-security.co.uk

Safetell International Ltd, Unit 46, Fawkes Avenue, Dartford, DA1 1JQ Tel: (01322) 223233 Fax: (01322) 277751

SECURITY SEALS

Bond R S C Associates Ltd, Unit 3 Mercy Terrace, Ladywell, London, SE13 7UX Tel: (020) 8314 1188 Fax: (020) 8314 1221 E-mail: info@bondmailrooms.com

SECURITY SERVICES

1st Choice Security Services Ltd, Unit 4 Hall Court, Bridge Street, Polesworth, Tamworth, Staffordshire, B78 1DT Tel: (01827) 899972 Fax: (01827) 899953 E-mail: pgrace@1stcss.co.uk

Ace Security, Security House, 248 Pellon Lane, Halifax, West Yorkshire, HX1 4PZ Tel: (01422) 342444 E-mail: sales@acesecurity.com

ADT Fire & Security plc, Adt House, Kilmartin Place, Uddingston, Glasgow, G71 5PH Tel: (01698) 486000 Fax: (01698) 486100 E-mail: info@adtfireandsecurity.co.uk

▶ Advanced Security, Chevron House, 346 Long Lane, Hillingdon, Uxbridge, Middlesex, UB10 9PF Tel: (01895) 201800 Fax: (01895) 201801 E-mail: info@securiplan.co.uk

All Security Ltd, 1a Colston Avenue, Carshalton, Surrey, SM5 2PH Tel: (020) 8643 2151 Fax: (020) 8770 0038

▶ All Year Security, 1 Peall Road, Croydon, CR0 3EX Tel: (0845) 9000707 Fax: (0845) 9000808 E-mail: info@allyearsecurity.co.uk

Andron Contract Services Ltd, 7 Telford Place, Cumbernauld, Glasgow, G67 2NH Tel: (01236) 451143 Fax: (01236) 451134 E-mail: admin@andron.co.uk

▶ Anubis Protection (UK), 46 Yewlands Avenue, Higher Blackley, Manchester, M9 6QR Tel: 0845 456 8717 Fax: 08712 365 328 E-mail: enquiries@anubis-protection.co.uk

Armtrack Security Services, 127 Moresk Road, Truro, Cornwall, TR1 1BP Tel: (01872) 222022 Fax: (01872) 222022

SECURITY SERVICES – *continued*

Associated Security Ltd, 59 London Road, Wallington, Surrey, SM6 7HW Tel: (020) 8669 7811 Fax: (020) 8669 9890 E-mail: sales@associatedsecurity.co.uk
Associated Security Group Ltd, 277 Wandsworth Bridge Road, London, SW6 2TX Tel: (020) 7736 7092 Fax: (020) 8669 9890 E-mail: info@associatedsecuritygroup.co.uk
Associated Security Group Ltd, 277 Wandsworth Bridge Road, London, SW6 2TX Tel: (020) 7736 7092 Fax: (020) 8669 9890 E-mail: info@associatedsecuritygroup.co.uk
Associated Security Group Ltd, 59 London Road, Wallington, Surrey, SM6 7HW Tel: (020) 8669 7722 Fax: (020) 8669 9890 E-mail: sales@associatedsecuritygroup.co.uk
Audiotel International Ltd, Corby Road, Weldon, Corby, Northamptonshire, NN17 3AR Tel: (01536) 266677 Fax: (01586) 277711 E-mail: sales@audiotel-international.com
A-Z Windscreens, 17 Boar Green Close, Manchester, M40 3AW Tel: 0161-682 2399 Fax: 0161-682 2399
Bowman & Porter Security Ltd, 678 High Road, North Finchley, London, N12 9PT Tel: (020) 8446 2541 Fax: (020) 8445 6016
Carlisle Facility Ltd, Block C, Albany Place, Hyde Way, Welwyn Garden City, Hertfordshire, AL7 3BG Tel: (01707) 824200 E-mail: mail@carlislefacility.com
Carlisle Staffing plc, 3 Albany Place, Hyde Way, Welwyn Garden City, Hertfordshire, AL7 3BG Tel: (01707) 323000 Fax: (020) 8498 8851
Chesterfield Auto Electrical Ltd, Storforth La Trading Estate, Hasland, Chesterfield, Derbyshire, S41 0QL Tel: (01246) 554404 Fax: (01246) 554404 E-mail: sales@cae-auto-electrical.co.uk
Chubb Emergency Response, 5 Repton Court, Repton Close, Basildon, Essex, SS13 1LN Tel: (01268) 522066 Fax: (01268) 273070 E-mail: andrew.vaccari@chubb.co.uk
Chubb Security Personnel Ltd, 2nd Floor The Brooke Building, Shepcote Lane, Sheffield, S9 1QT Tel: 0114-272 6552 Fax: 0114-242 5641
Churchill Recruitment Consultants Ltd, Arodene House, 41-55 Perth Road, Ilford, Essex, IG2 6BX Tel: (020) 8518 6969 Fax: (020) 8518 6970 E-mail: recruit@churchillrecruitment.com
Contract Security Services Ltd, Challenger House, 125 Gunnersbury Lane, London, W3 8LH Tel: (020) 8752 0160 Fax: (020) 8992 9536 E-mail: cssltd1@aol.com
Cromwell Security & Fire Services Ltd, 72 Fortune Green Road, London, NW6 1DS Tel: (020) 7435 0334 Fax: (020) 7794 3384
▶ D & G Short, 19 Station Road, Flitwick, Bedford, MK45 1JT Tel: (01525) 753819 Fax: (01525) 716687 E-mail: info@dandgshort.com
Dawes Security Systems, 74 Hulme Hall Road, Cheadle Hulme, Cheadle, Cheshire, SK8 6LF Tel: 0161-485 8100 Fax: 0161-486 6500 E-mail: sales@dawessecurity.co.uk
▶ Detect International Ltd, Hulmes Bridge House, North Moor Lane, Halsall, Ormskirk, Lancashire, L39 8RF Tel: (0870) 3007201 Fax: (0870) 3007202 E-mail: Info@dik9.com
▶ Diamond Event Security Ltd, 60 Heol Collen, Cardiff, CF5 5TX Tel: (029) 2059 1340 Fax: (029) 2059 6091 E-mail: info@diamondeventsecurity.co.uk
Dyno-Locks, 143 Maple Road, Surbiton, Surrey, KT6 4BJ Tel: (020) 8481 2200 Fax: (020) 8481 2288 E-mail: postmaster@dyno.com
▶ E J C, PO Box 103, Aylesbury, Buckinghamshire, HP17 8WL Tel: (0845) 3510603 E-mail: enquiries@essenjay.com
Eagle Security Solutions Ltd, 162 Trafalgar Road, London, SE10 9TZ Tel: (0845) 9002950 E-mail: info@eaglesecuritysolutions.co.uk
Elite Contract Security Ltd, Elite House, 83-85 Badsley Moor Lane, Rotherham, South Yorkshire, S65 2PH Tel: (01709) 382120 Fax: (01709) 376000 E-mail: ecs2004@aol.com
European Research & Investigations Ltd, 52 Upper Brook Street, Mayfair, London, W1K 5BB Tel: (020) 7499 9822 Fax: (020) 7493 4220 E-mail: sipinternational@aol.com
Harling Security Products, 237 Church Road, Hayes, Middlesex, UB3 2LG Tel: (020) 8561 3787 Fax: (020) 8848 0999 E-mail: harlingsec@aol.com
Horan Fencing Ltd, 220 Easter Road, Edinburgh, EH6 8LE Tel: 0131-555 3155 Fax: 0131-555 4610
Initial Security Ltd, Unit 14 Sovereign Enterprise Park, King William Street, Salford, M50 3UP Tel: 0161-848 0141 Fax: 0161-848 0520
Isl Dardan Security Ltd, Aston House, 18a Bidwell Road, Rackheath, Norwich, NR13 6PT Tel: (01603) 263000 Fax: (01603) 263070 E-mail: sales@isldarden.co.uk
Kinetic Products Ltd, Unit B1, Brookside Business Park, Greengate Middleton, Manchester, M24 1GS Tel: 0161-654 9595 Fax: 0161-654 9596 E-mail: sales@kinetic-security.co.uk
L3 Comunications Ltd, Astro House, Brants Bridge, Bracknell, Berkshire, RG12 9HW Tel: (01344) 477900 Fax: (01344) 477901 E-mail: matthew.woodman@l-3.com
Legion Security, 351-353 Newmarket Road, Cambridge, CB5 8JG Tel: (01223) 352328 Fax: (01223) 355223
▶ Lion Watch Security Services Ltd, 143 High Street, Chesterton, Cambridge, CB4 1NL Tel: (07903) 960665 E-mail: info@lionwatch.co.uk
Lisburn Security Services Ltd, Security House, Lissea Industrial Estate East, Lisburn, County Antrim, BT28 2RD Tel: (028) 9260 5859 Fax: (028) 9262 2423 E-mail: gsmith@lisburnsecurityservices.co.uk
Lodge Service (Midland) Ltd, Scala House, Holloway Circus, Queensway, Birmingham, B1 1EQ Tel: 0121-643 2400 Fax: 0121-643 1807 E-mail: lodgeserv@virgin.net
Lothian Alarms, Cooper Business Park, Buchan Lane, Broxburn, West Lothian, EH52 5QD Tel: (01506) 855978 Fax: (01506) 855666
Mainline Security Systems, 39 Wrawby Street, Brigg, South Humberside, DN20 9BS Tel: (01652) 650567 Fax: (01652) 658818
Masterguard Security Services Ltd, Masterguard House, 1 Ipsley Street, Redditch, Worcestershire, B98 7AR Tel: (01527) 65344 Fax: (01527) 63888 E-mail: mastergaurd_2000@yahoo.co.uk
▶ Metropolitan Security Services Group Ltd, 384 Poynters Road, Luton, LU4 0TW Tel: (0870) 2424557 Fax: (01582) 570001 E-mail: sales@metropolitansecurity.co.uk
Millers Alarms Ltd, Moorley House, 539 Woodborough Road, Mapperly, Nottingham, NG3 5FR Tel: 0115-960 4232 Fax: 0115-955 2552 E-mail: millersalarms@ntlworld.com
Mison Security Ltd, 5 Skyline, Lime Harbour, London, E14 9TS Tel: (020) 7093 1177 Fax: (020) 7923 0493 E-mail: mail@misonsecurity.com
▶ Monarch Security Ltd, 20-24 Constitution Street, Edinburgh, EH6 7BT Tel: 0131-554 3553 Fax: 0131-555 2100
Northern Protection, Unit 38 The Brampton Centre, Brampton Road, Wath-upon-Dearne, Rotherham, South Yorkshire, S63 6BB Tel: (01709) 879333 Fax: (01709) 879443 E-mail: cm@nightforce.co.uk
Orbis Property Protection, 106 Oxford Road, Uxbridge, Middlesex, UB8 1NA Tel: (01895) 465500 Fax: (01895) 465499 E-mail: pat.sullivan@ux.orbis-opp.com
Peter Tomas & Co., 50 Lancaster Street, Higham Ferrers, Rushden, Northamptonshire, NN10 8HY Tel: (01933) 359688
Pro Tect Security, 91 Albion Street, Birmingham, B1 3AA Tel: 0121-248 5522 Fax: 0121-248 5523
Protectall Lock & Safe Co. Ltd, 445b Stratford Road, Sparkhill, Birmingham, B11 4LB Tel: 0121-773 1609 Fax: 0121-773 8401 E-mail: sales@protectall-security.co.uk
R & R Security Services, 171 South Ealing Road, London, W5 4QP Tel: (020) 8560 3413 Fax: (020) 8560 3413 E-mail: info@randrsecurity.com
Reliance Security Services Ltd, London Street, 2-4 Old Pye Street, London, SW1P 2LE Tel: (020) 7222 6044 Fax: (020) 7222 9415 E-mail: info@reliancesecurity.co.uk
Reliance Security Services Ltd, Surety House Kingsway Industrial Estate, Kingsway, Luton, LU1 1LP Tel: (01582) 452278 Fax: (01582) 720505 E-mail: info@reliancesecurity.co.uk
▶ S F R Systems For Retailers Ltd, 23 Paterson Road, Finedon Road Industrial Estate, Wellingborough, Northamptonshire, NN8 4BZ Tel: (01933) 224101 Fax: (01933) 274598 E-mail: sales@sfr.co.uk
▶ Scion Electronics, 161 Hospital Street, Birmingham, B19 3XA Tel: 0121-359 6366 Fax: 0121-359 6448 E-mail: lee.davis@scionelectronics.co.uk
Scotshield Burglar Alarm Systems, 1 Dryden Vale, Bilston Glen, Loanhead, Midlothian, EH20 9HN Tel: 0131-448 0583 Fax: 0131-448 0584 E-mail: admin@scotshield.com
Securicor Cash Services, Unit 8, Blackburn Trading Estate, Northumberland Close, Stanwell, Staines, Middlesex, TW19 7LN Tel: (01784) 421311 Fax: (01784) 420324
Securi-Guard Ltd, Darklake View, Estover, Plymouth, PL6 7TL Tel: (01752) 204900 Fax: (01752) 204912 E-mail: david.campbell@securi-guard.co.uk
Security Patrol Services Ltd, Roseland, Church Lane, Norton, Worcester, WR5 2PS Tel: (01905) 821000 Fax: (01905) 821408
Selectamark Security Systems Ltd, 1 Locks Court, 429 Crofton Road, Orpington, Kent, BR6 8NL Tel: (01689) 860757 Fax: (01689) 860693 E-mail: sales@selectamark.co.uk
Siteguard UK Ltd, Unit 30 Canal Bridge Enterprise Centre, Meadow Lane, Ellesmere Port, CH65 4EH Tel: 0151-355 3456 Fax: 0151-355 7809 E-mail: info@siteguarduk.com
Steel Security Services, 121 Boothferry Road, Hull, HU4 6EX Tel: (01482) 563732 Fax: (01482) 568353
Swallow Security Services Ltd, Swallow House, Theaklen Drive, St. Leonards-on-Sea, East Sussex, TN38 9AZ Tel: (01424) 425999 Fax: (01424) 421666 E-mail: swallowsecurity@btconnect.com
Temple Security Ltd, Temple House, 83-93 Staines Road, Hounslow, TW3 3JB Tel: (020) 8607 7500 Fax: (020) 8607 7510 E-mail: sales@templesecurity.co.uk
Thames Manufacturing Co. Ltd, 29 Mansfields, Writtle, Chelmsford, CM1 3NH Tel: (01245) 422062 Fax: (01245) 422062
Universal Locks, 894 Plymouth Road, Slough, SL1 4LP Tel: (01753) 696630 Fax: (01753) 568461 E-mail: info@universalsecurity.co.uk
Visionsec Building Service, Kings Road, Basingstoke, Hampshire, RG22 6DJ Tel: (01256) 336286 Fax: (01256) 471977
W F Joy & Co. Ltd, Unit 1a Parnall Industrial Estate, Parnall Road, Bristol, BS16 3JF Tel: 0117-958 5865 Fax: 0117-958 5865
Wackenhut U K Ltd, 875 Sidcup Road, London, SE9 3PP Tel: (020) 8850 4647 Fax: (020) 8850 0612
Whitehall Security Services, 137-139 High Street, Beckenham, Kent, BR3 1AG Tel: (020) 8658 3933 Fax: (020) 8663 3467 E-mail: sales@whitehallsecurity.com

SECURITY SERVICES, ON SITE

Consortium Support Services Ltd, 99 Wheatcroft Grove, Gillingham, Kent, ME8 9JE Tel: (01634) 232343 Fax: (01634) 232365 E-mail: derekrainham@blueyonder.co.uk
▶ Duel, Unit 1 Parkers Yard, Marlborough Road, Ilfracombe, Devon, EX34 8JP Tel: (01271) 863397 Fax: (01271) 863024 E-mail: enquiries@duel-investigations.com
▶ Metro Security Services, Liverpool, L28 1YX Tel: (0845) 2269185 E-mail: metrosecurity@lycos.co.uk

SECURITY SHREDDING

Anglia Recycling Ltd, Crow Hall Farm, Northfield Road, Soham, Ely, Cambridgeshire, CB7 5UF Tel: (01353) 624004 Fax: (01353) 723888 E-mail: sales@angliarecycling.co.uk
▶ Bettershred, Thornborough Road, Thornton, Milton Keynes, MK17 0HE Tel: (01280) 821444 Fax: (01280) 821190
C & J Blackburn, West End Mills, Watergate Road, Dewsbury, West Yorkshire, WF12 9QB Tel: (01924) 465958 Fax: (01924) 454155 E-mail: carol@cjblackburn.co.uk
CDS, 3 Avon Path, South Croydon, Surrey, CR2 6AX Tel: (020) 8651 4240 Fax: (020) 8651 0812
Confidential Destruction Services Ltd, Unit 2, Peterboat Close, Greenwich, London, SE10 0PX Tel: (020) 8293 1999 Fax: (020) 8293 5222 E-mail: admin@shredding.info
Data Shred Ltd, Bradfield Road, London, E16 2AX Tel: (020) 8450 6282 Fax: (020) 7476 2548
Data Shredding Services Ltd, 38 Pound Lane, Upper Beeding, Steyning, West Sussex, BN44 3JD Tel: (01903) 814949 Fax: (01903) 813925 E-mail: info@datashreddingservices.com
Deadman Confidential, 17 Golf Side, Sutton, Surrey, SM2 7HA Tel: (020) 8642 3600 Fax: (020) 8642 8378 E-mail: info@deadmanconfidential.co.uk
Effective Case Management Ltd, The Depository, Lewes Road, Lindfield, Haywards Heath, West Sussex, RH16 2LE Tel: (01444) 483968 Fax: (01444) 484852 E-mail: sales@casedocs.co.uk
Houghtons Waste Paper Ltd, York Street Mill, York Street, Audenshaw, Manchester, M34 5TN Tel: 0161-330 4971 Fax: 0161-343 4055 E-mail: info@houghtons-wp.co.uk
M & J Bowers, Lucott, Limington, Yeovil, Somerset, BA22 8EQ Tel: (01935) 840308 Fax: (01935) 841544
Perrys Recycling, Rimpton Road, Marston Magna, Yeovil, Somerset, BA22 8DL Tel: (01935) 850111 Fax: (01935) 851555 E-mail: sam@perrys-recycling.co.uk
▶ Premier Shredding Ltd, Unit 3J, North Road, Marchwood Industrial Park, Marchwood, Southampton, SO40 4BL Tel: (023) 8086 8888 Fax: (023) 8086 7475 E-mail: sales@premiershredding.co.uk
Restore Ltd, Redhill Distribution Centre, Salbrook Road, Redhill, RH1 5DY Tel: (01293) 446270 Fax: (01293) 446276 E-mail: john.minton@restore.co.uk
Riverdele Paper plc, Earlsway, Team Valley Trading Estate, Gateshead, Tyne & Wear, NE11 0RQ Tel: 0191-482 4271 Fax: 0191-482 4214 E-mail: info@riverdalepaper.co.uk
Robert Hough (Fibres) Ltd, 50-52 Thomas Road, London, E14 7BJ Tel: (07976) 558234 Fax: (020) 7537 2838 E-mail: enquiries@robert-hough.u-net.com
Sheard Properties Ltd, Solar Works, Calder Street, Greetland, Halifax, West Yorkshire, HX4 8AQ Tel: (01422) 373649 Fax: (01422) 310090 E-mail: sales@sheard.co.uk
The Shred Safe Ltd, Whitehall Farm Units, Cambridge Road, Croxton, St. Neots, Cambridgeshire, PE19 6SS Tel: (01480) 880088 Fax: (01480) 880044 E-mail: sales@shred-safe.co.uk
Shredders Direct, Bath Road, Speen, Newbury, Berkshire, RG14 1QY Tel: (01635) 43828 Fax: (01635 43820 E-mail: shreddersdirect@talk21.com
Shredsure Ltd, White House, Padhams Green, Mountnessing, Brentwood, Essex, CM13 1UL Tel: (01277) 354500 Fax: (01277) 356988
Sita Recycling Services Ltd, Unit 34 Coneygre Industrial Estate, Tipton, West Midlands, DY4 8XP Tel: 0121-522 2216 Fax: 0121-522 2942
Sita Security Shredding Ltd, 64-76 River Road, Barking, Essex, IG11 0DS Tel: (020) 8532 7990 Fax: (020) 8591 9345 E-mail: securityshredding@sita.co.uk

SECURITY SHREDDING MACHINES

Babs UK Ltd, Plot 1 Oakwood Hill Industrial Estate, Oakwood Hill, Loughton, Essex, IG10 3TZ Tel: (020) 8965 9821 Fax: (020) 8502 4187 E-mail: info@babs.co.uk
C L Shredders, Unit 1, Angeldown Farm, Manor Rd, Wantage, Oxon, OX12 8NQ Tel: (0800) 9757235 Fax: (01235) 765474 E-mail: cluton@clshredders.co.uk
Confidential Destruction Services Ltd, Unit 2, Peterboat Close, Greenwich, London, SE10 0PX Tel: (020) 8293 1999 Fax: (020) 8293 5222 E-mail: admin@shredding.info
M & Y Air Systems Ltd, Twickenham Trading Centre, Rugby Road, Twickenham, TW1 1DN Tel: (020) 8892 8893 Fax: (020) 8891 6175 E-mail: sales@myairsystems.fsnet.co.uk

SECURITY STORAGE CAGES

Carlton Downs Holdings Ltd, Hulley Road, Hurdsfield, Macclesfield, Cheshire, SK10 2LZ Tel: (01625) 616570 Fax: (01625) 427427 E-mail: enquiries@carltondowns.co.uk
▶ Lockheed Martin UK INSYS Ltd, Reddings Wood, Bedford, MK45 2HD Tel: (01525) 843883 Fax: (01525) 843446 E-mail: nigel.urquhart@lmco.com

SECURITY STREET FURNITURE

Bailey Streetscene Ltd, Bailey Business Park, Grimshaw Lane, Bollington, Macclesfield, Cheshire, SK10 5NY Tel: (0870) 0928928 Fax: (0870) 0929929 E-mail: info@baileystreetscene.co.uk
▶ Blueton Ltd, 19c Winchester Avenue, Winchester Industrial Estate, Denny, Stirlingshire, FK6 6QE Tel: (01324) 829661 Fax: (01324) 829551 E-mail: blueton@btinternet.com

SECURITY SYSTEM COMPONENTS

C S E Alarms, 13 Haigh Close, Chorley, Lancashire, PR7 2QR Tel: (01257) 275549

SECURITY SYSTEM OR EQUIPMENT INSTALLATION OR MAINTENANCE OR SERVICING

A B Rooms & Son Ltd, 4 Field Street, Hull, HU9 1HS Tel: (01482) 320260 Fax: (01482) 219384 E-mail: enquiries@abrooms.co.uk
A D K (Northwest) Ltd, 215 Accrington Road, Blackburn, BB1 2AQ Tel: (01254) 278999 Fax: (01254) 278970 E-mail: jemimah@london.com
A M Security Group Ltd, Unit 7 English Business Park, Hove, East Sussex, BN3 7ET Tel: (01273) 740400 Fax: (01273) 740401
A S Security Alarms Ltd, Springclose House Post Office Lane, South Chard, Chard, Somerset, TA20 2PL Tel: (01460) 221137 Fax: (01460) 221137 E-mail: assecurityalarms@btconnect.com
A Solo Security Ltd, 22a Horseshoe Park, Pangbourne, Reading, RG8 7JW Tel: 0118-984 4083 Fax: 0118-984 4204 E-mail: sales@asolosecurity.co.uk
A V Communication Solutions Ltd, Boston Buildings, 14-16 Yellow House Lane, Southport, Merseyside, PR8 1ER Tel: (01704) 531469 Fax: (01704) 539326 E-mail: av_comm_sols@btinternet.com
Abel Alarm Co. Ltd, 84 Barden Road, Tonbridge, Kent, TN9 1UB Tel: (01732) 355592 Fax: (01732) 365241 E-mail: info.tonbridge@abelalarm.co.uk
Ability Security Systems Ltd, Eton House, 156 High Street, Ruislip, Middlesex, HA4 8LJ Tel: (01895) 677070 Fax: (01895) 677055 E-mail: info@ability-security.co.uk
Access Control Services, 20-26 High Street, Greenhithe, Kent, DA9 9NN Tel: (01322) 370777 Fax: (01322) 370076 E-mail: admin@xplan.com
Acorn Security Alarms Ltd, Swan House, Bonds Mill, Stonehouse, Gloucestershire, GL10 3RF Tel: (01453) 794050 Fax: (01453) 794051 E-mail: info@acornsecurityalarms.co.uk
Adpro Securities, 28a Highgate, Cherry Burton, Beverley, North Humberside, HU17 7RR Tel: (01964) 550555 Fax: (01964) 551954
Advanced Alarms Lincs Ltd, 44 Richmond Road, Cleethorpes, South Humberside, DN35 8PE Tel: (01472) 236749 Fax: (01472) 315848 E-mail: sales@advancedalarms.co.uk
AIS Fire Tech Tech, Unit 12 Riverside Business Park, 33 River Road, Barking, Essex, IG11 0DA Tel: (020) 8591 3433 Fax: (020) 8594 1226 E-mail: enquiries@firetech.co.uk
Aleck J Shone, 16 High Street, Saltney, Chester, CH4 8SE Tel: (01244) 683531 Fax: (01244) 659770
Altrincham & Cheshire Security Systems, 16 Trafford Drive, Timperley, Altrincham, Cheshire, WA15 6EJ Tel: 0161-976 3752 Fax: 0161-976 3752
Arm Sure Security, 97 Occupation Road, Corby, Northamptonshire, NN17 1EE Tel: (01536) 202631 Fax: (01536) 202102
Associated Security Group Ltd, 59 London Road, Wallington, Surrey, SM6 7HW Tel: (020) 8669 7722 Fax: (020) 8669 9890 E-mail: sales@associatedsecuritygroup.co.uk
Aston Security, Walthamstow Business Centre, Clifford Road, London, E17 4SX Tel: (020) 8527 6888 Fax: (020) 8527 6969

SECURITY SYSTEM OR EQUIPMENT INSTALLATION OR MAINTENANCE OR SERVICING – *continued*

Automatic Protection Equipment & Crown Security Se, 73 Lower High Street, Bristol, BS11 0AW Tel: 0117-982 5045 Fax: 0117-982 6046 E-mail: info@apealarms.co.uk

▶ Axxess 28 Ltd, 18 Rosemary Lane, Blackwater, Camberley, Surrey, GU17 0LS Tel: (01276) 36915 Fax: (01276) 36917 E-mail: sales@axxess28.com

B & D Electrical Security & Surveillance Ltd, Unit 12 Grinnall Business Centre, Sandy Lane, Stourport-on-Severn, Worcestershire, DY13 9QB Tel: (01299) 822758 Fax: (01299) 827995

B & E Security Systems, 10 Oakland Avenue, Portrush, County Antrim, BT56 8JP Tel: (028) 7082 5119 Fax: (028) 7082 3757 E-mail: team@eonde.prestel.co.uk

Birmingham Alarm Technicians Ltd, 28-30 Hall Street, Birmingham, B18 6BS Tel: 0121-236 7828 Fax: 0121-236 6114

C J Security Systems Ltd, Unit 3 Fence Avenue, Macclesfield, Cheshire, SK10 1LT Tel: (01625) 613707 Fax: (01625) 617898 E-mail: sales@cheshirelock.co.uk

C P S Engineering, Wentworth Road, Mapplewell, Barnsley, South Yorkshire, S75 6DU Tel: (01226) 386515 Fax: (01226) 380165 E-mail: cpsengineering@aol.com

Chris Lewis, Faraday House, 38 Poole Road, Bournemouth, BH4 9DW Tel: (01202) 751599 Fax: (01202) 759500 E-mail: sales@chrislewissecurity.co.uk

Chroma Visual, 61 Leyland Trading Estate, Wellingborough, Northamptonshire, NN8 1RS Tel: (01933) 443737 Fax: (01933) 271770 E-mail: cvl@globalnet.co.uk

Circle Security, 170 Lanark Road West, Currie, Midlothian, EH14 5NY Tel: (0800) 0723712 Fax: 0131-476 9578

Clayman Electronics Ltd, 91 Stour View Gardens, Corfe Mullen, Wimborne, Dorset, BH21 3TL Tel: (01202) 849777

Crimewatch Security Ltd, Magpie House, 57 Earle Street, Crewe, CW1 2AS Tel: (01270) 589627 Fax: (01270) 584087 E-mail: kevinvickers@crimewatch-security.co.uk

Cromwell Security & Fire Services Ltd, 72 Fortune Green Road, London, NW6 1DS Tel: (020) 7435 0334 Fax: (020) 7794 3384

Davenheath, Unit 3 Kingfisher House, Trinity Business Park, London, E4 8TD Tel: (020) 8531 2003 Fax: (020) 8531 9105

Electronic & Security Services Ltd, 50 Boucher Place, Belfast, BT12 6HT Tel: (028) 9066 3510 Fax: (028) 9066 1995 E-mail: info@ess-security.co.uk

Expert Security Systems Ltd, 26 Wellowgate, Grimsby, South Humberside, DN32 0RA Tel: (01472) 241279

Fastsigns, 630-642 Chesterfield Road, Sheffield, S8 0SA Tel: 0114-255 2553 Fax: 0114-258 8444

Fourway Communication Ltd, Delamare Road, Cheshunt, Waltham Cross, Hertfordshire, EN8 9SH Tel: (01992) 629182 Fax: (01992) 639227 E-mail: info@fourway.co.uk

Fwa, 28 Tynemouth Road, North Shields, Tyne & Wear, NE30 4AA Tel: 0191-259 1099 Fax: 0191-258 2737 E-mail: sales@fwa.uk.com

G A Car Alarms, 9 Hudson Cl, Haverhill, Suffolk, CB9 0LF Tel: 01440 705855 Fax: 01440 705855

G C Electronics, 6 Deighton Avenue, Sherburn in Elmet, Leeds, LS25 6BR Tel: (01977) 683576

Harrison Locks, Pump Street, Worcester, WR1 2QX Tel: (01905) 20999 Fax: (01527) 892612 E-mail: harrison.lock@btinternet.com

Higgins Electronics, 116-120 High Street, Aberlour, Banffshire, AB38 9PA Tel: (01340) 871275 Fax: (01340) 871275

▶ Initial Electronic Security Systems Ltd, Unit A Sett End Road North, Shadsworth Business Park, Blackburn, BB1 2PT Tel: (01254) 844600 Fax: (01254) 696218

▶ Interphone CCTV Ltd, PO Box 1, Harrow, Middlesex, HA3 5UH Tel: (020) 8621 6000 Fax: (020) 8621 6100

Interphone CCTV Ltd, Interphone House, P O Box 1, Harrow, Middlesex, HA3 5UH Tel: (020) 8621 6000 Fax: (020) 8621 6100 E-mail: security@interphone.co.uk

Jaguar Alarm Co., Jaguar House, 191 Old Oak Road, London, W3 7HH Tel: (020) 8743 1358 Fax: (020) 8743 1358

Katana Installations, 20 Muirfield Avenue, Swinton, Mexborough, South Yorkshire, S64 8SX Tel: (01709) 590678 Fax: (01709) 590678

Knighthood Security Systems Ltd, 132 Talbot Road, London, W11 1JA Tel: (020) 8541 4725 Fax: (020) 8255 9190 E-mail: sales@knighthoodsecurity.co.uk

Locktec Ltd, Unit 7-11, Pentlandfield Business Park, Roslin, Midlothian, EH25 9RE Tel: 0131-445 7788 Fax: 0131-445 7527 E-mail: sales@locktec.net

Lynx Security, The Old Pump Station, Furnace Lane, Finedon, Wellingborough, Northamptonshire, NN9 5NZ Tel: (01604) 621727 Fax: (01536) 724666 E-mail: enquiries@lynxsecurity.net

Magnum Security Ltd, 50 Alexandra Rd, Acocks Green, Birmingham, B27 6HE Tel: 0121-706 0087 Fax: 0121-243 2712

Masterguard Security & Fire Services, The Paddocks, Greenacres Drive, Uttoxeter, Staffordshire, ST14 7EB Tel: (01889) 566040 Fax: (01889) 566040

Midland Security Systems, 544a Burton Road, Littleover, Derby, DE23 6FN Tel: (01332) 296664 Fax: (01332) 298238

MRFS Group, 8 Canbury Business Park, Elm Crescent, Kingston upon Thames, Surrey, KT2 6HJ Tel: (020) 8547 4333 Fax: (020) 8547 4334

Nationwide Alarm Call, 154 Wollaton Road, Beeston, Nottingham, NG9 2PH Tel: 0115-943 0981 Fax: 0115-922 2038

Newton Fabrications Ltd, 9 York Street, Ayr, KA8 8AN Tel: (01292) 269135 Fax: (01292) 610258 E-mail: davidcorson@newtonholdings.com

Nu Fire & Security Ltd, Unit 8A, Kayley Industrial Estate, Richmond Street, Ashton-under-Lyne, Lancashire, OL7 0AU Tel: 0161-331 7430 Fax: (0845) 4022309 E-mail: sales@nufire.co.uk

P C B Security Systems, 60 Kingswood Cresent, Rayleigh, Essex, SS6 7BH Tel: (01268) 741006 Fax: (01268) 741006

Perimeter Internal Protection, Office 32, The Valley, 67 Church Road, Newtownabbey, County Antrim, BT36 7LS Tel: (028) 9086 8413 Fax: (028) 9086 8718 E-mail: info@pipsecurity.com

Principal Security Systems Ltd, 180 Bridge Road, Sarisbury Green, Southampton, SO31 7EH Tel: (01489) 886677 Fax: (01489) 886699 E-mail: sales@setonsecurities..co.uk

Reliant High-Tec Ltd, Surety House, 70 Barweel Business Park, Leather Head Road, Chessington, Surrey, KT9 2NY Tel: (020) 8391 2200 Fax: (01689) 890738 E-mail: sales@relitech.co.uk

Safe & Sound Security Systems, 3 Chestnut Avenue, Manchester, M21 8BE Tel: 0161-861 8980 Fax: 0161-861 8980 E-mail: safeandsoundmcr@hotmail.com

Safe & Sound Security Systems Security Alarms, 9 Devonshire Road, Gravesend, Kent, DA12 5AA Tel: (01474) 350613 Fax: (01474) 350613

Safeholme Burglar Alarm Systems, 3 Lead Lane, Brompton, Northallerton, North Yorkshire, DL6 2TZ Tel: (01609) 772624 Fax: (01609) 761101 E-mail: sales@safeholme.co.uk

Secure Alarm Co. Ltd, Unit 28 Shaftesbury St South, Derby, DE23 8YH Tel: (0870) 0429999 Fax: (0870) 0420099 E-mail: info@securealarm.co.uk

Securi Plex Ltd, Swordfish Way, Sherburn in Elmet, Leeds, LS25 6NG Tel: (01977) 680700 Fax: (01977) 680701 E-mail: business@securi-plex.co.uk

Security 201, 332 Goring Road, Goring-by-Sea, Worthing, West Sussex, BN12 4PE Tel: (01903) 242902 Fax: (01903) 242618 E-mail: info@security201.co.uk

Security Surveillance Systems, Boundary Farm, Grave Yard Lane, Bickerstaffe, Ormskirk, Lancashire, L39 9EG Tel: (01695) 420968 Fax: (01695) 424790 E-mail: mark-fitzgerald@btconnect.com

Sightguard I O W Ltd, 39 High Street, Wootton Bridge, Ryde, Isle of Wight, PO33 4LU Tel: (01983) 884000 Fax: (01983) 884000

Squirealarms Ltd, 165-171 Humberstone Road, Leicester, LE5 3AF Tel: 0116-262 3916 E-mail: info@squirealarms.co.uk

Systems Intelligence Ltd, 21 Decimus Park, Kingstanding Way, Tunbridge Wells, Kent, TN2 3GP Tel: (01892) 509940 Fax: (01892) 509941 E-mail: sales@vitechsecurity.co.uk

Team Technology (South West) Ltd, Riverside Road, Pottington Business Park, Barnstaple, Devon, EX31 1TE Tel: (01271) 370420 Fax: (01271) 375977 E-mail: sales@teamtechnologysw.co.uk

Waveney Security Ltd, 1 Southend Road, Bungay, Suffolk, NR35 1DN Tel: (01986) 895588 Fax: (01986) 892288 E-mail: suffolk@waveneysecurity.co.uk

West Mercia Security, 52 Walker Avenue, Stourbridge, West Midlands, DY9 9EL Tel: (01384) 396316 Fax: (01384) 396316

▶ Westmorland Fire & Security Ltd, Beezon Chambers, Sandes Avenue, Kendal, Cumbria, LA9 6BL Tel: (01539) 724919 Fax: (01539) 740589 E-mail: service@westmorlandsecurity.co.uk

Wilson Alarms, Ruyton XI Towns, Shrewsbury, SY4 1WX Tel: (0845) 2306966 Fax: (0845) 2306967 E-mail: enquiries@wilson-alarms.co.uk

Xtal Security Systems Ltd, 191 Replingham Road, London, SW18 5LY Tel: (020) 8877 9802 Fax: (020) 8877 3427 E-mail: info@xtalsecurity.com

SECURITY SYSTEM OR EQUIPMENT MONITORING

Bell Security, Roding House, 970 Romford Road, London, E12 5LP Tel: (020) 8477 7500 Fax: (020) 8478 8052 E-mail: info@bellsec.com

M J Security Systems Ltd, PO Box 6, Nottingham, NG10 4PN Tel: 0115-946 1280 Fax: (0870) 7482040

Sterling Security Systems Ltd, PO Box 999, Tamworth, Staffordshire, B79 8EY Tel: (01827) 310059 Fax: (0870) 0558852 E-mail: info@sterling-security.co.uk

SECURITY SYSTEMS OR EQUIPMENT

A D T Fire & Security P.L.C., Security House, The Summit, Hanworth Road, Sunbury-on-Thames, Middlesex, TW16 5DB Tel: (0800) 0111111

Audiotel International Ltd, Corby Road, Weldon, Corby, Northamptonshire, NN17 3AR Tel: (01536) 266677 Fax: (01586) 277711 E-mail: sales@audiotel-international.com

C X Access Systems Ltd, Unit 5, Cricketts Lane Industrial Park, Chippenham, Wiltshire, SN15 3EQ Tel: (01249) 443898 Fax: (01249) 443336 E-mail: cxaccess@aol.com

Capital Fire & Security Alarm Systems, Ferry Road, Beauly, Inverness-Shire, IV4 7EA Tel: (01463) 782475 Fax: (01463) 782475

Castle Care Tech Ltd, North Street, Winkfield, Windsor, Berkshire, SL4 4SY Tel: (01344) 890582 Fax: (01344) 890024 E-mail: sales@castle-caretech.com

Civic Security Ltd, Vision House, 182 Landells Road, London, SE22 9PP Tel: (020) 8299 5150 Fax: (020) 8299 5160 E-mail: sales@civicsecurity.com

▶ Computerguard Ltd, Hazlewell House, Graffham, Petworth, West Sussex, GU28 0QA Tel: (01798) 867133 Fax: (01798) 867135

Coopers Security Ltd, Security House, Xerox Business Park, Mitcheldean, Gloucestershire, GL17 0SZ Tel: (01594) 543343 Fax: (01594) 545401 E-mail: marketing@menviersecurity.co.uk

Dedicated Micros Ltd, Aegon House, Daresbury Park, Daresbury, Warrington, WA4 4HS Tel: (01928) 706400 Fax: (01928) 706350 E-mail: customerservice@dmicros.com

Dennard Ltd, 55 Fleet Road, Fleet, Hampshire, GU51 3PN Tel: (01252) 614884 Fax: (01252) 626013 E-mail: sales@dennard-cctv.com

Fort Knox, 1 Mount Vernon Road, Liverpool, L7 8TY Tel: 0151-708 9333 Fax: 0151-709 8908

Gardiner Technology Ltd, Queensway, Rochdale, Lancashire, OL11 1TQ Tel: (0845) 7328328 Fax: (01706) 510100 E-mail: sales@gardiner-technology.com

Guardall Ltd, Lochend Industrial Estate, Queen Anne Drive, Newbridge, Midlothian, EH28 8PL Tel: 0131-333 2900 Fax: 0131-333 4919 E-mail: sales@guardall.co.uk

Hunter Security Ltd, Walnut Tree Farm, Cockmannings Lane, Orpington, Kent, BR5 4HF Tel: (01689) 870951 Fax: (01689) 822363 E-mail: enquiries@huntersecurity.com

Luminite Security Equipment, 2a Bellevue Road, London, N11 3ER Tel: (020) 8368 7887 Fax: (020) 8368 3952 E-mail: sales@luminite.co.uk

Maxhunt Ltd, Yelverton Road, Bristol, BS4 5HP Tel: 0117-977 9001 Fax: 0117-971 5971 E-mail: sales@maxhunt.com

Pyronix Security Equipment Ltd, Pyronix House, Braithwell Way, Hellaby, Rotherham, South Yorkshire, S66 8QY Tel: (01709) 700100 Fax: (01709) 701042 E-mail: sales@pyronix.co.uk

R K R Security Ltd, 6 Bilton Road, Erith, Kent, DA8 2AN Tel: (01322) 334881

Safetell International Ltd, Unit 46, Fawkes Avenue, Dartford, DA1 1JQ Tel: (01322) 223233 Fax: (01322) 277751

Securit World Ltd, Spectrum House, Hillview Gardens, London, NW4 2JQ Tel: (020) 8266 3300 Fax: (020) 8203 1027 E-mail: support@securitworld.com

SRB Technologies, 6 Portland Business Centre, Manor House Lane, Datchet, Slough, SL3 9EG Tel: (01753) 592492 Fax: (01753) 592692 E-mail: sales@betalight.com

Standfast Security Systems Ltd, 120 Coldharbour Road, Redland, Bristol, BS6 7SL Tel: 0117-942 3366 Fax: 0117-944 6241 E-mail: sales@standfast.co.uk

Strathclyde Firemans Personal Alarm Co. Ltd, 234 Allison Street, Glasgow, G42 8RT Tel: 0141-423 7011 E-mail: ellis.cohen@amserve.net

Tag Guard Ltd, Unit 2 Blendworth Farm House, Blendworth, Waterlooville, Hampshire, PO8 0AG Tel: (023) 9259 8218 Fax: (023) 9259 8918 E-mail: sales@tag-guard.co.uk

Tam Fabrications Ltd, Unit 5 Rexmore Way, Liverpool, L15 0HX Tel: 0151-734 0018

Tate Fire & Security Protection, 3 Cheddar Business Park, Wedmore Road, Cheddar, Somerset, BS27 3EB Tel: (01934) 744111 Fax: (01934) 744304 E-mail: sales@tatefire.co.uk

Tynetec Ltd, Cowley Road, Blyth Industrial Estate, Blyth, Northumberland, NE24 5TF Tel: (01670) 352371 Fax: (01670) 362807 E-mail: sales@tynetec.co.uk

SECURITY SYSTEMS OR EQUIPMENT INSTALLERS APPROVAL OR CERTIFICATION BODY

A D K (Northwest) Ltd, 215 Accrington Road, Blackburn, BB1 2AQ Tel: (01254) 278999 Fax: (01254) 278970 E-mail: jemimah@london.com

A & S Security Systems, 8 Woodcroft Rise, Ballymena, County Antrim, BT42 1TA Tel: (028) 2565 8969 Fax: (028) 2565 8969

Abbot Security, Unit 4, The Courtyard, Fore Street, Saltash, Cornwall, PL12 6JR Tel: (01752) 841007

Ace Security & Electrical Ltd, 150-152 Loughton Way, Buckhurst Hill, Essex, IG9 6AR Tel: (020) 8506 1421 Fax: (020) 8506 6666

Avantgarde Security Systems, 190 Frant Road, Thornton Heath, Surrey, CR7 7JW Tel: (020) 8239 6989 Fax: (020) 8251 8311 E-mail: avantgardesecurity@blueyonder.co.uk

Beta Security Systems, Llandegai Industrial Estate, Llandygai, Bangor, Gwynedd, LL57 4YH Tel: (01248) 364967 Fax: (01248) 364967

Britannia Security Services Ltd, Eden Business Centre, South Stour Avenue, Ashford, Kent, TN23 7RS Tel: (01233) 628684 Fax: (01233) 628684

▶ Chester Security Systems, 32 Church Road, Saughall, Chester, CH1 6EN Tel: (01244) 881399 Fax: (01244) 880935 E-mail: info@chestersecurity.co.uk

Clayman Electronics Ltd, 91 Stour View Gardens, Corfe Mullen, Wimborne, Dorset, BH21 3TL Tel: (01202) 849777

Concept Security Systems, 21 Park Avenue, London, NW10 7EX Tel: (020) 8965 3657 Fax: (020) 8965 3657

D G H Security & Electrical Installations, 35 Lansdowne Road, Sevenoaks, Kent, TN13 3XU Tel: (01732) 464165 Fax: (01732) 464166

Kirby Electrical Ltd, 4 Storforth La Trading Estate, Hasland, Chesterfield, Derbyshire, S41 0QD Tel: (01246) 220202 Fax: (01246) 208638

NSI, Queensgate House, 14 Cookham Road, Maidenhead, Berkshire, SL6 8AJ Tel: (0870) 2050000 Fax: (01628) 773367 E-mail: nacoss@nsi.org.uk

Retainagroup Ltd., 134-136 Buckingham Palace Road, London, SW1W 9SA Tel: (020) 7823 6868 Fax: (020) 7823 6864 E-mail: general.sales@retainagroup.co.uk

Sterling Security Systems Ltd, PO Box 999, Tamworth, Staffordshire, B79 8EY Tel: (01827) 310059 Fax: (0870) 0558852 E-mail: info@sterling-security.co.uk

T I Security Ltd, Enterprise Industrial Estate, Aberford Road, Barwick in Elmet, Leeds, LS15 4EF Tel: 0113-281 2106 Fax: 0113-281 3279

West Country Security, Security House, Newham Road, Truro, Cornwall, TR1 3QG Tel: (01872) 275596 Fax: (01872) 264834

SECURITY SYSTEMS/ EQUIPMENT, MOTOR VEHICLE

▶ A F S Security Ltd, 582-584 Barking Road, London, E13 9JU Tel: (020) 8471 9000 Fax: (020) 8475 0877 E-mail: afssecurity@btconnect.com

Advanced Vehicle Security of Bath, 5 Gabrial Crescent, Swindon, SN25 2AT Tel: (0800) 328 4082

SECURITY SYSTEMS/ EQUIPMENT, TELEVISION

Peca Electronics, 1 Parnell Court, Andover, Hampshire, SP10 3LX Tel: (01264) 355975 Fax: (01264) 366536 E-mail: sales@peca-electronics.co.uk

SECURITY TAGS, RETAIL

▶ Bluerock Security Ltd, St. James Road, Brackley, Northamptonshire, NN13 7XY Tel: (01280) 706969 Fax: (01280) 706969 E-mail: sales@bluerocksecurity.com

▶ Maxtag (UK) Ltd, 8 Suttons Bussiness Park, Reading, RG6 1AZ Tel: 0118-935 6180 Fax: 0118-935 6181 E-mail: sales@maxtag.com

▶ Solutions Distributors Ltd, Unit 1 Hixon Industrial Estate, Church Lane, Hixon, Stafford, ST18 0PY Tel: (0871) 4341510 Fax: (0871) 4341514 E-mail: sales@solutions-distributors.co.uk

▶ Tag Company UK Ltd, Duval House, High Street Harmondsworth, Harmondsworth, West Drayton, Middlesex, UB7 0BT Tel: (020) 8283 4999 E-mail: info@tagcompany.com

SECURITY VEHICLE SYSTEMS

Auto Guard Security Centre Ltd, Unit 3 Sandy La Industrial Estate, Stourport-on-Severn, Worcestershire, DY13 9QB Tel: (01299) 878111 Fax: (01299) 871990

Bri-Stor Systems Ltd, Church Lane, Hixon, Stafford, ST18 0PS Tel: (01889) 271202 Fax: (01889) 271178 E-mail: systems@bristor.co.uk

Brushstrokes Signs, Station Road, Buckhaven, Leven, Fife, KY8 1JH Tel: (01592) 714804 Fax: (01592) 714103

▶ Intact Electronics Ltd, 455 Chorley Old Road, Bolton, BL1 6AH Tel: (01204) 491000 Fax: (01204) 455575

Maple Fleet Services Ltd, Maple House, High Street, Slamannan, Falkirk, FK1 3EY Tel: 0161-477 3476 Fax: 0161-477 6377 E-mail: sales@mapletechnology.co.uk

SECURITY VEHICLE SYSTEMS – *continued*

Stadium Consumer Products, Stadium North, Tofts Farm Industrial Estate East, Hartlepool, Cleveland, TS25 2DH Tel: (01429) 862616 Fax: (01429) 272126 E-mail: julie.morrissey@stadiumcp.co.uk
Tomorrows World, 555 Shields Road, Newcastle Upon Tyne, NE6 4QL Tel: 0191-240 0555 E-mail: info@cpswbay.co.uk
Tracker Network Ltd, Otter House 5 Cowley Business Park, High Street, Cowley, Uxbridge, Middlesex, UB8 2AD Tel: (01895) 234567 Fax: (01895) 234117 E-mail: info@tnuk.co.uk
Van Locks Ltd, 76 Portland Street, Manchester, M1 4GU Tel: 0161-236 1231 Fax: 0161-236 2885 E-mail: vanlock@talk21.com
W A S O 2000, 15 Park Avenue, Cheadle Hulme, Cheadle, Cheshire, SK8 6EU Tel: (0870) 9027979 Fax: 0161-428 1790 E-mail: sales@waso.co.uk

SECURITY VEHICLE SYSTEMS ENGINEERS, INSTALLATION OR SERVICE

001 Mobile Car Audio & Security, 1 Esher Road, Walton-on-Thames, Surrey, KT12 4JZ Tel: (01932) 253001 E-mail: sales@001mobile.com
A Z Sunroof Services, 21 Lilley Lane, Birmingham, B31 3JU Tel: 0121-411 1222 Fax: 0121-608 6008
Acousticar Car Entertainment Systems, 4 Kingsley Industrial Park, New Road, Kibworth, Leicester, LE8 0LE Tel: 0116-279 3113 Fax: 0116-279 3224 E-mail: sales@acousticar.co.uk
Alarm Shop, 110 Balls Pond Road, London, N1 4AG Tel: (020) 7275 9990
Cheltenham Auto Security, 22 Oak Av, Charlton Kings, Cheltenham, Glos, GL52 6JG Tel: 01242 239283
Grange Vehicle Security, 36 The Crescent, Bricket Wood, St. Albans, Hertfordshire, AL2 3NF Tel: (01923) 673456
J R Roberts & Sons, 67 Eagle Road, Wembley, Middlesex, HA0 4SL Tel: (020) 8903 1884 Fax: (020) 8903 1884
Knightwatch Ltd, PO Box 319, Sevenoaks, Kent, TN15 8JL Tel: (01732) 886777 Fax: (01732) 886888 E-mail: sales@autowatch.co.uk
Liteon Automotive Electronics Ltd, 11 Ptarmigan Place, Attleborough Fields Industrial Estate, Nuneaton, Warwickshire, CV11 6RX Tel: (024) 7637 4222 Fax: (024) 7637 5444
The London Car Alarm Co, 14 Pennine Drive, London, NW2 1PB Tel: (020) 8264 7227 E-mail: londoncaralarmco@yohoo.co.uk
Mobile Systems, 2 Greaves Way Industrial Estate, Stanbridge Road, Leighton Buzzard, Bedfordshire, LU7 4UB Tel: (01525) 853267 Fax: (01525) 853268 E-mail: info@mobilesystems.co.uk
Niclec Services, 16 Gladstone Road, Orpington, Kent, BR6 7EA Tel: (01689) 858318
Precision Alarms, Pauls Court, 12b Meppel Avenue, Canvey Island, Essex, SS8 9RZ Tel: (01268) 696787 Fax: (01268) 696922 E-mail: sales@precisionalarms.co.uk
R's Electrics, 815 High Road, London, N17 8ER Tel: (0870) 7746333 Fax: (020) 8808 4955 E-mail: sales@rs-electrics.co.uk
Safe & Sound Car Technology, 247-249 Bradford Road, Keighley, West Yorkshire, BD21 4AW Tel: (01535) 691611 Fax: (01535) 610033
Tamworth Auto Electrics Ltd, Unit 6-7 Mariner, Tamworth, Staffordshire, B79 7UL Tel: (01827) 67539 Fax: (01827) 57473
Tracker Network Ltd, Otter House 5 Cowley Business Park, High Street, Cowley, Uxbridge, Middlesex, UB8 2AD Tel: (01895) 234567 Fax: (01895) 234117 E-mail: info@tnuk.co.uk
Turnbulls Truro Ltd, 97 Kenwyn Street, Truro, Cornwall, TR1 3BX Tel: (01872) 245155 Fax: (01872) 245150
Vehicle Security, 159 Balby Rd, Doncaster, S. Yorkshire, DN4 0RG Tel: 01302 311390 Fax: 01302 310114

SECURITY VEHICLES

Johnson Security Ltd, Orchard Industrial Estate, Toddington, Cheltenham, Gloucestershire, GL54 5EB Tel: (01242) 621362 Fax: (01242) 621554 E-mail: sales@johnson-security.co.uk
Tracker Network Ltd, Otter House 5 Cowley Business Park, High Street, Cowley, Uxbridge, Middlesex, UB8 2AD Tel: (01895) 234567 Fax: (01895) 234117 E-mail: info@tnuk.co.uk

SECURITY VISUAL DISPLAY (VDU) OR VIDEO MONITOR UNITS

B C Technology Ltd, 3 Wallis Close, Park Farm Industrial Estate, Wellingborough, Northamptonshire, NN8 6AG Tel: (01933) 405050 Fax: (01933) 405454 E-mail: info@bctechnologyltd.co.uk
Calibre UK Ltd, Cornwall House, Cornwall Terrace, Bradford, West Yorkshire, BD8 7JS Tel: (01274) 394125 Fax: (01274) 730960 E-mail: lisas@calibreuk.com

SECURITY WASTE DISPOSAL SERVICES

Anglia Recycling Ltd, Crow Hall Farm, Northfield Road, Soham, Ely, Cambridgeshire, CB7 5UF Tel: (01353) 624004 Fax: (01353) 723888 E-mail: sales@angliarecycling.co.uk
Confidential Destruction Services Ltd, Unit 2, Peterboat Close, Greenwich, London, SE10 0PX Tel: (020) 8293 1999 Fax: (020) 8293 5222 E-mail: admin@shredding.info

SECURITY WINDOW BARS

C.P. Belcher (Welding) Ltd, 115B Blythswood Road, Tyseley, Birmingham, B11 2BX Tel: 0121-706 9689 Fax: 0121-706 8477 E-mail: steve@cpbsteel.fsnet.co.uk
C A T Engineering Ltd, Glendale Works, 25 Sandhurst Road, Crowthorne, Berkshire, RG45 7HR Tel: (01344) 772934 Fax: (01344) 779283 E-mail: len@categ.fsnet.co.uk
K S Security Ltd, Units 2-6, Warsop Trading Estate, Hever Road, Edenbridge, Kent, TN8 5LD Tel: (01732) 867199 Fax: (01732) 867102 E-mail: info@ks-security.co.uk

SEED POTATOES

▶ P.J.P Ltd, Paul Jackson Potatoes, Station Road, Firsby, Spilsby, Lincolnshire, PE23 5QS Tel: (01754) 830330 E-mail: sales@pjp.org.uk

SEEDS

Armstrong Richardson & Co.Limited, Mount Pleasant Way, Stokesley Business Park, Stokesley, Middlesbrough, Cleveland, TS9 5NZ Tel: (01642) 718280 Fax: (01642) 710993 E-mail: sales@armstrongrichardson.co.uk
Jim Hall, Jacksoms Lane, Langley Burrell, Chippenham, Wiltshire, SN15 5LU Tel: (01249) 750291 Fax: (01249) 750291
▶ Seed Developments Ltd, The Factory, Aller, Langport, Somerset, TA10 0QN Tel: (01458) 250762

SEISMIC CABLE MAINTENANCE/ REPAIR SPECIALIST SERVICES

Syntron Europe Ltd, Birchwood Way, Cotes Park Industrial Estate, Somercotes, Alfreton, Derbyshire, DE55 4QQ Tel: (01773) 605078 Fax: (01773) 605078 E-mail: chris.toner@sercelengland.com

SEISMIC CABLES, BUNDLE/ UMBILICAL

Syntron Europe Ltd, Birchwood Way, Cotes Park Industrial Estate, Somercotes, Alfreton, Derbyshire, DE55 4QQ Tel: (01773) 605078 Fax: (01773) 605078 E-mail: chris.toner@sercelengland.com

SEISMIC EXPLORATION CONTRACTORS

Fugro Seismic Imaging, Horizon House, Azalea Drive, Swanley, Kent, BR8 8JR Tel: (01322) 668011 Fax: (01322) 613650 E-mail: info@fugro-fsi.com

SEISMIC SURVEY SERVICES

Read Well Services Ltd, Viking House, 1 Claymore Avenue, Bridge of Don, Aberdeen, AB23 8GW Tel: (01224) 336600 Fax: (01224) 336611 E-mail: sales@readgroupuk.com
Veritas DGC Ltd, Crompton Way, Crawley, West Sussex, RH10 9QN Tel: (01293) 443000 Fax: (01293) 443010 E-mail: info@veritasdgc.com

SELF ACTING TEMPERATURE CONTROL SYSTEMS

▶ A P S Engineering Ltd, Mountford House, Grafton Street, High Wycombe, Buckinghamshire, HP12 3AJ Tel: (01494) 511533 Fax: (01494) 511566 E-mail: sales@apsworldwide.com

SELF ADHESIVE COMPUTER LABEL SYSTEMS

A & H Europe Ltd, Unit 24 B, Star Road, Partridge Green, Horsham, West Sussex, RH13 8RA Tel: (01403) 710055 Fax: (01403) 711082 E-mail: sale@aandheurope.com
Cliffstar Ltd, Unit 2 Stafford Mill Trading Estate, London Road, Thrupp, Stroud, Gloucestershire, GL5 2AZ Tel: (01453) 750057 Fax: (01453) 757448
Danro Ltd, 68 Station Road, Earl Shilton, Leicester, LE9 7GA Tel: (01455) 847061 Fax: (01455) 841272 E-mail: info@danroltd.co.uk
Douglas Storrie Labels Ltd, Tudor Works, Tudor Rd, Lytham St. Annes, Lancashire, FY8 2LA Tel: (01253) 643000 Fax: (01253) 643001 E-mail: sales@storrielabels.com
Fisher Clark, Horncastle Road, Boston, Lincolnshire, PE21 9HZ Tel: (01205) 365501 Fax: (01205) 364825 E-mail: fisherclark@fisherclark.co.uk
Iml Labels & Systems Ltd, 6 Brookdale Road, Thorncliffe Park Estate, Chapeltown, Sheffield, S35 2PW Tel: 0114-246 5771 Fax: 0114-240 3410 E-mail: sales@iml-labels.co.uk
Impact Boston Ltd, Victoria Road, Skegness, Lincolnshire, PE25 3SN Tel: (01754) 767275 Fax: (01754) 613100 E-mail: sales@impactboston.ltd.uk
Newfoil Ltd, Bradford Street, Farnworth, Bolton, BL4 9LS Tel: (01204) 861110 Fax: (01204) 862201 E-mail: info@newfoil.co.uk
Oki Buyer, 31a St. Neots Road, Eaton Ford, St. Neots, Cambridgeshire, PE19 7BA Tel: 0845 5314237 Fax: (01480) 403909 E-mail: sales@okibuyer.co.uk
R B Labels Ltd, 37 Grove Road, Ilkley, West Yorkshire, LS29 9PF Tel: (01943) 468302 Fax: (01943) 850406 E-mail: sales@tradelabels.co.uk
Renaddress Ltd, Target House, Lea Road, Waltham Abbey, Essex, EN9 1AE Tel: (01992) 712592 Fax: (01992) 760902 E-mail: reg@target-sys.co.uk
Simpson Label Co. Ltd, Newbattle Industrial Estate, Mayfield, Dalkeith, Midlothian, EH22 4AF Tel: 0131-654 2800 Fax: 0131-663 6185 E-mail: mail@simpsonlabel.co.uk
Sprint Labels & Co., 4 Barn Road, Carmarthen, Dyfed, SA31 1DE Tel: (01267) 231920 Fax: (01267) 231921
Worldmark, 4 Redwood CR, East Kilbride, Glasgow, G74 5PA Tel: (01355) 249191 Fax: (01355) 230875 E-mail: info@donprint.com
Worldmark, 4 Redwood CR, East Kilbride, Glasgow, G74 5PA Tel: (01355) 249191 Fax: (01355) 230875 E-mail: info@donprint.com
Zebra Technologies Europe, Pittman Way, Fulwood, Preston, PR2 9ZD Tel: (01772) 797555 Fax: (01772) 693000 E-mail: zebra_ap@zebra.com

SELF ADHESIVE CORKS

Cantrill Cork Products, 3 Alma Works, Darlaston Road, Wednesbury, West Midlands, WS10 7TG Tel: 0121-567 3140 Fax: 0121-567 3149E-mail: cancork@cantrill.fsbusiness.co.uk

SELF ADHESIVE ENVELOPES

▶ Ad3 Envelope Printers Ltd, Unit 143 Aireplace Mills, Kirkstall Road, Leeds, LS3 1JL Tel: 0113-244 3700 Fax: 0113-244 9400 E-mail: andy.martin@ad3envelope.co.uk
Smith Anderson Envelopes Ltd, Whiteside Industrial Estate, Bathgate, West Lothian, EH48 2RX Tel: (01506) 634463 Fax: (01506) 634366 E-mail: sales@eagle-envelopes.com
Tenza Technologies Ltd, Carlton Park Industrial Estate, Saxmundham, Suffolk, IP17 2NL Tel: (01728) 602811 Fax: (01728) 605282 E-mail: enquiries@tenzatech.com
Wegener Sefton, G 7 Unit Liver Industrial Estate, Long Lane, Walton, Liverpool, L9 7ES Tel: 0151-521 7070 Fax: 0151-525 2458 E-mail: howardpaul@btconnect.com

SELF ADHESIVE FOIL

P A L Adhesive Products Ltd, Old Park Industrial Estate, Old Park Road, Wednesbury, West Midlands, WS10 9LR Tel: 0121-556 6686 Fax: 0121-505 1487 E-mail: sales@paladhesives.co.uk

SELF ADHESIVE GRAPHICS

Graphic Innovation Ltd, 35 Chequers Hill, Amersham, Buckinghamshire, HP7 9DQ Tel: (01494) 431500 Fax: (01494) 431500 E-mail: info@graphicinnovation.com

SELF ADHESIVE LABEL PRINTERS

Prima Tapes & Labels Ltd, Prima House, Faraday Way, Orpington, Kent, BR5 3QW Tel: (01689) 816111 Fax: (01689) 816010 E-mail: sales@prima-tapes.com

SELF ADHESIVE LABEL PRINTING

Bemrosebooth Ltd, Stockholm Road, Hull, HU7 0XY Tel: (01482) 826343 Fax: (01482) 826667 E-mail: contact@bemrosebooth.co.uk
▶ Boxstar Ltd, Hill Street, Clayton-le-moors, Accrington, Lancashire, BB5 5EA Tel: 01254 395631 Fax: 01254 391573 E-mail: info@boxstarltd.com
Centralised Services, Piccadilly, Nottingham, NG6 9FN Tel: 0115-913 5000 Fax: 0115-977 0744 E-mail: centser@btconnect.com
Codeway Ltd, 13 Telford Way, Severalls Industrial Park, Colchester, CO4 9QP Tel: (01206) 756738 Fax: (01206) 756705 E-mail: sales@codeway.com
Crown Labels, 102 Walkley Rd, Sheffield, S6 2XP Tel: 0114-232 1152 Fax: 0114-232 1301 E-mail: sales@crownlabels.co.uk
▶ Go Labels International Co. Ltd, Albion Park, Warrington Road, Glazebury, Warrington, WA3 5PG Tel: (01925) 763091 Fax: (01925) 765741 E-mail: email@golabels.co.uk
▶ J H Davenport & Sons Ltd, Harehills Lane, Leeds, LS9 6JF Tel: 0113-249 5561 Fax: 0113-249 1381 E-mail: info@jhdavenport.co.uk
▶ Labels Galore, PO BOX 114, Newcastle upon Tyne, NE20 9ZQ Tel: (07739) 960871 E-mail: info@labelsgalore.co.uk
Ormerod Developments Rochdale Ltd, Ormerod House, Caldershaw Business Park, Rochdale, Lancashire, OL12 7LQ Tel: (01706) 646808 Fax: (01706) 640694 E-mail: sales@ormerods.com
▶ Swiss Valley Print Ltd, Unit 9 Trostre Industrial Park, Llanelli, Dyfed, SA14 9UU Tel: (01554) 758758 Fax: (01554) 758758 E-mail: cambrian@clara.net

SELF ADHESIVE LABEL ROLLS

Applied Labels, 4 Cronin Road, Weldon South Industrial Estate, Corby, Northamptonshire, NN18 8AQ Tel: (01536) 406572 Fax: (01536) 406972 E-mail: applied@btinternet.com
Double R Labels Ltd, 17-21 Redhills Road, South Woodham Ferrers, Chelmsford, CM3 5UL Tel: (01245) 325455 Fax: (01245) 325001 E-mail: info@doublerlabels.co.uk
End To End Labels Ltd, Vale Road, Spilsby, Lincolnshire, PE23 5HE Tel: (01790) 753475 Fax: (01790) 752979 E-mail: sales@endtoendlabels.co.uk
Stephen Fossler Co. Inc., 24 The Business Village, Wexham Road, Slough, SL2 5HF Tel: (01753) 553413 Fax: (01753) 518532 E-mail: fossleruk@aol.com
I D Labels Ltd, 1 Eagle Estate, Brookers Road, Billingshurst, West Sussex, RH14 9RZ Tel: (01403) 786800 Fax: (01403) 786700
M P S Labels Ltd, The Brick Store, Gallants Farm, Gallants Lane, East Farleigh, Maidstone, Kent, ME15 0LD Tel: (01622) 727510 Fax: (01622) 725210 E-mail: sales@mpslabels.co.uk

SELF ADHESIVE LABELS

A C Labels Ltd, 3 Centurion Way Business Park, Alfreton Road, Derby, DE21 4AY Tel: (01332) 366117 Fax: (01332) 291292 E-mail: d.clouston@aclabels.co.uk
A D S Worldwide Ltd, West Carr Lane, Sutton Fields, Hull, HU7 0BW Tel: (01482) 820219 Fax: (01482) 831596 E-mail: sales@ads-worldwide.com
Advance Bunzl Ltd, West Point, New Hive Lane, Larkfield, Kent, ME20 6XJ Tel: (01622) 764504 Fax: (01622) 208157 E-mail: sales@advancebunzl.com
Alpha Print & Design, Unit 12, Sedgemount Industrial Park, Bristol Road, Bridgwater, Somerset, TA6 4AR Tel: (01278) 426958 Fax: (01278) 424001 E-mail: alphaprint@ukonline.co.uk
Anglia, Oldmedow Road, King's Lynn, Norfolk, PE30 4JJ Tel: (01553) 776790 Fax: (01553) 776790
Anglia Labels Sales Ltd, Bull Lane Industrial Estate, Bull Lane, Acton, Sudbury, Suffolk, CO10 0BD Tel: (01787) 379118 Fax: (01787) 378840 E-mail: sales@anglialabels.co.uk
Applied Labels, 4 Cronin Road, Weldon South Industrial Estate, Corby, Northamptonshire, NN18 8AQ Tel: (01536) 406572 Fax: (01536) 406972 E-mail: applied@btinternet.com
Arc Labels Ltd, The Maltings Industrial Estate, Doncaster Road, Whitley Bridge, Goole, North Humberside, DN14 0HH Tel: (01977) 663063 Fax: (01977) 663064 E-mail: sales@arclabels.com
Arrow Screen Print Ltd, 3 Fletcher Way, Weston Road, Norwich, NR3 3ST Tel: (01603) 485942 Fax: (01603) 485385 E-mail: sales@arrowscreenprint.co.uk
▶ Ashfield Labels, Unit E Draycott Business Park, Cam, Dursley, Gloucestershire, GL11 5DQ Tel: (01453) 890825 Fax: (01453) 890579 E-mail: sales@ashfieldlabels.co.uk
Aydon Silver & Co. Ltd, Units 1-2 Stoney Lane Industrial Estate, Red Suns Road, Kidderminster, Worcestershire, DY10 2LG Tel: (01562) 820107 Fax: (01562) 822253 E-mail: enquiries@aydonsilver.co.uk

SELF ADHESIVE LABELS – *continued*

Aztec Labels, Kidderminster Industrial Estate, Spennells Valley Road, Kidderminster, Worcestershire, DY10 1XS Tel: (01562) 66518 Fax: (01562) 69802 E-mail: sales@azteclabel.co.uk

B M G Industries Ltd, Amwell Lane, Stanstead Abbotts, Ware, Hertfordshire, SG12 8EB Tel: (01920) 870240 Fax: (01920) 870652 E-mail: bmgprint@aol.com

B S Labels Ltd, Wood Street, Earl Shilton, Leicester, LE9 7NE Tel: (01455) 844451 Fax: (01455) 842607 E-mail: sales@bslabels.co.uk

The Baker Self-Adhesive Label Company Ltd, 37 Sutherland Road, London, E17 6BH Tel: (020) 8523 2174 Fax: (020) 8527 6556

Bemrosebooth Ltd, Stockholm Road, Hull, HU7 0XY Tel: (01482) 826343 Fax: (01482) 826667 E-mail: contact@bemrosebooth.co.uk

Berkshire Labels Ltd, Swangate, Hungerford, Berkshire, RG17 0YX Tel: (01488) 683628 Fax: (01488) 684186 E-mail: sales@berkshirelabels.co.uk

Berrington Press, Barton Yard, Hereford, HR4 0AZ Tel: (01981) 241360 Fax: (01432) 353877 E-mail: david@berrington-press.co.uk

Blackdown Plant Ltd, The Cross, 2 Midhurst Road, Haslemere, Surrey, GU27 3EE Tel: (01428) 643309 Fax: (01428) 661630 E-mail: sales@blackdownpress.co.uk

Bolton Labelling Systems, 53-55 Bridgeman Place, Bolton, BL2 1DE Tel: (01204) 526079 Fax: (01204) 384348 E-mail: sales@boltonlabelling.co.uk

Bondlabels Ltd, Wollaston Way, Burnt Mills Industrial Area, Basildon, Essex, SS13 1DJ Tel: (01268) 590555 Fax: (01268) 590999 E-mail: sales@bondlabels.co.uk

▶ Brackley Labels Ltd, A Nigel Court, Ward Road, Buckingham Road Industrial Estate, Brackley, Northamptonshire, NN13 7LF Tel: (01280) 704979 Fax: (01280) 705256 E-mail: sales@brackleylabels.net

Britannia Labels Ltd, 22b Centurion Way, Meridian Business Park, Leicester, LE19 1WH Tel: 0116-281 5300 Fax: 0116-281 5301 E-mail: sales@britannialabels.com

Brodie Label Services Ltd, 4 Dunnwoods Road, Cumbernauld, Glasgow, G67 3EN Tel: (01236) 736984 Fax: (01236) 731953 E-mail: info@brodielabels.co.uk

Burall, PO Box 7, Wisbech, Cambs, PE13 2SZ Tel: (0870) 728 7272 Fax: (0870) 728 7273

Burkett Quicksign, Unit 19 Carbrook Hall Industrial Estate, Dunlop Street, Sheffield, S9 2HR Tel: 0114-256 0720 Fax: 0114-256 0192 E-mail: sales@burkettquicksign.co.uk

C & S Nameplate Co. Ltd, 37 Vale Road, Portslade, Brighton, BN41 1GD Tel: (01273) 419646 Fax: (01273) 411316 E-mail: sales@candsnameplate.com

The Classic Label Company Ltd, Unit 9-14 Whitehall Properties, Town Gate, Wyke, Bradford, West Yorkshire, BD12 9JQ Tel: (01274) 690217 Fax: (01274) 690046 E-mail: info@classiclabels.co.uk

Clearprint Labels Ltd, 1-2 Essex Street, Preston, PR1 1QE Tel: (01772) 258185 Fax: (01772) 256622 E-mail: sales@clearprint.co.uk

Compass Printing Packaging Ltd, 49-51 Bridgeman Place, Bolton, BL2 1DE Tel: (01204) 527130 Fax: (01204) 381629 E-mail: mail@compasslabels2002.freeserve.co.uk

Crestline Printers Ltd, 1 Atlas Court, Coalville, Leicestershire, LE67 3FL Tel: (01530) 838761 Fax: (01530) 812582 E-mail: enquiries@crestline.co.uk

Crown Labels, 102 Walkley Rd, Sheffield, S6 2XP Tel: 0114-232 1152 Fax: 0114-232 1301 E-mail: sales@crownlabels.co.uk

D R Labelling Systems Ltd, 12 Westgarth Place, College Milton Industrial Estate, East Kilbride, Glasgow, G74 5NT Tel: (01355) 221200 Fax: (01355) 221737 E-mail: sales@drlabelling.co.uk

Danro Ltd, 68 Station Road, Earl Shilton, Leicester, LE9 7GA Tel: (01455) 847061 Fax: (01455) 841272 E-mail: info@danroltd.co.uk

Davand Lables Ltd, Unit 19 Offerton Industrial Estate, Hempshaw Lane, Stockport, Cheshire, SK2 5TJ Tel: 0161-474 7133 Fax: 0161-429 9265 E-mail: davandlabels@tiscali.co.uk

Daymark Ltd, Unit 70 Hartlebury Trading Estate, Hartlebury, Kidderminster, Worcestershire, DY10 4JB Tel: (01299) 251365 Fax: (01299) 251386 E-mail: sales@labelsandtags.com

Dippon Label Co. Ltd, 125 Dartmouth Middleway, Aston, Birmingham, B7 4UA Tel: 0121-359 8183 Fax: 0121-359 2749 E-mail: sales@dippon.co.uk

Ditone Labels, Harvard Industrial Estate, Kimbolton, Huntingdon, Cambridgeshire, PE28 0NJ Tel: (01480) 862600 Fax: (01480) 862623 E-mail: enquire@ditone.co.uk

Double R Labels Ltd, 17-21 Redhills Road, South Woodham Ferrers, Chelmsford, CM3 5UL Tel: (01245) 325455 Fax: (01245) 325001 E-mail: info@doublerlabels.co.uk

Easdale Labels Ltd, Unit 1 Enterprise Way, Sherburn in Elmet, Leeds, LS25 6NA Tel: (01977) 686300 Fax: (01977) 681971 E-mail: sales@reflexlabels.co.uk

Electro Graph Ltd, 177 Lower High Street, Stourbridge, West Midlands, DY8 1TG Tel: (01384) 378436 Fax: (01384) 392542 E-mail: sales@eguk.com

Elite Signs, 8 Cavendish Road, Salford, M7 4WW Tel: 0161-792 0232 Fax: 0161-792 0232 E-mail: elitesignsprint@aol.com

End To End Labels Ltd, Vale Road, Spilsby, Lincolnshire, PE23 5HE Tel: (01790) 753475 Fax: (01790) 752979 E-mail: sales@endtoendlabels.co.uk

Enterprise Graphics Ltd, 1 Earls Close, Earls Close Industrial Estate, Thurmaston, Leicester, LE4 8FZ Tel: 0116-260 0879 Fax: 0116-269 7729 E-mail: fiona@enterprisegraphics.wannado.co.uk

Evans Graphics Ltd, G Boyn Valley Industrial Estate, Boyn Valley Road, Maidenhead, Berkshire, SL6 4EJ Tel: (0870) 7773630 Fax: (0870) 7773632 E-mail: sales@evansgraphics.co.uk

Fast Stik Labels, 41 Norwood Road, London, SE24 9AA Tel: (020) 8671 1818 Fax: (020) 8671 1818 E-mail: fast-sticklables@tiscali.co.uk

Fastabs Ltd, Unit 3 Oswin Road, Brailsford Industrial Estate, Leicester, LE3 1HR Tel: 0116-291 6660 Fax: 0116-291 6661 E-mail: fastabs@virgin.net

Field Box More Labels, Roman Bank, Bourne, Lincolnshire, PE10 9LQ Tel: (01778) 426444 Fax: (01778) 421862

Field Boxmore, Millennium Way West, Nottingham, NG8 6AW Tel: 0115-979 6300 Fax: 0115-979 6333

Field First Label Access, Label House Kingsland Rading Estate, St. Philips Road, Bristol, BS2 0JZ Tel: 0117-954 3131 Fax: 0117-955 0739 E-mail: sales.labelaccess@fieldgroup.com

Fisher Clark, Horncastle Road, Boston, Lincolnshire, PE21 9HZ Tel: (01205) 365501 Fax: (01205) 364825 E-mail: fisherclark@fisherclark.co.uk

Flexcon Glenrothes Ltd, Whitworth Road, Glenrothes, Fife, KY6 2TF Tel: (01592) 663200 Fax: (01592) 663201 E-mail: enquiries@flexcon-europe.nl

Stephen Fossler Co. Inc., 24 The Business Village, Wexham Road, Slough, SL2 5HF Tel: (01753) 553413 Fax: (01753) 518532 E-mail: fossleruk@aol.com

Goldcrest Adhesive Products Ltd, Unit A, Telford Road, Bicester, Oxfordshire, OX26 4LD Tel: (01869) 243201 Fax: (01869) 244734 E-mail: sales@adhesivelabels.co.uk

Hamilton Adhesive Labels Ltd, 3 Highmeres Road, Troon Industrial Area, Leicester, LE4 9LZ Tel: 0116-246 0064 Fax: 0116-246 1645 E-mail: gcook@hamilton-labels.co.uk

Harlands of Hull Ltd, Burma Drive, Hull, HU9 5SD Tel: (01482) 785300 Fax: (01482) 785329 E-mail: enquiries@harlands.co.uk

Heron Labels Ltd, Unit 24 Pier Road Industrial Estate, Pier Road, Gillingham, Kent, ME7 1RZ Tel: (01634) 581979 Fax: (01634) 582120 E-mail: heron@heron-labels.co.uk

Hovat, Westmead, New Hythe Lane, Larkfield, Aylesford, Kent, ME20 6XJ Tel: (01622) 791193 Fax: (01622) 791192 E-mail: executive.hovat@btinternet.com

I D Labels Ltd, 1 Eagle Estate, Brookers Road, Billingshurst, West Sussex, RH14 9RZ Tel: (01403) 786800 Fax: (01403) 786700

Image Grafix, 6 Manse Parade, London Road, Swanley, Kent, BR8 8DA Tel: (01322) 614669 Fax: (01322) 614878 E-mail: imagegrafix@btconnect.com

Impact Boston Ltd, Victoria Road, Skegness, Lincolnshire, PE25 3SN Tel: (01754) 767275 Fax: (01754) 613100 E-mail: sales@impactboston.ltd.uk

Industrial Self Adhesives Ltd, Robey Close, Linby, Nottingham, NG15 8AA Tel: 0115-968 1895 Fax: 0115-963 2821 E-mail: sales@isatape.co.uk

Instrument Component Labels Ltd, Unit L1, Beversbrook Centre, Redman Road, Calne, Wiltshire, SN11 9PR Tel: (01249) 822010 Fax: (01249) 821330 E-mail: robertbromley@ic-labels.com

Intereel Group Ltd, Unit 11, Mountbatten Road, Tiverton, Devon, EX16 6SW Tel: (01884) 256364 Fax: (01884) 257898 E-mail: sales@intereel.co.uk

Itstick Labels Ltd, 8-9 Bath Road Trading Estate, Lightpill, Stroud, Gloucestershire, GL5 3QF Tel: (01453) 758010 Fax: (01453) 764089 E-mail: enquiries@itsticklabels.co.uk

Kroy (Europe) Ltd, Worton Drive, Worton Grange Ind Estate, Reading, RG2 0LZ Tel: 0118-986 1411 Fax: 0118-986 5205 E-mail: hamilton@kroy.com

L S Francis, Unit 12a Mayfair Industrial Area, Maldon Road, Latchingdon, Chelmsford, CM3 6LF Tel: (01621) 740924 Fax: (01621) 740924

Label Apeel Ltd, James House, Murrayfield Road, Leicester, LE3 1UW Tel: 0116-231 4555 Fax: 0116-231 4552 E-mail: info@labelapeel.co.uk

Label Link, The Old Bakery, High Street, Angmering, Littlehampton, West Sussex, BN16 4AG Tel: (01903) 782588 Fax: (01903) 782588 E-mail: sales@label-link.co.uk

The Label Makers Ltd, Labmak House, Prince Street, Bradford, West Yorkshire, BD4 6HQ Tel: (01274) 681151 Fax: (01274) 651090 E-mail: info@labmak.co.uk

Label Spec, Unit 2, Drummond Crescent, Riverside Business Park, Irvine, Ayrshire, KA11 5AN Tel: (01563) 550990 Fax: (01563) 550991 E-mail: sales@labelspec.co.uk

Label Supply Eastbourne Ltd, North Street, Eastbourne, East Sussex, BN21 3HG Tel: (01323) 645264 Fax: (01323) 727488 E-mail: enquiries@labelsupply.co.uk

Labelman Labels & Tags, 52b Salop Road, Oswestry, Shropshire, SY11 2RQ Tel: (01691) 679333 Fax: (01691) 679444 E-mail: sales@1abelman.demon.co.uk

Labelpower Ltd, 6 Kingsbury Trading Estate, Church Lane, London, NW9 8AU Tel: (020) 8205 8255 Fax: (020) 8200 1769 E-mail: sales@labelpower.co.uk

Labels Plus Ltd, Unit 3, River Side Industrial Estate, Bordercot Lane, Wickham Market, Woodbridge, Suffolk, IP13 0TA Tel: (0870) 7705161 Fax: (01728) 745385

Lancastrian Labels Ltd, 183 Great Howard Street, Liverpool, L3 7DL Tel: 0151-298 1212 Fax: 0151-298 1432 E-mail: sales@lancastrian.co.uk

Last Bros Ltd, Delamare Road, Cheshunt, Waltham Cross, Hertfordshire, EN8 9TE Tel: (01992) 638283 Fax: (01992) 638286 E-mail: sales@lastbros.co.uk

Le Mark Self Adhesives Ltd, Houghton Hill Industries, Houghton Hill Farm, Houghton, Huntingdon, Cambridgeshire, PE28 2DH Tel: (01480) 494540 Fax: (01480) 494206 E-mail: info@lemark.co.uk

Links Labels & Tapes Ltd, Pinfold Road, Bourne, Lincolnshire, PE10 9HT Tel: (01778) 426282 Fax: (01778) 425003 E-mail: enquiries@linkslabels-tapes.co.uk

M.L.P.S., PO Box 27, Grantham, Lincs, NG31 6SJ Tel: (01476) 590400 Fax: (01476) 590400 E-mail: sales@mlps.co.uk

M Latchford, 10 Alstone Lane, Cheltenham, Gloucestershire, GL51 8EG Tel: (01242) 584588 Fax: (01242) 529251 E-mail: sales@marklatchford-screenprint.co.uk

M P S Labels Ltd, The Brick Store, Gallants Farm, Gallants Lane, East Farleigh, Maidstone, Kent, ME15 0LD Tel: (01622) 727510 Fax: (01622) 725210 E-mail: sales@mpslabels.co.uk

Macfarlane Group Ukltd, 22 Bentinck Street, Kilmarnock, Ayrshire, KA1 4AS Tel: (01563) 525151 Fax: (01563) 539963 E-mail: kwoodhouse@macfarlanelabels.com

Marsh Labels Ltd, 6 Lady Bee Marina Industrial Estate, Albion Street, Southwick, Brighton, BN42 4EP Tel: (01273) 595744 Fax: (01273) 870425 E-mail: sales@marshlabels.co.uk

Martek, Unit 12b, Ridings Park, Eastern Way, Cannock, Staffordshire, WS11 7FJ Tel: (01543) 502202 Fax: (01543) 467726 E-mail: info@martekonline.co.uk

Maxwell Labels, Unit 8, Moorbridge Road, Bingham Industrial Estate, Nottingham, NG13 8GG Tel: (01949) 837831 Fax: (01949) 831128

Medway Engraving Products, 62 High Street, Newington, Sittingbourne, Kent, ME9 7JL Tel: (01795) 842617 Fax: (01795) 843782

Mid Lancs Labels Ltd, 1 High Street, Standish, Wigan, Lancashire, WN6 0HA Tel: (01257) 400700 Fax: (01257) 422871

Midland Regional Printers Ltd, Nottingham Road, Nottingham, NG7 7BT Tel: 0115-955 1000 Fax: 0115-955 1012 E-mail: sales@midlandregionalprinters.co.uk

Montgomery Engravers Ltd, Red Doles Road, Huddersfield, HD2 1AT Tel: (01484) 429520 Fax: (01484) 435022

Martin Mulligan (UK) Ltd, Barcode House, Shaw Street, St. Helens, Merseyside, WA10 1EN Tel: (01744) 744200 Fax: (01744) 744216 E-mail: sales@martinmulligan.com

Nelsons Labels MCR Ltd, Unit 3 Waterside, Trafford Park, Manchester, M17 1WD Tel: 0161-873 4500 Fax: 0161-873 4505 E-mail: sales@nelsons-labels.co.uk

Norprint Ltd, Horncastle Road, Boston, Lincolnshire, PE21 9HZ Tel: (01205) 365161 Fax: (01205) 364825 E-mail: norprint@norprint.co.uk

North Cheshire Labels, 16 Vernon Street, Hyde, Cheshire, SK14 1QH Tel: 0161-368 1345 Fax: 0161-351 7142

Nu Tac Trade Labels Ltd, Bradford Street, Farnworth, Bolton, BL4 9LS Tel: (01204) 861436 Fax: (01204) 862923 E-mail: info@newfoil.co.uk

Nutan Printers, 67-69 Harrison Road, Leicester, LE4 6BT Tel: 0116-266 9405 Fax: 0116-261 0251 E-mail: sales@nutan-printers.co.uk

Ovalring Ltd, 60 Prince of Wales Lane, Birmingham, B14 4JY Tel: 0121-436 6060 Fax: 0121-436 6061

Overprinting Machines UK Ltd, Speedprint House, Halifax Road, Cross Roads, Keighley, West Yorkshire, BD22 9DH Tel: (01535) 642528 Fax: (01535) 643958 E-mail: info@opmlabels.com

P M E Engraving & Screen Printing Ltd, 11 Robert Cort Industrial Estate, Britten Road, Reading, RG2 0AU Tel: 0118-986 4858 Fax: 0118-975 3415 E-mail: pms-sales@compuserve.com

Panel Print Industrial Screen Printers, 7-12 Morris Road, Poole, Dorset, BH17 0GG Tel: (01202) 686575 Fax: (01202) 675733 E-mail: panelprint@btconnect.com

Pat's Labels Ltd, 23 Newfield Road, Ash Vale, Aldershot, Hampshire, GU12 5LG Tel: (01252) 524245 Fax: (01252) 524257

Piroto Labelling Ltd, 9 Pond Wood Close, Moulton Park Industrial Estate, Northampton, NN3 6RT Tel: (01604) 646600 Fax: (01604) 492090 E-mail: info@piroto-labelling.com

Polycrown Ltd, Unit 3 Smiths Forge, North End Road, Yatton, Bristol, BS49 4AU Tel: (01934) 876349 Fax: (01934) 835406 E-mail: sales@polycrown.com

Precision Labelling Systems (Print) Ltd, Bridge Mill, Gauxholme Fold, Todmorden, Lancashire, OL14 7PW Tel: (01706) 815094 Fax: (01706) 816411 E-mail: production@precision-labelling.com

Premier Labels, 29 Gloucester St, Cirencester, Gloucestershire, GL7 2DJ Tel: (01285) 656255 Fax: 01285 656255

Premier Labels & Name Plates, Harrow Lane, Farncombe Street, Godalming, Surrey, GU7 3LD Tel: (01483) 423424

R B Labels Ltd, 37 Grove Road, Ilkley, West Yorkshire, LS29 9PF Tel: (01943) 468302 Fax: (01943) 850406 E-mail: sales@tradelabels.co.uk

Ranger Labels, Unit 2, Reach Road Industrial Estate, Burwell, Cambridge, CB25 0GH Tel: (01638) 743506 Fax: (01638) 743507

Renlim Labels, 1065 Thornton Road, Bradford, West Yorkshire, BD8 0PA Tel: (01274) 882222 Fax: (01274) 884449 E-mail: renlim@netserv.net

Royston Labels Ltd, 18 Orchard Road, Royston, Hertfordshire, SG8 5HD Tel: (01763) 212020 Fax: (01763) 248004 E-mail: info@roystonlabels.co.uk

S A Labels Ltd, Station Road, Oakworth, Keighley, West Yorkshire, BD22 0ED Tel: (01535) 646177 Fax: (01535) 646739 E-mail: sales@salabels.co.uk

S L Conyers & Son Ltd, Hawthorns Industrial Estate, Middlemore Road, Handsworth, Birmingham, B21 0BH Tel: 0121-551 2875 Fax: 0121-554 5267 E-mail: webmaster@conyers-labels.com

Secura Labels Ltd, Unit L2 Westminster Industrial Estate, Measham, Swadlincote, Derbyshire, DE12 7DS Tel: (01530) 515170 Fax: (01530) 515171 E-mail: sales@securalabels.co.uk

Simpson Label Co. Ltd, Newbattle Industrial Estate, Mayfield, Dalkeith, Midlothian, EH22 4AF Tel: 0131-654 2800 Fax: 0131-663 6185 E-mail: mail@simpsonlabel.co.uk

Skanem, 2 Princesway, Team Valley Trading Estate, Gateshead, Tyne & Wear, NE11 0TU Tel: 0191-482 8000 Fax: 0191-482 8001 E-mail: reception.newcastle@skanem.com

South East Labels, 7 Broomers Hill Park, Broomers Hill Lane, Pulborough, West Sussex, RH20 2RY Tel: (01798) 873738 Fax: (01798) 874538 E-mail: sales@southeastlabels.co.uk

Speedyprint Ltd, 67 Stockport Road, Stockport, Cheshire, SK3 0JG Tel: 0161-480 6038 Fax: 0161-480 5166 E-mail: sales@speedyprint.co.uk

Sprint Signs Ltd, Holmes Way, Horncastle, Lincolnshire, LN9 6JW Tel: (01507) 522247 Fax: (01507) 522017 E-mail: sales@sprintsigns.co.uk

Stayprint Labels & Tags, Brow Lane, Shelf, Halifax, West Yorkshire, HX3 7QJ Tel: (01274) 699200 Fax: (01274) 699209 E-mail: sales@stayprint.com

Suffolk Pricing Systems, 66a Canhams Road, Great Cornard, Sudbury, Suffolk, CO10 0ES Tel: (01787) 375192 Fax: (01787) 375192

T W Parker (Paper) Ltd, Farriers Way, Bootle, Merseyside, L30 4XL Tel: 0151-523 7308 Fax: 0151-530 1318

▶ Tinsley Robor Labels, 12 Arndale Road, Wick, Littlehampton, West Sussex, BN17 7HD Tel: (01903) 731212 Fax: (01903) 738204 E-mail: sales@agilabels.com

Tormax UK Ltd, Tormax HS Unit 21 Mole Bus Park, Randalls Road, Leatherhead, Surrey, KT22 7BD Tel: (01372) 377711 Fax: (01372) 378044 E-mail: tormax@langleysystems.co.uk

Trilogybrookes Printing, Ashbourne Way, Shirley, Solihull, West Midlands, B90 4QU Tel: 0121-745 9600 Fax: 0121-745 6200 E-mail: tkeatet@trilogymediagroup.com

Tungate Forms & Labels Ltd, Brookhouse Way, Cheadle, Stoke-on-Trent, ST10 1SR Tel: (01538) 755755 Fax: (01538) 756062

Valley Screenprint Co., Units 1-2, Browells Lane, Feltham, Middlesex, TW13 7EQ Tel: (020) 8890 8271 Fax: (020) 8890 8485 E-mail: post@vspcm.demon.co.uk

Vari Labels, 44a Waldeck Road, Dartford, DA1 1UA Tel: (01322) 293186 Fax: (01322) 442225

Vernham Labels Ltd, 6 Mayfield Avenue Industrial Park, Fyfield Road, Weyhill, Andover, Hampshire, SP11 8HU Tel: (01264) 773501 Fax: (01264) 773065 E-mail: malcolm@vernhamlabels.co.uk

Vision Printers Ltd, 25 Colne Valley Business Park, Huddersfield, HD7 5QG Tel: (01484) 847307 Fax: (01484) 846581 E-mail: sales@visionprint.com

Vista Labels Limited, Vista House, Hempshaw Lane, Stockport, Cheshire, SK1 4NB Tel: 0161-477 5151 Fax: 0161-477 9203 E-mail: sales@vistalabels.com

W H P Labels Ltd, 48 Smith Street, Birmingham, B19 3EN Tel: 0121-523 0007 Fax: 0121-523 2221 E-mail: rhwhp@aol.com

Wellan Studios Printers)Ltd, Unit 1, Grange Valley Road, Batley, West Yorkshire, WF17 6GG Tel: (01924) 473481 Fax: (01924) 477353 E-mail: sales@wellanstudios.com

Zebra Technologies Europe, Pittman Way, Fulwood, Preston, PR2 9ZD Tel: (01772) 797555 Fax: (01772) 693000 E-mail: zebra_ap@zebra.com

SELF ADHESIVE LETTERING

David Etchells Signs, Unit 5 Brassey Close, Peterborough, PE1 2AZ Tel: (01733) 347847 Fax: (01733) 311242 E-mail: sales@etchells-signs.co.uk
E S P Technologies Group Ltd, 2 Euroway, Wood Close, Quarry Wood, Aylesford, Kent, ME20 7UB Tel: (01622) 715000 Fax: (01622) 797000 E-mail: sales@esptech.co.uk
Riviera Signs Ltd, 2 104 Barton Road, Torquay, TQ2 7NY Tel: (01803) 324303 Fax: (01803) 314105 E-mail: sales@rivierasigns.co.uk
Signpost Engraving, 5 Dalton Court, Astmoor Industrial Estate, Runcorn, Cheshire, WA7 1PU Tel: (01928) 574777 Fax: (01928) 567314 E-mail: signpost.eng@btconnect.com
Slater Signs, Unit 32 Crayford Industrial Estate, Swaisland Drive, Crayford, Dartford, DA1 4HS Tel: (01322) 558409 Fax: (01322) 554474 E-mail: sales@slatersigns.co.uk
Staffordshire Signs & Graphics Ltd, 154 Lime Lane, Pelsall, Walsall, WS3 5AP Tel: (01543) 373006 Fax: (01543) 374550 E-mail: richard@signs-and-graphics.co.uk

SELF ADHESIVE PAPER

Avery Dennison Material (UK) Ltd, Unit 5/6, Gardner Road, Maidenhead, Berkshire, SL6 7PP Tel: (01628) 764095 Fax: (01628) 623713
Mactac UK Ltd, Unit 4-6 Britannia Trade Centre, Ryehill Close, Lodge Farm Industrial Estate, Northampton, NN5 7UA Tel: (01604) 756521 Fax: (01604) 758150 E-mail: bridings@bemis.com
Newfoil Ltd, Bradford Street, Farnworth, Bolton, BL4 9LS Tel: (01204) 861110 Fax: (01204) 862201 E-mail: info@newfoil.co.uk
Raflatac Ltd, Wareham Road, Eastfield, Scarborough, North Yorkshire, YO11 3DX Tel: (01723) 583661 Fax: (01723) 584896 E-mail: raflatac@raflatac.com
Scannedstick UK Ltd, Butterfly House, St. Neots, Cambridgeshire, PE19 6EE Tel: (01480) 362000 Fax: (01480) 217722 E-mail: sales@scannedstick.co.uk
Smith & McLaurin Ltd, Cartside Mill, Kilbarchan, Renfrewshire, PA10 2AF Tel: (01505) 707700 Fax: (01505) 704992 E-mail: info@smcl.co.uk
Tenza Technologies Ltd, Carlton Park Industrial Estate, Saxmundham, Suffolk, IP17 2NL Tel: (01728) 602811 Fax: (01728) 605282 E-mail: enquiries@tenzatech.com

SELF ADHESIVE PAPER CONVERTERS

Lynvale Ltd, Unit 6, Lime Grove Estate, Falconer Road, Haverhill, Suffolk, CB9 7XU Tel: (0870) 1609255 Fax: (0870) 1609256 E-mail: info@lynvale.co.uk

SELF ADHESIVE PAPER LABELS

A C Labels Ltd, 3 Centurion Way Business Park, Alfreton Road, Derby, DE21 4AY Tel: (01332) 366117 Fax: (01332) 291292 E-mail: d.clouston@aclabels.co.uk
Anglia Labels Sales Ltd, Bull Lane Industrial Estate, Bull Lane, Acton, Sudbury, Suffolk, CO10 0BD Tel: (01787) 379118 Fax: (01787) 378840 E-mail: sales@anglialabels.co.uk
Applied Labels, 4 Cronin Road, Weldon South Industrial Estate, Corby, Northamptonshire, NN18 8AQ Tel: (01536) 406572 Fax: (01536) 406972 E-mail: applied@btinternet.com
BP Self Adhesive Labels Ltd, Cypress Drive, St Mellons Business Park, St. Mellons, Cardiff, CF3 0EG Tel: (029) 2077 8500 Fax: (029) 2077 8388 E-mail: hello@bplabels.co.uk
▶ Go Labels International Co. Ltd, Albion Park, Warrington Road, Glazebury, Warrington, WA3 5PG Tel: (01925) 763091 Fax: (01925) 765741 E-mail: email@golabels.co.uk
▶ Labels Galore, PO BOX 114, Newcastle upon Tyne, NE20 9ZQ Tel: (07739) 960871 E-mail: info@labelsgalore.co.uk
▶ Robstock Ltd, Unit 9-10, Rope Walk, Ilkeston, Derbyshire, DE7 5HX Tel: 0115-930 3308 Fax: 0115-932 4726 E-mail: sales@robstock.co.uk

SELF ADHESIVE PHOTOLUMINESCENT LABELS

Globright Ltd, 530 Woodbridge Road, Ipswich, IP4 4PN Tel: (01473) 721561 Fax: (01473) 714069 E-mail: sales@globritephotoluminescent.com

SELF ADHESIVE PLASTIC FILM

Cherrie Adhesive Coatings Ltd, Unit 14 Raikes Clough Industrial, Estate Raikes Lane, Bolton, BL3 1RP Tel: (01204) 371645 Fax: (01204) 371645
Mactac UK Ltd, Unit 4-6 Britannia Trade Centre, Ryehill Close, Lodge Farm Industrial Estate, Northampton, NN5 7UA Tel: (01604) 756521 Fax: (01604) 758150 E-mail: bridings@bemis.com
Madico Graphic Films Ltd, 9 Cordwallace Park, Clivemont Road, Maidenhead, Berkshire, SL6 7BU Tel: (01628) 777766 Fax: (01628) 776666 E-mail: info@madico.co.uk
Neschen UK Ltd, Emerald Way, Stone Business Park, Stone, Staffordshire, ST15 0SR Tel: (01785) 610110 Fax: (01785) 610111 E-mail: neschen@neschen.co.uk
Ritrama UK Ltd, Lynwell Road, Lyntown Trading Estate, Eccles, Manchester, M30 9QG Tel: 0161-786 1700 Fax: 0161-786 1701 E-mail: info@ritrama.co.uk
Smith & McLaurin Ltd, Cartside Mill, Kilbarchan, Renfrewshire, PA10 2AF Tel: (01505) 707700 Fax: (01505) 704992 E-mail: info@smcl.co.uk

SELF ADHESIVE PLASTIC LABELS

Adcal Labels Ltd, Jayem Works, Gomm Road, High Wycombe, Buckinghamshire, HP13 7DJ Tel: (01494) 530761 Fax: (01494) 461651 E-mail: sales@adcal-labels.co.uk
Anglo Scottish Packaging, Montrose Avenue, Hillington Industrial Estate, Glasgow, G52 4LA Tel: 0141-882 5151 Fax: 0141-882 5500 E-mail: sales@angloscottish.net
The Baker Self-Adhesive Label Company Ltd, 37 Sutherland Road, London, E17 6BH Tel: (020) 8523 2174 Fax: (020) 8527 6556
Banbury Nameplates Ltd, Dashwood Road, Banbury, Oxfordshire, OX16 5HD Tel: (01295) 267638 Fax: (01295) 271745 E-mail: sales@banburynameplates.co.uk
▶ Brackley Labels Ltd, A Nigel Court, Ward Road, Buckingham Road Industrial Estate, Brackley, Northamptonshire, NN13 7LF Tel: (01280) 704979 Fax: (01280) 705256 E-mail: sales@brackleylabels.net
Castle Packaging Ltd, Bott Lane, Walsall, WS1 2JG Tel: (01922) 625451 Fax: (01922) 722202 E-mail: sales@castlepackaging.co.uk
The Danielson Group Ltd, 29 Pembroke Road, Aylesbury, Buckinghamshire, HP20 1DB Tel: (01296) 319000 Fax: (01296) 392141 E-mail: sales@danielson.co.uk
Daymark Ltd, Unit 70 Hartlebury Trading Estate, Hartlebury, Kidderminster, Worcestershire, DY10 4JB Tel: (01299) 251365 Fax: (01299) 251386 E-mail: sales@labelsandtags.com
Diametric Technical Manufacturing Ltd, 26-28 Manners View, Newport, Isle of Wight, PO30 5FA Tel: (01983) 826611 Fax: (01983) 826622 E-mail: tad.james@diemetric-manufacturing.co.uk
Goldcrest Adhesive Products Ltd, Unit A, Telford Road, Bicester, Oxfordshire, OX26 4LD Tel: (01869) 243201 Fax: (01869) 244734 E-mail: sales@adhesivelabels.co.uk
GPS Developments Ltd, 14 Darlington Close, Sandy, Bedfordshire, SG19 1RW Tel: (01767) 681560 Fax: (01767) 691685 E-mail: sales@gpsdevelopments.co.uk
Industrial Self Adhesives Ltd, Robey Close, Linby, Nottingham, NG15 8AA Tel: 0115-968 1895 Fax: 0115-963 2821 E-mail: sales@isatape.co.uk
L S Francis, Unit 12a Mayfair Industrial Area, Maldon Road, Latchingdon, Chelmsford, CM3 6LF Tel: (01621) 740924 Fax: (01621) 740924
M P S Labels Ltd, The Brick Store, Gallants Farm, Gallants Lane, East Farleigh, Maidstone, Kent, ME15 0LD Tel: (01622) 727510 Fax: (01622) 725210 E-mail: sales@mpslabels.co.uk
Sutterton Labels, Pinfold Road, Bourne, Lincolnshire, PE10 9HT Tel: (01778) 391637 Fax: (01778) 391638E-mail: sales@slpp.co.uk

SELF ADHESIVE PLASTIC STICKERS

Ad-Stik Enterprise, Bromley, BR1 2WN Tel: (020) 8468 7924 Fax: (020) 8468 7924
J A M Design Screen Print, 143a Croydon Road, Caterham, Surrey, CR3 6PF Tel: (01883) 343444 Fax: (01883) 343444 E-mail: jim.rimmington@btinternet.com
London Screen Printing, St. Clare Business Park, Holly Road, Hampton, Middlesex, TW12 1PZ Tel: (020) 8941 8285 Fax: (020) 8941 8806
Solito Graphics, 1137 Yardley Wood Road, Birmingham, B14 4LS Tel: 0121-474 4640 Fax: 0121-474 4640
Zed Team Ltd, 13 Mead Lane, Hertford, SG13 7AG Tel: (01992) 551777 Fax: (01992) 500697 E-mail: zteam@cix.compulink.co.uk

SELF ADHESIVE PVC SHEETING

Webmaster Ltd, Units 5-6 Astra Industrial Centre, Royle Barn Road, Rochdale, Lancashire, OL11 3DT Tel: (01706) 656122 Fax: (01706) 764400 E-mail: sales@webmasterltd.co.uk

SELF ADHESIVE SEALANTS

Winn & Coales Denso Ltd, Denso House, 33-35 Chapel Road, London, SE27 0TR Tel: (020) 8670 7511 Fax: (020) 8761 2456 E-mail: mail@denso.net

SELF ADHESIVE TAPE CONVERTERS

Lynvale Ltd, Unit 6, Lime Grove Estate, Falconer Road, Haverhill, Suffolk, CB9 7XU Tel: (0870) 1609255 Fax: (0870) 1609256 E-mail: info@lynvale.co.uk

SELF ADHESIVE TAPES, *See also headings under Adhesive Tape*

Adhere Industrial Tapes Ltd, Unit 1 Whitehall Road, Whitehall Industrial Estate, Colchester, CO2 8WA Tel: (01206) 871999 Fax: (01206) 871998 E-mail: sales@adhere.co.uk
▶ Industrial Tape Solutions Ltd, 2-6 Station Road, Shipley, West Yorkshire, BD18 2JL Tel: (01274) 592244 Fax: (01274) 591144 E-mail: sales@tapesolutions.co.uk
Limpet Printed Tapes Ltd, The Causeway, Bassingbourn, Royston, Hertfordshire, SG8 5JB Tel: (01763) 252420 Fax: (01763) 252421 E-mail: print@limpettapes.com
Mactac UK Ltd, Unit 4-6 Britannia Trade Centre, Ryehill Close, Lodge Farm Industrial Estate, Northampton, NN5 7UA Tel: (01604) 756521 Fax: (01604) 758150 E-mail: bridings@bemis.com
Swallow Tapes Ltd, 2 Cotton Hall Barns, Middlewich Road, Holmes Chapel, Crewe, CW4 7ET Tel: (01477) 535599 Fax: (01477) 535440 E-mail: sales@swallowtapes.sagehost.co.uk
V S A Products Ltd, Hardwick Trading Estate, Rollesby Road, King's Lynn, Norfolk, PE30 4JS Tel: (01553) 761521 Fax: (01553) 691464 E-mail: vsa-enquiries@btconnect.com
R.A. Wood Adhesive Tapes Ltd, Unit 2 Waterside Business Centre, Wolverhampton Road, Cannock, Staffordshire, WS11 1SN Tel: (01543) 578331 Fax: (01543) 572301

SELF ADHESIVE TAPES, PRINTED/ADVERTISING

Border Label Company Ltd, Glenview Catrail Road, Galashiels, Selkirkshire, TD1 1NW Tel: (01896) 759074 Fax: (01896) 759074
Test Valley, Watt Road, Salisbury, SP2 7UD Tel: (01722) 414800 Fax: (0870) 2240449
Tritel Ltd, Unit 1 Bolney Grange Business Park, Hickstead, Haywards Heath, West Sussex, RH17 5PB Tel: (01444) 871188 Fax: (01444) 871199 E-mail: sales@tritel.co.uk
Windmill Tapes & Labels, 6 Mackenzie Industrial Estate, Bird Hall Lane, Stockport, Cheshire, SK3 0SB Tel: 0161-495 3959 Fax: 0161-428 1603 E-mail: sales@windmilltapes.co.uk

SELF ADHESIVE TRANSFERS

Butchers Printed Products Ltd, 498-506 Moseley Road, Birmingham, B12 9AL Tel: 0121-440 2612 Fax: 0121-440 3239 E-mail: md@bppscreengraphics.co.uk
Dry Transfers Ltd, 1 Jubilee Street, Melton Mowbray, Leicestershire, LE13 1ND Tel: (01664) 565785 Fax: (01664) 410344 E-mail: sales@dry-transfers.co.uk
Graphicraft Ltd, 6-8 Singer Way, Woburn Road Industrial Estate, Kempston, Bedford, MK42 7AN Tel: (01234) 846000 Fax: (01234) 843601 E-mail: sales@cgi-visual.com
Kaylee Transfers Ltd, New Tythe Street, Long Eaton, Nottingham, NG10 2DP Tel: 0115-973 5247 Fax: 0115-946 0801 E-mail: sales@kayleetransfers.uk
Sherwood Transfer Co., 28 Victoria Road, Nottingham, NG5 2NB Tel: 0115-960 3995 Fax: 0115-969 1948

SELF ASSEMBLY FURNITURE

Addspace Furniture Ltd, Lowfield Road, Bolton-upon-Dearne, Rotherham, South Yorkshire, S63 8JF Tel: (01709) 899400 Fax: (01709) 897369 E-mail: paul.hakes@addspacefl.co.uk
Advanced Computer Furniture, Unit 2 Masons Road Industrial Estate, Masons Road, Stratford-upon-Avon, Warwickshire, CV37 9NF Tel: (01789) 414449 Fax: (01789) 415553
Ashwood Designs Ltd, Robertstown House, Aberdare Business Park, Aberdare, Mid Glamorgan, CF44 8ER Tel: (01685) 883388 Fax: (01685) 883399
Chillington Wolverhampton Ltd, Chillington Fields, Wolverhampton, WV1 2BY Tel: (01902) 451326 Fax: (01902) 452010
Justwise Group Ltd, Shire Hill, Saffron Walden, Essex, CB11 3AP Tel: (01799) 513466 Fax: (01799) 525657 E-mail: mail@justwise.demon.co.uk
Teemo Designs Ltd, Roman Bank, Cherry Holt Road, Bourne, Lincolnshire, PE10 9LQ Tel: (01778) 421421 Fax: (01778) 393135 E-mail: teemo@globalnet.co.uk

SELF CLINCH FASTENERS

Blakeacre Ltd, Austin Way, Hampstead Industrial Estate, Birmingham, B42 1DU Tel: 0121-358 5066 Fax: 0121-358 1721 E-mail: sales@blakeacre.co.uk
Normandy Air Compressors, Unit 1d Cranborne Industrial Estate, Cranborne Road, Potters Bar, Hertfordshire, EN6 3JN Tel: (01707) 662248

SELF CLINCH STUDS

Blakeacre Ltd, Austin Way, Hampstead Industrial Estate, Birmingham, B42 1DU Tel: 0121-358 5066 Fax: 0121-358 1721 E-mail: sales@blakeacre.co.uk

SELF CLOSING NON CONCUSSIVE VALVES

Barber Wilson & Co. Ltd, Crawley Road, London, N22 6AH Tel: (020) 8888 3461 Fax: (020) 8888 2041 E-mail: sales@barwil.co.uk

SELF CONTAINED SKID MOUNTED WATER PURIFICATION EQUIPMENT

DSI International Ltd, Unit 6, Abbey Road Enterprise Park, Neath, West Glamorgan, SA10 7DN Tel: (01639) 645400 Fax: (01639) 644664 E-mail: sales@aquapur950.com

SELF COPYING PAPER

Torras Paper Ltd, Creator House, Maidstone Road, Kingston, Milton Keynes, MK10 0BD Tel: (01908) 288000 Fax: (01908) 288001 E-mail: info@torraspapel.es

SELF DRILLING SCREWS

Bolt & Bearing London, 21s Queensway, Enfield, Middlesex, EN3 4UL Tel: (020) 8805 7250 Fax: (020) 8804 0126 E-mail: sales@boltandbearing.co.uk
Construction Fastener Techniques, C F T House, Mill Race Lane, Stourbridge, West Midlands, DY8 1JN Tel: (01384) 442277 Fax: (01384) 442999 E-mail: sales@cftltd.co.uk
Fastbolt Distributors (UK) Ltd, Sherbourne Drive, Tilbrook, Milton Keynes, MK7 8AW Tel: (01908) 650100 Fax: (01908) 650101 E-mail: fastbolt-uk@compuserve.com
Garrison Dales Ltd, Unit 8, North St Industrial Estate, Droitwich, Worcestershire, WR9 8JB Tel: (01905) 794555 Fax: (01905) 794592 E-mail: sales@garrisondales.co.uk

SELF DRIVE COMMERCIAL VEHICLE HIRE

▶ Charter Self Drive Ltd, Charter House, Forge Way Cleveland Street, Darlington, County Durham, DL1 2PB Tel: (01325) 481814 Fax: (01325) 484636 E-mail: info@charterselfdrive.co.uk
▶ Liberte' Horsebox Hire, Unit 7, Greetby Place, East Gillibrands, Skelmersdale, Lancashire, WN8 9UL Tel: (01928) 740020 E-mail: info@libertehorseboxes.co.uk
▶ Mayes Self Drive, 155 Chingford Road, London, E17 4PN Tel: (020) 8531 1123 Fax: (020) 8531 1330 E-mail: sales@mayesselfdrive.co.uk
▶ Metro Rentals Limited, Unit 2, Colne Way, Colne Way Court, Watford, WD24 7NE Tel: 01923 630630 Fax: 01923 639191 E-mail: enquiries@metrorentals.co.uk
▶ Practical Car & Van Rental, Unit 6 Willow Road, Trent Lane Indust Estate, Derby, DE74 2NP Tel: (01332) 812151 Fax: (01332) 853530 E-mail: andrewsherwood1@hotmail.com
▶ Walsall Van Hire, 305-317 Wednesbury Road, Pleck, Walsall, WS2 9QJ Tel: 01922 639652 E-mail: andrew@walsallvanhire.co.uk

SELF INKING RUBBER STAMPS

▶ Long Neck Stamps, 4 Leacroft Close, Kenley, Surrey, CR8 5EX Tel: 0709 288 7252 Fax: 0709 288 7252 E-mail: kwalexander@longneck.co.uk
Malling Press, Unit 4b Diplocks Way, Hailsham, East Sussex, BN27 3JF Tel: (01323) 847157 Fax: (01323) 847457
Polydiam Instant Rubber Stamp Co., 70-72 Markfield Road, London, N15 4QF Tel: (020) 8493 1060 Fax: (020) 8885 5711 E-mail: sales@rubberstamp.co.uk

SELF LOCKING NUTS

D S Fasteners Ltd, Unit 7, Hill Fort Close, Fison Way Industrial Estate, Thetford, Norfolk, IP24 1HS Tel: (01842) 763000 Fax: (01842) 764055

SELF LUBRICATING BEARINGS

F K F UK Ltd, Strode Road, Clevedon, Avon, BS21 6QQ Tel: (01275) 876021 Fax: (01275) 878480 E-mail: mail@fkf.co.uk
Oilite Bowman, 10 Isis Court, Wyndyke Furlong, Abingdon Business Park, Abingdon, Oxfordshire, OX14 1DZ Tel: (01235) 815816 Fax: (01235) 811234 E-mail: steve@bowman.co.uk
Railko Ltd, Boundary Rd, Loudwater, High Wycombe, Bucks, HP10 9QU Tel: (01628) 524901 Fax: (01628) 810761 E-mail: info@railko.co.uk

SELF PRIMING PUMPS

Dab Pumps Ltd, 4 Stortford Hall Industrial Park, Dunmow Road, Bishop's Stortford, Hertfordshire, CM23 5GZ Tel: (01279) 652776 Fax: (01279) 655147 E-mail: info@dabpumps.com
Godwin Pumps Ltd, Quenington, Cirencester, Gloucestershire, GL7 5BX Tel: (01285) 750271 Fax: (01285) 750352 E-mail: sales@godwinpumps.co.uk
Hilta TW, Flowplant House, Unit 8A-B Summit Crescent, Summit Estate, Smethwick, West Midlands, B66 1BT Tel: 0121-525 9955 Fax: 0121-525 0748 E-mail: hilta@hiltapumps.com
Hydromarque Ltd, 21 Stapledon Road, Orton Southgate, Peterborough, PE2 6TD Tel: (01733) 370545 Fax: (01733) 361249 E-mail: mail@hydromarque.com
Mack Engineering, Montrose Avenue, Hillington Industrial Estate, Glasgow, G52 4LA Tel: 0141-882 1030 Fax: 0141-882 7330 E-mail: mackengineering@btinternet.com
Pioneer Pump Ltd, Corner Farm Industrial Estate, Woolpit Road, Rattlesden, Bury St. Edmunds, Suffolk, IP30 0RZ Tel: (01449) 736777

SELF REGULATING FLOOR HEATING CABLES

▶ Discount Floor Heating Ltd, Studio 24, Torfaen Business Centre, Gilchrist Thomas Industrial Estate, Blaenavon, Gwent, NP4 9RL Tel: (0845) 6581511 Fax: (0845) 6613557 E-mail: info@discountfloorheating.co.uk
▶ Pedarson Heating, Unit 16, Martlesham Creek Industrial Estate, Sandy Lane, Martlesham, Woodbridge, Suffolk, IP12 4SD Tel: (01394) 384077 Fax: (01394) 387177 E-mail: info@pedarson.com
Stabilag (E.S.H.) Ltd, 34 Mark Road, Hemel Hempstead, Hertfordshire, HP2 7DD Tel: (0870) 9906763 Fax: (0870) 9906762 E-mail: sales@stabilag.com

SELF SEALING COUPLINGS

Covflex Hydraulic & Engineering Co. Ltd, Rowleys Green Industrial Estate, Rowleys Green Lane, Coventry, CV6 6AN Tel: (024) 7668 8714 Fax: (024) 7668 8720 E-mail: sales@covflex.freeserve.co.uk
▶ Millennium Coupling Co. Ltd, 72b Roman Way Industrial Estate, Ribbleton, Preston, PR2 5BE Tel: (01772) 653530 Fax: (01772) 653531 E-mail: sales@mcc-ltd.com

SELF STORAGE UNITS

▶ 1st Storage Centres, Stoneygate Close, Gateshead, Tyne & Wear, NE10 0AZ Tel: 0191-469 7777 Fax: 0191-469 7999 E-mail: gateshead@storagecentres.co.uk
Access Self Storage Ltd, 93 Park Lane, London, W1K 7TB Tel: (020) 7297 4100 E-mail: enquiries@accessstorage.com
Easystore, Church Close, Chedgrave, Norwich, NR14 6NH Tel: (01508) 520579
▶ Lock N Store Ltd, Walker Road, Newcastle upon Tyne, NE6 2HL Tel: 0191-224 3411 Fax: 0191-276 6476
▶ Newbury Self Store Ltd, A3 Cyril Vokins Road, Newbury, Berkshire, RG14 5XB Tel: (01635) 581811
▶ Pickfords Ltd, Unit 3 Treliske Industrial Estate, Treliske, Truro, Cornwall, TR1 3LP Tel: (01208) 76083 Fax: (01872) 270339 E-mail: enquiries5@pickfords.com
▶ Warrington Self Storage, Athertons Quay, Warrington, WA5 1AH Tel: (01925) 417007

SELF TAPPING SCREWS

Fred Balls, Unit 3 National Avenue Industrial Estate, Bontoft Avenue, Hull, HU5 4HF Tel: (01482) 445447 Fax: (01482) 492162
John Sylvester Fasteners & Plastics Ltd, Vulcan Street, Bradford, West Yorkshire, BD4 9QU Tel: (01274) 684040 Fax: (01274) 684240 E-mail: sales.fp@btconnect.com
Lancaster Fastener Co. Ltd, Middlegate, White Lund Industrial Estate, Morecambe, Lancashire, LA3 3BN Tel: (01524) 62645 Fax: (01524) 66367 E-mail: enquiries@lancasterfastener.co.uk

SELF TIPPING SKIPS

A R C, Ripley Drive, Normanton Business Park, Normanton Industrial Estate, Normanton, West Yorkshire, WF6 1QT Tel: (01924) 223333 Fax: (0871) 4330708 E-mail: sales@arccomputers.co.uk
G J F Fabrications Ltd, The Chase Link, Lichfield Road, Brownhills, Walsall, WS8 6LA Tel: (01543) 360777 Fax: (01543) 360977 E-mail: gjf@btconnect.com
Invicta Forks & Attachments, Westland Square, Dewsbury Road, Leeds, LS11 5SS Tel: 0113-277 1222 Fax: 0113-271 6860 E-mail: sales@invictaforks.co.uk
P M Bradley Fabrications Ltd, 8 Lodge Lane Industrial Estate, Lodge Lane, Tuxford, Newark, Nottinghamshire, NG22 0NL Tel: (01777) 871222 Fax: (01777) 871922 E-mail: info@pmbfabrications.co.uk

SEMI PRECIOUS STONES

▶ Cheshires Jewellers, 95 Spencer Street, Birmingham, B18 6DA Tel: 0121 5231124 Fax: 0121 523 1222 E-mail: info@cheshiresjewellers.co.uk
▶ T A Henn & Son Ltd, 38-41 Princess Street, Wolverhampton, WV1 1HD Tel: (01902) 428486 Fax: (01902) 420406 E-mail: info@exclusiveessentials.co.uk

SEMI TRAILERS

Montracon Ltd, Carr Hill, Doncaster, S. Yorkshire, DN4 8DE Tel: (01302) 739292 Fax: (01302) 730660 E-mail: enquiries@montracon.com

SEMICONDUCTOR ACCESSORIES

Charntec Electronics Ltd, PO Box 477, Eastleigh, Hampshire, SO5 0AR Tel: (01962) 735718 Fax: (01962) 736756 E-mail: charntec@btinternet.com
Compugraphics International Ltd, Unit F Newark Road North, Glenrothes, Fife, KY7 4NT Tel: (01592) 772557 Fax: (01592) 775359 E-mail: enquiries@cgi.co.uk

SEMICONDUCTOR BASES

Eltek Semiconductors Ltd, Nelson Road, Townstal Industrial Estate, Dartmouth, Devon, TQ6 9LA Tel: (01803) 834455 Fax: (01803) 833011 E-mail: sales@eltek-semi.com
Harris Systems Ltd, Eskdale Road, Winnersh, Wokingham, Berkshire, RG41 5TS Tel: 0118-969 8787 Fax: 0118-964 8001
Intel Investments UK Ltd, Pipers Way, Swindon, SN3 1RJ Tel: (01793) 403000 Fax: (01793) 641440
IsoCom Components Ltd, Unit 25B, Park View Road West, Park View Industrial Estate, Brenda Road, Hartlepool, Cleveland, TS25 1UD Tel: (01429) 863609 Fax: (01429) 863581 E-mail: sales@isocom.co.uk
Mintech Semiconductors Ltd, 2 Hellesdon Park Road, Drayton High Road, Norwich, NR6 5DR Tel: (01603) 788967 Fax: (01603) 788920 E-mail: sales@mintech.co.uk
National Semi-Conductor (U K) Ltd, Milford House, Milford St, Swindon, SN1 1DW Tel: (01793) 614141 Fax: (01793) 427551 E-mail: elspethmurrin@nsc.com
Photronics UK Ltd, 1 Technology Drive, Bridgend, Mid Glamorgan, CF31 3LU Tel: (01656) 662171 Fax: (01656) 656183 E-mail: wales@photronics.com
St Micro Electronics Ltd, Planer House, Parkway, Marlow, Buckinghamshire, SL7 1YL Tel: (01628) 890800 Fax: (01628) 890391
Wafer Technology Ltd, 34 Maryland Road, Tongwell, Milton Keynes, MK15 8HJ Tel: (01908) 210444 Fax: (01908) 210443 E-mail: sales@wafertech.co.uk

SEMICONDUCTOR CHIPS

Austria Mikrosysteme International Ltd, Coliseum Business Centre, Watchmoore Park, Riverside Way, Camberley, Surrey, GU15 3YL Tel: 0118-973 1797 Fax: (01276) 29353 E-mail: info@amsint.com
Conexant Systems UK Ltd, 1210 Parkview, Arlington Business Park, Theale, Reading, RG7 4TY Tel: 0118-965 7831
Filtronic, Millennium Way, Heighington Lane Business Park, Newton Aycliffe, County Durham, DL5 6JW Tel: (01325) 301111 Fax: (01325) 306177
Forward Microsystems Leicester Ltd, 40 Northgate Street, Leicester, LE3 5BY Tel: 0116-262 7974 Fax: 0116-262 4864 E-mail: sales@formicro.co.uk
Globe Electronics (UK) Ltd, 19 Westmorland Drive, Warfield, Bracknell, Berkshire, RG42 3QJ Tel: (01344) 420775 Fax: (01344) 421194 E-mail: globeuk@btinternet.com
Highland Scientific, Unit 16 Bedford Business Centre, Mile Road, Bedford, MK42 9TW Tel: (01234) 216636 Fax: (01234) 271991 E-mail: sales@highland-scientific.com
Infineon Technologies UK Ltd, Infineon House, Fleet Mill, Minley Road, Fleet, Hampshire, GU51 2RD Tel: (01252) 772200 Fax: (01252) 772201 E-mail: wendy.walker@infineon.com
▶ Sanyo Component Europe GmbH, Unit 1, Walton Lodge, Bridge Street, Walton-on-Thames, Surrey, KT12 1BT Tel: (01932) 233600 Fax: (01932) 230104

SEMICONDUCTOR COMPONENT MANUFRS, *See also headings under Transistor*

Abacus Choice, Rooks Street, Cottenham, Cambridge, CB24 8QZ Tel: (01954) 287070 Fax: (01954) 252078
Acal Technology Ltd, 3 The Business Centre, Molly Millers Lane, Wokingham, Berkshire, RG41 2EY Tel: 0118-902 9702 Fax: 0118-902 9614 E-mail: admin@amega-group.com
Advent Electronics Ltd, 4 Forward Drive, Pennington, Lymington, Hampshire, SO41 8GA Tel: (023) 8028 2703 Fax: (023) 8028 3275 E-mail: mail@advent-elect.co.uk
Alex Nangle Electrical Ltd, Unit 3 Oakbank Park Way, Mid Calder, Livingston, West Lothian, EH53 0TH Tel: (01506) 449400 Fax: (01506) 449404 E-mail: info@nangle.co.uk
▶ Analogue Integration Ltd, The Old Village Store, Corston, Malmesbury, Wiltshire, SN16 0HJ Tel: (01666) 823290 Fax: (01666) 825154 E-mail: enquiry@analog.co.uk
Atmel UK Ltd, Coliseum Business Centre, Riverside Way, Camberley, Surrey, GU15 3YL Tel: (01344) 390060 Fax: (01344) 390070 E-mail: jane.sorrell@atmel.com
Avnet Memec Ltd, 64-65 Rabans Close, Aylesbury, Buckinghamshire, HP19 8TW Tel: (01296) 330061 Fax: (01296) 330065 E-mail: sales@insightuk.memec.com
B F Group Ltd, Unit 6 Cobhan Centre, Westmead Industrial Estate, Westlea, Swindon, SN5 7UJ Tel: (01793) 498020 Fax: (01793) 542019 E-mail: sales@bfgroup.co.uk
Consumer Microcircuits Ltd, Ovel Park, Langford, Maldon, Essex, CM9 6WG Tel: (01621) 875500 Fax: (01621) 875600 E-mail: sales@cmlmicro.com
Contact Components Ltd, 5 Parkend, Harlow BSNS Park, Harlow, Essex, CM19 5QF Tel: (01279) 424211 Fax: (01279) 424213
Cricklewood Electronics Ltd, 40-42 Cricklewood Broadway, London, NW2 3ET Tel: (020) 8452 0161 Fax: (020) 8208 1441 E-mail: sales@cricklewoodelectronics.com
Die Technology Ltd, Corbrook Road, Chadderton, Oldham, OL9 9SD Tel: 0161-626 3827 Fax: 0161-627 2341E-mail: info@ditech.co.uk
Distributed Technology Ltd, Howard House, Amy Road, Oxted, Surrey, RH8 0PW Tel: (01883) 716161 Fax: (01883) 716865 E-mail: mail@dtl-connectors.co.uk
Force Components 89 Ltd, Suit 8 Grove Park Industrial Estate, Waltham Road, White Waltham, Maidenhead, Berkshire, SL6 3LW Tel: (01628) 820066 Fax: (01628) 825530 E-mail: sales@force89ltd.co.uk
Just Rams plc, 6 Iron Bridge Close, Great Central Way, London, NW10 0UF Tel: (020) 8451 8700 Fax: (020) 8459 6301 E-mail: sales@justrams.co.uk
Langrex, Unit 4, Daux Road, Billingshurst, West Sussex, RH14 9SJ Tel: (01403) 785600 Fax: (01403) 785656E-mail: langrex@aol.com
▶ M P S Ltd, 57 Woodroffe Drive, Basingstoke, Hampshire, RG22 6NH Tel: (01256) 817933 Fax: (08707) 625402 E-mail: sales@mpsintl.com
Magnatec Ltd, Coventry Road, Lutterworth, Leicestershire, LE17 4JB Tel: (01455) 554711 Fax: (01455) 558843 E-mail: sales@semelab.co.uk
National Semiconductor UK Ltd, Larkfield Industrial Estate, Greenock, Renfrewshire, PA16 0EQ Tel: (01475) 633733 Fax: (01475) 638515
Pacer Components plc, Unit 4 Horseshoe Park, Pangbourne, Reading, RG8 7JW Tel: 0118-984 5280 Fax: 0118-984 5425 E-mail: pacer@pacer.co.uk
Powersem Ltd, Dawill, Lower Road, Little Hallingbury, Bishop's Stortford, Hertfordshire, CM22 7RA Tel: (01279) 726911 Fax: (01279) 600589 E-mail: pb@pbentley.com
Profusion plc, Aviation Way, Southend Airport, Southend-on-Sea, SS2 6UN Tel: (01702) 543500 Fax: (01702) 543700 E-mail: sales@profusionplc.com
Raedek Electronics, Unit 12 Avenue Fields Industrial Estate, Avenue Farm, Stratford-upon-Avon, Warwickshire, CV37 0HT Tel: (01789) 209294 Fax: (01789) 295757 E-mail: sales@raedek.com
▶ Sanyo Component Europe GmbH, Unit 1, Walton Lodge, Bridge Street, Walton-on-Thames, Surrey, KT12 1BT Tel: (01932) 233600 Fax: (01932) 230104
Semelab plc, Coventry Road, Lutterworth, Leicestershire, LE17 4JB Tel: (01455) 556565 Fax: (01455) 558371 E-mail: sales@semelab.co.uk
Semiconductor Specialists (UK) Ltd, Lincoln Business Park, Osbaldwick, York, YO10 3JB Tel: (01904) 436450 Fax: (01904) 436550 E-mail: sales@semispecs.com
Semikron UK Ltd, Martin House, 7 Fountain Drive, Hertford, SG13 7UB Tel: (01992) 584677 Fax: (01992) 554942 E-mail: sales.skuk@semikron.com
Silicon Glen Technologies Ltd, South Avenue, Blantyre Industrial Estate, Blantyre, Glasgow, G72 0XB Tel: (01698) 307070 Fax: (01698) 327979 E-mail: mail@sgtsiliconglen.com
H C Starck Ltd, Unit 1 Harris Road, Calne, Wiltshire, SN11 9PT Tel: (01249) 822122 Fax: (01249) 823800 E-mail: sally.field@hcstarck.co.uk
▶ TC Components, Castletown Windmill, 1 Arbory Road, Castletown, Isle of Man, IM9 1HA Tel: (01624) 829689 Fax: (01624) 829686 E-mail: tcatiom@hotmail.com
Toshiba Electronics (Europe) Ltd, Riverside Way, Camberley, Surrey, GU15 3YA Tel: (01276) 694600 Fax: (01276) 694800 E-mail: infobox@teu.toshiba.co.uk
Vanguard Microelectronics Ltd, 2 The Stocks, Cosgrove, Milton Keynes, MK19 7JD Tel: (01908) 563399 Fax: (01908) 263003 E-mail: sales@sunrise.co.uk

SEMICONDUCTOR CRYSTALS

A D I American Distributors Inc, Units 3-4 Peckworth Industrial Estate, Bedford Road, Lower Standon, Henlow, Bedfordshire, SG16 6EE Tel: (01462) 850804 Fax: (01462) 819596 E-mail: sales@americandistr.com
Crystalox Ltd, 1 Limborough Road, Wantage, Oxfordshire, OX12 9AJ Tel: (01235) 770044 Fax: (01235) 770111 E-mail: sales@crystalox.com
Oxford Semiconductor Ltd, 25 Milton Park, Milton, Abingdon, Oxfordshire, OX14 4SH Tel: (01235) 824900 Fax: (01235) 821141 E-mail: sales@oxsemi.com

SEMICONDUCTOR DIODES, *See also heading for particular types*

G D Technik, 24 High Street, Twyford, Reading, RG10 9AG Tel: 0118-934 2277 Fax: 0118-934 2896 E-mail: sales@gd-technik.com

SEMICONDUCTOR DISCRETE MANUFRS

Philips, Cross Oak Lane, Redhill, RH1 5HA Tel: (01293) 815000 Fax: (01293) 815511

SEMICONDUCTOR GAS SUPPLY SYSTEMS

Microgas Systems Ltd, Aztec Ho, Perrywood Business Pk Honeycrock La, Salfords, Redhill, RH1 5DZ Tel: (01737) 378000 Fax: (01737) 378055 E-mail: rsmith@microgas.uk.com

SEMICONDUCTOR INFORMATION SERVICES

Powersem Ltd, Dawill, Lower Road, Little Hallingbury, Bishop's Stortford, Hertfordshire, CM22 7RA Tel: (01279) 726911 Fax: (01279) 600589 E-mail: pb@pbentley.com

SEMICONDUCTOR INTERCONNECT PACKAGING PRODUCTS

▶ Microstencil Limited, Starlaw Park, Starlaw Road, Livingston, West Lothian, EH54 8SF Tel: 01506 409190 Fax: 01506 409181 E-mail: n.gorman@microstencil.com

SEMICONDUCTOR INTERFACE LOAD BOARD TEST EQUIPMENT

Synergie-Cad UK Ltd, Greetwell Place, 2 Lime Kiln Way, Lincoln, LN2 4US Tel: (01522) 520222 Fax: (01522) 531222 E-mail: rogercooke@synergie-cad.co.uk

SEMICONDUCTOR MATERIALS, CUSTOM MADE

I Q E Europe Ltd, Cypress Drive, St. Mellons, Cardiff, CF3 0EG Tel: (029) 2083 9400 Fax: (029) 2083 9401 E-mail: info@iqep.com
O M C UK Ltd, Candela House, Cardrew Industrial Estate, Redruth, Cornwall, TR15 1SS Tel: (01209) 215424 Fax: (01209) 215197 E-mail: omc-sales@omc-uk.com

SEMICONDUCTOR MATERIALS, CUSTOM MADE – *continued*

Wafer Technology Ltd, 34 Maryland Road, Tongwell, Milton Keynes, MK15 8HJ Tel: (01908) 210444 Fax: (01908) 210443 E-mail: sales@wafertech.co.uk

SEMICONDUCTOR MEMORIES

Infineon Technologies UK Ltd, Infineon House, Fleet Mill, Minley Road, Fleet, Hampshire, GU51 2RD Tel: (01252) 772200 Fax: (01252) 772201 E-mail: wendy.walker@infineon.com

SEMICONDUCTOR PRODUCTION CHEMICALS/ MATERIALS

Rockwood Electronic Materials, Amber Business Centre, Greenhill Industrial Estate, Riddings, Alfreton, Derbyshire, DE55 4DA Tel: (01773) 844200 Fax: (01773) 844244

SEMICONDUCTOR PRODUCTION MACHINERY/ EQUIPMENT MANUFRS

Advanced Energy Industries UK Ltd, 5 Minton Place, Victoria Road, Bicester, Oxfordshire, OX26 6QB Tel: (01869) 320022 Fax: (01869) 325004

Alliance Sales (Europe) Ltd, Units 22-24, Brunel Way, Thetford, Norfolk, IP24 1HP Tel: (01842) 822150 Fax: (01842) 820300 E-mail: info@alliance-sales.com

Aviza Technology Ltd, Coed Rhedyn, Ringland Way, Newport, Gwent, NP18 2TA Tel: (01633) 414000 Fax: (01633) 414141 E-mail: sales@trikon.com

Charntec Electronics Ltd, PO Box 477, Eastleigh, Hampshire, SO5 0AR Tel: (01962) 735718 Fax: (01962) 736756 E-mail: charntec@btinternet.com

CVT Ltd, 4-6 Carters Lane, Kiln Farm, Milton Keynes, MK11 3ER Tel: (01908) 563267 Fax: (01908) 568354

Orbis Technologies Ltd, 5 Thorpe Close, Banbury, Oxfordshire, OX16 4SW Tel: (01295) 273179 Fax: (01295) 276394 E-mail: orbis@orbitech.demon.co.uk

Pyramid Engineering Services Co. Ltd, 4 Orchard Business Centre, Kangley Bridge Road, London, SE26 5AQ Tel: (020) 8776 5545 Fax: (020) 8768 7650 E-mail: enquiries@pyramideng.com

Rem Electronic Equipment, Arkle House, Mill Lane, Birch, Colchester, CO2 0NG Tel: (01206) 331657 Fax: (01206) 331657

Silicon Glen Technologies Ltd, South Avenue, Blantyre Industrial Estate, Blantyre, Glasgow, G72 0XB Tel: (01698) 307070 Fax: (01698) 327979 E-mail: mail@sgtsiliconglen.com

Tokyo Electron Europe Ltd, Crawley Business Quarter, Fleming Way, Crawley, West Sussex, RH10 9QL Tel: (01293) 655800 Fax: (01293) 655888

SEMICONDUCTOR PROGRAMMING

Lewmax Programming, Unit 1, Fowke Street, Rothley, Leicester, LE7 7PJ Tel: 0116-212 2133 Fax: 0116-212 2136 E-mail: sales@lewmax.co.uk

SEMICONDUCTOR RECTIFIER STACK MANUFRS

Powersem Ltd, Dawill, Lower Road, Little Hallingbury, Bishop's Stortford, Hertfordshire, CM22 7RA Tel: (01279) 726911 Fax: (01279) 600589 E-mail: pb@pbentley.com

SEMICONDUCTOR RECTIFIERS, POWER TYPE

Challenge Innovations, 41-43 Mill Street, Bedford, MK40 3EU Tel: (01234) 354025 Fax: (01234) 354025

SEMICONDUCTOR TEST EQUIPMENT MANUFRS

Alliance Sales (Europe) Ltd, Units 22-24, Brunel Way, Thetford, Norfolk, IP24 1HP Tel: (01842) 822150 Fax: (01842) 820300 E-mail: info@alliance-sales.com

Challenge Innovations, 41-43 Mill Street, Bedford, MK40 3EU Tel: (01234) 354025 Fax: (01234) 354025

▶ Megatech Ltd, Littleton Drive, Cannock, Staffordshire, WS12 4TS Tel: (01543) 500044 Fax: (01543) 500066 E-mail: web@megatechlimited.co.uk

Wentworth Laboratories Ltd, 1 Gosforth Close, Sandy, Bedfordshire, SG19 1RB Tel: (01767) 681221 Fax: (01767) 691951

SEMICONDUCTOR TESTING SERVICES

Eltek Semiconductors Ltd, Nelson Road, Townstal Industrial Estate, Dartmouth, Devon, TQ6 9LA Tel: (01803) 834455 Fax: (01803) 833011 E-mail: sales@eltek-semi.com

Everrett Charles Technology, Homer House, Sibthorp Street, Lincoln, LN5 7SL Tel: (01522) 548220 Fax: (01522) 568419

Unisem (Europe) Ltd, Pen Y Fan Industrial Estate, Croespenman, Crumlin, Newport, Gwent, NP11 3XT Tel: (01495) 244111 Fax: (01495) 244828 E-mail: enquiries@atlantic1.co.uk

SEMICONDUCTORS, *See also headings for particular types*

Ace Components Ltd, 4 Priory Gardens, Scorton, Preston, PR3 1AQ Tel: (01524) 793893 Fax: (01524) 793894 E-mail: colinbabbs.ace@ukonline.co.uk

Advent Electronics Ltd, 4 Forward Drive, Pennington, Lymington, Hampshire, SO41 8GA Tel: (023) 8028 2703 Fax: (023) 8028 3275 E-mail: mail@advent-elect.co.uk

Arrow International Technologies Ltd, Arrow House, 4 Malabar Fields, Daventry, Northamptonshire, NN11 4DP Tel: (01327) 301160 Fax: (01327) 301180 E-mail: arrowteks@aol.com

Astute Electronics Ltd, Church House, Church Street, Ware, Hertfordshire, SG12 9EN Tel: (01920) 483800 Fax: (01920) 486399 E-mail: insales@astute.co.uk

Austin Semiconductor (Europe) Ltd, Test House, 1 Mill Lane, Alton, Hampshire, GU34 2QG Tel: (01420) 88022 Fax: (01420 87259 E-mail: sales@austinsemi.com

Carsem Europe, 1 Potters Walk, 134 High Street, Wootton Bassett, Swindon, SN4 7AY Tel: (01793) 853888 Fax: (01793) 855388

Conexant Systems UK Ltd, 1210 Parkview, Arlington Business Park, Theale, Reading, RG7 4TY Tel: 0118-965 7831

E B V Elektronik, Thames House, 17 Marlow Road, Maidenhead, Berkshire, SL6 7AA Tel: (01628) 770707 Fax: (01628) 783811

Filtronic, Millennium Way, Heighington Lane Business Park, Newton Aycliffe, County Durham, DL5 6JW Tel: (01325) 301111 Fax: (01325) 306177

Infineon Technologies UK Ltd, Infineon House, Fleet Mill, Minley Road, Fleet, Hampshire, GU51 2RD Tel: (01252) 772200 Fax: (01252) 772201 E-mail: wendy.walker@infineon.com

Just Rams plc, 6 Iron Bridge Close, Great Central Way, London, NW10 0UF Tel: (020) 8451 8700 Fax: (020) 8459 6301 E-mail: sales@justrams.co.uk

Neoware Systems, Asmec Centre Eagle House, The Ring, Bracknell, Berkshire, RG12 1HB Tel: (01344) 382164 Fax: (01344) 303192 E-mail: info@neoware.com

St Microelectronics, 1000 Aztec West, Almondsbury, Bristol, BS32 4SQ Tel: (01454) 616616 Fax: (01454) 617910 E-mail: postmaster@st.com

T E C, Trinity Bus Park, Turner Way, Wakefield, West Yorkshire, WF2 8EF Tel: (01924) 387979 Fax: (01924) 387989

SEMICONDUCTORS, RECONDITIONED/REFURBISHED

W W E Semiconductors Ltd, The Beeches, Grange Rd, Uckfield, E. Sussex, TN22 1QU Tel: (01825) 746900 Fax: (01825) 746911

SENSING EDGE OR SENSOR SAFETY DOORS

Tapeswitch Ltd, Unit 38 Drumhead Road, Chorley North Industrial Estate, Chorley, Lancashire, PR6 7BX Tel: (01257) 249777 Fax: (01257) 246600 E-mail: sales@tapeswitch.co.uk

Triton Controls Ltd, 2 Randolph Industrial Estate, Evenwood, Bishop Auckland, County Durham, DL14 9SJ Tel: (01388) 833000 Fax: (01388) 833680 E-mail: info@tritoncontrols.co.uk

SENSITISED PAPER/FILM/FOIL

Kernow Coatings Ltd, Kernick Road, Penryn, Cornwall, TR10 9DQ Tel: (01326) 373147 Fax: (01326) 376614 E-mail: kc@sensitisers.com

SENSOR MANUFRS, *See also headings for particular types under Sensors*

A B Electronic Ltd, Colbern House, Spring Gardens, Romford, RM7 9LP Tel: (01708) 762222 Fax: (01708) 762981 E-mail: info@abelectronic.com

Acam Instrumentation Ltd, 23 Thomas Street, Northampton, NN1 3EN Tel: (01604) 628700 Fax: (01604) 628700 E-mail: tom@acamltd.co.uk

Anton Test & Measurement, Park House, 15-23 Greenhill Crescent, Watford, WD18 8PH Tel: (08704) 280073 Fax: (08704) 280076 E-mail: sales@anton-group.com

Charnwood Instrumentation Services, 81 Park Road, Coalville, Leicestershire, LE67 3AF Tel: (01530) 510615 Fax: (01530) 510950 E-mail: graham@instrumentationservices.net

▶ Forest Engineering, Tulliemet, Ballinluig, Pitlochry, Perthshire, PH9 0NY Tel: (01796) 482408

Instruments & Controls Hull, Faraday Works, Crowle Street, Hull, HU9 1RH Tel: (01482) 225607 Fax: (01482) 217122 E-mail: sales@instco.co.uk

Kempston Controls, Shirley Road, Rushden, Northamptonshire, NN10 6BZ Tel: (01933) 414500 Fax: (01933) 410211 E-mail: sales@kempstoncontrols.co.uk

R D P Group Ltd, Grove Street, Heath Town, Wolverhampton, WV10 0PY Tel: (01902) 457512 Fax: (01902) 452000 E-mail: sales@rdpelectronics.com

Radun Controls Ltd, Unit 42 Aberaman Industrial Estate, Aberaman, Aberdare, Mid Glamorgan, CF44 6UZ Tel: (01685) 887600 Fax: (01685) 887601 E-mail: general@radun.com

Richmond Industries UK Ltd, C11 Acre Business Park, Acre Road, Reading, RG2 0SA Tel: 0118-931 0396

Russell Sub Surface Systems Ltd, Unit 2 Isbourne Way, Winchcombe, Cheltenham, Gloucestershire, GL54 5NS Tel: (01242) 603975 Fax: (01242) 602614 E-mail: rss-sales-uk@natoil.com

Transmission Of Power Ltd, 37 Sketchley Meadows, Hinckley, Leicestershire, LE10 3ES Tel: (01455) 616538 Fax: (01455) 250237

▶ Vydas International Marketing, Swan House, Passfield Business Centre, Lynchborough Road, Passfield, Liphook, Hampshire, GU30 7SB Tel: (01428) 751822 Fax: (01428) 751833 E-mail: info@vydas.co.uk

Wenglor Sensoric, Suite B Secondfloor Aspen House, 15 Medlicott Close, Corby, Northamptonshire, NN18 9NF Tel: (01536) 747299 Fax: (01536) 742301 E-mail: info.uk@wenglor.de

▶ Wild Insight Ltd, 5 Cambridge Road, Ely, Cambridgeshire, CB7 4HJ Tel: (01353) 665304 Fax: (01353) 610466 E-mail: enquiries@wildinsight.co.uk

Zettlex Printed Technologies Ltd, Newton Court, Town Street, Newton, Cambridge, CB22 7PE Tel: (01223) 874444 Fax: (01223) 874111 E-mail: info@zettlex.com

SENSORS, CURRENT, CUSTOM BUILT

Toroid Technology Ltd, 50 Mill Lane, Purley Way, Croydon, CR0 4AA Tel: (020) 8686 8646 Fax: (020) 8686 7177 E-mail: toroids@toroid-tech.com

SENSORS, MOTION/POSITION

Kavlico Corporation, 11-15 Columbus Walk, Brigantine Place, Cardiff, CF10 4BZ Tel: (029) 2046 3449 Fax: (029) 2045 0852 E-mail: kavlico@btinternet.co.uk

Muirhead Vactric Components Ltd, Oakfield Road, London, SE20 8EW Tel: (020) 8659 9090 Fax: (020) 8659 9906 E-mail: sales@muirheadaerospace.com

TSS (International) Ltd, 1 Garnet Close, Greycaine Industrial Estate, Watford, WD24 7JZ Tel: (01923) 470800 Fax: (01923) 470838 E-mail: tssmail@tssuk.co.uk

W + S Measuring Systems Ltd, Queens House, The Square, Corwen, Clwyd, LL21 0DG Tel: (01490) 413550 Fax: (01490) 413014 E-mail: info.uk@globalencoder.com

SENSORS, RELATIVE HUMIDITY, WITH APPLICATION SPECIFIC INTEGRATED CIRCUIT (ASIC)

Swindon Silicon Systems Ltd, Radnor Street, Swindon, SN1 3PR Tel: (01793) 649400 Fax: (01793) 616215 E-mail: info@sssl.co.uk

SEPARATORS, *See also headings for particular types*

Hydroflow Europe Ltd, Gillmans Industrial Estate, Billingshurst, West Sussex, RH14 9EZ Tel: (01403) 783741 Fax: (01403) 784442 E-mail: hydroflowe@aol.com

SEPARATORS, DIESEL ENGINE FUEL/WATER

Glencoe Ltd, Glenco House, Drake Avenue, Staines, Middlesex, TW18 2AW Tel: (01784) 493555 Fax: (01784) 493222 E-mail: sales@fuelsystem.co.uk

SEPIOLITE

Steetley Bentonite & Absorbents Ltd, West Carr Road, Retford, Nottinghamshire, DN22 7ZF Tel: (01777) 712828 Fax: (01777) 700344 E-mail: hq@steetley.com

SEPTIC TANKS

Hydroserve Sewage Disposal, Kingsley House, Ganders Park, Kingsley, Bordon, Hampshire, GU35 9LU Tel: (01420) 470800 Fax: (01420) 470820 E-mail: enquiries@conderproducts.com

Klargester Environmental Ltd, College Road, Aston Clinton, Aylesbury, Buckinghamshire, HP22 5EW Tel: (01296) 633000 Fax: (01296) 633001 E-mail: sales@kingspanec.com

Titan Pollution Control, West Portway, Andover, Hampshire, SP10 3LF Tel: (01264) 352444 Fax: (01264) 366446 E-mail: sales@titanpc.co.uk

W C Stopher, Homeview, Halesworth Road, Redisham, Beccles, Suffolk, NR34 8NF Tel: (01986) 781253

SEQUENCE CONTROL HYDRAULIC VALVES

Hi-Press Hydraulics Ltd, Riverside Works, Forge Road, Whaley Bridge, High Peak, Derbyshire, SK23 7HY Tel: (01663) 735089 Fax: (01663) 735090 E-mail: sales@hi-press.co.uk

SEQUIN OR SEQUIN TRIMMINGS

Brody International Ltd, Units 1-2, 18 Gillender Street, London, E3 3JW Tel: (020) 7538 5666 Fax: (020) 7510 1099 E-mail: sales@brody.co.uk

SERIAL INTERFACE CABLES

Suna Supplies Ltd, B 91 Ewell Road, Surbiton, Surrey, KT6 6AH Tel: (020) 8390 8811 Fax: (020) 8390 4331 E-mail: sales@suna.co.uk

SERVICE LIFTS

Ace Elevators Southern Ltd, Millennium House, 74 South Street, Keighley, West Yorkshire, BD21 1DQ Tel: (01535) 602239 Fax: (01535) 661268 E-mail: sales@ace-elevators.co.uk

The Britannic Lift Company plc, Riverview Buildings, Bradford Road, Riddlesden, Keighley, West Yorkshire, BD20 5JH Tel: (01535) 600066 Fax: (01535) 600077 E-mail: sales@lifts.co.uk

▶ Classic Lifts Ltd, Jubilee House, Altcar Road, Formby, Liverpool, L37 8DL Tel: (01704) 833255 Fax: (01704) 833880 E-mail: dave.markman@lift-engineers.co.uk

County Lifting Equipment & Safety Co Ltd, Unit 2 Telford Way, Telford Way Industrial Estate, Kettering, Northamptonshire, NN16 8UN Tel: (01536) 417878 Fax: (01536) 417877

Husbands Group Ltd, Shelah Road, Halesowen, West Midlands, B63 3PP Tel: 0121-550 1560 Fax: 0121-585 5285 E-mail: sales@servicelifts.co.uk

Pickerings Europe Ltd, 9 Glasgow Road, Baillieston, Glasgow, G69 6JT Tel: 0141-771 7575 Fax: 0141-771 8585 E-mail: info@pickerings.co.uk

Thyssen Lifts & Esculators Ltd, 4Th Floor Maple House, High Street, Potters Bar, Hertfordshire, EN6 5BS Tel: (01707) 672000 Fax: (01707) 672011

SERVICE MANAGEMENT SYSTEM SOFTWARE

Hewlett Packard Ltd, Cain Road, Bracknell, Berkshire, RG12 1HN Tel: (01344) 360000 Fax: (01344) 363344E-mail: info@jobshp.com

Infogrames UK Ltd, 21 Castle Street, Manchester, M3 4SW Tel: 0161-827 8000 Fax: 0161-827 8001

Infor, Needles House, Birmingham Road, Studley, Warwickshire, B80 7AS Tel: (01527) 496200 Fax: (01527) 496300

Open Seas, 7 Nuffield Way, Abingdon, Oxfordshire, OX14 1RJ Tel: (01235) 537391 Fax: (01235) 535168 E-mail: info@openseas.co.uk

Pinnacle Computer Systems Ltd, BRE Complex, Bucknalls Lane, Watford, WD25 9XX Tel: (01923) 686000 Fax: (01923) 686001 E-mail: sales@pinnaclecomputers.co.uk

Proquis Ltd, Building 1050 Cornforth Drive, Sittingbourne Research Centre, Sittingbourne, Kent, ME9 8PX Tel: (01795) 479001 Fax: (01795) 479009 E-mail: mark.fowler@proquis.com

SERVICE TO SHIPPING CONFERENCES

Far Eastern Freight Conference, Bridge House, 4 Borough High Street, London, SE1 9QZ Tel: (020) 7403 1700 Fax: (020) 7378 6691 E-mail: info@fefclondon.com

SERVIETTES, PAPER

Haji Cash & Carry Wholesalers, Haji House, Lower Tweedale Street, Rochdale, Lancashire, OL11 1HG Tel: (01706) 715959 Fax: (01706) 715960

Swan Mill Paper Co. Ltd, Goldsel Road, Swanley, Kent, BR8 8EU Tel: (01322) 665566 Fax: (01322) 661406 E-mail: sales@swantex.com

William Walton & Sons, 152 Stamford Street Central, Ashton-under-Lyne, Lancashire, OL6 6AD Tel: 0161-330 1506

SERVO ALTERNATING CURRENT (AC) ELECTRIC MOTOR DRIVES

Control Techniques Dynamics Ltd, South Way, Andover, Hampshire, SP10 5AB Tel: (01264) 387600 Fax: (01264) 356561 E-mail: sales@ctdynamics.com

SERVO COMPONENTS

Motor Technology Ltd, Motec House, Chadkirk Business Park, Stockport, Cheshire, SK6 3NE Tel: 0161-217 7100 Fax: 0161-217 7101 E-mail: sales@motec.co.uk

Norwin Electronics Ltd, Unit 6 Industrial Estate, Station Road, Gamlingay, Sandy, Bedfordshire, SG19 3HB Tel: (01767) 651485 Fax: (01767) 651623 E-mail: sales@norwin.co.uk

SERVO CONTROL EQUIPMENT

Kelectronic, 1 Waterworks Road, Portsmouth, PO6 1NG Tel: (023) 9237 2077 Fax: (023) 9237 2077 E-mail: kelectronic.uk@aol.com

NUM (UK) Ltd, Unit 3, Fairfield Court, Seven Stars Industrial Estate, Coventry, CV3 4LJ Tel: (0871) 7504020 Fax: (0871) 7504021 E-mail: solutions@schneider-num.co.uk

Osai UK Ltd, Mount House, Bond Avenue, Bletchley, Milton Keynes, MK1 1SF Tel: (01908) 642687 Fax: (01908) 642688 E-mail: sales@osai.co.uk

SERVO CONTROLLED TEST SYSTEMS

R D P Howden Ltd, Southam, Warwickshire, CV47 0ZD Tel: (01926) 813141 Fax: (01926) 810007 E-mail: info@rdphowden.co.uk

SERVO DRIVE MAINTENANCE/ REPAIR SERVICES

European Drives & Motor Repairs Ltd, 9 Mansion Close, Moulton Park Industrial Estate, Northampton, NN3 6RU Tel: (01604) 499777 Fax: (01604) 492777 E-mail: sales@edmr.co.uk

SERVO DRIVE MANUFRS

Norwin Electronics Ltd, Unit 6 Industrial Estate, Station Road, Gamlingay, Sandy, Bedfordshire, SG19 3HB Tel: (01767) 651485 Fax: (01767) 651623 E-mail: sales@norwin.co.uk

SSD Drives Ltd, New Courtwick Lane, Wick, Littlehampton, West Sussex, BN17 7RZ Tel: (01903) 737000 Fax: (01903) 737100 E-mail:

Unico UK Ltd, Garamonde Drive, Wymbush, Milton Keynes, MK8 8LF Tel: (01908) 260000 Fax: (01908) 260360 E-mail: drives@unico.co.uk

SERVO DRIVE POSITIONING SYSTEMS

Mclennan Servo Supplies Ltd, Unit 1, The Royston Centre, Lynchford Road, Ash Vale, Aldershot, Hampshire, GU12 5PQ Tel: (0870) 7700700 Fax: (0870) 7700699 E-mail: sales@mclennan.co.uk

Trio Motion Technology Ltd, Shannon Way, Tewkesbury, Gloucestershire, GL20 8ND Tel: (01684) 292333 Fax: (01684) 297929 E-mail: sales@triomotion.com

Valtec Controls Ltd, Halifax Works, St. Marys Lane, Tewkesbury, Gloucestershire, GL20 5SF Tel: (01684) 292383 Fax: (01684) 294498 E-mail: valtec.controls@btinternet.com

SERVO ELECTRIC MOTOR CONTROLLERS

Chapmore Controls Ltd, 64 Junction Road, Northampton, NN2 7HS Tel: (01604) 714431 Fax: (01604) 714431 E-mail: info@chapmore.co.uk

Control Techniques, Business Development Centre, Stafford Park 4, Telford, Shropshire, TF3 3BA Tel: (01952) 213727 Fax: (01952) 213701 E-mail: uksales@controltechniques.com

Trio, Treetops House, Gillotts Lane, Henley-On-Thames, Oxfordshire, RG9 1PT Tel: (01491) 579118 Fax: (01491) 412211

SERVO MECHANISMS

K & N International Office Systems Ltd, 52 Britton Street, London, EC1M 5UQ Tel: (020) 7490 9340 Fax: (020) 7490 9349 E-mail: sales@kn-international.co.uk

SERVO MOTOR MAINTENANCE/ REPAIR SERVICES

European Drives & Motor Repairs Ltd, 9 Mansion Close, Moulton Park Industrial Estate, Northampton, NN3 6RU Tel: (01604) 499777 Fax: (01604) 492777 E-mail: sales@edmr.co.uk

SERVO MOTOR MANUFRS

Norwin Electronics Ltd, Unit 6 Industrial Estate, Station Road, Gamlingay, Sandy, Bedfordshire, SG19 3HB Tel: (01767) 651485 Fax: (01767) 651623 E-mail: sales@norwin.co.uk

Stebon Ltd, Unit 2C Chase Park Industrial Estate, Ring Road, Burntwood, Staffordshire, WS7 8JQ Tel: (01543) 677211 Fax: (01543) 675005 E-mail: sales@stebon.net

SERVO VALVES

Star Hydraulics Ltd, 8a Beta Close, Tewkesbury, Gloucestershire, GL20 8SR Tel: (01684) 296176 Fax: (01684) 850714 E-mail: sales@star-hydraulics.co.uk

Valtec Controls Ltd, Halifax Works, St. Marys Lane, Tewkesbury, Gloucestershire, GL20 5SF Tel: (01684) 292383 Fax: (01684) 294498 E-mail: valtec.controls@btinternet.com

SESAME OIL, ORGANIC

▶ Bushy Tail Ltd, Staveley Mill Yard, Back Lane, Staveley, Kendal, Cumbria, LA8 9LR Tel: (01539) 822244 Fax: 0870 8362158

SEWAGE CUTTER SUBMERSIBLE PUMPS

M B Pumps Ltd, 2 Royle Park, Congleton, Cheshire, CW12 1JJ Tel: (01260) 299438 Fax: (01260) 297595 E-mail: sales@mbpumps.co.uk

SEWAGE OR EFFLUENT TREATMENT MACERATORS

Hydrostal Ltd, 4-5 The Galloway Centre, Newbury, Berkshire, RG14 5TL Tel: (01635) 550440 Fax: (01635) 550140 E-mail: sales@hidrostal.co.uk

SEWAGE OR SLUDGE PUMPS

A B S Waste Water Treatment Technology, Unit 1 Bridges Industrial Estate, Bridge Road, Horshay, Telford, Shropshire, TF4 3EE Tel: (01952) 632030 Fax: (01952) 632040 E-mail: roger.youngman@absgroup.com

Blandford Engineering, Unit 7 Littletowns Estate, Blandford Heights, Blandford Forum, Dorset, DT11 7UR Tel: (01258) 454222 Fax: (01258) 480433 E-mail: blandfordpumps@btinternet.com

Egger Turo Pumps (U.K.) Ltd, Fountain House, Cleeve Road, Leatherhead, Surrey, KT22 7NH Tel: (01372) 377688 Fax: (01372) 373587 E-mail: info.uk@eggerpumps.com

Energy Chemical & Equipment Co, Southwell Business Park, Crew Lane, Southwell, Nottinghamshire, NG25 0TX Tel: (01636) 816600 Fax: (01636) 816602 E-mail: energypumps@aol.com

Fluid Equipment International Ltd, 10 Blandford Heights Industrial Estate, Blandford Forum, Dorset, DT11 7TE Tel: (01258) 459401 Fax: (01258) 459068 E-mail: sales.feil@btconnect.com

G & G Pump Services Ltd, Dragons Wharf, Dragons Lane, Sandbach, Cheshire, CW11 3PA Tel: (01270) 759270 Fax: (01270) 759280

Gilbert Gilkes & Gordon Ltd, Canal Iron Works, Kendal, Cumbria, LA9 7BZ Tel: (01539) 720028 Fax: (01539) 732110 E-mail: sales@gilkes.com

Grundfos Pumps Ltd, Grovebury Road, Leighton Buzzard, Bedfordshire, LU7 4TL Tel: (01525) 850000 Fax: (01525) 850011 E-mail: ukindustry@grundfos.com

Landia UK Ltd, Waymills Indust Estate, Waymills, Whitchurch, Shropshire, SY13 1TT Tel: (01948) 661200 Fax: (01948) 661201 E-mail: info@landia.co.uk

P C M Group UK Ltd, Pilot Road, Corby, Northamptonshire, NN17 5YF Tel: (01536) 740200 Fax: (01536) 740201 E-mail: sales@pcmgroupuk.eu

▶ P D Pumps Ltd, 8 Stuart Road, Bredbury, Stockport, Cheshire, SK6 2SR Tel: 0161-494 5522 Fax: 0161-406 8889 E-mail: sales@pdpumpsltd.co.uk

Seepex UK Ltd, Unit 3 Armtech Row, Houndstone Business Park, Yeovil, Somerset, BA22 8RW Tel: (01935) 472376 Fax: (01935) 479836 E-mail: sales@seepex.co.uk

T T Pumps Ltd, Onneley Works, Newcastle Road, Woore, Crewe, CW3 9RU Tel: (01630) 647200 Fax: (01630) 642100 E-mail: response@ttpumps.com

W H Hendy & Sons, Units 1-5, Station Road Industrial Estate, Wiveliscombe, Taunton, Somerset, TA4 2LX Tel: (01984) 623386 Fax: (01984) 624343

SEWAGE PUMPING STATIONS

Bethell Group plc, Dane House Europa Trading Estate, Stoneclough Road, Radcliffe, Manchester, M26 1GE Tel: (01204) 439100 Fax: (01204) 439101 E-mail: mail@bethell.co.uk

Causeway Electricial Services, Catherine Street, Warrington, WA5 0LH Tel: (01925) 633390 Fax: (01925) 243214

▶ Flowrite Drainage Services Ltd, The Kilns, Lynwick Street, Rudgwick, Horsham, West Sussex, RH12 3DG Tel: (01403) 822485 E-mail: info@flowrite-drainage.co.uk

P F S (Helston) Ltd, Unit 9, Water-Ma-Trout Industrial Estate, Helston, Cornwall, TR13 0LW Tel: (01326) 565454 Fax: (01326) 565505 E-mail: sales@pfs-uk.co.uk

Pims Group, Unit 1 106 Hawley Lane, Farnborough, Hampshire, GU14 8JE Tel: (01252) 513891 Fax: (01252) 516404 E-mail: sales@pimsgroup.co.uk

SEWAGE PUMPING SYSTEM INSTALLATION OR SERVICING

A M Pumps & Spares Ltd, 429 Jockey Road, Sutton Coldfield, West Midlands, B73 5XH Tel: 0121-321 3488 Fax: 0121-321 3499 E-mail: ampumpsltd@aol.com

Pims Group, Unit 1 106 Hawley Lane, Farnborough, Hampshire, GU14 8JE Tel: (01252) 513891 Fax: (01252) 516404 E-mail: sales@pimsgroup.co.uk

SEWAGE PUMPING SYSTEMS

A M Pumps & Spares Ltd, 429 Jockey Road, Sutton Coldfield, West Midlands, B73 5XH Tel: 0121-321 3488 Fax: 0121-321 3499 E-mail: ampumpsltd@aol.com

Binder Ltd, Progress Works, Ipswich Road, Claydon, Ipswich, IP6 0AG Tel: (01473) 830582 Fax: (01473) 832175 E-mail: info@binder.co.uk

Pims Group, Unit 1 106 Hawley Lane, Farnborough, Hampshire, GU14 8JE Tel: (01252) 513891 Fax: (01252) 516404 E-mail: sales@pimsgroup.co.uk

Pump Technology Ltd, Unit 56 Youngs Industrial Estate, Paices Hill, Aldermaston, Reading, RG7 4PW Tel: 0118-982 1555 Fax: 0118-982 1666 E-mail: sales@pump-technology.co.uk

Wendage Pollution Control Ltd, Rangeways Farm, Conford, Liphook, Hampshire, GU30 7QP Tel: (01428) 751296 Fax: (01428) 751541 E-mail: info@wpc.uk.net

SEWAGE TREATMENT CHEMICALS

▶ Bio-Plus, PO Box 6726, Northampton, NN5 6WQ Tel: (01604) 751222 Fax: (01604) 592777 E-mail: sales@bio-plus.co.uk

SEWAGE TREATMENT PLANT AND EQUIPMENT

Adams Hydraulics Ltd, PO Box 15, York, YO30 4XE Tel: (01904) 695695 Fax: (01904) 695600 E-mail: sales@adamshydraulics.co.uk

Allerton Construction Ltd, Woodbridge Road, Sleaford, Lincolnshire, NG34 7EW Tel: (01529) 305757 Fax: (01529) 414232 E-mail: sales@allertonuk.com

Brightwater Engineering, Unit 2 The Business Centre, Avenue One, Letchworth, Letchworth Garden City, Hertfordshire, SG6 2HB Tel: (01462) 485005 Fax: (01462) 485003 E-mail: enquiries@brightwater.uk.com

Clearwater Process Control Ltd, Clearwater House, Clearwater Industrial Park, Bristol Road, Bridgwater, Somerset, TA6 4AW Tel: (01278) 433443 Fax: (01278) 453653

Copa Ltd, Copa House, Crest Industrial Estate, Pattenden Lane, Marden, Tonbridge, Kent, TN12 9QJ Tel: (01622) 833900 Fax: (01622) 831466 E-mail: enquiries@copa.co.uk

Effluent Engineering Contracts Ltd, 16 The Promenade, Mayland, Chelmsford, CM3 6AR Tel: (01621) 740729 Fax: (01621) 744033 E-mail: paulbrinson@effluenteng.co.uk

The Haigh Group Ltd, Alton Road, Ross-on-Wye, Herefordshire, HR9 5NG Tel: (01989) 763131 Fax: (01989) 766360 E-mail: sales@haigh.co.uk

Hydroserve Sewage Disposal, Kingsley House, Ganders Park, Kingsley, Bordon, Hampshire, GU35 9LU Tel: (01420) 470800 Fax: (01420) 470820 E-mail: enquiries@conderproducts.com

Klargester Environmental Ltd, College Road, Aston Clinton, Aylesbury, Buckinghamshire, HP22 5EW Tel: (01296) 633000 Fax: (01296) 633001 E-mail: sales@kingspanec.com

Marine Ventures Ltd, Marven House, 1 Field Road, Reading, RG1 6AP Tel: 0118-950 3707 Fax: 0118-950 4066 E-mail: info@marineventures.co.uk

The Plastic Mountain UK Ltd, Oakwood BSNS Park, Stephenson Road West, Clacton-on-Sea, Essex, CO15 4TL Tel: (01255) 221534 Fax: (01255) 476817 E-mail: info@mantair.com

Titan Pollution Control, West Portway, Andover, Hampshire, SP10 3LF Tel: (01264) 352444 Fax: (01264) 366446 E-mail: sales@titanpc.co.uk

Tuke & Bell, Galaxy Point, Patent Drive Moorcroft Park, Wednesbury, West Midlands, WS10 7XD Tel: 0121-506 7330 Fax: 0121-506 7333 E-mail: reception@tukeandbell.co.uk

Valance Glass Fibre Co. Ltd, Unit 8 Netherwood Indsl Estate, Atherstone, Warwickshire, CV9 1JA Tel: (01827) 715619 Fax: (01827) 715619

W P L Ltd, 1-2 Aston Road, Waterlooville, Hampshire, PO7 7UX Tel: (023) 9224 2600 Fax: (023) 9224 2624 E-mail: admin@wpl-limited.co.uk

Wci Pollution Control Ltd, Unit 1 Old Brewery Road, Wiveliscombe, Taunton, Somerset, TA4 2PW Tel: (01984) 623404 Fax: (01984) 624449 E-mail: wcipc@aol.com

Webs Ltd, Ashborne House Waterperry Court, Middleton Road, Banbury, Oxfordshire, OX16 4QG Tel: (01295) 277272 Fax: (01295) 264070 E-mail: enquiries@websint.com

SEWAGE TREATMENT PLANT AND EQUIPMENT CONSULTANTS, CONTRACTORS OR DESIGNERS

Brightwater Engineering, Unit 2 The Business Centre, Avenue One, Letchworth, Letchworth Garden City, Hertfordshire, SG6 2HB Tel: (01462) 485005 Fax: (01462) 485003 E-mail: enquiries@brightwater.uk.com

Carillion Mowlems, Foundation House, Eastern Road, Bracknell, Berkshire, RG12 2UZ Tel: (01344) 720001

Ecobug Ltd, Llanteg, Narberth, Dyfed, SA67 8PY Tel: (07000) 326284 Fax: (01834) 831842 E-mail: phil@ecobug.com

Fostech Ltd, 10 Carnreagh Road, Hillsborough, County Down, BT26 6LH Tel: (028) 9268 2652 Fax: (028) 9268 9091 E-mail: fostech@nireland.com

G & G Pump Services Ltd, Dragons Wharf, Dragons Lane, Sandbach, Cheshire, CW11 3PA Tel: (01270) 759270 Fax: (01270) 759280

Summerfield & Lang Ltd, 60 Allerton Road, Woolton, Liverpool, L25 7RG Tel: 0151-428 7000 Fax: 0151-428 7172 E-mail: peter.summerfield@btinternet.com

SEWAGE TREATMENT PLANT AND EQUIPMENT INSTALLATION/MAINTENANCE SERVICES

Allerton Construction Ltd, Woodbridge Road, Sleaford, Lincolnshire, NG34 7EW Tel: (01529) 305757 Fax: (01529) 414232 E-mail: sales@allertonuk.com

Aquacare services, 7 Austin cottages, Potters gate, Farnham, Surrey, GU9 7BA Tel: 01252 711126 E-mail: mike@aquacareservices.co.uk

Wyatt Ltd, Unit 3, Whittington Buissness Park, Oswestry, Shropshire, SY11 4ND Tel: (01691) 662592 Fax: (01691) 658346 E-mail: wyattltd@aol.com

SEWAGE TREATMENT PLANT, PACKAGE

▶ Farley Groundworks, 44 Bath Road, Calcot Row, Reading, RG31 7QJ Tel: 0118-945 4223 Fax: 0118-945 4223 E-mail: contact@farleygroundworks.com

SEWAGE TREATMENT SERVICES

▶ S L R Consulting Ltd, No. 4 The Roundal, Roddinglaw Business Park, Gogar, Edinburgh, EH12 9DB Tel: 0131-335 6830 Fax: 0131-335 6831

SEWAGE TREATMENT SYSTEM INSTALLATION OR MAINTENANCE OR REFURBISHMENT

Advanced Main Drain, 109 High Street, Edenbridge, Kent, TN8 5AX Tel: (01732) 863607 Fax: (01732) 866931

C D Bissell Engineering Services Ltd, Unit 28, Moorfields Industrial Estate, Cotes Heath, Stafford, ST21 6QY Tel: (01782) 791711 Fax: (01782) 791511 E-mail: mick@cdbissell.com

Damar Group Ltd, Unit 15-19, Mill Road, Radstock, BA3 5TX Tel: (01761) 439111 Fax: (01761) 439123 E-mail: info@damarnet.com

Itsc Ltd, 9 Northfields Prospect, Northfields, London, SW18 1PE Tel: (020) 8874 7282 Fax: (020) 8874 7539 E-mail: itscuk@aol.com

Latham International Ltd, Rowhurst Close, Rowhurst Industrial Estate, Newcastle, Staffordshire, ST5 6BD Tel: (01782) 565364 Fax: (01782) 564886 E-mail: info@lathaminternational.com

Panks Engineers, 8 Heigham Street, Norwich, NR2 4TE Tel: (01603) 620297 Fax: (01603) 762679 E-mail: sales@panks.co.uk

SEWER CLEANING EQUIPMENT

Drain Brain Ltd, Meadowlands, Bibury, Cirencester, Gloucestershire, GL7 5LZ Tel: (01285) 740682 Fax: (01285) 740638 E-mail: enquiries@dbigroup.co.uk

SEWER CONTRACTORS

Balfour Beatty Construction International Ltd, 7 Mayday Road, Thornton Heath, Surrey, CR7 7XA Tel: (020) 8684 6922 Fax: (020) 8710 5222

Draincare Services, 23 Faraday Court, Park Farm Industrial Estate, Wellingborough, Northamptonshire, NN8 6XY Tel: (01933) 679292 Fax: (01933) 676161 E-mail: info@draincare.com

Effluent Engineering Contracts Ltd, 16 The Promenade, Mayland, Chelmsford, CM3 6AR Tel: (01621) 740729 Fax: (01621) 744033 E-mail: paulbrinson@effluenteng.co.uk

SEWER INSPECTION OR SURVEYING

Bethell Group plc, Dane House Europa Trading Estate, Stoneclough Road, Radcliffe, Manchester, M26 1GE Tel: (01204) 439100 Fax: (01204) 439101 E-mail: mail@bethell.co.uk

Free Flow Ltd, Free Flow House, Eple Bay Avenue, Birchington, Kent, CT7 9HT Tel: (0800) 7316261 Fax: (01843) 840934 E-mail: Alan@FreeFlowKent.co.uk

SEWER RELINING CONTRACTORS

Ferro Monk Systems Ltd, 16 Astley Way, Astley Lane Industrial Estate, Swillington, Leeds, LS26 8XT Tel: 0113-287 7577 Fax: 0113 287 7778 E-mail: info@ferromonk.co.uk

Planned Maintenance (Pennine) Ltd, Vine Grove Works, Commerce St, Haslingden, Rossendale, Lancashire, BB4 5JT Tel: (01706) 227865 Fax: (01706) 836111 E-mail: info@pmp-ltd.co.uk

SEWERAGE REPAIR OR REFURBISHMENT MACHINERY OR EQUIPMENT

S A Clough Ltd, 252-252a Newchurch Road, Bacup, Lancashire, OL13 0UE Tel: (01706) 875908 Fax: (01706) 875908

SEWING AIDS, *See also headings for particular types*

Affordable Machines, 185 Hoylake Road, Wirral, Merseyside, CH46 9QA Tel: 0151-677 7755 Fax: 0151-677 7755

Croft Mill, Croft Mill, Lowther Lane, Foulridge, Colne, Lancashire, BB8 7NG Tel: (01282) 869625 Fax: (01282) 870038 E-mail: info@croftmill.co.uk

Dowlings Sewing Machines, Unit 3, Orwell Court, Hurricane Way, Wickford, Essex, SS11 8YJ Tel: (01268) 570248 Fax: (01268) 562023 E-mail: sales@dowlings-sew.co.uk

Ilkeston Sewing & Janone Centre, Market Place, Ilkeston, Derbyshire, DE7 5QG Tel: 0115-930 7664 Fax: 0115-930 7664 E-mail: sales@ilkestonsewingcentre.co.uk

Martin Land Sewing Machine Co. Ltd, Mulberry House, Hall Lane, Morley St. Botolph, Wymondham, Norfolk, NR18 9TB Tel: (01953) 603139

Sewing Machine Supplies, 4 Tai Rhos, Pentre Berw, Gaerwen, Gwynedd, LL60 6LN Tel: (01248) 421692 Fax: (01248) 421692

Singer Sewing Centre, 7 Vine Street, Evesham, Worcestershire, WR11 4RE Tel: (01386) 765844 Fax: (01386) 765844

Singer Sewing Centre, 60 Fife Road, Kingston upon Thames, Surrey, KT1 1SP Tel: (020) 8546 1828 Fax: (020) 8546 8029

Singer Sewing Centre, 4 Market Street, Rhyl, Clwyd, LL18 1RL Tel: (01745) 351175

SEWING MACHINE AUTOMATED SYSTEMS

L. Gent Ltd, Unit 9 Hemlock Park, Hyssop Close, Cannock, Staffordshire, WS11 7FB Tel: (01543) 578383 Fax: (01543) 573797 E-mail: info@directron.co.uk

L Gent Ltd, 54 Syston Street East, Leicester, LE1 2JW Tel: 0116-253 8727 Fax: 0116-251 4761 E-mail: info@lgent.co.uk

SEWING MACHINE HIRE

Cotton Conquest, 42-44 Heron Street, Stoke-on-Trent, ST4 3AS Tel: (01782) 312173 Fax: (01782) 593340

L. Gent Ltd, Unit 9 Hemlock Park, Hyssop Close, Cannock, Staffordshire, WS11 7FB Tel: (01543) 578383 Fax: (01543) 573797 E-mail: info@directron.co.uk

▶ Independent Sewing Machines, 87 Barnoldswick Road, Barrowford, Nelson, Lancashire, BB9 6BQ Tel: (01282) 601012 Fax: (01282) 601012

L Gent Ltd, 54 Syston Street East, Leicester, LE1 2JW Tel: 0116-253 8727 Fax: 0116-251 4761 E-mail: info@lgent.co.uk

M & K Sewing Machines, 257-259 Barlow Road, Levenshulme, Manchester, M19 3HQ Tel: 0161-225 2074 Fax: 0161-257 3057

M & N Sewing Machines, 41 Tennyson Road, Kettering, Northamptonshire, NN16 0DD Tel: (01536) 514880 Fax: (01536) 411169

Sewplant UK Ltd, 20 Whitcliffe Road, Cleckheaton, West Yorkshire, BD19 3NU Tel: (01274) 875218 Fax: (01274) 875218

Sovereign Sewing Machines Ltd, 32 Stoke Newington Road, London, Greater London, N16 7XJ Tel: 020 72491839

SEWING MACHINE IMPORT MERCHANTS OR AGENTS

Janome Group UK Ltd, Southside, Bredbury, Stockport, Cheshire, SK6 2SP Tel: 0161-430 6011 Fax: 0161-494 0179

Merrow Sales UK Ltd, 17 Glebe Road, Groby, Leicester, LE6 0GT Tel: 0116-232 1779 Fax: 0116-287 8099

Sewing Machine Services Luton Ltd, Unit 6-52 High Town Enterprise Centre, York Street, Luton, LU2 0HA Tel: (01582) 455112

Stocks Sewing Machines, King House, 17 Regent Street, Leeds, LS2 7UZ Tel: 0113-243 6800 Fax: 0113-242 9830 E-mail: accounts@stocks.co.uk

World Of Sewing, 56-64 Camden Road, Tunbridge Wells, Kent, TN1 2QP Tel: (01892) 536314 Fax: (01892) 520810 E-mail: sales@sewing-world.co.uk

SEWING MACHINE NEEDLES

▶ Barnstaple Sewing Machines, Hallsannery, Bideford, Devon, EX39 5HE Tel: (01237) 470032 Fax: (01237) 470032 E-mail: sewingmachines@hallsannery.go-plus.net

Groz-Beckert UK Ltd, Groz-Beckert House, Gloucester Crescent, Wigston, Leicestershire, LE18 4YL Tel: 0116-264 3500 Fax: 0116-264 3505

▶ Hampshire Sewing Machines, 122-124 West Street, Fareham, Hampshire, PO16 0EP Tel: (01329) 280499 Fax: (01329) 280499 E-mail: machines@sewingmachines.co.com

SEWING MACHINE PARTS OR ACCESSORIES

Central Parts Ltd, 222 New John Street West, Birmingham, B19 3UA Tel: 0121-523 4067 Fax: 0121-507 0960 E-mail: centralparts@supanet.com

Franklins Sewing Centre, 48 Fisherton Street, Salisbury, SP2 7RB Tel: (01722) 554466 Fax: (01722) 554466

M & K Sewing Machines, 257-259 Barlow Road, Levenshulme, Manchester, M19 3HQ Tel: 0161-225 2074 Fax: 0161-257 3057

Newport Sewing Centre, Curlew Close, Queensway Meadows Industrial Estate, Newport, Gwent, NP19 4SY Tel: (01633) 284646

Rowlson Industrial Sewing Engineers Ltd, Westbury Road, Nottingham, NG5 1EJ Tel: 0115-979 1333 Fax: 0115-979 1444 E-mail: sales@rowlson.com

S B T Machine Co Stockport Ltd, Christie Street Industrial Estate, Christie Street, Stockport, Cheshire, SK1 4LR Tel: 0161-429 6929 Fax: 0161-480 6603 E-mail: sbtworldwide@aol.com

Sewing World Industrial Bolton, 130 Belmont Road, Bolton, BL1 7AN Tel: (01204) 309598 Fax: (01204) 306933

Sew-Quick Sewing Machine Services Ltd, The Workshop, Waterloo Road, Falmouth, Cornwall, TR11 3NU Tel: (01326) 318450 Fax: (01326) 318450 E-mail: sew-quick@tiscali.co.uk

Singer Sewing Centre, 14 Donegall Road, Belfast, BT12 5JN Tel: (028) 9032 6002 Fax: (028) 9032 6002

▶ Singer Sewing Centre, 126 Park View, Whitley Bay, Tyne & Wear, NE26 3QN Tel: 0191-252 5825 Fax: 0191-292 5826 E-mail: sales@singermachines.co.uk

Triumph Needle Co. Ltd, 14 Albion Street, Wigston, Leicestershire, LE18 4SA Tel: 0116-222 9222 Fax: 0116-222 9200 E-mail: triumphneedle@btclick.com

SEWING MACHINE REPAIR SPECIALIST SERVICES

Alan Godrich, 17-20 Charter Street, Leicester, LE1 3UD Tel: 0116-253 2322 Fax: 0116-262 9887 E-mail: sales@alan-godrich.com

Barcham Sewing Machinery, 59 Harbour Street, Whitstable, Kent, CT5 1AG Tel: (01227) 264271 Fax: (01227) 264271 E-mail: sales@barchams.co.uk

▶ Barnstaple Sewing Machines, Hallsannery, Bideford, Devon, EX39 5HE Tel: (01237) 470032 Fax: (01237) 470032 E-mail: sewingmachines@hallsannery.go-plus.net

Bateman Sewing Machines, 14 Helena Close, Hockley, Essex, SS5 4DJ Tel: (01702) 203306

Fast Signs Scotland Ltd, Unit 1, Millstreet Industrial Estate, Airdrie, Lanarkshire, ML6 6JJ Tel: (01236) 766050 Fax: (01236) 751647 E-mail: fastsigns@btconnect.com

Field Textiles Sewing Machines, Brewery House, Station Road, Bulwell, Nottingham, NG6 9AA Tel: 0115-979 7676 Fax: 0115-913 3244

G & G Sewing, 402 St Helens Road, Bolton, BL3 3RR Tel: (01204) 650878

Bob Green Sewing Machines, Moor Lane Business Centre, Moor Lane, Widnes, Cheshire, WA8 7AQ Tel: 0151-420 5565 Fax: 0151-420 5565

Husqvarna Studio, 27 Charles Street, Bath, BA1 1HU Tel: (01225) 482413 Fax: (01225) 482420 E-mail: enquiries@husqvarnastudio.co.uk

▶ Independent Sewing Machines, 87 Barnoldswick Road, Barrowford, Nelson, Lancashire, BB9 6BQ Tel: (01282) 601012 Fax: (01282) 601012

Industrial Sewing Services Birmingham Ltd, 225 Lozells Road, Birmingham, B19 1RJ Tel: 0121-554 5073 Fax: 0121-554 5073

▶ K & L Sewing Machines, PO Box 1305, Oxford, OX4 3BN Tel: (01865) 721915 Fax: (01865) 721915

L & M Nutt, 418 Chester Road, Sutton Coldfield, West Midlands, B73 5BS Tel: 0121-373 5497 Fax: 0121-373 5497

Lofthus Signs & Engraving Ltd, 5 St. Machar Drive, Aberdeen, AB24 3YJ Tel: (01224) 487377 Fax: (01224) 487580

N J Sewing, 2 Pretoria Place, Station Road, Brightons, Falkirk, FK2 0UF Tel: (01324) 711333 Fax: (01324) 711333

Parr Sewing Machines, 17 Lower Quest Hills Road, Malvern, Worcestershire, WR14 1RP Tel: (01684) 563106 Fax: (01684) 563106

Rush Machine Co., Shelton House Barns, Shelton, Newark, Nottinghamshire, NG23 5JQ Tel: (01949) 850131 Fax: (01949) 850131 E-mail: johnandirush@yahoo.co.uk

S M Sewing Machines, 566 North Circular Road, London, NW2 7QA Tel: (020) 8452 4257

Sew & Sew Machine Co., 5 Olympia Arcade, High Street, Kirkcaldy, Fife, KY1 1QF Tel: (01592) 261352 Fax: (01592) 261352

Sewing Is Fun, 77-79 High Street, Ruislip, Middlesex, HA4 8JL Tel: (01895) 634848 Fax: (01895) 632417

Sewing & Knitting Machine Centre, 193 Burton Stone Lane, York, YO30 6DG Tel: (01904) 655751 Fax: (01904) 655751

Sewing Machine Repair Co., 9 Morkinshire Cresent, Cotgrave, Nottingham, NG12 3HL Tel: 0115-989 2539

Sewing Machine Services, 200 Studfall Avenue, Corby, Northamptonshire, NN17 1LJ Tel: (01536) 269080

Sewing Machine Services, Fallady Cottage, Idvies, Forfar, Angus, DD8 2SP Tel: (01307) 818853 Fax: (01307) 818720

Sewing Machine Services Luton Ltd, Unit 6-52 High Town Enterprise Centre, York Street, Luton, LU2 0HA Tel: (01582) 455112

Sewmatic Sewing Machine Repair Services, Harlington Centre, Harlington Way, Fleet, Hampshire, GU51 4AE Tel: (01276) 32564

Singer Sewing Centre, 94 Church Street, Croydon, CR0 1RD Tel: (020) 8688 1128 Fax: (020) 8688 1128

Sueco UK Domestic & Industrial Sewing Machines, 162b Copnor Road, Portsmouth, PO3 5BZ Tel: (023) 9269 7621 Fax: (023) 9269 7621 E-mail: info@sueco.co.uk

Supreme Sewing & Knitting Machines Ltd, 114-116 Narborough Road, Leicester, LE3 0BS Tel: 0116-254 9029 Fax: 0116-254 9029

Sussex Sewing Machines, 148 Willingdon Park Drive, Eastbourne, East Sussex, BN22 0DG Tel: (01323) 509874 Fax: (01323) 509874

Tullys Sewing Machines & Accessories, 5 Holmeside, Sunderland, SR1 3JG Tel: 0191-565 7995 Fax: 0191-565 7209 E-mail: tullysew@aol.com

World Of Sewing, 56-64 Camden Road, Tunbridge Wells, Kent, TN1 2QP Tel: (01892) 536314 Fax: (01892) 520810 E-mail: sales@sewing-world.co.uk

SEWING MACHINES, *See also headings for particular types*

Bogod Machine Co., Bogod House, 50-52 Great Sutton Street, London, EC1V 0DJ Tel: (020) 7253 1198 Fax: (020) 7250 0016 E-mail: info@bernina.co.uk

Brother (U K) Ltd, Shepley St, Guide Bridge, Manchester, M34 5JD Tel: 0161-330 6531 Fax: 0161-308 3281 E-mail: sales@brother-uk.com

Clare Sewing Machine Shop, 13 Great Darkgate Street, Aberystwyth, Dyfed, SY23 1DE Tel: (01970) 617786

Crescent Sewing Machines Centre, 3a Crescent East, Thornton-Cleveleys, Lancashire, FY5 3LJ Tel: (01253) 856894

Danter Automatics, 11a Copse Cross Street, Ross-on-Wye, Herefordshire, HR9 5PD Tel: (01989) 563604 Fax: (01989) 563604

Express Sewing Machines, 196 Pasley Street, Stoke, Plymouth, PL2 1DT Tel: (01752) 606262 Fax: (01752) 708999

Fox Sewing Machine Ltd, 60 Babington Lane, Derby, DE1 1SX Tel: (01332) 347941 Fax: E-mail: fox sawing machine@tiscali.co.uk

Fried Jerry & Co. Ltd, Saltmeadows Road, Gateshead, Tyne & Wear, NE8 3BQ Tel: 0191-490 1313 Fax: 0191-490 1907 E-mail: lionel@jerryfried.co.uk

L. Gent Ltd, Unit 9 Hemlock Park, Hyssop Close, Cannock, Staffordshire, WS11 7FB Tel: (01543) 578383 Fax: (01543) 573797 E-mail: info@directron.co.uk

Industrial Sewing Services Birmingham Ltd, 225 Lozells Road, Birmingham, B19 1RJ Tel: 0121-554 5073 Fax: 0121-554 5073

Janome Group UK Ltd, Southside, Bredbury, Stockport, Cheshire, SK6 2SP Tel: 0161-430 6011 Fax: 0161-494 0179

Jaycotts Sewing Centre, Unit 14 Brierley Business Centre, Mirion Street, Crewe, CW1 2AZ Tel: (01270) 617171 E-mail: info@jaycotts.co.uk

George Kaccouris, 74 Aubert Pk, London, N5 1TS Tel: (020) 7704 1900

L Gent Ltd, 54 Syston Street East, Leicester, LE1 2JW Tel: 0116-253 8727 Fax: 0116-251 4761 E-mail: info@lgent.co.uk

L & M Nutt, 418 Chester Road, Sutton Coldfield, West Midlands, B73 5BS Tel: 0121-373 5497 Fax: 0121-373 5497

Lennox Sewing Machines, 2 Red Lion Yard, Rotherham, South Yorkshire, S60 1PN Tel: (01709) 377797 Fax: (01709) 377797

M & K Sewing Machines, 257-259 Barlow Road, Levenshulme, Manchester, M19 3HQ Tel: 0161-225 2074 Fax: 0161-257 3057

Maury Sewing Machine Co., Unit 12 Peterley Business Centre, Hackney Road, London, E2 9EQ Tel: (020) 7729 7328 Fax: (020) 7729 7534 E-mail: maurysew@aol.com

Merrow Sales UK Ltd, 17 Glebe Road, Groby, Leicester, LE6 0GT Tel: 0116-232 1779 Fax: 0116-287 8099

Pembertons Sewing Machine Centre, 21-25 Friars Street, Stirling, FK8 1HA Tel: (01786) 462993 Fax: (01786) 461998 E-mail: sales@pembertons.org

▶ R & G Industrial Sewing Machines, 6 Mossfield Road, Swinton, Manchester, M27 6EN Tel: 0161-793 4555 Fax: 0161-793 4224

J.J. & J. Read (Sewing Machines) Ltd, 336 Shirley Road, Southampton, SO15 3HJ Tel: (023) 8077 1398 Fax: (023) 8077 1398

Rowlson Industrial Sewing Engineers Ltd, Westbury Road, Nottingham, NG5 1EJ Tel: 0115-979 1333 Fax: 0115-979 1444 E-mail: sales@rowlson.com

S A Sewing Machines, 1 Halifax Road, Rochdale, Lancashire, OL12 9BD Tel: (01706) 355529 Fax: (01706) 355529 E-mail: sa.sewmac@ntlworld.com

S B T Machine Co Stockport Ltd, Christie Street Industrial Estate, Christie Street, Stockport, Cheshire, SK1 4LR Tel: 0161-429 6929 Fax: 0161-480 6603 E-mail: sbtworldwide@aol.com

Sew Knit, 9 Chapel Street, Lancaster, LA1 1NZ Tel: (01524) 64436

▶ Sew Northampton, 173 Wellingborough Road, Northampton, NN1 4DX Tel: (01604) 637200 Fax: (01604) 637200 E-mail: sales@sewing-centres.co.uk

SEWING MACHINES – *continued*

Sew & Save, 12 King Street, Sutton-in-Ashfield, Nottinghamshire, NG17 1AT Tel: (01623) 554886 Fax: (01623) 554886

Sewing Knitting & Handicraft Centre, 125 Mostyn Street, Llandudno, Gwynedd, LL30 2PE Tel: (01492) 875269 Fax: (01492) 875269 E-mail: wyn20@btinternet.com

Sewing Machine Co., 17 Top Row, Kirkgate Market Hall, Leeds, LS2 7HN Tel: 0113-243 5798

▶ Sewing Machine Centre, Lisburn Enterprise Centre, Enterprise Crescent, Lisburn, County Antrim, BT28 2BP Tel: (028) 9260 1200 Fax: (028) 9260 1200

Sewing Machine Exchange, 15 Daniel Owen Precinct, Mold, Clwyd, CH7 1AP Tel: (01352) 758925 Fax: (01352) 758925

Sewing Machine Exchange, 21 Charles Street, Wrexham, Clwyd, LL13 8BT Tel: (01978) 266746 Fax: (01978) 266746 E-mail: enquiries@sewingmachinesdirect.co.uk

Sewing World, 308-310 Wimborne Road, Bournemouth, BH9 2HN Tel: (01202) 770055 Fax: (01202) 775590 E-mail: sales@sewingworld.co.uk

Singer Sewing Centre, 59 Green Street, Gillingham, Kent, ME7 1AE Tel: (01634) 570254

▶ Singer Sewing Centre, 126 Park View, Whitley Bay, Tyne & Wear, NE26 3QN Tel: 0191-252 5825 Fax: 0191-292 5826 E-mail: sales@singermachines.co.uk

▶ T E Solutions, Unit 44 Canal Bridge Enterprise Centre, Ellesmere Port, CH65 4EH Tel: 0151 3562010

Tameside Sewing Machine Services, 266a Stamford St West, Ashton-under-Lyne, Lancashire, OL6 7NJ Tel: 0161-308 3112

Tyson Sewing Machines Ltd, 4 High Street, Southall, Middlesex, UB1 3DA Tel: (020) 8574 1587 E-mail: sales@tysonsewingmachines.co.uk

Welling Sewing Centre, 104-106 Welling High Street, Welling, Kent, DA16 1TJ Tel: (020) 8304 0470 Fax: (020) 8298 1582

Wimbledon Sewing Machine Co.Ltd, 292-312 Balham High Road, London, SW17 7AA Tel: (020) 8767 4724 Fax: (020) 8767 4726 E-mail: wimbledonsewingmachinecoltd@btinternet.com

SEWING MACHINES, USED

▶ Gur Sewing Machine Co., 162 Halesowen Street, Rowley Regis, West Midlands, B65 0ES Tel: 0121-561 5169 Fax: 0121-559 3449 E-mail: sales@gur.co.uk

SEWING SERVICES TO THE TRADE/CONTRACTORS

Golden Finishes Ltd, 4 Malvern Drive, Llanishen, Cardiff, CF14 5DR Tel: (029) 2075 5733 Fax: (029) 2076 3993 E-mail: gfinishes@aol.com

Harvey Quilting, 11 Robin Hood Industrial Estate, Alfred St South, Nottingham, NG3 1GE Tel: 0115-958 5777 Fax: 0115-950 3339 E-mail: tonyatharveys@hotmail.com

J H Cunliffe & Company Ltd, Duke Street Mill, Whitehall Street, Rochdale, Lancashire, OL12 0LW Tel: (01706) 631133 Fax: (01706) 527950 E-mail: brian@jhcunliffe.co.uk

Livingdale Ltd, 4 Candleby Lane, Cotgrave, Nottingham, NG12 3JG Tel: 0115-989 9070 Fax: 0115-989 4763 E-mail: sales@livingdale.co.uk

Manuals Sewing Services Ltd, Unit 3-4, London Road Industrial Estate, Baldock, Hertfordshire, SG7 6NG Tel: (01462) 491828 Fax: (01462) 491829 E-mail: mail@manualz.co.uk

Singer Sewing Centre, 14 Donegall Road, Belfast, BT12 5JN Tel: (028) 9032 6002 Fax: (028) 9032 6002

Stroud Sewing Services, 5 Meadow Mills Eastington Trading Estate, Churchend, Eastington, Stonehouse, Gloucestershire, GL10 3RZ Tel: (01453) 791487 Fax: (01453) 791487 E-mail: stroudsewingservices@tiscali.co.uk

Yateley Industries For The Disabled Ltd, Mill Lane, Yateley, Hampshire, GU46 7TF Tel: (01252) 872337 Fax: (01252) 860620

SEWING THREADS, *See also headings for particular types*

American & Efird GB Ltd, Chapelfield, Radcliffe, Manchester, M26 1JF Tel: 0161-766 1333 Fax: 0161-766 9965 E-mail: sales@amefird.co.uk

Astra Threads & Trimmings Ltd, Ladderedge, Leek, Staffordshire, ST13 7AG Tel: (01538) 373704 Fax: (01538) 373704 E-mail: astra@ladderedge.fsnet.co.uk

Barbra Coats Ltd, Hilden Mill, Lisburn, County Antrim, BT27 4RR Tel: (028) 9267 2231 Fax: (028) 9267 8048E-mail: mail@coats.com

C A Sperati The Special Agency plc, 54 Westcombe Hill, London, SE10 0LR Tel: (020) 8858 7069 Fax: (020) 8853 5349 E-mail: enquires@casperatiplc.com

Coats UK Ltd, Netherplace, Newton Mearns, Glasgow, G77 6PP Tel: 0141-616 1000 Fax: 0141-616 1060 E-mail: coats@coatsviyella.com

DMC Creative World, 62 Pullman Road, Wigston, Leicestershire, LE18 2DY Tel: 0116-281 1040 Fax: 0116-281 3592 E-mail: salesandmarketing@dmc.com

Donisthorpe, PO Box 137, Leicester, LE4 1BF Tel: 0116-234 7920 Fax: 0116-234 7901 E-mail: sales@amann.com

Empress Mills (1927) Ltd, Glen Mill, North Valley Road, Colne, Lancashire, BB8 9DT Tel: (01282) 863181 Fax: (01282) 870935 E-mail: chris@empressmill.co.uk

Gutermann Ltd, Bullsbrook Road, Hayes, Middlesex, UB4 0JR Tel: (020) 8589 1600 Fax: (020) 8589 1636 E-mail: christine.williams@gutermann.com

Leicester Thread & Trimming Manufacturers Ltd, 105 Barkby Road, Leicester, LE4 9LG Tel: 0116-276 5858 Fax: 0116-246 0451

Oxley Threads Ltd, Guide Mills, South Street, Ashton-under-Lyne, Lancashire, OL7 0PJ Tel: 0161-339 6400 Fax: 0161-343 1705 E-mail: information@oxley-threads.com

S & T Trimmings Ltd, 56-66 Cambridge Street, Coventry, CV1 5HW Tel: (024) 7622 3366 Fax: (024) 7666 4401 E-mail: info@sttrimmings.com

▶ T C Threads Ltd, King Edward Street, Hucknall, Nottingham, NG15 7JR Tel: 0115-968 0089 Fax: 0115-968 0346 E-mail: sales@tcthreads.ltd.uk

SEX AIDS

Hose Depot Direct Ltd, Units 8 Brunel Park, Blyth Road, Harworth, Doncaster, South Yorkshire, DN11 8NE Tel: (01302) 746969 Fax: (01302) 746974

Kinkz Love Store, 45 Banister Way, Wymondham, Norfolk, NR18 0TY Tel: (01953) 857517 E-mail: sales@kinkz.co.uk

Scala Agenturen UK, West Midland House, Temple Way, Coleshill, Birmingham, B46 1HH Tel: (01675) 430300 Fax: (01675) 430444 E-mail: scalab46@yahoo.co.uk

SHACKLES OR ANCHOR LINKS

Aqualift Ltd, Meeting Lane, Brierley Hill, West Midlands, DY5 3LB Tel: (01384) 77255 Fax: (01384) 77254 E-mail: sales@aqualift.co.uk

Bembridge & Jenkins Ltd, Moland Forge, Central Trading Estate, Shaw Road, Dudley, West Midlands, DY2 8QX Tel: (01384) 243833 Fax: (01384) 455628

Petersen Stainless Rigging Ltd, Blaydon Business Centre, Cowen Road, Blaydon-on-Tyne, Tyne & Wear, NE21 5TW Tel: 0191-414 0156 Fax: 0191-499 0041 E-mail: admin@petersen-stainless.co.uk

Tensile Forgings, Portersfield Road, Cradley Heath, West Midlands, B64 7BN Tel: (01384) 566758

SHADED POLE ELECTRIC MOTORS

Merkle-Korff, Treetops House, Gillotts Lane, Henley-On-Thames, Oxfordshire, RG9 1PT Tel: (01543) 255995 Fax: (01491) 412211 E-mail: sales@acdcsystems.com

SHAFT COUPLINGS, FLEXIBLE

Ondrives, Unit 15 Foxwood Industrial Park, Foxwood Road, Chesterfield, Derbyshire, S41 9RN Tel: (01246) 455500 Fax: (01246) 455522

SHAFT MAINTENANCE/REPAIR SERVICES

Garnett Wire Ltd, Scholes Lane, Scholes, Checkheaton, Cleckheaton, West Yorkshire, BD19 6NJ Tel: (01274) 875741 Fax: (01274) 851675 E-mail: sales@garnettwire.com

SHAFT SEALS, MARINE

Deep Sea Seals Ltd, 4 Marples Way, Havant, Hampshire, PO9 1NX Tel: (023) 9249 2123 Fax: (023) 9249 2470

SHAFT SEALS, ROTARY

▶ Action Seals Ltd, Westfield Road, Wallasey, Merseyside, CH44 7JA Tel: 0151-652 6661 Fax: 0151-653 4994 E-mail: sales@actionseals.co.uk

Autospin (Oil Seals) Ltd, Birkdale Avenue, Selly Oak, Birmingham, B29 6UB Tel: 0121-472 1243 Fax: 0121-471 3348 E-mail: sales@autospin.co.uk

Flowserve Ltd, Dakota Avenue, Salford, M50 2PU Tel: 0161-869 1200 Fax: 0161-869 1235

Sealmac Technology Ltd, 1645 Pershore Road, Kings Norton, Birmingham, B30 3DR Tel: 0121-459 4944 Fax: 0121-459 8420 E-mail: sales@sealmac.co.uk

SHAFT SINKING CONTRACTORS

Cementation Skanska, Bentley House, Jossey Lane, Doncaster, South Yorkshire, DN5 9ED Tel: (01302) 821100 Fax: (01302) 821111

SHAKERS, ELECTRODYNAMIC, VIBRATION TESTING

Gearing & Watson Electronics Ltd, South Road, Hailsham, East Sussex, BN27 3JJ Tel: (01323) 846464 Fax: (01323) 847550 E-mail: sales@dataphysics.com

SHALE SHAKER AND MUD SCREENS

Brandt, Badentoy Way, Badentoy Park, Portlethen, Aberdeen, AB12 4YS Tel: (01224) 787700 Fax: (01224) 784555 E-mail: sales@brandt-uk.com

Potter & Soar Ltd, Beaumont Road, Banbury, Oxfordshire, OX16 1SD Tel: (01295) 253344 Fax: (01295) 272132 E-mail: potter.soar@btinternet.com

SHAPED CUTTERS

A T Laser Dies, Unit 1B Elizabeth Trading Estate, Juno Way, London, SE14 5RW Tel: (020) 8691 7843 Fax: (020) 8692 8720 E-mail: sales@atlaser.co.uk

City Press Knives, 101 Weymouth Street, Leicester, LE4 6FR Tel: 0116-266 0709 Fax: 0116-266 0711

M P Vineis Ltd, 34 Henry Road, Barnet, Hertfordshire, EN4 8BD Tel: (020) 8449 4206 Fax: (020) 8449 4206 E-mail: vineis@btconnect.com

Charles Robinson (Cutting Tools) Ltd, Unit C1, Castle Park Industrial Estate, Bower Street, Oldham, OL1 3LN Tel: 0161-628 5550 Fax: 0161-628 5599 E-mail: sales@c-robinson.co.uk

Supreme Die Cutters, Unit 7 Forest Hill Business Centre, Clyde Vale, London, SE23 3JF Tel: (020) 8291 0473 Fax: (020) 8291 0402

Woodley Engineering Stockport Ltd, Whitefield Road, Bredbury, Stockport, Cheshire, SK6 2QR Tel: 0161-430 7488 Fax: 0161-406 6061

SHAVER PLUGS OR SOCKETS

Loblite International Ltd, 3rd Avenue, Team Valley Trading Estate, Gateshead, Tyne & Wear, NE11 0QQ Tel: 0191-487 8103 Fax: 0191-482 0270 E-mail: info@loblite.co.uk

SHEDS

A E Cox & Sons, Caretakers Caravan, North Street, Winterton, Scunthorpe, South Humberside, DN15 9QN Tel: (01724) 732676 Fax: (01724) 732676

A M J Fencing, Unit 7 Arden Street, Swindles Yard, Stockport, Cheshire, SK12 4NS Tel: (01663) 744560 Fax: (01663) 744560

A Neaverson & Sons Ltd, St Pegas Road, Peakirk, Peterborough, PE6 7NN Tel: (01733) 252225 Fax: (01733) 252121

Andy's Sheds, 46 Church Street, Warsop, Mansfield, Nottinghamshire, NG20 0AR Tel: (01623) 844439 E-mail: sales@andys-sheds.co.uk

Castle Portable Buildings Ltd, Wharf Street, Dukinfield, Cheshire, SK16 4PG Tel: 0161-339 3911 Fax: 0161-339 3911 E-mail: info@castleportable.co.uk

Coastal Sheds, Alpha Works, Common Road, Gorleston, Great Yarmouth, Norfolk, NR31 0QG Tel: (01493) 650050

D&B, Unit 3 Birds Industrial Estate, Risca, Newport, Gwent, NP11 6EW Tel: (01633) 619030 Fax: (01633) 619030

E C Walton & Co. Ltd, Old North Road, Sutton-on-Trent, Newark, Nottinghamshire, NG23 6QN Tel: (01636) 821215 Fax: (01636) 822027 E-mail: waltons@waltons.co.uk

Evans Windows Ltd, Cambrian Place, Pool Road, Newtown, Powys, SY16 1DH Tel: (01686) 626465 Fax: (01686) 627695

Hall B W Of Oxford, 13 Elmthorpe Road, Wolvercote, Oxford, OX2 8PA Tel: (01865) 310857 Fax: (01865) 310857

J & W Milligan, Galston Road, Hurlford, Kilmarnock, Ayrshire, KA1 5HS Tel: (01563) 527572 Fax: (01563) 536758 E-mail: sales@millicabin.com

KDM International plc, The Havens, Ransomes Europark, Ipswich, IP3 9SJ Tel: (01473) 276900 Fax: (01473) 276911 E-mail: sales@kdm.co.uk

▶ M & G Sheds & Fencing, Unit J9 Dudley Trading Estate, Shaw Road, Dudley, West Midlands, DY2 8QX Tel: (01384) 240956 Fax: (01384) 255741

New Line Sheds Ltd, Padworth Saw Mills, Rag Hill, Aldermaston, Reading, RG7 4NU Tel: 0118-971 2245 Fax: 0118-942 6391 E-mail: sales@newlinesheds.co.uk

Norfolk Greenhouses Ltd, Chiswick Avenue, Mildenhall, Bury St. Edmunds, Suffolk, IP28 7AZ Tel: (01638) 713418 Fax: (01638) 714715 E-mail: sales@norfolk-greenhouses.co.uk

Perrys Portables, Goatsmoor Lane, Stock, Ingatestone, Essex, CM4 9RS Tel: (01277) 652036 Fax: (01277) 652036

▶ Russell's Garden Buildings, Gelsmoor Road, Coleorton, Coalville, Leicestershire, LE67 8JF Tel: (01530) 222295 E-mail: shedsrus@hotmail.co.uk

S & B Sheds, 706 Oldham Road, Manchester, M40 2AA Tel: 0161-205 1642

▶ Sticks & Stones, Colchester Main Road, Alresford, Colchester, CO7 8DD Tel: (01206) 826835 Fax: (01206) 827655 E-mail: info@stixandstones.co.uk

Timber Line DIY, 1 Nicholson Buildings, South Shields, Tyne & Wear, NE33 5BD Tel: 0191-428 6645 Fax: 0191-428 0789 E-mail: sales@timberline.co.uk

Timbergarden, Unit 31 Lancaster Way Business Park, Ely, Cambridgeshire, CB6 3NW Tel: (01353) 668333 Fax: (01353) 668440

Titan Garden Buildings Ltd, Titan Works, Blacksmith Lane, Chilworth, Guildford, Surrey, GU4 8NQ Tel: (01483) 451009 Fax: (01483) 451258E-mail: info@titangardenbuildings.com

▶ Veerman's Shed Centre, 130 High Street, Tranent, East Lothian, EH33 1HJ Tel: (01875) 613090 Fax: (01875) 617492 E-mail: email@veermans.co.uk

SHEEP FOOD

John Loader (Wessex) Ltd, Station Mill, Ashford Road, Fordingbridge, Hampshire, SP6 1BY Tel: (01425) 652394 Fax: (01425) 652625 E-mail: info@wessex-feeds.co.uk

SHEEP SHEARING MACHINES

W & M Horner, Bolton by Bowland, Clitheroe, Lancashire, BB7 4PQ Tel: (01200) 441284 Fax: (01200) 440069 E-mail: shearinguk@hotmail.co.uk

SHEEPSKIN CLOTHING

Antartex Village, Lomond Industrial Estate, Alexandria, Dunbartonshire, G83 0TP Tel: (01389) 754263 Fax: (01389) 750656 E-mail: alexav141@ewm.com

Morlands Glastonbury, 3 Creeches Lane, Walton, Street, Somerset, BA16 9RR Tel: (01458) 446969 Fax: (01458) 840108 E-mail: morlands@btinternet.com

Nursey & Son Ltd, 12 Upper Olland Street, Bungay, Suffolk, NR35 1BQ Tel: (01986) 892821 Fax: (01986) 892823 E-mail: sales@nurseyleather.co.uk

Owen Barry, 32 Orchard Road, Street, Somerset, BA16 0BT Tel: (01458) 442858 Fax: (01458) 447319 E-mail: info@owenbarry.com

SHEEPSKIN LEATHER

Hanlin Export & Import Agents, 167a Wood Lane, Earlswood, Solihull, West Midlands, B94 5JL Tel: (01564) 702116 Fax: (01564) 703978 E-mail: hanlin.uk@btinternet.com

Owen Barry, 32 Orchard Road, Street, Somerset, BA16 0BT Tel: (01458) 442858 Fax: (01458) 447319 E-mail: info@owenbarry.com

SHEEPSKIN SADDLE PADS

▶ S O S Saddlery, Little Pengelly Farm, Lower Sticker, St. Austell, Cornwall, PL26 7JJ Tel: (01726) 65022 Fax: (01726) 72727

SHEET METAL

Abtek Ltd, Unit 10, Camperdown Industrial Estate, Newcastle upon Tyne, NE12 5UJ Tel: 0191-268 8555 Fax: 0191-268 8777 E-mail: sales@abtekltd.co.uk

Ackerman Engineering Ltd, Corbin Way, Gore Cross Business Park, Bradpole, Bridport, Dorset, DT6 3UX Tel: (01308) 422185 Fax: (01308) 458276 E-mail: sales@ackerman-eng.com

Amtec Ltd, Throop Business Park, Throop Road, Bournemouth, BH8 0DW Tel: (01202) 533557 Fax: (01202) 533567 E-mail: info@amteccorrosion.co.uk

Ashwell Engineering Services Ltd, Unit 12, Pinfold Road, Thurmaston, Leicester, LE4 8AT Tel: 0116-260 4050 E-mail: ashwelleng@hotmail.com

▶ Baytree Industries Ltd, Resource House, Brunel Road, St. Leonards-on-Sea, East Sussex, TN38 9RT Tel: (01424) 854460 Fax: (01424) 854461 E-mail: sales@bt-ind.com

Canal Engineering Ltd, Lenton Lane, Nottingham, NG7 2PQ Tel: 0115-986 6321 Fax: 0115-986 0211 E-mail: enquiries@canalengineering.co.uk

Chadfort Engineering Ltd, Unit 6c, Blakewater Road, Blackburn, BB1 5QH Tel: (01254) 582075 Fax: (01254) 661062 E-mail: andrew.chadwick@chadfort.co.uk

▶ indicates data change since last edition

SHEET METAL – *continued*

Ductmann Ltd, Withy Road Industrial Estate, Withy Road, Bilston, West Midlands, WV14 0RX Tel: (01902) 492292 Fax: (01902) 408199 E-mail: sales@ductmann.co.uk

Gridfeed Thornber Ltd, Brearley Mill, Halifax Road, Todmorden, Lancashire, OL14 6EF Tel: (01706) 815131 Fax: (01706) 815455 E-mail: gridthorn@aol.com

Mettech Ltd, Ramsden Road, Rotherwas Industrial Estate, Hereford, HR2 6LR Tel: 01432 341630

S M L Engineering Co. Ltd, Benlow Works, Silverdale Road, Hayes, Middlesex, UB3 3BW Tel: (020) 8573 5907 Fax: (020) 8561 5033

▶ John Tainton, 2 Broomhills Industrial Estate, Rayne Road, Braintree, Essex, CM7 2RG Tel: (01376) 528992 Fax: (01376) 528993 E-mail: southernsales@johntainton.co.uk

▶ John Tainton, Blackvein Industrial Estate, Cross Keys, Newport, Gwent, NP11 7PX Tel: (01495) 279247 Fax: (01495) 279243 E-mail: jtcksales@johntainton.co.uk

▶ John Tainton, 5 Cromwell Road, Bredbury, Stockport, Cheshire, SK6 2RF Tel: 0161-406 1006 Fax: 0161-406 6614 E-mail: northernsales@johntainton.co.uk

SHEET METAL CIRCLE SHEARS

Frost Rochdale Ltd, Eagle Iron Works, Crawford Street, Rochdale, Lancashire, OL16 5NU Tel: (01706) 644929 Fax: (01706) 860338 E-mail: sales@frost.co.uk

SHEET METAL CNC PUNCH PRESS SERVICES

Hitherbest Ltd, Heath Hill Court, Heath Hill Industrial Estate, Dawley, Telford, Shropshire, TF4 2RH Tel: (01952) 632100 Fax: (01952) 632109 E-mail: sales@hitherbest.co.uk

K J B Engineering (West Tanfield) Ltd, Unit 2 The Sawmills, West Tanfield, Ripon, North Yorkshire, HG4 5JU Tel: (01677) 470511 Fax: (01677) 470811 E-mail: sales@kjblaser.co.uk

SHEET METAL DUCTING OR DUCTS, *See also headings under Ventilation*

A E Engineering Services, 8 Eye Green Industries, Crowland Road, Eye, Peterborough, PE6 7SZ Tel: (01733) 223355 Fax: (01733) 222330 E-mail: tony@aeengineering.co.uk

A J Metal Fabrications Ltd, 21 Walthamstow Business Centre, Clifford Road, London, E17 4SX Tel: (020) 8527 4860 Fax: (020) 8527 4870 E-mail: steve@ajmetalfabs.co.uk

A K L Sheet Metal Co., 7 Embassy Industrial Estate, Attwood Street, Stourbridge, West Midlands, DY9 8RY Tel: (01384) 892361 Fax: (01384) 892361

Abbey Sheetmetal Ltd, Unit 3 Apex Pk, Diplocks Way, Hailsham, East Sussex, BN27 3JF Tel: (01323) 848454 Fax: (01323) 848456 E-mail: post@abbeysheetmetal.co.uk

Adams Sheet Metal Ltd, Mill Street, Wibsey, Bradford, West Yorkshire, BD6 3BQ Tel: (01274) 693630 Fax: (01274) 693631 E-mail: sales@a-s-m.co.uk

Airducts Design, Unit 45 Wassage Way, Hampton Lovett, Droitwich, Worcestershire, WR9 0NX Tel: (01905) 775454 Fax: (01905) 775656

Airomet Ltd, Unit 4 Millenium Court, Bunsford Park Road, Bromsgrove, Worcestershire, B60 3DX Tel: (01527) 837500 Fax: (01527) 833818

Airpro Systems, 265 Holton Road, Barry, South Glamorgan, CF63 4HT Tel: (01446) 729900 Fax: (01446) 729909

Alkie Ltd, Millwood View, Stalybridge, Cheshire, SK15 3AU Tel: 0161-338 8070 Fax: 0161-338 3191 E-mail: alkie.ltd@virgin.net

Alter Air, 6 Holly Grove, Basildon, Essex, SS16 6SB Tel: (01268) 540862 Fax: (01268) 540862

B H L Manufacturing Ltd, Llewellyns Quay, Port Talbot, West Glamorgan, SA13 1RG Tel: (01639) 884878 Fax: (01639) 890317

B J Doughty Engineering Ltd, Hereford Way, King's Lynn, Norfolk, PE30 4JD Tel: (01553) 773537 Fax: (01553) 767859 E-mail: admin@bjdoughty.co.uk

B & L Sheetmetal (2003) Ltd, Ramsden Road, Rotherwas Industrial Estate, Hereford, HR2 6LR Tel: (01432) 355040 Fax: (01432) 343844 E-mail: bandl2003@btconnect.com

B T M Services, Unit 16 The Lays Farm Trading Estate, Charlton Road, Keynsham, Bristol, BS31 2SE Tel: 0117-986 8390 Fax: 0117-986 1031 E-mail: btmservs@yahoo.co.uk

Bishop & Smith Stainless Fabrication, Unit 2 Thorn Business Park, Rotherwas, Hereford, HR2 6JT Tel: (01432) 342355 Fax: (01432) 352399E-mail: alan@bishop-smith.fsnet.co.uk

Boyd & Co (Metalworkers) Ltd, Chainbridge Road, Blaydon-on-Tyne, Tyne & Wear, NE21 5SW Tel: 0191-414 3331 Fax: 0191-414 0340 E-mail: info@boydduct.co.uk

Boydell Pipeworks & Fabrications, Poplar Street, Leigh, Lancashire, WN7 4HL Tel: (01942) 672951 Fax: (01942) 262042 E-mail: info@boydellfab.com

C D M Ductwork, 19 Prince William Road, Loughborough, Leicestershire, LE11 5GU Tel: (01509) 611118 Fax: (01509) 232345 E-mail: cdmductwork@aol.com

C D Stone Dunstable Ltd, Fairway Works, Southfields Road, Dunstable, Bedfordshire, LU6 3EP Tel: (01582) 605353 Fax: (01582) 660103

C J & L Fenwick, 2 Station Industrial Estate, Low Prudhoe, Prudhoe, Northumberland, NE42 6NP Tel: (01661) 833474 Fax: (01661) 833474

Catterall & Wood Ltd, Unit 2 Primrose Bank Mill, Friday Street, Chorley, Lancashire, PR6 0AA Tel: (01257) 272192 Fax: (01257) 261432

Coleman Manufacturing Ltd, Graycar Business Park, Barton Turn, Barton under Needwood, Burton-on-Trent, Staffordshire, DE13 8EN Tel: (01283) 716688 Fax: (01283) 712370 E-mail: simon.denning@colemans.uk.net

Complete Air Systems, Unit H & I Maybrook Industrial Estate, Maybrook Road, Walsall, WS8 7DG Tel: (01543) 361301 Fax: (01543) 372530

Contract Components, Unit 37 Pitcliffe Way, Bradford, West Yorkshire, BD5 7SG Tel: (01274) 721982 Fax: (01274) 306876 E-mail: sales@ccIveloduct.co.uk

Cool Air Co, 14 Seaforth Avenue, New Malden, Surrey, KT3 6JP Tel: (020) 8949 5259 Fax: (020) 8949 4490 E-mail: coolairco@aol.com

Crayford Sheet Metal Fabrications, Unit 37 Crayford Industrial Estate, Swaisland Drive, Crayford, Dartford, DA1 4HS Tel: (01322) 551555 Fax: (01322) 553124

Crossley Charles & Son Ltd, 9-11 Astley Street, Stockport, Cheshire, SK4 1AW Tel: 0161-480 2858 Fax: 0161-429 7353 E-mail: mail@charlescrossley.com

D & L Sheet Metal, 9 Whitehouse Enterprise Centre, Whitehouse Road, Newcastle upon Tyne, NE15 6EP Tel: 0191-275 0286 Fax: 0191-275 0286

D M C Ltd, 7 Sherwood Court, Thurston Road, Lewisham, London, SE13 7SD Tel: (020) 8297 1001 Fax: (020) 8297 1002

Domglade Ltd, 1a Desborough Avenue, High Wycombe, Buckinghamshire, HP11 2RS Tel: (01494) 437771 Fax: (01494) 462357

Ducted Air Systems Ltd, 101 Sadler Road, Lincoln, LN6 3RS Tel: (01522) 682239 Fax: (01522) 883002 E-mail: nev@ductedair.com

Ductmann Ltd, Withy Road Industrial Estate, Withy Road, Bilston, West Midlands, WV14 0RX Tel: (01902) 492292 Fax: (01902) 408199 E-mail: sales@ductmann.co.uk

Ductwork By Design Ltd, Unit 7, 193 Garth Rd, Morden, Surrey, SM4 4LZ Tel: (020) 8330 0091 Fax: (020) 8330 0103 E-mail: info@dbdltd.com

Ductwork & Fabrication Ltd, Dashwood Avenue, High Wycombe, Buckinghamshire, HP12 3DP Tel: (01494) 523935 Fax: (01494) 461970 E-mail: enquiries@cas-hw.demon.co.uk

Ductwork Projects Ltd, Unit 303-305 Woolsbridge Industrial Park, Woolsbridge Industrial Estate, Three Legged Cross, Wimborne, Dorset, BH21 6SX Tel: (01202) 823621 Fax: (01202) 823744 E-mail: enquiries@dpl-kvd.co.uk

Ductwork Wolverhampton Ltd, Unit 10-11, Spring Road, Ettingshall, Wolverhampton, WV4 6JT Tel: (01902) 353984 Fax: (01902) 353985

Dy-rect Services Ltd, Unit 8 Hikers Way, Crendon Industrial Park, Long Crendon, Aylesbury, Buckinghamshire, HP18 9RW Tel: (01844) 202233 Fax: (01844) 208748 E-mail: info@dy-rect.co.uk

E Chambers Mechanical Engineering Ltd, 32 Regal Drive, Soham, Ely, Cambridgeshire, CB7 5BE Tel: (01353) 624126 Fax: (01353) 624127 E-mail: info@ecl-ductwork.co.uk

Engineering Systems Ltd, Lifford Way, Binley Industrial Estate, Binley Industrial Estate, Coventry, CV3 2RN Tel: (024) 7645 7555 Fax: (024) 7645 7888 E-mail: engsysltd@tiscali.co.uk

Fan Maintenance Ltd, Eastern Works 4 Eastern Road, Walthamstow, London, E17 9DU Tel: (020) 8521 1856 Fax: (020) 8521 9421

Firth Sheet Metal Ltd, Barrys Lane, Scarborough, North Yorkshire, YO12 4HA Tel: (01723) 376771 Fax: (01723) 351325 E-mail: info@firmac.co.uk

Form Fabrications, 21-25 The Crescent, Hockley, Birmingham, B18 5LU Tel: 0121-551 3561 Fax: 0121-551 6258 E-mail: enquiries@formfabs.com

Forman Metal Products Ltd, Portrack Grange Road, Stockton-on-Tees, Cleveland, TS18 2PH Tel: (01642) 674314 Fax: (01642) 672899 E-mail: info@formanmetalproducts.co.uk

Frankham Ventilation Ltd, 4 Oak St Trading Estate, Oak Street, Quarry Bank, Brierley Hill, West Midlands, DY5 2JQ Tel: (01384) 262755 Fax: (01384) 70468

G B Ductwork Ltd, Station Road, Whitworth, Rochdale, Lancashire, OL12 8LJ Tel: (01706) 854900 Fax: (01706) 854990

G B Logan Fabrications Ltd, Deacon Road, Lincoln, LN2 4JB Tel: (01522) 523622 Fax: (01522) 527408 E-mail: logan@enterprise.net

Gen-Vent Metalworkers Ltd, Manor Works, Manor Road, London, SE25 4TA Tel: (020) 8656 3000 Fax: (020) 8655 4038

Halifax Sheet Metal & Ventilation, Pellon Industrial Estate, Queens Road, Halifax, West Yorkshire, HX1 4PR Tel: (01422) 362361 Fax: (01422) 340591E-mail: info@hsmv.co.uk

Harbridge (Sheet Metal) Ltd, Philip Street, St. Philips Marsh, Bristol, BS2 0TA Tel: 0117-977 8850 Fax: 0117-977 5145 E-mail: harbridge@totalise.co.uk

Harrison Industrial Ltd, Rodney Road, Southsea, Hampshire, PO4 8SY Tel: (023) 9275 1687 Fax: (023) 9281 8564 E-mail: harrison.indl@btclick.com

Impact Ducting Sales Ltd, 45 Oakland Road, Leicester, LE2 6AN Tel: 0116-244 8151 Fax: 0116-244 8343 E-mail: impactducting@impactholdings.com

J D W Engineering Ltd, Tameside Mill, Park Road, Dukinfield, Cheshire, SK16 5LP Tel: 0161-330 1989 Fax: 0161-343 1905 E-mail: sales@jdwengineering.com

J T Services Ltd, 99 Reindeer Road, Fazeley, Tamworth, Staffordshire, B78 3SP Tel: (01827) 250280 Fax: (01827) 281363

K J Engineering Ltd, Unit 4, 55 Albert Road North, Reigate, Surrey, RH2 9EL Tel: (01737) 223392 Fax: (01737) 224365 E-mail: kj.engineering@talk21.com

K M S Hardrange, Unit 5 Manor Industrial Estate, Flint, Clwyd, CH6 5UY Tel: (01352) 732291 Fax: (01352) 762886 E-mail: kmshardrange01@btconnect.com

Ladwa Engineering Ltd, Sanders Lodge Industrial Estate, Rushden, Northamptonshire, NN10 6BQ Tel: (01933) 359204 Fax: (01933) 410583 E-mail: info@ladwaengineering.co.uk

Mackley & Co. Ltd, Chatham Street, Sheffield, S3 8EJ Tel: 0114-272 3991 Fax: 0114-272 1004

Macklow Industrial Ltd, The Mill, Station Road, Salhouse, Norwich, NR13 6NY Tel: (01603) 720950 Fax: (01603) 720033 E-mail: info@macklow.co.uk

Maine Engineering Services Ltd, West Line Industrial Estate, Birtley, Chester le Street, County Durham, DH2 1AU Tel: 0191-410 0004 Fax: 0191-410 2053 E-mail: mick.main@dsl.pipex.com

Mansfield, Pollard & Co. Ltd, Edward House, Parry Lane, Bradford, West Yorkshire, BD4 8TL Tel: (01274) 774050 Fax: (01274) 775424 E-mail: admin@manpo.co.uk

Mastervent Ventilation Systems, 2 Engine Street, Smethwick, West Midlands, B66 3DT Tel: 0121-558 1559 Fax: 0121-565 4047 E-mail: home@masterventltd.go-plus.net

Merseyside Metalwork Ltd, Cotton Street, Liverpool, L3 7DY Tel: 0151-236 7349 Fax: 0151-236 6397

Middleton Sheet Metal Co. Ltd, Spring Vale, Middleton, Manchester, M24 2HS Tel: 0161-643 2462 Fax: 0161-643 3490 E-mail: info@msmgroup.org

Millwrights Liverpool Ltd, 31-33 Naylor Street, Liverpool, L3 6DR Tel: 0151-236 0479 Fax: 0151-255 0198

Norwich Sheet Metal Co. Ltd, 11 Hurricane Way, Norwich, NR6 6EZ Tel: (01603) 419490 Fax: (01603) 404590 E-mail: nsmetal@btconnect.com

John Patrick Engineering Ltd, Merlin Way, Quarry Hill Industrial Park, Ilkeston, Derbyshire, DE7 4RA Tel: 0115-944 0360 Fax: 0115-944 0373 E-mail: info@jpen.co.uk

Phoenix Ventilation & Engineering Ltd, Unit 6 Camphill Industrial Estate, Camphill Road, West Byfleet, Surrey, KT14 6EW Tel: (01932) 336125 Fax: (01932) 336132 E-mail: sales@phoenixventilation.co.uk

Pinnacle Ductwork Manufacturers Ltd, Unit 8 Seagull Lane, Emsworth, Hampshire, PO10 7QH Tel: (01243) 377214 Fax: (01243) 376448 E-mail: pinnacleductwork@aol.com

Prodrive Holdings Ltd, Acorn Way, Banbury, Oxfordshire, OX16 3ER Tel: (01295) 273355 Fax: (01295) 271188 E-mail: enquiries@prodrive.com

Prompt Profiles Ltd, Liberator House, Bidwell Road, Norwich, NR13 6PT Tel: (01603) 720090 Fax: (01603) 720202

Pure Air Ventilation Ltd, 9b 25 Osiers Road, London, SW18 1NL Tel: (020) 8874 2885 Fax: (020) 8877 1739

R & B Fabrications, 4 Vulcan Road, Solihull, West Midlands, B91 2JY Tel: 0121-711 3279 Fax: 0121-711 3279

Ray Rushin Ltd, Whiteley Road, Ripley, Derbyshire, DE5 3QL Tel: (01773) 512155 Fax: (01773) 512156 E-mail: sales@rayrushin.co.uk

Sansome Construction, Bond Street, Southampton, SO14 5AN Tel: (023) 8022 2349

Senior Hargreaves Ltd, Lord Street, Bury, Lancashire, BL9 0RG Tel: 0161-764 5082 Fax: 0161-762 2333 E-mail: postbox@senior-hargreaves.co.uk

Serco, Unit 63 Hillgrove Business Park, Nazeing Road, Nazeing, Waltham Abbey, Essex, EN9 2HB Tel: (01992) 893917 Fax: (01992) 893759

Sheet Metal Services, Hill Street, Kidderminster, Worcestershire, DY11 6TD Tel: (01562) 824995 Fax: (01562) 743998 E-mail: sales@saferack-sheetmetalservices.com

Sheetmetal Developments, Unit 1 Wessex Park, Bancombe Road Trading Estate, Somerton, Somerset, TA11 6SB Tel: (01458) 272212 Fax: (01458) 272212 E-mail: rosser@aol.com

Small Geared Motors Ltd, Villa Nova, Spurlands End Rd, Great Kingshill, High Wycombe, Bucks, HP15 6HX Tel: 01494 715642 Fax: 01494 711527

Charles Smethurst Ltd, Castlemill Street, Oldham, OL1 3HL Tel: 0161-624 4505 Fax: 0161-628 4282 E-mail: info@charlessmethurst.co.uk

Soho Sheet Metal Ltd, Furlong Lane, Stoke-on-Trent, ST6 3LE Tel: (01782) 817930 Fax: (01782) 575656

Southern Ductwork Manufacturing Ltd, Unit 15, Woodlands Business Park, Maidenhead, Berkshire, SL6 3UA Tel: (01628) 828446 Fax: (01628) 828448 E-mail: southernductwork@btconnect.com

T A B Sheet Fabrications Ltd, Unit 3 Galliford Road Industrial Estate, Heybridge, Maldon, Essex, CM9 4XX Tel: (01621) 858848 Fax: (01621) 583847 E-mail: info@tabfab.co.uk

Tatetone Ventilation Systems, 4 Bridgewater Close, Reading, RG30 1JT Tel: 0118-950 8914 Fax: 0118-950 8913 E-mail: enquiries@tateoneltd.co.uk

Tees Insulation Ltd, 138 Lynn Street, Hartlepool, Cleveland, TS24 7LX Tel: (01429) 265433 Fax: (01429) 863149 E-mail: info@teesgroup.com

Thermafabrications Ltd, New Craven Gate, Leeds, LS11 5NF Tel: 0113-245 7510 Fax: 0113-244 9430

Unicorn Sheet Metal Works, Unit 28, Point Pleasant Industrial Estate, Wallsend, Tyne & Wear, NE28 6HA Tel: 0191 2622882 E-mail: sales@unicornlasercutting.co.uk

Universal Sheetmetal Works, 317 Blucher Road, London, SE5 0LH Tel: (020) 7703 4575

V & C Installation Ltd, 24 Severnside Industrial Estate, Sudmeadow Road, Gloucester, GL2 5HS Tel: (01452) 415236 Fax: (01452) 309324 E-mail: paulvye@btconnect.com

V Installations Mechanical Handling Ltd, Saxon Business Park, Stoke Prior, Bromsgrove, Worcestershire, B60 4AD Tel: 01527 833248

Vaughan Mechanical Services (Scotland) Ltd, Aercon Works, East Mains Industrial Estate, Broxburn, West Lothian, EH52 5ND Tel: (01506) 853506 Fax: (01506) 854006 E-mail: vel@vaughan-group.co.uk

Ventilate Ltd, Solent Industrial Estate, Shamblehurst Lane, Hedge End, Southampton, SO30 2FX Tel: (01489) 782262 Fax: (01489) 781822 E-mail: info@peelfabs.co.uk

W M Spence Ltd, PO Box 344, Bradford, West Yorkshire, BD3 9TH Tel: (01274) 661824 E-mail: enquiries@wmspence.co.uk

Wallace Sheetmetal & Fabrication Ltd, Old Jam Works Lane, Station Road, Wigton, Cumbria, CA7 9AX Tel: (01697) 342918 Fax: (01697) 344617E-mail: mail@wallacesheetmetal.co.uk

Wessex Ducting Ltd, 11a Dawkins Road, Poole, Dorset, BH15 4JP Tel: (01202) 661222 Fax: (01202) 661888

West Engineering Ltd, Olympus Close, Ipswich, IP1 5LN Tel: (01473) 467930 Fax: (01473) 467931 E-mail: info@westengineering.co.uk

Whitehouse Engineering Co. Ltd, 14 Trench Road, Newtownabbey, County Antrim, BT36 4UU Tel: (028) 9084 8311 Fax: (028) 9034 2773 E-mail: info@whitehouse-eng.com

Woodford Sheet Metal Ltd, 14 Wham Street, Heywood, Lancashire, OL10 4QU Tel: (01706) 364295 Fax: (01706) 621996 E-mail: woodford-sm@lineone-net.co.uk

The Woodwork Dust Control Company Ltd, Wotton Road, Brill, Aylesbury, Buckinghamshire, HP18 9UB Tel: (01844) 238833 Fax: (01844) 238899 E-mail: woodworkdust@ukonline.co.uk

Worthside Engineering, Dalton Lane, Keighley, West Yorkshire, BD21 4JU Tel: (01535) 605698 Fax: (01535) 610302

Zephyr Ducts & Fittings Ltd, 8 Commerce Way, Leighton Buzzard, Bedfordshire, LU7 4RW Tel: 01525 376446

SHEET METAL ENCLOSURES

Hane Instruments Ltd, 691 Stirling Road, Slough, SL1 4ST Tel: (01753) 530313 Fax: (01753) 823301 E-mail: info@haneinstruments.co.uk

Lund Bros & Co. Ltd, Brookside Avenue, Rustington, Littlehampton, West Sussex, BN16 3LF Tel: (01903) 784242 Fax: (01903) 787126 E-mail: sales@lunds.co.uk

Sure Punch Precision Ltd, Tameside Mills, Park Road, Dukinfield, Cheshire, SK16 5PU Tel: 0161-343 7999 Fax: 0161-343 8999 E-mail: surepunch@surepunch.co.uk

SHEET METAL FABRICATION

▶ Kent Ductwork Ltd, Unit 7-9 Crayford Industrial Estate, Swaisland Drive, Crayford, Dartford, DA1 4HS Tel: (01322) 558887 Fax: (01322) 559991

▶ Paveford Holdings Ltd, Units 3 & 4 East Park Industrial Estate, Purbrook Road, Wolverhampton, WV1 2EJ Tel: (01902) 871282 Fax: (01902) 457309

▶ Rackham Engineering, Hellesdon Park Industrial Estate Road, Norwich, NR6 5DR Tel: (01603) 485038 Fax: (01603) 787106 E-mail: sale@rackhamengineering.co.uk

▶ Sheet Metal & General (Engineers), Unit D7-D8, Aldred Close, Killamarsh, Sheffield, S21 2JH Tel: 0114-251 1455

▶ T I S Insulations, 9 The Pines, Kingswood, Hull, HU7 3GT Tel: (01482) 829888 Fax: (07970) 318994 E-mail: pete@tisinsulation.com

▶ Ventilation & Hygiene Specialists, Unit 2 Wilson Street, Thornaby, Stockton-on-Tees, Cleveland, TS17 7AR Tel: (01642) 675755 Fax: (01642) 675760

SHEET METAL FABRICATION EQUIPMENT

Knaresborough Engineering, Sandbeck Way, Wetherby, West Yorkshire, LS22 7DN Tel: (01937) 589000 Fax: (01937) 585566

SHEET METAL FASTENERS

Components & Technology, Unit M Valley Way, Market Harborough, Leicestershire, LE16 7PS Tel: (01858) 439503 Fax: (01858) 466536 E-mail: sales@coldform.co.uk

Normandy Air Compressors, Unit 1d Cranborne Industrial Estate, Cranborne Road, Potters Bar, Hertfordshire, EN6 3JN Tel: (01707) 662248

SHEET METAL FORMING

A J Metal Fabrications Ltd, 21 Walthamstow Business Centre, Clifford Road, London, E17 4SX Tel: (020) 8527 4860 Fax: (020) 8527 4870 E-mail: steve@ajmetalfabs.co.uk

Ashwell Engineering Services Ltd, Unit 12, Pinfold Road, Thurmaston, Leicester, LE4 8AT Tel: 0116-260 4050 E-mail: ashwelleng@hotmail.com

Cad Fab Ltd, 7 The Courtyards, Victoria Road, Leeds, LS14 2LB Tel: 0113-265 5010 Fax: 0113-265 5012 E-mail: cadfab@aol.com

Calne Engineering Ltd, Stanier Road, Porte Marsh Industrial Estate, Calne, Wiltshire, SN11 9PX Tel: (01249) 813288 Fax: (01249) 821266E-mail: sales@calne-engineering.co.uk

Central Fabrications, 72 Burnmoor Street, Leicester, LE2 7JJ Tel: 0116-247 1515 Fax: 0116-247 1117

Coleman Manufacturing Ltd, Graycar Business Park, Barton Turn, Barton under Needwood, Burton-on-Trent, Staffordshire, DE13 8EN Tel: (01283) 716688 Fax: (01283) 712370 E-mail: simon.denning@colemans.uk.net

Counterhouse Systems Ltd, PO Box 381, Worcester, WR6 5YB Tel: (01886) 833044 Fax: (01886) 833152 E-mail: robert@counterhouse.co.uk

First Choice Business Systems Ltd, Unit 4-6 Murray Business Centre, Murray Road, Orpington, Kent, BR5 3RE Tel: (01689) 828182 Fax: (01689) 899399 E-mail: sales@firstchoiceltd.co.uk

J L Fabrications, Unit 7 Winstanley Industrial Estate, Long Lane, Warrington, WA2 8PR Tel: (01925) 633887 Fax: (01925) 630087

SHEET METAL PATTERNING/ RIGIDIZING SERVICES/ SUPPLIERS

F S C Stainless & Alloys, Ledra Works, Reservoir Place, Walsall, WS2 9SN Tel: (01922) 612545 Fax: (01922) 637755 E-mail: sales@fscstainless.co.uk

Fablink UK Ltd, Arcwell Works, Stafford Road, Fordhouses, Wolverhampton, WV10 7EJ Tel: (01902) 397766 Fax: (01902) 788912 E-mail: sales@fablink.co.uk

▶ Food Process Engineering Ltd, The Creamery, Sheriffiats Road, Thankerton, Biggar, Lanarkshire, ML12 6PA Tel: (01899) 308591 Fax: (01899) 308776 E-mail: sales@foodprocess.co.uk

Hollinwood Sheet Metal Co., Under Lane, Chadderton, Oldham, OL9 7PP Tel: 0161-683 5277 Fax: 0161-684 8608

Rimex Metals, Aden Road, Ponders End, Enfield, Middlesex, EN3 7SU Tel: (020) 8804 0633 Fax: (020) 8804 7275 E-mail: sales@rimexmetals.com

SHEET METAL PRESSINGS

Aircraft & Commercial Tools (Sheffield) Ltd, Bowling Green Street, Shalesmoor, Sheffield, S3 8SU Tel: 0114-272 8112 Fax: 0114-275 9273 E-mail: aircraft@globalnet.co.uk

Alinco Ltd, 22 Albert Drive, Burgess Hill, West Sussex, RH15 9TN Tel: (01444) 232719 Fax: (01444) 871680 E-mail: alinco@btinternet.com

B S B Engineering Co. Ltd, Phoenix Street, Bolton, BL1 2SY Tel: (01204) 535343 Fax: (01204) 389287 E-mail: enquiries@bsbengineering.com

Fred Baker Ltd, 30 Park Street, Birmingham, B5 5JH Tel: 0121-643 5409 Fax: 0121-643 0914

Binns Security Fencing Ltd, Pressmetal House St. Augustines Business Park, Estuary Close, Whitstable, Kent, CT5 2QJ Tel: (01227) 794490 Fax: (01227) 794488

BMR Presswork, Market Street, Draycott, Derby, DE72 3NB Tel: (01332) 875384 Fax: (01332) 874022

Bolyer Engineering Co. Ltd, Bayton Road, Bayton Road Industrial Estate, Exhall, Coventry, CV7 9EL Tel: (024) 7636 1600 Fax: (024) 7636 5151 E-mail: info@bolyer.co.uk

Broadway Stamping Ltd, Denbigh Road, Bletchley, Milton Keynes, MK1 1DT Tel: (01908) 647703 Fax: (01908) 649279 E-mail: broadways@broadwaysstampings.co.uk

D W O'Brien Ltd, 64 Trafalgar Road, Kettering, Northamptonshire, NN16 8DD Tel: (01536) 484495 Fax: (01536) 410976 E-mail: sales@dwobrien.co.uk

Harlow Pressings Ltd, 57-60 Llantarnam Industrial Park, Cwmbran, Gwent, NP44 3AW Tel: (01633) 487400 Fax: (01633) 863010

K M Pressings Ltd, 37B Copenhagen Road, Sutton Field Industrial Estate, Hull, HU7 0XQ Tel: (01482) 877900 Fax: (01482) 877909 E-mail: jonathon@kmpressing.karew.co.uk

Kaybee Engineering, Station Street, Bromsgrove, Worcestershire, B60 2BS Tel: (01527) 870845 Fax: (01527) 870845 E-mail: andy.knight@kpe.demon.co.uk

Leigh & Letcher, Chequers Lane, Dagenham, Essex, RM9 6QD Tel: (020) 8984 1015 Fax: (020) 8984 1735 E-mail: sales@leighandletcher.co.uk

Lenic Engineering Ltd, Unit 24 Cradle Hill Industrial Estate, Afriston Road, Seaford, East Sussex, BN25 3JE Tel: (01323) 896783 Fax: (01323) 491416 E-mail: info@metalpressings.co.uk

Middleton Metal Spinning, Clough Road, Manchester, M9 4FP Tel: 0161 2058687

Notts Industries Ltd, Carley Works, Garsdale, Frome, Somerset, BA11 1PR Tel: (01373) 452231 Fax: (01373) 451139

P A G Sheet Metal Ltd, 4 River Brent Business Park, Trumpers Way, London, W7 2QA Tel: (020) 8574 3577 Fax: (020) 8893 5370 E-mail: sales@pagsheetmetal.com

Panton (Sheet Metalworks) Ltd, 67 Swaisland Drive, Crayford Industrial Estate, Crayford, Dartford, DA1 4HS Tel: (01322) 554180 Fax: (01322) 555157 E-mail: enquiries@pantonsheetmetal.co.uk

Pegrex, Unit 1e Pearsall Drive, Oldbury, West Midlands, B69 2RA Tel: 0121-511 1475 Fax: 0121-511 1474 E-mail: nstruman@aol.com

Phoenix Pressings Ltd, Wakefield Road, Brighouse, West Yorkshire, HD6 1PE Tel: (01484) 712422 Fax: (01484) 716471 E-mail: sales@phoenixpressings.co.uk

Prescott Powell Ltd, 466 Moseley Road, Birmingham, B12 9AN Tel: 0121-446 4411 Fax: 0121-446 4681 E-mail: liam.duggan@prescottpowell.co.uk

Production Presswork & Tooling Ltd, Unit 12 Enterprise Court, Rankin Road, Basingstoke, Hampshire, RG24 8GE Tel: (01256) 816836 Fax: (01256) 812970

R S M Industries Ltd, School Lane, Exhall, Coventry, CV7 9NN Tel: (024) 7636 2082 Fax: (024) 7655 3715 E-mail: admin@rsmindustries.co.uk

Redfern Stevens Ltd, 40 Brickfield Road, Birmingham, B25 8HE Tel: 0121-766 6464 Fax: 0121-766 6651 E-mail: info@redfernstevens.co.uk

Romo (Engineering) Ltd, Unit 12B, Waterfall Lane Trading Estate, Waterfall Lane, Cradley Heath, West Midlands, B64 6PU Tel: 0121-559 5966 Fax: 0121-559 5952 E-mail: press@romo.co.uk

Salop Design & Engineering Ltd, Brixton Way, Shrewsbury, SY1 3LB Tel: (01743) 450501 Fax: (01743) 440904 E-mail: info@salopdesign.co.uk

Shermaynes Welders Engineers Ltd, Units 2d 3a/3b Southgate Industrial Centre, Southgate, Lancaster, Morecambe, LA3 3PB Tel: (01524) 69333

Peter Sowter & Co. Ltd, Components House, 5 Holmes Close, Wokingham, Berkshire, RG41 2SG Tel: 0118-978 2691 Fax: 0118-978 2691

Sullivan Engineering Co., 9 Doman Road, Camberley, Surrey, GU15 3DF Tel: (01276) 20931 Fax: (01276) 27168 E-mail: sullivaneng42@netscapeonline.co.uk

▶ Traker Engineering Ltd, Garth Works, Taffs Well, Cardiff, CF15 7RN Tel: (029) 2081 1088 Fax: (029) 2081 3520 E-mail: info@traker-eng.co.uk

W R R Pedley & Co. Ltd, Ann Street, Willenhall, West Midlands, WV13 1EW Tel: (01902) 366060 Fax: (01902) 603411

W Thacker & Sons Ltd, Field Gate, Walsall, WS1 3DJ Tel: (01922) 622302 Fax: (01922) 647790

Wardtec Ltd, Unit 92, Heming Road, Washford, Redditch, Worcestershire, B98 0DH Tel: (01527) 520594 Fax: (01527) 502235 E-mail: ward-tec@btconnect.com

Willis & Bates, Reservoir Road, Halifax, West Yorkshire, HX2 0ES Tel: (01422) 361228 Fax: (01422) 340480 E-mail: sales@bairstowbrothers.co.uk

Woodseats Engineering, 3 Canal Works, Cadman Street, Sheffield, S4 7ZG Tel: 0114-279 6143 Fax: 0114-279 6143 E-mail: sales@woodseatsengineering.com

Wye Valley Engineering Ltd, Unit 260 Netherwood Road Rotherwas Indust Estate, Rotherwas Industrial Estate, Hereford, HR2 6JU Tel: (01432) 266507 Fax: (01432) 341645 E-mail: enquries@durabase.co.uk

SHEET METAL PROFILING TO SPECIFICATION

It C M L Ltd, Unit 26 Cam Centre, Wilbury Way, Hitchin, Hertfordshire, SG4 0TW Tel: (01462) 635455 Fax: (01462) 635454 E-mail: salesitcml@btconnect.com

SHEET METAL PUNCHING

B & Z, O2, Cherrycourt Way, Leighton Buzzard, Bedfordshire, LU7 4UH Tel: (01525) 373018 Fax: (01525) 851439 E-mail: enquiries@bandz.co.uk

▶ Bell Bros Pudsey Ltd, Green Lane, Pudsey, West Yorkshire, LS28 8JN Tel: 0113-256 5715 Fax: 0113-256 9255E-mail: info@bellbros.com

Bondation Fabrications, 4-6 Abingdon Road, Nuffield Industrial Estate, Poole, Dorset, BH17 0UG Tel: (01202) 677828 Fax: (01202) 677861

Colmet Precision Ltd, Unit 15 Upper Wingbury Courtyard Business Centre, Leighton Road, Wingrave, Aylesbury, Buckinghamshire, HP22 4LW Tel: (01296) 681658 Fax: (01296) 681726 E-mail: sales@colmet.co.uk

Comvek Engineering Ltd, Station Drive, Unit 1, Breener Industrial Estate, Brierley Hill, West Midlands, DY5 3JZ Tel: (01384) 571515 Fax: (01384) 262088 E-mail: clbradley@btconnect.com

Gemflex Engineering Ltd, Unit 4, Cossall Industrial Estate, Coronation Road, Ilkeston, Derbyshire, DE7 5UA Tel: 0115-944 2414 Fax: 0115-944 2771 E-mail: sales@gemflex.co.uk

H T Fabrications Ltd, 420 Thurmaston Boulevard, Leicester, LE4 9LE Tel: 0116-276 1814 Fax: 0116-246 0576 E-mail: ht@fabs.freeserve.co.uk

E.E. Ingleton Engineering Ltd, Adelaide Works, 55 Mowbray St, Sheffield, S3 8EZ Tel: 0114-275 7834 Fax: 0114-272 9672 E-mail: sales@eeingleton.co.uk

J S J Precision, Milburn Road, Stoke-on-Trent, ST6 2QF Tel: (01782) 269694 Fax: (01782) 279138

Jarrobs Ltd, Units 1-5, Excalibur Industrial Estate, Fields Road, Alsager, Stoke-on-Trent, ST7 2LX Tel: (01270) 878711 Fax: (01270) 882464 E-mail: sales@jarrobs.co.uk

M & M Fabrications Ltd, Disraeli Street, Aylestone, Leicester, LE2 8LX Tel: 0116-245 2800 Fax: 0116-245 2801 E-mail: mandm@b-on-line.com

Metfab Design Ltd, Unit 220 Foley Industrial Estate, Kidderminster, Worcestershire, DY11 7DH Tel: (01562) 864129 Fax: (01562) 864129

Paragon Pressings, 3b Harpings Road, Hull, HU5 4JF Tel: (01482) 462822 Fax: (01482) 462833

Ryeford Engineering, 14 Ebley Road, Stonehouse, Gloucestershire, GL10 2LH Tel: (01453) 825841 Fax: (01453) 827732 E-mail: nick@ryefordeng.co.uk

SHEET METAL/PLATE BENDING ROLLS

Morgan Rushworth Ltd, Bromley Street, Lye, Stourbridge, West Midlands, DY9 8HS Tel: (01384) 895491 Fax: (01384) 424448 E-mail: sales@morganrushworth.com

Waltons Of Radcliffe Sales Ltd, Unit 14 Bradley Fold Trading Estate, Radcliffe Moor Road, Bradley Fold, Bolton, BL2 6RT Tel: (01204) 393633 Fax: (01204) 363196 E-mail: sales@waltons-of-radcliffe.com

SHEET METALWORK ENGINEERS OR FABRICATORS

A A Sheet Metals, 1 Fletcher Way, Weston Road, Norwich, NR3 3ST Tel: (01603) 417030 Fax: (01603) 417128 E-mail: alan.harrowing@aasheetmetalnorwich.fsnet.co.uk

A Barraclough, 72 Tyler Street, Sheffield, S9 1DH Tel: 0114-243 1683 Fax: 0114-243 2804 E-mail: sales@abarraclough.co.uk

A D E Engineering Ltd, Prospect Close, Lowmoor Business Park, Kirkby-In-Ashfield, Nottingham, NG17 7LF Tel: (01623) 753888 Fax: (01623) 750543

A D Fabrications Telford Ltd, Unit B5 Dawley Bank Industrial Estate, Cemetery Road, Dawley Bank, Telford, Shropshire, TF4 2BS Tel: (01952) 505525 Fax: (01952) 505489

A D J Fabrications Ltd, Unit 8a Bowes Road, Riverside Park Industrial Estate, Middlesbrough, Cleveland, TS2 1LU Tel: (01642) 225726 Fax: (01642) 242738

▶ A D P, 29 Invincible Drive, Armstrong Industrial Park, Newcastle upon Tyne, NE4 7HX Tel: 0191-256 8071 Fax: 0191-256 8072 E-mail: adpengineering@aol.com

▶ A D Precision Engineering Ltd, Unit 3a-C, Rink Road Indust Estate, Ryde, Isle of Wight, PO33 1LP Tel: (01983) 810708 Fax: (01983) 613987 E-mail: adprecision@btconnect.com

A E Engineering Services, 8 Eye Green Industries, Crowland Road, Eye, Peterborough, PE6 7SZ Tel: (01733) 223355 Fax: (01733) 222330 E-mail: tony@aeengineering.co.uk

A F Hussey London Ltd, Unit B10 Down Bounds Green Industrial Estate, Ringway, London, N11 2UD Tel: (020) 8368 3680 Fax: (020) 8361 2992

A & I Engineering Ltd, 49 Depot Road, Cwmavon, Port Talbot, West Glamorgan, SA12 9BA Tel: (01639) 896141 Fax: (01639) 896141

A J Fabrications, 28A Somerset Street, Northampton, NN1 3LW Tel: (01604) 628070 Fax: (01604) 627929

A J Metal Fabrications Ltd, 21 Walthamstow Business Centre, Clifford Road, London, E17 4SX Tel: (020) 8527 4860 Fax: (020) 8527 4870 E-mail: steve@ajmetalfabs.co.uk

A K L Sheet Metal Co., 7 Embassy Industrial Estate, Attwood Street, Stourbridge, West Midlands, DY9 8RY Tel: (01384) 892361 Fax: (01384) 892361

A L Gordon Engineering, Abbotshaugh Works, Abbots Road, Bankside Industrial Estate, Falkirk, FK2 7UU Tel: (01324) 622055 Fax: (01324) 613383 E-mail: info@al-gordon.co.uk

▶ A & L Mechanical Installations, 35 Portree Avenue, Kilmarnock, Ayrshire, KA3 2GA Tel: (01563) 525425 Fax: (01563) 525952

A P V Products, 3 Earlsfield Close, Lincoln, LN6 3RT Tel: (01522) 690774 Fax: (01522) 690723

A & R Sheet Metal Ltd, 68-70 College Street, Kempston, Bedford, MK42 8LU Tel: (01234) 348841 Fax: (01234) 262784 E-mail: sales@arsheetmetal.co.uk

A W Fabrications Ltd, Unit 3 Parsons Hall, High Street, Irchester, Wellingborough, Northamptonshire, NN29 7AB Tel: (01933) 357163 Fax: (01933) 410021

▶ Aaran Sheet Metal Ltd, Unit 6 Crossley Hall Works, York Street, Bradford, West Yorkshire, BD8 0HR Tel: (01274) 549100 Fax: (01274) 549300 E-mail: aaranmetal@aol.com

Abaca Engineering, Unit 2, Jackson Road, Holbrooks, Coventry, CV6 4BT Tel: (024) 7666 7390 Fax: (024) 7668 2845 E-mail: sales@abacaengineering.co.uk

Abbott Fabrications Ltd, Unit 1b Woodleys Yard, Newton Road, Higham Ferrers, Rushden, Northamptonshire, NN10 8HW Tel: (01933) 419942 Fax: (01933) 411619 E-mail: enquiries@abbott-fabrications.co.uk

▶ About Engineering Ltd, Thistleton Road Industrial Estate, Market Overton, Rutland, Oakham, Leicestershire, LE15 7PP Tel: (01572) 768007

Absolute, Convent Drive, Waterbeach, Cambridge, CB25 9QT Tel: (01223) 440022 Fax: (01223) 440033 E-mail: mail.winborn_products@virgin.net

▶ Abt Engineering Ltd, Unit 1, Cargo Terminal Campsie Drive, Abbotsinch, Paisley, Renfrewshire, PA3 2SG Tel: 0141-887 4404

Abtek Ltd, Unit 10, Camperdown Industrial Estate, Newcastle upon Tyne, NE12 5UJ Tel: 0191-268 8555 Fax: 0191-268 8777 E-mail: sales@abtekltd.co.uk

Acclaim Fabrications, 7b Meadow Road, Reading, RG1 8LB Tel: 0118-939 3413 Fax: 0118-939 3413

▶ Accranut Co. Ltd, 1 Closers Business Centre, Avenue Road, Nuneaton, Warwickshire, CV11 4ND Tel: (024) 7638 4062 Fax: (024) 7638 7889

Adamson Fabrications (Dundee) Ltd, 360 Strathmore Avenue, Dundee, DD3 6RU Tel: (01382) 812101 Fax: (01382) 832189 E-mail: sales@adamsonfabrications.co.uk

Adept Precision Sheet Metal Ltd, Ardglen Trading Estate, Whitchurch, Hampshire, RG28 7BB Tel: (01256) 893177 Fax: (01256) 893904 E-mail: info@adept-sheetmetal.co.uk

Adnor Ltd, Mill Place, Kingston upon Thames, Surrey, KT1 2RL Tel: (020) 8549 4728 Fax: (020) 8549 8989 E-mail: sales@adnor.co.uk

▶ ADS Precision Ltd, 716 Penistone Road, Hillsbough, Sheffield, S6 2DF Tel: 0114-234 7352 Fax: 0114-234 7362 E-mail: sales@adprecision.com

Advanced Metal Engineering Ltd, 200 Rickmansworth Road, Watford, WD18 7JS Tel: (01923) 211133 Fax: (01923) 241124 E-mail: ameltd@btconnect.com

Advanced Sheet Metal Engineering Ltd, 4 Lisle Road, High Wycombe, Buckinghamshire, HP13 5SH Tel: (01494) 451251 Fax: (01494) 535274

▶ Aerospace Machining Technology Ltd, 20 West Shore Road, Edinburgh, EH5 1QD Tel: 0131-552 4271 Fax: 0131-552 2552

▶ Aerospace & Technical Engineering, Units 5-6, Station Road, Leatherhead, Surrey, KT22 7AG Tel: (01372) 379929 Fax: (01372) 386973 E-mail: sales@at-engineering.co.uk

▶ Alex Aiken & Son Ltd, Dales Industrial Estate, Peterhead, Aberdeenshire, AB42 3GY Tel: (01779) 475121

James Aiken (Sheetmetal) Ltd, 10 Wellington Street, Aberdeen, AB11 5BT Tel: (01224) 572555 Fax: (01224) 571214 E-mail: enquiries@jasm.com

Air Domestique Ltd, Unit 4b Benbridge Industrial Estate, Holloway Road, Heybridge, Maldon, Essex, CM9 4ER Tel: (01621) 852994 Fax: (01621) 850643 E-mail: mail@ad-manufacturing.fsnet.co.uk

▶ Air Duct Systems (Southern) Ltd, 5 Oxford Road, Pen Mill Trading Estate, Yeovil, Somerset, BA21 5HR Tel: (01935) 431809

Air Marks Systems Ltd, A3-A4 Salcombe Road, Alfreton, Derbyshire, DE55 7RG Tel: (01773) 832228 Fax: (01773) 830186 E-mail: sales@airmarkssystems.ltd.uk

Air Steel Ltd, Furnace Hill, Halesowen, West Midlands, B63 3LZ Tel: 0121-550 2968 Fax: 0121-520 1346

Aire Valley Metal Products Ltd, Shaw House, Goulbourne Street, Keighley, West Yorkshire, BD21 1PG Tel: (01535) 600162 Fax: (01535) 600162 E-mail: aire@valleymetals.fsnet.co.uk

SHEET METALWORK ENGINEERS OR FABRICATORS – *continued*

Alco Engineering (Sheet Metal) Co.Ltd, High Bullen, St. Giles, Torrington, Devon, EX38 7JA Tel: (01805) 622461 Fax: (01805) 624011 E-mail: sales@alcoeng.co.uk

▶ Alderside Engineering, Biggar Road, Cleland, Motherwell, Lanarkshire, ML1 5PB Tel: (01698) 860157 Fax: (01698) 861966

Aldridge Bros Sheetmetal Ltd, Balfour Road, Altrincham, Cheshire, WA14 5LS Tel: 0161-928 4810 Fax: 0161-941 7765

Alex J Cheetham Ltd, Morton Street, Failsworth, Manchester, M35 0BP Tel: 0161-681 1115 Fax: 0161-681 0339 E-mail: mark@alexjcheetham.co.uk

▶ All Round Engineering Ltd, 498-499 Ipswich Road, Slough, SL1 4EP Tel: (01753) 516996 Fax: (01753) 692746 E-mail: sales@allroundengineering.co.uk

Allsops Ltd, Hope Bank Works, New Mil Road, Honley, Holmfirth, HD9 6QG Tel: (01484) 661447 Fax: (01484) 666808 E-mail: info@allsops.co.uk

Alma Sheet Metal Ltd, Unit 4 Mottram Way, Hurdsfield Industrial Estate, Macclesfield, Cheshire, SK10 2DH Tel: (01625) 427159 Fax: (01625) 669166 E-mail: sales@almasheetmetal.co.uk

Almar Services Ltd, 33 Marathon Place, Moss Side Industrial Estate, Leyland, PR26 7QN Tel: (01772) 623336 Fax: (01772) 623486

Almick Sheet Metal, Unit 7h Claymore, Wilnecote, Tamworth, Staffordshire, B77 5DQ Tel: (01827) 251530 Fax: (01827) 260390

▶ Alpha Engineering Solutions Ltd, 2 Pit Lane, Talke Pits, Stoke-on-Trent, ST7 1UH Tel: (01782) 774444 Fax: (01782) 775525 E-mail: enquires@alphaeng.co.uk

Alpha Sheet Metal Work, Unit 3A, Butlerfield Industrial Estate, Newton Grange, Bonnyrigg, Midlothian, EH19 3JQ Tel: (01875) 822588

Alpha Systems, Imperial Works, Coalpit Hill, Talke, Stoke-on-Trent, ST7 1PN Tel: (01782) 783267 Fax: (01782) 776240 E-mail: info@alphasystems-tec.co.uk

▶ Alpine Sheet Metal Ltd, 21 Porte Marsh Road, PorteMarsh Industrial Estate, Calne, Wiltshire, SN11 9BW Tel: (01249) 813412 Fax: (01249) 815184 E-mail: sales@alpinesheetmetal.co.uk

Alrog Engineering Ltd, Halifax Road, Cressex Business Park, High Wycombe, Buckinghamshire, HP12 3SD Tel: (01494) 447213 Fax: (01494) 528104

Alroy Sheet Metal Ltd, Gunnels Wood Road, Stevenage, Hertfordshire, SG1 2BL Tel: (01438) 355687 Fax: (01438) 367608 E-mail: lorna@alroys.com

Altech Engineering, Brighton Road, Bolney, Haywards Heath, West Sussex, RH17 5NA Tel: (01444) 881964 Fax: (01444) 881816 E-mail: sales@altechengineering.com

▶ Altissimo Ltd, Arnish Point, Stornoway, Isle Of Lewis, HS2 9JZ Tel: (01851) 707180 Fax: (01851) 705529 E-mail: mdm@camcal.co.uk

Aluminium Copper & Stainless Co. Ltd, 22-24 Crittall Road, Witham, Essex, CM8 3DR Tel: (01376) 513419 Fax: (01376) 511615

Ambery Metalform Components, Unit F6 Newton Business Park, Talbot Road, Hyde, Cheshire, SK14 4UQ Tel: 0161-367 9616 Fax: 0161-368 0689 E-mail: sales@ambery-metalform.co.uk

Amc Sheet Metal Fabrication, 1 2 3 The Chilterns, Marlborough Road, Lancing, West Sussex, BN15 8SU Tel: (01903) 752127 Fax: (01903) 750426

▶ Amco Engineering Services, Willow Tree House, Inchture, Perth, PH14 9RN Tel: (01828) 686963 Fax: (01828) 685385 E-mail: chatts@callnet.co.uk

Amenco (Poole) Ltd, Units 14-18, Willis Way, Fleets Industrial Estate, Poole, Dorset, BH15 3ST Tel: 0845 1306660 Fax: (01202) 671436 E-mail: office@amenco.co.uk

Anglia Engineering Ltd, Estate Road, 2 South Humberside Industrial Estate, Grimsby, South Humberside, DN31 2TG Tel: (01472) 359455 Fax: (01472) 242478 E-mail: sales@anglia-eng.co.uk

Anglosax Ltd, 3 Pomeroy Drive, Oadby Industrial Estate, Oadby, Leicester, LE2 5NE Tel: 0116-271 1005

Angus Mcmurtrie Blacksmiths Ltd, 1 Kellas Road, Wellbank, Broughty Ferry, Dundee, DD5 3PE Tel: (01382) 350301 Fax: (01382) 350573

▶ Anhop Metalwork Ltd, 109 Glenpark Street, Glasgow, G31 1NY Tel: 0141-554 7667

▶ APC Engineering, Unit 8, Flightway Business Park, Dunkeswell, Honiton, Devon, EX14 4RD Tel: (01404) 891105 Fax: (01404) 891107 E-mail: andy@apcengineering.co.uk

Apex Security Engineering Ltd, Flint Road, Letchworth Garden City, Hertfordshire, SG6 1HJ Tel: (01462) 673431 Fax: (01462) 671518 E-mail: sales@apexsecuritiesfurniture.com

▶ Apollo Sheet Metal Products, Bayton Road, Bayton Road Industrial Estate, Exhall, Coventry, CV7 9EJ Tel: (024) 7636 0822 Fax: (024) 7664 4415

▶ Applelec Sign Components, Walker Terrace, Bradford, West Yorkshire, BD4 7HP Tel: (01274) 774477 Fax: (01274) 774478 E-mail: sales@applelecsign.co.uk

▶ Applied Metal Technology Ltd, 3 Ashfield Close Whitehall Industrial Estate, Whitehall Road, Leeds, LS12 5JB Tel: 0113-279 3708 Fax: 0113-279 3816

Arben Sheet Metal Ltd, 204 Bedford Avenue, Slough Trading Estate, Slough, SL1 4RY Tel: (01753) 531066 Fax: (01753) 694724 E-mail: arben@globalnet.co.uk

Arc Gas Welding Co. Ltd, The Croft, Cheadle Road, Tean, Stoke-on-Trent, ST10 4DR Tel: (01538) 722460 Fax: (01538) 723293

Arch Motor & Manufacturing Co Co. Ltd, Redwongs Way, Huntingdon Trading Estate, Huntingdon, Cambridgeshire, PE29 7HD Tel: (01480) 459661 Fax: (01480) 450923 E-mail: info@archmotor.co.uk

Arcoe Metal Products, 11 Fairway Drive, Greenford, Middlesex, UB6 8PW Tel: (020) 8575 5541 Fax: (020) 8575 8678 E-mail: metalman@arcoe.freeserve.co.uk

▶ Argyle Engineering Ltd, 21-29 Regent Street, Liverpool, L3 7BW Tel: 0151-236 0777 Fax: 0151-236 8073

Armer Quality Components Ltd, Hope Mill, Greenacres Road, Oldham, OL4 2AB Tel: 0161-620 5203 Fax: 0161-627 5139 E-mail: mail@armerqc.co.uk

Armthorpe Fabrication, Renny's Lane, Dragonville Industrial Estate, Gilesgate, Durham, DH1 2RS Tel: 0191-386 9502 Fax: 0191-386 2092

Arrow Engineering Scunthorpe, Dawes Lane, Scunthorpe, South Humberside, DN15 6UW Tel: (01724) 869371 Fax: (01724) 270190

Ashdale Engineering, Mitchell Close, Andover, Hampshire, SP10 3TJ Tel: (01264) 355642 Fax: (01264) 333641

▶ Asseal, 139a Hillsborough Old Road, Lisburn, County Antrim, BT27 5QE Tel: (028) 9266 9966 Fax: (028) 9266 9977

▶ Auty Precision Engineering, 5-7 Colndale Road, Colnbrook, Slough, SL3 0HQ Tel: (01753) 770012 Fax: (01753) 770014

Azimex Fabrications Ltd, Cartwright Road, Northampton, NN2 6HF Tel: (01604) 717712 Fax: (01604) 791087

▶ Aztec Assemblies Ltd, Bryn Brithdir, Oakdale Business Park, Blackwood, Gwent, NP12 4AA Tel: (01495) 247788 Fax: (01495) 247080

▶ B & B Fabrications Ltd, Units B & D, Bedewell Industrial Park, Adair, Hebburn, Tyne & Wear, NE31 2XQ Tel: 0191-430 1908 Fax: 0191-428 0615

B D & J M Heslop, Newton Grange, Shipton by Beningbrough, York, YO30 1BA Tel: (01347) 848206 Fax: (01347) 848443

▶ B E C Engineering, Richmond Road, Atherstone, Warwickshire, CV9 2AH Tel: (01827) 718198 Fax: (01827) 715498

B H R Ltd, Unit 16, Peerglow Industrial Estate, Watford, WD18 9SR Tel: (01923) 776683 Fax: (01923) 776683

B J Doughty Engineering Ltd, Hereford Way, King's Lynn, Norfolk, PE30 4JD Tel: (01553) 773537 Fax: (01553) 767859 E-mail: admin@bjdoughty.co.uk

B & J Engineering Co., 7 Brampton Sidings Industrial Estate, Hempstalls Lane, Newcastle, Staffordshire, ST5 0SR Tel: (01782) 632132 Fax: (01782) 628591 E-mail: bjengltd@aol.com

B & K Fabrications Ltd, 60-64 Heath Mill Lane, Deritend, Birmingham, B9 4AR Tel: 0121-772 2667 Fax: 0121-772 2667

B L C Scotland Ltd, 20 Garrell Road, Kilsyth, Glasgow, G65 9JX Tel: (01236) 822365 Fax: (01236) 826446

▶ B & M Sheet Metal Ltd, Building 32 Bay 4 Second Avenue, The Pensnett Estate, Pensnett Trading Estate, Kingswinford, West Midlands, DY6 7PP Tel: (01384) 402558 Fax: (01384) 402557

B & P Fabrications Ltd, 6 Euston Street, Leicester, LE2 7ST Tel: 0116-249 4440 Fax: 0116-249 4444 E-mail: bandp@webleicester.co.uk

▶ B S & A Power Press, Unit 7-8 Tanfield Lea Industrial Estate South, Tanfield Lea, Stanley, County Durham, DH9 9QX Tel: (01207) 283377 Fax: (01207) 283366 E-mail: bsassociates@aol.com

B T M Services, Unit 16 The Lays Farm Trading Estate, Charlton Road, Keynsham, Bristol, BS31 2SE Tel: 0117-986 8390 Fax: 0117-986 1031 E-mail: btmservs@yahoo.co.uk

▶ Bailstar Ltd, Unit 7-8 Zennor Road Industrial Estate, Zennor Road, London, SW12 0PS Tel: (020) 8675 3419 Fax: (020) 8673 5951

Bakewell Engineering Ltd, 99 North Western Street, Ardwick, Manchester, M12 6JL Tel: 0161-273 2822 Fax: 0161-273 3829

Bambury Metal Fabrications, Short Street, Bristol, BS2 0SW Tel: 0117-971 9216 Fax: 0117-971 1898

Bankside Patterson Ltd, Catwick Lane, Brandesburton, Driffield, East Yorkshire, YO25 8RW Tel: (01964) 545454 Fax: (01964) 545459 E-mail: sales@bankside-patterson.co.uk

▶ Bar Products & Services Ltd, Hanworth Road, Low Moor, Bradford, West Yorkshire, BD12 0SG Tel: (01274) 699249

Barbour Engineering Ltd, 3 Balloo Avenue, Bangor, County Down, BT19 7QT Tel: (028) 9146 6622 Fax: (028) 9146 6535

▶ Barnfield Engineering Services Ltd, Lane End Farm, Hatt Common, East Woodhay, Newbury, Berkshire, RG20 0NG Tel: (01635) 255330 Fax: (01635) 255338 E-mail: barnfield@btclick.com

▶ Barton Engineering & Export Ltd, Diamond Road, Whitstable, Kent, CT5 1LN Tel: (01227) 272141 Fax: (01227) 771653 E-mail: susan@bartoneng.co.uk

Beagle Aircraft Ltd, Stony Lane, Christchurch, Dorset, BH23 1EX Tel: (01202) 482296 Fax: (01202) 499449

▶ Beddis Kenley Engineering Ltd, Unit 6, Astra Park, Parkside Lane, Leeds, LS11 5TD Tel: 0113-270 9674

▶ Bell Bros Pudsey Ltd, Green Lane, Pudsey, West Yorkshire, LS28 8JN Tel: 0113-256 5715 Fax: 0113-256 9255E-mail: info@bellbros.com

Bennett Engineering, Mintsfeet Industrial Estate, Mintsfeet Road, Kendal, Cumbria, LA9 6LU Tel: (01539) 722275 Fax: (01539) 730516 E-mail: s.bennett@bennett-engineering.co.uk

BFS Sheet Metal & Engineering Ltd, 42 Woodham Lane, New Haw, Addlestone, Surrey, KT15 3NA Tel: (01932) 848142 Fax: (01932) 841937 E-mail: stephen@bfssheetmetal.co.uk

Biggleswade Sheet Metal Co, The Old Forge, Rose Lane, Biggleswade, Bedfordshire, SG18 0JT Tel: (01767) 318509 Fax: (01767) 318509

Bilston Engineering Ltd, Spring Road, Wolverhampton, WV4 6LF Tel: (01902) 492004 Fax: (01902) 354510 E-mail: sales@bilston-engineering.co.uk

Birchfield Sheet Metal Sheet Metal, 15 Hadfield Industrial Estate, Waterside, Hadfield, Glossop, Derbyshire, SK13 1BS Tel: (01457) 865536 Fax: (01457) 865536

Bird Stevens & Co. Ltd, Sun Street, Brierley Hill, West Midlands, DY5 2JE Tel: (01384) 567381 Fax: (01384) 637357 E-mail: sales@birdstevens.co.uk

▶ Blackburn Heavy Engineering Ltd, Spring Bank Works, Albert Street, Blackburn, BB2 4BL Tel: (01254) 677817 Fax: (01254) 673260 E-mail: info@millhillpaper.com

▶ Blackhill Engineering Services Ltd, Blackhill Quarry, Woodbury, Exeter, EX5 1JL Tel: (01395) 232701 Fax: (01395) 232571

Blandon Group, Unit 12, Spring Mill Industrial Estate, Old Bristol Road, Avening Road, Nailsworth, Stroud, Gloucestershire, GL6 0BS Tel: (01453) 832358 Fax: (01453) 834878 E-mail: admin@blandon.com

▶ Block Engineers, 87 Church Road, Kessingland, Lowestoft, Suffolk, NR33 7SJ Tel: (01502) 740293 Fax: (01502) 742003 E-mail: agblockkessingland@hotmail.com

Bluntray Ltd, 55 Lonsdale Road, London, NW6 6RA Tel: (020) 7624 8151 Fax: (020) 7624 2533

Boden Sheet Metal Ltd, Drake House, Drake Avenue, Staines, Middlesex, TW18 2AW Tel: (01784) 452683 Fax: (01784) 465889 E-mail: info@bodensheetmetal.co.uk

Bondation Fabrications, 4-6 Abingdon Road, Nuffield Industrial Estate, Poole, Dorset, BH17 0UG Tel: (01202) 677828 Fax: (01202) 677861

▶ Bosus, 8 Dickson Street, Liverpool, L3 7EB Tel: 0151-298 9393 Fax: 0151-298 9500 E-mail: sales@bosus.com

Boulting Mechanical Services, Unit 11, Warrington Central Trading Estate Bewsey Road, Warrington, WA2 7LP Tel: (01925) 831151 Fax: (01925) 581120

Bowson Engineering Ltd, Oak House, Dewsbury Road, Fenton Industrial Estate, Stoke-on-Trent, ST4 2TE Tel: (01782) 749000 Fax: (01782) 749299 E-mail: sales@bowson.co.uk

Boydell Pipeworks & Fabrications, Poplar Street, Leigh, Lancashire, WN7 4HL Tel: (01942) 672951 Fax: (01942) 262042 E-mail: info@boydellfab.com

Bradshaw Sheet Metal Works Ltd, Bradshaw Works, Printers Lane, Bolton, BL2 3DW Tel: (01204) 303300 Fax: (01204) 595797

Braefield Precision Engineers Ltd, High Lane, Stanstead, Stansted, Essex, CM24 8LQ Tel: (01279) 815686 Fax: (01279) 815647 E-mail: braefield@tiscali.co.uk

Bragman Flett Ltd, 34 Holmethorpe Avenue, Redhill, RH1 2NL Tel: (01737) 779200 Fax: (01737) 779600 E-mail: bragman.flett@btopenworld.com

Brailsford Bros Barnsley Ltd, Langdale Road, Barnsley, South Yorkshire, S71 1AF Tel: (01226) 282703 Fax: (01226) 204897 E-mail: brailsfordbros@smartone.co.uk

▶ Brasscraft E K Ltd, 3a Hawbank Road, East Kilbride, Glasgow, G74 5EG Tel: (01355) 221089

Bridgwater Metalcraft Ltd, Brue Avenue, Bridgwater, Somerset, TA6 5LT Tel: (01278) 452867 Fax: (01278) 423167

Brighton Sheet Metal Ltd, The Hyde, Brighton, BN2 4JW Tel: (01273) 602216 Fax: (01273) 674153 E-mail: sales@brightonsheetmetal.co.uk

R. Bristoll Ltd, Timothy Bridge Road, Stratford-upon-Avon, Warwickshire, CV37 9NQ Tel: (01789) 204881 Fax: (01789) 204883

Broomstair Metal Co., 328 Hyde Road, Denton, Manchester, M34 3EH Tel: 0161-336 3240 Fax: 0161-336 8888

▶ Brown Engineering (Fochabers) Ltd, Garmouth Road, Mosstodloch Industrial Estate, Garmouth Road, Fochabers, Morayshire, IV32 7LH Tel: (01343) 820753 Fax: (01343) 821400 E-mail: enquiries@brownengineering.fochabers.co.uk

Francis Brown Ltd, Church Road, Stockton-on-Tees, Cleveland, TS18 2HL Tel: (01642) 806000 Fax: (01642) 806001 E-mail: sales@francisbrown.co.uk

Brunstock Engineering, Brunstock Works, Brunstock, Carlisle, CA6 4QG Tel: (01228) 525334 Fax: (01228) 525334

▶ Bryce Metalwork Ltd, 111 Deerdykes View, Cumbernauld, Glasgow, G68 9HN Tel: (01236) 453503 Fax: (01236) 453503

▶ Buckler Engineering Services Ltd, King Road Avenue, Bristol, BS11 9HG Tel: 0117-982 9135 Fax: 0117-982 6197

Bunce Sheet Metal Work, Unit B5 Crabtree Road, Thorpe Industrial Estate, Egham, Surrey, TW20 8RN Tel: (01784) 433556 Fax: (01784) 433556 E-mail: sales@buncesheetmetal.co.uk

▶ Burnhouse Engineering Ltd, Lochlibo Road, Burnhouse, Beith, Ayrshire, KA15 1LE Tel: (01560) 484433 Fax: (01560) 484632 E-mail: enquiry@burnhouse-eng.co.uk

Burton Sheet Metal Ltd, Wetmore Road, Burton-on-Trent, Staffordshire, DE14 1SN Tel: (01283) 564019 Fax: (01283) 562626

C & D Sheet Metal Engineering Ltd, Station Road North, Belvedere, Kent, DA17 6JL Tel: (020) 8311 2056 Fax: (020) 8310 7727 E-mail: sales@cdsheetmetal.com

C & F Fabrications Ltd, Cross Street, Darwen, Lancashire, BB3 2PN Tel: (01254) 772418 Fax: (01254) 760830

C H Barnett Ltd, 18 Tyseley Industrial Estate, Seeleys Road, Birmingham, B11 2LQ Tel: 0121-773 5222 Fax: 0121-773 7800 E-mail: sales@chbarnett.co.uk

C H S M, Victoria Mill, Manchester Road, Droylsden, Manchester, M43 6EQ Tel: 0161-370 3600 Fax: 0161-370 8454

C H W (Metal Components) Ltd, Unit 1A, Abercromby Industrial Estate, Abercromby Avenue, High Wycombe, Buckinghamshire, HP12 3AX Tel: (01494) 530883 Fax: (01494) 463581

C J & L Fenwick, 2 Station Industrial Estate, Low Prudhoe, Prudhoe, Northumberland, NE42 6NP Tel: (01661) 833474 Fax: (01661) 833474

C N C Punching Ltd, 47 Percy Road, Leicester, LE2 8FQ Tel: 0116-283 2350 Fax: 0116-244 0374

C & S Fabrications Ltd, Club Mill Road, Sheffield, S6 2FH Tel: 0114-234 7567 Fax: 0114-231 4513 E-mail: postmaster@scfabs.co.uk

▶ C Sharp Ltd, 76-80 Old Road, Morley, Leeds, LS27 7TH Tel: 0113-270 9944 Fax: 0113-270 9955 E-mail: enquiries@bsharpconstructions.com

C W R General Fabrications Ltd, 93-94, Leechmere East Industrial Estate, Sunderland, SR2 9TE Tel: 0191-521 2106 Fax: 0191-523 6216 E-mail: cwrfabrications@btconnect.com

▶ Caledus G P E Ltd, Linton Industrial Estate, The Haughs, Inverbervie, Montrose, Angus, DD10 0QB Tel: (01561) 361660 Fax: (01561) 362823

Callaghan Engineering, Pembroke Avenue, Waterbeach, Cambridge, CB25 9QP Tel: (01223) 863330 Fax: (01223) 863223

Calne Engineering Ltd, Stanier Road, Porte Marsh Industrial Estate, Calne, Wiltshire, SN11 9PX Tel: (01249) 813288 Fax: (01249) 821266E-mail: sales@calne-engineering.co.uk

Cambridge Rapid Components Ltd, Unit 4-5 Shire Hill, Saffron Walden, Essex, CB11 3AQ Tel: (01799) 522151 Fax: (01799) 521686 E-mail: sales@cambridgerapid.co.uk

Camco Metalcraft Ltd, Eastern Avenue Industrial Estate, Eastern Avenue, Dunstable, Bedfordshire, LU5 4JY Tel: (01582) 476204 Fax: (01582) 475602 E-mail: sales@camcometalcraft.co.uk

Cansco Greig Engineering Ltd, Souter Head Road, Altens Industrial Estate, Aberdeen, AB12 3LF Tel: (01224) 898810 Fax: (01224) 878542 E-mail: mail@cansco.co.uk

▶ Canwell Engineering, Redhouse Industrial Estate, Anglian Road, Walsall, WS9 8EP Tel: (01922) 745100

Carford Group Ltd, Units 1-4, Mitchell Road, Ferndown Industrial Estate, Wimborne, Dorset, BH21 7SG Tel: (01202) 851900 Fax: (01202) 851921 E-mail: sales@carford.co.uk

Carlton Sheet Metal Works Ltd, 16-18 Ashley Street, Nottingham, NG3 1JG Tel: 0115-950 5304 Fax: 0115-950 4976 E-mail: info@bagfast.com

Casargon Ltd, Genei House, Bentinck Street, Bolton, BL1 4QG Tel: (01204) 840500 Fax: (01204) 840600 E-mail: sales@casargon.sagenet.co.uk

▶ Castle Engineering Ltd, Unit 1, Palmbourne Industrial Park, Castle Street, Stafford, ST16 2TB Tel: (01785) 228808 Fax: (01785) 257883

Catterall & Wood Ltd, Unit 2 Primrose Bank Mill, Friday Street, Chorley, Lancashire, PR6 0AA Tel: (01257) 272192 Fax: (01257) 261432

Central Fabrications, 72 Burnmoor Street, Leicester, LE2 7JJ Tel: 0116-247 1515 Fax: 0116-247 1117

Central Metal Manufacturing Ltd, Leeside, Merrylees Industrial Estate, Desford, Leicester, LE9 9FS Tel: (01530) 230833 Fax: (01530) 230302

Central Steel Fabrications North West, Unit 5 Brickfields, Wilson Road Huyton, Liverpool, L36 6HY Tel: 0151-480 7504 Fax: 0151-480 7504 E-mail: enquiries@centralsteel.co.uk

Cerberus Engineering Services Ltd, Coker Road, Weston-super-Mare, Avon, BS22 6BX Tel: (01934) 517747 Fax: (01934) 512633 E-mail: info@ceberus-eng.co.uk

Chadderton Metal Products Ltd, Unit F2 Westwood Industrial Estate, Arkwright Street, Oldham, OL9 9LZ Tel: 0161-620 7907 Fax: 0161-627 4486 E-mail: sales@cmplimited.wanadoo.co.uk

Chadfort Engineering Ltd, Unit 6c, Blakewater Road, Blackburn, BB1 5QH Tel: (01254) 582075 Fax: (01254) 661062 E-mail: andrew.chadwick@chadfort.co.uk

SHEET METALWORK ENGINEERS OR FABRICATORS – *continued*

Chaggar Engineering, Murdock Road, Manton Industrial Estate, Bedford, MK41 7PE Tel: (01234) 360557 Fax: (0871) 2422493 E-mail: premchaggar@hotmail.com

▶ Chaner Engineering Ltd, Norwest Quarry Yard, Quarry Lane, Sandside, Milnthorpe, Cumbria, LA7 7HG Tel: (01539) 564376 Fax: (01539) 564753 E-mail: jacky@chaner-ltd.co.uk

Clifford Chapman Metalworks Ltd, Armstrong Estate, District 2, Washington, Tyne & Wear, NE37 1PB Tel: 0191-417 3135 Fax: 0191-417 8519 E-mail: email@cliffordchapman.com

Charlestown Engineering Services Ltd, Rayner House, Bayley Street, Stalybridge, Cheshire, SK15 1PZ Tel: 0161-338 7300 Fax: 0161-338 4884 E-mail: sales@charlestown1.com

Chum Engineering Ltd, Churchill Way, Trafford Park, Manchester, M17 1BS Tel: 0161-872 3253 Fax: 0161-872 0484 E-mail: info@chumengineering.co.uk

▶ Cic Omec Ltd, Moor Lane Trading Estate, Sherburn In Elmet, Leeds, LS25 6ES Tel: (01977) 682966

Cinmech Services Ltd, 63 Colvilles Place, Kelvin Industrial Estate, Glasgow, G75 0XE Tel: (01355) 244544 Fax: (01355) 248717 E-mail: cinmech@cinmech.com

▶ Clarke Chapman Syncrolift Division, H M N B Clyde, Faslane, Helensburgh, Dunbartonshire, G84 8HL Tel: (01436) 810001

Clarke Lane Engineering Ltd, 6 Belgrave Industrial Estate, Belgrave Road, Southampton, SO17 3EA Tel: (023) 8067 1564 Fax: (023) 8067 6774 E-mail: clarke-lane@supernet.com

▶ Clive View Engineering Ltd, Block 5, New Albion Industrial Estate, Halley St Yoker, Glasgow, G13 4DT Tel: 0141-952 3186

Clwyd Precision Engineering, Bridge Road, Wrexham Industrial Estate, Wrexham, Clwyd, LL13 9PS Tel: (01978) 660259 Fax: (01978) 661069 E-mail: cpe@bytecraft.net

Coast & County Engineering, Enterprise Road, Mablethorpe, Lincolnshire, LN12 1NB Tel: (01507) 473170 Fax: (01507) 473170

Coates & Shaw, Unit 23 Moss La Industrial Estate, Moss Lane, Royton, Oldham, OL2 6HR Tel: (01706) 840238 Fax: (01706) 881633

Coday Sheet Metal Fabrications Great Yarmouth Ltd, Salmon Road, Great Yarmouth, Norfolk, NR30 3QS Tel: (01493) 857566 Fax: (01493) 331446 E-mail: stevegraham@codaygy.co.uk

Coleman Manufacturing Ltd, Graycar Business Park, Barton Turn, Barton under Needwood, Burton-on-Trent, Staffordshire, DE13 8EN Tel: (01283) 716688 Fax: (01283) 712370 E-mail: simon.denning@colemans.uk.net

Comet-Pramesco Services, 30 Holywell Avenue, Folkestone, Kent, CT19 6JZ Tel: (01303) 255585 Fax: (01303) 243122 E-mail: steve_baxter@lineone.net

Complete Air Systems, Unit H & I Maybrook Industrial Estate, Maybrook Road, Walsall, WS8 7DG Tel: (01543) 361301 Fax: (01543) 372530

▶ Component Erectors, 77 Main Road, East Wemyss, Kirkcaldy, Fife, KY1 4RQ Tel: (01592) 716600 Fax: (01592) 716237 E-mail: davecel@tiscali.co.uk

Comtec Precision Sheet Metal, 60 Loverock Road, Reading, RG30 1DY Tel: 0118-958 8050 Fax: 0118-958 8040 E-mail: sales@comtecsheet.softnet.co.uk

Connect Engineering Ltd, Thomas Brown House, Edwin Road, Manchester, M11 3ER Tel: 0161-273 6333 Fax: 0161-273 8351 E-mail: connectengineering@yahoo.co.uk

Constant Aluminium Supplies Ltd, Unit B2 Junction 22 Business, Park Tweedale Way, Oldham, OL9 7LD Tel: 0161-681 9917 Fax: 0161-683 4182 E-mail: sales@constant-engineering.co.uk

Contracts Engineering Ltd, Chapel Park, Stadium Way, Sittingbourne, Kent, ME10 3RW Tel: (01795) 479284 Fax: (01795) 477812 E-mail: contracts@totalserve.co.uk

Coolmetal Steel Fabricators, 68-72 Bromley Street, Stourbridge, West Midlands, DY9 8JA Tel: (01384) 424424 Fax: (01384) 892810 E-mail: info@coolmetal.co.uk

▶ Cotswold Decorative Ironworkers, Marsh Farm, Stourton, Shipston-on-Stour, Warwickshire, CV36 5HS Tel: (01608) 685134 Fax: (01608) 685135 E-mail: sales@cd-ironworkers.co.uk

Cotswold Engineering, The Downs, Wickwar, Wotton-under-Edge, Gloucestershire, GL12 8JD Tel: (01454) 294609 Fax: (01454) 299427

Counterhouse Systems Ltd, PO Box 381, Worcester, WR6 5YB Tel: (01886) 833044 Fax: (01886) 833152 E-mail: robert@counterhouse.co.uk

Country Custom Engineering, Units 11-13 Enterprise Units, 21-27 Hollands Road, Haverhill, Suffolk, CB9 8PU Tel: (01440) 763881 Fax: (01440) 763880 E-mail: countrycustom@hotmail.co.uk

County Fabrications Leicester Ltd, B1 Valley Way, Market Harborough, Leicestershire, LE16 7PS Tel: (01858) 433958 Fax: (01858) 410463 E-mail: contact@countyfabs.co.uk

▶ CR Building Services Ltd, 24 Percival Lane, Runcorn, Cheshire, WA7 4UX Tel: (01928) 565069 Fax: (01928) 560297

▶ Crabb Engineering Ltd, 12 Aber Park, Aber Road, Flint, Clwyd, CH6 5EX Tel: (01352) 762121 Fax: (01352) 763040 E-mail: sales@crabbengineering.co.uk

▶ Craddock Engineering Ltd, 7 Hall Lane, Walsall Wood, Walsall, WS9 9AS Tel: (01543) 454572 Fax: (01543) 454585

▶ Craigie Engineering Ltd, Grainshore Road, Hatston, Kirkwall, Orkney, KW15 1FL Tel: (01856) 874680 Fax: (01856) 875255

Crayford Sheet Metal Fabrications, Unit 37 Crayford Industrial Estate, Swaisland Drive, Crayford, Dartford, DA1 4HS Tel: (01322) 551555 Fax: (01322) 553124

Crescent Sheet Metal Co., 6 Wood End No 2 Mill, Manchester Road, Mossley, Ashton-under-Lyne, Lancashire, OL5 9RR Tel: (01457) 836518 Fax: (01457) 833611

▶ Cromwall Fabrications (Sayrank) Ltd, Unit 10A, Palatine Industrial Estate, Causeway Avenue, Warrington, WA4 6QQ Tel: (01925) 637665 Fax: (01925) 417979

Crossman Engineering Ltd, Downsview Road, Wantage, Oxfordshire, OX12 9FA Tel: (01235) 772885 Fax: (01235) 772886 E-mail: sales@crossmaneng.co.uk

Crouch Bros Engineering Ltd, The Britannia Centre, Langston Road, Loughton, Essex, IG10 3SQ Tel: (020) 8508 3622 Fax: (020) 8508 4481

Cruz Yardy Engineering, Roundwell Works, Dereham Road, New Costessey, Norwich, NR5 0SQ Tel: (01603) 746774 Fax: (01603) 746774

Curbridge Motor Co. Ltd, Unit 8a Bury Farm, Botley, Southampton, SO30 2HB Tel: (01489) 780782 Fax: (01489) 783982 E-mail: ian@curbridge-engineering.fsnet.co.uk

Custom Metalcraft Ltd, 36 Bennet Road, Reading, RG2 0QX Tel: 0118-986 8077 Fax: 0118-986 8078

▶ Cylinder Resurfacing Co UK Ltd, Harwood Street, Blackburn, BB1 3DW Tel: (01254) 697300 Fax: (01254) 697199

▶ D B H (Dorset) Ltd, Unit 14, 4-6 Abingdon Road, Nuffield Industrial Estate, Poole, Dorset, BH17 0UG Tel: (01202) 684899 Fax: (01202) 677429

D B Sheetmetals, 1 Coopers Park, Cooper Drive, Braintree, Essex, CM7 2TN Tel: (01376) 552951 Fax: (01376) 552951

D C M Group Ltd, Bayton Road Industrial Estate, 41 Bayton Road, Exhall, Coventry, CV7 9EL Tel: (024) 7636 1601 Fax: (024) 7636 7914 E-mail: sales@dcm.co.uk

D D Fabrications, Blackdyke Road, Kingstown Industrial Estate, Kingstown, Carlisle, CA3 0PJ Tel: (01228) 536595 Fax: (01228) 536595 E-mail: enquiries@ddfabrications.co.uk

D & D Fine Limits, 2 St Clare Business Park, Holly Road, Hampton, Middlesex, TW12 1PZ Tel: (020) 8979 3545 Fax: (020) 8979 3545 E-mail: info@sheetmetalproduction.com

D G C Engineering Ltd, Sabhal Mor, Loan Dykes, Hillside, Montrose, Angus, DD10 9JN Tel: (01674) 830922

▶ D Harker Fabrications, D.H.F. Ltd, Greeves Road, Dewsbury, West Yorkshire, WF13 1EP Tel: (01924) 457614 Fax: (01924) 462291 E-mail: sales@dhfltd.co.uk

▶ D J R Engineering, 1 Station Road, Oldmeldrum, Inverurie, Aberdeenshire, AB51 0EZ Tel: (01651) 873377 Fax: (01651) 873388 E-mail: sales@djrengineering.com

D K M Sheet Metal Co. Ltd, Unit 9 Oldends Industrial Estate, Oldends, Stonehouse, Gloucestershire, GL10 3RQ Tel: (01453) 827661 Fax: (01453) 824094 E-mail: gill@dkmsheetmetal.co.uk

D & L Sheet Metal, 9 Whitehouse Enterprise Centre, Whitehouse Road, Newcastle upon Tyne, NE15 6EP Tel: 0191-275 0286 Fax: 0191-275 0286

D M D Electronic Engineers Ltd, 2 Nags Head Road, Enfield, Middlesex, EN3 7AJ Tel: (020) 8805 5056 Fax: (020) 8443 4160

▶ D M H Blacksmiths, 5 Carsegate Road, Inverness, IV3 8EX Tel: (01463) 233736 Fax: (01463) 236650

D P L, Elliott Works, Elliott Road, Bromley, BR2 9NT Tel: (020) 8460 2147 Fax: (020) 8313 3072 E-mail: sales@dplaw.co.uk

▶ D R Diesel, 1 Harbour Road, Fraserburgh, Aberdeenshire, AB43 9TB Tel: (01346) 517444 Fax: (01346) 517222

▶ D Swinley Engineering Ltd, 1 Midfield Road, Mitchelston Industrial Estate, Kirkcaldy, Fife, KY1 3NL Tel: (01592) 650300 Fax: (01592) 651469 E-mail: mail@dse.me.uk

D V R Fabrications, Unit 10 Winster Grove Industrial Estate, Winster Grove, Birmingham, B44 9EG Tel: 0121-325 0087 Fax: 0121-325 0087

D W Engineering, Unit A1 Industrial Estate, Watling Street, Consett, County Durham, DH8 6TA Tel: (01207) 505608 Fax: (01207) 505608

▶ D W Fabrications Ltd, Charles Street, Bury, Lancashire, BL9 5AJ Tel: 0161-761 6731 Fax: 0161-761 6731 E-mail: dwfabs@aol.com

▶ Dalesman Fabrications Ltd, 3 Astley Way, Astley La Industrial Estate, Swillington, Leeds, LS26 8XT Tel: 0113-287 5732 Fax: 0113-287 2319

Dappat Engineering Ltd, Hodgson Street, Hull, HU8 7JB Tel: (01482) 328872 Fax: (01482) 223265

Dar-Val Engineering Ltd, Ground Floor Unit B, 443-449 Holloway Road, London, N7 6LJ Tel: (020) 7263 7017 Fax: (020) 7263 7003

▶ Das Engineering Services Ltd, 5 Aire & Calder Industrial Park, Lock Lane, Castleford, West Yorkshire, WF10 2JA Tel: (01977) 559955 Fax: (01977) 520777

Datum Fabrications, 66 Redhill Road, Yardley, Birmingham, B25 8EX Tel: 0121-753 0119 Fax: 0121-753 0272

▶ David Paterson, 18 Linkwood Way, Linkwood Industrial Estate, Elgin, Morayshire, IV30 1HY Tel: (01343) 545190 Fax: (01343) 540444

Davis Cash & Co. Ltd, Alexandra Road, Enfield, Middlesex, EN3 7EN Tel: (020) 8804 4028 Fax: (020) 8805 2896 E-mail: sales@daviscash.co.uk

Daws Engineering Ltd, Curtis Road, Dorking, Surrey, RH4 1XD Tel: (01306) 881546 Fax: (01306) 740407 E-mail: rob.collinson@dawseng.co.uk

Dealpage Ltd, Station Road, Uppingham, Rutland, Leicestershire, LE15 9TX Tel: (01572) 823198 Fax: (01572) 823199

Deeside Engineering Services, Park Road, Rhosymedre, Wrexham, Clwyd, LL14 3YR Tel: (01978) 824335 Fax: (01978) 810696 E-mail: johnevans@deesideengineeringfsnet.co.uk

▶ Denholm Industrial Services, King George V Dock, Renfrew Road, Glasgow, G51 4SP Tel: 0141-445 3939 Fax: 0141-445 3020

Derbrich Fabrications, Estate Road 7, South Humberside Industrial Estate, Grimsby, South Humberside, DN31 2TP Tel: (01472) 885888 Fax: (01472) 884965 E-mail: fabrications@derbrich.freeserve.co.uk

▶ Derek Anthony Ltd, Units 4-5 White Swan Industrial Estate, Derker Street, Oldham, OL1 3LY Tel: 0161-627 4200 Fax: 0161-627 3616 E-mail: derekanthony@talk21.com

Dero Fabrication Ltd, Unit 67, Blackpole Trading Estate West, Blackpole Road, Worcester, WR3 8TJ Tel: (01905) 455199 Fax: (01905) 754152 E-mail: sales@dero.co.uk

Detail Sheet Metal Ltd, Unit 26 Fawkes Avenue, Questor, Dartford, DA1 1JQ Tel: (01322) 222122 Fax: (01322) 291794 E-mail: sales@kentech.co.uk

Edward Dewhurst Ltd, Grierson House, Chain Call Way, Preston Riversway Docklands, Preston, PR2 2DG Tel: (01772) 761777 Fax: (01772) 761666 E-mail: pad@edewhurst.com

Diametric Metal Fabrications Ltd, The Brookland, Blithbury Road, Rugeley, Staffordshire, WS15 3HQ Tel: (01889) 577243 Fax: (01889) 584672 E-mail: sales@diametricmetalfabrications.co.uk

▶ Diamould Ltd, 10 Peter Green Way, Furness Business Park, Barrow-in-Furness, Cumbria, LA14 2PE Tel: (01229) 825888 Fax: (01229) 825950 E-mail: sales@diamould.com

Dimension Engineering, Unit 21 The Business Village, Wexham Road, Slough, SL2 5HF Tel: (01753) 538166 Fax: (01753) 518966

Domic Welding Services, Unit 8, Victor Business Centre, Arthur St, Redditch, Worcestershire, B98 8JY Tel: (01527) 510041 Fax: (01527) 510403 E-mail: paul@pjwelding.fsnet.co.uk

Domic Welding & Sheetmetal Ltd, Unit 8 Victor Business Centre, Arthur Street, Redditch, Worcestershire, B98 8JY Tel: (01527) 515445 Fax: (01527) 510403 E-mail: touv@domic-pjwelding.fsnet.co.uk

Ductaire Fabrications Ltd, G Marmi Works, 23 Grafton Road, Croydon, CR0 3RP Tel: (020) 8688 5188 Fax: (020) 8681 2606 E-mail: sales@ductaire.co.uk

Durham Sheet Metal Works Ltd, Progress House, Templetown, South Shields, Tyne & Wear, NE33 5TE Tel: 0191-455 3558 Fax: 0191-456 8837 E-mail: paul@durhamsheetmetal.co.uk

Durose Ltd, 33-35 Adams Street, Birmingham, B7 4LT Tel: 0121-333 3096 Fax: 0121-359 6408 E-mail: sales@durose.co.uk

E B Hayward & Co., Sheet Metal Works, Nupend, Ashleworth, Gloucester, GL19 4JJ Tel: (01452) 700384 Fax: (01452) 700740 E-mail: simon@ebhayward.demon.co.uk

▶ E C Creative Services Ltd, 1 Lansdowne Road, Chadderton, Oldham, OL9 9EF Tel: 0161-628 7723 Fax: 0161-284 6654

▶ E C F Special Alloys Ltd, Lawn Road, Carlton-in-Lindrick, Worksop, Nottinghamshire, S81 9LB Tel: (01909) 540520 Fax: (01909) 540522

E Farrington & Co. Ltd, Regent Engineering Works, Robert Street, Hyde, Cheshire, SK14 1BN Tel: 0161-368 1675 Fax: 0161-367 8868E-mail: info@farringtons.fsbusiness.co.uk

▶ E I S Ltd, Mckean Street, Paisley, Renfrewshire, PA3 1QP Tel: 0141-887 7888 Fax: 0141-887 2887 E-mail: sales@electricaltrade.co.uk

E & M Engineering Services, Riverside, Thurso, Caithness, KW14 8BU Tel: (01847) 893702 Fax: (01847) 896511

E Poppleton & Son Ltd, Conway Road, Mochdre, Colwyn Bay, Clwyd, LL28 5HL Tel: (01492) 546061 Fax: (01492) 544076 E-mail: sales@poppleton.co.uk

E Reg Sheet Metal Fabricators, Unit 7 Kirby Road, Lomeshaye Industrial Estate, Nelson, Lancashire, BB9 6RS Tel: (01282) 697748 Fax: (01282) 697749

▶ Earnshaw Engineering Ltd, Unit 2 Barton Park Industrial Estate, Eastleigh, Hampshire, SO50 6RR Tel: (023) 8061 3137 Fax: (023) 8062 9151

▶ Earthy Industrial Systems Ltd, Unit D, Wylds Road, Bridgwater, Somerset, TA6 4BH Tel: (01278) 455877

▶ East Lancashire Fabrications Ltd, Unit 5-6 Springhill, Edleston Street, Accrington, Lancashire, BB5 0HG Tel: (01254) 871734 Fax: (01254) 872379

East Midlands Instrument Co. Ltd, Laughton Lane, Morton, Gainsborough, Lincolnshire, DN21 3ET Tel: (01427) 616721 Fax: (01427) 810804 E-mail: emi@eminst.co.uk

Eastern Hardware Co. Ltd, Hamilton Road, Lowestoft, Suffolk, NR32 1XF Tel: (01502) 573257 Fax: (01502) 586235 E-mail: eastern_hardware@btconnect.com

▶ Easton Sheet Metal Ltd, 31-38 South Road, Harlow, Essex, CM20 2AR Tel: (01279) 427842 Fax: (01279) 450761 E-mail: info@eastonsheetmetal.co.uk

Edgar Engineering Co., Woods Way Industrial Estate, Goring-By-Sea, Worthing, West Sussex, BN12 4QY Tel: (01903) 505056 Fax: (01903) 506456 E-mail: edgareng@btconnect.com

J. & M. Edwards Precision Engineers Ltd, Lefevre Way, Gapton Hall Industrial Estate, Great Yarmouth, Norfolk, NR31 0NW Tel: (01493) 604312 Fax: (01493) 655719 E-mail: sales@jmedwards.co.uk

▶ Elcadant Ltd, Lea Mills, Lea Road, Batley, West Yorkshire, WF17 8BB Tel: (01924) 479973 Fax: (01924) 443368

Elder Repetition Sheet Metal Ltd, 30 Oxford Road, Denham, Uxbridge, Middlesex, UB9 4DQ Tel: (01895) 258968 Fax: (01895) 252651 E-mail: sales@eldersheetmetal.co.uk

Elecon Sheet Metal, Ravensfield Industrial Estate, Charles Street, Dukinfield, Cheshire, SK16 4SD Tel: 0161-339 6210 Fax: 0161-343 1006

Electrobase RP Ltd, 7 Maxim Road, Dartford, DA1 4BG Tel: (01322) 555938 Fax: (01322) 555099 E-mail: sales@electrobaserp.co.uk

Electronic Metal Work Services Ltd, Hampstead Avenue, Mildenhall, Bury St. Edmunds, Suffolk, IP28 7AS Tel: (01638) 712054 Fax: (01638) 713832E-mail: info@emws.co.uk

Elite Metalcraft, 9 Walmgate Road, Perivale, Greenford, Middlesex, UB6 7LH Tel: (020) 8810 5555 Fax: (020) 8810 5133 E-mail: sales@elitemetalcraft.co.uk

Elston Manufacturing Wolverhampton Co., 30 Mander Street, Wolverhampton, WV3 0JZ Tel: (01902) 422159 Fax: (01902) 429465

▶ Emcor Drake & Scull Ltd, 51 Great North Road, Hatfield, Hertfordshire, AL9 5EN Tel: (01707) 630300 Fax: (01707) 630333

Enterprise Engineering Services Ltd, Craigshaw Drive, West Tullos Industrial Estate, Aberdeen, AB12 3TH Tel: (01224) 288400 Fax: (01224) 871327 E-mail: sales@eesl.com

Enterprise Fabrication Co., Virginia Street, Southport, Merseyside, PR8 6RZ Tel: (01704) 541544 Fax: (01704) 544260 E-mail: enterprise@e-fabs.co.uk

Environair Systems Ltd, The Old Foundery, Norwich Road, Great Yarmouth, Norfolk, NR29 5QD Tel: (01692) 678123 Fax: (01692) 678124 E-mail: kelly@environair.co.uk

▶ Environmental Engineering (UK) Ltd, Riverside Bridge Street, Dukinfield, Cheshire, SK16 4RX Tel: 0161-339 7100 Fax: 0161-339 7211 E-mail: email@envenguk.co.uk

Euro Sheet Metal Ltd, 6 Aintree Road, Perivale, Greenford, Middlesex, UB6 7LA Tel: (020) 8810 5026 Fax: (020) 8991 5008 E-mail: info@eurosheetmetal.co.uk

▶ F A S E, 16 Bridge St, Bailie Gate Industrial Estate, Sturminster Marshall, Wimborne, Dorset, BH21 4DB Tel: (01258) 858101

F Brinklow & Co. Ltd, 121 Clare Street, Northampton, NN1 3JA Tel: (01604) 636845 Fax: (01604) 636862

F C Hammonds, 13-17 Dove Lane, Newfoundland Road, Bristol, BS2 9HS Tel: 0117-955 1377 Fax: 0117-987 2377 E-mail: f.c.hammonds@btclick.com

F C Walker, The Archway, Bracondale, Norwich, NR1 2EE Tel: (01603) 626903 Fax: (01603) 762194

F.C. Whittle(Birmingham) Ltd, Unit 7, Union Road, Oldbury, West Midlands, B69 3EX Tel: 0121-544 7572 Fax: 0121-544 8132

F E M, Bradware Industrial Park, Leonard Street, Bingley, West Yorkshire, BD16 1DP Tel: (01274) 511911 Fax: (01274) 511913

▶ F F A Concepts, Rutherford Drive, Park Farm Industrial Estate, Wellingborough, Northamptonshire, NN8 6AQ Tel: (01933) 671980

▶ Fab Serv, Unit 2, Underbank Way, Cars Industrial Estate, Haslingden, Rossendale, Lancashire, BB4 5HH Tel: (01706) 230817 Fax: (01706) 230033 E-mail: enquiries@fabserv.co.uk

Fab Vent Engineering, North Road, Stoke-on-Trent, ST6 2BZ Tel: (01782) 219995 Fax: (01782) 219995

Fabcon Projects Ltd, Delta Close, Norwich, NR6 6BG Tel: (01603) 482338 Fax: (01603) 484064 E-mail: andrew@fabcon.co.uk

Fabfold Ltd, Amington Industrial Estate, 30 Sandy Way, Tamworth, Staffordshire, B77 4DS Tel: (01827) 313396 Fax: (01827) 313289 E-mail: fabfold@fabfold.fsnet.co.uk

Fabrenco Ltd, Wilton Road, Humberston, Grimsby, South Humberside, DN36 4AW Tel: (01472) 814845 Fax: (01472) 210412 E-mail: fabrenco@quista.net

Fabricate UK Ltd, Kelwood Mill, Farnham Road, Bradford, West Yorkshire, BD7 3JF Tel: (01274) 575126 Fax: (01274) 575127 E-mail: info@fabricateuk.com

Fabrication & Welding Services, Aldred Close, Norwood Industrial Estate, Killamarsh, Sheffield, S21 2JH Tel: 0114-247 7785 Fax: 0114-247 7785

▶ Falburn Engineering, Unit 1 Plean Industrial Estate, Plean, Stirling, FK7 8BJ Tel: (01786) 818549 Fax: (01786) 812350 E-mail: falburneng@aol.com

SHEET METALWORK ENGINEERS OR FABRICATORS – *continued*

Falcon Precision Ltd, Victory Close, Chandler's Ford Industrial Estate, Eastleigh, Hampshire, SO53 4BU Tel: (023) 8027 1666 Fax: (023) 8027 1771
E-mail: sales@falconprecision.co.uk

Fam Sheet Metal Work Co., Unit 14 Droicon Industrial Estate, Portway Road, Rowley Regis, West Midlands, B65 9BY Tel: 0121-559 6374

Fayton Developments (Precision Sheet Metal), Unit D 3, Dominion Way, Rustington, Littlehampton, West Sussex, BN16 3HQ Tel: (01903) 770192 Fax: (01903) 850498
E-mail: admin@fayton.co.uk

Federated Industries Ltd, 30-36 Virginia Street, Aberdeen, AB11 5AU Tel: (01224) 591323 Fax: (01224) 572858
E-mail: federated@btconnect.com

Feldman Fabrication Co. Ltd, Unit 83, Owen Road Industrial Estate, Owen Road, Willenhall, West Midlands, WV13 2PX Tel: 0121-526 4434 Fax: 0121-526 4201
E-mail: feldmanfabs@btconnect.com

Fielde Engineering Ltd, Unit 6-7 The Warren, East Goscote, Leicester, LE7 3XA Tel: 0116-260 8217 Fax: 0116-260 7921
E-mail: field@btconnect.com

▶ Findlay Campbell Blacksmiths Ltd, Waverley Street, Coatbridge, Lanarkshire, ML5 2BE Tel: (01236) 626662 Fax: (01236) 626664

▶ Finish Architectural, Unit 9 12, Westwood Business Park, Dulverton Road, Birmingham, B6 7EQ Tel: 0121-327 0523

First Choice Business Systems Ltd, Unit 4-6 Murray Business Centre, Murray Road, Orpington, Kent, BR5 3RE Tel: (01689) 828182 Fax: (01689) 899399
E-mail: sales@firstchoiceltd.co.uk

Firth Sheet Metal Ltd, Barrys Lane, Scarborough, North Yorkshire, YO12 4HA Tel: (01723) 376771 Fax: (01723) 351325
E-mail: info@firmac.co.uk

▶ Fitzsimmons G & Son, 25 Thornton Road, Rosewell, Midlothian, EH24 9DP Tel: 0131-448 2186 Fax: 0131-448 2186

▶ FMC Measurement Solutions, Unit 6 Baird Way, Thetford, Norfolk, IP24 1JA Tel: (01842) 822900 Fax: (01842) 765402
E-mail: sales@fmcmeasurementsolutions.com

Ford, 25 Poyser Street, London, E2 9RE Tel: (020) 7739 7779 Fax: (020) 7739 3307
E-mail: sales@wgford.co.uk

▶ Foredowel Welders, 4 Seaway Drive, Seaway Parade Industrial Estate, Port Talbot, West Glamorgan, SA12 7BR Tel: (01639) 814578 Fax: (01639) 823184

Form Weld Ltd, Unit 3C, Cutters Close, Narborough, Leicester, LE19 2FZ Tel: 0116-286 6654 Fax: 0116-275 0877
E-mail: formweld@btconnect.com

Forman Metal Products Ltd, Portrack Grange Road, Stockton-on-Tees, Cleveland, TS18 2PH Tel: (01642) 674314 Fax: (01642) 672899
E-mail: info@formanmetalproducts.co.uk

Formet Ltd, Harley Works, Paxton Hill, St. Neots, Cambridgeshire, PE19 6TA Tel: (01480) 475041 Fax: (01480) 472820
E-mail: sales@4met.co.uk

Formet Sheet Metal Ltd, Unit F Hoo Farm Industrial Estate, Worcester Road, Kidderminster, Worcestershire, DY11 7RA Tel: (01562) 744440 Fax: (01562) 829976

Formtech Sheet Metal Work, Royds Close, Leeds, LS12 6LL Tel: 0113-231 1030 Fax: 0113-279 4125
E-mail: sales@formtech.co.uk

Forrest Fabrications, York Street, Accrington, Lancashire, BB5 4BT Tel: (01254) 381386 Fax: (01254) 399571

Four-Tec Fabrications Ltd, Unit 2 Whieldon Industrial Estate, Whieldon Road, Stoke-on-Trent, ST4 4JP Tel: (01782) 844434 Fax: (01782) 744351
E-mail: fourtecfabs@aol.com

▶ Fraser & Evans, Newhouse Industrial Estate, Newhouse, Motherwell, Lanarkshire, ML1 5RX Tel: (01698) 833173 Fax: (01698) 833855
E-mail: sales@fraserandevans.com

▶ Philip Freeman Mobile Welders Ltd, Bertram House, 7 Bertram Street, Hamilton, Lanarkshire, ML3 0QS Tel: (01698) 712920 Fax: (01698) 712990
E-mail: sales@philipfreeman.co.uk

Frixos Metal Works Ltd, Unit 4, 30 Aden Road, Brimsdown, Enfield, Middlesex, EN3 7SY Tel: (020) 8443 1050 Fax: (020) 8440 1233
E-mail: jimmy@frixosmetalworks.co.uk

▶ Fulcrum Manufacturing, 19 Challenge Enterprise Centre, Sharps Close, Portsmouth, PO3 5RJ Tel: (023) 9269 9331

G B Logan Fabrications Ltd, Deacon Road, Lincoln, LN2 4JB Tel: (01522) 523622 Fax: (01522) 527408
E-mail: logan@enterprise.net

G & C Engineering plc, Cobham Road, Pershore, Worcestershire, WR10 2DL Tel: (01386) 553934 Fax: (01386) 555725
E-mail: sales@gandc.co.uk

▶ G D C Precision Engineering Ltd, Unit 2b Princess Road, New Stevenston, Motherwell, Lanarkshire, ML1 4HP Tel: (01698) 834001 Fax: (01698) 834001

▶ G & G Engineering Mechanical Services Ltd, Unit 5 Rockingham Business, Park Rockingham Row Birdwell, Birdwell, Barnsley, South Yorkshire, S70 5TW Tel: (01226) 747684 Fax: (01226) 740901
E-mail: ggeng@btconnect.com

▶ G G S Engineering Derby Ltd, Atlas Works, Litchurch Lane, Derby, DE24 8AQ Tel: (01332) 299345 Fax: (01332) 299678

G S Precision, North Weylands Industrial Estate, Molesey Road, Walton-on-Thames, Surrey, KT12 3PL Tel: (01932) 246477 Fax: (01932) 231345
E-mail: chris.brewall@gsprecision.co.uk

G S Robinson & Co. Ltd, Unit B T 4 30 Exmouth Road, West Chirton Industrial Estate South, North Shields, Tyne & Wear, NE29 7TY Tel: 0191-257 5374 Fax: 0191-296 1341

G & S Sheet Metals Ltd, 4a Lea Road, Waltham Abbey, Essex, EN9 1AE Tel: (01992) 713800 Fax: (01992) 713800

▶ G T M Engineering Co., Station Road, Newent, Gloucestershire, GL18 1BB Tel: (01531) 820118 Fax: (01531) 820698
E-mail: gtmengineering@logimail.co.uk

G T Pressing Co. Ltd, 46 Freehold Terrace, Brighton, BN2 4AB Tel: (01273) 601222 Fax: (01273) 682367
E-mail: enquiries@gtpressing.co.uk

▶ G & V A Engineering, Seddon Place, Skelmersdale, Lancashire, WN8 8EB Tel: (01695) 729994 Fax: (01695) 729940

▶ G W Lomas & Sons, Back Spinnerbottom, Birch Vale, High Peak, Derbyshire, SK22 1BN Tel: (01663) 742536 Fax: (01663) 742890
E-mail: info@gwlomasandsons.co.uk

G W Smith Fabrications, Unit G1 Elvington Industrial Estate, York Road, Elvington, York, YO41 4AR Tel: (01904) 608722 Fax: (01904) 607171

V. Garcia & Son, Malakoff Works, Malakoff Street, Stalybridge, Cheshire, SK15 1TD Tel: 0161-303 7383 Fax: 0161-338 2151
E-mail: bill-garcia@btconnect.com

Garrick Engineering Co. Ltd, Crowland Street Industrial Estate, Crowland Street, Southport, Merseyside, PR9 7RQ Tel: (01704) 534906 Fax: (01704) 537952
E-mail: info@garrickeng.co.uk

▶ Gartsherrie Engineering Ltd, Gartsherrie Road, Coatbridge, Lanarkshire, ML5 2EU Tel: (01236) 436464 Fax: (01236) 432044
E-mail: info@patersonsquarries.co.uk

▶ Gas Turbine Engineering Services, Nasmyth Building, Nasmyth Avenue, East Kilbride, Glasgow, G75 0QR Tel: (01355) 272660 Fax: (01355) 272665

▶ Gase Marine & General Engineering Services Ltd, 7 Tower Park Road, Crayford, Dartford, DA1 4LB Tel: (01322) 552980 Fax: (01322) 552986 E-mail: info@gaseaero.com

Gatehouse Scientific Instruments, 94c Hampstead Avenue, Mildenhall, Bury St. Edmunds, Suffolk, IP28 7AS Tel: (01638) 510555 Fax: (01638) 510555
E-mail: sales@gatehouseindustrial.com

▶ Gazzard Engineering Co. Ltd, Swinbourne Road, Burnt Mills Industrial Estate, Basildon, Essex, SS13 1EH Tel: (01268) 724585 Fax: (01268) 724536
E-mail: enquiries@gazshocks.com

Gemflex Engineering Ltd, Unit 4, Cossall Industrial Estate, Coronation Road, Ilkeston, Derbyshire, DE7 5UA Tel: 0115-944 2414 Fax: 0115-944 2771
E-mail: sales@gemflex.co.uk

▶ Gemweld (UK) Ltd, 2 Glenburn Road, Prestwick, Ayrshire, KA9 2NS Tel: (01292) 478008

Geomount Ltd, Unit 8 Cranleigh Gardens Industrial Estate, Southall, Middlesex, UB1 2BZ Tel: (020) 8571 7046 Fax: (020) 8571 6992
E-mail: pphillips@geomont.fsnet.co.uk

George Lister & Sons Ltd, 505 Coldhams Lane, Cambridge, CB1 3JS Tel: (01223) 518888 Fax: (01223) 504700
E-mail: martin@georgelister.co.uk

Gibbs (General Engineering) Ltd, 7 High Street, Prestatyn, Clwyd, LL19 9AF Tel: (01745) 853759 Fax: (01745) 854360
E-mail: office@gibbsge.com

Giffhorn & Co. Ltd, Unit 14, West Point Trading Park, Liverpool Street, Hull, HU3 4UU Tel: (01482) 323844 Fax: (01482) 213198
E-mail: egon@giffhornengkaroo.co.uk

James C. Gillespie (Engineering) Ltd, Block 4 Muirhead, Midfield Road, Mitchelston Industrial Estate, Kirkcaldy, Fife, KY1 3PS Tel: (01592) 650333 Fax: (01592) 650729
E-mail: sales@jcgillespie.co.uk

M.G. Godfrey & Co. Ltd, 174a Perry Vale, London, Greater London, SE23 2LR Tel: 020 82914168

Graham Engineering Ltd, Edward Street, Whitewalls Industrial Estate, Nelson, Lancashire, BB9 8SY Tel: (01282) 695121 Fax: (01282) 698498
E-mail: sales@graham-eng.co.uk

J.M. Grail (General Engineers) Ltd, Newtown Road, Steam Mills, Cinderford, Gloucestershire, GL14 3JE Tel: (01594) 822054 Fax: (01594) 826654
E-mail: info@grail.eu.com

▶ Gravaton Engineering Systems, H-J Fort Wallington Industrial Estate, Military Road, Fareham, Hampshire, PO16 8TT Tel: (01329) 237010 Fax: (01329) 287492

▶ Greenfield Engineering, Unit 2a Dobles Lane Industrial Estate, Holsworthy, Devon, EX22 6HL Tel: (01409) 254400 Fax: (01409) 254898
E-mail: sales@greenfieldengineering.co.uk

Grenville Engineering Stoke On Trent Ltd, 3 Newfields Industrial Estate, High Street, Stoke-on-Trent, ST6 5PD Tel: (01782) 577929 Fax: (01782) 575672
E-mail: greneng@greneng.co.uk

GSB Fabrication Ltd, Unit 3, Castle Trading Estate, Fareham, Hampshire, PO16 9SF Tel: (023) 9221 0787 Fax: (023) 9220 1252

Guilform Ltd, 5 Alban Park Industrial Estate, Hatfield Road, St. Albans, Hertfordshire, AL4 0JJ Tel: (01727) 841111 Fax: (01727) 832710

H B Humphries & Co. Ltd, Telford Way, Telford Way Industrial Estate, Kettering, Northamptonshire, NN16 8UN Tel: (01536) 512588 Fax: (01536) 410140
E-mail: enquiries@hbhumphries.co.uk

H & H Metals Fabrications Ltd, Unit 1, New Railway St, Willenhall, West Midlands, WV13 1LJ Tel: (01902) 635418 Fax: (01902) 635418

H & S Sheetmetal Fabrication Co., Unit 1, All Saints Industrial Estate, Shildon, County Durham, DL4 2RD Tel: (01388) 777172 Fax: (01388) 775034

Halifax Sheet Metal & Ventilation, Pellon Industrial Estate, Queens Road, Halifax, West Yorkshire, HX1 4PR Tel: (01422) 362361 Fax: (01422) 340591E-mail: info@hsmv.co.uk

▶ Halmond Engineering Products Ltd, 3 Mosshall Industrial Estate, Blackburn, Bathgate, West Lothian, EH47 7LY Tel: (01506) 633476 Fax: (01506) 656022

Hamilton Engineering, 65-67 Corporation Road, Birkenhead, Merseyside, CH41 3NG Tel: 0151-647 6444 Fax: 0151-666 1065

Hamilton Fabrications Ltd, Crab Tree Lane, Atherton, Manchester, M46 0AG Tel: (01942) 883745 Fax: (01942) 897481
E-mail: sales@hamiltonfab.co.uk

▶ Hammersmith Engineering Ltd, 4 Berkeley Court Earl Russell Way, Lawrence Hill, Bristol, BS5 0BX Tel: 0117-955 1800
E-mail: sales@hammersmith-engineering.co.uk

▶ Hamnavoe Engineering, Cairston Road, Stromness, Orkney, KW16 3JS Tel: (01856) 850576 Fax: (01856) 851200

Hane Instruments Ltd, 691 Stirling Road, Slough, SL1 4ST Tel: (01753) 530313 Fax: (01753) 823301 E-mail: info@haneinstruments.co.uk

Harbridge (Sheet Metal) Ltd, Philip Street, St. Philips Marsh, Bristol, BS2 0TA Tel: 0117-977 8850 Fax: 0117-977 5145
E-mail: harbridge@totalise.co.uk

Hardy Sheet Metal, 156 Sandridge Road, St. Albans, Hertfordshire, AL1 4AP Tel: (01727) 837833 Fax: (01727) 837833

Harrison Sheetmetal, Smyrna Street, Radcliffe, Manchester, M26 4BN Tel: 0161-723 4122 Fax: 0161-723 4122

Harrocell Ltd, 15e Wintersells Road, Byfleet, West Byfleet, Surrey, KT14 7LF Tel: (01932) 356347 Fax: (01932) 356347
E-mail: harrocell@btconnect.com

Harwoods For Steel Ltd, Whitegate Farm, Waterlooville, Hampshire, PO8 0TG Tel: (023) 9259 3442 Fax: (023) 9259 6010

Havant Sheet Metal Co. Ltd, Downley Road, Havant, Hampshire, PO9 2NN Tel: 0845 5314135 Fax: (023) 9247 0563
E-mail: sales@havantsheetmetal.co.uk

Heasman & Sadler Ltd, 29 Park Road, Faringdon, Oxfordshire, SN7 7BP Tel: (01367) 240286 Fax: (01367) 242056

▶ Heat Radiation Ltd, Belvedere Trading Estate, Taunton, Somerset, TA1 1BH Tel: (01823) 253177 Fax: (01823) 336076

Heatherside Engineering Ltd, Old Oak Close Industrial Estate, Old Oak Close, Arlesey, Bedfordshire, SG15 6XD Tel: (01462) 731575 Fax: (01462) 731575
E-mail: heatherside@btconnect.com

▶ Herbert Pool Engineering Ltd, 28 Waterfront Business Park, Fleet, Hampshire, GU51 3QT Tel: (01252) 614824 Fax: (01252) 625585

Hermitage S M Ltd, 25 Knowl Piece, Wilbury Way, Hitchin, Hertfordshire, SG4 0TY Tel: (01462) 422421 Fax: (01462) 422026
E-mail: sales@hermitagesm.co.uk

▶ Hewston Engineering (Midlands) Ltd, Unit 7 Modulrate Court, Enterprise Drive, Four Ashes, Wolverhampton, WV10 7DF Tel: (01902) 791492

High Speed Piercing Ltd, Pindar Road, Hoddesdon, Hertfordshire, EN11 0DE Tel: (01992) 445123 Fax: (01992) 466541
E-mail: admin@highspeedpiercing.co.uk

▶ Highbell Ltd, Unit 20, Ivanhoe Road, Hogwood Lane Industrial Estate, Wokingham, Berkshire, RG40 4QQ Tel: 0118-973 0357 Fax: 0118-973 1991 E-mail: barriehighbell@btconnect.com

Hindles Ltd, 22 Moorland Way, Lincoln, LN6 7JP Tel: (01522) 683000 Fax: (01522) 500127
E-mail: sales@psm-sportswear.co.uk

Hitherbest Ltd, Heath Hill Court, Heath Hill Industrial Estate, Dawley, Telford, Shropshire, TF4 2RH Tel: (01952) 632100 Fax: (01952) 632109 E-mail: sales@hitherbest.co.uk

▶ Hivac Engineering Ltd, 14 Ivyhouse Lane, Hastings, East Sussex, TN35 4NN Tel: (01424) 461007 Fax: (01424) 461009

Hoblongs Engineering, Hoblongs Industrial Estate, Chelmsford Road, Dunmow, Essex, CM6 1JA Tel: (01371) 874550 Fax: (01371) 872698

Hocklynn Ltd, Netham Road, Bristol, BS5 9PQ Tel: 0117-955 6294 Fax: 0117-935 1062
E-mail: hocklynnlimited@aol.com

Holder's Sheet Metal, Back Clare Street, Blackpool, FY1 6HS Tel: (01253) 341147 Fax: (01253) 341404

Holt Broadcast Services Ltd, Unit 13 Nimrod Industrial Estate, Nimrod Way, Reading, RG2 0EB Tel: 0118-931 0770 Fax: 0118-931 0696 E-mail: sales@holtbs.co.uk

Hooper Engineering Ltd, Nelson St, Oldbury, West Midlands, B69 4NY Tel: 0121-552 2835 Fax: 0121-552 3821
E-mail: hooper.sheetmetal@virgin.net

▶ Horizontal Boring Services, 1 Lamberhead Industrial Estate, Leopold Street, Wigan, Lancashire, WN5 8EG Tel: (01942) 224805 Fax: (01942) 224848

Horsham Sheet Metal, Foundry Lane, Horsham, West Sussex, RH13 5PX Tel: (01403) 264137 Fax: (01403) 272386
E-mail: sales@horshamsheetmetal.co.uk

Howarth 1985 Ltd, Alma St Work Meadow Croft, Alma Street, Radcliffe, Manchester, M26 4FU Tel: 0161-723 2024 Fax: 0161-723 2024

▶ Howden Blacksmiths Ltd, 15 Castle Road, Bankside Industrial Estate, Falkirk, FK2 7UY Tel: (01324) 630930 Fax: (01324) 670888
E-mail: scotthowden@aol.com

▶ Hugh K Gillies Ltd, 23 Kyle Road, Irvine Industrial Estate, Irvine, Ayrshire, KA12 8LE Tel: (01294) 274296 Fax: (01294) 277284
E-mail: hkgillies@btconnect.com

▶ Hunslet Engine Co., 2 Maple Park, Lowfields Avenue, Leeds, LS12 6HH Tel: 0113-277 4007 Fax: 0113-277 3005
E-mail: info@hunsletenginw.com

▶ Hunt Engineering Ltd, Swanston Road, Great Yarmouth, Norfolk, NR30 3NQ Tel: (01493) 332847 Fax: (01493) 330520

Hunter Neil Packaging Ltd, Unit 5, Hilltop Meadows, Old London Road, Knockholt, Sevenoaks, Kent, TN14 7JW Tel: (01959) 532200 Fax: (01959) 534400
E-mail: info@hunterneil.co.uk

Hutcheon Services Ltd, Bowtree House, Minto Drive, Altens Industrial Estate, Aberdeen, AB12 3LW Tel: (01224) 874875 Fax: (01224) 895975 E-mail: info@hutcheon-services.ltd.uk

▶ Hymec Precision Engineering Ltd, Darklake View, Estover, Plymouth, PL6 7TL Tel: (01752) 511002 Fax: (01752) 511003

▶ Ilott Engineering Ltd, 25 Cowley Road, Nuffield Industrial Estate, Poole, Dorset, BH17 0UJ Tel: (01202) 661038 Fax: (01202) 661150
E-mail: info@acurate-controls.co.uk

Imes, Clyde Submarine Base, Faslane, Helensburgh, Dunbartonshire, G84 8HL Tel: (01436) 811000 Fax: (01436) 811477

▶ Imes Engineers, 32 South Court The Courtyard, Woodlands, Bradley Stoke, Bristol, BS32 4NH Tel: (01454) 202288 Fax: (01454) 202123

Imperial, 65 North Acton Road, London, NW10 6PJ Tel: (020) 8965 8596 Fax: (020) 8961 9352 E-mail: info@iwsm.co.uk

▶ Imperial Ductwork Manufacturing, 140 Burnham Road, Dartford, DA1 5AZ Tel: (01322) 285328 Fax: (01322) 285428

▶ Independent Forgings & Alloys Ltd, Victoria Forge, Livesey Street, Sheffield, S6 2BL Tel: 0114-234 3000 Fax: 0114-234 0261

Indmar Sheet Metal, Swan Lane, Hindley Green, Wigan, Lancashire, WN2 4HD Tel: (01942) 520200 Fax: (01942) 520201

▶ Innovar Engineering Services Ltd, Unit 53 131 Lower Bathville, Armadale, Bathgate, West Lothian, EH48 2JS Tel: (01501) 732265 Fax: (01501) 733111
E-mail: ian.pope@btconnect.com

Instafab Sheet Metal Work, 5 Sunshine Mills, Wortley Road, Leeds, LS12 3HT Tel: 0113-263 4810 Fax: 0113-263 0444
E-mail: instafab@hotmail.com

Inventair Fabrications, Carnaby Industrial Estate, Lancaster Road, Carnaby, Bridlington, North Humberside, YO15 3QY Tel: (01262) 400919 Fax: (01262) 401358
E-mail: david@inventair.co.uk

Irwin & Campbell (Glasgow) Ltd, 22-24 Polmadie Street, Glasgow, G42 0PQ Tel: 0141-423 8377 Fax: 0141-423 8292

▶ Isleburn Ltd, Industrial Estate, Evanton, Dingwall, Ross-Shire, IV16 9XJ Tel: (01349) 832000 Fax: (01349) 832001
E-mail: enquiries@isleburn.com

Isotemp Heating & Ventilating Ltd, Station Road, Loudwater, High Wycombe, Buckinghamshire, HP10 9UD Tel: (01494) 534364 Fax: (01494) 461716

▶ Itasco Precision Ltd, 18 Faraday Road, Glenrothes, Fife, KY6 2RU Tel: (01592) 771285 Fax: (01592) 775164
E-mail: sales@itasco.co.uk

J A Glover Ltd, 23 Lordswood Industrial Estate, Revenge Road, Chatham, Kent, ME5 8UD Tel: (01634) 684419 Fax: (01634) 200423
E-mail: chatham@jagglover.demon.co.uk

▶ J B Fabrication Wrexham Ltd, Bryn Lane, Wrexham Industrial Estate, Wrexham, Clwyd, LL13 9UT Tel: (01978) 664446 Fax: (01978) 664447

J C Engineering, 136 High Street, Cottenham, Cambridge, CB24 8RX Tel: (01954) 206357 Fax: (01954) 206358

▶ J C Engineering Co., 6 Market Overton Industrial Estate, Thistleton Road, Market Overton, Oakham, Leicestershire, LE15 7PP Tel: (01572) 767888 Fax: (01572) 767999

J C Engineering Products, 17-19 Loverock Road, Battle Farm Trading Estate, Reading, RG30 1DZ Tel: 0118-958 1926 Fax: 0118-950 4018 E-mail: sales@jceng.co.uk

J D Fabrications Leicester Ltd, 38 Boston Road, Gorse Hill Industrial Estate, Beaumont Leys, Leicester, LE4 1AU Tel: 0116-236 8622 Fax: 0116-235 6220
E-mail: jdfabsleicesltd@aol.com

▶ J D Services (Hvac) Ltd, Suite 7, Matrix Business Centre, Victoria Road, Dartford, DA1 5AJ Tel: (01322) 271809

J E Gordon Ltd, 60 Whitworth St West, Manchester, M1 5WW Tel: 0161-236 1892 Fax: 0161-228 7803

J E Jenkins, 7 Eye Green Industries, Crowland Road, Eye, Peterborough, PE6 7SZ Tel: (01733) 223650 Fax: (01733) 223650

SHEET METALWORK ENGINEERS OR FABRICATORS – *continued*

J G B Steelcraft (U K) Ltd, Victoria Works, Mary St, Johnstone, Renfrewshire, PA5 8BT Tel: (01505) 326589 Fax: (01505) 382506 E-mail: brendan@jgb-steelcraft.co.uk

▶ J G Turnbull Ltd, Station Approach, East Boldon, Tyne & Wear, NE36 0AD Tel: 0191-536 2090 Fax: 0191-519 0218 E-mail: info@jgturnbullltd.demon.co.uk

J Harper & Sons Welding Fabrications Ltd, Willenhall La Industrial Estate, Willenhall Lane, Bloxwich, Walsall, WS3 2XN Tel: (01922) 478419 Fax: (01922) 409553

J Hill & Co. Ltd, Charlotte St, Melton Mowbray, Leicestershire, LE13 1NA Tel: (01664) 562219 Fax: (01664) 410258 E-mail: sales@hilltrident.co.uk

J & J Products Ashford Ltd, 3 River Gardens Business Centre, Spur Road, Feltham, Middlesex, TW14 0SN Tel: (020) 8890 5085 Fax: (020) 8751 1896 E-mail: jj.products@cwcom.net

J & K Sheet Metal, Unit 33 Joseph Wilson Industrial Estate, Whitstable, Kent, CT5 3PS Tel: (01227) 274763 Fax: (01227) 773021

J L Fabrications, Unit 7 Winstanley Industrial Estate, Long Lane, Warrington, WA2 8PR Tel: (01925) 633887 Fax: (01925) 630087

J & P Contracts Angus Ltd, 73 Dundee Street, Carnoustie, Angus, DD7 7PN Tel: (01241) 854911 Fax: (01241) 855860 E-mail: sales@jp-coatech.com

J & S Sheet Metal Products, Unit 30 South Hampshire Industrial Park, Totton, Southampton, SO40 3SA Tel: (023) 8087 2827 Fax: (023) 8086 0033 E-mail: sales@jssheetmeta1.com

J T Blythe Ltd, Kings Mill Lane, Redhill, RH1 5JY Tel: (01737) 823314 Fax: (01737) 822937 E-mail: harry@jtblythe.co.uk

J W Entwistle Co. Ltd, 41 Cobden Street, Salford, M6 6WF Tel: 0161-736 2297 Fax: 0161-745 7897 E-mail: adam@jwentwistle.com

J&J, Unit 1 20 Paynes Lane, Rugby, Warwickshire, CV21 2UH Tel: (01788) 568217 Fax: (01788) 547125 E-mail: jjsheetmetal@dialstart.net

James Smellie Fabrications Ltd, F Leona Trading Estate, Nimmings Road, Halesowen, West Midlands, B62 9JQ Tel: 0121-561 1167 Fax: 0121-559 0336

Jaroken Sheet Metal Ltd, 502-503 Ipswich Road, Trading Estate, Slough, SL1 4EP Tel: (01753) 578728 Fax: (01753) 578730 E-mail: sales@jarokensheetmetal.co.uk

▶ Jay Cee Lichfield Engineering Ltd, Coppice Side Industrial Estate, Brownhills, Walsall, WS8 7EX Tel: (01543) 377633 Fax: (01543) 374100 E-mail: jc@jaycee-eng.co.uk

▶ Jig Boring Services Ltd, Ordnance Street, Blackburn, BB1 3AE Tel: (01254) 680143

John Dent Engineering Co. Ltd, 1432a Clock Tower Road, Isleworth, Middlesex, TW7 6DT Tel: (020) 8560 4414 Fax: (020) 8847 4582 E-mail: info@johndentengineering.com

John E Dale & Son, Fletchers Yard, Wellowgate, Grimsby, South Humberside, DN32 0RG Tel: (01472) 354662

▶ John S Feather Ltd, Cherry Street Works, Cherry Street, Keighley, West Yorkshire, BD21 4JX Tel: (01535) 662693 Fax: (01535) 662693

Johnstone Metal Works, 2a Park Road, Ramsgate, Kent, CT11 7QE Tel: (01843) 593451 Fax: (01843) 850615

Jolibar Metal Works Ltd, Howe Moss Drive, Dyce, Aberdeen, AB21 0GL Tel: (01224) 770445 Fax: (01224) 770019 E-mail: sales@jolibarmetalworks.co.uk

▶ Jordan Engineering UK Ltd, Pillar Building, The Dockyard, Pembroke Dock, Dyfed, SA72 6TD Tel: (01646) 681999 Fax: (01646) 681998 E-mail: info@jordanengineering.co.uk

K & A Furness Ltd, Trent Industrial Estate, Duchess Street, Shaw, Oldham, OL2 7UT Tel: (01706) 843411 Fax: (01706) 882289 E-mail: sales@jet-vac.co.uk

K C Engineering, R/O 89 Upper Brockley Road, London, SE4 1TF Tel: (020) 8691 0219 Fax: (020) 8691 0219

K E P Engineering Ltd, Mosley Street, New Basford, Nottingham, NG7 7FQ Tel: 0115-978 0616 Fax: 0115-942 2280 E-mail: info@kepengineering.com

K J Wykes Ltd, Goosey Lodge, Wymington Lane, Wymington, Rushden, Northamptonshire, NN10 9LU Tel: (01933) 315818 Fax: (01933) 355808

K M S Hardrange, Unit 5 Manor Industrial Estate, Flint, Clwyd, CH6 5UY Tel: (01352) 732291 Fax: (01352) 762886 E-mail: kmshardrange01@btconnect.com

K P S Ltd, 3 Lyon Close, Woburn Road Industrial Estate, Kempston, Bedford, MK42 7SB Tel: (01234) 852915 Fax: (01234) 840124 E-mail: sales@kpssheetmetal.co.uk

K T Fabrications Ltd, Unit B Heath Place, Bognor Regis, West Sussex, PO22 9SL Tel: (01243) 861426 Fax: (01243) 826108

▶ K V A Power Ltd, Unit 12, Spring Mill Industrial Estate, Avening Road, Nailsworth, Stroud, Gloucestershire, GL6 0BS Tel: (01453) 832358

▶ K Young & Sons (Stroud) Ltd, Gaineys Wells, Stroud, Gloucestershire, GL5 1LQ Tel: (01453) 764503

Kab Metal Works, Rospeath Industrial Estate, Crowlas, Penzance, Cornwall, TR20 8DU Tel: (01736) 740803 Fax: (01736) 740803

Kathglade Ltd, 20 Aston Road, Waterlooville, Hampshire, PO7 7XE Tel: (023) 9226 9777 Fax: (023) 9226 2190

KBR, Wellheads Place, Wellheads Industrial Estate, Aberdeen, AB21 7GB Tel: (01224) 777000 Fax: (01224) 777710

▶ Keeble Bros, Eastern Industrial Estate, Bancrofts Road, South Woodham Ferrers, Chelmsford, CM3 5UG Tel: (01245) 321930 Fax: (01245) 321930

▶ Keiton Engineering Ltd, 2 William Burton Works, St. James Street, Wednesbury, West Midlands, WS10 7DY Tel: 0121-556 9919 Fax: 0121-556 1398

Kejan Sheet Metal Work, 9 Railway St Industrial Estate, Railway Street, Gillingham, Kent, ME7 1YQ Tel: (01634) 571016 Fax: (01634) 575789 E-mail: alan@kejan.f2s.com

▶ Ken Ware Engineers Ltd, Brailwood Road, Bilsthorpe, Newark, Nottinghamshire, NG22 8UA Tel: (01623) 871173 Fax: (01623) 871904

▶ Kenard Engineering (Tewkesbury) Ltd, Newtown Trading Estate, Green Lane, Tewkesbury, Gloucestershire, GL20 8SJ Tel: (01684) 271400

Kendal Metal Works Ltd, Mintsfeet Road, Kendal, Cumbria, LA9 6NN Tel: (01539) 722050 Fax: (01539) 741190

▶ Keweld Ltd, 109 Sadler Road, Lincoln, LN6 3RS Tel: (01522) 691723 Fax: (01522) 500855 E-mail: keweldltd@btconnect.com

King & Rawlings, 278-284 High Street, Waltham Cross, Hertfordshire, EN8 7EA Tel: (01992) 623575 Fax: (01992) 640570

Kirkbride Sheet Metal Work, 47 Wenlock Way, Leicester, LE4 9HU Tel: 0116-276 0131 Fax: 0116-246 1001 E-mail: kirkmfabs@aol.com

▶ Kisa Engineering Ltd, 45 Lady La Industrial Estate, Hadleigh, Ipswich, IP7 6BQ Tel: (01473) 823152 Fax: (01473) 828165

▶ D.W. Knight Engineering Co. Ltd, Unit 1, Sywell Airport, Sywell, Northampton, NN6 0BN Tel: (01604) 647689 Fax: (01604) 494637 E-mail: d-w-knight@tiscali.co.uk

W.G. Knight & Son, 18 Main Ridge, Boston, Lincolnshire, PE21 6SS Tel: 01205 363084

▶ Knowsley Engineering Services, 6 Peel Road, Skelmersdale, Lancashire, WN8 9PT Tel: (01695) 556108 Fax: (01695) 556649 E-mail: mail@knowsleyengineeringservices.co.uk

Kram Sheet Metal, Whitacre Road Industrial Estate, Nuneaton, Warwickshire, CV11 6BZ Tel: (024) 7664 1272 Fax: (024) 7635 2520

Krisco Engineering Ltd, Unit B2 Oldmixon Cresent, Weston-super-Mare, Avon, BS24 9AY Tel: (01934) 413800 Fax: (01934) 412620 E-mail: sales@kriscoengineering.co.uk

Kuhr Engineering Ltd, Ivy Arch Road, Worthing, West Sussex, BN14 8BX Tel: 0845 5314280 Fax: (01903) 205208 E-mail: ralf.kuhr@kuhr-engineering.co.uk

L L Potter & Sons Taplow Ltd, Taplow Road, Marshgate Trading Estate, Taplow, Maidenhead, Berkshire, SL6 0ND Tel: (01628) 667167 Fax: (01628) 667801 E-mail: potters@globalnet.co.uk

▶ L & S Engineers Calberto Ltd, Spire Road, District 10, Washington, Tyne & Wear, NE37 3ES Tel: 0191-416 8339 Fax: 0191-415 4615 E-mail: calberto@btopenworld.co.uk

▶ L S Fabrications Ltd, Swallowfields, Welwyn Garden City, Hertfordshire, AL7 1JD Tel: (01707) 885885

Lada Engineering Services, Vickers House, Vickers Business Centre Priestley Road, Basingstoke, Hampshire, RG24 9NP Tel: (01256) 333571 Fax: 01256 353130 E-mail: info@ladaengineering.co.uk

Ladwa Engineering Ltd, Sanders Lodge Industrial Estate, Rushden, Northamptonshire, NN10 6BQ Tel: (01933) 359204 Fax: (01933) 410583 E-mail: info@ladwaengineering.co.uk

Lall Engineering Ltd, 343 Bedworth Road, Longford, Coventry, CV6 6BN Tel: (024) 7636 4904 Fax: (024) 7636 2083

▶ Lanner Manufacturing Ltd, J Telford Road, Basingstoke, Hampshire, RG21 6YU Tel: (01256) 464288 Fax: (01256) 464209

▶ Laplace Electrical Ltd, Unit 26 42 Dalsetter Avenue, Glasgow, G15 8TE Tel: 0141-949 0099 Fax: 0141-949 1154

Laroc (Coventry) Ltd, Curriers Close, Charter Avenue Industrial Estate, Coventry, CV4 8AW Tel: (024) 7646 6085 Fax: (024) 7646 6085

Laser Steel Ltd, Chartwell Drive, Wigston, Leicestershire, LE18 2FL Tel: 0116-288 4933 Fax: 0116-288 4966

Lathe Trays Fabricators Ltd, Station Road, Rowley Regis, West Midlands, B65 0JX Tel: 0121-559 1115 Fax: (0870) 4202912 E-mail: admin@lathetrays.co.uk

Lazenbys Ltd, Main Street, Hull, HU2 0LF Tel: (01482) 329519 Fax: (01482) 216152

LDJ, Bridge Works, Iver Lane, Uxbridge, Middlesex, UB8 2JG Tel: (01895) 231880 Fax: (01895) 271825

▶ Leckie, Allanshaw Industrial Estate, Wellhall Road, Hamilton, Lanarkshire, ML3 9BG Tel: (01698) 283754 Fax: (01698) 281037

Leedsheath Ltd, Westfield Road, Slyfield Industrial Estate, Guildford, Surrey, GU1 1RR Tel: (01483) 503248 Fax: (01483) 575627 E-mail: tonycoker@btconnect.com

Leicester Fabrications Ltd, Hazel Drive, Narborough Road South, Leicester, LE3 2JE Tel: 0116-289 8154 Fax: 0116-289 2768

Leighton Carter Insulation Co. Ltd, 25 Argyle Street, Newport, Gwent, NP20 5NE Tel: (01633) 856624 Fax: (01633) 856178

▶ Leighwill Engineering, 61c & 61d Gorse Industrial Estate, Barnham, Thetford, Norfolk, IP24 2PH Tel: (01842) 890686 Fax: (01842) 890686

Lenesco Ltd, Grove Road, Northfleet, Gravesend, Kent, DA11 9AX Tel: (01474) 564692 Fax: (01474) 327329

Leniks Motor Panels Ltd, Lenik Motor Panels, Slingsby Close, Attleborough Fields Industrial Estate, Nuneaton, Warwickshire, CV11 6RP Tel: (024) 7638 4728 Fax: (024) 7638 4728

Leominster Engineering Co., Southern Avenue, Leominster, Herefordshire, HR6 0QF Tel: (01568) 613284 Fax: (01568) 614734

▶ Lerwick Engineering & Fabrication Ltd, Greenhead, Lerwick, Shetland, ZE1 0PY Tel: (01595) 692349

Letchford Swifts Ltd, Leamore Lane, Walsall, WS2 7BU Tel: (01922) 402460 Fax: (01922) 402460

Leton Engineering, Unit 14 Cockshades Farm, Stock Lane, Wybunbury, Nantwich, Cheshire, CW5 7HA Tel: (01270) 841977 Fax: (01270) 569226 E-mail: sales@1eton.net

▶ Level One Engineering Ltd, Birchill Road, Knowsley Industrial Park, Liverpool, L33 7TG Tel: 0151-547 1300 Fax: 0151-546 7877

Lewis & Raby (Engineers) Ltd, Birchill Road, Knowsley Industrial Park, Liverpool, L33 7TG Tel: 0151-546 2882 Fax: 0151-549 1585

Leyletts Engineering Co. Ltd, Cornwallis Road, Lyng, West Bromwich, West Midlands, B70 7JF Tel: 0121-544 6669 Fax: 0121-544 8483 E-mail: sales@leyletts.co.uk

Leytoner De Montfort Ltd, 8 Layton Road, Leicester, LE5 0PU Tel: 0116-276 7272 E-mail: leytoner@aol.com

Lilleker Engineering Co. Ltd, Unit 3b Lincoln Street, Rotherham, South Yorkshire, S60 1RP Tel: (01709) 829541 Fax: (01709) 829542 E-mail: sales@lilleker.co.uk

Livingston Precision (Engineering) Ltd, 28 Firth Road, Houstoun Industrial Estate, Livingston, West Lothian, EH54 5DJ Tel: (01506) 435281 Fax: (01506) 433973

▶ Lofting Services North West Ltd, Unit 7c-7d Arrow Trading Estate, Corporation Road, Audenshaw, Manchester, M34 5LR Tel: 0161-337 9111 Fax: 0161-337 9222 E-mail: sales@cncprecision.co.uk

Loubec Sheet Metal Ltd, Throstle Nest Mill, Leeds Road, Nelson, Lancashire, BB9 9XG Tel: (01282) 604737 Fax: (01282) 611897

▶ Loughborough Sheet Metal Specialists, 2 Royal Way, Loughborough, Leicestershire, LE11 5XR Tel: (01509) 233874 Fax: (01509) 241277 E-mail: sales@lborosheetmetal.co.uk

Lowland Sheet Metal Ltd, Unit 2 Coppice Trading Estate, Kidderminster, Worcestershire, DY11 7QY Tel: (01562) 743215 Fax: (01562) 863436

LPA Haswell Engineers Ltd, Oakwood Business Park, Stephenson Road West, Clacton-On-Sea, Essex, CO15 4TL Tel: (01255) 253900 Fax: (01255) 432963 E-mail: enquiries@lpa-haswell.com

Luxomation Ltd, 5 Worton Hall Industrial Estate, Worton Road, Isleworth, Middlesex, TW7 6ER Tel: (020) 8568 6373 Fax: (020) 8847 2603

Lynx Engineering Kent Ltd, 2 Denton Slipways Site, Wharf Road, Gravesend, Kent, DA12 2RU Tel: (01474) 328877 Fax: (01474) 327744

▶ M B Wellclad, PO Box 4, Motherwell, Lanarkshire, ML1 3NP Tel: (01698) 266111 Fax: (01698) 275487 E-mail: info@mbgroup.com

▶ M D P Engineering Ltd, Unit 21, Cornton Business Park, Cornton Road, Stirling, FK9 5AT Tel: (01786) 449600

M H V Products Ltd, 33 Woodthorpe Road, Ashford, Middlesex, TW15 2RP Tel: (01784) 241628 Fax: (01784) 255610 E-mail: sales@mhvproducts.co.uk

▶ M J M Engineering Services Ltd, 26 Poplar Road, Glenrothes, Fife, KY7 4AA Tel: (01592) 610771 Fax: (01592) 610088

M J R Fabrications, B Cranborne Industrial Estate, Cranborne Road, Potters Bar, Hertfordshire, EN6 3JN Tel: (01707) 646825 Fax: (01707) 649089

M J Sheet Metal Co., 158 Crow Lane, Romford, RM7 0ES Tel: (01708) 737050 Fax: (01708) 737096

M K W Engineering Ltd, Stargate Industrial Estate, Ryton, Tyne & Wear, NE40 3EX Tel: 0191-413 0000 Fax: 0191-413 2736 E-mail: sales@mkw.co.uk

M & M Fabrications Ltd, Disraeli Street, Aylestone, Leicester, LE2 8LX Tel: 0116-245 2800 Fax: 0116-245 2801 E-mail: mandm@b-on-line.com

▶ M M W Welding Ltd, Gremista, Lerwick, Shetland, ZE1 0PX Tel: (01595) 695600 Fax: (01595) 695474

M P L Fabrications, Dutton Road, Aldermans Green Industrial Estate, Coventry, CV2 2LE Tel: (024) 7661 0778 Fax: (024) 7661 9499 E-mail: sales@mplfabrications.com

M P M Engineering Services Ltd, Unit 2 192 Camford Way, Luton, LU3 3AN Tel: (01582) 582811 Fax: (01582) 491865 E-mail: enquiries@mpm-eng.co.uk

M T Perry Ltd, 5 Rawcliffe House, Howarth Road, Maidenhead, Berkshire, SL6 1AP Tel: (01628) 630330 Fax: (01628) 630330 E-mail: enquiries@perryfabs.co.uk

M V M Sheet Metal Fabrications Ltd, 7-9 Dawkins Road Industrial Estate, Poole, Dorset, BH15 4JP Tel: (01202) 677244 Fax: (01202) 679762 E-mail: enquiries@mvm-uk.com

▶ M & W Engineering Ltd, Sea View Business Park, North Road Industrial Estate, Berwick-upon-Tweed, TD15 1UP Tel: (01289) 330524 Fax: (01289) 303595 E-mail: mwengineering@btconnect.com

Mcbain George & Co., 2 Whitemyres Avenue, Aberdeen, AB16 6HQ Tel: (01224) 683921 Fax: (01224) 685562

▶ W.J. McCullough Services Ltd, Units 5-6, Brighton, BN1 4GD Tel: 01273 675487

Mcdonald Insulation & Maintenance Ltd, 7 Eastbury Road, London, E6 6LP Tel: (020) 7511 8899 Fax: (020) 7473 1133 E-mail: info@mcdonaldbrownltd.co.uk

Machined Components Ltd, 11 Ailsa Road, Irvine Industrial Estate, Irvine, Ayrshire, KA12 8LR Tel: (01294) 278112 Fax: (01294) 277698

Mackley & Co. Ltd, Chatham Street, Sheffield, S3 8EJ Tel: 0114-272 3991 Fax: 0114-272 1004

The Maine Group, Home Park Industrial Estate, Station Road, Kings Langley, Hertfordshire, WD4 8LZ Tel: (01923) 260411 Fax: (01923) 267136 E-mail: sales@maine.co.uk

Major Air Systems Ltd, Union Works, Andover Street, Birmingham, B5 5RG Tel: 0121-634 1580 Fax: 0121-643 2320

Major Fabrications Kent Ltd, Broad Lane, Betteshanger, Deal, Kent, CT14 0LX Tel: (01304) 614541 Fax: (01304) 614544 E-mail: enquiries@majorfabrications.com

Major Sheet Metals, 483 Bradford Road, Batley, West Yorkshire, WF17 8LB Tel: (01924) 441610 Fax: (01924) 420535

Malton Laser Ltd, Unit E3 The Pyramid Estate, Showfield Lane, Malton, North Yorkshire, YO17 6BT Tel: (01653) 697770 Fax: (01653) 690970 E-mail: info@maltonlaser.co.uk

Manesty Fabrication Services, Holmfield Industrial Estate, Holmfield, Halifax, West Yorkshire, HX2 9TP Tel: (01422) 241122 Fax: (01422) 241100 E-mail: chris.clarke@manesty.com

Marl Bank Sheet Metal Co. Ltd, Newtown Road, Worcester, WR5 1HA Tel: (01905) 22801 Fax: (01905) 726235 E-mail: marlbank@marlbank77.wannadoo.co.uk

Marsden Metal Products Ltd, Cedar Works, Ryebourne Street, Oldham, OL4 2BP Tel: 0161-624 9217 E-mail: info@marsdenmetal.co.uk

Mason & King Ltd, 11 Birstall Street, Leicester, LE1 2HJ Tel: 0116-253 6491 Fax: 0116-251 2403 E-mail: ray@masonking.co.uk

Masterford Ltd, Lyon Road, Bletchley, Milton Keynes, MK1 1EX Tel: (01908) 373106 Fax: (01908) 377181 E-mail: john-forder@btconnect.com

Matann Metal Fabrication Ltd, 5 Blatchford Road, Horsham, West Sussex, RH13 5QR Tel: (01403) 249994 Fax: (01403) 249355

Matt's Sheet Metal, Whitefield Mill, St. Marys Street, Nelson, Lancashire, BB9 7BA Tel: (01282) 602228 Fax: (01282) 602228

Maydown Precision Engineering Ltd, 11 Carrakeel Drive, Maydown, Londonderry, BT47 6UH Tel: (028) 7186 0531 Fax: (028) 7186 0496 E-mail: info@maydown.com

MBN Fabrications Ltd, Units 2-3, Northbridge Road, Berkhamsted, Hertfordshire, HP4 1EF Tel: (01442) 877888 Fax: (01442) 877862

Meakin & Son, 270 Abbey Street, Derby, DE22 3SX Tel: (01332) 344144 Fax: (01332) 292420 E-mail: metalwork@dial.pipex.com

▶ Mechserv Ltd, Sir William Smith Road, Kirkton Industrial Estate, Arbroath, Angus, DD11 3RD Tel: (01241) 439070 Fax: (01241) 439074

Mercantile Met-Tech Ltd, Plumpton House, Plumpton Road, Hoddesdon, Hertfordshire, EN11 0LB Tel: (01992) 445709 Fax: (01992) 467217 E-mail: info@mercantilemettech.co.uk

Merseyside Metalwork Ltd, Cotton Street, Liverpool, L3 7DY Tel: 0151-236 7349 Fax: 0151-236 6397

▶ Mertek Engineering Ltd, 7 Baylys Road, Plymouth, PL9 7NQ Tel: (01752) 480497 Fax: (01752) 480497

Metal Fabrication Services, Unit 3-4 Soaphouse Industrial Estate, Howard Street, Bristol, BS5 7AZ Tel: 0117-955 4132 Fax: 0117-935 0185 E-mail: enquries@wcltd.co.uk

▶ Metalcraft Architectural Engineering Co. Ltd, Unit 1 Ravenscroft Way, Barnoldswick, Lancashire, BB18 6JA Tel: (01282) 817517 Fax: (01282) 851300

Metalcraft Willenhall Ltd, Ezekiel Lane, Willenhall, West Midlands, WV12 5QX Tel: (01922) 476954 Fax: (01922) 409588

▶ Metalduct Nottingham Ltd, C12 Haydn Road, Nottingham, NG5 1DG Tel: 0115-962 3482 Fax: 0115-969 2881

Metasmith Edinburgh Ltd, Unit 12 Bilston Glen Industrial Estate, Dryden Road, Loanhead, Midlothian, EH20 9LZ Tel: 0131-440 7002 Fax: 0131-440 7003

Mice Kay Mar Ltd, Brookhill Industrial Estate, Pinxton, Nottingham, NG16 6NS Tel: (01773) 810107 Fax: (01773) 580286 E-mail: sales@micekaymar.com

▶ Mid Beds Development Ltd, N Cradock Road, Luton, LU4 0JF Tel: (01582) 580327 Fax: (01582) 565248

Mid Fab Developments Ltd, 84 Cliveland Street, Birmingham, B19 3SN Tel: 0121-359 1641 Fax: 0121-333 3228 E-mail: sales@midfabdevelopments.co.uk

▶ Midas, Unit 3 Singer Way, Kempston, Bedford, MK42 7AW Tel: (01234) 857770 Fax: (01234) 857771

Middleton Sheet Metal Co. Ltd, Spring Vale, Middleton, Manchester, M24 2HS Tel: 0161-643 2462 Fax: 0161-643 3490 E-mail: info@msmgroup.org

Midland Precision Ltd, Unit 3a Peckleton Lane Business Park, Peckleton, Leicester, LE9 7RF Tel: (01455) 828998 Fax: (01455) 828993 E-mail: sales@mid-precision.co.uk

▶ indicates data change since last edition

SHEET METALWORK ENGINEERS OR FABRICATORS – *continued*

Midland Tank & Ironplate Co. Ltd, 241-243 Heneage Street, Birmingham, B7 4LY Tel: 0121-359 0298 Fax: 0121-333 3035 E-mail: sales@mti.uk.com

Midway Metalcraft, Ridgeway Court, Grovebury Rd, Leighton Buzzard, Bedfordshire, LU7 4SW Tel: (01525) 374861 Fax: (01525) 374082 E-mail: enquiries@midwaymetalcraft.com

Adam Millar & Sons Ltd, 22 Muriel Street, Barrhead, Glasgow, G78 1QB Tel: 0141-881 6000 Fax: 0141-881 6060 E-mail: info@adammiller.com

Minster Engineering Co. Ltd, Ebor Industrial Estate, 74 Hallfield Road, York, YO31 7XD Tel: (01904) 717220 Fax: (01904) 717222 E-mail: gregallison@minstereng.freeserve.co.uk

▶ Mitsui Babcock Ltd, Torness Power Station, Torness, Dunbar, East Lothian, EH42 1QU Tel: (01368) 865188 Fax: (01368) 865183

Molesey Metal Works, 22 Island Farm Avenue, West Molesey, Surrey, KT8 2UA Tel: (020) 8979 1772 Fax: (020) 8979 7337

▶ Moor Insulation Ltd, Unit 29 Woodend Industrial Estate, Woodend Avenue, Speke, Liverpool, L24 9NB Tel: 0151-486 8272 Fax: 0151-486 8252

▶ Moore R D Ltd, Brunel Way, Stephenson Industrial Estate, Coalville, Leicestershire, LE67 3HF Tel: (01530) 510224 Fax: (01530) 836200

MRF Design & Fabrications Ltd, Unit 2, Jubilee Trading Centre, 130 Pershore Street, Birmingham, B5 6ND Tel: 0121-622 4447

MSK Fabrication, Unit 4 Orchard Park Industrial Estate, Sandiacre, Nottingham, NG10 5BP Tel: 0115-949 1500 Fax: 0115-949 1600 E-mail: info@mskfab.co.uk

Multishape Sheet Metal Work, 120 Camford Way, Luton, LU3 3AN Tel: (01582) 581133 Fax: (01582) 581158 E-mail: custserv@multishape.co.uk

▶ N E L Technologies Ltd, 269b Queensway South, Team Valley Trading Estate, Gateshead, Tyne & Wear, NE11 0SD Tel: 0191-487 4181 Fax: 0191-264 0994 E-mail: sales@nel-ltd.co.uk

N K F Metal Services, Unit 5 East Thamesmead Business Park, Kencot Close, Erith, Kent, DA18 4AB Tel: (020) 8310 2199 Fax: (020) 8310 2204 E-mail: john.oshea60@virgin.net

Nci, 2 Nelsons Lane, Hurst, Reading, RG10 0RR Tel: 0118-934 5316 Fax: 0118-934 2010 E-mail: info@nciservices.co.uk

Nelson Sheetmetal Fabricators Ltd, Walton St Works, Walton St, Colne, Lancashire, BB8 0EW Tel: (01282) 866966 Fax: (01282) 866990 E-mail: nsc@fsmail.net

Neptune Fabrications Ltd, 5 Ibrox Industrial Estate, Carmichael Street, Glasgow, G51 2QU Tel: 0141-427 3773 Fax: 0141-427 3703 E-mail: nepfab@btconnect.co.uk

▶ Nevis Heating & Vent Ltd, Unit 2a Caol Industrial Estate, Ardgour Road, Caol, Fort William, Inverness-Shire, PH33 7PH Tel: (01397) 705656 Fax: (01397) 701656

New Holland Sheet Metal Co. Ltd, Unit 30 Jubilee Trading Estate, Jubilee Road, Letchworth Garden City, Hertfordshire, SG6 1NE Tel: (01462) 674265 Fax: (01462) 480699 E-mail: newholland@btconnect.co.uk

▶ Newarthill Engineers & Fabricators Ltd, 102-110 Carfin Road, Newarthill, Motherwell, Lanarkshire, ML1 5JZ Tel: (01698) 732684 Fax: (01698) 733177

Newfold Ltd, Bridgewater Close, Reading, RG30 1NS Tel: 0118-957 3074 E-mail: sales@newfold.co.uk

▶ Nexus Precision Engineering, 1a Ligget Syke Place, East Mains Industrial Estate, Broxburn, West Lothian, EH52 5NA Tel: (01506) 855995 Fax: (01506) 854044

Nicholls Fabrications Ltd, New Hold Industrial Estate, Garforth, Leeds, LS25 2LD Tel: 0113-232 0847 Fax: 0113-232 0718

Nobles Engineering Solutions Ltd, 11 Mallard Close, Earls Barton, Northampton, NN6 0JF Tel: (01604) 810695 Fax: (01604) 812586

Nokell Fabrications Ltd, 18 Radway Industrial Estate, Radway Road, Shirley, Solihull, West Midlands, B90 4NR Tel: 0121-705 4771 Fax: 0121-711 3681

▶ Norstead Mechanical Engineers, 261 Springhill Parkway, Glasgow Business Park, Baillieston, Glasgow, G69 6GA Tel: 0141-781 2100 Fax: 0141-781 2101 E-mail: sales@norstead.co.uk

North Notts Sheet Metal Ltd, Unit 3 Welsh Croft Close, Kirkby-in-Ashfield, Nottingham, NG17 8EP Tel: (01623) 722123 Fax: (01623) 720562

North West Fabrications Ltd, Station Works, Berry Street, Bootle, Merseyside, L20 8AT Tel: 0151-922 9518 Fax: 0151-933 6395

▶ Northern Engineering & Welding Co. Ltd, Claggan Road, Fort William, Inverness-Shire, PH33 6PH Tel: (01397) 702588 Fax: (01397) 705091 E-mail: sales@newcolimited.co.uk

Norwest Engineering Ltd, Low Stripes, The Stripes, Cumwhinton, Carlisle, CA4 0AW Tel: (01228) 560408 Fax: (01228) 561696 E-mail: norwest@btclick.com

Norwich Sheet Metal Co. Ltd, 11 Hurricane Way, Norwich, NR6 6EZ Tel: (01603) 419490 Fax: (01603) 404590 E-mail: nsmetal@btconnect.com

Oakham Sheet Metal Co. Ltd, Brickhouse Lane, Great Bridge, West Bromwich, West Midlands, B70 0DS Tel: 0121-557 9656 Fax: 0121-522 2186

Oasis Metal Products, Wonastow Road, Monmouth, Gwent, NP25 5AH Tel: (01600) 715732 Fax: (01600) 714878

▶ Oem Fabrication Ltd, 47 Sandilands Street, Glasgow, G32 0HT Tel: 0141-764 2150

▶ P & A Engineering, Crown Works, Parry Lane, Bradford, West Yorkshire, BD4 8TJ Tel: (01274) 744887 Fax: (01274) 733335 E-mail: info@panda-engineering.co.uk

P A G Sheet Metal Ltd, 4 River Brent Business Park, Trumpers Way, London, W7 2QA Tel: (020) 8574 3577 Fax: (020) 8893 5370 E-mail: sales@pagsheetmetal.com

▶ P & C Precision Engineers Ltd, Unit 3c Heron Trading Estate, Whitefield Avenue, Luton, LU3 3BB Tel: (01582) 581735 Fax: (01582) 581735

▶ P D S C N C Engineering Ltd, Unit 10 Riverside Business Centre, Cliffe Street, Nelson, Lancashire, BB9 7QR Tel: (01282) 619848 Fax: (01282) 611024

▶ P & F Engineering, Unit C The Poplars, Beeston, Nottingham, NG9 2PD Tel: 0115 9220777

▶ P J D Engineering Ltd, 4 Henlow Industrial Estate, Henlow, Bedfordshire, SG16 6DS Tel: (01462) 815544 Fax: (01462) 816677

P J Mcgowan, Gethceln House, Dawley Road, Hayes, Middlesex, UB3 1EH Tel: (020) 8573 1571 Fax: (020) 8561 3750

P M Fabrication, Unit F3 Doulton Trading Estate, Doulton Road, Rowley Regis, West Midlands, B65 8JQ Tel: (01384) 561498 Fax: (01384) 561498

P & P Supplies Ltd, Units 9-11, Ely Distribution Centre, Heol Trelai, Ely, Cardiff, CF5 5NJ Tel: (029) 2059 7593 Fax: (029) 2059 1268 E-mail: info@pandpsupplies.co.uk

▶ P Pritchard Sheet Metal Ltd, Unit 15 White Horse Business Park, Ware Road, Stanford in the Vale, Faringdon, Oxfordshire, SN7 8NY Tel: (01367) 710060 Fax: (01367) 710105

Panton (Sheet Metalworks) Ltd, 67 Swaisland Drive, Crayford Industrial Estate, Crayford, Dartford, DA1 4HS Tel: (01322) 554180 Fax: (01322) 555157 E-mail: enquiries@pantonsheetmetal.co.uk

Paramount Precision Engineering Ltd, Unit D Wellington CR, New Malden, Surrey, KT3 3NE Tel: (020) 8949 7766 Fax: (020) 8949 0042 E-mail: paramount@technicalwebservices.com

Park Sheet Metal Co. Ltd, Bayton Road, Exhall, Coventry, CV7 9DJ Tel: (024) 7636 1606 Fax: (024) 7664 4078 E-mail: office@parksheetmetal.co.uk

Park Welding & Fabrication Co. Ltd, Slade Lane, Brighouse, West Yorkshire, HD6 3PP Tel: (01484) 716651 Fax: (01484) 723022 E-mail: sales@parkwelding.co.uk

Parkway Sheet Metal Works Ltd, Rawmarsh Road, Rotherham, South Yorkshire, S60 1RZ Tel: (01709) 374726 Fax: (01709) 829739

Pass Fabrications Ltd, Trent Street, Sheffield, S9 3XU Tel: 0114-244 2276 Fax: 0114-244 2276

J. Paterson, Gaywood Farm, Hole La, Edenbridge, Kent, TN8 6SL Tel: (01732) 864673 Fax: (01732) 864673

Patterns Ltd, Darley Abbey Mills, Darley Abbey, Derby, DE22 1DZ Tel: (01332) 342127 Fax: (01332) 298242 E-mail: enquiries@patternsderby.co.uk

▶ Paveford Holdings Ltd, Units 3 & 4 East Park Industrial Estate, Purbrook Road, Wolverhampton, WV1 2EJ Tel: (01902) 871282 Fax: (01902) 457309

Pearlgreen Engineering Ltd, 300 Hawthorn Avenue, Hull, HU3 5LL Tel: (01482) 618441

Pegasus, Old Surrenden Farm, Bethersden, Ashford, Kent, TN26 3DF Tel: (01233) 820867 Fax: (01233) 820867

▶ Pentland Precision Engineering, Unit 1-4 Pentland View, Pentland Industrial Estate, Loanhead, Midlothian, EH20 9QH Tel: 0131-448 2224

Joseph Percival & Co., Shawcross Street, Stockport, Cheshire, SK1 3EZ Tel: 0161-480 3858 Fax: 0161-480 7394

Perfab Engineering Ltd, Unit 3 Northway Lane, Tewkesbury, Gloucestershire, GL20 8HA Tel: (01684) 298423 Fax: (01684) 850427

▶ Peter Grant Associates Ltd, 18 Bakewell Road, Loughborough, Leicestershire, LE11 5QY Tel: (01509) 610580 Fax: (01509) 217346

Peterborough Sheet Metal Ltd, Unit 12 Towermead Business Centre, High Street, Peterborough, PE2 9DY Tel: (01733) 344880 Fax: (01733) 898421

Phillips Engineering, Bulmer Road Industrial Estate, Bulmer Road, Sudbury, Suffolk, CO10 7HJ Tel: (01787) 373549 Fax: (01787) 880276

Pierceton Engineering Ltd, 2 Macadam Place, South Newmoor Industrial Estate, Irvine, Ayrshire, KA11 4HP Tel: (01294) 214427 Fax: (01294) 214440

▶ Pignone Engineering, Badentoy CR, Portlethen, Aberdeen, AB12 4YD Tel: (01224) 784400 Fax: (01224) 785130

Pinnacle Ductwork Manufacturers Ltd, Unit 8 Seagull Lane, Emsworth, Hampshire, PO10 7QH Tel: (01243) 377214 Fax: (01243) 376448 E-mail: pinnacleductwork@aol.com

Pioneer Finishers, Pioneer Business Park, Princess Road, Ramsgate, Kent, CT11 7RX Tel: (01843) 596615 Fax: (01843) 580933 E-mail: pioneer.paul@talk21.com

Pre Fab Southern Ltd, 10 Alphage Road, Gosport, Hampshire, PO12 4DU Tel: (023) 9251 0200 Fax: (023) 9251 0300 E-mail: admin@pre-fab.co.uk

▶ Precise Engineering, Penrhiwfer Road, Tonypandy, Mid Glamorgan, CF40 1RL Tel: (01443) 435341 Fax: (01443) 423666

Precision Metal Products, Lady Indust Estate Albion Street, Southwick, Brighton, BN42 4EG Tel: (01273) 592886 Fax: (01273) 592711 E-mail: info@precisionmetalproducts.co.uk

Precision Sheets Products Ltd, 60 Victoria Road, Burgess Hill, West Sussex, RH15 9LR Tel: (01444) 247010 Fax: (01444) 233335

Preform Insulations Ltd, Unit 29 & 30 Enterprise Works, 13 & 14 Bergen Way, North Lynn Industrial Estate, King's Lynn, Norfolk, PE30 2JG Tel: (01553) 776382 Fax: (01603) 881254 E-mail: sales@preforminsulations.co.uk

Premier Sheet Metal & Engineering Co. Ltd, 4 Premier Building, Brockhampton Road, Havant, Hampshire, PO9 1JU Tel: (023) 9247 2633 Fax: (023) 9249 8210 E-mail: sales@premiersheetmetal.co.uk

Press Fab Ltd, 10 Bayton Way, Exhall, Coventry, CV7 9ER Tel: (024) 7636 2509

▶ Presscut Components, Station Road, Bagworth, Coalville, Leicestershire, LE67 1BH Tel: (01530) 230220 Fax: (01530) 230218 E-mail: sales@presscutcomponents.co.uk

▶ Preston Components Ltd, 19 Watt Road, Hillington Industrial Estate, Glasgow, G52 4RY Tel: 0141-882 1766 Fax: 0141-882 6363

Priest Engineering Co Poole Ltd, Holton Heath Trading Park, Poole, Dorset, BH16 6LE Tel: (01202) 631663 Fax: (01202) 632573 E-mail: sales@priest-engineering.co.uk

▶ Pro Metal Manufacturing Ltd, 3b Maitland Road, Lion Barn Industrial Estate, Needham Market, Ipswich, IP6 8NZ Tel: (01449) 723082 Fax: (01449) 723080

Process Pipe Work Services, North Lonsdale Road, Ulverston, Cumbria, LA12 9DL Tel: (01229) 583954 Fax: (01229) 581531 E-mail: admin@pps-ulv.co.uk

Prodrive Holdings Ltd, Acorn Way, Banbury, Oxfordshire, OX16 3ER Tel: (01295) 273355 Fax: (01295) 271188 E-mail: enquiries@prodrive.com

Production & Development Services Ltd, 1-2 Marshlands Road, Portsmouth, PO6 1ST Tel: 023 92215288

▶ Profile Engineering, 10 Lower Clark St Industrial Estate, Scarborough, North Yorkshire, YO12 7PP Tel: (01723) 350111 Fax: (01723) 350222

Propak Sheet Metal Ltd, Unit C-D Gunnels Wood Park, Gunnels Wood Road, Stevenage, Hertfordshire, SG1 2BH Tel: (01438) 728885 Fax: (01438) 740298 E-mail: bruce@propak.co.uk

Pro-Tech Precision Ltd, Station Road West, Ash Vale, Aldershot, Hampshire, GU12 5QD Tel: (01252) 516242 Fax: (01252) 524025 E-mail: sales@pro-techprecision.com

Quality Metal Fabrication, Unit 2 Meadow View Industrial Estate, Ruckinge, Ashford, Kent, TN26 2NR Tel: (01233) 733544 Fax: (01233) 733544

▶ Quality Products General Engineering Ltd, The Green, Old Sodbury, Bristol, BS37 6LY Tel: (01454) 325022 Fax: (01454) 315464 E-mail: info@sheetmetal.qualityproducts.co.uk

Quality Tool & Engineering Ltd, Maesyllan, Llanidloes, Powys, SY18 6DF Tel: (01686) 412679 Fax: (01686) 413554 E-mail: qualitytools@btconnect.com

Quante Telecommunications Ltd, Snailwell Business Pk, Fordham Rd, Snailwell, Newmarket, Suffolk, CB8 7NY Tel: (01638) 721333 Fax: (01638) 721233 E-mail: service@quante.co.uk

▶ Queensferry Metals Ltd, Port Edgar Marina, Port Edgar, South Queensferry, West Lothian, EH30 9SQ Tel: 0131-331 1791 Fax: 0131-331 4603

▶ Quintec Associates Ltd, Merlin House Gifford Court, Fox Den Road, Stoke Gifford, Bristol, BS34 8TT Tel: 0117-979 2888 Fax: 0117-979 2666

R & B Fabrications, 4 Vulcan Road, Solihull, West Midlands, B91 2JY Tel: 0121-711 3279 Fax: 0121-711 3279

R B Punching Services Ltd, College Road, Aston Clinton, Aylesbury, Buckinghamshire, HP22 5EZ Tel: (01296) 630262 Fax: (01296) 630485 E-mail: rbpunch@globalnet.co.uk

▶ R D T Precision Engineers Ltd, 3 Colvilles Road, Kelvin Industrial Estate, East Kilbride, Glasgow, G75 0RS Tel: (01355) 248072 Fax: (01355) 264380 E-mail: info@rdtprecision.com

▶ R G L Contracts, North Tay Works, Balfield Road, Dundee, DD3 6AG Tel: (01382) 641842 Fax: (01382) 642169

R I N C Engineering, 22 Singer Road, Kelvin Industrial Estate, East Kilbride, Glasgow, G75 0XS Tel: (01355) 248610 Fax: (01355) 248610 E-mail: rinc@wwwmail.co.uk

R J Barrington Ltd, 3 Barrington Buildings, Clinton Road, Leominster, Herefordshire, HR6 0RJ Tel: (01568) 612101 Fax: (01568) 612501 E-mail: mary@rjbarringtonltd.co.uk

▶ R J Engineering Ltd, 19 Enterprise Way, Jubilee Business Park, Derby, DE21 4BB Tel: (01332) 367611 Fax: (01332) 291635

▶ R M P Products Ltd, Unit 26 G W S Trading Estate, Leabrook Road, Wednesbury, West Midlands, WS10 7NB Tel: 0121-505 3066 Fax: 0121-505 3077 E-mail: rmpproducts@btconnect.com

R M R Engineering Ltd, 90-92 Tontine Street, Folkestone, Kent, CT20 1JW Tel: (01303) 253166 Fax: (01303) 220380 E-mail: sales@rmrengineering.co.uk

▶ R P Metal Co. Ltd, Toutley Industrial Estate, Toutley Road, Wokingham, Berkshire, RG41 1QN Tel: 0118-978 8006 Fax: 0118-977 6388 E-mail: rpmetalwork@btconnect.com

R & R Sheet Metal Fabrications Ltd, R & R House, North Bridge Road, Berkhamsted, Hertfordshire, HP4 1EH Tel: (01442) 876969 Fax: (01442) 877979

R S Taylor & Co UK Ltd, 18 Merchant Drive, Mead Lane, Hertford, SG13 7AY Tel: (01992) 551881 Fax: (01992) 500177

R Y Thomson & Son, 15 Ash Street, Dundee, DD1 5AR Tel: (01382) 221460 Fax: (01382) 907005 E-mail: rythomson@btconnect.com

▶ Rackham Engineering, Hellesdon Park Industrial Estate Road, Norwich, NR6 5DR Tel: (01603) 485038 Fax: (01603) 787106 E-mail: sale@rackhamengineering.co.uk

Radshape Sheet Metal Ltd, Shefford Road, Birmingham, B6 4PL Tel: 0121-242 3323 Fax: 0121-242 3385 E-mail: info@radshape.co.uk

▶ Rainey Engineering Solutions, Enterprise Crescent, Lisburn, County Antrim, BT28 2BP Tel: (028) 9266 9233 Fax: (028) 9266 9239

Rapier Precision Sheet Metal Ltd, 1 Princes Works, Princes Road, Teddington, Middlesex, TW11 0RW Tel: (020) 8943 4788 Fax: (020) 8977 1686 E-mail: info@rapierprecision.co.uk

Redfern & Birchall, 6 Fernhill Street, Bury, Lancashire, BL9 5BG Tel: 0161-764 4929 Fax: 0161-764 4929

Redman Sheet Metal Ltd, Unit 13 Isis Trading Estate, Swindon, SN1 2PG Tel: (01793) 692781 Fax: (01793) 491688 E-mail: jim@redman-sheet-metal.co.uk

Redmill Fabrication Ltd, 19 Inchmuir Road, Whitehill Industrial Estate, Bathgate, West Lothian, EH48 2EP Tel: (01506) 634333 Fax: (01506) 634999

Reeves Engineering Ltd, 15 Swinbourne Drive, Springwood Industrial Estate, Braintree, Essex, CM7 2YP Tel: (01376) 322613 Fax: (01376) 551522

▶ Remik Engineering Ltd, 61 Nasmyth Road, Glenrothes, Fife, KY6 2SD Tel: (01592) 631260 Fax: (01592) 631262

▶ Renson Products Ltd, Stainland Road, Greetland, Halifax, West Yorkshire, HX4 8LR Tel: (01422) 344222 Fax: (01422) 344766

Repfab Engineering Ltd, Unit 6 Whiteleather Square, Billingborough, Sleaford, Lincolnshire, NG34 0QP Tel: (01529) 240600 Fax: (01529) 240647

Retail Display Solutions, St. Andrew House, St. Andrews Trading Estate, Bridport, Dorset, DT6 3EX Tel: (01308) 459950 Fax: (01308) 424410 E-mail: sales@retaildisplaysolutions.co.uk

▶ Rhyal Engineering Ltd, Unit 8 Thornton Industrial Trading Estate, Milford Haven, Dyfed, SA73 2RX Tel: (01646) 699191 Fax: (01646) 699192

Rictor Engineering Ltd, Derby Street, Denton, Manchester, M34 3SD Tel: 0161-320 8842 Fax: 0161-335 0973

▶ Rig Engineering Sas, 621 George Street, Aberdeen, AB25 3YE Tel: (01224) 627200 Fax: (01224) 647308 E-mail: info@rigengineering.com

Riley Metal Works Ltd, 23 Yorkshire Road, London, E14 7LR Tel: (020) 7790 3597

▶ Rippleside Metal Works Ltd, Thames Road, Grays, Essex, RM17 6JP Tel: (01375) 383741 Fax: (01375) 391514

▶ Risbridger Engineering Services, 25 Trowers Way, Redhill, RH1 2LH Tel: (0845) 6442323 Fax: (0845) 6442453 E-mail: info@risbridger.com

▶ Ritetrak Engineering Wales Ltd, Gilfach Farm, Cwmbach, Whitland, Dyfed, SA34 0DN Tel: (01994) 448666 Fax: (01994) 448687

Riverdale Mahoney Ltd, Unit 3 Dicker Mill, Hertford, SG13 7AE Tel: (01992) 583988 Fax: (01992) 583988 E-mail: riverdalema@btinternet.com

▶ Robinson Instrument Machinery, Unit 2, 24 Battle Road, Heathfield Industrial Estate, Newton Abbot, Devon, TQ12 6XU Tel: (01626) 836789 Fax: (01626) 836790 E-mail: ron@robinsoninst.co.uk

Robric Engineering Co., Baldock Road, Stotfold, Hitchin, Hertfordshire, SG5 4NZ Tel: (01462) 732143 Fax: (01462) 735273

Rochdale Metal Units Ltd, Victoria Road, Adamroyd Mills, Todmorden, Lancashire, OL14 5LN Tel: (01706) 813071 Fax: (01706) 814916 E-mail: rmunits@btconnect.com

▶ Roger Bullivant Ltd, Cooperage Way, Alloa, Clackmannanshire, FK10 3LP Tel: (01259) 272050 Fax: (01259) 272051

Rolls Royce plc, Watnall Road, Hucknall, Nottingham, NG15 6EU Tel: 0115-963 3111 Fax: 0115-964 2345

Rom Metals Ltd, Wonastow Road Industrial Estate, Monmouth, Gwent, NP25 5AH Tel: (01600) 712312 Fax: (01600) 712312

Romar Process Engineering Ltd, 12 Faraday Road, Leigh-on-Sea, Essex, SS9 5JU Tel: (01702) 523351 Fax: (01702) 421402 E-mail: info@romar.uk.net

David Ross Fabrications Ltd, Unit 1E, Peckleton Lane Business Estate, Peckleton, Leicester, LE9 7RN Tel: (01455) 823721 Fax: (01455) 828339 E-mail: metalwork@davidrossfabrications.co.uk

▶ Ross-Shire Engineering Ltd, The Industrial Estate, Muir Of Ord, Ross-Shire, IV6 7UA Tel: (01463) 870049 E-mail: info@ross-ing.com

▶ Rotary Engineering Reading Ltd, Unit A8 Grovelands Avenue Workshops, Winnersh, Wokingham, Berkshire, RG41 5LB Tel: 0118-979 2200 Fax: 0118-979 2211

SHEET METALWORK ENGINEERS OR FABRICATORS – *continued*

Round Green Engineering Ltd, 199 Camford Way, Luton, LU3 3AN Tel: (01582) 503808 Fax: (01582) 503898 E-mail: barrie@roundgreen.com

Round House Ltd, 57 Pinbush Road, Lowestoft, Suffolk, NR33 7NL Tel: (01502) 515220 Fax: (01502) 500954 E-mail: sales@roundhouse.biz

Rowan Engineering, Garland Works, Desborough Avenue, High Wycombe, Buckinghamshire, HP11 2RN Tel: (01494) 531213 Fax: (01494) 465226 E-mail: enquiries@drjeng.fsnet.co.uk

▶ Rushmore plc, Victoria Works, Victoria Road, Hebden Bridge, West Yorkshire, HX7 8LN Tel: (01422) 844866 Fax: (01422) 844466 E-mail: sales@rushmoreplc.com

Ryeford Engineering, 14 Ebley Road, Stonehouse, Gloucestershire, GL10 2LH Tel: (01453) 825841 Fax: (01453) 827732 E-mail: nick@ryefordeng.co.uk

Rylandes Engineering Ltd, Broomfield Barn, Coolham Road, Shipley, Horsham, West Sussex, RH13 8PF Tel: (01403) 741268 Fax: (01403) 741605 E-mail: sales@rylandesengineering.co.uk

S A Jones, Unit 3 Gwyrfai Mills, Bontnewydd, Caernarfon, Gwynedd, LL54 7UN Tel: (01286) 678683 Fax: (01286) 678683

▶ S & E Engineering, 22 Wentworth Road, Southpark Industrial Estate, Scunthorpe, South Humberside, DN17 2AX Tel: (01724) 858661 Fax: (01724) 281168

S & G Fabrications Lowestoft Ltd, Horn Hill, Lowestoft, Suffolk, NR33 0PX Tel: (01502) 566734 Fax: (01502) 573900

S L S Fabrications Ltd, 2 Hythe Works, Diplocks Way, Hailsham, East Sussex, BN27 3JF Tel: (01323) 846061 Fax: (01323) 841009

S M P Security Ltd, Halesfield 24, Telford, Shropshire, TF7 4NZ Tel: (01952) 585673 Fax: (01952) 582816

S P B Metal Works, Unit 32a Bourne End Mills, Upper Bourne End Lane, Hemel Hempstead, Hertfordshire, HP1 2UJ Tel: (01442) 878165 Fax: (01442) 878444 E-mail: sales@spbmetalworks.co.uk

S T G Fabrications Ltd, Monument Way East, Woking, Surrey, GU21 5LY Tel: (01483) 769222 Fax: (01483) 769666 E-mail: stgfab@btclick.com

S W Asgood Engineering Ltd, Unit A1 Empress Park, Empress Road, Southampton, SO14 0JX Tel: (023) 8022 3880 Fax: (023) 8033 5131

S Ward & Co., 622 Commercial Road, London, E14 7HS Tel: (020) 7790 1172 Fax: (020) 7790 6616 E-mail: swardco@fsmail.net

Salisbury Switchgear Ltd, Warminster Road, South Newton Industrial Estate, Salisbury, SP2 0QW Tel: (01722) 744388 Fax: (01722) 742882 E-mail: j.robinson@salisburyswitchgear.co.uk

Sam's Fabrication, Unit 17 Morgan Way, Bowthorpe Employment Area, Norwich, NR5 9JJ Tel: (01603) 743252 Fax: (01603) 746927 E-mail: sales@samsfabrications.co.uk

Sandersons T C M, Unit 5 Wallis Court, Road Three, Winsford Industrial Estate, Winsford, Cheshire, CW7 3PD Tel: (01606) 550668

▶ Sandy Allan Blacksmiths Ltd, 5 Small Holdings, Thornton Road, Kirkcaldy, Fife, KY1 3NN Tel: (01592) 655444 Fax: (01592) 655978 E-mail: joe.currie1@btopenworld.com

▶ Sarll Metal Products, Leyton Avenue, Mildenhall, Bury St. Edmunds, Suffolk, IP28 7BL Tel: (01638) 718394 Fax: (01638) 718421 E-mail: info@sarl1.co.uk

Saturn Engineering Ltd, 68 Wilbury Way, Hitchin, Hertfordshire, SG4 0TP Tel: (01462) 458511 Fax: (01462) 458515 E-mail: saturneng@hotmail.com

SB Fabrications, Unit 7 Hammond Business Centre, Hammond Close, Attleborough Fields Industrial Estate, Nuneaton, Warwickshire, CV11 6RY Tel: (024) 7632 9011 Fax: (024) 7632 9011

▶ Score Europe Ltd, Howley Park Road East, Morley, Leeds, LS27 0SW Tel: 0113-289 8420 Fax: 0113-253 5649

▶ Scott Engineering Co. Ltd, Block 3 Unit 1 Moorpark Industrial Estate, Moorpark Place, Stevenston, Ayrshire, KA20 3JT Tel: (01294) 602045 Fax: (01294) 604601

Scrutton Engineering Ltd, Duck Lees Lane Industrial Estate, 73 East Duck Lees Lane, Enfield, Middlesex, EN3 7SR Tel: (020) 8443 4010 Fax: (020) 8609 0050 E-mail: info@selfab.com

Serco, Unit 63 Hillgrove Business Park, Nazeing Road, Nazeing, Waltham Abbey, Essex, EN9 2HB Tel: (01992) 893917 Fax: (01992) 893759

Shaw Sheet Metal Rugby Ltd, 13 Paynes Lane, Rugby, Warwickshire, CV21 2UH Tel: (01788) 536033 Fax: (01788) 536922 E-mail: sales@shawsheetmetal.co.uk

Shearwell Sheet Metal Works Ltd, 10 Boston Road, Leicester, LE4 1AU Tel: 0116-235 7669 Fax: 0116-235 7669

▶ The Sheet Metal Co. Ltd, Holme End Works, Burnley Road, Hebden Bridge, West Yorkshire, HX7 8NX Tel: (01422) 846283 E-mail: accountants@sheetmet.co.uk

Sheet Metal Products, St. Michaels Road, Newcastle upon Tyne, NE6 1QS Tel: 0191-276 3028 Fax: 0191-276 3028

▶ Sheet Metal Technology Ltd, Cradley Business Park, Overend Road, Cradley Heath, West Midlands, B64 7DW Tel: (01384) 411190 Fax: (01384) 412101

Sheet Metals Sherwood Ltd, Dako House, Vernon Road, Nottingham, NG6 0AR Tel: 0115-978 4456 Fax: 0115-978 4456

▶ Sheet Tech Fabrications, 6 Doman Road, Camberley, Surrey, GU15 3DF Tel: (01276) 684800 Fax: (01276) 20696

Sheet Tech Fabrications, 6 Doman Road, Camberley, Surrey, GU15 3DF Tel: (01276) 684800 Fax: (01276) 20696 E-mail: cliffdottson@sheettech.fsnet.co.uk

Sheetmetal Developments, Unit 1 Wessex Park, Bancombe Road Trading Estate, Somerton, Somerset, TA11 6SB Tel: (01458) 272212 Fax: (01458) 272212 E-mail: rosser@aol.com

▶ Shepley Engineers Ltd, Westlakes Science & Technology Park, Moor Row, Cumbria, CA24 3JZ Tel: (01946) 599022 Fax: (01946) 591933E-mail: engineers@sheepley.vhe.co.uk

Shermaynes Welders Engineers Ltd, Units 2d 3a/3b Southgate Industrial Centre, Southgate, Lancaster, Morecambe, LA3 3PB Tel: (01524) 69333

Shrub Hill Fabrications, Unit 3 British Rail Industrial Estate, Tolladine Road, Worcester, WR4 9PT Tel: (01905) 20644 Fax: (01905) 20644

Simister & Chorlton Ltd, 27 Edna Street, Hyde, Cheshire, SK14 1LD Tel: 0161-368 2309 Fax: 0161-367 8264

▶ Simstler, Riverside Way, Riverside Business Park, Irvine, Ayrshire, KA11 5DJ Tel: (01294) 557911

▶ Sitemech Fabrications Ltd, Porritt Street, Bury, Lancashire, BL9 6HJ Tel: 0161-764 3901 Fax: 0161-763 3109 E-mail: sales@sitemechfabs.co.uk

Charles Smethurst Ltd, Castlemill Street, Oldham, OL1 3HL Tel: 0161-624 4505 Fax: 0161-628 4282 E-mail: info@charlessmethurst.co.uk

▶ Smiths Engineering Works N I Ltd, Larne Road, Ballymena, County Antrim, BT42 3HA Tel: (028) 2564 1621 Fax: (028) 2564 3724 E-mail: info@smiths-engineering.com

SMJ Fabrications Ltd, Unit 12 Rookwood Hall, Abbess Roding, Ongar, Essex, CM5 0JL Tel: (01279) 876497 Fax: (01279) 876419

Solectron Systems UK, Arisdale Avenue, South Ockendon, Essex, RM15 5TT Tel: (01708) 852223 Fax: (01708) 850217

▶ Sontrest Surrounds, Mount Road, Kidsgrove, Stoke-on-Trent, ST7 4AZ Tel: (01782) 776271 Fax: (01782) 783357

Southern Sheetmetal Ltd, Unit 9 Bury Farm, Curbridge, Botley, Southampton, SO30 2HB Tel: (01489) 789143 Fax: (01489) 789069

▶ Southway Engineering Cornwall Ltd, Station Road, Kelly Bray, Callington, Cornwall, PL17 8ER Tel: (01579) 382261 Fax: (01579) 383935

Specialised Production Technology Ltd, 3 Monometer Business Park, Woodrolfe Road, Tollesbury, Maldon, Essex, CM9 8SB Tel: (01621) 868200 Fax: (01621) 868860

▶ Spruce Engineering Co. Ltd, Flanshaw Lane, Wakefield, West Yorkshire, WF2 9JE Tel: (01924) 378637 Fax: (01924) 383157 E-mail: mail@spruceeng.co.uk

Stace Yates Ltd, Unit 24 Bamfurlong Industrial Park, Staverton, Cheltenham, Gloucestershire, GL51 6SX Tel: (01452) 713722 Fax: (01452) 713282

Stadium Power Ltd, 23-29 Owen Road, Vinces Road Industrial Estate, Diss, Norfolk, IP22 4YU Tel: (01379) 644233 Fax: (01379) 650118 E-mail: sales@stadiumpower.co.uk

Stanham Engineering Ltd, 31a Cobble Lane, London, N1 1SF Tel: (020) 7226 3730 Fax: (020) 7226 2746

Stead & Wilkins Fabrications Ltd, Jolly Farmers Wharf, Thames Road, Crayford, Dartford, DA1 4QH Tel: (01322) 529134 Fax: (01322) 550314 E-mail: alanbaynton@steadandwilkins.co.uk

▶ Steels Engineering Services Ltd, Unit 4b Apollo House, Calleva Park, Aldermaston, Reading, RG7 8TN Tel: 0118-981 7868 Fax: 0118-981 6291

Stevenage Sheet Metal Co. Ltd, Unit 1, Jubilee Trade Centre, Jubilee Road, Letchworth Garden City, Hertfordshire, SG6 1SP Tel: (01462) 674794 Fax: (01462) 481132 E-mail: richard@stevenagesheetmetal.com

Stiles Metal Craft, Brickfield Industrial Estate, New Road, Gillingham, Dorset, SP8 4LT Tel: (01747) 824240 Fax: (01747) 824240

Stokes & Parry Ltd, Kelsey Close, Attleborough Fields Industrial Estate, Nuneaton, Warwickshire, CV11 6RS Tel: (024) 7638 2096 Fax: (024) 7634 2006 E-mail: stokesandparry@tiscali.co.uk

Stonaco Fabrications Ltd, Wilton Road, Haine Industrial Estate, Ramsgate, Kent, CT12 5HG Tel: (01843) 596448 Fax: (01843) 593548

▶ Stone Hardy, 1 Aubrey Street, Salford, M50 3UT Tel: 0161-868 2880 Fax: 0161-868 2899

▶ Stonehenge Services Ltd, Faraday Road, Salisbury, SP2 7NR Tel: (01722) 414161 Fax: (01722) 335343 E-mail: stonehenge.serve@btconnect.com

▶ Stratford Precision Engineering Ltd, 5 The Rubicon Centre, Broad Ground Road, Redditch, Worcestershire, B98 8YP Tel: (01527) 502567 Fax: (01527) 501921 E-mail: info@stratfordprecision.co.uk

Sullivan Engineering Co., 9 Doman Road, Camberley, Surrey, GU15 3DF Tel: (01276) 20931 Fax: (01276) 27168 E-mail: sullivaneng42@netscapeonline.co.uk

Summit Engineering Co., Wharf Way, Glen Parva, Leicester, LE2 9TF Tel: 0116-277 1083 Fax: 0116-277 3518 E-mail: summit@webleicester.co.uk

George Sumner Ltd, Bridge Street, Oldham, OL1 1EB Tel: 0161-678 6111 Fax: 0161-624 7773 E-mail: terry@georgesumner.co.uk

Surestep Sheet Metal Ltd, Unit J2 Northfleet Industrial Estate, Lower Road, Northfleet, Gravesend, Kent, DA11 9BL Tel: (01474) 560511 Fax: (01474) 354396 E-mail: info@surestepsheetmetal.com

Survirn Engineering Ltd, 1581 Bristol Road South, Rednal, Birmingham, B45 9UA Tel: 0121-453 7718 Fax: 0121-453 6915 E-mail: sales@survirn.co.uk

Swan Engineering, 70 Scarborough Street, Hull, HU3 4TG Tel: (01482) 890140 Fax: (01482) 323077E-mail: sales@swan-engineering.co.uk

Swanells & Grylls Ltd, 330-332 Selborne Road, Luton, LU4 8NU Tel: (01582) 573066

▶ SWC Trailers & Spares, Manor Farm, Abbotts Ann, Andover, Hampshire, SP11 7DB Tel: (01264) 710610

Swefco Ltd, 188 Corporation Road, Newport, Gwent, NP19 0DQ Tel: (01633) 250170 Fax: (01633) 250171E-mail: swefco@aol.com

Swindon Engineering Metalworkers, Unit 10 Bramble Close, Swindon, SN2 8DW Tel: (01793) 641808 Fax: (01793) 513029

▶ Syncro Ltd, 175 Trident House, Renfrew Road, Paisley, Renfrewshire, PA3 4EF Tel: 0141-849 7800 Fax: 0141-849 7844 E-mail: admin@letsco-operate.com

T A B Sheet Fabrications Ltd, Unit 3 Galliford Road Industrial Estate, Heybridge, Maldon, Essex, CM9 4XX Tel: (01621) 858848 Fax: (01621) 583847 E-mail: info@tabfab.co.uk

▶ T C Fabrications Ripley Ltd, Whiteley Road, Ripley, Derbyshire, DE5 3QL Tel: (01773) 513911 Fax: (01773) 512811 E-mail: dave@tcfabs.co.uk

T Eccleston & Son Leigh Ltd, Welch Hill Street, Leigh, Lancashire, WN7 4DU Tel: (01942) 672993 Fax: (01942) 261964

Tadley Engineering Ltd, Oak Tree Works, Silchester Road, Tadley, Hampshire, RG26 3PX Tel: 0118-981 0621 Fax: 0118-981 0787 E-mail: info@tadleyengineering.co.uk

Tanfield Group plc, Vigo Centre, Birtley Road, Washington, Tyne & Wear, NE38 9DA Tel: 0191-417 2170 Fax: (0845) 1557756 E-mail: sales@tanfieldgroup.com

▶ Tanfield Metal Spinners, 6 Parsons Road, Parsons Industrial Estate, Washington, Tyne & Wear, NE37 1HB Tel: 0191-419 3377

Tates, 4 Knightwood Court, Shuttleworth Close, Gapton Hall Industrial Estate, Great Yarmouth, Norfolk, NR31 0NQ Tel: (01493) 604197 Fax: (01493) 652816 E-mail: enquiries@tatesengineering.com

Taylor Made Fabrication, 6 Pipers Industrial Estate, Pipers Lane, Thatcham, Berkshire, RG19 4NA Tel: (01635) 873737 Fax: (01635) 874747 E-mail: info.request@taylormadefabrication.co.uk

▶ Taylor Manufacturing Ltd, 21 Denmark Street, Fraserburgh, Aberdeenshire, AB43 9EY Tel: (01346) 519399 Fax: (01346) 515781 E-mail: enquiries@taylormfg.co.uk

Tayside Sheet Metal Ltd, 8 Angus Works, Neish Street, Dundee, DD3 7JN Tel: (01382) 828822 Fax: (01382) 828833 E-mail: vent@taysidesheetmetal.freeserve.co.uk

Technicraft Anglia Ltd, Wilford Bridge Road, Melton, Woodbridge, Suffolk, IP12 1RB Tel: (01394) 385213 Fax: (01394) 387914 E-mail: technicraft@technicraft.co.uk

Tecproof Ltd, 266 Dansom Lane North, Hull, HU8 7RS Tel: (01482) 215886 Fax: (01482) 215886

Tegrel Ltd, Tundry Way, Blaydon-on-Tyne, Tyne & Wear, NE21 5TT Tel: 0191-414 6111 Fax: 0191-414 0660 E-mail: sales@tegrel.co.uk

Tharsus Vision Ltd, Unit 8/9, Spencer Road, Blyth, Northumberland, NE24 5TG Tel: (01670) 367030 Fax: (01670) 352012 E-mail: sales@directmessage.co.uk

Tharsus Welding & Sheet Metal Co. Ltd, Glen Street, Hebburn, Tyne & Wear, NE31 1NG Tel: 0191-483 2816 Fax: 0191-428 0063 E-mail: sales@tharsus.co.uk

▶ Thermodynamix Ltd, 3 Princes Park, Princesway, Team Valley Trading Estate, Gateshead, Tyne & Wear, NE11 0NF Tel: 0191-440 7000 Fax: 0191-440 7001

Thomas Shaw & Son (M/C) Ltd, Star Works, Holt Town, Manchester, M40 7FQ Tel: 0161-273 7686 Fax: 0161-274 3699 E-mail: tommy.shaw@virgin.net

▶ Thomson & Wallace Ltd, 25 Shuna Place, Glasgow, G20 9ED Tel: 0141-945 0433

Tiernan Automation Ltd, 308a Melton Road, Leicester, LE4 7SL Tel: 0116-266 4000 Fax: 0116-261 0090 E-mail: sales@t-automation.fsnet.co.uk

Tobel Sheetmetal Ltd, Diplocks Way, Hailsham, East Sussex, BN27 3JF Tel: (01323) 442244 Fax: (01323) 440408 E-mail: sales@tobel.co.uk

▶ Todd Engineering Ltd, 6 Prospect House, Prospect Road, Burntwood, Staffordshire, WS7 0AL Tel: (01543) 677749 Fax: (01543) 677749 E-mail: sales@todengineering.co.uk

▶ Tooling & Developments Ltd, Waterside Road, Hamilton Indutrsial Park, Leicester, LE5 1TL Tel: 0116-246 1808 Fax: 0116-246 1659

Topline Fabrications, Crown Works, Clayton Road, Hayes, Middlesex, UB3 1DU Tel: (020) 8813 5353 Fax: (020) 8561 3114

▶ Total Engineering Vibration Analysis, 2 Andrews Court, Andrews Way, Barrow-in-Furness, Cumbria, LA14 2UE Tel: (01229) 835500 Fax: (01229) 834400

Towrite Fabrications Ltd, Albert Road, Market Harborough, Leicestershire, LE16 7LU Tel: (01858) 467805 Fax: (01858) 434209 E-mail: sales@towrite.co.uk

Transforge UK Ltd, 19 Edmondthorpe Road, Wymondham, Melton Mowbray, Leicestershire, LE14 2AD Tel: (01572) 787504 Fax: (01572) 787565

▶ Transversal Sheet Metal Co. Ltd, Maypole Fields, Halesowen, West Midlands, B63 2QB Tel: (01384) 411135 Fax: (01384) 413674

Triad Fabrications, Globe Works, Queensway, Rochdale, Lancashire, OL11 2QY Tel: (01706) 655099 Fax: (01706) 658712 E-mail: admin@triadfabs.com

Trifab Steel Fabrication Co. Ltd, Unit 2 Lakeland Business Centre, Parish Lane, Pease Pottage, Crawley, West Sussex, RH10 5NY Tel: (01293) 511263 Fax: (01293) 512899 E-mail: a7bsl@aol.co.uk

▶ Trimet Engineering, 14 Tullylagan Road, Cookstown, County Tyrone, BT80 9AY Tel: (028) 8676 9937 Fax: (028) 8676 3484

Trinity Engineering Northampton Ltd, 15 Horsley Road, Northampton, NN2 6LJ Tel: (01604) 719803 Fax: (01604) 716670 E-mail: alan@trinityengnorth.co.uk

Trueline Engineering Services Ltd, Unit 15 King Street Trading Estate, Middlewich, Cheshire, CW10 9LF Tel: (01606) 836961 Fax: (01606) 836528

▶ Tumble Forge, 76 Bethesda Road, Tumble, Llanelli, Dyfed, SA14 6LG Tel: (01269) 841612 Fax: (01269) 832107 E-mail: sales@tumbleforge.co.uk

Tupman & Hainey Ltd, Louisa Street, Worsley, Manchester, M28 3GA Tel: 0161-790 2664 Fax: 0161-703 8435

Tyne Tunnel Engineering Ltd, B3 Narvik Way, Tyne Tunnel Trading Estate, North Shields, Tyne & Wear, NE29 7XJ Tel: 0191-258 0585 Fax: 0191-296 1745 E-mail: enquiries@ttengineering.co.uk

▶ U R S Corporation Ltd, 243 West George Street, Glasgow, G2 4QY Tel: 0141-226 3611 Fax: 0141-248 3773

Uniseed Engineering Ltd, Shepherds Grove Industrial Estate, Stanton, Bury St. Edmunds, Suffolk, IP31 2AR Tel: (01359) 250469 Fax: (01359) 252245

Unit Metal Construction Co. Ltd, Dale Street, Bilston, West Midlands, WV14 7JY Tel: (01902) 491436 Fax: (01902) 491665 E-mail: unitmetal@btconnect.com

▶ Universal Contract Management, Unit 16 Thornton Industrial Trad Est, Milford Haven, Dyfed, SA73 2RR Tel: 01646 690115

▶ Universal Fabrications (Coventry) Ltd, Whitacre Road Ind Estate, Nuneaton, Warwickshire, CV11 6BX Tel: 024 76370272

Universal Fabrications North West Ltd, Star Iron Works, Taurus Street, Oldham, OL4 2BN Tel: 0161-620 0550 Fax: 0161-620 0247 E-mail: sales@universal-fabrications.co.uk

Universal Sheet Metal Co., Dunlop Road, Hunt End Industrial Estate, Redditch, Worcestershire, B97 5XP Tel: (01527) 402202 Fax: (01527) 403030 E-mail: usm@usmlimited.co.uk

Upton Metal Works, Magdalene Road, Torquay, TQ1 4AF Tel: (01803) 814326 Fax: (01803) 200598

▶ V A Tech Reyrolle Ltd, 15 Bessemer Drive, Kelvin Industrial Estate, East Kilbride, Glasgow, G75 0QX Tel: (01355) 570970 Fax: (01355) 570971

V & C Installation Ltd, 24 Severnside Industrial Estate, Sudmeadow Road, Gloucester, GL2 5HS Tel: (01452) 415236 Fax: (01452) 309324 E-mail: paulvye@btconnect.com

Vacflo, Unit 14, Bingswood Industrial Estate, Whaley Bridge, High Peak, Derbyshire, SK23 7LY Tel: (01663) 719519 Fax: (01663) 719519 E-mail: mail@vacflo.com

Vacuum Systems Ltd, Unit 11 Lexden Lodge Industrial Estate, Crowborough Hill, Crowborough, East Sussex, TN6 2NQ Tel: (01892) 665633 E-mail: krizek@vacsys.co.uk

Vangard Ltd, Schofield Street, Royton, Oldham, OL2 6PT Tel: 0161-652 1249 Fax: 0161-678 6790

▶ Varis Engineering, 10-12 West Road, Greshop Industrial Estate, Forres, Morayshire, IV36 2GW Tel: (01309) 671211 Fax: (01309) 671241

Varivane Industries Ltd, William Road, Nursteed Industrial Estate, Devizes, Wiltshire, SN10 3EW Tel: (01380) 723624 Fax: (01380) 728367 E-mail: varivane.industries@btinternet.com

Vent Duct, The Hollies, Campton Road, Meppershall, Shefford, Bedfordshire, SG17 5PB Tel: (01462) 815018 Fax: (01462) 817045

Ventrac Sheet Metal Ltd, 20 Nimmo Drive, Glasgow, G51 3SX Tel: 0141-440 2221 Fax: 0141-425 1550 E-mail: john@ventrac.co.uk

Vertex Precision Engineering Ltd, 7 Armoury Road, Lufton Trading Estate, Yeovil, Somerset, BA22 8RL Tel: (01935) 477310 Fax: (01935) 706212 E-mail: vertex@vertexeng.demon.co.uk

▶ Viatech Ltd, Unit 16A, Klondyke Industrial Estate, Rushenden Road, Queenborough, Kent, ME11 5HN Tel: (01795) 666601

Viper Metal Products Ltd, Oldmixon Cresent, Weston-super-Mare, Avon, BS24 9AX Tel: (01934) 621912 Fax: (01934) 614347 E-mail: tony@viparmetal.co.uk

SHEET METALWORK ENGINEERS OR FABRICATORS – *continued*

Vision Sheet Metal Works, 3 Block 3, Inveresk Industrial Estate, Musselburgh, Midlothian, EH21 7UL Tel: 0131-665 7193 Fax: 0131-665 7193

▶ Vittoria Fabrication, Unit 4&5 Vittoria Street, Smethwick, West Midlands, B66 2ND Tel: 0121-565 4343 Fax: 0121-555 5792

W A Mcgarrie & Son Ltd, Friarton Road, Perth, PH2 8BB Tel: (01738) 631194 Fax: (01738) 633814 E-mail: office@mcgarrie.net

W F Joy & Co. Ltd, Unit 1a Parnall Industrial Estate, Parnall Road, Bristol, BS16 3JF Tel: 0117-958 5865 Fax: 0117-958 5865

W & G Pollard Ltd, Jacob Street, Accrington, Lancashire, BB5 1HU Tel: (01254) 391628 Fax: (01254) 382897

W H Pettit & Co Long Eaton Ltd, Bonsall Street, Long Eaton, Nottingham, NG10 2AH Tel: 0115-973 2577 Fax: 0115-946 1212

W M Spence Ltd, PO Box 344, Bradford, West Yorkshire, BD3 9TH Tel: (01274) 661824 E-mail: enquiries@wmspence.co.uk

W Speirs & Sons Ltd, 4 Portland Avenue, The Industrial Estate, Irvine, Ayrshire, KA12 8JD Tel: (01294) 275434 Fax: (01294) 312008

▶ Waders Welding & Fabrication Ltd, Elliott Road, Love Lane Industrial Estate, Cirencester, Gloucestershire, GL7 1YS Tel: (01285) 640725 Fax: (01285) 641698 E-mail: garywaders@tiscali.co.uk

▶ Walker Macleod Ltd, 8-36 Bulldale Street, Glasgow, G14 0NU Tel: 0141-954 0297 Fax: 0141-950 1351 E-mail: sales@walkermacleod.co.uk

▶ Wallace Whittle & Partners, Broughton Street Lane, Edinburgh, EH1 3LY Tel: 0131-524 5800 Fax: 0131-557 5801 E-mail: sales@wwpltd.co.uk

Wardons Metal Co. Ltd, Unit D4 Riverside Industrial Estate, Riverside Way, Dartford, DA1 5BS Tel: (01322) 276711 Fax: (01322) 288278 E-mail: wardons@jacobwhite-hospquip.co.uk

Ware Sheet Metal Ltd, Units 3-6, Charlton Mead Lane, Hoddesdon, Hertfordshire, EN11 0DJ Tel: (01992) 466483 Fax: (01992) 469604 E-mail: sales@waresheetmetal.co.uk

Warmflow Engineering Co. Ltd, Lissue Industrial Estate, Moira Road, Lisburn, County Antrim, BT28 2RF Tel: (028) 9262 1515 Fax: (028) 9262 1199 E-mail: mail@warmflow.co.uk

Warwick Engineering, 3 River Gardens, Feltham, Middlesex, TW14 0RD Tel: (020) 8844 2268 Fax: (020) 8751 0509

Watchwise Ltd, 20 North River Road, Great Yarmouth, Norfolk, NR30 1SG Tel: (01493) 842216 Fax: (01493) 857703 E-mail: ngraver@watchwise.co.uk

Waterton Engineering Co. Ltd, 2 Raymond Avenue, Chadderton, Oldham, OL9 7HW Tel: 0161-624 0004 Fax: 0161-624 8276

Watts Construction Ltd, Unit 1 & 2 Beacon Road Works, Beacon Road, Chatham, Kent, ME5 7BP Tel: (01634) 409149 Fax: (01634) 403005 E-mail: wattsgroupltd@btconnect.com

Wednesbury Fabrications, 1 Upper Chapel Street, Tividale, Oldbury, West Midlands, B69 2PG Tel: 0121-557 5171 Fax: 0121-557 7003

Weldtec Welding Services, Mackleys Industrial Estate, Henfield Road, Small Dole, Henfield, West Sussex, BN5 9XE Tel: (01273) 493493 Fax: (01273) 493493 E-mail: weldtecwelding@aol.com

Wenda Electronics & Engineering, 47 Cobham Road, Ferndown Industrial Estate, Wimborne, Dorset, BH21 7QZ Tel: (01202) 874961 Fax: (01202) 861260 E-mail: wendasheetmetal@cwcom.net

West Bromwich Sheet Metal Ltd, Unit 43n Siddons Factory Estate, Howard Street, West Bromwich, West Midlands, B70 0SU Tel: 0121-556 9120 Fax: 0121-556 9120

Western Metalcraft, 79d Grove Road, Fishponds, Bristol, BS16 2BP Tel: 0117-965 3865 Fax: 0117-965 3865

Westman Engineering Ltd, Units 15-18 Block 3, Old Mill ParkIndustrial Estate, Mansfield Woodhouse, Nottinghamshire, NG19 9BG Tel: (01623) 648740 Fax: (01623) 420376

Wheeler Fabrications Ltd, Orchard House, Sherbourne Road, Balsall Heath, Birmingham, B12 9DJ Tel: 0121-440 2345 Fax: 0121-440 4008 E-mail: wheelerfabs@btconnect.com

▶ Whitbybird, 60 Newman Street, London, W1T 3DA Tel: (020) 7631 5291 Fax: (020) 7323 4645

White Bros Ltd, Gosforth Industrial Estate, Newcastle Upon Tyne, NE3 1XD Tel: 0191-213 0455 Fax: 0191-284 1351 E-mail: enquiries@whitebros.co.uk

James White & Son (Engineering) Co. Ltd, Commercial Road, Reading, RG2 0RU Tel: 0118-987 3421 Fax: 0118-975 0521 E-mail: mark@jameswhite.freeserve.co.uk

▶ Whitefield Fabrications Ltd, Kirklees St, Bury, Lancashire, BL8 3NJ Tel: 01204 887700

Whitehouse Engineering Co. Ltd, 14 Trench Road, Newtownabbey, County Antrim, BT36 4UU Tel: (028) 9084 8311 Fax: (028) 9034 2773 E-mail: info@whitehouse-eng.com

Whitland Engineering Ltd, West Street, Whitland, Dyfed, SA34 0AE Tel: (01994) 240442 Fax: (01994) 240937 E-mail: whitland.engineering@btinternet.com

▶ Whitwick Engineering Coalville Ltd, 117 London Road, Coalville, Leicestershire, LE67 3JE Tel: (01530) 510770 Fax: (01530) 510068

William Hinsley Engineers Ltd, 1 Croft Street, Sowerby Bridge, West Yorkshire, HX6 2AJ Tel: (01422) 839968

William Oliver North Shields Ltd, Little Bedford Street, North Shields, Tyne & Wear, NE29 6NW Tel: 0191-257 5011 Fax: 0191-296 3140 E-mail: sales@worr.co.uk

Wilson Bros Sheffield Ltd, 35 Kirk Street, Sheffield, S4 7JX Tel: 0114-272 6179 Fax: 0114-276 5889

Winston Fabrications, Dale Road Trading Estate, Dale Road, Shildon, County Durham, DL4 2RE Tel: (01388) 777989 Fax: (01388) 776296 E-mail: anthony@winstonfabrications.co.uk

Bernard J. Wood, 13-17 Hayes Lane, Stourbridge, West Midlands, DY9 8QJ Tel: (01384) 892775 Fax: (01384) 892662

T. Wood Ltd, Canal Street, Stockport, Cheshire, SK1 3BZ Tel: 0161-480 5012 Fax: 0161-474 7266 E-mail: info@waterloo-sheetmetal.co.uk

Woodford Sheet Metal Ltd, 14 Wham Street, Heywood, Lancashire, OL10 4QU Tel: (01706) 364295 Fax: (01706) 621996 E-mail: woodford-sm@lineone-net.co.uk

▶ Woodward Peet Engineering Services Ltd, 21 Offerton Industrial Estate, Hempshaw Lane, Stockport, Cheshire, SK2 5TH Tel: 0161-474 1348 Fax: 0161-480 9261

Wooler Ltd, North Way, Andover, Hampshire, SP10 5AZ Tel: (01264) 324181 Fax: (01264) 333554

Wragg Bros Ltd, Robert Way, Wickford, Essex, SS11 8DQ Tel: (01268) 732607 Fax: (01268) 768499 E-mail: wragg.bros@btclick.com

▶ Wright & Maclennan Ltd, Camps Industrial Estate, Kirknewton, Midlothian, EH27 8DF Tel: (01506) 881486

Wyvern Sheet Metal & Fabrications Ltd, Three Springs Trading Estate, Vincent Road, Worcester, WR5 1BW Tel: (01905) 357830 Fax: (01905) 357830 E-mail: sales@wyvernsheetmetal.wanadoo.co.uk

Yellowpatter Sussex Ltd, Chantry Lane, Storrington, West Sussex, RH20 4TA Tel: (01903) 745741 Fax: (01903) 742668 E-mail: sales@yellowpatter.co.uk

Yorkshire design Fabrications Ltd, Unit B Cleres Mount Works, Clere Mount Road, Halifax, West Yorkshire, HX3 6AUU Tel: (01422) 345396 Fax: (01422) 349593 E-mail: www.ydfltd@btconnect.com

Yorkshire Laser & Fabrications Ltd, Phillips Street, Castleford, West Yorkshire, WF10 1NR Tel: (01977) 553120 Fax: (01977) 552527 E-mail: garnett.orford@louvres.co.uk

Youmac Sheet Metal Ltd, 250 Halley Street, Glasgow, G13 4DT Tel: 0141-952 3186 Fax: 0141-951 1557

▶ Tom Young Ltd, Wishaw Low Road, Cleland, Motherwell, Lanarkshire, ML1 5QU Tel: (01698) 860516 Fax: (01698) 861529

Young & Woods Ltd, 12-13 Burnt Mill Industrial Estate, Elizabeth Way, Harlow, Essex, CM20 2HS Tel: (01279) 443247 Fax: (01279) 420698 E-mail: antony@young-woods.com

▶ Zeus Engineering Co. Ltd, Stirling Road Industrial Estate, Airdrie, Lanarkshire, ML6 7UD Tel: (01236) 762398 Fax: (01236) 753554 E-mail: enquiries@zeusengineering.co.uk

Zot Engineering Ltd, Inveresk Mills Industrial Park, Musselburgh, Midlothian, EH21 7UQ Tel: 0131-653 6834 Fax: 0131-653 6025 E-mail: data@zot.co.uk

SHEET METALWORK PRECISION FINE LIMIT ENGINEERS OR FABRICATORS

A A Sheet Metals, 1 Fletcher Way, Weston Road, Norwich, NR3 3ST Tel: (01603) 417030 Fax: (01603) 417128 E-mail: alan.harrowing@aasheetmetalnorwich.fsnet.co.uk

A G Precision Sheet Metal Ltd, Unit 2-3 Bay Close, Progress Way, Luton, LU4 9UP Tel: (01582) 570391 Fax: (01582) 583339 E-mail: rgovier@agpsm.com

Acorn Precision, 19 Stairbridge Lane, Bolney, Haywards Heath, West Sussex, RH17 5PA Tel: (01444) 248160 Fax: (01444) 246354

Adept Precision Sheet Metal Ltd, Ardglen Trading Estate, Whitchurch, Hampshire, RG28 7BB Tel: (01256) 893177 Fax: (01256) 893904 E-mail: info@adept-sheetmetal.co.uk

Advanced Metal Engineering Ltd, 200 Rickmansworth Road, Watford, WD18 7JS Tel: (01923) 211133 Fax: (01923) 241124 E-mail: ameltd@btconnect.com

Air Domestique Ltd, Unit 4b Benbridge Industrial Estate, Holloway Road, Heybridge, Maldon, Essex, CM9 4ER Tel: (01621) 852994 Fax: (01621) 850643 E-mail: mail@ad-manufacturing.fsnet.co.uk

Air Heating & Manufacturing, Seaton Lane, St. Helier, Jersey, JE2 3QJ Tel: (01534) 734830 Fax: (01534) 767681 E-mail: airheating@hotmail.com

Alinco Ltd, 22 Albert Drive, Burgess Hill, West Sussex, RH15 9TN Tel: (01444) 232719 Fax: (01444) 871680 E-mail: alinco@btinternet.com

Alrog Engineering Ltd, Halifax Road, Cressex Business Park, High Wycombe, Buckinghamshire, HP12 3SD Tel: (01494) 447213 Fax: (01494) 528104

Alsager Precision Sheet Metal Ltd, Unit 1C Wistaston Business Centre, Wistaston Road, Crewe, CW2 7RP Tel: (01270) 251271 Fax: (01270) 215614 E-mail: alssheetmetal@talk21.com

Altech Engineering, Brighton Road, Bolney, Haywards Heath, West Sussex, RH17 5NA Tel: (01444) 881964 Fax: (01444) 881816 E-mail: sales@altechengineering.com

Apex Security Engineering Ltd, Flint Road, Letchworth Garden City, Hertfordshire, SG6 1HJ Tel: (01462) 673431 Fax: (01462) 671518 E-mail: sales@apexsecuritiesfurniture.com

Arben Sheet Metal Ltd, 204 Bedford Avenue, Slough Trading Estate, Slough, SL1 4RY Tel: (01753) 531066 Fax: (01753) 694724 E-mail: arben@globalnet.co.uk

Arbour Engineering Ltd, Unit 23, West Station Yard Industrial Estate, Spital Road, Maldon, Essex, CM9 6TS Tel: (01621) 857320 Fax: (01621) 874609

Archer Woodnutt Ltd, Pit Lane, Talke Pits, Stoke-on-Trent, ST7 1UH Tel: (01782) 785016 Fax: (01782) 776273 E-mail: info@archerwoodnutt.com

Automatic Devices Ltd, London Road, Pampisford, Cambridge, CB22 3EE Tel: (01223) 832485 Fax: (01223) 837758 E-mail: info@automaticdevices.co.uk

Ava Matic U K Ltd, 24 Padgets Lane, Redditch, Worcestershire, B98 0RB Tel: (01527) 518520 Fax: (01527) 518526 E-mail: info@avamatic.co.uk

B H R Ltd, Unit 16, Peerglow Industrial Estate, Watford, WD18 9SR Tel: (01923) 776683 Fax: (01923) 776683

B K Engineering Ltd, Kingswood Works, Heath and Reach, Leighton Buzzard, Bedfordshire, LU7 0AZ Tel: (01525) 237411 Fax: (01525) 237827 E-mail: sales@bkengineering.com

Bellshill Metal Works Glasgow Ltd, 60-82 Hamilton Road, Bellshill, Lanarkshire, ML4 1AG Tel: (01698) 747132 Fax: (01698) 746908

Bullet Engineering Ltd, Vale Road, Spilsby, Lincolnshire, PE23 5HE Tel: (01790) 753320 Fax: (01790) 754530

Bunce Sheet Metal Work, Unit B5 Crabtree Road, Thorpe Industrial Estate, Egham, Surrey, TW20 8RN Tel: (01784) 433556 Fax: (01784) 433556 E-mail: sales@buncesheetmetal.co.uk

C J Armstrong Manufacturing Co. Ltd, Unit 7-8 River Brent Business Park, Trumpers Way, London, W7 2QA Tel: (020) 8574 4602 Fax: (020) 8574 1078 E-mail: cjarmstrong@lycos.co.uk

Cad Fab Ltd, 7 The Courtyards, Victoria Road, Leeds, LS14 2LB Tel: 0113-265 5010 Fax: 0113-265 5012 E-mail: cadfab@aol.com

Callaghan Engineering, Pembroke Avenue, Waterbeach, Cambridge, CB25 9QP Tel: (01223) 863330 Fax: (01223) 863223

Carlton Engineering Products Ltd, Unit 1 Airborne Industrial, Estate Arterial Road, Leigh-on-Sea, Essex, SS9 4EX Tel: (01702) 420300 Fax: (01702) 529542 E-mail: sales@cep.uk.com

Chaggar Engineering, Murdock Road, Manton Industrial Estate, Bedford, MK41 7PE Tel: (01234) 360557 Fax: (0871) 2422493 E-mail: premchaggar@hotmail.com

Cheshire Specialist Engineering, L & M Business Park, Norman Road, Altrincham, Cheshire, WA14 4ES Tel: 0161-928 6138 Fax: 0161-928 6139 E-mail: sales@cseng.co.uk

Cliffsend Ltd, Falconer Road, Haverhill, Suffolk, CB9 7XU Tel: (01440) 762664 Fax: (01440) 762428 E-mail: mail@ccsheetmetal.co.uk

Coates Holdings Ltd, 3 Brindley Road, Cardiff, CF11 8TX Tel: (029) 2034 4554 Fax: (029) 2034 4545 E-mail: coates-co@fsmail.net

Colbree Precision Ltd, Units 10-12 Beacon Court, Pitstone Green Business Park, Quarry Road, Pitstone, Leighton Buzzard, Bedfordshire, LU7 9GY Tel: (01296) 664200 Fax: (01296) 664201 E-mail: sales@colbree.com

Comtec Precision Sheet Metal, 60 Loverock Road, Reading, RG30 1DY Tel: 0118-958 8050 Fax: 0118-958 8040 E-mail: sales@comtecsheet.softnet.co.uk

Contacta Engineering Ltd, Unit 21 Laurence Industrial Estate, Eastwoodbury Lane, Southend-on-Sea, SS2 6RH Tel: (01702) 511887 Fax: (01702) 420631 E-mail: info@contacta.co.uk

Contracts Engineering Ltd, Chapel Park, Stadium Way, Sittingbourne, Kent, ME10 3RW Tel: (01795) 479284 Fax: (01795) 477812 E-mail: contracts@totalserve.co.uk

Craintern Ltd, 13-17 Haltwhistle Road, South Woodham Ferrers, Chelmsford, CM3 5ZA Tel: (01245) 322438 Fax: (01245) 328926 E-mail: mailbox@ctlmedical.co.uk

D & D Fine Limits, 2 St Clare Business Park, Holly Road, Hampton, Middlesex, TW12 1PZ Tel: (020) 8979 3545 Fax: (020) 8979 3545 E-mail: info@sheetmetalproduction.com

D K M Sheet Metal Co. Ltd, Unit 9 Oldends Industrial Estate, Oldends, Stonehouse, Gloucestershire, GL10 3RQ Tel: (01453) 827661 Fax: (01453) 824094 E-mail: gill@dkmsheetmetal.co.uk

D P L, Elliott Works, Elliott Road, Bromley, BR2 9NT Tel: (020) 8460 2147 Fax: (020) 8313 3072 E-mail: sales@dplaw.co.uk

Davidson Sheet Metal, Bourtree House, Minto Drive, Altens, Aberdeen, AB12 3LW Tel: (01224) 897676 Fax: (01224) 895199 E-mail: enquiry@hutcheon-services.ltd.uk

Davrek Engineering, Finmere Road, Eastbourne, East Sussex, BN22 8QL Tel: (01323) 643788 Fax: (01323) 431266

Detail Sheet Metal Ltd, Unit 26 Fawkes Avenue, Questor, Dartford, DA1 1JQ Tel: (01322) 222122 Fax: (01322) 291794 E-mail: sales@kentech.co.uk

Enterprise Fabrication Co., Virginia Street, Southport, Merseyside, PR8 6RZ Tel: (01704) 541544 Fax: (01704) 544260 E-mail: enterprise@e-fabs.co.uk

Euro Sheet Metal Ltd, 6 Aintree Road, Perivale, Greenford, Middlesex, UB6 7LA Tel: (020) 8810 5026 Fax: (020) 8991 5008 E-mail: info@eurosheetmetal.co.uk

Formet Ltd, Harley Works, Paxton Hill, St. Neots, Cambridgeshire, PE19 6TA Tel: (01480) 475041 Fax: (01480) 472820 E-mail: sales@4met.co.uk

Gardner Aerospace Basildon Ltd, 2-4 Rowhedge Close, Basildon, Essex, SS13 1QQ Tel: (01268) 729311 Fax: (01268) 728951 E-mail: info@gardener-aerospace-basildon.com

Gemflex Engineering Ltd, Unit 4, Cossall Industrial Estate, Coronation Road, Ilkeston, Derbyshire, DE7 5UA Tel: 0115-944 2414 Fax: 0115-944 2771 E-mail: sales@gemflex.co.uk

Guilform Ltd, 5 Alban Park Industrial Estate, Hatfield Road, St. Albans, Hertfordshire, AL4 0JJ Tel: (01727) 841111 Fax: (01727) 832710

H Q C Ltd, North Florida Road, Haydock, St. Helens, Merseyside, WA11 9UB Tel: (01942) 722770 Fax: (01942) 270235 E-mail: hqcsales@hqc.co.uk

Havant Sheet Metal Co. Ltd, Downley Road, Havant, Hampshire, PO9 2NN Tel: 0845 5314135 Fax: (023) 9247 0563 E-mail: sales@havantsheetmetal.co.uk

Hillcrest Machinery Engineering Portchester Ltd, 1 Pennant Park, Standard Way, Fareham, Hampshire, PO16 8XU Tel: (01329) 231245 Fax: (01329) 822753 E-mail: office@hillcresteng.co.uk

Hi-Tech Sheet Metal Ltd, Molyneux House, Unit B, Fort Road Ind Est, Fort Road, Littlehampton, West Sussex, BN17 7QU Tel: 01903 711222 Fax: 01903 711227 E-mail: sales@htsm-ltd.co.uk

Holt Broadcast Services Ltd, Unit 13 Nimrod Industrial Estate, Nimrod Way, Reading, RG2 0EB Tel: 0118-931 0770 Fax: 0118-931 0696 E-mail: sales@holtbs.co.uk

Ilford Engineering Co. Ltd, Bentalls, Basildon, Essex, SS14 3BY Tel: (01268) 526756 Fax: (01268) 531485 E-mail: mike@ilfordengineering.co.uk

Ipeco Europe, Aviation Way, Southend-on-Sea, SS2 6UN Tel: (01702) 549371 Fax: (01702) 540782 E-mail: sales@ipeco.co.uk

J M J Precision Sheet Metal Ltd, 11 Boulton Road, Stevenage, Hertfordshire, SG1 4QX Tel: (01438) 360711 Fax: (01438) 360721

J R Nobbs & Sons Ltd, Rembrandt House, King Georges Avenue, Watford, WD18 7PW Tel: (01923) 234176 Fax: (01923) 211146 E-mail: sales@imp-engineering.co.uk

J&J, Unit 1 20 Paynes Lane, Rugby, Warwickshire, CV21 2UH Tel: (01788) 568217 Fax: (01788) 547125 E-mail: jjsheetmetal@dialstart.net

Jarrobs Ltd, Units 1-5, Excalibur Industrial Estate, Fields Road, Alsager, Stoke-on-Trent, ST7 2LX Tel: (01270) 878711 Fax: (01270) 882464 E-mail: sales@jarrobs.co.uk

JDR, 131 Grenfell Road, Maidenhead, Berkshire, SL6 1EX Tel: (01628) 629450 Fax: (01628) 625459 E-mail: ralph@jdrmhead.fsnet.co.uk

Jomar Engineering, 119 Sandycombe Road, Richmond, Surrey, TW9 2ER Tel: (020) 8332 6692 Fax: (020) 8948 4269

K P K (Sheet Metal) Ltd, Parkwood Works, Brooklands Close, Sunbury-On-Thames, Middlesex, TW16 7DX Tel: (01932) 789866 Fax: (01932) 789794 E-mail: sales@kpk-sheetmetal.co.uk

Keihan Systems, Unit 24 Padgets Lane, Redditch, Worcestershire, B98 0RB Tel: (01527) 518525 Fax: (01527) 518526 E-mail: info@keihan.co.uk

Kempston Ltd, Brunel Road, Bedford, MK41 9TG Tel: (01234) 341144 Fax: (01234) 348281

Kendal Metal Works Ltd, Mintsfeet Road, Kendal, Cumbria, LA9 6NN Tel: (01539) 722050 Fax: (01539) 741190

Kendrick Sheet Metal, 3 Peacocks Estate, Providence Street, Cradley Heath, West Midlands, B64 5DG Tel: (01384) 638363 Fax: (01384) 637881

Lightning Aerospace Ltd, Falkland Close, Charter Avenue Industrial Estate, Coventry, CV4 8AU Tel: (024) 7646 1238 Fax: (024) 7646 4745 E-mail: info@lightningaerospace.co.uk

Luxomation Ltd, 5 Worton Hall Industrial Estate, Worton Road, Isleworth, Middlesex, TW7 6ER Tel: (020) 8568 6373 Fax: (020) 8847 2603

M J Sheet Metal Co., 158 Crow Lane, Romford, RM7 0ES Tel: (01708) 737050 Fax: (01708) 737096

M P L Fabrications, Dutton Road, Aldermans Green Industrial Estate, Coventry, CV2 2LE Tel: (024) 7661 0778 Fax: (024) 7661 9499 E-mail: sales@mplfabrications.com

Macklow Industrial Ltd, The Mill, Station Road, Salhouse, Norwich, NR13 6NY Tel: (01603) 720950 Fax: (01603) 720033 E-mail: info@macklow.co.uk

Major Sheet Metals, 483 Bradford Road, Batley, West Yorkshire, WF17 8LB Tel: (01924) 441610 Fax: (01924) 420535

Malordale Engineering Ltd, Unit 10E, Britannia Estate, Leagrave Road, Luton, LU3 1RJ Tel: (01582) 421138 Fax: (01582) 412894 E-mail: tonyfuller@malordale.co.uk

SHEET METALWORK PRECISION FINE LIMIT ENGINEERS OR FABRICATORS – *continued*

Masterford Ltd, Lyon Road, Bletchley, Milton Keynes, MK1 1EX Tel: (01908) 373106 Fax: (01908) 377181 E-mail: john-forder@btconnect.com

MBN Fabrications Ltd, Units 2-3, Northbridge Road, Berkhamsted, Hertfordshire, HP4 1EF Tel: (01442) 877888 Fax: (01442) 877862

Mice Kay Mar Ltd, Brookhill Industrial Estate, Pinxton, Nottingham, NG16 6NS Tel: (01773) 810107 Fax: (01773) 580286 E-mail: sales@micekaymar.com

Millthorne Engineering Co., 82 Tewin Road, Welwyn Garden City, Hertfordshire, AL7 1BD Tel: (01707) 371695 Fax: (01707) 372141

Mulhouse Ltd, 36 Nobel Square, Burnt Mills Industrial Estate, Basildon, Essex, SS13 1LT Tel: (01268) 726222 Fax: (01268) 590424 E-mail: info@mulhouseltd.com

N F F Precision Ltd, 4 Enterprise Way Aviation Park, Bournemouth Int Airp, Hurn, Christchurch, Dorset, BH23 6EW Tel: (01202) 583000 Fax: (01202) 583058 E-mail: sales@nff.uk.com

New Holland Sheet Metal Co. Ltd, Unit 30 Jubilee Trading Estate, Jubilee Road, Letchworth Garden City, Hertfordshire, SG6 1NE Tel: (01462) 674265 Fax: (01462) 480699 E-mail: newholland@btconnect.com

Nortek Precision Sheet Steel Ltd, Priesty Fields, Congleton, Cheshire, CW12 4AQ Tel: (01260) 278839 Fax: (01260) 278201

North Notts Sheet Metal Ltd, Unit 3 Welsh Croft Close, Kirkby-in-Ashfield, Nottingham, NG17 8EP Tel: (01623) 722123 Fax: (01623) 720562

P E M Sheetmetal Ltd, 3 Springfield Road Industrial Estate, Burnham-on-Crouch, Essex, CM0 8TE Tel: (01621) 783367 Fax: (01621) 785086 E-mail: sales@pemltd.co.uk

P K D Precision Sheet Metal Ltd, Unit 7 Furlong Industrial Estate, Dain Street, Stoke-on-Trent, ST6 3LN Tel: (01782) 824800 Fax: (01782) 811746 E-mail: sales@pkdsheetmetal.co.uk

Panton (Sheet Metalworks) Ltd, 67 Swaisland Drive, Crayford Industrial Estate, Crayford, Dartford, DA1 4HS Tel: (01322) 554180 Fax: (01322) 555157 E-mail: enquiries@pantonsheetmetal.co.uk

Paul James Precision Sheet Metal Ltd, Unit B4 Sneyd Hill Industrial Estate, Stoke-on-Trent, ST6 2EB Tel: (01782) 812003 Fax: (01782) 812213 E-mail: pauljamessheetmetal@msn.com

Phoenix Precision Ltd, Crompton Road, Southfield Industrial Estate, Glenrothes, Fife, KY6 2SF Tel: (01592) 772077 Fax: (01592) 773535 E-mail: sales@phoenixprecision.com

Pierceton Engineering Ltd, 2 Macadam Place, South Newmoor Industrial Estate, Irvine, Ayrshire, KA11 4HP Tel: (01294) 214427 Fax: (01294) 214440

Precision Components & Equipment Ltd, Railway Street, Heywood, Lancashire, OL10 1LX Tel: (01706) 621421 Fax: (01706) 621319 E-mail: mike-pce@johnbradleygroup.co.uk

Precision Fabrications Ltd, Units 8-9 Sea Vixen Industrial Estate, 3 Wilverley Road, Christchurch, Dorset, BH23 3RU Tel: (01202) 474406 Fax: (01202) 473821 E-mail: enquiries@precisionfabricationsltd.co.uk

Propak Sheet Metal Ltd, Unit C-D Gunnels Wood Park, Gunnels Wood Road, Stevenage, Hertfordshire, SG1 2BH Tel: (01438) 728885 Fax: (01438) 740298 E-mail: bruce@propak.co.uk

Protec Metal Work Ltd, 7 H T H Complex, Blackwater Way, Aldershot, Hampshire, GU12 4DN Tel: (01252) 310443 Fax: (01252) 341787 E-mail: protecmetal@btconnect.com

Pro-Tech Precision Ltd, Station Road West, Ash Vale, Aldershot, Hampshire, GU12 5QD Tel: (01252) 516242 Fax: (01252) 524025 E-mail: sales@pro-techprecision.com

Quante Telecommunications Ltd, Snailwell Business Pk, Fordham Rd, Snailwell, Newmarket, Suffolk, CB8 7NY Tel: (01638) 721333 Fax: (01638) 721233 E-mail: service@quante.co.uk

R J W Sheet Metal Ltd, 40 Cobham Road, Ferndown Industrial Estate, Wimborne, Dorset, BH21 7NP Tel: (01202) 875852 Fax: (01202) 893953 E-mail: enquiries@rjwsheetmetal.com

Redman Sheet Metal Ltd, Unit 13 Isis Trading Estate, Swindon, SN1 2PG Tel: (01793) 692781 Fax: (01793) 491688 E-mail: jim@redman-sheet-metal.co.uk

Ringwood Precision, 2 Millstream Trading Estate, Christchurch Road, Ringwood, Hampshire, BH24 3SA Tel: (01425) 476296 Fax: (01425) 476296 E-mail: ukroy@freenetname.co.uk

Ripley Engineering Ltd, Rankine Road, Basingstoke, Hampshire, RG24 8PP Tel: (01256) 473940 Fax: (01256) 479991 E-mail: services@ripley-eng.co.uk

Rolls Royce plc, Watnall Road, Hucknall, Nottingham, NG15 6EU Tel: 0115-963 3111 Fax: 0115-964 2345

Rowan Engineering, Garland Works, Desborough Avenue, High Wycombe, Buckinghamshire, HP11 2RN Tel: (01494) 531213 Fax: (01494) 465226 E-mail: enquiries@drjeng.fsnet.co.uk

S B Engineering (Precision) Ltd, 1 Dyke Road Mews, Brighton, BN1 3JD Tel: 01273 821397

Shearline Precision Engineering Ltd, Cambridgeshire Business Park, Angel Drove, Ely, Cambridgeshire, CB7 4EX Tel: (01353) 668668 Fax: (01353) 668203 E-mail: sales@shearline.co.uk

Sheet Metal Services, Hill Street, Kidderminster, Worcestershire, DY11 6TD Tel: (01562) 824995 Fax: (01562) 743998 E-mail: sales@saferack-sheetmetalservices.com

Simclar International Ltd, Pitreavie Business Park, Queensferry Road, Dunfermline, Fife, KY11 8UN Tel: (01383) 735161 Fax: (01383) 739986 E-mail: sales@simclar.com

Speedy Sheet Metal Ltd, 5 Teknol House, Victoria Road, Burgess Hill, West Sussex, RH15 9LH Tel: (01444) 248764 Fax: (01444) 247767

Stanham Engineering Ltd, 31a Cobble Lane, London, N1 1SF Tel: (020) 7226 3730 Fax: (020) 7226 2746

Stevenage Sheet Metal Co. Ltd, Unit 1, Jubilee Trade Centre, Jubilee Road, Letchworth Garden City, Hertfordshire, SG6 1SP Tel: (01462) 674794 Fax: (01462) 481132 E-mail: richard@stevenagesheetmetal.com

Stewart & Allen Ltd, The Runnings, Cheltenham, Gloucestershire, GL51 9NW Tel: (01242) 523298 Fax: (01242) 226416

Strand Engineering North West Ltd, Ironworks Road, Barrow-in-Furness, Cumbria, LA14 2PH Tel: (01229) 821991 Fax: (01229) 811104 E-mail: strandeng@yahoo.co.uk

Supercraft Ltd, Canada Road, Byfleet, West Byfleet, Surrey, KT14 7JL Tel: (01932) 351941 Fax: (01932) 340807 E-mail: sales@supercraft.co.uk

Surestep Sheet Metal Ltd, Unit J2 Northfleet Industrial Estate, Lower Road, Northfleet, Gravesend, Kent, DA11 9BL Tel: (01474) 560511 Fax: (01474) 354396 E-mail: info@surestepsheetmetal.com

Swan Engineering, 70 Scarborough Street, Hull, HU3 4TG Tel: (01482) 890140 Fax: (01482) 323077E-mail: sales@swan-engineering.co.uk

Swanells & Grylls Ltd, 330-332 Selborne Road, Luton, LU4 8NU Tel: (01582) 573066

Sweetnam & Bradley Ltd, Gloucester Road, Malmesbury, Wiltshire, SN16 0DY Tel: (01666) 823491 Fax: (01666) 826010 E-mail: mike@sweetnam-bradley.com

T A D Precision Ltd, The Mount Toft, Cambridge, CB3 7RL Tel: (01223) 263421 Fax: (01223) 264135 E-mail: terryeasey@hotmail.co.uk

Taurus Engineering, Commerce Way, Lancing, West Sussex, BN15 8TA Tel: (01903) 761188 Fax: (01903) 767268 E-mail: sales@taurusengineering.co.uk

Taylor Made Fabrication, 6 Pipers Industrial Estate, Pipers Lane, Thatcham, Berkshire, RG19 4NA Tel: (01635) 873737 Fax: (01635) 874747 E-mail: info.request@taylormadefabrication.co.uk

▶ Tek Neek, Unit 10, Glenfield Park, Philips Rd, Blackburn, BB1 5PS Tel: (01254) 583008 Fax: (01254) 682965

Tharsus Vision Ltd, Unit 8/9, Spencer Road, Blyth, Northumberland, NE24 5TG Tel: (01670) 367030 Fax: (01670) 352012 E-mail: sales@directmessage.co.uk

Trelawney Engineering, Old Yard Workshop, Vansittart, Windsor, Berkshire, SL4 1SE Tel: (01753) 850300 E-mail: info@trelawneyengineering.co.uk

Ware Sheet Metal Ltd, Units 3-6, Charlton Mead Lane, Hoddesdon, Hertfordshire, EN11 0DJ Tel: (01992) 466483 Fax: (01992) 469604 E-mail: sales@waresheetmetal.co.uk

Wedge Engineering Ltd, 16 Darlington Close, Sandy, Bedfordshire, SG19 1RW Tel: (01767) 683527 Fax: (01767) 683529 E-mail: wedgeeng@btconnect.com

Wenda Electronics & Engineering, 47 Cobham Road, Ferndown Industrial Estate, Wimborne, Dorset, BH21 7QZ Tel: (01202) 874961 Fax: (01202) 861260 E-mail: wendasheetmetal@cwcom.net

Westcom Engineers, Global Park, East Gates Industrial Estate, Colchester, CO1 2TW Tel: (01206) 794114 Fax: (01206) 792749 E-mail: admin@westcomeng.fsnet.co.uk

Wren Metal Co. Ltd, Russell Street, Chadderton, Oldham, OL9 9LD Tel: 0161-624 9835 Fax: 0161-627 2746

SHEET METALWORKING MACHINERY MANUFRS, *See also headings for particular types*

Baltec UK Ltd, Danehill, Lower Earley, Reading, RG6 4UT Tel: 0118-931 1191 Fax: 0118-931 1103 E-mail: sales@baltec.co.uk

Bystronic UK Ltd, Chard Junction, Chard, Somerset, TA20 4QR Tel: (01460) 222100 Fax: (01460) 222108 E-mail: sales@bystronic.com

C M Z Machinery Ltd, Fullers End, Elsenham, Bishop's Stortford, Hertfordshire, CM22 6DU Tel: (01279) 814491 Fax: (01279) 814541 E-mail: info@cmzweb.co.uk

Crescent Machinery Ltd, Unit 1 Moderna Business Park, Moderna Way, Mytholmroyd, Hebden Bridge, West Yorkshire, HX7 5QQ Tel: (01422) 884888 Fax: 01422 881338 E-mail: info@crescentmachinery.co.uk

Frost Rochdale Ltd, Eagle Iron Works, Crawford Street, Rochdale, Lancashire, OL16 5NU Tel: (01706) 644929 Fax: (01706) 860338 E-mail: sales@frost.co.uk

Kee Engineering, Unit 14a Miller Business Park, Station Road, Liskeard, Cornwall, PL14 4DA Tel: (01579) 344285 Fax: (01579) 348635 E-mail: chris@kee.co.uk

Keeton,Sons & Co.,Limited, Keetona House, Acres Hill Lane, Sheffield, S9 4LR Tel: 0114-242 0328 Fax: 0114-261 8860 E-mail: keetons@keetons.com

Kingsland Engineering, Eagle Industrial Estate, Bagnall Street, Great Bridge, Tipton, West Midlands, DY4 7BS Tel: 0121-522 4929 Fax: 0121-522 3174 E-mail: sales@kingsland.com

Phoenix Machinery Ltd, Riverside Studios, Mill Lane, Dronfield, Derbyshire, S18 2XL Tel: (01246) 290027 Fax: (01246) 290093

Joseph Rhodes Ltd, Bell Vue, Elm Tree Street, Wakefield, West Yorkshire, WF1 5EQ Tel: (01924) 371161 Fax: (01924) 370928 E-mail: sales@joseph-rhodes.co.uk

Waltons Of Radcliffe Sales Ltd, Unit 14 Bradley Fold Trading Estate, Radcliffe Moor Road, Bradley Fold, Bolton, BL2 6RT Tel: (01204) 393633 Fax: (01204) 363196 E-mail: sales@waltons-of-radcliffe.com

SHEET METALWORKING MACHINERY MERCHANTS OR AGENTS

Carter Machine Tool Co. Ltd, Aldon Road, Poulton Industrial Estate, Poulton-le-Fylde, Lancashire, FY6 8JL Tel: (01253) 890289 Fax: (01253) 891615 E-mail: sales@cartermachinery.co.uk

Chiviott Machine Tools Ltd, Unit C1 Rudford Industrial Estate, Ford Road, Ford, Arundel, West Sussex, BN18 0BD Tel: (01903) 721281 Fax: (01903) 730868 E-mail: sales@chiviott.co.uk

Cinmech Services Ltd, 63 Colvilles Place, Kelvin Industrial Estate, Glasgow, G75 0XE Tel: (01355) 244544 Fax: (01355) 248717 E-mail: cinmech@cinmech.com

Coburg Engineering Ltd, Unit 22F, Wincombe Business Park, Shaftesbury, Dorset, SP7 9QJ Tel: (01747) 855022 Fax: (01747) 854744 E-mail: info@coburg.co.uk

Hatfield Machine Tool Co. Ltd, 2 Sandiford Road, Sutton, Surrey, SM3 9RD Tel: (020) 8644 6661 Fax: (020) 8644 4233 E-mail: sales@hatmac.co.uk

Multiform Machine Tool Ltd, Avaition House, Aviation Way, Southend Airport, Southend-on-Sea, SS2 6UN Tel: (0845) 0690290 Fax: (0845) 0690291 E-mail: info@mfmtl.co.uk

P & F Machine Tools Co. Ltd, 1 Glentrool Mews, Bolton, BL1 5JH Tel: (01204) 840545 Fax: (01204) 841804

Powell Mcneil Machinery Co. Ltd, Newcombe Drive, Hawkesworth Trading Estate, Swindon, SN2 1DZ Tel: (01793) 533675 Fax: (01793) 616171 E-mail: powellmcneil@compuserve.com

Sampson International Machine Tools, Keeley Lane, Wootton, Bedford, MK43 9HS Tel: (01234) 851200 Fax: (01234) 851123 E-mail: sales@sampsonmachinetools.com

SHEET METALWORKING, COMPONENTS

▶ Armstrong Blacksmiths & Engineers, Lichfield Road Industrial Estate, Tamworth, Staffordshire, B79 7TA Tel: (01827) 316663 Fax: (01827) 66833 E-mail: armstrong.blacksmiths@btopenworld.com

Quality Industries Ltd, Unit C 18 Stafford Park, Telford, Shropshire, TF3 3BN Tel: (01952) 292166 Fax: (01952) 292167 E-mail: sales@qivansystems.co.uk

SHEET METALWORKING/ FABRICATORS, CNC

A L Spinnings - CNC Punch Weld, Unit 499-101 Newhall Street, Willenhall, West Midlands, WV13 1LQ Tel: (01902) 601318 Fax: (01902) 601318 E-mail: adacncpunch@aol.com

▶ Class Sheet Metal, Ynyshir Road, Porth, Mid Glamorgan, CF39 0AT Tel: (01443) 682277 Fax: (01443) 682285

Euro Sheet Metal Ltd, 6 Aintree Road, Perivale, Greenford, Middlesex, UB6 7LA Tel: (020) 8810 5026 Fax: (020) 8991 5008 E-mail: info@eurosheetmetal.co.uk

Fablink UK Ltd, Arcwell Works, Stafford Road, Fordhouses, Wolverhampton, WV10 7EJ Tel: (01902) 397766 Fax: (01902) 788912 E-mail: sales@fablink.co.uk

Havant Sheet Metal Co. Ltd, Downley Road, Havant, Hampshire, PO9 2NN Tel: 0845 5314135 Fax: (023) 9247 0563 E-mail: sales@havantsheetmetal.co.uk

Pengrave Engineering Ltd, Fairway, Off Delta Way, Bridgtown, Cannock, Staffordshire, WS11 0BE Tel: (01543) 577142 Fax: (01543) 577930 E-mail: pengrave@compuserve.com

Premier Sheet Metal & Engineering Co. Ltd, 4 Premier Building, Brockhampton Road, Havant, Hampshire, PO9 1JU Tel: (023) 9247 2633 Fax: (023) 9249 8210 E-mail: sales@premiersheetmetal.co.uk

Redman Sheet Metal Ltd, Unit 13 Isis Trading Estate, Swindon, SN1 2PG Tel: (01793) 692781 Fax: (01793) 491688 E-mail: jim@redman-sheet-metal.co.uk

▶ Tek Neek, Unit 10, Glenfield Park, Philips Rd, Blackburn, BB1 5PS Tel: (01254) 583008 Fax: (01254) 682965

SHEET METALWORKING/ FABRICATORS, ELECTRICAL/ ELECTRONICS INDUSTRY

Ad Tek Products Ltd, 35 Broton Drive, Halstead, Essex, CO9 1HB Tel: (01787) 474470 Fax: (01787) 475880 E-mail: ad-tek@lineone.net

F1 Manufacturing, 350 Melton Road, Leicester, LE4 7SL Tel: 0116-268 8484 Fax: 0116-268 8489 E-mail: sales@f1manufacturing.com

SHEET METALWORKING/ FABRICATORS, MASS PRODUCTION

Mettech Ltd, Ramsden Road, Rotherwas Industrial Estate, Hereford, HR2 6LR Tel: 01432 341630

SHEET METALWORKING/ FABRICATORS, PROTOTYPE

Alsager Precision Sheet Metal Ltd, Unit 1C Wistaston Business Centre, Wistaston Road, Crewe, CW2 7RP Tel: (01270) 251271 Fax: (01270) 215614 E-mail: alssheetmetal@talk21.com

Bondation Fabrications, 4-6 Abingdon Road, Nuffield Industrial Estate, Poole, Dorset, BH17 0UG Tel: (01202) 677828 Fax: (01202) 677861

Chapel Sheet Metal Ltd, Bowden Lane, Chapel-en-le-Frith, High Peak, Derbyshire, SK23 0QG Tel: (01298) 813041 Fax: (01298) 816256 E-mail: paul_csm@btinternet.com

Cheltenham Patterns 1983 Ltd, Gloucestershire Airport, Staverton, Cheltenham, Gloucestershire, GL51 6SP Tel: (01452) 713037 Fax: (01452) 713270 E-mail: mike@cheltpatts.fsnet.co.uk

Colval Engineering, Unit 1a Bury Farm, Curbridge, Botley, Southampton, SO30 2HB Tel: (01489) 799100 Fax: (01489) 799100

Cotswald Design & Manufacture Ltd, The Daniel Gooch Building, Whitehill Lane, Wootton Bassett, Swindon, SN4 7DB Tel: (01793) 848007 Fax: (01793) 848526 E-mail: heather@ergotec-cdm.co.uk

E Reg Sheet Metal Fabricators, Unit 7 Kirby Road, Lomeshaye Industrial Estate, Nelson, Lancashire, BB9 6RS Tel: (01282) 697748 Fax: (01282) 697749

▶ JayWolfe, 64 Kingsley Road, Northampton, NN2 7BL Tel: 01604 821066 E-mail: jay.wolfe@ntlworld.com

Matt's Sheet Metal, Whitefield Mill, St. Marys Street, Nelson, Lancashire, BB9 7BA Tel: (01282) 602228 Fax: (01282) 602228

Multishape Sheet Metal Work, 120 Camford Way, Luton, LU3 3AN Tel: (01582) 581133 Fax: (01582) 581158 E-mail: custserv@multishape.co.uk

QFS Technologies Ltd, Unit 10-11 Chelmsley Wood Industrial Estate, Waterloo Avenue, Birmingham, B37 6QQ Tel: 0121-770 1200 Fax: 0121-770 1232

Quality Metal Fabrication, Unit 2 Meadow View Industrial Estate, Ruckinge, Ashford, Kent, TN26 2NR Tel: (01233) 733544 Fax: (01233) 733544

Ringwood Precision, 2 Millstream Trading Estate, Christchurch Road, Ringwood, Hampshire, BH24 3SA Tel: (01425) 476296 Fax: (01425) 476296 E-mail: ukroy@freenetname.co.uk

SHEET METALWORKING/ FABRICATORS, PUNCHING AND FORMING, CNC

Colmet Precision Ltd, Unit 15 Upper Wingbury Courtyard Business Centre, Leighton Road, Wingrave, Aylesbury, Buckinghamshire, HP22 4LW Tel: (01296) 681658 Fax: (01296) 681726 E-mail: sales@colmet.co.uk

Raydon Sheet Metal Co. Ltd, Birch Walk, Fraser Road, Erith, Kent, DA8 1QX Tel: (01322) 431535 Fax: (01322) 433637

SHEET METALWORKING/ FABRICATORS, SMALL BATCH/ PRODUCTION

▶ Sunbeam Woodworks Ltd, 17 & 21 Sunbeam Road, Park Royal, London, NW10 6JP Tel: (020) 8357 1000 Fax: (020) 8357 1021 E-mail: admin@sunbeamgroup.com

SHEET METALWORKING/ FABRICATORS, STAINLESS STEEL

▶ A1 Stainless Steel Fabrications, Redhill Works, 200 Prospect Row, Dudley, West Midlands, DY2 8SG Tel: (01384) 253738 Fax: (01384) 256157 E-mail: info@a1stainless.co.uk

▶ Bute Blacksmiths, 88 High Street, Rothesay, Isle of Bute, PA20 9BB Tel: (01700) 504235 Fax: (01700) 504235 E-mail: enquiries@buteblacksmiths.fsnet.co.uk

▶ Protosheet Engineering Ltd, 73 Swaisland Drive, Crayford, Dartford, DA1 4HY Tel: (01322) 550545 Fax: (01322) 555719 E-mail: sales@protosheet.co.uk

Raydon Sheet Metal Co. Ltd, Birch Walk, Fraser Road, Erith, Kent, DA8 1QX Tel: (01322) 431535 Fax: (01322) 433637

Riverdale Mahoney Ltd, Unit 3 Dicker Mill, Hertford, SG13 7AE Tel: (01992) 583988 Fax: (01992) 583988 E-mail: riverdalema@btinternet.com

Wyvern Sheet Metal & Fabrications Ltd, Three Springs Trading Estate, Vincent Road, Worcester, WR5 1BW Tel: (01905) 357830 Fax: (01905) 357830 E-mail: sales@wyvernsheetmetal.wanadoo.co.uk

SHEET METALWORKING/ FABRICATORS, TO SPECIFICATION

Aerotech Precision Manufacturing Ltd, 1 Stone Lane, Wimborne, Dorset, BH21 1HB Tel: (01202) 848484 Fax: (01202) 848989 E-mail: sales@aero-tech.co.uk

Aire Valley Metal Products Ltd, Shaw House, Goulbourne Street, Keighley, West Yorkshire, BD21 1PG Tel: (01535) 600162 Fax: (01535) 600162 E-mail: aire@valleymetals.fsnet.co.uk

Argent Fabrications Ltd, Unit 4 Avery Dell, Lifford Lane, Birmingham, B30 3DZ Tel: 0121-459 9617 Fax: 0121-458 6604 E-mail: enquiries@argentfabs.com

Catterall & Wood Ltd, Unit 2 Primrose Bank Mill, Friday Street, Chorley, Lancashire, PR6 0AA Tel: (01257) 272192 Fax: (01257) 261432

Colval Engineering, Unit 1a Bury Farm, Curbridge, Botley, Southampton, SO30 2HB Tel: (01489) 799100 Fax: (01489) 799100

Derbrich Fabrications, Estate Road 7, South Humberside Industrial Estate, Grimsby, South Humberside, DN31 2TP Tel: (01472) 885888 Fax: (01472) 884965 E-mail: fabrications@derbrich.freeserve.co.uk

E Reg Sheet Metal Fabricators, Unit 7 Kirby Road, Lomeshaye Industrial Estate, Nelson, Lancashire, BB9 6RS Tel: (01282) 697748 Fax: (01282) 697749

F1 Manufacturing, 350 Melton Road, Leicester, LE4 7SL Tel: 0116-268 8484 Fax: 0116-268 8489 E-mail: sales@f1manufacturing.com

Hooper Engineering Ltd, Nelson St, Oldbury, West Midlands, B69 4NY Tel: 0121-552 2835 Fax: 0121-552 3821 E-mail: hooper.sheetmetal@virgin.net

It C M L Ltd, Unit 26 Cam Centre, Wilbury Way, Hitchin, Hertfordshire, SG4 0TW Tel: (01462) 635455 Fax: (01462) 635454 E-mail: salesitcml@btconnect.com

J & K Sheet Metal, Unit 33 Joseph Wilson Industrial Estate, Whitstable, Kent, CT5 3PS Tel: (01227) 274763 Fax: (01227) 773021

M J P Tube & Fittings Ltd, Regil Lane, Winford, Bristol, BS40 8AX Tel: (01275) 474758 Fax: (01275) 472753

Major Sheet Metals, 483 Bradford Road, Batley, West Yorkshire, WF17 8LB Tel: (01924) 441610 Fax: (01924) 420535

Matt's Sheet Metal, Whitefield Mill, St. Marys Street, Nelson, Lancashire, BB9 7BA Tel: (01282) 602228 Fax: (01282) 602228

Planet Merchandising Products Ltd, Unit 219b, Aldington Road, London, SE18 5TS Tel: (020) 8855 9594 Fax: (020) 8316 2745 E-mail: sales@planetmerchandising.co.uk

Prodrive Holdings Ltd, Acorn Way, Banbury, Oxfordshire, OX16 3ER Tel: (01295) 273355 Fax: (01295) 271188 E-mail: enquiries@prodrive.com

R W M C Engineering Ltd, Harrow Wood Farm & Caravan Park, Poplar Lane, Bransgore, Christchurch, Dorset, BH23 8JE Tel: (01425) 674450 Fax: (01425) 674450

Retail Display Solutions, St. Andrew House, St. Andrews Trading Estate, Bridport, Dorset, DT6 3EX Tel: (01308) 459950 Fax: (01308) 424410 E-mail: sales@retaildisplaysolutions.co.uk

Warwick Engineering, 3 River Gardens, Feltham, Middlesex, TW14 0RD Tel: (020) 8844 2268 Fax: (020) 8751 0509

Western Metalcraft, 79d Grove Road, Fishponds, Bristol, BS16 2BP Tel: 0117-965 3865 Fax: 0117-965 3865

Westwood Automation Ltd, Bell Close, Newnham Industrial Estate, Plympton, Plymouth, PL7 4JH Tel: (01752) 202113 Fax: (01752) 202117

SHEETING MACHINES, PAPER/ PLASTIC ETC

Doel Engineering Ltd, 5 Europa Park, Croft Way, Witham, Essex, CM8 2FN Tel: (01376) 515515 Fax: (01376) 500015 E-mail: info@doelengineering.com

SHELF EDGE LABELS

Amco Print Solutions Ltd, 3 Beech Close, Menston, Ilkley, West Yorkshire, LS29 6NU Tel: (01943) 873 455 Fax: (01943) 884 786 E-mail: sales@amcoprint.com

SHELL AND TUBE HEAT EXCHANGERS

A C R Heat Transfer Ltd, Rollesby Road, King's Lynn, Norfolk, PE30 4LN Tel: (01553) 763371 Fax: (01553) 771322 E-mail: acrheat@msn.com

A M I Exchanges Ltd, Apex Workshops, Graythorp Industrial Estate, Hartlepool, Cleveland, TS25 2DF Tel: (01429) 860187 Fax: (01429) 860673 E-mail: sales@ami-exchangers.co.uk

Britannia Cooling Ltd, Britannia Road, Morley, Leeds, LS27 0DD Tel: 0113-253 6159 Fax: 0113-253 0111

Corsair Vacuum Systems Ltd, The Avenue, Endon, Stoke-On-Trent, ST9 9BY Tel: (01782) 504459 Fax: (01782) 504459 E-mail: corsair@vacpumps.co.uk

County Engineering Southern Ltd, Unit 9, Annington Commercial Centre, Annington Road, Bramber, Steyning, West Sussex, BN44 3WA Tel: (01903) 879428 Fax: (01903) 815077 E-mail: ces@countyeng.demon.co.uk

J M Heat Exchangers Ltd, 3 Albion Place, Doncaster, South Yorkshire, DN1 2EG Tel: (01302) 325179 Fax: (01302) 760353 E-mail: bryan@jmheatexchanges.com

Poole Process Equipment Ltd, 43-49 Nuffield Road, Nuffield Industrial Estate, Poole, Dorset, BH17 0RA Tel: (01202) 674683 Fax: (01202) 665265 E-mail: postmaster@poole-process.co.uk

R M F Engineering Ltd, Rotherham Road, Dinnington, Sheffield, S25 3RF Tel: (01909) 567683 Fax: (01909) 562725 E-mail: sales@rmf-engineering.co.uk

Ross Heat Exchangers Ltd, Units 6 & 7, Dryden Glen, Loanhead, Midlothian, EH20 9NA Tel: 0131-440 0066 Fax: 0131-440 4188 E-mail: sales@ross-heatexchangers.co.uk

S S T Process Engineering Ltd, Unit 22 Autumn Park, Dysart Road, Grantham, Lincolnshire, NG31 7DD Tel: (01476) 590112 Fax: (01476) 590113 E-mail: sales@sstpe.co.uk

Stanref International Ltd, Northern Way, Bury St. Edmunds, Suffolk, IP32 6NL Tel: 01284 763501

Unit Superheater Engineering Ltd, Unit Works, 2-8 Morfa Road, Swansea, SA1 2ET Tel: (01792) 654091 Fax: (01792) 456198 E-mail: eng@unit.co.uk

Wellman Hunt Graham Ltd, Astley Street, Dukinfield, Cheshire, SK16 4QT Tel: 0161-331 4400 Fax: 0161-331 4434

SHELL MOULDED CASTINGS

▶ B A S Castings Ltd, Wharf Road Industrial Estate, Pinxton, Nottingham, NG16 6LE Tel: (01773) 812028 Fax: (01773) 861948 E-mail: sales@bascastings.com

Bevan Simpson Foundry Ltd, Hainge Road, Tividale, Oldbury, West Midlands, B69 2PB Tel: 0121-557 3621 Fax: 0121-520 6622

Myriad Services Ltd, 111 Woods Lane, Derby, DE22 3UE Tel: (01332) 380763 Fax: (01332) 380763

R S M Castings Ltd, 7 North Portway Close, Round Spinney Industrial Estate, Northampton, NN3 8RQ Tel: (01604) 671333 Fax: (01604) 491012 E-mail: enquiries@rsm-castings.co.uk

William Cook, Cross Green Approach, Leeds, LS9 0SG Tel: 0113-249 6363 Fax: 0113-249 1376 E-mail: sales@william-cook.co.uk

SHELL MOULDING EQUIPMENT

Micra Pattern Co. Ltd, 91 Sorby Street, Sheffield, S4 7LA Tel: 0114 2720724

SHELLAC

Thew, Arnott & Co. Ltd, Newman Works, 270 London Road, Wallington, Surrey, SM6 7DJ Tel: (020) 8669 3131 Fax: (020) 8669 7747 E-mail: sales@thewarnott.co.uk

SHELLFISH

▶ A D M Seafoods, 1 Bedale Walk, Dartford, DA2 6HS Tel: (0871) 2447305 Fax: (0871) 2113186 E-mail: sales@admseafoods.com

Bruce's Shellfish, 9 Balconie Street, Evanton, Dingwall, Ross-Shire, IV16 9UN Tel: (01349) 830187 Fax: (01349) 830187

R J Noble, 2 Stainsacre La Industrial Estate, Fairfield Way, Whitby, North Yorkshire, YO22 4PU Tel: (01947) 820413 Fax: (01947) 820413

SHELTERS, BUS/SMOKING/ PUBLIC

Abacus Holdings Ltd, Oddicroft Lane, Sutton-in-Ashfield, Nottinghamshire, NG17 5FT Tel: (01623) 511111 Fax: (01623) 552133 E-mail: sales@abacuslighting.com

Autocross Plastics, Units 26-27 New Hall Hey Business Park, New Hall Hey Road, Rossendale, Lancashire, BB4 6HL Tel: (01706) 216794 Fax: (01706) 230758 E-mail: bill@euroshel.com

Bus Shelters (Wales) Ltd, Unit 60, Llantwit Major Road, Dyffryn Business Park, Cowbridge, South Glamorgan, CF71 7PY Tel: (01446) 795444 Fax: (01446) 793344 E-mail: bus@shelters.co.uk

▶ Nim (Ltd Engineering), Yardley House, 100 Chase Park Road, Yardley Hastings, Northampton, NN7 1HF Tel: (01604) 696120 Fax: (01604) 696122 E-mail: info@nimltdengineering.com

Woodhouse UK plc, Harrison Way, Leamington Spa, Warwickshire, CV31 3HL Tel: (01926) 314313 Fax: (01926) 883778 E-mail: enquires@woodhouse.co.uk

SHELVING

Abbey Racking, 1-7 Ruby Mews, Ruby Road, London, E17 4RB Tel: (020) 8521 6176 Fax: (020) 8521 2214 E-mail: sales@usedshelving.co.uk

Abbey Storage & Office Systems Ltd, International House, 30 Villa Road, Benfleet, Essex, SS7 5QL Tel: (01268) 794070 Fax: (01268) 566141 E-mail: doug@abbeystorage.freeserve.co.uk

Ace Systems Ltd, Rose Green Road, Bristol, BS5 7XE Tel: 0117-952 0624 Fax: 0117-935 4255 E-mail: sales@acestorage.co.uk

Amracks Ltd, 2 Cockerell Road, Corby, Northamptonshire, NN17 5DU Tel: (01536) 401361 Fax: (01536) 275909 E-mail: info@amracks.co.uk

Astor-Rack, 579 Gale Street, Dagenham, Essex, RM9 4TS Tel: (020) 8984 8499 Fax: (020) 8984 8412 E-mail: sales@astor-rack.co.uk

Axis Scotland Ltd, 12 Auchingramont Road, Hamilton, Lanarkshire, ML3 6JT Tel: (01698) 785000 Fax: (01698) 785111 E-mail: enquiries@axis.gb.com

▶ Base Line, 4 The Square, Notley Green, Great Notley, Braintree, Essex, CM77 7WT Tel: (01376) 551030 Fax: (01376) 551251 E-mail: sales@base-line.co.uk

Birchmoor Associates, 16 Norris Way Industrial Estate, Norris Way, Rushden, Northamptonshire, NN10 6BP Tel: (01933) 314499 Fax: (01933) 410495 E-mail: lionel@birchmoorassociates.co.uk

▶ Bridledene Steel Fabricators, Little Marsh Quarter, Sandhurst, Cranbrook, Kent, TN18 5NY Tel: (01580) 850860 Fax: (01580) 850870 E-mail: info@bridledene.com

Britannia Storage Systems, Airfield, Earls Colne, Colchester, CO6 2NS Tel: (01787) 223884 Fax: (01787) 223038 E-mail: enquires@britannia-storage.co.uk

Butler & Willow Ltd, 7 Harrington Mills, Leopold Street, Long Eaton, Nottingham, NG10 4QE Tel: 0115-946 8687 Fax: 0115-946 9446 E-mail: sales@butler-willow.co.uk

Cornish Maintenance Co, 4 Bilton Road, Perivale, Greenford, Middlesex, UB6 7FB Tel: (020) 8998 9247 Fax: (020) 8998 9149 E-mail: d.cornish@theseshelvingcentre.co.uk

CPS, 53 Bank Top Road, Rotherham, South Yorkshire, S65 3DY Tel: (01709) 543338 Fax: (01709) 543338

Crest Erection Services, 44a Bristol Road, Keynsham, Bristol, BS31 2BE Tel: 0117-986 6111 Fax: 0117-986 6333

▶ Cumbria Storage Systems Ltd, 52a Main Street, Cockermouth, Cumbria, CA13 9LU Tel: (01900) 827333 Fax: (01900) 827334 E-mail: sales@cumstore.co.uk

Design Masters Ltd, 2 Marlows Court, Marlows, Hemel Hempstead, Hertfordshire, HP1 1LE Tel: (01442) 256756 Fax: (01442) 260602 E-mail: designmasters@aol.com

Duval Products Ltd, Dexion Storage Centre, Armoury Way, London, SW18 1EU Tel: (020) 8870 7541 Fax: (020) 8870 2657 E-mail: sales@duvalproducts.co.uk

F Eastwood & Sons plc, London Works, Ripple Road, Barking, Essex, IG11 0SY Tel: (020) 8591 7200 Fax: (020) 8591 4193 E-mail: sales@feastwood.co.uk

Fastrack Used Racking, Unit 14 Hurricane Way, North Weald Airfield, North Weald, Epping, Essex, CM16 6AA Tel: (01992) 523500 Fax: (01992) 523900 E-mail: janice.cullin@unitedstorage.co.uk

Frodex, Everitt Close, Denington Industrial Estate, Wellingborough, Northamptonshire, NN8 2QE Tel: (01933) 225564 Fax: (01933) 226093

Greenoaks Ltd, Greenoaks House, Siemens Road, Irlam, Manchester, M44 5AH Tel: 0161-775 0956 Fax: 0161-776 1951 E-mail: info@greenoaks.ltd.uk

Headway Storage Systems Ltd, 142 Bath Road, Totterdown, Bristol, BS4 3EF Tel: 0117-971 2222 Fax: 0117-972 4912

Independent Storage Installation Services Ltd, 1 Calder Vale Mills, Healey Road, Ossett, West Yorkshire, WF5 8NF Tel: (01924) 281219 Fax: (01924) 281219 E-mail: info@independentstorage.co.uk

Kane Bros, 4 Divis Road, Hannahstown, Belfast, BT17 0NG Tel: (028) 9061 8235 Fax: (028) 9062 0067

Kingstonian Storage Equipment Ltd, 1 Phoenix Enterprise Park, Grovehill Road, Beverley, North Humberside, HU17 0JG Tel: (01482) 868055 Fax: (01482) 872558 E-mail: paul@kingsstorage.fsnet.co.uk

Link 51 (Shelving Storage) Ltd, 16 Mill St, Brierley Hill, West Midlands, DY5 2TB Tel: (01384) 472500 Fax: (01384) 472599 E-mail: shelving@link51.co.uk

Maxi Storage Systems Ltd, Walkley Mills, Spen Vale Street, Heckmondwike, West Yorkshire, WF16 0PS Tel: (01924) 411706 Fax: (01924) 411711 E-mail: keith@maxistorage.co.uk

Metalrax, Bordesley Green Road, Birmingham, B9 4TP Tel: 0121-772 8151 Fax: 0121-772 6135 E-mail: sales@metalrax-storage.co.uk

Monarch Shelving Ltd, Unit 7, Moss Lane Industrial Estate, Heyside, Oldham, OL2 6HR Tel: (01706) 880355 Fax: (0870) 7505477 E-mail: sales@monarchdirect.co.uk

Moresecure Ltd, Haldane House, Halesfield 1, Telford, Shropshire, TF7 4EH Tel: (01952) 683900 Fax: (01952) 683982 E-mail: sales@moresecure.co.uk

Pallet Handling Ltd, Chiddingstone Causeway, Tonbridge, Kent, TN11 8JD Tel: (01892) 870655 Fax: (01892) 870746

Randall Storage Systems Ltd, 5 Beaucroft Road, Wimborne, Dorset, BH21 2QW Tel: (01202) 848059 Fax: (01202) 848059

Rochdale Equipment Centre Ltd, Howard Street, Rochdale, Lancashire, OL12 0LU Tel: (01706) 656092 Fax: (01706) 641825 E-mail: sales@officefurniture-online.co.uk

S T S Storage Systems Ltd, 49-51 Yew Tree Road, Slough, SL1 2AG Tel: (01753) 821166 Fax: (01753) 576192 E-mail: sales@stsstorage.co.uk

Shelfstore Shelving & Racking, 158 Finchley Road, London, NW3 5HD Tel: (020) 7794 0313 Fax: (020) 7435 3927 E-mail: info@shelfstore.co.uk

Stockport Racking Co. Ltd, 12 Hammond Avenue, Whitehill Industrial Estate, Stockport, Cheshire, SK4 1PQ Tel: 0161-477 0155 Fax: 0161-477 0159

Storage Logic, 24 High Street, Bovingdon, Hemel Hempstead, Hertfordshire, HP3 0HG Tel: (01442) 831133 Fax: (01442) 831144 E-mail: info@storage-logic.co.uk

Storplan Racking Ltd, The Airfield, Full Sutton, York, YO41 1HS Tel: (01759) 371553 Fax: (01759) 372451 E-mail: storplan@ic24.net

▶ Surestore, 7, Kingsway, Hayling Island, Hampshire, PO11 0LZ Tel: (023) 9246 3239 Fax: (023) 9246 0302

▶ Systematic Creative Interiors Ltd, Red Shute Hill Industrial Estate, Red Shute Hill, Hermitage, Thatcham, Berkshire, RG18 9QL Tel: (01635) 201789 Fax: (01635) 200996 E-mail: sale@systematicinteriors.co.uk

T P G Storage, 7 Hudsons Way, Canvey Island, Essex, SS8 9FE Tel: (01268) 696336 Fax: (01268) 514048

Techniform Sales Ltd, 14 250 Milkwood Road, London, SE24 0HG Tel: (020) 7274 1999 Fax: (020) 7274 0199

Thiel Technics UK, 66 Tonacliffe Road, Whitworth, Rochdale, Lancashire, OL12 8SS Tel: (01706) 868822 Fax: (01706) 343402 E-mail: sales@thiel-technics.co.uk

Top Floor Ltd, 100 Cobham Road, Ferndown Industrial Estate, Wimborne, Dorset, BH21 7PQ Tel: (01202) 876339 Fax: (01202) 891047 E-mail: sales@topfloor.co.uk

Tyler Storage Ltd, 2 Compton Drive, Poole, Dorset, BH14 8PW Tel: (01202) 733344 Fax: (01202) 730228

United Storage Systems Ltd, United House, The Street, Takeley, Bishop's Stortford, Hertfordshire, CM22 6QR Tel: (01279) 871787 Fax: (01279) 871636 E-mail: sales@unitedstorage.co.uk

West Pennine Storage Equipment Ltd, West Pennine Business Park, Burnley Road, Bacup, Lancashire, OL13 8PJ Tel: (01706) 875500 Fax: (01706) 875600 E-mail: westpenninesd@aol.com

SHELVING UNITS, STAINLESS STEEL

P.W.S SYSTEMS, Unit 22D, Barking Industrial Park, RIPPLE ROAD, BARKING, ESSEX, IG11 0TJ Tel: (020) 8594 7574 E-mail: tws_office@yahoo.co.uk

SHELVING, ADJUSTABLE, ROLL OUT SHELVES

A.B. Allen Engineering Ltd, Phoenix House, 20 Duncrue Crescent, Belfast, BT3 9BW Tel: (028) 9037 0269 Fax: (028) 9077 7817 E-mail: sales@allen-engineering.co.uk

D M Interiors Ltd, 37 Enstone Road, Uxbridge, Middlesex, UB10 8EZ Tel: (01895) 674479 Fax: (01895) 621383

SHELVING, ADJUSTABLE, STEEL

Equip4work Ltd, 1st Floor, 1 St. Michael Street, Dumfries, DG1 2QD Tel: (0844) 4999222 Fax: (0844) 4999322 E-mail: sales@equip4work.co.uk

SHELVING, SHOP/STORE FIXTURE

Crosby Plant Sales Ltd, Church Street, Bootle, Merseyside, L20 1AF Tel: 0151-933 9920 Fax: 0151-933 7735
Cubex Contracts Ltd, 8 Desborough Road, Rothwell, Kettering, Northamptonshire, NN14 6JG Tel: (01536) 712729 Fax: (01536) 418990 E-mail: sales@cubexcontracts.com
Murray Services Ltd, Prospect Avenue, Seaton Delaval, Whitley Bay, Tyne & Wear, NE25 0DP Tel: 0191-237 3893 Fax: 0191-237 3801 E-mail: sales@murray-services.ltd.uk
UK Shelving Ltd, Northwick Road, Canvey Island, Essex, SS8 0PS Tel: (01268) 515247 Fax: (01268) 510829

SHERARDISING METAL TREATMENT SERVICES

Bodycote Metallurgical Coatings Ltd, Shakespeare Street, Wolverhampton, WV1 3LR Tel: (01902) 452915 Fax: (01902) 352917 E-mail: sales.bmc@bodycote.co.uk

SHIELD /SHIELDING COATINGS, RADIO FREQUENCY INTERFERENCE (RFI) AND ELECTROMAGNETIC INTERFERENCE (EMI)

▶ G & L Coatings, 8 Wallace Way, Hitchin, Hertfordshire, SG4 0SE Tel: (01462) 436668 Fax: (01462) 438982 E-mail: george.cooney@talk21.com

SHIELD/SHIELDING ELECTROMAGNETIC DISCHARGE (EMD) COATING SERVICES, RADIO FREQUENCY INTERFERENCE (RFI)

Leabank Coatings Ltd, Wycombe Road, Stokenchurch, High Wycombe, Buckinghamshire, HP14 3RJ Tel: (01494) 483737 Fax: (01494) 484239 E-mail: info@leabank.net
Pwe Coatings, 9 Nobel Square, Burnt Mills Industrial Estate, Basildon, Essex, SS13 1LS Tel: (01268) 729983 Fax: (01268) 727955

SHIELD/SHIELDING, RADIO FREQUENCY INTERFERENCE (RFI) AND ELECTROMAGNETIC INTERFERENCE (EMI)

E M C Plastics UK Ltd, Wychwood Business Centre, Shipton-Under-Wychwobusiness, Chipping Norton, Oxfordshire, OX7 6XU Tel: (01993) 832000 Fax: (01993) 831444 E-mail: sales@emc-uk.com
European Emc Products Ltd, Unit 8, Saffron Business Centre, Elizabeth Close, Saffron Walden, Essex, CB10 2BL Tel: (01799) 523073 Fax: (01799) 521191 E-mail: info@euro-emc.co.uk
P & P Technology Ltd, 1 Kestrel Park, Finch Drive, Springwood Industrial Estate, Braintree, Essex, CM7 2SF Tel: (01376) 550525 Fax: (01376) 552389 E-mail: info@p-p-t.co.uk
R F Shielding Ltd, Unit 16, Rising Sun Industrial Estate, Blaina, Abertillery, Gwent, NP13 3JW Tel: (01495) 292399 Fax: (01495) 292550 E-mail: info@rfshielding.co.uk
Surrey Management Consultants Ltd, Newmet House, Rue de St Lawrence, Waltham Abbey, Essex, EN9 1PF Tel: (01992) 703401 Fax: (01992) 768393 E-mail: materials@newmet.co.uk
Zytronic Displays Ltd, Patterson Street, Blaydon-on-Tyne, Tyne & Wear, NE21 5SG Tel: 0191-414 5511 Fax: 0191-414 0545 E-mail: info@zytronic.co.uk

SHIELDED FILTER WINDOWS

E M C Plastics UK Ltd, Wychwood Business Centre, Shipton-Under-Wychwobusiness, Chipping Norton, Oxfordshire, OX7 6XU Tel: (01993) 832000 Fax: (01993) 831444 E-mail: sales@emc-uk.com

SHIFT MANAGEMENT OR ROSTERING SOFTWARE

Computaphile Software Soltuions Ltd, 13 Surrey Close, Rugeley, Staffordshire, WS15 1JZ Tel: (01889) 579572 Fax: (01889) 579572 E-mail: brian@computaphile.com
Misco, Darby Close, Park Farm South, Wellingborough, Northamptonshire, NN8 6GS Tel: (08707) 208720 Fax: (08707) 208686 E-mail: salesdesk@misco.co.uk
P T C (UK) Ltd, Inavation House, Harvest Crescent, Fleet, Hampshire, GU51 2QR Tel: (01252) 817000 Fax: (01252) 817000
Smart People Time plc, Node Court, Drivers End, Codicote, Hitchin, Hertfordshire, SG4 8TR Tel: (01438) 822222 Fax: (01438) 822240 E-mail: info@smarthumanlogistics.com
Wisbech Computer Services Ltd, 107 Norwich Road, Wisbech, Cambridgeshire, PE13 2BB Tel: (01945) 464146 Fax: (01945) 464680 E-mail: sales@wisbech.com

SHIMS, *See also headings for particular types*

Attewell Ltd, 4 Southbridge Way, Southall, Middlesex, UB2 4BY Tel: (020) 8571 0055 Fax: (020) 8571 7139 E-mail: sales@attewell.co.uk

SHIP BROKERS

Amundsen & Smith Ltd, Cargo Durham Distribution Centre, Seaham, County Durham, SR7 7NZ Tel: 0191-581 2315 Fax: 0191-581 7360 E-mail: enquiries@amundsen-smith.co.uk
Anglo Caribbean Shipping Co. Ltd, 14 Skylines Village, Limeharbour, London, E14 9TS Tel: (020) 7537 7420 Fax: (020) 7537 4778
Atkinson & Prickett, Crowle House, Hull, HU1 1RJ Tel: (01482) 324191 Fax: (01482) 224914 E-mail: hull@kettlewell.com
B E Moors Ltd, Kemp House, 152-160 City Road, London, EC1V 2NP Tel: (020) 7855 5300 Fax: (020) 7454 9090 E-mail: admin@bemoors.co.uk
Bright Cook & Co Shipbrokers Ltd, 139 Upper Richmond Road, London, SW15 2TX Tel: (020) 8785 4288 Fax: (020) 8785 2571 E-mail: ships@brightcook.com
C M Los (London) Ltd, Coppergate House, 16 Brune Street, London, E1 7NJ Tel: (020) 7721 7977 Fax: (020) 7721 7967 E-mail: mail@cmlos.com
Capeside Steamship Co. Ltd, Charter House, 13-15 Carteret Street, London, SW1H 9DJ Tel: (020) 7222 4923 Fax: (020) 7222 0493
D S B Offshore Ltd, Eden House, 59 Fulham High Street, London, SW6 3JJ Tel: (020) 7384 2882 Fax: (020) 7731 8163 E-mail: sales@dsboffshore.com
Denholm Shipping Company Ltd, Liner House, Test Road, Eastern Docks, Southampton, SO14 3GE Tel: (023) 8071 3100 Fax: (023) 8071 3129 E-mail: finadmin@denshipsouth.co.uk
Embiricos Ship Brokers Ltd, Commonwealth House, 1-19 New Oxford Street, London, WC1A 1NU Tel: (020) 7404 0420 Fax: (020) 7400 0887
Express Tanker (UK) Limited, 17 Ensign House, ADMIRALS WAY, CANARY WHARF, LONDON, E14 9XQ Tel: 0207 863 1790 Fax: 0700 597 6260 E-mail: info@expresstanker.com
Galbraith's Ltd, Bridge Gate House, 124-126 Borough High Street, London, SE1 1BL Tel: (020) 7378 6363 Fax: (020) 7959 1086 E-mail: admin@galbraiths.co.uk
E.A. Gibson Shipbrokers Ltd, PO Box 278, London, EC1P 1HP Tel: (020) 7667 1000 Fax: (020) 7831 8762 E-mail: tanker@eagibson.co.uk
Gillie & Blair, 178 New Bridge Street, Newcastle upon Tyne, NE1 2TE Tel: 0191-230 4747 Fax: 0191-230 8255 E-mail: mail@gillieblair.com
Gourdomichalis & Co. (Chartering) Ltd, Mitre House, 12-14 Mitre Street, London, EC3A 5BU Tel: (020) 7283 9621 Fax: (020) 7283 3108 E-mail: mail@gourdochart.co.uk
Graypen Ltd, Prince Henry Drive, Queens Road, Immingham, South Humberside, DN40 1QY Tel: (01482) 794323 Fax: (01469) 552900 E-mail: info@graypen.co.uk
Harwin Shipping Agency Ltd, 40 Bowling Green Lane, London, EC1R 0NE Tel: (020) 7837 3759 Fax: (020) 7278 0745 E-mail: harwinship@aol.com
Howard Houlder & Partners Ltd, Osborn House, 74-80 Middlesex Street, London, E1 7EZ Tel: (020) 7247 9090 Fax: (020) 7360 4201
J R Rix & Sons Ltd, 45 Spyvee Street, Hull, HU8 7JJ Tel: (01482) 222250 Fax: (01482) 338590
Jeppesen Heaton Ltd, 17 Church Street, Epsom, Surrey, KT17 4PF Tel: (01372) 745678 Fax: (01372) 724111 E-mail: ian@jeppesen.freeserve.co.uk
John Gargan Chartering Ltd, Trident House, 105 Derby Road, Bootle, Merseyside, L20 8LZ Tel: 0151-922 0066 Fax: 0151-922 5006 E-mail: john@johngargan.co.uk
John Jolly, P O Box 2, Kirkwall, Orkney, KW15 1HS Tel: (01856) 872268 Fax: (01856) 875002 E-mail: operations@johnjolly.co.uk
Killick Martin & Co. Ltd, Bowden Freight Terminal, Luckyn Lane, Pips Hill Industrial Estate, Basildon, Essex, SS14 3AX Tel: (01268) 274382 Fax:
W. Knight Watson & Co. Ltd, Mandal House, South Shore Road, Grangemouth, Stirlingshire, FK3 8AE Tel: (01324) 486721 Fax: (01324) 473096 E-mail: enquiries@wkwat.co.uk
Leafe & Hawkes Ltd, 5 Merrick Street, Hull, HU9 1NF Tel: (01482) 325951 Fax: (01482) 225406E-mail: s.leafe@leafeandhawkes.co.uk
G.G. Lucas & Company Ltd, 17-18 Old Bond Street, London, W1S 4PT Tel: (020) 7629 1680 Fax: (020) 7629 7309 E-mail: shipping@gglucas.com
Lyras Financial Services Ltd, 24 26 Baltic Street, London, EC1Y 0RP Tel: (020) 7251 1313 Fax: (020) 7608 1783 E-mail: all@lyras-maritime.demon.co.uk
Macfarlane Shipping Co. Ltd, Grianan, Thurlow Road, Nairn, IV12 4HJ Tel: (01667) 451671 Fax: (01667) 455383 E-mail: macship@btinternet.com
Mctaggart Shipping & Management Co. Ltd, 1 Great Cumberland Place, London, W1H 7AL Tel: (020) 7468 8500 Fax: (020) 7468 8625 E-mail: chadring@macnav.com
Mason Shipbrokers Ltd, Unit 5-6 Blake House, Admirals Way, London, E14 9UJ Tel: (020) 7538 5366 Fax: (020) 7538 4677 E-mail: masonshp@globalnet.co.uk
N S Lemos & Co. Ltd, St Clare House, 30-33 Minories, London, EC3N 1DD Tel: (020) 7481 8921 Fax: (020) 7481 4177 E-mail: nslemos@nslemos.com
NJ Goulandris Ltd, Berkeley Square House, Berkeley Square, London, W1J 6BE Tel: (020) 7304 4900 Fax: (020) 7304 4802 E-mail: general@njgoulandris.com
North Atlantic Shipping Agency Ltd, Kingsway House, 103 Kingsway, London, WC2B 6QX Tel: (020) 7405 5554 Fax: (020) 7405 5125
O B C Shipping Ltd, Osprey House, Richmond Road, Pembroke Dock, Dyfed, SA72 6TS Tel: (01646) 622220 Fax: (01646) 622221 E-mail: pembroke.agency@obcgroup.com
Obc Shipping Ltd, 2a Gateway Business Park, Beancross Road, Grangemouth, Stirlingshire, FK3 8WX Tel: (01324) 482811 Fax: (01324) 665197 E-mail: grangemouth.agency@obcgroup.com
Oceanic Maritime Ltd, 32 The Mall, London, W5 3TJ Tel: (020) 8566 1100 Fax: (020) 8579 0443E-mail: containers@oceanicmaritime.com
Offshore Marine Contractors Ltd, Magellan House, James Watt Close, Gapton Hall Industrial Estate, Great Yarmouth, Norfolk, NR31 0NX Tel: (01493) 658489 Fax: (01493) 658490 E-mail: yarmouth@omcon.com
Pearl Carriers, 123 Aldersgate Street, London, EC1A 4JQ Tel: (020) 7253 3660 Fax: (020) 7608 2512
Pike Ward Ltd, Old Quay, Teignmouth, Devon, TQ14 8EU Tel: (01626) 772311 Fax: (01626) 770218 E-mail: agency@pikeward.co.uk
Quality Freight (UK) Ltd, 1st Floor Port Office, Manisty Wharf, Ellesmere Port, CH65 1AF Tel: 0151-355 6006 Fax: 0151-355 3273 E-mail: info@quality-freight.co.uk
Ramsey Steamship Co. Ltd, 8 Auckland Terrace, Parliament Street, Ramsey, Isle of Man, IM8 1AF Tel: (01624) 816202 Fax: (01624) 816206 E-mail: tony@ramsey-steamship.com
Rosenvinge & Co. Ltd, Suite 20 Albion House, Sidney Street, North Shields, Tyne & Wear, NE29 0DW Tel: 0191-258 0030 Fax: 0191-296 0520
S C Chambers & Co. Ltd, 1 Water Street, Liverpool, L2 0RD Tel: 0151-236 4151 Fax: 0151-227 2921 E-mail: sandp@scchambers.co.uk
John Samonas & Sons Ltd, Princeton Mews, 167-169 London Road, Kingston upon Thames, Surrey, KT2 6PT Tel: (020) 8547 2244 Fax: (020) 8547 1949 E-mail: samonas@johnsamonas.com
Seascope Offshore, 25 Carden Place, Aberdeen, AB10 1UQ Tel: (01224) 628470 Fax: (01224) 621444 E-mail: sales@seascope.co.uk
Seven Seas Chartering Ltd, Berger House, 38 Berkeley Square, London, W1J 5AD Tel: (020) 7495 6776 Fax: (020) 7491 9491 E-mail: sevenseas@sevsea.co.uk
Smit International (Scotland) Ltd, The Exchange, 62 Market Street, Aberdeen, AB11 5PT Tel: (01224) 560400 Fax: (01224) 581485
Smith, Hogg & Co. Ltd, Dock Offices, Cleveland Road, Hartlepool, Cleveland, TS24 0UZ Tel: (01429) 273157 Fax: (01429) 270693
Somerset Shipbrokers Ltd, Walsingham House, 35 Seething Lane, London, EC3N 4AN Tel: (020) 7488 4401 Fax: (020) 7265 0238
Southern Steamship, Victoria House, 1-3 College Hill, London, EC4R 2RA Tel: (020) 7236 2955 Fax: (020) 7248 4383 E-mail: southern@southernsteam.co.uk
Stewart Offshore Services, 1 Tranquil Bale, Black Heath, London, SE3 0BU Tel: (020) 8297 7474
▶ T T S Shipping Ltd, Charter House, 14 Park Road, Melton Mowbray, Leicestershire, LE13 1TT Tel: (01664) 410441 Fax: (01664) 410208 E-mail: admin@tts.co.uk
T Ward Shipping Ltd, 3 Johns Place, Leith, Edinburgh, EH6 7EL Tel: 0131-554 1231 Fax: 0131-553 3631 E-mail: shipping@tward.co.uk
V Ships Ltd, Gate House, 1 Farringdon Street, London, EC4M 7NS Tel: (020) 7489 0088 Fax: (020) 7489 0529 E-mail: ships@vships.com
Wainwright Bros & Co. Ltd, Lambourn House, 7 Western Road, Romford, RM1 3LD Tel: (01708) 756622 Fax: (01708) 756633 E-mail: freight@wainwrightgroup.com
Warrenpoint Harbour Authority, The Docks, Warrenpoint, Newry, County Down, BT34 3JR Tel: (028) 4177 3381 Fax: (028) 4177 3962 E-mail: info@warrenpointharbour.co.uk
Wigham-Richardson Ship Brokers Ltd, 36 Spital Square, London, E1 6DY Tel: (020) 7730 5200 Fax: (020) 7377 1495 E-mail: wigrich@btclick.com

SHIP BUILDERS

Appledore Shipbuilders Ltd, Bidna Yard, Hubbastone Road, Appledore, Bideford, Devon, EX39 1LZ Tel: (01237) 473281 Fax: (01237) 426500 E-mail: info@appledore-shipbuilders.co.uk
B A E Systems Marine Ltd, 1048 Govan Road, Glasgow, G51 4XP Tel: 0141-445 8000 Fax: 0141-445 2325 E-mail: sales.marketing@baesystems.com
Buckie Shipyard Ltd, Commercial Road, Buckie, Banffshire, AB56 1UR Tel: (01542) 832727 Fax: (01542) 831825 E-mail: office@buckieshipyard.com
Ferguson Marine plc, Castle Road, Port Glasgow, Renfrewshire, PA14 5NG Tel: (01475) 742300 Fax: (01475) 741269 E-mail: davehe@fergusons6.demon.co.uk
Garvel Clyde, James Watt Dock, Greenock, Renfrewshire, PA15 2AJ Tel: (01475) 725372 Fax: (01475) 725377
Graig Consultants Ltd, 25 Heol Cefn Onn, Lisvane, Cardiff, CF14 0TP Tel: (029) 2044 0200 Fax: (029) 2044 0207 E-mail: mail@graig.com
Harland & Wolff Ltd, Queens Island, Belfast, BT3 9DU Tel: (028) 9045 8456 Fax: (028) 9045 8515 E-mail: webmaster@harland-wolff.com
Hepworths Shipyard Ltd, Main Street, Paull, Hull, HU12 8AN Tel: (01482) 338817 Fax: (01482) 338820 E-mail: hepworths@rix.co.uk
Hyundai Heavy Industries Co. Ltd, Second Floor The Triangle, 5-17 Hammersmith Grove, London, W6 9LT Tel: (020) 8741 0501 Fax: (020) 8741 5620
I H I Europe Ltd, America House, 2 America Square, London, EC3N 2LU Tel: (020) 7481 8180 Fax: (020) 7481 4955 E-mail: vicki@ihieuro.co.uk
▶ I S S Machinery Services Ltd, 37 Eastcheap, London, EC3M 1DT Tel: (020) 7626 3505 Fax: (020) 7626 3606
Macduff Shipyards Ltd, The Harbour, Macduff, Banffshire, AB44 1QT Tel: (01261) 832234 Fax: (01261) 833541 E-mail: macduffshipyards@btconnect.com
Pendennis Shipyard (Composite) Ltd, Falmouth Docks, Falmouth, Cornwall, TR11 4NR Tel: (01326) 211344 Fax: (01326) 319253 E-mail: info@pendennis.com
R W Davis & Son Ltd, Junction Dry Dock, Canal Bank, Saul, Gloucester, GL2 7LA Tel: (01452) 740233 Fax: (01452) 741307 E-mail: sales@rwdavis.co.uk
Swan Hunter Tyneside Ltd, Station Road, Wallsend, Tyne & Wear, NE28 6EQ Tel: 0191-295 0295 Fax: 0191-262 0374 E-mail: john.mitchell@swanhunter.com
Tough Surveys Ltd, 27 Ferry Road, Teddington, Middlesex, TW11 9NN Tel: (020) 8977 4494 Fax: (020) 8977 7546 E-mail: johntough@ctinternet.com

SHIP CHANDLERS SUPPLIES

Falcon Ltd, Little Hendra, Treamble, Rose, Truro, Cornwall, TR4 9PS Tel: (01872) 573534

SHIP CHANDLERS/SHIP STORE SERVICES

▶ A E Monsen, West End Industrial Estate, West End, Penryn, Cornwall, TR10 8RT Tel: (01326) 373581 Fax: (01326) 377213 E-mail: falmouth@aemonsen.com
The Arbroath Fishermens Association Ltd, 2 Marketgate, Arbroath, Angus, DD11 1AY Tel: (01241) 873132 Fax: (01241) 875442
Bell Dunn & Keenlyside Ltd, Dale House, 21 Sussex St, Blyth, Northumberland, NE24 2AY Tel: (01670) 352213 Fax: (01670) 352767
Bembridge & Jenkins Ltd, Moland Forge, Central Trading Estate, Shaw Road, Dudley, West Midlands, DY2 8QX Tel: (01384) 243833 Fax: (01384) 455628
Bristol Boats Ltd, Mead Lane, Saltford, Bristol, BS31 3ER Tel: (01225) 872032 Fax: (01225) 872032
C I A Ltd, Froghall Road, Aberdeen, AB24 3JL Tel: (01224) 626364 Fax: (01224) 624005 E-mail: sales@c-i-a.co.uk
Cantell & Son Ltd, Robinson Road, Newhaven, East Sussex, BN9 9BL Tel: (01273) 514118 Fax: (01273) 513375
Crinan Boatyard Ltd, Crinan, Lochgilphead, Argyll, PA31 8SW Tel: (01546) 830232 Fax: (01546) 830281 E-mail: info@crinanboatyard.co.uk
Dale Sailing Co Ltd, Brunel Quay, Neyland, Milford Haven, Dyfed, SA73 1PY Tel: (01646) 601061 Fax: (01646) 601061 E-mail: enquiries@dale-sailing.co.uk

SHIP CHANDLERS/SHIP STORE SERVICES - *continued*

Darthaven Marina Ltd, Brixham Road, Kingswear, Dartmouth, Devon, TQ6 0SG Tel: (01803) 752733 Fax: (01803) 752722

Davey & Co London Ltd, 1 Commerce Way, Colchester, CO2 8HR Tel: (01206) 500945 Fax: (01206) 500949 E-mail: chandlery@davey.co.uk

Falcon Ltd, Little Hendra, Treamble, Rose, Truro, Cornwall, TR4 9PS Tel: (01872) 573534

Fleetwood Trawlers Supply Company, 1 Denham Way, Fleetwood, Lancashire, FY7 6PR Tel: (01253) 873476 Fax: (01253) 773230 E-mail: info@ftsgroup.co.uk

G W Elliott & Son, 105 Alexandra Road, Newport, Gwent, NP20 2JG Tel: (01633) 264929 Fax: (01633) 246242 E-mail: sales@elliotshipchandler.com

Frank Halls & Son, Mill Lane, Walton on the Naze, Essex, CO14 8PF Tel: (01255) 675596 Fax: (01255) 677772

Harbour Marine Services Ltd, Blackshore, Southwold, Suffolk, IP18 6TA Tel: (01502) 724721 Fax: (01502) 722060 E-mail: johnbuckley@harbourmarine.uk.com

Harding Bros Shipping Contractors Ltd, Avonmouth Way, Bristol, BS11 8DD Tel: 0117-982 5961 Fax: 0117-982 7276 E-mail: sc@hardingbros.co.uk

Hutton & Co. (Ships Chandlers) Ltd, Connaught Road, Kingswood, Hull, HU7 3AP Tel: (01482) 329925 Fax: (01482) 580588 E-mail: sales@huttons-chandlers.com

Hutton & Co. (Ships Chandlers) Ltd, Connaught Road, Kingswood, Hull, HU7 3AP Tel: (01482) 329925 Fax: (01482) 580588 E-mail: sales@huttons-chandelers.com

J Mccready & Co. Ltd, 123 Corporation Street, Belfast, BT1 3EJ Tel: (028) 9023 2842 Fax: (028) 9023 6187

J & R Starbuck, Chandlery House, Warrior Way, Pembroke Dock, Dyfed, SA72 6UB Tel: (01474) 350671 Fax: (01474) 536788 E-mail: sales@jrstarbuck.co.uk

James Gibb & Co. Ltd, Royston Works, Royston Avenue, Southend-on-Sea, SS2 5JY Tel: (01702) 614927 Fax: (01702) 601382

Jeckells & Son Ltd, Riverside Road, Hoveton, Norwich, NR12 8UQ Tel: (01603) 784488 Fax: (01603) 783234 E-mail: jeckellstrimmers@ukgateway.net

Norman Pearn & Co. Ltd, Mill Pool Boatyard, Bridgend, Looe, Cornwall, PL13 2AE Tel: (01503) 262244 Fax: (01503) 262244 E-mail: sales@looeboats.co.uk

Sea Cruisers Of Rye, 28 Winchelsea Road, Rye, East Sussex, TN31 7EL Tel: (01797) 222070 E-mail: info@sea-cruisers.co.uk

Wessex Marine Equipment Ltd, Logistics House, 1 Park Road, Southampton, SO15 3US Tel: (023) 8063 5215 Fax: (023) 8063 5216

SHIP CLASSIFICATION SOCIETIES

DNV, Cromarty House, Regent Quay, Aberdeen, AB11 5AR Tel: (01224) 335000 Fax: (01224) 593311

Nippon Kaiji Kyokai, Finsbury Circus House, 12-15 Finsbury Circus, London, EC2M 7EB Tel: (020) 7621 0963 Fax: (020) 7626 0383 E-mail: ln@classnk.or.jp

SHIP FURNISHERS OR FITTERS

M.J.M Marine Ltd, 10 Loughbrickland Road, Rathfriland, Newry, County Down, BT34 5AA Tel: (028) 4063 8396 Fax: (028) 4063 8973 E-mail: sales@mjmmarine.com

Newark Joiners Ltd, Newark Works, Castle Road, Port Glasgow, Renfrewshire, PA14 5NG Tel: (01475) 743555 Fax: (01475) 741269

SHIP MANAGEMENT/MANAGING AGENTS

Aberdeen Inshore Fish Selling Co., 154 North Esplanade East, Aberdeen, AB11 5QD Tel: (01224) 573317 Fax: (01224) 583568

Crescent Group, Brunswick House, 8-13 Brunswick Place, Southampton, SO15 2AP Tel: (023) 8063 9777 Fax: (023) 8063 9888 E-mail: sales@crescentplc.com

Droveleigh Ltd, Murray Street, Grimsby, South Humberside, DN31 3RD Tel: (01472) 352131 Fax: (01472) 240956

Farstad Shipping Ltd, Farstad House Badentoy Avenue, Badentoy Industrial Estate, Portlethen, Aberdeen, AB12 4YB Tel: (01224) 784000 Fax: (01224) 783340 E-mail: aberdeen@farstad.co.uk

J & A Gardner & Company Ltd, The Office Craigmaddie, Milngavie, Glasgow, G62 8LB Tel: 0141-956 6453 Fax: 0141-956 6685 E-mail: admin@jandagardner.co.uk

J Mckee & Partners Ltd, 34 South Quay, Great Yarmouth, Norfolk, NR30 2RG Tel: (01493) 850131 Fax: (01493) 330149 E-mail: mckeeships@aol.com

Mermaid Marine Management Ltd, Hoopers Hill, Lymington Road, New Milton, Hampshire, BH25 5PZ Tel: (01425) 619262 Fax: (01425) 619237 E-mail: mermaid.marine@btinternet.com

Norbulk Shipping (UK) Ltd, 68 Glassford Street, Glasgow, G1 1UP Tel: 0141-552 3000 Fax: 0141-559 5250 E-mail: mail@norbulkshipping.com

North Star Shipping Aberdeen Ltd, 207 Albert Quay, Aberdeen, AB11 5FS Tel: (01224) 592206 Fax: (01224) 584174 E-mail: callum.bruce@craig-group.com

O S G Ship Management (UK) Ltd, Horsley House, Regent Centre, Gosforth, Newcastle Upon Tyne, NE3 3HW Tel: 0191-285 0621 Fax: 0191-284 5644

Smit International (Scotland) Ltd, The Exchange, 62 Market Street, Aberdeen, AB11 5PT Tel: (01224) 560400 Fax: (01224) 581485

Southern Shipping & Finance Co. Ltd, Fourth Floor, 3 London Wall Buildings, London, EC2M 5RL Tel: (020) 7588 3711 Fax: (020) 7696 9971 E-mail: mail@southershipping.co.uk

V Ships Ltd, Gate House, 1 Farringdon Street, London, EC4M 7NS Tel: (020) 7489 0088 Fax: (020) 7489 0529 E-mail: ships@vships.com

Warwick & Esplen Ltd, Telfords Yard, London, E1W 2BS Tel: (020) 7480 7614 Fax: (020) 7265 0950 E-mail: info@hadleyshipping.com

SHIP REPAIR/REFURBISHMENT/ REFITTING SERVICES

A & P Falmouth Ltd, The Docks, Falmouth, Cornwall, TR11 4NR Tel: (01326) 212100 Fax: (01326) 211635 E-mail: falmouth@ap-group.co.uk

A & P Tyne, Wagonway Road, Hebburn, Tyne & Wear, NE31 1SP Tel: 0191-430 8600 Fax: 0191-428 6228 E-mail: tyne@ap-group.co.uk

Able Steel Fabrications Ltd, Unit 1 Park Street, Gosport, Hampshire, PO12 4UH Tel: (023) 9242 5425 Fax: (023) 9242 5444

Gordon Alison Ltd, 16 Jordan Street, Liverpool, L1 0BP Tel: 0151-709 4687 Fax: 0151-709 4723 E-mail: edwards@gordon-alison.fsnet.co.uk

Amethyst Marine Services Ltd, Amethyst House, Royal Stuart Lane, Cardiff, CF10 5EL Tel: (029) 2048 8149 Fax: (029) 2048 6928

Baymarine Industrial Services Ltd, Aqua-Plan House, Burt Street, Cardiff, CF10 5FZ Tel: (029) 2045 3700 Fax: (029) 2045 0077

Cantell & Son Ltd, Robinson Road, Newhaven, East Sussex, BN9 9BL Tel: (01273) 514118 Fax: (01273) 513375

Compass Shipping & Trading Co. Ltd, Office No. 10, 34-35 Hatton Garden, London, EC1N 8DX Tel: (020) 7242 6116 Fax: (020) 7242 3143

Crinan Boatyard Ltd, Crinan, Lochgilphead, Argyll, PA31 8SW Tel: (01546) 830232 Fax: (01546) 830281 E-mail: info@crinanboatyard.co.uk

Dales Engineering Ltd, Dales Industrial Estate, Peterhead, Aberdeenshire, AB42 3JF Tel: (01779) 478778 Fax: (01779) 471846 E-mail: sales@dalesgroup.co.uk

Dunston Ship Repaires Ltd, William Wright Dock, Hull, HU3 4PG Tel: (01482) 326774 Fax: (01482) 226815 E-mail: sales@dunstons.co.uk

Forth Estuary Engineering Ltd, Edinburgh Dock, Leith Docks, Edinburgh, EH6 7DW Tel: 0131-554 6434 Fax: 0131-555 1890 E-mail: info@forthestuary.co.uk

Garvel Clyde, James Watt Dock, Greenock, Renfrewshire, PA15 2AJ Tel: (01475) 725372 Fax: (01475) 725377

Grangemouth Ship Repairs Ltd, Carron Dock, Grangemouth, Stirlingshire, FK3 8UH Tel: (01324) 665745 Fax: (01324) 665742 E-mail: emple@gsrship.co.uk

Haggart Commercial Marine, 98-100 Vauxhall Street, Plymouth, PL4 0DD Tel: (01752) 660117 Fax: (01752) 660117

Hepworths Shipyard Ltd, Main Street, Paull, Hull, HU12 8AN Tel: (01482) 338817 Fax: (01482) 338820 E-mail: hepworths@rix.co.uk

Keller Bryant & Co. Ltd, Swan Centre, Fishers Lane, London, W4 1RX Tel: (020) 8996 9525 E-mail: mail@keller-bryant.co.uk

Keller Bryant Shipping Ltd, Ibex House, Minories, London, EC3N 1DY Tel: (020) 7481 8833 Fax: (0870) 4104312 E-mail: keller-bryant@dial.pipex.com

Larssen Engineering Ltd, Globe Industrial Estate, Rectory Road, Grays, Essex, RM17 6ST Tel: (01375) 371909 Fax: (01375) 390582 E-mail: sales@larssen.com

Matatec, Station Road, Seaton Delaval, Seaton Delaval, Whitley Bay, Tyne & Wear, NE25 0PT Tel: 0191-237 9900 Fax: 0191-237 9999 E-mail: msl@matatec.co.uk

Newson Boatbuilders Ltd, 3 Sea Lake Road, Lowestoft, Suffolk, NR32 3LQ Tel: (01502) 574902 Fax: (01502) 574902 E-mail: keith@newson.co.uk

North East Contract Services Ltd, Howdon Terminal, Willington Quay, Wallsend, Tyne & Wear, NE28 6UL Tel: 0191-234 5511 Fax: 0191-234 0888 E-mail: newcastle@ofsprayltd.com

George Prior Engineering Ltd, ABC Wharf, Southgates Road, Great Yarmouth, Norfolk, NR30 3LQ Tel: (01493) 852311 Fax: (01493) 330074

Rollo UK Ltd, Womersley Road, Grimsby, South Humberside, DN31 3SH Tel: (01472) 358989 Fax: (01472) 241141 E-mail: b.merrison@rollouk.com

Specialist Heavy Engineers plc, Alexandra Docks, Newport, Gwent, NP20 2NP Tel: (01633) 262961 Fax: (01633) 246342 E-mail: she.industrial@btinternet.com

Testbank Ship Repair & Boiler Co. Ltd, Western Avenue, Western Docks, Southampton, SO15 0HH Tel: (023) 8078 7878 Fax: (023) 8078 7826 E-mail: admin@testbank.co.uk

Timbacraft Ltd, Shandon, Helensburgh, Dunbartonshire, G84 8HP Tel: (01436) 810391 Fax: (01436) 811308

Tyne Slipway & Engineering, Commercial Road, South Shields, Tyne & Wear, NE33 1RP Tel: 0191-455 4893 Fax: 0191-456 6396

U N C (International) plc, Mayflower Close, Chandlers Ford Industrial Esta, Chandlers Ford, Eastleigh, Hampshire, SO53 4AR Tel: (023) 8026 9866 Fax: (023) 8025 3198 E-mail: sales@umc.co.uk

Us Marine & Industrial Pump Repair, Site 20 Grangefield Industrial Estate, Richardshaw Lane, Pudsey, West Yorkshire, LS28 6QW Tel: 0113-256 3721 Fax: 0113-255 9820 E-mail: sales@usmarine.co.uk

Wear Dockyard Ltd, South Docks, Sunderland, SR1 2EE Tel: 0191-567 4749 Fax: 0191-510 0765

SHIP RIGGERS/MAINTENANCE SERVICES

GRM Rigging Services, 7 Tarbet Street, Gourock, Renfrewshire, PA19 1UF Tel: (01475) 638811 Fax: (01475) 638811

J Mccready & Co. Ltd, 123 Corporation Street, Belfast, BT1 3EJ Tel: (028) 9023 2842 Fax: (028) 9023 6187

Tedford Rigging & Rafts, Unit 24 Ormeau Business Park, 8 Gromac Avenue, Belfast, BT7 2JA Tel: (028) 9032 6763 Fax: (028) 9023 4566 E-mail: info@tedfords.co.uk

Towne Lifting & Testing, Pennine Avenue, North Tees Industrial Estate, Stockton-on-Tees, Cleveland, TS18 2RJ Tel: (01642) 611035 Fax: (01642) 611036

SHIP SERVICING REPRESENTATIVES OR AGENTS

Harwin Shipping Agency Ltd, 40 Bowling Green Lane, London, EC1R 0NE Tel: (020) 7837 3759 Fax: (020) 7278 0745 E-mail: harwinship@aol.com

SHIP STABILISERS

Rolls Royce plc, Taxi Way, Hillend Industrial Park, Hillend, Dunfermline, Fife, KY11 9JT Tel: (01383) 823188 Fax: (01383) 824038 E-mail: post.master@vickersmarine.com

SHIP WIRING CABLES

Rexel Senate Electrical Wholesalers Ltd, Senate House, 6-16 Southgate Road, Potters Bar, Hertfordshire, EN6 5DS Tel: (01707) 640000 Fax: (01707) 640111

SHIP/TANKER SLUDGE/SLURRY CLEANING SERVICES

T C Repair & Supply, Sheddingdean Industrial Centre, Marchants Way, Burgess Hill, West Sussex, RH15 8QY Tel: (01444) 242564 Fax: (01444) 236683 E-mail: info@tcrepair.com

SHIPBUILDING STEELS, *See Steel Plate, Shipbuilding*

SHIPPING AGENCIES/LINER AGENCIES

A B P H, Manby Road, Immingham, South Humberside, DN40 3EG Tel: (01469) 551308 Fax: (01469) 571588

Altred & Harrison, Wellington House, 108 Beverley Road, Hull, HU3 1XA Tel: (01482) 611200 Fax: (01482) 225452 E-mail: info@oandh.co.uk

▶ Bishops Move, Unit 11, South Hampshire Industrial Park, Totton, Southampton, SO40 3SA Tel: (023) 8023 7100 Fax: (023) 8086 7888 E-mail: southampton@bishopsmove.com

John Burke & Co. Ltd, 141 York Street, Belfast, BT15 1AB Tel: (028) 9032 2841 Fax: (028) 9032 3395 E-mail: smcready@burkebelfast.com

Containerships UK Ltd, Teesport Container Terminal, Teesport, Middlesbrough, Cleveland, TS6 7SA Tel: (01642) 468592 Fax: (01642) 770737

Crete Shipping, 42 Battersea Rise, London, SW11 1EE Tel: (020) 7223 1244 Fax: (020) 7924 3895 E-mail: sales@creteshipping.co.uk

Davies Turner & Co. Ltd, London House, Hide Street, Stoke-on-Trent, ST4 1NF Tel: (01782) 413617 Fax: (01782) 744063

Denholm Barwil, Avonmouth Dock, Bristol, BS11 9DN Tel: 0117-982 5836 Fax: 0117-982 6272 E-mail: agency.brf@denholm-barwil.com

Denholm Forwarding Ltd, 1 First Way, Avonmouth, Bristol, BS11 9EF Tel: 0117-982 5313 Fax: 0117-982 5885

▶ Eurofreight Shipping Agencies Ltd, Pioneer House, Birmingham Street, Halesowen, West Midlands, B63 3HN Tel: 0121-585 0303 Fax: 0121-585 0636

Evergreen UK Ltd, Evergreen House, 160 Euston Road, London, NW1 2DX Tel: (020) 7559 8000 Fax: (020) 7559 8103

Fraserburgh Commercial Co. Ltd, Harbour Office, Whitehall Buildings, Shore Street, Fraserburgh, Aberdeenshire, AB43 5BR Tel: (01346) 512111 Fax: (01346) 514068 E-mail: steve@euroline-shipping.co.uk

Grimaldi Agencies Ltd, 28-29 St. James's Square, London, SW1Y 4JH Tel: (020) 7930 5683 Fax: (020) 7839 1961 E-mail: switchboard@grimaldi.co.uk

Halcyon (Shipping) Ltd, 40 South Quay, Great Yarmouth, Norfolk, NR30 2RL Tel: (01493) 856831

Hapag-Lloyd UK Ltd, Hapag-Lloyd House, 50 Cambridge Road, Barking, Essex, IG11 8HH Tel: (020) 8507 4000 Fax: (020) 8507 4193 E-mail: info.de@hlcl.com

Helexco Co. Ltd, 31 High Street Colliers Wood, London, SW19 2JE Tel: (020) 8542 4916 Fax: (020) 8540 8047 E-mail: kookies@btconnect.com

Helikon Shipping Enterprises Ltd, St Clare House, 30-33 Minories, London, EC3N 1DH Tel: (020) 7481 8601 Fax: (020) 7488 2226

Hull Blyth & Co. Ltd, 2 Coldbath Square, London, EC1R 5HL Tel: (020) 7696 9688 Fax: (020) 7696 9686 E-mail: enquiries@hull-blyth.com

▶ Hyundai Merchant Marine Europe Ltd, 204-207 Berth, Western Docks, Southampton, SO15 1DA Tel: (023) 8078 7700 Fax: (023) 8078 7233

Immediate Transportation Co. Ltd, Mckay Trading Estate, Blackthorne Road, Colnbrook, Slough, SL3 0AH Tel: (01753) 684644 Fax: (01753) 683338 E-mail: itcolhr@itcolhr.co.uk

Imorex, Dooley Road, Felixstowe, Suffolk, IP11 3HG Tel: (01394) 607743 Fax: (01394) 607767 E-mail: info@imorex.co.uk

Intrada Shipping & Trading Associates Ltd, 75 Main Road, Gidea Park, Romford, RM2 5EL Tel: (01708) 739353 Fax: (01708) 739252

John Gargan Chartering Ltd, Trident House, 105 Derby Road, Bootle, Merseyside, L20 8LZ Tel: 0151-922 0066 Fax: 0151-922 5006 E-mail: john@johngargan.co.uk

John Stronach Ltd, The Docks, Silloth, Wigton, Cumbria, CA7 4JQ Tel: (01697) 331456 Fax: (01697) 332808

Johnson Stevens Agencies Ltd, Johnson Stevens House, 2 Abbey Road, Barking, Essex, IG11 7AX Tel: (020) 8591 6200 Fax: (020) 8594 2161 E-mail: sales@j-s-agencies.co.uk

John Jolly, P O Box 2, Kirkwall, Orkney, KW15 1HS Tel: (01856) 872268 Fax: (01856) 875002 E-mail: operations@johnjolly.co.uk

Killick Martin & Co. Ltd, Bowden Freight Terminal, Luckyn Lane, Pips Hill Industrial Estate, Basildon, Essex, SS14 3AX Tel: (01268) 274382 Fax:

Little Whiting & Tedford Ltd, Princes Dock, 14 Clarendon Road, Belfast, BT1 3BG Tel: (028) 9053 3302 Fax: (028) 9053 3222 E-mail: agency@hamiltonshipping.com

Lombard Shipping & Forwarding Ltd, Lombard Centre, Link Road, Huyton, Liverpool, L36 6AP Tel: 0151-449 3535 Fax: 0151-489 1229 E-mail: sales@1ombardshipping.co.uk

Mann & Son London Ltd, The Navel House, Kings Quay Street, Harwich, Essex, CO12 3JJ Tel: (01255) 245200 Fax: (01255) 245219 E-mail: enquiries@manngroup.co.uk

Mediterranean Shipping Company UK Ltd, The Havens, Ipswich, IP3 9SJ Tel: (01473) 277777 Fax: (01473) 277700 E-mail: enquiries@medite.co.uk

Niarchos London Ltd, 41-43 Park Street, London, W1A 2JR Tel: (020) 7314 8400 Fax: (020) 7499 5481

Northern Containers Ltd, Haigh Park Road, Leeds, LS10 1RT Tel: 0113-270 8515 Fax: 0113-271 9687 E-mail: mailing@norcon.co.uk

P & O Cruises Ltd, Castlewood House, 77 New Oxford Street, London, WC1A 1PP Tel: (0845) 3585585 Fax: (023) 8052 3720

▶ P & O Nedlloyd Ltd, Northfleet Hope House, Tilbury, Essex, RM18 7HX Tel: (01375) 812200

River Plate Shipping & Trading Agency Ltd, Ingersol House, 9 Kingsway, London, WC2B 6XF Tel: (020) 7836 1155 Fax: (020) 7836 9922

Andrew Smith & Schultze Ltd, 54 Broad Street, Peterhead, Aberdeenshire, AB42 1BX Tel: (01779) 472210 Fax: (01779) 470638 E-mail: stevedores@rapidial.co.uk

▶ T T S Shipping Ltd, Charter House, 14 Park Road, Melton Mowbray, Leicestershire, LE13 1TT Tel: (01664) 410441 Fax: (01664) 410208 E-mail: admin@tts.co.uk

Zela Shipping Co. Ltd, 4 Paul Street, London, EC2A 4UG Tel: (020) 7247 6715 Fax: (020) 7377 6699 E-mail: mail@zelashipping.com

Zim UK, Suite 249 2nd Floor, India Buildings Water Street, Liverpool, L2 0QD Tel: 0151-258 1118 Fax: 0151-258 1117 E-mail: sales@zim.uk.com

SHIPPING CONSULTANCY, *See Marine Consultants etc*

SHIPPING EXCHANGE (RESTRICTED USAGE)

Baltic Exchange Ltd, 24 St.Mary Axe, London, EC3A 8EX Tel: (020) 7623 5501 Fax: (020) 7369 1622
E-mail: admin@balticexchange.com

Purvers International Ltd, Gateway House, Fareham Road, Gosport, Hampshire, PO13 0FW Tel: (01329) 238111 Fax: (01329) 825888 E-mail: mail@purvers.co.uk

SHIPPING LINES/SHIP OWNERS

▶ APL Ltd, Eagle Court, 9 Vine Street, Uxbridge, Middlesex, UB8 1QE Tel: (01895) 202600 Fax: (01895) 202698

Boddingtons Shipping Ltd, Blackbirds, Little Bardfield, Braintree, Essex, CM7 4TU Tel: (01371) 810983 Fax: (01371) 811854
E-mail: robinbodd@aol.com

Borchard Lines Ltd, 24 Chiswell Street, London, EC1Y 4XY Tel: (020) 7628 6961 Fax: (020) 7588 1884 E-mail: headoffice@borlines.com

Boyd Line, The Orangery Hesslewood Country Office Park, Ferriby Road, Hessle, North Humberside, HU13 0LH Tel: (01482) 324024 Fax: (01482) 323737
E-mail: info@boydline.co.uk

Caledonian Macbrayne Ltd, The Pier, Station Road, Gourock, Renfrewshire, PA19 1QP Tel: (01475) 650100 Fax: (01475) 637607
E-mail: marketing@calmac.co.uk

Charles M Willie & Co (Shipping) Ltd, Celtic House, Brittania Road, Roath Basin, Cardiff, CF10 4SF Tel: (029) 2047 1000 Fax: (029) 2047 5799 E-mail: mail@williegroup.co.uk

Costa Cruises, Carnival House, 5 Gainsford Street, London, SE1 2NE Tel: (020) 7940 4499 Fax: (020) 7940 5378
E-mail: sales@costacruises.co.uk

Crescent Group, Brunswick House, 8-13 Brunswick Place, Southampton, SO15 2AP Tel: (023) 8063 9777 Fax: (023) 8063 9888
E-mail: sales@crescentplc.com

DP World, 16 Palace Street, London, SW1E 5JQ Tel: (020) 7930 4343 Fax: (020) 7901 4015

Eastern Mediterranean Maritime (London) Ltd, Fountain House, 130 Fenchurch Strret, London, EC3M 5DJ Tel: (020) 7283 9591 Fax: (020) 7444 1909

Edda Supply Ships UK Ltd, Seaforth Centre, 30 Waterloo Quay, Aberdeen, AB11 5BS Tel: (01224) 587788 Fax: (01224) 583276
E-mail: info@eddasupplyships.com

Eggar Forrester Group, Rodwell House, Middlesex Street, London, E1 7HJ Tel: (020) 7377 1077 Fax: (020) 7247 2144

Eimskip UK Ltd, Middleplatt Road, Immingham, South Humberside, DN40 1AH Tel: (01469) 550200 Fax: (01469) 550394
E-mail: info@eimskip-uk.co.uk

EMS Ship Management Ltd, 3 Commercial Quay, 80 Commercial Street, Edinburgh, EH6 6LX Tel: 0131-554 4466 Fax: 0131-554 3843
E-mail: admin.uk@ems-asa.com

▶ Escombe Lambert Ltd, London Road, Barking, Essex, IG11 8BB Tel: (020) 8709 1600

F.T. Everard & Sons Ltd, Blake House, Admiral Park, Crossway, Dartford, DA2 6QQ Tel: (01322) 394500 Fax: (01322) 311943

Everard Shipping Companies, Peninsular House, 36 Monument Street, London, EC3R 8LJ Tel: (020) 7398 4450 Fax: (020) 7398 4480

James Fisher & Sons P.L.C., Fisher House, Michaelson Road, Barrow-in-Furness, Cumbria, LA14 1HR Tel: (01229) 615400 Fax: (01229) 836761
E-mail: postmaster@james-fisher.co.uk

Fred Olsen Cruise Lines, 42 Whitehouse Road, Ipswich, IP1 5LL Tel: (01473) 292200 Fax: (01473) 292345
E-mail: reservations@fredolsen.co.uk

Giles W Pritchard-Gordon (Shipowning) Ltd, Slaughan Park, Slaugham, Haywards Heath, West Sussex, RH17 6AH Tel: (01444) 400000 Fax: (01444) 401150

Gillie & Blair, 178 New Bridge Street, Newcastle upon Tyne, NE1 2TE Tel: 0191-230 4747 Fax: 0191-230 8255
E-mail: mail@gillieblair.com

Graig Consultants Ltd, 25 Heol Cefn Onn, Lisvane, Cardiff, CF14 0TP Tel: (029) 2044 0200 Fax: (029) 2044 0207
E-mail: mail@graig.com

Grimaldi Agencies Ltd, 28-29 St. James's Square, London, SW1Y 4JH Tel: (020) 7930 5683 Fax: (020) 7839 1961
E-mail: switchboard@grimaldi.co.uk

Hanson Aggregates Ltd, Marine Parade, Southampton, SO14 5JF Tel: (023) 8023 7210 Fax: (023) 8082 8248

Hapag-Lloyd UK Ltd, Hapag-Lloyd House, 50 Cambridge Road, Barking, Essex, IG11 8HH Tel: (020) 8507 4000 Fax: (020) 8507 4193
E-mail: info.de@hlcl.com

Helexco Co. Ltd, 31 High Street Colliers Wood, London, SW19 2JE Tel: (020) 8542 4916 Fax: (020) 8540 8047
E-mail: kookies@btconnect.com

Irish Ferries General Enquiries Passenger Reservations, Fenwick Street, Liverpool, L2 7RB Tel: (0870) 5171717 Fax: 0151-236 0562

Isles Of Scilly Steamship Co. Ltd, Hugh Street, St. Mary's, Isles of Scilly, TR21 0LJ Tel: (01720) 422357 Fax: (01720) 422192

Italian General Shipping Ltd, Berth 21 Powell Duffryn Ho, Tilbury Docks, Tilbury, Essex, RM18 7JT Tel: (020) 7488 9821 Fax: (020) 7480 5472

J & A Gardner & Company Ltd, The Office Craigmaddie, Milngavie, Glasgow, G62 8LB Tel: 0141-956 6453 Fax: 0141-956 6685
E-mail: admin@jandagardner.co.uk

J J Prior (Transport) Ltd, Ballat Quay, Fingringhoe, Colchester, CO5 7DB Tel: (01206) 729412 Fax: (01206) 729551
E-mail: sales@jjprior.co.uk

J R Rix & Sons Ltd, 45 Spyvee Street, Hull, HU8 7JJ Tel: (01482) 222250 Fax: (01482) 338590

John H Whitaker Holdings, Crown Dry Dock, Tower Street, Hull, HU9 1TY Tel: (01482) 595300 Fax: (01482) 226270

John H Whitaker Holdings, Crown Dry Dock, Tower Street, Hull, HU9 1TY Tel: (01482) 595300 Fax: (01482) 226270

K Line LNG Shipping UK Ltd, River Plate House, 7-11 Finsbury Circus, London, EC2M 7EA Tel: (020) 7382 6500

Macandrews, Lancaster House Mercury Court, Tithebarn Street, Liverpool, L2 2QP Tel: 0151-479 5555 Fax: 0151-236 2644
E-mail: reservations@aws.co.uk

Maersk Line (UK), 58 Robertson Street, Glasgow, G2 8DU Tel: 0141-275 6380 Fax: 0141-248 3496

Maersk Sealand (UK), Silkhouse Court, Tithebarn Street, Liverpool, L2 2LZ Tel: (08703) 330804 Fax: 0151-236 4199
E-mail: lplmng@maersk.com

The Maersk Company UK Ltd, Maersk House, Brayham Street, London, E1 8EP Tel: (020) 7441 1439 Fax: (020) 7712 5100
E-mail: gbrmkt@maersk.com

Mitsui O S K Bulk Shipping Europe Ltd, Dexter House, Royal Mint Court, London, EC3N 4JR Tel: (020) 7265 7500 Fax: (020) 7265 7560

North Star Shipping Aberdeen Ltd, 207 Albert Quay, Aberdeen, AB11 5FS Tel: (01224) 592206 Fax: (01224) 584174
E-mail: callum.bruce@craig-group.com

O O C L UK Ltd, Oocl House, Bridge Road, Levington, Ipswich, IP10 0NE Tel: (01473) 659000 Fax: (01473) 654200

Oocl UK Ltd, Furness House, Furness Quay, Salford, M50 3XZ Tel: 0161-872 4466 Fax: 0161-876 7318

Ot Africa Line, Marc House, 13-14 Great St. Thomas Apostle, London, EC4V 2BB Tel: (020) 7332 6000 Fax: (020) 7332 6003
E-mail: enquiries@otal.com

P & O Cruises Ltd, Castlewood House, 77 New Oxford Street, London, WC1A 1PP Tel: (0845) 3585585 Fax: (023) 8052 3720

The P & O Cruises Ltd, Richmond House, Terminus Terrace, Southampton, SO14 3PN Tel: (023) 8053 4200 Fax: (023) 8022 7920

P & O European Ferries Ltd, Copse Road, Fleetwood, Lancashire, FY7 6RP Tel: (01253) 615700 Fax: (01253) 615702
E-mail: info@poisfreight.com

P & O Ferries, King George Dock, Hedon Road, Hull, HU9 5QA Tel: (01482) 795141 Fax: (01482) 708255
E-mail: sales@ponsf.com

P & O Nedlloyd Global Logistics Ltd, Capital Gate, 320 New North Road, Ilford, Essex, IG6 3ES Tel: (020) 8918 6000 Fax: (020) 8918 6088 E-mail: centraladmin@mersk.com

P & O Steam Navigation Co, Peninsular House, 79 Pall Mall, London, SW1Y 5EJ Tel: (020) 7930 4343 Fax: (020) 7930 8572
E-mail: groupinformation@pogroup.com

Ramsey Steamship Co. Ltd, 8 Auckland Terrace, Parliament Street, Ramsey, Isle of Man, IM8 1AF Tel: (01624) 816202 Fax: (01624) 816206 E-mail: tony@ramsey-steamship.com

Red Funnel Group Ltd, 12 Bugle Street, Southampton, SO14 2JY Tel: (0870) 4448889 Fax: (0870) 4448897
E-mail: post@redfunnel.co.uk

Seascope Offshore, 25 Carden Place, Aberdeen, AB10 1UQ Tel: (01224) 628470 Fax: (01224) 621444 E-mail: sales@seascope.co.uk

W. Stowell (Shipping) Ltd, 37 Coleridge Avenue, Low Fell, Gateshead, Tyne & Wear, NE9 6EN Tel: 0191-487 3222 Fax: 0191-491 0056
E-mail: sparestan@stowellshipping.co.uk

John Swire & Sons Ltd, Swire House, 59 Buckingham Gate, London, SW1E 6AJ Tel: (020) 7834 7717 Fax: (020) 7630 0353

Tesma UK Ltd, 3 Commercil Quay, 88 Commercial Street, Edinburgh, EH6 6LX Tel: 0131-554 4466 Fax: 0131-554 3843
E-mail: administration@gibsongas.co.uk

Tidewater Marine North Sea Ltd, Souter Head Road, Altens Industrial Estate, Aberdeen, AB12 3LF Tel: (01224) 293000 Fax: (01224) 293001 E-mail: info@tdw.com

Andrew Weir Shipping Ltd, Dexter House, 2 Royal Mint Court, London, EC3N 4XX Tel: (020) 7265 0808 Fax: (020) 7481 4784
E-mail: aws@aws.co.uk

West Of England Mutual War Risks Association Ltd, Tower Bridge Court, 224 Tower Bridge Road, London, SE1 2UP Tel: (020) 7716 6000 Fax: (020) 7716 6100
E-mail: mail@westpandi.com

SHIPS' ACCOMMODATION LADDERS

Tyne Gangway Structures Ltd, Howdon Lane, Wallsend, Tyne & Wear, NE28 0AL Tel: 0191-262 3657 Fax: 0191-262 1498
E-mail: info@tynegangway.co.uk

SHIPS' AGENTS

A Nielson & Co. Ltd, Kings Dock, Swansea, SA1 1RJ Tel: (01792) 652421 Fax: (01792) 476466 E-mail: a_nielsen@talk21.com

Amundsen & Smith Ltd, Cargo Durham Distribution Centre, Seaham, County Durham, SR7 7NZ Tel: 0191-581 2315 Fax: 0191-581 7360
E-mail: enquiries@amundsen-smith.co.uk

Anglo Norden Forest Products Ltd, Orwell Terminal Eagle Wharf, Helena Road, Ipswich, IP3 0BT Tel: (01473) 233244 Fax: (01473) 230805 E-mail: sales@anglonorden.co.uk

Ariel Maritime (UK) Ltd, Unit 26, Waters Edge Business Park, Salford, M5 3EZ Tel: 0161-848 9009 Fax: 0161-848 9511
E-mail: manchester@arielmaritime.co.uk

B E Moors Ltd, Kemp House, 152-160 City Road, London, EC1V 2NP Tel: (020) 7855 5300 Fax: (020) 7454 9090
E-mail: admin@bemoors.co.uk

Balkan & Black Sea Shipping Co. Ltd, Black Sea House, 72 Wilson Street, London, EC2A 2DH Tel: (020) 7684 2800 Fax: (020) 7684 2790
E-mail: enquiries@bbss.uk

Bellamy & Co Plymouth Ltd, Millbay Docks, Plymouth, PL1 3SA Tel: (01752) 665154 Fax: (01752) 263572
E-mail: ballamyagency@plymouth-chamber.co.uk

Briton Ferry Stevedoring Ltd, Giants Wharf, Briton Ferry, Neath, West Glamorgan, SA11 2LP Tel: (01639) 825700 Fax: (01639) 822912 E-mail: bfss@dial.pipex.com

C M Shaw Ltd, Clarence Row, Stockton-on-Tees, Cleveland, TS18 2HD Tel: (01642) 606668 Fax: (01642) 617845
E-mail: cmshaw@stkn.freeserve.co.uk

Chandris England Ltd, 17 Old Park Lane, London, W1K 1QT Tel: (020) 7412 3900 Fax: (020) 7412 0901

The Dundee Perth & London Shipping Company Ltd, 26 East Dock Street, Dundee, DD1 9HY Tel: (01382) 203111 Fax: (01382) 200575
E-mail: agency@dpandl.co.uk

▶ Euroship Logistics Ltd, PO Box 515, Grimsby, South Humberside, DN37 9QD Tel: (01472) 353333 Fax: (01472) 595695
E-mail: dchristie@euroshiplogistics.co.uk

Flixborough Wharf Ltd, Trent Port House, Flixborough, Scunthorpe, North Lincolnshire, DN15 8RS Tel: (01724) 867691 Fax: (01724) 851207 E-mail: info@flixboroughwharf.co.uk

G C Fox (SW) Ltd, The Docks, Falmouth, Cornwall, TR11 4NJ Tel: (01326) 311300 Fax: (01326) 211334

G Heyn & Sons Ltd, 1 Corry Place, Belfast, BT3 9AH Tel: (028) 9035 0000 Fax: (028) 9035 0011 E-mail: info@heyn.co.uk

Gdynia America Shipping Lines (London) Ltd, 5 St. Johns Lane, London, EC1M 4DH Tel: (020) 7549 1693 Fax: (020) 7549 1694
E-mail: shipping@gdynia-america.co.uk

Gillie & Blair, 178 New Bridge Street, Newcastle upon Tyne, NE1 2TE Tel: 0191-230 4747 Fax: 0191-230 8255
E-mail: mail@gillieblair.com

Harwin Shipping Agency Ltd, 40 Bowling Green Lane, London, EC1R 0NE Tel: (020) 7837 3759 Fax: (020) 7278 0745
E-mail: harwinship@aol.com

J & A Gardner & Company Ltd, The Office Craigmaddie, Milngavie, Glasgow, G62 8LB Tel: 0141-956 6453 Fax: 0141-956 6685
E-mail: admin@jandagardner.co.uk

J G Oldfield & Co., Prince of Wales Dock, Workington, Cumbria, CA14 1BN Tel: (01900) 603701 Fax: (01900) 604823

John C Hadjipateras & Sons Ltd, 24 Baltic Street West, London, EC1Y 0UR Tel: (020) 7490 4010 Fax: (020) 7253 4043

Killick Martin & Co. Ltd, Bowden Freight Terminal, Luckyn Lane, Pips Hill Industrial Estate, Basildon, Essex, SS14 3AX Tel: (01268) 274382 Fax:

Lewis & Peat Produce Ltd, 79 Knightsbridge, London, SW1X 7RB Tel: (020) 7235 0099 Fax: (020) 7235 2055
E-mail: lewisandpeat@compuserve.com

G.Y. Line (Agency) Ltd, East Quay, 51 South Denes Road, Great Yarmouth, Norfolk, NR30 3PR Tel: (01493) 852411 Fax: (01493) 857583 E-mail: gyline@gywc.uk

Lykiardopulo & Co. Ltd, 2-3 Gough Square, London, EC4A 3DE Tel: (020) 7353 6633 Fax: (020) 7353 6645
E-mail: office@lykiardopulo.co.uk

M M D (Shipping Services) Ltd, Flathouse Quay, Prospect Road, Portsmouth, PO2 7SP Tel: (023) 9282 6351 Fax: (023) 9229 1910

Mctaggart Shipping & Management Co. Ltd, 1 Great Cumberland Place, London, W1H 7AL Tel: (020) 7468 8500 Fax: (020) 7468 8625
E-mail: chadring@macnav.com

Mann & Son London Ltd, The Navel House, Kings Quay Street, Harwich, Essex, CO12 3JJ Tel: (01255) 245200 Fax: (01255) 245219
E-mail: enquiries@manngroup.co.uk

O B C Shipping Ltd, Osprey House, Richmond Road, Pembroke Dock, Dyfed, SA72 6TS Tel: (01646) 622220 Fax: (01646) 622221
E-mail: pembroke.agency@obcgroup.com

Obc Shipping Ltd, 2a Gateway Business Park, Beancross Road, Grangemouth, Stirlingshire, FK3 8WX Tel: (01324) 482811 Fax: (01324) 665197
E-mail: grangemouth.agency@obcgroup.com

Obc Shipping, O B C House, Sabatier Close, Thornaby, Stockton-on-Tees, Cleveland, TS17 6EW Tel: (01642) 637500 Fax: (01642) 637502

Piggins & Rix Ltd, Meridian Street, Montrose, Angus, DD10 8DS Tel: (01674) 672827 Fax: (01674) 676135

John Samonas & Sons Ltd, Princeton Mews, 167-169 London Road, Kingston upon Thames, Surrey, KT2 6PT Tel: (020) 8547 2244 Fax: (020) 8547 1949
E-mail: samonas@johnsamonas.com

Santa-Cruz Travel & Shipping Agency Ltd, 2 Crampton Road, Pende, London, SE20 7AT Tel: (020) 8689 3373 Fax: (020) 8689 0493
E-mail: santacruzship@talk21.com

Small & Co. Shipping Ltd, Europa House, 40 South Quay, Great Yarmouth, Norfolk, NR30 2RL Tel: (01502) 572301 Fax: (01493) 857533
E-mail: smallandcoshipping@halcyonshipping.com

W. Stowell (Shipping) Ltd, 37 Coleridge Avenue, Low Fell, Gateshead, Tyne & Wear, NE9 6EN Tel: 0191-487 3222 Fax: 0191-491 0056
E-mail: sparestan@stowellshipping.co.uk

T Ward Shipping Ltd, 3 Johns Place, Leith, Edinburgh, EH6 7EL Tel: 0131-554 1231 Fax: 0131-553 3631
E-mail: shipping@tward.co.uk

Torbay & Brixham Shipping Agents, The Quay, Brixham, Devon, TQ5 8AS Tel: (01803) 882214 Fax: (01803) 882579
E-mail: sales@tbsa.co.uk

Transport Distribution Ltd, Dock Gate 2, Felixstowe, Suffolk, IP11 3SW Tel: (01394) 675601 Fax: (01394) 674278

Edward W. Turner & Son, Logistics House, 80 Regent Road, Liverpool Freeport, Bootle, Merseyside, L20 1BL Tel: 0151-922 1888 Fax: 0151-933 3488
E-mail: eddie.magnall@dfwltd.com

Yeoward Shipping Ltd, The Logistics Office, Port of Liverpool, Liverpool, L21 1JR Tel: 0151-928 8173 Fax: 0151-928 8174
E-mail: yeowardshipping@btconnect.com

SHIPS' BOILER MAINTENANCE/ REPAIR SERVICES

A & P Tyne, Wagonway Road, Hebburn, Tyne & Wear, NE31 1SP Tel: 0191-430 8600 Fax: 0191-428 6228
E-mail: tyne@ap-group.co.uk

SHIPS' FITTINGS

Beaconsfield Products Halesowen Ltd, Foxoak Street, Cradley Heath, West Midlands, B64 5DE Tel: (01384) 569571 Fax: (01384) 566328 E-mail: sales@beacoproducts.co.uk

Tyne Gangway Structures Ltd, Howdon Lane, Wallsend, Tyne & Wear, NE28 0AL Tel: 0191-262 3657 Fax: 0191-262 1498
E-mail: info@tynegangway.co.uk

SHIPS' HULL MAINTENANCE/ REPAIR SERVICES

Penzance Dry Dock Ltd, Wharf Road, Penzance, Cornwall, TR18 4BW Tel: (01736) 363838 Fax: (01736) 351207
E-mail: admiral.1@btconnect.com

SHIPS' MACHINERY MAINTENANCE/REPAIR SERVICES

Unitor UK Ltd, Kelvin House, 40 Kelvin Road, Wallasey, Merseyside, CH44 7JW Tel: 0151-630 3869 Fax: 0151-637 0151
E-mail: sales@unitor.com

SHIPS' TACKLE, *See also headings for particular types*

Aqualift Ltd, Meeting Lane, Brierley Hill, West Midlands, DY5 3LB Tel: (01384) 77255 Fax: (01384) 77254
E-mail: sales@aqualift.co.uk

Solid Stampings Ltd, Porters Field Road, Cradley Heath, West Midlands, B64 7BL Tel: (01384) 636421 Fax: (01384) 639163
E-mail: info@solidswivel.co.uk

SHIRTING FABRICS

Combined Trading (Garments) Ltd, 77-79 Great Eastern Street, London, EC2A 3HU Tel: (020) 7739 0551 Fax: (020) 7729 2556

SHIRTS

▶ Atr, 35 Spring Lane, Wellingborough, Northamptonshire, NN8 1EY Tel: (01933) 229965 Fax: 01933 229965 E-mail: info@atruk.com
Denby Dale Shirt Co. Ltd, The Old School House, Spark Lane, Mapplewell, Barnsley, South Yorkshire, S75 6AB Tel: (01226) 390211 Fax: (01226) 388192 E-mail: charles@denbydaleshirt.co.uk
H R Denne Ltd, 40 Bedford Street, Belfast, BT2 7FF Tel: (028) 9024 2866 Fax: (028) 9033 3117 E-mail: dennesbel@btconnect.com
Graham Hunter (Shirts) Ltd, Springtown Road, Springtown Industrial Estate, Londonderry, BT48 0LY Tel: (028) 7126 2542 Fax: (028) 7126 3556 E-mail: info@hunterapparelsolutions.com
JL 2007 Realisations Ltd, Hastings House, Park Industrial Estate, St. Albans, Hertfordshire, AL2 2DR Tel: (01727) 875369 Fax: (01727) 875367
Perry Ellis Europe Ltd, Crittall Road, Witham, Essex, CM8 3DJ Tel: (01376) 502345 Fax: (01376) 500733 E-mail: custserv@farah.co.uk
Polyfashion Ltd, 34 Parliament Street, Small Heath, Birmingham, B10 0QJ Tel: 0121-772 7754 Fax: 0121-766 6744 E-mail: info@polyfashion.co.uk
▶ Prowse & Hargood Ltd, Unit 3, Jessop Close, Clacton-on-Sea, Essex, CO15 4LY Tel: (0870) 2467740 Fax: (0870) 2467780 E-mail: info@prowseandhargood.com
Rael Brook (Group) Ltd, Grosvenor Street, Ashden Underline, Ashton-Under-Lyne, Lancashire, OL7 0JY Tel: 0161-344 5618 Fax: 0161-308 5060 E-mail: admin@raelbrookshirts.com
Revelation Shirts Ltd, Bewsey Street, Warrington, WA2 7JF Tel: (01925) 634372 Fax: (01925) 418438 E-mail: infomation@revelationshirts.co.uk
Saville Row Shirt Co (Castledowsan) Ltd, Curran Road, Castledawson, Magherafelt, County Londonderry, BT45 8AF Tel: (028) 7946 5000 Fax: (028) 7946 8074
▶ Sprint Design Ltd, Unit 46 John Player Building, Stirling Enterprise Park, Stirling, FK7 7RP Tel: (01786) 447707 Fax: (01786) 447707 E-mail: info@sprintdesign.co.uk

SHOCK ABSORBENT PROTECTIVE CLOTHING

Derby Unitex Ltd, Derbyshire Business Development Centre, Beaufort Street, Derby, DE21 6AX Tel: (01332) 298988 Fax: (01322) 295696 E-mail: derby@unitex.co.uk

SHOCK ABSORBER RING SPRINGS

Spax Performance Ltd, 2 Launton Business Centre, Murdock Road, Bicester, Oxfordshire, OX26 4PL Tel: (01869) 244771 Fax: (01869) 240536 E-mail: sales@spaxperformance.com

SHOCK ABSORBERS, *See also headings for particular types*

Ace Controls International, 1 Belvedere Road, Newton-le-Willows, Merseyside, WA12 0JJ Tel: (01925) 227171 Fax: (01925) 229323 E-mail: sales@ace-controls.co.uk
Anthan Engineering Ltd, Watford, WD19 4EZ Tel: (01923) 249474 Fax: (01923) 249477 E-mail: anthan@anthan.co.uk
▶ Avo UK Ltd, Caswell Road, Brackmills Industrial Estate, Northampton, NN4 7PW Tel: (01604) 708101 Fax: (01604) 761030 E-mail: sales@avouk.com
Roadlink International Ltd, Strawberry Lane, Willenhall, West Midlands, WV13 3RL Tel: (01902) 606210 Fax: (01902) 606604 E-mail: j.darwin@roadlink-international.co.uk
Spax Performance Ltd, 2 Launton Business Centre, Murdock Road, Bicester, Oxfordshire, OX26 4PL Tel: (01869) 244771 Fax: (01869) 240536 E-mail: sales@spaxperformance.com
Transhock Distribution Ltd, Unit 1, Industrial Estate, Arden Road, Saltley, Birmingham, B8 1DL Tel: 0121-322 4200 Fax: 0121-327 6239 E-mail: transhock@aol.com

SHOCK OR VIBRATION RECORDING DATA LOGGERS

Environmental Equipments Ltd, 12, Eleanor House, Kingsclere Park, Kingsclere, Newbury, Berkshire, RG20 4SW Tel: (01635) 298502 Fax: (01635) 296499 E-mail: sales@e-equipments.com

SHOE COMPONENTS

Ashford & Campion Ltd, Westfield Terrace, Higham Ferrers, Rushden, Northamptonshire, NN10 8BB Tel: (01933) 359321 Fax: (01933) 410403
Chick Plastics Ltd, 42 Kenilworth Drive, Oadby, Leicester, LE2 5LG Tel: 0116-271 3377
City Leather Co Leicester Ltd, 47 Kenilworth Drive, Oadby, Leicester, LE2 5LT Tel: 0116-271 3322 Fax: 0116-272 0828
Dickinson Shoe Services Ltd, 345 Shields Road, Newcastle upon Tyne, NE6 2UD Tel: 0191-265 4858 Fax: 0191-224 2245 E-mail: westgaterubbers@aol.com
Gillson Bros Ltd, 4 Conder Quay, East Quay, Bridgwater, Somerset, TA6 4DB Tel: (01278) 422932 Fax: (01278) 453958 E-mail: gillsoles@hotmail.com
Hide & Hides Ltd, Portishead Road, Leicester, LE5 0JN Tel: 0116-276 6514
Portch Trimmings Ltd, 2 Ireton Avenue, Leicester, LE4 9EW Tel: (0116) 276 6537 Fax: (0116) 246 0778
Punch Sales Ltd, Lower Farm Road, Moulton Park Industrial Estate, Northampton, NN3 6XF Tel: (01604) 646426 Fax: (01604) 495245 E-mail: info@punchindustries.com
Savvas Georgiou, 207-209 Langham Road, London, N15 3LH Tel: (020) 8889 7999 Fax: (020) 8888 8927
W Smart & Son Ltd, 44 Park Road, Rushden, Northamptonshire, NN10 0RG Tel: (01933) 312038 Fax: (01933) 318891

SHOE FINISHES

A & G Toseland Ltd, St. Michael Road, Kettering, Northamptonshire, NN15 6AU Tel: (01536) 414401 Fax: (01536) 414402 E-mail: premierfinishes_uk@yahoo.co.uk

SHOE LACES

Barrowfield Leather Co. Ltd, 47 Solway Street, Glasgow, G40 4JG Tel: 0141-554 7863 Fax: 0141-554 8053 E-mail: office@barrowfield.com

SHOE LASTS

▶ The Slipper . Com, Brantwood Lodge, Coniston, Cumbria, LA21 8AD Tel: 015394 41997 Fax: 015394 41998 E-mail: lasts@theslipper.com

SHOE LINING FABRICS

Camtex Fabrics Ltd, Blackwood Road, Lillyhall Industrial Estate, Lillyhall, Workington, Cumbria, CA14 4JJ Tel: (01900) 602646 Fax: (01900) 66827 E-mail: info@cambrelle.com
Milton Leicester Ltd, North Street, Wigston, Leicestershire, LE18 1PR Tel: 0116-288 5871 Fax: 0116-288 0116 E-mail: sales@miltons.ltd.uk

SHOE MERCERY, *See also headings for individual items*

Archbond Ltd, Mill Hill Factory, Desford Road, Enderby, Leicester, LE19 4AD Tel: 0116-284 1222 Fax: 0116-284 9954 E-mail: lizhayes@archbond.co.uk
Excel Adhesives, 18 Low Farm Place, Moulton Park Industrial Estate, Northampton, NN3 6HY Tel: (01604) 648484 Fax: (01604) 790370

SHOE POLISHES

Dunkelman & Son Ltd, 15 Jermyn Street, London, SW1Y 6LT Tel: (020) 7734 7340 Fax: (020) 7287 0933 E-mail: info@dunkelman.com
Punch Sales Ltd, Lower Farm Road, Moulton Park Industrial Estate, Northampton, NN3 6XF Tel: (01604) 646426 Fax: (01604) 495245 E-mail: info@punchindustries.com

SHOE REPAIR MACHINES

Standard Engineering Ltd, Lawson Street, Kettering, Northamptonshire, NN16 8XU Tel: (01536) 517070 Fax: (01536) 410755
Trophy World, 12 Bourtree Pl, Hawick, Roxburghshire, TD9 9HW Tel: 01450 372174

SHOE SOLES, *See Soles etc*

SHOE TOOLS

Moulding Bros & Merry Leicester Ltd, 11 Hilltop Road, Hamilton, Leicester, LE5 1TT Tel: 0116-276 5112 Fax: 0116-276 6596
▶ Woodware Repetitions Ltd, 47 Mowbray Street, Sheffield, S3 8EN Tel: 0114-272 6060 Fax: 0114-279 7475

SHOE TREES

Dunkelman & Son Ltd, 15 Jermyn Street, London, SW1Y 6LT Tel: (020) 7734 7340 Fax: (020) 7287 0933 E-mail: info@dunkelman.com

SHOE UPPER FABRICS

Milton Leicester Ltd, North Street, Wigston, Leicestershire, LE18 1PR Tel: 0116-288 5871 Fax: 0116-288 0116 E-mail: sales@miltons.ltd.uk

SHOES

▶ A Wedding to Talk About, 1 Brennan Close, Barrow-in-Furness, Cumbria, LA13 0TD Tel: (01229) 812921
Bowhill & Elliott East Anglia Ltd, 65 London Street, Norwich, NR2 1HL Tel: (01603) 620116 Fax: (01603) 620066
▶ Inglis James Shoemaker, Cavalry Park, Peebles, EH45 9BU Tel: (01721) 722422 Fax: (0845) 8951051 E-mail: sales@jamesinglis.com
Shoe Zone Ltd, Haramead Business Centre, Humberstone Road, Leicester, LE1 2LH Tel: 0116-222 3000 Fax: 0116-222 3001 E-mail: info@shoezone.net
▶ Taylors Keighley Ltd, 60 Cavendish Street, Keighley, West Yorkshire, BD21 3RL Tel: (01535) 603693 Fax: (01535) 603693 E-mail: info@taylorsshoes.co.uk
Edward Woodley & Sons Ltd, Newton Road, Higham Ferrers, Rushden, Northamptonshire, NN10 8HR Tel: (01933) 353373 Fax: (01933) 358275 E-mail: ewoodley@globalnet.co.uk

SHOES, LADIES'

Bacup Shoe Co. Ltd, Atherton Holme Mill, Railway Street, Bacup, Lancashire, OL13 0UF Tel: (01706) 873304 Fax: (01706) 873216 E-mail: admin@bacupshoe.co.uk
Barker Shoes Sales Ltd, 3 Station Road, Earls Barton, Northampton, NN6 0NT Tel: (01604) 810387 Fax: (01604) 812350 E-mail: barker@barkersshoes.co.uk
Beaconsfield Footwear Ltd, 2 Peel Road, Skelmersdale, Lancashire, WN8 9PT Tel: (01695) 712720 Fax: (01695) 712715 E-mail: info@hotter.co.uk
Bowhill & Elliott East Anglia Ltd, 65 London Street, Norwich, NR2 1HL Tel: (01603) 620116 Fax: (01603) 620066
Brevitt Rieker Ltd, 37 Tenter Road, Moulton Park Industrial Estate, Northampton, NN3 6AX Tel: (01604) 491222 Fax: (01604) 499512 E-mail: sales@rieker.net
W.J. Brookes Sraigh Devine, 44 King Street, Earls Barton, Northampton, NN6 0LQ Tel: (01604) 810217 Fax: (01604) 812511 E-mail: providerwb@aol.com
Chuckle Shoes, 3 New Bridge Street, Exeter, EX4 3JW Tel: (01392) 270321 Fax: (01392) 207003
Church & Co (Footwear Ltd), St James, Northampton, NN5 5JB Tel: (01604) 593333 Fax: (01604) 754405 E-mail: sales@church-footwear.com
C. & J. Clark International Ltd, 40 High Street, Street, Somerset, BA16 0YA Tel: (01458) 443131 Fax: (01458) 447547 E-mail: john.keery@clarks.com
D B Shoes Ltd, Irchester Road, Rushden, Northamptonshire, NN10 9XF Tel: (01933) 359217 Fax: (01933) 410218 E-mail: denton@dbshoes.freeserve.co.uk
E Sutton & Son Ltd, Riverside, Bacup, Lancashire, OL13 0DT Tel: (01706) 874961 Fax: (01706) 879268 E-mail: firstname@esutton.co.uk
Equity Shoes Ltd, Western Road, Leicester, LE3 0GQ Tel: 0116-254 9313 Fax: 0116-255 3769 E-mail: equity@equityshoes.com
Florentine Shoes, European Cargo Centre, Motherwell Way, Grays, Essex, RM20 3XD Tel: (01708) 867111 Fax: (01708) 862110 E-mail: mikeluff@florentineshoes.freeserve.co.uk
The Florida Group Ltd, Dibden Road, Norwich, NR3 4RR Tel: (01603) 426341 Fax: (01603) 424354 E-mail: mailroom@floridagroup.co.uk
Gina Shoes Ltd, Fitzroy House, Abbot Street, London, E8 3DP Tel: (020) 7254 9811 Fax: (020) 7249 1984 E-mail: ginashoes@aol.com
▶ Heel2toe.co.uk Ltd, Unit 9 Meadow Heights, Fir Street, Ramsbottom, Bury, Lancashire, BL0 0BN Tel: (07779) 151881
▶ Inglis James Shoemaker, Cavalry Park, Peebles, EH45 9BU Tel: (01721) 722422 Fax: (0845) 8951051 E-mail: sales@jamesinglis.com
Lambert Howarth Group P.L.C., Healeywood Road, Burnley, Lancashire, BB11 2HL Tel: (01282) 471200 Fax: (01282) 471279
▶ Plus in Boots Ltd, 150 Magna Road, Poole, Dorset, BH11 9NB Tel: 01202 581566
R E Ormerod & Sons Ltd, Union Mill, Bacup Road, Rossendale, Lancashire, BB4 7JN Tel: (01706) 215391 Fax: (01706) 210368
RSS Edge Shoes, 184 Wellington Road, Bilston, West Midlands, WV14 6BE Tel: (01902) 353007 Fax: (01902) 353823 E-mail: sales@edgeshoes.com
White & Co. Ltd, 50a Main Road, Hackleton, Northampton, NN7 2AB Tel: (01604) 870982 Fax: (01604) 870529 E-mail: shoes@whiteeb.co.uk

SHOES, SAFETY, WOMENS

Hamilton & Pollock, Kenton Lane Farm, Kenton Lane, Harrow, Middlesex, HA3 8RT Tel: (020) 8909 0601 Fax: (020) 8909 0602 E-mail: info@hampol.co.uk

SHOP BLINDS

Coverlite Blinds & Awnings, 9-11 Hanover Street, Bolton, BL1 4TG Tel: (01204) 364444 Fax: (01204) 397232
Lelliotts Sunblinds Ltd, 80 Sopmting Road, Worthing, West Sussex, BN14 9ES Tel: (01273) 330077 Fax: (01903) 538052 E-mail: lelliottsblinds@btclick.com
Olympic Blinds Ltd, Olympic House Bilton Court, Bilton Way, Luton, LU1 1LX Tel: (01582) 737878 Fax: (01582) 402182 E-mail: sales@olympicblindsltd.co.uk
Rogers Blinds & Awnings Ltd, Unit 6 Castle Buildings, Gilston Road, Saltash, Cornwall, PL12 6TW Tel: (01752) 840616 Fax: (01752) 840571 E-mail: rogersblinds@supanet.com

SHOP CHANGING ROOM CALL SYSTEMS

▶ Tricom, Unit 4, Turner Street, Dudley, West Midlands, DY1 1TX Tel: (01384) 456560

SHOP DISPLAY FURNITURE INSTALLATION

Recordpass Ltd, 4 Glencoe Business Park, Warne Road, Weston-super-Mare, Avon, BS23 3TS Tel: (01934) 629220 E-mail: warn.joinery@virgin.net

SHOP ESTATE AGENTS

James Andrew International Ltd, 72-75 Marylebone High Street, London, W1U 5JW Tel: (020) 7224 4436 Fax: (020) 7486 5277 E-mail: hms@jamesandrew.co.uk
bValued Ltd, Unit 2, Dyfrig Road Industrial Estate, Cardiff, CF5 5AD Tel: (0845) 1309438 Fax: (0845) 1309439 E-mail: enquiries@bvalued.co.uk
Alan Croft Property Services, 48 Conduit Street, London, W1S 2YR Tel: (020) 7434 9799 Fax: (020) 7734 0217
▶ Donaldsons, 48 Warwick Street, London, W1B 5NL Tel: (020) 7534 5000 Fax: (020) 7424 0045
Garner & Sons, 15 St Petersgate, Stockport, Cheshire, SK1 1EB Tel: 0161-480 3013 Fax: 0161-477 9125 E-mail: enquiries@garnerandsons.co.uk
Harvey Spack Field, 33 Bruton Street, London, W1J 6QU Tel: (020) 7629 9663 Fax: (020) 7491 1964
▶ Kingsley Commercial, Chenil House, 181-183 Kings Road, London, SW3 5EB Tel: (020) 7352 3130 Fax: (020) 7352 5111 E-mail: sales@kingsleycommercial.co.uk
Knight Frank Property Company, Knight Frank 20 Hanover Square, London, W1S 1HZ Tel: (020) 7408 1100 Fax: (020) 7493 4114 E-mail: farms.estates@knightfrank.com
▶ My Home Bulgaria Ltd, 129 Wellington Road, London, london, E6 6EB Tel: (020) 8552 5920 Fax: (0870) 7622839 E-mail: zaur@pochta.ws

SHOP FITTING JOINERY

Applied Shopfitting Ltd, Hamlyn House, Mardle Way, Buckfastleigh, Devon, TQ11 0NS Tel: (01364) 643855 Fax: (01364) 643888 E-mail: info@appliedshopfitting.co.uk
Masher Bros, 97-103 Florence Road, London, SE14 6QL Tel: (020) 8691 1632 Fax: (020) 8691 1496 E-mail: sales@masherbros.com
▶ Roebuck & Holmes Ltd, 1-6 Farnley Mill, Farnley Road, Farnley Tyas, Huddersfield, HD4 6UN Tel: (01484) 665553 Fax: (01484) 664828 E-mail: admin@roebuckandholmes.co.uk

SHOP FITTING LIGHTING

Jerrards plc, Arcadia House Cairo New Road, Croydon, CR0 1XP Tel: (020) 8251 5522 Fax: (020) 8251 5500
Lloyd & Son, Copthall Farm, Breakspear Road South, Ickenham, Uxbridge, Middlesex, UB10 8HB Tel: (01895) 679000 Fax: (01895) 679000 E-mail: lloydandson640@btinternet.com
▶ VP Commercial Ltd, 22 Timor Grove, Stoke-on-Trent, ST4 8RR Tel: (01782) 646660 Fax: 01782 646672 E-mail: vp@vp-com.co.uk

SHOP FITTING SERVICES

A A Z Aluminium & uPVC Centre, Satya-Niwas, 53 Hencroft Street South, Slough, SL1 1RF Tel: (01753) 539248 Fax: (01753) 539248

▶ A & D Joinery, Premier Partnership Estate, Leys Road, Brierley Hill, West Midlands, DY5 3UP Tel: (01384) 265165 Fax: (01384) 265464

A E Hadley Ltd, Limberline Spur, Portsmouth, PO3 5JR Tel: (023) 9266 4341 Fax: (023) 9266 4940 E-mail: info@aehadley.com

Alken Construction Ltd, Redmoss Business Centre, Greenbank Road, East Tullos Industrial Estate, Aberdeen, AB12 3BQ Tel: (01224) 875265 Fax: (01224) 879023

▶ Amj Services UK Ltd, 21a Whirlow Grove, Whirlow, Sheffield, S11 9NR Tel: 0114-249 8380 Fax: 0114 2817979 E-mail: tony@amjservices.com

Anglia Shopfitting Norwich Ltd, Diamond Road, Norwich, NR6 6AB Tel: (01603) 426297 Fax: (01603) 483644

Antone Displays Ltd, Wanstead Road, Leicester, LE3 1TR Tel: 0116-232 4700 Fax: 0116-287 8012

Apc Group Ltd, Crown Street, Thornton Road, Bradford, West Yorkshire, BD1 2LA Tel: (01274) 306970 Fax: (01274) 730900 E-mail: info@a-p-c.biz

Arrow Display Fittings Ltd, 21 Bartleet Road, Redditch, Worcestershire, B98 0DG Tel: (01527) 527941 Fax: (01527) 510205 E-mail: sales@arrowdisplay.co.uk

B Batch Electrical Ltd, 2025 Spring Bank West, Hull, HU5 5ER Tel: (01482) 506903 Fax: (01482) 571900 E-mail: tristan@bbatch.karou.co.uk

Baldwin & Moore Ltd, Unit 7 Elton Road Business Park, Derby, DE24 8EG Tel: (01332) 385356 Fax: (01332) 385377 E-mail: baldwinandmoore@derby22.fsnet.co.uk

Bassett & Findley Ltd, Talbot Road North, Wellingborough, Northamptonshire, NN8 1QS Tel: (01933) 224898 Fax: (01933) 227731 E-mail: info@bassettandfindley.ltd.uk

Malcolm Baucher Ltd, Cavendish House, Brighton Road, Waterloo, Liverpool, L22 5NG Tel: 0151-920 8030 Fax: 0151-949 0527 E-mail: baucherbuild@aol.com

Beacon Woodcraft Ltd, Queen Street, Premier Business Park, Walsall, WS2 9NT Tel: (01922) 613255 Fax: (01922) 634720 E-mail: info@beaconwoodcraft.co.uk

Beasley (Joiners) Ltd, Bangor Terrace, Leeds, LS12 5PS Tel: 0113-263 0524 Fax: 0113-279 2389 E-mail: sales@beasleyjoiners.co.uk

Beaver Leeds Ltd, Elder Mills, Elder Road, Leeds, LS13 4DL Tel: 0113-239 3363 Fax: 0113-236 1264 E-mail: info@beaverleeds.ltd.uk

Benbow Interiors, Bradley Mill, Newton Abbot, Devon, TQ12 1NF Tel: (01626) 367861 Fax: (01626) 355591 E-mail: mail@benbow-interiors.co.uk

Blow & Scrimshaw Ltd, 10 Dixon Way, Lincoln, LN6 7XN Tel: (01522) 521319 Fax: (01522) 545718 E-mail: contact@blowandscrimshaw.com

V.J. Bowers & Sons, 11 Rydal Road, Little Lever, Bolton, BL3 1DT Tel: (01204) 578358 Fax: (01204) 578358

Boygle & Co. Ltd, Chichester Road, Romiley, Stockport, Cheshire, SK6 4BL Tel: 0161-406 8280 Fax: 0161-406 8244

C A B Joinery Services Ltd, C A B Joinery Services Ltd, Unit 3, Block A, Bescot Industrial Estate, Woden Road West, Wednesbury, West Midlands, WS10 7SG Tel: 0121-556 5445 Fax: 0121-505 4352 E-mail: enquiries@cab-joinery.co.uk

C D Contracts Ltd, 50 Garendon Road, Shepshed, Loughborough, Leicestershire, LE12 9NX Tel: (01509) 505511 Fax: (01509) 505522 E-mail: cdcontractsltd@aol.com

C D L Co. Ltd, 29 Grafton Road, Croydon, CR0 3RP Tel: (020) 8680 3077 Fax: (020) 8686 9225 E-mail: annaaustin@cdlco.fsnet.co.uk

C R Gibbs & Sons (Sheffield) Ltd, Nunnery Drive, Sheffield, S2 1TA Tel: 0114-273 7003 Fax: 0114-275 3500 E-mail: crgibbs@btconnect.com

Cambridge Joinery Ltd, 23 Fen End, Over, Cambridge, CB4 5NE Tel: (01954) 231008 Fax: (01954) 232263 E-mail: jim@cambridgejoinery.co.uk

Canon Davis Hangers, Cranford House, Coombe Way, Byfleet, West Byfleet, Surrey, KT14 7DP Tel: (01932) 411288 Fax: (01932) 411289

Carlisle Refrigeration Thermoking Ltd, Brunthill Road, Kingstown Industrial Estate, Carlisle, CA3 0EH Tel: (01228) 531449 Fax: (01228) 511514E-mail: info@carlislerefrigeration.co.uk

Carterian Joinery, 38 Brearley Street, Hockley, Birmingham, B19 3NR Tel: 0121-359 4340 Fax: 0121-333 4115 E-mail: ian.carter@carterian.co.uk

▶ Casco Ltd, Unit 21, Lawson Hunt Industrial Park, Guildford Road, Broadbridge Heath, Horsham, West Sussex, RH12 3JR Tel: (01403) 248244 Fax: (01403) 218347 E-mail: contactus@casco-group.com

Castles Shopfitters Limited, Bowland Street Works, Bowland Street, Bradford, West Yorkshire, BD1 3BW Tel: (01274) 724271 E-mail: mail@castle_shopfitters.co.uk

Cheshire Contracts Shopfitting Ltd, Imperial Works, 151 Bennett Street, Manchester, M12 5BH Tel: 0161-273 6253 Fax: 0161-274 3454 E-mail: enquiries@cheshire-contracts.co.uk

Classic Holdings, 55 Cradley Road, Cradley Heath, West Midlands, B64 7BB Tel: (01384) 637825 Fax: (01384) 564079 E-mail: classicholdings@aol.com

Construction & Shopfitting Ltd, 117, Piccotts End, Hemel Hempstead, Hertfordshire, HP1 3AU Tel: (01442) 244117 Fax: (01442) 233274 E-mail: cs.co@virgin.net

County Shopfitting Ltd, 7 Portsmouth Enterprise Centre, Quartermaine Road, Portsmouth, PO3 5QT Tel: (023) 9269 8365 Fax: (023) 9267 3647 E-mail: enquiries@countyshopfitting.co.uk

Coutts & Findlater Ltd, 15-18 Hudson Road, Sunderland, SR1 2LL Tel: 0191-567 1291 Fax: 0191-564 0590 E-mail: john@jfwilsonshopfittersltd.fsnet.co.uk

▶ Daleside Group Shopfitters Ltd, Park Road East, Calverton, Nottingham, NG14 6LL Tel: 0115-965 6696 Fax: 0115-965 6328 E-mail: info@dalesidegroup.com

Dayman Display Ltd, Sidney House, 262 Aylestone Lane, Wigston, Leicestershire, LE18 1BD Tel: 0116-288 3338 E-mail: sales@daymandisplay.fsnet.co.uk

Deane & Amos Group Ltd, South Portway Close, Round Spinney, Northampton, NN3 8RH Tel: (01604) 790990 Fax: (01604) 644644 E-mail: mail@deane-amos.co.uk

R. Dillon (Clacton) Ltd, Ford Road Industrial Estate, Clacton-On-Sea, Essex, CO15 3DT Tel: (01255) 423059 Fax: (01255) 222836

▶ Dodson Shop Fitters, Loders Cottage, Gaunts, Wimborne, Dorset, BH21 4JJ Tel: (01258) 840509 E-mail: info@dodsonshopfitters.co.uk

Dollar Rae Ltd, 47 Haggs Road, Glasgow, G41 4AR Tel: 0141-649 9331 Fax: 0141-632 9882 E-mail: sales@dollarrae.co.uk

E L Shopfitters, 45 Huntly Road, Hillington Industrial Estate, Glasgow, G52 4DZ Tel: 0141-882 9979 Fax: 0141-882 9979

Edmont Joinery Ltd, Hyde Road, Swindon, SN2 7RB Tel: (01793) 825765 Fax: (01793) 825725 E-mail: admin@edmont.co.uk

Enhurst Ltd, 65-69 County Street, London, SE1 4AD Tel: (020) 7403 0630 Fax: (020) 7407 5940 E-mail: office@enhurst.freeserve.co.uk

Euro Shopfitting Ltd, Unit 3 Bilton Way, Lutterworth, Leicestershire, LE17 4JA Tel: (01455) 559999 Fax: (01455) 559898 E-mail: info@euroshopfitting.co.uk

Europa Shop & Office Fitting, 3 Maxted Road, Hemel Hempstead Industrial Estate, Hemel Hempstead, Hertfordshire, HP2 7DX Tel: (01442) 213412 Fax: (01442) 267672 E-mail: postmaster@europa-shopfitting.co.uk

Fabframe Ltd, 2 Whiting Street, Sheffield, S8 9QR Tel: 0114-258 8808 Fax: 0114-255 4465

Fitzroy Group, Radford Court Industrial Estate, Nottingham, NG7 3DY Tel: (0870) 4289102 Fax: (0870) 4289186

G F Joinery (Contract) Ltd, Gooder Lane, Brighouse, West Yorkshire, HD6 1HB Tel: (01484) 715116 Fax: (01484) 400089 E-mail: gfgroupltd@freenetname.co.uk

G T Morgan & Co, Desford Lane, Kirby Muxloe, Leicester, LE9 2BF Tel: (01455) 828022 Fax: (01455) 828001 E-mail: contract@gtmorgan.demon.co.uk

Gariff Construction Ltd, Village House, Eleventh Street, Trafford Park, Manchester, M17 1JF Tel: 0161-848 9983 Fax: 0161-848 9984 E-mail: leeunsworth@gariff.co.uk

H M S Designs, Wenlock Way, Leicester, LE4 9HU Tel: 0116-274 1244 Fax: 0116-276 4086 E-mail: hmsdesigns@freeuk.com

H W D Shopfitters Ltd, 65 Marlborough Road, Newport, Gwent, NP19 0BY Tel: (01633) 211761 Fax: (01633) 843014 E-mail: enquire@hwdshopfitters.co.uk

Heaton Shopfitters Ltd, 88 Tatton Road South, Stockport, Cheshire, SK4 4LX Tel: 0161-442 5786 Fax: 0161-718 3519

Hemming & Morris (Shopfitters) Ltd, 60 Lincoln Road, Olton, Birmingham, B27 6NZ Tel: 0121-706 5740 Fax: 0121-706 6192 E-mail: sales@hemmingmorris.co.uk

Henry Hall Displays Fittings Ltd, Cherrytree, Union Road, Sheffield, S11 9EF Tel: 0114-255 1351 Fax: 0114-250 0006 E-mail: sales@retaildisplay.com

I D E SS Ltd, 3 West Road, Harlow, Essex, CM20 2BQ Tel: (01279) 400140 Fax: (01279) 400141

Interlink Design & Display Ltd, Unit 2-4 Station Road Industrial Estate, Station Road, Coleshill, Birmingham, B46 1HT Tel: (01675) 467870 Fax: (01675) 467871 E-mail: enquiries@interlinkdesign.co.uk

Itab G.W.S Group Ltd, Unit E2 Imperial Business Estate, West Mill, Gravesend, Kent, DA11 0DL Tel: (01474) 537744 Fax: (01474) 537860 E-mail: info@gwsgroup.com

Jones & Andrews Ltd, Melrose Close, Swansea Enterprise Park, Swansea, SA6 8QE Tel: (01792) 701797 Fax: (01792) 701793

Keyplan Shopfitting Ltd, Whatfside, Festival Way, Stoke-on-Trent, ST1 5PU Tel: (01782) 285596 Fax: (01782) 204365 E-mail: mike@keyplanshopfit.co.uk

Kier Western, 27-37 Martin Street, Plymouth, PL1 3NQ Tel: (01752) 201123 Fax: (01392) 261789 E-mail: info.plymouth@kier.co.uk

Kirkman & Jourdain Holdings Ltd, 150 Brooker Road, Waltham Abbey, Essex, EN9 1JH Tel: (01992) 788588 Fax: (01992) 788643 E-mail: k.j@kirkmanandjourdain.com

L P R Services Ltd, 6 Cantors Way, Minety, Malmesbury, Wiltshire, SN16 9QZ Tel: (01666) 860992 Fax: (01666) 860992 E-mail: info@lprservices.co.uk

Leslie Atkins & Partners Ltd, 3 Airfield Road, Christchurch, Dorset, BH23 3TG Tel: (01202) 499444 Fax: (01202) 499223 E-mail: reception@latkins.co.uk

Lester & Lester Ltd, 1-9 Tennyson Road, London, SW19 8SH Tel: (020) 8540 8687 Fax: (020) 8543 4322 E-mail: darren@lesters.ssworld.co.uk

The LodgeTaylor's Shopfitters, 280 Birchanger Lane, Birchanger, Bishop's Stortford, Hertfordshire, CM23 5QP Tel: (01279) 817003

London Shopfitters Ltd, 6 Blackwater Close, Rainham, Essex, RM13 8UA Tel: (01708) 552225 Fax: (01708) 557567

Lynn & Jones Storefitters Ltd, Falcon House, Kenneth Street Off Ingram Road, Holbeck, Leeds, LS11 9RF Tel: 0113-234 0737 Fax: 0113-245 6130 E-mail: enquiries@lynnandjones.co.uk

Lynton Shopfitters Ltd, Hose Street, Stoke-on-Trent, ST6 5AL Tel: (01782) 819902 Fax: (01782) 839919 E-mail: admin@lynton-shopfitters.co.uk

M C H Design & Shopfitting Ltd, 27 Fergusson Drive, Knockmoore Hill Industrial Park, Lisburn, County Antrim, BT28 2EX Tel: (028) 9266 8000 Fax: (028) 9267 8008 E-mail: ask@makeit-fit.com

M.J.M Marine Ltd, 10 Loughbrickland Road, Rathfriland, Newry, County Down, BT34 5AA Tel: (028) 4063 8396 Fax: (028) 4063 8973 E-mail: sales@mjmmarine.com

M J M Suspended Ceilings, Melville Road, Sidcup, Kent, DA14 4LX Tel: (020) 8300 8400 E-mail: smarks.mjm@ntlworld.com

M & S Aluminium Systems Ltd, Unit 19 Van Alloys Industrial Estate, Busgrove Lane, Stoke Row, Henley-on-Thames, Oxfordshire, RG9 5QW Tel: (01491) 680600 Fax: (01491) 680700 E-mail: sales@ms-ali.com

Madden Construction & Display Ltd, Unit 26-27 Watery La Industrial Estate, Watery Lane, Willenhall, West Midlands, WV13 3SU Tel: (01902) 366234 Fax: (01902) 366500

Marco Joinery Ltd, 17-19 Downing Street, Sutton-in-Ashfield, Nottinghamshire, NG17 4EF Tel: (01623) 556684 Fax: (01623) 556664

Maskame & Tait, 9-11 St. Peter Street, Peterhead, Aberdeenshire, AB42 1QB Tel: (01779) 473661 Fax: (01779) 481482 E-mail: info@maskameandtait.co.uk

Mentha & Halsall (Shopfitters) Ltd, 95a Linaker St, Southport, Merseyside, PR8 5BU Tel: (01704) 530800 Fax: (01704) 500601 E-mail: info@mentha-halsall.com

Mercia Interiors, 8 Victoria Buildings, Newhall Street, Willenhall, West Midlands, WV13 1LN Tel: (01902) 636685 Fax: (01902) 637086 E-mail: info@mimltd.freeserve.co.uk

Morgans, 102 Borstal Road, Rochester, Kent, ME1 3BD Tel: (01634) 370370 Fax: (01634) 370037 E-mail: sales@shopfitting.com

▶ Multilines Ltd, 1 255 Water Road, Wembley, Middlesex, HA0 1JW Tel: (020) 8997 7788 Fax: (020) 8997 9988 E-mail: sales@multilines.co.uk

Nason Foster Ltd, Moor Lane, Birmingham, B6 7HH Tel: 0121-356 5693 Fax: 0121-356 3818 E-mail: sales@nasonfoster.co.uk

New Quay Developments Ltd, 68 Armagh Road, Tandragee, Craigavon, County Armagh, BT62 2HS Tel: (028) 3884 0444 Fax: (028) 3884 1811 E-mail: info@newquayconstruction.com

▶ Newman Scott Ltd, 1 Sadler Foster Way, Teesside Industrial Estate, Stockton-on-Tees, Cleveland, TS17 9JY Tel: (01642) 769696 Fax: (01642) 769669 E-mail: columbr@newmanscott.co.uk

Nova Display, Unit 1, Peckfield Business Park, Phoenix Avenue, Micklefield, Leeds, LS25 4DY Tel: 0113-385 0200 Fax: 0113-385 0201 E-mail: howard@novadisplay.co.uk

Ocean Refit Ltd, The Barnyard, Stennack, St. Ives, Cornwall, TR26 1QR Tel: (01736) 799440 Fax: (01736) 799440 E-mail: oceanrefit@btopenworld.com

Optical Marketing Ltd, Unit 2, 28 Park Street, London, SE1 9EQ Tel: (020) 7378 1268 Fax: (020) 7378 8690 E-mail: omretail@aol.com

Peerless Designs Ltd, Unit 9, Brunswick Industrial Estate, Brunswick Way, London, N11 1JL Tel: (020) 8362 8500 Fax: (020) 8362 8525 E-mail: enquiries@peerlessdesigns.com

Pennant P B M Ltd, 8 Locarno Avenue, Luton, LU4 9EJ Tel: (01582) 576422 Fax: (01582) 581792 E-mail: pennant@email.com

F.J. Pike (Ramsgate) Ltd, 111-115 Hardres Street, Ramsgate, Kent, CT11 8QU Tel: (01843) 593438 Fax: (01843) 595639 E-mail: contact@fjpike.co.uk

Platonoff & Harris, Suite 206 Mill Studio Business Centre, Crane Mead, Ware, Hertfordshire, SG12 9PY Tel: (01920) 444255 Fax: (01920) 487673 E-mail: tony.ph@shopfitters.net

Pollards Fyrespan, Units 3-5 Haslemere Business Centre, Lincoln Way, Enfield, Middlesex, EN1 1AY Tel: (020) 8443 5511 Fax: (020) 8443 3804 E-mail: info@pollardsfyrespan.co.uk

Portview Fitout Ltd, 46 Florenceville Avenue, Belfast, BT7 3GZ Tel: (028) 9064 4765 Fax: (028) 9064 1330 E-mail: info@portview.co.uk

R W Joinery Stockport Ltd, Unit 26 Vernon Mill, Mersey Street, Stockport, Cheshire, SK1 2HX Tel: 0161-480 8722 Fax: 0161-474 7646 E-mail: info@rwjoinery.co.uk

R W M C Engineering Ltd, Harrow Wood Farm & Caravan Park, Poplar Lane, Bransgore, Christchurch, Dorset, BH23 8JE Tel: (01425) 674450 Fax: (01425) 674450

G.K. Raw & Co. Ltd, Claro Way, Claro Road, Harrogate, North Yorkshire, HG1 4DE Tel: (01423) 501241 Fax: (01423) 530865

▶ Robert H Leach T/A Whitaker, Eurocam Technology Park, Chase Way, Bradford, West Yorkshire, BD5 8HW Tel: (01274) 391460

▶ Rockingham Display & Cabinet Makers Ltd, Highfields Farm Enterprise Centre, Huncote Road, Stoney Stanton, Leicester, LE9 4DJ Tel: (01455) 273912 Fax: (01455) 271106

S J C Shopfitters, 3 Britannia Road, Waltham Cross, Hertfordshire, EN8 7NY Tel: (01992) 711151 Fax: (01992) 714441 E-mail: sales@sjcshopfitters.co.uk

Scriven Electrical Contractors Ltd, Unit 11, Brandon Way Industrial Estate, Brandon Way, West Bromwich, West Midlands, B70 9PW Tel: 0121-553 7243 Fax: 0121-553 7872 E-mail: building@scrivenelectric.demon.uk

▶ J Seamer & Son Ltd, 35 Shaftesbury Street South, Derby, DE23 8YH Tel: (01332) 348303 Fax: (01332) 291617

Shopfit UK Ktd, West End Works, Staithes Road, Preston, Hull, HU12 8TJ Tel: (01482) 896240 Fax: (01482) 896510 E-mail: info@shopfituk.co.uk

Sign World 2000, Drome Road, Deeside Industrial Park, Deeside, Clwyd, CH5 2NY Tel: (01244) 281955 Fax: (01244) 281949 E-mail: mail.signworld@btinternet.com

Stansted Pine, Stansted Saw Mills, Stansted Park, Rowland's Castle, Hampshire, PO9 6DU Tel: (023) 9241 3595

Stopps Ltd, Lyon Road, Walton-on-Thames, Surrey, KT12 3RU Tel: (01932) 242086 Fax: (01932) 228893 E-mail: mail@stopps.co.uk

▶ Syntec, Unit 1 Parkside, Ravenscourt Park, London, W6 0UU Tel: (020) 8834 7544 Fax: (020) 8762 0604 E-mail: syntec_projects@blueyonder.co.uk

Trent Shopfitters, Gateway House, Beechdale Road, Nottingham, NG8 3EZ Tel: 0115-942 5151 Fax: 0115-942 5656

Triplar Ltd, Baron Avenue, Earls Barton, Northampton, NN6 0JE Tel: (01604) 812999 Fax: (01604) 812992 E-mail: office@triplar.co.uk

Tudor Storefitters Ltd, 17 Southfield, Welwyn Garden City, Hertfordshire, AL7 4ST Tel: (01707) 333048 Fax: (01707) 372626 E-mail: tudor999@aol.com

Turnercraft Cabinet Makers, 5 Furlong Parade, Stoke-on-Trent, ST6 3AX Tel: (01782) 837618 Fax: (01782) 837618

Turners Bar Fitters & Joiners Ltd, Martins Mill, Pellon Lane, Halifax, West Yorkshire, HX1 5QJ Tel: (01422) 354984 Fax: (01422) 342770

▶ Vale (UK) Ltd, Kitling Road, Knowsley Industrial Park South, Knowsley, Prescot, Liverpool, L34 9JA Tel: 0151-546 4684

Vincents Shopfitters Ltd, Priory Works, Newton Street, Newton Saint Faith, Norwich, NR10 3AD Tel: (01603) 891050 Fax: (01603) 890689 E-mail: post@vincents.co.uk

▶ Walker & Kitching Ltd, Sandall Stones Road, Kirk Sandall Estate, Kirk Sandall, Doncaster, South Yorkshire, DN3 1QR Tel: (01302) 880044

Wanzl Ltd, Europa House, Heathcote Lane, Heathcote, Warwick, CV34 6SP Tel: (01926) 451951 Fax: (01926) 451952

Wattson Shopfitters Ltd, 4-6 Countess Wear Road, Countess Wear, Exeter, EX2 6LG Tel: (01392) 258781 Fax: (01392) 420866 E-mail: wattson@theshopfitters.co.uk

William Tilston, 3a-3c The Borders Industrial Park, River Lane, Saltney, Chester, CH4 8RJ Tel: (01244) 678786 Fax: (01244) 683935

Anthony Willis Shopfitters Ltd, 55 Grosvenor Street, Cardiff, CF5 1NJ Tel: (029) 2034 5582 Fax: (029) 2023 7260 E-mail: mail@anthonywillis-shopfitters.co.uk

▶ Willyn Contracts Ltd, Common Lane, Watnall, Nottingham, NG16 1HD Tel: 0115-938 9606 Fax: 0115-938 4027

Withey Contracts Ltd, Waburn House, Adams Close, Kempston, Bedford, MK42 7JE Tel: (01234) 844600 Fax: (01234) 844601 E-mail: info@withey.co.uk

SHOP FITTINGS, *See also headings for particular types*

A & E Plastic Fabrications Ltd, 40 St. Peters Street, Radford, Nottingham, NG7 3FF Tel: 0115-978 0048 Fax: 0115-979 1351 E-mail: info@aaep.co.uk

▶ A P T Fixing Ltd, Unit C1 Doulton Trading Estate, Doulton Road, Rowley Regis, West Midlands, B65 8JQ Tel: (01384) 560059 Fax: (01384) 560059

▶ A & S Glazing, Greets Green Road, West Bromwich, West Midlands, B70 9EG Tel: 0121-557 3150 Fax: 0121-557 3150

John Anthony Organistation, Greenwood House, Unity Road, Lowmoor Business Park, Kirkby-in-Ashfield, Nottingham, NG17 7LE Tel: (01623) 755090 Fax: (01623) 755110 E-mail: sales@jao.co.uk

▶ Apex Displays, 18-20 Gladstone Street, Leicester, LE1 2BN Tel: 0116-251 1999 Fax: 0116-251 2022 E-mail: team@apex-displays.co.uk

Arrow Display Fittings Ltd, 21 Bartleet Road, Redditch, Worcestershire, B98 0DG Tel: (01527) 527941 Fax: (01527) 510205 E-mail: sales@arrowdisplay.co.uk

Arrow Wire Products Ltd, 15 Boulton Road, Reading, RG2 0NF Tel: 0118-987 4521 Fax: 0118-931 3456 E-mail: sales@arrowwireproducts.co.uk

▶ indicates data change since last edition

SHOP FITTINGS – *continued*

Aspect Graphics & Displays, Units 35-36 Bury Business Centre, Kay Street, Bury, Lancashire, BL9 6BU Tel: 0161-763 9955 Fax: 0161-763 9355 E-mail: sales@aspectdisplays.co.uk

B Plan Shop Equipment, Unit 4e Bellair, Musker Street, Liverpool, L23 0UB Tel: 0151-932 1002 Fax: 0151-932 1002

B & W Joinery Ltd, 2 50 Bradfield Road, Finedon Road Industrial Estate, Wellingborough, Northamptonshire, NN8 4HB Tel: (01933) 279800 Fax: (01933) 279881 E-mail: r.webb@bwjoinery.fsnet.co.uk

▶ Bacchus Interiors Exhibition & Display, Stadium Works, Dogford Road, Royton, Oldham, OL2 6UA Tel: 0161-652 6520 Fax: 0161-652 6529 E-mail: sales@bacchusgroup.co.uk

Beaver Leeds Ltd, Elder Mills, Elder Road, Leeds, LS13 4DL Tel: 0113-239 3363 Fax: 0113-236 1264 E-mail: info@beaverleeds.ltd.uk

Bennett Architectural Aluminium Solutions Ltd, Parsonage Street, Stoke-on-Trent, ST6 5HL Tel: (01782) 834633 Fax: (01782) 835395 E-mail: helpdesk@baasl.co.uk

V.J. Bowers & Sons, 11 Rydal Road, Little Lever, Bolton, BL3 1DT Tel: (01204) 578358 Fax: (01204) 578358

Brassworld Bar Equipment, Unit 22 Royal Industrial Estate, Jarrow, Tyne & Wear, NE32 3HR Tel: 0191-428 2233 Fax: 0191-483 8893 E-mail: lisa@ahlpipework.co.uk

Bray Display Ltd, 23 Woodside Industrial Park, Works Road, Letchworth Garden City, Hertfordshire, SG6 1LA Tel: (01462) 482323 Fax: (01462) 482324 E-mail: jim@braydisplay.co.uk

Brimglades Ltd, 1 Deans Factory Estate, Lambs Lane, Rainham, Essex, RM13 9XL Tel: (01708) 552085 Fax: (01708) 520237

Cameo Shop Fitting Ltd, 47 Broughton Street, Manchester, M8 8AN Tel: 0161-839 6799 Fax: 0161-839 6798 E-mail: joanne@cameoshopfitting.co.uk

Caranco Ltd, Caranco House, Wilford Road, Nottingham, NG2 1EB Tel: 0115-986 2272 Fax: 0115-986 3705 E-mail: sales@caranco.co.uk

▶ Casco Ltd, Unit 21, Lawson Hunt Industrial Park, Guildford Road, Broadbridge Heath, Horsham, West Sussex, RH12 3JR Tel: (01403) 248244 Fax: (01403) 218347 E-mail: contactus@casco-group.com

Chilfen Joinery Ltd, 1 Flint Road, Letchworth Garden City, Hertfordshire, SG6 1HJ Tel: (01462) 705390 Fax: (01462) 674327 E-mail: michelled@chilfen.co.uk

County Shopfitting Ltd, 7 Portsmouth Enterprise Centre, Quartermaine Road, Portsmouth, PO3 5QT Tel: (023) 9269 8365 Fax: (023) 9267 3647 E-mail: enquiries@countyshopfitting.co.uk

▶ Creative Timber Ltd, Unit 9A, Luton Business Park, Ilminster, Somerset, TA19 9DU Tel: (01460) 57915 Fax: (01460) 57903

Cube Arts Ltd, 14-18 Abbotsbury Road, Morden, Surrey, SM4 5LQ Tel: (020) 8685 9108 Fax: (020) 8085 9089 E-mail: info@cubearts.com

D & H Display Ltd, Facet Road, Birmingham, B38 9PT Tel: 0121-451 3666 Fax: 0121-451 3666

D & S Shopfitters, 103 Brinksway Trading Estate, Stockport, Cheshire, SK3 0BZ Tel: 0161-477 3142 Fax: 0161-477 3142

▶ Daleside Group Shopfitters Ltd, Park Road East, Calverton, Nottingham, NG14 6LL Tel: 0115-965 6696 Fax: 0115-965 6328 E-mail: info@dalesidegroup.com

▶ Dawson Peebles Ltd, 5 Morris Road, Leicester, LE2 6BR Tel: 0116-274 5270 Fax: 0116-274 5271

Deane & Amos Aluminium Systems Ltd, Queens Park Indust Estate, Studland Road, Northampton, NN2 6NA Tel: (01604) 718708 Fax: (01604) 717170

Deniet & Son Ltd, Finchley Avenue, Mildenhall, Bury St. Edmunds, Suffolk, IP28 7BG Tel: (01638) 713442 Fax: (01638) 712783 E-mail: bob@deniet.flexnet.co.uk

▶ Dialogue Commercial Interiors Ltd, New Farm Buildings, Northampton Road, Stoke Bruerne, Towcester, Northants, NN12 7XU Tel: (01604) 864401 Fax: (01604) 862519

Display, Unit 1 White Road, Off Charfleets Road, Canvey Island, Essex, SS8 0PQ Tel: (01268) 696509 Fax: (01268) 696587 E-mail: display.uk@virgin.co.uk

The Display Centre UK Ltd, 2 The Avenue, Westside Fareham Railway Station, Fareham, Hampshire, PO14 1NP Tel: (01329) 231333 Fax: (01329) 823262 E-mail: sales@displaycentre.co.uk

Drakes Display & Shop Aids, 45 Wessex Trade Centre, Ringwood Road, Poole, Dorset, BH12 3PG Tel: (01202) 735858 Fax: (01202) 733979 E-mail: sales@drakesdisplay.co.uk

Duram Ltd, Duram House, Cemetery Road, Bradford, West Yorkshire, BD8 9RZ Tel: (01274) 542603 Fax: (01274) 548526 E-mail: sales@duram.co.uk

▶ Dymond Engineering & Metal Products Ltd, Combrew Lane, Bickington, Barnstaple, Devon, EX31 2ND Tel: (01271) 372662 Fax: (01271) 322077 E-mail: sales@dymondengineering.co.uk

Eastern Shop Equipment Ltd, Anson Road, Airport Industrial Estate, Norwich, NR6 6ED Tel: (01603) 424294 Fax: (01603) 405106 E-mail: sales@easternshopequipment.co.uk

▶ Eden, Field Road, Mildenhall, Bury St. Edmunds, Suffolk, IP28 7AR Tel: (0870) 7258826 Fax: (0870) 7258827 E-mail: fiona.diviney@eden-industries.co.uk

England Brothers Ltd, Higham Mead, Chesham, Buckinghamshire, HP5 2AH Tel: (01494) 792633 Fax: (01494) 793633 E-mail: info@englandbro.co.uk

Eyeline Visual Merchandising Ltd, Amsterdam Road, Hull, HU7 0XF Tel: (01482) 824191 Fax: (01482) 824193 E-mail: enquiries@eyeline.co.uk

F Eastwood & Sons plc, London Works, Ripple Road, Barking, Essex, IG11 0SY Tel: (020) 8591 7200 Fax: (020) 8591 4193 E-mail: sales@feastwood.co.uk

F & G Smart (Shop Fittings) Ltd, Tyseley Industrial Estate, Seeleys Road, Birmingham, B11 2LA Tel: 0121 7725634 Fax: 0121 7668995 E-mail: info@smartshopfittings.co.uk

First Manufacturing Ltd, Bagley Road, Wellington, Somerset, TA21 9PZ Tel: (01823) 667879 Fax: (01823) 661317 E-mail: sales@firstman.co.uk

Fylde Shopfitting, 293 Church Street, Blackpool, FY1 3PF Tel: (01253) 620257 Fax: (01253) 291150

G B Projects Ltd, The Mill, Pepperoyd Street, Dewsbury, West Yorkshire, WF13 1PA Tel: (01924) 467147 Fax: (01924) 458511 E-mail: sales@gbprojects.co.uk

Goldenline Ltd, 7 Providence Industrial Estate, Providence Street, Stourbridge, West Midlands, DY9 8HQ Tel: (01384) 892578 Fax: (01384) 423855 E-mail: sales@goldenline.ltd.uk

▶ H S Retail Design Ltd, Tadman Street, Wakefield, West Yorkshire, WF1 5QU Tel: (01924) 371333 Fax: (01924) 372191 E-mail: enquiries@tjhowley.co.uk

Hanson & Beards Ltd, Garden Field, Wyke, Bradford, West Yorkshire, BD12 9NH Tel: (01274) 601010 Fax: (01274) 601666 E-mail: sales@hansonandbeards.co.uk

Hass Interiors, 14 Union Road, Sheffield, S11 9EF Tel: 0114-249 3142 Fax: 0114-250 0006

Hobday Ltd, Aston Brook St East, Aston, Birmingham, B6 4RR Tel: 0121-359 4431 Fax: 0121-608 2008

Interior Fitting Services Ltd, Manor House Farm, 10 Addington Road, Woodford, Kettering, Northamptonshire, NN14 4ES Tel: (01832) 733999 Fax: (01832) 737978

Itab G.W.S Group Ltd, Unit E2 Imperial Business Estate, West Mill, Gravesend, Kent, DA11 0DL Tel: (01474) 537744 Fax: (01474) 537860 E-mail: info@gwsgroup.com

J D S Group Ltd, 19 Park Road, Faringdon, Oxfordshire, SN7 7BP Tel: (01367) 241507 Fax: (01367) 241705 E-mail: jdsgroup@btinternet.com

The J Marshall Partnership Ltd, Brunel Drive, Northern Road Ind Estate, Newark, Nottinghamshire, NG24 2EG Tel: (01636) 705702 Fax: (01636) 677939

JDS Plaswood Ltd, Threxton House, Threxton Road Industrial Estate, Watton, Thetford, Norfolk, IP25 6NG Tel: (01953) 881799 Fax: (01953) 884774

Jem Ltd, Springfield Mills, Spa Street, Ossett, West Yorkshire, WF5 0HW Tel: (01924) 277626 Fax: (01924) 270759 E-mail: jayne@jemltd.co.uk

Jubilee Joinery Hull Ltd, Eagle House, Cleveland Street, Hull, HU8 7AU Tel: (01482) 224275 Fax: (01482) 217672 E-mail: jubilee@sagehost.co.uk

K L S Ltd, 22-23 Austin Fields, King's Lynn, Norfolk, PE30 1PH Tel: (01553) 772935 Fax: (01553) 769118 E-mail: sales@klsonline.co.uk

Lazawood Ltd, 79 Farleigh Road, Warlingham, Surrey, CR6 9EJ Tel: (01883) 622151 Fax: (01883) 624533

Leslie Atkins & Partners Ltd, 3 Airfield Road, Christchurch, Dorset, BH23 3TG Tel: (01202) 499444 Fax: (01202) 499223 E-mail: reception@latkins.co.uk

Lime Bright Ltd, 29B Marlborough Road, Newport, Gwent, NP19 0BX Tel: (01633) 244225 Fax: (01633) 665777

Lofthus Signs & Engraving Ltd, 5 St. Machar Drive, Aberdeen, AB24 3YJ Tel: (01224) 487377 Fax: (01224) 487580

London Shopfitters Ltd, 6 Blackwater Close, Rainham, Essex, RM13 8UA Tel: (01708) 552225 Fax: (01708) 557567

M C H Design & Shopfitting Ltd, 27 Fergusson Drive, Knockmoore Hill Industrial Park, Lisburn, County Antrim, BT28 2EX Tel: (028) 9266 8000 Fax: (028) 9267 8008 E-mail: ask@makeit-fit.com

▶ M G Shopfronts Ltd, Units 5f-2c Albion Works, Moor Street, Brierley Hill, West Midlands, DY5 3SZ Tel: (01384) 571227 Fax: (01384) 573006 E-mail: sales@mgshopfronts.com

Micron Engineering Ltd, Unit 5 Earls Way, Earl Way Industrial Estate, Thurmaston, Leicester, LE4 8DL Tel: 0116-264 0040 Fax: 0116-289 1402 E-mail: e.muddimer@btconnect.com

Millers Retail Design Ltd, Granby House, Greenwood Street, Salford, M6 6PD Tel: 0161-743 1026 Fax: 0161-743 1598

Morplan Shop Fittings Mnfrs, 56 Great Titchfield Street, London, W1W 7DF Tel: (020) 7636 1887 Fax: (020) 7637 9597 E-mail: enquiries@morplan.co.uk

Multifab Sheet Metal & Light Fabrication, Unit 31 Upper Mills, Cannal Side, Slaithwaite, Huddersfield, HD7 5HA Tel: (01484) 841222 Fax: (01484) 841333

Opto International Ltd, Bayley Street, Stalybridge, Cheshire, SK15 1QQ Tel: 0161-330 9136 Fax: 0161-343 7332 E-mail: enquiry@optoint.co.uk

▶ Opus Fabrication, Unit 3, Phoenix Works, Windsor Road, Enfield, Redditch, Worcestershire, B97 6DJ Tel: (01527) 68533 Fax: (01527) 68534 E-mail: opus-fab@btconnect.com

P M S Morley Ltd, 3 High Mill Business Park, Mill Street, Morley, Leeds, LS27 0WJ Tel: 0113-259 7557 Fax: 0113-259 7251

Panelslot Ltd, The Crossways, Nettleden, Hemel Hempstead, Hertfordshire, HP1 3DQ Tel: (01442) 878681 Fax: (01442) 878682

Peerless Designs Ltd, Unit 9, Brunswick Industrial Estate, Brunswick Way, London, N11 1JL Tel: (020) 8362 8500 Fax: (020) 8362 8525 E-mail: enquiries@peerlessdesigns.com

Planet Merchandising Products Ltd, Unit 219b, Aldington Road, London, SE18 5TS Tel: (020) 8855 9594 Fax: (020) 8316 2745 E-mail: sales@planetmerchandising.co.uk

Point Eight Ltd, Unit 14 Blackbrook Valley Industrial Estate, Narrowboat Way, Dudley, West Midlands, DY2 0EZ Tel: (01384) 238282 Fax: (01384) 455746 E-mail: sales@point8.co.uk

Punchline Engineering Ltd, 9 Horton Road, West Drayton, Middlesex, UB7 8JL Tel: (01895) 420626 Fax: (01895) 443938

R T Display Systems Ltd, 10 Lyon Road, South Wimbledon, London, SW19 2RL Tel: (020) 8545 2945 Fax: (020) 8545 2955 E-mail: sales@octanorm.co.uk

R W Joinery Stockport Ltd, Unit 26 Vernon Mill, Mersey Street, Stockport, Cheshire, SK1 2HX Tel: 0161-480 8722 Fax: 0161-474 7646 E-mail: info@rwjoinery.co.uk

Radford Customer Guidance & Checkouts Division, Sherbourne Drive, Tilbrook, Milton Keynes, MK7 8BA Tel: (01908) 366688 Fax: (01908) 368811 E-mail: sales@radford.co.uk

Retail Display Ltd, 6 Clarendon Drive, Wymbush, Milton Keynes, MK8 8DA Tel: (01908) 262822 Fax: (01908) 564604 E-mail: sales@retaildisplay.co.uk

Retail Display Centre Ltd, 42 Kirkfield View, Livingston Village, Livingston, West Lothian, EH54 7BP Tel: (01506) 462228 Fax: (01506) 857730 E-mail: retaildisplaycentre@hotmail.com

Retail Equipment Ltd, 21-22 Chilton Industrial Estate, Addison Road, Sudbury, Suffolk, CO10 2YW Tel: (01787) 372488 Fax: (01787) 311941

▶ Retail Furniture Ltd, Unit E, Halesfield 13, Telford, Shropshire, TF7 4PL Tel: (01952) 587277 Fax: (01952) 201269

Retif, 33-37 Admiral Street, Glasgow, G41 1HP Tel: 0141-429 0537 Fax: 0141-420 1036

Sebix Ltd, 2 Crittle Drive, Springwood Industrial Estate, Braintree, Essex, CM7 2RD Tel: (01376) 550552 Fax: (01376) 550547 E-mail: mick-p@selbix.co.uk

Sev, Lilac Grove, Beeston, Nottingham, NG9 1QX Tel: 0115-907 8233 Fax: 0115-907 8823

Shop Fitting Suppliers Ltd, Aqueduct Street, Preston, PR1 7JH Tel: (01772) 886276 Fax: (01772) 201440 E-mail: sales@shopfittingsupplies.co.uk

Shop Fittings Warehouse, Derby Mill, 13 Thomas Street, Bolton, BL3 6JU Tel: (01204) 396395 Fax: (01204) 396395 E-mail: sales@shopfittingswarehouse.co.uk

Stag Shopfronts Ltd, 16B Kings Mill Way, Mansfield, Nottinghamshire, NG18 5ER Tel: (01623) 631356 Fax: (01623) 421653

▶ Stanley J Murphy Ltd, Crompton Road, Stevenage, Hertfordshire, SG1 2EE Tel: (01438) 359923 Fax: (01438) 350651 E-mail: enquiries@sjmgroup.co.uk

Stuart Shop Fittings Ltd, Unit 10 Alexandra Mill, Baker Street, Morley, Leeds, LS27 0QH Tel: 0113-259 7092 Fax: 0113-259 7093

Summit Retail Display Ltd, Church Street, Milton Regis, Sittingbourne, Kent, ME10 2JZ Tel: (01795) 425552 Fax: (01795) 475552

▶ Sunbeam Woodworks Ltd, 17 & 21 Sunbeam Road, Park Royal, London, NW10 6JP Tel: (020) 8357 1000 Fax: (020) 8357 1021 E-mail: admin@sunbeamgroup.com

Thermotech Building Maintenance Ltd, Northminster Business Park, Northfield Lane, Upper Poppleton, York, YO26 6QU Tel: (01904) 788900 Fax: (01904) 788990

▶ Thomas Muckle & Sons, Bridge Street, Cragside, Morpeth, Northumberland, NE65 7SG Tel: (01669) 620321 Fax: (01669) 620505 E-mail: enquiries@thomasmuckle.co.uk

Three R Display Ltd, 28 Whiteley Croft Rise, Otley, West Yorkshire, LS21 3NR Tel: (01943) 466553 Fax: (01943) 466552 E-mail: threer@btconnect.com

▶ Timber Design Bedrooms, Unit 20 Riverside Mill, Lune Street, Padiham, Burnley, Lancashire, BB12 8DG Tel: (01282) 777926 Fax: (01282) 777926 E-mail: tdsshopfitting@aol.com

Topfit Ltd, 1 Aston Road North, Birmingham, B6 4DS Tel: 0121-608 6711 Fax: 0121-608 2008 E-mail: sales@e-shopfittings.com

Topslot Shop Fittings Systems Ltd, Unit 37, Aneurin Bevan Avenue, Brynmenyn Industrial Estate, Brynmenyn, Bridgend, CF32 9SZ Tel: (01656) 721900 Fax: (01656) 721926

Trade Systems, 48-56 Hawks Road, Kingston Upon Thames, Surrey, KT1 3EE Tel: (020) 8549 5281 Fax: (020) 8541 5637 E-mail: sales@tradesystems.co.uk

Trent Shopfitters, Gateway House, Beechdale Road, Nottingham, NG8 3EZ Tel: 0115-942 5151 Fax: 0115-942 5656

V R M, Dorset Avenue, Thornton-Cleveleys, Lancashire, FY5 2DE Tel: (01253) 852461 Fax: (01253) 852461

Versatile Fittings Ltd, Bicester Road, Aylesbury, Buckinghamshire, HP19 8AU Tel: (01296) 483481 Fax: (01296) 437596 E-mail: info@versatile-fittings.co.uk

W M S Displays Ltd, Unit 2/3, Southways Industrial Estate, Coventry Road, Hinckley, Leicestershire, LE10 0NJ Tel: (01455) 619966 Fax: (01455) 619988 E-mail: info@wmsdisplays.com

▶ Walker Bros (Elland) Ltd, Ainleys Industrial Estate, Huddersfield Road, Elland, West Yorkshire, HX5 9JP Tel: (01422) 310767 Fax: (01422) 377837 E-mail: sales@wbelland.com

Walker Metalwork (Elland) Ltd, Castle Mills, Elland, West Yorkshire, HX5 0RY Tel: 01422 310011

Wilfield Shopfitting & Exhibitions, 53-59 New Tythe Street, Long Eaton, Nottingham, NG10 2DL Tel: 0115-946 6960 Fax: 0115-946 6969 E-mail: sales@wilfield.com

Willey & Bunker Ltd, Park Avenue Industrial Estate, Sundon Park Road, Luton, LU3 3BP Tel: (01582) 574382 Fax: (01582) 490043 E-mail: willey&bunker@itnet.co.uk

Woodstyle, Swinnow View, Leeds, LS13 4TZ Tel: 0113-255 9098 Fax: 0113-220 9727

Wyndham Plastics Ltd, Ogmore Terrace, Bridgend, Mid Glamorgan, CF31 1SU Tel: (01656) 652869 Fax: (01656) 669915 E-mail: steve@wyndham-plastics.co.uk

SHOP FLOOR DATA CAPTURE SYSTEMS

Zetes Ltd, Carrington Business Park, Carrington, Urmston, Manchester, M31 4DD Tel: 0161-776 4593 Fax: 0161-775 2544

SHOP FRONT DOOR HARDWARE

▶ Zero Seal Systems Ltd, Unit 6, Ladford Covert, Ladfordfields Business Park, Seighford, Stafford, ST18 9QG Tel: (01785) 282910 Fax: (01785) 282498 E-mail: sales@zeroplus.co.uk

SHOP FRONT FITTINGS

Access Industrial Door Co Midlands Ltd, 148a Crankhall Lane, Wednesbury, West Midlands, WS10 0ED Tel: 0121-505 1435 Fax: 0121-505 3318 E-mail: neelsangha@aol.com

C D Contracts Ltd, 50 Garendon Road, Shepshed, Loughborough, Leicestershire, LE12 9NX Tel: (01509) 505511 Fax: (01509) 505522 E-mail: cdcontractsltd@aol.com

Paignton Glassworks Ltd, 16 Marldon Road, Paignton, Devon, TQ3 3QZ Tel: (01803) 558096 Fax: (01803) 522044 E-mail: enquiries@paigntonglass.co.uk

UK Shopfront Shutters Ltd, Bridge Road, Southall, Middlesex, UB2 4AB Tel: (020) 8571 5553 Fax: (020) 8574 7066 E-mail: ukshopfronts@aol.com

SHOP FRONTS

▶ Galloway Windows, Creebridge Mill, Creebridge, Newton Stewart, Wigtownshire, DG8 6NP Tel: (01671) 404848 Fax: (01671) 404969

SHOP FURNISHINGS, DISPLAY,

See Display etc

SHOP INTERIOR/RETAIL DESIGNERS

Apiffany Interior Design Ltd, Yandell Publishing Ltd, 9 Vermont Place, Tongwell, Milton Keynes, MK15 8JA Tel: (0870) 1212617 Fax: (0870) 1212618 E-mail: info@apiffany.co.uk

Arno GB Ltd, Discovery House, 125 Redcliff Street, Bristol, BS1 6HU Tel: 0117-929 2541 Fax: 0117-929 4684 E-mail: display@arno-online.co.uk

▶ Chameleon Products Ltd, 8 Grange Close, Bradley Stoke, Bristol, BS32 0AH Tel: (01425) 655952 Fax: (01425) 655607 E-mail: tsw@chameleonproducts.net

Checkland Kindleysides Ltd, Charnwood Edge, Syston Road, Cossington, Leicester, LE7 4UZ Tel: 0116-264 4700 Fax: 0116-264 4701 E-mail: info@checkind.com

▶ CheekyTiki Ltd, Unit E, 2 Leswin Place, Stoke Newington, London, N16 7NJ Tel: (020) 7241 0742 Fax: (020) 7241 0742 E-mail: info@cheekytiki.com

Dunsmore Blinds, 69 Lawford Lane, Rugby, Warwickshire, CV22 7JS Tel: (01788) 811517 Fax: (01788) 811517

SHOP INTERIOR/RETAIL DESIGNERS – *continued*

Every Body's Display, Scrubs Lane, London, W10 6AH Tel: (020) 8960 6121 Fax: (020) 8960 9894E-mail: info@universaldisplay.co.uk
Henry Hall Displays Fittings Ltd, Cherrytree, Union Road, Sheffield, S11 9EF Tel: 0114-255 1351 Fax: 0114-250 0006 E-mail: sales@retaildisplay.com
▶ Interior Matters UK Ltd, 18 Cecil Avenue, Bournemouth, BH8 9EH Tel: (01202) 528152 E-mail: sue@interiormatters.co.uk
James Pringle, Unit 1 Mill Lane, Pitlochry, Perthshire, PH16 5BH Tel: (01796) 472315
▶ Christina Lees, Cocoa Court, 21a Pillory Street, Nantwich, Cheshire, CW5 5BZ Tel: (01270) 611142 Fax: (01270) 842822
Momentum Ltd, Unit 27, Verey Road, Woodside Estate, Dunstable, Bedfordshire, LU5 4TT Tel: (01582) 607301 Fax: (01582) 607302
▶ Quinn Interiors Ltd, Number 4, Moorhey Street, Oldham, OL4 1JD Tel: 0161-785 3150 E-mail: sales@quinninteriors.co.uk
Sloane Group (Holdings) Ltd, 2-20 Booth Drive, Park Farm Estate, Wellingborough, Northamptonshire, NN8 6GR Tel: (01933) 401555 Fax: (01933) 400507 E-mail: info@sloanegroup.co.uk
Spice Design Consultants, Hop Studios, 2 Jamaica Road, London, SE1 2BX Tel: (020) 7252 0808 Fax: (020) 7237 7199 E-mail: studio@spicehop.com
Springfield Stores, Buck Street, Challock, Ashford, Kent, TN25 4AR Tel: (01233) 740327 Fax: (01233) 740327
▶ Visual Communications, 209 Lynchford Road, Farnborough, Hampshire, GU14 6HF Tel: (01252) 540044 Fax: (01252) 516616 E-mail: tara@vis-com.net
World Visual Ltd, 35 Lower Richmond Road, London, SW14 7EZ Tel: (020) 8876 4444 Fax: (020) 8392 9200 E-mail: info@worldvisual.co.uk
▶ Zemira Designs, 26 Fairwood Park, Marton-in-Cleveland, Middlesbrough, Cleveland, TS8 9XP Tel: (01642) 271440 E-mail: zemiradesigns@hotmail.com

SHOP MACHINED METAL PARTS

Micron Engineering Ltd, Unit 5 Earls Way, Earl Way Industrial Estate, Thurmaston, Leicester, LE4 8DL Tel: 0116-264 0040 Fax: 0116-289 1402 E-mail: e.muddimer@btconnect.com
Punchline Engineering Ltd, 9 Horton Road, West Drayton, Middlesex, UB7 8JL Tel: (01895) 420626 Fax: (01895) 443938
Retail Display Ltd, 6 Clarendon Drive, Wymbush, Milton Keynes, MK8 8DA Tel: (01908) 262822 Fax: (01908) 564604 E-mail: sales@retaildisplay.co.uk
World Visual Ltd, 35 Lower Richmond Road, London, SW14 7EZ Tel: (020) 8876 4444 Fax: (020) 8392 9200 E-mail: info@worldvisual.co.uk

SHOP OR STORE SECURITY ALARM SYSTEMS

Checkpoint Meto, 43 Western Road, Bracknell, Berkshire, RG12 1RF Tel: (01344) 701200 Fax: (01344) 701333 E-mail: lfardell@eur.checkpt.com
Dent Ltd, 191-195 Sturton St., Cambridge, CB1 2QH Tel: (01223) 350038 Fax: (01223) 300996 E-mail: dentsecur@aol.com
F M Electronics Ltd, 12 - 14 Forest Vale Road, Forest Vale Industrial Estate, Cinderford, Gloucestershire, GL14 2PH Tel: (01594) 827070 Fax: (01594) 827066 E-mail: sales@fmelectronics.co.uk
▶ Oracle Vision Ltd, 11 Penarth Terrace, Upton, Pontefract, West Yorkshire, WF9 1DZ Tel: (0870) 7587676 Fax: (0870) 7587944 E-mail: sales@oracle-vision.com
ProTag Retail Security, Units 2-3, Short Way, The Industrial Estate, Thornbury, Bristol, BS35 3UT Tel: (01454) 418500 Fax: (01454) 413708 E-mail: martin@touchpanels.co.uk
▶ Spa Security Solutions, 8 Spa Road, Ballynahinch, County Down, BT24 8LU Tel: (028) 9756 1065 Fax: (028) 9756 1065 E-mail: sales@spacctv.com
▶ Sparc Systems Ltd, 430 Allesley Old Road, Coventry, CV5 8GF Tel: (07930) 854033 E-mail: wilson@sparcsys.co.uk

SHORT CIRCUIT TESTING SERVICES

Polar Instruments Ltd, Garenne Park, St. Sampson, Guernsey, GY2 4AF Tel: (01481) 253081 Fax: (01481) 252476 E-mail: mail@polarinstruments.com

SHORT MESSAGE SERVICE (SMS) SOFTWARE

4productions, 1-3 Lime Hill Road, Tunbridge Wells, Kent, TN1 1LJ Tel: (01892) 524428 Fax: 01892 614811 E-mail: info@4productions.co.uk
▶ Niche Technologies Ltd, Ternion Court, 264-268 Upper Fourth Street, Milton Keynes, MK10 1DP Tel: 0870 7504471 Fax: 0870 1335371 E-mail: sales@niche-technologies.co.uk
Reach2Mobile Ltd, Keswick House, 26 Myrtle Avenue, Ruislip, Middlesex, HA4 8RZ Tel: 08707 665232 E-mail: infok@reach2mobile.co.uk
▶ Text-Messaging 4 Business, 6 Station Road, London, NW4 4PZ Tel: (0870) 7606836 Fax: (0870) 7606836 E-mail: fambizzari@yahoo.co.uk

SHORTBREAD

Campbell's Shortbread, Ancaster Square, Callander, Perthshire, FK17 8BL Tel: (01877) 330013 Fax: (01877) 331290 E-mail: sales@campbellsshortbread.co.uk

SHOT BLASTING CONTRACTORS

▶ A1 Blast Services, 26 Camborne Close, Northampton, NN4 8PH Tel: (07901) 972536
A1 Blasting Cleaning & Painting, Riverside House Wallerscote Island, Winnington Lane, Northwich, Cheshire, CW8 4YF Tel: (01606) 783203 Fax: (01606) 781581
Aberdeen Blast Cleaning Services Ltd, Hillview Road, East Tullos Industrial Estate, Aberdeen, AB12 3HB Tel: (01224) 896565 Fax: (01224) 894989
Advanced Food Technology, 3a Wenman Road, Thame, Oxfordshire, OX9 3UF Tel: (01844) 217303 Fax: (01844) 212341 E-mail: info@appliedfood.co.uk
Aldeby Painting Services Ltd, Britannia Way, Thurmaston, Leicester, LE4 8JY Tel: 0116-269 5699 Fax: 0116-260 2887 E-mail: kevin.aldeby@virgin.net
Anglia Rustguard Ltd, 26 Crittall Road, Western Industrial Estate, Witham, Essex, CM8 3DR Tel: 01376 514152 Fax: 01376 512802 E-mail: angliarustguard@btconnect.com
Aquablast Blast Cleaning, Crutched Friars, Little Whelnetham, Bury St. Edmunds, Suffolk, IP30 0UH Tel: (01284) 388700 Fax: (01284) 388701 E-mail: sales@aquablast.uk.com
B G Penny & Co. Ltd, Unit 3, Three Spires Industrial Estate, Ibstock Road, Coventry, CV6 6JR Tel: (024) 7636 7636 Fax: (024) 7636 7636
Baker Engineering Co., Unit 11 Paramount Industrial Estate, Sandown Road, Watford, WD24 7XA Tel: (01923) 229309 Fax: (01923) 801182 E-mail: sales@bakereng.co.uk
G. Banks (Nu-Co), Unit 9, Atlantic Trading Estate, Barry, South Glamorgan, CF63 3RF Tel: (01446) 742861 Fax: (01446) 742861
F. Bemrose Ltd, Manby Road, Immingham, South Humberside, DN40 2LL Tel: (01469) 572961 Fax: (01469) 571498 E-mail: frankbemrose@aol.com
Blastpride Holdings Ltd, Units 7-8 Curran Buildings, Curran Road, Cardiff, CF10 5NE Tel: (029) 2037 1959 Fax: (029) 2022 2351
Blastreat Arundel Ltd, 14 Fitzalan Road, Arundel, West Sussex, BN18 9JS Tel: (01903) 883262 Fax: (01903) 884185 E-mail: blastreat@btconnect.com
Brian Plant, Wickham Road, Grimsby, South Humberside, DN31 3SL Tel: (01472) 241342 Fax: (01472) 354329
Carillion, Webb Road, Skippers Lane Industrial Estate, Middlesbrough, Cleveland, TS6 6HD Tel: (01642) 459000 Fax: (01642) 454111
Cas Coatings, Old Mill, Victoria Road, Bradford, West Yorkshire, BD2 2BH Tel: (01274) 634493 Fax: (01274) 634493
Cotswold Blast Cleaning, Linenfields, Old Boars Hill, Oxford, OX1 5JJ Tel: (07831) 705205 Fax: (01865) 326134
Countrywide Industrial Coatings, Thwaite Lodge, Thwaite Close, Erith, Kent, DA8 1DP Tel: (01322) 338639 Fax: (01322) 359060
Cray Metal Finishers, D1-D2 Unit Riverside Industrial Estate, Riverside Way, Dartford, DA1 5BS Tel: (01322) 220662 Fax: (01322) 288032 E-mail: sales@craymetalfinishers.co.uk
▶ Davidsons, Seagate, Peterhead, Aberdeenshire, AB42 1JP Tel: (01779) 474455 Fax: (01779) 475218
R.L. Dumelow & Son, St. Matthews Street, Burton-On-Trent, Staffordshire, DE14 3DE Tel: (01283) 564292 Fax: (01283) 564292
Edinburgh Painting Contractors, 30 Christiemiller Avenue, Edinburgh, EH7 6ST Tel: (0131) 669 4691 Fax: (0131) 669 4691
European Coatings Ltd, Sandwich Industrial Estate, Ramsgate Road, Sandwich, Kent, CT13 9LY Tel: (01304) 621121 Fax: (01304) 621535
▶ Express Heat Treatments, Unisant Trading Estate, Powke Lane, Cradley Heath, West Midlands, B64 5PY Tel: 0121-561 6500 Fax: 0121-561 6509 E-mail: sales@expressheat.co.uk
Express Metal Finishers, Manchester Road, Mossley, Ashton-under-Lyne, Lancashire, OL5 9QN Tel: (01457) 837718 Fax: (01457) 835801
G & N Shotblasting Ltd, Brindley Close, Drayton Fields Industrial Estate, Daventry, Northamptonshire, NN11 8RP Tel: (01327) 872569 Fax: (01327) 300878 E-mail: sales@shotblast.co.uk
Gemini Corrosion Services Ltd, Spurryhillock Industrial Estate, Broomhill Road, Stonehaven, Kincardineshire, AB39 2NH Tel: (01569) 765488 Fax: (01569) 766315 E-mail: enquiries@gemini-corrosion.co.uk
Griffin & Son, 106 Pavenhill, Purton, Swindon, SN5 4DB Tel: (01793) 770807 Fax: (01793) 771807 E-mail: pete@griffinandson.uk.com
Hereford Abrasives Co. Ltd, Unit 702, Fordshill Road, Rotherwas Industrial Estate, Hereford, HR2 6NS Tel: (01432) 270289 Fax: (01432) 274278E-mail: sales@blasting.freeserve.co.uk
Heritage Restoration Services Ltd, 18 Derby Road, Burton-on-Trent, Staffordshire, DE14 1RU Tel: (01283) 546266 Fax: (01283) 546266 E-mail: davekeytes@btopenworld.co.uk
Herrington Industrial Services Ltd, Crown Works, Crown Road, Sunderland, SR5 2BS Tel: 0191-516 0634 Fax: 0191-548 1553
Hunter Steel Coatings Ltd, Pinfold Lane, Alltami, Mold, Flintshire, CH7 6NZ Tel: (01244) 541177 Fax: (01244) 549310 E-mail: huntersteel@btconnect.com
Johnson Walsh Engineering Ltd, 47 Newford Crescent, Stoke-on-Trent, ST2 7EB Tel: (01782) 544555 Fax: (01782) 544116 E-mail: jwesshot@btclick.com
K G D Industrial Services, Willow Court, Netherwood Road, Rotherwas Industrial Estate, Hereford, HR2 6JU Tel: (01432) 374374 Fax: (01432) 353419 E-mail: sales@kgdprocess.com
K G Sprayers Aldershot Ltd, 3a Holder Road, Aldershot, Hampshire, GU12 4RH Tel: (01252) 324309 Fax: (01252) 345895
K M H Powder Coating & Shotblasting, 10b Radnor Road, Wigston, Leicestershire, LE18 4XY Tel: 0116-277 0050 Fax: 0116-277 7229 E-mail: hackmower@aol.com
Kemach Services, 34 Singer Way, Woburn Road Industrial Estate, Kempston, Bedford, MK42 7AF Tel: (01234) 857340 Fax: (01234) 857340 E-mail: tworr46530@aol.com
Langwith Metal Finishers, Unit 21 Doublegate Lane, Rawreth, Wickford, Essex, SS11 8UD Tel: (01268) 570020 Fax: (01268) 570700 E-mail: enquiries@langwithmetal.com
M O S Cold Cutting Systems Ltd, Acorn Park Industrial Estate, Charlestown, Shipley, W. Yorkshire, BD17 7SW Tel: (01274) 588066 Fax: (01274) 588077 E-mail: stm@constructionplus.net
Metex Engineering Ltd, 5 Holly Lane, Beeston, Nottingham, NG9 4AB Tel: 0115-943 0155 Fax: 0115-943 6365
Midland Surface Finishing, 42 Bayton Road, Exhall, Coventry, CV7 9EJ Tel: (024) 7636 0436 Fax: (024) 7636 0721
▶ MTW Blasting, Morley Barn Farm, Kegworth Road, Gotham, Nottingham, NG11 0LG Tel: 07788 110197 E-mail: cars_r_me@msn.com
N K Coatings Ltd, 4 Michelin Road, Newtownabbey, County Antrim, BT36 4PT Tel: (028) 9083 3725 Fax: (028) 9083 7433 E-mail: mail@nkcoatings.com
R.J. Nash Ltd, 74 Livery Street, Birmingham, B3 1RG Tel: (0121) 200 3900 Fax: (0121) 200 3906 E-mail: brookwelding@btinternet.com
Nemac Fabrications Ltd, 5 Staition Road Industrial Estate, Station Road, Reddish, Stockport, Cheshire, SK5 6ND Tel: 0161-432 1030 Fax: 0161-443 2096 E-mail: neil@nemac.co.uk
North West Enamellers, Unit 14-15 Catheralls Industrial Estate, Brookhill Way, Buckley, Clwyd, CH7 3PS Tel: (01244) 549185 Fax: (01244) 544739
Ormac Coatings Ltd, Thorncliffe Works, Thorncliffe Park Estate, Chapeltown, Sheffield, S35 2PH Tel: 0114-246 1237 Fax: 0114-257 0151 E-mail: orrmac@aol.com
P & R Finishing, 1 Site 2 North Bridge Road, Berkhamsted, Hertfordshire, HP4 1EH Tel: (01442) 873962 Fax: (01442) 873962
Powa Pak Cleaners Ltd, Bletchley, Market Drayton, Shropshire, TF9 3RZ Tel: (01630) 638276 Fax: (01630) 638548 E-mail: sales@powapak.co.uk
Precision Component Blasting, Unit13 Fazeley Industrial Estate, Fazeley Street, Birmingham, B5 5RS Tel: 0121-643 1478 Fax: 0121-643 1478
Prepcraft, 11 Hunsdon, Welwyn Garden City, Hertfordshire, AL7 2PN Tel: (07775) 928822 Fax: (01707) 371413 E-mail: enquiries@prepcraft.co.uk
Quality Coatings Ltd, Russell Street, Chadderton, Oldham, OL9 9LD Tel: 0161-620 0008 Fax: 0161-627 2746
Ramco Tubular Services Ltd, Badentoy Road Badentoy Park, Badentoy Industrial Estate, Portlethen, Aberdeen, AB12 4YA Tel: (01224) 782278 Fax: (01224) 783001 E-mail: info@ramco-plc.com
Roften Galvanising Ltd, North Road, Ellesmere Port, CH65 1AB Tel: 0151-355 4257 Fax: 0151-355 0753 E-mail: creditacc_roften@yahoo.co.uk
Rust Proofing Company (Manchester) Ltd, Vauxhall Works, Greg Street, Reddish, Stockport, Cheshire, SK5 7BR Tel: 0161-480 8341 Fax: 0161-480 8820
South Staffs Group Ltd, Churchfield House, 36 Vicar Street, Dudley, West Midlands, DY2 8RG Tel: (01384) 458300 Fax: (01384) 233670 E-mail: sales@southstaffsindustries.com
▶ South Staffs Industries Ltd, Bloomfield Road, Tipton, West Midlands, DY4 9EE Tel: 0121-522 2373 Fax: 0121-522 3528
Standish Metal Treatments, Potter Place, Skelmersdale, Lancashire, WN8 9PW Tel: (01695) 455977 Fax: (01695) 728835 E-mail: smtltd@aol.com
▶ Steadblast Special Projects, 4 Buckland Road, Parkside, Stafford, ST16 1TZ Tel: 0788 4433851 Fax: 01785 603506 E-mail: doctorearwax60@hotmail.com
Supablast Nationwide Ltd, 11 Gorsey Lane, Coleshill, Birmingham, B46 1JU Tel: (01675) 464446 Fax: (01675) 464447 E-mail: enquiries@supablast.co.uk
Surface Dynamics (UK) Ltd, 348 SPON LANE SOUTH, WEST BROMWICH, WEST MIDLANDS, B70 6AZ Tel: (0121) 553 7772 Fax: (0121) 553 4746 E-mail: sales@surfacedynamics.co.uk
Surface Engineers Manchester Ltd, Globe Works Off Astley Street, Dukinfield, Cheshire, SK16 4QZ Tel: 0161-330 9224 Fax: 0161-343 2650
Systematic Servicing Equipment Ltd, Field Works, Broadway Road, Willersey, Broadway, Worcestershire, WR12 7PH Tel: (01386) 852342 Fax: (01386) 858556 E-mail: sales@systematic-servicing.co.uk
Tayblast Services Ltd, Corrosion Centre, Lunan Bay, Montrose, Angus, DD10 9TG Tel: (01241) 830513 Fax: (01241) 830533 E-mail: colinkennedy@tayblast.com
Jack Tighe Coatings Ltd, Sandall Stones Road, Kirk Sandall Industrial Estate, Doncaster, South Yorkshire, DN3 1QR Tel: (01302) 880360 Fax: (01302) 880370
Tramontana Bros, Foxglove Cottage, Mamble, Kidderminster, Worcestershire, DY14 9JL Tel: (01299) 832422 Fax: (01299) 832026
Unimet Enamellers Ltd, 183-185 Cardiff Road, Reading, RG1 8HD Tel: 0118-959 5528
Universal Applied Coatings Ltd, Parish Lane, Pease Pottage, Crawley, West Sussex, RH10 5NY Tel: (01293) 514943 Fax: (01293) 552619
Watford Coatings Ltd, Park House, Greenhill CR, Watford, WD18 8QU Tel: (01923) 235640 Fax: (01923) 449229 E-mail: sales@watfordcoatings.co.uk
Wednesfield Shotblasting Ltd, Planetary Road, Willenhall, West Midlands, WV13 3SW Tel: 01902 731781
▶ Zinga UK, 2-4 Arkwright Way, North Newmoor Industrial Estate, Irvine, Ayrshire, KA11 4JU Tel: (01294) 224412 Fax: (01294) 215003 E-mail: sales@zinga-uk.com

SHOT BLASTING EQUIPMENT

Blastline Ltd, Grove Street, Mansfield Woodhouse, Mansfield, Nottinghamshire, NG19 8BU Tel: (01623) 623333 Fax: (01623) 655208 E-mail: sales@blastline.co.uk
Blastman Robotics Ltd, 68 Cunliffe Cl, Oxford, OX2 7BL Tel: (01865) 512654 Fax: (01865) 311874
Electrogenerators Ltd, 14 Australia Road, Slough, SL1 1SA Tel: (01753) 522877 Fax: (01753) 824653
I S P C Surface Preperation Ltd, Wakefield Road, Ossett, West Yorkshire, WF5 9AW Tel: (01924) 276303 Fax: (01924) 277829 E-mail: uk-info@surfacepreperation.com
Ispc Surface Preperation Ltd, Craven Road, Craven Road, Altrincham, Cheshire, WA14 5EP Tel: 0161-928 6388 Fax: 0161-929 8017 E-mail: uk-info@wheelabrator.co.uk
J Reid Engineering Ltd, Factory Road, Sandycroft, Deeside, Clwyd, CH5 2QJ Tel: (01244) 520688 Fax: (01244) 535921 E-mail: linda@jreidtrading.demon.co.uk
Kemach Services, 34 Singer Way, Woburn Road Industrial Estate, Kempston, Bedford, MK42 7AF Tel: (01234) 857340 Fax: (01234) 857340 E-mail: tworr46530@aol.com
Power Blast International, 9 Colhook Industrial Park, Petworth, West Sussex, GU28 9LP Tel: (01428) 707895 Fax: (01428) 707894 E-mail: sales@powerblast.co.uk
Shotblast Supplies Ltd, 10-20 Kilton Terrace, Worksop, Nottinghamshire, S80 2DQ Tel: (01909) 530107 Fax: (01909) 482982 E-mail: sales@shotblast-supplies.co.uk

SHOT BLASTING EQUIPMENT COMPONENTS OR SPARE PARTS

Pangborn UK Ltd, Riverside House Brymau Three Trading Estate, River Lane, Saltney, Chester, CH4 8RQ Tel: (01244) 659852 Fax: (01244) 659853 E-mail: sales@pangborn.co.uk
Pangborn (UK) Ltd, Orgreave Drive, Sheffield, S13 9NR Tel: 0114-288 0786 Fax: 0114-288 0791 E-mail: panguk@aol.com
Purser Plant Ltd, Nyes Wharf, Frensham Street, London, SE15 6TH Tel: (020) 7639 1344 Fax: (020) 7639 2155

SHOT BLASTING EQUIPMENT HIRE

A-Plant Ltd, Nuthall Road, Nottingham, NG8 5BU Tel: 0115-942 0567 Fax: 0115-978 8868 E-mail: nottinghamwest@aplant.com
Purser Plant Ltd, Nyes Wharf, Frensham Street, London, SE15 6TH Tel: (020) 7639 1344 Fax: (020) 7639 2155

SHOT BLASTING INSTALLATION OR SERVICING

Brian Cook Engineering Ltd, Calder Road Works, Ravensthorpe, Dewsbury, West Yorkshire, WF13 3JT Tel: (01924) 469469 Fax: (01924) 849099
Industrial Wear Parts Sheffield Ltd, Speedlock Works, Petre Street, Sheffield, S4 8LN Tel: 0114-261 0651 Fax: 0114-242 3030 E-mail: sales@iwp-ltd.co.uk
Steeltek, Serpentine Works, Serpentine Road, Cleckheaton, West Yorkshire, BD19 3HU Tel: (01274) 852131 Fax: (01274) 851486

SHOT BLASTING SERVICES, COATINGS

▶ Rosler UK, Unity Grove, Knowsley Business Park, Prescot, Merseyside, L34 9GT Tel: 0151-482 0444 Fax: 0151-482 4400
Westcountry Shotblasting Ltd, Armidale, Fenny Bridges, Honiton, Devon, EX14 3BG Tel: (07870) 606116 E-mail: blasting@btinternet.com

SHOT PEENING CONTRACTORS

Ceratex Engineering Ltd, Church La Works, Church Lane, Kelbrook, Barnoldswick, Lancashire, BB18 6UF Tel: (01282) 842900 Fax: (01282) 844093 E-mail: sales@ceratex.co.uk
Elgamec, Unit 9-11 Enterprise Industrial Estate, Station Road West, Ash Vale, Aldershot, Hampshire, GU12 5QJ Tel: (01252) 518177 Fax: (01252) 541331 E-mail: info@elgamec.com
Metal Improvement Company, European Corporate Office, Hambridge Lane, Newbury, Berkshire, RG14 5TU Tel: (01635) 279621 Fax: (01635) 279629 E-mail: eurosales@metalimprovement.com

SHOTGUN CARTRIDGES

Lyalvale Ltd, Express Estate, Fisherwick Road, Lichfield, Staffordshire, WS13 8XA Tel: (01543) 434400 Fax: (01543) 434420 E-mail: sales@lyalvaleexpress.com

SHOTGUNS

A A Brown & Sons, 1 Snake Lane, Alvechurch, Birmingham, B48 7NT Tel: 0121-445 5395 Fax: 0121-445 2113 E-mail: sales@aabrownandsons.com
Accles & Shelvoke Ltd, Selco Way Off First Avenue, Minworth Industrial Estate, Minworth, Sutton Coldfield, West Midlands, B76 1BA Tel: 0121-313 4567 Fax: 0121-313 4569 E-mail: sales@eley.co.uk
Asi, Alliance House, Snape, Saxmundham, Suffolk, IP17 1SW Tel: (01728) 688555 Fax: (01728) 688950
David Mckay Brown (Gunmakers) Ltd, 32 Hamilton Road, Bothwell, Glasgow, G71 8NA Tel: (01698) 853727 Fax: (01698) 854207 E-mail: info@mckaybrown.com
J Roberts & Son Ltd, 22 Wyvil Road, London, SW8 2TG Tel: (020) 7622 1131 Fax: (020) 7627 4442 E-mail: shop@jroberts-gunmakers.co.uk
Clive C. Lemon, The Gun Room, Park Cottage, Upper Bentley, Redditch, Worcestershire, B97 5TD Tel: (01527) 550080 Fax: (01527) 550080
James Purdey & Sons Ltd, 57 South Audley Street, London, W1K 2ED Tel: (020) 7499 1801 Fax: (020) 7355 3297 E-mail: sales@james-purdey.co.uk

SHOULDER PADS

Ashcott Equestuirn Ltd, Reme Drive, Heath Park Industrial Estate, Honiton, Devon, EX14 1SE Tel: (01404) 44680 Fax: (01404) 46688
D P M (Padding) Ltd, Glover Centre, Egmont Street, Mossley, Ashton-under-Lyne, Lancashire, OL5 9PY Tel: (01457) 833899 Fax: (01457) 837931
Profit Manufacturing Ltd, Unit 36 Albion Mills, Albion Road, Bradford, West Yorkshire, BD10 9TF Tel: (01274) 610590 Fax: (01274) 610541 E-mail: sales@pro-fit-int.com
Rayflex Ltd, Unit 6-9, 35 River Road, Barking, Essex, IG11 0DA Tel: (020) 8591 9418 Fax: (020) 8591 9419 E-mail: info@rayflexltd.co.uk

SHOWCARD DESIGNERS/ FINISHERS/PRODUCERS/ WRITERS

C O S Print, Blakehill Works, Bradford Road, Idle, Bradford, West Yorkshire, BD10 8SQ Tel: (01274) 615142 Fax: (01274) 615129 E-mail: cospresentation@ndirect.co.uk

SHOWCASES

Astabridge Ltd, Earlstrees Road, Earlstrees Industrial Estate, Corby, Northamptonshire, NN17 4AZ Tel: (01536) 267796 Fax: (01536) 402079 E-mail: info@astabmnge.co.uk
Technacryl Ltd, Shakenhurst, Cleobury Mortimer, Kidderminster, Worcestershire, DY14 9AR Tel: (01299) 832406 Fax: (01299) 832676
Woodstyle, Swinnow View, Leeds, LS13 4TZ Tel: 0113-255 9098 Fax: 0113-220 9727

SHOWER BATHS

▶ Richmonds Bathrooms, 21 Berridale Avenue, Cathcart, Glasgow, G44 3AF Tel: 0141 571 7261 E-mail: steve@richmondsbathrooms.co.uk

SHOWER CABINET OR CUBICLE OR ENCLOSURE

Cit Realisations Ltd, 6 Wedgwood Road, Bicester, Oxfordshire, OX26 4UL Tel: (01869) 327173 Fax: (01869) 247214 E-mail: sales@chilterninvadex.co.uk
Contour Showers Ltd, Siddorn Street, Winsford, Cheshire, CW7 2BA Tel: (01606) 592586 Fax: (01606) 861260 E-mail: sales@contour-showers.co.uk
Coram Showers Ltd, Stanmore Industrial Estate, Bridgnorth, Shropshire, WV15 5HP Tel: (01746) 766466 Fax: (01746) 764140 E-mail: sales@coram.co.uk
Esl Healthcare Ltd, 9 Eastbourne Road, Westham, Pevensey, East Sussex, BN24 6EP Tel: (01323) 465800 Fax: (01323) 460248 E-mail: sales@eslindustries.co.uk
Kohler Daryl Ltd, Alfred Road, Wallasey, Merseyside, CH44 7HY Tel: 0151-606 5000 Fax: 0151-638 0303 E-mail: daryl@daryl-showers.co.uk
Majestic Shower Co. Ltd, 1 North Place, Edinburgh Way, Harlow, Essex, CM20 2SL Tel: (01279) 443644 Fax: (01279) 635074 E-mail: info@majesticshowers.com
Matki Public Ltd Company, Churchward Road, Yate, Bristol, BS37 5PL Tel: (01454) 322888 Fax: (01454) 315284 E-mail: sales@matki.co.uk
Nordic Saunas Ltd, Unit 5, Fairview Industrial Estate, Holland Road, Oxted, Surrey, RH8 9BD Tel: (01883) 732400 Fax: (01883) 716970 E-mail: info@nordic.co.uk
Selecta International, Dodgson Street, Rochdale, Lancashire, OL16 5SJ Tel: (01706) 350191 Fax: (01706) 525129
Showerlux UK Ltd, Stonebridge Trading Estate, Sibree Road, Coventry, CV3 4FD Tel: (024) 7663 9400 Fax: (024) 7630 5457 E-mail: sales@showerlux.co.uk
Sovereign Excel Ltd, Globe Lane, Dukinfield, Cheshire, SK16 4RQ Tel: 0161-330 3091 Fax: 0161-343 1610 E-mail: info@sovereignshowers.co.uk

SHOWER CABINET OR CUBICLE OR ENCLOSURE SEALS

Linear Ltd, Coatham Avenue, Aycliffe Industrial Park, Newton Aycliffe, County Durham, DL5 6DB Tel: (01325) 310151 Fax: (01325) 307200 E-mail: enquiries@linear-ltd.com

SHOWER CURTAINS, CUSTOM MADE

Aqualona Products, 50 Moxon Street, Barnet, Hertfordshire, EN5 5TS Tel: (020) 8449 7321 Fax: (020) 8449 7496 E-mail: sales@aqualona.com

SHOWER FITTINGS OR SPRAYS

A & J Gummers Ltd, Unit H Redfern Park Way, Birmingham, B11 2DN Tel: 0121-706 2241 Fax: 0121-706 2960 E-mail: sales@gummers.co.uk
Aqualisa Products Ltd, Westerham Trade Centre, The Flyers Way, Westerham, Kent, TN16 1DE Tel: (01959) 560000 Fax: (01959) 560030 E-mail: marketing@aqualisa.co.uk
Avilion, Gateway X111 Industrial Estate, Ferry Lane, Rainham, Essex, RM13 9YH Tel: (01708) 526361 Fax: (01708) 550220 E-mail: sales@avilion.co.uk
Chowart Ltd, 58 Heming Road, Redditch, Worcestershire, B98 0EA Tel: (01527) 501601 Fax: (01527) 510217 E-mail: admin@chowart.co.uk
Croydex Ltd, Central Way, Andover, Hampshire, SP10 5AW Tel: (01264) 365881 Fax: (01264) 356437 E-mail: admin@croydex.co.uk
Dolphin Bathrooms, Dolphin House, Springvale Industrial Park, Bilston, West Midlands, WV14 0QL Tel: (01902) 407000 E-mail: dolphin_reception@dolphin-mail.co.uk
Marleton Cross Ltd, Alpha Close, Tewkesbury, Gloucestershire, GL20 8JF Tel: (01684) 293311 Fax: (01684) 293900 E-mail: rhj@mxgroup.demon.co.uk

Opella Ltd, Twyford Road, Rotherwas Industrial Estate, Hereford, HR2 6JR Tel: (01432) 357331 Fax: (01432) 264014 E-mail: sales@opella.co.uk
Peglar, Belmont Works, St. Catherines Avenue, Doncaster, South Yorkshire, DN4 8DF Tel: (0870) 1200285 Fax: (01302) 367661 E-mail: export@pegler.com
Showerdrape STD Ltd, Rammon House, 3 Longacre Street, Manchester, M1 2WN Tel: 0161-272 8700 Fax: 0161-272 8840 E-mail: info@showerdrape.co.uk
Spiral Hardware Ltd, Unit 36, Wimbledon Avenue, Brandon, Suffolk, IP27 0NZ Tel: (01842) 816086 Fax: (01842) 813867 E-mail: info@spiralhardware.co.uk

SHOWER PUMPS

Damixa Ltd, Edison Courtyard, Brunel Road, Earlstrees Industrial Estate, Corby, Northamptonshire, NN17 4LS Tel: (01536) 409222 Fax: (01536) 400144 E-mail: uksales@damixa.com

SHOWER UNITS, INDUSTRIAL/ SAFETY

Casargon Ltd, Genei House, Bentinck Street, Bolton, BL1 4QG Tel: (01204) 840500 Fax: (01204) 840600 E-mail: sales@casargon.sagenet.co.uk
Davroc Ltd, Ibroc House, Essex Road, Hoddesdon, Hertfordshire, EN11 0QS Tel: (01992) 441672 Fax: (01992) 708308 E-mail: info@davroc.co.uk
Hughes Safety Showers Ltd, Whitefield Road, Bredbury, Stockport, Cheshire, SK6 2SS Tel: 0161-430 6618 Fax: 0161-430 7928 E-mail: sales@hughes-safety-showers.co.uk
Kays Medical, 3-7 Shaw Street, Liverpool, L6 1HH Tel: 0151-482 2830 Fax: 0151-207 3384 E-mail: kays@kaysmedical.com
Maestro International Ltd, 11-17 Powerscroft Road, Sidcup, Kent, DA14 5NH Tel: (020) 8302 4035 Fax: (020) 8302 8933 E-mail: info@maestrointl.co.uk

SHOWER VACUUM FORMED PLASTIC TRAYS

Contour Showers Ltd, Siddorn Street, Winsford, Cheshire, CW7 2BA Tel: (01606) 592586 Fax: (01606) 861260 E-mail: sales@contour-showers.co.uk
E S P Plastics Ltd, Prospect Road, Crook, County Durham, DL15 8JL Tel: (01388) 765400 Fax: (01388) 765300 E-mail: sales@esp-plastics.co.uk

SHREDDED PAPER PACKAGING

Corpak Film Converters, Unit 19 Dinting Lane Industrial Estate, Glossop, Derbyshire, SK13 7NU Tel: (01457) 860758 Fax: (01457) 856008
Shredhouse Gift Packaging, Salisbury Road Business Park, Salisbury Road, Pewsey, Wiltshire, SN9 5PZ Tel: (01672) 564333 Fax: (01672) 564301

SHREDDER BLADES

Edge Tool Co. Ltd, Unit 2a Dronfield, Callywhite Lane, Dronfield, Derbyshire, S18 2XR Tel: (01246) 415111 Fax: (01246) 415222 E-mail: sales@etmblades.co.uk

SHREDDING MACHINE HIRE

M A C Tool Hire, 25 Park Street, Congleton, Cheshire, CW12 1EG Tel: (01260) 299751 Fax: (01260) 299698

SHREDDING MACHINES

▶ Datashred, Units 1-2, Rennys Lane Industrial Estate, Gilesgate, Durham, DH1 2RW Tel: 0191-386 4966 Fax: 0191-370 9850 E-mail: sales@securishred.com
▶ Trim A Tree, Wharley Farm, College Road, Cranfield, Bedford, MK43 0AH Tel: (0800) 7831665 Fax: (0800) 7831665 E-mail: info@trimatree.co.uk

SHRINK FILM/WRAPPING MATERIALS

Galley-Pak, Galley-Pak House, 38 Greenfields, Shillington, Hitchin, Hertfordshire, SG5 3NX Tel: (01462) 711545 Fax: (01462) 712970 E-mail: john@galley-pak.com
J R S Packaging Ltd, Unit 6, The Vineyards Industrial Estate, Gloucester Road, Cheltenham, Gloucestershire, GL51 8NJ Tel: (01242) 226269 Fax: (01242) 261954 E-mail: jrspackaging@lineone.net

Normec, PO Box 116, Leeds, LS13 9AP Tel: (0870) 7570078 Fax: (0870) 7570079 E-mail: normecleeds@aol.com
Sanders Polyfilms Ltd, Westfields Trading Estate, Hereford, HR4 9NS Tel: (01432) 277558 Fax: (01432) 357409 E-mail: sales@polyfilms.co.uk
Shrinkfast Ltd, Bridgewater Close, Hawkesworth TRDG Estate, Hawkesworth Trading Estate, Swindon, SN2 1ED Tel: (01793) 612072 Fax: (01793) 534649 E-mail: sales@shrinkfast.co.uk
Wrapid Holdings Ltd, 250 Thornton Road, Bradford, West Yorkshire, BD1 2LB Tel: (01274) 220220 Fax: (01274) 736195 E-mail: mail@wrapid.co.uk

SHRINK SLEEVING AND BANDING MACHINES

Turpins Packaging Systems Ltd, Kennedy Way, Clacton-on-Sea, Essex, CO15 4AB Tel: (01255) 423402 Fax: (01255) 473312 E-mail: sales@sleevit.com

SHRINK SLEEVING PACKING SERVICES

Allgo Ltd, Unit 9c Bank Hall Park, Wharf Street, Warrington, WA1 2DG Tel: (01925) 570150 Fax: (01925) 570155 E-mail: david.snitch@allgo.biz
R.C. Warren Packers Ltd, Unit C Valley Park, Tolpits Lane, Watford, WD18 9LT Tel: (01923) 770747 Fax: (01923) 770731 E-mail: twarren@warrenpackers.co.uk

SHRINK SLEEVING, PACKING

Decorative Sleeves, Unit 6 Pioneer Way, Castleford, West Yorkshire, WF10 5QU Tel: (01977) 510030 Fax: (01977) 521240
Decorative Sleeves Holdings, Rollesby Road, Hardwick Industrial Estate, King's Lynn, Norfolk, PE30 4LS Tel: (01553) 769319 Fax: (01553) 767097 E-mail: mktg@decorativesleeves.co.uk
Fuji Seal Europe Ltd, Scimitar Close, Gillingham Business Park, Gillingham, Kent, ME8 0RJ Tel: (01634) 378656 Fax: (01634) 379179 E-mail: sales@uk.fujiseal.com

SHRINK WRAP MACHINE MANUFRS

Aaron Packaging Machinery, Leeds 12 Business Park, Barras Garth Road, Leeds, LS12 4JY Tel: (07802) 886250 E-mail: sales@aaron-pack-mart.co.uk
Advanced Dynamics Ltd, 250 Thornton Road, Bradford, West Yorkshire, BD1 2LB Tel: (01274) 220300 Fax: (01274) 308953 E-mail: info@advanceddynamics.co.uk
Bluebird Packaging Machines Ltd, 43 Boulton Road, Reading, RG2 0NU Tel: 0118-987 4611 Fax: 0118-987 4575 E-mail: sales@bluebird-machines.co.uk
Ceco Packaging Services, The Forge, Kirk Eaton, Huddersfield, HD5 0JS Tel: (01484) 424673 Fax: (01484) 519727 E-mail: james@kirkeng.co.uk
E D L Packaging, Oswald Street, Burnley, Lancashire, BB12 0BY Tel: (01282) 429305 Fax: (01282) 429350 E-mail: sales@johnquinn.co.uk
Lachenmeier (UK) Ltd, Wilsons Park, Monsall Road, Newton Heath, Manchester, M40 8PA Tel: 0161-205 3666 Fax: 0161-205 3777 E-mail: kl@lachenmeier.com
Meco Pak (UK) Ltd, Greenway House, Sugarswell Business Park, Shenington, Banbury, Oxfordshire, OX15 6HW Tel: (01295) 688910 Fax: (01295) 688911 E-mail: info@mecopak.co.uk
Novopac (UK) Ltd, Fieldhead Broomers Corner, Shipley, Horsham, West Sussex, RH13 8PR Tel: (01403) 740003 Fax: (01403) 740071 E-mail: richard@novopac.co.uk
Samarose Engineering Services Ltd, Unit 3 West Side, Ash Industrial Estate, Flex Meadow, Harlow, Essex, CM19 5TJ Tel: (01279) 421395 Fax: (01279) 421612 E-mail: ses@samarose.co.uk
Wrapid Holdings Ltd, 250 Thornton Road, Bradford, West Yorkshire, BD1 2LB Tel: (01274) 220220 Fax: (01274) 736195 E-mail: mail@wrapid.co.uk
Wraps UK, 2 Nimrod Way, East Dorset Trade Park, Wimborne, Dorset, BH21 7SH Tel: (01202) 880204 Fax: (01202) 842632 E-mail: sales@wrapsuk.com

SHRINKWRAP FILM, POLYOLEFIN

▶ CeeT UK, 20 Lewis Street, Eccles, Manchester, M30 0PX Tel: (07793) 537512 Fax: 0161-707 9145 E-mail: sales@ceetuk.co.uk

SHRINKWRAP FILM, PVC

Boyce & Co., Exeter Airport Industrial Estate, Exeter Airport, Clyst Honiton, Exeter, EX5 2LJ Tel: (01392) 368891 Fax: (01392) 365598
Makkipak Ltd, Mallard Close, Earls Barton, Northampton, NN6 0JF Tel: (01604) 812755 Fax: (01604) 812413 E-mail: sales@makkipak.com

SHUTTER DOORS

Lifestyle Shutters, Unit 8 The Enterprise Centre, Bell Lane Industrial Estate, Uckfield, East Sussex, TN22 1QL Tel: (01825) 760722 Fax: (01825) 769305 E-mail: info@lifestyleshutters.co.uk

SHUTTLE TRANSIT SYSTEMS, *See Rapid Transit Systems, Passenger Carrying etc*

SIDE CHANNEL BLOWERS

Northey Technologies Ltd, Nortech House, Allens Lane, Poole, Dorset, BH16 5DG Tel: (01202) 668600 Fax: (01202) 668500 E-mail: info@northey.net

SIEVING EQUIPMENT/SYSTEMS/UNITS

Combine Fabrications Ltd, Fen Lane, Long Bennington, Newark, Nottinghamshire, NG23 5ED Tel: (01400) 281506 Fax: (01400) 282100 E-mail: enquiries@combinefabs.co.uk
Endecotts Ltd, 9 Lombard Road, London, SW19 3UP Tel: (020) 8542 8121 Fax: (020) 8543 6629 E-mail: sales@endecotts.com
Filter Screen Supply Ltd, 2 Paynes Place Farm, Cuckfield Road, Burgess Hill, West Sussex, RH15 8RG Tel: (01444) 244406 Fax: (01444) 230303E-mail: sales@filterscreensupply.co.uk
Gericke Ltd, Victoria House, Cavendish Street, Ashton-under-Lyne, Lancashire, OL6 7DJ Tel: 0161-344 1140 Fax: 0161-308 3403 E-mail: sales@gericke.co.uk

SIFTING PLANT, POWDER/CHEMICAL

Filter Screen Supply Ltd, 2 Paynes Place Farm, Cuckfield Road, Burgess Hill, West Sussex, RH15 8RG Tel: (01444) 244406 Fax: (01444) 230303E-mail: sales@filterscreensupply.co.uk

SIGHT FLOW INDICATORS

Visilume Ltd, Unit 30 Moor Park Industrial Estate, Tolpits Lane, Watford, WD18 9SP Tel: (01923) 211131 Fax: (01923) 211432 E-mail: sales@visilume.co.uk

SIGHT GLASSES

Delta Fluid Products Ltd, Delta Road, St. Helens, Merseyside, WA9 2ED Tel: (01744) 611811 Fax: (01744) 611818 E-mail: enquiries@deltafluidproducts.com
GlasTechnik, Sagana Lodge, Scotton Rd, Scotter, Gainsborough, Lincs, DN21 3SB Tel: (01724) 761172 Fax: (01724) 764352 E-mail: sightglasses@aol.com
▶ Harrier Fluid Power Ltd, Parys Road, Ludlow Business Park, Ludlow, Shropshire, SY8 1XY Tel: (01584) 876033 Fax: (01584) 876044 E-mail: sales@harrieronline.co.uk
Monax Glass Ltd, 22 Charles Jarvis Court, Cupar, Fife, KY15 5EJ Tel: (01334) 657800 Fax: (01334) 657857 E-mail: monax@sol.co.uk
John Moncrieff Ltd, The Glassworks, Scotlandwell Farmhouse, Main Street, Scotlandwell, Kinross, KY13 9JA Tel: (01592) 840064 Fax: (01592) 840065 E-mail: enquiries@jmoncrieff.co.uk
Rhodes, Delta Road, Parr, St. Helens, Merseyside, WA9 2ED Tel: (01744) 451616 Fax: (01744) 26791 E-mail: enquiries@deltafluidproducts.com
Visilume Ltd, Unit 30 Moor Park Industrial Estate, Tolpits Lane, Watford, WD18 9SP Tel: (01923) 211131 Fax: (01923) 211432 E-mail: sales@visilume.co.uk

SIGN ADHESIVES

Robert Tate Signs Ltd, 15 East Campbell Street, Glasgow, G1 5DT Tel: 0141-552 7610 Fax: 0141-553 1725

SIGN CONSULTANTS OR DESIGNERS

Ace Signs Group, 1 Bentalls, Basildon, Essex, SS14 3BS Tel: (01268) 706800 Fax: (01702) 294325 E-mail: enquiries@asg.co.uk
Ace Signs Group, Oak Tree Road, Binley, Coventry, CV3 2RR Tel: (024) 7660 8200 Fax: (024) 7660 8201 E-mail: info@asg.co.uk
Arthur Diamond, Atkinson House, 43 Duke Street, Liverpool, L1 5AP Tel: 0151-706 0336 Fax: 0151-706 0336
Assign Technology, Unit 1 Wadsworth Business Centre, 21 Wadsworth Road, Greenford, Middlesex, UB6 7LQ Tel: (020) 8998 0806 Fax: (020) 8998 1272 E-mail: info@assigntechnology.com
Aztec Group, Unit 18 Chiltern Business Village, Arundel Road, Uxbridge, Middlesex, UB8 2SN Tel: (01895) 520600 Fax: (01895) 520650 E-mail: sales@aztecgroup.net
Bill Dawson Sign Consultants, Nailford House, Brewery Lane, Bridge, Canterbury, Kent, CT4 5LF Tel: (01227) 831044 Fax: (01227) 831044
Brook Signs, 6 Cedar House, Caen Street, Braunton, Devon, EX33 1AH Tel: (01271) 812300
Coursamis Ltd, Unit 3 11 Tait Road, Croydon, CR0 2DP Tel: (020) 8684 7973 Fax: (020) 8684 6532 E-mail: sgv@csgroup.fsnet.co.uk
Dan Display & Imaging Ltd, Harlequin House, Coedcad Lane, Pontyclun, Mid Glamorgan, CF72 9EW Tel: (01443) 225656 Fax: (01443) 226544 E-mail: info@dandisplay.co.uk
Design Systems, The Old School, Exton St, London, SE1 8UE Tel: 020 79289275
Esprit Communications, Supreme House, 300 Regents Park Road, London, N3 2JX Tel: (020) 8346 4499 Fax: (020) 8346 6969 E-mail: beter@espritcommunications.com
Falcon Signs Ltd, 109 Grove Technology Park, Wantage, Oxfordshire, OX12 9FA Tel: (01235) 768872 Fax: (01235) 768822 E-mail: sales@falconsigns.co.uk
Frodsham Sign & Display Ltd, 1 Millfield Lane, Haydock, St. Helens, Merseyside, WA11 9TW Tel: (01942) 272330 Fax: (01942) 272331 E-mail: sales@frodshamsigns.co.uk
G R S Sign Co. Ltd, Tateshall Way, Fairfield Industrial Estate, Louth, Lincolnshire, LN11 0YZ Tel: (01507) 609485 Fax: (01507) 609489 E-mail: sales@grssigns.co.uk
Graphical Impact, 61 Hoe Street, London, E17 4SA Tel: (020) 8925 2333 Fax: (020) 8925 2332 E-mail: info@graphicalimpact.com
Graphics By Jeff & Chris, 85 Market Street, Hollingworth, Hyde, Cheshire, SK14 8JA Tel: (01457) 765995 Fax: (01457) 765995 E-mail: grafixgrafix@aol.com
The Harris Sign Group Ltd, Springfield Road, Coventry, CV1 4GN Tel: (024) 7622 9950 Fax: (024) 7638 1320
M L Signs, 3a Bessemer Road, Cardiff, CF11 8BA Tel: (029) 2022 7694 Fax: (029) 2038 8148
McKay Signs & Graphics, Unit 7 Chipping Edge Estate, Hatters Lane, Chipping Sodbury, Bristol, BS37 6AA Tel: (01454) 319483 Fax: (01454) 312912
Mercury & Phillips, 51-59 Waterworks Road, Norwich, NR2 4DA Tel: (01603) 666699 Fax: (01603) 616781 E-mail: sales@mercuryphillipssigns.co.uk
Midland Graphics Sign Depot, 14 Victoria Terrace, Leamington Spa, Warwickshire, CV31 3AB Tel: (01926) 452009 Fax: (01926) 470767
R G Services, PO Box 1864, Radstock, BA3 3ZA Tel: (01761) 435858 Fax: (01761) 435858 E-mail: sales@rgservices.co.uk
Rac Signs, Rac Ho, 1 Forest Rd, Feltham, Middx, TW13 7RR Tel: (0845) 6010000 Fax: (0845) 2082502
Reflex Design, 10 Pelham Street, Oadby, Leicester, LE2 4DJ Tel: 0116-272 1239 Fax: (0870) 0111611 E-mail: sales@reflexdesign.uk.com
Re-Graphics, Unit 10 Freshways House, 16 Eastman Road, London, W3 7YG Tel: (020) 8743 3529 Fax: (020) 8743 3629
Royal Signs, 167 Culford Road, London, N1 4DT Tel: (020) 7254 6969 Fax: (020) 7249 0880
▶ Scorpio Signs (Design & Display) Ltd, Hartford House Yard, School Lane, Hartford, Northwich, Cheshire, CW8 1NP Tel: (01606) 74912 Fax: (01606) 76036 E-mail: mail@scorpiosigns.co.uk
Sign & Design, 31 Hospital Lane, Blaby, Leicester, LE8 4FE Tel: 0116-277 1957 Fax: 0116-277 5755 E-mail: signs@freenet.co.uk
▶ Sign Express Northampton, Collingwood Business Centre, Lower Harding Street, Northampton, NN1 2JL Tel: (01604) 472972 Fax: (01604) 472373 E-mail: northampton@signsexpress.co.uk
Sign It, Beehive Works, Beehive Lane, Chelmsford, CM2 9JY Tel: (01245) 492294 Fax: (01245) 262147 E-mail: sales@sign-it.co.uk
Sign Logic, Gatehead Business Park, Delph New Road, Delph, Oldham, OL3 5DE Tel: (01457) 878806 Fax: (01457) 820592 E-mail: sales@signlogic.co.uk
Sign Studio, 5 Croft Street, Cheltenham, Gloucestershire, GL53 0EE Tel: (01242) 228866 Fax: (01242) 228777 E-mail: sales@chelt-signstudio.co.uk
Sign Studio, 158 Cromwell Road, Salford, M6 6DE Tel: 0161-792 7254 Fax: 0161-792 1873
▶ Signs Express Ltd, 140 Appin Road, Birkenhead, Merseyside, CH41 9HJ Tel: 0151-650 2344 Fax: 0151-650 2355 E-mail: liverpool@signsexpress.co.uk
▶ Signs Express Ltd, Unit 17 Avonbank Industrial Centre, West Town Road, Bristol, BS11 9DE Tel: 0117-982 4004 Fax: 0117-982 5005 E-mail: bristol.north@signsexpress.co.uk
▶ Signs Express Ltd, Barnwell Drbarnwell Business Park, Cambridge, CB5 8UZ Tel: (01223) 414005 Fax: (01223) 413801 E-mail: cambridge@signsexpress.co.uk
▶ Signs Express Ltd, 2 Ketlan Court, River Lane, Saltney, Chester, CH4 8SB Tel: (01244) 681682 Fax: (01244) 681600 E-mail: chester@signsexpress.co.uk
Signs Express Ltd, 19a Westside Centre, London Road, Stanway, Colchester, CO3 8PH Tel: (01206) 213111 Fax: (01206) 212110 E-mail: colchester@signsexpress.co.uk
▶ Signs Express Ltd, 1 Henson Road, Darlington, County Durham, DL1 4QD Tel: (01325) 382444 Fax: (01325) 382777 E-mail: southdurham@signsexpress.co.uk
▶ Signs Express Ltd, 3 Parker Industrial Centre, 275-289 Watling Street, Dartford, DA2 6EP Tel: (01322) 221771 Fax: (01322) 221597 E-mail: dartford@signsexpress.co.uk
Signs Express Ltd, Unit S2 & S4 Didcot Enterprise Centre, Hawksworth, Didcot, Oxfordshire, OX11 7PH Tel: (01235) 811177 Fax: (01235) 818805 E-mail: oxford@signsexpress.co.uk
Signs Express Ltd, 3 Guildhall Industrial Estate, Sandall Stones Road, Kirk Sandall Industrial Estate, Doncaster, South Yorkshire, DN3 1QR Tel: (01302) 888173 Fax: (01302) 888234 E-mail: doncaster@signsexpress.co.uk
▶ Signs Express Ltd, Unit G2 Marabout Industrial Estate, Dorchester, Dorset, DT1 1YA Tel: (01305) 260042 Fax: (01305) 260052 E-mail: w.dorset@signsexpress.co.uk
▶ Signs Express Ltd, 25 Dumbryden Road, Edinburgh, EH14 2AB Tel: 0131-453 1232 Fax: 0131-453 1238 E-mail: edinburgh.w@signsexpress.co.uk
▶ Signs Express Ltd, 19 Eastville Close, Eastern Avenue, Gloucester, GL4 3SJ Tel: (01452) 309390 Fax: (01452) 309396 E-mail: gloucester@signsexpress.co.uk
▶ Signs Express Ltd, Unit 2e Westmains Industrial Estate, Grangemouth, Stirlingshire, FK3 8YE Tel: (01324) 666966 Fax: (01324) 666969 E-mail: falkirk@signsexpress.co.uk
▶ Signs Express Ltd, 1 Maple River Industrial Estate, River Way, Harlow, Essex, CM20 2DP Tel: (01279) 641300 Fax: (01279) 641400 E-mail: info@signsexpress.co.uk
▶ Signs Express Ltd, 4 Hookstone Centre, Hookstone Chase, Harrogate, North Yorkshire, HG2 7HW Tel: (01423) 885111 Fax: (01423) 885222E-mail: harrogate@signsexpress.co.uk
▶ Signs Express Ltd, Unit 20 The Hawthorn Centre, Elmgrove Road, Harrow, Middlesex, HA1 2RF Tel: (020) 8424 9920 Fax: (020) 8424 9940 E-mail: wembley@signsexpress.co.uk
▶ Signs Express Ltd, Unit 16 Priory Tec Park Saxon Way, Priory Park, Hessle, North Humberside, HU13 9PB Tel: (01482) 629966 Fax: (01482) 629967 E-mail: sales@signsexpress.co.uk
▶ Signs Express Ltd, 6 Greenwich Close, Ipswich, IP3 0DD Tel: (01473) 281414 Fax: (01473) 281456 E-mail: ipswich@signsexpress.co.uk
▶ Signs Express Ltd, Unit 30 Lake Enterprise Park, Ladies Walk, Lancaster, LA1 3NX Tel: (01524) 389966 Fax: (01524) 389977 E-mail: lancaster@signsexpress.co.uk
▶ Signs Express Ltd, 2 Leodis Court, Leeds, LS11 5JJ Tel: 0113-243 6711 Fax: 0113-243 6744 E-mail: leeds.east@signsexpress.co.uk
▶ Signs Express Ltd, 3 Cardinal Close, Lincoln, LN2 4SY Tel: (01522) 530202 Fax: (01522) 539007 E-mail: lincoln@signsexpress.co.uk
▶ Signs Express Ltd, Unit 5 Simcox Court, Riverside Park Industrial Estate, Middlesbrough, Cleveland, TS2 1UX Tel: (01642) 249999 Fax: (01642) 240444 E-mail: teesside@signsexpress.co.uk
▶ Signs Express Ltd, 99 Alston Drive, Bradwell Abbey, Milton Keynes, MK13 9HF Tel: (01908) 221330 Fax: (01908) 221227 E-mail: miltonkeynes@signsexpress.co.uk
Signs Express Ltd, 25 Kingsway, Norwich, NR2 4UE Tel: (01603) 762680 Fax: (01603) 762681 E-mail: norwich@signsexpress.co.uk
▶ Signs Express Ltd, 9 Greenhill Road, Paisley, Renfrewshire, PA3 1RJ Tel: 0141-883 0304 Fax: 0141-840 1955 E-mail: info@signexpress.co.uk
▶ Signs Express Ltd, Unit 14 Wolseley Business Park, Wolseley Close, Plymouth, PL2 3BY Tel: (01752) 563336 Fax: (01752) 500120 E-mail: plymouth@signsexpress.co.uk
▶ Signs Express Ltd, Unit G3 Railway Triangle, Walton Road, Portsmouth, PO6 1TQ Tel: (023) 9238 3821 Fax: (023) 9238 3822 E-mail: portsmouth@signsexpress.co.uk
▶ Signs Express Ltd, 14 Long Barn Lane, Reading, RG2 7SZ Tel: 0118-975 1155 Fax: 0118-975 1133 E-mail: reading@signsexpress.co.uk
▶ Signs Express Ltd, Unit 38 City Industrial Park, Southern Road, Southampton, SO15 1HA Tel: (023) 8022 7676 Fax: (023) 8022 7678 E-mail: southampton@signsexpress.co.uk
▶ Signs Express Ltd, Unit 3 Crabtree Close, Fenton Industrial Estate, Stoke-on-Trent, ST4 2SW Tel: (01782) 416930 Fax: (01782) 416931 E-mail: stokeontrent@signsexpress.co.uk
▶ Signs Express Ltd, 9-23 Third Cross Road, Twickenham, TW2 5DY Tel: (020) 8893 3221 Fax: (020) 8893 3233 E-mail: twickenham@signsexpress.co.uk
▶ Signs Express Ltd, Unit 4b Glover Industrial Estate, Spire Road, Washington, Tyne & Wear, NE37 3ES Tel: 0191-415 1234 Fax: 0191-415 3222 E-mail: wearside@signsexpress.co.uk
▶ Signs Express Ltd, 2 Osbaldwick Industrial Estate, Outgang Lane, Osbaldwick, York, YO19 5UX Tel: (01904) 431343 Fax: (01904) 431344 E-mail: york@signsexpress.co.uk
▶ Signs Express Taunton, 13a-13b Unit, Cornishway South, Galmington Trading Estate, Taunton, Somerset, TA1 5NQ Tel: (01823) 289366 Fax: (01823) 289377 E-mail: taunton@signsexpress.co.uk
Smithbrewer Ltd, Sunnyside Road North, Weston-super-Mare, Avon, BS23 3PZ Tel: (01934) 642642 Fax: (01934) 642646 E-mail: sales@smithbrewer.co.uk
Solar Graphics, 8 Finch Drive, Braintree, Essex, CM7 2SF Tel: (01376) 552209 Fax: (01376) 320077 E-mail: sales@solargraphics.net
Star Signs, Pioneer Business Park, Princes Road, Ramsgate, Kent, CT11 7RX Tel: (01843) 579003 Fax: (01843) 583002
Swift Signs & Shirts, Tutin Road, Leeming Bar Industrial Estate, Northallerton, North Yorkshire, DL7 9UJ Tel: (01677) 424175 Fax: (01677) 426550 E-mail: swiftsigns@tiscali.co.uk
Tatlow Signs Ltd, Unit 1 2 Gate Street, Blackburn, BB1 3AQ Tel: (01254) 667666 Fax: (01254) 503101 E-mail: sales@tatlowsigns.co.uk
Tribune Graphics Ltd, Unit 11 New Road Industrial Estate, Grace Road, Sheerness, Kent, ME12 1DB Tel: (01795) 580261 Fax: (01795) 663318 E-mail: mail@tribunegraphics.co.uk
V G Signs, 46 Seaforth Road, Leeds, LS9 6AJ Tel: 0113-248 8737 Fax: 0113-248 8737
Viz Biz Design, 4 24 Ings Road, Wakefield, West Yorkshire, WF1 1DZ Tel: (01924) 377888 Fax: (01924) 385573 E-mail: vizbiz@btconnect.com

SIGN CONTRACTORS OR SIGN MAKERS OR SUPPLIERS OR INSTALLERS, *See also headings under Signs*

1st Call Mercury Signs, Highfield View, Park Lane, Stokenchurch, Buckinghamshire, HP14 3TQ Tel: (01494) 482288 Fax: (01494) 483152 E-mail: mcgillsign@aol.com
1st Call Rotosign Ltd, Pressmetal House, St Augustines Business Park, Whitstable, Kent, CT5 2QJ Tel: (01227) 794490 Fax: (01227) 794488 E-mail: sales@amp-uk.co.uk
4d Signs, The Old Dairy, Wonston, Hazelbury Bryan, Sturminster Newton, Dorset, DT10 2EE Tel: (01258) 817878 Fax: (01258) 817879 E-mail: info@4dsigns.co.uk
A D Signs & Engraving Ltd, Unit 3 Webner Industrial Estate, Alltingshaw Road, Wolverhampton, WV2 2LD Tel: (01902) 353535 Fax: (01902) 496775 E-mail: sales@ad-signs.co.uk
A P H Signs, 4 The Nurseries, Cymau, Wrexham, Clwyd, LL11 5LE Tel: (01978) 761487 Fax: (01978) 856568
A S A P Sign Services, 9 Bradley Road, Wrexham, Clwyd, LL13 7TG Tel: (01978) 353265 Fax: (01978) 354689 E-mail: asap.sign-services@dail.pipex.com
A Weston, 23 Marsh St South, Stoke-on-Trent, ST1 1JA Tel: (01782) 214580 Fax: (01782) 214581
A1 Supreme Sales Signs, 24 Nuneaton Way, Newcastle upon Tyne, NE5 1QN Tel: 0191-267 9333 Fax: 0191-229 0759
Abbott Signs, 29 Victoria Road, Northampton, NN1 5ED Tel: (01604) 636793 Fax: (01604) 632302 E-mail: info@abbottsigns.co.uk
Abbott Signs, Unit 12 Kendal Court, Hurricane Way, Wickford, Essex, SS11 8YB Tel: (01268) 572626 Fax: (01268) 574626 E-mail: abbotsignltd@btconnect.com
Aberdeen Sign & Engraving Co. Ltd, 93 Victoria Road, Aberdeen, AB11 9LU Tel: (01224) 898984 Fax: (01224) 898954 E-mail: sales@absign.co.uk
Abstract Signs & Graphics Ltd, Unit 4 High Hazels Court, Coombe Road, Nottingham, NG16 3SU Tel: (01773) 711611 Fax: 0115-963 3711 E-mail: info@abstractsigns.co.uk
Ace Marine, Bankside, Thorpe Lane, Trimley St. Martin, Felixstowe, Suffolk, IP11 0RY Tel: (01394) 277357 Fax: (01394) 276828
Ace Signs Group, 1 Bentalls, Basildon, Essex, SS14 3BS Tel: (01268) 706800 Fax: (01702) 294325 E-mail: enquiries@asg.co.uk
Acme Neon, Fitzroy Terrace, Grafton Street, Northampton, NN1 2NU Tel: (01604) 631068 Fax: (01604) 631068 E-mail: sales@acmeneon.co.uk
Acorn Signs, 16 Church Street, Hadfield, Glossop, Derbyshire, SK13 2AD Tel: (01457) 861211 E-mail: acorn@signs95.fsnet.co.uk
Acorn Signs, Oaktree Business Park, Oakwood Road, Mansfield, Nottinghamshire, NG18 3HQ Tel: (01623) 414004 Fax: (01623) 414005 E-mail: signsfromacorn@btconnect.com

SIGN CONTRACTORS OR SIGN MAKERS OR SUPPLIERS OR INSTALLERS – *continued*

Adco Signs, 15 Cleggs Buildings, Bolton, BL1 4AN Tel: (01204) 529167 Fax: (01204) 399214 E-mail: adcoinfo.signs@virgin.net

Addax Signs & Displays Ltd, 22 Eastmuir Street, Annick Industrial Estate, Glasgow, G32 0HS Tel: 0141-778 8881 Fax: 0141-778 5490

Addison Signs, Unit 16 Links Business Centre, Raynham Road, Bishop's Stortford, Hertfordshire, CM23 5NZ Tel: (01279) 507407 Fax: (01279) 507477 E-mail: enquiries@addisonsigns.co.uk

Admiral Signs Ltd, 121 Oak Street, Norwich, NR3 3BP Tel: (01603) 627573 Fax: (01603) 619954 E-mail: info@admiral-signs.co.uk

Advance Trade Signs, Unit 18, Moorside Maltings, Burton Row, Leeds, LS11 5NX Tel: 0113-276 5621 Fax: 0113-276 5621

Advasign, Gelli Industrial Estate, Gelli, Pentre, Mid Glamorgan, CF41 7UW Tel: (01443) 441112 E-mail: info@advasign.co.uk

Alchemy Lettering Co. Ltd, 11-15 Wade Street, Bristol, BS2 9DR Tel: 0117-941 1800 Fax: 0117-941 2800 E-mail: alchemyltd@btconnect.com

Aldermaston Signs, Unit 24 Youngs Industrial Estate, Paices Hill, Aldermaston, Reading, RG7 4PW Tel: 0118-981 1170 Fax: 0118-981 7690 E-mail: info@aldermastonsigns.co.uk

▶ All Signs & Design Ltd, Unit 24 Knightcott Industrial Estate, Banwell, Avon, BS29 6JN Tel: (01934) 822800 Fax: (01934) 822800

Alljay Plastics Sheet Sales, 321 Sutton Road, Southend-on-Sea, SS2 5PF Tel: (01702) 600320 Fax: (01702) 600325 E-mail: alljayplastics@aol.com

Alpha Sign Systems, Oakwood Bussiness Park, Oldmixon Crescent, Weston-Super-Mare, Avon, BS24 9AY Tel: (01934) 625444 Fax: (01934) 625358 E-mail: sales@alphasignsystems.com

Alpha Signs, Hamperden End, Debden Green, Saffron Walden, Essex, CB11 3NA Tel: (01279) 850555

Alpha Signs (Northampton) Ltd, Clarence Avenue, Northampton, NN2 6NY Tel: (01604) 712233 Fax: (01604) 717131

▶ Alphabet Signs (south west) Ltd, Mary Seacole Rd, The Millfields, Plymouth, PL1 3JY Tel: 08447 255456

▶ Andesign Sign Writers, F 11-13 Coleshill Road, Sutton Coldfield, West Midlands, B75 7AA Tel: 0121-354 2272 Fax: 0121-355 8883 E-mail: info@andesignuk.co.uk

A-Ok Signs Ltd, Units 21-23 Phoenix Court, Hawkins Road, Colchester, CO2 8JY Tel: (01206) 793683 Fax: (01206) 792895 E-mail: sales@aoksigns.com

Apex Signs, 2a West Telferton, Edinburgh, EH7 6UL Tel: 0131-657 3530 Fax: 0131-669 7305 E-mail: info@apex-signs.co.uk

Apollo Signs & Engraving, Wigwam Lane Unit E1, Imex Enterprise Park, Hucknall, Nottingham, NG15 7SZ Tel: 0115-963 1366 Fax: 0115-961 1355 E-mail: dexterapolo@aol.com

Applied Lettering, 2 Junction Road, Andover, Hampshire, SP10 3QT Tel: (01264) 357438 Fax: (01264) 357438

▶ Argoneon Ltd, Unit A6 Continental Approach, Westwood Industrial Estate, Margate, Kent, CT9 4JG Tel: (01843) 226420 Fax: 01843 226420 E-mail: michael@argoneon.co.uk

Aristocrat Signs, Unit 6 Mitchell Close, Fareham, Hampshire, PO15 5SE Tel: (01489) 589292 Fax: (01489) 584909 E-mail: aristocrat@zoom.co.uk

Art All, 34 Britannia Way, Britannia Enterprise Park, Lichfield, Staffordshire, WS14 9UY Tel: (01543) 258222 Fax: (01543) 258444 E-mail: signs@artall.co.uk

Ashford Signmakers Ltd, Unit 11q Godinton Way Industrial Estate, Godinton Way, Ashford, Kent, TN23 1JB Tel: (01233) 621447 Fax: (01233) 624327 E-mail: coneysigns@aol.com

Ashford Signs, 7 Roberts Close, Hempnall, Norwich, NR15 2ND Tel: (01508) 498242 Fax: (01508) 498242

Assign Technology, Unit 1 Wadsworth Business Centre, 21 Wadsworth Road, Greenford, Middlesex, UB6 7LQ Tel: (020) 8998 0806 Fax: (020) 8998 1272 E-mail: info@assigntechnology.com

Assignment Signs & Nameplates, 26 Brindley Road, Dodwells Bridge Industrial Estate, Hinckley, Leicestershire, LE10 3BY Tel: (01455) 891200 Fax: (01455) 619426

AST Signs, Unit 2, Gilwilly Road, East Lakes Business Park, Penrith, Cumbria, CA11 9BF Tel: (01768) 892292 Fax: (01768) 892294 E-mail: mark@astsigns.com

Autograph, Block 2 Beechfield Road, Willowyard Industrial Estate, Beith, Ayrshire, KA15 1LN Tel: (01505) 506366 Fax: (01505) 506344

Autograph, The Malthouse, 139-141 Eastgate, Worksop, Nottinghamshire, S80 1QS Tel: (01909) 488500 Fax: (01909) 482687 E-mail: autographsigns.uk@btconnect.com

Autographic Sign Co., Offerton Lodge, Offerton, Sunderland, SR4 9JL Tel: 0191-534 6295 Fax: 0191-534 6157

Autotop Signs & Nameplates, Council Street West, Llandudno, Gwynedd, LL30 1ED Tel: (01492) 860667 Fax: (01492) 878050

Avia Signs & Labels, Shore Head, Stonehaven, Kincardineshire, AB39 2JY Tel: (01569) 767290 Fax: (01569) 767290 E-mail: david@aviasigns.freeserve.co.uk

Avonmouth Shipping & Salvage, Chittening Industrial Estate, Chittening, Bristol, BS11 0YB Tel: 0117-982 9608 Fax: 0117-982 9559 E-mail: avonmouthsigns@btconnect.com

B E P Signs Ltd, 8a South Street, Greenock, Renfrewshire, PA16 8TX Tel: (01475) 784423 Fax: (01475) 729213 E-mail: enquiries@bepsigns.co.uk

Baillie Sign Services, 184-186 Queensferry Road, Edinburgh, EH4 2BW Tel: 0131-315 2800 Fax: 0131-315 2797 E-mail: sales@bailliesigns.co.uk

Barrett Inter Signs Co Ltd, 18 Farlow Road, Northfield, Birmingham, B31 3AE Tel: 0121-477 7396 Fax: 0121-477 7414

Bastow & Ryder Ltd, 157 Sunbridge Road, Bradford, West Yorkshire, BD1 2NU Tel: (01274) 724358

BBS Graphix Group, Market St, Bingley, W. Yorkshire, BD16 2HP Tel: (01274) 510562 Fax: (01274) 510562 E-mail: info@bbsgraphixs.com

BCC, B Station Road, Newcastle Emlyn, Dyfed, SA38 9BY Tel: (01239) 710823 Fax: (01239) 711449 E-mail: sales@bccit.co.uk

Beach Signs Ltd, Leigh Street, Sheffield, S9 2PR Tel: 0114-243 7382 Fax: 0114-262 6550 E-mail: sales@beachsign.net

Benegraph & Academie Signs, 12 Market Place, Adlington, Chorley, Lancashire, PR7 4EZ Tel: (01257) 480366 Fax: (01257) 483499

Bernlite Ltd, 3 Brookside, Colne Way, Watford, WD24 7QJ Tel: (01923) 200160 Fax: (01923) 246057

Beta Signs, Unit 1 Block 6 Shenstone Trading Estate, Bromsgrove Road, Halesowen, West Midlands, B63 3XB Tel: 0121-501 3535 Fax: 0121-501 3545 E-mail: sales@betasigns.co.uk

Blizzard Signs, 13 Schoolhall Lane, Bury St. Edmunds, Suffolk, IP33 1HA Tel: (01284) 754651 Fax: (01284) 754651 E-mail: sales@blizzardsigns.com

Bodylines, Autograph House, Frank Street, Preston, PR1 1PB Tel: (01772) 561177 Fax: (01772) 556993

Booth Signs, 45 Stafford Road, Wallington, Surrey, SM6 9AP Tel: (020) 8669 1625 Fax: (020) 8773 3429 E-mail: boothsigns@lineone.net

Boston Signs & Displays, Unit 1, Spalding Road, Boston, Lincolnshire, PE21 8XL Tel: (01205) 363849 Fax: (01205) 367725 E-mail: boston_signs@yahoo.co.uk

Bowden & Dolphin Ltd, 16 Cherrywood Road, Birmingham, B9 4UD Tel: 0121-773 6000 Fax: 0121-773 4070 E-mail: info@bowdenanddolphinsigns.com

Bpe Signs, B135 Stourvale Road, Bournemouth, BH6 5HF Tel: (01202) 430066 Fax: (01202) 430066 E-mail: info@bpesigns.co.uk

Branch Signs, 7 Dalmeny Road, Worcester Park, Surrey, KT4 8UU Tel: (020) 3277 1060 Fax: (020) 8949 3690 E-mail: michaelbranch@freenet.co.uk

Brighton Sign Co., Foredown House, 2-4 Foredown Drive, Portslade, Brighton, BN41 2BB Tel: (01273) 424900 Fax: (01273) 412006 E-mail: sales@brightonsigns.co.uk

Brilliant Signs & Fabrications, Unit 2 Forty Green, Bledlow, Princes Risborough, Buckinghamshire, HP27 9PN Tel: (01844) 273602 Fax: (0871) 4330112 E-mail: peter.snellgrove@brilliant-signs.com

Brinsmoor Solutions, Unit 2 Aerial Way, Hucknall, Nottingham, NG15 6DW Tel: 0115-964 0961 Fax: 0115-964 1819

▶ Britelite Signage, 1 Wallis Court, James Carter Road, Mildenhall, Bury St. Edmunds, Suffolk, IP28 7DD Tel: (01638) 583879 Fax: (01638) 515237

Broadway Signs, Unit 18 Elmbourne Industrial Estate, Crabtree Manorway, Belvedere, Kent, DA17 6AW Tel: (020) 8310 8100 Fax: (020) 8310 1950E-mail: curwood1954@hotmail.com

Brock Signs & Graphics Ltd, 32 Kansas Avenue, Salford, M50 2GL Tel: 0161-877 8484 Fax: 0161-877 8444 E-mail: sales@brocksigns.co.uk

Broome Signs, Old Bridge Way, Shefford, Bedfordshire, SG17 5HQ Tel: (01462) 851919 Fax: (01462) 851595 E-mail: sales@broomesigns.com

George Brown, 12 Crosby Street, Bangor, County Down, BT20 5EE Tel: (028) 9146 6136 Fax: (028) 9146 6136

M. & A. Brown (Engravers) Ltd, Stable Fold, Barton Road, Worsley, Manchester, M28 2PE Tel: 0161-794 2397 Fax: 0161-794 4982 E-mail: masigns@ukonline.co.uk

Brunel Signs, Unit 8b, St. Marks Road, St. James Industrial Estate, Corby, Northamptonshire, NN18 8AN Tel: (01536) 205335 Fax: (01536) 408509 E-mail: brunelsign@aol.com

Brushstrokes Signs, Station Road, Buckhaven, Leven, Fife, KY8 1JH Tel: (01592) 714804 Fax: (01592) 714103

Bull Signs, Bayhorne Lane, Horley, Surrey, RH6 9ES Tel: (01293) 821313 Fax: (01293) 821414 E-mail: sales@bullsigns.com

Butterfield Signs Ltd, 174 Sunbridge Road, Bradford, West Yorkshire, BD1 2RZ Tel: (01274) 722244 Fax: (01274) 848998 E-mail: general@butterfield-signs.co.uk

C Adams, Unit 18 Barton Hill Trading Estate, Maze Street, Bristol, BS5 9TE Tel: 0117-954 2331 Fax: 0117-954 2331

C H Reynolds & Sons Ltd, 1358 Stratford Road, Hall Green, Birmingham, B28 9EH Tel: 0121-777 3675 Fax: 0121-777 4883 E-mail: reysigns@aol.com

C Stanley Jones Paints, Plot 8a Plough Lane Industrial Estate, Hereford, HR4 0EH Tel: (01432) 278613 Fax: (01432) 341089 E-mail: signs.stan@ukonline.co.uk

Car & Business Cosmetics, 1 Maxwell Street, South Shields, Tyne & Wear, NE33 4PU Tel: 0191-456 3795 Fax: 0191-454 4078

Caractor Graphics, 330 Moorhey Road, Liverpool, L31 5LR Tel: 0151-520 0500 Fax: 0151-520 0900 E-mail: caractorgraphics@yahoo.co.uk

Care Signs, 1 Sutton Industrial Park, Sea Road, Winchelsea Beach, Winchelsea, East Sussex, TN36 4LZ Tel: (01797) 223999 Fax: (01797) 222264 E-mail: sales@caresigns.co.uk

▶ CB Neon Signmakers, Humberstone Lane, Leicester, LE4 9HA Tel: 0116-246 1838 Fax: 0116-246 1838 E-mail: justin@aol.com

Cee-Jay, 4-6 Beeching Close, Bexhill-on-Sea, East Sussex, TN39 3YF Tel: (01424) 734126 Fax: (01424) 734126

Celtic Displays, Unit 17 Newport Business Centre, Corporation Road, Newport, Gwent, NP19 4RF Tel: (01633) 271133 Fax: (01633) 271135 E-mail: jackie@celticdisplays.co.uk

Central Signs & Graphics, 6 Saltley Industrial Centre, Adderley Road, Birmingham, B8 1AW Tel: 0121-326 7744 Fax: 0121-326 8123 E-mail: reginold1@aol.com

Centurion Components Ltd, 38 Carron Place, East Kilbride, Glasgow, G75 0TS Tel: (01355) 265222 Fax: (01355) 230331 E-mail: sales@centurionsigns.co.uk

Centurion Europe Ltd, Hunt Lane, Doncaster, South Yorkshire, DN5 9SH Tel: (01302) 788700 Fax: (01302) 390004 E-mail: sales@centurioneurope.co.uk

Certa Ceto Sandbach, 45 Hightown, Crewe, CW1 3BZ Tel: (01270) 251333 Fax: (01270) 251444 E-mail: mellorremstar@aol.com

Characters Signs, Aston Bury, Aston, Stevenage, Hertfordshire, SG2 7EG Tel: (01438) 880181 Fax: (01438) 880182 E-mail: info@characterssigns.com

Charterbrook Signs, 1 Acorn Court, Clarion Close, Swansea Enterprise Park, Swansea, SA6 8QU Tel: (01792) 799888 Fax: (01792) 795400 E-mail: nigel.hillman@charterbrook.co.uk

Citisigns Ltd, 2a Church Lane, Dinnington, Sheffield, S25 2LY Tel: (01909) 567474 Fax: (01909) 564141 E-mail: mail@citysigns.co.uk

City County Screen Print, 7 Adco Business Centre, Bobbers Mill, Nottingham, NG8 5AH Tel: 0115-970 1130 Fax: 0115-970 4557 E-mail: paul@ccsigns.co.uk

City & County Signs, 209 Pinhoe Road, Exeter, EX4 8AB Tel: (01392) 434366 Fax: (01392) 434366

City Signs, Darley Abbey Mills, Darley Abbey, Derby, DE22 1DZ Tel: (01332) 349772 Fax: (01332) 341164

City Signs Midlands Ltd, 34 Jasper Street, Stoke-on-Trent, ST1 3DA Tel: (01782) 281069 Fax: (01782) 281609 E-mail: citysignuk@netscapeonline.co.uk

▶ Cka Signs, 61 High Street, Felling, Gateshead, Tyne & Wear, NE10 9LU Tel: 0191-469 3555 Fax: 0191-469 3555 E-mail: ckasignsandgraphics@blueyonder.co.uk

Clarke W R Signs Ltd, Scholars Lane, Stratford-upon-Avon, Warwickshire, CV37 6HE Tel: (01789) 292898 Fax: (01789) 414653

▶ Classic Signs Of London, 11 Redburn Industrial Estate, Woodall Road, Enfield, Middlesex, EN3 4LQ Tel: (020) 8805 4649 Fax: (020) 8805 1847

Coalville Signs, Units 2 3 Stephenson Indust Estate, Stephenson Way, Coalville, Leicestershire, LE67 3HB Tel: (01530) 811398 Fax: (01530) 830958

Coates Signs, 84 Holme Lane, Sheffield, S6 4JW Tel: 0114-234 4834 Fax: 0114-234 4834 E-mail: info@coatesigns.co.uk

Cobal Sign Systems Ltd, Brookway Industrial Estate, Brookway, Hambridge Lane, Newbury, Berkshire, RG14 5PE Tel: (01635) 570600 Fax: (01635) 32432 E-mail: info@cobal.co.uk

Coleman Signs, 44 Revell Road, Kingston upon Thames, Surrey, KT1 3SW Tel: (020) 8949 2693 E-mail: afcol@waitrose.com

Combined Signs, 4 Carpenters Place, London, SW4 7TD Tel: (020) 7720 5797 Fax: (020) 7720 2318 E-mail: signs@combinedsigns.co.uk

Commercial Nameplate Manufacturing Co., Butt End Mills, Chadwick Fold Lane, Mirfield, West Yorkshire, WF14 8PW Tel: (01924) 498652 Fax: (01924) 491167 E-mail: sales@commercialnameplates.co.uk

Complete Sign Experience Ltd, 20 Fox Croft, Tibshelf, Alfreton, Derbyshire, DE55 5QR Tel: (01773) 590163 Fax: (01773) 590163

Concept Signs, 40-42 Albert Road, Braintree, Essex, CM7 3JQ Tel: (01376) 329240 Fax: (01376) 331937 E-mail: signsconcept@aol.com

Concept Signs Ltd, Unit 7, Collingwood Industrial Estate, Maidstone Road, Sutton Valence, Maidstone, Kent, ME17 3QS Tel: (01622) 844884 Fax: (01622) 843884 E-mail: signletters2003@yahoo.co.uk

Connswater Graphics Ltd, 1 Dargan Court, Dargan Cresent, Belfast, BT3 9JP Tel: (028) 9077 7395 Fax: (028) 9077 7065 E-mail: info@connswatergraphics.com

Contract Sign Systems Ltd, John Davey Drive, Treleigh Industrial Estate, Redruth, Cornwall, TR16 4AX Tel: (01209) 313449 Fax: (0870) 8706929 E-mail: sales@contractsigns.co.uk

Contrast Signs, 135 Roxeth Green Avenue, Harrow, Middlesex, HA2 0QJ Tel: (020) 8864 9242

Cotswold Graphics Ltd, 10 Draycott Business Village, Draycott, Moreton-in-Marsh, Gloucestershire, GL56 9JY Tel: (01386) 701222 Fax: (01386) 701228 E-mail: johnl@cotswold-graphics.co.uk

County Engravers & Signs, Unit 5 Trentview Court, Nottingham, NG2 3FX Tel: 0115-985 1171 Fax: 0115-986 1007 E-mail: sales@countyengravers-signs.co.uk

County Signs, Unit 13 Orchard Industrial Estate, Christen Way, Parkwood, Maidstone, Kent, ME15 9YE Tel: (01622) 672232 Fax: (01622) 752559 E-mail: mail@county-signs.co.uk

Cousins Dave, 42 The Roundway, Kingskerswell, Newton Abbot, Devon, TQ12 5BW Tel: (01803) 404431 Fax: (01803) 391998 E-mail: dcsigns@hotmail.com

Cranmer Signs, 117a Sutton Avenue North, Peacehaven, East Sussex, BN10 7QJ Tel: (01273) 583706 Fax: (01273) 583706 E-mail: terrysignman@dsl.pipex.com

▶ Creative Graphics International, Unit 21, Weston Road Industrial Estate, Stratford-upon-Avon, Warwickshire, CV37 0AH Tel: (01789) 415141 Fax: (01789) 414160

Creative Signage, 60 Station Avenue, West Ewell, Epsom, Surrey, KT19 9UH Tel: (020) 8224 0056E-mail: info@creativesignage.co.uk

Creative Signs, 10 Worcester Road Industrial Estate, Chipping Norton, Oxfordshire, OX7 5XW Tel: (01608) 643557 Fax: (01608) 643557 E-mail: sales@creativepubsigns.co.uk

Creative Signs, Sandbach Road, Stoke-on-Trent, ST6 2DG Tel: (01782) 214589 Fax: (01782) 214589 E-mail: creative.signs@btopenworld.com

Creative Solutions, Swanston's Road, Great Yarmouth, Norfolk, NR30 3NQ Tel: (01493) 851899 Fax: (01493) 330178 E-mail: sales@creativesolutionsprinting.co.uk

Crescent Signs & Engraving, Unit 5q, Faraday Road, Newbury, Berkshire, RG14 2AD Tel: (01635) 528037 Fax: (01635) 49549 E-mail: enquiries@crescentsigns.co.uk

Cybersign, 1 Newtown Road, Camlough, Newry, County Down, BT35 8NN Tel: (028) 3083 7070 Fax: (028) 3083 7028 E-mail: sales@cybersign.co.uk

D B Sign Associates Ltd, Dukeries Industrial Estate, Claylands Avenue, Worksop, Nottinghamshire, S81 7BQ Tel: (01909) 472922 Fax: (01909) 478698 E-mail: office@dbsigns.com

D E Signs, Cartref, Chelmsford Road, Barnston, Dunmow, Essex, CM6 1LS Tel: (01371) 874011 Fax: (01371) 874011 E-mail: tim@de-signs.co.uk

D G Design & Graphics, 11 Industrial Centre, Gower Street, Ipswich, IP2 8EX Tel: (01473) 681077 Fax: (01473) 690604 E-mail: dgdesigngraphics@aol.com

D J N Signs, The Banks, Sileby, Loughborough, Leicestershire, LE12 7RE Tel: (01509) 813359 Fax: (01509) 814374 E-mail: sales@djn.co.uk

D M A Signs, Unit 5-6 Bridge Works, Kingston Road, Leatherhead, Surrey, KT22 7SU Tel: (01372) 363808 Fax: (01372) 363801 E-mail: sale@dmasigns.co.uk

D T Signs Ltd, Willow Court, Bracewell Avenue, Poulton Industrial Estate, Poulton-le-Fylde, Lancashire, FY6 8JF Tel: (01253) 892410 Fax: (01253) 899802 E-mail: admin@dtsigns.co.uk

Dale Signs, 19 Woodhouse Road, Sheffield, S12 2AY Tel: 0114-253 1461 Fax: 0114-239 8127

Daniels, 27-29 Cross Green Lane, Leeds, LS9 8LJ Tel: 0113-245 4020 Fax: 0113-245 5528

A.J. Darling & Sons Ltd, Unit 1, Mereway Road, Twickenham, TW2 6RF Tel: (020) 8898 5555 Fax: (020) 8898 9874 E-mail: darlingsigns@aol.com

Dart Fire Protection Ltd, Dart Fire Protection Centre, Plymouth Road, Totnes, Devon, TQ9 5PH Tel: (01803) 862416 Fax: (01803) 867183 E-mail: sales@dartfire.co.uk

David Etchells Signs, Unit 5 Brassey Close, Peterborough, PE1 2AZ Tel: (01733) 347847 Fax: (01733) 311242 E-mail: sales@etchells-signs.co.uk

Day Signs, 1 Ford Road, Totnes, Devon, TQ9 5LQ Tel: (01803) 865880 Fax: (01803) 868466 E-mail: sales@daysigns.net

Deltaband Ltd, 2280 Coventry Road, Sheldon, Birmingham, B26 3JR Tel: 0121-742 9922 Fax: 0121-742 9933 E-mail: enquiries@deltaband.co.uk

▶ Design Signs, 8 Queen Mary Works, Queen Marys Avenue, Watford, WD18 7JR Tel: (01923) 497087 E-mail: design_signs@hotmail.com

Design of Walton, 3 Lyln Road, Hersham Trading Estate, Walton-on-Thames, Surrey, KT12 3PU Tel: (01932) 240376 Fax: (01932) 241110 E-mail: signs@designofwalton.co.uk

The Designer Sign Company Ltd, Unit 11 Ebblake Enterprise Park, Black Moor Road, Ebblake Industrial Estate, Verwood, Dorset, BH31 6YS Tel: (01202) 813575 Fax: (01202) 813606

Designs, 53 Middleton Road, Banbury, Oxfordshire, OX16 3QR Tel: (01295) 254777 Fax: (01295) 254541 E-mail: david@designs-uk.com

Devon Signs Exmouth, The Old Dairyworks, New North Road, Exmouth, Devon, EX8 1RU Tel: (01395) 276618 Fax: (01395) 276618

Dial A Sign, Bessemer Road, Cardiff, CF11 8BA Tel: (029) 2039 8208 Fax: (029) 2039 8209 E-mail: signs@dialasign.fsnet.co.uk

SIGN CONTRACTORS OR SIGN MAKERS OR SUPPLIERS OR INSTALLERS – *continued*

Display, Unit 1 White Road, Off Charfleets Road, Canvey Island, Essex, SS8 0PQ Tel: (01268) 696509 Fax: (01268) 696587 E-mail: display.uk@virgin.co.uk

Dixon Signs, Stratford Rd, Drayton, Banbury, Oxon, OX15 6EE Tel: (01295) 730707 Fax: (01295) 730026 E-mail: mail@dixonsigns.co.uk

Dockerills Brighton Ltd, 3abc Church Street, Brighton, BN1 1UJ Tel: (01273) 607434 Fax: (01273) 679771 E-mail: dockerills@dockerills.demon.co.uk

▶ Don Valley Signs, Unit 4, Valley Works, Grange Lane, Sheffield, S5 0DQ Tel: 0114-246 6111 Fax: 0114-240 1928 E-mail: sales@donvalleysigns.co.uk

Douglas Signs Ltd, Unit 1 Moorings Close, Lower Hollin Bank Street, Blackburn, BB2 4AH Tel: (01254) 694284 Fax: (01254) 694292 E-mail: sales@douglas-signs.co.uk

Douthwaite Signs, 14 Lumley Street, Castleford, West Yorkshire, WF10 5LB Tel: (01977) 603605 Fax: (01977) 603605 E-mail: chris@chrisarcher.wanadoo.co.uk

▶ Dreamprint, Unit 36, Royds Enterprise Park, Future Fields, Buttershaw, Bradford, West Yorkshire, BD6 3EW Tel: (01274) 355661 Fax: (01274) 355662 E-mail: bob@dreamprint.co.uk

▶ Peter Dudley Exhibitions & Displays, Uttoxer Road, Blithbury, Rugeley, Staffordshire, WS15 3JG Tel: (01889) 504284 Fax: (01889) 504284

E C Signs, Unit 33, Leyton Ind Village, Argall Ave, London, E10 7QP Tel: (020) 8556 7222 Fax: (020) 8518 7676

E S L Displays & Graphics, Units 3-5 Hillside Mews, Riding Barn Hill, Wick, Bristol, BS30 5PA Tel: 0117-937 4777 Fax: 0117-937 4550 E-mail: info@eslgroupuk.co.uk

Eagle Signs Ltd, 56 Oreston Road, Pomphlett, Plymouth, PL9 7JQ Tel: (01752) 402559 Fax: (01752) 481126 E-mail: info@eaglesigns.co.uk

East Herts Signs & Engraving, 3 Old Cross, Hertford, SG14 1HX Tel: (01992) 553004 Fax: (01992) 501165

▶ Eberhardt Signs Ltd, Victory Trading Estate, Kiln Road, Portsmouth, PO3 5LP Tel: (023) 9266 5466 Fax: (023) 9266 5681 E-mail: sales@eberhardtsigns.com

▶ Echo, 2 Sloefield Drive, Carrickfergus, County Antrim, BT38 8GX Tel: (028) 9335 8165 Fax: (028) 9335 8154 E-mail: info@echosigns.co.uk

Eden, 1 Little Dockray, Penrith, Cumbria, CA11 7HL Tel: (01768) 869000 Fax: (01768) 865578 E-mail: david@edengraphics.co.uk

▶ Effective Screen & Photographic, 11 Malborough Way, Yardley Gobion, Towcester, Northamptonshire, NN12 7TU Tel: (01908) 543547 Fax: 01908 542536

Effective Screen & Photographic, 11 Malborough Way, Yardley Gobion, Towcester, Northamptonshire, NN12 7TU Tel: (01908) 543547 E-mail: 40quatro@tesco.net

Electro Signs Ltd, 97 Vallentin Road, London, E17 3JJ Tel: (020) 8521 8066 Fax: (020) 8520 8127 E-mail: info@electrosigns.co.uk

Elite Signs, 8 Cavendish Road, Salford, M7 4WW Tel: 0161-792 0232 Fax: 0161-792 0232 E-mail: elitesignsprint@aol.com

Ellis Signs, Dunstan Road Railway Street, Gateshead, Tyne & Wear, NE11 9EE Tel: 0191-477 1600 Fax: 0191-460 4460 E-mail: bernerd@ellisssigns.fsnet.co.uk

Elmtree Signs, 62 Empress Road, Southampton, SO14 0JU Tel: (023) 8023 0903 Fax: (023) 8023 0904 E-mail: rod@elmtreesigns.co.uk

Embassy Signs Ltd, 83 Bellenden Road, London, SE15 4QJ Tel: (020) 7732 1055 Fax: (020) 7732 4163E-mail: sales@embassysigns.co.uk

Ensign, Wakefield Place, Sandgate, Kendal, Cumbria, LA9 6HT Tel: (01539) 724433 Fax: (01539) 724499 E-mail: anne@sunsigns.co.uk

Ensign, 5 Cannon Park Road, Cannon Park Industrial Estate, Middlesbrough, Cleveland, TS1 5JP Tel: (01642) 800222 Fax: (01642) 241239 E-mail: info@ensign.co.uk

Ensign, 44 Nelson Avenue, Minster on Sea, Sheerness, Kent, ME12 3SE Tel: (01795) 873993 Fax: (01795) 874720

Escott Signs Ltd, Princesway, Team Valley Trading Estate, Gateshead, Tyne & Wear, NE11 0TU Tel: 0191-487 1010 Fax: 0191-491 0762 E-mail: sales@escottsigns.co.uk

Esprit Communications, Supreme House, 300 Regents Park Road, London, N3 2JX Tel: (020) 8346 4499 Fax: (020) 8346 6969 E-mail: beter@espritcommunications.com

▶ Essential Graphics, Graphics House, Heyford Park, Upper Heyford, Bicester, Oxfordshire, OX25 5HA Tel: (01869) 233435 Fax: (01869) 232287E-mail: essentialsigns@btconnect.com

Essex Graphic Signs, Cobwebs, 26 Scarletts, Basildon, Essex, SS14 2HZ Tel: (01268) 293293 Fax: (01268) 452525 E-mail: sign.sales@virgin.net

Estate Signs, 176 Christchurch Road, Ringwood, Hampshire, BH24 3AS Tel: (01425) 475574 Fax: (01425) 479906 E-mail: sales@estate-signs.co.uk

Euro Signs UK Ltd, 92 Cato Street, Hartlands, Birmingham, B7 4TS Tel: 0121-359 5566 Fax: 0121-359 5354 E-mail: sales@europlate.com

▶ Exposure Sign and Promotions, Lower Gosford Street, Middlesbrough, Cleveland, TS2 1NU Tel: (01642) 252500 Fax: (01642) 248988 E-mail: contactus@exposuresigns.co.uk

Express Signs, 1 Vulcan House, Vulcan Road, Solihull, West Midlands, B91 2JY Tel: 0121-709 0749 Fax: 0121-709 1059

Fabrisign Ltd, 42 Lower Addiscombe Road, Croydon, CR0 6AA Tel: (020) 8688 7764 Fax: (020) 8680 8331

Fair Sign Co., Unit E6 Aladdin Workspace, 426 Long Drive, Greenford, Middlesex, UB6 8UH Tel: (020) 8578 3080 Fax: (020) 8578 3082 E-mail: sales@fairsign.co.uk

Falcon Signs Ltd, 109 Grove Technology Park, Wantage, Oxfordshire, OX12 9FA Tel: (01235) 768872 Fax: (01235) 768822 E-mail: sales@falconsigns.co.uk

Fastsigns, Galbraith House 142 Lombard House, Great Charles St Queensway, Birmingham, B3 3LG Tel: 0121-236 2123 Fax: 0121-212 9970 E-mail: martin.drury@fastsigns.com

Fastsigns, 11 Colman Parade, Southbury Road, Enfield, Middlesex, EN1 1YY Tel: (020) 8367 3777 Fax: (020) 8367 3863

Fastsigns, 55 Western Road, Hove, East Sussex, BN3 1JD Tel: (01273) 726600 Fax: (01273) 722200 E-mail: mike.heath@fastsigns.com

Fazeley Signs, Unit 118 Bonehill Mill, Lichfield Street, Fazeley, Tamworth, Staffordshire, B78 3QS Tel: (01827) 261711 Fax: (01827) 261711 E-mail: info@fazeleysigns.co.uk

Fine Sign, Oldcotes Road, Dinnington, Sheffield, S25 2QX Tel: (01909) 518886 Fax: (01909) 518662

First Signs & Labels Ltd, Unit 1, Raynham Close, Raynham Road Industrial Estate, Raynham Road, Bishop's Stortford, Hertfordshire, CM23 5PJ Tel: (01279) 467999 Fax: (01279) 467888 E-mail: sales@firstsafetysigns.co.uk

Fitt Signs Ltd, 60-62 Pitt Street, Norwich, NR3 1DF Tel: (01603) 619128 Fax: (01603) 760524 E-mail: info@fitt-signs.co.uk

Flying Monk Graphics, 9 Malmesbury Business Park, Beuttell Way, Malmesbury, Wiltshire, SN16 9JU Tel: (01666) 829228 Fax: (01666) 829229 E-mail: sales@flyingmonkgraphics.co.uk

Ford Signs, 1A Burgess Street, Leicester, LE1 4QJ Tel: 0116-251 8185 Fax: 0116-251 6595 E-mail: sales.fordsigns@virgin.net

Forward Signs Ltd, 81-83 Cato Street, Birmingham, B7 4TS Tel: 0121-333 3338 Fax: 0121-333 3341 E-mail: rpg@forwardsigns.co.uk

Freeway Signs Ltd, Chalkwell Road, Sittingbourne, Kent, ME10 2LJ Tel: (01795) 426724 Fax: (01795) 431180 E-mail: freewaysigns@lineone.net

Frome Sign Co. Ltd, Unit 3 Lakeside Park, Mells, Frome, Somerset, BA11 3RH Tel: (01373) 813666 Fax: (01373) 813777 E-mail: fromesigns@aol.com

G B D Signs Services, 17 Lloyd Goring Cl, Angmering, Littlehampton, W. Sussex, BN16 4LG Tel: (01903) 779999 Fax: (01903) 779777

G B Signs, 274 High Street, Waltham Cross, Hertfordshire, EN8 7EA Tel: (01992) 623819 Fax: (01992) 623819

Gemini Group, Unit 21 Derryloran Industrial Estate, Sandholes Road, Cookstown, County Tyrone, BT80 9LU Tel: (028) 8676 1292 Fax: (028) 8676 5566 E-mail: sales@thegeminigroup.co.uk

Gemini Group, Unit 21 Derryloran Industrial Estate, Sandholes Road, Cookstown, County Tyrone, BT80 9LU Tel: (028) 8676 1292 Fax: (028) 8676 5566

Ghinn Signs, 98 Wickham Street, Welling, Kent, DA16 3LU Tel: (020) 8316 5501 Fax: (020) 8854 7612 E-mail: ghinnsigns@aol.com

Glendining Signs, 7 The Markham Centre, Station Road, Theale, Reading, RG7 4PE Tel: 0118-932 3788 Fax: 0118-932 3804 E-mail: sales@glendining.co.uk

Gordon Signs & Interior Displays Ltd, St. Faiths Road, Norwich, NR6 7BW Tel: (01603) 486142 Fax: (01603) 486172 E-mail: simon@gordonsigns.co.uk

Gpa Signs & Graphics, 51 Rowms Lane, Swinton, Mexborough, South Yorkshire, S64 8AA Tel: (01709) 588856 Fax: (01405) 815503 E-mail: gpa.signs@virgin.net

▶ Grafico, Unit 9, Holmbush Farm, Crawley Road, Faygate, Horsham, West Sussex, RH12 4SE Tel: (01293) 852002 Fax: (01293) 852004

Grafityp (UK) Ltd, 103 Mariner, Tamworth, Staffordshire, B79 7UL Tel: (01827) 300500 Fax: (01827) 51333 E-mail: sales@grafityp.co.uk

Grafix Signmakers Ltd, Parkhill Road, Kingstown Industrial Estate, Carlisle, CA3 0EX Tel: (01228) 541456 Fax: (01228) 511000 E-mail: info@grafixsigns.co.uk

Graphic Co, 35 Oldacres, Maidenhead, Berkshire, SL6 1XH Tel: (01628) 638541 Fax: (01628) 776564

Graphic Engravers, 354 Halliwell Road, Bolton, BL1 8AP Tel: (01204) 844159 Fax: (01204) 849445 E-mail: graphicengravers@btconnect.com

Graphic Services UK Ltd, 26 Eastcott Hill, Swindon, SN1 3JG Tel: (01793) 542678 Fax: (01793) 430788

Graphics Factory, 339 Church Road, St. George, Bristol, BS5 8AA Tel: 0117-902 6318 Fax: 0117-902 6318 E-mail: sales@thegraphicsfactory.co.uk

Gratel Signs & Nameplates, 4 Blatchford Close, Horsham, West Sussex, RH13 5RG Tel: (01403) 210385 Fax: (01403) 218282

Green Field Signs, 23 Oak Road, Newcastle, Staffordshire, ST5 6DE Tel: (01782) 768031 Fax: (01782) 768031 E-mail: greenfieldsigns@ntlworld.com

Greens The Signmakers Ltd, Brighton Street, Kingston-upon-Hull, East Riding of Yorkshire, HU3 4UW Tel: (01482) 327371 Fax: (01482) 228050 E-mail: davidragan@greens-signmakers.co.uk

Griffin & General Fire Services Ltd, 7 Willow Street, London, EC2A 4BH Tel: (020) 7251 9379 Fax: (020) 7729 5652 E-mail: headoffice@griffinfire.co.uk

Griffon Studios, PO Box 5047, Alexandria, Dunbartonshire, G83 8YR Tel: (01389) 830600 Fax: (01389) 830600

H & M Graphics, 1 Kinneil Road, Bo'ness, West Lothian, EH51 0AY Tel: (01506) 829388 Fax: (01506) 829393 E-mail: hm.graphics@btconnect.com

Hallam Signs, Cherry Tree, Union Road, Sheffield, S11 9EF Tel: 0114-249 3141 Fax: 0114-249 3145 E-mail: hallamsigns@talk21.com

Hardy Signs, Unit 10 Falcon Close, Burton-on-Trent, Staffordshire, DE14 1SG Tel: (01283) 569102 Fax: (01283) 540001 E-mail: sales@hardysigns.co.uk

Harmony Signs & Design Services Ltd, 18 Fisher St, Paignton, Devon, TQ4 5EL Tel: (01803) 559317 Fax: (01803) 522357 E-mail: admin@harmonysigns.co.uk

Hawes Group Ltd, Sandfield Close, Moulton Park, Northampton, NN3 6EU Tel: (01604) 790000 Fax: (01604) 790190 E-mail: info@hawes.co.uk

J.S. Heaton Ltd, 11 Provident Way, Timperley, Altrincham, Cheshire, WA15 6PR Tel: 0161-980 0531 Fax: 0161-980 0531

Hi-lite Signs Ltd, 100 Sinclair Road, Aberdeen, AB11 9PP Tel: (01224) 248532 Fax: (01224) 248479

Hitech Signmakers Ltd, 65-81 Townsend St, Glasgow, G4 0LA Tel: 0141-332 4111 Fax: 0141-331 1906 E-mail: sales@hitechsigns.co.uk

Hollywood Signs Ltd, Coal Valley Business Park, Westwood Avenue, Birmingham, B11 3RF Tel: 0121-773 3123 Fax: 0121-773 3324 E-mail: sales@hollywoodsigns.co.uk

Howson Signs & Screenprint, 52-54 Thompson Close, Chesterfield, Derbyshire, S41 9AZ Tel: (01246) 454676 Fax: (01246) 260302 E-mail: howsons@aol.com

Hunter Signs Ltd, 5 Pill Farm Industrial Estate, Caldicot, Gwent, NP26 5JG Tel: (01291) 430617 Fax: (01291) 430070 E-mail: alison@westbase.uk.com

I P D Signs, 162 Walsall Road, Norton Canes, Cannock, Staffordshire, WS11 9RB Tel: (01543) 270033 Fax: (01543) 279911 E-mail: info@ipdsigns.co.uk

I S Group, Unit 1 Enterprise House Aber Park, Aber Road, Flint, Clwyd, CH6 5EX Tel: (01352) 792000 Fax: (01352) 792001 E-mail: sales@impactsigns.co.uk

Icon Sign Manufacturing, 16 East Parade, Ilkley, West Yorkshire, LS29 8EZ Tel: (01535) 211456 Fax: (01943) 433400

Id Signs Scotland Ltd, 200 Swniton Road, Baillieston, Glasgow, G69 6DB Tel: 0141-773 3666 Fax: 0141-773 1690

▶ Identity Signs (London) Ltd, Identity House, Chase Farm, Southgate Road, Potters Bar, Hertfordshire, EN6 5ER Tel: (01707) 644715

Image Sign Co, Stretham Station Road, Wilburton, Ely, Cambridgeshire, CB6 3QD Tel: (01353) 648208 Fax: (01353) 648208

Impact Graphics, 2 Smitham Bridge Road, Hungerford, Berkshire, RG17 0QP Tel: (01488) 685001 Fax: (01488) 685395 E-mail: info@impact-graphics.co.uk

Impact Signs, 13-14 Hutton Street, Boldon Colliery, Tyne & Wear, NE35 9LW Tel: 0191-536 0536 Fax: 0191-536 5536 E-mail: info@inpact3dsigns.co.uk

Impact Signs & Design Ltd, Unit 59 Atlantic Business Centre, Atlantic Street, Broadheath, Altrincham, Cheshire, WA14 5NQ Tel: 0161-929 9594 Fax: 0161-929 9597 E-mail: sales@impact-signs.co.uk

▶ In Signs, The Old Council Yard, Dane Valley Road, St. Peters, Broadstairs, Kent, CT10 3JJ Tel: (01843) 871321 Fax: (01843) 871321 E-mail: insigns@tiscali.co.uk

Infosigns Signs & Nameplates, Unit 1 Howsell Road Industrial Estate, Malvern, Worcestershire, WR14 1UJ Tel: (01684) 577744 Fax: (01684) 566862 E-mail: info@infosigns.uk.com

Insignia, 20 Common Road, Bristol, BS15 3LL Tel: (01249) 460006 Fax: 0117-935 3916 E-mail: richard@insignia-signs.co.uk

Insignia Signs & Services, Unit 7 Albion Park, Albion Way, Armley Road, Leeds, LS12 2EJ Tel: 0113-243 8533 Fax: 0113-243 8733 E-mail: sales@insigniasigns.biz

▶ Intergraphics, 2, Nightingale Court, Weston-super-Mare, Avon, BS22 8SX Tel: (01934) 511001 Fax: (01934) 511006

Intersign Signs & Nameplates, 92 Bowesfield Lane, Stockton-on-Tees, Cleveland, TS18 3EU Tel: (01642) 674242 Fax: (01642) 617203 E-mail: intersign@lineone.net

Iolair Signs, Hardengreen Coach Works, Dalkeith, Midlothian, EH22 3LD Tel: 0131-663 2483 Fax: 0131-663 2497 E-mail: iolairsigns@aol.com

J Knight, 15 Sycamore Avenue, Oldham, OL4 2EL Tel: 0161-633 1222 E-mail: jeff.knightsigns@btinternet.com

J P Prints & Signs, Pantone House, 124 Abertillery Road, Blaina, Gwent, NP13 3DR Tel: (01495) 291795 Fax: (01495) 291716 E-mail: john@jpprint.co.uk

J S M Signs Ltd, Unit 24a Daniels Industrial Estate, Bath Road, Stroud, Gloucestershire, GL5 3TJ Tel: (01453) 751812 Fax: (01453) 751999 E-mail: jsm.signs@btconnect.com

J T S Engravers, 30-34 Aire Street, Leeds, LS1 4HT Tel: 0113-242 2158 Fax: 0113-242 8903 E-mail: jtsengravers@hotmail.co.uk

Jepsons Signs Ltd, 124A King William Street, Stourbridge, West Midlands, DY8 4EU Tel: (01384) 444588 Fax: (01384) 444589

JKN Digital Ltd, 13e Chain Caul Road, Ashton-on-Ribble, Preston, PR2 2PD Tel: (01772) 722735 Fax: (01772) 760560 E-mail: sales@jkndigital.co.uk

John Eley, 17-18 Leofric Square, Peterborough, PE1 5TU Tel: (01733) 344293 Fax: (01733) 344293 E-mail: eleysigns@johneleysigns.com

Joules Signs, Philomel, 542 Abbott Street, Pamphill, Wimborne, Dorset, BH21 4EF Tel: (01202) 885847 Fax: (01202) 885847

JT Displays Ltd, Rear of, 211-213 High Town Road, Luton, LU2 0BZ Tel: (01582) 723295 Fax: (01582) 417600

Judson Signs Ltd, Unit 4C, Gibbons Road, Sheepbridge Lane, Mansfield, Nottinghamshire, NG18 5DZ Tel: (01623) 659444 Fax: (01623) 659222 E-mail: judson.signs@btconnect.com

Jupiter Signs, 20 Singer Way, Kempston, Bedford, MK42 7AE Tel: (01234) 854577 Fax: (01234) 841401 E-mail: sales@jupitersigns.com

K B S Group, 41 Marsh Green Road West, Marsh Barton Trading Estate, Exeter, EX2 8PN Tel: (01392) 208208 Fax: (01392) 208200 E-mail: sales@kbs-group.com

K W Signs, 11 Burnside Road, Bolton, BL1 6EP Tel: (01204) 491487 Fax: (01204) 491488

Kensworth Sawmills Ltd, Dovehouse Lane, Kensworth, Dunstable, Bedfordshire, LU6 2PQ Tel: (01582) 873124 Fax: (01582) 873024 E-mail: kensworthsawmillsltd@hotmail.com

Kershaw Signs, 31 Harrowby Road, Leeds, LS16 5HX Tel: 0113-278 5873

Kingfisher Facilities Group, Kingfisher House, Rowan Way, New Balderton, Newark, Nottinghamshire, NG24 3AU Tel: (01636) 610776 Fax: (01636) 610150 E-mail: kingfisher.graphics@ntlworld.com

Kremer Signs, 300 New Greenham Park, Greenham, Thatcham, Berkshire, RG19 6HN Tel: (01635) 46125 Fax: (01635) 523170 E-mail: sales@kremersigns.co.uk

Lamb Signs, 62 West Harbour Road, Edinburgh, EH5 1PW Tel: 0131-552 3900 Fax: 0131-552 1093

Lamb's Signs, Unit B3 Sapphire Way, Rhombus Business Park, Norwich, NR6 6NN Tel: (01603) 410400 Fax: (01603) 410700 E-mail: lambsigns@talk21.com

Lancashire County Engineering Services, Dewhurst Row, Bamber Bridge, Preston, PR5 6BB Tel: (01772) 628323 Fax: (01772) 532343 E-mail: hq@lces.lancscc.gov.uk

Lane Signs, Peartree Farm, Welwyn Garden City, Hertfordshire, AL7 3UW Tel: (01707) 326084 Fax: (01707) 372366

Langton Signs & Graphics, 499a Saffron Lane, Leicester, LE2 6UJ Tel: 0116-283 4484 Fax: 0116-283 4484

▶ Lazar Signs, 4 Period Works, 1 Lammas Road, London, E10 7QT Tel: (020) 8558 5656 Fax: (020) 8556 4725 E-mail: sales@lazarsigns.co.uk

Leek Signs & Graphics, Unit 10 Town Yard Industrial Estate, Station Street, Leek, Staffordshire, ST13 8BF Tel: (01538) 385262 Fax: (01538) 385262

Legend Signs Ltd, 1 Benham Business Park, Ashford Road, Newingreen, Hythe, Kent, CT21 4JD Tel: (01303) 261278 Fax: (01303) 261280 E-mail: info@kullasigns.co.uk

Leighton Signs Ltd, Unit 2 3 Water Hall Farm, Wavendon Road, Salford, Milton Keynes, MK17 8AZ Tel: (01908) 282283 Fax: (01908) 282284 E-mail: info@leightonsigns.co.uk

Libra Signs Ltd, Great Keelings, Lower Stock Road, West Hanningfield, Chelmsford, CM2 8UY Tel: (01277) 841944 Fax: (01277) 841629 E-mail: sales@librasigns.com

Limelight Signs Ltd, Plantation Works, Heys Street, Bacup, Lancashire, OL13 9QL Tel: (01706) 873866 Fax: (01706) 879102 E-mail: sales@limelight-signs.co.uk

Liskeard Signs & Trophies, 8 Pike Street, Liskeard, Cornwall, PL14 3JE Tel: (01579) 347098 Fax: (01579) 347098

London House Signs, 28 High Street, Bluntisham, Huntingdon, Cambridgeshire, PE28 3LD Tel: (01480) 453922 Fax: (01480) 411077 E-mail: john@londonhousesigns.com

▶ The Look Signs & Graphics Ltd, Unit B, Little Moor Lane, Loughborough, Leicestershire, LE11 1SF Tel: (01509) 232614 Fax: (01509) 232617 E-mail: info@thelook.co.uk

Lush Signs, 64 Old Milton Road, New Milton, Hampshire, BH25 6DX Tel: (01425) 616905 Fax: (01425) 628830 E-mail: lushsigns@newmilton.fsbusiness.co.uk

M B C Signs London Ltd, Unit 33 Leyton Industrial Village, Argall Avenue, London, E10 7QP Tel: (020) 8532 8321 Fax: (020) 8518 7676

M B C Signs London Ltd, Unit 33 Leyton Industrial Village, Argall Avenue, London, E10 7QP Tel: (020) 8532 8321 Fax: (020) 8518 7676 E-mail: mcassanova@btconnect.com

▶ indicates data change since last edition

SIGN CONTRACTORS OR SIGN MAKERS OR SUPPLIERS OR INSTALLERS – *continued*

M C M, 26 Donisthorpe Street, Leeds, LS10 1PL Tel: 0113-245 1020 Fax: 0113-243 1971 E-mail: info@mcmpos.co.uk

M E C Signs Ltd, Boxshall Court, Pound Street, Newbury, Berkshire, RG14 6AB Tel: (01635) 41745 Fax: (01635) 31923 E-mail: sales@mecsigns.co.uk

M G S Signs Ltd, Quickjay House, Bilston Street, Willenhall, West Midlands, WV13 2AW Tel: (01902) 366223 Fax: (01902) 366340

M L Signs, 3a Bessemer Road, Cardiff, CF11 8BA Tel: (029) 2022 7694 Fax: (029) 2038 8148

M3 Signs, 3 Hursley Road, Chandler's Ford, Eastleigh, Hampshire, SO53 2FW Tel: (023) 8025 3632 Fax: (023) 8025 4444

▶ Mac Signs & Graphics, 49 Long Lane, Holbury, Southampton, SO45 2LG Tel: (023) 8089 2228 Fax: (023) 8089 9268 E-mail: info@mac-signs.co.uk

Mcbride Signs & Engraving Services, 2 Henderson Drive, Inverness, IV1 1TR Tel: (01463) 237303 Fax: (01463) 713373 E-mail: mcbsigns@aol.com

Mcgarrigle Signs, Aubery Street, Londonderry, BT48 6RX Tel: (028) 7126 0699 Fax: (028) 7126 0699

Mcrobb Display, 70 Montgomery Street, Edinburgh, EH7 5JA Tel: 0131-556 9633 Fax: 0131-556 7657 E-mail: info@mcrobb.co.uk

Magna Display Systems Ltd, Unit 13 Alliance Close, Attleborough Fields Industrial Estate, Nuneaton, Warwickshire, CV11 6SD Tel: (024) 7632 0032 Fax: (024) 7635 0213 E-mail: info@magnadisplaysystems.co.uk

Magnetex Sign Systems, 20 Junction Road, Saintfield, Ballynahinch, County Down, BT24 7JU Tel: (028) 9751 0093 Fax: (028) 9751 1044

Major Signs, 189 Meanwood Road, Leeds, LS7 1NB Tel: 0113-243 8792 Fax: 0113-243 8792

▶ Mark 1 Signs, Charleston, Nigg, Aberdeen, AB12 3LN Tel: (01224) 899311 Fax: (01224) 899311 E-mail: info@mark1signs.co.uk

Marneon Signs Ltd, 11 Pontyglasdwr Street, Swansea, SA1 2BH Tel: (01792) 646949 Fax: (01792) 652227 E-mail: andrew-cotford@marneonsigns.com

Maxwell Jones Studios Ltd, 58K Arthur Street, Redditch, Worcestershire, B98 8JY Tel: (01527) 502900 Fax: (01527) 510265 E-mail: sales@maxwelljones.com

▶ MB Sign Design, 4 Newtown Grange Farm Business Centre, Desford Road, Newtown Unthank, Leicester, LE9 9FL Tel: (01455) 824102 Fax: (01455) 824102

Mendip Signs, Unit 14 Keyford Court, Manor Furlong, Frome, Somerset, BA11 4BD Tel: (01373) 461460 Fax: (01373) 461305 E-mail: sales@mendipsigns.co.uk

Mercury Engraving & Diesinking Ltd, Unit A5 Up Ringway, Bounds Green Industrial Estate, London, N11 2UD Tel: (0800) 1077118 Fax: (020) 8368 9018 E-mail: sales@mercuryengraving.co.uk

▶ Mersey Signs, Unit 24, Junction 8 Business Park, Ross Cliffe Road, Ellesmere Port, CH65 3AS Tel: 0151-355 0478 Fax: 0151-356 5352 E-mail: info@merseysigns.co.uk

Mico Signs & Blinds Ltd, 123 Kentish Town Road, London, NW1 8PB Tel: (020) 7284 2698 Fax: (020) 7267 5191 E-mail: sales@micosigns.co.uk

Micro Data Systems Ltd, 65 Lower Olland Street, Bungay, Suffolk, NR35 1BY Tel: (01986) 895004 Fax: (01986) 896563 E-mail: sales@microdata.co.uk

Mid Wales Signs, Llanbrynmair, Powys, SY19 7AA Tel: (01650) 521250 Fax: (01650) 521250 E-mail: ibwilliams88@hotmail.com

Mike Brown, 21 Horsecroft, Stanford in the Vale, Faringdon, Oxfordshire, SN7 8LL Tel: (01367) 718993 Fax: (01367) 718993

Miller Signs, 52 Berry Street, Liverpool, L1 4JQ Tel: 0151-708 0072 Fax: 0151-708 0072

Momentum Design Management Ltd, Robert Denholm House, Bletchingley Road Nutfield, Nutfield, Redhill, RH1 4HW Tel: (01737) 822555 E-mail: contact@momentum-dm.com

Monwel Hankinson Signs & Services, Letchworth Road, Ebbw Vale, Gwent, NP23 6UZ Tel: (01495) 301333 Fax: (01495) 350323 E-mail: monwel@blaner-gwent.co.uk

Morgan Associates, Unit 15 Ilford Trading Estate, Paycocke Road, Basildon, Essex, SS14 3DR Tel: (01268) 288587 Fax: (01268) 288587 E-mail: info@ma4.co.uk

Morley Signs, Unit 5 Station Avenue, Bridlington, North Humberside, YO16 4LZ Tel: (01262) 678800 Fax: (01262) 678830

N B Sign Services, 72 Winner Street, Paignton, Devon, TQ3 3BH Tel: (01803) 521160 Fax: (01803) 521135

N J M Sign & Display Ltd, 52 Bunting Road Industrial Estate, Northampton, NN1 3JY Tel: (01604) 250777 Fax: (01604) 250777 E-mail: njmsigns@aol.com

N M Signs, Baltimore Road, Birmingham, B42 1DG Tel: 0121-357 9357 Fax: 0121-358 5600 E-mail: designssignsandgraphics@yahoo.co.uk

N M Signs, Baltimore Road, Birmingham, B42 1DG Tel: 0121-357 9357 Fax: 0121-358 5600

National Signshop, Courtney Street, Hull, HU8 7QF Tel: (01482) 225050 Fax: (01482) 323077 E-mail: info@nationalsignshop.co.uk

▶ Neon Effects, 70 Stanley Gardens, London, W3 7SZ Tel: (020) 8743 8801 Fax: (020) 8749 7347

Neon & Sign Shop, 992-994 Argyle Street, Glasgow, G3 8LU Tel: 0141-248 9001 Fax: 0141-248 9002

Newman Display Ltd, 23a Pakenham Street, London, WC1X 0LB Tel: (020) 7278 1400 Fax: (020) 7278 0996 E-mail: info@newman-displays.com

The Newport Sign Company Ltd, 47 Dolphin Street, Newport, Gwent, NP20 2AT Tel: (01633) 263301 Fax: (01633) 676497 E-mail: bernie@aol.com

Newsigns Sign Writers, Unit 6a The Arches, Loveridge Road, London, NW6 2DS Tel: (020) 7328 9251 Fax: (020) 7624 7465

Nibra Sign Ltd, Ivy House Farm, Wolvershill Road, Banwell, Somerset, BS29 6LB Tel: (01934) 822772 Fax: (01934) 822517 E-mail: nibra.signs@btopenworld.com

Nichols Sign Ltd, Units 1 & 14 Treeton Enterprise, Rother Crescent, Treeton, Rotherham, South Yorkshire, S60 5QY Tel: 0114-288 9998 Fax: 0114-288 9998

Nordis Industries, Cornhill Close, Lodge Farm Industrial Estate, Northampton, NN5 7UB Tel: (01604) 596910 Fax: 01604 758470

▶ North Star Signs, 6-7 Doncaster Road, Barnsley, South Yorkshire, S70 1TH Tel: (01226) 288228 Fax: (01226) 288228 E-mail: info@northstarsigns.co.uk

North West Graphics, 195 St Helens Road, Bolton, BL3 3PY Tel: (01204) 657123

Northallerton Sign Co., The Units, Morton On Swale, Northallerton, N. Yorkshire, DL7 9RJ Tel: (01609) 777687 Fax: (01609) 777687 E-mail: sales@allertonsigns.co.uk

Northampton Signs Ltd, Unit 5,, Stour Road,, Weedon Road Industrial Estate,, Northampton, NN5 5AA Tel: (01604) 758198 E-mail: sales@northamptonsigns.co.uk

Northern Plastics 84 Ltd, Mount Street, Hyde, Cheshire, SK14 1NT Tel: 0161-368 2968 Fax: 0161-368 2183 E-mail: np84ltd@btconnect.com

Olympiad Signs Ltd, 7 Dorma Trading Park, Staffa Road, London, E10 7QX Tel: (020) 8539 3006 Fax: (020) 8556 1075 E-mail: sales@olympiadsigns.co.uk

Olympic Sign Services, Unit 5, Bradbauy Drive, Springwood Indutrial Estate, Braintree, Essex, CM7 2SD Tel: (01376) 551300 Fax: (01376) 328121 E-mail: sales@olypicsignservices.co.uk

Olympic Signs Ltd, Units 30-31 Colebrook Industrial Estate, Longfield Road, Tunbridge Wells, Kent, TN2 3DG Tel: (01892) 548444 Fax: (01892) 538444 E-mail: sales@olympicsigns.co.uk

O'Neill Signs, Bankes Lane, Weston Point, Runcorn, Cheshire, WA7 4HQ Tel: (01928) 592393 Fax: (01928) 592393 E-mail: oneillsigns@zoom.co.uk

P J Drew Engravers Ltd, Lower Vicarage Road, Southampton, SO19 7RJ Tel: (023) 8044 6062 Fax: (023) 8042 2981 E-mail: sales@pjdrew.co.uk

P & N Corporate Media Ltd, 9c Aven Industrial Park, Tickhill Road, Maltby, Rotherham, South Yorkshire, S66 7QR Tel: (01709) 818999 Fax: (01709) 769911 E-mail: studio@cncorpmedia.co.uk

P & S Promotions Sign & Print, 16 Hodgsons Court, Hodgsons Way, Wickford, Essex, SS11 8XR Tel: (01268) 572616 Fax: (01268) 572122

▶ Palm Pro Ltd, Unit 5 South John Street, Carlisle, CA2 5AJ Tel: (01228) 591911 Fax: (01228) 591241 E-mail: mail@palmprosigns.co.uk

Pannell Signs Ltd, Chelsea House, Chelsea Street, New Basford, Nottingham, NG7 7HN Tel: 0115-970 0371 Fax: 0115-942 2452 E-mail: sales@pannellsigns.co.uk

Parry's Signs, Link Industrial Estate, 8 Howsell Road, Malvern, Worcestershire, WR14 1TF Tel: (01684) 892998 Fax: (01684) 572754 E-mail: enquires@parryssigns.co.uk

Peel Graphics, 104-106 Bridge Street, Heywood, Lancashire, OL10 1JG Tel: (01706) 621960 Fax: (01706) 625249 E-mail: sales@peelgraphics.co.uk

Perspective Signs Ltd, 21 Riverside Industrial Park, Rapier Street, Ipswich, IP2 8JX Tel: (01473) 681684 Fax: (01473) 601746

Phoenix Signs, 49 North Bridge Street, Sunderland, SR5 1AH Tel: 0191-567 5021 Fax: 0191-567 5021 E-mail: phoenix.sings@virgin.net

Photocast Products Ltd, Unit 78 Venture Point West, Speke, Liverpool, L24 9PB Tel: 0151-486 2826 Fax: 0151-486 2826 E-mail: photocastproducts@btinternet.com

▶ Pinders Dewsbury Ltd, 241 Bradford Road, Batley, West Yorkshire, WF17 6JQ Tel: (01924) 437123 Fax: (01924) 437124 E-mail: info@pindersign.co.uk

Plastengrave Ltd, Unit 29 77-87 Trafalgar Business Centre, River Road, Barking, Essex, IG11 0JU Tel: (020) 8591 2595 Fax: (020) 8594 0459 E-mail: sales@plastengrave.co.uk

Polysigns Signs & Nameplates, 121-123 Newfoundland Road, Bristol, BS2 9LU Tel: 0117-954 0888 Fax: 0117-935 0213 E-mail: polysigns@aol.com

Powergraphic Displays Ltd, 6 Blenheim Road, Cressex Business Park, High Wycombe, Buckinghamshire, HP12 3RS Tel: (01494) 450936 Fax: (01494) 461975 E-mail: edwardbutler@powergraphicdisplays.com

▶ Premier Signs, 3 Hedgend Industrial Estate, Shuart Lane, St. Nicholas at Wade, Birchington, Kent, CT7 0NB Tel: (01843) 843895 Fax: (01843) 843895

Premier Signs, 5 Somers Road, Rugby, Warwickshire, CV22 7DB Tel: (01788) 565361 Fax: (01788) 569165

Pro-Active Signs, 5 New Mill, Post Office Road, Inkpen, Hungerford, Berkshire, RG17 9PU Tel: (01488) 669152 Fax: (01488) 669267 E-mail: sales@pro-activesigns.co.uk

Pryorsign, Unit 3a, Denby Way, Hellaby, Rotherham, South Yorkshire, S66 8HR Tel: (01709) 700408 Fax: (01709) 532745 E-mail: david.fordham@pryorsign.com

PW Signs, 21 Southgate, Pontefract, West Yorkshire, WF8 1LN Tel: (01977) 701701 Fax: (01977) 701701 E-mail: pwsigns@btconnect.com

Pyramid Visuals, Pyramid House, 105-109 Oyster Lane, Byfleet, Surrey, KT14 7JR Tel: (01932) 338899 Fax: (01932) 338888 E-mail: info@pyramidvisuals.co.uk

Quality Signs & Engraving, Victoria Buildings, Stringes Lane, Willenhall, West Midlands, WV13 1LN Tel: (01902) 604844 Fax: (01902) 604844 E-mail: qualitysigns@tinyworld.co.uk

Quick Sign, Unit 2 Evercreech Way, Walrow, Highbridge, Somerset, TA9 4AR Tel: (01278) 787268 Fax: (01278) 784611 E-mail: sales@quick-sign.co.uk

Quicksign Signs & Nameplates, 7 Hightown Industrial Estate, Crow Arch Lane, Ringwood, Hampshire, BH24 1ND Tel: (01425) 470445 Fax: (01425) 476289 E-mail: steve@quicksign.co.uk

R & D Signs Ltd, 37 Lichfield Road, Birmingham, B6 5RW Tel: 0121-327 3041 Fax: 0121-326 6983 E-mail: info@rdsigns.co.uk

R G Services, PO Box 1864, Radstock, BA3 3ZA Tel: (01761) 435858 Fax: (01761) 435858 E-mail: sales@rgservices.co.uk

R & M Signmakers, 2 Whitehill Lane, Gravesend, Kent, DA12 5LY Tel: (01474) 568358 Fax: (01474) 568358

Radar Signs, 143 Beehive Lane, Ilford, Essex, IG4 5DR Tel: (020) 8551 0216 Fax: (020) 8551 1458 E-mail: radarsigns@btclick.com

▶ Rainbow Graphics, 14 Hilton Avenue, Scunthorpe, South Humberside, DN15 8BD Tel: (01724) 282455 Fax: (01724) 343823 E-mail: rainbowgraphics@ntlworld.com

Ram Signs, 4 Brighton Road, Lower Kingswood, Tadworth, Surrey, KT20 6SY Tel: (01737) 833444 Fax: (01737) 833432 E-mail: rsgsales@aol.com

Randle Signs, 29 Blackdown Avenue, Chesterfield, Derbyshire, S40 4QQ Tel: (01246) 205905 Fax: (01246) 205905

Raymac Signs Ltd, Prospect Works, Showfield Lane, Malton, North Yorkshire, YO17 6BT Tel: (01653) 600015 Fax: (01653) 691600 E-mail: sales@raymac.co.uk

Raysigns Ltd, 11-13 Tower Hamlets Road, Dover, Kent, CT17 0BJ Tel: (01304) 214506 Fax: (01304) 202915 E-mail: andrew@raysigns.fsnet.co.uk

Reade Signs Ltd, 4 Holder Road, Aldershot, Hampshire, GU12 4RH Tel: (01252) 333535 Fax: (01252) 333535 E-mail: sales@readesigns.com

Readwell Signs Ltd, 357 Hedon Road, Hull, HU9 1RA Tel: (01482) 227233 Fax: (01482) 219823 E-mail: sales@readwell.co.uk

Red Leaver Signs, 80 Dalling Road, London, W6 0JA Tel: (020) 8741 4306 Fax: (020) 8741 4307

Red Signs, Unit 14 105 Hopewell Business Centre, Hopewell Drive, Chatham, Kent, ME5 7DX Tel: (01634) 309434 Fax: (01634) 309436 E-mail: info@redsigns.co.uk

Regal Signs & Graphics, 2 Restmor Way, Wallington, Surrey, SM6 7AH Tel: (020) 8835 2332 Fax: (020) 8835 2326 E-mail: sales@regalsigns.co.uk

Regency Signs, 5 Knowle Farm Bus Centre, Wadhurst Road, Frant, Tunbridge Wells, Kent, TN3 9EJ Tel: (01892) 510738 Fax: (01892) 515352 E-mail: sales@regencysigns.co.uk

Regis Plastic Signs, Providence Street, Stourbridge, West Midlands, DY9 8HN Tel: (01384) 892366 Fax: (01384) 892367

Remco Signs Ltd, Mundy Street, Ilkeston, Derbyshire, DE7 8DH Tel: 0115-930 7769 Fax: 0115-932 7714 E-mail: sales@remcosigns.com

Resistek Ltd, 46 Holton Road, Holton Heath Trading Park, Poole, Dorset, BH16 6LT Tel: (01202) 625605 Fax: (01202) 632438 E-mail: sales@resistek.co.uk

Ricochet Signs & Designs, B3 Browings Farm Workshops, Blackboys, Uckfield, East Sussex, TN22 5HG Tel: (01825) 890088 Fax: (01825) 890088 E-mail: info@ricochetsigns.co.uk

▶ Ringway Signs Ltd, Twenty Twenty Industrial Estate, St. Laurence Avenue, Allington, Maidstone, Kent, ME16 0LL Tel: (01622) 693476 Fax: (01622) 685992

Rivermeade Signs Ltd, Rowley Industrial Park, Roslin Road, London, W3 8BH Tel: (020) 8896 6900 Fax: (020) 8752 1691 E-mail: info@rivermeade.com

Riverway Building & Signage Ltd, Riverway, Trowbridge, Wiltshire, BA14 8LL Tel: (01225) 760131 Fax: (01225) 777207 E-mail: mail@riverwaywilts.co.uk

Alan Roberts (Engravers) Ltd, 39A-43A Knight Street, Liverpool, L1 9DT Tel: 0151-709 3404 Fax: 0151-707 8081 E-mail: mail@alanrobertsengravers.co.uk

Rock Foundry, Lakeside, Duncote, Towcester, Northamptonshire, NN12 8AL Tel: (01327) 351561 Fax: (01327) 353344 E-mail: rockfoundry@aol.com

Rowthorn Signs, 19 Milton Road, Portsmouth, PO3 6AN Tel: (023) 9273 7210 Fax: (023) 9229 3955E-mail: rowthorn@btopenworld.com

Royal British Legion Industries, Royal British Legion Village, Hall Road, Aylesford, Kent, ME20 7NL Tel: (01622) 795900 Fax: (01622) 882195 E-mail: enquiries@rbli.co.uk

Roys Signs, 15 Hoobrook Industrial Estate, Worcester Road, Kidderminster, Worcestershire, DY10 1HY Tel: (01562) 829299 Fax: (01562) 829299

Rushden Graphics Co., 25 Alfred Street, Rushden, Northamptonshire, NN10 9YS Tel: (01933) 418419 Fax: (01933) 317790 E-mail: sales@rgc.org.uk

Russell Signs Ltd, Units J-L Forest Industrial Park, Forest Road, Hainault, Ilford, Essex, IG6 3HL Tel: (020) 8501 2418 Fax: (020) 8500 4628 E-mail: vikki@russellsigns.co.uk

Rydon Signs Ltd, Unit 3 Peek House, Pinhoe Trading Estate, Exeter, EX4 8JN Tel: (01392) 466653 Fax: (01392) 466671 E-mail: sales@rydonsigns.com

S B M Signmaking & Engraving, 8-9 Lawson Way, Middlesbrough, Cleveland, TS3 6LN Tel: (01642) 227268 Fax: (01642) 271033 E-mail: sbmsigns@sc.com

S B Signs, 16 Blandford Square, Newcastle upon Tyne, NE1 4HZ Tel: 0191-222 0852 Fax: 0191-232 2065

▶ S L Signs, 9 Georges Road, London, N7 8HD Tel: (020) 7697 0444 Fax: (020) 7697 0444

Safety 1st Signs, 34 Millersdale Avenue, Mansfield, Nottinghamshire, NG18 5HS Tel: (01623) 429947 Fax: (01623) 640540

Sanbar Signs Ltd, 21 Argyll Road, Westcliff-on-Sea, Essex, SS0 7HL Tel: (01702) 344611 Fax: (01702) 344611 E-mail: sanbarsignssouthend@aol.com

Sandblast Sign Co., The Lodge, Barking Road, Barking, Ipswich, IP6 8HG Tel: (01449) 722252 Fax: (01449) 722355 E-mail: lorrraine@ssc.gb.com

▶ Scorpio Signs (Design & Display) Ltd, Hartford House Yard, School Lane, Hartford, Northwich, Cheshire, CW8 1NP Tel: (01606) 74912 Fax: (01606) 76036 E-mail: mail@scorpiosigns.co.uk

Scriptus Ltd, 3 Campus Road, Listerhills Science Park, Bradford, West Yorkshire, BD7 1HR Tel: 0113-278 0367 Fax: (01274) 391973 E-mail: stylus.marketing@virgin.net

Semaphore Cardiff Ltd, Bessemer Road, Cardiff, CF11 8BA Tel: (029) 2022 4111 Fax: (029) 2022 5401

▶ Severnside Safety Supplies Ltd, Malmesbury Road, Kingsditch Trading Estate, Cheltenham, Gloucestershire, GL51 9PL Tel: (01242) 525811 Fax: (01242) 224184 E-mail: sales@sevsafe.co.uk

Shawcross Ltd, Priory Street, Priory Industrial Estate, Birkenhead, Merseyside, CH41 5JH Tel: 0151-647 6692 Fax: 0151-666 1569 E-mail: info@shawcrosssigns.co.uk

Sigma Signs Ltd, Unit 4B, Arun Buildings, Arundel Road, Uxbridge, Middlesex, UB8 2RP Tel: (01895) 273268 Fax: (01895) 271614 E-mail: signs@sigmasigns.com

Sign Co., 18 Homedale Drive, Luton, LU4 9TE Tel: (01582) 492075 E-mail: sales@sign-co.com

Sign 2000 Ltd, Maidstone Road, Paddock Wood, Tonbridge, Kent, TN12 6QJ Tel: (01892) 834383 Fax: (01892) 838349 E-mail: info@sign2000.co.uk

Sign A Rama, 91 Ringway, Preston, PR1 2QD Tel: (01772) 258494 Fax: (01772) 259845 E-mail: preston@sign-a-rama.co.uk

Sign A Rama, Unit A Whiteknights Retail Centre, Shinfield Road, Reading, RG2 8HA Tel: 0118-931 1122 Fax: 0118-931 4040 E-mail: reading@sign-a-rama.co.uk

Sign A Rama, 328-330 Hobs Moat Road, Solihull, West Midlands, B92 8JT Tel: 0121-742 5888 Fax: 0121-742 5656 E-mail: birminghamsouth@sign-a-rama.co.uk

Sign A Rama, 1 Parker Street, Warrington, WA1 1LT Tel: (01925) 445577 Fax: (01925) 244555 E-mail: signarama.warrington@talk21.com

The Sign & Blind Centre Ltd, 24 Cavendish Road, New Malden, Surrey, KT3 6DE Tel: (020) 8337 1538 E-mail: signblindcoltd@aol.com

The Sign Centre, Newark Road South, Glenrothes, Fife, KY7 4NS Tel: (01592) 630101 Fax: (01592) 630188

Sign Centre, 1 Farrier Road, Lincoln, LN6 3RU Tel: (01522) 500024 Fax: (01522) 500054 E-mail: enquires@signcentre-uk.com

Sign Connections Ltd, Unit 5 Sinclair Court, Great Yarmouth, Norfolk, NR31 0NH Tel: (01493) 440285 Fax: (01493) 653888 E-mail: info@signconnections.com

Sign & Design, 31 Hospital Lane, Blaby, Leicester, LE8 4FE Tel: 0116-277 1957 Fax: 0116-277 5755 E-mail: signs@freenet.co.uk

Sign Designs, 147-149 Hutcheon Street, Aberdeen, AB25 3RY Tel: (01224) 645361 Fax: (01224) 643647 E-mail: dundee@signdesigns.co.uk

▶ Sign & Digital Print Solutions, The Sign Workshop, Rear of 78 Ham Lane, Longham, Ferndown, Dorset, BH22 9DP Tel: (01202) 572625

Sign & Display Centre, 253 Barlow Moor Road, Manchester, M21 7GJ Tel: 0161-861 7311 Fax: 0161-861 7306 E-mail: sales@signanddisplay.co.uk

The Sign Experience Ltd, 12 Dukes Court, Bognor Road, Chichester, West Sussex, PO19 8FX Tel: (01243) 779991 Fax: (01243) 779992 E-mail: info@sign-ex.co.uk

SIGN CONTRACTORS OR SIGN MAKERS OR SUPPLIERS OR INSTALLERS – *continued*

Sign Factory, Unit 12 Kingston Industrial Estate, Ardgowan Street, Port Glasgow, Renfrewshire, PA14 5DG Tel: (01475) 743624 Fax: (01475) 745677 E-mail: signfactory@btconnect.com

Sign Group, Cathedral Road, Cardiff, CF11 9HA Tel: (029) 2022 5250 Fax: (029) 2078 6666

▶ Sign Group, Unit 1del Guerra Courtgelligron Industrail Estatetonyrefa, Tonyrefail, Porth, Mid Glamorgan, CF39 8ES Tel: (01443) 670300 Fax: (01443) 670404

▶ Sign Guy, The Old School House, St Peters Lane, Bickenhill Village, Solihull, West Midlands, B92 0DP Tel: 07869 296579 Fax: 01675 443 080 E-mail: signguys@btinternet.com

Sign House Ltd, Unit H Burley Hill Trading Estate, Leeds, LS4 2PU Tel: 0113-274 0476 Fax: 0113-274 0477 E-mail: enq@thesignhouse.com

Sign Installations Ltd, Unit 2 1-7 Ernest Avenue, London, SE27 0DQ Tel: (020) 8681 1971 Fax: (020) 8670 7721

Sign It, Beehive Works, Beehive Lane, Chelmsford, CM2 9JY Tel: (01245) 492294 Fax: (01245) 262147 E-mail: sales@sign-it.co.uk

Sign Makers Products Ltd, Hawthorne House, Ipswich Road, Long Stratton, Norwich, NR15 2XB Tel: (01508) 531183 Fax: (01508) 531139 E-mail: sales@sign-makers-products.co.uk

Sign & Poster Specialists, 23 Meadow Place, Shrewsbury, SY1 1PD Tel: (01743) 353320 Fax: (01743) 235053 E-mail: david@signandposter.co.uk

▶ Sign & Print, 11 Colchester Road, Great Totham, Maldon, Essex, CM9 8BZ Tel: (01621) 891289 E-mail: sales@click4signs.co.uk

Sign & Print Centre, 162 Top Road, Calow, Chesterfield, Derbyshire, S44 5TD Tel: (01246) 209691 Fax: (01246) 209690

▶ Sign & Print Here, 4 Long Lane, Wrington, Bristol, BS40 5SA Tel: (01934) 861144 Fax: (01934) 861155

Sign Specialists Ltd, 19 Oxleasow Road, East Moons Moat, Redditch, Worcestershire, B98 0RE Tel: (01527) 504250 Fax: (01527) 504251 E-mail: sales@sign-specialists.co.uk

Sign Stop, 71 Station Road, Flitwick, Bedford, MK45 1JU Tel: (01525) 714949 Fax: (01525) 719498

The Sign Studio, The Ferrers Centre, Staunton Harold, Ashby-de-la-Zouch, Leicestershire, LE65 1RU Tel: (01332) 694545 Fax: (01332) 864863 E-mail: info@ferrerscentre.co.uk

Sign Studio, 5 Croft Street, Cheltenham, Gloucestershire, GL53 0EE Tel: (01242) 228866 Fax: (01242) 228777 E-mail: sales@chelt-signstudio.co.uk

Sign Studio, 391 Durnsford Road, London, SW19 8EE Tel: (020) 8946 7193

Sign Studio, 158 Cromwell Road, Salford, M6 6DE Tel: 0161-792 7254 Fax: 0161-792 1873

The Sign Studio N E Ltd, 7 Tees Court, Skippers Lane Industrial Estate, Middlesbrough, Cleveland, TS6 6DX Tel: (01642) 465999 Fax: (01642) 465888 E-mail: sign.studio@btconnect.com

Sign Studios Ltd, 16 Broomhills Industrial Estate, Rayne Road, Braintree, Essex, CM7 2RG Tel: (01376) 349529 Fax: (01376) 552635 E-mail: sign.studios@btinternet.com

Sign Supply Ltd, 20 Station Road, Chertsey, Surrey, KT16 8BE Tel: (0870) 2402678 Fax: (0870) 2402679 E-mail: sales@signsupply.co.uk

Sign Wizards, 27 Upper High Street, Cradley Heath, West Midlands, B64 5HX Tel: (01384) 413223 Fax: (01384) 413223

Sign Wizzard, Griffin Lane, Aylesbury, Buckinghamshire, HP19 0GH Tel: (01296) 398022 Fax: (01296) 398028 E-mail: sign.wizzard@virgin.net

Sign Work Of Cambridge Sign Manufacturers, 303 St.Neots Road Hardwick, Hardwick, Cambridge, CB23 7QL Tel: (01954) 211611 Fax: (01954) 211010 E-mail: admin@signwork.co.uk

Sign Works, 12 Clarendon Avenue, Leamington Spa, Warwickshire, CV32 5PZ Tel: (01926) 311791 Fax: (01926) 311791 E-mail: simon@thesignworks.co.uk

Sign Workshop The, Doods Road, Reigate, Surrey, RH2 0NT Tel: (01737) 240479 Fax: (01737) 223694

Sign World 2000, Drome Road, Deeside Industrial Park, Deeside, Clwyd, CH5 2NY Tel: (01244) 281955 Fax: (01244) 281949 E-mail: mail.signworld@btinternet.com

Signarc Services, 1 Cording Street, London, E14 6NL Tel: (020) 7517 3979 Fax: (020) 7538 8657 E-mail: info@tcsigns.co.uk

Signature Signs, 188 Church Road, Hove, East Sussex, BN3 2DJ Tel: (01273) 774775

Signbusters Of Ayr, 132 Hunters Avenue, Ayr, KA8 9EQ Tel: (01292) 281224 Fax: (01292) 477552 E-mail: signhouseayrcc@aol.com

Signconex Ltd, St. Johns Works, Fern Street, Bury, Lancashire, BL9 5BP Tel: 0161-764 9500 Fax: 0161-764 9600 E-mail: sales@signconex.co.uk

Signcraft Ltd, St. Stephens Road, West Drayton, Middlesex, UB7 7RL Tel: (01895) 442768 Fax: (01895) 442153 E-mail: sales@signcraft.org

Signcraft Signs, 244 High Road, Romford, RM6 6AP Tel: (020) 8599 4747 Fax: (020) 8599 1616 E-mail: signcraft@signcraft.fsnet.co.uk

▶ Signcraft Signs & Graphics, 157 Heathhall Industrial Estate, Heathhall, Dumfries, DG1 3PH Tel: (01387) 251595 Fax: (01387) 251820 E-mail: sales@signcraft-signs.co.uk

Signet Signs, Unit 11 Islwyn Workshops, Pontymister Industrial Estate, Risca, Newport, Gwent, NP11 6NP Tel: (01633) 601305 Fax: (01633) 601305 E-mail: deansignet@aol.com

Signgrave Signs & Nameplates, Tudor Court, Harold Court Road, Romford, RM3 0AE Tel: (01708) 373827 Fax: (01708) 381069 E-mail: sign.grave@virgin.net

Significant Signs, Unit 34 Mahatma Gandhi Industrial Estate, Milkwood Road, London, SE24 0JF Tel: (020) 7924 9343 Fax: (020) 7924 9343

Signline, Unit 5a Ridge Hill Farm, Nash, Milton Keynes, MK17 0EH Tel: (01908) 379600 Fax: (01908) 715113

The Signmaster, 25 Whessoe Road, Darlington, County Durham, DL3 0QP Tel: (01325) 351374 Fax: (01325) 351374

Signmaster, 276 Smithdown Road, Allerton, Liverpool, L15 5AJ Tel: 0151-722 4009 Fax: 0151-722 4008 E-mail: andyg@fitwell-ltd.co.uk

Signpost Signs, 137 Upper Wickham Lane, Welling, Kent, DA16 3AL Tel: (020) 8854 8777 Fax: (020) 8855 0577 E-mail: enquiries@signpostsigns.co.uk

SignRight, 157-161 West Road, Westcliff-On-Sea, Essex, SS0 9DH Tel: (01702) 308486 Fax: (0870) 7061711 E-mail: info@signright.co.uk

Signrise Signs & Nameplates, Tirmynydd Road, Three Crosses, Swansea, SA4 3PB Tel: (01792) 872536 Fax: (01792) 872536

Signrite Ltd, 41C Green Street, Ayr, KA8 8BQ Tel: (01292) 285908 Fax: (01292) 261539 E-mail: mail@signritesignmakers.co.uk

Signs Incorporated, 77 Lowfield Street, Dartford, DA1 1HP Tel: (01322) 221181 Fax: (01322) 221185

Signs 2000 Ltd, 6 North Street, Liverpool, L3 2AY Tel: 0151-227 1033 Fax: 0151-227 1032 E-mail: signs2000@cybase.co.uk

Signs By Morrell Ltd, Tarran Way South, Tarran Industrial Estate, Wirral, Merseyside, CH46 4TP Tel: 0151-678 8989 Fax: 0151-678 8816 E-mail: sales@signs-by-morrell.com

Signs & Designs, Riverside House, Lock Lane, Castleford, West Yorkshire, WF10 2JZ Tel: (01977) 512095 Fax: (01977) 603695 E-mail: sales@signs-designs.co.uk

Signs Direct, 23 Kingsway, Scarborough, North Yorkshire, YO12 6SG Tel: (01723) 500425 Fax: (01723) 500425 E-mail: kevin@signsdirect.freeserve.co.uk

Signs Express Ltd, Unit 16 Priory Industrial Park, Christchurch, Dorset, BH23 4HE Tel: (01425) 277676 Fax: (01425) 277694 E-mail: bournemouth@signsexpress.co.uk

Signs Express Ltd, Unit 4 Bishopgate Business Park, Widdrington Road, Coventry, CV1 4NN Tel: (024) 7622 3380 Fax: (024) 7625 6377 E-mail: coventry@signsexpress.co.uk

Signs Express Ltd, Unit D1 Amberley Drive, Sinfin Lane, Sinfin, Derby, DE24 9RE Tel: (01332) 769450 Fax: (01332) 769470 E-mail: derby@signsexpress.co.uk

Signs Express Ltd, 257b Dukesway, Team Valley Trading Estate, Gateshead, Tyne & Wear, NE11 0PZ Tel: 0191-487 4900 Fax: 0191-487 5900 E-mail: gateshead@signsexpress.co.uk

Signs Express Ltd, 2 St Andrews Court, Rollesby Road, King's Lynn, Norfolk, PE30 4LS Tel: (01553) 761762 Fax: (01553) 761769 E-mail: kingslynn@signsexpress.co.uk

Signs Express, Unit 14 Abbey Enterprise Park, Mill Road, Newtownabbey, County Antrim, BT36 7BA Tel: (028) 9086 5647 Fax: (028) 9086 9224E-mail: belfast@signsexpress.co.uk

Signs Express Ltd, Kingsland Grangeaston Ctwoolston, Woolston, Warrington, WA1 4SG Tel: (01925) 822990 Fax: (01925) 822120 E-mail: warrington@signsexpress.co.uk

Signs & Labels Of Shrewsbury, Unit 7a Hardwicke Stables Industrial Estate, Hadnall, Shrewsbury, SY4 4AS Tel: (01939) 210230 Fax: (01939) 210231

Signs Now, 36a Ashley Road, Bournemouth, BH1 4LH Tel: (01202) 392727 Fax: (01202) 392728 E-mail: signsnowbmth@aol.com

Signs & Safety Ltd, Unit 6 Fairlawn Enterprise Park, Bonehurst Road, Redhill, RH2 7QT Tel: (01737) 246969 Fax: (01737) 247979 E-mail: info@signsandsafety.co.uk

Signs Of The Times Ltd, Wingfield Road, Tebworth, Leighton Buzzard, Bedfordshire, LU7 9QQ Tel: (01525) 874185 Fax: (01525) 875746 E-mail: enquiries@sott.co.uk

Signs Xtra, Unit 6 Grange Lane Industrial Estate, Carrwood Road, Barnsley, South Yorkshire, S71 5AS Tel: (01226) 731334 Fax: (01226) 731335 E-mail: signsxtra@btconnect.com

Signs4you, 35 East St, Crediton, Devon, EX17 3AY Tel: 01363 776877 Fax: 01363 776877 E-mail: shsigns@aol.com

Signsense, 240 Ashley Road, Poole, Dorset, BH14 9BZ Tel: (01202) 252627 Fax: (01202) 250300

Signtech, Hereford Way, King's Lynn, Norfolk, PE30 4JD Tel: (01553) 770800 Fax: (01553) 691931 E-mail: sales@signtech.uk.com

Signtech Plastics & Signs, 82 Moorland Road, Weston-super-Mare, Avon, BS23 4HT Tel: (01934) 416137 Fax: (01934) 628008 E-mail: signtech1@tiscali.co.uk

Signtek Sign Writers, Unit 5e Southbourne Business Park, Courtlands Road, Eastbourne, East Sussex, BN22 8UY Tel: (01323) 642625 Fax: (01323) 439559 E-mail: info@signtek.co.uk

Signtrade Letters Ltd, 225 Long Lane, Finchley, London, N3 2RL Tel: (0500) 456700 Fax: (0208) 349 5806 E-mail: sales@signtrade.co.uk

Signwise, Unit 26 Enterprise Way, Newport, Gwent, NP20 2AQ Tel: (01633) 841766 Fax: (01633) 841766 E-mail: info@signwise.net

Signwise Sign Services Ltd, Unit 7 Bodolph Bridge Trading, Estate Oundle Road, Peterborough, PE2 9QP Tel: (01733) 558554 Fax: (01733) 563384 E-mail: sign.wise@btclick.com

Signwork, Crosshouse Road, Southampton, SO14 5GZ Tel: (023) 8063 8243 Fax: (023) 8023 4512 E-mail: info@signwork.net

Signworks Signs & Nameplates, Station Yard, Grange-over-Sands, Cumbria, LA11 6DW Tel: (01539) 534077 Fax: (01539) 535047

▶ Signworx Scotland Ltd, Unit 4, Guards Road Industrial Estate, Coldstream, Berwickshire, TD12 4EE Tel: (01890) 885885 Fax: (01890) 882138 E-mail: signworx@ospreyco.com

Simplex Ltd, Unit C Peter Road, Lancing, West Sussex, BN15 8TH Tel: (01903) 750333 E-mail: sales@simplexltd.com

▶ Simply Signs Ltd, The Old Dairy, Well Street, Winsford, Cheshire, CW7 1HN Tel: (01606) 869123 Fax: (01606) 869169

Simply Stripes Signmakers Ltd, Unit 33 Enterprise City, Meadowfield Avenue, Spennymoor, County Durham, DL16 6JF Tel: (01388) 420460 Fax: (01388) 420009

Simpsons Of Aberdeen, 30 Anderson Drive, Aberdeen, AB15 4TY Tel: (01224) 316260 Fax: (01224) 316260

Smithbrewer Ltd, Sunnyside Road North, Weston-super-Mare, Avon, BS23 3PZ Tel: (01934) 642642 Fax: (01934) 642646 E-mail: sales@smithbrewer.co.uk

Smiths Of Buckie, 27 East Church Street, Buckie, Banffshire, AB56 1ET Tel: (01542) 832488 Fax: (01542) 834896

Snell Signs & Supplies Ltd, 243-245 Cleethorpe Road, Grimsby, South Humberside, DN31 3BE Tel: (01472) 342000 Fax: (01472) 240027

Solar Graphics, 8 Finch Drive, Braintree, Essex, CM7 2SF Tel: (01376) 552209 Fax: (01376) 320077 E-mail: sales@solargraphics.net

Solar Signs, Normanby Road, Nettleton, Market Rasen, Lincolnshire, LN7 6TB Tel: (01472) 851914 Fax: (01472) 851037 E-mail: enquires@solarsigns.co.uk

Solihull Signs, 270 Lode Lane, Solihull, West Midlands, B91 2HY Tel: 0121-704 1624 Fax: 0121-704 1624 E-mail: sales@solihullsigns.co.uk

Solito Graphics, 1137 Yardley Wood Road, Birmingham, B14 4LS Tel: 0121-474 4640 Fax: 0121-474 4640

Southern Neon Lights, 57a Rockstone Lane, Southampton, SO14 6JA Tel: (023) 8071 0300 Fax: (023) 8033 8481 E-mail: sales@southernneon.com

Spectrum Signs, 290 Northholt Road, South Harrow, Harrow, Middlesex, HA2 8EB Tel: (020) 8422 1168 Fax: (020) 8864 4220 E-mail: spectrumsigns@webtribe.net

Spectrum Signs, Unit R5 Elvington Industrial Estate, York Road, Elvington, York, YO41 4AR Tel: (01904) 607000 Fax: (01904) 607060 E-mail: sales@signsbyspectrum.com

Speedy Signs Ltd, 39 Waterhead Road, Stoke-on-Trent, ST3 5NG Tel: (01782) 327077 Fax: (01782) 593276

Spicer Arts, Wharley Farm, College Road, Cranfield, Bedford, MK43 0AH Tel: (01234) 750029 Fax: (01234) 750029

Sprint Graphics, Station Road, Irthlingborough, Wellingborough, Northamptonshire, NN9 5QE Tel: (01933) 651908 Fax: (01933) 655688 E-mail: sales@sprintgraphics.co.uk

Sprint Signs Ltd, Holmes Way, Horncastle, Lincolnshire, LN9 6JW Tel: (01507) 522247 Fax: (01507) 522017 E-mail: sales@sprintsigns.co.uk

Stalite Signs Ltd, 7 Apple Lane, Exeter, EX2 5GL Tel: (01392) 447001 Fax: (01392) 447002 E-mail: sales@stalite.co.uk

Standing Stone, Llwynteg, Ffynnonddrain, Carmarthen, Dyfed, SA33 6EE Tel: (01267) 223226 Fax: (01267) 223495 E-mail: sales@standingstone.co.uk

Star Signs, Pioneer Business Park, Princes Road, Ramsgate, Kent, CT11 7RX Tel: (01843) 579003 Fax: (01843) 583002

Sterling Signs Ltd, Millmead Business Centre, Milmead Industrial Centre, London, N17 9QU Tel: (020) 8885 4206 Fax: (020) 8801 8714 E-mail: tim@sterlingsigns.co.uk

Stewart Signs Ltd, Trafalgar Close, Chandler's Ford, Eastleigh, Hampshire, SO53 4BW Tel: (023) 8025 4781 Fax: (023) 8025 5620 E-mail: sales@stewartsigns.co.uk

Stick 'Em Signs, Hyde Bank Road, New Mills, High Peak, Derbyshire, SK22 4NN Tel: (01663) 741160 Fax: (01663) 741162

Stretford Industrial Services Ltd, 8 Radnor Street, Stretford, Manchester, M32 8LE Tel: 0161-865 4235 Fax: 0161-865 0139 E-mail: sales@sisgroup.co.uk

Studio 2, 101 Lockhurst Lane, Coventry, CV6 5SF Tel: (024) 7663 8144 Fax: (024) 7666 1457 E-mail: sales@studio2exhibitions.co.uk

Studio Signs, 10-12 High Street, Goldthorpe, Rotherham, South Yorkshire, S63 9LR Tel: (01709) 891160 Fax: (01709) 891160 E-mail: dean@studiosigns.co.uk

Style Engravers, Unit 2 Warneford Avenue, Ossett, West Yorkshire, WF5 9NJ Tel: (01924) 270506 Fax: (01924) 265156 E-mail: sales@engravers.fsbusiness.co.uk

Style Graphics Ltd, 38 Decima Street, London, SE1 4QQ Tel: (01689) 609477 Fax: (020) 7407 7625

Sullivan Signs, Unit 8 Coatbank Way, Coatbridge, Lanarkshire, ML5 3AG Tel: (01236) 432892 Fax: (01236) 440744 E-mail: jimsullivansigns@btopenworld.com

▶ Sun Signs & Blinds Ltd, Unit 27 Sheraton Business Centre, Wadsworth Road, Greenford, Middlesex, UB6 7JB Tel: (020) 8998 3368 Fax: (020) 8998 3365 E-mail: info@sun-sign.co.uk

▶ Supersigns Sign Writers, 114-116 The Hornet, Chichester, West Sussex, PO19 7JR Tel: (01243) 532045 Fax: (01243) 532062 E-mail: sales@supersignschichester.co.uk

Sussex Sign Centre, 4 Mill Road, Burgess Hill, West Sussex, RH15 8DR Tel: (01444) 246884 Fax: (01444) 871871 E-mail: sales@sussexsigncentre.co.uk

Swan Signs Ltd, Lynton House, Golden Hill, Leyland, PR25 3NN Tel: (01772) 455011 Fax: (01772) 457936

Swesco, Unit 3E Treloggan Industrial Estate, Newquay, Cornwall, TR7 2SX Tel: (01637) 878160 Fax: (01637) 871115 E-mail: sales@swesco.net

Swift Signs, 73 Kingsmead Avenue, Worcester Park, Surrey, KT4 8UZ Tel: (020) 8337 1080 Fax: (020) 8337 1080 E-mail: swiftsign@btconnect.com

Symbol Signs, Unit 18 Abenglen Industrial Estate, Betam Road, Hayes, Middlesex, UB3 1SS Tel: (020) 8561 0240 Fax: (020) 8561 0920 E-mail: symbolsign@aol.com

System One Signs, Unit 24 H T M Business Park, Abergele Road, Rhuddlan, Rhyl, Clwyd, LL18 5UZ Tel: (01745) 590880 Fax: (01745) 590880

System Signs, 7 Greystone Road, Carlisle, CA1 2DJ Tel: (01228) 545558 Fax: (01228) 545558 E-mail: admin@systemsigns.co.uk

T C P Construction, River Road, Barking, Essex, IG11 0DG Tel: (020) 8594 9228 Fax: (020) 8594 9227

T J'S Sign Co. Ltd, Unit C4, Portland Business Park, Portland Road, Hove, East Sussex, BN3 5RY Tel: (01273) 431134 Fax: (01273) 431135 E-mail: sales@tjsignco.com

▶ Taktyle Science Europe Ltd, Bentwaters Parks, Rendlesham, Woodbridge, Suffolk, IP12 2TW Tel: (01394) 420741 Fax: (01394) 420664

Target Signs, Unit 27 Baltic Works, Effingham Road, Sheffield, S9 3QA Tel: 0114-243 6600 Fax: 0114-243 6633

Taylor & Pickles Ltd, Bushell St Mills, Bushell Street, Preston, PR1 2SP Tel: (01772) 251520 Fax: (01772) 561610 E-mail: info@taylorandpickles.co.uk

Techniform Graphics Ltd, 172 Bexley Road, London, SE9 2PH Tel: (020) 8850 9191 Fax: (020) 7703 6001 E-mail: sales@techniformgraphics.co.uk

Technosign Ltd, Unit 3 35a Stanbridge Road, Leighton Buzzard, Bedfordshire, LU7 4PZ Tel: (01525) 382111 Fax: (01525) 382382

▶ Thrower Signs, 54 Linersh Wood Close, Bramley, Guildford, Surrey, GU5 0EQ Tel: (01483) 894257 Fax: (01483) 890329 E-mail: simon@throwersigns.co.uk

Totem Signs, 31b Albion Road, Edinburgh, EH7 5QJ Tel: 0131-476 3777 Fax: 0131-467 7446 E-mail: info@totemsigns.com

Town & Country Signs Ltd, 125 Poplar High Street, London, E14 0AE Tel: (020) 7515 8383 Fax: (020) 7538 8657 E-mail: info@tcsigns.co.uk

Tradesigns Signs & Nameplates, 1124 Pershore Road, Stirchley, Birmingham, B30 2YG Tel: 0121-471 1381 Fax: 0121-471 1381

Traffic Sign Contracting Ltd, P O Box 102, Burton-on-Trent, Staffordshire, DE13 0BN Tel: (01283) 515595 Fax: (01283) 515915

Tribune Graphics Ltd, Unit 11 New Road Industrial Estate, Grace Road, Sheerness, Kent, ME12 1DB Tel: (01795) 580261 Fax: (01795) 663318 E-mail: mail@tribunegraphics.co.uk

Triwonder Signs, Unit 4, Tannery Road, Tonbridge, Kent, TN9 1RF Tel: (01732) 770444 Fax: (01732) 363888

Trojan Signs Ltd, 11 Lyon Road, Hersham Industrial Estate, Walton-On-Thames, Surrey, KT12 3PU Tel: (01932) 232400 Fax: (01932) 987687 E-mail: troy@trojansigns.com

▶ Tudor Signs, 6 CWRT Y Coed, Brackla, Bridgend, Mid Glamorgan, CF31 2ST Tel: (01656) 650901 Fax: (01656) 650901

Tullford Marketing, 37 Europa Way, Martineau Lane, Norwich, NR1 2EN Tel: (01603) 629649 Fax: (01603) 630186 E-mail: andrew@tullford.co.uk

Twenty Twenty Displays Ltd, Unit 25, Tregoniggie Industrial Estate, Falmouth, Cornwall, TR11 4SN Tel: (01326) 372520 Fax: (01326) 377243 E-mail: info@twentytwentydisplays.com

Ultimate Signs, Business House, 1 Calow Lane, Hasland, Chesterfield, Derbyshire, S41 0AL Tel: (01246) 222555 Fax: (01246) 271030 E-mail: ian@ultimate-signs.com

Universal Silk Screen Printers, Unit 5 Leeside Works, Stanstead Abbotts, Ware, Hertfordshire, SG12 8JL Tel: (01920) 877274 Fax: (01920) 877114

▶ V Signs, Unit 27, Evesham Road, Fladbury, Pershore, Worcestershire, WR10 2QS Tel: (01386) 861700 Fax: (01386) 861700

▶ indicates data change since last edition

SIGN CONTRACTORS OR SIGN MAKERS OR SUPPLIERS OR INSTALLERS – *continued*

Valvil Services, 533 Rayleigh Road, Benfleet, Essex, SS7 3TN Tel: (01268) 745333 Fax: (01268) 745333
VDC, 86 Oxford Road, Clacton-on-Sea, Essex, CO15 3TG Tel: (01255) 221884 Fax: (01255) 429242
Victory Imaging, Forest Buildings, 41 Creswell Road, Clowne, Chesterfield, Derbyshire, S43 4PN Tel: (01246) 570771 Fax: (01246) 570772 E-mail: sales@victory-imaging.co.uk
Viking Signs, Unit 2 Alma Park Road, Grantham, Lincolnshire, NG31 9SE Tel: (01476) 590261 Fax: (01476) 590261 E-mail: sales@vikingsigns.co.uk
Vinatec Signs & Nameplates, 244 Bentley Road, Doncaster, South Yorkshire, DN5 9QP Tel: (01302) 822777 Fax: (01302) 822777 E-mail: sales@vinatec.co.uk
Vinter Sign, Rear Of 37 Chipstead Valley Rd, Coulsdon, Surrey, CR5 2RB Tel: 020 86609603 Fax: 020 86609640
The Vinyl Cut, Newmill Farm, Stonehaven, Kincardineshire, AB39 3YJ Tel: (0845) 0565589 Fax: (01569) 740102
Vinyl Graphics Flags Banners, 109 Bell Hill Road, Flat, Bristol, BS5 7LY Tel: 0117-935 3705 Fax: 0117-940 1446 E-mail: sales@vinylgraphicsonline.co.uk
Vision Visual Solutions Ltd, 1 Solent Industrial Estate, Shamblehurst Lane, Hedge End, Southampton, SO30 2FX Tel: (01489) 781000 Fax: (01489) 781100 E-mail: sales@vvsltd.co.uk
Vista Signs, 267 Nottingham Road, Nottingham, NG7 7DA Tel: 0115-942 1511 Fax: 0115-942 2462 E-mail: sales@vista-signs.co.uk
▶ Visual Image Signs, Staple Close, West Quantoxhead, Taunton, Somerset, TA4 4DF Tel: (01984) 639211 Fax: (01984) 639511 E-mail: postmaster@visualimagesigns.co.uk
Vital Signs & Graphics Ltd, 326 Great Cheetham Street East, Salford, M7 4UJ Tel: 0161-792 7557 Fax: 0161-792 7677 E-mail: sales@vitalsignsandgraphics.co.uk
W Andrews (Signs), 17 Rees House, Burnhall Industrial Estate, Fleetwood, Lancashire, FY7 8RS Tel: (01253) 826862 Fax: (01253) 826862
W E A Group Ltd, Unit 4 Hales Road Industrial Estate, Hales Road, Leeds, LS12 4PL Tel: 0113-279 9442 Fax: 0113-279 0703 E-mail: info@wae-group.co.uk
Walker Signs, Cook Lane, Heckmondwike, West Yorkshire, WF16 9JG Tel: (01924) 407918 Fax: (01924) 404058 E-mail: enquiries@walkersigns.co.uk
Ward & Co. Ltd, Unit 18, Maze St, Barton Hill Trading Estate, Bristol, BS5 9TE Tel: 0117-955 3385 Fax: 0117-955 7518 E-mail: sales@ward-signs.co.uk
Watson Signs, Unit 1 Dunaverig, Ruskie, Thornhill, Stirling, FK8 3QW Tel: (01786) 850501 Fax: (01259) 720022 E-mail: Admin@watsonsigns.co.uk
Webb Display Services Ltd, Canalside Harris Business Park, Hanbury Road, Stoke Prior, Bromsgrove, Worcestershire, B60 4DJ Tel: (01527) 837306 Fax: (01527) 575230 E-mail: graphics@webbdisplay.co.uk
West Midland Signs, 56 Station Road, Cradley Heath, West Midlands, B64 6NU Tel: (01384) 635577 Fax: (01384) 635577
▶ West Sussex Signs, Clovelly Road, Southbourne, Emsworth, Hampshire, PO10 8PF Tel: (01243) 377702 Fax: (01243) 376454 E-mail: sales@westsussexsigns.co.uk
Weston Designs, Unit G9 Rudford Industrial Estate, Ford Road, Arundel, West Sussex, BN18 0BD Tel: (01403) 274639 Fax: (01403) 274665 E-mail: sales@westondesigns.ndo.co.uk
Gerald Whittaker Signs, The Workshop Iron Hill, Hollycombe, Liphook, Hampshire, GU30 7LP Tel: (01428) 722260 Fax: (01428) 722260
Wildan Sign Services Ltd, Unit 5, Plot 7f Claymore, Time Valley Industrial Estate, Tamworth, Staffordshire, B77 5DQ Tel: (01827) 283400 Fax: (01827) 283808 E-mail: sales@wildan-signs.co.uk
Williams & Brown, Unit 11 Ketlan Court, River Lane, Saltney, Chester, CH4 8RH Tel: (01244) 678302 Fax: (01244) 681519 E-mail: williamsandbrownsigns@btopenword.com
Wirral Sign Service, Thorndale Business Centre, Wallasey Road, Wallasey, Merseyside, CH44 2AG Tel: 0151-638 6382 Fax: 0151-638 6382 E-mail: info@wirralsigns.co.uk
Woollen & Co. Ltd, Old Lane, Halfway, Sheffield, S20 3GZ Tel: 0114-276 4411 Fax: 0114-248 9980 E-mail: woollens@hotmail.co.uk
Wright Sign Service, 1 Greenside, Pudsey, West Yorkshire, LS28 8PU Tel: 0113-255 7259 Fax: 0113-255 7259 E-mail: jon808@btclick.com
▶ Wright Signs, 4 Teal Business Park, Dodwells Road, Hinckley, Leicestershire, LE10 3BZ Tel: (01455) 616151 Fax: (0845) 8906151 E-mail: sales@asg.co.uk
X L B Signs, 5 Hayes Metro Centre, Springfield Road, Hayes, Middlesex, UB4 0LE Tel: (020) 8561 5664 Fax: (020) 8561 5665
▶ Xcalibur Sign Writers, 241 Torquay Road, Paignton, Devon, TQ3 2HW Tel: (01803) 666125 Fax: (01803) 666126
Xpose Media Ltd, Unit 3 Mona Industrial Park, Gwalchmai, Holyhead, Gwynedd, LL65 4RJ Tel: (01407) 720222 Fax: (01407) 720066 E-mail: sales@angleseysigns.co.uk
▶ Zebra Signs & Graphics, 4 Hill Street Industrial Estate, Hill Street, Ardrossan, Ayrshire, KA22 8HE Tel: (01294) 608476 Fax: (01294) 608476
Zedi Signs, Connaught House, 32 Connaught Street, Northampton, NN1 3BP Tel: (01604) 231525 Fax: (01604) 231527 E-mail: zedisigns@aol.com
▶ Zeitgeist, 8 Pettycur Bay, Kinghorn, Burntisland, Fife, KY3 9SB Tel: (01592) 890952
Zero Signs Ltd, Grosvenor Works, Derby Street, Crewe, CW1 3ER Tel: (01270) 256258 Fax: (01270) 501603 E-mail: sales@zerosigns.co.uk
Zillwoods Signmasters, Britannia Road, Southampton, SO14 5RH Tel: (023) 8071 4900 Fax: (023) 8071 4901 E-mail: team@zillwoods.co.uk

SIGN CONTRACTORS' SUPPLY SERVICES

Allsigns, 122 Connaught Road, Brookwood, Woking, Surrey, GU24 0AS Tel: (01483) 799100 Fax: (01483) 799188
Band-Tite Co. Ltd, 9 Aizlewood Road, Sheffield, S8 0YX Tel: 0114-250 0393 Fax: 0114-250 0394 E-mail: sales@band-tite.co.uk
Bill Dawson Sign Consultants, Nailford House, Brewery Lane, Bridge, Canterbury, Kent, CT4 5LF Tel: (01227) 831044 Fax: (01227) 831044
Blazeneon Ltd, Units 3-4 Arden Road, Rednal, Birmingham, B45 0JA Tel: 0121-457 7715 Fax: 0121-453 9356 E-mail: victorl@blazeneon.com
Frank Layton (Display), 9 Broadway Place, London, SW19 3TP Tel: (020) 8946 5041 Fax: (020) 8944 7324
Fylde Signs, The Warehouse, Cross Street, Blackpool, FY1 2EA Tel: (01253) 291414 Fax: (01253) 291415
Services Supply Co., 26 Penybont Road, Pencoed, Bridgend, Mid Glamorgan, CF35 5RA Tel: (01656) 860344 Fax: (01656) 862555 E-mail: sales@goldleafsupplies.com
Sign Designs, 5 Whorterbank, Dundee, DD2 3AA Tel: (01382) 622407 Fax: (01382) 624344
Sign & Image Works, 115 Blackburn Road, Bolton, BL1 8HF Tel: (01204) 393824 Fax: (01204) 365123 E-mail: sales@silentimage.com
Signcast, 14 Sherwood Forest Art & Craft Centre, Forest Corner, Edwinstowe, Mansfield, Nottinghamshire, NG21 9RN Tel: (01623) 825595 Fax: (01623) 825595 E-mail: sales@signcast.co.uk
Signflair Ltd, 10-54 Ainsworth Avenue, Belfast, BT13 3EN Tel: (028) 9032 6007 Fax: (028) 9033 1936 E-mail: signflair@dnet.co.uk
Signs Direct Trade, 2 Rancorn Road, Margate, Kent, CT9 5DG Tel: (01843) 224400 Fax: (01843) 296092
G.H. Tomlin & Co. Ltd, 11 Sandon Industrial Estate, Sandon Way, Liverpool, L5 9YN Tel: 0151-207 7216 Fax: 0151-298 2347 E-mail: mark@tomlinsighns.com
Treble Nine Signs, 8 Whittingham Road, Halesowen, West Midlands, B63 3TE Tel: 0121-550 1581 Fax: 0121-550 1581 E-mail: russ@treble-nine-signs.freeserve.co.uk
Vision Visual Solutions Ltd, 1 Solent Industrial Estate, Shamblehurst Lane, Hedge End, Southampton, SO30 2FX Tel: (01489) 781000 Fax: (01489) 781100 E-mail: sales@vvsltd.co.uk
Vulcascot Ltd, Braintree Road, Ruislip, Middlesex, HA4 0XX Tel: (020) 8841 4211 Fax: (020) 8841 3544

SIGN FIXING CLIPS

K.W. Hyde Ltd, 16 Blackthorne Road, Canvey Island, Essex, SS8 7BJ Tel: (07970) 461172 Fax: (07970) 110690 E-mail: kevin@kwhyde.com

SIGN FRAMES

Nationwide Signs Ltd, Derry Street, Wolverhampton, WV2 1EY Tel: (01902) 871116 Fax: (01902) 351195 E-mail: roadframes@aol.com

SIGN GANTRY ANCHORS

▶ Cesano Signs & Graphics, 20 St. Georges Road, Badshot Lea, Farnham, Surrey, GU9 9LX Tel: (01252) 341491 E-mail: dragonheartz@btinternet.com

SIGN MAINTENANCE, NEON

▶ A & S Signs, 240 Holliday Street, Birmingham, B1 1SJ Tel: 0121-632 6222 Fax: 0121-632 6222 E-mail: designwithsigns@btinternet.com
E Signs, 118 Piccadilly, Mayfair, London, W1J 7NW Tel: (0800) 7312259 Fax: (0845) 0042259 E-mail: info@e-signs.co.uk

SIGN MAKING EQUIPMENT

Alliance Engraving & Lettering Co. Ltd, Unit 18 Barton Hill Trading Estate, Maze Street, Bristol, BS5 9TE Tel: 0117-955 5292 Fax: 0117-955 7518 E-mail: sales@alliance-signs.co.uk
Alpha Systems, 63-65 High Street, Standish, Wigan, Lancashire, WN6 0HD Tel: (01257) 426617 Fax: (01257) 472148 E-mail: info@alphasolutions.co.uk
Assignments Ltd, Unit 6 Broadway Green Farm, Broadway Road, Lightwater, Surrey, GU18 5SU Tel: (01276) 452110 Fax: (01276) 453312 E-mail: sales@assimen.com
Becc Signs, 9a Orchard Rise, Croydon, CR0 7QZ Tel: (020) 8777 9377 Fax: (020) 8776 2224 E-mail: mail@beccs.co.uk
Birchdale Associates, Unit A, Chiltern Trading Estate, Leighton Buzzard, Bedfordshire, LU7 4TU Tel: (01525) 852513 Fax: (01525) 850462 E-mail: sales@signtec.co.uk
Craft Signs, 1 Hermitage Lane, Mansfield, Nottinghamshire, NG18 5HA Tel: (01623) 626166 Fax: (01623) 420977
DEWA Moving Signs, 140 Heanor Road, Ilkeston, Derbyshire, DE7 8TB Tel: 0115-932 1577 Fax: 0115-930 3976
Dragon Signs Of North Wales, Unit 1-2 Plot 11 Llandegai Industrial Estate, Llandygai, Bangor, Gwynedd, LL57 4YH Tel: (01248) 352286 Fax: (01248) 352286
Gee Tee Signs Ltd, Bestwood Road, Nottingham, NG6 8SS Tel: 0115-976 1188 Fax: 0115-976 1213 E-mail: sales@geeteesigns.com
Gloster Photographic Services Ltd, 6 Francis Woodcock Trading Estate, Barton Street, Gloucester, GL1 4JD Tel: (01452) 413444 Fax: (01452) 413444 E-mail: glosterphoto@fsmail.net
Grafityp (UK) Ltd, 103 Mariner, Tamworth, Staffordshire, B79 7UL Tel: (01827) 300500 Fax: (01827) 51333 E-mail: sales@grafityp.co.uk
I Spi Ltd, 47 Mansionhouse Road, Mount Vernon, Glasgow, G32 0RP Tel: 0141-764 1600 Fax: 0141-764 1600
Ideal Signs, Lerburn Place, The Lerburne, Wedmore, Somerset, BS28 4ED Tel: (01934) 712888 Fax: (01934) 713777
Jim Watts Signs, 27 Abbey Street, Market Harborough, Leicestershire, LE16 9AA Tel: (01858) 467763 Fax: (01858) 434826 E-mail: sales@jwsigns.co.uk
N-Grave Ltd, Legion Hall, Magdalen Road, Tilney St. Lawrence, King's Lynn, Norfolk, PE34 4RE Tel: (01945) 881133 Fax: (01945) 881144 E-mail: ngrave@btinternet.com
Prestige Signs, 33 Daryl Road, Wirral, Merseyside, CH60 5RD Tel: 0151-342 6372 Fax: 0151-342 6372
Select Signs, 25 West Street, Newport, Isle of Wight, PO30 1PR Tel: (01983) 529477 Fax: (01983) 520177
Sign Fit, 482 Barking Road, London, E6 2LT Tel: (020) 8552 1194 Fax: (020) 8548 1047
Signs Of The Times, 25 Townhead, Glasgow, G66 1NG Tel: 0141-776 7962 Fax: 0141-776 3322
Signs Unlimited, 60 Lincoln Road, Birmingham, B27 6NZ Tel: 0121-706 9021 Fax: 0121-706 6192
Signtech Plastics & Signs, 82 Moorland Road, Weston-super-Mare, Avon, BS23 4HT Tel: (01934) 416137 Fax: (01934) 628008 E-mail: signtech1@tiscali.co.uk
Signwise (Scotland) Ltd, 61 Dykehead Street, Queenslie Industrial Estate, Glasgow, G33 4AQ Tel: 0141-774 5261 Fax: 0141-774 9683 E-mail: signwise@cairnleck.co.uk
T G S, 4 Armstrong Court, Armstrong Way, Yate, Bristol, BS37 5NG Tel: (01454) 322033 Fax: (01454) 322077 E-mail: tgsbristol@btconnect.com
Touch Print Ltd, 49 Maple Avenue, Bulwark, Chepstow, Gwent, NP16 5RG Tel: (01291) 621401 Fax: (01291) 621403 E-mail: sales@touchprint.co.uk
Universal Components Ltd, Universal House, Pennywell Road, Bristol, BS5 0ER Tel: 0117-955 9091 Fax: 0117-955 6091 E-mail: info@universal-aluminium.co.uk
Williams & Brown, Unit 11 Ketlan Court, River Lane, Saltney, Chester, CH4 8RH Tel: (01244) 678302 Fax: (01244) 681519 E-mail: williamsandbrownsigns@btopenword.com

SIGN MAKING MATERIALS

A P A UK Ltd, Unit 10 Capital Industrial Estate, Crabtree Manorway South, Belvedere, Kent, DA17 6BJ Tel: (020) 8311 4400 Fax: (020) 8312 4777 E-mail: apauk@apaspa.com
Acorn Signs, Unit 3, 42 Harbour Road, Inverness, IV1 1UF Tel: (01463) 713708 Fax: (01463) 710332 E-mail: sales@acornsigns.co.uk
Artifax Signs & Print, 9f New Yard, Clay Flatts Industrial Estate, Workington, Cumbria, CA14 3YE Tel: (01900) 606452 Fax: (01900) 608395 E-mail: m.laidlow@btopenworld.com
Creative Signs, Sandbach Road, Stoke-on-Trent, ST6 2DG Tel: (01782) 214589 Fax: (01782) 214589 E-mail: creative.signs@btopenworld.com
FOCUS Signs Ltd, 136a St. Johns Road, Woking, Surrey, GU21 7PS Tel: (01483) 776716 Fax: (01483) 776716
W. Habberley Meadows Ltd, 5 Saxon Way, Chelmsley Wood, Birmingham, B37 5AY Tel: 0121-770 0103 Fax: 0121-770 6512 E-mail: gold@habberleymeadows.co.uk
Lowestoft Sign Centre Design Manufacture Installation, Ellough Industrial Estate, Ellough, Beccles, Suffolk, NR34 7TD Tel: (01502) 710717 Fax: (01502) 717233 E-mail: sales@lowestoftsigns.co.uk
Masonlite Ltd, 36 Second Avenue, Chatham, Kent, ME4 5AX Tel: (01634) 812751 Fax: (01634) 811883 E-mail: neon@masonlite.com
Robert Horne Group plc, Huntsman House, B2 Evelyn Street, London, SE8 5DL Tel: (020) 7231 9634 Fax: (020) 7231 5641
Rockwell Signs, 341 Southmead Road, Westbury-on-Trym, Bristol, BS10 5LW Tel: 0117-950 4506 Fax: 0117-950 4506
S A S Materials Ltd, 956 Kingsbury Road, Erdington, Birmingham, B24 9QA Tel: 0121-377 6005 Fax: 0121-377 7402 E-mail: sales@easystick.co.uk
Signs UK, Winsor Farm Studio, Yealmpton, Plymouth, PL8 2LL Tel: 01752 881144 Fax: 01752 881172

SIGNAL CONDITIONING EQUIPMENT

Amelec Instruments Ltd, 3-5 Cochran Close, Crownhill, Milton Keynes, MK8 0AJ Tel: (01908) 567003 Fax: (01908) 566735 E-mail: sales@amelec-uk.com
Sky Electronic Systems Ltd, Unit D Cavendish Courtyard, Weldon North Industrial Estate, Corby, Northamptonshire, NN17 5DZ Tel: (01536) 267000 Fax: (01536) 267666 E-mail: ian@skyd.fsnet.co.uk

SIGNAL GENERATORS

M & B Radio (Leeds), 86 Bishopgate Street, Leeds, LS1 4BB Tel: 0113-243 5649 Fax: 0113-242 6881

SIGNAL PROCESSING INTEGRATED CIRCUITS (IC)

Entegra Ltd, Entergra House, Woodside Lane, Lymington, Hampshire, SO41 8FJ Tel: (01590) 671700 E-mail: sales@entegra.co.uk
Sundance Multiprocessor Technology Ltd, Chiltern Ho, Waterside, Chesham, Buckinghamshire, HP5 1PS Tel: (01494) 793167 Fax: (01494) 793168 E-mail: sales@sundance.com

SIGNS TO SPECIFICATION

Able Signs, Unit 5, 1-2 Davey Road, Clacton-On-Sea, Essex, CO15 4XD Tel: (01255) 427350 Fax: (01255) 221658
Acorn Signs, 203 London Road, Stoke-on-Trent, ST4 5RW Tel: (01782) 412020 Fax: (01782) 412259
All About Signs Ltd, 19 Ordnance Court, Ackworth Road Hilsea, Portsmouth, PO3 5RZ Tel: (023) 9265 4720 Fax: (023) 9265 4721 E-mail: admin@allaboutsigns.co.uk
Amber Signs, Pledgdon Hall, Henham, Bishop's Stortford, Hertfordshire, CM22 6BJ Tel: (01279) 850836 Fax: (01279) 850995 E-mail: ambersigns@btconnect.com
Artd'Sign Sign Manufacturer, Victoria Road, Unit 8, Teknol House, Burgess Hill, West Sussex, RH15 9LH Tel: (01444) 241215 Fax: (01444) 239136 E-mail: info@artdsigns.co.uk
Aztec Signs, 10 Lound Road, Kendal, Cumbria, LA9 7DT Tel: (01539) 724897 Fax: (01539) 724897
CGS Signs Ltd, 23 Railway Road, Adlington, Chorley, Lancashire, PR6 9RG Tel: (01257) 482790 Fax: (01257) 482791 E-mail: sales@cgssigns.co.uk
Chadfield Signs, 6 Highfield Road, Stockton-on-Tees, Cleveland, TS18 5HG Tel: (01642) 582082
Characters Signs, Aston Bury, Aston, Stevenage, Hertfordshire, SG2 7EG Tel: (01438) 880181 Fax: (01438) 880182 E-mail: info@characterssigns.com
Classic Signs, 52 Cardigan Road, Bridlington, North Humberside, YO15 3HQ Tel: (01262) 673131 Fax: (01262) 673131 E-mail: sales@classic-signs.co.uk
Concept Signs Ltd, Unit 7, Collingwood Industrial Estate, Maidstone Road, Sutton Valence, Maidstone, Kent, ME17 3QS Tel: (01622) 844884 Fax: (01622) 843884 E-mail: signletters2003@yahoo.co.uk
Contract Sign Systems Ltd, John Davey Drive, Treleigh Industrial Estate, Redruth, Cornwall, TR16 4AX Tel: (01209) 313449 Fax: (0870) 8706929 E-mail: sales@contractsigns.co.uk
Craft Signs, 1 Hermitage Lane, Mansfield, Nottinghamshire, NG18 5HA Tel: (01623) 626166 Fax: (01623) 420977
Creative Image Signs & Displays Ltd, 8 Spibton Abbey, Bedford, MK41 0UQ Tel: (01234) 356588 Fax: (01234) 346898 E-mail: signsplusbeford@aol.com
Creative Signwriting Co., 64 Englands Lane, Gorleston, Great Yarmouth, Norfolk, NR31 6BE Tel: (01493) 600742 Fax: (01493) 653984 E-mail: info@creativesign.co.com

SIGNS TO SPECIFICATION – *continued*

▶ Cube Display Ltd, Downham Street, Bradford, West Yorkshire, BD3 9QY Tel: (01274) 746611 Fax: (01274) 746622

Custom Grafix, Knighton-On-Teme, Tenbury Wells, Worcestershire, WR15 8LZ Tel: (0800) 5421646 Fax: (01584) 781077

Cyclops Signs, 76 London Road, Bexhill-on-Sea, East Sussex, TN39 3LE Tel: (0845) 1991814 Fax: (01424) 215025 E-mail: sales@cyclopssigns.co.uk

Dorling Signs Ltd, 66-74 Virgil Street, Liverpool, L5 5BY Tel: 0151-298 1511 Fax: 0151-298 1512 E-mail: info@dorling-signs.co.uk

▶ Peter Dudley Exhibitions & Displays, Uttoxer Road, Blithbury, Rugeley, Staffordshire, WS15 3JG Tel: (01889) 504284 Fax: (01889) 504284

Euro Signs, 70 Lower Dock Street, Newport, Gwent, NP20 1EH Tel: (01633) 216486 Fax: (01633) 216486

Fair Sign Co., Unit E6 Aladdin Workspace, 426 Long Drive, Greenford, Middlesex, UB6 8UH Tel: (020) 8578 3080 Fax: (020) 8578 3082 E-mail: sales@fairsign.co.uk

Fastsigns, 86 Walcot Street, Bath, BA1 5BD Tel: (01225) 447797 Fax: (01225) 444010

Fastsigns, 449 Cowbridge Road East, Cardiff, CF5 1JH Tel: (029) 2034 4455 Fax: (029) 2034 4488 E-mail: 868@fastsigns.com

Fastsigns Ltd, 36 High St, New Malden, Surrey, KT3 4HE Tel: 020 83360802 Fax: 020 83360914

Ford Signs, 1A Burgess Street, Leicester, LE1 4QJ Tel: 0116-251 8185 Fax: 0116-251 6595 E-mail: sales.fordsigns@virgin.net

Hayward Signs, Unit 1-2 Bay Works, Marine Road, Pevensey Bay, Pevensey, East Sussex, BN24 6EG Tel: (01323) 740266 Fax: (01323) 460245 E-mail: superscreen@btconnect.com

Henley Sign People, Unit 1b Vines Farm, Reading Road, Cane End, Reading, RG4 9HE Tel: 0118-972 4567 Fax: 0118-972 3205 E-mail: sales@signpeople.com

Horwich Signs Ltd, 4 Stirling Industrial Estate, Chorley New Road, Horwich, Bolton, BL6 6DU Tel: (01204) 669500 Fax: (01204) 669500

Instant Image, Park Farm, Colchester Road, Elmstead, Colchester, CO7 7BA Tel: (01206) 822121 Fax: (01206) 822121 E-mail: instant.7b@virgin.net

J D Signs, PO Box 317, Camberley, Surrey, GU17 0QG Tel: (01276) 600562 Fax: (01273) 600562

Joules Signs, Philomel, 542 Abbott Street, Pamphill, Wimborne, Dorset, BH21 4EF Tel: (01202) 885847 Fax: (01202) 885847

Legend Signs Ltd, 1 Benham Business Park, Ashford Road, Newingreen, Hythe, Kent, CT21 4JD Tel: (01303) 261278 Fax: (01303) 261280 E-mail: info@kullasigns.co.uk

Letters & Logos Ltd, Crow La Bus Park, Crow, Ringwood, Hampshire, BH24 3EA Tel: (01425) 477281 Fax: (01425) 480094 E-mail: team@lettersandlogos.co.uk

Mamba Signs, 9 Wyndham Lane, Plymouth, PL1 5ED Tel: (01752) 227434 Fax: (01752) 260310

Morris & Laken Signs Ltd, 14 Ravenswood Industrial Estate, Shernhall Street, London, E17 9HQ Tel: (020) 8521 1910 Fax: (020) 8509 3803

Pearce Forecourt Signs Ltd, 456 Margate Road, Broadstairs, Kent, CT10 2PU Tel: (01843) 869585 Fax: (01843) 868340

Peterborough Signs, 17-18 Leofric Square, Peterborough, PE1 5TU Tel: (01733) 555060 Fax: (01733) 344293 E-mail: info@peterborough-signs.co.uk

Phoenix Signs Ltd, Unit 7, Continental Approach, Westwood Industrial Estate, Margate, Kent, CT9 4JG Tel: (01843) 228682 Fax: (01843) 227373 E-mail: vince@phoenixsignsuk.ltd.uk

Raccoon Signs & Display Ltd, 9 Warsop Trading Estate, Hever Road, Edenbridge, Kent, TN8 5LD Tel: (01732) 864966 Fax: (01732) 867612 E-mail: enquiries@raccoon.co.uk

Randle Signs, 29 Blackdown Avenue, Chesterfield, Derbyshire, S40 4QQ Tel: (01246) 205905 Fax: (01246) 205905

Rivermeade Signs Ltd, Rowley Industrial Park, Roslin Road, London, W3 8BH Tel: (020) 8896 6900 Fax: (020) 8752 1691 E-mail: info@rivermeade.com

Roys Signs, 15 Hoobrook Industrial Estate, Worcester Road, Kidderminster, Worcestershire, DY10 1HY Tel: (01562) 829299 Fax: (01562) 829299

Rufford Studios Ltd, 3 Monks Dairy, Isle Brewers, Taunton, Somerset, TA3 6QL Tel: (01460) 281878

S & P M Signs & Graphics, Sign & Graphic Centre, Bath Road, Padworth, Reading, RG7 5HR Tel: 0118-971 4713 Fax: 0118-971 4723 E-mail: sales@spmsigns.com

▶ Shingle Berry Signs, Unit 4, Lloyd Court, Dunston, Gateshead, Tyne & Wear, NE11 9EP Tel: 0191-461 0084 Fax: 0191-460 3929 E-mail: sales@shingleberrysigns.com

Sign Engineering, George Street, High Wycombe, Buckinghamshire, HP11 2RZ Tel: (01494) 459915 Fax: (01494) 459915

Sign Fx, Signs F X, Unit 4 Bradmash Court, Bradmarsh Way, Rotherham, South Yorkshire, S60 1BW Tel: (01709) 360057 E-mail: signfxsales@btconnect.com

Sign Solutions, Unit 6-7, Brympton Way, Yeovil, Somerset, BA20 2HP Tel: (01935) 425864 Fax: (01935) 425533 E-mail: sales@ss4signs.co.uk

Signature Signs, Timbercot, Waterside, Bradwell-on-Sea, Southminster, Essex, CM0 7QT Tel: (01621) 776772 Fax: (01621) 776772

▶ Signs & Design Ltd, 22-23 King Street Trading Estate, Middlewich, Cheshire, CW10 9LF Tel: (01606) 738833 Fax: (01606) 738547 E-mail: info@golfcoursesigns.co.uk

Signs & Print, 21-23 Dudley Road, Brierley Hill, West Midlands, DY5 1HA Tel: (01384) 261333 Fax: (01384) 261666

Signsense, 240 Ashley Road, Poole, Dorset, BH14 9BZ Tel: (01202) 252627 Fax: (01202) 250300

Signwaves Ltd, Lefevre Way, Great Yarmouth, Norfolk, NR31 0NW Tel: (01493) 419300 Fax: (01493) 419301 E-mail: equiries@signwavesgroup.com

Signwise, Unit B3 Spectrum Business Estate, Anthonys Way, Medway City Estate, Rochester, Kent, ME2 4NP Tel: (01634) 297200 Fax: (01634) 297222 E-mail: info@signwise.co.uk

Signworx, Unit 16 Ellingham Industrial Centre, Ellingham Way, Ashford, Kent, TN23 6NF Tel: (01233) 632244 Fax: (01233) 632255 E-mail: info@msignworx.com

Spectrum Sign & Display Ltd, 11a Brindley Road, Reginald Road Industrial Estate, St. Helens, Merseyside, WA9 4HY Tel: (01744) 815005 Fax: (01744) 813920 E-mail: sales@spectrumsigns.net

Standing Stone, Llwynteg, Ffynnonddrain, Carmarthen, Dyfed, SA33 6EE Tel: (01267) 223226 Fax: (01267) 223495 E-mail: sales@standingstone.co.uk

Stockport Signs, 26 Middle Hillgate, Stockport, Cheshire, SK1 3AY Tel: 0161-429 7604 Fax: 0161-429 7604 E-mail: cheshiresigns@aol.com

Superior Signs Ltd, 1-7 Taylor Street, Bury, Lancashire, BL9 6DT Tel: 0161-764 5170 Fax: 0161-762 9068 E-mail: sales@superiorsigns.co.uk

Swift Signs, 26 Stradey Park Avenue, Llanelli, Dyfed, SA15 3EF Tel: (01554) 757781 Fax: (01554) 774024

Synergy Sign Design Ltd, Hi-Spec House, Liverpool Road, Great Sankey, Warrington, WA5 1EE Tel: (01925) 487951 Fax: (01925) 492794 E-mail: sales@synergysigns.com

Trilogy, 189 Castleblany Road, Keady, Armagh, BT60 3HY Tel: (028) 3753 0950 Fax: (028) 3753 0950

Triwonder Signs, Unit 4, Tannery Road, Tonbridge, Kent, TN9 1RF Tel: (01732) 770444 Fax: (01732) 363888

Vinatec Signs & Nameplates, 244 Bentley Road, Doncaster, South Yorkshire, DN5 9QP Tel: (01302) 822777 Fax: (01302) 822777 E-mail: sales@vinatec.co.uk

Vision Signs & Ceilings, 151-153 New Road, Portsmouth, PO2 7QS Tel: (023) 9267 2525 Fax: (023) 9262 4462 E-mail: sales@visionsigns.com

Viz Biz Design, 4 24 Ings Road, Wakefield, West Yorkshire, WF1 1DZ Tel: (01924) 377888 Fax: (01924) 385573 E-mail: vizbiz@btconnect.com

Wingate Signs Ltd, 23 Pilsworth Way, Bury, Lancashire, BL9 8RE Tel: 0161-767 9383 Fax: 0161-796 3827 E-mail: wingatesigns@btinternet.com

SIGNS, A-FRAME

Burnham Signs Ltd, Burnham Way, London, SE26 5AG Tel: (020) 8659 1525 Fax: (020) 8659 4707 E-mail: sales@burnhamsigns.com

SIGNS, ELECTRONIC/ CHANGEABLE INFORMATION

Blaze Maintenance Ltd, 15 Tonbridge Road, Hildenborough, Tonbridge, Kent, TN11 9BH Tel: (01732) 832555 Fax: (01732) 833002 E-mail: info@blazemaintenance.co.uk

C W Micro-Systems, 11 Mitchell Point, Ensign Way, Southampton, SO31 4RF Tel: (023) 8045 6888 Fax: (023) 8045 6542 E-mail: info@signblazer.com

E D C Technology, Suite 24, Mountbatten House, Hillcrest, Highgate, London, N6 4HJ Tel: (020) 8341 2689

Electro Signs Ltd, 97 Vallentin Road, London, E17 3JJ Tel: (020) 8521 8066 Fax: (020) 8520 8127 E-mail: info@electrosigns.co.uk

Esprit Communications, Supreme House, 300 Regents Park Road, London, N3 2JX Tel: (020) 8346 4499 Fax: (020) 8346 6969 E-mail: beter@espritcommunications.com

Ferrograph Ltd, New York Way, New York Industrial Park, Newcastle upon Tyne, NE27 0QF Tel: 0191-280 8800 Fax: 0191-280 8810

Piers-Roger (Electronics) Ltd, Knights Court, Magellan Close, Walworth Industrial Estate, Andover, Hampshire, SP10 5NT Tel: (01264) 400800 Fax: (01264) 400900 E-mail: sales@polycomp.co.uk

Racecourse Information Systems Ltd, Chapland Cottage, Lanark, ML11 7RH Tel: (01555) 663285 Fax: (01555) 663285

Vision Options Ltd, York House, 22 Old Shoreham Road, Brighton, BN1 5DD Tel: (01273) 385000 Fax: (01273) 549549 E-mail: voptions@aol.com

SIGNS, ESTATE AGENT/BOARD ERECTORS

C S Howard, 73 Grasscroft, Northampton, NN2 8QL Tel: (01604) 845888 Fax: (01604) 820213 E-mail: colin@the-boardman.co.uk

City & County Signs, 209 Pinhoe Road, Exeter, EX4 8AB Tel: (01392) 434366 Fax: (01392) 434366

Kremer Signs Ltd, Units 18, East Road Industrial Estate, Sleaford, Lincolnshire, NG34 7EQ Tel: (01529) 415511 Fax: (01529) 415444 E-mail: sales@kremersigns.co.uk

Kremer Signs, 300 New Greenham Park, Greenham, Thatcham, Berkshire, RG19 6HN Tel: (01635) 46125 Fax: (01635) 523170 E-mail: sales@kremersigns.co.uk

Signline, Unit 5a Ridge Hill Farm, Nash, Milton Keynes, MK17 0EH Tel: (01908) 379600 Fax: (01296) 715113

▶ So Estates, 20 Russell Road, West Wittering, Chichester, West Sussex, PO20 8EF Tel: (01243) 674444 Fax: (01243) 674444 E-mail: info@soestates.co.uk

SIGNS, FIRE EXTINGUISHER

Fire Protection Centre, Atkinsons Way, Foxhills Industrial Estate, Scunthorpe, South Humberside, DN15 8QJ Tel: (01724) 854199 Fax: 01724 854213 E-mail: bthloden@fireprotectioncentre.com

Fire Safety Express, Tesla Court, Innovation Way, Lynch Wood, Peterborough, PE2 6FL Tel: (01733) 234504 Fax: 01733 234504 E-mail: enquiries@firesafetyexpress.co.uk

▶ Fire Solutions, Units 1 & 2 The Great Barn, Earls Croome, Worcester, WR8 9DF Tel: (01905) 371321 Fax: E-mail: info@firesolutions.co.uk

▶ Nordal Fire Protection Services Ltd, Nordalmere House, 46 Midland Road, Raunds, Northamptonshire, NN9 6JF Tel: (01933) 625407 Fax: (01933) 626939 E-mail: sales@nordal.co.uk

SIGNS, MAGNETIC, VEHICLE

▶ Hollographics Ltd, 2 Wynford, The Pastures, Kings Worthy, Winchester, Hampshire, SO23 7LX Tel: (01962) 882422 Fax: (01962) 882422 E-mail: info@hollographics.com

▶ Magic Signs, 167 Ash Hill Road, Ash, Aldershot, Hampshire, GU12 5DW Tel: (01252) 337776 Fax: (01252) 337776 E-mail: sales@magicsigns.co.uk

Prescott Graphics Services, Unit 17M, Westside Ind Est, St. Helens, Merseyside, WA9 3AT Tel: (0800) 9546172 E-mail: enquiries@precottgraphics.co.uk

▶ Sign Impact, 1 High House Cottage, Woodham Road, Battlesbridge, Wickford, Essex, SS11 7QL Tel: (01268) 761116 E-mail: sales@sign-impact.co.uk

▶ Signs Express Ltd, Unit 16 Anglo Business Park, Smeaton Close, Aylesbury, Buckinghamshire, HP19 8UP Tel: (01296) 339998 Fax: (01296) 331118 E-mail: aylesbury@signsexpress.co.uk

▶ www.fullcoloursigns.biz, Unit 3 Granville Court, Leighton Street, Nottingham, NG3 2FU Tel: 0115-841 8416 Fax: 0115-841 8417 E-mail: sales@fullcoloursigns.biz

SIGNS, MOVING/MULTIPOSTER

Powergraphic Displays Ltd, 6 Blenheim Road, Cressex Business Park, High Wycombe, Buckinghamshire, HP12 3RS Tel: (01494) 450936 Fax: (01494) 461975 E-mail: edwardbutler@powergraphicdisplays.com

SIGNS, TACTILE, BRAILLE

Recognition Express, 10-16 Victoria Parade, Urmston, Manchester, M41 9RE Tel: 0161-748 1716 Fax: 0161-755 3650 E-mail: sales@re-manchester.co.uk

SIGNS, TIN

Admiral Signs Of Hull Ltd, Sainsbury Way, Hessle, North Humberside, HU13 9NX Tel: (01482) 575007 Fax: (01482) 219098 E-mail: info@admiral-signs-hull.co.uk

SIGNS, TRADEWORK

Fife Signs Screen Printers, 3 Waverley Road, Kirkcaldy, Fife, KY1 3NH Tel: (01592) 655646 Fax: (01592) 655330 E-mail: sales@caledoniasigns.co.uk

Midland Signs Systems Ltd, 2 Stour Road, Weedon Road Industrial Estate, Northampton, NN5 5AA Tel: (01604) 580966 Fax: (01604) 581878

Phoenix Signs Ltd, Unit 7, Continental Approach, Westwood Industrial Estate, Margate, Kent, CT9 4JG Tel: (01843) 228682 Fax: (01843) 227373 E-mail: vince@phoenixsignsuk.ltd.uk

Signature Signs, Timbercot, Waterside, Bradwell-on-Sea, Southminster, Essex, CM0 7QT Tel: (01621) 776772 Fax: (01621) 776772

Spectrum Menu Systems Ltd, Units 12 &13, Hixon Industrial Estate, Church Lane, Hixon, Stafford, ST18 0PY Tel: (01889) 271440 Fax: (01889) 271449

SIGNWRITING OR LETTERING SERVICES

A R Dixon Display Ltd, 7a Waterloo Industrial Estate, Waterloo Road, Bidford-on-Avon, Alcester, Warwickshire, B50 4JH Tel: (01789) 772233 Fax: (01789) 490928

A W S Metal Finishers, 79 Baltimore Road, Birmingham, B42 1DG Tel: 0121-357 3127 Fax: 0121-357 3127 E-mail: airbrush12@aol.com

Action Graphics (Birmingham) Ltd, Units 3 & 5 Phoenix Park Industrial Estate, Avenue Close, Aston, Birmingham, B7 4NU Tel: 0121-242 4000 Fax: 0121-242 4030 E-mail: info@action-graphics.co.uk

Admiral Signs Ltd, 121 Oak Street, Norwich, NR3 3BP Tel: (01603) 627573 Fax: (01603) 619954 E-mail: info@admiral-signs.co.uk

Arro Signs, Unit 4 Three Springs Industrial Estate, Vincent Road, Worcester, WR5 1BW Tel: (01905) 356333 Fax: (01905) 764406

Arrow Signs, Nairn Road, Cramlington, Northumberland, NE23 1RQ Tel: (01670) 735922 Fax: (01670) 716269

Artd'Sign Sign Manufacturer, Victoria Road, Unit 8, Teknol House, Burgess Hill, West Sussex, RH15 9LH Tel: (01444) 241215 Fax: (01444) 239136 E-mail: info@artdsigns.co.uk

Bolton Sign Contractors, Unit 4 Printers Lane, Bolton, BL2 3DW Tel: (01204) 594700 Fax: (01204) 595424 E-mail: info@boltonsign.co.uk

Booth Signs, 45 Stafford Road, Wallington, Surrey, SM6 9AP Tel: (020) 8669 1625 Fax: (020) 8773 3429 E-mail: boothsigns@lineone.net

Alexander Boyd Displays Ltd, Lambeg Mills, Ballyskeagh Road, Lisburn, County Antrim, BT27 5SX Tel: (028) 9030 1115 Fax: (028) 9030 1305E-mail: sboyd@alexanderboyd.com

Brewer Sign Services, 24 Meredith Road, Portsmouth, PO2 9NN Tel: (023) 9266 8602 Fax: (023) 9266 8602

Cambrian Signs, 10 Burnell Road, Sheffield, S6 2AX Tel: 0114-233 0233 Fax: 0114-233 0233

Castleton Signs Ltd, 25 Mitcham Lane, London, SW16 6LQ Tel: (020) 8769 8741 Fax: (020) 8769 9699E-mail: sales@castletonsigns.co.uk

Commercial Signs & Displays Ltd, Commercial Road, Devizes, Wiltshire, SN10 1EH Tel: (01380) 721068 Fax: (01380) 721068 E-mail: commercialsigns@btconnect.com

Contrast Signs, 135 Roxeth Green Avenue, Harrow, Middlesex, HA2 0QJ Tel: (020) 8864 9242

Countrywide Signs, Church Villa, 23 Brinkley Road, Dullingham, Newmarket, Suffolk, CB8 9UW Tel: (01638) 508077 Fax: (01638) 507880 E-mail: sales@countrywide-signs.com

D3 Display, 1 Cyril Road, Small Heath, Birmingham, B10 0SS Tel: 0121-772 1815 Fax: 0121-766 6052 E-mail: info@d3display.co.uk

Dale Signs, 19 Woodhouse Road, Sheffield, S12 2AY Tel: 0114-253 1461 Fax: 0114-239 8127

▶ Dartmoor Memorials, Westbridge Trading Centre, Westbridge Indust Estate, Tavistock, Devon, PL19 8DE Tel: (01822) 617700 Fax: (01822) 617702 E-mail: enquiries@dartmoor-memorials.com

Decor Signs, Unit 22 Oldbury Business Centre, Oldbury Road, Cwmbran, Gwent, NP44 3JU Tel: (01633) 866349 Fax: (01633) 866349 E-mail: marketing@decorsigns.co.uk

E S P Technologies Group Ltd, 2 Euroway, Wood Close, Quarry Wood, Aylesford, Kent, ME20 7UB Tel: (01622) 715000 Fax: (01622) 797000 E-mail: sales@esptech.co.uk

▶ Ensign UK, 21 Polesworth Close, Redditch, Worcestershire, B98 0EE Tel: (07791) 381048 E-mail: ensign-uk@blueyonder.co.uk

Ghinn Signs, 98 Wickham Street, Welling, Kent, DA16 3LU Tel: (020) 8316 5501 Fax: (020) 8854 7612 E-mail: ghinnsigns@aol.com

▶ Kevin Glashier, 93 Sussex Way*, London, N7 6RU Tel: (020) 7281 7821 E-mail: kevin@kevinglashier.co.uk

Gould Autoplates & Signs Ltd, 2 Blackfriars Trading Estate, Blackfriars Road, Nailsea, Bristol, BS48 4DJ Tel: (01275) 853853 Fax: (01275) 859426

Graphic Signs, 157 Fulford Road, York, YO10 4HH Tel: (01904) 621499 Fax: (01904) 621499

David A. Green, 5 Ruskin Grove, Stockport, Cheshire, SK6 1DP Tel: 0161-430 7099 Fax: 0161-430 7099

Harmony Signs & Design Services Ltd, 18 Fisher St, Paignton, Devon, TQ4 5EL Tel: (01803) 559317 Fax: (01803) 522357 E-mail: admin@harmonysigns.co.uk

The Harris Sign Group Ltd, Springfield Road, Coventry, CV1 4GN Tel: (024) 7622 9950 Fax: (024) 7638 1320

Jag Signs Supplies, Mitre Ct, Winterland La, Holsworthy, Devon, EX22 6NF Tel: (01409) 254370

▶ indicates data change since last edition

SIGNWRITING OR LETTERING SERVICES – *continued*

K B S Group, 41 Marsh Green Road West, Marsh Barton Trading Estate, Exeter, EX2 8PN Tel: (01392) 208208 Fax: (01392) 208200 E-mail: sales@kbs-group.com

K W Signs, 11 Burnside Road, Bolton, BL1 6EP Tel: (01204) 491487 Fax: (01204) 491488

▶ Kentish Sign Writers, 139 Ballens Road, Chatham, Kent, ME5 8PG Tel: (01634) 309295 Fax: E-mail: sales@kentishsigns.com

Kershaw Signs, 31 Harrowby Road, Leeds, LS16 5HX Tel: 0113-278 5873

Kremer Signs Ltd, Units 18, East Road Industrial Estate, Sleaford, Lincolnshire, NG34 7EQ Tel: (01529) 415511 Fax: (01529) 415444 E-mail: sales@kremersigns.co.uk

Kullasigns Sign Writers, 1 Benham Water Farm, Ashford Road, Newingreen, Hythe, Kent, CT21 4JD Tel: (01303) 261279 Fax: (01303) 261280 E-mail: sales@legendsigns.co.uk

L A H Signs, 47 Gaol Lane, Sudbury, Suffolk, CO10 1JJ Tel: (01787) 373073 Fax: (01787) 373073

L & M Signs, Unit 1 Highlands Close, St Helens Way, Thetford, Norfolk, IP24 1HG Tel: 01842 821990 Fax: 01842 750706 E-mail: trevor@lmsigns.co.uk

Mcquillan Signs, Cleves, Keymer Road, Burgess Hill, West Sussex, RH15 0AP Tel: (01444) 471847 Fax: (01444) 248592 E-mail: johntmcquillan@fsnet.co.uk

Millsigns Sign Writers, 26 Bell Street, Romsey, Hampshire, SO51 8GW Tel: (01794) 830088

Monwel Hankinson Signs & Services, Letchworth Road, Ebbw Vale, Gwent, NP23 6UZ Tel: (01495) 301333 Fax: (01495) 350323

▶ Morgan Signs, Fairoak House, Fairoak Road, Cardiff, CF24 4YA Tel: (029) 2023 2022 Fax: (029) 2023 2017 E-mail: ceri@morgan-signs.co.uk

Motor Mode, The Art Works, 53 Butchers Lane, Mereworth, Maidstone, Kent, ME18 5QA Tel: (01622) 817400 Fax: (01732) 868167 E-mail: office@motormode.com

Newsigns Sign Writers, Unit 6a The Arches, Loveridge Road, London, NW6 2DS Tel: (020) 7328 9251 Fax: (020) 7624 7465

Reade Signs Ltd, 4 Holder Road, Aldershot, Hampshire, GU12 4RH Tel: (01252) 333535 Fax: (01252) 333535 E-mail: sales@readesigns.com

Riviera Signs Ltd, 2 104 Barton Road, Torquay, TQ2 7NY Tel: (01803) 324303 Fax: (01803) 314105 E-mail: sales@rivierasigns.co.uk

Rondar Signs Ltd, 2 Outram Road, Dukinfield, Cheshire, SK16 4XE Tel: 0161-339 0194 Fax: 0161-339 1370E-mail: info@rondar.co.uk

Royle & Gemmell, Booth House, Suthers Street, Oldham, OL9 7TQ Tel: 0161-628 9292 Fax: 0161-628 9292

Samark Signs Sign Design, 6 Rosshill Industrial Park, Sutton Road, Southend-on-Sea, SS2 5PZ Tel: (01702) 616655 E-mail: samarksigns@yahoo.co.uk

Showprint Photographics Ltd, 29 High Street, Hampton Wick, Kingston Upon Thames, Surrey, KT1 4DA Tel: (020) 8943 9572 Fax: (020) 8943 5372

Sign 7 Ltd, Unit 10 Fox Oak Enterprise Centre, Foxoak Street, Cradley Heath, West Midlands, B64 5DP Tel: (01384) 413704 Fax: (01384) 413705

Signs Of The Times, Whitchurch Business Park, Shakespeare Way, Whitchurch, Shropshire, SY13 1LJ Tel: (01948) 666609 Fax: (01948) 666681 E-mail: admin@signsofthetimes.uk.com

Solihull Signs, 270 Lode Lane, Solihull, West Midlands, B91 2HY Tel: 0121-704 1624 Fax: 0121-704 1624 E-mail: sales@solihullsigns.co.uk

Stourport Sign Studio, 3 Sandy La Industrial Estate, Stourport-on-Severn, Worcestershire, DY13 9QB Tel: (01299) 826044 Fax: (01299) 826044

Sussex Sign Centre, 4 Mill Road, Burgess Hill, West Sussex, RH15 8DR Tel: (01444) 246884 Fax: (01444) 871871 E-mail: sales@sussexsigncentre.co.uk

Symbol Signs, 3 Rennie Road, Skippers Lane Industrial Estate, Middlesbrough, Cleveland, TS6 6PX Tel: (01642) 467533 Fax: (01642) 463393 E-mail: symbolsigns@btconnect.com

Tanton Signs, 2 Ladycroft Way, Orpington, Kent, BR6 7BX Tel: (01689) 859642 Fax: (01689) 859642

▶ The Traditional Signwriting & Signmaking Company, 3 Berryfield Road, London, SE17 3QE Tel: (020) 7708 3271 Fax: (020) 7701 9766 E-mail: james@signwriting-london.co.uk

Truk Mark, 391 Holywood Road, Belfast, BT4 2LS Tel: (028) 9065 8837 Fax: (028) 9065 7225 E-mail: devansco@btinternet.com

Martin West Signs, 200 Pyotts Hill, 20 Pyotts Hill, Old Basing, Basingstoke, Hants, RG24 8AP Tel: (01256) 464005

SILAGE BAGS, POLYETHYLENE (PE)

Nelson Packaging, Waidshouse Mill, Townsley Street, Nelson, Lancashire, BB9 0RY Tel: (01282) 690215 Fax: (01282) 699976

SILAGE PROTECTION SHEETS

▶ Secure Covers, Edgton, Craven Arms, Shropshire, SY7 8HN Tel: 01588 680661 Fax: 01588 680416 E-mail: gerardthomas@securecovers.com

SILENCED CONTAINERISED GENERATOR SETS

Eagle Power, Johnson Bridge Road, Off Church Lane, West Bromwich, West Midlands, B71 1DG Tel: 0121-580 3222 Fax: 0121-525 4796 E-mail: eagle@kw1.com

▶ Kentec Power Systems Ltd, Unit 18 Cannel Road, Chasetown Industrial Estate, Burntwood Business Park, Burntwood, Staffordshire, WS7 3FU Tel: (01543) 677802 Fax: (01543) 677508 E-mail: sales@kentec.uk.com

SILENCED GENERATOR SETS

Arc-Gen Ltd, Station Road, Four Ashes Industrial Estate, Four Ashes, Wolverhampton, WV10 7DB Tel: (01902) 790824 Fax: (01902) 790355 E-mail: andymunford@arc-gen.co.uk

Cummins Power Generation Ltd, Manston Park, Columbus Avenue, Manston, Ramsgate, Kent, CT12 5BF Tel: (01843) 255000 Fax: (01843) 255902 E-mail: graham.n.baldock@cummins.com

SILENCER COMPONENTS/ FITTINGS

Burgess Architectural Products Ltd, Brookfield Road, Burbage, Hinckley, Leicestershire, LE10 2LL Tel: (01455) 618787 Fax: (01455) 251061 E-mail: sales@fleetguard.com

Vegem Ltd, PO Box 9, Leeds, LS27 0QN Tel: 0113-253 0451 Fax: 0113-252 1161 E-mail: enquiries@vegem.co.uk

SILICA GEL SACHETS

GeeJay Chemicals Ltd, 1 Beamish Close, Sandy, Bedfordshire, SG19 1SD Tel: (01767) 682774 Fax: (01767) 699697 E-mail: sales@geejaychemicals.co.uk

SILICA SAND

Bathgate Silica Sand Ltd, Arclid Quarry, Congleton Road, Arclid, Sandbach, Cheshire, CW11 4SN Tel: (01270) 762492 Fax: (01270) 759449 E-mail: info@bathgatesilica.co.uk

Bucbricks Ardleigh Sands, Martells Industrial Estate, Slough Lane, Ardleigh, Colchester, CO7 7RU Tel: (01206) 230310 Fax: (01206) 231057 E-mail: sands@bucbricks.co.uk

J Stoddard & Sons Ltd, Pinsley Green, Wrenbury, Nantwich, Cheshire, CW5 8HE Tel: (01270) 780996 Fax: (01270) 780027

▶ Maple Arenas, 41 Newlands Road, Riddings, Alfreton, Derbyshire, DE55 4EQ Tel: (01773) 606068 Fax: (01773) 606068 E-mail: info@maneges.co.uk

Sand In A Bottle, 47 St. Denys Avenue, Sleaford, Lincolnshire, NG34 8AS Tel: (01529) 414861 Fax: (01529) 414861 E-mail: dave@sandinabottle.co.uk

SILICON CARBIDE PRODUCTS/ COMPONENTS

Morgan Advanced Materials & Technology, Unit 13, Madeley Road, North Moons Moat, Redditch, Worcestershire, B98 9NB Tel: (01527) 69205 Fax: (01527) 62195

SILICON CHIPS, *See Microelectronic etc*

SILICON RELEASE PACKAGING

Kalico Products Ltd, Panty Buarth, Gwernaffield, Mold, Clwyd, CH7 5ER Tel: (01352) 742100 Fax: (01352) 742102E-mail: info@kalico.co.uk

Siliconepak Ltd, Amber Business Centre, Hill Top Rd, Riddings, Alfreton, Derbyshire, DE55 4BR Tel: (01773) 607967 Fax: (01773) 540283

SILICON WAFER RECLAIM/ RECOVERY SERVICES

Rockwood Electronic Materials, Amber Business Centre, Greenhill Industrial Estate, Riddings, Alfreton, Derbyshire, DE55 4DA Tel: (01773) 844200 Fax: (01773) 844244

SILICON WAFERS

I Q E Europe Ltd, Cypress Drive, St. Mellons, Cardiff, CF3 0EG Tel: (029) 2083 9400 Fax: (029) 2083 9401 E-mail: info@iqep.com

Shin-Etsu Handotai Europe Ltd, Wilson Road, Livingston, West Lothian, EH54 7DA Tel: (01506) 415555 Fax: (01506) 417171

SILICONE ADHESIVES

Bentley Chemicals Ltd, Unit 17 Hoo Farm Industrial Estate, Worcester Road, Kidderminster, Worcestershire, DY11 7RA Tel: (01562) 515121 Fax: (01562) 515847 E-mail: info@bentleychemicals.co.uk

ThreeBond Europe SAS, 5 Newmarket Court, Kingston, Milton Keynes, MK10 0AS Tel: (01908) 285000 Fax: (01908) 285001 E-mail: mark.beeson@threebond.co.uk

SILICONE COMPOUNDS

Clwyd Compounders Ltd, Gardden Industrial Estate, Ruabon, Wrexham, Clwyd, LL14 6RG Tel: (01978) 810551 Fax: (01978) 810740 E-mail: sales@clwydcompounders.com

I Q E Europe Ltd, Cypress Drive, St. Mellons, Cardiff, CF3 0EG Tel: (029) 2083 9400 Fax: (029) 2083 9401 E-mail: info@iqep.com

SILICONE GREASE

Bentley Chemicals Ltd, Unit 17 Hoo Farm Industrial Estate, Worcester Road, Kidderminster, Worcestershire, DY11 7RA Tel: (01562) 515121 Fax: (01562) 515847 E-mail: info@bentleychemicals.co.uk

SILICONE LUBRICANTS

GBR Technology Ltd, 6 Jupiter House, Calleva Park, Aldermaston, Reading, RG7 8NN Tel: 0118-982 0567 Fax: 0118-982 0590 E-mail: sales@gbrtech.co.uk

Spanjaard UK Ltd, PO Box 21, Huntingdon, Cambridgeshire, PE29 2EQ Tel: (01480) 457022 Fax: (01480) 457022

SILICONE PIGMENTS

Holland Colours UK Ltd, Unit 16 Sabre Court, Gillingham Business Park, Gillingham, Kent, ME8 0RW Tel: (01634) 388727 Fax: (01634) 388910 E-mail: hcuk@hollandcolours.com

SILICONE PRODUCT DESIGN

Aspex Technology, Rapid House, 40 Oxford Road, High Wycombe, Buckinghamshire, HP11 2EE Tel: (01494) 558121 Fax: (01494) 558016 E-mail: sales@aspex-semi.com

SILICONE PRODUCTS, *See also headings for particular types*

James Dawson & Son Ltd, Tritton Road, Lincoln, LN6 7AF Tel: (01522) 531821 Fax: (01522) 510029 E-mail: sales@james-dawson.co.uk

Elite Industrial Services, 41 Mafeking Road, Walderslade, Chatham, Kent, ME5 9HG Tel: (01634) 683334 Fax: (01634) 683334

Jamak Fabrication Europe Ltd, 52-53 Oakhill Industrial Estate, Devonshire Road, Worsley, Manchester, M28 3PT Tel: (01204) 794554 Fax: (01204) 574521 E-mail: mail@jamak.co.uk

Samco Silicone Products, 4 Secton Court, Veasey Close, Attleborough Fields Industrial Estate, Nuneaton, Warwickshire, CV11 6RT Tel: (024) 7664 1270 Fax: (024) 7634 4992 E-mail: sales@samco.co.uk

Silex Ltd, Units 4 & 5, Broxhead Trading Estate, Lindford, Bordon, Hants, GU35 0NY Tel: (01420) 487130 Fax: (01420) 489274 E-mail: info@silex.co.uk

Universal Rubber Co., The Old Bakery, 2 Tithe Barn Road, Stafford, ST16 3PQ Tel: (01785) 252793 Fax: (01785) 225379

SILICONE REMOVERS

Creative Polymer Developments, 24 Brookfield Drive, Littleborough, Lancashire, OL15 8RH Tel: (01706) 374631 Fax: (01706) 370189 E-mail: michaelgooder@creativepolymer.co.uk

SILICONE RUBBER

Alchemie Ltd, Warwick Road, Kineton, Warwick, CV35 0HU Tel: (01926) 640600 Fax: (01926) 641698 E-mail: sales@alchemie.com

T Y M Seals & Gaskets, A Hopton Park, London Road, Devizes, Wiltshire, SN10 2EY Tel: (01380) 734510 Fax: (01380) 734511 E-mail: admin@tym.co.uk

Viking Extrusions Ltd, 4 Ivy Arch Road, Worthing, West Sussex, BN14 8BX Tel: (01903) 205532 Fax: (01903) 205534 E-mail: sales@vikext.co.uk

SILICONE RUBBER COMPOUNDS

Primasil Silicones Ltd, Kington Rd, Weobley, Hereford, HR4 8QU Tel: (01544) 312600 Fax: (01544) 312601 E-mail: sales@primasil.com

SILICONE RUBBER EXTRUSION SECTIONS

▶ Rubber Extrusions & Seal Ltd, Lancashire House, 251 Higginshaw Lane, Royton, Oldham, OL2 6HW Tel: 0161-622 0020 Fax: 0161-622 0010 E-mail: gculley251@aol.com

SILICONE RUBBER EXTRUSIONS

▶ Apex GB Ltd, Station Approach, Victoria, Roche, St. Austell, Cornwall, PL26 8LG Tel: (0870) 7373771 Fax: (0870) 7373772 E-mail: sales@apexgb.com

Capital Rubber & Plastics Ltd, Units 9-11 Deans Factory Estate, Lambs Lane, Rainham, Essex, RM13 9XL Tel: (01708) 552214 Fax: (01708) 524004 E-mail: sales@capitalrubber.co.uk

Viking Extrusions Ltd, 4 Ivy Arch Road, Worthing, West Sussex, BN14 8BX Tel: (01903) 205532 Fax: (01903) 205534 E-mail: sales@vikext.co.uk

SILICONE RUBBER EXTRUSIONS TO SPECIFICATION

Silex Ltd, Units 4 & 5, Broxhead Trading Estate, Lindford, Bordon, Hants, GU35 0NY Tel: (01420) 487130 Fax: (01420) 489274 E-mail: info@silex.co.uk

SILICONE RUBBER GASKETS

Avon Group Manufacturing Ltd, 30 Vale Lane, Bristol, BS3 5RU Tel: 0117-904 3355 Fax: 0117-904 3366 E-mail: admin@avon-group.co.uk

Silex Ltd, Units 4 & 5, Broxhead Trading Estate, Lindford, Bordon, Hants, GU35 0NY Tel: (01420) 487130 Fax: (01420) 489274 E-mail: info@silex.co.uk

T Y M Seals & Gaskets, A Hopton Park, London Road, Devizes, Wiltshire, SN10 2EY Tel: (01380) 734510 Fax: (01380) 734511 E-mail: admin@tym.co.uk

Viking Extrusions Ltd, 4 Ivy Arch Road, Worthing, West Sussex, BN14 8BX Tel: (01903) 205532 Fax: (01903) 205534 E-mail: sales@vikext.co.uk

SILICONE RUBBER HOSES

Artel Rubber Co., The Studio Unit 3/A, Waterloo Industrial Estate, Waterloo Road, Bidford-on-Avon, Alcester, Warwickshire, B50 4JH Tel: (01789) 774099 Fax: (01789) 774599 E-mail: sales@artelrubber.co.uk

James Dawson & Son Ltd, Tritton Road, Lincoln, LN6 7AF Tel: (01522) 531821 Fax: (01522) 510029 E-mail: sales@james-dawson.co.uk

Universal Rubber Co., The Old Bakery, 2 Tithe Barn Road, Stafford, ST16 3PQ Tel: (01785) 252793 Fax: (01785) 225379

SILICONE RUBBER KEYPAD SWITCHES

Elma Electronic UK Ltd, Premier Business Centre, Speedfields Park, Fareham, Hampshire, PO14 1TY Tel: (01329) 289100 Fax: (01329) 289101 E-mail: info@elma-electronic.co.uk

SILICONE RUBBER MOULDING OR EXTRUSION SERVICES

Cynflex Ltd, Highfield Street, Long Eaton, Nottingham, NG10 4GY Tel: 0115-973 5689 Fax: 0115-972 2149 E-mail: sales@cynflex.com

Deerness Rubber Co. Ltd, Coulson Street, Spennymoor, County Durham, DL16 7RS Tel: (01388) 420301 Fax: (01388) 420284 E-mail: sales@deerness-rubber.co.uk

Primasil Silicones Ltd, Kington Rd, Weobley, Hereford, HR4 8QU Tel: (01544) 312600 Fax: (01544) 312601 E-mail: sales@primasil.com

SILICONE RUBBER MOULDING OR EXTRUSION SERVICES – *continued*

Roe, Salop Street, Bolton, BL2 1DZ Tel: (01204) 523188 Fax: (01204) 523178 E-mail: p_roe@btconnect.com
Samco Silicone Products, 4 Secton Court, Veasey Close, Attleborough Fields Industrial Estate, Nuneaton, Warwickshire, CV11 6RT Tel: (024) 7664 1270 Fax: (024) 7634 4992 E-mail: sales@samco.co.uk
Silverstream Engineering, 60 Bridge Road East, Welwyn Garden City, Hertfordshire, AL7 1JU Tel: (01707) 322552 Fax: (01707) 334124
T Y M Seals & Gaskets, A Hopton Park, London Road, Devizes, Wiltshire, SN10 2EY Tel: (01380) 734510 Fax: (01380) 734511 E-mail: admin@tym.co.uk

SILICONE RUBBER MOULDS

Alec Tiranti Ltd, 3 Pipers Court, Berkshire Drive, Thatcham, Berkshire, RG19 4ER Tel: 0118-930 2775 Fax: (0845) 1232101 E-mail: enquiries@tiranti.co.uk

SILICONE RUBBER PROFILE EXTRUSIONS

▶ Rubber Extrusions & Seal Ltd, Lancashire House, 251 Higginshaw Lane, Royton, Oldham, OL2 6HW Tel: 0161-622 0020 Fax: 0161-622 0010 E-mail: gculley251@aol.com

SILICONE RUBBER SEALS

Kingfisher Rubber & Plastics, Unit 1alfred Court Saxon Business Park, Hanbury Road, Stoke Prior, Bromsgrove, Worcestershire, B60 4AD Tel: (01527) 570570 Fax: (01527) 575200 E-mail: marklewis.kingfisher@virgin.net

SILICONE RUBBER SHEETS

Samco Silicone Products, 4 Secton Court, Veasey Close, Attleborough Fields Industrial Estate, Nuneaton, Warwickshire, CV11 6RT Tel: (024) 7664 1270 Fax: (024) 7634 4992 E-mail: sales@samco.co.uk

SILICONE RUBBER TUBING EXTRUSIONS

Kingfisher Rubber & Plastics, Unit 1alfred Court Saxon Business Park, Hanbury Road, Stoke Prior, Bromsgrove, Worcestershire, B60 4AD Tel: (01527) 570570 Fax: (01527) 575200 E-mail: marklewis.kingfisher@virgin.net
Piltec Rubber & Plastic Ltd, Waterloo Park, Bidford-on-Avon, Alcester, Warwickshire, B50 4JG Tel: (01789) 778271 Fax: (01789) 772886 E-mail: sales@piltec.com

SILICONE SEALANTS

Adshead Ratcliffe, Derby Road, Belper, Derbyshire, DE56 1WJ Tel: (01773) 596300 Fax: (01773) 821215 E-mail: admin@arbo.co.uk
Hodgson Sealants Ltd, Belprin Road, Beverley, North Humberside, HU17 0LN Tel: (01482) 868321 Fax: (01482) 870729 E-mail: sales@hodgson-sealants.co.uk
M C Building Chemicals, Stechford Trading Estate Lyndon Road, Unit 17, Stechford, Birmingham, B33 8BU Tel: 0121-789 8333 Fax: 0121-789 8595 E-mail: sales@mc-bauchemie.de
Tecseal Ltd, 4 East Chorley Business Centre, East Way, Chorley, Lancashire, PR6 0BJ Tel: (01257) 249933 Fax: (01257) 249944

SILICONE SPONGE FABRICATED GASKETS

Silicon Fabrication Services Ltd, Unit E Kingsway, Kingsway Industrial Estate, Luton, LU1 1LP Tel: (01582) 412697 Fax: (01582) 412277 E-mail: sfs.ltd@btinternet.com

SILICONES

A P S Ltd, Sea King Road, Lynx Trading Estate, Yeovil, Somerset, BA20 2NZ Tel: (01935) 410710 Fax: (01935) 410888 E-mail: aps@rtv2.co.uk
Dow Corning, Copse Drive, Coventry, CV5 9RG Tel: (01676) 528000 Fax: (01676) 528001
Jacobson Chemicals Ltd, Unit 4, Newman Lane, Alton, Hampshire, GU34 2QR Tel: (01420) 86934 Fax: (01420) 549574 E-mail: sales@jacobsonchemicals.co.uk
Silicon Fabrication Services Ltd, Unit E Kingsway, Kingsway Industrial Estate, Luton, LU1 1LP Tel: (01582) 412697 Fax: (01582) 412277 E-mail: sfs.ltd@btinternet.com

SILK FABRICS

Bennett Silks Ltd, Crown Royal Park, Higher Hill Gate, Stockport, Cheshire, SK1 3HB Tel: 0161-476 8600 Fax: 0161-480 5385 E-mail: sales@bennett-silks.co.uk
Biddle Sawyer Silks, 22 Rook Street, St Mary"s Courtyard, Manchester, M15 5PS Tel: 0161-227 9428 Fax: 0161-227 8023 E-mail: info@biddlesawyersilks.com
Bradshaw & Bradshaw, 18 Hanson Street, London, W1W 6UE Tel: (020) 7255 2333 Fax: (020) 7255 3131
Bulmer & Lumb Group Ltd, Albert Street, Lockwood, Huddersfield, HD1 3PE Tel: (01484) 423231 Fax: (01484) 435313 E-mail: headoffice@taylor-and-lodge.co.uk
Creative Club Ties, The Whitehouse, 84 Cromley Road, High Lane, Stockport, Cheshire, SK6 8BU Tel: (01663) 762173 Fax: (01663) 810243 E-mail: julian.hyde@talk21.com
D C Dalgleish Ltd, Dunsdale Mill, Dunsdale Road, Selkirk, TD7 5EB Tel: (01750) 20781 Fax: (01750) 20502
David Evans & Co, Bourne Road, Crayford, Dartford, DA1 4BP Tel: (01322) 557521 Fax: (01322) 550476 E-mail: sales@davidevans.co.uk
Gainsborough Silk Weaving Co. Ltd, Alexandra Road, Sudbury, Suffolk, CO10 2XH Tel: (01787) 372081 Fax: (01787) 881785 E-mail: sales@gainsborough.co.uk
Gale Furs, 65 Regents Park Road, London, NW1 8XD Tel: (020) 7722 5870 Fax: (020) 7722 8830
Hansson Of Guildford, 108 Woodbridge Road, Guildford, Surrey, GU1 4PY Tel: (01483) 451625 Fax: (01483) 451602 E-mail: sales@hansson-silks.co.uk
James Hare Ltd, PO Box 72, Leeds, LS1 1LX Tel: 0113-243 1204 Fax: 0113-234 7648 E-mail: sales@jameshareslks.co.uk
Mason's Textiles Ltd, Cricketers Close, Carleton New Road, Skipton, North Yorkshire, BD23 2AZ Tel: (01756) 799333 Fax: (01756) 700182 E-mail: sales@masonsdesign.demon.co.uk
Pongees Ltd, 28-30 Hoxton Square, London, N1 6NN Tel: (020) 7739 9130 Fax: (020) 7739 9132 E-mail: sales@pongees.co.uk
▶ ThaiStyle(UK) Ladies Apparel, 23 Fleet Street, Torquay, TQ1 1DB Tel: (0845) 6440241 Fax: (0845) 2269949 E-mail: jim@thaistyle.co.uk
Vanners Silks, Weavers Lane, Sudbury, Suffolk, CO10 1BB Tel: (01787) 372396 Fax: (01787) 310674 E-mail: rcroft@vanners.com
Stephen Walters & Sons Ltd, Sudbury Silk Mills, Sudbury, Suffolk, CO10 2XB Tel: (01787) 372266 Fax: (01787) 880126 E-mail: sales@stephenwalters.co.uk

SILK SCREEN PRINTING, *See headings under Screen*

SILK SCREENING

R & T Industrial Engravers, 26 The Tanneries, Brockhampton Lane, Havant, Hampshire, PO9 1JB Tel: (023) 9245 4751 Fax: (023) 9247 2709 E-mail: rt.engraving@tinyworld.co.uk

SILK YARN

Richard Atkinson & Co. Ltd, 10 Nicholson Drive, Mallusk, Newtownabbey, County Antrim, BT36 4FD Tel: (028) 9084 3323 Fax: (020) 8908 4850 E-mail: info@atkinsons-irishpoplin-ties.com
Glemsford Silk Mills Ltd, Chequers Lane, Glemsford, Sudbury, Suffolk, CO10 7PW Tel: (01787) 280244 Fax: (01787) 281730

SILO CLEANING CONTRACTORS

▶ Silocare Ltd, Grayingham Road, Blyborough, Gainsborough, Lincolnshire, DN21 4EY Tel: (01427) 668061 Fax: (01427) 668062 E-mail: silocare@aol.com

SILO DISCHARGING EQUIPMENT

Portasilo Ltd, New Lane, Huntington, York, YO32 9PR Tel: (01904) 624872 Fax: (01904) 611760 E-mail: bulk@portasilo.co.uk

SILO DISTRIBUTORS OR AGENTS

Bagfast Ltd, Unit 2, Morris Court, Colwick Industrial Estate, Nottingham, NG4 2JN Tel: 0115-940 1658 Fax: 0115-961 1714 E-mail: sales@bagfast.com
Barton Fabrication Ltd, Harbour Road Trading Estate, Portishead, Bristol, BS20 7BL Tel: (01275) 845901 Fax: (01275) 849462 E-mail: barton.fabrication@virgin.net
Eurpa Silos Ltd, Unit 15, Prydwen Road, Swansea West Industrial Estate, Swansea, SA5 4HN Tel: (01792) 410450 Fax: (01792) 410455
H Cooper & Sons Bristol, Westerleigh Road, Yate, Bristol, BS37 8QA Tel: (01454) 312081 Fax: (01454) 318880E-mail: info@hcooper.net
Rapid International Ltd, 96 Mullavilly Road, Tandragee, Craigavon, County Armagh, BT62 2LX Tel: (028) 3884 0671 Fax: (028) 3884 0880E-mail: info@rapidinternational.com
Regal Tanks, Ellough Park, Benacre Road, Beccles, Suffolk, NR34 7XD Tel: (01502) 710100 Fax: (01502) 710103 E-mail: info@regaltanks.co.uk
Romar Process Engineering Ltd, 12 Faraday Road, Leigh-on-Sea, Essex, SS9 5JU Tel: (01702) 523351 Fax: (01702) 421402 E-mail: info@romar.uk.net
Spencer Construction & Engineering, Royal Albert Works, Bradfield Road, London, E16 2AT Tel: (020) 7511 1711 Fax: (020) 7474 2195
Weldon Engineering Ltd, Unit 4B Climpy Industrial Park, Climpy Road, Forth, Lanark, ML11 8EW Tel: (01555) 812233 Fax: (01555) 812454 E-mail: sales@weldon-engineering.com

SILO HIRE

Regal Tanks, Ellough Park, Benacre Road, Beccles, Suffolk, NR34 7XD Tel: (01502) 710100 Fax: (01502) 710103 E-mail: info@regaltanks.co.uk

SILO WEIGHING SYSTEMS

▶ Advanced Micropower Ltd, 2a Loughaghrey Road, Annahilt, Hillsborough, County Down, BT26 6DB Tel: (028) 9263 8225 Fax: (028) 9263 8225 E-mail: sales@advancedmicropower.co.uk

SILOS, GLASS COATED/FUSED

Permastore Ltd, Airfield Industrial Park, Eye Airfield Industrial Estate, Eye, Suffolk, IP23 7HS Tel: (01379) 870723 Fax: (01379) 870530 E-mail: sales@permastore.co.uk

SILVER BRAZING ALLOYS

Johnson Matthey Plc, York Way, Royston, Hertfordshire, SG8 5HJ Tel: (01763) 253200 Fax: (01763) 253168 E-mail: webbp@matthey.com
Thessco Ltd, Royds Mill, Windsor Street, Sheffield, S4 7WB Tel: 0114-272 0966 Fax: 0114-275 2655 E-mail: metals@thessco.co.uk

SILVER FUSE STRIPS

Thessco Ltd, Royds Mill, Windsor Street, Sheffield, S4 7WB Tel: 0114-272 0966 Fax: 0114-275 2655 E-mail: metals@thessco.co.uk

SILVER OXIDE BATTERIES

▶ The Small Battery Co., 70 Cromford Road, London, SW18 1NY Tel: (020) 8871 3730 Fax: (020) 8871 3686 E-mail: info@smallbattery.company.org.uk

SILVER PLATED GIFTWARE

Francis Howard Ltd, Aberdeen Works, Trafalgar Street, Sheffield, S1 3RL Tel: 0114-249 3314 Fax: 0114-249 3316
Hugh Crawshaw, 94 Matilda Street, Sheffield, S1 4QF Tel: 0114-273 9799 Fax: 0114-270 0229
Queen Anne Tableware Ltd, Holyhead Road, Wednesbury, West Midlands, WS10 7PD Tel: 0121-556 1471 Fax: 0121-556 4966 E-mail: queen.anne@btconnect.com
Sorrill & Coley, 22 New John St West, Birmingham, B19 3NB Tel: 0121-359 7428 Fax: 0121-359 5508
Tregawne, PO Box 48, Pershore, Worcestershire, WR10 3YE Tel: (01386) 861800 Fax: (01386) 861900 E-mail: sales@tregawne.freeserve.co.uk
Watson Group Ltd, Tudor House, Highlands Road, Shirley, Solihull, West Midlands, B90 4ND Tel: 0121-705 4624 Fax: 0121-711 1086 E-mail: jean@wapwatson.com
Widdop Bingham & Co. Ltd, Broadgate, Broadway Business Park, Chadderton, Oldham, OL9 9XE Tel: 0161-688 1200 Fax: 0161-682 6808 E-mail: sales@widdop.co.uk

SILVER PLATED WARE

John Barker & Dixon Ltd, Lincoln Works, Smithfield, Sheffield, S3 7AR Tel: 0114-272 4962 Fax: 0114-276 0299
British Silverware Ltd, Windsor Street, Sheffield, S4 7WB Tel: 0114-286 0500 Fax: 0114-286 0501 E-mail: office@britishsilverware.co.uk
Camelot Silverware Ltd, 173 Gibraltar Street, Sheffield, S3 8UA Tel: 0114-272 4935 Fax: 0114-273 7149 E-mail: enquiries@camelotsilverware.co.uk
Cannon.Co.Uk, 214-224 Barr Street, Birmingham, B19 3AG Tel: 0121-551 4131 Fax: 0121-554 9292 E-mail: peter.cannon@cannon.co.uk
J W Evans & Sons Ltd, 52-57 Albion Street, Birmingham, B1 3EA Tel: 0121-236 1775 Fax: 0121-236 7966
Special Efx Ltd, Ettington Park Bus Centre, Stratford-upon-Avon, Warwickshire, CV37 8BT Tel: (01789) 450005
W A Humphries Ltd, 65 Hunters Vale, Birmingham, B19 2XH Tel: 0121-554 0125 Fax: 0121-554 0155

SILVER PLATING PROCESSORS OR SERVICES

Antique Renovating Co., 43 Bent Street, Manchester, M8 8NW Tel: 0161-834 8000
F H Lambert Ltd, Rembrandt House, King Georges Avenue, Watford, WD18 7PW Tel: (01923) 229444 Fax: (01923) 255717 E-mail: info@fhlambert.co.uk
H Quibell & Sons, 20 Hockley Street, Birmingham, B18 6BL Tel: 0121-554 1250 E-mail: enquiries@hquibell-silversmiths.co.uk
Hastings Metal Finishers, Unit 7-8 Prince Consort Industrial Estate, Hebburn, Tyne & Wear, NE31 1EH Tel: 0191-483 9213 Fax: 0191-483 9213 E-mail: hmf.sales@tiscali.co.uk
J.W.Rudge & Co.Limited, Anne Road, Smethwick, West Midlands, B66 2NZ Tel: 0121-558 5519 Fax: 0121-558 0053 E-mail: millssteve@btconnect.co.uk
T C Plating Co. Ltd, Unit 6b Ada St Workshops, 8 Andrews Road, London, E8 4QN Tel: (020) 7249 2603 Fax: (020) 7923 3640
Twickenham Plating Group Ltd, 12-13 Balena Close, Poole, Dorset, BH17 7DB Tel: (01202) 692416 Fax: (01202) 600628 E-mail: info@pender.co.uk
Y & B Plating Ltd, 6 Priestley Way, Crawley, West Sussex, RH10 9NT Tel: (01293) 528974 Fax: (01293) 552877

SILVERWARE REPAIR/ RESTORATION SERVICES

H Quibell & Sons, 20 Hockley Street, Birmingham, B18 6BL Tel: 0121-554 1250 E-mail: enquiries@hquibell-silversmiths.co.uk
Hampton Utillities, Meeting House Lane, Balsall Common, Coventry, CV7 7GD Tel: (01676) 534438 E-mail: colin.harrison1@tinyworld.co.uk
Hugh Crawshaw, 94 Matilda Street, Sheffield, S1 4QF Tel: 0114-273 9799 Fax: 0114-270 0229

SILVERWARE, MANUFACTURING SILVERSMITHS

Arthur Price, Britannia Way, Lichfield, Staffordshire, WS14 9UY Tel: (01543) 267324 Fax: (01543) 414488 E-mail: catering@arthur-price.com
John Barker & Dixon Ltd, Lincoln Works, Smithfield, Sheffield, S3 7AR Tel: 0114-272 4962 Fax: 0114-276 0299
Baxter, 103 Arundel Street, Sheffield, S1 2NT Tel: 0114-272 1575 Fax: 0114-272 5354 E-mail: anne@wjabaxter.co.uk
British Silverware Ltd, Windsor Street, Sheffield, S4 7WB Tel: 0114-286 0500 Fax: 0114-286 0501 E-mail: office@britishsilverware.co.uk
Broadway & Co. Ltd, Shady Lane, Birmingham, B44 9ER Tel: 0121-360 0606 Fax: 0121-360 7880 E-mail: information@broadwaysilver.uk.com
Camelot Silverware Ltd, 173 Gibraltar Street, Sheffield, S3 8UA Tel: 0114-272 4935 Fax: 0114-273 7149 E-mail: enquiries@camelotsilverware.co.uk
Cannon.Co.Uk, 214-224 Barr Street, Birmingham, B19 3AG Tel: 0121-551 4131 Fax: 0121-554 9292 E-mail: peter.cannon@cannon.co.uk
▶ Carrs Of Sheffield Manufacturing Ltd, Troy House 2 Holbrook Avenue, Holbrook Industrial Estate, Holbrook, Sheffield, S20 3FH Tel: 0114-251 0610 Fax: 0114-251 0685
Chimo Holdings, White Rose Works, 61 Eyre Lane, Sheffield, S1 3GF Tel: 0114-272 4656 Fax: 0114-249 0922 E-mail: sales@chimoholdings.co.uk
Crescent Silver Repairs & Restoration, 85 Spencer Street, Birmingham, B18 6DE Tel: 0121-236 9006 Fax: 0121-212 1466 E-mail: mail@cresent-silver.co.uk
▶ David Baggaley, 79 West Bar, Sheffield, S3 8PS Tel: (07877) 162431 E-mail: david.baggaley1@btinternet.com
Dragon Workshop, 47 Princess Victoria Street, Bristol, BS8 4BX Tel: 0117-973 2656
F. Drury Ltd, 5 Gilleyfield Avenue, Sheffield, S17 3NS Tel: 0114-236 7907 Fax: 0114-236 7907

▶ indicates data change since last edition

SILVERWARE, MANUFACTURING SILVERSMITHS – *continued*

Richard Fox & Associates, 8-28 Luton Avenue, Croydon, CR0 2BP Tel: (020) 8683 3331 Fax: (020) 8683 2223 E-mail: richard@foxsilver.net
Gainsborough, 34-44 Northwood Street, Birmingham, B3 1TU Tel: 0121-236 2335 Fax: 0121-236 2846 E-mail: sales@gainsboroughsilver.co.uk
H Quibell & Sons, 20 Hockley Street, Birmingham, B18 6BL Tel: 0121-554 1250 E-mail: enquiries@hquibell-silversmiths.co.uk
Hamilton & Inches Ltd, 87 George Street, Edinburgh, EH2 3EY Tel: 0131-225 4898 Fax: 0131-220 6994
Hampton Utillities, Meeting House Lane, Balsall Common, Coventry, CV7 7GD Tel: (01676) 534438 E-mail: colin.harrison1@tinyworld.co.uk
Francis Howard Ltd, Aberdeen Works, Trafalgar Street, Sheffield, S1 3RL Tel: 0114-249 3314 Fax: 0114-249 3316
Hugh Crawshaw, 94 Matilda Street, Sheffield, S1 4QF Tel: 0114-273 9799 Fax: 0114-270 0229
▶ J. A. Campbell London Sterling Silver, 18 Perseverance Works, 38 Kingsland Road, London, E2 8DD Tel: 020 72534560 Fax: 020 76132729 E-mail: info@jacampbell.co.uk
J W Evans & Sons Ltd, 52-57 Albion Street, Birmingham, B1 3EA Tel: 0121-236 1775 Fax: 0121-236 7966
Jane Chantler Ltd, Clifford House, Market Street, Brough, Kirkby Stephen, Cumbria, CA17 4AX Tel: (01768) 341296 E-mail: jane@touchstone2000.freeserve.co.uk
Jones Bros & Warriss Ltd, 104 Mary St, Sheffield, S1 4RU Tel: 0114-272 0820 Fax: 0114-272 9011 E-mail: warriss@gxn.co.uk
Alexander Kirkwood & Son, 13 Albany Street, Edinburgh, EH1 3PY Tel: 0131-556 7843 Fax: 0131-556 4779
Mappin & Webb Ltd, 170 Regent Street, London, W1B 5BQ Tel: (020) 7734 3801 Fax: (020) 7494 3766
Martyn Pugh Ltd, Unit 8 Winyates Centre, Redditch, Worcestershire, B98 0NR Tel: (01527) 502513 Fax: (01527) 502513
Padgett & Braham Ltd, 10 Shacklewell Road, London, N16 7TA Tel: (020) 7254 6362 Fax: (020) 7254 7175 E-mail: pandb@tinyworld.co.uk
Padgett & Braham Ltd, 10 Shacklewell Road, London, N16 7TA Tel: (020) 7254 6362 Fax: (020) 7254 7175 E-mail: p&b@tinyworld.co.uk
Premier-Ware Ltd, Vander House, Starn Hill Close, Ecclesfield, Sheffield, S35 9TG Tel: 0114-257 2700 Fax: 0114-257 1364 E-mail: sales@premier-ware.co.uk
Quarrier Ward Ltd, PO Box 8104, Birmingham, B15 3JY Tel: 0121-454 2818 Fax: 0121-454 2818
Remane Bros Ltd, 63-66 Hatton Garden, London, EC1N 8RF Tel: (020) 7405 6794 Fax: (020) 7831 6289 E-mail: remanegems@aol.com
S J Phillips Ltd, 139 New Bond Street, London, W1S 2TL Tel: (020) 7629 6261 Fax: (020) 7495 6180 E-mail: enquiries@sjphillips.com
Smith & Harris, 31 Hatton Garden, London, EC1N 8DH Tel: (020) 7405 1056 Fax: (020) 7405 1056
Sorrill & Coley, 22 New John St West, Birmingham, B19 3NB Tel: 0121-359 7428 Fax: 0121-359 5508
Stear & Bright Silversmiths, Studio 1 Clevedon Craft Centre, Moor Lane, Clevedon, Avon, BS21 6TD Tel: (01275) 872149
Swatkins Group Ltd, Leamore House, Leamore Lane, Walsall, WS2 7DQ Tel: (01922) 711700 Fax: (01922) 710410 E-mail: sales@swatkins.com
John Taylor Poston & Co. Ltd, 19-21 Great Queens Street, London, WC2B 5BE Tel: (020) 7242 0471 Fax: (020) 7831 8692 E-mail: gqs@toye.demon.co.uk
Toghill Jewellers, 16 Hockley Street, Birmingham, B18 6BL Tel: 0121-554 2727
W A Humphries Ltd, 65 Hunters Vale, Birmingham, B19 2XH Tel: 0121-554 0125 Fax: 0121-554 0155

SIMULATION SYSTEMS

C A E UK plc, Innovation Drive, York Road, Burgess Hill, West Sussex, RH15 9TW Tel: (01444) 247535 Fax: (01444) 244895 E-mail: cae_plc@cae.co.uk
Domian Electronics Ltd, The Bungalow, Portland Road, Burgess Hill, West Sussex, RH15 9RL Tel: (01444) 254583 Fax: (01444) 254584 E-mail: domianelec@aol.com
▶ Rockfield Software Ltd, Ethos Building, Kings Road, St. Thomas, Swansea, SA1 8AS Tel: (01792) 455577 Fax: (01792) 455648 E-mail: sales@rockfield.co.uk

SIMULATION SYSTEMS, NUMERICALLY BASED

▶ Rockfield Software Ltd, Ethos Building, Kings Road, St. Thomas, Swansea, SA1 8AS Tel: (01792) 455577 Fax: (01792) 455648 E-mail: sales@rockfield.co.uk

SIMULATORS, *See also headings for particular types*

Argon Electronics, Unit 16, Progress Park, Ribocon Way, Luton, LU4 9UR Tel: (01582) 491616 Fax: (01582) 492780 E-mail: sales@argonelectronics.com
▶ Esd Simulation Training Ltd, Craigearn Business Park, Morrison Way, Kintore, Inverurie, Aberdeenshire, AB51 0TH Tel: (01467) 634934 Fax: (01467) 634949
Quadrant Systems Ltd, Victoria Gardens, Burgess Hill, West Sussex, RH15 9NB Tel: (01444) 246226 Fax: (01444) 870172 E-mail: pmasters@quadrant-systems.co.uk

SIMULATORS, DRILLING

Drilling Systems UK Ltd, Hurnview House, Bournemouth International Airport, Hurn, Christchurch, Dorset, BH23 6EW Tel: (01202) 582255 Fax: (01202) 582288 E-mail: info@drillingsystems.com

SINGLE BOARD COMPUTERS

Phytec Technology Holding AG, 24 Leek Lane, Biddulph Moor, Stoke-on-Trent, ST8 7NE Tel: (01782) 514652 Fax: (01782) 514652 E-mail: info@phytec.co.uk
TMC Technology UK Co., Ltd, 12 Wedgwood Court, Stevenage, Hertfordshire, SG1 4QR Tel: (01438) 842300 Fax: (01438) 842308 E-mail: sales@tmc-uk.com

SINGLE BOARD MICROCONTROLLER KITS

Phytec Technology Holding AG, 24 Leek Lane, Biddulph Moor, Stoke-on-Trent, ST8 7NE Tel: (01782) 514652 Fax: (01782) 514652 E-mail: info@phytec.co.uk

SINGLE BUYER TRADE CREDIT INSURANCE

Rycroft Associates LLP, 16 Queens Avenue, Shirley, Solihull, West Midlands, B90 2NT Tel: 0121 7458978 Fax: 0121 7443562 E-mail: mikestott@rycroftassociates.com

SINGLE CRYSTALS

Metal Crystals & Oxides Ltd, Unit B4 Button End Industrial Estate, Harston, Cambridge, CB22 7GX Tel: (01223) 872072 Fax: (01223) 872517 E-mail: sales@metal-crystals.com

SINGLE ESCAPE SET BREATHING EQUIPMENT CABINETS

Jo Bird & Co. Ltd, Factory Lane, Bason Bridge, Highbridge, Somerset, TA9 4RN Tel: (01278) 785546 Fax: (01278) 780541 E-mail: info@jobird.co.uk

SINGLE LANE CONVEYOR AUTOMATIC CONVERGING EQUIPMENT

Converging Solutions Holdings Ltd, Unit 13, Waterloo Business Park, Bidford-on-Avon, Alcester, Warwickshire, B50 4JG Tel: (01789) 491144 Fax: (01789) 491155 E-mail: sale@convergingsolutions.co.uk

SINGLE LENS REFLEX (SLR) CAMERA BODIES

Sino West Business Consultancy Ltd, 32 William Bristow Road, Coventry, CV3 5LQ Tel: (024) 7650 2465 Fax: (024) 7650 3215 E-mail: enquiry@sinowest.co.uk

SINGLE PHASE CONVERTERS

Isomatic UK Ltd, 9 Pimms Close, Guildford, Surrey, GU4 7YG Tel: (01483) 534634 Fax: (01483) 573624 E-mail: peter.burton@isomatics.biz

SINGLE POLE PUSH BUTTON SWITCHES

Eao Ltd, Albert Drive, Burgess Hill, West Sussex, RH15 9TN Tel: (01444) 236000 Fax: (01444) 236641 E-mail: sales.euk@eao.com

SINGLE REVOLUTION CLUTCHES

Stieber Brakes, Wichita Building, Ampthill Road, Bedford, MK42 9RD Tel: (01234) 355499 Fax: (01234) 214264 E-mail: diane.lawman@wichita.co.uk

SINK FIXING CLAMPS

Springfast Ltd, Unit 6F, Morelands Trading Estate, Bristol Road, Gloucester, GL1 5RZ Tel: (01452) 416688 Fax: (01452) 308723 E-mail: admin@springfast.co.uk

SINK UNITS

Stoneham plc, Powerscroft Road, Sidcup, Kent, DA14 5DZ Tel: (020) 8300 8181 Fax: (020) 8300 8183 E-mail: kitchens@stoneham.plc.uk

SINKS

Pyramif UK Ltd, Unit 1, Alexandra Way, Ashchurch Industrial Estate, Tewkesbury, Gloucestershire, GL20 8NB Tel: (01684) 298040 Fax: (01684) 293114 E-mail: sales@pyramifuk.com
Teka Products Ltd, 177 Milton Park, Milton, Abingdon, Oxfordshire, OX14 4SE Tel: (01235) 861916 Fax: (01235) 832137 E-mail: sales@teka.co.uk
Waterline Ltd, Jenna House, 6 Mollins Court, Cumbernauld, Glasgow, G68 9HP Tel: (0870) 5561560 Fax: (01236) 453868 E-mail: sales@waterline.co.uk

SINTERED METAL COMPONENTS/SHAPED PARTS

A & M Tungsten Powders Ltd, 11 Maxted Road, Hemel Hempstead, Hertfordshire, HP2 7DX Tel: (01442) 254691 Fax: (01442) 255503 E-mail: info.amtp@virgin.net
B S A Advanced Sintering Ltd, Hadleigh Road, Ipswich, IP2 0HX Tel: (01473) 233300 Fax: (01473) 230424 E-mail: Sales@bsasintering.com
GKN Sinter Metals Ltd, PO Box 3, Lichfield, Staffordshire, WS13 6HB Tel: (01543) 403000 Fax: (01543) 403001 E-mail: info@gknsintermetals.co.uk

SINTERED METAL FRICTION PRODUCTS

Barbrak Ltd, 5 Eden Court, Eden Way, Leighton Buzzard, Bedfordshire, LU7 4FY Tel: (01525) 376605 Fax: (01525) 370505 E-mail: chris@barbrak.co.uk

SINTERED POWDER METALLURGY PRODUCTS, *See also Sintered Metal etc*

Hoganas GB Ltd, Munday Works, Morley Road, Tonbridge, Kent, TN9 1RP Tel: (01732) 362243 Fax: (01732) 770262 E-mail: sales@powdrex.com

SIRENS

▶ E2S European Safety Systems Ltd, Impress House, Mansell Road, London, W3 7QH Tel: 020 8743 8880 Fax: 020 8740 4200 E-mail: sales@e2s.com

SITE ACCOMMODATION FACILITIES MANAGEMENT

▶ Lauriston Park Guest House, 6 Lauriston Park, Edinburgh, EH3 9JA Tel: 0131-228 5557 E-mail: info@lauristonpark.com

SITE CLEARANCE CONTRACTORS

Castlemoor Demolition Ltd, Transfer House, 53 Marshgate Lane, Stratford, London, E15 2NQ Tel: (020) 8503 1505 Fax: (020) 8519 5035
Davis & Samson Contractors, Billet Lane, Berkhamsted, Hertfordshire, HP4 1DP Tel: (01442) 878800 Fax: (01442) 878801 E-mail: sales@davisandsamson.co.uk
Morecambe Metals Ltd, Northgate, White Lund Industrial Estate, Morecambe, Lancashire, LA3 3AZ Tel: (01524) 69191 Fax: (01524) 843987 E-mail: sales@morecambemetals.co.uk
P & R Pallets & Cases, 2 Bridge Industrial Estate, Hot Lane, Stoke-on-Trent, ST6 2DL Tel: (01782) 822555 Fax: (01782) 822555
▶ Projects (SW) Ltd, 3 Huntersway, Culmstock, Cullompton, Devon, EX15 3HJ Tel: (01884) 841621 Fax: (01884) 841621 E-mail: info@projects-sw.co.uk
W Hayden & Son Ltd, Webb Street, Bilston, West Midlands, WV14 8XL Tel: (01902) 402341 Fax: (01902) 491832
Walsh Demolition, 257 Moorland Road, Cardiff, CF24 2LJ Tel: (029) 2046 0645 Fax: (029) 2046 0645

SITE ELECTRICAL SUPPLIERS, *See Electrical Equipment, Temporary, Building Site etc*

SITE ENGINEER RECRUITMENT CONSULTANCY

▶ Corinne Dauncey, PO Box 2448, Slough, SL1 1ZB Tel: 0870 8701193 Fax: 0870 8701194 E-mail: coz.dauncey@theengineeringjob.com

SITE INVESTIGATION CONSULTANCY

Eldred Geotechnics, Veitchi Barn, Newbarn Road, Swanley, Kent, BR8 7PW Tel: (01322) 663222

SITE SLEEPING ACCOMMODATION MODULES

Manchester Cabins Ltd, Tweedale Way, Oldham, OL9 7LD Tel: 0161-684 3333 Fax: 0161-684 1111 E-mail: info@manchestercabins.co.uk

SITE SUPPORT SERVICES

Baltic Wharf Boatyard Ltd, Baltic Wharf Business Centre, St. Peters Quay, Totnes, Devon, TQ9 5EW Tel: (01803) 867922 Fax: (01803) 866795 E-mail: sales@balticwharf.co.uk
Site Services Construction Ltd, 3 Inglewhite Road, Goosnargh, Preston, PR3 2EB Tel: (01772) 782583 Fax: (01772) 784166 E-mail: fredwareing@aol.com

SKATEBOARDS

▶ Bitch Skateboards, 11 Flag Square, Shoreham-by-Sea, West Sussex, BN43 5RZ Tel: (07766) 001121 E-mail: bitchskates@yahoo.co.uk
▶ Newdeal Skates, Auriol Drive, Greenford, Middlesex, UB6 0DU Tel: (020) 8515 5000 Fax: (020) 8422 0422

SKATES, INDUSTRIAL/ MACHINERY SKATES, MACHINE MOVING, MANUFRS

Skate Systems Ltd, 55 London Road, Hurst Green, Etchingham, East Sussex, TN19 7QP Tel: (01580) 860020 Fax: (01580) 860021 E-mail: sales@skatesystems.co.uk

SKATING ACCESSORIES AND EQUIPMENT

▶ Bigfoot Play Systems Ltd, Hamilton House, 111 Marlowes, Hemel Hempstead, Hertfordshire, HP1 1BB Tel: (01442) 243355 Fax: (01442) 244330 E-mail: info@bigfootplay.com

SKID PACKAGE UNITS

Jordan Division Ltd, Millbrook Road, Yate, Bristol, BS37 5PB Tel: (01454) 328300 Fax: (01454) 325866 E-mail: sales@jordanengineering.co.uk
Multi Process, Unit 8 Stroud Enterprise Centre, Lightpill, Stroud, Gloucestershire, GL5 3NL Tel: (01453) 750002 Fax: (01453) 758271
Proweld Quality Vessels Ltd, Units 22-23, Lion Court, Daneshill, Basingstoke, Hampshire, RG24 8QU Tel: (01256) 814184 Fax: (01256) 814164 E-mail: simon@proweld.uk.com

SKID PREVENTION OR ANTISKID OR ANTILOCK BRAKE SYSTEM (ABS) COMPONENTS

Haldex Brake Products Ltd, Moons Moat Drive, Redditch, Worcestershire, B98 9HA Tel: (01527) 499499 Fax: (01527) 499500 E-mail: info@hbpuk.haldex.com

SKID PREVENTION OR ANTISKID OR ANTILOCK BRAKE SYSTEM (ABS) COMPONENTS – *continued*

Squires Gear & Engineering Ltd, 98 Swan Lane, Coventry, CV2 4GB Tel: (024) 7623 1110 Fax: (024) 7623 1112 E-mail: djs@squires-gear.co.uk

SKID PREVENTION OR ANTISKID OR ANTILOCK BRAKE SYSTEMS (ABS)

Knorr Bremse Systems for Commercial Vehicles Ltd, Century House, Follybook Road, Emerald Park East, Emmersons Green, Bristol, BS16 7SE Tel: 0117-984 6100 Fax: 0117-984 6101

SKID STEER LOADER ASPHALT CUTTERS

▶ M.T.S Nationwide Ltd, Unit 2, Flanshaw Way, Wakefield, West Yorkshire, WF2 9LP Tel: (01924) 387007 Fax: (01924) 384011 E-mail: mtsnationwidelimited@btinternet.com

SKID STEER LOADERS

Beddoes Bros, Pentre Hyling, Church Stoke, Montgomery, Powys, SY15 6HU Tel: (01588) 620199 Fax: (01588) 620499 E-mail: paul@beddoesplant.co.uk

Hurst Plant Sales Ltd, Station Yard Station Road, Haxey Junction, Doncaster, South Yorkshire, DN9 2NL Tel: (01427) 753030 Fax: (01427) 752030 E-mail: sales@hurstplantsales.co.uk

▶ M.T.S Nationwide Ltd, Unit 2, Flanshaw Way, Wakefield, West Yorkshire, WF2 9LP Tel: (01924) 387007 Fax: (01924) 384011 E-mail: mtsnationwidelimited@btinternet.com

SKIN CARE PREPARATIONS

Kingfisher Sales & Marketing, PO Box 100, Aberdare, Mid Glamorgan, CF44 8YX Tel: (01685) 879879

▶ Lotus Sales & Marketing Ltd, 35 Windsor Avenue, Sutton, Surrey, SM3 9RR Tel: (020) 8644 2717 Fax: (020) 8641 3082

▶ Primavera Aromatherapy Ltd, Manor House, Manor Road, Frome, Somerset, BA11 4BN Tel: (01373) 467103 Fax: (01373) 451532 E-mail: mail@primavera.co.uk

▶ Pur Natural Skincare, Unit 4 Hubert Johns Buildings, Pant Industrial Estate, Dowlais, Merthyr Tydfil, CF48 2SR Tel: (029) 2055 2691 E-mail: simonfford@btinternet.com

▶ SPA MOMENTS UK (Pure Fiji Retailers), c/o The Perfect Balance, Dunston Hole Farm, Dunston Road, Chesterfield, Derbyshire, S41 9RL Tel: 01246 269819 E-mail: products@spamoments.co.uk

▶ Wild Wood & Rose, 110 Johnson Road, Emersons Green, Bristol, BS16 7JG Tel: 0117-957 1420 Fax: 0117-970 2285 E-mail: shop@wildwoodrose.com

SKIN CARE PREPARATIONS, INDUSTRIAL

A K Supplies, 5 Regent Road, Handsworth, Birmingham, B21 8AB Tel: 0121-554 7107 Fax: 0121-682 3958

Airvert Ltd, Ghyll Road Industrial Estate, Ghyll Road, Heathfield, East Sussex, TN21 8AW Tel: (01435) 868292 Fax: (01435) 864838 E-mail: mthompson@airvert.co.uk

Apaseal Ltd, Unit 32 The Willow Estate, Avis Way, Newhaven, East Sussex, BN9 0DD Tel: (01273) 517995 Fax: (01273) 611061

Ashfarm Personal Care Ltd, 33 Croft Street, Manchester, M11 4RQ Tel: 0161-223 8265 Fax: 0161-223 7100 E-mail: mark@mpmconsumerproducts.com

Fine English Toiletries Ltd, 15-17 Landsdown Road, Shirley, Southampton, SO15 4HD Tel: (023) 8077 8080 Fax: (023) 8077 5545

David Somerset Skincare, Henley-On-Thames, Oxfordshire, RG9 6YZ Tel: (01491) 578080 E-mail: info@somersets.com

SKIN CARE PRODUCTS, HERBAL

▶ Bay House, Unit 1 New Rookery Farm, Little London, Silverstone, Towcester, Northamptonshire, NN12 8UP Tel: (01327) 856988 Fax: (01327) 856967 E-mail: sales@bay-house.co.uk

[illegible]llament Limited, Manor Farm, Ashton, [illegible]ster, CH3 8DG Tel: 0870 2426995 [illegible]: info@ellament.com

[illegible] Cosmetics, Unit 2, Alpine House, [illegible] Lane, London, NW9 9RX Tel: (020) [illegible] Fax: (020) 8204 9955 [illegible]in@hazafro.co.uk

▶ Natural Alternative Products, PO BOX 3, Whitefield, M45 6WS Tel: 0161 7980671 E-mail: sales@natural-alternative-products.co.uk

▶ Natural Care Products, Highcroft, 30 Old Lodge Lane, Purley, Surrey, CR8 4DF Tel: 020 86452552 E-mail: Andrew@natural-care-products.co.uk

▶ Organic Towel Co., 108 Weston Street, London, SE1 3QB Tel: (0870) 0501261 Fax: (0870) 7622371 E-mail: contact@organictowel.co.uk

▶ Pur Natural Skincare, Unit 4 Hubert Johns Buildings, Pant Industrial Estate, Dowlais, Merthyr Tydfil, CF48 2SR Tel: (029) 2055 2691 E-mail: simonfford@btinternet.com

▶ Quinessence Aromatherapy, 2 Forest Court, Linden Way, Coalville, Leicestershire, LE67 3JY Tel: (01530) 838358 Fax: (01530) 814171 E-mail: sales@quinessence.com

▶ Tavoy Investments Ltd, 25 Bartel Close, Leverstock Green, Hemel Hempstead, Hertfordshire, HP3 8LY Tel: (0845) 2261978 Fax: (0845) 2261978

▶ Vitamin UK, PO Box 98, Manchester, M20 6PZ Tel: (0800) 0568148 Fax: 0161-445 4939 E-mail: info@vitaminuk.com

SKIN FELLMONGERS

B Webster & Sons Eastrington Ltd, Lilac Villa, Eastrington, Goole, North Humberside, DN14 7XL Tel: (01430) 440336 Fax: (01430) 441826

Chas Paisley & Sons, 2 Caroline Street, Langholm, Dumfriesshire, DG13 0AF Tel: (01387) 380308 Fax: (01387) 381048

Nettletons & Porters Ltd, Wakefield Road, Ossett, West Yorkshire, WF5 9JX Tel: (01924) 273047 Fax: (01924) 280584 E-mail: nettletons@freezone.co.uk

SKIN IRRITATION PHARMACEUTICALS

▶ Hygieia Healthcare Ltd, PO Box 117, Bideford, Devon, EX39 1AA Tel: (01237) 473128 Fax: (01237) 425742 E-mail: sales@hygieia.co.uk

SKIN PACKAGING CARDS

Arthur W. Clowes Ltd, Unit 2 Pepper Road Hazel Grove, Hazel Grove, Stockport, Cheshire, SK7 5BW Tel: 0161-483 1827 Fax: 0161-483 1827 E-mail: sales@clowesprinters.co.uk

SKIN PACKAGING EQUIPMENT

Quickpack UK Ltd, 14 Linnell Way, Telford Way Industrial Estate, Kettering, Northamptonshire, NN16 8PS Tel: (01536) 510910 Fax: (01536) 410568 E-mail: quickpackuk@quickpack.com

SKIN PACKAGING SERVICES

Skincross (Cheshire) Ltd, 6 Riverside, Dukinfield, Cheshire, SK16 4HE Tel: 0161-343 7323 Fax: 0161-343 7324

Sportsmatch UK Ltd, 16 Summer Street, Leighton Buzzard, Bedfordshire, LU7 1HT Tel: (01525) 381638 Fax: (01525) 851236 E-mail: info@sportsmatch-uk.com

SKINCARE PRODUCTS

▶ Light Fantastic Ipl, Clattern House, 8-10 High Street, Kingston upon Thames, Surrey, KT1 1EY Tel: (020) 8546 6262 E-mail: lightfanlinks@yahoo.co.uk

SKIP BODIES/SKIP CONTAINERS

Marshall Cooke Ltd, Burrell Way, Thetford, Norfolk, IP24 3RW Tel: (01842) 764312 Fax: (01842) 761033 E-mail: sales@marshallcooke.com

Firber Engineering Ltd, Sidings Road, Lowmoor Business Park, Kirkby-in-Ashfield, Nottingham, NG17 7JZ Tel: (01623) 757794 Fax: (01623) 688990 E-mail: sales@firber.co.uk

G B Fabrication & Welding Services, Bunkers Hill, Bunkers Hill, Kidlington, Oxfordshire, OX5 3EL Tel: (07770) 761599 Fax: (01869) 331759 E-mail: julian.gbfabf@virgin.net

GWR Engineering Ltd, 36 Derby Road, Liverpool, L20 1AB Tel: 0151-933 3150 Fax: 0151-944 2410 E-mail: gwrengineering@aol.com

Mayfly Containers Ltd, Bridge St Industrial Estate, Bridge Street, Clay Cross, Chesterfield, Derbyshire, S45 9NU Tel: (01246) 862456 Fax: (01246) 862711

Randalls Fabrications Ltd, Randall Fabrication, Hoyle Mill Road, Kinsley, Pontefract, West Yorkshire, WF9 5JB Tel: (01977) 615132 Fax: (01977) 610059 E-mail: sales@randallsfabrications.co.uk

Reform & Weld, Building A, Gobowen, Oswestry, Shropshire, SY10 7JZ Tel: (01691) 650479 Fax: (01691) 650461

Skip Units Ltd, Industrial Estate, Sinfin Lane, Derby, DE24 9GL Tel: (01332) 761361 Fax: (01332) 270013 E-mail: sales@skipunits.co.uk

Skyglass Ltd, Morgans Yard, Arundel Road Industrial Estate, Uxbridge, Middlesex, UB8 2RP Tel: (01895) 234432 Fax: (01895) 271118

Stronga Ltd, Ashendene Farm, White Stubbs Lane, Bayford, Hertford, SG13 8PZ Tel: (01992) 519000 Fax: (01992) 519011 E-mail: info@stronga.co.uk

Terbergmatec UK Ltd, Highgrounds Way, Rhodesia, Worksop, Nottinghamshire, S80 3AF Tel: (01909) 484000 Fax: (01909) 489000

Thomson Engineering, 66 Whitehill Road, Glenrothes, Fife, KY6 2RP Tel: 01592 774345

Webb Truck Equipment, Acton Place, Melford Road, Acton, Sudbury, Suffolk, CO10 0BB Tel: (01787) 377368 Fax: (01787) 880618 E-mail: sales@web-extrareach.co.uk

SKIP CONTRACTORS

A R C, Ripley Drive, Normanton Business Park, Normanton Industrial Estate, Normanton, West Yorkshire, WF6 1QT Tel: (01924) 223333 Fax: (0871) 4330708 E-mail: sales@arccomputers.co.uk

Barnes E A & Sons Ltd, Unit 5, Vulcan Road, Lichfield, Staffordshire, WS13 6RW Tel: (01543) 250480 Fax: (01543) 250480 E-mail: sales@eabarnes.co.uk

Brisco Waste Disposal Ltd, 87 Ystrad Road, Fforestfach, Swansea, SA5 4BU Tel: (01792) 584585 Fax: (01792) 586811

C H Middleton Ltd, 65-71 Sprotbrough Road, Doncaster, South Yorkshire, DN5 8BW Tel: (01302) 783731 Fax: (01302) 390024 E-mail: c.h.middleton@btconnect.com

C & J Blackburn, West End Mills, Watergate Road, Dewsbury, West Yorkshire, WF12 9QB Tel: (01924) 465958 Fax: (01924) 454155 E-mail: carol@cjblackburn.co.uk

Constructional Steel & Alloy, Unit 7 Salamons Way, Rainham, Essex, RM13 9UL Tel: (01708) 551967 Fax: (01708) 555453

Alistair Corrie, 3 Station Drive, Hurlford, Kilmarnock, Ayrshire, KA1 5AU Tel: (01563) 543315 Fax: (01563) 543315

Curtis Power & Co. Ltd, Carter La Farm, 5 Carterhall Lane, Sheffield, S12 3XD Tel: 0114-239 8764 Fax: 0114-265 4441

F. Davis & Co., 64 London Road, Bexhill-On-Sea, East Sussex, TN39 3LE Tel: (01424) 211248 Fax: (01424) 730568

Dunstable Waste Group Ltd, Townsend Farm Indust Estate, Blackburn Road, Houghton Regis, Dunstable, Bedfordshire, LU5 5DD Tel: (01582) 476600 Fax: (01582) 664117 E-mail: admin@dwg.uk.com

Evans Skip Hire, Park Lane, Halesowen, West Midlands, B63 2RA Tel: (01384) 412289 Fax: (01384) 412289 E-mail: sales@evansskips.com

F & W Collins Waste Materials Ltd, 139 Upper Allen Street, Sheffield, S3 7GW Tel: 0114-272 5808 Fax: 0114-272 5808 E-mail: info@collins-skips.co.uk

G B N Removal Co. Ltd, Estate Way, London, E10 7JN Tel: (020) 8556 2211 Fax: (020) 8532 8519 E-mail: Gbnremoval@aol.com

G & M Industrial Services Ltd, Shaw Road, Dudley, West Midlands, DY2 8TP Tel: (01384) 236400 Fax: (01384) 235454 E-mail: enquiries@gmskips.com

G & R Metals Skip Hire, 64 London Rd, Bexhill-on-Sea, E. Sussex, TN39 3LE Tel: (01424) 730568

H Brown, 172-180 St Andrews Road, Northampton, NN2 6DB Tel: (01604) 714121

Hales Waste Control Ltd, Coronation Road, Cressex Business Park, High Wycombe, Buckinghamshire, HP12 3TZ Tel: (01494) 521221 Fax: (01992) 640212 E-mail: marketing@biffa.co.uk

Holborn Waste Ltd, Massie Works, 305 A -335 Lichfield Road, Aston, Birmingham, B6 7ST Tel: 0121-327 1046 Fax: 0121-327 3968 E-mail: hwsales@btconnect.com

Holden Environmental Ltd, Shore Road, Perth, PH2 8BH Tel: (01738) 634747 Fax: (01738) 637150 E-mail: sales@holden-enviro.com

Holmes T Skip Hire Ltd, 14 Pleasant Street, West Bromwich, West Midlands, B70 0RF Tel: 0121-553 2495 Fax: 0121-500 5845

J W Burford Metals, Russell Gardens, Wickford, Essex, SS11 8BH Tel: (01268) 732112 Fax: (01268) 573080

Lanz Transport Ltd, Galleymead House, Old Bath Road, Colnbrook, Slough, SL3 0NT Tel: (01753) 682005 Fax: (01753) 682040

Latham & Sons Beckenham Ltd, Latham House, Kangley Bridge Road, London, SE26 5BA Tel: (020) 8778 9008 Fax: (020) 8659 2360

Monway Builders Supplies Ltd, Portway Road, Wednesbury, West Midlands, WS10 7EQ Tel: 0121-502 0911 Fax: 0121-556 9427

Thomas Muir Haulage Ltd, Randolph Industrial Estate, Kirkcaldy, Fife, KY1 2TX Tel: (01592) 651076 Fax: (01592) 651138

J. & M. Murdoch & Son Ltd, Crofthead Industrial Estate, Lochlibo Road, Neilston, Glasgow, G78 3NE Tel: 0141-580 6322 Fax: 0141-580 6323 E-mail: info@jmmurdoch.com

A.C. Nurden Plant Hire Ltd, Park Road, Malmesbury, Wiltshire, SN16 0BX Tel: (01666) 823518 Fax: (01666) 824810

Oakley Arnold Ltd, Cockshot Lane, Broseley, Shropshire, TF12 5NE Tel: (01952) 882322 Fax: (01952) 882707

▶ Oldham Bros Scrap Merchants Dismantlers Demolition, Kirkby Bank Road, Clarence House, Knowsley Industrial Park, Liverpool, L33 7SY Tel: 0151-546 5233 Fax: 0151-546 1258 E-mail: demolition@oldhambros.co.uk

Owen Skip Hire, Lingard Lane, Bredbury Park Industrial Estate, Bredbury, Stockport, Cheshire, SK6 2RN Tel: 0161-430 5650 Fax: 0161-430 5650 E-mail: owenskiphire@tiscalli.co.uk

Porthmadog Skip Hire, Penamser Industrial Estate, Porthmadog, Gwynedd, LL49 9NZ Tel: (07979) 506624 Fax: (01766) 515217 E-mail: welshskips@supanet.com

R & H Tomlinson Ltd, The Recycling Centre, Hackworth Industrial Park, Shildon, County Durham, DL4 1HF Tel: (01388) 778222 Fax: (01388) 778333 E-mail: nicktomlinson007@aol.com

Savetime Skip Company, Henrys House, Challenge Road, Ashford, Middlesex, TW15 1AX Tel: (01784) 247207

Shanks Waste Solutions, Loughborough Road, Bunny, Nottingham, NG11 6QN Tel: 0115-945 6069 Fax: 0115-940 5170

Simpson Environmental Services Ltd, Simpsons Way, Stoke Poges Lane, Slough, SL1 3GD Tel: (01753) 533311 Fax: (01753) 533311 E-mail: jeff@simpsonrecycling.com

Tar Skips & Transport Ltd, Rear of 97 King William Street, Amblecote, Stourbridge, West Midlands, DY8 4EY Tel: (01384) 390711 Fax: (01384) 828060 E-mail: peggy.tristram@btconnect.com

Thompson (Metals) Ltd, Winterton Road, Scunthorpe, South Humberside, DN15 0BA Tel: (01724) 843831 Fax: (01724) 847786 E-mail: thompsonmetals@fsnet.co.uk

Wildman Transport (Bedford) Ltd, Postley Road, Kempston, Bedford, MK42 7BU Tel: (01234) 854244 Fax: (01234) 841362 E-mail: roy@wildmantransport.com

Willard Skip Hire Ltd, 4 Folgate Road, North Walsham, Norfolk, NR28 0AJ Tel: (01692) 405820 Fax: (01692) 500058

Williams Plant Hire Ltd, Henfaes Lane, Welshpool, Powys, SY21 7BE Tel: (01938) 552337 Fax: (01938) 555650

A. Winchester & Sons, 9 Great Queen Street, Dartford, DA1 1TJ Tel: (01322) 221388 Fax: (01322) 227659 E-mail: dartfordskips@aol.com

Wright Brothers (Clayton) Ltd, Victoria Works, Barnard Road, Bradford, West Yorkshire, BD4 7DY Tel: (01274) 587777 Fax: (01274) 394629

Wye Valley Reclemation, Llyod George House, Fordshill Road, Rotherwas Industrial Estate, Hereford, HR2 6NS Tel: (01432) 353606 Fax: (01432) 340020 E-mail: info@wyevalleygroup.co.uk

Yph Waste Management Ltd, Lufton Park, Lufton Way, Lufton Trading Estate, Lufton, Yeovil, Somerset, BA22 8HP Tel: (01935) 412211 Fax: (01935) 411963

SKIP HIRE

▶ A M White, Daytona, Whittington Hill, Whittington, King's Lynn, Norfolk, PE33 9TE Tel: (01366) 500212 Fax: (01366) 500880

▶ Cappagh Contractors Construction London Ltd, 8 Waterside Way, London, SW17 0HB Tel: (020) 8947 4000 Fax: (020) 8944 9447

▶ J T M Skip Hire, 73 High Street, Blaenavon, Pontypool, Gwent, NP4 9PZ Tel: (01495) 791380 Fax: (01495) 791380 E-mail: john@jmahoney399.freeserve.co.uk

▶ Mcfletch Ltd, The Barn, The Street, Pebmarsh, Halstead, Essex, CO9 2NH Tel: (01787) 269964 Fax: (01787) 269909 E-mail: mcfletch@demo-ltd.fsnet.co.uk

▶ Peter Norris Haulage Ltd, Station Approach, St. Mary Cray, Orpington, Kent, BR5 2NB Tel: (01689) 832228 Fax: (01689) 896299

▶ R.S Skips Ltd, 25, Darnley Road, Gravesend, Kent, DA11 0RZ Tel: 01474 362862 Fax: 01474 362862E-mail: info@rsskips.co.uk

Redgate Holdings Ltd, Redgate Lane, West Gorton, Manchester, M12 4RY Tel: 0161-273 5575 Fax: 0161-274 4113 E-mail: redgateholdings@hotmail.co.uk

▶ Sheehan Haulage, Woodstock Road, Yarnton, Kidlington, Oxfordshire, OX5 1PH Tel: (01865) 379931

▶ T B Williamson, Unit 39 Mayfield Industrial Estate, Dalkeith, Midlothian, EH22 4AD Tel: 0131-654 2900 Fax: 0131-654 2909

T J Cottis Transport, 17 Rawreth Industrial Estate, Rawreth Lane, Rayleigh, Essex, SS6 9RL Tel: (01702) 200119 Fax: (01268) 780026

SKIPS

▶ Anglia Landscapes, Brooklands, Straight Road, Boxted, Colchester, CO4 5QY Tel: (01206) 272357 E-mail: sales@anglialandscapes.co.uk

▶ Transport (U K) Ltd, Hydrauch Estate, St Andrews Rd, Avonmouth, Bristol, BS11 9HW Tel: 0117-982 9816 Fax: 0117-982 1243

SKIRTS

Arthur Elkin Holdings Ltd, Progress Mill, Parsonage Street, Macclesfield, Cheshire, SK11 7LY Tel: (01625) 423502 Fax: (01625) 612994 E-mail: elkin.sales@arthurelkin.co.uk

▶ indicates data change since last edition

SKIRTS – *continued*

Baltex Clothing, 63 Hume Street, Smethwick, West Midlands, B66 3PN Tel: (07956) 365202
Fashion Craft Ltd, 11 Dolphin Street, Ardwick, Manchester, M12 6BG Tel: 0161-273 3947 Fax: 0161-273 3947
Glenisla Kilts Ltd, Braidhurst Industrial Estate, Motherwell, Lanarkshire, ML1 3ST Tel: (01698) 254579 Fax: (01698) 275372
G.D. Golding Ltd, 220 Hatfield Road, St. Albans, Hertfordshire, AL1 4LW Tel: (01727) 841321 Fax: (01727) 831462 E-mail: tailors@goldings.co.uk
Kathrina Fashions (Marketing) Ltd, 41-45 Little Donegall Street, Belfast, BT1 2JD Tel: (028) 9032 6963 Fax: (028) 9023 3427 E-mail: kathrina@tinyonline.co.uk
Kinloch Anderson Ltd, 4 Dock Street, Leith, Edinburgh, EH6 6EY Tel: 0131-555 1355 Fax: 0131-555 1392 E-mail: enquiries@kinlochanderson.com
Lakeland Skirts, Unit 1b Boundary Bank, Kendal, Cumbria, LA9 5RR Tel: (01539) 725341 Fax: (01539) 741403
M Waldman Ltd, 8 224 Iverson Road, London, NW6 2HL Tel: (020) 7624 6527 Fax: (020) 7625 7326 E-mail: contactus@waldmanskirts.com
Strathmore Woollen Co. Ltd, Station Works, North Street, Forfar, Angus, DD8 3BN Tel: (01307) 462135 Fax: (01307) 468603 E-mail: info@tartanbystrathmore.co.uk

SKYLIGHT INSTALLATION

Solalighting Ltd, 17 High Street, Olney, Buckinghamshire, MK46 4EB Tel: (0845) 4580101 Fax: (01234) 241766

SLACKS, LADIES' TAILORED

▶ ReetPetite, The Cottage, Ragnall Lane, Walkley Wood, Nailsworth, Gloucestershire, GL6 0RX Tel: 01453 833996 E-mail: reet@reetpetite.biz

SLAG

Tarmac Western, Morfe Bank, Corus Works, Port Talbot, West Glamorgan, SA13 2NG Tel: (01639) 883052 Fax: (01639) 884435
W R Winton Ltd, Richmond House, Forsyth Road, Woking, Surrey, GU21 5SB Tel: (01483) 770121 Fax: (01483) 715630 E-mail: info@winton-antlia.com

SLAT CONVEYOR SYSTEMS

G P M Engineering Systems Ltd, 1585 Bristol Road South, Rednal, Birmingham, B45 9UA Tel: 0121-457 7132 Fax: 0121-457 9035 E-mail: scrow@gpmengineering.com
Newland Engineering Co. Ltd, Captain Clarke Road, Hyde, Cheshire, SK14 4RF Tel: 0161-368 0326 Fax: 0161-367 8004 E-mail: info@newland-conveyors.com
Quality Conveyors Ltd, 10 Elland Lane, Elland, West Yorkshire, HX5 9DU Tel: (01422) 377166 Fax: (01422) 377238 E-mail: qconveyor@aol.com
Romech Spiral Systems Ltd, Carnaby Industrial Estate, Lancaster Road, Carnaby, Bridlington, North Humberside, YO15 3QY Tel: (01262) 601128 Fax: (01262) 671905 E-mail: sales@romech.co.uk
Rusmail Conveyor Systems Ltd, 33-35 Adams Street, Birmingham, B7 4LT Tel: 0121-359 1549 Fax: 0121-333 3104 E-mail: sales@rusmailconveyors.co.uk

SLATE

Burlington Slate Production Ltd, Cavendish House, Kirkby-in-Furness, Cumbria, LA17 7UN Tel: (01229) 889661 Fax: (01229) 889466 E-mail: sales@burlingtonstone.co.uk
Matthew Charlton & Sons (Slaters) Ltd, Chareway Lane, Hexham, Northumberland, NE46 3HW Tel: (01434) 606177 Fax: (01434) 601679 E-mail: slaters@matthewcharlton.com
H Butterfield Ltd, Selbourne Road, Luton, LU4 8QF Tel: (01582) 491100 Fax: (01582) 490969 E-mail: enquiries@butterfieldnatstone.co.uk
Inigo Jones & Co. Ltd, Tudor Slate Works, Caernarfon, Gwynedd, LL54 7ST Tel: (01286) 830242 Fax: (01286) 831247 E-mail: slate@inigojones.co.uk
J & R Marble Company Ltd, Unit 9, Period Works, London, E10 7QT Tel: (020) 8539 6471 Fax: (020) 8539 9264 E-mail: sales@jrmarble.co.uk
▶ K R Venning Ltd, Castle Farm, Raisbeck, Penrith, Cumbria, CA10 3SG Tel: (01539) 624481 Fax: (01539) 624483
Lomax Demolition & Timber Yard, Albion Street, Bury, Lancashire, BL8 2AD Tel: 0161-764 5845
Alfred McAlpine Slate Ltd, Penrhyn Quarry, Bethesda, Bangor, Gwynedd, LL57 4YG Tel: (01248) 600656 Fax: (01248) 601171 E-mail: slate@mcalpineplc.co.uk
R J Sharples, Riverside Sawmill, Fishwick Bottoms, Preston, PR2 5AU Tel: (01772) 556019 Fax: (01772) 250708 E-mail: info@rjsharples.co.uk
▶ Rustic Stone House Signs, 8 Burstow Park Business Centre, Antlands Lane, Shipley Bridge, Horley, Surrey, RH6 9TF Tel: (01293) 823673 Fax: (01293) 821462 E-mail: stone@rusticstone.net
Wincilate Ltd, Quarry Offices, Aberllefenni, Upper Corris, Machynlleth, Powys, SY20 9RT Tel: (01654) 761602 Fax: (01654) 761418 E-mail: slate@wincilate.co.uk

SLATE FLOORING

▶ Delabole Slate Co. Ltd, Pengelly Road, Delabole, Cornwall, PL33 9AZ Tel: (01840) 212242 Fax: (01840) 212948 E-mail: sales@delaboleslate.com

SLATE TILES

▶ Fairford Roof Tile Manufacturers, The Rhymes Yard, Rhymes Lane, Fairford, Gloucestershire, GL7 4RD Tel: (01285) 713653 Fax: (01285) 712169 E-mail: fairfordrooftile@aol.com

SLATE, GRANULATED/ POWDERED

▶ Delabole Slate Co. Ltd, Pengelly Road, Delabole, Cornwall, PL33 9AZ Tel: (01840) 212242 Fax: (01840) 212948 E-mail: sales@delaboleslate.com

SLATING CONTRACTORS

A & E Elkins Ltd, 6 Insulcrete Works, Yeoman Street, London, SE8 5DT Tel: (020) 7231 8808 Fax: (020) 7252 3758 E-mail: sales@roofingspecialistuk.com
A E S Roofing Contractors Ltd, Lingens Bungalow, Sledgemoor, Broadwas, Worcester, WR6 5NR Tel: (01905) 333697 Fax: (01905) 333650 E-mail: info@aesroofing.co.uk
Joseph Hardgrave Ltd, 42-44 Church Lane, Bishopthorpe, York, YO23 2QG Tel: (01904) 704161 Fax: (01904) 703711
Kinder Roofing Ltd, Conservation House, 116 Darwen Road, Bromley Cross, Bolton, BL7 9BQ Tel: (01204) 592200 Fax: (01204) 597700 E-mail: roofing@kinders.co.uk
North Eastern Slating & Building Co., 6 Balmoral Terrace, Aberdeen, AB10 6HH Tel: (01224) 211179 Fax: (01224) 211180

SLATWALL SHOP FITTINGS

Surrey Wholesale, Fleming Way, Crawley, West Sussex, RH10 9JY Tel: (01293) 611111 Fax: (01293) 550555
Tameside Metal Components, Dove House, Thorncliffe Wood, Hollingworth, Hyde, Cheshire, SK14 8NJ Tel: (01457) 766300 Fax: (01457) 766300

SLEEPING BAGS

Bedcrest Ltd, Old Hall Street, Middleton, Manchester, M24 1AG Tel: (0870) 7662324
▶ The Sleep Factory, PO Box 28859, London, SW13 0YX Tel: (020) 8332 7467
Snug Company Ltd, Stonegate House, Stoneygate Lane, Gateshead, Tyne & Wear, NE10 0HJ Tel: 0191-495 2322 Fax: 0191-495 2321 E-mail: admin@snug-ltd.com

SLEEPING GAS ATTACK ALARMS

▶ Nereus Alarms Ltd, 9 Britannia Road, Lower Parkstone, Poole, Dorset, BH14 8AZ Tel: (01202) 731886 Fax: (01202) 739060 E-mail: info@nereusalarms.co.uk

SLEEVE WRAPPING MACHINES

Lachenmeier (UK) Ltd, Wilsons Park, Monsall Road, Newton Heath, Manchester, M40 8PA Tel: 0161-205 3666 Fax: 0161-205 3777 E-mail: kl@lachenmeier.com
Novopac (UK) Ltd, Fieldhead Broomers Corner, Shipley, Horsham, West Sussex, RH13 8PR Tel: (01403) 740003 Fax: (01403) 740071 E-mail: richard@novopac.co.uk
Turpins Packaging Systems Ltd, Kennedy Way, Clacton-on-Sea, Essex, CO15 4AB Tel: (01255) 423402 Fax: (01255) 473312 E-mail: sales@sleevit.com

SLICING MACHINES

Exeter Scale & Equipment Co., Grace Road Central, Marsh Barton Trading Estate, Exeter, EX2 8QA Tel: (01392) 275324
J A Lorrimar & Co., Lorrimar House Hatfield Hi-Tech Park, Goulton Street, Hull, HU3 4DD Tel: (01482) 228173 Fax: (01482) 214106 E-mail: info@lorrimar.co.uk

SLIDE ON FLANGE DUCTING

Doby Ltd, Doby Ltd, Hare Law Industrial Estate, Stanley, County Durham, DH9 8UJ Tel: (01207) 299861 Fax: (01207) 283563 E-mail: sales@dobyverrolec.com
Ductmate (Europe) Ltd, Arrol Road, Wesker Gourdie Industrial Estate, Dundee, DD2 4TH Tel: (01382) 622111 Fax: (01382) 621444 E-mail: sales@ductmate.co.uk

SLIDE VALVES

Kempster Engineering Ltd, 1 Astra Centre, Royle Barn Road, Rochdale, Lancashire, OL11 3DT Tel: (01706) 345599 Fax: (01706) 657396 E-mail: sales@kempsteruk.com

SLIDEWAY GRINDING

Birmingham Machine Tool Services Ltd, 312-314 Bradford Street, Birmingham, B5 6ET Tel: 0121-622 6339 Fax: 0121-666 6406 E-mail: bhammctool@aol.com
Odin Engineering Ltd, Unit 4, Fullwood Close, Aldermans Green Industrial Estate, Coventry, CV2 2SS Tel: (024) 7660 2622 Fax: (024) 7660 2649

SLIDING BATHROOM DOORS

▶ JOHN MONAGHAN (southern) Ltd, Units 24/25, Mount Pleasant Industrial Estate, Northam, Southampton, SO14 0SP Tel: (023) 8023 2238 Fax: (023) 8021 1218 E-mail: info@monaghansouthern.co.uk

SLIDING DOOR FITTINGS OR RUNNING GEAR

▶ Apex Enterprises, Kern House, Corporation Road, Birkenhead, Merseyside, CH41 1HB Tel: 0151-647 9323 Fax: 0151-647 9324
Hillaldam Coburn Ltd, 6 Wyvern Estate, Beverley Way, New Malden, Surrey, KT3 4PH Tel: (020) 8336 1515 Fax: (020) 8336 1414 E-mail: sales@hillaldam.co.uk
King Sliding Doors Gear, Invest House, Bruce Road, Fforestfach, Swansea, SA5 4HS Tel: (01792) 583555 Fax: (01792) 587046 E-mail: enquiries@kingslidingdoorgear.com
P C Henderson Ltd, Durham Road, Bowburn, Durham, DH6 5NG Tel: 0191-377 0701 Fax: 0191-377 1309 E-mail: sales@pchenderson.com
Runners, Signal Hill, Lenborough Road, Gawcott, Buckingham, MK18 4BU Tel: (01280) 822288

SLIDING DOORS

BID Group Ltd, Elland Close, Wingates Industrial Estate, Westhoughton, Bolton, BL5 3XE Tel: 0870 607 5050 Fax: 0870 6081271 E-mail: sales@bidgroup.co.uk
C R F Sections Ltd, Hale Trading Estate, Lower Church Lane, Tipton, West Midlands, DY4 7PQ Tel: 0121-557 1234 Fax: 0121-522 3003
Martin Elliott, The Laurels, Sling, Coleford, Gloucestershire, GL16 8JJ Tel: 01594 836758
Horton Automatics Ltd, Hortonwood 31, Telford, Shropshire, TF1 7YZ Tel: (01952) 670169 Fax: (01952) 670181 E-mail: sales@horton-automatics.ltd.uk
Sunfold Systems, Unit 12 Chestnut Drive, Wymondham, Norfolk, NR18 9SB Tel: (01953) 423423 Fax: (01953) 423430 E-mail: info@sunfold.com

SLIDING HEAD LATHES

Star Micronics GB Ltd, Chapel Street, Melbourne, Derby, DE73 8JF Tel: (01332) 864455 Fax: (01332) 864005E-mail: sales@stargb.net

SLIDING PARTITIONING

Dividers Ltd, Unit 1, Llanelli Gate, Dafen, Llanelli, Dyfed, SA14 8LQ Tel: (01269) 844877 Fax: (01269) 831112 E-mail: sales@esperowalls.com

SLIDING WROUGHT IRON GATES

ALL SEASONS WROUGHT IRON UK LTD, UNIT 15 PARKWAY COURT, GLAISDALE PARKWAY, BILBOROUGH, NOTTINGHAM, NG8 4GN Tel: 0115 928 6688 E-mail: jimbrowne701@hotmail.com

SLIP OR BLOCK GAUGES

Broadleaf Engineering, 1 Craven Street, Leicester, LE1 4BX Tel: 0116-253 9200 Fax: 0116-253 0598
Alan Browne Gauges Ltd, Blackdown Mill, Blackdown, Leamington Spa, Warwickshire, CV32 6QT Tel: (01926) 424278 Fax: (01926) 451865 E-mail: sales@alanbrowne.co.uk

SLIP RESISTANT OR ANTISLIP OR SAFETY FLOORING

Ashland Resources Ltd, PO Box 3694, Colchester, CO4 5QJ Tel: (01206) 273658 Fax: (01206) 273199 E-mail: sales@ashland.co.uk
Epoxy Products, 7 Haviland Road, Ferndown Industrial Estate, Wimborne, Dorset, BH21 7RZ Tel: (01202) 891899 Fax: (01202) 896983 E-mail: sales@epoxyproducts.co.uk
Evertile Ltd, 6 Moresby Road, London, E5 9LF Tel: (020) 8806 3167 Fax: (020) 8806 7434 E-mail: sales@evertile.com
Glendining Road Marks Ltd, 4 Marsh Lane, Tottenham, London, N17 0XE Tel: (020) 8808 2929 Fax: (020) 8880 9161 E-mail: roadmarks@glendining.com
▶ Graepel Perforators Ltd, Unit 5 Burtonwood Industrial Centre, Phipps La, Burtonwood, Warrington, WA5 4HX Tel: (01925) 229809 Fax: (01925) 228069 E-mail: sales@graepeluk.com
▶ Island Leisure Products Ltd, Unit 1a Eurolink Industrial Centre, Castle Road, Sittingbourne, Kent, ME10 3RN Tel: (01795) 436500 Fax: (01795) 436700 E-mail: info@islandleisureproducts.co.uk
Jaymart Rubber & Plastics Ltd, Woodlands Trading Estate, Eden Vale Road, Westbury, Wiltshire, BA13 3QS Tel: (01373) 864926 Fax: (01373) 858454 E-mail: matting@jaymart.net
Jobling Purser Ltd, Paradise Works, Scotswood Road, Newcastle Upon Tyne, NE15 6BZ Tel: 0191-273 2331 Fax: 0191-226 0129 E-mail: info@joblingpurser.com
Maresco Ltd, 2 The Alcorns, Cambridge Road, Stansted, Essex, CM24 8DF Tel: (01279) 817333 Fax: (01279) 817334
Permadeck Systems Ltd, Unit 12 Westside Industrial Estate, Jackson Street, St. Helens, Merseyside, WA9 3AT Tel: (01744) 751869 Fax: (01744) 22551 E-mail: enquiries@safteysurfacing.uk.com
Polyflor Ltd, P O Box 3965, Manchester, M45 7NR Tel: 0161-767 1111 Fax: 0161-767 1100 E-mail: info@polyflor.com
R P S Industrial Flooring Contractors Ltd, Woodhouse, Packhorse Lane, Headley Heath, Birmingham, B38 0DN Tel: (01564) 824900 Fax: (01564) 823447
Safemate Antislip Ltd, Unit 1 Bankhead Avenue, Bucksburn, Aberdeen, AB21 9ET Tel: (01224) 716283 Fax: (01224) 714653 E-mail: safemate@ifb.co.uk
Safety Flooring Supplies, 132-134 Stanwell Road, Ashford, Middlesex, TW15 3QP Tel: (01784) 244577 Fax: (0870) 4020124
Scotgrip (U K) Ltd, Units 8-9, North Deeside Road, Banchory, Kincardineshire, AB31 5YR Tel: (01330) 825335 Fax: (01330) 825260 E-mail: info@scotgrip.com
Sortimo International Ltd, Old Sarum Park, Old Sarum, Salisbury, SP4 6EB Tel: (01722) 411585 Fax: (01722) 320831 E-mail: sales@sortimo.co.uk
Stanmor Floors Ltd, Holly Park Industrial Estate Unit 6, Spitfire Road, Birmingham, B24 9PB Tel: 0121-384 8868 Fax: 0121-384 6424 E-mail: bmorton@stanmorfloors.co.uk
Tarkett Ltd, Dickley Lane, Lenham, Maidstone, Kent, ME17 2QX Tel: (01622) 854000 Fax: (01622) 854500 E-mail: uksales@tarkett.com

SLIP RING MANUFRS

Conductix Ltd, 1 Michigan Avenue, Salford, M50 2GY Tel: 0161-848 0161 Fax: 0161-873 7017 E-mail: info@conductix.co.uk
Courtney Bell Ltd, Lawson Road, Dartford, DA1 5BP Tel: (01322) 221833 Fax: (01322) 228581
MOOG Components Group Ltd, 30 Suttons Park Avenue, Suttons Business Park, Reading, RG6 1AW Tel: 0118-966 6044 Fax: 0118-966 6524 E-mail: mcg@moog.com
Morgan Rekofa Tinsley Division, 37 John Swains Way, Long Sutton, Spalding, Lincolnshire, PE12 9DQ Tel: (01406) 366400 Fax: (01406) 366626 E-mail: sales@morgan-rekofa.co.uk
Morganite Electro Carbon, Stanhope Street, Birmingham, B12 0UZ Tel: 0121-773 3738 Fax: 0121-771 4473E-mail: sales@mecl.co.uk
Rotadata Ltd, Bateman Street, Derby, DE23 8JQ Tel: (01332) 348008 Fax: (01332) 331023 E-mail: sales@rotadata.com
Schleifring Systems Ltd, Abex Road, Newbury, Berkshire, RG14 5EY Tel: (01635) 36363 Fax: (01635) 582118 E-mail: sales@schleifring.co.uk
Southern Commutators Ltd, 16B Mill Lane, Carshalton, Surrey, SM5 2JY Tel: (020) 8669 3876 Fax: (020) 8773 4082 E-mail: southerncommutators@tiscali.co.uk

SLIP RING MANUFRS – *continued*

T E L Engineering Ltd, Newby Road, Hazel Grove, Stockport, Cheshire, SK7 5DA Tel: 0161-456 6545 Fax: 0161-456 3810 E-mail: mail@trolexengineering.co.uk

SLIPPERS

Bowhill & Elliott East Anglia Ltd, 65 London Street, Norwich, NR2 1HL Tel: (01603) 620116 Fax: (01603) 620066

Church & Co (Footwear Ltd), St James, Northampton, NN5 5JB Tel: (01604) 593333 Fax: (01604) 754405 E-mail: sales@church-footwear.com

Delmore, Chiswick Avenue, Mildenhall, Bury St. Edmunds, Suffolk, IP28 7AY Tel: (01638) 714805 Fax: (01638) 713043

Essanti Textiles, Waterloo Road, Llandrindod Wells, Powys, LD1 6BH Tel: (01597) 825825 Fax: (01597) 825281 E-mail: sales@slippers.co.uk

▶ Inglis James Shoemaker, Cavalry Park, Peebles, EH45 9BU Tel: (01721) 722422 Fax: (0845) 8951051 E-mail: sales@jamesinglis.com

Morlands Glastonbury, 3 Creeches Lane, Walton, Street, Somerset, BA16 9RR Tel: (01458) 446969 Fax: (01458) 840108 E-mail: morlands@btinternet.com

Nursey & Son Ltd, 12 Upper Olland Street, Bungay, Suffolk, NR35 1BQ Tel: (01986) 892821 Fax: (01986) 892823 E-mail: sales@nurseyleather.co.uk

SLITTING AND REWINDING MACHINES, COMBINED, FILM/ VINYL ETC

Ab Graphic International, Carnaby Industrial Estate, Lancaster Road, Carnaby, Bridlington, North Humberside, YO15 3QY Tel: (01262) 671138 Fax: (01262) 606359 E-mail: info@abgint.com

Parkland Machines Ltd, 6 Portland Street, Bury, Lancashire, BL9 6EY Tel: 0161-762 9737 Fax: 0161-762 9738 E-mail: sales@parkland-international.com

SLITTING KNIFE HOLDERS

Fife Tidland Ltd, 70-72 Manchester Road, Denton, Manchester, M34 3PR Tel: 0161-320 2000 Fax: 0161-320 4513 E-mail: sales_uk@maxcess.de

SLITTING SERVICES, PAPER/ PLASTIC, ETC

Magnum Materials Ltd, Globe Lane Indust Estate Broadway, Dukinfield, Cheshire, SK16 4UU Tel: 0161-343 1131 Fax: 0161-343 1132 E-mail: sales@magnum-uk.com

SLOTTED NUTS

J Cooke Engineering Ltd, Ashwell Street, Baldock, Hertfordshire, SG7 5QT Tel: (01462) 742236 Fax: (01462) 742188 E-mail: sales@jcooke.co.uk

SLUDGE OR SLURRY OR DIRTY WATER DISPOSAL SERVICES

Morrison Mud Engng Services, Sandford Lane, Everdene House, Wareham, Dorset, BH20 4DY Tel: (01929) 551245 Fax: (01929) 554245 E-mail: enquiries@morrisonmud.co.uk

SLUDGE/SLURRY MONITORING EQUIPMENT

▶ Precise Solutions, Cote House, Wetheral, Carlisle, CA4 8HZ Tel: (01228) 562234 Fax: (01228) 501912 E-mail: derekjohnston@precise-solutions.co.uk

SLUDGE/SLURRY SCRAPERS

▶ Yardscrapers UK, 82 Cheetham Meadow, Leyland, PR26 7UA Tel: (01772) 434484 Fax: (01772) 434484 E-mail: maxiscrape@aol.com

SLUDGE/SLURRY TANKERS

Whale Tankers Ltd, Ravenshaw, Solihull, West Midlands, B91 2SU Tel: 0121-704 5700 Fax: 0121-704 5701 E-mail: whalemail@whale.co.uk

SLUDGE/SLURRY TANKS

Permastore Ltd, Airfield Industrial Park, Eye Airfield Industrial Estate, Eye, Suffolk, IP23 7HS Tel: (01379) 870723 Fax: (01379) 870530 E-mail: sales@permastore.co.uk

SLUDGE/SLURRY TREATMENT PLANT

Mitchell Dryers Ltd, Denton Holme, Carlisle, CA2 5DU Tel: (01228) 534433 Fax: (01228) 633555 E-mail: sales@mitchell-dryers.co.uk

SLUDGE/SLURRY/DIRTY WATER DISPOSAL SYSTEMS

The Haigh Group Ltd, Alton Road, Ross-on-Wye, Herefordshire, HR9 5NG Tel: (01989) 763131 Fax: (01989) 766360 E-mail: sales@haigh.co.uk

Wyatt Ltd, Unit 3, Whittington Buissness Park, Oswestry, Shropshire, SY11 4ND Tel: (01691) 662592 Fax: (01691) 658346 E-mail: wyattltd@aol.com

SLURRY FLOWMETERS

G L Flow Ltd, Hanson Park, Hanson Close, Middleton, Manchester, M24 2QZ Tel: 0161-643 9833 Fax: 0161-643 9835 E-mail: info@glflow.co.uk

SLURRY PUMPS

▶ P D Pumps Ltd, 8 Stuart Road, Bredbury, Stockport, Cheshire, SK6 2SR Tel: 0161-494 5522 Fax: 0161-406 8889 E-mail: sales@pdpumpsltd.co.uk

Weir Minerals Europe Ltd, Halifax Road, Todmorden, Lancashire, OL14 5RT Tel: (01706) 814251 Fax: (01706) 815350 E-mail: sales.uk@weirminerals.com

Wright Rain Irrigation, 4 Christchurch Road, Ringwood, Hampshire, BH24 3SB Tel: (01425) 472251 Fax: (01425) 472258 E-mail: sales@wrightrain.com

SLURRY SEPARATORS

Morrison Mud Engng Services, Sandford Lane, Everdene House, Wareham, Dorset, BH20 4DY Tel: (01929) 551245 Fax: (01929) 554245 E-mail: enquiries@morrisonmud.co.uk

SLUSH MACHINES

▶ Us 4 Slush Ltd, 8C Canford Business Park, Magna Road, Poole, Dorset, BH21 3AP Tel: (01202) 572104 E-mail: sales@us4slush.com

SMALL BATCH INJECTION MOULDINGS

A G M Plastics, 3-4 The Drove, West Wilts Trading Estate, Bratton, Westbury, Wiltshire, BA13 4JE Tel: (01373) 827771 Fax: (01373) 827772 E-mail: alan@agmplastics.co.uk

Engineering Plastic Products Ltd, Unit 6, Shaw Road, Dudley, West Midlands, DY2 8TS Tel: (01384) 235881 Fax: (01384) 255260

Vertex Moulding Ltd, 4 Shorncliffe Industrial Estate, North Close, Folkestone, Kent, CT20 3UH Tel: (01303) 253198 Fax: (01303) 253198 E-mail: vml01@vml01.fsnet.co.uk

SMALL BORE PIPE CLEANING EQUIPMENT

▶ Whirlwind Technologies Ltd, 1 Poplar Street, (Off Buck Street), Leigh, Lancashire, WN7 4HL Tel: (01942) 671300 Fax: (01942) 262042 E-mail: info@whirltech.co.uk

SMALL BUSINESS COMPUTER SYSTEMS

Alpha Computer Services UK Ltd, 69 Bransgrove Road, Edgware, Middlesex, HA8 6HZ Tel: (020) 8905 7245 Fax: (020) 8905 7245

Applied Electronics, Onslow House, Magham Down, Hailsham, East Sussex, BN27 1PL Tel: (01323) 844709 Fax: (01323) 844725

▶ Auxilior Ltd, 6 Steventon Road, Southampton, SO18 5HA Tel: (023) 8047 3441 E-mail: kevin.haynes@auxilior.co.uk

Baniftec Ltd, Farley Edge, Farley Common, Westerham, Kent, TN16 1UB Tel: (01959) 564526 E-mail: enquiries@baniftec.com

Barnsley Yesco, 17 Fishdam La, Monk Bretton, Barnsley, S. Yorkshire, S71 2PX Tel: (01226) 200338 Fax: (01226) 200338 E-mail: yesco@computers97.freeserve.co.uk

▶ BCS, 364 Two Mile Hill Road, Bristol, BS15 1AH Tel: 0117-967 5707 Fax: 0117-940 7555 E-mail: b.c.s@virgin.net

Cynetix Group Ltd, Unit C1, Aven Industrial Park, Tickhill Road, Maltby, Rotherham, South Yorkshire, S66 7QR Tel: (01709) 819922 Fax: (01709) 798804 E-mail: sales@cynetix.co.uk

Dragon Systems, Gyllellog, Pennal, Machynlleth, Powys, SY20 9DU Tel: (01654) 791642 Fax: (01654) 791277 E-mail: dragoncom@aol.com

▶ Ikonik Ltd, Unit 19, Victoria Way, Pride Park, Derby, DE24 8AN Tel: (01332) 224176

NKC Computers Ltd, Unit 22 Ogmore Crescent, Bridgend, Mid Glamorgan, CF31 3TE Tel: (01656) 655009 Fax: (01656) 669025

▶ Pyranha Solutions Ltd, 4 Monkswell Drive, Bolton le Sands, Carnforth, Lancashire, LA5 8JZ Tel: (07808) 054533 E-mail: andrew@pyranha.co.uk

SMALL BUSINESS SUPPORT SERVICES

▶ Jo Branagan Business Support Services, 188 Danube Road, Hull, HU5 5UX Tel: (07973) 511026 E-mail: info@jo-branagan.co.uk

▶ Business Advisor Partnership, Hamlet House, 63 High Street, Eccleshall, Stafford, ST21 6BW Tel: (01785) 851536 Fax: (01785) 859437 E-mail: pat@thebusinessadvisor.org

▶ DiGi-Masters.Com, 24 Franche Road, Wolverley, Kidderminster, Worcestershire, DY11 5TP Tel: (01562) 636213 E-mail: info@digi-masters.com

▶ E-Module, 7 Legion Court, Bennochy Road, Kirkcaldy, Fife, KY2 5JE Tel: (01592) 644744 E-mail: sales@e-module.co.uk

▶ Fitzpatrick Wilkes & Co. Ltd, The Old Forge Cottages, The Green, Beeston, Sandy, Bedfordshire, SG19 1PF Tel: (01767) 692473 E-mail: info@fitzpatrick-wilkes.co.uk

▶ G D S Computer Systems Ltd, 19 St. Lawrence Way, Hurstpierpoint, Hassocks, West Sussex, BN6 9SH Tel: (01273) 832841 E-mail: info@gdsit.co.uk

▶ Mba Businessense Ltd, Skiers Hall Farm, Elsecar, Barnsley, South Yorkshire, S74 8EU Tel: (01226) 748338 Fax: (01226) 748338 E-mail: info@mbabusinessense.co.uk

▶ myHotDesk, 27 John Player Building, Stirling Enterprise Park, Stirling, Stirling, FK7 7RP Tel: 01786 450022 E-mail: advice@www.myhotdesk.com

▶ Omagh Business Forum, 33 Market Street, Omagh, County Tyrone, BT78 1EE Tel: (028) 8225 9595 Fax: (028) 8225 9596 E-mail: info@omaghchamber.com

▶ Powerview Consulting Services, 44 Rectory Avenue, Corfe Mullen, Wimborne, Dorset, BH21 3EZ Tel: (01202) 699977 Fax: (01202) 699977 E-mail: business.growth@powerview-services.com

▶ SF Consultants, 31 Austins Mead, Bovingdon, Hertfordshire, HP3 0JU Tel: 01442 380120 Fax: 01442 380334 E-mail: stephanie.farrer@ntlworld.com

▶ Steve Parker ICD International Company Development, 24 Shearwater Drive, Amblecote, Brierley Hill, West Midlands, DY5 2RD Tel: 01384 893346 Fax: 01384 893346 E-mail: steveparker1@ukonline.co.uk

SMALL COMPUTER SYSTEM INTERFACE (SCSI) CONNECTORS

Bridgeworks Ltd, 135 Summerford Road, Christchurch, Dorset, BH23 3PY Tel: (01425) 478811 Fax: (0870) 1210709 E-mail: sales@4bridgeworks.com

SMALL HOLE DRILLING

Amco Drilling International, PO Box 1, Barnsley, South Yorkshire, S75 1HT Tel: (01226) 243413 Fax: (01226) 320202 E-mail: info@amco-constrction.co.uk

Electro-Discharge Ltd, Unit 14, Bagley Industrial Pk, Northfield Rd, Netherton, Dudley, West Midlands, DY2 9DY Tel: (01384) 238451 Fax: (01384) 245971 E-mail: ron@electro-discharge.co.uk

▶ Oxford Lasers Ltd, Moorbrook Park, Didcot, Oxfordshire, OX11 7HP Tel: (01235) 814433 Fax: (01235) 810060 E-mail: admin@oxfordlasers.com

Partridge Microdrilling Services, Priestley Way, Crawley, West Sussex, RH10 9NT Tel: (01293) 526525 Fax: (01293) 526525 E-mail: partridrill@aol.com

Saxton Drilling Ltd, Cardrew Industrial Estate, Redruth, Cornwall, TR15 1SS Tel: (01209) 315100 Fax: (01209) 315000

SMALL PARTS STORAGE CABINETS

▶ Storageshop, Brookfield, Horsham Road, Alfold, Cranleigh, Surrey, GU6 8JE Tel: (07767) 821194 E-mail: sales@storageshop.co.uk

SMART CARD OPERATED TIMERS/CONTROLLERS

Wayfarer Transit Systems Ltd, 10 Willis Way, Fleets Industrial Estate, Poole, Dorset, BH15 3SS Tel: (01202) 670671 Fax: (01202) 339369 E-mail: sales@wayfarer.co.uk

SMART CARD READER/WRITER MANUFRS

Dione P.L.C., Dione House, Oxford Road, Stokenchurch, High Wycombe, Buckinghamshire, HP14 3SX Tel: (01494) 486000 Fax: (01494) 486050 E-mail: info@dionecorp.com

Euclid Ltd, Euclid House, Parklands Business Park, Waterlooville, Hampshire, PO7 6XP Tel: (023) 9226 6333 Fax: (023) 9226 6555 E-mail: sales@euclid.ltd.uk

Neuroscot Ltd, 8 Meadow Street, Falkirk, FK1 1RP Tel: 0131-453 3845 Fax: 0131-453 3838 E-mail: neuroscot@compuserve.com

SMART CARDS

Crown Hill Associates Ltd, Station House, Station Road, Wilburton, Ely, Cambridgeshire, CB6 3PZ Tel: (01353) 749990 Fax: (01353) 749991 E-mail: sales@crownhill.co.uk

Cubic Transportation Systems Ltd, Honeycrock Lane, Redhill, RH1 5LA Tel: (01737) 782200 Fax: (01737) 789759 E-mail: cubicafc@cts-ltd.co.uk

Datum Automation Ltd, 18 Aston Road, Waterlooville, Hampshire, PO7 7XG Tel: (023) 9224 1154 Fax: (023) 9224 1156 E-mail: sales@datum-automation.com

▶ Oberthur Card Systems Ltd, Alexandre Way, Ashchurch Business Centre, Tewkesbury, Gloucestershire, GL20 8GA Tel: (01684) 290290 Fax: (01684) 290111 E-mail: s.west@oberthurcs.com

SMART MEDIA MEMORY CARDS

Lexicon Distribution, 11 Ackroyd St, Morley, Leeds, LS27 8QX Tel: 0113-252 2727 Fax: 0113-252 3177 E-mail: rob@xic.co.uk

Verbatim Ltd, Prestige House, 23-26 High St, Egham, Surrey, TW20 9DU Tel: (01784) 439781 Fax: (01784) 470760 E-mail: info@verbatim-europe.com

SMELTING, *See headings for particular ore or metal*

SMOKE ALARMS

▶ Progress Fire & Security Ltd, 54 Ashfield Road, Sale, Cheshire, M33 7DT Tel: 0161-976 4802 Fax: 0161-905 3948

Sprue Aegis P.L.C., The Techno Centre, Puma Way, Coventry, CV1 2TT Tel: (024) 7623 6600 Fax: (024) 7623 6603 E-mail: info@sprueaegis.com

SMOKE CURTAINS, GLASS FIBRE OR FIBREGLASS

Sheffield Ceilings S E Ltd, 165 Bow Road, Wateringbury, Maidstone, Kent, ME18 5EA Tel: (01622) 814477 Fax: (01622) 813555 E-mail: sheffield.ceilings@btinternet.com

SMOKE DAMPERS

Disys Technologies Ltd, 24-25 Cross Hands Business Centre, Heol Parc Mawr, Cross Hands, Llanelli, Dyfed, SA14 6RE Tel: (01269) 842496 Fax: (01269) 844708 E-mail: info@disystechnologies.com

Halton Products Ltd, 5 Waterside Business Park, Eastways, Witham, Essex, CM8 3YQ Tel: (01376) 503040 Fax: (01376) 503060 E-mail: enquiries@haltongroup.com

SMOKE DENSITY EQUIPMENT, DETECT/ANALYSE ETC

No Climb Products, 163 Dixons Hill Road, North Mymms, Hatfield, Hertfordshire, AL9 7JE Tel: (01707) 282760 Fax: (01707) 282777 E-mail: info@noclimb.com

SMOKE DISPERSAL VENTILATORS

Aircare Europe Ltd, Unit 27 Tatton Court, Kingsland Grange, Woolston, Warrington, WA1 4RR Tel: (08707) 445588 Fax: (01925) 850325 E-mail: info@aircareeurope.com

SMOKE DISPERSAL VENTILATORS

– continued

K G Smoke Dispersal, 3 Foundry Lane, Horsham, West Sussex, RH13 5PX Tel: (01403) 242299 Fax: (01403) 255577 E-mail: kgsmoke@hotmail.co.uk
Powrmatic Ltd, Hort Bridge, Ilminster, Somerset, TA19 9PS Tel: (01460) 53535 Fax: (01460) 52341 E-mail: info@powrmatic.co.uk
Smoke Vent Services Ltd, 27 Pandy Road, Bedwas, Caerphilly, Mid Glamorgan, CF83 8EH Tel: (029) 2088 9173 Fax: (029) 2088 5026 E-mail: sales@smokevent.co.uk

SMOKE GENERATING EQUIPMENT

Brock's Explosives Ltd, Gateside Factory, Sanquhar, Dumfriesshire, DG4 6JP Tel: (01659) 50531 Fax: (01659) 50526
Martin Manufacturing UK plc, Belvoir Way, Fairfield Industrial Estate, Louth, Lincolnshire, LN11 0LQ Tel: (01507) 604399 Fax: (01507) 601956 E-mail: sales@martin.dk

SMOKE HOODS/FIRE ESCAPE MASKS

S M Alexander Plastics Ltd, Little End Road, Eaton Socon, St. Neots, Cambridgeshire, PE19 8JH Tel: (01480) 473140 Fax: (01480) 406968 E-mail: smalexanderplastics@btinternet.com

SMOKED BACON

▶ Encore Catering, Blair Court, Port Dundas Business Park, 100 Borron Street, Glasgow, G4 9XE Tel: 0141-353 9148 Fax: 0141-353 9145

SMOKED CHEESE

▶ Summer Isles Foods Ltd, The Smoke House, Altandhu, Achiltibuie, Ullapool, Ross-Shire, IV26 2YR Tel: (01854) 622353 Fax: (01854) 622335

SMOKED FISH

▶ Brid Fish Ltd, Old Laundry Trading Estate, Sea Road North, Bridport, Dorset, DT6 3BD Tel: (01308) 456306 Fax: (01308) 456367 E-mail: info@thegourmetworld.com
R J Noble, 2 Stainsacre La Industrial Estate, Fairfield Way, Whitby, North Yorkshire, YO22 4PU Tel: (01947) 820413 Fax: (01947) 820413

SMOKED SALMON

▶ A D M Seafoods, 1 Bedale Walk, Dartford, DA2 6HS Tel: (0871) 2447305 Fax: (0871) 2113186 E-mail: sales@admseafoods.com
Springs Smoked Salmon, Edburton Road, Edburton, Henfield, West Sussex, BN5 9LN Tel: (01273) 857338 Fax: (01273) 857228
▶ West Coast Smoked Foods Ltd, Stonebarn, Gilgarran, Workington, Cumbria, CA14 4RF Tel: (01946) 834475 Fax: (01946) 833996 E-mail: info@westcoastseafoods.co.uk

SMOKELESS FUELS

Coalite Smokeless Fuels, PO Box 21, Chesterfield, Derbyshire, S44 6AB Tel: (01246) 822281 Fax: (01246) 240044 E-mail: enquiries@coalite.co.uk
▶ Fergusson Group, Castlecraig Business Park, Players Road, Stirling, FK7 7SH Tel: (01786) 477222 Fax: (01786) 463522

SMOKERS' REQUISITES MANUFACTURE, *See headings for particular types*

SMOKING SHELTER EQUIPMENT

▶ Nim (Ltd Engineering), Yardley House, 100 Chase Park Road, Yardley Hastings, Northampton, NN7 1HF Tel: (01604) 696120 Fax: (01604) 696122 E-mail: info@nimltdengineering.com

SNACK FOOD PACKAGING

▶ The Food & Packaging Company, 84 Tenter Road, Moulton Park, Northampton, NN3 6AX Tel: 01604 493020 Fax: 01604 492228 E-mail: info@thefandp.com

SNACK FOOD PROCESSING MACHINERY

Berkshire Foods, 210 166 Fareham Road, Gosport, Hampshire, PO13 0FW Tel: (01329) 230000 Fax: (01329) 236611
Glennans Ltd, Dovefields, Dovefields Industrial Estate, Uttoxeter, Staffordshire, ST14 8HU Tel: (01889) 567338 Fax: (01889) 562701 E-mail: richard.thompson@glennans.co.uk

SNACK FOOD VENDING MACHINES

Vendcare Nationwide Services Ltd, Avenue 3, Station Lane Trading Estate, Witney, Oxfordshire, OX28 4BQ Tel: (01993) 703959 Fax: (01993) 776045 E-mail: sales@vendcare.com

SNAP ACTING THERMOSTATS

Capri Electrical Developments Ltd, 45-47 Whalley Road, Clitheroe, Lancashire, BB7 1EE Tel: (01200) 425070 Fax: (01200) 423070 E-mail: roger@storageheater.co.uk
Sunvic Controls Ltd, Bellshill Road, Uddingston, Glasgow, G71 6NP Tel: (01698) 812944 Fax: (01698) 813637 E-mail: sales@sunvic.co.uk

SNOOKER/BILLIARD CHALK

Alliance Snooker Ltd, 45-47 Edge Lane, Edge Hill, Liverpool, L7 2PD Tel: 0151-264 8174 Fax: 0151-281 1490 E-mail: sales@alliancesnooker.co.uk
Baizecraft Snooker & Pool Tables, 120a Saintfield Road, Lisburn, County Antrim, BT27 5PG Tel: (028) 9263 8649 Fax: (028) 9263 8994 E-mail: sales@baizecraft.com
Blue Moon Leisure, Unit 9 The Old Retort House Hele Business Park, Witheridge Place, Ilfracombe, Devon, EX34 9RA Tel: (01271) 864922 Fax: (01271) 864922 E-mail: sales@bluemoonleisure.com

SNOOKER/BILLIARD CUES

Cue Doctor, 120 Prince Avenue, Westcliff-on-Sea, Essex, SS0 0NW Tel: (01702) 391323 Fax: (01702) 391323 E-mail: poolandsnooker@googlemail.co.uk
Cuecraft Ltd, Unit 3 Coach Close, Shireoaks, Worksop, Nottinghamshire, S81 8AP Tel: (01909) 474461 Fax: (01909) 483197 E-mail: sales@cuecraft.com
Peradon Ltd, 128 Richmond Row, Liverpool, L3 3BL Tel: 0151-298 1470 Fax: 0151-298 2988 E-mail: peradon@eaclare.co.uk

SNOOKER/BILLIARD TABLE CLOTH

Blue Moon Leisure, Unit 9 The Old Retort House Hele Business Park, Witheridge Place, Ilfracombe, Devon, EX34 9RA Tel: (01271) 864922 Fax: (01271) 864922 E-mail: sales@bluemoonleisure.com
Glenroyd Mills Ltd, Occupation Lane, Pudsey, West Yorkshire, LS28 8HW Tel: 0113-256 5667 Fax: 0113-257 6859 E-mail: sales@glenroyd.com
Milliken Woolen Speciality, Lodgemore Mills, Stroud, Gloucestershire, GL5 3EJ Tel: (01453) 760800 Fax: (01453) 752919 E-mail: wsp-sales@milliken.com
P H B Textiles Ltd, PO Box 35586, London, NW4 1XG Tel: (07958) 492545 Fax: (020) 8203 5388
Thurston, Clare House, 46-48 St. Anne Street, Liverpool, L3 3DW Tel: 0151-482 2700 Fax: 0151-298 1134 E-mail: thurston@eaclare.co.uk

SNOOKER/BILLIARD TABLE/ REQUISITES SUPPLIERS

A & D Billiards & Pool Services Ltd, 1421 Pershore Road, Stirchley, Birmingham, B30 2JL Tel: 0121-689 9988 Fax: 0121-451 3261 E-mail: andy@aanddbilliards.co.uk
A Shade Above The Rest, 22 Lamb House, Elmington Estate, London, SE5 7JF Tel: 07956 459892 Fax: (020) 7701 5404 E-mail: enquiries@snookerman.co.uk
Aleena Pool & Snooker Services, 1 Golden Triangle Industrial Estate, Hale Road, Widnes, Cheshire, WA8 8TN Tel: 0151-420 8071 Fax: 0151-420 8071
B S C Snooker Equipment, 24 Newbiggin Road, Grangemouth, Stirlingshire, FK3 0LF Tel: (01324) 473069 Fax: (01324) 473069
Bce Ltd, 9 Whitehall Trading Estate, Gerrish Avenue, Whitehall, Bristol, BS5 9DF Tel: 0117-955 1770 Fax: 0117-955 2271 E-mail: admin@bce-uk.com
Billiard Supply Co., 21 Beacon Street, Huddersfield, HD2 2RS Tel: (01484) 424333 Fax: (01484) 424333
Birmingham Export Billiards, 2 Red Rooster Industrial Estate, Tintagel Way, Aldridge, Walsall, WS9 8ER Tel: (01922) 455554 Fax: (01922) 455558 E-mail: sales@birminghambilliards.com
Blackpool Snooker Co., 245 Dickson Road, Blackpool, FY1 2JH Tel: (01253) 299710 Fax: (01253) 299710
Cheadle Snooker, 11 Carrs Road, Cheadle, Cheshire, SK8 2EE Tel: 0161-491 0868
Cue Above The Rest, 5 Demontfort Rise, Ware, Hertfordshire, SG12 0DQ Tel: (01920) 484847 Fax: (01920) 484847 E-mail: queabovetherest@yahoo.co.uk
Elston & Hopkin, Unit 3a, Heapham Road Industrial Estate, Sandars Road, Gainsborough, Lincolnshire, DN21 1RZ Tel: (01427) 839271 Fax: (01427) 839271 E-mail: info@elstonandhopkin.co.uk
Tim Franklin, 379a-379b Gloucester Road, Horfield, Bristol, BS7 8TN Tel: 0117-983 5511 Fax: 0117-983 5512 E-mail: sales@poolandsnooker.com
IG Block, 49 Nags Head Lane, Brentwood, Essex, CM14 5NL Tel: (01277) 848884 Fax: (01277) 848885 E-mail: sales@coinscope.co.uk
International Agencies, 670 Pollokshaws Road, Glasgow, G41 2QE Tel: 0141-424 3995 Fax: 0141-424 1357 E-mail: sales@snookpool.co.uk
Kevin's Cloth Emporium, 39 Victoria Road, Ruislip, Middlesex, HA4 9AB Tel: (01895) 624333 Fax: (01895) 623114
Kingswood Leisure Ltd, 9 Graiseley Row, Wolverhampton, WV2 4HJ Tel: (01902) 713303 Fax: (01902) 713117 E-mail: info@kwlonline.com
M & N Pool Table Services, Leisure House, Billington Road, Leighton Industrial Park, Leighton Buzzard, Bedfordshire, LU7 4TN Tel: (01525) 381133 Fax: 01525 381133
On Cue With Michael Lowcock, 12 Hatfield Lane, Armthorpe, Doncaster, South Yorkshire, DN3 3EX Tel: (01302) 832978 Fax: (01302) 832978
Peradon Ltd, 128 Richmond Row, Liverpool, L3 3BL Tel: 0151-298 1470 Fax: 0151-298 2988 E-mail: peradon@eaclare.co.uk
T.& F. Rowley, 22 Lamb Ho, Elmington Estate, London, SE5 7JF Tel: 020 77015404

SNOOKER/BILLIARD TABLES

A Shade Above The Rest, 22 Lamb House, Elmington Estate, London, SE5 7JF Tel: 07956 459892 Fax: (020) 7701 5404 E-mail: enquiries@snookerman.co.uk
Ambassador Billiard Co., Priesthorpe Lane, Farsley, Pudsey, West Yorkshire, LS28 5RF Tel: 0113-204 7500 Fax: 0113-204 7501 E-mail: sales@snookermarket.co.uk
Barker Billiards, 32 Greenhead Gardens, Chapeltown, Sheffield, S35 1AR Tel: 0114-245 6738 Fax: 0114-245 6738
Birmingham Export Billiards, 2 Red Rooster Industrial Estate, Tintagel Way, Aldridge, Walsall, WS9 8ER Tel: (01922) 455554 Fax: (01922) 455558 E-mail: sales@birminghambilliards.com
Dayboard Ltd, Unit 6 Ravenstone Road Industrial Estate, Coalville, Leicestershire, LE67 3NB Tel: (01530) 813279 Fax: (01530) 510602 E-mail: richard@dayboard.co.uk
Kingswood Leisure Ltd, 9 Graiseley Row, Wolverhampton, WV2 4HJ Tel: (01902) 713303 Fax: (01902) 713117 E-mail: info@kwlonline.com
Rainbow Equipment Ltd, 5 Great Groves, Goffs Oak, Waltham Cross, Hertfordshire, EN7 6SX Tel: (01707) 879876 Fax: (01707) 879876
Thurston, 110 High Street, Edgware, Middlesex, HA8 7HF Tel: (020) 8952 2002 Fax: (020) 8952 0222 E-mail: thurston@eaclare.co.uk

SNORKELING EQUIPMENT

▶ The Outdoor Pursuits Co-operative, 22-24 Radford Street, Stone, Staffordshire, ST15 8DA Tel: (01785) 818500

SNOW CLEARANCE EQUIPMENT, *See also headings for particular equipment*

Eagle Airfield Equipment Ltd, Nebo Road, Llanrwst, Gwynedd, LL26 0SE Tel: (01492) 642201 Fax: (01492) 641992 E-mail: eagle@downline.co.uk
Schmidt Holdings Ltd, Southgate Way, Orton Southgate, Peterborough, PE2 6GP Tel: (01733) 363300 Fax: (01733) 363333 E-mail: sales@schmidt.co.uk

SOAP POWDERS

ACDOCO Ltd, Mallison Street, Bolton, BL1 8PP Tel: (01204) 600500 Fax: (01204) 600501 E-mail: specialist@acdo.co.uk
Powles Hunt International, Stirling Road Industrial Estate, Airdrie, Lanarkshire, ML6 7UJ Tel: (01236) 626306 Fax: (01236) 626301 E-mail: sales@powleshunt.co.uk

SOAPS, TOILET/PERFUMED

Broad Oak Toiletries Ltd, Tiverton Way, Tiverton Business Park, Tiverton, Devon, EX16 6TG Tel: (01884) 242626 Fax: (01884) 242602
Christina May, Rotherdale, Fir Toll Road, Mayfield, East Sussex, TN20 6NB Tel: (01435) 873673 Fax: (01435) 873673 E-mail: bob@christinamay.com
H Bronnley & Co. Ltd, Bronnley Works, Radstone Road, Brackley, Northamptonshire, NN13 5AU Tel: (01280) 702291 Fax: (01280) 703912 E-mail: uksales@bronnley.co.uk
John Gosnell & Co. Ltd, North Street, Lewes, East Sussex, BN7 2QG Tel: (01273) 473772 Fax: (01273) 472217 E-mail: info@johngosnell.com
Kays Ramsbottom Ltd, Britannia Works, Kenyon Street, Ramsbottom, Bury, Lancashire, BL0 0AE Tel: (01706) 824010 Fax: (01706) 828615 E-mail: sales@kays-soap.com
Lever Faberge, PO Box 69, Wirral, Merseyside, CH62 4ZD Tel: 0151-641 4000 Fax: 0151-641 4029
Mitchells Wool Fat Soap Co. Ltd, 46 St Helena Road, Bradford, West Yorkshire, BD6 1QH Tel: (01274) 693063 Fax: (01274) 693057 E-mail: info@mitchellwoolfatsoap.co.uk
Nimbus Laboratories Ltd, Lower Farm Road, Moulton Park Industrial Estate, Northampton, NN3 6XF Tel: (01604) 646411 Fax: (01604) 647375 E-mail: keith@nimbus-labs.co.uk
Standard Soap Co. Ltd, Derby Road, Ashby-de-la-Zouch, Leicestershire, LE65 2HG Tel: (01530) 410000 Fax: (01530) 410001 E-mail: sales@standardsoap.co.uk

SOCIAL CARE CONSULTANCY

Institute of Public Care, 8 Palace Yard Mews, Bath, BA1 2NH Tel: (01225) 484088 Fax: (01225) 330313 E-mail: ipc@brookes.ac.uk
▶ P & L Meals, Oswin House, Oswin Avenue, Balby, Doncaster, South Yorkshire, DN4 0NR Tel: (01302) 850885 Fax: (01302) 850885

SOCKET ADAPTERS

Emulation Technology UK Ltd, 78 Asheridge Road, Chesham, Buckinghamshire, HP5 2PY Tel: (01494) 791336 Fax: (01494) 792336
Lloyd Research Ltd, 7-7A Brook Lane, Warsash, Southampton, SO31 9FH Tel: (01489) 885515 Fax: (01489) 885853 E-mail: progs@lloydres.co.uk

SOCKET SCREW MANUFRS

A1 Turning, 7 Holbrook Lane, Coventry, CV6 4AD Tel: (024) 7668 6333 Fax: (024) 7668 6222 E-mail: salesa1turning@btconnect.com
Clyde Fasteners Ltd, Hawbank Road, East Kilbride, Glasgow, G74 5ET Tel: (01355) 225451 Fax: (01355) 263191 E-mail: info@clydefasteners.com
Non Standard Socket Screw Ltd, Unit 2, Liddall Way, Horton Road, West Drayton, Middlesex, UB7 8PG Tel: (01895) 430003 Fax: (01895) 430004 E-mail: salestsa@aol.com
Socket & Allied Screws Ltd, 121 Camden Street, Birmingham, B1 3DJ Tel: 0121-200 2880 Fax: 0121-236 8991 E-mail: sales@socket-allied.com
Unbrako, 12-14 Tower Street, BIRMINGHAM, B19 3RR Tel: 0121 333 4610 Fax: 0121 333 4525 E-mail: unbrako.uk@spstech.com
▶ Vaughan Jones Socket Screws Ltd, Unit 352 Thorp Arch Trading Estate, Thorp Arch, Wetherby, West Yorkshire, LS23 7BJ Tel: (01937) 843298 Fax: (01937) 843501 E-mail: enquiries@vaughanjones.co.uk

SOCKET SCREWS, NON STANDARD

Non Standard Socket Screws Ltd, 358-364 Farm Street, Birmingham, B19 2TZ Tel: 0121-515 0121 Fax: 0121-523 4440 E-mail: sales@nssocketscrews.com

SOCKETS

Globe Electrical Co., 25 Crown Street, Ayr, KA8 8AG Tel: (01292) 269529 Fax: (01292) 611918

SOCKETS, SWITCH, DOUBLE

▶ Household Electrics, The Workshop, Terregleestown Farm, Terregles, Dumfries, DG2 9RW Tel: (01387) 268672

SOCKS

Angell Hosiery Ltd, Ashford Road, Leicester, LE2 6AA Tel: 0116-270 0698 Fax: 0116-270 1040

SOCKS – *continued*

Cautaulds UK, West Mill, Bridge Foot, Belper, Derbyshire, DE56 1BH Tel: (01773) 525525 Fax: (01773) 525545 E-mail:
Cavendish Hosiery Ltd, 77 Cannock Street, Leicester, LE4 9HR Tel: 0116-276 6477 E-mail: cavendishhos@aol.com
Commando Knitwear Ltd, Countesthorpe Road, Wigston, Leicestershire, LE18 4PJ Tel: 0116-278 5288 E-mail: info@commando-knitwear.co.uk
Samuel Eden & Son Ltd, Station Road, Sutton-in-Ashfield, Nottinghamshire, NG17 5FQ Tel: (01623) 553521 Fax: (01623) 552115 E-mail: sales@samueleden.co.uk
F J Bamkin & Son Ltd, Unit 3 Washdyke Lane Workshops, Washdyke Lane, Hucknall, Nottingham, NG15 6NH Tel: 0115-963 2020 Fax: 0115-968 0013 E-mail: info@penninebamkin.co.uk
Faisaltex Ltd, Faisal House, 107-109 Fletcher Road, Preston, PR1 5JG Tel: (01772) 704440 Fax: (01772) 794837
▶ Fimex Ltd, 4 Fimex Industrial Park, Victoria Road, Leeds, LS14 2LA Tel: 0113-218 8855 Fax: 0113-218 8866
Humphreys & Sons Ltd, Newton Lane, Wigston, Leicestershire, LE18 3SG Tel: 0116-288 1105 Fax: 0116-288 0661 E-mail: ian@europasports.co.uk
J Alex Swift Ltd, Cross Street, Hathern, Loughborough, Leicestershire, LE12 5LB Tel: (01509) 842284 Fax: (01509) 646106 E-mail: socks@jalexswift.co.uk
Madison Hosiery, Mill Green, Leeds, LS12 6HE Tel: 0113-244 3434 Fax: 0113-242 5634
David Mason Textiles Ltd, 2-4 Frog Island, Leicester, LE3 5AG Tel: 0116-253 9929 Fax: 0116-253 8458 E-mail: greg.dmt@btinternet.com
Medella Manufacturing Ltd, 1 Palmer Street, Leicester, LE4 5PT Tel: 0116-233 3299 Fax: 0116-233 3431 E-mail: jgarner-socks@aol.com
Nylon Hosiery, 44 Upper Bond Street, Hinckley, Leicestershire, LE10 1RJ Tel: (01455) 631413 Fax: (01455) 636345 E-mail: rob@nylonhosiery.co.uk
Pantherella Ltd, Hallaton St, Leicester, LE2 8QY Tel: 0116-283 1111 Fax: 0116-283 0695 E-mail: mail@pantherella.co.uk
Pep Socks, 3 Clyde Street, Leicester, LE1 2BG Tel: 0116-251 1467 Fax: 0116-251 1467
▶ polat socks, Flat 39, Langbourne Mansions, Langbourne Avenue, Highgate, London, N6 6PT Tel: (020) 8348 9995 Fax: (020) 8349 9995 E-mail: tarik@polat.wanadoo.co.uk
▶ Prowse & Hargood Ltd, Unit 3, Jessop Close, Clacton-on-Sea, Essex, CO15 4LY Tel: (0870) 2467740 Fax: (0870) 2467780 E-mail: info@prowseandhargood.com
John Scott-Nichol Ltd, Old Station Close, Shepshed, Loughborough, Leicestershire, LE12 9AJ Tel: (01509) 502261 Fax: (01509) 600364 E-mail: info@scott-nichol.com
Sihad Textiles Ltd, 3 Camden Street, Leicester, LE1 2AP Tel: 0116-253 9258
Swallow Hosiery, 2 Swallow Street, Manchester, M12 4GH Tel: 0161-225 6336 Fax: 0161-225 6336
Wolsey, Abbey Meadows, Leicester, LE4 5AD Tel: 0116-262 6755 Fax: 0116-253 0154 E-mail: sales@wolsey.com

SODA BLASTING EQUIPMENT

▶ Ecologic Systems Ltd, Brook House, Birmingham Road, Henley-in-Arden, West Midlands, B95 5QR Tel: (0870) 2863730 Fax: (0870) 2863731 E-mail: info@ecologicsystems.co.uk

SODA CRYSTALS

Dri Pak Ltd, Furnace Road, Ilkeston, Derbyshire, DE7 5EP Tel: 0115-932 5165 Fax: 0115-944 0297 E-mail: sales@dripak.co.uk

SODA LIME GLASS BEADS

▶ Bead Envy, 4 Killerby Lane, Cayton, Scarborough, North Yorkshire, YO11 3TP Tel: 01262 470229 E-mail: emma@beadenvy.co.uk
▶ Judith Johnston Lampwork Beads, 21 Kendal Road, Hove, East Sussex, BN3 5HZ Tel: (01273) 776985

SODIUM ACTIVATED BENTONITE CLAYS

▶ AMCOL Specialty Minerals, Wharton Lodge Mills, Weaver Valley Road, Winsford, Cheshire, CW7 3BU Tel: (01606) 868200 Fax: (01606) 868268E-mail: asm@amcol.com
Castle Clay Sales, Podmore Street, Stoke-on-Trent, ST6 2EZ Tel: (01782) 575992 Fax: (01782) 575995 E-mail: claysales@ukonline.co.uk
Steetley Bentonite & Absorbents Ltd, West Carr Road, Retford, Nottinghamshire, DN22 7ZF Tel: (01777) 712828 Fax: (01777) 700344 E-mail: hq@steetley.com

SODIUM BROMATE

Apollo Scientific Ltd, Bredbury, Stockport, Cheshire, SK6 2QR Tel: (01256) 336097 Fax: (01256) 336097 E-mail: johncaparn@fsmail.net

SODIUM CARBONATE

Brunner Mond Group Ltd, PO Box 4, Northwich, Cheshire, CW8 4DT Tel: (01606) 724000 Fax: (01606) 781353 E-mail: sales.enquiries@brunnermond.com

SODIUM HYDRIDE METAL TREATMENT SERVICES

Lenton Treatment Holdings Ltd, 68 Cannock Street, Barkby Thorpe Road, Leicester, LE4 9HR Tel: 0116-276 7162 Fax: 0116 2767446 E-mail: mail@lentontreatments.co.uk

SOFA BEDS

B & A Quilting Co. Ltd, Oxford Mill, Oxford Street East, Ashton-under-Lyne, Lancashire, OL7 0LT Tel: 0161-330 5030 Fax: 0161-339 0418 E-mail: info@ba-quilting.co.uk
▶ Bott Shaun Upholstery, 18 Leicester Road, Blaby, Leicester, LE8 4GQ Tel: 0116-277 9705 E-mail: info@handmadesofas.co.uk
Europa Sofabeds Ltd, Grindon Way, Heighington Lane Business Park, Newton Aycliffe, County Durham, DL5 6SH Tel: (01325) 318871 Fax: (01325) 300492
Nehl (UK) Ltd, Unit 2, Stafford Park 12, Telford, Shropshire, TF3 3BJ Tel: (01952) 292296 Fax: (01952) 290409 E-mail: enquiries@www.nehl(uk).com
▶ Sleep Right, Shop 4 Marine Court, St. Leonards-on-Sea, East Sussex, TN38 0DN Tel: (01424) 447246 Fax: (01424) 447246 E-mail: sales@futonsfirst.co.uk
Sofa Bed Factory Shop, Oxford House, Lower Oxford Street, Hartlepool, Cleveland, TS25 1PT Tel: (01429) 866607 Fax: (01429) 297001 E-mail: sales@sofabedfactoryshop.co.uk
Sofa Design, 1a Queen Street, Stourbridge, West Midlands, DY8 1TP Tel: (01384) 440546 Fax: (01384) 440546 E-mail: enquiries@sofadesign.co.uk

SOFAS

▶ Bed Shops, 2a Buckland Road, Pen Mill Trading Estate, Yeovil, Somerset, BA21 5EA Tel: (01935) 431331
▶ Bott Shaun Upholstery, 18 Leicester Road, Blaby, Leicester, LE8 4GQ Tel: 0116-277 9705 E-mail: info@handmadesofas.co.uk

SOFT DRINK DISPENSER INSTALLATION/MAINTENANCE CONTRACTORS

▶ County Contractors, Unit 17, Leeway Court, Leeway Industrial Estate, Newport, Gwent, NP19 4SJ Tel: (0870) 2434241 Fax: (01633) 270970 E-mail: info@countycontractors.co.uk

SOFT DRINK DISPENSERS

Ben Shaws Western, 5 Avon Gorge Industrial Estate, Portview Road, Bristol, BS11 9LQ Tel: 0117-982 4742 Fax: 0117-938 1169
Bon Accord Sparkling Drinks Ltd, 12 Station Rd, Larkhall, Lanarkshire, ML9 2DB Tel: 01698 883295 Fax: 01698 883295
Frujet Beverages Ltd, 4 Manor Road, London, N16 5SA Tel: (020) 8809 4646 Fax: (020) 8809 4747
I M I Cornelius UK Ltd, 1-3 Tything Road East, Kinwarton, Alcester, Warwickshire, B49 6EU Tel: (01789) 763101 Fax: (01789) 763644 E-mail: sales@cornelius.com
Matthew Clark, Holford Way, Holford, Birmingham, B6 7AX Tel: 0121-344 3773 Fax: 0121-331 8506
Scotsman Beverage Systems, 13 Halesowen Industrial Park, Chancel Way, Halesowen, West Midlands, B62 8SE Tel: 0121-501 2566 Fax: 0121-550 0873
Take Five Beverages, 271 Camp Road, St. Albans, Hertfordshire, AL1 5NR Tel: (01727) 851826 Fax: (01727) 869068 E-mail: sales@take-five.co.uk

SOFT DRINK PRODUCTION MACHINERY

England Worthside Ltd, Hope Mills, South Street, Keighley, West Yorkshire, BD21 1AG Tel: (01535) 682222 Fax: (01535) 682223 E-mail: enquiries@worthside.co.uk

SOFT DRINK VENDING MACHINES

▶ Us 4 Slush Ltd, 8C Canford Business Park, Magna Road, Poole, Dorset, BH21 3AP Tel: (01202) 572104 E-mail: sales@us4slush.com

SOFT DRINKS

Aberdeen Mineral Water Co. Ltd, Greyhope Road, Aberdeen, AB11 9RD Tel: (01224) 876888 Fax: (01224) 876676
Alderwicks Ltd, Clay Lane, Haverfordwest, Dyfed, SA61 1UH Tel: (01437) 762298 Fax: (01437) 765195
Barrett's, Tivoli Road, Margate, Kent, CT9 5TA Tel: (01843) 228581 Fax: (01843) 228878
Beer on Tap Ltd, Units 1-3 Townsend Farm Business Park, Melbury Osmond, Dorchester, Dorset, DT2 0LP Tel: (01935) 83683 Fax: (01935) 83683 E-mail: beerontapsales@aol.com
Benbrook Foods Ltd, The Manor Crown Business Centre, 5 Market Place, Whittlesey, Peterborough, PE7 1AB Tel: (01733) 350003 Fax: (01733) 350565 E-mail: jeanette.benner@benbrookfoods.co.uk
Britannia Soft Drinks Ltd, Britvic House, Broomfield Road, Chelmsford, CM1 1TU Tel: (01245) 261871 Fax: (01245) 267147 E-mail: forename.surname@britvic.co.uk
Britvic Northern Ireland, 468-472 Castlereagh Road, Belfast, BT5 6RG Tel: (028) 9079 9335 Fax: (028) 9070 7206 E-mail: james.simpson@candcgroup.ie
Britvic Soft Drinks Ltd, Wellington Parkway, Magna Park, Lutterworth, Leicestershire, LE17 4XW Tel: (01455) 559772 Fax: (01455) 551449
Britvic Soft Drinks Ltd, Aventine Way, Glebe Farm Industrial Estate, Rugby, Warwickshire, CV21 1HA Tel: (01788) 538800 Fax: (01788) 538817
Cadbury Schweppes P.L.C., Franklin House, Bournville Lane, Bournville, Birmingham, B30 2NB Tel: 0121-625 7000 Fax: 0121-458 2826
Cadbury Schweppes P.L.C., 25 Berkeley Square, London, W1J 6HB Tel: (020) 7409 1313 Fax: (020) 7830 5200 E-mail: info@cadburyschweppes.com
Calypso Soft Drinks Ltd, Spectrum Business Park, Wrexham Industrial Estate, Wrexham, Clwyd, LL13 9QA Tel: (01978) 668400 Fax: (01978) 668440 E-mail: contactus@calypso.co.uk
Cater Direct Ltd, Unit 6 Pasadena Close, Hayes, Middlesex, UB3 3NQ Tel: (020) 8561 7706 Fax: (020) 8561 7748 E-mail: info@caterdirect.co.uk
Coca Cola Enterprises Ltd, Cray Road, Sidcup, Kent, DA14 5DF Tel: (020) 8302 2600 Fax: (020) 8565 3309
Coca Cola GB & Ireland, 1 Queen Caroline Street, London, W6 9HQ Tel: (020) 8237 3000 Fax: (020) 8237 3700
Coca-Cola Bottlers Ulster, The Green, Lambeg, Lisburn, County Antrim, BT27 5SS Tel: (028) 9267 4231 Fax: (028) 9267 1049
Coca-Cola Enterprises Europe Ltd, Charter Place, Vine Street, Uxbridge, Middlesex, UB8 1EZ Tel: (01895) 231313
Cott Beverages Ltd, Bondgate, Pontefract, West Yorkshire, WF8 2XA Tel: (01977) 601600 Fax: (01977) 708447E-mail: sales@cott.co.uk
W. & J. Cruickshank & Co., Cunningholes Industrial Estate, Rathven, Buckie, Banffshire, AB56 4DA Tel: (01542) 832132 Fax: (01542) 835573 E-mail: cruickshank@wheenet.com
Crystal Drinks (UK) Ltd, 14 Wakefield Road, Featherstone, Pontefract, West Yorkshire, WF7 5HJ Tel: (01977) 797171 Fax: (01977) 791753 E-mail: gmcgoldrick@crystaldrinks.co.uk
Davies Brook & Co Ltd, Moreton-on-Lugg, Hereford, HR4 8DY Tel: (01432) 760666 Fax: (01432) 761477
▶ Dunns Food & Drink Ltd, 32 Glasgow Road, Blantyre, Glasgow, G72 0JY Tel: (01698) 727700 Fax: (01698) 727770 E-mail: sales@dunnsfoodanddrinks.co.uk
Edicos Ltd, Unit 8-9 Cromwell Industrial Estate, Staffa Road, London, E10 7QZ Tel: (020) 8539 6102 Fax: (020) 8539 8061
▶ Feel Good Drinks Co., 5 Hardwick Street, London, EC1R 4RG Tel: (020) 7687 7651 Fax: (020) 7687 7654 E-mail: team@feelgooddrinks.co.uk
Glaxosmithkline, 11 Stoke Poges Lane, Slough, SL1 3NW Tel: (01753) 533433 Fax: (01753) 502000
Gold Star Soft Drinks, 4 Abbots Close, Lee Mill Industrial Estate, Ivybridge, Devon, PL21 9GA Tel: (01752) 690051 Fax: (01752) 691147 E-mail: goldstardrinks@btinternet.com
Hartridges Ltd, West Street, Hambledon, Waterlooville, Hampshire, PO7 4SN Tel: (023) 9263 2882 Fax: (023) 9263 2540 E-mail: sales@hartridges.co.uk
Heath & Smith Ltd, Cherry Tree Road, Hexthorpe, Doncaster, South Yorkshire, DN4 0BJ Tel: (01302) 342097 Fax: (01302) 739513 E-mail: heathandsmith@aol.com
Histogram Ltd, Belmont Industrial Estate, Durham, DH1 1ST Tel: 0191-386 7111 Fax: 0191-383 3481
Incup Soft Drinks, Unit 2d Drum Industrial Estate, Chester le Street, County Durham, DH2 1SS Tel: (07966) 733394 Fax: 0191-492 0394 E-mail: sales@incupdrinks.com
Kassero Edible Oils Ltd, 6-8 Albert Road, St. Philips, Bristol, BS2 0XA Tel: 0117-971 4331 Fax: 0117-972 4183 E-mail: sales@kassero.co.uk
L A Drinks, 3 College Grove, Lurgan, Craigavon, County Armagh, BT66 6DA Tel: (028) 3832 6601 Fax: (028) 3832 9937 E-mail: sales@ladrinks.com
Lakeland Spring Soft Drinks Ltd, Red Lonning Industrial Estate, Whitehaven, Cumbria, CA28 6SJ Tel: (01946) 690777 Fax: (01946) 690888 E-mail: lakelandspring@aol.com
Liquid Measure, Gelli-Hirion Industrial Estate, Pontypridd, Mid Glamorgan, CF37 5SX Tel: (01443) 844622 Fax: (01443) 844623 E-mail: liquidmeasure@treforest.wannadoo.co.uk
Maine Soft Drinks Ltd, 35 Ballymena Road, Ballymoney, County Antrim, BT53 7EX Tel: (028) 2766 2088 Fax: (028) 2766 6112 E-mail: bruce@mainesoftdrinksltd.co.uk
Nichols plc, Laurel House 3 Woodlands Park, Ashton Road, Newton-le-Willows, Merseyside, WA12 0HH Tel: (01925) 222222 Fax: (01925) 222233
▶ Pete & Johnny, Unit 28 Talina Centre, Bagleys Lane, London, SW6 2BW Tel: (020) 7348 7464 Fax: (020) 7384 2032
Prem Fill Ltd, Chambers Road, Hoyland, Barnsley, South Yorkshire, S74 0EZ Tel: (01226) 741944 Fax: (01226) 351005 E-mail: office@prem-fill.freeserve.co.uk
Princes, 45-75 Bogmoor Road, Glasgow, G51 4TJ Tel: 0141-440 2585 Fax: 0141-445 3053
Princes Soft Drinks, West Yorkshire Industrial Estate, Toftshaw Lane, Bradford, West Yorkshire, BD4 6SX Tel: (01274) 651777 Fax: (01274) 651088 E-mail: info@princes.co.uk
▶ Rush Drinks, Ashpool House, Sandy Lane, Lowton, Warrington, WA3 1BG Tel: (01942) 680006 Fax: (01942) 607412 E-mail: enquiries@rushdrink.com
Sangs Banff Ltd, 22 St Machar Road, Aberdeen, AB24 2UU Tel: (01224) 276699 Fax: (01224) 276100 E-mail: sales@sangs.co.uk
Sangs Banff Ltd, Macduff Industrial Estate, Old Gamrie Road, Macduff, Banffshire, AB44 1GD Tel: (01261) 832911 Fax: (01261) 833637 E-mail: sales@sangs.co.uk
Silver Spring Mineral Water Co. Ltd, Park Farm Road, Park Farm Industrial Estate, Folkestone, Kent, CT19 5EA Tel: (01303) 856500 Fax: (01303) 256524 E-mail: eddie@silverspring.co.uk
Snapple Europe Ltd, 1 Castle Yard, Richmond, Surrey, TW10 6TF Tel: (020) 8332 9990 Fax: (020) 8332 6998 E-mail: snapple_europe@compuserve.com
Taylor & Co (Mineral Waters) Ltd, 215 London Road, Staines, Middlesex, TW18 4JF Tel: (01784) 459923 Fax: (01784) 441595 E-mail: admin@taylordrinks.co.uk
Tekno Fuel Sports Drinks, Crest Complex, Courteney Road, Gillingham, Kent, ME8 0RX Tel: (01634) 233272 E-mail: graham@teknofuel.co.uk
Thomas & Son, Darren Road, Ystalyfera, Swansea, SA9 2LL Tel: (01639) 842158
Tilloreys Soft Drinks, Creeches Lane, Walton, Street, Somerset, BA16 9RR Tel: (01458) 841534 Fax: (01458) 840740 E-mail: tilloreysdrinks@btconnect.com
Vimto, Laurel House Woodlands Park, Ashton Road, Newton-le-Willows, Merseyside, WA12 0HH Tel: (01925) 294080 Fax: (01925) 294090
W & J Cruickshank & Co., 31 Telford Street, Wick, Caithness, KW1 5EQ Tel: (01955) 602674 Fax: (01955) 602674
Waters & Robson Abbeywell Ltd, Abbey Well, 12 Coopies Lane, Morpeth, Northumberland, NE61 6JF Tel: (01670) 513113 Fax: (01670) 515821 E-mail: enquiries@abbey-well.co.uk

SOFT FACED HAMMERS

Thor Hammer Co. Ltd, Highlands Road, Shirley, Solihull, West Midlands, B90 4NJ Tel: 0121-705 4695 Fax: 0121-705 4727 E-mail: info@thorhammer.com

SOFT FURNISHING ACCESSORIES

A Davenport Trimmings Ltd, 1 Snell Street, Manchester, M4 7EL Tel: 0161-273 6539 Fax: 0161-273 6295 E-mail: info@adtrimmings.co.uk
▶ Digitata Ltd, Old Academy, Back Road, Stromness, Orkney, KW16 3AW Tel: (01856) 851740 Fax: (0870) 0518821 E-mail: info@digitatadesign.co.uk
▶ Flamboyance, 483 Green Lanes, London, N13 4BS Tel: (0845) 8382542 Fax: (0871) 2423304E-mail: sales@FlamboyanceLtd.co.uk
Handmade Curtain Co., 49 Turner Rise, Oadby, Leicester, LE2 5SH Tel: 0116-271 6954 E-mail: info@handmade-curtains.co.uk
▶ Onevillage.com, St. Benets, Church Lane, Charlbury, Chipping Norton, Oxfordshire, OX7 3SQ Tel: (01608) 811811

SOFT FURNISHING FABRICS

Apiffany Interior Design Ltd, Yandell Publishing Ltd, 9 Vermont Place, Tongwell, Milton Keynes, MK15 8JA Tel: (0870) 1212617 Fax: (0870) 1212618 E-mail: info@apiffany.co.uk

Denholme Velvets Ltd, Halifax Rd, Denholme, Bradford, West Yorkshire, BD13 4EZ Tel: (01274) 832185 Fax: (01274) 832646 E-mail: sales@denholme-velvets.co.uk

▶ Fisher Brian, 40 Fuller Road, Harleston, Norfolk, IP20 9EA Tel: (01379) 853052 Fax: (01379) 854713 E-mail: furnish@brianfisher.co.uk

Lloyd Furnishings, Albert Close Trading Estate, Whitefield, Manchester, M45 8EH Tel: 0161-796 1920 Fax: 0161-796 1921 E-mail: sales@curtains.co.uk

SOFT FURNISHING GOODS MAKERS/DESIGNERS/ PLANNERS/RENOVATION SERVICES

African Cloth Co., 7 Hurstmere Close, Grayshott, Hindhead, Surrey, GU26 6TR Tel: (01428) 607516 Fax: (01428) 607164

Albert E Chapman Ltd, 17 Crouch Hill, London, N4 4AP Tel: (020) 7272 2536 Fax: (020) 7263 1033

Angus Classic Interiors, 13-17 Bank Street, Brechin, Angus, DD9 6AU Tel: (01356) 623982 E-mail: sales@classicint.fsnet.co.uk

▶ Ayshire Curtain Makers, 3 Montgomery Place, Irvine, Ayrshire, KA12 8PN Tel: (01294) 275603 Fax: (01294) 275603

▶ Azura Soft Furnishings, Chapter Street, Manchester, M40 2AY Tel: 0161-202 4148

Beau-Monde, Unit 7 Old Pottery Court, Fore Street, Chudleigh, Newton Abbot, Devon, TQ13 0HX Tel: (01626) 852500 Fax: (01626) 852500

Bruva Renaissance, The Old Mill, Miry Lane, Yeadon, Leeds, LS19 7ER Tel: 0113-250 4499

Butterfly Collection Ltd, Rutland Street, Ilkeston, Derbyshire, DE7 8DG Tel: 0115-944 7469 Fax: 0115-944 7158 E-mail: lester.price@btinternet.com

▶ Casada Cushions, 20 Museum Street, London, WC1A 1JN Tel: (020) 7580 8878 Fax: (020) 7580 8870 E-mail: casadacushions@aol.com

Chiltern Mills, Enterprise House, Belle Isle Road, Leeds, LS10 2DG Tel: 0113-277 6226 Fax: 0113-277 6220

Clarke S.J Company Ltd, Caxton Park, Caxton Road Elm Farm Indusrial Estate, Elm Farm Industrial Estate, Bedford, MK41 0TY Tel: (01234) 346513 Fax: (01234) 364047 E-mail: sales@sjclarke.co.uk

▶ Collage Trading Services, 81 Lower Manor Lane, Burnley, Lancashire, BB12 0EF Tel: (01282) 439993 Fax: (01282) 439993

▶ Cosy Home Furnishings Ltd, Premier House, Premier Road, Manchester, M8 8HE Tel: 0161-819 5145 Fax: 0161-819 5152

Crowson Fabrics, Crowson House, Bellbrook Industrial Estate, Uckfield, East Sussex, TN22 1QZ Tel: (01825) 761044 Fax: (01825) 764283 E-mail: sales@crowsonfabrics.com

Curtain Studio, Unit 10, Swallow Mill, Swallow Street, Higher Hillgate, Stockport, Cheshire, SK1 3HJ Tel: 0161-480 6480

Future Furnishings Ltd, 41 Hollywood Rd, Bolton, BL1 6HP Tel: 01204 495711 Fax: 01204 495711

Gale Furs Ltd, Unit 7 Plough Yard, London, EC2A 3LP Tel: (020) 7247 2014 Fax: (020) 7377 6792

V.J. Herington, 11 South Park Rd, Harrogate, N. Yorkshire, HG1 5QU Tel: 01423 531721 Fax: 01423 531721

J&R Designs Ltd, 5-7 Shepherds Lane, London, E9 6JJ Tel: (020) 8985 0717 Fax: (020) 8985 7987

Daniel James Furnishings Ltd, Hilltop Works, Old Oak Common Lane, London, NW10 6DY Tel: (020) 8961 1070 E-mail: info@daniel-james.com

Jameson Curtains Ltd, 320 Cheapside, Birmingham, B5 6AX Tel: 0121-622 6620 Fax: 0121-622 6779 E-mail: furnishings@jamesons.demon.co.uk

▶ K W Curtain Designs, 59 Holt Drive, Loughborough, Leicestershire, LE11 3HZ Tel: (01509) 210585 E-mail: kwalmsley@kwdesigns.fsnet.co.uk

Krams Ugo Ltd, 18 Deans Drive, Edgware, Middlesex, HA8 9NU Tel: (020) 8906 8656 Fax: (020) 8906 8822 E-mail: enquiries@kramsugo.co.uk

▶ London Quilting Co., Unit C 25 Stable Way, London, W10 6QX Tel: (020) 8964 5782 Fax: (020) 8964 5782

Loraine Shaw, 602a Liverpool Road, Irlam, Manchester, M44 5AA Tel: 0161-776 2360 Fax: 0161-776 2360 E-mail: info@laineshawdesign.co.uk

Lyn Plan Ltd, 43 Imperial Way, Croydon, CR9 4LP Tel: (020) 8681 1833 Fax: (020) 8680 5727 E-mail: sales@lynplan.com

Mcewan Layne Soft Furnishings, 83 Canal Street, Long Eaton, Nottingham, NG10 4GA Tel: 0115-973 6330 Fax: 0115-973 6330

Lynne Marsden, Heatherdean, Llwynygroes, Tregaron, Dyfed, SY25 6PY Tel: (01974) 821271 Fax: (01974) 821271 E-mail: lynne.marsden@btopenworld.com

Oh Sew Pretty, 11 Shore Road, Skelmorlie, Ayrshire, PA17 5EQ Tel: (01475) 520101

Sally Penfold, Imasas, Middletown, Hailey, Witney, Oxfordshire, OX29 9UB Tel: (01993) 822922 Fax: (01993) 822922

Ponden Mill Ltd, 13 Westgate, Wakefield, West Yorkshire, WF1 1JZ Tel: (01924) 377777

▶ Portofino Studio Collection Ltd, Gore Road, New Milton, Hampshire, BH25 6SH Tel: (01425) 611722 Fax: (01425) 611218

▶ Anne Roche, Robertson Street, Barrhead, Glasgow, G78 1QW Tel: 0141-880 7789

Roseline Group, Unit 10 Cadzow Industrial Estate, Old Waters Road, Hamilton, Lanarkshire, ML3 7QU Tel: (01698) 459390 Fax: (01698) 459567

S J Dixon & Son Ltd, Garden Street, Walsall, WS2 8EG Tel: (01922) 647244 Fax: (01922) 722965

Sabre, 122 Fieldside, Ely, Cambs, CB6 3AT Tel: 01353 667616 Fax: 01353 667444

Sandringham Soft Furnishings, 10 Barn Green, Wolverhampton, WV3 7AY Tel: (01902) 344522

Sewcreative, 52 Prospect Rd, Market Drayton, Shropshire, TF9 3BH Tel: 01939 200266 Fax: 01939 200266

▶ Sofa Plan, 39 Phoenix Road, Washington, Tyne & Wear, NE38 0AD Tel: 0191-417 3511 Fax: 0191-417 5477

Suttons Furnishings Ltd, 56 Church Road, Hove, East Sussex, BN3 2FP Tel: (01273) 723728 Fax: (01273) 730837

▶ Swaggs & Tails, Unit 26, Rake Industries, Rogate, Petersfield, Hampshire, GU31 5DU Tel: (01730) 891006 Fax: (01730) 891006

Swan Lake Ltd, Harris Way, Sunbury-on-Thames, Middlesex, TW16 7EL Tel: (01932) 783620 Fax: (01932) 772207 E-mail: swanlake@totalise.co.uk

A.J. Tear & Co. Ltd, 76 Overstone Road, Northampton, NN1 3JS Tel: (01604) 639280 Fax: (01604) 633832 E-mail: sales@glanmar.co.uk

▶ Unique Crafts, Oldham Road, Middleton, Manchester, M24 1QZ Tel: 0161-653 4477 Fax: 0161-653 4488

Work Space, Chequers Street, Wigan, Lancashire, WN1 1HN Tel: (01942) 230512 Fax: (01942) 238800

SOFT MAGNETIC ALLOYS

Imphy Ugine Precision UK Ltd, Wessex Road, Bourne End, Buckinghamshire, SL8 5DT Tel: (01628) 850234 Fax: (01628) 850119

SOFT START ELECTRIC MOTORS

Central Electrical Co., West Midland House, Gipsy Lane, Willenhall, West Midlands, WV13 2HA Tel: (01902) 482477 Fax: (01902) 482478 E-mail: sales@centralelec.co.uk

Zeitlauf, Treetops House, Gillotts Lane, Henley-On-Thames, Oxfordshire, RG9 1PT Tel: (01491) 579118 Fax: (01491) 412211 E-mail: sales@acdcsystems.com

SOFT TOYS

▶ Class Creations Ltd, The Lippiatt, Cheddar Gorge, Cheddar, Somerset, BS27 3QP Tel: (01934) 740240 Fax: (01934) 740234 E-mail: mail@classcreations.co.uk

▶ Magicboxgifts, Optec House, Westfield Avenue, Wigston, Leicester, LE18 1HY Tel: 0116-229 0232 Fax: 0116-229 0232 E-mail: sales@magicboxgifts.com

▶ Special Treasures, 193 Hylton Road, Millfield, Sunderland, SR4 7YE Tel: (07931) 756051 E-mail: emahoward@yahoo.co.uk

SOFTWARE ENGINEERING TOOLS

▶ Exact Designs Ltd, Neep Cottage, Pencaitland, East Lothian, EH34 5DE Tel: (01875) 340859

▶ Phemisters Software, 64 Columbia Avenue, Livingston, West Lothian, EH54 6PR Tel: (01506) 413733 Fax: (08701) 322096

SOFTWOOD IMPORT MERCHANTS OR AGENTS

Dawson Bros Timber Ltd, Blowers Green Cresent, Dudley, West Midlands, DY2 8XQ Tel: (01384) 253816 Fax: (01384) 457248 E-mail: sales@dawsontimber.co.uk

Evans Bellhouse Ltd, South 3, Huskisson Dock, Regant Road, Liverpool, L3 0AT Tel: 0151-707 0000 Fax: 0151-922 7356 E-mail: james@evansbellhouse.co.uk

Finnforest UK Ltd, 46 Berth Tilbury Docks, Tilbury, Essex, RM18 7HS Tel: (01375) 856855 Fax: (01375) 851555 E-mail: email@finnforest.com

James Latham, Badminton Road Trading Estate, Badminton Road, Yate, Bristol, BS37 5JX Tel: (01454) 315421 Fax: (01454) 323488 E-mail: panals.yate@lathams.co.uk

Palmer Timber Ltd, 104 Station Road, Cradley Heath, West Midlands, B64 6PW Tel: 0121-559 5511 Fax: 0121-561 4562 E-mail: sales@palmertimber.com

Ridgeons Ltd, Alexandra Road, Sudbury, Suffolk, CO10 2XH Tel: (01787) 881777 Fax: (01787) 881186 E-mail: sudburysales@ridgens.net

Robert Duncan Ltd, Green Lane, Gateshead, Tyne & Wear, NE10 0JS Tel: 0191-469 8743 Fax: 0191-469 8903 E-mail: enquiries@robertduncan.co.uk

SOIL MECHANICS ANALYSTS OR CONSULTANCY OR RESEARCH OR TEST SERVICES

A-Z Analytical Services, 82 Allens Rd, Poole, Dorset, BH16 5BX Tel: (01202) 624985 Fax: (01202) 624985

Cambridge Insitu Ltd, Rectory Farm, 39 High Street, Little Eversden, Cambridge, CB3 7HE Tel: (01223) 262361 Fax: (01223) 263947 E-mail: caminsitu@aol.com

Hydraulic Transmission Services Ltd, Whitehall Road, Leeds, LS12 5JB Tel: 0113-279 3017 Fax: 0113-279 5505 E-mail: hts@btinternet.com

Masstock Arable UK Ltd, Station Road, Andoversford, Cheltenham, Gloucestershire, GL54 4LZ Tel: (01242) 821100 Fax: (01242) 820807

Oakley Soils & Concrete Engineering Ltd, Rede Hall, Chedburgh, Bury St. Edmunds, Suffolk, IP29 4UG Tel: (01284) 850555 Fax: (01284) 850345

Peter Hunter Seeds, Keepers Cottage, Oulton Park, Oulton, Tarporley, Cheshire, CW6 9BL Tel: (01829) 760397 Fax: (01829) 760526 E-mail: peter.hunter.associates@farming.co.uk

Soil Mechanics, Glossop House, Hogwood Lane, Finchampstead, Wokingham, Berkshire, RG40 4QW Tel: 0118-932 8888 Fax: 0118-932 8383 E-mail: sm@wokingham.mesgl.co.uk

SOIL MECHANICS EQUIPMENT

Cambridge Insitu Ltd, Rectory Farm, 39 High Street, Little Eversden, Cambridge, CB3 7HE Tel: (01223) 262361 Fax: (01223) 263947 E-mail: caminsitu@aol.com

Hydraulic Transmission Services Ltd, Whitehall Road, Leeds, LS12 5JB Tel: 0113-279 3017 Fax: 0113-279 5505 E-mail: hts@btinternet.com

SOIL PREPARATION EQUIPMENT

Kuhn Farm Machinery (UK) Ltd, Stafford Park 7, Telford, Shropshire, TF3 3BQ Tel: (01952) 239300 Fax: (01952) 290091 E-mail: infouk@kuhn.co.uk

SOIL REMEDIATION OR TREATMENT

▶ V H E Construction P.L.C., Phoenix House, 6 Hawthorn Park, Coal Road, Leeds, LS14 1PQ Tel: 0113 273 9200 Fax: 0113 273 9202 E-mail: s.maloney@construction.vhe.co.uk

SOIL REMEDIATION PLANT

▶ V H E Construction P.L.C., Phoenix House, 6 Hawthorn Park, Coal Road, Leeds, LS14 1PQ Tel: 0113 273 9200 Fax: 0113 273 9202 E-mail: s.maloney@construction.vhe.co.uk

SOIL STABILISATION CONTRACTORS

▶ Uretek UK Ltd, Peel House, Peel Rd, Skelmersdale, Lancs, WN8 9PT Tel: (01695) 50525 Fax: (01695) 555212 E-mail: sales@uretek.co.uk

SOIL STABILISATION EQUIPMENT

DNS Midlands Ltd, 1 Bridge Street, Derby, DE1 3HZ Tel: (01332) 363187 Fax: (01332) 371615 E-mail: enquiries@dnsmidlands.co.uk

SOIL STABILISATION SYSTEMS

A G A Group, Crawfold Farm, Balls Cross, Petworth, West Sussex, GU28 9JT Tel: (01403) 820999 Fax: (01403) 820011 E-mail: info@agagroup.org.uk

Kent Grouting Services Ltd, 10 Gun Lane, Rochester, Kent, ME2 4UB Tel: (01634) 717554 Fax: (01634) 711396 E-mail: martinstromsoy@freenetname.co.uk

SOIL TEST EQUIPMENT

Wykeham Farrance International Ltd, Chiltern House, Unit 4B, Knaves Beech Business Centre, Loudwater, High Wycombe, Buckinghamshire, HP10 9QY Tel: (01628) 521000 Fax: (01628) 530300 E-mail: sales@wfi.co.uk

SOIL TESTING SERVICES

▶ The Contamination Investigation Co. Ltd, 60 Elan Avenue, Stourport-on-Severn, Worcestershire, DY13 8LX Tel: (01299) 877539 Fax: (0845) 2991523 E-mail: sales@contamination-investigation.co.uk

SOIL TOP DRESSINGS

Alan Hadley Ltd, Colthrop Lacolthrop Business Park, Thatcham, Berkshire, RG19 4NB Tel: 0118-988 3266 Fax: 0118-988 4538 E-mail: waste@hadleys.co.uk

SOIL WARMING EQUIPMENT

Thermocable (Flexible Elements) Ltd, Pasture Lane, Clayton, Bradford, West Yorkshire, BD14 6LU Tel: (01274) 882359 Fax: (01274) 882229 E-mail: info@thermocable.com

SOLAR ENERGY CONSULTANCY

Solar Energy Alliance, 8 Battery Green Road, Lowestoft, Suffolk, NR32 1DE Tel: (01502) 515532 Fax: (01502) 589159 E-mail: info@solarenergyalliance.com

Sun X UK Ltd, 2 Madeira Parade, Madeira Avenue, Bognor Regis, West Sussex, PO22 8DX Tel: (01243) 826441 Fax: (01243) 829691 E-mail: sales@sun-x.co.uk

SOLAR GARDEN LIGHTING

▶ Garden Options Ltd, 3 The Wynd, Melrose, Roxburghshire, TD6 9LD Tel: (01896) 820630 E-mail: enquiries@gardenoptions.co.uk

▶ Growlighting.co.uk, Unit 19 Chatsworth Green, Basingstoke, Hampshire, RG22 4QA Tel: (01256) 320350 Fax: (01256) 320350 E-mail: rob@growlighting.co.uk

▶ Snowdrop Gardening & Design Services, 3 Stapeley Farm Cottages, Odiham, Hampshire, RG29 1JE Tel: (01256) 862020 E-mail: info@snowdropgardening.co.uk

Solar Illuminations, P.O. Box 19, Rye, East Sussex, TN31 6WZ Tel: (020) 8144 0847 E-mail: sales@solarilluminations.co.uk

SOLAR HEAT CONTROLS

Armour Guard Films Ltd, 6 Maple Court, Crystal Drive, Smethwick, West Midlands, B66 1RB Tel: 0121-544 4884 Fax: 0121-544 4885 E-mail: sales@armourguardfilms.co.uk

SOLAR HEAT EQUIPMENT OR SYSTEMS

Automation Control & Technology Ltd, 149 Tavistock Road, Fleet, Hampshire, GU51 4EE Tel: (01252) 623316 Fax: (01252) 623316 E-mail: sales@automationcontrol.co.uk

Filsol Solar, Unit 15 Ponthenry Industrial Estate, Ponthenry, Llanelli, Dyfed, SA15 5RA Tel: (01269) 860229 Fax: (01269) 860979 E-mail: info@filsol.co.uk

▶ Revolution Power Ltd, Office 1-1st Floor-Block B, Technology Court, Bradbury Road, Newton Aycliffe, County Durham, DL5 6DA Tel: (01325) 320910 E-mail: info@revolutionpower.co.uk

Sundwell Solar Ltd, 7 Tower Road, Washington, Tyne & Wear, NE37 2SH Tel: 0191-416 3001 Fax: 0191-415 4297 E-mail: solar@sundwel.com

Thermomax Ltd, Balloo Industrial Estate, Bangor, County Down, BT19 7UP Tel: (028) 9127 0411 Fax: (028) 9127 0572 E-mail: sales@thermomax.com

SOLAR HEAT REFLECTING OR CONTROL FILM

Commercial Window Films, Unit 12 Parkside Industrial Estate, Edge La Street, Royton, Oldham, OL2 6DS Tel: 0161-627 5274 Fax: 0161-627 0533 E-mail: sales@commercialblinds.co.uk

Durable, 1 498 Reading Road, Winnersh, Wokingham, Berkshire, RG41 5EX Tel: (0870) 2402480 Fax: 0118-989 5209 E-mail: mail@durable.co.uk

Eclipse Blind Systems Ltd, 10 Fountain Crescent, Inchinnan Business Park, Renfrew, PA4 9RE Tel: 0141-812 3322 Fax: 0141-812 5253 E-mail: orrd@eclipseblinds.co.uk

SOLAR HEAT REFLECTING OR CONTROL FILM – *continued*

Northgate Solar Controls, Barnet, Hertfordshire, EN4 9EW Tel: (020) 8441 4545 Fax: (020) 8441 4888

Reflex-Rol, Ryeford Hall, Ryeford, Ross-on-Wye, Herefordshire, HR9 7PU Tel: (01989) 750704 Fax: (01989) 750768 E-mail: reflexrol@btinternet.com

Stock Films, PO Box 11, Barnet, Hertfordshire, EN4 8AR Tel: (020) 8441 0449 Fax: (020) 8441 4888

Westgate Solar Control, PO Box 21, Stafford, ST16 3YJ Tel: (01785) 242181

SOLAR OR PHOTOVOLTAIC ELECTRICAL POWER SUPPLIES

Becosolar, 8-10 Speedwell Units, Nelson Road Industrial Estate, Dartmouth, Devon, TQ6 9SZ Tel: (01803) 833636 Fax: (01803) 835379 E-mail: info@becosolar.com

SOLAR PANELS

▶ Dabbrook Power Systems, Unit 23, Bells Marsh Rd, Gorleston, Great Yarmouth, Norfolk, NR31 6PT Tel: (01493) 441711 Fax: (01493) 440322 E-mail: info@dabbrook.com

▶ Genersys Ireland Ltd, 44 Victoria Square, Rostrevor, Newry, County Down, BT34 3EU Tel: (028) 4173 7777 Fax: (028) 4173 8456 E-mail: genersys@genersys-ireland.com

▶ Sun Save, 37 The Meadway, Shoreham-by-Sea, West Sussex, BN43 5RN Tel: (01273) 455500 Fax: (01273) 441631 E-mail: sales@sun-save.co.uk

SOLAR PANELS, DIRECT CURRENT (DC)

▶ Solar Watts Ltd, Holly Road, Horsham, West Sussex, RH12 4PA Tel: (0796) 6160126

Solstice Energy Ltd, 14 Gladwyn Road, Putney, London, SW15 1JY Tel: 020 8789 4717 Fax: 020 8789 4717 E-mail: info@solsticeenergy.co.uk

SOLAR POWERED BATTERIES

▶ Dabbrook Power Systems, Unit 23, Bells Marsh Rd, Gorleston, Great Yarmouth, Norfolk, NR31 6PT Tel: (01493) 441711 Fax: (01493) 440322 E-mail: info@dabbrook.com

SOLAR POWERED BATTERY CHARGERS

Becosolar, 8-10 Speedwell Units, Nelson Road Industrial Estate, Dartmouth, Devon, TQ6 9SZ Tel: (01803) 833636 Fax: (01803) 835379 E-mail: info@becosolar.com

SOLAR POWERED ELECTRICITY SUPPLY SYSTEMS

Invertec Ltd, Whelford Road, Fairford, Gloucestershire, GL7 4DT Tel: (01285) 713550 Fax: (01285) 713548 E-mail: sales@invertec.co.uk

SOLAR SHADING LOUVRES

Guthrie Douglas Ltd, Collins Rd, Heathcote Industrial Estate, Warwick, CV34 6TF Tel: (01926) 452452 Fax: (01926) 336417 E-mail: sales@guthrie-douglas.uk.com

SOLDER PASTES/POWDER

Henkel, Technologies House, Wood La End, Hemel Hempstead, Hertfordshire, HP2 4RQ Tel: (01442) 278000 Fax: (01442) 278071 E-mail: customer.enquiry@henkel.com

Tecnicon Precision, Unit 20 Euro Business Park, New Road, Newhaven, East Sussex, BN9 0DQ Tel: (01273) 510952 Fax: (01273) 513579

SOLDERABILITY TESTING SERVICES

Specific Components, Unit 23, Common Bank Industrial Estate, Ackhurst Road, Chorley, Lancashire, PR7 1NH Tel: (01257) 279944 Fax: (01257) 279922 E-mail: sales@specific-components.co.uk

SOLDERING (AUTOMATIC PROCESS/ROBOTIC) PRODUCTION EQUIPMENT/ SYSTEMS MANUFRS

Kuka Automation & Robotics, Hereward Rise, Halesowen, West Midlands, B62 8AN Tel: 0121-585 0800 Fax: 0121-585 0900 E-mail: sales@kuka.co.uk

Pillerhouse International Ltd, Rodney Way, Chelmsford, CM1 3BY Tel: (01245) 491333 Fax: (01245) 491331 E-mail: sales@pillarhouse.co.uk

Planer plc, 110 Windmill Road, Sunbury-on-Thames, Middlesex, TW16 7HD Tel: (01932) 755000 Fax: (01932) 755001 E-mail: sales@planer.co.uk

Seho UK Ltd, Unit C5, Brookside Business Park, Greengate, Middleton, Manchester, M24 1GS Tel: 0161-654 9117 Fax: 0161-654 7817 E-mail: pb@sehouk.demon.co.uk

Sensbey, 36 Carters Lane, Kiln Farm, Milton Keynes, MK11 3HL Tel: (01908) 569630 Fax: (01908) 562457 E-mail: sensbeyuk@compuserve.com

SOLDERING EQUIPMENT MANUFRS

B T U (Europe) Ltd, Unit 14 Armstrong Mall, Southwood Business Park, Farnborough, Hampshire, GU14 0NR Tel: (01252) 660010 Fax: (01252) 660011 E-mail: sales@btu.co.uk

Eurotec Industries Ltd, Unit 3 Stanley Centre, Kelvin Way, Crawley, West Sussex, RH10 9SE Tel: (01293) 846000 Fax: (01293) 613600 E-mail: sales@pdrsmt.com

Reef Engineering, Unit 2 Mayfair Industrial Estate, Maldon Road, Lachingdon, Chelmsford, CM3 6LF Tel: (01621) 744689 Fax: (01621) 744285 E-mail: reefengineering@btconnect.com

SOLDERING FLUID OR FLUXES, *See also headings for particular types*

Almit Technology Ltd, 7 Forest Row Business Park, Station Road, Forest Row, East Sussex, RH18 5DW Tel: (01342) 822844 Fax: (01342) 824155 E-mail: info@almit.co.uk

SOLDERLESS CONNECTOR TERMINALS

Kompress Holdings Ltd, Unit 5 Little Tennis Street, Nottingham, NG2 4EL Tel: 0115-958 1029 Fax: 0115-958 4180 E-mail: info@kompress.com

SOLDERS, *See also headings for particular types*

Jastac, 341 Court Road, Orpington, Kent, BR6 9BZ Tel: (01689) 873175 Fax: (01689) 873175

M B O (U K) Ltd, Mill End, Standon, Ware, Hertfordshire, SG11 1LR Tel: (01920) 823999 Fax: (01920) 823631 E-mail: sales@mbouk.co.uk

Reef Engineering, Unit 2 Mayfair Industrial Estate, Maldon Road, Lachingdon, Chelmsford, CM3 6LF Tel: (01621) 744689 Fax: (01621) 744285 E-mail: reefengineering@btconnect.com

Spanesi Automotive Mechanic Ltd, 33-37 Second Avenue Ind Estate, Chatham, Kent, ME4 5AY Tel: (01634) 845580 Fax: (01634) 401515

SOLENOID VALVES

Alpha Controls Ltd, Hindley Industrial Estate, Off Swan Lane, Hindley Green, Wigan, Lancashire, WN2 4HR Tel: (01942) 525833 Fax: (01942) 523413 E-mail: technicalsales@alphacontrols.co.uk

Beta Valve Systems Ltd, Parkhouse Business Centre, Desborough Park Road, High Wycombe, Buckinghamshire, HP12 3DJ Tel: (01494) 459511 Fax: (01494) 461136 E-mail: info@betavalve.com

Bifold Fluidpower Ltd, Greenside Way, Middleton, Manchester, M24 1SW Tel: 0161-345 4777 Fax: 0161-345 4780 E-mail: sales@bifold-fluidpower.co.uk

Copeland Corporation Ltd, Unit 17, Theale Lakes Business Park, Moulden Way, Sulhamsted, Reading, RG7 4GB Tel: 0118-983 8000 Fax: 0118-983 8001 E-mail: uksales@ecopeland.com

Goyen Controls Co. UK Ltd, Unit 3B, Beechwood, Chineham Business Park, Basingstoke, Hampshire, RG24 8WA Tel: (01256) 817800 Fax: (01256) 843164 E-mail:

Grange Controls Ltd, Unit 3 Midland Way, Thornbury, Bristol, BS35 2BS Tel: (01454) 418256 Fax: (01454) 415214 E-mail: sales@grangecontrols.co.uk

J & P Supplies Ltd, Junction Road, Audnam, Stourbridge, West Midlands, DY8 4YH Tel: (01384) 393329 Fax: (01384) 440212 E-mail: info@jpsupplies.co.uk

Pressure & Flow Ltd, Victoria House, 50 Albert Street, Rugby, Warwickshire, CV21 2RH Tel: (01788) 560426 Fax: (01788) 561228 E-mail: uk@sensortechnics.com

Process Control Equipment, 45 Dukesway, Teesside Industrial Estate, Stockton-on-Tees, Cleveland, TS17 9LT Tel: (01642) 768250

R G S Electro Pneumatics Ltd, West End Business Park, Oswaldtwistle, Accrington, Lancashire, BB5 4WZ Tel: (01254) 872277 Fax: (01254) 390133 E-mail: sales@rgs-e-p.co.uk

Valvekits Ltd, Brookside Way, Huthwaite, Sutton-in-Ashfield, Nottinghamshire, NG17 2NL Tel: (01623) 446700 Fax: (01623) 440214 E-mail: valvekits@valvekits.co.uk

Zoedale P.L.C., Stannard Way, Priory Business Park, Bedford, MK44 3WG Tel: (01234) 832832 Fax: (01234) 832800 E-mail: enquiries@zoedale.co.uk

SOLENOIDS, *See also headings for particular types*

Albright Engineers Ltd, 125 Red Lion Road, Surbiton, Surrey, KT6 7QS Tel: (020) 8390 5357 Fax: (020) 8390 1927 E-mail: sales@albright.co.uk

Diamond H Controls Ltd, Vulcan Road North, Norwich, NR6 6AH Tel: (01603) 425291 Fax: (01603) 424907 E-mail: sales@diamond-h-controls.co.uk

N S F Controls Ltd, Ingrow Bridge Works, Keighley, West Yorkshire, BD21 5EF Tel: (01535) 661144 Fax: (01535) 661474 E-mail: sales@nsfcontrols.co.uk

Solentec Ltd, 82a Jubilee Road, Waterlooville, Hampshire, PO7 7RE Tel: (023) 9226 1651 Fax: (023) 9226 9487 E-mail: sales@solentec.co.uk

Valley Systems Ltd, 26 Moorfields Close, Staines, Middlesex, TW18 3LU Tel: (01784) 457645 Fax: (01784) 438777 E-mail: trushton@magsol.co.uk

SOLES/HEELS, LEATHER

Ashford & Campion Ltd, Westfield Terrace, Higham Ferrers, Rushden, Northamptonshire, NN10 8BB Tel: (01933) 359321 Fax: (01933) 410403

Dickinson Shoe Services Ltd, 345 Shields Road, Newcastle upon Tyne, NE6 2UD Tel: 0191-265 4858 Fax: 0191-224 2245 E-mail: westgaterubbers@aol.com

▶ Dressed by Scotland, 57 Main Street, Pathhead, Edinburgh, EH37 5WT Tel: 0131-467 7508 Fax: 0131-467 7508

E A Tailby Ltd, Bath Road, Kettering, Northamptonshire, NN16 8NL Tel: (01536) 512639 Fax: (01536) 414816

SOLES/HEELS, PLASTIC

E A Tailby Ltd, Bath Road, Kettering, Northamptonshire, NN16 8NL Tel: (01536) 512639 Fax: (01536) 414816

SOLES/HEELS, RUBBER

Dickinson Shoe Services Ltd, 345 Shields Road, Newcastle upon Tyne, NE6 2UD Tel: 0191-265 4858 Fax: 0191-224 2245 E-mail: westgaterubbers@aol.com

E A Tailby Ltd, Bath Road, Kettering, Northamptonshire, NN16 8NL Tel: (01536) 512639 Fax: (01536) 414816

Fussell's Rubber Co. Ltd, 2 Brimbleworth Lane, St. Georges, Weston-Super-Mare, Avon, BS22 7XS Tel: (01934) 513473 Fax: (01934) 521019

Texon International Ltd, 16A Firtree Lane, Groby, Leicester, LE6 0FH Tel: (0870) 2255845 Fax: (0870) 225443 E-mail: enquiries@texon.com

SOLICITORS

Anna Arthur & Associates Solicitors, 5 Fieri Facais House, High Street, Ripley, Surrey, GU23 6AF Tel: (01483) 222499 Fax: (01483) 222766

▶ Campbell Fitzpatrick, 51 Adelaide Street, Belfast, BT2 8FE Tel: (028) 9032 7388 Fax: (028) 9032 7732 E-mail: sales@campbell-fitzpatrick.co.uk

▶ Corren Troen, 4 Buckingham Place, London, SW1 6HR Tel: (020) 7798 9344 Fax: (020) 7798 9349 E-mail: office@correntroen.com

Ferdinand Kelly Solicitors, Yew House, Tamworth, Staffordshire, B78 2EY Tel: (01827) 895039 Fax: (01827) 895039 E-mail: info@ferdinandkelly.co.uk

▶ Gill Akaster, 25 Lockyer Street, Plymouth, PL1 2QW Tel: (01752) 512000 Fax: (01752) 203503 E-mail: steve.turner@gillakaster.com

Gray Purdue Solicitors, Wellesley House, 202 London Road, Waterlooville, Hampshire, PO7 7AN Tel: (023) 9226 5251 Fax: (023) 9224 1597 E-mail: contact@graypurdue.co.uk

▶ Hughes Walker Solicitors Ltd, 82, Bolton Street, Bury, Lancs, BL9 0LL Tel: 0161 7633388 Fax: 0161 7637558 E-mail: enquiry@hughes-walker.co.uk

James Chan & Co., 37 Ludgate Hill, London, EC4M 7JN Tel: (020) 7236 8880 Fax: (020) 7236 8883 E-mail: law@chanlegal.com

Lovells Solicitors, Atlantic House, 50 Holborn Viaduct, London, EC1A 2FG Tel: (020) 7296 2000 Fax: (020) 7296 2001 E-mail: information@lovells.com

Masons, 1-4 Portland Square, Bristol, BS2 8RR Tel: 0117-924 5678 Fax: 0117-924 6699 E-mail: enquiries@pinsentmasons.com

▶ Masons, 123 St. Vincent Street, Glasgow, G2 5EA Tel: 0141-248 4858 Fax: 0141-248 6655 E-mail: enquiries@pinsentmasons.com

▶ Ms Solicitors, 9 Marlborough Place, Brighton, BN1 1UB Tel: (01273) 609944 Fax: (01273) 609944 E-mail: info@ms-solicitors.co.uk

▶ Pi Solicitors Specialists In Dental Negligence, Quinney View, Marshbrook, Church Stretton, Shropshire, SY6 6QE Tel: (01694) 781247 Fax: 01694 781387 E-mail: sales@personalinjuryplus.co.uk

▶ Pinsent Masons, 18-22 Melville Street, Edinburgh, EH3 7NS Tel: 0131-225 0000 Fax: 0131-225 0099 E-mail: enquiries@pinsentmasons.com

Pinsent Masons LLP, 1 Park Row, Leeds, LS1 5AB Tel: 0113-244 5000 Fax: 0113-244 8000 E-mail: enquiries@pinsentmasons.com

▶ Randle Thomas, 2 Wendron St, Helston, Cornwall, TR13 8PP Tel: (01326) 572951 Fax: 01326 563122 E-mail: rt@randlethomas.co.uk

Reed Smith, Park House, Station Square, Coventry, CV1 2FL Tel: (024) 7629 3020 Fax: (024) 7629 3031 E-mail: coventry-email@warner-cranston.com

▶ Reid Cooper Partnership, 78 Carlton Place, Glasgow, G5 9TH Tel: 0141-429 4656 Fax: 0141-429 1494

▶ Richard Hutchinson & Co., 9 College Street, Nottingham, NG1 5AQ Tel: 0115-959 9700 Fax: 0115-959 9234 E-mail: enquiries@richard-hutchinson.co.uk

▶ Steen & Co., Magdalen Centre, The Oxford Science Park, Oxford, OX4 4EA Tel: (01865) 784101 Fax: (01865) 784103 E-mail: mail@steenandco.co.uk

▶ Sterling Ward, 18 Charlotte Road, London, EC2A 3PB Tel: (020) 7729 4513 Fax: (020) 7033 0589 E-mail: gary.ward@stirling-ward.com

▶ Whitehead Woodward & Co., Gleniffer, Hoseley Lane, Marford, Wrexham, Clwyd, LL12 8YE Tel: (01978) 855478 Fax: 0161-237 3595 E-mail: fwhitehead@wwsolicitors.co.uk

▶ Windsor Bronzite Solicitors, 43 Bargates, Christchurch, Dorset, BH23 1QD Tel: 0870 4020555 Fax: 0870 4020556 E-mail: info@windsorbronzite.co.uk

SOLICITORS, DEBT RECOVERY

▶ Campbell Fitzpatrick, 51 Adelaide Street, Belfast, BT2 8FE Tel: (028) 9032 7388 Fax: (028) 9032 7732 E-mail: sales@campbell-fitzpatrick.co.uk

▶ Credit Tel International, Network House, 45 Warwick Road, Thames Ditton, Surrey, KT7 0PR Tel: (020) 8398 9555 Fax: (020) 8398 7831 E-mail: info@credittel.com

▶ D E A Associates, 154 Wickham Road, Croydon, CR0 8BF Tel: (020) 8654 0706 Fax: (020) 8654 0706 E-mail: collect@deaassociates.org.uk

Ferdinand Kelly Solicitors, Yew House, Tamworth, Staffordshire, B78 2EY Tel: (01827) 895039 Fax: (01827) 895039 E-mail: info@ferdinandkelly.co.uk

▶ Gill Akaster, 25 Lockyer Street, Plymouth, PL1 2QW Tel: (01752) 512000 Fax: (01752) 203503 E-mail: steve.turner@gillakaster.com

▶ Grant Saw, Norman House, 110-114 Norman Road, London, SE10 9EH Tel: (020) 8858 6971 Fax: (020) 8858 5796 E-mail: enquiries@grantsaw.co.uk

▶ Hughes Walker Solicitors Ltd, 82, Bolton Street, Bury, Lancs, BL9 0LL Tel: 0161 7633388 Fax: 0161 7637558 E-mail: enquiry@hughes-walker.co.uk

▶ Insolvency Network, 79 Manor Rise, Burntwood, Staffordshire, WS7 4TR Tel: (01543) 686362

Recover Debt Solutions Ltd, 24 Winckley Square, Preston, PR1 3JJ Tel: (0870) 8532090 Fax: (0870) 8532091 E-mail: enquiries@recoveryourdebts.com

▶ Renaissance, 1 Emperor Way, Exeter Business Park, Exeter Business Park, Exeter, EX1 3QS Tel: (01803) 404047 Fax: (01803) 404048 E-mail: enquiries@debt-recovery-services.com

SOLID CARBIDE CUTTERS

Drill Service Horley Ltd, 23 Albert Road, Horley, Surrey, RH6 7HR Tel: (01293) 774911 Fax: (01293) 820463 E-mail: sales@drill-service.co.uk

▶ S G S Carbide Tool UK Ltd, Unit 1 Metro Centre, Toutley Road, Wokingham, Berkshire, RG41 1QW Tel: 0118-979 5200 Fax: 0118-979 5295 E-mail: sales@sgstool.com

SOLID CARBIDE DRILL BITS

Cirbo Ltd, 16 Normandy Way, Bodmin, Cornwall, PL31 1EX Tel: (01208) 74174 Fax: (01208) 76801
Floyd Automatic Tooling Ltd, 17 Bondor Business Centre, London Road, Baldock, Hertfordshire, SG7 6HP Tel: (01462) 491919 Fax: (01462) 490835 E-mail: info@floydautomatic.co.uk
Peak Test Services, 152a Front Street, Chester le Street, County Durham, DH3 3AY Tel: 0191-387 1923 Fax: 0191-387 1994 E-mail: peak.test@thepeakgroup.com

SOLID FIRE DOORS

▶ John A Russell Joinery Ltd, 8 Dilwara Avenue, Glasgow, G14 0QS Tel: 0141-958 0444 Fax: 0141-958 0333

SOLID FORGED HANDRAILS

Glendale Developments Ltd, Unit 2a Union Road Trading Estate, Oldbury, West Midlands, B69 3EU Tel: 0121-541 1752 Fax: 0121-544 8774 E-mail: glendaledevelpoments@hotmail.com

SOLID FUEL APPLIANCES

Farm 2000 - Teisen Products Ltd, Bradley Green, Redditch, Worcestershire, B96 6RP Tel: (01527) 821621 Fax: (01527) 821665 E-mail: heat@farm2000.co.uk
Talbotts Biomass Energy Ltd, Tollgate drive, Tollgate Industrial Estate, Stafford, ST16 3HS Tel: (01785) 213366 Fax: (01785) 256418 E-mail: sales@talbotts.co.uk

SOLID FUEL COMBUSTION SYSTEMS

Moldow Ltd, Unit 31 Britannia Way, Britannia Enterprise Park, Lichfield, Staffordshire, WS14 9UY Tel: (01543) 258844 Fax: (01543) 416311
▶ James Proctor Ltd, PO Box 19, Burnley, Lancashire, BB11 1NN Tel: (01282) 453816 Fax: (01282) 416178 E-mail: sales@jamesproctor.com

SOLID FUEL FIRED BOILERS

Hoval Ltd, North Gate, Newark, Nottinghamshire, NG24 1JN Tel: (01636) 672711 Fax: (01636) 673532 E-mail: boilersales@hoval.co.uk

SOLID HANDLING VALVES

Dab Valves Ltd, White Meadow Farm, Parwich, Ashbourne, Derbyshire, DE6 1QY Tel: (01335) 390572 Fax: (01335) 390633 E-mail: sales@dabsystems.co.uk

SOLID O RING SILICONE RUBBER CORD EXTRUSIONS

▶ Rubber Extrusions & Seal Ltd, Lancashire House, 251 Higginshaw Lane, Royton, Oldham, OL2 6HW Tel: 0161-622 0020 Fax: 0161-622 0010 E-mail: gculley251@aol.com

SOLID RIVETS

▶ Aero Fasteners Co. Ltd, Unit 2, Block 4 Northherbour, Ayr, KA1 8BN Tel: (0870) 0509005 Fax: (0870) 0509006 E-mail: aerofastuk@btconnect.com
Amfast Fasteners & Fixing Devices, Clifton House Southdown Industrial Estate, Southdown Road, Harpenden, Hertfordshire, AL5 1PW Tel: (01582) 715150 Fax: (01582) 712120 E-mail: ritagill@am-fast.co.uk
L J Bearing & Engineering Services, Unit A5 Imex Business Park, Kings Rd, Tyseley, Birmingham, B11 2AL Tel: 0121-604 7131 Fax: 0121-604 7122 E-mail: enquiries@bearings-uk.com

SOLID STATE RELAYS

Kempston Controls, Shirley Road, Rushden, Northamptonshire, NN10 6BZ Tel: (01933) 414500 Fax: (01933) 410211 E-mail: sales@kempstoncontrols.co.uk
System Devices Ltd Automation Di, 17 Beeston Court, Stuart Road, Manor Park, Runcorn, Cheshire, WA7 1SS Tel: (01928) 571977 Fax: (01928) 571988 E-mail: sales@systemdevices.co.uk

SOLID STATE VARIABLE SPEED CONTROL SYSTEMS

Laurence, Scott & Electromotors Ltd, Po Box 25, Norwich, NR1 1JD Tel: (01603) 628333 Fax: (01603) 610604 E-mail: sales@laurence-scott.com

SOLID SURFACE KITCHEN UNITS OR WORKTOPS

▶ Artisan Work Surfaces, Units 3-4, Shelton Court, Shelton Road, Willowbrook Industrial Estate, Corby, Northamptonshire, NN17 5YU Tel: (01536) 409771 Fax: (01536) 201641 E-mail: sales@artisanworksurfaces.co.uk
Granit Ops Ltd, West Dean Road, West Tytherley, Salisbury, SP5 1QG Tel: (01980) 862253 Fax: (01980) 863073 E-mail: stone@granit-ops.co.uk
▶ International Kitchens & Bedrooms, 753 Holderness Road, Hull, HU8 9AR Tel: (01482) 375251 Fax: (01482) 711364 E-mail: enquiries@internationalkitchens.co.uk
▶ Rocky Tops, Unit 12c4, Anniesland Business Park, Glasgow, G13 1EU Tel: 0141-954 2455 Fax: 0141-954 2455 E-mail: kkirchmann@rockytops.co.uk

SOLID SURFACE MATERIAL FABRICATORS

Clarendon Fabrications, 25 Morris Road, Leicester, LE2 6AL Tel: 0116-244 8057 Fax: 0116-270 9214 E-mail: sales@clarendonfab.co.uk
W H Foster & Sons Ltd, Stourdale Road, Cradley, Cradley Heath, West Midlands, B64 7BG Tel: (01384) 415170 Fax: (01384) 415185 E-mail: sales@whfoster.co.uk

SOLID SURFACE SINKS

Athena Solid Surfaces, 14 Sedling Road, Wear Industrial Estate, Washington, Tyne & Wear, NE38 9BZ Tel: 0191-416 7275 Fax: 0191-417 7510 E-mail: admin@athenasolidsurfaces.co.uk

SOLID SURFACE WORKTOPS

▶ Artisan Work Surfaces, Units 3-4, Shelton Court, Shelton Road, Willowbrook Industrial Estate, Corby, Northamptonshire, NN17 5YU Tel: (01536) 409771 Fax: (01536) 201641 E-mail: sales@artisanworksurfaces.co.uk

SOLID TYRES

Green Tyre Co. P.L.C., Riverside Park Road, Middlesbrough, Cleveland, TS2 1UU Tel: (01642) 223322 Fax: (01642) 223313 E-mail: sales@greentyre.co.uk

SOLID WOOD FLOORING

▶ Disney Flooring, Albert Avenue, Weston-super-Mare, Avon, BS23 1YJ Tel: (01934) 628320 Fax: (01934) 615006 E-mail: enquiries@disney-flooring.com
▶ G D Floors Ltd, 8 Broomhill Court, Kilwinning, Ayrshire, KA13 6UL Tel: (01294) 559745 E-mail: info@gdfloors.co.uk
Holland & Welsh Ltd, Unit 13 Riverside Industrial Park, Treforest, Pontypridd, Mid Glamorgan, CF37 5TG Tel: (01443) 660255 Fax: (01443) 660651 E-mail: sales@hollandandwelsh.com
▶ Mckay Flooring Ltd, 123 Harmony Row, Glasgow, G51 3NB Tel: 0141-440 1586 Fax: 0141-425 1020 E-mail: enquires@mckay.co.uk
▶ Pivotal Holdings Ltd, 143 New Bond Street, London, W1S 2TP Tel: (020) 7493 5550 Fax: (020) 7493 5559 E-mail: enquiries@pivotalwoodflooring.com

SOLIDS HANDLING PUMPS

Egger Turo Pumps (U.K.) Ltd, Fountain House, Cleeve Road, Leatherhead, Surrey, KT22 7NH Tel: (01372) 377688 Fax: (01372) 373587 E-mail: info.uk@eggerpumps.com
Pioneer Pump Ltd, Corner Farm Industrial Estate, Woolpit Road, Rattlesden, Bury St. Edmunds, Suffolk, IP30 0RZ Tel: (01449) 736777

SOLUBLE OILS

D A Stuart Ltd, Lincoln Street, Wolverhampton, WV10 0DZ Tel: (01902) 456111 Fax: (01902) 453764 E-mail: dastuart@dastuart.co.uk

SOLVENT/SOLVENT VAPOUR RECOVERY PLANT/EQUIPMENT

David Clouting Ltd, 7B Perry Road, Witham, Essex, CM8 3UD Tel: (01376) 518037 Fax: (01376) 500104 E-mail: sales@davidclouting.co.uk
Land & Marine Project Engineering, Dock Road North, Wirral, Merseyside, CH62 4TQ Tel: 0151-641 5600 Fax: 0151-644 9990 E-mail: matthew.osullivan@landandmarine.com

SOLVENT/SOLVENT VAPOUR RECOVERY/RECYCLING SERVICES

Beolia Enviromental Services plc, 154a Pentonville Road, London, N1 9PE Tel: (020) 7812 5000 Fax: (020) 7812 5026 E-mail: edward.demaslatrie@veolia.co.uk
Chemical Recoveries, Rockingham Works Smoke Lane, Bristol, BS11 0YA Tel: 0117-982 0303 Fax: 0117-982 0301 E-mail: info@chemrec.co.uk
Envirosol Ltd, Unit 28 Thornleigh Trading Estate, Dudley, West Midlands, DY2 8UB Tel: (01384) 241808 Fax: (01384) 237519 E-mail: sales@envirosol.co.uk
Machine Mart Ltd, 50 Lobley Hill Road, Gateshead, Tyne & Wear, NE8 4XA Tel: 0191-493 2520 Fax: 0191-493 2212
Midland Oil Refinery Ltd, Shelah Road, Halesowen, West Midlands, B63 3PN Tel: 0121-585 6006 Fax: 0121-585 5405
P & R Disposal Services, 117 Clydesdale Place, Leyland, PR26 7QS Tel: (01772) 454129 Fax: (01772) 622258 E-mail: sales@distillex.xo.uk
Solvent Resource Management Ltd, Middleton Road, Middleton, Morecambe, Lancashire, LA3 3JW Tel: (01524) 853053 Fax: (01524) 851284 E-mail: sales@srm-ltd.com
Solvent Resource Management Ltd, Hendon Dock, Sunderland, SR1 2EW Tel: 0191-566 0000 Fax: 0191-566 0025 E-mail: sales@srm-ltd.com
Southern Refining Services Ltd, Membury Airfield, Lambourn Woodlands, Hungerford, Berkshire, RG17 7TJ Tel: (01488) 72898 Fax: (01488) 72762 E-mail: richard.srs@btconnect.com
SRM, Northumberland Dock, Hayhole Road, North Shields, Tyne & Wear, NE29 6DY Tel: 0191-258 4579 Fax: 0191-257 1646

SOLVENTS

Banner Chemicals Ltd, Unit B, Hampton Court, Manor Park, Runcorn, Cheshire, WA7 1TU Tel: (01928) 597000 Fax: (01928) 597001 E-mail: reception@bannerchemicals.co.uk
Caldic UK Ltd, Stainsby Close, Holmewood Industrial Estate, Holmewood, Chesterfield, Derbyshire, S42 5UG Tel: (01246) 854111 Fax: (01246) 856222 E-mail: info@caldic.com
Hammond Chemicals Ltd, Canal Street, Brierley Hill, West Midlands, DY5 1JR Tel: (01384) 480600 Fax: (01384) 480680
Hobstar Ltd, Palace Chemicals Ltd, Speke Hall Industrial Estate, Liverpool, L24 4AB Tel: 0151-486 6101 Fax: 0151-448 1982 E-mail: sales@palacechemicals.co.uk
Industrial Suppliers (Wimborne) Ltd, Higher Merley Lane, Corfe Mullen, Wimborne, Dorset, BH21 3EG Tel: (01202) 882331 Fax: (01202) 841282 E-mail: enquiries@iswgroup.co.uk
Solvents With Safety Ltd, Plumtree Road, Bircotes, Doncaster, South Yorkshire, DN11 8EW Tel: (01302) 711733 Fax: (01302) 711744 E-mail: sales@solventswithsafety.co.uk
Tewtrell Ltd, Limekiln Lane, Birmingham, B14 4SP Tel: 0121-430 2161 Fax: 0121-430 2741 E-mail: sales@tewtrell.com

SOLVENTS, HYDROCARBON, AROMATIC

▶ Multisol Ltd, Sorby Road, Irlam, Manchester, M44 5BA Tel: 0161-775 1622 Fax: 0161-777 9783 E-mail: sales@multisol.co.uk

SONAR EQUIPMENT

Chelsea Technologies Group, 55 Central Avenue, West Molesey, Surrey, KT8 2QZ Tel: (020) 8941 0044 Fax: (020) 8941 9349 E-mail: sales@chelsea.co.uk
Echopilot Ltd, 1 Endeavour Park, Crow Arch Lane, Ringwood, Hampshire, BH24 1SF Tel: (01425) 476211 Fax: (01425) 474300 E-mail: info@echopilot.com
Geoacoustics Ltd, Shuttleworth Close, Gapton Hall Industrial Estate, Great Yarmouth, Norfolk, NR31 0NQ Tel: (01493) 600666 Fax: (01493) 651100 E-mail: sales@geoacoustics.co.uk
Navico UK Ltd, Premier Way, Abbey Park, Romsey, Hampshire, SO51 9DH Tel: (01794) 510010 Fax: (01794) 510006 E-mail: sales.uk@navico.com
Thales Underwater Systems, Ocean House, Throop Road, Templecombe, Somerset, BA8 0DH Tel: (01963) 370551 Fax: (01963) 372200 E-mail: sales@tms-ltd.com
▶ Ultra Electronics Ltd, 419 Bridport Road, Greenford, Middlesex, UB6 8UA Tel: (020) 8813 4444 Fax: (020) 8813 4568 E-mail: information@ultra-scs.com

SONOCHEMISTRY/FLUIDSONIC/ ULTRASONIC PROCESSING SERVICES

Apollo, Pond House, Bulmer Lane, Holme-on-Spalding-Moor, York, YO43 4HE Tel: (01430) 860049 Fax: (01430) 861550 E-mail: sales@apolloultrasonics.co.uk

SOOT BLOWERS

Clyde Bergenann Ltd, 47 Broad Street, Glasgow, G40 2QR Tel: 0141-550 5400 Fax: 0141-550 5401 E-mail: icarruthers@clydebergemann.co.uk
Diamond Power Specialty Ltd, Glasgow Road, Dumbarton, G82 1ES Tel: (01389) 744000 Fax: (01389) 762669 E-mail: sales@diamondpower.co.uk

SORTATION CONVEYOR SYSTEMS

Vanriet UK Ltd, W Riverside Industrial Estate, Atherstone Street, Fazeley, Tamworth, Staffordshire, B78 3RW Tel: (01827) 288871 Fax: (01827) 250810 E-mail: sales@vanriet.co.uk

SOUND DEADENING STEEL

▶ Acousteel, Naylor Court, Patterson Street, Blaydon-on-Tyne, Tyne & Wear, NE21 5SD Tel: (0870) 7072000 Fax: (0870) 7072001 E-mail: info@acousteel.com

SOUND EQUIPMENT HIRE

▶ Direct Sound Hire, Unit 52 Imex Business Park, Ormonde Street, Fenton, Stoke-on-Trent, ST4 3NP Tel: (01782) 596666 E-mail: info@directsoundhire.co.uk

SOUND INSULATION, COMMERCIAL/OFFICE, *See Acoustic etc*

SOUND LEVEL METERS

▶ A V Calibration Ltd, 13C Old Bridge Way, Shefford, Bedfordshire, SG17 5HQ Tel: (01462) 638600 Fax: (01462) 638601 E-mail: lab@avcalib.co.uk
Gracey & Associates Ltd, Threeways, High Street, Chelveston, Wellingborough, Northamptonshire, NN9 6AS Tel: 01933 624212 Fax: 01933 624608 E-mail: hire@gracey.com

SOUND OR ACOUSTIC INSULATING MATERIALS

Beco Products Ltd, Becco House, Wrawby Road, Brigg, North Lincolnshire, DN20 8DT Tel: (01652) 651641 Fax: (01652) 652796 E-mail: info@becowallform.co.uk
C E P Cladding Ltd, Wainwright Close, St. Leonards-On-Sea, East Sussex, TN38 9PP Tel: (01424) 852641 Fax: (01424) 852797 E-mail: claddings@cepgroup.co.uk
Caledonian Ferguson Timpson Ltd, 5 Atholl Avenue, Hillington Park, Glasgow, G52 4UA Tel: 0141-882 4691 Fax: 0141-810 3402 E-mail: ask@caledonian-group.co.uk
Encon, 1 Rippleside Commercial Estate, Ripple Road, Barking, Essex, IG11 0RJ Tel: (020) 8595 2121 Fax: (020) 8595 9003 E-mail: info@encon.co.uk
Encon Ltd, Langage Science Park, Western Wood Way, Plympton, Plymouth, PL7 5BG Tel: (01752) 333720 Fax: (01752) 348938
Encon Insulation Ltd, Unit F1-F2, St. Michaels Close, Aylesford, Kent, ME20 7BU Tel: (01622) 713400 Fax: (01622) 713403 E-mail: maidstone@encon.co.uk
Encon Insulation Ltd, Unit 2 Elmbank, Channel Commercial Park, Queens Road, Belfast, BT3 9DT Tel: (028) 9045 4646 Fax: (028) 9045 4656 E-mail: t.patterson@encon.co.uk
Encon Insulation Ltd, 3-4 Tamebridge Industrial Estate, Aldridge Road, Perry Barr, Birmingham, B42 2TX Tel: 0121-356 0606 Fax: 0121-356 4828
Encon Insulation Ltd, 23 Nettlefold Road, Cardiff, CF24 5JQ Tel: (029) 2089 5040 Fax: (029) 2089 5044

SOUND OR ACOUSTIC INSULATING MATERIALS – *continued*

Encon Insulation Ltd, Unit 500, Fareham Reach, 166 Fareham Road, Gosport, Hampshire, PO13 0FP Tel: (01329) 230555 Fax: (01329) 230615 E-mail: fareham@encon.co.uk
Encon Insulation Ltd, Unit 9-10, Gelderd Road, Morley, Leeds, LS27 7JN Tel: 0113-289 7666 Fax: 0113-289 7555 E-mail: leeds@encon.co.uk
Encon Insulation Ltd, Unit E2, High Flatworth, Tyne Tunnel Trading Estate, Northshields, Newcastle Upon Tyne, NE29 7UZ Tel: 0191-293 1090 Fax: 0191-293 1099
Encon Insulation Ltd, Brunswick House, Deaghton Close, Wetherby, West Yorkshire, LS22 7GZ Tel: (01937) 524200 Fax: (01937) 524222
Encon Insulation Ltd, Unit 3, Industrial Estate, Stanton Harcourt, Witney, Oxfordshire, OX29 5UX Tel: (01865) 734500 Fax: (01865) 734518
Encon Insulation Materials, Unit 17-19, Bloomsgrove Industrial Estate, Nottingham, NG7 3JB Tel: 0115-978 0040 Fax: 0115-942 0264
Encon Insulation Northampton, 21 Saddleback Road, Westgate Industrial Estate, Northampton, NN5 5HL Tel: (01604) 580580 Fax: (01604) 580585 E-mail: info@encon.co.uk
Encon Insulation Scotland, 80 Cambuslang Road, Cambuslang, Clydesmill Industrial Estate, Glasgow, G32 8NB Tel: 0141-641 0011 Fax: 0141-641 5170
Encon Insulations, Unit 13 Studlands Park Industrial Estate, Newmarket, Suffolk, CB8 7AU Tel: (01638) 667292 Fax: (01638) 664081 E-mail: northampton@encon.co.uk
Encon Manchester Ltd, Chaddock Lane, Worsley, Manchester, M28 1DR Tel: 0161-703 7400 Fax: 0161-703 7411 E-mail: manchester@encon.co.uk
Fabric Service Oxford Ltd, 55 West End, Witney, Oxfordshire, OX28 1NJ Tel: (01993) 772995 Fax: (0845) 363 7151 E-mail: sales@soundservice.co.uk
Morrell Products Ltd, Halesfield 5, Telford, Shropshire, TF7 4QJ Tel: (01952) 587306 Fax: (01952) 582456 E-mail: enquiries@morrellproducts.com
Rockwool Rockpanel B V, Pencoed, Bridgend, Mid Glamorgan, CF35 6NY Tel: (01656) 862621 Fax: (01656) 862302 E-mail: info@rockwool.co.uk
Sheffield Insulations Ltd, Lower Mill Street, Blairgowrie, Perthshire, PH10 6AQ Tel: (01250) 873611 Fax: (01250) 875252 E-mail: blairgowrie@sheffins.co.uk

SOUND PRODUCTION EQUIPMENT

▶ H D L Audio Visual Services Ltd, 4 Hop Gardens, Henley-on-Thames, Oxfordshire, RG9 2EH Tel: (01491) 579020 Fax: (01491) 579037 E-mail: hires@hdlaudiovisualservices.com

SOUND RECORDING EQUIPMENT

Audio Developments Ltd, 23 Portland Road, Walsall, WS9 8NS Tel: (01922) 457007 Fax: (01922) 457008 E-mail: sales@audio.co.uk
Av Niche Recording Systems, 5 Heron Court, Cranes Farm Road, Basildon, Essex, SS14 3DF Tel: (01268) 474608 Fax: (01268) 531482 E-mail: avniche@btconnect.com
Common Heard Productions Ltd, Elizabeth House, 40 Lagland Street, Poole, Dorset, BH15 1QG Tel: (01202) 679671 Fax: (01202) 691672 E-mail: mail@commonheard.com
Klark Teknik Group UK plc, Coppice Industrial Trading Estate, Walter Nash Road, Kidderminster, Worcestershire, DY11 7HJ Tel: (01562) 741515 Fax: (01562) 745371
Langley Sound & Light, 104 Meadfield Road, Langley, Slough, SL3 8HR Tel: (01753) 543389 Fax: (01753) 549690
Nice Cti Systems UK Ltd, Tollbar Way, Hedge End, Southampton, SO30 2ZP Tel: (0870) 7224000 Fax: (0870) 7224500 E-mail:
P & G Stage Electrical Ltd, Studio House, North Stage, Broadway, Salford, M50 2UW Tel: 0161-877 4933 Fax: 0161-877 4944 E-mail: sales@pgstage.co.uk
Penny & Giles Controls Ltd, Unit 36 Nine Mile Point Industrial Estate, Cwmfelinfach, Ynysddu, Newport, Gwent, NP11 7HZ Tel: (01495) 202000 Fax: (01495) 202006 E-mail: sales@pennyandgiles.com
Preco Broadcast Systems Ltd, Unit 3 Four Seasons Crescent, Sutton, Surrey, SM3 9QR Tel: (020) 8644 4447 Fax: (020) 8644 0474 E-mail: sales@preco.co.uk
Raindirk Audio Ltd, 15 Thieves Bridge Road, Watlington, King's Lynn, Norfolk, PE33 0HL Tel: (01553) 810096E-mail: cyril@raindirk.com
Recording Systems Ltd, 111 Upper Bristol Road, Weston-super-Mare, Avon, BS22 8DN Tel: (01934) 616162 E-mail: sales@recordingsystems.co.uk
Sony Business Europe, Viables Industrial Estate, Jays Close, Basingstoke, Hampshire, RG22 4SB Tel: (01256) 355011 Fax: (01256) 474585
Sound Technology plc, 17 Letchworth Point, Dunhams Lane, Letchworth Garden City, Hertfordshire, SG6 1ND Tel: (01462) 480500 Fax: (01462) 480800 E-mail: sales@soundtech.co.uk
Soundcraft, Cranbourne House Cranborne Industrial Estate, Cranborne Road, Potters Bar, Hertfordshire, EN6 3JN Tel: (01707) 665000 Fax: (01707) 660482 E-mail: sales@soundcraft.com
Sounds Inc, Poundsbridge, Penshurst, Tonbridge, Kent, TN11 8AP Tel: (01892) 861099 Fax: (01892) 863485 E-mail: sales@soundsinc.co.uk
Spectra Sound, Unit 1-2 The Chambers, St. Edmunds Road, Northampton, NN1 5ET Tel: (01604) 634100 Fax: E-mail: dondix@lineone.net

SOUND RECORDING EQUIPMENT HIRE

Gracey & Associates Ltd, Threeways, High Street, Chelveston, Wellingborough, Northamptonshire, NN9 6AS Tel: 01933 624212 Fax: 01933 624608 E-mail: hire@gracey.com
▶ M R Studio, Liverpool, L12 0WW Tel: (07876) 518390 E-mail: info@mrstudio.biz
Sound & Light Hire Pa Co, 14 Exeter St, North Tawton, Devon, EX20 2HB Tel: (01837) 89066 Fax: (01837) 89065
Sound Services, Button Street, Swanley, Kent, BR8 8DX Tel: (01322) 667709 Fax: 0208-196 2387 E-mail: mail@sound-services.co.uk
Walker Sound Ltd, 8 Somerset Road, Southsea, Hampshire, PO5 2NL Tel: (023) 9273 0259

SOUND RECORDING STUDIO EQUIPMENT MAINTENANCE OR REPAIR

▶ Prestige Computer Services, 3-4 Park Road, Malmesbury, Wiltshire, SN16 0BX Tel: (01666) 825620 Fax: (01666) 826686 E-mail: service@pcs-uk.net
▶ Studio Designers, Shireshead Old Church, Stony Lane, Forton, Preston, PR3 1DE Tel: (01524) 792020 Fax: (01524) 792305 E-mail: info@studio-designers.co.uk
Television Systems, Vanwall Road, Maidenhead, Berkshire, SL6 4UB Tel: (01628) 676200 Fax: (01628) 676299 E-mail: sales@televisionsystems.ltd.uk
▶ Trenton Technical Services Ltd, 6 Botley Road, Hedge End, Southampton, SO30 2HE Tel: (01489) 796243 Fax: (01489) 797503 E-mail: sales@trentontechnical.com

SOUND RECORDING STUDIOS

▶ Classical Location Recording Services, Hope Cottage, 10 Middle Road, Berkhamsted, Hertfordshire, HP4 3EQ Tel: 01442 877698 E-mail: jules@julesmusic.co.uk
▶ Groove Yard, 79 Larkswood Road, London, E4 9DU Tel: (020) 8523 8083 E-mail: info@groove-yard-productions.com
▶ MLK Music, 5 Madeline Grove, Ilford, Essex, IG1 2RG Tel: 07951 302734 E-mail: info@mlkmusic.co.uk

SOUND RECORDINGS

▶ Activity Media Ltd, 7 Conway Drive, Flitwick, Bedford, MK45 1DE Tel: (01525) 759047
▶ The Bisky Batz, Wix's Lane, London, SW4 0AH Tel: (0870) 7659867 E-mail: sales@biskybatz.com
▶ Microphonic Ltd, Unit G25 Waterfront Studios Business Centre, Dock Road, London, E16 1AG Tel: (020) 7474 6696 E-mail: info@microphonic.biz

SOUND REPRODUCTION EQUIPMENT CONSULTANTS OR DESIGNERS

South West Audio Ltd, Vine House, Northwick Road, Pilning, Bristol, BS35 4HA Tel: (01454) 633635 Fax: (01454) 633668

SOUND REPRODUCTION EQUIPMENT HIRE

Cardiff M Light & Sound, Unit 2 The Highway Man Pub, Castle View, Bridgend, Mid Glamorgan, CF31 1NJ Tel: (01656) 648170 Fax: (01656) 648412 E-mail: sales@cardiffm.co.uk
Rayburn Sound Services, 138 Gooch Street, Birmingham, B5 7HF Tel: 0121-622 6066 Fax: 0121-622 6065 E-mail: sales@4dj.co.uk
Stage Two Ltd, Unit J Penfold Trading Estate, Imperial Way, Watford, WD24 4YY Tel: (01923) 230789 Fax: (01923) 255048 E-mail: info@stage-two.co.uk

SOUND REPRODUCTION EQUIPMENT INSTALLATION ENGINEERS

Fairbank Harding Ltd, 38 Chapeltown, Pudsey, West Yorkshire, LS28 8BL Tel: 0113-257 0020 Fax: 0113-257 0732 E-mail: sales@fairbankharding.co.uk
Rayburn Sound Services, 138 Gooch Street, Birmingham, B5 7HF Tel: 0121-622 6066 Fax: 0121-622 6065 E-mail: sales@4dj.co.uk

SOUND REPRODUCTION EQUIPMENT MAINTENANCE/ REPAIR ENGINEERS

Hocken Sound Contracts Ltd, 50 Sovereign Road, Kings Norton Business Centre, Birmingham, B30 3HN Tel: 0121-459 4242 Fax: 0121-433 5362 E-mail: sales@hockensound.co.uk
Pacific Sound & Light, 505 Bristol Road, Selly Oak, Birmingham, B29 6AU Tel: 0121-471 3110 Fax: 0121-471 3103 E-mail: enquiries@pacificsoundandlight.co.uk

SOUND REPRODUCTION EQUIPMENT MANUFRS

Baldwin Boxall Communications Ltd, Wealden Industrial Estate, Farningham Road, Crowborough, East Sussex, TN6 2JR Tel: (01892) 664422 Fax: (01892) 663146 E-mail: mail@baldwinboxall.co.uk
Broadland Stainless Ltd, New Road, Acle, Norwich, NR13 3BD Tel: (01493) 753933 Fax: (01493) 753944 E-mail: sales@broadlandstainless.co.uk
D N H Worldwide Ltd, 31 Clarke Road, Mount Farm, Bletchley, Milton Keynes, MK1 1LG Tel: (01908) 275000 Fax: (01908) 275100 E-mail: dnh@dnh.co.uk
Fwa, 28 Tynemouth Road, North Shields, Tyne & Wear, NE30 4AA Tel: 0191-259 1099 Fax: 0191-258 2737 E-mail: sales@fwa.uk.com
Lynx Lighting Ltd, 3 Oxford Road, Pen Mill Trading Estate, Yeovil, Somerset, BA21 5HR Tel: (01935) 429290 Fax: (01935) 845045 E-mail: sales@lynxlighting.co.uk
Mustang Communications Ltd, Dunslow Road, Eastfield, Scarborough, North Yorkshire, YO11 3UT Tel: (01723) 582555 Fax: (01723) 581673 E-mail: kelly@mustang.co.uk
National Sound Reproducers Ltd, Lower Priory Farm, Clamp Hill, Stanmore, Middlesex, HA7 3JJ Tel: (020) 8954 7677 Fax: (020) 8954 9329
Omega Enclosures, 1 Dellmount Avenue, Bangor, County Down, BT20 4TZ Tel: (028) 9147 2536
Path Group plc, 8 Dormer Road, Thame, Oxfordshire, OX9 3UD Tel: (01844) 219000 Fax: (01844) 219099
Rossco Ltd, Croft Court, Grammar School Walk, Hitchin, Hertfordshire, SG5 1JD Tel: (01462) 431413 Fax: (01462) 431423
Sound Technology plc, 17 Letchworth Point, Dunhams Lane, Letchworth Garden City, Hertfordshire, SG6 1ND Tel: (01462) 480500 Fax: (01462) 480800 E-mail: sales@soundtech.co.uk
West London Electric Acton Ltd, 9-11 High Street, London, W3 6NQ Tel: (020) 8992 2155 Fax: (020) 8992 4067E-mail: sales@wle.co.uk
Willow Communications Ltd, Kilvey Road, Brackmills Industrial Estate, Northampton, NN4 7BQ Tel: (01604) 877001 Fax: (01604) 877100 E-mail: mail@wcl.biz
Xta Electronics Ltd, Riverside Business Centre, Worcester Road, Stourport-on-Severn, Worcestershire, DY13 9BZ Tel: (01299) 879977 Fax: (01299) 879969 E-mail: sales@xta.co.uk

SOUND REPRODUCTION EQUIPMENT, STAGE/MOBILE

Avw Controls Ltd, Finningham Road, Rickinghall, Diss, Norfolk, IP22 1LT Tel: (01379) 898340 Fax: (01379) 898386 E-mail: info@avw.co.uk
H W Audio Ltd, 180-198 St. Georges Road, Bolton, BL1 2PH Tel: (01204) 385199 Fax: (01204) 364057 E-mail: sales@hwaudio.co.uk
Pacific Sound & Light, 505 Bristol Road, Selly Oak, Birmingham, B29 6AU Tel: 0121-471 3110 Fax: 0121-471 3103 E-mail: enquiries@pacificsoundandlight.co.uk
Walker Sound Ltd, 8 Somerset Road, Southsea, Hampshire, PO5 2NL Tel: (023) 9273 0259

SOUND SYSTEMS

▶ Chip Ltd, 46a Grahams Road, Falkirk, FK1 1HR Tel: (01324) 628853
Rossco Ltd, Croft Court, Grammar School Walk, Hitchin, Hertfordshire, SG5 1JD Tel: (01462) 431413 Fax: (01462) 431423
Sound Systems, 30 Station Road, Alvechurch, Birmingham, B48 7SD Tel: 0121-445 2757 Fax: 0121-445 2757
▶ Wise Productions UK Ltd, 3 Star Works, Salter Street, London, NW10 6UN Tel: (020) 8960 5111 Fax: (020) 8960 5151 E-mail: sales@wiseproductions.co.uk

SOUND SYSTEMS, MOBILE

▶ Cee-Lite & Sound Ltd, Unit 52, Imex Business Park, Ormonde Street, Stoke-on-Trent, ST4 3NP Tel: (01782) 596666 Fax: (01782) 596666 E-mail: sales@cee-lite.com
▶ J P L Sound & Communications, 267 Holton Road, Barry, South Glamorgan, CF63 4HT Tel: (01446) 722711 Fax: (01446) 722711 E-mail: info@jplsound.com
▶ S R D Sound & Lighting, Dry Hill Farm, Shipbourne Road, Tonbridge, Kent, TN10 3DJ Tel: (01732) 373920 Fax: (01732) 373921 E-mail: info@srdgroup.co.uk

SOUP HEATERS

Primal Foods Ltd, Unit 8, The Nelson Centre, Portfield Road, Portsmouth, PO3 5SF Tel: (023) 9262 0020 Fax: (023) 92620021 E-mail: info@primalfoods.co.uk

SOUPS

▶ Campbells Grocery Products, 2020 Cambourne Business Park, Cambourne, Cambridge, CB3 6EZ Tel: (01954) 714100 Fax: (01954) 714101

SOURCING AND PROCUREMENT AGENTS OR SERVICES, PLASTIC RAW MATERIALS

Prosource Europe Ltd, The Timbers, Horsemans Green, Whitchurch, Shropshire, SY13 3DY Tel: (07834) 387979 Fax: (0870) 1128449 E-mail: info@pro-source.co.uk
▶ Satara Ltd, Towcester, Northamptonshire, NN12 6WJ Tel: (07769) 973503 Fax: (01327) 358738 E-mail: dfdsatara@hotmail.co.uk

SOURCING AND PROCUREMENT AGENTS/ SERVICES, *See also headings listed for particular types*

B Plan Information Sytems, The Square, Basing View, Basingstoke, Hampshire, RG21 4EB Tel: (01256) 691111 Fax: (01256) 692450 E-mail: enquiries@fiinfo.com
▶ Berkeley Trade Management Limited, PO Box 25, Darlington, County Durham, DL2 3WX Tel: 01325 710111 Fax: 01325 710108 E-mail: info@trademanagement.co.uk
▶ BROWNWARRIORSOURCING, 112 Findhorn Street, Fintry, Dundee, DD4 9PN Tel: 01382 506814 E-mail: duncanscott@brownwarriorsourcing.co.uk
▶ BusinessGrowth UK, Bristol & West House, Post Office Road, Bournemouth, BH1 1BL Tel: (01202) 313611 Fax: (01202) 313601 E-mail: info@businessgrowthuk.com
Component Logistics Ltd, Milton Court Horsfield Way, Bredbury Park Industrial Estate, Bredbury, Stockport, Cheshire, SK6 2TD Tel: 0161-406 2800 Fax: 0161-406 2809 E-mail: cll@component-logistics.com
▶ Dawnthrive, Unit 7 Belbins Business Park, Cupernham Lane, Romsey, Hampshire, SO51 7JF Tel: (01794) 830352 Fax: (01794) 523539 E-mail: info@dawnthrive.com
▶ Edivorp Ltd, 4 Bowland Rise, Chandlers Ford, Chandler's Ford, Eastleigh, Hampshire, SO53 4QW Tel: (023) 8025 2600 E-mail: enquiries@edivorp.co.uk
▶ Effectual Storage Services, 5 Benfield Way, Braintree, Essex, CM7 3YS Tel: (01376) 551234 Fax: (01376) 551515 E-mail: sales@effectualstorage.co.uk
Entec International Ltd, B Belfont Trading Estate, Mucklow Hill, Halesowen, West Midlands, B62 8DR Tel: 0121-585 8800 Fax: 0121-585 8899 E-mail: info@entec-int.com
▶ Iubeo Europe Ltd, 82 Tenter Road, Moulton Park, Northampton, NN3 6AX Tel: +44 (01604) 646433 Fax: +44 (01604) 643737 E-mail: david@iubeo-europe.com
Richard James International Ltd, 48 Davis Street, Bristol, BS11 9JW Tel: 0117-982 8575 Fax: 0117-982 6361 E-mail: mail@richard-james.co.uk
▶ Jovia Ltd, 3 Linden Crescent, Great Ayton, Middlesbrough, Cleveland, TS9 6AF Tel: (01642) 723211 Fax: (01642) 724681

SOURCING AND PROCUREMENT AGENTS/ SERVICES, ELECTRONIC COMPONENTS

Anchor Components Ltd, 1 John Street, Biddulph, Stoke-on-Trent, ST8 6BB Tel: (01782) 522844 Fax: (01782) 522828 E-mail: sales@anchorcomponents.co.uk

Cursey Technology Ltd, Siddington, Cirencester, Gloucestershire, GL7 6EU Tel: (01285) 650090 Fax: (01285) 650091 E-mail: sales@cursey.co.uk

▶ Dawnthrive, Unit 7 Belbins Business Park, Cupernham Lane, Romsey, Hampshire, SO51 7JF Tel: (01794) 830352 Fax: (01794) 523539 E-mail: info@dawnthrive.com

▶ LMC Purchasing Solutions Ltd, 13 Hope Park Gardens, Bathgate, West Lothian, EH48 2QT Tel: (01506) 651276 Fax: (01506) 651276

Nitronics Ltd, Nitronics House, The Maltings Centre, Station Road, Sawbridgeworth, Hertfordshire, CM21 9JX Tel: (01279) 307555 Fax: (01279) 307700 E-mail: sales@nitronics.co.uk

T K O Procurement Services Ltd, Unit 18 Hassocks Workshop, Stroudley Rd, Basingstoke, Hants, RG24 8UQ Tel: (01256) 819000 Fax: (01256) 842100 E-mail: tony.osborn@btconnect.com

SOURCING AND PROCUREMENT AGENTS/ SERVICES, ELECTRONIC CONSUMABLES

▶ LMC Purchasing Solutions Ltd, 13 Hope Park Gardens, Bathgate, West Lothian, EH48 2QT Tel: (01506) 651276 Fax: (01506) 651276

SOURCING AND PROCUREMENT AGENTS/ SERVICES, ELECTRONIC EQUIPMENT

Cursey Technology Ltd, Siddington, Cirencester, Gloucestershire, GL7 6EU Tel: (01285) 650090 Fax: (01285) 650091 E-mail: sales@cursey.co.uk

Ex-Eltronics UK Ltd, Grove House, Headley Road Greyshott, Grayshott, Hindhead, Surrey, GU26 6LE Tel: (01428) 606060 Fax: (01428) 606593 E-mail: sales@exeluk.com

Peter Hall Export Services, Flaunden Lane, Bovingdon, Hemel Hempstead, Hertfordshire, HP3 0QA Tel: (01442) 833241 Fax: (01442) 834142 E-mail: peter@exportservices.co.uk

▶ LMC Purchasing Solutions Ltd, 13 Hope Park Gardens, Bathgate, West Lothian, EH48 2QT Tel: (01506) 651276 Fax: (01506) 651276

Wadco International, Unit 3 15 Nimrod Way, Wimborne, Dorset, BH21 7SH Tel: (01202) 890103 Fax: (01202) 890101 E-mail: sales@wadcointernational.ltd.uk

SOURCING AND PROCUREMENT AGENTS/ SERVICES, ENGINEERING PLANT AND EQUIPMENT

Ascott Clark, 42 Western Lane, Buxworth, High Peak, Derbyshire, SK23 7NS Tel: (01663) 734221 Fax: (01663) 734318 E-mail: info@ascottclark.com

Kvaerner E & C, 68 Hammersmith Road, London, W14 8YW Tel: (020) 7339 1000 Fax: (020) 7339 1100

T T C Lifting Gear Ltd, Newlyn Road, Cradley Heath, West Midlands, B64 6BE Tel: (01384) 564059 Fax: (01384) 410587

SOURCING AND PROCUREMENT AGENTS/ SERVICES, OIL AND GAS INDUSTRY

Creative Lighting & Sound, 6 Spires Business Units, Mugiemoss Road, Bucksburn, Aberdeen, AB21 9NY Tel: (01224) 683111 Fax: (01224) 686611 E-mail: cls_aberdeen@btconnect.com

M U C L, Suite 10, Berkeley House, Barnett Road, London Colney, St. Albans, Hertfordshire, AL2 1BD Tel: (01727) 822520 Fax: (01727) 822008 E-mail: eras@muscl.co.uk

▶ Visintini-Jones, Capel Barn, Capel Road, Orlestone, Ashford, Kent, TN26 2EH Tel: (01233) 733617 Fax: (01233) 733511 E-mail: rayjones@talktalk.net

SOURCING AND PROCUREMENT AGENTS/ SERVICES, REPLACEMENT PARTS ETC

Wadco International, Unit 3 15 Nimrod Way, Wimborne, Dorset, BH21 7SH Tel: (01202) 890103 Fax: (01202) 890101 E-mail: sales@wadcointernational.ltd.uk

SOYA PRODUCTS

A One Feed Supplements Ltd, North Hill, Dishforth Airfield, Thirsk, North Yorkshire, YO7 3DH Tel: (01423) 322706 Fax: (01423) 323260 E-mail: sales@a-one.co.uk

SPA OR WHIRLPOOL BATHS

A G Budget Discount Swimming Pools & Spas, Aqua Garden House, East Molesey, Surrey, KT8 0PA Tel: (0870) 1283185 Fax: (0870) 1283188 E-mail: info@agbudget.co.uk

Armitage Shanks Group Pension Trustees Ltd, Old Road, Armitage, Rugeley, Staffordshire, WS15 4BT Tel: (01543) 490253 Fax: (01543) 491677 E-mail: merrickj1@aseur.com

Casachi Hydrotheraphy Ltd, Unit A, 1 Wanborough Business Centre, Wanborough, Guildford, Surrey, GU3 2JS Tel: (01483) 813181 Fax: (01483) 813182

Crystal Waters Spas UK Ltd, Island Road, Hersden, Canterbury, Kent, CT3 4JD Tel: (01227) 361163 Fax: (01227) 361163 E-mail: mike@crystalwatersspas.co.uk

▶ Eden Steam Showers., 5 Bagshot Road, Chobham, Surrey, GU24 8BP Tel: 01276 856240 Fax: 0118-979 4565 E-mail: contact@edensteamshowers.co.uk

Jetform Services Ltd, Heath Road, Ramsden Heath, Billericay, Essex, CM11 1HU Tel: (01268) 711700 Fax: (01268) 711600 E-mail: sales@jetformservices.co.uk

Harold Moore & Son Ltd, 16 Rawson Spring Road, Sheffield, S6 1PD Tel: 0114-233 6161 Fax: 0114-232 6375 E-mail: admin@haroldmoorebaths.co.uk

Nordic Saunas Ltd, Unit 5, Fairview Industrial Estate, Holland Road, Oxted, Surrey, RH8 9BD Tel: (01883) 732400 Fax: (01883) 716970 E-mail: info@nordic.co.uk

Plumb Center, Station Approach, Coulsdon, Surrey, CR5 2YB Tel: (020) 8668 4121 Fax: (020) 8660 8795 E-mail: bk.colcon@woloseley.co.uk

▶ Premier Service & Installation, Premier House, Unit 6, Station Terrace, Station Road,, Kegworth, Derbyshire, DE74 2GE Tel: 01509 670600 Fax: 01509 673275 E-mail: info@premservices.co.uk

▶ Sundance Spas, Unit 23 Waterhouse Business Centre, Cromar Way, Chelmsford, CM1 2QE Tel: (01245) 392288

Tanby Swimming Pools & Hot Tubs, 620-622 Limpsfield Road, Warlingham, Surrey, CR6 9DS Tel: (01883) 622335 Fax: (01883) 626775 E-mail: martin@tanby.freeserve.co.uk

▶ Timber-Cabins.Co.Uk, Red Mayes Farm, Limewalk, Long Sutton, Spalding, Spalding, Lincolnshire, PE12 9HG Tel: (01406) 363978 Fax: (01406) 365689 E-mail: enquires@timber-cabins.co.uk

Young Leisure Ltd, 11 Industrial Estate, Priory Way, Taunton, Somerset, TA1 2AL Tel: (01823) 274569 Fax: (01823) 324147

SPACE FRAME STRUCTURES

Space Decks Holdings Ltd, Leach Road, Chard Business Park, Chard, Somerset, TA20 1FA Tel: (01460) 260800 Fax: (01460) 66123 E-mail: skysystems@spacedecks.co.uk

SPACE HEATERS, *See also headings under Space Heaters*

Coil Products Ltd, Evington Valley Road, Leicester, LE5 5LU Tel: 0116-249 0044 Fax: 0116-249 0033

Elan Dragonair Ltd, 162 Southampton Road, Portsmouth, PO6 4RY Tel: (023) 9237 6451 Fax: (023) 9237 0411

Energy Services Ltd, Utility Management Centre, Mucklow Hill, Halesowen, West Midlands, B62 8DR Tel: 0121-585 4000 Fax: 0121-585 4103 E-mail: simon.steed@energy-services.co.uk

▶ Eurostove Ltd, Littlemoor Road, Mark, Highbridge, Somerset, TA9 4NG Tel: (01278) 641367 Fax: (01278) 641419 E-mail: info@eurostove.co.uk

Kaloric Heater Co. Ltd, 31 33 Beethoven Street, London, W10 4LJ Tel: (020) 8969 1367 Fax: (020) 8968 8913 E-mail: admin@kaloricheater.co.uk

▶ Kroll, 49 Azura Close, Woolsbridge Industrial Est/Three Legg, Three Legged Cross, Wimborne, Dorset, BH21 6SZ Tel: (01202) 822221 Fax: (01202) 822222 E-mail: sales@krolluk.com

Nomoco Ltd, 77 Shaftesbury Avenue, Roundhay, Leeds, LS8 1DR Tel: (0870) 7001925 Fax: (0870) 7002024 E-mail: contactus@warmco.co.uk

Robinson Willey Ltd, Mill Lane, Old Swan, Liverpool, L13 4AJ Tel: 0151-228 9111 Fax: 0151-228 6661 E-mail: info@robinson-willey.com

SPACE PLANNING

▶ Accommodation Services Management Ltd, Greenhole Park, Greenhole Place, Bridge of Don Industrial Estate, Aberdeen, AB23 8EU Tel: (01224) 826100 Fax: (01224) 826101 E-mail: info@asm.co.uk

Clear Water Interiors, 69 Anglesmede Crescent, Pinner, Middlesex, HA5 5ST Tel: (020) 8863 1732

SPANNERS

Abingdon King Dick, Unit 11 Roman Way, Coleshill, Birmingham, B46 1HG Tel: (01675) 467776 Fax: (01675) 464277 E-mail: sales@kingdicktools.co.uk

Snap On Tools, Telford Way, Telford Way Industrial Estate, Kettering, Northamptonshire, NN16 8SN Tel: (01536) 413800 Fax: (01536) 413900 E-mail: max.christmas@snapon.com

SPARK ARRESTERS

Pyroban Ltd, Endeavour Works, Dolphin Road, Shoreham-By-Sea, West Sussex, BN43 6QG Tel: (01273) 463311 Fax: (01273) 465313 E-mail: customerservice@pyroban.com

SPARK EROSION ELECTRODE MANUFRS

Agie Charmilles Ltd, North View, Coventry Walsgrave Triangle, Coventry, CV2 2SJ Tel: (024) 7653 8666 Fax: (024) 7653 0023

Erodex UK Ltd, 42 Station Street, Wednesbury, West Midlands, WS10 8BW Tel: 0121-526 7368 Fax: 0121-526 6582 E-mail: sales@afshaw.com

Excel Precision Wse Ltd, Unit 2 Woodrow Way, Gloucester, GL2 5DX Tel: (01452) 419743 Fax: (01452) 307135 E-mail: sales@excel-precision.co.uk

Gaugemaster Co. Ltd, 93 Leopold Street, Birmingham, B12 0UD Tel: 0121-773 6331 Fax: 0121-772 4046 E-mail: enquiries@gaugemaster.net

Welo UK Ltd, Dunlop Road, Hunt End Industrial Estate, Redditch, Worcestershire, B97 5XP Tel: (01527) 546897 Fax: (01527) 545191 E-mail: welo.uk@btinternet.com

▶ Wire Cut Technologies Ltd, 115 Saturn Way, Hemel Hempstead, Hertfordshire, HP2 5PD Tel: (01442) 401856 Fax: (01442) 401856 E-mail: dshew@wire-cut.co.uk

SPARK EROSION MACHINE FILTERS

Agie Charmilles Ltd, North View, Coventry Walsgrave Triangle, Coventry, CV2 2SJ Tel: (024) 7653 8666 Fax: (024) 7653 0023

SPARK EROSION MACHINE MANUFRS

Electro Arc Co. Ltd, The Wallows Industrial Estate, Fens Pool Avenue, Brierley Hill, West Midlands, DY5 1QA Tel: (01384) 263426 Fax: (01384) 79017 E-mail: sales@electroarc.co.uk

Ells Machinery (Spark Erosion), 49 The Rise, Partridge Green, Horsham, West Sussex, RH13 8JB Tel: (01403) 710609 Fax: (01403) 710609

L V W Auto Motive Components Ltd, 118 Cleveland Street, Birkenhead, Merseyside, CH41 3QP Tel: 0151-666 2000 Fax: 0151-647 7220 E-mail: precision@senareng.demon.co.uk

Layton-Fine Machine Technologies Ltd, Units E8-E9, Park La, Castle Vale, Birmingham, B35 6LJ Tel: 0121-776 8883 Fax: 0121-776 8884 E-mail: enquiries@layton-fine.co.uk

SPARK EROSION MACHINING SERVICES (INCLUDING ON SITE)

Albe (England) Ltd, 51 Bideford Avenue, Perivale, Greenford, Middlesex, UB6 7PR Tel: (020) 8997 7282 Fax: (020) 8998 2932 E-mail: sales@albe.com

Ash Tool Co. Ltd, Lord Street, Ashton-under-Lyne, Lancashire, OL6 6HZ Tel: 0161-330 2325 Fax: 0161-343 2229 E-mail: ash.tool@zen.co.uk

Atkins Precision, 59 Fairmile Road, Christchurch, Dorset, BH23 2LA Tel: (01202) 478824

Automatic Engineers (Hinckley) Ltd, Burbage Road, Burbage, Hinckley, Leicestershire, LE10 2TP Tel: (01455) 238033 Fax: (01455) 615101 E-mail: roger@automaticengineers.com

Boundary Precision Engineering Ltd, Limber Road, Lufton, Yeovil, Somerset, BA22 8RR Tel: (01935) 472094 Fax: (01935) 382488

Classic Precision Engineering Ltd, Unit 2, New Line Road, Kirkby-In-Ashfield, Nottingham, NG17 8JQ Tel: (01623) 720402 Fax: (01623) 720353 E-mail: russ@cpeng.freeserve.co.uk

Diespark Precision Engineers, Phillips Street Industrial Estate, 99 Phillips Street, Birmingham, B6 4PT Tel: 0121-359 5800 Fax: 0121-359 5800

Di-Spark Ltd, Unit 3B Wessex Gate, Portsmouth Road, Horndean, Waterlooville, Hampshire, PO8 9LP Tel: (023) 9259 6338 Fax: (023) 9259 4077 E-mail: sales@dispsrks.co.uk

Electro-Discharge Ltd, Unit 14, Bagley Industrial Pk, Northfield Rd, Netherton, Dudley, West Midlands, DY2 9DY Tel: (01384) 238451 Fax: (01384) 245971 E-mail: ron@electro-discharge.co.uk

Erodatools Ltd, Unit 4 Laurence Works, Sheffield Road, Penistone, Sheffield, S36 6HF Tel: (01226) 763725 Fax: (01226) 767139 E-mail: krolfe@aol.com

Erode All, Queens Road, High Wycombe, Buckinghamshire, HP13 6AQ Tel: (01494) 521038 Fax: (01494) 531700 E-mail: sales@erode-all.com

G K Precision 96, 4 Sidings Road, Lowmoor Industrial Estate, Kirkby-in-Ashfield, Nottingham, NG17 7JZ Tel: (01623) 721919 Fax: (01623) 751616

Gibbs & Rustage Ltd, Albert Works, Victoria Road, Dukinfield, Cheshire, SK16 4UP Tel: 0161-339 3379 Fax: 0161-343 2207

H C M Engineering Ltd, Pedmore Road, Stourbridge, West Midlands, DY9 7DZ Tel: (01384) 422643 Fax: (01384) 899210 E-mail: simonh@hcmeng.co.uk

▶ Hardmetal Engineering Cornwall Ltd, Treleigh Industrial Estate, Jon Davey Drive, Redruth, Cornwall, TR16 4AX Tel: (01209) 202809 Fax: (01209) 202819 E-mail: sales@tungsten-carbide.com

Hewes Products, Wren Park, Cinques Road, Gamlingay, Sandy, Bedfordshire, SG19 3NJ Tel: (01767) 651333 Fax: (01767) 651311 E-mail: info@hewes.co.uk

Hi Tech E D M Services Ltd, 18 Bayton Road, Bayton Road Industrial Estate, Exhall, Coventry, CV7 9EJ Tel: (024) 7664 4404 Fax: (024) 7636 3777 E-mail: sales@hitechaerospace.com

Joal Engineering, 13 Orchard Road, Melbourn, Royston, Hertfordshire, SG8 6HL Tel: (01763) 245490 Fax: (01763) 247582

Kelland Precision Tooling, Quebec Street, Elland, West Yorkshire, HX5 9BX Tel: (01422) 370715 Fax: (01422) 370523 E-mail: sales@kellandtools.co.uk

Le Craft Products, Unit 10-11 Ebblake Industrial Estate, Forest Close, Ebblake Industrial Estate, Verwood, Dorset, BH31 6DE Tel: (01202) 827171 Fax: (01202) 813020

Mould Import Solutions Ltd, Units A, Crewe Close, Blidworth Industrial Park, Blidworth, Mansfield, Nottinghamshire, NG21 0TA Tel: (01623) 490070 Fax: (01623) 795687

Moulton & Cooper, 15 Shaw Lane Industrial Estate, Ogden Road, Doncaster, South Yorkshire, DN2 4SE Tel: (01302) 320831 Fax: (01302) 320831

Multispark Erosion Ltd, 145 Camford Way, Luton, LU3 3AN Tel: (01582) 502015 Fax: (01582) 507836 E-mail: sales@multispark.co.uk

Pascoe Engineering Ltd, 127 Nitshill Road, Glasgow, G53 7TD Tel: 0141-880 6444 Fax: 0141-881 4832 E-mail: info@pascoelimited.com

Pearton Tooling Ltd, Unit 8 Manor Way, Old Woking, Woking, Surrey, GU22 9JY Tel: (01483) 773648 Fax: (01483) 756639 E-mail: pearton@pearton.com

Preformtools Ltd, First Avenue, Bletchley, Milton Keynes, MK1 1DY Tel: (01908) 370788 Fax: (01908) 362802 E-mail: sales@preformtools.co.uk

R S T Spark Erosion Ltd, 7 Firbank Court, Leighton Buzzard, Bedfordshire, LU7 4YJ Tel: 01525 850797

Ryeland Toolmakers, Units 17-18 Barton Road, Water Eaton Industrial Estate, Milton Keynes, MK2 3JJ Tel: (01908) 647746 Fax: (01908) 270236 E-mail: info@ryelandtoolmakers.co.uk

S S E Precision Engineering, 37a Douglas Road, Poole, Dorset, BH12 2AU Tel: (01202) 463573 Fax: (01202) 463564

Sertrix Tools Ltd, Clayton Road, Hayes, Middlesex, UB3 1BQ Tel: (020) 8848 9545 Fax: (020) 8561 7077

Sheen Spark Ltd, 1 Ewhurst Avenue, Birmingham, B29 6EY Tel: 0121-472 6241 Fax: 0121-472 5396

Springfield Tools Ltd, Unit 14B, 54 College Road, Perry Barr, Birmingham, B44 8BS Tel: 0121-356 3403 Fax: 0121-356 2155 E-mail: andrewregan@btconnect.com

T G Engineering, Grove Street, Cheltenham, Gloucestershire, GL50 3LZ Tel: (01242) 235403 Fax: (01242) 226637

Teal Engineering, Breckland Business Park, Norwich Road, Watton, Thetford, Norfolk, IP25 6UP Tel: (01953) 885312 Fax: (01953) 883666 E-mail: info@tealengineering.co.uk

Travelling Wire, Unit 3 Teknol House, Victoria Road, Burgess Hill, West Sussex, RH15 9LH Tel: (01444) 239920 Fax: (01444) 239920 E-mail: twire@btconnect.com

SPARK EROSION MACHINING SERVICES (INCLUDING ON SITE) – *continued*

Triune Precision Engineering Co. Ltd, Spring Lane, Malvern, Worcestershire, WR14 1AJ Tel: (01684) 573331 Fax: (01684) 893201
Wire Erosion Co. Ltd, Units 8-9, Springfield Business Centre, Oldends Lane, Stonehouse, Gloucestershire, GL10 3SX Tel: (01453) 827771 Fax: (01453) 827761

SPARK EROSION TOOLING

▶ Mckenzie Engineering, 32 Cutlers Road, South Woodham Ferrers, Chelmsford, CM3 5XJ Tel: (01245) 425413
Penico Systems Ltd, Albion Works, Keighley Road, Bingley, West Yorkshire, BD16 2RD Tel: (01274) 511044 Fax: (01274) 510770
Rem Systems Ltd, Unit 24 26, Sabre Close, Quedgeley, Gloucester, GL2 4NZ Tel: (01452) 314100 Fax: (01452) 314101 E-mail: sales@remsystems.co.uk
System 3R, Redvale House, New Road, Princes Risborough, Buckinghamshire, HP27 0JN Tel: (01844) 274455 Fax: (01844) 348800 E-mail: info.uk@system3r.com
Welo UK Ltd, Dunlop Road, Hunt End Industrial Estate, Redditch, Worcestershire, B97 5XP Tel: (01527) 546897 Fax: (01527) 545191 E-mail: welo.uk@btinternet.com

SPARK EROSION WIRE

Agie Charmilles Ltd, North View, Coventry Walsgrave Triangle, Coventry, CV2 2SJ Tel: (024) 7653 8666 Fax: (024) 7653 0023
Welo UK Ltd, Dunlop Road, Hunt End Industrial Estate, Redditch, Worcestershire, B97 5XP Tel: (01527) 546897 Fax: (01527) 545191 E-mail: welo.uk@btinternet.com
▶ Wire Cut Technologies Ltd, 115 Saturn Way, Hemel Hempstead, Hertfordshire, HP2 5PD Tel: (01442) 401856 Fax: (01442) 401856 E-mail: dshew@wire-cut.co.uk
Wiretech International Ltd, 194 Fletchamstead Highway Industrial Estate, Fletchamstead Highway, Coventry, CV4 7BB Tel: (024) 7667 3366 Fax: (024) 7671 3030

SPARK PREVENTING OR ANTISPARK CONTRACTORS TOOLS

Safety Tools Ltd, Highlands Road, Shirley, Solihull, West Midlands, B90 4NJ Tel: 0121-705 3508 Fax: 0121-713 2505 E-mail: info@safetytools.co.uk

SPARKING PLUGS

Federal-Mogul Camshaft Castings Ltd, Tutnalls, Lydney, Gloucestershire, GL15 5PX Tel: (01594) 842112 Fax: (01594) 841037

SPARKLING WINE

▶ Genesis Wines Ltd, 78Tachbrook Street, London, SW1V 2NE Tel: (020) 7963 9060 Fax: (0870) 8502038 E-mail: sales@genesiswines.com

SPARKPROOF CHAIN BLOCKS

Ansell Jones Ltd, Satellite Industrial Park, Neachells Lane, Wolverhampton, WV11 3PQ Tel: (01902) 722117 Fax: (01902) 725533 E-mail: sales@anselljones.com
William Hackett Chains Ltd, Maypole Fields, Halesowen, West Midlands, B63 2QE Tel: (01384) 569431 Fax: (01384) 639157 E-mail: info@williamhackett.co.uk

SPATIAL DATA PROVIDERS

Harper Collins Publisher Ltd, Westerhill Rd, Glasgow, G64 2QT Tel: 0141-772 3200 Fax: 0141-306 3104 E-mail: vivion.mccormack@harpercollins.co.uk

SPECIAL ALLOYS

Non Ferrous Stockholders Ltd, Dock Meadow Drive, Wolverhampton, WV4 6LE Tel: (01902) 353747 Fax: (01902) 491030 E-mail: info@non-ferrous.co.uk

SPECIAL BATCH POWDER COATINGS

A1 Powder Coatings Ltd, Unit 5 Beta Buildings Willments Industrial Estate, Hazel Road, Southampton, SO19 7HS Tel: (023) 8044 6874 Fax: (023) 8044 6879 E-mail: enquiries@a1powdercoatings.co.uk
Atlas Coating Ltd, Unit 15a Hixon Airfield Estate, New Road, Hixon, Stafford, ST18 0PF Tel: (01889) 271002 Fax: (01889) 271178 E-mail: mail@atlascoating.co.uk

SPECIAL EFFECT DISCO LIGHTING

▶ Ampire Productions, Marino Way, Finchampstead, Wokingham, Berkshire, RG40 4RF Tel: 0118-973 5050
Arcane Lighting Ltd, 1f Avenue One, Chilton Industrial Estate, Chilton, Ferryhill, County Durham, DL17 0SF Tel: (01388) 720103 Fax: (01388) 720126
B K Electronics, Unit 1 3 & 5 Comet Way, Southend-on-Sea, SS2 6TR Tel: (01702) 527572 Fax: (01702) 420243 E-mail: sales@bkelec.com
▶ Intelligent Service, Unit 13, Marino Way, Finchampstead, Wokingham, Berkshire, RG40 4RF Tel: 0118-973 5050 Fax: 0118-973 5544 E-mail: nigel@4repair.co.uk
Lightbulb Co. (UK) Ltd, Thomas Edison House, 74-77 Magdalen Road, Oxford, OX4 1RE Tel: (01865) 794500 Fax: (01865) 203996 E-mail: sales@thelightbulb.co.uk
Lynx Lighting Ltd, 3 Oxford Road, Pen Mill Trading Estate, Yeovil, Somerset, BA21 5HR Tel: (01935) 429290 Fax: (01935) 845045 E-mail: sales@lynxlighting.co.uk
Pulsar Light Of Cambridge, 3 Coldhams Business Park, Norman Way, Cambridge, CB1 3LH Tel: (01223) 403500 Fax: (01223) 403501 E-mail: sales@pulsarlight.com
Sound Tech Ltd, 137 Western Road, Hockley, Birmingham, B18 7QD Tel: 0121-523 6344 Fax: 0121-507 0151 E-mail: chris@soundtech-ltd.freeserve.co.uk
Thanet Disco Centre, 16 North Foreland Road, Broadstairs, Kent, CT10 3NN Tel: (01843) 864001 Fax: (01843) 865666 E-mail: julie.jackson10@btiternet.com

SPECIAL EFFECT LIGHTING DESIGN

Arcane Lighting Ltd, 1f Avenue One, Chilton Industrial Estate, Chilton, Ferryhill, County Durham, DL17 0SF Tel: (01388) 720103 Fax: (01388) 720126
Brilliant Stages Ltd, 2 Hillgate, Hitchin, Hertfordshire, SG4 0RY Tel: (01462) 455366 Fax: (01462) 436219 E-mail: sales@brilliantstages.com
▶ Starry Night Ceilings, 37A Bolton Street, Ramsbottom, Bury, Lancashire, BL0 9HU Tel: (07904) 811480 E-mail: info@starrynightceilings.net

SPECIAL EFFECT LIGHTING FITTINGS

Arcane Lighting Ltd, 1f Avenue One, Chilton Industrial Estate, Chilton, Ferryhill, County Durham, DL17 0SF Tel: (01388) 720103 Fax: (01388) 720126
▶ Starry Night Ceilings, 37A Bolton Street, Ramsbottom, Bury, Lancashire, BL0 9HU Tel: (07904) 811480 E-mail: info@starrynightceilings.net

SPECIAL EFFECT PAINTS

▶ Imaginative Interiors, 11 Burnside Close, Harrogate, North Yorkshire, HG1 2BQ Tel: (01423) 565959

SPECIAL EFFECTS CONSULTANTS OR DESIGNERS, FILM/ADVERTISING ETC

Artem Ltd, Perivale Park, Horsenden Lane South, Perivale, Greenford, Middlesex, UB6 7RH Tel: (020) 8997 7771 Fax: (020) 8997 1503 E-mail: info@artem.com
▶ Jonk Design & Film Boutique, 30 High Street, Eton, Windsor, Berkshire, SL4 6AX Tel: (07793) 122586 Fax: (01753) 840240 E-mail: info@jonkproductions.com

SPECIAL EFFECTS EQUIPMENT

▶ Confetti Magic Ltd, Rocket Park, Pepperstock, Luton, LU1 4LL Tel: (01582) 723502 Fax: (01582) 485545 E-mail: ian@confettimagic.com
Parallel House Ltd, 70 The Green, Christian Malford, Chippenham, Wiltshire, SN15 4BQ Tel: (0870) 0762538 Fax: (07002) 226262
Side Effects, 4 Camberwell Trading Estate, 117-119 Denmark Road, London, SE5 9LB Tel: (020) 7738 5199 Fax: (020) 7738 5198

SPECIAL EFFECTS MAKE UP

▶ 3k Make-up, Showroom & Studio, 84, Queens Road, North Camp, Farnborough, Hampshire, GU14 6JR Tel: (01252) 371123 Fax: (01252) 377110 E-mail: info@3kmake-up.com
System Enterprises Ltd, Unit 21, Hartley Fold, Hartley, Kirkby Stephen, Cumbria, CA17 4JA Tel: (0845) 6430556 E-mail: info@systementerprises.com

SPECIAL EVENT MARQUEE HIRE

▶ Apna Marquee.com, 6 Copinger Walk, Edgware, Middlesex, HA8 0AH Tel: (07956) 895677 E-mail: info@ApnaMarquee.com
▶ Apple Marquees Ltd, Cranford House, 20 Harborough Rd, Kingsthorpe, Northampton, NN2 7AZ Tel: 01604 627290 E-mail: info@applemarquees.co.uk
▶ Brooks Marquee Hire, Chart Hill Road, Staplehurst, Tonbridge, Kent, TN12 0DE Tel: (0800) 7837089 Fax: (01622) 844662
▶ Carlinden Marquees, 12 Wordsworth Close, Bishops Waltham, Southampton, SO32 1RT Tel: (01489) 893151 Fax: (01489) 893151 E-mail: info@hampshire-marquees.co.uk
▶ The Organisation, 168 Edward Street, Brighton, BN2 0JB Tel: (01273) 891770 Fax: (01273) 891771 E-mail: admin@the-organisation.co.uk
▶ Sawtry Marquees, 4 Shawley Road, Sawtry, Cambridgeshire, PE28 5UH Tel: 01487 831852 E-mail: sawtrymarquees@btinternet.com
▶ Southport Marquees, PO Box 356, Southport, Merseyside, PR9 7WD Tel: (01704) 508646 Fax: (01704) 508646

SPECIAL GASES

C K Gas Products Ltd, Unit 3, Murrell Green Business Park, London Road, Hook, Hampshire, RG27 9GR Tel: (01256) 766633 Fax: (01256) 766630 E-mail: sales@ckgas.com
Linde Gas UK Ltd, 160 Leyton Road, London, E15 1DT Tel: (020) 8555 5544 Fax: (020) 8519 8627

SPECIAL OR SPECIALITY STEEL

Aviation Metals Ltd, Michigan Drive, Tongwell, Milton Keynes, MK15 8JE Tel: (01908) 210012 Fax: (01908) 210066 E-mail: sales@aviationmetals.co.uk
Brown & Glegg Edinburgh Ltd, Bankhead Crossway South, Sighthill Industrial Estate, Edinburgh, EH11 4EZ Tel: 0131-453 6611 Fax: 0131-453 1848 E-mail: info@brownglegg.co.uk
Caldervale Forge Co. Ltd, Dunrobin Road, Airdrie, Lanarkshire, ML6 8LS Tel: (01236) 763388 Fax: (01236) 765259 E-mail: rockeater@btinternet.com
Carpenter Technology UK Ltd, 6 The I O Centre, Nash Road, Redditch, Worcestershire, B98 7AS Tel: (01527) 512200 Fax: (01527) 512201 E-mail: afoulkes@cartech.com
Corus, Mossend Works, Main Street, Bellshill, Lanarkshire, ML4 1DJ Tel: (01698) 748424 Fax: (01698) 747191
Gould Alloys Ltd, Carrwood Road, Chesterfield, Derbyshire, S41 9QB Tel: (01246) 263300 Fax: (01246) 260999 E-mail: sales@gouldalloys.co.uk
Hillfoot Special Steels Ltd, 16 Hertburn Estate, Hertburn, Washington, Tyne & Wear, NE37 2SF Tel: 0191-417 0185 Fax: 0191-415 4740 E-mail: washington@hillfoot.com
Milford Steel, Unit 18 Thornton Industrial Trading Estate, Milford Haven, Dyfed, SA73 2RZ Tel: (01646) 698821 Fax: (01646) 697403 E-mail: millfodd@ellissteelgroup.co.uk
Quenched & Tempered Steels Ltd, 60 Green Road, Leeds, LS6 4JP Tel: 0113-225 0400 Fax: 0113-228 6333 E-mail: sales@qandtsteels.fsnet.co.uk
Union Steel Products Ltd, Row End, Berrow Green Road, Martley, Worcester, WR6 6PQ Tel: (01886) 888828 Fax: (01886) 888853

SPECIAL PURPOSE BELTING

Beltech Belting Mnfrs, 7 Acacia Close Business Estate, Off Cherrycourt Way, Leighton Buzzard, Bedfordshire, LU7 4QE Tel: (01525) 851155 Fax: (01525) 851156 E-mail: beltech@globalnet.co.uk

SPECIAL PURPOSE BOLTS

Greenaway & Co. Ltd, Penybont Bryncrug, Tywyn, Gwynedd, LL36 9PT Tel: (01654) 710073 Fax: (01654) 711846 E-mail: mail@greenawayuk.fsnet.co.uk
Pilgrim International Ltd, Southlink Business Park Unit 10, Oldham, OL4 1DE Tel: 0161-785 7700 E-mail: info@pilgrim-international.co.uk

SPECIAL PURPOSE BRUSHES

G B Kent & Sons plc, London Road, Hemel Hempstead, Hertfordshire, HP3 9SA Tel: (01442) 251531 Fax: (01442) 231672 E-mail: info@kentbrushes.com

SPECIAL PURPOSE CABLES

Haani Cables Ltd, Tofts Farm Industrial Estate East, Brenda Road, Hartlepool, Cleveland, TS25 2BS Tel: (01429) 221184 Fax: (01429) 272714 E-mail: info@haanicables.co.uk

SPECIAL PURPOSE CHAINS

B & S Chains (Midlands) Ltd, 29 Toys Lane, Halesowen, West Midlands, B63 2JX Tel: (01384) 413088 Fax: (01384) 413066 E-mail: enquiries@bandschains.co.uk
Howth Chains & Chain Assemblies, Unit 6 Brierley Trading Estate, North St, Brierley Hill, W. Midlands, DY5 3SL Tel: (01384) 79458 Fax: (01384) 79458
▶ Powel Automation Ltd, Commerce Way, Lancing Industrial Estate, Lancing, West Sussex, BN15 8TA Tel: (01903) 762700 Fax: (01903) 763652 E-mail: sales@powel.co.uk

SPECIAL PURPOSE CHASSIS

Planet Engineering, Unit 1, Southampton Road, Petersfinger, Salisbury, SP5 3DB Tel: (01722) 410010 Fax: (01722) 410010
Wheelbase Engineering Ltd, Lower Eccleshill Road, Darwen, Lancashire, BB3 0RP Tel: (01254) 819399 Fax: (01254) 776920 E-mail: sales@wheelbase.net

SPECIAL PURPOSE CHUCKS

P W T, Park Works, Lister Lane, Halifax, West Yorkshire, HX1 5JH Tel: (01422) 358361 Fax: (01422) 359379

SPECIAL PURPOSE COMPUTERS

A C S Office Solutions Ltd, 11 The Spinney, Bradwell, Milton Keynes, MK13 9BX Tel: (01604) 704000 Fax: (01604) 704001
Hamilton Grant Software Ltd, Seymour House, Lower South Street, Godalming, Surrey, GU7 1BZ Tel: (01483) 422404 Fax: (01483) 422401 E-mail: sales@hamilton-grant.com
J L A Computer Services Ltd, 1 Enterprise Court, Lakes Road, Braintree, Essex, CM7 3QS Tel: (01376) 343456 Fax: (01376) 321277 E-mail: sales@jla-computers.co.uk
Netlogic Consulting Ltd, Harlow, Essex, CM18 7NT Tel: (01279) 413355 Fax: (020) 8830 4173 E-mail: info@netlogicconsulting.com
SIR Learning Systems Ltd, Blackbrook House, Ashbourne Road, Blackbrook, Belper, Derbyshire, DE56 2DB Tel: (01773) 820011 Fax: (01773) 820206 E-mail: sales@sirplc.co.uk

SPECIAL PURPOSE CONNECTORS

Connectors & Switchgear Ltd, 25 Chacombe Road, Middleton Cheney, Banbury, Oxfordshire, OX17 2QS Tel: (01295) 710505 Fax: (01295) 712667 E-mail: sales@connectorandswitchgear.co.uk
Multipulse Electronics Ltd, Unit 3 Goldsworth Park Trading Estate, Kestrel Way, Woking, Surrey, GU21 3BA Tel: (01483) 713600 Fax: (01483) 729851 E-mail: sales@multipulse.com
Rockford Group Ltd, Rockford House, Renalsham, Woodbridge, Suffolk, IP12 2GJ Tel: (01394) 420800 Fax: (01394) 420820 E-mail: sales@rockford.co.uk

SPECIAL PURPOSE CONVEYOR BELTING

Conveyor Belt Systems Ltd, 19 Kewferry Road, Northwood, Middlesex, HA6 2NS Tel: (01923) 820121 Fax: (01923) 835699

SPECIAL PURPOSE CUSTOM BUILT MACHINERY

A B Hobley Ltd, Victoria Road, Bradford, West Yorkshire, BD2 2DD Tel: (01274) 639619 Fax: (01274) 641877 E-mail: paulhobley@abhobley.co.uk
A G R Automation Ltd, Elliot Industrial Estate, Arbroath, Angus, DD11 2NJ Tel: (01241) 872961 Fax: (01241) 871723 E-mail: agr@agr-automation.com

SPECIAL PURPOSE CUSTOM BUILT MACHINERY – *continued*

A T M Automation Ltd, Winchester Avenue, Blaby Industrial Park, Blaby, Leicester, LE8 4GZ Tel: 0116-277 3607 Fax: 0116-277 9800 E-mail: sales@atmautomation.com

Acorn Engineering, 6 Kingscroft Court, Ridgway, Havant, Hampshire, PO9 1LS Tel: (023) 9249 2040 Fax: (023) 9247 0377 E-mail: mail@acorn-engineering.co.uk

Anlyn Engineering, Taylor Street, Liverpool, L5 5AD Tel: 0151-207 5592 Fax: 0151-207 5594E-mail: anlynsales@agjengineering.co.uk

Apple Engineering Ltd, Unit 23 Gothenburg Way, Hull, HU7 0YG Tel: (01482) 824200 Fax: (01482) 824196 E-mail: sales@appleng.co.uk

Askey Precision Engineering, Neachells Lane, Willenhall, West Midlands, WV13 3SJ Tel: (01902) 306300 Fax: (01902) 306400

Autarky Co. Ltd, Charlwoods Industrial Estate, Charlwoods Place, East Grinstead, West Sussex, RH19 2HY Tel: (01342) 311388 Fax: (01342) 323733 E-mail: sales@autarky.com

Avon Hydraulics Ltd, Waterloo Road, Bidford-on-Avon, Alcester, Warwickshire, B50 4JN Tel: (01789) 772613 Fax: (01789) 490051

B S Ellis, Unit 5 Chillington Fields, Wolverhampton, WV1 2BY Tel: (01902) 459111 Fax: (01902) 459111

B T M Automation Products (UK) Ltd, Unit 6, Stephenson Road, St. Ives, Cambridgeshire, PE27 3WJ Tel: 0845 5314209 Fax: (01480) 497479 E-mail: btmautomation@btconnect.com

James Brown & Sons Ltd, 92 The Grove, Marton-in-Cleveland, Middlesbrough, Cleveland, TS7 8AP Tel: (01642) 318370 Fax: (01642) 318370

Burman Tool Co Ltd, Rye Road, Hoddesdon, Hertfordshire, EN11 0DZ Tel: (01992) 466311 Fax: 01992 468900 E-mail: info@burman.co.uk

C & L Developments, 25 Lyon Road, Walton-on-Thames, Surrey, KT12 3PU Tel: (01932) 244699 Fax: (01932) 241660 E-mail: info@cl-devs.co.uk

C P E Precision Engineering Co. Ltd, Sutherland House, Arlington Way, Sundorne Retail Park, Shrewsbury, SY1 4YA Tel: (01743) 444250 Fax: (01743) 462563

Cambridge Systems Engineering Ltd, Fordham Technology Centre, 5 Station Road, Fordham, Ely, Cambridgeshire, CB7 5LW Tel: (01638) 720727 Fax: (01638) 720724 E-mail: mailbox@cseltd.co.uk

Carnwood Engineering Ltd, Penn Industrial Estate, Providence Street, Cradley Heath, West Midlands, B64 5DJ Tel: (01384) 569787 Fax: (01384) 633508 E-mail: sales@carnwoodeng.co.uk

Central Engineering Services Ltd, Star Works, Burton St, Leek, Staffordshire, ST13 8BX Tel: (01538) 398127 Fax: (01538) 373774 E-mail: inquire@cepltd.co.uk

Clarke Web Ltd, 9 Poplar Industrial Estate, Redditch Road, Studley, Warwickshire, B80 7AY Tel: (01527) 857535 Fax: (01527) 857315 E-mail: clarkeweb@btconnect.com

Colin Mackenzie Engineering Ltd, 3 Murray Street, Paisley, Renfrewshire, PA3 1QG Tel: 0141-889 3031 Fax: 0141-889 3031

Comau Estil Systems, Midland Road, Luton, LU2 0HR Tel: (01582) 817600 Fax: (01582) 817700

Comet-Pramesco Services, 30 Holywell Avenue, Folkestone, Kent, CT19 6JZ Tel: (01303) 255585 Fax: (01303) 243122 E-mail: steve_baxter@lineone.net

▶ Concept Automated Systems Ltd, Trinity House, 160 John Wilson Business Park, Chestfield, Whitstable, Kent, CT5 3RA Tel: (01227) 770677 Fax: (01227) 771392 E-mail: sales@conceptautomatedsystems.co.uk

Concept (Design & Engineering), Unit 29, Palmerston Business Park, Palmerston Drive, Fareham, Hampshire, PO14 1DJ Tel: (023) 9250 3532 Fax: (023) 9260 2311 E-mail: cde.eng@virgin.net

Custom Enclosures Ltd, Concorde House, Concorde Street, Luton, LU2 0JD Tel: (01582) 480425 Fax: (01582) 414372 E-mail: custom.enclosures@btconnect.com

D & D Engineering Hull Ltd, Stockholm Road, Hull, HU7 0XW Tel: (01482) 879175 Fax: (01482) 838449 E-mail: info@ddeng.co.uk

D L I Precision Engineering Ltd, Trimdon Grange Industrial Estate, Trimdon Grange, Trimdon Station, County Durham, TS29 6PA Tel: (01429) 880454 Fax: (01429) 880369 E-mail: info@dlipe.plus.com

Denray Machine Tools & Automation Ltd, Westwood House, Westwood Road, Earlsdon, Coventry, CV5 6GF Tel: (024) 7667 8916 Fax: (024) 7669 1478

District Tooling Co., 7 Harolds Road, Harlow, Essex, CM19 5BJ Tel: (01279) 424302 Fax: (01279) 451186

Dual Brown, Ross Road, Stockton-on-Tees, Cleveland, TS18 2NH Tel: (01642) 602226 Fax: (01642) 602227

Electro Mechanical Services Ltd, 24B Portman Road, Reading, RG30 1EA Tel: 0118-956 1222 Fax: 0118-956 1220 E-mail: info@emssolutions.co.uk

Electrogenerators Ltd, 14 Australia Road, Slough, SL1 1SA Tel: (01753) 522877 Fax: (01753) 824653

Enco Engineering (Hants) Ltd, Block C, Stirling Business Park, Nimrod Way, Ferndown Industrial Estate, Ferndown, Dorset, BH21 7SH Tel: (01202) 875200 Fax: (01202) 866160 E-mail: sales@encoengineering.com

F Askew Engineers Ltd, Thorpe Road, Howden, Goole, North Humberside, DN14 7AY Tel: (01430) 430035 Fax: (01430) 431869 E-mail: enquries@askewengineers.co.uk

Falcon Engineering Ltd, 28 Wash Road, Hutton, Brentwood, Essex, CM13 1TB Tel: (01277) 226861 Fax: (01277) 230091 E-mail: neil@faleng.demon.co.uk

Ferrostatics International Ltd, Kings Court, 5 Waterloo Road, Stalybridge, Cheshire, SK15 2AU Tel: 0161-303 2200 Fax: 0161-303 2211 E-mail: sales@ferrostatics-int.com

Forward & Thompson Ltd, Atlas Road, North York Trading Estate, Clifton Moor, York, YO30 4UR Tel: (01904) 690999 Fax: (01904) 690960

J.M. Grail (General Engineers) Ltd, Newtown Road, Steam Mills, Cinderford, Gloucestershire, GL14 3JE Tel: (01594) 822054 Fax: (01594) 826654 E-mail: info@grail.eu.com

Group 4 Engineering, Pontardawe Industrial Estate, Pontardawe, Swansea, SA8 4EN Tel: (01792) 865000 Fax: (01792) 865099 E-mail: mail@group4engineering.co.uk

H & H Tool & Engineering Ltd, Unit 4, Harvey Industrial Estate, Shelah Road, Halesowen, West Midlands, B63 3PG Tel: 0121-550 2231 Fax: 0121-585 5789 E-mail: office@hhtools.com

Hawk Cars Ltd, Oakdene, Wadhurst Road, Frant, Tunbridge Wells, Kent, TN3 9EP Tel: (01892) 750341 Fax: (01892) 750071 E-mail: gerry@hawkcars.co.uk

Heavey & Co Engineers Ltd, Fielding Street, Eccles, Manchester, M30 0GJ Tel: 0161-789 1469 Fax: 0161-787 8226 E-mail: gedheavey@supanet.com

Helbar Automation Ltd, 478 Rayleigh Rd, Eastwood, Leigh-on-Sea, Essex, SS9 5HZ Tel: (01702) 522425 Fax: (01702) 522425 E-mail: info@helbar.com

Holmes, 15 Ffordd Derwyn, Penyffordd, Chester, CH4 0JT Tel: (01244) 545532 Fax: (01244) 545532 E-mail: nigel.holmes1@virgin.net

Horizon Instruments Ltd, Unit 12 Ghyll Industrial Estate, Heathfield, East Sussex, TN21 8AW Tel: (01435) 864239 Fax: (01435) 865222 E-mail: mail@horizoninstruments.co.uk

William Hustler & Sons Ltd, Henshaw Works, Henshaw Lane, Yeadon, Leeds, LS19 7RW Tel: 0113-250 3166 Fax: 0113-250 1272

Ishida Qualitech Ltd, Unit 1 19 Willis Way, Poole, Dorset, BH15 3SS Tel: (01202) 466300 Fax: (01202) 466302 E-mail: sales@ishidaeurope.com

K R G Industries Ltd, Russellcolt Street, Coatbridge, Lanarkshire, ML5 2BN Tel: (01236) 435659 Fax: (01236) 434812 E-mail: sales@krgindustries.com

Kall Kwik UK Ltd, Heaton Mersey Industrial Estate, Battersea Road, Stockport, Cheshire, SK4 3EA Tel: 0161-486 1911 Fax: 0161-431 8069 E-mail: sales@kallkwik.uk.com

Lambert Engineering Ltd, Station Estate, Tadcaster, North Yorkshire, LS24 9SG Tel: (01937) 832921 Fax: (01937) 835604 E-mail: le@lamberteng.com

Legend Engineering Ltd, Unit B1, Meadow Lane Industrial Estate, Alfreton, Derbyshire, DE55 7EZ Tel: (01773) 520192 Fax: (01773) 830267 E-mail: legend@fsbdial.co.uk

Linear Systems & Equipment Ltd, 9 Sampson House, Arterial Road, Laindon, Basildon, Essex, SS15 6DR Tel: (01268) 419558 Fax: (01268) 417034 E-mail: linsys@btconnect.com

M & S Developments, 9 Brittania Court, Basildon, Essex, SS13 1EU Tel: (01268) 728988 Fax: (01268) 724034

M S Precision Ltd, 3 Bristows Brickfield, Walters Ash, High Wycombe, Buckinghamshire, HP14 4UX Tel: (01494) 564200 Fax: (01494) 564200

Machine Tool & Engineering Services Ltd, Unit 14 Quay Lane Industrial Estate, Hardway, Gosport, Hampshire, PO12 4LJ Tel: (023) 9251 1666 Fax: (023) 9251 1164 E-mail: info@mtes.co.uk

Mikon, 15 Horwood Court, Bletchley, Milton Keynes, MK1 1RD Tel: (01908) 379333 Fax: (01908) 379900

Millthorne Engineering Co., 82 Tewin Road, Welwyn Garden City, Hertfordshire, AL7 1BD Tel: (01707) 371695 Fax: (01707) 372141

Needham Specialised Machines Ltd, Riverside Works, Storforth Lane, Chesterfield, Derbyshire, S40 2TU Tel: (01246) 238008 Fax: (01246) 277264 E-mail: sales@needhams.uk.com

Nixon Engineering Ltd, 7 Peterfield Road, Kingstown Industrial Estate, Carlisle, CA3 0EY Tel: (01228) 523956 Fax: (01228) 401919 E-mail: eddie@nixonengltd.freeserve.co.uk

Northampton Machinery Co., 7 Deer Park Road, Moulton Park Industrial Estate, Northampton, NN3 6RX Tel: (01604) 782220 Fax: (01604) 782230 E-mail: sales@mgshall.com

Orwin (North East) Ltd, 1-3 Brockwell Road, Crowther Industrial Estate, District 3, Washington, Tyne & Wear, NE38 0AF Tel: 0191-417 7092 Fax: 0191-416 7277

P J Engineering Products Ltd, Elswick Way Industrial Estate, Newcastle Road, South Shields, Tyne & Wear, NE34 0LW Tel: 0191-454 5553 Fax: 0191-455 0892 E-mail: sales@pjeng.co.uk

Paramode Ltd, Harbour Road, Lowestoft, Suffolk, NR32 3LZ Tel: (01502) 574213 Fax: (01502) 501503 E-mail: sales@paramode.co.uk

Peak Precision Engineering Ltd, Alexandra Works, St Annes Road, Manchester, M34 3DY Tel: 0161-303 4800 Fax: 0161-303 4801

Precision Engineers Pontefract Ltd, South Baileygate, Pontefract, West Yorkshire, WF8 2JL Tel: (01977) 702439 Fax: (01977) 600284

Production Pneumatics, 10 Townsend Close, Bristol, BS14 8TS Tel: (01275) 835204 Fax: (01275) 835204 E-mail: sales@productionpneumatics.co.uk

Project Management Services, The Brow, Lothersdale, Keighley, West Yorkshire, BD20 8EQ Tel: (01535) 633802 E-mail: peter@pmservice.co.uk

R G Engineering, 3 Stoney Court, Hotchkiss Way, Binley, Coventry, CV3 2RL Tel: (024) 7644 0508 Fax: (024) 7663 6680 E-mail: r.g.eng@dial.pipex.com

Rad Machinery Ltd, 3 Queens Road, Walsall, WS5 3NF Tel: (01922) 725602 Fax: (01922) 725503 E-mail: sales@radmachinery.co.uk

D.A. Ratchford, 6 Chester Hall Lane, Basildon, Essex, SS14 3BG Tel: (01245) 322720 Fax: (01268) 534828

Reef Engineering, Unit 2 Mayfair Industrial Estate, Maldon Road, Lachingdon, Chelmsford, CM3 6LF Tel: (01621) 744689 Fax: (01621) 744285 E-mail: reefengineering@btconnect.com

Regal Engineering Co. Ltd, Speedwell House, West Quay Road, Southampton, SO15 1GY Tel: (023) 8036 6407 Fax: (023) 8036 6301 E-mail: engineering@bsa-regal.co.uk

Rhoda Precision Tooling Ltd, Unit 2 Lansdown Industrial Estate, Cheltenham, Gloucestershire, GL51 8PL Tel: (01242) 233791 Fax: (01242) 226236 E-mail: rhodaprecision@btinternet.com

Rovic Engineering, 36 Dawkins Road, Poole, Dorset, BH15 4JD Tel: (01202) 683446 Fax: (01202) 684824 E-mail: rovic@roviceng.co.uk

S P Technology Ltd, Camperdown Industrial Park, George Buckman Drive, Dundee, DD2 3SP Tel: (01382) 880088 Fax: (01382) 880099 E-mail: info@sptechnology.co.uk

S R B Engineering 2000 Ltd, Unit 5 Enterprise Court, Newton Close, Park Farm Industrial Estate, Wellingborough, Northamptonshire, NN8 6UW Tel: (01933) 679161 Fax: (01933) 400363 E-mail: sales@srb-engineering.co.uk

Salford Engineering Ltd, Unit 9 Seaford Industrial Estate, Seaford Road, Salford, M6 6AQ Tel: 0161-737 7670 Fax: 0161-745 9224

Sewtec Automation Ltd, 3 Riverside Way, Dewsbury, West Yorkshire, WF13 3LG Tel: (01924) 494047 Fax: (01924) 480949 E-mail: sales@sewtec.co.uk

Shilldown Ltd, 16g Chalwyn Industrial Estate, Old Wareham Road, Poole, Dorset, BH12 4PE Tel: (01202) 722711 Fax: (01202) 722711

Skeens Precision Engineering Ltd, 55-55a Jubilee Road, Waterlooville, Hampshire, PO7 7RE Tel: (023) 9226 2191 Fax: (023) 9225 4219 E-mail: skeens@deans.freeserve.co.uk

South Western Tools Ltd, 26 New Station Road, Bristol, BS16 3RU Tel: 0117-965 9596 Fax: 0117-965 9566

Special Equipment Ltd, 1 United Mill, Suffolk Street, Oldham, OL9 7DJ Tel: 0161-624 6636 Fax: 0161-628 6340

T & S Overseas Ltd, PO Box 248, Rochdale, Lancashire, OL11 4YA Tel: (01706) 350406 Fax: (01706) 526809

Tilling Engineering Ltd, 1 Dale House, Craven Road, Broadheath, Altrincham, Cheshire, WA14 5HJ Tel: 0161-926 9995 Fax: 0161-926 9995 E-mail: clive.tilling@tillingeng.co.uk

Tokyo TV Ltd, Kennington Avenue, Kingswood, Bristol, BS15 1SH Tel: 0117-975 4374 Fax: 0117-975 4374 E-mail: blestwoe@lineone.net

Sam Tooling Ltd, 60 Newland Street, Coleford, Gloucestershire, GL16 8AL Tel: (01594) 835542 Fax: (01594) 837293

Topside Group Ltd, Daimler Drive, Cowpen Lane Industrial Estate, Billingham, Cleveland, TS23 4JD Tel: (01642) 566611 Fax: (01642) 561196

Volkobind Engineering Company Ltd, Unit 1 Tansey Green Trading Estate, Tansey Green Road, Brierley Hill, West Midlands, DY5 4TA Tel: (01384) 79746 Fax: (01384) 75737 E-mail: sales@volkobind.co.uk

Wells Fabrications & Developments Ltd, Unit 39a Wyrley Trading Estate, Wyrley Road, Birmingham, B6 7DB Tel: 0121-327 3354 Fax: 0121-327 3418 E-mail: ian.godwin@btconnect.com

West Surrey Engineering Ltd, Enterprise House, Ashford Road, Ashford, Middlesex, TW15 1XG Tel: (01784) 254085 Fax: (01784) 247785 E-mail: sales@wse.co.uk

Wroughton Developments, 14 Barcelona Cresent, Wroughton, Swindon, SN4 9EE Tel: (01793) 812292 Fax: (01793) 812292

SPECIAL PURPOSE CUSTOM BUILT MACHINERY DESIGN SERVICES

Ak Developments, 5 Station Road, Isleham, Ely, Cambridgeshire, CB7 5QT Tel: (01638) 720727 Fax: (01638) 720724 E-mail: cse@akd.co.uk

C J Uniques Ltd, Unit 12 Magnus, Tame Valley Industrial Estate, Wilnecote, Tamworth, Staffordshire, B77 5BY Tel: (01827) 261682 Fax: (01827) 261682

Eoin Technology Ltd, 35 Warwick Terrace, East Street, Olney, Buckinghamshire, MK46 4BU Tel: (07775) 935422 Fax: (0871) 2564641 E-mail: postbox@eointech.co.uk

M & S Developments, 9 Brittania Court, Basildon, Essex, SS13 1EU Tel: (01268) 728988 Fax: (01268) 724034

Orwin (North East) Ltd, 1-3 Brockwell Road, Crowther Industrial Estate, District 3, Washington, Tyne & Wear, NE38 0AF Tel: 0191-417 7092 Fax: 0191-416 7277

Practical Designs, South Road, Harlow, Essex, CM20 2AS Tel: (01279) 432509 Fax: (01279) 431971 E-mail: sales@practical-design.co.uk

SPECIAL PURPOSE DRILLING MACHINES

Drill Service Horley Ltd, 23 Albert Road, Horley, Surrey, RH6 7HR Tel: (01293) 774911 Fax: (01293) 820463 E-mail: sales@drill-service.co.uk

SPECIAL PURPOSE ELECTRIC MOTORS

BEVI Group UK, 62 Alleyn Park, London, SE21 8SF Tel: (020) 8670 0806 Fax: (0870) 4601131 E-mail: sales@bevi.co.uk

SPECIAL PURPOSE FASTENERS

Flintnine Fasteners Ltd, Highfield Road, Little Hulton, Manchester, M38 9ST Tel: 0161-790 7817 Fax: 0161-703 8314 E-mail: sales@flintnine.co.uk

Hollinwood Wood Precision Engineering Ltd, 8 Victoria Trading Estate, Drury Lane, Chadderton, Oldham, OL9 7PJ Tel: 0161-682 7900 Fax: 0161-681 4900 E-mail: sales@hollinwood.com

Nuts & Bolts (Cannock) Ltd, Unit 40 Rumer Hill Business Estate, Rumer Hill Rd, Cannock, Staffordshire, WS11 0ET Tel: (01543) 466100 Fax: (01543) 466699 E-mail: sales@nutsandbolts-staffs.co.uk

SPECIAL PURPOSE FURNACES

Hengelmolen Engineering Ltd, Great Bridge Industrial Estate, Tipton, West Midlands, DY4 0HR Tel: 0121-520 1181 Fax: 0121-557 5201 E-mail: hengelmolen@btconnect.com

SPECIAL PURPOSE GAUGING EQUIPMENT

Cadar Measurement Solutions Ltd, 100 Fitzwalter Road, Sheffield, S2 2SP Tel: 0114-275 0722 Fax: 0114-275 2912 E-mail: info@cadar.co.uk

SPECIAL PURPOSE GRINDING MACHINES

Earlsdon Technology Properties Ltd, Unit 11 Spitfire Close, Coventry Business Park, Coventry, CV5 6UR Tel: (024) 7671 7062 Fax: (024) 7671 7062 E-mail: sales@e-tech.co.uk

SPECIAL PURPOSE HEATING ELEMENTS

Elmatic (Cardiff) Ltd, Wentloog Road, Rumney, Cardiff, CF3 1XH Tel: (029) 2077 8727 Fax: (029) 2079 2297 E-mail: sales@elmatic.co.uk

Heater Bands Ltd, Bott Lane, Walsall, WS1 2JQ Tel: (01922) 636888 Fax: (01922) 622360 E-mail: brian@heaterbands.freeserve.co.uk

San Electroheat, PO Box 259, Hereford, HR1 9AU Tel: (01432) 851999 Fax: (01432) 851299 E-mail: h_comerford@btconnect.com

SPECIAL PURPOSE HINGES

Ames Stokes Stevens & Son, Hanley Works, Hanley Street, Birmingham, B19 3SP Tel: 0121-359 5561 Fax: 0121-359 2336 E-mail: sales@amesstokes.com

Gold & Wassall (Hinges) Ltd, Castle Works, Lichfield Road Industrial Estate, Tamworth, Staffordshire, B79 7TH Tel: (01827) 63391 Fax: (01827) 310819 E-mail: enquiries@goldwassallhinges.co.uk

SPECIAL PURPOSE HYDRAULIC PRESSES

Palamine Ltd, Homefield Road, Haverhill, Suffolk, CB9 8QP Tel: (01440) 762616 Fax: (01440) 762573 E-mail: sales@palamine.co.uk

SPECIAL PURPOSE KNIVES, *See headings for particular types according to usage*

SPECIAL PURPOSE MACHINE TOOLS

Acecutter Engineers Ltd, Unit 3 The Acre, Dappers Lane, Angmering, West Sussex, BN16 4EN Tel: (01903) 779977 Fax: (01903) 779966 E-mail: eng@seivad.co.uk
Cinetic Landis Grinding Ltd, Skipton Road, Cross Hills, Keighley, West Yorkshire, BD20 7SD Tel: (01535) 633211 Fax: (01535) 635493 E-mail: sales@cinetic-landis.co.uk
Curtis Machine Tools Ltd, Martells Industrial Estate, Ardleigh, Colchester, CO7 7RU Tel: (01206) 230032 Fax: (01206) 231426 E-mail: cnt@douglascurtis.co.uk
Evridge Precison Engineering Ltd, Holmesdale Works, Holmesdale Road, South Darenth, Dartford, DA4 9JP Tel: (01322) 868961 Fax: (01322) 868962 E-mail: mailbox@evridgeengineering.com
G & M Tools, Mill Lane, Ashington, Pulborough, West Sussex, RH20 3BX Tel: (01903) 892510 Fax: (01903) 892221 E-mail: sales@gandmtools.co.uk
Hay Machine Tools Ltd, Lythalls Lane, Coventry, CV6 6FX Tel: (024) 7668 8641 Fax: (024) 7663 7162 E-mail: office@heymachinetools.co.uk
Larkshill Engineering Ltd, 8 Bond Street, Hockley, Birmingham, B19 3LB Tel: 0121-236 2617 Fax: 0121-236 6963 E-mail: frankmurphy@larkshilleng.com

SPECIAL PURPOSE MACHINERY

Atkins Precision, 59 Fairmile Road, Christchurch, Dorset, BH23 2LA Tel: (01202) 478824
Autotech UK Ltd, Unit 1, Dyehouse Lane, Glastonbury, Somerset, BA6 9LZ Tel: (01458) 835551 Fax: (01458) 835903 E-mail: colin.autotechukltd@btinternet.com
Bartling Designs Ltd, Staplehurst Road, Sittingbourne, Kent, ME10 1TA Tel: (01795) 476424 Fax: (01795) 475751 E-mail: bartlingdesigns@bartlingdesigns.com
▶ Helix Precision Machining, Unit 18, Unitfactory Estate, Hull, HU8 7QF Tel: (01482) 323131 Fax: (01482) 226639 E-mail: office@helixprecision.co.uk

SPECIAL PURPOSE NAILS

Corufix UK Ltd, 28 Sidney Street, Gloucester, GL1 4DB Tel: (01452) 551860 Fax: (01452) 551860
R J Engineering, Derby Works, Liverpool Road South, Burscough, Ormskirk, Lancashire, L40 7SU Tel: (01704) 897771 Fax: (01704) 897772 E-mail: r.j.engineering@amserve.net

SPECIAL PURPOSE PACKAGING MACHINERY

Avery Dennison UK Ltd, Business Media Division Thomas Road, Wooburn Industrial Park, Wooburn Green, High Wycombe, Buckinghamshire, HP10 0PE Tel: (01628) 859500 Fax: (01628) 859599 E-mail: sales@averydennison.com
Senior Design Associates Ltd, Unit 4 Dukes Street, Windsor, Berkshire, SL4 1SE Tel: (01753) 833382 Fax: (01753) 833709 E-mail: contactus@sda.uk.com

SPECIAL PURPOSE PAINT BRUSHES

▶ The Traditional Paint Co., 1 North End, Bury Mead Road, Hitchin, Hertfordshire, SG5 1RT Tel: 0845 8903434 Fax: 01462 421337 E-mail: traditionalpaint@yahoo.co.uk

SPECIAL PURPOSE PAINTS

Hammerite Products Ltd, Eltringham Works, Prudhoe, Northumberland, NE42 6LP Tel: (01661) 830000 Fax: (01661) 835760 E-mail: sales@hammerite.com
Neogene Paints Ltd, 14 Caxton Way, Watford, WD18 8UJ Tel: (01923) 213737 Fax: (01923) 213617 E-mail: sales@neogenepaints.co.uk
Witham Oil & Paint (Lowestoft) Ltd, Stanley Road, Oulton Broad, Lowestoft, Suffolk, NR33 9ND Tel: (01502) 563434 Fax: (01502) 500010 E-mail: kathy.rowlands@withamoil-lowestoft.co.uk

SPECIAL PURPOSE PUMPS

Flowserve Pumps Ltd, PO Box 17, Newark, Nottinghamshire, NG24 3EN Tel: (01636) 705151 Fax: (01636) 705991 E-mail: newark@flowserve.com

SPECIAL PURPOSE RAIL EQUIPMENT

Polysafe Level Crossing Systems Ltd, Unit26 King St Industrial Estate, Langtoft, Peterborough, PE6 9NF Tel: (01778) 560555 Fax: (01778) 560773 E-mail: sales@polysafe.co.uk
Railtec Engineering Ltd, Wakefield Road, Dearne Works, Scissett, Huddersfield, HD8 9HS Tel: (01484) 862001 Fax: (01484) 864793 E-mail: john@railtec.co.uk

SPECIAL PURPOSE ROLLED STEEL SECTIONS

Ayrshire Metal Products plc, Pocket Nook Street, St. Helens, Merseyside, WA9 1LT Tel: (01744) 29145 Fax: (01744) 451257 E-mail: ampsth@compuserve.com

SPECIAL PURPOSE ROLLERS

Highland Roller Shutters, Unit 3 Evanton Industrial Estate, Evanton, Dingwall, Ross-Shire, IV16 9XJ Tel: (01349) 830555 Fax: (01349) 830530 E-mail: highlandrollerdoors@hotmail.com

SPECIAL PURPOSE SCAFFOLDING

NSS (Roofing & Cladding) Ltd, Access House, Aviation Park Flint Road, Saltney Ferry, Chester, CH4 0GZ Tel: (01244) 504900 Fax: (0845) 4501901 E-mail: enquiries@nssgroupplc.com

SPECIAL PURPOSE SHAFTS

Paragon Precision Products, 36 Camford Way, Luton, LU3 3AN Tel: (01582) 505005 Fax: (01582) 505010 E-mail: info@paragon-precision.co.uk

SPECIAL PURPOSE STRUCTURAL STEEL FABRICATORS

Carter Origin Ltd, Holmes Street, Rochdale, Lancashire, OL12 6AQ Tel: (01706) 656600 Fax: (01706) 524909 E-mail: sales@carterorigin.co.uk
Coventry Construction Ltd, Torrington Avenue, Coventry, CV4 9AP Tel: (024) 7646 2321 Fax: (024) 7669 4020 E-mail: info@covcon.co.uk
Dorchester Fabrications, Unit 32 Casterbridge Industrial Estate, Casterbridge, Dorchester, Dorset, DT1 1PL Tel: (01305) 267733
Mifflin Construction Ltd, Worcester Road, Leominster, Herefordshire, HR6 8AY Tel: (01568) 613311 Fax: (01568) 614935 E-mail: sales@mifflin.co.uk

SPECIAL PURPOSE TEST EQUIPMENT

A D M Automation, Nest Road, Gateshead, Tyne & Wear, NE10 0ES Tel: 0191-438 7888 Fax: 0191-438 7899 E-mail: sales@adm-automation.co.uk
Eland Engineering Company, 29 Lyon Road, Walton-on-Thames, Surrey, KT12 3PU Tel: (01932) 252666 Fax: (01932) 252583 E-mail: info@elandeng.co.uk
H.R. Smith Techtest Ltd, Street Court, Kingsland, Leominster, Herefordshire, HR6 9QA Tel: (01568) 708744 Fax: (01568) 708713 E-mail: sales@hr-smith.com
Specialist Engineering, Unit 17, Little Ridge, Knella Road Industrial Estate, Welwyn Garden City, Hertfordshire, AL7 2BH Tel: (01707) 336075 Fax: (01707) 330215
Turner Aviation Ltd, Spiersbridge Terrace, Thornliebank, Glasgow, G46 8JQ Tel: 0141-638 2265 Fax: 0141-638 9694 E-mail: enquiries@turner-aviation.co.uk
Weller Patents Development, 1-8 Grand Parade Mews Rear of, 96-110 Upper Richmond Road, London, SW15 2SP Tel: (020) 8788 6684 Fax: (020) 8788 4669

SPECIAL PURPOSE THERMOCOUPLES

Hasco-Thermic Ltd, 134 Birchfield Lane, Oldbury, West Midlands, B69 2AY Tel: 0121-552 4911 Fax: 0121-544 8143E-mail: mail@hasco.co.uk

SPECIAL PURPOSE TOOLS

Heenan Multiform Machines, Unit 34 Springvale Industrial Estate, Millfield Road, Bilston, West Midlands, WV14 0ST Tel: (01902) 401781 Fax: (01902) 401781

SPECIAL PURPOSE WINDOWS

Colorminium, 356-358 Prince Avenue, Westcliff-On-Sea, Essex, SS0 0NF Tel: (01702) 390091 Fax: (01702) 432840
Financial Strategies South Yorks, Unit 27 53 Mowbray Street, Sheffield, S3 8EN Tel: 0114-221 2632 Fax: 0114-276 6013
▶ H H Aluminium & Building Products Ltd, Unit 1/3, Park Gate Business Centre, Chandlers Way, Park Gate, Southampton, SO31 1FQ Tel: (01489) 589655 Fax: (01489) 589322 E-mail: peter@hhali.co.uk
Scandinavian Timber Ltd, 30a Roxborough Park, Harrow, Middlesex, HA1 3AY Tel: (020) 8864 0131 Fax: (020) 8426 9151 E-mail: enquiries@scandanaviantimber.com
Severn Valley Metal Window & Door Maintenance Co., Faraday Drive, Bridgnorth, Shropshire, WV15 5BB Tel: (01746) 761127 Fax: (01746) 765652
Specialists In Traditional Sash Windows, 24 Stoughton Road, Guildford, Surrey, GU1 1LL Tel: (01483) 823161 Fax: (01483) 823161
▶ Ventrolla Thames Valley, Friar Park Stables, Badgemore, Henley-On-Thames, Oxfordshire, RG9 4NR Tel: (01491) 412141 Fax: (01491) 412341 E-mail: info@ventrollathamesvalley.com

SPECIAL PURPOSE WIRE

▶ Carrington Wire, P O Box 56, Cardiff, CF24 2WR Tel: (029) 2025 6100 Fax: (029) 2025 6101 E-mail: sales@carringtonwiregroup.co.uk

SPECIAL PURPOSE WOODWORKING MACHINES

Woods Radio Frequency Services Ltd, Bullocks Farm, Bullocks Lane, Takeley, Bishop's Stortford, Hertfordshire, CM22 6TA Tel: (01279) 870432 Fax: (01279) 871689

SPECIAL SPECIFICATION BOLTS AND NUTS

3d Machine Shop Engineering Ltd, 23 The Business Centre, 20 James Road, Tyseley, Birmingham, B11 2BA Tel: 0121-628 6628 Fax: 0121-628 2008 E-mail: cliffdavies1@btconnect.com
A1 Turning, 7 Holbrook Lane, Coventry, CV6 4AD Tel: (024) 7668 6333 Fax: (024) 7668 6222 E-mail: salesa1turning@btconnect.com
Arduous Manufacturing, The Old Brewery, Norton Fitzwarren, Taunton, Somerset, TA2 6RN Tel: (01823) 339000 Fax: (01823) 339000
Arnold Wragg Ltd, Unit 2, Parkway One, Parkway Drive, Sheffield, S9 4WU Tel: 0114 2519050 Fax: 0114 2446635 E-mail: sales@arnold-wragg.com
Barnes & Thomas Ltd, Cheetham Mill, Park Street, Stalybridge, Cheshire, SK15 2BT Tel: 0161-338 3630 Fax: 0161-304 8055 E-mail: brian_richard@barnesandthomas.com
Bolt & Nut Manufacturing, White Lee Road, Swinton, Mexborough, South Yorkshire, S64 8BH Tel: (01709) 570212 Fax: (01709) 584125 E-mail: sales@tachart.com
C F E Fasteners Ltd, Unit 18, Central Trading Estate, Cable Street, Wolverhampton, WV2 2HX Tel: (01902) 871777 Fax: (01902) 351410 E-mail: sales@cfe.co.uk
Clarkwood Engineering Ltd, 7 Blackenhall Industrial Estate, Sunbeam Street, Wolverhampton, WV2 4PF Tel: (01902) 710868 Fax: (01902) 712840 E-mail: enquiries@clarkwood.co.uk
Dinstock Ltd, Unit C1, Hortonwood row 10, Telford, Shropshire, TF1 7ES Tel: (01952) 676700 Fax: (01952) 676800
Doran Engineering Co Holdings Ltd, Planetary Industrial Estate, Planetary Road, Willenhall, West Midlands, WV13 3XW Tel: (01902) 866000 Fax: (01902) 866222
Forward Industrial Products Group Ltd, Unit 2 Tyseley Park, Wharfedale Road Tyseley, Birmingham, B11 2DF Tel: 0121-707 2555 Fax: 0121-708 3081 E-mail: info@forwardindustrial.com
Hampshire Bolt & Tool Supplies Ltd, Armstrong Road, Daneshill East, Basingstoke, Hampshire, RG24 8NU Tel: (01256) 329781 Fax: (01256) 817150 E-mail: jillcorreale@aol.com
Ivyplus Fasteners & Fixing Devices, 41 Colmore Flats, Henrietta Street, Birmingham, B19 3PT Tel: 0121-212 2485 Fax: 0121-212 2485
J Hall & Son Fasteners Ltd, Bentley Mill Industrial Estate, Longmore Avenue, Walsall, WS2 0BW Tel: (01922) 626652 Fax: (01922) 649942 E-mail: jhallsales@btconnect.com
Jaton, Patriot Drive, Rooksley, Milton Keynes, MK13 8PB Tel: (01908) 690055 Fax: (01908) 690401 E-mail: milton.keynes@outlet-jaton.com
Lydford Precision Engineering Ltd, Sutherland Avenue, Monmore Green, Wolverhampton, WV2 2JH Tel: (01902) 351353 Fax: (01902) 351616 E-mail: sales@lydford-eng.co.uk
M & C Engineering, Unit 12 West Bowhouse Workshops, Girdle Toll, Irvine, Ayrshire, KA11 1BU Tel: (01294) 215986 Fax: (01294) 215986
Maxwell Engineering Co. Ltd, Waterloo Road, Llandrindod Wells, Powys, LD1 6BH Tel: (01597) 822414 Fax: (01597) 823067 E-mail: sales@maxwell-engineering.co.uk
R P M Fasteners Ltd, Ashland St, Wolverhampton, WV3 0BN Tel: (01902) 421252 Fax: (01902) 715585 E-mail: sales@rolevet.com
Spechtread Ltd, Unit 20, Field Close, Bloxwich, Walsall, WS3 3JS Tel: (01922) 710180 Fax: (01922) 710181
Spensall Engineering Ltd, Kitson Road, Leeds, LS10 1NR Tel: 0113-245 0726 Fax: 0113-242 0047
Stainless Steel Fasteners Ltd, Broombank Road, Chesterfield, Derbyshire, S41 9QJ Tel: (01246) 451818 Fax: (01246) 455268 E-mail: sales@ssfast.co.uk

SPECIAL SPECIFICATION SCREWS

Griffin Fastener Supplies Ltd, PO Box 7098, Solihull, West Midlands, B93 9LD Tel: (01564) 772161 Fax: (01564) 772162
Masons Fasteners Ltd, 3-4 Doris Road, Bordesley Green, Birmingham, B9 4SJ Tel: 0121-766 7500 Fax: 0121-766 8551
Rosch Engineering, Units 1 2, Calibre Indust Park, Four Ashes, Wolverhampton, WV10 7DZ Tel: (01902) 798100 Fax: (01902) 798844 E-mail: info@rosch.co.uk

SPECIALISED FURNITURE

Simon Thomas Pirie, Slepe Farm Workshop, Dorchester Road, Lytchett Minster, Poole, Dorset, BH16 6HT Tel: (01202) 625725 Fax: (01202) 625725 E-mail: sales@simonthomaspirie.co.uk
Robins Cabinet Makers, Lodge Farm Bungalow, Kineton, Warwick, CV35 0JH Tel: (01926) 640151 Fax: (01926) 640151
▶ Sandywood Furniture, 8 Boundary Business Court, Church Road, Mitcham, Surrey, CR4 3TD Tel: (020) 8687 7070 Fax: (020) 8648 7020 E-mail: sandywoodfurnitureltd@gmill.com
Special Branch, 5 Brailwood Close, Bilsthorpe, Newark, Nottinghamshire, NG22 8UG Tel: (01623) 871306

SPECIALISED OR SPECIAL PURPOSE ENGINEERING

A E Jones, 11 Mortimer Street, Cleckheaton, West Yorkshire, BD19 5AR Tel: (01274) 851126 Fax: (01274) 870155 E-mail: sales@aejones.co.uk
A Hodgson & Sons, Church Bank, Terrington St. Clement, King's Lynn, Norfolk, PE34 4NA Tel: (01553) 828361 Fax: (01553) 827262 E-mail: info@ajhodgesoneng.co.uk
Agp, Mussons Path, Luton, LU2 7RQ Tel: (01582) 735446 Fax: (01582) 400875 E-mail: alanwithy@hotmail.com
Ainscough Crane Hire Ltd, Harewood Works, Middlesbrough Road, Thornaby, Stockton-on-Tees, Cleveland, TS17 7BN Tel: (01642) 661111 Fax: (01642) 612422 E-mail: general@ainscough.co.uk
Atlas Marine Contractors Ltd, Imperial Dock Road, Leith Docks, Edinburgh, EH6 7DR Tel: 0131-555 6030 Fax: 0131-555 6040
Billington Structures Ltd, Barnsley Road, Wombwell, Barnsley, South Yorkshire, S73 8DS Tel: (01226) 340666 Fax: (01226) 755947 E-mail: sales@billington-structures.co.uk
D S Gear Company Ltd, Knights Bridge, Kirton Holme, Boston, Lincolnshire, PE20 1TH Tel: (01205) 290601 Fax: (01205) 290601 E-mail: ds.gears@virgin.net
Andrew Davies Construction Ltd, The Manor House, High Street, Buntingford, Hertfordshire, SG9 9AB Tel: (01763) 274334 Fax: (01763) 274335
J B Engineering, Unit 16b, 16 Balloo Avenue, Bangor, County Down, BT19 7QT Tel: (028) 9127 4742
J T Electrons, 42 Torridge Road, Thornton Heath, Surrey, CR7 7EY Tel: (020) 8665 6595 Fax: (020) 8665 6595 E-mail: istc@istc.org.uk
Manhick Engineering Ltd, 7 Wise Street, Leamington Spa, Warwickshire, CV31 3AP Tel: (01926) 332323 Fax: (01926) 315950 E-mail: dick.hickman@manhick.co.uk

SPECIALISED OR TO SPECIFICATION FREIGHT CONTAINERS

Elliott Sargeant Ltd, 4 Rushington Business Park, Rushington Lane, Totton, Southampton, SO40 9AH Tel: (023) 8066 1666 Fax: (023) 8066 1567

▶ Stonehaven Engineering Ltd, 2 Spurryhillock Industrial Estate, Broomhill Road, Stonehaven, Kincardineshire, AB39 2NH Tel: (01569) 766700 Fax: (01569) 766147 E-mail: info@stonehaven-eng.com

SPECIALISED PACKAGING

B M Packaging Ltd, Unit 4 Crosland Road Industrial Estate, Netherton, Huddersfield, HD4 7DQ Tel: (01484) 667855 Fax: (01484) 663280 E-mail: sales@bmpackaging.co.uk

Burton Box Co. Ltd, Burton Road Works, Burton-On-Trent, Staffordshire, DE14 3DH Tel: (01283) 540023 Fax: (01283) 565985

Dairi Pak, Platt Bridge, Ruyton XI Towns, Shrewsbury, SY4 1LS Tel: (01939) 260342 Fax: (01939) 260275 E-mail: sales@dairi-pak.co.uk

Field Boxmore, 9a Delta Drive, Tewkesbury, Gloucestershire, GL20 8HB Tel: (01684) 850020 Fax: (01684) 850141

K E B Packaging Ltd, Mills Hill Road, Middleton, Manchester, M24 2FT Tel: 0161-655 3464 Fax: 0161-655 3460 E-mail: sales@keb.co.uk

K M Packaging Services Ltd, 44 West Street, Oundle, Peterborough, PE8 4EF Tel: (01832) 274944 Fax: (01832) 274898 E-mail: louise@kmpack.co.uk

Kite Packaging, PO Box 50, Blackwood, Gwent, NP12 2XF Tel: (01495) 230976 Fax: (01495) 230080 E-mail: southwales@packwithkite.com

Kite Packaging, 186 Torrington Avenue, Coventry, CV4 9AJ Tel: (024) 7642 0088 Fax: (024) 7642 0062 E-mail: sales@packwithkite.com

Kite Packaging, H Park 34, Collett, Didcot, Oxfordshire, OX11 7WB Tel: (01235) 815615 Fax: (01235) 750760 E-mail: thamesvalley@packwithkite.com

Kite Packaging, Unit 24-28, Stakehill Industrial Estate, Middleton, Manchester, M24 2RW Tel: 0161-643 1001 Fax: 0161-643 1122 E-mail: manchester@packwithkite.com

Kite Packaging, Portfield Road, Portsmouth, PO3 5SF Tel: (023) 9265 2676 Fax: (023) 9265 2677 E-mail: southcoast@packwithkite.com

Kite Packaging Ltd (Sheffield), Unit 3, Grange Mill Lane, Sheffield, S9 1HW Tel: (01709) 565010 Fax: (01709) 565011 E-mail: sheffield@packwithkite.com

Line Packaging & Display, Centre 2000, St. Michaels Road, Sittingbourne, Kent, ME10 3DZ Tel: (01795) 429986 Fax: (01795) 439748

M Y Cartons Ltd, Grosvenor Road, Gillingham Business Park, Gillingham, Kent, ME8 0SA Tel: (01634) 388777 Fax: (01634) 377733 E-mail: sales@mypackaging.com

M Y Healthcare, E Railway Triangle, Walton Road, Portsmouth, PO6 1TY Tel: (023) 9221 0229 Fax: (023) 9221 9263 E-mail: sales@mypackaging.com

Saklok, Roughway Mill, Dunks Green, Tonbridge, Kent, TN11 9SG Tel: (01732) 810813 Fax: (01732) 810838 E-mail: roughway@btconnect.com

Sintec Keramik Ltd, Lake Road, Leeway Industrial Estate, Newport, Gwent, NP19 4SR Tel: (01633) 636500 Fax: (01633) 636501 E-mail: info.uk@sintec-keramik.com

Sportsmatch UK Ltd, 16 Summer Street, Leighton Buzzard, Bedfordshire, LU7 1HT Tel: (01525) 381638 Fax: (01525) 851236 E-mail: info@sportsmatch-uk.com

Waddingtons Cartons Ltd, Cockburn Fields, Middleton Grove, Leeds, LS11 5LX Tel: 0113-276 0730 Fax: 0113-276 0165 E-mail: enquiries@myholdings.co.uk

Wipak UK Ltd, Unit 3 Buttington Cross Enterprise Park, Buttington, Welshpool, Powys, SY21 8SL Tel: (01938) 555255 Fax: (01938) 555277 E-mail: sales@wipak.com

SPECIALISED WEIGHTS

Taw Engineering North West Ltd, 194 Price Street, Birkenhead, Merseyside, CH41 3PR Tel: 0151-647 6198 Fax: 0151-666 1347 E-mail: taw.engineering@virgin.net

SPECIALIST ANIMAL FENCING

Bude Angling Supplies, 6 Queen Street, Bude, Cornwall, EX23 8BB Tel: (01288) 353396 Fax: (01288) 353396 E-mail: petsgalorebude@aol.com

SPECIALIST DEMOLITION CONTRACTORS

▶ C A J Services Ltd, Unit K,, Higham Business Park, Bury Close, Higham Ferrers, Northamptonshire, NN10 8HQ Tel: (01933) 355001 Fax: (01933) 355009 E-mail: mail@cajservices.co.uk

▶ Pennine Plant Services, Woodlands, Dale Street, Longwood, Huddersfield, HD3 4TG Tel: (01484) 647129 Fax: (01484) 647290

SPECIALIST JOINERY

A G Duck & Sons Ltd, Charlton Mead Lane, Hoddesdon, Hertfordshire, EN11 0DJ Tel: (01992) 462188 Fax: (01992) 450991

A J B Joinery, Little Merebrook, Hanley Swan, Worcester, WR8 0EH Tel: (01684) 310610 Fax: (01684) 311917

A R Manley & Son Ltd, Rodington, Shrewsbury, SY4 4RF Tel: (01952) 770278 Fax: (01952) 770976 E-mail: sales@armanley.co.uk

Aldwick Doors & Windows, 59 Sunnymead Drive, Selsey, Chichester, West Sussex, PO20 0DG Tel: (01243) 778557 Fax: (01243) 778557 E-mail: sales@aldwickdoorsandwindows.co.uk

▶ Ambleside Joinery Sales, 18, Graystones Close, West Bridgford, Nottingham, NG2 6QU Tel: 01159 819853 Fax: 01159 819853 E-mail: ambleside.sales@ntlworld.com

▶ Apex Building Supplies & Joinery Ltd, Lower Street, Baylham, Ipswich, IP6 8JP Tel: (01473) 832484 Fax: (01473) 832494

Avon Joinery Manufacturers, 8 Minto Road Industrial Centre, Ashley Parade, Bristol, BS2 9YW Tel: 0117-955 8142

B & P Joiners Ltd, Thomas Street, Crewe, CW1 2BD Tel: (01270) 250969 Fax: (01270) 250969

B W Dove & Son, The Old Dairy, Darrow Green Road, Denton, Harleston, Norfolk, IP20 0BA Tel: (01986) 788377

Bartholomew Joinery Ltd, The Workshop Great Hidden Farm, Wantage Road, Eddington, Hungerford, Berkshire, RG17 0PW Tel: (01488) 685407 Fax: (01488) 681624 E-mail: bart.joinery@amserve.net

Beard Evans Joinery, Shepherd Road, Gloucester, GL2 5EL Tel: (01452) 423123 Fax: (01452) 501055 E-mail: sales@beardevansjoinery.co.uk

Bishopton Joinery, Burton Farm, Bishopton, Stratford-upon-Avon, Warwickshire, CV37 0RW Tel: (01789) 298448 Fax: (01789) 298448

Brent Taunton Joinery, 3 Coopers Industrial Estate, Littlehampton Road, Ferring, Worthing, West Sussex, BN12 6PW Tel: (01903) 248169 Fax: (01903) 248169

Brian Fawcett Joinery, Ellifoot Lane, Burstwick, Hull, HU12 9EF Tel: (01964) 670818 Fax: (01964) 671138 E-mail: enquiries@brianfawcett-joinery.com

Bristol & West Joinery & Turnings, 56-58 Park Rd, Stapleton, Bristol, BS16 1AU Tel: 0117-965 8662 Fax: 0117-965 8662

T.A. Brooks, 1 Staffa Drive, Tibshelf, Alfreton, Derbyshire, DE55 5PJ Tel: (01773) 872361 Fax: (01773) 872361

Brookthorpe Joinery, Stroud Road, Brookthorpe, Gloucester, GL4 0UQ Tel: (01452) 813007 Fax: (01452) 813007

Broxbarn Joineries, Millbrook House, Chertsey Road, Shepperton, Middlesex, TW17 9LA Tel: (01932) 877600 Fax: (01932) 269261

Burns & Churchill, Unit 10 Tudor Yard, Lawnside Road, Ledbury, Herefordshire, HR8 2BZ Tel: (01531) 636177 Fax: (01531) 636177

C B H (Joinery) Ltd, Meadow Street, Walsall, WS1 3QP Tel: (01922) 646690 Fax: (01922) 615244

Carlton Smith Projects Ltd, Station Approach, Station Road, Pershore, Worcestershire, WR10 2DB Tel: (01386) 555770 Fax: (01386) 556432 E-mail: info@carlton-smith.co.uk

N. Carpenter Custom Made Joinery & Furniture, Unit 7, Parklands Farm, Parklands, Shere, Guildford, Surrey, GU5 9JQ Tel: (01483) 203759 Fax: (01483) 203759

Charlotte Street Joinery, Unit A1 New Normanton Mills, Charlotte Street, Derby, DE23 6QG Tel: (01332) 367962 Fax: (01332) 748452 E-mail: charlottestreet@hotmail.com

Chelford Joinery Co. Ltd, Boundary Cottage, Chelford Road, Ollerton, Knutsford, Cheshire, WA16 8TA Tel: (01565) 751012 Fax: (01565) 652087

Chilton Joinery Ltd, 3 Chilton Industrial Estate, Martins Road, Sudbury, Suffolk, CO10 2FT Tel: (01787) 378667 Fax: (01787) 880632 E-mail: lee@chiltonjoinery.co.uk

Clark & Kemp Joinery Ltd, Units 8-10 Baddow Park, West Hanningfield Road, Great Baddow, Chelmsford, CM2 7SY Tel: (01245) 476667 Fax: (01245) 474857 E-mail: clark@clark-kemp.freeserve.co.uk

Clarman Joinery, Ferry Road, Fiskerton, Lincoln, LN3 4HW Tel: (01522) 751988 Fax: (01522) 751988

Classic Holdings, 55 Cradley Road, Cradley Heath, West Midlands, B64 7BB Tel: (01384) 637825 Fax: (01384) 564079 E-mail: classicholdings@aol.com

Classic Images Ltd, Oakcroft Works, Oakcroft Road, Chessington, Surrey, KT9 1RH Tel: (020) 8391 1133 Fax: (020) 8397 5040 E-mail: classicimages@ukonline.co.uk

Classic Joinery, 324 Guildford Road, Bisley, Woking, Surrey, GU24 9AE Tel: (01932) 354333 Fax: (01483) 797713 E-mail: john@classicjoinery.co.uk

Cleveland Joinery Ltd, Cleveland Place, Farncombe Street, Godalming, Surrey, GU7 3LP Tel: (01483) 415522 Fax: (01483) 861103

Cliffside Joinery, Cliff Side, Wakebridge, Matlock, Derbyshire, DE4 5HD Tel: (01773) 853077 Fax: (01773) 853077

D. & J. Cole (Joinery), Palmers Yard, London Road, Newbury, Berkshire, RG14 2BA Tel: (01635) 49748 Fax: (01635) 528413

Collinswood Joinery, 2 Rutherglen Road, Corby, Northamptonshire, NN17 1ER Tel: (01536) 201885 Fax: (01536) 409474

Cottingham Joinery Co. Ltd, Beckside North, Beverley, North Humberside, HU17 0PR Tel: (01482) 868145 Fax: (01482) 870728 E-mail: info@cottjoinery.co.uk

County Joinery, The Workshop, 13 Felpham Road, Bognor Regis, West Sussex, PO22 7AS Tel: (01243) 842714 E-mail: info@countyjoinery.co.uk

Critchley & Curtis, 7 Clegg Street, Liverpool, L5 3SP Tel: 0151-207 2437 Fax: 0151-207 2437

Croft Joinery, Castle Garage Yard, Croft Road, Neath, West Glamorgan, SA11 1RW Tel: (01639) 633355

Crown Joinery, Unit 6 Farthing Road, Ipswich, IP1 5AP Tel: (01473) 740030 Fax: (01473) 744231 E-mail: crownjoinery@aol.com

D Davies & Sons, Cornerswell Road, Penarth, South Glamorgan, CF64 2UZ Tel: (029) 2070 8524 Fax: (029) 2051 3189

D & P Joinery Manufacturers, 32a George Road, Carlton, Nottingham, NG4 3AE Tel: 0115-987 0128 Fax: 0115-956 0095 E-mail: dpjoinery@ntlworld.com

Dale Joinery Lichfield Ltd, Europa Way, Britannia Enterprise Park, Lichfield, Staffordshire, WS14 9TY Tel: (01543) 414223 Fax: (01543) 255538

▶ Daleside Group Shopfitters Ltd, Park Road East, Calverton, Nottingham, NG14 6LL Tel: 0115-965 6696 Fax: 0115-965 6328 E-mail: info@dalesidegroup.com

Dalton Joinery, Glendale Works, Dacre, Penrith, Cumbria, CA11 0HL Tel: (01768) 486684 Fax: (01768) 486684 E-mail: radjoinery@aol.com

Datone Joiners, Cemetery Road, Pudsey, West Yorkshire, LS28 7LW Tel: 0113-255 5532 Fax: 0113-255 5532

Delta Joiners Ltd, Brewsters Corner, Pendicke Street, Southam, Warwickshire, CV47 1PN Tel: (01926) 815253 Fax: (01926) 811040 E-mail: mail@deltajoiners.co.uk

Derek De'Ath Ltd, New Line, Bacup, Lancashire, OL13 9RY Tel: (01706) 879456 Fax: (01706) 878080 E-mail: office@derekd.co.uk

Design Research Shopfittings Ltd, 7 Cam Centre, Wilbury Way, Hitchin, Hertfordshire, SG4 0TW Tel: (01462) 420725 Fax: (01462) 421196

Design Woodworking, 7 Vernon Place, Northern Court, Nottingham, NG6 0DE Tel: 0115-977 0302

Dove Tail Joinery, 7 Field Barn Lane Industrial Estate, Field Barn Lane, Cropthorne, Pershore, Worcestershire, WR10 3LY Tel: (01386) 861123 Fax: (01386) 860975

E & R Joinery Ltd, Old Laughton Sawmills, Park Lane, Laughton, Lewes, East Sussex, BN8 6BP Tel: (01323) 811190 Fax: (01323) 811191 E-mail: sales@er-joinery.com

East Joinery, Unit 2 Willow Lane, Rugby, Warwickshire, CV22 5LX Tel: (01788) 568427 Fax: (01788) 574252 E-mail: r.ingram@ntlworld.com

Eckersley Joinery Ltd, Dawson Street, Swinton, Manchester, M27 4FJ Tel: 0161-794 5812 Fax: 0161-794 8586

Elmwood Joinery, Unit 9 Blackmore Park Road, Hanley Swan, Worcester, WR8 0EF Tel: (01684) 569097 Fax: (01684) 569097

Elvet Structures Ltd, Low Willington Industrial Estate, Willington, Crook, County Durham, DL15 0UH Tel: (01388) 747120 Fax: (01388) 745861 E-mail: gordan.pearson@elvetstructures.co.uk

Emerson Joinery, 50a Durham Road, Blackhill, Consett, County Durham, DH8 8NP Tel: (01207) 507805 Fax: (01207) 507805

England Joinery, Holehouse Lane, Glue Hill, Sturminster Newton, Dorset, DT10 2AA Tel: (01258) 472846 Fax: (01258) 472846 E-mail: info@englandjoinery.co.uk

Essex Woodcraft, Commerce Way, Colchester, CO2 8HJ Tel: (01206) 795464 Fax: (01206) 796596 E-mail: sales@essexwoodcraft.co.uk

Eves Joinery, Edwards Lane, Liverpool, L24 9HX Tel: 0151-486 1896 Fax: 0151-448 1548

F A North Carlton Ltd, 179 Carlton Hill, Carlton, Nottingham, NG4 1GZ Tel: 0115-987 2339 Fax: 0115-987 7504

Field Developments Hull Ltd, Staithes Road, Hull, HU12 8TJ Tel: (01482) 896240 Fax: (01482) 896510 E-mail: info@shopfituk.co.uk

Fineline Joinery, Littlemoor Road, Mark, Highbridge, Somerset, TA9 4NQ Tel: (01278) 641352 Fax: (01278) 641352

Firth Manufacturing Ltd, Hole House Lane, Stocksbridge, Sheffield, S36 1BS Tel: 0114-288 3298 Fax: 0114-288 4176 E-mail: info@firths.co.uk

Flacke Turner & James, Elm Street Lane, Cardiff, CF24 3QQ Tel: (029) 2049 2023 Fax: (029) 2049 2023

Flaxton Street Auto Spares, Fifield Indust Estate, Usworth Road, Longhill Industrial Estate, Hartlepool, Cleveland, TS25 1PD Tel: (01429) 260592 Fax: (01429) 273339

Fletcher Joinery, 261 Whessoe Road, Darlington, County Durham, DL3 0YL Tel: (01325) 357347 Fax: (01325) 357347 E-mail: enquiries@fletcherjoinery.co.uk

Forest Joinery Ltd, 47 Framfield Road, Uckfield, East Sussex, TN22 5AJ Tel: (01825) 766466 Fax: (01825) 766468 E-mail: info@forestjoineryltd.com

Forrest Contracts, Pleckgate Road, Blackburn, BB1 8QW Tel: (01254) 245122 Fax: (01254) 245259

D.E. Fox (Joinery) Ltd, Chapel Works, Bamforth St, Sheffield, S6 2HE Tel: 0114-234 8036 Fax: 0114-234 8036

Fryer's Ltd, Old Church Hall, Battle Green, Pelton Fell, Chester le Street, County Durham, DH2 2QW Tel: 0191-388 4914 Fax: 0191-388 4974 E-mail: fryersltd@aol.com

Fulton Joinery, 144 Fulton Road, Sheffield, S6 3JP Tel: 0114-234 7676

G Empson & Sons Ltd, Station Road, Gunness, Scunthorpe, South Humberside, DN15 8TR Tel: (01724) 782459 Fax: (01724) 783077

Gariff Construction Ltd, Village House, Eleventh Street, Trafford Park, Manchester, M17 1JF Tel: 0161-848 9983 Fax: 0161-848 9984 E-mail: leeunsworth@gariff.co.uk

I Fay, 93 Ridgeway, Sherborne, Dorset, DT9 6DB Tel: (01935) 814018 Fax: (01935) 816950

Linden Bauer Ltd, Mid Kent Business Park, Sortmill Road, Snodland, Kent, ME6 5UA Tel: (01634) 243137 Fax: (01634) 249306 E-mail: christian@lindenbauer.freeserve.co.uk

Magnet Ltd, 2a Hillbottom Road, Sands Industrial Estate, High Wycombe, Buckinghamshire, HP12 4HJ Tel: (01494) 445243 Fax: (01494) 538685 E-mail: highwycombe@magnettrade.co.uk

Masher Bros, 97-103 Florence Road, London, SE14 6QL Tel: (020) 8691 1632 Fax: (020) 8691 1496 E-mail: sales@masherbros.com

Michael Pepper Joinery, Ascot Drive, Derby, DE24 8GW Tel: (01332) 371133 Fax: (01332) 371132 E-mail: enquires@npeperjoinery.co.uk

Moss Joinery, 96 Leckhampton Road, Cheltenham, Gloucestershire, GL53 0BP Tel: (01242) 222622 Fax: (01242) 260265 E-mail: moss.cheltenham@kier.co.uk

Poldark Cabinet Makers, Woodbine Cottage, Gerrards Cross Road, Stoke Poges, Slough, SL2 4EL Tel: (01753) 662920 Fax: (01753) 662920

Quayside Joinery Ltd, 24 Ullswater Close, Kitty Brewster Industrial Estate, Blyth, Northumberland, NE24 4RG Tel: (01670) 540111 Fax: (01670) 360479

Romiley Glass & Windows Ltd, Green Lane, Romiley, Stockport, Cheshire, SK6 3JN Tel: 0161-494 0864 Fax: 0161-406 6290

Stanton Group, Laxcon Close, London, NW10 0TG Tel: (020) 8459 4640 Fax: (020) 8830 3377 E-mail: sales@stantongroup.co.uk

T Edson & Sons Ltd, Main Road, Plumtree, Nottingham, NG12 5NB Tel: 0115-937 2247 Fax: 0115-937 2486 E-mail: sales@edsons.co.uk

W France Successors, Luck Lane, Huddersfield, HD1 4QU Tel: (01484) 426032 Fax: (01484) 426032

William R Pinchin, Unit 22, Ravenswood Industrial Estate Shernhall Street, London, E17 9HQ Tel: (020) 8521 5590 Fax: (020) 8509 2070 E-mail: williamrpinchin@aol.com

Wratten Joinery, Aylesford Cottage, Guildford Road, Normandy, Guildford, Surrey, GU3 2AS Tel: (01483) 235324 Fax: (01483) 232131

SPECIALIST METALS, *See also headings for particular metals*

Aldruscilla, 8 Deer Park Road, London, SW19 3UU Tel: (020) 8543 8710 Fax: (020) 8543 0605 E-mail: metal@aldruscilla.co.uk

Power Metal Supplies, 2-4 Winton Square, Basingstoke, Hampshire, RG21 8EN Tel: (01256) 811821 Fax: (01256) 811824 E-mail: powermetal@ukonline.co.uk

SPECIALIST PACKING SERVICES

Blue Box Design Ltd, 2a Craig Leith Road, Broadleys Industrial Park, Stirling, FK7 7LQ Tel: (01786) 446098 Fax: (01786) 446097

Bottling & Packaging Enterprises, 2 Becklands Park Industrial Estate, York Road, Market Weighton, York, YO43 3GA Tel: (01430) 871990 Fax: (01430) 871999

▶ Reactive Solutions, 6 Lakeside Business Park, Pinfold Road, Thurmaston, Leicester, LE4 8AT Tel: 0116-260 3930 Fax: 0116-260 3931 E-mail: dean@reactive-solutions.com

SPECIALIST PATENT SERVICES

Forrester Ketley & Co., 105 Piccadilly, London, W1J 7NJ Tel: (020) 8889 6622 Fax: (020) 8881 1088 E-mail: fklondon@forresters.co.uk

▶ Innovation 2 Market Ltd, Kings Rd, The Docks, Swansea, SA1 8PH Tel: (01792) 295520 Fax: (01792) 295588 E-mail: sales@i2m-uk.com

Institute of Inventors, 19-23 Fosse Way, Ealing, London, W13 0BZ Tel: (020) 8998 3540

Intellectual Property Office, Patent Office, Concept House, Cardiff Road, Newport, Gwent, NP10 8QQ Tel: (0645) 500505 Fax: (01633) 817777 E-mail: enquiries@ipo.gov.uk

G.F. Redfern & Co., 7 Staple Inn, Holborn, London, WC1V 7QF Tel: (020) 7242 7680 Fax: (020) 7831 7957

Thomson Reuters (Scientific) Ltd, 77 Hatton Gardens, London, EC1N 8JS Tel: (020) 7433 4000 Fax: (020) 7433 4001 E-mail: ts.info.emea@thomson.com

SPECIALIST PRINTING

Color Communications Inc, Rowan House, 28 Queens Road, Hethersett, Norwich, NR9 3DB Tel: (01603) 813930 Fax: (01603) 813933
Flaps Envelopes Ltd, 70 Summer Lane, Birmingham, B19 3NG Tel: 0121-693 7377 Fax: 0121-693 0354
Global Link, Yew Tree House, Maerway Lane, Maer, Newcastle, Staffordshire, ST5 5EN Tel: (0870) 2201626 Fax: (01630) 647524 E-mail: sales@printingconsumables.com
Graphic Resources Group Ltd, Cedan House, 102 Kirkstall Road, Leeds, LS3 1JA Tel: 0113-228 8400 Fax: 0113 2284426
Hartham Press Ltd, 5a Marshgate Trading Estate, Hertford, SG13 7AB Tel: (01992) 589334 Fax: (01992) 554826 E-mail: sales@harthampress.com
Jones & Brooks Ltd, Duchess Street Industrial Estate, Shaw, Oldham, OL2 7UX Tel: (01706) 843121 Fax: (01706) 882985 E-mail: sales@jones-brooks.co.uk
Mersey Mirror Ltd, The Foundry, 36 Henry Street, Liverpool, L1 5BS Tel: 0151-709 7567 E-mail: post@merseymirror.com
Micro Laser Designs, 105 Midford Road, Bath, BA2 5RX Tel: (01225) 833266 Fax: (01225) 832200 E-mail: sales@mld.co.uk
PDQ Direct, Sureline House, Easting Close, Worthing, West Sussex, BN14 8HQ Tel: (01903) 282500 Fax: (01903) 282599 E-mail: sales@pdqdirect.co.uk
Print Consultants Ltd, Waterside Business Park, Waterside, Hadfield, Glossop, Derbyshire, SK13 1BE Tel: (01457) 860582 Fax: (01457) 856700 E-mail: sales@printconsultants.co.uk
Program Products (Services) Ltd, Enterprise House, Station Approach, West Byfleet, Surrey, KT14 6NJ Tel: (01932) 345566 Fax: (01932) 336333 E-mail: info@program-products.co.uk
UK Marketing (1998) & Co Ltd, 4 Wicklow St, Middlesbrough, Cleveland, TS1 4RG Tel: 01642 456789
Universal Press Ltd, Bridge House, Chilton Foliat, Hungerford, Berkshire, RG17 0TG Tel: (01488) 682328 Fax: (01488) 681899 E-mail: adviser@universal-press.co.uk

SPECIALIST SHEET METALWORKING

▶ Loughborough Sheet Metal Specialists, 2 Royal Way, Loughborough, Leicestershire, LE11 5XR Tel: (01509) 233874 Fax: (01509) 241277 E-mail: sales@lborosheetmetal.co.uk
Stockall Precision Sheet Metal Work Ltd, Unit 10 Wansdyke Business Centre, Oldfield Lane, Bath, BA2 3LY Tel: (01225) 422404 Fax: (01225) 422404 E-mail: sales@stockall.co.uk

SPECIALIST STATIONERY, *See Computer Stationery etc; also other headings for particular types sometimes listed under paper*

SPECIALIST VEHICLE TOWING EQUIPMENT FITTING SERVICES

Eagle Trailers, 241A Blandford Road, Hamworthy, Poole, Dorset, BH15 4AZ Tel: (01202) 671057 Fax: (01202) 671057
Edwards Brighouse Ltd, Vine Industrial Estate, Elland Road, Brookfoot, Brighouse, West Yorkshire, HD6 2QS Tel: (01484) 713335 Fax: (01484) 713335 E-mail: sales@edwardstowbars.co.uk
Gordon Love Trailers, 192 Bridge St West, Birmingham, B19 2YT Tel: 0121-359 6387 Fax: 0121-359 0317 E-mail: sales@wessex-trailers.co.uk
Harrogate Trailer & Towbar Centre, 6 Provincial Works, The Avenue, Harrogate, North Yorkshire, HG1 4QE Tel: (01423) 884962 Fax: (01423) 888953
R P Towing, Unit 1d Abercromby Avenue, High Wycombe, Buckinghamshire, HP12 3BW Tel: (01494) 528233 Fax: (01494) 638802 E-mail: rp.towing@ntlworld.com
Tow B Fabs, Unit 5-6 Kents Avenue, Hemel Hempstead, Hertfordshire, HP3 9XH Tel: (01442) 256764 Fax: (01442) 256764

SPECIALIST VIDEO EQUIPMENT HIRE

G H A Group Ltd, 9 Dean St, London, W1D 3RW Tel: (020) 7439 8705 Fax: (020) 7437 5880 E-mail: sales@ghagroup.co.uk
H Preston, 103 Worcester Road, Malvern, Worcestershire, WR14 1EP Tel: (01684) 575486 Fax: (01684) 575594 E-mail: jpreston@hpreston.co.uk
Midland Audio Visual Ltd, 210 New Road, Rubery, Rednal, Birmingham, B45 9JA Tel: 0121-453 3141 Fax: 0121-453 4626 E-mail: sales@midlandaudiovisual.co.uk
P E C Video Ltd, 65-66 Dean Street, London, W1D 4PL Tel: (020) 7437 4633 Fax: (020) 7025 1320 E-mail: sales@pec.co.uk
Regent Rentals, 1-1a Margaret Street, Coalville, Leicestershire, LE67 3LY Tel: (01530) 836611 Fax: (01530) 836611
T & R Rentals, 109 Southway, Westborough, Guildford, Surrey, GU2 8DQ Tel: (01483) 573029
Todd Herbert, Percys Lane, York, YO1 9TP Tel: (01904) 628676 Fax: (01904) 653328 E-mail: graham@htodd.co.uk
TT Visuals, 205 Royal College Street, London, NW1 0SG Tel: (020) 7419 9555 Fax: (020) 7419 9556 E-mail: ttvisuals@mac.com

SPECIALIST WELDING

A B R Specialists Welding Ltd, 2 Haines Street, West Bromwich, West Midlands, B70 7DS Tel: 0121-525 1319 Fax: 0121-525 1311 E-mail: enquiries@abrspecialistwelding.co.uk
▶ Wood Group Heavy Industrial Turbines, Unit D Worcester Trading Estate, Worcester, WR3 8HR Tel: (01905) 459570 Fax: (01905) 754651

SPECIALITY BEER

▶ Brune & Blond, PO Box 4143, Lichfield, Staffordshire, WS14 9WT Tel: (01543) 411458 E-mail: info@bruneandblond.co.uk
▶ Northern Ale Distributors, Holmcliffe Avenue, Bankfield Park, Huddersfield, HD4 7RN Tel: (01484) 302986 E-mail: sales@northernaledistributors.co.uk

SPECIALITY CHEMICALS

Blackburn Chemicals Ltd, Cunliffe Road, Whitebirk Industrial Estate, Blackburn, BB1 5SX Tel: (01254) 52222 Fax: (01254) 664224 E-mail: info@bbchem.co.uk
Cognis Performance Chemicals Ltd, Hardley, Hythe, Southampton, SO45 3ZG Tel: (023) 8089 4666 Fax: (023) 8024 3113 E-mail:
Conren Ltd, Astwith Close, Holmewood, Chesterfield, Derbyshire, S42 5UR Tel: (01246) 853900 Fax: (01246) 856348 E-mail: info@conren.com
Environmental & Remediation Services, Unit 11 12 Mercia Business Village, Torwood Close, Westwood Business Park, Coventry, CV4 8HX Tel: (024) 7642 6600 Fax: (024) 7642 6610 E-mail: ears@cel-international.com
Euram Chemicals Ltd, PO Box 346, Marlow, Buckinghamshire, SL7 1WH Tel: (01628) 472848 Fax: (01628) 890095 E-mail: sales@euramchemicals.co.uk
Glaxosmithkline, Harmire Road, Barnard Castle, County Durham, DL12 8DT Tel: (01833) 690600 Fax: (01833) 692300
Goldschmidt UK Ltd, Flimby Works, Main Road, Flimby, Maryport, Cumbria, CA15 8RP Tel: (01900) 813333 Fax: (01900) 815622
Honeywill & Stein Ltd, Times House, Throwley Way, Sutton, Surrey, SM1 4AF Tel: (020) 8770 3455 Fax: (020) 8770 3464 E-mail: schuelerm@honeywill.co.uk
▶ Ionic Solutions, Manningham Mills, Heaton Road, Bradford, West Yorkshire, BD9 4SH Tel: (01274) 549399 Fax: (0845) 6585599 E-mail: information@ionicsolutions.co.uk
Pentagon Chemicals, Dock Road, Northside, Workington, Cumbria, CA14 1JJ Tel: (01900) 604371 Fax: (01900) 66943 E-mail: sales@pentagonchemicals.co.uk
James Robinson Ltd, PO Box B3, Huddersfield, HD1 6BU Tel: (01484) 320500 Fax: (01484) 320300 E-mail: sales@james-robinson.ltd.uk
Scott Bader Co. Ltd, Wollaston Hall, Wollaston, Wellingborough, Northamptonshire, NN29 7RL Tel: (01933) 663100 Fax: (01933) 663028 E-mail: sales@scottbader.com
Shepherd Widnes Ltd, Moss Bank Road, Widnes, Cheshire, WA8 0RU Tel: 0151-424 9156 Fax: 0151-495 1446 E-mail: sales@shepwidnes.co.uk
Venchem Ltd, Knotts Lane, Colne, Lancashire, BB8 8AA Tel: (01282) 861198 Fax: (01282) 860020 E-mail: sales@venchem.co.uk

SPECIALITY FIBRE TOPS

Laycock International Ltd, Stanley Mills, Whitley Street, Bingley, West Yorkshire, BD16 4JH Tel: (01274) 562563 Fax: (01274) 562823 E-mail: mohair@legend.co.uk

SPECIALITY GLASS

Art Glass Ltd, Ellis Ashton Street, Liverpool, L36 6BN Tel: 0151-489 2214 Fax: 0151-489 2214 E-mail: sales@artglass.co.uk
C G I International Ltd, International House, Millfield Lane, Haydock, St. Helens, Merseyside, WA11 9GA Tel: (01942) 710720 Fax: (01942) 710730 E-mail: info@cgii.co.uk
Walker Engineering (Essex) Ltd, Unit 2A North Hill Business Park, North Hill, Horndon-On-The-Hill, Stanford-Le-Hope, Essex, SS17 8QA Tel: (01375) 361428 Fax: (01375) 361428 E-mail: walkereng@btconnect.com

SPECIALITY TEA

Steenbergs Organic, 1 Hallikeld Close, Melmerby, Ripon, North Yorkshire, HG4 5GZ Tel: (01765) 640101 Fax: (01765) 640101 E-mail: enquiriesl@steenbergs.co.uk

SPECIFIED METAL FABRICATION

Acomb Engineering Ltd, Catfoss, Hull, HU11 5SP Tel: (01964) 542724 Fax: (01964) 543939
Caithness Creels Ltd, 17c Airport Industrial Estate, Wick Airport, Wick, Caithness, KW1 4QS Tel: (01955) 602979 Fax: (01955) 602993
Foyle Vent Fabrications, Blighs Lane, Londonderry, BT48 9PJ Tel: (028) 7127 9494 Fax: (028) 7127 9495
L R Engineering, Milton Farm Workshop, West End Gardens, Fairford, Gloucestershire, GL7 4JB Tel: (01285) 713163 Fax: (01285) 713632 E-mail: lrengineering@btconnect.com
Sheffield Art Metal Co., Charter Works, 20 Hodgson Street, Sheffield, S3 7WQ Tel: 0114-244 4444 Fax: 0114-270 1549 E-mail: sheff.artmetal@btconnect.com
Underhill Building Services, Valley Road, Plymouth, PL7 1RF Tel: (01752) 283280 Fax: (01752) 344410

SPECTACLE CASES

▶ Roope Robert Opticians Ltd, 20 George Street, St. Albans, Hertfordshire, AL3 4ES Tel: (01727) 857798 E-mail: robert@roope.co.uk

SPECTACLE FRAMES

Brenal Optical Services, Great Western Street, Wednesbury, West Midlands, WS10 7LL Tel: 0121-556 1506 Fax: 0121-556 9792
Oliver Goldsmith Eyewear Ltd, The Studio, St Nicholas Close, Elstree, Borehamwood, Hertfordshire, WD6 3EW Tel: (020) 8207 5153 Fax: (020) 8207 2747 E-mail: oliver@ogspecs.force9.net
Pennine Optical Group Ltd, Pennine House, Manchester Road, Stockport, Cheshire, SK4 1TX Tel: 0161-477 8964 Fax: 0161-477 6949 E-mail: pennine@pog.co.uk
Wyvern Optical Ltd, 87 Narborough Road, Leicester, LE3 0LF Tel: 0116-254 8431 E-mail: wyvern1947@aol.com

SPECTACLE LENSES

Select Specs Ltd, PO Box 2, Westgate-on-Sea, Kent, CT8 8RX Tel: (01843) 835568 E-mail: reg1@selectspecs.com

SPECTACLES, READING GLASSES, READY-MADE

Besafe Protective Clothing Ltd, Somerton Works, Prince Avenue, Westcliff-on-Sea, Essex, SS0 0ER Tel: (01702) 333344 Fax: (01702) 433590 E-mail: sales@besafe.co.uk
Parmelee Ltd, Middlemore Lane West, Aldridge, Walsall, WS9 8BH Tel: (01922) 457421 Fax: (01922) 473275 E-mail: sales@parmelee-safety.com

SPECTROCHEMICAL ANALYSERS

Datech Scientific Ltd, Unit 13 Step Business Centre, Wortley Road, Deepcar, Sheffield, S36 2UH Tel: (0870) 7469810 Fax: (0870) 7469811E-mail: sales@datech-scientific.co.uk

SPECTROMETER ACCESSORIES/COMPONENTS

European Spectrometry Systems, Genesis House, Denton Drive, Northwich, Cheshire, CW9 7LU Tel: (01606) 49400 Fax: (01606) 330937 E-mail: service@essco.u-net.com

SPECTROMETER TESTING SERVICES INCLUDING ON SITE

Mass Spec UK Ltd, Regal House, Highfield Street, Oldham, OL9 6DT Tel: 0161-785 0828 Fax: 0161-785 0838 E-mail: service@massspecuk.ltd.uk

SPECTROMETERS, *See also headings for particular types*

Astranet Systems Ltd, PO Box 734, Cambridge, CB2 5PE Tel: (01223) 872197 Fax: (01223) 872197 E-mail: info@astranetsystems.com
European Spectrometry Systems, Genesis House, Denton Drive, Northwich, Cheshire, CW9 7LU Tel: (01606) 49400 Fax: (01606) 330937 E-mail: service@essco.u-net.com

SPECTROPHOTOMETER ACCESSORIES

Optiglass Ltd, 52-54 Fowler Road, Hainault, Ilford, Essex, IG6 3UT Tel: (020) 8500 1264 Fax: (020) 8500 1955 E-mail: info@optiglass.co.uk

SPECTROPHOTOMETER CELLS

Chandos Intercontinental, 6 St Anns Close, Chapel-en-le-Frith, High Peak, Derbyshire, SK23 9SG Tel: (01298) 814949 Fax: (01298) 814949 E-mail: chandos6@highpeak14.freeserve.co.uk

SPECTROPHOTOMETERS, *See also headings for particular types*

Astranet Systems Ltd, PO Box 734, Cambridge, CB2 5PE Tel: (01223) 872197 Fax: (01223) 872197 E-mail: info@astranetsystems.com
X-Rite Ltd, The Acumen Centre, First Avenue, Poynton, Stockport, Cheshire, SK12 1FJ Tel: (01625) 871100 Fax: (01625) 871444

SPECTROPHOTOMETRY EQUIPMENT

Cecil Instruments Ltd, Cambridge Road Industrial Estate, Milton, Cambridge, CB24 6AZ Tel: (01223) 420821 Fax: (01223) 420475 E-mail: info@cecilinstruments.com

SPECTROSCOPES

Paton Hawksley Education Ltd, 59 Wellsway, Keynsham, Bristol, BS31 1PG Tel: 0117-986 2364 Fax: 0117-986 8285

SPECTRUM ANALYSERS

Aeroflex Co. Ltd, Long Acres House, 6 Hills Way, Stevenage, Hertfordshire, SG1 2AN Tel: (01438) 742200 Fax: (01438) 727601 E-mail: deb.stockman@ifrsys.com
Bentham Instruments Ltd, 2 Boulton Road, Reading, RG2 0NH Tel: 0118-975 1355 Fax: 0118-931 2971 E-mail: sales@bentham.co.uk
Huntleigh Healthcare Ltd, 35 Portmanmoor Road Industrial Estate, East Moors, Cardiff, CF24 5HN Tel: (029) 2048 5885 Fax: (029) 2049 2520 E-mail: info@huntleigh-diagnostics.co.uk

SPEECH RECOGNITION COMPUTER SOFTWARE DEVELOPMENT

Philips Speech Processing, 8 The Courtyards, Wyncolls Road, Severalls Industrial Park, Colchester, CO4 9PE Tel: (01206) 755755 Fax: (01206) 755888 E-mail: info@speech.philips.com

SPEECH RECOGNITION SOFTWARE

▶ Cameo It, 5 Elizabeth Drive, Wantage, Oxfordshire, OX12 9YA Tel: (01235) 768660 Fax: (01235) 768660
Zest Computing Ltd, Summerhayes House, Croxeaston, Newbury, Berkshire, RG20 9QF Tel: (01635) 250559 Fax: (01635) 255337 E-mail: richard.holt@zestcomputing.com

SPEED BOATS

▶ Atlantic Focus, 17 Leachkin Avenue, Inverness, IV3 8LH Tel: 01463 712638 E-mail: info@atlanticfocus.co.uk
▶ Network Conwy, Conwy Marina, Ellis Way, Conwy, Gwynedd, LL32 8GU Tel: (01492) 580001 Fax: (01492) 580004 E-mail: info@nybconwy.co.uk
▶ Sailcats, 2 Furzebeam Row, Torrington, Devon, EX38 8DH Tel: (01805) 624489 E-mail: info@sailcats.co.uk

SPEEDOMETER CABLES

Speedograph Ltd, 104 Rolleston Drive, Arnold, Nottingham, NG5 7JR Tel: 0115-926 4235 Fax: 0115-920 9912 E-mail: info@speedograph-richfield.co.uk

SPEEDOMETERS

Siemans V D O, 36 Gravelly Industrial Park, Birmingham, B24 8TA Tel: 0121-326 1234 Fax: 0121-326 1299

SPHERICAL BEARINGS

F K F UK Ltd, Strode Road, Clevedon, Avon, BS21 6QQ Tel: (01275) 876021 Fax: (01275) 878480 E-mail: mail@fkf.co.uk
N M B Minebea UK Ltd, Doddington Road, Lincoln, LN6 3RA Tel: (01522) 500933 Fax: (01522) 500975
Silvertown UK Ltd, Horninglow Road, Burton-on-Trent, Staffordshire, DE13 0SN Tel: (01283) 510510 Fax: (01283) 510052 E-mail: sales.enq@silvertown.co.uk
Tuthill Linkage Ltd, Unit 41 Suttons Industrial Park, Reading, RG6 1AZ Tel: 0118-929 9900 Fax: 0118-966 5978 E-mail: dneave@tuthill.com

SPHEROIDAL GRAPHITE (SG) IRON CASTINGS

Castings plc, Lichfield Road, Brownhills, Walsall, WS8 6JZ Tel: (01543) 374341 Fax: (01543) 377483 E-mail: mail@castings.plc.uk
Cerdic Foundries Ltd, Beeching Close, Chard, Somerset, TA20 1BB Tel: (01460) 64301 Fax: (01460) 63961 E-mail: sales@cerdicfoundries.co.uk
H Downs & Sons Huddersfield Ltd, Peacock Works, Leeds Road, Huddersfield, HD2 1XR Tel: (01484) 428203 Fax: (01484) 546993 E-mail: sales@hdowns.co.uk
Hillsyde Foundry (Staffordshire) Ltd, Apedale Works, Rowhurst Industrial Estate, Chesterton, Newcastle, Staffordshire, ST5 6BD Tel: (01782) 564411 Fax: (01782) 562546 E-mail: sales@hillsyde.com
Incanite Foundries Ltd, Solar Works, Cornwall Road, Smethwick, West Midlands, B66 2JR Tel: 0121-565 2882 Fax: 0121-555 5190 E-mail: sales@incanite.co.uk
International Meehanite Metal Co. Ltd, 38 Albert Road North, Reigate, Surrey, RH2 9EH Tel: (01737) 244786 Fax: (01737) 226644 E-mail: meehaniteltd@btconnect.com
Jennings Winch & Foundry Co. Ltd, Tatham Street, Sunderland, SR1 2AG Tel: 0191-567 4408 Fax: 0191-510 1549 E-mail: jwf.co.ltd@aol.com
John Rhodes & Son Ltd, Hightown Foundry, Rhodes Street, Castleford, West Yorkshire, WF10 5LN Tel: (01977) 552324 Fax: (01977) 668011E-mail: richardshaw@johnrhodes.co.uk
Joseph & Jesse Siddons Ltd, Howard Street, Hill Top, West Bromwich, West Midlands, B70 0TB Tel: 0121-556 0218 Fax: 0121-556 3843 E-mail: info@jjsiddons.co.uk
Masstech, 9 Valley Road, Markfield, Leicestershire, LE67 9QS Tel: (01530) 244467 Fax: (01530) 244467 E-mail: masstech@bigfoot.com
Rhodes Nicholson Ltd, Emerald Ironworks, Emerald Street, Huddersfield, HD1 6BY Tel: (01484) 537383 Fax: (01484) 542931 E-mail: gerry@rhodes-nicholson.co.uk
Russell Castings Ltd, Bonchurch Street, Leicester, LE3 5EP Tel: 0116-299 2000 Fax: 0116-299 8844 E-mail: general@russellductile.co.uk
T H Dick & Co Ltd, Church Row, Cleveland St, Hull, HU8 7BD Tel: (01482) 329652 Fax: (01482) 589986E-mail: info@thdick.co.uk
Vald Birn (UK) Ltd, Cambois, Blyth, Northumberland, NE24 1SW Tel: (01670) 818111 Fax: (01670) 855511 E-mail: sales@valdbirn.co.uk

SPHYGMOMANOMETERS

A C Cossor & Son Surgical Ltd, Accoson Works, Vale Road, London, N4 1PS Tel: (020) 8800 1172 Fax: (020) 8809 5170 E-mail: accoson@accoson.com

SPIDER ACCESS PLATFORMS

Max Access Ltd, Unit 17 Bankside, Station Approach, Kidlington, Oxfordshire, OX5 1JE Tel: (01865) 373566 Fax: (01865) 378021 E-mail: info@maxaccess.co.uk

SPIN DRYERS

Merloni Domestic Appliances Ltd, Merloni Ho, 3 Cowley Business Pk, High St, Cowley, Uxbridge, Middx, UB8 2AD Tel: (01895) 858200 Fax: (01895) 858270

SPIN GALVANISING

▶ Yorkshire Spin Galvanising Ltd, Unit 152, B M K Industrial Estate, Wakefield Road, Liversedge, West Yorkshire, WF15 6BS Tel: (01924) 412317 Fax: (01924) 412318 E-mail: ysgr@aol.com

SPINDLE BALL BEARINGS

New Hampshire Ball Bearings (Europe), Suite 2.2, Doncastle House, Doncastle Road, Bracknell, Berkshire, RG12 8PE Tel: (01344) 308888 Fax: (01344) 485522

SPINDLE REBUILDING

S K F Spindle Service Centre (U K) Ltd, 8 Dencora Way, Sundon Business Park, Luton, LU3 3HP Tel: (01582) 494674 Fax: (01582) 494808 E-mail: skfspindleserviceuk@skf.com
▶ Spindle Services, Unit 9-10 Central City Industrial Estate, Red Lane, Coventry, CV6 5RY Tel: (024) 7663 7771 Fax: (024) 7663 7772 E-mail: simon.emms@btconnect.com
Technova Precision, Unit 8a Paragon Way, Bayton Road Industrial Estate, Coventry, CV7 9QS Tel: (024) 7636 7246 Fax: (024) 7636 1979 E-mail: will@technovaprecision.com

SPINDLES, MACHINE TOOL

▶ Spindle Services, Unit 9-10 Central City Industrial Estate, Red Lane, Coventry, CV6 5RY Tel: (024) 7663 7771 Fax: (024) 7663 7772 E-mail: simon.emms@btconnect.com

SPINNING MACHINERY

Allertex Ltd, Paradise Street, Bradford, West Yorkshire, BD1 2HP Tel: (01274) 723783 Fax: (01274) 728267 E-mail: info@allertex.co.uk

SPIRAL BEVEL GEARS

▶ Freedom Engineering Co. Ltd, 34 Springfield Way, Anlaby, Hull, HU10 6RJ Tel: (01482) 565566 Fax: (01482) 500826 E-mail: mike@freedomgears.fsnet.co.uk
Guest Gear Services, Higham Mead, Higham Road, Chesham, Buckinghamshire, HP5 2AF Tel: (01494) 794667 Fax: (01494) 794668 E-mail: guestgears@yahoo.com
Northern Tool & Gear Co. Ltd, John St West, Arbroath, Angus, DD11 1RT Tel: (01241) 872626 Fax: (01241) 870040 E-mail: general@ntgear.co.uk

SPIRAL COOLERS

▶ European Marine & Machinery Agencies, Nutsey House, Nutsey Lane, Totton, Southampton, SO40 3NB Tel: (023) 8058 0020 Fax: (023) 8058 0021 E-mail: sales@europeanmarine.co.uk

SPIRAL PAPER TUBE CONVERTING MACHINERY

C Perkin Ltd, 6 Shaw Cross Court, Horace Waller V C Parade, Shaw Cross Business Park, Dewsbury, West Yorkshire, WF12 7RF Tel: (01924) 439449 Fax: (01924) 438908 E-mail: info@cperkin.com

SPIRAL STAIRCASES

Albion Design of Cambridge Ltd, 131 Mereside, Soham, Ely, Cambridgeshire, CB7 5EG Tel: (01223) 836128 Fax: (01353) 722567 E-mail: sales@albionspirals.co.uk
Blanc De Bierges, Eastrea Road, Whittlesey, Peterborough, PE7 2AG Tel: (01733) 202566 Fax: (01733) 205405 E-mail: sales@blancdebierges.com
Bradfabs Ltd, 61A Plane Trees Road, Laisterdyke, Bradford, West Yorkshire, BD4 8AE Tel: (01274) 400401 Fax: (01274) 773335 E-mail: sales@bradfabs.co.uk
Cambridge Structures Ltd, 2 Huntingdon Street, St. Neots, Cambridgeshire, PE19 1BG Tel: (01480) 477700 Fax: (01480) 477766 E-mail: contact@cambridgestructures.com
Cornish Stairways Ltd, Kernick Industrial Estate, Penryn, Cornwall, TR10 9DQ Tel: (01326) 374662 Fax: (01326) 376596 E-mail: mikejordan@cornishstairways.co.uk
Hough Engineering, 138A High Street, Silverdale, Newcastle, Staffordshire, ST5 6LX Tel: (01782) 633984 Fax: (01782) 715987 E-mail: houghengineering@supnet.com
Humber Joiners Ltd, Stepney Lane, Hull, HU5 1HX Tel: (01482) 341954 Fax: (01482) 449516
J & B Novak Metalcraft Ltd, White Cottage Farm, Lucas Green Road, West End, Woking, Surrey, GU24 9LZ Tel: (01483) 474979 Fax: (01483) 472487
J F Payne, Enterprise House, Herbert Road, Newport, Gwent, NP19 7BH Tel: (01633) 223959 Fax: (01633) 266927 E-mail: jfp@ukonline.co.uk
Lewes Design Contracts Ltd, The Mill, Glynde, Lewes, East Sussex, BN8 6SS Tel: (01273) 858341 Fax: (01273) 858200 E-mail: info@spiralstairs.co.uk
R M J Alloys Ltd, 48 Bayton Road, Exhall, Coventry, CV7 9EJ Tel: (024) 7636 7508 Fax: (024) 7636 0280 E-mail: sales@rmjalloys.co.uk
Vista Products, 219 Kings Road, Tyseley, Birmingham, B11 2AA Tel: 0121-707 3242 Fax: 0121-706 5666
Weland Ltd, Hardley Industrial Estate, Hardley, Southampton, SO45 3NQ Tel: (023) 8084 9747 Fax: (023) 8084 9054 E-mail: info@weland.co.uk

SPIRAL WOUND DUCTING

Alpha Tube Co., Tameside Works, Park Road, Dukinfield, Cheshire, SK16 5PT Tel: 0161-339 8901 Fax: 0161-343 1750 E-mail: alpha@alphatube.freeserve.co.uk
Contract Components, Unit 37 Pitcliffe Way, Bradford, West Yorkshire, BD5 7SG Tel: (01274) 721982 Fax: (01274) 306876 E-mail: sales@cclveloduct.co.uk
Hotchkiss Air Supply (HAS), Heath Mill Road, Wombourne, Wolverhampton, WV5 8AP Tel: (01902) 895161 Fax: (01902) 892045 E-mail: info@hotchkissairsupply.co.uk
Lindab Ltd, Unit 9 - 10 Carousel Way, Riverside Business Park, Northampton, NN3 9HG Tel: (01604) 788350 Fax: (01604) 788351
West Engineering Ltd, Olympus Close, Ipswich, IP1 5LN Tel: (01473) 467930 Fax: (01473) 467931 E-mail: info@westengineering.co.uk

SPIRAL WOUND GASKETS

Nicholsons Sealing Technologies Ltd, Hamsterley, Newcastle upon Tyne, NE17 7SX Tel: (01207) 560505 Fax: (01207) 561004 E-mail: info@nicholsons.co.uk

SPIRAL WOUND PRODUCTS,

See also Ducting, Spiral Wound: also other headings for particular types

J F B Cores Ltd, 7 Boleyn Court, Manor Park, Runcorn, Cheshire, WA7 1SR Tel: (01928) 571812 Fax: (01928) 571813 E-mail: sales@cores.co.uk

SPIRIT GLASSES

▶ Dillon's Ltd, Hardres Court, Canterbury, Kent, CT4 6EN Tel: (01227) 700236 E-mail: info@dillonsspirits.com

SPIRIT LEVELS

▶ P R Engineering Ltd, 6a Aizlewood Road, Sheffield, S8 0YX Tel: 0114-250 9077 E-mail: sales@laser-level.co.uk
Sebor Absinth Ltd, PO Box 1111, Kingston Upon Thames, Surrey, KT1 4YX Tel: (020) 8943 9526 Fax: (020) 8977 3507 E-mail: info@seborabsinth.com

SPIRIT MEASURE DISPENSERS

Aubic Bar Supplies, Unit 7, Dominion Way, Rustington, Littlehampton, West Sussex, BN16 3HQ Tel: (01903) 775002 Fax: (01903) 775112 E-mail: info@aubic.co.uk
Centek International, Unit 30 Lawson Hunt Industrial Park, Guildford Road, Broadbridge Heath, Horsham, West Sussex, RH12 3JR Tel: (01403) 263323 Fax: (01403) 270651 E-mail: info@nuplas.co.uk
▶ I M I Cornelius (UK) Ltd, Rawson Spring Way, Sheffield, S6 1PG Tel: 0114-285 2345 Fax: 0114-285 3087 E-mail: gaskellsales@corneliusuk.com

SPLASH PROOF ELECTRIC MOTORS

Franklin Electric (Henley), Treetops House, Gillotts Lane, Henley-On-Thames, Oxfordshire, RG9 1PT Tel: (01491) 579118 Fax: (01491) 412211 E-mail: fesales@acdcsystems.com
Powertronic Drive Systems Ltd, Treetops House, Gillotts Lane, Henley-On-Thames, Oxfordshire, RG9 1PT Tel: (01491) 579118 Fax: (01491) 412211 E-mail: sales@powertronic.co.uk

SPLINE CUTTING SERVICES

▶ Freedom Engineering Co. Ltd, 34 Springfield Way, Anlaby, Hull, HU10 6RJ Tel: (01482) 565566 Fax: (01482) 500826 E-mail: mike@freedomgears.fsnet.co.uk

SPLINE GAUGES

Frenco International, 11 Fortnum Close, Birmingham, B33 0LG Tel: 0121-789 7895 Fax: 0121-789 7050 E-mail: sales@frenco.co.uk
Precision Technologies International Ltd, 22 Mariner, Tamworth, Staffordshire, B79 7UL Tel: (01827) 54371 Fax: (01827) 310406 E-mail: sales@ptiltd.co.uk

SPLINED GEAR SHAFTS

Comma Tech Ltd, Carlyon Road, Atherstone, Warwickshire, CV9 1LW Tel: (01827) 714741 Fax: (01827) 718943 E-mail: sales@commatech.co.uk

SPLIT RINGS

J P Olives Ltd, 31a Heming Road, Redditch, Worcestershire, B98 0DH Tel: (01527) 516600 Fax: (01527) 516611 E-mail: sales@jpolives.co.uk

SPONGE RUBBER PRODUCTS

Atlantic Rubber & Plastic Ltd, 6 St. Annes Road, Willenhall, West Midlands, WV13 1ED Tel: (01902) 634400 Fax: 01902 634413 E-mail: hintons@blueyonder.co.uk
Fabprene Ltd, Broadway, Globe Lane Industrial Estate, Dukinfield, Cheshire, SK16 4UU Tel: 0161-342 6902 Fax: 0161-342 6903 E-mail: sales@fabprene.co.uk

SPONGE RUBBER STRIPS

Atlantic Rubber & Plastic Ltd, 6 St. Annes Road, Willenhall, West Midlands, WV13 1ED Tel: (01902) 634400 Fax: 01902 634413 E-mail: hintons@blueyonder.co.uk

SPOON OR FORK BLANKS

Nickel Blanks Co. Ltd, 6 Smithfield, Sheffield, S3 7AR Tel: 0114-272 5792 Fax: 0114-276 8519 E-mail: shefcutler@aol.com

SPOONS OR FORKS

M & G Catering, 69/79 Hadfield Street, Old Trafford, Manchester, M16 9FE Tel: 0161-848 0959 Fax: 0161-848 0959 E-mail: mg-catering@ntlworld.com

SPORT AND LEISURE PROPERTY INSURANCE

▶ Alan Boswell, High Street, Attleborough, Norfolk, NR17 2EH Tel: (01953) 455600 Fax: (01953) 456400 E-mail: insurance@alanboswell.co.uk

SPORTS AWARD MEDALS

H.B. Sale Ltd, 390 Summer Lane, Birmingham, B19 3PN Tel: 0121-236 5661 Fax: 0121-233 3817

SPORTS BAGS

A W Bag Manufacturers, 84 Silk Street, Manchester, M4 6BJ Tel: 0161-205 6661 Fax: 0161-205 6661
Chilham Darts, Station Approach, Chilham, Canterbury, Kent, CT4 8EG Tel: (01227) 730310 Fax: (01227) 730630
Freedom, Gate Lane, Sutton Coldfield, West Midlands, B73 5TX Tel: 0121-355 8668 Fax: 0121-355 2113 E-mail: sales@swimcap.com
Halbro Sportswear Ltd, Chorley New Road, Horwich, Bolton, BL6 7JG Tel: (01204) 696476 Fax: (01204) 699479 E-mail: sales@halbro.com
M C Products, Unit 1-2 Yardley Centre, Yardley Road, Knowsley Industrial Park, Liverpool, L33 7SS Tel: 0151-548 0144 Fax: 0151-549 2283 E-mail: sales@mcproducts.co.uk
M1 Sport Ltd, Phoenix House, Waller Avenue, Luton, LU4 9RS Tel: (01582) 580000 Fax: (01582) 580040
Mapat Group Ltd, Unit 6, Mowat Trading Estate, Sandon Road, Watford, WD24 7UZ Tel: (01923) 255525 Fax: (01923) 250737
E. Skorski & Son Ltd, Cortress House, Julia Street, Strangeways, Manchester, M3 1DQ Tel: 0161-831 7017 Fax: 0161-832 7097 E-mail: mark@skorski.freeserve.co.uk

SPORTS CLOTHING FABRICS

A E Mccandless & Co. Ltd, 23 Bishop Street, Londonderry, BT48 6PR Tel: (028) 7136 2071 Fax: (028) 7126 8996

Alder Sportswear Ltd, Alder, Lewdown, Okehampton, Devon, EX20 4PJ Tel: (01566) 783444 Fax: (01566) 783483

Armley Fashions, Wesley Road, Leeds, LS12 1UH Tel: (07812) 766023 Fax: 0113-263 7053

Clarkson Knitting Ltd, Western Industrial Estate, Lon-Y-Llyn, Caerphilly, Mid Glamorgan, CF83 1XJ Tel: (029) 2086 1411 Fax: (029) 2086 0127 E-mail: paulslevin@clarksonknitting.com

Cloverbrook, Peel Mill, Gannow Lane, Burnley, Lancashire, BB12 6JJ Tel: (01282) 712000 Fax: (01282) 457723 E-mail: info@cloverbrook.co.uk

Newrooss Impex Ltd, New Skopes House, 2 Cross Green Garth, Cross Green Industrial Estate, Leeds, LS9 0SF Tel: 0113-240 2211 Fax: 0113-248 9544 E-mail: sales@skopes.com

Nicoll & Jack Ltd, Locarno Works, Brown Street, Dundee, DD1 5EE Tel: (01382) 224398 Fax: (01382) 228591

Roch Valley Manufacturing Ltd, 157 Glodwick Road, Oldham, OL4 1AR Tel: 0161-633 2536 Fax: 0161-627 5652

Sports Express GWCC, 75 Commercial Road, Oldgate, London, E1 1RD Tel: (020) 7377 5037 Fax: (020) 7247 1951

Todd & Reed, 32a Lily Road, London, E17 8HY Tel: (020) 8558 0722 Fax: (020) 8558 0722

Trophy Sportswear, 7a Forest La, London, E15 1HA Tel: (020) 8534 1687

UK Sportgear International Ltd, UK House, Freer Street, Nuneaton, Warwickshire, CV11 4PR Tel: (0870) 4031400 Fax: (0870) 4031399 E-mail: info@ukgear.com

SPORTS CLOTHING, PROTECTIVE

Central Safety Ltd, 30 North Street Industrial Estate, Droitwich, Worcestershire, WR9 8JB Tel: (01905) 774737 Fax: (01905) 796356

SPORTS CLOTHING, SURFING

▶ Blue Skin, Blue Skin, Hoxton Works, 128 Hoxton Street, London N1 6SH, London, United Kingdom, N1 6SH Tel: 020 7012 1720 E-mail: info@blueskin.com

▶ Channel Sports Boats, PO Box 872, Canterbury, Kent, CT4 6WA Tel: (01227) 831611 Fax: (01227) 831671 E-mail: sales@channel-sportsboats.com

▶ DevilWear Ltd, The Fashion House, Seaside Lane, Easington Colliery, Peterlee, County Durham, SR8 3PF Tel: (0870) 3217353 Fax: (0870) 7652757 E-mail: karl@devilwear.co.uk

▶ Ski Rack Surfboard Car Roof Rack Cheap Car Roof Rack, 15 Ambridge Close, Northampton, NN4 9RW Tel: (01604) 710106 E-mail: sales@rackinabag.co.uk

▶ The Wetsuit Factory, 24 Bay Tree Hill, Liskeard, Cornwall, PL14 4BG Tel: (01579) 343573 Fax: (01579) 342062 E-mail: sales@thewetsuitfactory.com

SPORTS CLOTHING, SWIMWEAR, LADIES'

▶ David Frank Hair & Beauty, 18 Dalton Square, Lancaster, LA1 1PL Tel: (01524) 843434 Fax:

▶ Rival, 116 West Street, Faversham, Kent, ME13 7JB Tel: (01795) 590473 E-mail: sales@rivaldancewear.co.uk

SPORTS CLOTHING, TRAINING TOPS, LADIES'

▶ Rival, 116 West Street, Faversham, Kent, ME13 7JB Tel: (01795) 590473 E-mail: sales@rivaldancewear.co.uk

SPORTS CLOTHING/FOOTWEAR WHOLESALE DISTRIBUTORS OR AGENTS

▶ 1stUniversal Trading Ltd, 86 Victoria Road, Stoke-on-Trent, ST4 2JX Tel: (01782) 763700 Fax: (01782) 763636 E-mail: universalfirst@hotmail.co.uk

28 Black London, Unit 3A, Trafalgar Business Park, Broughton Lane, Manchester, M8 9TZ Tel: 0161-839 2224 Fax: 0161-839 6661

Be That Body, Christs Hospital Sports Centre, Christs Hospital, Horsham, West Sussex, RH13 0YP Tel: (023) 8025 1125 E-mail: enquiries@bethatbody.com

▶ Beamshape Rhinosports, Rotherside Road, Eckington, Sheffield, S21 4HL Tel: 0114-276 2233 E-mail: info@rhinosports.co.uk

Climax Pro Squash, 3 St. Marys Drive, Greenfield, Oldham, OL3 7DT Tel: (01457) 829966 E-mail: headoffice@cxprosport.com

Explosive Fibres Direct Ltd, Middlewood House, North Hill, Launceston, Cornwall, PL15 7NN Tel: (01566) 782973 Fax: 01566 782973

Falcon Sportswear Ltd, Falcon House, Hutson Street, Bradford, West Yorkshire, BD5 7LZ Tel: (01274) 306186 Fax: (01274) 390937 E-mail: email@falconsports.co.uk

Foster Group UK Ltd, Unit 41 Golds Nurseries Business Park, Jenkins Drive, Elsenham, Bishop's Stortford, Hertfordshire, CM22 6JX Tel: (01279) 815596 Fax: (01279) 815526 E-mail: sales@fostergroup.co.uk

▶ Front Runner, 144-146 Chorley Old Road, Bolton, BL1 3AT Tel: (01204) 361837 Fax: (01204) 361837

▶ Gymphlex Ltd, Stamford Buildings, Stamford Street, Leicester, LE1 6NJ Tel: 0116-255 6326 Fax: 0116-247 1215 E-mail: enquiries@gymphlex.co.uk

Halbro Sportswear Ltd, Chorley New Road, Horwich, Bolton, BL6 7JG Tel: (01204) 696476 Fax: (01204) 699479 E-mail: sales@halbro.com

J. & N. Herz Ltd, Broadstone House, Broadstone Road, Reddish, Stockport, Cheshire, SK5 7DL Tel: 0161-443 3030 Fax: 0161-443 0345 E-mail: jherz@herz.co.uk

▶ Image Scotland Ltd, Fisherrow Industrial Estate, Newhailes Road, Musselburgh, Midlothian, EH21 6RU Tel: 0131-665 1414 Fax: 0131-665 1919 E-mail: sales@imagescotland.com

▶ Kings Road Sporting Club Ltd, 40-42 Kings Road, London, SW3 4UD Tel: (020) 7589 5418

▶ Leisurewear-actecs, 6 Penhill Industrail Park, Beaumont Road, Banbury, Oxon, OX16 1RW Tel: (01295) 703165 Fax: (01295) 255059 E-mail: sales@actecs.co.uk

William Lindop Ltd, PO Box 46, Manchester, M60 3DP Tel: 0161-832 9467 Fax: 0161-833 1961 E-mail: info@lindopsports.co.uk

Manchester Sports Ltd, Unit G5, Newton Business Park, Talbot Road, Hyde, Cheshire, SK14 4UQ Tel: 0161-366 1212 Fax: 0161-366 1177 E-mail: sales@manchestersports.co.uk

Maybury Sports Ltd, 139 Northwood Road, Thornton Heath, Surrey, CR7 8HX Tel: (020) 8653 5440 Fax: (020) 8771 3497 E-mail: sales@mayburysports.co.uk

Nike UK Ltd, 1 Victory Way, Doxford International Business, Sunderland, SR3 3XF Tel: 0191-401 6453 Fax: 0191-401 2012 E-mail: enquiries@nike.com

▶ Nineplus Ltd, Unit 1b, Goonhavern Industrial Estate, Truro, Cornwall, TR4 9QL Tel: (01872) 572280 Fax: (01872) 572280

Pacific Brands (UK) Ltd, Unit 1 Stretton Green Distribution Park, Langford Way, Barleycastle Lane, Appleton, Warrington, WA4 4TQ Tel: (01925) 212212 Fax: (01925) 212222

Peak Sports Ltd, Unit 4, Ford Street, Brinksway, Stockport, Cheshire, SK3 0BT Tel: 0161-480 2502 Fax: 0161-480 1652 E-mail: sales@peaksports.co.uk

Pro Image Ltd, 20 Briddon Street, Manchester, M3 1LS Tel: 0161-839 2845 Fax: 0161-839 5830 E-mail: kuldipproimage@aol.com

Procella, 10 Ashby Road, Coalville, Leicestershire, LE67 3LA Tel: (01530) 810112 Fax: (01530) 510721 E-mail: enquiries@procella.co.uk

▶ QS Discount Outlets, ENA MILL, Flapper fold lane, Atherton, M46 0HB Tel: 01942 879349 E-mail: sales@dsdiscount.com

R & R Country, Hull Road, Hemingbrough, Selby, North Yorkshire, YO8 6QJ Tel: (01757) 638555 Fax: (01757) 630770 E-mail: randrcountry@btconnect.com

Ratan Sports Ltd, 23 Claremont Road, Wolverhampton, WV3 0EA Tel: (01902) 339833 Fax: (01902) 339833

Reynolds Sports, 12-13 Crofton Close, Lincoln, LN3 4NT Tel: (01522) 513333 Fax: (01522) 530383

▶ Snow + Rock - Romford, Unit 1A, Davidson Way, Rom Valley Way, Romford, RM7 0AZ Tel: (01708) 436400 E-mail: direct@snowandrock.com

▶ Snow + Rock - Wirral Ltd, Unit 1, Eastham Point, 1062 New Chester Road, Wirral, Merseyside, CH62 8HJ Tel: 0151-328 5500 Fax: 0151-328 5501 E-mail: manager.liverpool@snowandrock.com

▶ Snow & Rock, 188 Kensington High Street, London, W8 7RG Tel: (020) 7937 0872 Fax: (020) 7938 2758 E-mail: manager.kensington@snowandrock.com

▶ Snow & Rock Sports Ltd, 14-16 The Priory Queensway, Birmingham, B4 6BS Tel: 0121-236 8280 Fax: 0121-212 2177

▶ Snow & Rock Sports Ltd, Units 1-3, Gloucester Road North, Filton, Bristol, BS34 7BQ Tel: 0117-914 3000 Fax: 0117-907 4278

▶ Snow & Rock Sports Ltd, 97 Fordwater Road, Chertsey, Surrey, KT16 8HH Tel: (01932) 566886 Fax: (01932) 561553

▶ Snow & Rock Sports Ltd, 31 The Boardwalk, Port Solent, Portsmouth, PO6 4TP Tel: (023) 9220 5388 Fax: (023) 9220 5399

▶ Snow & Rock Sports Ltd, Sheffield Ski Village, Vale Road, Sheffield, S3 9SJ Tel: 0114-275 1700 Fax: 0114-273 0003

▶ Sportsworld Promotions, 18 Truemper Grove, Caversfield, Bicester, Oxfordshire, OX27 8FD Tel: (01869) 320321 Fax: (01869) 320321

Tag, Unit 1 Derby Road Business Park, Burton-on-Trent, Staffordshire, DE14 1RW Tel: (01283) 531855 Fax: (01283) 741411 E-mail: sales@tagleisure.co.uk

Team Colours, The Maltings, Roydon Road, Stanstead Abbotts, Ware, Hertfordshire, SG12 8HG Tel: (01920) 871453 Fax: (01920) 872278 E-mail: sales@teamcolours.co.uk

▶ Tejay Sportswear Ltd, 67 Grace Road, Leicester, LE2 8AD Tel: 0116-283 9427 Fax: 0116-244 0193E-mail: sales@tejay.co.uk

▶ Tradelane Limited, 1 Victoria Avenue, Birmingham, B1 1BD Tel: 0121 6322240 Fax: 0121 6322241 E-mail: info@tradelane.co.uk

▶ Twistyfish, 38 Overnhill Road, Bristol, BS16 5DP Tel: (07729) 290896 E-mail: sales@twistyfish.co.uk

▶ United Safety, Unit 25b Station Lane Industrial Estate, Station Lane, Old Whittington, Chesterfield, Derbyshire, S41 9QX Tel: (01246) 268990 Fax: (01246) 268889 E-mail: unitedsafety@tiscali.co.uk

Willow Sportswear Ltd, 70 Harden Lane, Wilsden, Bradford, West Yorkshire, BD15 0EU Tel: (01535) 275854 Fax: (01535) 275854 E-mail: willowsportswear@hotmail.com

▶ X5 Ltd, Unit 6, 77 London Road, Newbury, Berkshire, RG14 1JN Tel: (0870) 2863666 Fax: (0870) 2863866 E-mail: sales@x5.ltd.uk

SPORTS EQUIPMENT, INDOOR

Allied Sports & Leisure Ltd, 2 Westminster House, Thorley Street, Failsworth, Manchester, M35 9PA Tel: 0161-688 7049 Fax: 0161-681 9851 E-mail: sales@asll.co.uk

▶ ezyShopping4u, 59 Valentine Rd, Kings Heath, Birmingham, B14 7AJ Tel: (07929) 140030 E-mail: sam@ezyshopping4u.com

▶ Kirtlington Park Polo School, Park Farm Technology Centre, Akeman Street, Kirtlington, Kidlington, Oxfordshire, OX5 3JQ Tel: (01869) 350083 Fax: (01869) 350083 E-mail: melissawadley@hotmail.com

Refkit Ltd, 25 Nash Avenue, Wolverhampton, WV6 7SS Tel: (01902) 746329 E-mail: sales@refkit.co.uk

▶ Snow & Rock Sports Ltd, Thorneberry Way, Guildford, Surrey, GU1 1QB Tel: (01483) 445200 Fax: (01483) 445336 E-mail: admin@snowandrock.com

▶ Ruth White Yoga Products Ltd, Building 188 First Street, New Greenham Park, Newbury, Berkshire, RG19 6HW Tel: (01635) 277494 Fax: (01635) 277497 E-mail: sales@ruthwhiteyoga.com

SPORTS EQUIPMENT, USED

▶ Kirtlington Park Polo School, Park Farm Technology Centre, Akeman Street, Kirtlington, Kidlington, Oxfordshire, OX5 3JQ Tel: (01869) 350083 Fax: (01869) 350083 E-mail: melissawadley@hotmail.com

SPORTS EQUIPMENT, WINTER

I & M Steiner Ltd, 5 Reynard Business Park, Windmill Road, Brentford, Middlesex, TW8 9LY Tel: (020) 8847 4422 Fax: (020) 8847 3322

▶ Kirtlington Park Polo School, Park Farm Technology Centre, Akeman Street, Kirtlington, Kidlington, Oxfordshire, OX5 3JQ Tel: (01869) 350083 Fax: (01869) 350083 E-mail: melissawadley@hotmail.com

▶ Office Star Group, Crucible Close, Mushet Industrial Park, Coleford, Gloucestershire, GL16 8RE Tel: (01594) 810081 Fax: (01594) 810111E-mail: 4schools@officestar-group.com

Refkit Ltd, 25 Nash Avenue, Wolverhampton, WV6 7SS Tel: (01902) 746329 E-mail: sales@refkit.co.uk

▶ Skeleton Coast, Unit B11, The Seedbed Centre, Wyncolls Road, Severalls Industrial Park, Colchester, CO4 9HT Tel: (01206) 855333 E-mail: terry@skeletoncoast.co.uk

▶ Snow & Rock Sports Ltd, Thorneberry Way, Guildford, Surrey, GU1 1QB Tel: (01483) 445200 Fax: (01483) 445336 E-mail: admin@snowandrock.com

▶ SnowTubes.co.uk, Hill Cottage, Lanfine Estate, Newmilns, Ayrshire, KA16 9JR Tel: 08700 664373

SPORTS FOOTWEAR, *See also headings for particular types*

Mitre Sports International Ltd, Pentland Centre, Lakeside, Squires Lane, London, N3 2QL Tel: (020) 8346 2600 Fax: (020) 8970 2887

Total Restraint Systems Ltd, Unit 4 Hurricane Close, Old Sarum, Salisbury, SP4 6LG Tel: (01722) 326080 Fax: (01722) 334437 E-mail: post@totalrestarint.com

SPORTS GOODS/EQUIPMENT/ ACCESSORIES MANUFRS

A Different Calibre Ltd, 16 The Wynd, Letchworth Garden City, Hertfordshire, SG6 3EL Tel: (01462) 674861

Abbey Supply Co. Ltd, 8 Balena Close, Poole, Dorset, BH17 7DB Tel: (01202) 603067 Fax: (01202) 601966

Allied Sports & Leisure Ltd, 2 Westminster House, Thorley Street, Failsworth, Manchester, M35 9PA Tel: 0161-688 7049 Fax: 0161-681 9851 E-mail: sales@asll.co.uk

▶ Allstar Sports Equipment, 1 Mid Road Industrial Estate, Mid Road, Prestonpans, East Lothian, EH32 9ER Tel: (01875) 811255 Fax: (01875) 811880 E-mail: sales@allstar-fencing.co.uk

▶ Alpha Distribution Sales & Service, Old Doncaster Road, Wath-upon-Dearne, Rotherham, South Yorkshire, S63 7EU Tel: (01709) 515157 Fax: (01709) 515158

Alternative Services, Cartref, Laurels Road, Offenham Cross, Evesham, Worcestershire, WR11 8RE Tel: (01386) 443795 Fax: (01386) 423893

Amazon Leisure UK Ltd, The Fitness Centre, Hargham Road, Shropham, Attleborough, Norfolk, NR17 1DS Tel: (01953) 498098 Fax: (01953) 498340 E-mail: sales@amazonamazon-leisure.co.uk

Amer Sports Ltd, Ayr Road, Irvine, Ayrshire, KA12 8HG Tel: (01294) 316200 Fax: (01294) 316300

Anthony & Pykett, 1 Park Road, Carlton, Nottingham, NG4 3DE Tel: 0115-940 0268 Fax: 0115-956 2494 E-mail: sales@anthonyandpykett.co.uk

Apollo Leisure, Unit 1 Forest Close, Ebblake Industrial Estate, Verwood, Dorset, BH31 6DE Tel: (01202) 812000 Fax: (01202) 827040 E-mail: sales@apolloleisure.co.uk

▶ Aquashoe Ltd, Unit 25 Lamberhurst Farm, Dargate, Faversham, Kent, ME13 9EP Tel: (01227) 752752 Fax: (01227) 752750

▶ Arfary Group, Parliament View APTS, D Block, No. 1 Albert Embankment, London, London, SE1 7XQ Tel: 0870 0053923 E-mail: sales@arfary.com

Arrowhead, Barn Owl Cottage, Moretonhmpstead, North Bovey, Newton Abbot, Devon, TQ13 8QT Tel: (01647) 441212 Fax: (01647) 441212 E-mail: info@arrowheaduk.com

Arten Co. Ltd, New Bongate Mill, Jedburgh, Roxburghshire, TD8 6DU Tel: (01835) 863380 Fax: (01835) 862148 E-mail: info@halfttern.co.uk

G.L. Ball Components Ltd, 41 Lancaster Road, Bowerhill Industrial Estate, Melksham, Wiltshire, SN12 6SS Tel: (01225) 702657 Fax: (01225) 790066 E-mail: gb.sherwood@btconnect.com

▶ Banner Batons Majorette Cheerleading Supplies, 9 Cornfield Lane, Eastbourne, East Sussex, BN21 4NE Tel: (01323) 439914 Fax: (01323) 439485 E-mail: sales@bannerbatons.co.uk

Bendcrete Climbing Walls, Aquaduct Mill, Tame Street, Stalybridge, Cheshire, SK15 1ST Tel: 0161-338 3046 Fax: 0161-338 7956 E-mail: mail@bendcrete.com

Bishop Sports & Leisure Ltd, Bishops House, Crown Lane, Farnham Royal, Slough, SL2 3SF Tel: (01753) 648666 Fax: (01753) 648989 E-mail: sales@bishopsport.co.uk

Body Sculpture (International Europe) Ltd, Morley Carr Road, Low Moor, Bradford, West Yorkshire, BD12 0RW Tel: (01274) 693888 Fax: (01274) 693700 E-mail: hi-markgroup@btinternet.co.uk

C C I International, 5 Priors Haw Road, Corby, Northamptonshire, NN17 5JG Tel: (01536) 260933 Fax: (01536) 401138 E-mail: info@cci-international.com

C J Wade & Co., 4 Warden Street, Ballymena, County Antrim, BT43 7DT Tel: (028) 2564 0370 Fax: (028) 2564 2823

C M S Sports & Leisure, 57 Pen Street, Boston, Lincolnshire, PE21 6TF Tel: (01205) 366730 Fax: (01205) 359119

Carr Of Nottingham Ltd, Ronald Street, Radford, Nottingham, NG7 3GY Tel: 0115-942 2252 Fax: 0115-942 2276 E-mail: carrofnottm@btconnect.com

▶ Challenge & Response, 16 Whiteladies Road, Bristol, BS8 2LG Tel: (0870) 2403893 Fax: 0117-973 6403 E-mail: sales@aquapacer.com

Charles Owen & Co (Bow) Ltd, Royal Works, Croesfoel Industrial Estate, Rhostyllen, Wrexham, Clwyd, LL14 4BJ Tel: (01978) 317777 Fax: (01978) 317778 E-mail: charles.owen@ukonline.co.uk

▶ Continental Shooting Supplies, Blackstone Farm, Dalry, Ayrshire, KA24 5HN Tel: (01294) 833297 Fax: (01294) 833312

Cordatec, 22 Marlborough Road, Southend-on-Sea, SS1 2UA Tel: (01702) 613339 Fax: (01702) 613339 E-mail: sales@cordatec.co.uk

Corporate Promotions Ltd, 47 Morriston Park Drive, Cambuslang, Glasgow, G72 7LJ Tel: 0141-641 3166 Fax: 0141-641 3166 E-mail: sales@promotionsworld.co.uk

▶ Decorum, 209 Tedco Business Works, Henry Robson Way, South Shields, Tyne & Wear, NE33 1RF Tel: 0191-456 7667 Fax: 0191-427 4858

Dunlop Slazenger International Ltd, Wakefield 41 Business Park, Wakefield, West Yorkshire, WF2 0XB Tel: (01924) 880000 Fax: (01924) 888287 E-mail: info@dsil.co.uk

Edwards Sports Products Ltd, Unit 8 & 9 Hounsell Building, North Mills, Bridport, Dorset, DT6 3BE Tel: (01308) 424111 Fax: (01308) 455800 E-mail: sales@edsports.co.uk

SPORTS GOODS/EQUIPMENT/ ACCESSORIES MANUFRS – *continued*

Emerald Sportswear, 47 Ballykine Road, Ballynahinch, County Down, BT24 8JE Tel: (028) 9756 1982 Fax: (028) 9756 4669 E-mail: sales@emerald-sportswear.co.uk

Esher Angling Centre, Pond House, Weston Green, Thames Ditton, Surrey, KT7 0JX Tel: (020) 8398 2405

▶ Euro-sport.co.uk, Monteagle Lane, Yateley, Hampshire, GU46 6NB Tel: (01252) 660670 E-mail: enquiries@euro-sport.co.uk

Field & Stream, 24 Charlemont Street, Moy, Dungannon, County Tyrone, BT71 7SL Tel: (028) 8778 9533 Fax: (028) 8778 9533 E-mail: sales@fieldandstream.ie

Fitness Focus, Little Farm, St. Neots Road, Bolnhurst, Bedford, MK44 2EP Tel: (01234) 376246 Fax: (01234) 378936 E-mail: sales@fitnessfocus.co.uk

▶ Foxer Leisure, Sheppey Way, Bobbing, Sittingbourne, Kent, ME9 8PD Tel: (01795) 841717 Fax: (01795) 841717

Gamestick Ltd, 68H Wyrley Road, Birmingham, B6 7BN Tel: 0121-327 2500 Fax: 0121-327 2500

Glenmore Shop, Glenmore, Aviemore, Inverness-Shire, PH22 1QU Tel: (01479) 861253 Fax: (01479) 861253

Glenway Products Ltd, Newton Works, Harcourt Road, Wigston, Leicestershire, LE18 3SB Tel: 0116-281 1455 Fax: 0116-281 3389

▶ GMK Ltd, Concorde Way, Fareham, Hampshire, PO15 5RL Tel: (01489) 579999 Fax: (01489) 579950

▶ GNG Group, Units 60/70 BMK Industrial Estate, Wakefield Road, Liversedge, West Yorkshire, WF15 6BS Tel: (01924) 400501 Fax: (01924) 408541 E-mail: sara@gng-group.co.uk

Grays Of Cambridge (International) Ltd, Whitwell Way, Coton, Cambridge, CB23 7PW Tel: (01954) 210446 Fax: (01954) 212225

Grays International Ltd, Station Road, Robertsbridge, East Sussex, TN32 5DH Tel: (0845) 0661823 Fax: (01580) 881156 E-mail: sales@grays-hockey.co.uk

Greaves Sports Ltd, 82 Sauchiehall Street, Glasgow, G2 3DF Tel: 0141-333 0030 Fax: 0141-333 9443

Greengauge (Sports) Ltd, 5 Gateside, Commercial Park, Haddington, East Lothian, EH41 3SE Tel: (0845) 5400012 Fax: (0845) 1308029

H R West, 19 Melton Road, Burton Lazars, Melton Mowbray, Leicestershire, LE14 2UR Tel: (01664) 562182 Fax: (01664) 567862

Hargreaves Sports Ltd, 2-3 Solent Twentyseven, Walton Road, Portsmouth, PO6 1SX Tel: (023) 9232 1200 Fax: (023) 9237 1212 E-mail: sales@hargreaves-sports.co.uk

Harris Active Sports, PO Box 1292, Basildon, Essex, SS15 6PY Tel: (01268) 491036 Fax: (01268) 544008 E-mail: sales@harris-active.co.uk

Harrod UK Ltd, 1 Pinbush Road, Lowestoft, Suffolk, NR33 7NL Tel: (01502) 583515 Fax: (01502) 582456 E-mail: sales@harrod.uk.com

▶ Hawk Cricket & Leisure, The Forge, Drayton, Belbroughton, Stourbridge, West Midlands, DY9 0BN Tel: (01562) 731115

Henry Krank & Co. Ltd, 100-104 Lowtown, Pudsey, West Yorkshire, LS28 9AY Tel: 0113-256 9163 Fax: 0113-257 4962

Hippo Sports Ltd, 1 Woodcroft Farm, Water End Road, Potten End, Berkhamsted, Hertfordshire, HP4 2SH Tel: (01442) 876010 Fax: (01442) 876020 E-mail: sales@zoppohippo.com

Hy Pro International, Arenson Centre, Arenson Way, Houghton Regis, Dunstable, Bedfordshire, LU5 5BN Tel: (01582) 670100

Icon Health & Fitness, 4 Revie Road, Leeds, LS11 8JG Tel: 0113-387 7122 Fax: 0113-387 7124 E-mail: sales@iconeurope.com

Inch's Saddlery, Unit 5 Hannington Farm, Hannington, Tadley, Hampshire, RG26 5TZ Tel: (01635) 297090 Fax: (01635) 297993 E-mail: inches@btinternet.com

JC-One, Lomia House, Falmouth Crescent, Normanton, West Yorkshire, WF6 2SW Tel: (01924) 891793 Fax: (01924) 223681 E-mail: sales@jc-one.co.uk

▶ JMS Cricket Ltd, Parkside Works, Parkwood Street, Keighley, West Yorkshire, BD21 4PJ Tel: (01535) 606777 Fax: (01535) 606777

John Jaques & Sons Ltd, House of Jaques, 1 Fircroft Way, Edenbridge, Kent, TN8 6EL Tel: (01732) 500200 Fax: (01732) 500111 E-mail: gameon@jaques.co.uk

K D Engineering Merseyside Ltd, Unit 33b-33c Garston Industrial Estate, Blackburne Street, Liverpool, L19 8JB Tel: 0151-427 8996 Fax: 0151-427 9397 E-mail: kengine@mersinet.co.uk

Karakal U K, The Old Tanks, Penpole Lane, Bristol, BS11 0EA Tel: 0117-982 9057 Fax: 0117-982 9004 E-mail: sales@karakal.com

Karrimor Ltd, Petre Road, Clayton Le Moors, Accrington, Lancashire, BB5 5JZ Tel: (01254) 893000 Fax: (01254) 893100 E-mail: webmaster@karrimor.co.uk

Kays Of Scotland, 9 Barskimming Road, Mauchline, Ayrshire, KA5 5AJ Tel: (01290) 550256 Fax: (01290) 552438 E-mail: sales@kaysofscotland.co.uk

Kettler (GB) Ltd, Merse Road, North Moons Moat, Redditch, Worcestershire, B98 9HL Tel: (01527) 591901 Fax: (01527) 62423 E-mail: sales@kettler.co.uk

▶ Kings Road Sporting Club Ltd, 40-42 Kings Road, London, SW3 4UD Tel: (020) 7589 5418

▶ Kookaburra Sport, 3 Brakey Road, Weldon North Industrial Estate, Corby, Northamptonshire, NN17 5LU Tel: (01536) 209210 Fax: (01536) 209211 E-mail: sales@kookaburra.co.uk

▶ Kukri Sports Ltd, Ranglet Road, Walton Summit Centre, Bamber Bridge, Preston, PR5 8AR Tel: (01772) 338899 Fax: (01772) 330055

Lazer Kits Ltd, Lissadel Street, Salford, M6 6GG Tel: 0161-743 1400 Fax: 0161-743 1411 E-mail: info@lazerkits.co.uk

Leisure Systems International Ltd, Northfield Road, Kineton Road Industrial Estate, Southam, Leamington Spa, Warwickshire, CV47 0RD Tel: (01926) 811611 Fax: (01926) 816102

Lloyd Ltd, Vale Business Park, Llandow, Cowbridge, South Glamorgan, CF71 7PF Tel: (01446) 773231 Fax: (01446) 771039 E-mail: enquiries@plmortgages.co.uk

M S Michael & Co. Ltd, 4 Batchelor Street, Chatham, Kent, ME4 4BJ Tel: (01634) 844994 Fax: (01634) 844995

Mccready's Sailboats Ltd, Priory Park, Holywood, County Down, BT18 0LG Tel: (028) 9042 1821 Fax: (028) 9042 2998 E-mail: sales@mccreadysailboats.co.uk

▶ Macs Sports, 4 Bridge Street, Cushendall, Ballymena, County Antrim, BT44 0RP Tel: (028) 2177 2121 Fax: (028) 2177 2315

Manchester Sports Ltd, Unit G5, Newton Business Park, Talbot Road, Hyde, Cheshire, SK14 4UQ Tel: 0161-366 1212 Fax: 0161-366 1177 E-mail: sales@manchestersports.co.uk

Marquesman Sports Services Ltd, 11c Salamanca Road, Tharston, Norwich, NR15 2PF Tel: (01508) 531010 Fax: (01508) 530660

Maxtrack Sports Equipment, New Rock House, Kempley Road, Dymock, Gloucestershire, GL18 2BB Tel: (01531) 890955 Fax: (01531) 890950 E-mail: sales@maxtrack.com

Mercury Sports Equipment Ltd, Victoria Road, Stoke-on-Trent, ST4 2HS Tel: (01782) 845577 Fax: (01782) 744998 E-mail: mercurysports@clara.net

Mike's Uk's No 1 Dive Stores, 268-270 Hillmorton Road, Rugby, Warwickshire, CV22 5BW Tel: (01788) 551800 Fax: (01788) 551900 E-mail: sales@scubagear.co.uk

Mountain Fever, 25 Brunswick Street, Stoke-on-Trent, ST1 1DR Tel: (01782) 266137 Fax: (01782) 285541 E-mail: sales@mountainfever.co.uk

Outdoor & Country Store, Stone Road, Blackbrook, Newcastle, Staffordshire, ST5 5EG Tel: (01782) 680068 Fax: (01782) 680068 E-mail: sales@outdoorandcountry.co.uk

Outdoor & Sports Co. Ltd, Redfern House, Dawson Street, Hyde, Cheshire, SK14 1RD Tel: 0161-366 5020 Fax: 0161-366 9732 E-mail: info@ronhill.com

Parker Clay Pigeon Traps, Marshland Farm, Middle Drove, St. Johns Fen End, Wisbech, Cambridgeshire, PE14 8JP Tel: (01945) 430465 Fax: (01945) 430465 E-mail: sales@parkertraps.com

Peak Sports Ltd, Unit 4, Ford Street, Brinksway, Stockport, Cheshire, SK3 0BT Tel: 0161-480 2502 Fax: 0161-480 1652 E-mail: sales@peaksports.co.uk

Personalized Sports Equipment, 4 Geralds Grove, Banstead, Surrey, SM7 1NE Tel: (01737) 210224 Fax: (01737) 360046

Pointfore, Old Priory Road, Easton-in-Gordano, Bristol, BS20 0PB Tel: (01275) 374212 Fax: (01275) 374212

Powerglide Billiards & Snooker Ltd, 119-121 Stanstead Road, Forest Hill, London, SE23 1HJ Tel: (020) 8291 3344 Fax: (020) 8699 4008 E-mail: assist@unicorngroup.com

Premier Sport & Fitness, 7-11 Darlington Street, Wigan, Lancashire, WN1 1DL Tel: (01942) 495695 Fax: (01942) 495695 E-mail: enquiries@fitness-equipment.uk.com

Primo Play Ltd, Thornhill Road, Dewsbury, West Yorkshire, WF12 9QQ Tel: (01924) 466684 Fax: (01924) 468614 E-mail: sales@primoplay.co.uk

Procella, 10 Ashby Road, Coalville, Leicestershire, LE67 3LA Tel: (01530) 810112 Fax: (01530) 510721 E-mail: enquiries@procella.co.uk

Puma UK Trustees Ltd, Challenge Court, Barnett Wood Lane, Leatherhead, Surrey, KT22 7LW Tel: (01372) 360255 Fax: (01372) 362081

Q Sports, 99a High Street, Staple Hill, Bristol, BS16 5HF Tel: 0117-957 5599 Fax: 0117-956 3331

Quality Gunslips Ltd, Sarnau, Llanymynech, Powys, SY22 6QJ Tel: (01938) 590204 Fax: (01938) 590411 E-mail: sales@gunslips.co.uk

R A B Enterprises, Rexon Meadows, Broadwoodwidger, Lifton, Devon, PL16 0JJ Tel: (01566) 784841 Fax: (01566) 784673 E-mail: sales@r-a-b.com

R & J Hill Engineering Ltd, Parker Drive Business Centre, 47 Parker Drive, Leicester, LE4 0JP Tel: 0116-236 6888 Fax: 0116-236 8777 E-mail: sales@hillsport.com

Ransome Sporting Goods, Wood Street, Middlesbrough, Cleveland, TS1 1JP Tel: (01642) 224444 Fax: (01642) 226000

Ratan Sports Ltd, 23 Claremont Road, Wolverhampton, WV3 0EA Tel: (01902) 339833 Fax: (01902) 339833

Reeds Of Cambridge, 70 Water Street, Cambridge, CB4 1PA Tel: (01223) 425348 Fax: (01223) 566717 E-mail: reedsofcambridge@dsl.tipex.com

▶ Reevu Ltd, Parsons House, Parsons Road, Washington, Tyne & Wear, NE37 1EZ Tel: 0191-418 7755 Fax: 0191-418 7799 E-mail: enquires@reevu.com

Robin Hood Golf Centre, 200 Robin Hood Lane, Birmingham, B28 0LG Tel: 0121-778 5557 Fax: 0121-777 7544 E-mail: promo@golfcentre.com

The Salix Cricket Bat Company Ltd, Butlers Farm, Horseshoes Lane, Langley, Maidstone, Kent, ME17 3JY Tel: (01622) 863380 Fax: (01622) 863380

▶ Samba Sports, Walton Street Work, Walton Street, Colne, Lancashire, BB8 0EN Tel: (01282) 860077 Fax: (01282) 860033 E-mail: info@sambasports.co.uk

Sanders Pool Table Hire Ltd, 75 Hatherley Cresent, Fareham, Hampshire, PO16 9TN Tel: (01329) 239979

Sandford & Down, 24 Pier Street, Plymouth, PL1 3BT Tel: (01752) 266248 Fax: (01752) 226131 E-mail: dive@sandfordanddown.co.uk

▶ Scope GB Ltd, 70a Ilford Lane, Ilford, Essex, IG1 2LA Tel: (020) 8270 9891 Fax: (020) 8252 1727 E-mail: mansoor98@yahoo.com

Shiner Ltd, 22 Church Road, Lawrence Hill, Bristol, BS5 9JB Tel: 0117-955 7432 Fax: 0117-955 4686 E-mail: admin@shiner.co.uk

Shogun International, 87 Gayford Road, London, W12 9BY Tel: (020) 8749 2022 Fax: (020) 8740 1086

Simply Scuba, Unit 111 112 John Wilson Business Park, Harvey Drive, Chestfield, Whitstable, Kent, CT5 3QY Tel: (0870) 9707000 Fax: (0870) 9707001 E-mail: customer.services@simplyscuba.com

Skorpion Sports Ltd, 103a Oak Lane, Bradford, West Yorkshire, BD9 4QU Tel: (01274) 548761 Fax: (01274) 544301 E-mail: info@skorpionsports.com

SLR Sportequip Co., 21 Ferndale Drive, Ratby, Leicester, LE6 0LH Tel: 0116-239 5020 Fax: 0116-239 0489 E-mail: sales@slrsportequip.co.uk

▶ Snow + Rock - Romford, Unit 1A, Davidson Way, Rom Valley Way, Romford, RM7 0AZ Tel: (01708) 436400 E-mail: direct@snowandrock.com

▶ Snow + Rock - Wirral Ltd, Unit 1, Eastham Point, 1062 New Chester Road, Wirral, Merseyside, CH62 8HJ Tel: 0151-328 5500 Fax: 0151-328 5501 E-mail: manager.liverpool@snowandrock.com

▶ Snow & Rock, 188 Kensington High Street, London, W8 7RG Tel: (020) 7937 0872 Fax: (020) 7938 2758 E-mail: manager.kensington@snowandrock.com

▶ Snow & Rock, 150 Holborn, London, EC1N 2LR Tel: (020) 7831 6900 Fax: (020) 7831 8545 E-mail: phil@mackechnie.co.nz

▶ Snow & Rock, 4 Mercer Street, London, WC2H 9QA Tel: (020) 7420 1444 Fax: (020) 7420 1445 E-mail: manager.coventgarden@snowandrock.com

▶ Snow & Rock Sports Ltd, 14-16 The Priory Queensway, Birmingham, B4 6BS Tel: 0121-236 8280 Fax: 0121-212 2177

▶ Snow & Rock Sports Ltd, Units 1-3, Gloucester Road North, Filton, Bristol, BS34 7BQ Tel: 0117-914 3000 Fax: 0117-907 4278

▶ Snow & Rock Sports Ltd, 97 Fordwater Road, Chertsey, Surrey, KT16 8HH Tel: (01932) 566886 Fax: (01932) 561553

▶ Snow & Rock Sports Ltd, 31 The Boardwalk, Port Solent, Portsmouth, PO6 4TP Tel: (023) 9220 5388 Fax: (023) 9220 5399

▶ Snow & Rock Sports Ltd, Sheffield Ski Village, Vale Road, Sheffield, S3 9SJ Tel: 0114-275 1700 Fax: 0114-273 0003

▶ Sportswear, Unit 12 Sharpes Industrial Estate, Alexandra Road, Swadlincote, Derbyshire, DE11 9AZ Tel: (01283) 225234 Fax: (01283) 552132 E-mail: k3552_@hotmail.com

▶ Sportzone Marketing, PO Box 332, Bushey, WD23 3XZ Tel: 0700 5938868 Fax: 0700 5938869 E-mail: john@sportzone-marketing.co.uk

SSL International plc, Venus Building, 1 Old Park Lane, Manchester, M41 7HA Tel: 0161-638 2560 Fax: 0161-615 8817 E-mail: andrea.smith@durex.co.uk

Stadia Sports, 19-20 Lancaster Way Business Park, Ely, Cambridgeshire, CB6 3NW Tel: (01353) 668686 Fax: (01353) 669444 E-mail: sales@stadia-sports.co.uk

T S Hattersley & Son Ltd, 63 Weymouth Road, Eccles, Manchester, M30 8TH Tel: 0161-789 1374 Fax: 0161-787 8632 E-mail: info@hattersleys.org

Tanera Camans, 39 Lochy Road, Inverlochy, Fort William, Inverness-Shire, PH33 6NW Tel: (01397) 705119

Taylor Made Golf Ltd, Spectrum House, Jays Close, Basingstoke, Hampshire, RG22 4BS Tel: (01256) 408600 Fax: (01256) 465562

Thomas Taylor (Bowls) Ltd, 217 Bernard Street, Glasgow, G40 3NB Tel: 0141-554 5255 Fax: 0141-551 0594 E-mail: info@taylor-bowls.co.uk

▶ Team Sports Distribution, 755a Lea Bridge Road, London, E17 9DZ Tel: (020) 8521 8700 Fax: (020) 8520 5280

▶ Tennsport Sports Equipment, 372 St. Albans Road, Watford, WD24 6PQ Tel: (01923) 227987 E-mail: tenn66jm@aol.com

Third Generation, 24 Metford Ground, Bristol, BS6 7LG Tel: 0117-935 0690 Fax: 0117-935 0690

Three D Sports, The Runnings, Cheltenham, Gloucestershire, GL51 9NJ Tel: (01242) 241819 Fax: (01242) 222994 E-mail: sales@3dsports.co.uk

Thule Ltd, Five C Business Centre, Concorde Drive, Clevedon, Avon, BS21 6UH Tel: (01275) 340404 Fax: (01275) 340686 E-mail: sales@thule.co.uk

Toco Sport Ltd, PO Box 128, Aberdeen, AB12 3LW Tel: (01224) 895700 Fax: (01224) 896057

Top Flight UK, 16-19 Trafalgar Way, Bar Hill, Cambridge, CB3 8SQ Tel: (01954) 786600 Fax: (01954) 786645

Trisport Ltd, 38 Amber Close, Tamworth Business Park, Amington, Tamworth, Staffordshire, B77 4RP Tel: (01827) 56544 Fax: (01827) 53181 E-mail: salesinfo@trisportgolf.com

Unicorn Products Ltd, South Barn, Crockham Park, Crockham Hill, Edenbridge, Kent, TN8 6UP Tel: 0115-985 3500 Fax: (01732) 782801 E-mail: assist@unicorngroup.com

Bill Upsall Ltd, Charlotte Street, South Shields, Tyne & Wear, NE33 1PX Tel: 0191-455 6305 Fax: 0191-455 6305 E-mail: phil@billupsalltrophies.fslife.co.uk

Vitrition UK Ltd, 7 Victoria Spring Business Park, Wormald Street, Liversedge, West Yorkshire, WF15 6RA Tel: (01924) 410400 Fax: (01924) 410500 E-mail: jo.pollard@btconnect.com

Volkl Tennis (UK) Ltd, Unit38 Chadkirk Business Park, Vale Road, Romiley, Stockport, Cheshire, SK6 3NE Tel: 0161-484 5151 Fax: 0161-427 8000

W A S P Hockey, 5 Healey New Mills, Healey Road, Ossett, West Yorkshire, WF5 8NF Tel: (01924) 278053 Fax: (01924) 278053 E-mail: sales@wasphockey.co.uk

Webex Sports Ltd, 5 Parade, Exmouth, Devon, EX8 1RS Tel: (01395) 260000 Fax: (01395) 260111

Webley & Scott Ltd, Frankly Industrial Park, Tay Road, Rednal Rubery, Birmingham, B45 0PA Tel: (0121) 453 1864 Fax: (0121) 457 7846 E-mail: guns@webley.co.uk

Wellington Country Sports, 24 High Street, Wellington, Somerset, TA21 8RA Tel: (01823) 662120 Fax: (01823) 667970 E-mail: sales@wellingtoncountrysports.co.uk

Witzig's Ltd, Unit 5, George Edwards Road Industrial Estate, Fakenham, Norfolk, NR21 8NL Tel: (01328) 864941 Fax: (01328) 864943 E-mail: info@witzigs.co.uk

Yehlex UK, 321f Mayoral Way, Team Valley Trading Estate, Gateshead, Tyne & Wear, NE11 0RT Tel: 0191-491 5502 Fax: 0191-491 5503 E-mail: sales@yehlex.co.uk

SPORTS GROUND EQUIPMENT MANUFRS

Bowcom Ltd, Florence Works, Brindley Road, Cardiff, CF11 8TX Tel: (029) 2038 8349 Fax: (029) 2034 3235 E-mail: info@bowcom.co.uk

Bytomic Distribution, Unit 15-17 Top Angel, Angel Vale Business Park, Buckingham Industrial Estate, Buckingham, MK18 1TH Tel: (01280) 818640 Fax: (01280) 823083 E-mail: sales@bytomic.com

Dennis Motor Mowers, Howardson Works, Ashbourne Road, Kirk Langley, Ashbourne, Derbyshire, DE6 4NJ Tel: (01332) 824777 Fax: (01332) 824525 E-mail: sales@dennisuk.com

Johnsons Health Tech, 27-61 City Road, Stoke-on-Trent, ST4 1DP Tel: (01782) 749100 Fax: (01782) 572000

K & T Sports Ltd, Po Box 183, Ashford, Kent, TN23 4ZY Tel: 01233 631447 Fax: 01233 611845

Massey & Harris Engineering Ltd, Cook Street Works, King Street West, Stockport, Cheshire, SK3 0AF Tel: 0161-480 5243 Fax: 0161-476 0151 E-mail: masseyharris@btconnect.com

R & J Hill Engineering Ltd, Parker Drive Business Centre, 47 Parker Drive, Leicester, LE4 0JP Tel: 0116-236 6888 Fax: 0116-236 8777 E-mail: sales@hillsport.com

Radford Ezy-Net, Charford House, Machinefarm, Hill Furze, Pershore, Worcestershire, WR10 2NE Tel: (01386) 861029 Fax: (01386) 861029E-mail: enquiries@radfordezynet.co.uk

Rigby Taylor Paints Ltd, Crown Lane, Horwich, Bolton, BL6 5HP Tel: (01204) 677776 Fax: (01204) 677785 E-mail: sales@rigbytaylor.com

Touchline Flags, 4 Seven House, 36-40 Town End, Caterham, Surrey, CR3 5UG Tel: (01883) 331550 Fax: (01883) 331555

SPORTS GROUND MAINTENANCE

▶ Horta Soils Ltd, 4 Carn Court Road, Portadown, Craigavon, County Armagh, BT63 5YX Tel: (028) 3833 7160

SPORTS GROUND MARKING COMPOUNDS

Fleet Line Markers Ltd, Spring La South, Malvern, Worcestershire, WR14 1AT Tel: (01684) 573535 Fax: (01684) 892784 E-mail: sales@fleetlinemarkers.com

SPORTS GROUND MARKING EQUIPMENT/MATERIALS DISTRIBUTORS OR AGENTS

Fleet Line Markers Ltd, Spring La South, Malvern, Worcestershire, WR14 1AT Tel: (01684) 573535 Fax: (01684) 892784 E-mail: sales@fleetlinemarkers.com

Regal Paints Ltd, Meadow Lane Indust Estate, Meadow Lane, Alfreton, Derbyshire, DE55 7EZ Tel: (01773) 830700 Fax: (01773) 832652 E-mail: regalpaintslimited@tiscali.co.uk

SLR Sportequip Co., 21 Ferndale Drive, Ratby, Leicester, LE6 0LH Tel: 0116-239 5020 Fax: 0116-239 0489 E-mail: sales@slrsportequip.co.uk

SPORTS GROUND TURF MAINTENANCE EQUIPMENT

Burrows GM Ltd, Wigan Road, Leyland, PR25 5UE Tel: (01772) 421778 Fax: (01772) 622530

John Bourne & Co. Ltd, Rye Road, Newenden, Cranbrook, Kent, TN18 5QG Tel: (01797) 252298 Fax: (01797) 253115 E-mail: enquiries@bourne.uk.com

Sisis Equipment Macclesfield Ltd, Hurdsfield Industrial Estate, Macclesfield, Cheshire, SK10 2LZ Tel: (01625) 503030 Fax: (01625) 427426 E-mail: info@sisis.com

Supaturf Products Ltd, Office 7 Grange Farm Business Park, Desford Road, Newtown Unthank, Leicester, LE9 9FL Tel: (01455) 825440 Fax: (01455) 828945 E-mail: sales@supaturf-products.co.uk

Techneat Engineering Ltd, 2a Henry Crabb Road, Littleport, Ely, Cambridgeshire, CB6 1SE Tel: (01353) 862044 Fax: (01353) 862644 E-mail: info@techneat.co.uk

▶ Turfmech Machinery Ltd, Hanger 5, New Road, Hixon, Stafford, ST18 0PF Tel: (01889) 271503 Fax: (01889) 271321 E-mail: sales@turfmech.co.uk

SPORTS NETS

Advanced Netting, 157 St Osyth Road, Clacton-on-Sea, Essex, CO15 3HD Tel: (01255) 428988 Fax: (01255) 220668 E-mail: sales@advancednetting.co.uk

Henry Cowls & Sons, Gilly Gabben Industrial Estate, Mawgan, Helston, Cornwall, TR12 6BB Tel: (01326) 221514 Fax: (01326) 221382

Harrod UK Ltd, 1 Pinbush Road, Lowestoft, Suffolk, NR33 7NL Tel: (01502) 583515 Fax: (01502) 582456 E-mail: sales@harrod.uk.com

Redport Net Ltd, Broadgauge Business Park, Bishops Lydeard, Taunton, Somerset, TA4 3RU Tel: (01823) 431885 Fax: (01823) 431886 E-mail: sales@ptwinchester.co.uk

SPORTS SKIRTS

▶ Blue Skin, Blue Skin, Hoxton Works, 128 Hoxton Street, London N1 6SH, London, United Kingdom, N1 6SH Tel: 020 7012 1720 E-mail: info@blueskin.com

SPORTS SURFACE COATINGS

Britannia Paints Ltd, Units 7-8, King Street Trading Estate, Middlewich, Cheshire, CW10 9LF Tel: (01606) 834015 Fax: (01606) 837006 E-mail: sales@britanniapaints.co.uk

SPORTS SURFACE FLOORING CONTRACTORS

▶ B U Interiors Ltd, Unit 15 Nonsuch Industrial Estate, Kiln Lane, Epsom, Surrey, KT17 1DH Tel: (01372) 747677 Fax: (01372) 747706 E-mail: sales@buinteriors.co.uk

▶ Layfix Flooring Ltd, PO Box 2764, Calne, Wiltshire, SN11 9QY Tel: (01249) 816713 Fax: (01249) 816713 E-mail: enquiries_layfix@hotmail.com

Parkett Borse Ltd, 81 Bolton Street, Chorley, Lancashire, PR7 3AG Tel: (01257) 270148 Fax: (01257) 270147 E-mail: info@parkettborse.com

SPORTS SURFACE RAW MATERIALS

B R G International Ltd, Carrington Field Street, Stockport, Cheshire, SK1 3JN Tel: 0161-477 4487 Fax: 0161-480 3573 E-mail: sales@brginternational.co.uk

SPORTS SURFACE REFURBISHMENT OR LINE MARKING

▶ Banner Solutions, Banner House, Central Buildings, Parkfield Road, Rugby, Warwickshire, CV21 1QJ Tel: (01788) 559300 Fax: (01788) 559333 E-mail: joanne.lewis@bannerholdings.co.uk

British Estate Services Ltd, 132 Bath Road, Reading, RG30 2EU Tel: 0118-957 2263 Fax: 0118-951 2267

Peter Dorrell & Co., PO Box 14, Malvern, Worcestershire, WR13 5AS Tel: (01684) 567504 Fax: (01684) 563101 E-mail: sales@peterdorrell.freeserve.co.uk

SPORTS TROPHIES

A1 Trophies, PO Box 200, Sutton Coldfield, West Midlands, B75 7TR Tel: 0121-378 2828 Fax: 0121 378 0500

▶ A1 Trophies & Engraving, Whitworth Road, South West Industrial Estate, Peterlee, County Durham, SR8 2LY Tel: 0191-586 1159 Fax: 0191-587 2970 E-mail: info@a1trophiesandengraving.com

Allsports Darts & Trophies Ltd, 34 Fairview Drive, Chigwell, Essex, IG7 6HS Tel: (020) 8500 8283 Fax: (020) 8500 8283

Almonds Engravers, 12 Duke Street, Darlington, County Durham, DL3 7AA Tel: (01325) 464808 Fax: (01325) 464808

Anglian Awards, The Grove, Hyde Lane, Danbury, Chelmsford, CM3 4LJ Tel: (01245) 223132 Fax: (01245) 222189 E-mail: info@anglianawards.com

▶ Atticus Trophies, 244 Manley Road, Manchester, M21 0RD Tel: 0161-746 7115 Fax: (0800) 6528551

Awardco Group, Mile Road, 9 Bedford Business Centre, Bedford, MK42 9TW Tel: (01234) 300555 Fax: (01234) 348871 E-mail: sales@awardco.co.uk

Aylesbury Trophies, 102 Tring Road, Aylesbury, Buckinghamshire, HP20 1LS Tel: (01296) 421475 Fax: (01296) 421475

B J Promotions & Trophies, 68 Church Street, Gainsborough, Lincolnshire, DN21 2JR Tel: (01427) 614976

Birkdale Trophies, 97 Old Watford Road, Bricket Wood, St. Albans, Hertfordshire, AL2 3UN Tel: (01923) 671225 Fax: (01923) 662522 E-mail: sales@birkdale-trophies.co.uk

Birmingham Trophies & Awards, Unit 10 Summerhill Industrial Estate, 4 Goodman Street, Birmingham, B1 2SS Tel: 0121-236 1327 Fax: 0121-233 9021

▶ Bloomfield Trophies, 72 St. Osyth Road, Clacton-on-Sea, Essex, CO15 3BU Tel: (01255) 435888 Fax: (01255) 221450

Roger Brown Trophies, 372 Carden Avenue, Brighton, BN1 8LJ Tel: (01273) 559110 Fax: (01273) 500298

Bullseye Awards & Garments Ltd, 127 Bath Road, Slough, SL1 3UW Tel: (01753) 578830 Fax: (01753) 825679 E-mail: admin@bullseyeuk.com

Cannon.Co.Uk, 214-224 Barr Street, Birmingham, B19 3AG Tel: 0121-551 4131 Fax: 0121-554 9292 E-mail: peter.cannon@cannon.co.uk

▶ Capital Trophies, Unit B1-B2 Peills Yard, Bourne Road, Bromley, BR2 9NS Tel: (020) 8466 9577 Fax: (020) 8466 9579

Challenger Trophies & Awards Ltd, 195 Salisbury Road, Totton, Southampton, SO40 3LL Tel: (023) 8086 8119 Fax: (023) 8086 3244 E-mail: challengertrophiesandawards@btinternet.com

Christo Trophies, 49 Broad Street, Banbury, Oxfordshire, OX16 5BT Tel: (01295) 262330 Fax: (01295) 262330

Classic Engravers, 6 Old Bridge Street, Truro, Cornwall, TR1 2AQ Tel: (01872) 241960 Fax: (01872) 241960

▶ Claudy Tackle & Sports, 630 Baranailt Road, Claudy, Londonderry, BT47 4EA Tel: (028) 7133 7323

Club Sports Trophies, Unit 6A Bombay Street, Bermondsey, London, SE16 3UX Tel: (020) 7639 5401 Fax: (0870) 7059029 E-mail: marc@munichtrophies.co.uk

▶ Coalville Trophy Centre, 42 Belvoir Road, Coalville, Leicestershire, LE67 3PN Tel: (01530) 810100

Cobblers Den, 11 St.Davids Road South, Lytham St. Annes, Lancashire, FY8 1TF Tel: (01253) 714391 E-mail: thecobblersden@hotmail.com

Cockney Trophies & Darts Centre, 1 Waterloo Road, Stoke-on-Trent, ST6 2EH Tel: (01782) 838404 Fax: (01782) 817791

Colborne Ltd, Park Road, Trowbridge, Wiltshire, BA14 8AP Tel: (01225) 764101 Fax: (01225) 762009 E-mail: sales@awards.uk.com

Concord Sportswear, 1 Ware Road, Hertford, SG13 7DY Tel: (01992) 583165 Fax: (01992) 553662 E-mail: sales@concordsportswear.co.uk

Concorde Trophies, 85 Victoria Street, Crewe, CW1 2JH Tel: (01270) 213753 Fax: (01270) 213753

Cornwall Trophies, Unit 7b Pool Industrial Estate, Pool, Redruth, Cornwall, TR15 3RH Tel: (01209) 313733 Fax: (01209) 313733

D J Morgan Engravers Ltd, 53 Warwick Street, Coventry, CV5 6ET Tel: (024) 7671 1232 Fax: (024) 7671 1232 E-mail: djmorgan@btconnect.com

D J Trophies, 30 Fairfield Approach, Wraysbury, Staines, Middlesex, TW19 5DS Tel: (01784) 483483 Fax: (01784) 482563

D & N Design, 2 Weston Road, Thames Ditton, Surrey, KT7 0HN Tel: (020) 8398 9639 Fax: (020) 8398 9639

Darlow Medals & Rosettes, 8 Verney Close, Butlers Marston, Warwick, CV35 0NP Tel: (01926) 640050 Fax: (01926) 640050 E-mail: darlowro@supanet..com

Dewhurst Trophies, 101 Norfolk Street, King's Lynn, Norfolk, PE30 1AQ Tel: (01553) 773355 Fax: (01553) 773355

Direct Auto Electrics, 126 Myton Drive, Shirley, Solihull, West Midlands, B90 1HH Tel: (07966) 398848 Fax: 0121-436 6235 E-mail: sales@directautoelectrics.co.uk

DKS, 32 Fir Trees Cresent, Lostock Hall, Preston, PR5 5SL Tel: (01772) 312466

▶ Don Rogers Ltd, 29 Faringdon Road, Swindon, SN1 5AR Tel: (01793) 527378 Fax: (01793) 527378

Durham Throphies UK, 69 Buckinghamshire Road, Durham, DH1 2BE Tel: 0191-386 9045

Enquire Within, 1 North Road, Reigate, Surrey, RH2 8LY Tel: (01737) 243938 Fax: (01737) 243938

Frost's Rosettes, 365 Totnes Road, Paignton, Devon, TQ4 7DE Tel: (01803) 664848 Fax: (01803) 664848

G H Rainey & Sons Ltd, 81 Spencer Street, Birmingham, B18 6DE Tel: 0121-236 8060

▶ G L Sports, 47 Rydal Crescent, Manchester, M28 7JD Tel: 0161-790 7444 Fax: 0161-790 7444

Gainsborough, 34-44 Northwood Street, Birmingham, B3 1TU Tel: 0121-236 2335 Fax: 0121-236 2846 E-mail: sales@gainsboroughsilver.co.uk

Geoff Happs Trophies, 21 High Street, Bentley, Doncaster, South Yorkshire, DN5 0AA Tel: (01302) 872296

Harlequin Sports Trophies, 1 Bloomfield Place, Bathgate, West Lothian, EH48 1PB Tel: (01506) 634069 Fax: (01506) 634069

Invertrophy.com, Suit 90, 24 Station Square, Academy Street, Inverness, IV1 1LD Tel: (01463) 238495 Fax: (01463) 729719 E-mail: sales@invertorphy.com

Ironside Trophies & Engraving, 1b Harmony Shopping Centre, Skyline Drive, Lisburn, County Antrim, BT27 4HP Tel: (028) 9267 8427 Fax: (028) 9267 8427 E-mail: info@ironsidetrophies.con

J C Trophies, 14 Beech Lane, St. Leonards, Ringwood, Hampshire, BH24 2QD Tel: (01202) 868896 Fax: (01202) 868895 E-mail: sales@jctrophies.com

J S Trophies, 2 Rood Hill, Congleton, Cheshire, CW12 1LG Tel: (01260) 272505 Fax: (01260) 272505 E-mail: jstrophies@tiscali.co.uk

▶ Jamie's Trophies, 31 Westgate, Ripon, North Yorkshire, HG4 2BQ Tel: (01765) 692233

Just Engraving, 138 St. Neots Road, Eaton Ford, St. Neots, Cambridgeshire, PE19 7AL Tel: (01480) 472715 Fax: (01480) 386716 E-mail: engraving@endersby.com

K & E K Sports Trophies, 16 Holderness Road, Hull, HU9 1EG Tel: (01482) 212138 Fax: (01482) 212138

K L M Trophy Centre, 2-3 The Parade, Southfields, Letchworth Garden City, Hertfordshire, SG6 4NB Tel: (01462) 684242 Fax: (01462) 684242 E-mail: klmengravers@aol.com

K P Badges & Trophies, 4 Antrim Road, Bristol, BS9 4BS Tel: 0117-962 0191 Fax: 0117-975 4264 E-mail: sales@trophiesuk.biz

K P M Trophies & Engraving, 88 Duke Street, St. Helens, Merseyside, WA10 2JN Tel: (01744) 603021

Lanes Trophies, 121 Higher Parr Street, St. Helens, Merseyside, WA9 1AG Tel: (01744) 732229 Fax: (01744) 732293

Len Fowler Trophies Ltd, 55 Lambs Conduit Street, London, WC1N 3NB Tel: (020) 7405 6130 Fax: (020) 7405 6130

Majestic Trophies Ltd, David Lane, Nottingham, NG6 0JU Tel: 0115-970 8509 Fax: 0115-942 0712

Mearns Trophy Centre, 60 Riverside Drive, Stonehaven, Kincardineshire, AB39 2GP Tel: (01569) 764762 Fax: (01569) 764762

Millington's Angling Equipment, 32 Steeley Lane, Chorley, Lancashire, PR6 0RD Tel: (01257) 272392

▶ Natural Interventions Ltd, Redwood House, Middleton Road, Eggleston, Barnard Castle, County Durham, DL12 0AQ Tel: (01833) 650022 Fax: (01833) 650033 E-mail: info@natural-interventions.co.uk

New Mourne Trophies, 14 Margaret Street, Newry, County Down, BT34 1DF Tel: (028) 3026 9736

North Wales Trophies & Engravers, 34 Tan-Y-Bryn Road, Llandudno, Gwynedd, LL30 1UU Tel: (01492) 860363

Northern Trophies Engravers, 41 Union Street, Middlesbrough, Cleveland, TS1 4EA Tel: (01642) 247877 Fax: (01642) 247877

Oaklands Signs, 70 Draycott, Cam, Dursley, Gloucestershire, GL11 5DH Tel: (01453) 542312 Fax: (01453) 543353 E-mail: jilldavis.oaklands@btinternet.com

Onlinetrophies, The Smiddy, Glass, Huntly, Aberdeenshire, AB54 4XR Tel: (0870) 7570640 Fax: (0870) 7570641 E-mail: info@onlinetrophies.co.uk

John Parker, The Market, Aberdare, Mid Glamorgan, CF44 7EB Tel: (01685) 875749 Fax: (01685) 875749

Paul Hett, 2-4 Market Street, Hyde, Cheshire, SK14 1AY Tel: 0161-368 9200 Fax: 0161-368 9200

Peter's Trophies, 10 West Street, Weston-super-Mare, Avon, BS23 1JT Tel: (01934) 620206 Fax: (01934) 620206 E-mail: monty19452003@yahoo.co.uk

Plymouth Trophyman, 75 Hyde Park Road, Plymouth, PL3 4JN Tel: (01752) 226787

Premier Trophies, 42-44 Outram Street, Sutton-in-Ashfield, Nottinghamshire, NG17 4FS Tel: (01623) 512849 Fax: (01623) 480443

R & B Trophies, 16 St Nicholas Street, Weymouth, Dorset, DT4 8AA Tel: (01305) 776826 Fax: (01305) 776826 E-mail: rbtrophys@tiscali.co.uk

R & D Trophy Supplies, Unit 1 Phoenix Park, Coldred Road, Maidstone, Kent, ME15 9XN Tel: (01622) 753884 Fax: (01622) 688443 E-mail: sales@rdtrophy.co.uk

Ramsgate Trophies, 111 King Street, Ramsgate, Kent, CT11 8PH Tel: (01843) 593872 Fax: (01843) 593872

Read T, 30 Elmtree Road, Basildon, Essex, SS16 4TN Tel: (01268) 456160

S B Services, 86 Chelwood Avenue, Hatfield, Hertfordshire, AL10 0RE Tel: (01707) 256644 Fax: (01707) 262599 E-mail: s.brayshaw@btopenworld.com

S D L Trophies Ltd, Britannia Centre Bentley Wood Way, Network 65 Business Park, Hapton, Burnley, Lancashire, BB11 5ST Tel: (01282) 418418 Fax: (01282) 418419 E-mail: admin@midfield.bromley.sch.uk

Shropshire Trophies Centre & Bowling Centre, 6 Milk Street, Shrewsbury, SY1 1SZ Tel: (01743) 369688 Fax: (01743) 360674 E-mail: stbc@lineone.net

Charles Smith & Reddish Ltd, 11a Lever Street, London, EC1V 3QU Tel: (020) 7253 2457 Fax: (020) 7490 4612 E-mail: info@csr-chartinstruments.co.uk

Star Trophies, 61 High Street, Bilston, West Midlands, WV14 0EZ Tel: (01902) 403655 Fax: (01902) 403655

Stewart R Trophies, 90 Titchfield Street, Kilmarnock, Ayrshire, KA1 1PH Tel: (01563) 522594 Fax: (01563) 522594 E-mail: ltd@btconnect.com

Swatkins Group Ltd, Leamore House, Leamore Lane, Walsall, WS2 7DQ Tel: (01922) 711700 Fax: (01922) 710410 E-mail: sales@swatkins.com

Swinnertons Of Walsall, 1 Holtshill Lane, Walsall, WS1 2JA Tel: (01922) 626081 Fax: (01922) 626082

Target Trophy & Engraving Centre, 312a Lytham Road, Blackpool, FY1 6EY Tel: (01253) 348798 Fax: (01253) 348798 E-mail: sales@targettrophies.co.uk

John Taylor Poston & Co. Ltd, 19-21 Great Queens Street, London, WC2B 5BE Tel: (020) 7242 0471 Fax: (020) 7831 8692 E-mail: gqs@toye.demon.co.uk

Team Strides, 6 Fleet Road, Fleet Holbeach, Holbeach, Spalding, Lincolnshire, PE12 7AX Tel: (01406) 425999 Fax: (01406) 425717 E-mail: sales@teamstrides.co.uk

Teesside & Cleveland Trophies, 32 Borough Road, Middlesbrough, Cleveland, TS1 5DW Tel: (01642) 240176 Fax: (01642) 240176

Town Street Jewellers, 69 Town Street, Armley, Leeds, LS12 3HD Tel: 0113-231 9991 Fax: 0113-231 9991

Trent Trophies & Engraving, 63 George Street, Newcastle, Staffordshire, ST5 1JT Tel: (01782) 619828 Fax: (01782) 619828

Tripp's Trophies, 49 Long Row, Felinfoel, Llanelli, Dyfed, SA15 4LW Tel: (01554) 772995 Fax: (01554) 772995 E-mail: trippstrophies@btopenworld.com

Trophy Centre Ltd, 266 High Street, Ayr, KA7 1NB Tel: (01292) 610638

The Trophy Centre Ltd, 18 Kilmarnock Road, Glasgow, G41 3NH Tel: 0141-649 3843 Fax: 0141-649 3843

Trophy Centre, 12 Reynolds Street, Warrington, WA4 1PP Tel: (01925) 444365 Fax: (01925) 444365

▶ Trophy Distributors, 4 West Gate Park, Tintagel Way, Aldridge, Walsall, WS9 8ER Tel: (01922) 455545 Fax: (01922) 459966 E-mail: info@trophydistributors.co.uk

Trophy Distributors UK Ltd, Queensway Trading Estate, 16/17 Bartholomew Row, Birmingham, B5 5JU Tel: 0121-236 7843 Fax: 0121-236 3229 E-mail: sales@trophydistributors.co.uk

The Trophy Shop, 48 Victoria Street, Perth, PH2 8JT Tel: (01738) 632245 E-mail: sales@perth-trophy-shop.com

Trophy World Awards Engraving, 50 Albert Street, Dundee, DD4 6QQ Tel: (01382) 461004 Fax: (01382) 461004

Trophyman Supplies Ltd, Olympic Works, 2-4 Kathleen Road, Southampton, SO19 8EX Tel: (023) 8043 8888 Fax: (023) 8068 5604 E-mail: sales@trophyman.co.uk

Tyrella Rosettes Ltd, 3 4 Ewart Street Workshops, 2 Ewart Street, Saltney Ferry, Chester, CH4 0BL Tel: (01244) 680204 Fax: (01244) 671410 E-mail: sales@tyrella.com

SPORTS TROPHIES – *continued*

Bill Upsall Ltd, Charlotte Street, South Shields, Tyne & Wear, NE33 1PX Tel: 0191-455 6305 Fax: 0191-455 6305 E-mail: phil@billupsalltrophies.fslife.co.uk

▶ V B Trophies, Unit 1 Lumen Road, Royston, Hertfordshire, SG8 7AF Tel: (01763) 244116 Fax: (01763) 250850 E-mail: sales@vbgroup.co.uk

Varley Trophies, 78 Beaumont Road, Plymouth, PL4 9BP Tel: (01752) 665984 Fax: (01752) 229567 E-mail: chris@howe11.fsbusiness.co.uk

W A Humphries Ltd, 65 Hunters Vale, Birmingham, B19 2XH Tel: 0121-554 0125 Fax: 0121-554 0155

W & K Rossiter, 79 Aldwick Road, Bognor Regis, West Sussex, PO21 2NW Tel: (01243) 828017 Fax: (01243) 828017 E-mail: trophieswk@yahoo.co.uk

W S S Windsor, 58 St. Leonards Road, Windsor, Berkshire, SL4 3BY Tel: (01753) 864483 Fax: (01753) 621102 E-mail: sales@wsswindsor.com

▶ Wordleys, 9 Bennington Street, Cheltenham, Gloucestershire, GL50 4ED Tel: 01242 525208 Fax: 01242 525208

SPORTS TROPHY CENTRES

▶ Purple Patch Promotions, 3 Gowers Close, Kesgrave, Ipswich, IP5 2XE Tel: (01473) 333388 Fax: (01473) 333388 E-mail: sales@purplepatch.org

SPORTS TROPHY STANDS

Birmingham Woodcrafts, Units 9-10 All Saints Industrial Estate, Hockley, Birmingham, B18 7RJ Tel: 0121-523 8007 Fax: 0121-507 0685

SPORTS VESTS

▶ Blue Skin, Blue Skin, Hoxton Works, 128 Hoxton Street, London N1 6SH, London, United Kingdom, N1 6SH Tel: 020 7012 1720 E-mail: info@blueskin.com

▶ DevilWear Ltd, The Fashion House, Seaside Lane, Easington Colliery, Peterlee, County Durham, SR8 3PF Tel: (0870) 3217353 Fax: (0870) 7652757 E-mail: karl@devilwear.co.uk

▶ Planet Dance, PO Box 233, Leeds, LS16 0AQ Tel: (0870) 1453995 Fax: 0113-226 9295 E-mail: info@planetdancedirect.co.uk

SPOT RESISTANCE WELDING EQUIPMENT

Chiltern Electrical Services, 1 Shenstone Drive, Burnham, Slough, SL1 7HJ Tel: (01628) 665090 Fax: (01628) 665090 E-mail: miketerry@chilelecserv.freeserve.co.uk

SPOT WELDING

▶ Traker Engineering Ltd, Garth Works, Taffs Well, Cardiff, CF15 7RN Tel: (029) 2081 1088 Fax: (029) 2081 3520 E-mail: info@traker-eng.co.uk

SPOT WELDING EQUIPMENT

R W M Wolverhampton Ltd, 34 Commercial Road, Wolverhampton, WV1 3RD Tel: (01902) 871272

Spanesi Automotive Mechanic Ltd, 33-37 Second Avenue Ind Estate, Chatham, Kent, ME4 5AY Tel: (01634) 845580 Fax: (01634) 401515

SPRAY BALLS, STAINLESS STEEL, CLEAN IN PLACE (CIP)

S B I Industries, Unit 10a Oakendene Industrial Estate, Bolney Road, Cowfold, Horsham, West Sussex, RH13 8AZ Tel: (01403) 864858 Fax: (01403) 864858 E-mail: richardball@sbindustries.co.uk

SPRAY BOOTH AIR FILTERS

Burntwood Spray Booth & Systems, Prospect Road, Burntwood, Staffordshire, WS7 0BU Tel: (01543) 685565 Fax: (01543) 684931 E-mail: spraybooths@unitech.uk.com

E M M UK Ltd, Old Road, Southam, Warwickshire, CV47 1RA Tel: (01926) 812419 Fax: (01926) 817425 E-mail: sales@emm.co.uk

Filtermax Filtration Services Ltd, Unit 17, Bradwell Works, Davenport Street, Stoke-on-Trent, ST6 4LL Tel: (01782) 816300 Fax: (01782) 790767 E-mail: sales@filterspares.com

Leyland Filtration Ltd, Yarrow Road, Chorley, Lancashire, PR6 0LP Tel: (01257) 269292 Fax: (01257) 261056 E-mail: layland.filtration@talk21.com

SPRAY BOOTH CHEMICALS

C T Supplies Ltd, Unit 94 Northwick Business Centre, Blockley, Moreton-in-Marsh, Gloucestershire, GL56 9RF Tel: (01386) 700884 Fax: (01386) 700126 E-mail: sales@ct-supplies.co.uk

SPRAY BOOTHS, *See also headings for particular types*

C T Composites, 2 Industrial Estate, Kempshott Park, Beggarwood, Basingstoke, Hampshire, RG23 7LP Tel: (01256) 396400 Fax: (01256) 397664 E-mail: sales@ctcomposites.co.uk

Eurotecno Spraybooths, 120a Green Road, Bournemouth, BH9 1EF Tel: (01202) 549286 E-mail: sales@eurotecno.co.uk

Galito Ltd, 357 Thorp Arch Trading Estate, Thorp Arch, Wetherby, West Yorkshire, LS23 7BJ Tel: (01937) 844698 Fax: (01937) 844509 E-mail: info@gallito.co.uk

Spraybake Spraybooth Manufacturers, Unit 1, Milner Road Chilton Road Indust Area, Sudbury (Suffolk), Sudbury, Suffolk, CO10 2XG Tel: (01787) 888650 Fax: 01787 882305 E-mail: b.baird@spraybake.co.uk

Xtreme Engineering Limited, 335 Blandford Road, Poole, Dorset, BH15 4HP Tel: (01202) 682051 Fax: (01202) 682051 E-mail: sales@xtreme-engineering.co.uk

SPRAY CONTACT ADHESIVES

Bondloc UK Ltd, Alton Works, Long Bank, Bewdley, Worcestershire, DY12 2UJ Tel: (01299) 269269 Fax: (01299) 269210 E-mail: sales@bondloc.co.uk

Cleftbridge Coatings Ltd, Unit 8a, Lower Road Trading Estate, Ledbury, Herefordshire, HR8 2DH Tel: (01531) 633771 Fax: (01531) 633719 E-mail: enquiries@cleftbridge.co.uk

SPRAY DISPENSING PUMPS

Coster Aerosols Ltd, Babbage Rd, Stevenage, Hertfordshire, SG1 2EQ Tel: (01438) 367763 Fax: (01438) 728305 E-mail: sales.uk@coster.com

Spraychem Ltd, Cardrew Industrial Estate, Redruth, Cornwall, TR15 1ST Tel: (01209) 315222 Fax: (01209) 314333 E-mail: sales@contico.co.uk

Titus Pumps Ltd, 3 Chiphouse Road, Bristol, BS15 4TR Tel: 0117-940 6293 Fax: (0870) 7877472 E-mail: sales@tituspumps.co.uk

SPRAY DRYERS

Delavan Ltd, Gorsey Lane, Widnes, Cheshire, WA8 0RJ Tel: 0151-424 6821 Fax: 0151-495 1043 E-mail: sales@delavan.co.uk

Spray Processes Ltd, 49A Bromham Road, Bedford, MK40 2AA Tel: (01234) 273922 Fax: (01234) 269436 E-mail: sales@spraypro.com

SPRAY EQUIPMENT, *See also headings under Spray Equipment for particular types*

Airmark, 6 Becket Road, London, N18 3PN Tel: (020) 8807 7891 Fax: (020) 8884 3898 E-mail: airmarkcom@aol.com

Allman Sprayers Ltd, Birdham Business Park, Birdham Road, Chichester, West Sussex, PO20 7BT Tel: (01243) 512511 Fax: (01243) 511171 E-mail: sales@allman-sprayers.co.uk

Anest Iwata UK Ltd, Little End Road, Eaton Socon, St. Neots, Cambridgeshire, PE19 8JH Tel: (01480) 405419 Fax: (01480) 217610 E-mail: enquiries@anest-iwata.co.uk

Best Pneumatics Ltd, Units 6-7, Short Way, Thornbury Industrial Estate, Thornbury, Bristol, BS35 3UT Tel: (01454) 415761 Fax: (01454) 414607

Delavan Ltd, Gorsey Lane, Widnes, Cheshire, WA8 0RJ Tel: 0151-424 6821 Fax: 0151-495 1043 E-mail: sales@delavan.co.uk

Dexter Paints Ltd, Albert Works, Trafalgar Street, Burnley, Lancashire, BB11 1RE Tel: (01282) 423361 Fax: (01282) 414573

Exel Industrial UK Ltd, Unit 4 Lockflight Buildings, Wheatlea Industrial Estate, Wigan, Lancashire, WN3 6XR Tel: (01942) 829111 Fax: (01942) 820491 E-mail: enquiries@exel-uk.com

Express Contracts Drying, Unit 8 Rassau Industrial Estate, Rassau, Ebbw Vale, Gwent, NP23 5SD Tel: (01495) 303363 Fax: (01495) 308683 E-mail: info@expresscontractdrying.com

Finishing Connect Ltd, 865 Plymouth Road, Slough, SL1 4LP Tel: (01753) 676788 Fax: (01753) 676790 E-mail: fincon@technocom.com

Gray Campling Ltd, 91a Southcote Road, Bournemouth, BH1 3SN Tel: (01202) 291828 Fax: (01202) 297304 E-mail: sales@graycampling.co.uk

L E Went Ltd, 52-56 Burlington Road, New Malden, Surrey, KT3 4NU Tel: (020) 8949 0626 Fax: (020) 8715 1116 E-mail: iew.paint@virgin.net

Lindsay Ellacott UK Ltd, Newton Farm Boyton, Boyton, Launceston, Cornwall, PL15 9RL Tel: (01566) 772208 Fax: (01566) 777228 E-mail: lellacott@aol.com

Mason Morley Ltd, Spray Quip House, St Pauls Street, Morley, Leeds, LS27 9EP Tel: 0113-253 8681 Fax: 0113-252 3179 E-mail: info@masonmorley.co.uk

Microcide Ltd, Shepherd's Grove, Stanton, Bury St. Edmunds, Suffolk, IP31 2AR Tel: (01359) 251077 Fax: (01359) 251545 E-mail: microcide@microcide.co.uk

Multi Spray & Pneumatics Ltd, Unit 1 Hanley Business Park, Cooper Street, Hanley, Stoke-on-Trent, ST1 4DW Tel: (01782) 281376 Fax: (01782) 204426 E-mail: technical@multisprayandpneumatics.co.uk

Spray-Trac Systems Ltd, Legram Lane, Marton-Cum-Grafton, Boroughbridge, York, YO51 9PS Tel: (01423) 322377 Fax: (01423) 324678 E-mail: sales@spraytrac.com

SPRAY GUN CLEANING

Safety-Kleen UK Ltd, 390 London Road, Isleworth, Middlesex, TW7 5AN Tel: (020) 8490 9084 Fax: (020) 8490 3859 E-mail: skuk@sk-europe.com

SPRAY GUN CLEANING EQUIPMENT

Redashe Ltd, Unit 8 The Brook Trading Estate, Deadbrook Lane, Aldershot, Hampshire, GU12 4XB Tel: (01252) 785010 Fax: (01252) 329328 E-mail: info@redashe.co.uk

SPRAY HIRE

Mason Morley Ltd, Spray Quip House, St Pauls Street, Morley, Leeds, LS27 9EP Tel: 0113-253 8681 Fax: 0113-252 3179 E-mail: info@masonmorley.co.uk

SPRAY NOZZLE MANUFRS

Cadar Ltd, Unit 3 The Point, Market Harborough, Leicestershire, LE16 7QU Tel: (01858) 410101 Fax: (01858) 433934 E-mail: sales@cadar.ltd.uk

Cleanacres Machinery Ltd, Hazleton, Cheltenham, Gloucestershire, GL54 4DX Tel: (01451) 860721 Fax: (01451) 860139 E-mail: info@cleanacres.co.uk

Laidler Products, 35 Fairfield Rise, Stourbridge, West Midlands, DY8 3PQ Tel: (01384) 442815 Fax: (01384) 441065 E-mail: mail@laidlerproducts.co.uk

Lechler Ltd, 1 Fell Street, Sheffield, S9 2TP Tel: 0114-249 2020 Fax: 0114-249 3600 E-mail: info@lechler.com

Newland Design Ltd, Lodge Quarry, Lancaster Road, Carnforth, Lancashire, LA5 9DW Tel: (01524) 733424

P N R UK Ltd, 13 16 Sugarbrook Road, Bromsgrove, Worcestershire, B60 3DW Tel: (01527) 579066 Fax: (01527) 579067 E-mail: sales@pnr.co.uk

Sealpump Engineering Ltd, Innovation Centre, Kirkleatham Business Park, Redcar, Cleveland, TS10 5SH Tel: (01642) 777720 Fax: (01642) 777730 E-mail: sales@sealpump.com

Spraying Systems Ltd, Farnham Business Park, Weydon Lane, Farnham, Surrey, GU9 8QT Tel: (01252) 727200 Fax: (01252) 712211 E-mail: info.uk@spray.com

SPRAYERS, EMULSION

▶ Fine Interiors Ltd, 78 Croydon Road, West Wickham, Kent, BR4 9HY Tel: (020) 8462 3994 Fax: (020) 8462 8808

▶ Jura-Spray Ltd, Wandle Trading Estate, Goat Road, Mitcham Junction, Mitcham, Surrey, CR4 4HW Tel: (020) 8640 1775

SPRAYERS, TURF

Techneat Engineering Ltd, 2a Henry Crabb Road, Littleport, Ely, Cambridgeshire, CB6 1SE Tel: (01353) 862044 Fax: (01353) 862644 E-mail: info@techneat.co.uk

▶ Turfmech Machinery Ltd, Hanger 5, New Road, Hixon, Stafford, ST18 0PF Tel: (01889) 271503 Fax: (01889) 271321 E-mail: sales@turfmech.co.uk

▶ Turfonline, Westminster Chambers, 106 Lord Street, Southport, Merseyside, PR8 1LF Tel: (01704) 501555 Fax: (01704) 501333 E-mail: jenny.knight@turfland.co.uk

SPREADS, PROCESSED FISH/ MEAT

Coldwater Seafood UK Ltd, Estate Road 2, South Humberside Industrial Estate, Grimsby, South Humberside, DN31 2TG Tel: (01472) 321100 Fax: (01472) 321220 E-mail: reception@coldwater-seafood.co.uk

Fresh Bacon Co., Ty Verlon Industrial Estate, Cardiff Road, Barry, South Glamorgan, CF63 2BE Tel: (01446) 700900

Princes Foods International Trading Group, Royal Liver Building, Pier Head, Liverpool, L3 1NX Tel: 0151-236 9282 Fax: 0151-236 1057

SPRING ASSISTED ACCESS COVERS OR FRAMES

▶ Arcova Manhole Cover Manufacturers, Willow Tree Farm, Main Street, Laneham, Retford, Nottinghamshire, DN22 0NG Tel: (01777) 228931 Fax: (01777) 228504 E-mail: sales@arcova.co.uk

Bilco UK Ltd, 3 Park Farm Business Centre, Fornham Park, Fornham St. Genevieve, Bury St. Edmunds, Suffolk, IP28 6TS Tel: (01284) 701696 Fax: (01284) 702531 E-mail: admin@bilco.com

Rhodes Engineering Group Ltd, High Street Mills, High Street, Heckmondwike, West Yorkshire, WF16 0DL Tel: (01924) 410740 Fax: (01924) 410164 E-mail: tranter@rhodesengineering.co.uk

SPRING ASSISTED CEILING ACCESS DOORS

Albion Spring Co Ltd, Oldbury Road, West Bromwich, West Midlands, B70 9EE Tel: 0121-557 3081 Fax: 0121-520 4983 E-mail: sales@albionspring.co.uk

C P D Distribution P.L.C., Unit 94 Roding Road, The London Industrial Park, Beckton, London, E6 6LS Tel: (020) 7474 5485 Fax: (020) 7474 6374

Ceiling Installation Ltd, Sanserra House, Mayfield Road, Bournemouth, BH9 1TW Tel: (01202) 539700 Fax: (01202) 535652 E-mail: cil2srs@aol.com

Cochrane & Watt Ceilings, Sonas, Forth, Lanark, ML11 8HD Tel: (01555) 811934 Fax: (01555) 811934

H & L Ceilings Ltd, The Old Workhouse, Hudds Vale Road, Bristol, BS5 7HY Tel: 0117-941 4222 Fax: 0117-941 2678 E-mail: johnhawke_hl@hotmail.com

SPRING ASSISTED FLOOR AND PIT DOORS

Bilco UK Ltd, 3 Park Farm Business Centre, Fornham Park, Fornham St. Genevieve, Bury St. Edmunds, Suffolk, IP28 6TS Tel: (01284) 701696 Fax: (01284) 702531 E-mail: admin@bilco.com

SPRING ASSISTED MANHOLE COVERS OR FRAMES

Technocover Ltd, Henfaes Lane, Welshpool, Powys, SY21 7BE Tel: (01938) 555511 Fax: (01938) 555527 E-mail: terry.batten@technocover.co.uk

SPRING BALANCES

Express Electrical & Engineering Supplies, 37 Cable Depot Road, Clydebank, Dunbartonshire, G81 1UY Tel: 0141-941 3689 Fax: 0141-952 8155 E-mail: sales@expresselectrical.co.uk

SPRING BRAKES

Albion Spring Co Ltd, Oldbury Road, West Bromwich, West Midlands, B70 9EE Tel: 0121-557 3081 Fax: 0121-520 4983 E-mail: sales@albionspring.co.uk

SPRING CLAMPS

Albion Spring Co Ltd, Oldbury Road, West Bromwich, West Midlands, B70 9EE Tel: 0121-557 3081 Fax: 0121-520 4983 E-mail: sales@albionspring.co.uk

SPRING CLIPS

▶ Anglia Springs Ltd, Unit N Loddon Industrial Estate, Little Money Road, Loddon, Norwich, NR14 6JD Tel: (01508) 528396 Fax: (01508) 528240 E-mail: info@angliasprings.com

Brayman Springs & Production Engineering, 7 28 Heming Road, Redditch, Worcestershire, B98 0DH Tel: (01527) 510004 Fax: (01527) 510004

Lancashire Spring Company, Meadowhead Spring Works, Off Dale Street, Milnrow, Rochdale, Lancashire, OL16 4HG Tel: (01706) 715800 Fax: (01706) 715801 E-mail: info@lancashire-spring.co.uk

Lesjofors Springs (U K) Ltd, Unit J4, Lowfields Way, Lowfields Business Park, Elland, West Yorkshire, HX5 9DA Tel: (01422) 377335 Fax: (01422) 373336 E-mail: info.ell@lesjoforsab.com

SPRING CLIPS – *continued*

▶ Oswald Springs, 76 Arthur Street, Redditch, Worcestershire, B98 8LJ Tel: (01527) 527777 Fax: (01527) 527785 E-mail: oswald@oswaldsprings.co.uk

Peterson Spring Europe Ltd, Unit 21, Trescott Road, Trafford Park, Redditch, Worcestershire, B98 7AH Tel: (01527) 585657 Fax: (01527) 588317 E-mail: sales@peterson.co.uk

Peterson Spring (UK) Ltd, Reddings Lane, Tyseley, Birmingham, B11 3HA Tel: 0121-706 2236 Fax: 0121-708 1253 E-mail: enquiries@psprings.euroe.co.uk

Protaform Components Ltd, Orchard Works, 76 Arthur Street, Redditch, Worcestershire, B98 8LJ Tel: (01527) 517500 Fax: (01527) 502373 E-mail: sales@protaform.com

S G Springs Ltd, 43 Crossgate Road, Park Farm Industrial Estate, Redditch, Worcestershire, B98 7SN Tel: (01527) 500955 Fax: (01527) 510278

Springfast Ltd, Unit 6F, Morelands Trading Estate, Bristol Road, Gloucester, GL1 5RZ Tel: (01452) 416688 Fax: (01452) 308723 E-mail: admin@springfast.co.uk

SPRING COILING MACHINE MANUFRS

Pave Automation Design & Development Ltd, Padholme Road East, Peterborough, PE1 5XL Tel: (01733) 342519 Fax: (01733) 563500 E-mail: pave@enterprise.net

SPRING COILING TOOLING

Spring Tooling Ltd, Alfred Court Saxon Business Park, Hanbury Road, Stoke Prior, Bromsgrove, Worcestershire, B60 4AD Tel: (01527) 876412 Fax: (01527) 878990 E-mail: andy@spring-tooling.co.uk

SPRING CONTACT TEST PROBES

Everrett Charles Technology, Homer House, Sibthorp Street, Lincoln, LN5 7SL Tel: (01522) 548220 Fax: (01522) 568419

Probus Electronics Ltd, Findon, Southill Lane, Pinner, Middlesex, HA5 2EQ Tel: (020) 8866 7272 Fax: (020) 8866 2999 E-mail: sales@probus.freeserve.co.uk

SPRING DESIGN

Juraise (Springs) Ltd, Sugarbrook Mill, Buntsford Hill, Stoke Pound, Bromsgrove, Worcestershire, B60 3AR Tel: (01527) 878811 Fax: (01527) 877537 E-mail: adrian@juraise.com

Southern Springs & Pressings Ltd, Stem Lane, New Milton, Hampshire, BH25 5NE Tel: (01425) 611517 Fax: (01425) 638142 E-mail: enquiries@southernsprings.co.uk

SPRING END GRINDING MACHINES

Bennett-Mahler Ltd, Merse Road, North Moons Moat, Redditch, Worcestershire, B98 9HL Tel: (01527) 62304 Fax: (01527) 591668 E-mail: bennettmahler@msn.com

SPRING HANGERS, CONSTANT/ VARIABLE

Carpenter & Paterson Holdings Ltd, Crown Works, Henfaes Lane, Welshpool, Powys, SY21 7BE Tel: (01938) 552061 Fax: (01938) 555306 E-mail: info@cp-ltd.co.uk

SPRING INTERIOR MATTRESSES

Baynell, 85-86 Darlington Street, Wolverhampton, WV1 4NG Tel: (01902) 425616 Fax: (01902) 311242

Burgess Bedding Ltd, 123 Pollard Street, Manchester, M4 7JB Tel: 0161-273 5528 Fax: 0161-273 5563

Dovetail Enterprises Ltd, Dunsinane Avenue, Dunsinane Industrial Estate, Dundee, DD2 3QN Tel: (01382) 810099 Fax: (01382) 814816 E-mail: enquiries@dovetailenterprises.co.uk

Downland Bedding Co. Ltd, 23 Blackstock Street, Liverpool, L3 6ER Tel: 0151-236 7166 Fax: 0151-236 0062 E-mail: sales@downlandbedding.co.uk

Heal & Son Ltd, The Heals Buildings, 196 Tottenham Court Road, London, W1T 7LQ Tel: (020) 7896 7555 Fax: (020) 7637 5582

Highland Blindcraft, 38 Ardconnel Street, Inverness, IV2 3EX Tel: (01463) 233662 Fax: (01463) 710809 E-mail: sales@highlandblindcraft.co.uk

Jay Be Ltd, Spen Lane, Gomersal, Cleckheaton, West Yorkshire, BD19 4PN Tel: (01924) 517820 Fax: (01924) 517910 E-mail: sales@jaybe.co.uk

Moffett & Sons Ltd, Seymour Hill Industrial Estate, Dunmurry, Belfast, BT17 9PW Tel: (028) 9030 1411 Fax: (028) 9061 0785 E-mail: enquiries@moffett.co.uk

MSS, Taffs Fall Road, Treforest Industrial Estate, Pontypridd, Mid Glamorgan, CF37 5TT Tel: (01443) 849200 Fax: (01443) 843377 E-mail: info@medsys.co.uk

Northsleep Ltd, 19-21 St Clair Street, Aberdeen, AB24 5TA Tel: (01224) 632334 Fax: (01224) 649282

Royal Strathclyde Blindcraft Industries Beds Mattresses Office Re, 12 Edgefauld Avenue, Glasgow, G21 4BB Tel: 0141-287 0800 Fax: 0141-287 0880

Sealy, Station Road, Aspatria, Wigton, Cumbria, CA7 2AS Tel: (0870) 7473259 Fax: (0870) 7429884 E-mail: salesorders@sealyuk.co.uk

Simmons Bedding Group P.L.C., Knight Road, Strood, Kent, ME2 2BP Tel: (01634) 723557 Fax: (01634) 290257

Staples Uk Ltd, Windover Road, Huntingdon, Cambridgeshire, PE29 7EF Tel: (01480) 442222 Fax: (01480) 442266 E-mail: enquiries@staplesbeds.co.uk

A.J. Tear & Co. Ltd, 76 Overstone Road, Northampton, NN1 3JS Tel: (01604) 639280 Fax: (01604) 633832 E-mail: sales@glanmar.co.uk

Towersleep Ltd, King Edward Street, Grimsby, South Humberside, DN31 3JW Tel: (01472) 355371 Fax: (01472) 242915 E-mail: sales@towersleep.co.uk

Vi Spring Ltd, Ernesettle Lane, Plymouth, PL5 2TT Tel: (01752) 366311 Fax: (01752) 355109 E-mail: info@vispring.co.uk

Warren Evans, 158a Camden Street, London, NW1 9PA Tel: (020) 7284 1132 Fax: (020) 7267 6604 E-mail: info@warrenevans.com

SPRING MANUFRS, *See also headings under Springs*

A Poole & Son Ltd, Hewell Road, Redditch, Worcestershire, B97 6AY Tel: (01527) 63676 Fax: (01527) 60136

The Active Spring Company Ltd, Sibleys Green, Sibleys Lane, Thaxted, Dunmow, Essex, CM6 2NU Tel: (01371) 830557 Fax: (01371) 831151 E-mail: sales@tascuk.com

Active Springs, Redditch Road, Studley, Warwickshire, B80 7AY Tel: (01527) 854932 Fax: (01527) 854969 E-mail: robert@active-springs.co.uk

All Spring Ltd, C/O Multistroke Ltd, King Street, Old Hill, Cradley Heath, West Midlands, B64 6JJ Tel: (01384) 567773 Fax: (01304) 566589 E-mail: allspringltd@btconnect.com

Alliance Spring Co Ltd, 44-46 Queensland Road, London, N7 7AR Tel: (020) 7607 3767 Fax: (020) 7609 2994 E-mail: sales@tascuk.co.uk

▶ Anglia Springs Ltd, Unit N Loddon Industrial Estate, Little Money Road, Loddon, Norwich, NR14 6JD Tel: (01508) 528396 Fax: (01508) 528240 E-mail: info@angliasprings.com

Ashfield Springs Ltd, Nunn Brook Rise, Huthwaite, Sutton-in-Ashfield, Nottinghamshire, NG17 2PD Tel: 0845 4941745 Fax: (01623) 455502 E-mail: bryan.smith@ashfield-springs.com

Ashworth Springs, 32 Tong Lane, Whitworth, Rochdale, Lancashire, OL12 8BE Tel: (01706) 854161 Fax: (01706) 854171

Baron Springs, Unit 3 70 Strathclyde Street, Glasgow, G40 4JR Tel: 0141-550 3477 Fax: 0141-554 7240

Batley Wire Products, 268 Bradford Road, Batley, West Yorkshire, WF17 6HT Tel: (01924) 470739 Fax: (01924) 520946

Baumann Springs & Pressings UK Ltd, East Mill Lane, Sherborne, Dorset, DT9 3DR Tel: (01935) 818100 Fax: (01935) 814141 E-mail: info@baumann-springs.com

Bevans Holdings Leicester Ltd, Gloucester Cresent, Wigston, Leicestershire, LE18 4YR Tel: 0116-278 2331 Fax: 0116-277 8307 E-mail: sales@bevanscomponents.co.uk

John Binns Springs Co. Ltd, Ghyll Way, Airedale Business Centre, Keighley Road, Skipton, North Yorkshire, BD23 2TZ Tel: (01434) 681111 Fax: (01434) 681100 E-mail: sales@jbsprings.co.uk

G.E. Bissell & Co. Ltd, Malt Mill Lane, Halesowen, West Midlands, B62 8JL Tel: 0121-559 2241 Fax: 0121-559 1168 E-mail: sales@bissell.co.uk

Charles Blyth & Co. Ltd, Carnival Way, Castle Donington, Derby, DE74 2NJ Tel: (01332) 810283 Fax: (01332) 855810 E-mail: info@charlesblyth-co.co.uk

John Bradley & Son Ltd, Spring Works, Russell Street, Heywood, Lancashire, OL10 1NU Tel: (01706) 360353 Fax: (01706) 366154 E-mail: jbs@johnbradleygroup.co.uk

Brayman Springs & Production Engineering, 7 28 Heming Road, Redditch, Worcestershire, B98 0DH Tel: (01527) 510004 Fax: (01527) 510004

Bywell Springs & Pressings Ltd, Unit 4, Millsborough House, Ipsley St, Redditch, Worcestershire, B98 7AL Tel: (01527) 66551 Fax: (01527) 66024 E-mail: sales@bywell.co.uk

Capital Springs & Pressings Ltd, Commerce Way, Edenbridge, Kent, TN8 6ED Tel: (01732) 867130 Fax: (01732) 867140 E-mail: sales@capitalsprings.com

Claridge Presswork Co. Ltd, 11 Bolton Road, Reading, RG2 0NH Tel: 0118-986 0114 Fax: 0118-931 3842 E-mail: sales@springsandwireforms.co.uk

D B Springs Ltd, 1 Double Century Works, High Street, Astwood Bank, Redditch, Worcestershire, B96 6AR Tel: (01527) 893220 Fax: (01527) 893220

Dene Spring UK Ltd, Bridge Works, Allum Lane, Borehamwood, Hertfordshire, WD6 3LT Tel: (020) 8953 6888 Fax: (020) 8207 5872 E-mail: deor@denespringuk.co.uk

DJD Components Wolverhampton, 2 Showell Road, Wolverhampton, WV10 9LN Tel: (01902) 426228 Fax: (01902) 424706 E-mail: steve@djd.co.uk

Doig Springs, Unit 1 Fairview Estate, Beech Road, Wycombe Marsh, High Wycombe, Buckinghamshire, HP11 1RY Tel: 01494 556700 Fax: 01494 511002 E-mail: enquiries@springs.co.uk

Don Springs (Sheffield) Ltd, 340 Coleford Road, Sheffield, S9 5PH Tel: 0114-244 1545 Fax: 0114-243 5291 E-mail: tony@donsprings.co.uk

Euro Springs, Unit 58 Dungannon Enterprise Centre, 2 Coalisland Road, Dungannon, County Tyrone, BT71 6JT Tel: (028) 8772 6169 Fax: (028) 8772 6524 E-mail: matt@eurosprings.co.uk

European Springs Ltd, 1 Indian Queens Industrial Estate, Lodge Way, Indian Queens, St. Columb, Cornwall, TR9 6TF Tel: (01726) 861444 Fax: (01726) 861555 E-mail: cornwallsales@europeansprings.com

European Springs & Pressings Ltd, Chaffinch Business Park, Croydon Road, Beckenham, Kent, BR3 4DW Tel: (020) 8663 1800 Fax: (020) 8663 1900 E-mail: sales@europeansprings.com

F B A Spring Engineers, 4 Howard Road, Park Farm Industrial Estate, Redditch, Worcestershire, B98 7SE Tel: (01527) 523524 Fax: (01527) 523524

Flexal Springs UK, 179 Park Avenue, London, NW10 7XH Tel: (020) 8453 0867 Fax: (020) 8961 9181 E-mail: flexalspringsuk@btconnect.com

Flexo Springs Ltd, Hill Street, Kingswood, Bristol, BS15 4HB Tel: 0845 4941786 Fax: 0117-935 2597 E-mail: sales@flexosprings.com

Goss Components Ltd, 43 Fulbourne Road, London, E17 4AF Tel: (020) 8527 5599 Fax: (020) 8527 1142 E-mail: enquiries@gosscomponent.com

A. & J. Green Engineering Ltd, Units 12-13, Enfield Industrial Estate, Redditch, Worcestershire, B97 6BG Tel: (01527) 62666 Fax: (01527) 584298 E-mail: ddptools@aol.com

Hanson Springs Ltd, Lincoln Street, Rochdale, Lancashire, OL11 1NP Tel: (01706) 522124 Fax: (01706) 640571 E-mail: sales@hanson-springs.co.uk

Harlow Springs Ltd, Unit B Cartel Business Estate, Edinburgh Way, Harlow, Essex, CM20 2TT Tel: (01279) 429004 Fax: (01279) 635953 E-mail: sales@harlowsprings.co.uk

Harris Springs Ltd, Ruscombe Works Tavistock Industrial Estate, Ruscombe Lane, Ruscombe, Reading, RG10 9LR Tel: 0118-934 0024 Fax: 0118-934 1365 E-mail: sales@harris-springs.com

Helical Technology Ltd, Dock Road, Lytham, Lancashire, FY8 5AQ Tel: (01253) 733122 Fax: (01253) 794880 E-mail: sales@helical-technology.co.uk

Industrial Springs Ltd, 2 Whitefield Road, Glasgow, G51 2YB Tel: 0141-427 6717 Fax: 0141-427 1680 E-mail: ind.spring@which.net

Innovative Springs & Wireforms, Unit 17 Millard Industrial Estate, Cornwallis Road, Lyng, West Bromwich, West Midlands, B70 7JF Tel: 0121-553 3373 Fax: 0121-553 3375

Irvine Spring Co. Ltd, 6 Kyle Road, Irvine Industrial Estate, Irvine, Ayrshire, KA12 8JS Tel: (01294) 279396 Fax: (01294) 277073 E-mail: info@irvinesprings.com

J B S Springs & Pressings Ltd, 7 Fordhouse Road Industrial Estate, Steel Drive, Wolverhampton, WV10 9XB Tel: (01902) 784396 Fax: (01902) 784396 E-mail: sales@jbsspringsltd.co.uk

J G Ross & Co Components Ltd, 19b Pershore Trading Estate, Station Road, Pershore, Worcestershire, WR10 2DD Tel: (01386) 552140 Fax: (01386) 555628 E-mail: info@jgross.co.uk

Kato Entex Ltd, Glaisdale Dr East, Nottingham, NG8 4JY Tel: 0115-929 3931 Fax: 0115-929 5773 E-mail: springs@kato-entex.co.uk

L & P Springs UK Ltd, Ravenscroft Way, Barnoldswick, Lancashire, BB18 6JA Tel: (01282) 814054 Fax: (01282) 814064 E-mail: sales@leggett.com

Lancashire Spring Company, Meadowhead Spring Works, Off Dale Street, Milnrow, Rochdale, Lancashire, OL16 4HG Tel: (01706) 715800 Fax: (01706) 715801 E-mail: info@lancashire-spring.co.uk

Lee Spring Ltd, Latimer Road, Wokingham, Berkshire, RG41 2WA Tel: 0118-978 1800 Fax: 0118-977 4832 E-mail: abinding@leespring.co.uk

Leeming & Peel Ltd, Duncombe Street Works, Bradford, West Yorkshire, BD8 9AJ Tel: (01274) 491464 Fax: (01274) 481690 E-mail: lpsprings@aol.com

Lion Springs Ltd, Summer Street, Rochdale, Lancashire, OL16 1SY Tel: (01706) 861352 Fax: (01706) 657863 E-mail: sales@lionsprings.co.uk

Litchfield Bros Ltd, Ripley Road, Ambergate, Belper, Derbyshire, DE56 2EP Tel: (01773) 852435 Fax: (01773) 852661 E-mail: aksimmons@lbplastics.co.uk

Long Technology Ltd, 1 Richmond Lane, Huntly, Aberdeenshire, AB54 8FJ Tel: (01466) 794646 Fax: (01466) 794111 E-mail: sales@longtechnology.com

Longcroft Engineering Ltd, Rochdale Road Industrial Estate, Walsden, Todmorden, Lancashire, OL14 6UD Tel: (01706) 819955 Fax: (01706) 819966 E-mail: paul@longcroftengineering.co.uk

Mercury Spring Ltd, Unit 2 Leamore Enterprise Park, Wall End Close, Walsall, WS2 7PH Tel: (01922) 712271 Fax: (01922) 409947 E-mail: mercuryspring@mail.net

Micro Spring & Presswork Co. Ltd, Enfield Industrial Estate, Redditch, Worcestershire, B97 6BW Tel: (01527) 69121 Fax: (01527) 61758 E-mail: email@microspring.co.uk

Mortimer Springs Ltd, Coleman Works, Villiers Road, London, NW2 5PU Tel: (020) 8459 1420 Fax: (020) 8451 7614 E-mail: sales@mortimersprings.com

C. Norris (Spring Specialists) Ltd, Ladyhouse Spring Works, Newhey Road, Milnrow, Rochdale, Lancashire, OL16 4JD Tel: (01706) 642555 Fax: (01706) 648347 E-mail: andrewward@btconnect.com

North Belfast Spring Works, 2 Cosgrave Street, Belfast, BT15 2JN Tel: (028) 9035 1813

Owen Springs Ltd, Aldwarke Terrace, Parkgate, Rotherham, South Yorkshire, S62 6BX Tel: (01709) 710700 Fax: (01709) 710666 E-mail: sales@owensprings.co.uk

Penning Springs, Bolton Road North, Ramsbottom, Bury, Lancashire, BL0 0LY Tel: (01706) 824614 Fax: (01706) 821636

Performance Springs Ltd, Queensway Industrial Estate, Scafell Road, St Annes, Lytham St. Annes, Lancashire, FY8 3HE Tel: (01253) 716900 Fax: (01253) 716911 E-mail: sales@performance-springs.com

Peterson Spring Europe Ltd, Unit 21, Trescott Road, Trafford Park, Redditch, Worcestershire, B98 7AH Tel: (01527) 585657 Fax: (01527) 588317 E-mail: sales@peterson.co.uk

Peterson Spring (UK) Ltd, Reddings Lane, Tyseley, Birmingham, B11 3HA Tel: 0121-706 2236 Fax: 0121-708 1253 E-mail: enquiries@psprings.euroe.co.uk

Protaform Components Ltd, Orchard Works, 76 Arthur Street, Redditch, Worcestershire, B98 8LJ Tel: (01527) 517500 Fax: (01527) 502373 E-mail: sales@protaform.com

Race Engine Components, Kingswood Farm, Kingswood, Albrighton, Wolverhampton, WV7 3AQ Tel: (01902) 373770 Fax: (01902) 373772 E-mail: jivey10194@aol.com

Recoil Springs International Ltd, Anchor Lane, Abbess Roding, Ongar, Essex, CM5 0JR Tel: (01279) 876020 Fax: (01279) 876747

Reliable Spring & Manufacturing Co. Ltd, Unit 4a Princes End Industrial Estate, Nicholls Road, Tipton, West Midlands, DY4 9LG Tel: 0121-557 4999 Fax: 0121-557 6959 E-mail: sales@reliablespring.co.uk

S D Precision, 3 Stevenage Enterprise Centre, Orchard Road, Stevenage, Hertfordshire, SG1 3HH Tel: (01438) 361587 Fax: (01438) 721217 E-mail: sales@sdprecision.co.uk

S M J Products, Richardshaw Lane, Stanningley, Pudsey, West Yorkshire, LS28 6BZ Tel: 0113-236 0396 Fax: 0113-261 2357

Skegness Springs Ltd, Hassall Road, Skegness, Lincolnshire, PE25 3TB Tel: (0845) 4305000 Fax: (01754) 610584 E-mail: sales@skegsprings.co.uk

Skelding's Ltd, 126 Oldbury Road, Smethwick, West Midlands, B66 1JE Tel: 0121-558 0622 Fax: 0121-558 6115

South West Precision, Mill Road, Barnstaple, Devon, EX31 1JQ Tel: (01271) 344221 Fax: (01271) 344355

Spring Developments Ltd, Lyng Lane, West Bromwich, West Midlands, B70 7RP Tel: 0121-553 6543 Fax: 0121-553 7552

Frederick Spring Co., Princes End Industrial Park, Nicholls Road, Tipton, West Midlands, DY4 9LG Tel: 0121-557 4080 Fax: 0121-557 6959 E-mail: robjenkins@btclick.com

Spring & Press Developments Ltd, Unit 49 Enfield Industrial Estate, Redditch, Worcestershire, B97 6DE Tel: (01527) 67602 Fax: (01527) 60183 E-mail: sales@kn-products.co.uk

Springco (N I) Ltd, Tavanagh Factory, Armagh Road, Craigavon, County Armagh, BT62 3EG Tel: (028) 3833 3482 Fax: (028) 3833 8721 E-mail: sales@springco.co.uk

Springcoil Spring Distributors, 2 Woodbourn Hill, Sheffield, S9 3NE Tel: 0114-273 1111 Fax: 0114-273 0222 E-mail: enquiries@springcoil.co.uk

Springmakers Redditch Ltd, Unit 2b Ipsley Street, Redditch, Worcestershire, B98 7BU Tel: (01527) 65300 Fax: (01527) 65300

Springmakers Redditch, Doward Crest, The Doward, Whitchurch, Ross-on-Wye, Herefordshire, HR9 6DZ Tel: (01600) 890325 Fax: (01600) 890325

Springmasters Ltd, Arthur Street, Redditch, Worcestershire, B98 8LF Tel: (01527) 521000 Fax: (01527) 528866 E-mail: sales@springmasters.com

Springstop Ltd, Unit 11 Block 3, Nuneaton Street, Glasgow, G40 3JU Tel: 0141-554 4424 Fax: 0141-554 4423 E-mail: springstop1@aol.com

SPRING MANUFRS – *continued*

Stevenage Spring Co. Ltd, 9 Hyatt Trading Estate, Babbage Road, Stevenage, Hertfordshire, SG1 2EQ Tel: (01438) 740078 Fax: (01438) 741065 E-mail: stan.copper@stevenagesprings.co.uk
Tested Spring Co. Ltd, 20 Hainge Road, Tividale, Oldbury, West Midlands, B69 2NG Tel: 0121-557 2308 Fax: 0121-557 4031 E-mail: sales@testedspring.com
Tinsley Bridge (Exports) Ltd, P O Box 89, Sheffield, S9 2DZ Tel: 0114-221 1111 Fax: 0114-243 1331 E-mail: general@tinsleybridge.co.uk
Trafalgar Textile Co. Ltd, Greenbrook Works, Lowerhouse Lane, Burnley, Lancashire, BB12 6ND Tel: (01282) 772923 Fax: (01282) 772923
Trusprings Ltd, Lodge Mill, Lodge Street, Wardle, Rochdale, Lancashire, OL12 9JR Tel: (01706) 648550 Fax: (01706) 377130
UK Spring Supplies, 7 Elmwood, Sawbridgeworth, Hertfordshire, CM21 9NL Tel: (01279) 723666 Fax: (01279) 723729 E-mail: larryelmwood@aol.com
United Springs Ltd, Mandale Park, Norman Road, Rochdale, Lancashire, OL11 4HP Tel: 01706 644551 Fax: 01706 630516 E-mail: amay@united-springs.co.uk
Valley Spring Co. Ltd, Pottery Lane East, Chesterfield, Derbyshire, S41 9BH Tel: (01246) 451981 Fax: (01246) 454327 E-mail: sales@valleyspring.com
Vernier Springs and Pressings Ltd, Edward Street, Redditch, Worcestershire, B97 6HA Tel: (01527) 582950 E-mail: roger@verniersprings.com
Wade Spring Ltd, Bennett Street, Long Eaton, Nottingham, NG10 4HL Tel: 0115-946 3000 Fax: 0115-946 1361 E-mail: mchiltern@wade-spring.com

SPRING PINS

G.E. Bissell & Co. Ltd, Malt Mill Lane, Halesowen, West Midlands, B62 8JL Tel: 0121-559 2241 Fax: 0121-559 1168 E-mail: sales@bissell.co.uk

SPRING PRESSINGS

Southern Springs & Pressings Ltd, Stem Lane, New Milton, Hampshire, BH25 5NE Tel: (01425) 611517 Fax: (01425) 638142 E-mail: enquiries@southernsprings.co.uk
United Springs Ltd, Mandale Park, Norman Road, Rochdale, Lancashire, OL11 4HP Tel: 01706 644551 Fax: 01706 630516 E-mail: amay@united-springs.co.uk

SPRING PRODUCTION MACHINERY MANUFRS

Damar Industrial Machinery Ltd, Clipper Road, Troon Industrial Estate, Leicester, LE4 9JE Tel: 0116-276 4144 Fax: 0116-246 0663 E-mail: sales@damar.biz
Mattress Production Technology Ltd, New Line Industrial Estate, The Sidings, Bacup, Lancashire, OL13 9RW Tel: (01706) 878558 Fax: (01706) 878288 E-mail: enquiries@mptg.demon.co.uk
Wafios-Metoma Ltd, 21 Colemeadow Road, North Moons Moat, Redditch, Worcestershire, B98 9PB Tel: (01527) 65396 Fax: (01527) 67570 E-mail: sales@wafios-metoma.com
Whitelegg Machines Ltd, Horsham Road, Beare Green, Dorking, Surrey, RH5 4LQ Tel: (01306) 713200 Fax: (01306) 711865 E-mail: sales@whitelegg.com

SPRING STEEL

Argent Steel Ltd, 1 Matthew Street, Sheffield, S3 7BE Tel: 0114-270 1428 Fax: 0114-272 3717 E-mail: enquiries@argentsteel.co.uk
Bond Precision Grinding Ltd, Trafalgar Works, Effingham Road, Sheffield, S9 3QA Tel: 0114-273 1212 Fax: 0114-276 5387 E-mail: bondpreci@aol.com
Corus Engineering Steels Pension Scheme Trustee Ltd, PO Box 50, Rotherham, South Yorkshire, S60 1DW Tel: (01709) 371234 E-mail: christianname.surname@corusgroup.com
George Ibbotson Steels Ltd, 16 Atlas Way, Sheffield, S4 7QQ Tel: 0114-244 7400 Fax: 0114-244 7412 E-mail: sales@ibbotsonsteels.co.uk
Graham Oxley Tool Steels Ltd, 55-57 Bridge Street, Sheffield, S3 8NS Tel: 0114-272 0403 Fax: 0114-275 2489
Shearline Steels Strip Ltd, 3 Gibbons Industrial Park, Dudley Road, Kingswinford, West Midlands, DY6 8XF Tel: (01384) 401533 Fax: (01384) 294892 E-mail: sales@shearlinesteel.com
Springstop Ltd, Unit 11 Block 3, Nuneaton Street, Glasgow, G40 3JU Tel: 0141-554 4424 Fax: 0141-554 4423 E-mail: springstop1@aol.com

SPRING STEEL STRIPS

Brite Band 1990 Ltd, Manywells Brow Industrial Estate, Cullingworth, Bradford, West Yorkshire, BD13 5DX Tel: (01535) 271427 Fax: (01535) 275676 E-mail: j.hanson@briteband.co.uk

SPRING WATER

▶ WaterPromotions, PO Box 27, Richmond, Surrey, TW10 6XN Tel: (020) 8948 5551

SPRING WIRE MANUFRS

Knight Precision Wire, Hadley Works, Cranborne Road, Potters Bar, Hertfordshire, EN6 3JL Tel: (01707) 645261 Fax: (01707) 649225 E-mail: kpw.sales@knight-group.co.uk
R & S Wire Ltd, Grove Street, Kirklees Steel Works, Brighouse, West Yorkshire, HD6 1PL Tel: (01484) 715120 Fax: (01484) 711882
Reddiwire Ltd, 9 Dunlop Road, Hunt End, Redditch, Worcestershire, B97 5XP Tel: (01527) 550202 Fax: (01527) 546856 E-mail: reddiwire@dial.pipex.com
Stride Supplies Ltd, 33 Monkspath Business Park, Highlands Road, Shirley, Solihull, West Midlands, B90 4NZ Tel: 0121-733 3010 Fax: 0121-733 3360 E-mail: sales@stride-technical.co.uk

SPRINGS TO SPECIFICATION

Capital Springs & Pressings Ltd, Commerce Way, Edenbridge, Kent, TN8 6ED Tel: (01732) 867130 Fax: (01732) 867140 E-mail: sales@capitalsprings.com

SPRINGS, SUSPENSION (VEHICLE)

A & B Pneumatics, 117 Halftown Road, Lisburn, County Antrim, BT27 5RF Tel: (028) 9268 3440 Fax: (028) 9268 3440 E-mail: abpneumaticsltd@hotmail.com
Brigg Motor Springs Ltd, 79 Bridge Street, Brigg, South Humberside, DN20 8NF Tel: (01652) 653280 Fax: (01652) 659029
Brost Forge Motorspring Service, Unit 7 149 Roman Way, London, N7 8XH Tel: (020) 7607 2311 Fax: (020) 7619 0370
Firestone Industrial Products Inc, Church Street, Staines, Middlesex, TW18 4EP Tel: (01784) 462326 Fax: (01784) 462327 E-mail: sales@firestoneindustrial.com
G M E Motor Engineers (Coventry) Ltd, Boston Place, Foleshill, Coventry, CV6 5NN Tel: (024) 7666 4911 Fax: (024) 7666 3020 E-mail: sales@gmesprings.co.uk
Jones Springs Engineering Ltd, Gladstone Street, Wednesbury, West Midlands, WS10 8BE Tel: 0121-568 7575 Fax: 0121-568 7692 E-mail: sales@jones-springs.co.uk
K & L Commercials, 2 Shelah Road, Halesowen, West Midlands, B63 3PG Tel: 0121-585 1349
N A R Gorup Ltd, Unit 6, Quorn Way, Grafton Street Industrial Estate, Northampton, NN1 2PN Tel: (01604) 631666 Fax: (01604) 232673 E-mail: nargroup@btconnect.com
Paddington Motor Springs, Unit 46 Stadium Business Centre, North End Road, Wembley, Middlesex, HA9 0AT Tel: (020) 8795 3300 Fax: (020) 8795 5954
S & M Springs, 3-4 Benner Road, Pinchbeck, Spalding, Lincolnshire, PE11 3TZ Tel: (01775) 712125 Fax: (01775) 712126

SPRINKLER DESIGN

▶ D I S Sprinklers, 183 Westgate Street, Gloucester, GL1 2RN Tel: (01452) 330585 Fax: (01452) 306692 E-mail: sprinklers@dis-ltd.co.uk

SPRINKLER SYSTEM COMPONENTS

▶ D I S Sprinklers, 183 Westgate Street, Gloucester, GL1 2RN Tel: (01452) 330585 Fax: (01452) 306692 E-mail: sprinklers@dis-ltd.co.uk

SPRINKLER SYSTEMS HOLDING TANKS

Galglass Ltd, 321 Hough Lane, Wombwell, Barnsley, South Yorkshire, S73 0LR Tel: (01226) 340370 Fax: (01226) 344200 E-mail: sscott@galglass.co.uk

SPRINKLERS, IRRIGATION

▶ Bei Giardini, 69 Braycourt Avenue, Walton-on-Thames, Surrey, KT12 2BA Tel: (01932) 244403 Fax: (01932) 244403 E-mail: beigiardini@aol.com
▶ City Irrigation Ltd, Bencewell Granary, 39 Oakley Road, Bromley, BR2 8HD Tel: (020) 8462 4630 Fax: (020) 8462 3810 E-mail: sales@cityirrigation.co.uk

SPRINKLERS, RESIDENTIAL PROPERTIES

Autoquench Ltd, 132 Priory Road, Hall Green, Birmingham, B28 0TB Tel: 0121-693 6888 Fax: 0121-430 6007 E-mail: mail@autoquench.co.uk

SPUN METAL PRODUCTS

Metal Spinners Group Ltd, Clough Road, Manchester, M9 4FP Tel: 0161-205 2286 Fax: 0161-203 4376 E-mail: msg@metal-spinners.co.uk

SPUR GEARS

M. Clarke Engineering, 566 Attercliffe Road, Sheffield, S9 3QP Tel: 0114-244 7234 Fax: 0114-244 7234
Compact Orbitial Gears Ltd, Unit A Brynberth Industrial Estate, Rhayader, Powys, LD6 5EW Tel: (01597) 811676 Fax: (01597) 811677 E-mail: info@compactorbitalgears.com
Derwentside Precision Gears Ltd, Morrison Industrial Estate, Stanley, County Durham, DH9 7XW Tel: (01207) 231274 Fax: (01207) 231274
Pentag Gears & Oilfield Equipment Ltd, 5 John Street, Sheffield, S2 4QR Tel: 0114-258 3473 Fax: 0114-258 4264 E-mail: meril@pentage-gears.com
Shaw Gears, Unit 5 Duchess St Industrial Estate, Shaw, Oldham, OL2 7UX Tel: (01706) 847220 Fax: (01706) 847220
T B Engineering Ltd, Network House, Perry Road, Harlow, Essex, CM18 7NS Tel: (01279) 418300 Fax: (01279) 418100
WMH Transmissions Ltd, Lichfield Road Industrial Estate, 24 Cavendish, Tamworth, Staffordshire, B79 7XH Tel: (01827) 310311 Fax: (01827) 307118 E-mail: sales@wmh-trans.co.uk

SPURS

Clark Electrical Services, 78 Milnrow Road, Shaw, Oldham, OL2 8ER Tel: (01706) 290837 Fax: (01706) 290837 E-mail: electricalspurs@aol.com
W Raybould & Sons Ltd, Croxstalls Close, Walsall, WS3 2XT Tel: (01922) 479196 Fax: (01922) 494616 E-mail: sales@raybould.co.uk

SQUEEGEES

Trelleborg Applied Technology, Halfpenny Lane, Knaresborough, North Yorkshire, HG5 0PP Tel: (01423) 862677 Fax: (01423) 868340 E-mail: sales@unitex.co.uk

STABLE AND HARNESS ROOM HARDWARE

Horse Requisites Newmarket Ltd, Black Bear Lane, Newmarket, Suffolk, CB8 0WB Tel: (01638) 664619 Fax: (01638) 661562

STABLE DESIGN AND BUILDING CONTRACTORS

Kingsland Saw Mills Ltd, Kingsland, Leominster, Herefordshire, HR6 9SF Tel: (01568) 708206 Fax: (01568) 708258 E-mail: info@kingslandstabling.com
Monarch Equestrian, King Street, Willenhall, West Midlands, WV13 1QT Tel: (01902) 605566 Fax: (01902) 633556 E-mail: sales@monarch-equestrian.co.uk
National Stables, Badlesmere, Faversham, Kent, ME13 0JX Tel: (01233) 740933 Fax: (01233) 740950
Norcroft Equestrian Development, 1 Norton Road, Loddon, Norwich, NR14 6JN Tel: (01508) 520743 Fax: (01508) 528879

STABLE DOORS

▶ Gibbs Bros, Kitesbridge Farm, Asthall, Burford, Oxfordshire, OX18 4HL Tel: (01993) 878600 E-mail: info@gibbsbrothers.co.uk

STABLES

Warwick Buildings Ltd, Southam Road, Long Itchington, Southam, Warwickshire, CV47 9QL Tel: (01926) 815757 Fax: (01926) 815162 E-mail: sales@warwickbuildings.com

STACK EMISSION MONITORING EQUIPMENT

Codel International Ltd, Station Yard, Station Road, Bakewell, Derbyshire, DE45 1GE Tel: (01629) 814351 Fax: (0870) 0566307 E-mail: sales@codel.co.uk

STACKER CRANES

▶ Production Lines Northern Ltd, 14 Pleasant Row, Queensbury, Bradford, West Yorkshire, BD13 2BW Tel: (01274) 812035 E-mail: philip@productionlines.co.uk

STACKER TRUCKS

Jungheinrich GB Ltd, Sherbourne House, Sherbourne Drive, Tilbrook, Milton Keynes, MK7 8HX Tel: (01908) 363100 Fax: (01908) 363180 E-mail: info@jungheinrich.co.uk
Manual Handling Solutions, 58, Paige Close, The Meadows, Watlington, King's Lynn, Norfolk, PE33 0TQ Tel: (01553) 811977 Fax: (01553) 811004 E-mail: sales@manualhandlingsolutions.co.uk
Yale Europe, Flagship House, Reading Road North, Fleet, Hampshire, GU51 4WD Tel: (01252) 770700 Fax: (01252) 770890

STACKING MACHINES

▶ Buffers & Stackers Ltd, Creative Industries Centre, Wolverhampton Science Park, Wolverhampton, WV10 9TG Tel: (01902) 420877 Fax: (01902) 716312 E-mail: info@buffstack.co.uk
▶ Worswick Engineering Ltd, Philips Road, Blackburn, BB1 5SG Tel: (01254) 261351 Fax: (01254) 682208 E-mail: sales@worswick.com
WRH Marketing UK Ltd, 6 Stanstead Courtyard, Parsonage Road, Takeley, Bishop's Stortford, Hertfordshire, CM22 6PU Tel: (01279) 635657 Fax: (01279) 445666 E-mail: productinfo@wrh-marketing-uk.com

STACKING STORAGE BINS

Bott Ltd, Bude-Stratton Business Park, Bude, Cornwall, EX23 8LY Tel: (01288) 357788 Fax: (01288) 352692 E-mail: info@bottltd.co.uk

STAGE LIGHTING CONTROL SYSTEM DESIGN

Avw Controls Ltd, Finningham Road, Rickinghall, Diss, Norfolk, IP22 1LT Tel: (01379) 898340 Fax: (01379) 898386 E-mail: info@avw.co.uk
Brilliant Stages Ltd, 2 Hillgate, Hitchin, Hertfordshire, SG4 0RY Tel: (01462) 455366 Fax: (01462) 436219 E-mail: sales@brilliantstages.com
▶ Nimulus Sound & Light, Ring Road, West Park, Leeds, LS16 6RA Tel: 0113-230 5222 E-mail: info@nimulus.co.uk

STAGE SET DESIGN

▶ Andy Dixon, PO Box 164, Hertford, SG13 7ZJ Tel: (0845) 3308770 Fax: (0870) 6611554 E-mail: andy@scene2.co.uk

STAGE SET HIRE

Dunkenhalgh Hotel, Blackburn Road, Clayton Le Moors, Accrington, Lancashire, BB5 5JP Tel: (01254) 398021 Fax: (01254) 872230 E-mail: reception.dunkenhalgh@mcdonald-hotels.co.uk
Ec Display Associates Ltd, Unit 1 Winsor, 50 Windsor Avenue, London, SW19 2TJ Tel: (020) 8545 0505 Fax: (020) 8545 0042 E-mail: info@ecdisplay.com
Executive Hotel Services, 165 Victoria Road, Swindon, SN1 3BU Tel: (01793) 615831 Fax: (01793) 513521 E-mail: ehs@btconnect.com
Macdonald Bower Hotel, Hollinwood Avenue, Chadderton, Oldham, OL9 8DE Tel: 0161-682 7254 Fax: 0161-683 4605 E-mail: admin@macdonaldhotels.co.uk
▶ Soundsounds, Balmoral Close, Earls Barton, Northampton, NN6 0LZ Tel: (01604) 811768 E-mail: sales@soundsounds.com
Steeldeck, Kings Cross Freight Depot, York Way, London, N1 0UZ Tel: (020) 7833 2031 Fax: (020) 7278 3403 E-mail: info@aolsteeldeck.co.uk

STAGES, VERTICAL TRANSLATION

▶ Codestrata Ltd, 21 Melbourn Road, Royston, Hertfordshire, SG8 7DE Tel: (01763) 222876 E-mail: codestrata@ntlworld.com

STAGES, VERTICAL TRANSLATION

– continued

▶ Language Link UK, Mooregate House, 7B Station Road West, Oxted, Surrey, RH8 9EE Tel: (020) 7484 0999 Fax: (020) 7830 9331 E-mail: london@languagelinkuk.com

STAGING HIRE

▶ Prosceneium Ltd, Sladen Wood Mill, Todmorden Road, Littleborough, Lancashire, OL15 9EW Tel: (01706) 377226 Fax: (01706) 371953
Steeldeck Ltd, 30 Arklow Road, London, SE14 6EB Tel: (020) 8692 9721 Fax: (020) 7278 3403

STAINED GLASS CONTRACTORS/WORKING EQUIPMENT/MATERIALS

Art Glass Ltd, Ellis Ashton Street, Liverpool, L36 6BN Tel: 0151-489 2214 Fax: 0151-489 2214 E-mail: sales@artglass.co.uk
Birmingham Glass Studios Ltd, Units 5 & 6 The Stained Glass Centre, 100-102 Edward Road, Balsall Heath, Birmingham, B12 9LS Tel: 0121-706 3131 Fax: 0121706 3130 E-mail: bhamglass@aol.com
Elegance In Glass Ltd, Hill Lane Close, Markfield, Leicestershire, LE67 9PY Tel: (01530) 243838 Fax: (01530) 249122E-mail: sales@eing.co.uk
John Hardman Trading Co. Ltd, Lightwoods House, Lightwoods Park, Hagley Road West, Birmingham, B67 5DP Tel: 0121-429 7609 Fax: 0121-420 2316 E-mail: info@hardmantrading.com
I W F Ltd, Ilderton Station, West Lilburn, Alnwick, Northumberland, NE66 4PH Tel: (01668) 217900 Fax: (01668) 217909 E-mail: neil@iwf.co.uk
John Baker & Partners, 35 Whitecross Road, Weston-super-Mare, Avon, BS23 1EN Tel: (01934) 627767 Fax: (01934) 616319 E-mail: jbandptns@btinternet.com
▶ Rainbow Glass Studios, 82 Berelands Road, Prestwick, Ayrshire, KA9 1ER Tel: (01292) 474279 Fax: (01292) 471426 E-mail: info@rainbowglass.biz
S G O Decorative Glass, Unit 41 John Wilson Busn Park, Whitstable, Kent, CT5 3QY Tel: (01227) 265259 Fax: (01227) 265299
Stained Glass Experience, Studio 7 Art At Cedar Farm, Back Lane, Mawdesley, Ormskirk, Lancashire, L40 3SY Tel: (01704) 823121 Fax: (01704) 823121 E-mail: enquiries@stainedglassexperience.co.uk
Tenby & Penny Co. Ltd, 38a Beulah Road, London, E17 9LQ Tel: (020) 8520 7706 Fax: (020) 8521 1632 E-mail: tenbypenny@supanet.com

STAINED GLASS MIRRORS

Steve Amin Glaziers, 14-16 St. Ronans Road, Whitley Bay, Tyne & Wear, NE25 8AX Tel: 0191-251 4893 Fax: 0191-251 4893 E-mail: stevenamin@hotmail.com

STAINED GLASS PANELS

▶ Rainbow Glass Studios, 172 Stoke Newington Church Street, London, N16 0JL Tel: (020) 7249 0276 Fax: E-mail: richard@rainbowglassstudios.co.uk
Steve Amin Glaziers, 14-16 St. Ronans Road, Whitley Bay, Tyne & Wear, NE25 8AX Tel: 0191-251 4893 Fax: 0191-251 4893 E-mail: stevenamin@hotmail.com

STAINED GLASS WINDOW SOLDERING IRONS

▶ Rainbow Glass Studios, 82 Berelands Road, Prestwick, Ayrshire, KA9 1ER Tel: (01292) 474279 Fax: (01292) 471426 E-mail: info@rainbowglass.biz

STAINED GLASS WINDOWS

▶ Rainbow Glass Studios, 172 Stoke Newington Church Street, London, N16 0JL Tel: (020) 7249 0276 Fax: E-mail: richard@rainbowglassstudios.co.uk
▶ Specialized Glazing Ltd, Unit 6, Marshlands Road, Portsmouth, PO6 1ST Tel: (023) 9221 4113 Fax: (023) 9221 4118 E-mail: sales@specializedglazing.co.uk
Steve Amin Glaziers, 14-16 St. Ronans Road, Whitley Bay, Tyne & Wear, NE25 8AX Tel: 0191-251 4893 Fax: 0191-251 4893 E-mail: stevenamin@hotmail.com
▶ Tempsford Stained Glass, Tempsford, Sandy, Bedfordshire, SG19 2AW Tel: (01767) 640235 Fax: (01767) 641124

STAINLESS STEEL ACCESS COVERS OR GRATING

ACO Buildings Drainage, Hitchin Road, Shefford, Bedfordshire, SG17 5TE Tel: (01462) 816666 Fax: (01462) 851490 E-mail: buildingdrainage@aco.co.uk
Duplex Engineering (Scotland) Ltd, 34-36 Napier Court, Wardpark North, Cumbernauld, Glasgow, G68 0LG Tel: (01236) 612757 Fax: (01236) 612757 E-mail: enquiries@duplex-engineering.co.uk
▶ R & A Sheet Metal, 30-31 Sedling Road, Wear Industrial Estate, Washington, Tyne & Wear, NE38 9BZ Tel: (07801) 768398 Fax: 0191-419 2700 E-mail: randasheetmetal@aol.com

STAINLESS STEEL ADJUSTABLE FEET

Nu Tech Engineering Services Ltd, Unit 7 & 14 Newtown Business Park, Albion Close, Poole, Dorset, BH12 3LL Tel: (01202) 724100 Fax: (01202) 724114 E-mail: sales@nutech-eng.com

STAINLESS STEEL ALLOYS

Heymark Metals Ltd, Becklands Close, Bar Lane, Roecliffe, York, YO51 9NR Tel: (01423) 323388 Fax: (01423) 326888 E-mail: enquiries@heymark.co.uk

STAINLESS STEEL ARCHITECTURAL METALWORK

radley fabrications, 16 St Michaels Drive, Roxwell, Chelmsford, CM1 4NU Tel: 01245 248983 Fax: 01245 248983 E-mail: jennick@mcgregor247.fsnet.co.uk

STAINLESS STEEL BALL BEARINGS

Anglia Bearing Co. Ltd, 17 Lealand Way, Boston, Lincolnshire, PE21 7SW Tel: (01205) 357200 Fax: (01205) 351663
▶ Arc Euro Trade Ltd, 10 Archdale Street, Syston, Leicester, LE7 1NA Tel: 0116-269 5693 Fax: 0116-260 5805 E-mail: information@arceurotrade.co.uk
Denton Engineering Co. Ltd, The Bearing Shop, 194 Talbot Road, Hyde, Cheshire, SK14 4HJ Tel: 0161-368 2097 Fax: 0161-368 0881
E B Bright Engineering Sales, Unit 1 Tennis Court Industrial Estate, Nottingham, NG2 4EW Tel: 0115-950 6570 Fax: 0115-959 0921 E-mail: brightbearings@supanet.com
P B I International Ltd, Unit 29-30, Roper Close, Canterbury, Kent, CT2 7EP Tel: (01227) 455800 Fax: (01227) 458838 E-mail: sales@ball-bearings.co.uk

STAINLESS STEEL BALUSTRADES

All Metal Fabrications Services Ltd, Thundridge Business Park, Great Cambridge Road, Thundridge, Ware, Hertfordshire, SG12 0SS Tel: (01920) 485200 Fax: (01920) 485055
▶ Escafeld Art Metalwork, Novo Works, Bessemer Road, Sheffield, S9 3XN Tel: 0114-256 2868 Fax: 0114-256 2898 E-mail: geoff@escafeld-art-metalwork.co.uk
▶ M-Tech Engineering, 1 Third Avenue, Greasley Street, Nottingham, NG6 8ND Tel: 0115-979 4448 Fax: 0115-979 4449 E-mail: matt@mtechengineering.co.uk
Quest Machining & Engineering Ltd, Units 5-9 Hewitt Business Pk, Winstanley Rd, Billinge, Wigan, Lancs, WN5 7XB Tel: (01695) 627555 Fax: (01695) 627666 E-mail: vickihunterq@aol.com
Steel People Ltd, Unit 3e Priory Park, Mills Road, Aylesford, Kent, ME20 7PP Tel: (01622) 715900 Fax: (01622) 715905 E-mail: mail@thesteelpeople.com
SWR Ltd, 3 Eastman Way, Hemel Hempstead Industrial Estate, Hemel Hempstead, Hertfordshire, HP2 7DU Tel: (01442) 219611 Fax: (01442) 259918 E-mail: sales@swrgaragedoors.com
Tecni-Cable Ltd, 54 Merryfields, Mark, Highbridge, Somerset, TA9 4NB Tel: (01278) 641930 Fax: 0870 7669578 E-mail: sales@tecni-cable.co.uk

STAINLESS STEEL BANDS

Band-Tite Co. Ltd, 9 Aizlewood Road, Sheffield, S8 0YX Tel: 0114-250 0393 Fax: 0114-250 0394 E-mail: sales@band-tite.co.uk
Brite Band 1990 Ltd, Manywells Brow Industrial Estate, Cullingworth, Bradford, West Yorkshire, BD13 5DX Tel: (01535) 271427 Fax: (01535) 275676 E-mail: j.hanson@briteband.co.uk
Morris Gordon Engineering, Unit 1 New Mill End Farm, Chiltern Green Rd, Luton, LU1 3TS Tel: (01582) 460002 Fax: (01582) 460038 E-mail: sales@morrisgordon.co.uk

STAINLESS STEEL BAR GRINDING

Effingham Steel Services Ltd, Butterthwaite Lane, Ecclesfield, Sheffield, S35 9WA Tel: 0114-246 8977 Fax: 0114-245 4272 E-mail: sales@effinghamsteel.co.uk

STAINLESS STEEL BAR MANUFRS

A K Steel (Stainless Steel Stockholders), Lloyds Bank Chmbrs, 3 High St, Baldock, Hertfordshire, SG7 6BB Tel: (01462) 499400 Fax: (01462) 896763 E-mail: sales@aksteel.co.uk
A S D Metal Services, Unit 6-8 Vernon House Walker Industrial Estate, Walker Road, Guide, Blackburn, BB1 2QE Tel: (01254) 696969 Fax: (01254) 696988 E-mail: sales@asdmetalservices.co.uk
Amodil Supplies Ltd, Enterprise Trading Estate, Guinness Road, Trafford Park, Manchester, M17 1SG Tel: 0161-877 4539 Fax: 0161-877 4541 E-mail: mcl@amodilmanchester.demon.co.uk
Arminox UK, PO Box 39, Peterborough, PE8 4JT Tel: (01832) 272109 Fax: (01832) 275759 E-mail: info@arminox.com
Barpoint Ltd, Willenhall Trading Estate, Midacre, Willenhall, West Midlands, WV13 2JW Tel: (01902) 608021 Fax: (01902) 601652
Carpenter Technology UK Ltd, 6 The I O Centre, Nash Road, Redditch, Worcestershire, B98 7AS Tel: (01527) 512200 Fax: (01527) 512201 E-mail: afoulkes@cartech.com
Carrs Special Steels, Wadsley Bridge, Penistone Road North, Sheffield, S6 1LL Tel: 0114-285 5866 Fax: 0114-285 5734 E-mail: info@elgcarrs.co.uk
Columbia Metals Ltd, Union Street South, Halifax, West Yorkshire, HX1 2LA Tel: (01422) 343026 Fax: (01422) 346587 E-mail: export@columbiametals.co.uk
Corus, Unit 2 Pullman Court, Bolton, BL2 1HL Tel: (01204) 370999 Fax: (01204) 396684 E-mail: chris.deacon@corusgroup.com
Corus, Hetton Lyons Industrial Estate, Hetton-le-Hole, Houghton le Spring, Tyne & Wear, DH5 0RD Tel: 0191-526 3288 Fax: 0191-517 0138 E-mail: paul.brown@corusgroup.com
K K S (Stainless Steels) Co. Ltd, Unit 2A, Charlton Mead Lane South, Hoddesdon, Hertfordshire, EN11 0DJ Tel: (01992) 445222 Fax: (01992) 446887
Rotherham Stainless & Nickel Alloys Ltd, Northfield Road, Rotherham, South Yorkshire, S60 1RR Tel: (01709) 828055 Fax: (01709) 829716
Schlolz+Bickenbach UK Ltd, Speedwell Industrial Estate, Staveley, Chesterfield, Derbyshire, S43 3JW Tel: (01246) 280280 Fax: (01246) 280445
Ugitech UK Ltd, Units 14-15 Erdington Industrial Park, Chester Road, Birmingham, B24 0RD Tel: 0121-382 9494 Fax: 0121-386 1328 E-mail: sales@uginesavoie.usinor.com
Valbruan UK Ltd, 36a Walworth Road, Andover, Hampshire, SP10 5LH Tel: (01264) 333390 Fax: (01264) 333315

STAINLESS STEEL BEARINGS

Countrose Bearings, PO Box 376, Birmingham, B42 2TB Tel: 0121-356 7220 Fax: 0121-356 7322 E-mail: c.bennett@tufnol.co.uk

STAINLESS STEEL BELLOWS

Heitz GmbH, 8 Priory Close, Deeping St. James, Peterborough, PE6 8PR Tel: (01778) 347164 Fax: (01778) 349240 E-mail: heitzbellows@yahoo.co.uk
Palatine Precision Ltd, Airport Industrial Estate, 45 Laker Road, Rochester, Kent, ME1 3QX Tel: (01634) 684571 Fax: (01634) 200836 E-mail: sales@palatineprecision.co.uk

STAINLESS STEEL BILLET MANUFRS

A S D Metal Services, Unit 6-8 Vernon House Walker Industrial Estate, Walker Road, Guide, Blackburn, BB1 2QE Tel: (01254) 696969 Fax: (01254) 696988 E-mail: sales@asdmetalservices.co.uk
Carrs Special Steels, Wadsley Bridge, Penistone Road North, Sheffield, S6 1LL Tel: 0114-285 5866 Fax: 0114-285 5734 E-mail: info@elgcarrs.co.uk
J B Stainless Ltd, 61 Washford Road, Sheffield, S9 3XW Tel: 0114-242 0042 Fax: 0114-243 0043 E-mail: michael@jbstainless.co.uk
Rotherham Stainless & Nickel Alloys Ltd, Northfield Road, Rotherham, South Yorkshire, S60 1RR Tel: (01709) 828055 Fax: (01709) 829716

STAINLESS STEEL BOLT AND NUT MANUFRS

Acclaim Fasteners & Turned Parts, Unit 17 Premier Park Estate, Leys Road, Brierley Hill, West Midlands, DY5 3UP Tel: (01384) 76263 Fax: (01384) 76268
Avon Stainless Fasteners, Unit 10 Riverside Business Park, St. Annes Road, St. Annes Park, Bristol, BS4 4ED Tel: 0117-972 8560 Fax: 0117-972 8570 E-mail: sales@avonstainlessfasteners.co.uk
Capital Supplies Ltd, 87 Boston Road, Croydon, CR0 3EJ Tel: (020) 8665 5520 Fax: (020) 8665 5838 E-mail: info@capitalsupplies.co.uk
D J T Engineering, Willenhall Lane, Bloxwich, Walsall, WS3 2XN Tel: (01922) 491919 Fax: (01922) 497332 E-mail: djtsales@btconnect.com
Everbright Stainless, Brimington Road North, Chesterfield, Derbyshire, S41 9BE Tel: (01246) 451600 Fax: (01246) 451611 E-mail: everbright.sales@infast.com
Ivyplus Fasteners & Fixing Devices, 41 Colmore Flats, Henrietta Street, Birmingham, B19 3PT Tel: 0121-212 2485 Fax: 0121-212 2485
J & T Locks Bolts & Bars Ltd, Victoria Works, Victoria Street, Stoke-On-Trent, ST4 6HA Tel: (01782) 349440 Fax: (01782) 349449 E-mail: sales@storagebins.co.uk
▶ Sea Screw, 4 Churchdale Road, Eastbourne, East Sussex, BN22 8PS Tel: (01323) 430294 Fax: (01323) 411778
South West Fasteners, 1 Shepherd Road, Gloucester, GL2 5EL Tel: (01452) 424346 Fax: (01452) 309313
Sovereign Fasteners Ltd, 70 Morgan Close, Willenhall, West Midlands, WV12 4LH Tel: (01902) 636191 Fax: (01902) 634508
Stainless Steel Fasteners Ltd, Broombank Road, Chesterfield, Derbyshire, S41 9QJ Tel: (01246) 451818 Fax: (01246) 455268 E-mail: sales@ssfast.co.uk
Stainless Threaded Fasteners Ltd, 7 Beldray Park, Beldray Road, Bilston, West Midlands, WV14 7NH Tel: (01902) 490490 Fax: (01902) 496583 E-mail: sales@stf.fasteners.co.uk
Tipper Engineering Ltd, Hall Lane, Walsall Wood, Walsall, WS9 9AS Tel: (01543) 452266 Fax: (01543) 452288
W J L Engineering, 30-31 Sapcote Trading Centre, Powke Lane, Cradley Heath, West Midlands, B64 5QR Tel: (01384) 567782 Fax: (01384) 412692 E-mail: wjlengineering@btconnect.com
Westgate Fastenings, 5-6 Cumberland Place, Lowestoft, Suffolk, NR32 1UQ Tel: (01502) 560061 Fax: (01502) 517505
Williams Fasteners, Unit 4a, Shepcote Way, Tinsley Industrial Estate, Sheffield, S9 1TH Tel: 0114-256 5200 Fax: 0114-256 5210 E-mail: sales@williamsfasteners.com

STAINLESS STEEL BRAID BANDS

Austin Wolstencroft & Co. Ltd, 56 Broadbent Road, Oldham, OL1 4HY Tel: 0161-624 5236 Fax: 0161-620 8413 E-mail: avrilbrooks20944@aol.com

STAINLESS STEEL BREWERY FITTINGS

C B Tool Engineers (Cambridge) Ltd, 5 Viking Way, Bar Hill, Cambridge, CB3 8EE Tel: (01954) 780411 Fax: (01954) 781075 E-mail: chapman.c@cbtoolengineers.com
Concept Stainless Ltd, Little Fields Way, Oldbury, West Midlands, B69 2BT Tel: 0121-552 8881 Fax: 0121-552 9981 E-mail: sales@concept-stainless.co.uk
Kayel Engineering Ltd, Guildford Road, Broadbridge Heath, Horsham, West Sussex, RH12 3JR Tel: (01403) 261026 Fax: (01403) 217340 E-mail: kayel@talk2121.com

STAINLESS STEEL BUCKLES

Make Fast Ltd, 31 Mochdre Industrial Estate, Mochdre, Newtown, Powys, SY16 4LE Tel: (01686) 629010 Fax: (01686) 626700 E-mail: sales@makefast.com

STAINLESS STEEL CABLE MANAGEMENT SYSTEMS

Uni Trunk Ltd, Altona Road, Lisburn, County Antrim, BT27 5QB Tel: (028) 9262 5100 Fax: (028) 9262 5101 E-mail: lisburn@unitrunk.co.uk

STAINLESS STEEL CABLE TIES

Eurolok Ltd, Tame Park, Vanguard, Wilnecote, Tamworth, Staffordshire, B77 5DY Tel: (01827) 287439 Fax: (01827) 287485 E-mail: sales@eurolok.com

STAINLESS STEEL CAPILLARY COMPRESSION FITTINGS

Euro Fluid Power Ltd, St. Marys Works, Brierley Street, Stoke-on-Trent, ST6 1LB Tel: (01782) 575306 Fax: (01782) 575534 E-mail: eurofluid@aol.com

STAINLESS STEEL CASTORS

A U T (Wheels & Castors) Co. Ltd, The Wheel House, Egmont Street, Mossley, Ashton-under-Lyne, Lancashire, OL5 9NB Tel: (01457) 837772 Fax: (01457) 832472 E-mail: sales@aut.co.uk

Blickle Castors & Wheels Ltd, 30 Vincent Avenue, Crownhill, Milton Keynes, MK8 0AB Tel: (01908) 560904 Fax: (01908) 260510 E-mail: sales@blickle.co.uk

▶ Castor Services Ltd, The Wheel House, Egmont Street, Mossley, Ashton-Under-Lyne, Lancashire, OL5 9NB Tel: (01457) 838001 Fax: (01457) 838998 E-mail: sales@castorserviceslimited.co.uk

STAINLESS STEEL CATERING EQUIPMENT

Alomgate Ltd, Unit 1, Shaw Road, Dudley, West Midlands, DY2 8TS Tel: (01384) 238786 Fax: (01384) 455261 E-mail: john@alomgate.com

Aluline T/A Olympic, 59-62 Brindley Road, Astmoor Industrial Estate, Runcorn, Cheshire, WA7 1PF Tel: (01928) 563532 Fax: (01928) 580224 E-mail: accounts@barolympics.co.uk

Birmingham Catering Equipment Ltd, Unit 139a, Middlemore Road, Middlemore Industrial Estate, Birmingham, B21 0AY Tel: 0121-558 2451 Fax: 0121-558 2452 E-mail: enquiries@bceltd.com

C C K Stainless Products Ltd, Units 17-18, SDH Industrial Estate, West Street, Sowerby Bridge, Halifax, West Yorkshire, HX6 3BS Tel: (01422) 834293 Fax: (01422) 839306

Camel Tableware, Camel House, Six Ashes, Bridgnorth, Shropshire, WV15 6ER Tel: (01746) 781610 Fax: (01746) 781607 E-mail: info@cameltableware.com

Comet Catering Equipment Co. Ltd, 45 Brimsdown Industrial Estate, Lockfield Avenue, Brimsdown, Enfield, Middlesex, EN3 7XZ Tel: (020) 8804 4779 Fax: (020) 8804 9470

Corsair Manufacturing Ltd, Beaumont Close, Banbury, Oxfordshire, OX16 1SH Tel: (01295) 267021 Fax: (01295) 270396 E-mail: general@corsair-mfg.co.uk

H L Hazeltine Aveley Ltd, Arcany Road, South Ockendon, Essex, RM15 5TB Tel: (01708) 852030 Fax: (01708) 856464 E-mail: hazelstinest@aol.com

Hospitality Equipment Supplies Ltd, Calderwood House, 7 Montpellier Parade, Cheltenham, Gloucestershire, GL50 1UA Tel: (01242) 573227 Fax: (01242) 226121 E-mail: sales@h-e-s.co.uk

▶ In Stainless, Unit 5, Hookstone Chase, Harrogate, North Yorkshire, HG2 7HW Tel: (01423) 885885 Fax: (01423) 819819 E-mail: sales@instainless.co.uk

Madison Grant, Freightmaster Estate, Ferry Lane, Rainham, Essex, RM13 9BJ Tel: (01708) 477377 Fax: (01708) 456552 E-mail: madisongrant@freeserve.co.uk

MG Stainless Ltd, Unit 1 & 2, Shaw Rd, Netherton, Dudley, West Midlands, DY2 8TS Tel: (01384) 232175 Fax: (01384) 232177 E-mail: mail@mgstainless.co.uk

E & R Moffat Ltd, Bonnymuir Works, Seabegs Road, Bonnybridge, Stirlingshire, FK4 2BS Tel: (01324) 812272 Fax: (01324) 814107 E-mail: sales@ermoffat.co.uk

Old Ford Ltd, 381 Old Ford Road, London, E3 2LU Tel: (020) 8981 7373 Fax: (020) 8981 2784 E-mail: catering@oldford.co.uk

P J Stainless Steel Products, 22 Skidmore Road, Coseley, Bilston, West Midlands, WV14 8SE Tel: (01902) 401053 Fax: (01902) 405548

Pedrette Engineering Ltd, Unit 1, Ashville Trading Estate, Bristol Road, Gloucester, GL2 5EU Tel: (01452) 410447

Samuel Groves & Co. Ltd, Norton Street, Birmingham, B18 5RQ Tel: 0121-554 2001 Fax: 0121-523 2924 E-mail: sales@samuelgroves.co.uk

Franke Sissons Ltd, Carrwood Road, Chesterfield, Derbyshire, S41 9QB Tel: (01246) 450255 Fax: (01246) 451276 E-mail: ws.uk@franke.com

Stellex Ltd, Hadston Industrial Estate, Hadston, Morpeth, Northumberland, NE65 9YG Tel: (01670) 760082 Fax: (01670) 761404 E-mail: sales@stellex.co.uk

Swift Catering Equipment, Harper Hill Industrial Estate, Buxton, Derbyshire, SK17 9JN Tel: (01298) 79381

Tube & Marine Products Bingley Ltd, Albion Garage, Keighley Road, Bingley, West Yorkshire, BD16 2RD Tel: (01274) 567534 Fax: (01274) 567539 E-mail: sales@tmpeng.co.uk

W K Thomas & Co. Ltd, Mount House, Mount Road, Chessington, Surrey, KT9 1HY Tel: (020) 8391 2211 Fax: (020) 8391 2980 E-mail: info@wkthomas.com

Wardpark Gardner, 30 Winchester Avenue, Denny, Stirlingshire, FK6 6QE Tel: 01324 825136

Wilman Universal Industries, Green Lane, Hounslow, TW4 6DF Tel: (020) 8570 4455 Fax: (020) 8572 2389 E-mail: sales@universaldispensesystems.com

STAINLESS STEEL CENTRIFUGAL CASTINGS

Doncasters F B C Ltd, PO Box 160, Sheffield, S4 7QY Tel: 0114-243 1041 Fax: 0114-243 1358

STAINLESS STEEL CHAINS

F B Chain Ltd, Jubilee Road, Letchworth Garden City, Hertfordshire, SG6 1NE Tel: (01462) 670844 Fax: (01462) 480745 E-mail: phil.taylor@fbchain.com

STAINLESS STEEL CLADDING CONTRACTORS OR WELDING OR FIXING SERVICES

▶ Sorba UK, The Barn, Witham, Essex, CM8 2BU Tel: 01376 507750

STAINLESS STEEL COIL CUTTING/DECOILING/SLITTING FACILITIES/SERVICES

Allied Stainless Ltd, Newtown Works, Cradley Road, Dudley, West Midlands, DY2 9SW Tel: (01384) 635000 Fax: (01384) 633000 E-mail: info@alliedstainless.co.uk

Knight Strip Metals Ltd, Saltley Business Park, Cumbria Way, Saltley, Birmingham, B8 1BH Tel: 0121-322 8400 Fax: 0121-322 8401 E-mail: kms.sales@knight-group.co.uk

Thyssenkrupp Stainless UK Ltd, Unit F Elliott Way, Holford, Birmingham, B6 7AP Tel: 0121-331 3600 Fax: 0121-331 3621 E-mail: b.newitt@acciaiterni.co.uk

STAINLESS STEEL COIL MANUFRS

Allied Stainless Ltd, Newtown Works, Cradley Road, Dudley, West Midlands, DY2 9SW Tel: (01384) 635000 Fax: (01384) 633000 E-mail: info@alliedstainless.co.uk

STAINLESS STEEL COLD ROLLED SHEET

Stainless International Ltd, George Henry Rd, Great Bridge, Tipton, West Midlands, DY4 7BU Tel: 0121-522 3111 Fax: 0121-522 3377 E-mail: a.holland@stainlessinternational.com

STAINLESS STEEL COMPONENTS

BWB Engineering, 145-149 Stanwell Road, Ashford, Middlesex, TW15 3QN Tel: (01784) 254321 Fax: (01784) 243451

Cooney Marine Intl Ltd, Telford Way, Telford Way Industrial Estate, Kettering, Northamptonshire, NN16 8UN Tel: (01536) 484481 Fax: (01536) 411580 E-mail: sales@cooneymarine.co.uk

Daver Steels Ltd, 395 Petre Street, Sheffield, S4 8LN Tel: 0114-261 1999 Fax: 0114 261 1888 E-mail: sales@daversteels.co.uk

G C Supplies UK Ltd, 13-15a Reliance Trading Estate, Reliance Street, Manchester, M40 3ET Tel: 0161-681 8114 Fax: 0161-947 0148 E-mail: sales@gcstainless.co.uk

H A England, Comtech Business Park, Manchester Road, Westhoughton, Bolton, BL5 3QY Tel: (01942) 814435 Fax: (01942) 814943 E-mail: sales@haengland.co.uk

High Lee Engineering Co. Ltd, Unti 1 Princess Street, Rochdale, Lancashire, OL12 0HA Tel: (01706) 644269 Fax: (01706) 524810

▶ In Stainless, Unit 5, Hookstone Chase, Harrogate, North Yorkshire, HG2 7HW Tel: (01423) 885885 Fax: (01423) 819819 E-mail: sales@instainless.co.uk

Petersen Stainless Rigging Ltd, Blaydon Business Centre, Cowen Road, Blaydon-on-Tyne, Tyne & Wear, NE21 5TW Tel: 0191-414 0156 Fax: 0191-499 0041 E-mail: admin@petersen-stainless.co.uk

Rushforth & Co. Ltd, Unit 3 Westfield Industrial Estate, Kirk Lane, Leeds, LS19 7LX Tel: 0113-250 9162 Fax: 0113-239 1394

Warren Engineering, B4-B5 Unit Northway Trading Estate, Northway Lane, Tewkesbury, Gloucestershire, GL20 8JH Tel: (01684) 298000 Fax: (01684) 295981 E-mail: warrenengineering@aol.com

Wincro Metal Industries Ltd, 3 Fife Street, Sheffield, S9 1NJ Tel: 0114-242 2171 Fax: 0114-243 4306 E-mail: sales@wincro.com

STAINLESS STEEL CONVEYOR SYSTEMS

▶ B & Y Engineering, 5 The Cross, Baltonsborough, Glastonbury, Somerset, BA6 8QW Tel: (01458) 850136 Fax: (01458) 851291 E-mail: info@byengineering.co.uk

Braham & Dixon Ltd, 88 Hodgson Street, Hull, HU8 7JB Tel: (01482) 211853 Fax: (01482) 211865 E-mail: eric@bd-eng.co.uk

Bringate Sheet Metals, Cross Green Industrial Estate, Cross Green, Leeds, LS9 0SG Tel: 0113-240 7711 Fax: 0113-240 7722 E-mail: sales@bringate.co.uk

Clow Group Ltd, 90 Camlachie Street, Glasgow, G31 4AD Tel: 0141-556 6324 Fax: 0141-551 9087 E-mail: engineering@clowgroup.co.uk

STAINLESS STEEL COOKWARE MANUFRS

Broadland Stainless Ltd, New Road, Acle, Norwich, NR13 3BD Tel: (01493) 753933 Fax: (01493) 753944 E-mail: sales@broadlandstainless.co.uk

Catering-Suppliers.com, PO Box 12976, Witton, B6 7AP Tel: 0121-331 4200 E-mail: cateringsuppliers@gmail.com

Walter Dix & Co., 1 Stirling Court, Team Valley Trading Estate, Gateshead, Tyne & Wear, NE11 0JF Tel: 0191-482 0033 Fax: 0191-491 1488 E-mail: sales@wdix.co.uk

Horwood Homewares Ltd, Avonmouth Way, Bristol, BS11 9HX Tel: 0117-940 0000 Fax: 0117-940 1100 E-mail: sales@horwood.co.uk

Kuhn Rikon (UK) Ltd, Landport Road, Wolverhampton, WV2 2QJ Tel: (01902) 458410 Fax: (01902) 458160 E-mail: gourmets@kuhnrikon.demon.co.uk

Metal Craft Industries UK Ltd, Allen House, 17-21 Paterson Road, Finedon Road Industrial Estate, Wellingborough, Northamptonshire, NN8 4BZ Tel: (01933) 440573 Fax: (01933) 440574 E-mail: sales@store-equipment.co.uk

Philbar & Co. Ltd, 254 Kilburn High Road, London, NW6 2BX Tel: (020) 7624 8681 Fax: (020) 7624 8683

STAINLESS STEEL DAIRY FITTINGS

C B Tool Engineers (Cambridge) Ltd, 5 Viking Way, Bar Hill, Cambridge, CB3 8EE Tel: (01954) 780411 Fax: (01954) 781075 E-mail: chapman.c@cbtoolengineers.com

C T Flow Solutions, 24 Second Drove, Peterborough, PE1 5XA Tel: (01733) 319009 Fax: (01733) 319906 E-mail: ctflowsolutions@yahoo.co.uk

Concept Stainless Ltd, Little Fields Way, Oldbury, West Midlands, B69 2BT Tel: 0121-552 8881 Fax: 0121-552 9981 E-mail: sales@concept-stainless.co.uk

STAINLESS STEEL DRAINAGE PRODUCTS

ACO Buildings Drainage, Hitchin Road, Shefford, Bedfordshire, SG17 5TE Tel: (01462) 816666 Fax: (01462) 851490 E-mail: buildingdrainage@aco.co.uk

R N D O Services Ltd, Colchester Road, Coggeshall, Colchester, CO6 1RR Tel: (01376) 563636 Fax: (01376) 563635

STAINLESS STEEL DRUMS

Deva Manufacturing Services, Unit 3 Chester Gates, Dunkirk, Chester, CH1 6LT Tel: (01244) 851183 Fax: (01244) 851187 E-mail: sales@deva-uk.com

Graham Engineering Ltd, Edward Street, Whitewalls Industrial Estate, Nelson, Lancashire, BB9 8SY Tel: (01282) 695121 Fax: (01282) 698498 E-mail: sales@graham-eng.co.uk

STAINLESS STEEL DUCTWORK

C S Struthers, Valletta Street, Hull, HU9 5NU Tel: (01482) 707766 Fax: (01482) 787479 E-mail: sales@csstruthers.co.uk

STAINLESS STEEL (DUPLEX TYPE)

Offshore Stainless Supplies, Gorsey Lane, Great Wyrley, Walsall, WS6 6AL Tel: (01922) 414003 Fax: (01922) 414606 E-mail: chris@off-shore.stainless.co.uk

STAINLESS STEEL (DUPLEX TYPE) BARS

Taylor Forgings, Effingham Road, Sheffield, S4 7ZB Tel: 0114-275 9155 Fax: 0114-272 8440 E-mail: sales@taylorforgings.com

STAINLESS STEEL (DUPLEX TYPE) FORGINGS

Abbey Stainless Steel Co Ltd, Admiral Steel Works, Sedgley Road, Sheffield, S6 2DN Tel: 0114-231 2271 Fax: 0114-232 4983 E-mail: info@abbeystainless.co.uk

Firth Rixson Forgings Ltd, Dale Road North, Darley Dale, Matlock, Derbyshire, DE4 2JB Tel: 0114-219 3005 E-mail: info@firthrixson.com

North West Forgings Ltd, Unit F2 Nasmyth Business Park, James Nasmyth Way, Eccles, Manchester, M30 0SN Tel: 0161-785 2785 Fax: 0161-785 2777 E-mail: sales@nationalforge.com

Rotherham Stainless & Nickel Alloys Ltd, Northfield Road, Rotherham, South Yorkshire, S60 1RR Tel: (01709) 828055 Fax: (01709) 829716

STAINLESS STEEL DURBAR PLATES

Heskin Fabrications Ltd, Whalley Works, Whalley Road, Heskin, Chorley, Lancashire, PR7 5NY Tel: (01257) 451483 Fax: (01257) 453242 E-mail: heskinfabs@btconnect.co.uk

STAINLESS STEEL EXTRUSIONS

Osborn Steel Extrusions Ltd, Brighouse Road, Low Moor, Bradford, West Yorkshire, BD12 0QL Tel: (01274) 677331 Fax: (01274) 607858 E-mail: extrusion@osbornbujon.com

STAINLESS STEEL FABRICATION INSTALLATION

A & B Fabrications, 1 Morrell Street, Maltby, Rotherham, South Yorkshire, S66 7LL Tel: (01709) 816402

A D R Art Metalwork, 109 Railway Arches, Cannon Street Road, London, E1 2LY Tel: (020) 7488 3776 Fax: (020) 7488 3776

A M P S Fabrications Ltd, Arch 36 Miles Street, London, SW8 1RY Tel: (020) 7587 1444 Fax: (020) 7587 5141 E-mail: ampsfabs@aol.com

▶ Access Design & Engineering, Halesfield 18, Telford, Shropshire, TF7 4JS Tel: (01952) 588788 Fax: (01952) 685139 E-mail: sales@access-design.co.uk

Birchall Engineering Ltd, Birchwood Park Old School, Cottingham Street, Goole, North Humberside, DN14 5RR Tel: (01405) 767930 Fax: (01405) 767876

C B Construction, 96 North Ormesby Road, Middlesbrough, Cleveland, TS4 2AG Tel: (01642) 231928 Fax: (01642) 211949 E-mail: keith@cbcon-cleveland.co.uk

Highland Smiddy Ltd, 54 Thornbush Road, Inverness, IV3 8AF Tel: (01463) 232905 Fax: (01463) 711529

STAINLESS STEEL FABRICATIONS

Alifab, New Hall Mills, Milton Road, Stoke-on-Trent, ST1 6LE Tel: (01782) 544844 Fax: (01782) 544866 E-mail: sales@alifab.co.uk

C R F (UK) Ltd, Unit B8 Wem Industrial Estate, Soulton Road, Wem, Shrewsbury, SY4 5SD Tel: (01939) 235000 Fax: (01939) 235111 E-mail: crf-sales@spunwebs.net

F E Philcox & Sons, 24 Church Road, Catsfield, Battle, East Sussex, TN33 9DP Tel: (01424) 892391 Fax: (01424) 892141 E-mail: mail@fep-gates.co.uk

Highland Smiddy Ltd, 54 Thornbush Road, Inverness, IV3 8AF Tel: (01463) 232905 Fax: (01463) 711529

▶ In Stainless, Unit 5, Hookstone Chase, Harrogate, North Yorkshire, HG2 7HW Tel: (01423) 885885 Fax: (01423) 819819 E-mail: sales@instainless.co.uk

Metal Fabrication Services, Unit 3-4 Soaphouse Industrial Estate, Howard Street, Bristol, BS5 7AZ Tel: 0117-955 4132 Fax: 0117-935 0185 E-mail: enquries@wcltd.co.uk

R M S Engineering Prestwick Ltd, 5 Glenburn Industrial Estate, Shawfarm Road, Prestwick, Ayrshire, KA9 2NS Tel: (01292) 671160 Fax: (01292) 671404 E-mail: info@rmstainlesssteelexhausts.com

Stellier Stainless Services, 6 Shipston Close, Brockhill, Redditch, Worcestershire, B97 6UN Tel: 07966 665974 E-mail: contact@stellierstainless.com

▶ indicates data change since last edition

STAINLESS STEEL FABRICATIONS TO SPECIFICATION

Abbott Fabrications Ltd, Unit 1b Woodleys Yard, Newton Road, Higham Ferrers, Rushden, Northamptonshire, NN10 8HW Tel: (01933) 419942 Fax: (01933) 411619 E-mail: enquiries@abbott-fabrications.co.uk

▶ Aller Engineering, Chantry Farmhouse, Unit 1, Aller, Langport, Somerset, TA10 0RA Tel: (01458) 259550 Fax: (01458) 259512 E-mail: allerengineering@hotmail.co.uk

Burton Fabrications, 1a Pearson Street, Netherfield, Nottingham, NG4 2JA Tel: 0115-961 8261 Fax: 0115-961 8261

Fair Deal Fabrications, Hammond Avenue, Stockport, Cheshire, SK4 1PQ Tel: 0161-474 1316 Fax: 0161-480 0635 E-mail: sales@fairdealfab.co.uk

Gem Engineering Ltd, Factory Road, Sandycroft, Deeside, Clwyd, CH5 2QJ Tel: (01244) 520859 Fax: (01244) 520328 E-mail: sales@gemengineering.co.uk

STAINLESS STEEL FABRICATORS

A B C Stainless Ltd, Empson Road, Peterborough, PE1 5UP Tel: (01733) 314515 Fax: (01733) 315273 E-mail: abcstainless@aol.com

A B G Fabrications, Old Tin Plate Works, Old Tin Works Road, Pontypridd, Mid Glamorgan, CF37 1UD Tel: (01443) 402085 Fax: (01443) 491664

A & B Welding Services Ltd, 1a Woodside Road, Bridge of Don Industrial Estate, Aberdeen, AB23 8EF Tel: (01224) 823444 Fax: (01224) 825079 E-mail: sales@abweld.com

A D E Engineering Ltd, Prospect Close, Lowmoor Business Park, Kirkby-In-Ashfield, Nottingham, NG17 7LF Tel: (01623) 753888 Fax: (01623) 750543

A & M Engineering Hull Ltd, Unit 30 B, Foster Street, Hull, HU8 8BT Tel: (01482) 820806 Fax: (01482) 824614 E-mail: sales@am-engineering.co.uk

A Stanley Engineering, Gee House, Holborn Hill, Birmingham, B7 5JR Tel: 0121-326 0014 Fax: 0121-326 1779

A W Fabrications Ltd, Unit 3 Parsons Hall, High Street, Irchester, Wellingborough, Northamptonshire, NN29 7AB Tel: (01933) 357163 Fax: (01933) 410021

Able Steel Fabrications Ltd, Unit 1 Park Street, Gosport, Hampshire, PO12 4UH Tel: (023) 9242 5425 Fax: (023) 9242 5444 E-mail: ablesteelfab@btconnect.com

James Aiken (Sheetmetal) Ltd, 10 Wellington Street, Aberdeen, AB11 5BT Tel: (01224) 572555 Fax: (01224) 571214 E-mail: enquiries@jasm.com

Alan Davies Stainless Ltd, 62 Westhoughton Road, Adlington, Chorley, Lancashire, PR7 4ET Tel: (01257) 481652 Fax: (01257) 483110 E-mail: ads@stainless316.fsnet.co.uk

Alex J Cheetham Ltd, Morton Street, Failsworth, Manchester, M35 0BP Tel: 0161-681 1115 Fax: 0161-681 0339 E-mail: mark@alexjcheetham.co.uk

Anglia Engineering Ltd, Estate Road, 2 South Humberside Industrial Estate, Grimsby, South Humberside, DN31 2TG Tel: (01472) 359455 Fax: (01472) 242478 E-mail: sales@anglia-eng.co.uk

Anvil Tubesmiths Southern Ltd, Sedlescombe Sawmills, Hawkhurst Road, Staplecross, Robertsbridge, East Sussex, TN32 5SA Tel: (01580) 830770 Fax: (01580) 830220 E-mail: barry.luckham@btopenworld.com

Aquarius Engineering Ltd, 52 Bergen Way, North Lynn Industrial Estate, King's Lynn, Norfolk, PE30 2JG Tel: (01553) 771716 Fax: (01553) 765164 E-mail: aquarius.eng@easynet.co.uk

Arc Energy Resources Ltd, Unit 12 Eastington Industrial Estate, Meadow Mill, Eastington, Stonehouse, Gloucestershire, GL10 3RZ Tel: (01453) 823523 Fax: (01453) 823623 E-mail: sales@arcenergy.co.uk

▶ Arcwell Mobile Welding, 64 Tansey Green Road, Brierley Hill, West Midlands, DY5 4TE Tel: (07860) 419626 Fax: (01384) 78009 E-mail: patricia@hopton8339fsnet.co.uk

Argent Engineering Services Ltd, 52 Stockholm Road, Hull, HU7 0XW Tel: (01482) 838698 Fax: (01482) 838668

Argon Arc Ltd, South Nelson Road, South Nelson Industrial Estate, Cramlington, Northumberland, NE23 1WF Tel: (01670) 707888 Fax: (01670) 707889 E-mail: argonarc@btinternet.com

Armthorpe Fabrication, Renny's Lane, Dragonville Industrial Estate, Gilesgate, Durham, DH1 2RS Tel: 0191-386 9502 Fax: 0191-386 2092

B H L Manufacturing Ltd, Llewellyns Quay, Port Talbot, West Glamorgan, SA13 1RG Tel: (01639) 884878 Fax: (01639) 890317

B J Doughty Engineering Ltd, Hereford Way, King's Lynn, Norfolk, PE30 4JD Tel: (01553) 773537 Fax: (01553) 767859 E-mail: admin@bjdoughty.co.uk

Barton Fabrication Ltd, Harbour Road Trading Estate, Portishead, Bristol, BS20 7BL Tel: (01275) 845901 Fax: (01275) 849462 E-mail: barton.fabrication@virgin.net

Bedford Stainless Ltd, 11c Dock Road, Connah's Quay, Deeside, Clwyd, CH5 4DS Tel: (01244) 830271 E-mail: bedfordstainless@hotmail.co.uk

Blackburns, Fircroft Way, Edenbridge, Kent, TN8 6ES Tel: (01732) 582700 Fax: (01732) 582799 E-mail: edenbridge@blackburnsmetals.com

Bolenda Engineering Ltd, Birds Hill, Clopton, Woodbridge, Suffolk, IP13 6SE Tel: (01473) 601982 Fax: (01473) 690954 E-mail: lee@bolenda.ndo.co.uk

Bradford Welding & Sheet Metal Co. Ltd, 340b Thornton Road, Bradford, West Yorkshire, BD8 8LD Tel: (01274) 480288 Fax: (01274) 480284

Bragman Flett Ltd, 34 Holmethorpe Avenue, Redhill, RH1 2NL Tel: (01737) 779200 Fax: (01737) 779600 E-mail: bragman.flett@btopenworld.com

Burton Fabrications, 1a Pearson Street, Netherfield, Nottingham, NG4 2JA Tel: 0115-961 8261 Fax: 0115-961 8261

Bush Welding & Engineering, 6 Grainger Road Industrial Estate, Southend-on-Sea, SS2 5DD Tel: (01702) 610871 Fax: (01702) 610871

C & B Engineering Ltd, I Edison Courtyard, Brunel Road, Earlstrees Industrial Estate, Corby, Northamptonshire, NN17 4LS Tel: (01536) 202583 Fax: (01536) 269402 E-mail: ian.candbeng@btopenworld.com

C & B Marine Ltd, Chichester Marina, Chichester, West Sussex, PO20 7EJ Tel: (01243) 511273 Fax: (01243) 511273

C J & L Fenwick, 2 Station Industrial Estate, Low Prudhoe, Prudhoe, Northumberland, NE42 6NP Tel: (01661) 833474 Fax: (01661) 833474

Cables Direct Ltd, C Industrial Estate, Heage Road, Ripley, Derbyshire, DE5 3GH Tel: (01773) 514514 Fax: (01773) 514515 E-mail: sales@cablesdirect.co.uk

Cansco Greig Engineering Ltd, Souter Head Road, Altens Industrial Estate, Aberdeen, AB12 3LF Tel: (01224) 898810 Fax: (01224) 878542 E-mail: mail@cansco.co.uk

▶ Carbro Sheet Metal Co. Ltd, Unit 7, 106 Richardson Street, Stockport, Cheshire, SK1 3JL Tel: 0161-477 0900 Fax: 0161-477 0370 E-mail: info@carbro.co.uk

Caroway Fabrications Ltd, 40 Aston Road, Waterlooville, Hampshire, PO7 7XF Tel: (023) 9226 7614 Fax: (023) 9226 2290

Centurian Products Ltd, 3-7 Bombay Street, London, SE16 3UX Tel: (020) 7237 2273 Fax: (020) 7231 8285 E-mail: sales@cent.demon.co.uk

Chapel Sheet Metal Ltd, Bowden Lane, Chapel-en-le-Frith, High Peak, Derbyshire, SK23 0QG Tel: (01298) 813041 Fax: (01298) 816256 E-mail: paul_csm@btinternet.com

Chelmer Precision Welding, Marks Hall, Marks Hall Lane, Margaret Roding, Dunmow, Essex, CM6 1QT Tel: (01245) 231269 Fax: (01245) 231842 E-mail: cpweld@aol.com

Chum Engineering Ltd, Churchill Way, Trafford Park, Manchester, M17 1BS Tel: 0161-872 3253 Fax: 0161-872 0484 E-mail: info@chumengineering.co.uk

Clow Group Ltd, 185 Broad Street, Glasgow, G40 2QR Tel: 0141-554 1739 Fax: 0141-551 0813 E-mail: clow@ladders-direct.co.uk

Coates Holdings Ltd, 3 Brindley Road, Cardiff, CF11 8TX Tel: (029) 2034 4554 Fax: (029) 2034 4545 E-mail: coates-co@fsmail.net

Colne Valley Engineering, Unit 12 Olds Close, Watford, WD18 9RU Tel: (01923) 776212 Fax: (01923) 896587 E-mail: alanhughes@tesco.net

Cooney Marine Intl Ltd, Telford Way, Telford Way Industrial Estate, Kettering, Northamptonshire, NN16 8UN Tel: (01536) 484481 Fax: (01536) 415580 E-mail: sales@cooneymarine.co.uk

Cruz Yardy Engineering, Roundwell Works, Dereham Road, New Costessey, Norwich, NR5 0SQ Tel: (01603) 746774 Fax: (01603) 746774

D M S Stainless Fabrications Ltd, 1 St Peters Works, St Peters Road, Maidenhead, Berkshire, SL6 7QU Tel: (01628) 777391 Fax: (01628) 777396 E-mail: sales@stainless.demon.co.uk

D Steer Fabrication, 4 Riverside Avenue West, Lawford, Manningtree, Essex, CO11 1UN Tel: (01206) 391767 Fax: (01206) 391767 E-mail: thesteers@virgin.net

Datum Fabrications, 66 Redhill Road, Yardley, Birmingham, B25 8EX Tel: 0121-753 0119 Fax: 0121-753 0272

Daver Steels Ltd, 395 Petre Street, Sheffield, S4 8LN Tel: 0114-261 1999 Fax: 0114 261 1888 E-mail: sales@daversteels.co.uk

Davley Fabrications Ltd, Drakes Indust Estate, Shay Lane, Ovenden, Halifax, West Yorkshire, HX3 6RL Tel: (01422) 355982 Fax: (01422) 355984 E-mail: sales@davleyfabrications.co.uk

Delta Systems Electrical, 65 Boleness Road, Wisbech, Cambridgeshire, PE13 2RB Tel: (01945) 466866 Fax: (01945) 466108 E-mail: sales@deltasystems-uk.co.uk

Demarchi Engineering, Vincients Road, Bumpers Farm, Chippenham, Wiltshire, SN14 6NQ Tel: (01249) 448860 Fax: (01249) 445496 E-mail: sales@demarchi.co.uk

Denbar Fabrications, Archers Yard, Springwell Lane, Northallerton, North Yorkshire, DL7 8QJ Tel: (01609) 770658 Fax: (01609) 770658

▶ Dendrite Fabrications, 18 Gordon Close, Leek, Staffordshire, ST13 8NZ Tel: (07785) 325342 Fax: (01538) 384789 E-mail: jasonbanks@worldonline.co.uk

Derbrich Fabrications, Estate Road 7, South Humberside Industrial Estate, Grimsby, South Humberside, DN31 2TP Tel: (01472) 885888 Fax: (01472) 884965 E-mail: fabrications@derbrich.freeserve.co.uk

Design Engineering & Fabrications International Ltd, 14 Newbridge Way, Pennington, Lymington, Hampshire, SO41 8BH Tel: (01590) 671411 Fax: (01590) 676021 E-mail: info@defint.com

Direct Fabrications (Banbury) Ltd, Unit 2, Bridge Wharf, Lower Cherwell Street, Banbury, Oxfordshire, OX16 5AY Tel: (01295) 270808 Fax: (01295) 270808 E-mail: info@directfabrications.co.uk

Dorset Stainless, 39 Balena Close, Poole, Dorset, BH17 7EB Tel: (01202) 697469 Fax: (01202) 658899 E-mail: solutions@robton.co.uk

Drawn Metal Ltd, 50 Swinnow Lane, Leeds, LS13 4NE Tel: 0113-256 5661 Fax: 0113-239 3194 E-mail: sales@drawnmetal.co.uk

East Goscote Fabrications 1992 Ltd, 2 The Warren, East Goscote, Leicester, LE7 3XA Tel: 0116-260 6161 Fax: 0116-264 0759

Eden Fabrication Ltd, Primrose Hall, Green End, Threeholes, Wisbech, Cambridgeshire, PE14 9JD Tel: (01354) 638446 Fax: (01354) 638467

Ellco UK Ltd, Nile Street, Stoke-on-Trent, ST6 2AZ Tel: (01782) 837160 Fax: (01782) 837160

Endless Supply Ltd, Unit 31, Darlaston Centre Estate, Salisbery Street, Darlaston, West Midlands, WS10 8BQ Tel: 0121-568 7676 Fax: 0121-568 6787 E-mail: sales@endlessupply.co.uk

Enterprise Engineering Services Ltd, Craigshaw Drive, West Tullos Industrial Estate, Aberdeen, AB12 3TH Tel: (01224) 288400 Fax: (01224) 871327 E-mail: sales@eesl.com

Equinox International Ltd, 1 Castle Gate Business Park, Old Sarum, Salisbury, SP4 6QX Tel: (01722) 415709 Fax: (01722) 424001 E-mail: sales@eqx.com

▶ Escafeld Art Metalwork, Novo Works, Bessemer Road, Sheffield, S9 3XN Tel: 0114-256 2868 Fax: 0114-256 2898 E-mail: geoff@escafeld-art-metalwork.co.uk

Evans Ltd, 11 St James Industrial Estate, Westhampnett Road, Chichester, West Sussex, PO19 7JU Tel: (07976) 444316 Fax: (01243) 530828 E-mail: john@evanswelding.com

Expertplan Ltd, 471-473 The Arches, Dereham Place, London, EC2A 3HJ Tel: (020) 7739 1080 Fax: (020) 7739 9384

F C Hammonds, 13-17 Dove Lane, Newfoundland Road, Bristol, BS2 9HS Tel: 0117-955 1377 Fax: 0117-987 2377 E-mail: f.c.hammonds@btclick.com

F E Philcox & Sons, 24 Church Road, Catsfield, Battle, East Sussex, TN33 9DP Tel: (01424) 892391 Fax: (01424) 892141 E-mail: mail@fep-gates.co.uk

Fabcon Projects Ltd, Delta Close, Norwich, NR6 6BG Tel: (01603) 482338 Fax: (01603) 484064 E-mail: andrew@fabcon.co.uk

Feldman Fabrication Co. Ltd, Unit 83, Owen Road Industrial Estate, Owen Road, Willenhall, West Midlands, WV13 2PX Tel: 0121-526 4434 Fax: 0121-526 4201 E-mail: feldmanfabs@btconnect.com

Fellows, 1 Wattville Road, Smethwick, West Midlands, B66 2NU Tel: 0121-555 8550 Fax: 0121-555 8660 E-mail: trevor@hsfellowsltd.com

Fussey Piling Ltd, Lancaster Approach, North Killingholme, Immingham, South Humberside, DN40 3JZ Tel: (01469) 540644 Fax: (01469) 540849 E-mail: info@fusseyengineering.com

G B Welding Services Rutland Ltd, Unit 8 Pillings Road Industrial Estate, Oakham, Leicestershire, LE15 6QF Tel: (01572) 722764 Fax: (01572) 724347 E-mail: admin@gbwelding.co.uk

G M P (Banbury) Ltd, Unit 2, Power Park, Station Approach, Banbury, Oxfordshire, OX16 5AB Tel: (01295) 275300 Fax: (01295) 275400 E-mail: gmpb@globalnet.co.uk

G N J Engineering Ltd, Meeting Lane, Brierley Hill, West Midlands, DY5 3LB Tel: (01384) 480818 Fax: (01384) 78176 E-mail: info@gnjengineering.co.uk

G W Smith Fabrications, Unit G1 Elvington Industrial Estate, York Road, Elvington, York, YO41 4AR Tel: (01904) 608722 Fax: (01904) 607171

W. & G.W. Garratt Ltd, Upper Allen Street Works, Upper Allen Street, Sheffield, S3 7HA Tel: 0114-272 7094 Fax: 0114-272 0115 E-mail: enquiries@garrattsonline.com

General Engineering, 11 Seymour Street, Ballymoney, County Antrim, BT53 6JR Tel: (028) 2766 2454

Gilwood (Fabricators) Co. Ltd, Bradshaw Street, Heywood, Lancashire, OL10 1PL Tel: (01706) 360131 Fax: (01706) 625666 E-mail: sales@gilwood.co.uk

Graham Engineering Ltd, Edward Street, Whitewalls Industrial Estate, Nelson, Lancashire, BB9 8SY Tel: (01282) 695121 Fax: (01282) 698498 E-mail: sales@graham-eng.co.uk

Grant & Livingston Ltd, Kings Road, Canvey Island, Essex, SS8 0RA Tel: (01268) 696855 Fax: (01268) 697018 E-mail: gandl.canvey@btconnect.com

Grove Engineering Services Ltd, Unit C, The Grove, Corby, Northamptonshire, NN18 8EW Tel: (01536) 402732 Fax: (01536) 401133 E-mail: grove_engineering@ic24.net

E. Harding & Sons Ltd, Units 10 & 11, Walker Industrial Estate, Walker Road, Guide, Blackburn, BB1 2QE Tel: (01254) 581276 Fax: (01254) 677012 E-mail: sales@ehardings.co.uk

Heating & Industrial Pipework Ltd, 19-35 Warwick Street, Coventry, CV5 6ET Tel: (024) 7667 2224 Fax: (024) 7671 3391 E-mail: hipcov@aol.com

Heavey & Co Engineers Ltd, Fielding Street, Eccles, Manchester, M30 0GJ Tel: 0161-789 1469 Fax: 0161-787 8226 E-mail: gedheavey@supanet.com

Hercules C S M D, Unit 14-16 Nelson Road, Townstal Industrial Estate, Dartmouth, Devon, TQ6 9LA Tel: (01803) 833736 Fax: (01803) 834846 E-mail: herculescsmd@aol.com

Hiatco Ltd, West Road, Annfield Plain, Stanley, County Durham, DH9 8NJ Tel: (01207) 282314 Fax: (01207) 283599 E-mail: hiatco@btinternet.com

Hillend, Ridge Way, Hillend Industrial Park, Hillend, Dunfermline, Fife, KY11 9JH Tel: (01383) 823621 Fax: (01383) 823090 E-mail: nat.hillend@btconnect.com

Holden Engineering (U K) Ltd, 35a Oxford Road, Penmill Trading Estate, Yeovil, Somerset, BA21 5HR Tel: (01935) 410615 Fax: (01935) 410617 E-mail: holden.uk@talk21.com

Hopefield Fabrications Ltd, Windacre Works, Mather Road, Bury, Lancashire, BL9 6RA Tel: 0161-797 1991 Fax: 0161-764 1461 E-mail: gary@hopefieldfab.fsnet.co.uk

Horsham Sheet Metal, Foundry Lane, Horsham, West Sussex, RH13 5PX Tel: (01403) 264137 Fax: (01403) 272386 E-mail: sales@horshamsheetmetal.co.uk

William Hustler & Sons Ltd, Henshaw Works, Henshaw Lane, Yeadon, Leeds, LS19 7RW Tel: 0113-250 3166 Fax: 0113-250 1272

Hydrapower Ltd, Middlemore Lane, Aldridge, Walsall, WS9 8SP Tel: (01922) 458760 Fax: (01922) 743186

I M Products Ltd, 2 London Hill Farm, London Road, Stockbridge, Hampshire, SO20 6EN Tel: (01264) 810261 Fax: (01264) 810642

Icon Engineering, Europa Way, Wisbech, Wisbech, Cambridgeshire, PE13 2TZ Tel: (01945) 474411 Fax: (01945) 474144 E-mail: paul@icon-eng.co.uk

Ireflo Products Ltd, 120 Broughton Road, London, SW6 2LB Tel: (020) 7736 2048 Fax: (020) 7384 2391 E-mail: sales@london-music.co.uk

J & J Engineering, 10 Misson Mill, Bawtry Road, Misson, Doncaster, South Yorkshire, DN10 6DP Tel: (01302) 719531 Fax: (01302) 719531

J W Baker & Sons Bradford Ltd, Premier Works, Newman Street, Bradford, West Yorkshire, BD4 9NT Tel: (01274) 651650 Fax: (01274) 681984 E-mail: bakerfabrications@btconnect.com

Kingswinford Engineering Co. Ltd, Shaw Road, Dudley, West Midlands, DY2 8TS Tel: (01384) 253411 Fax: (01384) 258107 E-mail: kfordengcoltd@aol.com

Knights Design & Manufacturer, Trident Business Park, 6 Park Street, Nuneaton, Warwickshire, CV11 4NS Tel: (024) 7634 4822 Fax: (024) 7634 4822

L M Engineering Services Ltd, Unit 226D, Redwither Industrial Complex, Wrexham, Clwyd, LL13 9XU Tel: (01978) 660111 Fax: (01978) 660227 E-mail: steel@lmeng.fsbusiness.co.uk

Lancashire Fittings Ltd, 16 Back Devonshire Place, Harrogate, North Yorkshire, HG1 4AF Tel: (01423) 522355 Fax: (01423) 506111 E-mail: sales@lancashirefittings.com

Lathe Trays Fabricators Ltd, Station Road, Rowley Regis, West Midlands, B65 0JX Tel: 0121-559 1115 Fax: (0870) 4202912 E-mail: admin@lathetrays.co.uk

Leton Engineering, Unit 14 Cockshades Farm, Stock Lane, Wybunbury, Nantwich, Cheshire, CW5 7HA Tel: (01270) 841977 Fax: (01270) 569226 E-mail: sales@1eton.net

Lilleker Engineering Co. Ltd, Unit 3b Lincoln Street, Rotherham, South Yorkshire, S60 1RP Tel: (01709) 829541 Fax: (01709) 829542 E-mail: sales@lilleker.co.uk

Lindsey Fabrication & Engineering, 4 Pytchley Lodge Road, Kettering, Northamptonshire, NN15 6JQ Tel: (01536) 485770 Fax: (01536) 410730 E-mail: sales@1indseyfabs.co.uk

M T Perry Ltd, 5 Rawcliffe House, Howarth Road, Maidenhead, Berkshire, SL6 1AP Tel: (01628) 630330 Fax: (01628) 630330 E-mail: enquiries@perryfabs.co.uk

Mcgrath Bros (Engineering) Ltd, Lisnagarvagh House, Lissue Road, Lisburn, County Antrim, BT28 2SU Tel: (028) 9262 1186 Fax: (028) 9262 1955 E-mail: cmccann@mcgrath-group.com

Magma Fabrication (Glenrothes) Ltd, 21 Faraday Road, Southfield Industrial Estate, Glenrothes, Fife, KY6 2RU Tel: (01592) 773046 Fax: (01592) 773046 E-mail: admin@magmafabrication.co.uk

Manesty Fabrication Services, Holmfield Industrial Estate, Holmfield, Halifax, West Yorkshire, HX2 9TP Tel: (01422) 241122 Fax: (01422) 241100 E-mail: chris.clarke@manesty.com

Marl Bank Sheet Metal Co. Ltd, Newtown Road, Worcester, WR5 1HA Tel: (01905) 22801 Fax: (01905) 726235 E-mail: marlbank@marlbank77.wannadoo.co.uk

▶ indicates data change since last edition

STAINLESS STEEL FABRICATORS - *continued*

Marpet Fabrications Ltd, Unit 04 Clyde Workshops, Fullarton Road, Glasgow East Investment Park, Glasgow, G32 8YL Tel: 0141-641 1778 Fax: 0141-641 7118 E-mail: marpetfabs@aol.com

▶ Martec Engineering Group Ltd, Block 7 20 Clydesmill Drive, Cambuslang Investment Park, Clydesmill Industrial Estate, Glasgow, G32 8RG Tel: 0141-646 5220 Fax: 0141-646 1056E-mail: martec@martecengineering.co.uk

Metal Fabrication Services, Unit 3-4 Soaphouse Industrial Estate, Howard Street, Bristol, BS5 7AZ Tel: 0117-955 4132 Fax: 0117-935 0185 E-mail: enquries@wcltd.co.uk

Metal Prefabrications Dartford Ltd, Dewlands Estate, London Road, Stone, Dartford, DA2 6AS Tel: (01322) 220171 Fax: (01322) 288089

Modern Equipment & Foundry Engineering Ltd, 1 Dalton Lane, Keighley, West Yorkshire, BD21 4HW Tel: (01535) 605501 Fax: (01535) 602816

Northbourne Engineering Ltd, The Old Malt House, Easole Street, Nonington, Dover, Kent, CT15 4HF Tel: (01304) 842858 Fax: (01304) 842868 E-mail: northbourneeng@talk21.com

Northern Fabrications, Albion Road, Bradford, West Yorkshire, BD10 9LT Tel: 01274 613874

Northern Fabricators Ltd, Chanonry Industrial Estate, Elgin, Morayshire, IV30 6ND Tel: (01343) 546139 Fax: (01343) 549420 E-mail: enquiries@norfabs.co.uk

Norwich Sheet Metal Co. Ltd, 11 Hurricane Way, Norwich, NR6 6EZ Tel: (01603) 419490 Fax: (01603) 404590 E-mail: nsmetal@btconnect.com

P K D Precision Sheet Metal Ltd, Unit 7 Furlong Industrial Estate, Dain Street, Stoke-on-Trent, ST6 3LN Tel: (01782) 824800 Fax: (01782) 811746 E-mail: sales@pkdsheetmetal.co.uk

Park Engineering, Manor Farm, Manor Road, South Hinksey, Oxford, OX1 5AS Tel: (01865) 327050 Fax: (01865) 327050

Parkway Sheet Metal Works Ltd, Rawmarsh Road, Rotherham, South Yorkshire, S60 1RZ Tel: (01709) 374726 Fax: (01709) 829739

Pedrette Engineering Ltd, Unit 1, Ashville Trading Estate, Bristol Road, Gloucester, GL2 5EU Tel: (01452) 410447

Perfab Engineering Ltd, Unit 3 Northway Lane, Tewkesbury, Gloucestershire, GL20 8HA Tel: (01684) 298423 Fax: (01684) 850427

Peterborough Sheet Metal Ltd, Unit 12 Towermead Business Centre, High Street, Peterborough, PE2 9DY Tel: (01733) 344880 Fax: (01733) 898421

Phoenix Marine Ltd, 2 Marrowbone Slip, Sutton Rd, Plymouth, PL4 0HX Tel: (01752) 267428 Fax: (01752) 267415 E-mail: info@phoenix316.com

Plancraft Marine Ltd, 4 Little Shellwood Farm, Clayhill Road, Leigh, Reigate, Surrey, RH2 8PA Tel: (01306) 611100 Fax: (01306) 611101 E-mail: sales@plancraft.co.uk

Plymol Tubes Ltd, 6 Ravells Yard, Carr Lane, Hoylake, Wirral, Merseyside, CH47 4AZ Tel: 0151-632 1354 Fax: 0151-632 4912 E-mail: sales@flagstaffs.co.uk

PMF, N Quarry Road, Newhaven, East Sussex, BN9 9DG Tel: (01273) 517333 Fax: (01273) 517222 E-mail: sales@pmfdesigns.co.uk

▶ Porteous Fabrication, 1 Baronscourt Road, Willowbrae, Edinburgh, EH8 7ET Tel: 0131 6610907

Prep Tec Systems Ltd, Fern Hill Business Centre, Todd Street, Bury, Lancashire, BL9 5BJ Tel: 0161-761 5214 Fax: 0161-764 1914 E-mail: info@prep-tec.co.uk

Protech Fabrications Ltd, Rushden Road, Milton Ernest, Bedford, MK44 1RU Tel: (01234) 826233 Fax: (01234) 822762 E-mail: info@protech-food-systems.co.uk

Pulling, Sweetlands Way, Gosberton, Spalding, Lincolnshire, PE11 4HH Tel: (01775) 841070 Fax: (01775) 840167 E-mail: info@andypullingengineering.co.uk

R E Rose, 4 Oakwood Business Park, Stephenson Road West, Clacton-on-Sea, Essex, CO15 4TL Tel: (01255) 428928 Fax: (01255) 434937

R G Abercrombie, Caledonian Road, Alloa, Clackmannanshire, FK10 1NB Tel: (01259) 222500 Fax: (01259) 222528 E-mail: info@diageo.com

R I N C Engineering, 22 Singer Road, Kelvin Industrial Estate, East Kilbride, Glasgow, G75 0XS Tel: (01355) 248610 Fax: (01355) 248610 E-mail: rinc@wwwmail.co.uk

R S M Engineering Tamworth Ltd, Unit 14 Two Gates Industrial Estate, Watling Street, Two Gates, Tamworth, Staffordshire, B77 5AE Tel: (01827) 250816 Fax: (01827) 287898

R Sanderson & Sons Ltd, Cannon Street, Hull, HU2 0AB Tel: (01482) 226286 Fax: (01482) 327220 E-mail: info@robert-sanderson.co.uk

Redfern & Birchall, 6 Fernhill Street, Bury, Lancashire, BL9 5BG Tel: 0161-764 4929 Fax: 0161-764 4929

Renegade Engineering Co. Ltd, Unit F Penfold Works, Imperial Way, Watford, WD24 4YY Tel: (01923) 230788 Fax: (01923) 219496

Resurgem Engineering Co. Ltd, Bury Manor, High Street, Wick, Bristol, BS30 5SH Tel: 0117-937 2987 Fax: 0117-937 3516 E-mail: sales@resurgem.co.uk

Rictor Engineering Ltd, Derby Street, Denton, Manchester, M34 3SD Tel: 0161-320 8842 Fax: 0161-335 0973

Risuda Fabrications Ltd, Hare Street, Hopwood Lane, Halifax, West Yorkshire, HX1 4DJ Tel: (01422) 369782 Fax: (01422) 348251

Roaches International Ltd, Upperhulme, Leek, Staffordshire, ST13 8TY Tel: (01538) 300425 Fax: (01538) 300364 E-mail: info@roaches.co.uk

Round House Ltd, 57 Pinbush Road, Lowestoft, Suffolk, NR33 7NL Tel: (01502) 515220 Fax: (01502) 500954 E-mail: sales@roundhouse.biz

N. Rourke & Son (Engineering) Ltd, 4-6 Barkan Way, Swinton, Manchester, M27 8SF Tel: 0161-793 5171 Fax: 0161-794 4760 E-mail: nrourkeson@hotmail.com

Rowlands & Naylor, Unit 2 Aerial Business Park, Lambourn Woodlands, Hungerford, Berkshire, RG17 7RZ Tel: (01488) 72229 Fax: (01488) 73048 E-mail: rowlands@rowlandsandnaylor.co.uk

S A Jones, Unit 3 Gwyrfai Mills, Bontnewydd, Caernarfon, Gwynedd, LL54 7UN Tel: (01286) 678683 Fax: (01286) 678683

Sam's Fabrication, Unit 17 Morgan Way, Bowthorpe Employment Area, Norwich, NR5 9JJ Tel: (01603) 743252 Fax: (01603) 746927 E-mail: sales@samsfabrications.co.uk

Sandersons T C M, Unit 5 Wallis Court, Road Three, Winsford Industrial Estate, Winsford, Cheshire, CW7 3PD Tel: (01606) 550668

Satin Stainless Fabrications, Bridge Road, Weston-super-Mare, Avon, BS23 3NE Tel: 01934 632870

Sheet Tech Fabrications, 6 Doman Road, Camberley, Surrey, GU15 3DF Tel: (01276) 684800 Fax: (01276) 20696 E-mail: cliffdottson@sheettech.fsnet.co.uk

Site Engineering Services, Reverdane Road, Congleton, Cheshire, CW12 1UN Tel: (01260) 275252 Fax: (01260) 270211 E-mail: sales@phoenixengineering.co.uk

Skillforce Ltd, Eton Hill Road, Radcliffe, Manchester, M26 2ZT Tel: 0161-724 6634 Fax: 0161-723 1661 E-mail: sales@parsonsreiss.com

Southcroft Engineering Co. Ltd, Thurcroft Industrial Estate, New Orchard Road, Thurcroft, Rotherham, South Yorkshire, S66 9HY Tel: (01709) 545147 Fax: (01709) 700259

Speedfab Ltd, Unit 10, Credenda Road, West Bromwich, West Midlands, B70 7JE Tel: 0121-541 1761 Fax: 0121-544 0028 E-mail: speedfabltd@aol.com

Sshteel, The Lodge, Cefn Bychan Woods, Pantymwyn, Mold, Clwyd, CH7 5EP Tel: (01352) 742111 Fax: (01352) 742101

Stace Yates Ltd, Unit 24 Bamfurlong Industrial Park, Staverton, Cheltenham, Gloucestershire, GL51 6SX Tel: (01452) 713722 Fax: (01452) 713282

Stainfab Sheet Metal Ltd, 50 Offerton Industrial Estate, Hempshaw Lane, Stockport, Cheshire, SK2 5TJ Tel: 0161-480 5009 Fax: 0161-480 5509 E-mail: sales@stainfab.com

Stainfree Fabrications Ltd, Cockersdale Works, Whitehall Road, Drighlington, Bradford, West Yorkshire, BD11 1NQ Tel: 0113-285 4299 Fax: 0113-285 2706 E-mail: mail@stainfree-fabrications.ltd.uk

Stainless & Alloy Products Ltd, 8 Greets Green Road Industrial Estate, Greets Green Road, West Bromwich, West Midlands, B70 9EW Tel: 0121-557 0033 Fax: 0121-557 7775

Stainless Metalcraft, Chatteris Engineering Works, Honeysome Road, Chatteris, Cambridgeshire, PE16 6SA Tel: (01354) 692391 Fax: (01354) 695281 E-mail: infoline@metalcraft.co.uk

Stevend Ltd, Fieldhouse Lane, Marlow, Buckinghamshire, SL7 1LW Tel: (01628) 472374 Fax: (01628) 475050 E-mail: ralph@stevend.co.uk

Stoneman Engineering Ltd, Parks Works, Station Road, Tiverton Junction, Cullompton, Devon, EX15 2QA Tel: (01884) 820369 Fax: (01884) 821533 E-mail: sales@stoneman-engineering.co.uk

T A M Engineering, Leverington Common, Leverington, Wisbech, Cambridgeshire, PE13 5JG Tel: (01945) 410494 Fax: (01945) 410476

A. Taylor & Son (Leeds) Ltd, Weaver Street, Leeds, LS4 2AY Tel: 0113-263 9036 Fax: 0113-231 0286 E-mail: sales@ataylor.co.uk

Technical Fabrications, Unit 28 Rowfant Business Centre, Wallage Lane, Rowfant, Crawley, West Sussex, RH10 4NQ Tel: (01342) 717523 Fax: (01342) 715392

Technical Welding Services, Corporation Road, Rochdale, Lancashire, OL11 4HJ Tel: (01706) 655402 Fax: (01706) 657735 E-mail: sales@technicalwelding.co.uk

Technicraft Anglia Ltd, Wilford Bridge Road, Melton, Woodbridge, Suffolk, IP12 1RB Tel: (01394) 385213 Fax: (01394) 387914 E-mail: technicraft@technicraft.co.uk

Teme Valley Engineering, 1-3 Rosemary Lane, Leintwardine, Craven Arms, Shropshire, SY7 0LP Tel: (01547) 540321 Fax: (01547) 540486

Terry Gregory Metal Fabrications Ltd, 599 Kingston Road, London, SW20 8SA Tel: (020) 8542 9941 Fax: (020) 8543 6091 E-mail: metal@terrygregory.freeserve.co.uk

Tilewind Ltd, Carcroft Industrial Estate, Adwick Le St, Doncaster, South Yorkshire, DN6 7BD Tel: 01302 721205

Tiverton Fabrications Ltd, Tiverton Business Park, Tiverton Way, Tiverton, Devon, EX16 6TG Tel: (01884) 255701 Fax: (01884) 253047

Tyne Tunnel Engineering Ltd, B3 Narvik Way, Tyne Tunnel Trading Estate, North Shields, Tyne & Wear, NE29 7XJ Tel: 0191-258 0585 Fax: 0191-296 1745 E-mail: enquiries@ttengineering.co.uk

Uniseed Engineering Ltd, Shepherds Grove Industrial Estate, Stanton, Bury St. Edmunds, Suffolk, IP31 2AR Tel: (01359) 250469 Fax: (01359) 252245

Unitech Engineering Ltd, Prospect Road, Burntwood, Staffordshire, WS7 0AL Tel: (01543) 675800 Fax: (01543) 687070 E-mail: info@unitech.uk.com

Universal Fabrications North West Ltd, Star Iron Works, Taurus Street, Oldham, OL4 2BN Tel: 0161-620 0550 Fax: 0161-620 0247 E-mail: sales@universal-fabrications.co.uk

Universal Sheet Metal Co., Dunlop Road, Hunt End Industrial Estate, Redditch, Worcestershire, B97 5XP Tel: (01527) 402202 Fax: (01527) 403030 E-mail: usm@usmlimited.co.uk

V P Welding Ltd, VP Square, Storeys Bar Road, Peterborough, PE1 5YS Tel: (01733) 552888 Fax: (01733) 311972

Vacflo, Unit 14, Bingswood Industrial Estate, Whaley Bridge, High Peak, Derbyshire, SK23 7LY Tel: (01663) 719519 Fax: (01663) 719519 E-mail: mail@vacflo.com

Vertex Precision Engineering Ltd, 7 Armoury Road, Lufton Trading Estate, Yeovil, Somerset, BA22 8RL Tel: (01935) 477310 Fax: (01935) 706212 E-mail: vertex@vertexeng.demon.co.uk

Viking Stainless Products, Unit 9 Castlelaurie Industrial Estate, Falkirk, FK2 7XF Tel: (01324) 636298 Fax: (01324) 634818

Warren Engineering, B4-B5 Unit Northway Trading Estate, Northway Lane, Tewkesbury, Gloucestershire, GL20 8JH Tel: (01684) 298000 Fax: (01684) 295981 E-mail: warrenengineering@aol.com

Watermark Systems UK Ltd, 18 Cotton Brook Road, Derby, DE23 8YJ Tel: (01332) 366000 Fax: (01332) 372006 E-mail: sales@watermark-uk.com

Watts Construction Ltd, Unit 1 & 2 Beacon Road Works, Beacon Road, Chatham, Kent, ME5 7BP Tel: (01634) 409149 Fax: (01634) 403005 E-mail: wattsgroupltd@btconnect.com

Weldon Engineering Ltd, Unit 4B Climpy Industrial Park, Climpy Road, Forth, Lanark, ML11 8EW Tel: (01555) 812233 Fax: (01555) 812454 E-mail: sales@weldon-engineering.com

White Bros Ltd, Gosforth Industrial Estate, Newcastle Upon Tyne, NE3 1XD Tel: 0191-213 0455 Fax: 0191-284 1351 E-mail: enquiries@whitebros.co.uk

Willand Engineering Co Halifax Ltd, Hopwood Lane, Halifax, West Yorkshire, HX1 5EL Tel: (01422) 369000 Fax: (01422) 380821

William Oliver North Shields Ltd, Little Bedford Street, North Shields, Tyne & Wear, NE29 6NW Tel: 0191-257 5011 Fax: 0191-296 3140 E-mail: sales@worr.co.uk

Wisbech Fabrications Ltd, Unit 3, 62 Weasenham Lane, Wisbech, Cambridgeshire, PE13 2RU Tel: (01945) 466477 Fax: (01945) 466456 E-mail: wisfabltd@aol.com

Woking Sheet Metal & Coachworks Ltd, 141 Goldsworth Road, Woking, Surrey, GU21 6LT Tel: (01483) 761898 Fax: (01483) 755605 E-mail: woking.sheetmetal@btinternet.com

Bernard J. Wood, 13-17 Hayes Lane, Stourbridge, West Midlands, DY9 8QJ Tel: (01384) 892775 Fax: (01384) 892662

Wytkin Services, Waterswallows Industrial Park, Waterswallows Road, Buxton, Derbyshire, SK17 7JB Tel: (01298) 70069 Fax: (01298) 70069 E-mail: Wytkinservices@aol.com

X Tech Stainless Steel Fabrications Ltd, Unit A2 Trecenydd Industrial Estate, Caerphilly, Mid Glamorgan, CF83 2RZ Tel: 029 20886639

Yellowpatter Sussex Ltd, Chantry Lane, Storrington, West Sussex, RH20 4TA Tel: (01903) 745741 Fax: (01903) 742668 E-mail: sales@yellowpatter.co.uk

Yorkshire design Fabrications Ltd, Unit B Cleres Mount Works, Clere Mount Road, Halifax, West Yorkshire, HX3 6AUU Tel: (01422) 345396 Fax: (01422) 349593 E-mail: www.ydfltd@btconnect.com

STAINLESS STEEL FASTENERS OR FIXINGS

Coburn Fasteners, Unit 1-3 Brunel Way, Stroudwater Business Park, Stonehouse, Gloucestershire, GL10 3SX Tel: (01453) 828515 Fax: (01453) 791040 E-mail: andy@coburnfasteners.co.uk

Demarchi Engineering, Vincients Road, Bumpers Farm, Chippenham, Wiltshire, SN14 6NQ Tel: (01249) 448860 Fax: (01249) 445496 E-mail: sales@demarchi.co.uk

Everbright Stainless, Brimington Road North, Chesterfield, Derbyshire, S41 9BE Tel: (01246) 451600 Fax: (01246) 451611 E-mail: everbright.sales@infast.com

▶ Excalibur Screwbolts Ltd, 10 Aldermans Hill, Hockley, Essex, SS5 4RW Tel: (01702) 206962 Fax: (01702) 207918 E-mail: charles.bickford@screwbolt.com

Fixmart Services, 80 A The Brent, Dartford, DA1 1YW Tel: (01322) 274226 Fax: (01322) 278178

Millwood Stainless Fasteners, Unit 20 Lea Hall Enterprise Park, Rugeley, Staffordshire, WS15 1LH Tel: 01889 577712

Monofix Ltd, 4 Premier Trading Estate, Dartmouth Middleway, Birmingham, B7 4AT Tel: 0121-359 2117 Fax: 0121-359 2187 E-mail: sales@monofix.co.uk

Moorhouse Fasteners, 17 Malmesbury Road, Kingsditch Trading Estate, Cheltenham, Gloucestershire, GL51 9PL Tel: (01242) 690392 Fax: (01242) 690391 E-mail: peterhamer@hambury.fsnet.co.uk

Precision Stainless Fasteners, Unit 5 Bilston Industrial Estate, Oxford Street, Bilston, West Midlands, WV14 7EG Tel: (01902) 408222 Fax: (01902) 409222 E-mail: apexbilston@btinternet.com

Priority Metals & Fasteners Ltd, 17 Murrills Estate, Fareham, Hampshire, PO16 9RD Tel: (023) 9220 0300 Fax: (023) 9220 0302 E-mail: sales@prioritymetals.co.uk

Stainless Steel Fixings Ltd, 10 Charlwoods Road, East Grinstead, West Sussex, RH19 2HU Tel: (01342) 328608 Fax: (01342) 314861

STAINLESS STEEL FILTERS

Filters For Industry, 12c Queensway, New Milton, Hampshire, BH25 5NN Tel: (01425) 628533 Fax: (01425) 621767 E-mail: sales@porvairfiltration.com

STAINLESS STEEL FINISHING/ POLISHING SERVICES

A P N Polishing, Unit 9, 54 Shernall Street, London, E17 9HP Tel: (020) 8520 3538 Fax: (020) 8520 3538

A S D Metal Services, Suit 107, 1111 Parkway, Whiteley, Fareham, Hampshire, PO15 7AB Tel: (01489) 611660 Fax: (01489) 611750

All Metal Polishers, Unit 41 65 Caroline Street, Birmingham, B3 1UG Tel: 0121-236 1162

Almond & Mellor Services Ltd, Hampden Mill, Grimshaw Street, Darwen, Lancashire, BB3 2QJ Tel: (01254) 705498 Fax: (01254) 873680 E-mail: sales@almondmellor.freeserve.co.uk

Amian J Ltd, Lord Nelson Industrial Estate, Commercial Road, Stoke-On-Trent, ST1 3QF Tel: (01782) 267501 Fax: (01782) 267501

Apperley Honing Ltd, Alpha Works, Alstone La, Cheltenham, Glos, GL51 8ES Tel: (01242) 525868 Fax: (01242) 224738 E-mail: sales@apperleyhoning.co.uk

E A E Polishing Services Ltd, Green Street, Oldham, OL8 1TA Tel: 0161-678 8273 Fax: 0161-628 5144 E-mail: sales@eaepolishingservices.co.uk

Elite Metal Polishing Services, 81 Bunting Road, Northampton, NN2 6EE Tel: (01604) 712191 Fax: (01604) 712191

▶ Euro Polishing Technology, 83 Moorhey Street, Oldham, OL4 1JE Tel: 0161-628 4466 Fax: 0161-628 4477 E-mail: europolishing@hotmail.co.uk

High Class Metal Polishing, Unit 1-2 Lower Mills, Bridgend, Stonehouse, Gloucestershire, GL10 2BB Tel: (01453) 825464 Fax: (01453) 825464

Professional Polishing Services Ltd, 18b Parkhouse Industrial Estate, Middlemore Road, Smethwick, West Midlands, B66 2DR Tel: 0121-555 6569 Fax: 0121-555 6613 E-mail: sales@professionalpolishing.co.uk

Sillavan Metal Polishes, Sillavan Works, Wood Street, Bury, Lancashire, BL8 2SL Tel: 0161-797 6666 Fax: 0161-797 3454 E-mail: bury@sillavan.co.uk

Stainless Equipment Co. (Metal Finishers) Ltd, Alma Road, Ponders End, Enfield, Middx, EN3 7BB Tel: (020) 8805 0884 Fax: (020) 8804 8167 E-mail: david@stainlesssteelpolishers.co.uk

Thyssenkrupp Stainless UK Ltd, Unit F Elliott Way, Holford, Birmingham, B6 7AP Tel: 0121-331 3600 Fax: 0121-331 3621 E-mail: b.newitt@acciaiterni.co.uk

STAINLESS STEEL FITTINGS

▶ Pumpac Pump Mnfrs, Unit 16 Pentood Industrial Estate, Cardigan, Dyfed, SA43 3AG Tel: (01239) 621308 Fax: (01239) 614942 E-mail: sales@pumpac.co.uk

STAINLESS STEEL FLANGES

All Stainless Ltd, 21 Camford Way, Luton, LU3 3AN Tel: (01582) 584075 Fax: (01582) 585234 E-mail: info@stainlesssteelsupplies.com

All Stainless Ltd, 21 Camford Way, Luton, LU3 3AN Tel: (01582) 584075 Fax: (01582) 585234 E-mail: info@allstainlessltd.co.uk

Chemipetro Ltd, Plant A Peartree Indust Park, Pear Tree Lane, Dudley, West Midlands, DY2 0UW Tel: (01384) 239441 Fax: (01384) 238430 E-mail: sales@chemipetro.com

Alexander Comley Ltd, Pensnett Trading Estate, Kingswinford, West Midlands, DY6 7ND Tel: (01384) 401080 Fax: (01384) 273935 E-mail: sgwilliams@alexandercomley.co.uk

Evenort Ltd, Houghton Road, North Anston, Sheffield, S25 4JJ Tel: (01909) 569361 Fax: (01909) 550631 E-mail: sales@evenort.co.uk

STAINLESS STEEL FLANGES – *continued*

Formula One Pipelines Ltd, Unit 20, Delph Road, Delph Road Industrial Estate, Brierley Hill, West Midlands, DY5 2TW Tel: (01384) 482211 Fax: (01384) 482223

Kays Medical, 3-7 Shaw Street, Liverpool, L6 1HH Tel: 0151-482 2830 Fax: 0151-207 3384 E-mail: kays@kaysmedical.com

Linvic Engineering Ltd, Hickman Avenue, Wolverhampton, WV1 2DW Tel: (01902) 456333 Fax: (01902) 455856 E-mail: sales@linvic.co.uk

MDS Petrochemical Supplies, Unit 48b Premier Partnership Estate, Leys Road, Brierley Hill, West Midlands, DY5 3UP Tel: (01384) 485055 Fax: (01384) 480053 E-mail: sales@mdspetrochemical.co.uk

Nikal Steels, Block 3 Unit 14 Grazebrook Industrial Park, Peartree Lane, Dudley, West Midlands, DY2 0XW Tel: (01384) 243717 Fax: (01384) 243718 E-mail: sales@nikalsteels.co.uk

STAINLESS STEEL FORGINGS

Abbey Stainless Steel Co Ltd, Admiral Steel Works, Sedgley Road, Sheffield, S6 2DN Tel: 0114-231 2271 Fax: 0114-232 4983 E-mail: info@abbeystainless.co.uk

M S I - Quality Forgings Ltd, Balby Carr Bank, Balby, Doncaster, South Yorkshire, DN4 8DH Tel: (01302) 325906 Fax: (01302) 760511 E-mail: sales@msi-forge.com

North West Forgings Ltd, Unit F2 Nasmyth Business Park, James Nasmyth Way, Eccles, Manchester, M30 0SN Tel: 0161-785 2785 Fax: 0161-785 2777 E-mail: sales@nationalforge.com

Offshore Stainless Supplies, Gorsey Lane, Great Wyrley, Walsall, WS6 6AL Tel: (01922) 414003 Fax: (01922) 414606 E-mail: chris@off-shore.stainless.co.uk

Frank Pickering & Co. Ltd, Beeley Wood Works, Claywheels Lane, Sheffield, S6 1ND Tel: 0114-231 8819 Fax: 0114-285 2564

Taylor Forgings, Effingham Road, Sheffield, S4 7ZB Tel: 0114-275 9155 Fax: 0114-272 8440 E-mail: sales@taylorforgings.com

STAINLESS STEEL FOUNDATION NUTS

▶ Sea Screw, 4 Churchdale Road, Eastbourne, East Sussex, BN22 8PS Tel: (01323) 430294 Fax: (01323) 411778

STAINLESS STEEL FRAMED GLASS DOORS

North 4 Design, Unit 12, 2 Somerset Road, London, N17 9EJ Tel: (020) 8885 4404 Fax: (0870) 1308374 E-mail: websales@north4.co.uk

STAINLESS STEEL FURNITURE

D S M Industrial Engineering Ltd, Nottingham Road, Beeston, Nottingham, NG9 6DP Tel: 0115-925 5927 Fax: 0115-925 8456 E-mail: dsmengineering@tiscali.co.uk

STAINLESS STEEL HANDLES

Sshteel, The Lodge, Cefn Bychan Woods, Pantymwyn, Mold, Clwyd, CH7 5EP Tel: (01352) 742111 Fax: (01352) 742101

STAINLESS STEEL HIGH VACUUM CHAMBERS

Instrument Technology Ltd, Menzies Road, Ponswood Industrial Estate, St. Leonards-On-Sea, East Sussex, TN38 9BB Tel: (01424) 442121 Fax: (01424) 719696 E-mail: sales@itl-vacuum.com

Nte Vacuum Technology Ltd, 190-192 Stanley Green Road, Poole, Dorset, BH15 3AH Tel: (01202) 677715 Fax: (01202) 677723 E-mail: sales@ntepoole.co.uk

STAINLESS STEEL HOLLOW BAR MANUFRS

Intamet Ltd, Unit 11 The iO Centre, Stephenson Rd, Segensworth, Fareham, Hampshire, PO15 5RU Tel: (01329) 843355 Fax: (01329) 847799 E-mail: sales@intamet.co.uk

STAINLESS STEEL HOSE CLIP AND CLAMPS

Morris Gordon Engineering, Unit 1 New Mill End Farm, Chiltern Green Rd, Luton, LU1 3TS Tel: (01582) 460002 Fax: (01582) 460038 E-mail: sales@morrisgordon.co.uk

L. Robinson & Co., London Chambers, Mill Road, Gillingham, Kent, ME7 1HJ Tel: (01634) 851182 Fax: (01634) 280101 E-mail: sales@jubileeclips.co.uk

STAINLESS STEEL HOSE FITTINGS

Carlton Hydraulics Ltd, Chesterton Road, Eastwood Trading Estate, Rotherham, South Yorkshire, S65 1SU Tel: (01709) 378999 Fax: (01709) 820292 E-mail: sales@carlton-hydraulics.co.uk

Metalflex Industrial Supplies Ltd, Unit 9 Adlington Court, Birchwood, Warrington, WA3 6PL Tel: (01925) 814999 Fax: (01925) 838999 E-mail: john.milsom@metalflex.co.uk

Seagull Fittings Ltd, 90 Roebuck Lane, West Bromwich, West Midlands, B70 6QX Tel: 0121-525 0020 Fax: 0121-525 1116 E-mail: sales@seagullfittings.co.uk

STAINLESS STEEL HOT WATER CYLINDERS OR BOILERS

Viessmann Ltd, Hortonwood 30, Telford, Shropshire, TF1 7YP Tel: (01952) 675000 Fax: (01952) 675040 E-mail: info-uk@viessmann.com

STAINLESS STEEL INGOTS

Carrs Special Steels, Wadsley Bridge, Penistone Road North, Sheffield, S6 1LL Tel: 0114-285 5866 Fax: 0114-285 5734 E-mail: info@elgcarrs.co.uk

STAINLESS STEEL LIGHT STRUCTURAL FABRICATIONS

Conder Structures Ltd, Wellington Road, Burton-on-Trent, Staffordshire, DE14 2AA Tel: (01283) 545377 Fax: (01283) 530483 E-mail: sales@conderstructures.co.uk

Tartan Manufactoring Ltd, 35 Soho Mills Industrial Estate, Wooburn Green, High Wycombe, Buckinghamshire, HP10 0PF Tel: (01628) 810119 Fax: (01628) 810177

STAINLESS STEEL MERCHANTS (INTERNATIONAL), IMPORTERS, EXPORTERS OR TRADERS

Elg Haniel Metals Ltd, Templeborough Works, Sheffield Road, Sheffield, S9 1RT Tel: 0114-244 3333 Fax: 0114-256 1742 E-mail: enquiries@elg.co.uk

SMS Scotland Ltd, 6 Albion Way, Kelvin Industrial Estate, East Kilbride, Glasgow, G75 0YN Tel: (01355) 264949 Fax: (01355) 264545 E-mail: sales@stockmetal.co.uk

STAINLESS STEEL MIXING VESSELS

Able Engineering, Cadley Hill Road, Swadlincote, Derbyshire, DE11 9EQ Tel: (01283) 227160 Fax: (01283) 222375 E-mail: dave@able-engineering.co.uk

Coldstream (Engineering) Ltd, Olympus House, Mill Green Road, Haywards Heath, West Sussex, RH16 1XQ Tel: (01444) 440091 Fax: (01444) 472329 E-mail: sales@adelphi.uk.com

Lindsey Fabrication & Engineering, 4 Pytchley Lodge Road, Kettering, Northamptonshire, NN15 6JQ Tel: (01536) 485770 Fax: (01536) 410730 E-mail: sales@1indseyfabs.co.uk

Stainfree Fabrications Ltd, Cockersdale Works, Whitehall Road, Drighlington, Bradford, West Yorkshire, BD11 1NQ Tel: 0113-285 4299 Fax: 0113-285 2706 E-mail: mail@stainfree-fabrications.ltd.uk

STAINLESS STEEL NAILS

Stone Fasteners Ltd, Woolwich Road, London, SE7 8SL Tel: (020) 8293 5080 Fax: (020) 8293 4935 E-mail: sales@stonefasteners.com

STAINLESS STEEL NAMEPLATES

Mercury Engraving & Diesinking Ltd, Unit A5 Up Ringway, Bounds Green Industrial Estate, London, N11 2UD Tel: (0800) 1077118 Fax: (020) 8368 9018 E-mail: sales@mercuryengraving.co.uk

STAINLESS STEEL PANELS

DC Welding Fabrication, Pegs Farm, Staplow, Ledbury, Herefordshire, HR8 1NQ Tel: (01531) 640779 Fax: (01531) 640779 E-mail: dc.welding@btinternet.com

STAINLESS STEEL PICKLING/ CLEANING SERVICES

Alkemi M F Technology, 15 Central Trade Park, Marley Way, Saltney, Chester, CH4 8SX Tel: (01244) 674800 Fax: (01244) 681063

Vecom Stainless Finishers Ltd, Unit 7, Claycliffe Business Park, Cannon Way, Barnsley, South Yorkshire, S71 1HT Tel: (0845) 2309704 Fax: (0845) 2309604 E-mail: sales@vecom.co.uk

STAINLESS STEEL PIPE FITTINGS

▶ Asset Brokers (Int) Ltd, 123 Ashgrove Road West, Aberdeen, AB16 5FA Tel: (01224) 666308 Fax: (01224) 698154 E-mail: info@abil.org.uk

▶ Pumpac Pump Mnfrs, Unit 16 Pentood Industrial Estate, Cardigan, Dyfed, SA43 3AG Tel: (01239) 621308 Fax: (01239) 614942 E-mail: sales@pumpac.co.uk

STAINLESS STEEL PIPELINE MANIFOLDS

Sse Pipe Fittings Ltd, Pedmore Road, Dudley, West Midlands, DY2 0RE Tel: (01384) 480333 Fax: (01384) 480805 E-mail: sales@ssepipefittings.co.uk

STAINLESS STEEL PIPES

Eden Material Services (UK) Ltd, Unit 42A No 1 Industrial Estate, Medomsley Road, Consett, County Durham, DH8 6TT Tel: (01207) 590055 Fax: (01207) 590059 E-mail: sales@edenmaterials.co.uk

RDMG Aerospace, Boardman Road, Swadlincote, Derbyshire, DE11 9EN Tel: (01283) 550960 Fax: (01283) 550961 E-mail: administration@tecalemitaero.co.uk

STAINLESS STEEL PIPEWORK

Cleanline Engineering Co. Ltd, 27 Acacia Grove, New Malden, Surrey, KT3 3BJ Tel: (07909) 983648 E-mail: c.mence@cleanline-eng.co.uk

Gem Engineering Ltd, Factory Road, Sandycroft, Deeside, Clwyd, CH5 2QJ Tel: (01244) 520859 Fax: (01244) 520328 E-mail: sales@gemengineering.co.uk

Pipextra Stainless Ltd, 2b Red Rose Court, Sunnyhurst Road, Blackburn, BB2 1PS Tel: (01254) 672999 Fax: (01254) 676784 E-mail: sales@stainlesscutpipe.co.uk

T W Metals Ltd, Unit 43 Nursling Industrial Estate, Majestic Road, Nursling, Southampton, SO16 0AF Tel: (023) 8073 9333 Fax: (023) 8073 9601 E-mail: enquiries@twmetals.co.uk

STAINLESS STEEL PIPEWORK ENGINEERS OR FABRICATORS OR INSTALLATION

Ashington Fabrication Co. Ltd, Ennerdale Road, Kitty Brewster Industrial Estate, Blyth, Northumberland, NE24 4RD Tel: (01670) 365666 Fax: (01670) 364466 E-mail: enquiries@afc-ltd.com

BPS Knowsley Ltd, Haven House, Kirkby Bank Road, Knowsley Industrial Park, Liverpool, L33 7RG Tel: 0151-548 1882 Fax: 0151-548 3884

Hi Line Services Lichfield Ltd, 56 Britannia Way, Britannia Enterprise Park, Lichfield, Staffordshire, WS14 9UY Tel: (01543) 258741 Fax: (01543) 250925 E-mail: info@hilineservices.co.uk

Jordan Division Ltd, Millbrook Road, Yate, Bristol, BS37 5PB Tel: (01454) 328300 Fax: (01454) 325866 E-mail: sales@jordanengineering.co.uk

Metcraft Engineering Ltd, Unit 10 Fenn FLD Indust Estate, Homefield Road, Haverhill, Suffolk, CB9 8QP Tel: (01440) 712227 Fax: (01440) 712274

Microgas Systems Ltd, Aztec Ho, Perrywood Business Pk Honeycrock La, Salfords, Redhill, RH1 5DZ Tel: (01737) 378000 Fax: (01737) 378055 E-mail: rsmith@microgas.uk.com

Millside Ltd, Niagra Works, Beeley Wood Road, Sheffield, S6 1NH Tel: 0114-233 3091 Fax: 0114-232 6776

Orbital Specialist Contracting Services, Unit 22 Business Development Centre, Telford, Shropshire, TF3 3BA Tel: (01952) 290777 Fax: (01952) 293277

STAINLESS STEEL PLATE SAWING

E. Harding & Sons Ltd, Units 10 & 11, Walker Industrial Estate, Walker Road, Guide, Blackburn, BB1 2QE Tel: (01254) 581276 Fax: (01254) 677012 E-mail: sales@ehardings.co.uk

STAINLESS STEEL PRESSINGS

A E Oscroft & Sons, 49d Pipers Road, Park Farm Industrial Estate, Redditch, Worcestershire, B98 0HU Tel: (01527) 502203 Fax: (01527) 510378 E-mail: info@aeoscroft.co.uk

C B Tool Engineers (Cambridge) Ltd, 5 Viking Way, Bar Hill, Cambridge, CB3 8EE Tel: (01954) 780411 Fax: (01954) 781075 E-mail: chapman.c@cbtoolengineers.com

David Bowler & Sons Ltd, Hardley Industrial Estate, Hardley, Hythe, Southampton, SO45 3YQ Tel: (023) 8084 3109 Fax: (023) 8084 0034 E-mail: bowler.group@virgin.net

Howard S Cooke & Co Holdings Ltd, Arrow Road, Redditch, Worcestershire, B98 8PA Tel: (01527) 63231 Fax: (01527) 66770 E-mail: sales@protex.com

Mackays Of Cambridge Ltd, 120 Church End, Cambridge, CB1 3LB Tel: (01223) 508222 Fax: (01223) 510222 E-mail: engineering@mackay.co.uk

P F C Industries, 1 Livingstone Road, Sheffield, S9 3XX Tel: 0114-256 1508 Fax: 0114-256 1485

Romo (Engineering) Ltd, Unit 12B, Waterfall Lane Trading Estate, Waterfall Lane, Cradley Heath, West Midlands, B64 6PU Tel: 0121-559 5966 Fax: 0121-559 5952 E-mail: press@romo.co.uk

V.C.W. Engineering Ltd, Unit 8 Ailwin Road, Morton Hall industrial Estate, Bury St. Edmunds, Suffolk, IP32 7DS Tel: (01284) 768371 Fax: (01284) 768371 E-mail: brucewhiteman@aol.com

G W Waite Ltd, North Lonsdale Road, Ulverston, Cumbria, LA12 9DN Tel: (01229) 582046 Fax: (01229) 583893 E-mail: sales@gwwaite.com

West Bromwich Pressings Ltd, Pleasant Street, Lyng, West Bromwich, West Midlands, B70 7DT Tel: 0121-525 5540 Fax: 0121-525 0581

STAINLESS STEEL PRESSURE VESSELS

▶ Baskerville, 30 Long Wood Road, Trafford Park, Manchester, M17 1PZ Tel: 0161-888 2345 Fax: 0161-888 2345 E-mail: admin@baskervilleautoclaves.co.uk

Cookson & Zinn PTL Ltd, Station Road Works, Station Road, Hadleigh, Ipswich, IP7 5PN Tel: (01473) 825200 Fax: (01473) 828446 E-mail: info@czltd.com

Crew Stainless & Special Alloys, Unit 17 Coneygre Industrial Estate, Tipton, West Midlands, DY4 8XP Tel: 0121-520 1066 Fax: 0121-520 7600 E-mail: sales@crewstainless.co.uk

H Pontifex & Sons Ltd, Pepper Road, Leeds, LS10 2NJ Tel: 0113-271 3411 Fax: 0113-277 7985 E-mail: info@pontifex.co.uk

J E T Engineering, Ditton Road, Widnes, Cheshire, WA8 0TH Tel: 0151-423 5273 Fax: 0151-495 1390 E-mail: sales@jet-engineering.co.uk

John R Boone Ltd, 18 Silk Street, Congleton, Cheshire, CW12 4DH Tel: (01260) 272894 Fax: (01260) 281128 E-mail: sales@jrboone.com

K G D Industrial Services, Willow Court, Netherwood Road, Rotherwas Industrial Estate, Hereford, HR2 6JU Tel: (01432) 374374 Fax: (01432) 353419 E-mail: sales@kgdprocess.com

Langfields Ltd, 158 Liverpool Street, Salford, M5 4LJ Tel: 0161-736 4506 Fax: 0161-745 7108 E-mail: sales@langfields.com

Newson Gale Ltd, Omega House, Private Road 8, Colwick, Nottingham, NG4 2JX Tel: 0115-940 7500 Fax: 0115-940 7501 E-mail: sales@newson-gale.co.uk

Edwin Snowden & Co. Ltd, 173 Fountain Road, Hull, HU2 0LJ Tel: (01482) 320143 Fax: (01482) 225589 E-mail: info@edwin-snowden.co.uk

Stainless Metalcraft, Chatteris Engineering Works, Honeysome Road, Chatteris, Cambridgeshire, PE16 6SA Tel: (01354) 692391 Fax: (01354) 695281 E-mail: infoline@metalcraft.co.uk

Whiteley Read Engineering Ltd, Gateway Indust Estate, Rotherham, South Yorkshire, S62 6JL Tel: (01709) 710661 Fax: (01709) 710961 E-mail: sales@whitely-read.co.uk

STAINLESS STEEL PRODUCERS, *See also headings for individual semifinished products*

Metal Supermarkets, 1 Overland Trading Estate Gelderd Road, Gildersome, Morley, Leeds, LS27 7JN Tel: 0113-238 0900 Fax: 0113-238 0060 E-mail: headoffice@metalsupermarkets.com

Milton Keynes Metals Ltd, Ridge Hill Farm, Nash, Milton Keynes, MK17 0EH Tel: (01296) 713631 Fax: (01296) 714155 E-mail: sales@mkmetals.co.uk

Morecroft Engineers Ltd, 14 Churchfield Road, Sudbury, Suffolk, CO10 2YA Tel: (01787) 374717 Fax: (01787) 881016

R B Stainless, Unit 6 West Stockwith Park, Stockwith Road, Misterton, Doncaster, South Yorkshire, DN10 4ES Tel: (01427) 891988 Fax: (01427) 891988

STAINLESS STEEL PRODUCTS,
See also headings for particular types

Associated Metal Stainless Ltd, 101 Brook Street, Glasgow, G40 3AP Tel: 0141-551 0707 Fax: 0141-551 0690 E-mail: info@assoc-metal.co.uk

Coldstream (Engineering) Ltd, Olympus House, Mill Green Road, Haywards Heath, West Sussex, RH16 1XQ Tel: (01444) 440091 Fax: (01444) 472329 E-mail: sales@adelphi.uk.com

F D Products, 1-5 Olympus Park Business Centre, Quedgeley, Gloucester, GL2 4NF Tel: (01452) 722944 Fax: (01452) 722825

Smart Manufacturing Ltd, Clovelly Road Ind Estate, Bideford, Devon, EX39 3HN Tel: 01237 471977

STAINLESS STEEL PROFILE CUTTING SERVICES

▶ Carbro Sheet Metal Co. Ltd, Unit 7, 106 Richardson Street, Stockport, Cheshire, SK1 3JL Tel: 0161-477 0900 Fax: 0161-477 0370 E-mail: info@carbro.co.uk

Essex Laser Job Shop Ltd, Unit D4, Frogmore Industrial Estate, Motherwell Way, Grays, Essex, RM20 3XD Tel: (01708) 689658 Fax: (01708) 865433 E-mail: sales@essexlaser.co.uk

Intec Laser Services, Woolaston Road, Park Farm North, Redditch, Worcestershire, B98 7SG Tel: (01527) 518550 Fax: (01527) 518551 E-mail: sales@intec.uk.net

J & M Profile Services Ltd, Vauxhall Iron Works, Beauford Road, Birkenhead, Merseyside, CH41 1HE Tel: 0151-653 6006 Fax: 0151-652 1425 E-mail: jmprofiles@jmprofiles.co.uk

K K S (Stainless Steels) Co. Ltd, Unit 2A, Charlton Mead Lane South, Hoddesdon, Hertfordshire, EN11 0DJ Tel: (01992) 445222 Fax: (01992) 446887

Laser Line Engineering Ltd, Unit 14 Avon Business Park, Lodge Causeway, Bristol, BS16 3JP Tel: 0117-965 7002 Fax: 0117-965 7004 E-mail: sales@laser-line.net

Loks Plasma Services, Unit 10 11 Walker Road Industrial Park, Blackburn, BB1 1BG Tel: (01254) 689111 Fax: (01254) 689222 E-mail: sales@loksplasma.co.uk

Pearson Profilers, Skippers Lane, Skippers Lane Industrial Estate, Middlesbrough, Cleveland, TS6 6HA Tel: (01642) 466566 Fax: (01642) 466299 E-mail: sales@pearsonprofilers.co.uk

Plascut Stainless, Coleford Road, Darnall, Sheffield, S9 5PJ Tel: 0114-251 9535 Fax: 0114-251 9536 E-mail: sheffield.zi2@centers.co.uk

Precision Profiles, Southway Drive, Bristol, BS30 5LW Tel: 0117-960 9922 Fax: 0117-960 9944 E-mail: info@precisionprofiles.co.uk

Springfield Stainless, Springfield Works, Stocks Lane, Batley, West Yorkshire, WF17 8PA Tel: (01924) 420303 Fax: (01924) 423333 E-mail: info@springfield-stainless.co.uk

D.S. Willetts (Stainless) Ltd, Murdoch Road, Bilston, West Midlands, WV14 7HG Tel: (01902) 404221 Fax: (01902) 405705 E-mail: sales@dswilletts.co.uk

STAINLESS STEEL ROAD STUDS

Arden Winch & Co. Ltd, 116 Station Road, Beeston, Nottingham, NG9 2AY Tel: 0115-925 8222 Fax: 0115-925 8444 E-mail: roger.graves@ardenwinch.co.uk

STAINLESS STEEL RODS

Outokumpu Ltd, Stevenson Road, Sheffield, S9 3XG Tel: 0114-242 1124 Fax: 0114-242 2152

STAINLESS STEEL SANITARY WARE

Associated Metal Stainless Ltd, 101 Brook Street, Glasgow, G40 3AP Tel: 0141-551 0707 Fax: 0141-551 0690 E-mail: info@assoc-metal.co.uk

Bellshill Metal Works Glasgow Ltd, 60-82 Hamilton Road, Bellshill, Lanarkshire, ML4 1AG Tel: (01698) 747132 Fax: (01698) 746908

C C K Stainless Products Ltd, Units 17-18, SDH Industrial Estate, West Street, Sowerby Bridge, Halifax, West Yorkshire, HX6 3BS Tel: (01422) 834293 Fax: (01422) 839306

D S M Industrial Engineering Ltd, Nottingham Road, Beeston, Nottingham, NG9 6DP Tel: 0115-925 5927 Fax: 0115-925 8456 E-mail: dsmengineering@tiscali.co.uk

MG Stainless Ltd, Unit 1 & 2, Shaw Rd, Netherton, Dudley, West Midlands, DY2 8TS Tel: (01384) 232175 Fax: (01384) 232177 E-mail: mail@mgstainless.co.uk

Franke Sissons Ltd, Carrwood Road, Chesterfield, Derbyshire, S41 9QB Tel: (01246) 450255 Fax: (01246) 451276 E-mail: ws.uk@franke.com

STAINLESS STEEL SCRAP MERCHANTS/PROCESSORS

Elg Haniel Metals Ltd, Templeborough Works, Sheffield Road, Sheffield, S9 1RT Tel: 0114-244 3333 Fax: 0114-256 1742 E-mail: enquiries@elg.co.uk

European Metal Recycling Ltd, Sirius House, Delta CR, Westbrook, Warrington, WA5 7NS Tel: (01925) 715400 Fax: (01925) 713480

Ray Pillinger, Aldred Close, Norwood Industrial Estate, Killamarsh, Sheffield, S21 2JH Tel: 0114-248 3739 Fax: 0114-248 8081

Tinico Alloys Ltd, Unit 1 North Drive, Greasborough Road, Rotherham, South Yorkshire, S60 1QF Tel: (01709) 376844 Fax: (01709) 828210E-mail: tinicoltd@aol.com

STAINLESS STEEL SCREW CONVEYOR SYSTEMS

PJH Engineering Ltd, Unit 15e Bergen Way, Sutton Fields Industrial Estate, Hull, HU7 0YQ Tel: (01482) 370375 Fax: (01482) 370385

STAINLESS STEEL SCREWS

Avon Stainless Fasteners, Unit 10 Riverside Business Park, St. Annes Road, St. Annes Park, Bristol, BS4 4ED Tel: 0117-972 8560 Fax: 0117-972 8570 E-mail: sales@avonstainlessfasteners.co.uk

G T C Fixings Ltd, 84 Witt Road, Fair Oak, Eastleigh, Hampshire, SO50 7FQ Tel: 0845 5261414 Fax: (0800) 1975000 E-mail: sales@gtc-direct.com

Stainless Threaded Fasteners Ltd, 7 Beldray Park, Beldray Road, Bilston, West Midlands, WV14 7NH Tel: (01902) 490490 Fax: (01902) 496583 E-mail: sales@stf.fasteners.co.uk

STAINLESS STEEL SECTIONS

D & D Stainless, Unit 16 Nettlehill Road, Houstoun Industrial Estate, Livingston, West Lothian, EH54 5DL Tel: (01506) 434325 Fax: (01506) 435345 E-mail: sales@danddstainless.co.uk

Legg Brothers Holdings Ltd, Spring Road, Ettingshall, Wolverhampton, WV4 6JT Tel: (01902) 408188 Fax: (01902) 408228 E-mail: mail@leggbrothers.co.uk

Perchcourt Ltd, Unit 6b Heath St Industrial Estate, Abberley Street, Smethwick, West Midlands, B66 2QZ Tel: 0121-555 6161 Fax: 0121-555 6176 E-mail: sales@perchcourt.co.uk

STAINLESS STEEL SHEARING

Barnshaws Plate Bending, Anchor Lane, Bilston, West Midlands, WV14 9NE Tel: (01902) 880250 Fax: (01902) 880505

Mackays Of Cambridge Ltd, 120 Church End, Cambridge, CB1 3LB Tel: (01223) 508222 Fax: (01223) 510222 E-mail: engineering@mackay.co.uk

P P Plasma, New Factory, Vere Street, Salford, M50 2GQ Tel: 0161-736 9299 Fax: 0161-745 7915

Stainless Steel Services Ltd, Middlemore Road, Handsworth, Birmingham, B21 0BH Tel: 0121-523 8100 Fax: 0121-523 8102 E-mail: info@stainlesssteelservices.co.uk

STAINLESS STEEL SHEET CNC FORMING

Burton Fabrications, 1a Pearson Street, Netherfield, Nottingham, NG4 2JA Tel: 0115-961 8261 Fax: 0115-961 8261

Calne Engineering Ltd, Stanier Road, Porte Marsh Industrial Estate, Calne, Wiltshire, SN11 9PX Tel: (01249) 813288 Fax: (01249) 821266E-mail: sales@calne-engineering.co.uk

Counterhouse Systems Ltd, PO Box 381, Worcester, WR6 5YB Tel: (01886) 833044 Fax: (01886) 833152 E-mail: robert@counterhouse.co.uk

First Choice Business Systems Ltd, Unit 4-6 Murray Business Centre, Murray Road, Orpington, Kent, BR5 3RE Tel: (01689) 828182 Fax: (01689) 899399 E-mail: sales@firstchoiceltd.co.uk

STAINLESS STEEL SHEET CNC PUNCHING

J T Blythe Ltd, Kings Mill Lane, Redhill, RH1 5JY Tel: (01737) 823314 Fax: (01737) 822937 E-mail: harry@jtblythe.co.uk

STAINLESS STEEL SHEET MANUFRS

Caterform Works, Victoria Road, Eccleshill, Bradford, West Yorkshire, BD2 2BN Tel: (01274) 626751 Fax: (01274) 626752 E-mail: aireseal@airedale-group.co.uk

Rimex Metals, Aden Road, Ponders End, Enfield, Middlesex, EN3 7SU Tel: (020) 8804 0633 Fax: (020) 8804 7275 E-mail: sales@rimexmetals.com

STAINLESS STEEL SHEET METALWORK ENGINEERS OR FABRICATORS

A B C Stainless Ltd, Empson Road, Peterborough, PE1 5UP Tel: (01733) 314515 Fax: (01733) 315273 E-mail: abcstainless@aol.com

A & H Fabrications, Unit 2-3 Rawreth Industrial Estate, Rawreth Lane, Rayleigh, Essex, SS6 9RL Tel: (01268) 781118 Fax: (01268) 781118

Ab Light Engineering, Hollygrove Farm, Upper Northam Drive, Hedge End, Southampton, SO30 4BG Tel: (023) 8046 6657 Fax: (023) 8046 6657

Acorn Industrial Developments, 3 Wallbrook Court, Netherwood Road, Rotherwas Industrial Estate, Hereford, HR2 6JG Tel: (01432) 276600 Fax: (01432) 341268

Ava Matic U K Ltd, 24 Padgets Lane, Redditch, Worcestershire, B98 0RB Tel: (01527) 518520 Fax: (01527) 518526 E-mail: info@avamatic.co.uk

Burgess & Co. Ltd, New North Road, Heckmondwike, West Yorkshire, WF16 9DP Tel: (01924) 402406 Fax: (01924) 410175 E-mail: info@cburgess.co.uk

▶ Carbro Sheet Metal Co. Ltd, Unit 7, 106 Richardson Street, Stockport, Cheshire, SK1 3JL Tel: 0161-477 0900 Fax: 0161-477 0370 E-mail: info@carbro.co.uk

Carlton Engineering Products Ltd, Unit 1 Airborne Industrial, Estate Arterial Road, Leigh-on-Sea, Essex, SS9 4EX Tel: (01702) 420300 Fax: (01702) 529542 E-mail: sales@cep.uk.com

Centurian Products Ltd, 3-7 Bombay Street, London, SE16 3UX Tel: (020) 7237 2273 Fax: (020) 7231 8285 E-mail: sales@cent.demon.co.uk

Chapel Sheet Metal Ltd, Bowden Lane, Chapel-en-le-Frith, High Peak, Derbyshire, SK23 0QG Tel: (01298) 813041 Fax: (01298) 816256 E-mail: paul_csm@btinternet.com

Coast & County Engineering, Enterprise Road, Mablethorpe, Lincolnshire, LN12 1NB Tel: (01507) 473170 Fax: (01507) 473170

E Farrington & Co. Ltd, Regent Engineering Works, Robert Street, Hyde, Cheshire, SK14 1BN Tel: 0161-368 1675 Fax: 0161-367 8868E-mail: info@farringtons.fsbusiness.co.uk

Elite Metalcraft, 9 Walmgate Road, Perivale, Greenford, Middlesex, UB6 7LH Tel: (020) 8810 5555 Fax: (020) 8810 5133 E-mail: sales@elitemetalcraft.co.uk

▶ JayWolfe, 64 Kingsley Road, Northampton, NN2 7BL Tel: 01604 821066 E-mail: jay.wolfe@ntlworld.com

Jomar Engineering, 119 Sandycombe Road, Richmond, Surrey, TW9 2ER Tel: (020) 8332 6692 Fax: (020) 8948 4269

Keihan Systems, Unit 24 Padgets Lane, Redditch, Worcestershire, B98 0RB Tel: (01527) 518525 Fax: (01527) 518526 E-mail: info@keihan.co.uk

Letchford Swifts Ltd, Leamore Lane, Walsall, WS2 7BU Tel: (01922) 402460 Fax: (01922) 402460

Loubec Sheet Metal Ltd, Throstle Nest Mill, Leeds Road, Nelson, Lancashire, BB9 9XG Tel: (01282) 604737 Fax: (01282) 611897

Manesty Fabrication Services, Holmfield Industrial Estate, Holmfield, Halifax, West Yorkshire, HX2 9TP Tel: (01422) 241122 Fax: (01422) 241100 E-mail: chris.clarke@manesty.com

Marl Bank Sheet Metal Co. Ltd, Newtown Road, Worcester, WR5 1HA Tel: (01905) 22801 Fax: (01905) 726235 E-mail: marlbank@marlbank77.wannadoo.co.uk

Preform Insulations Ltd, Unit 29 & 30 Enterprise Works, 13 & 14 Bergen Way, North Lynn Industrial Estate, King's Lynn, Norfolk, PE30 2JG Tel: (01553) 776382 Fax: (01603) 881254 E-mail: sales@preforminsulations.co.uk

Quality Metal Fabrication, Unit 2 Meadow View Industrial Estate, Ruckinge, Ashford, Kent, TN26 2NR Tel: (01233) 733544 Fax: (01233) 733544

Quest Machining & Engineering Ltd, Units 5-9 Hewitt Business Pk, Winstanley Rd, Billinge, Wigan, Lancs, WN5 7XB Tel: (01695) 627555 Fax: (01695) 627666 E-mail: vickihunterq@aol.com

R S M Engineering Tamworth Ltd, Unit 14 Two Gates Industrial Estate, Watling Street, Two Gates, Tamworth, Staffordshire, B77 5AE Tel: (01827) 250816 Fax: (01827) 287898

Raydon Sheet Metal Co. Ltd, Birch Walk, Fraser Road, Erith, Kent, DA8 1QX Tel: (01322) 431535 Fax: (01322) 433637

Rictor Engineering Ltd, Derby Street, Denton, Manchester, M34 3SD Tel: 0161-320 8842 Fax: 0161-335 0973

Shaw Sheet Metal Rugby Ltd, 13 Paynes Lane, Rugby, Warwickshire, CV21 2UH Tel: (01788) 536033 Fax: (01788) 536922 E-mail: sales@shawsheetmetal.co.uk

Speedfab Ltd, Unit 10, Credenda Road, West Bromwich, West Midlands, B70 7JE Tel: 0121-541 1761 Fax: 0121-544 0028 E-mail: speedfabltd@aol.com

Stainfab Sheet Metal Ltd, 50 Offerton Industrial Estate, Hempshaw Lane, Stockport, Cheshire, SK2 5TJ Tel: 0161-480 5009 Fax: 0161-480 5509 E-mail: sales@stainfab.com

Stainfree Fabrications Ltd, Cockersdale Works, Whitehall Road, Drighlington, Bradford, West Yorkshire, BD11 1NQ Tel: 0113-285 4299 Fax: 0113-285 2706 E-mail: mail@stainfree-fabrications.ltd.uk

▶ Trueform Engineering Ltd, Unit 4 Pasadena Close, Pump Lane, Hayes, Middlesex, UB3 3NQ Tel: (020) 8561 4959 Fax: (020) 8589 0545 E-mail: sales@trueform.co.uk

Tupman & Hainey Ltd, Louisa Street, Worsley, Manchester, M28 3GA Tel: 0161-790 2664 Fax: 0161-703 8435

Vacflo, Unit 14, Bingswood Industrial Estate, Whaley Bridge, High Peak, Derbyshire, SK23 7LY Tel: (01663) 719519 Fax: (01663) 719519 E-mail: mail@vacflo.com

STAINLESS STEEL SHEET/PLATE STOCKHOLDERS

Brite Band 1990 Ltd, Manywells Brow Industrial Estate, Cullingworth, Bradford, West Yorkshire, BD13 5DX Tel: (01535) 271427 Fax: (01535) 275676 E-mail: j.hanson@briteband.co.uk

Corus Ltd, PO Box 4, Wolverhampton, WV5 8AT Tel: (01902) 324444 Fax: (01902) 324204 E-mail: enquiries@corus.com

Metal Supermarkets, Unit 381a Jedburgh Court, Team Valley Trading Estate, Gateshead, Tyne & Wear, NE11 0BQ Tel: 0191-487 2144 Fax: 0191-487 2155 E-mail: gateshead@metalsupermarkets.org.uk

S E S Multimetal Stock, 1 Caldershaw Centre, Ings Lane, Rochdale, Lancashire, OL12 7LQ Tel: (01706) 711999 Fax: (01706) 651999 E-mail: sales@sesmultimetal.co.uk

Stainless International Ltd, George Henry Rd, Great Bridge, Tipton, West Midlands, DY4 7BU Tel: 0121-522 3111 Fax: 0121-522 3377 E-mail: a.holland@stainlessinternational.com

Thyssenkrupp Stainless UK Ltd, Unit F Elliott Way, Holford, Birmingham, B6 7AP Tel: 0121-331 3600 Fax: 0121-331 3621 E-mail: b.newitt@acciaiterni.co.uk

STAINLESS STEEL SHOP FITTINGS

C D Contracts Ltd, 50 Garendon Road, Shepshed, Loughborough, Leicestershire, LE12 9NX Tel: (01509) 505511 Fax: (01509) 505522 E-mail: cdcontractsltd@aol.com

STAINLESS STEEL SINKS

Astracast P.L.C., PO Box 20, Birstall, West Yorkshire, WF17 9XD Tel: (01924) 477466 Fax: (01924) 475801 E-mail: marketing@astracast.co.uk

Bellshill Metal Works Glasgow Ltd, 60-82 Hamilton Road, Bellshill, Lanarkshire, ML4 1AG Tel: (01698) 747132 Fax: (01698) 746908

Carron Phoenix, Carron Works, Carron, Falkirk, FK2 8DW Tel: (01324) 638321 Fax: (01324) 620978 E-mail: fgp-sales@carron.com

Ced Fabrications Ltd, Clayton House, Clayton Business Park, Clayton le Moors, Accrington, Lancashire, BB5 5JD Tel: (01254) 238282 Fax: (01254) 238228 E-mail: sales@cedfabsltd.demon.co.uk

Power Electronic Measurement Ltd, 164 Lower Regent Street, Beeston, Nottingham, NG9 2DJ Tel: 0115-925 4212 Fax: 0115-967 7685 E-mail: info@pemuk.com

Franke Sissons Ltd, Carrwood Road, Chesterfield, Derbyshire, S41 9QB Tel: (01246) 450255 Fax: (01246) 451276 E-mail: ws.uk@franke.com

Southcroft Engineering Co. Ltd, Thurcroft Industrial Estate, New Orchard Road, Thurcroft, Rotherham, South Yorkshire, S66 9HY Tel: (01709) 545147 Fax: (01709) 700259

STAINLESS STEEL SINTERED FILTERS

Sintamesh Ltd, Unit 2, Bentinck Workshops, Park Lane, Kirkby-in-Ashfield, Nottingham, NG17 9LE Tel: (01623) 753401 Fax: (01623) 753408 E-mail: sinta@btconnect.com

STAINLESS STEEL SPRINGS

Alliance Spring Co Ltd, 44-46 Queensland Road, London, N7 7AR Tel: (020) 7607 3767 Fax: (020) 7609 2994 E-mail: sales@tascuk.co.uk
Springpart Manufacturing Ltd, 50 Heming Road, Redditch, Worcestershire, B98 0EA Tel: (01527) 527302 Fax: (01527) 520215 E-mail: info@springpart.com

STAINLESS STEEL STAIRCASES

Euro Spec, Unit 7 Drakes Lane, Boreham, Chelmsford, CM3 3BE Tel: (01245) 362551 Fax: (01245) 360522 E-mail: sales@euro-spec.co.uk
H L Hazeltine Aveley Ltd, Arcany Road, South Ockendon, Essex, RM15 5TB Tel: (01708) 852030 Fax: (01708) 856464 E-mail: hazelstinest@aol.com

STAINLESS STEEL STOCKHOLDERS, *See also headings for particular products*

A K Steel (Stainless Steel Stockholders), Lloyds Bank Chmbrs, 3 High St, Baldock, Hertfordshire, SG7 6BB Tel: (01462) 499400 Fax: (01462) 896763 E-mail: sales@aksteel.co.uk
A S C Metals Ltd, 3 Jackdaw Close, Crow Lane Industrial Estate, Northampton, NN3 9ER Tel: (01604) 415036 Fax: (01604) 415019
A S C Metals Ltd, 20a Maxwell Road, Peterborough, PE2 7JD Tel: (01733) 370626 Fax: (01733) 370392
A S C Metals Ltd, Shaw Road, Bushbury, Wolverhampton, WV10 9LA Tel: (01902) 371700 Fax: (01902) 424324
A S D Metal Services, Unit 6-8 Vernon House Walker Industrial Estate, Walker Road, Guide, Blackburn, BB1 2QE Tel: (01254) 696969 Fax: (01254) 696988 E-mail: sales@asdmetalservices.co.uk
A S D Metal Services, Suit 107, 1111 Parkway, Whiteley, Fareham, Hampshire, PO15 7AB Tel: (01489) 611660 Fax: (01489) 611750
Abbey Stainless Steel Co Ltd, Admiral Steel Works, Sedgley Road, Sheffield, S6 2DN Tel: 0114-231 2271 Fax: 0114-232 4983 E-mail: info@abbeystainless.co.uk
Acton Bright Steel Ltd, Gordon Road, Staines, Middlesex, TW18 3BG Tel: (01784) 463595 Fax: (01784) 451748 E-mail: sales@actonbrightsteel.co.uk
All Stainless Ltd, 21 Camford Way, Luton, LU3 3AN Tel: (01582) 584075 Fax: (01582) 585234 E-mail: info@stainlesssteelsupplies.com
Alloy Sales Ltd, B G K House, Travellers Lane, North Mymms, Hatfield, Hertfordshire, AL9 7HF Tel: (01707) 268222 Fax: (01707) 274655 E-mail: info@alloysales.co.uk
Anglia Alloys Ltd, Unit 5 Riverside Industrial Estate, Riverside Road, Gorleston, Great Yarmouth, Norfolk, NR31 6PU Tel: (01493) 651028 Fax: (01493) 655391
Argent Steel Ltd, 1 Matthew Street, Sheffield, S3 7BE Tel: 0114-270 1428 Fax: 0114-272 3717 E-mail: enquiries@argentsteel.co.uk
Asc Metals Lincoln Ltd, Westminster Industrial Estate, Station Road, North Hykeham, Lincoln, LN6 3QY Tel: (01522) 501777 Fax: (01522) 501700 E-mail: sales@ascmetals.com
Avon Steel Co. Ltd, Unit 18 Midsomer Enterprise Park, Radstock Road, Midsomer Norton, Radstock, BA3 2BB Tel: (01761) 416721 Fax: (01761) 412870 E-mail: charles@avonsteel.co.uk
BACO Metal Centres, Unit 1 Lombard Centre, Kirkhill Pl, Dyce, Aberdeen, AB21 0GU Tel: (01224) 802600 Fax: (01224) 802699 E-mail: bmc.marketing@british-aluminium.ltd.uk
Baco Metal Centres, Edison Road, Elm Farm Industrial Estate, Bedford, MK41 0HU Tel: (01234) 684100 Fax: (01234) 684199 E-mail: bmc.sales@alcoa.com
Baco Metal Centres, Coegnant Close, Brackla Industrial Estate, Bridgend, Mid Glamorgan, CF31 2AH Tel: (01656) 683900 Fax: (01656) 683999 E-mail: bridgend@bacometalcentres.co.uk
Baco Metal Centres, Unit 14 St Andrews Trading Estate, Third Way, Avonmouth, Bristol, BS11 9YE Tel: 0117-948 2600 Fax: 0117-948 2699 E-mail: bmc.sales@alcoa.com
Baco Metal Centres, 13 Concorde Road, Norwich, NR6 6BJ Tel: (01603) 243900 Fax: (01603) 243999 E-mail: norwich@blackburnsm.com
Baco Metal Centres, 1 Eagle Road, Plympton, Plymouth, PL7 5JY Tel: (01752) 612400 Fax: (01752) 612499 E-mail: plymouth@bacometalcentres.co.uk
Baco Metal Centres, Unit 4 Stadium Way, Tilehurst, Reading, RG30 6BX Tel: 0118-980 3300 Fax: 0118-980 3399 E-mail: bmc.sales@alcoa.com
Barpoint Ltd, Willenhall Trading Estate, Midacre, Willenhall, West Midlands, WV13 2JW Tel: (01902) 608021 Fax: (01902) 601652
Bird Stainless Ltd, Box Mill, Sheffield Road, Penistone, Sheffield, S36 6HQ Tel: (01226) 766766 Fax: (01226) 766841 E-mail: sales@birdstst.com
Blackburns, Fircroft Way, Edenbridge, Kent, TN8 6ES Tel: (01732) 582700 Fax: (01732) 582799 E-mail: edenbridge@blackburnsmetals.com
▶ Blackburns Metal Centres, Units 3-4, Haydock Lane, Haydock Industrial Estate, Haydock, St. Helens, Merseyside, WA11 9UY Tel: 0161-254 8800 Fax: (01942) 758899 E-mail: haydock@blackburnsmetalcentre.com
Blackburns Metals Ltd, 4 Wellington Road, Leeds, LS3 1LE Tel: 0113-296 1500 Fax: 0113-296 1599 E-mail: leeds@blackburnsmetals.com
Cashmores, Upper Brook Street, Walsall, WS2 9PD Tel: (01922) 720930 Fax: (01922) 648304 E-mail: sales@cashmores.co.uk
D & D Stainless, Unit 16 Nettlehill Road, Houstoun Industrial Estate, Livingston, West Lothian, EH54 5DL Tel: (01506) 434325 Fax: (01506) 435345 E-mail: sales@danddstainless.co.uk
Damstahl Stainless Ltd, Halesfield 4, Telford, Shropshire, TF7 4AP Tel: (01952) 583999 Fax: (01952) 583958 E-mail: stainless@damstahl.com
Direct Metal Services Ltd, 2 Swan Business Park, Sandpit Road, Dartford, DA1 5ED Tel: (01322) 287878 Fax: (01322) 287567 E-mail: info@directmetalservices.co.uk
Eden Material Services (UK) Ltd, Unit 42A No 1 Industrial Estate, Medomsley Road, Consett, County Durham, DH8 6TT Tel: (01207) 590055 Fax: (01207) 590059 E-mail: sales@edenmaterials.co.uk
Enpar Special Alloys Ltd, Station Road, Ecclesfield, Sheffield, S35 9YR Tel: 0114-219 3002 Fax: 0114-219 1145 E-mail: sales.esa@firthrixson.com
Enterprise Metals, Kemys Way, Swansea Enterprise Park, Swansea Enterprise Park, Swansea, SA6 8QF Tel: (01792) 796774 Fax: (01792) 792974 E-mail: sales@ellissteelgroup.co.uk
F S C Stainless & Alloys, Ledra Works, Reservoir Place, Walsall, WS2 9SN Tel: (01922) 612545 Fax: (01922) 637755 E-mail: sales@fscstainless.co.uk
Fabricast Multi Metals Ltd, Main Street, Hull, HU2 0LF Tel: (01482) 327944 Fax: (01482) 216670 E-mail: sales@fabricast.co.uk
Ferrari Stainless & Alloys Ltd, Unit 89, Woolsbridge Industrial Park, Three Legged Cross, Wimborne, Dorset, BH21 6SU Tel: (01202) 823346 Fax: (01202) 823903
H & H Alloy Sales Ltd, J A S House, Titford Lane, Rowley Regis, West Midlands, B65 0PY Tel: 0121-559 6466 Fax: 0121-559 8723 E-mail: signs@warleyholdings.co.uk
Harbour, Unit 4 Premier Industrial Units, Castle Street, Castlepark Industrial Estate, Ellon, Aberdeenshire, AB41 9RF Tel: (01358) 722422 Fax: (01358) 722880 E-mail: harboureng@btinternet.com
Howco UK Ltd, 3 Blairlinn Road, Cumbernauld, Glasgow, G67 2TF Tel: (01236) 454111 Fax: (01236) 454222
Intamet Ltd, Unit 11 The iO Centre, Stephenson Rd, Segensworth, Fareham, Hampshire, PO15 5RU Tel: (01329) 843355 Fax: (01329) 847799 E-mail: sales@intamet.co.uk
K K S (Stainless Steels) Co. Ltd, Unit 2A, Charlton Mead Lane South, Hoddesdon, Hertfordshire, EN11 0DJ Tel: (01992) 445222 Fax: (01992) 446887
Kelvin Steels Ltd, Spiersbridge Lane, Thornliebank Industrial Estate, Thornliebank, Glasgow, G46 8JT Tel: 0141-638 7988 Fax: 0141-638 1097 E-mail: info@kelvinsteels.com
Newgate Stainless Ltd, Victoria Mills, Cleckheaton, West Yorkshire, BD19 5DR Tel: (01274) 852040 Fax: (01274) 852142 E-mail: newgatesales@btconnect.com
Offshore Stainless Supplies, Gorsey Lane, Great Wyrley, Walsall, WS6 6AL Tel: (01922) 414003 Fax: (01922) 414606 E-mail: chris@off-shore.stainless.co.uk
Opus Signs Ltd, Rollins House, Mimram Road, Hertford, SG14 1NW Tel: (01992) 501355 Fax: (01992) 501398 E-mail: sales@opussigns.co.uk
Orchard Materials Ltd, 7 Brunel Way, Thornbury, Bristol, BS35 3UR Tel: (01454) 415222 Fax: (01454) 415333 E-mail: sales@orchardmaterials.com
Orion Alloys, Unit 3f River Way, Harlow, Essex, CM20 2DP Tel: (01279) 434422 Fax: (01279) 420044 E-mail: sales@orionalloys.co.uk
P & P Supplies Ltd, Units 9-11, Ely Distribution Centre, Heol Trelai, Ely, Cardiff, CF5 5NJ Tel: (029) 2059 7593 Fax: (029) 2059 1268 E-mail: info@pandpsupplies.co.uk
Philip Cornes & Co. Ltd, Lanner Building, Clews Road, Redditch, Worcestershire, B98 7ST Tel: (01527) 555000 Fax: (01527) 547000 E-mail: philipcornes.sales@twmetals.co.uk
Quest 4 Alloys Ltd, Alloys House, Dale Street, Bilston, West Midlands, WV14 7JY Tel: (01902) 409316 Fax: (01902) 409304 E-mail: info@quest4alloys.co.uk
S E S Multimetal Stock, 1 Caldershaw Centre, Ings Lane, Rochdale, Lancashire, OL12 7LQ Tel: (01706) 711999 Fax: (01706) 651999 E-mail: sales@sesmultimetal.co.uk
Sandvik Material Technology UK, Manor Way, Halesowen, West Midlands, B62 8QZ Tel: 0121-504 5111
Sandvik Materials Technology, Manor Way, Halesowen, West Midlands, B62 8QZ Tel: (01224) 725494 Fax: 0121-504 5152 E-mail: sales.smtuk@sandvik.com
Sandvik Materials Tecnology Ltd, Manor Way, Halesowen, Smethwick, West Midlands, B62 8QZ Tel: 0121-504 5000 Fax: 0121-504 5151 E-mail: sales.smtuk@sandvic.com
Severn Metals Ltd, Unit 22 Hither Green Industrial Estate, Clevedon, Avon, BS21 6XU Tel: (01275) 343430 Fax: (01275) 343469 E-mail: sales@severnmetals.co.uk
Sinderby Stainless Ltd, J Alanbrooke Business Park, Station Road, Topcliffe, Thirsk, North Yorkshire, YO7 3SE Tel: (01845) 577550 Fax: (01845) 577800 E-mail: sales@sinderbystainless.co.uk
Spectrum Alloys Ltd, Milton Road, Stoke-on-Trent, ST1 6LE Tel: (01782) 532800 Fax: (01782) 532809 E-mail: info@spectrumalloys.co.uk
The Stainless Centre, Hurricane Way, Wickford, Essex, SS11 8YB Tel: (01621) 785578 E-mail: sales@stainless-centre.co.uk
Surrey Stainless Steels Ltd, Unit 5 Stirling Way, Beddington Farm Road, Croydon, CR0 4XN Tel: (020) 8684 9596 Fax: (020) 8689 9651 E-mail: surreystainless.steels@btinternet.com
Taybroh Alloys & Stainless Steels Ltd, Unit 2 Eastington Trading Estate, Stonehouse, Gloucestershire, GL10 3RY Tel: (01453) 828991 Fax: (01453) 828988 E-mail: sales@taybrohalloys.co.uk
Taylor Forgings, Effingham Road, Sheffield, S4 7ZB Tel: 0114-275 9155 Fax: 0114-272 8440 E-mail: sales@taylorforgings.com
ThyssenKrupp Aerospace Ltd, Kiltonga Industrial Estate, Belfast Road, Newtownards, County Down, BT23 4TJ Tel: (028) 9184 4100 Fax: (028) 9184 4199
U K F Stainless Ltd, 12 Buntsford Park Road, Bromsgrove, Worcestershire, B60 3DX Tel: (01527) 578686 Fax: (01527) 837792
Ugitech UK Ltd, Units 14-15 Erdington Industrial Park, Chester Road, Birmingham, B24 0RD Tel: 0121-382 9494 Fax: 0121-386 1328 E-mail: sales@uginesavoie.usinor.com
Valbruan UK Ltd, 36a Walworth Road, Andover, Hampshire, SP10 5LH Tel: (01264) 333390 Fax: (01264) 333315
Valgram Stainless Steel Ltd, Unit 28 Parkrose Industrial Estate, Middlemore Road, Smethwick, West Midlands, B66 2DZ Tel: 0121-555 6241 Fax: 0121-555 5650
Villamead, 203 Inkerman Street, Birmingham, B7 4SA Tel: 0121-359 7498 Fax: 0121-359 7498 E-mail: villamead@aol.com

STAINLESS STEEL STRIP COATING SERVICES

Corus, Brockhurst Crescent, Walsall, WS5 4AX Tel: (01922) 629593 Fax: (01922) 648202

STAINLESS STEEL STRIP MANUFRS

Phillip Chapman Of Malton, York Road Industrial Estate, Malton, North Yorkshire, YO17 6YD Tel: (01653) 699030
Staystrip Group Ltd, 11-16 Eyre Street, Birmingham, B18 7AA Tel: 0121-455 0111 Fax: 0121-454 5524 E-mail: sales@staystrip.co.uk

STAINLESS STEEL STRIP PROCESSING

Equinox International Ltd, 1 Castle Gate Business Park, Old Sarum, Salisbury, SP4 6QX Tel: (01722) 415709 Fax: (01722) 424001 E-mail: sales@eqx.com
Stafford Stainless Steels, Meaford Power Station, Meaford, Stone, Staffordshire, ST15 0UU Tel: (01782) 796868 Fax: (01782) 374410 E-mail: sales@stainless.st
Staystrip Group Ltd, 11-16 Eyre Street, Birmingham, B18 7AA Tel: 0121-455 0111 Fax: 0121-454 5524 E-mail: sales@staystrip.co.uk

STAINLESS STEEL STRIP STOCKHOLDERS

Inmet Aluminium & Stainless Ltd, D Boomes Industrial Estate, New Road, Rainham, Essex, RM13 8BS Tel: (01708) 522673 Fax: (01708) 555743 E-mail: inmet@netcomuk.co.uk
Quest 4 Alloys Ltd, Alloys House, Dale Street, Bilston, West Midlands, WV14 7JY Tel: (01902) 409316 Fax: (01902) 409304 E-mail: info@quest4alloys.co.uk
Reddiwire Ltd, 9 Dunlop Road, Hunt End, Redditch, Worcestershire, B97 5XP Tel: (01527) 550202 Fax: (01527) 546856 E-mail: reddiwire@dial.pipex.com

STAINLESS STEEL STRIPS, SPRING

Staystrip Group Ltd, 11-16 Eyre Street, Birmingham, B18 7AA Tel: 0121-455 0111 Fax: 0121-454 5524 E-mail: sales@staystrip.co.uk

STAINLESS STEEL SWIMMING POOL FITTINGS

All Swim, Link Trade Park, Cardiff, CF11 8TT Tel: (029) 20 705059 Fax: (029) 2071 3340 E-mail: sales@allswimltd.com

STAINLESS STEEL TABLEWARE

Anchor Food Service Equipment, Unit F1, Valley Way, Market Harborough, Leicestershire, LE16 7PS Tel: (01858) 468181 Fax: (01858) 467506 E-mail: pennywashtech@1dial.co.uk
Chomette Ltd, 307 Merton Road, London, SW18 5JS Tel: (020) 8877 7000 Fax: (020) 8874 8627 E-mail: paulb@chomettedornberger.co.uk
Comet Catering Equipment Co. Ltd, 45 Brimsdown Industrial Estate, Lockfield Avenue, Brimsdown, Enfield, Middlesex, EN3 7XZ Tel: (020) 8804 4779 Fax: (020) 8804 9470
Emwood Co., 43 Broom Hill Road, Rochester, Kent, ME2 3LF Tel: (01634) 719242 Fax: (01634) 719242

STAINLESS STEEL TANKS

Allister Welding Co. Ltd, Unit 30, Horndon Industrial Park, Station Road, West Horndon, Brentwood, Essex, CM13 3XL Tel: (01277) 812534 Fax: (01277) 812616 E-mail: enquiry@allister.co.uk
Argent Engineering Services Ltd, 52 Stockholm Road, Hull, HU7 0XW Tel: (01482) 838698 Fax: (01482) 838668
E G Reeve & Sons Ltd, Burton Road, Norwich, NR6 6AT Tel: (01603) 427228 Fax: (01603) 789548 E-mail: alan@egreeve.co.uk
Goodwin Tanks Ltd, Pontefract Street, Derby, DE24 8JD Tel: (01332) 363112 Fax: (01332) 294683 E-mail: sales@goodwintanks.co.uk
Greenline Tanks Ltd, Townwell, Cromhall, Wotton-under-Edge, Gloucestershire, GL12 8AG Tel: (01454) 294801 Fax: (01454) 294799 E-mail: chris@greenlinetanks.co.uk
H Pontifex & Sons Ltd, Pepper Road, Leeds, LS10 2NJ Tel: 0113-271 3411 Fax: 0113-277 7985 E-mail: info@pontifex.co.uk
Hillend, Ridge Way, Hillend Industrial Park, Hillend, Dunfermline, Fife, KY11 9JH Tel: (01383) 823621 Fax: (01383) 823090 E-mail: nat.hillend@btconnect.com
Morecheck Ltd, Unit 449, Walton Summit Centre, Bamber Bridge, Preston, PR5 8AU Tel: (01772) 629708 Fax: (01772) 629709 E-mail: sales@morecheck.com
Oval 316 Ltd, 10 Cowley Road, Nuffield Industrial Estate, Poole, Dorset, BH17 0UJ Tel: (01202) 682830 Fax: (01202) 665572 E-mail: office@oval316.co.uk
R Sanderson & Sons Ltd, Cannon Street, Hull, HU2 0AB Tel: (01482) 226286 Fax: (01482) 327220 E-mail: info@robert-sanderson.co.uk
Sinclair Stainless Fabrications Ltd, Chalk Lane, Snetterton, Norwich, NR16 2JZ Tel: (01953) 887473 Fax: (01953) 888405 E-mail: info@sinclair-stainless.com

STAINLESS STEEL TEMPER ROLLED STRIPS

▶ Firebird Metals Ltd, 1 Canal Street, Sheffield, S4 7ZE Tel: (0870) 7622333 Fax: (0870) 7622334 E-mail: neil@firebirdmetals.com

STAINLESS STEEL THREADED FASTENERS

B D M Fastenings, 10 Royce Road, Crawley, West Sussex, RH10 9NX Tel: (01293) 548186 Fax: (01293) 553274 E-mail: sales@bdm-fastenings.demon.co.uk

STAINLESS STEEL TIE BARS OR ROCK BOLTS

Daver Steels Ltd, 395 Petre Street, Sheffield, S4 8LN Tel: 0114-261 1999 Fax: 0114 261 1888 E-mail: sales@daversteels.co.uk
SSR Stainless Steel Reinforcement Ltd, Units B & C Burnt Common, London Road, Send, Woking, Surrey, GU23 7LN Tel: (01483) 226426 Fax: (01483) 226427 E-mail: ssr@btconnect.com
Stainless UK Ltd, Newhall Works, Newhall Road, Sheffield, S9 2QL Tel: 0114-244 1333 Fax: 0114-244 1444

STAINLESS STEEL TUBE FITTINGS MANUFRS

Advance Couplings Ltd, Thwaites Lane, Keighley, West Yorkshire, BD21 4LJ Tel: (01535) 669216 Fax: (01535) 610243 E-mail: sales@advanced-couplings.co.uk
All Stainless Ltd, 21 Camford Way, Luton, LU3 3AN Tel: (01582) 584075 Fax: (01582) 585234 E-mail: info@allstainlessltd.co.uk

STAINLESS STEEL TUBE FITTINGS MANUFRS – *continued*

Aston Fittings, Springcroft Road, Birmingham, B11 3EL Tel: 0121-778 6001 Fax: 0121-778 6002 E-mail: sales@astonfittings.com
Berkeley Stainless Fittings Ltd, 5 Novers Hill Trading Estate, Novers Hill, Bedminster, Bristol, BS3 5QY Tel: 0117-966 5544 Fax: 0117-966 5548 E-mail: bristol@berkeleystainless.co.uk
Alexander Comley Ltd, Pensnett Trading Estate, Kingswinford, West Midlands, DY6 7ND Tel: (01384) 401080 Fax: (01384) 273935 E-mail: sgwilliams@alexandercomley.co.uk
Custom Fittings Ltd, Pavilion, Cleckheaton, West Yorkshire, BD19 3UD Tel: (01274) 852066 Fax: (01274) 852029 E-mail: sales@customfittings.co.uk
Dairy Pipe Lines Ltd, Commercial Centre, Ashdon Road, Saffron Walden, Essex, CB10 2NH Tel: (01799) 520188 Fax: (01799) 520183 E-mail: dairypipelines@dpluk.co.uk
G C Supplies UK Ltd, 13-15a Reliance Trading Estate, Reliance Street, Manchester, M40 3ET Tel: 0161-681 8114 Fax: 0161-947 0148 E-mail: sales@gcstainless.co.uk
Inoxta-Realm Ltd, 29-35 Gladstone Road, Croydon, CR0 2BQ Tel: (020) 8689 5521 Fax: (020) 8689 0245 E-mail: inoxta@realm.co.uk
International Pipeline Supplies Ltd, 3 Cookson House, River Drive, South Shields, Tyne & Wear, NE33 1TL Tel: 0191-455 9648 Fax: 0191-454 0505 E-mail: office@internationalgroup.fsbusiness.co.uk
Lancashire Fittings Ltd, 16 Back Devonshire Place, Harrogate, North Yorkshire, HG1 4AF Tel: (01423) 522355 Fax: (01423) 506111 E-mail: sales@lancashirefittings.com
Newgate Stainless Ltd, Victoria Mills, Cleckheaton, West Yorkshire, BD19 5DR Tel: (01274) 852040 Fax: (01274) 852142 E-mail: newgatesales@btconnect.com
Process Control Equipment, 45 Dukesway, Teesside Industrial Estate, Stockton-on-Tees, Cleveland, TS17 9LT Tel: (01642) 768250
Proteus Fittings Ltd, Unit 6 Stonegravels Lane, Chesterfield, Derbyshire, S41 7LF Tel: (01246) 211303 Fax: (01246) 209700 E-mail: info@proteusfittings.co.uk
Sse Pipe Fittings Ltd, Pedmore Road, Dudley, West Midlands, DY2 0RE Tel: (01384) 480333 Fax: (01384) 480805 E-mail: sales@ssepipefittings.co.uk
Suncombe Ltd, Jade House, Lockfield Avenue, Brimsdown, Enfield, Middlesex, EN3 7JY Tel: (020) 8443 3454 Fax: (020) 8443 3969 E-mail: sales@suncombe.com

STAINLESS STEEL TUBE MANIPULATION/BENDING SERVICES OR FABRICATORS

Atlas Tube Bending Ltd, Albert Street, Oldham, OL8 3QP Tel: 0161-683 5556 Fax: 0161-683 5557 E-mail: admin@atlastubebending.co.uk
Dhap Ltd, The Headlands, Downton, Salisbury, SP5 3HT Tel: (01725) 513639 Fax: (01725) 513698
Formbend Ltd, Unit 4-5 Charles St Industrial Estate, Charles Street, West Bromwich, West Midlands, B70 0AZ Tel: 0121-557 0555 Fax: 0121-557 0888 E-mail: sales@formbend.com
Kewtube Ltd, 63 Bideford Avenue, Perivale, Greenford, Middlesex, UB6 7PT Tel: (020) 8991 0062 Fax: (020) 8991 2883 E-mail: info@kewtube.com
Malvern Tubular Components Ltd, Spring Lane, Malvern, Worcestershire, WR14 1DA Tel: (01684) 892600 Fax: (01684) 892337 E-mail: sales@mtc.uk.com
Pipework Fabrication Services Ltd, Western Industrial Estate, Caerleon, Newport, NP18 3NN Tel: (01633) 430099 Fax: (01633) 430099
Plant & Automation Ltd, Lord North St, Miles Platting, Manchester, M40 8HT Tel: 0161-205 5756 Fax: 0161-205 0503
Tubetech Ltd, Arundel Road, Uxbridge, Middlesex, UB8 2RP Tel: (01895) 233268 Fax: (01895) 231933

STAINLESS STEEL TUBE MANUFRS

Accellent, Unit E3 Brookside Business Park, Greengate, Middleton, Manchester, M24 1GS Tel: 0161-643 0018 Fax: 0161-643 0019 E-mail: susan.ward@accellent.com
All Stainless Ltd, 21 Camford Way, Luton, LU3 3AN Tel: (01582) 584075 Fax: (01582) 585234 E-mail: info@stainlesssteelsupplies.com
All Stainless Ltd, 21 Camford Way, Luton, LU3 3AN Tel: (01582) 584075 Fax: (01582) 585234 E-mail: info@allstainlessltd.co.uk
Amodil Supplies Ltd, Enterprise Trading Estate, Guinness Road, Trafford Park, Manchester, M17 1SG Tel: 0161-877 4539 Fax: 0161-877 4541 E-mail: mcl@amodilmanchester.demon.co.uk
Concept Stainless Ltd, Little Fields Way, Oldbury, West Midlands, B69 2BT Tel: 0121-552 8881 Fax: 0121-552 9981 E-mail: sales@concept-stainless.co.uk
Coopers Needleworks Ltd, 261-265 Aston Lane, Handsworth, Birmingham, B20 3HS Tel: 0121-356 4719 Fax: 0121-356 3050 E-mail: sales@coopernw.com
Doncasters F B C Ltd, PO Box 160, Sheffield, S4 7QY Tel: 0114-243 1041 Fax: 0114-243 1358
Intamet Ltd, Unit 11 The iO Centre, Stephenson Rd, Segensworth, Fareham, Hampshire, PO15 5RU Tel: (01329) 843355 Fax: (01329) 847799 E-mail: sales@intamet.co.uk
Kay Electronics & Materials, 52 Albany Park Road, Kingston Upon Thames, Surrey, KT2 5SU Tel: (020) 8546 3235 Fax: (020) 8549 5712 E-mail: jaqueline_babinet@hotmail.com
Le Guellec, Stone Road, Tittensor, Stoke-On-Trent, ST12 9HA Tel: (01782) 374111 Fax: (01782) 373488 E-mail: info@wlmetals.co.uk
Non-Corrosive Control Lines Ltd, 25 Blake House, Gunwharf Quays, Portsmouth, PO1 3TH Tel: (023) 9273 1178 Fax: (023) 9273 1196 E-mail: nccl@btconnect.com
Perchcourt Ltd, Unit 6b Heath St Industrial Estate, Abberley Street, Smethwick, West Midlands, B66 2QZ Tel: 0121-555 6161 Fax: 0121-555 6176 E-mail: sales@perchcourt.co.uk
Profins Ltd, Burdon Drive, North West Industrial Estate, Peterlee, County Durham, SR8 2JH Tel: 0191-586 7669 Fax: 0191-586 0777 E-mail: info@profins.com
S E S Multimetal Stock, 1 Caldershaw Centre, Ings Lane, Rochdale, Lancashire, OL12 7LQ Tel: (01706) 711999 Fax: (01706) 651999 E-mail: sales@sesmultimetal.co.uk
Sandvik Materials Tecnology Ltd, Manor Way, Halesowen, Smethwick, West Midlands, B62 8QZ Tel: 0121-504 5000 Fax: 0121-504 5151 E-mail: sales.smtuk@sandvic.com
Schiedel Right Vent Ltd, Crowther Road, Crowther Industrial Estate, Washington, Tyne & Wear, NE38 0AQ Tel: 0191-416 1150
Southern Metals, 29 St. James Industrial Estate, Westhampnett Road, Chichester, West Sussex, PO19 7JU Tel: (01243) 781814 Fax: (01243) 781814
Swagelock London, Unit 11, Kingley Park, Station Road, Kings Langley, Hertfordshire, WD4 8GW Tel: (020) 8200 1677 Fax: (020) 8200 9819 E-mail: info@london.swagelock.com
U K F Stainless Ltd, 12 Buntsford Park Road, Bromsgrove, Worcestershire, B60 3DX Tel: (01527) 578686 Fax: (01527) 837792
W E Bates Ltd, Bath Meadow Cottage, Gaydon Road, Bishops Itchington, Southam, Warwickshire, CV47 2QZ Tel: (01926) 613222 Fax: (01926) 614222 E-mail: sales@w-e-bates.co.uk

STAINLESS STEEL TURNED PARTS

Bonut Engineering Ltd, Universal Works, Hibbert Street, Stockport, Cheshire, SK4 1NS Tel: 0161-480 1068 Fax: 0161-480 6173 E-mail: info@bonutengineering.co.uk
C N F Precision Engineering Ltd, C N F Factory, Southern Road, Aylesbury, Buckinghamshire, HP19 9AY Tel: (01296) 481727 Fax: (01296) 434940 E-mail: sales@cnfengineering.com
Harris Repair Consultancy Service Ltd, Unit 3, Crondal Road, Exhall, Coventry, CV7 9NH Tel: (024) 7636 4848 Fax: (024) 7664 4411 E-mail: g.harris@harrisrcs.com
Hawk Engineering, Bessemer Road, Sheffield, S9 3XN Tel: 0114-281 7111 Fax: 0114-281 7222 E-mail: sales@hawkengineering.co.uk

STAINLESS STEEL VALVES

Albion Distribution Ltd, Unit 9a Fall Bank Industrial Estate, Dodworth, Barnsley, South Yorkshire, S75 3LS Tel: (01226) 729900 Fax: (01226) 288011 E-mail: dist@albiongroup.co.uk
B I S Valves Ltd, Unit 17 Kingfisher Park, Three Cross Road, West Moors, Wimborne, Dorset, BH21 6US Tel: (01202) 896322 Fax: (01202) 896718 E-mail: info@bisvalves.co.uk
Dairy Pipe Lines Ltd, Commercial Centre, Ashdon Road, Saffron Walden, Essex, CB10 2NH Tel: (01799) 520188 Fax: (01799) 520183 E-mail: dairypipelines@dpluk.co.uk
H S Pipequipment Ltd, Red Shute Hill Industrial Estate, Hermitage, Thatcham, Berkshire, RG18 9QL Tel: (01635) 201329 Fax: (01635) 201941 E-mail: info@hso.co.uk
Inoxta-Realm Ltd, 29-35 Gladstone Road, Croydon, CR0 2BQ Tel: (020) 8689 5521 Fax: (020) 8689 0245 E-mail: inoxta@realm.co.uk
Lancashire Fittings Ltd, 16 Back Devonshire Place, Harrogate, North Yorkshire, HG1 4AF Tel: (01423) 522355 Fax: (01423) 506111 E-mail: sales@lancashirefittings.com
Valvetech Ltd, Unit 9, Brookside Industrial Estate, Sawtry, Huntingdon, Cambridgeshire, PE28 5SB Tel: (01487) 830080 Fax: (01487) 833081 E-mail: sales@valvetech.co.uk
Versatile Controls Ltd, Unit R1 Innsworth Technology Park, Innsworth Lane, Gloucester, GL3 1DL Tel: (01452) 731447 Fax: (01452) 731621 E-mail: sales@versatilecontrols.co.uk
Zoedale P.L.C., Stannard Way, Priory Business Park, Bedford, MK44 3WG Tel: (01234) 832832 Fax: (01234) 832800 E-mail: enquiries@zoedale.co.uk

STAINLESS STEEL VESSELS

Coldstream (Engineering) Ltd, Olympus House, Mill Green Road, Haywards Heath, West Sussex, RH16 1XQ Tel: (01444) 440091 Fax: (01444) 472329 E-mail: sales@adelphi.uk.com
Hi Line Services Lichfield Ltd, 56 Britannia Way, Britannia Enterprise Park, Lichfield, Staffordshire, WS14 9UY Tel: (01543) 258741 Fax: (01543) 250925 E-mail: info@hilineservices.co.uk
Nte Vacuum Technology Ltd, 190-192 Stanley Green Road, Poole, Dorset, BH15 3AH Tel: (01202) 677715 Fax: (01202) 677723 E-mail: sales@ntepoole.co.uk
Sinclair Stainless Fabrications Ltd, Chalk Lane, Snetterton, Norwich, NR16 2JZ Tel: (01953) 887473 Fax: (01953) 888405 E-mail: info@sinclair-stainless.com
Stekko Co Ltd, 4 Avocet Trading Estate, Richardson Street, High Wycombe, Buckinghamshire, HP11 2SB Tel: (01494) 459332 Fax: (01494) 459313 E-mail: sales@stekko.co.uk

STAINLESS STEEL WALL TIES

B P C Building Products Ltd, Flanshaw Way, Wakefield, West Yorkshire, WF2 9LP Tel: (01924) 364794 Fax: (01924) 373846 E-mail: sales@bpcfixings.com
Powerplace Ltd, The Firs, Newton-By-Frodsham, Frodsham, WA6 6TE Tel: (01928) 787127 Fax: (01928) 788448 E-mail: powerplace@fsbdial.co.uk
The Stainless Wire Tie Company Ltd, 3 Fife Street, Sheffield, S9 1NJ Tel: 0114-261 9966 Fax: 0114-242 6333 E-mail: sales@wiretie.com

STAINLESS STEEL WASHERS

Surrey Fastners, Course Road, Ascot, Berkshire, SL5 7HQ Tel: (01344) 876104 Fax: (01344) 620185 E-mail: surreyfast@aol.com

STAINLESS STEEL WATER FEATURES

▶ SPECTRUM PRODUCTS LTD, The Workshop, 8 Church Street, Little Lever, Bolton, BL3 1BE Tel: 01204 452731 Fax: 01204 452731 E-mail: spectrummail@aol.com

STAINLESS STEEL WELDED MESH

J & T Locks Bolts & Bars Ltd, Victoria Works, Victoria Street, Stoke-On-Trent, ST4 6HA Tel: (01782) 349440 Fax: (01782) 349449 E-mail: sales@storagebins.co.uk
Midland Wire Mesh Ltd, Lodgefield Road, Halesowen, West Midlands, B62 8AX Tel: 0121-559 4020 Fax: 0121-561 4030 E-mail: waltmesh@aol.co.uk

STAINLESS STEEL WELDED TUBE MANUFRS

Tiverton Fabrications Ltd, Tiverton Business Park, Tiverton Way, Tiverton, Devon, EX16 6TG Tel: (01884) 255701 Fax: (01884) 253047
U K F Stainless Ltd, 12 Buntsford Park Road, Bromsgrove, Worcestershire, B60 3DX Tel: (01527) 578686 Fax: (01527) 837792
W E Bates Ltd, Bath Meadow Cottage, Gaydon Road, Bishops Itchington, Southam, Warwickshire, CV47 2QZ Tel: (01926) 613222 Fax: (01926) 614222 E-mail: sales@w-e-bates.co.uk

STAINLESS STEEL WELDING

Express Fabrications Ltd, 85 Cyncoed Road, Cardiff, CF23 5SD Tel: (029) 2046 4365 Fax: (029) 2073 6898
Fastweld '93 Welding Services, Unit 8, Old Farm Buildings, Maiden Lane, Crayford, Dartford, DA1 4LX Tel: (01322) 553145 Fax: (01322) 553145
Metalstyle Fabrications Ltd, Unit 25, Harvest Drive, South Lowestoft Industrial Estate, Lowestoft, Suffolk, NR33 7NJ Tel: (01502) 515758 Fax: (01502) 589927 E-mail: metalstylefab@btconnect.com
Oxford Welding, Unit 1 Wharf Farm Buildings, Eynsham Road, Cassington, Witney, Oxfordshire, OX29 4DB Tel: (01865) 884366 Fax: (01865) 884366
Patera Engineering Ltd, Unit 2a Galveston Grove, Oldfields Business Park, Stoke-on-Trent, ST4 3ES Tel: (01782) 318822 Fax: (01782) 318822 E-mail: pateraeng@cs.com
Q A Weldtech Ltd, 1a Bowes Road, Middlesbrough, Cleveland, TS2 1LU Tel: (01642) 222831 Fax: (01642) 242003 E-mail: quality@qaweldtech.co.uk
Ray Weld, Dayton Drive, Darent Industrial Park, Erith, Kent, DA8 2LE Tel: (01322) 334499
Welding Services (Weldon) Ltd, Trevithick Road, Willowbrook South Industrial E, Corby, Northamptonshire, NN17 5XY Tel: (01536) 266623 Fax: (01536) 403159 E-mail: weldingservices@aol.com

STAINLESS STEEL WELDING FABRICATION

Advance Fabrications Ltd, 1 Harrow Garage, Newbury Road, Headley, Thatcham, Berkshire, RG19 8LG Tel: (01635) 268234 Fax: (01635) 268704
Alfreton Fabrications Ltd, Unit 5b Wimsey Way, Somercotes, Alfreton, Derbyshire, DE55 4LS Tel: (01773) 608163 Fax: (01773) 608163 E-mail: sales@alfertonfabs.co.uk
Archer Engineering (Leeds) Ltd, Pepper Road, Hunslet, Leeds, LS10 2RU Tel: 0113-270 5478 Fax: 0113-271 9886 E-mail: richard@archereng.co.uk
Arminhall Engineering, Shire Hill Industrial Estate, Saffron Walden, Essex, CB11 3AQ Tel: (01799) 524510 Fax: (01799) 526680
Cadnam Metalcraft, Southampton Road, Cadnam, Southampton, SO40 2NB Tel: (023) 8081 2489 Fax: (023) 8081 2976 E-mail: cadnammetalcraft@btconnect.com
Chapway Fabrications, Charlton Mead Lane, Hoddesdon, Hertfordshire, EN11 0DJ Tel: (01992) 468028 Fax: (01992) 479720
▶ Metaltech Sheet Metal Work, Arundel Street, Halifax, West Yorkshire, HX1 4LE Tel: (01422) 355760 Fax: (01422) 344294 E-mail: sales@metaltech.org
Reed Fabrications, Station Road, North Hykeham, Lincoln, LN6 3QY Tel: (01522) 693974 Fax: (01522) 501731
Tab Fabs Ltd, Unit 4 Lower Wield, Alresford, Hampshire, SO24 9AJ Tel: (01256) 389123 Fax: (01256) 389188

STAINLESS STEEL WELDING SUPPLIES

Allied Stainless Ltd, Newtown Works, Cradley Road, Dudley, West Midlands, DY2 9SW Tel: (01384) 635000 Fax: (01384) 633000 E-mail: info@alliedstainless.co.uk

STAINLESS STEEL WIRE MANUFRS

K T S Wire Industries Ltd, Park Mills, South Street, Morley, Leeds, LS27 8AT Tel: 0113-253 2421 Fax: 0113-307 6868 E-mail: mail@ktswire.com
Knight Precision Wire, Hadley Works, Cranborne Road, Potters Bar, Hertfordshire, EN6 3JL Tel: (01707) 645261 Fax: (01707) 649225 E-mail: kpw.sales@knight-group.co.uk
Navtec North Europe Ltd, South Moore Lane, Havant, Hampshire, PO9 1JJ Tel: (023) 9248 5777 Fax: (023) 9248 5770 E-mail: navnor@navtec.net
Shaped Wires Ltd, Prospect Mills, Scholes, Cleckheaton, West Yorkshire, BD19 6NJ Tel: (01274) 855635 Fax: (01274) 851116 E-mail: sales@shapedwires.com
Webster & Horsfall Ltd, Fordrough, Birmingham, B25 8DW Tel: 0121-772 2555 Fax: 0121-772 0762 E-mail: sales@websterandhorsfall.co.uk

STAINLESS STEEL WIRE SHAPE/SHAPED/FORMED COMPONENTS/PRODUCTS

Gargsales (UK) Ltd, 240 Fleetside, West Molesey, Surrey, KT8 2NL Tel: (020) 8783 9007 Fax: (020) 8783 9007 E-mail: gargwireuk@yahoo.co.uk

STAINLESS STEEL, MIRROR POLISHED

Outlook Stockholders (Metals) Ltd, Woodcote Grove Farm, Meadow Hill, Coulsdon, Surrey, CR5 2QQ Tel: (020) 8668 9656 Fax: (020) 8668 5111

STAIR LIFT SPARE PARTS

▶ Just Stairlifts, Woodside, Crowhurst Lane End, Oxted, Surrey, RH8 9NT Tel: (0800) 0830513 Fax: (01342) 893466 E-mail: enquiries@juststairlifts.co.uk

STAIR LIFTS

Bison Bede Ltd, Unit 9 Number One Industrial Estate, Consett, County Durham, DH8 6ST Tel: (01207) 585000 Fax: (01207) 585085 E-mail: sales@bisonbede.co.uk

▶ indicates data change since last edition

STAIR LIFTS – *continued*

Brooks Stairlifts Ltd, Telecom House Millenium Business Park, Station Road, Steeton, Keighley, West Yorkshire, BD20 6RB Tel: (0800) 834730 Fax: (01535) 290014 E-mail: brooks@stairlifts.co.uk

▶ Just Stairlifts, Woodside, Crowhurst Lane End, Oxted, Surrey, RH8 9NT Tel: (0800) 0830513 Fax: (01342) 893466 E-mail: enquiries@juststairlifts.co.uk

▶ Mangini Stairlifts, 48 Dunkerley Avenue, Failsworth, Manchester, M35 0EB Tel: (07960) 012276 Fax: 0161-681 0329 E-mail: mangini.stairlifts@virgin.net

▶ Stairglide, Unit 8, Barshaw Park, Leycroft Road, Leicester, LE4 1ET Tel: (0800) 7812020 E-mail: info@equilift.com

Stannah Lift Service Ltd, Unit 6 Ambassador Industrial Estate, 9 Airfield Road, Christchurch, Dorset, BH23 3TG Tel: (01202) 476781

Stannah Lift Service Ltd, 48 Bleak Hill Way, Mansfield, Nottinghamshire, NG18 5EZ Tel: (01623) 631010 Fax: (01623) 636182

Sunrise Medical Ltd, Sunrise Business Park, High Street, Wollaston, Stourbridge, West Midlands, DY8 4PS Tel: (01384) 446688 Fax: (01384) 446699 E-mail: sunmail@sunmed.co.uk

ThyssenKrupp Accessibility, 62 Boston Road, Leicester, LE4 1AW Tel: 0116-234 4310 Fax: 0116-236 4134 E-mail: info@TKAccessibility.com

STAIR RETURN HANDRAIL SECTIONS

StairRopes.com, Tallowater, Braddock, Lostwithiel, Cornwall, PL22 0RH Tel: (07624) 172799 E-mail: jameswatson@stairropes.com

STAIR SPINDLES OR NEWELS

▶ UK Stairparts, 18 Bowlers Croft, Basildon, Essex, SS14 3EE Tel: (01268) 284000 Fax: (01268) 534800

STAIR WREATH HANDRAIL SECTIONS

StairRopes.com, Tallowater, Braddock, Lostwithiel, Cornwall, PL22 0RH Tel: (07624) 172799 E-mail: jameswatson@stairropes.com

STAIRCASE INSTALLATION

Charles Grosvenor Ltd, 300 Birchfield Road, Redditch, Worcestershire, B97 4LZ Tel: (01527) 543668 Fax: (01527) 550125 E-mail: cgltg@btconnect.com

▶ Lyndale Stairs, 1 Mount Road, Burntwood, Staffordshire, WS7 0AJ Tel: (01543) 677780

STAIRCASE ROPES

Period Flooring, Commerce House, 4 High Street, Nutfield, Redhill, RH1 4HQ Tel: (01737) 823053 Fax: (01737) 822862 E-mail: info@stairropes.co.uk

STAIRCASES

All Metal Fabrications Services Ltd, Thundridge Business Park, Great Cambridge Road, Thundridge, Ware, Hertfordshire, SG12 0SS Tel: (01920) 485200 Fax: (01920) 485055

Amber Valley Engineering Ltd, Pye Bridge Industrial Estate, Pye Bridge, Alfreton, Derbyshire, DE55 4NX Tel: (01773) 604753 Fax: (01773) 540136 E-mail: ambervalleyeng@hotmail.com

▶ Ambleside Joinery Sales, 18, Graystones Close, West Bridgford, Nottingham, NG2 6QU Tel: 01159 819853 Fax: 01159 819853 E-mail: ambleside.sales@ntlworld.com

▶ C N C Joinery Ltd, Unit 5, Venture Court, Bradley Lane, Newton Abbot, Devon, TQ12 1NB Tel: (01626) 332203 Fax: (01626) 332204 E-mail: customer.service@cncjoinery.co.uk

Glazzard (Dudley) Ltd, The Washington Centre, Netherton, Dudley, West Midlands, DY2 9RE Tel: (01384) 233151 Fax: (01384) 250224 E-mail: acg@glazzard.co.uk

Charles Grosvenor Ltd, 300 Birchfield Road, Redditch, Worcestershire, B97 4LZ Tel: (01527) 543668 Fax: (01527) 550125 E-mail: cgltg@btconnect.com

▶ Keating & King, Unit 13-14, The Bridge, Narberth, Dyfed, SA67 8QZ Tel: (01834) 861676 Fax: (01834) 861858 E-mail: keatingjoinery@aol.com

Leigh Joinery Co. Ltd, Clifton Street, Leigh, Lancashire, WN7 5AD Tel: (01942) 608182 Fax: (01942) 608182

Nailsworth Services Ltd, Unit 5 Strensham Business Park, Strensham, Worcester, WR8 9JZ Tel: (01684) 274758 Fax: (01684) 274758 E-mail: helen@nailsworth.eclipse.co.uk

P M Bradley Fabrications Ltd, 8 Lodge Lane Industrial Estate, Lodge Lane, Tuxford, Newark, Nottinghamshire, NG22 0NL Tel: (01777) 871222 Fax: (01777) 871922 E-mail: info@pmbfabrications.co.uk

▶ Rembrand Timber Ltd, Shielhill Wood, Tealing, Dundee, DD4 0PW Tel: (01382) 323200 Fax: (01382) 382520

Safety Stairways Ltd, Unit 45 Owen Road Industrial Estate, Willenhall, West Midlands, WV13 2PX Tel: 0121-526 3133 Fax: 0121-526 2833 E-mail: info@safety-stairways.com

Top Notch Ltd, Kingsley, Summercourt, Newquay, Cornwall, TR8 5AG Tel: (01872) 510652 Fax: (01872) 510652

▶ UK Stairparts, 18 Bowlers Croft, Basildon, Essex, SS14 3EE Tel: (01268) 284000 Fax: (01268) 534800

STAIRWAY COMPONENTS

Eglinton Wood Turners, Mid Lodge Cottage, Eglinton, Irvine, Ayrshire, KA12 8TA Tel: (01294) 558145 Fax: (01294) 558145

STAKES/STAVES, WOODEN

▶ Cheviot Trees Ltd, Newton Brae, Berwick-upon-Tweed, TD15 1UL Tel: (01289) 386755 Fax: (01289) 386750 E-mail: katherine@cheviot-trees.co.uk

STAMP PAD INKS

Cambridge Rubber Stamps Direct, 58 Victoria Road, Cambridge, CB4 3DU Tel: (01223) 361600 Fax: (01223) 461391 E-mail: admin@stampsdirect.co.uk

English Stamp Co., French Grass Quarry, Kingston Road, Worth Matravers, Swanage, Dorset, BH19 3JP Tel: (01929) 439117 Fax: (01929) 439150 E-mail: sales@englishstamp.com

Rollers' Inks & Marking Ltd, PO Box 69, Hull, HU2 8HS Tel: (01482) 218172 Fax: (01482) 214999 E-mail: info@markcbrown.co.uk

STAMP PADS, *See Rubber Stamp Pads etc*

STAMPINGS, SILVER/ ELECTROPLATE

J W Evans & Sons Ltd, 52-57 Albion Street, Birmingham, B1 3EA Tel: 0121-236 1775 Fax: 0121-236 7966

STANDBY POWER SUPPLIES

▶ Alpha Technologies, Twyford House, Pig Lane, Thorley, Bishop's Stortford, Hertfordshire, CM22 7PA Tel: (01279) 501110 Fax: (01280) 659870 E-mail: sales@alphaeurope.com

STANDBY UNINTERRUPTIBLE POWER SUPPLIES (UPS)

▶ Archer Power, Archer House, Twyford Road, Wokingham, Berkshire, RG40 5QT Tel: (0845) 8330333 Fax: (0845) 8330222 E-mail: admin@archerpower.com

STAPLE GUNS, AIR

Clipfast, Lancaster House, Lancaster Fields, Crewe, CW1 6FF Tel: (01270) 585959 E-mail: info@clipfast.co.uk

STAPLE (WIRE) MANUFRS

Senior Packaging Ltd, 4 Borrowdale Road, Dewsbury, West Yorkshire, WF12 7PF Tel: (01924) 430201 Fax: (01924) 510065 E-mail: info@seniorpackaging.co.uk

Super Hanger Manufacturing Co. Ltd, 100 Vale Road, Windsor, Berkshire, SL4 5JL Tel: (01753) 622500 Fax: (01753) 622770 E-mail: sales@super-hanger.co.uk

STAPLING MACHINES/ STAPLERS, INDUSTRIAL

Colt Staplers, 10 Bunting Close, Mitcham, Surrey, CR4 4ND Tel: (020) 8687 5500 Fax: (020) 8687 5501 E-mail: sales@coltstaplers.co.uk

Galino Ltd, 2 South Caldeen Road, Coatbridge, Lanarkshire, ML5 4EG Tel: (01236) 449898 Fax: (01236) 449899 E-mail: galino.ltd@virgin.net

Stapling Centre P.L.C., Rapesco House, One Connections Business Place, Otford Road, Sevenoaks, Kent, TN14 5DF Tel: (01732) 464800 Fax: (01732) 464888

STAPLING MACHINES/ STAPLERS/STAPLES

Bea Fastening Systems Ltd, Waterside Road, Beverley, North Humberside, HU17 0ST Tel: (01482) 889911 Fax: (01482) 871804 E-mail: sales@uk.bea-group.com

Betco Packaging Supplies, 12 Gregston Industrial Estate, Birmingham Road, Oldbury, West Midlands, B69 4EX Tel: 0121-552 8400 Fax: 0121-511 1324 E-mail: sales@betcofasteners.co.uk

Josef Kihlberg Ltd, The Bridgewater Complex, Canal Street, Bootle, Merseyside, L20 8AH Tel: 0151-550 0085 Fax: 0151-550 0086 E-mail: reception.ltd@kihlberg.co.uk

Nailfast, 3 Nobel Court, Nobel Road, West Gourdie Industrial Estate, Dundee, DD2 4UH Tel: (01382) 622993 Fax: (01382) 612993 E-mail: sale@nailfast.co.uk

T K Stapling Supplies, Radnor Cliff, Folkestone, Kent, CT20 2JL Tel: (07074) 782753 Fax: (01303) 226845 E-mail: info@tk-supplies.co.uk

Young Black Industrial Stapling Ltd, Radway Road, Swindon, SN3 4ND Tel: (01793) 838400 Fax: (01793) 838401 E-mail: info@youngblack.co.uk

STARCH AND STARCH DERIVATIVES

Avebe U K Ltd, Thornton Hall, Thornton Curtis, Ulceby, South Humberside, DN39 6XD Tel: (01469) 532222 Fax: (01469) 531488

Cargill P.L.C., Cargill, Guiness Road, Trafford Park, Manchester, M17 1PA Tel: 0161-872 5959 Fax: 0161-848 9034 E-mail: graham_fletcher@cargill.com

National Starch & Chemical, Prestbury Court Greencourts Business Park, Styal Road, Manchester, M22 5LW Tel: 0161-435 3200 Fax: 0161-435 3351

STARCHES, SPECIALITY/ MODIFIED

National Starch & Chemical, Prestbury Court Greencourts Business Park, Styal Road, Manchester, M22 5LW Tel: 0161-435 3200 Fax: 0161-435 3351

Stadex Industries Ltd, Coed Aben Road, Wrexham Industrial Estate, Wrexham, Clwyd, LL13 9UH Tel: (01978) 660266 Fax: (01978) 660316 E-mail: sales@stadex.co.uk

START UP BUSINESS KITS

▶ Enterprise Works, Beach Road, Newhaven, East Sussex, BN9 0BX Tel: (01273) 511560 Fax: (01273) 611345 E-mail: info@enterpriseworks.co.uk

▶ TWD Hosting Limited, 76 Oak Street, Shaw, Oldham, OL2 8EJ Tel: 01706 881126 E-mail: sales@twdhosting.co.uk

STARTER MOTOR REPAIR

Charles Kenward Motors Ltd, 14 Sherwood Road, Bromsgrove, Worcestershire, B60 3DR Tel: (01527) 875432 Fax: (01527) 570088

STARTER SYSTEMS

Jetter Distributors Ltd, Leighswood House, 43 Leighswood Road, Walsall, WS9 8AH Tel: (01922) 745200 Fax: (01922) 745045 E-mail: jetteruk@btinternet.com

Pepperl & Fuchs, 77 Ripponden Road, Oldham, OL1 4EL Tel: 0161-633 6431 Fax: 0161-624 6537 E-mail: sales@pepperl-fuchs.com

Western Automation, Unit 1 Boston Court, Salford, M50 2GN Tel: 0161-877 0910 Fax: 0161-876 5243 E-mail: westernautomation@yahoo.co.uk

STATIC CHARGE ELIMINATORS

Advanced Dynamics Ltd, 250 Thornton Road, Bradford, West Yorkshire, BD1 2LB Tel: (01274) 220300 Fax: (01274) 308953 E-mail: info@advanceddynamics.co.uk

Envetron Standby Power Ltd, 28 Wash Road, Hutton, Brentwood, Essex, CM13 1TB Tel: (01277) 214455 Fax: (01277) 227341 E-mail: enquiry@nvtools.co.uk

Fraser Anti Static Techniques Ltd, 1 Station Road, Pinhoe, Exeter, EX1 3SA Tel: (01398) 331114 Fax: (01398) 331411 E-mail: sales@fraser-antistatic.co.uk

Schleising Consultancy Ltd, 10 Victoria Mead, Thame, Oxfordshire, OX9 3HY Tel: (01844) 213492 Fax: (01844) 216751 E-mail: eddie.schleising@dsl.pipex.com

STATIC CONTROL EQUIPMENT

Process Control Co, Griffin Lane, Aylesbury, Buckinghamshire, HP19 8BF Tel: (01296) 484877 Fax: (01296) 393122

STATIC CONTROL MATERIALS

Sirus Microtech, The Old Stables, Linden Hill, Wellington, Somerset, TA21 0DW Tel: (01823) 660665 Fax: (01823) 665321 E-mail: sales@sirus.co.uk

STATIC CONTROL SERVICES

Fraser Anti Static Techniques Ltd, 1 Station Road, Pinhoe, Exeter, EX1 3SA Tel: (01398) 331114 Fax: (01398) 331411 E-mail: sales@fraser-antistatic.co.uk

STATIC DISCHARGE/EARTHING EQUIPMENT

Pix Electrical Co. Ltd, Unit 6, Muslin Street, Salford, M5 4NF Tel: (0161) 925 9829 Fax: (0161) 737 9438 E-mail: phillip.hall@pixelectrical.co.uk

STATIC FREQUENCY CONVERTERS

Chloride Power Ltd, Kempston Court, Manor Road, Kempston Hardwick, Bedford, MK43 9PQ Tel: (01234) 840282 Fax: (01234) 841156

Powernetics International Ltd, Jason Works, Clarence Street, Loughborough, Leicestershire, LE11 1DX Tel: (01509) 214153 Fax: (01509) 262460 E-mail: sales@powernetics.co.uk

STATIC INVERTERS

Socomec Sicon Ltd, 401-402 Love Lane, Cirencester, Gloucestershire, GL7 1YG Tel: (01285) 644444 Fax: (01285) 644414 E-mail: enquires@socomec.com

STATIC VAR COMPENSATORS

Nichicon Europe Ltd, Riverside Way, Camberley, Surrey, GU15 3YL Tel: (01276) 405500 Fax: (01276) 686531

STATIONARY POWER TOOLS

Power Tools Plus, 131 Gloucester Road, Bishopston, Bristol, BS7 8AX Tel: 0117-949 9700 Fax: 0117-914 7758

STATIONERS REQUISITES, COMMERCIAL/OFFICE, *See also headings for particular types*

A A A Stationery, 15-19 Benwell Road, London, N7 7BL Tel: (020) 7700 4246 Fax: (020) 7700 3150 E-mail: info@galaxywholesalers.com

A C Midas, 102-104 Rockingham Road, Corby, Northamptonshire, NN17 1AE Tel: (01536) 267711 Fax: (01536) 262214

A & K Office Products Ltd, 7 Crraftsman Square, Temple Farm Industrial Estate, Southend-on-Sea, SS2 6RH Tel: (01702) 313233 Fax: (0800) 614051

A Tec Group, Units 6-9 Buckley Road Industrial Estate, Buckley Road, Rochdale, Lancashire, OL12 9EF Tel: (01706) 643050 Fax: (01706) 632767 E-mail: info@atecgroup.co.uk

Abbotts Office Solutions, Station Yard, Thame, Oxfordshire, OX9 3UH Tel: (01844) 268360 Fax: (01844) 268370 E-mail: abbott@officesolutions.co.uk

Abc Axworthy's Ltd, Cotswold House, Kingsland Trading Estate, St Phillips Road, Bristol, BS2 0JZ Tel: 0117-927 2700 Fax: 0117-927 3345 E-mail: abc@axworthys.co.uk

Acorn Business Supplies Ltd, Acorn House Motorway Industrial Estate, Forstal, Aylesford, Kent, ME20 7AF Tel: (01622) 882233 Fax: (01622) 882101 E-mail: sales@acorn-business-supplies.co.uk

Alpha Business Centre Ltd, 12 Princes Drive, Colwyn Bay, Clwyd, LL29 8LA Tel: (01492) 531813 Fax: (01492) 531708 E-mail: sales@alpha-business-centre.co.uk

Anker International plc, Howard House, Howard Way, Interchange Park, Newport Pagnell, Buckinghamshire, MK16 9PX Tel: (01908) 618811 Fax: (01908) 612612 E-mail: info@anker.co.uk

Archway Business Centre, The Mill, Boden Street, Chard, Somerset, TA20 2DD Tel: (01460) 65439 Fax: (01460) 61136 E-mail: sales@archway-uk.com

Astute, 44-46 Brechin Road, Forfar, Angus, DD8 3JX Tel: (01307) 464467 Fax: (01307) 464561 E-mail: sales@astute.uk.com

STATIONERS REQUISITES, COMMERCIAL/OFFICE – *continued*

Atlas Office Supplies, 36 Trafalgar Road, Kettering, Northamptonshire, NN16 8DA Tel: (01536) 417414 Fax: (01536) 417528

Albert E. Bailey & Sons Ltd, 25 Holywell Row, London, EC2A 4XE Tel: (020) 7729 1442 E-mail: baileyprintgroup@talk21.com

Bates Office Service Ltd, Unit 26-29 Ropery Business Park, Anchor & Hope Lane, London, SE7 7RX Tel: (020) 8858 0988 Fax: (020) 8858 1136 E-mail: sales@thestationers.co.uk

Blairgowrie Printers, 7 Reform Street, Blairgowrie, Perthshire, PH10 6BD Tel: (01250) 872102

Boston Office Solutions, Moor La Trading Estate, Sherburn in Elmet, Leeds, LS25 6ES Tel: (01977) 681068 Fax: (01977) 681619 E-mail: sales@bostonoffice.co.uk

Business Needs.Co.UK, Elwin House, 13 Alford Road, Cromer, Norfolk, NR27 9AN Tel: (01263) 512170

C R Business Equipment Ltd, Unit 11 Stephenson Way, Formby Business Park, Formby, Liverpool, L37 8EG Tel: (01704) 834083 Fax: (01704) 834083

Carson Stationery & Print Ltd, 107-109 West Street, Sheffield, S1 4EQ Tel: 0114-272 0342 Fax: 0114-281 2996 E-mail: carson-sp@zoom.co.uk

Cathedral Stationery, 2 Park Avenue, Lincoln, LN6 0BY Tel: (01522) 692366 Fax: (01522) 684015

Colemans, 34-36 St Giles Street, Northampton, NN1 1JW Tel: (01604) 636708 Fax: (01604) 622533

Colemans Office Supplies, 8a Berrington Road, Leamington Spa, Warwickshire, CV31 1NB Tel: (01926) 451751 Fax: (01926) 450973 E-mail: info@colemansofficesupplies.co.uk

Coleridge Business Supplies, Dollis Hill Estate, Brook Road, London, NW2 7BZ Tel: (020) 8208 7711 Fax: (020) 8208 7722

Cooper Office Supplies Ltd, 61c Lord Avenue, Thornaby, Stockton-on-Tees, Cleveland, TS17 9JX Tel: (01642) 760414 Fax: (01642) 750991 E-mail: sales@cooperoffice.co.uk

Corporate Express, Tameside Drive, Birmingham, B6 7AY Tel: 0121-331 3400 Fax: 0121-331 3002 E-mail: dylan.jones@cexp.co.uk

Cross's, Brenchley House, Week Street, Maidstone, Kent, ME14 1RF Tel: (01622) 677436 Fax: (01622) 752254

Cubix Ltd, 34 Candlemas Lane, Beaconsfield, Buckinghamshire, HP9 1AF Tel: (01494) 678661 Fax: (01494) 678663 E-mail: sales@cubix.co.uk

David Richards Ltd, 1-2 The Deacon Estate, Cabinet Way, London, E4 8QF Tel: (020) 8523 2051 Fax: (020) 8523 2746 E-mail: enquiries@davidrichards.co.uk

Dialstat Office Supplies, 1 Sovereign Business Park, 46-48 Willis Way, Poole, Dorset, BH15 3TB Tel: (01202) 774400 Fax: (01202) 666818 E-mail: info@dialstat.co.uk

Dick Thomas York Ltd, Hallfield Road, York, YO31 7XQ Tel: (01904) 430920 Fax: (01904) 430911

Don Ruffles, 53 Bell Street, Reigate, Surrey, RH2 7AQ Tel: (01737) 245755 Fax: (01737) 244095 E-mail: sales@rufflesstationery.com

Draw Write, 72-74 Sandgate, Ayr, KA7 1BX Tel: (01292) 610735 Fax: (01292) 263877 E-mail: dwrite7274@aol.com

Dudley Inkwell, Howerine House, 5-6 Empire Way, Wembley, Middlesex, HA9 0XA Tel: (0870) 4442882 Fax: (0870) 4442883 E-mail: sales@dudley.co.uk

Dudley Office Products Ltd, 5-6 Empire Way, Wembley, Middlesex, HA9 0XA Tel: (020) 8980 7199 Fax: (0870) 4442883 E-mail: sales@dudley.co.uk

East London Graphics, 86-88 Upton Lane, London, E7 9LW Tel: (020) 8470 1028 Fax: (020) 8470 0898

Egan Reid Stationery Co. Ltd, Horsfield Way, Bredbury Park Industrial Estate, Bredbury, Stockport, Cheshire, SK6 2SU Tel: 0161-406 6000 Fax: 0161-406 6591 E-mail: sales@eganreid.co.uk

Ensiform Type Products Ltd, 2 Nafcot Street, Watford, WD17 4RB Tel: (01923) 442020 Fax: (0800) 838097

Envelopes Wholesale Ltd, 37 Blythswood Drive, Paisley, Renfrewshire, PA3 2ES Tel: 0141-840 5210 Fax: 0141-840 5211 E-mail: sales@envelopeswholesale.co.uk

F Tollman & Co. Ltd, 85 Tavistock Street, Bedford, MK40 2RH Tel: (01234) 267009 Fax: (01234) 217826 E-mail: sales@tollman.co.uk

J.G. Fenn Ltd, Fenn House, Duke Street, Stoke-on-Trent, ST4 3PT Tel: (01782) 315782 Fax: (01782) 344060 E-mail: enquiries@fenns.co.uk

G M Business Print & Systems Ltd, Cornhill, Liverpool, L1 8DZ Tel: 0151-709 0676 Fax: 0151-709 0678 E-mail: sales@gmbusinessprint.co.uk

George Anderson Stationers Ltd, 36 Standish Street, Burnley, Lancashire, BB11 1AP Tel: (01282) 426858 Fax: (01282) 415728 E-mail: kevin@ga-stationers.freeserve.co.uk

Graham Systems, Lagan Mills, Dromore, County Down, BT25 1AS Tel: (028) 9269 0291 Fax: (028) 9269 3854 E-mail: info@grahamsystems.co.uk

H Jenkinsons & Co. Ltd, Kitling Road, Knowsley Business Park, Prescot, Merseyside, L34 9JR Tel: (0870) 7517744 Fax: (0870) 7525374 E-mail: sales@jenkinsons.co.uk

Henry Cowan & Son Ltd, 40 Bethnal Green Road, London, E1 6HZ Tel: (020) 7739 8627 Fax: (020) 7739 0729 E-mail: sales@cowansdirect.co.uk

Hussey & Greaves Ltd, 94 Hutton Road, Shenfield, Brentwood, Essex, CM15 8ND Tel: (01277) 226262 Fax: (01277) 261287 E-mail: sales@husseyandgreaves.co.uk

Hussey & Knights Ltd, 60 Bethel Street, Norwich, NR2 1NR Tel: (01603) 428110 Fax: (01603) 761032 E-mail: sales@hussey-knights.co.uk

Imprint, Victory House, Dalton Lane, Keighley, West Yorkshire, BD21 4JH Tel: (01535) 667954 Fax: (01535) 600072 E-mail: info@inprintkeighley.co.uk

Imprint (Bournemouth) Ltd, 2-4 Acland Road, Bournemouth, BH9 1JJ Tel: (01202) 520552 Fax: (01202) 521949

Index Business Supplies Ltd, 127-129 Becontree Avenue, Dagenham, Essex, RM8 2UL Tel: (020) 8598 9912 Fax: (020) 8598 8658 E-mail: info@indexbs.com

Inglis Allen Ltd, 40 Townsend Place, Kirkcaldy, Fife, KY1 1HF Tel: (01592) 267201 Fax: (01592) 206049 E-mail: info@scottishcalendars.com

J Greenwood & Sons, 13 North Terrace, Seaham, County Durham, SR7 7EU Tel: 0191-581 2372 Fax: 0191-581 1619

Johnston Reid & Co., 224 Hardgate, Aberdeen, AB10 6AA Tel: (01224) 212255 Fax: (01224) 211146 E-mail: sales@johnstonreid.co.uk

JPS Stationery, 5 Arena Parade, Letchworth Garden City, Hertfordshire, SG6 3BY Tel: (01462) 480223 Fax: (01462) 480223

Kami Office Supplies, 620 Western Avenue, London, W3 0TE Tel: (020) 8896 9399

Kenroy Thompson Ltd, 25 Cobourg Street, Plymouth, PL1 1SR Tel: (01752) 227693 Fax: (0800) 7836322 E-mail: sales@kenroythompson.co.uk

Robert Kenyon Ltd, PO Box 18, Bolton, BL3 6NH Tel: (01204) 523810 Fax: (01204) 364819

L B M Office Supplies Ltd, 88 Bancroft, Hitchin, Hertfordshire, SG5 1NG Tel: (01462) 431201 Fax: (01462) 420476

Langstane Press Ltd, Palmerston Road, Aberdeen, AB11 5QJ Tel: (01224) 212212 Fax: (01224) 210066 E-mail: sales@langstane.co.uk

Laser Traders, 83 Horton Road, Datchet, Slough, SL3 9LY Tel: (01753) 580082 Fax: (01753) 580082

Ludgate Office Equipment Ltd, 7 Stevens Lane, Claygate, Esher, Surrey, KT10 0TD Tel: (01372) 466091 Fax: (01372) 464960 E-mail: sales@ludgateoe.co.uk

M & A Office Supplies Ltd, Unit 12 Westwood Court, Brunel Road, Totton, Southampton, SO40 3WX Tel: (023) 8066 7110 Fax: (023) 8066 7136 E-mail: simon@maoffice.demon.co.uk

Magnum Office Products, 4-5 Priestley Way, Crawley, West Sussex, RH10 9NT Tel: (01293) 547220 Fax: (01293) 543572 E-mail: ray.butler@magnumoffice.co.uk

Manton Office Equipment Ltd, 4 Clipstone Brook Industrial Estate, Cherrycourt Way, Leighton Buzzard, Bedfordshire, LU7 4GP Tel: (01525) 852350 Fax: (01525) 852352 E-mail: info@mantonoffice.com

Martin Reprographics Ltd, Wrightsway, Lincoln, LN2 4JY Tel: (01522) 526268 Fax: (01522) 546514 E-mail: martinrepro@talk21.com

Mason's Paper Ltd, 1 Island House, Bluestem Road, Ipswich, IP3 9RR Tel: (01473) 711123 Fax: (01473) 270109

Merlin Office Supplies, 7-8 Northbrook Close, Worcester, WR3 8BP Tel: (01905) 24240 Fax: (01905) 726747 E-mail: merlinoffice@aol.com

Metrik Office Supplies, 20 Market Square, Dumfries, DG2 7AB Tel: (01387) 253844 Fax: (01387) 257343 E-mail: scallender@metrik.co.uk

Millway Stationery Ltd, Chapel Hill, Stansted, Essex, CM24 8AP Tel: (01279) 812009 Fax: (01279) 812741

Modern Typewriting Supplies Ltd, 69 Choumert Road, London, SE15 4AS Tel: (020) 7639 6317 Fax: (020) 7358 1079 E-mail: modern@btconnect.com

Moss Office Equipment Ltd, Unit 14 Beauchamp Industrial Park, Watling Street, Wilnecote, Tamworth, Staffordshire, B77 5BZ Tel: (01827) 289155 Fax: (01827) 251847

Normans O E B, 30-32 Victoria Road, Scarborough, North Yorkshire, YO11 1SD Tel: (01723) 364307 Fax: (01723) 352775 E-mail: scarb@normansoffice.co.uk

North Shropshire Conservative & Unionist Association, Sambrook Hall, Noble Street, Wem, Shrewsbury, SY4 5DT Tel: (01939) 235222 Fax: (01939) 232220 E-mail: sales@nsprint.co.uk

North Wilts Office Supplies, Ford, Chippenham, Wiltshire, SN14 8RT Tel: (01225) 742569 Fax: (01249) 783207 E-mail: sales@nwos.co.uk

Office Equipment Workshop, 2 Elm Lane, Tongham, Farnham, Surrey, GU10 1BX Tel: (01252) 316700 Fax: (01252) 316705 E-mail: offequipworkshop@btinternet.com

Office Outlet, 38-40 Hastings Road, Leicester, LE5 0HL Tel: 0116-274 3308 Fax: 0116-276 1254 E-mail: sales@theofficeoutlet.co.uk

Office Plus Ltd, 1 Industrial Estate, Thomas Road, London, E14 7BN Tel: (020) 7537 0340 Fax: (020) 7537 0348 E-mail: sales@officeplus.ltd.uk

Office Solutions Organisation Ltd, Unit 4-5, Silver End Industrial Estate, Brettell Lane, Brierley Hill, West Midlands, DY5 3LA Tel: (01384) 351080 Fax: (01384) 351090 E-mail: birmingham@osol.co.uk

Offitec Ltd, 72 West Hill, London, SW15 2UJ Tel: (020) 8871 2525 Fax: (020) 8871 0243

Orchard Stationery, 1 Parkway, Harlow Business Park, Harlow, Essex, CM19 5QF Tel: (01279) 635234 Fax: (01279) 454564 E-mail: sales@orchardstationary.co.uk

Osco Office Supplies Ltd, H E M House, Kirkstall Road, Leeds, LS4 2BT Tel: 0113-279 3511 Fax: 0113-231 0926 E-mail: sales@oscodirect.com

Oyez Straker Office Supplies Ltd, Guild House, Wesley Drive, Newcastle upon Tyne, NE12 9UP Tel: 0191-215 0844 Fax: 0191-266 8450

P D M Office Supplies, 3 Parklands Parade, Bath Road, Hounslow, TW5 9AX Tel: (020) 8570 4488 Fax: (020) 8569 6050

Polypress Ltd, 20 Bridgeland Street, Bideford, Devon, EX39 2QE Tel: (01237) 472272 Fax: (01237) 421414

H. Portsmouth & Son, 1033-1043 London Road, Leigh-On-Sea, Essex, SS9 3JY Tel: (01702) 478255 Fax: (01702) 473640 E-mail: print@hportsmouth.freeserve.co.uk

Probyns Office Stationery Supplies, 25 Tyrrel Street, Bradford, West Yorkshire, BD1 1RU Tel: (01274) 721717 Fax: (01274) 732349 E-mail: probyns@probyns.co.uk

Promocorp Ltd, Unit 98 Springvale Industrial Estate, Cwmbran, Gwent, NP44 5BH Tel: (01633) 861291 Fax: (01633) 876543 E-mail: promocorp@oeugroup.co.uk

Purbrook Ltd, 22-26 Stannary Street, London, SE11 4AA Tel: (020) 7735 9142 Fax: (020) 7793 0609 E-mail: info@purbrooks.co.uk

R D Industries Ltd, Estover Road, Plymouth, PL6 7PS Tel: (01752) 844148

Rippin's Books, 77 Coleman Road, Leicester, LE5 4LE Tel: 0116-246 0044 Fax: 0116-246 0404

Scott Computer Supplies, Unit A3, Sumervell Street, Cambuslang, Glasgow, G62 7EB Tel: 0141-646 2690 Fax: 0141-646 2838 E-mail: info@scottcomputersupplies.co.uk

Scrogie Scottaspress, 23 Broad Street, Peterhead, Aberdeenshire, AB42 1HY Tel: (01779) 490869 Fax: (01779) 477853

Set (Cardiff) Ltd, 6-7 Duke St, Cardiff, CF10 1AY Tel: (029) 2037 3328 Fax: (029) 2038 3344

Shepshed Knight Printing Service Ltd, 91 Charnwood Road, Shepshed, Loughborough, Leicestershire, LE12 9NL Tel: (01509) 502246 Fax: (01509) 503179 E-mail: sales@shepshedknight.com

Sidney Graham Business Supplies Ltd, 236-240 Station Road, Kings Heath, Birmingham, B14 7TE Tel: 0121-443 3377 Fax: 0121-441 1456 E-mail: matt@sidneygraham.plus.com

Ian Smith Stationers Ltd, 205 Great Bridge Street, West Bromwich, West Midlands, B70 0DJ Tel: 0121-557 5451 Fax: 0121-557 2507 E-mail: head.office@iansmithstationers.btinternet.com

Snows Office Supplies, Unit 8 Hounsdown Business Park, Newmans Copse Road, Totton, Southampton, SO40 9LX Tel: (0870) 6092027 Fax: (0870) 6092028 E-mail: sales@snowsoffice.co.uk

Staples Uk Ltd, Lady Bay Retail Park, Meadow Lane, Nottingham, NG2 3GZ Tel: 0115-986 0714 Fax: 0115-986 0721

Stat Plus Ltd, Greenlea Park, Prince Georges Road, London, SW19 2PU Tel: (020) 8646 5500 Fax: (020) 8640 2905 E-mail: enquiries@statplus.co.uk

Stationery Express, 15 The Metro Centre, St. Johns Road, Isleworth, Middlesex, TW7 6NJ Tel: (020) 8568 1771 Fax: (020) 8569 8168 E-mail: sales@stationeryexpress.net

Stevenson Office Furniture, 863-865 Harrow Road, London, NW10 5NG Tel: (020) 8969 3850 Fax: (020) 8968 1790

Stonehill Office Supplies, Unit 16, Chapel Way, St. Annes Park, Bristol, BS4 4EU Tel: 0117-300 5661 Fax: 0117-300 5662 E-mail: mail@stonehill.co.uk

Tab Business Machines & Equipment Ltd, 2-3 London Road, London, SE1 6JZ Tel: (020) 7620 3366 Fax: (020) 7633 0206 E-mail: sales@tab.uk.com

Tag Instantprint Ltd, 182 London Road, Kingston Upon Thames, Surrey, KT2 6QW Tel: (020) 8546 6833 Fax: (020) 8547 1441 E-mail: taginstantprint@aol.com

Tannas Office Supplies Ltd, 76 High Road, London, NW10 2PU Tel: (020) 8459 0521 Fax: (020) 8459 8603 E-mail: info@tannas.co.uk

Telfac Services & Supply, 23 Treesmill Drive, Maidenhead, Berkshire, SL6 3HR Tel: (01628) 671111 Fax: (01628) 674928 E-mail: sales@telfacofficesupplies.co.uk

Thomas Bower & Son Ltd, 111 Broomfield Avenue, Palmers Green, London, N13 4JR Tel: (020) 8882 1888

John Till Printers, 32 Woodside Close, Walsall, WS5 3LU Tel: 0121-357 3267 Fax: 0121-357 3267 E-mail: info@johntill.co.uk

Toms Office Technology Ltd, 26 Adelaide Road, Leamington Spa, Warwickshire, CV31 3PL Tel: (01926) 425842 Fax: (01926) 832017 E-mail: sales@tomsoffice.co.uk

Tutill Nicol Ltd, 1 Richmond Street, Liverpool, L1 1EE Tel: 0151-709 3319 Fax: 0151-707 8785

W F Arber & Co. Ltd, 459 Roman Road, London, E3 5LX Tel: (020) 8980 2067

WB Office Equipment Ltd, 16 Mandervell Road, Oadby, Leicester, LE2 5LQ Tel: 0116-271 1033 Fax: 0116-271 1022

West End Stationers Ltd, 231 Kentish Town Road, London, NW5 2JT Tel: (020) 7485 4472 Fax: (020) 7267 5231

Westway Business Services, 2 St. Marys Way, Baldock, Hertfordshire, SG7 6JF Tel: (01462) 490900 Fax: (01462) 490411

Wheatley Dyson & Son Ltd, 1 Quarry Court, Beacon Hill Road, Halifax, West Yorkshire, HX3 6AQ Tel: (0800) 6342010 Fax: (0800) 0424329 E-mail: sales@wheatley-dyson.co.uk

The Whistle Fish Gallery, Unit 1 Barncoose Industrial Estate, Barncoose, Redruth, Cornwall, TR15 3RQ Tel: (01209) 202424 Fax: (01209) 202434 E-mail: sales@milkwoodpublishing.com

Paul White Ltd, 69 Upper Accomodation Road, Leeds, LS9 8LS Tel: 0113-248 9898 Fax: 0113-248 4863 E-mail: leeds@paulwhiteltd.co.uk

Whitegrove Group P.L.C., Units 5-7, Goodwood Road, Boyatt Wood Industrial Estate, Eastleigh, Hampshire, SO50 4NT Tel: (023) 8064 2643 Fax: (023) 8064 2647

Wight Business Services, 3 Daish Way, Newport, Isle of Wight, PO30 5XB Tel: (01983) 822229 Fax: (01983) 521899 E-mail: wbs@freenet.co.uk

Williams Weddings, 17 Albany Way, Bristol, BS30 8UA Tel: 0117-949 0297 Fax: 0117-949 0297

Word Processing Services, 107 Dashwood Avenue, High Wycombe, Buckinghamshire, HP12 3EB Tel: (01494) 538090 Fax: (01494) 538088 E-mail: info@wordproc.co.uk

STATIONERS, WHOLESALE/ STATIONERY SUNDRIES DISTRIBUTORS OR AGENTS

21st Century, Security House, 65 Canterbury Street, Blackburn, BB2 2HT Tel: (01254) 661199 Fax: (01254) 699969 E-mail: sales@cctv-uk.com

A B Parker & Sons, 7 Franklyn Street, Bristol, BS2 9LA Tel: 0117-955 6544 Fax: 0117-955 6544

A T S S (East Anglia) Ltd, Station Road East, Stowmarket, Suffolk, IP14 1RQ Tel: (01449) 674944 Fax: (01449) 678678 E-mail: sales@atssea.co.uk

Aldon Brearley Print, The Engine House, Ashley Lane, Shipley, West Yorkshire, BD17 7DB Tel: (01274) 583192 Fax: (01274) 532862 E-mail: aldon.brearley@btconnet.co.uk

Apperley Business Supplies Ltd, 1 St Andrews Road, Montpelier, Bristol, BS6 5EH Tel: 0117-942 4972 Fax: 0117-942 4400 E-mail: marklaval@blueyonder.co.uk

Arcraft Products 2005 Ltd, 1 Mousell Street, Cheetham, Manchester, M8 8HY Tel: 0161-833 2269 Fax: 0161-833 2269 E-mail: greetings16@hotmail.com

Armour Supplies Ltd, Units 2-3, Brunel Road, Churchfield Industrial Estate, St. Leonards-on-Sea, East Sussex, TN38 9RT Tel: (01424) 853717 Fax: (01424) 853719

Barkshire Group, 40 Ivanhoe Road, Hogwood Industrial Estate, Finchampstead, Wokingham, Berkshire, RG40 4QQ Tel: 0118-973 2919 Fax: 0118-973 0899 E-mail: sales@barkshiregroup.co.uk

Barry Bennett Ltd, Unit 15a Bankfield Business Park, Quebec Street, Bolton, BL3 5JN Tel: (01204) 534311 Fax: (01204) 362783 E-mail: info@baarybennett.co.uk

Beith Printing Co. Ltd, 1-7 Earl Haig Road, Hillington Industrial Estate, Glasgow, G52 4JU Tel: 0141-882 9088 Fax: 0141-882 3204 E-mail: mail@beith-printing.co.uk

Bennett Sykes Group, 84 Vaughan Way, Leicester, LE1 4SH Tel: 0116-253 0454 Fax: 0116-253 6127 E-mail: enquiries@bennettsykes.co.uk

Brewers Business Solutions Ltd, Water-Ma-Trout, Helston, Cornwall, TR13 0LW Tel: (01326) 563424 Fax: (01326) 563606

Burke Office Furniture & Equipment, Unit 28 Ormeau Business Park, 8 Cromac Avenue, Belfast, BT7 2JA Tel: (028) 9087 6020 Fax: (028) 9087 6677 E-mail: enquiries@burke-office.co.uk

C & F Office Supplies Ltd, Units 16 Lye Business Centre, Enterprise Drive, Stourbridge, West Midlands, DY9 8QH Tel: (01384) 898370 Fax: (01384) 898370

Campsie Paper Co. Ltd, Courtauld Way, Eglinton, Londonderry, BT47 3DN Tel: (028) 7181 1243 Fax: (028) 7181 1626

Cell Ltd, Hallsteads, Dove Holes, Buxton, Derbyshire, SK17 8BJ Tel: (01298) 816692 Fax: (01298) 816277 E-mail: sales@cell-limited.co.uk

Central Business Machines Ltd, 112-118 Kingsland Road, London, E2 8DJ Tel: (020) 7729 5588 Fax: (020) 7729 9137

Chase Group Printing & Stationery Ltd, Unit 11 Heston Industrial Mall, Church Rd, Hounslow, TW5 0LD Tel: (020) 8577 1930 Fax: (020) 8572 3065 E-mail: info@chasegrp.co.uk

Cluine Group Ltd, 15 Lochside Street, Oban, Argyll, PA34 4HP Tel: (01631) 562572 Fax: (01631) 565286 E-mail: info@officesupplies-printing.co.uk

Coral Press Ltd, 115 Hatfield Road, St. Albans, Hertfordshire, AL1 4JS Tel: (01727) 854466 Fax: (01727) 851331 E-mail: sales@coralpress.co.uk

STATIONERS, WHOLESALE/ STATIONERY SUNDRIES DISTRIBUTORS OR AGENTS – *continued*

Corporate Express, Brunel Road, Wakefield 41 Industrial Estate, Wakefield, West Yorkshire, WF2 0XG Tel: (0870) 4205359 Fax: (0870) 0660707

Coubrough & McKeracher (Printers) Ltd, 8 Falfield Street, Glasgow, G5 8HL Tel: 0141-429 0487 Fax: 0141-429 0515 E-mail: enquiries@cmckprinters.com

Crescent Office Ltd, 71-73 Beverley Road, Hull, HU3 1XL Tel: (01482) 224444 Fax: (01482) 213505 E-mail: user@crescent-office.com

Data Consultants, 49 Leander Crescent, Bellshill, Lanarkshire, ML4 1JA Tel: (01698) 834343 Fax: (01698) 834343

Eason & Son Ni Ltd, 21-25 Boucher Road, Belfast, BT12 6QU Tel: (028) 9038 1200 Fax: (028) 9068 2544 E-mail: accountsreceivable@eason.co.uk

Econoprint UK Ltd, Cooper Drive, Springwood Industrial Estate, Braintree, Essex, CM7 2RF Tel: (01376) 349955 Fax: (01376) 346853 E-mail: sales@econoprint.co.uk

Electronic Print Systems, 51 Bells Road, Gorleston, Great Yarmouth, Norfolk, NR31 6AN Tel: (01493) 664204 Fax: (01493) 440241 E-mail: gabform@gtyarmouth.co.uk

Excel Office Equipment, 24 Mannamead Road, Plymouth, PL4 7AA Tel: (01752) 660151 Fax: (01752) 225778 E-mail: sales@exeloffice.co.uk

Foxe Graphics Ltd, Enterprise Road, Golf Road Industrial Estate, Mablethorpe, Lincolnshire, LN12 1NB Tel: (01507) 477748 Fax: (01507) 473128 E-mail: alex@foxe.co.uk

▶ GBA Pen Co. Ltd, Fyfield Business & Research Park, 7 Fyfield Road, Ongar, Essex, CM5 0GN Tel: (01277) 369620 Fax: (01277) 369629 E-mail: gbapen@btconnect.com

Geometrix Ltd, Chase Road, Brownhills, Walsall, WS8 6JU Tel: (01543) 452424 Fax: (01543) 453012 E-mail: enquiries@geometrix.co.uk

George Anderson Stationers Ltd, 36 Standish Street, Burnley, Lancashire, BB11 1AP Tel: (01282) 426858 Fax: (01282) 415728 E-mail: kevin@ga-stationers.freeserve.co.uk

Gilmex International Ltd, 78 Conington Road, London, SE13 7LH Tel: (020) 8318 3921 Fax: (020) 8463 0565 E-mail: sales@gilmex.com

Grosvenor House Papers, Westmorland Business Park, Gilthwaiterigg Lane, Kendal, Cumbria, LA9 6NP Tel: (01539) 726161 Fax: (01539) 733678 E-mail: info@ghpkendal.co.uk

Hamelin Stationery Ltd, River Street, Brighouse, West Yorkshire, HD6 1LU Tel: (01484) 385600 Fax: 01484 385602 E-mail: sales@oxfordstationery.com

Hannaford & Marshall Ltd, Hanmar House, 42 Bethnal Green Road, London, E1 6HZ Tel: (020) 7739 2834 Fax: (020) 7613 0011 E-mail: mail@hanmar.co.uk

Hughes & Coleman Ltd, Delta Close, Norwich, NR6 6BG Tel: (01603) 426159 Fax: (01603) 486853 E-mail: sales@hughesandcoleman.co.uk

Infolist Ltd, Valley Business Centre Church Road, Newtownabbey, County Antrim, BT36 7LP Tel: (028) 9085 1133 Fax: (028) 9085 4708 E-mail: info@infolistltd.com

J A Magson Ltd, Magson House, Kettlestring Lane, York, YO30 4XF Tel: (01904) 690097 Fax: (01904) 691018 E-mail: sales@magson.co.uk

J J Newland Ltd, 10 Brown Avenue, Leeds, LS11 0DX Tel: 0113-271 7340 Fax: 0113-277 9877

J M Tatler & Son Ltd, Abbey Street Works, Derby, DE22 3SW Tel: (01332) 342120 Fax: (01332) 293699 E-mail: willtat@fsbdial.co.uk

Jim Barlow Stationers Ltd, 18 Park Road, Worsley, Manchester, M28 7DA Tel: 0161-799 9558 Fax: 0161-703 8789 E-mail: sales@jimbarlows.co.uk

Jubilee Printers, 430 Edgware Road, London, W2 1EG Tel: (020) 7724 1094 Fax: (020) 7706 0518 E-mail: info@jubileeprinters.co.uk

Kardwell Hobs Ltd, Sunrise House, Sunrise Business Park, Higher Shaftsbury Road, Blandford Forum, Dorset, DT11 8ST Tel: (01258) 452125 Fax: (01258) 486709 E-mail: hobbs.blandford@virgin.net

Kingfield Cotswold, Cotswold House, St. Philips Road, Bristol, BS2 0JZ Tel: 0117-900 6000 Fax: 0117-900 6100

KTC Office Stationery Supplies, 21 Pudding Lane, Maidstone, Kent, ME14 1TY Tel: (01622) 758853 Fax: (01622) 753741 E-mail: ktcoffice@btconnect.com

Lianda Business Services, Lianda House, Camphill Road, West Byfleet, Surrey, KT14 6EW Tel: (01932) 341444 Fax: (01932) 349220 E-mail: sales@lianda.co.uk

M S A In Print, 115 Graingers Lane, Cradley Heath, West Midlands, B64 6AD Tel: (01384) 568790 Fax: (01384) 410320 E-mail: msainprint@fsb.dial.co.uk

Mcgregor Business Equipment, Unit 2 Fence Avenue, Macclesfield, Cheshire, SK10 1LT Tel: (01625) 618182 Fax: (01625) 618545 E-mail: officesupplies@mcgregors.co.uk

Magson Stationery, Bluestem Road, Ransomes Industrial Estate, Ipswich, IP3 9RR Tel: (01473) 727667 Fax: (01473) 727863

Offizone Office Stationery Supplies, 1-15 Middle Hillgate, Stockport, Cheshire, SK1 3AY Tel: 0161-480 2010 Fax: 0161-480 4133 E-mail: sales@offizone.co.uk

P L G Distributors Ltd, 6 Francis Road, Yardley, Birmingham, B25 8HP Tel: 0121-766 1000 Fax: 0121-766 1002

PDQ Direct, Sureline House, Easting Close, Worthing, West Sussex, BN14 8HQ Tel: (01903) 282500 Fax: (01903) 282599 E-mail: sales@pdqdirect.co.uk

Playwrite Group plc, 25-27 Curtain Road, London, EC2A 3PN Tel: (020) 7247 6611 Fax: (020) 7247 5450 E-mail: sales@playwritegroup.com

Postglow Printers, 139 Francis Road, London, E10 6NT Tel: (020) 8539 7559 Fax: (020) 8556 1970 E-mail: sales@frankel.co.uk

Print Systems Ltd, 11 Merse Road, Moons Moat North Industrial Estate, Redditch, Worcestershire, B98 9HL Tel: (01527) 64555 Fax: (01527) 62100 E-mail: info@print-systems.co.uk

Projects XL Ltd, Glenville House, Spring Gardens, Romford, RM7 9LD Tel: (01708) 751919 Fax: (01708) 725294 E-mail: info@projectsxl.com

▶ R M S International Ltd, 66 Pendlebury Road, Swinton, Manchester, M27 4GY Tel: 0161-727 8182 Fax: 0161-727 8191 E-mail: jmcdermott@rmsint.com

R & S Greeting Cards Ltd, 157 Fallsbrook Road, London, SW16 6DY Tel: (020) 8677 5212 Fax: (020) 8664 7108

Rabbitt Recycling, 27-29 New Street, Charfield, Wotton-under-Edge, Gloucestershire, GL12 8ES Tel: (01453) 844343 Fax: (01453) 521330 E-mail: info@rabbittrecycling.co.uk

Rogate Paper Supplies, Bowness Avenue, Sompting, Lancing, West Sussex, BN15 9TP Tel: (01903) 755208 Fax: (01903) 751898 E-mail: sales@rogatepaper.co.uk

Ryman The Stationer, 64 High Street, Bedford, MK40 1NT Tel: (01234) 216175 Fax: (01234) 351888

Ryman The Stationer, 62 Old Christchurch Road, Bournemouth, BH1 1LL Tel: (01202) 295390 Fax: (01202) 554866

Ryman The Stationer, 43 High Street, Bromley, BR1 1LE Tel: (020) 8460 6606 Fax: (020) 8460 6606

Ryman The Stationer, 53 Sidney Street, Cambridge, CB2 3HX Tel: (01223) 312095 Fax: (01223) 315130

Ryman The Stationer, 24 Burgate, Canterbury, Kent, CT1 2HA Tel: (01227) 470573 Fax: (01227) 470573

Ryman The Stationer, 175-177 High Street, Guildford, Surrey, GU1 3AW Tel: (01483) 454088 Fax: (01483) 454088

Ryman The Stationer, 63 Borough High Street, London, SE1 1NF Tel: (020) 7407 0288 Fax: (020) 7378 7960

Ryman The Stationer, 191 Camden High Street, London, NW1 7BT Tel: (020) 7267 1276 Fax: (020) 7267 1276

Ryman The Stationer, 57 Charing Cross Road, London, WC2H 0NE Tel: (020) 7439 2058 Fax: (020) 7439 2058

Ryman The Stationer, 146 Edgware Road, London, W2 1ET Tel: (020) 7723 2496 Fax: (020) 7723 0807

Ryman The Stationer, 149 Fleet Street, London, EC4A 2BU Tel: (020) 7353 4985 Fax: (020) 7353 4985

Ryman The Stationer, 19-20 High Holborn, London, WC1V 6BS Tel: (020) 7405 1642 Fax: (020) 7242 1463

Ryman The Stationer, 96 Kensington High Street, London, W8 4SG Tel: (020) 7938 3531 Fax: (020) 7376 2284 E-mail: info@ryman.co.uk

Ryman The Stationer, 50 London Wall, London, EC2M 5TE Tel: (020) 7588 6707 Fax: (020) 7256 7010

Ryman The Stationer, 336 North End Road, London, SW6 1NB Tel: (020) 7381 8885 Fax: (020) 7381 8885

Ryman The Stationer, 68 Notting Hill Gate, London, W11 3HT Tel: (020) 7229 5308 Fax: (020) 7792 3044

Ryman The Stationer, 64 Old Brompton Road, London, SW7 3LQ Tel: (020) 7581 0858 Fax: (020) 7581 0858

Ryman The Stationer, 105 Putney High Street, London, SW15 1SS Tel: (020) 8788 6220 Fax: (020) 8789 8563

Ryman The Stationer, 121 Queensway, London, W2 4SJ Tel: (020) 7229 5957 Fax: (020) 7727 0755

Ryman The Stationer, 4 Shepherd Market, London, W1J 7QB Tel: (020) 7493 2270 Fax: (020) 7493 2270

Ryman The Stationer, 430 The Strand, London, WC2R 0QN Tel: (020) 7240 4408 Fax: (020) 7497 0975

Ryman The Stationer, 24-27 Thayer Street, London, W1U 2QL Tel: (020) 7935 8261 Fax: (020) 7224 3280

Ryman The Stationer, 66 Tottenham Court Road, London, W1T 2EX Tel: (020) 7636 7306 Fax: (020) 7636 5120

Ryman The Stationer, 31-35 Victoria Street, London, SW1H 0EU Tel: (020) 7222 4020 Fax: (020) 7630 0975

Ryman The Stationer, 4 Montpelier Vale, London, SE3 0TA Tel: (020) 8318 1445 Fax: (020) 8318 3852

Ryman The Stationer, 11 Regent Street, London, SW1Y 4ST Tel: (020) 7930 9538 Fax: (020) 7930 0975

Ryman The Stationer, 104 Baker Street, London, W1U 6TN Tel: (020) 7487 2570 Fax: (020) 7487 2570

Ryman The Stationer, 6-10 Great Portland Street, London, W1W 8QL Tel: (020) 7636 3468 Fax: (020) 7637 0975

Ryman The Stationer, 15 Hanover Street, London, W1S 1YJ Tel: (020) 7629 8397 Fax: (020) 7355 2081

Ryman The Stationer, 26 New Broadway, London, W5 2XA Tel: (020) 8579 2839 Fax: (020) 8566 0934

Ryman The Stationer, 48 Albemarle Street, London, W1S 4DH Tel: (020) 7493 9777 Fax: (020) 7493 9777 E-mail: info@ryman.co.uk

Ryman The Stationer, 27 Earl Street, Maidstone, Kent, ME14 1PF Tel: (01622) 750889 Fax: (01622) 766141

Ryman The Stationer, High Street, Oxford, OX1 4AB Tel: (01865) 246571 Fax: (01865) 728427

Ryman The Stationer, 3-5 Duke Street, Reading, RG1 4SA Tel: 0118-950 0493 Fax: 0118-950 0493

Ryman The Stationer, 11 The Quadrant, Richmond, Surrey, TW9 1BP Tel: (020) 8948 8090 Fax: (020) 8948 8090

Ryman The Stationer, 52 High Street, Staines, Middlesex, TW18 4DY Tel: (01784) 462981 Fax: (01784) 465208

Ryman The Stationer, 119 High Street, Sutton, Surrey, SM1 1JF Tel: (020) 8643 5281 Fax: (020) 8643 5281

Ryman The Stationer, 107 Peascod Street, Windsor, Berkshire, SL4 1DN Tel: (01753) 857310 Fax: (01753) 857310

Ryman The Stationer, 23 Chertsey Road, Woking, Surrey, GU21 5AB Tel: (01483) 723608 Fax: (01483) 723608

Ryman The Stationer, 3 Middle Street, Yeovil, Somerset, BA20 1LE Tel: (01935) 431305 Fax: (01935) 477098

Shire Business Solutions, Shire House, Highlands Road, Shirley, Solihull, West Midlands, B90 4LR Tel: 0121-711 3030 Fax: 0121-711 3060 E-mail: sales@shire-bs.com

▶ Shooting Star, 18 Homfray Avenue, Morecambe, Lancashire, LA3 3AG Tel: (01524) 400181 E-mail: nickipilkington@yahoo.com

Sigma Group, 12 Don Road, St. Helier, Jersey, JE2 4QD Tel: (01534) 733561 Fax: (01534) 768546 E-mail: cdpsigma@itl.net

Arthur C. Smith Ltd, Oldmedow Road, Hardwick Industrial Estate, King's Lynn, Norfolk, PE30 4LD Tel: (01553) 817220 Fax: (0845) 0500864 E-mail: sales@acssupplies.com

South Eastern Printing & Stationery Co. Ltd, Unit 5H Horndon Industrial Park, Station Road, West Horndon, Brentwood, Essex, CM13 3XL Tel: (01277) 812111 Fax: (01277) 811388

Sprintprint Printers, Aston Road, Waterlooville, Hampshire, PO7 7UD Tel: (023) 9226 7131 Fax: (023) 9224 1448 E-mail: sales@sprintprint.co.uk

Stewarts of Edinburgh Ltd, Meadowbank Works, 67 Marionville Road, Edinburgh, EH7 6AJ Tel: 0131-659 6010 Fax: 0131-652 1348 E-mail: mail@stewarts.eu.com

J. Stott & Sons Ltd, 7 Richmond Hill, Blackburn, BB1 7LB Tel: (01254) 51567 Fax: (01254) 682780 E-mail: tony@jstott.com

Stratford Paper Co. Ltd, 50 Holness Road, London, E15 4EW Tel: (020) 8534 1639 Fax: (020) 8519 1810

Summit Drawing Office Supplies Ltd, 1 Grove Street, Woodston, Peterborough, PE2 9AG Tel: (01733) 555789 Fax: (01733) 555004 E-mail: summit@summitdos..co.uk

Swift Business Equipment Ltd, Northgate, Aldridge, Walsall, WS9 8TR Tel: (01922) 743454 Fax: (01922) 743134 E-mail: sales@swiftbe.co.uk

Swiftprint, 186 Campden Hill Road, London, W8 7TH Tel: (020) 7229 5012 Fax: (020) 7229 3068 E-mail: mail@swiftprint.co.uk

Trickey Of Ewell, Blenheim Road, Epsom, Surrey, KT19 9AH Tel: (01372) 747727 Fax: (01372) 729103 E-mail: online@trickeys.fsnet.co.uk

Unicorn Office Products Ltd, Unit 25 Station Road Workshops, Station Road, Bristol, BS15 4PJ Tel: 0117-907 6662 Fax: 0117-907 6663 E-mail: sales@unicornonline.net

W G Office Supplies Ltd, Unit 3 Crayford Industrial Estate, Swaisland Drive, Crayford, Dartford, DA1 4HS Tel: (01322) 526527 Fax: (01322) 556249E-mail: sales@wgo.co.uk

WH Smith Retail Ltd, Greenbridge Road, Swindon, SN3 3LD Tel: (01793) 616161 Fax: (01793) 426410 E-mail: info@whsmithonline.com

Wholesale Stationers (Devon) Ltd, Brunel Road, Brunel Industrial Estate, Newton Abbot, Devon, TQ12 4PB Tel: (01626) 365007 Fax: (01626) 367269 E-mail: sales@wholesalestationers.co.uk

Wilcox Desk Top Equipment, Unison House, 46 George Street, Kidderminster, Worcestershire, DY10 1PY Tel: (01562) 824470 Fax: (01562) 829867 E-mail: sales@wilcoxdesktop.co.uk

Wilkinson Richmond, Unit E11 Countess Avenue, Cheadle Hulme, Cheadle, Cheshire, SK8 6QS Tel: 0161-485 1655 Fax: 0161-486 6097

Sid Wilson (Newcastle) Ltd, 3-5 Tundry Way, Chainbridge Road Industrial Estate, Blaydon-On-Tyne, Tyne & Wear, NE21 5SJ Tel: 0191-414 3344 Fax: 0191-414 5962 E-mail: sidwilsonsweets@aol.com

Wordflow, 32-38 Scrutton Street, London, EC2A 4RQ Tel: (020) 7377 1182 Fax: (020) 7377 2942 E-mail: help@wordflow.co.uk

Wyatt & Ackerman Ltd, 30 North Street, Bedminster, Bristol, BS3 1HW Tel: 0117-966 1675 Fax: 0117-966 1775 E-mail: sales@wyattandackerman.co.uk

STATIONERY BATTERIES

▶ UK Business Print Ltd, 15 Hendersyde Park, Kelso, Roxburghshire, TD5 7TU Tel: (01573) 224889 Fax: (01573) 223854 E-mail: sales@ukbrand.com

STATIONERY (CONTINUOUS) DISTRIBUTORS OR AGENTS

Anca, Leyton Avenue, Mildenhall, Bury St. Edmunds, Suffolk, IP28 7BL Tel: (01638) 717611 Fax: (01638) 717711

STATIONERY (CONTINUOUS) MANUFRS/PRINTING SERVICES

A P Litho Ltd, Units 9-10 Bourne Road Industrial Park, Bourne Road, Dartford, DA1 4BZ Tel: (01322) 523289 Fax: (01322) 527343 E-mail: alan@printapl.fsnet.co.uk

Adare Halcyon Ltd, Park Mill, Clayton West, Huddersfield, HD8 9QQ Tel: (01484) 863411 Fax: (01484) 862355 E-mail: info@adare.com

Albert Taylor & Sons,Limited, Thames House, Thames Street, Rotherham, South Yorkshire, S60 1LU Tel: (01709) 515131 Fax: (01709) 515135 E-mail: info@taylorsprint.com

Centrereed Ltd, Thames House, Thames Street, Rotherham, South Yorkshire, S60 1LU Tel: (01709) 827700 Fax: (01709) 827715 E-mail: sales@centrereed.co.uk

Charter Business Forms Ltd, Harris Industrial Estate, Hanbury Road, Stoke Prior, Bromsgrove, Worcestershire, B60 4AD Tel: (01527) 575166 Fax: (01527) 579152

Claymore Graphics Ltd, 63 Cotton Street, Aberdeen, AB11 5EG Tel: (01224) 576176 Fax: (01224) 584431 E-mail: mail@claymoregraphics.co.uk

Coda Systemforms Ltd, Harbour House, Coldharbour Lane, Rainham, Essex, RM13 9YA Tel: (01708) 520100 Fax: (01708) 550073 E-mail: neilcook@codasystemforms.co.uk

Coubrough & McKeracher (Printers) Ltd, 8 Falfield Street, Glasgow, G5 8HL Tel: 0141-429 0487 Fax: 0141-429 0515 E-mail: enquiries@cmckprinters.com

A.B. Crick (Printers) Ltd, 762 Ampthill, Bedford, MK45 2XH Tel: (01234) 742292 Fax: (01234) 742292

Darley Ltd, Wellington Road, Burton-on-Trent, Staffordshire, DE14 2AD Tel: (01283) 564936 Fax: (01283) 545688 E-mail: mailbox@darley.co.uk

Datagraphic UK Ltd, Cottage Leap, Butler's Leap, Rugby, Warwickshire, CV21 3XP Tel: (01788) 535383 Fax: (01788) 535351 E-mail: sales@datagraphic.co.uk

Dataproof, The Bond, 180-182 Fazeley Street, Birmingham, B5 5SE Tel: 0121-753 7930 Fax: 0121-753 7939 E-mail: office@dataproof.biz

DTS Computer Print Ltd, Adams Street, Birmingham, B7 4LT Tel: 0121-359 5551 Fax: 0121-359 7300E-mail: sales@dts-ltd.com

Duffields Business Forms Ltd, 4 Nunn Brook Road, Huthwaite, Sutton-in-Ashfield, Nottinghamshire, NG17 2HU Tel: (01623) 440140 Fax: (01623) 440124

F B Jesper & Son Ltd, 14 Oxford St, Harrogate, North Yorkshire, HG1 1PU Tel: (01423) 503998 E-mail: harrogate@jespers.co.uk

FT Print, Centrus Business Park, Mead Lane, Hertford, SG13 7AW Tel: (01992) 501500 Fax: (01992) 501352 E-mail: printed@forms-technology.co.uk

Graphico Printing Ltd, 69-71 London Road, Croydon, CR0 2RF Tel: (020) 8681 1101 Fax: (020) 8688 8588 E-mail: sales@graphico.com

▶ Ips, Executive House, Mill Lane, Blaby, Leicester, LE8 4FG Tel: 0116-277 2666 Fax: 0116-276 1199 E-mail: susan@direct-ips.co.uk

J F A Printing plc, Wellington CR, New Malden, Surrey, KT3 3NE Tel: (020) 8640 7777 Fax: (020) 8942 7228 E-mail: sales@jfaprint.co.uk

Jaguar Business Forms, 9-17 Crompton Way, Crawley, West Sussex, RH10 9QG Tel: (01293) 512688 Fax: (01293) 551703 E-mail: sales@jagforms.co.uk

John L R James & Co. Ltd, Victoria Road Industrial, Estate, Skegness, Lincolnshire, PE25 3SW Tel: (01754) 768521 Fax: (01754) 768936 E-mail: sales@jlrjames.com

Kestrel Group Ltd, Unit 1-2 York Street, St. Werburghs, Bristol, BS2 9XT Tel: 0117-955 7524 Fax: 0117-955 8157

Lion F P G Ltd, Oldbury Road, West Bromwich, West Midlands, B70 9DQ Tel: 0121-585 0000 Fax: 0121-503 0419 E-mail: sales@lionfpg.co.uk

Lonsdale Print Solutions Ltd, Denington Road, Denington Industrial Estate, Wellingborough, Northamptonshire, NN8 2RA Tel: (01933) 228855 Fax: (01933) 442405 E-mail: info@lonsdaleps.co.uk

M B F Business Forms Ltd, 20 Rectory Road, West Bridgford, Nottingham, NG2 6BG Tel: 0115-981 3786 Fax: 0115-945 5249 E-mail: info@mbf-business-forms.co.uk

Mailtime Services Ltd, 490 Gorton Road, Reddish, Stockport, Cheshire, SK5 6PP Tel: 0161-223 0044 Fax: 0161-223 0055

STATIONERY (CONTINUOUS) MANUFRS/PRINTING SERVICES – *continued*

Malling Press, Unit 4b Diplocks Way, Hailsham, East Sussex, BN27 3JF Tel: (01323) 847157 Fax: (01323) 847457

Merchants Systems, 11 Paul Street, Liverpool, L3 6DX Tel: 0151-236 2253 Fax: 0151-236 0861 E-mail: sales@merchants-systems.co.uk

▶ Micro Computer Forms Ltd, 9 Blackbrook Valley Industrial Estate, Narrowboat Way, Dudley, West Midlands, DY2 0XQ Tel: (01384) 455221 Fax: (01384) 455223 E-mail: lsm@mcforms.co.uk

N W C Business Forms Ltd, Unit 17-19, Greenfield Business Park, Holywell, Clwyd, CH8 7HW Tel: (01352) 712965 Fax: (01352) 713092

Orchestra Wotton Group Ltd, Walk Mills, Kingswood, Wotton-under-Edge, Gloucestershire, GL12 8JT Tel: (01453) 845019 Fax: (01453) 845019 E-mail: enquiries@orchestrawotton.co.uk

P F C Group Ltd, Roman Way Business Centre, Berry Hill Industrial Estate, Droitwich, Worcestershire, WR9 9AJ Tel: (01905) 797000 Fax: (01905) 797274 E-mail: marketsales@pfcgroup.co.uk

Paragon Ltd, Park Road, Castleford, West Yorkshire, WF10 4RR Tel: (01977) 669700 Fax: (01977) 603036 E-mail: sales@paragon-castleford.com

R P Business Forms Ltd, Unit 17 Fallings Park Industrial Estate, Park Lane, Wolverhampton, WV10 9QB Tel: (01902) 723500 Fax: (01902) 723116 E-mail: rpbusinessforms@btinternet.com

Redlin Print Ltd, 33 Hanbury Road, Chelmsford, CM1 3AE Tel: 01245 280555 E-mail: sales@redlin.co.uk

Reelprint Register Sets Ltd, Spring Road Industrial Estate, 13 Lanesfield Drive, Wolverhampton, WV4 6UA Tel: (01902) 405177 Fax: (01902) 405178 E-mail: reelprint@lineone.net

Robrook Press Ltd, Queens Road, Morley, Leeds, LS27 0PF Tel: 0113-253 5753 Fax: 0113-238 0231 E-mail: paul@robrook.com

Specialist Print Sevices Ltd, Mallard Close, Birmingham, B27 6BW Tel: 0121-707 7166 Fax: 0121-706 1383 E-mail: specialist-print@aol.com

Tate Fastforms Ltd, Wingate House, Wingate Road, Luton, LU4 8PU Tel: (01582) 586700 Fax: (01582) 586725 E-mail: enquiries@tateconsumables.co.uk

Weston Business Forms, Unit 23-24 Solent Industrial Estate, Shamblehurst Lane, Hedge End, Southampton, SO30 2FY Tel: (01489) 780707 Fax: (01489) 780200 E-mail: sales@westonbusinessforms.co.uk

STATIONERY (CONTINUOUS) PRINTING MACHINE MANUFRS

Chase Design & Print, White Cottage Works, Rumer Hill Road, Cannock, Staffordshire, WS11 8EX Tel: (01543) 462334 Fax: (01543) 505707 E-mail: chasedesign2000@hotmail.com

Tom Gutherless Ltd, 34 & 34a St James Street, Hull, HU3 2DH Tel: (01482) 214184 Fax: (01482) 215211 E-mail: print@tom-guther.co.uk

STATIONERY ENGRAVING SERVICES

▶ The Design Station Ltd, 9 Turnstone Drive, Featherstone, Wolverhampton, WV10 7TA Tel: (01902) 722192 E-mail: jackie@thedesignstation.co.uk

Wren Press Stationary Ltd, Unit 1 Chelsea Wharf, 15 Lots Road, London, SW10 0QJ Tel: (020) 7351 5887 Fax: (020) 7352 7063 E-mail: orders@wrenpress.com

STATIONERY IMPORT/EXPORT MERCHANTS OR AGENTS

Crown Trading Ltd, 26a Sidney Road, London, SW9 0TS Tel: (020) 7733 4607 Fax: (020) 7733 8100

Stationery Express, 15 The Metro Centre, St. Johns Road, Isleworth, Middlesex, TW7 6NJ Tel: (020) 8568 1771 Fax: (020) 8569 8168 E-mail: sales@stationeryexpress.net

STATIONERY TO SPECIFICATION

▶ Caricature/Cartoon Portrait Wedding Invitations, 5 Hillview Cottages (Off Plough Hill), Basted, Borough Green, Sevenoaks, Kent, TN15 8PS Tel: (01732) 883555 E-mail: weddings@christmanncreative.co.uk

STATOR COILS

Robson & Francis Ltd, Unit 2 Hardess Street Industrial Estate, London, SE24 0HN Tel: (020) 7733 2353 E-mail: info@rewinds.co.uk

S & S Windings Ltd, 5 Focus 303 Business Centre, South Way, Andover, Hampshire, SP10 5NY Tel: (01264) 334095 Fax: (01264) 334095 E-mail: sswindings@btclick.com

STATUTORY INSPECTION SERVICES, ENGINEERING

▶ Skypark Freight, 16 Owen Drive, Liverpool, L24 1YL Tel: 0151-448 0048 Fax: 0151-448 0007 E-mail: steve@skylog.freeserve.co.uk

STEAM ACCUMULATORS

Collins Walker Ltd, Unit 7a Nottingham South & Wilford Industrial Estate, Ruddington Lane, Nottingham, NG11 7EP Tel: 0115-981 8044 Fax: 0115-945 5376 E-mail: sales@collins-walker.co.uk

STEAM AND STEAM GENERATOR WATER TREATMENT SHELL AND TUBE HEAT EXCHANGERS

Brade Engineering Ltd, Atlas Works, Gibbet Street, Halifax, West Yorkshire, HX1 4DB Tel: (01484) 711003 Fax: (01422) 350066 E-mail: sales@ormandyltd.com

STEAM BOILER/GENERATOR/ RAISER

Babcock Wanson UK Ltd, 7 Elstree Way, Borehamwood, Hertfordshire, WD6 1SA Tel: (020) 8953 7111 Fax: (020) 8207 5177 E-mail:

Boiler Tech Services, Unit 22 Demmings Road, Cheadle, Cheshire, SK8 2PE Tel: 0161-428 2967 Fax: 0161-428 6487 E-mail: peter@mead4656.fsnet.co.uk

Controlled Flame Boilers Ltd, Gorse Lane Industrial Estate, Brunel Road, Clacton-on-Sea, Essex, CO15 4LU Tel: (01255) 224500 Fax: (01255) 224555 E-mail: sales@steamboilers.co.uk

Vapac Humidity Control Ltd, Station Road, Edenbridge, Kent, TN8 6EG Tel: (01732) 863447 E-mail: peter.dewdney@eton_williams.com

STEAM BOILERS, *See also Steam Boiler, Generator, Raiser etc*

Israel Newton & Sons Ltd, Summerley Works, Idle, Bradford, West Yorkshire, BD10 8TT Tel: (01274) 612059 Fax: (01274) 612059

STEAM CABINS

▶ Premier Service & Installation, Premier House, Unit 6, Station Terrace, Station Road,, Kegworth, Derbyshire, DE74 2GE Tel: 01509 670600 Fax: 01509 673275 E-mail: info@premservices.co.uk

STEAM CLEANERS, INDUSTRIAL

▶ GP Cleaners, Unit F3, Innsworth Technology Park, Innsworth Lane, Gloucester, GL3 1DL Tel: (01452) 731630 Fax: (01452) 739212 E-mail: sales@gpcleaners.com

STEAM CLEANING EQUIPMENT

CB Services, 5 Building 14 Mallusk Park, Mallusk Road, Newtownabbey, County Antrim, BT36 4FS Tel: (028) 9083 7738 Fax: (028) 9083 2093 E-mail: iaininfo@cb-services.com

Check Equipment, 2 Spencer Drive, Melbourn, Royston, Hertfordshire, SG8 6HP Tel: (01763) 261971 Fax: (01763) 262995 E-mail:

Checo 2000, Brailwood Road, Bilsthorpe, Newark, Nottinghamshire, NG22 8UA Tel: (01623) 871976 Fax: (01623) 871964 E-mail: info@checo200.co.uk

Earlex Ltd, Opus Park Moorfield Road, Slyfield Industrial Estate, Guildford, Surrey, GU1 1SZ Tel: (01483) 454666 Fax: (01483) 454548 E-mail: enquiries@earlex.co.uk

F & G Services, Charfield Road, Kingswood, Wotton-Under-Edge, Gloucestershire, GL12 8RL Tel: (01453) 842307 Fax: (01453) 844303

I R T S Ltd, Hillside, Sewell, Dunstable, Bedfordshire, LU6 1RP Tel: (01582) 600080 Fax: (01582) 666447

J L Clark & Co., 16 Alliance Close, Ptarmigan Place, Attleborough Fields Industrial Estate, Nuneaton, Warwickshire, CV11 6RX Tel: (024) 7635 2140 Fax: (024) 7635 3347 E-mail: jlandclarksonltd@aol.com

Jennychem, Jennychem House, Sort Mill Road, Mid Kent Business Park, Snodland, Kent, ME6 5UA Tel: (01634) 290770 Fax: (01634) 245777 E-mail: jenny@jennychem.com

Kleaning Equipment Western Ltd, Park Road, Dawley Bank, Telford, Shropshire, TF4 2BE Tel: (01952) 502600 Fax: (01952) 504703 E-mail: enquiries@cleaning-equipment.co.uk

Nailsea Power Cleaning Ltd, Cherry Orchard Farm, Youngwood Lane, Nailsea, Bristol, BS48 4NP Tel: (01275) 810881 Fax: (01275) 810885

P G & C Nottingham Ltd, Main Road, Tallington, Stamford, Lincolnshire, PE9 4RN Tel: (01778) 380666 Fax: (01778) 381707 E-mail: enquiries@pgcnottingham.co.uk

Phillard Pump Co., Unit B, Holmes Court, Horncastle, Lincolnshire, LN9 6AS Tel: (01507) 523281 Fax: (01507) 527437

Quill International, Quill International Group Ltd, Castle Lane, Melbourne, Derby, DE73 8JB Tel: (01332) 863292 Fax: (01332) 863292 E-mail: sales@quillinternational.com

Robinsons, Braybrooke Road, Great Oxendon, Market Harborough, Leicestershire, LE16 8LU Tel: (01858) 461900 Fax: (01858) 465646

Scotkleen Warwick Power Washers, 149a Glasgow Road, Wishaw, Lanarkshire, ML2 7QJ Tel: (0870) 8600600 Fax: (01698) 356697 E-mail: info@scotkleen.co.uk

STEAM CLEANING EQUIPMENT HIRE

Modern Tool Hire Ltd, Minerva Lane Works, Walsall Street, Wolverhampton, WV1 3LX Tel: (01902) 453044 Fax: (01902) 453221

Power Clean Services, 3 Regent Business Centre, Pump Lane, Hayes, Middlesex, UB3 3NP Tel: (020) 8573 9893 Fax: (020) 8573 7765

Simpsons, Trowbridge Road, Westbury, Wiltshire, BA13 3AY Tel: (01373) 826578 Fax: (01373) 865315 E-mail: simpson1979@aol.com

Total Cleaning Equipment Ltd, 223-225 Ilderton Road, London, SE15 1NS Tel: (020) 7732 0191 Fax: (020) 7732 0194 E-mail: tcelimited@aol.com

STEAM CLEANING EQUIPMENT MAINTENANCE/REPAIR SERVICES

Admor Services, Foxes Retreat, Worlds End, Beedon, Newbury, Berkshire, RG20 8SE Tel: (01635) 248088 Fax: (01635) 247877 E-mail: terry@admorservices.co.uk

J L Clark & Co., 16 Alliance Close, Ptarmigan Place, Attleborough Fields Industrial Estate, Nuneaton, Warwickshire, CV11 6RX Tel: (024) 7635 2140 Fax: (024) 7635 3347 E-mail: jlandclarksonltd@aol.com

Super Service, Frogs Island, Old Didcot Road, Brightwell-cum-Sotwell, Wallingford, Oxfordshire, OX10 0SW Tel: (01491) 837000 Fax: (01491) 839900

Total Cleaning Equipment Ltd, 223-225 Ilderton Road, London, SE15 1NS Tel: (020) 7732 0191 Fax: (020) 7732 0194 E-mail: tcelimited@aol.com

STEAM OR WATER SPACE HEATERS

Turnbull & Scott Engineers Ltd, Glenfield Park One, Philips Road, Blackburn, BB1 5PF Tel: (01254) 586460 Fax: (01254) 586490 E-mail: sales@turnbull-scott.co.uk

STEAM PACKINGS AND JOINTINGS

Harrison, J.A. & Co. Ltd, Britain Works, Sherborne Street, Manchester, M8 8HP Tel: 0161-832 2282 Fax: 0161-832 3263 E-mail: enquiries@jaharrison.co.uk

STEAM TRAP MANUFRS

Gardner Energy Management Ltd, 1 John Street, Bristol, BS1 Tel: 0117-917 7010 Fax: 0117-917 7011 E-mail: enq@gemtrap.co.uk

Smart Valves & Controls Ltd, Uxbridge Road, Leicester, LE4 7ST Tel: 0116-268 8130 Fax: 0116-261 0050 E-mail: sales@northvalekorting.co.uk

▶ TC Fluid Control Ltd, Broadgate, Broadway Business Park, Oldham, OL9 9XA Tel: 0161-684 7488 Fax: 0161-684 7487 E-mail: info@tc-fluidcontrol.com

STEAM TUBE ROTARY DRYERS

JND Technologies Ltd, Thrumpton Lane, Retford, Nottinghamshire, DN22 7AN Tel: (01777) 706777 Fax: (01777) 713192 E-mail: info@jnd.co.uk

STEAM TURBINE DRIVEN GENERATOR SETS

Alstom Power Generation Ltd, Silverlink Business Park, Silverlink, Wallsend, Tyne & Wear, NE28 9ND Tel: 0191-295 2000 Fax: 0191-295 2011

Combustion Energy & Steam Specialists Ltd, 77-79 John Street, Stromness, Orkney, KW16 3AD Tel: (01856) 851177 Fax: (01856) 851199 E-mail: enquiries@cess.co.uk

Dresser-Rand (U K) Ltd, C I Tower St. Georges Square, High Street, New Malden, Surrey, KT3 4DN Tel: (020) 8336 7300 Fax: (020) 8336 0773

KKK Limited, 7 Regent Park, Park Farm Industrial Estate, Off Booth Drive, Wellingborough, Northants, NN8 6GR Tel: (01933) 671480 Fax: (01933) 671470 E-mail: kkk.limited@agkkk.de

Seimens Power Generation Ltd, C A Parsons Works, Shields Road, Newcastle upon Tyne, NE6 2YL Tel: 0191-276 1188 Fax: 0191-276 0276 E-mail: spgl@siemens.co.uk

STEAM TURBINES

Converteam, Boughton Road, Rugby, Warwickshire, CV21 1BU Tel: (01788) 546600 Fax: (01788) 560767

Dresser-Rand (U K) Ltd, C I Tower St. Georges Square, High Street, New Malden, Surrey, KT3 4DN Tel: (020) 8336 7300 Fax: (020) 8336 0773

R J B Engineering, Westminster Industrial Estate, Station Road, North Hykeham, Lincoln, LN6 3QY Tel: (01522) 690491 Fax: (01522) 697543 E-mail: info@sje-engineering.co.uk

STEAM VALVES

Dynafluid Ltd, Units D1-D2, Halesfield 21, Telford, Shropshire, TF7 4NX Tel: (01952) 580946 Fax: (01952) 582546 E-mail: enquiries@dynafluid.com

Peter Smith Valve Co. Ltd, Occupation Road, Nottingham, NG6 8RX Tel: 0115-927 2831 Fax: 0115-977 0233 E-mail: sales@petersmithvalve.co.uk

Taylor Shaw, Albert St, Lockwood, Huddersfield, HD1 3QG Tel: (01484) 532425 Fax: (01484) 512426 E-mail: sales@taylor-shaw.co.uk

STEARIC ACID

H. Foster & Co. Ltd, 103 Kirkstall Road, Leeds, LS3 1JL Tel: 0113-243 9016 Fax: 0113-242 2418 E-mail: sales@hfoster.co.uk

STEEL, *See also headings for particular products*

A H Allen Ltd, Downing Road, West Meadows Industrial Estate, Derby, DE21 6HA Tel: (01332) 346400 Fax: (01332) 291023 E-mail: sales@aha-steel-derby.co.uk

A H Allen Steel Services Ltd, Liliput Road, Brackmills Industrial Estate, Northampton, NN4 7DT Tel: (01604) 762211 Fax: (01604) 765525 E-mail: sales@aha-steel.co.uk

A S D Anderson Brown, 24 South Gyle Crescent, South Gyle Industrial Estate, Edinburgh, EH12 9EB Tel: 0131-459 3200 Fax: 0131-459 3266 E-mail: customer.care@asdplc.co.uk

A S D Metal Services Ltd, Gibson Lane, Melton, North Ferriby, East Yorkshire, HU14 3HX Tel: (01482) 633360 Fax: (01482) 633370 E-mail: hull@asdmetalservices.co.uk

A S D Metal Services Ltd, Tunstall Road, Biddulph, Stoke-on-Trent, ST8 6JZ Tel: (01782) 515152 Fax: (01782) 522240 E-mail: asdmetalservices@asdplc.co.uk

A S D Metal Services Ltd, PO Box 5, Stoke-on-Trent, ST4 2NQ Tel: (01782) 202118 Fax: (01782) 283220 E-mail: stoke@asdmetalservices.co.uk

A S D Metal Services Cardiff, East Moors Road, Cardiff, CF24 5SP Tel: (029) 2046 0622 Fax: (029) 2049 0105 E-mail: cardiff@asdmetalservices.co.uk

A S D Metal Services Carlisle, Unit C Earls Way, Kingmoor Park Central, Carlisle, CA6 4SE Tel: (01228) 674766 Fax: (01228) 674197 E-mail: carlisle@asdmetalservices.co.uk

A S K Mcgowan Ltd, Coombs Wood Business Park, Steelpark Road, Halesowen, West Midlands, B62 8HD Tel: 0121-561 6800 Fax: 0121-561 6803 E-mail: central@askmcgowan.co.uk

▶ A Smith Sandwell Ltd, Union Road, Oldbury, West Midlands, B69 3EU Tel: 0121-544 6575 Fax: 0121-552 1537 E-mail: asmithsandwell@btconnect.com

STEEL – *continued*

Abbey Steel & Shearing Co. Ltd, 5 Cartwright Road, Pin Green Industrial Area, Stevenage, Hertfordshire, SG1 4QJ Tel: (01438) 741888 Fax: (01438) 740980 E-mail: sales@abbeysteel.co.uk

Accent Steel Ltd, 164 West Wycombe Road, High Wycombe, Buckinghamshire, HP12 3AE Tel: (01494) 465421 Fax: (01494) 524044 E-mail: accentsteel@ukonline.co.uk

Ace Metal, 10 Morgan Way, Bowthorpe Employment Area, Norwich, NR5 9JJ Tel: (01603) 731935 Fax: (01603) 748421 E-mail: acemetalsupplies@aol.com

Acton Bright Steel Ltd, Gordon Road, Staines, Middlesex, TW18 3BG Tel: (01784) 463595 Fax: (01784) 451748 E-mail: sales@actonbrightsteel.co.uk

▶ Adelphi Engineering & Construction, Unit 1 Imex Business Centre, Lugar, Cumnock, Ayrshire, KA18 3JG Tel: (01290) 426677 Fax: (01290) 425588

Adey Steel, Meadow Lane, Loughborough, Leicestershire, LE11 1JU Tel: (01509) 556677 Fax: (01509) 828622 E-mail: admin@adey-steel.co.uk

Alexander Stirling & Co., Meadowforth Road, Stirling, FK7 7SA Tel: (01786) 473333 Fax: (01786) 450408 E-mail: sales@alexanderstirling.co.uk

Allan Industrial Products Ltd, Suite 3, 30 Bancroft, Hitchin, Hertfordshire, SG5 1LE Tel: (01462) 454021 Fax: (01462) 421312 E-mail: sales@allanindustrial.co.uk

Amarex Ltd, Newburn Industrial Estate, Shelley Road, Newcastle upon Tyne, NE15 9RT Tel: 0191-264 4781 Fax: 0191-229 0405 E-mail: steel@amerex.demon.co.uk

Arkoss Metals Ltd, 112 Latimer Road, Chesham, Buckinghamshire, HP5 1QQ Tel: (01494) 776163 Fax: (01494) 771511

Armada Tube & Steel (SW) Ltd, Tube & Steel Service Centre, Pennygillam Industrial Estate, Launceston, Cornwall, PL15 7ED Tel: (01566) 776699 Fax: (01566) 776500 E-mail: des@armadatube.co.uk

Arraquip Ltd, Withambrook Industrial Estate, Grantham, Lincolnshire, NG31 9ST Tel: (01476) 573637 Fax: (01476) 590192 E-mail: arraquip@msn.com

Asd, Hamlin Way, King's Lynn, Norfolk, PE30 4LQ Tel: (01553) 761431 Fax: (01553) 692394 E-mail: info@asdplc.co.uk

Asd, Station Road, Stalbridge, Sturminster Newton, Dorset, DT10 2RW Tel: (01963) 362066 Fax: (01963) 363260 E-mail: yeovil@asdplc.co.uk

Asd Metal Services, South Humberside Industrial Estate, Grimsby, South Humberside, DN31 2TG Tel: (01472) 353851 Fax: (01472) 240028 E-mail: grimsby@asdmetalservices.co.uk

Ashton Steel Stockholders Ltd, Station Yard, Station Road, Hadfield, Glossop, Derbyshire, SK13 1AA Tel: (01457) 862438 Fax: (01457) 861325

George Ausden Ltd, 253 High Street, Watford, WD17 2HW Tel: (01923) 223530 Fax: (01923) 223530 E-mail: info@geo-ausden.com

Aviation Metals Ltd, Michigan Drive, Tongwell, Milton Keynes, MK15 8JE Tel: (01908) 210012 Fax: (01908) 210066 E-mail: sales@aviationmetals.co.uk

Avon Steel Co. Ltd, Unit 18 Midsomer Enterprise Park, Radstock Road, Midsomer Norton, Radstock, BA3 2BB Tel: (01761) 416721 Fax: (01761) 412870 E-mail: charles@avonsteel.co.uk

B I L Steels Ltd, Eyre Street, Birmingham, B18 7AA Tel: 0121-456 5886 Fax: 0121-454 6213

B S Steels, 1 Shawcross Industrial Park, Ackworth Road, Portsmouth, PO3 5HU Tel: (023) 9267 3778 Fax: (023) 9269 1528 E-mail: bssteels@btconnect.com

Ballachree Ltd, Canal Road, Frizinghall, Bradford, West Yorkshire, BD2 1AU Tel: (01274) 593131 Fax: (01274) 596752 E-mail: sales@ballachree.co.uk

Barclay & Mathieson Ltd, 180 Hardgate Road, Glasgow, G51 4TB Tel: 0141-445 6161 Fax: 0141-445 6964 E-mail: admin@bmsteel.co.uk

Barclay & Mathieson Ltd, Arnold Road, Nottingham, NG6 0EF Tel: 0115-970 1171 Fax: 0115-942 2181 E-mail: nottingham@bmsteel.co.uk

Barclay & Mathieson Ltd, Coleford Road, Sheffield, S9 5NF Tel: 0114-244 2094 Fax: 0114-243 5965 E-mail: sheffield@bmsteel.co.uk

Barnes Morris Steels, Bay 3 5 Grazebrook Industrial Park, Peartree Lane, Dudley, West Midlands, DY2 0XW Tel: (01384) 233393 Fax: (01384) 253111 E-mail: info@barnesmorris.co.uk

Barnetts Of Canterbury, 1 Wealden Forest Park, Herne Common, Herne Bay, Kent, CT6 7LQ Tel: (01227) 710174 Fax: (01227) 713113

Barton Steel Services Ltd, Unit 6 Severnside Trading Estate, Textilose Rd, Trafford Park, Manchester, M17 1WA Tel: 0161-872 3084 Fax: 0161-872 0759

C. Beech & Sons (Netherton) Ltd, Waterside Estate, Primrose Hill, Cradley Road, Netherton, Dudley, West Midlands, DY2 9RG Tel: (01384) 456654 Fax: (01384) 238656 E-mail: sales@cbeech-steel.co.uk

Berkshire Metals Ltd, 10-12 Armour Road, Tilehurst, Reading, RG31 6HS Tel: 0118-942 9476 Fax: 0118-942 4800

Bexley Steel, 8 Power Industrial Estate, Slade Green Road, Erith, Kent, DA8 2HU Tel: (01322) 335420 Fax: (01322) 335984 E-mail: bexleysteel@supernet.com

Henry T. Billson (Kettering) Ltd, Glendon Ironworks, Sackville St, Kettering, Northants, NN16 9EQ Tel: (01536) 512194 Fax: (01536) 484152 E-mail: sales@billsonssteel.co.uk

Bond Precision Grinding Ltd, Trafalgar Works, Effingham Road, Sheffield, S9 3QA Tel: 0114-273 1212 Fax: 0114-276 5387 E-mail: bondpreci@aol.com

Boswell & Co. (Steels) Ltd, Bassett Road, Park Lane Industrial Estate, Cradley, Halesowen, West Midlands, B63 2RE Tel: (01384) 637375 Fax: (01384) 410103 E-mail: boswellsteel@aol.com

Bowdell Steel Services Ltd, 57 Bradford Street, Walsall, WS1 3QD Tel: (01922) 720989 Fax: (01922) 635960 E-mail: bowdellsteel@tinyworld.co.uk

Bradley Steels Ltd, Dawley Brook, Kingswinford, West Midlands, DY6 7AS Tel: (01384) 293855 Fax: (01384) 297440

Brian Mccance Steel Ltd, 1 Dargan Road, Belfast, BT3 9JU Tel: (028) 9077 2326 Fax: (028) 9077 9698 E-mail: admin@mccancesteel.com

Bristol Steel Stockholders Ltd, Unit 13-14 Avonbridge Trading Estate, Atlantic Road, Bristol, BS11 9QD Tel: 0117-982 8131 Fax: 0117-982 8137 E-mail: steel@bristolsteel.co.uk

M. Brittain (York) Ltd, Unit 12 Barclay Curle Works, 739 South Street, Glasgow, G14 0AH Tel: 0141-950 1400 Fax: 0141-950 1393

Brockstock, Overend Road, Corngreaves Trading Estate, Cradley Heath, West Midlands, B64 7DD Tel: 0121-568 6161 Fax: (01384) 567191 E-mail: sales@brockstock.co.uk

Gary Brown Steels Ltd, Unit 21 Izons Industrial Estate, Oldbury Road, West Bromwich, West Midlands, B70 9BS Tel: 0121-525 2700 Fax: 0121-525 6200

Brown & Glegg Edinburgh Ltd, Bankhead Crossway South, Sighthill Industrial Estate, Edinburgh, EH11 4EZ Tel: 0131-453 6611 Fax: 0131-453 1848 E-mail: info@brownglegg.co.uk

Brown McFarlane Ltd, 239 Myreside Street, Glasgow, G32 6DR Tel: 0141-551 9191 Fax: 0141-554 6825 E-mail: info@brownmac.co.uk

C Brown & Sons Steel Ltd, Pedmore Road, Dudley, West Midlands, DY2 0RL Tel: (01384) 480048 Fax: (01384) 263838 E-mail: sales@cbrownsteels.co.uk

C L T (Essington) Ltd, Unit 2C Bloxwich Business Pk, Fryers Rd, Walsall, WS2 7LY Tel: (01922) 713367 Fax: (01922) 713368

C M T Steel Services Ltd, Overend Road, Corngreaves Trading Estate, Cradley Heath, West Midlands, B64 7DD Tel: (01384) 565166 Fax: (01384) 633586 E-mail: sales@cmt-steel.co.uk

C Roberts Steel Services Manchester Ltd, Clement Works, Long Wood Road, Trafford Park, Manchester, M17 1PZ Tel: 0161-874 5200 Fax: 0161-848 7820 E-mail: sales@roberts-steel-mcr.co.uk

C & S Steels Wolverhampton Ltd, Highfields Road, Bilston, West Midlands, WV14 0LQ Tel: (01902) 404771 Fax: (01902) 353348 E-mail: sales@prosol-electronics.co.uk

Camp Steel, 29 Grafton Road, Sparkbrook, Birmingham, B11 1JP Tel: 0121-772 7821 Fax: 0121-771 0435 E-mail: dave-campsteel@btconnect.com

Camtrex Ltd, Amington Road, Birmingham, B25 8ET Tel: 0121-706 1167 Fax: 0121-706 5565 E-mail: j.thomas@camtrex.co.uk

Canal Engineering Ltd, Lenton Lane, Nottingham, NG7 2PQ Tel: 0115-986 6321 Fax: 0115-986 0211 E-mail: enquiries@canalengineering.co.uk

Cannon Steels Ltd, 22 Walcot Road, Enfield, Middlesex, EN3 7NF Tel: (020) 8805 4070 Fax: (020) 8805 4525 E-mail: enquiries@cannonsteelsltd.co.uk

Carter Steel Ltd, Yarm Road, Stockton-on-Tees, Cleveland, TS18 3SA Tel: (01642) 679831 Fax: (01642) 670346

Castle Steel Services Ltd, Pensnett House, Pensnett Trading Estate, Kingswinford, West Midlands, DY6 7PP Tel: (01384) 401600 Fax: (01384) 292785 E-mail: mikeb@tidentsections.co.uk

▶ Castmaster Roll Co., Eagle Foundry, Stevenson Road, Sheffield, S9 3XG Tel: 0114-244 0381 Fax: 0114-243 1317 E-mail: sales@castmasterrolls.com

Central Plate Services Ltd, Phoenix Works Industrial Estate, Richards Street, Wednesbury, West Midlands, WS10 8BZ Tel: 0121-526 3770 Fax: 0121-526 4770

John Chorley & Co. Ltd, Dallam Lane, Warrington, WA2 7PZ Tel: (01925) 636552 Fax: (01925) 415812 E-mail: sales@johncholey.co.uk

Christmas Stockholders Ltd, Ainsdale Drive, Shrewsbury, SY1 3TL Tel: (01743) 462515 Fax: (01743) 464430

Classic Steels Stockholding Ltd, The Old Press House, Irwell Vale Road, Rossendale, Lancashire, BB4 6LF Tel: (01706) 244880 Fax: (01706) 219331 E-mail: classicsteels@lineone.net

Clifda Steels Ltd, Northwick Corner, Canvey Island, Essex, SS8 0PS Tel: (01268) 510066 Fax: (01268) 683815 E-mail: clifdasteels@yahoo.com

Clydeside Steel Fabrications Ltd, 180 Hardgate Road, Glasgow, G51 4TB Tel: 0141-445 2898 Fax: 0141-445 6964 E-mail: fabs@bmsteel.co.uk

Cogent Orb Electrical Steels, PO Box 30, Newport, Gwent, NP19 0XT Tel: (01633) 290033 Fax: (01633) 294592 E-mail: sales@cogent-power.com

College Gauge & Tool Co. Ltd, Unit 16 The Business Centre, 20 James Road, Tyseley, Birmingham, B11 2BA Tel: 0121-764 6433 Fax: 0121-764 6499

Color Steels Ltd, Blackvein Industrial Estate, Cross Keys, Newport, Gwent, NP11 7YD Tel: (01495) 279100 Fax: (01495) 271456

Combined Steel Services Ltd, 5 Boddis Industrial Park, Garratts Lane, Cradley Heath, West Midlands, B64 5SS Tel: 0121-559 3737 Fax: 0121-559 2500 E-mail: combinedsteels@btconnect.com

Consett Steel Services Ltd, Bradley Workshops, Consett, County Durham, DH8 6HG Tel: (01207) 590171 Fax: (01207) 592086 E-mail: sales@consett-steel.co.uk

Contisteel (Southern) Ltd, Wyvols Court, Swallowfield, Reading, RG7 1WY Tel: 0118-988 0258 Fax: 0118-988 0348 E-mail: well.joshi@contisteelarcelor.com

Richard Cooke Engineering Steels Ltd, 38 Moorgate Road, Rotherham, South Yorkshire, S60 2AG Tel: (01709) 830214 Fax: (01709) 830216 E-mail: sales@rces.co.uk

Corby Steel Supplies Ltd, Sondes Road, Willowbrook East Industrial Estate, Corby, Northamptonshire, NN17 5XL Tel: (01536) 261164 Fax: (01536) 402971

Corus, Mossend Works, Main Street, Bellshill, Lanarkshire, ML4 1DJ Tel: (01698) 748424 Fax: (01698) 747191

Corus, Mossend Works, Main Street, Bellshill, Lanarkshire, ML4 1DJ Tel: (01698) 748424 Fax: (01698) 747191

Corus, Walker Industrial Estate, Walker Road, Guide, Blackburn, BB1 2QE Tel: (01254) 55161 Fax: (01254) 677505

Corus, Sengate, The Drove, Brandon, Suffolk, IP27 0JY Tel: (01842) 816200 Fax: (01842) 813019

Corus, Station Road, South Darenth, Dartford, DA4 9LD Tel: (01322) 227272 Fax: (01322) 864893

▶ Corus Ltd, West Wing Midland House, New Road, Halesowen, West Midlands, B63 3HY Tel: 0121-585 5522 Fax: 0121-585 5241

Corus, Park Road, Halesowen, West Midlands, B63 2RN Tel: (01384) 897377 Fax: (01384) 898018

Corus, 11 Oldfield Lane, Leeds, LS12 4DH Tel: 0113-263 4242 Fax: 0113-231 0491 E-mail: angela.barnard@corusgroup.com

Corus, Wakefield Road, Leeds, LS10 1AY Tel: 0113-276 0660 Fax: 0113-272 7197

Corus, 216a Moira Road, Lisburn, County Antrim, BT28 2SN Tel: (028) 9266 0747 Fax: (028) 9266 0748

Corus Ltd, Brinsworth Strip Mills, Sheffield Road, Rotherham, South Yorkshire, S60 1BN Tel: (01709) 377113 Fax: (01709) 375250

Corus, Colndale Road, Colnbrook, Slough, SL3 0HL Tel: (01753) 683131 Fax: (01753) 684372 E-mail: customer-services@corusgroup.com

Corus, 202 Solent Business Centre, 343 Millbrook Road West, Southampton, SO15 0HW Tel: (023) 8023 3094 Fax: (023) 8023 3096

Corus, 96 Stourbridge Road, Lye, Stourbridge, West Midlands, DY9 7DD Tel: (01384) 424151 Fax: (01384) 424073

Corus, Steelpark Way, Wolverhampton, WV11 3SQ Tel: (01902) 631163 Fax: (01902) 484001 E-mail: enquiries@corus-servicecentres.co.uk

Corus, Steelpark Way, Wolverhampton, WV11 3SQ Tel: (01902) 631163 Fax: (01902) 484001 E-mail: enquiries@corus-servicecentres.co.uk

Corus Ltd, PO Box 4, Wolverhampton, WV5 8AT Tel: (01902) 324444 Fax: (01902) 324204 E-mail: enquiries@corus.com

Corus Bristol, Badminton Road Trading Estate, Yate, Bristol, BS37 5JU Tel: (01454) 316600 Fax: (01454) 321014 E-mail: info@corusgroup.com

Corus Engineering Steels Pension Scheme Trustee Ltd, PO Box 50, Rotherham, South Yorkshire, S60 1DW Tel: (01709) 371234 E-mail: christianname.surname@corusgroup.com

Corus Metal Centre, Fairfax Road, Heathfield Industrial Estate, Newton Abbot, Devon, TQ12 6UD Tel: (01626) 835008 Fax: (01626) 835009 E-mail: andrew.curtis@corusgroup.com

Corus Service Centre, Chainbridge Road Industrial Estate, Blaydon-On-Tyne, Tyne & Wear, NE21 5SS Tel: 0191-414 2181 Fax: 0191-414 2210

Corus Service Centre, Unit 4 Symondscliffe Way, Portskewett, Caldicot, Gwent, NP26 5PW Tel: (01291) 421732 Fax: (01291) 425085

Corus Service Centre, Garmouth Road, Mosstodloch, Fochabers, Morayshire, IV32 7LH Tel: (01343) 820606 Fax: (01343) 821295

Corus Service Centre, Spittlegate Industrial Estate, Grantham, Lincolnshire, NG31 7UP Tel: (01476) 565522 Fax: (01476) 562459

Corus Service Centre, The Steelpark, Steelpark Way, Wolverhampton, WV11 3SR Tel: (01902) 484200 Fax: (01902) 484049

Cotswold Steel Stockholders Ltd, Unit 1m2 Babdown Industrial Estate, Babdown, Tetbury, Gloucestershire, GL8 8YL Tel: (01666) 504889 Fax: (01666) 504891 E-mail: james@cotswoldsteels.com

Countrywide Steel & Tubes, 326-328 Coleford Road, Sheffield, S9 5PH Tel: 0114-244 8444 Fax: 0114-244 8555

Coventry Grinders Ltd, 7 Alpha Business Park, Deedmore Road, Coventry, CV2 1EQ Tel: (024) 7660 4377 Fax: (024) 7660 4975 E-mail: info@coventry-grinders.co.uk

Cudlow Steel Services Ltd, Unit H4 Rudford Industrial Estate, Ford Road, Ford, Arundel, West Sussex, BN18 0BD Tel: (01903) 714545 Fax: (01903) 716151 E-mail: cudlow@fsbdial.co.uk

Cutler & Woolf (Steel) Ltd, Unit 32, Jubilee Trade Centre, Jubilee Road, Letchworth Garden City, Hertfordshire, SG6 1SP Tel: (01462) 480420 Fax: (01462) 480430 E-mail: sales@cutlerandwoolfe.co.uk

D C Ould, Mount Pleasant, Roche, St. Austell, Cornwall, PL26 8LH Tel: (01726) 890349 Fax: (01726) 890910

D & F Steels Ltd, Valley Farm Road, Stourton, Leeds, LS10 1SD Tel: 0113-277 0951 Fax: 0113-276 0591 E-mail: dandf@asdplc.co.uk

Daniel Lewis & Son Ltd, 493-495 Hackney Road, London, E2 9ED Tel: (020) 7739 8881 Fax: (020) 7739 2136 E-mail: daniellewis@ad.com

Danson Steel Ltd, C Kingsbridge Wharf, Kingsbridge Road, Barking, Essex, IG11 0BD Tel: (020) 8507 8921 Fax: (020) 8507 8746 E-mail: danson@barking57.fsnet.co.uk

Davro Iron & Steel Co. Ltd, Ridgewell Works, Stourbridge Road, Wootton, Bridgnorth, Shropshire, WV15 6ED Tel: (01746) 780242 Fax: (01746) 780930 E-mail: mikenielen@davrodeal.co.uk

Stan Dawson Ltd, Kirkley Sawmills, Kirkley, Newcastle upon Tyne, NE20 0BD Tel: (01661) 860413 Fax: (01661) 822352

Denmay Steel & Hire Co., 137 Wellington Road, Portslade, Brighton, BN41 1DN Tel: (01273) 430399 Fax: (01273) 430799

Dent Steel Services (Yorkshire) Ltd, Unit 17, Chapel Lane, Airdrie, Lanarkshire, ML6 6GX Tel: (01236) 439511 Fax: (01744) 439512

Dent Steel Services Yorkshire Ltd, New Works Road, Low Moor, Bradford, West Yorkshire, BD12 0QN Tel: (01274) 607070 Fax: (01274) 672979 E-mail: enquiries@dentsteel.co.uk

Denvic Ltd, Greenhill Industrial Estate, Kidderminster, Worcestershire, DY10 2RN Tel: (01562) 755274 Fax: (01562) 755274 E-mail: denvic@btconnect.com

Direct Metal Services Ltd, 2 Swan Business Park, Sandpit Road, Dartford, DA1 5ED Tel: (01322) 287878 Fax: (01322) 287567 E-mail: info@directmetalservices.co.uk

Dixon Steelstock, Unit 2a Southgate, White Lund Industrial Estate, Morecambe, Lancashire, LA3 3PB Tel: (01524) 67241 Fax: (01524) 382641 E-mail: morcambe@bmsteel.co.uk

Dudley Iron & Steel Co. Ltd, Unit 8, Tividale, Oldbury, West Midlands, B69 3HU Tel: 0121-601 5000 Fax: 0121-601 5001 E-mail: sales@dudley-iron-steel.co.uk

▶ Dustacco Engineering Ltd, 83 Carron Place, Kelvin Industrial Estate, East Kilbride, Glasgow, G75 0YL Tel: (01355) 229191

E X Stock Steel Ltd, Units 2-4, Isca Foundary, Millman St, Newport, Gwent, NP20 2JL Tel: (01633) 253111 Fax: (01633) 264333

Eggleston Bros Ltd, Centurion Way Business Park, Alfreton Road, Derby, DE21 4AY Tel: (01332) 341536 Fax: (01332) 295715 E-mail: info@egglestonbros.co.uk

Eiffel Steelworks Ltd, Studio 2 D Power Road Studios, 114b Power Road, London, W4 5PY Tel: (020) 8747 5990 Fax: (020) 8747 5991 E-mail: mail@eiffel-uk.co.uk

Ellis (Faull), Kemys Way, Swansea Enterprise Park, Swansea, SA6 6QA Tel: (01792) 797722 Fax: (01792) 792974

Ellwood Steel Ltd, Unit 2 Park Lane, Halesowen, West Midlands, B63 2NT Tel: (01384) 564935 Fax: (01384) 410577

Energy Alloys, Chesterfield Trading Estate, Carrwood Road, Sheepbridge, Chesterfield, Derbyshire, S41 9QB Tel: (01246) 264500 Fax: (01246) 264550 E-mail: imsuk.energy@ims-group.com

Excel Steel Stock, Harbour Road Trading Estate, Portishead, Bristol, BS20 7AT Tel: (01275) 847997 Fax: (01275) 849855

F D O'Dell & Sons Ltd, Cow Close Langford Road, Langford Road, Biggleswade, Bedfordshire, SG18 9JT Tel: (01767) 313113 Fax: (01767) 313113

F H Warden (Steel) Ltd, Landor Street, Birmingham, B8 1AE Tel: 0121-327 7575 Fax: 0121-327 7212 E-mail: sales@fhwarden.co.uk

F T M Marketing Ltd, P O Box 163C, Esher, Surrey, KT10 0YH Tel: (020) 8286 6661 Fax: (020) 8286 2202 E-mail: info@sonneteer.co.uk

Fays Metals Ltd, 3 37 Colville Road, London, W3 8BL Tel: (020) 8993 8883 Fax: (020) 8993 7200 E-mail: sales@fays-metals.co.uk

Forsteel Ltd, 18 St Johns Road, Slough, SL2 5EY Tel: (01753) 517322 Fax: (01753) 517832 E-mail: lsimm42778@aol.com

Fowle & Co. Ltd, Tremlon House, Menzies Road, St. Leonards-on-Sea, East Sussex, TN38 9BQ Tel: (01424) 444666 Fax: (01424) 720442 E-mail: lauren.edwards@btconnect.com

STEEL – *continued*

Franklin Steel Stockholders P.L.C., Franklin Park, Patterson Street, Blaydon-On-Tyne, Tyne & Wear, NE21 5TL Tel: 0191-499 0222 Fax: 0191-499 0223 E-mail: sales@franklinsteel.co.uk

Freeston Stockholding Ltd, Unit 11, Eclipse Industrial Estate, Sedgley Road West, Tipton, West Midlands, DY4 8AB Tel: 0121-520 2281 Fax: 0121-522 3853

William Fry & Co. Ltd, Mitre Works, Neasden Goods Depot, Neasden Lane, London, NW10 2UG Tel: (020) 8459 5141 Fax: (020) 8459 2290 E-mail: md@metalandwaste.com

G T Coulson Fabrication Ltd, Ponders End Industrial Estate, East Duck Lees Lane, Enfield, Middlesex, EN3 7SR Tel: (020) 8804 5961 Fax: (020) 8804 0014 E-mail: info@gtcoulson.com

Goodman Steel Services Ltd, 98 Cardiff Road, Reading, RG1 8LL Tel: 0118-956 1212 Fax: 0118-956 1218 E-mail: sales@goodsteel.co.uk

Thomas Graham & Sons Ltd, The Maltings, Shaddongate, Carlisle, CA2 5TU Tel: (01228) 525364 Fax: (01228) 547313 E-mail: sales@thomas-graham.co.uk

Grampian Steel Services Ltd, Greenford, Oldmeldrum, Inverurie, Aberdeenshire, AB51 0BH Tel: (01651) 872040 Fax: (01651) 872069 E-mail: grampiansteel@compuserve.com

Grange Steels, P O Box 2, Stoke-on-Trent, ST8 6JZ Tel: (01782) 510210 Fax: (01782) 510211 E-mail: grangesteels@asdplc.co.uk

H K B Steels Services Ltd, Autobase Industrial Estate, Tipton Road, Tividale, Oldbury, West Midlands, B69 3HU Tel: 0121-557 8361 Fax: 0121-520 8810 E-mail: sales@hkb-steel.co.uk

A.D. Hall Ltd, Chemical Lane, Longbridge Hayes Indrustrial Estate, Stoke-on-Trent, ST6 4PB Tel: (01782) 577605

Hall & Pickles, Blackvein Industrial Estate, Cross Keys, Newport, Gwent, NP11 7PX Tel: (023) 8065 1815 Fax: (01495) 271563 E-mail: cksales@hallandpickles.co.uk

Hall & Pickles, Poynton Industrial Estate, Poynton, Stockport, Cheshire, SK12 1NB Tel: (01625) 878787 Fax: (01625) 855573 E-mail: sales@hallandpickles.co.uk

Handley Steel Ltd, Phoenix Works Industrial Estate, Richards Street, Wednesbury, West Midlands, WS10 8BZ Tel: 0121-568 6387 Fax: 0121-568 6387

Harbour, Unit 4 Premier Industrial Units, Castle Street, Castlepark Industrial Estate, Ellon, Aberdeenshire, AB41 9RF Tel: (01358) 722422 Fax: (01358) 722880 E-mail: harboureng@btinternet.com

Charles Head Ltd, 78 Tavistock Street, Bletchley, Milton Keynes, MK2 2PN Tel: (01908) 372250 Fax: (01908) 371023 E-mail: sales@charles-head.co.uk

Hi Tech Steel Services Ltd, Neills Road, Bold Industrial Park, Bold, St. Helens, Merseyside, WA9 4TU Tel: (01744) 818767 Fax: (01744) 818706 E-mail: sales@hitechsteels.co.uk

High Peak Steels Ltd, Thornfield House Brookfield Industrial Estate, Peakdale Road, Glossop, Derbyshire, SK13 6LQ Tel: (01457) 866911 Fax: (01457) 869178 E-mail: mark@highpeaksteels.com

▶ Hill Steels Ltd, Peartree Lane, Dudley, West Midlands, DY2 0XB Tel: (01384) 255455 Fax: (01384) 258333 E-mail: markpickering@hillsteels.co.uk

Hillfoot Special Steels Ltd, 16 Hertburn Estate, Hertburn, Washington, Tyne & Wear, NE37 2SF Tel: 0191-417 0185 Fax: 0191-415 4740 E-mail: washington@hillfoot.com

Hillsborough Steelstock Ltd, Penistone Road North, Sheffield, S6 1LE Tel: 0114-285 5525 Fax: 0114-232 0972

John Hornby & Sons Ltd, Old Crown Dyeworks, Birkshall Lane, Bradford, West Yorkshire, BD4 8TB Tel: (01274) 390856 Fax: (01274) 728825

Howco Quality Alloys Ltd, Carbrook Street, Sheffield, S9 2JN Tel: 0114-244 6711 Fax: 0114-244 7469 E-mail: sales@howcogroup.com

Frank Hughes & Son Ltd, Lunts Heath Road, Widnes, Cheshire, WA8 5SG Tel: 0151-424 5731 Fax: 0151-495 2063 E-mail: sales@frankhughes.co.uk

I S & G Steel Stockholders Ltd, Cooting Road Industrial Estate, Aylesham, Canterbury, Kent, CT3 3ER Tel: (01304) 840300 Fax: (01304) 840600 E-mail: aylesham@isg-steel.co.uk

I S & G Steel Stockholders Ltd, Temple Wood, Stock Road, West Hanningfield, Chelmsford, CM2 8LL Tel: (01277) 840471 Fax: (01277) 840234 E-mail: chelmsford@isg-steel.co.uk

Industrial Metal Services Ltd, Metalstock House, Metal Stock House, Vanguard Way, Southend-on-Sea, SS3 9RE Tel: (01702) 296922 Fax: (01702) 296444 E-mail: sales@industrialmetal.co.uk

Intersteel, European Business Pk, Taylors Lane, Oldbury, West Midlands, B69 2BN Tel: 0121-627 9279 Fax: 0121-627 9270 E-mail: sales@intersteel.co.uk

J C Y Steel Supplies Ltd, 35 Hovefield Avenue, Burnt Mills Industrial Area, Basildon, Essex, SS13 1EB Tel: (01268) 729886 Fax: (01268) 725262 E-mail: sales@jcysteel.com

J P L Steel Stock Ltd, Pinfold Road, Thurmaston, Leicester, LE4 8AS Tel: 0116-260 6464 Fax: 0116-260 6808 E-mail: sales@jplsteelstock.co.uk

▶ Jacquet UK Ltd, Rockingham House, Wentworth Way, Tankersley, Barnsley, South Yorkshire, S75 3DH Tel: (01226) 745000 Fax: (01226) 746000 E-mail: j.uk@myjacquet.com

James Brothers (Hamworthy) Ltd, 19 Blandford Road, Hamworthy, Poole, Dorset, BH15 4AW Tel: (01202) 673815 Fax: (01202) 684033 E-mail: inquiries@james-bros.co.uk

John Bell Pipeline Caspian, Units 3/4 Camiestone Road, Thainstone Industrial Park, Inverurie, Aberdeenshire, AB51 5GT Tel: (01224) 716079 Fax: (01224) 716079 E-mail: sales@jbpipeline.co.uk

John H Place Steels Ltd, 44 Black Park Road, Toomebridge, Antrim, BT41 3SL Tel: (028) 7965 0481 Fax: (028) 7965 0175 E-mail: sales@johnhplace.com

John Lawrie Aberdeen Ltd, Forties Road, Montrose, Angus, DD10 9ET Tel: (01674) 672005 Fax: (01674) 677911 E-mail: sales@johnlawrie.com

John S Shackleton Sheffield Ltd, 4 Downgate Drive, Sheffield, S4 8BU Tel: 0114-244 4767 Fax: 0114-242 5965

K L M Steels Ltd, Unit 2a/172, 172 Argyle Street, Birmingham, B7 5TE Tel: 0121-327 0600 Fax: 0121-327 4575 E-mail: klmsteels@virgin.net

Katoll Metals & Industrial Products Ltd, Central Avenue, Cradley Heath, West Midlands, B64 7BY Tel: (01384) 634001 Fax: (01384) 410776 E-mail: sales@katollmetals.co.uk

Keenans Steel Fabricators, 197-199 Highland Road, Southsea, Hampshire, PO4 9EZ Tel: (023) 9282 6841 Fax: (023) 9285 1401

Kennedy & Morrison Ltd, Boucher Road, Belfast, BT12 6QF Tel: (028) 9087 0870 Fax: (028) 9087 0871 E-mail: sales@kandm.co.uk

Laidler Steels Ltd, Stallings Lane, Kingswinford, West Midlands, DY6 7LE Tel: (01384) 400442 Fax: (01384) 294295

Lancaster & Winter Ltd, Brownroyd Street, Bradford, West Yorkshire, BD8 9AE Tel: (01274) 546303 Fax: (01274) 481143 E-mail: lancaster.winter.ltd@themail.co.uk

Laxford Steels, 21 Load Street, Bewdley, Worcestershire, DY12 2AE Tel: (01299) 400144 Fax: (01299) 400144

Lilleshall Steel Services Ltd, Steel House, 1 Bristol Road, Gloucester, GL1 5TF Tel: (01452) 526821 Fax: (01452) 300430 E-mail: sales@lilleshall-steel.co.uk

Lingwood Steels Ltd, Unit 1-2 Brymill Industrial Estate, Brown Lion Street, Tipton, West Midlands, DY4 9EG Tel: 0121-520 6161 Fax: 0121-522 2967 E-mail: paul@lingwoodsteels.co.uk

Liverpool Steel Services, 31-32 Byng Street, Millers Bridge Industrial Estate, Millers Bridge Industrial Esta, Bootle, Merseyside, L20 1EE Tel: 0151-922 4265 Fax: 0151-922 0400 E-mail: liverpool@bmsteel.co.uk

Locum Fine Steels Ltd, Little London Road, Sheffield, S8 0UH Tel: 0114-255 7371 Fax: 0114-250 9114 E-mail: info@locumfinesteels.com

Lothian Steel Services Ltd, Whitburn Road, Bathgate, West Lothian, EH48 2HR Tel: (01506) 633500 Fax: (01506) 633648 E-mail: sales@lothiansteels.co.uk

Luton Steels, Wharley Farm, College Road, Cranfield, Bedford, MK43 0AH Tel: (01234) 750003 Fax: (01234) 750084 E-mail: sales@lutonsteels.co.uk

M Brittain York Ltd, 8 Moneybroom Road, Lisburn, County Antrim, BT28 2QP Tel: (028) 9262 2270 Fax: (028) 9262 2280

M E T Steel Ltd, 51 Mallusk Road, Newtownabbey, County Antrim, BT36 4RU Tel: (028) 9083 7311 Fax: (028) 9084 3548

M G Steels Ltd, Phoenix House, Dudley Road West, Tividale, Oldbury, West Midlands, B69 2PJ Tel: 0121-522 4520 Fax: 0121-520 0191

M & M Steel Stockholders & Fabricators, Riverside Works Trevor St Industrial Estate, Trevor Street, Birmingham, B7 5RG Tel: 0121-327 1695 Fax: 0121-327 1708 E-mail: mmsteel@btconnect.com

M Q Metal Fabrication Ltd, Unit 11 Shaftesbury Industrial Centre, Bull Lane, London, N18 1SX Tel: (020) 8807 0098 Fax: (020) 8807 7318

Macward Steel Slitting Services Ltd, Unit 3 Polo Grounds, New Inn, Pontypool, Gwent, NP4 0TW Tel: (01495) 751122 Fax: (01495) 762369 E-mail: salesoffice@macwards.co.uk

Mancells Marfleet Ltd, Erimus Works, Valletta Street, Hull, HU9 5NU Tel: (01482) 375231 Fax: (01482) 706545 E-mail: sales@mancells.co.uk

Massey Engineering Ltd, Ludlow Business Park, Orleton Road, Ludlow Business Park, Ludlow, Shropshire, SY8 1XF Tel: (01584) 875210 Fax: (01584) 874089

Mattersons Ltd, Kingfield Road, Coventry, CV6 5AS Tel: (024) 7670 3713 Fax: (024) 7666 8156 E-mail: sales@matterson.co.uk

David Matthews Ltd, Clayton Tinplate Works, Pontardulais, Swansea, SA4 8SN Tel: (01792) 882766 Fax: (01792) 885195 E-mail: inquiries@dmlltd.demon.co.uk

Mealham Metal Products, Orchard Buildings, Chilmington Green, Great Chart, Ashford, Kent, TN23 3DL Tel: (01233) 621150 Fax: (01233) 621150

Mercer & Sons Ltd, Pump Street Warehouses, Blackburn, BB2 1PG Tel: (01254) 587000 Fax: (01254) 680875 E-mail: info@mercer-sons.co.uk

Metal Supermarkets, 1 Overland Trading Estate Gelderd Road, Gildersome, Morley, Leeds, LS27 7JN Tel: 0113-238 0900 Fax: 0113-238 0060 E-mail: headoffice@metalsupermarkets.com

Metropes Metals Ltd, Estate Road 3, South Humberside Industrial Estate, Grimsby, South Humberside, DN31 2TB Tel: (01472) 342440 Fax: (01472) 267815

Midland Tube & Fabrications, 4 Corngreaves Works, Corngreaves Road, Cradley Heath, West Midlands, B64 7DA Tel: (01384) 566364 Fax: (01384) 566365 E-mail: keithcadman@btconnect.com

Mi-King Ltd, Bentall Business Park, Glover District 11, Washington, Tyne & Wear, NE37 3JD Tel: 0191-415 5919 Fax: 0191-415 1300 E-mail: sales@mi-king.co.uk

Milden Steels Ltd, Unit 1 Park St Works, Kidderminster, Worcestershire, DY11 6TN Tel: (01562) 66615 Fax: (01562) 829293 E-mail: sales@milden-steels.fsnet.co.uk

Milford Steel, Unit 18 Thornton Industrial Trading Estate, Milford Haven, Dyfed, SA73 2RZ Tel: (01646) 698821 Fax: (01646) 697403 E-mail: millfodd@ellissteelgroup.co.uk

Mister Steel Ltd, Stewarts La Depot, Dickens Street, London, SW8 3EP Tel: (020) 7738 8858 Fax: (020) 7738 8893 E-mail: info@mistersteel.co.uk

Monkhouse & Brown, Teams Street, Gateshead, Tyne & Wear, NE8 2RF Tel: 0191-460 0220 Fax: 0191-460 0334

Mosgrove, Alan Ltd, Tranker Lane, Shireoaks, Worksop, Nottinghamshire, S81 8AQ Tel: (01909) 473250 Fax: (01909) 478877

Mountelm Ltd, 8 Junction Street, Carlisle, CA2 5XH Tel: (01228) 523136 Fax: (01228) 530550 E-mail: m.liddle@btconnect.com

Multimetals (Scotland), Unit 1 Atlantic Way, Wednesbury, West Midlands, WS10 7WW Tel: 0121-505 2323 Fax: 0121-505 2324 E-mail: enquiries@multimetals.com

Murray (International) Metals Ltd, Murray Works, Newbridge Industrial Estate, Newbridge, Midlothian, EH28 8PJ Tel: 0131-333 3333 Fax: 0131-333 4477 E-mail: mim_newbridge@murray-metals.co.uk

N S D Ltd, South Park Road, Scunthorpe, South Humberside, DN17 2BY Tel: (01724) 810000 Fax: (01724) 819981 E-mail: sales@nsc.ltd.uk

Newark Storage Co. Ltd, Bowbridge Road, Newark, Nottinghamshire, NG24 4EQ Tel: (01636) 680660 Fax: (01636) 673530 E-mail: sales@newark-steel.co.uk

Newbridge Steels Ltd, 14a High Street, Cowbridge, South Glamorgan, CF71 7AG Tel: (01446) 775517 Fax: (01446) 775355 E-mail: bronwennewbridge@yahoo.co.uk

Niagra Lasalle, Planetary Road, Willenhall, West Midlands, WV13 3SW Tel: (01902) 307007 Fax: (01902) 864269 E-mail: brightbar@niag.com

O I W (Steels) Ltd, 12 Benfleet Road, Benfleet, Essex, SS7 1QB Tel: (01702) 557373 Fax: (01702) 551762 E-mail: sales@oiwsteels.co.uk

Organically Coated Steels, Hoo Farm Industrial Estate, Worcester Road, Kidderminster, Worcestershire, DY11 7RA Tel: (01562) 821400 Fax: (01562) 865396 E-mail: ocs@asdmetalservices.co.uk

▶ Outokumpu Stainless Ltd, PO Box 161, Sheffield, S9 1TR Tel: 0114-244 3311 Fax: 0114-244 8280

Graham Oxley Tool Steels Ltd, 55-57 Bridge Street, Sheffield, S3 8NS Tel: 0114-272 0403 Fax: 0114-275 2489

P & D Northern Steels Ltd, Mosshey Street, Shaw, Oldham, OL2 8QL Tel: (01706) 848811 Fax: (01706) 841153 E-mail: sales@pdnorthern.co.uk

P W S Ltd, Strawberry Lane, Willenhall, West Midlands, WV13 3SE Tel: (01902) 365200 Fax: (01902) 365201

P W S Ltd, Strawberry Lane, Willenhall, West Midlands, WV13 3SE Tel: (01902) 365200 Fax: (01902) 365201

▶ Pab Coventry Ltd, Midland House Falkland Close, Charter Avenue Industrial Estate, Charter Avenue Industrial Esta, Coventry, CV4 8AU Tel: (024) 7669 4419 Fax: (024) 7646 7799 E-mail: info@pabconventry.co.uk

Paddington Steels Ltd, 6 Paddington Court, New Road, Kidderminster, Worcestershire, DY10 1AQ Tel: (01562) 827300 Fax: (01562) 827301

Parkes & Billingham Ltd, Peartree Lane, Dudley, West Midlands, DY2 0QW Tel: (01384) 480660 Fax: (01384) 70271 E-mail: parkesandbillingham@office01.fsnet.co.uk

Parkside Steel (Stockholders) Ltd, Waterways Business Centre, Navigation Drive, Enfield, Middlesex, EN3 6JJ Tel: (01992) 703500 Fax: (01992) 719857

Parson & Crosland Ltd, PO Box 10, Middlesbrough, Cleveland, TS2 1HG Tel: (01642) 244161 Fax: (01642) 230487 E-mail: sales@parson-crosland.co.uk

Philip Cornes & Co. Ltd, Lanner Building, Clews Road, Redditch, Worcestershire, B98 7ST Tel: (01527) 555000 Fax: (01527) 547000 E-mail: philipcornes.sales@twmetals.co.uk

Phoenix Metals, Firs Industrial Estate, Kidderminster, Worcestershire, DY11 7QN Tel: (01562) 822777 Fax: (01562) 822477

Phoenix Steels Co., Speedwell Road, Birmingham, B25 8EL Tel: 0121-707 0165 Fax: 0121-766 7767 E-mail: sales@phoenixsteels.com

Pipeline Centre, Shails Lane, Trowbridge, Wiltshire, BA14 8LQ Tel: (01225) 762331 Fax: (01225) 777370 E-mail: sales@pipeline.centre.co.uk

Pitchford Steelstock, Pedmore Road, Brierley Hill, West Midlands, DY5 1TH Tel: (01384) 489030 Fax: (01384) 480209

Prefab Steel Co. Ltd, 114 Brighton Road, Shoreham-by-Sea, West Sussex, BN43 6RH Tel: (01273) 597733 Fax: (01273) 597774 E-mail: prefabsteel@btinternet.com

Primetals Ltd, 282 Cutler Heights Lane, Bradford, West Yorkshire, BD4 9HU Tel: (01274) 654250 Fax: (01274) 651205 E-mail: sales@primetals.co.uk

Priory Steels Ltd, Cable Street, Wolverhampton, WV2 2HX Tel: (01902) 351001 Fax: (01902) 871345 E-mail: info@priorysteel.fsnet.co.uk

R H Steel, Church Farm, Hamerton, Huntingdon, Cambridgeshire, PE28 5QX Tel: (01832) 293501 Fax: 01832 293670

R S Lloyd Midlands, Unit 33 Dawley Trading Estate, Stallings Lane, Kingswinford, West Midlands, DY6 7AP Tel: (01384) 401030 Fax: (01384) 401023

Rainham Steel Co. Ltd, Kathryn House, Manor Way, Rainham, Essex, RM13 8RE Tel: (01708) 522311 Fax: (01708) 559024 E-mail: info@rainhamsteel.co.uk

Rayleigh Steel, Unit 7 Westfield Close Rawreth Industrial Estate, Rawreth Lane, Rayleigh, Essex, SS6 9RL Tel: (01268) 783600 Fax: (01268) 783620

▶ Rhi Refractories UK Ltd, Hillview Road, Bonnybridge, Stirlingshire, FK4 2EH Tel: (01324) 819400 Fax: (01324) 814218

Robert Smith Steels Ltd, Cathcart Quay, Cathcart Street, Birkenhead, Merseyside, CH41 3HZ Tel: 0151-647 4221 Fax: 0151-647 4839 E-mail: sales@robertsmithsteel.co.uk

Rowan Steels Ltd, 2 Park Street Works, Park Street, Kidderminster, Worcestershire, DY11 6TN Tel: (01562) 67476 Fax: (01562) 515412 E-mail: sales@rowansteels.co.uk

Rowham Steel Products Ltd, Lyons Road, Trafford Park, Manchester, M17 1RF Tel: 0161-786 3700 Fax: 0161-786 3707 E-mail: sales@rowhamsteel.co.uk

Royton Steel Stock Ltd, Caldershaw Centre, Ings Lane, Rochdale, Lancashire, OL12 7LQ Tel: (01706) 715555 Fax: (01706) 715443

Rubicon Ltd, Unit 11 Rockingham Business Park, Rockingham Row, Birdwell, Barnsley, South Yorkshire, S70 5TW Tel: (01226) 351515 Fax: (01226) 351535 E-mail: mail@rubiconsteel.co.uk

Rycon Steels, 2 Alexandra Industrial Estate, Wentloog Road, Rumney, Cardiff, CF3 1EY Tel: (029) 2036 2311 Fax: (029) 2036 2322 E-mail: rycon@rsteels.fsnet.co.uk

S M Thompson Ltd, Marathon Works, Newport Bridge, Middlesbrough, Cleveland, TS1 5TG Tel: (01642) 245161 Fax: (01642) 223392 E-mail: sales@smthompson.co.uk

S & S Steelstock Ltd, Dickens Street, Blackburn, BB1 1RN Tel: (01254) 699966 Fax: (01254) 674999

Sebden Steel, Broad Quay Road, Felnex Industrial Estate, Newport, Gwent, NP19 4PN Tel: (01633) 276054 Fax: (01633) 283355 E-mail: newport@sebden.com

Sebden Steel Service Centres Ltd, Craven Road, Broadheath, Altrincham, Cheshire, WA14 5HE Tel: 0161-928 8327 Fax: 0161-941 7061 E-mail: altrincham@sebden.com

Shaws Metals Ltd, Hartland Works, Haydock Park Road, Derby, DE24 8HW Tel: (01332) 383341 Fax: (01332) 294085 E-mail: sales@shawsmetalsltd.sagenet.co.uk

Simpson John Junior Glasgow Ltd, 28 Coxhill Street, Glasgow, G21 1HN Tel: 0141-332 3231 Fax: 0141-332 7325 E-mail: sales@simpsonsteel.co.uk

Skymetals Non Ferrous Metals, Unit 3 Trillennium Highway Point, Gorsey Lane, Coleshill, Birmingham, B46 1JU Tel: (01675) 430140 Fax: (01675) 430346 E-mail: birmingham@allmetal.co.uk

South Midland Steel Ltd, 19 Oaklands Avenue, Watford, WD19 4SD Tel: (01923) 252089 Fax: (01923) 250525 E-mail: smsteel@freeuk.com

Southend Aluminium Co., 24 Milton Road, Westcliff-on-Sea, Essex, SS0 7JX Tel: (01702) 331601 Fax: (01702) 330525

Southern Metals, 29 St. James Industrial Estate, Westhampnett Road, Chichester, West Sussex, PO19 7JU Tel: (01243) 781814 Fax: (01243) 781814

C.F. Sparrowhawk Ltd, 24 Epsom Lane North, Tadworth, Surrey, KT20 5EH Tel: (01737) 352889 Fax: (01737) 371088

Stainless & Alloy Supplies, Unit 75 Percy Business Park, Rounds Green Road, Oldbury, West Midlands, B69 2RE Tel: 0121-544 9969 Fax: 0121-544 9979 E-mail: stainandalloy1@btconnect.com

John Stansfeld Ltd, Springwell Works, Buslingthorpe Lane, Leeds, LS7 2DF Tel: 0113-262 8155 Fax: 0113-262 9730 E-mail: sales@gheuk.co.uk

Steel Stop Ltd, Methley Road, Castleford, West Yorkshire, WF10 1LX Tel: (01977) 555333 Fax: (01977) 603960

Steel Supplies Ltd, Arksey Lane, Bentley, Doncaster, South Yorkshire, DN5 0ST Tel: (01302) 874321 Fax: (01302) 876287 E-mail: sales@steelsupplies.co.uk

Steelco UK Ltd, 12 Blackbrook Business Park, Narrowboat Way, Dudley, West Midlands, DY2 0XQ Tel: (01384) 455535 Fax: (01384) 456860 E-mail: steelco@fowle.btinternet.com

▶ indicates data change since last edition

STEEL – *continued*

Steelfast, Kings Farm Estate, Stanbridge Road, Great Billington, Leighton Buzzard, Bedfordshire, LU7 9JH Tel: (01525) 851603 Fax: (01525) 851836
L.R. Stewart & Sons Ltd, Hampden Road, Hornsey, London, N8 0HG Tel: (020) 8348 5267 Fax: (020) 8340 7774 E-mail: info@lrstewartandsons.co.uk
Stockwell Steel, Goods Yard, Bangor, Gwynedd, LL57 2TX Tel: (01248) 364041 Fax: (01248) 353100 E-mail: bangor@bmsteel.co.uk
Struthers & Carter Ltd, Erimus Works, Valletta Street, Hedon Road, Hull, HU9 5NU Tel: (01482) 795171 Fax: (01482) 708926 E-mail: enquiries@struthers-carter.co.uk
Suffolk Steel Stockholders Ltd, Woodhall Business Park, Sudbury, Suffolk, CO10 1WH Tel: (01787) 370015 Fax: (01787) 379109
Summerhill Steels Ltd, Chiltern House, Leys Road, Brierley Hill, West Midlands, DY5 3UP Tel: (01384) 482048 Fax: (01384) 482022 E-mail: pmale@aol.com
Swift Steels Services Ltd, Unit 9 Leeway Industrial Estate, Newport, Gwent, NP19 4SL Tel: (01633) 271188 Fax: (01633) 278311
T Good & Sons Ltd, 36 Vulcan Way, New Addington, Croydon, CR0 9UG Tel: (01689) 848211 Fax: (01689) 841069 E-mail: dave@tgood.co.uk
T M (UK), Climpy Industrial Park, Climpy Road, Forth, Lanark, ML11 8EW Tel: (01555) 812600 Fax: (01555) 812753
John Tainton, Hoo Farm Industrial Estate, Worcester Road, Kidderminster, Worcestershire, DY11 7RA Tel: (01562) 740477 Fax: (01562) 68765 E-mail: jtsales@johntainton.co.uk
Tamworth Steel Stockholders Ltd, Gagarin, Apollo, Tamworth, Staffordshire, B79 7TA Tel: (01827) 61531 Fax: (01827) 310078 E-mail: sales@tamworth-steel.co.uk
F.H. Tapley & Sons, The Smithy, Moss Lane, Cheswardine, Market Drayton, Shropshire, TF9 2RE Tel: (01630) 661376 Fax: (01630) 661376
Tatham Steels Ltd, Duke Avenue, Stamley Green Industrial Estate, Cheadle Hulme, Cheadle, Cheshire, SK8 6QZ Tel: 0161-485 8535 Fax: 0161-485 7804 E-mail: tathem@bmsteel.co.uk
Taylor Steel Midlands Ltd, Autobase Industrial Estate, Tipton Road, Tividale, Oldbury, West Midlands, B69 3HU Tel: 0121-601 5081 Fax: 0121-601 5069 E-mail: info@taylor-steel-midlands.co.uk
Thomson McFarlane Ltd, West Brent, Forties Road Industrial Estate, Montrose, Angus, DD10 9PA Tel: (01674) 677077 Fax: (01674) 677999
Tipton & Mill Steels Ltd, Hobart Road, Tipton, West Midlands, DY4 9LQ Tel: 0121-557 7251 Fax: 0121-557 7258 E-mail: sales@tipton-steels.co.uk
Tomrods Ltd, Manse Lane, Knaresborough, North Yorkshire, HG5 8LF Tel: (01423) 867333 Fax: (01423) 867834 E-mail: sales@tomrods.co.uk
Uddeholm Steel Stockholders, European Business Park, Taylors Lane, Oldbury, West Midlands, B69 2BN Tel: 0121-552 5530 Fax: 0121-544 3036 E-mail: sales@uddeholm.co.uk
United Steel Services Leeds Ltd, 282 Cutler Heights Lane, Bradford, West Yorkshire, BD4 9HU Tel: (01274) 654254 Fax: (01274) 688208 E-mail: united@steels.co.uk
Universal Steels Ltd, 52 Peasehill Road, Rosyth, Dunfermline, Fife, KY11 2GB Tel: (01383) 418720 Fax: (01383) 411505
Van Leeuwen Tubes Ltd, Unit 7 Provincial Park, Nether Lane, Ecclesfield, Sheffield, S35 9ZX Tel: 0114-257 7577 Fax: 0114-257 0639 E-mail: sales@vanleeuwen.nl
VolkerSteel Foundations Ltd, Springwell Road, Springwell, Gateshead, Tyne & Wear, NE9 7SP Tel: 0191-417 3545 Fax: 0191-416 2894 E-mail: info.ss@volkerstevin.co.uk
W & D Peddie Ltd, 284 High Street, Perth, PH1 5QS Tel: (01738) 621449 Fax: (01738) 629232
W H Dale Ltd, Main Street, Thornton Curtis, Ulceby, South Humberside, DN39 6XW Tel: (01469) 531229 Fax: (01469) 530611 E-mail: sales@whdale.co.uk
W & J Smith Metal Stockists Ltd, Ashmore Lake Way, Willenhall, West Midlands, WV12 4LF Tel: (01902) 607336 Fax: (01902) 634905
W M Kenyon Macclesfield Ltd, 73 Great King Street, Macclesfield, Cheshire, SK11 6PN Tel: (01625) 422074 Fax: (01625) 617712
Wessex Steel Co. Ltd, Wessex House, 9 Station Parade, London, SW12 9AB Tel: (020) 8675 5331 Fax: (020) 8675 9525 E-mail: nigel@wessexsteel.co.uk
West Yorkshire Steel Co. Ltd, Sandbeck Works, Sandbeck Industrial Estate, Wetherby, West Yorkshire, LS22 7DN Tel: 01937 584440 Fax: (0845) 658 1305 E-mail: sales@westyorkssteel.com
Wightman Metals, Ringway, Bounds Green Industrial Estate, London, N11 2UD Tel: (020) 8368 1660 Fax: (020) 8368 9570
Willenhall Shearing Co, Leve Lane, Willenhall, West Midlands, WV13 1PS Tel: (01902) 605126 Fax: (01902) 631919
William Mellard & Son, River Works, Campbell Road, Stoke-on-Trent, ST4 4RN Tel: (01782) 744777 Fax: (01782) 744512 E-mail: sales@mellard.co.uk
Wood & Son, 3 Barrack Road, Guildford, Surrey, GU2 9RU Tel: (01483) 504012 Fax: (01483) 504012
Woodall Steels Ltd, Town Works, Washington Street, Dudley, West Midlands, DY2 9PH Tel: (01384) 456888 Fax: (01384) 457755
Worcestershire Steels Co., Unit 20 Enfield Industrial Estate, Redditch, Worcestershire, B97 6BY Tel: (01527) 67777 Fax: (01527) 64225E-mail: worcestershire.steels@virgin.net
Wrekin Steel Ltd, Unit A4 Hortonwood 10, Telford, Shropshire, TF1 7ES Tel: (01952) 677600 Fax: (01952) 677900

STEEL ACCESS COVERS OR GRATING

Castle Fabrication & Installation Ltd, 3a Cold Hesledon Industrial Estate, Cold Hesledon, Seaham, County Durham, SR7 8ST Tel: 0191-581 5177 Fax: 0191-581 4792 E-mail: sales@castlefab.com

STEEL ACCESS LADDERS

▶ BND UK Limited, Suite 501,, International House,, 223 Regent Street,, London, W1R 8QD Tel: 0870 2863725 Fax: 0870 7064636 E-mail: ht-sales@bndhardware.co.uk
Nailsworth Services Ltd, Unit 5 Strensham Business Park, Strensham, Worcester, WR8 9JZ Tel: (01684) 274758 Fax: (01684) 274758 E-mail: helen@nailsworth.eclipse.co.uk
Survequip.com, Centrix House, Ash 05, 26 Crow Lane East, Newton-le-Willows, Merseyside, WA12 9UY Tel: (0800) 13 13 435 Fax: (01925) 273001 E-mail: sales@survequip.com

STEEL AGRICULTURAL BUILDINGS

Ag Con Products Ltd, 45 Newtown Road, Rostrevor, Newry, County Down, BT34 3BZ Tel: (028) 4173 8963 Fax: (028) 4173 8971 E-mail: brian@ag.con.fsnet.co.uk
G.E. Baker (UK) Ltd, Heath Road, Woolpit, Bury St. Edmunds, Suffolk, IP30 9RN Tel: (01359) 240529 Fax: (01359) 242086 E-mail: baker@quality-equipment.co.uk
Browns of Wem Ltd, Four Lane Ends, Wem, SY4 5UQ Tel: (01939) 232382 Fax: (01939) 234032 E-mail: mail@brownsofwem.com
Bussens & Vigrass, Bexwell Road, Downham Market, Norfolk, PE38 9LH Tel: (01366) 382294 Fax: (01366) 382878
Conibear Bros, Unit 2 Commercial Road Businness Park, Lords Meadow Industrial Estate, Crediton, Devon, EX17 1ER Tel: (01363) 772911 Fax: (01363) 772185
Craven Construction Ltd, Butts Works, High Bentham, Lancaster, LA2 7AN Tel: (01524) 261145 Fax: (01524) 262060
Cumbrian Implement Co. Ltd, 4 King Street, Aspatria, Wigton, Cumbria, CA7 3ET Tel: (01697) 320269 Fax: (01697) 322677 E-mail: newdale@btconnect.com
D & D Construction Ringmer Ltd, 19-21 Cradle Hill Industrial Estate, Seaford, East Sussex, BN25 3JE Tel: (01323) 890403 Fax: (01323) 490140 E-mail: info@danddconstruction.co.uk
D J Contracts South Ltd, 7 Kent Close, Granby Industrial Estate, Weymouth, Dorset, DT4 9TF Tel: (01305) 780111 Fax: (01305) 761409 E-mail: mail@darrenholland.co.uk
DeVille & Lear Ltd, Mill Lane Works, Mill Lane, Roston, Ashbourne, Derbyshire, DE6 2EE Tel: (01335) 324302 Fax: (01335) 324568 E-mail: info@devilleandlear.co.uk
Ernest Leng & Son, Friars Hill Farm, Friars Hill, Sinnington, York, YO62 6SL Tel: (01751) 431774 Fax: (01751) 431774
Farm & Industrial Buildings Ltd, Ryehill Close, Lodge Farm Industrial Estate, Northampton, NN5 7UA Tel: (01604) 753937 Fax: (01604) 758206 E-mail: nigel@farmindustrial.fsnet.co.uk
G D L Air Systems Ltd, Air Diffusion Works, Woolley Bridge Road, Hadfield, Glossop, Derbyshire, SK13 1AB Tel: (01457) 861538 Fax: (01457) 866010 E-mail: sales@grille.co.uk
Integrated Piggery Systems Ltd, Showfield Lane, Malton, North Yorkshire, YO17 6BT Tel: (01653) 694994 Fax: (01653) 696685 E-mail: ipsltd@fsmail.net
J Thackray & Sons Ltd, Brawby, Malton, North Yorkshire, YO17 6PY Tel: (01653) 668246 Fax: (01653) 668592
K Freeman Ltd, Westgate, North Newbald, South Newbald, York, YO43 4SN Tel: (01430) 827671 Fax: (01430) 827459 E-mail: kfreemanltd@aol.com
Leominster Construction Co. Ltd, Leominster Industrial Estate, Southern Avenue, Leominster, Herefordshire, HR6 0QF Tel: (01568) 612943 Fax: (01568) 612910
Minshall Brothers, Adderley Road, Market Drayton, Shropshire, TF9 3SX Tel: (01630) 657647 Fax: (01630) 657202 E-mail: info@minshallconstruction.com
Newstyle Fabrications, Ifton Industrial Estate, St. Martins, Oswestry, Shropshire, SY11 3DA Tel: (01691) 773303 Fax: (01691) 773303
Northern Structures Ltd, Amble Industrial Estate, Amble, Morpeth, Northumberland, NE65 0PE Tel: (01665) 710746 Fax: (01665) 712738 E-mail: sales@northernstructures.co.uk
OZ-UK Innovations Ltd, Christmas Cottage, Hilgay Road, West Dereham, King's Lynn, Norfolk, PE33 9RN Tel: (01553) 619483 Fax: (01553) 828497 E-mail: peach@oz-uk.com
Philip Sidford, Bridzor Farm, Wardour, Tisbury, Salisbury, SP3 6RN Tel: (01747) 870456 Fax: (01747) 871656 E-mail: pjs@sidford.com
Tilke Engineering, Bell House Lane, Anslow, Burton-on-Trent, Staffordshire, DE13 9PA Tel: (01283) 563756 Fax: (01283) 541525
Waddington Buildings Ltd, Station Road, Brompton on Swale, Richmond, North Yorkshire, DL10 7SH Tel: (01748) 812323 Fax: (01748) 812145

STEEL ALLOY BLACK BARS

Corus, Unit 2 Pullman Court, Bolton, BL2 1HL Tel: (01204) 370999 Fax: (01204) 396684 E-mail: chris.deacon@corusgroup.com
Corus, Hetton Lyons Industrial Estate, Hetton-le-Hole, Houghton le Spring, Tyne & Wear, DH5 0RD Tel: 0191-526 3288 Fax: 0191-517 0138 E-mail: paul.brown@corusgroup.com
Corus Engineering Steels, Coleford Road, Sheffield, S9 3QE Tel: 0114-244 7264 Fax: 0114-243 0941 E-mail: chris.deacon@corusgroup.com
Corus Engineering Steels, PO Box 25, Wolverhampton, WV1 3DY Tel: (01902) 875000 Fax: (01902) 875011 E-mail: keith.grant@corusgroup.com

STEEL ALLOY FABRICATORS

Goddard Engineering Ltd, The Workshop, Rumbolds Farm, Plaistow, Billingshurst, West Sussex, RH14 0PZ Tel: (01403) 871144 Fax: (01403) 871134
M J Ellis Manufacturing, Forest Extra, Up Somborne, Stockbridge, Hampshire, SO20 6RA Tel: (01794) 388384
▶ Mormet Fabrications Ltd, Unit 9-10 Hale Trading Estate, Lower Church Lane, Tipton, West Midlands, DY4 7PQ Tel: 0121-522 2522 Fax: 0121-522 2551

STEEL ALLOY FORGINGS

Firth Rixson Forgings Ltd, Dale Road North, Darley Dale, Matlock, Derbyshire, DE4 2JB Tel: 0114-219 3005 E-mail: info@firthrixson.com

STEEL ARCHES

Burbage Iron Craft Ltd, Unit 16, Sketchley Industrial Estate, Hinckley, Leicestershire, LE10 3ER Tel: (01455) 251656 Fax: (01455) 614136 E-mail: sales@burbageironcraft.co.uk

STEEL BALLS

Royal Steel Ball Products, 6 Egerton Square, Knutsford, Cheshire, WA16 6EY Tel: (01565) 653881 Fax: (01565) 653870 E-mail: pmather@onetel.net.uk

STEEL BALUSTRADES

▶ Graepel Perforators Ltd, Unit 5 Burtonwood Industrial Centre, Phipps La, Burtonwood, Warrington, WA5 4HX Tel: (01925) 229809 Fax: (01925) 228069 E-mail: sales@graepeluk.com
Rees Engineering Services Ltd, 401-403 Rayleigh Road, Benfleet, Essex, SS7 3ST Tel: (01268) 778274 Fax: (01268) 745204 E-mail: reception@reesteel.com

STEEL BARRIERS

Blackburn Bailey Ltd, Wantz Road, Dagenham, Essex, RM10 8PS Tel: (020) 8593 7346 Fax: (020) 8984 0813 E-mail: info@blackburngroup.co.uk
Kewtube Ltd, 63 Bideford Avenue, Perivale, Greenford, Middlesex, UB6 7PT Tel: (020) 8991 0062 Fax: (020) 8991 2883 E-mail: info@kewtube.com

STEEL BARS, *See also headings under Steel Bars*

A S D Coil Processing, Tipton Road, Tividale, Oldbury, West Midlands, B69 3HU Tel: 0121-522 2215 Fax: 0121-522 2293 E-mail: customer.care@asdplc.co.uk
A S D Metal Services Ltd, Gibson Lane, Melton, North Ferriby, East Yorkshire, HU14 3HX Tel: (01482) 633360 Fax: (01482) 633370 E-mail: hull@asdmetalservices.co.uk
Ashton Steel Stockholders Ltd, Station Yard, Station Road, Hadfield, Glossop, Derbyshire, SK13 1AA Tel: (01457) 862438 Fax: (01457) 861325
Ayrshire Metal Products plc, Pocket Nook Street, St. Helens, Merseyside, WA9 1LT Tel: (01744) 29145 Fax: (01744) 451257 E-mail: ampsth@compuserve.com
Barclay & Mathieson Ltd, Coleford Road, Sheffield, S9 5NF Tel: 0114-244 2094 Fax: 0114-243 5965 E-mail: sheffield@bmsteel.co.uk
▶ Barmaid Joinery Manufacturers, 3 Wesley Street, Swinton, Manchester, M27 6AD Tel: 0161-728 1122 Fax: 0161-728 2233
Boswell & Co. (Steels) Ltd, Bassett Road, Park Lane Industrial Estate, Cradley, Halesowen, West Midlands, B63 2RE Tel: (01384) 637375 Fax: (01384) 410103 E-mail: boswellsteel@aol.com
Caparo Merchant Bar plc, Brigg Road, Scunthorpe, South Humberside, DN16 1XJ Tel: (01724) 853333 Fax: (01724) 403044 E-mail: sales@cmbplc.co.uk
Corus, 96 Stourbridge Road, Lye, Stourbridge, West Midlands, DY9 7DD Tel: (01384) 424151 Fax: (01384) 424073
Corus Engineering Steels, Coleford Road, Sheffield, S9 3QE Tel: 0114-244 7264 Fax: 0114-243 0941 E-mail: chris.deacon@corusgroup.com
Corus Engineering Steels Pension Scheme Trustee Ltd, PO Box 50, Rotherham, South Yorkshire, S60 1DW Tel: (01709) 371234 E-mail: christianname.surname@corusgroup.com
General Steel Services, 45 Sydenham Road, Belfast, BT3 9DH Tel: (028) 9045 6327 Fax: (028) 9045 8096 E-mail: gss@metsteel.co.uk
Grange Steels, P O Box 2, Stoke-on-Trent, ST8 6JZ Tel: (01782) 510210 Fax: (01782) 510211 E-mail: grangesteels@asdplc.co.uk
Howco Quality Alloys Ltd, Carbrook Street, Sheffield, S9 2JN Tel: 0114-244 6711 Fax: 0114-244 7469 E-mail: sales@howcogroup.com
Ledra Steels Ltd, Ledra Works, Reservoir Pl, Walsall, WS2 9SN Tel: (01922) 621542 Fax: (01922) 637755
Niagara Lasalle UK, Victoria Steelworks, Bull Lane, Wednesbury, West Midlands, WS10 8RS Tel: 0121-506 7500 Fax: 0121-506 7501 E-mail: hotrolled@niag.com
Niagara Lasalle UK, Victoria Steelworks, Bull Lane, Wednesbury, West Midlands, WS10 8RS Tel: 0121-506 7500 Fax: 0121 506 7501 E-mail: hotrolled@niag.com
Premier Alloys, Newbridge Industrial Estate, Newbridge, Midlothian, EH28 8PJ Tel: 0131-333 4140 Fax: 0131-333 4727 E-mail: premier_alloys@mih.co.uk
Summercliff Ltd, Bilport Lane, Wednesbury, West Midlands, WS10 0NT Tel: 0121-556 0888 Fax: 0121-556 5779 E-mail: sales@summercliffe.co.uk

STEEL BEARING HOUSINGS

Cast Iron Welding Service Ltd, 2 Samson Road, Hermitage Industrial Estate, Coalville, Leicestershire, LE67 3FP Tel: (01530) 811308 Fax: (01530) 835724 E-mail: sales@castironwelding.co.uk

STEEL BENCHES, *See also Work Bench Manufrs*

Hooper Knight & Co., St Albans Road, Gloucester, GL2 5FW Tel: (01452) 502888 Fax: (01452) 502960 E-mail: intray@hooperknight.com
J A S Engineering, Glover Centre, Egmont Street, Mossley, Ashton-under-Lyne, Lancashire, OL5 9PY Tel: (01457) 833181 Fax: (01457) 837981 E-mail: sales@jasengineering.co.uk
Sono UK Ltd, Enterprise House, Murdock Road, Dorcan, Swindon, SN3 5HY Tel: (01793) 488488 Fax: (01793) 522868 E-mail: info@sono-uk.com
Wybone Ltd, Mason Way, Hoyland, Barnsley, South Yorkshire, S74 9TF Tel: (01226) 744010 Fax: (01226) 350105 E-mail: sales@wybone.co.uk

STEEL BILLET GRINDING

Effingham Steel Services Ltd, Butterthwaite Lane, Ecclesfield, Sheffield, S35 9WA Tel: 0114-246 8977 Fax: 0114-245 4272 E-mail: sales@effinghamsteel.co.uk

STEEL BILLETS

Barretts Of Aspley Ltd, North Common Farm, Woburn Road, Marston Moretaine, Bedford, MK43 0NN Tel: (01525) 280136 Fax: (01525) 280137

STEEL BLACK BARS TO SPECIFICATION

Istil UK plc, Rushenden Road, Queenborough, Kent, ME11 5HS Tel: (01795) 580880 Fax: (01795) 580165 E-mail:

STEEL BOLSTER AND PLATE SUBCONTRACTORS

C & M Mould Tools Ltd, Unit 1-3 Brunel Close, Ebblake Industrial Estate, Verwood, Dorset, BH31 6BA Tel: (01202) 813019 Fax: (01202) 814219 E-mail: cmmoulds@aol.com

STEEL BRIDGES

Britain Fabricators Ltd, Watnall Road, Hucknall, Nottingham, NG15 6EP Tel: 0115-963 2901 Fax: 0115-968 0335 E-mail: sales@britonsltd.co.uk

Cleveland Bridge, PO Box 27, Darlington, County Durham, DL1 4DF Tel: (01325) 469735 Fax: (01325) 382320 E-mail: info@clevelandbridge.com

Fairfield Mabey Ltd, Off Station Road, Chepstow, Gwent, NP16 5YL Tel: (01291) 623801 Fax: (01291) 625453 E-mail: mail@fairfieldmabey.com

Lanarkshire Welding Co. Ltd, John Street, Wishaw, Lanarkshire, ML2 7TQ Tel: (01698) 264271 Fax: (01698) 265711 E-mail: johnhett@lanarkshirewelding.co.uk

Mabey & Johnson Ltd, Floral Mile, Twyfors, Reading, RG10 9SQ Tel: 0118-940 3921 Fax: 0118-940 3941 E-mail: sales@mabey.co.uk

Nusteel Structures Ltd, Lympne Industrial Estate, Hythe, Kent, CT21 4LR Tel: (01303) 268112 Fax: (01303) 266098 E-mail: general@nusteelstructures.com

STEEL BRIGHT DRAWN HEXAGONS

Ledra Steels Ltd, Ledra Works, Reservoir Pl, Walsall, WS2 9SN Tel: (01922) 621542 Fax: (01922) 637755

STEEL BRIGHT DRAWN SECTIONS

Ledra Steels Ltd, Ledra Works, Reservoir Pl, Walsall, WS2 9SN Tel: (01922) 621542 Fax: (01922) 637755

STEEL CABINS

▶ S G B plc, 86-88 Gresham Road, London, SW9 7NP Tel: (020) 7924 9000 Fax: (020) 7738 4144

▶ S G B plc, Richmond Walk, Plymouth, PL1 4LT Tel: (01752) 561575 Fax: (01752) 606892

▶ S G B Rovacabin, Green Lane, Felling, Gateshead, Tyne & Wear, NE10 0EZ Tel: (0800) 585383 Fax: 0191-469 5175

▶ S G B Rovacabin, 12 Dunnswood Road, Wardpark South, Cumbernauld, Glasgow, G67 3EN Tel: (01236) 729601 Fax: (01236) 738005

▶ S G B Rovacabin, 609 London Road, Grays, Essex, RM20 3BJ Tel: (0800) 585383 Fax: (01708) 869560

▶ S G B Rovacabin Haydock, Anglezarke Road, Sankey Valley Industrial Estate, Newton-le-Willows, Merseyside, WA12 8DJ Tel: (0800) 585383 Fax: (01925) 291045

▶ S G B Rovacabin Hire Ltd, Ainleys Industrial Estate, Huddersfield Road, Elland, West Yorkshire, HX5 9BZ Tel: 0161-620 3047 Fax: (01454) 322948

▶ S G B Rovacabin Hire Ltd, Ainleys Industrial Estate, Huddersfield Road, Elland, West Yorkshire, HX5 9BZ Tel: 0161-620 3047 Fax: (01422) 379142

▶ SGB Rovacabin, Unit 54 Hobbs Industrial Estate, Newchapel, Lingfield, Surrey, RH7 6HN Tel: (01342) 833869 Fax: (01342) 835550

STEEL CASTINGS

Anderson Stewart Castings Ltd, Block 1 Lochshore Industrial Estate, Caledonia Road, Glengarnock, Beith, Ayrshire, KA14 3DB Tel: (01505) 683368 Fax: (01505) 683771 E-mail: mail@ascast.co.uk

Blantyre Castings Ltd, Block 9a West Avenue, Blantyre, Glasgow, G72 0UZ Tel: (01698) 829572 Fax: (01698) 824093 E-mail: blantyrecastings@btconnect.com

Bonds Foundry Co., Wards End, Tow Law, Bishop Auckland, County Durham, DL13 4JS Tel: (01388) 730328 Fax: (01388) 731034 E-mail: bfc@bondsfoundry.com

Britcast Plant & Machinery Dealer, Green Acres, Shere Road, West Clandon, Guildford, Surrey, GU4 8SG Tel: (01483) 223696 Fax: (01483) 223696 E-mail: britcast@lineone.net

East Coast Castings Co. Ltd, The Foundry, Norwich Road, Carbrooke, Thetford, Norfolk, IP25 6TL Tel: (01953) 881741 Fax: (01953) 884769 E-mail: ecc@fsbdial.co.uk

▶ H I Quality Steel Castings Ltd, Foundry Street, Wittington Moor, Chesterfield, Derbyshire, S41 9AX Tel: (01246) 260303 Fax: (01246) 260245 E-mail: steven@hiqsc.com

Hean Studio, Kingsland, Leominster, Herefordshire, HR6 9QU Tel: (01568) 708966 Fax: (01568) 708901 E-mail: heanstudio@dial.pipex.com

Johnson Porter Industrial Services, Attwood Street, Stourbridge, West Midlands, DY9 8RY Tel: (01384) 897080 Fax: (01384) 897170

Lestercast Ltd, 14-16 Ireton Avenue, Leicester, LE4 9EU Tel: 0116-276 7284 Fax: 0116-246 0401 E-mail: sales@lestercast.co.uk

Lost Wax Castings Ltd, 23 Tithe Cl, Codicote, Hitchin, Herts, SG4 8UX Tel: (01438) 820822 Fax: (01438) 820822 E-mail: sjm3753735@gsk.com

Medical Technology Ltd, Parkway Close, Parkway Industrial Estate, Sheffield, S9 4WH Tel: 0114-273 8764 Fax: 0114-273 8764

Noirit Ltd, 17-18 Hatherton Street, Walsall, WS4 2LE Tel: (01922) 625471 Fax: (01922) 722339 E-mail: sales@noirit.com

P T S Ltd, 2 Academy Street, Coatbridge, Lanarkshire, ML5 3AU Tel: (01236) 431277 Fax: (01236) 431052 E-mail: mailbox@pts.ltd.uk

Sheffield Forgemasters Engineering Ltd, PO Box 286, Sheffield, S9 2RU Tel: 0114-244 9071 Fax: 0114-242 2103 E-mail: sales@sfel.com

Trefoil Steel Co. Ltd, Rotherfield Works, Deadmans Hole Lane, Sheffield, S9 1QQ Tel: (01709) 830701 Fax: (01709) 830737 E-mail: sales@trefoilsteel.com

Weardale Steel (Wolsingham) Ltd, Durham Road, Wolsingham, Bishop Auckland, County Durham, DL13 3HX Tel: (01388) 527201 Fax: (01388) 527838 E-mail: les.graham@weardalecastings.co.uk

Wearparts UK Ltd, Oaks Industrial Estate, Gilmorton Road, Lutterworth, Leicestershire, LE17 4HA Tel: (01455) 553551 Fax: (01455) 550907 E-mail: sales@wearparts.com

William Cook, Cross Green Approach, Leeds, LS9 0SG Tel: 0113-249 6363 Fax: 0113-249 1376 E-mail: sales@william-cook.co.uk

▶ William Cook Holbrook Precision Ltd, Station Road, Halfway, Sheffield, S20 3GD Tel: 0114-251 0410 Fax: 0114-251 0096 E-mail: admin@william-cook.co.uk

William Hunter & Sons (Ironfounders) Ltd, Halton House, Millrigg Road, Wiston, Biggar, Lanarkshire, ML12 6HT Tel: (01899) 850500 Fax: (01899) 850566

STEEL CASTORS

P & L Industrial Equipment Ltd, Lind Street, Manchester, M40 7ES Tel: 0161-273 2626 Fax: 0161-274 3633 E-mail: sales@plcastors.co.uk

STEEL CHAINS

Deacon Products Ltd, Unit 1, Penn Industrial Estate, Providence Street, Cradley Heath, West Midlands, B64 5DJ Tel: (01384) 416931 Fax: (01384) 635172 E-mail: info@chain-fittings.co.uk

STEEL CHIMNEY CONTRACTORS OR DESIGNERS

Rodell Chimneys Ltd, Ffrwdgrech Industrial Estate, Brecon, Powys, LD3 8LA Tel: (01874) 623723 Fax: (01874) 623725 E-mail: sales@rodell-chimneys.co.uk

STEEL CHIMNEY ERECTORS

A 1 Sheetmetal Flues Ltd, Maun Way, Boughton Industrial Estate, Newark, Nottinghamshire, NG22 9ZD Tel: (01623) 860578 Fax: (0870) 1602281 E-mail: info@a1flues.co.uk

J R F Chimney Specialists Ltd, 50 Nasmyth Road, Glenrothes, Fife, KY6 2SD Tel: (01592) 771199 Fax: (01592) 771135 E-mail: info@jrf-chimney-spec.co.uk

STEEL CHIMNEYS

A 1 Sheetmetal Flues Ltd, Maun Way, Boughton Industrial Estate, Newark, Nottinghamshire, NG22 9ZD Tel: (01623) 860578 Fax: (0870) 1602281 E-mail: info@a1flues.co.uk

E G Reeve & Sons Ltd, Burton Road, Norwich, NR6 6AT Tel: (01603) 427228 Fax: (01603) 789548 E-mail: alan@egreeve.co.uk

Flues & Flashings Ltd, Unit 246 Ikon Industrial Estate, Droitwich Road, Hartlebury, Kidderminster, Worcestershire, DY10 4EU Tel: (01299) 250049 Fax: (01299) 250947 E-mail: info@fluesandflashings.co.uk

J T Services Ltd, 99 Reindeer Road, Fazeley, Tamworth, Staffordshire, B78 3SP Tel: (01827) 250280 Fax: (01827) 281363

James Engineering Construction, Wood Street, Alfreton, Derbyshire, DE55 7JW Tel: (01773) 832425 Fax: (01773) 831000 E-mail: jamesengineering@btinternet.com

M M F Ltd, 55 Woodburn Road, Smethwick, West Midlands, B66 2PU Tel: 0121-555 6555 Fax: 0121-555 6816 E-mail: sales@fluepipes.com

John Patrick Engineering Ltd, Merlin Way, Quarry Hill Industrial Park, Ilkeston, Derbyshire, DE7 4RA Tel: 0115-944 0360 Fax: 0115-944 0373 E-mail: info@jpen.co.uk

Pennine Systems Ltd, Crossley Works, Stockfield Mount, Off Peel Street, Chadderton, Oldham, OL9 9LR Tel: 0161 678 2998 Fax: 0161 678 2997 E-mail: sales@penninesystems.co.uk

Rodell Chimneys Ltd, Ffrwdgrech Industrial Estate, Brecon, Powys, LD3 8LA Tel: (01874) 623723 Fax: (01874) 623725 E-mail: sales@rodell-chimneys.co.uk

Schiedel Right Vent Ltd, Crowther Road, Crowther Industrial Estate, Washington, Tyne & Wear, NE38 0AQ Tel: 0191-416 1150

Shropshire Flue & Duct Services, Unit 84, Condover Industrial Estate, Dorrington, Shrewsbury, SY5 7NH Tel: (01743) 718844 Fax: (01743) 718874

Thelkane Industrial Chimneys Ltd, Copse Road, Fleetwood, Lancashire, FY7 6RP Tel: (01253) 875121 Fax: (01253) 772106

STEEL COIL COATING SERVICES

Coilcolor Ltd, Docks Way, Newport, Gwent, NP20 2NW Tel: (01633) 254382 Fax: (01633) 243219 E-mail: sales@colorgroup.co.uk

Colorgroup Ltd, Whitehead Estate, Docks Way, Newport, Gwent, NP20 2NW Tel: (01633) 223854 Fax: (01633) 253992 E-mail: dave.burston@colorgroup.co.uk

Corus, Brockhurst Crescent, Walsall, WS5 4AX Tel: (01922) 629593 Fax: (01922) 648202

STEEL COIL CUTTING/ DECOILING/SLITTING FACILITIES/SERVICES

Butterworth Steel Processing, Bilport Lane, Wednesbury, West Midlands, WS10 0NT Tel: 0121-556 8541 Fax: 0121-502 4644

C S Alloys, Unit 32 Jubilee Trade Centre, Jubilee Road, Letchworth Garden City, Hertfordshire, SG6 1SP Tel: (01462) 481273 Fax: (01462) 481092 E-mail: csalloys@hotmail.com

Capital Coated Steel, East Tyndall Street, Cardiff, CF24 5DA Tel: (029) 2046 0606 Fax: (029) 2048 8687 E-mail: email@capitalcs.com

Castle Steel Services Ltd, Pensnett House, Pensnett Trading Estate, Kingswinford, West Midlands, DY6 7PP Tel: (01384) 401600 Fax: (01384) 292785 E-mail: mikeb@tidentsections.co.uk

Color Steels Ltd, Blackvein Industrial Estate, Cross Keys, Newport, Gwent, NP11 7YD Tel: (01495) 279100 Fax: (01495) 271456

▶ Colter Steels Ltd, Unit 10 Owen Road Industrial Estate, Willenhall, West Midlands, WV13 2PY Tel: 0121-526 6066 Fax: 0121-526 3044 E-mail: sales@coltersteels.co.uk

European Steel Sheets Ltd, Doris Road, Bordesley Green, Birmingham, B9 4SJ Tel: 0121-766 7677 Fax: 0121-766 7864 E-mail: dan.broadhurst@europeansteelsheets.com

Hi Tech Steel Services Ltd, Neills Road, Bold Industrial Park, Bold, St. Helens, Merseyside, WA9 4TU Tel: (01744) 818767 Fax: (01744) 818706 E-mail: sales@hitechsteels.co.uk

J & J Slitting Services Ltd, 217 Sams Lane, West Bromwich, West Midlands, B70 7EX Tel: 0121-553 1131 Fax: 0121-525 2411

Jayclem Products Ltd, Newbold Road, Kirkby Mallory, Leicester, LE9 7QG Tel: (01455) 823560 Fax: (01455) 824846 E-mail: jclem@webleicester.co.uk

Katoll Metals & Industrial Products Ltd, Central Avenue, Cradley Heath, West Midlands, B64 7BY Tel: (01384) 634001 Fax: (01384) 410776 E-mail: sales@katollmetals.co.uk

Knight Strip Metals Ltd, Saltley Business Park, Cumbria Way, Saltley, Birmingham, B8 1BH Tel: 0121-322 8400 Fax: 0121-322 8401 E-mail: kms.sales@knight-group.co.uk

Macward Steel Slitting Services Ltd, Unit 3 Polo Grounds, New Inn, Pontypool, Gwent, NP4 0TW Tel: (01495) 751122 Fax: (01495) 762369 E-mail: salesoffice@macwards.co.uk

Parkes & Billingham Ltd, Peartree Lane, Dudley, West Midlands, DY2 0QW Tel: (01384) 480660 Fax: (01384) 70271 E-mail: parkesandbillingham@office01.fsnet.co.uk

Phoenix Steel Services Ltd, Units 3-4, Charlotte Street, Dudley, West Midlands, DY1 1TD Tel: (01384) 458866 Fax: (01384) 455576 E-mail: sales@phoenixsteelservices.co.uk

▶ Professional Slitting Services, 6 Stourdale Road, Cradley Heath, West Midlands, B64 7BG Tel: (01384) 633322 Fax: (01384) 633323 E-mail: sales@reddifast.co.uk

Renforce Ltd, 26A Collegiate Crescent, Sheffield, S10 2BH Tel: 0114-266 7521 Fax: 0114-268 4331

Roberts Steels Ltd, Unit 2, Bay 3 Sovereign Works, Deepdale Lane, Dudley, West Midlands, DY3 2AF Tel: (01384) 259549 Fax: (01384) 456851 E-mail: sales@robertssteelsgroup.co.uk

Rowham Steel Products Ltd, Lyons Road, Trafford Park, Manchester, M17 1RF Tel: 0161-786 3700 Fax: 0161-786 3707 E-mail: sales@rowhamsteel.co.uk

Sebden Steel Midlands Ltd, Thorns Road, Brierley Hill, West Midlands, DY5 2PJ Tel: (01384) 424344 Fax: (01384) 892982 E-mail: brierleyhill@sebden.com

Sebden Steels, Chandler Road, Chichester, West Sussex, PO19 8UE Tel: (01243) 528311 Fax: (01243) 787038 E-mail: chichester@sebden.com

Steel & Alloy Processing Ltd, Trafalgar Works, Union Street, West Bromwich, West Midlands, B70 6BZ Tel: 0121-553 5292 Fax: 0121-553 3864 E-mail: info@steelalloy.co.uk

John Tainton, Hoo Farm Industrial Estate, Worcester Road, Kidderminster, Worcestershire, DY11 7RA Tel: (01562) 740477 Fax: (01562) 68765 E-mail: jtsales@johntainton.co.uk

STEEL COIL CUTTING/SLITTING MACHINE REBUILDERS/ REFURBISHMENT SERVICES

Orion Link Ltd, Unit 2 Lodge Ford Trading Estate, Cradley Heath, West Midlands, B64 7RW Tel: (01384) 565448 Fax: (01384) 565147 E-mail: sales@orion-link.co.uk

STEEL COILS

A S D Coil Processing, Tipton Road, Tividale, Oldbury, West Midlands, B69 3HU Tel: 0121-522 2215 Fax: 0121-522 2293 E-mail: customer.care@asdplc.co.uk

A S D Motor Services, Drum Industrial Estate, Drum Industrial Estate, Chester le Street, County Durham, DH2 1ST Tel: 0191-492 2322 Fax: 0191-410 0126

▶ A Smith Sandwell Ltd, Union Road, Oldbury, West Midlands, B69 3EU Tel: 0121-544 6575 Fax: 0121-552 1537 E-mail: asmithsandwell@btconnect.com

Gary Brown Steels Ltd, Unit 21 Izons Industrial Estate, Oldbury Road, West Bromwich, West Midlands, B70 9BS Tel: 0121-525 2700 Fax: 0121-525 6200

Castle Steel Services Ltd, Pensnett House, Pensnett Trading Estate, Kingswinford, West Midlands, DY6 7PP Tel: (01384) 401600 Fax: (01384) 292785 E-mail: mikeb@tidentsections.co.uk

Clifton Steel Ltd, 122 Fazeley Industrial Estate, Fazeley Street, Birmingham, B5 5RS Tel: 0121-603 4000 Fax: 0121-603 4001 E-mail: sales@cliftonsteel.co.uk

Corus, 216a Moira Road, Lisburn, County Antrim, BT28 2SN Tel: (028) 9266 0747 Fax: (028) 9266 0748

Corus Service Centre, Unit 4 Symondscliffe Way, Portskewett, Caldicot, Gwent, NP26 5PW Tel: (01291) 421732 Fax: (01291) 425085

Galvanised Sheet & Coil Ltd, Doris Road, Bordesley Green, Birmingham, B9 4SJ Tel: 0121-773 8341 Fax: 0121-771 0024

Hi Tech Steel Services Ltd, Neills Road, Bold Industrial Park, Bold, St. Helens, Merseyside, WA9 4TU Tel: (01744) 818767 Fax: (01744) 818706 E-mail: sales@hitechsteels.co.uk

Graham Perry Steels Ltd, Units 1-3 Dock Meadow Drive Industrial Estate, Lanesfield Drive, Spring Road, Ettingshall, Wolverhampton, WV4 6LE Tel: (01902) 490450 Fax: (01902) 490217 E-mail: sales@grahamperrysteels.co.uk

R S Lloyd Midlands, Unit 33 Dawley Trading Estate, Stallings Lane, Kingswinford, West Midlands, DY6 7AP Tel: (01384) 401030 Fax: (01384) 401023

Roberts Steels Ltd, Unit 2, Bay 3 Sovereign Works, Deepdale Lane, Dudley, West Midlands, DY3 2AF Tel: (01384) 259549 Fax: (01384) 456851 E-mail: sales@robertssteelsgroup.co.uk

Shearline Steels Strip Ltd, 3 Gibbons Industrial Park, Dudley Road, Kingswinford, West Midlands, DY6 8XF Tel: (01384) 401533 Fax: (01384) 294892 E-mail: sales@shearlinesteel.com

Steel & Alloy Processing Ltd, Trafalgar Works, Union Street, West Bromwich, West Midlands, B70 6BZ Tel: 0121-553 5292 Fax: 0121-553 3864 E-mail: info@steelalloy.co.uk

STEEL CONCRETE FORMWORK

Chart Engineering Ltd, Pivington Works, Pluckley, Ashford, Kent, TN27 0PG Tel: (01233) 840555 Fax: (01233) 840687 E-mail: sales@chartengineering.com

▶ Corus Special Profiles Ltd, Skinningrove, Saltburn-By-The-Sea, Cleveland, TS13 4ET Tel: (01287) 640212 Fax: (01287) 643467

Form Fab Worcester Ltd, 9-11 Bache Road, Sandy Lane Industrial Estate, Stourport-on-Severn, Worcestershire, DY13 9QB Tel: (01299) 879271 Fax: (01299) 877339 E-mail: sales@form-fab.com

Hanson Concrete Products plc, 21 Wilden Road, Pattinson Industrial Estate, Washington, Tyne & Wear, NE38 8QB Tel: 0191-417 0066 Fax: 0191-417 0131 E-mail: sales@omnideck.co.uk

Matravers Engineering Ltd, Isle Moor Works, Fivehead, Taunton, Somerset, TA3 6PA Tel: (01460) 281544 Fax: (01460) 281735 E-mail: info@matravers.co.uk

Special Formwork Ltd, Stubbers Green Road, Aldridge, Walsall, WS9 8BN Tel: (01922) 451909 Fax: (01922) 454520 E-mail: info@formwork.co.uk

STEEL CONTAINERS

Firber Engineering Ltd, Sidings Road, Lowmoor Business Park, Kirkby-in-Ashfield, Nottingham, NG17 7JZ Tel: (01623) 757794 Fax: (01623) 688990 E-mail: sales@firber.co.uk

L F E Material Handling, Units 3-5 Hibberd House, Curriers Close, Charter Avenue Industrial Esta, Coventry, CV4 8AW Tel: (024) 7647 0170 Fax: (024) 7669 4521 E-mail: lfemh@btconnect.com

Pensteel Ltd, Unit 1, Horndon Industrial Park, West Horndon, Essex, CM13 3XL Tel: (01277) 810211 Fax: (01277) 811971 E-mail: sales@pensteel.co.uk

Titan Containers (UK) Ltd, Suite 1, 1 Cecil Court, London Road, Enfield, Middlesex, EN2 6DE Tel: (020) 8362 1444 Fax: (01707) 664407 E-mail: uk@titancontainer.com

STEEL CYLINDERS

Harvey Fabrication Ltd, Hancock Road, Bow, London, E3 3DA Tel: (020) 8981 7811 Fax: (020) 8981 7815

► Icam Engineering Ltd, Dock Road Industrial Estate, Connah's Quay, Deeside, Clwyd, CH5 4DS Tel: (01244) 831143 Fax: (01244) 831338 E-mail: icam@daisyconnect.com

Wyko Tubes, Vauxhall Street, Queens Cross, Dudley, W. Midlands, DY1 1TA Tel: (01384) 237816 Fax: (01384) 457463 E-mail: sales@wyko-tubes.co.uk

STEEL DOOR FRAMES

Accent Hansen, Greengate Industrial Estate, Greenside Way, Middleton, Manchester, M24 1SW Tel: 0161-284 4100 Fax: 0161-655 3119 E-mail: operations@accenthansen.co.uk

Crittall Windows Ltd, Springwood Drive, Braintree, Essex, CM7 2YN Tel: (01376) 324106 Fax: (01376) 349662 E-mail: hq@crittall-windows.co.uk

Drawn Metal Ltd, 50 Swinnow Lane, Leeds, LS13 4NE Tel: 0113-256 5661 Fax: 0113-239 3194 E-mail: sales@drawnmetal.co.uk

Fitzpatrick Doors Ltd, Rushey Lane, Birmingham, B11 2BL Tel: 0121-706 6363 Fax: 0121-708 2250 E-mail: fitzuk1@aol.com

STEEL DOORS

Accent Hansen, Greengate Industrial Estate, Greenside Way, Middleton, Manchester, M24 1SW Tel: 0161-284 4100 Fax: 0161-655 3119 E-mail: operations@accenthansen.co.uk

Beck Engineering Co (Bridlington) Ltd, Camlock Works, 13 & 15 Bridlington Road, Hunmanby, Filey, North Yorkshire, YO14 0LR Tel: (01723) 890631 Fax: (01723) 891554 E-mail: shane@becktransglobal.co.uk

► Bradbury Security Grilles, Dunlop Way, Queensway Enterprise Estate, Scunthorpe, South Humberside, DN16 3RN Tel: (01724) 271999 Fax: (01724) 271888 E-mail: sales@bradburyuk.com

D W Industrial Doors, Unit 27 Farset Enterprise Park, Springfield Road, Belfast, BT12 7DY Tel: (028) 9023 7723 Fax: (028) 9023 7723

Doors & Hardware Ltd, Taskmaster Works, Maybrook Road, Minworth, Sutton Coldfield, West Midlands, B76 1AL Tel: 0121-351 5276 Fax: 0121-313 1228 E-mail: sales@doors-and-hardware.com

H M Doors, 620 Bradford Road, Batley, West Yorkshire, WF17 8HF Tel: (01924) 440114 Fax: (01924) 477761

Intellect Computers, 12 Scarsdale Place, Buxton, Derbyshire, SK17 6EF Tel: (01298) 70055 Fax: (01298) 70066 E-mail: enquiries@oxin.net

Ir Martin Roberts, Millen Road, Sittingbourne, Kent, ME10 2AA Tel: (01795) 476161 Fax: (01795) 422463

► J K Doors Ltd, Unit 4/6, Hanworth Road, Off Common Road, Low Moor, Bradford, West Yorkshire, BD12 0SG Tel: (0845) 0589420 Fax: (0845) 0589421 E-mail: kevin@jkdoors.co.uk

J.S. Millinton & Sons Ltd, Albert Buildings, Humberstone Road, Leicester, LE5 3AJ Tel: 0116-253 3333 Fax: 0116-251 4471 E-mail: webmaster@jsmillington.com

P C Henderson Ltd, Durham Road, Bowburn, Durham, DH6 5NG Tel: 0191-377 0701 Fax: 0191-377 1309 E-mail: sales@pchenderson.com

Secuirdoor North East Ltd, Commercial Road, South Shields, Tyne & Wear, NE33 1RP Tel: 0191-425 0000 Fax: 0191-425 0037

Soham Security Products Ltd, 22 Regal Drive, Soham, Ely, Cambridgeshire, CB7 5BE Tel: (01353) 722930 Fax: (01353) 624429 E-mail: sales@sohamsecurity.co.uk

Tyco Fire & Integrated Solutions, Tyco Park, Grimshaw Lane, Manchester, M40 2WL Tel: 0161-455 4475 Fax: 0161-455 4532 E-mail: wfs.doors.uk@tycoint.com

Vista-Brunswick Ltd, 105 Glenfrome Road, Bristol, BS2 9XA Tel: 0117 9551491

STEEL DOWEL PINS

Emkay Screw Supplies, 74 Pepys Way, Strood, Rochester, Kent, ME2 3LL Tel: (01634) 717256 Fax: (01634) 717256 E-mail: emkaysupplies@talktalk.net

STEEL DRUMS

Hearl Heaton Ltd, Halifax Road, Liversedge, West Yorkshire, WF15 6JJ Tel: (01924) 406721 Fax: (01924) 400803 E-mail: info@hearlheaton.co.uk

J E Jones S & D Ltd, Moor Lane, Birmingham, B6 7HH Tel: 0121-356 9169 Fax: 0121-356 0595 E-mail: jejdrums@aol.com

James J Carrick & Co. Ltd, 450 Petershill Road, Glasgow, G21 4PB Tel: 0141-558 6008 Fax: 0141-557 0318 E-mail: enquiries@jamesjcarrick.com

R L M Packaging Ltd, Dairycoates Industrial Estate, Wiltshire Road, Hull, HU4 6PA Tel: (01482) 505585 Fax: (01482) 568115 E-mail: info@rlm-packaging.co.uk

R Spivey & Son Ltd, 54 Upper Station Road, Batley, West Yorkshire, WF17 5TA Tel: (01924) 473372 Fax: (01924) 442921 E-mail: david@spiveydrums.co.uk

R. Spivey & Sons Ltd, 30 Pheasant Drive, Birstall, Batley, West Yorkshire, WF17 9LT Tel: (01924) 423200 Fax: (01924) 420006 E-mail: david@spiveydrums.co.uk

A.W. Stokes & Son (Drums) Ltd, Hall Street, West Bromwich, West Midlands, B70 7DN Tel: 0121-553 1713 Fax: 0121-553 0825 E-mail: sales@awsdrums.co.uk

STEEL DUCTING

► Greenbank Group Inc, Hartshorne Road, Woodville, Swadlincote, Derbyshire, DE11 7GT Tel: (0870) 6078880 Fax: (0870) 6078889 E-mail: info@greenbank.tv

The Woodwork Dust Control Company Ltd, Wotton Road, Brill, Aylesbury, Buckinghamshire, HP18 9UB Tel: (01844) 238833 Fax: (01844) 238899 E-mail: woodworkdust@ukonline.co.uk

STEEL EXTRUSIONS

Osborn Steel Extrusions Ltd, Brighouse Road, Low Moor, Bradford, West Yorkshire, BD12 0QL Tel: (01274) 677331 Fax: (01274) 607858 E-mail: extrusion@osbornbujon.com

STEEL FABRICATIONS

Aegis Security, Dane Road, Bletchley, Milton Keynes, MK1 1JQ Tel: (01908) 375451 Fax: (01908) 375044 E-mail: info@kemco-aegis.com

Alpha Fabrications, Unit 53c Notley Enterprise Park, Raydon Road, Great Wenham, Colchester, CO7 6QD Tel: (01473) 827263 Fax: (01473) 829762

► Amtin Ltd, Manor Barns, The Street, Brundish, Woodbridge, Suffolk, IP13 8BL Tel: (01379) 388385 Fax: (01379) 388386 E-mail: design@amtin.co.uk

Bendall, Brunthill Road, Kingstown Industrial Estate, Carlisle, CA3 0EH Tel: (01228) 526246 Fax: (01228) 525634 E-mail: info@bendalls.co.uk

► Bolt Fabrications & Site Services, Unit 5, Albany Trading Estate, Albany Street, Newport, Gwent, NP20 5NQ Tel: (07799) 835958 Fax: (01633) 872143 E-mail: mike@boltfabs.co.uk

Bowdell Steel Services Ltd, 57 Bradford Street, Walsall, WS1 3QD Tel: (01922) 720989 Fax: (01922) 635960 E-mail: bowdellsteel@tinyworld.co.uk

C R F (UK) Ltd, Unit B8 Wem Industrial Estate, Soulton Road, Wem, Shrewsbury, SY4 5SD Tel: (01939) 235000 Fax: (01939) 235111 E-mail: crf-sales@spunwebs.net

Cherrymill Ltd, 23 Hoylake Road, Scunthorpe, South Humberside, DN17 2AZ Tel: (01724) 867244 Fax: (01724) 858509 E-mail: cherrymill.co.uk@amserve.net

Leonard Cooper Ltd, Balm Road, Leeds, LS10 2JR Tel: 0113-270 5441 Fax: 0113-276 0659 E-mail: sales@leonardcooperltd.co.uk

► Crickhowell Joinery, Timbercraft Park, Llangattock, Crickhowell, Powys, NP8 1HW Tel: (01873) 810156 Fax: (01873) 810204

D & A Fabrications, Unit 23 Landgate Industrial Estate, Wigan Road, Ashton-in-Makerfield, Wigan, Lancashire, WN4 0BW Tel: (01942) 717183 Fax: (01942) 719880

Durham Sheet Metal Works Ltd, Progress House, Templetown, South Shields, Tyne & Wear, NE33 5TE Tel: 0191-455 3558 Fax: 0191-456 8837 E-mail: paul@durhamsheetmetal.co.uk

F C Curran Ltd, Duke Street, Nottingham, NG7 7JN Tel: 0115-970 6801 Fax: 0115-942 2221 E-mail: enquiries@fccurran.co.uk

F E Philcox & Sons, 24 Church Road, Catsfield, Battle, East Sussex, TN33 9DP Tel: (01424) 892391 Fax: (01424) 892141 E-mail: mail@fep-gates.co.uk

Fair Deal Fabrications, Hammond Avenue, Stockport, Cheshire, SK4 1PQ Tel: 0161-474 1316 Fax: 0161-480 0635 E-mail: sales@fairdealfab.co.uk

Four-Tec Fabrications Ltd, Unit 2 Whieldon Industrial Estate, Whieldon Road, Stoke-on-Trent, ST4 4JP Tel: (01782) 844434 Fax: (01782) 744351 E-mail: fourtecfabs@aol.com

G B H Services Ltd, 17-18 Mercia Way, Bells Close Industrial Estate, Newcastle Upon Tyne, NE15 6UF Tel: 0191-229 0488 Fax: 0191-264 4095 E-mail: sales@gbhservices.co.uk

Gardiners, The Batts, Frosterley, Bishop Auckland, County Durham, DL13 2SE Tel: (07711) 356444 Fax: (01388) 527295

GGD Engineering Ltd, Rashierieve Cottages, Newburgh, Ellon, Aberdeenshire, AB41 6AU Tel: (01358) 789920 Fax: (01358) 789919 E-mail: sales@ggdengineering.co.uk

Grange Engineering, Trenholme Bar, Northallerton, North Yorkshire, DL6 3LE Tel: (01642) 706074 Fax: (01642) 701641

Graythorpe Forge & Engineering Ltd, 99 Graythorp Industrial Estate, Hartlepool, Cleveland, TS25 2DP Tel: (01429) 273268 Fax: (01429) 236553

► H S Realisations Ltd, Unit 10 Locomotion Industrial Estate, Chorley New Road, Horwich, Bolton, BL6 5UE Tel: (01204) 695989 Fax: (01204) 669343

J J Welding Fabrication Ltd, Greenbank Road, East Tullos Industrial Estate, Aberdeen, AB12 3BQ Tel: (01224) 898889 Fax: (01224) 873139 E-mail: njohnston@twma.co.uk

M J P Tube & Fittings Ltd, Regil Lane, Winford, Bristol, BS40 8AX Tel: (01275) 474758 Fax: (01275) 472753

Metaltec Ltd, Unit 5 Hurricane Close, Old Sarum, Salisbury, SP4 6LG Tel: (01722) 339090 Fax: (01722) 321311 E-mail: metal_tec@btconnect.com

Minianchor, 3 Toledo Works, Neepsend Lane, Sheffield, S3 8UL Tel: 0114-275 6211 Fax: 0114-249 6211 E-mail: info@minianchorltd.co.uk

Nicoll Industries, 4 Steelfabs Industrial Estate, Victoria CR, Burton-on-Trent, Staffordshire, DE14 2QD Tel: (01283) 510570 Fax: (01283) 536188 E-mail: enquiries@nicoll-industries.co.uk

On Site Welding Solutions Ltd, 6b Sweetmans Yard, Plough Lane, Hereford, HR4 0EE Tel: (01432) 276639 Fax: (01432) 276639 E-mail: andrew-skinner@tiscaly.co.uk

► Plan Engineers, 1 Ashton Grange Industrial Estate, Bryn Road, Ashton-in-Makerfield, Wigan, Lancashire, WN4 8BX Tel: (01942) 271299 Fax: (01942) 721756

Profab Fabrications, Triton Works, Stringes Lane, Willenhall, West Midlands, WV13 1LD Tel: (01902) 633253 Fax: (01902) 633253

► Salmor Industries, 4 Silverwood Industrial Area, Silverwood Road, Lurgan, Craigavon, County Armagh, BT66 6LN Tel: (028) 3831 3100 Fax: (028) 3831 7770 E-mail: sales@salmor.co.uk

T P Fabrications, Bolton Road, Birmingham, B10 0AU Tel: 0121-773 3798 Fax: 0121-773 3798

► Thirsk Fabrications, Thirsk Industrial Park, York Road, Thirsk, North Yorkshire, YO7 3BX Tel: (01845) 525923 Fax: (01845) 524420

Wilbar Engineers, Patterson Street, Blaydon-on-Tyne, Tyne & Wear, NE21 5TL Tel: 0191-414 5697 Fax: 0191-499 0174 E-mail: wilbarengineer@aol.com

► Wilton Engineering Services, Port Clarence Road, Port Clarence, Middlesbrough, Cleveland, TS2 1RZ Tel: (01642) 546611 Fax: (01642) 546622 E-mail: info@wiltonengineering.co.uk

STEEL FABRICATORS

► A & A Fabrications, Unit 2 Athertons Quay, Warrington, WA5 1AH Tel: (01925) 419357 Fax: (01925) 419357

► A A Fabrications South West Ltd, Unit 10 Deverill Road Trading Estate, Deverill Road, Sutton Veny, Warminster, Wiltshire, BA12 7BZ Tel: (01985) 841441 Fax: (01985) 841441

A & B Fabrications, 12 Cherrywood Road, Birmingham, B9 4UD Tel: 0121-771 3143 Fax: 0121-771 3143

A & B Fabrications, 1 Morrell Street, Maltby, Rotherham, South Yorkshire, S66 7LL Tel: (01709) 816402

A B G Fabrications, Old Tin Plate Works, Old Tin Works Road, Pontypridd, Mid Glamorgan, CF37 1UD Tel: (01443) 402085 Fax: (01443) 491664

A & B Welding Services Ltd, 1a Woodside Road, Bridge of Don Industrial Estate, Aberdeen, AB23 8EF Tel: (01224) 823444 Fax: (01224) 825079 E-mail: sales@abweld.com

A Bush Engineering Services Ltd, 16-18 Manor Road, Leeds, LS11 9AH Tel: 0113-246 0581 Fax: 0113-246 0043E-mail: info@abush.co.uk

A C E Metalworks Ltd, 14 Stacey Avenue, London, N18 3PL Tel: (020) 8807 6533 Fax: (020) 8807 7145 E-mail: sales@acemetalworks.freeserve.co.uk

► A C Engineers & Fabricators, 9 Beacon Trading Estate, Middlemore Lane, Aldridge, Walsall, WS9 8DU Tel: (01922) 453494

A C L Structures Ltd, Holland Way, Blandford Forum, Dorset, DT11 7TA Tel: (01258) 456051 Fax: (01258) 450566 E-mail: enquiries@aclstructures.co.uk

A D Morton Ltd, New Line Industrial Estate, The Sidings, Bacup, Lancashire, OL13 9RW Tel: (01706) 878358 Fax: (01706) 878380

► A D Profiles, 534 Attercliffe Road, Sheffield, S9 3QP Tel: 0114-244 7184 Fax: 0114-244 7184

A D R Art Metalwork, 109 Railway Arches, Cannon Street Road, London, E1 2LY Tel: (020) 7488 3776 Fax: (020) 7488 3776

A F Drew Construction Ltd, 38 Mill Lane, Frampton Cotterell, Bristol, BS36 2AA Tel: (01454) 850004 Fax: (01454) 850061

► A H Fabrications, 1 Brean Farm, Warren Road, Brean, Burnham-on-Sea, Somerset, TA8 2RR Tel: (01278) 751930 Fax: (01278) 751930

A Hodgson Engineers & Smiths Ltd, 54 Guest Street, Leigh, Lancashire, WN7 2HD Tel: (01942) 673038 Fax: (01942) 673038 E-mail: hodgsoneng@fsnet.co.uk

A Hodgson & Sons, Church Bank, Terrington St. Clement, King's Lynn, Norfolk, PE34 4NA Tel: (01553) 828361 Fax: (01553) 827262 E-mail: info@ajhodgesoneng.co.uk

A Howe Light Engineering, 1 Priory Works, Priory Cresent, Southend-on-Sea, SS2 6LD Tel: (01702) 611451 Fax: (01702) 469078 E-mail: david.knight@steelfabricators1.co.uk

A J S Contracts Ltd, Unit 3, Craggs Industrial Park, Morven St, Worksop, Nottinghamshire, S80 4AJ Tel: (01909) 722239 Fax: (01909) 724411 E-mail: ajscontracts@aol.com

A M C Engineering Ltd, Unit 3, Blackhill Industrial Estate, Findon, Aberdeen, AB12 4RL Tel: (01224) 782232 Fax: (01224) 782480 E-mail: sales@amc-engineering.co.uk

A & M Engineering, Briercliffe Business Centre, Burnley Road, Briercliffe, Burnley, Lancashire, BB10 2HG Tel: (01282) 412706 Fax: (01282) 424880

A M Fabrications, Unit 2 Block 2, Newlands Avenue, Brackla Industrial Estate, Bridgend, Mid Glamorgan, CF31 2AG Tel: (01656) 658874 Fax: (01656) 658874

► A & M Metal Services Ltd, Horbury Wagon Works, Charles Roberts Street, Horbury, Wakefield, West Yorkshire, WF4 5QH Tel: (01924) 266333 Fax: (01924) 266600

A Mcpherson Blacksmiths Ltd, West Fulton Smithy, Craigends Road, Houston, Johnstone, Renfrewshire, PA6 7EH Tel: (01505) 321282 Fax: (01505) 331662

► A N T Welding Ltd, Collington Works, Collington, Bromyard, Herefordshire, HR7 4ND Tel: (01885) 410607 Fax: (01885) 410607 E-mail: ANTwelding@AOL.COM

A R C Welding Services, Lapthorne, Totnes Road, Ipplepen, Newton Abbot, Devon, TQ12 5TN Tel: (01803) 813092 Fax: (01803) 813091

A Stanley Engineering, Gee House, Holborn Hill, Birmingham, B7 5JR Tel: 0121-326 0014 Fax: 0121-326 1779

A & W Fabrications & Structural Services, Old Bush Street, Brierley Hill, West Midlands, DY5 1UB Tel: (01384) 573676 Fax: (01384) 573676

A W Jeffreys Southampton Ltd, 91-97 Dukes Road, Southampton, SO14 0ST Tel: (023) 8055 3730 Fax: (023) 8067 1345 E-mail: awj@awjefferys.co.uk

A W S Engineering, Unit F1, Shaw Road, Dudley, West Midlands, DY2 8TP Tel: (01384) 236488 Fax: (01384) 236489 E-mail: tony@steel-fabrications.co.uk

A1 Metal Fabrications, 22 Boston Road, Leicester, LE4 1AU Tel: 0116-235 0444 Fax: 0116-235 0444

► A1 Secure Fabrications, Unit 4 Clifton Avenue, Long Eaton, Nottingham, NG10 2GA Tel: 0115-946 1777 Fax: 0115-946 1777 E-mail: a1securefabs@aol.com

► Ab Welding, 13 Mode Wheel Road South, Salford, M50 1DG Tel: 0161-877 5757 E-mail: sales@abweld.co.uk

Aberdeen Fabrication Ltd, Links Place, Aberdeen, AB11 5DY Tel: (01224) 588321 Fax: (01224) 583898 E-mail: sales@afab.co.uk

Able Steel Fabrications Ltd, Unit 1 Park Street, Gosport, Hampshire, PO12 4UH Tel: (023) 9242 5425 Fax: (023) 9242 5444 E-mail: ablesteelfab@btconnect.com

Able Steel Fabrications Ltd, Unit 1 Park Street, Gosport, Hampshire, PO12 4UH Tel: (023) 9242 5425 Fax: (023) 9242 5444

Acclaim Fabrications, 7b Meadow Road, Reading, RG1 8LB Tel: 0118-939 3413 Fax: 0118-939 3413

Acorn Fabrications, Unit 4a, 179 Cardiff Road, Reading, RG1 8HD Tel: 0118-958 7466 Fax: 0118-958 7466 E-mail: dinoacornfabs@live.co.uk

Actem UK Ltd, 2 Sea View Industrial Estate, Peterlee, County Durham, SR8 4TQ Tel: 0191-518 0235 Fax: 0191-586 1139 E-mail: paula.w@btclick.com

Adam Engineering Fabrication, Acton Hall Enterprise Park, Station Lane, Featherstone, Pontefract, West Yorkshire, WF7 6EQ Tel: (01977) 600280 Fax: (01977) 602196

Adey Steel, Meadow Lane, Loughborough, Leicestershire, LE11 1JU Tel: (01509) 556677 Fax: (01509) 828622 E-mail: admin@adey-steel.co.uk

Adnor Ltd, Mill Place, Kingston upon Thames, Surrey, KT1 2RL Tel: (020) 8549 4728 Fax: (020) 8549 8989 E-mail: sales@adnor.co.uk

Advance Fabrications Ltd, 1 Harrow Garage, Newbury Road, Headley, Thatcham, Berkshire, RG19 8LG Tel: (01635) 268234 Fax: (01635) 268704

AFF Fabrication Services Ltd, Abbey Fruit Pk, Grange Rd, Butlocks Heath, Southampton, SO31 5FF Tel: 023 80454100 Fax: 023 80454260

► Agar Ltd, Unit F2 Blackpole Trading Estate East, Blackpole Road, Worcester, WR3 8SG Tel: (01905) 452717 Fax: (01905) 458589

STEEL FABRICATORS - *continued*

Agri Weld Services, Willow Bridge Mills, Dalton, Thirsk, North Yorkshire, YO7 3BN Tel: (01845) 577963 Fax: (01845) 577963

Aire Valley Metal Products Ltd, Shaw House, Goulbourne Street, Keighley, West Yorkshire, BD21 1PG Tel: (01535) 600162 Fax: (01535) 600162 E-mail: aire@valleymetals.fsnet.co.uk

Akd Engineering, Horn Hill, Lowestoft, Suffolk, NR33 0PX Tel: (01502) 527800 Fax: (01502) 527848 E-mail: info@akd-engineering.co.uk

Aker Kvaerner, Wellesley Road, Methil, Leven, Fife, KY8 3RA Tel: (01592) 268181 Fax: (01592) 715574 E-mail: peter.holt@akerkvaerner.com

Alban Engineering Services Ltd, Wood Street Passage, Wood Street, Kettering, Northamptonshire, NN16 9SQ Tel: (01536) 513225 Fax: (01536) 513225

Albion Welding & Fabrication, Unit 27 North Pontypool Industrial Park, Pontnewynydd, Pontypool, Gwent, NP4 6PB Tel: (01495) 750180 Fax: (01495) 769819 E-mail: arsamins@btconnect.com

Aldridge Bros Sheetmetal Ltd, Balfour Road, Altrincham, Cheshire, WA14 5LS Tel: 0161-928 4810 Fax: 0161-941 7765

▶ Aldridge Fabrications Ltd, Mount Road, Burntwood, Staffordshire, WS7 0AX Tel: (01543) 682121 Fax: (01543) 674680 E-mail: davidneville@aldridge-fabrications.co.uk

Alfreton Fabrications Ltd, Unit 5b Wimsey Way, Somercotes, Alfreton, Derbyshire, DE55 4LS Tel: (01773) 608163 Fax: (01773) 608163 E-mail: sales@alfertonfabs.co.uk

Alifab, New Hall Mills, Milton Road, Stoke-on-Trent, ST1 6LE Tel: (01782) 544844 Fax: (01782) 544866 E-mail: sales@alifab.co.uk

Allerton Engineering Ltd, Allerton House, Thurston Road, Northallerton, North Yorkshire, DL6 2NA Tel: (01609) 774471 Fax: (01609) 780364 E-mail: sales@allertonengineering.co.uk

▶ Allfabs Fence Suppliers, Kitson House, Watercock Street, Bradford, West Yorkshire, BD4 7DZ Tel: (01274) 740100 Fax: (01274) 689153

Allins Ltd, Southgate Works, Hartland, Bideford, Devon, EX39 6DG Tel: (01237) 441242

Allister Welding Co. Ltd, Unit 30, Horndon Industrial Park, Station Road, West Horndon, Brentwood, Essex, CM13 3XL Tel: (01277) 812534 Fax: (01277) 812616 E-mail: enquiry@allister.co.uk

Allslade plc, Dundas Lane, Portsmouth, PO3 5SD Tel: (023) 9266 7531 Fax: (023) 9267 9818 E-mail: accounts@allslade.co.uk

Allsops Ltd, Hope Bank Works, New Mil Road, Honley, Holmfirth, HD9 6QG Tel: (01484) 661447 Fax: (01484) 666808 E-mail: info@allsops.co.uk

Allyson Fabrications Ltd, Andersen Road, Goole, North Humberside, DN14 6UD Tel: (01405) 762214 Fax: (01405) 768505

Almick Sheet Metal, Unit 7h Claymore, Wilnecote, Tamworth, Staffordshire, B77 5DQ Tel: (01827) 251530 Fax: (01827) 260390

Alstone Engineering, Unit 1 Towers Business Park, Wheelhouse Road, Rugeley, Staffordshire, WS15 1UZ Tel: (01889) 577775 Fax: (01889) 575111

Altech Services, 1 Cemetery Road, Houghton Regis, Dunstable, Bedfordshire, LU5 5BZ Tel: (01582) 472882 Fax: (01582) 471887

Am PM Fabrications, Hatfield Cottage, Hardings Elms Road, Billericay, Essex, CM11 2UH Tel: (01268) 285115 Fax: (01268) 285117 E-mail: ampmfabrications@btconnect.com

Amber Valley Engineering Ltd, Pye Bridge Industrial Estate, Pye Bridge, Alfreton, Derbyshire, DE55 4NX Tel: (01773) 604753 Fax: (01773) 540136 E-mail: ambervalleyeng@hotmail.com

Amrob Engineering Ltd, Unit 14 Garth Works, Taffs Well, Cardiff, CF15 7RN Tel: (029) 2081 3033 Fax: (029) 2081 3272

Ams Steel Fabrications, St Nicholas Industrial Estate, Darlington, County Durham, DL1 2NL Tel: (01325) 254439 Fax: (01325) 254439

Andrew Young & Son (Engineers) Ltd, 45 Midwharf Street, Glasgow, G4 0LD Tel: (0141) 332 1165 Fax: (0141) 331 2690

Apollo Fabrications Ltd, Unit 20 Canalside Industrial Estate, Brettell Lane, Brierley Hill, West Midlands, DY5 3JU Tel: (01384) 484603 Fax: (01384) 484603 E-mail: ralph-apollo@supanet.com

J.F. Appelbe & Co. Ltd, Littlefair Road, Hedon Road, Hull, HU9 5LN Tel: (01482) 781191 Fax: (01482) 781235 E-mail: enquiries@applebes.com

Arc Engineering Fabrication Ltd, 311 Bexhill Road, St. Leonards-on-Sea, East Sussex, TN38 8AJ Tel: (01424) 715220 Fax: (01424) 442344 E-mail: steelwork@arcfab.freeserve.co.uk

Archer Engineering (Leeds) Ltd, Pepper Road, Hunslet, Leeds, LS10 2RU Tel: 0113-270 5478 Fax: 0113-271 9886 E-mail: richard@archereng.co.uk

Archibald Mcaulay & Son, Bankend Road, Broadmeadow Industrial Estate, Dumbarton, G82 2RB Tel: (01389) 762778 Fax: (01389) 742350 E-mail: steel@mcaulay.co.uk

Arc-Tec, Unit 4 Bound Oak, Eversley Road, Arborfield, Reading, RG2 9PN Tel: 0118-976 1777 Fax: 0118-976 1444

Arden Fabrications, Packwood Road, Lapworth, Solihull, West Midlands, B94 6EJ Tel: (01564) 770966 Fax: (01564) 771052 E-mail: guy@ardenfabrications.co.uk

Ark Site Fabrications, Unit 7b Greenhill Mills, Grange Road, Batley, West Yorkshire, WF17 6LH Tel: (01924) 420470 Fax: (01924) 359744 E-mail: brian@arksite.co.uk

▶ Arkay Engineering, Unit1 Budds Lane, Romsey, Hampshire, SO51 0HA Tel: (01794) 511644 Fax: (01794) 511678

Arminhall Engineering, Shire Hill Industrial Estate, Saffron Walden, Essex, CB11 3AQ Tel: (01799) 524510 Fax: (01799) 526680

▶ Armitech Ltd, 149 Mill Lane, Wallasey, Merseyside, CH44 3BJ Tel: 0151-639 0222 Fax: 0151-639 0222 E-mail: chris_wigins@armitec.co.uk

Arndrove Fabrications Ltd, Unit 3 Wyther Lane, Industrial Estate, Kirkstall, Leeds, LS5 3BT Tel: 0113-230 7722 Fax: 0113-230 7207

Ashwell Engineering Services Ltd, Unit 12, Pinfold Road, Thurmaston, Leicester, LE4 8AT Tel: 0116-260 4050 E-mail: ashwelleng@hotmail.com

Asset Engineering Ltd, 16 20 Black Lake Industrial Estate, Black Lake, West Bromwich, West Midlands, B70 9QP Tel: 0121-553 0231 Fax: 0121-525 4856

Astec Construction, Northfield, Hull Road, Cliffe, Selby, North Yorkshire, YO8 6NH Tel: (01757) 630374 Fax: (01757) 630609

Astral Fabrications Ltd, 5 Phoenix House, Castle Street, Tipton, West Midlands, DY4 8HP Tel: 0121-522 4761 Fax: 0121-522 4761

▶ Astralite Fabricators Ltd, 4 Marshall Road, Hampden Park Industrial Estate, Eastbourne, East Sussex, BN22 9AT Tel: (01323) 501221 Fax: (01323) 521452 E-mail: sales@astralitefabricators.co.uk

Atlantic Engineering UK Ltd, Depot Road, Middlesbrough, Cleveland, TS2 1LE Tel: (01642) 248525 Fax: (01642) 221950 E-mail: enquire@atlanticeng.co.uk

Attachments Ltd, 6 Peterborough Road, Crowland, Peterborough, PE6 0BA Tel: (01733) 210611 Fax: (01733) 211345 E-mail: sales@attachments.ltd.uk

Audenshaw Steel Ltd, Unit 12 Wharf Parade, Lower Wharf Street, Ashton-under-Lyne, Lancashire, OL6 7PE Tel: 0161-343 8550 Fax: 0161-343 8550

Aveco Teesside Ltd, The Slipways, Dockside Road, Middlesbrough, Cleveland, TS3 8AT Tel: (01642) 224994 Fax: (01642) 248138 E-mail: aveco.teeside@ntl.com

Aycliffe Plastics (Fabrications) Ltd, Ketton Way, Aycliffe Industrial Estate, Newton Aycliffe, County Durham, DL5 6AU Tel: (01325) 310000 Fax: (01325) 301987 E-mail: info@aycliffefabrications.co.uk

▶ Ayne Engineers Ltd, Cocker Avenue, Poulton Industrial Estate, Poulton-le-Fylde, Lancashire, FY6 8JU Tel: (01253) 896007 Fax: (01253) 896006 E-mail: sales@ayneengineers.co.uk

B B F Co. Ltd, Unit 5 Bishopsgate Industrial Estate, Cashs Lane, Coventry, CV1 4NN Tel: (024) 7622 7925 Fax: (024) 7655 3097 E-mail: nikki@bbfco.ltd.uk

B B & W W Erectors Ltd, 51 Uckfield Road, Enfield, Middlesex, EN3 6AS Tel: (01992) 717417 Fax: (01992) 767894

B C Barton & Son Ltd, Granville Iron Works, Oldbury, West Midlands, B69 2NJ Tel: 0121-557 2272 Fax: 0121-557 2276 E-mail: presworkers@b-c-b.co.uk

▶ B & C Fabrications, Unit I Stonebridge Court, Nottingham, NG3 2GY Tel: 0115-947 2444 Fax: 0115-947 2777

B C S Steel Fabrication, Carron Works, Stenhouse Road, Carron, Falkirk, FK2 8DR Tel: (01324) 631528 Fax: (01324) 630729

B D & J M Heslop, Newton Grange, Shipton by Beningbrough, York, YO30 1BA Tel: (01347) 848206 Fax: (01347) 848443

B & D Willett Fabrications Ltd, 131 Mereside, Soham, Ely, Cambridgeshire, CB7 5EG Tel: (01353) 721374 Fax: (01353) 722567 E-mail: rujwillett@bdwillett.co.uk

▶ B G Contracts, Unit 1 Brown Street, Coatbridge, Lanarkshire, ML5 4AS Tel: (01236) 435335 Fax: (01236) 449894

B Horrocks Fabrications, Mill Street Works, Mill Street, Adlington, Chorley, Lancashire, PR6 9QY Tel: (01257) 482560 Fax: (01257) 474259

B & J Engineering Co., 7 Brampton Sidings Industrial Estate, Hempstalls Lane, Newcastle, Staffordshire, ST5 0SR Tel: (01782) 632132 Fax: (01782) 628591 E-mail: bjengltd@aol.com

B & K Fabrications Ltd, 60-64 Heath Mill Lane, Deritend, Birmingham, B9 4AR Tel: 0121-772 2667 Fax: 0121-772 2667

B & K Steelwork Fabrications Ltd, High Edge Court, Church Street, Heage, Belper, Derbyshire, DE56 2BW Tel: (01773) 853400 Fax: (01773) 857389 E-mail: bksf@bksf.prestel.co.uk

B O'Leary & Sons Engineering Ltd, Blacklands, East Malling, West Malling, Kent, ME19 6DR Tel: (01732) 845313 Fax: (01732) 874397

B P Engineering Co. Ltd, 5 Railway Buildings, Carr Lane, Hoylake, Wirral, Merseyside, CH47 4AY Tel: 0151-632 1364 Fax: 0151-632 3364 E-mail: bpeng@btconnect.com

B & R Fabrication & Welding, 115 Spalding Road, Deeping St. James, Peterborough, PE6 8SD Tel: (01778) 341355 Fax: (01778) 341355

B S Steels, 1 Shawcross Industrial Park, Ackworth Road, Portsmouth, PO3 5HU Tel: (023) 9267 3778 Fax: (023) 9269 1528 E-mail: bssteels@btconnect.com

B V Senior Engineering Co. Ltd, Hall Road, Maltby, Rotherham, South Yorkshire, S66 8ET Tel: (01709) 818511 Fax: (01709) 812557

B Wilson & Sons, 4 Martins Lane, Newry, County Down, BT35 8PJ Tel: (028) 3026 3342 Fax: (028) 3026 7919

Banfield Engineering Wisbech Ltd, Unit 8b Tinkers Drove, Wisbech, Cambridgeshire, PE13 3PQ Tel: (01945) 585554 Fax: (01945) 463874 E-mail: sales@banfield-uk.com

Barnes Steel Fabrications, 3 Brooklyn Farm, North Hill, Horndon-on-the-Hill, Stanford-le-Hope, Essex, SS17 8QA Tel: (01375) 644048 Fax: (01375) 644049

Barnetts Of Canterbury, 1 Wealden Forest Park, Herne Common, Herne Bay, Kent, CT6 7LQ Tel: (01227) 710174 Fax: (01227) 713113

Beam Structural Services Ltd, Creek Road, March, Cambridgeshire, PE15 8RE Tel: (01354) 660895 Fax: (01354) 661361 E-mail: sales@bssmarchltd.co.uk

Beaumont Engineering, Unit G11 Rudford Industrial Estate, Ford Road, Ford, Arundel, West Sussex, BN18 0BD Tel: (01903) 730822 Fax: (01903) 730315

Bebbington Steps Ltd, Unit 1-2 Finnimore Industrial Estate, Ottery St. Mary, Devon, EX11 1NR Tel: (01404) 813817 Fax: (01404) 813817E-mail: martin@bebbingtonsteps.co.uk

Becro Engineering Services Ltd, 117 Brooker Road, Waltham Abbey, Essex, EN9 1JH Tel: (01992) 713045 Fax: (01992) 700157 E-mail: admin@becro.co.uk

Beejay Welding Engineers, 5 Newlyn Road, Cradley Heath, West Midlands, B64 6BE Tel: (01384) 566205 Fax: (01384) 565245

C.P. Belcher (Welding) Ltd, 115B Blythswood Road, Tyseley, Birmingham, B11 2BX Tel: 0121-706 9689 Fax: 0121-706 8477 E-mail: steve@cpbsteel.fsnet.co.uk

Belmont Fabrications Ltd, Unit 7, 15 Headley Road, Woodley, Reading, RG5 4JB Tel: 0118-944 8782 Fax: 0118-944 8757 E-mail: belmontfabltd@aol.com

Bexley Steel, 8 Power Industrial Estate, Slade Green Road, Erith, Kent, DA8 2HU Tel: (01322) 335420 Fax: (01322) 335984 E-mail: bexleysteel@supernet.com

Henry T. Billson (Kettering) Ltd, Glendon Ironworks, Sackville St, Kettering, Northants, NN16 9EQ Tel: (01536) 512194 Fax: (01536) 484152 E-mail: sales@billsonssteel.co.uk

Bilston Engineering Ltd, Spring Road, Wolverhampton, WV4 6LF Tel: (01902) 492004 Fax: (01902) 354510 E-mail: sales@bilston-engineering.co.uk

Birchall Engineering Ltd, Birchwood Park Old School, Cottingham Street, Goole, North Humberside, DN14 5RR Tel: (01405) 767930 Fax: (01405) 767876

Birley Ventures Ltd, Mountfield Road, New Romney, Kent, TN28 8LH Tel: (01797) 361100 Fax: (01797) 367700 E-mail: birleyventures@aol.com

Black Cat Fabrications Ltd, Unit 12, Marsland Street Industrial Centre, Hazel Grove, Stockport, Cheshire, SK7 4ER Tel: 0161-482 2272 Fax: 0161-482 2272 E-mail: blackcatfabs@hotmail.com

Blakey Engineering Ltd, Caleb Close, Dunstable Road, Luton, LU4 8DR Tel: (01582) 571640 Fax: (01582) 492055 E-mail: blakey@engineeringco.fsnet.co.uk

Bolenda Engineering Ltd, Birds Hill, Clopton, Woodbridge, Suffolk, IP13 6SE Tel: (01473) 601982 Fax: (01473) 690954 E-mail: lee@bolenda.ndo.co.uk

Boulting Mechanical Services, Unit 11, Warrington Central Trading Estate Bewsey Road, Warrington, WA2 7LP Tel: (01925) 831151 Fax: (01925) 581120 E-mail: mechanical@boulting.co.uk

Bowson Engineering Ltd, Oak House, Dewsbury Road, Fenton Industrial Estate, Stoke-on-Trent, ST4 2TE Tel: (01782) 749000 Fax: (01782) 749299 E-mail: sales@bowson.co.uk

Bradfabs Ltd, 61A Plane Trees Road, Laisterdyke, Bradford, West Yorkshire, BD4 8AE Tel: (01274) 400401 Fax: (01274) 773335 E-mail: sales@bradfabs.co.uk

Brican Fabrications Ltd, 12 Alder Road, Broadmeadow Industrial Estate, Dumbarton, G82 2EL Tel: (01389) 731410 Fax: (01389) 730711

Bridge Engineering Ltd, Station Road, Thorney, Peterborough, PE6 0QE Tel: (01733) 270308 Fax: (01733) 270985 E-mail: bridgeeng@btopenworld.com

Brightarc Welding, Newlands Farm, Canterbury Road, Selsted, Dover, Kent, CT15 7HL Tel: (01303) 844319 Fax: (01303) 844666

Bripat Engineering, Unit 7 Steel Close, Eaton Socon, St. Neots, Cambridgeshire, PE19 8TT Tel: (01480) 211322 Fax: (01480) 210761 E-mail: brian.raffaelli@btconnect.com

Broadcliffe Fabrications, Cragg Vale, Hebden Bridge, West Yorkshire, HX7 5RU Tel: (01422) 884030 Fax: (01422) 884030

Brooks & Jackson Engineering Ltd, P O Box 186, Macclesfield, Cheshire, SK10 4RE Tel: 01625 611550 Fax: 01625 611550

T.M. Brooks Ltd, Unit 4, Dawley Estate, Stallings Lane, Kingswinford, West Midlands, DY6 7AP Tel: (01384) 400777 Fax: (01384) 400167 E-mail: office@tmbrooks.co.uk

Brookside Services Ltd, Station Road, Harrietsham, Maidstone, Kent, ME17 1JA Tel: (01622) 858995 Fax: (01622) 859793

Francis Brown Ltd, Church Road, Stockton-on-Tees, Cleveland, TS18 2HL Tel: (01642) 806000 Fax: (01642) 806001 E-mail: sales@francisbrown.co.uk

Robert Brown Engineering Ltd, Douglas Close, Preston Farm Industrial Estate, Stockton-on-Tees, Cleveland, TS18 3SB Tel: (01642) 675201 Fax: (01642) 615902

Brumfitt Factory Equipment Ltd, Foundry Works, Gibson Street, Laisterdyke, Bradford, West Yorkshire, BD3 9TF Tel: (01274) 666760 Fax: (01274) 666760

Brunstock Engineering, Brunstock Works, Brunstock, Carlisle, CA6 4QG Tel: (01228) 525334 Fax: (01228) 525334

Brynmawr Tools & Engineering Co. Ltd, Heritage Court Road, Gilchrist Thomas Industrial Estate, Blaenavon, Pontypool, Gwent, NP4 9RL Tel: (01495) 790230 Fax: (01495) 792757 E-mail: wnquiries@gosengomeering.co.uk

Budget Steel Fabrications, 48 English Street, Hull, HU3 2DT Tel: (01482) 320346 Fax: (01482) 215799 E-mail: business@budgetsteel.co.uk

▶ Builders Beams Ltd, Unit 15 Cosgrove Way, Luton, LU1 1XL Tel: (01582) 429151 Fax: (01582) 429155

Buildswift Ltd, 2 Fleet La Industrial Estate, Fleet Lane, St. Helens, Merseyside, WA9 1TA Tel: (01744) 731494 Fax: (01744) 731506 E-mail: glee@buildswift.co.uk

Burntisland Fabrications, Seaforth Place, West Shore, Burntisland, Fife, KY3 9AU Tel: (01592) 222000 Fax: (01592) 874688 E-mail: enquiries@bifab.co.uk

Burton Sheet Metal Ltd, Wetmore Road, Burton-on-Trent, Staffordshire, DE14 1SN Tel: (01283) 564019 Fax: (01283) 562626

Bush Welding & Engineering, 6 Grainger Road Industrial Estate, Southend-on-Sea, SS2 5DD Tel: (01702) 610871 Fax: (01702) 610871

Bystone Engineers Ltd, Price Street, Bilston, West Midlands, WV14 7EE Tel: (01902) 494604 Fax: (01902) 353147

C B Construction, 96 North Ormesby Road, Middlesbrough, Cleveland, TS4 2AG Tel: (01642) 231928 Fax: (01642) 211949 E-mail: keith@cbcon-cleveland.co.uk

C & B Engineering Ltd, I Edison Courtyard, Brunel Road, Earlstrees Industrial Estate, Corby, Northamptonshire, NN17 4LS Tel: (01536) 202583 Fax: (01536) 269402 E-mail: ian.candbeng@btopenworld.com

C Biggs, Lankelly, Lankelly Lane, Fowey, Cornwall, PL23 1HN Tel: (01726) 833350 Fax: (01726) 833860 E-mail: chrisbiggs.engineering@virgin.net

C E Edwards Engineers Ltd, Eagle Works, Leek New Road, Stoke-on-Trent, ST6 2LD Tel: (01782) 202400 Fax: (01782) 262781 E-mail: sales@ceedwards.co.uk

C H E Coach House Engineering Ltd, 23 Squares Road, Chilton Trinity, Bridgwater, Somerset, TA5 2BW Tel: (01278) 456557 Fax: (01278) 456557

C H E Coach House Engineering Ltd, 23 Squares Road, Chilton Trinity, Bridgwater, Somerset, TA5 2BW Tel: (01278) 456557 Fax: (01278) 456557

C H K Engineering Ltd, Pyms Lane, Crewe, CW1 3PJ Tel: (01270) 255520 Fax: (01270) 211263 E-mail: sales@chk-engineering.co.uk

▶ C & J Fabrications Ltd, Unit 5 & 6 Scout Bottom Business, Park Waterfoot, Rossendale, Lancashire, BB4 9JR Tel: (01706) 250084 Fax: (01706) 211113

C L S Offshore Ltd, Bessemer Way, Harfreys Industrial Estate, Great Yarmouth, Norfolk, NR31 0LX Tel: (01493) 668730 Fax: (01493) 667548 E-mail: info@clsoffshore.co.uk

C M F Ltd, Falcon Way, Feltham, Middlesex, TW14 0XJ Tel: (020) 8844 0940 Fax: (020) 8751 5793 E-mail: info@cmf.co.uk

C & M Welding Services, Crabtree Road, Thorpe Industrial Estate, Egham, Surrey, TW20 8RN Tel: (01784) 438127 Fax: (01784) 470223

C P Steel, Salamanca Road, Tharston, Norwich, NR15 2PF Tel: (01508) 531316 Fax: (01508) 531364

C & R Fabrications, Abbey Hill Trading Estate, Stourton Way, Yeovil, Somerset, BA21 3AR Tel: (01935) 427940 Fax: (01935) 414728

C T Farr, Timothys Bridge Road, Stratford-upon-Avon, Warwickshire, CV37 9NQ Tel: (01789) 267161 Fax: (01789) 415719

C U Lighting Ltd, 35 Westgate, Cleckheaton, West Yorkshire, BD19 5LE Tel: (01274) 876887 Fax: (01274) 876888

C.W. (Industrial) Fans Ltd, Unit 25, Thornleigh Trading Estate, Dudley, West Midlands, DY2 8UB Tel: (01384) 211010 Fax: (01384) 238086

Cadnam Metalcraft, Southampton Road, Cadnam, Southampton, SO40 2NB Tel: (023) 8081 2489 Fax: (023) 8081 2976 E-mail: cadnammetalcraft@btconnect.com

Caldwell Metalwork Fabrication, Units 10-11 Shaftsbury Industrial Estate, Icknield Way, Letchworth Garden City, Hertfordshire, SG6 1HE Tel: (01462) 670505 Fax: (01462) 670500

Caletrim Fabrications Ltd, 7a Bowes Road, Middlesbrough, Cleveland, TS2 1LU Tel: (01642) 224121 Fax: (01642) 224121

Cambrian Foundry Ltd, Unit 34 Vastre Indust Estate, Kerry Road, Newtown, Powys, SY16 1DZ Tel: (01686) 626209 Fax: (01686) 629500 E-mail: camfound@hotmail.com

Cameo Engineering Ltd, Unit 20 Brookside Business Park, Cold Meece, Stone, Staffordshire, ST15 0RZ Tel: (01785) 761134 Fax: (01785) 761837

Camlock Engineering Ltd, Unit 12F, Thorn Business Park, Rotherwas, Hereford, HR2 6JT Tel: (01432) 279553 Fax: (01432) 266010 E-mail: camlock@tactronics.com

Campbell Engineering, Gosforth Road, Derby, DE24 8HU Tel: (01332) 347344 Fax: (01332) 364385

STEEL FABRICATORS – *continued*

Cannon Steels Ltd, 22 Walcot Road, Enfield, Middlesex, EN3 7NF Tel: (020) 8805 4070 Fax: (020) 8805 4525 E-mail: enquiries@cannonsteelsltd.co.uk

Caparo Fabrications Ltd, Macrome Road, Tettenhall, Wolverhampton, WV6 9HF Tel: (01902) 753041 Fax: (01902) 742375

Capital Steel Fabrications, 21-23 Parkhouse Street, London, SE5 7TQ Tel: (020) 7252 5445 Fax: (020) 7703 5212

▶ Capital Steelworks, Unit 1 Kingsnorth Works, Hoo, Rochester, Kent, ME3 9NZ Tel: (01634) 256420 Fax: (01634) 255938 E-mail: capsteelltd@aol.com

Carnwood Engineering Ltd, Penn Industrial Estate, Providence Street, Cradley Heath, West Midlands, B64 5DJ Tel: (01384) 569787 Fax: (01384) 633508 E-mail: sales@carnwoodeng.co.uk

Castle Fabrication & Installation Ltd, 3a Cold Hesledon Industrial Estate, Cold Hesledon, Seaham, County Durham, SR7 8ST Tel: 0191-581 5177 Fax: 0191-581 4792 E-mail: sales@castlefab.com

Castlerigg Engineering Co. Ltd, Browfoot Works, Penrith Road, Keswick, Cumbria, CA12 4LH Tel: (01768) 772876 Fax: (01768) 772885 E-mail: info@castlerigg-eng.co.uk

Ced Fabrications Ltd, Clayton House, Clayton Business Park, Clayton le Moors, Accrington, Lancashire, BB5 5JD Tel: (01254) 238282 Fax: (01254) 238228 E-mail: sales@cedfabsltd.demon.co.uk

Ceejay Maintenance Ltd, Unit 49 Fairways Business Park, Lammas Road, London, E10 7QB Tel: (020) 8518 7644 Fax: (020) 8518 7678

▶ Central Steel Fabrications, 75-77 Chequers Lane, Dagenham, Essex, RM9 6QJ Tel: (020) 8592 7292 Fax: (020) 8517 4848 E-mail: centralsteelltd@aol.com

Centurian Products Ltd, 3-7 Bombay Street, London, SE16 3UX Tel: (020) 7237 2273 Fax: (020) 7231 8285 E-mail: sales@cent.demon.co.uk

Cgi, Wigwam Lane, Hucknall, Nottingham, NG15 7TA Tel: 0115-963 5991 Fax: 0115-968 0334

Channel Steel Fabrications Ltd, Brocklebank Industrial Estate, Brocklebank Road, London, SE7 7SX Tel: (020) 8858 6666

Chapway Fabrications, Charlton Mead Lane, Hoddesdon, Hertfordshire, EN11 0DJ Tel: (01992) 468028 Fax: (01992) 479720

Charles Kendrew Metal Workers Ltd, 33-35 Tower Street, Harrogate, North Yorkshire, HG1 1HS Tel: (01423) 502025 Fax: (01423) 531028 E-mail: enquiries@kendrews.co.uk

Cheshire Fabrications, Villa Farm, Sound Lane, Sound, Nantwich, Cheshire, CW5 8BE Tel: (01270) 780707 Fax: (01270) 780707

Chieftain Contracts Ltd, 33 Broomhill Road, Bonnybridge, Stirlingshire, FK4 2AL Tel: (01324) 812911 Fax: (01324) 814927

Cladburn Engineering Co., C Block 17 South Avenue, Blantyre Industrial Estate, Blantyre, Glasgow, G72 0XB Tel: (01698) 822550 Fax: (01698) 825130

Claire Fabrications, 1 Abbey Street, Birkenhead, Merseyside, CH41 5JG Tel: 0151-647 3399

Robert Clark & Sons (Steel Fabricators) Ltd, Wallace Road, Sheffield, S3 9UA Tel: 0114-273 7233 Fax: 0114-272 3532

Clydefab Fabricators, Upper Ingleston, Greenock, Renfrewshire, PA15 3AD Tel: (01475) 888918 Fax: (01475) 888918

Clydeside Steel Fabrications Ltd, 180 Hardgate Road, Glasgow, G51 4TB Tel: 0141-445 2898 Fax: 0141-445 6964 E-mail: fabs@bmsteel.co.uk

Coast & County Engineering, Enterprise Road, Mablethorpe, Lincolnshire, LN12 1NB Tel: (01507) 473170 Fax: (01507) 473170

Code-A-Weld, Units 5-10, Bessemer Way, Harfreys Industrial Estate, Great Yarmouth, Norfolk, NR31 0LX Tel: (01493) 602844 Fax: (01493) 653331 E-mail: codeaweld@btinternet.com

▶ W. & D. Cole Ltd, Ashford Road, Bethersden, Ashford, Kent, TN26 3AT Tel: (01233) 820240 Fax: (01233) 820805 E-mail: emailus@wdcole.com

Coles, Steam Mill Lane, Great Yarmouth, Norfolk, NR31 0HP Tel: (01493) 602100 Fax: (01493) 602100

Colne Valley Engineering, Unit 12 Olds Close, Watford, WD18 9RU Tel: (01923) 776212 Fax: (01923) 896587 E-mail: alanhughes@tesco.net

▶ Composite Systems, Gortrush Industrial Estate, Great Northern Road, Omagh, County Tyrone, BT78 5LU Tel: (028) 8224 8046 Fax: (028) 8224 8047 E-mail: info@compositedesign.ltd.uk

Comtec Precision Sheet Metal, 60 Loverock Road, Reading, RG30 1DY Tel: 0118-958 8050 Fax: 0118-958 8040 E-mail: sales@comtecsheet.softnet.co.uk

Concept Balustrades Ltd, Unit 9, Papermill Road, Cardiff, CF11 8DH Tel: (029) 2022 0040 Fax: (029) 2034 4402 E-mail: enq@conceptbalustrades.co.uk

Conibear Bros, Unit 2 Commercial Road Businness Park, Lords Meadow Industrial Estate, Crediton, Devon, EX17 1ER Tel: (01363) 772911 Fax: (01363) 772185

▶ Constructional Steelwork, Unit 3, 204 Oldbury Road, West Bromwich, West Midlands, B70 9DE Tel: 0121-525 8766

Contact Services (W R) Ltd, Paddock Works, 149A Shay Lane, Halifax, West Yorkshire, HX3 6RR Tel: (01422) 349536 Fax: (01422) 349468

▶ Contour Steel Fabrication Services, Paynes Business Park, Dereham Road, Beeston, King's Lynn, Norfolk, PE32 2NQ Tel: (01328) 701574 Fax: (01328) 701542

Contract Trade And Professional Ltd, Duchy Business Centre, Wilson Way, Pool, Redruth, Cornwall, TR15 3RT Tel: (01209) 314644 Fax: (01209) 314944 E-mail: sales@cornish-steel.co.uk

Ron Cook Engineers, 48-50 Oxford Street, Hull, HU2 0QP Tel: (01482) 327187 Fax: (01482) 213658

W.A. Cooke & Sons Engineers (Est 1926) Ltd, Southern Street, Walkden, Worsley, Manchester, M28 3QN Tel: (01204) 574721 Fax: (01204) 861778 E-mail: admin@wacooke.co.uk

Leonard Cooper Ltd, Balm Road, Leeds, LS10 2JR Tel: 0113-270 5441 Fax: 0113-276 0659 E-mail: sales@leonardcooperltd.co.uk

Corkery Construction Ltd, 15 Linnet Avenue, Paddock Wood, Tonbridge, Kent, TN12 6XG Tel: (01892) 838097 Fax: (01892) 834030 E-mail: michcrkry@aol.com

Cotswold Steel Stockholders Ltd, Unit 1m2 Babdown Industrial Estate, Babdown, Tetbury, Gloucestershire, GL8 8YL Tel: (01666) 504889 Fax: (01666) 504891 E-mail: james@cotswoldsteels.com

County Fabrications Leicester Ltd, B1 Valley Way, Market Harborough, Leicestershire, LE16 7PS Tel: (01858) 433958 Fax: (01858) 410463 E-mail: contact@countyfabs.co.uk

Coventry Construction Ltd, Torrington Avenue, Coventry, CV4 9AP Tel: (024) 7646 2321 Fax: (024) 7669 4020 E-mail: info@covcon.co.uk

Cozens Smith, The Common, Cranleigh, Surrey, GU6 8SB Tel: (01483) 273131 Fax: (01483) 268238

Craft Metal Products, Unit 18 Birksland Industrial Estate, Bradford, West Yorkshire, BD4 8TY Tel: (01274) 731531 Fax: (01274) 731531

Craig & Buchanan Ltd, 23 Lochburn Road, Glasgow, G20 9AE Tel: 0141-946 2007 Fax: 0141-945 2100 E-mail: shona@craigbuchanan.co.uk

Craintern Ltd, 13-17 Haltwhistle Road, South Woodham Ferrers, Chelmsford, CM3 5ZA Tel: (01245) 322438 Fax: (01245) 328926 E-mail: mailbox@ctlmedical.co.uk

Craufurd Engineering Services Ltd, Unit 4-5 Lower Mount Farm, Cookham, Maidenhead, Berkshire, SL6 9EE Tel: (01628) 532288 Fax: (01628) 532424

Tony Craze Welding & Fabrication, 13 United Downs Industrial Park, St. Day, Redruth, Cornwall, TR16 5HY Tel: (01209) 821166 Fax: (01209) 821864 E-mail: steel@tonycraze.net

Creighton & Son Ltd, 2 Parr Road, Stanmore, Middlesex, HA7 1QA Tel: (020) 8952 8252 Fax: (020) 8951 1434 E-mail: metalman@btconnect.com

Crescent Engineering & Technical Services Ltd, Unit 5, Lee Smith Street, Hull, HU9 1SD Tel: (01482) 329625 Fax: (01482) 581130

Crime Beat Security, 388 High Road, Ilford, Essex, IG1 1TL Tel: (020) 8478 4999 Fax: (020) 8478 7722 E-mail: sales@crimebeatsecurity.co.uk

Crossways Tanks & Fabrications Ltd, Vanguard Road, Gapton Hall Industrial Estate, Great Yarmouth, Norfolk, NR31 0NT Tel: (01493) 661156 Fax: (01493) 661159 E-mail: sales@crossways-tanks.co.uk

Crown Engineering Co., Unit 9 Hedgend Industrial Estate, Shuart Lane, St. Nicholas at Wade, Birchington, Kent, CT7 0NB Tel: (01843) 845300 Fax: (01843) 848352 E-mail: enquiries@crownengineering.co.uk

▶ Crown Structural Engineering, Burma Road, Blidworth, Mansfield, Nottinghamshire, NG21 0RT Tel: (01623) 490555 Fax: (01623) 490666 E-mail: enquiries@crownstructuralengineering.co.uk

Currie Of Airdrie Ltd, Deanston Factory, 36 Glencraig Street, Airdrie, Lanarkshire, ML6 9AS Tel: (01236) 764218 Fax: (01236) 764218

CVH Fabrications, Unit 2a Crown Works, Little Poutney Street, Wolverhampton, WV2 4JH Tel: (01902) 426020 Fax: (01902) 425726

D & A Fabrications Ltd, Barn House, Red House Lane, Eccleston, Chorley, Lancashire, PR7 5RH Tel: (01257) 452181

▶ D B S Engineering, Tilbury Docks Industrial Complex, Tilbury, Essex, RM18 7EH Tel: (01375) 842202 Fax: (01375) 844144

D & D Fabrications, Mariner, Tamworth, Staffordshire, B79 7UL Tel: (01827) 53159 Fax: (01827) 53597

D & D Fabrications Runcorn, Old Power Station, Percival Lane, Runcorn, Cheshire, WA7 4YR Tel: (01928) 569203 Fax: (01928) 569203

D & D James, Bryn Myfyr, High Street, Coedpoeth, Wrexham, Clwyd, LL11 3UF Tel: (01978) 756611 Fax: (01978) 756611

D E S Fabrications Ltd, Littleton Lane, Shepperton, Middlesex, TW17 0NF Tel: (01932) 563616 Fax: (01932) 570933 E-mail: denise@desgroupltd.co.uk

D G T Steel & Cladding Ltd, Atlas Works, Norwich Road, Lenwade, Norwich, NR9 5SW Tel: (01603) 308200 Fax: (01603) 308201 E-mail: sales@dgt-steelandcladding.co.uk

D J Installations & Fabrications, The Cottage, Backworth, Newcastle upon Tyne, NE27 0AP Tel: 0191-268 4215 Fax: 0191-268 4215

D J Williams & Son, H Peblig Mill, Llanbeblig Road, Caernarfon, Gwynedd, LL55 2SE Tel: (01286) 673254 Fax: (01286) 672007

D.L.D. Engineering, Foundry Yard, Hall La, Walton On The Naze, Essex, CO14 8HW Tel: (01255) 671722 Fax: (01255) 671722 E-mail: sales@dldeng.fsnet.co.uk

▶ D M A Engineering, F Sams Lane, West Bromwich, West Midlands, B70 7EX Tel: 0121-553 7370 Fax: 0121-553 7626

D P L, Elliott Works, Elliott Road, Bromley, BR2 9NT Tel: (020) 8460 2147 Fax: (020) 8313 3072 E-mail: sales@dplaw.co.uk

D P S Fabrications Ltd, East Hanningfield Industrial Estate, Chelmsford, CM3 5BX Tel: (01245) 400161 Fax: (01245) 400435

D & R, Unit 4 Long Furrow, East Goscote, Leicester, LE7 3ZL Tel: 0116-260 6530 Fax: 0116-269 7283

D & R Fabrications Ltd, Mill Farm Yard, Darnhall, Winsford, Cheshire, CW7 4DG Tel: (01270) 528105 Fax: (01270) 528109 E-mail: info@drfabrications.co.uk

D & R Structures Ltd, 7 Lidsey Road, Woodgate, Chichester, West Sussex, PO20 3SU Tel: (01243) 544838 Fax: (01243) 544840

D V R Fabrications, Unit 10 Winster Grove Industrial Estate, Winster Grove, Birmingham, B44 9EG Tel: 0121-325 0087 Fax: 0121-325 0087

D W Engineering, Unit A1 Industrial Estate, Watling Street, Consett, County Durham, DH8 6TA Tel: (01207) 505608 Fax: (01207) 505608

Dales Engineering Ltd, Dales Industrial Estate, Peterhead, Aberdeenshire, AB42 3JF Tel: (01779) 478778 Fax: (01779) 471846 E-mail: sales@dalesgroup.co.uk

Daleside Welding, Gowrey Farm, Wandales Lane, Kirkby Lonsdale, Carnforth, Lancashire, LA6 2JN Tel: (01524) 272312 Fax: (01524) 273123

Danson Steel Ltd, C Kingsbridge Wharf, Kingsbridge Road, Barking, Essex, IG11 0BD Tel: (020) 8507 8921 Fax: (020) 8507 8746 E-mail: danson@barking57.fsnet.co.uk

Dappat Engineering Ltd, Hodgson Street, Hull, HU8 7JB Tel: (01482) 328872 Fax: (01482) 223265

Daro Engineering Stafford Ltd, Unit 7a & 7b Dewick Depot, Cannock Road, Brocton, Stafford, ST17 0SU Tel: (01785) 660391 Fax: (01785) 665347 E-mail: office@daroengineering.co.uk

▶ Dart Meet Services, Pipers Close, Pennygillam Industrial Estate, Launceston, Cornwall, PL15 7PJ Tel: (01566) 777488 Fax: (01566) 777488

Das Fabrications Ltd, Ajax Works, Whitehill Street, Stockport, Cheshire, SK4 1NT Tel: 0161-476 1222 Fax: 0161-476 1333 E-mail: dave@dasfabs.fsbusiness.co.uk

Datel Products Ltd, Morgan Rushford Trading Estate, Providence Street, Stourbridge, West Midlands, DY9 8HS Tel: (01384) 893589 Fax: (01384) 893589

Datona Ltd, Unit 1 Addington Park Industrial Estate, Irthlingborough Road, Little Addington, Kettering, Northamptonshire, NN14 4AS Tel: (01933) 651561 Fax: (01933) 411873

David Williams Llandudno Ltd, 4 Builder Street, Llandudno, Gwynedd, LL30 1DR Tel: (01492) 876869 Fax: (01492) 870664

Davidson Sheet Metal, Bourtree House, Minto Drive, Altens, Aberdeen, AB12 3LW Tel: (01224) 897676 Fax: (01224) 895199 E-mail: enquiry@hutcheon-services.ltd.uk

Davley Fabrications Ltd, Drakes Indust Estate, Shay Lane, Ovenden, Halifax, West Yorkshire, HX3 6RL Tel: (01422) 355982 Fax: (01422) 355984 E-mail: sales@davleyfabrications.co.uk

Dayton Engineering Ltd, Unit 1-4 Tir Llwyd Industrial Estate, Kinmel Bay, Rhyl, Clwyd, LL18 5JA Tel: (01745) 336457 Fax: (01745) 354247E-mail: info@dayton-engineering.co.uk

Dearneside Fabrications, Trafalgar Works, Wallace Road, Sheffield, S3 9SR Tel: 0114-241 9540 Fax: 0114-278 7681

▶ Deconsys Technology Ltd, Macart House, Farnham Road, Bradford, West Yorkshire, BD7 3JG Tel: (01274) 521700 Fax: (01274) 521700 E-mail: info@deconsys.co.uk

Delmark Engineering, Unit 26 V I P Trading Estate, 50 Anchor & Hope Lane, London, SE7 7TE Tel: (020) 8305 1919 Fax: (020) 8853 1509 E-mail: sales@delmark.co.uk

Delta, 15 Brook Road, Kimbolton, Huntingdon, Cambridgeshire, PE28 0LR Tel: (01480) 861154 Fax: (01480) 861134 E-mail: info@deltafabrications.com

Delta Systems Electrical, 65 Boleness Road, Wisbech, Cambridgeshire, PE13 2RB Tel: (01945) 466866 Fax: (01945) 466108 E-mail: sales@deltasystems-uk.co.uk

▶ Dendrite Fabrications, 18 Gordon Close, Leek, Staffordshire, ST13 8NZ Tel: (07785) 325342 Fax: (01538) 384789 E-mail: jasonbanks@worldonline.co.uk

Denmay Steel & Hire Co., 137 Wellington Road, Portslade, Brighton, BN41 1DN Tel: (01273) 430399 Fax: (01273) 430799

Denmic Engineering Ltd, 7 Linburn Close, Royston, Barnsley, South Yorkshire, S71 4NB Tel: (01226) 701887 Fax: (01226) 701096

▶ Designer Metal Products, 40 Cromwell Industrial Estate, Staffa Road, London, E10 7QZ Tel: (020) 8558 9239

Devoran Metals, Devoran Joinery Works, Greenbank Road, Devoran, Truro, Cornwall, TR3 6PQ Tel: (01872) 863376 Fax: (01872) 862123 E-mail: sales@devoran-metals.co.uk

Dial Precision Engineering Ltd, Dial House Dutton Green, Stanney Mill Industrial Park, Little Stanney, Chester, CH2 4SA Tel: 0151-357 2016 Fax: 0151-355 0751 E-mail: warren@dial-eng.co.uk

Diamar Fabrications Ltd, Unit 6 North St Trading Estate, Brierley Hill, West Midlands, DY5 3QF Tel: (01384) 480528 Fax: (01384) 480528

Discain Project Services Ltd, Crow Lane, Little Billing, Northampton, NN3 9BZ Tel: (01604) 787276 Fax: (01604) 407290 E-mail: discain@discain.co.uk

DJS Welding Services & R & J Pipe Work, Norwich Road, Brooke, Norwich, NR15 1HJ Tel: (01508) 550177 Fax: (01508) 558011 E-mail: mike@rjpipe.demon.co.uk

Donyal Holdings Ltd, Unit 7 Hobson Industrial Estate, Hobson, Newcastle upon Tyne, NE16 6EA Tel: (01207) 270909 Fax: (01207) 270333

Dorchester Fabrications, Unit 32 Casterbridge Industrial Estate, Casterbridge, Dorchester, Dorset, DT1 1PL Tel: (01305) 267733

Doublewood Engineering, 4 Enterprise Court, Station Road, Witham, Essex, CM8 2TJ Tel: (01376) 517337 Fax: (01376) 517337

Douglas Buildings, Syke Road, Wigton, Cumbria, CA7 9NG Tel: (01697) 478690 Fax: (01697) 349073

Drillfield Engineering Co. Ltd, Scott Works, Unit 1, Mannor Road, Mancetter, Atherstone, Warwickshire, CV9 1RG Tel: (01827) 712468 Fax: (01827) 714252

Droitwich Road Aquatics, Droitwich Road, Claines, Worcester, WR3 7SW Tel: (01905) 757376 Fax: (01905) 452242

Ductavent Ltd, Gerrard Place, Skelmersdale, Lancashire, WN8 9SG Tel: (01695) 720368 Fax: (01695) 50618 E-mail: ductavents@aol.com

Dunninghams Ltd, 16 Manor Road Dovercourt, Harwich, Essex, CO12 4DU Tel: (01255) 502497 Fax: (01255) 241707 E-mail: sales@g-dunningham.co.uk

Dyer Welding Services Ltd, West Bank Terminal, Wherstead Road, Ipswich, IP2 8NB Tel: (01473) 602101 Fax: (01473) 680459 E-mail: enquiries@dyerwelding.com

E A & H Sandford Lifting Ltd, Albion Parade, Gravesend, Kent, DA12 2RN Tel: (01474) 365361 Fax: (01474) 569036

E Jones Engineering, Gweldir, Bancyffordd, Llandysul, Dyfed, SA44 4SD Tel: (01559) 384941 Fax: (01559) 384941

E K W Fabrications Ltd, Coppice Side Industrial Estate, West Coppice Road, Walsall, WS8 7HB Tel: (01543) 378181 Fax: (01543) 361012

E & P Engineering Services, 16 St Nicholas Road, Littlestone, New Romney, Kent, TN28 8PT Tel: (01797) 366724

E S Hadley, Foundry Yard, Hall Lane, Walton on the Naze, Essex, CO14 8HW Tel: (01255) 679913 Fax: (01255) 850932 E-mail: efhadleyeng@aol.com

Easiflo Engineering Ltd, Providence Street, Stourbridge, West Midlands, DY9 8HR Tel: (01384) 894811 Fax: (01384) 422447 E-mail: easiflo.eng@btconnect.com

Easiflo Fabrications, 4 Building 64, Third Avenue, Pensnett Trading Estate, Kingswinford, West Midlands, DY6 7XX Tel: (01384) 279245 Fax: (01384) 400030

East Goscote Fabrications 1992 Ltd, 2 The Warren, East Goscote, Leicester, LE7 3XA Tel: 0116-260 6161 Fax: 0116-264 0759

East Yorkshire Engineering, Unit B 133 Marfleet Avenue, Hull, HU9 5SA Tel: (01482) 788008 Fax: (01482) 788008

Eastern Hardware Co. Ltd, Hamilton Road, Lowestoft, Suffolk, NR32 1XF Tel: (01502) 573257 Fax: (01502) 586235 E-mail: eastern_hardware@btconnect.com

Eden Wood Structures, 81 Ashgrove Road, Newry, County Down, BT34 1QJ Tel: (028) 3026 6863 Fax: (028) 3026 2599

Richard Edwards Fabrications Ltd, 15 Broadfield Close, Croydon, CR0 4XR Tel: (020) 8686 8616 Fax: (020) 8686 5313

Ellco UK Ltd, Nile Street, Stoke-on-Trent, ST6 2AZ Tel: (01782) 837160 Fax: (01782) 837160

Elliott & Wragg Ltd, Elliott & Wragg, Buxton Road, Tideswell, Buxton, Derbyshire, SK17 8PQ Tel: (01298) 871582 Fax: (01298) 871785

Ellis Engineering & Welding Services, Salmon Road, Great Yarmouth, Norfolk, NR30 3QS Tel: (01493) 842690 Fax: (01493) 842690 E-mail: ellisengineering@btconnect.com

Elsome Engineering Ltd, Welby Road, Asfordby Hill, Melton Mowbray, Leicestershire, LE14 3RD Tel: (01664) 813234 Fax: (01664) 813341 E-mail: sales@elsomes.com

Elstone Engineering Co., Earlsway, Teesside Industrial Estate, Stockton-on-Tees, Cleveland, TS17 9JU Tel: (01642) 769442 Fax: (01642) 763068

Engineering & Maintenance Services, Unit 75a Gibbons Industrial Park, Dudley Road, Kingswinford, West Midlands, DY6 8XF Tel: (01384) 400147 Fax: (01384) 400148

Enterpriseforce Metal Pressing, Unit 3c-Unit 3d Canal Estate, Station Road, Langley, Slough, SL3 6EG Tel: (01753) 585018 Fax: (01753) 542685 E-mail: david@dmpgroup.co.uk

Ermine Engineering Company Ltd, Francis House Silver Birch Park, Great Northern Terrace, Lincoln, LN5 8LG Tel: (01522) 510977 Fax: (01522) 510929 E-mail: info@ermineengineering.co.uk

Essex Wirework Company Ltd, PO Box 1, Hockley, Essex, SS5 5LD Tel: (01702) 205022 Fax: (01702) 207678

STEEL FABRICATORS – *continued*

Euro Spec, Unit 7 Drakes Lane, Boreham, Chelmsford, CM3 3BE Tel: (01245) 362551 Fax: (01245) 360522 E-mail: sales@euro-spec.co.uk

Euro Tanks, 4 Heritage Way, Corby, Northamptonshire, NN17 5XW Tel: (01536) 201006 Fax: (01536) 400140 E-mail: sales@eurotanks.co.uk

European Coatings Ltd, Sandwich Industrial Estate, Ramsgate Road, Sandwich, Kent, CT13 9LY Tel: (01304) 621121 Fax: (01304) 621535

Evadx Ltd, Tir Llwyd Enterprise Park, Kinmel Bay, Rhyl, Clwyd, LL18 5JZ Tel: (01745) 336413 Fax: (01745) 339639 E-mail: sales@evadx.com

Evans Ltd, 11 St James Industrial Estate, Westhampnett Road, Chichester, West Sussex, PO19 7JU Tel: (07976) 444316 Fax: (01243) 530828 E-mail: john@evanswelding.com

Evenwood Engineering Ltd, Evenwood, Bishop Auckland, County Durham, DL14 9NJ Tel: (01388) 832556 Fax: (01388) 832966

Excalibur Group Holdings, Excalibur House, First Avenue, Crewe, CW1 6UG Tel: (01270) 252405 Fax: (01270) 581010 E-mail: mark@radwayeng.co.uk

Exitile Ltd, 49-61 Jodrell Street, Nuneaton, Warwickshire, CV11 5EG Tel: (024) 7635 2771 Fax: (024) 7635 2761 E-mail: sales@exitile.com

Express Fabrications Ltd, 85 Cyncoed Road, Cardiff, CF23 5SD Tel: (029) 2046 4365 Fax: (029) 2073 6898

F G Stacy, Moor Park, Clawton, Holsworthy, Devon, EX22 6PQ Tel: (01409) 211201 Fax: (01409) 211565

F & J Hauck Ltd, Linney Lane, Shaw, Oldham, OL2 8HB Tel: (01706) 848797 Fax: (01706) 844973

▶ F L S Steel Structures Ltd, Garratt Street, Brierley Hill, West Midlands, DY5 1JU Tel: (01384) 484200 Fax: (01384) 484202

F R Fletcher & Son Ltd, Carterton Industrial Estate, Black Bourton Road, Carterton, Oxfordshire, OX18 3EZ Tel: (01993) 844887 Fax: (01993) 840499 E-mail: frfletcher@tiscali.co.uk

Fab Signs & Structures UK Ltd, The Boiler House, Thames Industrial Park, Princess Margaret Road, East Tilbury, Tilbury, Essex, RM18 8RL Tel: (01375) 846815 Fax: (01375) 845250 E-mail: fred@fabsignsandstructures.co.uk

Fabco, 33a Groganstown, Dunmurry, Belfast, BT17 0NR Tel: (028) 9062 6666 Fax: (028) 9062 6666

Fabfold Ltd, Amington Industrial Estate, 30 Sandy Way, Tamworth, Staffordshire, B77 4DS Tel: (01827) 313396 Fax: (01827) 313289 E-mail: fabfold@fabfold.fsnet.co.uk

Fabricolor Ltd, Foley Business Park, Kidderminster, Worcestershire, DY11 7PT Tel: (01562) 744587 Fax: (01562) 865825 E-mail: enquiries@fabricolor.co.uk

Fairfield Mabey Ltd, Off Station Road, Chepstow, Gwent, NP16 5YL Tel: (01291) 623801 Fax: (01291) 625453 E-mail: mail@fairfieldmabey.com

Fairwood Fabrications Ltd, Docks Road, The Docks, Port Talbot, West Glamorgan, SA13 1RA Tel: (01639) 898002 Fax: (01639) 881908 E-mail: ssharp@fairwoodfabrications.com

Falcon Fabrications, Southlands Farms, Oakhanger, Bordon, Hampshire, GU35 9JD Tel: (01420) 489444 Fax: (01420) 489444

Farnworth & Langan Blackburn Ltd, Unit 6 Stancliffe Street Industrial Estate, Blackburn, BB2 2QR Tel: (01254) 676935 Fax: (01254) 680113 E-mail: farnworth-langan@btconnect.com

Federated Industries Ltd, 30-36 Virginia Street, Aberdeen, AB11 5AU Tel: (01224) 591323 Fax: (01224) 572858 E-mail: federated@btconnect.com

Fenweld Steel Fabricators, Bramley Road, St. Ives, Cambridgeshire, PE27 3WS Tel: (01480) 300877 Fax: (01480) 492120

Ferguson Marine plc, Castle Road, Port Glasgow, Renfrewshire, PA14 5NG Tel: (01475) 742300 Fax: (01475) 741269 E-mail: davehe@fergusons6.demon.co.uk

Ferrite Fabrications Ltd, 1 Wrights Yard, Top Road, Wimbish, Saffron Walden, Essex, CB10 2XJ Tel: (01799) 599907 Fax: (01799) 599914

Findlay G W & Sons, 262 Alma Road, Enfield, Middlesex, EN3 7BB Tel: (020) 8805 0575 Fax: (020) 8805 0575

Fiscol Engineering, 85 Greenland CR, Southall, Middlesex, UB2 5ES Tel: (020) 8574 1065 Fax: (020) 8813 9780

Fix It Engineering, North Back Lane, Terrington, York, YO60 6NS Tel: (01653) 648446 Fax: (01653) 648293

FJS Services, Westfield Road, Manea, March, Cambridgeshire, PE15 0LN Tel: (01354) 680752 Fax: (01354) 680176

Fleming Fabrications Ltd, 2 Derby Road, London, N18 2PA Tel: (020) 8884 1752 Fax: (020) 8884 1756

Flexible Machining Systems Ltd, 2-3 Blatchford Road, Horsham, West Sussex, RH13 5QR Tel: (01403) 270466 Fax: (01403) 270458 E-mail: sales@fmsltd.co.uk

Flintshire Fabrications Ltd, St. Asaph Road, Lloc, Holywell, Clwyd, CH8 8RD Tel: (01352) 711701 Fax: (01352) 711817 E-mail: info@flintshirefabrications.com

Flowline Engineering (UK) Ltd, Trafford Park Road, Newbridge, Trafford Park, Manchester, M17 1HG Tel: 0161-872 1421 Fax: 0161-872 5247 E-mail: flowline01@aol.com

Ford Green Engineering Ltd, Clarence Road, Longton, Stoke-On-Trent, ST3 1AZ Tel: (01782) 342530 Fax: (01782) 599692 E-mail: mail@fge.co.uk

The Forge, 1 Alverstone Road, East Cowes, Isle of Wight, PO32 6NZ Tel: (01983) 292716 Fax: (01983) 282131 E-mail: forgewhip@rann5979.freeserve.co.uk

Forrest Precision Engineering Co. Ltd, 538 Edgefauld Road, Glasgow, G21 4NB Tel: 0141-557 3555 Fax: 0141-558 6216

Four Tees Engineers Ltd, 1 Dewar Close, Segensworth West, Fareham, Hampshire, PO15 5UB Tel: (01489) 885899 Fax: (01489) 885928 E-mail: admin@fourtees.co.uk

Foxhall Engineering, Delta House, Delta Way, Thorpe Industrial Estate, Egham, Surrey, TW20 8RX Tel: (01784) 472220 Fax: (01784) 472221 E-mail: foxhalleng@hotmail.co.uk

Frank Whitfield & Co., 126 English Street, Hull, HU3 2BT Tel: (01482) 227376 Fax: (01482) 227376

Franklin Mechanical Fittings, Unit 40 New Enterprise Workshop, Mount Street, Nechells, Birmingham, B7 5RD Tel: 0121-327 6493 Fax: 0121-327 6493

F.W. Frost (Engineers) Ltd, Bidewell Close, Drayton High Road, Norwich, NR8 6AP Tel: (01603) 867301 Fax: (01603) 261586 E-mail: sales@fwfrost-engineers.co.uk

William Fry & Co. Ltd, Mitre Works, Neasden Goods Depot, Neasden Lane, London, NW10 2UG Tel: (020) 8459 5141 Fax: (020) 8459 2290 E-mail: md@metalandwaste.com

Fulwood Fabrications Ltd, Farndale Road, Staveley, Chesterfield, Derbyshire, S43 3YN Tel: (01246) 477346 Fax: (01246) 280035 E-mail: sales@fulwood.uk.com

Fussey Piling Ltd, Lancaster Approach, North Killingholme, Immingham, South Humberside, DN40 3JZ Tel: (01469) 540644 Fax: (01469) 540849 E-mail: info@fusseyengineering.com

Fyfe Welding Services Ltd, Western Harbour, Leith Docks, Edinburgh, EH6 6NT Tel: 0131-553 5536

G B Fabrication & Welding Services, Bunkers Hill, Bunkers Hill, Kidlington, Oxfordshire, OX5 3EL Tel: (07770) 761599 Fax: (01869) 331759 E-mail: julian.gbfabf@virgin.net

G & B Fabrications Services, Unit 20 Newfields Industrial Estate, High Street, Stoke-on-Trent, ST6 5PD Tel: (01782) 824600 Fax: (01782) 824700

▶ G & B Steelwork, Hope Farm, Gibbons Brook, Sellindge, Ashford, Kent, TN25 6HJ Tel: (01303) 813906 Fax: (01303) 813906

G B Welding Services Rutland Ltd, Unit 8 Pillings Road Industrial Estate, Oakham, Leicestershire, LE15 6QF Tel: (01572) 722764 Fax: (01572) 724347 E-mail: admin@gbwelding.co.uk

G C W Fabrications Ltd, Unit 23, James Carter Road, Bury St. Edmunds, Suffolk, IP28 7DE Tel: (01638) 515478 Fax: (01638) 717554

G C Welding, Stonelands Farm House, Withyham, Hartfield, East Sussex, TN7 4BH Tel: (01892) 861106 Fax: (01892) 861422

G D C Steel Fabrications Ltd, Unit H Adamson Industrial Estate, Croft Street, Hyde, Cheshire, SK14 1EE Tel: 0161-367 8990 Fax: 0161-367 8992 E-mail: gdcsteelfab@btconnect.com

G D R Fabrication, Unit 5 Trevol Business Park, Trevol Road, Torpoint, Cornwall, PL11 2TB Tel: (01752) 816262 Fax: (01752) 816263

G Mullen Steelwork Ltd, 114 Milton Road, Gravesend, Kent, DA12 2PG Tel: (01474) 325664 Fax: (01474) 328917 E-mail: sales@gmullensteelworks.fsnet.co.uk

G N J Engineering Ltd, Meeting Lane, Brierley Hill, West Midlands, DY5 3LB Tel: (01384) 480818 Fax: (01384) 78176 E-mail: info@gnjengineering.co.uk

G P Fabrications Ltd, 10-13 Ashmount Industrial Park, Ford Street, Kinsley, Pontefract, West Yorkshire, WF9 5EE Tel: (01977) 612226 Fax: (01977) 617220 E-mail: gary.gpfabs@sales.com

G R M Engineering & Contract Services Ltd, Ferry Lane, Snaith, Goole, North Humberside, DN14 9LL Tel: (01405) 861720 Fax: (01405) 861991 E-mail: davegrm@btconnect.com

G S Robinson & Co. Ltd, Unit B T 4 30 Exmouth Road, West Chirton Industrial Estate South, North Shields, Tyne & Wear, NE29 7TY Tel: 0191-257 5374 Fax: 0191-296 1341

Galemain Engineering Services Ltd, New Street, Holbrook Industrial Estate, Holbrook, Sheffield, S20 3GH Tel: 0114-247 3347 Fax: 0114-248 7301 E-mail: galemain@aol.com

Garmendale Engineering Ltd, Dale Works, Manners Industrial Estate, Ilkeston, Derbyshire, DE7 8EF Tel: 0115-932 7082 Fax: 0115-930 9391 E-mail: garmendale@enquiries.com

W. & G.W. Garratt Ltd, Upper Allen Street Works, Upper Allen Street, Sheffield, S3 7HA Tel: 0114-272 7094 Fax: 0114-272 0115 E-mail: enquiries@garrattsonline.com

Garwards Engineering, 8 Progress Way, Mid Suffolk Business Park, Eye, Suffolk, IP23 7HU Tel: (01379) 871337 Fax: (01379) 873041 E-mail: gareth@garwards.com

Gasarc Engineering, Triangle Works, Triangle North, Bath, BA2 3JB Tel: (01225) 421234 Fax: (01225) 425287

▶ Gates Architectual Metal Work, Alice Street Works, Alice Street, Morecambe, Lancashire, LA4 5NH Tel: (01524) 413513

Gateway Fabrications Ltd, Broad Lane, Gilberdyke, Brough, North Humberside, HU15 2TS Tel: (01430) 440185 Fax: (01430) 441850 E-mail: sales@bathroompods.com

Gem Engineering Ltd, Factory Road, Sandycroft, Deeside, Clwyd, CH5 2QJ Tel: (01244) 520859 Fax: (01244) 520328 E-mail: sales@gemengineering.co.uk

Gemweld Fabrications & Engineering Co. Ltd, Lancaster Way, Market Deeping, Peterborough, PE6 8LA Tel: (01778) 344733 Fax: (01778) 343988 E-mail: cam@gemweld.co.uk

General Engineering, 11 Seymour Street, Ballymoney, County Antrim, BT53 6JR Tel: (028) 2766 2454

General Services Fabrications Ltd, Sudmeadow Road, Gloucester, GL2 5HS Tel: (01452) 304515 Fax: (01452) 504729

George H Rigby & Son Ltd, 3 Liverpool Road, Great Sankey, Warrington, WA5 1ED Tel: (01925) 635267 Fax: (01925) 416744

GGD Engineering Ltd, Rashierieve Cottages, Newburgh, Ellon, Aberdeenshire, AB41 6AU Tel: (01358) 789920 Fax: (01358) 789919 E-mail: sales@ggdengineering.co.uk

Gibbs (General Engineering) Ltd, 7 High Street, Prestatyn, Clwyd, LL19 9AF Tel: (01745) 853759 Fax: (01745) 854360 E-mail: office@gibbsge.com

Glomac Engineering Ltd, Little End Road, Eaton Socon, St. Neots, Cambridgeshire, PE19 8JH Tel: (01480) 215533 Fax: (01480) 405952 E-mail: sales@glomac.co.uk

Goodall Services Ltd, 7 Davenport Centre, Renwick Road, Barking, Essex, IG11 0SH Tel: (020) 8592 2707 Fax: (020) 8592 5716

A.W. Grace & Son, Unit 124, Culham Site 1, Culham, Abingdon, Oxfordshire, OX14 3DA Tel: (01235) 531462 Fax: (01235) 534021 E-mail: info@awgrace.co.uk

Grange Engineering, Trenholme Bar, Northallerton, North Yorkshire, DL6 3LE Tel: (01642) 706074 Fax: (01642) 701641

Grantham Welding Ltd, Unit3 & 4 North Bank, Berry Hill Industrial Estate, Droitwich, Worcestershire, WR9 9AU Tel: (01905) 773335 Fax: (01905) 773335

Gray Engineering, Hirfron, Mountain, Holyhead, Gwynedd, LL65 1YW Tel: (01407) 760525 Fax: (01407) 760525 E-mail: contact@graysengineering.co.uk

Great Bridge Welding Co., Bagnall Street, Golds Hill, West Bromwich, West Midlands, B70 0TS Tel: 0121-557 2325

Green Arc Fabrications Ltd, Market Farm, Honey Pot Lane, Kemsing, Sevenoaks, Kent, TN15 6NT Tel: (01732) 761243 Fax: (01732) 763705

Griffiths Fabrications, Unit A10 Dovers Corner Industrial Estate, New Road, Rainham, Essex, RM13 8QT Tel: (01708) 523797 Fax: (01708) 522698

Gurso Plant & Lining Ltd, Landywood Lane, Cheslyn Hay, Walsall, WS6 7AL Tel: (01922) 418005 Fax: (01922) 412641 E-mail: sales@gurso.demon.co.uk

H & B Fabrication Ltd, John Street, Walkley Lane, Heckmondwike, West Yorkshire, WF16 0NA Tel: (01924) 412609 Fax: (01924) 412609

▶ H B S Engineering Co., Unit 11 2 Palatine Industrial Estate, Causeway Avenue, Warrington, WA4 6QQ Tel: (01925) 632388 Fax: (01925) 445904

H Case & Son Cradley Heath Ltd, Mount Works, Foxoak Street, Cradley Heath, West Midlands, B64 5DQ Tel: (01384) 566358 Fax: (01384) 634601 E-mail: sales@h-caseandson.co.uk

H Langdon & Son Chatham Ltd, 51-53 Second Avenue, Chatham, Kent, ME4 5BA Tel: (01634) 842485 Fax: (01634) 831037

H W Engineering Ltd, Cemetery Road, Ince, Wigan, Lancashire, WN3 4NN Tel: (01942) 866091 Fax: (01942) 863158

Had Fab Ltd, Macmerry Industrial Estate, Tranent, East Lothian, EH33 1RD Tel: (01875) 611711 Fax: (01875) 612711 E-mail: sales@hadfabltd.co.uk

Hagley Engineering Ltd, Blackbrook Road, Holly Hall, Dudley, West Midlands, DY2 0QP Tel: (01384) 261858 Fax: (01384) 77394 E-mail: hagleye@btconnect.com

Haigh & Ellis, St Andrews Road, Huddersfield, HD1 6SB Tel: (01484) 421647 Fax: (01484) 428324 E-mail: mark@haighandellis.fsbusiness.co.uk

Hailsham Structures Ltd, 2 Wentworth House, George Street, Hailsham, East Sussex, BN27 1AD Tel: (01323) 847545 Fax: (01323) 442223

Haley Engineering Ltd, Bellcombe, Brent Road, East Brent, Highbridge, Somerset, TA9 4DB Tel: (01278) 760591 Fax: (01278) 760587 E-mail: sales@haleyengineering.co.uk

Hall & Blenkinsop Ltd, Hetton Lyons Industrial Estate, Hetton-Le-Hole, Houghton Le Spring, Tyne & Wear, DH5 0RF Tel: 0191-526 2114 Fax: 0191-517 0112

Halyard Fabrications Ltd, 4 Whittle Road, Ferndown Industrial Estate, Wimborne, Dorset, BH21 7RW Tel: (01722) 710922 Fax: (01202) 894705

Handley Steel Ltd, Phoenix Works Industrial Estate, Richards Street, Wednesbury, West Midlands, WS10 8BZ Tel: 0121-568 6387 Fax: 0121-568 6387

Handmark Engineering, Unit 3c Park Road Industrial Estate, Park Road, Barrow-in-Furness, Cumbria, LA14 4EQ Tel: (01229) 835922 Fax: (01229) 877461 E-mail: enquiries@handmark-engineering.co.uk

Hares Of Snape Holdings Ltd, Manor House, Snape, Bedale, North Yorkshire, DL8 2TA Tel: (01677) 470269 Fax: (01677) 470681

Hart Metal Craft, Wivenhoe Business Centre, 23-24 Brook Street, Wivenhoe, Colchester, CO7 9DP Tel: (01206) 822017 Fax: (01206) 822017

Harvey Fabrication Ltd, Hancock Road, Bow, London, E3 3DA Tel: (020) 8981 7811 Fax: (020) 8981 7815

J.A. Harvey (Bassingham) Ltd, The Old Dairy, Navenby Lane, Bassingham, Lincoln, LN5 9JF Tel: (01522) 788111 Fax: (01522) 788195 E-mail: ja.harvey@btconnect.com

Harwoods For Steel Ltd, Whitegate Farm, Waterlooville, Hampshire, PO8 0TG Tel: (023) 9259 3442 Fax: (023) 9259 6010

Hawkesley Engineering Ltd, Unit 3, Avery Dell Industrial Estate, Birmingham, B30 3DZ Tel: 0121-433 4277 Fax: 0121-433 4280 E-mail: enquiries@hawkesley.co.uk

Hawkins Roofing Ltd, Unit 9 Thorpe Way, Banbury, Oxfordshire, OX16 4SP Tel: (01295) 252363 Fax: (01295) 251008 E-mail: hawkins-roofing@telinco.co.uk

Hawthorne Engineering Ltd, Unit 5 Hexthorpe Trading Park, Littlewood Street, Hexthorpe, Doncaster, South Yorkshire, DN4 0EJ Tel: (01302) 321990 Fax: (01302) 349939 E-mail: sales@hawthorneengineeringltd.co.uk

Hayes Industries Ltd, 2 Marchington Industrial Estate, Stubby Lane, Marchington, Uttoxeter, Staffordshire, ST14 8LP Tel: (01283) 820402 Fax: (01283) 820648 E-mail: enquiries@able-engineering.co.uk

A.J. Hayton Ltd, Bainsbeck Garage, Arkholme, Carnforth, Lancashire, LA6 1BA Tel: (01524) 222242 Fax: (01524) 222242

Charles Head Ltd, 78 Tavistock Street, Bletchley, Milton Keynes, MK2 2PN Tel: (01908) 372250 Fax: (01908) 371023 E-mail: sales@charles-head.co.uk

Helios Fabrications Ltd, Lakeside Business Park, Broadway Lane, South Ferney, Cirencester, Gloucestershire, GL7 5XL Tel: (01285) 869988 Fax: (01285) 869999

Helm Exhibitions Ltd, 27-29 Speedwell Road, Haymills, Birmingham, B25 8HU Tel: 0121-766 6755 Fax: 0121-766 6752 E-mail: enquiries@helmx.co.uk

Henderson Engineering (N E) Ltd, Vickers Close, Preston Farm Industrial Estate, Stockton-on-Tees, Cleveland, TS18 3TD Tel: (01642) 608008 Fax: (01642) 612636 E-mail: enquiries@hendersonengineering.com

Henry Isaac Fireplaces, The Foundry, St. Ippolyts, Hitchin, Hertfordshire, SG4 7NX Tel: (01462) 442588 Fax: (01462) 421618

Henry Lewis & Son Ltd, 7 Bolling Road, Bradford, West Yorkshire, BD4 7HN Tel: (01274) 307359 Fax: (01274) 370784

Hercules C S M D, Unit 14-16 Nelson Road, Townstal Industrial Estate, Dartmouth, Devon, TQ6 9LA Tel: (01803) 833736 Fax: (01803) 834846 E-mail: herculescsmd@aol.com

Heron Fabrications, Unit 4, Berry court farm, Little london, Basingstoke, Hampshire, RG26 5AT Tel: 01256 850963 Fax: 01256 850963 E-mail: info@heronfabrications.co.uk

Heskin Fabrications Ltd, Whalley Works, Whalley Road, Heskin, Chorley, Lancashire, PR7 5NY Tel: (01257) 451483 Fax: (01257) 453242 E-mail: heskinfabs@btconnect.co.uk

Highcliffe Engineering Ltd, Unit C Old Housecraft Yard, Church Street, Mexborough, South Yorkshire, S64 0HH Tel: (01709) 581656 Fax: (01709) 581656

J Hill, 1 Culm View, Honiton Road, Cullompton, Devon, EX15 1NX Tel: (01884) 841557 Fax: (01884) 841134

Hill & Webster Ltd, Ashbourne Indust Estate, Ashbourne, Derbyshire, DE6 1HD Tel: (01335) 343119 Fax: (01335) 346400 E-mail: hillwebster@compuserve.com

Hillside Metals Ltd, Cranborne Industrial Estate, Cranborne Road, Potters Bar, Hertfordshire, EN6 3JU Tel: (01707) 658131 Fax: (01707) 650777 E-mail: sales@hillsidemetals.com

Himanet, 125 Moor Street, Mansfield, Nottinghamshire, NG18 5SG Tel: (01623) 420646 Fax: (01623) 420646

Hiscock Engineers Trowbridge Ltd, 28 Union Street, Trowbridge, Wiltshire, BA14 8RY Tel: (01225) 752106 Fax: (01225) 751326

Hi-Tech Sheet Metal Ltd, Molyneux House, Unit B, Fort Road Ind Est, Fort Road, Littlehampton, West Sussex, BN17 7QU Tel: 01903 711222 Fax: 01903 711227 E-mail: sales@htsm-ltd.co.uk

Hoblongs Engineering, Hoblongs Industrial Estate, Chelmsford Road, Dunmow, Essex, CM6 1JA Tel: (01371) 874550 Fax: (01371) 872698

Hogg Engineering Ltd, Lawson Street, North Shields, Tyne & Wear, NE29 6TF Tel: 0191-259 5181 Fax: 0191-296 0641 E-mail: hogg-engineering@talk21.com

▶ Hollygate Fabrications, Delta Road, Audenshaw, Manchester, M34 5HR Tel: 0161-371 2630 Fax: 0161-371 9694 E-mail: sales@hollygate.co.uk

Hollygate Fabrications Ltd, The Hollygate, Chestergate, Stockport, Cheshire, SK3 0BD Tel: 0161-371 2630 Fax: 0161-371 9694 E-mail: tony@hollygate.co.uk

Houston's Of Cupar Ltd, Station House, Station Road, Cupar, Fife, KY15 5HX Tel: (01334) 655331 Fax: (01334) 656437 E-mail: sales@houstons.co.uk

▶ Howard Berkin, Victoria Road, Ripley, Derbyshire, DE5 3FX Tel: (01773) 513800 Fax: (01773) 513600 E-mail: howardberkin@tiscalli.co.uk

▶ indicates data change since last edition

STEEL FABRICATORS – *continued*

Howard Cole Developments Ltd, 4 Peterborough Road, Crowland, Peterborough, PE6 0BA Tel: (01733) 211351 Fax: (01733) 211441

Hubert Davies & Sons, The Green, Neath, West Glamorgan, SA11 1SE Tel: (01639) 643022

William Hustler & Sons Ltd, Henshaw Works, Henshaw Lane, Yeadon, Leeds, LS19 7RW Tel: 0113-250 3166 Fax: 0113-250 1272

Hydrapower Ltd, Middlemore Lane, Aldridge, Walsall, WS9 8SP Tel: (01922) 458760 Fax: (01922) 743186

Hyzed Engineering Ltd, Old Colliery Road, Graddfa Industrial Estate, Llanbradach, Caerphilly, Mid Glamorgan, CF83 3QS Tel: (029) 2088 4874 Fax: (029) 2085 1557

Icon Engineering, Europa Way, Wisbech, Wisbech, Cambridgeshire, PE13 2TZ Tel: (01945) 474411 Fax: (01945) 474144 E-mail: paul@icon-eng.co.uk

▶ Icon Welding Co. Ltd, Station Lane Industrial Estate, Station Lane, Old Whittington, Chesterfield, Derbyshire, S41 9QX Tel: (01246) 454618 Fax: (01246) 455618

Ilford Engineering Co. Ltd, Bentalls, Basildon, Essex, SS14 3BY Tel: (01268) 526756 Fax: (01268) 531485

Index Fabrications Southampton Ltd, Rochester Street, Southampton, SO14 5QW Tel: (023) 8063 1484 Fax: (023) 8063 1484 E-mail: indexfabs@aol.com

Industrial Metal Forms Ltd, Units 15 Wynford Industrial Trading Estate, Wynford Road, Birmingham, B27 6JP Tel: 0121-765 4800 Fax: 0121-765 4810

Paul Innes Construction Ltd, 47 Tennyson Avenue, Hartlepool, Cleveland, TS25 5NX Tel: (01429) 294276 Fax: (01429) 294276

Instant Installations, Station Lane, New Whittington, Chesterfield, Derbyshire, S43 2AF Tel: (01246) 260056 Fax: (01246) 260056 E-mail: sales@instantinstallationsltd.co.uk

Inter Steels Ltd, Darent Indust Park, Wallhouse Road, Erith, Kent, DA8 2JT Tel: (01322) 337766 Fax: (01322) 335662 E-mail: sales@intergroupofcompanies.net

Intrim Fabrications, The Workshop, Tyte Farm, Sandford, St. Martin, Oxford, OX7 7AH Tel: (01608) 683338 Fax: (01608) 683338

Invicta, Westland Square, Leeds, LS11 5SS Tel: 0113-277 1222 Fax: 0113-271 6860 E-mail: sale@invictafork.co.uk

Ireflo Products Ltd, 120 Broughton Road, London, SW6 2LB Tel: (020) 7736 2048 Fax: (020) 7384 2391 E-mail: sales@london-music.co.uk

Isleburn Structural Services, Delny Industrial Estate, Invergordon, Ross-Shire, IV18 0QW Tel: (01862) 843910 Fax: (01862) 843919 E-mail: enquiries@isleburnss.demon.co.uk

J A Clark & Co Engineers Ltd, Charrold Works, Stephenson Way, Thetford, Norfolk, IP24 3RJ Tel: (01842) 752348 Fax: (01842) 755194 E-mail: sales@jaclark.co.uk

J A G Services Ltd, 13 Reform Road, Maidenhead, Berkshire, SL6 8BY Tel: (01628) 670909 Fax: (01628) 672016 E-mail: gstuart@jagservices.fsnet.co.uk

J B Developments, Rose Cottage, New Gilston, Leven, Fife, KY8 5TF Tel: (01334) 840512 Fax: (01334) 840640

J B Engineering, Scropton Road, Hatton, Derby, DE65 5DS Tel: (01283) 812348 Fax: (01283) 812230 E-mail: info@jbeng-hatton.co.uk

▶ J B Fabrication, 71 London Street, Leicester, LE5 3RW Tel: 0116-246 1204 Fax: 0116-246 1204

J & E Fabrications Ltd, Unit 25A, Blythe Park, Cresswell Lane, Cresswell, Stoke-on-Trent, ST11 9RD Tel: (01782) 388011 Fax: (01782) 388004 E-mail: jandefabs@aol.com

J E Jenkins, 7 Eye Green Industries, Crowland Road, Eye, Peterborough, PE6 7SZ Tel: (01733) 223650 Fax: (01733) 223650

J E Matthews & Sons Ltd, Southbridge, Cotton End, Northampton, NN4 8BS Tel: (01604) 762188 Fax: (01604) 705218 E-mail: matthews@cottonendfsbusiness.co.uk

J E T Engineering, Ditton Road, Widnes, Cheshire, WA8 0TH Tel: 0151-423 5273 Fax: 0151-495 1390 E-mail: sales@jet-engineering.co.uk

J Forrest, Knowepark, Meikle Wartle, Inverurie, Aberdeenshire, AB51 5BA Tel: (01467) 671415 Fax: (01467) 671415 E-mail: jfengineering@btinternet.com

J G Tinkler Ltd, Bowesfield Lane, Stockton-on-Tees, Cleveland, TS18 3HJ Tel: (01642) 675797 Fax: (01642) 673193 E-mail: jgtinklerltd@aol.com

J Hesketh Engineering Ltd, Wilcock Street, Wigan, Lancashire, WN3 4AR Tel: (01942) 245114 Fax: (01942) 820240

J Luke, 101B High Rd, Beeston, Nottingham, NG9 2LH Tel: 0115-925 5616 Fax: 0115-925 5616 E-mail: jdluke@btconect.com

J M Fabweld Ltd, Llewellyns Quay, Port Talbot, West Glamorgan, SA13 1RF Tel: (01639) 884550 Fax: (01639) 891015 E-mail: jmfabwellltd@btconnect.com

J & M Profile Services Ltd, Vauxhall Iron Works, Beauford Road, Birkenhead, Merseyside, CH41 1HE Tel: 0151-653 6006 Fax: 0151-652 1425 E-mail: jmprofiles@jmprofiles.co.uk

J.N.J. Fabrications Ltd, Ambrose Street, Gorton, Manchester, M12 5DD Tel: 0161-223 7277 Fax: 0161-223 7277 E-mail: sales@jnjfabs.co.uk

J O & R H Baird Ltd, Industry Road, Newcastle upon Tyne, NE6 5XF Tel: 0191-265 5538 Fax: 0191-265 5833

J P C Engineering, Greenhey Place, Skelmersdale, Lancashire, WN8 9SA Tel: (01695) 729552 Fax: (01695) 725552

J P Fabrications, C 4 Belcon Industrial Estate, Geddings Road, Hoddesdon, Hertfordshire, EN11 0NT Tel: (01992) 444428 Fax: (01992) 444428 E-mail: jpfabs@aol.com

J P Forrest & Son Ltd, Claylands Avenue, Worksop, Nottinghamshire, S81 7DJ Tel: (01909) 472031 Fax: (01909) 530124 E-mail: sales@jpforrest.com

J P G Site Services Ltd, Kerry Road Works, Kerry Road, Newtown, Powys, SY16 1DX Tel: (01686) 624815 Fax: (01686) 629336

J Pratley & Sons Ltd, Pingemead Farm, Pingewood, Reading, RG30 3UR Tel: 0118-975 7500 Fax: 0118-975 6787 E-mail: sales@j.pratleysons.co.uk

J Preston & Son, Pitt Street, Widnes, Cheshire, WA8 0TG Tel: 0151-424 3718 Fax: 0151-495 2360 E-mail: sales@prestonsofwidnes.co.uk

▶ J R R Engineering Ltd, 37 Highmeres Road, Leicester, LE4 9LZ Tel: 0116-276 8801 Fax: 0116-246 0015

J R S Fabrication Engineers Ltd, 3 Vauxhall Industrial Estate, Greg Street, Stockport, Cheshire, SK5 7BR Tel: 0161-477 4313 Fax: 0161-477 4616

J R Smith, East Redmyre Farm, Allanton Road, Shotts, Lanarkshire, ML7 5AH Tel: (01501) 821517 Fax: (01501) 821517

J & R Steel Fabrications Ltd, Unit 5a Caxton Trading Estate, Printing House Lane, Hayes, Middlesex, UB3 1BE Tel: (020) 8569 0129 Fax: (020) 8569 0139

J Robertson, Mill Lane, Walton on the Naze, Essex, CO14 8PF Tel: (01255) 672855 Fax: (01255) 850487

J Smith & Sons, 2a Hawthorne Road, Blyth, Northumberland, NE24 3DT Tel: (01670) 352185 Fax: (01670) 352185 E-mail: davidblacksm@aol.com

J V Fabrication & Engineering, 5a Station Road, Langley Mill, Nottingham, NG16 4BG Tel: (01773) 530524 Fax: (01773) 530524

J W Baker & Sons Bradford Ltd, Premier Works, Newman Street, Bradford, West Yorkshire, BD4 9NT Tel: (01274) 651650 Fax: (01274) 681984 E-mail: bakerfabrications@btconnect.com

J White Fabrications, South Cowton, Northallerton, North Yorkshire, DL7 0JB Tel: (01325) 378207 Fax: (01325) 378271

Jason Steel Fabrications, 1 Bangley Farm, Hints Road, Mile Oak, Tamworth, Staffordshire, B78 3DJ Tel: (01827) 287207 Fax: (01827) 287207

Jayville Engineering Ltd, Unit A2 Halesfield 24, Telford, Shropshire, TF7 4NS Tel: (01952) 583041 Fax: (01952) 586342

JCC Engineering Ltd, 50 Adderley Street, Birmingham, B9 4ED Tel: 0121-773 6900 Fax: 0121-766 7760 E-mail: jccengineering@btconnect.com

▶ Jes Ltd, Phoenix Wharf, The Docks, Port Talbot, West Glamorgan, SA13 1RA Tel: (01639) 898166 Fax: (01639) 899454

John Dylan Roberts, Pen Y Graig Fawr, Llansannan, Denbigh, Clwyd, LL16 5HE Tel: (01745) 870347 Fax: (01745) 870555 E-mail: dylanpencraig@aol.com

John Gibson & Sons Ltd, Unit 215 Heathhall Industrial Estate, Heathhall, Dumfries, DG1 3PH Tel: (01387) 254764 Fax: (01387) 266005 E-mail: gibsonblacksmith@aol.com

John Innes Gilkes Ltd, Bugbrooke Road, Kislingbury, Northampton, NN7 4AY Tel: (01604) 830098 Fax: (01604) 832190

John Lund Gisburn Ltd, Unit 1c & 1d Mill Lane, Gisburn, Clitheroe, Lancashire, BB7 4LN Tel: (01200) 445263 Fax: (01200) 445155

Jolibar Metal Works Ltd, Howe Moss Drive, Dyce, Aberdeen, AB21 0GL Tel: (01224) 770445 Fax: (01224) 770019 E-mail: sales@jolibarmetalworks.co.uk

Jomar Engineering, 119 Sandycombe Road, Richmond, Surrey, TW9 2ER Tel: (020) 8332 6692 Fax: (020) 8948 4269

Brian Jones Engineering (Fabrications), Heulwen, Penrhyndeudraeth, Gwynedd, LL48 6AH Tel: (01766) 770731 Fax: (01766) 770731

Joseph Maxwell, 1 Galabreck Road, Thornhill, Dumfriesshire, DG3 4LP Tel: (01848) 330365 Fax: (01848) 331734

Joy Steel Structures (London) Ltd, London Industrial Park, 1 Whitings Ways, East Ham, London, E6 6LR Tel: (020) 7474 0550 Fax: (020) 7473 0158 E-mail: info@joysteel.co.uk

JST Steel Fabrications Ltd, The Small Cord Workshop, The Fordrough Hay Mills, Birmingham, B25 8DW Tel: 0121-772 5460

▶ K A D Metal Work Ltd, Studio 101, 7-10 Riverside Yard, London, SW17 0BB Tel: (020) 8946 2429 Fax: (020) 8946 0684

K B S Fabrications, 2b Vulcan Works, Leckhampton Road, Cheltenham, Gloucestershire, GL53 0AL Tel: (01242) 572507 Fax: (01242) 572507

K D Design, Unit 2 Yonder Hill, Chard Junction, Chard, Somerset, TA20 4QR Tel: (01460) 221745 Fax: (01460) 221746 E-mail: kddf01@aol.co.uk

K E P Engineering Ltd, Mosley Street, New Basford, Nottingham, NG7 7FQ Tel: 0115-978 0616 Fax: 0115-942 2280 E-mail: info@kepengineering.com

K & H Engineering, 5 Morris Road, Newtongrange, Dalkeith, Midlothian, EH22 4ST Tel: 0131-663 0564 Fax: 0131-654 2699

K & M Welding & Fabrication Engineers Ltd, Unit 3, Dunton Trading Estate, Mount Street, Birmingham, B7 5QL Tel: 0121-327 4771 Fax: 0121-328 9203 E-mail: kmwelding@yahoo.com

K & R Fabrications Ltd, Old Station Close, Shepshed, Loughborough, Leicestershire, LE12 9NJ Tel: (01509) 506996 Fax: (01509) 506996 E-mail: kandrfabs@btconnect.com

K W Geere Engineering, 4 Lady Bee Marina Industrial Units, Albion Street, Southwick, Brighton, BN42 4EG Tel: (01273) 596211 Fax: (01273) 592196

K W Wait Reinforcing Services, 2 Hill View, Soundwell, Bristol, BS16 4RW Tel: 0117-975 3610

K W Welding & Fabrication, 60k Gorse Industrial Estate, Barnham, Thetford, Norfolk, IP24 2PH Tel: (01842) 890606 Fax: (01842) 890889 E-mail: kevinwhittred@aol.com

Kalfab Engineering, 25 Long Lane, Chapel-En-Le-Frith, High Peak, Derbyshire, SK23 0TF Tel: (01298) 816250 Fax: (01663) 733555

▶ Karris Engineering, Stephenson Way, Thetford, Norfolk, IP24 3RE Tel: (01842) 755204 Fax: (01842) 755380 E-mail: karris@btconnect.com

Kastle Engineering Ltd, Longbeck Trading Estate, Marske By The Sea, Redcar, Cleveland, TS11 6HR Tel: (01642) 485506 Fax: (01642) 488601 E-mail: kastle10@btinternet.com

KCG Services Ltd, Neptune Close, Medway City Estate, Rochester, Kent, ME2 4LT Tel: (01634) 294787 Fax: (01634) 714111

Keenans Steel Fabricators, 197-199 Highland Road, Southsea, Hampshire, PO4 9EZ Tel: (023) 9282 6841 Fax: (023) 9285 1401

Keith Collier Engineering, Riverview Farm, Overcote Road, Over, Cambridge, CB24 5NT Tel: (01954) 231760 Fax: (01954) 231979

Kejan Sheet Metal Work, 9 Railway St Industrial Estate, Railway Street, Gillingham, Kent, ME7 1YQ Tel: (01634) 571016 Fax: (01634) 575789 E-mail: alan@kejan.f2s.com

Kendley Ltd, Old Goods Yard, Station Road, Talacre, Holywell, Clwyd, CH8 9RD Tel: (01745) 887412 Fax: (01745) 888290 E-mail: kendley@btconnect.com

Kensington Engineering, Burton Street, Leek, Staffordshire, ST13 8DA Tel: (01538) 387578 Fax: (01538) 387578

Kingswinford Engineering Co. Ltd, Shaw Road, Dudley, West Midlands, DY2 8TS Tel: (01384) 253411 Fax: (01384) 258107 E-mail: kfordengcoltd@aol.com

Kirkton Engineering, The Works, Station Road, Monymusk, Inverurie, Aberdeenshire, AB51 7HJ Tel: (01467) 651276 Fax: (01467) 651616 E-mail: kirktoneng@lineone.net

Knight & Butler Ltd, 2 High Street, East Grinstead, West Sussex, RH19 3AW Tel: (01342) 318650 Fax: (01342) 318651 E-mail: email@knightandbutler.com

L D Engineering Ltd, Great Northern Works, Hartham Lane, Hertford, SG14 1QW Tel: (01992) 584049 Fax: (01992) 584927 E-mail: ldeng@tiscali.co.uk

L W Yates, Cooke Street Forge, Cooke Street, Bentley, Doncaster, South Yorkshire, DN5 0DD Tel: (01302) 874330 Fax: (01302) 874330

Lanarkshire Welding Co. Ltd, John Street, Wishaw, Lanarkshire, ML2 7TQ Tel: (01698) 264271 Fax: (01698) 265711 E-mail: johnhett@lanarkshirewelding.co.uk

Lantern Engineering Ltd, Hamilton Road, Maltby, Rotherham, South Yorkshire, S66 7NE Tel: (01709) 813636 Fax: (01709) 817130 E-mail: sales@lantern.co.uk

Larssen Engineering Ltd, Globe Industrial Estate, Rectory Road, Grays, Essex, RM17 6ST Tel: (01375) 371909 Fax: (01375) 390582 E-mail: sales@larssen.com

Lauderdale Coachworks, Kirk Wynd, Lauder, Berwickshire, TD2 6ST Tel: (01578) 722227 Fax: (01578) 722227 E-mail: jim@rabbittrap.co.uk

Ledbury Welding & Engineering Ltd, New Mills Industrial Estate, Leadon Way, Ledbury, Herefordshire, HR8 2SR Tel: (01531) 632222 Fax: (01531) 634718 E-mail: sales@lweltd.co.uk

Leeming Nelson Ltd, Bankhall Works, Juniper Street, Liverpool, L20 8EL Tel: 0151-922 7019 Fax: 0151-922 0795

Lemon Steel Services Ltd, Russell Gardens, Wickford, Essex, SS11 8BL Tel: (01268) 571666 Fax: (01268) 571555 E-mail: phil@lemonsteel.co.uk

Lenesco Ltd, Grove Road, Northfleet, Gravesend, Kent, DA11 9AX Tel: (01474) 564692 Fax: (01474) 327329

Leyletts Engineering Co. Ltd, Cornwallis Road, Lyng, West Bromwich, West Midlands, B70 7JF Tel: 0121-544 6669 Fax: 0121-544 8483 E-mail: sales@leyletts.co.uk

Leytoner De Montfort Ltd, 8 Layton Road, Leicester, LE5 0PU Tel: 0116-276 7272 E-mail: leytoner@aol.com

Liftech Engineering, 12d Tower Workshops, Riley Road, London, SE1 3DG Tel: (020) 7237 6580 Fax: (020) 7252 3785

Linkester Chemical & Supply Co. Ltd, Gaw End Lane, Macclesfield, Cheshire, SK11 0LB Tel: (01260) 252116

Linkweld Engineering & Construction Ltd, 56 High Street, Edenbridge, Kent, TN8 5AJ Tel: (01732) 864376

London Engineering Co. Ltd, 9-13 Valentia Place, London, SW9 8PJ Tel: (020) 7738 7338 Fax: (020) 7924 0331 E-mail: londonendco@aol.com

Long & Co Kent Ltd, Bybow Farm, Orchard Way, Dartford, DA2 7ER Tel: (01322) 273028 Fax: (01322) 228818

Lowe Engineering Midland Ltd, Stone Road, Bramshall, Uttoxeter, Staffordshire, ST14 8SH Tel: (01889) 563244 Fax: (01889) 563554 E-mail: sales@loweengineering.co.uk

Stephen D. Lowe, The Forge, 49 Claverham Road, Yatton, Bristol, BS49 4LD Tel: (01934) 834907 Fax: (01934) 876568

Lowes, Unit 8-9 Owen Road Industrial Estate, Willenhall, West Midlands, WV13 2PY Tel: 0121-526 2601 Fax: 0121-526 2612

Luton Fabrications Ltd, Tring Road, Dunstable, Bedfordshire, LU6 2JX Tel: (01582) 663330 Fax: (01582) 662333

Luton Steels, Wharley Farm, College Road, Cranfield, Bedford, MK43 0AH Tel: (01234) 750003 Fax: (01234) 750084 E-mail: sales@lutonsteels.co.uk

Lycett Fabrications Ltd, Mariner, Lichfield Road Industrial Estate, Tamworth, Staffordshire, B79 7UL Tel: (01827) 53231 Fax: (01827) 69650 E-mail: mckd@lycettfab13.freeserve.co.uk

M A P Structual Steel Manufacturing, Cross Pipes Road, Alverthorpe, Wakefield, West Yorkshire, WF2 8BG Tel: (01924) 367447 Fax: (01924) 366593 E-mail: info@mapss.com

▶ M Adams, 77 Colvend Street, Glasgow, G40 4DU Tel: 0141-556 2915

M & B Engineering Ltd, Bellotts Road, Bath, BA2 3RT Tel: (01225) 333944 Fax: (01225) 448395

▶ M C Services, 21a New Road, Earby, Barnoldswick, Lancashire, BB18 6UY Tel: (01282) 844801 Fax: (01282) 843159

M D Fabrications, 9 Marlow Road, Leicester, LE3 2BQ Tel: 0116-282 6771 Fax: 0116-282 6771 E-mail: md.fabrications@globaluk.net

M Fairclough, 41-42 Centurion Industrial Estate, Centurion Way, Farington, Leyland, PR25 4GU Tel: (01772) 436184 Fax: (01772) 436184

M G R Welding Ltd, Unit 13 Churchill Way, Fleckney, Leicester, LE8 8UD Tel: 0116-240 3215 Fax: 0116-240 3215

M G Steel Products, Morthen Road, Wickersley, Rotherham, South Yorkshire, S66 1DX Tel: (01709) 709545 Fax: (01709) 709546

M J Agar Steel Fabricators & Engineers 2004 Ltd, Weirhead Works, 1 Hobson Avenue, Sheffield, S6 2GR Tel: 0114-234 2911 Fax: 0114-232 3885

M J Mccleave & Co., 3 Hannahstown Hill, Hannahstown, Belfast, BT17 0LT Tel: (028) 9061 3377 Fax: (028) 9060 0001

M & K Fabrication, Hillsdene, Clockhouse Lane, Romford, RM5 2RR Tel: (01708) 769004 Fax: (01708) 769005

M L (UK) Ltd, Kettering Terrace, Mile End, Portsmouth, PO2 7AE Tel: (023) 9281 9114 Fax: (023) 9282 3386 E-mail: martin@mluk.co.uk

M & M Engineering Construction, 66 Templepatrick Road, Ballyclare, County Antrim, BT39 9AL Tel: (028) 9335 2891 Fax: (028) 9335 2891

▶ M & M's Metalwork, Winchester, Hampshire, SO21 3NT Tel: 01962 761663 Fax: 01962 761663

M P Welding Fabrications, Wareley Road, Peterborough, PE2 9PF Tel: (01733) 344455 Fax: (01733) 561628

M R F Fabrications Ltd, Unit 6, Holton Road, Poole, Dorset, BH16 6LT Tel: (01202) 631877 Fax: (01202) 631841 E-mail: larry@mrffabs.fsnet.co.uk

M S B Enginnering Ltd, Head Dyke Lane, Pilling, Preston, PR3 6SJ Tel: (01253) 790009 Fax: (01253) 790790

M & S Engineering Ltd, East Road, Eastriggs, Annan, Dumfriesshire, DG12 6TD Tel: 01461 40111

▶ M & S Fabrication, 1 Corunna Place, Edinburgh, EH6 5JG Tel: 0131-553 7134 Fax: 0131-554 4171

▶ Mac Steels, Woodhouse Farm, Robeys Lane, Alvecote, Tamworth, Staffordshire, B78 1AS Tel: (01827) 896699 Fax: (01827) 897799

Mcgrath Bros (Engineering) Ltd, Lisnagarvagh House, Lissue Road, Lisburn, County Antrim, BT28 2SU Tel: (028) 9262 1186 Fax: (028) 9262 1955 E-mail: cmccann@mcgrath-group.com

Harry Maiden Ltd, Lowfield, Croft Road, Montrose, Angus, DD10 9NL Tel: (01674) 673222 Fax: (01674) 673299 E-mail: info@harrymaiden.co.uk

Main Welding Co. Ltd, Shawclough Road, Shawclough, Rochdale, Lancashire, OL12 6LN Tel: (01706) 655131 Fax: (01706) 655135 E-mail: enquiries@mainltd.co.uk

Mainport Engineering (1990) Ltd, Pembroke Dock, Dyfed, SA72 6WD Tel: (01646) 621563 Fax: (01646) 621305 E-mail: mpe@my-office.co.uk

Maldon Marine Ltd, 16 West Station Yard, Spital Road, Maldon, Essex, CM9 6TW Tel: (01621) 859000 Fax: (01621) 858935 E-mail: info@maldon-marine.co.uk

Malthouse Engineering Co. Ltd, 3 Hainge Road, Tividale, Oldbury, West Midlands, B69 2NL Tel: 0121-557 8455 Fax: 0121-520 2034

Marland Fabrications Ltd, 3 Addison Street, Sunderland, SR2 8BL Tel: 0191-565 6010 Fax: 0191-565 6010

Marr Engineering Ltd, Green Acres Farm, Old Gloucester Road, Winterbourne, Bristol, BS36 1RZ Tel: (01454) 777150 Fax: (01454) 777152

STEEL FABRICATORS – *continued*

▶ Martec Engineering Group Ltd, Block 7 20 Clydesmill Drive, Cambuslang Investment Park, Clydesmill Industrial Estate, Glasgow, G32 8RG Tel: 0141-646 5220 Fax: 0141-646 1056E-mail: martec@martecengineering.co.uk

Matthews & Son Hanley Ltd, Howson Street, Stoke-on-Trent, ST1 3LG Tel: (01782) 213866 Fax: (01782) 213866

▶ MD Welding Services, Unit 1-3 MBJ Business Park, Kenny Hill, Bury St. Edmunds, Suffolk, IP28 8DS Tel: (01353) 675599 Fax: (01353) 675599

E.& R. Meakes Ltd, Forge Works, Lane End, High Wycombe, Buckinghamshire, HP14 3HJ Tel: (01494) 881262 Fax: (01494) 883279

Mealham Metal Products, Orchard Buildings, Chilmington Green, Great Chart, Ashford, Kent, TN23 3DL Tel: (01233) 621150 Fax: (01233) 621150

Meldan Fabrications Ltd, St Marys Works, Marsh Lane, Barton-upon-Humber, South Humberside, DN18 5HB Tel: (01652) 632075 Fax: (01652) 660389 E-mail: sales@meldan.co.uk

Melvin Bros, Unit 3 Baird Avenue, Strutherhill Industrial Estate, Larkhall, Lanarkshire, ML9 2PJ Tel: (01698) 887605 Fax: (01698) 884871 E-mail: melvinbrothers@aol.com

▶ Meridian Welded Structures, 4b Station Road, Harrietsham, Maidstone, Kent, ME17 1JA Tel: (01622) 853533 Fax: (01622) 853534

Metafab Solutions, Marine Shed, Cu Lighting Estate, Broadwell, Coleford, Gloucestershire, GL16 7EG Tel: (01594) 839220 Fax: (01594) 827878 E-mail: sales@metafabs.com

Metal Cabinets Sales Ltd, Moorfield Road Estate, Yeadon, Leeds, LS19 7BN Tel: 0113-250 8082 Fax: 0113-250 5138 E-mail: person@metalcabinets.co.uk

Metal Fabrications Darwen Ltd, Taylor Street, Darwen, Lancashire, BB3 1DQ Tel: (01254) 701829 Fax: (01254) 701829

Metal Railing Co. Ltd, Unit 28 Point Pleasant Industrial Estate, Wallsend, Tyne & Wear, NE28 6HA Tel: 0191-295 1685 Fax: 0191-262 2882

Metallic Fabrications Ltd, 212 Thorp Arch Trading Estate, Wetherby, West Yorkshire, LS23 7BJ Tel: (01937) 843485 Fax: (01937) 845517 E-mail: metfabs@aol.com

Metalstyle Fabrications Ltd, Unit 25, Harvest Drive, South Lowestoft Industrial Estate, Lowestoft, Suffolk, NR33 7NJ Tel: (01502) 515758 Fax: (01502) 589927 E-mail: metalstylefab@btconnect.com

Metalwork Structures, St Annes House, 399 Lees Hall Road, Dewsbury, West Yorkshire, WF12 9HB Tel: (01924) 461355 Fax: (01924) 450291 E-mail: sales@metalworkgroup.co.uk

Metcraft Engineering Ltd, Unit 10 Fenn FLD Indust Estate, Homefield Road, Haverhill, Suffolk, CB9 8QP Tel: (01440) 712227 Fax: (01440) 712274

Metex Engineering Ltd, 5 Holly Lane, Beeston, Nottingham, NG9 4AB Tel: 0115-943 0155 Fax: 0115-943 6365

Metfabs Ltd, Rope Walk, Littlehampton, West Sussex, BN17 5DE Tel: (01903) 717517 Fax: (01903) 713682

Metwin Ltd, 104 Chingford Mount Road, London, E4 9AA Tel: (020) 8523 2081 Fax: (020) 8531 8313 E-mail: metwin@btconnect.com

MFB Fabrications Ltd, High Street, Clay Cross, Chesterfield, Derbyshire, S45 9DX Tel: (01246) 861700 Fax: (01246) 861777 E-mail: sales@mfbfabs.co.uk

MGL Van Hire, Unit 8, Trench Lock Industrial Estate, Telford, Shropshire, TF1 5SW Tel: (01952) 252396

Mice Kay Mar Ltd, Brookhill Industrial Estate, Pinxton, Nottingham, NG16 6NS Tel: (01773) 810107 Fax: (01773) 580286 E-mail: sales@micekaymar.com

Michael Thorne, Bishops Court, Bishops Court Lane, Clyst St. Mary, Exeter, EX5 1DH Tel: (01392) 261350 Fax: (01392) 261390 E-mail: info@michaelthorne.co.uk

Mid Fab Developments Ltd, 84 Cliveland Street, Birmingham, B19 3SN Tel: 0121-359 1641 Fax: 0121-333 3228 E-mail: sales@midfabdevelopments.co.uk

The Mid Kent Steel Centre, Station Road, Harrietsham, Maidstone, Kent, ME17 1JA Tel: (01622) 859955 Fax: (01622) 858333

Middleton Forge Ltd, Station Bank, Middleton-in-Teesdale, Barnard Castle, County Durham, DL12 0NG Tel: (01833) 640595 Fax: (01833) 640157 E-mail: enquiries@middleton-forge.co.uk

▶ Midland Fabrication & Welding Ltd, Unit 18 Gregston Industrial Estate, Birmingham Road, Oldbury, West Midlands, B69 4EX Tel: 0121-544 8668

Midland Structural Holdings Ltd, Herald Business Park, Golden Acres Lane, Coventry, CV3 2RT Tel: (024) 7644 5584 Fax: (024) 7645 9995 E-mail: steel@mss-ltd.com

Midland Tank & Ironplate Co. Ltd, 241-243 Heneage Street, Birmingham, B7 4LY Tel: 0121-359 0298 Fax: 0121-333 3035 E-mail: sales@mti.uk.com

Midsomer Engineering, Coombend, Radstock, BA3 3AS Tel: (01761) 434929 Fax: (01761) 432271

Miktek Ltd, 2 Wetherden Business Park, Wetherden, Stowmarket, Suffolk, IP14 3JU Tel: (01359) 241456E-mail: mik@miktek.co.uk

K.C. Milner Engineering Ltd, Unit 7 Shepherd Cross Street, Bolton, BL1 3DE Tel: (01204) 843540 Fax: (01204) 493480

Milsteel, Monmouth Road, Abergavenny, Gwent, NP7 5HF Tel: (01873) 858295 Fax: (01873) 859808

Minianchor, 3 Toledo Works, Neepsend Lane, Sheffield, S3 8UL Tel: 0114-275 6211 Fax: 0114-249 6211 E-mail: info@minianchorltd.co.uk

Mister Steel Ltd, Stewarts La Depot, Dickens Street, London, SW8 3EP Tel: (020) 7738 8858 Fax: (020) 7738 8893 E-mail: info@mistersteel.co.uk

Mitregate Ltd, Slack Lane, Heanor, Derbyshire, DE75 7GX Tel: (01773) 762320 Fax: (01773) 530927

Morgan Blacksmiths Ltd, Chase Forge, Upper Chase Road, Malvern, Worcestershire, WR14 2BT Tel: (01684) 573848 Fax: (01684) 573848

Morgan Cooper Ltd, Salmon Road, Great Yarmouth, Norfolk, NR30 3QS Tel: (01493) 843233 Fax: (01493) 844068 E-mail: info@morgan-cooper.co.uk

Morgans UK Ltd, Roma Road, Birmingham, B11 2JH Tel: 0121-706 3216 Fax: 0121-765 4177

Mortimore Manufacturing Ltd, Burley Road, Cottesmore, Oakham, Leicestershire, LE15 7BN Tel: (01572) 813202 Fax: (01572) 813201 E-mail: mortimores@webleister.co.uk

Mosgrove, Alan Ltd, Tranker Lane, Shireoaks, Worksop, Nottinghamshire, S81 8AQ Tel: (01909) 473250 Fax: (01909) 478877

Mount Pleasant Steel Fabrications, Milton Street, Crook, County Durham, DL15 9JJ Tel: (01388) 763595 Fax: (01388) 768719

▶ MQM, Unit 5 Ashville Way, Whetstone, Leicester, LE8 6NU Tel: 0116-275 1564 Fax: 0116-275 3723 E-mail: andrew@mqmfabrications.co.uk

Multiform Ltd, Skipton Road, Cross Hills, Keighley, West Yorkshire, BD20 7DS Tel: (01535) 636095 Fax: (01535) 635047 E-mail: enquiries@multiform.ltd.uk

Namsbury Engineering Ltd, 56 Penistone Road, Sheffield, S6 3AE Tel: 0114-272 8111 Fax: 0114-270 1859 E-mail: enquiries@namsbury.demon.co.uk

Nationwide Signs Ltd, Derry Street, Wolverhampton, WV2 1EY Tel: (01902) 871116 Fax: (01902) 351195 E-mail: roadframes@aol.com

NB Structures Ltd, Unit 1a Apex Works, Hackhurst Lane, Lower Dicker, Hailsham, East Sussex, BN27 4BW Tel: (01323) 848401 Fax: (01323) 848402

Nemac Fabrications Ltd, 5 Staition Road Industrial Estate, Station Road, Reddish, Stockport, Cheshire, SK5 6ND Tel: 0161-432 1030 Fax: 0161-443 2096 E-mail: neil@nemac.co.uk

Nene Engineering Peterborough Ltd, Wareley Road, Peterborough, PE2 9PF Tel: (01733) 553946 Fax: (01733) 894155 E-mail: info@neneengineering.co.uk

Neville Fabrications, 1 Peet Street, Derby, DE22 3RF Tel: (01332) 294928 Fax: (01332) 294928

Newbrook Engineering Ltd, Quakers Coppice, Crewe, CW1 6FA Tel: (01270) 584836 Fax: (01270) 584837 E-mail: cbherri@aol.com

Newburgh Engineering Co. Ltd, Newburgh Works, Bradwell, Hope Valley, Derbyshire, S33 9NT Tel: (01709) 724260 E-mail: sales@newburgh.co.uk

Newfield Fabrications Co. Ltd, Hall Lane, Elton, Sandbach, Cheshire, CW11 3TU Tel: (01270) 762331 Fax: (01270) 768003 E-mail: sales@newfield.co.uk

Newport Fabrications Ltd, Unit 22, Leeway Industrial Estate, Newport, Gwent, NP19 4SL Tel: (01633) 270666 Fax: (01633) 270068 E-mail: mark.nsl@virgin.net

Nia Ltd, Unit 1 Churchill House, 114 Windmill Road, Brentford, Middlesex, TW8 9NB Tel: (020) 8847 5225 Fax: (020) 8560 1090 E-mail: peterchapman@niasteelworkltd.co.uk

Nicholson G Engineers Ltd, Blue House Lane, Washington, Tyne & Wear, NE37 2TD Tel: 0191-416 2041 Fax: 0191-415 5139

Nicoll Industries, 4 Steelfabs Industrial Estate, Victoria CR, Burton-on-Trent, Staffordshire, DE14 2QD Tel: (01283) 510570 Fax: (01283) 536188 E-mail: enquiries@nicoll-industries.co.uk

Nigel Ferguson Fabricators, Old School Buildings, Cemetery Road, Aberbeeg, Abertillery, Gwent, NP13 2AX Tel: (01495) 212471 Fax: (01495) 320051

Niweld Fabrications Ltd, Unit 18 Two Gates Trading Estate, Watling Street, Two Gates, Tamworth, Staffordshire, B77 5AE Tel: (01827) 285189 Fax: (01827) 282264

Nixon Engineering Ltd, 7 Peterfield Road, Kingstown Industrial Estate, Carlisle, CA3 0EY Tel: (01228) 523956 Fax: (01228) 401919 E-mail: eddie@nixonengltd.freeserve.co.uk

Norris Adams Fabrications, Unit 6, Upcott Avenue, Pottington Business Park, Barnstaple, Devon, EX31 1HN Tel: (01271) 322969 Fax: (01271) 322969

North Dean Fabrications Ltd, Grove Street, Wakefield Road, Brighouse, West Yorkshire, HD6 1PL Tel: (01484) 710845 Fax: (01484) 722397 E-mail: mail@northdeanfabs.co.uk

North East Profiling & Engineering Co. Ltd, Bellway Industrial Estate, Whitley Road, Longbenton, Newcastle upon Tyne, NE12 9SW Tel: 0191-266 4521 Fax: 0191-270 0983 E-mail: sales@northeastprofiling.com

Northbourne Engineering Ltd, The Old Malt House, Easole Street, Nonington, Dover, Kent, CT15 4HF Tel: (01304) 842858 Fax: (01304) 842868 E-mail: northbourneeng@talk21.com

Northern Machine Guard & Fabrications, Unit 14 Albert Mill, Albert Place, Lower Darwen, Darwen, Lancashire, BB3 0QE Tel: (01254) 662595 Fax: (01254) 662595

Norton Fabrications, 49 Light Pipe Hall Road, Stockton-on-Tees, Cleveland, TS18 4AH Tel: (01642) 674944 Fax: (01642) 890522

NRG Fabrications Ltd, Harlestone Road, Northampton, NN5 6UJ Tel: (01604) 580022 Fax: (01604) 580033

Nu Weld Engineering Services Ltd, 36 Oxford Street, Birmingham, B5 5NR Tel: 0121-633 0909 Fax: 0121-633 3124 E-mail: enquieries@nu-weld.co.uk

Oakwood Steel Fabrications, 260 Oakwood Lane, Leeds, LS8 3LE Tel: 0113-235 9853 Fax: 0113-235 9884

▶ O'Donnell Site Services Ltd, The Cabin - Walkley Works, Walkley Lane, Heckmondwike, West Yorkshire, WF16 0PH Tel: (01924) 409111 Fax: (01924) 409444

O'Hare Steel, 115 Newry Road, Kilkeel, Newry, County Down, BT34 4ET Tel: (028) 3085 1452 Fax: (028) 3085 1637

Mark Oldham Services, Somersby Street, Grimsby, South Humberside, DN31 1TT Tel: (01472) 344691 Fax: (01472) 344691

▶ Olympia Fabrications Ltd, Unit 16 Showell Road Industrial Estate, Showell Road, Wolverhampton, WV10 9LU Tel: (01902) 717708 Fax: (01902) 717708

On Site Services Gravesend Ltd, 1 Wharf Road, Gravesend, Kent, DA12 2RU Tel: (01474) 321552 Fax: (01474) 357778 E-mail: enquiries@onsiteservicesgravesend.co.uk

Onward Fabrications Ltd, Unit 65 Owen Road, Willenhall, West Midlands, WV13 2PZ Tel: 0121-526 5263 Fax: 0121-568 6138 E-mail: sales@onwardfabs.co.uk

Oswin & Johnson, Occupation Road, Stoney Stanton, Leicester, LE9 4JJ Tel: (01455) 271707 Fax: (01455) 271728

Ovenden Engineers, 2 Radnor Street, Folkestone, Kent, CT19 6AQ Tel: (01303) 254387 Fax: (01303) 254387

P & B Fabrications Ltd, Unit 5 Marston Moor Business Park, Tockwith, York, YO26 7QF Tel: (01423) 359016 Fax: (01423) 359084

P Burley & Son, Magna Mile, Ludford, Market Rasen, Lincolnshire, LN8 6AH Tel: (01507) 313620 Fax: (01507) 313620

▶ P D F Fabricators, Unit 2, Plumpton House, Plumpton Road, Hoddesdon, Hertfordshire, EN11 0LB Tel: 01992 446593 Fax: 01992 446593

P G Carmichael, B Toynbee Road, Eastleigh, Hampshire, SO50 9DH Tel: (023) 8061 5900 Fax: (023) 8026 6480

P Gillan & Sons, 1 Blezard Court, Transbritannia Enterprise Park, Blaydon-on-Tyne, Tyne & Wear, NE21 5NH Tel: 0191-499 0294 Fax: 0191-414 5353

P J Engineering Products Ltd, Elswick Way Industrial Estate, Newcastle Road, South Shields, Tyne & Wear, NE34 0LW Tel: 0191-454 5553 Fax: 0191-455 0892 E-mail: sales@pjeng.co.uk

P J Welding & Fabricating, Unit 12, Summerhill Industrial Estate, Goodman Street, Birmingham, B1 2SS Tel: 0121-236 8152 Fax: 0121-212 1705

P M Bradley Fabrications Ltd, 8 Lodge Lane Industrial Estate, Lodge Lane, Tuxford, Newark, Nottinghamshire, NG22 0NL Tel: (01777) 871222 Fax: (01777) 871922 E-mail: info@pmbfabrications.co.uk

P M Fabrication, Unit F3 Doulton Trading Estate, Doulton Road, Rowley Regis, West Midlands, B65 8JQ Tel: (01384) 561498 Fax: (01384) 561498

P S T Construction, 3 Brooke Street, Sunderland, SR5 1BN Tel: 0191-510 9241 Fax: 0191-567 6311

Pacc Engineering, 4b Tulnacross Road, Cookstown, County Tyrone, BT80 9NH Tel: (028) 8675 1796

Park Engineering, Manor Farm, Manor Road, South Hinksey, Oxford, OX1 5AS Tel: (01865) 327050 Fax: (01865) 327050

Park Engineering Derby Ltd, 123b Nottingham Road, Derby, DE1 3QP Tel: (01332) 342342 Fax: (01332) 385361

Parkway Sheet Metal Works Ltd, Rawmarsh Road, Rotherham, South Yorkshire, S60 1RZ Tel: (01709) 374726 Fax: (01709) 829739

Pass Fabrications Ltd, Trent Street, Sheffield, S9 3XU Tel: 0114-244 2276 Fax: 0114-244 2276

John Patrick Engineering Ltd, Merlin Way, Quarry Hill Industrial Park, Ilkeston, Derbyshire, DE7 4RA Tel: 0115-944 0360 Fax: 0115-944 0373 E-mail: info@jpen.co.uk

Payne & Son Engineers, 26 Bagthorpe Road, East Rudham, King's Lynn, Norfolk, PE31 8RA Tel: (01485) 528269

Pearson Engineering Services, Wincomblee Road, Newcastle Upon Tyne, NE6 3QS Tel: 0191 2340001

Penarth Industrial Services Ltd, 8 Gripoly Mills, Sloper Road, Cardiff, CF11 8AA Tel: (029) 2064 1555 Fax: (029) 2064 1899 E-mail: info@pisltd.com

Pernic Forge, Unit B1 Porthmellon Industrial Estate, Porth Mellon, St. Mary's, Isles of Scilly, TR21 0JY Tel: (01720) 423353 Fax: (01720) 423353

Peter Hope Metals Ltd, 2 Grange Road Business Park, Grange Road, Batley, West Yorkshire, WF17 6LL Tel: (01924) 440055 Fax: (01924) 442200E-mail: peterhope.metalsltd@virgin.net

Peter Marshall Ltd, Gelderd Road, Morley, Leeds, LS27 7LL Tel: 0113-307 6730 Fax: 0113-307 5968

PGS Engineering Ltd, Quayside Drive, Walsall, WS2 9LA Tel: (01922) 425555 Fax: (01922) 425556

Phillips Welding, Sedgedale Cottage, Killingworth Village, Newcastle upon Tyne, NE12 6BL Tel: 0191-268 6741 Fax: 0191-268 6741

Philrae Fabrications Ltd, 53 Circular Road, Storforth Lane Trading Estate, Chesterfield, Derbyshire, S41 0QR Tel: (01246) 279234 Fax: (01246) 234862

M. Pickering (Scarborough) Ltd, 66 Londesborough Road, Scarborough, North Yorkshire, YO12 5AF Tel: 01723 373852

Playle Engineering Co., Home Farm Works, Birch Park, Birch, Colchester, CO2 0LS Tel: (01206) 330315 Fax: (01206) 330138 E-mail: sales@playleengineering.com

Pleatward Engineering Ltd, Rawfolds Industrial Estate, Bradford Road, Rawfolds, Cleckheaton, West Yorkshire, BD19 5LT Tel: (01274) 874771 Fax: (01274) 851180 E-mail: sales@pleatward.co.uk

Plym Ironworks, Rear of 186 Exeter Street, Off Alma Street, Plymouth, PL4 0NQ Tel: (01752) 226316

Plymouth Metal Fabrications, 13 Porsham Close, Roborough, Plymouth, PL6 7DB Tel: (01752) 788883 Fax: (01752) 788228

PMR Fixers Ltd, Mayfield Road, Ashbourne, Derbyshire, DE6 2BJ Tel: (01335) 347629 Fax: (01335) 344051

Pocklington Steel Structures, Heron House, Carnaby Industrial Estate, Lancaster Road, Carnaby, Bridlington, North Humberside, YO15 3QY Tel: (01262) 402400 Fax: (01262) 402401

Popper & Carter, Billets Farm, Great Wigborough, Colchester, CO5 7RW Tel: (01206) 738222 Fax: (01206) 734535 E-mail: nigel@popperandcarter.co.uk

Portus & Rhodes (Fabrications) Ltd, 77 St Mary S Road, Garston, Liverpool, L19 2NN Tel: 0151-427 6885

Precision Components & Equipment Ltd, Railway Street, Heywood, Lancashire, OL10 1LX Tel: (01706) 621421 Fax: (01706) 621319 E-mail: mike-pce@johnbradleygroup.co.uk

Prefab Steel Co. Ltd, 114 Brighton Road, Shoreham-by-Sea, West Sussex, BN43 6RH Tel: (01273) 597733 Fax: (01273) 597774 E-mail: prefabsteel@btinternet.com

Prelude Fabrications Ltd, 129 Mereside, Soham, Ely, Cambridgeshire, CB7 5EG Tel: (01353) 722402 Fax: (01353) 624608

Prepcraft, 11 Hunsdon, Welwyn Garden City, Hertfordshire, AL7 2PN Tel: (07775) 928822 Fax: (01707) 371413 E-mail: enquiries@prepcraft.co.uk

▶ Pressed Steel Products, 11 All Saints Industrial Estate, Bishop Auckland, Shildon, County Durham, DL4 2RD Tel: (01388) 770490 Fax: (01388) 778068 E-mail: sales@pspuk.com

Priest Engineering Co Poole Ltd, Holton Heath Trading Park, Poole, Dorset, BH16 6LE Tel: (01202) 631663 Fax: (01202) 632573 E-mail: sales@priest-engineering.co.uk

Primarc Engineering Ltd, Unit 4 Esslemont Industrial Estate, Ellon, Aberdeenshire, AB41 8PA Tel: (01358) 724543 Fax: (01358) 724550

Priory Engineering Co Christchurch Ltd, 60 Purewell, Christchurch, Dorset, BH23 1ES Tel: (01202) 486538 Fax: (01202) 473740 E-mail: enquire@prioryengineering.co.uk

Promet Technology Ltd, 31 Chase Road, London, NW10 6PU Tel: (020) 8965 0500 Fax: (020) 8965 3030

Gareth Pugh Steel Framed Buildings, Agrimont Depot, Station Yard, Abermule, Montgomery, Powys, SY15 6NH Tel: (01686) 630500 Fax: (01686) 630441 E-mail: enquiry@garethpugh.co.uk

Purdy Gates, 1 Wards Farm, Greenmore, Woodcote, Reading, RG8 0RB Tel: (01491) 681181 Fax: (01491) 682933

Q P D Fabrications Ltd, Unit 2, Shelley Road, Preston, PR2 2DB Tel: (01772) 258992 Fax: (01772) 884371

Quadmost Engineering Ltd, Mallibee, Pett Road, Pett, Hastings, East Sussex, TN35 4HE Tel: (01424) 814244 Fax: (01424) 814522 E-mail: bob@quadmost.fsnet.co.uk

Quality Control Technology, 8 Gainsborough Close, Long Eaton, Nottingham, NG10 1PX Tel: 0115-946 9111 Fax: 0115-946 9222 E-mail: sales@q-c-t.demon.co.uk

R & A F Engineers, Unit 5b Britannia Park Industrial Estate, North Road, Stoke-on-Trent, ST6 2PZ Tel: (01782) 201212 Fax: (01782) 201212

R B Ross Steel Fabrictions Ltd, Moss-Side, Dyce, Aberdeen, AB21 7AS Tel: (01224) 770577 Fax: (01224) 772079 E-mail: info@rbross.co.uk

R B S Engineering Storage & Fabrications Ltd, Protection Works Martin Street, Rear of 934 Bradford Road, Birstall, Batley, West Yorkshire, WF17 9PJ Tel: (01924) 440021 Fax: (01924) 443674 E-mail: info@rbs.co.uk

R C T Manufacturing Services, Leona Trading Estate, Nimmings Road, Halesowen, West Midlands, B62 9JQ Tel: 0121-561 5492 Fax: 0121-561 2444 E-mail: rctmanufacturing@btconnect.com

R C Thanet Ltd, 20 Albion Road, Broadstairs, Kent, CT10 2UP Tel: (01843) 862288

R & D Engineering, Springfield Industrial Estate, Failsworth, Manchester, M35 0GA Tel: 0161-682 6068 Fax: 0161-682 6068

STEEL FABRICATORS – *continued*

R & D Fabrications, Units 65-67 Boughton Industrial Estate, New Ollerton, Newark, Nottinghamshire, NG22 9LD Tel: (01623) 862473 Fax: (01623) 862866 E-mail: sheila@randdfabs.fsnet.co.uk

R E S Ltd, Station Road, Queensferry, Deeside, Clwyd, CH5 2TB Tel: (01244) 831134 Fax: (01244) 822453 E-mail: sales@res-engineering.co.uk

R J D Fabrications Ltd, Hellaby Industrial Estate, Hellaby Lane, Rotherham, South Yorkshire, S66 8HN Tel: (01709) 531951 Fax: (01709) 700252 E-mail: sales@rjd-eng.com

▶ R J Edwards, Unit 15 Ashcroft Road, Knowsley Industrial Park, Liverpool, L33 7TW Tel: 0151-545 1060 Fax: 0151-545 1061

R J Kingston Engineering Ltd, Timothys Bridge Road, Stratford-upon-Avon, Warwickshire, CV37 9NQ Tel: (01789) 205008 Fax: (01789) 415645

R M B Engineering Services Ltd, Union Street, West Bromwich, West Midlands, B70 6BP Tel: 0121-500 1940 Fax: 0121-500 1941 E-mail: sales@rmbgroup.co.uk

▶ R M Fabrications, Ringwood Road, Three Legged Cross, Wimborne, Dorset, BH21 6QZ Tel: (01202) 828240 Fax: (01202) 828250

R M G Fabrications Ltd, 32a Heming Road, Redditch, Worcestershire, B98 0DH Tel: (01527) 525442 Fax: (01527) 527642

R & R Engineering Ltd, Oak Road, Wrexham Industrial Estate, Wrexham, Clwyd, LL13 9RG Tel: (01978) 661523 Fax: (01978) 661227 E-mail: sales@rrengineeringltd.com

R & S Steel Services Ltd, Haywood Industrial Complex, Hereford, HR4 0LT Tel: (01432) 830140 Fax: (01432) 830807

Rainham Welding Works Ltd, 152 New Road, Rainham, Essex, RM13 8RS Tel: (01708) 554107 Fax: (01708) 554107

Rank Fabrications Ltd, Finnington Industrial Estate, Feniscowles, Blackburn, BB2 5JD Tel: 01254 202315

Rapid Fabrications Ltd, Unit 1 Belgrave Mill, Fitton Hill Road, Oldham, OL8 2LZ Tel: 0161-628 6776 Fax: 0161-628 6776 E-mail: rapfab@btconnect.com

Redfab Ltd, 656 Portslade Road, London, SW8 3DH Tel: (020) 7622 2221 Fax: (020) 7622 2221 E-mail: redfablimited@hotmail.com

Regalspire Ltd, Ormonde Street, Stoke-on-Trent, ST4 3RR Tel: (01782) 335988 Fax: (01782) 598138

Reliance Engineering, Giles Lane, Landford, Salisbury, SP5 2BG Tel: (01794) 322904 Fax: (01794) 323620

Reliance Engineering & Fabrication Ltd, Retford, Nottinghamshire, DN22 1WS Tel: (07771) 634203 E-mail: gbrumpton@aol.com

Rennyco Ltd, West Tree Building, Whessoe Road, Darlington, County Durham, DL3 0QT Tel: (01325) 480502 Fax: (01325) 384278 E-mail: sales@rennycoltd.com

Renown Welding, Unit 12 Diplocks Way, Hailsham, East Sussex, BN27 3JF Tel: (01323) 847742 Fax: (01323) 440471

Len Riches & Son, Tricity Works, Hatherleigh, Okehampton, Devon, EX20 3LR Tel: (01837) 810480

Rippin Ltd, Unit 38 Thistle Industrial Estate, Church Street, Cowdenbeath, Fife, KY4 8LP Tel: (01383) 518610 Fax: (01383) 513099

Riteweld Engineering Ltd, Beaumont Road, Banbury, Oxfordshire, OX16 1RH Tel: 01295 250995 Fax: 01295 273505 E-mail: doug@riteweld.fsnet.co.uk

Riverside Engineering Services Ltd, Prince Charles Wharf, Stannergate Road, Dundee, DD1 3NA Tel: (01382) 450099 Fax: (01382) 450088 E-mail: enquiries@resl.co.uk

Robal Ltd, Station Road, Greenfield, Holywell, Clwyd, CH8 7EL Tel: (01352) 713052 Fax: (01352) 713502

Roberts Welding Ltd, Readmans Industrial Estate, Station Road, East Tilbury, Tilbury, Essex, RM18 8QR Tel: (01375) 857736 Fax: (01375) 851280

Robertson Fabrications, 88 Middlesex Street, Glasgow, G41 1EE Tel: 0141-429 0139 Fax: 0141-429 6688 E-mail: robsab@talk21.com

Roc Fencing Ltd, Firs Indust Estate, Kidderminster, Worcestershire, DY11 7QN Tel: (01562) 69440 Fax: (01562) 823718 E-mail: sales@rocfencing.co.uk

Roche Engineering, Spodden Mill, Station Road, Whitworth, Rochdale, Lancashire, OL12 8LJ Tel: (01706) 853385 Fax: (01706) 853385 E-mail: alan@rocheengineering.fsnet.co.uk

Anthony Rochford, 58 Walsingham Road, Wallasey, Merseyside, CH44 9DY Tel: 0151-691 1095 Fax: 0151-691 1095

Rodell Mechanical Services Ltd, Unit 14 Gardener Industrial Estate, Kent House Lane, Beckenham, Kent, BR3 1LF Tel: (020) 8778 2324 Fax: (020) 8676 9901 E-mail: rodellmsldt@hotmail.com

Rodway & Taylor Birmingham Ltd, 85 Buckingham Street, Birmingham, B19 3HU Tel: 0121-236 4027 Fax: 0121-233 2972 E-mail: paul.rodway@virgin.net

N. Rourke & Son (Engineering) Ltd, 4-6 Barkan Way, Swinton, Manchester, M27 8SF Tel: 0161-793 5171 Fax: 0161-794 4760 E-mail: nrourkeson@hotmail.com

Rowecord Holdings Ltd, Neptune Works, Usk Way, Newport, Gwent, NP20 2SS Tel: (01633) 256433 Fax: (01792) 467308 E-mail: enquiries@rowecord.com

Rowlands & Naylor, Unit 2 Aerial Business Park, Lambourn Woodlands, Hungerford, Berkshire, RG17 7RZ Tel: (01488) 72229 Fax: (01488) 73048 E-mail: rowlands@rowlandsandnaylor.co.uk

Rpa, Unit 3 Adams Close, Heanor, Derbyshire, DE75 7SW Tel: (01773) 764509 Fax: (01773) 764509

Rutland Engineering Services Ltd, Bridge Farm, Luffenham Road, Ketton, Stamford, Lincolnshire, PE9 3YA Tel: (01780) 721160 Fax: (01780) 722160 E-mail: sales@resl.fsnet.co.uk

RW Engineering, Threeways, High Street, Ixworth, Bury St. Edmunds, Suffolk, IP31 2HN Tel: (01359) 233098 Fax: (01359) 231832

S Ainsworth & Co., Chadwick Street, Blackburn, BB2 4AA Tel: (01254) 670668 Fax: (01254) 279887 E-mail: stan.ainsworth@zen.co.uk

S & D Fabricators Ltd, Greenbank CR, East Tullos Industrial Estate, Aberdeen, AB12 3BG Tel: (01224) 895564 Fax: (01224) 899065

S G D Engineers, Unit 14c Whitebridge Industrial Estate, Whitebridge Lane, Stone, Staffordshire, ST15 8LQ Tel: (01785) 811104 Fax: (01785) 811104 E-mail: andrew.ward6@btconnect.com

S G Welding & Fabrications, Freeman Road, North Hykeham, Lincoln, LN6 9AP Tel: (01522) 501569 Fax: (01522) 501560

S & I Structures, 4 Forge Way, Cleveland Trading Estate, Darlington, County Durham, DL1 2PJ Tel: (01325) 369930 Fax: (01325) 369940

S M L Engineering Co. Ltd, Benlow Works, Silverdale Road, Hayes, Middlesex, UB3 3BW Tel: (020) 8573 5907 Fax: (020) 8561 5033

S & S Engineering Ltd, Blackwell Industrial Estate, Station Road, Tilbrook, Huntingdon, Cambridgeshire, PE28 0JY Tel: (01480) 860426 Fax: (01480) 860355

▶ S & S Steel Fabrications, Greendale Mill, Brow Top, Grindleton, Clitheroe, Lancashire, BB7 4QR Tel: (01200) 440765 Fax: (01200) 440393

S T G Fabrications Ltd, Monument Way East, Woking, Surrey, GU21 5LY Tel: (01483) 769222 Fax: (01483) 769666 E-mail: stgfab@btclick.com

S Willetts (Fabrications) Ltd, Pleasant Street, Lyng, West Bromwich, West Midlands, B70 7DT Tel: 0121-553 2705 Fax: 0121-525 0581

Sabre Structures Ltd, 46a Bradford Road, Brighouse, West Yorkshire, HD6 1RY Tel: (01484) 722778 Fax: (01484) 722880

J.T. Salt Engineering Ltd, Woodbank Street, Burslem, Stoke-On-Trent, ST6 3AZ Tel: (01782) 577901 Fax: (01782) 790260

Salvage, Gordon Ltd, Power House, Embley Lane, West Wellow, Romsey, Hampshire, SO51 6DN Tel: (01794) 522196 Fax: (01794) 511429 E-mail: gsl.metalcraft@btconnect.com

Sandersons T C M, Unit 5 Wallis Court, Road Three, Winsford Industrial Estate, Winsford, Cheshire, CW7 3PD Tel: (01606) 550668

Savage Cranes Ltd, West Street, Hunton, Maidstone, Kent, ME15 0RR Tel: (01622) 820611 Fax: (01622) 820807

Savill Fabrications Ltd, 2 Milton Avenue, Croydon, CR0 2BP Tel: (020) 8683 2929 Fax: (020) 8683 2555 E-mail: savill1@btconnect.com

Scaife Don Steel Fabrications, Pipwell Gate, Moulton Seas End, Spalding, Lincolnshire, PE12 6LU Tel: (01406) 371750 Fax: (01406) 371671

Scarness Fabrications Ltd, 3 Riverside Park, Reservoir Road, Hull, HU6 7QD Tel: (01482) 446662 Fax: (01482) 446268

Schofield Fabrications Bromsgrove Ltd, Sugarbrook Road, Bromsgrove, Worcestershire, B60 3DN Tel: (01527) 870220 Fax: (01527) 575409 E-mail: schofab@aol.com

▶ Scorpion Metal Fabrications Ltd, 8 Longside Lane, Bradford, West Yorkshire, BD7 1DF Tel: (01274) 730055

J. Scott Engineering Ltd, Little Wold, North Dalton, Driffield, East Yorkshire, YO25 9UZ Tel: (01377) 217197 Fax: (01377) 217790

Sea Fab Ltd, Unit 4b Kings Court, Jarrow, Tyne & Wear, NE32 3QS Tel: 0191-489 9203 Fax: 0191-428 0357 E-mail: cfab@btclick.com

Seafab Consultants Ltd, Wellheads Terrace, Wellheads Industrial Estate, Aberdeen, AB21 7GF Tel: (01224) 770287 Fax: (01224) 723400 E-mail: info@seafab.co.uk

Seaweld Fabrications, Mylor Yacht Harbour, Mylor Churchtown, Falmouth, Cornwall, TR11 5UF Tel: (01326) 373155 Fax: (01326) 373155

Secure Fabrications, 1 Yew Street, Salford, M7 2HL Tel: 0161-705 0377

Seychell Engineering & Fabrication Ltd, 8 Arkwright Road, Bicester, Oxfordshire, OX26 4SU Tel: (01869) 322035 Fax: (01869) 321174 E-mail: seychellgroup@btconnect.com

Shaw Fabrication Ltd, Unit B4, Halesfield 9, Telford, Shropshire, TF7 4QW Tel: (01952) 580838 Fax: (01952) 581085

Shaws Metals Ltd, Hartland Works, Haydock Park Road, Derby, DE24 8HW Tel: (01332) 383341 Fax: (01332) 294085 E-mail: sales@shawsmetalsltd.sagenet.co.uk

Sheepbridge Steel, Bleak Hill Sidings, Mansfield, Nottinghamshire, NG18 5EP Tel: (01623) 623144 Fax: (01623) 623144

Sheffield Art Metal Co., Charter Works, 20 Hodgson Street, Sheffield, S3 7WQ Tel: 0114-244 4444 Fax: 0114-270 1549 E-mail: sheff.artmetal@btconnect.com

Shelley Engineering Redhill Ltd, Unit 31-33 Grace Business Centre, 23 Willow Lane, Mitcham, Surrey, CR4 4TU Tel: (020) 8685 0302 Fax: (020) 8687 0572 E-mail: mail@shelleyengineering.co.uk

Sherburn Hill Engineering Co. Ltd, Tanfield Lea Industrial Estate South, Tanfield Lea, Stanley, County Durham, DH9 9QT Tel: (01207) 236777 Fax: (01207) 231053 E-mail: sherburnhill@btconnect.com

Sherwen Engineering Co. Ltd, Mile End Green, Dartford, DA2 8EB Tel: (01474) 703220 Fax: (01474) 705016 E-mail: sales@sherwen-engineering.co.uk

Shire Mechanical Ltd, Highfield Farm, Binley, Andover, Hants, SP11 6HA Tel: (01264) 738898 Fax: (01264) 738551

Shrub Hill Fabrications, Unit 3 British Rail Industrial Estate, Tolladine Road, Worcester, WR4 9PT Tel: (01905) 20644 Fax: (01905) 20644

▶ Sian Fabrications, Deykin Avenue, Birmingham, B6 7HN Tel: 0121-328 9229 Fax: 0121-328 0990

Skip Units Ltd, Industrial Estate, Sinfin Lane, Derby, DE24 9GL Tel: (01332) 761361 Fax: (01332) 270013 E-mail: sales@skipunits.co.uk

Smart Metals Ltd, 3 Victoria Trading Estate, Drury Lane, Chadderton, Oldham, OL9 7PJ Tel: 0161-684 9545 Fax: 0161-684 9969

Snashall Steel Fabrications Co. Ltd, Pulham Business Park, Pulham, Dorchester, Dorset, DT2 7DX Tel: (01300) 345588 Fax: (01300) 345533 E-mail: malcolm@snashallsteel.co.uk

Solent Manufacturing Ltd, Unit 4-5 Pipers Wood Industrial Park, Waterberry Drive, Waterlooville, Hampshire, PO7 7XU Tel: (023) 9223 2348 Fax: (023) 9223 2358 E-mail: pam.a@solentmanufacturing.co.uk

Somdor Engineering Ltd, Gibbs Marsh Trading Estate, Stalbridge, Sturminster Newton, Dorset, DT10 2RY Tel: (01963) 362210 Fax: (01963) 362388

South Durham Structures Ltd, South Church Enterprise Park, Bishop Auckland, County Durham, DL14 6XR Tel: (01388) 777350 Fax: (01388) 775225 E-mail: name@southdurhamstructures.co.uk

South East Steel Fabrication & Engineering, Legge Street, London, SE13 6NP Tel: (020) 8690 6229 Fax: (020) 8690 6229

Southern Counties Steel Fabrications, Unit 1-2 17 Bessemer Close, Ebblake Industrial Estate, Verwood, Dorset, BH31 6AZ Tel: (01202) 820983 Fax: (01202) 820001 E-mail: info@southernsteel.co.uk

Sparta Ltd, Victoria Works, Hill End Lane, Rossendale, Lancashire, BB4 7AG Tel: (01706) 221111 Fax: (01706) 222309 E-mail: enquiries@sparta.co.uk

Specialised Engineering Services, 129 Monk Street, Derby, DE22 3QE Tel: (01332) 370994 Fax: (01332) 294513 E-mail: sales@ukbollards.com

Specialist Fabrications Ltd, Unit 4b, Heritage Business Park, Heritage Way, Gosport, Hampshire, PO12 4BG Tel: (023) 9252 5555 Fax: (023) 9250 3333 E-mail: sales@specfabs.co.uk

Speedgold Ltd, Pierhead, The Docks, Port Talbot, West Glamorgan, SA13 1RH Tel: (01639) 898519 Fax: (01639) 891611

Stallingborough Construction Ltd, Unit 5, Prince Edward Drive, Immingham, South Humberside, DN40 1QU Tel: (01469) 574867 Fax: (01469) 577760

Stamford Fabrications Ltd, Oliver Close, Grays, Essex, RM20 3EE Tel: (01708) 861665 Fax: (01708) 864123

Stead & Wilkins Fabrications Ltd, Jolly Farmers Wharf, Thames Road, Crayford, Dartford, DA1 4QH Tel: (01322) 529134 Fax: (01322) 550314 E-mail: alanbaynton@steadandwilkins.co.uk

Steel Construction, Molehill Road, Chestfield, Whitstable, Kent, CT5 3PB Tel: (01227) 792556 Fax: (01227) 794361

Steel Fab U K, Bold Street, Preston, PR1 7NX Tel: (01772) 883380 Fax: (01772) 883225 E-mail: sales@steelfabuk.co.uk

Steel Services Associates Ltd, 6 Barton Road Industrial Units, Barton Road, Torquay, TQ2 7NS Tel: (01803) 313383 Fax: (01803) 322299

Steel Services Great Yarmouth Ltd, South Denes Road, Great Yarmouth, Norfolk, NR30 3PF Tel: (01493) 856180 Fax: (01493) 852237 E-mail: info@steelservices.co.uk

Steel Services Winchester Ltd, London Road, Kings Worthy, Winchester, Hampshire, SO23 7QA Tel: (01962) 884588 Fax: (01962) 889366

Steelcraft Ltd, Unit 2-6 Drum Industrial Estate, Chester le Street, County Durham, DH2 1AG Tel: 0191-410 9996 Fax: 0191-410 9228 E-mail: sales@steelcraft.ltd.uk

▶ Steelcraft Site Service Ltd, 6 Dollymans Farm House, Doublegate Lane, Rawreth, Wickford, Essex, SS11 8UD Tel: (01268) 560100 Fax: (01268) 560102

Steelfix Ltd, Prestwick Old Plant Yard, Prestwick Road Ends, Ponteland, Newcastle upon Tyne, NE20 9BX Tel: (01661) 860660 Fax: (01661) 820083 E-mail: enquiries@wroughtirongates.co.uk

Steeltech Ltd, Pitts Cleave, Tavistock, Devon, PL19 0PW Tel: (01822) 611144 Fax: (01822) 611188

Steelware Co. UK Ltd, 36 Normandy Way, Walker Lines Industrial Estate, Bodmin, Cornwall, PL31 1EX Tel: (01208) 77766 Fax: (01208) 77779

Steelwise Steel Fabricators, Centurion House, Centurion Way, Farington, Leyland, PR25 3GR Tel: (01772) 454929 Fax: (01772) 454929

▶ Stephen Clark Fabrication Ltd, Castle Street, Alloa, Clackmannanshire, FK10 1EU Tel: (01259) 729729 Fax: (01259) 210000 E-mail: sales@scfabs.com

Robert Stevens & Sons Ltd, Unit 5 Crescent Court Business Centre, North Crescent, London, E16 4TG Tel: (020) 7511 6300

Stevenson & Cheyne, Unit 7 Butterfield Industrial Estate, Bonnyrigg, Midlothian, EH19 3JQ Tel: (01875) 822822 Fax: (01875) 823723 E-mail: sales@platerolling.co.uk

Stonaco Fabrications Ltd, Wilton Road, Haine Industrial Estate, Ramsgate, Kent, CT12 5HG Tel: (01843) 596448 Fax: (01843) 593548

Store Forge, 15 Lintonville Terrace, Ashington, Northumberland, NE63 9UN Tel: (01670) 522088 Fax: (01670) 522088

Stourbridge Engineering Services Ltd, 19a Oak Street, Quarry Bank, Brierley Hill, West Midlands, DY5 2JN Tel: (01384) 561600 Fax: (01384) 561600

Straits Construction, Bloomfield Road, Tipton, West Midlands, DY4 9ET Tel: 0121-557 8758 Fax: 0121-520 0435

Stronghold Welding & Engineering Co., Overend Road, Halesowen, West Midlands, B63 2SA Tel: (01384) 569441

Structural Steel Fabrications, Shilton Industrial Estate, Bulkington Road, Coventry, CV7 9JY Tel: (024) 7660 2900 Fax: (024) 7662 2111

Structures (Cordell) Ltd, Sotherby Road, Skippers Lane Industrial Estate, South Bank, Middlesbrough, Cleveland, TS6 6LP Tel: (01642) 452406 Fax: (01642) 464118 E-mail: structures@cordellgroup.com

Supreme Ironcraft Ltd, Unit 26 Brook Road Industrial Estate, Brook Road, Rayleigh, Essex, SS6 7XL Tel: (01268) 747774 Fax: (01268) 770449

Sussex Ironcraft South Eastern Ltd, 31b Avis Way, Newhaven, East Sussex, BN9 0DJ Tel: (01273) 515931 Fax: (01273) 513811

Sutcliffe Bros Bradford Ltd, Paradise Works, 164 Sunbridge Road, Bradford, West Yorkshire, BD1 2HF Tel: (01274) 733063 Fax: (01274) 304434 E-mail: sutbros@aol.com

Swan Hunter Tyneside Ltd, Station Road, Wallsend, Tyne & Wear, NE28 6HQ Tel: 0191-295 0295 Fax: 0191-262 0374 E-mail: john.mitchell@swanhunter.com

Swindon Engineering Metalworkers, Unit 10 Bramble Close, Swindon, SN2 8DW Tel: (01793) 641808 Fax: (01793) 513029

T A M Engineering, Leverington Common, Leverington, Wisbech, Cambridgeshire, PE13 5JG Tel: (01945) 410494 Fax: (01945) 410476

T Bland, Sandars Road, Heapham Road Industrial Estate, Gainsborough, Lincolnshire, DN21 1RZ Tel: (01427) 610116 Fax: (01427) 810287 E-mail: t.bland@virgin.net

T C Morgan, Caecwm, Huntington, Kington, Herefordshire, HR5 3PQ Tel: (01544) 370277 Fax: (01544) 370277 E-mail: tcmorganconst@aol.com

T D I Engineering, Block 7 Unit 2 Moorpark Industrial Estate, Moorpark Place, Stevenston, Ayrshire, KA20 3JT Tel: (01294) 471769

T E Watson & Son, Front Street, Blyth, Northumberland, NE24 4HN Tel: (01670) 823357 Fax: (01670) 823357

T & F Steel Designs, Ross Street, Brierfield, Nelson, Lancashire, BB9 5LQ Tel: (01282) 612663 Fax: (01282) 612663

T H Fabrications Ltd, Unit 22 Healey New Mills, Healey Road, Ossett, West Yorkshire, WF5 8NF Tel: (01924) 266599 Fax: (01924) 266599

T I Engineering, 1 Bookers Lane, Earnley, Chichester, West Sussex, PO20 7JG Tel: (01243) 673659 Fax: (01243) 673659

▶ T M Fabrications, Hicks Road, Markyate, St. Albans, Hertfordshire, AL3 8LG Tel: (01582) 842000 Fax: (01582) 842017 E-mail: tm-fabrications@btconnect.com

T R Engineering, Islwyn, Poplar Grove, Llanrwst, Gwynedd, LL26 0ED Tel: (01492) 641487 Fax: (01492) 641487

T Sargent, 9 Coulter Close, Cuffley, Potters Bar, Hertfordshire, EN6 4RR Tel: (01707) 874349 Fax: (01707) 876289

T W Fabrications, Green Acres, Duns Tew Road, Middle Barton, Chipping Norton, Oxfordshire, OX7 7DG Tel: (01869) 347014 Fax: (01869) 347014

Tab Fabs Ltd, Unit 4 Lower Wield, Alresford, Hampshire, SO24 9AJ Tel: (01256) 389123 Fax: (01256) 389188

Tadweld Ltd, Station Estate, Station Road, Tadcaster, North Yorkshire, LS24 9SG Tel: (01937) 832865 Fax: (01937) 835823 E-mail: info@tadweld.co.uk

Taw Engineering North West Ltd, 194 Price Street, Birkenhead, Merseyside, CH41 3PR Tel: 0151-647 6198 Fax: 0151-666 1347 E-mail: taw.engineering@virgin.net

A. Taylor & Son (Leeds) Ltd, Weaver Street, Leeds, LS4 2AY Tel: 0113-263 9036 Fax: 0113-231 0286 E-mail: sales@ataylor.co.uk

Taylor & Brown Ltd, 29 Enterprise Way, Thornton Road Industrial Estate, Pickering, North Yorkshire, YO18 7NA Tel: (01751) 477171 Fax: (01751) 477644

Taylor & Kilduff, 80 Main Road, West Huntspill, Highbridge, Somerset, TA9 3QX Tel: (01278) 788464 Fax: (01278) 792496

Taylor & Watson Ltd, Wentworth Road, Penistone, Sheffield, S36 6ET Tel: (01226) 762035 Fax: (01226) 370216 E-mail: taylorwatson65@hotmail.com

STEEL FABRICATORS – *continued*

Technocover, Whittington Road, Oswestry, Shropshire, SY11 1HZ Tel: (01691) 653251 Fax: (01691) 658222 E-mail: sales@jonesofoswestry.com

Teemore Engineering, Teemore, Derrylin, Enniskillen, County Fermanagh, BT92 9BL Tel: (028) 6774 8377 Fax: (028) 6774 8978

Teme Valley Engineering, 1-3 Rosemary Lane, Leintwardine, Craven Arms, Shropshire, SY7 0LP Tel: (01547) 540321 Fax: (01547) 540486

Terry Gregory Metal Fabrications Ltd, 599 Kingston Road, London, SW20 8SA Tel: (020) 8542 9941 Fax: (020) 8543 6091 E-mail: metal@terrygregory.freeserve.co.uk

Test Valley Engineers Ltd, Stoneymarsh, Michelmersh, Romsey, Hampshire, SO51 0LB Tel: (01794) 368308 Fax: (01794) 368693 E-mail: sales@test-valley.co.uk

Thanet-Ware Kent Ltd, Ellington Works, Princes Road, Ramsgate, Kent, CT11 7RZ Tel: (01843) 591076 Fax: (01843) 586198

Thomas Lane & Co. Ltd, Hope St Works, Hazel Grove, Stockport, Cheshire, SK7 4EL Tel: 0161-483 9666 Fax: 0161-456 4440 E-mail: fabwork@t-lane.demon.co.uk

Thomas's Forge, The Forge, Fownhope, Hereford, HR1 4NJ Tel: (01432) 860262 Fax: (01432) 860262

Thomfab Engineering Services, Unit 1 Blackhill Industrial Estate, Findon, Aberdeen, AB12 4RL Tel: (01224) 781615 Fax: (01224) 781615 E-mail: duncan@thomfab.com

Thornleigh Fabrications Ltd, Unit 25, Thornleigh Trading Estate, Dudley, West Midlands, DY2 8UB Tel: (01384) 238574 Fax: (01384) 238086

Titan Fabrications Ltd, 14 Thames Street, Louth, Lincolnshire, LN11 7AD Tel: (01507) 603264 Fax: (01507) 609080 E-mail: sales@titanltd.co.uk

Tombi, Unit 20, Limberline Industrial Estate, Limberline Spur, Hilsea, Portsmouth, PO3 5DY Tel: (023) 9269 0215 Fax: (023) 9269 1095

Tower Welding Ltd, 7 Abbey Trading Estate, London, Greater London, SE26 5TW Tel: 020 86599900

▶ Traker Engineering Ltd, Garth Works, Taffs Well, Cardiff, CF15 7RN Tel: (029) 2081 1088 Fax: (029) 2081 3520 E-mail: info@traker-eng.co.uk

Transforge UK Ltd, 19 Edmondthorpe Road, Wymondham, Melton Mowbray, Leicestershire, LE14 2AD Tel: (01572) 787504 Fax: (01572) 787565

▶ Treble R Fabrications, 42 Crossgate Road, Park Farm Industrial Estate, Redditch, Worcestershire, B98 7SN Tel: (01527) 510401 Fax: (01527) 503325

Tre-Fad Engineering, Unit 3, Cwmbraw Industrial Estate, Ebbw Vale, Gwent, NP23 5AE Tel: (01495) 350077

Trentex Engineering Ltd, Garner Street, Stoke-on-Trent, ST4 7AX Tel: (01782) 207171 Fax: (01782) 207272 E-mail: sales@trentex.co.uk

Trescher Fabrications Ltd, Ra1 & 2, Bermondsey Trading Estate, London, SE16 3LL Tel: (020) 7231 8692 Fax: (020) 7252 3303 E-mail: sales@trescherfabrications.co.uk

Treval Engineering Ltd, Crossways, Cray Avenue, Orpington, Kent, BR5 4AA Tel: (01689) 834301 Fax: (01689) 890660 E-mail: info@treval.co.uk

Trifab Steel Fabrication Co. Ltd, Unit 2 Lakeland Business Centre, Parish Lane, Pease Pottage, Crawley, West Sussex, RH10 5NY Tel: (01293) 511263 Fax: (01293) 512899 E-mail: a7bsl@aol.co.uk

Trimate Fabrications, Unit 10 Mearclough Works, Walker Lane, Sowerby Bridge, West Yorkshire, HX6 2AR Tel: (01422) 834665 Fax: (01422) 834665 E-mail: trimate@totalise.co.uk

Triple S Fabrications Ltd, Brooklands Business Centre, Taylor Lane, Loscoe, Heanor, Derbyshire, DE75 7TA Tel: (01773) 763246 Fax: (01773) 763246 E-mail: triplesfabsltd@aol.com

Triple T Engineering Ltd, Hackworth Industrial Park, Shildon, County Durham, DL4 1HF Tel: (01388) 774444 Fax: (01388) 774444 E-mail: sales@triple-t-eng.co.uk

Trueline Engineering Services Ltd, Unit 15 King Street Trading Estate, Middlewich, Cheshire, CW10 9LF Tel: (01606) 836961 Fax: (01606) 836528

Tupman & Hainey Ltd, Louisa Street, Worsley, Manchester, M28 3GA Tel: 0161-790 2664 Fax: 0161-703 8435

Turner, 8-9 171 Church Hill Road, Thurmaston, Leicester, LE4 8DH Tel: 0116-269 7714 Fax: 0116-269 7717 E-mail: enquiries@mturnerservices.co.uk

Twelco Fabrications Ltd, Old Airfield, Belton Road, Sandtoft, Doncaster, South Yorkshire, DN8 5SX Tel: (01724) 710844 Fax: (01724) 710188 E-mail: twelcofabltd@aol.com

▶ William Twigg (Matlock) Ltd, 26 Bakewell Road, Matlock, Derbyshire, DE4 3AX Tel: (01629) 56651 Fax: (01629) 56123 E-mail: sales@twiggs.co.uk

Tyne Tunnel Engineering Ltd, B3 Narvik Way, Tyne Tunnel Trading Estate, North Shields, Tyne & Wear, NE29 7XJ Tel: 0191-258 0585 Fax: 0191-296 1745 E-mail: enquiries@ttengineering.co.uk

Ultralift Lifting Equipment, 4 Shipyard Road, Selby, North Yorkshire, YO8 8BN Tel: (01757) 213850 Fax: (01757) 700681

Uniseed Engineering Ltd, Shepherds Grove Industrial Estate, Stanton, Bury St. Edmunds, Suffolk, IP31 2AR Tel: (01359) 250469 Fax: (01359) 252245

Unit Construction, 41 Cardinal Close, Tonbridge, Kent, TN9 2EN Tel: (01732) 355250 Fax: (01892) 355984

Unity Engineering Services, Unit 18 Wansdyke Workshops, Unity Road, Keynsham, Bristol, BS31 1NH Tel: 0117-986 6241 Fax: 0117-986 6241

Universal Balancing, Station Street, Cradley Heath, West Midlands, B64 6AJ Tel: (01384) 567550 Fax: (01384) 413997 E-mail: jblomer@unifabrcations.co.uk

Universal Fabrications, Mansfield Road, Edwinstowe, Mansfield, Nottinghamshire, NG21 9NJ Tel: (01623) 824212 Fax: (01623) 824212

Universal Steels Ltd, 52 Peasehill Road, Rosyth, Dunfermline, Fife, KY11 2GB Tel: (01383) 418720 Fax: (01383) 411505

Upton Metal Works, Magdalene Road, Torquay, TQ1 4AF Tel: (01803) 814326 Fax: (01803) 200598

Urban Design & Developments Ltd, Units 4-5, Incomol Business Park, Derby Road, Chesterfield, Derbyshire, S45 9AG Tel: (01246) 862319 Fax: (01246) 863192 E-mail: streetstructures@aol.com

V Installations Mechanical Handling Ltd, Saxon Business Park, Stoke Prior, Bromsgrove, Worcestershire, B60 4AD Tel: 01527 833248

V P Welding Ltd, VP Square, Storeys Bar Road, Peterborough, PE1 5YS Tel: (01733) 552888 Fax: (01733) 311972

Varley & Gulliver Ltd, Alfred Street, Sparkbrook, Birmingham, B12 8JR Tel: 0121-773 2441 Fax: 0121-766 6875 E-mail: sales@v-and-g.co.uk

Ventfix Fabrications Ltd, Unit 54-55 Youngs Industrial Estate, Aldermaston, Reading, RG7 4PW Tel: 0118 9816246

Victor Buyck Ltd, 20 Kingswood Creek, Wraysbury, Staines, Middlesex, TW19 5EN Tel: (01784) 483006 Fax: (01784) 483008 E-mail: sales@buyck.be

Victoria Fabrications Ltd, Station Road, Whittington Moor, Chesterfield, Derbyshire, S41 9ES Tel: (01246) 450605 Fax: (01246) 455987

Viking Stainless Products, Unit 9 Castlelaurie Industrial Estate, Falkirk, FK2 7XF Tel: (01324) 636298 Fax: (01324) 634818

VolkerBrooks Ltd, Whitegate, White Lund Industrial Estate, Morecambe, Lancashire, LA3 3BY Tel: (01524) 599400 Fax: (01524) 599401 E-mail: info.vb@volkerstevin.co.uk

W A Skinner & Co UK Ltd, Dorset Way, Byfleet, West Byfleet, Surrey, KT14 7LB Tel: (01932) 344228 Fax: (01932) 348517

W B Engineering, 13 Paynes Lane, Rugby, Warwickshire, CV21 2UH Tel: (01788) 565225 Fax: (01788) 565225

W Campbell & Son Ltd, Harpings Road, Hull, HU5 4JG Tel: (01482) 444422 Fax: (01482) 444424

W Dooher, 4 Loughan Road, Dunamanagh, Strabane, County Tyrone, BT82 0QE Tel: (028) 7139 8084 Fax: (028) 7139 8084

W G Fabrications Ltd, 69 High Street, Princes End, Tipton, West Midlands, DY4 9JF Tel: 0121-520 0024 Fax: 0121-520 0089

W H M Engineering Ltd, 24 Earl Haig Road, Hillington Industrial Estate, Glasgow, G52 4JU Tel: 0141 8834422

W H Ricketts & Sons, Forge Works, Ffynnon Gynydd, Hereford, HR3 5LX Tel: (01497) 847250 Fax: (01497) 847329

W M Codd Ltd, Marsh Lane, Barton-upon-Humber, South Humberside, DN18 5HB Tel: (01652) 632578 Fax: (01652) 660484

W S Britland & Co. Ltd, Tilmanstone Depot, Pike Road, Eythorne, Dover, Kent, CT15 4DH Tel: (01304) 831583 Fax: (01304) 831983 E-mail: britland.dover@dial.pipex.com

W & W Engineers Ltd, Farndon Road, Market Harborough, Leicestershire, LE16 9NP Tel: (01858) 466166 Fax: (01858) 464921

Waldridge Engineering, Greenham Business Park, Greenham, Wellington, Somerset, TA21 0LR Tel: (01823) 672444

Walker Products, Unit 71 Kage Buildings, Pye Bridge Industrial Estate, Pye Bridge, Alfreton, Derbyshire, DE55 4NU Tel: (01773) 609257 Fax: (01773) 609257

Maurice Walsah & Co. Ltd, Drumaness Industrial Estate, Old Park Road, Drumaness, Ballynahinch, County Down, BT24 8SE Tel: (028) 9756 2842 Fax: (028) 9756 2592 E-mail: info@mauricewalsh.com

Wantage Engineering Co. Ltd, 6 W & G Industrial Estate, Faringdon Road, East Challow, Wantage, Oxfordshire, OX12 9TF Tel: (01235) 764161 Fax: (01235) 764163 E-mail: sales@wantageengineer.f9.co.uk

Peter Ward Engineering, Sheaf Bank, Gleadless Road, Sheffield, S2 3DA Tel: 0114-255 0633 Fax: 0114-255 5371 E-mail: info@peterwardengineering.net

Warmglade Ltd, 2 College Farm, Church Street, Whaddon, Royston, Hertfordshire, SG8 5RU Tel: (01223) 208788

Washburn Fabrications Ltd, Riffa Business Park, Harrogate Road, Leathley, Otley, West Yorkshire, LS21 2RZ Tel: 0113-284 1111 Fax: 0113-284 2842

Waterman Offshore Ltd, Peters Works, Wouldham, Rochester, Kent, ME1 3XL Tel: (01634) 865341 Fax: (01634) 687447 E-mail: enquiries@watermanoffshoreltd.co.uk

Charles Watts Engineering Ltd, 94-102 Somers Road, Rugby, Warwickshire, CV22 7DH Tel: (01788) 543152 Fax: (01788) 575986 E-mail: sales@charleswatts.co.uk

Weardale Steel (Wolsingham) Ltd, Durham Road, Wolsingham, Bishop Auckland, County Durham, DL13 3HX Tel: (01388) 527201 Fax: (01388) 527838 E-mail: les.graham@weardalecastings.co.uk

Webgibb Welding & Fabrications, Unit 11 Bluebird Industrial Estate, Park Lane, Wolverhampton, WV10 9QQ Tel: (01902) 722040 Fax: (01902) 722040 E-mail: shane@webgibb.u-net.com

Weco Engineering Ltd, Griston Road, Watton, Thetford, Norfolk, IP25 6DL Tel: (01953) 881142 Fax: (01953) 882795

Wednesbury Fabrications, 1 Upper Chapel Street, Tividale, Oldbury, West Midlands, B69 2PG Tel: 0121-557 5171 Fax: 0121-557 7003

Weldametal Services Ltd, 10-12 Winfield Street, Dunstable, Bedfordshire, LU6 1LS Tel: (01582) 665246 Fax: (01582) 661443 E-mail: weldametal@aol.com

Welding & Site Services Ltd, Unit 18 Twin Lakes Industrial Park, Bretherton Road, Croston, Leyland, PR26 9RF Tel: (01772) 601300 Fax: (01772) 601496 E-mail: sales@welding-services.co.uk

Weldright Fabrications, Old Coal Yard, Green Lane West, Garstang, Preston, PR3 1NJ Tel: (01995) 604166 Fax: (01995) 600889 E-mail: garstangtruckbodys@hotmail.com

Weldrite Steel Fabricators, Providence Works, Norton Street, Miles Platting, Manchester, M40 8EH Tel: 0161-203 4541 Fax: 0161-205 1980 E-mail: weldriteuk@aol.com

Weldwork Ltd, Central Way, Feltham, Middlesex, TW14 0XJ Tel: (020) 8890 4141 Fax: (020) 8751 5793 E-mail: info@cmf.co.uk

Wells Fabrications & Developments Ltd, Unit 39a Wyrley Trading Estate, Wyrley Road, Birmingham, B6 7DB Tel: 0121-327 3354 Fax: 0121-327 3418 E-mail: ian.godwin@btconnect.com

Wenlock Installations Ltd, Unit 1 Holloway Street West, Dudley, West Midlands, DY3 2DZ Tel: (01902) 664472 Fax: (01902) 662261

West Cumberland Engineering Ltd, Joseph Noble Road, Lillyhall Industrial Estate, Lillyhall, Workington, Cumbria, CA14 4JX Tel: (01900) 872787 Fax: (01900) 872789 E-mail: wcel@wcel.vhe.co.uk

Westbournes Steel & Pipe, 1 Clovelly Road, Southbourne, Emsworth, Hampshire, PO10 8PE Tel: (01243) 376751 Fax: (01243) 376613

Westok Ltd, Horbury Junction Industrial Estate, Calder Vale Road, Horbury, Wakefield, West Yorkshire, WF4 5ER Tel: (01924) 264121 Fax: (01924) 280030 E-mail: info@westok.co.uk

Westpark Fabrications Ltd, Unit 4 Waterfield Mill, 4 Balmoral Road, Darwen, Lancashire, BB3 2EW Tel: (01254) 760136 Fax: (01254) 762116

Whale Engineering, Unit 9 Eldin Industrial Estate, Edgefield Road Loanhead, Loanhead, Midlothian, EH20 9DX Tel: 0131-440 4290 Fax: 0131-440 0272

White Cross Plant Ltd, 135 Engineer Road, West Wilts Trading Estate, Westbury, Wiltshire, BA13 4JW Tel: (01373) 824422 Fax: (01373) 825234

▶ Whitten Ltd, Unit 4, 39 Willow Lane, Mitcham, Surrey, CR4 4NA Tel: (020) 8640 3888 E-mail: whittenmetalworks@btconnect.com

Willas Engineering Ltd, 9-10 Village Farm Road, Village Farm Industrial Estate, Pyle, Bridgend, Mid Glamorgan, CF33 6BL Tel: (01656) 745000 Fax: (01656) 745175 E-mail: ian@willas.co.uk

William Oliver North Shields Ltd, Little Bedford Street, North Shields, Tyne & Wear, NE29 6NW Tel: 0191-257 5011 Fax: 0191-296 3140 E-mail: sales@worr.co.uk

▶ Williams, Old Barn Farm, Rosliston Road, Walton-on-Trent, Swadlincote, Derbyshire, DE12 8LR Tel: (01283) 711635 Fax: (01283) 711405 E-mail: fandjwilliams@btconnect.com

Winsford Fabrications, Road 5, Winsford Industrial Estate, Winsford, Cheshire, CW7 3SH Tel: (01606) 597305 Fax: (01606) 597308

Winston Fabrications, Dale Road Trading Estate, Dale Road, Shildon, County Durham, DL4 2RE Tel: (01388) 777989 Fax: (01388) 776296 E-mail: anthony@winstonfabrications.co.uk

Wood & Son, 3 Barrack Road, Guildford, Surrey, GU2 9RU Tel: (01483) 504012 Fax: (01483) 504012

Woodburn Engineering Ltd, Rosganna Works, Trailcock Road, Carrickfergus, County Antrim, BT38 7NU Tel: (028) 9336 6404 Fax: (028) 9336 7539 E-mail: tony@woodburnengineeringltd.co.uk

Woodend Fabrications Ltd, Manchester Road, Mossley, Ashton-under-Lyne, Lancashire, OL5 9AT Tel: (01457) 834880 Fax: (01457) 838261

Woodfield Systems Ltd, The Wharf, Crown Quay Lane, Sittingbourne, Kent, ME10 3JJ Tel: (01795) 421551 Fax: (01795) 421554

Yarmside Fabrications Ltd, Durham Lane, Eaglescliffe, Stockton-on-Tees, Cleveland, TS16 0PS Tel: (01642) 782920 Fax: (01642) 786060

Zendstate Invicta Ltd, Chegworth Court, Chegworth Road, Harrietsham, Maidstone, Kent, ME17 1DG Tel: (01622) 859941 Fax: (01622) 859941

STEEL FASTENERS

Britannia Fasteners, 4/6 Auckland Street, Hot Lane Industrial Estate, Stoke-on-Trent, ST6 2AT Tel: (01782) 833233 Fax: (01782) 833255E-mail: sales@britanniafasteners.co.uk

Phil Holden Fasteners Ltd, 23 Swannington Road, Cottage Lane Industrial Estate, Broughton Astley, Leicester, LE9 6TU Tel: (01455) 285888 Fax: (01455) 285105 E-mail: enquiries@phs-ltd.com

Non Standard Socket Screw Ltd, Unit 2, Liddall Way, Horton Road, West Drayton, Middlesex, UB7 8PG Tel: (01895) 430003 Fax: (01895) 430004 E-mail: salestsa@aol.com

Wirth Engineering, Birch House, Fraser Road, Erith, Kent, DA8 1QX Tel: (01322) 434345 Fax: (01322) 434346

STEEL FENCING

Arco Redman Ltd, The Boardroom Suite, Lingley House, Commissioners Road, Strood, Rochester, Kent, ME2 4EE Tel: (01634) 723372 Fax: (01634) 725572 E-mail: mail@arcoredman.co.uk

Coates Fencing Ltd, Unit 3 Barham Close, Bridgwater, Somerset, TA6 4DS Tel: (01278) 423577 Fax: (01278) 427760 E-mail: info@coatesfencing.co.uk

Dowlings Ltd, Duttons Farm, Bangors Road South, Iver, Buckinghamshire, SL0 0AY Tel: (01753) 630653 Fax: (0870) 2201684 E-mail: dowlingsltd@aol.com

Drayton Fencing, 93 Park View Road, Uxbridge, Middlesex, UB8 3LN Tel: (01895) 444727 Fax: (01895) 431054

F J Campion Ltd, Thames View, Upper Sunbury Road, Hampton, Middlesex, TW12 2DL Tel: (020) 8979 2351 Fax: (020) 8979 2351

Fabrikat Nottingham Ltd, Hamilton Road, Sutton-in-Ashfield, Nottinghamshire, NG17 5LN Tel: (01623) 442200 Fax: (01623) 442233

G L Jones Playgrounds Ltd, 1 Station Road, Bethesda, Bangor, Gwynedd, LL57 3NE Tel: (01248) 600372 Fax: (01248) 602085 E-mail: info@gljones-playgrounds.co.uk

J Hill & Co. Ltd, Charlotte St, Melton Mowbray, Leicestershire, LE13 1NA Tel: (01664) 562219 Fax: (01664) 410258 E-mail: sales@hilltrident.co.uk

Kingsforth Landscape & Construction Ltd, Mangham Way, Rotherham, South Yorkshire, S61 4RL Tel: (01709) 378977 Fax: (01709) 838992 E-mail: enquiries@kingsforthfencing.co.uk

Lanlee Supplies Ltd, Red Scar Works, Burnley Road, Colne, Lancashire, BB8 8ED Tel: (01282) 868204 Fax: (01282) 870116 E-mail: sales@lanleesupplies.co.uk

Orsogril UK, 4 Pentland Road, Edinburgh, EH13 0JA Tel: 0131-441 1255 Fax: 0131-441 4161 E-mail: sales@orsogril.co.uk

Paramount Steel Fence, Florida Close, Hot Lane Industrial Estate, Stoke-on-Trent, ST6 2DJ Tel: (01782) 833333 Fax: (01782) 832222 E-mail: steelfence@btinternet.com

Richards & Hewitt Sales Ltd, Dorset Way, Byfleet, West Byfleet, Surrey, KT14 7LB Tel: (01932) 346025 Fax: (01932) 348517

Rom Ltd, 710 Brightside Lane, Sheffield, S9 2BR Tel: 0114-231 7900 Fax: 0114-231 7095 E-mail: sales@rom.co.uk

Rom Group Ltd, Eastern Avenue, Trent Valley, Lichfield, Staffordshire, WS13 6RN Tel: (01543) 414111 Fax: (01543) 421605 E-mail: sales@rom.co.uk

J.T. Salt Engineering Ltd, Woodbank Street, Burslem, Stoke-On-Trent, ST6 3AZ Tel: (01782) 577901 Fax: (01782) 790260

Strongpoint Fencing Ltd, Unit 1 Boarshaw Industrial Estate, Clough Road, Middleton, Manchester, M24 2WH Tel: 0161-643 0045 Fax: 0161-653 8162

STEEL FIBRES

▶ Propex Concrete Systems, No. 9, Royal Court, Basil Close, Chesterfield, Derbyshire, S41 7SL Tel: 0845 5314078 Fax: (01246) 564201 E-mail: trevor.atkinson@propexinc.co.uk

STEEL FILING CABINETS

Amerson Ltd, 9 Albany Road, Granby Industrial Estate, Weymouth, Dorset, DT4 9TH Tel: (01305) 206101 Fax: (01305) 206106 E-mail: amersonsales@amerson.co.uk

Carter-Parratt Ltd, Crossens Way, Marine Drive, Southport, Merseyside, PR9 9YL Tel: (01704) 228990 Fax: (01704) 228981 E-mail: storage@carter-parratt.co.uk

Claughton Office Equipment Ltd, 53 Beverley Road, Hull, HU3 1XL Tel: (01482) 323235 Fax: (01482) 224201 E-mail: sales@claughtons.com

F C Brown Steel Equipment Ltd, 17 Queens Road, Bisley, Woking, Surrey, GU24 9BJ Tel: (01483) 474577 Fax: (01483) 489962

G G I Office Furniture (UK) Ltd, Global Way, Darwen, Lancashire, BB3 0RW Tel: (01254) 778500 Fax: (01254) 778519 E-mail: info@ggieurope.com

STEEL FIRE ESCAPE DOORS

▶ JA Architectural Ltd, Enterprise Park, Swansea, SA6 6ZW Tel: 07071 222455 Fax: 07071 222355 E-mail: enquiries@jaarchitectural.co.uk

Soham Security Products Ltd, 22 Regal Drive, Soham, Ely, Cambridgeshire, CB7 5BE Tel: (01353) 722930 Fax: (01353) 624429 E-mail: sales@sohamsecurity.co.uk

STEEL FLATS

Bromford Iron & Steel Co. Ltd, Bromford Lane, West Bromwich, West Midlands, B70 7JJ Tel: 0121-553 6121 Fax: 0121-525 0913 E-mail: enquiries@bromfordsteels.co.uk

Consett Steel Services Ltd, Bradley Workshops, Consett, County Durham, DH8 6HG Tel: (01207) 590171 Fax: (01207) 592086 E-mail: sales@consett-steel.co.uk

Goodman Steel Services Ltd, 98 Cardiff Road, Reading, RG1 8LL Tel: 0118-956 1212 Fax: 0118-956 1218 E-mail: sales@goodsteel.co.uk

H K B Steels Services Ltd, Autobase Industrial Estate, Tipton Road, Tividale, Oldbury, West Midlands, B69 3HU Tel: 0121-557 8361 Fax: 0121-520 8810 E-mail: sales@hkb-steel.co.uk

STEEL FLOORING

Arco Redman Ltd, The Boardroom Suite, Lingley House, Commissioners Road, Strood, Rochester, Kent, ME2 4EE Tel: (01634) 723372 Fax: (01634) 725572 E-mail: mail@arcoredman.co.uk

British Standard Gratings, 2 Springhill Trading Eastate, Aston Street, Shifnal, Shropshire, TF11 8DR Tel: (01952) 277777 Fax: (01952) 277778

Causeway Steel Products Ltd, Five Ash Road, Gravesend, Kent, DA11 0RF Tel: (01474) 567871 Fax: (01474) 328993 E-mail: causewaysteel@causeway-steel.co.uk

Corus, Station Road, South Darenth, Dartford, DA4 9LD Tel: (01322) 227272 Fax: (01322) 864893

Corus Service Centre, Spittlegate Industrial Estate, Grantham, Lincolnshire, NG31 7UP Tel: (01476) 565522 Fax: (01476) 562459

Eurogrid (Incorp) B I E Ltd, Halesfield 18, Telford, Shropshire, TF7 4JS Tel: (01952) 581988 Fax: (01952) 586285 E-mail: sales@eurogrid.co.uk

Lionweld Kennedy Ltd, Marsh Road, Middlesbrough, Cleveland, TS1 5JS Tel: (01642) 245151 Fax: (01642) 224710 E-mail: sales@lk-uk.com

P C P Gratings Ltd, Enterprise Drive, Four Ashes, Wolverhampton, WV10 7DF Tel: (01902) 791792 Fax: (01902) 791795 E-mail: sales@pcp.dk

Ward Insulated Panels Ltd, Sherburn, Malton, North Yorkshire, YO17 8PQ Tel: (01944) 710591 Fax: (01944) 710777 E-mail: wbc@wards.co.uk

STEEL FORGED SEMIFINISHED PRODUCTS, *See headings for particular products*

STEEL FORGING MANUFRS

Finkl UK Ltd, Langley Green Road, Oldbury, West Midlands, B69 4TR Tel: 0121-544 4506 Fax: 0121-544 1706 E-mail: sales@finkl-uk.co.uk

Firth Rixson Forgings Ltd, Meadowhall Road, Wincobank, Sheffield, S9 1HD Tel: 0114-219 3001 Fax: 0114-219 1131 E-mail: fsales@firthrixson.com

Floform Ltd, Henfaes Lane, Welshpool, Powys, SY21 7BJ Tel: (01938) 552611 Fax: (01938) 555339 E-mail: sales@floform.co.uk

G K N Hardy Spicer Ltd-Birfield Extrusions, Station Works, Old Walsall Rd, Great Barr, Birmingham, B42 1DZ Tel: 0121-623 8818 Fax: 0121-358 4033

Graythorpe Forge & Engineering Ltd, 99 Graythorp Industrial Estate, Hartlepool, Cleveland, TS25 2DP Tel: (01429) 273268 Fax: (01429) 236553

John Hesketh & Son Ltd, Castlecroft Ironworks, Bury Grounds, Bury, Lancashire, BL9 0HU Tel: 0161-764 1109 Fax: 0161-763 1285

Samuel Lewis Ltd, PO Box 65, Cradley Heath, West Midlands, B64 5PS Tel: 0121-561 2157 Fax: 0121-561 5273

Mills Forgings Ltd, Charterhouse Road, Coventry, CV1 2BJ Tel: (024) 7622 4985 Fax: (024) 7652 5453 E-mail: sales@millsforgings.co.uk

Frank Pickering & Co. Ltd, Beeley Wood Works, Claywheels Lane, Sheffield, S6 1ND Tel: 0114-231 8819 Fax: 0114-285 2564

Premier Stampings Ltd, Station Street, Cradley Heath, West Midlands, B64 6AJ Tel: (01384) 353100 Fax: (01384) 353101

Sheffield Forgemasters Engineering Ltd, PO Box 286, Sheffield, S9 2RU Tel: 0114-244 9071 Fax: 0114-242 2103 E-mail: sales@sfel.com

Somers Forge Ltd, Haywood Forge, Prospect Road, Halesowen, West Midlands, B62 8DZ Tel: 0121-585 5959 Fax: 0121-585 7154 E-mail: sales@somersforge.com

Spromak, 11g Wilson Road, Liverpool, L36 6AN Tel: 0151-480 0592 Fax: 0151-480 0656

Thomas C Wild, Vulcan Works, Tinsley Park Road, Sheffield, S9 5DP Tel: 0114-244 2471 Fax: 0114-244 2052E-mail: info@tc-wild.co.uk

W Burkinshaw, Bath Steel Works, Penistone Road, Sheffield, S6 3AJ Tel: 0114-272 3777 Fax: 0114-272 3777

Wyman Gordon Ltd, Houstoun Road, Houstoun Industrial Estate, Livingston, West Lothian, EH54 5BZ Tel: (01506) 446200 Fax: (01506) 446300

STEEL FOUNDERS, *See Castings, Steel etc*

STEEL FRAMED AGRICULTURAL BUILDINGS

DeVille & Lear Ltd, Mill Lane Works, Mill Lane, Roston, Ashbourne, Derbyshire, DE6 2EE Tel: (01335) 324302 Fax: (01335) 324568 E-mail: info@devilleandlear.co.uk

STEEL FRAMED WINDOWS

C B Metal Casements Ltd, Beardmore Place, Clydebank, Dunbartonshire, G81 4HS Tel: 0141-952 6431 Fax: 0141-941 1952 E-mail: cdmetal@supanet.co.uk

Cotswold Casement Co. Ltd, Cotswold Business Village, London Road, Moreton-in-Marsh, Gloucestershire, GL56 0PS Tel: (01608) 650568 Fax: (01608) 651699 E-mail: sales@cotswold-casements.co.uk

Crittall Windows Ltd, Springwood Drive, Braintree, Essex, CM7 2YN Tel: (01376) 324106 Fax: (01376) 349662 E-mail: hq@crittall-windows.co.uk

DNS Windows Ltd, Daniels Way, Hucknall, Nottingham, NG15 7LL Tel: 0115-963 6361 Fax: 0115-968 0183

Drury Casement Co. Ltd, Blakemore Road, West Bromwich, West Midlands, B70 8JF Tel: 0121-553 2198 Fax: 0121-553 2301 E-mail: garry.jones@btclick.com

K G Smoke Dispersal, 3 Foundry Lane, Horsham, West Sussex, RH13 5PX Tel: (01403) 242299 Fax: (01403) 255577 E-mail: kgsmoke@hotmail.co.uk

Lightfoot Windows Ltd, 31 Crouch Hill, London, N4 4AS Tel: (020) 7272 1622 Fax: (020) 7281 1404

Lightfoot Windows Ltd, 31 Crouch Hill, London, N4 4AS Tel: (020) 7272 1622 Fax: (020) 7281 1404

Metal Casements Ltd, Birch St, Walsall, WS2 8JB Tel: (01922) 724032 Fax: (01922) 723048

Metwin Ltd, 104 Chingford Mount Road, London, E4 9AA Tel: (020) 8523 2081 Fax: (020) 8531 8313 E-mail: metwin@btconnect.com

Monk Metal Windows Ltd, Hansons Bridge Road, Birmingham, B24 0QP Tel: 0121-351 4411 Fax: 0121-351 3673 E-mail: neil.holdings@monkmetal.co.uk

Olivand Metal Windows Ltd, 43a Chesley Gardens, London, E6 3LN Tel: (020) 8471 8111 Fax: (020) 8552 7015

Rea Metal Windows Ltd, 126-136 Green Lane, Stoneycroft, Liverpool, L13 7ED Tel: 0151-228 6373 Fax: 0151-254 1828 E-mail: all@reametal.co.uk

Senlac Windows & Doors Ltd, Station Road, Battle, East Sussex, TN33 0DF Tel: (01424) 772362 Fax: (01424) 773615 E-mail: sales@senlac-windows.co.uk

Vista-Brunswick Ltd, 105 Glenfrome Road, Bristol, BS2 9XA Tel: 0117 9551491

West Leigh Ltd, 11-13 Spa Road, London, SE16 3RB Tel: (020) 7232 0030 Fax: (020) 7232 1763 E-mail: info@west-leigh.co.uk

▶ Xtral Ltd, Pelham Works, Pelham Street, Wolverhampton, WV3 0BJ Tel: (01902) 425040

STEEL GRINDING BALLS

Helipebs Controls Ltd, Premier Works, Sisson Road, Gloucester, GL2 0RE Tel: (01452) 423201 Fax: (01452) 307665 E-mail: sales@helipebs.co.uk

Royal Steel Ball Products, 6 Egerton Square, Knutsford, Cheshire, WA16 6EY Tel: (01565) 653881 Fax: (01565) 653870 E-mail: pmather@onetel.net.uk

STEEL HANDLES

Avocet Hardware Taiwan Ltd, Brookfoot Mills, Elland Road, Brighouse, West Yorkshire, HD6 2RW Tel: (01484) 711700 Fax: (01484) 720124 E-mail: post@avocet-hardware.co.uk

Berger Tools Ltd, Units B 1-2 Chaucer Business Park, Watery Lane, Kemsing, Sevenoaks, Kent, TN15 6QY Tel: (01732) 763377 Fax: (01732) 763335 E-mail: sales@berger-tools.co.uk

Buxactic Ltd, Sedgwick Lane, Horsham, West Sussex, RH13 6QE Tel: (01403) 218880 Fax: (01403) 274111 E-mail: chris@buxatic.co.uk

STEEL (HIGH SPEED/HSS) MANUFRS

Bohler Special Steels, European Business Park, Taylors Lane, Oldbury, West Midlands, B69 2BN Tel: 0121-552 2575 Fax: 0121-552 0023 E-mail: sales@bohlersteels.co.uk

Crusteel Ltd, Rutland Way, Sheffield, S3 8DG Tel: 0114-276 0651 Fax: 0114-273 9005 E-mail: Sales@crusteel.co.uk

Duferco UK Ltd, Buntsford Park Road, Bromsgrove, Worcestershire, B60 3DX Tel: (01527) 570509 Fax: (01527) 575274

Fairway Form Tools, Unit B1-B5 Canklow Meadows Industrial Estate, West Bawtry Road, Rotherham, South Yorkshire, S60 2XL Tel: (01709) 820055 Fax: (01709) 820066 E-mail: sales@fairwayformtools.co.uk

Firth Rixson Superalloys Ltd, Shepley Street, Glossop, Derbyshire, SK13 7SA Tel: (01457) 854351 Fax: (01457) 855529 E-mail: lbrierley@firthrixson.com

STEEL (HIGH SPEED/HSS) POWDERS

Carpenter Technology UK Ltd, 6 The I O Centre, Nash Road, Redditch, Worcestershire, B98 7AS Tel: (01527) 512200 Fax: (01527) 512201 E-mail: afoulkes@cartech.com

Hoganas GB Ltd, Munday Works, Morley Road, Tonbridge, Kent, TN9 1RP Tel: (01732) 362243 Fax: (01732) 770262 E-mail: sales@powdrex.com

STEEL HOSPITAL FURNITURE

Associated Metal Stainless Ltd, 101 Brook Street, Glasgow, G40 3AP Tel: 0141-551 0707 Fax: 0141-551 0690 E-mail: info@assoc-metal.co.uk

Will Beck Ltd, Kitchener Road, High Wycombe, Buckinghamshire, HP11 2SW Tel: (0845) 4500444 Fax: (0845) 4500445 E-mail: sales@wil.co.uk

Castle Neroche Ltd, Neroche House, Bason Bridge, Highbridge, Somerset, TA9 4RN Tel: (01278) 787840 Fax: (01278) 781825 E-mail: sales@castleneroche.com

Philip Chapper & Co. Ltd, Unit 1, Orbital 25 Business Park, Dwight Road, Watford, WD18 9DA Tel: (01923) 235179 Fax: (01923) 242278

Deanestor Ltd, Deanestor Building, Warren Way, Forest Town, Mansfield, Nottinghamshire, NG19 0FL Tel: (01623) 420041 Fax: (01623) 420061 E-mail: sales@deanestor.co.uk

Hoskins Medical Equipment, Woodsbank Trading Estate, Woden Road West, Wednesbury, West Midlands, WS10 7BL Tel: 0121-707 6600 Fax: 0121-502 2092 E-mail: sales@hoskinsme.co.uk

Hospital Metalcraft Ltd, Blandford Heights, Blandford Forum, Dorset, DT11 7TG Tel: (01258) 451338 Fax: (01258) 455056 E-mail: sales@bristolmaid.com

Jacob, White (Hospital Equipment) Ltd, Unit I4, Riverside Industrial Estate, Riverside Way, Dartford, DA1 5BX Tel: (01322) 223267 Fax: (01322) 288278 E-mail: jacobwhite@jacobwhite-hoftquip.co.uk

Medisco Medical Systems Ltd, Unit 13, Isis Trading Estate, Strutton Road, Swindon, SN1 2PG Tel: (01793) 692781 Fax: (01793) 491688E-mail: jim@redman-sheet-metal.co.uk

Rastrick Engineering Ltd, 7 Martin Street, Brighouse, West Yorkshire, HD6 1DA Tel: (01484) 715748 Fax: (01484) 720639

STEEL INDUSTRY SOFTWARE

Guardbase Ltd, Far Cockcroft, Rishworth, Sowerby Bridge, West Yorkshire, HX6 4RE Tel: (01422) 822990 Fax: (01422) 824885

STEEL INGOTS

Goodwin Alloy Products, Goodwin House, Leek Road, Hanley, Stoke-On-Trent, ST1 3NR Tel: (01782) 220260 Fax: (01782) 228060 E-mail: goodwinplc@goodwin.co.uk

Goodwin International Ltd, Ivy House Foundry, Hanley, Stoke-on-Trent, ST1 3NR Tel: (01782) 220000 Fax: (01782) 208060 E-mail: goodwinplc@goodwin.co.uk

STEEL LADDERS

Alan Davies Stainless Ltd, 62 Westhoughton Road, Adlington, Chorley, Lancashire, PR7 4ET Tel: (01257) 481652 Fax: (01257) 483110 E-mail: ads@stainless316.fsnet.co.uk

Infometal, Moseley Street, Birmingham, B12 0RT Tel: 0121-693 3800 Fax: 0121-693 3803 E-mail: info@barnies.co.uk

J Gorstige Ltd, Unit 10 Carlton Mill, Pickering Street, Leeds, LS12 2QG Tel: 0113-279 5200 Fax: 0113-279 5200

Surespan Ltd, Leamore Industrial Estate, Leamore Close, Walsall, WS2 7NL Tel: (01922) 711185 Fax: (01922) 497943

STEEL LIBRARY SHELVING

Libraco Library Accessories, Filston Farm, Filston Lane, Sevenoaks, Kent, TN14 5JU Tel: (01959) 524074 Fax: (01959) 525218 E-mail: sales@1ibraco.uk.com

STEEL LINTELS

Allmat East Surrey Ltd, The Kenley Waterworks, Godstone Road, Kenley, Surrey, CR8 5AE Tel: (020) 8668 6666 Fax: (020) 8763 2110 E-mail: info@allmat.co.uk

Birtley Building Products Ltd, Mary Avenue, Birtley, Chester le Street, County Durham, DH3 1JF Tel: 0191-492 1059 Fax: 0191-410 0650 E-mail: info@birtley-building.co.uk

C F P Supplies, Unit 6-7 Building, 53b Third Avenue, Pensnett Trading Estate, Kingswinford, West Midlands, DY6 7XG Tel: (01384) 400220 Fax: (01384) 400160

▶ Catnic, Pontygwindy Industrial Estate, Caerphilly, Mid Glamorgan, CF83 2WJ Tel: (029) 2033 7900 Fax: (029) 2086 3178 E-mail: sali.morris@corusgroup.com

I G Ltd, Avondale Road, Cwmbran, Gwent, NP44 1XY Tel: (01633) 486486 Fax: (01633) 486492 E-mail: info@igltd.co.uk

Southern Nail Supplies, Ikon House, 3 Arkwright Road, Reading, RG2 0LU Tel: 0118-987 3344

Wade Building Services Ltd, Groveland Road, Tipton, West Midlands, DY4 7TN Tel: 0121-520 8121 Fax: 0121-557 7061 E-mail: sales@wade-bs.co.uk

STEEL LOCKERS

A B Lockers Ltd, Alvis Court, Alvis Close, Cowpen Lane Industrial Estate, Billingham, Cleveland, TS23 4JG Tel: (01642) 560170 Fax: (01642) 566784

Arkinstall Ltd, 6 Buntsford Park Road, Bromsgrove, Worcestershire, B60 3DX Tel: (01527) 872962 Fax: (01527) 837127 E-mail: info@arkinstall.co.uk

Astor-Rack, 579 Gale Street, Dagenham, Essex, RM9 4TS Tel: (020) 8984 8499 Fax: (020) 8984 8412 E-mail: sales@astor-rack.co.uk

Lion Steel Equipment Ltd, Johnson Brook Road, Hyde, Cheshire, SK14 4RB Tel: 0161-368 4286 Fax: 0161-367 8214 E-mail: sales@lionsteel.co.uk

M S Storage Equipment Ltd, 78 Park Lane, Poynton, Stockport, Cheshire, SK12 1RE Tel: (01625) 858555 Fax: (01625) 858262 E-mail: sales@msstorage.co.uk

Redditek Systems Ltd, Unit 53 South Moons Moat Industrial Estate, Padgets Lane, Redditch, Worcestershire, B98 0RD Tel: (01527) 501687 Fax: (01527) 510320 E-mail: sales@redditek.co.uk

Simon & Dean Ltd, Castle Works, Studley, Warwickshire, B80 7EE Tel: 01527 853131

▶ Simply Direct, Adelphi Mill, Grimshaw Lane, Bollington, Macclesfield, Cheshire, SK10 5JB Tel: (01625) 576527 Fax: (01625) 576545 E-mail: sales@simplydirect.net

Welco, 2 Parklands, Rednal, Birmingham, B45 9PZ Tel: (0800) 9549001 Fax: (0845) 6888900 E-mail: sales@welco.co.uk

STEEL MANHOLE COVERS OR FRAMES

Kastle Engineering Ltd, Longbeck Trading Estate, Marske By The Sea, Redcar, Cleveland, TS11 6HR Tel: (01642) 485506 Fax: (01642) 488601 E-mail: kastle10@btinternet.com

Peter Savage Ltd, Liberty House, Liberty Way, Attleborough Fields Ind Estate, Nuneaton, Warwickshire, CV11 6RZ Tel: (024) 7664 1777 Fax: (024) 7637 5250 E-mail: sales@peter-savage.co.uk

Technocover, Whittington Road, Oswestry, Shropshire, SY11 1HZ Tel: (01691) 653251 Fax: (01691) 658222 E-mail: sales@jonesofoswestry.com

STEEL MANUFACTURERS' AGENTS/REPRESENTATIVES/ TRADING SUBSIDIARIES

Apex Engineering South Ltd, Apex Business Centre, Queens Farm Road, Shorne, Gravesend, Kent, DA12 3HU Tel: (01474) 825700 Fax: (01474) 825717 E-mail: sales@apex-engineering.co.uk

Arcelor UK, Arcelor House, 4 Princes Way, Solihull, West Midlands, B91 3AL Tel: 0121-705 5444 Fax: 0121-703 0584

Bedford Stainless Engineering, Blyth Road, Harworth, Doncaster, South Yorkshire, DN11 8NE Tel: (01302) 752003 Fax: (01302) 752006

Bohler Special Steels, European Business Park, Taylors Lane, Oldbury, West Midlands, B69 2BN Tel: 0121-552 2575 Fax: 0121-552 0023 E-mail: sales@bohlersteels.co.uk

STEEL MANUFACTURERS' AGENTS/ REPRESENTATIVES/TRADING SUBSIDIARIES – *continued*

William Burns & Sons, 1 School Road, Millisle, Newtownards, County Down, BT22 2DZ Tel: (028) 9048 4140 Fax: (028) 9048 4140

Caparo Group Ltd, 101-103 Baker Street, London, W1U 6LN Tel: (020) 7486 1417 Fax: (020) 7224 4109 E-mail: sales@caparo.co.uk

Caparo Merchant Bar plc, Brigg Road, Scunthorpe, South Humberside, DN16 1XJ Tel: (01724) 853333 Fax: (01724) 403044 E-mail: sales@cmbplc.co.uk

Cookson Bros, Hornby Boulevard, Bootle, Merseyside, L20 5DX Tel: 0151-922 3394 Fax: 0151-922 3014

Corus, 202 Solent Business Centre, 343 Millbrook Road West, Southampton, SO15 0HW Tel: (023) 8023 3094 Fax: (023) 8023 3096

Corus Group, Hampton House, 20 Albert Embankment, London, SE1 7TJ Tel: (020) 7975 8000 Fax: (020) 7975 8400

D & A Fabrications, Unit 23 Landgate Industrial Estate, Wigan Road, Ashton-in-Makerfield, Wigan, Lancashire, WN4 0BW Tel: (01942) 717183 Fax: (01942) 719880

Eagle Structural Ltd, The Maples, Lordship Road, Great Carlton, Louth, Lincolnshire, LN11 8JS Tel: (01507) 450081 Fax: (01507) 450981

Eurofab Sheffield Ltd, Dixon Street, Sheffield, S6 3AW Tel: 0114-272 9339 Fax: 0114-278 6686

Eurosteel & Allied Ltd, 61 Washford Road, Sheffield, S9 3XW Tel: 0114-242 0066 Fax: 0114-242 0077 E-mail: frank@gsbaceroltd.co.uk

Handley Steel Ltd, 4 Burkitt Drive, Tipton, West Midlands, DY4 0QE Tel: 0121-556 7037 Fax: 0121-568 6387

Peter Macarthur & Co. Ltd, 17 Station Road, Biggar, Lanarkshire, ML12 6BW Tel: (01899) 221933 Fax: (01899) 221353 E-mail: petermacarthur@aol.com

Mito Construction & Engineering Ltd, Adams Wharf, 19 Yeoman Street, London, SE8 5DT Tel: (020) 7231 0918 Fax: (020) 7231 6307 E-mail: mitocons@aol.com

Neil's Steels Ltd, Westerman Complex, School Road, Hove, East Sussex, BN3 5HX Tel: (01273) 882323 Fax: (01273) 882323 E-mail: info@neilssteels.com

Newade Stainless Products Ltd, Jubilee Works, Jubilee Street North, Halifax, West Yorkshire, HX3 6QY Tel: (01422) 356658 Fax: (01422) 343793 E-mail: philwade@newade.co.uk

Oxborrow Engineering, Malting Forge, Malting Lane, Kirby-le-Soken, Frinton-on-Sea, Essex, CO13 0EH Tel: (01255) 850850 Fax: (01255) 852666 E-mail: sales@oxborrowengineering.co.uk

Radius Reinforcements Ltd, 1 Villa Place, Clackmannan, FK10 4HZ Tel: (01259) 215129 Fax: (01259) 215129 E-mail: radiusrebar1@freeuk.com

Sidenor UK, Northside House, Mount Pleasent, Barnet, Hertfordshire, EN4 9EB Tel: (020) 8447 1444 Fax: (020) 8447 1555

T A Kirkpatrick & Co Ltd, Beltenmont, Kirkpatrick Fleming, Lockerbie, Dumfriesshire, DG11 3NQ Tel: (01461) 800275 Fax: (01461) 800340 E-mail: info@takirkpatrick.com

UK Site Fix Ltd, 1 Spring Gardens, Frome, Somerset, BA11 2NU Tel: (01373) 452207 Fax: (01373) 452207 E-mail: jonhowell@tinyworld.co.uk

Voest Alpine Stahl Ltd, Albion Place, London, W6 0QT Tel: (020) 8600 5800 Fax: (020) 8741 3099 E-mail: officelondon@vosetalpine.com

STEEL MARKING PUNCHES

Davidson & Co. Ltd, 92 Harwood Street, Sheffield, S2 4SE Tel: 0114-272 4584 Fax: 0114-279 7309

Hamilton Rand, Paper Mill End Industrial Estate, Birmingham, B44 8NH Tel: 0121-344 3202 Fax: 0121-344 3202

William W Cope, Unit 34 Camp Hill Industrial Estate, John Kempe Way, Birmingham, B12 0HU Tel: 0121-766 8874 Fax: 0121-771 2866 E-mail: martingeer@williamcope.co.uk

STEEL MASTS

C U Lighting Ltd, 35 Westgate, Cleckheaton, West Yorkshire, BD19 5LE Tel: (01274) 876887 Fax: (01274) 876888 E-mail: sales@cuphosco.co.uk

Francis & Lewis International, Waterwells Drive, Waterwells Business Park, Quedgeley, Gloucester, GL2 2AA Tel: (01452) 722200 Fax: (01452) 722244 E-mail: sales@fli.co.uk

Noble Masts, A Shed, Canons Road, Bristol, BS1 5UH Tel: 0117-929 7450 Fax: 0117-925 6033

Saturn Communications Ltd, Park House, 27 Hartswood Road, Warley, Brentwood, Essex, CM14 5AE Tel: (01277) 234131 Fax: (01277) 234156 E-mail: len@saturncomms.co.uk

STEEL MEASURING TAPES

Arrow Fastener (U K) Ltd, Unit 5 ZK Park, 23 Commerce Way, Croydon, CR0 4ZS Tel: 0845 5314109 Fax: (020) 8686 9197 E-mail: arrowfast@aol.com

Fisco Ltd, 21 Brook Road, Rayleigh, Essex, SS6 7XD Tel: (01268) 747074 Fax: (01268) 782801 E-mail: sales@fisco.co.uk

Pi Tape Ltd, Dean Court, Upper Dean, Huntingdon, Cambridgeshire, PE28 0NL Tel: (01234) 708882 Fax: (01234) 708677 E-mail: sales@pitape.co.uk

STEEL MERCHANTS (INTERNATIONAL), IMPORTERS, EXPORTERS OR TRADERS

Allan Industrial Products Ltd, Suite 3, 30 Bancroft, Hitchin, Hertfordshire, SG5 1LE Tel: (01462) 454021 Fax: (01462) 421312 E-mail: sales@allanindustrial.co.uk

C M C (U K) Ltd, Bradwall Court, Bradwall Road, Sandbach, Cheshire, CW11 1GE Tel: (01270) 759444 Fax: (01270) 759888 E-mail: uksteeltrading@cmcukltd.com

Concept Control Services, Robson House, Robson Street, Stoke-on-Trent, ST1 4ER Tel: (01782) 261111 Fax: (01782) 261111 E-mail: simon.f@conceptcontrolservices.com

Daewoo International Ltd, 10TH Floor C I Tower, St. Georges Square, New Malden, Surrey, KT3 4HH Tel: (020) 8336 9130 Fax: (020) 8949 3783 E-mail: kelliedodds@daewoo.co.uk

Euro Asia Exports Ltd, 25 Uxendon Hill, Wembley, Middlesex, HA9 9RX Tel: (020) 8904 2575 Fax: (020) 8904 9187 E-mail: euro@euasia.demon.co.uk

▶ Euro Steel Products Ltd, Floor 5,24, Chiswell Street, London, EC1Y 4TY Tel: (020) 7248 5473 Fax: (020) 7248 3069 E-mail: eurosteel@uk.stemcor.com

Europa Import Export, 3-8 Porchester Gate, Bayswater Road, London, W2 3HP Tel: (020) 7221 3449 Fax: (020) 7221 7461 E-mail: eie@compuserve.com

J F E Steel Corporation, London Int Press Centre, 76 Shoe Lane, London, EC4A 3JB Tel: (020) 7583 1133 Fax: (020) 7583 1144 E-mail: london@jfe-steel.co.uk

Kubach & Sambrook (Metals) Ltd, 57 Manor Park Crescent, Edgware, Middlesex, HA8 7LY Tel: (020) 8951 0688 Fax: (020) 8951 4540 E-mail: info@kubach.co.uk

▶ Macedonia Steel Ltd, 93-99 Upper Richmond Road, London, SW15 2TG Tel: (020) 8780 5577 Fax: (020) 8780 5455 E-mail: macsteel@onetel.net.uk

Macsteel International UK Ltd, 1 Harbour Exchange Square, London, E14 9GE Tel: (020) 7971 5678 Fax: (020) 7531 9187 E-mail: admin@miuk.co.uk

Primary Industries UK Ltd, 1 Warwick Row, London, SW1E 5ER Tel: (020) 7347 1500 Fax: (020) 7347 1501 E-mail: info@primaryuk.co.uk

Samac Overseas Ltd, Alperton House, Bridgewater Road, Wembley, Middlesex, HA0 1EH Tel: (020) 8903 5611 Fax: (020) 8900 2373 E-mail: samac@stemcor.com

U S Steel Kosice UK Ltd, 46-54 High Street, Ingatestone, Essex, CM4 0DG Tel: (01277) 355155 Fax: (01277) 354649 E-mail: info@ussk.co.uk

Universal Steels Ltd, 52 Peasehill Road, Rosyth, Dunfermline, Fife, KY11 2GB Tel: (01383) 418720 Fax: (01383) 411505

STEEL MEZZANINE FLOORS

Allen Mezzanines, 42 Croft Lane, Letchworth Garden City, Hertfordshire, SG6 1AP Tel: (01462) 484022 Fax: (01462) 484022 E-mail: allenmezzanines@ntlworld.com

M H Group, M H House, Madeley Street, Hull, HU3 2AH Tel: (01482) 328896 Fax: (01482) 225867 E-mail: sales@mhindustrial.co.uk

STEEL OR CONCRETE BUILDING COMPOSITE FRAMES

Caerleon Ready Mixed Concrete Ltd, Western Industrial Estate, Caerleon, Newport, NP18 3NN Tel: (01633) 423549 Fax: (01633) 430413

Robinsons Scotland Ltd, Broomhouses 2 Industrial Estate, Old Glasgow Road, Lockerbie, Dumfriesshire, DG11 2SD Tel: (01576) 205905 Fax: (01576) 204466 E-mail: sales@rbscotland.com

STEEL OR CUT STEEL NAILS

John Reynolds & Sons Ltd, Units 5-6 Church Lane Industrial Estate, West Bromwich, West Midlands, B71 1AR Tel: 0121-553 2754 Fax: 0121-500 5460 E-mail: sales@johnreynolds.co.uk

Young Black Industrial Stapling Ltd, Radway Road, Swindon, SN3 4ND Tel: (01793) 838400 Fax: (01793) 838401 E-mail: info@youngblack.co.uk

STEEL OR STAINLESS STEEL HANDRAILS

▶ Access Design & Engineering, Halesfield 18, Telford, Shropshire, TF7 4JS Tel: (01952) 588788 Fax: (01952) 685139 E-mail: sales@access-design.co.uk

Alan Davies Stainless Ltd, 62 Westhoughton Road, Adlington, Chorley, Lancashire, PR7 4ET Tel: (01257) 481652 Fax: (01257) 483110 E-mail: ads@stainless316.fsnet.co.uk

British Standard Gratings, 2 Springhill Trading Eastate, Aston Street, Shifnal, Shropshire, TF11 8DR Tel: (01952) 277777 Fax: (01952) 277778

D G N Design, Unit 7 270 Lakey Lane, Birmingham, B28 8RA Tel: 0121-778 6878 Fax: 0121-778 6878

Delta Balustrades, Belpher Road, Stockport, Cheshire, SK4 3QW Tel: 0161-947 4747

Eurogrid (Incorp) B I E Ltd, Halesfield 18, Telford, Shropshire, TF7 4JS Tel: (01952) 581988 Fax: (01952) 586285 E-mail: sales@eurogrid.co.uk

Form Fab Worcester Ltd, 9-11 Bache Road, Sandy Lane Industrial Estate, Stourport-on-Severn, Worcestershire, DY13 9QB Tel: (01299) 879271 Fax: (01299) 877339 E-mail: sales@form-fab.com

Glendale Developments Ltd, Unit 2a Union Road Trading Estate, Oldbury, West Midlands, B69 3EU Tel: 0121-541 1752 Fax: 0121-544 8774 E-mail: glendaledevelpoments@hotmail.com

Grainger Tubolt Ltd, Unit A, Meyrick Owen Way, Pembroke Dock, Dyfed, SA72 6WS Tel: (01646) 683584 Fax: (01646) 621392 E-mail: sales@grainger-tubolt.co.uk

Greaves Art Metalwork Ltd, Ireland Close, Staveley, Chesterfield, Derbyshire, S43 3PE Tel: (01246) 280672 Fax: (01246) 280673

L H W Engineering Ltd, Iremonger Road, London Road, Nottingham, NG2 3HU Tel: 0115-986 1247 Fax: 0115-986 0684 E-mail: sales@lhw.co.uk

Lionweld Kennedy Ltd, Marsh Road, Middlesbrough, Cleveland, TS1 5JS Tel: (01642) 245151 Fax: (01642) 224710 E-mail: sales@lk-uk.com

Lothian Steel Services Ltd, Whitburn Road, Bathgate, West Lothian, EH48 2HR Tel: (01506) 633500 Fax: (01506) 633648 E-mail: sales@lothiansteels.co.uk

O S F Ltd, Unit 6 Station Road, Four Ashes Industrial Estate, Four Ashes, Wolverhampton, WV10 7DB Tel: (01902) 798080 Fax: (01902) 794750 E-mail: sales@jcshopfitters.co.uk

R S H Services Ltd, Southedge Works, Hipperholme, Halifax, West Yorkshire, HX3 8EF Tel: (01422) 202840 Fax: (01422) 206070 E-mail: rshservices@tiscali.co.uk

Riteweld Engineering Ltd, Beaumont Road, Banbury, Oxfordshire, OX16 1RH Tel: 01295 250995 Fax: 01295 273505 E-mail: doug@riteweld.fsnet.co.uk

J.T. Salt Engineering Ltd, Woodbank Street, Burslem, Stoke-On-Trent, ST6 3AZ Tel: (01782) 577901 Fax: (01782) 790260

Seagull Fittings Ltd, 90 Roebuck Lane, West Bromwich, West Midlands, B70 6QX Tel: 0121-525 0020 Fax: 0121-525 1116 E-mail: sales@seagullfittings.co.uk

Stainless International Ltd, George Henry Rd, Great Bridge, Tipton, West Midlands, DY4 7BU Tel: 0121-522 3111 Fax: 0121-522 3377 E-mail: a.holland@stainlessinternational.com

Steel Line Ltd, 415 Petre Street, Sheffield, S4 8LL Tel: 0114-231 7330 Fax: 0114-256 0330 E-mail: enquiries@steelline.co.uk

Structural Stairways Ltd, The Premier Estate, Leys Road, Brierley Hill, West Midlands, DY5 3UP Tel: (01384) 79256 Fax: (01384) 482412 E-mail: metalwork@stairways18.fsnet.co.uk

W A Mcgarrie & Son Ltd, Friarton Road, Perth, PH2 8BB Tel: (01738) 631194 Fax: (01738) 633814 E-mail: office@mcgarrie.net

STEEL OR STAINLESS STEEL ROOFING CONTRACTORS

Adstone Construction, Wassage Way, Hampton Lovett, Droitwich, Worcestershire, WR9 0NX Tel: (01905) 794561 Fax: (01905) 794040 E-mail: mail@adstone.org.uk

STEEL OR STAINLESS STEEL ROOFING MATERIALS

BCC Stockholders Ltd, Pontardulais Road, Gorseinon, Swansea, SA4 4FQ Tel: (01792) 893985 Fax: (01792) 893124 E-mail: sales@rollaclad.com

Panels & Profiles, Tewksbury Business Park, Severn Drive, Tewkesbury Business Park, Tewkesbury, Gloucestershire, GL20 8TX Tel: (01684) 856600 Fax: (01684) 856601 E-mail: sales@coruspanelsandprofiles.co.uk

STEEL OR STAINLESS STEEL SHOP FRONT FITTINGS

V.J. Bowers & Sons, 11 Rydal Road, Little Lever, Bolton, BL3 1DT Tel: (01204) 578358 Fax: (01204) 578358

Pollards Fyrespan, Units 3-5 Haslemere Business Centre, Lincoln Way, Enfield, Middlesex, EN1 1AY Tel: (020) 8443 5511 Fax: (020) 8443 3804 E-mail: info@pollardsfyrespan.co.uk

UK Shopfront Shutters Ltd, Bridge Road, Southall, Middlesex, UB2 4AB Tel: (020) 8571 5553 Fax: (020) 8574 7066 E-mail: ukshopfronts@aol.com

STEEL OR TUNGSTEN CARBIDE WHEEL GLASS CUTTERS

Shaw Cutters, Ashwellthorpe Industrial Estate, Ashwellthorpe, Norwich, NR16 1ER Tel: (01508) 488400 Fax: (01508) 488058 E-mail: sales@dcdevs.co.uk

STEEL PALLET OR STILLAGES

Action Handling Equipment Ltd, Maltings Industrial Estate, Station Road, Sawbridgeworth, Hertfordshire, CM21 9JY Tel: (01279) 724989 Fax: (01279) 600224 E-mail: sales@actionhandling.co.uk

Bache Pallets Ltd, Bromley Street, Stourbridge, West Midlands, DY9 8HU Tel: (01384) 897799 Fax: (01384) 891351 E-mail: sales@bache-pallets.co.uk

Clark Handling Ltd, Hobson Industrial Estate, Hobson, Newcastle upon Tyne, NE16 6EA Tel: (01207) 270825 Fax: (01207) 271393 E-mail: sales@clarkhandling.co.uk

J S Burgess Engineering Ltd, Units 18-20, Bingswood Trading Estate, Whaley Bridge, High Peak, Derbyshire, SK23 7LY Tel: (01663) 719300 Fax: (01663) 719301

M G K Engineering (Northern) Ltd, Polbeth Industrial Estate, Polbeth, West Calder, West Lothian, EH55 8TJ Tel: (01506) 871757 Fax: (01506) 873400 E-mail: sales@mgkscot.co.uk

Metal Products Arden Ltd, Prospect Road, Burntwood, Staffordshire, WS7 0AE Tel: (01543) 682627 Fax: (01543) 671901 E-mail: enquiries@metalproducts.co.uk

Palletower (GB) Ltd, Pallet Centre Europe, Dane Road Industrial Estate, Sale, Cheshire, M33 7BH Tel: 0161-905 2233 Fax: 0161-972 0922 E-mail: info@palletower.com

R Elliott & Sons Ltd, 21 Bridge Street, Uttoxeter, Staffordshire, ST14 8AR Tel: (01889) 565241 Fax: (01889) 563203

STEEL PANEL PINS

Frank Shaw (Bayonet) Ltd, Merse Road, North Moons Moat, Redditch, Worcestershire, B98 9HL Tel: (01527) 66241 Fax: (01527) 584455 E-mail: sales@frankshaw.co.uk

STEEL PARTITIONING

Alco Beldan Ltd, Accordial House, 35 Watford Metro Centre, Watford, WD18 9XN Tel: (01923) 246600 Fax: (01923) 245654 E-mail: enquiries@alcobeldan.com

D L Storage Handling Ltd, 20 Jessops Riverside, 800 Brightside Lane, Sheffield, S9 2RX Tel: 0114-244 0202 Fax: 0114-244 1222 E-mail: sales@thedlcompany.com

Edm Ceco Holdings Ltd, 1 Carryduff Business Park, Comber Road, Carryduff, Belfast, BT8 8AN Tel: (028) 9081 5303 Fax: (028) 9081 5449 E-mail: sales@edmspanwall.com

FOCUS Interiors Ltd, Wellsway Works, Wells Road, Radstock, BA3 3RZ Tel: (01761) 420055 Fax: (01761) 420077 E-mail: enquiries@focusinteriorsltd.co.uk

G B R Industries Ltd, Galebreaker House, New Mills Industrial Estate, Ledbury, Herefordshire, HR8 2SS Tel: (01531) 637900 Fax: (01531) 637901 E-mail: jps@galebreaker.co.uk

Interior & Facility Contracts Ltd, Excelsior House, Buntsford Park Road, Bromsgrove, Worcestershire, B60 3DX Tel: (01527) 573000 Fax: (01527) 573001 E-mail: enquiries@interior-facility.com

P K K Storage Systems Ltd, Gibbons Lane, Brierley Hill, West Midlands, DY5 4RY Tel: (01384) 79555 Fax: (01384) 75588 E-mail: pkkcontracts@aol.com

Thrislington Products Ltd, Durham Way South, Aycliffe Industrial Park, Newton Aycliffe, County Durham, DL5 6SW Tel: (01325) 301333 Fax: (01325) 301444 E-mail: sales@thrislington.co.uk

Troax UK Ltd, Enterprise House, Murdock Road, Dorcan, Swindon, SN3 5HY Tel: (01793) 542000 Fax: (01793) 618784 E-mail: info@troax.co.uk

WRG Partition Systems, 22 Bartleet Road, Redditch, Worcestershire, B98 0DQ Tel: (01527) 502299 Fax: (01527) 502288 E-mail: wrgpartitions@aol.com

STEEL PICKLING/OILING SERVICES

Central Steel Pickling Ltd, Nomex House, Powke Lane, Cradley Heath, West Midlands, B64 5PX Tel: (01384) 566373 Fax: (01384) 566376

STEEL PILING

Corus, 15 Great Marlborough Street, London, W1F 7HR Tel: (020) 7717 4444 Fax: (020) 7717 4455

Lemon Groundwork Supplies, Russell Gardens, Wickford, Essex, SS11 8BH Tel: (01268) 571571 Fax: (01268) 571555 E-mail: sales@lemon-gs.co.uk

VolkerSteel Foundations Ltd, Springwell Road, Springwell, Gateshead, Tyne & Wear, NE9 7SP Tel: 0191-417 3545 Fax: 0191-416 2894 E-mail: info.ss@volkerstevin.co.uk

STEEL PIPES, STRUCTURAL

▶ Mooreland Construction Ltd, Leabrook Road, Wednesbury, West Midlands, WS10 7LZ Tel: 0121-505 6248

STEEL PLATE BENDING

Barnshaw's Bending Centre Ltd, 2 Arrow Trading Estate, Corporation Road, Audenshaw, Manchester, M34 5LR Tel: 0161-320 9696 Fax: 0161-335 0918

STEEL PLATE FLATTENING

Ballachree Ltd, Canal Road, Frizinghall, Bradford, West Yorkshire, BD2 1AU Tel: (01274) 593131 Fax: (01274) 596752 E-mail: sales@ballachree.co.uk

STEEL PLATE MANUFRS

A S D Motor Services, Drum Industrial Estate, Drum Industrial Estate, Chester le Street, County Durham, DH2 1ST Tel: 0191-492 2322 Fax: 0191-410 0126

Armstrong Glen Metals, 14 Palacecraig Street, Coatbridge, Lanarkshire, ML5 4RY Tel: (01236) 424396 Fax: (01236) 433330 E-mail: glenmetals@asdmetalservices.co.uk

Asd Metal Services, South Humberside Industrial Estate, Grimsby, South Humberside, DN31 2TG Tel: (01472) 353851 Fax: (01472) 240028 E-mail: grimsby@asdmetalservices.co.uk

C. Beech & Sons (Netherton) Ltd, Waterside Estate, Primrose Hill, Cradley Road, Netherton, Dudley, West Midlands, DY2 9RG Tel: (01384) 456654 Fax: (01384) 238656 E-mail: sales@cbeech-steel.co.uk

Central Plate Services Ltd, Phoenix Works Industrial Estate, Richards Street, Wednesbury, West Midlands, WS10 8BZ Tel: 0121-526 3770 Fax: 0121-526 4770

Corus, Mossend Works, Main Street, Bellshill, Lanarkshire, ML4 1DJ Tel: (01698) 748424 Fax: (01698) 747191

Corus, 96 Stourbridge Road, Lye, Stourbridge, West Midlands, DY9 7DD Tel: (01384) 424151 Fax: (01384) 424073

Corus Construction & Industrial UK Ltd, Brigg Road, Scunthorpe, South Humberside, DN16 1BP Tel: (01724) 404040 Fax: (01724) 402191E-mail: andrew.page@corusgroup.com

Coventry Grinders Ltd, 7 Alpha Business Park, Deedmore Road, Coventry, CV2 1EQ Tel: (024) 7660 4377 Fax: (024) 7660 4975 E-mail: info@coventry-grinders.co.uk

Forth Steel Ltd, 28 South Gyle Cresent, Edinburgh, EH12 9EB Tel: 0131-316 4360 Fax: 0131-316 4343 E-mail: forth_steel@mih.co.uk

Industeel UK, Hallow Park, Hallow, Worcester, WR2 6PG Tel: (01905) 641444 Fax: (01905) 641555

Malcolm Clarke Haulage Ltd, Jubilee Works, Clifton St Miles, Manchester, M40 8HN Tel: 0161-205 7280 Fax: 0161-205 8473 E-mail: sales@clarke-steel.co.uk

Murray (International) Metals Ltd, Murray Works, Newbridge Industrial Estate, Newbridge, Midlothian, EH28 8PJ Tel: 0131-333 3333 Fax: 0131-333 4477 E-mail: mim_newbridge@murray-metals.co.uk

P & D Northern Steels Ltd, Mosshey Street, Shaw, Oldham, OL2 8QL Tel: (01706) 848811 Fax: (01706) 841153 E-mail: sales@pdnorthern.co.uk

Pearson Profilers, Skippers Lane, Skippers Lane Industrial Estate, Middlesbrough, Cleveland, TS6 6HA Tel: (01642) 466566 Fax: (01642) 466299 E-mail: sales@pearsonprofilers.co.uk

Quenched & Tempered Steels Ltd, 60 Green Road, Leeds, LS6 4JP Tel: 0113-225 0400 Fax: 0113-228 6333 E-mail: sales@qandtsteels.fsnet.co.uk

Readman Steel Ltd, Cochranes Wharf, Cargo Fleet, Middlesbrough, Cleveland, TS3 6AW Tel: (01642) 242641 Fax: (01642) 241912 E-mail: mail@wgrsteels.co.uk

Rubicon Ltd, Unit 11 Rockingham Business Park, Rockingham Row, Birdwell, Barnsley, South Yorkshire, S70 5TW Tel: (01226) 351515 Fax: (01226) 351535 E-mail: mail@rubiconsteel.co.uk

S M Thompson Ltd, Marathon Works, Newport Bridge, Middlesbrough, Cleveland, TS1 5TG Tel: (01642) 245161 Fax: (01642) 223392 E-mail: sales@smthompson.co.uk

Sleeman Engineering Ltd, Dawes Lane, Scunthorpe, South Humberside, DN16 1DN Tel: (01724) 272100 Fax: (01724) 272101 E-mail: info@firthrixson.com

John Stansfeld Ltd, Springwell Works, Buslingthorpe Lane, Leeds, LS7 2DF Tel: 0113-262 8155 Fax: 0113-262 9730 E-mail: sales@gheuk.co.uk

Swedish Steel, De Salis Court, De Salis Drive, Hampton Lovett, Droitwich, Worcestershire, WR9 0QE Tel: (01905) 795794 Fax: (01905) 794736 E-mail: ssabuk@ssab.com

Taylor Metals, 244 Bernard Street, Glasgow, G40 3NX Tel: 0141-556 1903 Fax: 0141-556 1903

Tipton & Mill Steels Ltd, Hobart Road, Tipton, West Midlands, DY4 9LQ Tel: 0121-557 7251 Fax: 0121-557 7258 E-mail: sales@tipton-steels.co.uk

Universal Steel, 9 Lindholme Gardens, Owlthorpe, Sheffield, S20 6TD Tel: (07870) 575523 Fax: 0114-248 4139 E-mail: peterjwatters@tiscali.co.uk

STEEL PLATE SHEARING

Clifda Steels Ltd, Northwick Corner, Canvey Island, Essex, SS8 0PS Tel: (01268) 510066 Fax: (01268) 683815 E-mail: clifdasteels@yahoo.com

Comvek Engineering Ltd, Station Drive, Unit 1, Breener Industrial Estate, Brierley Hill, West Midlands, DY5 3JZ Tel: (01384) 571515 Fax: (01384) 262088 E-mail: clbradley@btconnect.com

D Perkins, 3 Maltings Industrial Estate, Derby Road, Burton-on-Trent, Staffordshire, DE14 1RN Tel: (01283) 510451 Fax: (01283) 517977 E-mail: info@cncmetalproducts.co.uk

Marlborough Constructional Engineers Ltd, Winston Avenue, Croft, Leicester, LE9 3GQ Tel: (01455) 283500 Fax: (01455) 285147 E-mail: enquiries@marlboroughltd.com

Sebden Steel Midlands Ltd, Thorns Road, Brierley Hill, West Midlands, DY5 2PJ Tel: (01384) 424344 Fax: (01384) 892982 E-mail: brierleyhill@sebden.com

Willsden Steel Ltd, Airfield Business Park, Elvington, York, YO41 4AU Tel: (01904) 608773 Fax: (01904) 608754

STEEL PLATE TO SPECIFICATION

A S D Metal Services Cardiff, East Moors Road, Cardiff, CF24 5SP Tel: (029) 2046 0622 Fax: (029) 2049 0105 E-mail: cardiff@asdmetalservices.co.uk

James Bridge Steel Services Ltd, B S A Business Park, Armoury Road, Birmingham, B11 2RQ Tel: 0121-753 4444 Fax: 0121-753 4446 E-mail: sales@steelplates.co.uk

STEEL PORTAL FRAMES

Archibald Mcaulay & Son, Bankend Road, Broadmeadow Industrial Estate, Dumbarton, G82 2RB Tel: (01389) 762778 Fax: (01389) 742350 E-mail: steel@mcaulay.co.uk

STEEL PRECISION CUT LENGTH TUBES

Broson Ltd, Church Hill Road, Thurmaston, Leicester, LE4 8DJ Tel: 0116-269 8899 Fax: 0116-269 8898 E-mail: sales@broson.co.uk

Corus Ltd, West Wing Midland House, New Road, Halesowen, West Midlands, B63 3HY Tel: 0121-585 5522 Fax: 0121-585 5241 E-mail: cdtl@corusgroup.com

Kirkby Steel Tubes Ltd, Abbotsfield Road, Reginald Road Industrial Estat, St. Helens, Merseyside, WA9 4HU Tel: (01744) 830600 Fax: (01744) 830609E-mail: mail@kst.uk.com

Newman-Phoenix Drawn Tube Ltd, Phoenix Street, West Bromwich, West Midlands, B70 0AS Tel: 0121-543 5700 Fax: 0121-500 3030

Star Tubes (Southern) Ltd, Lilliput Road, Brackmills, Northampton, NN4 7DT Tel: (01908) 311777 Fax: (01908) 321874 E-mail: sales@startubes-southern.co.uk

STEEL PRESS TOOL CASTINGS

▶ J L Ornamental Castings, Unit 7, Old Ballynahinch Road, Lisburn, County Antrim, BT27 6TH Tel: (07710) 458636 Fax: (028) 9263 9808 E-mail: johnlavelle@btopenworld.com

STEEL PRESSINGS

Hall & Blenkinsop Ltd, Hetton Lyons Industrial Estate, Hetton-Le-Hole, Houghton Le Spring, Tyne & Wear, DH5 0RF Tel: 0191-526 2114 Fax: 0191-517 0112

Pegrex, Unit 1e Pearsall Drive, Oldbury, West Midlands, B69 2RA Tel: 0121-511 1475 Fax: 0121-511 1474 E-mail: nstruman@aol.com

Portland Pressings Ltd, Moor Lane, Birmingham, B6 7HH Tel: 0121-356 8187 Fax: 0121-344 3039

Pressrite Engineering Ltd, 24 Ogmore Crescent, Bridgend Industrial Estate, Bridgend, Mid Glamorgan, CF31 3TE Tel: (01656) 657067 Fax: (01656) 645857

Senior Press & Tool Co. Ltd, Unit 34b Marlborough Road, Churchill Industrial Estate, Lancing, West Sussex, BN15 8TR Tel: (01903) 762835 Fax: (01903) 762835

Shire Pressings Ltd, Doubak Works, Barton Industrial Estate, Bilston, West Midlands, WV14 7LH Tel: (01902) 490155 Fax: (01902) 490155

Taylor Pressform Ltd, 21 Rigby Close, Heathcote Industrial Estate, Warwick, CV34 6TH Tel: (01926) 339507 Fax: (01926) 451306

Waterhouse Pressings Ltd, Unit 4f Snaygill Industrial Estate, Keighley Road, Skipton, North Yorkshire, BD23 2QR Tel: (01756) 794577 Fax: (01756) 701481

STEEL PRESSURE VESSEL DOORS

Charles McNeil (Engineers), PO Box 4, Motherwell, Lanarkshire, ML1 3NP Tel: (01698) 266111 Fax: (01698) 269774 E-mail: lpowell@mbgroup.com

STEEL PRESSURE VESSELS

J E T Engineering, Ditton Road, Widnes, Cheshire, WA8 0TH Tel: 0151-423 5273 Fax: 0151-495 1390 E-mail: sales@jet-engineering.co.uk

Sheffield Forgemasters Engineering Ltd, PO Box 286, Sheffield, S9 2RU Tel: 0114-244 9071 Fax: 0114-242 2103 E-mail: sales@sfel.com

▶ Wefco (Gainsborough) Ltd, Brittania Works, Spring Gardens, Gainsborough, Lincolnshire, DN21 2AZ Tel: (01427) 611000 Fax: (01427) 612000 E-mail: glennb@wefco.net

Whiteley Read Engineering Ltd, Gateway Indust Estate, Rotherham, South Yorkshire, S62 6JL Tel: (01709) 710661 Fax: (01709) 710961 E-mail: sales@whitely-read.co.uk

STEEL PROCESSING MACHINERY, SHEET/STRIP

Concorde Precision Profile Ltd, Unit 86 Gibbons Industrial Park, Dudley Road, Kingswinford, West Midlands, DY6 8XF Tel: (01384) 400366 Fax: (01384) 402166 E-mail: carlconcorde@fsbdial.co.uk

M Brittain York Ltd, 29 Hospital Fields Road, Fulford Industrial Estate, York, YO10 4FZ Tel: (01904) 636021 Fax: (01904) 611627 E-mail: sales@mbrittainyork.co.uk

M F G Machinery, 6 Climax Works, Station Road, Reddish, Stockport, Cheshire, SK5 6YZ Tel: 0161-431 9125 Fax: 0161-432 2440

STEEL PROCESSING SERVICES, SHEET/STRIP

A S K Mcgowan Ltd, Coombs Wood Business Park, Steelpark Road, Halesowen, West Midlands, B62 8HD Tel: 0121-561 6800 Fax: 0121-561 6803 E-mail: central@askmcgowan.co.uk

Brockstock, Overend Road, Corngreaves Trading Estate, Cradley Heath, West Midlands, B64 7DD Tel: 0121-568 6161 Fax: (01384) 567191 E-mail: sales@brockstock.co.uk

Clifton Steel Ltd, 122 Fazeley Industrial Estate, Fazeley Street, Birmingham, B5 5RS Tel: 0121-603 4000 Fax: 0121-603 4001 E-mail: sales@cliftonsteel.co.uk

Corus UK Ltd, Glamorgan Works, Pontarddulais, Swansea, SA4 8SB Tel: (01792) 882548 Fax: (01792) 885196

Hillsborough Steelstock Ltd, Penistone Road North, Sheffield, S6 1LE Tel: 0114-285 5525 Fax: 0114-232 0972

J B & S Lees, Trident Steel Works, Albion Road, West Bromwich, West Midlands, B70 8BH Tel: 0121-553 3031 Fax: 0121-553 7680 E-mail: sales@jbslees.co.uk

Organically Coated Steels, Hoo Farm Industrial Estate, Worcester Road, Kidderminster, Worcestershire, DY11 7RA Tel: (01562) 821400 Fax: (01562) 865396 E-mail: ocs@asdmetalservices.co.uk

Paddington Steels Ltd, 6 Paddington Court, New Road, Kidderminster, Worcestershire, DY10 1AQ Tel: (01562) 827300 Fax: (01562) 827301

Rowham Steel Products Ltd, Lyons Road, Trafford Park, Manchester, M17 1RF Tel: 0161-786 3700 Fax: 0161-786 3707 E-mail: sales@rowhamsteel.co.uk

Sebden Steel, Broad Quay Road, Felnex Industrial Estate, Newport, Gwent, NP19 4PN Tel: (01633) 276054 Fax: (01633) 283355 E-mail: newport@sebden.com

Steelco UK Ltd, 12 Blackbrook Business Park, Narrowboat Way, Dudley, West Midlands, DY2 0XQ Tel: (01384) 455535 Fax: (01384) 456860 E-mail: steelco@fowle.btinternet.com

T J Thomson & Son Ltd, Millfield Works, Grangefield Road, Stockton-on-Tees, Cleveland, TS18 4AE Tel: (01642) 672551 Fax: (01642) 672556 E-mail: postbox@tjthomson.co.uk

STEEL PRODUCTS IMPORT/ EXPORT MERCHANTS OR AGENTS

Bohler Special Steels, European Business Park, Taylors Lane, Oldbury, West Midlands, B69 2BN Tel: 0121-552 2575 Fax: 0121-552 0023 E-mail: sales@bohlersteels.co.uk

Paignton Engineering, 3 Alders Way, Baytor Industrial Estate, Paignton, Devon, TQ4 7QJ Tel: (01803) 551302 Fax: (01803) 551302

STEEL PROFILES

▶ Accurist Fabrications Ltd, Wharf Foundry, Well Street, Bolton, BL1 1TZ Tel: (01204) 529383 Fax: (01204) 362896 E-mail: sales@accfabs.co.uk

West Yorkshire Steel Co. Ltd, Sandbeck Works, Sandbeck Industrial Estate, Wetherby, West Yorkshire, LS22 7DN Tel: 01937 584440 Fax: (0845) 658 1305 E-mail: sales@westyorkssteel.com

STEEL PROFILING

▶ E M E, 8 Robert Frazer Industrial, Station Road, Hebburn, Tyne & Wear, NE31 1BD Tel: 0191-428 4500 Fax: 0191-428 2767

STEEL RACKS

Ace Systems Ltd, Rose Green Road, Bristol, BS5 7XE Tel: 0117-952 0624 Fax: 0117-935 4255 E-mail: sales@acestorage.co.uk

Allcraft Metals, 69 Fleet Road, Fleet, Hampshire, GU51 3PJ Tel: (01252) 811901

Atol Racking & Building Ltd, Unit A3 Wymeswold Industrial Park, Wymeswold Road, Burton-on-the-Wolds, Loughborough, Leicestershire, LE12 5TY Tel: (01509) 881345 Fax: (01509) 881064E-mail: office@atol.co.uk

Flowstore Systems plc, 39 Frogmore Industrial Estate, Clayton Road, Hayes, Middlesex, UB3 1AU Tel: (020) 8581 5555 Fax: (020) 8581 5575 E-mail: sales@flowstore.co.uk

Planned Storage Systems Ltd, Murdock Road, Dorcan, Swindon, SN3 5HY Tel: (01793) 694071 Fax: (01793) 610516 E-mail: mail@hi-lo.co.uk

Rack International UK Ltd, Pant Industrial Estate, Dowlais, Merthyr Tydfil, CF48 2SR Tel: (01685) 383133 Fax: (01685) 383836 E-mail: sales@cavesystems.co.uk

Redirack Ltd, Wharf Road, Kilnhurst, Mexborough, South Yorkshire, S64 5SU Tel: (01709) 584711 Fax: (01709) 589821 E-mail: sales@redirack.co.uk

Wickens Engineering Ltd, 1 Shire Business Park, Wainwright Road, Worcester, WR4 9FA Tel: (01905) 456780 Fax: (01905) 456073 E-mail: info@wickens.co.uk

STEEL RAILWAY SLEEPERS

Coronet Rail Ltd, Castor Road, Sheffield, S9 2TL Tel: 0114-256 2225 Fax: 0114-261 7826 E-mail: sales@coronetrail.co.uk

Corus UK Ltd, Moss Bay Road, Workington, Cumbria, CA14 5AE Tel: (01900) 64321 Fax: (01900) 842237 E-mail: info@britishsteel.co.uk

STEEL RAINWATER GOODS

Konaflex Ltd, Unit 2 Northcote Road, Stechford, Birmingham, B33 9BE Tel: 0121-783 9778 Fax: 0121-784 8026E-mail: konaflex@aol.com

Lupton Fabrications Ltd, Unit A Aquatite House, Water Lane, Leeds, LS11 9UD Tel: 0113-242 6872 Fax: 0113-242 6874 E-mail: sales@lupton.uk.com

M R (Site Services) Ltd, Unit 6, Worcester Trading Estate, Blackpole, Worcester, WR3 8HR Tel: (01905) 755055 Fax: (01905) 755053 E-mail: info@mrsiteservices.com

Oakham Sheet Metal Co. Ltd, Brickhouse Lane, Great Bridge, West Bromwich, West Midlands, B70 0DS Tel: 0121-557 9656 Fax: 0121-522 2186

STEEL REFINING

S M S Mevac (UK) Ltd, Road Four, Winsford Industrial Estate, Winsford, Cheshire, CW7 3RS Tel: (01606) 551421 Fax: (01606) 553078 E-mail: mail@sms-mevac.co.uk

STEEL REFUSE CHUTES

▶ Hardall International Ltd, Fairway Works, Southfields Road, Dunstable, Bedfordshire, LU6 3EP Tel: (01582) 500860 Fax: (01582) 690975 E-mail: sales@hardall.co.uk

R.V. Weaver, Rectory Road, Grays, Essex, RM17 6BD Tel: (01375) 390820 Fax: (01375) 393333

STEEL RINGS

Doncasters Blaenavon Ltd, Forge Side, Blaenavon, Pontypool, Gwent, NP4 9XG Tel: (01495) 790345 Fax: (01495) 791565 E-mail: rhudson@doncasters.com

M J Sections Ltd, Unit 5 Marriott Road Industrial Estate, Netherton, Dudley, West Midlands, DY2 0JZ Tel: (01384) 230444 Fax: (01384) 456086 E-mail: sales@mjsections.co.uk

Thomas C Wild, Vulcan Works, Tinsley Park Road, Sheffield, S9 5DP Tel: 0114-244 2471 Fax: 0114-244 2052E-mail: info@tc-wild.co.uk

White Cross Ring Co. Ltd, Battye Street, Bradford, West Yorkshire, BD4 8AG Tel: (01274) 669933 Fax: (01274) 660137 E-mail: jason@whitecrossring.co.uk

STEEL ROLLERS

Tomah Engineers Ltd, 104 Fitzwalter Rd., Sheffield, S2 2SP Tel: 0114-272 1199 Fax: 0114-276 8675 E-mail: tomaheng@aol.com

STEEL ROLLERS FOR BEARINGS

Goldline F1 Ltd, Stafford Park 17, Telford, Shropshire, TF3 3DG Tel: (01952) 292401 Fax: (01952) 292403 E-mail: info@goldlinebearings.co.uk

STEEL ROUND BARS

Consett Steel Services Ltd, Bradley Workshops, Consett, County Durham, DH8 6HG Tel: (01207) 590171 Fax: (01207) 592086 E-mail: sales@consett-steel.co.uk

STEEL SAWING

Contract Cutting Services, Unit 19 Mill House Lane, Triangle, Sowerby Bridge, West Yorkshire, HX6 3LN Tel: (01422) 835313 Fax: (01422) 835320 E-mail: scott.thewlis@tiscali.co.uk

Corus, Sengate, The Drove, Brandon, Suffolk, IP27 0JY Tel: (01842) 816200 Fax: (01842) 813019

Corus, 202 Solent Business Centre, 343 Millbrook Road West, Southampton, SO15 0HW Tel: (023) 8023 3094 Fax: (023) 8023 3096

Corus Bristol, Badminton Road Trading Estate, Yate, Bristol, BS37 5JU Tel: (01454) 316600 Fax: (01454) 321014 E-mail: info@corusgroup.com

Corus Service Centre, Garmouth Road, Mosstodloch, Fochabers, Morayshire, IV32 7LH Tel: (01343) 820606 Fax: (01343) 821295

Hillsborough Steelstock Ltd, Penistone Road North, Sheffield, S6 1LE Tel: 0114-285 5525 Fax: 0114-232 0972

Precision Sawing Services Ltd, Union Road, Oldbury, West Midlands, B69 3EX Tel: 0121-544 9233 Fax: 0121-544 8846 E-mail: pssl2@aol.com

STEEL SCAFFOLDING

Hewaswater Ltd, Hewas Water Ltd, Hewas Water, St. Austell, Cornwall, PL26 7JF Tel: (01726) 885200 Fax: (01726) 885212 E-mail: info@heltd.demon.co.uk

Infometal, Moseley Street, Birmingham, B12 0RT Tel: 0121-693 3800 Fax: 0121-693 3803 E-mail: info@barnies.co.uk

Wade Building Services Ltd, Groveland Road, Tipton, West Midlands, DY4 7TN Tel: 0121-520 8121 Fax: 0121-557 7061 E-mail: sales@wade-bs.co.uk

Youngman Group, The Causeway, Heybridge, Maldon, Essex, CM9 4LJ Tel: (01621) 745900 Fax: (01621) 745710 E-mail: youngmansales@youngmangroup.com

STEEL SCREWS

Global Screw Co. Ltd, Business & Technology Centre, Eccles, Manchester, M30 0RJ Tel: 0161-787 3034 Fax: 0161-787 3112

STEEL SECTION CUTTING OR MITRE SERVICES

Corus Ltd, Brinsworth Strip Mills, Sheffield Road, Rotherham, South Yorkshire, S60 1BN Tel: (01709) 377113 Fax: (01709) 375250

Hanworth Timber Co. Ltd, White Post Road, Hanworth, Norwich, NR11 7HN Tel: (01263) 761766 Fax: (01263) 768903

STEEL SECTION MANUFRS, *See also other headings under Steel Sections*

Audenshaw Steel Ltd, Unit 12 Wharf Parade, Lower Wharf Street, Ashton-under-Lyne, Lancashire, OL6 7PE Tel: 0161-343 8550 Fax: 0161-343 8550

Ayrshire Metal Products, Royal Oak Way North, Royal Oak Industrial Estate, Daventry, Northamptonshire, NN11 8NR Tel: (01327) 300990 Fax: (01327) 300885 E-mail: sales@ayrshire.co.uk

Barclay & Mathieson Ltd, Cloverhill Road, Bridge of Don, Aberdeen, AB23 8FE Tel: (01224) 702771 Fax: (01224) 826227 E-mail: aberdeen@bmsteel.co.uk

Bexley Steel, 8 Power Industrial Estate, Slade Green Road, Erith, Kent, DA8 2HU Tel: (01322) 335420 Fax: (01322) 335984 E-mail: bexleysteel@supernet.com

Bradshaw Sheet Metal Works Ltd, Bradshaw Works, Printers Lane, Bolton, BL2 3DW Tel: (01204) 303300 Fax: (01204) 595797

Grange Steels, P O Box 2, Stoke-on-Trent, ST8 6JZ Tel: (01782) 510210 Fax: (01782) 510211 E-mail: grangesteels@asdplc.co.uk

Hickman Steels International Ltd, PO Box 6, Bridgnorth, Shropshire, WV16 5JJ Tel: (01746) 761733 Fax: (01746) 767299 E-mail: mikemansfield@hickmansteels.com

Inter Steels Ltd, Darent Indust Park, Wallhouse Road, Erith, Kent, DA8 2JT Tel: (01322) 337766 Fax: (01322) 335662 E-mail: sales@intergroupofcompanies.net

Morgan & Marlow Ltd, 93 Buckingham Street, Birmingham, B19 3JB Tel: 0121-212 9755 Fax: 0121-212 9756

Murray (International) Metals Ltd, Murray Works, Newbridge Industrial Estate, Newbridge, Midlothian, EH28 8PJ Tel: 0131-333 3333 Fax: 0131-333 4477 E-mail: mim_newbridge@murray-metals.co.uk

Readman Steel Ltd, Cochranes Wharf, Cargo Fleet, Middlesbrough, Cleveland, TS3 6AW Tel: (01642) 242641 Fax: (01642) 241912 E-mail: mail@wgrsteels.co.uk

Willsden Steel Ltd, Airfield Business Park, Elvington, York, YO41 4AU Tel: (01904) 608773 Fax: (01904) 608754

STEEL SECTIONS, STRUCTURAL

▶ 3D Structural Fabrications, Bull Street, Gornal Wood, Dudley, West Midlands, DY3 2NQ Tel: (01902) 656263 Fax: (01902) 656036 E-mail: structuralservices@blueyonder.co.uk

STEEL SEMI FINISHED PRODUCTS, *See headings for particular types*

STEEL SHEET LASER CUTTING SERVICES

▶ Laser Products UK Ltd, Phoenix Works, Hope Bank Honley, Holmfirth, HD9 6PR Tel: (01484) 665870 Fax: (01484) 663581 E-mail: sales@laserproductsuk.com

STEEL SHEET MANUFRS, *See also other headings under Steel Sheet*

A & C Steels Ltd, 7 Brookvale Trading Estate, Moor Lane, Birmingham, B6 7AQ Tel: 0121-356 1080 Fax: 0121-344 3731

A S D Metal Services Ltd, Gibson Lane, Melton, North Ferriby, East Yorkshire, HU14 3HX Tel: (01482) 633360 Fax: (01482) 633370 E-mail: hull@asdmetalservices.co.uk

A S D Motor Services, Drum Industrial Estate, Drum Industrial Estate, Chester le Street, County Durham, DH2 1ST Tel: 0191-492 2322 Fax: 0191-410 0126

Accent Steel Ltd, 164 West Wycombe Road, High Wycombe, Buckinghamshire, HP12 3AE Tel: (01494) 465421 Fax: (01494) 524044 E-mail: accentsteel@ukonline.co.uk

Armada Tube & Steel (SW) Ltd, Tube & Steel Service Centre, Pennygillam Industrial Estate, Launceston, Cornwall, PL15 7ED Tel: (01566) 776699 Fax: (01566) 776500 E-mail: des@armadatube.co.uk

Asd Metal Services, South Humberside Industrial Estate, Grimsby, South Humberside, DN31 2TG Tel: (01472) 353851 Fax: (01472) 240028 E-mail: grimsby@asdmetalservices.co.uk

Barclay & Mathieson Ltd, Coleford Road, Sheffield, S9 5NF Tel: 0114-244 2094 Fax: 0114-243 5965 E-mail: sheffield@bmsteel.co.uk

Barnet Metal Engineering Co. Ltd, Stirling Works, Tewin Road, Welwyn Garden City, Hertfordshire, AL7 1AG Tel: (01707) 324327 Fax: (01707) 371375

Butterworth Steel Processing, Bilport Lane, Wednesbury, West Midlands, WS10 0NT Tel: 0121-556 8541 Fax: 0121-502 4644

C J Upton & Sons Ltd, 7 Stamford Square, Ashton-under-Lyne, Lancashire, OL6 6QU Tel: 0161-339 3330 Fax: 0161-339 3304 E-mail: sales@cjupton.com

C L T (Essington) Ltd, Unit 2C Bloxwich Business Pk, Fryers Rd, Walsall, WS2 7LY Tel: (01922) 713367 Fax: (01922) 713368

Camp Steel, 29 Grafton Road, Sparkbrook, Birmingham, B11 1JP Tel: 0121-772 7821 Fax: 0121-771 0435 E-mail: dave-campsteel@btconnect.com

Cogent Orb Electrical Steels, PO Box 30, Newport, Gwent, NP19 0XT Tel: (01633) 290033 Fax: (01633) 294592 E-mail: sales@cogent-power.com

Color Steels Ltd, Blackvein Industrial Estate, Cross Keys, Newport, Gwent, NP11 7YD Tel: (01495) 279100 Fax: (01495) 271456

Combined Steel Services Ltd, 5 Boddis Industrial Park, Garratts Lane, Cradley Heath, West Midlands, B64 5SS Tel: 0121-559 3737 Fax: 0121-559 2500 E-mail: combinedsteels@btconnect.com

Cutler & Woolf (Steel) Ltd, Unit 32, Jubilee Trade Centre, Jubilee Road, Letchworth Garden City, Hertfordshire, SG6 1SP Tel: (01462) 480420 Fax: (01462) 480430 E-mail: sales@cutlerandwoolfe.co.uk

Davro Iron & Steel Co. Ltd, Ridgewell Works, Stourbridge Road, Wootton, Bridgnorth, Shropshire, WV15 6ED Tel: (01746) 780242 Fax: (01746) 780930 E-mail: mikenielen@davrodeal.co.uk

European Steel Sheets Ltd, Doris Road, Bordesley Green, Birmingham, B9 4SJ Tel: 0121-766 7677 Fax: 0121-766 7864 E-mail: dan.broadhurst@europeansteelsheets.com

Fowle & Co. Ltd, Tremlon House, Menzies Road, St. Leonards-on-Sea, East Sussex, TN38 9BQ Tel: (01424) 444666 Fax: (01424) 720442 E-mail: lauren.edwards@btconnect.com

H Powell Ltd, Booth Street, Smethwick, West Midlands, B66 2PF Tel: 0121-555 5527 Fax: 0121-555 6208

Hall & Pickles, Blackvein Industrial Estate, Cross Keys, Newport, Gwent, NP11 7PX Tel: (023) 8065 1815 Fax: (01495) 271563 E-mail: cksales@hallandpickles.co.uk

Katoll Metals & Industrial Products Ltd, Central Avenue, Cradley Heath, West Midlands, B64 7BY Tel: (01384) 634001 Fax: (01384) 410776 E-mail: sales@katollmetals.co.uk

Mossteel Ltd, Unit 22 Central Industrial Estate, Cable Street, Wolverhampton, WV2 2RJ Tel: (01902) 351832 Fax: (01902) 351231

Rowan Steels Ltd, 2 Park Street Works, Park Street, Kidderminster, Worcestershire, DY11 6TN Tel: (01562) 67476 Fax: (01562) 515412 E-mail: sales@rowansteels.co.uk

John Stansfield Ltd, Springwell Works, Buslingthorpe Lane, Leeds, LS7 2DF Tel: 0113-262 8155 Fax: 0113-262 9730 E-mail: sales@gheuk.co.uk

A. Steadman & Son Ltd, Warnell, Welton, Carlisle, CA5 7HH Tel: (01697) 478277 Fax: (01697) 478530 E-mail: info@steadmans.co.uk

Steelco UK Ltd, 12 Blackbrook Business Park, Narrowboat Way, Dudley, West Midlands, DY2 0XQ Tel: (01384) 455535 Fax: (01384) 456860 E-mail: steelco@fowle.btinternet.com

Tipton & Mill Steels Ltd, Hobart Road, Tipton, West Midlands, DY4 9LQ Tel: 0121-557 7251 Fax: 0121-557 7258 E-mail: sales@tipton-steels.co.uk

Willsden Steel Ltd, Airfield Business Park, Elvington, York, YO41 4AU Tel: (01904) 608773 Fax: (01904) 608754

STEEL SHEET SHEARING

A & C Steels Ltd, 7 Brookvale Trading Estate, Moor Lane, Birmingham, B6 7AQ Tel: 0121-356 1080 Fax: 0121-344 3731

Artrow Metals Co. Ltd, Landywood Lane, Cheslyn Hay, Walsall, WS6 7AL Tel: (01922) 412602 Fax: (01922) 414583

B I L Steels Ltd, Eyre Street, Birmingham, B18 7AA Tel: 0121-456 5886 Fax: 0121-454 6213

Barnet Metal Engineering Co. Ltd, Stirling Works, Tewin Road, Welwyn Garden City, Hertfordshire, AL7 1AG Tel: (01707) 324327 Fax: (01707) 371375

Barnshaws Plate Bending, Anchor Lane, Bilston, West Midlands, WV14 9NE Tel: (01902) 880250 Fax: (01902) 880505

Butterworth Steel Processing, Bilport Lane, Wednesbury, West Midlands, WS10 0NT Tel: 0121-556 8541 Fax: 0121-502 4644

Byworth Engineering Ltd, Albion Works, Royd Ings Ave, Keighley, W. Yorkshire, BD21 4BZ Tel: (01535) 602780 Fax: (01535) 611319

C S Alloys, Unit 32 Jubilee Trade Centre, Jubilee Road, Letchworth Garden City, Hertfordshire, SG6 1SP Tel: (01462) 481273 Fax: (01462) 481092 E-mail: csalloys@hotmail.com

Davro Iron & Steel Co. Ltd, Ridgewell Works, Stourbridge Road, Wootton, Bridgnorth, Shropshire, WV15 6ED Tel: (01746) 780242 Fax: (01746) 780930 E-mail: mikenielen@davrodeal.co.uk

Ellwood Steel Ltd, Unit 2 Park Lane, Halesowen, West Midlands, B63 2NT Tel: (01384) 564935 Fax: (01384) 410577

European Steel Sheets Ltd, Doris Road, Bordesley Green, Birmingham, B9 4SJ Tel: 0121-766 7677 Fax: 0121-766 7864 E-mail: dan.broadhurst@europeansteelsheets.com

Galvanised Sheet & Coil Ltd, Doris Road, Bordesley Green, Birmingham, B9 4SJ Tel: 0121-773 8341 Fax: 0121-771 0024

H Powell Ltd, Booth Street, Smethwick, West Midlands, B66 2PF Tel: 0121-555 5527 Fax: 0121-555 6208

J & T Steel Shearing, 37 The Bridge Trading Estate, Bridge Street North, Smethwick, West Midlands, B66 2BZ Tel: 0121-565 2886 Fax: 0121-558 9670 E-mail: jtsteel@hotmail.co.uk

Marlborough Constructional Engineers Ltd, Winston Avenue, Croft, Leicester, LE9 3GQ Tel: (01455) 283500 Fax: (01455) 285147 E-mail: enquiries@marlboroughltd.com

Milden Steels Ltd, Unit 1 Park St Works, Kidderminster, Worcestershire, DY11 6TN Tel: (01562) 66615 Fax: (01562) 829293 E-mail: sales@milden-steels.fsnet.co.uk

Mossteel Ltd, Unit 22 Central Industrial Estate, Cable Street, Wolverhampton, WV2 2RJ Tel: (01902) 351832 Fax: (01902) 351231

Paddington Steels Ltd, 6 Paddington Court, New Road, Kidderminster, Worcestershire, DY10 1AQ Tel: (01562) 827300 Fax: (01562) 827301

Rowan Steels Ltd, 2 Park Street Works, Park Street, Kidderminster, Worcestershire, DY11 6TN Tel: (01562) 67476 Fax: (01562) 515412 E-mail: sales@rowansteels.co.uk

Sebden Steel Midlands Ltd, Thorns Road, Brierley Hill, West Midlands, DY5 2PJ Tel: (01384) 424344 Fax: (01384) 892982 E-mail: brierleyhill@sebden.com

Steel & Alloy Processing Ltd, Trafalgar Works, Union Street, West Bromwich, West Midlands, B70 6BZ Tel: 0121-553 5292 Fax: 0121-553 3864 E-mail: info@steelalloy.co.uk

Willenhall Shearing Co, Leve Lane, Willenhall, West Midlands, WV13 1PS Tel: (01902) 605126 Fax: (01902) 631919

STEEL SHELVING

Brysdales Interiors Ltd, Brysdale House Drumhead Road, Chorley North Business Park, Chorley, Lancashire, PR6 7DE Tel: (01257) 240000 Fax: (01257) 240024 E-mail: enquiries@brysdales.co.uk

Craven & Co. Ltd, Manse Lane, Knaresborough, North Yorkshire, HG5 8ET Tel: (01423) 796208 Fax: (01423) 869189 E-mail: sales@craven-solutions.com

E Z Rect Ltd, Witan Park, Avenue Two, Witney, Oxfordshire, OX28 4FH Tel: (01993) 779494 Fax: (01993) 704111 E-mail: sales@e-z-rect.com

East Anglian Shelving Ltd, 20/21 Denny Rd, Hardwick Industrial Estate, King's Lynn, Norfolk, PE30 4HG Tel: (01553) 765205 Fax: (01553) 768464 E-mail: sales@eais-shelving.co.uk

Itab G.W.S Group Ltd, Unit E2 Imperial Business Estate, West Mill, Gravesend, Kent, DA11 0DL Tel: (01474) 537744 Fax: (01474) 537860 E-mail: info@gwsgroup.com

Nicholl & Wood Ltd, Netherton Works, Holmfield, Halifax, West Yorkshire, HX3 6ST Tel: (01422) 244484 Fax: (01422) 248777 E-mail: sales@niwood.co.uk

Rackline Systems Storage Ltd, Oaktree Lane, Talke Pits, Stoke-on-Trent, ST7 1RX Tel: (01782) 777666 Fax: (01782) 777444 E-mail: sales@rackline.co.uk

Sperrin Metal Products Ltd, Cahore Road, Draperstown, Magherafelt, County Londonderry, BT45 7AP Tel: (028) 7962 8362 Fax: (028) 7962 8972 E-mail: sales@sperrin-metal.com

Ssi Schaefer Ltd, 83-84 Livingstone Road, Walworth Industrial Estate, Andover, Hampshire, SP10 5QZ Tel: (01264) 386600 Fax: (01264) 386611 E-mail: solutions@ssi-schaefer.co.uk

T P G Storage, 7 Hudsons Way, Canvey Island, Essex, SS8 9FE Tel: (01268) 696336 Fax: (01268) 514048

STEEL SILOS

Eurpa Silos Ltd, Unit 15, Prydwen Road, Swansea West Industrial Estate, Swansea, SA5 4HN Tel: (01792) 410450 Fax: (01792) 410455

STEEL SLITTING, *See Steel Coil Cutting etc*

STEEL SPRINGS

Woodhead R.S.R Springs Commercial Vehicle Spares, 41 Rothersthorpe Avenue, Rothersthorpe Avenue Industrial Estate, Rothersthorpe Avenue Industrial Estat,

Northampton, NN4 8JH Tel: (01604) 675777 Fax: (01604) 675808 E-mail: sales@serckintertruck.co.uk

STEEL STACKABLE CHAIRS

Southsea Deck Chairs Ltd, The Old Council Depot, Burrfields Road, Portsmouth, PO3 5LZ Tel: (023) 9265 2865 Fax: (023) 9265 5830 E-mail: info@deckchairs.co.uk

STEEL STAIRCASES

Euro Spec, Unit 7 Drakes Lane, Boreham, Chelmsford, CM3 3BE Tel: (01245) 362551 Fax: (01245) 360522 E-mail: sales@euro-spec.co.uk
Four-Tec Fabrications Ltd, Unit 2 Whieldon Industrial Estate, Whieldon Road, Stoke-on-Trent, ST4 4JP Tel: (01782) 844434 Fax: (01782) 744351 E-mail: fourtecfabs@aol.com
Lowe Engineering Midland Ltd, Stone Road, Bramshall, Uttoxeter, Staffordshire, ST14 8SH Tel: (01889) 563244 Fax: (01889) 563554 E-mail: sales@loweengineering.co.uk
S G Welding & Fabrications, Freeman Road, North Hykeham, Lincoln, LN6 9AP Tel: (01522) 501569 Fax: (01522) 501560
▶ Whitten Ltd, Unit 4, 39 Willow Lane, Mitcham, Surrey, CR4 4NA Tel: (020) 8640 3888 E-mail: whittenmetalworks@btconnect.com

STEEL STOCKHOLDERS

▶ Bone Steel Ltd, Pickering Park Works, Netherton Road, Wishaw, Lanarkshire, ML2 0EQ Tel: (01698) 375000 Fax: (01698) 372727 E-mail: sales@bonesteel.co.uk
▶ Ford Steel Services, 33 Dawley Trading Estate, Stallings Lane, Kingswinford, West Midlands, DY6 7AP Tel: (01384) 288966 Fax: (01384) 292114
A.D. Hall Ltd, Chemical Lane, Longbridge Hayes Indrustrial Estate, Stoke-on-Trent, ST6 4PB Tel: (01782) 577605
▶ J L Steel Services, Unit 101, Bandeath Industrial Estate, Stirling, FK7 7NP Tel: (01786) 817081 Fax: (01786) 810981
L.W. Lambourn & Co. Ltd, 27 Citypoint, 1 Ropemakers Street, London, EC2Y 9ST Tel: (020) 7775 3600 Fax: (020) 7775 3829 E-mail: info@stemcor.com
Midland Motor Rewinds, 6 Factory Road, Birmingham, B18 5JU Tel: 0121-551 2323 Fax: 0121-554 2295
▶ PTC Alliance UK, Gander Lane, Barlborough, Chesterfield, Derbyshire, S43 4PZ Tel: (01246) 573437 Fax: (01246) 573431 E-mail: darren.hunt@ptcalliance.com
Supreme Steels, 578 Queslett Road, Birmingham, B43 7DY Tel: 0121-325 1393 Fax: 0121-325 1409 E-mail: supremesteels@aol.com

STEEL STREET LIGHTING STANDARDS OR COLUMNS

Abacus Holdings Ltd, Oddicroft Lane, Sutton-in-Ashfield, Nottinghamshire, NG17 5FT Tel: (01623) 511111 Fax: (01623) 552133 E-mail: sales@abacuslighting.com
Fabrikat Nottingham Ltd, Hamilton Road, Sutton-in-Ashfield, Nottinghamshire, NG17 5LN Tel: (01623) 442200 Fax: (01623) 442233

STEEL STRIP SHEARING

Cudlow Steel Services Ltd, Unit H4 Rudford Industrial Estate, Ford Road, Ford, Arundel, West Sussex, BN18 0BD Tel: (01903) 714545 Fax: (01903) 716151 E-mail: cudlow@fsbdial.co.uk

STEEL STRIP, CARBON

BSS Steelstrip Ltd, 42 Gatcombe Way, Priorslee, Telford, Shropshire, TF2 9GZ Tel: (01952) 290313 E-mail: bss@steelstrip.co.uk

STEEL STRIPS, *See also headings for particular types*

A & C Steels Ltd, 7 Brookvale Trading Estate, Moor Lane, Birmingham, B6 7AQ Tel: 0121-356 1080 Fax: 0121-344 3731
A S D Coil Processing, Tipton Road, Tividale, Oldbury, West Midlands, B69 3HU Tel: 0121-522 2215 Fax: 0121-522 2293 E-mail: customer.care@asdplc.co.uk
C S Alloys, Unit 32 Jubilee Trade Centre, Jubilee Road, Letchworth Garden City, Hertfordshire, SG6 1SP Tel: (01462) 481273 Fax: (01462) 481092 E-mail: csalloys@hotmail.com
Corus Ltd, Brinsworth Strip Mills, Sheffield Road, Rotherham, South Yorkshire, S60 1BN Tel: (01709) 377113 Fax: (01709) 375250
Corus (U K) Ltd, Llanwern Works, Newport, Gwent, NP19 4QZ Tel: (01633) 290022
Corus UK Ltd, Glamorgan Works, Pontarddulais, Swansea, SA4 8SB Tel: (01792) 882548 Fax: (01792) 885196
Ductile Stourbridge Cold Mills Ltd, PO Box 13, Willenhall, West Midlands, WV13 1HQ Tel: (01902) 365400 Fax: (01902) 365444 E-mail: info@dscm.co.uk
Harry Fisher & Co., London Works, Bridge St, Sheffield, S3 8NT Tel: 0114-272 1998 Fax: 0114-275 2489
George Ibbotson Steels Ltd, 16 Atlas Way, Sheffield, S4 7QQ Tel: 0114-244 7400 Fax: 0114-244 7412 E-mail: sales@ibbotsonsteels.co.uk
Reddiwire Ltd, 9 Dunlop Road, Hunt End, Redditch, Worcestershire, B97 5XP Tel: (01527) 550202 Fax: (01527) 546856 E-mail: reddiwire@dial.pipex.com
Uddeholm Steel Stockholders, European Business Park, Taylors Lane, Oldbury, West Midlands, B69 2BN Tel: 0121-552 5530 Fax: 0121-544 3036 E-mail: sales@uddeholm.co.uk

STEEL SURPLUS/LIQUIDATED/ REDUNDANT JOB AND STOCK BULK BUYERS

Mark James Ltd, 9 Churchill Close, Streatley, Luton, LU3 3PJ Tel: (01582) 881534 Fax: (01582) 883486

STEEL TANKS

Allied Tank & Fabrications Ltd, Phoenix Works Industrial Estate, Richards Street, Wednesbury, West Midlands, WS10 8BZ Tel: 0121-568 8166 Fax: 0121-568 8177 E-mail: sales@alliedtanks.co.uk
▶ James Blake & Co. (Engineers) Ltd, 30-32 South Fort Street, Leith, Edinburgh, EH6 5NU Tel: 0131-554 1646 Fax: 0131-553 4128 E-mail: info@blakegroup.co.uk
Bradshaw Sheet Metal Works Ltd, Bradshaw Works, Printers Lane, Bolton, BL2 3DW Tel: (01204) 303300 Fax: (01204) 595797
Braithwaite Engineers Ltd, Neptune Works Cork Wharf, Mill Parade, Newport, Gwent, NP20 2UY Tel: (01633) 262141 Fax: (01633) 250631 E-mail: tanks@braithwaite.co.uk
Castle Engineering Resources Ltd, 4 Central Works, Peartree Lane, Dudley, West Midlands, DY2 0QU Tel: (01384) 230233 Fax: (01384) 230757 E-mail: castle.eng@btclick.com
E G Reeve & Sons Ltd, Burton Road, Norwich, NR6 6AT Tel: (01603) 427228 Fax: (01603) 789548 E-mail: alan@egreeve.co.uk
Easiflo Engineering Ltd, Providence Street, Stourbridge, West Midlands, DY9 8HR Tel: (01384) 894811 Fax: (01384) 422447 E-mail: easiflo.eng@btconnect.com
Eddison & Wanless Ltd, Unit 1, Mallard Industrial Estate, Horbury, Wakefield, West Yorkshire, WF4 5QH Tel: (01924) 271128 Fax: (01924) 271251 E-mail: info@eddisonwanless.co.uk
Galglass Ltd, 321 Hough Lane, Wombwell, Barnsley, South Yorkshire, S73 0LR Tel: (01226) 340370 Fax: (01226) 344200 E-mail: sscott@galglass.co.uk
Greenline Tanks Ltd, Townwell, Cromhall, Wotton-under-Edge, Gloucestershire, GL12 8AG Tel: (01454) 294801 Fax: (01454) 294799 E-mail: chris@greenlinetanks.co.uk
Harvey Fabrication Ltd, Hancock Road, Bow, London, E3 3DA Tel: (020) 8981 7811 Fax: (020) 8981 7815
J T Services Ltd, 99 Reindeer Road, Fazeley, Tamworth, Staffordshire, B78 3SP Tel: (01827) 250280 Fax: (01827) 281363
Koronka Agriculture & Tanks Ltd, Bridgend, Kinross, KY13 8EN Tel: (01577) 862189 Fax: (01577) 864773 E-mail: sales@koronka.co.uk
Ledbury Welding & Engineering Ltd, New Mills Industrial Estate, Leadon Way, Ledbury, Herefordshire, HR8 2SR Tel: (01531) 632222 Fax: (01531) 634718 E-mail: sales@lweltd.co.uk
M1 Engineering Ltd, 5 Commondale Way, Bradford, West Yorkshire, BD4 6SQ Tel: (01274) 416000 Fax: (01274) 420307
Mayweld Engineering Co. Ltd, Banners Lane, Halesowen, West Midlands, B63 2SD Tel: (01384) 560285 Fax: (01384) 411456
North Hunts Welding & Engineering Co., America Farm Cottage, Oxney Road, Peterborough, PE1 5YR Tel: (01733) 222632 Fax: (01733) 222732
Spencer Construction & Engineering, Royal Albert Works, Bradfield Road, London, E16 2AT Tel: (020) 7511 1711 Fax: (020) 7474 2195
Taylor Fuel Control, Unit 4a New England Estate, Off Pindar Road, Hoddesdon, Hertfordshire, EN11 0BZ Tel: (01992) 451101 Fax: (01992) 444954
Telford Tanks Ltd, Unit 3c Central Works, Peartree Lane, Dudley, West Midlands, DY2 0QU Tel: (01384) 212167 Fax: (01384) 457757
▶ Vulcan Tanks Ltd, Cotes Park Lane, Cotes Park Industrial Estate, Somercotes, Alfreton, Derbyshire, DE55 4NJ Tel: (01773) 835321 Fax: (01773) 836578 E-mail: sales@vulcantanks.co.uk
Winsford Fabrications, Road 5, Winsford Industrial Estate, Winsford, Cheshire, CW7 3SH Tel: (01606) 597305 Fax: (01606) 597308

STEEL THREADED PRESSURE PLUGS

B B R Engineering (Shropshire) Ltd, King Street, Broseley, Shropshire, TF12 5LT Tel: (01952) 882597 Fax: (01952) 883955 E-mail: sales@bbrengineering.co.uk

STEEL TOWER ERECTION OR INSTALLATION

Bradley Hire Southern Ltd, Biltam Farm, Stan Hill, Charlwood, Horley, Surrey, RH6 0EP Tel: 01293 863205 Fax: 01293 862775
▶ Hi-Point Scaffolding Ltd, Valley Works, Grange Lane, Sheffield, S5 0DQ Tel: 0114-257 7600 E-mail: info@hi-pointscaffolding.co.uk
▶ S C H Site Services, Units G511 A, B & C, Whinbank Road, Aycliffe Industrial Estate, Newton Aycliffe, County Durham, DL5 6AY Tel: (01325) 327149 Fax: (01325) 327148 E-mail: b.smithies@schsiteservices.co.uk
Saturn Communications Ltd, Park House, 27 Hartswood Road, Warley, Brentwood, Essex, CM14 5AE Tel: (01277) 234131 Fax: (01277) 234156 E-mail: len@saturncomms.co.uk

STEEL TOWERS

12 VoltZ Ltd, 5 Fleetwood St, Preston, PR2 2PT Tel: (0871) 2500555 Fax: (0871) 2500554 E-mail: help@12voltz.com
Cambrian Caledonian Ltd, Llandygai Industrial Estate, Bangor, Gwynedd, LL57 4YH Tel: (01248) 370248 Fax: (01248) 370406
Crofton Engineering Ltd, Cambridge Road, Linton, Cambridge, CB21 4NN Tel: (01223) 892138 Fax: (01223) 893547 E-mail: info@crofton-eng.co.uk
Alan Dick & Co. Ltd, The Barlands, London Road, Charlton Kings, Cheltenham, Gloucestershire, GL52 6UT Tel: (01242) 518500 Fax: (01242) 510191 E-mail: contact@uk.alandickgroup.com
Francis & Lewis International, Waterwells Drive, Waterwells Business Park, Quedgeley, Gloucester, GL2 2AA Tel: (01452) 722200 Fax: (01452) 722244 E-mail: sales@fli.co.uk
Nusteel Structures Ltd, Lympne Industrial Estate, Hythe, Kent, CT21 4LR Tel: (01303) 268112 Fax: (01303) 266098 E-mail: general@nusteelstructures.com
Painter Bros Ltd, Holmer Road, Hereford, HR4 9SW Tel: (01432) 374400 Fax: (01432) 374427E-mail: enquiries@painterbrothers.com
Tower Structures Marketing Ltd, 44 Westbourne Terrace, London, W2 3UH Tel: (020) 7402 4452 Fax: (020) 7706 8643

STEEL TUBE FITTINGS

Atom Hydraulics, 1 Wicks Close, Springwood Industrial Estate, Braintree, Essex, CM7 2GE Tel: (01376) 348889 Fax: (01376) 348311
Blackwater Manufacturing Ltd, 2 Faraday Road, Glenrothes, Fife, KY6 2RU Tel: (01592) 774637 Fax: (01592) 775160 E-mail: sales@blackwatermfg.co.uk

STEEL TUBE FITTINGS (HEAVY WALL) MANUFRS

H P F Energy Services, 99 Sadler Foster Way, Teeside Industrial Estate, Stockton-on-Tees, Cleveland, TS17 9JY Tel: (01642) 750009 Fax: (01642) 750044 E-mail: thornaby@hpf-energy.com

STEEL TUBE MANIPULATION, *See Tube Manipulation etc*

STEEL TUBE MANUFRS, *See also other headings under Steel Tubes/Pipes*

Alexander Stirling & Co., Meadowforth Road, Stirling, FK7 7SA Tel: (01786) 473333 Fax: (01786) 450408 E-mail: sales@alexanderstirling.co.uk
Armada Tube & Steel (SW) Ltd, Tube & Steel Service Centre, Pennygillam Industrial Estate, Launceston, Cornwall, PL15 7ED Tel: (01566) 776699 Fax: (01566) 776500 E-mail: des@armadatube.co.uk
Arrow Hydraulics, 76 Heming Road, Redditch, Worcestershire, B98 0EA Tel: (01527) 517120 Fax: (01527) 517123
Asd, Hamlin Way, King's Lynn, Norfolk, PE30 4LQ Tel: (01553) 761431 Fax: (01553) 692394 E-mail: info@asdplc.co.uk
Benteler UK Ltd, 31 Waterloo Road, Wolverhampton, WV1 4DP Tel: (01902) 712212 Fax: (01902) 712899 E-mail: sales@benteleruk.com
Broson Ltd, Church Hill Road, Thurmaston, Leicester, LE4 8DJ Tel: 0116-269 8899 Fax: 0116-269 8898 E-mail: sales@broson.co.uk
Cleveland Steel & Tubes Ltd, Dalton Airfield, Dalton, Thirsk, North Yorkshire, YO7 3JN Tel: (01845) 577789 Fax: (01845) 578373 E-mail: admin@cleveland-steel.com
Corus Ltd, West Wing Midland House, New Road, Halesowen, West Midlands, B63 3HY Tel: 0121-585 5522 Fax: 0121-585 5241 E-mail: cdtl@corusgroup.com
Corus Ltd, 20 Inch Pipe Mill Tube Works, Hartlepool, Cleveland, TS25 2EG Tel: (01429) 266611 Fax: (01429) 527283
Corus Tubes plc, PO Box 101, Corby, Northamptonshire, NN17 5UA Tel: (01536) 402121 Fax: (01536) 404111
D Berry & Co. Ltd, Middlemoor Industrial Estate, Kentish Road, Middlemore Industrial Estate, Birmingham, B21 0AY Tel: 0121-558 4411 Fax: 0121-555 5546 E-mail: enquires@dberryandco.co.uk
Dudley Iron & Steel Co. Ltd, Unit 8, Tividale, Oldbury, West Midlands, B69 3HU Tel: 0121-601 5000 Fax: 0121-601 5001 E-mail: sales@dudley-iron-steel.co.uk
Dudley Tubes Ltd, Meadow Lane, Bilston, West Midlands, WV14 9NQ Tel: (01902) 671747 Fax: (01902) 354049 E-mail: dudleytubes@btconnect.com
Duright Engineering Co., Portway Road, Wednesbury, West Midlands, WS10 7DZ Tel: 0121-556 7718 Fax: 0121-556 7745 E-mail: sales@duright.co.uk
E M T Steels Ltd, 5 Gleneld Drive, Stourbridge, West Midlands, DY8 2PF Tel: (01384) 373888 Fax: (01384) 395712 E-mail: ajroden@btconnect.com
Euro Tube West Midlands Ltd, Navigation Road, Worcester, WR5 3DE Tel: (01905) 767833 Fax: (01905) 764305 E-mail: sales@eurotube.biz
F W B Cymru Co. Ltd, Five Crosses Industrial Estate, Ruthin Road, Minera, Wrexham, Clwyd, LL11 3RD Tel: (01978) 720720 Fax: (01978) 720721 E-mail: sales@fwbcymru.co.uk
▶ H B S Bar Stock Ltd, 125 Lodgefield Road, Halesowen, West Midlands, B62 8AX Tel: 0121-559 4251 Fax: 0121-561 4565
Hall & Pickles, Poynton Industrial Estate, Poynton, Stockport, Cheshire, SK12 1NB Tel: (01625) 878787 Fax: (01625) 855573 E-mail: sales@hallandpickles.co.uk
Harvard Industries Ltd, Wood Lane, Erdington, Birmingham, B24 9QR Tel: 0121-386 6621 Fax: 0121-386 6721 E-mail: johncauser@aol.com
Hayes Tubes Ltd, Balds Lane, Lye, Stourbridge, West Midlands, DY9 8NN Tel: (01384) 422373 Fax: (01384) 422877 E-mail: hayestubes@enterprise.net
Hilmar Tubes Ltd, Hardy Street, Eccles, Manchester, M30 7NB Tel: 0161-787 7747 Fax: 0161-787 7748 E-mail: graham@hilmar.co.uk
Hub Le Bas, Rose Street, Bilston, West Midlands, WV14 8TS Tel: (01902) 493506 Fax: (01902) 353687 E-mail: westsales@hublebas.co.uk
▶ Jackson & Keay Ltd, Private Road No. 7, Colwick Industrial Estate, Colwick, Nottingham, NG4 2JW Tel: 0115-961 7113 Fax: 0115-961 8664
John Bell Pipeline Caspian, Units 3/4 Camiestone Road, Thainstone Industrial Park, Inverurie, Aberdeenshire, AB51 5GT Tel: (01224) 716079 Fax: (01224) 716079 E-mail: sales@jbpipeline.co.uk
M & N Fabrications Ltd, Wharf Road, Woodston, Peterborough, PE2 9PS Tel: (01733) 342408 Fax: (01733) 342408 E-mail: deegeorge@aol.com
▶ Marcegaglia UK Ltd, New Road, Dudley, West Midlands, DY2 8TA Tel: (01384) 242812 Fax: (01384) 242813 E-mail: uk@marcegaglia.com
Midland Tube & Fabrications, 4 Corngreaves Works, Corngreaves Road, Cradley Heath, West Midlands, B64 7DA Tel: (01384) 566364 Fax: (01384) 566365 E-mail: keithcadman@btconnect.com
Monarch Tubes Ltd, Autobase Industrial Estate, Tipton Road, Tividale, Oldbury, West Midlands, B69 3HU Tel: 0121-601 5039 Fax: 0121-601 5038
National Tube Stockholders Ltd, Dalton Industrial Estate, Dalton, Thirsk, North Yorkshire, YO7 3HE Tel: (01845) 577440 Fax: (01845) 577165 E-mail: nts@nationaltube.co.uk
Ogden Transteel, Butler Way, Town Street, Stanningley, Pudsey, West Yorkshire, LS28 6EZ Tel: 0113-257 8221 Fax: 0113-236 2340 E-mail: ogdentransteel@aol.com
Phillips Products Dudley Ltd, Dawley Brook, Kingswinford, West Midlands, DY6 7AS Tel: (01384) 273592 Fax: (01384) 400036
Pipeline Centre, Unit 303a Dean Road, Bristol, BS11 8AT Tel: 0117-982 4828 Fax: 0117-982 4832
Pipeline Centre Ltd, Leads Road, Hull, HU7 0BY Tel: (01482) 838880 Fax: (01482) 878827 E-mail: sales@piplinecenter.co.uk
Preferred Tubes Ltd, Bird Hall Lane, Stockport, Cheshire, SK3 0SZ Tel: 0161-428 5355 Fax: 0161-428 7555
Readman Steel Ltd, Cochranes Wharf, Cargo Fleet, Middlesbrough, Cleveland, TS3 6AW Tel: (01642) 242641 Fax: (01642) 241912 E-mail: mail@wgrsteels.co.uk
Rothley Ltd, Macrome Road, Wolverhampton, WV6 9HG Tel: (01902) 756461 Fax: (01902) 745554 E-mail: sales@rothley.com
S J Andrew & Sons, South Turnpike, Redruth, Cornwall, TR15 2LZ Tel: (01209) 213171 Fax: (01209) 219459 E-mail: nathan@sjandrew.com

▶ indicates data change since last edition

STEEL TUBE MANUFRS – *continued*

Smith Brothers Stores Ltd, Battern Street, Aylestone Road, Leicester, LE2 7PB Tel: 0116-283 3511 Fax: 0116-244 0430 E-mail: sales@sbs-1897.co.uk

Star Tubes (Southern) Ltd, Lilliput Road, Brackmills, Northampton, NN4 7DT Tel: (01908) 311777 Fax: (01908) 321874 E-mail: sales@startubes-southern.co.uk

Star Tubes (UK) Ltd, Airfield Industrial Estate, York Road, Elvington, York, YO41 4AU Tel: (01904) 608681 Fax: (01904) 608649 E-mail: enkayo@aol.com

▶ Tube Engineers Ltd, Ardgraft Works, Newtoft Business Park, Newtoft, Market Rasen, Lincolnshire, LN8 3WA Tel: (01673) 862286 Fax: (01673) 885562 E-mail: sales@tubeengineers.co.uk

Union Steel Tubes, Wellington House, Wellington Industrial Estate, Bilston, West Midlands, WV14 9EE Tel: (01902) 881222 Fax: (01902) 880500 E-mail: enquiries@unionsteel.co.uk

▶ Vector International Ltd, Unit 31, Wellheads Crescent, Wellheads Industrial Estate, Aberdeen, AB21 7GA Tel: (01224) 775242 E-mail: sales@vector-supplies.ltd.uk

Yardley Holland Ltd, 154 Stafford Street, Walsall, WS2 8EA Tel: (01922) 633877 Fax: (01922) 634868

STEEL TUBES TO SPECIFICATION

Jourdans Sheet Metal Work, Marsh End, Lords Meadow Industrial Estate, Crediton, Devon, EX17 1DN Tel: (01363) 773562 Fax: (01363) 773365 E-mail: pluxton@jourdansmetal.co.uk

STEEL TUBES, ALLOY

Nomax Ltd, 22 Hyde Street, Winchester, Hampshire, SO23 7DR Tel: (01962) 840850 Fax: (01962) 841512 E-mail: quote@nomax.co.uk

STEEL TUBES, COLD ROLLED

▶ Gatehill Trading Ltd, 18 Gatehill Road, Northwood, Middlesex, HA6 3QD Tel: (01923) 820206 Fax: (01923) 450999 E-mail: gatehill@gtrad.co.uk

STEEL VALVE BALLS

Sheridan Engineering Hereford, 4 Parkwood Court, Rotherwas Industrial Estate, Hereford, HR2 6NU Tel: (01432) 269683 Fax: (01432) 354410 E-mail: sales@sheridanengineering.co.uk

STEEL VINYL LINED SWIMMING POOLS

Fox Pool (UK) Ltd, Mere House, Stow Road, Sturton By Stow, Lincoln, LN1 2BZ Tel: (01427) 788662 Fax: (01427) 788526 E-mail: grayfoxswi@aol.com

STEEL WALL CLADDING

Panels & Profiles, Tewksbury Business Park, Severn Drive, Tewkesbury Business Park, Tewkesbury, Gloucestershire, GL20 8TX Tel: (01684) 856600 Fax: (01684) 856601 E-mail: sales@coruspanelsandprofiles.co.uk

STEEL WHEELS

Titan Steel Wheels Ltd, Bridge Road, Cookley, Kidderminster, Worcestershire, DY10 3SD Tel: (01562) 850561 Fax: (01562) 851576 E-mail: sales@titansteelwheels.com

STEEL WIRE

Barnfather Wire Ltd, Willenhall Road, Wednesbury, West Midlands, WS10 8JG Tel: 0121-526 2880 Fax: 0121-526 3130 E-mail: sales@barnfatherwire.co.uk

Boswell Rod & Wire Ltd, 4 The Wallows Industrial Estate, Wallows Road, Brierley Hill, West Midlands, DY5 1QB Tel: (01384) 263238 Fax: (01384) 480223 E-mail: sales@boswellrod.co.uk

Kiveton Park Holdings Ltd, Kiveton Park, Sheffield, S26 6NQ Tel: (01909) 770252 Fax: (01909) 772949 E-mail: sales@kpsteel.co.uk

G. John Power Ltd, Hayseech Road, Halesowen, West Midlands, B63 3PF Tel: 0121-550 3112 Fax: 0121-585 5147 E-mail: sales@gjohnpower.co.uk

R & S Wire Ltd, Grove Street, Kirklees Steel Works, Brighouse, West Yorkshire, HD6 1PL Tel: (01484) 715120 Fax: (01484) 711882

Rotosound Manufacturing Ltd, Unit 3B, Morewood Close, Sevenoaks, Kent, TN13 2HU Tel: (01732) 450838 Fax: (01732) 458994 E-mail: jason@rotosound.com

Unsco, Manor Road, Kiveton Park Station, Sheffield, S26 6PB Tel: (01909) 770431 Fax: (01909) 772848 E-mail: galdrich@unsco.com

The Willing Wire Company Ltd, Middlemore Lane, Walsall, WS9 8SP Tel: (01922) 452814 Fax: (01922) 743248 E-mail: mail@willing-wire.com

STEEL WIRE RODS

Macelloy Ltd, Hawke Street, Sheffield, S9 2LN Tel: 0114-242 6704 Fax: 0114-243 1324 E-mail: info@macalloy.com

Voest Alpine Stahl Ltd, Albion Place, London, W6 0QT Tel: (020) 8600 5800 Fax: (020) 8741 3099 E-mail: officelondon@vosetalpine.com

STEEL WIRE RODS TO SPECIFICATION

G. John Power Ltd, Hayseech Road, Halesowen, West Midlands, B63 3PF Tel: 0121-550 3112 Fax: 0121-585 5147 E-mail: sales@gjohnpower.co.uk

STEEL WIRE TO SPECIFICATION

G. John Power Ltd, Hayseech Road, Halesowen, West Midlands, B63 3PF Tel: 0121-550 3112 Fax: 0121-585 5147 E-mail: sales@gjohnpower.co.uk

The Willing Wire Company Ltd, Middlemore Lane, Walsall, WS9 8SP Tel: (01922) 452814 Fax: (01922) 743248 E-mail: mail@willing-wire.com

STEEL WOOL PRODUCTS

Metallic Wool Co. Ltd, Bredgar Road, Gillingham, Kent, ME8 6PL Tel: (01634) 239444 Fax: (01634) 239888 E-mail: enquiries@metallic-wool.co.uk

Trollull Ltd, 17-18 Brunel Gate, West Portway Industrial Estate, Andover, Hampshire, SP10 3SL Tel: (01264) 333443 Fax: (01264) 334428 E-mail: trollull@trollull.co.uk

STEEL, STRUCTURAL, HOT ROLLED

▶ 3D Structural Fabrications, Bull Street, Gornal Wood, Dudley, West Midlands, DY3 2NQ Tel: (01902) 656263 Fax: (01902) 656036 E-mail: structuralservices@blueyonder.co.uk

STEELS, CARBON

Corby Steel Supplies Ltd, Sondes Road, Willowbrook East Industrial Estate, Corby, Northamptonshire, NN17 5XL Tel: (01536) 261164 Fax: (01536) 402971

Harry Fisher & Co., London Works, Bridge St, Sheffield, S3 8NT Tel: 0114-272 1998 Fax: 0114-275 2489

STEELS, MARAGING

Maher Ltd, 2 Brightside Way, Sheffield, S9 2RQ Tel: 0114-290 9200 Fax: 0114-290 9290 E-mail: sales@maher.co.uk

STEELS, PRECOATED, SHEET/ COIL/STRIP ETC, *See also headings for particular coating*

Cooper 2005 Ltd, Great Bridge Street, West Bromwich, West Midlands, B70 0DJ Tel: 0121-521 1500 Fax: 0121-521 1526 E-mail: stevet@coopercoated.co.uk

STEELWORKS CONTRACTORS OR DESIGNERS

▶ Allott Steelwork Ltd, Worthing Road, Sheffield, S9 3JB Tel: 0114-276 6882 Fax: 0114-275 4922 E-mail: info@allottsteelwork.co.uk

Assistance Teknica Ltd, York House, Borough Road, Middlesbrough, Cleveland, TS1 2HJ Tel: (01642) 224545 Fax: (01642) 243514 E-mail: enquiries@teknica.co.uk

▶ D H Structures Ltd, Tollgate Drive, Tollgate Industrial Estate, Stafford, ST16 3HS Tel: (01785) 246269 Fax: (01785) 222077 E-mail: enquiries@dhstructures.co.uk

Foregale Ltd, Union Road, Liversedge, West Yorkshire, WF15 7JS Tel: (01924) 401020 Fax: (01924) 405872

Jackson Steel Structures Ltd, Densfield Works, Tannadice Street, Dundee, DD3 7QP Tel: (01382) 858439 Fax: (01382) 833964 E-mail: sales@jacksonsteel.co.uk

Mayflower Engineering Ltd, Coleridge Road, Sheffield, S9 5DA Tel: 0114-244 1353 Fax: 0114-244 5977 E-mail: sales@mayflower-engineering.co.uk

▶ Multiserve Group, Aldwarke Works, Rotherham, South Yorkshire, S65 3SR Tel: (01709) 527743 Fax: (01709) 529458

Wall Engineering Co. Ltd, Cromer Road, North Walsham, Norfolk, NR28 0NB Tel: (01692) 403701 Fax: (01692) 406610 E-mail: info@wallengineering.co.uk

STEELWORKS PLANT AND EQUIPMENT MANUFRS

Corus Process Engineering, Old Frame RM, Derwent Howe, Workington, Cumbria, CA14 3YZ Tel: (01900) 68000 Fax: (01900) 601111 E-mail: cpe@corusgroup.com

Gega Lotz Ltd, Kiln Way, Woodville, Swadlincote, Derbyshire, DE11 8EA Tel: (01283) 214281 Fax: (01283) 222108 E-mail: sales@gegalotz.co.uk

S M S Mevac (UK) Ltd, Road Four, Winsford Industrial Estate, Winsford, Cheshire, CW7 3RS Tel: (01606) 551421 Fax: (01606) 553078 E-mail: mail@sms-mevac.co.uk

V A I Industries UK Ltd, Warren Road, Scunthorpe, North Lincolnshire, DN15 6XH Tel: (01724) 280360 Fax: (01724) 864405 E-mail: j.harris@fuchsuk.com

STEEPLEJACK SERVICES

A J Restoration Co Ltd, Restoration House, Second Avenue, Greasley St, Nottingham, NG6 8NE Tel: 0115-927 7044 Fax: 0115-976 3476 E-mail: ajrestoration.co@btconnect.com

Aboval & Co. Ltd, 24 Firtrees Close, Rothershide, London, SE16 5NG Tel: (07774) 852505 Fax: (020) 7252 3793

B E S T, Morton Street, Brooke House, Middleton, Manchester, M24 6AN Tel: 0161-655 3000 Fax: 0161-655 3001 E-mail: info@bestservices.co.uk

▶ H & A Hight Services Ltd, 8 Snowdon Road, Middlesbrough, Cleveland, TS2 1LP Tel: (01642) 218607 Fax: (01642) 217149

John Devlin & Son Dukinfield Ltd, 1 Platt Street, Dukinfield, Cheshire, SK16 4QZ Tel: 0161-330 5074 Fax: 0161-330 5074

▶ Northern Steeplejacks Edinburgh Ltd, 7 Newbattle Road, Newtongrange, Dalkeith, Midlothian, EH22 4RA Tel: 0131-654 2700 Fax: 0131-654 2600

Pendrich Hype Services Ltd, 78-82 Carnethie Street, Rosewell, Midlothian, EH24 9AW Tel: 0131-440 1991 Fax: 0131-448 2157 E-mail: enquiries@pendrich.com

Richardson, Courville House, 1 Ellerbeck Court, Stokesley, Middlesbrough, Cleveland, TS9 5PT Tel: (01642) 714791 Fax: (01642) 714387 E-mail: enquiries@pcrichardson.co.uk

Rodell Chimneys Ltd, Ffrwdgrech Industrial Estate, Brecon, Powys, LD3 8LA Tel: (01874) 623723 Fax: (01874) 623725 E-mail: sales@rodell-chimneys.co.uk

▶ T & T Steeplejacks Ltd, Snowdon House, Snowdon Road, Middlesbrough, Cleveland, TS2 1DY Tel: (01642) 247972 Fax: (01642) 247972

Tarrant S C S Ltd, 1st Floor Victoria Court, St. Pancras, Chichester, West Sussex, PO19 7GD Tel: (01243) 839992 Fax: (01243) 839993 E-mail: rita.brown.tarrant@breathemail.net

W E Harrison Sheffield Ltd, 33 Regent Terrace, Sheffield, S3 7QA Tel: 0114-272 0561 Fax: 0114-272 0564 E-mail: weh@quista.net

▶ Zenith S A S Ltd, Unit 7, Dryden Vale Bilston Glen, Loanhead, Midlothian, EH20 9HN Tel: 0131-440 3000 Fax: 0131-448 2260

STEERING GEAR/SYSTEMS/ UNITS, MARINE

Hamilton Jet UK Ltd, Unit 4a Birches Industrial Estate, East Grinstead, West Sussex, RH19 1XZ Tel: (01342) 313437 Fax: (01342) 313438 E-mail: info@hamjetuk.com

Lewmar Ltd, Crescent House, Latimer Road, Luton, LU1 3UZ Tel: (01582) 404400 Fax: (01582) 400331 E-mail: sales@whitlocksteering.com

Rolls Royce plc, Taxi Way, Hillend Industrial Park, Hillend, Dunfermline, Fife, KY11 9JT Tel: (01383) 823188 Fax: (01383) 824038 E-mail: post.master@vickersmarine.com

Wills Ridley, Kernick Industrial Estate, Unit One, Annear Road, Penryn, Cornwall, TR10 9EW Tel: (01326) 376015 Fax: (01326) 376212 E-mail: info@wills-ridley.com

STEERING GEAR/SYSTEMS/ UNITS, MOTOR VEHICLE

D & A Steering Ltd, 27 Nursey Road, Hockley, Birmingham, B19 2XN Tel: 0121-523 8444 Fax: 0121-523 8136

Euro Steer Ltd, Shay La Industrial Estate, Shay Lane, Longridge, Preston, PR3 3BT Tel: (01772) 786022 Fax: (01772) 786237

Steering Developments Group Ltd, Unit 5 Eastman Way, Hemel Hempstead, Hertfordshire, HP2 7HF Tel: (01442) 212918 Fax: (01442) 240254 E-mail: enquiries@steeringdevelopments.co.uk

T R W Systems Ltd, Resolven, Neath, West Glamorgan, SA11 4HN Tel: (01639) 665000 Fax: (01639) 665350

STEERING GEAR/SYSTEMS/ UNITS, MOTOR VEHICLE, RECONDITIONED

Euro Steer Ltd, Shay La Industrial Estate, Shay Lane, Longridge, Preston, PR3 3BT Tel: (01772) 786022 Fax: (01772) 786237

J Mccartney Ltd, 168 Park View Road, London, N17 9BL Tel: (020) 8808 0582 Fax: (020) 8365 1884 E-mail: jmccartneylimited@parkviewroad.fsnet.co.uk

Kiley & Clinton, 52-53 Birchall Street, Birmingham, B12 0RP Tel: 0121-772 8000 Fax: 0121-772 3215 E-mail: kileyclinton@btconnect.com

Power Steering Specialists, Unit 1-2 Brocklebank Industrial Estate, Brocklebank Road, London, SE7 7SX Tel: (020) 8858 0168 Fax: (020) 8858 7595E-mail: sales@powersteering.co.uk

STEERING WHEELS

Key Steering System Ltd, Unit 2675 Kings Court, The Crescent, Birmingham Business Park, Birmingham, B37 7YE Tel: 0121-717 5230 Fax: 0121-717 5236 E-mail: aston.c@keysafetyinc.com

STENCIL BOARDS

Pyramid Engineering & Manufacturing Co. Ltd, 8 Palace Road, East Molesey, Surrey, KT8 9DL Tel: (020) 8979 4814 Fax: (020) 8979 4814

STENCIL CLEANING SYSTEMS

M & D Wheeler Ltd, Avondale Business Centre, Woodland Way, Woodland Way, Bristol, BS15 1AW Tel: 0117-960 3358 Fax: E-mail: m.d.wheeler@btinternet.com

STENCIL CUTTING/PLATE CUTTING MACHINES

Pyramid Engineering & Manufacturing Co. Ltd, 8 Palace Road, East Molesey, Surrey, KT8 9DL Tel: (020) 8979 4814 Fax: (020) 8979 4814

STENCIL CUTTING/PLATE CUTTING SERVICES/ ENGINEERS

Roger Needham & Sons Ltd, Units 15-16 Salford Enterprise Centre, Guide Street, Salford, M50 1EW Tel: 0161-745 7277 Fax: 0161-745 7826 E-mail: frankrnsl@aol.com

Pakmark, Units 1-2 Benson Industrial Estate, Benson Rd, Birmingham, B18 5TS Tel: 0121-523 0665 Fax: 0121-523 5343 E-mail: pakmark@btconnect.com

STENCIL GUMMING

Packaids Ltd, Ruscombe Park, Ruscombe Lane, Ruscombe, Reading, RG10 9LU Tel: 0118-934 3877 Fax: 0118-934 0273 E-mail: sales@packaids.co.uk

STEP LADDERS

Globe Ladders, Vincent Street, Birmingham, B12 9SG Tel: 0121-440 6636 Fax: 0121-440 5475 E-mail: info@globeladders.co.uk

Hewitt Ladders Ltd, 37 Melrose Street, Leicester, LE4 6FD Tel: 0116-266 3304 Fax: 0116-261 3033 E-mail: hewittladdersltd@btconnect.com

J Gorstige Ltd, Unit 10 Carlton Mill, Pickering Street, Leeds, LS12 2QG Tel: 0113-279 5200 Fax: 0113-279 5200

▶ Loadlift Ltd, Winchester House, Winchester Road, Frinton-on-Sea, Essex, CO13 9JB Tel: (01255) 671187 Fax: (01255) 672236 E-mail: sales@loadlift.com

Redhill Manufacturing Ltd, Unit 6, Padgets Lane, South Moons Moat Industrial Estate, Redditch, Worcestershire, B98 0RA Tel: (01527) 529002 Fax: (01527) 523950 E-mail: sales@redhillmanufacturing.co.uk

STEREOTYPE PLATE PRINTING

Plastotype Ltd, Crustable Close, Mushep Industrial Park, Coleford, Gloucestershire, GL16 8RE Tel: (01594) 837374 Fax: (01594) 837312 E-mail: info@plastotype.com

STERILE SAMPLING EQUIPMENT

Clifton Enterprises Ltd, Clifton House, 32 Cavendish Road, Sheffield, S11 9BH Tel: 0114-258 7229 Fax: 0114-250 0239 E-mail: vanasyl@aol.com

STERILISERS, HOSPITAL/ MEDICAL/SURGICAL

Andersen Products Ltd, Davy Road, Gorse Lane Industrial Estate, Clacton-On-Sea, Essex, CO15 4XA Tel: (01255) 428328 Fax: (01255) 222987 E-mail: uk@andersenmedical.com

Getinge UK Ltd, Orchard Way, Sutton-in-Ashfield, Nottinghamshire, NG17 1JU Tel: (01623) 510033 Fax: (01623) 440456

Jacob, White (Hospital Equipment) Ltd, Unit I4, Riverside Industrial Estate, Riverside Way, Dartford, DA1 5BX Tel: (01322) 223267 Fax: (01322) 288278 E-mail: jacobwhite@jacobwhite-hoftquip.co.uk

Steri Products Ltd, 10 Towerfield Road, Shoeburyness, Southend-on-Sea, SS3 9QE Tel: (01702) 296266 Fax: (01702) 296267 E-mail: steriproducts@btconnect.com

William G. Fuller & Co. Ltd, 43 Earl Street, Hastings, East Sussex, TN34 1SG Tel: (01424) 426094 Fax: (01424) 444763 E-mail: sales@fullermedical.co.uk

STERNGEAR SYSTEMS, MARINE

J Crowther Royton Ltd, Eden Works Belgrave Mill, Honeywell Lane, Oldham, OL8 2JP Tel: 0161-652 4234 Fax: 0161-627 4265 E-mail: crowther.marine@tiscali.co.uk

Sillette Sonic, 2 Beverley Trading Estate, Garth Road, Morden, Surrey, SM4 4LU Tel: (020) 8337 7543 Fax: (020) 8330 9014 E-mail: sales@sillette.co.uk

Teignbridge Propellers Ltd, Great Western Way, Forde Road, Newton Abbot, Devon, TQ12 4AW Tel: (01626) 333377 Fax: (01626) 360783 E-mail: sales@teignbridge.co.uk

STEVEDORING SERVICES

Associated British Ports, Old Custom House, Key St, Ipswich, IP4 1BY Tel: (01473) 231010 Fax: (01473) 230914 E-mail: ipswich@abports.co.uk

Briton Ferry Stevedoring Ltd, Giants Wharf, Briton Ferry, Neath, West Glamorgan, SA11 2LP Tel: (01639) 825700 Fax: (01639) 822912 E-mail: bfss@dial.pipex.com

Convoys Chatham Ltd Head Office, No 3 Basin, Chatham Docks, Chatham, Kent, ME4 4SR Tel: (01634) 892099 Fax: (01634) 895235 E-mail: enquiries@convoys.co.uk

Denholm Shipping Company Ltd, Liner House, Test Road, Eastern Docks, Southampton, SO14 3GE Tel: (023) 8071 3100 Fax: (023) 8071 3129 E-mail: finadmin@denshipsouth.co.uk

Ferris Stevedores Ltd, 2 Corry Place, Belfast Harbour Estate, Belfast, BT3 9HY Tel: (028) 9074 8371 Fax: (028) 9074 6500 E-mail: robert@ferris-belfast.freeuk.com

James Fisher & Sons P.L.C., Fisher House, Michaelson Road, Barrow-in-Furness, Cumbria, LA14 1HR Tel: (01229) 615400 Fax: (01229) 836761 E-mail: postmaster@james-fisher.co.uk

Gunness Wharf Ltd, Gunness Wharf, Gunness, Scunthorpe, South Humberside, DN15 8SY Tel: (01724) 867691 Fax: (01724) 851207 E-mail: info@flixboroughwharf.co.uk

Hamilton Shipping Ltd, 14 Clarendon Road, Belfast, BT1 3BG Tel: (028) 9053 3200 Fax: (028) 9053 3222 E-mail: containers@hamiltonshipping.com

Jacob Pickwell & Co. Ltd, Pickwell House, Immingham Dock, Immingham, South Humberside, DN40 2LZ Tel: (01469) 572415 Fax: (01469) 572897 E-mail: j.pickwell@cargohandling.uk

James Jack Listing Services Ltd, Oilfield Support Base, Shore Road, Invergordon, Ross-Shire, IV18 0EX Tel: (01349) 853000 Fax: (01349) 853416E-mail: invergordon@james-jack.co.uk

John Sutcliffe & Son Grimsby Ltd, Alexandra Chambers, Flour Square, Grimsby, South Humberside, DN31 3LS Tel: (01472) 359101 Fax: (01472) 241935 E-mail: admin@jsutcliffe.co.uk

Kent United Contractors Ltd, Unit 4 Regis Business Park, New Road, Sheerness, Kent, ME12 1NB Tel: (01795) 583475 Fax: (01795) 583476 E-mail: kuc@lineone.net

Larne Harbour Ltd, 9 Olderfleet Road, Larne, County Antrim, BT40 1AS Tel: (028) 2887 2100 Fax: (028) 2887 2209 E-mail: info@portoflarne.co.uk

M M D (Shipping Services) Ltd, Flathouse Quay, Prospect Road, Portsmouth, PO2 7SP Tel: (023) 9282 6351 Fax: (023) 9229 1910

Mistley Quay & Forwarding, High Street, Mistley, Manningtree, Essex, CO11 1HB Tel: (01206) 394431 Fax: (01206) 393882 E-mail: enquiries@twlogistics.co.uk

Read & Sutcliffe Ltd, St. Johns Road, Boston, Lincolnshire, PE21 6HG Tel: (01205) 310444 Fax: (01205) 310500 E-mail: info@rsboston.com

S H S Freight Services Ltd, Unit 20 Riverside Development, Chesterton Road, Eastwood Trading Estate, Rotherham, South Yorkshire, S65 1SU Tel: (01709) 377071 Fax: (01709) 820959 E-mail: davidmaw@aol.com

Small & Co. Shipping Ltd, Europa House, 40 South Quay, Great Yarmouth, Norfolk, NR30 2RL Tel: (01502) 572301 Fax: (01493) 857533 E-mail: smallandcoshipping@halcyonshipping.com

Andrew Smith & Schultze Ltd, 54 Broad Street, Peterhead, Aberdeenshire, AB42 1BX Tel: (01779) 472210 Fax: (01779) 470638 E-mail: stevedores@rapidial.co.uk

Sussex Port Forwarding Ltd, Shoreham Port, Harbour Office, 84-86 Albion Street, Southwick, Brighton, BN42 4ED Tel: (01273) 598100 Fax: (01273) 592492 E-mail: info@shoreham-port.co.uk

Teignmouth Quay Co Holdings Ltd, Old Quay, Teignmouth, Devon, TQ14 8ES Tel: (01626) 774044 Fax: (01626) 776240 E-mail: teignmouth@abports.co.uk

STILL MINERAL WATER

Berrington Spring Water Co., Little Berrington Farm, Marden, Hereford, HR1 3EY Tel: (01568) 797552 Fax: (01568) 797224 E-mail: sales@berringtonwater.com

Brecon Beacon Natural Waters, Llwyn Dewi, Trapp, Llandeilo, Dyfed, SA19 6TT Tel: (01269) 850175 Fax: (01269) 851181 E-mail: info@breconwater.co.uk

Buxton Mineral Water, Station Road, Buxton, Derbyshire, SK17 6AQ Tel: (01298) 766000 Fax: (01298) 72088

Campsie Spring Scotland Ltd, Veich Place, Lennoxtown, Glasgow, G66 7JQ Tel: (01360) 312121 Fax: (01360) 312672

Chiltern Hills Watercoolers Ltd, Toms Hill, Aldbury, Tring, Hertfordshire, HP23 5SD Tel: (0870) 1678899 Fax: (01442) 851538

Davies Brook & Co Ltd, Moreton-on-Lugg, Hereford, HR4 8DY Tel: (01432) 760666 Fax: (01432) 761477

Hildon Ltd, Broughton, Hampshire, SO20 8DQ Tel: (01794) 302056 Fax: (01794) 301033 E-mail: hildon@hildon.com

Kings Hill Forest Glade, Newmains, Wishaw, Lanarkshire, ML2 9PJ Tel: (01501) 823085 Fax: (01501) 822161 E-mail: sales@kmwl.co.uk

Minerale Water Co., PO Box 2798, London, NW10 0DG Tel: (020) 8450 8082 Fax: (020) 8450 8083 E-mail: sales@minerale-water.co.uk

Nestle Waters Powwow, St Georges Well, Long Hanborough, Witney, Oxfordshire, OX29 8BT Tel: (01993) 882802 Fax: (01993) 883872

Nestle Waters UK Ltd, Trinity Court, Church Street, Rickmansworth, Hertfordshire, WD3 1LD Tel: (01923) 897700 Fax: (01923) 897608 E-mail: enquiries@waters.nestle.com

Princes Gate Springwater Ltd, New House Farm, Princes Gate, Ludchurch, Narberth, Dyfed, SA67 8JD Tel: (01834) 831225 Fax: (01834) 831305 E-mail: sales@princesgatespringwater.com

Purely Scottish Ltd, Woollands, Cockburnspath, Berwickshire, TD13 5XW Tel: (01368) 860600 Fax: (01368) 861960 E-mail: sales@purelyscottish.com

Strathmore Mineral Water Co. Ltd, 126 West High St, Forfar, Angus, DD8 1BP Tel: (01307) 466147 Fax: (01307) 466072 E-mail: bobwatson@matthewclark.co.uk

Waters & Robson Abbeywell Ltd, Abbey Well, 12 Coopies Lane, Morpeth, Northumberland, NE61 6JF Tel: (01670) 513113 Fax: (01670) 515821 E-mail: enquiries@abbey-well.co.uk

Windsor House Natural Water Co Ltd, Park Road, Emsworth, Hampshire, PO10 8NY Tel: (01243) 376156 Fax: (01243) 379100

Yorkshire Spring Watercoolers Ltd, The Exchange, Hard Ings Road, Keighley, West Yorkshire, BD21 3ND Tel: (01535) 611122 Fax: (01535) 663373

STITCHING MACHINE (PACKAGING) MANUFRS

Davies Machinery, 21 Harris Road, Lostock Gralam, Northwich, Cheshire, CW9 7PE Tel: (01606) 48683 Fax: (01606) 48683

STOCK AND SHARE BROKERS,

See headings under Broker Dealers

STOCK CONTROL COMPUTER SYSTEMS

Ammnet Ltd, Wentworth House, 3 Lichfield Road, Burntwood, Staffordshire, WS7 0HQ Tel: (01543) 305133 Fax: (0870) 0547750 E-mail: sales@ammnet.com

Compere Systems Ltd, Ivy Street, Birkenhead, Merseyside, CH41 5EE Tel: 0151-647 7457 Fax: 0151-666 2569 E-mail: davidj@comperesystems.com

Computacentre, 1 West Point Court, Great Park Road, Bradley Stoke, Bristol, BS32 4PS Tel: (01454) 614444 Fax: (01454) 620803

Counter Solutions Ltd, Lakeside Business Centre, Shipley, Heanor, Derbyshire, DE75 7JQ Tel: (01773) 530303 Fax: (01773) 530404 E-mail: sales@countersolutions.com

Delta Software Ltd, Whitwood Lodge, Whitwood Lane, Whitwood, Wakefield, West Yorkshire, WF10 5QD Tel: (01204) 529171 Fax: (01977) 668378 E-mail: info@deltasoftware.co.uk

Keystone Software Developments Ltd, 84 Commercial Road, Grantham, Lincolnshire, NG31 6DB Tel: (01476) 562447 E-mail: info@keystonesoftware.co.uk

Sly Development Ltd, 15 The Avenue, Acocks Green, Birmingham, B27 6NG Tel: 0121-707 0060 Fax: 0121-707 0032 E-mail: info@slynet.co.uk

STOCK CONTROL SYSTEMS

Keystone Software Developments Ltd, 84 Commercial Road, Grantham, Lincolnshire, NG31 6DB Tel: (01476) 562447 E-mail: info@keystonesoftware.co.uk

STOCKINETTE

A Bennett Hosiery Ltd, North End Mills, North End, Wirksworth, Matlock, Derbyshire, DE4 4FG Tel: (01629) 822677 Fax: (01629) 824731

Alan Appleton Oldham Ltd, Jowett Street, Oldham, OL1 4JQ Tel: 0161-652 0327 Fax: 0161-633 0019 E-mail: sales@alanappleton.freeserve.co.uk

James Hargreaves (Bacup) Ltd, Irwell Mill, Lee Street, Bacup, Lancashire, OL13 0AG Tel: (01706) 874701 Fax: (01706) 877005 E-mail: info@jameshargreaves.co.uk

Martin Cox, Jacksons Lane, Wellingborough, Northamptonshire, NN8 4LB Tel: (01933) 276935 Fax: (01933) 277127 E-mail: sales@martincoxchamois.com

Warner Textile Machinery, Magna Road, Wigston, Leicestershire, LE18 4ZH Tel: 0116-278 7578 Fax: 0116-278 7588 E-mail: wtm@warnertextilemachinery.co.uk

Yorkshire Cleaning Fabrics Ltd, Drakes Industrial Estate, Shay Lane, Ovenden, Halifax, West Yorkshire, HX3 6RL Tel: (01422) 358286 Fax: (01422) 346891 E-mail: sales@ycfcleaning.co.uk

STOCKINGS, LADIES'

Andrea Hosiery Manufacturing Co. Ltd, 107-115 Humberstone Road, Leicester, LE5 3AN Tel: 0116-262 5543 Fax: 0116-262 8732

Cautaulds UK, West Mill, Bridge Foot, Belper, Derbyshire, DE56 1BH Tel: (01773) 525525 Fax: (01773) 525545 E-mail:

▶ Cheeky Legs Wholesale Tights and Hosiery, Unit 10 Coombe Park, Ashprington, Totnes, Devon, TQ9 7DY Tel: (0845) 2576847 E-mail: admin@cheekylegs.co.uk

Flude Hosiery, Rugby Road, Hinckley, Leicestershire, LE10 0QQ Tel: (01455) 615543 Fax: (01455) 615543 E-mail: sales@flude.co.uk

Nylon Hosiery, 44 Upper Bond Street, Hinckley, Leicestershire, LE10 1RJ Tel: (01455) 631413 Fax: (01455) 636345 E-mail: rob@nylonhosiery.co.uk

▶ Seductive Lingerie, 14 Enderby Road, Scunthorpe, South Humberside, DN17 2HD Tel: (01724) 332874 E-mail: seller.seller@ntlworld.com

STOCKTAKING SERVICES

▶ Portland Stock Taking & Inventories, PO Box 7526, Newark, Nottinghamshire, NG22 9ZR Tel: (01623) 836000 Fax: 01623 862502 E-mail: audit@portlandhq.co.uk

R Harris Systems Ltd, 89 University Street, Belfast, BT7 1HP Tel: (028) 9032 6802 Fax: (028) 9032 5269 E-mail: pframe@harrissystems.co.uk

▶ Stockies Inventory Services, 105 Birkdale, Whitley Bay, Tyne & Wear, NE25 9LZ Tel: 0191-251 5584 E-mail: sales@stockies.com

STOCKTAKING SERVICES, LICENSING, CATERING AND HOTEL TRADE

▶ Portland Stock Taking & Inventories, PO Box 7526, Newark, Nottinghamshire, NG22 9ZR Tel: (01623) 836000 Fax: 01623 862502 E-mail: audit@portlandhq.co.uk

▶ Stockies Inventory Services, 105 Birkdale, Whitley Bay, Tyne & Wear, NE25 9LZ Tel: 0191-251 5584 E-mail: sales@stockies.com

▶ Wontner Smith (Stocktakers & Gaugers) Ltd, 9 Springfield Road, Bexleyheath, Kent, DA7 6DX Tel: (01322) 523186 E-mail: tonylast@wontnersmith.co.uk

STONE BALLS

▶ Recycles Africa, Walnut Cottage, Brockhampton Lane, Swindon Village, Cheltenham, Gloucestershire, GL51 9RS Tel: (01242) 572161 Fax: (01242) 530774 E-mail: tony@recyclesafrica.com

STONE BREAKING MACHINES

Haith Industrial, Cowhouse Lane, Armthorpe, Doncaster, South Yorkshire, DN3 3EE Tel: (01302) 831911 Fax: (01302) 300173 E-mail: sales@haith.co.uk

STONE CLADDING CONTRACTORS

Firthglow Ltd, 1 Papyrus Road, Werrington, Peterborough, PE4 5BH Tel: (01733) 570345 Fax: (01733) 576115

Grants Of Shoreditch Ltd, 25 Hackney Road, London, E2 7NX Tel: (020) 7729 3380 Fax: (020) 7613 3610 E-mail: sales@grantsint.com

Midland Marble Ltd, Masonry Works, 80 Dollman Street, Birmingham, B7 4RP Tel: 0121-359 3699 Fax: 0121-333 3052 E-mail: enquiries@midlandmarbleltd.co.uk

▶ Vetter UK Ltd, Barford Road, Little Barford, St. Neots, Cambridgeshire, PE19 6WB Tel: (01480) 402900 Fax: (01480) 402572 E-mail: vetteruk@laingorourke.com

STONE CLEANING CONTRACTORS

Archers Stone Restoration Ltd, Winters Farm, North Common Road, Wivelsfield Green, Haywards Heath, West Sussex, RH17 7RJ Tel: (01444) 471090 Fax: (01444) 471095 E-mail: info@archerstone.com

▶ Bolton Stone Restoration Ltd, Winter House, Winter Street, Bolton, BL1 8AZ Tel: (01204) 843853 Fax: (01204) 849841 E-mail: enquiries@boltonstone.co.uk

Bonsers Cleaning Nottingham, 19a Forester Street, Netherfield, Nottingham, NG4 2LJ Tel: 0115-988 7520 Fax: (01636) 815926 E-mail: contact@bonsersrestoration.co.uk

Building Restoration & Cleaning (Leeds) Ltd, Abbey Mills, Kirkstall, Leeds, LS5 3HP Tel: 0113-278 6472 Fax: 0113-275 4644 E-mail: brcleeds@btconnect.com

Construction Cosmetics, Red Mill House Centurion Way Business Park, Alfreton Road, Derby, DE21 4AY Tel: (01332) 867740 Fax: (01332) 867741 E-mail: info@concos.co.uk

Crips Ltd, 40 Oxford Drive, Berdmonsey Street, London, SE1 2FB Tel: (020) 7403 1190 Fax: (020) 7407 4734 E-mail: enquiries@crips.co.uk

Edinburgh Painting Contractors, 30 Christiemiller Avenue, Edinburgh, EH7 6ST Tel: (0131) 669 4691 Fax: (0131) 669 4691

Hunter & Clark Ltd, 1173 Gallowgate, Glasgow, G31 4EG Tel: 0141-554 2327 Fax: 0141-554 4974 E-mail: enquires@hunterandclark.co.uk

Just Developments, 4 Sunnybank, Holly Road, Wilmslow, Cheshire, SK9 1ND Tel: (01625) 530752 Fax: (01625) 530752 E-mail: jurgstaubli@hotmail.com

Negus Ken Ltd, 90 Garfield Road, London, SW19 8SB Tel: (020) 8543 9266 Fax: (020) 8543 9100 E-mail: enquiries@kennegus.co.uk

Proclean Tectonics Ltd, 19 Bourton Road, Solihull, West Midlands, B92 8AY Tel: 0121-707 8090 Fax: 0121-707 2896

Rominar UK Ltd, 106 Columbia Road, London, E2 7RG Tel: (020) 7739 8567 Fax: (020) 7729 7099 E-mail: rominarukltd@aol.com

Stonewest Holdings Ltd, Lamberts Place, St James's Road, Croydon, CR9 2HX Tel: (020) 8684 6646 Fax: (020) 8684 9323 E-mail: info@stonewest.co.uk

▶ Westone Masonry, Unit 4 Knightcott Industrial Estate, Banwell, Avon, BS29 6JN Tel: (01934) 824488 Fax: (01934) 824499

STONE CLEANING EQUIPMENT

Blastline Ltd, Grove Street, Mansfield Woodhouse, Mansfield, Nottinghamshire, NG19 8BU Tel: (01623) 623333 Fax: (01623) 655208 E-mail: sales@blastline.co.uk

Tensid UK plc, 70a Wheatash Road, Addlestone, Surrey, KT15 2ES Tel: (01932) 564133 Fax: (01932) 562046 E-mail: info@tensid.com

STONE DRESSING TOOLS

Harbro Supplies Ltd, Morland Street, Bishop Auckland, County Durham, DL14 6JG Tel: (01388) 605363 Fax: (01388) 603263 E-mail: harbrosupplies@hotmail.com

STONE FIREPLACES

▶ Firecraft Manufacturing, 1159 Melton Road, Syston, Leicester, LE7 2JS Tel: 0116-269 7030 Fax: 0116-269 7031

▶ Mann's Fireplaces, 96-98 Scotland Road, Nelson, Lancashire, BB9 7XJ Tel: (01282) 614789 Fax: (01282) 614789 E-mail: info@mannsfireplaces.co.uk

STONE FLOOR TILES

Bon Accord Glass, Bon Accord House, Riverside Drive, Aberdeen, AB11 7SL Tel: (01224) 588944 Fax: (01224) 582731

▶ Ivybridge Tile & Slate Centre, Unit 17 Erme Court, Leonards Road, Ivybridge, Devon, PL21 0SZ Tel: (01752) 690856 Fax: (01752) 690856

▶ Martin & Sons, 103-109 Efford Road, Plymouth, PL3 6NG Tel: (01752) 771586 Fax: (01752) 706388 E-mail: martinsandsons@plymstonewannado.co.uk

▶ Stamford Stone Co. Ltd, Stamford Road, Marholm, Peterborough, PE6 7HX Tel: (01780) 740970 Fax: (01780) 740755 E-mail: sales@stamfordstone.co.uk

▶ West Country Tile Centre Ltd, Pool Indust Park, Wilson Way, Pool, Redruth, Cornwall, TR15 3RX Tel: (01209) 212909 Fax: (01209) 711992 E-mail: info@westcountrytilecentre.co.uk

STONE FLOORING

▶ Downs Stone Co. Ltd, Lower Buildings, Sarsden, Chipping Norton, Oxfordshire, OX7 6PN Tel: (01608) 658357 Fax: (01608) 658882 E-mail: sales@downstone.com

STONE GRINDING OR POLISHING EQUIPMENT OR MACHINERY

Harbro Supplies Ltd, Morland Street, Bishop Auckland, County Durham, DL14 6JG Tel: (01388) 605363 Fax: (01388) 603263 E-mail: harbrosupplies@hotmail.com

STONE MASONRY CONTRACTORS

A Elfes Ltd, 155-157 Green Lane, Ilford, Essex, IG1 1XW Tel: (020) 7788 3290 Fax: (020) 8478 7979

Axtell Perry Simm Masonry Ltd, Osney Mead, Oxford, OX2 0EQ Tel: (01865) 254600 Fax: (01865) 254617 E-mail: sales@apsmasonry.com

W.R. Bedford Stonemasonry Ltd, 57-65 Whitehouse Lane, Bedminster, Bristol, BS3 4DN Tel: 0117-963 7756 Fax: 0117-963 4223 E-mail: wr.bedford@1way.co.uk

Border Concrete Products Ltd, Jedburgh Road, Kelso, Roxburghshire, TD5 8JG Tel: (01573) 224393 Fax: (01573) 226360 E-mail: sales@borderconcrete.co.uk

Bowman E Sons Building Contractors, Cherryholt Road, Stamford, Lincolnshire, PE9 2EP Tel: (01780) 751015 Fax: (01780) 759051 E-mail: mail@ebowman.co.uk

Cathedral Works Organisation, Terminus Road, Chichester, West Sussex, PO19 8TX Tel: (01243) 784225 Fax: (01243) 813700 E-mail: info@cwo.uk.com

▶ Classic Formai, Crofton House, Lindal Road, London, SE4 1EJ Tel: (020) 8469 2340 Fax: (020) 8694 8020 E-mail: sales@classicformi.com

Coulson, William James House, Cowley Road, Cambridge, CB4 0WX Tel: (01223) 423800 Fax: (01223) 420550 E-mail: group@coulson.co.uk

▶ Dartmoor Memorials, Westbridge Trading Centre, Westbridge Indust Estate, Tavistock, Devon, PL19 8DE Tel: (01822) 617700 Fax: (01822) 617702 E-mail: enquiries@dartmoor-memorials.com

Davis Memorials, 1 Park Street, Kidderminster, Worcestershire, DY11 6TN Tel: (01384) 566958 Fax: (01562) 861160

Easton Masonry UK Ltd, 99 Easton Street, Portland, Dorset, DT5 1BP Tel: (01305) 861020 Fax: (01305) 820401

▶ Fairhaven of Anglesey Abbey Ltd, Northfield Farm, Lode Road, Bottisham, Cambridge, CB5 9DN Tel: (01223) 812555

▶ Mike Gibson Stonework Ltd, 5 Scawfell Crescent, Seascale, Cumbria, CA20 1LF Tel: (01946) 727122 E-mail: gibstones@tiscali.co.uk

Hunter & Clark Ltd, 1173 Gallowgate, Glasgow, G31 4EG Tel: 0141-554 2327 Fax: 0141-554 4974 E-mail: enquiries@hunterandclark.co.uk

I R S Structural Solutions Ltd, Unit 6, Beta Terrace, Masterlord Business Park, West Road, Ransomes Europark, Ipswich, IP3 9SX Tel: (0870) 7607607 Fax: (0870) 7607607 E-mail: info@irs-group.com

J Oldham & Co. Ltd, Tearne House, Hollington, Stoke-on-Trent, ST10 4HR Tel: (01889) 507353 Fax: (01889) 507212 E-mail: enquiries@joldham.co.uk

Jersey Monumental Co, 82 New Street, St. Helier, Jersey, JE2 3TE Tel: (01534) 730252 Fax: (01534) 731374 E-mail: jmco@jerseymail.co.uk

▶ Bruce Kirby, Sycamore Cottage, Hemsford, Littlehempston, Totnes, Devon, TQ9 6NE Tel: (01803) 762136 E-mail: bruce@acanthus.org.uk

Landers Quarries Ltd, Kingston Road, Worth Matravers, Swanage, Dorset, BH19 3JP Tel: (01929) 439205 Fax: (01929) 439268 E-mail: landers@purbeckstone.co.uk

Leakes Masonry Ltd, James Street, Louth, Lincolnshire, LN11 0JW Tel: (01507) 604828 Fax: (01507) 600826 E-mail: info@leakes-masonry.com

Linford-Bridgeman Ltd, Quonians, Lichfield, Staffordshire, WS13 7LB Tel: (01543) 414234 Fax: (01543) 258250 E-mail: clare.millington@linfordgroup.co.uk

London Stone Conservation, 42 Sekforde Street, Clerkenwell, London, EC1R 0HA Tel: (020) 7251 0592 Fax: (020) 7251 0592 E-mail: lsc@londonstoneconservation.co.uk

Rhead, Meir Road, Stoke-on-Trent, ST3 7JD Tel: (01782) 599770 Fax: (01782) 599771 E-mail: peter.stephenson@normanrhead.co.uk

Sarsfields Memorials, 1 Old Thomas Lane, Liverpool, L14 3NA Tel: 0151-259 2762 Fax: 0151-254 2067

Scottish Natural Stones Ltd, Westwood Estate, West Calder, West Lothian, EH55 8PN Tel: (01506) 874222 Fax: (01506) 874285

Staffordshire Stone Hollington Ltd, Quarry Bank, Hollington, Stoke-on-Trent, ST10 4HQ Tel: (01889) 507435 Fax: (01889) 507365

Stonewest Holdings Ltd, Lamberts Place, St James's Road, Croydon, CR9 2HX Tel: (020) 8684 6646 Fax: (020) 8684 9323 E-mail: info@stonewest.co.uk

▶ T A Law Stonework Contractors, The Bield, Ravenstonedale, Kirkby Stephen, Cumbria, CA17 4NQ Tel: (01539) 623215 Fax: (01539) 623436 E-mail: enquirues@masonry.co.uk

Turner & Co., 240 Sebert Road, London, E7 0NP Tel: (020) 8534 1843 Fax: (020) 8519 0057

W J Haysom & Son, St Adhelms Quarry, Swanage, Dorset, BH19 3LN Tel: (01929) 439217 Fax: (01929) 439215 E-mail: haysom@purbeckstone.co.uk

Wells Masonry Services Ltd, Ilsom Farm, Ilsom, Tetbury, Gloucestershire, GL8 8RX Tel: (01666) 504251 Fax: (01666) 502285 E-mail: sales@wells-group.co.uk

STONE OR RECONSTITUTED STONE WALL CLADDING

Chevron Lifts Ltd, The I O Centre, Barn Way, Lodge Farm Industrial Estate, Northampton, NN5 7UW Tel: (01604) 750080 Fax: (01604) 750081 E-mail: email@chevron-lift.com

Derwent Stone Products Ltd, Unit 16 Greencroft Industrial Estate, Stanley, County Durham, DH9 7XP Tel: (01207) 521482 Fax: (01207) 521455 E-mail: derwentstone@aol.com

Firthglow Ltd, 1 Papyrus Road, Werrington, Peterborough, PE4 5BH Tel: (01733) 570345 Fax: (01733) 576115

Sedgemoor Stone Products Ltd, Pen Mill, Station Yard, Yeovil, Somerset, BA21 5DD Tel: (01935) 429797 Fax: (01935) 432392 E-mail: info@sedgemoorestone.co.uk

Stoneflex URP Ltd, Units 1-4, Vauxhall Industrial Estate, Ruabon, Wrexham, Clwyd, LL14 6HA Tel: (01978) 812111 Fax: (01978) 810399 E-mail: info@stoneflex.com

STONE PRODUCTS

▶ A & H Interiors Ltd, Unit 40 Minerva Works, Crossley Lane, Huddersfield, HD5 9SA Tel: (01484) 432422 Fax: (01484) 426228

▶ Aboyne Fire & Stoves Ltd, Bourtreebush Smithy, Bruntland Road, Portlethen, Aberdeen, AB12 4QN Tel: (01224) 781150

▶ Adams Fireplaces, 117 London Road, King's Lynn, Norfolk, PE30 5ES Tel: (01553) 760541

▶ Akaray, North Circular Road, London, NW2 7AX Tel: (020) 8438 8222

▶ Architectural Stone Ltd, 10 Sheepwalk Road, Lisburn, County Antrim, BT28 3RD Tel: (028) 9264 8048 Fax: (028) 9264 8775

▶ Aspects Of Stone, Broughton Grounds, Broughton, Newport Pagnell, Buckinghamshire, MK16 0HZ Tel: (01908) 830061 Fax: (01908) 830062 E-mail: sales@aspectsofstone.co.uk

▶ Brachot Hermant UK Ltd, Wood Lane, Erdington, Birmingham, B24 9QJ Tel: 0121-382 8778 Fax: 0121-382 8700

▶ Caithness Stone Industries Ltd, The Shore, Wick, Caithness, KW1 4JX Tel: (01955) 605472 Fax: (01955) 605907

▶ Capital Fireplaces Ltd, Units 12-17, Henlow Trading Estate, Henlow, Bedfordshire, SG16 6DS Tel: (01462) 813138 Fax: (0800) 9804847

▶ Cast Tec, Unit 3b East Side, Tynedock, South Shields, Tyne & Wear, NE33 5SP Tel: 0191-497 5438 Fax: 0191-497 4288 E-mail: sales@casttec.co.uk

▶ Cheshire Marble Industries Ltd, Unit 6 Atlantic Point, Atlantic St, Broadheath, Altrincham, Cheshire, WA14 5DE Tel: 0161-926 8775 Fax: 0161-926 9381 E-mail: info@chesiremarble.co.uk

▶ Churwell Art Stone, Hill Top Farm, Rooms Lane, Gildersome, Morley, Leeds, LS27 7NJ Tel: 0113-252 3855

▶ Classic Formai, Crofton House, Lindal Road, London, SE4 1EJ Tel: (020) 8469 2340 Fax: (020) 8694 8020

▶ Classic Formai, Crofton House, Lindal Road, London, SE4 1EJ Tel: (020) 8469 2340 Fax: (020) 8694 8020 E-mail: sales@classicformi.com

▶ Classic Masonry Ltd, Church Hall, Albion Road, North Shields, Tyne & Wear, NE30 2RQ Tel: 0191-257 6666 Fax: 0191-258 4411 E-mail: info@classicmasonry.co.uk

▶ Co-Operative Monumental Services, 217 Bogmoor Road, Glasgow, G51 4TH Tel: 0141-445 1886 Fax: 0141-440 5391

▶ Dunedin Stone Ltd, 3 Lower, London Road, Edinburgh, EH7 5TL Tel: 0131-661 0130

▶ E Moorhouse & Son, Park House, Springfield Road, Bigrigg, Egremont, Cumbria, CA22 2TL Tel: (01946) 811152 Fax: (01946) 811052

▶ Eurocraft Distributors Ltd, Coxwell Avenue, Wolverhampton Science Park, Wolverhampton, WV10 9RT Tel: (01902) 718020 Fax: (01902) 718021

▶ Fairhaven of Anglesey Abbey Ltd, Northfield Farm, Lode Road, Bottisham, Cambridge, CB5 9DN Tel: (01223) 812555

▶ G & E Interiors, 27-29 Liverpool Road, Kidsgrove, Stoke-On-Trent, ST7 1EA Tel: (01782) 785965

▶ George McAlpine & Sons Ltd, 90 Seaward Street, Glasgow, G41 1HJ Tel: 0141-420 1392 Fax: 0141-420 3906 E-mail: info@georgemcalpine.co.uk

▶ Gibson & Goold Ltd, 165-167 Whitletts Road, Ayr, KA8 0JH Tel: (01292) 268478 Fax: (01292) 611949

▶ Gordon Greaves Slate Ltd, The Mill, Troutbeck Bridge, Windermere, Cumbria, LA23 1HS Tel: (01539) 446737 Fax: (01539) 442049 E-mail: sales@gordongreaves.co.uk

▶ Grant Ameristone Ltd, Cawdor House, London Road, Woolmer Green, Knebworth, Hertfordshire, SG3 6JE Tel: (01438) 811009

▶ Grassby & Sons Ltd, Dorchester Road, Grimstone, Dorchester, Dorset, DT2 9NA Tel: (01305) 269678 Fax: (01305) 250309 E-mail: info@glassby-stone.co.uk

▶ Hestia Fireside Design, Unit 6, Newhailes Industrial Estate, Newhailes Road, Musselburgh, Midlothian, EH21 6SY Tel: 0131-653 1900

▶ Home & Hearth, 451 Hillington Road, Hillington Industrial Estate, Glasgow, G52 4BL Tel: 0141-891 4891 Fax: 0141-882 7807

▶ I K M Tiles Marble & Granite, 55 Bangor Road, Edinburgh, EH6 5JX Tel: 0131-467 8900 Fax: 0131-467 8901

▶ Ivett & Reed Ltd, 615 Newmarket Road, Cambridge, CB5 8PA Tel: (01223) 213500 Fax: (01223) 249150 E-mail: sales@ivettandreed.co.uk

▶ J & G Mossman Ltd, 42 Parkhead Road, Sauchie, Alloa, Clackmannanshire, FK10 3BH Tel: (01259) 722319 Fax: (01259) 219793

▶ Keystone Restoration Ltd, 39 Station Road, Longfield, Kent, DA3 7QD Tel: (01474) 703600 Fax: (01474) 703100 E-mail: mail@kystm.co.uk

▶ Kingstone (London) Ltd, Unit 37A, Grace Business Centre, Willow Lane, Mitcham, Surrey, CR4 4TU Tel: (020) 8640 3560 Fax: (020) 8640 3160 E-mail: martin@optionsmarble.demon.co.uk

▶ Kirk Natural Stone Ltd, Bridgend, Fyvie, Turriff, Aberdeenshire, AB53 8LL Tel: (01651) 891891 Fax: (01651) 891891 E-mail: info@kirknaturalstone.com

▶ Living Flames, 751 Pollokshaws Road, Glasgow, G41 2AX Tel: 0141-422 1540

▶ Marble Building Products Ltd, The Airfield, Full Sutton, York, YO41 1HS Tel: (01759) 373352 Fax: (01759) 373394 E-mail: ethurlow@mbpltd.uk.com

▶ Marbles Ltd, 9 South Street, Bromley, BR1 1RH Tel: (020) 8313 3467 Fax: (020) 8313 3509E-mail: graham@marbellimited.com

▶ Marlborough Marble & Stone Work Ltd, 30 Welbeck Road, Glasgow, G53 7SD Tel: 0141-881 8200 Fax: 0141-880 4468

▶ Marshalls plc, Birkby Grange, Birkby Hall Road, Huddersfield, HD2 2TJ Tel: (01484) 438900 Fax: (01484) 438944

▶ Mega Marble, 5 Premier Park Road, London, NW10 7NZ Tel: (020) 8965 5007 Fax: (020) 8965 8552 E-mail: info@megamarble.co.uk

▶ Melmar Stone, Hallcroft Industrial Estate, Aurilac Way, Retford, Nottinghamshire, DN22 7PX Tel: (01777) 870444 Fax: (01777) 860060

Muggins Pottery Ltd, Burton Bandalls Farm, Burton Lane, Burton-on-the-Wolds, Loughborough, Leicestershire, LE12 5TE Tel: (01509) 266582 E-mail: info@muggins.com

▶ Natural Stone Features, 3B Kingston Industrial Estate, Ardgowan Street, Port Glasgow, Renfrewshire, PA14 5DG Tel: (01475) 744436

▶ Natural Stone Quarries Ltd, The Shore, Forth Bank Industrial Estate, Alloa, Clackmannanshire, FK10 1HA Tel: (01259) 721977 Fax: (01259) 723383

▶ NBS Stone Products Ltd, Co Bam House, Pleasant Street, Stoke-on-Trent, ST6 3DL Tel: (01782) 838559 Fax: (01782) 838442

▶ New Forest Woodburning Centre Ltd, The Old School House, Church Lane, Sway, Lymington, Hampshire, SO41 6AD Tel: (01590) 683585 Fax: (01590) 683587 E-mail: sales@woodburners.com

▶ North Stone (NI) Ltd, Shinny Road, Macosquin, Coleraine, County Londonderry, BT51 4PS Tel: (028) 7032 1100 Fax: (028) 7035 7333

▶ P Challen Ltd, Norfolk Estate Saw Mill, London Road, Arundel, West Sussex, BN18 9AU Tel: (01903) 885000 Fax: (01903) 885050 E-mail: info@pchallen.co.uk

▶ P Lipton & Sons Ltd, 7-11 Gourock Street, Glasgow, G5 9RY Tel: 0141-429 7341 Fax: 0141-418 0470

▶ P M Fireplaces, 56 Ballygawley Road, Dungannon, County Tyrone, BT70 1TZ Tel: (028) 8772 5215 Fax: (028) 8772 2505

▶ Prima, 60 West Hendon Broadway, London, NW9 7AE Tel: (020) 8201 5857 Fax: (020) 8202 8282

▶ Realstone Ltd, Barclay Curle Complex, 739 South Street, Glasgow, G14 0BX Tel: 0141-954 1161 Fax: 0141-958 1261

▶ Roma Marble Ltd, 3 Munro Drive, Cline Road, London, N11 2LZ Tel: (020) 8361 7818 Fax: (020) 8361 7819 E-mail: sales@romamarble.co.uk

▶ Sandy Mclean & Co., 1 East High Street, Greenlaw, Duns, Berwickshire, TD10 6YF Tel: (01361) 810405 Fax: (01361) 810676

▶ Silestone Of London, Unit 2 Octinum Business Park, Albert Drive, Woking, Surrey, GU21 5RW Tel: (01483) 757345 Fax: (01483) 757346 E-mail: sales@silestoneoflondon.co.uk

▶ Stone Tec Ltd, 34 Russell Road, Edinburgh, EH11 2LP Tel: 0131-313 4111 Fax: 0131-313 4222

▶ Strettle Memorials, Moor Edge Road, Shiremoor, Newcastle upon Tyne, NE27 0HU Tel: 0191-253 3222 Fax: 0191-297 1775

▶ Templestone Fire Surrounds Ltd, Station Wharf, Castle Cary, Somerset, BA7 7PE Tel: (01963) 350242 Fax: (01963) 350258 E-mail: sales@templestone.co.uk

▶ Tudorstone Stone Products, The Dale, Stoney Middleton, Hope Valley, Derbyshire, S32 4TF Tel: (01433) 639005 Fax: (01433) 639656 E-mail: darlstone@ukonline.co.uk

▶ Unimar Ltd, 5 Perivale Industrial Park, Horsenden La South, Greenford, Middlesex, UB6 7RL Tel: (020) 7870 5695 Fax: (020) 8810 7766 E-mail: info@unimarltd.co.uk

▶ Venice Marble Ltd, 254 Kilburn High Road, London, NW6 2BX Tel: (020) 7372 3191 Fax: (020) 7372 3196

▶ Walkers Bros Cockermouth Ltd, 6 Market Place, Cockermouth, Cumbria, CA13 9NQ Tel: (01900) 823302 Fax: (01900) 823302

▶ Welcome Fireplace Co Ltd, 44 Seaward Street, Glasgow, G41 1HJ Tel: 0141-429 8242 Fax: 0141-429 1067

▶ Welters Organisation Worldwide, D Kingmoor Park, Heathlands Estate, Carlisle, CA6 4RE Tel: (0870) 2416422 Fax: (01228) 674959 E-mail: sales@welters-worldwide.com

▶ Wessex Memorials, 2 Clump Farm Industrial Estate, Higher Shaftesbury Road, Blandford Forum, Dorset, DT11 7TD Tel: (01258) 450252 Fax: (01258) 450253 E-mail: info@wessexmemorials.co.uk

▶ Worcestershire Marble, Button Bridge, Kinlet, Bewdley, Worcestershire, DY12 3AW Tel: (01299) 841206 Fax: (01299) 841516

STONE RESTORATION CONTRACTORS

A J Restoration Co Ltd, Restoration House, Second Avenue, Greasley St, Nottingham, NG6 8NE Tel: 0115-927 7044 Fax: 0115-976 3476 E-mail: ajrestoration.co@btconnect.com

Baker & Sons Danbury Ltd, Eves Corner, Danbury, Chelmsford, CM3 4QB Tel: (01245) 225876 Fax: (01245) 226821 E-mail: enq@bakersofdanbury.co.uk

J. Battle, Pipers Drier Studio, Clarendon Park, Salisbury, SP5 3ES Tel: (01722) 711770 Fax: (01722) 506707 E-mail: jay.battle@ntlworld.com

W.R. Bedford Stonemasonry Ltd, 57-65 Whitehouse Lane, Bedminster, Bristol, BS3 4DN Tel: 0117-963 7756 Fax: 0117-963 4223 E-mail: wr.bedford@1way.co.uk

▶ Bolton Stone Restoration Ltd, Winter House, Winter Street, Bolton, BL1 8AZ Tel: (01204) 843853 Fax: (01204) 849841 E-mail: enquiries@boltonstone.co.uk

Brick & Stone Doctors, 139 Newgate Lane, Mansfield, Nottinghamshire, NG18 2LG Tel: (01623) 402427 Fax: (01623) 402208 E-mail: brick.stonedoctors@ntlworld.com

▶ DG Stone, 33 Farm Crescent, Wexham, Slough, SL2 5TQ Tel: 01753 524316 Fax: 01753 524316 E-mail: dgstone@hotmail.co.uk

George Sweeney Junior, 39 Whitehill Road, Glenrothes, Fife, KY6 2RW Tel: (01592) 774325 Fax: (01592) 774325

Grants Of Shoreditch Ltd, 25 Hackney Road, London, E2 7NX Tel: (020) 7729 3380 Fax: (020) 7613 3610 E-mail: sales@grantsint.com

▶ L B Stone, Hatton Court, Hatton Close, Moulton Park Industrial Estate, Northampton, NN3 6SU Tel: (01604) 670333 Fax: (01604) 648764

Metropolitan Stone, 5 Wells Place, Merstham, Redhill, RH1 3DR Tel: (01737) 644111 Fax: (01737) 648300

Natural Stone Co., Elm Cottage, Ockham Road North, Ockham, Woking, Surrey, GU23 6NW Tel: (01483) 211311 Fax: (01483) 211555

Negus Ken Ltd, 90 Garfield Road, London, SW19 8SB Tel: (020) 8543 9266 Fax: (020) 8543 9100 E-mail: enquiries@kennegus.co.uk

Rominar UK Ltd, 106 Columbia Road, London, E2 7RG Tel: (020) 7739 8567 Fax: (020) 7729 7099 E-mail: rominarukltd@aol.com

STONE RESTORATION CONTRACTORS – *continued*

William Sapcote & Sons Ltd, 87 Camden Street, Birmingham, B1 3DE Tel: 0121-233 1200 Fax: 0121-236 2731 E-mail: enquiries@sapcote.co.uk

Watson Construction Group Ltd, Westwood, West Calder, West Lothian, EH55 8PN Tel: (01506) 871561 Fax: (01506) 871770 E-mail: info@watsongroup.co.uk

▶ Westone Masonry, Unit 4 Knightcott Industrial Estate, Banwell, Avon, BS29 6JN Tel: (01934) 824488 Fax: (01934) 824499

STONE SAWING MACHINES

Harbro Supplies Ltd, Morland Street, Bishop Auckland, County Durham, DL14 6JG Tel: (01388) 605363 Fax: (01388) 603263 E-mail: harbrosupplies@hotmail.com

STONE, DRESSED

▶ A & D Sutherland Ltd, Spittal Mains Quarry, Spittal, Wick, Caithness, KW1 5XR Tel: (01847) 841239 Fax: (01847) 841321

▶ A S Ballantine Ltd, 214 Lisnaragh Road, Dunamanagh, Strabane, County Tyrone, BT82 0SB Tel: (028) 7139 8276 Fax: (028) 7139 8189 E-mail: asballantine@btconnect.com

▶ Aggregate Industries Ltd, Croy Quarry Constarry Road, Kilsyth, Glasgow, G65 9HY Tel: (01236) 823274 Fax: (01236) 825311

▶ Aggregate Industries Ltd, Marybank, Isle of Lewis, HS2 0DD Tel: (01851) 703342 Fax: (01851) 705282

▶ Aggregate Industries Ltd, Melbur Works, Summercourt, Newquay, Cornwall, TR8 5UA Tel: (01726) 862233 Fax: (01726) 862240

▶ Aggregate Industries, Duntilland Quarry, Salsburgh, Shotts, Lanarkshire, ML7 4NZ Tel: (01698) 870811

▶ Ambrisbeg Ltd, 68 Marine Road, Port Bannatyne, Isle Of Bute, PA20 0LT Tel: (01700) 502719

▶ Balmedie Quarry, Balmedie Quarry, Belhelvie, Aberdeen, AB23 8WT Tel: (01358) 742203 Fax: (01358) 742203

▶ Barr Ltd, Barr Quarry, Glenluce, Newton Stewart, Wigtownshire, DG8 0JQ Tel: (01581) 300329 Fax: (01581) 300523

▶ The Bath Stone Co. Ltd, Stoke Hill Mine, Midford Lane, Limpley Stoke, Bath, BA2 7GP Tel: (01225) 723792

J. Battle, Pipers Drier Studio, Clarendon Park, Salisbury, SP5 3ES Tel: (01722) 711770 Fax: (01722) 506707 E-mail: jay.battle@ntlworld.com

▶ Cemex UK Ltd, Core Utilities, Kilmartin Place, Glasgow, G71 5PH Tel: (01355) 243011 Fax: (01698) 816068

▶ Cemex Uk Materials Ltd, Airdrie Road, Caldercruix, Airdrie, Lanarkshire, ML6 8PA Tel: (01236) 843040 Fax: (01236) 842529

▶ Chap Quarries Ltd, Park Quarry, Durris, Banchory, Kincardineshire, AB31 6BA Tel: (01330) 811771 Fax: (01330) 811497

▶ Cursiter Quarry, Finstown, Kirkwall, Orkney, KW15 1TT Tel: (01856) 761295

▶ Downs Stone Co. Ltd, Lower Buildings, Sarsden, Chipping Norton, Oxfordshire, OX7 6PN Tel: (01608) 658357 Fax: (01608) 658882 E-mail: sales@downstone.com

▶ Enstone Thistle Ltd, Dunecht, Westhill, Aberdeenshire, AB32 7ED Tel: (01330) 833361 Fax: (01330) 833565

▶ Geddes Group, Ardownie Quarry, Monifieth, Dundee, DD5 4HW Tel: (01382) 533382 Fax: (01382) 535655

▶ Geddes Group, Beanston, Haddington, East Lothian, EH41 3SB Tel: (01620) 861165 Fax: (01620) 861311 E-mail: enquiries@geddesgroup.co.uk

▶ Hanson Aggregates Ltd, Caer Glaw Quarry, Gwalchmai, Holyhead, Gwynedd, LL65 4PW Tel: (01407) 720292 Fax: (01407) 720106

▶ Hanson Aggregates Ltd, Clee Hill Quarry, Clee Hill, Ludlow, Shropshire, SY8 3QA Tel: (01584) 890516

▶ Hanson Aggregates, Brindister Quarry, Gulberwick, Shetland, ZE2 9EX Tel: (01595) 692401

▶ J Boyd & Sons Carnmoney, 38 The Square, Ballyclare, County Antrim, BT39 9BB Tel: (028) 9334 0866 Fax: (028) 9332 4850

▶ J Joslin (Contractors) Ltd, Lower Road, Long Hanborough, Witney, Oxfordshire, OX29 8LR Tel: (01993) 882153 E-mail: enquires@j-jocklin.co.uk

▶ John Maclachlan Quarries Ltd, Soroba, Oban, Argyll, PA34 4SB Tel: (01631) 566295 Fax: (01631) 566758

▶ Leighs Quarries, New Forres Quarry, Forres, Morayshire, IV36 2RQ Tel: (01309) 671144 Fax: (01309) 671199

▶ Mcgirr Engineering, Lurganbuoy, Sixmilecross, Omagh, County Tyrone, BT79 9EJ Tel: (028) 8075 8694 Fax: (028) 8075 8694

▶ O I Manufacturing Ltd, Devilla Quarry, Alloa, Clackmannanshire, FK10 3QD Tel: (01259) 730621 Fax: (01259) 730340 E-mail: barry.chalmers@eu.o-i.com

▶ Patersons Of Greenoakhill Ltd, Greenoakhill Quarry, Uddingston, Glasgow, G71 7SN Tel: 0141-771 3939 Fax: 0141-773 4248

▶ R M C Russell, Cowieslinn Crossing, Peebles, EH45 8QZ Tel: (01721) 730251 Fax: (01721) 730379

▶ Tarmac Ltd, Upper Cruiks, Inverkeithing, Fife, KY11 1HH Tel: (01383) 413241 Fax: (01383) 413244

▶ Tarmac Central Ltd, Dene Quarry, The Hill, Cromford, Matlock, Derbyshire, DE4 3QS Tel: (01629) 822104 Fax: (01629) 826185

▶ Tarmac Northern Ltd, Ravelrigg Quarry, Kirknewton, Midlothian, EH27 8EF Tel: 0131-449 5523 Fax: 0131-451 5771

▶ Tayside Contracts, Collace Quarry, Collace, Perth, PH2 6JB Tel: (01821) 650222 Fax: (01821) 650440

▶ W B B Minerals Ltd, Levenseat Quarry, Fauld House, Bathgate, West Lothian, EH47 9AD Tel: (01270) 752752 Fax: (01501) 772621

▶ Yeoman (Morven) Ltd, Rhugh Garbh Depot, Barcaldine, Oban, Argyll, PA37 1SE Tel: (01631) 720489 Fax: (01631) 720639

STONEWARE

Dunoon Ceramics Ltd, 5 Walton Industrial Estate, Beacon Road, Stone, Staffordshire, ST15 0RY Tel: (01785) 817414 Fax: (01785) 812322 E-mail: sales@dunoonmugs.co.uk

STONEWARE TILES

Dunoon Ceramics Ltd, 5 Walton Industrial Estate, Beacon Road, Stone, Staffordshire, ST15 0RY Tel: (01785) 817414 Fax: (01785) 812322 E-mail: sales@dunoonmugs.co.uk

Fired Earth Ltd, 1-3 Twyford Mill, Oxford Road, Adderbury, Banbury, Oxfordshire, OX17 3SX Tel: (01295) 812088 Fax: (01295) 810832 E-mail: info@firedearth.com

▶ Leafcutter Design, 119 Penn Hill Avenue, Poole, Dorset, BH14 9LY Tel: (01202) 716969 Fax: (01202) 716969 E-mail: sales@leafcutterdesign.co.uk

Tranasco Co. Ltd, Unit 28 Greenhill Industrial Estate, Coatbridge, Lanarkshire, ML5 2AG Tel: (01236) 424400 Fax: (01236) 424477

STOOLS, ADJUSTABLE HEIGHT

▶ James Upholstery, 3 Booth Road, Little Lever, Bolton, BL3 1JY Tel: (01204) 408993 E-mail: jamesupholstery@ntlworld.com

STOPPED FLOW SPECTROMETERS

Applied Photophysics, 203 Kingston Road, Leatherhead, Surrey, KT22 7PB Tel: (01372) 386537 Fax: (01372) 386477 E-mail: sales@photophysics.com

STORAGE BIN OR CONTAINER HIRE

▶ Pentalver Container Sales, West Bay Road, Western Docks, Southampton, SO15 0GN Tel: (023) 8070 6070 Fax: (023) 8070 6074 E-mail: soupentsal@pentalver.com

STORAGE BINS OR CONTAINERS, *See also separate headings for particular materials stored*

Empteezy Ltd, Alpha House, 4 Muir Road, Houstoun Industrial Estate, Livingston, West Lothian, EH54 5DR Tel: (01506) 430309 Fax: (01506) 441466 E-mail: sales@empteezy.co.uk

Garrods of Barking Ltd, Abbey Wharf, Kings Bridge Road, Barking, Essex, IG11 0BD Tel: (020) 8594 0224 Fax: (020) 8594 0225 E-mail: info@garrods.com

Kardex Sysytems, 26, Regency Park, Newtownards, County Down, BT23 8ZG Tel: (028) 9181 4242 Fax: (028) 9181 5599

Marc Containers Ltd, Unit 33b Westerton Road, East Mains Industrial Estate, Broxburn, West Lothian, EH52 5AU Tel: (01506) 852804 Fax: (01506) 857083

U B H International Ltd, Orrell Lane, Burscough, Ormskirk, Lancashire, L40 0SL Tel: (01704) 898500 Fax: (01704) 898518 E-mail: tanks@ubh.co.uk

STORAGE CABINETS

James Bedford & Co. Ltd, Pennine View, Birstall, Batley, West Yorkshire, WF17 9NF Tel: (01924) 442048 Fax: (01924) 472117 E-mail: sales@jbedford.co.uk

Mark Brazier Jones, Hyde Hall Barn, Sandon, Buntingford, Hertfordshire, SG9 0RU Tel: (01763) 273599 Fax: (01763) 273410 E-mail: studio@braizer-jones.com

▶ Traditional Values Ltd, 10-14 West Street, Southend-on-Sea, SS2 6HJ Tel: (01702) 300087 Fax: (01702) 390766 E-mail: info@traditional-values.co.uk

Treston Ltd, 5b Bone Lane, Newbury, Berkshire, RG14 5SH Tel: (01635) 521521 Fax: (01635) 37452 E-mail: salesuk@treston.com

STORAGE CONTAINERS

ACS Cabins, Midlands Farm, Mill Lane, Headley, Bordon, Hampshire, GU35 0PB Tel: (01428) 714900

▶ Fife Warehousing Co. Ltd, Wemyss Road, Dysart, Kirkcaldy, Fife, KY1 2XZ Tel: (01592) 651065 Fax: (01592) 652360 E-mail: sales@fifegroup.com

▶ K Carriers, Continental House, Avis Way, Newhaven, East Sussex, BN9 0DH Tel: (01273) 514599 Fax: (01273) 515939

Leavesley Container Services, Lichfield Rd, Branston, Burton-on-Trent, Staffordshire, DE14 3HD Tel: (01283) 537382 Fax: (01283) 511740 E-mail: sales@leavesley-containers.com

Manchester Cabins Ltd, Tweedale Way, Oldham, OL9 7LD Tel: 0161-684 3333 Fax: 0161-684 1111 E-mail: info@manchestercabins.co.uk

Mobile Storage UK, New Millerdam Industrial, Barnsley Road, Newmillerdam, Wakefield, West Yorkshire, WF2 6QW Tel: (01924) 254254 Fax: (01924) 249249

▶ Nelson The Removal Co., Irongrey Park, Irongray Road, Dumfries, DG2 0JE Tel: (01387) 722320 Fax: (01387) 722321 E-mail: info@nelsonremovals.co.uk

▶ Southampton Containers Limited, Eling Container Base, Eling Wharf, High Street, Totton, Southampton, SO40 4TE Tel: (023) 8066 8505 Fax: (023) 8066 8504 E-mail: info@southamptoncontainers.co.uk

Stalkers Transport Ltd, Townfoot Industrial Estate, Brampton, Cumbria, CA8 1SW Tel: (01697) 73699 Fax: (01697) 73176 E-mail: enquiries@stalkerstransport.co.uk

STORAGE CONTRACTORS/ SERVICES

A Storage Solution Ltd, Riverside House, Leaside Road, London, E5 9LU Tel: (020) 8806 3155 Fax: (020) 8806 7265E-mail: storsol@aol.com

Abbey Self Storage, Abbey Business Centre, Ingate Place, London, SW8 3NS Tel: (020) 7627 8000 Fax: (020) 7720 6633

Access Self Storage Ltd, 93 Park Lane, London, W1K 7TB Tel: (020) 7297 4100 E-mail: enquiries@accessstorage.com

J.R. Adams (Newcastle) Ltd, Hannington Works, Longrigg, Swalwell, Newcastle Upon Tyne, NE16 3AS Tel: 0191-488 7911 Fax: 0191-488 3101

Albatross, 63 Orchard Way, Croydon, CR0 7NQ Tel: (020) 8777 2665 E-mail: albatrossremoval@aol.com

Baird Lends A Hand Ltd, 75 Beardmore Way, Clydebank, Dunbartonshire, G81 4HT Tel: 0141-952 0962 Fax: 0141-941 2205 E-mail: jb@baird-uk.com

Baylis Distribution Ltd, New Potter Grange Road, Goole, North Humberside, DN14 6BZ Tel: (01405) 766174 Fax: (01405) 766270

Baylis Distribution Ltd, Hamilton House, Birchwood Lane, Moore, Warrington, WA4 6XJ Tel: (01925) 656770 Fax: (01925) 571049

Belgrave Shipping Co. Ltd, Fishers Way, Belvedere, Kent, DA17 6BS Tel: (020) 8310 1890 Fax: (020) 8312 3505 E-mail: belgrave@ukfraite.co.uk

▶ Bishops Move, Unit 11, South Hampshire Industrial Park, Totton, Southampton, SO40 3SA Tel: (023) 8023 7100 Fax: (023) 8086 7888 E-mail: southampton@bishopsmove.com

Bishops Move Chichester Ltd, 3 The Nelson Centre, Portfield Road, Portsmouth, PO3 5SF Tel: (023) 9266 9350 Fax: (023) 9266 9399 E-mail: portsmouth@bishopsmove.co.uk

Boathunters Boatbuilders, The Docks, Burry Port, Dyfed, SA16 0LT Tel: (01554) 834030

Bonner International, 19 Kennet Road, Dartford, DA1 4QN Tel: (020) 8303 6261 Fax: (01322) 556882 E-mail: moving@dbonner.co.uk

Bretts Transport Ltd, Thorney Road, Guyhirn, Wisbech, Cambridgeshire, PE13 4AG Tel: (01733) 849245 Fax: (01733) 849363

Burke Bros, Foxs Lane, Wolverhampton, WV1 1PA Tel: (01902) 714555 Fax: (01902) 427837 E-mail: sales@burkebros.co.uk

C S Ellis Group Ltd, Wireless Hill Ind Estate, South Luffenham, Oakham, Leicestershire, LE15 8NF Tel: (01780) 720133 Fax: (01780) 721801 E-mail: mail@csellis.co.uk

Charles W Michie Ltd, 54 Park Road, Aberdeen, AB24 5PA Tel: (01224) 632281 Fax: (01224) 649012E-mail: carolyn@michietransport.co.uk

City Moving & Storage Ltd, Canada House Business Centre, 272 Field End Road, Ruislip, Middlesex, HA4 9NA Tel: (020) 8582 0420 Fax: (020) 8582 0421 E-mail: info@citymoving.co.uk

City Space Services Ltd, 37-39 Holmesdale Road, North Holmwood, Dorking, Surrey, RH5 4HS Tel: (0800) 592058 Fax: (01306) 884552

Commercial & Personal Relocations Ltd, Space Centre, Legg Brothers Industrial Estate, Spring Road, Wolverhampton, WV4 6JT Tel: (01902) 491001 Fax: (01902) 491002 E-mail: liz@cpr-uk.com

▶ Dalepak Packing, The Business Centre, Ross Road, Weedon Road Industrial Estate, Northampton, NN5 5AX Tel: (01604) 580777 Fax: (01604) 756600

Dashwood Metal Products, PO Box 23, St. Neots, Cambridgeshire, PE19 8UZ Tel: (01480) 477339

Davies Turner Worldwide Movers Ltd, 49 Wates Way, Mitcham, Surrey, CR4 4HR Tel: (020) 7622 4393 Fax: (020) 7720 3897 E-mail: removals@daviesturner.co.uk

Delivery Service Ltd, Stoke Hall Road, Ipswich, IP2 8EJ Tel: (01473) 601564 Fax: (01473) 602789 E-mail: sales@ipswichdeliveryservice.co.uk

Domain Selfstorage, 21-31 Shacklewell Lane, London, E8 2DA Tel: (020) 7923 3003 Fax: (020) 7923 7799 E-mail: info@domainselfstorage.co.uk

Drury Smart, 148 Brierley Road, Walton Summit Centre, Bamber Bridge, Preston, PR5 8AH Tel: (01704) 533243 Fax: (01772) 318400

East Coast Storage (Handling) Ltd, Clenchwarton Road, West Lynn, King's Lynn, Norfolk, PE34 3LW Tel: (01553) 772689 Fax: (01553) 691578 E-mail: ecoast@globalnet.co.uk

▶ Easymove (Bristol) Ltd, Albert Crescent, Bristol, BS2 0SU Tel: 0117-977 1460

Edwards, Strathmore Avenue, Luton, LU1 3NZ Tel: (01582) 730256 Fax: (01582) 730256

Evans Transport, Braunton Road, Barnstaple, Devon, EX31 1LE Tel: (01271) 326632 Fax: (01271) 326616 E-mail: evanstransport@btconnect.com

Alan Firmin Ltd, Mid Kent Business Park, Sortmill Road, Snodland, Kent, ME6 5GP Tel: (01634) 241200 Fax: (01622) 820823 E-mail: transport@alanfirmin.co.uk

Firmin Coates Ltd, The Pines, Fordham Road, Newmarket, Suffolk, CB8 7LG Tel: (01638) 720481 Fax: (01638) 721240 E-mail: i.murfitt@firmincoates.co.uk

▶ Five Valleys Removals, 22 Quedgeley Trading Estate East, Haresfield, Stonehouse, Gloucestershire, GL10 3EX Tel: (01452) 729056 Fax: (01452) 729494

Fletchers Removals, Racecourse Industrial Park, Mansfield Road, Derby, DE21 4SX Tel: (01332) 371470 Fax: (01332) 294397 E-mail: sales@webbesremovals.net

G B Liners Ltd, 8 Haslemere Industrial Estate, Third Way, Avonmouth, Bristol, BS11 9TP Tel: 0117-982 8141 E-mail: bristol@gbliners.com

G & J Ping Ltd, 63 Coates Road, Eastrea, Whittlesey, Peterborough, PE7 2BA Tel: (01733) 203383 Fax: (01733) 351204

G R Warehousing Ltd, Old Station Road, Mendlesham, Stowmarket, Suffolk, IP14 5RT Tel: (01449) 768009 Fax: (01449) 766823 E-mail: mike@grwarehousing.fsnet.co.uk

G T W Storage Services Ltd, 41-45 James Watt Street, Glasgow, G2 8NF Tel: 0141-221 4727 Fax: 0141-224 4520

Gardner Freight International Ltd, Mersey Chambers, Covent Garden, Liverpool, L2 8XT Tel: 0151-236 7366 Fax: 0151-243 3463 E-mail: harrisons@liverpool.co.uk

Gilbert Norris Removals, Wakefield Road, Netherton, Bootle, Merseyside, L30 6TZ Tel: 0151-530 1196 Fax: 0151-524 1808

Harrow Green Ltd, Cooks Road, London, E15 2PW Tel: (020) 8522 0101 Fax: (020) 8522 0252 E-mail: info@harrowgreen.com

Hartgrove Bros, Station Road, Redcar, Cleveland, TS10 1RD Tel: (01642) 489937 Fax: (01642) 489937

Horsehay Ltd, Horsehay Estate, Telford, Shropshire, TF4 3PY Tel: (01952) 503344 Fax: (01952) 503356 E-mail: richard@horsehay.uk.com

IMG Industrial Maintenance Group Ltd, Unit M Riverside Industrial Estate, Fazeley, Tamworth, Staffordshire, B78 3RW Tel: (01827) 283322 Fax: (01827) 250143

Interdean Interconex Ltd, Interdean House, 15 Central Way, London, NW10 7XW Tel: (020) 8961 4141 Fax: (020) 8965 4484 E-mail: interdean@interconex.com

Iron Mountain Ltd, Cottons Centre, Tooley Street, London, SE1 2TT Tel: (0800) 270270 Fax: (020) 7939 1501

Island Removals, Manners View, Newport, Isle of Wight, PO30 5FA Tel: (01983) 526374 Fax: (01983) 526374 E-mail: info@islandremovals.co.uk

J Newby & Sons, Mintsfeet Road South, Kendal, Cumbria, LA9 6ND Tel: (01539) 720819 Fax: (01539) 734607 E-mail: pickfords.preston@pickfords.com

L A Reed & Son Haulage Ltd, 47 Low Street, Swinefleet, Goole, North Humberside, DN14 8DF Tel: (01405) 704351 Fax: (01405) 766654

L V Transport Ltd, Norfolk Road, Gravesend, Kent, DA12 2PS Tel: (01474) 567361 Fax: (01474) 564455 E-mail: lv.transport@btopenworld.com

Lait Storage & Distribution Ltd, Northern Road, Chilton Industrial Estate, Sudbury, Suffolk, CO10 2ZB Tel: (01787) 376493 Fax: (01787) 312707 E-mail: admin@lait-storage.co.uk

▶ Lanes Storage & Removals, Greenbottom, Chacewater, Truro, Cornwall, TR4 8QW Tel: (01872) 560147 Fax: (01872) 561051

Le Marquand Bros, 5-6 Peirson Road, St. Helier, Jersey, JE2 3PD Tel: (01534) 723261 Fax: (01534) 768971

Lewis & Sons, 8 Silver Street, Barnstaple, Devon, EX32 8HR Tel: (01271) 342336 Fax: (01271) 323330

▶ Lingfield Warehousing Ltd, Lingfield Point, Mcmullen Road, Darlington, County Durham, DL1 1RW Tel: (01325) 359795

▶ Marcus (Bradford) Ltd, Unit 10, Northside Industrial Estate, Northside Road, Bradford, West Yorkshire, BD7 2QT Tel: (01274) 573488

Martells Of Sutton Ltd, Unit 3, 4, Charlwoods Road, East Grinstead, West Sussex, RH19 2HG Tel: (01342) 321303 Fax: (01342) 302145 E-mail: removals@martells.co.uk

STORAGE CONTRACTORS/ SERVICES – *continued*

▶ Metrans Processing Ltd, Unit 5, North Orbital Trading Estate, Napsbury Lane, St. Albans, Hertfordshire, AL1 1XB Tel: (01727) 848160

A.J. & R.J. Mew, 20 Mayfield Road, Ryde, Isle Of Wight, PO33 3TR Tel: (01983) 852835 Fax: (01983) 568758

Moreton C Cullimore & Son Ltd, Fromebridge Lane, Whitminster, Gloucester, GL2 7PD Tel: (01452) 740436 Fax: (01452) 740866

F.C. Morgan (Removals) Ltd, 30 Crosby Road North, Liverpool, L22 4QF Tel: 0151-928 3154 Fax: 0151-928 2848

Morleys, 2 Waterworks Road, Eastbourne, East Sussex, BN22 8LR Tel: (01323) 725793 Fax: (01323) 734193

Northover & Gilbert Removals, Gundry Lane, Bridport, Dorset, DT6 3RJ Tel: (01308) 423939 Fax: (01308) 423939

▶ Osbornes Removals & Storage Ltd, Remco House, Wharf Road, Sale, Cheshire, M33 2AF Tel: 0161-236 0358 Fax: 0161-969 9879

P Fahey & Sons Holdings Ltd, 92 Chorlton Road, Stretford, Manchester, M15 4AL Tel: 0161-226 5959 Fax: 0161-227 9747 E-mail: removals@faheygroup.co.uk

Page The Packers, Old Station Road, Ventnor, Isle of Wight, PO38 1DX Tel: (01983) 852951 Fax: (01983) 855956 E-mail: info@page-packers.fsnet.co.uk

Peter Evans Ltd, Wickwar Road, Chipping Sodbury, Bristol, BS37 6BQ Tel: (01278) 793339 Fax: (01278) 793251 E-mail: mail@peforktrucks.co.uk

Pickfords Ltd, 2a Brunel Way, Fareham, Hampshire, PO15 5TX Tel: (023) 9282 1325 Fax: (01489) 573128

▶ Pickfords Ltd, Pickfords House, Foxbridge Way, Normanton Industrial Estate, Normanton, West Yorkshire, WF6 1TN Tel: (01482) 878866 Fax: (01924) 899387

Porters Of Woking, 5 North Road, Woking, Surrey, GU21 5DS Tel: (01483) 765432 Fax: (01483) 756432 E-mail: sales@portersremovals.co.uk

▶ R H Cambidge Storage Ltd, Argoed Farm, Kinnerley, Oswestry, Shropshire, SY10 8DH Tel: (01691) 682361 Fax: (01691) 682513

Reads Removal, Westwood Farm, Westwood, Peterborough, PE3 9UW Tel: (01733) 334411 Fax: (01733) 334320 E-mail: sales@readsremovals.co.uk

Rhys Davies & Sons Ltd, Moy Road Industrial Estate, Taffs Well, Cardiff, CF15 7QR Tel: (029) 2081 0587 Fax: (029) 2081 0717 E-mail: sales@rhysdavies.co.uk

▶ Richardson Removal & Storage Contractors Ltd, Vickers Close, Preston Farm Industrial Estate, Stockton-on-Tees, Cleveland, TS18 3TD Tel: (01642) 673207 Fax: (01642) 671080

Richman's Removals (Swindon) Ltd, Transfer Bridge Industrial Estate, County Road, Swindon, SN1 2EL Tel: (01793) 526621 Fax: (01793) 542795 E-mail: enquiries@richmansswindon.co.uk

A. Robins & Sons Ltd, Unit 9 Spring Lakes Industrial Estate, Deadbrooke Lane, Aldershot, Hampshire, GU12 4UH Tel: (0800) 243433 Fax: (01252) 345861 E-mail: sales@overs.co.uk

Robinsons International Removals Ltd, Nuffield Way, Abingdon, Oxfordshire, OX14 1TN Tel: (01235) 552266 Fax: (01235) 553573 E-mail: oxford@robinsons-intl.com

Robinsons International Removals Ltd, Bartleet Road, Redditch, Worcestershire, B98 0DG Tel: (01527) 830850 Fax: (01527) 526812 E-mail: redditch@robinsons-intl.com

Romstor Ltd, Unit 22,, West Station Ind. Estate, Spital Road,, Maldon, Essex, CM9 6TS Tel: 01621 855600 Fax: 01621 875919 E-mail: sales@romstor.co.uk

Rumsey & Sons, Market House, Market Road, Richmond, Surrey, TW9 4LZ Tel: (020) 8892 1896 Fax: (020) 8876 9969 E-mail: removals@rumseyandson.com

Ryans Move International Ltd, Unit 14 Gateway Industrial Estate, Hythe Road, London, NW10 6RJ Tel: (020) 8969 7047 Fax: (020) 8969 1326E-mail: britannia@ryansmove.co.uk

S J Sharp (Nuneaton) Ltd, Weddington Road, Nuneaton, Warwickshire, CV10 0AE Tel: (024) 7638 3232 Fax: (024) 7638 2362

Saunders of Harpenden, 31 Frogmore, Park Street, St. Albans, Hertfordshire, AL2 2NH Tel: (01727) 875348 Fax: (01727) 875068

Scroby Fayre Ltd, 31 Clydesdale Rise, Bradwell, Great Yarmouth, Norfolk, NR31 9UG Tel: (01493) 652833 Fax: (01493) 441707

Shepherd Offshore P.L.C., Offshore Technology Park, Walker, Newcastle Upon Tyne, NE6 3NL Tel: 0191-262 9614 Fax: 0191-263 9872 E-mail: headoffice@shepherdoffshore.com

Smarts Of Northolt, Unit 15 The Metropolitan Centre, Derby Road, Greenford, Middlesex, UB6 8UJ Tel: (0500) 030609 Fax: (020) 8575 8804 E-mail: sales@smartsremovals.co.uk

Solihull Storage Ltd, Beresford House, Highlands Road, Shirley, Solihull, West Midlands, B90 4ND Tel: 0121-705 2323 Fax: 0121-705 7683 E-mail: sales@storage-removals.co.uk

Storehire UK Ltd, Stansted Distribution Centre, Start Hill, Great Hallingbury, Bishop's Stortford, Hertfordshire, CM22 7DG Tel: (01279) 505202 Fax: (01279) 505233

Strank's Removals, Unit 5 Wotton Trading Estate, Ashford, Kent, TN23 6LL Tel: (01233) 646478 Fax: (01233) 645653 E-mail: admin@stranks-removals.co.uk

D. Sully & Son Ltd, Unit 4 Coldharbour Lane Industrial Estate, 129 Coldharbour Lane, London, SE5 9NY Tel: (020) 7733 3559 E-mail: sales@sully.co.uk

Team Relocations plc, Drury Way, Brentpark, Neasden, London, NW10 0JN Tel: (020) 8784 0100 Fax: (020) 8451 0061

TNT Logistics Ltd, Parkside Lane, Leeds, LS11 5TD Tel: 0113-276 2244 Fax: 0113-276 2928

Tomhead Ltd, 2a Ramsden Road, Rotherwas Industrial Estate, Hereford, HR2 6NP Tel: (01432) 358420 Fax: (01432) 354448 E-mail: info@tomhead.co.uk

▶ Town & Country Removals Ltd, Unit 3, 100 Church Street, Staines, Middlesex, TW18 4YA Tel: (01784) 464188 Fax: 01784 464484 E-mail: info@townandcountryremovals.net

Turner Removal Services, Huyton Road, Adlington, Chorley, Lancashire, PR7 4JR Tel: (01254) 56182 Fax: (01257) 484324

U T S Johnsons Removals Storage, Unit 1 Parker Industrial Estate, Mansfield Road, Derby, DE21 4SZ Tel: (01332) 371452 Fax: (01332) 298803 E-mail: moves@johnsons-rs.co.uk

Varlin Ltd, Rookery Farm, West Charlton, Charlton Mackrell, Somerton, Somerset, TA11 7AL Tel: (01458) 224080 Fax: (01458) 224090 E-mail: sales@varlin.co.uk

W Baybutt Ltd, Plantation Road, Burscough Industrial Estate, Ormskirk, Lancashire, L40 8JT Tel: (01704) 892905 Fax: (01704) 892262

W G & H Horsley, Ashville, Main Street, Newton on Derwent, York, YO41 4DA Tel: (01904) 608742 Fax: (01904) 608755

▶ W H Barley Transport & Storage Ltd, Old Wolverton Road, Old Wolverton, Milton Keynes, MK12 5NL Tel: (01908) 227222 Fax: (01908) 227370 E-mail: sales@whbarley.co.uk

W Mcmullin & Sons, 27 Desborough Lane, Plymouth, PL4 9PJ Tel: (01752) 660874 Fax: (01752) 660874 E-mail: wmcmullinandsons@btconnect.com

Wansdyke Security Ltd, PO Box 179, Corsham, Wiltshire, SN13 9TL Tel: (01225) 810225 Fax: (01225) 810625 E-mail: sales@wansdyke.co.uk

Wardle & Keach, Mill Lane, Kislingbury, Northampton, NN7 4BD Tel: (01604) 891133 Fax: (01604) 891155 E-mail: sales@wardleandkeach.co.uk

We 'R' Storage Ltd, Richmond Street, West Bromwich, West Midlands, B70 0DD Tel: 0121-520 3532 Fax: 0121-522 3862 E-mail: johnlee@werstorage.freeserve.co.uk

West Cornwall Storage & Distribution Ltd, Calloose, Leedstown, Hayle, Cornwall, TR27 5ET Tel: (01736) 850146 Fax: (01736) 850148

Western Self Storage, A Phoenix Trading Estate, London Road, Thrupp, Stroud, Gloucestershire, GL5 2BX Tel: (01453) 883743 Fax: (01453) 231033 E-mail: info@westernselfstorage.co.uk

C. Oliver Whitby & Sons Ltd, Hospital Fields, Fulford Road, York, YO10 4FS Tel: (01904) 655106 Fax: (01904) 627663 E-mail: wcoliver@aol.com

Whitehead, Unit 4 Coomber Way, Croydon, CR0 4TQ Tel: (020) 8684 4507 Fax: (020) 8683 3100 E-mail: info@pfwhitehead.com

Willmotts Transport Ltd, Willmotts Business Park, Waterlip, Shepton Mallet, Somerset, BA4 4RN Tel: (01749) 880333 Fax: (01749) 880337 E-mail: enquiries@willmottsbusinesspark.co.uk

Woodrush Distribution, Unit 6 Greenfield Road, Pulloxhill, Bedford, MK45 5EY Tel: (01525) 717199 Fax: (01525) 717606 E-mail: sales@woodrush.co.uk

Worthing Removals & Storage Co P & H Ltd, Ivy Arch Road, Worthing, West Sussex, BN14 8BX Tel: (01903) 204280 Fax: (01903) 824245E-mail: sales@worthingremovals.co.uk

Wyards Removals, Knightsdale Road, Ipswich, IP1 4HE Tel: (01473) 463708 Fax: (01473) 744447 E-mail: sales@wyardsremovals.co.uk

STORAGE CONTRACTORS/ SERVICES, ARCHIVE/ COMMERCIAL RECORD

▶ 3D Space Ltd, Warwick Way, Pimlico, London, SW1V 1QT Tel: (020) 7840 8130 E-mail: enquiries@3dspacestorage.co.uk

▶ Archive Management Systems Ltd, Unit 2 Sterling Way, Reading, RG30 6HW Tel: 0118-943 1443 Fax: 0118-942 6631 E-mail: postmaster@archivems.co.uk

Cade Brothers Ramsey Ltd, 94 Great Whyte, Ramsey, Huntingdon, Cambridgeshire, PE26 1HR Tel: (01487) 813318 Fax: (01487) 710449

Crown Records Management Ltd, Marshgate Business Centre, 10-12 Marshgate Lane, London, E15 2NH Tel: (020) 8555 1880 Fax: (020) 8555 2110

Domain Selfstorage, 21-31 Shacklewell Lane, London, E8 2DA Tel: (020) 7923 3003 Fax: (020) 7923 7799 E-mail: info@domainselfstorage.co.uk

Easistore, Enterprise House, Enterprise Way, Edenbridge, Kent, TN8 6HF Tel: (0800) 3162323 Fax: (01732) 868087 E-mail: customerservice@easistore.co.uk

Exclusive Move Solutions, 1 Cooks Road, London, E15 2PW Tel: (020) 8555 5179 Fax: (020) 8555 5172 E-mail: info@move-ems.com

Horsehay Ltd, Horsehay Estate, Telford, Shropshire, TF4 3PY Tel: (01952) 503344 Fax: (01952) 503356 E-mail: richard@horsehay.uk.com

M & G Transport, Highlands Road, Shirley, Solihull, West Midlands, B90 4ND Tel: 0121-705 2323 Fax: 0121-705 9163 E-mail: sales@storage-removals.co.uk

▶ Newark Storage Co. Ltd, Bowbridge Road, Newark, Nottinghamshire, NG24 4EQ Tel: (01636) 680660

Paper Flow Ltd, Unit 5 & 6, 20 Bugsby Way, London, SE7 7SJ Tel: (020) 8331 2090 Fax: (020) 8331 2001 E-mail: sales@paperflowonline.com

▶ Rapide Reprographics, St. James House, Pendleton Way, Salford, M6 5FW Tel: 0161-743 0302 Fax: 0161-743 0305 E-mail: sales@rapide-repro.co.uk

▶ Red Devil Storage, Units 1 - 2, The Wynne Jones Centre, Tring Road, Aylesbury, Buckinghamshire, HP21 7RL Tel: (01296) 397215 Fax: (01296) 397216 E-mail: tringroad@reddevilstorage.co.uk

▶ Red Devil Storage Ltd, 381 Kennington Road, London, SE11 4PT Tel: (0800) 0561773 Fax: (020) 7480 8120 E-mail: enquiries@reddevilstorage.co.uk

Restore Ltd, Redhill Distribution Centre, Salbrook Road, Redhill, RH1 5DY Tel: (01293) 446270 Fax: (01293) 446276 E-mail: john.minton@restore.co.uk

Solihull Storage Ltd, Beresford House, Highlands Road, Shirley, Solihull, West Midlands, B90 4ND Tel: 0121-705 2323 Fax: 0121-705 7683 E-mail: sales@storage-removals.co.uk

Vintage Archives, LT Braxted Hall, Witham Road, Little Braxted, Witham, Essex, CM8 3EU Tel: (01376) 501311 Fax: (01376) 504982 E-mail: mail@vintagearchives.co.uk

We 'R' Storage Ltd, Richmond Street, West Bromwich, West Midlands, B70 0DD Tel: 0121-520 3532 Fax: 0121-522 3862 E-mail: johnlee@werstorage.freeserve.co.uk

STORAGE EQUIPMENT OR SYSTEMS, TEMPORARY

▶ Envelope Structures Ltd, The Old Mill, Wallops Wood Farm, Sheardley Lane, Droxford, SO32 3QY Tel: (01489) 878101 Fax: (0871) 6617326 E-mail: enquiries@envelopestructures.co.uk

STORAGE EQUIPMENT SAFETY INSPECTION SERVICES

Storage Equipment Safety Service Ltd, Trafalgar Court, South Nelson Road, South Nelson Industrial Estate, Cramlington, Northumberland, NE23 1WF Tel: (01670) 736444 Fax: (01670) 739903 E-mail: sess@sess.co.uk

STORAGE EQUIPMENT TO SPECIFICATION

Bott, Unit 9 Ivanhoe Industrial Estate, Tournament Way, Ashby-de-la-Zouch, Leicestershire, LE65 2UU Tel: (01530) 410600 Fax: (01530) 410629 E-mail: v-sales@bottltd.co.uk

STORAGE EQUIPMENT/ SYSTEMS DISTRIBUTORS OR AGENTS

A T Tool Centre Ltd, 26-27 Buckingham Trade Park, Buckingham Avenue, Slough, SL1 4QA Tel: 01753 536811 Fax: 01753 532709 E-mail: slough@at-toolcentre.co.uk

Abbey Racking, 1-7 Ruby Mews, Ruby Road, London, E17 4RB Tel: (020) 8521 6176 Fax: (020) 8521 2214 E-mail: sales@usedshelving.co.uk

C & H Storage & Handling Systems Ltd, PO Box 42, Uttoxeter, Staffordshire, ST14 7ED Tel: (01889) 567662 Fax: (01889) 562493 E-mail: jhunt@chstorage.co.uk

D L Storage Handling Ltd, 20 Jessops Riverside, 800 Brightside Lane, Sheffield, S9 2RX Tel: 0114-244 0202 Fax: 0114-244 1222 E-mail: sales@thedlcompany.com

Design Masters Ltd, 2 Marlows Court, Marlows, Hemel Hempstead, Hertfordshire, HP1 1LE Tel: (01442) 256756 Fax: (01442) 260602 E-mail: designmasters@aol.com

Dexion Storage Centre Anglia Ltd, 43 Hurricane Way, Norwich, NR6 6HE Tel: (01603) 418121 Fax: (01603) 418124 E-mail: sales@dexion-anglia.co.uk

Dialrack Ltd, 8 Bilton Industrial Estate, Bilton Road, Basingstoke, Hampshire, RG24 8LJ Tel: (01256) 810907 Fax: (01256) 810942 E-mail: sales@dialrack.co.uk

Duval Products Ltd, Dexion Storage Centre, Armoury Way, London, SW18 1EU Tel: (020) 8870 7541 Fax: (020) 8870 2657 E-mail: sales@duvalproducts.co.uk

Exel Ltd, Storage & Interiors Centre, Northbank Industrial Park, Cadishead, Manchester, M44 5AH Tel: 0161-775 1611 Fax: 0161-775 4753 E-mail: sales@brookstore.co.uk

Fast Engineering Ltd, 5 Windmill Court, Antrim, BT41 2TX Tel: (028) 9442 8686 Fax: (028) 9442 9929 E-mail: info@fastank.com

Forth Systems, 36-40 Yardley Road, Olney, Buckinghamshire, MK46 5ED Tel: (01234) 717007 Fax: (01234) 717010 E-mail: steven@forthsystems.co.uk

Hertfordshire Storage Systems Ltd, 6 Winton Road, Ware, Hertfordshire, SG12 7AX Tel: (01920) 467027 Fax: (01920) 462563 E-mail: info@hertfordshirestorage.co.uk

Kingstonian Storage Equipment Ltd, 1 Phoenix Enterprise Park, Grovehill Road, Beverley, North Humberside, HU17 0JG Tel: (01482) 868055 Fax: (01482) 872558 E-mail: paul@kingsstorage.fsnet.co.uk

Pallet Handling Ltd, Chiddingstone Causeway, Tonbridge, Kent, TN11 8JD Tel: (01892) 870655 Fax: (01892) 870746

Pallet Racking Co., Sandfield Mill, Saul, Gloucester, GL2 7JY Tel: (01452) 740000 Fax: (01452) 740440

Pearson Knight, 65 Pitcairn Road, Smethwick, West Midlands, B67 5NE Tel: 0121-429 4396 Fax: 0121-420 1699

Polstore Storage Systems Ltd, PO Box 408, Dorking, Surrey, RH5 5YF Tel: (0870) 8504012 Fax: (0870) 8504013 E-mail: info@polstore.co.uk

Polypal Ltd, Polypal House, Monckton Road Industrial Estate, Wakefield, West Yorkshire, WF2 7AL Tel: (01924) 200015 Fax: (01924) 201160 E-mail: enquiry@polypal.co.uk

Rack, 25 Burrowfield, Welwyn Garden City, Hertfordshire, AL7 4SS Tel: (01707) 394847 Fax: (01707) 391523 E-mail: sales@rackstorage.co.uk

Ross Storage Equipment Co., 2 Abbotsford, Bishopbriggs, Glasgow, G64 1ED Tel: 0141-772 2453 Fax: 0141-772 2453

Rotaglade Ltd, 85 Park Road, Hale, Altrincham, Cheshire, WA15 9LQ Tel: 0161-980 3102 Fax: 0161-980 3102

Sandring Ltd, 224 Burley Road, Leeds, LS4 2EU Tel: 0113-274 4488 Fax: 0113-275 8030 E-mail: sales@sandring.co.uk

Storage Equipment Systems, A Bumpers Farm Industrial Estate, Bristol Road, Bumpers Farm, Chippenham, Wiltshire, SN14 6LH Tel: (01249) 445593 Fax: (01249) 658779 E-mail: aashelving@aol.com

Storage Logic, 24 High Street, Bovingdon, Hemel Hempstead, Hertfordshire, HP3 0HG Tel: (01442) 831133 Fax: (01442) 831144 E-mail: info@storage-logic.co.uk

Storplan Racking Ltd, The Airfield, Full Sutton, York, YO41 1HS Tel: (01759) 371553 Fax: (01759) 372451 E-mail: storplan@ic24.net

Techniform Sales Ltd, 14 250 Milkwood Road, London, SE24 0HG Tel: (020) 7274 1999 Fax: (020) 7274 0199

Technirack Systems Ltd, Unit 18 Avenue One, Witney, Oxfordshire, OX28 4XZ Tel: (01993) 893602 Fax: (01993) 893601

Thiel Technics UK, 66 Tonacliffe Road, Whitworth, Rochdale, Lancashire, OL12 8SS Tel: (01706) 868822 Fax: (01706) 343402 E-mail: sales@thiel-technics.co.uk

Till & Whitehead Ltd, Ellesmere Street, Manchester, M15 4JX Tel: 0161-827 3901 Fax: 0161-827 3915E-mail: sales@tillwite.com

Trade Systems, 48-56 Hawks Road, Kingston Upon Thames, Surrey, KT1 3EE Tel: (020) 8549 5281 Fax: (020) 8541 5637 E-mail: sales@tradesystems.co.uk

Trademark Interiors, 8 March Monte Gate, Hemel Hempstead, Hertfordshire, HP2 7BF Tel: (01442) 260022 Fax: (01442) 232244 E-mail: info@tmark.co.uk

Tri-Stor Products Ltd, 23 Weetwood Drive, Sheffield, S11 9QL Tel: 0114-236 3052 Fax: 0114-236 4429 E-mail: pdconstantine@aol.com

U F G Storage Systems, 1a Lalleford Road, Luton, LU2 9JG Tel: (01582) 414173 Fax: (01582) 414173

West Pennine Storage Equipment Ltd, West Pennine Business Park, Burnley Road, Bacup, Lancashire, OL13 8PJ Tel: (01706) 875500 Fax: (01706) 875600 E-mail: westpenninesd@aol.com

Wigan Storage Systems Ltd, 1 Edale Drive, Standish, Wigan, Lancashire, WN6 0LN Tel: (01257) 424345 Fax: (01257) 423958 E-mail: sales@wiganstorage.co.uk

Wyvern Handling & Storage Equipment Ltd, PO Box 5483, Stourport-on-Severn, Worcestershire, DY13 3BG Tel: (01299) 829300 Fax: (01299) 825799 E-mail: sales@wyvernhandling.co.uk

STORAGE EQUIPMENT/ SYSTEMS INSPECTION SERVICES

Autoscan Ltd, 61 High Road, Beeston, Nottingham, NG9 4AJ Tel: 0115-922 4249 Fax: 0115-922 9142 E-mail: info@autoscanuk.co.uk

STORAGE EQUIPMENT/ SYSTEMS MANUFRS, *See also headings for particular types*

Autoscan Ltd, 61 High Road, Beeston, Nottingham, NG9 4AJ Tel: 0115-922 4249 Fax: 0115-922 9142 E-mail: info@autoscanuk.co.uk

STORAGE EQUIPMENT/SYSTEMS MANUFRS – *continued*

▶ Base Line, 4 The Square, Notley Green, Great Notley, Braintree, Essex, CM77 7WT Tel: (01376) 551030 Fax: (01376) 551251 E-mail: sales@base-line.co.uk

Bri-Stor Systems Ltd, Church Lane, Hixon, Stafford, ST18 0PS Tel: (01889) 271202 Fax: (01889) 271178 E-mail: systems@bristor.co.uk

Coltran Products Ltd, 17-31 Church Street, Mexborough, South Yorkshire, S64 0EW Tel: (01709) 584031 Fax: (01709) 584431 E-mail: sales@coltran.com

Denios Ltd, Unit 1 - 3, Audley Avenue Enterprise Park, Newport, Shropshire, TF10 7DW Tel: (01952) 811991 Fax: (01952) 825687 E-mail: sales@denios.co.uk

Keeping Storage Systems, Beaufoys Avenue, Ferndown, Dorset, BH22 9RJ Tel: (01202) 894122 Fax: (01202) 891642

L M S Constructional Engineers Ltd, 8 Swinton Meadows Industrial Estate, Meadow Way, Swinton, Mexborough, South Yorkshire, S64 8AB Tel: (01709) 571001 Fax: (01709) 571021 E-mail: sales@lmskan.co.uk

L S E Storage Equipment Ltd, 15 Aintree Road, Bootle, Merseyside, L20 9PL Tel: 0151-476 2478 Fax: 0151-476 2482 E-mail: sales@lsestorage.com

▶ Midland Shelving Ltd, 8 Coventry Road, Bulwell, Nottingham, NG6 8RA Tel: 0115-977 1400 Fax: 0115-977 1600 E-mail: sales@midlandshelving.com

▶ Moduflex Ltd, Fourth Way, Bristol, BS11 8DX Tel: 0117-982 2882 Fax: 0117-982 2881 E-mail: info@moduflex.co.uk

▶ Mole Storage, Aston Down, Frampton Mansell, Stroud, Gloucestershire, GL6 8HX Tel: (01285) 760444

Raaco GB Ltd, Wenrisc House Meadow Court, High Street, Witney, Oxfordshire, OX28 6ER Tel: (01993) 776333 Fax: (01993) 776444 E-mail: sales@raaco.com

Spartan Storage Ltd, Fairgate House, 205 Kings Road, Birmingham, B11 2AA Tel: 0121-706 3591 Fax: 0121-707 8950

▶ Travhydro Ltd, R B R House, Hawksworth Road, Central Park, Telford, Shropshire, TF2 9TU Tel: (01952) 210163 Fax: (01952) 210157

STORAGE EQUIPMENT/ SYSTEMS, ARCHIVE/ COMMERCIAL RECORD

Conservation Resources (UK) Ltd, Unit 2 Ashville Way, Watlington Road, Cowley, Oxford, OX4 6TU Tel: (01865) 747755 Fax: (01865) 747035 E-mail: conservarts@aol.com

▶ Dixon Timber Products Ltd, Roberts Road, Balby, Doncaster, South Yorkshire, DN4 0JT Tel: (01302) 341833 Fax: (01302) 341839 E-mail: dixontimber@btconnect.com

Edm, Daisyfield Business Centre, Appleby Street, Blackburn, BB1 3BL Tel: (01254) 722033 Fax: (01254) 583003

ESE (Scotland) Ltd, 3 Dunlop Court, Deans Industrial Estate, Deans, Livingston, West Lothian, EH54 8SL Tel: (01506) 413313 Fax: (01506) 416550 E-mail: info@ese-scotland.co.uk

G Ryder & Co. Ltd, Denbigh Road, Bletchley, Milton Keynes, MK1 1DG Tel: (01908) 375524 Fax: (01908) 373658 E-mail: john.discombe@ryderbox.co.uk

Neat Ideas Ltd, Sandall Stones Road, Kirk Sandall Industrial Estate, Doncaster, South Yorkshire, DN3 1QU Tel: (01302) 890089 Fax: (01302) 886605 E-mail: sales@neat-ideas.com

Ssi Schaefer Ltd, 83-84 Livingstone Road, Walworth Industrial Estate, Andover, Hampshire, SP10 5QZ Tel: (01264) 386600 Fax: (01264) 386611 E-mail: solutions@ssi-schaefer.co.uk

Stockport Racking Co. Ltd, 12 Hammond Avenue, Whitehill Industrial Estate, Stockport, Cheshire, SK4 1PQ Tel: 0161-477 0155 Fax: 0161-477 0159

Storofile, Shirewood Store, Woodlands, Wimborne, Dorset, BH21 8LX Tel: (01202) 822115 Fax: (01202) 822866 E-mail: sales@storofile.com

STORAGE EQUIPMENT/ SYSTEMS, AUTOMATED

Digitron Translift Ltd, Hallcroft Road, Retford, Nottinghamshire, DN22 7PT Tel: (01777) 707511 Fax: (01777) 860778

Kardex Systems UK Ltd, Kestrel House Falconry Court, Bakers Lane, Epping, Essex, CM16 5LL Tel: (0870) 2422224 Fax: (0870) 2400420 E-mail: moreinfo@kardex.co.uk

▶ Xyratex, Langstone Technology Park, Langstone Road, Havant, Hampshire, PO9 1SA Tel: (023) 9249 6000 Fax: (023) 9249 6001 E-mail: info@uk.xyratex.com

STORAGE EQUIPMENT/ SYSTEMS, HUMIDITY CONTROLLED

Farm Electronics Ltd, Alma Park Industrial Estate, Grantham, Lincolnshire, NG31 9SR Tel: (01476) 591592 Fax: (01476) 591188 E-mail: info@farmelec.co.uk

STORAGE EQUIPMENT/ SYSTEMS, LIVE

Flowstore Systems plc, 39 Frogmore Industrial Estate, Clayton Road, Hayes, Middlesex, UB3 1AU Tel: (020) 8581 5555 Fax: (020) 8581 5575 E-mail: sales@flowstore.co.uk

STORAGE EQUIPMENT/ SYSTEMS, LOW TEMPERATURE

Hogg Pneumatics Ltd, Collingwood House, Lawson Street, North Shields, Tyne & Wear, NE29 6TG Tel: 0191-258 2623 Fax: 0191-296 1445 E-mail: sales@james-hogg.demon.co.uk

STORAGE EQUIPMENT/ SYSTEMS, SMALL COMPONENTS

Northern Storage Systems Ltd, 5 Liff Park, Liff, Dundee, DD2 5PH Tel: 01382 581475

STORAGE EQUIPMENT/ SYSTEMS, STEEL

A B Lockers Ltd, Alvis Court, Alvis Close, Cowpen Lane Industrial Estate, Billingham, Cleveland, TS23 4JG Tel: (01642) 560170 Fax: (01642) 566784

Atol Racking & Building Ltd, Unit A3 Wymeswold Industrial Park, Wymeswold Road, Burton-on-the-Wolds, Loughborough, Leicestershire, LE12 5TY Tel: (01509) 881345 Fax: (01509) 881064E-mail: office@atol.co.uk

N.C. Brown (Storage Equipment) Ltd, Firwood Industrial Estate, Thicketford Road, Bolton, BL2 3TR Tel: (01204) 590200 Fax: (01204) 590210

Brysdales Interiors Ltd, Brysdale House Drumhead Road, Chorley North Business Park, Chorley, Lancashire, PR6 7DE Tel: (01257) 240000 Fax: (01257) 240024 E-mail: enquiries@brysdales.co.uk

Carter-Parratt Ltd, Crossens Way, Marine Drive, Southport, Merseyside, PR9 9YL Tel: (01704) 228990 Fax: (01704) 228981 E-mail: storage@carter-parratt.co.uk

Davicon Structural Engineers, The Wallows Industrial Estate, Fens Pool Avenue, Brierley Hill, West Midlands, DY5 1QA Tel: (01384) 572851 Fax: (01384) 265098 E-mail: sales@davicon.com

P K K Storage Systems Ltd, Gibbons Lane, Brierley Hill, West Midlands, DY5 4RY Tel: (01384) 79555 Fax: (01384) 75588 E-mail: pkkcontracts@aol.com

Planned Storage Systems Ltd, Murdock Road, Dorcan, Swindon, SN3 5HY Tel: (01793) 694071 Fax: (01793) 610516 E-mail: mail@hi-lo.co.uk

Rack International UK Ltd, Pant Industrial Estate, Dowlais, Merthyr Tydfil, CF48 2SR Tel: (01685) 383133 Fax: (01685) 383836 E-mail: sales@cavesystems.co.uk

Rackline Systems Storage Ltd, Oaktree Lane, Talke Pits, Stoke-on-Trent, ST7 1RX Tel: (01782) 777666 Fax: (01782) 777444 E-mail: sales@rackline.co.uk

Redirack Ltd, Wharf Road, Kilnhurst, Mexborough, South Yorkshire, S64 5SU Tel: (01709) 584711 Fax: (01709) 589821 E-mail: sales@redirack.co.uk

▶ Steel Storage (UK) Ltd, Unit C1, Twickenham Trading Estate, Rugby Road, Twickenham, TW1 1DG Tel: (020) 8744 9444

United Storage Systems Ltd, United House, The Street, Takeley, Bishop's Stortford, Hertfordshire, CM22 6QR Tel: (01279) 871787 Fax: (01279) 871636 E-mail: sales@unitedstorage.co.uk

W K D Storage Systems Ltd, 3-4 Bourne Industrial Estate, Wrotham Road, Borough Green, Sevenoaks, Kent, TN15 8DF Tel: (01732) 882042 Fax: (01732) 885763 E-mail: sales@wkdstorage.co.uk

STORAGE FACILITIES

▶ Boughey Distribution Ltd, Wardle Industrial Estate, Wardle, Nantwich, Cheshire, CW5 6RS Tel: (01829) 260704

Domain Selfstorage, 21-31 Shacklewell Lane, London, E8 2DA Tel: (020) 7923 3003 Fax: (020) 7923 7799 E-mail: info@domainselfstorage.co.uk

▶ European Van Lines International Ltd, Unit 3 100 Church Street, Staines, Middlesex, TW18 4YA Tel: (01784) 466117 Fax: (01784) 464484 E-mail: info@evl.co.uk

▶ Ferryman Ltd, Unit 2, Newbridge Road Industrial Estate, Pontllanfraith, Blackwood, Gwent, NP12 2XF Tel: (01495) 222300 Fax: (01495) 222302 E-mail: sales@ferryman.org.uk

▶ Immingham Storage Co. Ltd, East Riverside, Immingham Dock, Immingham, South Humberside, DN40 2LZ Tel: (01469) 578889 Fax: (01469) 572001

▶ Nationwide Self Storage Ltd, 620 Western Avenue, London, W3 0TE Tel: (020) 8992 1700

▶ NYK Logistics Ltd, 99 Bailliestion Road, Glasgow, G32 0TF Tel: 0141-778 5481 Fax: 0141-778 3022

STORAGE PRODUCTS

▶ B C Connections Ltd, 27a Erewash Square, Ilkeston, Derbyshire, DE7 5SP Tel: 0115-977 0586 Fax: (0870) 1319548 E-mail: bcconnection@emailaccount.com

Bott, Unit 9 Ivanhoe Industrial Estate, Tournament Way, Ashby-de-la-Zouch, Leicestershire, LE65 2UU Tel: (01530) 410600 Fax: (01530) 410629 E-mail: v-sales@bottltd.co.uk

Davian Systems, 46 Bank Road, Dawley Bank, Telford, Shropshire, TF4 2BB Tel: (01952) 507377 Fax: (01952) 507377 E-mail: info@daviansystemsltd.co.uk

Tom Hamilton Transport, Burnside, Kinglassie, Lochgelly, Fife, KY5 0UP Tel: (01592) 882307 E-mail: tom@tht.co.uk

Moresecure Ltd, Haldane House, Halesfield 1, Telford, Shropshire, TF7 4EH Tel: (01952) 683900 Fax: (01952) 683982 E-mail: sales@moresecure.co.uk

STORAGE RACKS, *See also Rack etc*

Range Storage & Material Handling Equipment Ltd, Parry Lane, Bradford, West Yorkshire, BD4 8TJ Tel: (01274) 736363 Fax: (01274) 743322 E-mail: range.storage@lineone.net

Wesbart UK Ltd, Daux Road, Billingshurst, West Sussex, RH14 9YR Tel: (01403) 782738 Fax: (01403) 784180 E-mail: wesbart@talk21.com

STORAGE RACKS, WAREHOUSE

▶ Butchers Removals & Storage Co., 6b Quarry Wood Industrial Estate, Mills Road, Aylesford, Kent, ME20 7NA Tel: (01622) 725888 Fax: (01622) 725219 E-mail: info@butchersremovals.co.uk

Davian Systems, 46 Bank Road, Dawley Bank, Telford, Shropshire, TF4 2BB Tel: (01952) 507377 Fax: (01952) 507377 E-mail: info@daviansystemsltd.co.uk

▶ Mitchell Storage & Distribution Ltd, Unit 12 The Warren, East Goscote, Leicester, LE7 3XA Tel: 0116-260 4080 Fax: 0116-260 4081 E-mail: sales@ncexpress.com

▶ Racks Industries Ltd, Unit 8 Castlefields Trad Estate, Bradford, Bingley, West Yorkshire, BD16 2AF Tel: (01274) 551170 Fax: (01274) 560594 E-mail: enquiries@racks-industries.co.uk

▶ Storage Equipment Centre, Entrance Two, Gunnels Wood Road, Stevenage, Hertfordshire, SG1 2BT Tel: (0870) 2410872 Fax: (0870) 2410873 E-mail: info@sec-online.co.uk

STORAGE SOLUTIONS

▶ George Varney (Bulk Services) Ltd, Varneys Yard, Watford, Northampton, NN6 7UF Tel: (01327) 872288

▶ Move It Man, 1 Cranage Road, Crewe, CW2 8NJ Tel: (01270) 650888 E-mail: admin@the-move-it-man.com

STORAGE SYSTEMS TO SPECIFICATION

Optimum Storage Systems Ltd, Unit 14 Bowers Mill, Branch Road, Barkisland, Halifax, West Yorkshire, HX4 0AD Tel: (01422) 379549 Fax: (01422) 377334 E-mail: sales@optstore.co.uk

STORAGE VESSELS, *See headings for particular types*

STORAGE/DISTRIBUTION COMBINED SERVICES

A C R Logistics, 2300 Park Avenue, Dove Valley Park, Foston, Derby, DE65 5BY Tel: (01283) 586200 Fax: (01283) 586419

Agricultural Bulk Services Bristol Ltd, Royal Portbury Dock, Portbury, Bristol, BS20 7XL Tel: (01275) 375777 Fax: (01275) 374932

B D & J M Heslop, Newton Grange, Shipton by Beningbrough, York, YO30 1BA Tel: (01347) 848206 Fax: (01347) 848443

Baylis Distribution Ltd, New Potter Grange Road, Goole, North Humberside, DN14 6BZ Tel: (01405) 766174 Fax: (01405) 766270

Bondelivery, TT Complex, Dundrod Road, Crumlin, County Antrim, BT29 4SS Tel: (028) 9082 5151 Fax: (028) 9068 3300 E-mail: bondelivery@demon.co.uk

Denholm Barwil, Avonmouth Dock, Bristol, BS11 9DN Tel: 0117-982 5836 Fax: 0117-982 6272 E-mail: agency.brf@denholm-barwil.com

Dodds Ltd, Mansfield Road, Aston, Sheffield, S26 2BS Tel: 0114-287 4187 Fax: 0114-287 2251 E-mail: traffic@dodds.co.uk

Euro Forklifts Ltd, St. Michaels Road, Sittingbourne, Kent, ME10 3DN Tel: (01795) 425536 Fax: (01795) 476192

Firmin Coates Ltd, The Pines, Fordham Road, Newmarket, Suffolk, CB8 7LG Tel: (01638) 720481 Fax: (01638) 721240 E-mail: i.murfitt@firmincoates.co.uk

▶ Freightroute Ltd, 90 Bristol Road, Gloucester, GL1 5SQ Tel: (01452) 310301 Fax: (01452) 310300

Gibbs & Ball Ltd, St Margarets Road, South Darenth, Dartford, DA4 9LB Tel: (01322) 862232 Fax: (01322) 864954

J. Jackson (Transport) Ltd, 31-33 Midland Road, Scunthorpe, North Lincolnshire, DN16 1DQ Tel: (01724) 856925 Fax: (01724) 859835

K L M Storage Ltd, Rushock Trading Estate, Droitwich, Worcestershire, WR9 0NR Tel: (01299) 250885 Fax: (01299) 251450 E-mail: info@klmstorage.com

Lait Storage & Distribution Ltd, Northern Road, Chilton Industrial Estate, Sudbury, Suffolk, CO10 2ZB Tel: (01787) 376493 Fax: (01787) 312707 E-mail: admin@lait-storage.co.uk

Leen Valley Engineering Ltd, Station Terrace, Hucknall, Nottingham, NG15 7TQ Tel: 0115-963 3822 Fax: 0115-968 0131

Lightwood plc, Hangar 2, North Weald Airfield, North Weald, Epping, Essex, CM16 6AA Tel: (01992) 524237 Fax: (01992) 524501 E-mail: store@lightwoodplc.demon.co.uk

▶ Mark James Distribution Ltd, March Way, Battlefield Enterprise Park, Shrewsbury, SY1 3JE Tel: (01743) 460500 Fax: (01743) 441222

Momart Ltd, 199-205 Richmond Road, London, E8 3NJ Tel: (020) 8986 3624 Fax: (020) 8533 0122 E-mail: enquiries@momart.co.uk

New Move, Tenmore House, Kennford Road, Marsh Barton Trading Estate, Exeter, EX2 8LY Tel: (01392) 491000 Fax: (01392) 491911

Noakes T Partners Cold Stores, Goudhurst Road, Horsmonden, Tonbridge, Kent, TN12 8AY Tel: (01892) 722682 Fax: (01892) 723557 E-mail: admin@noakes-coldstores.co.uk

Optimum Storage Systems Ltd, Po Box 121, Elland, West Yorkshire, HX5 9AJ Tel: (01422) 379549 Fax: (01422) 377344

Pos Direct Ltd, 99 Boston Road, Leicester, LE4 1AW Tel: 0116-234 4400 Fax: 0116-235 8947 E-mail: sales@pos-direct.co.uk

Quickpak-UK Ltd, Office 2 Imex Business Centre, Oxleasow Road, Redditch, Worcestershire, B98 0RE Tel: (0845) 838 5979 Fax: (01527) 830 568 E-mail: sales@quickpak-uk.com

Richard & Osborne Ltd, Goss Moor, Fraddon, St. Columb, Cornwall, TR9 6EU Tel: (01726) 860308 Fax: (01726) 861135

Round Oak Rail Terminal Ltd, Round Oak Terminal, Pedmore Road, Brierley Hill, West Midlands, DY5 1LJ Tel: (01384) 263109 Fax: (01384) 265428

▶ Tanner Business Centre, Waterside Mill, Chew Valley Road, Greenfield, Oldham, OL3 7NH Tel: (01457) 872273 Fax: (01457) 870133 E-mail: info@tannerbrothers.co.uk

TDG plc, 25 Victoria Street, London, SW1H 0EX Tel: (020) 7222 7411 Fax: (020) 7222 2806 E-mail: businessenquiries@tdg.co.uk

J. & W. Watt Ltd, London Road, Carlisle, CA1 2NN Tel: (01228) 522311 Fax: (01228) 511926 E-mail: office@wattstorage.com

STOVE ENAMEL FINISHES

Bob Jackson Cycles 1993 Ltd, 320-322 Stanningley Road, Leeds, LS13 3EG Tel: 0113-255 9844 Fax: 0113-255 4444 E-mail: factory@bobjacksoncycles.demon.co.uk

Custom Coatings Ltd, 450 Blandford Road, Poole, Dorset, BH16 5BN Tel: (01202) 621155 Fax: (01202) 627622 E-mail: custom_coatings@hotmail.com

Protega Coatings Ltd, Kelvin Way, West Bromwich, West Midlands, B70 7JZ Tel: 0121-525 5665 Fax: 0121-553 2787 E-mail: info@tikkurila.co.uk

Vaz Finishers, 25 Mallet Road, London, SE13 6SP Tel: (020) 8852 0711

STOVE ENAMELLING

A J Finishers Ltd, 45 Barton Road, Bletchley, Milton Keynes, MK2 3BA Tel: (01908) 648437 Fax: (01908) 645016

A W Fabrications Ltd, Unit 3 Parsons Hall, High Street, Irchester, Wellingborough, Northamptonshire, NN29 7AB Tel: (01933) 357163 Fax: (01933) 410021

Alpha Stove Enamelling Ltd, Unit 17 Green Lane Industrial Estate, Green Lane, Letchworth Garden City, Hertfordshire, SG6 1HP Tel: (01462) 670761 Fax: (01462) 684466 E-mail: alphastoveltd@aol.com

STOVE ENAMELLING – *continued*

Alw, Tweedale Industrial Estate, Madeley, Telford, Shropshire, TF7 4JR Tel: (01952) 684100 Fax: (01952) 581611 E-mail: bruce@alws.freeserve.co.uk

Armacoating North West Ltd, Moores Mill, Cathrine Street East, Denton, Manchester, M34 3RQ Tel: 0161-320 9856 Fax: 0161-320 0772

Ascot Metal Finishers Ltd, 6 David Road, Colnbrook, Slough, SL3 0DG Tel: (01753) 682416 Fax: (01753) 680493

Base Enamellers Ltd, 1 Power Works, Slade Green Road, Erith, Kent, DA8 2HU Tel: (01322) 338052 Fax: (01322) 334360 E-mail: info@base-enamellers.co.uk

Bell Polishing & Engineering Ltd, Pool Street, Wolverhampton, WV2 4HN Tel: (01902) 421714 Fax: (01902) 424517 E-mail: bell.polishing@virgin.net

Blastreat Arundel Ltd, 14 Fitzalan Road, Arundel, West Sussex, BN18 9JS Tel: (01903) 883262 Fax: (01903) 884185 E-mail: blastreat@btconnect.com

Bristol Product Coating Ltd, The Mill Bath Road, Swineford, Bitton, Bristol, BS30 6LW Tel: 0117-932 3647 Fax: 0117-932 6183

BT Products Engineering, Unit U Penfold Works, Imperial Way, Watford, WD24 4YY Tel: (01923) 240950 Fax: (01923) 255932

Cambridge Electro Plating Ltd, 21 25 Union Lane, Cambridge, CB4 1PR Tel: (01223) 352464 Fax: (01223) 361085 E-mail: cep@btinternet.com

Conqueror Industries Ltd, Units 3-9, Royston Trading Estate, South Close, Royston, Hertfordshire, SG8 5UH Tel: (01763) 249535 Fax: (01763) 247276E-mail: info@c-i-ltd.co.uk

Cray Metal Finishers, D1-D2 Unit Riverside Industrial Estate, Riverside Way, Dartford, DA1 5BS Tel: (01322) 220662 Fax: (01322) 288032 E-mail: sales@craymetalfinishers.co.uk

Crewe Stove Enamelling Co. Ltd, Springvale Industrial Estate, Moston Road, Sandbach, Cheshire, CW11 3HL Tel: (01270) 769069 Fax: (01270) 768003

Crystal Finishes Ltd, Blackwater Way, Aldershot, Hampshire, GU12 4DP Tel: (01252) 325999 Fax: (01252) 330256

D & T Industrial Finishers Ltd, 9 Commerce Way, Stanbridge Road, Leighton Buzzard, Bedfordshire, LU7 4RW Tel: (01525) 376135 Fax: (01525) 217595 E-mail: info@dtindustrialfinishings.co.uk

Darrenpalm Ltd, 33 Highmeres Road, Leicester, LE4 9LZ Tel: 0116-276 9872

Davies (Stove Enamellers) Ltd, Unit M Cradock Road Industrial Estate, Cradock Road, Luton, LU4 0JF Tel: (01582) 572582 Fax: (01582) 594703 E-mail: tom@lth.co.uk

R.L. Dumelow & Son, St. Matthews Street, Burton-On-Trent, Staffordshire, DE14 3DE Tel: (01283) 564292 Fax: (01283) 564292

Ele Flex Ltd, Quarry Lane, Chichester, West Sussex, PO19 8NY Tel: (01243) 782205 Fax: (01243) 532416 E-mail: eleflex@btconnect.com

Elland Metal Finishers, Woodman Works, South Lane, Elland, West Yorkshire, HX5 0PA Tel: (01422) 375974 Fax: (01422) 375974

Express Metal Finishers, Manchester Road, Mossley, Ashton-under-Lyne, Lancashire, OL5 9QN Tel: (01457) 837718 Fax: (01457) 835801

Finishright Powder Coatings, Horsham Trading Estate, Foundry Lane, Horsham, West Sussex, RH13 5PX Tel: (01403) 274374 Fax: (01403) 210057

Fleetwood Engineering Co. Ltd, 1 Lechmere Rd, London, NW2 5DA Tel: (020) 8459 3444 Fax: (020) 8459 3444

Fowlers Specialist Treatments Ltd, 126 129 Pritchett Street, Aston, Birmingham, B6 4EH Tel: 0121-359 8571 Fax: 0121-359 4037 E-mail: enquiries@fowlersindustrial.co.uk

Full Range Finishing Ltd, Unit 14 Jubilee Trade Centre, Jubilee Road, Letchworth Garden City, Hertfordshire, SG6 1SP Tel: (01462) 684294 Fax: (01462) 683312 E-mail: sales@fullrange.fsnet.co.uk

Hanman Surface Technology, Unit 1-2 Springmill Industrial Estate, Avening Road, Nailsworth, Stroud, Gloucestershire, GL6 0BS Tel: (01453) 833416 Fax: (01453) 834775

Ipf, 37 Whitehill Road, Glenrothes, Fife, KY6 2RW Tel: (01592) 771805 Fax: (01592) 771805

J Hambleton Stove Enamellers, Egerton Street, Droylsden, Manchester, M43 7EL Tel: 0161-301 4444 Fax: 0161-371 0944

J R Tyson & Sons Ltd, 5 Rawreth Industrial Estate, Rawreth Lane, Rayleigh, Essex, SS6 9RL Tel: (01268) 783555 Fax: (01268) 782655

K G Sprayers Aldershot Ltd, 3a Holder Road, Aldershot, Hampshire, GU12 4RH Tel: (01252) 324309 Fax: (01252) 345895

K N P Finishing Ltd, Unit 10, Commerce Way, Leighton Buzzard, Bedfordshire, LU7 4RW Tel: (01525) 850478 Fax: (01525) 850479 E-mail: andykendall@btconnect.com

Kempston Ltd, Brunel Road, Bedford, MK41 9TG Tel: (01234) 341144 Fax: (01234) 348281

L B L Finishers, Gunstore Road, Portsmouth, PO3 5HL Tel: (023) 9269 2020 Fax: (023) 9267 0379 E-mail: sales@tomburn.co.uk

Lap Tab Ltd, 205 Tyburn Road, Birmingham, B24 8NB Tel: 0121-328 1697 Fax: 0121-328 9787 E-mail: sales@lap-tab.co.uk

Le Carousel, 35 Easter Park, Benyon Road, Silchester, Reading, RG7 2PQ Tel: 0118-970 0228 Fax: 0118-970 1944

Leicester Enamellers Ltd, Coventry Road, Narborough, Leicester, LE19 2GG Tel: 0116-275 1231 Fax: 0116-275 1330

Lemin & Co. Ltd, Unit 4 Albone Way, Biggleswade, Bedfordshire, SG7 5AN Tel: (01767) 600120 Fax: (01767) 600121 E-mail: enquiries@lemin.co.uk

Metafin Group Holdings Ltd, Green Lane, Walsall, WS2 8JG Tel: (01922) 626073 Fax: (01922) 720673

Midland Enamellers, 1 Pinfold Road, Thurmaston, Leicester, LE4 8AS Tel: 0116-269 7861 Fax: 0116-264 0739

Nationwide Coatings UK Ltd, 5 Canal Estate, Station Road, Langley, Slough, SL3 6EG Tel: (01753) 671612 Fax: (01753) 671613 E-mail: sales@nationwidecoatings.co.uk

North West Enamellers, Unit 14-15 Catheralls Industrial Estate, Brookhill Way, Buckley, Clwyd, CH7 3PS Tel: (01244) 549185 Fax: (01244) 544739

P & R Finishing, 1 Site 2 North Bridge Road, Berkhamsted, Hertfordshire, HP4 1EH Tel: (01442) 873962 Fax: (01442) 873962

P.W.S Metal Finishing, Coppen Road, Unit A, Dagenham, Essex, RM8 1HJ Tel: (020) 8595 9994 Fax: (020) 8592 3740 E-mail: mjratpws@aol.com

Palace Perma Signs Ltd, Lowmoor Industrial Estate, Prospect Close, Kirkby-in-Ashfield, Nottingham, NG17 7LF Tel: (01623) 754899 Fax: (01623) 752341

Paraid Ltd, Unit 4 Bond Street, West Bromwich, West Midlands, B70 7DQ Tel: 0121-580 0111 Fax: 0121-580 0222

Phoenix Corporation UK Ltd, Unit 5 North Weylands Industrial Estate, Molesey Road, Walton-on-Thames, Surrey, KT12 3PL Tel: (01932) 246236 Fax: (01932) 246236

Quality Surface Coatings Ltd, Hackworth Industrial Park, Shildon, County Durham, DL4 1HE Tel: 01388 776197

R A Peatey & Sons Ltd, Green Lane, Yeadon, Leeds, LS19 7BY Tel: 0113-250 1046 Fax: 0113-250 7364

R B Industrial Finishers, Unit 4 Kents Avenue, Hemel Hempstead, Hertfordshire, HP3 9XH Tel: (01442) 244343 Fax: (01442) 235127

Rainbow Spray Services, 5 Berrite Works, Ironbridge Road, West Drayton, Middlesex, UB7 8HY Tel: (01895) 430852 Fax: (01895) 430853

Reflec plc, Road One, Winsford Industrial Estate, Winsford, Cheshire, CW7 3QQ Tel: (01606) 593911 Fax: (01606) 559535 E-mail: info@reflec.co.uk

Relion Broma Ltd, Avenue Industrial Estate, Gallows Corner, Romford, RM3 0BY Tel: (01708) 341177 Fax: (01708) 384999

Rollem Fabrications Ltd, The Common, Ecclesfield, Sheffield, S35 9WN Tel: 0114 2468119

Rowland Way Ltd, Unit 2 Southmoor Lane, Havant, Hampshire, PO9 1JW Tel: (023) 9245 3879 Fax: (023) 9245 5593 E-mail: rowlandway@aol.com

Rust Proofing Company (Manchester) Ltd, Vauxhall Works, Greg Street, Reddish, Stockport, Cheshire, SK5 7BR Tel: 0161-480 8341 Fax: 0161-480 8820

Sandwell Stove Enamellers & Powder Coaters Ltd, Unit 12 Blankenhall Industrial Estate, Sunbeam Street, Wolverhampton, WV2 4PF Tel: (01902) 422899 Fax: (01902) 423380

Scruse & Crossland Ltd, 2 Wingate Road, Gosport, Hampshire, PO12 4DR Tel: (023) 9250 2403 Fax: (023) 9251 1728 E-mail: sales@scruse.co.uk

Slough Plastic Coatings, 2 David Road, Colnbrook, Slough, SL3 0DG Tel: (01753) 683907 Fax: (01753) 682571 E-mail: sloughplastic@btconnect.com

Solo Product Finishing, 4 Highbury Road, Brandon, Suffolk, IP27 0ND Tel: (01842) 813355 Fax: (01842) 813377

South West Industrial Finishers Co. Ltd., 117-119 Severn Road, Weston-Super-Mare, Avon, BS23 1DS Tel: (01934) 414613 Fax: (01934) 636243

Specialist Coating Ltd, All Saints Industrial Estate, Darlington Road, Shildon, County Durham, DL4 2RD Tel: (01388) 774034 Fax: (01388) 777010 E-mail: sales@specialistcoatings.co.uk

Spray Finishers (Poole), 14 Abingdon Road, Nuffield Industrial Estate, Poole, Dorset, BH17 0UG Tel: (01202) 685488 Fax: (01202) 676260 E-mail: info@sprayfinishes.co.uk

Steadhall Finishing, Unit 1, Bay Close, Progress Way, Luton, LU4 9UP Tel: (01582) 561518 Fax: (01582) 493350 E-mail: rainbowfinishers@aol.com

Stewart & Allen Ltd, The Runnings, Cheltenham, Gloucestershire, GL51 9NW Tel: (01242) 523298 Fax: (01242) 226416

T O C Ltd, Brandon Road, Binley, Coventry, CV3 2AN Tel: (024) 7645 0020 Fax: (024) 7663 5722 E-mail: sales@toc-ltd.co.uk

T T C Engineering Ltd, Unit 13, Chalwyn Industrial Estate, Old Wareham Road, Poole, Dorset, BH12 4PE Tel: (01202) 738181

Teversham Engineering Ltd, Hall Farm, Church Road, Teversham, Cambridge, CB1 9AP Tel: 01223 293904

Tombs & Bliss, Unit K, Chosen View Road, Kingsditch Trading Estate, Cheltenham, Gloucestershire, GL51 9LT Tel: (01242) 525957 Fax: (01242) 525957

Trestan Finishers Ltd, Unit B, 26 Hazel Road, Southampton, SO19 7GA Tel: (023) 8043 3081 E-mail: info@trestanfinishers.co.uk

Trevon Industrial Finishers, Whitewalls Industrial Estate, Regent Street, Colne, Lancashire, BB8 8LJ Tel: (01282) 861786 Fax: (01282) 863829

Trico Services Ltd, The Old Powder Mill, Powder Mill Lane, Dartford, DA1 1NT Tel: (01322) 276777 Fax: (01322) 276776

Unimet Enamellers Ltd, 183-185 Cardiff Road, Reading, RG1 8HD Tel: 0118-959 5528

Vanden Powder Coatings Ltd, 79 Manchester Road, Westhoughton, Bolton, BL5 3QD Tel: (01942) 818953 Fax: (01942) 840678

Vangard Ltd, Schofield Street, Royton, Oldham, OL2 6PT Tel: 0161-652 1249 Fax: 0161-678 6790

Vulcan Stove Enamelling Ltd, Station Road, East Preston, Littlehampton, West Sussex, BN16 3AA Tel: (01903) 770287 Fax: (01903) 783426

W H Greaves & Son Electroplating Ltd, 2 Lock Street, Sheffield, S6 3BJ Tel: 0114-232 3272 Fax: 0114-232 3273

Watford Coatings Ltd, Park House, Greenhill CR, Watford, WD18 8QU Tel: (01923) 235640 Fax: (01923) 449229 E-mail: sales@watfordcoatings.co.uk

Willow Stove Enamellers, Unit 11 Eagle Trading Estate, Willow Lane, Mitcham, Surrey, CR4 4UY Tel: (020) 8646 7169 Fax: (020) 8646 7169

STOVED PAINT FINISHES

Custom Coatings Ltd, 450 Blandford Road, Poole, Dorset, BH16 5BN Tel: (01202) 621155 Fax: (01202) 627622 E-mail: custom_coatings@hotmail.com

STOVES

Acle Stove Centre, Beaconsfield Barn, The Street, Acle, Norwich, NR13 3DX Tel: (01493) 751575

Bower & Child Ltd, 91 Wakefield Road, Huddersfield, HD5 9AB Tel: (01484) 425416 Fax: (01484) 517353

Chase Heating Ltd, Somerfield Stores, Racecourse Road, Pinvin, Pershore, Worcestershire, WR10 2EY Tel: (01386) 553542 Fax: (01386) 552269 E-mail: chasehtg@gxn.co.uk

Clearview Stoves, Dinham House, Dinham, Ludlow, Shropshire, SY8 1EH Tel: (01584) 878100 Fax: (01584) 872010 E-mail: info@clearviewstoves.com

Edwards & Godding Reading Ltd, 9d Loverock Road, Reading, RG30 1DZ Tel: 0118-939 3046 Fax: 0118-959 0294 E-mail: aga@edgod.globalnet.co.uk

Heating World, 53 Whitchurch Road, Shrewsbury, SY1 4DT Tel: (01743) 446775 Fax: (01743) 460385 E-mail: info@heatingworld.com

Individual Fires & Stoves, Chimneys, Brookgate Farm, London Road, Hurstgreen, Etchingham, East Sussex, TN19 7QY Tel: (01580) 860976 Fax: (01580) 860988

Levi (Europa), 44 Mill Street, Kidderminster, Worcestershire, DY11 6XB Tel: (01562) 69957 Fax: (01562) 824321

Morley Stoves Co Ltd, Marsh Lane, Ware, Hertfordshire, SG12 9QB Tel: (01920) 468001 Fax: (01920) 463893 E-mail: info@morley-stoves.co.uk

R W Knight & Son, Castle Farm, Marshfield, Chippenham, Wiltshire, SN14 8HU Tel: (01225) 891469 Fax: (01225) 892369 E-mail: enquires@knight-stoves.co.uk

Yorkshire Stove & Plumbing Centre, 39 High Street, Boroughbridge, York, YO51 9AW Tel: (01423) 323200 Fax: (01423) 323200

STOVES, GAS, MOBILE

▶ Stovesonline Ltd, Box and Rose Cottage, Capton, Dartmouth, Devon, TQ6 0JE Tel: 0845 226 5754 Fax: 0870 220 0920 E-mail: info@stovesonline.co.uk

STRAIGHT EDGES, GRANITE

▶ Amg Stone Products Ltd, Rosedale, Stonehaven Road, Aberdeen, AB12 5UT Tel: (01224) 877283 Fax: (01224) 873462 E-mail: info@amgstoneproducts.com

STRAIN GAUGE BONDING SERVICES

▶ Gauge Factors Ltd, Units 5-6 Towergate Industrial Park, Colebrook Way, Andover, Hampshire, SP10 3BB Tel: (01264) 336396 Fax: (01264) 336826 E-mail: sales@gaugefactors.com

STRAIN GAUGE SYSTEMS

Accurate Controls, 25 Cowley Road, Nuffield Industrial Estate, Poole, Dorset, BH17 0UJ Tel: (01202) 678108 Fax: (01202) 670161 E-mail: info@accurate-controls.ltd.uk

Astech Electronics Ltd, Forge Industrial Estate, The Street, Binsted, Alton, Hampshire, GU34 4PF Tel: (01420) 22689 Fax: (01420) 22636 E-mail: astech@astech.demon.co.uk

Force Measurement Systems Ltd, 3-5 Lister Road, Glasgow, G52 4BH Tel: 0141-882 8858 Fax: 0141-810 3434 E-mail: sales@forcemeasurement.co.uk

H B M UK Ltd, 1 Churchill Court, 58 Station Road, North Harrow, Harrow, Middlesex, HA2 7SA Tel: (020) 8515 6100 Fax: (020) 8515 6149 E-mail: info@uk.hbm.com

Vishay Measurements Group UK Ltd, 1 Cartel Units, Stroudley Road, Basingstoke, Hampshire, RG24 8FW Tel: (01256) 462131 Fax: (01256) 471441 E-mail: email@measurementsgroup.co.uk

STRAIN GAUGE TRANSDUCERS

H B M UK Ltd, 1 Churchill Court, 58 Station Road, North Harrow, Harrow, Middlesex, HA2 7SA Tel: (020) 8515 6100 Fax: (020) 8515 6149 E-mail: info@uk.hbm.com

▶ Strain Measurement Devices Ltd, Bury Road, Chedburgh, Bury St. Edmunds, Suffolk, IP29 4UQ Tel: (01284) 852000 Fax: (01284) 852371 E-mail: askus@smdsensors.co.uk

STRAIN GAUGES

Ellison Sensors International Ltd, Sensor House, Wrexham Technology Park, Wrexham, Clwyd, LL13 7YP Tel: (01978) 262255 Fax: (01978) 262233 E-mail: info@esi-tec.com

T S M Ltd, Sensor House, Wrexham Technology Park, Wrexham, Clwyd, LL13 7YP Tel: (01978) 291800 Fax: (01978) 291888 E-mail: tsm@esi-tec.com

STRAPPING MACHINE MANUFRS

Orgapack, 58 Heatherhouse Road, Irvine, Ayrshire, KA12 8HQ Tel: (01294) 311911 Fax: (01294) 311920

Securit Ropes & Packaging Ltd, Unit 6 Phoenix Court, Dominion Way, Rustington, West Sussex, BN16 3HQ Tel: 0845 5261818 Fax: (0845) 634 0262 E-mail: sales@securit-ropes-packaging.co.uk

▶ Dick Smith Services Ltd, 3 Shannon Centre, Shannon Way, Canvey Island, Essex, SS8 0PE Tel: (01268) 510963 Fax: (01268) 510977E-mail: sales@dicksmithservices.co.uk

STRAPPING SYSTEMS

Acre Packaging Supplies Ltd, 15 Kepler, Lichfield Road Industrial Estate,, Tamworth, Staffordshire, B79 7XE Tel: (01827) 310330 Fax: (01827) 310337 E-mail: sales@acrepackaging.co.uk

Bandapac Packaging Materials, 9 Fieldings Road, Cheshunt, Waltham Cross, Hertfordshire, EN8 9TL Tel: (01992) 622799 Fax: (01992) 628873

Clingfoil Ltd, Unit 1 Second Avenue, Poynton, Stockport, Cheshire, SK12 1ND Tel: (01625) 878953 Fax: (01625) 859005 E-mail: sales@clingfoil.co.uk

▶ Cobden, 4-5 Laundry Street, Salford, M6 6WJ Tel: 0161-745 7744 Fax: 0161-745 9027 E-mail: info@cobdensupplies.co.uk

K P Packaging, Eastwood Avenue, Grimsby, South Humberside, DN34 5BE Tel: (01472) 750006 Fax: (01472) 349975

▶ Lawtons Group Ltd, 60 Vauxhall Road, Liverpool, L3 6DL Tel: 0151-479 3000 Fax: 0151-479 3001 E-mail: info@lawtonsgroup.co.uk

Reid Bros Glasgow, Unit 64 Elderpark Workspace, 100 Elderpark Street, Glasgow, G51 3TR Tel: 0141-425 1060 Fax: 0141-440 2257 E-mail: scottishsales@thorneandderrick.co.uk

Securit Ropes & Packaging Ltd, Unit 6 Phoenix Court, Dominion Way, Rustington, West Sussex, BN16 3HQ Tel: 0845 5261818 Fax: (0845) 634 0262 E-mail: sales@securit-ropes-packaging.co.uk

▶ Signode Machines Group Europe, Queensway, Fforestfach, Swansea, SA5 4ED Tel: (01792) 585758 Fax: (01792) 585078 E-mail: machinesuk@signodeuk.com

Strapex, Unit 50 Empire Industrial Park, Aldridge, Walsall, WS9 8UQ Tel: (01922) 742500 Fax: (01922) 742501 E-mail: info@strapex.co.uk

STRATA OR GROUND CONTROL SERVICES

Weldgrip, 2d Redbrook Business Park, Wilthorpe Road, Barnsley, South Yorkshire, S75 1JN Tel: (01226) 785553 Fax: (01226) 731563 E-mail: info@weldgrip.com

STRATEGIC MANAGEMENT CONSULTANCY

Aware Marketing Consultants, 16 Craigweil Close, Stanmore, Middlesex, HA7 4TR Tel: (020) 8954 9121 Fax: (020) 8954 2102 E-mail: aweiss@marketing-intelligence.co.uk

STRATEGIC MANAGEMENT CONSULTANCY – *continued*

Mercuri International UK Ltd, 6 Olton Bridge, 245 Warwick Road, Solihull, West Midlands, B92 7AH Tel: 0121-706 3400 Fax: 0121-706 3900 E-mail: admin.london@mercuri.co.uk

STRATIGRAPHIC OR SEDIMENTOLOGICAL ANALYSIS

Halliburton Manufacturing & Services Ltd, Kirkhill Industrial Estate, Howemoss Cresent, Aberdeen, AB21 0GN Tel: (01224) 795000 Fax: (01224) 771438

STRAW

L R & Sons, Laindon Common Road, Little Burstead, Billericay, Essex, CM12 9SY Tel: (01277) 652381 Fax: (01277) 652381 E-mail: lrandsons@aol.com

STREET FURNITURE

Abacus Holdings Ltd, Oddicroft Lane, Sutton-in-Ashfield, Nottinghamshire, NG17 5FT Tel: (01623) 511111 Fax: (01623) 552133 E-mail: sales@abacuslighting.com

Ballantine Engineering Ltd, Links Road, Bo'Ness, West Lothian, EH51 9PW Tel: (01506) 822721 Fax: (01506) 827326 E-mail: sales@ballantineboness.co.uk

Blanc De Bierges, Eastrea Road, Whittlesey, Peterborough, PE7 2AG Tel: (01733) 202566 Fax: (01733) 205405 E-mail: sales@blancdebierges.com

Branson Leisure Ltd, Fosters Croft, Foster Street, Harlow, Essex, CM17 9HS Tel: (01279) 432151 Fax: (01279) 450542 E-mail: sales@bransonleisure.co.uk

Bruce & Hyslop (Brucast) Ltd, 1 Well Lane, Bootle, Merseyside, L20 3BS Tel: 0151-922 2404 Fax: 0151-922 5994 E-mail: colin.appleton@bruceandhyslop.com

Bus Shelters (Wales) Ltd, Unit 60, Llantwit Major Road, Dyffryn Business Park, Cowbridge, South Glamorgan, CF71 7PY Tel: (01446) 795444 Fax: (01446) 793344 E-mail: bus@shelters.co.uk

The Cast Iron Company Ltd, 8 Old Lodge Place, Twickenham, TW1 1RQ Tel: (020) 8744 9992 Fax: (020) 8744 1121 E-mail: info@castiron.co.uk

D W Windsor Ltd, Pindar Road, Hoddesdon, Hertfordshire, EN11 0DX Tel: (01992) 474600 Fax: (01992) 474601 E-mail: sales@dwwindsor.co.uk

Earth Anchors Ltd, 15 Campbell Road, Croydon, CR0 2SQ Tel: (020) 8684 9601 Fax: (020) 8684 2230 E-mail: enquiries@earth-anchors.com

Ebor Concretes Ltd, Ripon, North Yorkshire, HG4 1JE Tel: (01765) 604351 Fax: (01765) 690065 E-mail: sales@eborconcrete.co.uk

▶ Environmental Street Furniture, 67 Valley Business Centre, Church Road, Newtownabbey, County Antrim, BT36 7LS Tel: (028) 9055 2876 Fax: (028) 9055 1661 E-mail: sales@streetfurniture-uk.com

Furnitubes International Ltd, Meridian House, Royal Hill, London, SE10 8RD Tel: (020) 8378 3200 Fax: (020) 8378 3250 E-mail: sales@furnitubes.com

G L Jones Playgrounds Ltd, 1 Station Road, Bethesda, Bangor, Gwynedd, LL57 3NE Tel: (01248) 600372 Fax: (01248) 602085 E-mail: info@gljones-playgrounds.co.uk

Inpine Ltd, Anglia Way Industrial Estate, Anglia Way, Mansfield, Nottinghamshire, NG18 4LP Tel: (01623) 625468

▶ J C Decaux (UK) Ltd, Nottingham South & Wilford Industrial Estate, Nottingham, NG11 7EP Tel: 0115-982 2776 Fax: 0115-982 1467

Macemain Engineering Ltd, Boyle Road, Willowbrook East Indust, Corby, Northamptonshire, NN17 5XU Tel: (01536) 401331 Fax: (01536) 401298 E-mail: sales@macemainamstad.com

Mallatite Ltd, Hardwick View Road, Holmewood, Chesterfield, Derbyshire, S42 5SA Tel: (01246) 593280 Fax: (01246) 593281 E-mail: info@mallatite.co.uk

Marshalls Mono Ltd, Landscape House, Premiere Way, Housefield Business Park, Elland, West Yorkshire, HX5 9HT Tel: (01422) 306400 Fax: (0870) 6002426

N A L Ltd, Kinloch Drive, Bolton, BL1 4LZ Tel: (01204) 496772 Fax: (01204) 845952 E-mail: sales@nal.ltd.uk

Orsogril UK, 4 Pentland Road, Edinburgh, EH13 0JA Tel: 0131-441 1255 Fax: 0131-441 4161 E-mail: sales@orsogril.co.uk

Peter S Neale, Clays Road, Sling, Coleford, Gloucestershire, GL16 8LJ Tel: (01594) 837309 Fax: (01594) 835363 E-mail: sales@peter-s-neale.demon.co.uk

Russell Leisure Ltd, Newbridge Industrial Estate, Newbridge, Midlothian, EH28 8PJ Tel: 0131-335 5400 Fax: 0131-335 5401 E-mail: sales@russell-leisure.co.uk

S M P Playgrounds Ltd, Thorpe Industrial Estate, Ten Acre Lane, Egham, Surrey, TW20 8RJ Tel: (01784) 489100 Fax: (01784) 431079 E-mail: sales@smp.co.uk

Sign Trade Supplies, Britannia House, Granville Road, Maidstone, Kent, ME14 2BJ Tel: (01622) 689410 Fax: (01622) 689416 E-mail: orders@signtradesupplies.co.uk

Specialised Engineering Services, 129 Monk Street, Derby, DE22 3QE Tel: (01332) 370994 Fax: (01332) 294513 E-mail: sales@ukbollards.com

Townscape Products Ltd, Fulwood Road South, Sutton-in-Ashfield, Nottinghamshire, NG17 2JZ Tel: (01623) 513355 Fax: (01623) 440267 E-mail: sales@townscape-products.co.uk

▶ Urban Elements, Glebe Farm, Cross Street, Barrow-upon-Humber, North Lincolnshire, DN19 7AL Tel: (01469) 533253 Fax: (01469) 533253 E-mail: info@urbanelements.co.uk

Urbis Lighting Ltd, 1-5 Telford Road, Basingstoke, Hampshire, RG21 6YW Tel: (01256) 354446 Fax: (01256) 841314 E-mail: sales@urbislighting.com

Woodhouse UK plc, Harrison Way, Leamington Spa, Warwickshire, CV31 3HL Tel: (01926) 314313 Fax: (01926) 883778 E-mail: enquires@woodhouse.co.uk

Wybone Ltd, Mason Way, Hoyland, Barnsley, South Yorkshire, S74 9TF Tel: (01226) 744010 Fax: (01226) 350105 E-mail: sales@wybone.co.uk

STREET FURNITURE DESIGN

▶ Blueton Ltd, 19c Winchester Avenue, Winchester Industrial Estate, Denny, Stirlingshire, FK6 6QE Tel: (01324) 829661 Fax: (01324) 829551 E-mail: blueton@btinternet.com

▶ Garrick Outdoor Ltd, Unit 4, Langley Place, Burscough Industrial Estate, Ormskirk, Lancashire, L40 8JS Tel: (01772) 816414 Fax: (01772) 816415 E-mail: enquires@garrickoutdoor.co.uk

▶ Isu Ltd, PO Box 4370, Wolverhampton, WV1 9AE Tel: (01902) 636588 Fax: (01902) 636588 E-mail: studio@isu-design.co.uk

▶ Satellite GB Ltd, 15-20 The Oval, Bethnal Green, London, E2 9DX Tel: (020) 7739 5830 Fax: (020) 7739 5305 E-mail: roger@radar.gb.com

▶ Suite Leather, New Victoria Mills, Wellington Street, Bury, Lancashire, BL8 2AL Tel: 0161-763 4500 Fax: 0161-763 3500 E-mail: suiteleatheruk@btconnect.com

STREET LIGHTING CONTRACTORS

▶ Adams, Vale House, 19 Hainge Road, Tividale, Oldbury, West Midlands, B69 2NR Tel: 0121-522 0560 Fax: 0121-522 0570

▶ Aylesbury Mains Ltd, Colts Holm Road, Old Wolverton, Milton Keynes, MK12 5QD Tel: (01908) 222041 Fax: (01908) 222037

Deeco Lighting, Highfield, Bryn Awelon, Mold, Clwyd, CH7 1LT Tel: (01352) 700380 Fax: (01352) 700380

Eldridge Electrical Ltd, Binders Industrial Estate, Cryers Hill Road, Cryers Hill, High Wycombe, Buckinghamshire, HP15 6LJ Tel: (01494) 715956 Fax: (01494) 716176 E-mail: info@eldridgeelectricalltd.co.uk

Lightways (Contractors) Ltd, Lochlands Industrial Estate, Larbert, Stirlingshire, FK5 3NS Tel: (01324) 553025 Fax: (01324) 557870 E-mail: head.office@lightways.co.uk

STREET LIGHTING CONTROL EQUIPMENT

Zodion Ltd, Zodion House, Station Road, Sowerby Bridge, West Yorkshire, HX6 3AF Tel: (01422) 317337 Fax: (01422) 836717 E-mail: sales@zodionltd.eu.com

STREET LIGHTING COVERS

Vacuum Formers Ltd, Brunswick Mill, Pickford Street, Macclesfield, Cheshire, SK11 6JN Tel: (01625) 428389 Fax: (01625) 619808 E-mail: info@vacuumformers.co.uk

STREET LIGHTING CUT OUT FUSES

Tofco CPP Ltd, Meadowfield, Ponteland, Newcastle Upon Tyne, NE20 9SD Tel: (01661) 860001 Fax: (01661) 860002 E-mail: info@tofco.co.uk

STREET LIGHTING EQUIPMENT,

See also headings for particular types

B E I Distribution, Wyndham Way, Brackla, Bridgend, Mid Glamorgan, CF31 2NB Tel: (01656) 645414 Fax: (01656) 669231 E-mail: info@beilighting.com

Charles Lighting Ltd, Priestlands Lane, Sherborne, Dorset, DT9 4HL Tel: (01935) 817444 Fax: (01935) 816778

Farmers Cottage Lamps, Castle Lane, Coleshill, Birmingham, B46 2RA Tel: (01675) 464705 Fax: (01675) 462857

Metcraft Lighting Ltd, Bourne Street, Chadderton, Oldham, OL9 7LX Tel: 0161-683 4298 Fax: 0161-688 8004 E-mail: info@metcraftlighting.com

▶ Pudsey Diamond Engineering Ltd, Macadam Way, Andover, Hampshire, SP10 3LF Tel: 01264 336677

Seesaw Design, PO Box 100, Bury, Lancashire, BL8 2FU Tel: (01204) 882222 Fax: (01204) 882200 E-mail: mikeyounge@btconnect.com

Snapfast Fasteners & Fixing Devices, Unit 1-2 Park Court, Ninth Avenue, Team Valley Trading Estate, Gateshead, Tyne & Wear, NE11 0EH Tel: 0191-482 4075 Fax: 0191-491 1799 E-mail: snapfast@natlineuk.net

STREET LIGHTING FIXTURES

Pettitt Joinery Co. Ltd, Royce Road, Peterborough, PE1 5YB Tel: (01733) 567742 Fax: (01733) 567742

STREET LIGHTING LAMPS

▶ Pudsey Diamond Engineering Ltd, Macadam Way, Andover, Hampshire, SP10 3LF Tel: 01264 336677

STREET LIGHTING LANTERNS

C U Thosco Lighting Ltd, Charles House, Furlong, Ware, Hertfordshire, SG12 9TA Tel: (01920) 462272 Fax: (01920) 485915 E-mail: export@cuphosco.co.uk

D W Windsor Ltd, Pindar Road, Hoddesdon, Hertfordshire, EN11 0DX Tel: (01992) 474600 Fax: (01992) 474601 E-mail: sales@dwwindsor.co.uk

▶ Pudsey Diamond Engineering Ltd, Macadam Way, Andover, Hampshire, SP10 3LF Tel: 01264 336677

Scroll Gates, Southampton Road, Eastleigh, Hampshire, SO50 5QT Tel: (023) 8061 2028 Fax: (023) 8061 2028 E-mail: sales@scrollgates.com

Sugg Lighting Ltd, Sussex Manor Business Park, Gatwick Road, Crawley, West Sussex, RH10 9GD Tel: (01293) 540111 Fax: (01293) 540114 E-mail: admin@sugglighting.co.uk

Urbis Lighting Ltd, 1-5 Telford Road, Basingstoke, Hampshire, RG21 6YW Tel: (01256) 354446 Fax: (01256) 841314 E-mail: sales@urbislighting.com

STREET NAMEPLATES

Midland Signs Leicester Ltd, 15 Foxholes Road, Golfcourse Lane, Leicester, LE3 1TH Tel: 0116-254 4445 Fax: 0116-254 2020 E-mail: info@ggstreetnameplates.com

Signwise Sign Services Ltd, 4 Challenger Way, Peterborough, PE1 5EX Tel: (01733) 565770 Fax: (01733) 563384 E-mail: info@signwisesignservices.co.uk

STRESS ANALYSIS SERVICES, ENGINEERING

▶ Asmet Engineering & Technical Services Ltd, 27 Highcroft Crescent, Leamington Spa, Warwickshire, CV32 6BN Tel: (01926) 314536 Fax: 0871 2439203E-mail: asmet@clara.co.uk

Cordell Group Ltd, 159-160 High Street, Stockton-on-Tees, Cleveland, TS18 1PL Tel: (01642) 662400 Fax: (01642) 662402 E-mail: enquiries@cordellgroup.com

Sharples Stress Engineers Ltd, Unit 29 Old Mill Industrial Estate, Bamber Bridge, Preston, PR5 6SY Tel: (01772) 323359 Fax: (01772) 316017 E-mail: sharplesstress@aol.com

STRESS MANAGEMENT CONSULTANCY

▶ Capita Learning & Development, 17-19 Rochester Row, London, SW1P 1LA Tel: (0870) 1648900 Fax: (0870) 1658974 E-mail: cpdwebinfo@capita.co.uk

▶ Coady Consultants Ltd, 87 The Straits Lower Gornal, Dudley, West Midlands, DY3 3AL Tel: (01902) 664837 Fax: (01902) 664837 E-mail: enquiries@coadyconsultants.co.uk

Keenan Research Ltd, Victoria House, 15 Gay Street, Bath, BA1 2PH Tel: (01225) 336569 Fax: (01225) 442685 E-mail: kmkeenan@keenan-research.com

STRESS MANAGEMENT TRAINING

Keenan Research Ltd, Victoria House, 15 Gay Street, Bath, BA1 2PH Tel: (01225) 336569 Fax: (01225) 442685 E-mail: kmkeenan@keenan-research.com

▶ Orchid Indulgence Ltd, 5 Swann Lane, Cheadle Hulme, Cheadle, Cheshire, SK8 7HU Tel: 0161 221 2673 E-mail: enquiries@orchidindulgence.com

STRESS RELIEVING ENGINEERING

Middleton Heat Treatments Ltd, 315 Whapload Road, Lowestoft, Suffolk, NR32 1UL Tel: (01502) 561721 Fax: (01502) 517712

STRESS RELIEVING SERVICES, VIBRATORY

V S R Co., Unit 13A, Shrub Hill Industrial Estate, Worcester, WR4 9EL Tel: (01905) 452800 Fax: (01905) 731811E-mail: sales@v-s-r.co.uk

STRESS SCREENING EQUIPMENT

Sharetree Ltd, Unit 3 Meadow Mill Eastington Trading Estate, Churchend, Eastington, Stonehouse, Gloucestershire, GL10 3RZ Tel: (01453) 828642 Fax: (01453) 828076 E-mail: sales@sharetree.com

STRETCH WRAP FILM EXTRUDING/REWINDING MACHINES

Wittey Machinery Ltd, Unit 17 Haddenham Aerodrome Industrial Estate, Dollicott, Haddenham, Aylesbury, Buckinghamshire, HP17 8LJ Tel: (01844) 344723 Fax: (01844) 342004

STRETCH WRAP FILM MANUFRS

Ambassador Packaging Ltd, Road One, Winsford Industrial Estate, Winsford, Cheshire, CW7 3QB Tel: (01606) 567000 Fax: (01606) 567001 E-mail: ambassador@pregis.com

M J Maillis UK Ltd, Monarch House, Chrysalis Way, Eastwood, Nottingham, NG16 3RY Tel: (01773) 539000 Fax: (01773) 539090 E-mail: info@mallis.co.uk

Primopost Ltd, 1 Staden Park, Staden Lane, Buxton, Derbyshire, SK17 9RZ Tel: (01298) 79113 Fax: (01298) 70435

▶ Signode Machines Group Europe, Queensway, Fforestfach, Swansea, SA5 4ED Tel: (01792) 585758 Fax: (01792) 585078 E-mail: machinesuk@signodeuk.com

Simpson Packaging, Shawcross, Owl Lane, Dewsbury, West Yorkshire, WF12 7RQ Tel: (01924) 869010 Fax: (01924) 437666 E-mail: sales@simpson-packaging.co.uk

Test Valley, Watt Road, Salisbury, SP2 7UD Tel: (01722) 414800 Fax: (0870) 2240449

STRETCH WRAPPING MACHINES

E D L Packaging, Oswald Street, Burnley, Lancashire, BB12 0BY Tel: (01282) 429305 Fax: (01282) 429350 E-mail: sales@johnquinn.co.uk

Lancopak Ltd, Central Indust Estate, St.Marks Street, Bolton, BL3 6NR Tel: (01204) 395959 Fax: (01204) 383161 E-mail: barrie@lancopak.co.uk

Propack Automation Machinery Ltd, Unit 8 Binns Close, Coventry, CV4 9TB Tel: (024) 7647 0074 Fax: (024) 7647 1190 E-mail: sales@propack.co.uk

STRING MUSICAL INSTRUMENTS

▶ Blake-Robson Northumbria Tuning Machines, Low Lambton Farm, Penshaw, Houghton le Spring, Tyne & Wear, DH4 7NQ Tel: 0191-246 2007 Fax: 0191-385 8013 E-mail: tuningmachines@aol.com

Bow Brand International Ltd, Highgate, King's Lynn, Norfolk, PE30 1PT Tel: 0800 282355 Fax: (01553) 762887 E-mail: sales@bowbrand.co.uk

STRIP AND CIRCULAR CHART RECORDERS

Roger's Machine Tools, Unit 21 Two Gates Trading Estate, Watling Street, Two Gates, Tamworth, Staffordshire, B77 5AE Tel: (01827) 283247 Fax: (01827) 262049 E-mail: rmtools@btopenworld.com

STRIP FASCIA SIGNS

Studio 127, 127 East Parade, Keighley, West Yorkshire, BD21 5HX Tel: (01535) 605148 Fax: (01535) 691521 E-mail: enquiries@studio127.co.uk

STRIP FORMING/MULTIPLE SLIDE MACHINES/PRESSES

Lamba Welding Systems, 31 Racecourse Road, Gallowfields Trading Estate, Richmond, North Yorkshire, DL10 4SU Tel: (01748) 850292 Fax: (01748) 850343

STRIP STRAIGHTENING, *See Straightening etc*

STRIPPABLE OR PROTECTIVE COATING SYSTEMS

Factory Improvements Supplies Ltd, 24-26 Imperial Ave, Shirley, Southampton, SO15 8QH Tel: (023) 8078 6759 Fax: (023) 8070 2989
▶ Plastidip UK, Unit 1, Harvesting Lane, East Meon, Petersfield, Hampshire, GU32 1QR Tel: (01730) 823823 Fax: (01730) 823321 E-mail: info@plastidip.co.uk

STROBOSCOPE (ELECTRONIC) MANUFRS

Compact Instruments Ltd, 61-65 Lever Street, Bolton, BL3 2AB Tel: (01204) 532544 Fax: (01204) 522285 E-mail: info@compactinstruments.co.uk
Sandhurst Instruments Ltd, 30 Sudley Road, Bognor Regis, West Sussex, PO21 1ER Tel: (01243) 820200 Fax: (01243) 860111 E-mail: sandhurst.instruments@freenet.co.uk

STRONGROOM BUILDING OR ENGINEERING OR INSTALLATION OR SERVICING

Midland Safe, Halesfield 2, Telford, Shropshire, TF7 4QH Tel: (01952) 682000 Fax: (01952) 682009 E-mail: sales@midland-safe.co.uk

STRUCTURAL ADHESIVES

Building Adhesives Ltd, Longton Road, Stoke-on-Trent, ST4 8JB Tel: (01782) 591100 Fax: (01782) 591101 E-mail: info@building-adhesives.com
Cytec Engineered Materials Ltd, Abenbury Way, Wrexham Industrial Estate, Wrexham, Clwyd, LL13 9UZ Tel: (01978) 665200 Fax: (01978) 665222 E-mail: info@cytec.com
Henkel Ltd, Apollo Court, Bishops Square Business Park, Hatfield, Hertfordshire, AL10 9EY Tel: (01707) 635000 Fax: (01707) 635099 E-mail: ukcorp.communications@henkel.co.uk
Hitek Electronic Materials Ltd, 15 Wentworth Road, Scunthorpe, South Humberside, DN17 2AX Tel: (01724) 851678 Fax: (01724) 280586 E-mail: sales@hitek-ltd.co.uk
I T W Plexus, Unit 3, Shipton Way, Express Business Park, Rushden, Northamptonshire, NN10 6GL Tel: (0870) 4587588 Fax: (0870) 4589077 E-mail: sales@itwplexus.co.uk
Leeson Polyurethanes Ltd, Hermes Close, Tachbrook Park, Warwick, CV34 6NW Tel: (01926) 833367 Fax: (01926) 881469 E-mail: sales@lpultd.com

STRUCTURAL BEAMS

▶ Osborne Business Enterprises Ltd, Selsey Road, Sidlesham, Chichester, West Sussex, PO20 7NE Tel: 01243 641974

STRUCTURAL CANOPIES

Central Canopies & Car Ports, PO Box 32, Nuneaton, Warwickshire, CV11 9XU Tel: (024) 7634 4680 Fax: (024) 7634 4667
Conservatory Supplies Ltd, The Conservatory Centre, Leighsinton Road, Malvern, Worcestershire, WR14 1JP Tel: (01684) 575588 Fax: (01684) 576077 E-mail: sales@csltd.net
Global M S I plc, Cannon Lane, Tonbridge, Kent, TN9 1PP Tel: (01732) 351358 Fax: (01732) 770563 E-mail: sales@global-msi.com
Performance Sails, Victoria Loft, Hill Furze, Pershore, Worcestershire, WR10 2NB Tel: (01386) 861161 Fax: (01386) 861253 E-mail: performancesails@hotmail.com

STRUCTURAL CAVITY TRAYS

Cavity Trays Ltd, Boundary Avenue, Lufton Trading Estate, Lufton, Yeovil, Somerset, BA22 8HU Tel: (01935) 474769 Fax: (01935) 428223 E-mail: sales@cavitytrays.co.uk
The Expanded Metal Company, PO Box 14, Hartlepool, Cleveland, TS25 1PR Tel: (01429) 867388 Fax: (01429) 866795 E-mail: sales@expamet.co.uk
Gap Ltd, 12 Ridge Way, Donibristle Industrial Park, Hillend, Dunfermline, Fife, KY11 9JN Tel: (01383) 824181 Fax: (01383) 824722 E-mail: mark.adams@gap.uk
Hamer Jack & Son Tottington Ltd, 200a Bury Road, Tottington, Bury, Lancashire, BL8 3DX Tel: (01204) 883867 Fax: (01204) 888592 E-mail: info@jackhamer-son.co.uk
I G Ltd, Avondale Road, Cwmbran, Gwent, NP44 1XY Tel: (01633) 486486 Fax: (01633) 486492 E-mail: info@igltd.co.uk
Z LED Ltd, Brookhill Industrial Estate, Pinxton, Nottingham, NG16 6NF Tel: (01732) 363443 Fax: (01732) 363553 E-mail: info@z-led.com

STRUCTURAL DEMOLITION

▶ First Refurbishment & Demolition Ltd, 16 Lyon Road, Walton-on-Thames, Surrey, KT12 3PU Tel: (01932) 269301 Fax: (01932) 269303
▶ L & W Wilson Ltd, Gatebeck Road, Endmoor, Kendal, Cumbria, LA8 0HL Tel: (01539) 567601 Fax: (01539) 567775 E-mail: office@landwwilson.co.uk

STRUCTURAL DRY LINING EQUIPMENT ACCESSORIES

C F I, Unit 9B, Thorpe Close, Banbury, Oxfordshire, OX16 4SW Tel: (01295) 257014 Fax: (01295) 272405 E-mail: sales@cfiswin.co.uk
Cornercare Ltd, Unit 3-4 Walter Nash Road West, Birchen Coppice Trading Estate, Kidderminster, Worcestershire, DY11 7QY Tel: (01562) 515200 Fax: (01562) 864063 E-mail: cornercare@compuserve.com
Partitions & Ceilings Ltd, 13 Gloucester Road, London, E11 2ED Tel: (020) 8989 9384 Fax: (020) 8989 2892 E-mail: part.ceilings@ntlworld.com

STRUCTURAL DRY LINING SERVICES

Lloyd Davenport Ltd, Unit 10 Kingfisher Court, Hambridge Road, Newbury, Berkshire, RG14 5SJ Tel: (01635) 529191 Fax: (01635) 524278
Decke Newcastle Ltd, 244 Park View, Whitley Bay, Tyne & Wear, NE26 3QX Tel: 0191-251 2606 Fax: 0191-251 4880 E-mail: decke.newcastle@contactbox.co.uk
▶ E A C Group Of Companies, Jubilee House, Broadway, Silver End, Witham, Essex, CM8 3RQ Tel: (01376) 585855 Fax: (01376) 587910 E-mail: mail@eacgroup.net
Excel Plastering Ilford Ltd, 1 Natal Road, Ilford, Essex, IG1 2HA Tel: (020) 8553 2244 Fax: (020) 8553 4489 E-mail: excelplastering1@btopenworld.com
▶ JP taping & jointing, 57 Huntington terrace road, Cannock, Staffordshire, WS11 5HB Tel: 07976 284152 Fax: 01543 428578 E-mail: phasey@tiscli.co.uk
Marmox UK Ltd, 3 Rochester Airport Industrial Estate, Laker Road, Rochester, Kent, ME1 3QX Tel: (01634) 862277 Fax: (01634) 864223 E-mail: sales@marmox.com
Partitions & Ceilings Ltd, 13 Gloucester Road, London, E11 2ED Tel: (020) 8989 9384 Fax: (020) 8989 2892 E-mail: part.ceilings@ntlworld.com
Thermofelt (Contracts) Ltd, Kingswood House, 31-39 Miles Road, Mitcham, Surrey, CR4 3DA Tel: (020) 8646 9300 E-mail: thermofeltcontracts@woodcote.com
Thistlebrook Ltd, 14-16 Chase Street, Luton, LU1 3QZ Tel: (01582) 453753 Fax: (01582) 481825
Toveglen Ltd, Unit 1 Drakes Lane, Boreham, Chelmsford, CM3 3BE Tel: (01245) 360435 Fax: (01245) 362322 E-mail: mbladon@toveglen.co.uk
Warwick Ceilings, 10 Blackall Industrial Estate, Hamberts Road, South Woodham Ferrers, Chelmsford, CM3 5UW Tel: (01245) 325533 Fax: (01245) 323363 E-mail: info@warwick.gb.com

STRUCTURAL ENGINEERING CONSULTANCY

Abbott Holliday Partnership, 9 Greens Court, Lansdowne Mews, London, W11 3AP Tel: (020) 7792 1147 Fax: (01233) 820755 E-mail: enquiries@peter-holliday.co.uk
Alan White, Woodside House, 20-23 Woodside Place, Glasgow, G3 7QF Tel: 0141-582 1419 Fax: 0141-582 1484 E-mail: alan@alanwhitedesign.com
▶ Baynham Meikle Partnership, 8 Meadow Road, Harborne, Birmingham, B17 8BU Tel: 0121-434 4100 Fax: 0121-434 4073
Cherrymill Ltd, 23 Hoylake Road, Scunthorpe, South Humberside, DN17 2AZ Tel: (01724) 867244 Fax: (01724) 858509 E-mail: cherrymill.co.uk@amserve.net
Consulting Engineers' Co-Partnership London Ltd, 1528 London Road, London, SW16 4EU Tel: (020) 8679 5621 Fax: (020) 8679 7922 E-mail: mail@cecp.co.uk
Cooper Beal & Ross, 33 Shaw Road, Stockport, Cheshire, SK4 4AG Tel: 0161-442 9770 Fax: 0161-442 9775 E-mail: cooperbealross@aol.com
▶ Fordham Johns, 31 Regent Street, Great Yarmouth, Norfolk, NR30 1RR Tel: (01493) 843012 Fax: (01493) 330084
Frazer Nash Consultancy Ltd, Stonebridge The Dorking Business Park, Station Road, Dorking, Surrey, RH4 1HJ Tel: (01306) 885050 Fax: (01306) 886464 E-mail: info@fnc.co.uk
Frazer-Nash Consultancy Ltd, Quay Head House, Colston Ave., Bristol, BS1 1EB Tel: 0117-922 6242 Fax: 0117-922 6524 E-mail: sales@fnc.co.uk
Greenwood Structures, 67 Trafalgar Road, Moseley, Birmingham, B13 8BL Tel: 0121-449 0278 Fax: 0121-249 2499
H A Ross Structural Engineers, Workshop, Stephen Road Industrial Estate, Huntly, Aberdeenshire, AB54 8SX Tel: (01466) 793153 Fax: (01466) 794395
Hilbre Engineering Design Services, 71 Park Rd, Meols, Wirral, Merseyside, CH47 7BD Tel: 0151-632 2995 Fax: 0151-632 2850 E-mail: heds@tinyonline.co.uk
▶ Kilngrove, Ivory House, Cockfield, Bury St. Edmunds, Suffolk, IP30 0LN Tel: 01284 827474 Fax: 01284 827475 E-mail: enquiries@kilngrove.co.uk
Michael Barclay Partnership, 105 Strand, London, WC2R 0AB Tel: (020) 7240 1191 Fax: (020) 7240 2241
Modular Robotic Systems Ltd, Cale Lane, Aspull, Wigan, Lancashire, WN2 1HQ Tel: (01942) 820088 Fax: (01942) 820431 E-mail: info@modular-ltd.co.uk
Nash Mynard Design Ltd, Dodford Mill, Dodford, Northampton, NN7 4SS Tel: (01327) 341643 Fax: (01327) 341801
R Hatton, 3 Drapers Way, Stevenage, Hertfordshire, SG1 3DT Tel: (01438) 350933 Fax: (01438) 740297 E-mail: mail@richardhatton.co.uk
Rowen Structures Ltd, Fulwood Road South, Sutton-in-Ashfield, Nottinghamshire, NG17 2JW Tel: (01623) 558558 Fax: (01623) 558866 E-mail: sales@rowenstructures.co.uk
▶ Rupee Design Ltd, 12a Sutherland Avenue, Maida Vale, London, W9 2HQ Tel: (020) 7289 3201 E-mail: rupeedesign@yahoo.co.uk
Scott Wilson, Central Boulevard, Blythe Valley Park, Shirley, Solihull, West Midlands, B90 8AH Tel: 0121-746 6200 Fax: 0121-746 6201 E-mail: birmingham@camerontaylor.co.uk
▶ Shire Consulting, 8 Spicer Street, St. Albans, Hertfordshire, AL3 4PQ Tel: (01727) 838455 Fax: (01727) 835047 E-mail: enquiries@shire-uk.com
W A Fairhurst & Partners, 1 Amgrove Court, Newcastle upon Tyne, NE4 6DB Tel: 0191-221 0505 Fax: 0191-221 0949 E-mail: newcastle@fairhurst.co.uk
Leslie Wilks Associates, 1 Sunnyside, Claygate Road, Laddingford, Maidstone, Kent, ME18 6BQ Tel: (01892) 730863 Fax: (01892) 730864 E-mail: info@leslie-wilks.co.uk
WSP, Colston Avenue 33, Bristol, BS1 4UA Tel: 0117-930 2000 Fax: 0117-929 4624 E-mail: admin@wspgroup.com
Zakiewicz Associates Ltd, Unit 3 Level 4 New England House, New England Street, Brighton, BN1 4GH Tel: (01273) 670370

STRUCTURAL ENGINEERS OR ENGINEERING

▶ A F Crudden Associates, 209 High Street, Elgin, Morayshire, IV30 1DJ Tel: (01343) 550500 Fax: (01343) 550886
A J Alder & Son Ltd, Unit 7 108 Nathan Way, London, SE28 0AU Tel: (020) 8854 8375 Fax: (020) 8855 1918
Advanced Structures Ltd, 227 Bristol Road, Birmingham, B5 7UB Tel: 0121-446 4809 Fax: 0121-446 4986 E-mail: advanced@freeuk.com
Alan White, Woodside House, 20-23 Woodside Place, Glasgow, G3 7QF Tel: 0141-582 1419 Fax: 0141-582 1484 E-mail: alan@alanwhitedesign.com
Alliance Piling Northwest Ltd, Unit 3-4 Victoria Works, Wallgate, Wigan, Lancashire, WN1 1BA Tel: (01942) 820001 Fax: (01942) 322282 E-mail: enquiries@alliancepiling.co.uk
Applied Design Group, Berberis House, 22 Hollowfields Way, Southcrest, Redditch, Worcestershire, B98 7NR Tel: (01527) 550474 E-mail: applieddesigngrp@btinternet.com
Arch Henderson & Partners, 26 Rubislaw Terrace, Aberdeen, AB10 1XE Tel: (01224) 631122 Fax: (01224) 632233 E-mail: headoffice@arch-henderson.co.uk
Archibald Mcaulay & Son, Bankend Road, Broadmeadow Industrial Estate, Dumbarton, G82 2RB Tel: (01389) 762778 Fax: (01389) 742350 E-mail: steel@mcaulay.co.uk
Atlasco Constructional Engineers Ltd, Rowhurst Close, Rowhurst Industrial Estate, Newcastle, Staffordshire, ST5 6BD Tel: (01782) 564711 Fax: (01782) 564591 E-mail: atlasco@steelweb.co.uk
B & K Steelwork Fabrications Ltd, High Edge Court, Church Street, Heage, Belper, Derbyshire, DE56 2BW Tel: (01773) 853400 Fax: (01773) 857389 E-mail: bksf@bksf.prestel.co.uk
▶ Babcock International Group PLC, Rosyth Business Park, Rosyth, Dunfermline, Fife, KY11 2YD Tel: (01383) 412131 Fax: (01383) 417774
Baldwin & Wiser Ltd, Urban Road, Kirkby-in-Ashfield, Nottingham, NG17 8AP Tel: (01623) 754982 Fax: (01623) 754983
Benaim (UK) Ltd, Dilke House, 1 Malet Street, London, WC1E 7JN Tel: (020) 7580 6000 Fax: (020) 7580 6090 E-mail: london@benaimgroup.com
Billington Modern Structures Ltd, 456 Badminton Road, Yate, Bristol, BS37 5HY Tel: (01454) 318181 Fax: (01454) 318231 E-mail: postroom@billington-modern.co.uk
Michael Birchell Structural Engineers, 61 Cotton Road, Potters Bar, Hertfordshire, EN6 5JJ Tel: (01707) 657996 Fax: (01707) 657996
Bird Associates, 7 Larksfield, Englefield Green, Egham, Surrey, TW20 0RB Tel: (01784) 438963 Fax: (01784) 432319
Bourne Steel Ltd, St. Clements House, St. Clements Road, Poole, Dorset, BH12 4GP Tel: (01202) 746666 Fax: (01202) 732002 E-mail: sales@bourne-steel.demon.co.uk
Britain Fabricators Ltd, Watnall Road, Hucknall, Nottingham, NG15 6EP Tel: 0115-963 2901 Fax: 0115-968 0335 E-mail: sales@britonsltd.co.uk
Bryan Packman Marcel, 26 Moreton Street, London, SW1V 2PE Tel: (020) 7834 7899 Fax: (020) 7931 0568 E-mail: consulting@bpm.uk.com
▶ Bulk Lift Europe Ltd, Monkswell House, Manse Lane, Knaresborough, North Yorkshire, HG5 8NQ Tel: (01423) 860100 Fax: (0845) 4301296 E-mail: agh@eds.gb
Buxton Associates Consulting Engineers Ltd, Dawson House, 131-135 High Street, New Malden, Surrey, KT3 4BH Tel: (020) 8949 8779 Fax: (020) 8942 9941 E-mail: mail@buxtonassociates.co.uk
Byrom Clark Roberts Ltd, Maclaren House, Talbot Road, Stretford, Manchester, M32 0FP Tel: 0161-875 0600 Fax: 0161-875 0601 E-mail: bcrmcr@bcr.uk.com
C E C P Ltd, 819a Chorley Old Road, Bolton, BL1 5SL Tel: (01204) 849484 Fax: (01204) 849192
C & P Structural Engineers, 169 Cromford Road, Langley Mill, Nottingham, NG16 4EU Tel: (01773) 530189 Fax: (01773) 530446 E-mail: candp@btconnect.com
Cadogan Consultants, 4th Floor The Market Building, 72-82 Rosebury Avenue, Clerkenwell, London, EC1R 4RW Tel: (020) 7837 5918 Fax: (020) 7490 2160
Calvert Brain & Fraulo, 3 Portland Street, King's Lynn, Norfolk, PE30 1PB Tel: (01553) 761771 Fax: (01553) 766033 E-mail: info@c-b-f.co.uk
Cambrian Caledonian Ltd, Llandygai Industrial Estate, Bangor, Gwynedd, LL57 4YH Tel: (01248) 370248 Fax: (01248) 370406
Carter Fielding Associates Ltd, 19 Dryden Court, Parkleys, Richmond, Surrey, TW10 5LJ Tel: (020) 8546 7211 Fax: (020) 8546 7008 E-mail: surveyors@carterfielding.co.uk
M.J. Carter Associates, Baddesley Colliery Offices, Main Road, Baxterley, Atherstone, Warwickshire, CV9 2LE Tel: (01827) 717891 Fax: (01827) 718507 E-mail: mailbox@mjca.co.uk
Cellbeam Ltd, Unit 516, Thorp Arch Trading Estate, Thorp Arch, Wetherby, West Yorkshire, LS23 7DB Tel: (01937) 840600 Fax: (01937) 840601 E-mail: sales@cellbeam.co.uk
Chalcross Ltd, Unit 7, Cromford Road Industrial Estate, Langley Mill, Nottingham, NG16 4FL Tel: (01773) 530178 Fax: (01773) 530178
Chiffon Engineering Services Ltd, 11 Almond Rd, Bermondsey, London, SE16 3LR Tel: (020) 7231 8831 Fax: (020) 7231 1997
Clarke Nicholls & Marcel, Galena House, 8-30 Galena Road, London, W6 0LT Tel: (020) 8748 8611 Fax: (020) 8741 8771 E-mail: cnm@cnmlondon.com
Cleveland Bridge, PO Box 27, Darlington, County Durham, DL1 4DF Tel: (01325) 469735 Fax: (01325) 382320 E-mail: info@clevelandbridge.com
W.A. Cooke & Sons Engineers (Est 1926) Ltd, Southern Street, Walkden, Worsley, Manchester, M28 3QN Tel: (01204) 574721 Fax: (01204) 861778 E-mail: admin@wacooke.co.uk
Leonard Cooper Ltd, Balm Road, Leeds, LS10 2JR Tel: 0113-270 5441 Fax: 0113-276 0659 E-mail: sales@leonardcooperltd.co.uk
Country Custom Engineering, Units 11-13 Enterprise Units, 21-27 Hollands Road, Haverhill, Suffolk, CB9 8PU Tel: (01440) 763881 Fax: (01440) 763880 E-mail: countrycustom@hotmail.co.uk
Coventry Construction Ltd, Torrington Avenue, Coventry, CV4 9AP Tel: (024) 7646 2321 Fax: (024) 7669 4020 E-mail: info@covcon.co.uk
Cundell, Saffron House, 6-10 Kirby Street, London, EC1N 8TS Tel: (020) 7438 1600 Fax: (020) 7438 1601 E-mail: info@cundall.com
Dixon Hurst Kemp Ltd, Station House, Bepton Road, Midhurst, West Sussex, GU29 9RE Tel: (01243) 787888 Fax: (01243) 787180 E-mail: chichester@dhk.co.uk
Doyle Partnership, 5 Waverley Road, Huddersfield, HD1 5NA Tel: (01484) 516977 Fax: (01484) 516958
Expert Engineering Ltd, Queen Mary, University of London, Mile End Road, London, E1 4NS Tel: (0845) 6586933 E-mail: jshaikh@expertengineering.co.uk
Frank H Dale Ltd, Mill Street, Leominster, Herefordshire, HR6 8EF Tel: (01568) 612212 Fax: (01568) 619402 E-mail: sales@fhdale.co.uk

STRUCTURAL ENGINEERS OR ENGINEERING – *continued*

▶ G W F Engineering Ltd, Woodhouse Road, Scunthorpe, South Humberside, DN16 1BD Tel: (01724) 868646 Fax: (01724) 867747 E-mail: enquiries@gwf.co.uk

Goddard & Co 1992 Ltd, Copley Mill, Demesne Drive, St. Pauls Trading Estate, Stalybridge, Cheshire, SK15 2QF Tel: 0161-304 9690 Fax: 0161-304 9694 E-mail: goddardco1992@btinternet.com

Peter Goodhind Associates Ltd, Brunel House, George Street, Gloucester, GL1 1BZ Tel: (01452) 503501 Fax: (01452) 308794 E-mail: mail@goodhindassociates.co.uk

Goodwin L F P, Wallis House, 24 High Street, Ewell, Epsom, Surrey, KT17 1SJ Tel: (020) 8394 1555 Fax: (020) 8393 7002

Greenwood Structures, 67 Trafalgar Road, Moseley, Birmingham, B13 8BL Tel: 0121-449 0278 Fax: 0121-249 2499

Gregg & Patterson Engineers Ltd, Ballyskeagh Road, Lisburn, County Antrim, BT27 5TD Tel: (028) 9061 8131 Fax: (028) 9062 2813

H Langdon & Son Chatham Ltd, 51-53 Second Avenue, Chatham, Kent, ME4 5BA Tel: (01634) 842485 Fax: (01634) 831037

Hadfield Cawkwell Davidson, 17 Broomgrove Road, Sheffield, S10 2LZ Tel: 0114-266 8181 Fax: 0114-266 6246 E-mail: sales@hcd.co.uk

Halcrow Crouch Ltd, City Park, 368 Alexandra Parade, Glasgow, G31 3AU Tel: 0141-552 2000 Fax: 0141-552 2525 E-mail: hcglasgow@halcrow.com

Halesowen Fabricators Ltd, Unit 8 Granada Industrial Estate, Oldbury, West Midlands, B69 4LH Tel: 0121-552 4360 Fax: 0121-511 1247

John Hally, Moray Street, Blackford, Auchterarder, Perthshire, PH4 1PY Tel: (01764) 682277 Fax: (01764) 663817

Hampco Ltd, Blairs College, South Deeside Road, Blairs, Aberdeen, AB12 5LF Tel: (01224) 860300 Fax: (01224) 860301 E-mail: admin@hampco.com

William Hare Ltd, Brandlesholme House, Brandlesholme Road, Bury, Lancashire, BL8 1JJ Tel: 0161-609 0000 Fax: 0161-609 0491 E-mail: hq@hare.co.uk

Harry Peers & Co. Ltd, Elton Street, Mill Hill, Bolton, BL2 2BS Tel: (01204) 528393 Fax: (01204) 362363 E-mail: sales@peers.co.uk

Hawksley Engineering Ltd, Burringham Road, Gunness, Scunthorpe, South Humberside, DN17 3LT Tel: (01724) 782511 Fax: (01724) 783577 E-mail: hawkeng@ic24.net

Charles Head Ltd, 78 Tavistock Street, Bletchley, Milton Keynes, MK2 2PN Tel: (01908) 372250 Fax: (01908) 371023 E-mail: sales@charles-head.co.uk

Hemsley Orrell Partnership, 41 Church Road, Hove, East Sussex, BN3 2BE Tel: (01273) 223900 Fax: (01273) 326767

Henry Smith Constructional Engineer Ltd, Wharton Steel Works, Deakins Road, Winsford, Cheshire, CW7 3BW Tel: (01606) 592121 Fax: (01606) 559134 E-mail: admin@hs-steel.co.uk

Highland Smiddy Ltd, 54 Thornbush Road, Inverness, IV3 8AF Tel: (01463) 232905 Fax: (01463) 711529

Hurst Pierce & Malcolm, Celtic House, 33 Johns Mews, London, WC1N 2QL Tel: (020) 7242 3593 Fax: (020) 7405 5274 E-mail: hurstpm@globalnet.co.uk

J M Feerick & Partners, 3-5 Church Street, Brierley Hill, West Midlands, DY5 3PT Tel: (01384) 77885 Fax: (01384) 76181 E-mail: johnfeerick@jmfeerickandpatns.co.uk

Jackson Steel Structures Ltd, Densfield Works, Tannadice Street, Dundee, DD3 7QP Tel: (01382) 858439 Fax: (01382) 833964 E-mail: sales@jacksonsteel.co.uk

Jampel Davison & Bell, 210a Tufnell Park Road, London, N7 0PZ Tel: (020) 7272 0562 Fax: (020) 7263 4005 E-mail: info@jamdavbell.co.uk

Jim Mccoll Associates, 6a Mill Lane, Edinburgh, EH6 6TJ Tel: 0131-555 0721 Fax: 0131-555 0723 E-mail: enquiries@mccollassoc.co.uk

K & M Arrowsmith, 81 West Street, Alford, Lincolnshire, LN13 9HT Tel: (01507) 463258 Fax: (01507) 462312 E-mail: steve@kandmarrowsmith.fsnet.co.uk

Killan Structural Ltd, 626 Huddersfield Road, Lees, Oldham, OL4 3NL Tel: 0161-624 2033 Fax: 0161-627 0793 E-mail: info@killan.co.uk

Lamby Engineering Ltd, East Moors Road, Cardiff, CF24 5EE Tel: (029) 2049 7716 Fax: (029) 2049 7701

R.E. Leach (Engineers) Ltd, Brockles Way, Garstang, Preston, PR3 0PZ Tel: 01995 640133

Leedsheath Ltd, Westfield Road, Slyfield Industrial Estate, Guildford, Surrey, GU1 1RR Tel: (01483) 503248 Fax: (01483) 575627 E-mail: tonycoker@btconnect.com

Leyletts Engineering Co. Ltd, Cornwallis Road, Lyng, West Bromwich, West Midlands, B70 7JF Tel: 0121-544 6669 Fax: 0121-544 8483 E-mail: sales@leyletts.co.uk

Lockerbie & Wilkinson Engineering Ltd, Alexandra Works, Locarno Road, Tipton, West Midlands, DY4 9SD Tel: 0121-557 1861 Fax: 0121-557 4804 E-mail: locwiltipton@aol.com

M G C Engineering Ltd, Bradfords Quay, Wadebridge, Cornwall, PL27 6DB Tel: (01208) 812585 Fax: (01208) 814066 E-mail: mgceng@tiscali.co.uk

M H I Ltd, 10 Appleton Gate, Newark, Nottinghamshire, NG24 1JY Tel: (01636) 704814 Fax: (01636) 671113 E-mail: enquiries@mhidesign.co.uk

William McDowell & Partners, Aldersgate House, 13-19 University Road, Belfast, BT7 1NA Tel: (028) 9024 5444 Fax: (028) 9024 5916

Marks Heeley & Brothwell Ltd, The Stables, Cannons Mill Lane, Bishop's Stortford, Hertfordshire, CM23 2BN Tel: (01279) 465900 Fax: (01279) 465999 E-mail: general@mhb.co.uk

Melliss & Partners, Boundary House The Pines Business Park, Broad Street, Guildford, Surrey, GU3 3BH Tel: (01483) 567879 Fax: (01483) 574616 E-mail: mail@melliss.com

Midland Erection Ltd, Roetan House, Thorns Road, Brierley Hill, West Midlands, DY5 2PF Tel: (01384) 424227 Fax: (01384) 424906 E-mail: miderect1@btconnect.com

Milton Steel Ltd, 20 Queensway, Stem Lane Industrial Estate, New Milton, Hampshire, BH25 5NN Tel: (01425) 613582 Fax: (01425) 623929 E-mail: sales@miltonsteel.co.uk

Morgan Cooper Ltd, Salmon Road, Great Yarmouth, Norfolk, NR30 3QS Tel: (01493) 843233 Fax: (01493) 844068 E-mail: info@morgan-cooper.co.uk

Mott Macdonald Ltd, Prince House, 49-51 Prince Street, Bristol, BS1 4PS Tel: 0117-906 9500 Fax: 0117-922 1924

Harold Newsome Ltd, Paragon Works, Elder Road, Leeds, LS13 4DJ Tel: 0113-257 0156 Fax: 0113-256 4095 E-mail: h.newsome@btconnect.com

North West Construction Services Ltd, Bleasby Street, Oldham, OL4 2AJ Tel: 0161 6261816

Northend Construction, Maypole Crescent, Wallhouse Road, Erith, Kent, DA8 2JZ Tel: (01322) 333441 Fax: (01322) 333441

Oak Tree Forge, Oak Tree Yard, Upper Manor Road, Paignton, Devon, TQ3 2TP Tel: (01803) 550436 Fax: (01803) 529277

Pell Frischmann Group Ltd, 4 Manchester Square, London, W1A 1AU Tel: (020) 7486 3661 Fax: (020) 7487 4153 E-mail: pflondon@pellfrischmann.com

Posford Haskoning, Eastchester House, Harlands Road, Haywards Heath, West Sussex, RH16 1PG Tel: (01444) 458551 Fax: (01444) 440665 E-mail: sales@royalhaskoing.com

R C Murray, 17 Woodland Gardens, North Wootton, King's Lynn, Norfolk, PE30 3PX Tel: (01553) 631770 Fax: (01553) 631770 E-mail: rcmkl@freeuk.com

R M J M Ltd, 83 Paul Street, London, EC2A 4UT Tel: (020) 7549 8900 Fax: (020) 7250 3131 E-mail: london@rmjm.com

Rennie & Kirkwood Ltd, 95 Morrison Street, Glasgow, G5 8BE Tel: 0141-429 2810 Fax: 0141-420 3728 E-mail: mail@rkglasgow.fsnet.co.uk

Renoco Engineering Ltd, Unit 36, Station Lane Industrial Estate, Old Whittington, Chesterfield, Derbyshire, S41 9QX Tel: (01246) 454725 Fax: (01246) 454599 E-mail: renocoeng@aol.com

Rowecord Holdings Ltd, Neptune Works, Usk Way, Newport, Gwent, NP20 2SS Tel: (01633) 256433 Fax: (01792) 467308 E-mail: enquiries@rowecord.com

Rowen Structures Ltd, Fulwood Road South, Sutton-in-Ashfield, Nottinghamshire, NG17 2JW Tel: (01623) 558558 Fax: (01623) 558866 E-mail: sales@rowenstructures.co.uk

Ken Rush Associates, Bowman House, 191 South Street, Braintree, Essex, CM7 3QB Tel: (01376) 326789 Fax: (01376) 342711 E-mail: engineer@ken-rush-assoc.demon.co.uk

S H Structures Ltd, Moor La Trading Estate, Sherburn in Elmet, Leeds, LS25 6ES Tel: (01977) 681931 Fax: (01977) 681930 E-mail: mail@shstructures.com

S M Cooper & Associates, Churchfield House, 36 Vicar Street, Dudley, West Midlands, DY2 8RG Tel: (01384) 257227 Fax: (01384) 211973

Charles Scott & Partners (London) Ltd, 23 Skylines, Limeharbour, London, E14 9TS Tel: (020) 7538 1333 Fax: (020) 7538 3747 E-mail: cspll@aol.com

Scott-White & Hookins, Fountain House, 26 St. Johns Street, Bedford, MK42 0AQ Tel: (01234) 213111 Fax: (01234) 213333 E-mail: bed@swh.co.uk

SCS Structural Steel Ltd, Hotham Street, Hull, HU9 1RD Tel: (01482) 585599 Fax: (01482) 620100 E-mail: scs@scsfirm.co.uk

Sinclair Johnston & Partners, Eagle House, 2b Narbonne Avenue, London, SW4 9JS Tel: (020) 8682 8920 Fax: (020) 8673 1419 E-mail: email@sjandp.co.uk

Southon Engineering Ltd, Aveley Indust Estate, Ardmore Road, Sth Ockendon, South Ockendon, Essex, RM15 5TH Tel: (01708) 858757 Fax: (01708) 858757 E-mail: john@southonengineering.co.uk

Stirling Maynard & Partners Ltd, Stirling House, Rightwell, Bretton, Peterborough, PE3 8DJ Tel: (01733) 262319 Fax: (01733) 331527 E-mail: enquires@stirlingmaynard.com

T Good & Sons Ltd, 36 Vulcan Way, New Addington, Croydon, CR0 9UG Tel: (01689) 848211 Fax: (01689) 841069 E-mail: dave@tgood.co.uk

Test Valley Engineers Ltd, Stoneymarsh, Michelmersh, Romsey, Hampshire, SO51 0LB Tel: (01794) 368308 Fax: (01794) 368693 E-mail: sales@test-valley.co.uk

John Tooke & Partners, 1a Montford Place, London, SE11 5DE Tel: (020) 7582 0255 Fax: (020) 7820 0297 E-mail: lloyd@john-tooke.co.uk

Train & Kemp, 10 Kennington Park Place, London, SE11 4AS Tel: (020) 7582 1276 Fax: (020) 7582 5728 E-mail: mail@trainandkemp.co.uk

Underpin & Makegood (Contracting) Ltd, 37 Millmarsh Lane, Enfield, Middx, EN3 7UY Tel: (020) 8805 4000 Fax: (020) 8805 4222 E-mail: david@underpin.com

Upfield Engineering, Rutherfords Business Park, Marley Lane, Battle, East Sussex, TN33 0TY Tel: (01424) 775373 Fax: (01424) 777164 E-mail: enquiries@upfieldengineering.co.uk

Victoria Fabrications Ltd, Station Road, Whittington Moor, Chesterfield, Derbyshire, S41 9ES Tel: (01246) 450605 Fax: (01246) 455987

Wall Engineering Co. Ltd, Cromer Road, North Walsham, Norfolk, NR28 0NB Tel: (01692) 403701 Fax: (01692) 406610 E-mail: info@wallengineering.co.uk

Watson Hallam, Burlington House, 369 Wellingborough Road, Northampton, NN1 4EU Tel: (01604) 230823 Fax: (01604) 230923

Westbury Park Engineering Ltd, Brook Lane, Westbury, Wiltshire, BA13 4ES Tel: (01373) 825500 Fax: (01373) 825511 E-mail: jamesbrain@westparkeng.co.uk

Wheeler & Jupp, 11b Holywell Hill, St. Albans, Hertfordshire, AL1 1EU Tel: (01727) 868127 Fax: (01727) 840931 E-mail: sales@wheelerandjupp.com

Wilson & Collins Ltd, Balthane Industrial Estate, Balthane, Ballasalla, Isle of Man, IM9 2AJ Tel: (01624) 822854 Fax: (01624) 824995

Ken Wilson Associates, 52 Union Road, Inverness, IV2 3JY Tel: (01463) 237375 Fax: (01463) 237666 E-mail: enquiries@kwa.uk.net

Zentech International Ltd, 103 Mytchett Road, Mytchett, Camberley, Surrey, GU16 6ES Tel: (01252) 376388 Fax: (01252) 376389 E-mail: sales@zentech.co.uk

STRUCTURAL FABRICATING ENGINEERING

▶ 3D Structural Fabrications, Bull Street, Gornal Wood, Dudley, West Midlands, DY3 2NQ Tel: (01902) 656263 Fax: (01902) 656036 E-mail: structuralservices@blueyonder.co.uk

▶ 3D Structural Services, 35 Humphrey Street, Lower Gornal, Dudley, West Midlands, DY3 2AW Tel: (01902) 656263 Fax: (01902) 656263 E-mail: structuralservices@blueyonder.co.uk

Action Group, Garston Business Park, Blackburne Street, Liverpool, L19 8JB Tel: 0151-427 1084 Fax: 0151-427 7130 E-mail: dkeen@theactiongroup.co.uk

AMS Group Consultants, PO Box 5586, Milton Keynes, MK4 1ZG Tel: (0870) 0923392 Fax: (0870) 0923393 E-mail: ams@amsgroup.demon.co.uk

▶ Linian North West Ltd, Unit 9 Shaw Street, St. Helens, Merseyside, WA10 1DQ Tel: (01744) 736330 Fax: (01744) 22013 E-mail: sales@linian.co.uk

▶ T. Shanks Engineering Ltd, 141 Greengairs Road, Greengairs, Airdrie, Lanarkshire, ML6 7SY Tel: (01236) 830325 Fax: (01236) 830736 E-mail: sales@shanksgroup.co.uk

▶ Structural Surveys Direct, 1-2 Aire House, Richmond Business Park, Sidings Court, Doncaster, South Yorkshire, DN4 5NL Tel: (0808) 144 8899 Fax: (08081) 448898 E-mail: info@structuralsurveysdirect.co.uk

STRUCTURAL FIRE PROTECTION CLADDING

Mitie Mccartney Fire Protection Ltd, 8 Lawmoor Place, Glasgow, G5 0XW Tel: 0141-429 4646 Fax: 0141-429 4442 E-mail: charlesa@mccartney.co.uk

▶ Mitie Mccartney Fire Protection Ltd, 3 Abbey Mead Industrial Park, Brooker Road, Waltham Abbey, Essex, EN9 1HU Tel: (01992) 761666 Fax: (01992) 761777 E-mail: paulas.waide@mitie.co.uk

Pyricon Ltd, PO Box 4641, London, SE11 4XE Tel: (020) 7735 8777

STRUCTURAL FIRE PROTECTION CONTRACTORS

John Atkinson Interiors Ltd, Deanfield Mill, Asquith Avenue, Morley, Leeds, LS27 9QT Tel: 0113-253 5661 Fax: 0113-238 0323 E-mail: atkinsoninteriors@btopenworld.com

Brimset Ltd, 2 Stocks Lane, Rawmarsh, Rotherham, South Yorkshire, S62 6NL Tel: (01709) 522270 Fax: (01709) 527240 E-mail: contracts@brimset.f9.co.uk

Merryhill Envirotec Ltd, Merryhill House, Budds Lane, Romsey, Hampshire, SO51 0HA Tel: (01794) 515848 Fax: (01794) 524386 E-mail: enquiries@merryhill-idm.co.uk

Perkins Contracts Ltd, Knights Court, South Chailey, Lewes, East Sussex, BN8 4QF Tel: (01273) 401401 Fax: (01273) 401400 E-mail: info@perkinscontracts.co.uk

S L (Thermal Insulation) Contracts & Supplies Co. Ltd, Unit 16 Blue Chalet Industrial Park, London Road, West Kingsdown, Sevenoaks, Kent, TN15 6BT Tel: (01474) 854465 Fax: (01474) 854393 E-mail: les@slcontracts.com

Specialist Coatings UK Ltd, 5 Tramsheds Industrial Estate, Coomber Way, Croydon, CR0 4TQ Tel: (020) 8665 5888 Fax: (020) 8665 6888 E-mail: info@specialistcoatingsuk.com

W R R, 5 The Arianne Business Centre Blackburn Road, Townsend Industrial, Houghton Regis, Dunstable, Bedfordshire, LU5 5DZ Tel: (01582) 665718 Fax: (01582) 664490 E-mail: wroberts@wrr-uk.com

STRUCTURAL FOUNDATION CONTRACTORS

A C Baker & Son Ltd, Wood Cottage, The Green, Sarratt, Rickmansworth, Hertfordshire, WD3 6AT Tel: (01923) 269190 Fax: (01923) 269190

Agritask Construction Ltd, Tanhouse Farm, Rusper Road, Newdigate, Dorking, Surrey, RH5 5BX Tel: (01306) 631334 Fax: (01306) 631891 E-mail: info@agritask.co.uk

AMEC Piling, Cold Meeth, Swynnton, Stone, Staffordshire, ST15 0UD Tel: (01785) 760022 Fax: (01785) 760762

B & B Construction Ltd, Baulker Farm, Baulker Lane, Farnsfield, Newark, Nottinghamshire, NG22 8HP Tel: (01623) 883771 Fax: (01623) 883771 E-mail: bernard@bbconstruction.freeserve.co.uk

B T M Sports Services, Columbia House, Columbia Avenue, Worcester Park, Surrey, KT4 7SP Tel: (020) 8337 3327 Fax: (020) 8337 3328

Bachy Soletanche, Units 2 & 5 Prospect Place, Mill Lane, Alton, Hampshire, GU34 2SX Tel: (01420) 594700 Fax: (01420) 86971 E-mail: geotech@bacsol.co.uk

Baram Ltd, Unit 1 Station Hill, Curdridge, Southampton, SO30 2DN Tel: (01489) 785086 Fax: (01489) 785929 E-mail: baramltd@aol.com

Bon Groundwork Ltd, 47 Windsor Drive, Orpington, Kent, BR6 6EY Tel: (01689) 862285 Fax: (01689) 850917

Roger Bullivant Ltd, Walton Road, Drakelow, Burton-on-Trent, Staffordshire, DE15 9UA Tel: (01283) 511115 Fax: (01283) 540826 E-mail: marketing@roger-bullivant.co.uk

Buxton & Cawthorne, 48 Cheney Hill, Heacham, King's Lynn, Norfolk, PE31 7BS Tel: (01485) 570139 Fax: (01485) 570545

Cannon Groundwork, 9 Cannon Street, Lydd, Romney Marsh, Kent, TN29 9AS Tel: (01797) 320988 Fax: (01797) 320988

Carroll & Son Fleet Ltd, Willow Cottage, The Hurst, Winchfield, Hook, Hampshire, RG27 8DF Tel: (01252) 843214 Fax: (01252) 845159

Coastel Groundworks Ltd, 5 Somerset Road, Walmer, Deal, Kent, CT14 7TD Tel: (01304) 361126 Fax: (01304) 361126

Conlon Ltd, 6 Kendrick Trading Estate, Galton Way, Swindon, SN2 2DU Tel: (01793) 644956 Fax: (01793) 535116 E-mail: survey@conlon.co.uk

D Kennedy & Son Ltd, 6 Ashcombe Drive, Radcliffe, Manchester, M26 3NL Tel: 0161-723 5136 Fax: 0161-723 5136 E-mail: j.kennedy33@ntlworld.com

Eakins Plant Hire & Ground Work Ltd, Manor Farm, Prestwood Lane, Ifield Wood, Crawley, West Sussex, RH11 0LA Tel: (01293) 871311 Fax: (01293) 871770

Fitfield Ltd, Unit 21 Chanters Industrial Estate, Tyldesley Old Road, Atherton, Manchester, M46 9BE Tel: (01942) 886888 Fax: (01942) 891921

Fitzgerald Contractors Ltd, 125 Cheston Road, Birmingham, B7 5EA Tel: 0121-326 0402 Fax: 0121-328 1963 E-mail: sales@fitzgerald-uk.com

Foundation Developments Ltd, Foundation House, Clarendon Road, Wallington, Surrey, SM6 8QX Tel: (020) 8669 8600

▶ Fox Plant (Owmby) Ltd, Caenby Hall, Caenby Corner, Market Rasen, Lincolnshire, LN8 2BU Tel: (01673) 878444 Fax: (01673) 878644 E-mail: office@foxowmby.com

Hartcrown Ltd, 3 Mantle Road, London, SE4 2DU Tel: (020) 7252 9380 Fax: (020) 7277 9606

Houlihan & Co Excavations Ltd, Ashford House, 46-48 Littleton Road, Ashford, Middlesex, TW15 1UQ Tel: (01784) 250650 Fax: (01784) 248296

Howard Construction, Boot Street, Great Bealings, Woodbridge, Suffolk, IP13 6PB Tel: (01473) 735315 Fax: (01473) 738383 E-mail: glenn@howardconstruction.co.uk

J A Kent Services East Midlands Ltd, Chestnut Farmhouse, Chestnut Lane, Barton-in-Fabis, Nottingham, NG11 0AE Tel: 0115-983 0691 Fax: 0115-983 1229 E-mail: info@kentservices.fsnet.co.uk

J C Edwardson Ltd, Unit 13 Wigan Enterprise Park, Seaman Way, Ince, Wigan, Lancashire, WN2 2LE Tel: (01942) 820943 Fax: (01942) 829185

Keller Ltd, Oxford Road, Ryton on Dunsmore, Coventry, CV8 3EG Tel: (024) 7651 1266 Fax: (024) 7630 5230 E-mail: marketing@keller-ge.co.uk

M Kember Groundworks, 20 Knottesford Close, Studley, Warwickshire, B80 7RL Tel: (01527) 854254

Kilwuddie Construction, 5 Wilson Place, East Kilbride, Glasgow, G74 4QD Tel: (01355) 266700 Fax: (01355) 261962

STRUCTURAL FOUNDATION CONTRACTORS – *continued*

L F Nugent Ltd, High Street, Handcross, Haywards Heath, West Sussex, RH17 6BN Tel: (01444) 401097 Fax: (01444) 401103 E-mail: lenn@nugentgroup.co.uk

Lydfield Construction Ltd, Meadow House, Cooks Lane, Calmore, Southampton, SO40 2RU Tel: (023) 8081 4466 Fax: (023) 8081 3785

M J Spencer, The Range, Hawkesbury Road, Hillesley, Wotton-under-Edge, Gloucestershire, GL12 7RE Tel: (01453) 843059 Fax: (01453) 843059

M Lambe Construction Ltd, Newton House, Newton Place, Birmingham, B18 5JY Tel: 0121-523 0666 Fax: 0121-554 8896

Mcmahon Contractors Services Ltd, Old Station Yard, Station Road, Stratford-upon-Avon, Warwickshire, CV37 8RP Tel: (01789) 720836 Fax: (01789) 721048 E-mail: sales@mcmahon-holdings.co.uk

Meaden Civil Engineering, 71 Micheldever Road, Whitchurch, Hampshire, RG28 7JH Tel: (01256) 893270

Myston Services Ltd, Foxhanger House, Curtis Lane, Headley, Bordon, Hampshire, GU35 8PH Tel: (01428) 713174

P J Wade Site Engineering Ltd, 38 Tuffley CR, Gloucester, GL1 5NE Tel: (01452) 304228 Fax: 01452 304359

Park Lane Groundworks Ltd, 54 Park Lane, Fen Drayton, Cambridge, CB24 4SW Tel: (01954) 232886 Fax: (01954) 232639 E-mail: enquiries@parklanegroundworks.co.uk

David Paul Construction, The Old Malthouse, Bridgnorth, Shropshire, WV15 5PJ Tel: (01746) 716310 Fax: (01746) 716581

R Campbell, 6 Oaklands Park, Hatherleigh Road, Okehampton, Devon, EX20 1LN Tel: (01837) 52540 Fax: (01837) 52540

R J Canning Ltd, Highbank House, Pear Tree Lane, Newbury, Berkshire, RG14 2LU Tel: (01635) 33606 Fax: (01635) 33607 E-mail: highbanks@supanet.com

R W Bennett & Son, 7 Paget Cottages, Munden Road, Dane End, Ware, Hertfordshire, SG12 0NL Tel: (01920) 438781

Rapidgrid Ltd, Progress Industrial Estate, Station Road, Rogiet, Caldicot, Gwent, NP26 3UE Tel: (01291) 424576 Fax: (01291) 424320

Renelec Ltd, Brownstone House, New Park Street, Devizes, Wiltshire, SN10 1DS Tel: (01380) 726363 Fax: (01380) 729255 E-mail: postmaster@renelec.co.uk

S & C Bennett Construction, The Workshop, Kingscote, Tetbury, Gloucestershire, GL8 8XZ Tel: (01453) 860180 Fax: (01453) 860180

S & J Contractors, 81 Vicarage Hill, Benfleet, Essex, SS7 1PD Tel: (01268) 755761

Solent Groundworks Ltd, 32 Dean Road, Southampton, SO18 6AP Tel: (023) 8044 8446 Fax: (023) 8044 3226 E-mail: solentgroundworks@btconnect.com

South Eastern Road & Groundworks Ltd, Highlands Yard, Queenborough Road, Southminster, Essex, CM0 7AD Tel: (01621) 774901 Fax: (01621) 773988

Springfield Construction, 10 The Fields, Donnington Wood, Telford, Shropshire, TF2 7PW Tel: (01952) 603233 Fax: (01952) 603233

Sylvia Plant Hire Ltd, 46 Sheepcote Dell Road, Holmer Green, High Wycombe, Buckinghamshire, HP15 6TL Tel: (01494) 717881 Fax: (01494) 488516

T King & Son Groundwork Ltd, Summerfield, Gentles Lane, Passfield, Liphook, Hampshire, GU30 7RY Tel: (01428) 751129 Fax: (01428) 751569

V Jackson, 103 Fairview Road, Stevenage, Hertfordshire, SG1 2NP Tel: (01438) 722016

W P Gallagher, 22 Blagden Lane, Huddersfield, HD4 6JZ Tel: (01484) 422644

STRUCTURAL GRP ENGINEERS OR ERECTORS OR FABRICATORS OR FIXERS

Sharp Site Services Ltd, 49 Mountain Road, Brynaman, Upper Brynamman, Ammanford, Dyfed, SA18 1AE Tel: (01269) 825932 Fax: (01269) 825932 E-mail: margaret@sharpsiteservices.com

STRUCTURAL HOLLOW SECTIONS

Corus Tubes plc, PO Box 101, Corby, Northamptonshire, NN17 5UA Tel: (01536) 402121 Fax: (01536) 404111

Hall & Pickles, Blackvein Industrial Estate, Cross Keys, Newport, Gwent, NP11 7PX Tel: (023) 8065 1815 Fax: (01495) 271563 E-mail: cksales@hallandpickles.co.uk

National Tube Stockholders Ltd, Dalton Industrial Estate, Dalton, Thirsk, North Yorkshire, YO7 3HE Tel: (01845) 577440 Fax: (01845) 577165 E-mail: nts@nationaltube.co.uk

Worcestershire Steels Co., Unit 20 Enfield Industrial Estate, Redditch, Worcestershire, B97 6BY Tel: (01527) 67777 Fax: (01527) 64225E-mail: worcestershire.steels@virgin.net

STRUCTURAL INSULATING GLASS

Abbseal (U K) Ltd, Broadway, Broadway, Hyde, Cheshire, SK14 4QW Tel: 0161-368 5711 Fax: 0161-366 8155

All Trim Plastics, Unit 1-2, Spring Lane, Willenhall, West Midlands, WV12 4HL Tel: (0845) 6099922 Fax: (01422) 370953 E-mail: sales@dqs.co.uk

▶ Pittsburgh Corning UK Ltd, 63 Milford Road, Reading, RG1 8LG Tel: 0118-950 0655 Fax: 0118-950 9019 E-mail: sales@foamglass.co.uk

STRUCTURAL INSULATION MATERIALS, *See Insulating etc*

STRUCTURAL INSULATION PANEL INFORMATION

▶ Just Insulation, 27 Massetts Road, Horley, Surrey, RH6 7DQ Tel: (0845) 2606232 Fax: (0845) 2606242 E-mail: purchases@just-insulation.com

STRUCTURAL LATTICE BEAMS

Metsec plc, Broadwell Works, Birmingham Road, Oldbury, West Midlands, B69 4HE Tel: 0121-552 1541 E-mail: windows@metsec.com

Tecton Timber Products, Abbey Road, Hempsted, Gloucester, GL2 5HU Tel: (01452) 381146 Fax: (01452) 381147 E-mail: paul@tecton.freeserve.co.uk

STRUCTURAL MONITORING

Mecon Ltd, 5a Pound Hill, Cambridge, CB3 0AE Tel: (01223) 355990 Fax: (01223) 354297 E-mail: enquiries@mecon.ltd.uk

Poulton Remedial Services Ltd, 86-88 Church Street, Old Town, Eastbourne, East Sussex, BN21 1QJ Tel: (01424) 422122 Fax: (01323) 734596 E-mail: enquiries@structuralrepairs.com

Structural Statics Ltd, Burntwood, Martyr Worthy, Winchester, Hampshire, SO21 1AD Tel: (01962) 886644 Fax: (01962) 886788 E-mail: info@structuralstatics.co.uk

STRUCTURAL OR CONSTRUCTION INDUSTRY FIXING SYSTEMS

2K Polymer Systems Limited, PO Box 7, Alfreton, Derbyshire, DE55 7RA Tel: (01773) 540440 Fax: (01773) 607638 E-mail: info@2kps.net

A & A Time Ltd, 13 Rutherford Road, Maghull, Liverpool, L31 3DD Tel: 0151-531 6913 Fax: 0151-531 7353 E-mail: sales@aandatime.co.uk

A C Fixings, 10 Montrose Road, Chelmsford, CM2 6TX Tel: (01245) 451234 Fax: (01245) 451701 E-mail: acfixingsltd@blueyonder.com

Abell Fasteners, Unit 337 Rushock Trading Estate, Rushock, Droitwich, Worcestershire, WR9 0NR Tel: (01299) 251533 Fax: (01299) 251533

Alderdale Fixing Systems, New John Street, Halesowen, West Midlands, B62 8HT Tel: 0121-561 5500 Fax: 0121-561 3535 E-mail: sales@alderdale.com

Allman Fasteners Ltd, PO Box 5, Wilmslow, Cheshire, SK9 2EF Tel: (01625) 537535 Fax: (01625) 537635

Alpha, Goudhurst Road, Marden, Tonbridge, Kent, TN12 9NW Tel: (01622) 832488 Fax: (01622) 832488

Apollo Construction Products, Unit 4 Weights Lane, Redditch, Worcestershire, B97 6RG Tel: (01527) 63999 Fax: (01527) 64999 E-mail: sales@apollofix.co.uk

Avery Knight & Bowlers Engineering Ltd, 33-35 James St West, Bath, BA1 2BT Tel: (01225) 425894 Fax: (01225) 445753 E-mail: sales@averyknight.co.uk

Bedford Fixings, 1a Dean Street, Bedford, MK40 3EQ Tel: (01234) 360747 Fax: (01234) 217414

Bluebird Fixings Ltd, Westminster Industrial Estate, Station Road, North Hykeham, Lincoln, LN6 3QY Tel: (01522) 697776 Fax: (01522) 697771 E-mail: info@bluebird-fixings.ltd.uk

Bryant Fixings Ltd, 21 Blatchford Road, Horsham, West Sussex, RH13 5QR Tel: (01403) 265652 Fax: (01403) 218070

Bunny's Bolts, The Depot The Mayford Centre, Mayford Green, Woking, Surrey, GU22 0PP Tel: (01483) 727227 Fax: (01483) 727995 E-mail: sales@bunnysbolt.com

Corroy Products Ltd, 25 Queen Street, Premier Business Park, Walsall, WS2 9NT Tel: (01922) 644884 Fax: (01922) 471370 E-mail: sales@corroy.co.uk

D Fix Bridgend Ltd, Newton Yard, Cemetery Road, Bridgend, Mid Glamorgan, CF31 1NA Tel: (01656) 669609 Fax: (01656) 767584 E-mail: mikecoleman@datapowertool.co.uk

Derbyshire Industrial Sales Ltd, Unit 17 Vanguard Trading Estate, Britannia Road, Chesterfield, Derbyshire, S40 2TZ Tel: (01246) 208963 Fax: (01246) 277139

Eagle Tools & Fixings, The Willows, Eardisland, Leominster, Herefordshire, HR6 9BN Tel: (01544) 388830 Fax: (01544) 388830

Earth Anchors Ltd, 15 Campbell Road, Croydon, CR0 2SQ Tel: (020) 8684 9601 Fax: (020) 8684 2230 E-mail: enquiries@earth-anchors.com

Eca Tool Fast, 26 Oswin Road, Leicester, LE3 1HR Tel: 0116-247 0402

Eland Fixings, Tree Tops, Broadshard, Crewkerne, Somerset, TA18 7NF Tel: (01460) 72219 Fax: (01460) 72219

Emhart Fastening Technology Ltd, Walsall Road, Perry Barr, Birmingham, B42 1BP Tel: 0121-331 2408 Fax: 0121-356 1598 E-mail: uk.marketing@bdk.com

Emlux Holdings Ltd, The Industrial Estate, Black Bourton Road, Brize Norton, Carterton, Oxfordshire, OX18 3LY Tel: (01993) 841574 Fax: (01993) 843186 E-mail: info@walraven.com

Essex Fixing & Abrasives Supplies Ltd, Unit 12 Featherby Way, Purdey's Industrial Estate, Rochford, Essex, SS4 1LD Tel: (01702) 549222 Fax: (01702) 541465

▶ Excalibur Screwbolts Ltd, 10 Aldermans Hill, Hockley, Essex, SS5 4RW Tel: (01702) 206962 Fax: (01702) 207918 E-mail: charles.bickford@screwbolt.com

Fixfast Fasteners & Fixing Devices Ltd, Forge Works, Horsham Road, Mid Holmwood, Dorking, Surrey, RH5 4EJ Tel: (01306) 880299 Fax: (01306) 880038 E-mail:

Fixing Point Ltd, Runnings Road, Kingsditch Trading Estate, Cheltenham, Gloucestershire, GL51 9NQ Tel: (01242) 265100 Fax: (01242) 236155 E-mail: sales@fixing.point.co.uk

The Fixings Co. Ltd, Fixings House, 658 Oldham Road, Failsworth, Manchester, M35 9DU Tel: 0161-682 7822 Fax: 0161-682 7099

Fixings & Power Tool Center, Brighton Road, Salfords, Redhill, RH1 5EQ Tel: (01293) 820088 Fax: (01293) 820099

Fixmart Services, 80 A The Brent, Dartford, DA1 1YW Tel: (01322) 274226 Fax: (01322) 278178

Freeway Tools & Fixings, 14 Victoria Way, Burgess Hill, West Sussex, RH15 9NF Tel: (01444) 873000 Fax: (01444) 873001 E-mail: admin@freewayfixings.com

Friulsider UK Ltd, Unit 16 Court Farm Business Park, Bishops Frome, Worcester, WR6 5AY Tel: (01885) 490445 Fax: (01885) 490452 E-mail: sales@friulsider.co.uk

General Fixings Ltd, Unit 54 Beeches Industrial Estate, Waverley Road, Yate, Bristol, BS37 5QR Tel: (01454) 310015 Fax: (01454) 273164 E-mail: sales@generalfixings.co.uk

H T C Fastenings Ltd, Lyon Way, Hatfield Road, St. Albans, Hertfordshire, AL4 0LR Tel: (01727) 832131 Fax: (01727) 843234 E-mail: info@hertstools.co.uk

Halfen Ltd, 31 Humphrys Road, Woodside Estate, Dunstable, Bedfordshire, LU5 4TP Tel: (01582) 470300 Fax: (0870) 5316304 E-mail: sales@halfen.co.uk

Harlequin Fixings & Sealants Ltd, 23 East Main Street, Darvel, Ayrshire, KA17 0HR Tel: (01560) 323832 Fax: (01560) 320361

Helifix Ltd, 21 Warple Way, London, W3 0RX Tel: (020) 8735 5200 Fax: (020) 8735 5201 E-mail: info@helifix.co.uk

Kernow Fixings, Manfield Way, Holmbush Industrial Estate, St. Austell, Cornwall, PL25 3HQ Tel: (01726) 624600 Fax: (01726) 624604

Liebig Bolts Ltd, Silica Road, Amington Industrial Estate, Tamworth, Staffordshire, B77 4DT Tel: (01827) 50547 Fax: (01827) 310524 E-mail: sales@liebigbolts.co.uk

Lindapter International, Brackenbeck Road, Bradford, West Yorkshire, BD7 2NF Tel: (01274) 521444 Fax: (01274) 521130 E-mail: enquiries@lindapter.com

Midland Fixing Services Ltd, Unit 20 Bordesley Trading Estate, Bordesley Green Road, Birmingham, B8 1BZ Tel: 0121-327 5713 Fax: 0121-328 1842

Monofix Ltd, 4 Premier Trading Estate, Dartmouth Middleway, Birmingham, B7 4AT Tel: 0121-359 2117 Fax: 0121-359 2187 E-mail: sales@monofix.co.uk

Pepcon Ltd, PO Box 272, Sunbury-on-Thames, Middlesex, TW16 6WB Tel: (01932) 788545 Fax: (01932) 788496 E-mail: sales@pepcon.org

Polycones Bolt Boxes Ltd, 9 Ashfold Avenue, Findon Valley, Worthing, West Sussex, BN14 0AP Tel: (01903) 526538 Fax: (01903) 526538

Porta Tool Fixings Ltd, Units 6-8, Brunel Road, Leigh-on-Sea, Essex, SS9 5JL Tel: (01702) 510080 Fax: (01702) 510030 E-mail: portatools@btconnect.com

Power Tool Supplies Ltd, 379 Kingsway, Hove, East Sussex, BN3 4QD Tel: (01273) 420111 Fax: (01273) 422313

Premier Fixings, Clarence Street, Aberdeen, AB11 5BH Tel: (01224) 585810 Fax: (01224) 575710

Quickfix, Arch 13 Bridgewater, Goswell Road, Windsor Castle, Windsor, Berkshire, SL4 1QY Tel: (01753) 840508 Fax: (01753) 831189 E-mail: fixings@quickfix.demon.co.uk

Ranger Fixings Ltd, 8 Central Business Park, Southcote Road, Bournemouth, BH1 3SJ Tel: (01202) 297125 Fax: (01202) 294087 E-mail: ranger.fixings@tiscali.co.uk

Rapierstar, Star Business Park, Buxton Road, Bosley, Macclesfield, Cheshire, SK11 0PS Tel: 0870 300 3313 Fax: 0870 300 3314 E-mail: sih@rapierstar.com

Rawlplug Ltd, Skibo Drive, Thornliebank Industrial Estate, Thornliebank, Glasgow, G46 8JR Tel: 0141-638 7961 Fax: 0141-273 2333 E-mail: info@rawlplug.co.uk

Rex Crystal Fixings, Commercial St, Wakefield, West Yorkshire, WF1 5RN Tel: (01924) 374099 Fax: (01924) 370045 E-mail: sales@rexcrystal.co.uk

SFS Intec Ltd, 153 Kirkstall Road, Leeds, LS4 2AT Tel: 0113-208 5500 Fax: 0113-208 5519 E-mail: gb.leeds@sfsintec.biz

Simpson Strong-Tie International Inc, Cardinal Point, Winchester Road, Tamworth, Staffordshire, B78 3HG Tel: (01827) 255600 Fax: (01827) 255616 E-mail: swilkes@strongtie.com

Southwest Fasteners Ltd, Unit 7-8 306 Industrial Estate, 242-244 Broomhill Road, Bristol, BS4 5RG Tel: 0117-972 3242 Fax: 0117-971 7555 E-mail: southwestfastners@dial.pipex.com

Stainless Steel Fixings Ltd, 10 Charlwoods Road, East Grinstead, West Sussex, RH19 2HU Tel: (01342) 328608 Fax: (01342) 314861

Sterling Power Tools & Fixings, 103 Newland Road, Worthing, West Sussex, BN11 1LB Tel: (01903) 211543 Fax: (01903) 523066

T L M Construction Fasteners Ltd, 13 Davy Road, Astmoor Industrial Estate, Runcorn, Cheshire, WA7 1PZ Tel: (01928) 576193 Fax: (01928) 581308 E-mail: sales@tlmfasteners.co.uk

Tackburn Ltd, Unit 11A Imex Business Centre, Oxleason Road, East Moons Moat, Redditch, Worcestershire, B98 8LG Tel: (01527) 68559 Fax: (01527) 68559

Techfix Products Ltd, Unit 10 Two Woods Industrial Estate, Talbots Lane, Brierley Hill, West Midlands, DY5 2YX Tel: (01384) 77551 Fax: (01384) 77552 E-mail: sales@techfixproducts.com

Techmarkets Ltd, Fourth Avenue, Trafford Park, Manchester, M17 1DB Tel: 0161-876 4125 Fax: 0161-876 4146 E-mail: techmarkets@btconnect.com

Thames Fixings & Fasteners Ltd, Collett, Southmead Industrial Estate, Didcot, Oxfordshire, OX11 7TA Tel: (01235) 511711 Fax: (01235) 511710 E-mail: enquires@thamesfixings.co.uk

Three Counties Fixings Ltd, 6 Capital Place, Harlow, Essex, CM19 5AS Tel: (01279) 451631 Fax: (01279) 451617 E-mail: tcfltd@msn.com

Torque Control Ltd, 60 Alstone Lane, Cheltenham, Gloucestershire, GL51 8HE Tel: (01242) 261233 Fax: (01242) 221115 E-mail: torquecontrolltd@btinternet.com

Unifix Ltd, Bridge House, Grove Lane, Smethwick, West Midlands, B66 2QT Tel: 0121-609 0099 Fax: 0121-626 0587 E-mail: marketing@unifix.com

V J Technology Ltd, Technology House Cobbswood Industrial Estate, Brunswick Road, Ashford, Kent, TN23 1EN Tel: (01233) 637695 Fax: (01233) 664361

Wessex Fixings, Unit 60 South Way, Andover, Hampshire, SP10 5AF Tel: (01264) 332332 Fax: (01264) 332550

STRUCTURAL OR CONSTRUCTION STEEL PROTECTIVE COATINGS

Practical Compounds Ltd, West Side, Tyne Dock, South Shields, Tyne & Wear, NE34 9PL Tel: 0191-456 9191 Fax: 0191-454 5523 E-mail: practical.comp@btinternet.com

STRUCTURAL OR TO SPECIFICATION FABRICATING ENGINEERS

A & J Fab Tech Ltd, Walkley Works, Walkley Lane, Heckmondwike, West Yorkshire, WF16 0PH Tel: (01924) 402151 Fax: (01924) 412966

A S Allman Ltd, Newmarket Drive, Ascot Drive Indust Estate, Derby, DE24 8HT Tel: (01332) 753167 Fax: (01332) 296250

A V Birch Ltd, Aldenham Mill, Muckley Cross, Acton Round, Bridgnorth, Shropshire, WV16 4RR Tel: (01746) 714418 Fax: (01746) 714419 E-mail: enquiries@avbirch.co.uk

Action Group, Garston Business Park, Blackburne Street, Liverpool, L19 8JB Tel: 0151-427 1084 Fax: 0151-427 7130 E-mail: dkeen@theactiongroup.co.uk

Advanced Process Fabrications Ltd, Unit 19 Worton Hall Industrial Estate, Worton Road, Isleworth, Middlesex, TW7 6ER Tel: (020) 8568 2964 Fax: (020) 8569 7034

▶ Allott Steelwork Ltd, Worthing Road, Sheffield, S9 3JB Tel: 0114-276 6882 Fax: 0114-275 4922 E-mail: info@allottsteelwork.co.uk

Amman Valley Fabrication Ltd, Llandeilo Road, Llandybie, Ammanford, Dyfed, SA18 3JG Tel: (01269) 851266 Fax: (01269) 851340

Arcrite Fabrications, Fleming Road, Corby, Northamptonshire, NN17 4SW Tel: (01536) 204969 Fax: (01536) 402456 E-mail: email@genbridge.fsnet.co.uk

▶ indicates data change since last edition

STRUCTURAL OR TO SPECIFICATION FABRICATING ENGINEERS – *continued*

Ashington Fabrication Co. Ltd, Ennerdale Road, Kitty Brewster Industrial Estate, Blyth, Northumberland, NE24 4RD Tel: (01670) 365666 Fax: (01670) 364466 E-mail: enquiries@afc-ltd.com

B & K Steelwork Fabrications Ltd, High Edge Court, Church Street, Heage, Belper, Derbyshire, DE56 2BW Tel: (01773) 853400 Fax: (01773) 857389 E-mail: bksf@bksf.prestel.co.uk

Babcock Scientific Services, Rosyth Dockyard, Rosyth, Dunfermline, Fife, KY11 2YD Tel: (01383) 412131 Fax: (01383) 422699 E-mail: bs-info@babcock.co.uk

Baldwin & Wiser Ltd, Urban Road, Kirkby-in-Ashfield, Nottingham, NG17 8AP Tel: (01623) 754982 Fax: (01623) 754983

Benruss Fabrications Ltd, 10 Derby Road, Bootle, Merseyside, L20 8LN Tel: 0151-922 5478 Fax: 0151-922 7835

Blaker Specialised Welding Repairs Ltd, Worthing Road, Dial Post, Horsham, West Sussex, RH13 8NJ Tel: (01403) 710333 Fax: (01403) 711234 E-mail: simon@blaker.co.uk

Boar Engineering Ltd, 39a Barking Industrial Park, Alfreds Way, Barking, Essex, IG11 0TJ Tel: (020) 8594 0526 Fax: (020) 8507 8050 E-mail: boareng@aol.com

C Hargreaves, Stockfield Mill, Melbourne Street, Chadderton, Oldham, OL9 9ES Tel: 0161-633 5330 Fax: 0161-633 5330

C & S Fabrications Ltd, Club Mill Road, Sheffield, S6 2FH Tel: 0114-234 7567 Fax: 0114-231 4513 E-mail: postmaster@scfabs.co.uk

C T Farr, Timothys Bridge Road, Stratford-upon-Avon, Warwickshire, CV37 9NQ Tel: (01789) 267161 Fax: (01789) 415719

Caldicot Engineering Ltd, Sudbrook Shipyard, Sudbrook, Caldicot, Gwent, NP26 5SY Tel: (01291) 421452 Fax: (01291) 422965

J.S. Chinn Engineering Co. Ltd, Faraday Road, Harrowbrook Industrial Estate, Hinckley, Leicestershire, LE10 3DE Tel: (01455) 238333 Fax: (01455) 890585 E-mail: enquiries@jschinn.com

Clifton Partners Co. Ltd, 18a Shaw Road, Newhey, Rochdale, Lancashire, OL16 4LT Tel: (01706) 848224 Fax: (01706) 881441 E-mail: clifton.partners@jtemail.co.uk

Crossley Charles & Son Ltd, 9-11 Astley Street, Stockport, Cheshire, SK4 1AW Tel: 0161-480 2858 Fax: 0161-429 7353 E-mail: mail@charlescrossley.com

Delron Services Ltd, Carlton House, Hall Road, Aylesford, Kent, ME20 7HR Tel: (01622) 790111 Fax: (01622) 792170

Delta, 15 Brook Road, Kimbolton, Huntingdon, Cambridgeshire, PE28 0LR Tel: (01480) 861154 Fax: (01480) 861134 E-mail: info@deltafabrications.com

Demarchi Engineering, Vincients Road, Bumpers Farm, Chippenham, Wiltshire, SN14 6NQ Tel: (01249) 448860 Fax: (01249) 445496 E-mail: sales@demarchi.co.uk

Denormo Technics Ltd, 8 Teal Business Pk, Dudwell Bridge, Hinckley, Leics, LE10 3BZ Tel: (01455) 250153 Fax: (01455) 617061

Alan Dick Engineering Ltd, Middleton Road, Heysham, Morecambe, Lancashire, LA3 2SE Tel: (01524) 855011 Fax: (01524) 859158 E-mail: adeheysham@btclick.com

Echo Engineering Southern Ltd, Chapel Land Farm, Ashford Road, New Romney, Kent, TN28 8TH Tel: (01797) 367670 Fax: (01797) 367671 E-mail: sales@echo-eng.com

Elmpark Engineering Services Ltd, Washington Street Industrial Estate, Halesowen Road, Dudley, West Midlands, DY2 9RE Tel: (01384) 239301 Fax: (01384) 457378 E-mail: anything@elmparkeng.co.uk

Fabweld New Mills Ltd, 5 Canal Foundry, Albion Road, New Mills, High Peak, Derbyshire, SK22 3EZ Tel: (01663) 746156 Fax: (01663) 747960 E-mail: fabweld@ntlworld.com

Fredan Engineering Ltd, London Road, Little Irchester, Wellingborough, Northamptonshire, NN8 2EA Tel: (01933) 440135 Fax: (01933) 273490

Gainsthorpe Furniture Ltd, Unit 5 Cromwell Centre, Roebuck Road, Ilford, Essex, IG6 3UG Tel: (020) 8501 3712 Fax: (020) 8501 5448 E-mail: info@gainsthorpe.co.uk

Gordon S Davidson, The Smiddy, Tyrie, Fraserburgh, Aberdeenshire, AB43 7BX Tel: (01346) 541270 Fax: (01346) 541270

Howells Group plc, Longley Lane, Sharston Industrial Area, Manchester, M22 4SS Tel: 0161-945 5567 Fax: 0161-945 5597 E-mail: j.dolan@howells-railway.co.uk

I E P Gardening Products, Unit 3 Budds Lane, Romsey, Hampshire, SO51 0HA Tel: (01794) 830899 Fax: (01794) 830923 E-mail: iepgp@btinternet.com

J J Engineering, Rowleys Green Lane, Longford, Coventry, CV6 6AL Tel: (024) 7668 2492 Fax: (024) 7668 2492

J Johnstone Engineering Ltd, 86 Skinburness Road, Silloth, Wigton, Cumbria, CA7 4QH Tel: (01697) 332399 Fax: (01697) 332579

K A D Metal Work Ltd, Studio 101, 7-10 Riverside Yard, London, SW17 0BB Tel: (020) 8946 2429 Fax: (020) 8946 0684 E-mail: info@kadmetalworks.co.uk

L E S Engineering Ltd, Armstrong Street, Grimsby, South Humberside, DN31 1XD Tel: (01472) 320200 Fax: (01472) 345337 E-mail: info@les-engineering.co.uk

Lam-art Dundee Ltd, 122 Liff Road, Dundee, DD2 2TL Tel: (01382) 612222 Fax: (01382) 612233 E-mail: lamartdundee@btopenworld.com

Levenbridge Engineering Ltd, 50 Perry Avenue, Teesside Industrial Estate, Thornaby, Stockton-on-Tees, Cleveland, TS17 9LN Tel: (01642) 750456 Fax: (01642) 750567 E-mail: enquiries@levenbridge.com

Longhope Welding Engineers, Church Road, Longhope, Gloucestershire, GL17 0LA Tel: (01452) 830572 Fax: (01452) 830983

M K W Engineering Ltd, Stargate Industrial Estate, Ryton, Tyne & Wear, NE40 3EX Tel: 0191-413 0000 Fax: 0191-413 2736 E-mail: sales@mkw.co.uk

M Tech Engineering, Plot 16 Tufthorn Industrial Estate, Stepbridge Road, Coleford, Gloucestershire, GL16 8PJ Tel: (01594) 837172 Fax: (01594) 832999

Macdonald Fabrication, Unit 2 Glebe Industrial Estate, Douglas, Lanark, ML11 0RH Tel: (01555) 851948 Fax: (01555) 851174

Motherwell Bridge (Holdings) Ltd, PO Box 4, Motherwell, Lanarkshire, ML1 3NP Tel: (01698) 266111 Fax: (01698) 269774 E-mail: info@mbgroup.com

Mudd Farm Equipment, Park View, Marthwaite, Sedbergh, Cumbria, LA10 5HS Tel: (01539) 620704 Fax: (01539) 621573

Nelsons Birstall Ltd, Perseverance Works, Gelderd Road, Batley, West Yorkshire, WF17 9PX Tel: (01924) 474981 Fax: (01924) 440871 E-mail: sales@nelsonseng.co.uk

Nicholson G Engineers Ltd, Blue House Lane, Washington, Tyne & Wear, NE37 2TD Tel: 0191-416 2041 Fax: 0191-415 5139

P Stratford Engineering, 4 Russell Gardens, Wickford, Essex, SS11 8QG Tel: (01268) 769844 Fax: (01268) 769844

Peter Hope Metals Ltd, 2 Grange Road Business Park, Grange Road, Batley, West Yorkshire, WF17 6LL Tel: (01924) 440055 Fax: (01924) 442200E-mail: peterhope.metalsltd@virgin.net

Plymol Tubes Ltd, 6 Ravells Yard, Carr Lane, Hoylake, Wirral, Merseyside, CH47 4AZ Tel: 0151-632 1354 Fax: 0151-632 4912 E-mail: sales@flagstaffs.co.uk

Pollards Engineering, Mundy Street, Ilkeston, Derbyshire, DE7 8EU Tel: 0115-932 4787 Fax: 0115-930 3559 E-mail: info@pollardengineering.com

Power Precision & Fabrication Ltd, Greenhill Works, Delaware Road, Gunnislake, Cornwall, PL18 9AS Tel: (01822) 832608 Fax: (01822) 834796

R H Mawson Engineers Ltd, Avenue D Thorp Arch Trading Estate, Thorp Arch, Wetherby, West Yorkshire, LS23 7BJ Tel: (01937) 845333 Fax: (01937) 843768

Rally Industrial Services Ltd, Beacon Works, Bilston Street, Dudley, West Midlands, DY3 1JE Tel: (01902) 884341 Fax: (01902) 880333

Riber Engineering Ltd, Brindley Way, Speedwell Industrial Estate, Staveley, Chesterfield, Derbyshire, S43 3JF Tel: (01246) 471244 Fax: (01246) 471233 E-mail: ribereng@aol.com

Roach Manufacturing Ltd, Off Whitemoor Lane, Ower, Romsey, Hampshire, SO51 6AJ Tel: (023) 8081 4287 Fax: (023) 8081 3970

Sharand Ltd, Churnetside Business Park, Station Road, Cheddleton, Leek, Staffordshire, ST13 7EE Tel: (01538) 360178 Fax: (01538) 360111

Sharples & Yates, Chorley Road, Westhoughton, Bolton, BL5 3PJ Tel: (01942) 815942 Fax: (01942) 815942

George Shaw Engineering (Sheffield) 1994 Ltd, Carlisle Street East, Sheffield, S4 7QN Tel: 0114-276 7011 Fax: 0114-270 0365 E-mail: peter@shaweng.fsnet.co.uk

Shilldown Ltd, 16g Chalwyn Industrial Estate, Old Wareham Road, Poole, Dorset, BH12 4PE Tel: (01202) 722711 Fax: (01202) 722711

Speed Engineering, Station Yard, Broome, Aston-on-Clun, Craven Arms, Shropshire, SY7 0NT Tel: (01588) 660427 Fax: (01588) 660771

Steel Technic Ltd, Mells, Frome, Somerset, BA11 3RH Tel: (01373) 813323 Fax: (01373) 813325

Straight Line Services Ltd, Westwood Farm, Highcross Road, Southfleet, Gravesend, Kent, DA13 9PH Tel: (01474) 832244 Fax: (01474) 834414

Strand Engineering North West Ltd, Ironworks Road, Barrow-in-Furness, Cumbria, LA14 2PH Tel: (01229) 821991 Fax: (01229) 811104 E-mail: strandeng@yahoo.co.uk

Swinton Fabrications Ltd, Unit 10 Cliffton Units, Rake Lane, Manchester, M27 8LJ Tel: 0161-793 9969

T M R, Canal Street, Brierley Hill, West Midlands, DY5 1JJ Tel: (01384) 75531 Fax: (01384) 573353 E-mail: sales@tmrracking.com

Test Valley Engineers Ltd, Stoneymarsh, Michelmersh, Romsey, Hampshire, SO51 0LB Tel: (01794) 368308 Fax: (01794) 368693 E-mail: sales@test-valley.co.uk

Timac, Unit 8 Stratton Business Park, Edworth, Biggleswade, Bedfordshire, SG18 8QB Tel: (01767) 312849 Fax: (01767) 601388 E-mail: timac.engineering@freenet.co.uk

Trafalgar Fabrications Co., Canon House, Harvest Lane, Sheffield, S3 8EF Tel: 0114-275 2521 Fax: 0114-275 2521

Underhill Building Services, Valley Road, Plymouth, PL7 1RF Tel: (01752) 283280 Fax: (01752) 344410

W I G Engineering Ltd, Barnfield, Chesterton, Bicester, Oxfordshire, OX26 1TE Tel: (01869) 320515 Fax: (01869) 320513 E-mail: wig@oxford38.fsnet.co.uk

Wallace Sheetmetal & Fabrication Ltd, Old Jam Works Lane, Station Road, Wigton, Cumbria, CA7 9AX Tel: (01697) 342918 Fax: (01697) 344617E-mail: mail@wallacesheetmetal.co.uk

Waverley Engineering Ltd, Waverley Street, Coatbridge, Lanarkshire, ML5 2BE Tel: (01236) 429099 Fax: (01236) 602710 E-mail: sales@waverleyfabs.co.uk

Winstanley & Co. Ltd, Racecourse Road, Pershore, Worcestershire, WR10 2DG Tel: (01386) 552278 Fax: (01386) 556531 E-mail: winstanleyco@compuserve.com

Yorkshire design Fabrications Ltd, Unit B Cleres Mount Works, Clere Mount Road, Halifax, West Yorkshire, HX3 6AUU Tel: (01422) 345396 Fax: (01422) 349593 E-mail: www.ydfltd@btconnect.com

STRUCTURAL ROOF DECKING

Conder Structures Ltd, Wellington Road, Burton-on-Trent, Staffordshire, DE14 2AA Tel: (01283) 545377 Fax: (01283) 530483 E-mail: sales@conderstructures.co.uk

STRUCTURAL SEALANT CONTRACTORS

Hookings Mastics Ltd, Unit B11 Suttons Business Park, New Road, Rainham, Essex, RM13 8DE Tel: (01708) 522090 Fax: (01708) 526147 E-mail: ken@hookingsmastics.com

Sealtite Sealants Ltd, 66 Woodbrooke Way, Corringham, Stanford-le-Hope, Essex, SS17 9DW Tel: (01375) 641607 Fax: (01375) 361283

Universal Sealants UK Ltd, Kingston House, Pattinson North, Washington, Tyne & Wear, NE38 8QA Tel: 0191-416 1530 Fax: 0191-415 4377 E-mail: info@usluk.com

STRUCTURAL SEALANTS

Adshead Ratcliffe, Derby Road, Belper, Derbyshire, DE56 1WJ Tel: (01773) 596300 Fax: (01773) 821215 E-mail: admin@arbo.co.uk

Building Adhesives Ltd, Longton Road, Stoke-on-Trent, ST4 8JB Tel: (01782) 591100 Fax: (01782) 591101 E-mail: info@building-adhesives.com

Tremco Illbruck Production Ltd, 393 Edinburgh Avenue, Slough, SL1 4UF Tel: (01753) 691696 Fax: (01753) 822640

Winn & Coales Denso Ltd, Denso House, 33-35 Chapel Road, London, SE27 0TR Tel: (020) 8670 7511 Fax: (020) 8761 2456 E-mail: mail@denso.net

STRUCTURAL SEALING EXPANSION JOINT CONTRACTORS

Maurer (UK) Ltd, Unit 4 Field End, Crendon Industrial Estate, Aylesbury, Buckinghamshire, HP18 9EJ Tel: (01844) 201481 Fax: (01844) 201355 E-mail: sjb@maurer.co.uk

▶ Route One Highways Ltd, Suite 3, 14 Rishworth Street, Wakefield, West Yorkshire, WF1 3BY Tel: (01924) 381970 Fax: (01924) 381971E-mail: gary@routeonehighways.co.uk

STRUCTURAL SPORTS HALL FABRICATORS

Bicester Products Squash Court Manufacturers Ltd, 55 West End, Witney, Oxfordshire, OX28 1NJ Tel: (01993) 774426 Fax: (01993) 779569 E-mail: sales@squashcourts.co.uk

STRUCTURAL STEEL FABRICATING EQUIPMENT

Allen Fabrications Ltd, Davies Road, Four Pools Industrial Estate, Evesham, Worcestershire, WR11 1DR Tel: (01386) 47277 Fax: (01386) 765450 E-mail: info@allenfabs.co.uk

▶ Jes Ltd, Phoenix Wharf, The Docks, Port Talbot, West Glamorgan, SA13 1RA Tel: (01639) 898166 Fax: (01639) 899454

James Killelea & Co. Ltd, Stoneholme Road, Crawshawbooth, Rossendale, Lancashire, BB4 8BA Tel: (01706) 229411 Fax: (01706) 228388 E-mail: info@killelea.co.uk

Press & Shear Machinery Ltd, 12/14 Ninian Park Ninian Way, Wilnecote, Tamworth, Staffordshire, B77 5ES Tel: (01827) 250000 Fax: (01827) 250022 E-mail: sales@pressandshear.com

Rishton Welding Co. Ltd, Heys Lane, Great Harwood, Blackburn, BB6 7UA Tel: (01254) 886361 Fax: (01254) 888530 E-mail: mrpilling@btconnect.com

Steeltek, Serpentine Works, Serpentine Road, Cleckheaton, West Yorkshire, BD19 3HU Tel: (01274) 852131 Fax: (01274) 851486

STRUCTURAL STEEL SUPPORT SYSTEMS

Ash & Lacy Building Systems, Bromford Lane, West Bromwich, West Midlands, B70 7JJ Tel: 0121-525 1444 Fax: 0121-524 8435 E-mail: kay.hall@ashandlacy.com

STRUCTURAL STEEL SYSTEMS

Mifflin Construction Ltd, Worcester Road, Leominster, Herefordshire, HR6 8AY Tel: (01568) 613311 Fax: (01568) 614935 E-mail: sales@mifflin.co.uk

STRUCTURAL STEELWORK DESIGN

Rees Engineering Services Ltd, 401-403 Rayleigh Road, Benfleet, Essex, SS7 3ST Tel: (01268) 778274 Fax: (01268) 745204 E-mail: reception@reesteel.com

STRUCTURAL STEELWORK DRAFTING SERVICES

▶ Inmac Engineering, 13-15 Parc Erissey Industrial Estate, New Portreath Road, Redruth, Cornwall, TR16 4HZ Tel: (01209) 313088 Fax: (01209) 313099 E-mail: admin@inmac-pl3.co.uk

STRUCTURAL STEELWORK ENGINEERS OR ERECTORS OR FABRICATORS OR FIXERS

A B G Fabrications, Old Tin Plate Works, Old Tin Works Road, Pontypridd, Mid Glamorgan, CF37 1UD Tel: (01443) 402085 Fax: (01443) 491664

A C Bacon Engineering Ltd, Norwich Road, Hingham, Norwich, NR9 4LS Tel: (01953) 850611 Fax: (01953) 851445 E-mail: steel@acbacon.co.uk

A & J Stead Ltd, 31 Derwent Road, York Road Business Park, Malton, North Yorkshire, YO17 6YB Tel: (01653) 693742 Fax: (01653) 691594 E-mail: admin@steadandson.co.uk

Adstone Construction, Wassage Way, Hampton Lovett, Droitwich, Worcestershire, WR9 0NX Tel: (01905) 794561 Fax: (01905) 794040 E-mail: mail@adstone.org.uk

Algo Business Centre, Glenearn Road, Perth, PH2 0NJ Tel: (01738) 450450 Fax: (01738) 450460 E-mail: pa@algo.co.uk

Allott Bros & Leigh Ltd, Fullerton Road, The Ickles, Rotherham, South Yorkshire, S60 1DJ Tel: (01709) 364115 Fax: (01709) 364696 E-mail: reception@uwilperengineering.com

▶ Allott Steelwork Ltd, Worthing Road, Sheffield, S9 3JB Tel: 0114-276 6882 Fax: 0114-275 4922 E-mail: info@allottsteelwork.co.uk

Ashington Fabrication Co. Ltd, Ennerdale Road, Kitty Brewster Industrial Estate, Blyth, Northumberland, NE24 4RD Tel: (01670) 365666 Fax: (01670) 364466 E-mail: enquiries@afc-ltd.com

Atd Fabrications, Unit D Bromcliffe Park, Barnsley, South Yorkshire, S71 5RN Tel: (01226) 718400 Fax: (01226) 718411

Atlantic Engineering UK Ltd, Depot Road, Middlesbrough, Cleveland, TS2 1LE Tel: (01642) 248525 Fax: (01642) 221950 E-mail: enquire@atlanticeng.co.uk

Atlasco Constructional Engineers Ltd, Rowhurst Close, Rowhurst Industrial Estate, Newcastle, Staffordshire, ST5 6BD Tel: (01782) 564711 Fax: (01782) 564591 E-mail: atlasco@steelweb.co.uk

B C Dyson & Co., Prescott Lodge, Prescott Street, Halifax, West Yorkshire, HX1 2QW Tel: (01422) 360934 Fax: (01422) 320379 E-mail: b.c.dyson@bt.openworld.com

B & R Fabrication, 3g Lyncastle Way, Barley Castle Lane, Appleton, Warrington, WA4 4ST Tel: (01925) 601728 Fax: (01925) 602261 E-mail: brfabrications@lineone.net

Barnes Steel Fabrications, 3 Brooklyn Farm, North Hill, Horndon-on-the-Hill, Stanford-le-Hope, Essex, SS17 8QA Tel: (01375) 644048 Fax: (01375) 644049

Barrier Offshore Engineering Ltd, Joyce Buildings, Haverton Hill Industrial Estate, Billingham, Cleveland, TS23 1PZ Tel: (01642) 565202 Fax: (01642) 563061

BCP Fabrication Ltd, Dormston Trading Estate, Burton Road, Dudley, West Midlands, DY1 2UF Tel: (01902) 885777 Fax: (01902) 883344

Becro Engineering Services Ltd, 117 Brooker Road, Waltham Abbey, Essex, EN9 1JH Tel: (01992) 713045 Fax: (01992) 700157 E-mail: admin@becro.co.uk

Bennett & Skelland Ltd, 306 Liverpool Road, Warrington, WA5 1DP Tel: (01925) 634066 Fax: (01925) 445505 E-mail: bennettandskelland@tiscali.co.uk

Billington Structures Ltd, Barnsley Road, Wombwell, Barnsley, South Yorkshire, S73 8DS Tel: (01226) 340666 Fax: (01226) 755947 E-mail: sales@billington-structures.co.uk

STRUCTURAL STEELWORK ENGINEERS OR ERECTORS OR FABRICATORS OR FIXERS – *continued*

Birtley Construction North East, West Line Industrial Estate Station Lane, Birtley, Ouston, Chester le Street, County Durham, DH2 1ZZ Tel: 0191-410 2707 Fax: 0191-492 0583

Blitz Communications Ltd, Unit 100 Centennial Park, Centennial Avenue, Elstree, Borehamwood, Hertfordshire, WD6 3SA Tel: (0870) 1621000 Fax: (0870) 1621111 E-mail: enquiries@blitzvision.com

Blueline Buildings, Rowms Lane, Swinton, Mexborough, South Yorkshire, S64 8AA Tel: (01709) 578333 Fax: (01709) 578444 E-mail: sales@bluelinebuildings.com

Bourne Steel Ltd, St. Clements House, St. Clements Road, Poole, Dorset, BH12 4GP Tel: (01202) 746666 Fax: (01202) 732002 E-mail: sales@bourne-steel.demon.co.uk

T.M. Brooks Ltd, Unit 4, Dawley Estate, Stallings Lane, Kingswinford, West Midlands, DY6 7AP Tel: (01384) 400777 Fax: (01384) 400167 E-mail: office@tmbrooks.co.uk

C M D Ltd, Flixborough Industrial Estate, Ninth Avenue, Flixborough, Scunthorpe, South Humberside, DN15 8SL Tel: (01724) 851873 Fax: (01724) 874411 E-mail: cm.developments@virgin.net

Cairnhill Structures Ltd, Watson Towers, Waverley St, Coatbridge, Lanarkshire, ML5 2BE Tel: (01236) 449393 Fax: (01236) 449334 E-mail: enquiries@cairnhillstructures.co.uk

Caldicot Engineering Ltd, Sudbrook Shipyard, Sudbrook, Caldicot, Gwent, NP26 5SY Tel: (01291) 421452 Fax: (01291) 422965

Caldwell Metalwork Fabrication, Units 10-11 Shaftsbury Industrial Estate, Icknield Way, Letchworth Garden City, Hertfordshire, SG6 1HE Tel: (01462) 670505 Fax: (01462) 670500

Capital Structures plc, 6 Blackstone Road, Stukeley Meadows Industrial Es, Huntingdon, Cambridgeshire, PE29 6EF Tel: (01480) 431188 Fax: (01480) 434210 E-mail: info@capital-structures.com

Caunton Engineering Ltd, Moorgreen Industrial Park, Engine Lane, Newthorpe, Nottingham, NG16 3QU Tel: (01773) 531111 Fax: (01773) 532020 E-mail: sales@caunton.co.uk

Centristic Ltd, 1 Cavalier Road, Heathfield Industrial Estate, Newton Abbot, Devon, TQ12 6TQ Tel: (01626) 834310 Fax: (01626) 834681 E-mail: centristic@btconnect.com

Cherrymill Ltd, 23 Hoylake Road, Scunthorpe, South Humberside, DN17 2AZ Tel: (01724) 867244 Fax: (01724) 858509 E-mail: cherrymill.co.uk@amserve.net

Chris Hodgson Engineering Ltd, Seven Acres, Hollocombe, Chulmleigh, Devon, EX18 7QH Tel: (01769) 520422 Fax: (01769) 520544

Churngold Construction Ltd, St. Andrews House, St. Andrews Road, Avonmouth, Bristol, BS11 9DQ Tel: 0117-900 7100 Fax: 0117-900 7111 E-mail: construction@churngold.co.uk

Clydeforth Engineers & Contractors Ltd, Barclay Curle Complex, 739 South Street, Glasgow, G14 0BX Tel: 0141-958 0628 Fax: 0141-959 0912 E-mail: louise@clydeforth.fsnet.co.uk

Conder Structures Ltd, Wellington Road, Burton-on-Trent, Staffordshire, DE14 2AA Tel: (01283) 545377 Fax: (01283) 530483 E-mail: sales@conderstructures.co.uk

Corfix Structures Ltd, No 3 Hoobrook Industrial Estate, Kidderminster, Worcestershire, DY10 1HY Tel: (01562) 60226 Fax: (01562) 60227

Costello London Ltd, Unit 8, 274 Queenstown Road, Battersea, London, SW8 4LP Tel: (020) 7720 4779 Fax: (020) 7498 7388

Cringate Engineering Ltd, 31-51 Blundell Street, Liverpool, L1 0AJ Tel: 0151-708 6082 Fax: 0151-708 5612 E-mail: cringate.eng.ltd@btconnect.com

Cumbrian Implement Co. Ltd, 4 King Street, Aspatria, Wigton, Cumbria, CA7 3ET Tel: (01697) 320269 Fax: (01697) 322677 E-mail: newdale@btconnect.com

D A Green & Sons Ltd, High Road, Whaplode, Spalding, Lincolnshire, PE12 6TL Tel: (01406) 370585 Fax: (01406) 370766 E-mail: sales@dagreen.co.uk

▶ D H Structures Ltd, Tollgate Drive, Tollgate Industrial Estate, Stafford, ST16 3HS Tel: (01785) 246269 Fax: (01785) 222077 E-mail: enquiries@dhstructures.co.uk

D & R Structures Ltd, 7 Lidsey Road, Woodgate, Chichester, West Sussex, PO20 3SU Tel: (01243) 544838 Fax: (01243) 544840

Denvic Ltd, Greenhill Industrial Estate, Kidderminster, Worcestershire, DY10 2RN Tel: (01562) 755274 Fax: (01562) 755274 E-mail: denvic@btconnect.com

Down & Francis Industrial Products Ltd, Ardath Road, Kings Norton, Birmingham, B38 9PN Tel: 0121-433 3300 Fax: 0121-433 3325 E-mail: reception@downandfrancis.co.uk

E K W Fabrications Ltd, Coppice Side Industrial Estate, West Coppice Road, Walsall, WS8 7HB Tel: (01543) 378181 Fax: (01543) 361012

E & P Engineering Services, 16 St Nicholas Road, Littlestone, New Romney, Kent, TN28 8PT Tel: (01797) 366724

E S Hadley, Foundry Yard, Hall Lane, Walton on the Naze, Essex, CO14 8HW Tel: (01255) 679913 Fax: (01255) 850932 E-mail: efhadleyeng@aol.com

▶ Elland Steel Structures Ltd, Philmar House, Gibbet Street, Halifax, West Yorkshire, HX2 0AR Tel: (01422) 380262 Fax: (01422) 380263 E-mail: sales@ellandsteel.com

Elliott & Wragg Ltd, Elliott & Wragg, Buxton Road, Tideswell, Buxton, Derbyshire, SK17 8PQ Tel: (01298) 871582 Fax: (01298) 871785

Engineering Systems Ltd, Lifford Way, Binley Industrial Estate, Binley Industrial Estate, Coventry, CV3 2RN Tel: (024) 7645 7555 Fax: (024) 7645 7888 E-mail: engsysltd@tiscali.co.uk

Esmanco Engineering Ltd, Hadfield Industrial Estate, Waterside, Hadfield, Glossop, Derbyshire, SK13 1BS Tel: (01457) 861673 Fax: (01457) 864044 E-mail: esmanco@btconnect.com

Evadx Ltd, Tir Llwyd Enterprise Park, Kinmel Bay, Rhyl, Clwyd, LL18 5JZ Tel: (01745) 336413 Fax: (01745) 339639 E-mail: sales@evadx.com

F J Booth & Partners Ltd, Dockside Road, Middlesbrough, Cleveland, TS3 8AT Tel: (01642) 241581 Fax: (01642) 223398 E-mail: enquiries@boothandpartners.co.uk

Fisher Engineering Ltd, Main Street, Ballinamallard, Enniskillen, County Fermanagh, BT94 2FY Tel: (028) 6638 8521 Fax: (028) 6638 8706 E-mail: info@fisher-engineering.co.uk

Folbigg Fabrications, Ramsden Road, Rotherwas Industrial Estate, Hereford, HR2 6LR Tel: (01432) 271481 Fax: (01432) 268773 E-mail: folbigg@rotherwas.fsbusiness.co.uk

Forman Metal Products Ltd, Portrack Grange Road, Stockton-on-Tees, Cleveland, TS18 2PH Tel: (01642) 674314 Fax: (01642) 672899 E-mail: info@formanmetalproducts.co.uk

G B H Services Ltd, 17-18 Mercia Way, Bells Close Industrial Estate, Newcastle Upon Tyne, NE15 6UF Tel: 0191-229 0488 Fax: 0191-264 4095 E-mail: sales@gbhservices.co.uk

G & T Evans, Dulas Mill, Mochdre Lane, Newtown, Powys, SY16 4JD Tel: (01686) 622100 Fax: (01686) 622220 E-mail: sales@gtevans.co.uk

General Erections, 103 Woodville Road, Hartshorne, Swadlincote, Derbyshire, DE11 7EX Tel: (01283) 216669 Fax: (01283) 216669

Graham Wood, Chartwell Road, Lancing, West Sussex, BN15 8TY Tel: (01903) 755991 Fax: (01903) 755384 E-mail: mail@grahamwoodstructural.co.uk

Grays Engineering Contracts Ltd, Globe Industrial Estate, Rectory Road, Grays, Essex, RM17 6ST Tel: (01375) 372367 Fax: (01375) 375079 E-mail: grayseng@btopenworld.com

Helm Exhibitions Ltd, 27-29 Speedwell Road, Haymills, Birmingham, B25 8HU Tel: 0121-766 6755 Fax: 0121-766 6752 E-mail: enquiries@helmx.co.uk

H.C. Hill Ltd, PO Box 137, Beckenham, Kent, BR3 4WY Tel: (020) 8650 7890 Fax: (020) 8650 0535 E-mail: enquiries@hchill.co.uk

Hill & Webster Ltd, Ashbourne Indust Estate, Ashbourne, Derbyshire, DE6 1HD Tel: (01335) 343119 Fax: (01335) 346400 E-mail: hillwebster@compuserve.com

I C T S Ltd, Solent Road, Havant, Hampshire, PO9 1JH Tel: (023) 9249 9123 Fax: (023) 9249 9108 E-mail: sales@ictsltd.co.uk

Ironbridge Construction Ltd, Unit B6 Hortonwood 10, Telford, Shropshire, TF1 7ES Tel: (01952) 676555 Fax: (01952) 676567 E-mail: sales@ironbridgeconstruction.co.uk

Island Structural, Bowcombe Works, Bowcombe Road, Newport, Isle of Wight, PO30 3HZ Tel: (01983) 525070 Fax: (01983) 521632

J B Taylor Construction Ltd, Sycamore Farm, Holmefield Lane, Orby, Skegness, Lincolnshire, PE24 5JB Tel: (01754) 811406 Fax: (01754) 811300

J G Turnbull Ltd, Station Approach, East Boldon, Tyne & Wear, NE36 0AD Tel: 0191-536 2090 Fax: 0191-519 0218 E-mail: office@jgturnballltd.co.uk

J W Engineering Ltd, Barker Gate, Ilkeston, Derbyshire, DE7 8DS Tel: 0115-877 0444 Fax: 0115-877 0791 E-mail: steelwork@jwestructures.co.uk

James Brothers (Hamworthy) Ltd, 19 Blandford Road, Hamworthy, Poole, Dorset, BH15 4AW Tel: (01202) 673815 Fax: (01202) 684033 E-mail: inquiries@james-bros.co.uk

Jamieson-Macgregor Ltd, Kelliebank, Alloa, Clackmannanshire, FK10 1NU Tel: (01259) 722725 Fax: (01259) 217165 E-mail: admin@jmark.co.uk

JCC Engineering Ltd, 50 Adderley Street, Birmingham, B9 4ED Tel: 0121-773 6900 Fax: 0121-766 7760 E-mail: jccengineering@btconnect.com

Jenkins & Davies (Engineering) Ltd, Waterloo Industrial Estate, Pembroke Dock, Dyfed, SA72 6BS Tel: (01646) 685895 Fax: (01646) 621030 E-mail: stephensmedley@jenkinsanddavies.com

Jones Baker Engineering Co., Love Lane, London, N17 8HG Tel: (020) 8808 8196 Fax: (020) 8365 0180

K Freeman Ltd, Westgate, North Newbald, South Newbald, York, YO43 4SN Tel: (01430) 827671 Fax: (01430) 827459 E-mail: kfreemanltd@aol.com

K & M Arrowsmith, 81 West Street, Alford, Lincolnshire, LN13 9HT Tel: (01507) 463258 Fax: (01507) 462312 E-mail: steve@kandmarrowsmith.fsnet.co.uk

Leicester Fabrications Ltd, Hazel Drive, Narborough Road South, Leicester, LE3 2JE Tel: 0116-289 8154 Fax: 0116-289 2768

Lemon Steel Services Ltd, Russell Gardens, Wickford, Essex, SS11 8BL Tel: (01268) 571666 Fax: (01268) 571555 E-mail: phil@lemonsteel.co.uk

Levenbridge Engineering Ltd, 50 Perry Avenue, Teesside Industrial Estate, Thornaby, Stockton-on-Tees, Cleveland, TS17 9LN Tel: (01642) 750456 Fax: (01642) 750567 E-mail: enquiries@levenbridge.com

Linkweld Engineering & Construction Ltd, 56 High Street, Edenbridge, Kent, TN8 5AJ Tel: (01732) 864376

Lockerbie & Wilkinson Engineering Ltd, Alexandra Works, Locarno Road, Tipton, West Midlands, DY4 9SD Tel: 0121-557 1861 Fax: 0121-557 4804 E-mail: locwiltipton@aol.com

Lockstore Ltd, Unit 11 Greetby Place, Eastgillybrans, Skelmersdale, Lancashire, WN8 9UL Tel: (01744) 885757 Fax: (01695) 51413

M A P Structual Steel Manufacturing, Cross Pipes Road, Alverthorpe, Wakefield, West Yorkshire, WF2 8BG Tel: (01924) 367447 Fax: (01924) 366593 E-mail: info@mapss.com

M Hasson & Sons Ltd, 17 Glebe Road, Rasharkin, Ballymena, County Antrim, BT44 8SS Tel: (028) 2957 1281 Fax: (028) 2957 1575 E-mail: sales@hassons.com

Maldon Marine Ltd, 16 West Station Yard, Spital Road, Maldon, Essex, CM9 6TW Tel: (01621) 859000 Fax: (01621) 858935 E-mail: info@maldon-marine.co.uk

Manorway Fabrications Ltd, 9 Parsons Road, Manor Trading Estate, Benfleet, Essex, SS7 4PU Tel: (01268) 565565 Fax: (01268) 565761

Metalogics Sheet Metal Work, Whitehorse Industrial Estate, Bodmin Parkway, Bodmin, Cornwall, PL30 4BB Tel: (01208) 73696 Fax: (01208) 73696

Midland Erection Ltd, Roetan House, Thorns Road, Brierley Hill, West Midlands, DY5 2PF Tel: (01384) 424227 Fax: (01384) 424906 E-mail: miderect1@btconnect.com

Midland Structural Holdings Ltd, Herald Business Park, Golden Acres Lane, Coventry, CV3 2RT Tel: (024) 7644 5584 Fax: (024) 7645 9995 E-mail: steel@mss-ltd.com

P.J. Miller Ltd, The Old Baths, Main Road, Far Cotton, Northampton, NN4 8EN Tel: (01604) 767710 Fax: (01604) 764884

Modern Equipment & Foundry Engineering Ltd, 1 Dalton Lane, Keighley, West Yorkshire, BD21 4HW Tel: (01535) 605501 Fax: (01535) 602816

Monk Bridge Construction Co., B2 Airfield Industrial Estate, York Road, Elvington, York, YO41 4AR Tel: (01904) 608416 Fax: (01904) 608759

Multi Fab Construction Ltd, Lower Field, Stretford, Leominster, Herefordshire, HR6 9DQ Tel: (01568) 720330 Fax: (01568) 720115

Nemac Fabrications Ltd, 5 Staition Road Industrial Estate, Station Road, Reddish, Stockport, Cheshire, SK5 6ND Tel: 0161-432 1030 Fax: 0161-443 2096 E-mail: neil@nemac.co.uk

North West Construction Services Ltd, Bleasby Street, Oldham, OL4 2AJ Tel: 0161 6261816

Northend Construction, Maypole Crescent, Wallhouse Road, Erith, Kent, DA8 2JZ Tel: (01322) 333441 Fax: (01322) 333441

Nusteel Structures Ltd, Lympne Industrial Estate, Hythe, Kent, CT21 4LR Tel: (01303) 268112 Fax: (01303) 266098 E-mail: general@nusteelstructures.com

Ogilby Construction Ltd, 16 Endowood Road, Chesterfield, Derbyshire, S40 3LX Tel: (01246) 566082

On Site Services Gravesend Ltd, 1 Wharf Road, Gravesend, Kent, DA12 2RU Tel: (01474) 321552 Fax: (01474) 357778 E-mail: enquiries@onsiteservicesgravesend.co.uk

Oswestry Industrial Buildings Ltd, Maesbury Road, Oswestry, Shropshire, SY10 8HA Tel: (01691) 661596 Fax: (01691) 661597

P H Hardwill Ltd, Hurst Works, Blackdown, Beaminster, Dorset, DT8 3LE Tel: (01460) 30661 Fax: (01460) 30173

P James Fabrications Ltd, Dock Meadow Drive, Lanesfield, Wolverhampton, WV4 6LE Tel: (01902) 408818 Fax: (01902) 408818

Painter Bros Ltd, Holmer Road, Hereford, HR4 9SW Tel: (01432) 374400 Fax: (01432) 374427E-mail: enquiries@painterbrothers.com

Phoenix Erection Co. Ltd, 7 The Grove, Walton-on-Thames, Surrey, KT12 2HP Tel: (01932) 243074 Fax: (01932) 240743

M. Pickering (Scarborough) Ltd, 66 Londesborough Road, Scarborough, North Yorkshire, YO12 5AF Tel: (01723) 373852

Pinnacle Structures, Unit 7 Westwood Industrial Estate, Ewyas Harold, Hereford, HR2 0EL Tel: (01981) 241414 Fax: (01981) 241195 E-mail: mail@pinnaclestructures.co.uk

Prefab Steel Co. Ltd, 114 Brighton Road, Shoreham-by-Sea, West Sussex, BN43 6RH Tel: (01273) 597733 Fax: (01273) 597774 E-mail: prefabsteel@btinternet.com

Prentis Engineering, Prentis Quay, Sittingbourne, Kent, ME10 2QD Tel: 01795 477128

Profab Fabrications, Triton Works, Stringes Lane, Willenhall, West Midlands, WV13 1LD Tel: (01902) 633253 Fax: (01902) 633253

R Beal & Co. Ltd, Newtown Industrial Estate, Birtley, Chester le Street, County Durham, DH3 2QW Tel: 0191-492 0123 Fax: 0191-492 0567 E-mail: sales@bealandco.com

R J D Fabrications Ltd, Hellaby Industrial Estate, Hellaby Lane, Rotherham, South Yorkshire, S66 8HN Tel: (01709) 531951 Fax: (01709) 700252 E-mail: sales@rjd-eng.com

R S L South West Ltd, Unit 15 Millfield Industrial Estate, Chard, Somerset, TA20 2BB Tel: (01460) 67373 Fax: (01460) 61669 E-mail: sales@rslsouthwest.com

Reads Construction Ltd, 6 Speedwell Way, Harleston Industrial Estate, Harleston, Norfolk, IP20 9EH Tel: (01379) 853063 Fax: (01379) 853676 E-mail: readsconstruction@harleston.fsbusiness.co.uk

Red Alce, Spithurst, Barcombe, Lewes, East Sussex, BN8 5ED Tel: (01273) 400780 Fax: (01273) 400744 E-mail: redalce@ukbuilder.com

Rees Engineering Services Ltd, 401-403 Rayleigh Road, Benfleet, Essex, SS7 3ST Tel: (01268) 778274 Fax: (01268) 745204 E-mail: reception@reesteel.com

Riverside Engineering Services Ltd, Prince Charles Wharf, Stannergate Road, Dundee, DD1 3NA Tel: (01382) 450099 Fax: (01382) 450088 E-mail: enquiries@resl.co.uk

Ro Co Engineering Services, Unit 8 Sinclair Court, Great Yarmouth, Norfolk, NR31 0NH Tel: (01493) 602744 Fax: (01493) 658450

Roberts Engineering, Bergen Way, Hull, HU7 0YQ Tel: (01482) 838240 Fax: (01482) 830697 E-mail: admin@robertsengineering.co.uk

Roberts Welding Ltd, Readmans Industrial Estate, Station Road, East Tilbury, Tilbury, Essex, RM18 8QR Tel: (01375) 857736 Fax: (01375) 851280

Royden Engineering Ltd, Sandwash Close, Rainford Industrial Estate, Rainford, St. Helens, Merseyside, WA11 8LS Tel: (01744) 883636 Fax: (01744) 885730 E-mail: sbennett@royden.co.uk

S M K Engineering Ltd, 4 Old Foundry Estate, Victoria Street, Widnes, Cheshire, WA8 7UE Tel: 0151-423 2320 Fax: 0151-420 8201

Scorpion Engineering Construction Ltd, Brunel Court, Elcot Lane, Marlborough, Wiltshire, SN8 2AZ Tel: (01672) 514471 Fax: (01672) 518518 E-mail: sales@scorpionstructures.co.uk

SCS Structural Steel Ltd, Hotham Street, Hull, HU9 1RD Tel: (01482) 585599 Fax: (01482) 620100 E-mail: scs@scsfirm.co.uk

Selwyn Construction Engineering Ltd, Tarran Road, Tarran Industrial Estate, Wirral, Merseyside, CH46 4TU Tel: 0151-678 0236 Fax: 0151-678 8959 E-mail: enquiries@selwyngroup.co.uk

Senior Steel Ltd, Bamfurlong Industrial Park, Staverton, Cheltenham, Gloucestershire, GL51 6SX Tel: (01452) 712843 Fax: (01452) 856470 E-mail: sales@seniorsteel.co.uk

Severfield-Reeve International Ltd, Dalton Airfield Industrial Estate, Dalton, Thirsk, North Yorkshire, YO7 3JN Tel: (01845) 577896 Fax: (01845) 578508 E-mail: admin@severfield-reeve.co.uk

Sherborne Metal Masters, Ash Lane, Little London, Tadley, Hampshire, RG26 5EL Tel: (01256) 880096 Fax: (01256) 880096

Shipley Fabrications Ltd, Willoughby Road, Ancaster, Grantham, Lincolnshire, NG32 3RT Tel: (01400) 231115 Fax: (01400) 231220

Shufflebottom Ltd, Heol Parc Mawr, Cross Hands Industrial Estate, Cross Hands, Llanelli, Dyfed, SA14 6RE Tel: (01269) 831831 Fax: (01269) 831031 E-mail: sales@shufflebottom.co.uk

Smyth Steel Ltd, 15 Gorran Road, Garvagh, Coleraine, County Londonderry, BT51 4HA Tel: (028) 7086 8544 Fax: (028) 7086 8102 E-mail: mail@smyth-steel.co.uk

South Durham Structures Ltd, South Church Enterprise Park, Bishop Auckland, County Durham, DL14 6XR Tel: (01388) 777350 Fax: (01388) 775225 E-mail: name@southdurhamstructures.co.uk

South East Steel Fabrication & Engineering, Legge Street, London, SE13 6NP Tel: (020) 8690 6229 Fax: (020) 8690 6229

Spencer Construction & Engineering, Royal Albert Works, Bradfield Road, London, E16 2AT Tel: (020) 7511 1711 Fax: (020) 7474 2195

SSI Projects Ltd, 40 Dodington, Whitchurch, Shropshire, SY13 1EF Tel: (01948) 665331 Fax: (01948) 663001E-mail: cme@ssi.uk.com

Steel Options Ltd, Orion Business Centre, Surrey Canal Road, London, SE14 5RT Tel: (020) 7232 0293

Straits Construction, Bloomfield Road, Tipton, West Midlands, DY4 9ET Tel: 0121-557 8758 Fax: 0121-520 0435

Structures (Cordell) Ltd, Sotherby Road, Skippers Lane Industrial Estate, South Bank, Middlesbrough, Cleveland, TS6 6LP Tel: (01642) 452406 Fax: (01642) 464118 E-mail: structures@cordellgroup.com

T Good & Sons Ltd, 36 Vulcan Way, New Addington, Croydon, CR0 9UG Tel: (01689) 848211 Fax: (01689) 841069 E-mail: dave@tgood.co.uk

▶ T S I Structures Ltd, Ashgrove, Fakenham Road, Morton on the Hill, Norwich, NR9 5SP Tel: (01603) 870399 Fax: (01603) 871855

Tatham Steels Ltd, Duke Avenue, Stamley Green Industrial Estate, Cheadle Hulme, Cheadle, Cheshire, SK8 6QZ Tel: 0161-485 8535 Fax: 0161-485 7804 E-mail: tathem@bmsteel.co.uk

Thermal Energy Construction Ltd, Trent Lane, Castle Donington, Derby, DE74 2NP Tel: (01332) 810999 Fax: (01332) 855175 E-mail: info@thermalenergy.co.uk

STRUCTURAL STEELWORK ENGINEERS OR ERECTORS OR FABRICATORS OR FIXERS – *continued*

Vacuum Systems Ltd, Unit 11 Lexden Lodge Industrial Estate, Crowborough Hill, Crowborough, East Sussex, TN6 2NQ Tel: (01892) 665633 E-mail: krizek@vacsys.co.uk
W C Evans & Sons, Limes Avenue, London, SE20 8QR Tel: (020) 8676 0047 Fax: (020) 8676 8268 E-mail: wcevans.ltd@btinternet.com
W I G Engineering Ltd, Barnfield, Chesterton, Bicester, Oxfordshire, OX26 1TE Tel: (01869) 320515 Fax: (01869) 320513 E-mail: wig@oxford38.fsnet.co.uk
W M Codd Ltd, Marsh Lane, Barton-upon-Humber, South Humberside, DN18 5HB Tel: (01652) 632578 Fax: (01652) 660484
Waddington Buildings Ltd, Station Road, Brompton on Swale, Richmond, North Yorkshire, DL10 7SH Tel: (01748) 812323 Fax: (01748) 812145
Warley Construction Co. Ltd, Swinbourne Road, Burnt Mills Industrial Estate, Basildon, Essex, SS13 1LD Tel: (01268) 726020 Fax: (01268) 725285 E-mail: info@warleyconstruction.co.uk
Weldwork Ltd, Central Way, Feltham, Middlesex, TW14 0XJ Tel: (020) 8890 4141 Fax: (020) 8751 5793 E-mail: info@cmf.co.uk
Wickens Engineering Ltd, 1 Shire Business Park, Wainwright Road, Worcester, WR4 9FA Tel: (01905) 456780 Fax: (01905) 456073 E-mail: info@wickens.co.uk
Willis Engineering NI Ltd, 14 Silverwood Industrial Estate, Lurgan, Craigavon, County Armagh, BT66 6LN Tel: (028) 3834 8444 Fax: (028) 3831 6333
Winston Fabrications, Dale Road Trading Estate, Dale Road, Shildon, County Durham, DL4 2RE Tel: (01388) 777989 Fax: (01388) 776296 E-mail: anthony@winstonfabrications.co.uk

STRUCTURAL STEELWORK TO SPECIFICATION

Allott Bros & Leigh Ltd, Fullerton Road, The Ickles, Rotherham, South Yorkshire, S60 1DJ Tel: (01709) 364115 Fax: (01709) 364696 E-mail: reception@uwilperengineering.com
Arc Fabrication Ltd, 2 Gourley Place, London, N15 5NF Tel: (020) 8800 2557 Fax: (020) 7706 1248 E-mail: sales@arcfabrications.com
▶ Aspect Metalcraft, Unit 8, Potts Marsh Industrial Estate, Eastbourne Road, Westham, Pevensey, East Sussex, BN24 5NH Tel: (01323) 735537 Fax: (01323) 765666 E-mail: sales@aspectmetalcraft.com
Caparo Industries P.L.C., Caparo House, Popes Lane, Oldbury, West Midlands, B69 4PJ Tel: 0121-202 4400 Fax: 0121-202 4401
Cookson Bros, Hornby Boulevard, Bootle, Merseyside, L20 5DX Tel: 0151-922 3394 Fax: 0151-922 3014
H L C Engineering Ltd, 4 Harvey Road, Burnt Mills Industrial Estate, Basildon, Essex, SS13 1QJ Tel: (01268) 590080 Fax: (01268) 590141E-mail: steelwork@hlcengineering.com
Island Structural, Bowcombe Works, Bowcombe Road, Newport, Isle of Wight, PO30 3HZ Tel: (01983) 525070 Fax: (01983) 521632
Lynxcourt Ltd, Unit 9 Victoria Way, Newmarket, Suffolk, CB8 7SH Tel: (01638) 669214 Fax: (01638) 660209 E-mail: kiteley@lynxcourt.freeserve.co.uk
Profab Fabrications, Triton Works, Stringes Lane, Willenhall, West Midlands, WV13 1LD Tel: (01902) 633253 Fax: (01902) 633253

STRUCTURAL SURVEYING

Abbott Holliday Partnership, 9 Greens Court, Lansdowne Mews, London, W11 3AP Tel: (020) 7792 1147 Fax: (01233) 820755 E-mail: enquiries@peter-holliday.co.uk
Checkley & Co., Broad St House, 212 Broad Street, Birmingham, B15 1AY Tel: 0121-643 8538 Fax: 0121-643 7416 E-mail: mailbox@checkleys.co.uk
Mills & Wood, 18 Grosvenor Street, London, W1K 4QQ Tel: (020) 7499 0934 Fax: (020) 7408 0250 E-mail: sales@millsandwood.co.uk
Howard Ruse Associates Ltd, 2 Avery Hill Road, London, SE9 2BD Tel: (020) 8850 5678 E-mail: sales@hraconsulting.co.uk

STRUCTURAL WAREHOUSE FABRICATORS

G Broughton & Sons, Ferneries Road, Barnetby, South Humberside, DN38 6HN Tel: (01652) 688652 Fax: (01652) 688069

STRUCTURED CABLE SYSTEMS

A N I Ltd, Suite 1, 98A Castle Lane West, Bournemouth, BH9 3JU Tel: (01202) 598737 Fax: (01202) 598722 E-mail: info@ani-ltd.co.uk
ADC Communications (UK) Ltd, Runnings Road, Kingsditch Trading Centre, Cheltenham, Gloucestershire, GL51 9NQ Tel: (01242) 264400 Fax: (01242) 264488 E-mail: christianname.surname@adckrone.com
Advanced Computer Installations Ltd, Unit 7 Salford Enterprise Centre, 5 Guide St, Salford, M50 1EW Tel: 0161-737 5654 Fax: 0161-737 5227 E-mail: veronica@acimanchester.co.uk
▶ Cablecomm Voice & Data Solutions Ltd, Aztec House, 187-189 Kings Road, Reading, RG1 4EX Tel: (0800) 0582662 Fax: 0118-988 3716 E-mail: sales@cablecomm.co.uk
Cablelines (Nottingham) Ltd, Unit 4 Orchard Park Industrial Estate, Sandiacre, Nottingham, NG10 5BP Tel: 0115-949 1010 Fax: 0115-949 1019 E-mail: sales@cablelines.com
Century Business Systems, 19-21 Mid Stocket Road, Aberdeen, AB15 5JL Tel: (01224) 644064 Fax: (01224) 643407 E-mail: info@century.uk.net
Communication Centre (International) Ltd, 60 Riverside I I I, Sir Thomas Longley Road, Strood, Rochester, Kent, ME2 4BH Tel: (01634) 295295 Fax: (01634) 723895 E-mail: enquiries@commscentre.com
▶ Elan Networks Ltd, The Mews, 12 Fortrose Street, Glasgow, G12 0TB Tel: 0141-337 6540 Fax: 0141-337 2244 E-mail: enquiries@elannetworks.co.uk
▶ Ergix Data Communications Ltd, 39 Rotherham Road, Dinnington, Sheffield, S25 3RG Tel: (07970) 264144 E-mail: scott@cawthorne962.fsnet.co.uk
Excel I T Ltd, Trafalgar House, 712 London Road, Grays, Essex, RM20 3JT Tel: (01708) 865855 Fax: (01708) 866856 E-mail: enquiries@excelit.com
Ford Systems Ltd, Park La, Nottingham, NG6 0EU Tel: 0115-927 2821 Fax: 0115-976 1041 E-mail: arthur.ford@fordgroup.co.uk
Hellermann Tyton, Ratcliff House, 43-45 Salthouse Road, Brackmills Industrial Estate, Northampton, NN4 7EX Tel: (01604) 706633 Fax: (01604) 705454
Molex Premise Networks Ltd, Network House, Concorde Way, Fareham, Hampshire, PO15 5RL Tel: (01489) 572111 Fax: (01489) 559106 E-mail: sales@molexpn.co.uk
▶ P W Maintenance Services, 38 Richmond Avenue, Kettering, Northamptonshire, NN15 5JG Tel: (01536) 830070 Fax: (01536) 522564 E-mail: admin@pwmservices.com
▶ Xtreme Business Solutions Ltd, Unit 3 Westhill Business Centre, Arnhall Business Park, Westhill, Aberdeen, AB32 6UF Tel: (01224) 744666 Fax: (01224) 330566 E-mail: sales@xtremesolutionsltd.com

STRUCTURED CABLE SYSTEMS CONSULTANCY

▶ Ergix Data Communications Ltd, 39 Rotherham Road, Dinnington, Sheffield, S25 3RG Tel: (07970) 264144 E-mail: scott@cawthorne962.fsnet.co.uk
▶ Sharpe Systems, Westthorpe Innovation Centre, Killamarsh, Sheffield, S21 1TZ Tel: 0114-251 4775 Fax: (0870) 1221505 E-mail: tim.sharpe@sharpe-systems.co.uk

STUD WELDING

Circle Technical Services Ltd, Turulus Way, Midmill Business Park, Kintore, Aberdeenshire, AB51 0TG Tel: (01467) 632020 Fax: (01467) 632022 E-mail: info@circletechnical.co.uk
Studfast Studwelding Ltd, 5 Low Farm Place, Moulton Park Industrial Estate, Northampton, NN3 6HY Tel: (01604) 790901 Fax: (01604) 492946 E-mail: sales.studfast@btconnect.com

STUD WELDING EQUIPMENT

Studwelders, Millennium House Severn Link Distribution Centre, Newhouse Fa, Mathern, Chepstow, Gwent, NP16 6UN Tel: (01291) 626048 Fax: (01291) 629979 E-mail: info@studwelders.co.uk
Taylor Studwelding Systems Ltd, Commercial Road, Dewsbury, West Yorkshire, WF13 2BD Tel: (01924) 452123 Fax: (01924) 430059 E-mail: sales@taylor-studwelding.com

STUD WELDING FASTENER MANUFRS

Cutlass Fasteners Ltd, Dixon Close, Old Boston Trading Estate, Haydock, St. Helens, Merseyside, WA11 9SL Tel: (01942) 712387 Fax: (01942) 722306 E-mail: sales@cutlass-studwelding.com
Studwelders, Millennium House Severn Link Distribution Centre, Newhouse Fa, Mathern, Chepstow, Gwent, NP16 6UN Tel: (01291) 626048 Fax: (01291) 629979 E-mail: info@studwelders.co.uk

STUDENT DIARIES

▶ Waveney Publishing Ltd, Waveney House, 45-47 Stour Street, Birmingham, B18 7AJ Tel: 0121-454 9441 Fax: 0121-454 9529

STUDENT PLANNERS

The School Planner Co. Ltd, 80 Carolgate, Retford, Nottinghamshire, DN22 6EF Tel: (01777) 861980 Fax: (01777) 711782 E-mail: enquiries@school-planners.co.uk

STUDIO KILNS

Cromartie Kilns Ltd, Park Hall Road, Longton, Stoke-On-Trent, ST3 5AY Tel: (01782) 313947 Fax: (01782) 599723 E-mail: enquiries@cromartie.co.uk
Potterycrafts Ltd, Campbell Road, Stoke-on-Trent, ST4 4ET Tel: (01782) 745000 Fax: (01782) 746000 E-mail: sales@potterycraft.co.uk

STUDIO OR CINE OR STAGE OR TELEVISION LIGHTING

A J S Theatre Lighting & Stage Supplies Ltd, 25-26 Hightown Industrial Estate, Crow Arch Lane, Ringwood, Hampshire, BH24 1ND Tel: (01425) 481100 Fax: (01425) 471398 E-mail: enquiries@ajs.co.uk
Avolites Ltd, Park Avenue, London, NW10 7XL Tel: (020) 8965 8522 Fax: (020) 8965 0290 E-mail: sales@avolites.com
Celco Ltd, 14 Forest Hill Business Centre, Clyde Vale, London, SE23 3JF Fax: (020) 8699 5056 E-mail: sales@celco.co.uk
Helmsman Electronics Ltd, 31 Faringdon Avenue, Blackpool, FY4 3QQ Tel: (01253) 343056 Fax: (01253) 408004 E-mail: mail@helmsmanuk.co.uk
▶ David Lawrence Lighting, Unit 7, New Lydenburg Commercial Estate, New Lydenburg Street, London, SE7 8NF Tel: (020) 8858 2820 Fax: (020) 8858 2820 E-mail: david@davidlawrencelights.co.uk
P & G Stage Electrical Ltd, Studio House, North Stage, Broadway, Salford, M50 2UW Tel: 0161-877 4933 Fax: 0161-877 4944 E-mail: sales@pgstage.co.uk
Photon Beard Ltd, Unit K3, Cherrycourt Way, Stanbridge Road, Leighton Buzzard, Bedfordshire, LU7 4UH Tel: (01525) 850911 Fax: (01525) 850922 E-mail: info@photonbeard.com
Power Drive Drum Co. Ltd, Unit M1 Cherrycourt Way, Leighton Buzzard, Bedfordshire, LU7 4UH Tel: (01525) 370292 Fax: (01525) 852126 E-mail: info@mypowerdrive.com
Procameras, PO Box 461, Wolverhampton, WV10 7YX Tel: (01902) 791511 Fax: (01902) 791585 E-mail: david@davidcole.fsnet.co.uk
Projects Department Ltd, 26 Woodlands Road, Camberley, Surrey, GU15 3NA Tel: (01276) 681423 Fax: (01276) 537170 E-mail: info@projectsdepartment.com
James Thomas Engineering Ltd, Navigation Complex, Navigation Road, Worcester, WR5 3DE Tel: (01905) 363600 Fax: (01905) 363601 E-mail: sales@jamesthomas.co.uk

STUDIO OR CINE OR STAGE OR TELEVISION LIGHTING CONTRACTORS INCLUDING HIRE

Central Theatre Supplies, Midshire House, 1186 Stratford Road, Hall Green, Birmingham, B28 8AB Tel: 0121-778 6400 Fax: 0121-702 2046 E-mail: sales@centraltheatresupplies.co.uk
Event Lighting, 10 Palmerston Close, Kibworth, Leicester, LE8 0JJ Tel: 0116-279 3851
J P L Services, 15 High Street, Rampton, Cambridge, CB24 8QE Tel: (01954) 250851 Fax: (01954) 250543
Larn Ltd, Unit 5 The Stable Block, Brewer Street, Bletchingley, Redhill, RH1 4QP Tel: (01883) 744033 Fax: (01883) 743844
Lee Lighting Ltd, 110 Lancefield Street, Glasgow, G3 8JD Tel: 0141-221 5175 Fax: 0141-248 2751 E-mail: mark@lee.co.uk
Lighting & Sound Equipment, 118 Cowley Road, Oxford, OX4 1JE Tel: (01865) 722027 Fax: (01865) 202454
▶ Nimulus Sound & Light, Ring Road, West Park, Leeds, LS16 6RA Tel: 0113-230 5222 E-mail: info@nimulus.co.uk
P & G Stage Electrical Ltd, Studio House, North Stage, Broadway, Salford, M50 2UW Tel: 0161-877 4933 Fax: 0161-877 4944 E-mail: sales@pgstage.co.uk
R & G Theatre Services, 19-21 Foxes Bridge Road, Forest Vale Industrial Estate, Cinderford, Gloucestershire, GL14 2PQ Tel: (01594) 823197 Fax: (01594) 826045 E-mail: sales@lampo.co.uk
Tega Office, 58 Stockholm Road, Hull, HU7 0XW Tel: (01482) 831032 Fax: (01482) 831331 E-mail: sales@tega.co.uk
Vary-Lite, 20-22 Fairway Drive, Greenford, Middlesex, UB6 8PW Tel: (020) 8575 6666 Fax: (020) 8575 0424 E-mail: info@vari-lite.eu.com
White Light (Electrics) Ltd, 20 Merton Industrial Park, Jubilee Way, Wimbledon, London, SW19 3WL Tel: (020) 8254 4800 Fax: (020) 8254 4801 E-mail: info@whitelightgroup.co.uk

STUDS AND STUD BOLTS, ENGINEERS'

Bomet UK (Threaded Bar) Ltd, Unit H3, Eastacre, Off Longacre, Willenhall, West Midlands, WV13 2JZ Tel: (01902) 368400 Fax: (01902) 606877 E-mail: j.shuffe@bomet.com
Bon Accord Metal Supplies Ltd, 86 Sinclair Road, Aberdeen, AB11 9PP Tel: (01224) 878898 Fax: (01224) 879730 E-mail: info@bonaccordmetals.co.uk
Cutlass Fasteners Ltd, Dixon Close, Old Boston Trading Estate, Haydock, St. Helens, Merseyside, WA11 9SL Tel: (01942) 712387 Fax: (01942) 722306 E-mail: sales@cutlass-studwelding.com
Lydford Precision Engineering Ltd, Sutherland Avenue, Monmore Green, Wolverhampton, WV2 2JH Tel: (01902) 351353 Fax: (01902) 351616 E-mail: sales@lydford-eng.co.uk
Permafast Ltd, Derby Road, Clay Cross, Chesterfield, Derbyshire, S45 9AG Tel: (01246) 250150 Fax: (01246) 250085 E-mail: info@permafast.co.uk
Prosper Engineering, Minto Drive, Altens Industrial Estate, Aberdeen, AB12 3LW Tel: (01224) 877776 Fax: (01224) 890666
Prosper Engineering Ltd, 3 Arkwright Way, North Newmoor Industrial Estate, Irvine, Ayrshire, KA11 4JU Tel: (01294) 224422 Fax: (01294) 215003 E-mail: sales@prosper-engineering.com
R A K Fasteners Ltd, R A K Fasteners Ltd Unit 18 Pinfold Industrial Estate, Field Close, Bloxwich, Walsall, WS3 3JS Tel: (01922) 408508 Fax: (01922) 402037
Rollstud Ltd, 5 Denmore Industrial Estate, Denmore Road, Denmore Industrial Estate, Aberdeen, AB23 8JW Tel: (01224) 425300 Fax: (01224) 425333

STUDS AND STUD BOLTS, ENGINEERS, TO SPECIFICATION

P K Engineering West Bromwich Ltd, Unit 3 Kelvin Way, West Bromwich, West Midlands, B70 7TN Tel: 0121-500 5847 Fax: 0121-553 1622 E-mail: sales@pk-engineering.co.uk

SUBASSEMBLY INJECTION MOULDINGS

Carclo Engineering Group, PO Box 14, Ossett, West Yorkshire, WF5 9LR Tel: (01924) 268040 Fax: (01924) 283226 E-mail: investor.relations@carclo-plc.com
G M D Mouldings Ltd, Dec House, 143-145 Cardiff Road, Reading, RG1 8JF Tel: 0118-957 2188 Fax: 0118-957 1218 E-mail: martin@mclayton.fsbusiness.co.uk

SUBCONTRACT ASSEMBLY SERVICES

Connect 2 Technology Ltd, Longbeck Road, Marske-by-the-Sea, Redcar, Cleveland, TS11 6HQ Tel: (01642) 492220 Fax: (01642) 492223 E-mail: sales@connect2t.co.uk
Produmax Ltd, The Tannery, Station Road, Otley, West Yorkshire, LS21 3HX Tel: (01943) 461713 Fax: (01943) 850228 E-mail: mail@produmax.co.uk
Staffordshire Precision Engineering Ltd, 4 Red Mine Close, Newcastle, Staffordshire, ST5 9HZ Tel: (01782) 630500 Fax: (01782) 638440 E-mail: sales@staffsprecision.co.uk
Wire All Products, 42 New Road, Rochester, Kent, ME1 1DX Tel: (01634) 812984 Fax: 01634 409636 E-mail: sales@wireall.co.uk

SUBCONTRACT DEBURRING

Extrude Hone Ltd, 1 Sovereign Business Park, Joplin Court, Crownhill, Milton Keynes, MK8 0JP Tel: (01908) 263636 Fax: (01908) 262141 E-mail: miltonkeynes.sales@extrudehone.com
Norfinish Engineering Ltd, Sleekburn Business Centre, West Sleekburn, Bedlington, Northumberland, NE22 7DD Tel: (01670) 855087 Fax: (01670) 855079 E-mail: info@norfinish.co.uk

SUBCONTRACT ELECTRONIC EQUIPMENT MANUFACTURING

A F G Electronics, Fairfield House, Goose Hill, Headley, Thatcham, Berkshire, RG19 8AU Tel: (01635) 268496 Fax: (01635) 268020 E-mail: sales@afg.pins.co.uk
Connor Solutions Ltd, 1-2 Gadwall Road, Houghton le Spring, Tyne & Wear, DH4 5NL Tel: 0191-512 1555 Fax: 0191-512 1666
▶ E M F Electronics, 146 Portsmouth Road, Lee-on-the-Solent, Hampshire, PO13 9AE Tel: (023) 9255 6225 E-mail: sales@emf-electronics.co.uk

SUBCONTRACT ELECTRONIC EQUIPMENT MANUFACTURING – *continued*

Kingfield Electronics Ltd, Carrwood House, Carrwood Road, Chesterfield Trading Estate, Chesterfield, Derbyshire, S41 9QB Tel: (01246) 451701 Fax: (01246) 572390 E-mail: d.bailey@kingfield-electronics.co.uk

▶ Vantage Electronics Ltd, 4 Carlo Court, Finchampstead, Wokingham, Berkshire, RG40 4RF Tel: 0118-973 1186 Fax: 0118-973 1192

SUBCONTRACT PRINTED CIRCUIT BOARD (PCB) ASSEMBLY

▶ Dragon Design, 14a Cambridge Road, Granby Industrial Estate, Weymouth, Dorset, DT4 9TJ Tel: (01305) 750777 Fax: (01305) 784555 E-mail: info@dragondesignltd.com

SUBCONTRACT STRUCTURAL STEELWORK

▶ 3D Structural Services, 35 Humphrey Street, Lower Gornal, Dudley, West Midlands, DY3 2AW Tel: (01902) 656263 Fax: (01902) 656263 E-mail: structuralservices@blueyonder.co.uk

▶ Aventus Design, 7 Leaches Farm Business Centre, Bicester Road, Kingswood, Aylesbury, Buckinghamshire, HP18 0RR Tel: (01296) 770066 Fax: (08707) 066007 E-mail: mail@aventusdesign.co.uk

B & R Fabrication, 3g Lyncastle Way, Barley Castle Lane, Appleton, Warrington, WA4 4ST Tel: (01925) 601728 Fax: (01925) 602261 E-mail: brfabrications@lineone.net

Dracup (UK) Ltd, Lane Close Mills, Bartle Lane, Bradford, West Yorkshire, BD7 4QQ Tel: (01274) 571071 Fax: (01274) 501209 E-mail: email@dracupuk.com

Gray Fabrications UK Ltd, 57 Clement Way, Upminster, Essex, RM14 2NX Tel: (01708) 703505 Fax: (01708) 703505 E-mail: gray.fabrications@ntlworld.com

▶ Inmac Engineering, 13-15 Parc Erissey Industrial Estate, New Portreath Road, Redruth, Cornwall, TR16 4HZ Tel: (01209) 313088 Fax: (01209) 313099 E-mail: admin@inmac-pl3.co.uk

▶ Maltech UK Ltd, 1 Newgate, Malton, North Yorkshire, YO17 7LF Tel: (01653) 697092 Fax: (01653) 692486

▶ Jon Roscoe Outsourcing & Sub-Contract Specialist, 61, Bellevue Gardens, Shrewsbury, SY3 7JH Tel: (01743) 244829 Fax: (01743) 244829 E-mail: jonroscoeuk@aol.com

▶ SC Consulting, Victoria House, 28-32 Desborough Street, High Wycombe, Buckinghamshire, HP11 2NF Tel: (01494) 601170 Fax: (01494) 601171 E-mail: mail@scceng.co.uk

▶ T. Shanks Engineering Ltd, 141 Greengairs Road, Greengairs, Airdrie, Lanarkshire, ML6 7SY Tel: (01236) 830325 Fax: (01236) 830736 E-mail: sales@shanksgroup.co.uk

Spirex Metal Products Ltd, Marsh Lane, Ware, Hertfordshire, SG12 9QQ Tel: (01920) 460516 Fax: (01920) 487028 E-mail: info@spirex.co.uk

Streamline Outsource Ltd, The Innovation Centre, Rennes Drive, University Of Exeter Campus, Exeter, EX4 4RN Tel: (07743) 845124 Fax: (0870) 4584046 E-mail: sales@streamlineoutsource.com

▶ Structural Surveys Direct, 1-2 Aire House, Richmond Business Park, Sidings Court, Doncaster, South Yorkshire, DN4 5NL Tel: (0808) 144 8899 Fax: 08081 448898 E-mail: info@structuralsurveysdirect.co.uk

SUBLIMATION PRINTING, *See also Thermostatic Printing etc*

▶ Atlas Transfer Printers Ltd, 9 Wanstead Road, Leicester, LE3 1TR Tel: 0116-231 4500 Fax: 0116-231 4600 E-mail: atpl@btconnect.com

▶ Meesha Graphics Ltd, 37 Orchard Street, Leicester, LE1 3UG Tel: 0116-242 6300 Fax: 0116-242 6301 E-mail: raj@meeshagraphics.com

SUBMERSIBLE MIXERS

A B S Pumps Ltd, Astral Towers, 5TH Floor, Betts Way, Crawley, West Sussex, RH10 9UY Tel: (01293) 558140 Fax: (01293) 527972

Landia UK Ltd, Waymills Indust Estate, Waymills, Whitchurch, Shropshire, SY13 1TT Tel: (01948) 661200 Fax: (01948) 661201 E-mail: info@landia.co.uk

SUBMERSIBLE POND PUMPS

Q S S Aquarium & Koi Centre, 339 Wakefield Road, Bradford, West Yorkshire, BD4 7NJ Tel: (01274) 728361 Fax: (01274) 720718 E-mail: sales@qssaquarium.co.uk

SUBMERSIBLE PUMPS

A B S Waste Water Treatment Technology, Unit 1 Bridges Industrial Estate, Bridge Road, Horshay, Telford, Shropshire, TF4 3EE Tel: (01952) 632030 Fax: (01952) 632040 E-mail: roger.youngman@absgroup.com

Border Pumps & Transmissions, Station Road, Sandycroft, Deeside, Clwyd, CH5 2PT Tel: (01244) 533065 Fax: (01244) 535635

Centrilift, Howe Moss Place, Kirkhill Industrial Estate, Dyce, Aberdeen, AB21 0ES Tel: (01224) 772233 Fax: (01224) 771021 E-mail: sales@centrilift.com

Flowserve Pumps Ltd, PO Box 17, Newark, Nottinghamshire, NG24 3EN Tel: (01636) 705151 Fax: (01636) 705991 E-mail: newark@flowserve.com

Godwin Pumps Ltd, Quenington, Cirencester, Gloucestershire, GL7 5BX Tel: (01285) 750271 Fax: (01285) 750352 E-mail: sales@godwinpumps.co.uk

Lincolnshire Rewinds, Long Leys Road, Lincoln, LN1 1DX Tel: (01522) 524283 Fax: (01522) 521122

Liquified Gas Pumping Services Ltd, 18 Abbotsinch Road, Grangemouth, Stirlingshire, FK3 9UX Tel: (01324) 485475 Fax: (01324) 485677 E-mail: sales@lgpservices.co.uk

M B Pumps Ltd, 2 Royle Park, Congleton, Cheshire, CW12 1JJ Tel: (01260) 299438 Fax: (01260) 297595 E-mail: sales@mbpumps.co.uk

Mid Kent Electrical Engineering Co., The Street, Detling, Maidstone, Kent, ME14 3JT Tel: (01622) 735702 Fax: (01622) 734844 E-mail: pumpsales@mke.co.uk

Sparrow Quality Water Solutions, The Abbey, Preston Road, Yeovil, Somerset, BA20 2EN Tel: (01935) 479395 Fax: (01935) 848523

T T Pumps Ltd, Onneley Works, Newcastle Road, Woore, Crewe, CW3 9RU Tel: (01630) 647200 Fax: (01630) 642100 E-mail: response@ttpumps.com

Viking Pump Ltd, Viking House, Dannemore Drive, Sheffield, S9 5DF Tel: 0114-244 7701 Fax: 0114-243 2614

SUBMINIATURE D CONNECTORS

I T W McMurdo Connectors, Norway Road, Hilsea, Portsmouth, PO3 5HT Tel: (023) 9269 4971 Fax: (023) 9265 3356 E-mail: itwswitch1@aol.com

SUBSEA OR UNDERWATER CABLE INSTALLATION CONTRACTORS

Procon Industrial Automation Ltd, Unit 5 Arclid Industrial Estate, Hemmingshaw Lane, Arclid, Sandbach, Cheshire, CW11 4SY Tel: (01270) 759708 Fax: (01270) 766350 E-mail: rn@proconuk.freeserve.co.uk

SUBSEA OR UNDERWATER CABLE INSTALLATION MACHINERY

Fraser Hydraulic Power, Unit BT 96/4 Fisher Industrial Estate, Fisher St, Walker, Newcastle upon Tyne, NE6 4LT Tel: 0191-263 7272 Fax: 0191-263 4016 E-mail: joanner@fhpltd.co.uk

SUBSEA OR UNDERWATER CABLE TESTING SERVICES OR FACILITIES

Alcatel Submarine Networks Ltd, Christchurch Way, London, SE10 0AG Tel: (020) 8293 2000 Fax: (020) 8293 2433

SUBSEA OR UNDERWATER CABLES

Custom Design Mouldings Ltd, Unit 212-215, Springvale Industrial Estate, Cwmbran, Gwent, NP44 5BJ Tel: (01633) 861441 Fax: (01633) 876412 E-mail: sales@cdg-uk.com

Duco Ltd, Nelson Road, Newcastle upon Tyne, NE6 3NL Tel: 0191-295 0303 Fax: 0191-295 0842 E-mail: ducosbd@uk.coflaxip.com

▶ Hydro Bond Engineering Ltd, 2b Woodside Road, Bridge of Don Industrial Estate, Aberdeen, AB23 8EF Tel: (01224) 822996 Fax: (01224) 825142 E-mail: sales@hydrohouse.co.uk

J D R Cable Systems Ltd, 175 Wisbech Road, Littleport, Ely, Cambridgeshire, CB6 1RA Tel: (01353) 865800 Fax: (01353) 861388 E-mail: uk@jdrcables.com

Oceaneering Multiflex, Dundas Road, Rosyth, Dunfermline, Fife, KY11 2XS Tel: (01383) 643400 Fax: (01383) 643590 E-mail: enquiries@oceaneering.com

Rochester Corporation, 2nd Floor Taylor Building, 62-64 Bromham Road, Bedford, MK40 2QG Tel: (01234) 327013 Fax: (01234) 327062 E-mail: djharris@rochester-cables.com

SUBSEA OR UNDERWATER EARTH MOVING MACHINES

Con Mech Group Ltd, Cleary Court, Church Street East, Woking, Surrey, GU21 6HJ Tel: (01483) 714024 Fax: (01483) 714343

SUBSEA OR UNDERWATER ENGINEERING COMPONENTS OR EQUIPMENT

Aker Kvaerner Subsea Ltd, Unit 59, Clivemont Road, Cordwallis Industrial Estate, Maidenhead, Berkshire, SL6 7BZ Tel: (01628) 506560 Fax: (01628) 506501 E-mail: info@kvaerner.com

Bowtech Products Ltd, Howe Moss Cresent, Kirkhill Industrial Estate, Dyce, Aberdeen, AB21 0GN Tel: (01224) 772345 Fax: (01224) 772900 E-mail: bowtech@bowtech.co.uk

Perry Slingsby Systems Ltd, Ings Lane, Kirkbymoorside, York, YO62 6EZ Tel: (01751) 431751 Fax: (01751) 431388 E-mail: pssl@uk.perrymail.com

SUBSEA OR UNDERWATER FLANGES

Linvic Engineering Ltd, Hickman Avenue, Wolverhampton, WV1 2DW Tel: (01902) 456333 Fax: (01902) 455856 E-mail: sales@linvic.co.uk

SUBSEA OR UNDERWATER INSPECTION

Geoacoustics Ltd, Shuttleworth Close, Gapton Hall Industrial Estate, Great Yarmouth, Norfolk, NR31 0NQ Tel: (01493) 600666 Fax: (01493) 651100 E-mail: sales@geoacoustics.co.uk

Submersible Television Surveys Ltd, 4 Barratt Trading Estate, Denmore Road, Bridge of Don, Aberdeen, AB23 8JW Tel: (01224) 823333 Fax: (01224) 824639 E-mail: admin@stsrov.com

Subsea Vision Ltd, 15 Southlands Avenue, Corfe Mullen, Wimborne, Dorset, BH21 3JB Tel: (01202) 656861 Fax: (01202) 601530 E-mail: enquiries@subseavision.co.uk

SUBSEA OR UNDERWATER MARINE DETECTORS

Aquascan International Ltd, Aquascan House, Hill Street, Newport, Gwent, NP20 1LZ Tel: (01633) 841117 Fax: (01633) 254829 E-mail: info@aquascan.co.uk

SUBSEA OR UNDERWATER PIPELINE INSPECTION

▶ DC Voltage Gradient Technology & Supply Ltd, Corbett House, Swan Lane, Hindley Green, Wigan, Lancashire, WN2 4EY Tel: (01942) 522180 Fax: (01942) 522179 E-mail: dcvg@fsbdial.co.uk

SUBSEA OR UNDERWATER WELLHEAD CONNECTORS

M I B International Ltd, Sun Alliance House, Little Park Street, Coventry, CV1 2JZ Tel: (024) 7622 5202 Fax: (024) 7622 1752 E-mail: sales@mibinternational.com

SUBSEA/UNDERWATER BUOYANCY PRODUCTS

Seaflex Ltd, Samuel Whites, Bridge Road, Cowes, Isle of Wight, PO31 7RA Tel: (01983) 290525 Fax: (01983) 295853 E-mail: info@seaflex.co.uk

SUBSEA/UNDERWATER CABLES/UMBILICALS

Cortland Fibron B X Ltd, Unitc R D Park, Stephenson Close, Hoddesdon, Hertfordshire, EN11 0BW Tel: (01992) 471444 Fax: (01992) 471555

Duco Ltd, Nelson Road, Newcastle upon Tyne, NE6 3NL Tel: 0191-295 0303 Fax: 0191-295 0842 E-mail: ducosbd@uk.coflaxip.com

Oceaneering Multiflex, Dundas Road, Rosyth, Dunfermline, Fife, KY11 2XS Tel: (01383) 643400 Fax: (01383) 643590 E-mail: enquiries@oceaneering.com

SUBSEA/UNDERWATER CONSTRUCTORS/ CONTRACTORS

Donarm Construction Ltd, Viewfield Industrial Estate, Glenrothes, Fife, KY6 2RS Tel: (01592) 775201 Fax: (01592) 771751 E-mail: donarm_construction@compuserve.com

JonesMarine, Cumberland House, 1 Kensington Road, London, W8 5NX Tel: (020) 7938 3046 Fax: (020) 7938 3015 E-mail: jerry@jonesmarine.com

Saipem Ltd, Saipem House, Station Road, Motspur Park, New Malden, Surrey, KT3 6JJ Tel: (020) 8296 5000 Fax: (020) 8296 5100

SUBSEA/UNDERWATER CONSULTANTS

Ajt Engineering Ltd, Craigshaw Crescent, West Tullos Industrial Estate, Aberdeen, AB12 3TB Tel: (01224) 871791 Fax: (01224) 890251 E-mail: info@ajt-engineering.co.uk

B A E Systems, Elettra Avenue, Waterlooville, Hampshire, PO7 7XS Tel: (023) 9226 4466 Fax: (023) 9226 0246

Mckenzie-Midlane Ltd, PO Box 35, Whitby, North Yorkshire, YO21 3EZ Tel: (01947) 820243 Fax: (01947) 820488 E-mail: sales@mckmid.com

Pegasus International UK Ltd, The Academy, Belmont Street, Aberdeen, AB10 1LB Tel: (01224) 623300 Fax: (01224) 623301 E-mail: aberdeen@pegasus-international.com

SUBSEA/UNDERWATER CONTROL SYSTEMS

Applied Acoustic Engineering Ltd, 3 Marine House, Marine Park, Great Yarmouth, Norfolk, NR31 0NL Tel: (01493) 440355 Fax: (01493) 440720E-mail: general@appliedacoustics.com

Seaflex Ltd, Samuel Whites, Bridge Road, Cowes, Isle of Wight, PO31 7RA Tel: (01983) 290525 Fax: (01983) 295853 E-mail: info@seaflex.co.uk

Vetco Grey, 2 High Street, Nailsea, Bristol, BS48 1BS Tel: (01275) 810100 Fax: (01275) 851467 E-mail: paul.roberts@vetco.com

SUBSEA/UNDERWATER ENGINEERING SERVICES

Acergy Ltd, Bucksburn House, Howes Road, Aberdeen, AB16 7QU Tel: (01224) 718200 Fax: (01224) 715129 E-mail: uk-hr@acergy-group.com

Ajt Engineering Ltd, Craigshaw Crescent, West Tullos Industrial Estate, Aberdeen, AB12 3TB Tel: (01224) 871791 Fax: (01224) 890251 E-mail: info@ajt-engineering.co.uk

▶ All Oceans Engineering Ltd, Tyrebagger Works, Kinellar, Aberdeen, AB21 0TT Tel: (01224) 791001 Fax: (01224) 791002 E-mail: admin@alloceans.co.uk

BG Group, 100 Thames Valley Park Drive, Reading, RG6 1PT Tel: 0118-935 3222 Fax: 0118-929 3710 E-mail: admin@bg-group.com

Bowtech Products Ltd, Howe Moss Cresent, Kirkhill Industrial Estate, Dyce, Aberdeen, AB21 0GN Tel: (01224) 772345 Fax: (01224) 772900 E-mail: bowtech@bowtech.co.uk

Seaweld Engineering Ltd, The Limes, The Street, Acle, Norwich, NR13 3QJ Tel: (01493) 751421 Fax: (01493) 750064 E-mail: admin@seaweld.co.uk

Technip Offshore Ltd, Enterprise Drive, Westhill Industrial Estate, Westhill, Aberdeenshire, AB32 6TQ Tel: (01224) 744044 Fax: (01224) 271271

SUBSEA/UNDERWATER LOCATING SERVICES, CABLE/ PIPE ETC

Aquascan International Ltd, Aquascan House, Hill Street, Newport, Gwent, NP20 1LZ Tel: (01633) 841117 Fax: (01633) 254829 E-mail: info@aquascan.co.uk

SUBSIDENCE INVESTIGATION

Byrom Clark Roberts Ltd, Maclaren House, Talbot Road, Stretford, Manchester, M32 0FP Tel: 0161-875 0600 Fax: 0161-875 0601 E-mail: bcrmcr@bcr.uk.com

Howard Ruse Associates Ltd, 2 Avery Hill Road, London, SE9 2BD Tel: (020) 8850 5678 E-mail: sales@hraconsulting.co.uk

SUBSOILERS

Simba International Ltd, Woodbridge Road, Sleaford, Lincolnshire, NG34 7EW Tel: (01529) 304654 Fax: (01529) 413468 E-mail: sales@simba.co.uk

SUBSTATION CONSULTANTS OR DESIGNERS, HIGH VOLTAGE

Balfour Kilpatrick Ltd, Glasgow Road, Deanside, Renfrew, PA4 8XZ Tel: 0141-885 4321 Fax: 0141-885 4480 E-mail: enquiry@balfourkilpatrick.com

SUBSTATION TEST EQUIPMENT

Omicron Electronics UK Ltd, Unit 9, Marconi Gate, Staffordshire Technology Park, Stafford, ST18 0FZ Tel: (01785) 251000 Fax: (01785) 252000 E-mail: info@uk.omicron.at

SUBSURFACE RADAR DETECTION SERVICES

Brasec, Anchorage House, Stoke Street, Rodney Stoke, Cheddar, Somerset, BS27 3UP Tel: (01749) 870888 Fax: (01749) 870999 E-mail: bristec_radar_uk@compuserve.com

Ekaw Projects Ltd, Link House, Church Street, Haxey, Doncaster, South Yorkshire, DN9 2HY Tel: (01427) 752006 Fax: (01427) 753581

SUCCESSION PLANNING HUMAN RESOURCES (HR) COMPUTER SOFTWARE

▶ Human Concepts, Suite 10 The White House, 42 The Terrace, Torquay, TQ1 1DE Tel: (01803) 390490 Fax: (01803) 203304 E-mail: sales@orgplus.co.uk

SUCTION BELTING

R S Richardson Belting Co. Ltd, Crown Works, Staincliffe Road, Dewsbury, West Yorkshire, WF13 4SB Tel: (01924) 468191 Fax: (01924) 458065 E-mail: mail@diepress-richardson.co.uk

SUCTION FILTERS

Fenchurch Environmental Group Ltd, Dennow Farm, Firs Lane, Appleton, Warrington, WA4 5LF Tel: (01925) 269111 Fax: (01925) 269444 E-mail: sales@fengroup.com

SUEDE PRODUCERS OR DRESSERS

Charles F Stead & Co. Ltd, Tannery, Sheepscar Street North, Leeds, LS7 2BY Tel: 0113-262 8643 Fax: 0113-262 6309 E-mail: suede@cfstead.com

SUGAR

British Sugar plc, Cantley Sugar Factory, Cantley, Norwich, NR13 3ST Tel: (01493) 700351 Fax: (01493) 724203

SUGAR PRODUCTION MACHINERY

Fletcher Smith, 33 Brunel Parkway, Pride Park, Derby, DE24 8HR Tel: (01332) 636000 Fax: (01332) 636020 E-mail: info@fletchersmith.com

Sudeco International Ltd, Unit 1-2 Progress Business Park, Progress Way, Croydon, CR0 4XD Tel: (020) 8686 7000 Fax: (020) 8680 0068 E-mail: info@sudeco.com

Tate & Lyle Sugars, Thames Refinery, Factory Road, London, E16 2EW Tel: (020) 7476 4455 Fax: (020) 7511 5507 E-mail: CEO@qudos.com

SUGAR REFINERS

Tate & Lyle Sugars, Thames Refinery, Factory Road, London, E16 2EW Tel: (020) 7476 4455 Fax: (020) 7511 5507 E-mail: CEO@qudos.com

Walker S Nonsuch Ltd, Calverley Street, Stoke-on-Trent, ST3 1QS Tel: (01782) 321525 Fax: (01782) 599449 E-mail: walkersnonsuch@walkers-nonsuch.co.uk

SUGAR SACHETS

Bristow's Of Devon Holdings Ltd, Marsh Lane, Crediton, Devon, EX17 1ET Tel: (01363) 774631 Fax: (01363) 772792 E-mail: sweets@bristows-of-devon.co.uk

Melitta System Service, Unit 21 Grove Park Industrial Estate, Waltham Road, White Waltham, Maidenhead, Berkshire, SL6 3LW Tel: (01628) 829888 Fax: (01628) 825111

Nutshell Packaging, Telford Road, Salisbury, SP2 7PZ Tel: (01722) 321630 Fax: (01722) 341479

SULPHUR ANALYSERS

Onix Process Analysis, Ion Path, Road Three, Winsford Industrial Estate, Winsford, Cheshire, CW7 3GA Tel: (01606) 548704 Fax: (01606) 548711 E-mail: glewis@onixpa.com

SUNBED ULTRAVIOLET (UV) SCREENS

▶ Manor Beauty, Hove Manor, Hove Street, Hove, East Sussex, BN3 2DF Tel: (01273) 748483 E-mail: admin@blakeneymanor.co.uk

SUNBEDS

Browned Off, 10 Farr Avenue, Barking, Essex, IG11 0NZ Tel: (020) 8507 0707 E-mail: browned.off@btinternet.com

▶ Mambo's UK Tanning Supplies, 434 Preston Old Road, Blackburn, BB2 5LY Tel: (0800) 8496359 Fax: (01254) 209621 E-mail: info@iso-italia.co.uk

SUNGLASSES

▶ SunSpecs2u, 63 High West Street, Dorchester, Dorset, DT1 1UY Tel: (01305) 264922 E-mail: info@sunspecs2u.co.uk

SUPERMARKET TROLLEY MAINTENANCE/REPAIR SERVICES

Symonds Trolley Services Ltd, Wern Trading Estate, Rogerstone, Newport, Gwent, NP10 9XX Tel: (01633) 892362 Fax: (01633) 896618 E-mail: symonds@symondshydroclean.co.uk

SUPERVISORY CONTROL AND DATA ACQUISITION (SCADA) SYSTEMS, FOOD AND DRINK INDUSTRY

Anville Instruments, Unit 19 Pegasus Court, North Lane, Aldershot, Hampshire, GU12 4QP Tel: (01252) 351030 Fax: (01252) 323492 E-mail: stephen@anvilleinstrumemts.com

Castle View Services Ltd, Steuart Road, Bridge of Allan, Stirling, FK9 4JX Tel: (01786) 834060 Fax: (01786) 832658 E-mail: enquiries@castleview.co.uk

▶ Javelin Controls Ltd, 10 Warbleton Road, Chineham, Basingstoke, Hampshire, RG24 8RF Tel: 01256 812557 Fax: 01256 812557 E-mail: sales@javelin-controls.com

SUPERVISORY CONTROL AND DATA ACQUISITION SYSTEMS (SCADA)

Global Engineering Services, Yew Tree Cott, Sampford Moor, Wellington, Somerset, TA21 9QL Tel: (0870) 7651508 Fax: (0870) 7652508 E-mail: mauricepinner@compuserve.com

Grapevine Instruments, PO Box 598, Canterbury, Kent, CT4 7GW Tel: (07010) 707940 Fax: (01227) 730892 E-mail: sfigures@netcomuk.co.uk

Logicware Ltd, 16 Northfield Park Avenue, Annan, Dumfriesshire, DG12 5EX Tel: (01461) 204913 Fax: (0870) 7051744 E-mail: info@logic-ware.com

Ocean Technical Systems Ltd, Oceantech House, Station Approach, Cheam, Sutton, Surrey, SM2 7AU Tel: (020) 8643 2233 Fax: (020) 8643 6444 E-mail: ots@oceantechsys.com

Pacscom Ltd, 6 Majestic Road, Nursling Industrial Estate, Southampton, SO16 0YT Tel: (023) 8073 7557 Fax: (023) 8073 1600 E-mail: sales@pacscom.com

SUPPLY BASE/WAREHOUSE OPERATORS, OIL INDUSTRY

Aberdeen Harbour Board, 16 Regent Quay, Aberdeen, AB11 5SS Tel: (01224) 597000 Fax: (01224) 571507 E-mail: info@aberdeen-harbour.co.uk

Asco UK Ltd, Asco House, Sinclair Road, Aberdeen, AB11 9PL Tel: (01224) 580396 Fax: (01224) 576172 E-mail: info@ascoplc.com

Port Of Sunderland, Quayside House Wylam Wharf, Low Street, Sunderland, SR1 2BU Tel: 0191-553 2146 Fax: 0191-553 2145 E-mail: sales@portofsunderland.org.uk

SUPPLY BOAT/WORK BOAT SERVICES

Briggs Marine Contractors Ltd, West Dock, Seaforth Place, Burntisland, Fife, KY3 9AU Tel: (01592) 872939 Fax: (01592) 873975

Edda Supply Ships UK Ltd, Seaforth Centre, 30 Waterloo Quay, Aberdeen, AB11 5BS Tel: (01224) 587788 Fax: (01224) 583276 E-mail: info@eddasupplyships.com

North Star Shipping Aberdeen Ltd, 207 Albert Quay, Aberdeen, AB11 5FS Tel: (01224) 592206 Fax: (01224) 584174 E-mail: callum.bruce@craig-group.com

SUPPLY CHAIN EXECUTION (SCE) SOLUTION PROVIDERS

Catalyst International Ltd, Capital Court, 30 Windsor Street, Uxbridge, Middlesex, UB8 1AB Tel: (01895) 450400 Fax: (01895) 450401 E-mail: europe@catalystinternational.com

Finmatica Ltd, Finmatica House, Ashted Lock, Aston Science Park, Birmingham, B7 4AZ Tel: 0121-359 5096 Fax: 0121-359 0375 E-mail: enquiries@finmatica.com

Panalpina World Transport Ltd, Great South West Road, Feltham, Middlesex, TW14 8NE Tel: (020) 8587 9000 Fax: (020) 8587 9200

SUPPLY CHAIN MANAGEMENT (SCM) SERVICES

Allport Ltd, 2 The Faraday Centre, Faraday Road, Crawley, West Sussex, RH10 9PX Tel: (01293) 510246 Fax: (01293) 562044 E-mail: info@allport.co.uk

Exel Ltd, Solstice House, 251 Midsummer Boulevard, Central Milton Keynes, Milton Keynes, MK9 1EQ Tel: (01908) 244000 Fax: (01908) 244244 E-mail: business.enquiry@exel.com

Fossoft, Newstead House, Lake View Drive, Annesley, NG15 0DT Tel: (01623) 720012 Fax: (01623) 720006

Geologistics Ltd, Unit 12 The Brunel Centre, Newton Road, Crawley, West Sussex, RH10 9TU Tel: (01293) 652900 Fax: (01293) 652901 E-mail: gatwick@geo-logistics.com

I E S A Ltd, Dallon Lane, Warrington, WA2 7PZ Tel: (01925) 634301 Fax: (01925) 417762 E-mail: info@iesa.co.uk

▶ Kamino Ltd, 3b Gatwick Metro Centre, Balcombe Road, Horley, Surrey, RH6 9GA Tel: (01293) 874444 Fax: (01293) 874454

Kuehne + Nagel Ltd, Hays House, Sunrise Parkway, Linford Wood, Milton Keynes, MK14 6BW Tel: (01908) 255000 Fax: (01908) 255200

Kuehne & Nagel Ltd, Building 317, World Freight Terminal, Manchester Airport, Manchester, M90 5NA Tel: 0161-436 9400 Fax: 0161-436 9429 E-mail: manfa@kuehne-nagel.com

Meatingpoint A.B., 27 The Business Exchange, Rockingham Rd, Kettering, Northants, NN16 8JX Tel: (01536) 526477 Fax: (01536) 526478 E-mail: malcolm.morrison@meatingpoint.com

Motivated Engineering Techniques Ltd, Roseville, Tongue End, Spalding, Lincolnshire, PE11 3JJ Tel: (01775) 670361 Fax: (01775) 670371

Supply Control Ltd, Broomlea, Pacemuir Road, Kilmacolm, Renfrewshire, PA13 4JJ Tel: (01505) 873255 E-mail: neilm@supplycontrol.com

SUPPLY CHAIN MANAGEMENT (SCM) SOFTWARE

▶ Business Collaborator, North Reading Bridge House, George Street, Reading, RG1 8LS Tel: (0870) 1632555 Fax: (0870) 1632550 E-mail: sales@groupbc.com

▶ Openda Ltd, PO Box 2774, Swindon, SN5 3NY Tel: (0870) 0411890 Fax: (0870) 0411899 E-mail: enquiries@openda.com

▶ Synchro Ltd, Design Centre 2.3, Coventry Universtiy, Technology Park, Puma Way, Coventry, CV1 2TT Tel: (024) 7679 2200 E-mail: info@synchroltd.com

T I S Software Ltd, Regatta Place, Marlow Road, Bourne End, Buckinghamshire, SL8 5TD Tel: (01628) 532565 Fax: (01628) 532514 E-mail: info@tissoft.co.uk

SUPPLY TEACHER RECRUITMENT

A S A Law, Glade House, 52 Carter Lane, London, EC4V 5JL Tel: (020) 7236 2395 Fax: (020) 7246 4746

▶ Twenty Four Seven, 1 Marsel House, Stephensons Way, Ilkley, West Yorkshire, LS29 8DD Tel: (01943) 604777 Fax: (01943) 604800 E-mail: education@247recruitment.org.uk

SURFACE ACOUSTIC WAVE (SAW) COMPONENTS

Ridley Sawmill, Ansty, Salisbury, SP3 5QD Tel: (01747) 870351 Fax: (01747) 870351

SURFACE ACOUSTIC WAVE (SAW) FILTERS

Mircro Networks Ltd, Unit 5, Dorcan Bus Village, Murdoch Road, Swindon, SN3 5HY Tel: (01793) 613991 Fax: (01793) 613977 E-mail: sales@mnc.com

Thales Computers, Cornwell Business Park, 31 Salthouse Road, Brackmills Industrial Estate, Northampton, NN4 7EX Tel: (01604) 700221 Fax: (01604) 700112 E-mail: sales@thalescomputers.co.uk

SURFACE AND INSPECTION ENGINEERS TABLES

▶ Eley Metrology Ltd, Beaufort House Beaufort Court Industrial Estate, Mansfield Road, Derby, DE21 4FS Tel: (01332) 367475 Fax: (01332) 371435 E-mail: email@eleymet.com

W B J Ltd, Metrology House, Dukinfield Road, Hyde, Cheshire, SK14 4SD Tel: 0161-367 9898 Fax: 0161-367 9700 E-mail: admin@wbj.co.uk

SURFACE COATING CONTRACTORS

Color-Board, Cartersfield Road, Waltham Abbey, Essex, EN9 1JD Tel: (01992) 714382 Fax: (01992) 714938 E-mail: liz@color-board.co.uk

SURFACE COATING MATERIALS, *See Protective Coatings etc*

SURFACE ENERGY MEASUREMENT CONTACT ANGLE METERS

Tantec UK Ltd, P O Box 9593, Tamworth, Staffordshire, B78 3HS Tel: (01827) 284244 Fax: (01827) 286311 E-mail: chris@merciasystems.co.uk

SURFACE ENERGY MEASUREMENT INK TEST KITS

Tantec UK Ltd, P O Box 9593, Tamworth, Staffordshire, B78 3HS Tel: (01827) 284244 Fax: (01827) 286311 E-mail: chris@merciasystems.co.uk

SURFACE ENGINEERING

Tamworth Heat Treatment Ltd, 7 Darwell Park, Mica Close, Tamworth, Staffordshire, B77 4DR Tel: (01827) 318030 Fax: (01827) 318039

SURFACE FINISHING TOOLS/ EQUIPMENT

Balco Engineering Ltd, 35 Nursery Road, Hockley, Birmingham, B19 2XN Tel: 0121-523 0853 Fax: 0121-554 0597 E-mail: balcoeng@aol.com

SURFACE GRINDING

Accurate Grinding, Unit 6 Dawsons Lane, Barwell, Leicester, LE9 8BE Tel: (01455) 840888 Fax: (01455) 840888

Advance Metal Components Ltd, Units 12-14, Minters Industrial Estate, Southwall Road, Deal, Kent, CT14 9PZ Tel: (01304) 380574 Fax: (01304) 380619 E-mail: sales@amc-uk.com

Ajs Profiles, Unit 12a Parkrose Industrial Estate, Middlemore Road, Smethwick, West Midlands, B66 2DZ Tel: 0121-565 5379 Fax: 0121-565 5379 E-mail: ajsprofiles.ltd@virgin.net

▶ Charles Day Steels Ltd, Downgate Drive, Sheffield, S4 8BT Tel: 0114-244 5544 Fax: 0114-244 5588 E-mail: sales@daysteel.co.uk

Enterprise Grinding Ltd, 58 Sapcote Trading Centre, Powke Lane, Cradley Heath, West Midlands, B64 5QX Tel: (01384) 413598 Fax: (01384) 413599

SURFACE GRINDING – *continued*

General Utilities Stockport Ltd, Clough Works, Middlewood Road, Poynton, Stockport, Cheshire, SK12 1SJ Tel: (01625) 876321 Fax: (01625) 876284 E-mail: sales@generalutilities.co.uk

Kenworth Engineering Ltd, Jackson Place, Wilton Road Industrial Estate, Humberston, Grimsby, North East Lincolnshire, DN36 4AS Tel: (01472) 210678 Fax: (01472) 210912 E-mail: rob@kenworthengineering.co.uk

Premier Bodies Ltd, Llay Hall Industrial Estate, Mold Road, Cefn Y Bedd, Wrexham, Clwyd, LL12 9YG Tel: (01978) 762224 Fax: (01978) 762693

SURFACE GRINDING DIAMOND WHEELS

Dorey's Ltd, 13-15 Oakford, Kingsteignton, Newton Abbot, Devon, TQ12 3EQ Tel: (01626) 361200 Fax: (01626) 361205 E-mail: dorey's@btconnect.com

▶ Floor Prep Services Ltd, 38c Hoylake Road, South Park Industrial Estate, Scunthorpe, North Lincolnshire, DN17 2AZ Tel: (07710) 248677 Fax: (01724) 875353 E-mail: Info@floorprepservices.co.uk

SURFACE HEATING PANELS

Infro Heat Ltd, 2 Landport Road, Wolverhampton, WV2 2QJ Tel: (01902) 351025 Fax: (01902) 352552 E-mail: sales@infroheat.co.uk

SURFACE LIQUID DRAINAGE SYSTEMS

ElkinTatic, Hammond House, Holmestone Road, Poulton Close, Dover, Kent, CT17 0UF Tel: (01304) 203545 Fax: (01304) 215001 E-mail: acp@gaticdover.co.uk

SURFACE MOUNT (SM) REFLOW EQUIPMENT

Mekko Technologies, Matrix House, Unit 20, Leicester, LE1 1PL Tel: 0116-251 4648 E-mail: enquiries@mekko.co.uk

SURFACE MOUNT (SM) REWORK EQUIPMENT, SURFACE MOUNT TECHNOLOGY (SMT)

Cooper Rason Ltd, 30 Victoria Street, Irthlingborough, Wellingborough, Northamptonshire, NN9 5RG Tel: (01933) 650950 Fax: (01933) 652821 E-mail: sales@cooper-rason.co.uk

Eurotec Industries Ltd, Unit 3 Stanley Centre, Kelvin Way, Crawley, West Sussex, RH10 9SE Tel: (01293) 846000 Fax: (01293) 613600 E-mail: sales@pdrsmt.com

SURFACE MOUNT (SM) TAPING SERVICES

Iota Device Programming Ltd, Unit A1, Sandy Business Park, Gosforth Close, Sandy, Bedfordshire, SG19 1RB Tel: (01767) 692228 Fax: (01767) 699927 E-mail: sales@iotadpl.co.uk

SURFACE MOUNT TECHNOLOGY (SMT) INSPECTION EQUIPMENT

Cooper Rason Ltd, 30 Victoria Street, Irthlingborough, Wellingborough, Northamptonshire, NN9 5RG Tel: (01933) 650950 Fax: (01933) 652821 E-mail: sales@cooper-rason.co.uk

Rem Electronic Equipment, Arkle House, Mill Lane, Birch, Colchester, CO2 0NG Tel: (01206) 331657 Fax: (01206) 331657

SURFACE MOUNTED (SM) ASSEMBLY SERVICES

Brantham Engineering Ltd, 3l Moss Road, Witham, Essex, CM8 3UQ Tel: (01376) 518384 Fax: (01376) 518900 E-mail: mail@brantham.com

Challenger Solutions Ltd, Unit 85 Haltwhistle Road, South Woodham Ferrers, Chelmsford, CM3 5ZA Tel: (01245) 325252 Fax: (01245) 325301 E-mail: jon@challengersolutions.com

Ketech Systems, Glaisdale Dr East, Nottingham, NG8 4GR Tel: 0115-900 5600 Fax: 0115-900 5601 E-mail: enquiry@ketech.com

M R P Electronics plc, 59 Brunel Road, Bedford, MK41 9TJ Tel: (01234) 216222 Fax: (01234) 219000 E-mail: sales@mrpplc.co.uk

Technology Services, W2 Warrington Business Park, Long Lane, Warrington, WA2 8TX Tel: (01925) 444621 Fax: (01925) 492221

Wildtrax Electronics Ltd, Unit 11A Southcourt Road, Worthing, West Sussex, BN14 7DF Tel: 0845 5314279 Fax: (01903) 212003 E-mail: howard@wildtrax.com

SURFACE MOUNTED (SM) ASSEMBLY/COMPONENT MAINTENANCE/REPAIR SERVICES

Kelectronic, 1 Waterworks Road, Portsmouth, PO6 1NG Tel: (023) 9237 2077 Fax: (023) 9237 2077 E-mail: kelectronic.uk@aol.com

SURFACE MOUNTED (SM) ASSEMBLY/COMPONENT MANUFRS

B N Precision Assemblies, Unit 10, Portsmouth Enterprise Centre, Quartremaine Road, Portsmouth, PO3 5QT Tel: (023) 9266 6444 Fax: (023) 9266 6444

Coilcraft (U K), 21 Napier Place, Wardpark North, Cumbernauld, Glasgow, G68 0LL Tel: (01236) 730595 Fax: (01236) 730627 E-mail: sales@coilcraft-europe.com

Corintech Ltd, Ashford Mill, 118-122 Station Road, Fordingbridge, Hampshire, SP6 1DZ Tel: (01425) 655655 Fax: (01425) 652756 E-mail: info@corintech.co.uk

Partnertech Poole Ltd, Turnkey House, 31 Benson Road, Nuffield Industrial Estate, Poole, Dorset, BH17 0RY Tel: (01202) 674333 Fax: (01202) 678028 E-mail: info@hansatech.co.uk

Reel Service Ltd, 55-56 Nasmyth Road, Glenrothes, Fife, KY6 2SD Tel: (01592) 773208 Fax: (01592) 774696 E-mail: gchristison@reelserviceltd.com

Tekmar Electronics Ltd, Wincombe Business Park, Shaftesbury, Dorset, SP7 9QJ Tel: (01747) 855348 Fax: (01747) 851004 E-mail: tekmargroup@aol.com

SURFACE MOUNTED (SM) ASSEMBLY/COMPONENT PRODUCTION EQUIPMENT MANUFRS

Elite Engineering Ltd, 1 Davis Way, Fareham, Hampshire, PO14 1JF Tel: (01329) 231435 Fax: (01329) 822759 E-mail: sales@elite-eng.co.uk

Screen Art Enterprises, Industrial Estate, St. Ives, Cambridgeshire, PE27 3LE Tel: (01480) 464649 Fax: (01480) 496426

Tekmar Electronics Ltd, Wincombe Business Park, Shaftesbury, Dorset, SP7 9QJ Tel: (01747) 855348 Fax: (01747) 851004 E-mail: tekmargroup@aol.com

SURFACE MOUNTED (SM) CAPACITORS

Syfer Technology Ltd, Old Stoke Road, Arminghall, Norwich, NR14 8SQ Tel: (01603) 629721 Fax: (01603) 665001 E-mail: sales@syfer.co.uk

SURFACE MOUNTED (SM) INDUCTORS

Total Frequency Control Ltd, Units 3-4 Mill Lane, Storrington, West Sussex, RH20 4NF Tel: (01903) 740000 Fax: (01903) 742208 E-mail: sales@tfc.co.uk

SURFACE MOUNTED (SM) LED DISPLAYS

Oxley Developments Co. Ltd, Priory Park, Ulverston, Cumbria, LA12 9QG Tel: (01229) 582621 Fax: (01229) 483263 E-mail: sales@oxleygroup.com

SURFACE MOUNTED (SM) PRINTED CIRCUIT ASSEMBLIES

A C W Technology Ltd, Comines Way, Hedge End, Southampton, SO30 4XX Tel: (023) 8048 6000 Fax: (023) 8048 6001 E-mail: welcome@acw.co.uk

Davlec Ltd, Unit 16, Severn Farm Industrial Estate, Welshpool, Powys, SY21 7DF Tel: (01938) 555791 Fax: (01938) 555792 E-mail: sales@davlec.com

SURFACE MOUNTED (SM) PRINTED CIRCUIT BOARD (PCB) MAINTENANCE OR REPAIR

▶ Trenton Technical Services Ltd, 6 Botley Road, Hedge End, Southampton, SO30 2HE Tel: (01489) 796243 Fax: (01489) 797503 E-mail: sales@trentontechnical.com

SURFACE PREPARATION CLEANING ACCESSORIES

Meech S C T Ltd, 2 Network Point, Range Road, Witney, Oxfordshire, OX29 0YD Tel: (01993) 706700 Fax: (01933) 776977 E-mail: sales@meech.com

SURFACE PREPARATION CONTRACTORS OR SERVICES

▶ Preparation Group, Deacon Road, Lincoln, LN2 4JB Tel: (0870) 2243606 Fax: (0870) 2243607 E-mail: sales@ppcgroup.co.uk

SURFACE PREPARATION CONTRACTORS/SERVICES, FOR COATING ETC

Kue Engineering Ltd, Unit 6, Birksland Street, Bradford, West Yorkshire, BD3 9SU Tel: (01274) 669516 Fax: (01274) 720088

Tech-Ni-Plant Ltd, Unit 4 Holt Court North Heneage, Street West Aston Science Park, Birmingham, B7 4AX Tel: 0121-359 8545 Fax: 0121-333 4950

N.L. Williams Group Ltd, Westside Industrial Estate, Jackson Street, St. Helens, Merseyside, WA9 3AT Tel: (01744) 26526 Fax: (01744) 22551 E-mail: enquiries@safetysurfacing.uk.com

SURFACE PREPARATION EQUIPMENT

▶ Preparation Group, Deacon Road, Lincoln, LN2 4JB Tel: (0870) 2243606 Fax: (0870) 2243607 E-mail: sales@ppcgroup.co.uk

SURFACE PREPARATION EQUIPMENT FOR COATING

▶ Refina Ltd, Unit 7 Upton Industrial Estate, Factory Road, Poole, Dorset, BH16 5SL Tel: (01202) 632270 Fax: (01202) 632432 E-mail: sales@refina.co.uk

SURFACE ROUGHNESS GAUGE MANUFRS

Rubert & Co. Ltd, Acru Works, Demmings Road, Cheadle, Cheshire, SK8 2PG Tel: 0161-428 5855 Fax: 0161-428 1146 E-mail: info@rubert.co.uk

SURFACE TABLES, GRANITE

▶ Amg Stone Products Ltd, Rosedale, Stonehaven Road, Aberdeen, AB12 5UT Tel: (01224) 877283 Fax: (01224 873462 E-mail: info@amgstoneproducts.com

SURFACE TREATMENT EQUIPMENT

Odlings M C R Ltd, Rosscliffe Road, Junction 8 Business Centre, Ellesmere Port, CH65 3AS Tel: 0151-355 0261 Fax: 0151-356 4423 E-mail: sales@odlingsmcr.co.uk

SURFACE TREATMENT, CHEMICAL CONVERSION, ALUMINIUM

Honeyglen Anodising Limited, 62, Sampson Road North, Sparkbrook, Birmingham, B11 1BG Tel: 0121 7736179 Fax: 0121 7667021 E-mail: john@honeyglen.co.uk

SURFACE TREATMENT, CHEMICAL CONVERSION, ALUMINIUM ALLOYS

Honeyglen Anodising Limited, 62, Sampson Road North, Sparkbrook, Birmingham, B11 1BG Tel: 0121 7736179 Fax: 0121 7667021 E-mail: john@honeyglen.co.uk

SURFACE WATER FILTER OR FILTRATION SYSTEMS

K.K. Balers Ltd, Victory House, Victory Park Road, Addlestone, Surrey, KT15 2AX Tel: (01932) 852423 Fax: (01932) 847170 E-mail: sales@kkbalers.com

SURFACTANTS

Anikem Ltd, 18 North Gate, Harborne, Birmingham, B17 9EP Tel: 0121-428 1355 Fax: 0121-428 1366 E-mail: sales@anikem.co.uk

Stepan UK Ltd, Bridge House, Bridge Street, Stalybridge, Cheshire, SK15 1PH Tel: 0161-338 5511 Fax: 0161-338 4245 E-mail: sales@stepanuk.com

SURGE AND TRANSIENT PROTECTION DEVICES

Surgetech Ltd, Durlston House, North Street, Westbourne, Emsworth, Hampshire, PO10 8SN Tel: (01243) 379613 Fax: (01243) 370003 E-mail: bill.jones@surgetech.co.uk

SURGE ARRESTERS/CONTROL EQUIPMENT, HYDRAULIC/WATER

Fawcett Christie Hydraulics Ltd, Sandycroft Industrial Estate, Chester Road, Sandycroft, Deeside, Clwyd, CH5 2QP Tel: (01244) 535515 Fax: (01244) 533002 E-mail: sales@fch.co.uk

▶ Flowguard Ltd, Watford Bridge Road, New Mills, High Peak, Derbyshire, SK22 4HJ Tel: (01663) 745976 Fax: (01663) 742788 E-mail: sales@flowguard.com

G E Energy UK Ltd, Kvaerner House, Ten Pound Walk, Doncaster, South Yorkshire, DN4 5HW Tel: (01302) 761761 Fax: (01302) 760230

Morton & Bone Services, PO Box 1, Gairloch, Ross-Shire, IV21 2AY Tel: (01445) 712322 Fax: (01445) 712310 E-mail: stopsurge@aol.com

Mountfold, Roberts Farm, Mount Bures, Bures, Suffolk, CO8 5AZ Tel: 01787229955

SURGE ARRESTERS/DIVERTERS, ELECTRIC

A N Wallis, Greasley Street, Nottingham, NG6 8NG Tel: 0115-927 1721 Fax: 0115-875 6630 E-mail: info@an-wallis.com

Telematic Ltd, Pondwicks Road, Luton, LU1 3LH Tel: (01582) 429464 Fax: (01582) 459669 E-mail: admin@telematic.com

Tyco Electronics Ltd Bowthorpe Emp, Unit 8 A Freshfield Industrial Estate, Stevenson Road, Brighton, BN2 0DF Tel: (01273) 692591 Fax: (01273) 601741 E-mail: craig.sutton@bowthorpe-emp.com

SURGICAL APPLIANCES, *See also Medical Supply etc*

A H Shaw & Partner, Phoenix Works, Manor Road, Ossett, West Yorkshire, WF5 0LF Tel: (01924) 273474 Fax: (01924) 273474

Bodys Surgical Care Centre, 631 London Road, Westcliff-on-Sea, Essex, SS0 9PE Tel: (01702) 346204 Fax: (01702) 338631

Buchanan Orthotics Ltd, Suite 4-2 Sky Park SK5, 45 Finnieston Street, Glasgow, G3 8JU Tel: 0141-221 9997 Fax: 0141-221 1345 E-mail: sales@buchananorthotics.freeserve.co.uk

Charter Health Care, Unit 1, The Links, Bakewell Road, Orton Southgate, Peterborough, PE2 6BJ Tel: 0800 132787

Chiropody Appliance Service, P O Box 32, Colyton, Devon, EX24 6YR Tel: (01297) 553818 Fax: (01297) 553818

▶ Djo UK Ltd, 7 The Pines Business Park, Broad Street, Guildford, Surrey, GU3 3BH Tel: (01483) 452964 Fax: (01483) 459470

Dudley Surgical Appliances Ltd, Horseley Heath, Tipton, West Midlands, DY4 7AA Tel: 0121-557 4204 Fax: 0121-520 1283 E-mail: dudsurg@aol.com

E Smith & Co, Albion Street, Hull, HU1 3TE Tel: (01482) 324599 Fax: (01482) 588266

Gilbert & Mellish Ltd, 3 Lightning Way, Birmingham, B31 3PH Tel: 0121-475 1101 Fax: 0121-478 0163 E-mail: sales@gilbert-mellish.co.uk

P V O'Neill Ltd, 32a Commercial Street, Shipley, West Yorkshire, BD18 3SP Tel: (01274) 584716 Fax: (01274) 596598

Prescription Footwear Associates Ltd, P F A House, Lake Lane, Barnham, Bognor Regis, West Sussex, PO22 0JB Tel: (01243) 554407 Fax: (01243) 554407 E-mail: sales@pfa.sageweb.co.uk

RSL Steeper Ltd, Cavendish Road, Manchester, M20 1LB Tel: 0161-434 4167 Fax: 0161-448 9446

SURGICAL APPLIANCES – *continued*

Sallis Healthcare Ltd, Waterford Street, Nottingham, NG6 0DH Tel: 0115-978 7841 Fax: 0115-942 2272 E-mail: info@sallis.co.uk

Salts Healthcare Ltd, Unit 2 Richard Street, Birmingham, B7 4AA Tel: 0121-333 2000 Fax: 0121-359 0830 E-mail: salt@salts.co.uk

SURGICAL BANDAGES

G E Bridge & Co. Ltd, 123-125 Old Christchurch Road, Bournemouth, BH1 1HF Tel: (01202) 204802 Fax: (01202) 204800

Steroplast, Alpha Point, Bradnor Road, Sharston Industrial Area, Manchester, M22 4TE Tel: 0161-902 3030 Fax: 0161-902 3040 E-mail: sales@steroplast.co.uk

SURGICAL BIOPSY NEEDLES

Tomlinson Tube & Instrument Ltd, Unit 4C Waterloo Industrial Estate, Waterloo Road, Bidford-on-Avon, Alcester, Warwickshire, B50 4JH Tel: (01789) 778966 Fax: (01789) 490239 E-mail: keith@tomlinson-tube.co.uk

SURGICAL BLADES

▶ Lance Paragon Ltd, Owlerton Green, Sheffield, S6 2BJ Tel: 0114- 255 1063 E-mail: info@lance-paragon.co.uk

Unomedical Ltd, 26-27 Thornhill Road, Redditch, Worcestershire, B98 9NL Tel: (01527) 587700 Fax: (01527) 592111 E-mail: redditch@unomedical.com

SURGICAL DRESSINGS

Convatec Ltd, Milton Road, Uxbridge, Middlesex, UB10 8EF Tel: (01895) 628400 Fax: (01895) 628456

Johnson & Johnson Finance Ltd, Coronation Road, Ascot, Berkshire, SL5 9EY Tel: (01344) 864140 Fax: (01344) 871133 E-mail: enquiries@johnsonandjohnson.com

Naturellr Consumer Products Ltd, 21 Mountjoy Road, Omagh, County Tyrone, BT79 7EQ Tel: (028) 8224 9396 Fax: (028) 8224 7793 E-mail: info@naturelle.ie

Robinson Healthcare Ltd, Lawn Road, Carlton In Lindrick, Carlton-in-Lindrick, Worksop, Nottinghamshire, S81 9LB Tel: (01909) 735001 Fax: (01909) 731103 E-mail: enquiry@robinsoncare.com

Frank Sammeroff Ltd, 131 Woodhead Road, Glasgow, G53 7NN Tel: 0141-881 5701 Fax: 0141-881 4919 E-mail: info@sammeroff.co.uk

Steroplast, Alpha Point, Bradnor Road, Sharston Industrial Area, Manchester, M22 4TE Tel: 0161-902 3030 Fax: 0161-902 3040 E-mail: sales@steroplast.co.uk

Unomedical Ltd, 26-27 Thornhill Road, Redditch, Worcestershire, B98 9NL Tel: (01527) 587700 Fax: (01527) 592111 E-mail: redditch@unomedical.com

SURGICAL FOOTWEAR

Dudley Surgical Appliances Ltd, Horseley Heath, Tipton, West Midlands, DY4 7AA Tel: 0121-557 4204 Fax: 0121-520 1283 E-mail: dudsurg@aol.com

Moore Bros Ltd, 12 Cashel Road, Birkenhead, Merseyside, CH41 1DY Tel: 0151-639 6252 Fax: 0151-639 6252

Moore Bros Surgical Ltd, Unit 8, The Headlands, Salisbury Road, Salisbury, SP5 3JJ Tel: (01725) 512551 Fax: (01725) 512699 E-mail: moore.bros@virgin.net

R X Laboratories, Unit 12, Ryeland Farm Industrial Estate, Wellington, Somerset, TA21 9PZ Tel: (01823) 660429 Fax: (01823) 660429 E-mail: sales@rxlabs.com

Jane Saunders & Manning Ltd, 1070-1072 London Road, Thornton Heath, Surrey, CR7 7ND Tel: (020) 8684 2364 Fax: (020) 8665 5968 E-mail: sales@jsmltd.co.uk

Sterling Upper Co Surgical Ltd, 2 36-38 Beaconsfield Road, St. George, Bristol, BS5 8ER Tel: 0117-955 6520 Fax: 0117-941 2060

Taycare Medical Ltd, 351 Tong Road, Leeds, LS12 4QG Tel: 0113-231 1800 Fax: 0113-231 1805 E-mail: ben.taylor@taycare.com

SURGICAL HOSIERY, GOODS AND ORTHOPAEDIC SUNDRIES

Auto-Med Technologies Ltd, 127 North Gate, Nottingham, NG7 7FZ Tel: 0115-919 1234 Fax: 0115-919 1236 E-mail: sales@auto-med.com

B D S Ltd, Grangestone Industrial Estate, Ladywell Avenue, Girvan, Ayrshire, KA26 9PL Tel: (01465) 714848 Fax: (01465) 713857 E-mail: contact@bdf.ltd.uk

Credenhill Ltd, 10 Cossall Industrial Estate, Cossall Industrial Estate, Ilkeston, Derbyshire, DE7 5UG Tel: 0115-932 0144 Fax: 0115-944 0437 E-mail: sales@credenhill.co.uk

Dudley Surgical Appliances Ltd, Horseley Heath, Tipton, West Midlands, DY4 7AA Tel: 0121-557 4204 Fax: 0121-520 1283 E-mail: dudsurg@aol.com

Medi UK, Plough Lane, Hereford, HR4 0EL Tel: (01432) 373500 Fax: (01432) 373510 E-mail: enquiries@mediuk.co.uk

S T D Pharmaceutical Products Ltd, Plough Lane, Hereford, HR4 0EL Tel: (01432) 373555 Fax: (01432) 371314 E-mail: enquries@stdpharm.co.uk

W Brewin & Co Ltd, Eastern Boulevard, Leicester, LE2 7BE Tel: 0116-254 6372 Fax: 0116-254 2856

SURGICAL IMPORT/EXPORT MERCHANTS OR AGENTS

Derwick Ltd, 14 Westwood Close, Potters Bar, Hertfordshire, EN6 1LH Tel: (01707) 645855 Fax: (01707) 857291 E-mail: m.anjarwalla@btconnect.com

SURGICAL INSTRUMENT MAINTENANCE/REPAIR SERVICES

Abbey Surgical Repairs, Silver Wing Industrial Estate, Horatius Way, Croydon, CR0 4RU Tel: (020) 8688 8555 Fax: (020) 8688 8557 E-mail: info@abbeysurgical.com

B & H Surgical Instrument Makers, Unit C2 Up Bounds Green Industrial Estate, South Way, London, N11 2UL Tel: (020) 8368 1616 Fax: (020) 8368 0243 E-mail: office@bhsi.co.uk

Duckworth & Kent Ltd, Terence House, 7 Marquis Business Centre, Royston Road, Baldock, Hertfordshire, SG7 6XL Tel: (01462) 893254 Fax: (01462) 896288 E-mail: info@duckworth-and-kent.com

Orthoeurope Ltd, Orth House, Kimber Road, Abingdon, Oxfordshire, OX14 1SG Tel: (01235) 555001 Fax: (01235) 555004 E-mail: info@ortho-europe.com

Tricomed Surgical Ltd, 10 Tenterden Road, Croydon, CR0 6NN Tel: (020) 8656 1924 Fax: (020) 8656 7026 E-mail: tricomed@btconnect.com

SURGICAL INSTRUMENT MANUFRS

A C Cossor & Son Surgical Ltd, Accoson Works, Vale Road, London, N4 1PS Tel: (020) 8800 1172 Fax: (020) 8809 5170 E-mail: accoson@accoson.com

Abbey Surgical Repairs, Silver Wing Industrial Estate, Horatius Way, Croydon, CR0 4RU Tel: (020) 8688 8555 Fax: (020) 8688 8557 E-mail: info@abbeysurgical.com

Andante Medical Services Ltd, Brick Kiln Lane, Horsmonden, Tonbridge, Kent, TN12 8ES Tel: (01892) 724881 Fax: (01892) 535853 E-mail: sales@medicalpromotional.co.uk

B. Braun Medical Ltd, Brookdale Road, Thorncliffe Park Estate, Chapeltown, Sheffield, S35 2PW Tel: 0114-225 9000 Fax: 0114-225 9111 E-mail: info@bbraun.com

B & H Surgical Instrument Makers, Unit C2 Up Bounds Green Industrial Estate, South Way, London, N11 2UL Tel: (020) 8368 1616 Fax: (020) 8368 0243 E-mail: office@bhsi.co.uk

B M Brown, Pincents Kiln Industrial Park, Pincents Kiln, Calcot, Reading, RG31 7SB Tel: 0118-930 5333 Fax: 0118-930 5111 E-mail: enquiries@bmbrowne.co.uk

Beckett Instruments Ltd, 533 Rayleigh Road, Benfleet, Essex, SS7 3TN Tel: (01268) 773653 Fax: (01268) 745697 E-mail: beckettinstruments@btinternet.com

Biomerieux UK Ltd, Grafton Way, Basingstoke, Hampshire, RG22 6HY Tel: (01256) 461881 Fax: (01256) 816863

Biomet Merck Ltd, Waterton Industrial Estate, Waterton Industrial Estate, Bridgend, Mid Glamorgan, CF31 3XA Tel: (01656) 655221 Fax: (01656) 645454

C Bolter Ltd, Carlton Works, St Johns Hill, Sevenoaks, Kent, TN13 3NS Tel: (01732) 457010 Fax: (01732) 740904

Caterham Surgical Supplies Ltd, 89A Gloucester Road, Croydon, CR0 2DN Tel: (020) 8683 1103 Fax: (020) 8683 1105 E-mail: info@caterhamsurgical.co.uk

Central Surgical Co. Ltd, 82a-84a Hornsey Road, London, N7 7NN Tel: (020) 7609 7259 Fax: (020) 7700 1328 E-mail: info@centralsurgical.co.uk

▶ Dentafix UK Ltd, Unit 11-13, Helix Business Park, Camberley, Surrey, GU15 2QT Tel: (01276) 691821 Fax: (01276) 23490 E-mail: info@dentafix.co.uk

Dixey Instruments, 5 High Street, N Hykeham, Northampton, NN6 9DD Tel: (01522) 683152 Fax: (01604) 882488 E-mail: info@dixeyinstruments.com

Duckworth & Kent Ltd, Terence House, 7 Marquis Business Centre, Royston Road, Baldock, Hertfordshire, SG7 6XL Tel: (01462) 893254 Fax: (01462) 896288 E-mail: info@duckworth-and-kent.com

Exmoor Plastics, Unit 2 4 Trinity Business Centre, South Street, Taunton, Somerset, TA1 3AQ Tel: (01823) 276837 Fax: (01823) 334154 E-mail: sales@exmoorplastics.co.uk

Henleys Medical Supplies Ltd, Brownfields, Welwyn Garden City, Hertfordshire, AL7 1AN Tel: (01707) 333164 Fax: (01707) 334795 E-mail: sales@henleysmed.com

Innovision Surgical Ltd, 25 West Midlands Freeport, Birmingham International Airport, Birmingham, B26 3QD Tel: 0121-782 0105 Fax: 0121-782 2249 E-mail: ray@innovision.fsnet.co.uk

▶ Lance Paragon Ltd, Owlerton Green, Sheffield, S6 2BJ Tel: 0114- 255 1063 E-mail: info@lance-paragon.co.uk

Landmark Surgical Ltd, 21 Woodland Road, Birkenhead, Merseyside, CH42 4NT Tel: 0151-643 1323 Fax: 0151-643 9312 E-mail: landmarksurgical@btconnect.com

Lyall Willis & Co. Ltd, 49 Cooden Sea Road, Bexhill-on-Sea, East Sussex, TN39 4SL Tel: (01424) 848388 Fax: (01424) 848399 E-mail: info@lyallwillis.co.uk

Mediworld Ltd, 444 - 446 Streatham High Road, London, SW16 3PX Tel: (020) 8764 1806 Fax: (020) 8679 2489 E-mail: sales@mediworld.co.uk

Nikomed Ltd, Stuart Court, Salisbury Road, Romsey, Hampshire, SO51 6DJ Tel: (01794) 525100 Fax: (01794) 525101 E-mail: sales@nikomed.co.uk

R B Medical, 2 Alton Road Industrial Estate, Ross-on-Wye, Herefordshire, HR9 5ND Tel: (01989) 563958 Fax: (01989) 768267 E-mail: a.ross@rimbros.co.uk

Research Instruments Ltd, Kernick Road, Penryn, Cornwall, TR10 9DQ Tel: (01326) 372753 Fax: (01326) 378783 E-mail: sales@research-instruments.com

▶ Royal Surrey County Hospital, Egerton Road, Guildford, Surrey, GU2 7XX Tel: (01483) 464054 Fax: (01483) 406899

▶ S J T Medical, Spartan Works, 20 Carlisle Street, Sheffield, S4 7LJ Tel: 0114-272 8273 Fax: 0114-220 1172 E-mail: info@sjtmedical.com

S Murray & Co. Ltd, Holborn House, High Street, Old Woking, Woking, Surrey, GU22 9LB Tel: (01483) 740099 Fax: (01483) 755111 E-mail: sales@smurray.co.uk

Saharan Trading, 6 Blackburn Road, Rotherham, South Yorkshire, S61 2DR Tel: (01709) 557711 Fax: (01709) 557700 E-mail: info@saharantrading.co.uk

Scala Surgical Ltd, 200 Church Road, London, NW10 9NP Tel: (020) 8459 1816 Fax: (020) 8459 3416 E-mail: scala_impex@yahoo.co.uk

Surgical Holdings Ltd, 8 Parkside Centre, Potters Way, Southend-on-Sea, SS2 5SJ Tel: (01702) 602050 Fax: (01702) 460006 E-mail: office@surgicalholdings.co.uk

Tomlinson Tube & Instrument Ltd, Unit 4C Waterloo Industrial Estate, Waterloo Road, Bidford-on-Avon, Alcester, Warwickshire, B50 4JH Tel: (01789) 778966 Fax: (01789) 490239 E-mail: keith@tomlinson-tube.co.uk

Topline Instruments Co., 7 Craven Avenue, Southall, Middlesex, UB1 2DJ Tel: (020) 8867 9701 Fax: (020) 8867 9702

Tricomed Surgical Ltd, 10 Tenterden Road, Croydon, CR0 6NN Tel: (020) 8656 1924 Fax: (020) 8656 7026 E-mail: tricomed@btconnect.com

Uniplex (UK) Ltd, 11 Furnace Hill, Sheffield, S3 7AF Tel: 0114-272 6858 Fax: 0114-272 7288 E-mail: sales@uniplex-uk.com

John Weiss & Son Ltd, 89 Alston Drive, Bradwell Abbey, Milton Keynes, MK13 9HF Tel: (01908) 318017 Fax: (01908) 318708 E-mail: sales@johnweiss.com

SURGICAL NEEDLES

Entaco Ltd, Royal Victoria Works, Birmingham Road, Studley, Warwickshire, B80 7AP Tel: (01527) 852306 Fax: (01527) 857447 E-mail: sales@entaco.com

▶ Richard-Allan Medical Industries (UK) Ltd, 95 Bromsgrove Raod, Redditch, Worcestershire, B97 4RL Tel: (01527) 460302 Fax: (01527) 460303 E-mail: m.penver@blueyonder.co.uk

Sterimedix Ltd, Unit 6/7, Kingfisher Business Park, Arthur Street, Redditch, Worcestershire, B98 8LG Tel: (01527) 501480 Fax: (01527) 501491 E-mail: sales@sterimedix.com

Tomlinson Tube & Instrument Ltd, Unit 4C Waterloo Industrial Estate, Waterloo Road, Bidford-on-Avon, Alcester, Warwickshire, B50 4JH Tel: (01789) 778966 Fax: (01789) 490239 E-mail: keith@tomlinson-tube.co.uk

SURGICAL OR DENTAL OPTICAL LOUPES

▶ S J T Medical, Spartan Works, 20 Carlisle Street, Sheffield, S4 7LJ Tel: 0114-272 8273 Fax: 0114-220 1172 E-mail: info@sjtmedical.com

SURGICAL OR ORTHOPAEDIC IMPLANTS

B. Braun Medical Ltd, Brookdale Road, Thorncliffe Park Estate, Chapeltown, Sheffield, S35 2PW Tel: 0114-225 9000 Fax: 0114-225 9111 E-mail: info@bbraun.com

Biomet Merck Ltd, Waterton Industrial Estate, Waterton Industrial Estate, Bridgend, Mid Glamorgan, CF31 3XA Tel: (01656) 655221 Fax: (01656) 645454

Depuy International Holdings Ltd, St Anthonys Road, Beeston, Leeds, LS11 8DT Tel: 0113-270 0461 Fax: 0113-272 4101 E-mail: depuy@dpygb.jnj.com

J R I Ltd, Unit 18, Sheffield 35A Business Park, Churchill Way, Chapeltown, Sheffield, S35 2PY Tel: 0114-257 3200 Fax: 0114-257 3204 E-mail: manufacturing@jri-ltd.co.uk

Medasil (Surgical) Ltd, Medasil House, Hunslet Road, Leeds, LS10 1AU Tel: 0113-243 3491 Fax: 0113-242 9276 E-mail: medasil@dial.pipex.com

New Splint Ltd, Unitech House, Units B1 B2, Bond Close, Kingsland Buisiness Park, Basingstoke, Hampshire, RG24 8PZ Tel: (01256) 365480 Fax: (01256) 365486 E-mail: sales.dept@newsplint.co.uk

Ortho Dynamics Ltd, Ambassador Industrial Estate, 10 Airfield Road, Christchurch, Dorset, BH23 3TG Tel: (01202) 481153 Fax: (01202) 481150 E-mail: enquiries@orthodynamics.co.uk

Plasma Biotal Ltd, 1 Meverill Road, Tideswell, Buxton, Derbyshire, SK17 8PY Tel: (01298) 872348 Fax: (01299) 873708 E-mail: general@plasma-group.co.uk

▶ Ranier Technology Ltd, Greenhouse Farm, Newmarket Road, Teversham, Cambridge, CB5 8AA Tel: (01223) 505045 Fax: (01223) 505046E-mail: ranier.technology@ranier.co.uk

Sandvik Bioline, Longacre Way, Holbrook, Sheffield, S20 3FS Tel: 0114-263 3100 Fax: 0114-263 3111

Stratec Medical Ltd, 20 Tewin Road, Welwyn Garden City, Hertfordshire, AL7 1LG Tel: (01707) 332212 Fax: (01707) 338504

Stryker UK Ltd, Stryker House, Hambridge Road, Newbury, Berkshire, RG14 5EG Tel: (01635) 262400 Fax: (01635) 580300 E-mail: sales@emea.strykercorp.com

Symmetry Medical, Beulah Road, Sheffield, S6 2AN Tel: (0114) 285 5881 Fax: (0114) 233 6978 E-mail: info@tpcl.com

SURGICAL SCISSORS

Acme United Europe, Estate Office Thorncliffe Park Estate, Newton Chambers Road, Chapeltown, Sheffield, S35 2PH Tel: 0114-220 3709 Fax: 0114-220 3706 E-mail: sales@acmeunited.co.uk

Saharan Trading, 6 Blackburn Road, Rotherham, South Yorkshire, S61 2DR Tel: (01709) 557711 Fax: (01709) 557700 E-mail: info@saharantrading.co.uk

SURGICAL SUPPLY SERVICES OR AGENTS, *See Medical Supply etc*

SURPLUS BEARINGS

Ibd Ltd, 3 City Park Industrial Estate, Gelderd Road, Leeds, LS12 6DR Tel: 0113-279 6988 Fax: 0113-231 0336 E-mail: douglas@barclays.net

SURPLUS CHEMICALS

▶ Konrad Chemicals, Manchester Road, Wilmslow, Cheshire, SK9 2JW Tel: (01625) 531581 Fax: (01625) 529906 E-mail: konradchemicals@ntlworld.com

SURPLUS STEEL TUBES

Ogden Transteel, Butler Way, Town Street, Stanningley, Pudsey, West Yorkshire, LS28 6EZ Tel: 0113-257 8221 Fax: 0113-236 2340 E-mail: ogdentransteel@aol.com

SURPLUS/LIQUIDATED/ REDUNDANT GOODS JOB AND STOCK BULK BUYERS, *See also headings for particular commodities such as Metal etc*

Global Overstock Ltd, 27 Atwood Road, London, W6 0HX Tel: (0800) 0920363 Fax: (020) 8741 9935 E-mail: info@globaloverstock.com

Holroyds, 499 Bath Road, Saltford, Bristol, BS31 3HQ Tel: (01225) 873000 Fax: (01225) 873834 E-mail: info@holroyds.org

John Lawrie Aberdeen Ltd, Forties Road, Montrose, Angus, DD10 9ET Tel: (01674) 672005 Fax: (01674) 677911 E-mail: sales@johnlawrie.com

R W H Stock Solutions Ltd, Station Lane, Offord Cluny, St. Neots, Cambridgeshire, PE19 5ZA Tel: (01480) 813800 Fax: (01480) 813813 E-mail: sales@rwh-enterprises.com

Wheelhouse Ltd, 9-21 Bell Road, Hounslow, TW3 3NS Tel: (020) 8570 3501 Fax: (020) 8570 6666 E-mail: davidh@wheelhouse.ltd.uk

▶ www.liquidatedstocklots.com, 2 Blackburn House, Bedford Road, Aspley Guise, Milton Keynes, MK17 8DH Tel: (01908) 583847

SURROUND SOUND SPEAKER SYSTEMS

B & W Group Ltd, Dale Road, Worthing, West Sussex, BN11 2BH Tel: (01903) 221800 Fax: (01903) 221801 E-mail: info@bwgroup.com

▶ Must Av It, 28 Lattimore Road, Wheathampstead, Hertfordshire, AL4 8QE Tel: 0870 446 0146 Fax: 0870 762 6431 E-mail: info@webstract.co.uk

▶ PA Sound Hire.co.uk, 58 Newport Road, Countess Wear, Topsham, Exeter, EX2 7EE Tel: (01392) 875865 E-mail: andrew@pasoundhire.co.uk

▶ Sound Surround, 12 Belvedere Crescent, Bewdley, Worcestershire, DY12 1JX Tel: 01299 405077 E-mail: soundsurround@bewdley12.freeserve.co.uk

SURVEILLANCE EQUIPMENT (ELECTRONIC) MANUFRS

B S C Snooker Equipment, 24 Newbiggin Road, Grangemouth, Stirlingshire, FK3 0LF Tel: (01324) 473069 Fax: (01324) 473069

Confidential Communications Ltd, 344 Kilburn Lane, London, W9 3EF Tel: (020) 8968 0227 Fax: (020) 8968 0194 E-mail: info@spyestoreuk.com

Crown UK Ltd, Old Mill Road, Portishead, Bristol, BS20 7BX Tel: (01275) 818008 Fax: (01275) 818288 E-mail: mcross@crownukltd.com

First Secure Ltd, 157 Adnitt Rd, Northampton, NN1 4NH Tel: 01604 472060 Fax: 01604 472060

Geutebruck (UK) Ltd, 8 Central Park, Bellfield Road, High Wycombe, Buckinghamshire, HP13 5HG Tel: (01494) 510999 Fax: (01494) 510888 E-mail: info@geutebruck.co.uk

Identec Ltd, Mercantile Road, Rainton Bridge Industrial Estate, Houghton le Spring, Tyne & Wear, DH4 5PH Tel: 0191-584 4084 Fax: 0191-584 9077E-mail: info@identic.co.uk

Lorraine Electronics Surveillance, 716 Lea Bridge Road, London, E10 6AW Tel: (020) 8558 4226 Fax: (020) 8558 1338 E-mail: info@lorraine.co.uk

T R L Technology Ltd, Shannon Way, Ashchurch, Tewkesbury, Gloucestershire, GL20 8ND Tel: (01684) 278700 Fax: (01684) 850406 E-mail: d_hall@trltech.co.uk

Verifeye (UK) Ltd, 1 Branksome Business Centre, Cortry Close, Poole, Dorset, BH12 4BQ Tel: (023) 8028 4727 Fax: (01202) 733366 E-mail: sales@verifeye.co.uk

Visual Surveillance Systems Ltd, 18 Station Road, Drighlington, Bradford, West Yorkshire, BD11 1JU Tel: 0113-285 2324 Fax: 0113-285 3026

SURVEILLANCE EQUIPMENT SUPPORT SYSTEMS

Instro Precision Ltd, Hornet Close, Pysons Road Industrial Estate, Broadstairs, Kent, CT10 2YD Tel: (01843) 604455 Fax: (01843) 861032 E-mail: marketing@instro.com

SURVEILLANCE EQUIPMENT, MOBILE TELEPHONE DETECTION

▶ Pda Electronics Ltd, 7 Bevan Hill, Chesham, Buckinghamshire, HP5 2QS Tel: (01494) 794949 Fax: (01494) 791820 E-mail: info@pdaelectronics.com

SURVEY ELECTRONIC EQUIPMENT/SYSTEMS, SUBSEA/UNDERWATER

Applied Acoustic Engineering Ltd, 3 Marine House, Marine Park, Great Yarmouth, Norfolk, NR31 0NL Tel: (01493) 440355 Fax: (01493) 440720E-mail: general@appliedacoustics.com

Sonardyne Group Ltd, Ocean House, Blackbush Business Park, Yateley, Hampshire, GU46 6GD Tel: (01252) 872288 Fax: (01252) 876100 E-mail: sales@sonardyne.co.uk

SURVEY EQUIPMENT, *See also headings for particular application*

Ashtead Technology Ltd, Unit 3, Kirkton Avenue, Pimedden Road Industrial Estate, Aberdeen, AB21 0BF Tel: (01224) 771888 Fax: (01224) 770129 E-mail: rentals@ashtead-technology.com

Barrow (Don), Sandy Lane, Whirley, Macclesfield, Cheshire, SK10 4RJ Tel: (01625) 429092 Fax: (01625) 429092 E-mail: info@donbarrow.co.uk

Calserv Surveying Instruments, 5 Prospect Way, Rugby, Warwickshire, CV21 3UU Tel: (01788) 553666 Fax: (01788) 551666 E-mail: calserv@calserv.freeserve.co.uk

Holtwood Marketing Ltd, 11 Brassey Drive, Aylesford, Kent, ME20 7QL Tel: (01622) 710921 Fax: (01622) 717945 E-mail: ward@holtwood.co.uk

Leica Geosystems Ltd, 83 Inglis Green Road, Edinburgh, EH14 2EZ Tel: 0131-443 6966 Fax: 0131-443 7825

M B S, Nowhurst Lane, Broadbridge Heath, Horsham, West Sussex, RH12 3PJ Tel: (01403) 263303 Fax: (01403) 263839

Omega Laser Services, Wood End House, Cubley, Penistone, Sheffield, S36 9AW Tel: (01226) 767221 Fax: (01226) 766807

▶ S C C S, Great North Road, Eaton Socon, St. Neots, Cambridgeshire, PE19 8EB Tel: (01480) 404888 Fax: (01480) 404333 E-mail: sona@sccssurvey.co.uk

▶ Speedy Survey Ltd, Unit 3 12 Popes Lane, Oldbury, West Midlands, B69 4PN Tel: 0121-544 7726 Fax: 0121-552 0250 E-mail: sales@speedysurvey.co.uk

Survey Express Services, 9 Manor Parade, Hatfield, Hertfordshire, AL10 9JS Tel: (01707) 273172 Fax: (01707) 270085

Survey Supplies Ltd, The Forge, 1 Cross Street, Eye, Suffolk, IP23 7AB Tel: (01379) 870111 Fax: (01379) 870935

▶ Technology Plus Services Ltd, 28, Newcomen Road, Tunbridge Wells, Kent, TN4 9PA Tel: (01892) 615315 Fax: (01892) 615316

Topcon GB Ltd, 25 Breakfield, Coulsdon, Surrey, CR5 2HS Tel: (020) 8668 2233 Fax: (020) 8668 8322 E-mail: sales@topcon.co.uk

York Survey Supply, Prospect House, George Cayley Drive, Clifton Moor, York, YO30 4XE Tel: (01904) 692723 Fax: (01904) 690385 E-mail: sales@yorksurvey.co.uk

SURVEY EQUIPMENT HIRE

Applied Acoustic Engineering Ltd, 3 Marine House, Marine Park, Great Yarmouth, Norfolk, NR31 0NL Tel: (01493) 440355 Fax: (01493) 440720E-mail: general@appliedacoustics.com

Ashtead Technology Ltd, Unit 3, Kirkton Avenue, Pimedden Road Industrial Estate, Aberdeen, AB21 0BF Tel: (01224) 771888 Fax: (01224) 770129 E-mail: rentals@ashtead-technology.com

Hudsons Instruments & Lasers, 123 Foundry Lane, Southampton, SO15 3GB Tel: (023) 8070 4704 Fax: (023) 8070 2828 E-mail: sales@hudsons-uk.com

J B Sales Ltd, Fircroft Way, Edenbridge, Kent, TN8 6EL Tel: (01732) 867835 Fax: (01732) 867836 E-mail: colin@jbsales.co.uk

Kerryredd Surveying Equipment Ltd, 1206 London Road, London, SW16 4DN Tel: (020) 8679 7233 Fax: (020) 8679 9147

Speedy Survey Ltd, 6 Power Court, Luton, LU1 3JJ Tel: (01582) 722365 Fax: (01582) 424341

Survey Connection Scotland Ltd, Paragon House, Oakbank, Livingston, West Lothian, EH53 0JS Tel: (01506) 881090 Fax: (01506) 884488

Survey Supplies Ltd, The Forge, 1 Cross Street, Eye, Suffolk, IP23 7AB Tel: (01379) 870111 Fax: (01379) 870935

Topcon (Great Britain) Ltd, Unit 17 Swift Business Centre, Keen Road, Ocean Park, Cardiff, CF24 5JR Tel: (029) 2047 0776 Fax: (029) 2047 0779 E-mail: cardiff@topcon.co.uk

SURVEY EQUIPMENT MAINTENANCE OR REPAIR

KOREC, 34-44 Mersey View, Waterloo, Liverpool, L22 6QB Tel: 0845 6031214 Fax: 0151 9315559 E-mail: info@korecgroup.com

Seedy Servey, 122 Hide Park Street, Glasgow, G3 8BW Tel: 0141-204 1744 Fax: 0141-204 1696

Survey Supplies Ltd, The Forge, 1 Cross Street, Eye, Suffolk, IP23 7AB Tel: (01379) 870111 Fax: (01379) 870935

Swiss Tech UK Ltd, Harmill House, 31 Pebblemoor, Edlesborough, Dunstable, Bedfordshire, LU6 2HZ Tel: (01525) 222556 Fax: (01525) 221749 E-mail: fletcherswisstec@aol.com

Topcon (Great Britain) Ltd, Unit 17 Swift Business Centre, Keen Road, Ocean Park, Cardiff, CF24 5JR Tel: (029) 2047 0776 Fax: (029) 2047 0779 E-mail: cardiff@topcon.co.uk

SURVEY SERVICES, SUBSEA/ UNDERWATER

Dolphin Drilling Ltd, Howe Moss Drive, Kirkhill Industrial Estate, Dyce, Aberdeen, AB21 0GL Tel: (01224) 411411 Fax: (01224) 723627

Marine & Offshore Consultants Ltd, Magellan House, James Watt Close, Great Yarmouth, Norfolk, NR31 0NX Tel: (01493) 440166 Fax: (01493) 658490 E-mail: support@modgy.co.uk

Measurement Devices Ltd, Silverburn Crescent, Bridge of Don Industrial Estate, Aberdeen, AB23 8EW Tel: (01224) 246700 Fax: (01224) 824987 E-mail: info@mdl.co.uk

Submersible Television Surveys Ltd, 4 Barratt Trading Estate, Denmore Road, Bridge of Don, Aberdeen, AB23 8JW Tel: (01224) 823333 Fax: (01224) 824639 E-mail: admin@stsrov.com

SURVIVAL CRAFTS

Survival Craft, Findon Shore, Findon/Portlethen, Portlethen, Aberdeen, AB12 3RL Tel: (01224) 784488 Fax: (01224) 784111 E-mail: info@survivalcraft.com

Survival Systems International UK Ltd, Viking Road, Great Yarmouth, Norfolk, NR31 0NU Tel: (01493) 659411 Fax: (01493) 655425 E-mail: admin@survivalsystemsint.com

SURVIVAL EQUIPMENT/LIFE SUPPORT SYSTEMS, *See also headings for particular types*

Penrith Survival Equipment, Sandale, Coupland Beck, Appleby-in-Westmorland, Cumbria, CA16 6LN Tel: (01768) 351666 Fax: (01768) 353666 E-mail: hg@survival.u-net.com

SURVIVAL EQUIPMENT/LIFE SUPPORT SYSTEMS MAINTENANCE/REPAIR SERVICES

South Eastern Marine Services Ltd, Olympic Business Centre, Paycocke Road, Basildon, Essex, SS14 3EX Tel: (01268) 534427 Fax: (01268) 281009 E-mail: sems@btinternet.com

Survival Systems International UK Ltd, Viking Road, Great Yarmouth, Norfolk, NR31 0NU Tel: (01493) 659411 Fax: (01493) 655425 E-mail: admin@survivalsystemsint.com

SURVIVAL EQUIPMENT/LIFE SUPPORT SYSTEMS, AIRBORNE

Haynes & Cann Ltd, 1-9 Overstone Road, Northampton, NN1 3JL Tel: (01604) 626143 Fax: (01604) 604721

SURVIVAL EQUIPMENT/LIFE SUPPORT SYSTEMS, GENERAL PURPOSE

B C B International Ltd, Units 7-8, Clydesmuir Road Industrial Estate, Cardiff, CF24 2QS Tel: (029) 2043 3700 Fax: (029) 2043 3701 E-mail: info@bcbin.com

G Q Parachutes Ltd, Isfryn Industrial Estate, Blackmill, Bridgend, Mid Glamorgan, CF35 6EQ Tel: (01656) 840300 Fax: (01656) 840396

SURVIVAL SUIT SERVICES

Whirly Bird Services Ltd, Montrose Way, Dyce, Aberdeen, AB21 0JF Tel: (01224) 771423 Fax: (01224) 773789 E-mail: mail@whirlybird.co.uk

SUSPENDED ACCESS PLATFORMS

Clow Group Ltd, Garratts Lane, Cradley Heath, West Midlands, B64 5AW Tel: 0121-559 5222 Fax: 0121-559 0330 E-mail: clowgroup@btconnect.com

Electromec Access, Unit 11 Buslingthorpe Green, Leeds, LS7 2HG Tel: 0113-239 2818 Fax: 0113-237 4088 E-mail: sales@electromec-access.co.uk

SUSPENDED CEILING CLEANING OR REFURBISHMENT SERVICES

Above All, 178 High Road, Chilwell, Beeston, Nottingham, NG9 5BB Tel: 0115-925 1959 Fax: 0115-943 1408 E-mail: service@aboveall.co.uk

Acoustic Ceilings Ltd, Unit 16-18, Loftus Street, Cardiff, CF5 1HL Tel: (029) 2034 2918 Fax: (029) 2034 2919

Broadland Sevices Ltd, 2D Wellesley Road, Tharston, Norwich, NR15 2PD Tel: (01508) 532100 Fax: (01508) 532292 E-mail: info@bstrip.com

Ceiling Services, 4 North Grove, Dalry, Ayrshire, KA24 5DW Tel: (01294) 835336

Complete Interiors, Ansell Road, Inscape House, Dorking, Surrey, RH4 1QN Tel: (01306) 882198 Fax: (01306) 876427 E-mail: info@completeinteriors.co.uk

Crofton House Associates, Crofton House, The Moor, Hawkhurst, Cranbrook, Kent, TN18 4NN Tel: (01580) 752919 Fax: (01580) 754173 E-mail: info@crofton-house.co.uk

S. Gordon, 100 Blakenhale Road, Sheldon, Birmingham, B33 0XA Tel: 0121-786 2482 Fax: 0121-604 4662

A.N. Howorth, 11 Cleveleys Road, Accrington, Lancashire, BB5 5ET Tel: (01254) 233482 Fax: (01254) 233482

H.J. Mccammon, Hebbross, Perridge Close, Exeter, EX2 9PX Tel: (01392) 259111

Metfix Ceilings Ltd, 40b Humber Avenue, Coventry, CV3 1AY Tel: (024) 7645 7343 Fax: (024) 7663 5915

Suspended Ceiling Co Wales Ltd, 74a Westbourne Road, Penarth, South Glamorgan, CF64 3HB Tel: (029) 2071 1708 Fax: (029) 2071 2607

SUSPENDED CEILING COMPONENTS

Acoustilux Suspended Ceilings, 4a Old Lodge Lane, Purley, Surrey, CR8 4DE Tel: (020) 8660 3300 Fax: (020) 8660 6644

Advanced Industries Ltd, 4 Avocet Trading Estate, Richardson Street, High Wycombe, Buckinghamshire, HP11 2SB Tel: (01494) 450722 Fax: (01494) 448998 E-mail: sales@office-refurbishment.com

Armstrong Metal Ceilings Ltd, 9-10 Telford Drive, Tollgate Industrial Estate, Stafford, ST16 3ST Tel: (01785) 222414 Fax: (01785) 226084

Atlas Suspended Ceilings, 27 Beechwood Street, Belfast, BT5 5BQ Tel: (028) 9065 0532 Fax: (028) 9065 3905

Birmingham Partitioning Supplies Ltd, Unit 54 Rovex Business Park, Hay Hall Road, Birmingham, B11 2AQ Tel: 0121-706 0666 Fax: 0121-708 1355 E-mail: sales@bhampartitions.co.uk

Bristol Acoustic Ceilings Ltd, 40 Shellards Road, Longwell Green, Bristol, BS30 9DU Tel: 0117-932 2073 Fax: 0117-932 9950

C A P S Ltd, 80 Pike Helve St, Golds Hill, West Bromwich, West Midlands, B70 0TU Tel: 0121-557 9553 Fax: 0121-522 2795 E-mail: caps.ltd@lineone.net

C P Supplies Ltd, 95 Chester Street, Aston, Birmingham, B6 4AE Tel: 0121-380 1600 Fax: 0121-380 1616 E-mail: admin@cpsupplies.co.uk

▶ C P Supplies Ltd, Unit A389, Western Avenue, Team Valley Trading Estate, Gateshead, Tyne & Wear, NE11 0SZ Tel: 0191-296 2233 Fax: 0191-482 3500

C P Supplies Ltd, Sheridale Business Centre, Knight Road, Rochester, Kent, ME2 2EL Tel: (01634) 290029 Fax: (01634) 290888

C P Supplies Ltd, Twickenham Trading Estate, Rugby Road, Twickenham, TW1 1DQ Tel: (020) 8891 5971 Fax: (020) 8892 5218 E-mail: michellephelan@cpsupplies.co.uk

Capco Interior Supplies Ltd, Unit 5, Moreton Industrial Estate, Swanley, Kent, BR8 8DE Tel: (01322) 661199 Fax: (01322) 662299 E-mail: bmswanley@cpdplc.co.uk

Carratt Suspended Ceilings Ltd, 8 Whitehart Mews, Southgate, Sleaford, Lincolnshire, NG34 7RY Tel: (01529) 305704 Fax: (01529) 307263

▶ Cawdell Contracts, Malting Lane, Dagnall, Berkhamsted, Hertfordshire, HP4 1QY Tel: (01442) 843100 Fax: (01442) 842170

Ceiling Craft, 44 Vernon Drive, Stanmore, Middlesex, HA7 2BT Tel: (020) 8427 4560 Fax: (020) 8426 0599

Ceilings Distribution Ltd, 2a-Elland Way, Leeds, LS11 0EY Tel: 0113-270 0333 Fax: 0113-270 2839

▶ Ceilings Distribution Ltd, Cameron Court, Winwick Quay, Warrington, WA2 8RE Tel: (01925) 635405 Fax: (01925) 417291

Commercial Ceiling Factors Ltd, Malvern Drive, Llanishen, Cardiff, CF14 5DR Tel: (029) 2076 3311 Fax: (029) 2075 5910 E-mail: sales@ccfltd.com

CPD Distribution, 8 Commerce Way, Trafford Park, Manchester, M17 1HW Tel: 0161-874 5311 Fax: 0161-874 5312 E-mail: mikejennion@cpdplc.co.uk

Croydon Ceilings Ltd, 94-96 Drummond Road, Croydon, CR0 1TX Tel: (020) 8686 0500 Fax: (020) 8688 9229

Damar Ceilings Ltd, Owl House, Chathan Street, Macclesfield, Cheshire, SK11 6EE Tel: (01625) 511323 Fax: (01625) 610475 E-mail: damarceilings@btconnect.com

Ecophon Ltd, Old Brick Kiln, Ramsdell, Tadley, Hampshire, RG26 5PP Tel: (01256) 850989 Fax: (01256) 851550 E-mail: sales@ecophon.co.uk

▶ Elite Ceiling Manufacturers Ltd, Ridgeway Industrial Estate, Iver, Buckinghamshire, SL0 9HU Tel: (01753) 654411 Fax: (01753) 630002 E-mail: henry@ecmuk.com

Gildair Ltd, 18 Kings Road, Sale, Cheshire, M33 6GB Tel: 0161-973 2176 Fax: 0161-973 2176

H E P Rolled Sections, Bayton Road, Exhall, Coventry, CV7 9EJ Tel: (024) 7658 5600 Fax: (024) 7658 5649 E-mail: info@metsec.com

Hill Top, Ridgacre Road, West Bromwich, West Midlands, B71 1BB Tel: 0121-555 1470 Fax: 0121-555 1471 E-mail: sales.hts@hadleygroup.co.uk

I T A Ceilings Ltd, Unit 4 107 Summerway, Exeter, EX4 8DP Tel: (01392) 468781 Fax: (01392) 465476 E-mail: itacielings@aol.com

Interceil Ltd, Fairholme, Ridley Terrace, Cambois, Blyth, Northumberland, NE24 1QS Tel: (01670) 828008 Fax: (01670) 827749

SUSPENDED CEILING COMPONENTS – *continued*

J H C Interiors Ltd, 10 Lady Lane, Paisley, Renfrewshire, PA1 2LJ Tel: 0141-849 6349 Fax: 0141-849 7493 E-mail: sales@jhcinteriors.co.uk

Jeffrey Graham Ltd, 1 Crompton Avenue, Bolton, BL2 6PG Tel: (01204) 412721 Fax: (01204) 435274

JHH Contracts Ltd, 1 Italy Street, Middlesborough, Middlesbrough, Cleveland, TS2 1DP Tel: (01642) 240070 Fax: (01642) 241393 E-mail: sales@jhhcontracts.com

Komfort Office Environments Plc, Units 1-10, Whittle Way, Crawley, West Sussex, RH10 9RW Tel: (01293) 592500 Fax: (01293) 553271 E-mail: general@komfort.com

▶ Les White & Partners, 832 Whittingham Lane, Goosnargh, Preston, PR3 2AX Tel: (01772) 865490 Fax: (01772) 865490

▶ Level Best Solutions Ltd, Commerce Way, Edenbridge, Kent, TN8 6ED Tel: (01732) 868218 Fax: (01732) 860107 E-mail: info@levelbestsolutions.com

Metfix Ceilings Ltd, 40b Humber Avenue, Coventry, CV3 1AY Tel: (024) 7645 7343 Fax: (024) 7663 5915

Midland Interiors Ltd, Unit 58 G Arthur Street, Lakeside, Redditch, Worcestershire, B98 8JY Tel: (01527) 522566 Fax: (01527) 522562 E-mail: s.troth@midlandinteriors.co.uk

Nevill Long, Chartwell Drive, Wigston, Leicestershire, LE18 2FL Tel: 0116-257 0670 Fax: 0116-257 0044 E-mail: sales@longnevill.co.uk

Nevill Long Interior Building Products, Centre House, Victory Way, Hounslow, TW5 9NS Tel: (020) 8573 9898 Fax: (020) 8813 5127

▶ Proof Safe, Unit 17 Sealand Farm Workshops, Sealand Road, Sealand, Chester, CH1 6BS Tel: (01244) 881722 Fax: (01244) 880732 E-mail: djwalker@proofsafe.co.uk

Quickfix Midlands, Unit B1, The Haysfield Business Centre, Malvern, Worcestershire, WR14 1GF Tel: (01684) 560700 Fax: (01684) 560020 E-mail: sales@quick-fix.demon.co.uk

▶ Roe Dry Lining, 295 Drumsurn Road, Limavady, County Londonderry, BT49 0PX Tel: (028) 7776 3274 Fax: (028) 7776 7187

▶ Smart Interior, Watson House, 33 Burton Road, Sheffield, S3 8BX Tel: 0114-272 3929 Fax: 0114-272 3894 E-mail: john@smartinterior.net

Southern Suspended Ceilings Ltd, 151 Burges Road, Southend-on-Sea, SS1 3JN Tel: (01702) 584392 Fax: (01702) 584392

▶ Southwest Ceilings Ltd, 1, Queen Victoria Street, Bristol, BS2 0QR Tel: 0117-955 8552 Fax: 0117-955 8552

T T Carpets & Ceilings, The Red Barn, Harmony Hill, Milnthorpe, Cumbria, LA7 7QA Tel: (01539) 562898 Fax: (01539) 564404 E-mail: enquires@ttcarpets.fsnet.co.uk

Test Valley Ceilings & Partitioning, 16 Gover Road, Southampton, SO16 9BR Tel: (023) 8086 4546 Fax: (023) 8049 5831 E-mail: gary.fawson@ntlworld.com

Thomson's Suspended Ceilings, Balquharn Farm, Alva, Clackmannanshire, FK12 5NZ Tel: (01259) 763427 Fax: (01259) 769865 E-mail: fionathmsn@aol.com

U S G (U K) Ltd, 1 Swan Road, South West Industrial Estate, Peterlee, County Durham, SR8 2HS Tel: 0191-586 1121 Fax: 0191-586 0097 E-mail: sales@usg-europe.com

W P Ceiling Co. Ltd, 85 Mansfield Avenue, Barnet, Hertfordshire, EN4 8QF Tel: (020) 8449 9603 Fax: (020) 8449 2754 E-mail: rpayne7812@aol.com

Wiland Wines Ltd, Regent House, Ellis Street, Anstey, Leicester, LE7 7FG Tel: 0116-236 3479 Fax: 0116-234 0262

Wynn Ceilings, 200 The Broadway, London, NW9 7EE Tel: (020) 8202 0368 Fax: (020) 8202 2167

SUSPENDED CEILING SYSTEMS CONSTRUCTORS OR MANUFACTURERS OR CONTRACTORS

A J B Partitioning & Ceiling, 13 Long Lane, Billesdon, Leicester, LE7 9AL Tel: 0116-259 6347 E-mail: ajb@billesdon.fsbusiness.co.uk

A L M Partitioning, 9 East End, Langtoft, Peterborough, PE6 9LP Tel: (01733) 266333 Fax: (01733) 266333

A W R Ceilings & Partitions, Jack O Watton Industrial Estate, Lichfield Road, Water Orton, Birmingham, B46 1NU Tel: 0121-748 2608 Fax: 0121-776 7561 E-mail: triciaharris@eidosnet.co.uk

A30 Interiors, 167 Cannon Workshops, 3 Cannon Drive, London, E14 4AS Tel: (0800) 3161000 Fax: (0207) 719 844 E-mail: enq@a30interiors.com

▶ Aask Us, 1 Murdock Road, Bicester, Oxfordshire, OX26 4PP Tel: (01869) 322771 Fax: (01869) 322772

▶ Abbey Interior Systems Ltd, 82a High Street, Cosham, Portsmouth, PO6 3AJ Tel: 023 92325355 Fax: 023 92325355 E-mail: abbeyinterior@hotmail.com

Adex Interiors For Industry Ltd, 5 Avebury Court, Hemel Hempstead, Hertfordshire, HP2 7TA Tel: (01442) 232327 Fax: (01442) 262713 E-mail: adex@msn.com

Akron Construction, Unit 2 Baxter Street, Aberdeen, AB11 9QA Tel: (01224) 896959 Fax: (01224) 896875

▶ Alpine Construction Services, Ifield Green, Ifield, Crawley, West Sussex, RH11 0ND Tel: (01293) 412233 Fax: (01293) 514675 E-mail: sales@labour-hire.com

Anchor Interior Solutions Ltd, 97 Leyland Trading Estate, Wellingborough, Northamptonshire, NN8 1RT Tel: (01933) 275757 Fax: (01933) 270070

Anglia Partitions Ltd, Unit 3 Freisian Way, King's Lynn, Norfolk, PE30 4JQ Tel: (01553) 691202 Fax: (01553) 769808 E-mail: info@angliapartitions.demon.co.uk

Aronn Interiors Ltd, 17 West Avenue, Aldwick, Bognor Regis, West Sussex, PO21 3QP Tel: (01243) 823904 Fax: (01243) 841132 E-mail: ceilings@aronn.wanadoo.co.uk

Arrow Ceilings Ltd, A9 Hucknall Road, Nottingham, NG5 1FD Tel: 0115-985 7016 Fax: 0115-985 6883 E-mail: mail@arrowceilings.co.uk

Astec Projects Ltd, 187-189 Kings Road, Reading, RG1 4EX Tel: 0118-958 1333 Fax: 0118-958 1337 E-mail: astec@astecprojects.co.uk

Ata, 37 Smiths Way, Water Orton, Birmingham, B46 1TW Tel: 0121-748 5785 Fax: 0121-748 5785

John Atkinson Interiors Ltd, Deanfield Mill, Asquith Avenue, Morley, Leeds, LS27 9QT Tel: 0113-253 5661 Fax: 0113-238 0323 E-mail: atkinsoninteriors@btopenworld.com

B & K Ceilings Ltd, Unit B8 Manor Development Centre, 40 Alison Crescent, Sheffield, S2 1AS Tel: 0114-253 1620 Fax: 0114-239 4976

Bailey & Davidson Ltd, The Street, Bishop's Cannings, Devizes, Wiltshire, SN10 2LD Tel: (01380) 860386 Fax: (01380) 860897 E-mail: nbailey@kwikbuild.com

Bailey Johnson, Wyther Lane, Leeds, LS5 3BT Tel: 0113-275 9048 Fax: 0113-230 4328 E-mail: info@baileyjohnson.co.uk

Banfield Suspended Ceilings, Culzean, Wexham Park La, Wexham, Slough, SL3 6LX Tel: 01753 532421 Fax: 01753 532421

Barden Roofing Services, 199 Alverthorpe Road, Wakefield, West Yorkshire, WF2 9PT Tel: (01924) 378094 Fax: (01924) 378094

Barnards Ceilings & Partitions Ltd, Mulberry House, Holders Green, Lindsell, Dunmow, Essex, CM6 3QQ Tel: (01371) 870104 Fax: (01371) 870105

Beckett Construction Solutions Ltd, 99 Kingsway, Dunmurry, Belfast, BT17 9NU Tel: (028) 9066 3631 Fax: (028) 9055 1309 E-mail: mail@whbeckett.com

Blakiston Ltd, 38 St. Helens Road, Hayling Island, Hampshire, PO11 0BT Tel: (023) 9246 9698 Fax: (023) 9246 9716 E-mail: sales@partitions.net

Bolts Of Hereford, 5-7 Perseverance Road, Hereford, HR4 9SN Tel: (01432) 269508 Fax: (01432) 263835 E-mail: nick.bolt@btclick.com

Bowller Roofing Supplies, Station Road, Harston, Cambridge, CB22 7QP Tel: (01223) 872260 Fax: (01223) 871143 E-mail: admin@bowller.co.uk

Boygle & Co. Ltd, Chichester Road, Romiley, Stockport, Cheshire, SK6 4BL Tel: 0161-406 8280 Fax: 0161-406 8244

Bridger & Co Office Interiors, South Ease Cottage, Send Marsh Road, Ripley, Woking, Surrey, GU23 6JQ Tel: (01483) 224920 Fax: (01483) 211599

British Gypsum Ltd, Gotham Road, East Leake, Loughborough, Leicestershire, LE12 6JQ Tel: 0115-945 1050 Fax: 0115-945 1154 E-mail: bgtechnical.enquiries@bpb.com

▶ Broadland Interior Systems, The Bearings, Bowbridge Road, Newark, Nottinghamshire, NG24 4BZ Tel: (01636) 700744

Browns Ladders & Ceilings, Glen Way, Brierfield, Nelson, Lancashire, BB9 5NH Tel: (01282) 615517 Fax: (01282) 615515 E-mail: sales@brownsladders.co.uk

Buchan Ceilings Ltd, 7 Curtis Road, Coventry, CV2 3AG Tel: (024) 7644 5589 Fax: (024) 7644 5589E-mail: robbie@robbiebuchan.co.uk

Building Tecnics, Regents Trade Park, Barwell Lane, Gosport, Hampshire, PO13 0EQ Tel: (01329) 282900 Fax: (0870) 200517 E-mail: info@buildingtecnics.com

Burgess Architectural Products Ltd, Brookfield Road, Burbage, Hinckley, Leicestershire, LE10 2LL Tel: (01455) 618787 Fax: (01455) 251061 E-mail: info@burgessceilings.co.uk

C F C Group Ltd, Kilnbrook House, Rosekiln Lane, Reading, RG2 0BY Tel: (0845) 0540040 Fax: (0845) 0540041 E-mail: cfc@cfcgroup.co.uk

C F Ceilings, Howgill Garage, Low Road, Whitehaven, Cumbria, CA28 9HS Tel: (01946) 691188 Fax: (01946) 591770

C M Services, 22 Lowbell Lane, London Colney, St. Albans, Hertfordshire, AL2 1AZ Tel: (01727) 825535 Fax: (01727) 825568 E-mail: info@cmbservices.co.uk

Caledonian Contracts (Aberdeen) Ltd, 8 Holland Place, Aberdeen, AB25 3UW Tel: (01224) 630355 Fax: (01224) 639504

Caroline Construction Ltd, PO Box 267, Sittingbourne, Kent, ME10 4HX Tel: (01795) 470722 Fax: (01795) 470121

Carter Ceilings Ltd, 2 Cunningham Road, Stirling, FK7 7SW Tel: (01786) 464914 Fax: (01786) 450012 E-mail: info@carter.co.uk

Castell Ceilings Co, Willow View, 62 Marshfield Road, Castleton, Cardiff, CF3 2UW Tel: (01633) 681411 Fax: (01633) 681700

▶ Ceiling 2 Ltd, Hazel Grove, Linthwaite, Huddersfield, HD7 5TQ Tel: (01484) 300106 Fax: (01484) 300114

Ceiling Craft, 44 Vernon Drive, Stanmore, Middlesex, HA7 2BT Tel: (020) 8427 4560 Fax: (020) 8426 0599

Ceiling Grids Ltd, Branson Street, Manchester, M40 7FJ Tel: 0161-273 4511 Fax: 0161-274 3914

Ceiling Services Ltd, 3 West Hill, Dunstable, Beds, LU6 3PN Tel: 01582 668822 Fax: 01582 665586

▶ Ceilings & Partitions Ltd, Alexander House, Robinson Terrace, Washington, Tyne & Wear, NE38 7BD Tel: 0191-417 8089 Fax: 0191-417 1486

Ceipart Ltd, 1 Bowker Street, Worsley, Manchester, M28 0SG Tel: 0161-790 5905 Fax: 0161-703 8673 E-mail: ceipt@aol.com

▶ Cicada Interiors Limited, 64 Knightsbridge, London, United Kingdom, SW1X 7JF Tel: (020) 7590 3095 Fax: (020) 7590 9601 E-mail: peter@cicadainteriors.com

Clark & Fenn Skanska Ltd, Unit 19 Mitcham Industrial Estate, Streatham Road, Mitcham, Surrey, CR4 2AP Tel: (020) 8685 5000 Fax: (020) 8640 1986 E-mail: clark.and.fenn@skanska.co.uk

Classic Excel, William Jones House, Cambois, Blyth, Northumberland, NE24 1QY Tel: (01670) 530550 Fax: (01670) 531452 E-mail: info@classicceilings.co.uk

▶ Commercial Interior Specialists, Bowesfield Lane, Stockton-on-Tees, Cleveland, TS18 3HJ Tel: (01642) 611295 Fax: (01642) 611296 E-mail: sales@cis-interiors.co.uk

Construction & Shopfitting Ltd, 117, Piccotts End, Hemel Hempstead, Hertfordshire, HP1 3AU Tel: (01442) 244117 Fax: (01442) 233274 E-mail: cs.co@virgin.net

Contract Ceilings, Unit 3c Firlands Mill, South Parade, Pudsey, West Yorkshire, LS28 8AD Tel: 0113-239 4614 Fax: 0113-239 3638

Cowill Construction 1989 Ltd, The Mill, Congleton Road, Talke, Stoke-on-Trent, ST7 1NE Tel: (01782) 785319 Fax: (01782) 775404 E-mail: office@cowill89.freeserve.co.uk

CPS Interiors Ltd, 1 Prince William Way, Loughborough, Leicestershire, LE11 5DD Tel: (01509) 230429 Fax: (01509) 610617 E-mail: cpsinteriors@btconnect.com

▶ Davroy Contracts Ltd, 510 Queslett Road, Great Barr, Birmingham, B43 7EJ Tel: 0121-325 0899 Fax: 0121-360 6840 E-mail: post@davroy.co.uk

Dawber Williamson (Lincs) Ltd, Torrington House, Torrington Street, Grimsby, South Humberside, DN32 9QH Tel: (01472) 347532 Fax: (01472) 344223

Decke Newcastle Ltd, 244 Park View, Whitley Bay, Tyne & Wear, NE26 3QX Tel: 0191-251 2606 Fax: 0191-251 4880 E-mail: decke.newcastle@contactbox.co.uk

Diamond Ceilings Ltd, 227 Southborough Lane, Bromley, BR2 8AT Tel: (020) 7232 2122 Fax: (020) 8295 5941

Dobie Johnston Ltd, 151 Poplin Street, Glasgow, G40 4LW Tel: 0141-550 2345 Fax: 0141-550 1115

Drew Wylie Building Services, 352 Saintfield Road, Belfast, BT8 7SJ Tel: (028) 9081 7170 Fax: (028) 9079 3443 E-mail: drewwylie@hotmail.com

▶ E A C Group Of Companies, Jubilee House, Broadway, Silver End, Witham, Essex, CM8 3RQ Tel: (01376) 585855 Fax: (01376) 587910 E-mail: mail@eacgroup.net

East Midlands Ceilings, Dinnington Lane, Moorwood Moor, South Wingfield, Alfreton, Derbyshire, DE55 7NW Tel: (01629) 534845 Fax: (01629) 534811 E-mail: info@emceilings.com

Ek Partitions & Ceilings Ltd, 15 Arden Business Centre, Arden Road, Alcester, Warwickshire, B49 6HW Tel: (01789) 400404 Fax: (01789) 400505 E-mail: sales@ekpartitions.com

▶ Elite Ceiling Manufacturers Ltd, Ridgeway Industrial Estate, Iver, Buckinghamshire, SL0 9HU Tel: (01753) 654411 Fax: (01753) 630002 E-mail: henry@ecmuk.com

Elite Storage Ltd, New Holder Street, Bolton, BL1 4SN Tel: (01204) 522930 Fax: (01204) 366985

ESE (Scotland) Ltd, 3 Dunlop Court, Deans Industrial Estate, Deans, Livingston, West Lothian, EH54 8SL Tel: (01506) 413313 Fax: (01506) 416550 E-mail: info@ese-scotland.co.uk

Firsmere Engineering Ltd, Aston Lane, Sharnford, Hinckley, Leicestershire, LE10 3PA Tel: (01455) 273940 Fax: (01455) 273996

Flexi-Plan Partitions Ltd, Unit J1, Halesfield 19, Telford, Shropshire, TF7 4QT Tel: (01952) 586126 Fax: (01952) 581174 E-mail: flexplanpartitions@btopenworld.com

Alexander Gatey & Co. Ltd, Unit 89 West Avenue, Blantyre, Glasgow, G72 0XE Tel: (01698) 821919 Fax: (01698) 823946 E-mail: info@alexandergatey.co.uk

Glenside Commercial Interiors, Glenside House, Kitchener Road, High Wycombe, Buckinghamshire, HP11 2SW Tel: (01494) 529803 Fax: (01494) 452212

▶ Go Interiors, 3 Elizabeth Trading Estate, Juno Way, London, SE14 5RW Tel: (020) 8469 3716 Fax: (020) 8469 0037 E-mail: sales@gointeriors.co.uk

Group Interiors, Shingle Hall, Epping Upland, Epping, Essex, CM16 6PD Tel: (01992) 572373 Fax: (01992) 575543

H & R Interiors, 155 High Street, Rhyl, Clwyd, LL18 1UF Tel: (01745) 344443 Fax: (01745) 343303

Harrison Suspended Ceilings, Shirley House, Oldham Street, Hyde, Cheshire, SK14 1LJ Tel: 0161-368 1315 Fax: 0161-367 8005

Hatmet Ltd, Interiors House, Lynton Road, London, N8 8SL Tel: (020) 8341 0200 Fax: (020) 8341 9878 E-mail: info@hatmet.co.uk

Hemax Ceilings Ltd, 167 The Grove, Biggin Hill, Kent, TN16 3UJ Tel: (01959) 701554 Fax: (01959) 573006

Hitec Suspended Ceilings, 44 Inisclan Road, Mountfield, Omagh, County Tyrone, BT79 7QB Tel: (028) 8077 1422 Fax: (028) 8077 1122 E-mail: hitecceilings@hotmail.com

▶ Howe Suspended Ceilings, 12 Heatherbrae, Bishopbriggs, Glasgow, G64 2TA Tel: 0141-762 3915 Fax: 0141-762 3915 E-mail: enquiries@howesuspendedceilings.co.uk

Howe Suspended Ceilings, 78 Eastburn Road, Glasgow, G21 3NS Tel: 0141-557 5299

Howe Suspended Ceilings, Kirklands, Skegness Road, Ingoldmells, Skegness, Lincolnshire, PE25 1NL Tel: (01754) 763124 Fax: (01754) 763124 E-mail: info@howesuspendedceilings.co.uk

Peter Howell Office Interiors, 105 Dockfield Road, Shipley, West Yorkshire, BD17 7BE Tel: (01274) 592337 Fax: (01274) 531595 E-mail: info@peter-howell.com

I M Dunn, Quay Cottage, Salter Mill, Landulph, Saltash, Cornwall, PL12 6QG Tel: (01752) 845673 Fax: (01752) 845673

I T S Projects Ltd, 42-44 Portman Road, Reading, RG30 1EA Tel: 0118-950 0225 Fax: 0118-950 3267 E-mail: info@itsprojects.co.uk

Image Ceilings Ltd, 82 Lind Road, Sutton, Surrey, SM1 4PL Tel: (020) 8770 3300 Fax: (0870) 8901146 E-mail: info@imageceilings.co.uk

Interior Design Ceiling Co. Ltd, Sundorne House, Astley, Shrewsbury, SY4 4ED Tel: (01939) 250407 Fax: (01939) 250704

Interior & Facility Contracts Ltd, Excelsior House, Buntsford Park Road, Bromsgrove, Worcestershire, B60 3DX Tel: (01527) 573000 Fax: (01527) 573001 E-mail: enquiries@interior-facility.com

Interior Property Specialists Ltd, Interplan House, Chelmsford Road Industrial Estate, Dunmow, Essex, CM6 1HE Tel: (01371) 874241 Fax: (01371) 873848 E-mail: contact@ips-interiors.co.uk

Ivor Hopkins Suspended Ceilings & Partitions, 10 Kingsmead, Station Road, Kings Cliffe, Peterborough, PE8 6YH Tel: (01780) 470048 Fax: (01780) 470039 E-mail: sales@ivorhopkins.co.uk

J P C Interiors Ltd, 144 Whitworth Road, Swindon, SN25 3BJ Tel: (01793) 524311 Fax: (01793) 524808

Jaketone Ltd, 44 Millhouse Lane, Wirral, Merseyside, CH46 6HN Tel: 0151-677 6620 Fax: 0151-677 6620

K S Interiors Ltd, School Road, Nomansland, Salisbury, SP5 2BY Tel: (01794) 390683 Fax: (01794) 390683

Kewmill Construction Ltd, Dagnall Road, High Wycombe, Buckinghamshire, HP12 4AN Tel: (01442) 843333 Fax: (01442) 842297

G.R. Kinder (Ceilings) Ltd, Unit 1 Rochdale Road Industrial Estate, Church Street, Middleton, Manchester, M24 2PY Tel: (0161) 654 8084 Fax: (0161) 655 3762 E-mail: paul@kinderinteriors.co.uk

▶ Kosco Interiors Ltd, 500b Knutsford Road, Warrington, WA4 1DX Tel: (01925) 242555 Fax: (01925) 242818 E-mail: koscointeriors@aol.com

Lazer Partitions & Ceilings, 119a Tarring Road, Worthing, West Sussex, BN11 4HE Tel: (01903) 205719 Fax: (01903) 204041 E-mail: lazer@mistral.co.uk

Leemo (Partitions) Ltd, Essex House, Kelfall Street, Oldham, OL9 6HR Tel: 0161-665 4666 Fax: 0161-624 4376

Lifetime Interiors Ltd, Unit D2, 86-102 King Street, Farnworth, Bolton, BL4 7AS Tel: (01204) 574166 Fax: (01204) 574263 E-mail: mail@lifetimeinteriors.co.uk

Lining Systems Ltd, Unit 8 Woodcock Trading Estate, 277 Barton Street, Gloucester, GL1 4JE Tel: (01452) 387771 Fax: (01452) 387771 E-mail: sales@liningsystems.co.uk

Lohan Ceilings Ltd, 120 Ashton Road, Denton, Manchester, M34 3JE Tel: 0161-336 0954 Fax: 0161-337 8727 E-mail: lohanceiling@tiscali.co.uk

Lyntech Systems Ltd, Unit 11 Maguire Industrial Estate, Torrington Avenue, Coventry, CV4 9HN Tel: (024) 7646 8710 Fax: (024) 7646 6111 E-mail: sales@lyntech-systems.ltd.uk

Lyntons Ceiling & Partitions, 32-34 Albion Road, Sutton, Surrey, SM2 5TF Tel: (020) 8661 7875

M J M Suspended Ceilings, Melville Road, Sidcup, Kent, DA14 4LX Tel: (020) 8300 8400 E-mail: smarks.mjm@ntlworld.com

Mapgale Ltd, 1 Peppin Lane, Fotherby, Louth, Lincolnshire, LN11 0UW Tel: (01507) 600635 Fax: (01507) 600635

Mayflower Ceiling Services, 107 Lawn Lane, Hemel Hempstead, Hertfordshire, HP3 9HS Tel: (01442) 242005 Fax: (01442) 268555

Mayflower Ceiling Services, 107 Lawn Lane, Hemel Hempstead, Hertfordshire, HP3 9HS Tel: (01442) 242005 Fax: (01442) 268555

Medway Office Interiors Ltd, 10 Sherwood Close, Herne Bay, Kent, CT6 7DX Tel: (01227) 363505 Fax: (01227) 363505

T.J. Mee Contracts, 11 Tyler Road, Ratby, Leicester, LE6 0NQ Tel: 0116-238 7628 Fax: 0116-238 7628

▶ indicates data change since last edition

SUSPENDED CEILING SYSTEMS CONSTRUCTORS OR MANUFACTURERS OR CONTRACTORS – *continued*

▶ Metaflex Ltd, Milltown Industrial Estate, Greenan Road, Warrenpoint, Newry, County Down, BT34 3FN Tel: (028) 4177 3604 Fax: (028) 4177 3266
Midland Ceilings Ltd, 63 Chartwell Drive, Wigston, Leicestershire, LE18 2FS Tel: 0116-288 7721 Fax: 0116-288 7022
Midland Tool Manufacturing Co. Ltd, Unit 13, Belle Eau Park, Bilsthorpe, Newark, Nottinghamshire, NG22 8TX Tel: (01623) 870411 Fax: (01623) 871857 E-mail: midlandtoolmans@msn.com
Neo Interiors, The Old Dairy, Upper Thrift Street, Northampton, NN1 5HR Tel: (01604) 601981 Fax: (01604) 601989 E-mail: neointeriors@talk21.com
New Lyne Interiors, 1 Shrublands Drive, Lightwater, Surrey, GU18 5QS Tel: (01276) 474511 Fax: (01276) 474220
Newey Ceilings Ltd, 1-4 South Uxbridge Street, Burton-on-Trent, Staffordshire, DE14 3LD Tel: (01283) 569696 Fax: (01283) 569699
John Noad (Ceilings) Ltd, Bardfield Centre, Braintree Road, Great Bardfield, Braintree, Essex, CM7 4SL Tel: (01371) 811112 Fax: (01371) 811124 E-mail: enquiries@jnoad.co.uk
Nottingham Suspended Ceilings Ltd, Wright Street, Netherfield, Nottingham, NG4 2PG Tel: 0115-987 9880 Fax: 0115-940 0086 E-mail: info@nsceilings.co.uk
Omega Interiors, The Cavendish Centre, Winnall Close, Winchester, Hampshire, SO23 0LB Tel: (01962) 843542 Fax: (01962) 843062 E-mail: tony@omega-online.co.uk
P & M Ceilings, 10 Eastdale Place, Altrincham, Cheshire, WA14 5LG Tel: 0161-928 3631 Fax: 0161-928 3631
P M R Ceilings & Partitioning Ltd, Unit 3-4 Bridge Road Industrial Estate, Litherland, Liverpool, L21 6PH Tel: 0151-928 6668 Fax: 0151-920 2090
Parker Ceilings & Partitions Ltd, Park Lane, Laughton, Lewes, East Sussex, BN8 6BP Tel: (01323) 811000 Fax: (01323) 811130 E-mail: parkerceiling@bt-click.com
Partitioning Plus Ltd, 342b Farnham Rd, Slough, SL2 1BT Tel: 01753 572373 Fax: 01753 694422
Partitions & Ceilings Ltd, 13 Gloucester Road, London, E11 2ED Tel: (020) 8989 9384 Fax: (020) 8989 2892 E-mail: part.ceilings@ntlworld.com
Pba Interiors, 119 Chiltern Drive, Surbiton, Surrey, KT5 8LS Tel: (020) 8390 6855 Fax: (020) 8399 0653
Peveril Interiors Ltd, Peveril House, Alfreton Road, Derby, DE21 4AG Tel: (01332) 344956 Fax: (01332) 380893 E-mail: peverilinteriors@peveril-house.co.uk
Pheonix Systems, Phoenix House, 15-19 Norway Street, Portslade, Brighton, BN41 1GN Tel: (01273) 418874 Fax: (01273) 418363 E-mail: info@phoenix-sys.co.uk
Pinnacle Partition Systems Ltd, 6 Cawley Hatch, Harlow, Essex, CM19 5AN Tel: (01279) 641317 Fax: (01279) 641329 E-mail: sales@pinnacle-partitions.co.uk
Pyramid Contracts Ltd, 94 Walsall Road, West Bromwich, West Midlands, B71 3HN Tel: 0121-588 8411 Fax: 0121-588 7942
Quality Conveyors Ltd, 10 Elland Lane, Elland, West Yorkshire, HX5 9DU Tel: (01422) 377166 Fax: (01422) 377238
Quantock Ceilings Southern Ltd, Unit 27 Hamp Industrial Estate, Old Taunton Road, Bridgwater, Somerset, TA6 3NT Tel: (01278) 446611 Fax: (01278) 446612 E-mail: sales@quantockceilings.co.uk
R & D Ceilings (South West) Ltd, 232 Wells Road, Bristol, BS4 2PJ Tel: 0117-977 0222 Fax: 0117-977 0313 E-mail: info@randdceilings.co.uk
R P R Linings Ltd, Doctors Lane, Henley-in-Arden, West Midlands, B95 5AW Tel: (01564) 792940 Fax: (01564) 794795 E-mail: rpr_linnings@talk21.com
Rae Electrical Services, 116a Blackstock Road, London, N4 2DR Tel: (020) 7226 2962 Fax: (020) 7359 3354 E-mail: raeelectrical@aol.com
Joe Rooney Floors & Ceilings Ltd, 2 Duncan Street, Gateshead, Tyne & Wear, NE8 3PU Tel: 0191-477 0045 Fax: 0191-477 8879
Roskel Contracts Ltd, Suite 1a Old Bank House, 50 St Johns Close, Knowle, Solihull, West Midlands, B93 0JU Tel: (01564) 732292 Fax: (01564) 732296 E-mail: sales@roskel.co.uk
Roskell Contracts Ltd, 102 Lower Guildford Road, Knaphill, Woking, Surrey, GU21 2EW Tel: (01483) 489905 Fax: (01483) 489925
▶ S J D Commercial Interiors, 120 High Street, Lee-on-the-Solent, Hampshire, PO13 9DB Tel: (023) 9255 1469
S W Ceiling Co., Hillsboro, Brockworth Rd, Churchdown, Gloucester, GL3 2NH Tel: (01452) 714334 Fax: (01452) 714334 E-mail: m.rickards@cableinet.co.uk
Sapphire Contractors Ltd, 18 Gladstone Road, Croydon, CR0 2BQ Tel: (020) 8665 6226 Fax: (020) 8665 6282 E-mail: enquiries@sapphirecontractors.co.uk
Sheffield Ceilings S E Ltd, 165 Bow Road, Wateringbury, Maidstone, Kent, ME18 5EA Tel: (01622) 814477 Fax: (01622) 813555 E-mail: sheffield.ceilings@btinternet.com
Shepherd Interiors, Unit 4, 10 First Avenue, Bletchley, Milton Keynes, MK1 1DN Tel: (01908) 644688 Fax: (01908) 646606 E-mail: info@rgnsltd.co.uk
Sherwood Interiors Ltd, 38 Churchill Park, Colwick, Nottingham, NG4 2HF Tel: 0115-987 0158 Fax: 0115-961 5505 E-mail: info@sherwoodinteriors.co.uk
Shropshire Ceilings, 50 Longden Coleham, Shrewsbury, SY3 7DH Tel: (01743) 343456 Fax: 01743 343456 E-mail: lee@shropshireceilings.co.uk
Solo Interiors Ltd, Unit 3b, Brookfield Farm Industrial Estate, Gravel Pit Lane, Cheltenham, Gloucestershire, GL52 3NQ Tel: (01242) 220440 Fax: (01242) 220441 E-mail: info@solointeriors.com
Sound Interiots Ltd, 4 Levens Road, Newby Road Industrial Estate, Hazel Grove, Stockport, Cheshire, SK7 5DL Tel: 0161-456 8282 Fax: 0161-456 3030 E-mail: all@sound-interiors.co.uk
Spectra Group Ltd, Duchess Industrial Estate, Sievewright Street, Rutherglen, Glasgow, G73 1LL Tel: 0141-647 0831 Fax: 0141-643 0047 E-mail: office@spectragroup.co.uk
Star Ceilings Ltd, P O Box 6, Banbury, Oxfordshire, OX15 4RU Tel: (01295) 722777 Fax: (01295) 722778
Star Installation Ltd, Unit B Progress Business Centre, Cannock, Staffordshire, WS11 0JR Tel: (01543) 574146 Fax: (01543) 469312
Star Suspended Ceilings Ltd, 4 Lockwood Street, Hull, HU2 0HJ Tel: (01482) 229788 Fax: (01482) 588155 E-mail: info@star.co.uk
Stedeford Ceilings, 11 Carsic Lane, Sutton-in-Ashfield, Nottinghamshire, NG17 2AS Tel: (01623) 515355 Fax: (01623) 403046
Stroud Office Interiors Ltd, Alder Ho, Inchbrook Trading Estate, Woodchester, Stroud, Glos, GL5 5EY Tel: (01453) 834867 Fax: (01453) 835818 E-mail: derek@stroudofficeinteriors.co.uk
Sullivans Ceilings Ltd, 105 Hilldene Avenue, Romford, RM3 8DL Tel: (01708) 371038 Fax: (01708) 371038
▶ Systematic Creative Interiors Ltd, Red Shute Hill Industrial Estate, Red Shute Hill, Hermitage, Thatcham, Berkshire, RG18 9QL Tel: (01635) 201789 Fax: (01635) 200996 E-mail: sale@systematicinteriors.co.uk
T P P Interiors Ltd, Rysted Lane, Westerham, Kent, TN16 1EP Tel: (01959) 563575 Fax: (01959) 561032 E-mail: des@tppinteriors.co.uk
Tamworth Ceilings Partitions & Interiors, 152 Lichfield Road, Tamworth, Staffordshire, B79 7SF Tel: (01827) 52738
Tapper Interiors Ltd, Vantage Business Park, Bloxham Road, Banbury, Oxfordshire, OX16 9UX Tel: (01295) 221240 Fax: (01295) 221241
Technique Ceilings, 46 Weston Road, Doncaster, South Yorkshire, DN4 8NF Tel: (01302) 855552 Fax: (01302) 850347
Technirack Systems Ltd, Unit 18 Avenue One, Witney, Oxfordshire, OX28 4XZ Tel: (01993) 893602 Fax: (01993) 893601
Tedwood Storage Systems Ltd, 1489 Melton Road, Queniborough, Leicester, LE7 3FP Tel: 0116-269 3838
Templemead Ltd, 5 Ascot Road, Shotley Bridge, Consett, County Durham, DH8 0NU Tel: (01207) 581237 Fax: (01207) 581237
▶ Thames Ceilings Ltd, Greensands, Reading Road, East Hendred, Wantage, Oxfordshire, OX12 8JE Tel: (01235) 443690 Fax: (01235) 443699 E-mail: sales@thamesceilings.ltd.uk
Thermofelt (Contracts) Ltd, Kingswood House, 31-39 Miles Road, Mitcham, Surrey, CR4 3DA Tel: (020) 8646 9300 E-mail: thermofeltcontracts@woodcote.com
Top Floor Ltd, 100 Cobham Road, Ferndown Industrial Estate, Wimborne, Dorset, BH21 7PQ Tel: (01202) 876339 Fax: (01202) 891047 E-mail: sales@topfloor.co.uk
Trills, Enterprise House, 21 Sherwood Road, Bromsgrove, Worcestershire, B60 3DR Tel: (01527) 874920 Fax: (01527) 876857 E-mail: enquiries@trills.co.uk
Tru-Line Ltd, Unit 16, Victoria Street, Middlesbrough, Cleveland, TS1 5QZ Tel: (01642) 232411 Fax: (01642) 217457
Versatile Kent Ltd, 94 Dover Road, Folkestone, Kent, CT20 1LA Tel: (01303) 850219 Fax: (01303) 220929 E-mail: info@versatile-kent.co.uk
Walker Interiors Ltd, East Park Street, Morley, Leeds, LS27 0PW Tel: 0113-253 7566 Fax: 0113-387 8601 E-mail: walkerintltd@aol.com
▶ Watsons, Breach Barns Lane, Waltham Abbey, Essex, EN9 2AD Tel: (01992) 651900 Fax: (01992) 651900 E-mail: sales@watsonsbuilders.co.uk
Wynn Ceilings, 200 The Broadway, London, NW9 7EE Tel: (020) 8202 0368 Fax: (020) 8202 2167

SUSPENDED CEILING TILES

▶ Advance Ceilings Ltd, Foundation House, Lodge Lane, Grays, Essex, RM17 5RZ Tel: (01375) 396311 Fax: (01375) 392759 E-mail: sales@advancedceilings.co.uk

SUSPENDED FLOOR VOID VENTILATORS

Fans & Spares Ltd, Unit 25 Whitemoor Court Industrial Estate, Whitemoor Court, Nottingham, NG8 5BY Tel: 0115-929 4104 Fax: 0115-929 2710 E-mail: nottingham@fansandspares.co.uk

SUSPENSION SYSTEMS, *See also headings for particular types*

Friction Linings Southampton Ltd, Unit 2 Easton La Business Park, Easton Lane, Winchester, Hampshire, SO23 7RQ Tel: (01962) 867666 E-mail: info@frictionlinings.co.uk
Roc Wales Ltd, Plas Yn Bonwm House, Holyhead Road, Corwen, Clwyd, LL21 9EG Tel: (01490) 413440 Fax: (01490) 413452 E-mail: panelsys@aol.com

SUSPENSION SYSTEMS, TRAILER/SEMITRAILER

Fleet Factors Ltd, Unit G, South Orbital Trading Estate, Folland Way, Hull, HU9 1NB Tel: (01482) 227423 Fax: (01482) 325746 E-mail: hull@fleetfactors.co.uk

SWAGING MACHINE MAINTENANCE/REPAIR/ REFURBISHMENT SERVICES

R G Attachments, 86 Belper Street, Leicester, LE4 6EA Tel: 0116-261 1038 Fax: 0116-261 2403 E-mail: info@rga.co.uk

SWAGING MACHINES

Albion Hose Ltd, Albion Works, Alma Street, Smethwick, West Midlands, B66 2RL Tel: 0121-565 4103 Fax: 0121-558 7220 E-mail: sales@albionhose.co.uk
H M Machinery UK Ltd, 41 Scholey Close, Halling, Rochester, Kent, ME2 1JZ Tel: (01634) 244600 Fax: (01634) 244599

SWARF CENTRIFUGES

Filtration Service Engineering Ltd, Unit 15 Oldington Trading Estate, Kidderminster, Worcestershire, DY11 7QP Tel: (01562) 60233 Fax: (01562) 748387 E-mail: info@fse.co.uk

SWARF CONVEYORS

▶ Frederick Crowther & Son Ltd, 4b High Level Way, Halifax, West Yorkshire, HX1 4PN Tel: (01422) 367788 Fax: (01422) 363802 E-mail: sales@cromar.co.uk

SWARF EXTRACTION/ HANDLING/PROCESSING SYSTEMS/EQUIPMENT

Arboga Darenth Ltd, Darenth Works, Ray Lamb Way, Erith, Kent, DA8 2LA Tel: (01322) 342533 Fax: (01322) 331226 E-mail: info@arbogadarenth.co.uk
Filtration Service Engineering Ltd, Unit 15 Oldington Trading Estate, Kidderminster, Worcestershire, DY11 7QP Tel: (01562) 60233 Fax: (01562) 748387 E-mail: info@fse.co.uk
Haesler Machine Tools, 14 Leyden Road, Stevenage, Hertfordshire, SG1 2BW Tel: (01438) 350835 Fax: (01438) 229482 E-mail: ben.haesler@ntlworld.com

SWIMMING AIDS

Adrian March, 5 The Paddock, Kings Worthy, Winchester, Hampshire, SO23 7QR Tel: (01962) 882277 E-mail: adrian@adrianmarch.com

SWIMMING POOL CHEMICAL PRODUCTS

▶ B Z C International Ltd, Waterbury Hill, Horsted Keynes, Haywards Heath, West Sussex, RH17 7BA Tel: (01342) 813748 Fax: (01342) 813748 E-mail: info@bzc.co.uk
Primemix, Nether Compton, Sherborne, Dorset, DT9 4PZ Tel: (01935) 389069 Fax: (01935) 815699 E-mail: howard@primix.demon.co.uk
Surex (International) Ltd, Unit 5, Airport Trading Estate, Westerham, Kent, TN16 3BW Tel: (01959) 576000 Fax: (01959) 571000 E-mail: info@surex.co.uk

SWIMMING POOL CONSTRUCTION OR MAINTENANCE CONTRACTORS

Alan Bettin Holdings Ltd, Seale Lane, Seale, Farnham, Surrey, GU10 1LD Tel: (01252) 782022 Fax: (01252) 782283 E-mail: sales@abpools.co.uk
Anglian Pools, 7 Hurricane Way, Airport Industrial Estate, Norwich, NR6 6EZ Tel: (01603) 429441 Fax: (01603) 417274 E-mail: mail@spasandpools.net
Aquabuild Ltd, Woodland Dell, Byers Lane, South Godstone, Godstone, Surrey, RH9 8JH Tel: (01342) 893519 Fax: (01342) 892933 E-mail: aquabuild@yahoo.co.uk
Aquaplan, South Cadleigh House, Beech Road, Ivybridge, Devon, PL21 9HN Tel: (01752) 892908 Fax: (01752) 892908
Ardep UK Ltd, Unit 34, Spring Vale Industrial Estate, Cwmbran, Gwent, NP44 5BD Tel: (01633) 480496 Fax: (01633) 480497 E-mail: sales@ardep.com
Armadale UK Swimming Pools & Spas, Unit 11 Capenhurst Technology Park, Capenhurst Lane, Chester, CH1 6EH Tel: 0151- 347 1661 Fax: 0151-347 1658 E-mail: post@armadaleuk.com
B T U (Pool Services) Ltd, Wyevale Garden Centre, Egley Road, Woking, Surrey, GU22 0NH Tel: (01483) 727444 Fax: (01483) 766254 E-mail: sales@btu-poolservices.com
Baracuda UK, Unit 2, Swinford Farm, Swinford, Witney, Oxon, OX29 4BY Tel: (01865) 881988 Fax: (01865) 883717
Biwater International Ltd, Biwater House, Station App, Dorking, Surrey, RH4 1TZ Tel: (01306) 740740 Fax: (01306) 885233 E-mail: corporate.communications@biwater.com
Brickell Swimming Pools Ltd, 84a Oakley Lane, Basingstoke, Hampshire, RG23 7JU Tel: (01256) 780567 Fax: (01256) 782385 E-mail: info@brickellpools.co.uk
Buckingham Swimming Pools Ltd, Dalehouse Lane, Kenilworth, Warwickshire, CV8 2EB Tel: (01926) 852351 Fax: (01926) 512387 E-mail: info@buckinghampools.com
Clearwater Swimming Pools Ltd, The Studio, 81 Langley Close, Headington, Oxford, OX3 7DB Tel: (01865) 766112 Fax: (01865) 741373 E-mail: sales@clearwater-pools.co.uk
▶ Complete, Calcot Lane, Curdridge, Southampton, SO32 2BN Tel: (01489) 797979 Fax: (01489) 797978 E-mail: malcolm@completemaintenance.co.uk
Complete Gardeners Ltd, Timberyard, 2 Mile Lane, Highnam, Gloucester, GL2 8DW Tel: (01452) 523078 Fax: (01452) 309323 E-mail: cotswoldpools@aol.com
Crystalclear Leisure, Woodside Centre, Southend Arterial Road, Rayleigh, Essex, SS6 7TR Tel: (01268) 776690 Fax: (01268) 775842 E-mail: accleisure@aol.com
Dinefwr Gates, Cwmcib Ganol, Ffairfach, Llandeilo, Dyfed, SA19 6TE Tel: (01558) 822833 Fax: (01558) 824612
Elm Leisure, Hitherford, Over, Cambridge, CB24 5NY Tel: (01954) 230230 Fax: (01954) 231775 E-mail: info@elmleisure.com
Jetform Services Ltd, Heath Road, Ramsden Heath, Billericay, Essex, CM11 1HU Tel: (01268) 711700 Fax: (01268) 711600 E-mail: sales@jetformservices.co.uk
Lecrafern Pools, Eastcourt Yard, Lower Higham Road, Gravesend, Kent, DA12 2NZ Tel: (01474) 824151 Fax: (01474) 822486 E-mail: lecrafernpools@aol.com
Letts Swimming Pools Ltd, Semer, Ipswich, IP7 6HP Tel: (01473) 822375 Fax: (01473) 824223
Luton Swimming Pool Supplies, 86 Old Bedford Road, Luton, LU2 7PD Tel: (01582) 731819 Fax: (01582) 611054 E-mail: sales@lutonpools.com
Merlin Leisure Group, Bloomfield Garden Centre, 241 Berechurch Hall Road, Colchester, CO2 9NP Tel: (01206) 766402 Fax: (01206) 766406
Moormead Leisure Ltd, Moormead House, Fosters Hill, Holwell, Sherborne, Dorset, DT9 5LQ Tel: (01963) 23622 Fax: (01963) 23622
Origin Leisure, Summerhouse Business Park, Canal Way, Harefield, Uxbridge, Middlesex, UB9 6TH Tel: (01895) 823366 Fax: (01895) 824445 E-mail: info@origindfl.co.uk
Oyster Pools & Leisure Ltd, Raglan Garden Centre, Abergavenny Road, Raglan, Usk, Gwent, NP15 2BH Tel: (01291) 690614 Fax: (01291) 690951 E-mail: info@oysterpools.co.uk
▶ Peterborough Pools Ltd, 3 Fenlake Business Centre, Fengate, Peterborough, PE1 5BQ Tel: (01733) 319222 Fax: (01733) 319111 E-mail: enquiries@peterboroughpools.co.uk
Poly Advisory Services Ltd, 2 Hollygate Industrial Park, Hollygate Lane, Cotgrave, Nottingham, NG12 3JW Tel: 0115-989 4167 Fax: 0115-989 9215 E-mail: sales@polyadvisory.com
The Pool Co. Ltd, 50 Torwood Street, Torquay, TQ1 1DT Tel: (01803) 291900 Fax: (01803) 290399 E-mail: info@the-pool-co.com
▶ Pool Construction Standfield Ltd, Poplar Farm, Dean Road, West Tytherley, Salisbury, SP5 1NR Tel: (01794) 341909 Fax: (01794) 341795
Pool Filtration Ltd, 76 Stafford Road, Wallington, Surrey, SM6 9AY Tel: (020) 8669 0657 Fax: (020) 8773 0647 E-mail: poolfiltrationltd@tiscali.co.uk

SWIMMING POOL CONSTRUCTION OR MAINTENANCE CONTRACTORS

– continued

Pool Vac Ltd, 229 London Road, Camberley, Surrey, GU15 3EY Tel: (01276) 25252 Fax: (01276) 21796 E-mail: poolvac@web-hq.com

Poolserve Leisurebuild Ltd, 39 Windsor Road, Chobham, Woking, Surrey, GU24 8LD Tel: (01276) 856677 Fax: (01276) 856061 E-mail: mail@poolserveleisurebuild.co.uk

Premier Gunite Ltd, Heritage House, Worplesdon Road, Guildford, Surrey, GU2 9XN Tel: (01483) 235988 Fax: (01483) 233483

Rainbow Pools, The Tannery, Queen Street, Gomshall, Guildford, Surrey, GU5 9LY Tel: (0870) 4050567 Fax: (0870) 4050568 E-mail: info@rainbowgroup.com

Regency Swimming Pools, Regency House, 88A Great Brickkiln Street, Graisley, Wolverhampton, WV3 0PU Tel: (01902) 427709 Fax: (01902) 422632 E-mail: info@jwgswimming.co.uk

Rushden Pool Care Ltd, 7 Birchall Road, Rushden, Northamptonshire, NN10 9RQ Tel: (01933) 358256 Fax: (01933) 359911 E-mail: info@rushdenpoolcare.co.uk

Rutherford The Pool People, Marley Lane, Battle, East Sussex, TN33 0TY Tel: (01424) 775060 Fax: (01424) 777066 E-mail: info@rutherfordpools.co.uk

▶ Sea Blue Trading UK Ltd, New Park, Axminster, Devon, EX13 5UQ Tel: (01297) 32645 Fax: (0845) 2803125

Swimco A R Penny Ltd, 12 Coombend, Radstock, BA3 3AJ Tel: (01761) 432838 Fax: (01761) 437216 E-mail: info@swimcopools.co.uk

Tanby Swimming Pools & Hot Tubs, 620-622 Limpsfield Road, Warlingham, Surrey, CR6 9DS Tel: (01883) 622335 Fax: (01883) 626775 E-mail: martin@tanby.freeserve.co.uk

Unipools Leisure Construction Ltd, 621 Watford Way, Mill Hill, London, NW7 3JN Tel: (020) 8959 8686 Fax: (020) 8959 2037 E-mail: info@unipools.com

Vernon Swimming Pools, Thistley Hall, Widdington, Saffron Walden, Essex, CB11 3ST Tel: (01799) 541470 Fax: (01799) 541701

Wensum Pools Ltd, Parker Drive, Fakenham, Norfolk, NR21 8RP Tel: (01328) 838835 Fax: (01328) 855725 E-mail: sales@wensumpools.co.uk

Young Leisure Ltd, 11 Industrial Estate, Priory Way, Taunton, Somerset, TA1 2AL Tel: (01823) 274569 Fax: (01823) 324147

SWIMMING POOL CONTROL PANELS

▶ Homefield Leisure Ltd, Poolclean, Winterdown Road, Esher, Surrey, KT10 8LS Tel: (01372) 465531 Fax: (01372) 469117 E-mail: sales@homefieldleisure.co.uk

Thermalec Products Ltd, Kingsley Close, Lee Mill Industrial Estate, Ivybridge, Devon, PL21 9GD Tel: (01752) 313343 Fax: (01752) 313353 E-mail: sales@thermalec.com

SWIMMING POOL COVERS

Aquamat Ltd, Unit 8g Chalford Industrial Estate, Chalford, Stroud, Gloucestershire, GL6 8NT Tel: (01453) 884411 Fax: (01453) 884499 E-mail: admin@aquamatcovers.co.uk

Brickell Swimming Pools Ltd, 84a Oakley Lane, Basingstoke, Hampshire, RG23 7JU Tel: (01256) 780567 Fax: (01256) 782385 E-mail: info@brickellpools.co.uk

Dri Pool Accessories, 3 Westwood Court, Brunel Road, Totton, Southampton, SO40 3WX Tel: (023) 8066 3131 Fax: (023) 8066 3232 E-mail: sales@dripool.co.uk

Forge Leisure Ltd, Forge Industrial Centre, Morpeth Road, Ashington, Northumberland, NE63 8QG Tel: (01670) 522022 Fax: (01670) 522072 E-mail: forgeleisure@btconnect.com

Intermark Leisure Ltd, Winnington Avenue, Winnington, Northwich, Cheshire, CW8 4EE Tel: (01606) 871831 Fax: (01606) 782241 E-mail: sales@intermarkleisure.ltd.uk

▶ K T R Environmental Solutions Ltd, 1 Close Barn, Coberley Road, Coberley, Cheltenham, Gloucestershire, GL53 9QY Tel: (01242) 870134 Fax: (01242) 870134 E-mail: sales@ktrworld.com

Plastica Ltd, Perimeter House, Napier Road, St. Leonards-On-Sea, East Sussex, TN38 9NY Tel: (01424) 857857 Fax: (01424) 857858 E-mail: info@plastica.ltd.uk

Polybuild Ltd, Upper Chancton Farm, London Road, Washington, Pulborough, West Sussex, RH20 3DH Tel: (01903) 892333 Fax: (01903) 892777 E-mail: sales@polybuild.com

T & O Engineering Ltd, 10 Willow Wood Road, Meopham, Gravesend, Kent, DA13 0QT Tel: (01732) 822560 Fax: (01732) 822560 E-mail: peter4tno@aol.com

SWIMMING POOL DESIGN CONSULTANCY

Biwater International Ltd, Biwater House, Station App, Dorking, Surrey, RH4 1TZ Tel: (01306) 740740 Fax: (01306) 885233 E-mail: corporate.communications@biwater.com

Caromal Lesiure, The Willows, Foundry Lane, Copford, Colchester, CO6 1BH Tel: (01206) 210741 Fax: (01206) 212173

Certikin International Ltd, 2 Station Lane Industrial Park Estate, Witney, Oxfordshire, OX28 4FH Tel: (01993) 778855 Fax: (01993) 778620 E-mail: export@certikin.co.uk

▶ Peterborough Pools Ltd, 3 Fenlake Business Centre, Fengate, Peterborough, PE1 5BQ Tel: (01733) 319222 Fax: (01733) 319111 E-mail: enquiries@peterboroughpools.co.uk

Rainbow Pools, The Tannery, Queen Street, Gomshall, Guildford, Surrey, GU5 9LY Tel: (0870) 4050567 Fax: (0870) 4050568 E-mail: info@rainbowgroup.com

SWIMMING POOL EQUIPMENT AND ACCESSORIES

Alan Bettin Holdings Ltd, Seale Lane, Seale, Farnham, Surrey, GU10 1LD Tel: (01252) 782022 Fax: (01252) 782283 E-mail: sales@abpools.co.uk

All Swim, Link Trade Park, Cardiff, CF11 8TT Tel: (029) 20 705059 Fax: (029) 2071 3340 E-mail: sales@allswimltd.com

Aquamat Ltd, Unit 8g Chalford Industrial Estate, Chalford, Stroud, Gloucestershire, GL6 8NT Tel: (01453) 884411 Fax: (01453) 884499 E-mail: admin@aquamatcovers.co.uk

Aquaplan, South Cadleigh House, Beech Road, Ivybridge, Devon, PL21 9HN Tel: (01752) 892908 Fax: (01752) 892908

▶ B Z C International Ltd, Waterbury Hill, Horsted Keynes, Haywards Heath, West Sussex, RH17 7BA Tel: (01342) 813748 Fax: (01342) 813748 E-mail: info@bzc.co.uk

Caromal Lesiure, The Willows, Foundry Lane, Copford, Colchester, CO6 1BH Tel: (01206) 210741 Fax: (01206) 212173

Certikin International Ltd, 2 Station Lane Industrial Park Estate, Witney, Oxfordshire, OX28 4FH Tel: (01993) 778855 Fax: (01993) 778620 E-mail: export@certikin.co.uk

Clearwater Swimming Pools Ltd, The Studio, 81 Langley Close, Headington, Oxford, OX3 7DB Tel: (01865) 766112 Fax: (01865) 741373 E-mail: sales@clearwater-pools.co.uk

Easy Pools Ltd, PO Box 425, Haywards Heath, West Sussex, RH16 2YR Tel: (01825) 791122 Fax: (01825) 791128

Emco (UK) Ltd, Unit 65, Atcham Business Park, Upton Magna, Shrewsbury, SY4 4UG Tel: (0870) 1611617 Fax: (0870) 1611618 E-mail: enquiries@emcouk.co.uk

Fox Pool (UK) Ltd, Mere House, Stow Road, Sturton By Stow, Lincoln, LN1 2BZ Tel: (01427) 788662 Fax: (01427) 788526 E-mail: grayfoxswi@aol.com

Greaves Art Metalwork Ltd, Ireland Close, Staveley, Chesterfield, Derbyshire, S43 3PE Tel: (01246) 280672 Fax: (01246) 280673

Imperial Swimming Pool Supplies, Magerae, Marriotts Avenue, South Heath, Great Missenden, Buckinghamshire, HP16 9QN Tel: (01494) 863030 Fax: (01494) 891030 E-mail: imperialswimmingpools@btopenworld.com

Intermark Leisure Ltd, Winnington Avenue, Winnington, Northwich, Cheshire, CW8 4EE Tel: (01606) 871831 Fax: (01606) 782241 E-mail: sales@intermarkleisure.ltd.uk

Invarmex (UK) Ltd, Unit 5, Hollygate Lane Industrial Park, Cotgrave, Nottingham, NG12 3JW Tel: 0115-989 4420 Fax: 0115-989 4463 E-mail: uk@invarmex.com

J P Lennard Ltd, Hadrians Way, Glebe Farm Industrial Estate, Rugby, Warwickshire, CV21 1ST Tel: (01788) 544839 Fax: (01788) 541851 E-mail: sales@jpl.co.uk

▶ Jetstream Products Ltd, 206 Farnborough Road, Farnborough, Hampshire, GU14 7JL Tel: (01252) 545006 Fax: (01252) 372670 E-mail: info@jetstreamuk.com

Leisureteq Swimming Pool Equipment, Unit 15 Innage Park, Holly Lane Industrial Estate, Atherstone, Warwickshire, CV9 2QX Tel: (01827) 715750 Fax: (01827) 715550 E-mail: mailbox@leisureteq.co.uk

Luton Swimming Pool Supplies, 86 Old Bedford Road, Luton, LU2 7PD Tel: (01582) 731819 Fax: (01582) 611054 E-mail: sales@lutonpools.com

▶ Merlin Leisure, Ladds Garden Centre, Bath Road, Hare Hatch, Reading, RG10 9SB Tel: 0118-940 1444 E-mail: sales@advantagespas.co.uk

Plastica Ltd, Perimeter House, Napier Road, St. Leonards-On-Sea, East Sussex, TN38 9NY Tel: (01424) 857857 Fax: (01424) 857858 E-mail: info@plastica.ltd.uk

Pool Filtration Ltd, 76 Stafford Road, Wallington, Surrey, SM6 9AY Tel: (020) 8669 0657 Fax: (020) 8773 0647 E-mail: poolfiltrationltd@tiscali.co.uk

Pool N Spa Services Ltd, Falcon Road, Sowton Industrial Estate, Exeter, EX2 7LJ Tel: (01392) 446910 Fax: (01392) 446912 E-mail: poolnspaservicesltd@btconnect.com

Pools & Gardens Ltd, Walk Mills Farm, Wychbold, Droitwich, Worcestershire, WR9 0DH Tel: (01527) 861597 Fax: (01527) 861881

Pow Sport & Leisure Co., PO Box 28, London, W4 4WT Tel: (0870) 3503650 Fax: (0870) 3503651 E-mail: info@pow-sport.co.uk

▶ Q1 Leisure Ltd, Ruxley Manor, Maidstone Road, Sidcup, Kent, DA14 5BQ Tel: (020) 8309 0600 Fax: (020) 8300 7759

Reed Harris, 27 Carnwath Road, London, SW6 3HR Tel: (020) 7736 7511 Fax: (020) 7736 2988 E-mail: enquiries@reed-harris.co.uk

Rutherford The Pool People, Marley Lane, Battle, East Sussex, TN33 0TY Tel: (01424) 775060 Fax: (01424) 777066 E-mail: info@rutherfordpools.co.uk

S C P UK Ltd, 15-19 Pelham Court, Pelham Place, Crawley, West Sussex, RH11 9SH Tel: (01293) 546126 Fax: (01293) 528442 E-mail: scpuk@scppool.com

▶ Sabre Leisure, Home Orchard, Brim Hill, Maidencombe, Torquay, TQ1 4TR Tel: (01803) 316655

▶ Selective Covers Ltd, G Lumley Close, Thirsk Industrial Park, Thirsk, North Yorkshire, YO7 3TD Tel: (01845) 522856 Fax: (01845) 574227

▶ Splasher Pools, Culver Garden Centre, Cattlegate Road, Enfield, Middlesex, EN2 9DS Tel: (020) 8363 7249 Fax: (020) 8303 1398 E-mail: sales@splasherpools.com

Surex (International) Ltd, Unit 5, Airport Trading Estate, Westerham, Kent, TN16 3BW Tel: (01959) 576000 Fax: (01959) 571000 E-mail: info@surex.co.uk

▶ Swimming Pool Supplies, 224e Havant Road, Drayton, Portsmouth, PO6 1PA Tel: (023) 9238 7771 Fax: (023) 9238 7772

Unipools Leisure Construction Ltd, 621 Watford Way, Mill Hill, London, NW7 3JN Tel: (020) 8959 8686 Fax: (020) 8959 2037 E-mail: info@unipools.com

SWIMMING POOL FILTER PUMPS

All Swim, Link Trade Park, Cardiff, CF11 8TT Tel: (029) 20 705059 Fax: (029) 2071 3340 E-mail: sales@allswimltd.com

Brickell Swimming Pools Ltd, 84a Oakley Lane, Basingstoke, Hampshire, RG23 7JU Tel: (01256) 780567 Fax: (01256) 782385 E-mail: info@brickellpools.co.uk

Complete Gardeners Ltd, Timberyard, 2 Mile Lane, Highnam, Gloucester, GL2 8DW Tel: (01452) 523078 Fax: (01452) 309323 E-mail: cotswoldpools@aol.com

SWIMMING POOL HEAT PUMPS

A G Budget Discount Swimming Pools & Spas, Aqua Garden House, East Molesey, Surrey, KT8 0PA Tel: (0870) 1283185 Fax: (0870) 1283188 E-mail: info@agbudget.co.uk

Calorex Heat Pumps Ltd, Unit 2, The Causeway, Heybridge, Maldon, Essex, CM9 4XL Tel: (01621) 856611 Fax: (01621) 850871 E-mail: sales@calorex.com

Complete Gardeners Ltd, Timberyard, 2 Mile Lane, Highnam, Gloucester, GL2 8DW Tel: (01452) 523078 Fax: (01452) 309323 E-mail: cotswoldpools@aol.com

Fordwater Pumping Supplies Ltd, Unit 32 Forest Vale Road, Forest Vale Industrial Estate, Cinderford, Gloucestershire, GL14 2PH Tel: (01594) 826780 Fax: (01594) 826780 E-mail: fordwater@hotmail.com

Heatstar Ltd, 22 Daish Way, Newport, Isle of Wight, PO30 5XB Tel: (01983) 521465 Fax: (01983) 822016 E-mail: info@heatstar.co.uk

▶ The Pool Shop, 60 The Grove, Christchurch, Dorset, BH23 2HB Tel: (01202) 480232 Fax: (01202) 480222 E-mail: sales@pool-shop.co.uk

SWIMMING POOL HEATERS

▶ Elecro Engineering Ltd, Unit 14 Leyden Road, Stevenage, Hertfordshire, SG1 2BW Tel: (01438) 749474 Fax: (01438) 361329 E-mail: info@eleco.co.uk

▶ Jetstream Products Ltd, 206 Farnborough Road, Farnborough, Hampshire, GU14 7JL Tel: (01252) 545006 Fax: (01252) 372670 E-mail: info@jetstreamuk.com

Thermalec Products Ltd, Kingsley Close, Lee Mill Industrial Estate, Ivybridge, Devon, PL21 9GD Tel: (01752) 313343 Fax: (01752) 313353 E-mail: sales@thermalec.com

SWIMMING POOL LINERS

Aquaflex Ltd, 1 Edison Road, Salisbury, SP2 7NU Tel: (01722) 328873 Fax: (01722) 413068 E-mail: info@aquaflex.co.uk

Azure Leisure Pools, 150 London Road, Bagshot, Surrey, GU19 5DG Tel: (01276) 475566 Fax: (01276) 475201

Plastica Ltd, Perimeter House, Napier Road, St. Leonards-On-Sea, East Sussex, TN38 9NY Tel: (01424) 857857 Fax: (01424) 857858 E-mail: info@plastica.ltd.uk

SWIMMING POOL REFURBISHMENT

Active Water Systems, 122 Newport Road, Caldicot, Monmouthshire, NP26 4BT Tel: (01291) 420012 Fax: (0870) 4294048 E-mail: us@ActiveWater.co.uk

SWIMMING POOL WATER FILTERS OR FILTRATION SYSTEMS

Aqua Process Engineering Ltd, Aqua House, 27 Denison Road, London, SW19 2DJ Tel: (020) 8543 3647 Fax: (020) 8543 2163 E-mail: enquiries@aquaprocess.com

Ardep UK Ltd, Unit 34, Spring Vale Industrial Estate, Cwmbran, Gwent, NP44 5BD Tel: (01633) 480496 Fax: (01633) 480497 E-mail: sales@ardep.com

Biwater International Ltd, Biwater House, Station App, Dorking, Surrey, RH4 1TZ Tel: (01306) 740740 Fax: (01306) 885233 E-mail: corporate.communications@biwater.com

Buckingham Swimming Pools Ltd, Dalehouse Lane, Kenilworth, Warwickshire, CV8 2EB Tel: (01926) 852351 Fax: (01926) 512387 E-mail: info@buckinghampools.com

Certikin International Ltd, 2 Station Lane Industrial Park Estate, Witney, Oxfordshire, OX28 4FH Tel: (01993) 778855 Fax: (01993) 778620 E-mail: export@certikin.co.uk

Lacron UK Ltd, Radfield, London Road, Teynham, Sittingbourne, Kent, ME9 9PS Tel: (01795) 521733 Fax: (01795) 522085 E-mail: info@lacron.co.uk

SWIMMING POOL WATER TEST EQUIPMENT

Lovibond Water Testing, Waterloo Road, Salisbury, SP1 2JY Tel: (01722) 327242 Fax: (01722) 412322 E-mail: sales@tintometer.com

SWIMMING POOL WATER TREATMENT CONSULTANTS

Purple Prodjects, 9 Holtspur Close, Beaconsfield, Buckinghamshire, HP9 1DP Tel: (01494) 680855 Fax: (01494) 671670

SWIMMING POOL WATER TREATMENT SYSTEMS

Hydropath UK Ltd, Acorn Park, Lenton Lane Industrial Estate, Nottingham, NG7 2TR Tel: 0115-986 9966 Fax: 0115-986 9944 E-mail: sales@hydroflow.com

Surex (International) Ltd, Unit 5, Airport Trading Estate, Westerham, Kent, TN16 3BW Tel: (01959) 576000 Fax: (01959) 571000 E-mail: info@surex.co.uk

SWIMMING POOLS

A G Budget Discount Swimming Pools & Spas, Aqua Garden House, East Molesey, Surrey, KT8 0PA Tel: (0870) 1283185 Fax: (0870) 1283188 E-mail: info@agbudget.co.uk

▶ Alligator Pool Products, Unit 27, Station Road Industrial Estate, Southwater, Horsham, West Sussex, RH13 9UD Tel: (01403) 730505 Fax: (01403) 733888 E-mail: info@alligator-pools.co.uk

Aqua Home Pools Marketing Ltd, Oteley Road, Shrewsbury, SY2 6QW Tel: (01743) 235081 Fax: (01743) 271043 E-mail: enquiry@aquahome.com

Crystalclear Leisure, Woodside Centre, Southend Arterial Road, Rayleigh, Essex, SS6 7TR Tel: (01268) 776690 Fax: (01268) 775842 E-mail: accleisure@aol.com

Elm Leisure, Hitherford, Over, Cambridge, CB24 5NY Tel: (01954) 230230 Fax: (01954) 231775 E-mail: info@elmleisure.com

Fox Pool (UK) Ltd, Mere House, Stow Road, Sturton By Stow, Lincoln, LN1 2BZ Tel: (01427) 788662 Fax: (01427) 788526 E-mail: grayfoxswi@aol.com

▶ Leisure Design, 35 Dunvegan Avenue, Gourock, Renfrewshire, PA19 1AE Tel: (01475) 520912

Luton Swimming Pool Supplies, 86 Old Bedford Road, Luton, LU2 7PD Tel: (01582) 731819 Fax: (01582) 611054 E-mail: sales@lutonpools.com

Origin Leisure, Summerhouse Business Park, Canal Way, Harefield, Uxbridge, Middlesex, UB9 6TH Tel: (01895) 823366 Fax: (01895) 824445 E-mail: info@origindfl.co.uk

▶ Peterborough Pools Ltd, 3 Fenlake Business Centre, Fengate, Peterborough, PE1 5BQ Tel: (01733) 319222 Fax: (01733) 319111 E-mail: enquiries@peterboroughpools.co.uk

Premier Pool Services, 25A The Street, Charlwood, Horley, Surrey, RH6 0BY Tel: (01293) 863841 Fax: (01293) 863841

Rutherford The Pool People, Marley Lane, Battle, East Sussex, TN33 0TY Tel: (01424) 775060 Fax: (01424) 777066 E-mail: info@rutherfordpools.co.uk

Sterling Swimming Pools, Daniels Road, Norwich, NR4 6QP Tel: (01603) 503908 Fax: (01603) 811507 E-mail: duncan@sterlingpools.co.uk

SWIMMING POOLS, GLASS FIBRE OR FIBREGLASS

Elm Leisure, Hitherford, Over, Cambridge, CB24 5NY Tel: (01954) 230230 Fax: (01954) 231775 E-mail: info@elmleisure.com

SWIMMING SHORTS

▶ Just Hom.Com, 44 High Street, Shrewsbury, SY1 1ST Tel: (01743) 247246 Fax: E-mail: sales@justhom.com

SWIMMING TRUNKS

▶ Just Hom.Com, 44 High Street, Shrewsbury, SY1 1ST Tel: (01743) 247246 Fax: E-mail: sales@justhom.com

SWIMWEAR

Anthony Howard Eaton Ltd, Cursham Street, Sutton-in-Ashfield, Nottinghamshire, NG17 5FD Tel: (01623) 557444

Desiree Boutique, 26 High Street, Rottingdean, Brighton, BN2 7HR Tel: (01273) 303444 Fax: (01273) 303444

Hargreaves Sports Ltd, 2-3 Solent Twentyseven, Walton Road, Portsmouth, PO6 1SX Tel: (023) 9232 1200 Fax: (023) 9237 1212 E-mail: sales@hargreaves-sports.co.uk

▶ Just Hom.Com, 44 High Street, Shrewsbury, SY1 1ST Tel: (01743) 247246 Fax: E-mail: sales@justhom.com

T.H. Knightall, Hawksley Avenue, Sheffield, S6 2BG Tel: 0114-234 8886 Fax: 0114-285 4753 E-mail: thkltd@aol.com

Pak Nylon Hosiery Co, 31 Broughton Street, Cheetham Hill, Manchester, M8 8LZ Tel: 0161 832 7371 Fax: 0161 839 5134 E-mail: C_M_Afzal_Khan@hotmail.co.uk

Sherwood Group P.L.C., Fields Farm Road, Long Eaton, Nottingham, NG10 1GT Tel: 0115-946 1070 Fax: 0115-946 2720 E-mail: info@sherwoodgroup.co.uk

Speedo International Ltd, Ascot Road, Nottingham, NG8 5AJ Tel: 0115-916 7000 Fax: 0115-910 5005 E-mail: speedoinfo@pentland.com

W Fischer & Sons Luton Ltd, 4a William Street, Luton, LU2 7RE Tel: (01582) 404022 Fax: (01582) 400455

SWISS TYPE TURNING SERVICES

S J C Engineering Ltd, 5 Court Industrial Estate, Navigation Road, Chelmsford, CM2 6ND Tel: (01245) 492926 Fax: (01245) 494296 E-mail: enquiries@sjceng.co.uk

SWITCH DISTRIBUTORS OR AGENTS

Chartland Electronics Ltd, Chartland House Old Station Approach, Randalls Road, Leatherhead, Surrey, KT22 7TE Tel: (01372) 363666 Fax: (01372) 363833 E-mail: sales@chartlandelectronics.co.uk

E Preston Electrical Ltd, Unit 28 Broadway, Globe Lane, Dukinfield, Cheshire, SK16 4UU Tel: 0161-339 5177 Fax: 0161-343 1935 E-mail: sales@epreston.co.uk

Farcroft Electronic Services Ltd, Tanglewood 88 Jobs Lane, Coventry, CV4 9ED Tel: (024) 7646 0087 Fax: (024) 7647 0369 E-mail: enquires@farcroft-uk.com

Pennine Components Ltd, PO Box 1, Todmorden, Lancashire, OL14 5BB Tel: (01706) 815737 Fax: (01706) 817628 E-mail: sales@penninecomponents.co.uk

Read Cosine Ltd, Unit 1 Leanne Business Centre, Sandford Lane, Wareham, Dorset, BH20 4DY Tel: (01929) 550727 Fax: (01929) 550357 E-mail: sales@readcosine.com

SWITCH LEGENDS AND LABELS

Instyle Leather Goods Ltd, Publicity House, Tweedy Lane, Newport, Gwent, NP19 8DZ Tel: (01633) 282412 Fax: (01633) 282413 E-mail: m-freeman@btinternet.com

SWITCH MANUFRS, ELECTRIC,

See also headings under Switches

Itt Cannon Ltd, Viables Industrial Estate, Jays Close, Basingstoke, Hampshire, RG22 4BA Tel: (01256) 311200 Fax: (01256) 322356 E-mail: sales.uk@cannon.de.ittind.com

Knitter Switch UK Ltd, Grove House, Lutyens Close, Lychpit, Basingstoke, Hampshire, RG24 8AG Tel: (01256) 338670 Fax: (01256) 338671 E-mail: ksuk@knitter-switch.com

Robinson Seabrook Ltd, 16 Moat Way, Barwell, Leicester, LE9 8EY Tel: (01455) 846151 Fax: (01455) 846383 E-mail: rwells1047@aol.com

Stoneridge Pollak Ltd, The Moors, Tewkesbury Road, Cheltenham, Gloucestershire, GL51 9BP Tel: (01242) 283000 Fax: (01242) 283023 E-mail: stuart.felton@stoneridgepollak.co.uk

SWITCHBOARDS

Actemium, Meteor Business Park, Cheltenham Road East, Gloucester, GL2 9QL Tel: (01452) 713222 Fax: (01452) 713444 E-mail: actemium@actemium.co.uk

Aird, Walker & Ralston Ltd, 12F Lawson Street, Kilmarnock, Ayrshire, KA1 3JP Tel: (01563) 522236 Fax: (01563) 521304 E-mail: sales@airdwalker.co.uk

B & F Group Ltd, Sovereign Way, Chester West Employment Park, Chester, CH1 4QJ Tel: (01244) 390215 Fax: (01244) 382747

Ellison Switchgear, Mounts Road, Wednesbury, West Midlands, WS10 0DU Tel: 0121-505 2000 Fax: 0121-556 1981 E-mail: enquiries@ellison.co.uk

Howarth Switchgear Ltd, Finlas Street, Cowlairs Industrial Estate, Glasgow, G22 5DT Tel: 0141-557 3553 Fax: 0141-558 0614 E-mail: sales@howarthswitchgear.co.uk

Industrial & Marine Switchgear Ltd, Amsterdam Road, Sutton Fields Industrial Estate, Hull, HU7 0XF Tel: (01482) 831222 Fax: (01482) 826696 E-mail: information@ims-swgr.karoo.co.uk

M C R Electrical Services, 2 Factory Estate, English Street, Hull, HU3 2BE Tel: (01482) 589062 Fax: (01482) 589525 E-mail: mcr@unit2.fslife.co.uk

Moss Switchgear Services Ltd, Ashwood House, Aragon Road, Blackbushe Business Park, Yateley, Hampshire, GU46 6GA Tel: (01252) 876767 Fax: (01252) 877313 E-mail: info@moss-switchgear.co.uk

Northern Switch Gear & Controls, 2 Lloyd Court, Dunston, Gateshead, Tyne & Wear, NE11 9EP Tel: 0191-461 1130 Fax: 0191-461 1140 E-mail: nthnswitch@aol.com

Pandelco Ltd, Canal Street, Burton-on-Trent, Staffordshire, DE14 3TB Tel: (01283) 542738 Fax: (01283) 511774 E-mail: sales@pandelco.co.uk

Sperrin Switchgear, 1 20 Cahore Road, Draperstown, Magherafelt, County Londonderry, BT45 7LS Tel: (028) 7962 7770 Fax: (028) 7962 7771

Terasaki Europe Ltd, 80 Beardmore Way, Clydebank, Dunbartonshire, G81 4HT Tel: 0141-565 1600 Fax: 0141-952 9246 E-mail: marketing@terasaki.com

Wyke Electrical Control Ltd, Unit 1, St Marks Square, Hull, HU3 2DQ Tel: (01482) 328630 Fax: (01482) 320674

SWITCHBOARDS TO SPECIFICATION

Eaton Electric Ltd, Reddings Lane, Tysley, Birmingham, B11 3EZ Tel: 0121-685 2100 Fax: 0121-706 2012

Mertech Pumps Ltd, 39 Hastings Street, Luton, LU1 5BE Tel: (01582) 422622 Fax: (01582) 422922 E-mail: mail@mertech.co.uk

▶ Salem Automation Ltd, Sycamore Road, Eastwood Trading Estate, Rotherham, South Yorkshire, S65 1EN Tel: (01709) 538200 Fax: (01709) 376903 E-mail: sales@salemautomation.net

SWITCHED MODE POWER SUPPLIES (SMPS)

D P Energy Services, Unit 5 & 6, Heron Avenue, Wickford, Essex, SS11 8DL Tel: (01268) 560040 Fax: (01268) 560261 E-mail: sales@drakepower.com

Eltek Energy (UK) Ltd, Eltek House, Maxted Road, Hemel Hempstead, Hertfordshire, HP2 7DX Tel: (01442) 219355 Fax: (01442) 245894 E-mail: uksales@eltekenergy.com

G E Digital Energy, Wheatfield Way, Hinckley, Leicestershire, LE10 1YG Tel: 0116-290 5280 Fax: 0116-290 5281 E-mail: sales@imv.co.uk

Lite On Ltd, North Seaton Industrial Estate, Ashington, Northumberland, NE63 0YB Tel: (01670) 813648 Fax: (01670) 853787 E-mail: sales@liteon.co.uk

Lomond Electronic Services, 8 Silverston Avenue, Bognor Regis, West Sussex, PO21 2RB Tel: (01243) 842520 Fax: (01243) 842520 E-mail: lomondpsu@btclick.com

P S U Designs Ltd, 7 Bloomfield Park, Bloomfield Road, Tipton, West Midlands, DY4 9AP Tel: 0121-557 6499 Fax: 0121-557 6498 E-mail: sales@psudesigns.co.uk

Protolink, 6 Zone B Chelmsford Road Industrial Estate, Chelmsford Road, Dunmow, Essex, CM6 1HD Tel: (01371) 875726 Fax: (01371) 876381 E-mail: sales@protolink.co.uk

R T E Electronics, 568 Burnley Road, Rossendale, Lancashire, BB4 8AJ Tel: (01706) 227234 Fax: (01706) 227531 E-mail: brain@rtepower.co.uk

Tabuchi Electric UK Ltd, Tabuchi House, Robson Avenue, Teesside Industrial Estate, Stockton-on-Tees, Cleveland, TS17 9LS Tel: (01642) 750750 Fax: (01642) 750108

V X I Power Ltd, Westminster Industrial Estate, Station Road, North Hykeham, Lincoln, LN6 3QY Tel: (01522) 500511 Fax: (01522) 500515 E-mail: sales@vxipower.com

Young Ecc Electronics, Crown House, Coronation Road, Cressex Business Park, High Wycombe, Buckinghamshire, HP12 3TA Tel: (01494) 753500 Fax: (01494) 753501 E-mail: sales@youngelectronics.com

SWITCHED MODE TRANSFORMERS

Precision Windings Ltd, Unit J, Durban Road, South Bersted, Bognor Regis, West Sussex, PO22 9QT Tel: (01243) 823311 Fax: (01243) 823318E-mail: sales@precisionwindings.co.uk

Tabuchi Electric UK Ltd, Tabuchi House, Robson Avenue, Teesside Industrial Estate, Stockton-on-Tees, Cleveland, TS17 9LS Tel: (01642) 750750 Fax: (01642) 750108

SWITCHES, GIGABIT LOCAL AREA NETWORK (LAN)

▶ Internormen Technology, Unit G14, Westthorpe Fields Road, Killamarsh, Sheffield, S21 1TZ Tel: 0114-218 0614 Fax: 0114-218 0615 E-mail: northsales@reacttechnologies.com

▶ Khipu Networks Ltd, Infineon House, Minley Road, Fleet, Hampshire, GU51 2RD Tel: (01252) 773184 Fax: (01252) 629008 E-mail: sales@khipu-networks.com

▶ Premier Management, 18 Balmoral CR, Oswestry, Shropshire, SY11 2XG Tel: (01691) 653505 E-mail: carl.palmer@premierconsultancy.com

▶ Red Galleon Ltd, Beech House Docking Road, Sedgeford, Hunstanton, Norfolk, PE36 5LR Tel: (01485) 579363 Fax: (01485) 579396 E-mail: info@redgalleon.com

SWITCHES, LIMIT, ADJUSTABLE

▶ Sub-Atlantic, Blackburn Business Park, Woodburn Road, Blackburn, Aberdeen, AB21 0PS Tel: (01224) 798660 Fax: (01224) 798661

SWITCHES, MEMBRANE/ KEYBOARD/TOUCH

C & K Systems Ltd, Cunliffe Drive, Northfield Ave., Kettering, Northamptonshire, NN16 8LF Tel: (01536) 410595 Fax: (01536) 416602

The Danielson Group Ltd, 29 Pembroke Road, Aylesbury, Buckinghamshire, HP20 1DB Tel: (01296) 319000 Fax: (01296) 392141 E-mail: sales@danielson.co.uk

Diamond H Controls Ltd, Vulcan Road North, Norwich, NR6 6AH Tel: (01603) 425291 Fax: (01603) 424907 E-mail: sales@diamond-h-controls.co.uk

Electro Serigraphic Products Ltd, Unit 8 Collers Way, Reepham, Norwich, NR10 4SW Tel: (01603) 871227 Fax: (01603) 871237 E-mail: esp@membrane-switches.co.uk

John Mcgavigan Information Technology Ltd, 111 Westerhill Road, Bishopbriggs, Glasgow, G64 2QR Tel: 0141-302 0000 Fax: 0141-302 0290 E-mail: enquiries@mcgavigan.com

Touch Panel Products Ltd, Short Way, Thornbury, Bristol, BS35 3UT Tel: (01454) 417307 Fax: (01454) 413708 E-mail: sales@touchpanels.co.uk

SWITCHES, ROCKER

Apem Components Ltd, Drakes Drive, Long Crendon, Aylesbury, Buckinghamshire, HP18 9BA Tel: (01844) 202400 Fax: (01844) 202500 E-mail: info@apem.co.uk

SWITCHES, TEMPERATURE CONTROLLED/THERMOSTAT

Able Instruments & Controls Ltd, Danehill, Lower Earley, Reading, RG6 4UT Tel: 0118-931 1188 Fax: 0118-931 2161 E-mail: sales@able.co.uk

Amot Controls Ltd, Western Way, Bury St. Edmunds, Suffolk, IP33 3SZ Tel: (01284) 762222 Fax: (01284) 760256 E-mail: info@amot.com

Custom Control Sensors International, 13 Shrivenham Hundred Business Park, Majors Road, Watchfield, Swindon, SN6 8TZ Tel: (01793) 783545 Fax: (01793) 783532 E-mail: pswitch@ccsdualsnap.co.uk

Otter Controls Ltd, Hardwick Square South, Buxton, Derbyshire, SK17 6LA Tel: (01298) 762300 Fax: (01298) 72664 E-mail: sales@ottercontrols.com

P V L Ltd, 9 Lexden Lodge Industrial Estate, Crowborough Hill, Crowborough, East Sussex, TN6 2NQ Tel: (01892) 664499 Fax: (01892) 663690 E-mail: info@pd1.co.uk

SWITCHES, TILT/TIP

Polaron Cortina Ltd, 26 Greenhill Cresent, Watford Business Park, Watford, WD18 8XG Tel: (01923) 495495 Fax: (01923) 228796 E-mail: sales@polaron.co.uk

SWITCHGEAR CABINETS

Hooper Engineering Ltd, Nelson St, Oldbury, West Midlands, B69 4NY Tel: 0121-552 2835 Fax: 0121-552 3821 E-mail: hooper.sheetmetal@virgin.net

SWITCHGEAR CONTACT MATERIALS

Loxwood Contacts Ltd, Unit 11 Cardiff Road Industrial Estate, Cardiff Road, Watford, WD18 0DG Tel: (01923) 254521 Fax: (01923) 818027 E-mail: sales@loxwoodcontacts.co.uk

Vacuum Impregnated Products Ltd, Hew Cut Lane, Woolston, Warrington, WA1 4AG Tel: (01925) 817213 Fax: (01925) 823862 E-mail: sales@viproducts.co.uk

SWITCHGEAR MAINTENANCE/ REPAIR SERVICES

Bowers Electricals Ltd, Slack Lane, Heanor, Derbyshire, DE75 7GX Tel: (01773) 531531 Fax: (01773) 716171 E-mail: enquiries@bowerselec.co.uk

Burtonwood Generator & Switchgear Services Ltd, St Michaels Road, St. Helens, Merseyside, WA9 4WZ Tel: (01744) 814444 Fax: (01744) 814455 E-mail: sales@burtonwoodgroup.com

Electra Switch Ltd, Unit 4 Colne Way Court, Colne Way, Watford, WD24 7NE Tel: (01923) 246154 Fax: (01923) 246482 E-mail: esl@electra-switch.co.uk

G E Oil & Gas, Badentoy Crescent, Badentoy Park, Aberdeen, AB12 4YD Tel: (01224) 785100 Fax: (01224) 785120

Switchgear Engineering Services Ltd, Wright Street, Audenshaw, Manchester, M34 5TT Tel: 0161-371 0833 Fax: 0161-371 0834

Whippendell Electrical Ltd, 477-479 Whippendell Road, Watford, WD18 7PU Tel: (01923) 228201 Fax: (01923) 228007 E-mail: kevin@wippendale-marine.co.uk

SWITCHGEAR MANUFRS

A T S Panels Ltd, Unit B, Lammas Courtyard, Weldon Industrial Estate, Corby, Northamptonshire, NN17 5EZ Tel: (01536) 407474 Fax: (01536) 409443

Burtonwood Generator & Switchgear Services Ltd, St Michaels Road, St. Helens, Merseyside, WA9 4WZ Tel: (01744) 814444 Fax: (01744) 814455 E-mail: sales@burtonwoodgroup.com

E P Systems Ltd, Media House, 21 East Ways Industrial Estate, Witham, Essex, CM8 3YQ Tel: (01376) 531380 Fax: (01376) 531361 E-mail: neil-rowe@epsystems.co.uk

Electra Switch Ltd, Unit 4 Colne Way Court, Colne Way, Watford, WD24 7NE Tel: (01923) 246154 Fax: (01923) 246482 E-mail: esl@electra-switch.co.uk

Electrical Supplies Ltd, 7 The Broadway, Hampton Court Way, Thames Ditton, Surrey, KT7 0LX Tel: (020) 8398 9377 Fax: (020) 8398 8093

Ellison Switchgear, Mounts Road, Wednesbury, West Midlands, WS10 0DU Tel: 0121-505 2000 Fax: 0121-556 1981 E-mail: enquiries@ellison.co.uk

FKI Switchgear Ltd, Newport Road, Pontllanfraith, Blackwood, Gwent, NP12 2XH Tel: (01495) 223001 Fax: (01495) 225674

G K Switchgear Ltd, 4 Colts Holm Road, Old Wolverton, Milton Keynes, MK12 5QD Tel: (01908) 225777 Fax: (01908) 225818 E-mail: rjbgks@aol.com

Huggett Electrical Ltd, Twerton Mill, Lower Bristol Road, Bath, BA2 1EW Tel: (01225) 426271 Fax: (01225) 448154 E-mail: mail@huggettelectrical.co.uk

L C Switchgear Ltd, Unit 2, Hove Technology Centre, St Josephs Close, Hove, East Sussex, BN3 7ES Tel: (01273) 770540 Fax: (01273) 770547

Lucy Switchgear, Howland Road, Thame, Oxfordshire, OX9 3UJ Tel: (01844) 267222 Fax: (01844) 267223 E-mail: sales.switchgear@wlucy.co.uk

Parmley Graham Ltd, Saltmeadows Road, Gateshead, Tyne & Wear, NE8 3BG Tel: 0191-477 4625 Fax: 0191-478 6801 E-mail: hq@parmley-graham.co.uk

Proteus Switchgear, Stafford Park 12, Telford, Shropshire, TF3 3BJ Tel: (01952) 292001 Fax: (01952) 292837

R & B Switchgear Services Ltd, The Courtyard, Green Lane, Heywood, Lancashire, OL10 2EX Tel: (01706) 369933 Fax: (01706) 364564

Specialist Switchgear Systems Ltd, 9 Kay Street, Bury, Lancashire, BL9 6BU Tel: 0161-764 1297 Fax: 0161-762 9807

R. & B. Star Ltd, 14 Kennet Road, Crayford, Dartford, DA1 4SD Tel: (01322) 555125 Fax: (01322) 522465

Switchgear International Ltd, Farthing Road Industrial Estate, Ipswich, IP1 5AP Tel: (01473) 240280 Fax: (01473) 242929 E-mail: sales@switchgearinternational.co.uk

W F Wades, 12 Falcon Business Centre, Falcon Close, Burton-on-Trent, Staffordshire, DE14 1SG Tel: (01283) 541621 Fax: (01283) 510382

SWITCHGEAR MANUFRS – *continued*

W.F. Wades, Unit 11, Garrick Industrial Centre, Irving Way, London, NW9 6AQ Tel: (020) 8203 0055 Fax: (020) 8203 6570
Whipp & Bourne, Switchgear Works, Manchester Road, Rochdale, Lancashire, OL11 2SS Tel: (01706) 632051 Fax: (01706) 674236

SWITCHGEAR TRIPPING BATTERY UNITS

Dartpoint Ltd, Unit 1b Kitewell Lane, Lydd, Romney Marsh, Kent, TN29 9LP Tel: (01797) 320910 Fax: (01797) 320571 E-mail: sales@dartpoint.co.uk
Lohmeier-Comat UK Ltd, 1 Dunston Pl, Dunston Rd, Chesterfield, Derbyshire, S41 8XA Tel: (01246) 264300 Fax: (01246) 264301 E-mail: sales@edlcomat.co.uk

SWITCHGEAR, TRANSFORMER

▶ Jemelec Ltd, Unit 16 Vanguard Trading Estate, Britannia Road, Chesterfield, Derbyshire, S45 9DX Tel: (0870) 7871769

SWIVEL JOINTS

Anson Ltd, Team Valley Trading Estate, Seventh Avenue, Gateshead, Tyne & Wear, NE11 0JW Tel: 0191-482 0022 Fax: 0191-487 8835 E-mail: anson-gateshead@anson.co.uk
Deublin Ltd, Royce Close, Andover, Hampshire, SP10 3TS Tel: (01264) 333355 Fax: (01264) 333304 E-mail: deublin@deublin.co.uk
Glenthorpe Engineering Co. Ltd, 95 Railway Road, Teddington, Middlesex, TW11 8TE Tel: (020) 8977 5433 Fax: (020) 8943 4993
Rotaflow F V Ltd, Rotec House, Bingswood Trading Estate, Whaley Bridge, High Peak, Derbyshire, SK23 7LY Tel: (01663) 735003 Fax: (01663) 735006 E-mail: sales@rotaflow.com

SYNCHRONOUS ELECTRIC MOTORS

Haydon Switch (HSI) (Henley), Treetops House, Gillotts Lane, Henley-on-Thames, Oxfordshire, RG9 1PT Tel: (01491) 579118 Fax: (01491) 412211 E-mail: sales@acdcsystems.com
Rotalink Ltd, Cropmead, Crewkerne, Somerset, TA18 7HQ Tel: (01460) 72000 Fax: (01460) 74278 E-mail: info@rotalink.com

SYNTHETIC ADHESIVES

Ace Adhesives Ltd, Shenstone Drive, Walsall, WS9 8TP Tel: (01922) 459393 Fax: (01922) 743417 E-mail: sales@aceadhesives.com
C B Adhesives, Adlington Industrial Estate, Adlington, Macclesfield, Cheshire, SK10 4NL Tel: (01625) 850180 Fax: (01625) 875932
Forbo Swift Adhesives Ltd, Bridge Street, Chatteris, Cambridgeshire, PE16 6RD Tel: (01354) 692345 Fax: (01354) 696661
Strongbond Adhesives Ltd, Beehive Works, Hollins Lane, Bury, Lancashire, BL9 8AA Tel: 0161-766 2618 Fax: 0161-767 9024 E-mail: sales@strongbond.co.uk

SYNTHETIC CHAMOIS LEATHER

Lees Newsome Ltd, Ashley Mill, Ashley Street, Oldham, OL9 6LS Tel: 0161-652 1321 Fax: 0161-627 3362 E-mail: sales@leesnewsome.co.uk

SYNTHETIC FIBRE PRODUCERS/PROCESSORS OR SERVICES

Norfolk Textured Yarns Cromer Ltd, Holt Road, Cromer, Norfolk, NR27 9JW Tel: (01263) 513188 Fax: (01263) 515347

SYNTHETIC FIBRE ROPES

Linear Composites Ltd, Vale Mills, Oakworth, Keighley, West Yorkshire, BD22 0EB Tel: (01535) 643363 Fax: (01535) 643605 E-mail: mail@linearcomposites.com
Rope Services Tipton Ltd, St Georges Works, Bradleys Lane, Tipton, West Midlands, DY4 9EZ Tel: 0121-557 7521 Fax: 0121-557 8921

SYNTHETIC FIBRE TWINE

Independent Twine Manufacturing Co. Ltd, Westbank Road, Llay Industrial Estate, Llay, Wrexham, Clwyd, LL12 0PZ Tel: (01978) 854812 Fax: (01978) 854229 E-mail: keithmacguire@indtwineco.com

SYNTHETIC FIBRE WASTE MERCHANTS/PROCESSORS

Walbrad Wool Trading Co., White Rose Mill, Holdsworth Road, Halifax, West Yorkshire, HX3 6SN Tel: (01422) 241001 Fax: (01422) 246331 E-mail: info@cashmere-fibre.co.uk
Walter Smith Nelson Ltd, Wenning Street, Nelson, Lancashire, BB9 0LE Tel: (01282) 698142 Fax: (01282) 619109 E-mail: wsmith@provider.co.uk

SYNTHETIC FIBRE WEAVING SERVICES

Woodrow Universal Ltd, Junction Mills, Skipton Road, Cross Hills, Keighley, West Yorkshire, BD20 7SE Tel: (01535) 633364 Fax: (01535) 634439 E-mail: sales@woodrowuniversal.co.uk

SYNTHETIC FURNISHING FABRIC YARN

Robert Noble Ltd, March Street, Peebles, EH45 8ER Tel: (01721) 724311 Fax: (01721) 721893 E-mail: enquiries@robert-noble.co.uk

SYNTHETIC LATEX

Formulated Polymer Products Ltd, 8 Garden Street, Ramsbottom, Bury, Lancashire, BL0 9BQ Tel: (01706) 828208 Fax: (01706) 828820 E-mail: neil@polymers.co.uk

SYNTHETIC LUBRICANTS

Suff Marine (Europe) Ltd, 15 Allanfield Drive, Newton Stewart, Wigtownshire, DG8 6BP Tel: (01671) 401216 Fax: (01671) 401216 E-mail: sales@suffmarine.com

SYNTHETIC MOULDINGS

Oakleaf Reproductions Ltd, Ling Bob Mill, Main St, Wilsden, Bradford, West Yorkshire, BD15 0JP Tel: (01535) 272878 Fax: (01535) 275748 E-mail: sales@oakleaf.co.uk

SYNTHETIC PAPER

Tech Folium Ltd, Triumph Trading Park, Speke Hall Road, Speke, Liverpool, L24 9GQ Tel: 0151-486 4300 Fax: 0151-486 3335

SYNTHETIC PICTURE FRAME MOULDINGS

M G Framing, Unit 8 Islwyn Workshops, Pontymister Industrial Estate, Risca, Newport, Gwent, NP11 6NP Tel: (01633) 612034 Fax: (01633) 612034 E-mail: mgframing@btinternet.com

SYNTHETIC RESIN BONDED FABRIC (SRBF) BASE LAMINATED PLASTIC

C L S Fabrication Ltd, 1 Caswell Road, Leamington Spa, Warwickshire, CV31 1QD Tel: (01926) 336126 Fax: (01926) 312022 E-mail: sales@clsfab.co.uk
Vulcascot Ltd, Braintree Road, Ruislip, Middlesex, HA4 0XX Tel: (020) 8841 4211 Fax: (020) 8841 3544

SYNTHETIC RESIN, FOUNDRY USE, *See Foundry etc*

SYNTHETIC RESIN, PAINT/ VARNISH/WIRE ENAMEL

Schenectady (Europe) Ltd, Four Ashes, Wolverhampton, WV10 7BT Tel: (01902) 790555 Fax: (01902) 791640 E-mail:

SYNTHETIC RESINS, *See also headings for particular types*

B I P (Oldbury) Ltd, PO Box 3180, Oldbury, West Midlands, B69 4PG Tel: 0121-544 2333 Fax: 0121-552 4267 E-mail: enquiries@bip.co.uk
B I P Organics Ltd, Brooks Lane Industrial Estate, Middlewich, Cheshire, CW10 0JG Tel: (01606) 835271 Fax: (01606) 835274
Borden Chemical, Station Road, Cowie, Stirling, FK7 7BQ Tel: (01786) 814045 Fax: (01786) 816476
DSM, Delves Road, Heanor Gate Industrial Estate, Heanor, Derbyshire, DE75 7SG Tel: (01773) 536500 Fax: (01773) 536600
Dynea UK Ltd, Alyn Works, Denbigh Road, Mold, Clwyd, CH7 1BF Tel: (01352) 757657 Fax: (01352) 758914 E-mail: sales@dynea.com
Euroresins UK Ltd, Cloister Way, Ellesmere Port, CH65 4EL Tel: 0151-356 3111 Fax: 0151-355 3772 E-mail: sales@euroresins.com
Industrial Copolymers Ltd, Iotech House, Miller Street, Preston, PR1 1EA Tel: (01772) 201964 Fax: (01772) 255194 E-mail: info@incorez.com
Raschig UK Ltd, Trafford Road, Salford, M5 4QD Tel: 0161-877 3933 Fax: 0161-877 3944 E-mail: raschig.uk_ltd@virgin.net
Schenectady (Europe) Ltd, Four Ashes, Wolverhampton, WV10 7BT Tel: (01902) 790555 Fax: (01902) 791640 E-mail:
Scott Bader Co. Ltd, Wollaston Hall, Wollaston, Wellingborough, Northamptonshire, NN29 7RL Tel: (01933) 663100 Fax: (01933) 663028 E-mail: sales@scottbader.com
Spectrum Resin Systems Ltd, 69a Huddersfield Road, Elland, West Yorkshire, HX5 9AA Tel: (01422) 375851 Fax: (01422) 310291
V I L Resins Ltd, Union Road, Bolton, BL2 2DT Tel: (01204) 388800 Fax: (01204) 362775 E-mail: enquiries@vilresins.com
Wessex Resins & Adhesives Ltd, Cupernham Lane, Romsey, Hampshire, SO51 7LF Tel: (01794) 521111 Fax: (0870) 7701032 E-mail: info@wessex-resins.com

SYNTHETIC SAPPHIRE COMPONENTS

A Blundell Jewel Bearings Ltd, 203 Torrington Avenue, Coventry, CV4 9UT Tel: (024) 7647 3625 Fax: (024) 7646 6399
Image Optics Components, Harvey Road, Basildon, Essex, SS13 1ES Tel: (01268) 728477 Fax: (01268) 590445 E-mail: sales@image-optics.fsnet.co.uk
Pi-Kem Ltd, Yew Tree House, Tilley Wem, Wem, Shrewsbury, SY4 5HE Tel: (01939) 234801 Fax: (01939) 235394 E-mail: pikem.rouse@virgin.net

SYNTHETIC SPORTS SURFACE INSTALLATION OR LAYING CONTRACTORS

▶ Banner Sports Surfaces, Banner House, Parkfield Road, Rugby, Warwickshire, CV21 1QJ Tel: 01788 559332 Fax: 01788 559333 E-mail: joanne.lewis@bannerholdings.co.uk
Gerald Davies Ltd, Kenfig Industrial Estate, Margam, Port Talbot, West Glamorgan, SA13 2PE Tel: (01656) 745525 Fax: (01656) 746270 E-mail: enquiries@geralddavies.co.uk
Tim Bingham, 28 Main Street, Sutton-on-Trent, Newark, Nottinghamshire, NG23 6PF Tel: (01636) 821246 Fax: (01636) 821719 E-mail: sales@binghamgroundservices.co.uk

SYNTHETIC SPORTS SURFACES

Eldwick Ltd, Bentley Buildings, Glaisdale, Whitby, North Yorkshire, YO21 2QY Tel: (01947) 897337 Fax: (01947) 897660
Play Rite plc, Wellington Mills, Liversedge, West Yorkshire, WF15 7XA Tel: (01924) 412488 Fax: (01924) 412337 E-mail: info@play-rite.co.uk
Sports Surfaces (UK) Ltd, PO Box 1010, Chester, CH1 3WN Tel: (01244) 321200 Fax: (01244) 347735 E-mail: info@sportssurfacesuk.com
Tim Bingham, 28 Main Street, Sutton-on-Trent, Newark, Nottinghamshire, NG23 6PF Tel: (01636) 821246 Fax: (01636) 821719 E-mail: sales@binghamgroundservices.co.uk

SYNTHETIC SUEDE, *See Leathercloth etc*

SYNTHETIC TEXTILES, *See headings for particular types*

SYPHONING EQUIPMENT

Johnson Systems International Ltd, Little Lane, Ilkley, West Yorkshire, LS29 8HY Tel: (01943) 607550 Fax: (01943) 609463

SYSTEMS INTEGRATION AND DEVELOPMENT

Ecentric Media Ltd, PO Box 473, Horsham, West Sussex, RH12 5YL Tel: (01403) 253022 Fax: 01403 253022 E-mail: enquiries@ecentricmedia.co.uk
▶ Zentive Ltd, 25 Barnes Wallis Road, Segensworth East, Fareham, Hampshire, PO15 5TT Tel: (01489) 569440 Fax: (01489) 889854 E-mail: sales@zentive.com

SYSTEMS INTEGRATION SERVICES

A N Q, The Manor House, 14 Market Street, Lutterworth, Leicestershire, LE17 4EH Tel: (01455) 559446 Fax: (01455) 558523 E-mail: lgibson@anq.com
Active Information Systems, Unit 3 Brooks Green Road, Coolham, Horsham, West Sussex, RH13 8GR Tel: (01403) 740400 Fax: (01403) 741125 E-mail: active@activegrp.co.uk
▶ Advanced Control Systems Ltd, 140 Aberford Road, Woodlesford, Leeds, LS26 8LG Tel: 0113-282 7123 Fax: 0113-282 5252 E-mail: office@xcl.co.uk
Ampac System Integrators Ltd, Hilton Officers, Shobnall Road, Burton-On-Trent, Staffordshire, DE14 2BW Tel: (01283) 567888 Fax: (01283) 567606 E-mail: info@ampac.co.uk
Axiom Software Solutions Ltd, 1 Olympic Way, Wembley, Middlesex, HA9 0NP Tel: (0845) 2305665 E-mail: info@biztechsolutions.co.uk
B A E Systems plc, Stirling Square, 6 Carlton Gardens, London, SW1Y 5AD Tel: (01252) 373232 Fax: (01252) 383000
Bits N Bytes Computer Solutions Ltd, 22-24 Ravendale St North, Scunthorpe, South Humberside, DN15 6NJ Tel: (01724) 282627 Fax: (01724) 280605 E-mail: sales@bitsnbytes.co.uk
Blackburn Starling & Co. Ltd, Queens Drive, Nottingham, NG2 3AY Tel: 0115-986 6331 Fax: 0115-986 0301 E-mail: sales@blackburn-starling.co.uk
D C S Automotive Ltd, Clarendon House, Clarendon Square, Leamington Spa, Warwickshire, CV32 5QJ Tel: (01926) 831401 Fax: (01926) 450183 E-mail: info@dcs-automotive.co.uk
Diam Software Ltd, 4 Lincoln Avenue, Canterbury, Kent, CT1 3YD Tel: (01227) 479333 E-mail: enquiries@diam.co.uk
E B D Computing Solutions Ltd, 57 Woodside, Ponteland, Newcastle upon Tyne, NE20 9JB Tel: (01661) 820389 Fax: (01661) 820389 E-mail: akeogh@excellencebydesign.co.uk
Exel, Ocean House, The Ring, Bracknell, Berkshire, RG12 1AN Tel: (01344) 302000 Fax: (01344) 710037
Fca Computers, 185 Kingston Road, Epsom, Surrey, KT19 0AA Tel: (020) 8786 7492 Fax: (020) 8786 7493 E-mail: sales@fcacomputers.co.uk
Getronics UK Ltd, Cygnus House, 1 The Southwood Crescent, Apollo Rise, Farnborough, Hampshire, GU14 0NL Tel: (0870) 9068000 Fax: (020) 8874 3014 E-mail: getronics.helpdesk@getronics.com
I S Integration Ltd, Westpoint, 4 Redheughs Rigg, Edinburgh, EH12 9DQ Tel: (0131) 338 6106 Fax: (0131) 338 6700
Industrial Science & Technology Ltd, The Watch Oak, Chain La, Battle, E. Sussex, TN33 0YD Tel: (01424) 775001 Fax: (01424) 775002
Next Step Developments, Glamafan Court, Port Talbot, West Glamorgan, SA13 2BN Tel: (01792) 323230 Fax: (01792) 323225
Olympus Automation, 4 A1 Parkway, Southgate Way, Orton Southgate, Peterborough, PE2 6YN Tel: (01733) 394700 Fax: (01733) 394901 E-mail: sales@olympus-automation.co.uk
Orange Business Services, 217 Bath Road, Slough, SL1 4AA Tel: (020) 8321 4300 Fax: (020) 8321 4040
Osprey Networks & Communications, Tower House, High Street, Aylesbury, Buckinghamshire, HP20 1SQ Tel: (01296) 745000 Fax: (01296) 745055 E-mail: sales@ospreynet.co.uk
Riva Consulting Ltd, Chedeham House, Cot Lane, Chichester, West Sussex, PO18 8ST Tel: (01243) 575955 Fax: (01243) 575966 E-mail: sales@riva-consulting.com
S X Consultancy Ltd, 5 White Oak Square, London Road, Swanley, Kent, BR8 7AG Tel: (01322) 407070 Fax: (01322) 660669
Serco, Unit A-B Wellington Gate, Silverthorne Way, Waterlooville, Hampshire, PO7 7XY Tel: (023) 9278 4950 Fax: (023) 9226 9859
Thales Underwater Systems Ltd, Dolphin House, Ashurst Drive, Stockport, Cheshire, SK3 0XB Tel: 0161-491 4001 Fax: 0161-491 1796 E-mail: info@thales-is.com

SYSTEMS INTEGRATORS, PROCESS CONTROL APPLICATIONS

▶ Atlas Business plc, Globe House, The Gullet, Nantwich, Cheshire, CW5 5RT Tel: (01270) 613016 Fax: (01270) 613012 E-mail: sales@atlasbiz.com

T BOLTS

Harrison & Clough Ltd, PO Box 9, Keighley, West Yorkshire, BD21 4EG Tel: (0870) 8892222 Fax: (0870) 8892233

T SHIRTS, WOMEN'S

▶ The Jump Shop, C/o Skydive UK Ltd, Dunkeswell Airfield, Dunkeswell, Honiton, Devon, EX14 4LG Tel: (07939) 030339 Fax: (01246) 203487 E-mail: sales@thejumpshop.co.uk

T-SHIRT/SWEATSHIRT DRYING EQUIPMENT, INFRARED

Panther Dryers, Hillside House, Intwood Road, Norwich, NR4 6TG Tel: (01603) 505509 E-mail: charlie@pantherd.freeserve.co.uk

T-SHIRT/SWEATSHIRT PRINTING CONTRACT SERVICES

3S Balloon Printers, Unit 9, Hortonwood 33, Telford, Shropshire, TF1 7EX Tel: (01952) 677506 Fax: (01952) 677464 E-mail: sales@3sballons.com
Alexco Emblems, 94 Guildford Road, Croydon, CR0 2HJ Tel: (020) 8683 0546 Fax: (020) 8689 4749 E-mail: alexco@btconnect.com
Alfabet Screenprint Ltd, 9 Sargeant Turner Trading Estate, Bromley Street, Stourbridge, West Midlands, DY9 8HZ Tel: (01384) 897355 Fax: (01384) 893414E-mail: info@alfabet.com
Big Screen, 5 Dace Road, London, E3 2NG Tel: (020) 8986 3300 Fax: (020) 8986 3742 E-mail: sales@thebigscreen.co.uk
BTC Group Ltd, Unit 9 Millington Road, Hayes, Middlesex, UB3 4AZ Tel: (020) 8569 2250 Fax: (020) 8587 3350 E-mail: sales@btcgroup.co.uk
Custom Print, 2 Ashvale Road, Tooting, London, SW17 8PW Tel: (020) 8672 3511 Fax: (020) 8682 2904 E-mail: sales@customprint.com
▶ Dreamprint, Unit 36, Royds Enterprise Park, Future Fields, Buttershaw, Bradford, West Yorkshire, BD6 3EW Tel: (01274) 355661 Fax: (01274) 355662 E-mail: bob@dreamprint.co.uk
Elite Screen Printing & Embroidery Ltd, 45 Sartoris Road, Rushden, Northamptonshire, NN10 9TL Tel: (01933) 315930 Fax: (01933) 418364 E-mail: elitetex@aol.com
Express T-Shirts Ltd, 194 Kingston Road, New Malden, Surrey, KT3 3RJ Tel: (020) 8949 4099 Fax: (020) 8949 3121
Freshair Ltd, Unit 5 Horseshoe Close, London, NW2 7JJ Tel: (020) 8452 4266 Fax: (020) 8452 2954 E-mail: sales@freshair.co.uk
Goodlands Displays, Unit 16 College Fields Business Centre, Prince Georges Road, London, SW19 2PT Tel: (020) 8687 8254 Fax: (020) 8687 8257 E-mail: printing@goodlands.co.uk
Impressions Design Ltd, Sutherland Works, Beaufort Road, Stoke-on-Trent, ST3 1RH Tel: (01782) 329535 Fax: (01782) 329535 E-mail: info@impressionsdesignltd.co.uk
Logo Leisurewear, Unit 22, Caddsdown Industrial Estate, Clovelly Road, Bideford, Devon, EX39 3HN Tel: (01237) 459393 Fax: (01237) 459393 E-mail: sales@logoleisurewear.co.uk
M G A Corporation Ltd, Unit 6 Britannia Business Park, Mills Road Quarrywood, Quarry Wood, Aylesford, Kent, ME20 7NT Tel: (01622) 717332 Fax: (01622) 715508 E-mail: goldstaruk@ukonline.co.uk
Practivewear, 47-49 Park Royal Road, London, NW10 7LQ Tel: (020) 8963 0888 Fax: (020) 8963 0343
Print A Gift, 237 High Street, Acton, London, W3 9BY Tel: (020) 8993 4820 Fax: (020) 8993 2164 E-mail: info@pagl.co.uk
Screenprint Printers, Unit 14 Hall Barn Road Industrial Estate, Hall Barn Road, Isleham, Ely, Cambridgeshire, CB7 5RJ Tel: (01638) 780200 Fax: (01638) 780 300 E-mail: screenprint@mail.islehamnet.co.uk
Signagraphic Signs & Nameplates, 7 Russell St North, Coventry, CV1 4GD Tel: (024) 7625 8802 Fax: (024) 7625 8802 E-mail: neil@signagraphic.co.uk
Stourport Sign Studio, 3 Sandy La Industrial Estate, Stourport-on-Severn, Worcestershire, DY13 9QB Tel: (01299) 826044 Fax: (01299) 826044
Streamline Graphics, Banhaw Wood Lodge, Lower Benefield, Peterborough, PE8 5AG Tel: (01832) 205363 Fax: (01733) 205216 E-mail: streamline-graphics@tiscali.co.uk
T O T Shirts, Banksia Road, London, N18 3BF Tel: (020) 8887 7900 Fax: (020) 8345 6095 E-mail: paul@t-o-t-shirts.co.uk
T S S & P Ltd, Twickenham Trading Estate, Rugby Road, Twickenham, TW1 1DU Tel: (020) 8607 0500 Fax: (020) 8607 0547
T Shirt Products, Somers Road, Rugby, Warwickshire, CV22 7DG Tel: (0845) 0714405 Fax: (0845) 0714406 E-mail: sales@tsp-tshirts.co.uk
Top TS Kent Ltd, Unit 35 Blenheim Close, Pysons Road Industrial Estate, Broadstairs, Kent, CT10 2YF Tel: (01843) 863737 Fax: (01843) 863684 E-mail: cotts@aol.com
Tradewinds Merchandising Co. Ltd, Lynton Road, London, N8 8SL Tel: (020) 8341 9700 Fax: (0845) 2309006 E-mail: sales@tradewinds.eu.com
Upper & Lower Leisurewear, Leylands House, Molesey Road, Walton-On-Thames, Surrey, KT12 3PW Tel: (01932) 241174 Fax: (01932) 244947 E-mail: sales@upperandlower.co.uk
V M R Publicity, 241 Redcatch Road, Knowle, Bristol, BS4 2HQ Tel: 0117-972 0505 Fax: 0117-972 0606 E-mail: vmrviv@aol.com
Mick Wright Merchandising, 185 Weedon Road, Northampton, NN5 5DA Tel: (07000) 226397 Fax: (01604) 456129 E-mail: tshirts@mickwright.com

T-SHIRTS/SWEATSHIRTS

A & M Mclellan Ltd, 94-96 Moorside Road, Swinton, Manchester, M27 0HJ Tel: 0161-794 1169 Fax: 0161-794 3733 E-mail: sales@mclellan-sport.co.uk
Bedewear Manufacturing Co. Ltd, Bede Street, Leicester, LE3 5LD Tel: 0116-254 9031
BusinessGift.UK.Com, 92 Langdale Road, Leyland, PR25 3AS Tel: (01772) 435010 Fax: (01772) 457280 E-mail: steve@ad-options.co.uk
Chameleon, PO Box 34, Kilgetty, Pembrokeshire, SA68 0WZ Tel: (07792) 706440 E-mail: info@chameleoncreations.co.uk
Doppelgangers Ltd, 3 Fountain Cottages, South Park Lane, Bletchingley, Redhill, RH1 4NH Tel: (01883) 743324 Fax: (01883) 743324 E-mail: doppelgangers@btclick.com
Elms & Elms, 6-8 Brookfield Road, Cheadle, Cheshire, SK8 2PN Tel: 0161-428 8383 Fax: 0161-428 8855 E-mail: info@elmsandelms.co.uk
Goldgem Belvoir Ltd, Belvoir House, Paddock Street, Wigston, Leicestershire, LE18 2AN Tel: 0116-288 1909 Fax: 0116-257 0184
Hargreaves Sports Ltd, 2-3 Solent Twentyseven, Walton Road, Portsmouth, PO6 1SX Tel: (023) 9232 1200 Fax: (023) 9237 1212 E-mail: sales@hargreaves-sports.co.uk
▶ Image Scotland Ltd, Fisherrow Industrial Estate, Newhailes Road, Musselburgh, Midlothian, EH21 6RU Tel: 0131-665 1414 Fax: 0131-665 1919 E-mail: sales@imagescotland.com
Leicester Sports Wear Co. Ltd, 92a Ashfordby St, Leicester, LE5 3QH Tel: 0116-253 9804 Fax: 0116-253 9804
MTC Tees, 4 Forest Industrial Park, Forest Road, Ilford, Essex, IG6 3HL Tel: (020) 8501 0922 Fax: (020) 8559 8230
Print A Gift, 237 High Street, Acton, London, W3 9BY Tel: (020) 8993 4820 Fax: (020) 8993 2164 E-mail: info@pagl.co.uk
Ranks Enterprises, Ranks House, Unit B4 Neptune Road, Harrow, Middlesex, HA1 4HX Tel: (020) 8863 9993 Fax: (020) 8424 8887 E-mail: sales@ranksent.com
▶ Sprint Design Ltd, Unit 46 John Player Building, Stirling Enterprise Park, Stirling, FK7 7RP Tel: (01786) 447707 Fax: (01786) 447707 E-mail: info@sprintdesign.co.uk
T S S & P Ltd, Twickenham Trading Estate, Rugby Road, Twickenham, TW1 1DU Tel: (020) 8607 0500 Fax: (020) 8607 0547
Mick Wright Merchandising, 185 Weedon Road, Northampton, NN5 5DA Tel: (07000) 226397 Fax: (01604) 456129 E-mail: tshirts@mickwright.com

TAB WASHERS

Impress North East Limited, Ryton Industrial Estate, Newburn Bridge Road, Blaydon-on-Tyne, Tyne & Wear, NE21 4SQ Tel: 0191-414 8901 Fax: 0191-414 2400 E-mail: sales@impressltd.co.uk

TABLE CUTLERY

Arthur Price, Britannia Way, Lichfield, Staffordshire, WS14 9UY Tel: (01543) 267324 Fax: (01543) 414488 E-mail: catering@arthur-price.com
John Barker & Dixon Ltd, Lincoln Works, Smithfield, Sheffield, S3 7AR Tel: 0114-272 4962 Fax: 0114-276 0299
Bierton & Staniforth Ltd, Crescent Works, 71-73 St. Mary's Road, Sheffield, S2 4AN Tel: (0114) 272 0514
C Robathon & Sons Ltd, 63 Hunters Vale, Birmingham, B19 2XH Tel: 0121-554 6990 Fax: 0121-554 4389 E-mail: sales@c-robathan.com
Chimo Holdings, White Rose Works, 61 Eyre Lane, Sheffield, S1 3GF Tel: 0114-272 4656 Fax: 0114-249 0922 E-mail: sales@chimoholdings.co.uk
Samuel Eales Silverware Ltd, 26 Douglas Road, Sheffield, S3 9SA Tel: 0114 2720885
Harrison Fisher & Co. Ltd, 78 Milton Street, Sheffield, S3 7WJ Tel: 0114-272 4221 Fax: 0114-275 4187 E-mail: sales@harrison-fisher.co.uk
Francis Howard Ltd, Aberdeen Works, Trafalgar Street, Sheffield, S1 3RL Tel: 0114-249 3314 Fax: 0114-249 3316
David Mellor Design Ltd, The Round Building, Leadmill, Hathersage, Hope Valley, Derbyshire, S32 1BA Tel: (01433) 650220 Fax: (01433) 650944 E-mail: sales@davidmellordesign.com
Nickel Blanks Co. Ltd, 6 Smithfield, Sheffield, S3 7AR Tel: 0114-272 5792 Fax: 0114-276 8519 E-mail: shefcutler@aol.com
Pinder Bros Ltd, Sheaf Plate Works, Arundel Street, Sheffield, S1 1DJ Tel: 0114-275 2277 Fax: 0114-272 6718 E-mail: sales@pinder.co.uk
Premier-Ware Ltd, Vander House, Starn Hill Close, Ecclesfield, Sheffield, S35 9TG Tel: 0114-257 2700 Fax: 0114-257 1364 E-mail: sales@premier-ware.co.uk
Rutland Cutlery Co. Ltd, 73-101 Neepsend Lane, Sheffield, S3 8AT Tel: 0114-273 7056 Fax: 0114-273 1062 E-mail: shefcutler@aol.com
S & S Marketing, B8-B10 Unit Tenterfields Business Park, Burnley Road, Luddendenfoot, Halifax, West Yorkshire, HX2 6EQ Tel: (01422) 882754 Fax: (01422) 884978 E-mail: sales@sandsmarketing.co.uk
John Sanderson & Son (1929) Ltd, Eye Witness Works, 78 Milton Street, Sheffield, S3 7WJ Tel: 0114-272 2682 Fax: 0114-275 4187 E-mail: sales@harrison-fisher.co.uk
Sheffield Metal Co., Smithfield, Sheffield, S3 7AR Tel: 0114-275 9566 Fax: 0114-275 4675 E-mail: shefcutler@aol.com
William Turner Master Cutlers, Savanna, Holywell Bay, Newquay, Cornwall, TR8 5PQ Tel: (01637) 830925 Fax: (01637) 831032
William Yates Ltd, White Rose Works, 61 Eyre Lane, Sheffield, S1 3GF Tel: 0114-272 3518 Fax: (0845) 0958686 E-mail: sales@chimoholdings.co.uk

TABLE DECORATION BALLOONS

▶ Balloons For All Occasions, 52 King Street, Ramsgate, Kent, CT11 8NT Tel: (01843) 851087 Fax: (01843) 851087
Cti Balloons Ltd, 6 Consul Road, Rugby, Warwickshire, CV21 1PB Tel: (01788) 546299 Fax: (01788) 546114 E-mail: ctiballoon@aol.com
Great Western Balloons, 6 Redwood Close, Honiton, Devon, EX14 2XS Tel: (01404) 45968 Fax: (01404) 45968
Occasions, 96 Liverpool Road, Cadishead, Manchester, M44 5AN Tel: 0161-775 7979 Fax: 0161-775 7979
▶ Porosol Ltd, Tennis House, 249-251 Belper Road, Stanley Common, Ilkeston, Derbyshire, DE7 6FY Tel: 0115-930 7977 Fax: 0115-944 2147 E-mail: t.shaw@porosol.fsnet.co.uk
Sonic Party Time, 2a North Street, Heavitree, Exeter, EX1 2RH Tel: (01392) 848785

TABLE GLASSWARE

Brierley Hill Glass Co. Ltd, Mount Pleasant, Quarry Bank, Brierley Hill, West Midlands, DY5 2YS Tel: (01384) 77486 Fax: (01384) 77486 E-mail: sales@brierleycrystal.com
Caithness Crystal, 9-12 Hardwick Industrial Estate, Paxman Road, King's Lynn, Norfolk, PE30 4NE Tel: (01553) 765111 Fax: (01553) 767628 E-mail: sales@caithnessglass.co.uk
County Glassware Ltd, 4 Faraday Court, Park Farm Industrial Estate, Wellingborough, Northamptonshire, NN8 6XY Tel: (01933) 402204 Fax: (01933) 400433 E-mail: sales@countyglassware.co.uk
Glen Cairn Crystal Studio, 12 Tartraven Place, East Mains Industrial Estate, Broxburn, West Lothian, EH52 5LT Tel: (01506) 856775
▶ Italcomma UK Llp, 1 Bell Lane, Byfield, Daventry, Northamptonshire, NN11 6US Tel: (01327) 260070 Fax: (01327) 260065 E-mail: info@italcomma.co.uk
Royal Brierley Crystal Ltd, Tipton Road, Dudley, West Midlands, DY1 4SQ Tel: 0121-530 5607 Fax: (01384) 457302 E-mail: brierleyshop@dartington.co.uk

TABLE LAMPS

Brilliant (UK) Ltd, Hanworth Trading Estate, Hampton Road West, Feltham, Middlesex, TW13 6DR Tel: (020) 8898 3131 Fax: (020) 8898 3232 E-mail: sales@brilliant-ag.com
Derwent Lighting, Derwent Road, York Road Business Park, Malton, North Yorkshire, YO17 6YB Tel: (01653) 696444 Fax: (01653) 696965 E-mail: enquiries@derwentlighting.co.uk
Franklite Factory Shop, Snowdon Drive, Winterhill, Milton Keynes, MK6 1AP Tel: (01908) 443090 Fax: (01908) 691939 E-mail: info@franklite.ltd.uk
▶ Iceberg Trading (UK) Limited, 61 Strattondale Street, Poplar, London, E14 3HG Tel: 078 30311941 E-mail: info@icebergdesign.co.uk
Moss Lighting Ltd, Unit 2a Bordesley Street, Birmingham, B5 5PG Tel: 0121-643 0529 Fax: 0121-633 4576
▶ Rod Page Woodturning, 11 Southmead Crescent, Crewkerne, Somerset, TA18 8DH Tel: (01460) 271426 Fax: E-mail: rod@rodpage-woodturner.co.uk
Thornwood Designs, 6 Top Factory, Cringle Lane, Stoke Rochford, Grantham, Lincolnshire, NG33 5EF Tel: (01476) 530600 Fax: (01476) 577544 E-mail: info@lampstyle.com

TABLE LEGS, STEEL

▶ SPP Folding Tables, 8 Castle Street, Castle Gate, Hertford, SG14 1HD Tel: (01992) 410333 E-mail: enquiries@tables4sale.com

TABLE LINEN

Richard Haworth Ltd, Kearsley Mill, Stoneclough, Radcliffe, Manchester, M26 1RH Tel: (01204) 702300 Fax: (01204) 705772 E-mail: info@richardhaworth.co.uk
Midland Linen Services Ltd, 3 Klaxon Tysley Industrial Estate, 751 Warwick Road, Tyseley, Birmingham, B11 2HA Tel: 0121-708 1069 Fax: 0121-707 4686 E-mail: info@midlandlinen.co.uk
Quality Fabrics, 52 Leabourne Road, London, N16 6TA Tel: (020) 8826 5040 Fax: (05601) 162220 E-mail: qualityfabrics@btconnect.com
Reward Manufacturing Company Ltd, Sackville Mills, Sackville Street, Skipton, North Yorkshire, BD23 2PR Tel: (01756) 797755 Fax: (01756) 796644 E-mail: info@rewardtrolleys.com
Richard Haworth & Co. Ltd, Kearsley Mill, Stoneclough, Radcliffe, Manchester, M26 1RH Tel: (01204) 708508 Fax: (01204) 705772 E-mail: info@richardhaworth.co.uk
Samuel Lamont & Sons Ltd, Victoria Street, Lurgan, Craigavon, County Armagh, BT67 9DA Tel: (028) 3832 9066 Fax: (028) 3834 3095 E-mail: mail@samuellamont.co.uk

TABLE LININGS/LEATHER TABLE TOPS

Woolnough Ac Ltd, 7 Parmiter Industrial Centre, Parmiter Street, London, E2 9HZ Tel: (020) 8980 9813 Fax: (020) 8980 9814

TABLE MATS

Lady Clare Ltd, Oldends Lane Industrial Estate, Oldends, Stonehouse, Gloucestershire, GL10 3RQ Tel: (01453) 824482 Fax: (01453) 827855 E-mail: info@lady-clare.com

TABLES, BAR

Grosvenor Fabrications, Limes House, Silver Street, Stansted, Essex, CM24 8HE Tel: (01279) 814146 Fax: (01279) 814179 E-mail: sales@grosvenorfabrications.co.uk

TABLES, COFFEE, MARBLE

Morgan Masonry Ltd, Marble Yard, Carnon Valley, Carnon Downs, Truro, Cornwall, TR3 6LG Tel: (01872) 870091 Fax: (01872) 870092 E-mail: enquiries@morganmasonry.co.uk

TABLES, CRAFT

▶ A J Homecrafts, Coppins Rest, 25 Saxhorn Road, Lane End, High Wycombe, Bucks, HP14 3JN Tel: 01494 883138 Fax: 01494 883138 E-mail: ajhomecrafts@fsmail.net

TABLES, DINING, GLASS

▶ Shady Palm Ltd, 31 Boscombe Road, London, W12 9HT Tel: 0870 4604969 Fax: 0870 1126573 E-mail: info@shadypalm.co.uk

TABLES, DINING, OAK

▶ 1st For Furniture Ltd, Fairclough Hall Farm, Halls Green, Weston, Hitchin, Hertfordshire, SG4 7DP Tel: (01462) 790990 Fax: (01462) 790995 E-mail: info@1st-for-furniture.co.uk
▶ Shady Palm Ltd, 31 Boscombe Road, London, W12 9HT Tel: 0870 4604969 Fax: 0870 1126573 E-mail: info@shadypalm.co.uk

TABLES, FOLDING/TRESTLE

Gopak Ltd, Range Road, Hythe, Kent, CT21 6HG Tel: (01303) 265751 Fax: (01303) 268282 E-mail: sales@gopak.co.uk
Grosvenor Fabrications, Limes House, Silver Street, Stansted, Essex, CM24 8HE Tel: (01279) 814146 Fax: (01279) 814179 E-mail: sales@grosvenorfabrications.co.uk
Mobilite International Ltd, PO Box 236, Oxford, OX2 6XU Tel: (0870) 2410729 Fax: (0870) 2410730 E-mail: david@mobiliteuk.com
Muswell Manufacturing Co. Ltd, Unit D1 New Southgate Industrial Estate, Lower Park Road, London, N11 1QD Tel: (020) 8368 8738 Fax: (020) 8368 4726 E-mail: sales@muswell.co.uk
SICO Europe Ltd, The Link Park, Lympne Industrial Estate, Lympne, Kent, CT21 4LR Tel: (01303) 234000 Fax: (01303) 234001 E-mail: sales@sico-europe.com

TABLET COATINGS

Colorcon Ltd, Flagship House Victory Way, Crossways, Dartford, DA2 6QD Tel: (01322) 293000 Fax: (01322) 627200 E-mail: info@colorcon.co.uk

TABLEWARE, *See also individual material used*

Afe Online, Unit 20 Centurion Way, Meridian Business Park, Leicester, LE19 1WJ Tel: (01827) 309190 Fax: (0800) 525829 E-mail: sales@afeonline.net

Anchor Food Service Equipment, Unit F1, Valley Way, Market Harborough, Leicestershire, LE16 7PS Tel: (01858) 468181 Fax: (01858) 467506 E-mail: pennywashtech@1dial.co.uk

Brakes Catering Equipment, Unit 3 Gloucester Court, Gloucester Terrace, Armley Road, Leeds, LS12 2ER Tel: (0845) 9319494 Fax: 0113-231 9495

C Robathon & Sons Ltd, 63 Hunters Vale, Birmingham, B19 2XH Tel: 0121-554 6990 Fax: 0121-554 4389 E-mail: sales@c-robathan.com

Cater Hire Ltd, Bray House, Pottersheath Road, Welwyn, Hertfordshire, AL6 9TA Tel: (01438) 815428 Fax: (01438) 815428 E-mail: caterhireagd@aol.com

Catering Equipment (Newcastle Under Lyne) Ltd, Metfab House, Montrose Street, Stoke-On-Trent, ST4 3PB Tel: (01782) 313226 Fax: (01782) 327260

Caterquip (GB) Ltd, Unit 3 Euro-Seas Centre, Blyth, Northumberland, NE24 1LZ Tel: (01670) 546363 Fax: (01670) 546260 E-mail: enquiries@caterquip-gb.co.uk

Caterquip Midlands, 4 Albion Parade, Kingswinford, West Midlands, DY6 0NP Tel: (01384) 402345 Fax: (01384) 402345

Churchill Fine Bone China (Holdings) Ltd, Marlborough Works, High Street, Stoke-on-Trent, ST6 5NZ Tel: (01782) 577566 Fax: (01782) 810318 E-mail: churchill@churchillchina.com

County Glassware Ltd, 4 Faraday Court, Park Farm Industrial Estate, Wellingborough, Northamptonshire, NN8 6XY Tel: (01933) 402204 Fax: (01933) 400433 E-mail: sales@countyglassware.co.uk

Disposables & Catering Supplies, Haltwhistle House, Haltwhistle Road, South Woodham Ferrers, Chelmsford, CM3 5ZA Tel: (01245) 320839 Fax: (01245) 322256 E-mail: sales@dcs-swf.co.uk

DPS Tableware Ltd, 11-12 Beacon Road, Walton Industrial Estate, Stone, Staffs, ST15 0NN Tel: (01785) 826333 Fax: (01785) 826330 E-mail: sales@dpstableware.co.uk

Georgia Pacific GB Ltd, Lower Street, Newcastle, Staffordshire, ST5 2RS Tel: (01782) 615376 Fax: (01782) 712236

Heaton Catering Equipment Ltd, 160 Heaton Park Road, Newcastle Upon Tyne, NE6 5NR Tel: 0191-265 6709 Fax: 0191-265 6506 E-mail: sales@heatoncateringequipment.co.uk

Heritage Group, 62 Green Lane, Small Heath, Birmingham, B9 5DB Tel: 0121-773 0724 Fax: 0121-766 6073 E-mail: sales@heritage-silverware.com

Lambert & Blaber Ltd, 25 Kings Road, Haslemere, Surrey, GU27 2QA Tel: (01428) 658534 Fax: (01428) 658341 E-mail: sales@lambertblaber.co.uk

C.J. Lang & Son Ltd, 78 Longtown Road, Dundee, DD4 8JU Tel: (01382) 512000 Fax: (01382) 508222E-mail: info@cjlang.co.uk

▶ On The Table Ltd, 28 South Street, Dorchester, Dorset, DT1 1BY Tel: (01305) 257258 Fax: (01305) 257258 E-mail: sales@onthetable.biz

Oneida Silversmiths Ltd, Cheshire Oaks Outlet Village, Kinsey Road, Ellesmere Port, CH65 9LA Tel: 0151-356 1024 Fax: 0151-356 1024

▶ The Potters Friend, 6 Rawle Close, Cheadle, Stoke-On-Trent, ST10 1UX Tel: (01538) 751200 E-mail: thepottersfriend@aol.com

Royal Stafford, Royal Overhouse Pottery, Overhouse Street, Stoke-On-Trent, ST6 4EE Tel: (01782) 577244 Fax: (01782) 817336 E-mail: enquries@royalstafford.co.uk

Take One Ltd, Unit 1, Moor Barn, Sheldon Lane, Bakewell, Derbyshire, DE45 1QR Tel: (01629) 814610 Fax: (01629) 814610 E-mail: info@takeoneltd.com

Xing Xing, 2 Acton Hill Mews, Acton, London, W3 9QN Tel: (020) 8896 7618 Fax: (020) 8993 0785 E-mail: info@xingxingltd.com

TABLOID NEWSPAPERS

Robertsons, 2 West Port, Arbroath, Angus, DD11 1RE Tel: (01241) 872541

TACHOGRAPH CHART ANALYSIS

Foster Tachograph Ltd, 17 Fulwood Hall Lane, Fulwood, Preston, PR2 8DB Tel: (01772) 655155 Fax: (01772) 793739 E-mail: enquiries@fostertachographs.co.uk

Foster Tachographs, 189 Watling Street Road, Fulwood, Preston, PR2 8AE Tel: (01772) 655155 Fax: (01772) 793739 E-mail: enquiries@fostertachographs.co.uk

▶ J D'A B Consultancy Ltd, 17 Naseby Road, Congleton, Cheshire, CW12 4QX Tel: (01260) 297974 Fax: (01260) 291674 E-mail: mail@ex-pc.co.uk

Tachograph Analysis Consultants, 23 Westway, Maghull, Liverpool, L31 2PQ Tel: 0151-531 1004 Fax: 0151-531 1122 E-mail: nigelkirkwood@digital-tachograph.com

TACHOGRAPH CHART PRINTERS/PUBLISHERS

Eurodisc UK Ltd, Station Approach, Bridgnorth, Shropshire, WV16 5DP Tel: (01746) 764400 Fax: (01746) 764400

TACHOGRAPH CHART SELLERS OR AGENTS

Eurodisc UK Ltd, Station Approach, Bridgnorth, Shropshire, WV16 5DP Tel: (01746) 764400 Fax: (01746) 764400

SJD Computers, Medford House, East Common Lane, Scunthorpe, South Humberside, DN16 1DE Tel: (01724) 854424 Fax: (01724) 854424 E-mail: sjd@cwcom.net

Tachograph Analysis Consultants, 23 Westway, Maghull, Liverpool, L31 2PQ Tel: 0151-531 1004 Fax: 0151-531 1122 E-mail: nigelkirkwood@digital-tachograph.com

TACHOGRAPHS

A.B. Butt Ltd, Frog Island, Leicester, LE3 5AZ Tel: 0116-251 3344 Fax: 0116-253 6377 E-mail: sales@abbutt.co.uk

Eurodisc UK Ltd, Station Approach, Bridgnorth, Shropshire, WV16 5DP Tel: (01746) 764400 Fax: (01746) 764400

SJD Computers, Medford House, East Common Lane, Scunthorpe, South Humberside, DN16 1DE Tel: (01724) 854424 Fax: (01724) 854424 E-mail: sjd@cwcom.net

Tachodisc, 19 Kingsland Grange, Woolston, Warrington, WA1 4RW Tel: (01925) 820088 Fax: (01925) 831300 E-mail: info@tachodisc.co.uk

TACHOMETER MANUFRS

Control Ability, Unit 2, Ashworth Buildings, Heys Lane, Great Harwood, Blackburn, BB6 7BA Tel: (01254) 886685 Fax: (01254) 886068 E-mail: sales@controlability.com

James H Heal & Co. Ltd, Richmond Works, Lake View, Halifax, West Yorkshire, HX3 6EP Tel: (01422) 366355 Fax: (01422) 352440 E-mail: info@james-heal.co.uk

LS Controls, 270 Abbey Road, Leeds, LS5 3ND Tel: (01943) 872025 Fax: 0113-259 0243 E-mail: ls.lee@amserve.com

Oval Automation Ltd, Lake Lane, Barnham, Bognor Regis, West Sussex, PO22 0AD Tel: (01243) 555885 Fax: (01243) 554846 E-mail: paul@oval.org.uk

Sensors UK Ltd, 135-137 Hatfield Road, St. Albans, Hertfordshire, AL4 0DH Tel: (01727) 861110 Fax: (01727) 844272 E-mail: admin@sensorsuk.com

Siemans V D O, 36 Gravelly Industrial Park, Birmingham, B24 8TA Tel: 0121-326 1234 Fax: 0121-326 1299

Taylor Dynamic Controls, Unit W4 Blaby Industrial Park, Winchester Avenue, Blaby, Leicester, LE8 4GZ Tel: 0116-278 4100 Fax: 0116-278 4200 E-mail: sales@taylordynamics.com

TACHOMETERS, DENTAL LABORATORIES

▶ Trident Dental Laboratory, Rose Lane, Liverpool, L18 8AG Tel: 0151-724 4656 Fax: 0151-724 6855

TACKS

Crown Nail Co. Ltd, 48 Commercial Road, Wolverhampton, WV1 3QS Tel: (01902) 351806 Fax: (01902) 871212 E-mail: sales@crown-nail.com

Farringtons Saddle Co., 15 Butts Road, Walsall, WS4 2AR Tel: (01922) 634440 Fax: (01922) 634440

TACKY CLOTHS/TACK RAGS, IMPREGNATED

Starchem Ltd, Strawberry Lane, Willenhall, West Midlands, WV13 3RS Tel: (01902) 838880 Fax: (01902) 838881 E-mail: sales@starchem.co.uk

TACTILE SWITCHES

J A E Europe Ltd, Coliseum Business Centre, Riverside Way, Camberley, Surrey, GU15 3YL Tel: (01276) 404000 Fax: (01276) 404010 E-mail: sales@jae.co.uk

TAG LABELS

Eyetag Ltd, Albert Works, Melville Street, Bradford, West Yorkshire, BD7 1JD Tel: (01274) 721332 Fax: (01274) 740196

Fisher Clark, Horncastle Road, Boston, Lincolnshire, PE21 9HZ Tel: (01205) 365501 Fax: (01205) 364825 E-mail: fisherclark@fisherclark.co.uk

▶ Globalbagtag.Com, Everon Centre, 58 John Street, Filey, North Yorkshire, YO14 9NT Tel: (0870) 7657280 Fax: (0870) 7657281 E-mail: sales@globalbagtag.com

Lancastrian Labels Ltd, 183 Great Howard Street, Liverpool, L3 7DL Tel: 0151-298 1212 Fax: 0151-298 1432 E-mail: sales@lancastrian.co.uk

S O S Talisman, 21 Grays Corner, Ley Street, Ilford, Essex, IG2 7RQ Tel: (020) 8554 5579 Fax: (020) 8554 1090 E-mail: sostalisman@btinternet.com

TAGGED CORD CARRY HANDLES

Stribbons Ltd, 99 Sanders Road, Finedon Road Industrial Estate, Wellingborough, Northamptonshire, NN8 4NL Tel: (01933) 443446 Fax: (01933) 443435 E-mail: info@stribbons.co.uk

TAILBOARD LIFTING GEAR (VEHICLE) MAINTENANCE OR REPAIR SERVICES

Stone Hardy, London House, Chittening Industrial Estate, Chittening, Bristol, BS11 0YB Tel: 0117-938 0802 Fax: 0117-938 6229

Vehicle & Tail Lift Repairs, 4 Monarch Works, Elswick Road, Fenton Industrial Estate, Stoke-on-Trent, ST4 2SH Tel: (01782) 845386 Fax: (01782) 846175 E-mail: vtrstoke@vtrgroup.co.uk

TAILBOARD LIFTING GEAR (VEHICLE) MANUFRS

Lancashire Tippers, Kirkhall Workshops, Bilbao Street, Bolton, BL1 4HH Tel: (01204) 493750 Fax: (01204) 847966 E-mail: lanctip@masseytruckengineering.co.uk

Marshall Thermo King Ltd, 3b Andes Road, Nursling, Southampton, SO16 0YZ Tel: (023) 8073 9944 Fax: (023) 8073 9090 E-mail: southampton@marshall-thermoking.co.uk

Ratcliff Tail Lifts Ltd, Bessemer Road, Welwyn Garden City, Hertfordshire, AL7 1ET Tel: (01707) 325571 Fax: (01707) 327752 E-mail: info@ratcliffpalfinger.co.uk

Ray Smith Group plc, Fengate, Peterborough, PE1 5XG Tel: (01733) 563936 Fax: (01733) 377090

Ross & Bonnyman Ltd, Roberts Street, Forfar, Angus, DD8 3DG Tel: (01307) 469366 Fax: (01307) 461567

Smyth's Equipment Supply Co., Tamar Commercial Centre, Chater Street, Belfast, BT4 1BL Tel: (028) 9045 1355 Fax: (028) 9045 4838 E-mail: sescobelfast@aol.com

TAILORS' DUMMIES

Proportion Display Ltd, Galatix House, 9 Dallington Street, London, EC1V 0LN Tel: (020) 7251 6943 Fax: (020) 7250 1798 E-mail: mail@proportionlondon.com

Universal Display Fittings Co. Ltd, 51 Mortimer Street, London, W1W 8JH Tel: (020) 7580 9471 Fax: (020) 7436 9732 E-mail: info@universaldisplay.co.uk

TAKE AWAY FOOD CONTAINERS

Eawex International Trading Co. Ltd, Rear of 12 Burley Road, Oakham, Leicestershire, LE15 6DH Tel: (01572) 756322 Fax: (01572) 756322 E-mail: kimwahng@hotmail.com

TALKBACK INTERCOM SYSTEMS

Grandrew Securities, 7 Linden Avenue, Wembley, Middlesex, HA9 8BB Tel: (020) 8902 5674 Fax: (020) 8900 9218

TALLOW

Harris Tobias Ltd, 3 Station Road, Stansted, Essex, CM24 8BE Tel: (01279) 647164 Fax: (01279) 647038 E-mail: info@harristobias.com

TAMBOURS

The Tambour Company Ltd, Warren Road, Green Lane Business Park, Featherstone, Pontefract, West Yorkshire, WF7 6EL Tel: (01977) 600026 Fax: (01977) 600991

TAMPER EVIDENT LABELS

Ampack Security Products Ltd, Saxon Way, Melbourn, Royston, Hertfordshire, SG8 6DN Tel: (01763) 261900 Fax: (01763) 261234

Image Grafix, 6 Manse Parade, London Road, Swanley, Kent, BR8 8DA Tel: (01322) 614669 Fax: (01322) 614878 E-mail: imagegrafix@btconnect.com

Kroy (Europe) Ltd, Worton Drive, Worton Grange Ind Estate, Reading, RG2 0LZ Tel: 0118-986 1411 Fax: 0118-986 5205 E-mail: hamilton@kroy.com

L G L Protectaseal Ltd, Unit 8 & 9, Hitchin Road Industrial Estate, Oxen Road, Luton, LU2 0DZ Tel: (01582) 422976 Fax: (01582) 404082 E-mail: contact@protectaseal.com

Label Spec, Unit 2, Drummond Crescent, Riverside Business Park, Irvine, Ayrshire, KA11 5AN Tel: (01563) 550990 Fax: (01563) 550991 E-mail: sales@labelspec.co.uk

Madico Graphic Films Ltd, 9 Cordwallace Park, Clivemont Road, Maidenhead, Berkshire, SL6 7BU Tel: (01628) 777766 Fax: (01628) 776666 E-mail: info@madico.co.uk

Royston Labels Ltd, 18 Orchard Road, Royston, Hertfordshire, SG8 5HD Tel: (01763) 212020 Fax: (01763) 248004 E-mail: info@roystonlabels.co.uk

TAMPO PRINTERS OR PRINTING SERVICES, *See also Pad Printing Services*

▶ Printon Plastics & Assemblies Ltd, Unit 4 Attwood Business Centre, Attwood Street, Lye, Stourbridge, West Midlands, DY9 8RY Tel: (01384) 77007 Fax: (01384) 77747 E-mail: info@printonplastics.co.uk

TANDEM VIBRATORY ROLLERS

Finnpave, Thorbury Avenue, March Trading Estate, March, Cambridgeshire, PE15 0AZ Tel: (01354) 658600 Fax: (01354) 661888 E-mail: sales@finnpave.co.uk

H M Plant Ltd, 964 Weston Road, Slough Trading Estate, Slough, SL1 4HR Tel: (01753) 213900 Fax: (01753) 213901 E-mail: info@hmplant.ltd.uk

TANGENTIAL FANS

Consort 1996 Ltd, Thornton Industrial Estate, Milford Haven, Dyfed, SA73 2RT Tel: (01646) 692172 Fax: (01646) 695195 E-mail: enquiries@consortepl.com

TANK CLEANING EQUIPMENT

Breconcherry Ltd, Lower Road Trading Estate, Ledbury, Herefordshire, HR8 2DH Tel: (01531) 632476 Fax: (01531) 633839 E-mail: cip@breconcherry.com

Non Entry Systems Ltd, Bruce Road, Fforestfach, Swansea, SA5 4HS Tel: (01792) 580455 Fax: (01792) 578610 E-mail: sales@nonentrysystems.com

Sealpump Engineering Ltd, Innovation Centre, Kirkleatham Business Park, Redcar, Cleveland, TS10 5SH Tel: (01642) 777720 Fax: (01642) 777730 E-mail: sales@sealpump.com

Spraying Systems Ltd, Farnham Business Park, Weydon Lane, Farnham, Surrey, GU9 8QT Tel: (01252) 727200 Fax: (01252) 712211 E-mail: info.uk@spray.com

T C Repair & Supply, Sheddingdean Industrial Centre, Marchants Way, Burgess Hill, West Sussex, RH15 8QY Tel: (01444) 242564 Fax: (01444) 236683 E-mail: info@tcrepair.com

TANK CLEANING EQUIPMENT, ROTARY JET MIXER

▶ Stem Drive Ltd, Solway Works, Annan Road, Eastriggs, Annan, Dumfriesshire, DG12 6NJ Tel: (01461) 40904 Fax: (01461) 40801 E-mail: sales@stemdrivemixer.co.uk

TANK CLEANING SERVICES

Arrow Environmental Services Ltd, Exchange Works, Kelvin Way, West Bromwich, West Midlands, B70 7JW Tel: 0121-525 0757 Fax: 0121-525 1179 E-mail: arrow.environmental@virgin.net
Branchand Ltd, Ashwellthorpe Industrial Estate, Ashwellthorpe, Norwich, NR16 1ER Tel: (01508) 488450 Fax: (01508) 488451 E-mail: info@branchand.co.uk
Bristol Tank Ltd, Princess House, Princess Street, St Philips, Bristol, BS2 0RR Tel: 0117-954 0838 Fax: 0117-954 0839 E-mail: bristoltank@aol.com
Gordons Environmental Ltd, 66-68 Back Sneddon Street, Paisley, Renfrewshire, PA3 2BY Tel: 0141-842 1189 Fax: 0141-842 1139 E-mail: gordonsltd@aol.com
Hurn Waste Oil Ltd, 20 Winkham Business Park, Shaftesbury, Dorset, SP7 9QJ Tel: (01747) 858561 Fax: (01747) 858562 E-mail: oilwaterltd@hotmail.com
I N I Environmental Services Ltd, 77 Westwood Glen, Tilehurst, Reading, RG31 5NW Tel: 0118-942 7314 Fax: 0118-942 7313 E-mail: inienviro@aol.com
J W Hinchliffe Tanks Ltd, Weaver Street, Kirkstall Road, Leeds, LS4 2AU Tel: 0113-263 5163 Fax: 0113-263 5164 E-mail: jwhinchliffetanks.ltd@yahoo.co.uk
Mechanical Cleansing Services Ltd, Unit G, Salford Street Industrial Estate, Aston, Birmingham, B6 7SH Tel: (0845) 5314243 Fax: 0121-327 3105 E-mail: droemcsltd@aol.com
MTB Environmental Ltd, Dominion House, Copse Lane, Hamble, Southampton, SO31 4QB Tel: (023) 8045 8050 Fax: (023) 8045 7356 E-mail: mtb@mtbenv.demon.co.uk
Reynolds Industrial & Cleaning Services Ltd, Unit 21 Capstan Centre, Thurrock Park Way, Tilbury, Essex, RM18 7HH Tel: (01375) 856555 Fax: (01375) 856956 E-mail: reynoldsno1@aol.com
Rotherham Waste Oils, Quarry Oil Depot, Kilnhurst Road, Kilnhurst, Mexborough, South Yorkshire, S64 5TL Tel: (01709) 527131 Fax: (01709) 719729 E-mail: sales@rwoil.co.uk
▶ Sharpe Refinery Service Hydro Carbons Ltd, Arlington Works, Arlington Road, Twickenham, TW1 2BB Tel: (020) 8892 0502 Fax: (020) 8892 8193 E-mail: sales@sharpesoil.co.uk
Soptralentz UK Ltd, Ravell Drum Works, Gelderd Road, Leeds, LS12 6DL Tel: 0113-263 8573 Fax: 0113-263 7842 E-mail: ken@peaserecycling.co.uk
Tank Cleaners (Glasgow) Ltd, Robslee Drive, Giffnock, Glasgow, G46 7TY Tel: 0141-638 0906 Fax: 0141-638 9014 E-mail: simon@mitchellthomson.fsnet.co.uk
Taylors Industrial Services Ltd, Hareness Circle, Altens Industrial Estate, Aberdeen, AB12 3LY Tel: (01224) 872972 Fax: (01224) 872697 E-mail: taylors_industrial_services@btinternet.com
Valve Grove, Unit 15 16 Withy Road Industrial Estate, Withy Road, Bilston, West Midlands, WV14 0RX Tel: (01902) 498560 Fax: (01902) 498474
▶ Viridor Waste Management Ltd, 42 Kings Hill Avenue, Kings Hill, West Malling, Kent, ME19 4AJ Tel: (01732) 229200

TANK COVERS/DOMES

Armfibre Ltd, Unit 7, Wilstead Industrial Park, Kenneth Way, Wilstead, Bedford, MK45 3PD Tel: (01234) 741444 Fax: (01767) 651901 E-mail: sales@armfibre.com
Land & Marine Project Engineering, Dock Road North, Wirral, Merseyside, CH62 4TQ Tel: 0151-641 5600 Fax: 0151-644 9990 E-mail: matthew.osullivan@landandmarine.com
Sas Safe & Secure, Birchwoodmoor House, Roston, Ashbourne, Derbyshire, DE6 2EH Tel: (01889) 591595 Fax: (01889) 591595 E-mail: sales@legionnairesdisease.co.uk

TANK ERECTION OR INSTALLATION OR REPLACEMENT OR REMOVAL CONTRACTORS

Adler & Allan Ltd, 22-42 Livingstone Road, London, E15 2LJ Tel: (020) 8555 7111 Fax: (020) 8519 3090 E-mail: sales@adlerandallan.co.uk
D & S Services, Unit H2 & Unit H3 Rudford Industrial Estate, Ford Road, Ford, Arundel, West Sussex, BN18 0BD Tel: (01903) 732732 Fax: (01903) 716151 E-mail: sales@dandsservices.co.uk
Ellis Engineering & Welding Services, Salmon Road, Great Yarmouth, Norfolk, NR30 3QS Tel: (01493) 842690 Fax: (01493) 842690 E-mail: ellisengineering@btconnect.com
Interect Construction Services, St. Tewdric, Oakhanger, Bordon, Hampshire, GU35 9JW Tel: (01420) 472610 Fax: (01420) 475225 E-mail: instacliveowen@msn.com
▶ Sharpe Refinery Service Hydro Carbons Ltd, Arlington Works, Arlington Road, Twickenham, TW1 2BB Tel: (020) 8892 0502 Fax: (020) 8892 8193 E-mail: sales@sharpesoil.co.uk

TANK GAUGES

CTS, 41 Forge Lane, Minworth Industrial Park, Minworth, Sutton Coldfield, West Midlands, B76 1AH Tel: 0121-351 4445 Fax: 0121-351 4442 E-mail: sales@centretank.com

TANK GAUGING SYSTEMS

Ashridge Engineering Ltd, 58 North Road Indust Estate, Okehampton, Devon, EX20 1BQ Tel: (01837) 53381 Fax: (01837) 55022 E-mail: sales@ash-eng.co.uk
Motherwell Control Systems Ltd, 1 St Michaels Road, St. Helens, Merseyside, WA9 4WZ Tel: (01744) 815211 Fax: (01744) 814497 E-mail: sales@motherwellcs.com

TANK HIRE

Qualitank Services Ltd, Harrison Street, Widnes, Cheshire, WA8 8TN Tel: 0151-495 1116 Fax: 0151-424 6842 E-mail: sales@qualitank.co.uk
Swire Oil Field Services, Swire House, Souter Head Road, Altens Industrial Estate, Aberdeen, AB12 3LF Tel: (01224) 872707 Fax: (01224) 874516 E-mail: jlucas@swireos.com
Watkins Hire, Churwell Vale, Shaw Cross Business Park, Dewsbury, West Yorkshire, WF12 7RD Tel: (01924) 439733 Fax: (01924) 439732 E-mail: hire@watkinshire.co.uk

TANK LIDS, WATER

▶ Environmental Fabrications, Unit 26 Manor Development Centre, Alison CR, Sheffield, S2 1AS Tel: 0114-278 8777 Fax: 0114-254 4974 E-mail: info@watertankrefurbishment.com

TANK LINER/LINING SYSTEMS, PLASTIC

Linertech Ltd, Wellington Mills, Quebec Street, Elland, West Yorkshire, HX5 9BX Tel: (01422) 377551 Fax: (01422) 311636 E-mail: sales@linertech.co.uk

TANK LINER/LINING SYSTEMS, RUBBER

I Q L Ltd, Stirling Road, Cressex Business Park, High Wycombe, Buckinghamshire, HP12 3ST Tel: (01494) 463636 Fax: (01494) 439639 E-mail: sales@iqllimited.co.uk
P V H Rubber & Plastic Linings & Manufacturing Ltd, Unit 16, Webnor Industrial Estate, Ettingshall Road, Wolverhampton, WV2 2LD Tel: (01902) 409186 Fax: (01902) 497265 E-mail: kdelveir@aol.com
Premier Fuel Systems Ltd, Trent Lane Industrial Estate, Castle Donnington, Derby, DE74 2NP Tel: (01332) 850515 Fax: (01332) 850749 E-mail: info@premier-fuel-systems.com
Russetts Developments Ltd, 27 Burners Lane, Kiln Farm, Milton Keynes, MK11 3HA Tel: (0870) 7702800 Fax: (0870) 7702801 E-mail: info@russetts.co.uk

TANK LINING SERVICES

Corrocoat Services Ltd, Forster Street, Leeds, LS10 1PW Tel: 0113-276 0760 Fax: 0113-276 0700 E-mail: enquiries@corrocoat.com
Fabline Metal Finishing Services, Greenway Road, Bilston, West Midlands, WV14 0TJ Tel: (01902) 353511 Fax: (01902) 353511
Gurso Plant & Lining Ltd, Landywood Lane, Cheslyn Hay, Walsall, WS6 7AL Tel: (01922) 418005 Fax: (01922) 412641 E-mail: sales@gurso.demon.co.uk
Hesco Bastion Ltd, Unit 41 Knowsthorpe Way, Leeds, LS9 0SW Tel: 0113-248 6633 Fax: 0113-248 3501 E-mail: info@hescobastion.com
K T Tank Lining Services, Building 43, Kingsnorth Industrial Estate, Kingsnorth, Hoo, Rochester, Kent, ME3 9ND Tel: (01634) 846824 Fax: (01634) 845441
P V H Rubber & Plastic Linings & Manufacturing Ltd, Unit 16, Webnor Industrial Estate, Ettingshall Road, Wolverhampton, WV2 2LD Tel: (01902) 409186 Fax: (01902) 497265 E-mail: kdelveir@aol.com

TANK MANUFACTURE AND INSTALLATION DESIGN TO SPECIFICATION

A J D Instruments, 9 Lindfield Enterprise Park, Lewes Road, Lindfield, Haywards Heath, West Sussex, RH16 2LX Tel: (01444) 484055 Fax: (01444) 484042 E-mail: sales@ajdinstruments.co.uk
Broughton Mechanical & Civil Engineering Ltd, Ditton Road, Widnes, Cheshire, WA8 0TH Tel: 0151-423 5273 Fax: 0151-495 1390 E-mail: enquiries@jep-engineering.co.uk

TANK REPLACEMENT, WATER

▶ Environmental Fabrications, Unit 26 Manor Development Centre, Alison CR, Sheffield, S2 1AS Tel: 0114-278 8777 Fax: 0114-254 4974 E-mail: info@watertankrefurbishment.com

TANK ROTARY WASH HEADS

T C Repair & Supply, Sheddingdean Industrial Centre, Marchants Way, Burgess Hill, West Sussex, RH15 8QY Tel: (01444) 242564 Fax: (01444) 236683 E-mail: info@tcrepair.com

TANK STEAM HEATERS

Koch Heat Transfer Company, PO Box 790, Wimborne, Dorset, BH21 5BQ Tel: (01258) 840776 Fax: (01258) 840961 E-mail: bftuk@kochind.com

TANK VALVES

▶ Schuf UK Ltd, 157 Park Road, Teddington, Middlesex, TW11 0BP Tel: (020) 8977 2992 Fax: (020) 8943 3898 E-mail: sales@schuf.co.uk

TANKER DISCHARGE/LOAD EQUIPMENT

Emco Wheaton UK Ltd, Enterprise Road, Westwood Industrial Estate, Margate, Kent, CT9 4JR Tel: (01843) 221521 Fax: (01843) 295444 E-mail: sales@emcowheaton.co.uk
Gardner Denver UK Ltd, PO Box 468, Bradford, West Yorkshire, BD5 7HW Tel: (01274) 715240 Fax: (01274) 715241
Industrial Flow Control Ltd, Unit 1, Askews Farm Lane, Grays, Essex, RM17 5XR Tel: (01375) 387155 Fax: (01375) 387420 E-mail: sales@inflow.co.uk

TANKER (ROAD) COMPONENTS/ SPARE PARTS

Matano, Units 14-15 Whinfield Industrial Estate, Whinfield Way, Rowlands Gill, Tyne & Wear, NE39 1EH Tel: (01207) 549448 Fax: (01207) 549447 E-mail: james.harlend@metano.com
Steerforth Sales Ltd, Unit 7, Holder Road, Aldershot, Hampshire, GU12 4RH Tel: (01252) 333633 Fax: (01252) 343080 E-mail: sales@steerforth.co.uk

TANKER (ROAD) HIRE

▶ M F Compton & Son, Grovebury Road, Leighton Buzzard, Bedfordshire, LU7 4TS Tel: (01525) 371707 Fax: (01525) 851891 E-mail: enquiries@tankers-r-us.com
Qualitank Services Ltd, Harrison Street, Widnes, Cheshire, WA8 8TN Tel: 0151-495 1116 Fax: 0151-424 6842 E-mail: sales@qualitank.co.uk
Road Tankers Northern Ltd, Platts Common Industrial Estate, Barrowfield Road, Hoyland, Barnsley, South Yorkshire, S74 9TH Tel: (01226) 350650 Fax: (01226) 360528 E-mail: suzanne@rtnltd.co.uk
Thurroclean, Thompson Road, Trafford Park, Manchester, M17 1SE Tel: 0161-848 0821 Fax: 0161-848 0359 E-mail: info@tt-group.co.uk

TANKER (ROAD) MAINTENANCE OR REPAIR OR REFURBISHMENT SPECIALIST SERVICES

Isocon Engineering Ltd, 322 Broomloan Road, Glasgow, G51 2JQ Tel: 0141-440 5454 Fax: 0141-425 1344 E-mail: isoconengltd@ibrox4.demon.co.uk
Purfleet Commercials Ltd, 520 London Road, Grays, Essex, RM20 3BE Tel: (01708) 863931 Fax: (01708) 868226 E-mail: tmason@harris-group.co.uk
Road Tankers Northern Ltd, Platts Common Industrial Estate, Barrowfield Road, Hoyland, Barnsley, South Yorkshire, S74 9TH Tel: (01226) 350650 Fax: (01226) 360528 E-mail: suzanne@rtnltd.co.uk
Thurroclean, Thompson Road, Trafford Park, Manchester, M17 1SE Tel: 0161-848 0821 Fax: 0161-848 0359 E-mail: info@tt-group.co.uk
Ward Fabrication Ltd, Brick Street, Cleckheaton, West Yorkshire, BD19 5EH Tel: (01274) 861123 Fax: (01274) 852664
Widnes Tank Container Services Ltd, Ditton Road, Widnes, Cheshire, WA8 0NE Tel: 0151-424 6742 Fax: 0151-423 4210 E-mail: info@widnestcs.co.uk

TANKS, *See also headings for particular material or usage*

▶ C H F Supplies, Crane Hall, Wyreside, Out Rawcliffe, Preston, PR3 6TP Tel: (01995) 670888 Fax: (01995) 670305 E-mail: alex@chfsupplies.co.uk
Clarehill Plastics Ltd, New Building, 21 Clarehill Road, Moira, Craigavon, County Armagh, BT67 0PB Tel: (028) 9261 1077 Fax: (028) 9261 2672 E-mail: info@clarehill.com
D & S Services, Unit H2 & Unit H3 Rudford Industrial Estate, Ford Road, Ford, Arundel, West Sussex, BN18 0BD Tel: (01903) 732732 Fax: (01903) 716151 E-mail: sales@dandsservices.co.uk
▶ I E S Robust Tanks, Fountain House, Brindley Close, Holly Lane Industrial Estate, Atherstone, Warwickshire, CV9 2GA Tel: 0121-351 7219 Fax: (01827) 714534
Jessops plc, 257 High Street, Cheltenham, Gloucestershire, GL50 3HJ Tel: (0845) 4587074 Fax: (01242) 228054
K P Thomas & Son, Templeton, Narberth, Dyfed, SA67 8SR Tel: (0800) 3286033 Fax: (01834) 861686 E-mail: kpthomas@templeton22.fsnet.co.uk
Pipe Centre Plus, Unit 8, Spring Road Industrial Estate, Ettingshall, Wolverhampton, WV4 6JZ Tel: (01902) 409341 Fax: E-mail: p15.wolverhampton@wolsely.com
Regal Tanks, Ellough Park, Benacre Road, Beccles, Suffolk, NR34 7XD Tel: (01502) 710100 Fax: (01502) 710103 E-mail: info@regaltanks.co.uk
The Tank Exchange, Lewden House, Barnsley Road, Dodworth, Barnsley, South Yorkshire, S75 3JU Tel: (01226) 203852 Fax: (01226) 299424
Tanks & Vessels Industries, Bankwood Lane Industrial Estate, Bankwood Lane, New Rossington, Doncaster, South Yorkshire, DN11 0PS Tel: (01302) 866003 Fax: (01302) 864990 E-mail: sales@tanksandvessels.com
Whitby Tanks Ltd, Custom House, 1 Old Market Place, Whitby, North Yorkshire, YO21 3BT Tel: (01947) 606237 Fax: (01947) 602876 E-mail: sales@whitbytanks.co.uk

TANKS, AIR COMPRESSOR

Cathro Air Compressor Services, 48 Winpenny Road, Parkhouse Industrial Estate, Parkhouse Industrial Estate East, Newcastle, Staffordshire, ST5 7RH Tel: (01782) 561191 Fax: (01782) 563348 E-mail: tom@cathrocompressors.wanadoo.co.uk

TANKS, ALUMINIUM/ALLOY

Oval 316 Ltd, 10 Cowley Road, Nuffield Industrial Estate, Poole, Dorset, BH17 0UJ Tel: (01202) 682830 Fax: (01202) 665572 E-mail: office@oval316.co.uk

TANKS, GLASS COATED/FUSED

Goodwin Tanks Ltd, Pontefract Street, Derby, DE24 8JD Tel: (01332) 363112 Fax: (01332) 294683 E-mail: sales@goodwintanks.co.uk
Permastore Ltd, Airfield Industrial Park, Eye Airfield Industrial Estate, Eye, Suffolk, IP23 7HS Tel: (01379) 870723 Fax: (01379) 870530 E-mail: sales@permastore.co.uk
▶ Vulcan Tanks Ltd, Cotes Park Lane, Cotes Park Industrial Estate, Somercotes, Alfreton, Derbyshire, DE55 4NJ Tel: (01773) 835321 Fax: (01773) 836578 E-mail: sales@vulcantanks.co.uk

TANKS, GLASS FIBRE OR FIBREGLASS

Austin Roberts, Tarran Way South, Tarran Industrial Estate, Wirral, Merseyside, CH46 4UB Tel: 0151-678 6088 Fax: 0151-678 9448 E-mail: austin.roberts@virgin.net
Boatman Plastics, Newport Road, Market Drayton, Shropshire, TF9 2AA Tel: (01630) 657286 Fax: (01630) 655545
Brimar Plastic Ltd, North Road, Yate, Bristol, BS37 7PR Tel: (01454) 322111 Fax: (01454) 316955 E-mail: brimar@brimarplastics.co.uk
Capvond Plastics Ltd, 32 Welbeck Road, Glasgow, G53 7SD Tel: 0141-876 9000 Fax: 0141-876 4123 E-mail: office@capvond.co.uk
Conder Products Ltd, Whitehouse Way, South West Industrial Estate, Peterlee, County Durham, SR8 2HZ Tel: 0191-587 8660 Fax: 0191-586 1274 E-mail: sales@conderproducts.co.uk
Croy Glass Fibre Products, 3 Lower Dartmouth Street, Birmingham, B9 4LG Tel: 0121-773 8714 Fax: 0121-773 8714

TANKS, GLASS FIBRE OR FIBREGLASS – *continued*

Ian Flockton Developments Ltd, Estate Road 1, South Humberside Industrial Estate, Grimsby, South Humberside, DN31 2TB Tel: (01472) 359634 Fax: (01472) 241392 E-mail: info@ianflockton.co.uk

G & A Plastics Ltd, Springhill Works, Exchange St, Accrington, Lancashire, BB5 0LE Tel: (01254) 871919 Fax: (01254) 390967 E-mail: david@gaplastics.co.uk

▶ I E S Robust Tanks, Fountain House, Brindley Close, Holly Lane Industrial Estate, Atherstone, Warwickshire, CV9 2GA Tel: 0121-351 7219 Fax: (01827) 714534

Mottram Industrial Plastics, 99a North Street, Cannock, Staffordshire, WS11 0AZ Tel: (01543) 573735 Fax: (01543) 574925 E-mail: andy@mottramindustrialplastics.co.uk

Nicholson Plastics Ltd, Riverside Road, Kirkfieldbank, Lanark, ML11 9JS Tel: (01555) 664316 Fax: (01555) 663056 E-mail: sales@nicholsonplastics.co.uk

Parton Fibreglass Ltd, P F G House, Claymore, Tame Valley Industrial Estate, Tamworth, Staffordshire, B77 5DQ Tel: (01827) 261771 Fax: (01827) 261390 E-mail: sales@pfg-tanks.com

R M J Mouldings, 4B Centurion Park, Kendel Road, Shrewsbury, SY1 4EH Tel: (01743) 450470 Fax: (01743) 351584

Robby Tanks Ltd, Cruwys Morchard, Tiverton, Devon, EX16 8LY Tel: (01363) 866310 Fax: (01363) 866310

Spel Products Ltd, Lancaster Road, Shrewsbury, SY1 3NQ Tel: (01743) 445200 Fax: (08451) 300442

TANKS, SECTIONAL, GRP, WATER/CHEMICAL STORAGE

▶ I E S Robust Tanks, Fountain House, Brindley Close, Holly Lane Industrial Estate, Atherstone, Warwickshire, CV9 2GA Tel: 0121-351 7219 Fax: (01827) 714534

Nicholson Plastics Ltd, 20b Lansdowne Road, Croydon, CR0 2BX Tel: (020) 8760 0930 Fax: (020) 8688 1811

Parton Fibreglass Ltd, P F G House, Claymore, Tame Valley Industrial Estate, Tamworth, Staffordshire, B77 5DQ Tel: (01827) 261771 Fax: (01827) 261390 E-mail: sales@pfg-tanks.com

Pow Ltd, Conitor House, Denbury Road, Newton Abbot, Devon, TQ12 6AD Tel: (01626) 361490 Fax: (01626) 333359 E-mail: sales@powplastics.co.uk

TANKS, SEPTIC, CONCRETE

▶ Hydrorod Drainage Services, 48 Birchy Barton Hill, Exeter, EX1 3EX Tel: (01392) 498899 Fax: (01392) 498877 E-mail: mail@hydrorod.com

TANNING MACHINERY

A.M. Ede Technical Services Ltd, Conger Cottage, Market Square, Dunstable, Bedfordshire, LU5 6BP Tel: (01525) 873890 Fax: (01525) 873890

Melbourne Sun Rooms Ltd, 25 Victoria Street, Melbourne, Derby, DE73 8FR Tel: (01332) 863811 E-mail: melbournesunroom@aol.com

TANNING MATERIALS

Roy Dickson Wilson, Alrewas House, Main Street, Alrewas, Burton-on-Trent, Staffordshire, DE13 7ED Tel: (01283) 792255 Fax: (01283) 792041

TANTALUM TURNED PARTS

▶ BST Precision Ltd, Unit D 10, Hortonwood 7, Hortonwood, Telford, Shropshire, TF1 7XU Tel: (01952) 603952 Fax: (01952) 604947 E-mail: tony.edgley@bstprecision.co.uk

TAP (SCREWING/THREAD CUTTING/THREADING) AND DIE MANUFRS

Arc Tap & Die Co. Ltd, Delamare Road, Cheshunt, Waltham Cross, Hertfordshire, EN8 9SH Tel: (01992) 629247 Fax: (01992) 636268

Depo FHT, Lion House, Welsh Road East, Southam, Warwickshire, CV47 1NE Tel: (01926) 813969 Fax: (01926) 817722 E-mail: sales@fht-uk.com

Emuge (UK) Ltd, 2 Claire Court, Rawmarsh Road, Rotherham, South Yorkshire, S60 1RU Tel: (01709) 364494 Fax: (01709) 364540 E-mail: sales@emuge-uk.co.uk

Grayson Millward Ltd, Wharf Road Industrial Estate, Pinxton, Nottingham, NG16 6LE Tel: (01773) 810144 Fax: (01773) 860321 E-mail:

Guhring Ltd, Castle Bromwich Business Park, Tameside Drive, Castle Vale, Birmingham, B35 7AG Tel: 0121-749 5544 Fax: 0121-776 7224 E-mail: info@guhring.co.uk

Richard Lloyd Ltd, Cromwell Works, Tenbury Wells, Worcestershire, WR15 8LF Tel: (01584) 810381 Fax: (01584) 810080 E-mail: sales@galtona.co.uk

Nonpareil Taps & Dies Ltd, 15 Rookwood Way, Haverhill, Suffolk, CB9 8PB Tel: (01440) 703625 Fax: (01440) 712101 E-mail: info@nonpareiltapsanddies.co.uk

T-Tech Tooling Ltd, 70 Prince Of Wales Lane, Yardley Wood, Birmingham, B14 4JZ Tel: 0121-474 2255 Fax: 0121-474 2066 E-mail: sales@t-tech.co.uk

TAPER LEAF SPRINGS

G M E Motor Engineers (Coventry) Ltd, Boston Place, Foleshill, Coventry, CV6 5NN Tel: (024) 7666 4911 Fax: (024) 7666 3020 E-mail: sales@gmesprings.co.uk

TAPER PINS, *See also headings for particular types*

Griffvale Ltd, Alexandra Indust Estate, Alexandra Road, Denton, Manchester, M34 3DX Tel: 0161-335 0175 Fax: 0161-336 0513 E-mail: griffvaleltd@btconnect.com

TAPER ROLLER BEARINGS

Commerce International G B Ltd, 14 Dalston Gardens, Stanmore, Middlesex, HA7 1BU Tel: (020) 8206 1133 Fax: (020) 8204 6969 E-mail: commintl@aol.com

Gamet Bearings, Hythe Station Road, Colchester, CO2 8LD Tel: (01206) 862121 Fax: (01206) 868690 E-mail: sales@gamet-bearings.co.uk

TAPES

▶ Adhesive Coatings, Eagle Technology Park, Queensway, Rochdale, Lancashire, OL11 1TQ Tel: (01706) 356125 Fax: (01706) 524853 E-mail: postbox@adhesive-coatings.co.uk

TAPES, ADHESIVE

Coating & Converting Solutions Ltd, Bloomfield Park, Bloomfield Road, Tipton, West Midlands, DY4 9AP Tel: 0121-557 1155 Fax: 0121-557 9997 E-mail: sales@coatingconverting.co.uk

TAPES, IDENTIFICATION/ SAFETY, PIPELINE

▶ Industrial Tape Solutions Ltd, 2-6 Station Road, Shipley, West Yorkshire, BD18 2JL Tel: (01274) 592244 Fax: (01274) 591144 E-mail: sales@tapesolutions.co.uk

Premier Tape Converters Ltd, Unit 2, 24-26 Boulton Road, Stevenage, Hertfordshire, SG1 4QX Tel: (01732) 521122 Fax: (01438) 759555

TAPESTRIES

Coats Crafts U.K, Lingfield, McMullen Road, Darlington, County Durham, DL1 1YQ Tel: (01325) 394394 Fax: (01325) 394200 E-mail: consumer.services@coats.com

W H I Tapestry Shop, 85 Pimlico Road, London, SW1W 8PH Tel: (020) 7730 5366

TAPPING MACHINE MANUFRS

Datamach Ltd, Falkland Close, Charter Avenue Industrial Estate, Coventry, CV4 8AU Tel: (024) 7647 0707 Fax: (024) 7646 4059 E-mail: enquiries@datamach.co.uk

Harcross Engineering Barnstaple Ltd, Pilland Way, Pottington Business Park, Barnstaple, Devon, EX31 1LP Tel: (01271) 372235 Fax: (01271) 344642

TAPPING SERVICES

Tapping Services, 18-19 Broad Lanes, Bilston, West Midlands, WV14 0RY Tel: (01902) 404882 Fax: (01902) 403692

TAPS, *See also headings for particular types*

Bristan Group Ltd, 30 Lagrange, Lichfield Road Industrial Estate, Tamworth, Staffordshire, B79 7XD Tel: (01827) 68525 Fax: (01827) 68553 E-mail: enquire@bristan.com

Damixa Ltd, The Case Building, Watford Business Park, Caxton Way, Watford, WD18 8ZF Tel: (01923) 690100 Fax: (01923) 690101 E-mail: damixa@damixa.com

Prima Flow, Stargate Business Park, Cuckoo Road, Nechells, Birmingham, B7 5SE Tel: 0121-327 1234 Fax: (0121) 3274046 E-mail: info@muellerprimaflow.com

TAPS, DRUM, PLASTIC

Brassey Export Co., Starbell House, Carr Lane, Hoylake, Wirral, Merseyside, CH47 4FB Tel: 0151-632 6464 Fax: 0151-632 6392 E-mail: bec@starbell.com

▶ Capsolutions Ltd, 41 Airmyn Road, Goole, East Yorkshire, DN14 6XB Tel: (01405) 763040 Fax: (01405) 763041 E-mail: sales@capsolutions.co.uk

▶ Worldwide Dispensers, Merton Industrial Park, Lee Road, London, SW19 3WD Tel: (020) 8545 7500 Fax: (020) 8545 7502 E-mail: sales@dsswd.com

TAR DISTILLERS/DISTILLATION PRODUCTS

Koppers UK Ltd, Normanby Gateway, Lysaghts Way, Scunthorpe, North Lincolnshire, DN15 9YG Tel: (01724) 281555 Fax: (01724) 281343 E-mail: kuk@koppers-eu.com

TAR SPRAYING EQUIPMENT

Phoenix Engineering Co., Combe Street, Chard, Somerset, TA20 1JE Tel: (01460) 63531 Fax: (01460) 67388 E-mail: sales@phoenixeng.co.uk

TARMACADAM

Aggregate Industries UK Ltd, Hulland Ward, Ashbourne, Derbyshire, DE6 3ET Tel: (01335) 372222 Fax: (01335) 370074

Billown Lime Quarries Ltd, Billown Quarry, Ballasalla, Isle Of Man, IM9 3DW Tel: (01624) 828765 Fax: (01624) 824477

Cemex UK Ltd, Crown House, Evreux Way, Rugby, Warwickshire, CV21 2DT Tel: 0114-242 6050 Fax: (01788) 540166

Colordrives Ltd, 65 Knowle Wood Road, Dorridge, Solihull, West Midlands, B93 8JP Tel: (01564) 772755 Fax: (01564) 772755 E-mail: info@colordrives.co.uk

East Coast Surfacing, Europa Way, Atherton Way, Brigg, South Humberside, DN20 8AR Tel: (01652) 657651 Fax: (01652) 659636 E-mail: js.brown@btconnect.com

Fibresand International Ltd, Ash House Ransom Wood Business Park, Southwell Road, Rainworth, Mansfield, Nottinghamshire, NG21 0HJ Tel: (01623) 675305 Fax: (01623) 675308 E-mail: enquiries@fibresand.com

Instarmac Group plc, Kingsbury Link, Trinity Road, Piccadilly, Tamworth, Staffordshire, B78 2EX Tel: (01827) 872244 Fax: (01827) 874466 E-mail: enquiries@instarmac.co.uk

RMC Aggregates Eastern Ltd, Dowding Road, Lincoln, LN3 4PN Tel: (01522) 540721 Fax: (01522) 576438

▶ Tarmac Centre Ltd, Harrison Street, Rotherham, South Yorkshire, S61 1EE Tel: (01709) 740700

Tarmac Western Ltd, Railway Terrace, Terrace Road, Pinvin, Pershore, Worcestershire, WR10 2DP Tel: (01386) 555389 Fax: (01386) 556014

TARMACADAM OVERLAY STENCILLED PATTERN BLOCK PAVING

Colordrives Ltd, 65 Knowle Wood Road, Dorridge, Solihull, West Midlands, B93 8JP Tel: (01564) 772755 Fax: (01564) 772755 E-mail: info@colordrives.co.uk

Stencil Tech, 1 Upland Industrial Estate, Mere Way, Wyton, Huntingdon, Cambridgeshire, PE28 2JZ Tel: (01480) 435919 Fax: (01480) 435922 E-mail: sales@stencil-tech.co.uk

TARPAULIN DISTRIBUTORS OR AGENTS

B Sipling Covermakers, Broughton, Brigg, South Humberside, DN20 0BZ Tel: (01652) 652343 Fax: (01652) 652343 E-mail: becky@sipling.freeserve.co.uk

Bradshaws Direct Ltd, James Nicolson Link, Clifton Moore, York, YO30 4XX Tel: (01904) 691169 Fax: (01904) 691133 E-mail: ferrey@aol.com

Del Tarpaulins Ltd, Unit 39, Millers Bridge Industrial, Bootle, Merseyside, L20 8AB Tel: 0151-922 9461 Fax: 0151-922 9908 E-mail: sales@r-lunt.co.uk

Montrose Rope & Sail Co., 13 Bents Road, Montrose, Angus, DD10 8QA Tel: (01674) 672657 Fax: (01674) 675785 E-mail: neilpaton@montroseropeandsail.co.uk

Pritchard Tyrite, Crockford Lane, Chineham, Basingstoke, Hampshire, RG24 8NA Tel: (01256) 400600 Fax: (01256) 400622 E-mail: martin@calhoun.co.uk

Tom Morrow Ltd, 1 Anderson Avenue, Aberdeen, AB24 4LR Tel: (01224) 485567 Fax: (01224) 488607

TARPAULIN MAINTENANCE/ REPAIR SERVICES

B & H Canvas Products Ltd, 33a Chester Street, Cardiff, CF11 6PY Tel: (029) 2034 3610 Fax: (029) 2056 3753

Bolton Tarpaulins, Unit 16 Brownlow Business Centre, Darley Street, Bolton, BL1 3DX Tel: (01204) 380837 Fax: (01204) 380837 E-mail: boltontarps@btconnect.com

D & S Tarpaulins, Evergreen, Groves Farm Road, Eastchurch, Sheerness, Kent, ME12 3SY Tel: (01795) 880956

Del Tarpaulins Ltd, Unit 39, Millers Bridge Industrial, Bootle, Merseyside, L20 8AB Tel: 0151-922 9461 Fax: 0151-922 9908 E-mail: sales@r-lunt.co.uk

F Waites & Sons, Harper Street, Driffield, North Humberside, YO25 6LY Tel: (01377) 253310 Fax: (01377) 253310

P W Mobile Repairs, 40 Cornfields, Holbeach, Spalding, Lincolnshire, PE12 7QN Tel: (01406) 426630 Fax: (01406) 426909

Shrewsbury Tarpaulins Ltd, Unit 1ac Leaton Industrial Estate, Leaton, Bomere Heath, Shrewsbury, SY4 3AP Tel: (01939) 290692 Fax: (01939) 290692

Stuart Canvas Products, Warren Works, Hardwick Grange, Woolston, Warrington, WA1 4RF Tel: (01925) 814525 Fax: (01925) 831709

Tarpaulin Repair Services, Three Ways, Walkers Lane, Whittington, Worcester, WR5 2NN Tel: (01905) 767077 Fax: (01905) 767077

Woodlands Tarpaulins, 8 Middle Lickhurst, Bleasdale Road, Whitechapel, Preston, PR3 2ER Tel: (01995) 640779 Fax: (01995) 640277

TARPAULINS

A J S Tarpaulin Services, Mariner Way, Felnex Industrial Estate, Newport, Gwent, NP19 4PQ Tel: (01633) 290387 Fax: (01633) 277317 E-mail: ajstarpaulins@tinyworld.co.uk

A R D Tools & Patterns, 1 Roberts Drive, Bridgwater, Somerset, TA6 6BH Tel: (01278) 433177 Fax: (01278) 433160

Aberdeen Tarpaulins, 42a Seaforth Road, Aberdeen, AB24 5PU Tel: (01224) 631915 Fax: (01224) 631012

Ace Tarpaulins, Dovecot Street, Stockton-on-Tees, Cleveland, TS18 1HG Tel: (01642) 886216 Fax: (01642) 886244 E-mail: enquiries@acetarpaulinsltd.co.uk

Adams Tarpaulins, The Old Bakery, Ford Road, Wiveliscombe, Taunton, Somerset, TA4 2RE Tel: (01984) 623315 Fax: (01984) 623602

Allison Gray, Longtown Street, Dundee, DD4 8LF Tel: (01382) 505888 Fax: (01382) 507333 E-mail: allison-gray@dpandl.co.uk

Andrew Mitchell & Co. Ltd, Bishops Court Industrial Estate, Sidmouth Road, Exeter, EX2 7JH Tel: (01392) 432228 Fax: (01392) 211589

Awnings & Blinds By Morco, Riverside, Lombard Wall, London, SE7 7SG Tel: (020) 8858 2083 Fax: (020) 8305 2431 E-mail: sales@morcoblinds.co.uk

B & H Canvas Products Ltd, 33a Chester Street, Cardiff, CF11 6PY Tel: (029) 2034 3610 Fax: (029) 2056 3753

Tony Beal Ltd, 18 Station Road, Baillieston, Glasgow, G69 7UF Tel: 0141-773 2166 Fax: 0141-773 2904 E-mail: tbl@bealgroup.com

Bolton Tarpaulins, Unit 16 Brownlow Business Centre, Darley Street, Bolton, BL1 3DX Tel: (01204) 380837 Fax: (01204) 380837 E-mail: boltontarps@btconnect.com

C.D Tarpaulins, Unit W Rudford Industrial Estate, Ford Road, Ford, Arundel, West Sussex, BN18 0BD Tel: (01903) 732305 Fax: (01903) 732305

C J Covers Ltd, 30 Williamson Street, Hull, HU9 1EP Tel: (01482) 226970 Fax: (01482) 327218

Carter's, 99-113 Caversham Road, Reading, RG1 8AR Tel: 0118-959 9022 Fax: 0118-950 0618 E-mail: info@carterse.com

Contarps North West Ltd, Unit D4 Newton Business Park, Talbot Road, Hyde, Cheshire, SK14 4UQ Tel: 0161-367 9341 Fax: 0161-367 9352 E-mail: sales@contarps.co.uk

Controlla Covers Ltd, Brunswick Industrial Park, Hannah Street, Darwen, Lancashire, BB3 3HL Tel: (01254) 772020 Fax: (01254) 773030 E-mail: controlla@aol.com

Cosalt Young, 1 Liddell Street, North Shields, Tyne & Wear, NE30 1HE Tel: 0191-257 6121 Fax: 0191-296 1431 E-mail: northshields@cosalt.co.uk

▶ Covertec Wigan, Unit 3-4 Richard Street, Ince, Wigan, Lancashire, WN3 4JN Tel: (01942) 231377 Fax: (01942) 231377

Cunningham Covers Ltd, 42 Tobermore Road, Maghera, County Londonderry, BT46 5DR Tel: (028) 7964 2638 Fax: (028) 7964 3511 E-mail: info@cunninghamcovers.co.uk

▶ Curtain Tek, Acre Workshop, Blackburn Road, Haslingden, Rossendale, Lancashire, BB4 5AZ Tel: (01706) 212303 Fax: (01706) 212303

Custom Covers 1984 Ltd, Quayside Road, Southampton, SO18 1AD Tel: (023) 8033 5744 Fax: (023) 8022 5581 E-mail: sales@customcovers.co.uk

TARPAULINS – *continued*

D Haynes Ltd, 9-11 Hanover Street, Bolton, BL1 4TG Tel: (01204) 382122 Fax: (01204) 397232

Del Tarpaulins Ltd, Unit 39, Millers Bridge Industrial, Bootle, Merseyside, L20 8AB Tel: 0151-922 9461 Fax: 0151-922 9908 E-mail: sales@r-lunt.co.uk

Dobie Wyatt Ltd, Old School, Cadley, Marlborough, Wiltshire, SN8 4NE Tel: (01672) 512563 Fax: (01672) 516948 E-mail: dobiewyatt@cwcom.net

Emlyn Canvas & Cordage Co. Ltd, George Street Conservatory Centre, Granville Square, Newport, Gwent, NP20 2AB Tel: (01633) 262262 Fax: (01633) 222420

Fisher Tarpaulins, Unit 5-6 The Maltings, Navigation Drive, Hurst Business Park, Brierley Hill, West Midlands, DY5 1UT Tel: (01384) 571313 Fax: (01384) 261666

George Neville Transport Safety Systems Ltd, Southwell Lane Industrial Estate, Summit Close, Kirkby-in-Ashfield, Nottingham, NG17 8GJ Tel: (01623) 755300 Fax: (01623) 756563

Hastings & Henshaw, Bridgecroft Mills, Tanyard Road, Millsbridge, Huddersfield, HD3 4NF Tel: (01484) 647111 Fax: (01484) 647111

Intension Canvas Goods, 6 Anchor Industrial Estate, Dumballs Road, Cardiff, CF10 5FF Tel: (029) 2023 2031 Fax: (029) 2038 3583 E-mail: sales@intension.co.uk

J Clemishaw & Company Ltd, Barnbrook Building, Barnbrook Street, Bury, Lancashire, BL9 7DT Tel: 0161-764 4614 Fax: 0161-764 4615

J R Parkin Ltd, Whiteheads Mill, Young St, Bradford, West Yorkshire, BD8 9RQ Tel: (01274) 498567 Fax: (01274) 482023 E-mail: ian@jrparkin.wanadoo.co.uk

Jordans Sunblinds Ltd, York St, Hull, HU2 0QW Tel: (01482) 326657 Fax: (01482) 212486 E-mail: enquiries@jordansofhull.co.uk

K & T Tilts, Readmans Industrial Estate, Station Road, East Tilbury, Tilbury, Essex, RM18 8QR Tel: (01375) 840880 Fax: (01375) 840740 E-mail: info@kandttilts.co.uk

Kirklands Ltd, Kirkland House, Main Cross Road, Great Yarmouth, Norfolk, NR30 3NZ Tel: (01493) 843060 Fax: (01493) 853001 E-mail: sales@kirkgroup.co.uk

W. J. Leech & Sons Ltd, 275 Derby Road, Bootle, Merseyside, L20 8PL Tel: 0151-933 9334 Fax: 0151-933 5005 E-mail: david@wjleech.com

M & N Canvas Services Ltd, Butterthwaite Lane, Ecclesfield, Sheffield, S35 9WA Tel: 0114-246 1293 Fax: 0114-257 0311

Mayor & Son Ltd, 1 Brierley Street, Ashton-on-Ribble, Preston, PR2 2AU Tel: (01772) 254488 Fax: (01772) 259897

Metcalf Leenside Ltd, 139-143 Canal Street, Nottingham, NG1 7HD Tel: 0115-958 0865 Fax: 0115-959 8934 E-mail: sales@metcalf.co.uk

William Milne (Tarpaulins) Ltd, 42a Seaforth Road, Aberdeen, AB24 5PU Tel: (01224) 631012 Fax: (01224) 631012

Andrew Mitchell & Co. Ltd, 15 Dunivaig Road, Glasgow, G33 4TT Tel: 0141-773 5454 Fax: 0141-773 5455E-mail: info1@mitco.co.uk

G. Mudford & Sons Ltd, Aurillac Way, Hallcroft Road, Retford, Nottinghamshire, DN22 7PX Tel: (01777) 703489 Fax: (01777) 704743 E-mail: info@mudfordmarquees.co.uk

▶ Mudfords Sheffield Ltd, 400 Petre Street, Sheffield, S4 8LU Tel: 0114-243 3033 Fax: 0114-244 4536 E-mail: sales@mudfords.co.uk

R. Billson & Sons Ltd, 431 Thurmaston Boulevard, Off Claymill Road, Leicester, LE4 9LA Tel: 0116-276 2555 Fax: 0116-276 9234

Shrewsbury Tarpaulins Ltd, Unit 1ac Leaton Industrial Estate, Leaton, Bomere Heath, Shrewsbury, SY4 3AP Tel: (01939) 290692 Fax: (01939) 290692

▶ Simpers Ltd, 17 Mercers Row, Cambridge, CB5 8HY Tel: (01223) 351729 Fax: (01223) 311818 E-mail: info@simpers.co.uk

Speedings Flags Poles & Masts, 4 Carrmere Road, Leechmere Industrial Estate, Sunderland, SR2 9TW Tel: 0191-523 9933 Fax: 0191-523 9955 E-mail: speedingsltd@btconnect.com

Star Covers Ltd, 12 Manor Workswhitehall Road, Drighlington, Bradford, West Yorkshire, BD11 1LN Tel: 0113-285 4747 Fax: 0113-285 2293

Stronghold International, Nicholson Court, Geddings Road, Hoddesdon, Hertfordshire, EN11 0NE Tel: (01992) 460274 Fax: (01992) 479471 E-mail: sales@stronghold.co.uk

Stuart Brumby Cover Makers, 18 Park Farm Road, Foxhills Industrial Estate, Scunthorpe, South Humberside, DN15 8QP Tel: (01724) 280440 Fax: (01724) 280440

Stuart Canvas Products, Warren Works, Hardwick Grange, Woolston, Warrington, WA1 4RF Tel: (01925) 814525 Fax: (01925) 831709

Tees Tarpaulins Ltd, Skinner Street, Stockton-on-Tees, Cleveland, TS18 1EG Tel: (01642) 607772 Fax: (01642) 607633

Tom Morrow Tarpaulins Inverness Ltd, 14 Henderson Road, Inverness, IV1 1SN Tel: (01463) 220862 Fax: (01463) 243110 E-mail: enquiries@tommorrowtarpaulins.co.uk

Trailer Tilts Ltd, 15A Walton Avenue, Felixstowe, Suffolk, IP11 8HH Tel: (01394) 673635 Fax: (01394) 673635

W Oliver Allen & Sons, Loe Bar Road, Porthleven, Helston, Cornwall, TR13 9EN Tel: (01326) 562222 Fax: (01326) 562222 E-mail: woallen@porth-leven.com

W Sails, 51 Southsea Avenue, Leigh-on-Sea, Essex, SS9 2AX Tel: (01702) 714550 Fax: (01702) 714550

W W S Tarpaulins Ltd, 22 Bryggen Road, The Old Station Yard, Galton Road, King's Lynn, Norfolk, PE32 1LQ Tel: (01553) 777304 Fax: (01553) 849888 E-mail: info@wwstarpaulins.co.uk

John Waddon (1967) Ltd, 1 Sedgemount Industrial Estate, Bristol Road, Bridgwater, Somerset, TA6 4AR Tel: (01278) 422280 Fax: (01278) 444266 E-mail: sales@waddons.co.uk

William Arnold Tarpaulins Ltd, 30 Thames Road, Barking, Essex, IG11 0HZ Tel: (020) 8594 1500 Fax: (020) 8594 7773 E-mail: www.tarpaulins.co.uk

George Woodall & Sons Ltd, 35 & 37 Market Place, Malton, North Yorkshire, YO17 7LP Tel: (01653) 692086 Fax: (01653) 691488 E-mail: shop@gwoodall.com

TARTAN CLOTHS

D C Dalgleish Ltd, Dunsdale Mill, Dunsdale Road, Selkirk, TD7 5EB Tel: (01750) 20781 Fax: (01750) 20502

Lochcarron Weavers, Lochcarron, Strathcarron, Ross-Shire, IV54 8YH Tel: (01520) 722212 Fax: (01520) 722634

Mallalieu's Of Delph Ltd, Valley Mill, Millgate, Delph, Oldham, OL3 5DG Tel: (01457) 874811 Fax: (01457) 870231 E-mail: sales@mallalieus.com

Strathmore Woollen Co. Ltd, Station Works, North Street, Forfar, Angus, DD8 3BN Tel: (01307) 462135 Fax: (01307) 468603 E-mail: info@tartanbystrathmore.co.uk

TARTS

▶ Le Moulin, Mill Walk, Wheathampstead, St. Albans, Hertfordshire, AL4 8DT Tel: (01582) 831988 Fax: (01582) 831988 E-mail: julie.bell@can-do.co.uk

TATTOO MACHINE ACCESSORIES

▶ New Image Tattoo & Body Piercing Supplies, 66 Laughton Road, Dinnington, Sheffield, S25 2PS Tel: (01909) 560722 Fax: (0870) 7621361 E-mail: mark@tattookit.co.uk

TAXATION CONSULTANCY

Hamiltons Accountants & Business Advisors, Meriden House, 6 Great Cornbow, Halesowen, West Midlands, B63 3AB Tel: 0121-585 6655 Fax: 0121-585 6228 E-mail: enquiries@hamiltons-group.co.uk

▶ Montgomery Swann Ltd, Scotts Sufferance Wharf, 1 Mill Street, London, SE1 2DE Tel: (020) 7237 0537 Fax: (020) 7237 2661 E-mail: s.bradshaw@montgomeryswann.com

Shah & Co., 15 Stanier Street, Swindon, SN1 5QU Tel: (01793) 524084 E-mail: shahco@mrshah.com

▶ Teeac Associates, Unit 205 Camberwell Business Centre, Lomond Grove, London, SE5 7HN Tel: (020) 7708 2396 Fax: (0870) 7656230 E-mail: info@teeac.com

TAXI DATA SYSTEMS

▶ P & A Taxi Meters, 6 Foundation Units, Westfield Road, Slyfield Industrial Estate, Guildford, Surrey, GU1 1SF Tel: (01483) 535353 Fax: (01483) 450222 E-mail: don@novaxuk.com

▶ Pearce Real Kab Co., 24 New Houses, Pantygasseg, Pontypool, Torfaen, NP4 6UH Tel: (01495) 756511 Fax: (01495) 759911 E-mail: mikeyjpearce@hotmail.com

▶ Sercombe Taxis, 4 Copland Meadows, Totnes, Devon, TQ9 6ER Tel: (01803) 864745 Fax: 01803 864745 E-mail: sales@sercombetaxis.co.uk

TAXI METERS

▶ Clydewide Taxis, 99 High Street, Lanark, ML11 7LN Tel: (01555) 663813 Fax: (01555) 678937 E-mail: taxis@clydewide.co.uk

▶ colin bowen, 80Quarrysprings, Harlow, Essex, CM20 3HS Tel: 07916 245161 Fax: 01279 869605 E-mail: stanstedtaxis@yahoo.co.uk

Contact Radio Communications Ltd, Unit 19 Leeway Court, Leeway Industrial Estate, Newport, Gwent, NP19 4SJ Tel: (01633) 270005 Fax: (01633) 271305

▶ Digitax Electronics UK Ltd, The Smoke House, 31 Tanners Bank, North Shields, Tyne & Wear, NE30 1JH Tel: 0191-296 1294 E-mail: digitax2@aol.com

Halda Ltd, Quay Business Centre, 12 Harvard Court, Winwick Quay, Warrington, WA2 8LT Tel: (01925) 629926 Fax: (01925) 629929 E-mail: haldauk@aol.com

▶ TeePee Electronics, TeePee House, 61 Wavell Gardens, Slough, SL2 2EL Tel: (01753) 570546 Fax: (01753) 570546 E-mail: pulsarteepee@yahoo.co.uk

TAXI OR MINICAB INSURANCE

▶ Data Cars, 101 Eltham High Street, London, SE9 1TD Tel: (020) 8850 1111 Fax: (020) 8850 1000 E-mail: mail@datacars.com

▶ Taxi insurance from WYN Group Insurance Services, WYN House, 4 Eve Road, Woking, Surrey, GU21 5JT Tel: 01483 722266 E-mail: info@wyngroup.co.uk

TAXIS

▶ 1st Airports Express Cars, 104 Gloucester Road, London, SW7 4RH Tel: (020) 7244 6556

▶ 1st Kensington Riders Cars, 180-186 Cromwell Road, Kensington And Chelsea, London, SW5 0SS Tel: (020) 7244 7744

▶ Air-2-There.Co.Uk, 55 Leighswood Avenue, Walsall, WS9 8AT Tel: (01922) 864248 E-mail: enquires@air-2-there.co.uk

▶ Data Cars, 101 Eltham High Street, London, SE9 1TD Tel: (020) 8850 1111 Fax: (020) 8850 1000 E-mail: mail@datacars.com

▶ K & J Travel Direct, 15 Beechcombe Close, Pershore, Worcestershire, WR10 1PW Tel: (01386) 553243 Fax: 01386 553653 E-mail: knewbury@traveldirect-pershore.co.uk

▶ London Black Cab, Faircross Avenue, Romford, RM5 3UB Tel: (07956) 808896 E-mail: alan.smith222@virgin.net

▶ Serpentine Cars, 81 Hargate Way, Hampton Hargate, Peterborough, PE7 8DL Tel: (01733) 565058 E-mail: lee@serpentinecars.com

Sunland Airport Transfers, Castle Lane, Littleham, Exmouth, Devon, EX8 5BR Tel: 01395 269301 E-mail: sunlandcars@centralpets.com

TEA BAG FILTER PAPER

J R Crompton U S A Ltd, 12th Floor, Sunlight House, Manchester, M3 3JZ Tel: 0161-817 6500 Fax: 0161-817 6506 E-mail: info@crompton.co.uk

▶ Suki Teahouse, Unit 6a, Northumberland Street, Belfast, BT13 2JF Tel: (028) 9033 0938 Fax: (028) 9027 8491 E-mail: oscar@suki-tea.com

TEA BAG PRODUCTION MACHINE/EQUIPMENT, INSTALLATION OR SERVICE

Recon Services, Unit 3 Barratt Industrial Park, St. Oswalds Road, Gloucester, GL1 2SH Tel: (01452) 415116 Fax: (01452) 415124 E-mail: reconservi@aol.com

Teacraft Ltd, PO Box 190, Bedford, MK42 7EE Tel: (01234) 852121 Fax: (01234) 853232 E-mail: info@teacraft.com

TEA PROCESSING MACHINERY

Dickinson Legg Ltd, Moorside Road, Winchester, Hampshire, SO23 7SS Tel: (01962) 842222 Fax: (01962) 840567 E-mail: sales@dickinson.com

Teacraft Ltd, PO Box 190, Bedford, MK42 7EE Tel: (01234) 852121 Fax: (01234) 853232 E-mail: info@teacraft.com

TEA TOWELS

Thomas Ferguson & Co. Ltd, 54 Scarva Road, Banbridge, County Down, BT32 3QD Tel: (028) 4062 3491 Fax: (028) 4062 2453 E-mail: info@fergusonsirishlinen.com

Hanson Textiles Ltd, Surcon House, 11a Copson Street, Manchester, M20 3HE Tel: 0161-718 3888 Fax: 0161-718 3323 E-mail: sales@hansontextiles.co.uk

Samuel Lamont & Sons Ltd, Victoria Street, Lurgan, Craigavon, County Armagh, BT67 9DA Tel: (028) 3832 9066 Fax: (028) 3834 3095 E-mail: mail@samuellamont.co.uk

TEACHER TRAINING

International House, 106 Piccadilly, London, W1J 7NL Tel: (020) 7518 6999 Fax: (020) 7495 0284 E-mail: info@ihlondon.co.uk

▶ Telford Computer Training, The Rock, Telford, Shropshire, TF3 5DA Tel: 01952 504202 E-mail: jenny_urey@hotmail.com

TEACHING AIDS

Cochranes of Oxford Ltd, Grove Farm Barns, High Street, Shipton-under-Wychwood, Chipping Norton, Oxfordshire, OX7 6DG Tel: (01993) 832868 Fax: (01993) 832578 E-mail: cochranes@mailbox.co.uk

Connevans Ltd Equipment For The Deaf, 54 Albert Road North, Reigate, Surrey, RH2 9YR Tel: (01737) 247571 Fax: (01737) 223475 E-mail: mail@connevans.com

Crochet Design, 11 North Street, Morecambe, Lancashire, LA4 5LR Tel: (01524) 831752 Fax: (01524) 833099 E-mail: paulineturner@crochet.co.uk

E & L Instruments Ltd, Aerial Road, Llay, Wrexham, Clwyd, LL12 0TU Tel: (01978) 853920 Fax: (01978) 854564 E-mail: info@eandl-group.com

Goodwill Art Service Ltd, The Old School, Church Street, Upton, Didcot, Oxfordshire, OX11 9JB Tel: (01235) 831990 Fax: (01235) 831990 E-mail: goodwiilart@uptonoxon.demon.co.uk

▶ Kip Mcgrath Education Centre (Southall), The Arches, Merrick Road, Southall, Middlesex, UB2 4AU Tel: (020) 8574 7338 E-mail: enquiries@kmgsouthall.com

▶ Primary Tuition, 40 Gilderdale Close, Birchwood, Warrington, WA3 6TH Tel: (01925) 821995 E-mail: mary@cottam.freeserve.co.uk

TEAK GARDEN FURNITURE

▶ Cornwall Wood Treatment Services Ltd, 12, United Downs Industrial Park, St. Day, Redruth, Cornwall, TR16 5HY Tel: (01209) 820878 Fax: (01209) 822222 E-mail: sales@cornwallwood.co.uk

featureDECO.co.uk, Unit A5, Link One Industrial Park, George Henry Road, Tipton, West Midlands, DY4 7BU Tel: 0845 200 4956 E-mail: enquiries@featuredeco.co.uk

▶ GoAfrica, 34 St. Barnabas Street, Wellingborough, Northamptonshire, NN8 3HB Tel: (0845) 6447984 E-mail: gwen@goafrica.co.uk

▶ Kingshall Furniture, 5 Millennium Point, Broadfields, Aylesbury, Buckinghamshire, HP19 8ZU Tel: (01296) 339925 Fax: (01296) 392900 E-mail: info@kingshallfurniture.com

▶ Odd Ltd, Oxford, OX7 6WZ Tel: (01993) 830674 Fax: (01993) 832474 E-mail: mail@oddlimited.com

▶ Planet Leisure UK, The LnS Building, Unit 4, Crockford Lane, Chineham, Basingstoke, Hampshire, RG24 8NA Tel: (01256) 841950 Fax: (01256) 818255 E-mail: sales@planetleisureuk.co.uk

▶ Tills Innovations, Thingoe Cottage, The Street, Great Barton, Bury St. Edmunds, Suffolk, IP31 2QP Tel: (01284) 787479 Fax: (01284) 787507 E-mail: enquiries@tills-innovations.com

▶ Treehouse Furniture Ltd, 174 Penarth Road, Cardiff, CF11 6NL Tel: (029) 2023 0796 Fax: (029) 2023 0796 E-mail: ralph@intothewoods.co.uk

▶ treehousebuilders.co.uk, 60 Court Leet, Coventry, CV3 2JR Tel: (07879) 224260 E-mail: chris@treehousebuilders.co.uk

TECHNICAL AND IMPREGNATED FOAM

Vitec, Oldham Road, Middleton, Manchester, M24 2DB Tel: 0161-653 8231 Fax: 0161-654 8942 E-mail: vitec@kay-metzeler.co.uk

TECHNICAL AUTHORS

▶ Codelog Logistic Support Solutions Ltd, Unit 22B, Progress Business Park, Orders Lane, Kirkham, PR4 2TZ Tel: (01772) 672080 E-mail: info@codelog.com

Communication Arts, Horsemans Hill Barn, Gore Lane, Uplyme, Lyme Regis, Dorset, DT7 3RJ Tel: (01297) 444707 Fax: (01297) 444934 E-mail: info@communicationarts.co.uk

▶ Continental Data Graphics Ltd, Gate House, Fretherne Road, Welwyn Garden City, Hertfordshire, AL8 6RD Tel: (01707) 392520 Fax: (01707) 371813 E-mail: sales@cdgl.com

▶ Harrison Technical Publications Ltd, Glen Garth, Ireleth Road, Askam-in-Furness, Cumbria, LA16 7DP Tel: (07813) 890408 E-mail: info@htpl.co.uk

TECHNICAL BUILDING INFORMATION PUBLICATIONS

Building Research Establishment Ltd, Bucknalls Lane, Garston, Watford, WD25 9XX Tel: (01923) 664000 Fax: (01923) 664010 E-mail: enquiries@bre.co.uk

TECHNICAL CERAMIC FURNACES

Dytech Corporation Ltd, Stubley Lane, Dronfield, Derbyshire, S18 1LS Tel: (01246) 299700 Fax: (01246) 299720 E-mail: sales@hi-por.com

Kilnstruct, Walley St, Stoke-on-Trent, ST6 2AH Tel: (01782) 833383 Fax: (01782) 833411

TECHNICAL CERAMIC KILNS

Dytech Corporation Ltd, Stubley Lane, Dronfield, Derbyshire, S18 1LS Tel: (01246) 299700 Fax: (01246) 299720 E-mail: sales@hi-por.com

TECHNICAL COMPUTER SUPPORT SERVICES

▶ 1TeK Computer Services, Tor Close, Purbrook, Waterlooville, Hampshire, PO7 8SU Tel: (07963) 873799 Fax: (07092) 034359 E-mail: seocontact@1tek.net

▶ Ade Sims, 23 Heathfield, Chippenham, Wiltshire, SN15 1BQ Tel: 01249 461295 E-mail: adesims@supanet.com

▶ Advantech Ltd, 5 Clarence Road, Grays, Essex, RM17 6QA Tel: (01375) 392822 Fax: (01375) 392399 E-mail: enquiries@advantechltd.co.uk

▶ Anything It, 14 Mary Seacole Road, Plymouth, PL1 3JY Tel: (01752) 667771 Fax: (01752) 667771 E-mail: sales@anything-it.biz

▶ Arcam Consultancy Ltd, 24 Burghmuir Road, Perth, PH1 1LS Tel: (0845) 0550723 E-mail: rod@arcam-it.com

▶ BL1 : I.T. Specialists, 7 Trevarrick Court, Horwich, Bolton, BL6 6TF Tel: (07005) 968828 E-mail: bl1@hotmail.co.uk

▶ Broadnet Systems & Solutions, 1st Floor, 148 High Street, Berkhamsted, Hertfordshire, HP4 3AT Tel: (01442) 879090 Fax: (01442) 873210 E-mail: sales@broadnetsystems.com

▶ Cambit Support, 16 Chesterton Hall CR, Cambridge, CB4 1AP Tel: (01223) 576705 E-mail: sales@cambit.net

Computer Shack Ltd, 11 Church Street, Tewkesbury, Gloucestershire, GL20 5PA Tel: (01684) 275757 Fax: (01684) 275670

▶ computer-doctor.uk.com, 40 Graham Road, Worthing, West Sussex, BN11 1TL Tel: (01903) 868010 E-mail: surgery@computer-doctor.uk.com

Coxon E & J, 10 Park Road, Stonehouse, Gloucestershire, GL10 2DE Tel: (01453) 827100 Fax: (01453) 827100 E-mail: eric@ejcoxon.co.uk

Davian Systems, c/o The Punch Hotel, 25, Chapels, Darwen, Lancashire, BB3 OEE Tel: 07792 287416 E-mail: info@daviansystems.co.uk

▶ Doctor Software, Suite 3, Stanta Business Centre, 3 Soothouse Spring, St. Albans, Hertfordshire, AL3 6PF Tel: (01727) 869806 Fax: (0871) 4742864 E-mail: chris.beere@doctorsoftware.co.uk

▶ Dove Computer Solutions, Oak Cottage, Dove Street, Ellastone, Ashbourne, Derbyshire, DE6 2GY Tel: (0845) 2260522 Fax: (01335) 324317 E-mail: info@dovecomputers.com

▶ E-Logic Computer Services Ltd, 15 Wades Croft Freckleton, Preston, PR4 1SU Tel: (01772) 634446 Fax: (0870) 4869123 E-mail: mark.cooper@e-logic.co.uk

▶ Esynco Computer Services, 109 Park Court, London, SW11 4LE Tel: (0845) 6652897 E-mail: pcproblems@esynco.co.uk

▶ Fixit Systems Support, The Diary House Roxby Place, Rickett Street, London, SW6 1RU Tel: (0845) 1303595 Fax: (0870) 1374300 E-mail: sales@fixit.co.uk

▶ Hardy Technical Services Ltd, 69 Lake Drive, Hainworthy, Poole, Poole, Dorset, BH15 4LR Tel: (01202) 674916 Fax: (0871) 2420922 E-mail: info@hardytechnicalservices.co.uk

Ilkley It Services Ltd, Nat West Bank Chambers The, Grove Ilkley, Ilkley, West Yorkshire, LS29 9LS Tel: (01943) 601601 E-mail: info@ilkleyitservices.co.uk

▶ Imitza Systems, 26 High Street, Spennymoor, County Durham, DL16 6DB Tel: (01388) 818844 E-mail: info@imitza.co.uk

▶ Inform I T, 55 Beauchamp Place, London, SW3 1NY Tel: (020) 7350 0191 Fax: (07050) 616471 E-mail: info@inform-it.com

▶ iSolve IT Ltd, Haldo House, Western Way, Bury St. Edmunds, Suffolk, IP33 3SP Tel: (0808) 2000911 Fax: (020) 7681 2933 E-mail: info@isolveit.co.uk

▶ Isys Computer Services Ltd, 4 Charlotte Street, Dumbarton, G82 4JB Tel: (0845) 1434040 Fax: (0845) 1434039 E-mail: info@isys-computers.co.uk

IT Support Tech, 2 Wells Road, Upper Knowle, Bristol, BS4 2AX Tel: 07787 569913 E-mail: simonlovell_99@yahoo.com

▶ ITC Service Ltd, 45 Wedderlaw, Cramlington, Northumberland, NE23 6PA Tel: (07919) 154375 Fax: 0191-416 3003 E-mail: info@itcservive.co.uk

▶ Logicomm 2000 Ltd, 174 Watling Street, Bridgtown, Cannock, Staffordshire, WS11 0BD Tel: (0845) 2255816 Fax: (0845) 2255817 E-mail: sales@logicomm-2000.com

▶ M A Networks Ltd, 171 Warley Hill, Great Warley, Brentwood, Essex, CM13 3AG Tel: 07802 481688 Fax: 0870 706 2516 E-mail: info@manetworks.co.uk

Mcneill Associates Ltd, 14 Well Hall Parade, London, SE9 6SP Tel: (020) 8294 1565 Fax: (020) 8859 4562 E-mail: post@mcneill.co.uk

▶ N F M Solutions Ltd, 7 Standrigg Gardens, Brightons, Falkirk, FK2 0GJ Tel: (0870) 7776698 Fax: (0870) 7776398 E-mail: info@nfmsolutions.com

▶ Northern I T Consultancy, 5 Rishton Lane, Bolton, BL3 6QZ Tel: (0870) 7517444 Fax: 01204 456671 E-mail: Info@nitc.co.uk

▶ On-It Ltd, 32 Demesne Road, Wallington, Surrey, SM6 8PP Tel: (020) 8773 9900

▶ Ooh It, 49 Westcroft Gardens, Morden, Surrey, SM4 4DJ Tel: (020) 8543 6769 Fax: (0870) 705 8270 E-mail: Info@oohit.com

▶ PC Response, 3 Heathlands Court, Wokingham, Berkshire, RG40 3AY Tel: 01344 761880 E-mail: help@pcresponse.net

Premier Networks UK, Garsett House, St. Andrews Hall Plain, Norwich, NR3 1AU Tel: (01603) 305659 E-mail: info@premiernetworks.co.uk

▶ RedKite IT Solutions Ltd, 127 Stonegate, Hunmanby, Filey, North Yorkshire, YO14 0PU Tel: (01723) 890890 Fax: (07812) 356040 E-mail: enquiries@redkiteit.com

Regenersis Ltd, 1 James Wort Avenue, Westwood Park, Glenrothes, Fife, KY7 4UA Tel: (01592) 774704 Fax: (01592) 774150 E-mail: margaret.lessels@crc-group.com

▶ RGB Solutions Ltd, Bonnington Mill, 72 Newhaven Road, Edinburgh, EH6 5QG Tel: 0131-554 8888 Fax: 0131-555 1032 E-mail: info@rgbsolutions.co.uk

▶ Seca PCS Ltd, Unit E 7 Craigend Place, Anniesland, Glasgow, G13 2UN Tel: 0141-959 1440 E-mail: info@secapcs.co.uk

▶ SGP Computing Ltd, 1 Hinckley Road, Earl Shilton, Leicester, LE9 7LG Tel: (01455) 449372 Fax: (01455) 449372 E-mail: enquiries@sgpcomputing.com

Sidneyplus International Library System, Rodney House, Castle Gate, Nottingham, NG1 7AW Tel: 0115-955 5936 Fax: 0115-955 5937 E-mail: sales@sydneyplus.com

▶ Surrey Technology Management, Sandy Farm Business Centre, Sands Road, The Sands, Farnham, Surrey, GU10 1PX Tel: 08458 904040 E-mail: info@surreytm.com

▶ Tekksupport, 5 Kinghorn Court, Golspie, Sutherland, KW10 6SJ Tel: (01408) 633695 E-mail: info@tekksupport.co.uk

▶ Westside I T Solutions, 125 Murray Road, Sheffield, S11 7GH Tel: (07745) 121208 E-mail: rob@westside-it.net

▶ YMA Associates Ltd, 22 Chelmarsh Close, Redditch, Worcestershire, B98 8SQ Tel: (01527) 585090 Fax: (0870) 0521898 E-mail: ksenquiries@yma-associates.com

TECHNICAL DESIGNERS

C B Construction, 96 North Ormesby Road, Middlesbrough, Cleveland, TS4 2AG Tel: (01642) 231928 Fax: (01642) 211949 E-mail: keith@cbcon-cleveland.co.uk

▶ D S M Geodata Ltd, 3 Hope Street, Bo'Ness, West Lothian, EH51 0AA Tel: (01506) 518000 Fax: (01506) 517777 E-mail: info@dsmgeodata.com

Southampton Industrial Draughting Ltd, 33A Salisbury Road, Totton, Southampton, SO40 3HX Tel: (023) 8086 1651 Fax: (023) 8086 1651

TECHNICAL DOCUMENTATION SERVICES

Dats (Holdings) Ltd, 1 Springfield Street, Palmyra Square, Warrington, WA1 1BB Tel: (01925) 428559 Fax: (01925) 403801 E-mail: dats@dats.co.uk

Diafade Ltd, 4 Norfolk Road, Buntingford, Hertfordshire, SG9 9AN Tel: (01763) 273379 E-mail: mailroom@diafade.co.uk

Furness Engineering & Technology, Ellers Mill, The Ellers, Ulverston, Cumbria, LA12 0AQ Tel: (01229) 584043 Fax: (01229) 586440 E-mail: mail@fetl.co.uk

▶ Harrison Technical Publications Ltd, Glen Garth, Ireleth Road, Askam-in-Furness, Cumbria, LA16 7DP Tel: (07813) 890408 E-mail: info@htpl.co.uk

▶ Polygraphic Ltd, Raebarn House, Hulbert Road, Waterlooville, Hampshire, PO7 7JT Tel: (023) 9223 1888 Fax: (023) 9223 1999 E-mail: sales@inteqniq.com

Red House Consultancy, 10 Badger Lane, Blackshaw Head, Hebden Bridge, West Yorkshire, HX7 7JX Tel: (01422) 846846 Fax: (01422) 846846 E-mail: simon@red-house-consultancy.co.uk

▶ Serco Medway Ltd, Victory House, Meeting House Lane, Chatham, Kent, ME4 4YU Tel: (01322) 303118 Fax: (01634) 835537 E-mail: paul@uk.serco-ai.com

Stats NNC Ltd, South House, 2 Bond Avenue, Bletchley, Milton Keynes, MK1 1SW Tel: (01908) 271660 Fax: (01908) 271332 E-mail: diane.quick@stats-nnc.co.uk

TECHNICAL FELT

W E Rawson Ltd, Castlebank Mills, Portobello Road, Wakefield, West Yorkshire, WF1 5PS Tel: (01924) 373421 Fax: (01924) 290334

TECHNICAL GLASSWARE, *See Scientific Glassware etc; also other headings for particular types*

TECHNICAL ILLUSTRATION SERVICES

▶ Mdi-Digital, 130 Mansfield Lane, Norwich, NR1 2LT Tel: (01603) 632005 Fax: (01603) 632005 E-mail: info@mdi-digital.com

Trilobyte Design Ltd, Mersa House, Haroldslea Drive, Horley, Surrey, RH6 9DT Tel: (01293) 774747 E-mail: info@trilobytedesigns.co.uk

TECHNICAL INFORMATION SERVICES

Electrostatic Solutions Ltd, 13 Redhill Crescent, Southampton, SO16 7BQ Tel: (023) 8090 5600 E-mail: jeremys@static-sol.com

Intermediate Technology Development Group, Bourton Hall, Bourton On Dunsmore, Rugby, Warwickshire, CV23 9QZ Tel: (01926) 634400 Fax: (01926) 634401 E-mail: info@practicalaction.org.uk

Technologies Group Ltd, Hampstead Avenue, Mildenhall, Bury St. Edmunds, Suffolk, IP28 7AS Tel: (01638) 713631 Fax: (01638) 712271 E-mail: sales@tech-group.co.uk

TECHNICAL LABORATORY EQUIPMENT

A & D Instruments Ltd, 24-26 Blacklands Way, Abingdon, Oxfordshire, OX14 1DY Tel: (01235) 550420 Fax: (01235) 550485 E-mail: sales@aandd-eu.net

Cole Parmer Instrument Company Ltd, 3 River Brent Business Park, Trumpers Way, London, W7 2QA Tel: (020) 8574 7556 Fax: (020) 8574 7543 E-mail: sales@coleparmer.co.uk

Elemental Microanalysis Ltd, Okehampton Business Park, Okehampton, Devon, EX20 1UB Tel: (01837) 54446 Fax: (01837) 54544 E-mail: info@microanalysis.co.uk

Genevac Ltd, 6 Farthing Road, Ipswich, IP1 5AP Tel: (01473) 240000 Fax: (01473) 461176 E-mail: sales@genevac.co.uk

Jencons (Scientific) Ltd, Cherrycourt Way Industrial Estate, Stanbridge Road, Leighton Buzzard, Bedfordshire, LU7 4UA Tel: (01525) 372010 Fax: (01525) 379547 E-mail: export@jencons.co.uk

L T E Scientific Ltd, Greenbridge Lane, Greenfield, Oldham, OL3 7EN Tel: (01457) 876221 Fax: (01457) 870131 E-mail: info@lte-scientific.co.uk

Medical Wire & Equipment Co Bath Ltd, Unit 29 Leafield Industrial Estate, Leafield Way, Corsham, Wiltshire, SN13 9RT Tel: (01225) 810361 Fax: (01225) 810153 E-mail: sales@mwe.co.uk

Medicell International Ltd, 239 Liverpool Road, London, N1 1LX Tel: (020) 7607 2295 Fax: (020) 7700 4156 E-mail: all@medicell.co.uk

Mickle Laboratory Engineering Co. Ltd, Goose Green, Gomshall, Guildford, Surrey, GU5 9LJ Tel: (01483) 202178 Fax: (01483) 202178 E-mail: anthony@micklelab.freeserve.co.uk

Porvair Sciences Ltd, 6 Shepperton Business Park, Govett Avenue, Shepperton, Middlesex, TW17 8BA Tel: (01932) 224539 Fax: (01932) 254393 E-mail: int.sales@porvair.com

R.B. Radley & Co. Ltd, Shirehill, Saffron Walden, Essex, CB11 3AZ Tel: (01799) 513320 Fax: (01799) 513283 E-mail: sales@radleys.co.uk

Scilabub Ltd, Unit 9 Huntingdon Court, Huntingdon Way, Measham, Swadlincote, Derbyshire, DE12 7NQ Tel: (01530) 279996 Fax: (01530) 270759 E-mail: sales@scilabub.com

Seward Ltd, The Technology Centre, Eastling Close, Worthing, West Sussex, BN14 8HQ Tel: (01903) 524616 Fax: (01903) 524603 E-mail: info@seward.co.uk

Thermo Electron Ltd, 5 Ringway Centre, Edison Road, Basingstoke, Hampshire, RG21 6YH Tel: (01256) 817282 Fax: (01256) 817292 E-mail: info@thermols.com

Zinsser Analytic (UK) Ltd, Howarth Road, Stafferton Way, Maidenhead, Berkshire, SL6 1AP Tel: (01628) 773202 Fax: (01628) 672199 E-mail: officeuk@zinsser-analytic.com

TECHNICAL OR INDUSTRIAL TRAINING

▶ Achor Limited, 82 Northgate, Beccles, Suffolk, NR34 9AY Tel: (01502) 716870 Fax: (01502) 716587 E-mail: info@achor.co.uk

▶ D C W Training Services, 63 Barnwell Street, Kettering, Northamptonshire, NN16 0JD Tel: (07947) 641457 Fax: (01536) 392137 E-mail: sedcwe17@ntlworld.com

Delta Press Ltd, Cameron House, North Bridge Road, Berkhamsted, Hertfordshire, HP4 1EH Tel: (01442) 877794 Fax: (01442) 877828 E-mail: deltap98@aol.com

▶ Feenix E-Learning Ltd, 67 Vancouver Quay, Salford, M50 3TU Tel: 0161-872 5277 Fax: (07092) 115000 E-mail: info2@feenix.co.uk

Fortec T A Ltd, 5 Upminster Trading Park, Warley Street, Upminster, Essex, RM14 3PJ Tel: (01708) 224713 Fax: (01708) 641029 E-mail: kp@fortectraining.co.uk

Gaddon Consulants, 18 New Royd, Millhouse Green, Sheffield, S36 9NW Tel: (01226) 766999 E-mail: sales@gaddon.co.uk

Maxim Training Knowledgepool, 42 Bond Street, Brighton, BN1 1RD Tel: (01273) 827751 Fax: (01273) 738829 E-mail: tracy.capaldi-drewett@knowledgepool.com

▶ Rescue From Technology, 17 Linley Court, Thicket Road, Sutton, Surrey, SM1 4QA Tel: 0870 3831519 Fax: 07092 309964 E-mail: enquiries@rescuefrom.com

Rgit Montrose Ltd, Blackness Avenue, Altens Industrial Estate, Aberdeen, AB12 3PG Tel: (01224) 899707 Fax: (01224) 873221 E-mail: aberdeen@rgitmontrose.co.uk

Technique Training, Midland Court, Barlborough Links, Chesterfield, Derbyshire, S43 4UL Tel: (01246) 813703 Fax: (01246) 571090 E-mail: mark@techniquetraining.co.uk

▶ Teckchek Europe Ltd, 1a Church Road, Croydon, CR0 1SG Tel: (020) 8401 1188 Fax: (020) 8401 0808 E-mail: dbeer@ikmnet.com

Teesside Training Enterprise Ltd, Middlesbrough Road East, South Bank, Middlesbrough, Cleveland, TS6 6TZ Tel: (01642) 462266 Fax: (01642) 460873 E-mail: info@tte.co.uk

Thales Training & Simulation, Gatwick Road, Crawley, West Sussex, RH10 9RL Tel: (01293) 562822 Fax: (01293) 563366

TECHNICAL PUBLICATIONS

Arena Books, 6 Southgate Green, Bury St. Edmunds, Suffolk, IP33 2BL Tel: (01284) 754123 Fax: (01284) 754123 E-mail: arenabooks@tiscali.co.uk

Delta Press Ltd, Cameron House, North Bridge Road, Berkhamsted, Hertfordshire, HP4 1EH Tel: (01442) 877794 Fax: (01442) 877828 E-mail: deltap98@aol.com

Harquejas Publications Ltd, 2 Shenley Close, Leighton Buzzard, Bedfordshire, LU7 3DG Tel: (01525) 852370 E-mail: sales@harquejas.co.uk

Incisive Media, 32 & 34 Broadwick Street, London, W1A 2HG Tel: (020) 7316 9000 Fax: (020) 7316 9003

Intelligent Business Strategies Ltd, Springfield House, Water Lane, Wilmslow, Cheshire, SK9 5BG Tel: (01625) 520700 Fax: (01625) 520700

Jabb Technical Graphics, 17 Crown Lane, Thurlby, Bourne, Lincolnshire, PE10 0EZ Tel: (01778) 421412 Fax: (01778) 421412 E-mail: andybaker@jtechg.fsnet.co.uk

Lion Bridge, Copthall Terrace, Coventry, CV1 2FP Tel: (024) 7622 2844 Fax: (024) 7625 8892

The Morrisby Organisation Ltd, Focus 31 North, Cleveland Road, Hemel Hempstead, Hertfordshire, HP2 7EY Tel: (01442) 215521 Fax: (01442) 240531 E-mail: info@morrisby.co.uk

Wit Press, Ashurst Lodge, Lyndhurst Road, Ashurst, Southampton, SO40 7AA Tel: (023) 8029 3223 Fax: (023) 8029 2853 E-mail: witpress@witpress.com

TECHNICAL PUBLISHERS, SERVICES TO

Intras Ltd, Perseus House, Chapel Court Holly Walk, Leamington Spa, Warwickshire, CV32 4YS Tel: (01926) 334137 Fax: (01926) 314755 E-mail: intras@intras.co.uk

Omega Scientific, Fynamore, Reading Road, Wallingford, Oxfordshire, OX10 9DT Tel: (01491) 837736 Fax: (01491) 825454

Roles & Associates Ltd, 3 Pucks Corner, Lower Hampton Road, Sunbury-on-Thames, Middlesex, TW16 5PR Tel: (020) 8783 0777 Fax: (020) 8783 0088 E-mail: roles@easynet.co.uk

Allan H. Webb & Co. Ltd, Colne Lodge, Longbridge Way, Uxbridge, Middlesex, UB8 2YG Tel: (01895) 239387 Fax: (01895) 234429 E-mail: enquiries@ahw-ux.co.uk

Whittles Publishing Services, Roseleigh House, Latheronwheel, Latheron, Caithness, KW5 6DW Tel: (01593) 741240 Fax: (01593) 741360 E-mail: info@whittlespublishing.com

Wit Press, Ashurst Lodge, Lyndhurst Road, Ashurst, Southampton, SO40 7AA Tel: (023) 8029 3223 Fax: (023) 8029 2853 E-mail: witpress@witpress.com

TECHNICAL SALES RECRUITMENT CONSULTANCY

Garrett Lloyd Ltd, Unit 39-40 Derwent Business Centre, Clarke Street, Derby, DE1 2BU Tel: (01332) 206219 Fax: (01332) 206225 E-mail: recruitment@garrett-lloyd.com

▶ Pareto Law plc, Barfield House, 24-28 Alderley Road, Wilmslow, Cheshire, SK9 1PL Tel: (01625) 255255 Fax: (01625) 255256 E-mail: graduate@paretolaw.co.uk

TECHNICAL SERVICES TO THOSE ENGAGED IN PUBLIC RELATIONS

Institute Of Public Relations, 32 St James's Square, London, SW1Y 4JR Tel: (020) 7766 3333 Fax: (020) 7766 3344 E-mail: info@cipr.co.uk

TECHNICAL STAFF/PERSONNEL RECRUITMENT AGENCIES/ CONSULTANTS/SERVICES

Allied Technical Services Ltd, Aberdeen Studios, 22-24 Highbury Grove, London, N5 2EA Tel: (020) 7226 2220 Fax: (020) 7226 0297

Altus Recruitment Services Ltd, Moseley, Birmingham, B13 9ZQ Tel: 0121-442 4030 Fax: 0121-442 4030

Anders Elite Ltd, Capital House, Houndwell Place, Southampton, SO14 1HU Tel: (023) 8022 3511 Fax: (023) 8022 7911 E-mail: contactus@anderselite.com

Anglo European Workforce Ltd, 51 Waterloo Road, Wolverhampton, WV1 4QJ Tel: (01902) 426767 Fax: (01902) 421895 E-mail: contact@angloew.com

Applied Executive Selection Ltd, Shales House, 17-19 Mealcheapen St, Worcester, WR1 2DQ Tel: (01905) 23444 Fax: (01905) 23393 E-mail: info@aesco.co.uk

Aquatic Engineering & Construction Ltd, Palmerston Centre, 29-31 Palmerston Road, Aberdeen, AB11 5QP Tel: (01224) 573359 Fax: (01224) 577361 E-mail: admin@aquatic.co.uk

Aspectus Global Resource Solutions Ltd, Suite 353, 405 Kings Road, London, SW10 0BB Tel: (07002) 773288 Fax: (020) 8549 8592 E-mail: bmadmin@aspectusltd.co.uk

Atlan Ltd, Six Acre House, 17 Town Square, Sale, Cheshire, M33 7WZ Tel: 0161-282 1770 Fax: 0161-962 0316 E-mail: cbsnorth@atlanrecruitment.com

Avon Construction, 850 Wimborne Road, Bournemouth, BH9 2DS Tel: (01202) 523006

B C P Search & Selection Ltd, Unit 9b Intec 2, Wade Road, Basingstoke, Hampshire, RG24 8NE Tel: (01256) 470704 Fax: (01256) 844054 E-mail: mail@bcprecruitment.co.uk

Bulldog Engineering Recruitment & Management, 223a-225 South Coast Road, Peacehaven, East Sussex, BN10 8LB Tel: (01273) 580580 E-mail: recruitment@bulldog.co.uk

C P L Scientific Information Services Ltd, Nosworthy Way, Mongewell, Wallingford, Oxfordshire, OX10 8DE Tel: (01491) 829346 Fax: (01491) 836232 E-mail: sis@cplsis.com

C V Screen, 12 Octagon Court, High Wycombe, Buckinghamshire, HP11 2HS Tel: (01494) 769191 Fax: (01494) 447621 E-mail: matt@cvscreen.co.uk

Capital Engineering Personnel Ltd, Broadway House, 112-134 The Broadway, London, SW19 1RL Tel: (020) 8605 2800 Fax: (028) 8946 3899 E-mail: admin@cap-recruit.co.uk

Capital Group of Companies Ltd, Broadway House, 112-134 The Broadway, London, SW19 1RL Tel: (020) 8542 8131 Fax: (020) 8540 7385 E-mail: admin@cap-recruit.co.uk

Cappo International Ltd, Global House, 38-40 High Street, West Wickham, Kent, BR4 0NJ Tel: (020) 8776 1850 Fax: (020) 8777 9952 E-mail: info@cappo.co.uk

CBS Butler, Kings Mill, Kings Mill Lane, South Nutfield, Redhill, RH1 5NB Tel: (01737) 822000 Fax: (01737) 823031 E-mail: admin@uk.butler.com

Cliveden House, Taplow, Maidenhead, Berkshire, SL6 0JF Tel: (01628) 668561 Fax: (01628) 661837 E-mail: reservations@clivedenhouse.co.uk

Comms Resources, 1 Sherman Road, Bromley, BR1 3JH Tel: (020) 8663 1999 Fax: (020) 8313 6601 E-mail: mail@commsresources.com

Contact Technical Services, Jarodale House, 7 Gregory Boulevard, Nottingham, NG7 6LB Tel: 0115-911 9230 Fax: 0115-911 9231 E-mail: admin@makecontact.co.uk

Crownmain Ltd, 19 Buxton Avenue, Gorleston, Great Yarmouth, Norfolk, NR31 6HG Tel: (01493) 663639 Fax: (01493) 669622 E-mail: crownmain@aol.com

CSE Aviation, Langford Lane, Oxford Airport, Kidlington, Oxfordshire, OX5 1RA Tel: (01865) 844200 Fax: (01865) 840628 E-mail: jdg@cse-aviation.com

Dats (Holdings) Ltd, 1 Springfield Street, Palmyra Square, Warrington, WA1 1BB Tel: (01925) 428559 Fax: (01925) 403801 E-mail: dats@dats.co.uk

Design Services NW Ltd, 42 Long Street, Middleton, Manchester, M24 6UQ Tel: 0161-643 0088 Fax: 0161-643 6254 E-mail: info@designservicesltd.co.uk

Elan I T Computing, St Johns House, Barrington Road, Altrincham, Cheshire, WA14 1JY Tel: 0161-924 3900 Fax: 0161-924 3901 E-mail: info.alt@elanit.co.uk

Em-Jay Appointments, 17 Manor Road, Reigate, Surrey, RH2 9LA Tel: (01737) 224411 Fax: (01737) 224410 E-mail: recruitment@tinyonline.co.uk

Executive Facilities Ltd, 43 High Street, Marlow, Buckinghamshire, SL7 1BA Tel: (01628) 898556 Fax: (01628) 898139 E-mail: eft@efrecruitment.co.uk

Faststream Recruitment Ltd, Medina Chambers, Town Quay, Southampton, SO14 2AQ Tel: (023) 8033 4444 Fax: (023) 8033 5555 E-mail: ben@faststream.co.uk

▶ Format Recruitment, 44 Rutland Road, Hove, East Sussex, BN3 5FF Tel: (01273) 772200 Fax: (01273) 748735 E-mail: nadina@formatrecruitment.com

Institution of Fire Engineers, 148 Upper New Walk, Leicester, LE1 7QB Tel: 0116-255 3654 Fax: 0116-247 1231 E-mail: info@ife.org.uk

J L Communications Ltd, Ferry Lane, Pembroke, Dyfed, SA71 4RE Tel: (01646) 683123 Fax: (01646) 621111

Jobsearch Employment Agency, 25 Bridge Street, Burnley, Lancashire, BB11 1AD Tel: (01282) 412212 Fax: (01282) 412212 E-mail: sales@jobsearch-employment.co.uk

L A International, International House, Festival Way, Stoke-on-Trent, ST1 5UB Tel: (01782) 203000 Fax: (01782) 203050 E-mail: mail@lainternational.co.uk

Listgrove Ltd, 16 The Courtyard, Timothys Bridge Road, Stratford-upon-Avon, Warwickshire, CV37 9NP Tel: (01789) 207070 Fax: (01789) 207096 E-mail: contact@listgrove.co.uk

Matchtech Group plc, 1450 Parkway, Solent Business Park, Fareham, Hampshire, PO15 7AF Tel: (01489) 898150 E-mail: jdean@Matchtech.com

MB Careers Ltd, 8 High Street, Berkhamsted, Herts, HP4 2BL Tel: 0845 2263478 E-mail: info@mb-careers.co.uk

MDS Consultants, Tribune Avenue, Broadheath, Altrincham, Cheshire, WA14 5RX Tel: 0161-927 7744 Fax: 0161-927 7612

▶ NDF Associates, Chadwick House, Back Grange Avenue, Harrogate, North Yorkshire, HG1 2AN Tel: (01423) 529333 Fax: (01423) 529555E-mail: enquiries@ndfassociates.co.uk

Orion, 11b Baird House, Newark Road South, Glenrothes, Fife, KY7 4NS Tel: (01592) 775050 Fax: (01592) 772515 E-mail: fife@orioneng.com

Orion Technical Services Ltd, Springfield Street, Warrington, WA1 1BB Tel: (01925) 242020 Fax: (01925) 242040 E-mail: ots@orioneng.com

Park, 11 South Street, Havant, Hampshire, PO9 1BU Tel: (023) 9248 8500 Fax: (023) 9248 8501 E-mail: havent@parc-group.com

Plan Personnel, Stonemead House, 95 London Road, Croydon, CR0 2RF Tel: (020) 8681 0846 Fax: (020) 8253 5993 E-mail: speto@planpersonnel.co.uk

Polytec Personnel Ltd, Orwell House, Cowley Road, Cambridge, CB4 0PP Tel: (01223) 423267 Fax: (01223) 420268 E-mail: recruit@ppluk.net

Poole Computers Ltd, 865 Ringwood Road, Bournemouth, BH11 8LL Tel: (01202) 591548 Fax: (01202) 590944 E-mail: pcl@lds.co.uk

Premmit Associates Ltd, 33 Eccleston Square, London, SW1V 1PB Tel: (020) 7834 7253 Fax: (020) 7834 3544 E-mail: info@premmit.com

Prime Recruitment Ltd, 37 Locks Heath Centre, Centre Way, Locks Heath, Southampton, SO31 6DX Tel: (01489) 559090 Fax: (01489) 559995 E-mail: enquiries@prime-recruitment.co.uk

Pro Services Audio, 7 Pumbro, Stonesfield, Witney, Oxfordshire, OX29 8QF Tel: (01993) 891765 Fax: (01993) 891009 E-mail: psa@ggilbaud.deman.co.uk

▶ Proactive Recruitment Solutions Ltd, Jewellery Business Centre, 95 Spencer Street, Birmingham, B18 6DA Tel: 0121-523 1006 Fax: 0121-523 1016 E-mail: enquiries@proactiverecruitment.co.uk

Probe Technical Recruitment, 6 Emmanuel Court, Sutton Coldfield, West Midlands, B72 1TJ Tel: 0121-321 4311 Fax: 0121-321 4312 E-mail: recruitment@probe-uk.com

Project People Ltd, Whitefriars, Lewins Mead, Bristol, BS1 2NT Tel: 0117-908 7000 Fax: 0117-925 4676 E-mail: sales@handsets.com

R D Piper Recruitment, 1 Riverside House, Lower Southend Road, Wickford, Essex, SS11 8BB Tel: (01268) 561020 Fax: (01268) 571483 E-mail: enquiries@rdpiper.co.uk

Resource Group, 105 West George Street, Glasgow, G2 1PE Tel: 0141-226 1220 Fax: 0141-248 6782 E-mail: sales@trgrecruitment.net

Road Recruitment, Trioka House 2, East Union Street, Rugby, Warwickshire, CV22 6AJ Tel: (01788) 572841 Fax: (01788) 578609 E-mail: sales@rdrecruit.com

Roevin Management Services Ltd, 40-44 Rothesay Road, Luton, LU1 1QZ Tel: (01582) 727216 Fax: (01582) 732188 E-mail: luton@roevin.co.uk

Rosta Engineering Ltd, Resource House, 144 Castle Street, Stockport, Cheshire, SK3 9JH Tel: 0161-429 5300 Fax: 0161-429 5322 E-mail: mail@rosta.com

Rullion Engineering Personnel Ltd, PO Box 124, Altrincham, Cheshire, WA14 4RJ Tel: 0161-926 1717 Fax: 0161-926 1727 E-mail: engineering@rullion.co.uk

Seltek Consultants, 25a Hockerill Street, Bishop's Stortford, Hertfordshire, CM23 2DH Tel: (01279) 657716 Fax: (01279) 651119 E-mail: sales@seltekconsultants.co.uk

Source Logistics Ltd, 75 Bothwell Street, Glasgow, G2 6TS Tel: 0141-572 2100 Fax: 0141-572 2101 E-mail: mail@sourceuk.com

T.E.D. (Recruitment) Ltd, 2nd Floor, 277-279 Bethnal Green Road, London, E2 6AH Tel: (020) 7613 5555 Fax: (020) 7613 1191 E-mail: info@tedrecruitment.com

Technical Network Ltd, 81-82 Darlington Street, Wolverhampton, WV1 4JD Tel: (01902) 311313 Fax: (01902) 427235 E-mail: sales@netrec.co.uk

Towers Recruitment Services, Chiltern Chambers, St Peters Avenue, Caversham, Reading, RG4 7DH Tel: 0118-946 1200 Fax: 0118-946 3318 E-mail: jobs@towers.co.uk

▶ Unix Recruitment Ltd, Brightside Business Centre, 60 Lonnen Road, Wimborne, Dorset, BH21 7AX Tel: (01202) 888021 E-mail: richard@unixrecruitment.co.uk

TECHNICAL TAPES

Boston Tapes UK Ltd, Unit 12 Block 2, Wednesbury Trading Estate, Wednesbury, West Midlands, WS10 7JN Tel: 0121-556 9900 Fax: 0121-556 9034 E-mail: avantitapes@yahoo.co.uk

Fillmore Packaging Ltd, Unit 15, Bowthorpe Industrial Estate, Norwich, NR5 9JE Tel: (01603) 745911 Fax: (01603) 747519 E-mail: sales.norwich@fillmorepackaging.co.uk

Heskins Tapes, Churchill Road, Brinscall, Chorley, Lancashire, PR6 8RQ Tel: (01254) 832266 Fax: (01254) 832476 E-mail: mail@heskins.com

TECHNICAL TRANSLATION SERVICES

▶ Aplomb Ltd, 74 Chancery Lane, London, WC2A 1AD Tel: (020) 7831 9444 Fax: (020) 7831 9445 E-mail: admin@aplombonline.com

▶ China Interface, 39 Middlepark Drive, Northfield, Birmingham, B31 2FL Tel: 0121-476 0845 Fax: (0845) 2803140 E-mail: info@china-interface.co.uk

▶ Itt Ltd, 2b Bath Court, Bath Row, Birmingham, B15 1NE Tel: 0121-248 1632 Fax: 0121-248 1633 E-mail: richard.ashton@i-t-t.com

▶ Kerry Services Ltd, 6 The Walks East, Huntingdon, Cambridgeshire, PE29 3AP Tel: (01480) 391504 Fax: (01480) 386467 E-mail: info@kerrytrans.com

▶ LingoTec Translations, 4 Edith Cottages, Hansford Lane, St. Helier, Jersey, JE2 3JL Tel: 01534 498604E-mail: info@lingotec.co.uk

▶ Wolfestone Translation, Metropole Chambers, Salubrious Passage, Swansea, SA1 3RT Tel: (0845) 0000083 Fax: 0845 000 0083 E-mail: sales@wolfestone.co.uk

TECHNICAL WRITERS OR AGENCIES

Authordocs Ltd, 60 Purton Road, Swindon, SN2 2LZ Tel: (0845) 0940387 Fax: (01793) 539640 E-mail: info@authordocs.co.uk

▶ Brunswick Instrumentation Ltd, Maritime House, Basin Road North, Portslade, Brighton, BN41 1WR Tel: (01273) 704949 Fax: (01273) 248900 E-mail: info@brun-inst.co.uk

Harquejas Publications Ltd, 2 Shenley Close, Leighton Buzzard, Bedfordshire, LU7 3DG Tel: (01525) 852370 E-mail: sales@harquejas.co.uk

Leythorne Ltd, Hawthorns Business Centre, Halfords Lane, Smethwick, West Midlands, B66 1BB Tel: 0121-558 1181 Fax: 0121-555 4913 E-mail: sales@leythorne.co.uk

Red House Consultancy, 10 Badger Lane, Blackshaw Head, Hebden Bridge, West Yorkshire, HX7 7JX Tel: (01422) 846846 Fax: (01422) 846846 E-mail: simon@red-house-consultancy.co.uk

TECHNOLOGICAL KNOW HOW TRANSFER/LICENSING/ INFORMATION EXCHANGE

A.T.T.A.C. Aberdeen Technology Transfer & Consultancy, 26 Albert Terrace, Aberdeen, AB10 1XY Tel: (01224) 641953 Fax: (01224) 643651 E-mail: bill@aqa.co.uk

Fostech Ltd, 10 Carnreagh Road, Hillsborough, County Down, BT26 6LH Tel: (028) 9268 2652 Fax: (028) 9268 9091 E-mail: fostech@nireland.com

▶ Invest Northern Ireland, 44-58 May Street, Belfast, BT1 4NN Tel: (028) 9023 9090 Fax: (028) 9049 0490 E-mail: info@investni.com

Make It With Lasers, T W I, Granta Park, Great Abington, Cambridge, CB1 6AL Tel: (01223) 891162 Fax: (01223) 890661 E-mail: miwl@twi.co.uk

Tuv UK Quality Assurance Ltd, Surrey House, Surrey Street, Croydon, CR9 1XZ Tel: (020) 8686 3400 Fax: (020) 8680 4035 E-mail: london@tuv-uk.com

Umist Ventures Ltd, The Fairbairn Building, Manchester, M60 1QD Tel: 0161-200 3057 Fax: 0161-200 3052

TECHNOLOGY BASED EDUCATION SERVICES

▶ Lords College Ltd, 53 Manchester Road, Bolton, BL2 1ES Tel: (01204) 523731 Fax: (0870) 4299706 E-mail: principal@lordscollege.co.uk

▶ McIvor Tutorials, 6 Bushfield Mills, Feeny, Londonderry, BT47 4TL Tel: (0784) 3416283 Fax: E-mail: mcivortdr@yahoo.co.uk

TECHNOLOGY BASED PUBLIC RELATIONS

First Impression (Doncaster), PO Box 812, Doncaster, South Yorkshire, DN1 9AE Tel: 01302 874381 E-mail: contact@firstimpression.co.uk

▶ Impact Media, The Mm2 Building, 84 Pickford Street, Manchester, M4 5BT Tel: 0161-236 0008 Fax: 0161-236 0204 E-mail: info@impactmediapr.com

▶ P J M C Ltd, 4 Church End, Radford Semele, Leamington Spa, Warwickshire, CV31 1TA Tel: (01926) 312886 Fax: (01926) 435355 E-mail: info@pjmc.com

▶ Watch PR, 29 Gibbon Road, Kingston upon Thames, Surrey, KT2 6AD Tel: 020 8286 0654 E-mail: enquiries@watchpr.com

▶ Words Worth, Benfleet Water Tower, 335 Benfleet Road, Benfleet, Essex, SS7 1PW Tel: (01268) 756261 Fax: (01268) 750706

TECHNOLOGY PERSONNEL RECRUITMENT AGENCY

▶ Capita Social Housing Resourcing, Dean Bradley House, 52 Horseferry Road, London, SW1P 2AF Tel: (020) 7481 8383 Fax: (020) 7202 0045

D P Connect, Garrard House, 2-6 Homesdale Road, Bromley, BR2 9LZ Tel: (020) 8466 5666 Fax: (020) 8313 1716 E-mail: info@dpconnect.co.uk

G S A Tech Source Ltd, Cathedral House, 5 Beacon Street, Lichfield, Staffordshire, WS13 7AA Tel: (0845) 2267200 Fax: (0845) 2267210 E-mail: gsa@gsatechsource.com

▶ Just I T Training Ltd, The Dragon House, 37 Artillery Lane, London, E1 7LP Tel: (020) 7655 4600 E-mail: recruitment@justit.co.uk

Recruitment Initiative, St. Albans House, Portland Street, Leamington Spa, Warwickshire, CV32 5EZ Tel: (01926) 424111 Fax: (01926) 424142 E-mail: sales@therecruitmentinitiative.com

Skyblue, 23 Tavistock Street, London, WC2E 7NX Tel: (08701) 285430 Fax: (0870) 1285240 E-mail: ask@skybluesoloutions.com

▶ Unix Recruitment Ltd, Brightside Business Centre, 60 Lonnen Road, Wimborne, Dorset, BH21 7AX Tel: (01202) 888021 E-mail: richard@unixrecruitment.co.uk

TEDDY BEARS

▶ Bedford Bears Ltd, 21 Broom Hall, High Street, Broom, Biggleswade, Bedfordshire, SG18 9ND Tel: 01767 318626 Fax: 01767 631131 E-mail: ann@bedfordbears.wanadoo.co.uk

▶ GotchaSomething, 44 Penrhyn Road, Far Cotton, Northampton, NN4 8ED Tel: 0845 1565470 E-mail: general@gotchasomething.co.uk

▶ Heaven Sent, St Pauls Church, Darwall Street, Walsall, WS1 1DA Tel: (01922) 633073 E-mail: post@heaventsentgifts.uk.com

▶ Your Design, 84 New Court Way, Ormskirk, Lancashire, L39 2YT Tel: (01695) 574264 E-mail: contact@yourdesign.co.uk

TEE SHIRTS, PRINTED

▶ Europa Leisure Equipment, 1 Croft Way, Eastways, Witham, Essex, CM8 2FB Tel: (01376) 517717 Fax: (01376) 518018 E-mail: sales@europa-leisure.co.uk

▶ First Image, 54 Swinburne Avenue, Hitchin, Hertfordshire, SG5 2RA Tel: (01462) 457458 E-mail: firstimagesales@aol.com

▶ Fruit Of The Loom T-Shirt Printers, Unit 4C Dover House Industrial Estate, Witley, Godalming, Surrey, GU8 5QZ Tel: (01483) 860270 E-mail: sales@ucs-group.co.uk

▶ J L H Print & Promotions, Garth Works, Taffs Well, Cardiff, CF15 7YF Tel: (029) 2081 4195 Fax: (029) 2081 4195 E-mail: sales@jlhprintpromotions.co.uk

▶ J R H Enterprises, 33 Iveagh Close, Hackney, London, E9 7BW Tel: (020) 8525 0926 Fax: (020) 8525 0926 E-mail: sales@jrhenterprises.co.uk

▶ Magzs Group, 13 Woodhouse Grove, London, E12 6SR Tel: 0794 0549770 Fax: 0208 4716016 E-mail: sales@magzs.co.uk

▶ Manchester Print Co., 8 Lower Ormond Street, Manchester, M1 5QF Tel: 0161-228 0775 E-mail: msctshirt@yahoo.co.uk

▶ Mongrel Clothing -T-Shirts, PO Box 44, Newtown, Powys, SY16 1WD Tel: (07791) 081943E-mail: contact@mongrelclothing.co.uk

TEE SHIRTS, PRINTED – *continued*

▶ October Textiles Ltd, Unit C14 Hartley Workspace,, Hadyn Road, Sherwood,, Nottingham, NG5 1DG Tel: 0115-962 6636 Fax: 0115-962 6636 E-mail: fardad@october.co.uk
▶ P J Heaven, PO Box 164, Beverley, North Humberside, HU17 7AP Tel: (01482) 860777 Fax: (01482) 860777 E-mail: sales@pjheaven.co.uk
▶ Worlds Apart, Unit C Aldow Enterprise Park, Manchester, M12 6AE Tel: 0161-274 3737 Fax: 0161-274 3738 E-mail: sales@t-shirtprinter.com

TELECINE EQUIPMENT

Chitter Chatter Telecom Ltd, 92 North End, Croydon, CR0 1UJ Tel: (020) 8688 2616 Fax: (020) 8688 5523 E-mail: info@chitter-chatter.co.uk

TELECOMMUNICATION CABLES

Alcatel Submarine Networks Ltd, Christchurch Way, London, SE10 0AG Tel: (020) 8293 2000 Fax: (020) 8293 2433
C R Telecom, 27 Langcliffe Avenue, Warwick, CV34 5XT Tel: (01926) 408399 Fax: (01926) 408401 E-mail: clive@crtelecom.demon.co.uk
▶ Emerge Communications, 5 Cults Business Park, Station Road, Cults, Aberdeen, AB15 9PE Tel: (0870) 0500152 E-mail: sales@emerge-comms.co.uk
Hitel Communication Systems, 97 Stanley Road, Bootle, Merseyside, L20 7DA Tel: 0151-944 1276 Fax: 0151-933 1313 E-mail: info@hitelcommunications.com
KCC Global, Global House, Adlington Indust Estate, Prestbury, Macclesfield, Cheshire, SK10 4BF Tel: (01625) 874111 Fax: (0845) 3459006 E-mail: enquiries@kccglobal.co.uk
Lodge Radio Telephone Systems Ltd, Beccles Road, Raveningham, Norwich, NR14 6NX Tel: (01502) 717929 Fax: (01502) 712937
Low Cost Communications, 4 Hillcrest Avenue, Leigh, Lancashire, WN7 5HH Tel: (01942) 603812 Fax: (01942) 603812
M G Communications, 24 Durant Street, London, E2 7BP Tel: (020) 7729 2628 Fax: (020) 7729 2628
Phone-In, 34 Queensferry Street, Edinburgh, EH2 4QS Tel: 0131-220 4325 Fax: (0870) 1221438 E-mail: enquiries@phone-in.com
Phonelink Installations Ltd, 94 Sterry Road, Gowerton, Swansea, SA4 3BW Tel: (01792) 875999 Fax: (01792) 875111 E-mail: sales@phonelink-inst.co.uk
PTC Systems Ltd, 3 Priors, London Road, Bishop's Stortford, Hertfordshire, CM23 5ED Tel: (01279) 755855 Fax: (01279) 755923
Rochester Corporation, 2nd Floor Taylor Building, 62-64 Bromham Road, Bedford, MK40 2QG Tel: (01234) 327013 Fax: (01234) 327062 E-mail: djharris@rochester-cables.com
Stevesound Communications Services Ltd, 103 Comer Road, Worcester, WR2 5HY Tel: (01905) 425300 Fax: (01905) 425300
Viking Ltd, Chatsworth House, Portland Close, Houghton Regis, Dunstable, Bedfordshire, LU5 5AW Tel: (01582) 603600 Fax: (01582) 471114 E-mail: accounts@vikingltd.co.uk
Vocom Ltd, Unit 6 Budbrooke Indust Est, Budbrooke Rd, Warwick, CV34 5HG Tel: 01926 493322 Fax: 01926 492870

TELECOMMUNICATION COMPONENTS

Alpha Micro Components Ltd, Springfield House, Cranes Road, Sherborne St. John, Basingstoke, Hampshire, RG24 9LJ Tel: (01256) 851770 Fax: (01256) 851771 E-mail: sales@alphamicro.net
Consumer Microcircuits Ltd, Ovel Park, Langford, Maldon, Essex, CM9 6WG Tel: (01621) 875500 Fax: (01621) 875600 E-mail: sales@cmlmicro.com
Drallim Industries, Drury Lane, St. Leonards-on-Sea, East Sussex, TN38 9BA Tel: (01424) 205140 Fax: (01424) 202140 E-mail: sales@drallim.com
Fulcrum Systems, Hillbottom Road, Sands Industrial Estate, High Wycombe, Buckinghamshire, HP12 4HJ Tel: (0845) 4304060 Fax: (01494) 473324 E-mail: sales@fulcrum-systems.co.uk
Icomm Structured Wiring Systems, 5 Wychwood Close, New Duston, Northampton, NN5 6QL Tel: (01604) 584655 Fax: (01604) 584652
Q\Dos Networks Ltd, Ropers, Manor Lane, Stutton, Ipswich, IP9 2TB Tel: (01473) 326300 Fax: (01473) 238544 E-mail: sales@qdos.co.uk
Quante Telecommunications Ltd, Snailwell Business Pk, Fordham Rd, Snailwell, Newmarket, Suffolk, CB8 7NY Tel: (01638) 721333 Fax: (01638) 721233 E-mail: service@quante.co.uk
Solitek Ltd, Watermill House, Restmoor Way, Wallington, Surrey, SM6 7AH Tel: (020) 8669 6669 Fax: (020) 8669 6961 E-mail: sales@solitek.co.uk
T O C Ltd, Brandon Road, Binley, Coventry, CV3 2AN Tel: (024) 7645 0020 Fax: (024) 7663 5722 E-mail: sales@toc-ltd.co.uk

TELECOMMUNICATION CONSULTANCY OR DESIGN

Advance Communications, Business Development Centre, Main Avenue, Treforest Indust Estate, Pontypridd, Mid Glamorgan, CF37 5UR Tel: (01443) 843555 Fax: (01443) 841449
Advanced Topograhic Development & Images Ltd, 4-7 Kingsland Court, Three Bridges Road, Crawley, West Sussex, RH10 1HL Tel: (01293) 522052 Fax: (01293) 522521 E-mail: enquiries@atdi.co.uk
▶ Ayudar, Sheraton House, Castle Park, Cambridge, CB3 0AX Tel: (08709) 9 01090
Callscan Ltd, Callscan House Priestley Wharf, 20 Holt Street, Birmingham, B7 4BZ Tel: 0121-359 8941 Fax: 0121-359 1417 E-mail: info@epcuk.com
Cambridge Algorithmica Ltd, 9 Oakdene, Beaconsfield, Buckinghamshire, HP9 2BZ Tel: (01494) 678989 Fax: (01494) 678990 E-mail: info@camalg.co.uk
CMC Consulting, 2 Progress Business Centre, Whittle Parkway, Slough, SL1 6DQ Tel: (01628) 600870 Fax: (01628) 660688 E-mail: jason@sian-consulting.com
▶ Coach House Communications Ltd, The Coach House, Sherridge Road, Leigh Sinton, Malvern, Worcestershire, WR13 5DB Tel: (0870) 4440888 Fax: (0844) 8440124 E-mail: enquiries@coachhousecommunications.co.uk
E C I Telecom, Isis House, Gastons Wood, Chineham, Basingstoke, Hampshire, RG24 8TW Tel: (01256) 388000 Fax: (01256) 388143
East Midlands Technologies, 54 Beeston Fields Drive, Barmcote, Beeston, Nottingham, NG9 3DD Tel: 0115-922 3874 Fax: 0115-922 3874 E-mail: bob@bramcote.demon.co.uk
▶ Esys Plc, 1 Occam Court, Occam Road, Surrey Research Park, Guildford, Surrey, GU2 7HJ Tel: (01483) 304545 Fax: (01483) 303878 E-mail: info@esys.co.uk
Eurotel Communications Ltd, Foleshill Enterprise Park, Courtaulds Way, Coventry, CV6 5NX Tel: (024) 7686 7400 Fax: 0870 750334 E-mail: sales@hbtcommunications.com
▶ Fusion Four Telecoms Ltd, 7 Saffron Court, Southfields Business Park, Laindon, Basildon, Essex, SS15 6SS Tel: (01268) 417500 Fax: (01268) 543355 E-mail: fft@fusiontelecom.co.uk
Fusion ICS, Broadwall House, 21 Broadwall, London, SE1 9PL Tel: (020) 7960 5100 Fax: (020) 7928 5961 E-mail: info@fusion-ics.com
Genesys I B S Ltd, Singleton Court Business Centre, Wonastow Road, Monmouth, Gwent, NP25 5JA Tel: (01600) 710300 Fax: (01600) 710301 E-mail: nick@genesysibs.com
Global Telecommunications Laboratories Ltd, Gladstone House, Gladstone Drive, Bristol, BS16 4RU Tel: 0117-987 0044 Fax: 0117-987 0055 E-mail: gtl@gtlabs.co.uk
Hitel Communication Systems, 97 Stanley Road, Bootle, Merseyside, L20 7DA Tel: 0151-944 1276 Fax: 0151-933 1313 E-mail: info@hitelcommunications.com
Imagination Technologies, Turing House, Station Road, Chepstow, Gwent, NP16 5PB Tel: (01291) 625422 Fax: (01291) 620301 E-mail: info@ensigma.com
Improcom Ltd, Management House, Cottingham Road, Corby, Northamptonshire, NN17 1TD Tel: (01536) 207107 Fax: (01536) 265699 E-mail: admin@improcom.co.uk
Incom Telecommunications, Water Side, Trafford Park, Manchester, M17 1WD Tel: 0161-935 1000 Fax: 0161-935 1001 E-mail: sales@incomtelecoms.co.uk
Inenco Group Ltd, Petros House, St. Andrews Road North, Lytham St. Annes, Lancashire, FY8 2NF Tel: (01253) 785000 Fax: (01253) 785001 E-mail: enquiries@inenco.com
Interconnect Communications Ltd, Merlin House, Station Road, Chepstow, Gwent, NP16 5PB Tel: (01291) 638400 Fax: (01291) 638401 E-mail: enquiries@icc-uk.com
Logica UK Ltd, Stephenson House, 75 Hampstead Road, London, NW1 2PL Tel: (020) 7637 9111 Fax: (020) 7468 7006 E-mail: webmaster@logicacmg.com
▶ Milestone Technologies Ltd, 6 Jardine Cottages, Templewood Lane, Stoke Poges, Slough, SL2 4BQ Tel: 01753 662182 Fax: 0870 134 1924 E-mail: enquiries@milestonetechnologies.co.uk
Nus Consulting Group, Regent House, Queensway, Redhill, RH1 1QT Tel: (01737) 781200 Fax: (01737) 766799 E-mail: service@nusconsulting.co.uk
▶ Ortiga Ltd, Vienna House, Birmingham International Park, Bickenhill Lane, Birmingham, B37 7GN Tel: 0121-767 1934 Fax: 0121-705 3486 E-mail: enquiries@ortiga.co.uk
Paul Strachan Consulting Ltd, 30 Turfbeg Drive, Forfar, Angus, DD8 3LH Tel: (01307) 460667 Fax: (0870) 420 3597 E-mail: info@strachanconsulting.co.uk
Premier Voice & Data, Motokov House, North Lynn Indust Estate, North Lynn Industrial Estate, King's Lynn, Norfolk, PE30 2JG Tel: (01553) 779950 Fax: (01553) 779950 E-mail: info@premiervoiceanddata.co.uk
Reeves Lund, The Courtyard, 55 Charterhouse Street, London, EC1M 6HA Tel: (020) 7739 8888 Fax: (020) 7490 4488 E-mail: sales@reeveslund.com
Systems & Communications Ltd, 10 Moreland Close, Alton, Hampshire, GU34 2SA Tel: (01420) 88482 Fax: (01420) 544754
Talking Technology Ltd, Technology House, 11 Palmerston Road, Sutton, Surrey, SM1 4QL Tel: (020) 8770 9343 Fax: (020) 8770 9143 E-mail: sales@talktech.co.uk
Task Communications Ltd, 259 Church Road, Benfleet, Essex, SS7 4QN Tel: (01268) 793240 Fax: (01268) 881010 E-mail: sales@taskcomms.co.uk
Texcel Technology plc, Parkside Works, Thames Road, Crayford, Dartford, DA1 4SB Tel: (01322) 621700 Fax: (01322) 557733 E-mail: sales@texceltechnology.com
▶ Vernet Solutions Ltd, Wick Avenue, Wheathampstead, St. Albans, Hertfordshire, AL4 8PZ Tel: (0845) 4656655

TELECOMMUNICATION COST AND TARIFF CONSULTANCY

▶ West Wales Telecom, Camrose Lass, Portfield Gate, Haverfordwest, Dyfed, SA62 3LS Tel: (01437) 760984 E-mail: admin@westwalestelecom.com

TELECOMMUNICATION ELECTRONIC COMPONENTS

Abacus Eiger Northeast, Hall Mews, Clifford Road, Boston Spa, Wetherby, West Yorkshire, LS23 6DT Tel: (01937) 841312 Fax: (01937) 841062
Alpha Micro Components Ltd, Springfield House, Cranes Road, Sherborne St. John, Basingstoke, Hampshire, RG24 9LJ Tel: (01256) 851770 Fax: (01256) 851771 E-mail: sales@alphamicro.net
Enabling Communications Group Ltd, Unit 3 Wareley Yard, Wareley Road, Peterborough, PE2 9PF Tel: (01733) 892031 Fax: (01733) 891197 E-mail: sales@ecgcomms.co.uk
I D Installations, 202 Nuthurst Road, Manchester, M40 3PP Tel: 0161-682 4595 Fax: 0161-682 4595 E-mail: david@idinstallations.freeserve.co.uk
T T Electronics, East Field Industrial Estate, Glenrothes, Fife, KY7 4NX Tel: (01592) 662200 Fax: (01592) 662299
Telecoms UK (South) Ltd, Telegraph Cottage, Christchurch Road, Ringwood, Hampshire, BH24 3AS Tel: (01425) 461700

TELECOMMUNICATION EQUIPMENT POWER SUPPLIES

Constant Power Services Ltd (CPS), Units 3, Trust Industrial Estate, Wilbury Way, Hitchin, Hertfordshire, SG4 0UZ Tel: (01462) 422955 Fax: (01462) 422754 E-mail: sales@cps4ups.co.uk
Davtrend Ltd, 7a Fitzherbert Spur, Farlington, Portsmouth, PO6 1TT Tel: (023) 9237 2004 Fax: (023) 9232 6307 E-mail: sales@davtrend.co.uk
E R L Ltd, Iroko House, Bolney Avenue, Peacehaven, East Sussex, BN10 8HF Tel: (01273) 581007 Fax: (01273) 581555 E-mail: erl@fastnet.co.uk
Eaton Power Solutions Ltd, Heath Place, Ashgrove Industrial Park, Bognor Regis, West Sussex, PO22 9SJ Tel: (01243) 810500 Fax: (01243) 868613
G E Digital Energy, Wheatfield Way, Hinckley, Leicestershire, LE10 1YG Tel: 0116-290 5280 Fax: 0116-290 5281 E-mail: sales@imv.co.uk
M S N Network Power Ltd, Fourth Avenue, Globe Park, Marlow, Buckinghamshire, SL7 1YG Tel: (01628) 403200 Fax: (01628) 403203 E-mail: sales@emersonnetworkpower.com
R T E Electronics, 568 Burnley Road, Rossendale, Lancashire, BB4 8AJ Tel: (01706) 227234 Fax: (01706) 227531 E-mail: brain@rtepower.co.uk

TELECOMMUNICATION FIXED CELLULAR TERMINALS (FCT)

▶ Interquartz, Pennine House, Salford Street, Bury, Lancashire, BL9 6YA Tel: 0161-763 3122 Fax: 0161-763 4029 E-mail: roy.stephenson@interquartz.co.uk

TELECOMMUNICATION MANAGEMENT SERVICES PROVIDER

BTS Holdings plc, B T S House, 69-73 Manor Road, Wallington, Surrey, SM6 0DD Tel: (020) 8401 9000 Fax: (020) 8401 9101 E-mail: sales@bts.co.uk
Interconnect Communications Ltd, Merlin House, Station Road, Chepstow, Gwent, NP16 5PB Tel: (01291) 638400 Fax: (01291) 638401 E-mail: enquiries@icc-uk.com
KCC Global, Global House, Adlington Indust Estate, Prestbury, Macclesfield, Cheshire, SK10 4BF Tel: (01625) 874111 Fax: (0845) 3459006 E-mail: enquiries@kccglobal.co.uk
Swiftnet Ltd, Britannia House, 958-964 High Road, London, N12 9RY Tel: (020) 8446 9494 Fax: (020) 8446 7010 E-mail: sales@swiftnet.co.uk
▶ Switch Utilities Ltd, New Brook House, 385 Alfreton Road, Nottingham, NG7 5LR Tel: (0845) 6341005 Fax: (0845) 6341006 E-mail: james@switchutilities.com
▶ zamano ltd., Bedford Chambers, Covent Garden, London, WC2E 8HA Tel: 0207 557 6020 E-mail: sebastian@zamano.com

TELECOMMUNICATION MAST CONSULTANCY OR DESIGN

Minting Communications Ltd, Sebastopol Barn, Church Lane, Minting, Horncastle, Lincolnshire, LN9 5RS Tel: (01507) 578500 E-mail: collinrood@minting.ltd.co.uk

TELECOMMUNICATION NETWORK SYNCHRONISATION EQUIPMENT

▶ Gemini Telecommunications, 78 Britton Street, Gillingham, Kent, ME7 5ET Tel: (01634) 580510 Fax: (01634) 579628 E-mail: sales@gemini-telecom.com

TELECOMMUNICATION OPERATOR OUTSOURCING

Abacus, Omnicom House, 2 Alexandra Road, Reading, RG1 5PE Tel: 0118-376 6664 Fax: 0118-376 6660 E-mail: sales@abacus-billing.com
Leadline Services Ltd, 54 New Street, Worcester, WR1 2DL Tel: (01905) 724000 Fax: (01905) 726888 E-mail: sales@leadline.co.uk
▶ T R G Recruitment Services Ltd, 5th Floor, 4 St. Pauls Churchyard, London, EC4M 8AY Tel: (020) 7236 8844 Fax: (020) 7236 8181 E-mail: cv@thetrggroup.co.uk
▶ Vernet Solutions Ltd, Wick Avenue, Wheathampstead, St. Albans, Hertfordshire, AL4 8PZ Tel: (0845) 4656655

TELECOMMUNICATION OR INSTRUMENTATION BATTERY CHARGERS

Prepair Ltd, 11 Flowers Industrial Estate, Latimer Road, Luton, LU1 3XA Tel: (01582) 455000 Fax: (01582) 416000 E-mail: prepair@easynet.co.uk

TELECOMMUNICATION ORGANISATIONS

02 UK, 260 Bath Road, Slough, SL1 4DX Tel: (01753) 565000 Fax: (01753) 565010
Anglia Telecoms, 1 Gateshead Close, Sandy, Bedfordshire, SG19 1RS Tel: (01767) 692792 Fax: (01767) 692992 E-mail: info@angliatelecoms.co.uk
Arqrva Ltd, Crawley Court, Crawley, Winchester, Hampshire, SO21 2QA Tel: (01962) 823434 Fax: (01962) 822378
B S C L Ltd, Horndon Industrial Park, West Horndon, Brentwood, Essex, CM13 3XD Tel: 01268 578940 Fax: 01277 810157 E-mail: info@bscl.com
Clansey Communications Ltd, 68-70 Market Street, Cannock, Staffordshire, WS12 1AY Tel: (01543) 424485 Fax: (01543) 422256 E-mail: sales@clansey.co.uk
Kingston Communications Hull plc, 35-37 Carr Lane, Hull, HU1 3RE Tel: (01482) 602100 Fax: (01482) 320652 E-mail: publicrelations@kcom.com
Latitude Communications, 50 Regent St, London, W1B 5RD Tel: (020) 7470 7125 Fax: (020) 7470 7113
Liberty Bell Voice & Data Ltd, The Old Courthouse, Chapel Street, Dukinfield, Cheshire, SK16 4DT Tel: (0800) 5053373 Fax: (0800) 5053773
Network Business Communications, 57 London Road, Enfield, Middlesex, EN2 6DU Tel: (020) 8370 8370 Fax: (020) 8366 6844
Network Connect Ltd, Egret Mill, 162 Old Street, Ashton-under-Lyne, Lancashire, OL6 7ST Tel: 0161-214 2000 Fax: 0161-214 2001 E-mail: sales@networkconnect.co.uk
Nokia UK Ltd, Lancaster House, Lancaster Way, Ermine Business Park, Huntingdon, Cambridgeshire, PE29 6YJ Tel: (0870) 0555777 Fax: (01480) 435111 E-mail: firstname.surname@nokia.com
The Phone & Fax Co., 35 Norwich Street, Fakenham, Norfolk, NR21 9AF Tel: (01328) 856566 Fax: (01328) 856506 E-mail: fakenham@digital-phone.co.uk
PNC Telecom Services Ltd, Cavallino House, Corsley Heath, Corsley, Warminster, Wiltshire, BA12 7PL Tel: (07000) 707070 Fax: (07000) 707071

TELECOMMUNICATION ORGANISATIONS – *continued*

Telecommunications Users' Association, 7 Sylvan Court, Southfields Business Park, Basildon, Essex, SS15 6TD Tel: (0870) 2202071 Fax: (0870) 2202075 E-mail: tua@dial.pipex.com

▶ Vernet Solutions Ltd, Wick Avenue, Wheathampstead, St. Albans, Hertfordshire, AL4 8PZ Tel: (0845) 4656655

TELECOMMUNICATION PROTECTION SYSTEMS

▶ Bailey Teswaine, Etna House, 78 New Coventry Road, Birmingham, B26 3AY Tel: 0121-771 7288 Fax: 0121-771 7268 E-mail: enquiries@baileyteswaine.co.uk

TELECOMMUNICATION SERVICES OR CONTRACTORS

A T C Ltd, Greenway House, Greenway Business Centre, Harlow, Essex, CM19 5QD Tel: 0161-406 1000 Fax: (0870) 0558081 E-mail: sales@atc.co.uk

Alcatel Telecom Ltd, Bulding N140, Christchurch Way, London, SE10 0AG Tel: (0870) 9033600 Fax: (020) 8293 2433

Answerlink plc, Manton Lane, Manton Industrial Estate, Bedford, MK41 7TL Tel: (0845) 3305577 Fax: (0845) 3305588 E-mail: info@answerlink.com

Arian Communications Ltd, Unit 14, Gaugemaster Way, Ford, Arundel, West Sussex, BN18 0RX Tel: (0871) 2261481 Fax: (01903) 881510 E-mail: mike@ariancom.com

Axon Systems, 108 Bartholomew Street, Newbury, Berkshire, RG14 5DT Tel: (01635) 33033 Fax: (07050) 300603 E-mail: sales@axon-systems.co.uk

Boucon Network Solutions Ltd, 2 Minster Court, Valley Way, Swansea Enterprise Park, Swansea, SA6 8RN Tel: (01792) 762200 Fax: (01792) 762201

Cable and Wireless P.L.C., Redlion Square, London, WC1R 4HQ Tel: (020) 7315 4000 Fax: (020) 7315 5182

Charnwood Cabling Ltd, Ark Business Centre, Gordon Road, Loughborough, Leicestershire, LE11 1JP Tel: (01509) 236200 Fax: (01509) 236211 E-mail: kevin@charnwoodcabling.co.uk

Cloud Communications Ltd, 58 Broadoak Road, Langford, Bristol, BS40 5HB Tel: (01934) 853900 Fax: (01934) 853909 E-mail: brian@cloud-isdn.com

Comm-Unique Aquarious Ltd, 3 Sillins Hall, Sillins Lane, Callow Hill, Redditch, Worcestershire, B97 5TP Tel: (01527) 404100 Fax: (01527) 404503

Computel, 13 The Broadway, Thatcham, Berkshire, RG19 3JA Tel: (01635) 847701

▶ Corporate Communications Ltd, 45 Bank Street, Galashiels, Selkirkshire, TD1 1EP Tel: 0870 7460060 Fax: 0870 7460061 E-mail: info@corpcl.co.uk

Eastern Communications, Cavendish House, Happisburgh, Norwich, NR12 0RU Tel: (01692) 650077

Eurotel Communications Ltd, Foleshill Enterprise Park, Courtaulds Way, Coventry, CV6 5NX Tel: (024) 7686 7400 Fax: 0870 750334 E-mail: sales@hbtcommunications.com

Evante Fitness Ltd, 71-73 High Street North, Dunstable, Bedfordshire, LU6 1JF Tel: (01582) 477600 Fax: (01582) 471366

First Choice Technology Solutions Ltd, Broadhurst House, Bury Old Road, Salford, M7 4QX Tel: 0161-740 4400 Fax: 0161-740 4411

Genesis Scotland Ltd, The Douglas Centre, Marchmont Crescent, Buckie, Banffshire, AB56 4BT Tel: (01542) 834947 Fax: (0870) 3835549E-mail: genesisltd@btopenworld.com

Genesys Communications, Trenewth House, Michaelstow, St. Tudy, Bodmin, Cornwall, PL30 3PE Tel: (01208) 851158 Fax: (01208) 851199 E-mail: john@genesys.sfnet.co.uk

Hitel Communication Systems, 97 Stanley Road, Bootle, Merseyside, L20 7DA Tel: 0151-944 1276 Fax: 0151-933 1313 E-mail: info@hitelcommunications.com

I T C, 68 High Street, Witney, Oxfordshire, OX28 6HJ Tel: (01993) 709999 Fax: (01993) 778367

Infolink Communications Ltd, 2 Camden Road, London, NW1 9DL Tel: (020) 7482 1888 Fax: (020) 7482 2255

Intercept Telecom Ltd, 4 Angerstein Business Park, Horn Lane, London, SE10 0RT Tel: (020) 8305 4900 Fax: (020) 8305 4901 E-mail: info@intercept-telecom.com

Itc Ltd, 2-8 Park Road, Lytham St. Annes, Lancashire, FY8 1QX Tel: (01253) 783990 Fax: (01253) 783993 E-mail: info@itcoms.co.uk

The Logic Group Enterprises Ltd, Logic House, Waterfront Business Park, Fleet Road, Fleet, Hampshire, GU51 3SB Tel: (01252) 776755 Fax: (01252) 776738 E-mail: marketing@the-logic-group.com

Mcnicholas Construction Holdings Ltd, Lismirrane Industrial Park, Elstree Road, Borehamwood, Hertfordshire, WD6 3EA Tel: (020) 8953 4144 Fax: (020) 8953 1860 E-mail: sales@mcnicholas.co.uk

Masterpoint Communication Systems Ltd, 15 Tresham Street, Kettering, Northamptonshire, NN16 8RS Tel: (01536) 417744 Fax: (0870) 4428855

Network Europe Group plc, 14 Capricorn Centre, Cranes Farm Road, Basildon, Essex, SS14 3JJ Tel: (0870) 3330321 Fax: (0870) 3330320 E-mail: sales@negplc.com

Norgate Ltd, Unit 4b Newton Court, Wavertree Technology Park, Liverpool, L13 1EJ Tel: 0151-220 5556 Fax: 0151-254 1463 E-mail: sales@norgatetelecom.co.uk

North East Communications, 76 High Street, Elgin, Morayshire, IV30 1BJ Tel: (01343) 551551 Fax: (01343) 540340

P M A Ltd, Grant Thornton House, 24-26 Rothesay Road, Luton, LU1 1QX Tel: (01582) 400184 Fax: (01582) 487740

Phoenix Phones, 2 Stanley Cottages, London Road, Hartley Wintney, Hook, Hampshire, RG27 8RT Tel: (01252) 845845 Fax: (01252) 845888 E-mail: admin@phoenix-phones.co.uk

Phone-In, 34 Queensferry Street, Edinburgh, EH2 4QS Tel: 0131-220 4325 Fax: (0870) 1221438 E-mail: enquiries@phone-in.com

Powerdial Telecommunications Equipment, The Studio, East Batterlaw Farm, Hawthorn, Seaham, County Durham, SR7 8RP Tel: 0191-527 5000 Fax: 0191-527 0036

Powergen plc, Colliers Way, Nottingham, NG8 6AL Tel: (0870) 4191539 Fax: 0115-995 6738 E-mail: sales@eme.co.uk

▶ Redbox Consulting Ltd, 49 Clarendon Road, Watford, WD17 1HZ Tel: (0870) 4455660 Fax: (0870) 4455661 E-mail: info@redbox-group.com

S P Neworks Ltd, 2 Wallingford Road, Uxbridge, Middlesex, UB8 2BB Tel: (01895) 259066 Fax: (01895) 259150

SNC, 2 Denston Close, Prenton, Merseyside, CH43 9XU Tel: 0151-678 6471 Fax: 0151-257 9453

Sparks Business Systems, Kingsway House, Bank Buildings, Bridgend Industrial Estate, Bridgend, Mid Glamorgan, CF31 3SB Tel: (01656) 767231 Fax: (01656) 661106

Suretel Systems Ltd, 39 Chedworth Crescent, Portsmouth, PO6 4ES Tel: (023) 9264 6646 Fax: (023) 9264 6646

Systems & Communications Ltd, 10 Moreland Close, Alton, Hampshire, GU34 2SA Tel: (01420) 88482 Fax: (01420) 544754

Tekeda Telecom, Cygnet Court, Hawthorn Street, Wilmslow, Cheshire, SK9 5EL Tel: (01625) 416200 Fax: (01625) 539042 E-mail: enq@takeda-telecom.co.uk

Telefonix, 3 Albany Court, Albany Park, Camberley, Surrey, GU16 7QR Tel: (01252) 333888 Fax: (01252) 376167 E-mail: info@systems-supported.com

Telephone Connexions Ltd, Marconi Road, Burgh Road Industrial Estate, Carlisle, CA2 7NA Tel: (01228) 514369 Fax: (01228) 594369 E-mail: sales@telephoneconnexions.co.uk

Telephone Lines Ltd, 304 High Street, Cheltenham, Gloucestershire, GL50 3JF Tel: (01242) 583699 Fax: (01242) 690033 E-mail: info@telephonelines.net

UK Freephone, PO Box 800, South Ockendon, Essex, RM15 4WH Tel: (0870) 7485835 Fax: (0870) 7485329 E-mail: info@ukfreephone.co.uk

Utility Options, 78 Northgate Street, Chester, CH1 2HR Tel: (0800) 1950123 Fax: (01352) 781813 E-mail: enquiries@utility-options.co.uk

West Communications Ltd, The Estate Office, Charlestown Road, St. Austell, Cornwall, PL25 3NJ Tel: (01726) 222020 Fax: (01726) 68880 E-mail: info@west-comms.net

Yello Telecommunications Management Ltd, 23 Meadvale Road, Leicester, LE2 3WN Tel: 0116-224 4000 Fax: 0116-224 4010 E-mail: enquiries@yello.co.uk

TELECOMMUNICATION SYSTEMS AND SERVICES

Advance Communications & Rentals, 111 Kingsley Crescent, Stonebroom, Alfreton, Derbyshire, DE55 6HZ Tel: (01773) 874887 Fax: (01773) 874888

The ANPR Co. Ltd, Link House Unit 5, Bath Road Business Centre, Devizes, Wilts, SN10 1XA Tel: (01380) 739000 Fax: (01380) 739071 E-mail: sales@anpr.com

Atlas Security, 226 Psalter Lane, Sheffield, S11 8UT Tel: 0114-266 9850

C F Telecom, 36 Regent Street, Great Yarmouth, Norfolk, NR30 1RR Tel: (0845) 4582363 Fax: (0845) 4582364E-mail: sales@cftele.com

C2c Network Solutions Ltd, The Stripe, Riverside, Sinnington, York, YO62 6RY Tel: (01751) 430063 Fax: (01751) 431999

Combined Communications Ltd, 19 Lodge Lane, Grays, Essex, RM17 5RY Tel: (01375) 392600 Fax: (01375) 392008

Communication Systems, 82 Elm Grove, Worthing, West Sussex, BN11 5LJ Tel: (01903) 532323 Fax: (01903) 700238

Datasharp Telecom (Eastern) Ltd, 78 Chapel Street, King's Lynn, Norfolk, PE30 1EF Tel: (01553) 666111 Fax: (01553) 666112 E-mail: sales@datasharptelecom.com

Digitel Technology Ltd, 7 Cross Street, Barnstaple, Devon, EX31 1BA Tel: (01271) 311913 E-mail: sales@digitel.uk.net

Eastern Telephones, 2 Bowthorpe Workshops, Bowthorpe Hall Road, Norwich, NR5 9AA Tel: (01603) 743388 Fax: (01603) 743388 E-mail: webenquiries@eastern-telephones.co.uk

▶ The Link, 43-45 Fishergate, Preston, PR1 2AD Tel: (01772) 562396 Fax: (01772) 562409

Mcmillan Communications, 198b Newhouse Road, Blackpool, FY4 4PA Tel: (01253) 698885 Fax: (01253) 798474 E-mail: info@mcmillan-communications.co.uk

▶ Soneric Communications, Unit 24 Wren Court, Strathclyde Business Park, Bellshill, Lanarkshire, ML4 3NQ Tel: (01698) 742210 Fax: (01698) 840080 E-mail: sales@soneric.com

▶ Switch Utilities Ltd, New Brook House, 385 Alfreton Road, Nottingham, NG7 5LR Tel: (0845) 6341005 Fax: (0845) 6341006 E-mail: james@switchutilities.com

Talking Technology Ltd, Technology House, 11 Palmerston Road, Sutton, Surrey, SM1 4QL Tel: (020) 8770 9343 Fax: (020) 8770 9143 E-mail: sales@talktech.co.uk

TELECOMMUNICATION SYSTEMS DESIGN

▶ Coach House Communications Ltd, The Coach House, Sherridge Road, Leigh Sinton, Malvern, Worcestershire, WR13 5DB Tel: (0870) 4440888 Fax: (0844) 8440124 E-mail: enquiries@coachhousecommunications.co.uk

TELECOMMUNICATION SYSTEMS INTEGRATORS

C & M Communications Consultants Ltd, Tanners Court, Tanners Lane, East Wellow, Romsey, Hampshire, SO51 6DP Tel: (01794) 518508 Fax: (01794) 518182 E-mail: stephen.michaelides@candmcommunications.co.uk

Cti Data Solutions Ltd, Nordic House, 120 High Street, Purley, Surrey, CR8 2AD Tel: (020) 8763 3888 Fax: (020) 8763 3863 E-mail: info@ctidata.co.uk

▶ Felltech Ltd, St Johns House, Garrigill, Alston, Cumbria, CA9 3DS Tel: (01434) 380000 E-mail: info@felltech.com

▶ Milestone Technologies Ltd, 6 Jardine Cottages, Templewood Lane, Stoke Poges, Slough, SL2 4BQ Tel: 01753 662182 Fax: 0870 134 1924 E-mail: enquiries@milestonetechnologies.co.uk

▶ PNComms (UK) Ltd, 96 Wilsthorpe Road, Breaston, Derby, DE72 3AG Tel: (07977) 178771 E-mail: info@pncomms.com

▶ Zentive Ltd, 25 Barnes Wallis Road, Segensworth East, Fareham, Hampshire, PO15 5TT Tel: (01489) 569440 Fax: (01489) 889854 E-mail: sales@zentive.com

TELECOMMUNICATION SYSTEMS OR EQUIPMENT, *See also headings for particular types*

1 Communication Ltd, 4 Clearway Court, 139-141 Croydon Road, Caterham, Surrey, CR3 6PF Tel: (01883) 333880 Fax: (01883) 333881 E-mail: marketing@tisl.com

20/20 Telecom, 102 High Street, Canvey Island, Essex, SS8 7SQ Tel: (01268) 511700 Fax: (01268) 696151

A C H Access Control Ltd, High Point, South Hanningfield Road, Wickford, Essex, SS11 7PF Tel: (01268) 710636 Fax: (01268) 710556E-mail: markwetton@ach.demon.co.uk

A T C Ltd, 2 Thomas Holden Street, Bolton, BL1 2QG Tel: (01204) 550600 Fax: (01204) 381702 E-mail: enquiries@atc.co.uk

A T L Telecommunications Ltd, Cypress Drive, St Mellons, Cardiff, CF3 0EG Tel: (029) 2050 0700 Fax: (029) 2050 0701 E-mail: sales@atltelecom.com

▶ Active Voice & Data Ltd, Unit 14 Kendray Business Centre, Thornton Road, Barnsley, South Yorkshire, S70 3NA Tel: (01226) 704610 E-mail: sales@active-voicedata.co.uk

▶ Albertronic, Unit 305 Vale Enterprise Centre, Hayes Road, Sully, Penarth, South Glamorgan, CF64 5SY Tel: (01446) 709000 Fax: (01446) 709002

Anglia Telecom Centres plc, 166 Handford Road, Ipswich, IP1 2BH Tel: (01473) 382000 Fax: (01473) 225617 E-mail: mandy.stafford@angliatelecom.co.uk

Anglia Telecoms, 1 Gateshead Close, Sandy, Bedfordshire, SG19 1RS Tel: (01767) 692792 Fax: (01767) 692992 E-mail: info@angliatelecoms.co.uk

Ansacaller Telecommunication Ltd, Unity House, Main Road, Denholme, Bradford, West Yorkshire, BD13 4BL Tel: (01274) 834366 Fax: (01274) 834593

Ascom Tele Nova Ltd, Enterprise Drive, Sutton Coldfield, West Midlands, B74 2DY Tel: 0121-353 6151 Fax: 0121-352 1424

Ash Hill Communications & Electronics Ltd, Keepers Cottage, Combe Raleigh, Honiton, Devon, EX14 4TG Tel: (01404) 44080 Fax: (01404) 44122

Aston Communications, 2 St. Johns Buildings, Friern Barnet Road, London, N11 3DP Tel: (020) 8361 8711 Fax: (020) 8361 3633 E-mail: john@aston-telex.com

▶ Belfuse Eu, Riverside Estate, Sir Thomas Longley Road, Medway City Estate, Rochester, Kent, ME2 4DP Tel: (01634) 722890 Fax: (01634) 716677

Beta Telecom, 1 Southborough Terrace, Brunswick Street, Leamington Spa, Warwickshire, CV31 2DT Tel: (01926) 311479 Fax: (01926) 337704 E-mail: tara@betatelecom.co.uk

Bistech plc, 137 Victoria Road, Ferndown, Dorset, BH22 9HX Tel: (01202) 863200 Fax: (01202) 896465

Black & White Telephone Co., John Street, Royston, Hertfordshire, SG8 9BE Tel: (01763) 248216 Fax: (01763) 249475

Brian Green, D B H House, Boundary Street, Liverpool, L5 9YJ Tel: 0151-207 5225 Fax: 0151-207 3300 E-mail: sales@brian-green.co.uk

Brightel Datanet Ltd, Unit 3 Moulsecoomb Way, Brighton, BN2 4PB Tel: (01273) 244400 Fax: (01273) 244410

▶ Brighton Communications Systems, Scallow Wish, Moat Lane, Waldron, Heathfield, East Sussex, TN21 0RT Tel: (01273) 888788 Fax: (0845) 1232934 E-mail: mail@commsdirect.com

Brighton Electrical Assemblies Ltd, Cradle Hill Industrial Estate, Seaford, East Sussex, BN25 3JE Tel: (01323) 893295 Fax: (01323) 897429 E-mail: info@bealtd.co.uk

Britannic Technologies Ltd, Britannic House, Merrow Business Park, Guildford, Surrey, GU4 7WA Tel: (01483) 242526 Fax: 0845-050 1001 E-mail: enquiries@btlnet.co.uk

BT, Annandale House, 1 Hanworth Road, Sunbury-On-Thames, Middlesex, TW16 5DJ Tel: (01932) 765766 Fax: (01932) 772277

▶ Business Voice & Data, 324 Birmingham Road, Lickey End, Bromsgrove, Worcestershire, B61 0HJ Tel: (01527) 832552 Fax: (01527) 832542

C E S Telecom Ltd, 15-17 Newgate Street Village, Hertford, SG13 8RA Tel: (01707) 874775 Fax: (01707) 873165 E-mail: emily.dean@cestelecom.com

C F Telecom, 36 Regent Street, Great Yarmouth, Norfolk, NR30 1RR Tel: (0845) 4582363 Fax: (0845) 4582364E-mail: sales@cftele.com

C & M Communications Consultants Ltd, Tanners Court, Tanners Lane, East Wellow, Romsey, Hampshire, SO51 6DP Tel: (01794) 518508 Fax: (01794) 518182 E-mail: stephen.michaelides@candmcommunications.co.uk

C S Communication Services Ltd, 19 Sutton Oak Corner, Sutton Coldfield, West Midlands, B74 2DH Tel: (0845) 6771000 E-mail: sales@comms.co.uk

C S E Seprol Ltd, Rotherside Road, Eckington, Sheffield, S21 4HL Tel: (01246) 436331 Fax: (01246) 432461 E-mail: products@cse-seprol.com

▶ Cedardell Ltd, 3 Collingwood Street, Newcastle upon Tyne, NE1 1JW Tel: 0191-260 2600 Fax: 0191-260 2606 E-mail: sales@cedardell.com

▶ Cellular Surplus, Norwich Road, Colton, Norwich, NR9 5BZ Tel: (01603) 882800 Fax: (01603) 882015

Centurion Communications Ltd, Centurion House, Leyland Business Park, Centurion Way, Farington, Leyland, PR25 3GR Tel: (01772) 628362 Fax: (0870) 2113008 E-mail: post@telecomcentral.co.uk

▶ Challenge Technical Services Ltd, Alloa Business Centre, The Whins, Alloa, Clackmannanshire, FK10 3SA Tel: (01324) 556772

Check Communications Ltd, The Haven Communications House, 40 Chester Road West, Queensferry, Deeside, Clwyd, CH5 1SA Tel: (01244) 834800 Fax: (01244) 831606 E-mail: solutions@checkcomm.comm

Chiltern Telecom, 61 Union Street, Dunstable, Bedfordshire, LU6 1EX Tel: (01582) 604040 Fax: (0871) 2230230 E-mail: sales@chilterntelecom.co.uk

Cleartone Telecomms Ltd, Unit 15 Pontyfelin Industrial Estate, New Inn, Pontypool, Gwent, NP4 0DQ Tel: (01495) 752255 Fax: (01495) 752323 E-mail: admin@cleartone.co.uk

Comm Systems Ltd, Unit 17 Martello Enterprise Centre, Courtwick Lane, Wick, Littlehampton, West Sussex, BN17 7PA Tel: (01903) 722222 Fax: (01903) 726000 E-mail: enquiries@commsys.biz

Comm-Tech Martham Ltd, 2 Rollesby Road, Martham, Great Yarmouth, Norfolk, NR29 4RU Tel: (01493) 748274 Fax: (01493) 740185 E-mail: enquiries@comm-tech.co.uk

Communications South Ltd, 284 Hayling Avenue, Portsmouth, PO3 6EF Tel: (023) 9283 3993 Fax: (023) 9283 3288 E-mail: sales@commsouth.co.uk

Compass Communications Northern Ltd, 3 Lewis Road, Sidcup, Kent, DA14 4NB Tel: (020) 8309 1400 Fax: (020) 8300 2062 E-mail: compass@compass-comm.co.uk

Computertel Ltd, 53 Bath Street, Gravesend, Kent, DA11 0DF Tel: (01474) 561111 Fax: (01474) 561122 E-mail: sales@computertel.co.uk

D C S Telecom Ltd, Reculver Road, Herne Bay, Kent, CT6 6PB Tel: (01227) 741825 Fax: (01227) 361011 E-mail: sales@dcstelecom.co.uk

D S P G Ltd, 253a Kilburn Lane, London, W10 4BQ Tel: (020) 8964 0774 Fax: (020) 8964 0720 E-mail: info@dspg.co.uk

Dacon P.L.C., 1 Enterprise Way, Hemel Hempstead, Hertfordshire, HP2 7YJ Tel: (01442) 233222 Fax: (01442) 219656 E-mail: info@dacon.co.uk

▶ Data & Information Technology Ltd, Technology House, Normanton Lane, Bottesford, Nottingham, NG13 0EL Tel: (01949) 843757 Fax: (01949) 843758

TELECOMMUNICATION SYSTEMS OR EQUIPMENT – *continued*

Dataline Northern Ltd, 160-162 Cross Street, Sale, Cheshire, M33 7AQ Tel: 0161-905 1200 Fax: 0161-905 3001 E-mail: dataline@btconnect.com

Datasharp Telecom (Eastern) Ltd, 78 Chapel Street, King's Lynn, Norfolk, PE30 1EF Tel: (01553) 666111 Fax: (01553) 666112 E-mail: sales@datasharptelecom.com

Datasharp Wales, Unit 5b, Llangan, Bridgend, Mid Glamorgan, CF35 5DR Tel: (01656) 869999 Fax: (01656) 869990 E-mail: info@datasharpwales.com

Datel Solutions, 71 Elgin Street, Dunfermline, Fife, KY12 7SA Tel: (01383) 742752 Fax: (01383) 432223 E-mail: info@datel-solutions.co.uk

▶ Datex Systemcare Ltd, 6, Leeholme Road, Billingham, Cleveland, TS23 3TA Tel: (01642) 371033 Fax: (01642) 373461

▶ Dectel Ltd, 105 Horse St, Chipping Sodbury, Bristol, BS37 6DE Tel: (01454) 883300 Fax: (01454) 883300 E-mail: dectel@blueyonder.co.uk

Design Communications UK Ltd, Breckenwood Road, Ash House, Fulbourn, Cambridge, CB21 5DQ Tel: (01223) 882488 Fax: (01223) 882499 E-mail: sales@designcom.co.uk

Direct Telecom Services Ltd, 17 Bessemer Way, Harfreys Industrial Estate, Great Yarmouth, Norfolk, NR31 0LX Tel: (01493) 440000 Fax: (01493) 440063 E-mail: tim@direct-telecom-svs.co.uk

Direct Telecommunications Systems Ltd, Direct House, 16 Commercial Road, Skelmanthorpe, Huddersfield, HD8 9DA Tel: (01484) 867867 Fax: (01484) 867860 E-mail: info@direct-telecom.co.uk

Elmleigh Electrical Systems Ltd, Elmleigh House, Dawsons Lane, Barwell, LE9 8BE Tel: (01455) 847045 Fax: (01455) 844045 E-mail: belinda.jones@elmleigh.co.uk

Ension Technologies Ltd, Unit 14 The Capricorn Centre, Cranes Farm Road, Basildon, Essex, SS14 3JJ Tel: (01268) 795579 Fax: (01268) 461525

Ericsson Ltd, Maplewood Crockford Lane, Chineham Business Park, Chineham, Basingstoke, Hampshire, RG24 8YB Tel: (01256) 707874 Fax: (01256) 774373

Etrali UK Ltd, Piercy House, 7-9 Copthall Avenue, London, EC2R 7NJ Tel: (020) 7628 2795 Fax: (020) 7628 4972 E-mail: enquiries@aircharlie.com

Eurosonic Communications, 11 Sherborne Street, Manchester, M3 1JS Tel: 0161-831 7879 Fax: 0161-835 2125 E-mail: eurosonic@europasonic.com

Eurotel Communications Ltd, Foleshill Enterprise Park, Courtaulds Way, Coventry, CV6 5NX Tel: (024) 7686 7400 Fax: 0870 750334 E-mail: sales@hbtcommunications.com

Exchange Communications Ltd, Exchange House, Kerr Stree, Glasgow, G66 1LF Tel: (0870) 0855000 Fax: (0870) 0505555 E-mail: info@exchangecommunications.co.uk

▶ Faxco Maintenance Ltd, Irvine Industrial Estate, Irvine, Ayrshire, KA12 8JJ Tel: (01294) 311796

Fine Line Communications E A Ltd, Logic House, Harfreys Road, Great Yarmouth, Norfolk, NR31 0LS Tel: (01493) 441114 Fax: (01493) 441124 E-mail: clairey@finelinecoms.co.uk

▶ Fonefixation, 31-37 Etna Road, Falkirk, FK2 9EG Tel: (0871) 250 2555

Fortune Die & Tool Co. Ltd, 293 Knella Road, Welwyn Garden City, Hertfordshire, AL7 3NS Tel: (01707) 331430 Fax: (01707) 331430

Freerose Ltd, 26 Apex Business Centre, Boscombe Road, Dunstable, Bedfordshire, LU5 4SB Tel: (01582) 472274 Fax: (01582) 475574 E-mail: info@freerose.co.uk

Frequentis UK Ltd, Gainsborough House, 2 Sheen Road, Richmond, Surrey, TW9 1AE Tel: (020) 8973 2616

Fujitsu Telecommunications Europe Ltd, Solihull Parkway, Birmingham Business Park, Birmingham, B37 7YU Tel: 0121-717 6000 Fax: 0121-717 6014 E-mail: rcpt@ftel.co.uk

G B Telecoms, Galamoor House, Netherdale Industrial Estate, Galashiels, Selkirkshire, TD1 3EY Tel: (01896) 752607 Fax: (01896) 661308 E-mail: sales@gbtscotland.co.uk

G C S Ltd, Fingal House, East Street, Mayfield, East Sussex, TN20 6TU Tel: (01435) 872833 Fax: (01435) 873762

▶ Gooch Ict Ltd, 56 Coulson Road, Lincoln, LN6 7BG Tel: (01522) 546624 Fax: (01522) 546624 E-mail: hayley@goochict.co.uk

Grapevine Communications London, 488 St. Albans Road, Watford, WD24 6QU Tel: (01923) 219992 Fax: (01923) 219993 E-mail: info@grapevinecomms.co.uk

▶ Harris Stratex Networks UK. Ltd, 4 Bell Drive, Hamilton International Technology Park, Blantyre, Glasgow, G72 0FB Tel: (01698) 717200 Fax: (01698) 717204

▶ Helitune Ltd, Hatchmoor Industrial Estate, Torrington, Devon, EX38 7HP Tel: (01805) 624650 Fax: (01805) 624689

▶ I T Telecoms Ltd, 34 Avenue Parade, Accrington, Lancashire, BB5 6PP Tel: (01254) 394608 Fax: (01254) 395649 E-mail: sales@it-telecoms.org

▶ In Touch International, 43 Brace Street, Walsall, WS1 3PS Tel: (0870) 7507090 Fax: (0870) 7550033

Integrated Communications (Scotland) Ltd, Meikle Road, Kirkton Campus, Livingston, West Lothian, EH54 7DE Tel: (01506) 410780 Fax: (01506) 425400 E-mail: sales@icsscotland.com

Interalia Communications Ltd, Endahna House, Bridge End Road, Grantham, Lincolnshire, NG31 7TS Tel: (01476) 594207 Fax: (01476) 594208

Kenton Research Ltd, Unit 19 Bourne Road Industrial Park, Bourne Road, Dartford, DA1 4BZ Tel: (01322) 552000 Fax: (01322) 552020 E-mail: info@kentonresearch.co.uk

Kingston Communications Ltd, Elmbank Mill, Menstrie, Clackmannanshire, FK11 7BU Tel: (01259) 768700 Fax: (01259) 768709

Lane Telecommunications Ltd, Lane House, Priors Way, Maidenhead, Berkshire, SL6 2XJ Tel: (01628) 785351 Fax: (01628) 781611 E-mail: pfincham@lanetelecom.com

Lindfield Communications, 134 Islingword Road, Brighton, BN2 9SH Tel: (01273) 609008 E-mail: sales@1indfieldcomms.co.uk

The Link, 15 Market Centre, Crewe, CW1 2NG Tel: (01270) 254747 Fax: (01270) 254712

London Central Communications, 81 Southwark Street, London, SE1 0HX Tel: (020) 7401 3122 Fax: (020) 7357 8480

Lowe Electronics Ltd, Bentley Bridge, Chesterfield Road, Matlock, Derbyshire, DE4 5LE Tel: (01629) 580800 Fax: (01629) 580020 E-mail: info@lowe.co.uk

Lucent Technologies Holdings UK, Optimus, Windmill Hill Business Park, Swindon, SN5 6PP Tel: (01793) 883333 Fax: (01793) 883236

Mentor Communications Ltd, PO Box 21, Wellingborough, Northamptonshire, NN8 1PB Tel: (08454) 581552 Fax: (08708) 401553 E-mail: mentor.comms@fsbdial.co.uk

Mitel Networks, Mitel Business Park, Portskewett, Caldicot, Gwent, NP26 5YR Tel: (0870) 9092020 Fax: (0870) 9094040 E-mail: sales@mite1.com

▶ Monarch Business Systems Ltd, Unit 7, Drumhill Works, Clayton Lane, Clayton, Bradford, W. Yorkshire, BD14 6RF Tel: (01274) 883000

▶ Monx Electronic Engineers, County Park Road, Barrow-in-Furness, Cumbria, LA14 4BQ Tel: (01229) 837860 Fax: (01229) 837824

▶ N E C Infrontia, 75 Swingbridge Road, Loughborough, Leicestershire, LE11 5JB Tel: (01509) 643100 Fax: (01509) 610206 E-mail: sales@necinfrontia.co.uk

N T T Europe Ltd, Devon House, 58-60 St Katharines Way, London, E1W 1LB Tel: (020) 7977 1000 Fax: (020) 7977 1001 E-mail: info@ntt.co.uk

Network Business Communications, 57 London Road, Enfield, Middlesex, EN2 6DU Tel: (020) 8370 8370 Fax: (020) 8366 6844

Norgate Ltd, Unit 4b Newton Court, Wavertree Technology Park, Liverpool, L13 1EJ Tel: 0151-220 5556 Fax: 0151-254 1463 E-mail: sales@norgatetelecom.co.uk

Norsat International Ltd, The Old School, School Lane, South Carlton, Lincoln, LN1 2RL Tel: (01522) 730800 Fax: (01522) 730927 E-mail: smullery@norsat.com

Nortel Networks UK Ltd, Maidenhead Office Park, Westacott Way, Littlewick Green, Maidenhead, Berkshire, SL6 3QH Tel: (01628) 432000 Fax: (01628) 434318 E-mail: enquiries@nortelnetworks.com

Nortel Networks UK Ltd, Maidenhead Office Park, Westacott Way, Littlewick Green, Maidenhead, Berkshire, SL6 3QH Tel: (01628) 432000 Fax: (01628) 432812 E-mail: enquiries@nortelnetworks.com

Northern Communications Systems Ltd, Haigh Hall, Jebb Lane, Haigh, Barnsley, South Yorkshire, S75 4BT Tel: (01924) 830400 Fax: (01924) 830081

Northern Ireland Community Addiction Service, 219 Albertbridge Road, Belfast, BT5 4PU Tel: (028) 9073 1602 Fax: (028) 9046 0979

▶ Onesat Telecommunications Equipment, 34 Meadow Lane, Earith, Huntingdon, Cambridgeshire, PE28 3QE Tel: (01487) 741133 Fax: (01487) 843785 E-mail: sales@one-sat.com

Orion Telecom Ltd, Mays Farm, Sharnal Street, High Halstow, Rochester, Kent, ME3 8QL Tel: (01634) 255550 Fax: (01634) 251777 E-mail: sales@orion-telecom.co.uk

Palebeck Telecommunications Technology Ltd, 9 Little Portland Street, London, W1W 7JF Tel: (020) 7580 7226 Fax: (020) 7580 3115 E-mail: sales@pttl.co.uk

Philips Business Communication, Philips House Cambridge Business Park, Cowley Road, Cambridge, CB4 0HB Tel: (01223) 468000 Fax: (01223) 468444 E-mail: sales@sopho.philips.co.uk

▶ Phones 4U Ltd, Lower Level, White Rose Shopping Centre, Leeds, LS11 8LL Tel: 0113-270 3754

Pink Telecommunications, 15 The Broadway, Woodford Green, Essex, IG8 0HL Tel: (020) 8506 6464 Fax: (020) 8506 6400

Polysleeve Products Ltd, Groby Lodge Farm, Groby, Leicester, LE6 0GN Tel: (01530) 249719 Fax: (01530) 249729

Portal Telecommunications Equipment, Sapphire House, Roundtree Way, Norwich, NR7 8SQ Tel: (01603) 785300 Fax: (01603) 785303

Portman Electronics Ltd, 159 Commercial Road, Newport, Gwent, NP20 2PJ Tel: (01633) 841007 Fax: (01633) 222951

Postfield Structure Solutions Ltd, Old Barn Lane, Kenley, Surrey, CR8 5AT Tel: (020) 8668 8241 Fax: (020) 8660 1693 E-mail: info@postfieldcables.com

Powercom Trading Ltd, 5 Uxbridge Road, Slough, SL1 1SN Tel: (01753) 553838 Fax: (01753) 553828

Preformed Line Products GB Ltd, East Portway, Andover, Hampshire, SP10 3LH Tel: (01264) 366234 Fax: (01264) 356714 E-mail: sales@preformed.com

Premier Telecommunications Ltd, The Old Chapel, Main Street, Branston, Burton-on-Trent, Staffordshire, DE14 3EY Tel: (01283) 568301 Fax: (01283) 568352

▶ Protronix Ltd, Unit 13 14, Wren Court, Strathclyde Business Park, Bellshill, Lanarkshire, ML4 3NQ Tel: (01698) 741007 Fax: (01698) 846363 E-mail: sales@protronix-uk.com

▶ Qing Cables Ltd, Malmesbury Road, Kingsditch Trading Estate, Cheltenham, Gloucestershire, GL51 9PL Tel: (01242) 224141 Fax: (01242) 224134 E-mail: enquire@qingcables.co.uk

Quality Communications (S E), 5 Ribston Gardens, Paddock Wood, Tonbridge, Kent, TN12 6BA Tel: (01892) 835925 Fax: (01892) 832504 E-mail: sales@qualycom.co.uk

R G T Ltd, Chapel Road, Smallfield, Horley, Surrey, RH6 9NW Tel: (01342) 844411 Fax: (0870) 7771333 E-mail: sales@rgt.co.uk

Racal Acoustics, Waverley Industrial Park, Hailsham Drive, Harrow, Middlesex, HA1 4TR Tel: (020) 8515 6200 Fax: (020) 8427 0350 E-mail: email@racalacoustic.com

Recordacall Telecommunications Equipment, Recall House, 44 Main Road, Denholme, Bradford, West Yorkshire, BD13 4BL Tel: (01274) 832575 Fax: (01274) 834593

Red-M Services Ltd, Graylands, Langhurstwood Road, Horsham, West Sussex, RH12 4QD Tel: (01403) 211100 Fax: (01403) 248597

Reeves Lund, The Courtyard, 55 Charterhouse Street, London, EC1M 6HA Tel: (020) 7739 8888 Fax: (020) 7490 4488 E-mail: sales@reeveslund.com

▶ Renfrewshire Electronics, Block 15, Dubbs Road, Port Glasgow, Renfrewshire, PA14 5UG Tel: (01475) 794350 Fax: (01475) 744787 E-mail: sales@renfrew-elec.co.uk

Rocom Ltd, Thorp Arch Trading Estate, Thorp Arch, Wetherby, West Yorkshire, LS23 7RR Tel: (01937) 847777 Fax: (01937) 847788 E-mail: sales@rocon.co.uk

S3 Interactive, Unit 1a Dunrobin Court, 14 North Avenue, Clydebank Business Park, Clydebank, Dunbartonshire, G81 2QP Tel: 0141-952 2111 Fax: 0141-952 5255

Sapphire Communications Ltd, Herongate House, 76 Herongate Road, London, E12 5EQ Tel: (020) 8530 7272 Fax: (020) 8530 1141

Selex Communications Ltd, Marconi House, New Street, Chelmsford, CM1 1PL Tel: (01245) 353221 Fax: (01245) 287125 E-mail: alan.heritage@selex-comms.com

Shipton Communications Ltd, 1 Frogmore Road, Hemel Hempstead, Hertfordshire, HP3 9TG Tel: (01442) 345600 Fax: (01442) 345663

Siemens Communication, Turnells Mill Lane, Wellingborough, Northamptonshire, NN8 2RB Tel: (01933) 225000 Fax: (01933) 222650

Silver Telecom Ltd, Imperial House, Imperial Way, Coedkernew, Newport, Gwent, NP10 8UH Tel: (01633) 811833 Fax: (01633) 811834 E-mail: sales@silvertel.com

Skymasts Antennas Ltd, Equilibrium House, Mansion Close, Moulton Park Industrial Estate, Northampton, NN3 6RU Tel: (01604) 494132 Fax: (01604) 494133 E-mail: info@skymasts.com

Southern Cables, 5 Burwood Grove, Hayling Island, Hampshire, PO11 9DS Tel: (023) 9246 7337

Spitfire Technology Group, Unit 6-7 Southbank Business Centre, Ponton Road, London, SW8 5BL Tel: (020) 7501 3000 Fax: (020) 7501 3001 E-mail: sales@spitfire.co.uk

Sprint Communications, Unit F, Hove Technology Centre, St. Josephs Close, Hove, East Sussex, BN3 7ES Tel: (0870) 6082801 Fax: (0870) 6082802E-mail: sales@scsl.co.uk

Statcom Telecommunication Consultants, Unit 17d Shrub Hill Industrial Estate, Worcester, WR4 9EL Tel: (0870) 9909460 Fax: (08707) 872330

▶ Steve Cornish Solutions, Imex Business Centre, Brookfield Road, Arnold, Nottingham, NG5 7ER Tel: 0115-920 5740 Fax: 0115-966 7427 E-mail: steve@stevecornish.com

▶ Supercross Ltd, 3 Babington Close, Middleton, Milton Keynes, MK10 9HE Tel: (01908) 308180 Fax: (01908) 230750

Surrey Car Telephones Ltd, 3 The Riverside Business Centre, Walnut Tree Close, Guildford, Surrey, GU1 4UG Tel: (01483) 563999 Fax: (01483) 300813 E-mail: info@sctcomms.co.uk

Sytems (Telecom) Ltd, Unit 111 BMG Industrial Estate, Wakefield Road, Liversedge, West Yorkshire, WF15 6BS Tel: (01924) 402333 Fax: (01924) 402334

▶ T K P Electronics Ltd, Unit H5 Britannia Centre For Enterprise, Pengam Road, Pengam, Blackwood, Gwent, NP12 3SP Tel: (01443) 831052 Fax: (01443) 831052

▶ T M B Systems Ltd, Unit 10 Silver Business Park, Airfield Way, Christchurch, Dorset, BH23 3TA Tel: (01202) 488771 Fax: (01202) 488772 E-mail: paul@tmbonline.co.uk

▶ T R B Ltd, Rhodfa TRB, St. Asaph Business Park, St. Asaph, Clwyd, LL17 0JB Tel: (01745) 586500 Fax: (01745) 584111 E-mail: info@trb-ltd.co.uk

Talking Phones, Linotype House, L & M Business Park, Norman Road, Altrincham, Cheshire, WA14 4ES Tel: (0845) 4503435

Talking Technology Ltd, Technology House, 11 Palmerston Road, Sutton, Surrey, SM1 4QL Tel: (020) 8770 9343 Fax: (020) 8770 9143 E-mail: sales@talktech.co.uk

Task Communications Ltd, 259 Church Road, Benfleet, Essex, SS7 4QN Tel: (01268) 793240 Fax: (01268) 881010 E-mail: sales@taskcomms.co.uk

Taylor Bros Oldham Ltd, Lee Street, Oldham, OL8 1EE Tel: 0161-652 3221 Fax: 0161-626 1736 E-mail: karen.taylorbrs@btinternet.com

Telecom Solutions International, 23-27 Endsleigh Road, Redhill, RH1 3LX Tel: (0870) 6060380 Fax: (01377) 647801 E-mail: info@tsigroup.co.uk

Telecom Supply Line Ltd, Units 1&2, Treelyn Park, Welbeck Way, Woodston, Peterborough, PE2 7WH Tel: (01733) 390929 Fax: (01733) 391059E-mail: sales@telecomsupplyline.ltd.uk

Telephone Lines Ltd, 304 High Street, Cheltenham, Gloucestershire, GL50 3JF Tel: (01242) 583699 Fax: (01242) 690033 E-mail: info@telephonelines.net

Teletec International, Cranfield Innovation Centre, University Way, Cranfield, Bedford, MK43 0BT Tel: (01234) 756027 Fax: (01234) 756028

Teletech U K Ltd, 225 Bath Street, Glasgow, G2 4GZ Tel: 0141-420 2500 Fax: 0141-420 2590 E-mail: info@teletech.com

Teletronics Ltd, Unit C3-C5, Formal Industrial Estate, Treswithian, Camborne, Cornwall, TR14 0PY Tel: (01209) 716360 Fax: (01209) 716285

Telsis Direct Ltd, 16 Barnes Wallis Road, Segensworth East, Fareham, Hampshire, PO15 5TT Tel: (01489) 885877 Fax: (01489) 885826 E-mail: sales@telsis.com

Telspec plc, Lancaster Parker Road, Rochester, Kent, ME1 3QU Tel: (01634) 687133 Fax: (01634) 684984 E-mail: net@telspec.co.uk

Tertio Ltd, 1 Angel Square, Torrens Street, London, EC1V 1PL Tel: (01225) 478000 Fax: (01225) 478001

Texcel Technology plc, Parkside Works, Thames Road, Crayford, Dartford, DA1 4SB Tel: (01322) 621700 Fax: (01322) 557733 E-mail: sales@texceltechnology.com

▶ Time 24 Ltd, Empire Works, Parcel Terrace, Derby, DE1 1LY Tel: (01332) 200880 Fax: (01332) 349801 E-mail: enquiries@time24derby.co.uk

Tota Crontol Systems, 2 High St, Tattenhall, Chester, CH3 9PX Tel: (01829) 770900 Fax: (01829) 770900

Trafalgar Square Collectors Centre, 7 Whitcomb Street, London, WC2H 7HA Tel: (020) 7930 1979 Fax: (020) 7930 1152

Tyco Electronics, Kinmel Park, Bodelwyddan, Rhyl, Clwyd, LL18 5TZ Tel: (01745) 584545 Fax: (01745) 584780 E-mail: admin@pinacl.com

Videoquest 2004 Ltd, 27 Masson Avenue, Ruislip, Middlesex, HA4 6QT Tel: (020) 8842 2783 Fax: (020) 8842 2784 E-mail: videoquestltd@btconnect.com

Voice Connect Ltd, 10-12 Firtree Lane Trading Estate, Groby, Leicester, LE6 0FH Tel: 0116-232 2622 Fax: 0116-232 2433 E-mail: info@voiceconnect.co.uk

▶ Zycomm Electronics Ltd, 51 Nottingham Road, Ripley, Derbyshire, DE5 3AS Tel: (01773) 570123 Fax: (01773) 570155 E-mail: sales@zycomm.co.uk

TELECOMMUNICATION SYSTEMS OR EQUIPMENT INSTALLATION

▶ A C Systems, 42 St. James Road, Torquay, TQ1 4AY Tel: (0870) 4448995 Fax: (08704) 448996 E-mail: sales@acsystems.co.uk

A P R Telecoms Maintenance, Appointment House, Philip Ford Way, Silfield, Wymondham, Norfolk, NR18 9AQ Tel: (01953) 713333 Fax: (01953) 713345

Abbey Telecom, Logic House, Ordnance Street, Blackburn, BB1 3AE Tel: (01254) 272000 Fax: (01254) 272001 E-mail: sales@abbeytelecom.co.uk

Allied Communications Ltd, 7 Hepton Court, Leeds, LS9 6PW Tel: 0113-200 9000 Fax: 0113-200 9001 E-mail: info@alliedcom.co.uk

Anglia Telecoms, 1 Gateshead Close, Sandy, Bedfordshire, SG19 1RS Tel: (01767) 692792 Fax: (01767) 692992 E-mail: info@angliatelecoms.co.uk

Ash Hill Communications & Electronics Ltd, Keepers Cottage, Combe Raleigh, Honiton, Devon, EX14 4TG Tel: (01404) 44080 Fax: (01404) 44122

Ashland Communications Equipment Ltd, Ashland House, Dobson Park Way, Ince, Wigan, Lancashire, WN2 2DX Tel: (01942) 221122 Fax: (01942) 222127 E-mail: sales@ashlandcomm.com

Berkshire Telephone Systems Ltd, PO Box 4229, Reading, RG8 9XT Tel: (01491) 682552 Fax: (01491) 682551

Bistech plc, 137 Victoria Road, Ferndown, Dorset, BH22 9HX Tel: (01202) 863200 Fax: (01202) 869465

Black & White Telephone Co., John Street, Royston, Hertfordshire, SG8 9BE Tel: (01763) 248216 Fax: (01763) 249475

Britannic Technologies Ltd, Britannic House, Merrow Business Park, Guildford, Surrey, GU4 7WA Tel: (01483) 242526 Fax: 0845-050 1001 E-mail: enquiries@btlnet.co.uk

TELECOMMUNICATION SYSTEMS OR EQUIPMENT INSTALLATION – *continued*

Cable and Wireless P.L.C., Redlion Square, London, WC1R 4HQ Tel: (020) 7315 4000 Fax: (020) 7315 5182

Check Communications Ltd, The Haven Communications House, 40 Chester Road West, Queensferry, Deeside, Clwyd, CH5 1SA Tel: (01244) 834800 Fax: (01244) 831606 E-mail: solutions@checkcomm.com

Chiltern Telecom, 61 Union Street, Dunstable, Bedfordshire, LU6 1EX Tel: (01582) 604040 Fax: (0871) 2230230 E-mail: sales@chilterntelecom.co.uk

Clwyd Communications, 1 Llewelyn Drive, Bryn-y-Baal, Mold, Clwyd, CH7 6SW Tel: (01352) 700352 Fax: (01352) 759724 E-mail: sales@cymrucomms.co.uk

Communications UK Ltd, Comms House, Collingwood Road, Wimborne, Dorset, BH21 6QF Tel: (01202) 894222 Fax: (01202) 892262 E-mail: sales@comms.uk.com

Computer Links Ltd, 7 Grange Road, Houston Industrial Estate, Houstoun Industrial Estate, Livingston, West Lothian, EH54 5DE Tel: (01506) 434811 Fax: (01506) 441997 E-mail: service@computer-links.co.uk

Cumbria Communications 2000 Ltd, Westgate, Milburn, Penrith, Cumbria, CA10 1TW Tel: (01768) 361416 Fax: (01768) 362000

D C S Telecom Ltd, Reculver Road, Herne Bay, Kent, CT6 6PB Tel: (01227) 741825 Fax: (01227) 361011 E-mail: sales@dcstelecom.co.uk

Daly Telecom, The Point, Granite Way, Mountsorrel, Loughborough, Leicestershire, LE12 7TZ Tel: (01509) 410400 Fax: (0870) 2407755 E-mail: info@dalytelecom.co.uk

Darnell Consultants Ltd, 14a Kenworthy Lane, Manchester, M22 4EJ Tel: 0161-945 6996 Fax: 0161-945 6997 E-mail: bernard@darnellconsultants.com

Direct Telecom Services Ltd, 17 Bessemer Way, Harfreys Industrial Estate, Great Yarmouth, Norfolk, NR31 0LX Tel: (01493) 440000 Fax: (01493) 440063 E-mail: tim@direct-telecom-svs.co.uk

Eclipse Telecom 99, 36 Hertford Drive, Tyldesley, Manchester, M29 8LU Tel: (01942) 889900 Fax: (01942) 878060

Etrali UK Ltd, Piercy House, 7-9 Copthall Avenue, London, EC2R 7NJ Tel: (020) 7628 2795 Fax: (020) 7628 4972 E-mail: enquiries@aircharlie.com

Fine Line Communications E A Ltd, Logic House, Harfreys Road, Great Yarmouth, Norfolk, NR31 0LS Tel: (01493) 441114 Fax: (01493) 441124 E-mail: clairey@finelinecoms.co.uk

Fujitsu Telecommunications Europe Ltd, Solihull Parkway, Birmingham Business Park, Birmingham, B37 7YU Tel: 0121-717 6000 Fax: 0121-717 6014 E-mail: rcpt@ftel.co.uk

General Telecom & Data UK Ltd, 3-5 Berringtons Lane, Rainford, St. Helens, Merseyside, WA11 7PZ Tel: (01744) 885828 Fax: (01744) 889515 E-mail: enquiries@generaltel.co.uk

GPT Communications Systems Ltd, 11 Brunswick Road, Plymouth, PL4 0NP Tel: (01752) 660226 Fax: (01752) 601419

I D Installations, 202 Nuthurst Road, Manchester, M40 3PP Tel: 0161-682 4595 Fax: 0161-682 4595 E-mail: david@idinstallations.freeserve.co.uk

Internal Communications Network Ltd, 268 Hackney Road, London, E2 7SJ Tel: (020) 7613 0000 Fax: (020) 7723 7300 E-mail: icm@talk21.com

Invicta Telephone Sales Ltd, Unit 30 Branbridges Industrial Estate, Branbridges Road, East Peckham, Tonbridge, Kent, TN12 5HF Tel: (01622) 870550 Fax: (01622) 870569 E-mail: enquires@itslimited.com

ISDN Communications Ltd, The Stable Block, Ronans, Winkfield Row, Bracknell, Berkshire, RG42 6LY Tel: (01344) 899006 Fax: (01344) 899001

Kitel C S, Welldon, Askham, Penrith, Cumbria, CA10 2PG Tel: (01931) 712870

Livewire Telecommunication, Kineton Road, Gaydon, Warwick, CV35 0HB Tel: (01926) 640634

Medigen Telecommunications Ltd, 186 High Road, Ilford, Essex, IG1 1LR Tel: (020) 8477 0807 Fax: (020) 8478 3349

National Communications Group Ltd, Old Cider Works Lane, Abbotskersewell, Newton Abbot, Devon, TQ12 5GH Tel: (0870) 6084440 Fax: (0870) 5246642 E-mail: ops@nationalcommsgroup.co.uk

Network Business Communications, 57 London Road, Enfield, Middlesex, EN2 6DU Tel: (020) 8370 8370 Fax: (020) 8366 6844

Pink Telecommunications, 15 The Broadway, Woodford Green, Essex, IG8 0HL Tel: (020) 8506 6464 Fax: (020) 8506 6400

Premier Telecom, 1 Dungannon Park, Moy Road, Dungannon, County Tyrone, BT71 6BT Tel: (028) 8775 2986 Fax: (028) 8775 2986

Premier Telecommunications Ltd, The Old Chapel, Main Street, Branston, Burton-on-Trent, Staffordshire, DE14 3EY Tel: (01283) 568301 Fax: (01283) 568352

Premier Voice & Data, Motokov House, North Lynn Indust Estate, North Lynn Industrial Estate, King's Lynn, Norfolk, PE30 2JG Tel: (01553) 779950 Fax: (01553) 779950 E-mail: info@premiervoiceanddata.co.uk

Programmed Communications, Unit 9 Bluebird House, Povey Cross Road, Horley, Surrey, RH6 0AF Tel: (01293) 822033 Fax: (01293) 821958

Protel Communications Ltd, Raleigh House, 9a The Wellsway, Keynsham, Bristol, BS31 1HF Tel: 0117-986 4486 Fax: 0117-986 5144 E-mail: info@protelcomms.co.uk

Russell Systems Telecom, Communication House, The Watermark, Gateshead, Tyne & Wear, NE11 9SZ Tel: 0191-461 4200 Fax: 0191-461 4201

Sangikyo Corporation, Highbridge Industrial Estate, Oxford Road, Uxbridge, Middlesex, UB8 1HR Tel: (01895) 876101 Fax: (01895) 876257

Statcom Telecommunication Consultants, Unit 17d Shrub Hill Industrial Estate, Worcester, WR4 9EL Tel: (0870) 9909460 Fax: (08707) 872330

Strata Communications, 25 Hibson Avenue, Rochdale, Lancashire, OL12 7RU Tel: (01706) 344375 Fax: (01706) 633172 E-mail: info@stratacommunications.co.uk

STS, Unit 175 Dean Clough Office Park, Halifax, West Yorkshire, HX3 5AX Tel: (01422) 383071 Fax: (01422) 383072

Telecall Ltd, 1 Stratfield Park, Elettra Avenue, Waterlooville, Hampshire, PO7 7XN Tel: (023) 9225 0525 Fax: (023) 9226 5299 E-mail: sales@telecall.uk.com

Telephone Services Ltd, Phonex House, 18 Suffolk Street, Pendleton, Salford, M6 6DU Tel: 0161-737 7055 Fax: 0161-737 7055

Telwise Ltd, 7 Little Forge Road, Park Farm, Redditch, Worcestershire, B98 7SF Tel: (01527) 519930 Fax: (01527) 519939 E-mail: telwise@telwiseuk.com

Tricom Telecom, 9 Thorne Way, Kirton, Boston, Lincolnshire, PE20 1JP Tel: (01205) 724889 Fax: (01205) 724852 E-mail: tricom.telecom@fsbdial.co.uk

Wharfdale Telecom, 5 Park Terrace, Otley, West Yorkshire, LS21 1HH Tel: (01943) 465987 Fax: (01943) 463012

Widewell Communications, 49 Lulworth Drive, Plymouth, PL6 7DT Tel: (01752) 721226 Fax: (01752) 721236 E-mail: enquire@widewell.co.uk

Worth Installations Ltd, Bramwell House, Park Lane, Keighley, West Yorkshire, BD21 4QX Tel: (01535) 210510 Fax: (01535) 691508 E-mail: sales@worthcomms.co.uk

TELECOMMUNICATION SYSTEMS OR EQUIPMENT MAINTENANCE OR REPAIR

A P R Telecoms Maintenance, Appointment House, Philip Ford Way, Silfield, Wymondham, Norfolk, NR18 9AQ Tel: (01953) 713333 Fax: (01953) 713345

A S T Networks Ltd, Temple Court, Cathedral Road, Cardiff, CF11 9HA Tel: (0870) 1160110 Fax: (0870) 1160611 E-mail: enquiries@astnetworks.co.uk

Ashland Communications Equipment Ltd, Ashland House, Dobson Park Way, Ince, Wigan, Lancashire, WN2 2DX Tel: (01942) 221122 Fax: (01942) 222127 E-mail: sales@ashlandcomm.com

Automatic Response Telephone Systems Ltd, 153 Marine Drive, Saltdean, Brighton, BN2 8AA Tel: (01273) 304010 E-mail: director@1tripcamera.com

Bistech plc, 137 Victoria Road, Ferndown, Dorset, BH22 9HX Tel: (01202) 863200 Fax: (01202) 896465

Britannic Technologies Ltd, Britannic House, Merrow Business Park, Guildford, Surrey, GU4 7WA Tel: (01483) 242526 Fax: 0845-050 1001 E-mail: enquiries@btlnet.co.uk

C S Communication Services Ltd, 19 Sutton Oak Corner, Sutton Coldfield, West Midlands, B74 2DH Tel: (0845) 6771000 E-mail: sales@comms.co.uk

Comm-Tech Martham Ltd, 2 Rollesby Road, Martham, Great Yarmouth, Norfolk, NR29 4RU Tel: (01493) 748274 Fax: (01493) 740185 E-mail: enquiries@comm-tech.co.uk

Communications UK Ltd, Comms House, Collingwood Road, Wimborne, Dorset, BH21 6QF Tel: (01202) 894222 Fax: (01202) 892262 E-mail: sales@comms.uk.com

D C S Telecom Ltd, Reculver Road, Herne Bay, Kent, CT6 6PB Tel: (01227) 741825 Fax: (01227) 361011 E-mail: sales@dcstelecom.co.uk

Direct Telecom Services Ltd, 17 Bessemer Way, Harfreys Industrial Estate, Great Yarmouth, Norfolk, NR31 0LX Tel: (01493) 440000 Fax: (01493) 440063 E-mail: tim@direct-telecom-svs.co.uk

Eclipse Telecom 99, 36 Hertford Drive, Tyldesley, Manchester, M29 8LU Tel: (01942) 889900 Fax: (01942) 878060

Electronic Repair Technology, Signal Works, Talbot Road, Wellingborough, Northants, NN8 1QH Tel: (01933) 228866 Fax: (01933) 443623 E-mail: dave@autocontrol.freeserve.co.uk

Fujitsu Telecommunications Europe Ltd, Solihull Parkway, Birmingham Business Park, Birmingham, B37 7YU Tel: 0121-717 6000 Fax: 0121-717 6014 E-mail: rcpt@ftel.co.uk

Halton Communications Ltd, Unit 12 King Edward Industrial Estate, Gibraltar Row, Liverpool, L3 7HJ Tel: 0151-236 9323 Fax: 0151-236 2875 E-mail: admin@haltoncommunications.co.uk

Kingston Communications Ltd, Elmbank Mill, Menstrie, Clackmannanshire, FK11 7BU Tel: (01259) 768700 Fax: (01259) 768709

Leonard-Carter Communications Ltd, 113 Lavender Walk, London, SW11 1JS Tel: (020) 7738 0738 Fax: (020) 7738 0081

London Central Communications, 81 Southwark Street, London, SE1 0HX Tel: (020) 7401 3122 Fax: (020) 7357 8480

Margolis Technology, Laser House, 132-140 Goswell Road, London, EC1V 7DY Tel: (020) 7251 7000 Fax: (020) 7251 7600 E-mail: tdwyer@margolistechnology.com

Task Communications Ltd, 259 Church Road, Benfleet, Essex, SS7 4QN Tel: (01268) 793240 Fax: (01268) 881010 E-mail: sales@taskcomms.co.uk

Telecall Ltd, 1 Stratfield Park, Elettra Avenue, Waterlooville, Hampshire, PO7 7XN Tel: (023) 9225 0525 Fax: (023) 9226 5299 E-mail: sales@telecall.uk.com

Teleconnect Systems, Melford Pl, St Peters Rd, Hockley, Essex, SS5 6AA Tel: 01702 206606 Fax: 01702 206606

Telinet Ltd, 52 Southwark Bridge Road, London, SE1 0AR Tel: 0207 771 7700

Trac International Ltd, Unit 12 Kirkhill Industrial Estate, Howe Moss Drive, Dyce, Aberdeen, AB21 0GL Tel: (01224) 725800 Fax: (01224) 725801 E-mail: info@tracinternational.com

TELECOMMUNICATION SYSTEMS OR EQUIPMENT RESELLERS

▶ Gemini Telecommunications, 78 Britton Street, Gillingham, Kent, ME7 5ET Tel: (01634) 580510 Fax: (01634) 579628 E-mail: sales@gemini-telecom.com

TELECOMMUNICATION SYSTEMS SOFTWARE/ HARDWARE DESIGN SERVICES

Alcatel Telecom Ltd, Bulding N140, Christchurch Way, London, SE10 0AG Tel: (0870) 9033600 Fax: (020) 8293 2433

Communications UK Ltd, Comms House, Collingwood Road, Wimborne, Dorset, BH21 6QF Tel: (01202) 894222 Fax: (01202) 892262 E-mail: sales@comms.uk.com

Dalman Technical Services, Unit 36 Walworth Enterprise Centre Duke Close, West Way, Andover, Hampshire, SP10 5AP Tel: (01264) 357580 Fax: (01264) 351325 E-mail: sales@dalmants.co.uk

Kddi, Atlas House, 1-7 King Street, London, EC2V 8AU Tel: (020) 7397 1111 Fax: (020) 7600 3088

Mentat Systems Ltd, 3 Rutland Road, Southport, Merseyside, PR8 6PB Tel: (01704) 514506 E-mail: sale@mentat.co.uk

Telsis Direct Ltd, 16 Barnes Wallis Road, Segensworth East, Fareham, Hampshire, PO15 5TT Tel: (01489) 885877 Fax: (01489) 885826 E-mail: sales@telsis.com

TELECOMMUNICATION SYSTEMS/EQUIPMENT, AUDIO

Aur Telephone, 260 Tottenham Court Road, London, W1T 7RF Tel: (020) 7637 7353 Fax: (020) 7323 9790

Border Telecom, Heather Drive, Ascot, Berkshire, SL5 0HT Tel: (01344) 873873 Fax: (01344) 873872

ISDN Communications Ltd, The Stable Block, Ronans, Winkfield Row, Bracknell, Berkshire, RG42 6LY Tel: (01344) 899006 Fax: (01344) 899001

Murphy Telecommunications, 293 Salisbury Road, Totton, Southampton, SO40 3LZ Tel: (023) 8086 1479 Fax: (023) 8086 8483 E-mail: murtel@talktalk.net

R G Jones, 16 Endeavour Way, London, SW19 8UH Tel: (020) 8971 3100 Fax: (020) 8971 3101 E-mail: enquiries@rgjones.co.uk

Sarian Systems, Beacon House, Riverside Business Park, Leeds Road, Ilkley, West Yorkshire, LS29 8JZ Tel: (01943) 605055 Fax: (01943) 605056

TELECOMMUNICATION SYSTEMS/EQUIPMENT EXPORT MERCHANTS OR AGENTS

Canecrown Ltd, 34 London Road, Croydon, CR0 2TA Tel: (020) 8649 8349 Fax: (020) 8649 8349 E-mail: tilcluk@aol.com

▶ Fusion Four Telecoms Ltd, 7 Saffron Court, Southfields Business Park, Laindon, Basildon, Essex, SS15 6SS Tel: (01268) 417500 Fax: (01268) 543355 E-mail: fft@fusiontelecom.co.uk

In Touch Cellular Ltd, Newbury, Gillingham, Dorset, SP8 4HZ Tel: (01747) 822525 Fax: (01747) 825364

TELECOMMUNICATION SYSTEMS/EQUIPMENT INFORMATION SERVICES

▶ Ayudar, Sheraton House, Castle Park, Cambridge, CB3 0AX Tel: (08709) 9 01090

▶ Coach House Communications Ltd, The Coach House, Sherridge Road, Leigh Sinton, Malvern, Worcestershire, WR13 5DB Tel: (0870) 4440888 Fax: (0844) 8440124 E-mail: enquiries@coachhousecommunications.co.uk

TELECOMMUNICATION SYSTEMS/EQUIPMENT TEST SERVICES

Global Telecommunications Laboratories Ltd, Gladstone House, Gladstone Drive, Bristol, BS16 4RU Tel: 0117-987 0044 Fax: 0117-987 0055 E-mail: gtl@gtlabs.co.uk

TELECOMMUNICATION SYSTEMS/EQUIPMENT, LOCAL AREA NETWORK (LAN) AND WIDE AREA NETWORK (WAN)

Kenton Research Ltd, Unit 19 Bourne Road Industrial Park, Bourne Road, Dartford, DA1 4BZ Tel: (01322) 552000 Fax: (01322) 552020 E-mail: info@kentonresearch.co.uk

TELECOMMUNICATION SYSTEMS/EQUIPMENT, MOBILE DATA

▶ Corporate Communications Ltd, 45 Bank Street, Galashiels, Selkirkshire, TD1 1EP Tel: 0870 7460060 Fax: 0870 7460061 E-mail: info@corpcl.co.uk

Signature Industries Ltd, Unit 19 Atlas Industrial Estate, Foundry Street, Glasgow, G21 4PR Tel: 0141-558 7272 Fax: 0141-558 9696 E-mail: info@sigcom.co.uk

Team Simoco Ltd, Field House, Uttoxeter Old Road, Derby, DE1 1NH Tel: (01332) 375500 Fax: (01332) 375501 E-mail: marketing@teamsimoco.com

Thorcom Network Services Ltd, Unit 4 96b Blackpole Trading Estate We, St, Worcester, WR3 8TJ Tel: (01905) 756700 Fax: (01905) 755777 E-mail: sales@thorcom.co.uk

TELECOMMUNICATION TEST EQUIPMENT MANUFRS

Genesys I B S Ltd, Singleton Court Business Centre, Wonastow Road, Monmouth, Gwent, NP25 5JA Tel: (01600) 710300 Fax: (01600) 710301 E-mail: nick@genesysibs.com

T R L Technology Ltd, Shannon Way, Ashchurch, Tewkesbury, Gloucestershire, GL20 8ND Tel: (01684) 278700 Fax: (01684) 850406 E-mail: d_hall@trltech.co.uk

▶ Tempo Europe Ltd, Suit 8 Brecon House, William Brown Close, Llantarnam Industrial Park, Cwmbran, Gwent, NP44 3AB Tel: (01633) 225600 Fax: (01633) 627711 E-mail: tempo@klauke.txtron.com

TELECOMMUNICATIONS ADAPTERS

Check Communications Ltd, The Haven Communications House, 40 Chester Road West, Queensferry, Deeside, Clwyd, CH5 1SA Tel: (01244) 834800 Fax: (01244) 831606 E-mail: solutions@checkcomm.comm

▶ Connell Communications Ltd, 63 Brights Avenue, Rainham, Essex, RM13 9NW Tel: (01708) 521598 Fax: (01708) 521648 E-mail: doconnell@connellcommunications.com

TELECOMMUNICATIONS CIVIL ENGINEERING

▶ TeleFone Resources (UK) Ltd, Unit 7G, N17 Studios, 784-788 Tottenham High Road, Tottenham, London, N17 0DA Tel: (020) 8803 5050 Fax: (020) 8887 0455 E-mail: sales@telresuk.com

TELECOMMUNICATIONS CONNECTORS

Leotronics Ltd, London Road, Rake, Liss, Hampshire, GU33 7PQ Tel: (01730) 893838 Fax: (01730) 894442 E-mail: sales@leotronics.co.uk

TELECOMMUNICATIONS CONNECTORS – *continued*

Ringtel Electronics (UK) Ltd, Ringtel House, Lakeview, Llantarnam Industrial Park, Cwmbran, Gwent, NP44 3HP Tel: (01633) 489550 Fax: (01633) 489570 E-mail: sales@ringtel.com

Siemens Communications, Technology Drive, Beeston, Nottingham, NG9 1LA Tel: 0115-943 0300 Fax: 0115-925 9610 E-mail: firstname.surname@siemens.com

Spectrum Control GmbH, PO Box 34, Great Yarmouth, Norfolk, NR29 5RE Tel: (01692) 678041 Fax: (01692) 678042 E-mail: sales@spectrumcontrol.co.uk

Swale Components Ltd, Unit 88 John Wilson Business Park, Chestfield, Whitstable, Kent, CT5 3QT Tel: (01227) 771100 Fax: (01227) 771117 E-mail: sales@swalecomponents.com

Viking Ltd, Chatsworth House, Portland Close, Houghton Regis, Dunstable, Bedfordshire, LU5 5AW Tel: (01582) 603600 Fax: (01582) 471114 E-mail: accounts@vikingltd.co.uk

TELECOMMUNICATIONS EXTENSION SOUNDING ALARMS

A B M Security Systems Ltd, 20 Warrington Road, Prescot, Merseyside, L34 5RB Tel: 0151-426 0233 Fax: 0151-430 7962 E-mail: info@abmsecurity.co.uk

▶ Eft Systems Ltd, 39a Cobden Road, Southport, Merseyside, PR9 7TR Tel: (01704) 229662 Fax: (01704) 505391

TELECOMMUNICATIONS PROJECT MANAGEMENT

C P S-Lanmear Ltd, 158 Little Hardwick Rd, Aldridge, Walsall, WS9 0SF Tel: 0121-353 5705 Fax: 0121-353 5705 E-mail: csiddell@compuserve.com

Causeway Associates, Clophill House, High Street, Clophill, Bedford, MK45 4AA Tel: (01462) 810033

Grapevine, 83 Broadway, Southbourne, Bournemouth, BH6 4EJ Tel: (01202) 429232 Fax: (01202) 424559 E-mail: sales1@grapevine-comms.co.uk

M C I, Reading International Business Park, Reading, RG2 6DA Tel: 0118-905 5000 Fax: 0118-905 5711

TELECOMMUNICATIONS SALES STAFF RECRUITMENT

▶ Pareto Law plc, Barfield House, 24-28 Alderley Road, Wilmslow, Cheshire, SK9 1PL Tel: (01625) 255255 Fax: (01625) 255256 E-mail: graduate@paretolaw.co.uk

TELECOMMUNICATIONS SECURITY SYSTEMS

C & M Communications Consultants Ltd, Tanners Court, Tanners Lane, East Wellow, Romsey, Hampshire, SO51 6DP Tel: (01794) 518508 Fax: (01794) 518182 E-mail: stephen.michaelides@candmcommunications.co.uk

Stirling Solent Communications, 33 Portsmouth Enterprise Centre, Quartremaine Road, Portsmouth, PO3 5QT Tel: (0870) 7701702 Fax: (023) 9267 3518E-mail: csil@csil-uk.com

TELECOMMUNICATIONS SOFTWARE

A T Communications, Canon House, Thame Road, Haddenham, Aylesbury, Buckinghamshire, HP17 8LH Tel: (01844) 266266 Fax: (01844) 266262

Action Information Technologies Ltd, 1 Butler Road, Shrewsbury, SY3 7AJ Tel: (01743) 244377 Fax: (01743) 244367 E-mail: sales@actionit.demon.co.uk

Amdocs, Clarify Court, London Road, Earley, Reading, RG6 1BW Tel: 0118-955 5200 Fax: 0118-955 5201

C T A Services, 1 Drake Road, Newport, Isle of Wight, PO30 1EQ Tel: (01983) 524129 Fax: (01983) 528001 E-mail: sales@ctaservices.co.uk

Clansey Communications Ltd, 68-70 Market Street, Cannock, Staffordshire, WS12 1AY Tel: (01543) 424485 Fax: (01543) 422256 E-mail: sales@clansey.co.uk

The Computer Partnership Ltd, Berwick House, 8-10 Knoll Rise, Orpington, Kent, BR6 0EJ Tel: (01689) 898000 Fax: (01689) 898089 E-mail: marketing@tcplifesystems.com

Fone Installations, Unit 2 Douglas Buildings, Lodge Road, Staplehurst, Kent, TN12 0QZ Tel: (01580) 893377 Fax: (01580) 893434 E-mail: mail@foneinstallations.co.uk

Hazid Technologies, 21a S G C S Business Park, Technology Drive, Beeston, Nottingham, NG9 2ND Tel: 0115-922 4115 Fax: 0115-922 4115 E-mail: sales@hazid.com

Kingston Communications Ltd, Elmbank Mill, Menstrie, Clackmannanshire, FK11 7BU Tel: (01259) 768700 Fax: (01259) 768709

Mentat Systems Ltd, 21 Porthleven Crescent, Astley, Tyldesley, Manchester, M29 7FZ Tel: (01942) 749444 E-mail: sales@mentat.co.uk

Midland Phone Services plc, Unit 6-7 Two Woods Lane, Brierley Hill, West Midlands, DY5 1TA Tel: (01384) 74888 Fax: (01384) 76888

Network Europe Group plc, 14 Capricorn Centre, Cranes Farm Road, Basildon, Essex, SS14 3JJ Tel: (0870) 3330321 Fax: (0870) 3330320 E-mail: sales@negplc.com

TVM Systems, 2 Newgate Court, Paradise Street, Coventry, CV1 2RU Tel: (024) 7625 7875 Fax: (024) 7625 6433 E-mail: sales@tvm-systems.co.uk

TELECOMMUNICATIONS TRANSFORMERS

Northern Coil Services, Unit 6 Aston Court, Kingsland Grange, Woolston, Warrington, WA1 4SG Tel: (01925) 819642 Fax: (01925) 825865 E-mail: ncsdeakin@aol.com

Profec Holdings Ltd, 10 Betts Avenue, Martlesham Heath, Ipswich, IP5 3RH Tel: (01473) 611422 Fax: (01473) 611919 E-mail: sales@profec.com

Rolfe Industries, 14 High Street, Steyning, West Sussex, BN44 3GG Tel: (01903) 810600 Fax: (01903) 810611 E-mail: support@ri.uk.com

TELEMETRY CONTROL SYSTEMS

E D G S B Ltd, The Mews, 70 London Road, Burgess Hill, West Sussex, RH15 8NB Tel: (01444) 248691 Fax: (01444) 248721 E-mail: sales@edg.co.uk

Geutebruck (UK) Ltd, 8 Central Park, Bellfield Road, High Wycombe, Buckinghamshire, HP13 5HG Tel: (01494) 510999 Fax: (01494) 510888 E-mail: info@geutebruck.co.uk

Lee-Dickens Ltd, Rushton Rd, Desborough, Kettering, Northamptonshire, NN14 2QW Tel: (01536) 760156 Fax: (01536) 762552 E-mail: sales@lee-dickens.co.uk

Ocean Technical Systems Ltd, Oceantech House, Station Approach, Cheam, Sutton, Surrey, SM2 7AU Tel: (020) 8643 2233 Fax: (020) 8643 6444 E-mail: ots@oceantechsys.com

TELEMETRY DATA RECORDERS

Astro Med Inc, Astro Med House 11 Progress Business Centre, Whittle Parkway, Slough, SL1 6DQ Tel: (01628) 668836 Fax: (01628) 664994 E-mail: astromeduk@astromed.com

TELEMETRY REMOTE CONTROL SYSTEMS

Churchill Controls Ltd, Unit 12 Station Industrial Estate, Oxford Road, Wokingham, Berkshire, RG41 2YQ Tel: 0118-989 2200 Fax: 0118-989 2007 E-mail: sales@churchill-controls.co.uk

TELEMETRY SYSTEMS/ EQUIPMENT

Acksen Ltd, 42 University Road, Belfast, BT7 1NJ Tel: (028) 9020 1050 Fax: (028) 9020 1060 E-mail: sales@acksen.com

Addlestone Electronics, Kistadan, Church Lane, Bisley, Woking, Surrey, GU24 9EA Tel: (01483) 480969 Fax: (01483) 797268 E-mail: sales@addlestone-electronics.co.uk

Antec Instrumentation, Unit 1, 59 Queensway North, Team Valley Trading Estate, Gateshead, Tyne & Wear, NE11 0NX Tel: 0191-482 4241 Fax: 0191-487 8835

C S I P Ltd, Unit 11 Granby Court, Surrey Close, Granby Industrial Estate, Weymouth, Dorset, DT4 9XB Tel: (01305) 779020 Fax: (01305) 778095 E-mail: sales@csip.co.uk

Chelsea Technologies Group, 55 Central Avenue, West Molesey, Surrey, KT8 2QZ Tel: (020) 8941 0044 Fax: (020) 8941 9349 E-mail: sales@chelsea.co.uk

Churchill Controls Ltd, Unit 12 Station Industrial Estate, Oxford Road, Wokingham, Berkshire, RG41 2YQ Tel: 0118-989 2200 Fax: 0118-989 2007 E-mail: sales@churchill-controls.co.uk

Conway Security Products Ltd, Seymour House, Copyground Lane, High Wycombe, Buckinghamshire, HP12 3HE Tel: (01494) 461373 Fax: (01494) 531685 E-mail: sales@conway-cctv.co.uk

▶ Karlan Digital Ltd, 76 Howdale Road, Hull, HU8 9JZ Tel: (07841) 870659 E-mail: enquiries@karlandigital.co.uk

Lee-Dickens Ltd, Rushton Rd, Desborough, Kettering, Northamptonshire, NN14 2QW Tel: (01536) 760156 Fax: (01536) 762552 E-mail: sales@lee-dickens.co.uk

Measurement Devices Ltd, Silverburn Crescent, Bridge of Don Industrial Estate, Aberdeen, AB23 8EW Tel: (01224) 246700 Fax: (01224) 824987 E-mail: info@mdl.co.uk

Meteor Communications (Europe) Ltd, Hertfordshire Business Centre, Alexander Road, London Colney, St. Albans, Hertfordshire, AL2 1JG Tel: (01727) 828200 Fax: (01727) 828100

Mowden Controls Ltd, Mount View, Standard Way Industrial Estate, Northallerton, North Yorkshire, DL6 2YD Tel: (01609) 779535 Fax: (01609) 779539 E-mail: enquiries@mowden.co.uk

Pacscom Ltd, 6 Majestic Road, Nursling Industrial Estate, Southampton, SO16 0YT Tel: (023) 8073 7557 Fax: (023) 8073 1600 E-mail: sales@pacscom.com

Radio-Tech Ltd, Radio House, The Old Brewery, Lindsey Street, Epping, Essex, CM16 6RD Tel: (01992) 576107 Fax: (01992) 561994 E-mail: sales@radtec.demon.co.uk

SeNd Technology Ltd, Hunters End, Cox Green Lane, Maidenhead, Berkshire, SL6 3EU Tel: (0870) 4587363 Fax: (07092) 383861 E-mail: sales@sendtech.co.uk

Serck Controls Ltd, Stonebridge Trading Estate, Rowley Drive, Coventry, CV3 4FH Tel: (024) 7651 1069 Fax: (024) 7630 2437 E-mail: sales@serck-controls.co.uk

TELEPHONE ANSWERING MACHINES

Champ Telephones Holdings Ltd, 11-15 Station Street, Coventry, CV6 5FL Tel: (024) 7666 7757 Fax: (024) 7668 2290 E-mail: gary@champtel.co.uk

▶ Landline Phones, 27-29A New Broadway, Tarring Road, Worthing, West Sussex, BN11 4HP Tel: (0870) 7707191 Fax: (0870) 7707191 E-mail: info@landlinephones.co.uk

Lazerbuilt Ltd, 20 Gunnels Wood Park, Gunnels Wood Road, Stevenage, Hertfordshire, SG1 2BH Tel: (01438) 743753 Fax: (01438) 720077 E-mail: enquiries@lazerbuilt.co.uk

Retell, 53 Thames Street, Sunbury-on-Thames, Middlesex, TW16 5QH Tel: (01932) 779755 Fax: (01932) 780383 E-mail: sales@retell.co.uk

TELEPHONE ANSWERING SERVICES

▶ Abela Secretarial Services, 26 Campbell Road, Maidstone, Kent, ME15 6QA Tel: 01622 210552 Fax: 01622 210552 E-mail: info@abelasecretarial.com

Ansacom Telephone Answering Services, Basement Flat, 8 St. Johns Road, Tunbridge Wells, Kent, TN4 9NP Tel: (01892) 612700 Fax: (01892) 616323 E-mail: s.johnson@ansacom.co.uk

Answering (Scotland) Ltd, Suite 291, 93 Hope Street, Glasgow, G2 6LD Tel: 0141-221 9911 Fax: 0141-204 3998 E-mail: admin@answer4you.co.uk

▶ Arbell Ltd, Vickers House Vickers Business Centre, Priestley Road, Basingstoke, Hampshire, RG24 9NP Tel: (01256) 810100 Fax: (01256) 486588 E-mail: enquiries@arbell.co.uk

▶ Beserved Virtual Offices Ltd, Newlands, 13 The Green, Tuddenham, Bury St. Edmunds, Suffolk, IP28 6SD Tel: (0845) 2268064 E-mail: bev@beserved.co.uk

▶ Business Calls Direct, Pentland House, Pentland Park, Glenrothes, Fife, KY6 2AH Tel: (01592) 777800 Fax: (01592) 772860

Business Services Bureau, 11 Greenland Road, Barnet, Hertfordshire, EN5 2AL Tel: (020) 8440 3474 Fax: (020) 8440 3676 E-mail: bsb@busybee.demon.co.uk

Comverse Infosys U K Ltd, Hertford Place, Rickmansworth, Hertfordshire, WD3 9XB Tel: (01923) 717300 Fax: (01923) 717301

Concorde Agency, 28a High Street, Harpenden, Hertfordshire, AL5 2SX Tel: (01582) 715000 Fax: (01582) 461306 E-mail: sue.churchhouse@concord-agency.com

First Call Communications, St. Magnus House, 21 Guild Street, Aberdeen, AB11 6NJ Tel: (0500) 567500 Fax: (01224) 574448 E-mail: stuart.taylor@first/cal/comms.co.uk

▶ Havelock Secretarial Services, Havelock Secretarial Services, Enterprise 5, Five Lane Ends, Idle, Bradford, West Yorkshire, BD10 8EW Tel: 01274 618821 Fax: 01274 612604 E-mail: ltaylor@tayloredwebs.co.uk

Leadline Services Ltd, 54 New Street, Worcester, WR1 2DL Tel: (01905) 724000 Fax: (01905) 726888 E-mail: sales@leadline.co.uk

Mealbox Ltd, 235 Farnham Road, Slough, SL2 1DE Tel: (01753) 554391 E-mail: enq@mealbox.com

▶ Office Business & Services, 68 High Street, Witney, Oxfordshire, OX28 6HJ Tel: (01993) 200400 Fax: (01993) 200401 E-mail: info@obsl.co.uk

TELEPHONE CABINETS

Storacall Teleacoustics, 6 Enterprise Way, Cheltenham Trade Park, Cheltenham, Gloucestershire, GL51 8LZ Tel: (01242) 570995 Fax: (01242) 226131 E-mail: storacall.telea@btinternet.com

TELEPHONE CABLES

Euronetwork Ltd, 1 Horwood Court, Bletchley, Milton Keynes, MK1 1RD Tel: (01908) 371909 Fax: (01908) 378239 E-mail: info@euronetwork.co.uk

TELEPHONE CALL CENTRE SYSTEMS

Arden Direct Marketing Ltd, Island House, Arthur Street, Barwell, Leicester, LE9 8AH Tel: (0870) 4025220 Fax: (01455) 852249 E-mail: sales@ardendirect.co.uk

Avaya UK Ltd, Avaya House, Cathedral Hill, Guildford, Surrey, GU2 7YL Tel: (01483) 308000 Fax: (01483) 308001 E-mail: sales@avaya.co.uk

Clement Clarke International Ltd, Unit A Cartel Business Estate, Edinburgh Way, Harlow, Essex, CM20 2TT Tel: (01279) 414969 Fax: (01279) 456339 E-mail: info@c3headsets.com

Dacon P.L.C., 1 Enterprise Way, Hemel Hempstead, Hertfordshire, HP2 7YJ Tel: (01442) 233222 Fax: (01442) 219656 E-mail: info@dacon.co.uk

Datasharp Telecom (Eastern) Ltd, 78 Chapel Street, King's Lynn, Norfolk, PE30 1EF Tel: (01553) 666111 Fax: (01553) 666112 E-mail: sales@datasharptelecom.com

▶ Direct Response Ltd, 3 Angel Walk, London, W6 9HX Tel: (0870) 4149000 Fax: (0870) 4149001 E-mail: sales@drltd.com

Hays Technology, Appletree Road, Chipping Warden, Banbury, Oxfordshire, OX17 1LL Tel: (01295) 663000 Fax: (01295) 660361 E-mail: logistics@haystechnology.com

Hill Taylor Partnership, Alexandra House, Pound Lane, Exmouth, Devon, EX8 4NP Tel: (01395) 222242 Fax: (01395) 225858 E-mail: enquiries@hilltaylor.co.uk

Synergistic Software Co Ltd, Hughenden House, Main Street, Collingham, Wetherby, West Yorkshire, LS22 5AS Tel: (01937) 573446 Fax: (01937) 574211 E-mail: tony@syn.co.uk

TELEPHONE CALL LOGGING EQUIPMENT MANUFRS

BTS Holdings plc, B T S House, 69-73 Manor Road, Wallington, Surrey, SM6 0DD Tel: (020) 8401 9000 Fax: (020) 8401 9101 E-mail: sales@bts.co.uk

City Telecom, 36 Golders Gardens, London, NW11 9BU Tel: (0870) 9502750 Fax: (0870) 0118330 E-mail: sales@citytelecom.co.uk

Duplex Telecom Ltd, The Widford Hall, Widford Hall Lane, Chelmsford, CM2 8TD Tel: (0870) 7481408 Fax: (0870) 7481407 E-mail: sales@duplex.co.uk

Oak Telecom Ltd, 7 Albany Park, Cabot Lane, Poole, Dorset, BH17 7BX Tel: (01202) 607000 Fax: (01202) 607001

Soft-Ex UK Ltd, Unit 3b Juno House, Calleva Park, Aldermaston, Reading, RG7 8RA Tel: 0118-981 5555 Fax: 0118-981 5577 E-mail: sales@soft-ex.net

Solitaire Communications Ltd, 1 Yardley Business Park, Luckyn Lane, Basildon, Essex, SS14 3GL Tel: (0845) 8800180 Fax: (01268) 243903

Tiger Communications Ltd, 77-79 Christchurch Road, Ringwood, Hampshire, BH24 1DH Tel: (01425) 461566 Fax: (01425) 461484 E-mail: sales@tigercomms.com

TELEPHONE CALL LOGGING SOFTWARE

▶ Telephone Recorders Direct Ltd, 462 London Road, Isleworth, Middlesex, TW7 4ED Tel: (020) 8326 8282 E-mail: salesmanager@telephonerecordersdirect.com

TELEPHONE CALL SERVICE PROVIDERS, CARRIER PRE SELECTION (CPS)

The Utility Warehouse, PO Box 407, Huntingdon, Cambridgeshire, PE29 2ZG Tel: (0845) 1242201 Fax: (0870) 7773753

▶ Zimo Communications, 26 York Street, London, W1U 6PZ Tel: (0800) 3213000 E-mail: sales@ewcoms.com

TELEPHONE CONFERENCE SERVICES/BUREAU SERVICES

A C T Teleconferencing, Queens House, Kymberley Road, Harrow, Middlesex, HA1 1US Tel: (020) 8901 5401 Fax: (020) 8901 5492 E-mail: marketing@europe.acttel.com

TELEPHONE CONVERSATION RECORDING EQUIPMENT

Retell, 53 Thames Street, Sunbury-on-Thames, Middlesex, TW16 5QH Tel: (01932) 779755 Fax: (01932) 780383 E-mail: sales@retell.co.uk

TELEPHONE DOOR TO FLAT OR ENTRANCE TO RECEPTION SYSTEMS

Fermax UK Ltd, Fermax House, Bebington Close, Billericay, Essex, CM12 0DT Tel: (01277) 634777 Fax: (01277) 634666 E-mail: sales@fermaxuk.com

Livewire Telecommunication, Kineton Road, Gaydon, Warwick, CV35 0HB Tel: (01926) 640634

TELEPHONE DOOR TO FLAT OR ENTRANCE TO RECEPTION SYSTEMS CONTRACTORS OR INSTALLATION OR HIRE OR SERVICES

Anchor Sound & Security, 474 Hatfield Road, St. Albans, Hertfordshire, AL4 0XS Tel: (01727) 831402

Britelec Network Services Ltd, 39 London Road, Braintree, Essex, CM7 2LD Tel: (01376) 552323 Fax: (01376) 340006

Entryphone Company Ltd, 23 Granville Road, London, SW18 5SD Tel: (020) 8870 8635 Fax: (020) 8874 0066

▶ ToneTel Telecom, 86 Cabell Road, Guildford, Surrey, GU2 8JQ Tel: 01483 578456 Fax: 01483 871528 E-mail: sales@tonetel.co.uk

TELEPHONE EXCHANGE INSTALLATION CONTRACTORS/ RENTAL/SERVICE/SUPPLIERS

City Telecom, 36 Golders Gardens, London, NW11 9BU Tel: (0870) 9502750 Fax: (0870) 0118330 E-mail: sales@citytelecom.co.uk

Micro Plus Software Ltd, Continental House, 497 Sunleigh Road, Alperton, Middlesex, HA0 4LY Tel: (020) 8733 8233 Fax: (020) 8733 8237 E-mail: sales@tollring.co.uk

Palebeck Telecommunications Technology Ltd, 9 Little Portland Street, London, W1W 7JF Tel: (020) 7580 7226 Fax: (020) 7580 3115 E-mail: sales@pttl.co.uk

TELEPHONE INTERNAL SYSTEMS

Entryphone Company Ltd, 23 Granville Road, London, SW18 5SD Tel: (020) 8870 8635 Fax: (020) 8874 0066

Itc Ltd, 2-8 Park Road, Lytham St. Annes, Lancashire, FY8 1QX Tel: (01253) 783990 Fax: (01253) 783993 E-mail: info@itcoms.co.uk

Telequip Ltd, 5 Acorn Business Centre, Northarbour Road, Portsmouth, PO6 3TH Tel: (023) 9221 5215 Fax: (08707) 770778 E-mail: postmaster@telequip.co.uk

TELEPHONE INTERNAL SYSTEMS CONTRACTORS/ INSTALLATION/RENTAL/ SERVICE/SUPPLIERS

A T Communications, Canon House, Thame Road, Haddenham, Aylesbury, Buckinghamshire, HP17 8LH Tel: (01844) 266266 Fax: (01844) 266262

Anchor Sound & Security, 474 Hatfield Road, St. Albans, Hertfordshire, AL4 0XS Tel: (01727) 831402

B J C Communication Contracts Ltd, 198 Hydean Way, Stevenage, Hertfordshire, SG2 9YD Tel: (07879) 605543 Fax: (0844) 5875728 E-mail: mail@bjccommunications.co.uk

Commsplus Ltd, 51 Gazelle Road, Weston-super-Mare, Avon, BS24 9ES Tel: (01934) 882200 Fax: (01934) 411010 E-mail: julyanb@commsplus.co.uk

Datacom Communication Systems Ltd, Unit 11 Towngate Business Centre, Durham, DH7 8HG Tel: 0191-378 3409 Fax: 0191-378 3402

Eurolink Telecom Ltd, Exeter Road, Bournemouth, BH2 5AR Tel: (01202) 558228 Fax: (01202) 558227 E-mail: enq@eurolinltelecom.com

Genesis Scotland Ltd, The Douglas Centre, Marchmont Crescent, Buckie, Banffshire, AB56 4BT Tel: (01542) 834947 Fax: (0870) 3835549E-mail: genesisltd@btopenworld.com

King Communication Services, 19 Coatbank Street, Coatbridge, Lanarkshire, ML5 3SP Tel: (01236) 429445 Fax: (01236) 429445 E-mail: info@kingcoms.com

Leta Telephone Training Equipment, Unit 1, Edolph Farm, Norwood Hill Road, Charlwood, Horley, Surrey, RH6 0EB Tel: (01293) 865019 Fax: (01293) 863971

Micro Plus Software Ltd, Continental House, 497 Sunleigh Road, Alperton, Middlesex, HA0 4LY Tel: (020) 8733 8233 Fax: (020) 8733 8237 E-mail: sales@tollring.co.uk

Pennine Telecom Ltd, Pennine House, Salford Street, Bury, Lancashire, BL9 6YA Tel: 0161-763 3333 Fax: 0161-763 3332 E-mail: info@penninetelecom.com

Pink Telecommunications, 15 The Broadway, Woodford Green, Essex, IG8 0HL Tel: (020) 8506 6464 Fax: (020) 8506 6400

Symphony Telecom Ltd, Telford House, Corner Hall, Hemel Hempstead, Hertfordshire, HP3 9HN Tel: (01442) 283300 Fax: (01442) 283328 E-mail: symphony@symphony.com

Telephone Service Centre, 43 Wessex Estate, Ringwood, Hampshire, BH24 1XD Tel: (07970) 661519 Fax: (01425) 477589 E-mail: telephoneserv@aol.com

TELEPHONE JUNCTION BOXES

▶ Addaphone Telecommunication Services, 6 Cotswold Green, Aylesbury, Buckinghamshire, HP20 2HB Tel: (01296) 397322 E-mail: dj@addaphone.co.uk

▶ Xtel Communications (UK) Ltd, Commerce Court, Challenge Way, Bradford, West Yorkshire, BD4 8NW Tel: (0800) 8499066 Fax: (0800) 8499096 E-mail: sales@xtelcomms.net

TELEPHONE KIOSKS

F G G Plant, Fyfield Hall, Fyfield, Ongar, Essex, CM5 0SA Tel: (01277) 899495 Fax: (01277) 899613

Storacall Teleacoustics, 6 Enterprise Way, Cheltenham Trade Park, Cheltenham, Gloucestershire, GL51 8LZ Tel: (01242) 570995 Fax: (01242) 226131 E-mail: storacall.telea@btinternet.com

TELEPHONE LINE TEST EQUIPMENT

Advanced Telephone Systems, Willoughby House, Willoughby Road, Harpenden, Hertfordshire, AL5 4PS Tel: (01582) 767799 Fax: (01582) 762266

TELEPHONE LOW COST ROUTING (LCR) SYSTEMS

Digitel Technology Ltd, 7 Cross Street, Barnstaple, Devon, EX31 1BA Tel: (01271) 311913 E-mail: sales@digitel.uk.net

Nortec Production Ltd, 11 Fourways, Atherstone, Warwickshire, CV9 1LG Tel: (01827) 717896 Fax: (01827) 717842 E-mail: robin.clements@nortec-prod.demon.co.uk

Sprint Ltd, PO Box 2452, Hove, East Sussex, BN3 7WB Tel: (0870) 6082801 Fax: (0870) 6082802 E-mail: sales@scsl.co.uk

TELEPHONE MAINTENANCE/ REPAIR/REFURBISHMENT SERVICES

L B Technologies Ltd, 42 Medley Road, Rayne, Braintree, Essex, CM77 6TQ Tel: (01376) 345041 E-mail: bullimores@aol.com

Telequip Ltd, 5 Acorn Business Centre, Northarbour Road, Portsmouth, PO6 3TH Tel: (023) 9221 5215 Fax: (08707) 770778 E-mail: postmaster@telequip.co.uk

TELEPHONE MANUFRS

Advanced Telephone Systems, Willoughby House, Willoughby Road, Harpenden, Hertfordshire, AL5 4PS Tel: (01582) 767799 Fax: (01582) 762266

Arnesys Telecommunications Equipment, Queens Bridge Road, Nottingham, NG2 1NB Tel: 0115-985 2525 Fax: 0115-985 2526 E-mail: admin@arnesys.com

Azzurri Communications Ltd, 6 Manor Court, Barnes Wallis Road, Fareham, Hampshire, PO15 5TH Tel: (01489) 889300 Fax: (01489) 553554 E-mail: sales@azzu.co.uk

Bell Communications, 196-198 Cheltenham Road, Bristol, BS6 5QZ Tel: 0117-923 2323 Fax: 0117-923 2031 E-mail: info@bellcomm.co.uk

Freerose Ltd, 26 Apex Business Centre, Boscombe Road, Dunstable, Bedfordshire, LU5 4SB Tel: (01582) 472274 Fax: (01582) 475574 E-mail: info@freerose.co.uk

Geemarc Telecomm SA, Unit 5 Swallow Court, Swallowfields, Welwyn Garden City, Hertfordshire, AL7 1SB Tel: (01707) 372372 Fax: (01707) 372529 E-mail: sales@geemarc.com

I C S, Royal Mail House, 37 Terminus Terrace, Southampton, SO14 3FD Tel: (023) 80227878 Fax: (023) 80227878

K2 Kommunications, 37 Moulton Street, Manchester, M8 8FQ Tel: 0161-833 9952 Fax: 0161-833 9951

▶ Landline Phones, 27-29A New Broadway, Tarring Road, Worthing, West Sussex, BN11 4HP Tel: (0870) 7707191 Fax: (0870) 7707191 E-mail: info@landlinephones.co.uk

Lazerbuilt Ltd, 20 Gunnels Wood Park, Gunnels Wood Road, Stevenage, Hertfordshire, SG1 2BH Tel: (01438) 743753 Fax: (01438) 720077 E-mail: enquiries@lazerbuilt.co.uk

Leta Telephone Training Equipment, Unit 1, Edolph Farm, Norwood Hill Road, Charlwood, Horley, Surrey, RH6 0EB Tel: (01293) 865019 Fax: (01293) 863971

Local Telecom Service Ltd, The Business Communications Centre, 34 Auster Road, York, YO30 4XA Tel: (01904) 690550 Fax: (01904) 492064 E-mail: sales@lts.co.uk

Odyssey Systems Ltd, Lockheed Close, Preston Farm Industrial Estate, Stockton-on-Tees, Cleveland, TS18 3SE Tel: (01642) 661800 Fax: (01642) 661801 E-mail: sales@odyssey-systems.co.uk

Premier Managed Payphones Ltd, Unit 10 Alexandra Way, Ashchurch, Tewkesbury, Gloucestershire, GL20 8NB Tel: (01684) 298974 Fax: (01684) 290616

▶ Rika Telephone Equipment, 170-172 Honeypot Lane, Stanmore, Middlesex, HA7 1EE Tel: (020) 8204 5400 Fax: (020) 8206 1815 E-mail: ameed@rika.co.uk

▶ Soneric Communications, Unit 24 Wren Court, Strathclyde Business Park, Bellshill, Lanarkshire, ML4 3NQ Tel: (01698) 742210 Fax: (01698) 840080 E-mail: sales@soneric.com

Speech & Data Communications, 135 Glendale Gardens, Leigh-on-Sea, Essex, SS9 2BE Tel: (01702) 473478 Fax: (01702) 473478

TELEPHONE MARKETING/ TELEMARKETING/SALES SERVICES

▶ AgentPhone Ltd, P.O.Box 5064, Leighton Buzzard, Bedfordshire, LU7 3FT Tel: 01525 243000 Fax: 01525 379180 E-mail: mail@agentphone.com

B C C Marketing Services Ltd, Belgrade Centre, Denington Road, Denington Industrial Estate, Wellingborough, Northamptonshire, NN8 2QH Tel: (01933) 443322 Fax: (01933) 441844 E-mail: info@bccmarketing.co.uk

B P S, Pinnacle House, 17-25 Hartfield Road, London, SW19 3SE Tel: (020) 8296 1000 Fax: (020) 8296 1010

▶ Business Calls Direct, Pentland House, Pentland Park, Glenrothes, Fife, KY6 2AH Tel: (01592) 777800 Fax: (01592) 772860

▶ Chase Marketing, 26 Pine Walk, Cobham, Surrey, KT11 2HJ Tel: (01932) 586960

▶ Connor Associates, 7 Grangewood Terrace, Stobswood, Morpeth, Northumberland, NE61 5QE Tel: (01670) 791997 E-mail: ian@doors-opened.co.uk

▶ David Archibald, 3 Queen Charlotte Lane, Edinburgh, EH6 6AY Tel: 0845 0110184 E-mail: info@contactfoundry.com

Epic Marketing Services, Point Road, Canvey Island, Essex, SS8 7RT Tel: (01268) 514290 Fax: (01268) 695891 E-mail: sales@epictelemarketing.co.uk

F D S International Ltd, The Ground Floor, Hill House, London, N19 5NA Tel: (020) 7272 7766 Fax: (020) 7272 4468 E-mail: enquiries@fdf.co.uk

▶ Farmpro Mail Marketing Ltd, Stephenson Road, Groundwell Industrial Estate, Swindon, SN25 5AN Tel: (01793) 451000 Fax: (01793) 451010

▶ gsa Ltd, Unit 3, Devonshire Business Park, Borehamwood, Herts, WD6 1NA Tel: 0208 236 2531

Jupiter B2B Marketing, 82 Beech Farm Drive, Macclesfield, Cheshire, SK10 2ER Tel: (01625) 431166 Fax: (01625) 431177 E-mail: karriegrant@jupiterb2b.co.uk

Leadline Services Ltd, 54 New Street, Worcester, WR1 2DL Tel: (01905) 724000 Fax: (01905) 726888 E-mail: sales@leadline.co.uk

Mealbox Ltd, 235 Farnham Road, Slough, SL2 1DE Tel: (01753) 554391 E-mail: enq@mealbox.com

▶ Novacheck Ltd, 438 London Road, High Wycombe, Buckinghamshire, HP11 1LP Tel: (01494) 526553 Fax: (01494) 526553 E-mail: contactus@novacheck.com

Price Direct Ltd, 505A Norwood Road, London, SE27 9DL Tel: (020) 8761 7612 Fax: (020) 8761 7514 E-mail: info@pricedirect.com

▶ Prospects 4 Business Ltd, PO Box 6619, Derby, DE21 5AB Tel: (01332) 832518 Fax: (0870) 432518 E-mail: sales@prospects4business.co.uk

▶ Return On Investment Ltd, 7 Pepper Street, Nantwich, Cheshire, CW5 5AB Tel: (01270) 610400 Fax: (01270) 628135 E-mail: diane.hawkins@roiltd.co.uk

Sales Force GB Ltd, 1 Haven Green, Ealing, London, W5 2UU Tel: (020) 8998 9646 Fax: (020) 8248 7796 E-mail: g.gedge@btconnect.com

Salesnet Ltd, Sterling House, Teddington, Middlesex, TW11 8PB Tel: (020) 8410 3200 Fax: (020) 8410 3211 E-mail: info@salesnet.ltd.uk

Telecom Solutions International, 23-27 Endsleigh Road, Redhill, RH1 3LX Tel: (0870) 6060380 Fax: (01377) 647801 E-mail: info@tsigroup.co.uk

▶ VHO, Suite 24 Basepoint Business Centre, Rivermead Drive, Swindon, SN5 7EX Tel: 01793 608701 Fax: 01793 608704 E-mail: vivienne@vhorg.co.uk

TELEPHONE MOVING AND CHANGING ENGINEERING

▶ D G Tel Communications, Unit 10 Stammerham Business Centre, Capel Road, Rusper, Horsham, West Sussex, RH12 4PZ Tel: (01306) 710370 Fax: (01306) 710371 E-mail: dg.tel@btinternet.com

Grapevine, 83 Broadway, Southbourne, Bournemouth, BH6 4EJ Tel: (01202) 429232 Fax: (01202) 424559 E-mail: sales1@grapevine-comms.co.uk

TELEPHONE REAL TIME CALL MONITORING SYSTEMS

Callscan Ltd, Callscan House Priestley Wharf, 20 Holt Street, Birmingham, B7 4BZ Tel: 0121-359 8941 Fax: 0121-359 1417 E-mail: info@epcuk.com

TELEPHONE SERVICES

Remark Telecommunications, Unit 3 The Manor Grove Centre, Vicarage Farm Road, Peterborough, PE1 5UH Tel: (01733) 551255 Fax: (01733) 551755 E-mail: sales@remarktelecomm.com

TELEPHONE STERILISING/ CLEANING SERVICES

Astrocare Ltd, Bolton Enterprise Centre, Washington Street, Bolton, BL3 5EY Tel: (01204) 370861 Fax: (01204) 548742 E-mail: astrocare@aol.com

Deja Vu Computer Cleaners, 149 Bramley Close, London, E17 6EG Tel: (020) 8523 4661 Fax: (020) 8523 4661

S & M Computer Cleaning Services Ltd, Midland House, New Road, Halesowen, West Midlands, B63 3HY Tel: 0121-550 4008 Fax: 0121-550 5272 E-mail: sales@computercleaners.co.uk

TELEPHONE SYSTEM MAINTENANCE

▶ Harrogate Communications, 6 Nydd Vale Terrace, Harrogate, North Yorkshire, HG1 5HA Tel: (01423) 532977 Fax: (01423) 532979 E-mail: info@1stcoms.co.uk

▶ Phone It Ict Helston, 17 Marconi Close, Helston, Cornwall, TR13 8PD Tel: (01326) 565335 Fax: (01326) 573541 E-mail: philipeade@btconnect.com

▶ S T L Communications Ltd, Park House, Station Lane, Witney, Oxfordshire, OX28 4LH Tel: (01993) 777100 Fax: (01993) 777101 E-mail: sryan@spireholdings.com

TELEPHONIST OR RECEPTIONIST OR CALL CENTRE STAFF RECRUITMENT

▶ T R G Recruitment Services Ltd, 5th Floor, 4 St. Pauls Churchyard, London, EC4M 8AY Tel: (020) 7236 8844 Fax: (020) 7236 8181 E-mail: cv@thetrggroup.co.uk

TELEPRINTER STATIONERY, *See Telecommunication Stationery etc*

TELESCOPE ACCESSORIES/ SPARE PARTS

David Hinds Ltd, Unit B Chiltern Industrial Estate, Grovebury Road, Leighton Buzzard, Bedfordshire, LU7 4TU Tel: (01525) 852696 Fax: (0844) 170588 E-mail: astro@dhinds.co.uk

▶ Sussex Astronomy Centre, 16 Mulberry Lane, Goring By Sea, Worthing, West Sussex, BN12 4JL Tel: (01903) 247317 E-mail: worthingastronomy@tiscali.co.uk

TELESCOPE MAINTENANCE/ REPAIR SERVICES

Broadhurst Clarkson & Fuller Ltd, 63 Farringdon Road, London, EC1M 3JB Tel: (020) 7405 2156 Fax: (020) 7430 2471 E-mail: info@telescopehouse.co.uk

TELESCOPES, *See also headings for particular types*

▶ Action Optics, 16 Butts Ash Gardens, Hythe, Southampton, SO45 3BL Tel: (023) 8084 2801 Fax: (023) 8084 2801 E-mail: richard@actionoptics.co.uk

Braithwaite Telescopes, Old School, Manse Brae, Dalserf, Larkhall, Lanarkshire, ML9 3BN Tel: (01698) 881004 E-mail: john@dalserf.demon.co.uk

Broadhurst Clarkson & Fuller Ltd, 63 Farringdon Road, London, EC1M 3JB Tel: (020) 7405 2156 Fax: (020) 7430 2471 E-mail: info@telescopehouse.co.uk

Claritas Ltd, 2 Earlswood Street, London, SE10 9ES Tel: (020) 8858 2411 Fax: (020) 8305 2875 E-mail: claritasltd@amstrad.co.uk

David Hinds Ltd, Unit B Chiltern Industrial Estate, Grovebury Road, Leighton Buzzard, Bedfordshire, LU7 4TU Tel: (01525) 852696 Fax: (0844) 170588 E-mail: astro@dhinds.co.uk

In Focus Ltd, Wild Fowl Trust Newgrounds, Slimbridge, Gloucester, GL2 7BT Tel: (01453) 890978 Fax: (01453) 890267 E-mail: infocus@netcomuk.co.uk

Intro 2020 Ltd, Unit 1, Priors Way, Maidenhead, Berkshire, SL6 2HP Tel: (01628) 674411 Fax: (01628) 771055 E-mail: jane@intro2020.co.uk

Stockport Binocular & Telescope Centre, Mercian Way, Stockport, Cheshire, SK3 9DF Tel: 0161-429 8002 Fax: 0161-474 0440 E-mail: tloptics@aol.com

TELESCOPIC CRANE HIRE

South West Crane Hire Ltd, Tan Lane, Exeter, EX2 8EG Tel: (01392) 256148 Fax: (01392) 270603 E-mail: info@sw-crane-hire.co.uk

Telford Crane Hire Ltd, Halesfield 22, Telford, Shropshire, TF7 4QX Tel: (01952) 586304 Fax: (01952) 587848 E-mail: sales@telfordcrane.co.uk

▶ J. Thomas (Southern) Ltd, Bankside House, Henfield Road, Small Dole, Henfield, West Sussex, BN5 9XQ Tel: (01273) 494848 Fax: (01273) 497804 E-mail: cranes@jthomas.co.uk

TELESCOPIC FORKLIFT TRUCKS

▶ UK Forks, Central House, Beckwith Knowle, Otley Road, Beckwithshaw, Harrogate, North Yorkshire, HG3 1UD Tel: (0800) 123101 Fax: (01423) 565657 E-mail: info@ukforks.com

TELESCOPIC HANDLERS

▶ J S Clayton Plant Hire Ltd, Unit 1a Sefton La Industrial Estate, Liverpool, L31 8BX Tel: 0151-531 1210 Fax: 0151-531 9600 E-mail: jsclaytonplanthire@hotmail.com

TELESCOPIC TOWERS

Clark Masts Teksam Ltd, 18 Ringwood Road, Binstead, Ryde, Isle Of Wight, PO33 3PA Tel: (01983) 563691 Fax: (01983) 566643 E-mail: sales@clarkmasts.com

South Midlands Communications Ltd, SM House, School Close, Chandler's Ford, Eastleigh, Hampshire, SO53 4RA Tel: (023) 8024 6200 Fax: (023) 8024 6206 E-mail: sales@smc-comms.com

TELETEXT AND OPEN CAPTION SUBTITLING SYSTEMS

Screen Subtitling Systems Ltd, Old Rectory, Church Lane, Claydon, Ipswich, IP6 0EQ Tel: (01473) 831700 Fax: (01473) 830078 E-mail: sales@screen.subtitling.com

TELEVISION AERIALS

A1 Aerials Ltd, 14 Arden Oak Road, Sheldon, Birmingham, B26 3LX Tel: 0121-742 0026 Fax: 0121-742 7360 E-mail: a1aerials@btconnect.com

Aerialect Ltd, 34 High Street, Kelvedon, Colchester, CO5 9AG Tel: (01376) 570135 Fax: (01376) 571545

Antiference, Eastern Avenue, Lichfield, Staffordshire, WS13 7SB Tel: (01889) 272600 Fax: (01296) 84284 E-mail: sales@antiference.co.uk

Blake UK Ltd, 177-187 Rutland Road, Sheffield, S3 9PT Tel: 0114-275 9729 Fax: 0114-275 6061 E-mail: sales@blake.uk.com

D W Systems, 19 Cleveland Close, Highwoods, Colchester, CO4 9RD Tel: (01206) 842711

J B Television Services, 633 Abbeydale Road, Sheffield, S7 1TB Tel: 0114-255 2178 Fax: 0114-255 2178

▶ Matthew Aerial & Satellite Systems, 57a Glencoe Road, Bushey, WD23 3DP Tel: (020) 8950 2213 Fax: (020) 8950 4262

Switchit Service Ltd, 34 Brunswick Street West, Hove, East Sussex, BN3 1EL Tel: (01273) 325442 Fax: (01273) 208450

▶ Wight Aerials, 34 North Street, Ventnor, Isle of Wight, PO38 1NJ Tel: (07973) 511614 E-mail: sales@wightaerials.com

TELEVISION BROADCASTING, *See Broadcasting etc*

TELEVISION (CABLE) CONTRACTORS, INSTALLATION OR SERVICE

▶ Scope Security Systems Ltd, 66-68 Leigh Road, Leigh, Lancashire, WN7 1RX Tel: (01942) 674123 Fax: (01942) 680510

TELEVISION (CABLE) EQUIPMENT

NTL, Cambridge Research Park, Ely Road, Waterbeach, Cambridge, CB25 9TF Tel: (01223) 724040 Fax: (01223) 567222

TELEVISION (CABLE) TEST EQUIPMENT MANUFRS

Scientific Atlanta Western Europe Ltd, 49 Suttons Park Avenue, Reading, RG6 1AZ Tel: (0870) 8325400 Fax: (0870) 8325444

TELEVISION ENGINEERS TO THE TRADE

Avery Electronic Services, Unit 4 Wren Industrial Estate, Coldred Road, Parkwood, Maidstone, Kent, ME15 9XN Tel: (01622) 682138 Fax: (01622) 691232

TELEVISION EQUIPMENT

F W Patterson Television Ltd, 21C1 Ben Nevis Estate, Claggan, Fort William, Inverness-Shire, PH33 6RU Tel: (01397) 702612 Fax: (01397) 701054 E-mail: fwpatterson@btconnect.com

R C Snelling Investments Ltd, Blofield Corner, Blofield, Norwich, NR13 4SQ Tel: (01603) 712202 Fax: (01603) 716052 E-mail: sales@snellingtv.co.uk

TELEVISION FILM PRODUCTION COMPANIES/ORGANISATIONS/ PRODUCERS

ADI UK Ltd, Pittman Court, Pittman Way, Fulwood, Preston, PR2 9ZG Tel: (0800) 592346 Fax: (01772) 708201 E-mail: sales@theadigroup.com

ARC Facilities Ltd, 1 Park Circus, Glasgow, G3 6AX Tel: 0141-333 1200 Fax: 0141-332 6002 E-mail: arcfacilities@picardy.co.uk

Michael Barratt, Field House, Ascot Road, Holyport, Maidenhead, Berkshire, SL6 3LD Tel: (01628) 770800 Fax: (01628) 627737 E-mail: michael@mbarrett.co.uk

Bray Management Ltd, Bray Studios, Down Place, Water Oakley, Windsor, Berkshire, SL4 5UG Tel: (01628) 622111 Fax: (01628) 770381 E-mail: bray.studios@btinternet.com

Fremantlemedia Tems, 1 Stephen Street, London, W1T 1AL Tel: (020) 7691 6000 Fax: (020) 7691 6100

▶ Charles Garland Productions Ltd, PO Box 639, Bury St. Edmunds, Suffolk, IP33 9FE Tel: (01359) 244453 E-mail: charles.garland@talk21.com

Goldcrest Films International Ltd, 65-66 Dean Street, London, W1D 4PL Tel: (020) 7437 8696 Fax: (020) 7437 4448 E-mail: mail@goldcrestfilms.com

▶ Grasshopper Films Ltd, 3rd Floor 14 Bacon Street, London, E1 6LF Tel: (020) 7739 7154 Fax: (020) 7739 6359 E-mail: info@grasshopperfilms.com

Hammerwood Film Producers & Distributors, 110 Trafalgar Road, Portslade, Brighton, BN41 1GS Tel: (01273) 277333 Fax: (01273) 705451E-mail: filmangels@freenetname.co.uk

Jacaranda Productions Ltd, Felgate Mews Studland Street, London, W6 0LY Tel: (020) 8741 9088 Fax: (020) 8748 5670 E-mail: creatives@jacaranda.co.uk

Lilyville Screen Entertainment Ltd, 7 Lilyville Road, London, SW6 5DP Tel: (020) 7371 5940 Fax: (020) 7736 9431 E-mail: tony.cash@btclick.com

London Weekend Television Ltd, The London Television Centre, Upperground, London, SE1 9LT Tel: (020) 7620 1620 Fax: (020) 7928 7825

P S A Ltd, 52 The Downs, Altrincham, Cheshire, WA14 2QJ Tel: 0161-924 0011 Fax: 0161-924 0022 E-mail: sales@psafilms.co.uk

Paper Moon Productions, Wychwood House, Burchetts Green Lane, Burchetts Green, Maidenhead, Berkshire, SL6 3QW Tel: (01628) 829819 Fax: (01628) 825949 E-mail: info@paper-moon.co.uk

Picture Palace Films Ltd, 13 Egbert Street, London, NW1 8LJ Tel: (020) 7586 8763 Fax: (020) 7586 9048 E-mail: info@picturepalace.com

Silver Productions Ltd, 29 Castle Street, Salisbury, SP1 1TT Tel: (01722) 336227 Fax: (01722) 336227 E-mail: info@silver.co.uk

Squirrel Films Ltd, 119 Rotherhithe Street, London, SE16 4NF Tel: (020) 7231 2209 Fax: (020) 7231 2119 E-mail: ostockman@sandsfilms.co.uk

▶ Talent Television, Lion House, 72-75 Red Lion Street, London, WC1R 4NA Tel: (020) 7421 7800 Fax: (020) 7421 7811

▶ Western Eye, Kinley House, 43 The Crescent, Bristol, BS9 4RP Tel: (07803) 593833 E-mail: mail@western-eye.com

TELEVISION GRAPHIC DESIGN

▶ Brand Creative, Slackcote Lane, Delph, Oldham, OL3 5TP Tel: (01457) 874016 Fax: (01457) 874016 E-mail: design@brand-creative.co.uk

▶ Dynamite Pictures, 8 Wilkinson Terrace, Stutton, Tadcaster, North Yorkshire, LS24 9BP Tel: (07816) 319195 E-mail: richard.ball@lycos.co.uk

TELEVISION MONITORS

1a Productions Ltd, Langshot, Torrance, Glasgow, G64 4DL Tel: (01360) 620855 Fax: (01360) 620788

HCVF Video Production Companies, 67-69 Kenneth Street, Inverness, IV3 5QF Tel: (01463) 224788 Fax: (01463) 711460 E-mail: info@hcvf.co.uk

Ikegami Electronics, Unit E1 Cologne Court, Brooklands Close, Sunbury-on-Thames, Middlesex, TW16 7EB Tel: (01932) 769700 Fax: (01932) 769710 E-mail: info@ikegami.co.uk

Tatung UK Ltd, Stafford Park 10, Telford, Shropshire, TF3 3AB Tel: (01952) 290111 Fax: (01952) 290390 E-mail: service@tatung.co.uk

TELEVISION PROMPTING EQUIPMENT

Portaprompt Ltd, Spearmast Industrial Park, Lane End Road, High Wycombe, Buckinghamshire, HP12 4JQ Tel: (01494) 450414 Fax: (01494) 437591 E-mail: helen@portaprompt.co.uk

TELEVISION RECEIVERS

Bang & Olufsen, Unit 630 Wharfdale Road, Winnersh Triangle, Wokingham, Berkshire, RG41 5TP Tel: 0118-969 2288 Fax: 0118-969 3388

▶ Freeview Receiver, Returns Department, Sequoia Technical Services, County Estate Nunn Brook Road, Huthwaite, Sutton-in-Ashfield, Nottinghamshire, NG17 2HU Tel: (0870) 4430638 E-mail: sales@freeviewreceivers.co.uk

J V C Manufacturing U K Ltd, 2 Glenburn Road, East Kilbride, Glasgow, G74 5BA Tel: (01355) 241166 Fax: (01355) 265231 E-mail: enquiries@jvc.co.uk

Tatung UK Ltd, Stafford Park 10, Telford, Shropshire, TF3 3AB Tel: (01952) 290111 Fax: (01952) 290390 E-mail: service@tatung.co.uk

TELEVISION REPAIR

▶ S J S TV Services Ltd, 22 Becksbourne Close, Penenden Heath, Maidstone, Kent, ME14 2ED Tel: (01622) 664500 Fax: (01622) 664500 E-mail: sales@sjstv.co.uk

Synapse Electronics, Old Crofters Yard, Combi Street, Oban, Argyll, PA34 4HU Tel: (01631) 565055

TELEVISION SERVICE EQUIPMENT

Omnibus Systems Ltd, Main Street, Stanford on Soar, Loughborough, Leicestershire, LE12 5PY Tel: (0870) 5004300 Fax: (0870) 5040003 E-mail: sales@omnibus.co.uk

TELEVISION STANDS

Dalen Ltd, Garretts Green Trading Estate, Valepits Road, Birmingham, B33 0TD Tel: 0121-783 3838 Fax: 0121-784 6348 E-mail: sales@top-tec.co.uk

TELEVISION STUDIO CAMERA MOUNTING EQUIPMENT

Vinten Broadcast Ltd, Western Way, Bury St. Edmunds, Suffolk, IP33 3TB Tel: (01284) 752121 Fax: (01284) 750560 E-mail: contact@vinten.com

TELEVISION STUDIO CONTROL SYSTEMS/EQUIPMENT

Courtyard Electronics Ltd, 13 Riverside Park, Dogflud Way, Farnham, Surrey, GU9 7UG Tel: (01252) 712030 Fax: (01252) 722060 E-mail: info@courtyard.co.uk

D E G A Broadcast Systems, 1 Newton Court, Rankine Road, Basingstoke, Hampshire, RG24 8GF Tel: (01256) 816220 Fax: (01256) 843952 E-mail: david@dega.co.uk

Sony Business Europe, Viables Industrial Estate, Jays Close, Basingstoke, Hampshire, RG22 4SB Tel: (01256) 355011 Fax: (01256) 474585

Trilogy Broadcast, 26 Focus Way, Walworth Industrial Estate, Andover, Hampshire, SP10 5NY Tel: (01264) 384000 Fax: (01264) 334806 E-mail: sales@trilogycomms.com

TELEVISION TEST EQUIPMENT

Electronic Visuals Ltd, 20 Ferry Lane, Wraysbury, Staines, Middlesex, TW19 6HG Tel: (01784) 483311 Fax: (01784) 483918 E-mail: info@electronic-visuals.com

TELEVISION TRANSMITTERS

Harris Systems Ltd, Eskdale Road, Winnersh, Wokingham, Berkshire, RG41 5TS Tel: 0118-969 8787 Fax: 0118-964 8001

TELEVISIONS, PLASMA SCREEN

▶ Visual Service Centre, Unit 1 Derby Trading Estate, Stores Road, Derby, DE21 4BE Tel: (01332) 291119 Fax: (01332) 291119 E-mail: info@visualservicecentre.co.uk

TELEX MANUFRS

Aston Communications, 2 St. Johns Buildings, Friern Barnet Road, London, N11 3DP Tel: (020) 8361 8711 Fax: (020) 8361 3633 E-mail: john@aston-telex.com

Network Telex Ltd, Kingsland House, 514 Wimborne Road, Ferndown, Dorset, BH22 9NG Tel: (01202) 874156 Fax: (01202) 897827 E-mail: info.uk@telex-net.co.uk

TELEX PAPER TAPE EQUIPMENT

G N T Ltd, Waterside Estate, Cradley Road, Dudley, West Midlands, DY2 9RG Tel: (01384) 236007 Fax: (01384) 236929 E-mail: info@gnt.co.uk

TELEX SHARING AGENCIES/ BUREAU SERVICES

Senator Communications Ltd, 5 Newton Court, Wavertree Technology Park, Liverpool, L13 1EJ Tel: 0151-259 5959 Fax: 0151-259 0099 E-mail: sales@senatorinternational.uk

TELEX SOFTWARE

Network Telex Ltd, Kingsland House, 514 Wimborne Road, Ferndown, Dorset, BH22 9NG Tel: (01202) 874156 Fax: (01202) 897827 E-mail: info.uk@telex-net.co.uk

TEMPERATURE CONTROL CONSULTANTS

F G H Instrument Services, 29 Oldmill Street, Stoke-on-Trent, ST4 2RP Tel: (01782) 414445 Fax: (01782) 414486 E-mail: sales@fghinst.fsbusiness.co.uk

S B S Engineering Services, Tynewydd, Horeb, Llandysul, Dyfed, SA44 4JG Tel: (01559) 363708 Fax: (01559) 363708

Stanton Kilns, Foley Works, King Street, Stoke-on-Trent, ST4 3DE Tel: (01782) 312316 Fax: (01782) 598978 E-mail: sales@stanton-kilns.co.uk

TEMPERATURE CONTROL INSTRUMENTATION

Cal Controls Ltd, Bury Mead Road, Hitchin, Hertfordshire, SG5 1RT Tel: (01462) 436161 Fax: (01462) 451801 E-mail: sales@cal-controls.com

Contrel Ltd, PO Box 4127, Sudbury, Suffolk, CO10 1AB Tel: (01787) 881292 Fax: (01787) 881926 E-mail: intray7@contrel.co.uk

TEMPERATURE CONTROL PANELS

Active Controls, 6 Court Yard Workshops, Bath Street, Market Harborough, Leicestershire, LE16 9EW Tel: (01858) 466504 Fax: (01858) 463650 E-mail: activecontrols@ukonline.co.uk

Alpha, Westbury, Sherborne, Dorset, DT9 3RB Tel: (01935) 813722 Fax: (01935) 811822

C N Controls Ltd, Thorpe Way Indust Estate, Thorpe Way, Banbury, Oxfordshire, OX16 4SP Tel: (01295) 266704 Fax: (01295) 266704 E-mail: sales@cncontrols.co.uk

Electroserv Control Panel Mnfrs, Unit A Wentworth Industrial Court, Goodwin Road, Slough, SL2 2ER Tel: (01753) 539606 Fax: (01753) 539606

TEMPERATURE CONTROL SYSTEM RECORDERS

Inviron Ltd, Deben House, 1 Selsdon Way, City Harbour, London, E14 9GL Tel: (020) 7515 5511 Fax: (020) 7515 5551 E-mail: admin@inviron.co.uk

TEMPERATURE CONTROLLED ROAD TRANSPORT AND HAULAGE

▶ Direct Chilled Ltd, Edward Street, Redditch, Worcestershire, B97 6HA Tel: 0845 6010348 E-mail: dcdsredditch@aol.com

TEMPERATURE CONTROLLER MANUFRS

A B B Ltd, Howard Road, St. Neots, Cambridgeshire, PE19 8EU Tel: (01480) 475321 Fax: (01480) 217948 E-mail: automationltd.sales@gb.abb.com

Abacus, Unit 29, Ardent Way, Mountheath Industrial Park, Prestwich, Manchester, M25 9WE Tel: 0161-773 7594 Fax: 0161-773 0093 E-mail: info@abacusweighing.com

Accurate Controls, 25 Cowley Road, Nuffield Industrial Estate, Poole, Dorset, BH17 0UJ Tel: (01202) 678108 Fax: (01202) 670161 E-mail: info@accurate-controls.ltd.uk

Cal Controls Ltd, Bury Mead Road, Hitchin, Hertfordshire, SG5 1RT Tel: (01462) 436161 Fax: (01462) 451801 E-mail: sales@cal-controls.com

Caltec Electronic Equipment, L Quarry Road, Newhaven, East Sussex, BN9 9DG Tel: (01273) 517516 Fax: (01273) 517278

Central Cold Storage Co., Leamore Lane, Walsall, WS2 7DQ Tel: (01922) 401307 Fax: (01922) 710033 E-mail: johncoxcoldstoresltd@btinternet.com

The Control Shop Ltd, 17 Bilton Industrial Estate, Stockmans Close, Birmingham, B38 9TS Tel: 0121-451 1030 Fax: 0121-459 1511 E-mail: sales@controlshop.co.uk

Coster Environmental Controls Ltd, Unit 5 Sir Francis Ley Indust Park, Derby, DE23 8XA Tel: (01332) 200555 Fax: (01332) 204181

Eagle Controls International Ltd, PO Box 42, Letchworth Garden City, Hertfordshire, SG6 1HQ Tel: (01462) 670566 Fax: (01462) 673992 E-mail: info@eaglecontrols.co.uk

Electroserv International, 30a Townley Street, Macclesfield, Cheshire, SK11 6HZ Tel: (01625) 615626 Fax: (01625) 617559

Electroserv (T C & S) Ltd, PO Box 163, Macclesfield, Cheshire, SK11 6JY Tel: (01625) 618526 Fax: (01625) 500746 E-mail: dh@electroserv.co.uk

Eukero Controls Ltd, Unit 7 Worton Court, Worton Road, Isleworth, Middlesex, TW7 6ER Tel: (020) 8568 4664 Fax: (020) 8568 4115 E-mail: info@eukero.co.uk

▶ J.W. Fairbairn Process Solutions Ltd, 120 Woodneuk Road, Darnley Industrial Estate, Glasgow, G53 7QS Tel: 0141-880 7455 Fax: 0141-880 5290 E-mail: sales@jwfltd.com

Tom Granby Liverpool, Caddick Road, Knowsley Business Park, Prescot, Merseyside, L34 9HP Tel: 0151-548 8768 Fax: 0151-549 1979 E-mail: a.smith@dbcfoodservice.co.uk

▶ Horne Engineering Ltd, PO Box 7, Johnstone, Renfrewshire, PA5 8BD Tel: (01505) 321455 Fax: (01505) 336287E-mail: info@horne.co.uk

Hotset UK Ltd, Unit M, Bowen Industrial Estate, Aberbargoed, Bargoed, Mid Glamorgan, CF81 9EP Tel: (01443) 875581 Fax: (01443) 831422 E-mail: sales@hotset.u-net.com

M H Weltronic Systems Ltd, Unit 1 Crowles Ash Business Centre, Crowles Ash, Bromyard, Herefordshire, HR7 4SW Tel: (01885) 400777 Fax: (01885) 400777 E-mail: weltronic_sysltd@lineone.net

Monika, 10 Brook Park, Gaddesby Lane, Rearsby, Leicester, LE7 4YL Tel: (01664) 423900 Fax: (01664) 420033 E-mail: info@monika.com

R T D Products, Unit 10-11 A K Business Park, Russell Road, Southport, Merseyside, PR9 7SA Tel: (01704) 507696 Fax: (01704) 507055 E-mail: rnice@rtd-products.co.uk

Sirco Controls Ltd, Swaines Industrial Estate, Ashingdon Road, Rochford, Essex, SS4 1RQ Tel: (01702) 545125 Fax: (01702) 546873 E-mail: sales@sirco-controls.co.uk

Stanton Kilns, Foley Works, King Street, Stoke-on-Trent, ST4 3DE Tel: (01782) 312316 Fax: (01782) 598978 E-mail: sales@stanton-kilns.co.uk

Storm Products, 28 Hawbank Road, East Kilbride, Glasgow, G74 5EX Tel: (01355) 249358 Fax: (01355) 249197 E-mail: sales@cvcs.co.uk

T C Ltd, PO Box 130, Uxbridge, Middlesex, UB8 2YS Tel: (01895) 252222 Fax: (01895) 273540 E-mail: sales@tc.co.uk

Tactical Controls Ltd, Unit 4 Parkland Business Centre, Chartwell Road, Lancing, West Sussex, BN15 8UE Tel: (01903) 750800 Fax: (01903) 750678 E-mail: email@tacticalcontrols.co.uk

West Instruments Ltd, The Hyde, Brighton, BN2 4JU Tel: (01273) 606271 Fax: (01273) 609990 E-mail: info@westinstruments.com

TEMPERATURE GAUGES

Bourdon Haenni Ltd, Unit A Central Estate, Albert Road, Aldershot, Hampshire, GU11 1SZ Tel: (01252) 354000 Fax: (01252) 354009 E-mail: info@bourdon-haenni.co.uk

Roxar Ltd, Heritage Gate, Sandy Lane West, Littlemore, Oxford, OX4 6LB Tel: (01865) 712828 Fax: (01865) 712829

Siemens V D O Automotive Ltd, The Broadlands, 120 Holford Drive, Holford, Birmingham, B6 7UG Tel: 0121-344 2000 Fax: 0121-344 2072 E-mail: admin@vdodayton.com

Star Instruments Ltd, Barkway, Royston, Hertfordshire, SG8 8EH Tel: (01763) 848886 Fax: (01763) 848881 E-mail: sales@star-instruments.co.uk

Wika Instruments Ltd, 4 Gatton Park Business Centre, Wells Place Merstham, Redhill, RH1 3LG Tel: (01737) 644008 Fax: 01737 644403 E-mail: info@wika.co.uk

TEMPERATURE INDICATING LABELS

Hallcrest Temperature Monitoring Systems Mnfrs, 20 Downing Road, West Meadows Industrial Estate, Derby, DE21 6HA Tel: (01332) 382421 Fax: (01332) 291208 E-mail: sales@hallcrest.com

TEMPERATURE INDICATING STRIP MANUFRS

Hallcrest Temperature Monitoring Systems Mnfrs, 20 Downing Road, West Meadows Industrial Estate, Derby, DE21 6HA Tel: (01332) 382421 Fax: (01332) 291208 E-mail: sales@hallcrest.com

Hallcrest Temperature Monitoring Systems Mnfrs, 20 Downing Road, West Meadows Industrial Estate, Derby, DE21 6HA Tel: (01332) 382421 Fax: (01332) 291208 E-mail: sales@hallcrest.com

Thermographics Measurements Ltd, Riverside Buildings, Dock Road, Connah's Quay, Deeside, Clwyd, CH5 4DS Tel: (01244) 818348 Fax: (01244) 818502 E-mail: sales@t-m-c.com

TEMPERATURE INDICATOR SYSTEMS

British Rototherm Co. Ltd, Kenfig Industrial Estate, Margam, Port Talbot, West Glamorgan, SA13 2PW Tel: (01656) 740551 Fax: (01656) 745915 E-mail: rototherm@rototherm.co.uk

Contarnex Europe Ltd, 252 Martin Way, Morden, Surrey, SM4 4AW Tel: (020) 8540 1034 Fax: (020) 8543 3058 E-mail: enquiries@contarnex.com

Data Track Process Instruments Ltd, 153 Somerford Road, Christchurch, Dorset, BH23 3TY Tel: (01425) 271900 Fax: (01425) 271978 E-mail: dtpi.sales@dtrack.com

R & J Engineering, Gate House Cam Centre, Wilbury Way, Hitchin, Hertfordshire, SG4 0TW Tel: (01462) 620444 Fax: (01462) 620777

TEMPERATURE INFRARED SENSORS

Exergen Corp, Tollgate House, 69-71 High Street, Harpenden, Hertfordshire, AL5 2SL Tel: (01582) 461123 Fax: (01582) 461117 E-mail: sales@qhigroup.com

I P L, Unit 16, Llys y Fedwen, Parc Menai, Poundbury, Bangor, Gwynedd, LL57 4BN Tel: (01248) 672122 E-mail: sales@ipl-int.com

Wenglor Sensoric, Suite B Secondfloor Aspen House, 15 Medlicott Close, Corby, Northamptonshire, NN18 9NF Tel: (01536) 747299 Fax: (01536) 742301 E-mail: info.uk@wenglor.de

TEMPERATURE MEASURING INSTRUMENTS/SYSTEMS

B K W Instruments Ltd, Weymouth Road, Winton, Eccles, Manchester, M30 8NN Tel: 0161-707 4838 Fax: 0161-787 7580 E-mail: sales@bkwinstruments.co.uk

Comark Ltd, Comark House Gunnels Wood Park, Gunnels Wood Road, Stevenage, Hertfordshire, SG1 2TA Tel: (01438) 367367 Fax: (01438) 367400 E-mail: salesuk@comarkltd.com

Farm Electronics Ltd, Alma Park Industrial Estate, Grantham, Lincolnshire, NG31 9SR Tel: (01476) 591592 Fax: (01476) 591188 E-mail: info@farmelec.co.uk

Pyrometrics Ltd, Unit 1a Westthorpe Business Park, Killamarsh, Sheffield, S21 1TZ Tel: 0114-251 1201 Fax: 0114-248 4453 E-mail: mail@pyrometrics.co.uk

R A G, The Malthouse, Old Bexley Heath Business Park, 19 Bourne Road, Bexley, Kent, DA5 1LR Tel: (0800) 0431416 Fax: (0870) 850 1417 E-mail: info@ragcomms.com

TEMPERATURE MONITORING INFRARED SYSTEMS

Exergen Corp, Tollgate House, 69-71 High Street, Harpenden, Hertfordshire, AL5 2SL Tel: (01582) 461123 Fax: (01582) 461117 E-mail: sales@qhigroup.com

TEMPERATURE MONITORING SYSTEMS MANUFRS

▶ Anville Censors, Westward House, Glebeland Road, Camberley, Surrey, GU15 3DB Tel: (01276) 684613 Fax: (01276) 692606 E-mail: camberleycensorsfuk@online.co.uk

Chauvin Arnoux UK Ltd, Waldeck House, Waldeck Road, Maidenhead, Berkshire, SL6 8BR Tel: (01628) 788888 Fax: (01628) 628099 E-mail: sales@chauvin-arnoux.co.uk

Contronics Ltd, Greenfield Farm Industrial Estate, Congleton, Cheshire, CW12 4TU Tel: (01260) 298383 Fax: (01260) 298387 E-mail: sales@contronics.co.uk

▶ Global Measurements & Control Ltd, Unit 17, Ford Lane, Ford, Arundel, West Sussex, BN18 0UZ Tel: (01243) 555277 Fax: (01243) 555177 E-mail: sales@globalltd.co.uk

J T L Systems Ltd, Unit 41, Kingfisher Court, Hambridge Road, Newbury, Berkshire, RG14 5SJ Tel: (01635) 263646 Fax: (01635) 263647 E-mail: sales@jtl.co.uk

Monika, 10 Brook Park, Gaddesby Lane, Rearsby, Leicester, LE7 4YL Tel: (01664) 423900 Fax: (01664) 420033 E-mail: info@monika.com

Ronan Engineering Ltd, Factory 1-2 Tilley Road, Crowther, Washington, Tyne & Wear, NE38 0AE Tel: 0191-416 1689 Fax: 0191-416 5856 E-mail: sales@ronan.com

▶ Stirling Sensors, Cowling Street, Oldham, OL8 1UY Tel: 0161-785 8788 Fax: 0161-627 0507 E-mail: sales@stirlingsensors.co.uk

TEMPERATURE OR RAIN OR WIND OR SMOKE ROOF VENT OR WINDOW ELECTRONIC CONTROL SYSTEMS

▶ L & R Loft Services, 8 Stonehill Crescent, Bognor Regis, West Sussex, PO21 3PQ Tel: (0800) 2984350 E-mail: enq@loftservices.co.uk

TEMPERATURE PROBES

The Control Shop Ltd, 17 Bilton Industrial Estate, Stockmans Close, Birmingham, B38 9TS Tel: 0121-451 1030 Fax: 0121-459 1511 E-mail: sales@controlshop.co.uk

GMF Equipment Ltd, 9A High Street, Kegworth, Derby, DE74 2DA Tel: (01509) 673656 Fax: (01509) 674729 E-mail: sales@gmfequipment.co.uk

TEMPERATURE RECORDER MANUFRS

British Rototherm Co. Ltd, Kenfig Industrial Estate, Margam, Port Talbot, West Glamorgan, SA13 2PW Tel: (01656) 740551 Fax: (01656) 745915 E-mail: rototherm@rototherm.co.uk

Cold Chain Instruments Ltd, 1 Martlets Way, Goring-by-Sea, Worthing, West Sussex, BN12 4HF Tel: (01903) 249000 Fax: (01903) 248740 E-mail: sales@transcan.co.uk

Minta Instrumentation Ltd, Caddick Road, Knowsley Business Park, Prescot, Merseyside, L34 9HP Tel: 0151-548 6818 Fax: 0151-548 5578 E-mail: sales@mintasensors.co.uk

Sar Ltd, Highfield, Row Dow Lane, Knatts Valley, Sevenoaks, Kent, TN15 6XN Tel: (01959) 524444 Fax: (01959) 524455 E-mail: sales@sarltd.co.uk

Storm Products, 28 Hawbank Road, East Kilbride, Glasgow, G74 5EX Tel: (01355) 249358 Fax: (01355) 249197 E-mail: sales@cvcs.co.uk

TEMPERATURE SENSORS

Cold Chain Instruments Ltd, 1 Martlets Way, Goring-by-Sea, Worthing, West Sussex, BN12 4HF Tel: (01903) 249000 Fax: (01903) 248740 E-mail: sales@transcan.co.uk

Crossland Components Ltd, Unit L Tanfield Lea Industrial Estate South, Tanfield Lea, Stanley, County Durham, DH9 9XA Tel: (01207) 230269 Fax: (01207) 283849 E-mail: info@crossland.co.uk

Data Harvest Group Ltd, 1 Eden Court, Eden Way, Leighton Buzzard, Bedfordshire, LU7 4FY Tel: (01525) 373666 Fax: (01525) 851638 E-mail: sales@data-harvest.co.uk

Dynisco (UK) Ltd, Unit 2B Crowood House, Gipsy Lane, Swindon, SN2 8YY Tel: (01527) 577077 Fax: (01527) 577070 E-mail: dyniscouk@dynisco.com

Minta Instrumentation Ltd, Caddick Road, Knowsley Business Park, Prescot, Merseyside, L34 9HP Tel: 0151-548 6818 Fax: 0151-548 5578 E-mail: sales@mintasensors.co.uk

Sensing Devices Ltd, 97 Tithebarn Road, Southport, Merseyside, PR8 6AG Tel: (01704) 546161 Fax: (01704) 546231 E-mail: sales@sensing-devices.co.uk

TEMPORARY ACCESS ROADWAY CONTRACTORS

Trax Portable Access, Dukeries Industrial Estate, Claylands Avenue, Worksop, Nottinghamshire, S81 7DJ Tel: (0870) 240 2381

TEMPORARY BUILDING CONSTRUCTORS OR FABRICATORS

A V Group Ltd, Hall Road, Langley Mill, Nottingham, NG16 4HP Tel: (01773) 711079 Fax: (01773) 711246 E-mail: sales@avgroup.co.uk

Ably Shelters Ltd, 1700 Blueprint, Dundas Spur, Portsmouth, PO3 5RW Tel: (023) 9244 8040 Fax: (023) 9244 8049 E-mail: sales@ablyshelters.co.uk

▶ Dainton Portable Buildings Ltd, Dainton Business Park, Newton Abbot, Devon, TQ12 5TZ Tel: (01626) 835547 Fax: (01626) 830407 E-mail: info@dainton.com

Elliott Group Ltd, Mill Lane, Congresbury, Bristol, BS49 5JD Tel: (01934) 832103 Fax: (01934) 876198

Goods Protection Ltd, 11/12 Shuttleworth Road, Elm Farm Industrial Estate, Bedford, MK41 0EP Tel: (01234) 327522 Fax: (01234) 270885 E-mail: info@goods-protection.co.uk

Losberger Walter UK, 27 High Street, Collingham, Collingham, Newark, Nottinghamshire, NG23 7LA Tel: (01636) 893776 Fax: (01636) 893774 E-mail: losbergeruk@losberger.com

P R Portable Buildings, The Lawns, 52 West Street, Crewkerne, Somerset, TA18 8BA Tel: (01460) 72033 Fax: (01460) 72033

▶ Shed Scene, Brecklands Nursery, Siston Lane, Bristol, BS30 5LX Tel: (0845) 3108710 Fax: (0845) 3108711 E-mail: info@shedscene.com

▶ Temp Space, 5 Beechmore Road, London, SW11 4ET Tel: (0800) 3287554 E-mail: enquiries@temp-space.co.uk

▶ Wernick Hire Ltd, 1882190 Keyham Road, Devenport, Plymouth, PL2 1RD Tel: (01752) 567037 Fax: (01752) 567348 E-mail: hire@wernickplymouth.co.uk

TEMPORARY BUILDING HIRE

Elliott Group Ltd, Seckar Wood Industrial Park, Barnsley Road, Newmillerdam, Wakefield, West Yorkshire, WF2 6QW Tel: (01924) 254420 Fax: (01924) 241959 E-mail: info@elliotthire.co.uk

G E Capital Modular Space Ltd, G E House, Ten Pound Walk, Doncaster, South Yorkshire, DN4 5HW Tel: (01302) 732400 Fax: (01302) 732407 E-mail: mick-cleghorn@gecapital.com

▶ Ravenstock MSG Ltd, Chittening Industrial Estate, Chittening, Bristol, BS11 0YB Tel: 0117-938 0110 Fax: 0117-938 0220 E-mail: webenquiries@ravenstockmsg.com

▶ Spaciotempo UK Ltd, Dovefields, Dovefields Industrial Estate, Uttoxeter, Staffordshire, ST14 8HU Tel: (01889) 569569 Fax: (01889) 569555 E-mail: sales@spaciotempo.com

Wernick Hire Ltd, Baluniefield Trading Estate, Balunie Drive, Dundee, DD4 8YZ Tel: (01382) 477108 Fax: (01382) 778741

▶ indicates data change since last edition

TEMPORARY BUILDING HIRE – *continued*

Wernick Hire Ltd, Leeway Industrial Estate, Newport, Gwent, NP19 4SL Tel: (01633) 281118 Fax: (01633) 282242

TEMPORARY BUILDINGS

Finrone Ltd, 52C Strabane Road, Castlederg, County Tyrone, BT81 7HZ Tel: (028) 8167 9918 Fax: (028) 8167 9399 E-mail: info@finrone.com

G E Capital Modular Space Ltd, Grappenhall Lane, Appleton, Warrington, WA4 4QT Tel: (01925) 268361 Fax: (01925) 268763

Goods Protection Ltd, 11/12 Shuttleworth Road, Elm Farm Industrial Estate, Bedford, MK41 0EP Tel: (01234) 327522 Fax: (01234) 270885 E-mail: info@goods-protection.co.uk

Portakabin Ltd, 19-21 Glasgow Road, Newbridge, Midlothian, EH28 8SY Tel: 0131-335 3114 Fax: 0131-335 3110

TEMPORARY FENCING

Darfen Steelhoard, Herons Way, Balby, Doncaster, South Yorkshire, DN4 8WA Tel: (0845) 7023878 Fax: (01302) 327135 E-mail: sales@steelhoard.co.uk

TEMPORARY KITCHEN UNITS

PKL Group (UK) Ltd, Stella Way, Bishops Cleeve, Cheltenham, Glos, GL52 7DQ Tel: (01242) 663000 Fax: (01242) 677819 E-mail: postbox@pkl.co.uk

TEMPORARY PORTABLE BUILDINGS

Aganto Ltd, Unit 5, Saw Mill Road, Hermitage, Thatcham, Berkshire, RG18 9QL Tel: (01635) 202979 Fax: (01635) 202467 E-mail: info@aganto.co.uk

▶ Temp Space, 5 Beechmore Road, London, SW11 4ET Tel: (0800) 3287554 E-mail: enquiries@temp-space.co.uk

TEMPORARY ROOF PROTECTION SYSTEMS

▶ Special Fire Systems, Baston Hall, Crews Hill, Alfrick, Worcester, WR6 5HF Tel: (01886) 884747 Fax: (01886) 884125 E-mail: enquiries@special-fire.com

TEMPORARY ROOFING CONTRACTORS

Ably Shelters Ltd, 1700 Blueprint, Dundas Spur, Portsmouth, PO3 5RW Tel: (023) 9244 8040 Fax: (023) 9244 8049 E-mail: sales@ablyshelters.co.uk

▶ J W Lewis & Sons Ltd, Bojea Industrial Estate, Trethowel, St. Austell, Cornwall, PL25 5RJ Tel: (01726) 72764 Fax: (01726) 65858 E-mail: enquiries@jwlewisandsons.sagenet.co.uk

TEMPORARY STAFF PAYROLL SERVICES

ABCO Computer Services Ltd, Airways House, First Avenue, London Stansted Airport North, Stansted, Essex, CM24 1RY Tel: (01279) 680000 Fax: (01279) 661371 E-mail: abcopay@ndirect.co.uk

▶ Charterhouse Group International Plc, 2nd Floor, 37 Lombard Street, London, United Kingdom, EC3V 9BQ Tel: 0800 634 4848 Fax: 0800 634 4849 E-mail: sales@charterhouseplc.com

TEMPORARY STAFF RECRUITMENT AGENCIES

▶ Ann Pettengell Gold Helm Ltd, 1 Dover Street, Cambridge, CB1 1DY Tel: (01223) 350234 Fax: (01223) 462929 E-mail: jobs@annpettengell.co.uk

▶ Bennett Secretarial Services Ltd, 51a-52 Market Street, Hyde, Cheshire, SK14 2AB Tel: 0161-368 5511 Fax: 0161-627 1793 E-mail: hyde@bennettstaff.co.uk

▶ Bennett Staff Bureau, 22 St Petersgate, Stockport, Cheshire, SK1 1HD Tel: 0161-480 0411 Fax: 0161-474 7610 E-mail: stockport@bennettstaff.co.uk

D K Associates Ltd, 26-34 Friar Lane, Nottingham, NG1 6DQ Tel: 0115-947 3500 Fax: 0115-985 9007 E-mail: office@dk-recruit.co.uk

▶ Encore Personnel, 2 Plough Road, Wellington, Telford, Shropshire, TF1 1ET Tel: (01952) 262970 Fax: (01952) 641880 E-mail: sales@encorepersonnel.co.uk

▶ Encore Personnel Services, Market Chambers, Shelton Square, Coventry, CV1 1DG Tel: (024) 7623 8330 Fax: (024) 7625 6475 E-mail: coventry@encorepersonnel.co.uk

▶ Munnelly Support Services Ltd, The Heights, 59-65 Lowlands Road, Harrow, Middlesex, HA1 3AW Tel: (020) 8515 0300 Fax: (020) 8861 5837

▶ Parc UK Ltd, Claremont House, 20 North Claremont Street, Glasgow, G3 7LE Tel: 0141-331 2383 Fax: 0141-331 2385

▶ Scientific Staffing Solutions (Scotland) Ltd, Suite 26D, 8-10 Glasgow Road, Kirkintilloch, Glasgow, G66 1SH Tel: 0141-578 3600 Fax: 0141-578 0049

▶ XPT Solutions, One St. Colme Street, Edinburgh, EH3 6AA Tel: 0131-220 8253 Fax: 0131-220 8201

TEMPORARY STAFF RECRUITMENT AGENCIES, ENGINEERING

▶ Encore Personnel, 2 Plough Road, Wellington, Telford, Shropshire, TF1 1ET Tel: (01952) 262970 Fax: (01952) 641880 E-mail: sales@encorepersonnel.co.uk

▶ F E S Recruitment & Personnel, 298 Stanley Road, Bootle, Merseyside, L20 3ET Tel: 0151-922 9392 Fax: 0151-922 9592 E-mail: craig@fes-recruitment.co.uk

▶ J N F Employment, 2c The Parade, Edinburgh Drive, Didcot, Oxfordshire, OX11 7LT Tel: (01235) 811600 Fax: (01235) 811601 E-mail: oxfordshire@jnf-employment.co.uk

▶ Local Personnel, 26 High Street, Wetherby, Leeds, Leeds, LS22 6LT Tel: 01937 588111 Fax: 01937 588444 E-mail: john@localpersonnel.co.uk

TEMPORARY STAIR EDGE PROTECTION EQUIPMENT

▶ Special Fire Systems, Baston Hall, Crews Hill, Alfrick, Worcester, WR6 5HF Tel: (01886) 884747 Fax: (01886) 884125 E-mail: enquiries@special-fire.com

TEMPORARY STORAGE BIN OR CONTAINER HIRE

777 Waste Management, 158 Beddington Lane, Croydon, CR0 4TE Tel: (020) 8689 6861 Fax: (020) 8689 7176 E-mail: maxine.grew@777group.co.uk

▶ Site Equipment Ltd, Bowerhurst, Mill Lane, Crondall, Farnham, Surrey, GU10 5RP Tel: (01252) 851988 Fax: (01252) 851989 E-mail: hire@site-equip.co.uk

TEMPORARY TRAFFIC MANAGEMENT

▶ Direct Traffic Management Ltd, Unit 26 Frontier Works, King Edward Road, Thorne, Doncaster, South Yorkshire, DN8 4HU Tel: (01405) 817733 Fax: (01405) 813007 E-mail: info@direct-traffic.co.uk

TEMPORARY WAREHOUSE HIRE

Arena Structures, Needingworth Road, St. Ives, Cambridgeshire, PE27 3ND Tel: (01480) 468888 Fax: (01480) 462888

TEMPORARY WAREHOUSING

H D L Carson, Trafford Park Road, Trafford Park, Manchester, M17 1WH Tel: 0161-872 2694 Fax: 0161-877 9755 E-mail: fredrickcarson@aol.com

I A S Storage Systems, Newtonsyde, Charleston, Nigg, Aberdeen, AB12 3LL Tel: (01224) 897305 Fax: (01224) 897305 E-mail: ias@totalise.co.uk

▶ Spaciotempo UK Ltd, Dovefields, Dovefields Industrial Estate, Uttoxeter, Staffordshire, ST14 8HU Tel: (01889) 569569 Fax: (01889) 569555 E-mail: sales@spaciotempo.com

TENNIS BALL FELT

Milliken Industrials Ltd, Wellington Street, Bury, Lancashire, BL8 2AY Tel: 0161-764 2244 Fax: 0161-705 2148 E-mail: john.lancashire@milliken.com

Milliken Woolen Speciality, Lodgemore Mills, Stroud, Gloucestershire, GL5 3EJ Tel: (01453) 760800 Fax: (01453) 752919 E-mail: wsp-sales@milliken.com

TENNIS COURT SURROUND FENCING

Thames Steel & Equipment Ltd, Turkey Cottage, Curload, Stoke St. Gregory, Taunton, Somerset, TA3 6JE Tel: (01823) 698881 Fax: (01823) 698988 E-mail: douglas.billington@lineone.net

TENSILE FABRIC STRUCTURES

▶ Envelope Structures Ltd, The Old Mill, Wallops Wood Farm, Sheardley Lane, Droxford, SO32 3QY Tel: (01489) 878101 Fax: (0871) 6617326 E-mail: enquiries@envelopestructures.co.uk

▶ Meliar Design, Lower Cwm Barns, Llanafan Fawr, Builth Wells, Powys, LD2 3SG Tel: 01597 860291 E-mail: info@meliar.com

TENSILE TEST EQUIPMENT

T W L Force Systems, 15 Old Farm Lane, Fareham, Hampshire, PO14 2DB Tel: (01329) 665186 Fax: (01329) 668177 E-mail: sales@twlforce.co.uk

▶ Testometric Co. Ltd, Unit 1 Lincoln Business Park, Lincoln Close, Rochdale, Lancashire, OL11 1NR Tel: (01706) 654039 Fax: (01706) 646089 E-mail: info@testometric.co.uk

Tinius Olsen Ltd, Unit 6, Perrywood Business Park, Honeycrock Lane, Salfords, Redhill, RH1 5DZ Tel: (01737) 765001 Fax: (01737) 764768 E-mail: sales@tiniusolsen.co.uk

TENSILE/IMPACT TESTING SERVICES, MECHANICAL

Bodycote Materials Testing Ltd, Shields Road, Newcastle upon Tyne, NE6 2YD Tel: 0191-275 2800 Fax: 0191-276 0177 E-mail: sales-mt@bodycote-mt.com

TENSION LATCHES

Fairchild Fasteners UK Ltd, Unit 6 Bardon 22 Industrial Estate, Bardon Hill, Coalville, Leicestershire, LE67 1TE Tel: (01530) 518900 Fax: (01530) 518910 E-mail: sales@fairchildfasteners.com

TENSION SPRINGS

Lion Springs Ltd, Summer Street, Rochdale, Lancashire, OL16 1SY Tel: (01706) 861352 Fax: (01706) 657863 E-mail: sales@lionsprings.co.uk

Peterson Spring (UK) Ltd, Reddings Lane, Tyseley, Birmingham, B11 3HA Tel: 0121-706 2236 Fax: 0121-708 1253 E-mail: enquiries@psprings.euroe.co.uk

TENT CLOTH/MARQUEE CLOTH

Crocker Bros, 8-18 Station Road, Chellaston, Derby, DE73 5SU Tel: (01332) 700699 Fax: (01332) 705655 E-mail: sales@crockerbros.co.uk

TENT FRAMES

Ultramatrix Production Services Ltd, Farfield Works, Birds Green, Romsley, Bridgnorth, Shropshire, WV15 6HJ Tel: (01746) 780360 Fax: (01746) 780933

TENT HIRE

Owen Brown, Station Road, Castle Donington, Derby, DE74 2NL Tel: (01332) 850000 Fax: (01332) 850005 E-mail: info@owen-brown.co.uk

Compass Marquees, East Oakdene, Headcorn, Ashford, Kent, TN27 9JF Tel: (01622) 892254 Fax: (01622) 891473 E-mail: tents@compass-marquees.co.uk

Dover Marquee Co. Ltd, 30 Mayfield Avenue, Dover, Kent, CT16 2PL Tel: (01304) 215315 Fax: (01304) 202086 E-mail: sales@dover-marquee.co.uk

Tents & Marquees Ltd, Haughton Farm, Haughton, Shrewsbury, SY4 4GB Tel: (01743) 709246 Fax: (01743) 709106 E-mail: info@tentsandmarquees.com

TENTS

Aquila Shelters Ltd, Claremont House, St Georges Road, Bolton, BL1 2BY Tel: (01204) 522424 Fax: (01204) 365110 E-mail: sales@aquila-shelters.co.uk

C.F. Barker & Sons (Marquees) Ltd, 47 Osborne Road, Thornton Heath, Surrey, CR7 8PD Tel: (01883) 337099 Fax: (020) 8653 2932

▶ Blacktoe Ltd, 53 The Slough, Redditch, Worcestershire, B97 5JR Tel: (01527) 458954

Diaward Equipment (UK) Ltd, Firmin House, 82-86 New Town Row, Birmingham, B6 4HU Tel: 0121-359 6666 Fax: 0121-359 3292 E-mail: enquiries@firmin.co.uk

G Stanley, 5 Wyke Street, Hull, HU9 1PA Tel: (01482) 225590 Fax: (01482) 588764 E-mail: sales@gstanleys.co.uk

J & S Franklin Holdings & Management Services Ltd, Franklin House, 151 Strand, London, WC2R 1HL Tel: (020) 7836 2762 Fax: (020) 7836 2784 E-mail: defence@franklin.co.uk

Leith (U K) Ltd, Pier Road, Berwick-upon-Tweed, TD15 1JB Tel: (01289) 307264 Fax: (01289) 330517 E-mail: enquiries@wleithmarquees.co.uk

Roder UK Ltd, Unit 16 Earith Business Park, Meadow Drove, Earith, Huntingdon, Cambridgeshire, PE28 3QF Tel: (01487) 840840 Fax: (01487) 840843 E-mail: sales@roderuk.com

TERMINAL BLOCKS

D N A UK Ltd, Bighton Hill, Ropley, Alresford, Hampshire, SO24 9SQ Tel: (01962) 772666 Fax: (01962) 772660 E-mail: info@dnacap.com

R H Ling, 82 Forest Road, Frome, Somerset, BA11 2TQ Tel: (01373) 467592 Fax: (01373) 467592

Rush Industrial Sales, 126 Station Road, Tempsford, Sandy, Bedfordshire, SG19 2AY Tel: (01767) 640779 Fax: (01767) 640617 E-mail: sales@rushind.com

Termate Ltd, Leone Works, John Street, New Bassford, Nottingham, NG7 7HL Tel: 0115-978 4652 Fax: 0115-970 2106 E-mail: sales@termate.com

TERMINAL BLOCKS, TELECOMMUNICATION

▶ Inbound Solutions Ltd, Unit 8, Greenham Park, Common Road, Witchford, Ely, Cambridgeshire, CB6 2HF Tel: (0800) 0776907 Fax: (01353) 661147 E-mail: contact@inboundsolutions.co.uk

TERMINAL ENCLOSURES

Electrix International Ltd, 1a-1b Dovecot Hill, South Church Enterprise Park, Bishop Auckland, County Durham, DL14 6XP Tel: (01388) 774455 Fax: (01388) 777359 E-mail: enquiries@electrix.co.uk

TERMINAL INSULATORS

Selsmore (Marketing) Ltd, Unit 23 The Tanneries, Brockhampton Lane, Havant, Hampshire, PO9 1JB Tel: (023) 9249 2907 Fax: (023) 9247 3714 E-mail: selsmore@tiscali.co.uk

TERMINALS, BATTERY, BRASS

Eurowales Cable Accessories, Atlantic Trading Estate, Barry, South Glamorgan, CF63 3RF Tel: (01446) 739965 Fax: (01446) 739966 E-mail: sales@eurowales-cable-accessories.com

TERMINALS, COPPER

▶ Kompress Holdings Ltd, 34 Dalziel Road, Hillington Industrial Estate, Glasgow, G52 4NN Tel: 0141-883 0228 Fax: 0141-883 6123 E-mail: sales@kompress.com

TERMINALS/TERMINAL TAGS, ELECTRIC CABLE OR WIRE

Cablespeed, 447 Oakshott Place, Bamber Bridge, Preston, PR5 8AT Tel: (0870) 6098025 Fax: (0870) 6098026 E-mail: sales@cablespeed.co.uk

Takbro Ltd, Unit 5 Albert Drive, Burgess Hill, West Sussex, RH15 9TN Tel: (01444) 245601 Fax: (01444) 872316 E-mail: mail@takbro.co.uk

TERRA-COTTA PRODUCERS OR SUPPLIERS

Ceramicos, The Warehouse, Whitehill Cottage, Oxhill, Warwick, CV35 0RH Tel: 01295 680176 Fax: 01295 680174 E-mail: sales@ceramicos.co.uk

Henry Watson Potteries Ltd, Pottery House, Pottery Hill, Wattisfield, Diss, Norfolk, IP22 1NH Tel: (01359) 251239 Fax: (01359) 250984 E-mail: sales@henrywatson.com

Keymer Tiles Ltd, Nye Road, Burgess Hill, West Sussex, RH15 0LZ Tel: (01444) 232931 Fax: (01444) 871852 E-mail: info@keymer.co.uk

Shaws Of Darwen, Waterside, Darwen, Lancashire, BB3 3NX Tel: (01254) 771086 Fax: (01254) 873462 E-mail: sales@shaws-of-darwen.co.uk

TERRA-COTTA PRODUCTS IMPORT/EXPORT MERCHANTS OR AGENTS

Cocina Ceramics, Unit 5 Knighton Hill Business Centre, Knighton Hill, Wembury, Plymouth, PL9 0ED Tel: (01752) 863663 Fax: (01752) 863663 E-mail: cocinaceramics@ffmail.net
Patio Garden Centres, 100 Tooting Bec Road, London, SW17 8BG Tel: (020) 8672 2251 Fax: (020) 8682 2105

TERRACOTTA TILE CLADDING

Telling Lime Products, Primrose Avenue, Wolverhampton, WV10 8AW Tel: (01902) 789777 Fax: (01902) 398777 E-mail: m.wood@telling.co.uk

TERRAZZO CONTRACTORS

Fieldmount Terrazzo Ltd, 7-8 Liddell Road, London, NW6 2EW Tel: (020) 7624 8866 Fax: (020) 7328 1836 E-mail: enquiries@nftmms.co.uk
Marriott & Price Ltd, Station House Station Yard, Waterhouse Lane, Kingswood, Tadworth, Surrey, KT20 6EN Tel: (01737) 352735 Fax: (01737) 359192 E-mail: info@marriottandprice.co.uk
O Toffolo & Son Ltd, 42 Temple Street, Hull, HU5 1AE Tel: (01482) 342674 Fax: (01482) 441344 E-mail: carl@toffolo.co.uk
Pallam Precast Ltd, 41 Lockfield Avenue, Enfield, Middlesex, EN3 7PY Tel: (020) 8805 6811 Fax: (020) 8804 9825
Roman Mosaic Contracts Ltd, Bloomfield Road, Tipton, West Midlands, DY4 9ES Tel: 0121-557 2267 Fax: 0121-557 0975 E-mail: sales@romanmosaiccontracts.co.uk
Zanetti & Bailey, Verona House, Filwood Road, Bristol, BS16 3RY Tel: 0117-965 6565 Fax: 0117-965 1236 E-mail: info@marbleflooring.com

TERRAZZO TILES

Pilkingtons Tiles Group Plc, P O Box 4, Manchester, M27 8LP Tel: 0161-727 1000 Fax: 0161-727 1122 E-mail: info@pilkingtontiles.com
Quiligotti Terrazzo Ltd, PO Box 4, Manchester, M27 8LP Tel: 0161-727 1189 Fax: 0161-793 1173 E-mail: sales@pilkingtons.com

TERRY TOWELLING FABRICS

Floringo Ltd, Enterprise House, 133 Blyth Road, Hayes, Middlesex, UB3 1DD Tel: (020) 8587 3400 Fax: (020) 8569 1445 E-mail: floringo@globalnet.co.uk
Richard Haworth & Co. Ltd, Kearsley Mill, Stoneclough, Radcliffe, Manchester, M26 1RH Tel: (01204) 708508 Fax: (01204) 705772 E-mail: info@richardhaworth.co.uk

TEST BED SYSTEMS

Curran Engineering Ltd, Unit 15 Valley Enterprise, Bedwas House Industrial Estate, Bedwas, Caerphilly, CF83 8DW Tel: (029) 2085 0800 Fax: (029) 2085 0800 E-mail: rjh@curranltd.co.uk

TEST ENGINEERING SERVICES

C I A Ltd, Froghall Road, Aberdeen, AB24 3JL Tel: (01224) 626364 Fax: (01224) 624005 E-mail: sales@c-i-a.co.uk
E White, Watling Street, Clifton upon Dunsmore, Rugby, Warwickshire, CV23 0AQ Tel: (01788) 860526 Fax: (01788) 860150 E-mail: sales@ericwhite.co.uk
▶ Eclipse Petroleum Technology, Salvesen Tower, Blaikies Quay, Aberdeen, AB11 5PW Tel: (01224) 588355 Fax: (01224) 588356
R M R Materials Testing Co. Ltd, Deepdale Lane, Dudley, West Midlands, DY3 2AF Tel: (01384) 234515 Fax: (01384) 235511 E-mail: rmrmaterialstestingco@callnetuk.com

TEST EQUIPMENT, *See also headings under Test and also that which is tested, such as Aircrat Test*

Anton Test & Measurement, Park House, 15-23 Greenhill Crescent, Watford, WD18 8PH Tel: (08704) 280073 Fax: (08704) 280076 E-mail: sales@anton-group.com
Cal-Com Systems Ltd, Calibration House, Moorefield Grove, Bolton, BL2 2LQ Tel: (01204) 383311 Fax: (01204) 382556
Clare Instruments, Dominion Way, Worthing, West Sussex, BN14 8NW Tel: (01903) 233314 Fax: (01903) 216089 E-mail: sales@clareinstruments.com
Cooke International, Unit 9 Ford La Business Park, Ford, Arundel, West Sussex, BN18 0UZ Tel: (01243) 555590 Fax: (01243) 551455
D F D Instruments, Northpoint House, 52 High Street, Knaphill, Woking, Surrey, GU21 2PY Tel: (01483) 799333 Fax: (01483) 480199 E-mail: tore@dfdinstruments.co.uk
▶ East Coast Controls Ltd, Acre House, Stirling Road, Kilsyth, Glasgow, G65 0PT Tel: (01236) 825490 Fax: (01236) 822307
Euremica Ltd, Instrument House, Morgan Drive, Guisborough, Cleveland, TS14 7DG Tel: (01287) 204020 Fax: (01287) 204021 E-mail: sales@euremica.com
G A Assembly Ltd, Alma Works, Coke Hill, Rotherham, South Yorkshire, S60 2HX Tel: (01709) 839911 Fax: (01709) 838373 E-mail: sales@gaa-ltd.co.uk
G M C Instrumentation (UK) Ltd, Priest House, Priest Street, Cradley Heath, West Midlands, B64 6JN Tel: (01384) 638822 Fax: (01384) 639168 E-mail: sales@gmciuk.com
▶ Hartest Precision Instruments Ltd, 4 St Georges Industrial Estate, Richmond Road, Kingston upon Thames, Surrey, KT2 5BQ Tel: (020) 8541 4333 Fax: (020) 8549 3374 E-mail: sales@sheeninstruments.com
I R Group, Forbes House, Whitefriars Estate, Tudor Road, Harrow, Middlesex, HA3 5SS Tel: (020) 8420 0211
Imex Systems Ltd, 34 Old Kilmore Road, Moira, Craigavon, County Armagh, BT67 0LZ Tel: (028) 9261 9233 Fax: (028) 9261 9234 E-mail: sales@ulster.imex.co.uk
▶ Insight NDT Equipment Ltd, The Old Cider Mill, Wrigglebrook, Kingsthorne, Hereford, HR2 8AW Tel: (01981) 541122 Fax: (01981) 541133 E-mail: sales@insightndt.com
Instron, Coronation Road, High Wycombe, Buckinghamshire, HP12 3SY Tel: (01494) 464646 Fax: (01494) 456123 E-mail: info_news@instron.com
Instrotech Ltd, Unit A Penfold Trading Estate, Imperial Way, Watford, WD24 4YY Tel: (01923) 442244 Fax: (01923) 252959 E-mail: sales@instrotech.com
Kew Technik Ltd, Rankine Road, Basingstoke, Hampshire, RG24 8PP Tel: (01256) 864100 Fax: (01256) 864164 E-mail: sales@kewt.co.uk
▶ Land-Drill Geotechnics Ltd, Drilling & Exploration Centre, Pardovan Estate, Philipstoun, Linlithgow, West Lothian, EH49 7RX Tel: (01506) 830044 Fax: (01506) 830055 E-mail: info@land-drill.com
M & B Radio (Leeds), 86 Bishopgate Street, Leeds, LS1 4BB Tel: 0113-243 5649 Fax: 0113-242 6881
M T S Systems Ltd, Brook House Somerford Court, Somerford Road, Cirencester, Gloucestershire, GL7 1TW Tel: (01285) 648800 Fax: (01285) 658052
Micropoint Plus Ltd, 22 Laurel Avenue, Slough, SL3 7DG Tel: (01753) 790829 Fax: (01753) 790830E-mail: micropointplus@btconnect.com
N D T Kenged, 5 Keith Street, Hamilton, Lanarkshire, ML3 7BL Tel: (01698) 285914 Fax: (01698) 891975 E-mail: ken@kenged.co.uk
Paxton Instruments, Trillium House, 32 New Street, St. Neots, Cambridgeshire, PE19 1AJ Tel: (01480) 356472 Fax: (01480) 356598
Preco Broadcast Systems Ltd, Unit 3 Four Seasons Crescent, Sutton, Surrey, SM3 9QR Tel: (020) 8644 4447 Fax: (020) 8644 0474 E-mail: sales@preco.co.uk
Pullman Instruments (UK) Ltd, Chatsworth House, Chatsworth Terrace, Harrogate, North Yorkshire, HG1 5HT Tel: (01423) 720360 Fax: (01423) 720361 E-mail: info@pullman.co.uk
Rohde & Schwarz UK Ltd, Ansells Bus Park, Fleet, Hampshire, GU51 2UZ Tel: (01252) 811377 Fax: (01252) 811447 E-mail: sales@rsuk.rohde-shwartz.com
Sitest Ltd, Unit 9 Minster Park Collingwood Road, Verwood, Dorset, BH31 6QF Tel: (01202) 861733 Fax: (01202) 861734 E-mail: info@sitest.co.uk
Vann Draper Electronics, Barrow-on-Trent, Derby, DE73 7HL Tel: (01283) 704706 Fax: (01283) 704707 E-mail: admin@vanndraper.co.uk
Wentworth Laboratories Ltd, 1 Gosforth Close, Sandy, Bedfordshire, SG19 1RB Tel: (01767) 681221 Fax: (01767) 691951
Westlairds Ltd, Patrixbourne, The Green, Datchet, Slough, SL3 9JH Tel: (01753) 543939 Fax: (01753) 549933 E-mail: westlairds@westlairds.co.uk
▶ Wexham Developments 93, 2c Amity Road, Reading, RG1 3LJ Tel: 0118-966 1977 Fax: 0118-966 1981
Zwick Ltd, Main Enquiries, Southern Avenue, Leominster, Herefordshire, HR6 0QH Tel: (01568) 615201 Fax: (01568) 616626 E-mail: sales.info@zwick.co.uk

TEST EQUIPMENT CONSULTANTS OR DESIGNERS, AUTOMATIC, PERSONAL COMPUTER (PC) BASED

▶ Scilutions Ltd, Trinafour, Abingdon Road, Marcham, Abingdon, Oxfordshire, OX13 6NU Tel: (01865) 391460 Fax: (01865) 391385 E-mail: kellysweb@scilutions.co.uk

TEST EQUIPMENT HIRE

Aughton Automation Ltd, 66 Brindley Road, Astmoor Industrial Estate, Runcorn, Cheshire, WA7 1PF Tel: (01928) 589606 Fax: (01928) 589601 E-mail: brian.duffy@aughtonuk.com
HCS Control Systems Ltd, Unit V2, Viewfield Industrial Estate, Glenrothes, Fife, KY6 2RG Tel: (01592) 770786 Fax: (01592) 775737 E-mail: sales@hcscsl.com
I R Group, Forbes House, Whitefriars Estate, Tudor Road, Harrow, Middlesex, HA3 5SS Tel: (020) 8420 0211
Instrument Solutions, Old Bracknell Lane West, Bracknell, Berkshire, RG12 7AH Tel: (01344) 459314 Fax: (01344) 714868 E-mail: sales@bis.fm
Orix Rentec Ltd, 9 Falcon Park Industrial Estate, Neasden Lane, London, NW10 1RZ Tel: (020) 8208 8600 Fax: (020) 8208 8601 E-mail: info@orixrentec.co.uk
Water Weights, Unit 7 Gapton Hall Industrial Estate, Vanguard Road, Great Yarmouth, Norfolk, NR31 0NT Tel: (01493) 442591 Fax: (01493) 442535 E-mail: marketing@imes-group.com

TEST EQUIPMENT, BURN-IN

Sharetree Ltd, Unit 3 Meadow Mill Eastington Trading Estate, Churchend, Eastington, Stonehouse, Gloucestershire, GL10 3RZ Tel: (01453) 828642 Fax: (01453) 828076 E-mail: sales@sharetree.com

TEST EQUIPMENT, ELECTRICAL

M T I Instruments & Calibration, Littleburn Industrial Estate, Langley Moor, Durham, DH7 8HJ Tel: 0191-378 3990 Fax: 0191-378 3973
Martindale Electric Co. Ltd, Metrohm House, Penfold Trading Estate, Imperial Way, Watford, WD24 4YY Tel: (01923) 441717 Fax: (01923) 446900 E-mail: sales@martindale-electric.co.uk
Relay Engineering Services, 1a Dicker Mill, Hertford, SG13 7AA Tel: (01992) 586234 Fax: (01992) 582894 E-mail: info@relayeng.com
Seaward Electronic Ltd, 11 Bracken Hill, South West Industrial Estate, Peterlee, County Durham, SR8 2LS Tel: 0191-586 3511 Fax: 0191-586 0227 E-mail: sales@seaward.co.uk

TEST EQUIPMENT, ELECTRONIC, USED

▶ Alternative Test Equipment, PO Box 3470, Wokingham, Berkshire, RG40 9AH Tel: (0845) 3457791 Fax: (0845) 3457792 E-mail: sales@AlternativeTest.co.uk
▶ Isis Electronics Cheltentham Ltd, Building 66, Aston Down, Frampton Mansell, Stroud, Gloucestershire, GL6 8GA Tel: (01285) 760777 Fax: (01285) 760163 E-mail: sales@astondown.co.uk

TEST EQUIPMENT, INTERFACE, PLUG-IN

Synergie-Cad UK Ltd, Greetwell Place, 2 Lime Kiln Way, Lincoln, LN2 4US Tel: (01522) 520222 Fax: (01522) 531222 E-mail: rogercooke@synergie-cad.co.uk

TEST FIXTURES

Everett Charles, Fence Avenue Indust Estate, Fence Avenue, Macclesfield, Cheshire, SK10 1LT Tel: (01625) 500303 Fax: (01625) 500306
Forwessun Test Systems Ltd, Unit 2 Newton Court, 2 Wavertree Technology Park, Liverpool, L13 1EJ Tel: 0151-220 5558 Fax: 0151-259 6407 E-mail: admin@forwessun.com
Minderaty Solutions N I Ltd, 75 Belfast Road, Carrickfergus, County Antrim, BT38 8BX Tel: (028) 9335 7300 Fax: (028) 9335 7305 E-mail: infoni@mindready.com
Multex Ltd, Caputhall Road, Deans Industrial Estate, Deans, Livingston, West Lothian, EH54 8AS Tel: (01506) 460661 Fax: (01506) 460816

TEST HOUSES/FACILITIES/ CENTRES

3C Test Ltd, Technology Park, Silverstone Circuit, Silverstone, Towcester, Northamptonshire, NN12 8GX Tel: (01327) 857500 Fax: (01327) 857747 E-mail: sales@3ctest.co.uk
British Standards Institution, 389 Chiswick High Road, London, W4 4AL Tel: (020) 8996 9000 Fax: (020) 8996 7400 E-mail: info@bsi-global.com
Chelmsford Precision Services, 29 The Westerings, Great Baddow, Chelmsford, CM3 3UY Tel: (01245) 474901
Code-A-Weld, 2nd Avenue, Westfield Trading Estate, Midsomer Norton, Radstock, BA3 4BE Tel: (01761) 410410 Fax: (01761) 418388 E-mail: info@codeaweld.com
RFI Global Services Ltd, Ewhurst Park, Ramsdell, Tadley, Hampshire, RG26 5RQ Tel: (01256) 851193 Fax: (01256) 312001 E-mail: sales@rfi-global.com
Somerford Laboratories Ltd, 9 Horcott Industrial Estate, Horcott Road, Fairford, Gloucestershire, GL7 4BX Tel: (01285) 713737 Fax: (01285) 713733 E-mail: test@somlab.com
Veeco Instruments Ltd, Nanotech House Buckingway Business Park, Anderson Road, Swavesey, Cambridge, CB24 4UQ Tel: (01954) 233900 Fax: (01954) 231300 E-mail: info@veeco.co.uk

TEST PLUGS

Test Plugs Ltd, 12 Falklands Road, Haverhill, Suffolk, CB9 0EA Tel: (01440) 704201 Fax: (01440) 763121 E-mail: sales@test-plugs.com

TEST PROBES, *See also headings for particular types*

Peak Production Equipment Ltd, Peak House, Works Road, Letchworth Garden City, Hertfordshire, SG6 1GB Tel: (01462) 475605 Fax: (01462) 480294 E-mail: sales@thepeakgroup.com

TEST PROGRAMMING

Micropoint Plus Ltd, 22 Laurel Avenue, Slough, SL3 7DG Tel: (01753) 790829 Fax: (01753) 790830E-mail: micropointplus@btconnect.com

TEST RIGS

Sercon Controls Ltd, Clay Lane, Spar Fields, Slarthwate, Huddersfield, HD7 5BG Tel: (01484) 845548 Fax: (01484) 847846 E-mail: gln@serconcontrols.com

TEST SIEVES

Endecotts Ltd, 9 Lombard Road, London, SW19 3UP Tel: (020) 8542 8121 Fax: (020) 8543 6629 E-mail: sales@endecotts.com
Impact Test Equipment Ltd, Building 21, Stevenston Industrial Estate, Stevenston, Ayrshire, KA20 3LR Tel: (01294) 602626 Fax: (01294) 461168 E-mail: sales@impact-test.co.uk

TEST SYSTEMS/SYSTEMS DESIGN SERVICES

Hydramec Ltd, Haverscroft Industrial Estate, New Road, Attleborough, Norfolk, NR17 1YE Tel: (01953) 458500 Fax: (01953) 458509 E-mail: mail@hydramec.co.uk
Itochu Europe plc, 2 Ashbys Yard, Medway Wharf Road, Tonbridge, Kent, TN9 1RE Tel: (01732) 363003 Fax: (01732) 367775
Micro Technology Consultants, Unit 32 Business Centre, Main Street, Coatbridge, Lanarkshire, ML5 3RB Tel: (01236) 432205 Fax: (01236) 421933

TESTING, *See also headings for particular types of service*

Bodycote Materials Engineering, White Cross Industrial Estate, South Road, Lancaster, LA1 4XQ Tel: (01524) 841070 Fax: (01524) 62983 E-mail: sales-uk@bodycote-mt.com
▶ Invent Calibration Services, 85 Southdown Road, Harpenden, Hertfordshire, AL5 1PR Tel: (01582) 461666 Fax: (01582) 460077 E-mail: sales@invent-uk.com
N D T Consultants Ltd, Siskin Drive, Middlemarch Business Park, Coventry, CV3 4FJ Tel: (024) 7651 1151 Fax: (024) 7651 1696 E-mail: sales@ndt-consultants.co.uk
RFI Global Services Ltd, Ewhurst Park, Ramsdell, Tadley, Hampshire, RG26 5RQ Tel: (01256) 851193 Fax: (01256) 312001 E-mail: sales@rfi-global.com
▶ Stansted Laboratories, Unit 9, Riverside Industrial Estate, 27, Thames Road, Barking, Essex, IG11 0ND Tel: (020) 8594 5104 Fax: (020) 8591 8762 E-mail: sales@stanstedlabs.co.uk

TESTING, AERODYNAMICS

Flow Science Ltd, Goldstein Laboratory, Liverpool Road, Eccles, Manchester, M30 7RU Tel: 0161-787 8749 Fax: 0161-787 8749 E-mail: flowsci@fs1.ae.man.ac.uk

TESTING, ELECTRICAL

Goodmarriott & Hursthouse Ltd, Hooton Street, Nottingham, NG3 5GL Tel: 0115-950 5100 Fax: 0115-958 1200E-mail: mail@gandh.co.uk
Langston Jones & Co. Ltd, Station St West Business Park, Coventry, CV6 5BP Tel: (024) 7666 8592 Fax: (024) 7666 8593 E-mail: sales@langston-jones.co.uk
RH Industrial Electronics, Unit 11d Dabble Duck Industrial Estate, Shildon, County Durham, DL4 2RA Tel: (01388) 777823 Fax: (01388) 775902 E-mail: rhie@comp42.freeserve.co.uk

TESTING, ELECTRICAL, EARTH RESISTANT

▶ Eric Boam, 20 Meadowbank, Passage Hill, Mylor, Falmouth, Cornwall, TR11 5SW Tel: (01326) 375915 Fax: (01326) 375915 E-mail: eric@electricianscornwall.co.uk

TESTING, ELECTRONIC

Igg Component Technology Ltd, Waterside House, Waterside Gardens, Fareham, Hampshire, PO16 8RR Tel: (01329) 829311 Fax: (01329) 829312 E-mail: enquiries@igg.co.uk

TESTING, LOW VOLTAGE DIRECTIVE

Cranage E M C Testing Ltd, Stable Court, Oakley Hall, Market Drayton, Shropshire, TF9 4AG Tel: (01630) 658568 Fax: (01630) 658921 E-mail: info@cranage.co.uk

TESTING, MATERIALS, *See also specialist services*

A-Z Analytical Services, 82 Allens Rd, Poole, Dorset, BH16 5BX Tel: (01202) 624985 Fax: (01202) 624985
Birmingham Gun Barrel Proof House, Banbury Street, Birmingham, B5 5RH Tel: 0121-643 3860 Fax: 0121-643 7872 E-mail: sales@gunproof.com
Bodycote Materials Engineering, White Cross Industrial Estate, South Road, Lancaster, LA1 4XQ Tel: (01524) 841070 Fax: (01524) 62983 E-mail: sales-uk@bodycote-mt.com
Bodycote Radiography, 1 Blackbrook Valley Industrial Estate, Narrowboat Way, Dudley, West Midlands, DY2 0XQ Tel: (01384) 455880 Fax: (01384) 457250 E-mail: dudley@bodycote-mt.com
BSI Quality Assurance, 389 Chiswick High Road, London, W4 4AL Tel: (020) 8996 9000 Fax: (020) 8996 7400 E-mail: info@bsi-global.com
C Mac Microcircuits Ltd, South Denes, Great Yarmouth, Norfolk, NR30 3PX Tel: (01493) 856122 Fax: 01493 858536 E-mail: mssinfo@cmac.com
CMT (Testing) Ltd, Prime Park Way, Prime Enterprise Park, Derby, DE1 3QB Tel: (01332) 383333 Fax: (01332) 602607 E-mail: testing@cmt-ltd.co.uk
D T S Raeburn Ltd, Moor Lane, Witton, Birmingham, B6 7HG Tel: 0121-344 3826 Fax: 0121-344 4754 E-mail: enquiries@dts-raeburn.co.uk
M B Inspections Ltd, PO Box 4, Motherwell, Lanarkshire, ML1 3NP Tel: (01698) 262277 Fax: (01698) 269774
Co Mech Ltd, Victory House, Victory Road, Derby, DE24 8EL Tel: (01332) 275820 Fax: (01332) 275817 E-mail: sales@comech.co.uk
N Code International Ltd, Innovation Technology Center, Advanced Manufacturing Park, Brunel Way, Catcliffe, Rotherham, South Yorkshire, S60 5WG Tel: 0114-254 1246 Fax: 0114-254 1245 E-mail: info@ncode.com
Nicholls Colton & Partners Ltd, 7-11 Harding Street, Leicester, LE1 4DH Tel: 0116-253 6333 Fax: 0116-251 4709 E-mail: testing@nicholls-colton.co.uk
P M I Services, Glen Villa, Ashbrooke Range, Sunderland, SR2 9BP Tel: 0191-528 1469 Fax: 0191-511 0369
Quality Test & Measurement Services, 25 Chapelmere Close, Sandbach, Cheshire, CW11 1TB Tel: (01270) 767974 Fax: (01270) 766478 E-mail: martin@bissnet.co.uk
Rapra Technology, Shawbury, Shrewsbury, SY4 4NR Tel: (01939) 250383 Fax: (01939) 251118 E-mail: info@rapra.net
Sendt Ltd, Littlebrook Business Centre, Littlebrook Manorway, Dartford, DA1 5PZ Tel: (01322) 287347 Fax: (01322) 287493 E-mail: tony.blake@sendt.freeserve.co.uk
Sheffield Testing Laboratories Ltd, 56 Nursery Street, Sheffield, S3 8GP Tel: 0114-272 6581 Fax: 0114-272 3248 E-mail: hq@sheffieldtesting.com
Shirley Technologies Ltd, Unit 12 Westpoint Enterprise Park, Clarence Avenue, Trafford Park, Manchester, M17 1QS Tel: 0161-869 1610 Fax: 0161-872 6492 E-mail: info@shirleytech.co.uk
Special Testing Works Ltd, Bacon Lane, Sheffield, S9 3NH Tel: 0114-244 1061 Fax: 0114-244 0444

TESTING, MECHANICAL

Bodycote Materials Testing Ltd, Denison House, Hexthorpe Road, Doncaster, South Yorkshire, DN4 0BF Tel: (01302) 384340 Fax: (01302) 384341 E-mail: sales-uk@bodycote.com
Bodycote Materials Testing Ltd, Shields Road, Newcastle upon Tyne, NE6 2YD Tel: 0191-275 2800 Fax: 0191-276 0177 E-mail: sales-mt@bodycote-mt.com
Commercial Testing Services Ltd, Blackmore Street, Sheffield, S4 7TZ Tel: 0114-276 8758 Fax: 0114-272 0449 E-mail: cts@allvac.com

TESTING, METALLURGICAL

Commercial Testing Services Ltd, Blackmore Street, Sheffield, S4 7TZ Tel: 0114-276 8758 Fax: 0114-272 0449 E-mail: cts@allvac.com

TESTING, PRODUCTS, *See also specialist services*

D F D Instruments, Northpoint House, 52 High Street, Knaphill, Woking, Surrey, GU21 2PY Tel: (01483) 799333 Fax: (01483) 480199 E-mail: tore@dfdinstruments.co.uk
Foster Tachograph Ltd, 17 Fulwood Hall Lane, Fulwood, Preston, PR2 8DB Tel: (01772) 655155 Fax: (01772) 793739 E-mail: enquiries@fostertachographs.co.uk
Piper Test & Measurement Ltd, The Barn, Bilsington, Ashford, Kent, TN25 7JT Tel: (01233) 720130 Fax: (01233) 720140 E-mail: piper@piper-ltd.co.uk
Scientifics, 4-6 Wharfside, Oldbury, West Midlands, B69 2BU Tel: 0121-552 1565 Fax: 0121-544 8581 E-mail: admin@scientifics.com

TETHER MANAGEMENT SYSTEMS

▶ Sub-Atlantic, Blackburn Business Park, Woodburn Road, Blackburn, Aberdeen, AB21 0PS Tel: (01224) 798660 Fax: (01224) 798661

TEXT MESSAGING DISPLAYS

▶ Reverse Billed SMS, Canford Chambers, Lower Ground Floor, 22 St. Peters Road, Bournemouth, BH1 2LE Tel: (0870) 7504906 Fax: (0870) 7061094 E-mail: Alan@palmmedia.co.uk

TEXT MESSAGING INFORMATION SERVICES

Win plc, 1 Cliveden Office Village, Lancaster Road, Cressex Business Park, High Wycombe, Buckinghamshire, HP12 3YZ Tel: (01494) 750500 Fax: (01494) 750820 E-mail: enquiries@winplc.com

TEXTILE AGENTS/ REPRESENTATIVES

60 Plus Textiles Services Ltd, Ingsend Farm, Barley, Nelson, Lancashire, BB9 6LJ Tel: (01282) 614442 Fax: (01282) 694620
A Y Agencies, Millbank, 3 Cargill Avenue, Maybole, Ayrshire, KA19 8AD Tel: (01655) 883041 Fax: (01655) 883981
Bhallatex Fabric Importers, 93 Parker Drive, Leicester, LE4 0JP Tel: 0116-236 3660 Fax: 0116-236 3680
Bradshaw & Bradshaw, 18 Hanson Street, London, W1W 6UE Tel: (020) 7255 2333 Fax: (020) 7255 3131
Clayton UK Ltd, 12 Little Lane, Calverton, Nottingham, NG14 6JU Tel: 0115-965 5009 Fax: 0115-965 2333 E-mail: graham.clayton@claytonukltd.co.uk
Combined Trading (Garments) Ltd, 77-79 Great Eastern Street, London, EC2A 3HU Tel: (020) 7739 0551 Fax: (020) 7729 2556
David Burns, 44-46 Riding House Street, London, W1W 7EX Tel: (020) 7580 1422 Fax: (020) 7436 3046 E-mail: david@davidburnsinttex.com
Colin Devey Clearance Fabrics, 139 Blacker Lane, Netherton, Wakefield, West Yorkshire, WF4 4EZ Tel: (01924) 275087 Fax: (01924) 275087
Escotex International Ltd, 38-40 Eastcastle Street, London, W1W 8DT Tel: (020) 7580 4237 Fax: (020) 7436 5327
Glendale Textiles Ltd, 86 Main Street, Queniborough, Leicester, LE7 3DA Tel: 0116-269 5548 Fax: 0116-269 5564
D.C. Gwillim Enterprises Ltd, Charnwood House, 251 Loughborough Road, Mountsorrel, Loughborough, Leicestershire, LE12 7AS Tel: (01509) 621272 Fax: (01509) 620911
Simon Hacking & Associates, Cile Cotes House, Oxford Road, Marlow, Buckinghamshire, SL7 2NT Tel: (01628) 488475 Fax: (0870) 8918762
James Rickwood & Co.,Limited, 12 Ladybarn Crescent, Bramhall, Stockport, Cheshire, SK7 2EZ Tel: 0161-439 3778 Fax: 0161-439 7823
M M Textiles, 65 Anderton Road, Birmingham, B11 1LZ Tel: 0121-773 7522 Fax: 0121-773 7522
M S C A Ltd, The Seedbed Centre, Vanguard Way, Shoeburyness, SS3 9QY Tel: (01702) 382338 Fax: (01702) 382391 E-mail: ldmtt@ldn.xm.mitsui.co.jp
Mantex International Ltd, Millbank House, Bollin Walk, Wilmslow, Cheshire, SK9 1BJ Tel: (01625) 530555 Fax: (01625) 528323 E-mail: mantex@mantexintl.co.uk
Milliken Woollen Speciality Products, Cam Woollen Mills, Everlands, Cam, Dursley, Gloucestershire, GL11 5NN Tel: (01453) 542258 Fax: (01453) 548540
Rogerson Yarns Ltd, Heathside, 1 Clifton Road, Halifax, West Yorkshire, HX3 0BT Tel: (01422) 364088 Fax: (01422) 348709 E-mail: jonathan@rogersonyarnsltd.co.uk
S Frank Cook & Son, 215 West End Lane, London, NW6 1XJ Tel: (020) 7431 6565 Fax: (020) 7435 9862 E-mail: info@sfrankcook.co.uk
Ullman International, 1 Stable Court Beechwoods, Elmete Lane, Leeds, LS8 2LQ Tel: 0113-201 8844 Fax: 0113-201 8855
Wheeler, Hickson & Co., 10-11 Lower John Street, London, W1F 9EB Tel: (020) 7437 0186 Fax: (020) 7439 4994 E-mail: info@wheelerhickson.co.uk
Wood, Son & Fleming Ltd, 12 Nascot Street, Watford, WD17 4RB Tel: (01923) 253911 Fax: (01923) 243921

TEXTILE AUXILIARIES, *See Textile Chemical etc*

TEXTILE BAGS

▶ Scafclad Ltd, Canvas Works, Cox Lane, Chessington, Surrey, KT9 1SG Tel: (020) 8974 1271 Fax: (020) 8974 1957 E-mail: claire@protectivetextile.co.uk

TEXTILE BEAMING MACHINES

Crabtree Textile Machines Ltd, Norman Road, Oswaldtwistle, Accrington, Lancashire, BB5 4NF Tel: (01254) 304410 Fax: (01254) 304415 E-mail: info@crabtreelooms.com

TEXTILE BRAIDING MACHINES

▶ Oma UK Ltd, Unit 3-4 Greenfield Farm Industrial Estate, Hopkins Lane, Congleton, Cheshire, CW12 4TR Tel: (01260) 278585 Fax: (01260) 278590 E-mail: omauk@aol.com

TEXTILE CANVAS, *See also headings for particular types*

2canvas Limited, 155 Stockwell Street, Glasgow, G1 4LR Tel: 0141-552 0005 E-mail: design@2canvas.co.uk
Peter Greig & Co., Victoria Linen Works, 147-151 St Clair Street, Kirkcaldy, Fife, KY1 2BU Tel: (01592) 651901 Fax: (01592) 655596 E-mail: rosie@petergreig.co.uk
Ratsey & Lapthorn Ltd, 37 Medina Road, Cowes, Isle of Wight, PO31 7BX Tel: (01983) 294051 Fax: (01983) 294053 E-mail: ratseysails@ratsey.com
William Arnold Tarpaulins Ltd, 30 Thames Road, Barking, Essex, IG11 0HZ Tel: (020) 8594 1500 Fax: (020) 8594 7773 E-mail: www.tarpaulins.co.uk
Wolfin Textiles Ltd, 359 Uxbridge Road, Hatch End, Pinner, Middlesex, HA5 4JN Tel: (020) 8428 9911 Fax: (020) 8428 9955 E-mail: cotton@wolfintextiles.co.uk

TEXTILE CAPS

Failsworth Hats Ltd, Crown Street, Crown Street, Failsworth, Manchester, M35 9BD Tel: 0161-681 3131 Fax: 0161-683 4754 E-mail: sales@failsworth-hats.co.uk

TEXTILE CARD CLOTHING

Garnett Wire Ltd, Scholes Lane, Scholes, Checkheaton, Cleckheaton, West Yorkshire, BD19 6NJ Tel: (01274) 875741 Fax: (01274) 851675 E-mail: sales@garnettwire.com
James Holdsworth & Bros Ltd, Unit 18, West Slaithwaite Road, Huddersfield, HD7 6LS Tel: (01924) 494471 Fax: (01484) 847153 E-mail: info@jamesholdsworth.com

TEXTILE CARDING MACHINES

Alfred Briggs Sons & Co. Ltd, 108 Church Lane, Gomersal, Cleckheaton, West Yorkshire, BD19 4QL Tel: (01274) 873272 Fax: (01274) 869999 E-mail: sales@alfred-briggs.ltd.uk
Arthur Heaton & Co. Ltd, Valley Works, Station Lane, Heckmondwike, West Yorkshire, WF16 0NF Tel: (01924) 403731 Fax: (01924) 410069
James Holdsworth & Bros Ltd, Unit 18, West Slaithwaite Road, Huddersfield, HD7 6LS Tel: (01924) 494471 Fax: (01484) 847153 E-mail: info@jamesholdsworth.com

TEXTILE CHEESE CLOTH

A & I Holmes & Co. Ltd, Unit 8c Kayley Industrial Estate, Richmond Street, Ashton-under-Lyne, Lancashire, OL7 0AU Tel: 0161-343 1911 Fax: 0161-343 2959 E-mail: aiholmes@btconnect.com
Cheeses Cheese Makers, 13 Fortis Green Road, London, N10 3HP Tel: (020) 8444 9141
Stratton Sales Ltd, 1 Station Road, Shepton Mallet, Somerset, BA4 5DD Tel: (01749) 344071 Fax: (01749) 346134 E-mail: info@strattonsales.co.uk

TEXTILE CHEMICAL PRODUCTS

Albion Colours Ltd, High Level Way, Halifax, West Yorkshire, HX1 4PN Tel: (01422) 358431 Fax: (01422) 330867 E-mail: colours.sales@albionchemicals.co.uk
British Salt Ltd, Cledford Lane, Middlewich, Cheshire, CW10 0JP Tel: (01606) 832881 Fax: (01606) 835999 E-mail: sales@british-salt.co.uk
Chemische Fabrik Tubingen UK Ltd, 6 Newby Road Industrial Estate, Levens Road, Hazel Grove, Stockport, Cheshire, SK7 5DA Tel: 0161-456 3355 Fax: 0161-456 4153 E-mail: dbyrne@chtuk.co.uk
Stephenson Group Ltd, PO Box 305, Bradford, West Yorkshire, BD7 1HY Tel: (01274) 723811 Fax: (01274) 370108 E-mail: src@stephensongroup.co.uk
Thor Specialities UK Ltd, Wincham Avenue, Wincham, Northwich, Cheshire, CW9 6GB Tel: (01606) 818800 Fax: (01606) 818801 E-mail: info@thor.com
Wilkinson & Scott Ltd, 58 Nelson Street, Bradford, West Yorkshire, BD5 0DZ Tel: (01274) 724059 Fax: (01274) 305389 E-mail: anne@mac56.com

TEXTILE COMBED PRODUCTS, *See headings for particular fibre*

TEXTILE CURTAIN FABRICS, *See also Furnishing Fabrics etc*

Briman Contracts Ltd, Unit 2b Building B Wembley Commercial Centre, East Lane, Wembley, Middlesex, HA9 7UR Tel: (020) 8908 0102 Fax: (020) 8904 0664 E-mail: info@briman.co.uk
▶ Concorde Blind & Curtain Co. Ltd, 45 Waterside Park, Old Wolverton Road, Old Wolverton, Milton Keynes, MK12 5NP Tel: (01908) 320600 Fax: (01908) 227338
Evans Textile Sales Ltd, 22 Piccadilly Trading Estate, Manchester, M1 2NP Tel: 0161-274 4147 Fax: 0161-274 4070 E-mail: sales@evans-textiles.com
Fabric Place, 12 High Road, Chilwell, Beeston, Nottingham, NG9 4AE Tel: 0115-943 6636 Fax: 0115-943 1336 E-mail: info@fabricsinternational.com
Charles Holliday & Co., Railway Station, Green Road, Newmarket, Suffolk, CB8 9WT Tel: (01638) 661603 Fax: (01638) 665124 E-mail: brookefairbairn@btconnect.com
Instant Home Ltd, Beaulieu House, 78 Ermine Street, Huntingdon, Cambridgeshire, PE29 3EZ Tel: 01480 432230 Fax: 01480 432868 E-mail: hollie@instanthome.co.uk
Lloyd Furnishings, Albert Close Trading Estate, Whitefield, Manchester, M45 8EH Tel: 0161-796 1920 Fax: 0161-796 1921 E-mail: sales@curtains.co.uk
Premier Textiles Ltd, Green Lane Industrial Estate, Green Lane, Stockport, Cheshire, SK4 2JR Tel: 0161-429 5770 Fax: 0161-429 5777 E-mail: sales@premier-textiles.com
R C Kennedy Ltd, 1 North Street, Manchester, M8 8RE Tel: 0161-832 6182 Fax: 0161-834 3053
Reebitex Fabrics Ltd, Rope Walk, Ilkeston, Derbyshire, DE7 5HX Tel: 0115-930 9619 Fax: 0115-930 8769 E-mail: sales@reebitex.com
▶ RUF NECK, 463 Lichfield Road, Birmingham, B6 7SS Tel: 08456 446876 E-mail: raj@ruf-neck.com
▶ Shahina Textiles, Tivoli House, Derby Street, Bolton, BL3 6JY Tel: (01204) 361617 Fax: (01204) 261618 E-mail: sal92uk@yahoo.co.uk
Volvina Ltd, 1-3 Duke Street, Northampton, NN1 3BE Tel: (01604) 633044 Fax: (01604) 629868 E-mail: volvina@curtains-uk.com

TEXTILE CURTAIN FABRICS – *continued*

Walcott House Ltd, Lyneham, Chipping Norton, Oxfordshire, OX7 6QQ Tel: (01993) 832940 Fax: (01993) 832950

TEXTILE CUTTING MACHINES

Cappa Pinking Machinery Ltd, 25 Westgate, Otley, West Yorkshire, LS21 3AT Tel: (01943) 467655 Fax: (01943) 850362 E-mail: sales@emberfern.co.uk
T W Eaton & Co. Ltd, 247 Noel Street, Nottingham, NG7 6AR Tel: 0115-978 4084 Fax: 0115-942 2631

TEXTILE CUTTING, COMMISSION

S G Cuttings, Unit E4 Europa Trading Estate, Stoneclough Road, Radcliffe, Manchester, M26 1GG Tel: (01204) 574030 Fax: (01204) 574031 E-mail: simon.leigh@john-holden.com

TEXTILE DESIGNERS OR CONSULTANTS

D T Donan & Co., 8 Abercorn Commercial Centre, Manor Farm Road, Wembley, Middlesex, HA0 1YA Tel: (020) 8903 8288 Fax: (020) 8900 1533
Anna French Ltd, 36 Hinton Road, London, SE24 0HJ Tel: (020) 7737 6555 E-mail: info@annafrench.co.uk
H E Textiles, 20b The Nook, Cosby, Leicester, LE9 1RQ Tel: 0116-275 3353 Fax: 0116-275 3389 E-mail: nicola.pollock@pgen.net
Pattern Masters Ltd, 9 Norfolk Street, Peterborough, PE1 2NP Tel: (01733) 555171 Fax: (01733) 555191 E-mail: enquiries@patternmasters.co.uk
Schippel Design Ltd, 21B Graham Street, Birmingham, B1 3JR Tel: 0121-236 2635 Fax: 0121-236 9289
Textra Fabric Importers, Sheephouse Barn, Reading Road, East Hendred, Wantage, Oxfordshire, OX12 8HR Tel: (0870) 2414949 Fax: (08702) 414950 E-mail: sales@textra.co.uk

TEXTILE DRESS FABRICS

Denholme Velvets Ltd, Halifax Rd, Denholme, Bradford, West Yorkshire, BD13 4EZ Tel: (01274) 832185 Fax: (01274) 832646 E-mail: sales@denholme-velvets.co.uk
Glenroyd Mills Ltd, Occupation Lane, Pudsey, West Yorkshire, LS28 8HW Tel: 0113-256 5667 Fax: 0113-257 6859 E-mail: sales@glenroyd.com
James Hare Ltd, PO Box 72, Leeds, LS1 1LX Tel: 0113-243 1204 Fax: 0113-234 7648 E-mail: sales@jamesharesilks.co.uk
▶ Sherwoods Fabrics, 39 Church Street, Malvern, Worcestershire, WR14 2AA Tel: (01684) 572379 Fax: (01684) 563295 E-mail: info@sherwoodsfabrics.co.uk
Sidhu Textile Co. Ltd, 85-87 The Broadway, Southall, Middlesex, UB1 1LA Tel: (020) 8574 3385 Fax: (020) 8843 9229 E-mail: s_sidhu100@hotmail.com
D.H.J. Weisters Ltd, Anchor Mill, Darwen, Lancashire, BB3 0AH Tel: (01254) 873333 Fax: (01254) 873659 E-mail: customer-services@weisters.co.uk
Whaleys Bradford Ltd, Harris Court, Bradford, West Yorkshire, BD7 4EQ Tel: (01274) 576718 Fax: (01274) 521309 E-mail: whaleys@btinternet.com

TEXTILE DRYERS

Border Textiles UK Ltd, Whitechapel Road, Cleckheaton, West Yorkshire, BD19 6HY Tel: (01274) 866200 Fax: (01274) 866220 E-mail: sales@bordertextiles.co.uk
Caltherm UK Ltd, Rowhurst Industrial Estate, Newcastle, Staffordshire, ST5 6BD Tel: (01782) 563865 Fax: (01782) 561607 E-mail: info@caltherm.co.uk

TEXTILE DUST COVERS

Ernest Griffith & Sons Ltd, Praed Rd, Trafford Park, Manchester, M17 1PQ Tel: 0161-877 1655 Fax: 0161-877 6577 E-mail: pdbrearley@aol.com
Moorfield Of Lancashire, Perseverence Mill, Olive Lane, Eccleshill, Darwen, Lancashire, BB3 3BA Tel: (01254) 704131 Fax: (01254) 704141 E-mail: donelana@aol.com

TEXTILE DYEING MACHINES

James Bailey Ltd, Empire Works, Howgate Road, Huddersfield, HD7 5AX Tel: (01484) 842316 Fax: (01484) 846537 E-mail: sales@jamesbailey.co.uk
John Bradley Ltd, 1 Levens Road, Newby Road, Industrial Estate, Stockport, Cheshire, SK7 5DL Tel: 0161-483 5200 Fax: 0161-483 5101 E-mail: office@samuelbradley.com

TEXTILE DYERS CHEMICALS

A.E. Charlesworth & Co.Ltd, Rugby St, Leicester, LE3 5FG Tel: 0116-251 0552 Fax: 0116-251 8629
D P Dyers Ltd, Thirstin Dye Works, Thirstin Road, Honley, Holmfirth, HD9 6JL Tel: (01484) 661215 Fax: (01484) 665591

TEXTILE ELASTIC GOODS

Liberty Plc, 210-220 Regent St, London, W1B 5AH Tel: (020) 7734 1234 Fax: (020) 7573 9876 E-mail: info@liberty.co.uk

TEXTILE EMBOSSING SERVICES

Animm Textiles Ltd, Mangochi House, 107-115 Gwendolen Road, Leicester, LE5 5FL Tel: 0116-212 1234 Fax: 0116-273 3396 E-mail: info@animm.com

TEXTILE EXPORT MERCHANTS OR AGENTS

Alif UK Ltd, 33 Parker Drive, Leicester, LE4 0JP Tel: 0116-235 5050 Fax: 0116-235 5500 E-mail: sales@alifuk.co.uk
Clark & Terry, Unit 25-26-Newhaven Business Park, Barton Lane, Eccles, Manchester, M30 0HH Tel: 0161-787 7898 Fax: 0161-787 7728 E-mail: clarkandterry@talk21.com
I J Parkash Ltd, 30 Brunswick Street, Manchester, M13 9TQ Tel: 0161-273 5883 Fax: 0161-273 7262 E-mail: rajiv@absonline.net
Joseph Newman, Highgate Business Centre, 1h Greenwood Place, London, NW5 1LB Tel: (020) 7482 1769 Fax: (020) 7482 1766 E-mail: jnewmantext@aol.com
M H Spencer Ltd, Charter Avenue, Coventry, CV4 8AF Tel: (024) 7646 4044 Fax: (024) 7669 4011 E-mail: sales@weavingreeds.com
Narang Textiles, 121 City Road, Bradford, West Yorkshire, BD8 8JR Tel: (01274) 723157 Fax: (01274) 304334 E-mail: textiles@narang.co.uk
William Root Ltd, White Rose Mill, Holdsworth Road, Halifax, West Yorkshire, HX3 6SN Tel: (01422) 246161 Fax: (01422) 246331 E-mail: info@cashmere-fibre.co.uk
Tashglen Ltd, 3 Mountington Park Close, Harrow, Middlesex, HA3 0NW Tel: (020) 8907 9428 Fax: (020) 8909 1661 E-mail: tashglen@compuserve.com

TEXTILE FABRIC PLEATING MACHINES

J.B. Landers, 6 Stonebridge Centre, 51 Rangemoor Rd, London, N15 4LP Tel: (020) 8808 0066 Fax: (020) 8808 0066

TEXTILE FINISHING CHEMICALS

A.E. Charlesworth & Co.Ltd, Rugby St, Leicester, LE3 5FG Tel: 0116-251 0552 Fax: 0116-251 8629

TEXTILE FINISHING MACHINES

James Bailey Ltd, Empire Works, Howgate Road, Huddersfield, HD7 5AX Tel: (01484) 842316 Fax: (01484) 846537 E-mail: sales@jamesbailey.co.uk
R G Foster Textile Machinery Ltd, Burnham Way, Queens Bridge Road, Nottingham, NG2 1NB Tel: 0115-988 2222 Fax: 0115-985 1881 E-mail: sales@foster-tm.co.uk
S P T Machines Ltd, Brookside Ave, Rustington, Littlehampton, W. Sussex, BN16 3LF Tel: (01903) 784212 Fax: (01903) 770288 E-mail: info@sptmachines.co.uk

TEXTILE GOODS, MADE-UP, *See also headings for particular types*

Bailey Textiles, 9-10 The Warren, East Goscote, Leicester, LE7 3XA Tel: 0116-269 4694 Fax: 0116-269 3956 E-mail: sales@baileysdirect.plus.com
Britannic Warehouse, 142 Sand Pits, Birmingham, B1 3RJ Tel: 0121-236 7271 Fax: 0121-236 8266 E-mail: sales@britannicwarehouse.co.uk
Cologne & Cotton Ltd, 39 Kensington Church Street, London, W8 4LL Tel: (020) 7376 0324 Fax: (020) 7376 0373
Dewhirst Accessories Ltd, Kitty Brewster Industrial Estate, Blyth, Northumberland, NE24 4RG Tel: (01670) 368587 Fax: (01670) 365773
F R Street Ltd, Frederick House, Hurricane Way, Wickford, Essex, SS11 8YB Tel: (01268) 766677 Fax: (01268) 764534 E-mail: val@street.co.uk
William Gee Ltd, William Gee House, 520-522 Kingsland Road, London, E8 4AH Tel: (020) 7254 2451 Fax: (020) 7249 8116 E-mail: wmgeetrims@aol.com
Harry G Smith Ltd, PO Box 89, Aberdeen, AB12 3DA Tel: (01224) 897044 Fax: (01224) 894648 E-mail: office@harrygsmith.co.uk
Kolon Imperial Graphics plc, Erico House, 93/99 Upper Richmond Road, London, SW15 2TG Tel: (020) 8780 1585 Fax: (020) 8785 7004 E-mail: junelee21@kolonuk.net
L Whitaker & Sons 1983 Ltd, Unit 4-5 Rochdale Industrial Centre, Albion Road, Rochdale, Lancashire, OL11 4HN Tel: (01706) 655611 Fax: (01706) 655611 E-mail: sales@lwhitaker.co.uk
Murmar-Phipps Ltd, PO Box 1, Northampton, NN4 8WN Tel: (01604) 763033 Fax: (01604) 23297
Natural Linens, 12 City Road, Littleport, Ely, Cambridgeshire, CB6 1NG Tel: (01353) 860849 Fax: (01353) 860849 E-mail: sales@natlin.force9.co.uk
J. Stott & Sons Ltd, 7 Richmond Hill, Blackburn, BB1 7LB Tel: (01254) 51567 Fax: (01254) 682780 E-mail: tony@jstott.com
Unique Bedding-parties, The Warehouse, 4-5 Mason St, Consett, County Durham, DH8 5DD Tel: 01207 592300

TEXTILE HOUSEHOLD GOODS, *See also headings for particular types*

Accent Textiles, Cambridge Industrial Estate, Dickinson Street, Salford, M3 7LW Tel: 0161-832 3003 Fax: 0161-832 9129 E-mail: info@accent-textiles.com
Albert Hartley Ltd, Crownest Mill, Skipton Road, Barnoldswick, Lancashire, BB18 5RH Tel: (01282) 666000 Fax: (01282) 666002 E-mail: ssmith@alberthartley.co.uk
Anglowide Marketing Ltd, County Ground Works, Deanstones Lane, Bradford, West Yorkshire, BD13 2AT Tel: (01274) 883668 Fax: (01274) 818980
Bedeck Ltd, 189 Lurgan Road, Craigavon, County Armagh, BT67 0QS Tel: (028) 3832 5836 Fax: (028) 3831 3001 E-mail: cust.services@bedeck.co.uk
Bolton Hemming Ltd, Halliwell Industrial Estate, Wapping Street, Bolton, BL1 8DP Tel: (01204) 492614 Fax: (01204) 492088 E-mail: enquiries@bolton-hemming.co.uk
Cliffridge Ltd, 83 Kempston Street, Liverpool, L3 8HE Tel: 0151-207 2770 Fax: 0151-207 2770
Dewhirst Accessories Ltd, Kitty Brewster Industrial Estate, Blyth, Northumberland, NE24 4RG Tel: (01670) 368587 Fax: (01670) 365773
Dorma Group Ltd, Newtown Mill Lees Street, Pendlebury, Swinton, Manchester, M27 6DB Tel: 0161-251 4400 Fax: 0161-251 4417 E-mail: info@dorma.co.uk
Harveys Furnishing Ltd, Amberley House, New Road, Rainham, Essex, RM13 8QN Tel: (01708) 521177 Fax: (01708) 521514
Hilden Manufacturing Co. Ltd, Clifton Mill, Pickup Street, Accrington, Lancashire, BB5 0EY Tel: (01254) 391131 Fax: (01254) 770770 E-mail: sales@hilden.co.uk
J H Cunliffe & Company Ltd, Duke Street Mill, Whitehall Street, Rochdale, Lancashire, OL12 0LW Tel: (01706) 631133 Fax: (01706) 527950 E-mail: brian@jhcunliffe.co.uk
J H Walker, Ravensthorpe Mills, Calder Road, Dewsbury, West Yorkshire, WF13 3JS Tel: (01924) 466544 Fax: (01924) 455977
Linden Textiles Ltd, Linden Court House, 52 Liverpool Street, Salford, M5 4LT Tel: 0161-745 9268 Fax: 0161-737 6061 E-mail: zedfred@aol.com
Linen Room, 482 Wilbraham Road, Manchester, M21 9AS Tel: 0161-860 4979 Fax: 0161-860 4979 E-mail: info@2tlr.co.uk
McCaw Allan & Co. Ltd, Victoria Street, Lurgan, Craigavon, County Armagh, BT67 9DU Tel: (028) 3834 1412 Fax: (028) 3834 3095 E-mail: sales@mccaw-allan.com
Manchester Pin Mill Textiles Ltd, Dreamscene House, Park House Bridge Estate, Langley Road, Salford, M6 6JQ Tel: 0161-737 3300 Fax: 0161-737 3100 E-mail: info@pinmill.com
Manchester Toiletries & Food Wholesale, 173-175 Cheetham Hill Road, Manchester, M8 8LG Tel: (0161) 839 7086 Fax: (0161) 839 7084 E-mail: zabarimports@aol.com
David Mather Supplies Ltd, 6 Knowsley Street, Manchester, M8 8GF Tel: 0161-834 6606 Fax: 0161-832 5066 E-mail: info@davidmather.com
S A N Ltd, 42 Bloom Street, Manchester, M1 3HR Tel: 0161-236 2246 Fax: 0161-236 5528 E-mail: sasltd@lineone.net
S Green & Sons Ltd, Fairfield Road, London, E3 2QA Tel: (020) 8981 7940 Fax: (020) 8981 3625 E-mail: sgreen@globalnet.o.uk
Ulster Weavers Home Fashions, Unit 1-6 St Helens Business Park, Holywood, County Down, BT18 9HQ Tel: (028) 9032 9494 Fax: (028) 9032 6612 E-mail: sales@ulsterweavers.com

TEXTILE HOUSEHOLD GOODS IMPORT MERCHANTS OR AGENTS

F & Y Products, 7a Thurswood House Cranborne Industrial Estate, Cranborne Road, Potters Bar, Hertfordshire, EN6 3JN Tel: (01707) 654221 Fax: (01707) 654224
Manchester Pin Mill Textiles Ltd, Dreamscene House, Park House Bridge Estate, Langley Road, Salford, M6 6JQ Tel: 0161-737 3300 Fax: 0161-737 3100 E-mail: info@pinmill.com
Manchester Toiletries & Food Wholesale, 173-175 Cheetham Hill Road, Manchester, M8 8LG Tel: (0161) 839 7086 Fax: (0161) 839 7084 E-mail: zabarimports@aol.com
Swiscot Textiles Ltd, Canada House, 3 Chepstow Street, Manchester, M1 5FW Tel: 0161-236 1025 Fax: 0161-236 6635 E-mail: info@swiscot.com

TEXTILE IMPORT MERCHANTS OR AGENTS

Alami International Ltd, 7 Dace Road, London, E3 2NG Tel: (020) 8533 7800 Fax: (020) 8533 0026 E-mail: sales@alami.co.uk
Alif UK Ltd, 33 Parker Drive, Leicester, LE4 0JP Tel: 0116-235 5050 Fax: 0116-235 5500 E-mail: sales@alifuk.co.uk
Aziz Textiles Ltd, 19-21 Portland St, Aston, Birmingham, B6 5RX Tel: 0121-328 4456 Fax: 0121-328 6941
Clark & Terry, Unit 25-26-Newhaven Business Park, Barton Lane, Eccles, Manchester, M30 0HH Tel: 0161-787 7898 Fax: 0161-787 7728 E-mail: clarkandterry@talk21.com
J.M. Clayton & Co. Ltd, Unit 3 Phoenix Court, Hammond Avenue, Stockport, Cheshire, SK4 1PQ Tel: 0161-474 0061 Fax: 0161-474 0071 E-mail: omar@jmclayton.co.uk
Francis Dinsmore Ltd, 25 Greenfield Road, Kells, Ballymena, County Antrim, BT42 3JL Tel: (028) 2589 1203 Fax: (028) 2589 2295 E-mail: info@dinsmore.co.uk
Eker & Albert Ltd, 293-295 Old Street, London, EC1V 9LA Tel: (020) 7739 0158 Fax: (020) 7739 7402
Frederick Thomas & Co. Ltd, Linden Court House, 52 Liverpool Street, Salford, M5 4LT Tel: 0161-745 7761 Fax: 0161-737 6061 E-mail: zedfred@aol.com
I J Parkash Ltd, 30 Brunswick Street, Manchester, M13 9TQ Tel: 0161-273 5883 Fax: 0161-273 7262 E-mail: rajiv@absonline.net
Joseph Newman, Highgate Business Centre, 1h Greenwood Place, London, NW5 1LB Tel: (020) 7482 1769 Fax: (020) 7482 1766 E-mail: jnewmantext@aol.com
B.L. Joshi UK Ltd, 212-214 Ealing Road, Wembley, Middlesex, HA0 4QG Tel: (020) 8903 0653 Fax: (020) 8902 2702 E-mail: bljoshiuk@aol.com
Lal & Co. (Glasgow), Laltex House, 12-18 Coburg Street, Glasgow, G5 9JF Tel: 0141-429 0935 Fax: 0141-429 8036
M S C A Ltd, The Seedbed Centre, Vanguard Way, Shoeburyness, SS3 9QY Tel: (01702) 382338 Fax: (01702) 382391 E-mail: ldmtt@ldn.xm.mitsui.co.jp
Narang Textiles, 121 City Road, Bradford, West Yorkshire, BD8 8JR Tel: (01274) 723157 Fax: (01274) 304334 E-mail: textiles@narang.co.uk
Paul Smith Foundation, Riverside Buildings, Riverside Way, Nottingham, NG2 1DP Tel: 0115-986 8877 Fax: 0115-986 2649
R Hardaker & Co. Ltd, Ashley House, Ashley Lane, Shipley, West Yorkshire, BD17 7DB Tel: (01274) 589166 Fax: (01274) 531511 E-mail: mail@hardakers.com

TEXTILE INDUSTRY BLADES

J W Stead & Son Ltd, Preserve Works, Thackley Old Road, Shipley, West Yorkshire, BD18 1QB Tel: (01274) 597814 Fax: (01274) 532177 E-mail: info@jwstead.com
W B Swift Ltd, Leafland Street, Halifax, West Yorkshire, HX1 4LX Tel: (01422) 358073 Fax: (01422) 330360 E-mail: wbswift@nildram.co.uk

TEXTILE INDUSTRY LUBRICANTS

Calder Oils Ltd, Netherfield Road, Dewsbury, West Yorkshire, WF13 3JX Tel: (01924) 461058 Fax: (01924) 459773 E-mail: sales@calder-oils.co.uk

TEXTILE LAMINATING SERVICES, COMMISSION

D P S Birmingham Ltd, 46 Hallam Street, Birmingham, B12 9PS Tel: 0121-440 3203 Fax: 0121-440 5220

▶ indicates data change since last edition

TEXTILE LAMINATING SERVICES, COMMISSION – *continued*

Decorshades LLP, 5 Brewery Mews Business Centre, St Johns Road, Isleworth, Middlesex, TW7 6PH Tel: (020) 8847 1939 Fax: (020) 8847 1939
E-mail: martin@decshade.demon.co.uk
J Clegg & Bros Rakewood Ltd, Rakewood Mill, Rakewood Road, Littleborough, Lancashire, OL15 0AP Tel: (01706) 378342
E-mail: peter@jclegg.co.uk

TEXTILE LOOMS

Alfred Briggs Sons & Co. Ltd, 108 Church Lane, Gomersal, Cleckheaton, West Yorkshire, BD19 4QL Tel: (01274) 873272 Fax: (01274) 869999 E-mail: sales@alfred-briggs.ltd.uk
Bonas Machine Co. Ltd., Dukesway, Team Valley Trading Estate, Gateshead, Tyne & Wear, NE11 0LF Tel: 0191-491 0444 Fax: 0191-491 0999 E-mail: sales@bonas.co.uk
Crabtree Textile Machines Ltd, Norman Road, Oswaldtwistle, Accrington, Lancashire, BB5 4NF Tel: (01254) 304410 Fax: (01254) 304415 E-mail: info@crabtreelooms.com

TEXTILE MACHINE ROLLMAKERS

Philip Lodge Ltd, Machine Works, New Mill Road, Brockholes, Holmfirth, HD9 7AE Tel: (01484) 661143 Fax: (01484) 661164

TEXTILE MACHINERY, *See also headings for particular types*

▶ A M S Manchester, 27 Honey Street, Manchester, M8 8RG Tel: 0161-819 2540 Fax: 0161-819 2541
E-mail: enquiries@ams-steam-eng.co.uk
Adelco Screen Process Ltd, 16 18 Highview, High Street, Bordon, Hampshire, GU35 0AX Tel: (01420) 488388 Fax: (01420) 476445
E-mail: sales@adelco.co.uk
Arndt Systems, 23 Falcons Rise, Belper, Derbyshire, DE56 0QN Tel: (01773) 827894 Fax: (01773) 827894
Barke Machinery Ltd, 274 Manchester Road, Audenshaw, Manchester, M34 5GL Tel: 0161-370 1313 Fax: 0161-301 5993
E-mail: info@barke.demon.co.uk
Bates Textile Machine Co. (Leicester) Ltd, Harding Street, Leicester, LE1 4DH Tel: 0116-262 9661 Fax: 0116-251 3041
E-mail: sales@bates-textile.demon.co.uk
Bonas Machine Co. Ltd., Dukesway, Team Valley Trading Estate, Gateshead, Tyne & Wear, NE11 0LF Tel: 0191-491 0444 Fax: 0191-491 0999 E-mail: sales@bonas.co.uk
Border Textiles UK Ltd, Whitechapel Road, Cleckheaton, West Yorkshire, BD19 6HY Tel: (01274) 866200 Fax: (01274) 866220
E-mail: sales@bordertextiles.co.uk
John Bradley Ltd, 1 Levens Road, Newby Road, Industrial Estate, Stockport, Cheshire, SK7 5DL Tel: 0161-483 5200 Fax: 0161-483 5101 E-mail: office@samuelbradley.com
Cobble Blackburn Ltd, Gate Street, Blackburn, BB1 3AH Tel: (01254) 55121 Fax: (01254) 671125 E-mail: info@cobble.co.uk
Cotec Converting Machinery Ltd, Unit 20 St. Johns Industrial Estate, Lees, Oldham, OL4 3DZ Tel: 0161-626 5350 Fax: 0161-626 5450 E-mail: jackcotten@btconnect.com
D B Grinders Ltd, Primrose Works, Primrose Bank, Oldham, OL8 1HQ Tel: 0161-626 4202 Fax: 0161-626 4210
E-mail: dbgrinders@btconnect.com
Arthur Heaton & Co. Ltd, Valley Works, Station Lane, Heckmondwike, West Yorkshire, WF16 0NF Tel: (01924) 403731 Fax: (01924) 410069
J B B Textile Agencies Ltd, 19 Bark Street East, Bolton, BL1 2BQ Tel: (01204) 528400 Fax: (01204) 528090
E-mail: info@jbbmachinery.co.uk
Macart Textiles Machinery Ltd, Macart House, Farnham Road, Bradford, West Yorkshire, BD7 3JG Tel: (01274) 525900 Fax: (01274) 525901 E-mail: enquiries@macart.com
Measuring Machines Ltd, 9 Oban Court, Hurricane Way, Wickford, Essex, SS11 8YB Tel: (01268) 560999 Fax: (01268) 561222
E-mail: info@measuringmachines.co.uk
N Schlumberger UK Ltd, Hillam Road, Bradford, West Yorkshire, BD2 1QN Tel: (01274) 394641 Fax: (01274) 370424
E-mail: n.schlumberber.uk@mail.com
Philip Lodge Ltd, Machine Works, New Mill Road, Brockholes, Holmfirth, HD9 7AE Tel: (01484) 661143 Fax: (01484) 661164
Platt UK, Macart House, Farnham Road, Bradford, West Yorkshire, BD7 3JG Tel: (01274) 525903 Fax: (01274) 524033
E-mail: eddif@platt.co.uk
R G Foster Textile Machinery Ltd, Burnham Way, Queens Bridge Road, Nottingham, NG2 1NB Tel: 0115-988 2222 Fax: 0115-985 1881
E-mail: sales@foster-tm.co.uk
Reliant Machinery Ltd, 17 Asheridge Road, Chesham, Buckinghamshire, HP5 2PY Tel: (01494) 792299 Fax: (01494) 791317
Robert S Maynard Ltd, P O Box 8, Wilmslow, Cheshire, SK9 5ER Tel: (01625) 524055 Fax: (01625) 524584
E-mail: robert.s.maynard.ltd@dial.pipex.com
Sellers Engineers Ltd, Chapel Hill, Huddersfield, HD1 3EH Tel: (01484) 540101 Fax: (01484) 544457 E-mail: admin@sellersengineers.com
T & S Overseas Ltd, PO Box 248, Rochdale, Lancashire, OL11 4YA Tel: (01706) 350406 Fax: (01706) 526809
T W Eaton & Co. Ltd, 247 Noel Street, Nottingham, NG7 6AR Tel: 0115-978 4084 Fax: 0115-942 2631
Tufting & Process Machinery Ltd, Commercial Mill, St. Pauls Court, Oswaldtwistle, Accrington, Lancashire, BB5 3HP Tel: (01254) 391400 Fax: (01254) 391332
E-mail: tpm@achinery.fslife.co.uk
Warner Textile Machinery, Magna Road, Wigston, Leicestershire, LE18 4ZH Tel: 0116-278 7578 Fax: 0116-278 7588
E-mail: wtm@warnertextilemachinery.co.uk
William Birch Engineers Ltd, Milton Street, Salford, M7 1UX Tel: 0161-834 9675 Fax: 0161-833 2268
E-mail: sales@william-birch.co.uk
Wilson Knowles & Sons, 6 Chapel Lane, Heckmondwike, West Yorkshire, WF16 9JT Tel: (01924) 402208 Fax: (01924) 406895
E-mail: sales@wilsonknowlesandsons.co.uk

TEXTILE MACHINERY ACCESSORIES/ANCILLARY EQUIPMENT/COMPONENTS MANUFRS

Ascotex Ltd, Calder Works, Simonstone, Burnley, Lancashire, BB12 7NL Tel: (01282) 772011 Fax: (01282) 773600
E-mail: sales@ascotex.com
Craft Engineering International Ltd, Lower Granby Street, Ilkeston, Derbyshire, DE7 8DJ Tel: 0115-932 2810 Fax: 0115-944 0048
E-mail: sales@craftex.co.uk
Crossley's Shuttles Ltd, Woodbottom Mill, Hollins Road, Walsden, Todmorden, Lancashire, OL14 6PG Tel: (01706) 812152 Fax: (01706) 813767 E-mail: sales@crossleysshuttles.co.uk
Eadie & Kanai Co. Ltd, 19 Scotts Road, Paisley, Renfrewshire, PA2 7AN Tel: 0141-889 4126 Fax: 0141-848 1290 E-mail: sales@ekcl.co.uk
Hugh G. Fyfe Ltd, 78-84 Bell Street, Dundee, DD1 1HW Tel: (01382) 322892 Fax: (01382) 202052
Arthur Heaton & Co. Ltd, Valley Works, Station Lane, Heckmondwike, West Yorkshire, WF16 0NF Tel: (01924) 403731 Fax: (01924) 410069
Hollingsworth Service Co. Ltd, Units 6-7 Norden Court, Hayes Lane Industrial Estate, Great Harwood, Blackburn, BB6 7UR Tel: (01254) 881100 Fax: (01254) 881101
E-mail: pat.turner@btconnect.com
J Thwaites Ltd, 31 Bretton Street, Dewsbury, West Yorkshire, WF12 9BJ Tel: (01924) 460480 Fax: (01924) 460607
E-mail: info@tufgrip.com
Lee, Crossley Hall Works, York Street, Bradford, West Yorkshire, BD8 0HR Tel: (01274) 496487 Fax: (01274) 487081
M H Spencer Ltd, Charter Avenue, Coventry, CV4 8AF Tel: (024) 7646 4044 Fax: (024) 7669 4011 E-mail: sales@weavingreeds.com
▶ Maytree Associates Ltd, 17 Maytree Drive, Kirby Muxloe, Leicester, LE9 2LP Tel: 0116-239 4275 Fax: (0870) 7515096
E-mail: maytreeass@btconnect.com
Micro Pneumatics, 1 Palmer Street, Leicester, LE4 5PT Tel: 0116-261 1055 Fax: 0116-261 1066 E-mail: sales@micropneumatics.co.uk
Muschamp Machine Services, 6-12 Whitebirk Road, Blackburn, BB1 3JD Tel: (01254) 263361 Fax: (01254) 697947
E-mail: info@muschamp.co.uk
Tuffa Bobbin Co., 10 Greycaines Industrial Estate, Bushey Mill Lane, Watford, WD24 7GG Tel: (01923) 222248 Fax: (01923) 817024
E-mail: sales@tuffabobbin.com
Walker & Smith, Lanes Mills, 403 Bradford Road, Batley, West Yorkshire, WF17 5LY Tel: (01924) 474469 Fax: (01924) 474460
E-mail: sales@walker-smith.co.uk

TEXTILE MACHINERY ENGINEERS, DISMANTLING/ERECTING/INSTALLING

Ascotex Ltd, Calder Works, Simonstone, Burnley, Lancashire, BB12 7NL Tel: (01282) 772011 Fax: (01282) 773600
E-mail: sales@ascotex.com
Hollingsworth Service Co. Ltd, Units 6-7 Norden Court, Hayes Lane Industrial Estate, Great Harwood, Blackburn, BB6 7UR Tel: (01254) 881100 Fax: (01254) 881101
E-mail: pat.turner@btconnect.com
Karl Mayer Textile Machinery Ltd, Kings Road, Shepshed, Loughborough, Leicestershire, LE12 9HT Tel: (01509) 502056 Fax: (01509) 508065 E-mail: mhyeabsley@karlmayer.co.uk
Walker & Smith, Lanes Mills, 403 Bradford Road, Batley, West Yorkshire, WF17 5LY Tel: (01924) 474469 Fax: (01924) 474460
E-mail: sales@walker-smith.co.uk

TEXTILE MACHINERY IMPORT/EXPORT MERCHANTS OR AGENTS

▶ A M S Manchester, 27 Honey Street, Manchester, M8 8RG Tel: 0161-819 2540 Fax: 0161-819 2541
E-mail: enquiries@ams-steam-eng.co.uk
I S C Textile Machinery Ltd, 1 Town St, Farsley, Pudsey, W. Yorkshire, LS28 5EN Tel: 0113-257 7015
Robert S Maynard Ltd, P O Box 8, Wilmslow, Cheshire, SK9 5ER Tel: (01625) 524055 Fax: (01625) 524584
E-mail: robert.s.maynard.ltd@dial.pipex.com
Texel, PO Box 19, Todmorden, Lancashire, OL14 8FB Tel: (01706) 815262 Fax: (01706) 815262

TEXTILE MEASURING MACHINES

Measuring Machines Ltd, 9 Oban Court, Hurricane Way, Wickford, Essex, SS11 8YB Tel: (01268) 560999 Fax: (01268) 561222
E-mail: info@measuringmachines.co.uk

TEXTILE MERCHANT-CONVERTERS

Bill Beaumont Textiles Ltd, Park Mills, Deighton Road, Chorley, Lancashire, PR7 2HP Tel: (01257) 263065 Fax: (01257) 241348
E-mail: sales@billbeaumont.co.uk
Benmar Textiles Ltd, Cheetwood Road, Off Broughton Street, Manchester, M8 8AQ Tel: 0161-839 7000 Fax: 0161-839 2500
E-mail: info@benmartextiles.co.uk
G.B. Brooks & Co. Ltd, Mackenzie Industrial Park, Bird Hall Lane, Cheadle Heath, Stockport, Cheshire, SK3 0SB Tel: 0161-428 7330 Fax: 0161-428 7294
E-mail: enquiries@gbbrooks.co.uk
C & H Textile Menders, Market Street, Milnsbridge, Huddersfield, HD3 4HT Tel: (01484) 640850 Fax: (01484) 640850
C & J Fabrics, 11 Norford Way, Rochdale, Lancashire, OL11 5QS Tel: (01706) 633973 Fax: (01706) 638445
E-mail: cjfabrics@compuserve.com
C Q C Ltd, Riverside Road, Pottington Business Park, Barnstaple, Devon, EX31 1NB Tel: (01271) 345678 Fax: (01271) 345090
E-mail: pjg@cqc.co.uk
J.M. Clayton & Co. Ltd, Unit 3 Phoenix Court, Hammond Avenue, Stockport, Cheshire, SK4 1PQ Tel: 0161-474 0061 Fax: 0161-474 0071 E-mail: omar@jmclayton.co.uk
Francis Dinsmore Ltd, 25 Greenfield Road, Kells, Ballymena, County Antrim, BT42 3JL Tel: (028) 2589 1203 Fax: (028) 2589 2295
E-mail: info@dinsmore.co.uk
Eker & Albert Ltd, 293-295 Old Street, London, EC1V 9LA Tel: (020) 7739 0158 Fax: (020) 7739 7402
Evans Textile Sales Ltd, 22 Piccadilly Trading Estate, Manchester, M1 2NP Tel: 0161-274 4147 Fax: 0161-274 4070
E-mail: sales@evans-textiles.com
Greenwood J.F, Barton Lane, Eccles, Manchester, M30 0HN Tel: 0161-786 1075 Fax: 0161-787 7613
E-mail: sjb@behrens.co.uk
Hammertex Ltd, Nationwide House, 7 Victoria Way, Burgess Hill, West Sussex, RH15 9NF Tel: (01444) 257733 Fax: (01444) 257744
E-mail: sales@hammertex.co.uk
Harlequin Fabric & Wallcoverings Ltd, Ladybird House, Beeches Road, Loughborough, Leicestershire, LE11 2HA Tel: (0870) 8300355 Fax: (0870) 8300359
E-mail: sales@harlequin.uk.com
James Walker & Sons Blankets Ltd, Station Road, Mirfield, West Yorkshire, WF14 8NA Tel: (01924) 492277 Fax: (01924) 480263
E-mail: sales@jwalker.co.uk
John Kaldor Fabric Maker UK Ltd, Portland House, 4 Great Portland Street, London, W1W 8QJ Tel: (020) 7631 3557 Fax: (020) 7580 8628 E-mail: info@johnkaldor.co.uk
Thomas Kershaw Ltd, Unit 10, Walnesley Court, Accrington, Lancashire, BB5 5JQ Tel: (01254) 875550 Fax: (01254) 875551
E-mail: tkfabrics@hotmail.com
▶ Kindon Textiles Ltd, 31 Belmont Way, Rochdale, Lancashire, OL12 6HR Tel: (01706) 656951 Fax: (01706) 345496
E-mail: g-kindon@msn.com
Marson, Unit 8 Kings Exchange, Tileyard Road, London, N7 9AH Tel: (020) 7619 6500 Fax: (020) 7619 6501
Moorfield Of Lancashire, Perseverence Mill, Olive Lane, Eccleshill, Darwen, Lancashire, BB3 3BA Tel: (01254) 704131 Fax: (01254) 704141 E-mail: donelana@aol.com
Norman Lyons & Co Exports Ltd, 106 Cleveland Street, London, W1T 6NX Tel: (020) 7380 1515 Fax: (020) 7388 4526
Phoenix Calico Ltd, Phoenix Works, 6 Huddersfield Road, Stalybridge, Cheshire, SK15 2QA Tel: 0161-304 7144 Fax: 0161-304 7244
Frank Preston (Textiles), Newhaven Business Park, Barton Lane, Eccles, Manchester, M30 0TH Tel: 0161-786 1080 Fax: 0161-786 1144
Protoleague Fabrics, Union Mill, Vernon Street, Bolton, BL1 2PT Tel: (01204) 528900 Fax: (01204) 528250
E-mail: sales@protoleague.co.uk
R & J Partington, Failsworth Mill, Ashton Road West, Failsworth, Manchester, M35 0FR Tel: 0161-934 4040 Fax: 0161-683 4280
E-mail: partington@fabric.co.uk
R K Ross & Co. Ltd, Unit 1 George Leigh Street, Manchester, M4 6BD Tel: 0161-205 1822 Fax: 0161-203 4609
Safe Textiles Ltd, 151 Whitechapel Road, London, E1 1DN Tel: (020) 7247 6641 Fax: (020) 7247 2497
Sandmoor Textile Co. Ltd, 30 Low Hall Road, Horsforth, Leeds, LS18 4EF Tel: 0113-258 5228 Fax: 0113-239 0155
Sangson Ltd, 221 Lozells Rd, Birmingham, B19 1RJ Tel: 0121-551 6530 Fax: 0121-551 6107
Severnside Fabrics Ltd, Gordon Road, Whitehall, Bristol, BS5 7DR Tel: 0117-951 0412 Fax: 0117-935 4165
E-mail: sales@severnsidefabrics.co.uk
Shawe Hall Textiles, 85 North Western Street, Manchester, M12 6DY Tel: 0161-273 6006 Fax: 0161-273 6006
Sir Jacob Behrens & Sons Ltd, Newhaven Business Park, Barton Lane, Eccles, Manchester, M30 0TH Tel: 0161-786 1000 Fax: 0161-787 7613
E-mail: sales@behrens.co.uk
Textra Fabric Importers, Sheephouse Barn, Reading Road, East Hendred, Wantage, Oxfordshire, OX12 8HR Tel: (0870) 2414949 Fax: (08702) 414950
E-mail: sales@textra.co.uk
H.L. Wilkinson & Co. Ltd, 49-51 Central Street, London, EC1V 8AB Tel: (020) 7253 5241 Fax: (020) 7250 1562
E-mail: info@hlwilkinson.co.uk
Wolfin Textiles Ltd, 359 Uxbridge Road, Hatch End, Pinner, Middlesex, HA5 4JN Tel: (020) 8428 9911 Fax: (020) 8428 9955
E-mail: cotton@wolfintextiles.co.uk

TEXTILE OIL PRODUCTS

Squire A Radcliffe & Sons Ltd, Gillbridge Works, Lowlands Road, Mirfield, West Yorkshire, WF14 8LU Tel: (01924) 491491 Fax: (01924) 498940

TEXTILE PRINTED FABRICS

Albert Hartley Ltd, Crownest Mill, Skipton Road, Barnoldswick, Lancashire, BB18 5RH Tel: (01282) 666000 Fax: (01282) 666002
E-mail: ssmith@alberthartley.co.uk
▶ Atlas Transfer Printers Ltd, 9 Wanstead Road, Leicester, LE3 1TR Tel: 0116-231 4500 Fax: 0116-231 4600
E-mail: atpl@btconnect.com
Barracks Fabrics Printing Co. Ltd, Caton Road, Lancaster, LA1 3PA Tel: (01524) 389308 Fax: (01524) 381057
▶ Digitalis, Llangoed Hall, Llyswen, Brecon, Powys, LD3 0YP Tel: (01874) 754631 Fax: (01874) 754588
E-mail: simon@digitalis.uk.com
Fibrous Ltd, Unit E2, Newton Business Park, Talbot Road, Newton, Hyde, Cheshire, SK14 4UQ Tel: (0845) 4508935 Fax: (0845) 4508936 E-mail: info@fibrous.com
P C I, Duke Street, New Basford, Nottingham, NG7 7JN Tel: 0115-970 3451 Fax: 0115-978 1547 E-mail: info@pacificconcept.com
Protoleague Fabrics, Union Mill, Vernon Street, Bolton, BL1 2PT Tel: (01204) 528900 Fax: (01204) 528250
E-mail: sales@protoleague.co.uk
S M D Textiles Ltd, Pittman Way, Fulwood, Preston, PR2 9ZD Tel: (01772) 651199 Fax: (01772) 654034
E-mail: enquiries@swatchbox.co.uk

TEXTILE PRINTER ENGRAVERS

Meshtex Ltd, Second Avenue, Poynton Industrial Estate, Poynton, Stockport, Cheshire, SK12 1ND Tel: (01625) 876949 Fax: (01625) 879529 E-mail: info@meshtex.com

TEXTILE PRINTING CHEMICALS

Magna Colours Ltd, 3 Dodworth Business Park, Upper Cliffe Road, Dodworth, Barnsley, South Yorkshire, S75 3SP Tel: (01226) 731751 Fax: (01226) 731752
E-mail: sales@magnacolours.com

TEXTILE PRINTING CONTRACT SERVICES

A M Screen Print, 5 Millsborough House, Millsborough Road, Redditch, Worcestershire, B98 7BU Tel: (01527) 62323 Fax: (01527) 62401 E-mail: amscreenprint@btconnect.com
Advartex Ltd, Pickforde Lane, Ticehurst, Wadhurst, East Sussex, TN5 7BL Tel: (01580) 200120 Fax: (01580) 201001
E-mail: andy@advartex.co.uk

TEXTILE PRINTING CONTRACT SERVICES – *continued*

Albert Hartley Ltd, Crownest Mill, Skipton Road, Barnoldswick, Lancashire, BB18 5RH Tel: (01282) 666000 Fax: (01282) 666002 E-mail: ssmith@alberthartley.co.uk
Cannon Street Jersey Fabrics Ltd, Ashley Works, Ashley Road, London, N17 9LJ Tel: (020) 8885 9400 Fax: (020) 8885 9410 E-mail: enquiries@csjf.co.uk
Continuous Transfer Paper Printers Ltd, Lotti Works, Two Bridges Road, Newhey, Rochdale, Lancashire, OL16 3SR Tel: (01706) 299015 Fax: (01706) 841159E-mail: sales@ctpp.co.uk
Imageon Ltd, White Cross Industrial Estate, South Road, Lancaster, LA1 4XQ Tel: (01524) 382777 Fax: (01524) 382777 E-mail: info@imageonltd.fsbusiness.co.uk
J Clegg & Bros Rakewood Ltd, Rakewood Mill, Rakewood Road, Littleborough, Lancashire, OL15 0AP Tel: (01706) 378342 E-mail: peter@jclegg.co.uk
Standfast Barracks, Caton Road, Lancaster, LA1 3PA Tel: (01524) 64334 Fax: (01524) 380157
T Shirt Products, Somers Road, Rugby, Warwickshire, CV22 7DG Tel: (0845) 0714405 Fax: (0845) 0714406 E-mail: sales@tsp-tshirts.co.uk
Tiviot Prints Ltd, Lymefield Mill, Broadbottom, Hyde, Cheshire, SK14 6AG Tel: (01457) 763297 Fax: (01457) 765499 E-mail: info@tiviotprintsltd.demon.co.uk

TEXTILE PRINTING MACHINES

L & S Prints, Export House, West Lane, Keighley, West Yorkshire, BD21 2LH Tel: (01535) 690030 Fax: (01535) 690133

TEXTILE PRINTING, DIGITAL

▶ Aneataprint Two Ltd, 170a New London Centre, Drury Lane, London, WC2B 5QA Tel: (020) 7841 1280 Fax: (020) 7841 1289 E-mail: sales@aneataprint.co.uk
▶ Digitalis, Llangoed Hall, Llyswen, Brecon, Powys, LD3 0YP Tel: (01874) 754631 Fax: (01874) 754588 E-mail: simon@digitalis.uk.com

TEXTILE PROCESSORS TO THE TRADE

Beaumont Blending Co. Ltd, Ings Dyeworks, Wakefield Road, Scissett, Huddersfield, HD8 9JL Tel: (01484) 863526 Fax: (01484) 865479
Craven Yarn Services, Milton House, Cononly, Keighley, West Yorkshire, BD20 8LL Tel: (01535) 630683 Fax: (01535) 630683 E-mail: john@cravenyarns.fsnet.co.uk

TEXTILE PRODUCTS, TO CUSTOMERS SPECIFICATION

Jarvis Manufacturing Ltd, 22b Hawthorn Road, Eastbourne, East Sussex, BN23 6QA Tel: (01323) 411993 Fax: (01323) 649662 E-mail: info@jarvismanufacturing.co.uk
M. Perkins & Son Ltd, 2 Weyside Park, Newman Lane, Mill Lane, Alton, Hampshire, GU34 2YY Tel: (01420) 541171 Fax: (01420) 541173 E-mail: sales@mperkins.co.uk
Profit Manufacturing Ltd, Unit 36 Albion Mills, Albion Road, Bradford, West Yorkshire, BD10 9TF Tel: (01274) 610590 Fax: (01274) 610541 E-mail: sales@pro-fit-int.com

TEXTILE SHODDY

Wilson Bros (Chickenley) Ltd, Chickenley Mills, Dewsbury, W. Yorkshire, WF12 8ND Tel: (01924) 463252 Fax: (01924) 463439 E-mail: chris@wilsonbros.demon.co.uk

TEXTILE SLITTING CONTRACT SERVICES

Jac & Co., Failsworth Mill, Ashton Road West, Failsworth, Manchester, M35 0FR Tel: 0161-934 4070 Fax: 0161-683 2074
Keenedge Ltd, Unit 7 Summerlands Industrial Estate, Endmoor, Kendal, Cumbria, LA8 0FB Tel: (01539) 561800 Fax: (01539) 561799 E-mail: info@cutting.co.uk

TEXTILE SLITTING MACHINES

Border Textiles UK Ltd, Whitechapel Road, Cleckheaton, West Yorkshire, BD19 6HY Tel: (01274) 866200 Fax: (01274) 866220 E-mail: sales@bordertextiles.co.uk
T W Eaton & Co. Ltd, 247 Noel Street, Nottingham, NG7 6AR Tel: 0115-978 4084 Fax: 0115-942 2631

TEXTILE SMALLWARES

W.N. Gutteridge Ltd, 11-13 Wellington Street, Leicester, LE1 6HH Tel: 0116-254 3825 Fax: 0116-247 0276 E-mail: buttons@gutteridge.co.uk

TEXTILE SPECIAL PURPOSE CUSTOM BUILT MACHINERY

Krupa Bros & Son Ltd, 14 Brook Street, Bury, Lancashire, BL9 6AH Tel: 0161-797 4499 Fax: 0161-764 8722

TEXTILE SPINNERS AND DOUBLERS, *See headings for particular yarn*

TEXTILE SPINNING RING TRAVELLERS

Eadie & Kanai Co. Ltd, 19 Scotts Road, Paisley, Renfrewshire, PA2 7AN Tel: 0141-889 4126 Fax: 0141-848 1290 E-mail: sales@ekcl.co.uk

TEXTILE TEST EQUIPMENT

James H Heal & Co. Ltd, Richmond Works, Lake View, Halifax, West Yorkshire, HX3 6EP Tel: (01422) 366355 Fax: (01422) 352440 E-mail: info@james-heal.co.uk
Roaches International Ltd, Upperhulme, Leek, Staffordshire, ST13 8TY Tel: (01538) 300425 Fax: (01538) 300364 E-mail: info@roaches.co.uk
S D L Atlas (International) Ltd, Crown Royal, Crown Royal, Shawcross St, Stockport, Cheshire, SK1 3JW Tel: 0161-480 8485 Fax: 0161-480 8580 E-mail: stephen.combes@dial.pipex.com
Testrite Ltd, Woodfield Works, Old Lane, Halifax, West Yorkshire, HX3 6TF Tel: (01422) 366963 Fax: (01422) 345431 E-mail: sales@testrite.co.uk

TEXTILE TESTING/PROVING SERVICES

Shirley Technologies Ltd, Unit 12 Westpoint Enterprise Park, Clarence Avenue, Trafford Park, Manchester, M17 1QS Tel: 0161-869 1610 Fax: 0161-872 6492 E-mail: info@shirleytech.co.uk
STR Ambergate, Dylan Laboratories, Ambergate, Belper, Derbyshire, DE56 2EY Tel: (01773) 854000

TEXTILE TRANSFERS

Britannia Transprint, 38 Burgess Road, Saffron Works, Leicester, LE2 8QL Tel: 0116-283 8485 E-mail: info@tranfereprint.co.uk
J & A International Ltd, Vale Road, Spilsby, Lincolnshire, PE23 5HE Tel: (01790) 752757 Fax: (01790) 754132 E-mail: ja-int@ja-int.co.uk
Technographics UK, Polymark House, Abbeydale Road, Wembley, Middlesex, HA0 1LQ Tel: (020) 8991 0011 Fax: (020) 8998 8080 E-mail: sales@technographics.co.uk

TEXTILE WASHING, *See Bleachers etc*

TEXTILE WASTE EXPORT MERCHANTS OR AGENTS

A Cohen, 10 Palace Gate, London, W8 5NF Tel: (020) 7225 0022 Fax: (020) 7584 9520
H S Wood Textiles, Park View Mills, Raymond Street, Bradford, West Yorkshire, BD5 8DT Tel: (01274) 734322 Fax: (01274) 744592 E-mail: wgroup@globalnet.co.uk

TEXTILE WASTE/RAG PULLING/ RECYCLING/DISPOSAL CONTRACTORS/PROCESSORS/ MERCHANTS

A Cohen, 10 Palace Gate, London, W8 5NF Tel: (020) 7225 0022 Fax: (020) 7584 9520
T.W. Beaumont Ltd, Spafield Mill, Upper Road, Batley, West Yorkshire, WF17 7LS Tel: (01924) 461401 Fax: (01924) 461378 E-mail: helen.miles@yorkshirewiter.co.uk
Cleaning Rag Supply Co. Ltd, 28 Brearley Street, Hockley, Birmingham, B19 3NR Tel: 0121-333 4446 Fax: 0121-333 4442 E-mail: enquiries@cleaningragsupply.co.uk
Clyde Recycling Ltd, 1650 London Road, Glasgow, G31 4QG Tel: 0141-554 8778 Fax: (0141) 554 6717
Jack Cohen & Sons, 107 Fairfield Street, Manchester, M1 2WG Tel: 0161-273 3788 Fax: 0161-273 3788
E Klein & Co., 122-126 Westferry Road, London, E14 3SG Tel: (020) 7987 1171 Fax: (020) 7538 0477
Fred Singleton Huddersfield Ltd, Cliffe End Mills, Dale Street, Longwood, Huddersfield, HD3 4TG Tel: (01484) 653153 Fax: (01484) 649009
H S Wood Textiles, Park View Mills, Raymond Street, Bradford, West Yorkshire, BD5 8DT Tel: (01274) 734322 Fax: (01274) 744592 E-mail: wgroup@globalnet.co.uk
I & G Cohen Ltd, Castle Works, Bazaar Street, Salford, M6 6GS Tel: 0161-736 8899 Fax: 0161-745 8697 E-mail: sales@igcohen.com
J Williams, Unit 2 Freeman Street, Birkenhead, Merseyside, CH41 1BR Tel: 0151-647 6532 Fax: 0151-647 6532
James Ronbinson Fibes Ltd, Wharfedale Road, Euroway Industrial Estate, Bradford, West Yorkshire, BD4 6SG Tel: (01274) 689400 Fax: (01274) 685986 E-mail: sales@jrfibres.co.uk
L Clancey & Sons, Murton Lane, Murton, York, YO19 5UF Tel: (01904) 489169 Fax: (01904) 489508 E-mail: clancey.l@btconnect.com
Lawrence M Barry & Co., Britannia Mill, North Cresent, London, E16 4TG Tel: (020) 7473 2898 Fax: (020) 7473 1381 E-mail: sales@1mb.co.uk
Mill Road Properties Ltd, Pressing Room Dye Works, Hartley Street, Dewsbury, West Yorkshire, WF13 2HR Tel: (01924) 465323 Fax: (01924) 502662
Nathan's Wastesavers Ltd, Unit 13 Winchester Avenue, Denny, Stirlingshire, FK6 6QE Tel: (01324) 826828 Fax: (01324) 826555
PJ's Workwear, 42 The Tything, Worcester, WR1 1JT Tel: (01905) 22051 Fax: (01905) 617476
Salvatex Holdings Ltd, 1 St. Marks Road, St. James Industrial Estate, Corby, Northamptonshire, NN18 8AN Tel: (01536) 400002 Fax: (01536) 400169
Smith Bros (Staincliffe) Ltd, Mohair Mills, Gibson Street, Bradford, West Yorkshire, BD3 9TS Tel: (01274) 662281 Fax: (01274) 656299 E-mail: strossltd@aol.com
George Stross Ltd, Providence Mills, Bradford Street, Dewsbury, West Yorkshire, WF13 1EN Tel: (01924) 466031 Fax: (01924) 466029 E-mail: sales@fabworks.co.uk
T.D. Whitfield & Sons Ltd, Oak Lea Mills, Meadow Rd, Apperley Bridge, Bradford, W. Yorkshire, BD10 0LY Tel: (01274) 613106 Fax: (01274) 617688

TEXTILE WATERPROOFING PROCESSORS OR SERVICES

Proofings Technology Ltd, Hare Hill Road, Littleborough, Lancashire, OL15 9HE Tel: (01706) 372314 Fax: (01706) 370473 E-mail:
Sealproof Ltd, Dan Lane Mill, Tyldesley Road, Atherton, Manchester, M46 9DA Tel: (01942) 878012 Fax: (01942) 878298

TEXTILE WATERPROOFING PRODUCTS

Grangers International Ltd, Grange Close, Clover Nook Industrial Park, Somercotes, Alfreton, Derbyshire, DE55 4QT Tel: (01773) 521521 Fax: (01773) 521262 E-mail: grangers@grangers.co.uk

TEXTILE WINDING MACHINES

S P T Machines Ltd, Brookside Ave, Rustington, Littlehampton, W. Sussex, BN16 3LF Tel: (01903) 784212 Fax: (01903) 770288 E-mail: info@sptmachines.co.uk
Stabel Ltd, Coney Green, Oswestry, Shropshire, SY11 2JL Tel: (01691) 650200 Fax: (01691) 654839 E-mail: george@stabel.co.uk
Texkimp Ltd, Manchester Road, Northwich, Cheshire, CW9 7NN Tel: (01606) 40345 Fax: (01606) 40366 E-mail: info@texkimp.co.uk

TEXTILE WIRE

W B Swift Ltd, Leafland Street, Halifax, West Yorkshire, HX1 4LX Tel: (01422) 358073 Fax: (01422) 330360 E-mail: wbswift@nildram.co.uk

TEXTILE WOVEN FABRICS

John Holdsworth & Co. Ltd, Shaw Lodge Mills, Halifax, West Yorkshire, HX3 9ET Tel: (01422) 433000 Fax: (01422) 433300 E-mail: sales@holdsworth.co.uk
John Spencer Textiles Ltd, Ashfield Mill, Active Way, Burnley, Lancashire, BB11 1BS Tel: (01282) 423111 Fax: (01282) 416283 E-mail: sales@johnspencer.com
Replin Fabrics, March Street Mills, March Street, Peebles, EH45 8ER Tel: (01721) 724310 Fax: (01721) 721893 E-mail: enquiries@replin-fabrics.co.uk
Somic plc, PO Box 8, Preston, PR1 5PS Tel: (01772) 790000 Fax: (01772) 795677 E-mail: somic@somic.co.uk
Vale Weavers Ltd, Caldervale Mill, Barrowford, Nelson, Lancashire, BB9 7BL Tel: (01282) 617692 Fax: (01282) 696530

TEXTILES, *See also headings for particular fabrics*

A B Textiles, 191 Wigston Lane, Leicester, LE2 8DJ Tel: 0116-283 3585 Fax: 0116-283 3533
A T Warping, Unit W8 Legrams Mill, Legrams Lane, Bradford, West Yorkshire, BD7 1NH Tel: (01274) 724836 Fax: (01274) 722846
Abakhan Fabrics, Llanerch-y-Mor, Holywell, Clwyd, CH8 9DX Tel: (01745) 562101 Fax: (01745) 562101 E-mail: enquiries@abakhan-fabricsfirst.co.uk
Albert Jones Textiles Ltd, 51-53 Richmond Street, Manchester, M1 3WB Tel: 0161-236 4043 Fax: 0161-236 0434
Allsorts, 33 Kirkby Road, Hemsworth, Pontefract, West Yorkshire, WF9 4BA Tel: (01977) 610955
Ashworth Bros Nelson Ltd, Whitefield Mill, Victoria Street, Nelson, Lancashire, BB9 7HL Tel: (01282) 613997 Fax: (01282) 613997
Aziz Textiles Ltd, 19-21 Portland St, Aston, Birmingham, B6 5RX Tel: 0121-328 4456 Fax: 0121-328 6941
B A E Systems, Spares Logistic Centre Vickers Drive South, Brooklands Busin, Weybridge, Surrey, KT13 0UJ Tel: (01932) 352611 Fax: (01932) 353355
Bradley Textiles Ltd, 6 Huss Row, Belfast, BT13 1EE Tel: (028) 9032 5434 Fax: (028) 9031 5350 E-mail: bradleytextiles@btopenworld.com
Calder Weaving Co. Ltd, Scout Road, Hebden Bridge, West Yorkshire, HX7 5HZ Tel: (01422) 882382 Fax: (01422) 883381 E-mail: sales@calderweaving.co.uk
Cavendish Fabrics Ltd, 140 New Cavendish Street, London, W1W 6YE Tel: (020) 7631 0768 Fax: (020) 7580 8481
Collins & Hayes Ltd, Menzies Road, Ponswood, St. Leonards-On-Sea, East Sussex, TN38 9XF Tel: (01424) 720027 Fax: (01424) 720270 E-mail: sales@collinsandhayes.com
Concept III Textiles International Ltd, 2 Marton Mills, Marton Street, Skipton, North Yorkshire, BD23 1TA Tel: (01756) 702100 Fax: (01756) 702101 E-mail: info@conceptiii.co.uk
Croft Mill, Croft Mill, Lowther Lane, Foulridge, Colne, Lancashire, BB8 7NG Tel: (01282) 869625 Fax: (01282) 870038 E-mail: info@croftmill.co.uk
▶ Crosrol UK Ltd, Macart House, Farnham Road, Bradford, West Yorkshire, BD7 3JG Tel: (01274) 525937 Fax: (01274) 525945 E-mail: sales@crosrol.co.uk
Dawson International plc, Lochleven Mills, Kinross, KY13 8GL Tel: (01577) 867000 Fax: (01577) 867010 E-mail: enquiries@dawson-international.co.uk
Dutton & Gavin Textiles Ltd, 62-66 Bermondsey Street, London, SE1 3UD Tel: (020) 7403 6388 Fax: (020) 7407 5814 E-mail: sales@dutgav.fsnet.co.uk
Empee Silk Fabrics, 31 Commercial Road, London, N18 1TP Tel: (020) 8887 6000 Fax: (020) 8887 6045 E-mail: empee@wholesalefabrics.co.uk
F R Street Ltd, Frederick House, Hurricane Way, Wickford, Essex, SS11 8YB Tel: (01268) 766677 Fax: (01268) 764534 E-mail: val@street.co.uk
Farago Fabrics Ltd, 333 Humberstone Lane, Leicester, LE4 9JR Tel: 0116-276 6556 Fax: 0116-246 1119
Fullwith Textiles Ltd, Sunnybank Mills, Town Street, Farsley, Pudsey, West Yorkshire, LS28 5UJ Tel: 0113-257 9811 Fax: 0113-257 7064
G B Wholesale Ltd, 439 Hackney Road, London, E2 9DY Tel: (020) 7729 7373
G & G Textiles Ltd, Unit 3a, St. Georges Houses, Moat Street, Wigston, Leicestershire, LE18 2NH Tel: 0116-257 1170 Fax: 0116-281 0330
Grewcock Fabrics Ltd, 15-29 Dartford Rd, Leicester, LE2 7PQ Tel: 0116-283 8551 Fax: 0116-244 0715
D.C. Gwillim Enterprises Ltd, Charnwood House, 251 Loughborough Road, Mountsorrel, Loughborough, Leicestershire, LE12 7AS Tel: (01509) 621272 Fax: (01509) 620911
Hume Sweet Hume, Pierowall, Westray, Orkney, KW17 2BZ Tel: (01857) 677259 Fax: (01857) 677259 E-mail: info@humesweethume.com
I J Parkash Ltd, 30 Brunswick Street, Manchester, M13 9TQ Tel: 0161-273 5883 Fax: 0161-273 7262 E-mail: rajiv@absonline.net
Image House Ltd, 67-73 Constitution Hill, Birmingham, B19 3JX Tel: 0121-233 3569 Fax: 0121-233 0139 E-mail: vchobera@compuserve.com
Indo African Exports Ltd, Failsworth Mill, Ashton Road West, Failsworth, Manchester, M35 0FR Tel: 0161-934 4004 Fax: 0161-683 4280 E-mail: indo@fabric.co.uk
Inter Weave Textiles, Whitwell Green Lane, Elland, West Yorkshire, HX5 9BJ Tel: (0870) 2242468 Fax: (0870) 2242469 E-mail: enquiries@interweavetextiles.com

TEXTILES – *continued*

J Stimler Ltd, Martin House, Downs Road, London, E5 8QJ Tel: (020) 7254 8499 Fax: (020) 7254 1270

Javaria Textiles Ltd, 4 Bay Street, Blackburn, BB1 5NJ Tel: (01254) 680777 Fax: (01254) 261688

K.Azmeh (Textiles) Ltd, Richmond House, Richmond Grove, Manchester, M13 0LN Tel: 0161-274 4827 Fax: 0161-274 4815 E-mail: info@katuk.com

K G Christys & Co. Ltd, Helmet Street, Manchester, M1 2NT Tel: 0161-274 4339 Fax: 0161-274 4322 E-mail: sales@kgchristys.co.uk

Leigh Knight Ltd, 82 Arnos Grove, London, N14 7AR Tel: (020) 8886 9806 Fax: (020) 8447 8332 E-mail: sales@leighknight.com

Kochane Bros Ltd, 29 Whitechapel Road, London, E1 1DU Tel: (020) 7247 9148 Fax: (020) 7247 2937

L Littlewood & Son Exports Ltd, 3 Edwin Road, Beswick, Manchester, M11 3ER Tel: 0161-273 1344 Fax: 0161-273 3013 E-mail: l-littlewood@btconnect.com

Lango Ltd, 101 Greenfield Road, London, E1 1EJ Tel: (020) 7247 8376 Fax: (020) 7247 3282

Lesterdale Ltd, Whitebirk Road, Blackburn, BB1 3JA Tel: (01254) 581607 Fax: (01254) 665425

Lewis & Wood Ltd, 5 The Green, Uley, Dursley, Gloucestershire, GL11 5SN Tel: (01453) 860080 Fax: (01453) 860054 E-mail: office@lewisandwood.co.uk

Linetex Clothing Co. Ltd, 56-58 Nelson Street, London, E1 2DE Tel: (020) 7790 0916 Fax: (020) 7790 9760 E-mail: linetex@hotmail.com

M & N Textiles Ltd, Wrengate House, 221 Palatine Road, Didsbury, Manchester, M20 2EE Tel: 0161-438 1050 Fax: 0161-438 1021 E-mail: mandn@wrengate.co.uk

Marson, Unit 8 Kings Exchange, Tileyard Road, London, N7 9AH Tel: (020) 7619 6500 Fax: (020) 7619 6501

Menzel UK, Preston Road, Charnock Richard, Chorley, Lancashire, PR7 5JZ Tel: (01257) 791503 Fax: (01257) 793980

Mickalan Ltd, 191 Granville Avenue, Long Eaton, Nottingham, NG10 4HE Tel: 0115-946 2761 Fax: 0115-973 3166

Mill Road Properties Ltd, Pressing Room Dye Works, Hartley Street, Dewsbury, West Yorkshire, WF13 2HR Tel: (01924) 465323 Fax: (01924) 502662

The Mill Shops, Buckfast Road, Buckfast, Buckfastleigh, Devon, TQ11 0ED Tel: (01364) 643325 Fax: (01364) 643183

Nelson Textiles, 31 Elizabeth Street, Nelson, Lancashire, BB9 7YA Tel: (01282) 612234 Fax: (01282) 612234 E-mail: nelsontextiles@tiscali.co.uk

Norman Lyons & Co Exports Ltd, 106 Cleveland Street, London, W1T 6NX Tel: (020) 7380 1515 Fax: (020) 7388 4526

▶ Padma Textile Manufacturing, 2b Heath Hurst Road, London, NW3 2RX Tel: (020) 7794 9988 Fax: (020) 7794 5599

Pam Textiles Ltd, 24,Manor Road, Lymm, Cheshire, WA13 0AU Tel: (07771) 644363 E-mail: murphypamtex@aol.com

Pendle Textiles Wholesale Textile Merchant, Halifax Road, Briercliffe, Burnley, Lancashire, BB10 3QU Tel: (01282) 454375 Fax: (01282) 412750 E-mail: sales@pendle-textiles.co.uk

Phoenix Calico Ltd, Phoenix Works, 6 Huddersfield Road, Stalybridge, Cheshire, SK15 2QA Tel: 0161-304 7144 Fax: 0161-304 7244

Precision Stiching, 7 Beck Street, Nottingham, NG1 1EQ Tel: 0115-955 7373 Fax: 0115-956 2230 E-mail: precisionstiching@yahoo.co.uk

Premier Textiles Ltd, 61 Bloom Street, Manchester, M1 3LY Tel: 0161-236 2212 Fax: 0161-236 9786 E-mail: info@premier-textiles.com

Protoleague Fabrics, Union Mill, Vernon Street, Bolton, BL1 2PT Tel: (01204) 528900 Fax: (01204) 528250 E-mail: sales@protoleague.co.uk

Pundit Drapery, 73-78 John Street Market, Bradford, West Yorkshire, BD1 3SS Tel: (01274) 739264

R A L Ltd, 449 Bethnal Green Road, London, E2 9QH Tel: (020) 7739 5149 Fax: (020) 7739 7856 E-mail: sales@ralphswimer.co.uk

R Chander, Alfred Street North, Nottingham, NG3 1AE Tel: 0115-950 2631 Fax: 0115-950 4668 E-mail: ashwansee@aol.com

R P Textiles, Castley Lane, Castley, Otley, West Yorkshire, LS21 2PY Tel: (01423) 734682 Fax: (01423) 734687 E-mail: ronpattex72@tiscali.co.uk

Ringtag International, 50 Whitehall Street, Rochdale, Lancashire, OL12 0LN Tel: (01706) 354854 Fax: (01706) 712181 E-mail: ring_tag@onetel.com

Rubitex Protective Clothing, 52 Lord Street, Manchester, M3 1HN Tel: 0161-834 3340 Fax: 0161-834 3326 E-mail: info@rubitex.co.uk

Ruby Fashions, 333-335 High Street North, London, E12 6PQ Tel: (020) 8472 7387 Fax: (020) 8472 7387

S K Fashions & Textiles, 33 Stonebridge Street, Leicester, LE5 3PB Tel: 0116-246 0960 Fax: 0116-274 2124

Sangson Ltd, 221 Lozells Rd, Birmingham, B19 1RJ Tel: 0121-551 6530 Fax: 0121-551 6107

The Scottish Collection, Unit O & P Floors Street Industrial Estate, Floors Street, Johnstone, Renfrewshire, PA5 8PE Tel: (01505) 335861 Fax: (01505) 335861

Selhide, Vulcan Works, Pollard Street, Manchester, M4 7AN Tel: 0161-273 1772 Fax: 0161-273 2437

Supreme Quilting Co plc, Brittania Works, Whitehall Road, Tipton, West Midlands, DY4 7JR Tel: 0121-520 7227 Fax: 0121-522 4245

Symon Of Edinburgh, Hardengreen, Dalkeith, Midlothian, EH22 3JY Tel: 0131-660 6611 Fax: 0131-663 9966 E-mail: sales@symon-edinburgh.co.uk

T N S Knitwear, Majid House, 37-49 Devonshire St North, Manchester, M12 6JR Tel: 0161-273 4406 Fax: 0161-272 8207 E-mail: info@tnsknitwear.com

Talk Talk Clothing Ltd, Unit 1, Spitfire Close Coventry, Coventry, CV5 6UR Tel: (024) 7667 6713 Fax: (024) 7671 5204

Tanaz International Ltd, 336 Humberstone Lane, Leicester, LE4 9JP Tel: 0116-274 0853 Fax: 0116-246 0346

Tandon Textile Merchants, 445 Moseley Road, Birmingham, B12 9BX Tel: 0121-440 0848 Fax: 0121-446 4563

Textile Team Ltd, Textile House, Cline Road, London, N11 2LX Tel: (020) 8361 0111 Fax: (020) 8361 7531

Thornbury Clothing Co., 25 Thornbury Road, Birmingham, B20 3DE Tel: 0121-356 6777 Fax: 0121-344 4050

Tonrose Ltd, Unit 1 Petre Road, Clayton le Moors, Accrington, Lancashire, BB5 5TZ Tel: (01254) 239900 Fax: (01254) 239111 E-mail: welcome@tonrose.com

Vartex (Textiles) Ltd, 54 Totara Park House, 34-36 Great Inn Road, London, WC1X 8HR Tel: (020) 7580 3866 Fax: (020) 7831 1515 E-mail: vtextiles@btclick.com

Wallass & Co. Ltd, Lumb Lane Mills, Lumb Lane, Bradford, West Yorkshire, BD8 7GA Tel: (01274) 724215 Fax: (01274) 724839 E-mail: sales@wallass.com

West Yorkshire Fabrics Ltd, 20 High Ash Drive, Leeds, LS17 8RA Tel: (0870) 4439842 Fax: 0113-225 6550 E-mail: info@stroud-brothers.demon.co.uk

White House Linen Specialists, 102 Waterford Road, London, SW6 2HA Tel: (020) 7629 3521 Fax: (020) 7629 8269 E-mail: john@the-white-house.co.uk

Whitley Willows Ltd, Addlecroft Lane, Lepton, Huddersfield, HD8 0NH Tel: (01484) 600800

Wilson Textiles Ltd, 22 Milnpark Street, Glasgow, G41 1BB Tel: 0141-429 0715 Fax: 0141-420 1627

TEXTILES, HOME FURNISHING

▶ Custom Images Ltd, 12 Mill Brow, Armathwaite, Carlisle, CA4 9PJ Tel: (01697) 472522 E-mail: julie@customimages.co.uk

featureDECO.co.uk, Unit A5, Link One Industrial Park, George Henry Road, Tipton, West Midlands, DY4 7BU Tel: 0845 200 4956 E-mail: enquiries@featuredeco.co.uk

▶ The Felbrigg Design Co, 51 Long Street, Tetbury, Gloucestershire, GL8 8AA Tel: (01666) 505026 Fax: (01666) 505026 E-mail: tetbury@felbriggdesign.com

▶ Oliver & Son Ltd, 11 Coinagehall Street, Helston, Cornwall, TR13 8ER Tel: (01326) 572082 Fax: (01326) 572515 E-mail: info@oliversofhelston.co.uk

▶ TD Textiles Direct, Wilson Road, Huyton, Liverpool, L36 6JG Tel: 0151-489 2121

▶ Tonder & Tonder, Bryants Farm, Kiln Road, Dunsden, Reading, RG4 9PB Tel: 0118-946 3704 Fax: 0118-946 3801 E-mail: sales@tonderandtonder.com

TEXTURED COATING PAINTS

Britannia Paints Ltd, Units 7-8, King Street Trading Estate, Middlewich, Cheshire, CW10 9LF Tel: (01606) 834015 Fax: (01606) 837006 E-mail: sales@britanniapaints.co.uk

▶ Nemacom Computer Mnfrs, 6 Morgans Business Park, Bettys Lane, Norton Canes, Cannock, Staffordshire, WS11 9UU Tel: (01543) 495020 Fax: (01543) 495021 E-mail: sales@nemacom.co.uk

▶ Renotex Ltd, Pollard Street, Lofthouse, Wakefield, West Yorkshire, WF3 3HG Tel: (01924) 820003 Fax: (01924) 829529 E-mail: sales@renotex.co.uk

TEXTURED PLASTIC WALL COATING SERVICES

Cornwall Bros Ltd, 2a Tovil Hill, Maidstone, Kent, ME15 6QS Tel: (01622) 755066 Fax: (01622) 755066

▶ South West Coatings Ltd, 8a The Lawn, Budleigh Salterton, Devon, EX9 6LR Tel: (0870) 0802978 E-mail: info@southwestcoatings.co.uk

TEXTURING MOULDS

Gravutex Eschmann International Ltd, Unit 10 Peakdale Road, Brookfield Industrial Estate, Glossop, Derbyshire, SK13 6LQ Tel: (01457) 867627 Fax: (01457) 855536 E-mail: aharrison@gravutexeshman.co.uk

THEATRE CURTAINS/DRAPES

▶ Renovation Seating Service, 96 Stone Cross La North, Lowton, Warrington, WA3 2SG Tel: (07766) 727811 Fax: (01942) 723033 E-mail: renovation.seating@fsmail.net

Rex Howard Drapes Ltd, Eastman Road, London, W3 7QS Tel: (020) 8740 5881 Fax: (020) 8740 5994 E-mail: rexdrapes@yahoo.com

THEATRE LIGHTING CONNECTORS

Lightfactor Sales, 20 Greenhill Crescent, Watford Business Park, Watford, WD18 8JA Tel: (01923) 698090 Fax: (01923) 698081 E-mail: info@lightfactor.co.uk

THEATRE STAGE EQUIPMENT

Blackfriars Scenery Ltd, Blackfriars Studio, 33 Bear Lane, London, SE1 0UH Tel: (020) 7928 6413 Fax: (020) 7261 1994 E-mail: staging@compuserve.com

Central Theatre Supplies, Midshire House, 1186 Stratford Road, Hall Green, Birmingham, B28 8AB Tel: 0121-778 6400 Fax: 0121-702 2046 E-mail: sales@centraltheatresupplies.co.uk

Le Maitre Fireworks Ltd, Unit 6 Forval Close, Mitcham, Surrey, CR4 4NE Tel: (020) 8646 2222 Fax: (020) 8646 1955 E-mail: info@lemaitreltd.com

Russell & Chapple Ltd, 68 Drury Lane, London, WC2B 5SP Tel: (020) 7836 7521 Fax: (020) 7497 0554 E-mail: sales@randc.net

THEATRICAL LIGHTING EQUIPMENT

A C Lighting Ltd, Centauri House, Hillbottom Road, High Wycombe, Buckinghamshire, HP12 4HQ Tel: (01494) 446000 Fax: (01494) 461024 E-mail: sales@aclighting.com

▶ Darkside Industries Ltd, 4 Hare Lane, Pudsey, West Yorkshire, LS28 9LH Tel: 0113-255 7191 Fax: 0113- 257 9799 E-mail: info@riggingsupplies.co.uk

Kave Theatre Services, 15 Western Road, Hurstpierpoint, Hassocks, West Sussex, BN6 9SU Tel: (01273) 835880 Fax: (01273) 834141 E-mail: sales@kave.co.uk

Kays Electronics of Chesterfield, 195 Sheffield Road, Chesterfield, Derbyshire, S41 7JQ Tel: (01246) 205361 E-mail: jk@kayselectronics.co.uk

Stage Services, C8 Ford Airfield Industrial Estate, Ford, Arundel, West Sussex, BN18 0HY Tel: (01903) 716333 Fax: (01903) 717187 E-mail: sales@stage-services.co.uk

THEATRICAL OR FILM OR TELEVISION ARTISTE AGENCIES

▶ R.C_ Annie Ltd, 34 Pullman Place, Eltham, London, SE9 9EG Tel: (07811) 390313 Fax: (0802) 3782880 E-mail: ruth@arty-annie.com

THEATRICAL SOUND SYSTEMS DESIGN SERVICES

A J S Theatre Lighting & Stage Supplies Ltd, 25-26 Hightown Industrial Estate, Crow Arch Lane, Ringwood, Hampshire, BH24 1ND Tel: (01425) 481100 Fax: (01425) 471398 E-mail: enquiries@ajs.co.uk

Stage Services, C8 Ford Airfield Industrial Estate, Ford, Arundel, West Sussex, BN18 0HY Tel: (01903) 716333 Fax: (01903) 717187 E-mail: sales@stage-services.co.uk

Warner Bros Distributors Ltd, Warner House, 98 Theobalds Road, London, WC1X 8WB Tel: (020) 7984 5200 Fax: (020) 7984 5001

THEATRICAL SPECIAL EFFECTS

▶ Confetti Magic Ltd, Rocket Park, Pepperstock, Luton, LU1 4LL Tel: (01582) 723502 Fax: (01582) 485545 E-mail: ian@confettimagic.com

Martin Manufacturing UK plc, Belvoir Way, Fairfield Industrial Estate, Louth, Lincolnshire, LN11 0LQ Tel: (01507) 604399 Fax: (01507) 601956 E-mail: sales@martin.dk

▶ V & W Animatronics, Unit 2, Cockles Lane, Weymouth, Dorset, DT4 9LT Tel: (01305) 768959 Fax: (01305) 768959 E-mail: info@animatronica.co.uk

THEATRICAL STAGE EQUIPMENT/PRODUCTS

▶ Darkside Industries Ltd, 4 Hare Lane, Pudsey, West Yorkshire, LS28 9LH Tel: 0113-255 7191 Fax: 0113- 257 9799 E-mail: info@riggingsupplies.co.uk

Steeldeck, Kings Cross Freight Depot, York Way, London, N1 0UZ Tel: (020) 7833 2031 Fax: (020) 7278 3403 E-mail: info@aolsteeldeck.co.uk

THEATRICAL STAGING

▶ Darkside Industries Ltd, 4 Hare Lane, Pudsey, West Yorkshire, LS28 9LH Tel: 0113-255 7191 Fax: 0113- 257 9799 E-mail: info@riggingsupplies.co.uk

THEATRICAL SUPPLY SERVICES

Central Theatre Supplies, Midshire House, 1186 Stratford Road, Hall Green, Birmingham, B28 8AB Tel: 0121-778 6400 Fax: 0121-702 2046 E-mail: sales@centraltheatresupplies.co.uk

Limitless Communications Ltd, 43 St Mour Road, London, SW6 4DR Tel: (020) 7371 5224 Fax: (020) 7371 9048 E-mail: enquiries@limitlesscommunications.com

Really Useful Group Ltd, 22 Tower Street, London, WC2H 9TW Tel: (020) 7240 0880 Fax: (020) 7240 1204

THEMED EVENT ORGANISING

▶ Bounce Krazee, 14 Green Leys, High Wycombe, Buckinghamshire, HP13 5UH Tel: (01494) 464902 E-mail: info@bouncekrazee.co.uk

Cubic Design & Construction Ltd, Ventureforth House, South Denes Road, Great Yarmouth, Norfolk, NR30 3PT Tel: (01493) 332031

Gekko Entertainments, 42 Theobalds Road, London, WC1X 8NW Tel: (020) 7404 1252 Fax: (020) 7242 1691 E-mail: info@gekkoentertainments.com

▶ IN GEAR EVENT SUPPORT, Unit 7 Coppen Road, Dagenham, Essex, RM8 1HJ Tel: 020 8593 0550 Fax: 020 8593 0552 E-mail: Glenn@ingearevents.fsbusiness.co.uk

▶ Pendleton Events Ltd, Pendleton House 37 Horseshoe, Close Pound Hill, Crawley, West Sussex, RH10 7YS Tel: (07984) 510856 Fax: 0845 330 7263 E-mail: info@pendletonevents.co.uk

▶ Tea Korrs Event Planning And Management, 159 Mellish Street, London, E14 8PJ Tel: 078 65054464 E-mail: teakorrs@gmail.com

▶ WonderWorks, Redemption House, 53 Theobald Street, Borehamwood, Herts, WD6 4RT Tel: 020 8953 7733 Fax: 020 8953 3388 E-mail: info@wworks.co.uk

THERAPY BIOFEEDBACK EQUIPMENT

Bard Holdings Ltd, Forest House, Brighton Road, Crawley, West Sussex, RH11 9BP Tel: (01293) 527888 Fax: (01293) 552428

THERMAL ANALYSERS

Gearing Scientific Ltd, 1 Ashwell Street Ashwell, Baldock, Hertfordshire, SG7 5QF Tel: (01462) 742007 Fax: (01462) 742565 E-mail: gearingsci@yahoo.com

Spectra Sensortech Ltd, Cowley Way, Crewe, CW1 6AG Tel: (01270) 250150 Fax: (01270) 251939

▶ Thermal Hazard Technology, 1 North House, Bond Avenue, Bletchley, Milton Keynes, MK1 1SW Tel: (01908) 646800 Fax: (01908) 645209 E-mail: info@thermalhazardtechnology.com

Thermometric Ltd, 10 Dalby Court, Gadbrook Business Centre, Rudheath, Northwich, Cheshire, CW9 7TN Tel: (01606) 49007 Fax: (01606) 48924

THERMAL ANALYSIS

Netzsch-Instruments, Hayward Industrial Park, Vigo Place, Walsall, WS9 8UG Tel: (01922) 459006 Fax: (01922) 453320 E-mail: sales@netzsch-therma1.co.uk

THERMAL COATINGS

Sontay Ltd, Four Elms Road, Edenbridge, Kent, TN8 6AB Tel: (0845) 3457253 Fax: (0845) 3457353 E-mail: sales@sontay.com

THERMAL COMPUTER PRINTER PRINT HEADS

▶ Barcodesolutions, Faraday House, Wolfreton Drive, Anlaby, Hull, HU10 7BY Tel: 08454 300798 Fax: 08454 300799 E-mail: david.newton@barcodesolutions.co.uk

THERMAL CONDUCTIVITY MEASUREMENT EQUIPMENT/ METERS

Gearing Scientific Ltd, 1 Ashwell Street Ashwell, Baldock, Hertfordshire, SG7 5QF Tel: (01462) 742007 Fax: (01462) 742565 E-mail: gearingsci@yahoo.com

THERMAL CUT OUT (TCO) FUSES

Capri Electrical Developments Ltd, 45-47 Whalley Road, Clitheroe, Lancashire, BB7 1EE Tel: (01200) 425070 Fax: (01200) 423070 E-mail: roger@storageheater.co.uk

THERMAL CUTOUTS (TCO)

▶ Rainer Schneider Ayres, 17 Shirlock Road, London, NW3 2HR Tel: (020) 7267 0812 Fax: (020) 7284 0672 E-mail: rsa_bxt@btinternet.com

THERMAL EXPANSION COMPENSATORS

▶ Flowguard Ltd, Watford Bridge Road, New Mills, High Peak, Derbyshire, SK22 4HJ Tel: (01663) 745976 Fax: (01663) 742788 E-mail: sales@flowguard.com

THERMAL FLUID HEATERS

Babcock Wanson UK Ltd, 7 Elstree Way, Borehamwood, Hertfordshire, WD6 1SA Tel: (020) 8953 7111 Fax: (020) 8207 5177 E-mail:

Faudler Balfour, P O Box 15, Leven, Fife, KY8 4RW Tel: (01333) 423020 Fax: (01333) 427432 E-mail: mailus@pfaudlerbalfour.co.uk

TP Fay Ltd, 57 Admin Road, Knowsley Industrial Park, Liverpool, L33 7TX Tel: (0870) 3505058 Fax: (0870) 3505059 E-mail: sales@tpfay.co.uk

THERMAL IMAGE LABELS

Labels & Data Systems (UK) Ltd, 9 Cresswell Close, Pinchbeck, Spalding, Lincolnshire, PE11 3TY Tel: 0161-929 8828 Fax: 0161-929 8518 E-mail: labelsdata@aol.com

Tormax UK Ltd, Tormax HS Unit 21 Mole Bus Park, Randalls Road, Leatherhead, Surrey, KT22 7BD Tel: (01372) 377711 Fax: (01372) 378044 E-mail: tormax@langleysystems.co.uk

THERMAL IMAGING

Epsilon Test Services Ltd, Epsilon House, The Square, Gloucester Business Park, Gloucester, GL3 4AD Tel: (0845) 2336600 Fax: (0845) 2336633 E-mail: enquiries@epsilontsl.co.uk

Thermaton Imaging (Thermal Imaging Services), 59 Queens Avenue, Meols, Wirral, Merseyside, CH47 0LS Tel: 0151-632 5192 Fax: 0151-632 5192 E-mail: povall@ic24.net

Thermoteknix Systems Ltd, Teknix House, 2 Pembroke Avenue, Waterbeach, Cambridge, CB5 9QR Tel: (01223) 204000 Fax: (01223) 204010 E-mail: sales@thermoteknix.co.uk

THERMAL IMAGING CONDITION MONITORING

Acumon Services UK, 27 The Oaks, Chorley, Lancashire, PR7 3QT Tel: (01257) 241624 Fax: (01257) 241624 E-mail: info@acmon.co.uk

Express Instrument Hire Ltd, Express House, Church Road, Tarleton, Preston, PR4 6UP Tel: (01772) 815600 Fax: (01772) 815937 E-mail: sales@expresshire.net

I R T Surveys Ltd, Unit D, Software Media Centre, Prospect House, Technology Park, Dundee, DD2 1TY Tel: (01382) 598510 Fax: (01382) 598533 E-mail: info@irtsurveys.co.uk

K C M Services Ltd, Mill View, Daisy Hill, Burstwick, Hull, HU12 9HE Tel: (01482) 227953 Fax: (08456) 445547 E-mail: info@kcmservices.com

THERMAL IMAGING ENERGY CONSERVATION SERVICES

▶ Stroma, Stroma Unit 4, Pioneer Way, Pioneer Business Park, Wakefield, West Yorkshire, WF10 5QU Tel: 0845 6211111 Fax: 0845 6211112 E-mail: info@stroma.com

Thermaton Imaging (Thermal Imaging Services), 59 Queens Avenue, Meols, Wirral, Merseyside, CH47 0LS Tel: 0151-632 5192 Fax: 0151-632 5192 E-mail: povall@ic24.net

THERMAL IMAGING EQUIPMENT

Goratec UK Ltd, 47 Cavendish Road, Eccles, Manchester, M30 9EE Tel: 0161-788 9929 Fax: 0161-788 9930

I R T Surveys Ltd, Unit D, Software Media Centre, Prospect House, Technology Park, Dundee, DD2 1TY Tel: (01382) 598510 Fax: (01382) 598533 E-mail: info@irtsurveys.co.uk

THERMAL IMAGING EQUIPMENT HIRE

Express Instrument Hire Ltd, Express House, Church Road, Tarleton, Preston, PR4 6UP Tel: (01772) 815600 Fax: (01772) 815937 E-mail: sales@expresshire.net

THERMAL IMAGING SENSORS

▶ Electcetra Ltd, 25 The Walk, Kilburn, Belper, Derbyshire, DE56 0PP Tel: (01332) 881320 E-mail: info@electcetra.com

THERMAL INDUSTRIAL INSULATION CONTRACTORS

A B C Insulation Co. Ltd, Alexandra Docks, Newport, Gwent, NP20 2NP Tel: (01633) 211473 Fax: (01633) 843212

A R G Europe Ltd, Unit 2, 58A Alexandra Road, Ponders End, Enfield, Middlesex, EN3 7EH Tel: (020) 8804 8008 Fax: (020) 8805 7600 E-mail: argeurope@aol.com

Aardvark Transatlantic Ltd, 106 New Road, Ascot, Berkshire, SL5 8QH Tel: (01344) 882314 Fax: (01344) 884506 E-mail: atlmonoglass@aol.com

Aerostill Insulation Co. Ltd, Gainsborough Road, London, E11 1HT Tel: (020) 8539 7587 Fax: (020) 8556 9140 E-mail: info@aerostill.co.uk

John Atkinson Interiors Ltd, Deanfield Mill, Asquith Avenue, Morley, Leeds, LS27 9QT Tel: 0113-253 5661 Fax: 0113-238 0323 E-mail: atkinsoninteriors@btopenworld.com

Baring Insulation Ltd, Unit A, 223A Hatfield Road, St. Albans, Hertfordshire, AL1 4TB Tel: (01727) 860004 Fax: (01727) 847253 E-mail: admin@baringinsulation.co.uk

Beacon Insulation Supplies Ltd, Bleak Hall Farm, Bleak Lane, Lathom, Ormskirk, Lancashire, L40 4BP Tel: (01704) 897878 Fax: (01704) 897879

Burton Insulations Ltd, Crown Industrial Estate, Anglesey Road, Burton-On-Trent, Staffordshire, DE14 3NX Tel: (01283) 536190 Fax: (01283) 540693

▶ C & D Industrial Services Ltd, 63 Portland Street, Mansfield Woodhouse, Mansfield, Nottinghamshire, NG19 8BE Tel: (01623) 781200 Fax: (01623) 420496

C G B Humbertherm Ltd, Middleplatt Road, Immingham, South Humberside, DN40 1AH Tel: (01469) 572726 Fax: (01469) 571728 E-mail: sales@cgbhumbertherm.com

Cape Industrial Services Ltd, Kirkton Drive, Dyce, Aberdeen, AB21 0BG Tel: (01224) 215800 Fax: (01224) 722879 E-mail: sales@capeindustrialservices.co.uk

CCF, Newark Road, Peterborough, PE1 5YX Tel: (01733) 551333 Fax: (01733) 311921

City Insulation Contractors Ltd, City House, Horspath Industrial Estate, Pony Road, Cowley, Oxford, OX4 2RD Tel: (01865) 715173 Fax: (01865) 770547 E-mail: info@cityins.co.uk

Cooks Insulations, Holly Cottage, 74 New Road, Tadley, Hampshire, RG26 3AN Tel: (07711) 241365 Fax: 0118-981 2552

Cristal Insulations Ltd, 48 Goodmayes Road, Ilford, Essex, IG3 9UR Tel: (020) 8597 0442 Fax: (020) 8597 0713

D B Industrial Services Ltd, Lyn Castle Way, Appleton, Warrington, WA4 4ST Tel: (01606) 597151 Fax: (01606) 597152 E-mail: sales@dbigroup.co.uk

D K & K Ltd, Unit 29, 64 Hoyland Road, Sheffield, S3 8AB Tel: 0114-276 9766 Fax: 0114-276 9755

Durable Contracts Ltd, Durable House, Crabtree Manorway, Belvedere, Kent, DA17 6AB Tel: (020) 8311 1211 Fax: (020) 8310 7893 E-mail: sales@durable-online.com

Dyson Insulations Ltd, Unit 16H, Sollingsby Park, Gateshead, Tyne & Wear, NE10 8YF Tel: 0191-416 5969 Fax: 0191-417 3817

Electrothermal Ltd, North Norfolk Ho, Pitmedden Road, Dyce, Aberdeen, AB21 0DP Tel: (01224) 722888 Fax: (01224) 772103 E-mail: eric.florence@rigblast.com

Gill Insulation Eastern Ltd, 39 Boss Hall Road, Ipswich, IP1 5BN Tel: (01473) 462822 Fax: (01473) 241153 E-mail: jon@gilleastern.co.uk

Gill Insulations Ltd, 5 33 Ebury Road, Nottingham, NG5 1BB Tel: 0115-962 6043 Fax: 0115-969 1688E-mail: sales@gillins.com

Haylock & Rolph, Unit 9 Hall Barn Road Industrial Estate, Hall Barn Road, Isleham, Ely, Cambridgeshire, CB7 5RJ Tel: (01638) 781715 Fax: (01638) 781716 E-mail: enquiries@haylockandrolph.co.uk

Hertel Services, Sotherby Road, Skippers Lane Idustrial Estate, Middlesbrough, Cleveland, TS6 6LP Tel: (01642) 469532 Fax: (01642) 445614 E-mail: info@hertel.co.uk

Highstone Insulation Co. Ltd, 6 Hasluck Gardens, New Barnet, Barnet, Hertfordshire, EN5 1HT Tel: (020) 8449 4273 Fax: (020) 8449 4273

Icopal, Barton Dock Road, Stretford, Manchester, M32 0YL Tel: 0161-865 4444 Fax: 0161-864 1178 E-mail: marketing.uk@icopal.com

Industrial Insulation Services, Unit 2 Osborne Mill, Osborne Street, Oldham, OL9 6QQ Tel: 0161-626 0973 Fax: 0161-627 4846

Instafoam & Fibre Ltd, Insta House, Ivanhoe Road, Hogwood Business Park, Wokingham, Berkshire, RG40 4PZ Tel: 0118-932 8811 Fax: 0118-932 8314 E-mail: info@instagroup.co.uk

Ipswich Insulation Ltd, Station House, Station Road, Bentley, Ipswich, IP9 2DB Tel: (01473) 327288 Fax: (01473) 327288

J Cullen Thermals Ltd, 202 Deykin Avenue, Birmingham, B6 7BH Tel: 0121-327 5260 Fax: 0121-327 1124 E-mail: info@jcollenthermals.com

Johnson's Insulation Supplies Ltd, 16 Victoria Way, Burgess Hill, West Sussex, RH15 9NF Tel: (01444) 243133 Fax: (01444) 871053

Kershaw Insulation Ltd, Willowcroft Works, Broad Lane, Cottenham, Cambridge, CB4 8SW Tel: (01954) 250155 Fax: (01954) 251628 E-mail: sales.office@kershaw-insulation.co.uk

Knight Thermal Insulation, 54 Factory Estate, College Road, Perry Barr, Birmingham, B44 8BS Tel: 0121-356 3980 Fax: 0121-356 1688

L Wynne & Co Manchester Ltd, Unit A7 The Dresser Centre, Whitworth Street, Openshaw, Manchester, M11 2NE Tel: 0161-223 2640 Fax: 0161-231 1367

Leighton Carter Insulation Co. Ltd, 25 Argyle Street, Newport, Gwent, NP20 5NE Tel: (01633) 856624 Fax: (01633) 856178

Mcgill Services Ltd, Vinci House Macklin Avenue, Cowpen Lane Industrial Estate, Billingham, Cleveland, TS23 4HF Tel: (01642) 379400 Fax: (01642) 379429 E-mail: mcgill@mcgillservices.co.uk

Marcalex Insulation Services, Hampstead Mill, Lake Street, Great Moor, Stockport, Cheshire, SK2 7NU Tel: 0161-456 7455 Fax: 0161-483 2529 E-mail: sales@marcalexservices.co.uk

Miller Pattison Ltd, 3 Eldon Way, Biggleswade, Bedfordshire, SG18 8NH Tel: (01767) 314444 Fax: (01767) 317601 E-mail: biggleswade@miller-patterson.co.uk

▶ Nevron Eurotherm Insulation Services Ltd, Unit 16, Valley Road Business Park, Birkenhead, Merseyside, CH41 7EL Tel: 0151-652 6213 Fax: 0151-652 6213 E-mail: info@nevroninsulation.co.uk

Newmarket Insulation Contracts, Exchange House, Wash Road, Wickhambrook, Newmarket, Suffolk, CB8 8XQ Tel: (01440) 820612 Fax: (01440) 820628 E-mail: newmarktinscon@hotmail.com

North Western Insulations Ltd, Redwither Road, Wrexham Industrial Estate, Wrexham, Clwyd, LL13 9RD Tel: (01978) 661708 Fax: (01978) 661570

Pinnacle Insulation Ltd, Sandgate Industrial Estate, Hartlepool, Cleveland, TS25 1TZ Tel: (01429) 233828 Fax: (01429) 861047 E-mail: mark@pinnacle-aic.com

Powertherm Contracts Insulation Ltd, C Crown Works, Rotherham Road, Beighton, Sheffield, S20 1AH Tel: 0114-248 9119 Fax: 0114-288 9882 E-mail: powertherm@aol.com

Preform Insulations Ltd, Unit 29 & 30 Enterprise Works, 13 & 14 Bergen Way, North Lynn Industrial Estate, King's Lynn, Norfolk, PE30 2JG Tel: (01553) 776382 Fax: (01603) 881254 E-mail: sales@preforminsulations.co.uk

R H Insulation Services Ltd, Unit 14, Wingate Road, Gosport, Hampshire, PO12 4DR Tel: (023) 9250 1141 Fax: (023) 9251 1409

Salamis International Ltd, 3 Greenhole Place, Bridge of Don Industrial Estat, Aberdeen, AB23 8EU Tel: (01224) 246001 Fax: (01224) 246100

Sandwell Insulation Services Ltd, Unit 1 Hale Trading Estate, Lower Church Lane, Tipton, West Midlands, DY4 7PJ Tel: 0121-520 3334 Fax: 0121-520 3334 E-mail: janxxx@ukonline.co.uk

Severn Insulation Co. Ltd, Somerton Works, Lloyd Street, Newport, Gwent, NP19 0JN Tel: (01633) 274239 Fax: (01633) 275252 E-mail: sales@severninsulation.co.uk

Sheffield Insulations Ltd, 303-305 Vale Road, Tonbridge, Kent, TN9 1TZ Tel: (01732) 370500 Fax: (01732) 370530

Southern Insulations, 2 Grove Rd, Strood, Rochester, Kent, ME2 4BY Tel: (01634) 291100 Fax: (01634) 290680

Stewart Energy Insulation Ltd, Connect House, 21 Willow Lane, Mitcham, Surrey, CR4 4NA Tel: (020) 8648 6601 Fax: (020) 8648 6602 E-mail: info@stewart-energy.com

T H Holroyd Ltd, Unit 15, Phoebe Lane Mills, Halifax, West Yorkshire, HX3 9EX Tel: (01422) 354793 Fax: (01422) 354255

▶ T I S Insulations, 9 The Pines, Kingswood, Hull, HU7 3GT Tel: (01482) 829888 Fax: (07970) 318994 E-mail: pete@tisinsulation.com

Tees Insulation Ltd, 138 Lynn Street, Hartlepool, Cleveland, TS24 7LX Tel: (01429) 265433 Fax: (01429) 863149 E-mail: info@teesgroup.com

Websters Insulation Ltd, Crowtree Farm, Crowtree Bank, Thorne Levels, Doncaster, South Yorkshire, DN8 5TF Tel: (01405) 812682 Fax: (01405) 817201 E-mail: info@webstersinsulation.com

Weld Lag (Preston) Ltd, Unit 11 Oysten Mill, Strand Road, Preston, PR1 8UR Tel: (01772) 768858 Fax: (01772) 768865 E-mail: enquiries@weldlag.co.uk

Western Industrial Insulation, Blakeney Business Park, High Street, Blakeney, Gloucestershire, GL15 4EB Tel: (01594) 517238 Fax: (01594) 516836

Yorkshire Sheeting & Insulation Services Ltd, Green Lane Trading Estate, Clifton, York, YO30 5PY Tel: (01904) 695800 Fax: (01904) 695815

THERMAL INSULATING ACCESSORIES OR PRODUCTS

Archbond Ltd, Mill Hill Factory, Desford Road, Enderby, Leicester, LE19 4AD Tel: 0116-284 1222 Fax: 0116-284 9954 E-mail: lizhayes@archbond.co.uk

Armstrong UK Investments, Armstrong House, 38 Market Square, Uxbridge, Middlesex, UB8 1NG Tel: (01895) 251122 Fax: (01895) 231571

Mothercare plc, 168 Commercial Street, Newport, Gwent, NP20 1JN Tel: (01633) 259938

Plysolene Ltd, Unit 21 Star Road Trading Estate, Star Road, Partridge Green, Horsham, West Sussex, RH13 8RA Tel: (01403) 713555 Fax: (01403) 713666 E-mail: info@wattsgroup.co.uk

Sas Thermal Insulation Service, Greenhill Mills, Grange Road, Batley, West Yorkshire, WF17 6LH Tel: (01924) 443999 Fax: (01924) 478628

THERMAL INSULATING MATERIAL PRODUCTION MACHINERY OR EQUIPMENT

CGB Engineering Services Ltd, 2 Britannia House, Gorton Road, Manchester, M11 2DA Tel: 0161-231 7347 Fax: 0161-231 7077 E-mail: cgbservices@aol.com

Insulation Machine Services, Coalbrookdale Road, Clayhill Light Industrial Park, Neston, CH64 3UG Tel: 0151-336 7242 Fax: 0151-336 2840 E-mail: timco@imsservices.freeserve.co.uk

Langtec Ltd, 1 Calder Court, Altham, Accrington, Lancashire, BB5 5YB Tel: (01282) 772544 Fax: (01282) 772740 E-mail: info@langtec.co.uk

THERMAL INSULATING MATERIALS

Brightcross Insulation Ltd, Shaftesbury Street, Derby, DE23 8XA Tel: (01332) 331808 Fax: (01332) 292697 E-mail: sales@brightcross.co.uk

Cheshire Ribbon Manufacturing Co., Kingston Mills, Manchester Road, Hyde, Cheshire, SK14 2BZ Tel: 0161-368 2048 Fax: 0161-367 8193 E-mail: sales@cheshirerib.co.uk

Chomerics, Unit 6 Century Point, Cressex Business Park, High Wycombe, Buckinghamshire, HP12 3SL Tel: (01628) 404000 Fax: (01628) 404091 E-mail: chomerics_europe@parker.com

Encon, 1 Rippleside Commercial Estate, Ripple Road, Barking, Essex, IG11 0RJ Tel: (020) 8595 2121 Fax: (020) 8595 9003 E-mail: info@encon.co.uk

Encon Ltd, Langage Science Park, Western Wood Way, Plympton, Plymouth, PL7 5BG Tel: (01752) 333720 Fax: (01752) 348938

Encon Insulation Ltd, Unit F1-F2, St. Michaels Close, Aylesford, Kent, ME20 7BU Tel: (01622) 713400 Fax: (01622) 713403 E-mail: maidstone@encon.co.uk

Encon Insulation Ltd, Unit 2 Elmbank, Channel Commercial Park, Queens Road, Belfast, BT3 9DT Tel: (028) 9045 4646 Fax: (028) 9045 4656 E-mail: t.patterson@encon.co.uk

Encon Insulation Ltd, 3-4 Tamebridge Industrial Estate, Aldridge Road, Perry Barr, Birmingham, B42 2TX Tel: 0121-356 0606 Fax: 0121-356 4828

Encon Insulation Ltd, 23 Nettlefold Road, Cardiff, CF24 5JQ Tel: (029) 2089 5040 Fax: (029) 2089 5044

Encon Insulation Ltd, Unit 500, Fareham Reach, 166 Fareham Road, Gosport, Hampshire, PO13 0FP Tel: (01329) 230555 Fax: (01329) 230615 E-mail: fareham@encon.co.uk

Encon Insulation Ltd, Unit 9-10, Gelderd Road, Morley, Leeds, LS27 7JN Tel: 0113-289 7666 Fax: 0113-289 7555 E-mail: leeds@encon.co.uk

THERMAL INSULATING MATERIALS
– *continued*

Encon Insulation Ltd, Unit E2, High Flatworth, Tyne Tunnel Trading Estate, Northshields, Newcastle Upon Tyne, NE29 7UZ Tel: 0191-293 1090 Fax: 0191-293 1099
Encon Insulation Ltd, Brunswick House, Deaghton Close, Wetherby, West Yorkshire, LS22 7GZ Tel: (01937) 524200 Fax: (01937) 524222
Encon Insulation Ltd, Unit 3, Industrial Estate, Stanton Harcourt, Witney, Oxfordshire, OX29 5UX Tel: (01865) 734500 Fax: (01865) 734518
Encon Insulation Materials, Unit 17-19, Bloomsgrove Industrial Estate, Nottingham, NG7 3JB Tel: 0115-978 0040 Fax: 0115-942 0264
Encon Insulation Northampton, 21 Saddleback Road, Westgate Industrial Estate, Northampton, NN5 5HL Tel: (01604) 580580 Fax: (01604) 580585 E-mail: info@encon.co.uk
Encon Insulation Scotland, 80 Cambuslang Road, Cambuslang, Clydesmill Industrial Estate, Glasgow, G32 8NB Tel: 0141-641 0011 Fax: 0141-641 5170
Encon Insulations, Unit 13 Studlands Park Industrial Estate, Newmarket, Suffolk, CB8 7AU Tel: (01638) 667292 Fax: (01638) 664081 E-mail: northampton@encon.co.uk
Encon Manchester Ltd, Chaddock Lane, Worsley, Manchester, M28 1DR Tel: 0161-703 7400 Fax: 0161-703 7411 E-mail: manchester@encon.co.uk
I S O Covers Ltd, Trent Valley Industrial Estate, Station Road, Rugeley, Staffordshire, WS15 2HQ Tel: (01889) 574333 Fax: (01889) 574111 E-mail: info@isocovers.com
Edward Keirby & Co. Ltd, Vine Works, Chichester Street, Rochdale, Lancashire, OL16 2BG Tel: (01706) 645330 Fax: (01706) 352882 E-mail: info@edwardkeirby.co.uk
Kingspan Industrial Insulation Ltd, PO Box 3, Glossop, Derbyshire, SK13 8LE Tel: (0870) 8508555 Fax: (0870) 8508444 E-mail: enquires.uk@insulation.kingspan.com
Panelbond Ltd, 1 King Edward Street, Grimsby, South Humberside, DN31 3JU Tel: (01472) 250130 Fax: (01472) 250784 E-mail: roybarber@panelbond.com
Permarock Products Ltd, Jubilee Drive, Loughborough, Leicestershire, LE11 5TW Tel: (01509) 262924 Fax: (01509) 230063 E-mail: sales@permarock.com
Pyrotek Engineering Materials Ltd, Garamonde Drive, Wymbush, Milton Keynes, MK8 8LN Tel: (01908) 561155 Fax: (01908) 560473 E-mail: petwin@pyrotek-inc.com
Recticel Insulation, Mitchell Hay Mills, College Road, Rochdale, Lancashire, OL12 6AE Tel: (01706) 715500 Fax: (01706) 715511
Rockwool Rockpanel B V, Pencoed, Bridgend, Mid Glamorgan, CF35 6NY Tel: (01656) 862621 Fax: (01656) 862302 E-mail: info@rockwool.co.uk
Weald Polyproducts Ltd, Unit 1, Heron Bussiness Park, White Field Avenue, Sundon Park, Luton, LU3 3BB Tel: (01582) 508517 Fax: (01582) 570188 E-mail: sales.wheels@btconnect.com
Yorkshire Building Services, Craggs Industrial Park, Morven Street, Creswell, Worksop, Nottinghamshire, S80 4AJ Tel: (01909) 721662 Fax: (01909) 721442 E-mail: sales@ybsinsulation.com

THERMAL INSULATION INFORMATION

▶ Just Insulation, 27 Massetts Road, Horley, Surrey, RH6 7DQ Tel: (0845) 2606232 Fax: (0845) 2606242 E-mail: purchases@just-insulation.com

THERMAL INSULATION TEST EQUIPMENT

Gearing Scientific Ltd, 1 Ashwell Street Ashwell, Baldock, Hertfordshire, SG7 5QF Tel: (01462) 742007 Fax: (01462) 742565 E-mail: gearingsci@yahoo.com

THERMAL INSULATION WINDOWS

▶ A J Framemaker, 3 Alrewas Road, Kings Bromley, Burton-on-Trent, Staffordshire, DE13 7HW Tel: (01543) 473791 Fax: (01543) 473932 E-mail: sales@ajframemaker.co.uk

THERMAL MANAGEMENT SYSTEMS

Ebm-Papst, The Barn, Sheepdown, East Ilsley, Newbury, Berkshire, RG20 7ND Tel: (0870) 7665170 Fax: (08707) 665180 E-mail: aanddsales@uk.ebmpapst.com
Environmental Process Systems Ltd, 32 Mere View Industrial Estate, Yaxley, Peterborough, PE7 3HS Tel: (01733) 243400 Fax: (01733) 243344 E-mail: sales@epsltd.co.uk

THERMAL PRINTING

Labelprint Identification Cards, 73 Imperial Drive, Harrow, Middlesex, HA2 7DU Tel: (020) 8424 9413 Fax: (020) 8424 9413

THERMAL PRINTING EQUIPMENT

Original Marketing, 4 Prospect Street, Bridlington, North Humberside, YO15 2AL Tel: (01262) 675916 Fax: (01262) 675916 E-mail: originalmarketing@ukonline.co.uk

THERMAL PROCESS OPTIMISATION SYSTEMS

Cal Gavin Ltd, 1 Station Road, Alcester, Warwickshire, B49 5ET Tel: (01789) 400401 Fax: (01789) 400411 E-mail: info@calgavin.co.uk

THERMAL PROCESS PLANT ENGINEERS, INSTALLATION OR SERVICE

J & B Insulations Ltd, Unit 1, Stanley St, Burton-on-Trent, Staffordshire, DE14 1DY Tel: (01283) 531287 Fax: (01283) 511953

THERMAL PROFILING EQUIPMENT

Link Hamson Ltd, 6 York Way, Lancaster Road, Cressex Business Park, High Wycombe, Buckinghamshire, HP12 3PY Tel: (01494) 439786 Fax: (01494) 526222 E-mail: sales@linkhamson.com

THERMAL PROTECTIVE CLOTHING

Penrith Survival Equipment, Sandale, Coupland Beck, Appleby-in-Westmorland, Cumbria, CA16 6LN Tel: (01768) 351666 Fax: (01768) 353666 E-mail: hg@survival.u-net.com

THERMAL SPRAYING

Silvey Engineering Ltd, Redstones, Haywicks Lane, Hardwick, Gloucester, GL2 3QE Tel: (01452) 720439

THERMAL STRUCTURAL CLADDING CONTRACTORS

Telling Lime Products, Primrose Avenue, Wolverhampton, WV10 8AW Tel: (01902) 789777 Fax: (01902) 398777 E-mail: m.wood@telling.co.uk

THERMAL STRUCTURAL INSULATION CONTRACTORS

Aerostill Insulation Co. Ltd, Gainsborough Road, London, E11 1HT Tel: (020) 8539 7587 Fax: (020) 8556 9140 E-mail: info@aerostill.co.uk
Baring Insulation Ltd, Unit A, 223A Hatfield Road, St. Albans, Hertfordshire, AL1 4TB Tel: (01727) 860004 Fax: (01727) 847253 E-mail: admin@baringinsulation.co.uk
Burton Insulations Ltd, Crown Industrial Estate, Anglesey Road, Burton-On-Trent, Staffordshire, DE14 3NX Tel: (01283) 536190 Fax: (01283) 540693
Domestic & General Insulation Ltd, 9 Bridges Business Park, Bridge Road, Horsehay, Telford, Shropshire, TF4 3EE Tel: (01952) 507777 Fax: (01952) 501111 E-mail: office@dgitelford.co.uk
Durable Contracts Ltd, Durable House, Crabtree Manorway, Belvedere, Kent, DA17 6AB Tel: (020) 8311 1211 Fax: (020) 8310 7893 E-mail: sales@durable-online.com
Highstone Insulation Co. Ltd, 6 Hasluck Gardens, New Barnet, Barnet, Hertfordshire, EN5 1HT Tel: (020) 8449 4273 Fax: (020) 8449 4273
J E D Insulations Ltd, 529 Kingston Road, Ewell, Epsom, Surrey, KT19 0DL Tel: (020) 8661 1050 Fax: (020) 8661 1052 E-mail: jedinsulations@bt.com
J & J Insulations Ltd, 27a New Road, Croxley Green, Rickmansworth, Hertfordshire, WD3 3EJ Tel: (01923) 897161 Fax: (01923) 897161 E-mail: jj.insulations@virgin.net
Knight Thermal Insulation, 54 Factory Estate, College Road, Perry Barr, Birmingham, B44 8BS Tel: 0121-356 3980 Fax: 0121-356 1688
Malrod Insulations Ltd, Glebe Mill, Library Street, Westhoughton, Bolton, BL5 3AU Tel: (01942) 811591 Fax: (01942) 814411 E-mail: enquiries@malrod.co.uk
Miller Pattison Ltd, 3 Eldon Way, Biggleswade, Bedfordshire, SG18 8NH Tel: (01767) 314444 Fax: (01767) 317601 E-mail: biggleswade@miller-patterson.co.uk
Nottingham Suspended Ceilings Ltd, Wright Street, Netherfield, Nottingham, NG4 2PG Tel: 0115-987 9880 Fax: 0115-940 0086 E-mail: info@nsceilings.co.uk
Perkins Contracts Ltd, Knights Court, South Chailey, Lewes, East Sussex, BN8 4QF Tel: (01273) 401401 Fax: (01273) 401400 E-mail: info@perkinscontracts.co.uk
R L Insulations, 4 Sentinel Works, Northgate Avenue, Bury St. Edmunds, Suffolk, IP32 6AZ Tel: (01284) 760937 Fax: (01284) 755031 E-mail: info@rlinsulation.fsnet.co.uk
S L (Thermal Insulation) Contracts & Supplies Co. Ltd, Unit 16 Blue Chalet Industrial Park, London Road, West Kingsdown, Sevenoaks, Kent, TN15 6BT Tel: (01474) 854465 Fax: (01474) 854393 E-mail: les@slcontracts.com
Sandwell Insulation Services Ltd, Unit 1 Hale Trading Estate, Lower Church Lane, Tipton, West Midlands, DY4 7PJ Tel: 0121-520 3334 Fax: 0121-520 3334 E-mail: janxxx@ukonline.co.uk
Sprayseal Contracts Ltd, Bollin House, Blakeley Lane, Mobberley, Knutsford, Cheshire, WA16 7LX Tel: (01565) 872303 Fax: (01565) 872599 E-mail: sales@sprayseal.co.uk
Star Installation Ltd, Unit B Progress Business Centre, Cannock, Staffordshire, WS11 0JR Tel: (01543) 574146 Fax: (01543) 469312

THERMAL TRANSFER LABELS

Anglo Scottish Packaging, Montrose Avenue, Hillington Industrial Estate, Glasgow, G52 4LA Tel: 0141-882 5151 Fax: 0141-882 5500 E-mail: sales@angloscottish.net
Excel Labels Ltd, 9 Crown Road, Kings Norton Business Centre, Birmingham, B30 3HY Tel: 0121-486 3300 Fax: 0121-486 3330 E-mail: enquiries@excellabels.co.uk
S L Conyers & Son Ltd, Hawthorns Industrial Estate, Middlemore Road, Handsworth, Birmingham, B21 0BH Tel: 0121-551 2875 Fax: 0121-554 5267 E-mail: webmaster@conyers-labels.com
Secura Labels Ltd, Unit L2 Westminster Industrial Estate, Measham, Swadlincote, Derbyshire, DE12 7DS Tel: (01530) 515170 Fax: (01530) 515171 E-mail: sales@securalabels.co.uk
Touch Print Ltd, 49 Maple Avenue, Bulwark, Chepstow, Gwent, NP16 5RG Tel: (01291) 621401 Fax: (01291) 621403 E-mail: sales@touchprint.co.uk

THERMAL TRANSFER RIBBONS

▶ Codepack Solutions Ltd, Woodhorn Lane, Oving, Chichester, West Sussex, PO20 2BX Tel: (01243) 792445 Fax: (01243) 792108 E-mail: sales@codepack.co.uk
GWR Systems, 258 Upper Shoreham Road, Shoreham-by-Sea, West Sussex, BN43 6BF Tel: (01273) 889333 Fax: (01273) 889556 E-mail: gwrsys@aol.com
Typerite Ltd, Upper Dromore Road, Warrenpoint, Newry, County Down, BT34 3PN Tel: (028) 4177 2111 Fax: (028) 4175 2022 E-mail: info@typerite.com

THERMISTOR MANUFRS

Crossland Components Ltd, Unit L Tanfield Lea Industrial Estate South, Tanfield Lea, Stanley, County Durham, DH9 9XA Tel: (01207) 230269 Fax: (01207) 283849 E-mail: info@crossland.co.uk

THERMOCOUPLE ASSEMBLIES

Ionic Instruments Ltd, Henfield Road, Small Dole, Henfield, West Sussex, BN5 9XE Tel: (01273) 493522 Fax: (01273) 493630 E-mail:
Universal Thermosensors Ltd, Units 10-11 Castle Road Technical Centre, Castle Road, Murston, Sittingbourne, Kent, ME10 3RG Tel: (01795) 470924 Fax: (01795) 476733 E-mail: sales@universal-thermosensors.co.uk

THERMOCOUPLE CABLES

▶ ITH Ltd, Unit 12, Prince Consort Road Industrial Estate, Hebburn, Tyne & Wear, NE31 1EH Tel: 0191-483 2020 Fax: 0191-483 2121 E-mail: sales@ithltd.co.uk

THERMOCOUPLE COMPENSATING CABLES

Heatsense Cables Ltd, 3 Astra Centre, Royle Barn Road, Rochdale, Lancashire, OL11 3DT Tel: (01706) 355330 Fax: (01706) 657691 E-mail: sales@heatsensecables.co.uk
T C Ltd, PO Box 130, Uxbridge, Middlesex, UB8 2YS Tel: (01895) 252222 Fax: (01895) 273540 E-mail: sales@tc.co.uk
Thermo Devices Ltd, Floats Road, Roundthorn Industrial Estate, Manchester, M23 9NF Tel: 0161-286 5100 Fax: 0161-286 5093 E-mail: sales@tdl.endress.com

THERMOCOUPLE CONNECTORS

Ionic Instruments Ltd, Henfield Road, Small Dole, Henfield, West Sussex, BN5 9XE Tel: (01273) 493522 Fax: (01273) 493630 E-mail:

THERMOCOUPLE MANUFRS

Caltec Electronic Equipment, L Quarry Road, Newhaven, East Sussex, BN9 9DG Tel: (01273) 517516 Fax: (01273) 517278
Carlingwood Ltd, 1 Bridge Green, Prestbury, Macclesfield, Cheshire, SK10 4HR Tel: (01625) 828342 Fax: (01625) 827471
Consolidated Ceramic Products, Rotherham Close, Norwood Industrial Estate, Killamarsh, Sheffield, S21 2JU Tel: 0114-247 8251 Fax: 0114-247 8253 E-mail: ccp.uk@btinternet.com
Cozier's Ltd, Littlebrook, Llangolman, Clynderwen, Dyfed, SA66 7XL Tel: (01437) 532660 Fax: (01437) 532670 E-mail: sales@coziers-ltd.co.uk
Electroserv International, 30a Townley Street, Macclesfield, Cheshire, SK11 6HZ Tel: (01625) 615626 Fax: (01625) 617559
Electroserv (T C & S) Ltd, PO Box 163, Macclesfield, Cheshire, SK11 6JY Tel: (01625) 618526 Fax: (01625) 500746 E-mail: dh@electroserv.co.uk
Minco Sampling-Techniques (UK) Ltd, Tofts Farm Industrial Estate, Brenda Road, Hartlepool, Cleveland, TS25 2BS Tel: (01429) 273252 Fax: (01429) 232611 E-mail: enquiries@mincouk.com
Seagas Industries Ltd, 152 Abbey Lane, Leicester, LE4 0DA Tel: 0116-266 9988 Fax: 0116-268 2557E-mail: sales@seagas.net
Sterling Sensors Ltd, Fitmec Works Hawksley Street, Oldham, OL8 4PQ Tel: 0161-627 0507 Fax: 0161-627 0507 E-mail: sales@sterlingsensors.co.uk
Thermal Detection Ltd, Unit 6 Orde Wingate Way, Stockton-on-Tees, Cleveland, TS19 0GA Tel: (01642) 602878 Fax: (01642) 618307 E-mail: tdl@thermal-detection.com
Thermo Devices Ltd, Floats Road, Roundthorn Industrial Estate, Manchester, M23 9NF Tel: 0161-286 5100 Fax: 0161-286 5093 E-mail: sales@tdl.endress.com
Universal Thermosensors Ltd, Units 10-11 Castle Road Technical Centre, Castle Road, Murston, Sittingbourne, Kent, ME10 3RG Tel: (01795) 470924 Fax: (01795) 476733 E-mail: sales@universal-thermosensors.co.uk
West Midlands Thermocouples, Unit 203 Telsen Industrial Centre, Thomas Street, Birmingham, B6 4TN Tel: 0121-359 0535 Fax: 0121-359 4005

THERMOELECTRIC COOLING DEVICES

Marlow Industries Europe, Aberdeen House, South Road, Haywards Heath, West Sussex, RH16 4NG Tel: (01444) 443404 Fax: (01444) 443334E-mail: support@marlow-europe.co.uk

THERMOFORMED PLASTIC PACKAGING

Daventry Thermoforming UK Ltd, West March Industrial Estate, West March, Daventry, Northamptonshire, NN11 4SA Tel: (01327) 878273 Fax: (01327) 300424 E-mail: diane@davthermoforming.demon.co.uk
Leeways Packaging Services Ltd, Lobstock, Churcham, Gloucester, GL2 8AN Tel: (01452) 750487 Fax: (01452) 750653 E-mail: info@leeways.co.uk
Mongoose Plastics Ltd, 57-58 Nasmyth Road, Glenrothes, Fife, KY6 2SD Tel: (01592) 774800 Fax: (01592) 775032 E-mail: george@mongoose-plastics.co.uk
Nelipak Thermoforming, PO Box 28, Bristol, BS31 1XT Tel: 0117-986 7163 Fax: 0117-986 7197
Nicholas Packaging Ltd, Ham Lane, Kingswinford, West Midlands, DY6 7JJ Tel: (01384) 400500 Fax: (01384) 270943 E-mail: sales@nicholaspackaging.com

THERMOFORMED PLASTIC PRODUCTS

Big Bear Plastic Products Ltd, Fantastic Works, Wassage Way, Hampton Lovett, Droitwich, Worcestershire, WR9 0NX Tel: (01905) 792500 Fax: (01905) 792501 E-mail: louises@big-bear.co.uk
Polyfab & Formings Ltd, Hindley Green Business Park Leigh Road, Hindley, Wigan, Lancashire, WN2 3LL Tel: (01942) 523617 Fax: (01942) 523533 E-mail: sales@polyfab.co.uk
Vacuum Formers Ltd, Brunswick Mill, Pickford Street, Macclesfield, Cheshire, SK11 6JN Tel: (01625) 428389 Fax: (01625) 619808 E-mail: info@vacuumformers.co.uk
Voestalpine Polynorm Plastics Ltd, PO Box 9, St. Helens, Merseyside, WA10 6FE Tel: (01744) 743333 Fax: (01744) 743300

THERMOFORMING EQUIPMENT

Formech International Ltd, 4 Thrales End Farm, Thrales End Lane, Harpenden, Hertfordshire, AL5 3NS Tel: (01582) 469797 Fax: (01582) 469646 E-mail: sales@formech.com

▶ Thermodynamix Ltd, 3 Princes Park, Princesway, Team Valley Trading Estate, Gateshead, Tyne & Wear, NE11 0NF Tel: 0191-440 7000 Fax: 0191-440 7001

THERMOFORMING FOOD PACKAGING

Convenience Food Systems, Interchange Park, Newport Pagnell, Buckinghamshire, MK16 9PS Tel: (01908) 513500 Fax: (01908) 513555

H F W Plastics Ltd, Albany Road, Gateshead, Tyne & Wear, NE8 3AT Tel: 0191-477 6519 Fax: 0191-490 1345 E-mail: sales@hfwplastics.co.uk

Hamilton Plastic Packaging, 18 Galowhill Road, Brackmills Industrial Estate, Northampton, NN4 7EE Tel: (01604) 766329 Fax: (01604) 701790 E-mail: sales@hamiltonpp.com

Sharp Interpack, Colley Lane, Bridgwater, Somerset, TA6 5YS Tel: (01278) 435000 Fax: (01278) 423019 E-mail: info@sharpinterpack.co.uk

THERMOGRAPHIC PRINTING MACHINES/EQUIPMENT

Martel Instruments Holdings Ltd, Stanelaw Way, Tanfield Lea Industrial Estate, Tanfield Lea, Stanley, County Durham, DH9 9XG Tel: (01207) 290266 Fax: (01207) 290239 E-mail: info@martelinstruments.com

THERMOGRAPHIC PRINTING SERVICES, EMBOSSED/RAISED SURFACE

Bryning & Wright Printers, Buckley House, Buckley Road Indust Estate, Rochdale, Lancashire, OL12 9EF Tel: (01706) 345897 Fax: (01706) 632767 E-mail: info@atecgroupe.co.uk

Camberley Printers Ltd, 357 London Road, Camberley, Surrey, GU15 3HQ Tel: (01276) 63048 Fax: (01276) 23477 E-mail: sales@camberleyprinters.co.uk

Carfax Cards Ltd, 76 Glentham Road, London, SW13 9JJ Tel: (020) 8748 1122 Fax: (020) 8748 7110 E-mail: carfax@business-cards.co.uk

Documedia, Northern Way, Bury St. Edmunds, Suffolk, IP32 6NR Tel: (01284) 762201 Fax: (01284) 764033 E-mail: sales@documedia.co.uk

Parkins of Aylesbury Ltd, Unit 15, Park Street Industrial Estate, Aylesbury, Buckinghamshire, HP20 1EB Tel: (020) 8539 7559 Fax: (01296) 483018 E-mail: orders@postglow.co.uk

R P Business Forms Ltd, Unit 17 Fallings Park Industrial Estate, Park Lane, Wolverhampton, WV10 9QB Tel: (01902) 723500 Fax: (01902) 723116 E-mail: rpbusinessforms@btinternet.com

Swift Printers, 7 Stephenson Way, Crawley, West Sussex, RH10 1TN Tel: (01293) 516507

T E Penny & Co. Ltd, Gosforth Close, Sunderland Road Industrial Estate, Sandy, Bedfordshire, SG19 1RB Tel: (01767) 681717 Fax: (01767) 680260

Thermofast Print Ltd, 2 Mills Road, Sudbury, Suffolk, CO10 2XX Tel: (01787) 880268 Fax: (01787) 880278 E-mail: sales@thermofast.co.uk

Unicorn Print & Design, 143 North Street, Romford, RM1 1ED Tel: (01708) 765017 Fax: (01708) 733491 E-mail: unicorndie@aol.com

W G Harrison Ltd, Dysart Road, Grantham, Lincolnshire, NG31 7LF Tel: (01476) 402041 Fax: (01476) 566999

THERMOGRAPHIC SURVEY OR SITE INVESTIGATION SERVICES

K C M Services Ltd, Mill View, Daisy Hill, Burstwick, Hull, HU12 9HE Tel: (01482) 227953 Fax: (08456) 445547 E-mail: info@kcmservices.com

THERMOINSULATED CLOTHING

Delf Freezer Wear Ltd, Delf House, Pool Close, West Molesey, Surrey, KT8 2HW Tel: 020 89412802 Fax: (020) 89417201 E-mail: david.barker@delf.co.uk

G R Bodycote Ltd, Orchard Works, Holliers Walk, Hinckley, Leicestershire, LE10 1QR Tel: (01455) 636271 Fax: (01455) 890025

Goldgem Belvoir Ltd, Belvoir House, Paddock Street, Wigston, Leicestershire, LE18 2AN Tel: 0116-288 1909 Fax: 0116-257 0184

Helly Hansen, 26a Pingle Drive, Bicester, Oxfordshire, OX26 6WD Tel: (01869) 325944 Fax: (01869) 325973

Musto Ltd, Christy Way, Laindon, Basildon, Essex, SS15 6TR Tel: (01268) 491555 Fax: (01268) 491440 E-mail: marketing@musto.co.uk

Stewardsons, Main Street, Hawkshead, Ambleside, Cumbria, LA22 0NT Tel: (01539) 436741 Fax: (01539) 436675 E-mail: sales@stewardsons.co.uk

Yeomans Outdoors, 3 Victoria Square, Ashbourne, Derbyshire, DE6 1GG Tel: (01335) 342468

THERMOMETER ASSEMBLIES

Thermal Detection Ltd, Unit 6 Orde Wingate Way, Stockton-on-Tees, Cleveland, TS19 0GA Tel: (01642) 602878 Fax: (01642) 618307 E-mail: tdl@thermal-detection.com

THERMOMETER MAINTENANCE/ REPAIR SERVICES

Instruments To Industry Ltd, Woodward Road, Knowsley Industrial Park North, Knowsley Industrial Park, Liverpool, L33 7UZ Tel: 0151-546 4943 Fax: 0151-548 6262 E-mail: sales@itiuk.com

THERMOMETER MANUFRS, *See also headings for particular types*

James Scientific Instruments Ltd, PO Box 18134, London, EC1R 4WD Tel: (020) 7837 1154 Fax: (020) 7278 7293 E-mail: sales@jamessciinst.com

Knowsley Instrument Services Ltd, Ashcroft Road, Knowsley Industrial Park North, Liverpool, L33 7TW Tel: 0151-548 8099 Fax: 0151-548 6599 E-mail: sales@kis-liverpool.co.uk

Mega-Quartz UK Ltd, 25 Boshers Gardens, Egham, Surrey, TW20 9NZ Tel: (01784) 437072 Fax: (01784) 435793 E-mail: megaquartzuk@aol.com

Stevenson Reeves Ltd, 40 Oxgangs Bank, Edinburgh, EH13 9LH Tel: 0131-445 7151 Fax: 0131-445 7323 E-mail: sales@stevenson-reeves.co.uk

Thermographics Measurements Ltd, Riverside Buildings, Dock Road, Connah's Quay, Deeside, Clwyd, CH5 4DS Tel: (01244) 818348 Fax: (01244) 818502 E-mail: sales@t-m-c.com

THERMOPLASTIC ELASTOMER (TPE) COMPOUNDS

Michael Ballance Plastics Ltd, Suite 8 Worthington House, 146 High Street, Burton-On-Trent, Staffordshire, DE14 1JE Tel: (01283) 511632 Fax: (01283) 517400 E-mail: mb@ballance-plastics.co.uk

THERMOPLASTIC EXTRUSIONS

Arrow Plastics Ltd, Arrow Works, Hampden Road, Kingston upon Thames, Surrey, KT1 3HQ Tel: (020) 8546 6258 Fax: (020) 8541 4654 E-mail: mail@arrow-plastics.co.uk

THERMOPLASTIC INJECTION MOULDING ULTRASONIC WELDING

DL Plastics Ltd, 9-11 Commerce Way, Lawford, Manningtree, Essex, CO11 1UT Tel: (01206) 396646 Fax: (01206) 396602 E-mail: enquiries@dlplastics.co.uk

THERMOPLASTIC MOULDINGS

A M A Plastics, Unit 1 Moreton Park Industrial Estate, Moreton Road South, Luton, LU2 0TL Tel: (01582) 734630 Fax: (01582) 419260

Eurotech Mouldings Ltd, Unit E Underwood Business Park, Wells, Somerset, BA5 1AF Tel: (01749) 676298 Fax: (01749) 670089

Plastic Engineering Ltd, Juno Drive, Leamington Spa, Warwickshire, CV31 3TA Tel: (01926) 334248 Fax: (01926) 461720 E-mail: plastic@pels.co.uk

Sarik Vacform, Unit 8-9 Pixash Business Centre, Pixash Lane, Keynsham, Bristol, BS31 1TP Tel: 0117-986 0404 Fax: 0117-986 0424 E-mail: info@sarik-vacform.com

Wyvern Mouldings Ltd, Unit 6 Britannia Business Park, Britannia Way Enigma Bus Park, Malvern, Worcestershire, WR14 1GZ Tel: (01684) 564563 Fax: (01684) 560862 E-mail: info@wyvernmouldings.co.uk

THERMOPLASTIC PRODUCTS

Almont Plastics Ltd, Lower Road, Ledbury, Herefordshire, HR8 2DH Tel: (01531) 633640 Fax: (01531) 635925

BC Plastic Mouldings Ltd, Commercial Road, Walsall, WS2 7NQ Tel: (01922) 497888 Fax: (01922) 478600 E-mail: cjms@btconnect.com

Caswick, Sandtoft Road, Belton, Doncaster, South Yorkshire, DN9 1PN Tel: (01427) 872017 Fax: (01427) 873541

Skar Precision Mouldings Ltd, Lady Lane Industrial Estate, Hadleigh, Ipswich, IP7 6AZ Tel: (01473) 828000 Fax: (01473) 828001 E-mail: sales@skar.co.uk

▶ Vulcascot Ltd, Gatwick Gate Industrial Estate, Lowfield Heath, Crawley, West Sussex, RH11 0TG Tel: (01293) 560130 Fax: (01293) 537743 E-mail: sales@vulcascot.co.uk

THERMOPLASTIC RUBBER MOULDINGS

Greene Tweed & Co. Ltd, Mere Way, Ruddington, Nottingham, NG11 6JS Tel: 0115-931 5777 Fax: 0115-931 5888 E-mail: mktng@gtweed.com

THERMOSET PLASTIC MOULDINGS

A E C Engineering, Unit 1a Conway Morfa Indust Estate, Aberconwy, Conwy, Gwynedd, LL32 8HB Tel: (01492) 584139 Fax: (01492) 584139

B F M Plastics Ltd, Unit 17c Orgreave Close, Sheffield, S13 9NP Tel: 0114-269 1688 Fax: 0114-269 3995 E-mail: sales@bfmplastics.com

Celect Tools, Ainsworth Street, Rochdale, Lancashire, OL16 5QX Tel: (07814) 349636 Fax: (01706) 648106 E-mail: sales@celect-tools.co.uk

▶ Cheshire Plastics, 1d Wellington Street, Clayton le Moors, Accrington, Lancashire, BB5 5HU Tel: (01254) 384222 Fax: (01254) 382555 E-mail: geoff@cheshireplastics.co.uk

K J Thermosets Ltd, Unit 8 & 9 Victoria Industrial Estate, Victoria Road, Bradford, West Yorkshire, BD2 2DD Tel: (01274) 626627 Fax: (01274) 626800 E-mail: sales@kjthermosets.co.uk

THERMOSET POWDER COATINGS

Becker Powder Coatings Ltd, Goodlass Road, Liverpool, L24 9HJ Tel: 0151-486 0486 Fax: 0151-486 0484

H & S Enamelling (U K) Ltd, Unit 10, Highbridge Industrial Estate, Oxford Rd, Uxbridge, Middlesex, UB8 1LX Tel: (01895) 233251 Fax: (01895) 810800 E-mail: sales@hsenamelling.co.uk

Paramount Powders UK Ltd, 4 Squirrels Trading Estate, Viveash Close, Hayes, Middlesex, UB3 4RZ Tel: (020) 8561 5588 Fax: (020) 8561 5599 E-mail: sales@paramountpowders.co.uk

Velspar, 95 Aston Church Road, Birmingham, B7 5RQ Tel: 0121-322 6900 Fax: 0121-322 6901 E-mail: infoeurope@powderstore.com

THERMOSTAT CONTROL ENGINEERING

W.J. Farvis & Sons Ltd, Temple Works, Morley Road, Southville, Bristol, BS3 1DT Tel: 0117-966 6677 Fax: 0117-966 9893 E-mail: sales@favis.co.uk

THERMOSTAT VALVES

Aqualisa Products Ltd, Westerham Trade Centre, The Flyers Way, Westerham, Kent, TN16 1DE Tel: (01959) 560000 Fax: (01959) 560030 E-mail: marketing@aqualisa.co.uk

▶ Horne Engineering Ltd, PO Box 7, Johnstone, Renfrewshire, PA5 8BD Tel: (01505) 321455 Fax: (01505) 336287E-mail: info@horne.co.uk

THERMOSTATS, *See also headings for particular types*

Hawco Direct, 8 Cranfield Road, Lostock Industrial Estate, Lostock, Bolton, BL6 4SB Tel: (01204) 675000 Fax: (01204) 675010 E-mail: catalogue@hawcodirect.co.uk

Hawco Refridgeration, The Wharf, Abbey Mill Business Park, Lower Eashing, Godalming, Surrey, GU7 2QN Tel: (01483) 869070 Fax: (01483) 869001 E-mail: sales@hawco.co.uk

▶ Heatmiser UK Ltd, Primrose House, Primrose Street, Darwen, Lancashire, BB3 2DE Tel: (01254) 776343 Fax: (01254) 704143 E-mail: info@heatmiser.co.uk

Infro Heat Ltd, 2 Landport Road, Wolverhampton, WV2 2QJ Tel: (01902) 351025 Fax: (01902) 352552 E-mail: sales@infroheat.co.uk

Radiotronic, Advance Park Rhonymedre, Wrexham, Clwyd, LL14 3YR Tel: (01978) 823900 Fax: (01978) 822913 E-mail: sales@aslgroup.uk.com

Raytech International, Coldnose Road, Rotherwas Industrial Estate, Hereford, HR2 6JL Tel: (01432) 340833 Fax: (01432) 340844 E-mail: sales@raytech.uk.com

Starkstrom (London) Ltd, 256 Field End Road, Eastcote, Ruislip, Middlesex, HA4 9UW Tel: (020) 8868 3732 Fax: (020) 8868 3736 E-mail: sales@starkstrom.com

Welbeck Catering Spares, 20 Bushey Hall Road, Bushey, WD23 2ED Tel: (01923) 801555

THERMOSTATS, DOMESTIC APPLIANCE

Capri Electrical Developments Ltd, 45-47 Whalley Road, Clitheroe, Lancashire, BB7 1EE Tel: (01200) 425070 Fax: (01200) 423070 E-mail: roger@storageheater.co.uk

Diamond H Controls Ltd, Vulcan Road North, Norwich, NR6 6AH Tel: (01603) 425291 Fax: (01603) 424907 E-mail: sales@diamond-h-controls.co.uk

E A C Ltd, PO Box 6023, Solihull, West Midlands, B93 0JN Tel: (01564) 770359 Fax: (01564) 774025 E-mail: eaccomps@aol.com

Strix UK Ltd, Taylor House, Minerva Close, Chester West Employment Park, Chester, CH1 4QL Tel: (01244) 394333 Fax: (01244) 390137 E-mail: sales@strix.com

Sunvic Controls Ltd, Bellshill Road, Uddingston, Glasgow, G71 6NP Tel: (01698) 812944 Fax: (01698) 813637 E-mail: sales@sunvic.co.uk

THERMOWELLS

Electro Mechanical Installations Ltd, 7 Mackenzie Industrial Estate, Bird Hall Lane, Stockport, Cheshire, SK3 0SB Tel: 0161-428 7800 Fax: 0161-428 8999 E-mail: office@emiltd.co.uk

THICKNESS GAUGES

▶ Mapra Technik Co., Unit D13, The Seedbed Centre, Langston Road, Loughton, Essex, IG10 3TQ Tel: (020) 8508 4207 Fax: (020) 8502 5107 E-mail: info@mapra.co.uk

Thermo Fisher Scientific, Shepherd Road, Gloucester, GL2 5HF Tel: (01452) 337800 Fax: (01452) 415156

THIN FILM COATINGS

▶ Ranier Technology Ltd, Greenhouse Farm, Newmarket Road, Teversham, Cambridge, CB5 8AA Tel: (01223) 505045 Fax: (01223) 505046E-mail: ranier.technology@ranier.co.uk

THIN FILM SPUTTERING SERVICES

Gigahertz Marketing Solutions, Croye Close, Andover, Hampshire, SP10 3AF Tel: (01264) 391539 Fax: (0870) 9124158 E-mail: sales@ghz-marketing.com

THIN FILM STRAIN GAUGES

▶ Strain Measurement Devices Ltd, Bury Road, Chedburgh, Bury St. Edmunds, Suffolk, IP29 4UQ Tel: (01284) 852000 Fax: (01284) 852371 E-mail: askus@smdsensors.co.uk

THIN JOINT MASONRY BUILDING SYSTEMS

B R C Special Products, Carver Road, Astonfields Industrial Estate, Stafford, ST16 3BP Tel: (01785) 222288 Fax: (01785) 240029

THIN WALL STEEL TUBES

Bull Tubes Ltd, Unit 4, Park Road, Willenhall, West Midlands, WV13 1AH Tel: (01902) 608881 Fax: (01902) 602221 E-mail: enquiries@bulltube.com

THREAD FORMING SCREWS

Lancaster Fastener Co. Ltd, Middlegate, White Lund Industrial Estate, Morecambe, Lancashire, LA3 3BN Tel: (01524) 62645 Fax: (01524) 66367 E-mail: enquiries@lancasterfastener.co.uk

THREAD MEASUREMENT GAUGES/INSTRUMENTS

Telford Threadgauge Ltd, Unit 1 Halesfield 18, Telford, Shropshire, TF7 4PP Tel: (01952) 588858 Fax: (01952) 588616

THREAD MILLING CUTTER AND DRILL COMBINED

Emuge (UK) Ltd, 2 Claire Court, Rawmarsh Road, Rotherham, South Yorkshire, S60 1RU Tel: (01709) 364494 Fax: (01709) 364540 E-mail: sales@emuge-uk.co.uk

THREAD PROTECTION CAPS,

See Masking Cap/Plug etc

THREAD ROLLING DIES

Grayson Millward Ltd, Wharf Road Industrial Estate, Pinxton, Nottingham, NG16 6LE Tel: (01773) 810144 Fax: (01773) 860321 E-mail:

Namco Tooling Ltd, New Road, Studley, Warwickshire, B80 7LZ Tel: (01527) 853667 Fax: (01527) 852668 E-mail: sales@namco-tooling.com

THREAD ROLLING ENGINEERING SERVICES

DJS Engineering, 11-12 Benedict Square, Peterborough, PE4 6GD Tel: (01733) 328214 Fax: (01733) 328214

THREAD ROLLING FASTENERS

Dobson & Beaumont Ltd, Appleby Street, Blackburn, BB1 3BH Tel: (01254) 53297 Fax: (01254) 676121 E-mail: philip@dobsonandbeaumont.co.uk

THREAD (SCREW) CUTTING MACHINE HIRE

D Berry & Co. Ltd, Middlemoor Industrial Estate, Kentish Road, Middlemore Industrial Estate, Birmingham, B21 0AY Tel: 0121-558 4411 Fax: 0121-555 5546 E-mail: enquires@dberryandco.co.uk

THREAD (SCREW) CUTTING MACHINE MANUFRS

Northwest Threading Services, 7 Suthers Street, Oldham, OL9 7TE Tel: 0161-628 5557 Fax: 0161-628 3339

Pipe Fabrication Equipment Services, Unit 4, Townley Business Park, Hanson Street, Middleton, Manchester, M24 2UF Tel: 0161-653 7459 Fax: 0161-654 7286

Ridge Tools, Arden Press Way, Pixmore Avenue, Letchworth Garden City, Hertfordshire, SG6 1LH Tel: (01462) 485335 Fax: (01462) 485315 E-mail: sales.uk@ridgid.com

Rotostock (Sales) Ltd, Porte Marsh Road, Calne, Wiltshire, SN11 8BW Tel: (01249) 822222 Fax: (01249) 822300 E-mail: sales@rotostock.co.uk

THREAD (SCREW) CUTTING TOOL MANUFRS

Depo FHT, Lion House, Welsh Road East, Southam, Warwickshire, CV47 1NE Tel: (01926) 813969 Fax: (01926) 817722 E-mail: sales@fht-uk.com

Posi-Thread (UK) Ltd, 4-5 Bridgewater Road, Hertburn Industrial Estate, District 11, Washington, Tyne & Wear, NE37 2SG Tel: 0191-417 8178 Fax: 0191-415 3120 E-mail: info@posithread.co.uk

Rothenberger UK Ltd, 2 Kingsthorne Park, Henson Way, Telford Way Industrial Estate, Kettering, Northamptonshire, NN16 8PX Tel: (01536) 310300 Fax: (01536) 310600 E-mail: info@rothenberger.co.uk

Wexco Ltd, Earlswood Trading Estate, Poolhead Lane, Earlswood, Solihull, West Midlands, B94 5EW Tel: (01564) 703624 Fax: (01564) 703066 E-mail: sales@wexco.co.uk

THREAD (SCREW) CUTTING/ GRINDING SERVICES

Aspin Engineering Ltd, Moss La Industrial Estate, Egremont Close, Whitefield, Manchester, M45 8FH Tel: 0161-766 9622 Fax: 0161-766 1423 E-mail: enquiries@aspin-engineering.com

B & S Threaded Products Ltd, 28 Newtown Street, Cradley Heath, West Midlands, B64 5LD Tel: (01384) 569899 Fax: (01384) 410392

Mercury Thread Gauges, 182-186 Fletchamstead Highway Industrial Estate, Fletchamstead Highway, Coventry, CV4 7BB Tel: (024) 7671 4185 Fax: (024) 7669 1234 E-mail: sales@mercurygauges.co.uk

THREADED FASTENER STUDDING

B D M Fastenings, 10 Royce Road, Crawley, West Sussex, RH10 9NX Tel: (01293) 548186 Fax: (01293) 553274 E-mail: sales@bdm-fastenings.demon.co.uk

Bomet UK (Threaded Bar) Ltd, Unit H3, Eastacre, Off Longacre, Willenhall, West Midlands, WV13 2JZ Tel: (01902) 368400 Fax: (01902) 606877 E-mail: j.shuffe@bomet.com

K Engineering, Unit 29 Parkrose Industrial Estate, Middlemore Road, Smethwick, West Midlands, B66 2DZ Tel: 0121-558 4367 Fax: 0121-565 1129 E-mail: sales@k-engineering.co.uk

Studwelders, Millennium House Severn Link Distribution Centre, Newhouse Fa, Mathern, Chepstow, Gwent, NP16 6UN Tel: (01291) 626048 Fax: (01291) 629979 E-mail: info@studwelders.co.uk

Studweldpro UK Ltd, Ollerton Road, Tuxford, Newark, Nottinghamshire, NG22 0PQ Tel: (01777) 874500 Fax: (01777) 874555 E-mail: sales@swpuk.com

THREADED FASTENERS, BRITISH STANDARDS

Lancaster Fastener Co. Ltd, Middlegate, White Lund Industrial Estate, Morecambe, Lancashire, LA3 3BN Tel: (01524) 62645 Fax: (01524) 66367 E-mail: enquiries@lancasterfastener.co.uk

THREADED INSERT TAPS

Spiralock Europe, 11 Court Yard Workshops, Bath Street, Market Harborough, Leicestershire, LE16 9EW Tel: (01858) 468646 Fax: (01858) 466808 E-mail: sl-europe@spiralock.com

THREADED INSERTS

Anchor Inserts, 11 Bayton Road Industrial Estate, Bayton Road, Exhall, Coventry, CV7 9EL Tel: (024) 7636 3979 Fax: (024) 7636 6303 E-mail: info@anchorinserts.com

Astley Components, 623-625 High Road Leyton, London, E10 6RF Tel: (020) 8556 9711 Fax: (020) 8556 6641 E-mail: sales@astleycomp.co.uk

Fairchild Fasteners UK Ltd, Unit 6 Bardon 22 Industrial Estate, Bardon Hill, Coalville, Leicestershire, LE67 1TE Tel: (01530) 518900 Fax: (01530) 518910 E-mail: sales@fairchildfasteners.com

HPS Group, 7 Spitfire Quay, Hazel Road, Southampton, SO19 7GB Tel: (023) 8044 4428 Fax: (023) 8042 0005

Powell Gee & Co Ltd, PO Box 15, Wednesbury, West Midlands, WS10 0UF Tel: 0121-556 6729 Fax: 0121-556 6729 E-mail: sales@powellgee.co.uk

Primary Fasteners Ltd, PO Box 571, Solihull, West Midlands, B90 4TA Tel: 0121 2475191 Fax: 0121 5357094 E-mail: mailroom@prifast.co.uk

THREADED INSERTS, WIRE/ HELICALLY COILED

Hillcliff Tools Ltd, 11 Catley Road, Sheffield, S9 5JF Tel: 0114-244 3665 Fax: 0114-242 3319 E-mail: jj@hillcliff-tools.com

W T I Fasteners Ltd, Unit 10 Huntingdon Court, Westminster Industrial Estate, Measham, Swadlincote, Derbyshire, DE12 7DS Tel: (01530) 273100 Fax: (01530) 273007 E-mail: admin@wireinserts.com

THREADED PRESSINGS

Bodill Parker Group Ltd, Barnfield Industrial Estate, Speed Road, Tipton, West Midlands, DY4 9DY Tel: 0121-557 4164 Fax: 0121-557 4177 E-mail: sales@bodill-parker.co.uk

THREADING TOOLS/TAPS/ MACHINES, SCREW, *See Thread (Screw) Cutting etc*

THREE DIMENSIONAL (3D) CNC MILLING

Abbey Die & Tool Ltd, Bentley Mill Close, Walsall, WS2 0BN Tel: (01922) 626545 Fax: (01922) 721717 E-mail: sales@abbeydieandtool.co.uk

Chase Precision Engineering Ltd, 10 7 Blackmoor Road, Ebblake Industrial Estate, Verwood, Dorset, BH31 6AX Tel: (01202) 813237 Fax: (01202) 813734

Lattimer Engineering Ltd, 79-83 Shakespeare Street, Southport, Merseyside, PR8 5AP Tel: (01704) 535040 Fax: (01704) 541046 E-mail: sales@lattimer.com

N C Geary (Precision Engineering), 10 Mill Road, Christchurch, Dorset, BH23 2JY Tel: (01202) 483585 Fax: (01202) 471163 E-mail: nick@geary-engineering.co.uk

Thunder Engineering, 1 Garfield Street, Leicester, LE4 5GF Tel: 0116-253 1105 Fax: 0116-253 1105

Wimborne Engineering, 58 Cobham Road, Ferndown Industrial Estate, Wimborne, Dorset, BH21 7QH Tel: (01202) 893043 E-mail: knud@moldtecknik.co.uk

THREE DIMENSIONAL (3D) DIGITISING/SCANNING/ PRODUCT DESIGN SERVICES

Frontier Design, 1 Capital Place, Lovet Road, Harlow, Essex, CM19 5AS Tel: (01279) 427945 Fax: (01279) 641330 E-mail: enquiries@frontierdesign.co.uk

▶ Glenelg Product Design, Low Barn, Church View, Menston, Ilkley, West Yorkshire, LS29 6EX Tel: (01943) 871117 Fax: (01943) 871002 E-mail: john@glenelgdesign.com

Optical Record Systems, Eagle Close, Chandler's Ford, Eastleigh, Hampshire, SO53 4NF Tel: (023) 8026 7755 Fax: (023) 8061 8861 E-mail: info@orsgroup.com

THREE DIMENSIONAL (3D) DOMING SERVICES

Dectek Ltd, Unit 29 Business Development Centre, Main Ave, Treforest Industrial Estate, Pontypridd, M. Glam, CF37 5UR Tel: (01443) 841840 Fax: (01443) 842815 E-mail: sales@dectek.co.uk

THREE DIMENSIONAL (3D) MACHINING

Formil Engineering Ltd, Coppice Side Industrial Estate, Brownhills, Walsall, WS8 7EX Tel: (01543) 371604 Fax: (01543) 372208 E-mail: formileng@ukonline.co.uk

THREE DIMENSIONAL (3D) MODELLING

▶ Isu Ltd, PO Box 4370, Wolverhampton, WV1 9AE Tel: (01902) 636588 Fax: (01902) 636588 E-mail: studio@isu-design.co.uk

▶ Vanity-Pure Design Ltd, 24 Hampshire Road, Derby, DE21 4EG Tel: 01332 727317 Fax: 01332 727317 E-mail: h.dunmore@vanity-puredesign.co.uk

THREE DIMENSIONAL (3D) MODELLING AND ANIMATION

▶ Happy Tuesdays Ltd, 11 Woodstock Avenue, West Ealing, London, W13 9UQ Tel: (0796) 6207504 Fax: (020) 8537 0849 E-mail: ianm@happytuesdays.co.uk

▶ Media Stations, 86 Smithbrook Kilns, Cranleigh, Surrey, GU6 8JJ Tel: (01483) 277765 E-mail: enquiries@mediastation.co.uk

T R S U, 1 Cranside Avenue, Bristol, BS6 7RA Tel: (07748) 740874 E-mail: ben@trsu.com

▶ Vanity-Pure Design Ltd, 24 Hampshire Road, Derby, DE21 4EG Tel: 01332 727317 Fax: 01332 727317 E-mail: h.dunmore@vanity-puredesign.co.uk

▶ Visuals 3D, 26 School Brow, Romiley, Stockport, Cheshire, SK6 3AT Tel: 0161-430 2623 E-mail: info@visuals-3d.co.uk

THREE DIMENSIONAL (3D) SURFACE WORKING

Frontier Design, 1 Capital Place, Lovet Road, Harlow, Essex, CM19 5AS Tel: (01279) 427945 Fax: (01279) 641330 E-mail: enquiries@frontierdesign.co.uk

THREE SEATER SOFAS

▶ Bott Shaun Upholstery, 18 Leicester Road, Blaby, Leicester, LE8 4GQ Tel: 0116-277 9705 E-mail: info@handmadesofas.co.uk

THROTTLE CONTROL CABLES

Catton Control Cables Ltd, 33-35 Kings Road, Yardley, Birmingham, B25 8JB Tel: 0121-772 4297 Fax: 0121-766 6075 E-mail: nick@catton.co.uk

THROUGH WALL VENTILATION UNITS

C.A. Martin & Son, Upper Bell Clive, Hartcliff Road, Penistone, Sheffield, S36 9FE Tel: (01226) 764444 Fax: (01226) 762336 E-mail: sales@camartinandson.co.uk

THRUST BEARINGS

Cooper Roller Bearings Co. Ltd, Wisbech Road, King's Lynn, Norfolk, PE30 5JX Tel: (01553) 767677 Fax: (01553) 761113 E-mail: sales@cooperbearings.com

THYRISTOR CONTROLLERS

Mobile Electro Service Ltd, Units 1-2 Buntsford Park Road, Bromsgrove, Worcestershire, B60 3DX Tel: (01527) 579795 Fax: (01527) 579963 E-mail: sales@mesuk.co.uk

Poerlink Electronic Ltd, Powerlink House, Ivy Arch Road, Worthing, West Sussex, BN14 8BX Tel: (01903) 209550 Fax: (01903) 215526 E-mail: admin@powerlinkelectronics.co.uk

Power Products International Ltd, Commerce Way, Edenbridge, Kent, TN8 6ED Tel: (01732) 866424 Fax: (01732) 866399 E-mail: sales@ppi-uk.com

Tactical Controls Ltd, Unit 4 Parkland Business Centre, Chartwell Road, Lancing, West Sussex, BN15 8UE Tel: (01903) 750800 Fax: (01903) 750678 E-mail: email@tacticalcontrols.co.uk

THYRISTOR STACKS

Caledon Controls Ltd, Unit 2, Block 4, Castlehill Industrial Estate, Carluke, Lanarkshire, ML8 5UF Tel: (01555) 773355 Fax: (01555) 772212 E-mail: info@caledoncontrols.co.uk

THYRISTORS

Caledon Controls Ltd, Unit 2, Block 4, Castlehill Industrial Estate, Carluke, Lanarkshire, ML8 5UF Tel: (01555) 773355 Fax: (01555) 772212 E-mail: info@caledoncontrols.co.uk

TICKET ISSUING MACHINE MAINTENANCE/REPAIR SERVICES

Cubic Transportation Systems Ltd, Honeycrock Lane, Redhill, RH1 5LA Tel: (01737) 782200 Fax: (01737) 789759 E-mail: cubicafc@cts-ltd.co.uk

Wayfarer Service Division, Workshop, 112 Gloucester Road, Croydon, CR0 2DE Tel: (020) 8404 1234 Fax: (020) 8689 9465

TICKET ISSUING MACHINES

Coinage (Bristol) Ltd, 91 Mayflower Street, Plymouth, PL1 1SB Tel: (0870) 1600992 Fax: (01364) 73799 E-mail: sales@coinage.co.uk

▶ Metric Group Ltd, Metric House Westmead Drive, Westmead Industrial Estate, Swindon, SN5 7AD Tel: (01793) 647800 Fax: (01793) 647802 E-mail: sales@metricgroup.co.uk

Shere Ltd, Guildford Indust Estate, Deaconfield, Guildford, Surrey, GU2 8YT Tel: (01483) 557400 Fax: (01483) 557401 E-mail: info@shere.com

Ticket Systems (UK) Ltd, 176 Hurwyn Avenue, Ruislip, Middlesex, HA4 6HJ Tel: (01895) 231575 Fax: (01895) 231575

Tor Systems Ltd, 58-60 Longton Road, Stoke-on-Trent, ST4 8YZ Tel: (01782) 644755 Fax: (01782) 644346 E-mail: djordan@torsystems.co.uk

TICKING FABRICS

J T Griffiths & Co. Ltd, Ticking Supplies, 61 Stockport Road, Ashton-under-Lyne, Lancashire, OL7 0LE Tel: 0161-330 5665 Fax: 0161-343 1684

TIGHTS, LADIES'

Cavendish Hosiery Ltd, 77 Cannock Street, Leicester, LE4 9HR Tel: 0116-276 6477 E-mail: cavendishhos@aol.com

Flude Hosiery, Rugby Road, Hinckley, Leicestershire, LE10 0QQ Tel: (01455) 615543 Fax: (01455) 615543 E-mail: sales@flude.co.uk

TILE ADHESIVES

C T D Carlisle, Viaduct Estate Road, Carlisle, CA2 5BN Tel: (01228) 536601 Fax: (01228) 520242 E-mail: sales@ctdtiles.co.uk

TILE ADHESIVES – *continued*

Granwood Flooring Ltd, Greenhill Lane, Riddings, Alfreton, Derbyshire, DE55 4AT Tel: (01773) 602341 Fax: (01773) 540043

TILE CUTTERS

Canaan Carbides Ltd, Unit 13, 13 Briar Close, Evesham, Worcestershire, WR11 4JQ Tel: (01386) 442818 Fax: (01386) 40564 E-mail: canaancarbides@btconnect.com

TILE PRODUCTION PLANT

Kengate Products Ltd, Littleton Lane, Shepperton, Middlesex, TW17 0NF Tel: (01932) 568672 Fax: (01932) 567171
S Cocker Tiles, Beckside Cottage, The Bridge, Bedale, North Yorkshire, DL8 1AN Tel: (01677) 424658

TILE TRIM OR SEALING STRIPS

Genesis Aps International Ltd, Ellerbeck Way, Stokesley Industrial Park, Stokesley, Middlesbrough, Cleveland, TS9 5JZ Tel: (01642) 713000 Fax: (01642) 713777 E-mail: enquiries@genesis-aps.com

TILES, *See also headings for particular types*

A.B.S. International Ltd, Persia House, 27 Aughton Road, Southport, Merseyside, PR8 2AG Tel: (01704) 564386 Fax: (01704) 550091 E-mail: abs@provider.co.uk
A Bleakley & Co., Winters Bridge, Portsmouth Road, Thames Ditton, Surrey, KT7 0ST Tel: (020) 8398 8137 Fax: (020) 8398 7877 E-mail: peter@ableakley.freeserve.co.uk
Advanced Ceramics, Fenton Barns Retail Village, North Berwick, East Lothian, EH39 5BW Tel: (01620) 850435 Fax: (01620) 850435
Bernard J Arnull & Co. Ltd, 17-21 Sunbeam Road, London, NW10 6JP Tel: (020) 8965 6094 Fax: (020) 8961 1585 E-mail: bernard.arnull@easynet.co.uk
▶ Betterplace Property Maintenance, T M S House, Cray Avenue, Orpington, Kent, BR5 3QB Tel: (01689) 875957 Fax: (01689) 885035 E-mail: betterplace1@aol.com
Bon Accord Glass, Bon Accord House, Riverside Drive, Aberdeen, AB11 7SL Tel: (01224) 588944 Fax: (01224) 582731
C S W Tiling Ltd, 22-24 Nuffield Road, Nuffield Industrial Estate, Poole, Dorset, BH17 0RB Tel: (01202) 675836 Fax: (01202) 668219 E-mail: csw.tiling@cswtiles.com
C T D Carlisle, Viaduct Estate Road, Carlisle, CA2 5BN Tel: (01228) 536601 Fax: (01228) 520242 E-mail: sales@ctdtiles.co.uk
Capital Tiles Supplies Ltd, P O Box 80, Coventry, CV1 2RJ Tel: (024) 7663 3336 Fax: (024) 7663 1447
Central Tiles, 19 Highfield Road, Hall Green, Birmingham, B28 0EL Tel: 0121-777 7422 Fax: 0121-778 2414 E-mail: sales@centraltilestudio.co.uk
Ceramic Tile Distributors, Quarry Lane, Chichester, West Sussex, PO19 8PE Tel: (01243) 787664 Fax: (01243) 776695
Ceramic Tiles Ltd, Unit 46, Bosshall Business Park, Bosshall Road, Ipswich, IP1 5BN Tel: (01473) 745478 Fax: (01473) 240133 E-mail: customer.support@ceramic-tiles.co.uk
Ceramique (International) Ltd, Unit 1, Royds Lane, Lower Wortley Ring Road, Leeds, LS12 6DU Tel: 0113-231 0218 Fax: 0113-231 0353 E-mail: info@ceramiqueinternationale.co.uk
Ceramodo Tiles, 236 Easterly Road, Leeds, LS8 3ES Tel: 0113-249 0041 Fax: 0113-248 5665 E-mail: sales@ceramodotiles.co.uk
Cladding Components Ltd, 17 Trinity Street, Leamington Spa, Warwickshire, CV32 5RH Tel: (01926) 420825 Fax: (01926) 313927 E-mail: clad.comp@ic24.net
Diamond Interior Design, Century Street, Stoke-on-Trent, ST1 5HT Tel: (01782) 212242 Fax: (01782) 202375 E-mail: sales@diamond-interior-design.co.uk
Eastern Glazed Ceramics Ltd, Tile House, Eversley Road, Norwich, NR6 6TA Tel: (01603) 423391 Fax: (01603) 789040 E-mail: enquiries@egctiles.co.uk
Euro Claddings Ltd, 9 Heathfield Road, Kings Heath, Birmingham, B14 7BT Tel: 0121-444 0375 Fax: 0121-441 1134 E-mail: eurocladdings@lineone.net
Euro Services Ltd, Unit 2C Rugby Road, Twickenham Trading Estate, Twickenham, TW1 1DG Tel: (020) 8744 1122 Fax: (020) 8744 0099 E-mail: eslceramics@aol.com
Evertile Ltd, 6 Moresby Road, London, E5 9LF Tel: (020) 8806 3167 Fax: (020) 8806 7434 E-mail: sales@evertile.com
John Frackelton & Son Ltd, 25 Imperial Drive, Belfast, BT6 8JH Tel: (028) 9073 2231 Fax: (028) 9073 1764 E-mail: tiles@frackeltons.co.uk
▶ GoodSource Global Trading Ltd, Unit 26, Cavans Way, Binley Industrial Estate, Coventry, CV3 2SF Tel: (08456) 448148 Fax: (08706) 622166 E-mail: contact@goodsource.co.uk
Hampshire Tile Warehouse Ltd, Hollybush Industrial Park, Hollybush Lane, Aldershot, Hampshire, GU11 2PX Tel: (01252) 333333 Fax: (0800) 3284481E-mail: admin@htw.co.uk
Hampshire Tile Warehouse Ltd, 5 Grange Industrial Estate, Albion Street, Southwick, Brighton, BN42 4EN Tel: (01273) 597070 Fax: (0800) 3284483E-mail: admin@htw.co.uk
▶ Iceni Printed Tiles, 8 Transopel House, Queens Square, Attleborough, Norfolk, NR17 2AE Tel: 01953 451313 E-mail: info@icenitiles.co.uk
▶ Ipm, Unit 31 Seymour Street, Millers Bridge Industrial Esta, Bootle, Merseyside, L20 1EE Tel: 0151-922 2252 Fax: 0151-922 2252 E-mail: enquiries@ipmgroup.co.uk
Langley London Ltd, Calver Quay, Calver Road, Warrington, WA2 8UD Tel: (0845) 2301515 Fax: (0845) 2301516 E-mail: mail@langleylondon.co.uk
▶ Lerwick Building Centre Ltd, 5d Gremista Industrial Estate, Gremista, Lerwick, Shetland, ZE1 0PX Tel: (01595) 696373 Fax: (01595) 692802 E-mail: billy@lerwickbuildingcentre.co.uk
Luton Ceramic Tile Co. Ltd, 6 Britannia Estate, Leagrave Road, Luton, LU3 1RJ Tel: (01582) 412121 Fax: (01582) 413061 E-mail: enquiries@lutonceramics.co.uk
▶ Maidenhead Tile Centre, 20 Cannon Court Road, Maidenhead, Berkshire, SL6 7QN Tel: (01628) 776333 Fax: (01628) 789206 E-mail: sales@maidenheadtiles.co.uk
Minoli Tiles, Watlington Road, Oxford, OX4 6LX Tel: (01865) 778225 Fax: (01865) 747642 E-mail: info@minoli.co.uk
Nicobond International Ltd, Cot Hill Trading Estate, Plymouth, PL7 1SR Tel: (01752) 339724 Fax: (01752) 342746
▶ Pietra Tile Distribution Ltd, 28 Silver Street, Bradford-on-Avon, Wiltshire, BA15 1JY Tel: (01225) 867678 Fax: (01225) 867678 E-mail: jakelewis@pietrastone.co.uk
Porcelanosa Yorkshire Ltd, Unit 15 Shaw Lane Industrial E, Ogden Rd, Doncaster, South Yorkshire, DN2 4SQ Tel: (01302) 341029 Fax: (01302) 739273
▶ Quadrant Modular Ltd, Unit 3d Priory Park, Mills Road, Aylesford, Kent, ME20 7PP Tel: (01622) 719090 Fax: (01622) 719191
Reed Harris, 27 Carnwath Road, London, SW6 3HR Tel: (020) 7736 7511 Fax: (020) 7736 2988 E-mail: enquiries@reed-harris.co.uk
Rogers Ceramics, Unit 3 Metcalf Way, Crawley, West Sussex, RH11 7SU Tel: (01293) 612057 Fax: (01293) 612047 E-mail: info@rogers-ceramics.com
Simmy Ceramics, Sayer House, Oxgate Lane, London, NW2 7JN Tel: (020) 8208 0416 Fax: (020) 8450 1140 E-mail: sales@simmyceramics.com
Stone & Ceramic Ltd, Unit 3 Kingside, Ruston Road, Woolwich, London, SE18 5BX Tel: (020) 8855 5400 Fax: (020) 8855 5404 E-mail: info@stone-ceramic.co.uk
▶ Stone House Tiles Ltd, Unit 42 Enterprise Industrial Estate, Bolina Road, London, SE16 3LF Tel: (020) 7237 5375 Fax: (020) 7231 7597E-mail: info@stonehousetiles.co.uk
Sunnyside Tiles, Sunnyside, Southrop, Lechlade, Gloucestershire, GL7 3PG Tel: (01367) 850510 Fax: (01367) 850508
▶ Suregrave UK Ltd, Unit 4 Faraday Close, Washington, Tyne & Wear, NE38 8QJ Tel: 0191-417 4505 Fax: 0191-415 3410
▶ Tile & Stone Gallery, Unit 3 Western Way, Bury St. Edmunds, Suffolk, IP33 3SP Tel: (01284) 706230 Fax: (01284) 765685
Tiles UK Ltd, 1-13 Monford St Off Langworthy Road, Salford, M50 2XD Tel: 0161-872 5155 Fax: 0161-848 7948 E-mail: info@tilesuk.com
Topps Tile, 2 Kittybrewster Retail Park, Bedford Road, Aberdeen, AB24 3LJ Tel: (01224) 488111 Fax: (01224) 488222
▶ Touchstone Tiles Ltd, 1 Ealing Road Trading Estate, Ealing Road, Brentford, Middlesex, TW8 0QY Tel: (020) 8758 2233 Fax: (020) 8758 2244 E-mail: sales@touchstonetiles.co.uk
Tower Ceramics, 91 Parkway, London, NW1 7PP Tel: (020) 7485 7192 Fax: (020) 7267 9571
Udny Edgar & Co. Ltd, 314 Balham High Road, London, SW17 7AA Tel: (020) 8767 8181 Fax: (020) 8767 7709
Zodiac Automotive UK Ltd, Wansbeck Bus Park, Rotary Parkway, Ashington, Northumberland, NE63 8QZ Tel: (01670) 562000 Fax: (01670) 855590

TILING TOOLS OR ACCESSORIES, *See also headings for particular types*

Shackerley (Holdings) Group Ltd, 139 Wigan Road, Euxton, Chorley, Lancashire, PR7 6JH Tel: (01257) 273114 Fax: (01257) 262386 E-mail: sales@shackerley.co.uk

TILT COVER MAINTENANCE/ REPAIR SERVICES, VEHICLE

C J Covers Ltd, 30 Williamson Street, Hull, HU9 1EP Tel: (01482) 226970 Fax: (01482) 327218
K & T Tilts, Readmans Industrial Estate, Station Road, East Tilbury, Tilbury, Essex, RM18 8QR Tel: (01375) 840880 Fax: (01375) 840740 E-mail: info@kandttilts.co.uk
Roland Tilts UK Ltd, Unit 1 Usher Street, Bradford, West Yorkshire, BD4 7DS Tel: (01274) 391645 Fax: (01274) 305156

TILT TRANSDUCERS

Clino Ltd, 54 Britten Drive, Malvern, Worcestershire, WR14 3LG Tel: (01684) 561525 Fax: (01684) 561721 E-mail: sales@clino.co.uk
Tilt Measurement Ltd, Horizon House Baldock Industrial Estate, London Road, Baldock, Hertfordshire, SG7 6NG Tel: (01462) 894566 Fax: (01462) 895990 E-mail: sales@tilt-measurement.com

TIMBER AGENTS

Denis Brown & Son (Nailsworth) Ltd, Broadmead, Bath Road, Woodchester, Stroud, Gloucestershire, GL5 5EG Tel: (01453) 873516 Fax: (01453) 873333
The Capworth Panel & Timber Company Ltd, 27 Capworth Street, London, E10 5AN Tel: (020) 8539 3374 Fax: (020) 8539 5872
Castle Milk & Corrie Estates, Norwood, Tundergarth, Lockerbie, Dumfriesshire, DG11 2QX Tel: (01576) 510203 Fax: (01576) 510362
Churchill & Sim Group Ltd, Ashdown Court, Lewes Road, Forest Row, East Sussex, RH18 5EZ Tel: (01342) 826333 Fax: (01342) 825103 E-mail: sales@churchillsim.com
Downey Engineering, Pontrilas, Hereford, HR2 0BB Tel: (01981) 240427 Fax: (01981) 240953
Edmiston & Mitchells, Haypark Business Centre, Marchmont Avenue, Polmont, Falkirk, FK2 0NZ Tel: (01324) 718728 Fax: (01324) 718738 E-mail: edmitch@compuserve.com
Flatau Dick & Co. Ltd, Bings, High Street, Limpsfield, Oxted, Surrey, RH8 0DR Tel: (01883) 730707 Fax: (01883) 717100 E-mail: sales@flataudick.co.uk
Fountain Timber Products Ltd, Brockley Combe Road, Backwell, Bristol, BS48 3DF Tel: (01934) 862710 Fax: (01934) 863298 E-mail: sales@fountaintimber.co.uk
Hunt Bros & Co. Ltd, Argyle Buildings, 69-71 Argyle Street, Birkenhead, Merseyside, CH41 6LQ Tel: 0151-647 4541 Fax: 0151-666 1045 E-mail: hardwoods@huntbros.co.uk
International Timber, Haven Road, Colchester, CO2 8HT Tel: (01206) 866822 Fax: (01206) 878000 E-mail: info@internationaltimber.com
J Bradnam & Sons, Melbourne Bridge, Withersfield, Haverhill, Suffolk, CB9 7RR Tel: (01440) 702110 Fax: (01440) 704463
J H Mayor Sons Ltd, Saw Mill, Ulnes Walton, Leyland, PR26 8LR Tel: (01257) 451303 Fax: (01257) 453736
James Mcgregor & Sons Ltd, 49 Sydenham Road, Belfast, BT3 9DR Tel: (028) 9045 1244 Fax: (028) 9045 6433 E-mail: sales@hardwoodni.com
Redrock Forestry, Felin Hen Farm, Felin Hen Road, Bangor, Gwynedd, LL57 4BB Tel: (01248) 364362 Fax: (01248) 364232
Craig Alan Thomas Ltd, 3rd Floor, 5 Covent Garden, Liverpool, L2 8UD Tel: 0151-227 2287 Fax: 0151-236 2165 E-mail: sales@atcraig.com
UCM Timber P.L.C., 3rd Floor, Suffolk House, College Road, Croydon, CR9 1TH Tel: (020) 8680 9900 Fax: (020) 8681 8776 E-mail: sales@ucmtimber.co.uk

TIMBER AGRICULTURAL BUILDINGS

A M Warkup Ltd, Aerodrome Works, Lissett, Driffield, North Humberside, YO25 8PT Tel: (01262) 468666 Fax: (01262) 468656 E-mail: amwarkup@amwarkup.co.uk
Browns of Wem Ltd, Four Lane Ends, Wem, SY4 5UQ Tel: (01939) 232382 Fax: (01939) 234032 E-mail: mail@brownsofwem.com
Farmplus Construction Ltd, Shay Lane, Longridge, Preston, PR3 3BT Tel: (01772) 785252 Fax: (01772) 782944 E-mail: enquiries@farmplus.co.uk
G D L Air Systems Ltd, Air Diffusion Works, Woolley Bridge Road, Hadfield, Glossop, Derbyshire, SK13 1AB Tel: (01457) 861538 Fax: (01457) 866010 E-mail: sales@grille.co.uk
Jones & Co., Severn Road, Welshpool, Powys, SY21 7AR Tel: (01938) 555340 Fax: (01938) 552592 E-mail: ifan@jones-co.co.uk
Minshall Brothers, Adderley Road, Market Drayton, Shropshire, TF9 3SX Tel: (01630) 657647 Fax: (01630) 657202 E-mail: info@minshallconstruction.com
Partridge Buildings, 2 Woodland Road, Broadclyst, Exeter, EX5 3LP Tel: (01392) 461771 Fax: (01392) 464352
T T Buildings Ltd, Kingsley Road, Bideford, Devon, EX39 2PF Tel: (01237) 475679 Fax: (01237) 421526 E-mail: sales@ttbuildings.co.uk

TIMBER CONNECTORS

Abru Ltd, Derwentside Industrial Park, Derby Road, Belper, Derbyshire, DE56 1WE Tel: (01773) 525700 Fax: (01773) 828059 E-mail: sales@abru.co.uk
Emstrey Timber Products, 2a Emstrey, Emstrey, Atcham, Shrewsbury, SY5 6QP Tel: (01743) 761131 Fax: (01743) 761825
Sandalwood Gates & Timber Products, Unit G7 Elvington Industrial Estate, York Road, Elvington, York, YO41 4AR Tel: (01904) 608542 E-mail: enquiries@sandalwoodgates.co.uk
Wolf Systems Ltd, Shilton Industrial Estate, Shilton, Coventry, CV7 9QL Tel: (0870) 7339933 Fax: (0870) 7339944 E-mail: mail@wolfsystem.co.uk

TIMBER CONSULTANTS AND RESEARCH

Trada Technology Ltd, Stocking Lane, Hughenden Valley, High Wycombe, Buckinghamshire, HP14 4ND Tel: (01494) 569600 Fax: (01494) 565487 E-mail: information@trada.co.uk

TIMBER CUTTING SERVICES

Wills Mill, mobile sawmilling and timber, The Woodshed, Home Farm, Baynards Park, Cranleigh, Surrey, GU6 8EQ Tel: 01483 548000 Fax: 01483 548000 E-mail: will@wills-mill.co.uk

TIMBER DRYING

Timber Dryers Ltd, 36-38 River Road, Barking, Essex, IG11 0DN Tel: (020) 8594 7752 Fax: (020) 8594 1089 E-mail: sales@blumsom.co.uk

TIMBER ENGINEERED/ SEMIFINISHED ASSEMBLIES

Fountain Timber Products Ltd, Brockley Combe Road, Backwell, Bristol, BS48 3DF Tel: (01934) 862710 Fax: (01934) 863298 E-mail: sales@fountaintimber.co.uk
Rte UK Ltd, 101a Hall Farm Road, Benfleet, Essex, SS7 5JW Tel: (01268) 569393 Fax: (01268) 751753 E-mail: rte-uk@lineone.net
Thomas Armstrong Timber Ltd, Workington Road, Flimby, Maryport, Cumbria, CA15 8RY Tel: (01900) 68226 Fax: (01900) 870800 E-mail: timber@thomasarmstrong.co.uk

TIMBER ENGINEERING SERVICES

A G Stuart Holdings Ltd, Old Rayne, Insch, Aberdeenshire, AB52 6RX Tel: (01464) 851208 Fax: (01464) 851202 E-mail: sales@sylvanstuart.com
H L D Ltd, Old Shipyard, Gainsborough, Lincolnshire, DN21 1NG Tel: (01427) 611800 Fax: (01427) 612867 E-mail: technical@hld.co.uk
David Smith St. Ives Ltd, Marley Road, St. Ives, Cambridgeshire, PE27 3EX Tel: (01480) 462323 Fax: (01480) 494832 E-mail: info@davidsmith.co.uk
Wright Ruffell (Joinery), Plough Road Centre, Great Bentley, Colchester, CO7 8LG Tel: (01206) 250601 Fax: (01206) 251443

TIMBER EXPORT MERCHANTS OR AGENTS

Smart & Emanuel, 93 Francklyn Gardens, Edgware, Middlesex, HA8 8SB Tel: (020) 8905 4114 Fax: (020) 8958 5100

TIMBER FENCING PANELS

▶ Direct Line Timber Ltd, 122 Liff Road, Dundee, DD2 2TL Tel: (01382) 624533 Fax: (01382) 400186 E-mail: sales@directlinetimber.co.uk
▶ Fast Fences Ltd, 44 Fountain Court, Waterside, Evesham, Worcestershire, WR11 1JX Tel: (0800) 0193019 E-mail: nigelrb@nigelrb.com
▶ Inwood (Cymru) Ltd, Units 65-65, Greenfield Business Centre, Greenfield, Holywell, Flintshire, CH8 7GR Tel: (01352) 718007 Fax: (01352) 719614 E-mail: enquiries@woodworkersuk.co.uk
Jacksons Garden Centre, 426-430 Stockfield Road, Yardley, Birmingham, B25 8JJ Tel: 0121-707 5066 Fax: 0121-707 5028 E-mail: martin@jacksons20.fsnet.co.uk
▶ Priory Paving (North East) Ltd, 1 Havelock Street, South Shields, Tyne & Wear, NE33 5DZ Tel: 0191-454 3111 Fax: 0191-454 5500 E-mail: sales@priorypaving.com
▶ Solid Timber Products, Heathfield Way, Gladstone Industry, Northampton, NN5 7QP Tel: (0845) 1297171 Fax: (0845) 1249499 E-mail: adam@solidonline.co.uk
▶ Sunny Aspects Ltd, 36 Udney Park Road, Teddington, Middlesex, TW11 9BG Tel: (020) 8977 4149 E-mail: info@sunnyaspects.co.uk

TIMBER FENCING PANELS - *continued*

▶ Wadham Fencing, 9 Rylands Farm Industrial Estate, Bagley Road, Wellington, Somerset, TA21 9PZ Tel: (01823) 662429 Fax: (01823) 666675
E-mail: enquires@wadhamfencing.co.uk

TIMBER FIRE RETARDANTS (FR)

▶ Cornwall Wood Treatment Services Ltd, 12, United Downs Industrial Park, St. Day, Redruth, Cornwall, TR16 5HY Tel: (01209) 820878 Fax: (01209) 822222
E-mail: sales@cornwallwood.co.uk

TIMBER FLOORING

Atkinson & Kirby Ltd, 2 Burscough Road, Ormskirk, Lancashire, L39 2XG Tel: (01695) 573234 Fax: (01695) 586902
E-mail: sales@akirby.co.uk

Carpet Services London Ltd, 79a Russell Road, London, SW19 1QN Tel: (020) 8543 9131 Fax: (020) 8540 2911
E-mail: csll@btconnect.com

Howarth Timber and Building Merchants Ltd, Medlock Sawmills, Shaw Road, Oldham, OL1 3LJ Tel: 0161-620 2128 Fax: 0161-620 9527 E-mail: htoldh@plp.howarth-timber.co.uk

Ken Hughes, 4 Keston Fruit Farm Cottages, Blackness Lane, Keston, Kent, BR2 6HR Tel: (07778) 285135 Fax: (01689) 855524
E-mail: kenhugheswoodfls@onetel.net.uk

Livingwood Floorcoverings, The Mount, Flimwell, Wadhurst, East Sussex, TN5 7QP Tel: (01580) 879888 Fax: (01580) 879444
E-mail: sales@livingwood.net

Merton Timber, Rowfant Sawmills, Wallage Lane, Rowfant, Crawley, West Sussex, RH10 4NQ Tel: (01342) 716633 Fax: (01342) 716655
E-mail: sales@merton-timber.co.uk

Priory Hardwoods, Unit 57 Bowers Mill, Branch Road, Barkisland, Halifax, West Yorkshire, HX4 0AD Tel: (01422) 311700 Fax: (01422) 311118 E-mail: info@prioryhardwoods.com

Westco Group Ltd, Penarth Road, Cardiff, CF11 8YN Tel: (029) 2037 6700 Fax: (029) 2038 3573 E-mail: westco@westcodiy.co.uk

▶ Woods of Wales, Henfaes Lane, Welshpool, Powys, SY21 7BE Tel: (01938) 554789 Fax: (01938) 554921
E-mail: sales@woodsofwalesffnet.co.uk

TIMBER FRAME KITS

Innovare Systems Ltd, Wray Coppice, Oaks Road, Reigate, Surrey, RH2 0LE Tel: (0845) 6740020 Fax: (0845) 0730800
E-mail: sales@innovaresystems.co.uk

▶ Karlin Timber Frame, 9 Maple Way, Aycliffe Industrial Park, Newton Aycliffe, County Durham, DL5 6BF Tel: (0845) 3454277 Fax: (0845) 3454299
E-mail: info@karlintimberframe.co.uk

TIMBER FRAMED BUILDING CONTRACTORS

A M A Carpentry Services Ltd, Unit 2 Caerbont Enterprise Park, Ystradgynlais, Swansea, SA9 1SW Tel: (01639) 730538 Fax: (01639) 730165 E-mail: ama-carpentry@fsmail.net

▶ Central Timber Frame Ltd, Unit 6, 31 Jubilee Drive, Loughborough, Leicestershire, LE11 5XS Tel: (01509) 269990

▶ Chisholme & Co., Lulham, Madley, Hereford, HR2 9JW Tel: (01981) 250642

Dalby Consultants Ltd, High Dalby House, Dalby, Pickering, North Yorkshire, YO18 7LP Tel: (01751) 460020

▶ Eurotech-NI, 11 Navan Manor, Armagh, BT61 7AP Tel: (028) 3751 1603
E-mail: info@eurotech-ni.com

▶ Global Timber Frames, Global House, Crompton Close, Basildon, Essex, SS14 3AY Tel: (01268) 272550 Fax: (01268) 272554

▶ Home & Office Ltd, 9 Mead Lane, Farnham, Surrey, GU9 7DY Tel: (01252) 820455 Fax: (01252) 820455

Innovare Systems Ltd, Wray Coppice, Oaks Road, Reigate, Surrey, RH2 0LE Tel: (0845) 6740020 Fax: (0845) 0730800
E-mail: sales@innovaresystems.co.uk

▶ J & C Bolton, West Green Cottage, Burgh-by-Sands, Carlisle, CA5 6AQ Tel: (01228) 576682

▶ Leisurewood, Unit 22, Diss Business Centre, Dark Lane, Scole, Diss, Norfolk, IP21 4HD Tel: (01379) 652620 Fax: (01379) 640590

▶ Q T F, 58A Drumarkin Road, Rathfriland, Newry, County Down, BT34 5ND Tel: (028) 4063 2494 Fax: (028) 4063 2495
E-mail: info@qtfhomes.co.uk

▶ The Room, 18 Molesworth Road, Cookstown, County Tyrone, BT80 8NR Tel: (028) 8675 8170

▶ Timcon Design, Unit 2, Fleets Lane, Rylstone, Skipton, North Yorkshire, BD23 6NA Tel: (01756) 730548

TIMBER FRAMED HOUSES

Innovare Systems Ltd, Wray Coppice, Oaks Road, Reigate, Surrey, RH2 0LE Tel: (0845) 6740020 Fax: (0845) 0730800
E-mail: sales@innovaresystems.co.uk

▶ Karlin Timber Frame, 9 Maple Way, Aycliffe Industrial Park, Newton Aycliffe, County Durham, DL5 6BF Tel: (0845) 3454277 Fax: (0845) 3454299
E-mail: info@karlintimberframe.co.uk

▶ Kingston Timber Frame Ltd, 14 Mill Hill Drive, Huntington, York, YO32 9PU Tel: (01904) 766686 Fax: (01904) 766686
E-mail: info@kingstontimberframe.co.uk

▶ Wessex Frame Buildings Ltd, Dovedale House, 16 Butts Road, Alton, Hampshire, GU34 1NB Tel: (01420) 82112 Fax: (01420) 82112
E-mail: enquiries@wessexframebuildings.co.uk

TIMBER FRAMED RESIDENTIAL AGRICULTURAL BUILDINGS

▶ Eurotech-NI, 11 Navan Manor, Armagh, BT61 7AP Tel: (028) 3751 1603
E-mail: info@eurotech-ni.com

▶ Karlin Timber Frame, 9 Maple Way, Aycliffe Industrial Park, Newton Aycliffe, County Durham, DL5 6BF Tel: (0845) 3454277 Fax: (0845) 3454299
E-mail: info@karlintimberframe.co.uk

TIMBER FRAMES

▶ The Forfar Roof Truss Company Ltd, Orchardbank Industrial Estate, Forfar, Angus, DD8 1TD Tel: (01307) 468030 Fax: (01307) 468817
E-mail: alan.hampton@forfarrooftruss.co.uk

Moreys, Trafalgar Road, Newport, Isle of Wight, PO30 1RT Tel: (01983) 525111 Fax: (01983) 520815

▶ Taylor Lane Timber Frame Ltd, Chapel Road, Rotherwas Industrial Estate, Hereford, HR2 6LD Tel: (01432) 271912 Fax: (01432) 351064 E-mail: tl@taylor-lane.co.uk

Top Notch Ltd, Kingsley, Summercourt, Newquay, Cornwall, TR8 5AG Tel: (01872) 510652 Fax: (01872) 510652

▶ Vasahus Ltd, Unit 4A, Wiston Business Park, London Road, Ashington, Pulborough, West Sussex, RH20 3DJ Tel: (01903) 891990 Fax: (01903) 892031E-mail: info@vasahus.biz

William Henry Martin Ltd, Allfield Court, Condover, Shrewsbury, SY5 7AP Tel: (01743) 874550 Fax: (01743) 874650

TIMBER I BEAMS

Tecton Timber Products, Abbey Road, Hempsted, Gloucester, GL2 5HU Tel: (01452) 381146 Fax: (01452) 381147
E-mail: paul@tecton.freeserve.co.uk

TIMBER IMPORT MERCHANTS OR AGENTS

A J Smith & Son Benfleet Ltd, 242 High Road, Benfleet, Essex, SS7 5LA Tel: (01268) 792771 Fax: (01268) 750780
E-mail: info@ajsmith.uk.com

A W Champion Properties Ltd, Champion House, Burlington Road, New Malden, Surrey, KT3 4NB Tel: (020) 8949 1621 Fax: (020) 8949 0271
E-mail: marketing@championtimber.com

Amerind Holdings Ltd, Bilsten House, Blackbushe Business Park, Yateley, Hampshire, GU46 6GE Tel: (01252) 861800 Fax: (01252) 861801 E-mail: admin@amerind.co.uk

Anglo Norden Forest Products Ltd, Orwell Terminal Eagle Wharf, Helena Road, Ipswich, IP3 0BT Tel: (01473) 233244 Fax: (01473) 230805 E-mail: sales@anglonorden.co.uk

Anthony Axford Ltd, Atlas Saw Mills, King Street, Farnworth, Bolton, BL4 7AD Tel: (01204) 571697 Fax: (01204) 795627
E-mail: sales@anthonyaxford.co.uk

Beecroft & Wightman Bradford Ltd, 94 Garnett Street, Bradford, West Yorkshire, BD3 9HB Tel: (01274) 725276 Fax: (01274) 725276

H & T Bellas Ltd, 14 Mountsandel Road, Coleraine, County Londonderry, BT52 1JD Tel: (028) 7034 2205 Fax: (028) 7035 2413
E-mail: info@bellas.co.uk

Bennetts & Co (Grimsby) Ltd, 101 Charlton St, Grimsby, South Humberside, DN31 1SW Tel: (01472) 350151 Fax: (01472) 250053
E-mail: bennettstimber@aol.com

Brooks Group (U K) Ltd, 27 Duncrue Street, Belfast, BT3 9AR Tel: (028) 9074 4201 Fax: (028) 9074 8952
E-mail: brooks.belfast@brooksgroup.ie

Bullock & Driffill Ltd, Staunton Works, Newark Road, Staunton in the Vale, Nottingham, NG13 9PF Tel: (01400) 280000 Fax: (01400) 280010
E-mail: bullock.driffill@btopenworld.com

C B North Ltd, 65 Hedon Road, Hull, HU9 1LW Tel: (01482) 329847 Fax: (01482) 215048

C L T Timber & Transport Ltd, Olds Approach, Coalpits Lane, Watford, WD18 9TD Tel: (01923) 711888 Fax: (01923) 711675
E-mail: wood@wattim.co.uk

Covers, Unit 1, Home Farm Business Centre Home Farm Road, Brighton, BN1 9HU Tel: (01273) 607044 Fax: (01273) 685208

D A Security Systems Ltd, 5 Cornfield Road, Lee-On-The-Solent, Hampshire, PO13 8HZ Tel: (023) 9255 0627

D W Mouldings Ltd, 58 Sunderland Road, Sandy, Bedfordshire, SG19 1QY Tel: (01767) 683400 Fax: (01767) 692296
E-mail: info@dwmouldings.co.uk

Drysdale Timber & Mouldings Ltd, 36-38 River Road, Barking, Essex, IG11 0DN Tel: (020) 8594 6004 Fax: (020) 8594 1089
E-mail: sales@blumsom.co.uk

E O Burton, Thorndon Sawmills, The Avenue, Brentwood, Essex, CM13 3RZ Tel: (01277) 260810 Fax: (01277) 262823
E-mail: timber@eoburton.com

William T. Eden Ltd, PO Box 3, Barking, Essex, IG11 0DU Tel: (020) 8477 8006 Fax: (020) 8477 8010 E-mail: headoffice@edens.co.uk

Edmund Robson & Co Ltd, West Side, Tyne Dock, South Shields, Tyne & Wear, NE34 9PJ Tel: 0191-489 8134 Fax: 0191-489 0696
E-mail: timber@edmundrobson.co.uk

Embercay, Units 1 & 2 Sadler Road, Doddington Road Industial Estate, Lincoln, LN6 3RS Tel: (01522) 500551 Fax: (01522) 500551

Evans Bellhouse Ltd, South 3, Huskisson Dock, Regant Road, Liverpool, L3 0AT Tel: 0151-707 0000 Fax: 0151-922 7356
E-mail: james@evansbellhouse.co.uk

George Barker & Sons Ltd, Backbarrow, Ulverston, Cumbria, LA12 8TA Tel: (01539) 531236 Fax: (01539) 530801
E-mail: sales@gbsltd.sagehost.co.uk

Glenmere Timber Co. Ltd, Hoptons Sawmill, Gores Lane, Market Harborough, Leicestershire, LE16 8AJ Tel: (01858) 466390 Fax: (01858) 466733

J.F. Goodwillie Ltd, Saw Mills, 154 London Road, Waterlooville, Hampshire, PO7 5SR Tel: (08707) 705433 Fax: (08707) 705435

Harry Goodwin & Sons Ltd, Canal Saw Mills, Barnfield Road Industrial Estate, Leek, Staffordshire, ST13 5QG Tel: (01538) 399027 Fax: (01538) 399472
E-mail: richard@goodwin4timber.co.uk

Frank Gresham & Co. Ltd, Kingston Chambers, 17 Princes Dock Street, Hull, HU1 2LT Tel: (01482) 324675 Fax: (01482) 226863
E-mail: mail@greshams.karoo.co.uk

Hardwood Dimensions Ltd, Trafford Park Road, Trafford Park, Manchester, M17 1WH Tel: 0161-872 5111 Fax: 0161-873 7004
E-mail: sales@hardwooddimensions.ltd.uk

Roger Haydock & Co. Ltd, Mersey View Road, Widnes, Cheshire, WA8 8LN Tel: 0151-425 2525 Fax: 0151-425 4141
E-mail: rdh@haydockwidnes.demon.co.uk

Hoppings Softwood Products, Bones Lane, Newchapel, Lingfield, Surrey, RH7 6HR Tel: (01342) 844449 Fax: (01342) 844449
E-mail: sales@hoppings.co.uk

Howarth Timber Ashton, Katherine Street, Ashton-under-Lyne, Lancashire, OL7 0AG Tel: 0161-330 1634 Fax: 0161-339 7618
E-mail: htasht@pop.howarth.timber.co.uk

Howarth (Timber Importers) Ltd, Lincoln Castle, Lincoln Castle Way, New Holland, Barrow-upon-Humber, South Humberside, DN19 7RR Tel: (01469) 532300 Fax: (01469) 531867 E-mail: info@howarth-timber.co.uk

International Timber, Haven Road, Colchester, CO2 8HT Tel: (01206) 866822 Fax: (01206) 878000 E-mail: info@internationaltimber.com

International Timber, Timber Division, Earls Road, Grangemouth, Stirlingshire, FK3 8UU Tel: (01324) 666000 Fax: (01324) 666111

International Timber, West Yard, Trafford Wharf Road, Trafford Park, Manchester, M17 1DJ Tel: 0161-848 2900 Fax: 0161-848 2901

Irvin & Sellers, 24-28 Duncrue Street, Belfast, BT3 9AR Tel: (028) 9035 1224 Fax: (028) 9035 1527 E-mail: info@ijktimber.co.uk

J Scadding & Son Ltd, Eugene Street, St. Judes, Bristol, BS5 0TW Tel: 0117-955 6032 Fax: 0117-941 4536
E-mail: timber@scadding-son-ltd.co.uk

James Latham, Longlands, Milner Way, Ossett, West Yorkshire, WF5 9JE Tel: (01924) 276111 Fax: (01924) 275156
E-mail: panels.ossett@lathams.co.uk

James Mcgregor & Sons Ltd, 49 Sydenham Road, Belfast, BT3 9DR Tel: (028) 9045 1244 Fax: (028) 9045 6433
E-mail: sales@hardwoodni.com

Lafford & Moore, Power House, Powerscroft Road, Sidcup, Kent, DA14 5EA Tel: (020) 8309 4224 Fax: (020) 8309 4222
E-mail: sales@laffordandmoore.co.uk

M H Southern & Co. Ltd, Church Bank Sawmills, Jarrow, Tyne & Wear, NE32 3EB Tel: 0191-489 8231 Fax: 0191-428 0146
E-mail: sales@mhsouthern.co.uk

Mackintosh & Partners (Timber) Ltd, Coopers Lane, Northaw, Potters Bar, Hertfordshire, EN6 4NE Tel: (01707) 642361 Fax: (01707) 646341 E-mail: jpaige@mackintosh.co.uk

Montague L Meyer, Lyncastle Road, Barley Castle Lane, Appleton, Warrington, WA4 4SN Tel: (01925) 211112 Fax: (01925) 211090
E-mail: sales.warrington@mlm.uk.com

Montague L Meyer (Pension Trustee) Ltd, Rippleway Wharf, Barking, Essex, IG11 0DU Tel: (020) 8477 8000 Fax: (020) 8594 8255
E-mail: info@mlmuk.com

Morgan (Timber & Boards), Park Lane Saw Mills, Kidderminster, Worcestershire, DY11 6TG Tel: (01562) 820620

Nicks & Co Timber Ltd, Canada Wharf, Bristol Road, Gloucester, GL1 5TE Tel: (01452) 300159 Fax: (01452) 307682

North London Business, Heron House, Ferry Lane, London, N17 9NF Tel: (020) 8885 9200 Fax: (020) 8801 4274
E-mail: banddsales@btconnect.com

Page & Taylor Ltd, Watery Lane, Ashton-on-Ribble, Preston, PR2 2XH Tel: (01772) 726222 Fax: (01772) 727207
E-mail: sales@pageandtaylor.co.uk

Plaut International Ltd, Heron Mews House, 1A Balfour Road, Ilford, Essex, IG1 4HP Tel: (020) 8553 3471 Fax: (020) 8478 1876
E-mail: panels@plautint.co.uk

Priday Sydney & Snewin Ltd, Oak Wharf, Timberwharf Road, London, N16 6DB Tel: (020) 8800 5661 Fax: (020) 8809 5521
E-mail: sales@pridays.sagehost.co.uk

Q-Deck, The Woodyard, Epping Road, Epping, Essex, CM16 6TT Tel: (01992) 561103
E-mail: sales@hoppings.co.uk

Rawle Gammon & Baker Holdings Ltd, Gammon House, Riverside Road, Pottington Business Park, Barnstaple, Devon, EX31 1LX Tel: (01271) 375501 Fax: (01271) 329982
E-mail: barnstable@rgbltd.co.uk

William Roberts & Co. Ltd, Water Street, Menai Bridge, Gwynedd, LL59 5DE Tel: (01248) 712596 Fax: (01248) 717303
E-mail: dolgellau@williamroberts.co.uk

S C A Ltd, Etruscan Street, Stoke-on-Trent, ST1 5PG Tel: (01782) 202122 Fax: (01782) 224200

Saint Gobain Building Distribution Ltd, Merchant House, Binley Business Park, Harry Weston Road, Coventry, CV3 2TT Tel: (024) 7643 8400 Fax: (024) 7643 8505
E-mail: shelley.knowles@jewson.co.uk

Smart & Emanuel, 93 Francklyn Gardens, Edgware, Middlesex, HA8 8SB Tel: (020) 8905 4114 Fax: (020) 8958 5100

Thornbridge Sawmills Ltd, Laurieston Road, Grangemouth, Stirlingshire, FK3 8XX Tel: (01324) 612121 Fax: (01324) 612100

Timber Marketing Corporation Ltd, Old House Mews, London Road, Horsham, West Sussex, RH12 1AF Tel: (01403) 255255 Fax: (01403) 210214 E-mail: tmchorsham@tmcorp.co.uk

Timbmet Ltd, PO Box 39, Oxford, OX2 9PP Tel: (01865) 862223 Fax: (01865) 860342
E-mail: marketing@timbmet.com

Tonge Bridge Timber Sales UK Ltd, Turner Bridge Works, Windley Street, Bolton, BL2 2DF Tel: (01204) 417676 Fax: (01204) 417583
E-mail: sales@tongebridgetimber.co.uk

Travis Perkins plc, Boyn Valley Road, Maidenhead, Berkshire, SL6 4EE Tel: (01628) 770577 Fax: (01628) 625919

Uynit 2, 1 Green Lane, Wardle, Nantwich, Cheshire, CW5 6BN Tel: (01829) 261010 Fax: (01829) 260884
E-mail: timber@rowlinson.co.uk

Vincent Timber Ltd, 8 Montgomery Street, Birmingham, B11 1DU Tel: 0121-772 5511 Fax: 0121-766 6002
E-mail: gdw@vincenttimber.co.uk

W Hanson Timber & Builders Merchants Ltd, Uxbridge Road, Southall, Middlesex, UB1 3EQ Tel: (020) 8571 3161 Fax: (020) 8574 3816
E-mail: sales@w-hanson.co.uk

Walker Timber Ltd, Carriden Sawmills, Bo'Ness, West Lothian, EH51 9SN Tel: (01506) 823331 Fax: (01506) 822590
E-mail: mail@walkertimber.com

G.R. Wiltshire & Co., Smoke Hall Lane, Winsford, Cheshire, CW7 3BE Tel: (01455) 202666 Fax: (01606) 555511
E-mail: sales@smeetimber.co.uk

Wood's Timber Co Ltd, Witham, Hull, HU9 1BG Tel: (01482) 320466 Fax: (01482) 212799

TIMBER JOINING CORRUGATED FASTENERS

W. & M. Joyce Engineers (Taurus Equipment) Ltd, Steele Road, London, NW10 7AR Tel: (020) 8965 2521 Fax: (020) 8961 0242
E-mail: barry@taurus-equipment.co.uk

R J Engineering, Derby Works, Liverpool Road South, Burscough, Ormskirk, Lancashire, L40 7SU Tel: (01704) 897771 Fax: (01704) 897772 E-mail: r.j.engineering@amserve.net

TIMBER LOG HANDLING EQUIPMENT

Soderhamn Errikson, Unit 17 Vauxhall Industrial Estate, Greg Street, Reddish, Stockport, Cheshire, SK5 7BR Tel: 0161-429 9437 Fax: 0161-477 0641
E-mail: info@se-saws.co.uk

TIMBER MARKING CRAYONS

Rowland Sandwith Ltd, 32 Canford Bottom, Wimborne, Dorset, BH21 2HD Tel: (01202) 882323 Fax: (01202) 842815
E-mail: hancocks@rowland-sandwith.co.uk

TIMBER MERCHANTS, *See also headings for particular types*

A Bertram Edwards Ltd, Old Coleham, Shrewsbury, SY3 7BU Tel: (01743) 357071 Fax: (01743) 357073 E-mail: info@bertram-edwards.co.uk

A Diamond & Son Timber Ltd, 35 New Mills Road, Coleraine, County Londonderry, BT52 2JB Tel: (028) 7034 3452 Fax: (028) 7034 3279 E-mail: sales@adiamondandson.co.uk

A J R Elsworth Ltd, Firwood Works, Firwood Industrial Estate, Thicketford Road, Firwood Fold, Bolton, BL2 3TR Tel: (01204) 595710 Fax: (01204) 302096

A J Smith & Son Benfleet Ltd, 242 High Road, Benfleet, Essex, SS7 5LA Tel: (01268) 792771 Fax: (01268) 750780 E-mail: info@ajsmith.uk.com

A K Williams & Sons Ltd, Queen Street, Madeley, Telford, Shropshire, TF7 4BH Tel: (01952) 585740 Fax: (01952) 582021

A W Champion Ltd, 2 Hartfield Cresent, London, SW19 3SD Tel: (020) 8542 1606 Fax: (020) 8540 7237

A W Champion Properties Ltd, Champion House, Burlington Road, New Malden, Surrey, KT3 4NB Tel: (020) 8949 1621 Fax: (020) 8949 0271 E-mail: marketing@championtimber.com

A & W Cushion Ltd, St Benedicts Sawmills, Barn Road, Norwich, NR2 4PW Tel: (01603) 628527 Fax: (01603) 765071 E-mail: cushion@kimbernorwich.demon.co.uk

Acutech, Unit 5 York House, Langston Road, Loughton, Essex, IG10 3TQ Tel: (020) 8502 2155 Fax: (020) 8508 8562 E-mail: sales@acuutech.com

Alan Walter (Timber), 7-23 Louisa St, Midland Road, Bristol, BS2 0LE Tel: 0117-926 8370 Fax: 0117-926 8370

Alexanders Sawmills Ltd, Heathfield Road, Ayr, KA8 9SS Tel: (01292) 267842 Fax: (01292) 610707

Alexandra Saw Mills Ltd, Byron Street, Carlisle, CA2 5TB Tel: (01228) 525368 Fax: (01228) 590282

Allen & Orr Ltd, The Albion Sawmills, Union Walk, Chesterfield, Derbyshire, S40 4SA Tel: (01246) 232426 Fax: (01246) 559099

Alsford Timber Ltd, Montague Road, Brielle Way, Sheerness, Kent, ME12 1YW Tel: (01795) 662363 Fax: (01795) 665806

Andersons, Denton Holme Sawmills, Denton Street, Carlisle, CA2 5EQ Tel: (01228) 526242 Fax: (01228) 515647

Andrew & Co Spalding Ltd, Welland Sawmills, Little London, Spalding, Lincolnshire, PE11 2UJ Tel: (01775) 723016 Fax: (01775) 722499 E-mail: derek@andrewdiy.co.uk

Anglian Timber Ltd, The Sawmill, Colchester Road, Wix, Manningtree, Essex, CO11 2RS Tel: (01255) 870881 Fax: (01255) 870480 E-mail: sales@angliantimber.co.uk

Arnold Laver, Manningham Sawmills, Canal Road, Bradford, West Yorkshire, BD2 1AR Tel: (01274) 732861 Fax: (01274) 737060 E-mail: sales@bradford.timberworld.co.uk

Arnold Laver, 478 Basingstoke Road, Reading, RG2 0QN Tel: 0118-975 1100 Fax: 0118-975 1900E-mail: sales@reading.timberworld.co.uk

A. Axford Ltd, The Workshop, Bark Street, Bolton, BL1 1AZ Tel: (01204) 520931 Fax: (01204) 520931

Anthony Axford Ltd, Atlas Saw Mills, King Street, Farnworth, Bolton, BL4 7AD Tel: (01204) 571697 Fax: (01204) 795627 E-mail: sales@anthonyaxford.co.uk

B B F Fencing, Victoria Street Sawmills, Stoke-on-Trent, ST4 6HD Tel: (01782) 717757 Fax: (01782) 712565 E-mail: trentwoodtimber@talktalkbusiness.net

B S W Timber plc, East End, Earlston, Berwickshire, TD4 6JA Tel: (01896) 849255 Fax: (01896) 848080E-mail: sales@bsw.co.uk

Mike Baker Timber Merchants, Boston Industrial Estate, Power Station Road, Rugeley, Staffordshire, WS15 2HS Tel: (01889) 583306 Fax: (01889) 575263

Barlows & Sons Hermitage Ltd, Red Shute Hill Industrial Estate, Red Shute Hill, Hermitage, Thatcham, Berkshire, RG18 9QL Tel: (01635) 200253 Fax: (01635) 201092

Barnes Branch & Co Ltd, Brook Street, High Wycombe, Buckinghamshire, HP11 2EQ Tel: (01494) 525761 Fax: (01494) 464582 E-mail: sales@barnesbranch.demon.co.uk

Barton Timber Co. Ltd, 50 North Street, Hornchurch, Essex, RM11 1SR Tel: (01708) 448805 Fax: (01708) 453561

Bearwood Builders Supply Co Smethwick Ltd, Three Shires Oak Road, Smethwick, West Midlands, B67 5BS Tel: 0121-429 2011 Fax: 0121-429 2226

Beaumont Forest Products Ltd, Swinley Sawmills, Swinley Road, Ascot, Berkshire, SL5 8AZ Tel: (01344) 874137 Fax: (01344) 874139 E-mail: sales@beaumontforest.co.uk

Bedford Timber Supplies Ltd, Cauldwell Walk, Bedford, MK42 9DT Tel: (01234) 272171 Fax: (01234) 269235 E-mail: matt@batfordtimbersupplies.co.uk

Beecroft & Wightman Bradford Ltd, 94 Garnett Street, Bradford, West Yorkshire, BD3 9HB Tel: (01274) 725276 Fax: (01274) 725276

Bell & Sime, Balunie Drive, Balunie Field Trading Estate, Dundee, DD4 8XE Tel: (01382) 730630 Fax: (01382) 739639 E-mail: dundee@buildbase.co.uk

Bendrey Bros, Bath Road, Bridgeyate, Bristol, BS30 5JW Tel: 0117-967 4382 Fax: 0117-967 4383

Bennetts & Co (Grimsby) Ltd, 101 Charlton St, Grimsby, South Humberside, DN31 1SW Tel: (01472) 350151 Fax: (01472) 250053 E-mail: bennettstimber@aol.com

Blandford Forum Timber Ltd, Holland Way, Blandford Forum, Dorset, DT11 7SX Tel: (01258) 452692 Fax: (01258) 459589 E-mail: talkwood@talk21.com

Boys & Boden Ltd, Mill Lane, Welshpool, Powys, SY21 7BL Tel: (01938) 556677 Fax: (01938) 555773

Bradford & Sons Ltd, 98 Hendford Hill, Yeovil, Somerset, BA20 2QR Tel: (01935) 845245 Fax: (01935) 845242 E-mail: bradfords@bradfords.co.uk

T. Brewer & Co. Ltd, 110 Dunmow Road, Bishop's Stortford, Hertfordshire, CM23 5HN Tel: (01279) 658338 Fax: (01279) 757023 E-mail: stortford@tbrewer.co.uk

Bristow Buildbase, Kensington Way, Oakengates, Telford, Shropshire, TF2 6ER Tel: (01952) 613561 Fax: (01952) 616555 E-mail: telford@buildbase.co.uk

Brooks Bros (London) Ltd, Kingsbridge Wharf, Kingsbridge Road, Barking, Essex, IG11 0BT Tel: (020) 8591 5300 Fax: (020) 8594 7133 E-mail: enquires@brooksbroslondon.com

Brooks Manson, Colne Rd, Earby, Barnoldswick, Lancs, BB18 6XT Tel: (01282) 842777 Fax: (01282) 843361 E-mail: brooks.earby@upm-kymmene.com

Buildbase, Simpson Road, Bletchley, Milton Keynes, MK1 1BB Tel: (01908) 644222 Fax: (01908) 270243

Builders Supplies (West Coast) Ltd, Kilbane Street, Fleetwood, Lancashire, FY7 7PF Tel: (01253) 776600 Fax: (01253) 776800 E-mail: sales@bswc.biz

Burcart Clacton Ltd, 259-265 Old Road, Clacton-on-Sea, Essex, CO15 3LU Tel: (01255) 422213 Fax: (01255) 476751 E-mail: burcart@supanet.com

Burnt Oak Builders Merchant Ltd, 41 Barnfield Road, Edgware, Middlesex, HA8 0AY Tel: (020) 8952 1257 Fax: (020) 8952 2538

Nelson Butler & Son Ltd, Elmhirst Road, Horncastle, Lincolnshire, LN9 5AU Tel: (01507) 523451 Fax: (01507) 522182

Buttle plc, 38-41 Castle Mews, London, NW1 8SY Tel: (020) 7485 8511 Fax: (020) 7482 3480 E-mail: bee@buttle.co.uk

C Blumsom Ltd, Maple Wharf, 36-38 River Road, Barking, Essex, IG11 0DN Tel: (020) 8594 5175 Fax: (020) 8507 1334 E-mail: sales@blumson.co.uk

C F Anderson & Son Ltd, 228 Old London Road, Marks Tey, Colchester, CO6 1HD Tel: (020) 7226 1212 Fax: (020) 7359 1112 E-mail: cfanderson@cfanderson.co.uk

C & W Berry Ltd, Golden Hill Lane, Leyland, Leyland, PR25 2YH Tel: (01772) 431216 Fax: (01772) 622314 E-mail: enquiries@cwberry.com

The Capworth Panel & Timber Company Ltd, 27 Capworth Street, London, E10 5AN Tel: (020) 8539 3374 Fax: (020) 8539 5872

Carver Gases Ltd, Littles Lane, Wolverhampton, WV1 1JY Tel: (01902) 577000 Fax: (01902) 712145 E-mail: mail@carvers.co.uk

Catford Timber Co., 161 Rushey Green, London, SE6 4BD Tel: (020) 8698 7277 Fax: (020) 8697 0790 E-mail: sales@catfordtimber.co.uk

Charles Gregory & Sons Ltd, Nottingham Road, Tansley, Matlock, Derbyshire, DE4 5FR Tel: (01629) 582376 Fax: (01629) 57112

Clanville Sawmills Ltd, Clanville, Castle Cary, Somerset, BA7 7PQ Tel: (01963) 350881 Fax: (01963) 351562 E-mail: admin@clanvillsawmills.co.uk

Clower & Son Ltd, 48-52 Nottingham Road, Ripley, Derbyshire, DE5 3AT Tel: (01773) 742351 Fax: (01773) 744610

Copeplan Co., Neath Road, Landore, Swansea, SA1 2JG Tel: (01792) 799895 Fax: (01792) 776670

▶ Cordiner, 5 Crombie Place, Aberdeen, AB11 9PJ Tel: (01224) 877611 Fax: (01224) 875510

J.P. Corry Ltd, 648 Springfield Road, Belfast, BT12 7EH Tel: (028) 9024 3661 Fax: (028) 9026 2123 E-mail: info@jpcorry.co.uk

Countryside Gates & Timber Products, Gressy Holme Farm, Bullpit Road, Balderton, Newark, Nottinghamshire, NG24 3LZ Tel: (01636) 679983 Fax: (01636) 703434

Cox Long Ltd, Airfield Industrial Estate, Hixon, Stafford, ST18 0PA Tel: (01889) 270166 Fax: (01889) 271041 E-mail: info@coxlong.com

Brian Curtis, 60 Park Avenue, Maidstone, Kent, ME14 5HL Tel: (01622) 757759

D A Brockwell, Mancetter Road, Hartshill, Nuneaton, Warwickshire, CV10 0RT Tel: (024) 7639 2283 Fax: (024) 7639 8259

D Sutherland & Son Ltd, Union Street, Wick, Caithness, KW1 5ED Tel: (01955) 602101 Fax: (01955) 602917

Dagless Ltd, Brigstock Road, Wisbech, Cambridgeshire, PE13 3JL Tel: (01945) 583826 Fax: (01945) 582673 E-mail: info@shiregb.co.uk

David Cover & Son Ltd, Chatfields Yard, Cooksbridge, Lewes, East Sussex, BN8 4TJ Tel: (01273) 476133 Fax: (01273) 400164 E-mail: sales@covers-group.co.uk

Davies Timber Ltd, Wythall Saw Mills Alcester Road, Wythall, Birmingham, B47 6JG Tel: (01564) 826861 Fax: (01564) 823505 E-mail: davistimber@davistimber.fsnet.co.uk

Dawson Bros Timber Ltd, Blowers Green Cresent, Dudley, West Midlands, DY2 8XQ Tel: (01384) 253816 Fax: (01384) 457248 E-mail: sales@dawsontimber.co.uk

Stan Dawson Ltd, Kirkley Sawmills, Kirkley, Newcastle upon Tyne, NE20 0BD Tel: (01661) 860413 Fax: (01661) 822352

Dobsons, 104-106 Stoke Road, Slough, SL2 5AP Tel: (01753) 520978 Fax: (01753) 823821 E-mail: dobsons@hotmail.com

East Bros Holdings Ltd, The Sawmills, West Dean, Salisbury, SP5 1JA Tel: (01794) 340270 Fax: (01794) 341317 E-mail: mail@eastbros.co.uk

Eastman & Co Timber Ltd, Princess Street, Bedminster, Bristol, BS3 4AG Tel: 0117-966 1596 Fax: 0117-907 3354 E-mail: andy@eastmantimber.wanadoo.co.uk

Edmund Robson & Co Ltd, West Side, Tyne Dock, South Shields, Tyne & Wear, NE34 9PJ Tel: 0191-489 8134 Fax: 0191-489 0696 E-mail: timber@edmundrobson.co.uk

Edwards Buildbase, 28 Elm Road, Wisbech, Cambridgeshire, PE13 2TB Tel: (01945) 584491 Fax: (01945) 475121 E-mail: wisbeck@billbase.co.uk

Embercay, Units 1 & 2 Sadler Road, Doddington Road Indusrial Estate, Lincoln, LN6 3RS Tel: (01522) 500551 Fax: (01522) 500551

Empress Fencing Ltd, Empress Sawmills, Clitheroe Road, Chatburn, Clitheroe, Lancashire, BB7 4JY Tel: (01200) 441215 Fax: (01200) 449931 E-mail: sales@empressfencing.co.uk

Enfield Timber Co., 1-23 Hertford Road, Enfield Highway, Enfield, Middlesex, EN3 5JD Tel: (020) 8804 1800 Fax: (020) 8443 4569

Evans Bellhouse Ltd, South 3, Huskisson Dock, Regant Road, Liverpool, L3 0AT Tel: 0151-707 0000 Fax: 0151-922 7356 E-mail: james@evansbellhouse.co.uk

F T Nixon & Son Ltd, Northend, Wisbech, Cambridgeshire, PE13 1TH Tel: (01945) 583231 Fax: (01945) 466902

Fallowfield Timber, Ladybarn Road, Fallowfield, Manchester, M14 6WW Tel: 0161-224 3636 Fax: 0161-224 0212

Firwood Timber & Building Supplies, 8 Greengate Lane, Prestwich, Manchester, M25 3HW Tel: 0161-798 8404 Fax: 0161-773 5386 E-mail: firwood@prestwichm25.wanadoo.co.uk

Fitchett & Woolacott, Willow Road, Nottingham, NG7 2PR Tel: 0115-993 1111 Fax: 0115-993 1151 E-mail: enquries@fitchett.co.uk

John Fleming & Co. Ltd, Silverburn Place, Bridge Of Don, Aberdeen, AB23 8EG Tel: (01224) 258200 Fax: (01224) 825377 E-mail: aberdeen@buildbase.co.uk

E. Fletcher (Timber) Ltd, Queen Street, Walsall, WS2 9PE Tel: (01922) 631254 Fax: (01922) 724589

Forest Products Ltd, Workshop Forestry Commission Lightmoor Dept, Speech House Road, Cinderford, Gloucestershire, GL14 3HU Tel: (01594) 822223 Fax: (01594) 826901 E-mail: enquiries@forest-products.com

Derek Fox & Sons (Timber) Ltd, Shay Lane Industrial Estate, Shay Lane, Longridge, Preston, PR3 3BT Tel: (01772) 784626 Fax: (01772) 785103 E-mail: info@derekfoxtimber.co.uk

G A Watts & Son, Podington Airfield, Hinwick, Wellingborough, Northamptonshire, NN29 7JQ Tel: (01234) 781003

Geo. Ashcroft & Co. Ltd, Sandy Road, Seaforth, Liverpool, L21 3TW Tel: 0151-928 2565 Fax: 0151-928 0342

George Barker & Sons Ltd, Backbarrow, Ulverston, Cumbria, LA12 8TA Tel: (01539) 531236 Fax: (01539) 530801 E-mail: sales@gbsltd.sagehost.co.uk

George Hill Timber Oldham Ltd, Boundary Industrial Estate, Millfield Road, Bolton, BL2 6QY Tel: (01204) 384867 Fax: (01204) 526601

Gibbon & Sons Ltd, Richmond Road, Cardiff, CF24 3XA Tel: (029) 2048 3331 Fax: (029) 2048 3333

Gilmore & Aitken Ltd, Auchincarroch Road, Alexandria, Dunbartonshire, G83 9EY Tel: (01389) 752333 Fax: (01389) 755659 E-mail: enquiries@aitkenhoward.co.uk

J.F. Goodwillie Ltd, Saw Mills, 154 London Road, Waterlooville, Hampshire, PO7 5SR Tel: (08707) 705433 Fax: (08707) 705435

Harry Goodwin & Sons Ltd, Canal Saw Mills, Barnfield Road Industrial Estate, Leek, Staffordshire, ST13 5QG Tel: (01538) 399027 Fax: (01538) 399472 E-mail: richard@goodwin4timber.co.uk

John Gordon & Son Ltd, Balblair Road, Nairn, IV12 5LY Tel: (01667) 453223 Fax: (01667) 452168 E-mail: enquiries@gordontimber.co.uk

Gregory Bros, The Timber Yard, Lucas Green Road, West End, Woking, Surrey, GU24 9YB Tel: (01483) 472264 Fax: (01483) 799548

Frank Gresham & Co. Ltd, Kingston Chambers, 17 Princes Dock Street, Hull, HU1 2LT Tel: (01482) 324675 Fax: (01482) 226863 E-mail: mail@greshams.karoo.co.uk

H A R Banfield & Son Ltd, 103-105 Barry Road, London, SE22 0HW Tel: (020) 8693 5022 Fax: (020) 8299 3197

H J Cooper Timber Ltd, Thornleigh Trading Estate, Dudley, West Midlands, DY2 8UB Tel: (01384) 254591 Fax: (01384) 237119 E-mail: info@cooperstimber.co.uk

H Lee & Son, The Woodyard, Belle Vue Road, Ashbourne, Derbyshire, DE6 1AT Tel: (01335) 342530

H M Lowe & Son Ltd, 476 Garrison Lane, Birmingham, B9 4NT Tel: 0121-772 0330 Fax: 0121-771 3759 E-mail: enquiries@hmlowe.co.uk

Haldane Fisher, Castle Street, Portadown, Craigavon, County Armagh, BT62 1BD Tel: (028) 3833 7321 Fax: (028) 3833 0896 E-mail: sales.portadown@haldane-fisher.com

Haldane & Fisher Ltd, Isle Of Man Business Park, Douglas, Isle Of Man, IM2 2QY Tel: (01624) 624466 Fax: (01624) 661335 E-mail: wigan@enterprize.net

Haldane Fisher, Carnbane Industrial Estate, Newry, County Down, BT35 6QQ Tel: (028) 3026 3201 Fax: (028) 3026 8101 E-mail: dgrayhaldanefisher@btinternet.com

Hanworth Timber Co. Ltd, White Post Road, Hanworth, Norwich, NR11 7HN Tel: (01263) 761766 Fax: (01263) 768903

Hardwood Dimensions Ltd, Trafford Park Road, Trafford Park, Manchester, M17 1WH Tel: 0161-872 5111 Fax: 0161-873 7004 E-mail: sales@hardwooddimensions.ltd.uk

Harris, Charlotte Road, Stirchley, Birmingham, B30 2BT Tel: 0121-451 1664 Fax: 0121-433 3864 E-mail: sales@harrisofstirchley.co.uk

Harry Adcock & Son, Saw Mills, Corby Glen, Grantham, Lincolnshire, NG33 4LB Tel: (01476) 550231 Fax: (01476) 550363 E-mail: richard@harryadcock.a-i-s.co.uk

Hartle Lane Sawmill, Hartle Lane, Belbroughton, Stourbridge, West Midlands, DY9 9TJ Tel: (01562) 730583

Harts Timber Buildings, 181 Broad Oak Road, St. Helens, Merseyside, WA9 2AQ Tel: (01744) 730004

Hawkesford Buildbase, Adderley Road, Market Drayton, Shropshire, TF9 3SW Tel: (01630) 652481 Fax: (01630) 655489 E-mail: marketdrayton@buildbase.co.uk

Herne Hill Timber Co, 301 Railton Road, London, SE24 0JN Tel: (020) 7274 2548

Hill Bros Building Supplies Ltd, Well Lane, Wolverhampton, WV11 1XS Tel: (01902) 731253 Fax: (01902) 306424

House & Patten, 1 Kennard Road, Kingswood, Bristol, BS15 8AA Tel: 0117-967 3347 Fax: 0117-967 3347

Howarth Timber and Building Merchants Ltd, Medlock Sawmills, Shaw Road, Oldham, OL1 3LJ Tel: 0161-620 2128 Fax: 0161-620 9527 E-mail: htoldh@plp.howarth-timber.co.uk

Percy A. Hudson Ltd, Northumberland Street, North Shields, Tyne & Wear, NE30 1DW Tel: 0191-257 5099 Fax: 0191-257 9461

Hughes & Allen Ltd, Canalside Industrial Estate, Oil Sites Road, Ellesmere Port, CH65 4EN Tel: 0151-355 3170 Fax: 0151-355 5074

International Timber, Haven Road, Colchester, CO2 8HT Tel: (01206) 866822 Fax: (01206) 878000 E-mail: info@internationaltimber.com

International Timber, West Yard, Trafford Wharf Road, Trafford Park, Manchester, M17 1DJ Tel: 0161-848 2900 Fax: 0161-848 2901

Irvin & Sellers, 24-28 Duncrue Street, Belfast, BT3 9AR Tel: (028) 9035 1224 Fax: (028) 9035 1527 E-mail: info@ijktimber.co.uk

J Bradnam & Sons, Melbourne Bridge, Withersfield, Haverhill, Suffolk, CB9 7RR Tel: (01440) 702110 Fax: (01440) 704463

J Callander & Son Ltd, Abbotshaugh Sawmill, Abbots Road, Falkirk, FK2 7XU Tel: (01324) 621563 Fax: (01324) 634386 E-mail: info@jcallander.co.uk

J J Mckinney & Sons, 120 Railway Street, Armagh, BT61 7ND Tel: (028) 3752 2844

J & M Elston, Washfield, Tiverton, Devon, EX16 9RF Tel: (01398) 351248 Fax: (01398) 351248

J P Corry, Ballydugan Indust Estate, Downpatrick, County Down, BT30 6HG Tel: (028) 4461 2011 Fax: (028) 4461 5635 E-mail: downpatrick@jpcorry.co.uk

J P Corry Ni Ltd, 136-210 Tennent Street, Belfast, BT13 3GF Tel: (028) 9075 1756 Fax: (028) 9035 2807

J Scadding & Son Ltd, Eugene Street, St. Judes, Bristol, BS5 0TW Tel: 0117-955 6032 Fax: 0117-941 4536 E-mail: timber@scadding-son-ltd.co.uk

J T Atkinsons Ltd, Ullswater Road, Penrith, Cumbria, CA11 7EH Tel: (01768) 865561 Fax: (01768) 890111

J T Dove Ltd, Orchard Street, Newcastle upon Tyne, NE1 3NB Tel: 0191-232 6151 Fax: 0191-222 1870 E-mail: newcastle@jtdove.co.uk

Jackson & Allen Ltd, 244 Chingford Mount Road, London, E4 8JP Tel: (020) 8529 7014 Fax: (020) 8520 8040

Jacobs Builder Centre, Loguestown Industrial Estate, Coleraine, County Londonderry, BT52 2NS Tel: (028) 7034 4751 Fax: (028) 7035 5963 E-mail: jacobs@macblair.com

James Latham, Longlands, Milner Way, Ossett, West Yorkshire, WF5 9JE Tel: (01924) 276111 Fax: (01924) 275156 E-mail: panels.ossett@lathams.co.uk

James Latham, 13 Chartwell Drive, Wigston, Leicestershire, LE18 2FN Tel: 0116-288 9161 Fax: 0116-281 3806 E-mail: panels.wigston@lathams.co.uk

James Latham Sales plc, Unit 2 Swallow Park, Finway Road, Hemel Hempstead Industrial Estate, Hemel Hempstead, Hertfordshire, HP2 7QU Tel: (01442) 849000 Fax: (01442) 239287 E-mail: marketing@lathams.co.uk

B. Jenkins & Sons Ltd, Watton Saw Mills, Brecon, Powys, LD3 7EN Tel: (01874) 622853 Fax: (01874) 622750 E-mail: sales.bjenkins@btconnect.com

Jennor Timber Co. Ltd, Lockfield Avenue, Enfield, Middlesex, EN3 7QL Tel: (020) 8805 2121 Fax: (020) 8804 2292

Jewson Ltd, 4 Beeching Road, Bexhill-on-Sea, East Sussex, TN39 3LG Tel: (01424) 731414 Fax: (01424) 731887

▶ indicates data change since last edition

TIMBER MERCHANTS – *continued*

Jewson Ltd, Nelson Way, Boston, Lincolnshire, PE21 8UA Tel: (01205) 362451 Fax: (01205) 365898

Jewson Ltd, Lyons Lane, Chorley, Lancashire, PR6 0PH Tel: (01257) 276211 Fax: (01257) 260098

Jewson, St. Peg Works, St. Peg Lane, Cleckheaton, West Yorkshire, BD19 3SH Tel: (01274) 872549 Fax: (01274) 864532

Jewsons Ltd, Cefndy Road, Rhyl, Denbighshire, LL18 2EU Tel: (01745) 334402 Fax: (01745) 344483

Job Earnshaw & Bros.Limited, Main Offices Stocksmoor Road, Midgley, Wakefield, West Yorkshire, WF4 4JG Tel: (01924) 830099 Fax: (01924) 830080 E-mail: john@job-earnshaw.co.uk

John Mcmurtry & Co. Ltd, 42 Douglas Terrace, Ballymena, County Antrim, BT42 3AP Tel: (028) 2564 8116 Fax: (028) 2564 2519

John Richardson & Son, Roper Street, Penrith, Cumbria, CA11 8HS Tel: (01768) 895000 Fax: (01768) 895007

Johnson & Co., Chapel Square, Deddington, Banbury, Oxfordshire, OX15 0SG Tel: (01869) 338275 Fax: (01869) 337014 E-mail: office@johnsonsofdeddington.co.uk

James Jones & Sons Ltd, Garmouth Road, Mosstodloch, Fochabers, Morayshire, IV32 7LH Tel: (01343) 821421 Fax: (01343) 821299 E-mail: mosstodloch@jamesjones.co.uk

James Jones & Sons Ltd, Broomage Avenue, Larbert, Stirlingshire, FK5 4NQ Tel: (01324) 562241 Fax: (01324) 558755 E-mail: sales@jamesjones.com

Joseph Parr Alco Ltd, Higginshaw Lane, Royton, Oldham, OL2 6JD Tel: 0161-633 1264 Fax: 0161-620 0866 E-mail: aellis@josephparr.co.uk

Joseph Thompson, Hendon Lodge Sawmills, Moor Terrace, Sunderland, SR1 2PA Tel: 0191-514 4663 Fax: 0191-514 3251

Keyline Ltd, Bentinck Street, Ashton-under-Lyne, Lancashire, OL7 0PT Tel: 0161-330 2214 Fax: 0161-343 2158

Keyline Ltd, Scotia Business Park, Scotia Road, Stoke-on-Trent, ST6 4HG Tel: (01782) 811999 Fax: (01782) 813999

Keyline Builders Merchants Ltd, 130 Salkeld Street, Glasgow, G5 8HD Tel: 0141-429 5141 Fax: 0141-429 4992

Keys Mcmahon, 15 Bay Road, Londonderry, BT48 7SH Tel: (028) 7136 6321 Fax: (028) 7136 4388 E-mail: info@rkeys.com

James Kingan & Sons Ltd, Townhead Sawmill, New Abbey, Dumfries, DG2 8DU Tel: (01387) 850282 Fax: (01387) 850492

Lambert Timber, Stanworth Road, Nelson, Lancashire, BB9 7DS Tel: (01282) 613333 Fax: (01282) 613933

Latchfords Timber Merchants, 24-28 Warner Street, London, EC1R 5EX Tel: (020) 7837 1461 Fax: (020) 7837 1462

James Latham, Badminton Road Trading Estate, Badminton Road, Yate, Bristol, BS37 5JX Tel: (01454) 315421 Fax: (01454) 323488 E-mail: panals.yate@lathams.co.uk

James Latham Ltd, Nest Road, Felling Industrial Estate, Gateshead, Tyne & Wear, NE10 0LU Tel: 0191-469 4211 Fax: 0191-469 2615 E-mail: denis@lathams.co.uk

Arnold Laver Birmingham Board Timberworld, Dudley Road, Oldbury, West Midlands, B69 3DA Tel: 0121-552 7788 Fax: 0121-544 7186 E-mail: sales@birminghamtimberworld.co.uk

Lawson Timber Ltd, White Hart Road, London, SE18 1DH Tel: (020) 8855 7621 Fax: (020) 8854 6552

Lawsons Whetstone Ltd, Woodcote Grove Road, Coulsdon, Surrey, CR5 2AG Tel: (020) 8660 0807 Fax: (020) 8668 4847

Leigh Timber Co. Ltd, 1388-1416 London Road, Leigh-on-Sea, Essex, SS9 2UJ Tel: (01702) 711366 Fax: (01702) 470993

Leyton Timber Merchants, 583-585 High Road, London, E10 6PY Tel: (020) 8539 6491 Fax: (020) 8539 6491

Linnell Bros Ltd, Silverstone Fields Farm, Silverstone, Towcester, Northamptonshire, NN12 8TB Tel: (01327) 354422 Fax: (01327) 355840 E-mail: info@linnellbros.co.uk

James Littler & Sons Ltd, Barons Quay Sawmills, Leicester Street, Northwich, Cheshire, CW9 5LD Tel: (01606) 46112 Fax: (01606) 43844 E-mail: sales@timbermerchantuk.com

Lomax Demolition & Timber Yard, Albion Street, Bury, Lancashire, BL8 2AD Tel: 0161-764 5845

Chas Lowe & Sons (Builders' Merchants) Ltd, 156 London Road, Knebworth, Hertfordshire, SG3 6HA Tel: (01438) 812740 Fax: (01438) 814324 E-mail: peter@chaslowe.co.uk

V.A. Luck Ltd, 414 Shaftmoor Lane, Hall Green, Birmingham, B28 8TA Tel: 0121-777 3366 Fax: 0121-778 5888

Lumber Mill Somerset, Haselbury Plucknett, Crewkerne, Somerset, TA18 7PH Tel: (01460) 73201

M & H Builders Merchants Ltd, 72-74 Wood Street, Walthamstow, London, E17 3HT Tel: (020) 8521 5900 Fax: (020) 8509 1933

M H Southern & Co. Ltd, Church Bank Sawmills, Jarrow, Tyne & Wear, NE32 3EB Tel: 0191-489 8231 Fax: 0191-428 0146 E-mail: sales@mhsouthern.co.uk

M & M Timber Ltd, Hunt House Sawmills, Clows Top, Kidderminster, Worcestershire, DY14 9HY Tel: (01299) 832611 Fax: (01299) 832536 E-mail: sales@mmtimber.co.uk

M Musgrove Ltd, 1 Gunnersbury Mews, London, W4 4AP Tel: (020) 8994 2941 Fax: (020) 8994 4484

M & N Fabrications Ltd, Wharf Road, Woodston, Peterborough, PE2 9PS Tel: (01733) 342408 Fax: (01733) 342408 E-mail: deegeorge@aol.com

Mackintosh & Partners (Timber) Ltd, Coopers Lane, Northaw, Potters Bar, Hertfordshire, EN6 4NE Tel: (01707) 642361 Fax: (01707) 646341 E-mail: jpaige@mackintosh.co.uk

Mcwiltons Ltd, 4 Basin Road North, Portslade, Brighton, BN41 1WA Tel: (01273) 423733 Fax: (01273) 430836

Merritt & Fryers Ltd, Firth Street Works, Firth Street, Skipton, North Yorkshire, BD23 2PX Tel: (01756) 792485 Fax: (01756) 700391 E-mail: info@merrittandfryers.co.uk

Merton Timber Ltd, 65-71 Grove Vale, London, SE22 8EQ Tel: (020) 8299 4131 Fax: (020) 8693 4136 E-mail: sales@mertontimber.co.uk

Merton Timber, 28 Goat Road, Mitcham, Surrey, CR4 4HU Tel: (020) 8687 0055 Fax: (020) 8648 5663 E-mail: sales@merton-timber.co.uk

Merton Timber, Central House, Murray Road, Orpington, Kent, BR5 3QY Tel: (01689) 890044 Fax: (01689) 890066 E-mail: sales@merton-timber.co.uk

Mid Sussex Timber Ltd, Ballards Yard, Park Road, Crowborough, East Sussex, TN6 2QS Tel: (01892) 652725 Fax: (01892) 653280 E-mail: mh@mstc.co.uk

Mid Sussex Timber Co. Ltd, Station Road, Forest Row, East Sussex, RH18 5EL Tel: (01342) 822191 Fax: (01342) 823052 E-mail: sales@mstc.co.uk

Millington & Ramstedt Ltd, 242-248 Bristol Road, Gloucester, GL1 5TA Tel: 0845 5260526 Fax: (01452) 306132 E-mail: sales@millingtonandramstedt.co.uk

Milton Keynes Buildbase, Simpson Road, Bletchley, Milton Keynes, MK1 1BB Tel: (01908) 369801 Fax: (01908) 270243 E-mail: miltonkeynes@buildbase.co.uk

Monmouthshire Timber Supplies Ltd, PO Box 20, Newport, Gwent, NP20 2YQ Tel: (01633) 213268 Fax: (01633) 257088 E-mail: mts@montimber.co.uk

Morgan & Co Strood Ltd, Knight Road, Rochester, Kent, ME2 2BA Tel: (01634) 290909 Fax: (01634) 290800 E-mail: info@morgantimber.co.uk

Morgan (Timber & Boards), Park Lane Saw Mills, Kidderminster, Worcestershire, DY11 6TG Tel: (01562) 820620

Moss, 92-94 King Street, London, W6 0QW Tel: (020) 8748 3884 Fax: (020) 8741 2470 E-mail: info@mosstimber.co.uk

N R Burnett Ltd, West Carr Lane, Hull, HU7 0AW Tel: (01482) 838800 Fax: (01482) 822110

Newfields Timber Yard Co. Ltd, 420 High Street, Stoke-on-Trent, ST6 5ES Tel: (01782) 834057 Fax: (01782) 839772

Nixon Knowles, Longwall Avenue, Nottingham, NG2 1LP Tel: 0115-986 5252 Fax: 0115-986 2198 E-mail: sales@nixonknowles.co.uk

Norman Ltd, 19 Commercial Buildings, St. Helier, Jersey, JE1 1BU Tel: (01534) 883388 Fax: (01534) 883334 E-mail: sales@normans.je

Odds W J Ltd, Crown Quay Lane, Sittingbourne, Kent, ME10 3JB Tel: (01795) 470844 Fax: (01795) 420463

P Hartwell Timber, Timber Yard, Weston-Subedge, Chipping Campden, Gloucestershire, GL55 6QH Tel: (01386) 840373 Fax: (01386) 841370 E-mail: info@hartwellfencing.co.uk

Page & Taylor Ltd, Watery Lane, Ashton-on-Ribble, Preston, PR2 2XH Tel: (01772) 726222 Fax: (01772) 727207 E-mail: sales@pageandtaylor.co.uk

Palgrave Brown UK Ltd, Pool Road Industrial Estate, Pool Road, Nuneaton, Warwickshire, CV10 9AE Tel: (024) 7634 4034 Fax: (024) 7634 5251

Palmer Timber Ltd, 104 Station Road, Cradley Heath, West Midlands, B64 6PW Tel: 0121-559 5511 Fax: 0121-561 4562 E-mail: sales@palmertimber.com

T.W. Parker Ltd, 90-118 Green Lane, London, N13 5UP Tel: (020) 8888 3477 Fax: (020) 8888 2273

Joseph Parr (Middlesbrough) Ltd, Blue House Point Road, Portrack Lane Trading Estate, Stockton-On-Tees, Cleveland, TS18 2PJ Tel: (01642) 679381 Fax: (01642) 617222 E-mail: jparrboro@aol.com

Pat'Erns Network UK Ltd, Stephenson Road, Clacton-on-Sea, Essex, CO15 4XA Tel: (01255) 427654 Fax: (01255) 420535

Paterson Timber Ltd, 140 Elliot Street, Glasgow, G3 8EX Tel: 0141-221 6445 Fax: 0141-221 1842 E-mail: info@paterson-timber.com

Porters, George Cayley Drive, Clifton Moore, York, YO30 4XE Tel: (01904) 690023 Fax: (01904) 692045

Richard Potter, Millstone Lane, Nantwich, Cheshire, CW5 5PN Tel: (01270) 625791 Fax: (01270) 610483 E-mail: richardpotter@fortimber.demon.co.uk

Priday Sydney & Snewin Ltd, Oak Wharf, Timberwharf Road, London, N16 6DB Tel: (020) 8800 5661 Fax: (020) 8809 5521 E-mail: sales@pridays.sagehost.co.uk

R J Sharples, Riverside Sawmill, Fishwick Bottoms, Preston, PR2 5AU Tel: (01772) 556019 Fax: (01772) 250708 E-mail: info@rjsharples.co.uk

R Thorne & Sons, Mannington Sawmills, Holt Road, Three Legged Cross, Wimborne, Dorset, BH21 6SE Tel: (01202) 822204 Fax: (01202) 824410 E-mail: robertthorne@fsbdial.co.uk

Red Joinery Ltd, Aquaduct Wharf, Hurst Lane, Bollington, Macclesfield, Cheshire, SK10 5LP Tel: (01625) 572128

Rembrand Timber Ltd, Bonnington Road Lane, Edinburgh, EH6 5BJ Tel: 0131-553 5351 Fax: 0131-554 2332 E-mail: leith@rembrand-timber.co.uk

Reynolds Trading Ltd, 364 Cleveland Street, Birkenhead, Merseyside, CH41 8EG Tel: 0151-670 1213 Fax: 0151-670 0064

Robbins Timber, 8-18 Brookgate, Bristol, BS3 2UN Tel: 0117-963 3136 Fax: 0117-963 7927 E-mail: sales@robbins.co.uk

Robert Ballantine & Son, East End, Star, Glenrothes, Fife, KY7 6LQ Tel: (01592) 758542 Fax: (01592) 610707

Robert Birkbeck & Son Ltd, Thurcroft Industrial Estate, New Orchard Road, Thurcroft, Rotherham, South Yorkshire, S66 9HY Tel: (01709) 546459 Fax: (01709) 546780 E-mail: robertbirkbeckandson@hotmail.com

Robert Duncan Ltd, Green Lane, Gateshead, Tyne & Wear, NE10 0JS Tel: 0191-469 8743 Fax: 0191-469 8903 E-mail: enquiries@robertduncan.co.uk

Robert Price Timber & Roofing merchants, Forest Road, Taffs Well, Cardiff, CF15 7YE Tel: (029) 2081 1681 Fax: (029) 2081 3605

William Roberts & Co. Ltd, Water Street, Menai Bridge, Gwynedd, LL59 5DE Tel: (01248) 712596 Fax: (01248) 717303 E-mail: dolgellau@williamroberts.co.uk

Robins Timber Co., Canalside Industrial Estate, Wedgebury Way, Brierley Hill, West Midlands, DY5 3JZ Tel: (01384) 78857 Fax: (01384) 485582

Robinson Timber & Building Supplies, Dansom Lane North, Hull, HU8 7RS Tel: (01482) 320081 Fax: (01482) 586741

Roman Timber Builders Merchants, 1 Roman Road, London, E6 3RX Tel: (020) 7476 8016 Fax: (020) 7473 3486 E-mail: romantimber@talk21.com

S C A Ltd, Etruscan Street, Stoke-on-Trent, ST1 5PG Tel: (01782) 202122 Fax: (01782) 224200

S Faulkner & Sons, Ashby Road East, Bretby, Burton-on-Trent, Staffordshire, DE15 0PS Tel: (01283) 550454

S Keeling & Co. Ltd, Forge Lane, Stoke-on-Trent, ST1 5PB Tel: (01782) 202660 Fax: (01782) 202019

M.W. Sales Ltd, 33-37 The Oval, Hackney Road, London, E2 0AS Tel: (020) 7739 5185 Fax: (020) 7729 3138

Salisbury Joinery, 3 Brunel Rd, Salisbury, SP2 7PU Tel: (01722) 337040 Fax: (01722) 337077

Selco Trade Centres Ltd, 1 Charlote Road, Stirchley, Birmingham, B30 2BT Tel: 0121-433 3355 Fax: 0121-458 5996

Smith Bros. Joinery Ltd, Pope Iron Road, Worcester, WR1 3HB Tel: (01905) 619830 Fax: (01905) 617294 E-mail: raymondwillden@smithbrothersjoinery.com

Southern & Darwent, Lissadel Street, Salford, M6 6BR Tel: 0161-745 9287 Fax: 0161-737 9744

Sterling Timber Ltd, White House, Bleasby Moor, Market Rasen, Lincolnshire, LN8 3QJ Tel: (01673) 844007 Fax: (01673) 844007 E-mail: admin@sterlingtimber.fsnet.co.uk

Sydenhams Ltd, 45-55 Ashley Road, Bournemouth, BH1 4LG Tel: (01202) 397454 Fax: (01202) 396465

Sydenhams Ltd, Mislingford, Fareham, Hampshire, PO17 5BA Tel: (01329) 832002 Fax: (01329) 834255

Sykes Timber, Carlyon Road, Atherstone, Warwickshire, CV9 1JD Tel: (01827) 718951 Fax: (01827) 714257 E-mail: wood@sykestimber.co.uk

T P Broombys Ltd, Currock Road, Carlisle, CA2 4AX Tel: (01228) 538511 Fax: (01228) 531488

Taylor Maxwell Timber, The Promenade, Clifton Down, Bristol, BS8 3NJ Tel: 0117-974 1382 Fax: 0117-974 1402 E-mail: tmtbristol@tmtimber.co.uk

F.H. Thompson-Felling & Sons Ltd, Poplar Sawmills, Factory Road, Blaydon-on-Tyne, Tyne & Wear, NE21 5RX Tel: 0191-499 0444 Fax: 0191-499 0220 E-mail: sales@fhthompson.co.uk

Thornbridge Sawmills Ltd, Laurieston Road, Grangemouth, Stirlingshire, FK3 8XX Tel: (01324) 612121 Fax: (01324) 612100

Thorogood Timber plc, Colchester Road, Ardleigh, Colchester, CO7 7PQ Tel: (01206) 233100 Fax: (01206) 233115 E-mail: sales@thorogood.co.uk

Tiger Timber Ltd, 36 Station Road, Chertsey, Surrey, KT16 8BE Tel: (01932) 560812 Fax: (01932) 570411

Timber Marketing Corporation Ltd, Old House Mews, London Road, Horsham, West Sussex, RH12 1AF Tel: (01403) 255255 Fax: (01403) 210214 E-mail: tmchorsham@tmcorp.co.uk

▶ Timber To Go, Newport Road, Coventry, CV6 4BQ Tel: (024) 7668 8886 Fax: (024) 7668 8869 E-mail: sales@timbertogo.com

Timbmet Ltd, PO Box 39, Oxford, OX2 9PP Tel: (01865) 862223 Fax: (01865) 860342 E-mail: marketing@timbmet.com

E.W. Tinegate Ltd, Lodge Road Saw Mills, 94 Lodge Road, Hockley, Birmingham, B18 5QZ Tel: 0121-554 1311 Fax: 0121-515 4464

Raymond Tisdale & Co. Ltd, Common Lane, Kenilworth, Warwickshire, CV8 2EL Tel: (01926) 852227 Fax: (01926) 850844

Totton Timber Co. Ltd, Maynard Road, Totton, Southampton, SO40 3DB Tel: (023) 8086 0077 Fax: (023) 8087 3168 E-mail: sales@tottontimber.com

Travis Perkins, 1 South Road, Hockley, Birmingham, B18 5LT Tel: 0121-554 3396 Fax: 0121-554 6811

Travis Perkins plc, Station Road, Chesterfield, Derbyshire, S41 9ET Tel: (01246) 450338 Fax: (01246) 453263

Travis Perkins plc, Recreation Lane, Felixstowe, Suffolk, IP11 9DQ Tel: (01394) 278999 Fax: (01394) 273486

Travis Perkins plc, 24-42 Palmerston Road, Harrow, Middlesex, HA3 7RR Tel: (020) 8861 1750 Fax: (020) 8861 3556

Travis Perkins plc, 26 Sangley Road, London, SE6 2JN Tel: (020) 8698 1081 Fax: (020) 8461 1229

Travis Perkins plc, Boyn Valley Road, Maidenhead, Berkshire, SL6 4EE Tel: (01628) 770577 Fax: (01628) 625919

Travis Perkins plc, Bond Street, Malvern, Worcestershire, WR14 1TQ Tel: (01684) 568401 Fax: (01684) 892745 E-mail: malvern@travisperkins.co.uk

Travis Perkins plc, Lodge Way House, Lodge Way, Northampton, NN5 7UG Tel: (01604) 752424 Fax: (01604) 758718 E-mail: careers@contemporary.co.uk

Travis Perkins plc, Lissadel Street, Salford, M6 6BR Tel: 0161-736 8751 Fax: 0161-737 9744

Travis Perkins Trading Co. Ltd, Bluebridge Industrial Estate, 11 Second Avenue, Colchester Road, Halstead, Essex, CO9 2HA Tel: (01787) 477882 Fax: (01787) 473761

Victoria Sawmill & Country Store, The Old Sawmills, Hawkerland Road, Colaton Raleigh, Sidmouth, Devon, EX10 0HP Tel: (01395) 568060 Fax: (01395) 567902 E-mail: admin@victoria-sawmills.co.uk

W Hanson Timber & Builders Merchants Ltd, Uxbridge Road, Southall, Middlesex, UB1 3EQ Tel: (020) 8571 3161 Fax: (020) 8574 3816 E-mail: sales@w-hanson.co.uk

W L West & Sons Ltd, Selham, Petworth, West Sussex, GU28 0PJ Tel: (01798) 861611 Fax: (01798) 861633

W Madden Insulation, Swinnow View, Leeds, LS13 4TZ Tel: 0113-257 9818 Fax: 0113-257 7586 E-mail: sales@wmadden.demon.co.uk

George Walker Ltd, Fosse Way Sawmills, Fosse Way, Syston, Leicester, LE7 1NH Tel: 0116-260 8330 Fax: 0116-269 7450 E-mail: info@george-walker.co.uk

Warrington Timber Co. Ltd, 1 Bowood Court, Winwick Quay, Warrington, WA2 8QZ Tel: (01925) 232687 Fax: (01925) 230167

Edgar Watson Ltd, Trent Lane, Nottingham, NG2 4DT Tel: 0115-950 3891 Fax: 0115-859 118

Websters Burn Ltd, Whitings Lane, Burn, Selby, North Yorkshire, YO8 8LG Tel: (01757) 270233 Fax: (01757) 270459

Wenban Smith Ltd, 14 Newland Road, Worthing, West Sussex, BN11 1JT Tel: (01903) 230311 Fax: (01903) 821780 E-mail: sales@wenban-smith.co.uk

W.H. Wesson (Fencing) Ltd, 126 Connaught Road, Brookwood, Woking, Surrey, GU24 0AS Tel: (01483) 472124 Fax: (01483) 472115

White & Etherington Ltd, New Farm Road, Alresford, Hampshire, SO24 9QE Tel: (01962) 732783 Fax: (01962) 735422

Whitmores Timber Co. Ltd, Main Road, Claybrooke Magna, Lutterworth, Leicestershire, LE17 5AQ Tel: (01455) 209121 Fax: (01455) 209041 E-mail: info@whitmores.co.uk

Whitten Timber Ltd, Eagle Wharf, Peckham Hill Street, London, SE15 5JT Tel: (020) 7732 3804 Fax: (020) 7635 3555

G.R. Wiltshire & Co., Smoke Hall Lane, Winsford, Cheshire, CW7 3BE Tel: (01455) 202666 Fax: (01606) 555511 E-mail: sales@smeetimber.com

Oscar Windebank & Son Ltd, The Bassetts, Box, Corsham, Wiltshire, SN13 8ER Tel: (01225) 742929

Wolseley Centre, Willow Lane, Lune Industrial Estate, Lancaster, LA1 5NA Tel: (01524) 67227 Fax: (01524) 844101

Wood's Timber Co Ltd, Witham, Hull, HU9 1BG Tel: (01482) 320466 Fax: (01482) 212799

TIMBER OR WOOD BUILDINGS,

See Prefabricated Timber etc

TIMBER PREFABRICATED HOUSES OR BUILDINGS

5 Star Homes Ltd, 104 Corkill Road, Omagh, County Tyrone, BT78 1UX Tel: (028) 8284 0900 Fax: (028) 8284 0281 E-mail: sales@5starhomes.co.uk

▶ Back To Natural, 115, Montagu Street, Kettering, Northants, NN16 8XJ Tel: (01536) 481881

Barrowmore Industries, Barrowmore Enterprise Estate, Barnhouse Lane, Great Barrow, Chester, CH3 7JA Tel: (01829) 742590 Fax: (01829) 742571 E-mail: kat@barrowmore.org.uk

Border Oak Ltd, Kingsland Sawmills, Kingsland, Leominster, Herefordshire, HR6 9SF Tel: (01568) 708752 Fax: (01568) 708295 E-mail: sales@borderoak.com

TIMBER PREFABRICATED HOUSES OR BUILDINGS - *continued*

British Timbermasters, Thame Road, Brill, Aylesbury, Buckinghamshire, HP18 9SA Tel: (01844) 237633 E-mail: sales@swedish-log-cabins.com

Canadian Log Homes UK Ltd, Maple Lodge, Rose Hill, Little Pertherick, Wadebridge, Cornwall, PL27 7QT Tel: (01841) 540680 Fax: (01841) 540580 E-mail: admin@canadianloghomes.co.uk

Carpenter Oak Ltd, The Framing Yard, Cornworthy, Totnes, Devon, TQ9 7HF Tel: (01803) 732900 Fax: (01803) 732901

▶ Cartledge, Brookenby Business Park, Brookenby, Binbrook, Market Rasen, Lincolnshire, LN8 6HF Tel: (01472) 399935 Fax: (01472) 399920

▶ Cartrefi Dyfed Homes, Unit 8a Glan Yr Afon Industrial Estate, Llanbadarn Fawr, Aberystwyth, Dyfed, SY23 3JQ Tel: (01970) 626686 Fax: (01970) 626026

Cosalt Holiday Homes Ltd, Stoneferry, Hull, HU8 8EH Tel: (01482) 227203 Fax: (01482) 210481 E-mail: info@coshomes.co.uk

D J R Roof Trusses Ltd, Winnards Perch, St. Columb, Cornwall, TR9 6DE Tel: (01637) 881333 Fax: (01637) 881315 E-mail: andy@djr-roof-trusses.demon.co.uk

Dagless Ltd, Brigstock Road, Wisbech, Cambridgeshire, PE13 3JL Tel: (01945) 583826 Fax: (01945) 582673 E-mail: info@shiregb.co.uk

Douglas W Standring, 20 Cae Gwastad, Harlech, Gwynedd, LL46 2GY Tel: (01766) 780483 Fax: (01766) 780483 E-mail: timberframestructures@btinternet.com

English Bros Ltd, Salts Road, Walton Highway, Wisbech, Cambridgeshire, PE14 7DU Tel: (01945) 587500 Fax: (01945) 582576 E-mail: customerservices@englishbrothers.co.uk

Eric Banks Associates Ltd, 136 Victoria Road, Walton-le-Dale, Preston, PR5 4AU Tel: (01772) 465213 Fax: (01772) 466252 E-mail: enquiries@dba-uk.com

Guildford Timber Frame Ltd, Brewhurst Sawmill, Roundstreet Common, Wisborough Green, Billingshurst, West Sussex, RH14 0AL Tel: (01403) 752888 Fax: (01403) 752471 E-mail: info@gtf.uk.com

Interbuild Components Ltd, Milton Mill, Ferry Road, Monifieth, Dundee, DD5 4NZ Tel: (01382) 534341 Fax: (01382) 534444

J Scott Thrapston Ltd, Bridge Street, Thrapston, Kettering, Northamptonshire, NN14 4LR Tel: (01832) 732366 Fax: (01832) 733703 E-mail: julia@scottsofthrapston.co.uk

▶ The Knotty Wood Co., The Ward, Strathaven, Lanarkshire, ML10 6AS Tel: (01357) 523366 Fax: (01357) 523366

Littleport Timber Buildings, 5a Saxon Business Park, Littleport, Ely, Cambridgeshire, CB6 1XX Tel: (01353) 861707

▶ Maple Timber Frame, Tarnacre Hall Business Park, Tarnacre Hall Mews, Preston, PR3 0SZ Tel: (01995) 679444 Fax: (01995) 679769

Moor Park Homes Ltd, The Sawmills, Whitelees Road, Lanark, ML11 7RX Tel: (01555) 665087 Fax: (01555) 666244 E-mail: sales@moorparkhomes.co.uk

Oak Frame Carpentry Co. Ltd, Nupend Farm, Nupend, Stonehouse, Gloucestershire, GL10 3SU Tel: (01453) 825092 Fax: (01453) 828788 E-mail: oakframe@btconnect.com

Purewell Timber, Unit 4 Lea Green Farm, Christchurch Road, Downton, Lymington, Hampshire, SO41 0LA Tel: (01590) 644477 Fax: (01590) 644477 E-mail: stephan@youworldtimber.com

Redmire Stables & Buildings Ltd, Five Oaks Sawmill, Five Oaks, Billingshurst, West Sussex, RH14 9BD Tel: (01403) 785508 Fax: (01403) 785333 E-mail: enquiries@redmire.co.uk

Robertson Timber Kit Ltd, 10 Perimeter Road, Elgin, Morayshire, IV30 6AE Tel: (01343) 549786 Fax: (01343) 552546 E-mail: sales@timberkit.co.uk

Rob Roy Homes (Crieff) Ltd, Dalchonzie, Comrie, Crieff, Perthshire, PH6 2LB Tel: (01764) 670425 Fax: (01764) 670419 E-mail: mail@robroyhomes.co.uk

Scandia Hus, Felcourt Road, Felcourt, East Grinstead, West Sussex, RH19 2LP Tel: (01342) 838060 Fax: (01342) 838061 E-mail: sales@scandia-hus.co.uk

Sherlock Of Oakwood, Oakwood, Chichester, West Sussex, PO18 9AL Tel: (01243) 786701 Fax: (01243) 775089 E-mail: sales@sherlocks.demon.co.uk

George Smith, Easter Tullochs, Rafford, Forres, Morayshire, IV36 2SL Tel: (01309) 674741 E-mail: info@georgecsmith.co.uk

Southern Timber Frame, Longdown Estate Yard, Longdown, Marchwood, Southampton, SO40 4UH Tel: (023) 8029 3062 Fax: (023) 8029 3969 E-mail: mail.stf@virgin.net

Stately Albion Ltd, Prince of Wales Industrial Estate, Abercarn, Newport, Gwent, NP11 5AR Tel: (01495) 244472 Fax: (01495) 248939 E-mail: sales@stately-albion.co.uk

▶ Swift Timber Homes Ltd, North Bridge House, North Bridge, St. Helen Auckland, Bishop Auckland, County Durham, DL14 9EY Tel: (01388) 835222 Fax: (01388) 835444 E-mail: enquires@swifttimberhomes.com

Thermatech Timber Structures Ltd, Bucklers Lane, St. Austell, Cornwall, PL25 3JN Tel: (01726) 71733 Fax: (01726) 71744

Truro Portable Buildings, Longdowns Industrial Estate, Longdowns, Penryn, Cornwall, TR10 9NA Tel: (01209) 860269 Fax: (01209) 860020 E-mail: sales@truro-portable-buildings.co.uk

Turriff Timber Products, Markethill Industrial Estate, Turriff, Aberdeenshire, AB53 4QY Tel: (01888) 563929 Fax: (01888) 563929

Warwick Buildings Ltd, Southam Road, Long Itchington, Southam, Warwickshire, CV47 9QL Tel: (01926) 815757 Fax: (01926) 815162 E-mail: sales@warwickbuildings.com

Westructure Timber Frames Ltd, Wichita Works, Water Lane, Exeter, EX2 8BU Tel: (01392) 411211 Fax: (01392) 411211

Westwind Oak Buildings Ltd, Laurel Farm, Yatton, Bristol, BS49 4QA Tel: (01934) 877317 Fax: (01934) 877317 E-mail: sales@westwindoak.com

Younger Homes Ltd, 1 Hall Street, Maghera, County Londonderry, BT46 5DA Tel: (028) 7964 3725 Fax: (028) 7964 4249

Ystwyth Homes Ltd, Ystwyth Works, Llanfarian, Aberystwyth, Dyfed, SY23 4NN Tel: (01970) 611321 Fax: (01970) 615679

TIMBER PRESERVATIVES

Ag Woodcare Products, 3a Waterloo Industrial Estate, Waterloo Road, Bidford-on-Avon, Alcester, Warwickshire, B50 4JH Tel: (01789) 778628 Fax: (01789) 490296 E-mail: email@agwoodcare.co.uk

▶ Marcher Chemicals Ltd, Rock Road, Rhosymedre, Wrexham, Clwyd, LL14 3YF Tel: (01978) 821245 Fax: (01978) 821169 E-mail: sales@aquatecpaint.co.uk

Palgrave Brown UK Ltd, Pool Road Industrial Estate, Pool Road, Nuneaton, Warwickshire, CV10 9AE Tel: (024) 7634 4034 Fax: (024) 7634 5251

▶ R K & J Jones, Southery Road, Seltwell, Thetford, Norfolk, IP26 4EH Tel: (01842) 828101

TIMBER PRODUCTS OR TIMBER

A Diamond & Son Timber Ltd, 35 New Mills Road, Coleraine, County Londonderry, BT52 2JB Tel: (028) 7034 3452 Fax: (028) 7034 3279 E-mail: sales@adiamondandson.co.uk

▶ Aberdeen Joinery, 43 Thistle Lane, Aberdeen, AB10 1TZ Tel: (01224) 644148

▶ Anderson Joinery Ltd, 3 Bradford Road, Stanningley, Pudsey, West Yorkshire, LS28 6AT Tel: 0113-255 0788 Fax: 0113-236 1681

▶ Andrew Mccall & Son, 11 Simonsburn Road, Loreny Industrial Estate, Kilmarnock, Ayrshire, KA1 5LA Tel: (01563) 571173 Fax: (01563) 571488

▶ Anglia Joinery Ltd, 28-29 Maitland Road, Lion Barn Industrial Estate, Needham Market, Ipswich, IP6 8NZ Tel: (01449) 720070 Fax: (01449) 722817

▶ Avc (Classic Woodworkers) Ltd, Newfield Works, High Street, Sandyford, Stoke-on-trent, ST6 5PQ Tel: 01782 832555 Fax: 01782 832666 E-mail: sales@avcwood.co.uk

▶ Aztec Conservatory Roof Systems Ltd, Haydock Lane, Haydock, St. Helens, Merseyside, WA11 0SN Tel: (01942) 720044 E-mail: sales@aztecsystems.co.uk

B G H Joinery Co. Ltd, Unicorn Business Centre, Ridgeway, Chiseldon, Swindon, SN4 0HT Tel: (01793) 741330 Fax: (01793) 741310 E-mail: sales@bghjoinery.wanadoo.co.uk

▶ Graham Ball Joiners & Builders Ltd, 11 Sedgwick Street, Preston, PR1 1TP Tel: (01772) 250481 Fax: (01772) 823383 E-mail: gbjb11s@awell.com

▶ Becher Joinery Ltd, 7 Worton Hall Industrial Estate, Worton Road, Isleworth, Middlesex, TW7 6ER Tel: (020) 8568 9488 Fax: (020) 8568 9311

H & T Bellas Ltd, 14 Mountsandel Road, Coleraine, County Londonderry, BT52 1JD Tel: (028) 7034 2205 Fax: (028) 7035 2413 E-mail: info@bellas.co.uk

▶ Brent Scaffold Boards Ltd, The Airfield, Breighton, Selby, North Yorkshire, YO8 6DJ Tel: (01757) 289199 Fax: (01757) 289105

Brooks Bros (London) Ltd, Kingsbridge Wharf, Kingsbridge Road, Barking, Essex, IG11 0BT Tel: (020) 8591 5300 Fax: (020) 8594 7133 E-mail: enquires@brooksbroslondon.com

▶ Bryant & Cairns, Borthwick View, Pentland Industrial Estate, Loanhead, Midlothian, EH20 9QH Tel: 0131-440 2855 Fax: 0131-448 2096 E-mail: sales@bryantandcairns.co.uk

▶ C 3 S Projects Ltd, Canal Mills, Elland, West Yorkshire, HX5 0SQ Tel: (01422) 313800 Fax: (01422) 313808

▶ C & G Joinery Services Ltd, Unit 13 W & G Industrial Estate, Faringdon Road, East Challow, Wantage, Oxfordshire, OX12 9TF Tel: (01235) 763233 Fax: (01235) 760259 E-mail: info@cgjoinery.co.uk

▶ C N C Joinery Ltd, Unit 5, Venture Court, Bradley Lane, Newton Abbot, Devon, TQ12 1NB Tel: (01626) 332203 Fax: (01626) 332204 E-mail: customer.service@cncjoinery.co.uk

▶ Cairnport Ltd, Lloyd Street, Rutherglen, Glasgow, G73 1NP Tel: 0141-613 1333 Fax: 0141-647 8444

▶ Caledonia Homes, Unit 10 Castle Street, Castlepark Industrial Estate, Ellon, Aberdeenshire, AB41 9RF Tel: (01358) 721661 Fax: (01358) 722955

The Capworth Panel & Timber Company Ltd, 27 Capworth Street, London, E10 5AN Tel: (020) 8539 3374 Fax: (020) 8539 5872

Cashmores Joinery Ltd, 86-88 Essex Road, Leicester, LE4 9EG Tel: 0116-276 9948 Fax: 0116-276 9948

▶ Charles Keith & Sons, Station Road, Cults, Aberdeen, AB15 9NP Tel: (01224) 868144

▶ Chrysalis Conservatories Windows & Doors Ltd, 95 Bridgwater Road, Bristol, BS13 8AE Tel: 0117-935 8580

Clinton Conservatories, 153 Cumbernauld Road, Chryston, Glasgow, G69 9AF Tel: 0141-779 4423

▶ Composite Entrance Doors Ltd, 7-9 Tannoch Drive, Cumbernauld, Glasgow, G67 2XX Tel: (01236) 739910 Fax: (01236) 782570

▶ Crendon Timber Engineering Ltd, Drakes Drive, Long Crendon, Aylesbury, Buckinghamshire, HP18 9BA Tel: (01844) 201020 Fax: (01844) 201625 E-mail: sales@crendon.co.uk

Brian Curtis, 60 Park Avenue, Maidstone, Kent, ME14 5HL Tel: (01622) 757759

▶ Custom Joinery, 37 Roseburn Street, Edinburgh, EH12 5PE Tel: 0131-337 3003 Fax: 0131-346 0333

▶ Deeside Homes, 8 Spurryhillock Industrial Estate, Broomhill Road, Stonehaven, Kincardineshire, AB39 2NH Tel: (01569) 767123 Fax: (01569) 767766

Derbybeech Ltd, Swinemoor Industrial Estate, Barmston Road, Beverley, North Humberside, HU17 0LA Tel: (01482) 868993 Fax: (01482) 872109 E-mail: info@derbybeech.com

Donaldson & Mcconnell Ltd, Grangemouth Road, Bo'Ness, West Lothian, EH51 0PU Tel: (01506) 828891 Fax: (01506) 829070

▶ Donaldson Timber Engineering, Brunswick Road Cobbswood Industrial Estate, Brunswick Road, Ashford, Kent, TN23 1ED Tel: (01233) 895222 Fax: (01233) 895220

▶ Dooria UK Ltd, 22 Glenburn Road, East Kilbride, Glasgow, G74 5BA Tel: (01355) 243918 Fax: (01355) 244137 E-mail: sales@doorian.co.uk

▶ Draks Shutters, Unit 316 Heyford Park, Camp Road, Upper Heyford, Bicester, Oxfordshire, OX25 5HA Tel: (01869) 232989 Fax: (01869) 232989 E-mail: sales@draksonline.co.uk

▶ Drumderg Joinery, 1a Lismacloskey Road, Antrim, BT41 3RA Tel: (028) 7965 0198 Fax: (028) 7965 9106

▶ Dunglass Designs, Old School, School Brae, West Barns, Dunbar, East Lothian, EH42 1UD Tel: (01368) 863590 Fax: (01368) 863590

▶ Eben Staircase Manufacturers, 4 Murieston Lane, Edinburgh, EH11 2LX Tel: 0131-477 3566 Fax: 0131-622 7759

▶ Edvic Ltd, 9a Burrell Way, Thetford, Norfolk, IP24 3RW Tel: (01842) 754333 Fax: (01842) 754411

▶ Edward Duckett & Son, Milnthorpe Road, Holme, Carnforth, Lancashire, LA6 1PS Tel: (01524) 781232 Fax: (01524) 782353 E-mail: office@duckett.ltd.uk

▶ Edwards & Hampson Ltd, 194 Rimrose Road, Bootle, Merseyside, L20 4QS Tel: 0151-922 9122 Fax: 0151-922 4127

▶ Empress Timber, 48 Empress Way, Euxton, Chorley, Lancashire, PR7 6QB Tel: (01257) 269596 Fax: (01257) 269596 E-mail: philwalsh@empresstimber.co.uk

▶ Erith Concrete Co., Landau Way, Darent Industrial Park, Erith, Kent, DA8 2LF Tel: (01322) 333263

▶ F Beardsell & Son Ltd, Spring Gardens, Huddersfield, HD1 3PL Tel: (01484) 420974 Fax: (01484) 431528 E-mail: sales@fbeardsell.com

▶ Felix Design, Unit 15, Tiverton Way, Tiverton Business Park, Tiverton, Devon, EX16 6SR Tel: (01884) 255420

▶ Finewood Joinery Products, Middlefield Industrial Estate, Falkirk, FK2 9HQ Tel: (01324) 673100 Fax: (01324) 673199 E-mail: sales@fine-wood.co.uk

▶ Flair Plastic Products Ltd, Unit 9d Minworth Industrial Estate, Stockton Close, Minworth, Sutton Coldfield, West Midlands, B76 1DH Tel: 0121-624 5001 Fax: 0121-624 5004 E-mail: sales@flairplasticproducts.co.uk

▶ Florada Garden Buildings Ltd, Unit W2 Continental Approach, Westwood Industrial Estate, Margate, Kent, CT9 4JG Tel: (01843) 223345 Fax: (01843) 298923 E-mail: admin@florada.co.uk

▶ Forest Craft, Unit 14-15 200 Woodville Park Industrial Estate, Woodville Street, Glasgow, G51 2RL Tel: 0141-445 4856

▶ Forever Warm Homes Ltd, 3a Ballymoyer Road, Newtownhamilton, Newry, County Down, BT35 0AH Tel: (028) 3087 8950 Fax: (028) 3087 8599 E-mail: seals@foreverwarmhomes.com

▶ Frame Wise Ltd, Unit 5 Presteigne Industrial Estate, Presteigne, Powys, LD8 2UF Tel: (01544) 260125 Fax: (01544) 260707 E-mail: sales@framewiseltd.co.uk

▶ G M Timber Systems, Haugh of Sluie, Banchory, Kincardineshire, AB31 4BA Tel: (01339) 884411 Fax: (01339) 884422 E-mail: info@gmtimbersystems.fsbusiness.co.uk

▶ G W Fleming, Gatehead Road, Crosshouse, Kilmarnock, Ayrshire, KA2 0HP Tel: (01563) 523853 Fax: (01563) 523853

▶ Gabriel Ash Ltd, Monument Farm, Churton Road, Farndon, Chester, CH3 6QP Tel: (01829) 271888 Fax: (01829) 271889 E-mail: sales@gabrielash.com

▶ H K Thorburn & Sons, Marjoriebanks, Lochmaben, Lockerbie, Dumfriesshire, DG11 1QH Tel: (01387) 810263 Fax: (01387) 810700

▶ Hardwood Timber Products Ltd, 3 West Coppice Road, Coppice Industrial Estate, Walsall, WS8 7HB Tel: (01543) 370370 Fax: (01543) 375280

George Harrison Ltd, Selsdon House, 212-220 Addington Road, South Croydon, Surrey, CR2 8LD Tel: (020) 8768 3200 Fax: (020) 8768 3201 E-mail: sales@ghuk.co.uk

▶ Hawthorne Timber Fabrications Ltd, 31 Markethill Road, Newtownhamilton, Newry, County Down, BT35 0BE Tel: (028) 3087 8283 Fax: (028) 3087 8926

▶ Henley Hill, Nimlett House, Nimlet, Cold Ashton, Chippenham, Wiltshire, SN14 8JX Tel: (01225) 891992 Fax: (01225) 891010

▶ Heritage Conservatories, 68 Tudor Road, Godmanchester, Huntingdon, Cambridgeshire, PE29 2DW Tel: (01480) 437774 Fax: (01480) 456184

▶ R.S. Hill, The Row, Douglastown, Forfar, Angus, DD8 1TL Tel: (01307) 466176 Fax: (01307) 468643

▶ Holywell Joinery Ltd, Unit 13, Delaval Trading Estate, Seaton Delaval, Whitley Bay, Tyne & Wear, NE25 0QT Tel: 0191-237 0190

▶ Horns Garden Sheds, 1 Winchester Drive, South West Industrial Estate, Peterlee, County Durham, SR8 2RJ Tel: 0191-518 1098 Fax: 0191-518 1098

Illingworth Bros, Unit 7 Greendykes Industrial Estate, Broxburn, West Lothian, EH52 6PG Tel: (01506) 854248 Fax: (01506) 856641

▶ Interlink Building Systems Ltd, 175 Glasgow Road, Edinburgh, EH12 9BH Tel: 0131-270 3534 Fax: 0131-270 3592

▶ Inwood (Cymru) Ltd, Units 65-65, Greenfield Business Centre, Greenfield, Holywell, Flintshire, CH8 7GR Tel: (01352) 718007 Fax: (01352) 719614 E-mail: enquiries@woodworkersuk.co.uk

▶ J M S Specialist Joinery Ltd, Unit B Bourne End, Kineton Road Industrial Estate, Southam, Warwickshire, CV47 0NA Tel: (01926) 813813 Fax: (01926) 812777 E-mail: jmsjoineryltd@aol.com

▶ Jack Stock Essex Fencing, The Old Bakery, Hawk Lane, Battlesbridge, Wickford, Essex, SS11 7RL Tel: (01268) 732184 Fax: (01268) 761675

▶ Jeld Wen UK Ltd, Grosvenor House, 112-114 Prince of Wales Road, Norwich, NR1 1NS Tel: (01603) 697800 Fax: (01603) 697809 E-mail: info@jeld-wen.co.uk

▶ Jeremy Uglow, Unit 5 Blacknest Industrial Estate, Blacknest Road, Blacknest, Alton, Hampshire, GU34 4PX Tel: (01420) 520009 Fax: (01420) 520463 E-mail: sales@jeremyuglow.com

Joinery Shop, Unit 16 Dockray Hall Industrial Estate, Dockray Hall Road, Kendal, Cumbria, LA9 4RU Tel: (01539) 731857

▶ K P Joinery Ltd, Unit J Chantry Industrial Estate, Storrington, Pulborough, West Sussex, RH20 4AD Tel: (01903) 745929 Fax: (01903) 746037

▶ Kildonan Homes Ltd, Bandeath Industrial Estate, Stirling, FK7 7NP Tel: (01786) 815656

▶ Kirkland Kitchens & Joinery Co. Ltd, The Old Cooperage, Gatebeck, Kendal, Cumbria, LA8 0HW Tel: (01539) 566999 Fax: (01539) 567733 E-mail: info@kirkland-kitchens.co.uk

▶ Lancashire Hill Joinery, 215 Chestergate, Stockport, Cheshire, SK3 0AN Tel: 0161-480 6928 Fax: 0161-476 3345

▶ Lenwood Conservatories, 6 Poplar Road, Broadmeadow Industrial Estate, Broadmeadow Industrial Estate, Dumbarton, G82 2RQ Tel: (01389) 761133 E-mail: sales@1enwood.co.uk

▶ McFadyen Conservatories, Crossford, Carluke, Lanarkshire, ML8 5QF Tel: (01555) 860123

▶ McFadyen Conservatories, Unit 3, Meadow Road, Motherwell, Lanarkshire, ML1 1QB Tel: (01698) 268862

Mackintosh & Partners (Properties) Ltd, The Sawmills, Small Dole, Henfield, West Sussex, BN5 9XG Tel: (01273) 497100 Fax: (01273) 497139 E-mail: sales@mackintosh.co.uk

▶ Macleod Building Services Contracts, 39 Turnhouse Road, Edinburgh, EH12 0AE Tel: 0131-339 2680 Fax: 0131-339 5829

▶ Magnet Ltd, Victoria House Corner, 24 London Road, Hadleigh, Benfleet, Essex, SS7 2QP Tel: (01702) 553112 Fax: (01702) 551892 E-mail: hadliegh.branch@magnet.co.uk

▶ Mel Wake Joinery Ltd, 4 Squire Drive, Brynmenyn, Bridgend, CF32 9TX Tel: (01656) 722500 Fax: (01656) 722723

▶ Merlin Network Ltd, Merlin Way, Hillend, Dunfermline, Fife, KY11 9JY Tel: (01383) 821182 Fax: (01383) 824682

Mitech Joinery, 234 Derby Road, Denby, Ripley, Derbyshire, DE5 8NN Tel: (01773) 570577 Fax: (01773) 570577 E-mail: roberts@mitechjoinery.co.uk

Moduspace Ltd, Burts Wharf, Crabtree Manorway North, Belvedere, Kent, DA17 6LJ Tel: (020) 8311 7070 Fax: (020) 8312 9908 E-mail: moduspace@aol.com

▶ Monzie Joinery Ltd, Monzie, Crieff, Perthshire, PH7 4HE Tel: (01764) 654877

▶ Nassau Industrial Doors Ltd, Dewsbury Road, Fenton Industrial Estate, Stoke-on-Trent, ST4 2TB Tel: (01782) 418700

▶ NClosure, Long Paddock, Peppershells Lane, Compton Dando, Bristol, BS39 4LL Tel: 01761 490374 Fax: 0871 6615701 E-mail: sales@nclosure.co.uk

TIMBER PRODUCTS OR TIMBER – *continued*

▶ North Wales Joinery Ltd, Builder St, Llandudno, Gwynedd, LL30 1DR Tel: (01492) 870418

▶ Ochil Timber Products Ltd, 5 Winchester Avenue, Denny, Stirlingshire, FK6 6QE Tel: (01324) 825503 Fax: (01324) 824333

▶ Oregon-Canadian Europe, Greenbank Business Park, 2-3 Swan Lane, Hindley Green, Wigan, Lancashire, WN2 4EZ Tel: (01942) 525040 Fax: (01942) 524240 E-mail: dan@oregoncanadian.com

▶ P B National Products Ltd, Unit 107 Marchington Industrial Estate, Stubby Lane, Marchington, Uttoxeter, Staffordshire, ST14 8LP Tel: (01283) 576860 Fax: (01283) 821180

Pagets Builders Merchants Ltd, 94 Broadfield Road, Sheffield, S8 0XL Tel: 0114-292 3000 Fax: 0114-250 9350 E-mail: info@c-paget.co.uk

▶ Paragon Joinery Ltd, Skitts Manor Farm, Moor Lane, Marsh Green, Edenbridge, Kent, TN8 5RA Tel: (01732) 867580 Fax: (01732) 865809 E-mail: paul.hemple@paragonjoinery.com

▶ Park Decking Timber, Ercall Park, High Ercall, Telford, Shropshire, TF6 6AU Tel: (01952) 770779 Fax: (01952) 770121

▶ Penicuik Home Improvements, Eastfield Industrial Estate, Penicuik, Midlothian, EH26 8HA Tel: (0845) 7515000 Fax: (01968) 664023

▶ Perkins & Perry, Wheal Chance, Radnor Road, Redruth, Cornwall, TR16 5EQ Tel: (01209) 820983 Fax: (01209) 821869 E-mail: mail@perkinsandperry.co.uk

▶ Rebate Ltd, Rebate House, Stourport Road, Kidderminster, Worcestershire, DY11 7BD Tel: (01562) 740065

▶ Redwells Joinery Ltd, 1 Crompton Road, Glenrothes, Fife, KY6 2SF Tel: (01592) 772010 Fax: (01592) 630093

▶ Bryn Roberts Workshops Ltd, Abbey Road North, Wrexham Industrial Estate, Wrexham, Clwyd, LL13 9RX Tel: (01978) 661828 Fax: (01978) 661553 E-mail: b.robertsryn@btconnect.com

▶ Roberts & Lyons, 59 A Wymeswold Industrial Estate, Wymeswold Lane, Burton On The Wolds, Loughborough, Leicestershire, LE12 5TY Tel: (01509) 881207 Fax: (01509) 880668 E-mail: sales@robertsandlyons.co.uk

▶ Colin Robertson, Charlesfield, St Boswells, Melrose, Roxburghshire, TD6 0HH Tel: (01835) 822480

▶ Robinson Wood Products Ltd, The Racks, Collin, Dumfries, DG1 4PU Tel: (01387) 750205 Fax: (01387) 750129

▶ Rom Joinery Ltd, 143 North Street, Romford, RM1 1ED Tel: (01708) 727512 Fax: (01708) 733089

▶ Romford Joinery, 10 Danes Road, Romford, RM7 0HL Tel: (01708) 720728 Fax: (01708) 720728

▶ Romiley Joinery Ltd, Green Lane, Romiley, Stockport, Cheshire, SK6 3JG Tel: 0161-494 0864 Fax: 0161-406 6290

▶ Roof Profiles Ltd, 7 Kyle Road, Irvine Industrial Estate, Irvine, Ayrshire, KA12 8JF Tel: (01294) 274488 Fax: (01294) 271199 E-mail: sales@roofprofiles.com

▶ The Roof Truss Company Ltd, Moycroft Industrial Estate, Elgin, Morayshire, IV30 1XZ Tel: (01343) 547474 Fax: (01343) 547990 E-mail: enquires@rtcts.co.uk

▶ S T P Joinery Ltd, Mildred Sylvester Way, Normanton Industrial Estate, Normanton, West Yorkshire, WF6 1TA Tel: (01924) 891988 Fax: (01924) 897252

▶ Scottish Prison Service, SPS HQ Industries, Central Store, Main Street, Fauldhouse, Bathgate, West Lothian, EH47 9DJ Tel: (01501) 773980 Fax: (01501) 771835 E-mail: anthony.apperley@sps.gov.uk

▶ Sheds & Shelters, Pilgrims Way, Hollingbourne, Maidstone, Kent, ME17 1UT Tel: (01622) 880031 Fax: (01622) 880031

▶ P Shipston & Sons, Victoria Mill, Watt Street, Sabden, Clitheroe, Lancashire, BB7 9ED Tel: (01282) 770225 Fax: (01282) 777146

▶ Sidlaw Windows Ltd, 2 Logie Avenue, Dundee, DD2 2AS Tel: (01382) 640200 Fax: (01382) 640118

▶ South Coast Fencing Ltd, Corn Dryer, Alresford Road, Winchester, Hampshire, SO21 1HH Tel: (01962) 843231 Fax: (01962) 843294 E-mail: sales@southcoastfencing.co.uk

▶ Specialists In Traditional Sash Windows, 5 Bramley Hedge Farm, Redhill Road, Cobham, Surrey, KT11 1EQ Tel: (01932) 866684 Fax: (01932) 590483 E-mail: sales@sashwindowspecialists.co.uk

▶ Spence & Grant Ltd, New Elgin Road, Elgin, Morayshire, IV30 6BA Tel: (01343) 541716

▶ Stackright Portable Buildings, 2 Bloxwich Road, Walsall, WS2 7BD Tel: (01922) 474455 Fax: (01922) 474477 E-mail: sales@stackright.co.uk

▶ Stafford Bridge Doors Ltd, Bedford Road, Pavenham, Bedford, MK43 7PS Tel: (01234) 826316 Fax: (01234) 826319 E-mail: sales@sbdoors.com

▶ Stockport Joinery Co., 10-16 King St West, Stockport, Cheshire, SK3 0DY Tel: 0161-477 5480 Fax: 0161-474 7248 E-mail: info@stockportjoinery.co.uk

▶ R.G. Stones (Buildings) Ltd, Rhoswiel Sawmills, Weston Rhyn, Oswestry, Shropshire, SY10 7TG Tel: (01691) 773391 Fax: (01691) 774316 E-mail: rgstones@btconnect.com

▶ Swift Joinery, Mylord CR, Camperdown Industrial Estate, Newcastle upon Tyne, NE12 5UJ Tel: 0191-216 9631

▶ T Clarke & Sons Joinery Ltd, The Workshop, Slippery Gowt Lane, Wyberton, Boston, Lincolnshire, PE21 7AA Tel: (01205) 354629 Fax: (01205) 358214 E-mail: sales@tclarkejoinery.co.uk

▶ T W Joinery South Wales Ltd, Heol Ffaldau, Brackla, Bridgend, Mid Glamorgan, CF31 2HQ Tel: (01656) 667745 Fax: (01656) 650887

▶ Tailor Made Conservatories Windows & Doors, Barlby Road, Selby, North Yorkshire, YO8 5BJ Tel: (01757) 705866

▶ Tate Fencing Ltd, 1 Chase Wood Works, Frant Road, Frant, Tunbridge Wells, Kent, TN3 9HG Tel: (01892) 750230 Fax: (01892) 750130 E-mail: sales@tate-fencing.co.uk

▶ Tate Fencing, Yellowcoat Mills, Hastings Road, Flimwell, Wadhurst, East Sussex, TN5 7PR Tel: (01580) 879900 Fax: (01580) 879677

▶ Taylor Lane Timber Frame Ltd, Chapel Road, Rotherwas Industrial Estate, Hereford, HR2 6LD Tel: (01432) 271912 Fax: (01432) 351064 E-mail: tl@taylor-lane.co.uk

Timber Store UK Ltd, Newton Road, Kingskerswell, Newton Abbot, Devon, TQ12 5ES Tel: (01803) 872400 Fax: (01803) 874072

▶ Timetra Ltd, 535 Main Street, Bellshill, Lanarkshire, ML4 1DG Tel: (01698) 746091 Fax: (01698) 843439

▶ Tomps Plaster Suppliers, 220 New Road, Sutton Bridge, Spalding, Lincolnshire, PE12 9QE Tel: (01406) 351001 Fax: (01406) 351513 E-mail: sales@tomps.com

▶ Traditional Joinery, Unit 1, Redding Industrial Estate, Redding, Falkirk, FK2 9TT Tel: (01324) 718400

Trafford Timber & Damp-Proofing Specialists Ltd, 1086 Chester Road, Stretford, Manchester, M32 0HL Tel: 0161-972 5777 Fax: 0161-972 5888 E-mail: admin@traffordtds.fsworld.co.uk

▶ Trinity Joinery, La Rue De La Hougette, St. Clement, Jersey, JE2 6LD Tel: (01534) 853567 Fax: (01534) 857191

▶ Truss Form Ltd, Hollin Bridge, Burnley Road East, Rossendale, Lancashire, BB4 9JR Tel: (01706) 212238 Fax: (01706) 223522

▶ W J Wicks & Sons, Bigadon Lane, Buckfastleigh, Devon, TQ11 0DT Tel: (01364) 643237 Fax: (01364) 642054

▶ W Parker & Sons, 6 Pierce Lane, Fulbourn, Cambridge, CB21 5DL Tel: (01223) 880464 Fax: (01223) 881694 E-mail: sales@wparkerandson.co.uk

▶ Walshaw Buildings Ltd, Unit 14 Dunscar Industrial Estate, Blackburn Road, Egerton, Bolton, BL7 9PQ Tel: (01204) 301671 Fax: (01204) 308782 E-mail: sales@dunscartimber.co.uk

▶ Weatherseal Holdings Ltd, 8 Darrows Industrial Estate, John Brannan Way, Bellshill, Lanarkshire, ML4 3HD Tel: (01698) 845468 Fax: (01698) 844807

▶ Wedgewood Homes, Tower Industrial Estate, London Road, Wrotham, Sevenoaks, Kent, TN15 7NS Tel: (01732) 824744 Fax: (01732) 824745

▶ Welsted Joinery Ltd, 31 Cutlers Road, South Woodham Ferrers, Chelmsford, CM3 5WA Tel: (01245) 329688 Fax: (01245) 329342

▶ Widnes Windows, 140 Birchfield Road, Widnes, Cheshire, WA8 9ED Tel: 0151-424 3332 Fax: 0151-420 4603 E-mail: info@widneswindows.co.uk

Willpack Case Mnfrs, Unit 1a Blackheath Trading Estate, Cakemore Road, Rowley Regis, West Midlands, B65 0QN Tel: 0121-559 4949 Fax: 0121-559 4545 E-mail: sales@willpack.net

▶ Windowseal & Distinctive Windows, Bradford Road, Winsford, Cheshire, CW7 2PD Tel: (01606) 594734 Fax: (01606) 598038

▶ Woods of Wales, Henfaes Lane, Welshpool, Powys, SY21 7BE Tel: (01938) 554789 Fax: (01938) 554921 E-mail: sales@woodsofwalesffnet.co.uk

▶ Woodscope Jordan Ltd, Hope Carr Way, Leigh, Lancashire, WN7 3DE Tel: (01942) 602266 Fax: (01942) 602277 E-mail: woodscopejordan@aol.com

▶ Woodworks, Unit 2 Moorside, Colchester, CO1 2TJ Tel: (01206) 862929 Fax: (01206) 862686

TIMBER RAILWAY SLEEPERS

Railway Sleeper.com, Kilgraney, Owthorpe Road, Cotgrave, Nottingham, NG12 3PU Tel: 0115-989 0445 Fax: 0115-989 3366 E-mail: enquiries@kilgraney.com

Weaver Demolition Ltd, Farrington Fields, Farrington Gurney, Bristol, BS39 6UU Tel: (01761) 452391 Fax: (01761) 453644 E-mail: mike@weaverdemolition.com

TIMBER ROOF TRUSSES

Anglian Timber Ltd, The Sawmill, Colchester Road, Wix, Manningtree, Essex, CO11 2RS Tel: (01255) 870881 Fax: (01255) 870480 E-mail: sales@angliantimber.co.uk

Bamber Roof Trusses, Church Farm Works, Oulton, Norwich, NR11 6NT Tel: (01263) 584255 Fax: (01263) 584166 E-mail: ronny.bamber@btinternet.com

Bullock & Driffill Ltd, Staunton Works, Newark Road, Staunton in the Vale, Nottingham, NG13 9PF Tel: (01400) 280000 Fax: (01400) 280010 E-mail: bullock.driffill@btopenworld.com

C B North Ltd, 65 Hedon Road, Hull, HU9 1LW Tel: (01482) 329847 Fax: (01482) 215048

Cox Long Ltd, Airfield Industrial Estate, Hixon, Stafford, ST18 0PA Tel: (01889) 270166 Fax: (01889) 271041 E-mail: info@coxlong.com

D J R Roof Trusses Ltd, Winnards Perch, St. Columb, Cornwall, TR9 6DE Tel: (01637) 881333 Fax: (01637) 881315 E-mail: andy@djr-roof-trusses.demon.co.uk

Howarth Timber Engineering Ltd, Howarth House, Hollow Road, Bury St. Edmunds, Suffolk, IP32 7QW Tel: (01284) 772700 Fax: (01284) 755567 E-mail: sales@howarthengineering.co.uk

J Scott Thrapston Ltd, Bridge Street, Thrapston, Kettering, Northamptonshire, NN14 4LR Tel: (01832) 732366 Fax: (01832) 733703 E-mail: julia@scottsofthrapston.co.uk

Jewson Ltd, Nelson Way, Boston, Lincolnshire, PE21 8UA Tel: (01205) 362451 Fax: (01205) 365898

Manderwood Timber Engineering Ltd, Unit 5, Great Honeyborough Trading Estate, Milford Haven, Dyfed, SA73 1SE Tel: (01646) 600621 Fax: (01646) 600784 E-mail: mwoodnyl@aol.com

Moreys, Trafalgar Road, Newport, Isle of Wight, PO30 1RT Tel: (01983) 525111 Fax: (01983) 520815

Pace Timber Engineering Ltd, Bleak Hall, Milton Keynes, MK6 1LA Tel: (01908) 302880 Fax: (01908) 397881 E-mail: enquiries@pacete.com

Palgrave Brown UK Ltd, St Andrews Road, Avonmouth, Bristol, BS11 9HT Tel: 0117-982 2375 Fax: 0117-982 9259 E-mail: info@palgravebrown.co.uk

Palgrave Brown UK Ltd, Canterbury Industrial Park, Island Road, Hersden, Canterbury, Kent, CT3 4HQ Tel: (01227) 712322 Fax: (01227) 712852

Pinewood Structures Ltd, 3 Station Road, Gamlingay, Sandy, Bedfordshire, SG19 3HB Tel: (01767) 651218 Fax: (01767) 651928 E-mail: enquiries@pinewood-structures.co.uk

Ridgeons Ltd, Alexandra Road, Sudbury, Suffolk, CO10 2XH Tel: (01787) 881777 Fax: (01787) 881186 E-mail: sudburysales@ridgerns.net

Rte UK Ltd, 101a Hall Farm Road, Benfleet, Essex, SS7 5JW Tel: (01268) 569393 Fax: (01268) 751753 E-mail: rte-uk@lineone.net

John B. Smith Ltd, Dugdale Street, Stockton-On-Tees, Cleveland, TS18 2NE Tel: (01642) 675096 Fax: (01642) 617701 E-mail: enquiries@johnbsmith.co.uk

▶ Truss 2 Frame, Catfoss Industrial Estate, Bewholme Lane, Brandesburton, Driffield, North Humberside, YO25 8ES Tel: (01964) 544777 Fax: (01964) 544888

Walker Timber Ltd, Carriden Sawmills, Bo'Ness, West Lothian, EH51 9SN Tel: (01506) 823331 Fax: (01506) 822590 E-mail: mail@walkertimber.com

Wyckham Blackwell Group Ltd, Old Station Road, Hampton-In-Arden, Solihull, West Midlands, B92 0HB Tel: (01675) 442233 Fax: (01675) 442227E-mail: info@wyckham-blackwell.co.uk

TIMBER SAW MILLS, *See Wood Saw Mills etc*

TIMBER STORAGE BUILDINGS

Warwick Buildings Ltd, Southam Road, Long Itchington, Southam, Warwickshire, CV47 9QL Tel: (01926) 815757 Fax: (01926) 815162 E-mail: sales@warwickbuildings.com

▶ Weatherstrong Timber Framed Buildings, Henfield Road, Cowfold, Horsham, West Sussex, RH13 8DU Tel: (01403) 865666 E-mail: andrwpar9@aol.com

TIMBER STRUCTURE CONSTRUCTION CONSULTANCY

▶ A & C Management Consultants Ltd, 13a Harben Parade, Finchley Road, London, NW3 6LH Tel: (020) 7564 7050 Fax: (020) 7564 8764 E-mail: acmanagement@tiscali.co.uk

TIMBER SURFACE COATING MATERIALS

C S Surface Coating Ltd, 2 Mackay Transport, Colonial Way, Watford, WD24 4JU Tel: (01923) 246982 Fax: (01923) 237841 E-mail: mail@cs-surface-coating.co.uk

▶ Timber Coaters, 187 Pensby Road, Heswall, Wirral, Merseyside, CH61 6UB Tel: (07778) 461644 Fax: 0151-342 5205 E-mail: timbercoaters@aol.com

TIMBER TREATMENT EQUIPMENT

Frank Key Nottingham Ltd, Portland Street, Daybrook, Nottingham, NG5 6BL Tel: 0115-920 8208 Fax: 0115-967 0393 E-mail: sales@frank-key.co.uk

Goodwood Timber Products, Plough Business Centre, Plough Road, Great Bentley, Colchester, CO7 7US Tel: (01206) 251711

TIMBER TREATMENT SERVICES

Advanced Remedial Treatments Ltd, 5 Stoke Road, Gosport, Hampshire, PO12 1LT Tel: (023) 9252 5244 Fax: (023) 9251 0750

Allen & Orr Ltd, The Albion Sawmills, Union Walk, Chesterfield, Derbyshire, S40 4SA Tel: (01246) 232426 Fax: (01246) 559099

Arch Chemicals UK, Wheldon Road, Castleford, West Yorkshire, WF10 2JT Tel: (01977) 714000 Fax: (01977) 714001

Complete Preservation Service Ltd, 4-5 Wyvern House, Harriers Trading Estate, Stadium Close, Kidderminster, Worcestershire, DY10 1NJ Tel: (01562) 69945 Fax: (01562) 69945 E-mail: complete.preservation@ukonline.co.uk

Dampcoursing Ltd, 10-12 Dorset Road, London, N15 5AJ Tel: (020) 8802 2233 Fax: (020) 8809 1839 E-mail: dampcoursingltd@london.com

Dampcure Luton Co., 1 Ashton Road, Luton, LU1 3QE Tel: (01582) 735650

▶ Dampcure Woodcure 30 Ltd, 41 Merton Road, Watford, WD18 0WJ Tel: (01923) 663322 Fax: (01923) 223842 E-mail: admin@dampcurewoodcure.com

Expertreat, Unit 3a Top Land Country Business Park, Cragg Road, Hebden Bridge, West Yorkshire, HX7 5HR Tel: (01422) 883535 Fax: (01422) 883535

Forest Products Ltd, Workshop Forestry Commission Lightmoor Dept, Speech House Road, Cinderford, Gloucestershire, GL14 3HU Tel: (01594) 822223 Fax: (01594) 826901 E-mail: enquiries@forest-products.com

Gulliver Timber Treatments Ltd, Bank Buildings, Station Road, Sevenoaks, Kent, TN14 5QX Tel: (01959) 524966 Fax: (01959) 525176 E-mail: enquiries@gullivertt.co.uk

Henry Jones & Sons Ltd, Wyvern, 1 Brynhedydd Road, Rhyl, Denbighshire, LL18 3UH Tel: (01745) 351314 Fax: (01745) 351314 E-mail: office@hjs1923.f9.co.uk

Kingsland Saw Mills Ltd, Kingsland, Leominster, Herefordshire, HR6 9SF Tel: (01568) 708206 Fax: (01568) 708258 E-mail: info@kingslandstabling.com

Lawson Timber Ltd, White Hart Road, London, SE18 1DH Tel: (020) 8855 7621 Fax: (020) 8854 6552

Mercian Preservation Ltd, 74 Cinder Bank, Dudley, West Midlands, DY2 9BH Tel: (01384) 250154 Fax: (01384) 456068

Pass & Co. (St. Albans) Ltd, 37 Thornton Road, Little Heath, Potters Bar, Hertfordshire, EN6 1JJ Tel: (01727) 851172 Fax: (01707) 654327

Plad Timber & Damp Proofing Specialists Ltd, 168 Birmingham Road, Shenstone Wood End, Lichfield, Staffordshire, WS14 0NX Tel: 0121-308 4241 Fax: 0121-323 3683

Protim Services Ltd, Cockersdale Works, Whitehall Road, Drighlington, Bradford, West Yorkshire, BD11 1NQ Tel: 0113-285 2173 Fax: 0113-285 2243 E-mail: leeds@protim-services.co.uk

R H Smith Worthing Ltd, Southdownview Way, Worthing, West Sussex, BN14 8NL Tel: (01903) 238316 E-mail: rhsmith1956@tiscali.co.uk

R Thorne & Sons, Mannington Sawmills, Holt Road, Three Legged Cross, Wimborne, Dorset, BH21 6SE Tel: (01202) 822204 Fax: (01202) 824410 E-mail: robertthorne@fsbdial.co.uk

RLH Developments, 3 Coombe Avenue, Croydon, CR0 5SD Tel: (020) 8681 8811 Fax: (020) 8666 0147 E-mail: info@rlhdevelopments.co.uk

S Keeling & Co. Ltd, Forge Lane, Stoke-on-Trent, ST1 5PB Tel: (01782) 202660 Fax: (01782) 202019

Sussex Timber Preservation Co. Ltd, Baltic Wharf, Wellington Road, Portslade, Brighton, BN41 1DX Tel: (01273) 420230 Fax: (01273) 430612

Edward Thomas & Son Ltd, Usk Sawmills, Sennybridge, Brecon, Powys, LD3 8RS Tel: (01874) 636321

TIMBER WINDOW FRAMES

▶ Ambleside Joinery Sales, 18, Graystones Close, West Bridgford, Nottingham, NG2 6QU Tel: 01159 819853 Fax: 01159 819853 E-mail: ambleside.sales@ntlworld.com

Rationel Windows (U K) Ltd, 7 Avonbury Business Park, Howes Lane, Bicester, Oxfordshire, OX26 2UA Tel: (01869) 248181 Fax: (01869) 249693 E-mail: sales@rationel.com

Top Notch Ltd, Kingsley, Summercourt, Newquay, Cornwall, TR8 5AG Tel: (01872) 510652 Fax: (01872) 510652

TIMBER WINDOW FRAMES – *continued*

▶ United Windows & Glazing Ltd, Mill Lane, Billinghay, LN4 4ES Tel: (01526) 861285 Fax: (01526) 861584 E-mail: unitedkel@dekker.demon.co.uk

TIME AND ATTENDANCE RECORDERS

▶ LTR, 3 Newtown Grange Farm Business Park, Desford Road, Newtown Unthank, Leicester, LE9 9FL Tel: (01455) 821999 Fax: (01455) 821949 E-mail: sales@ltrtech.co.uk

TIME AND ATTENDANCE SYSTEMS MANUFRS

A M Time Services, 8 Ivyside Close, Killamarsh, Sheffield, S21 1JT Tel: 0114-248 5855 Fax: 0114-248 5855 E-mail: info@amtime.co.uk

Addtime Recording Co. Ltd, 2 Eastwell Road, Ashton-in-Makerfield, Wigan, Lancashire, WN4 9QQ Tel: (01942) 272061 Fax: (01942) 274601E-mail: sales@addtimerecording.co.uk

Bodet UK Ltd, 4 Sovereign Park, Cleveland Way, Hemel Hempstead Industrial Estate, Hemel Hempstead, Hertfordshire, HP2 7DA Tel: (01442) 418800 Fax: (01442) 234345 E-mail: enquiries@bodet.co.uk

Face Time, 15 The Plain, Thornbury, Bristol, BS35 2BD Tel: (01454) 858590 Fax: (01454) 858589 E-mail: info@facetime.ltd.uk

▶ Human Recognition Systems Ltd, First Floor Vortex Court, Enterprise Way, Liverpool, L13 1FB Tel: 0151-254 2888 Fax: 0151-254 2999 E-mail: identify@hrsltd.com

Isgus International Ltd, Unit 10 Springfield Business Centre, Brunel Way, Stroudwater Business Park, Stonehouse, Gloucestershire, GL10 3SX Tel: (01453) 827373 Fax: (01453) 827360 E-mail: admin@isgus.co.uk

Time Systems UK Ltd, Systems House, Wavendon, Milton Keynes, MK17 8AA Tel: (01908) 281000 Fax: (01908) 281291 E-mail: sales@timesystemsuk.com

TIME AND FEE BILLING SOFTWARE

D S T, Afinity House, Beaufort Court, Rochester, Kent, ME2 4FD Tel: (01634) 292292 Fax: (01293) 554600

TIME AND FREQUENCY SYSTEMS

Quartzlock UK Ltd, Gothic, Plymouth Road, Totnes, Devon, TQ9 5LH Tel: (01803) 862062 Fax: (01803) 867962 E-mail: quartzlock@quartzlock.com

Rapco Electronics Ltd, 10 Joule Road, Basingstoke, Hampshire, RG21 6XF Tel: (01256) 325454 Fax: (01256) 322695 E-mail: info@rapco.co.uk

TIME AND MOTION PRODUCTIVITY MONITORING CONSULTANCY

▶ R W M Training, 3 Dunnet Place, Thurso, Caithness, KW14 8JE Tel: (01847) 894934 Fax: (07876) 844044 E-mail: info@rwm-training.co.uk

▶ Scott-Grant Technical Services, Portland Tower, Portland Street, Manchester, M1 3LD Tel: 0161-234 2121 Fax: 0161-234 2125 E-mail: training@scott-grant.co.uk

TIME CODE SYSTEMS

Infotec Ltd, The Maltings, Tamworth Road, Ashby-de-la-Zouch, Leicestershire, LE65 2PS Tel: (01530) 560600 Fax: (01530) 560111 E-mail: sales@infotech.co.uk

Rapco Electronics Ltd, 10 Joule Road, Basingstoke, Hampshire, RG21 6XF Tel: (01256) 325454 Fax: (01256) 322695 E-mail: info@rapco.co.uk

Wharton Electronics, Unit 15 Thame Park Business Centre, Wenman Road, Thame, Oxfordshire, OX9 3XA Tel: (01844) 260567 Fax: (01844) 218855 E-mail: info@wharton.co.uk

TIME CONTROL SYSTEMS

Meteor, 239 Drum Road, Cookstown, County Tyrone, BT80 9HP Tel: (028) 8675 1515 Fax: (028) 8672 8961 E-mail: sales@meteorelectrical.com

Prism Europe Ltd, Abbey Gate One, 8 Whitewell Road, Colchester, CO2 7DE Tel: (01206) 761300 Fax: (01206) 719900 E-mail: sales@prism-uk.com

Serco Integrated Transport Ltd, Cavendish House, Prince's Wharf, Stockton-On-Tees, Cleveland, TS17 6QY Tel: (01642) 636700 Fax: (01642) 636701

T-Data, 57 Skylark Way, Shinfield, Reading, RG2 9AD Tel: 0118-988 8810 Fax: (07092) 312381 E-mail: info@t-data.co.uk

Timeguard Ltd, Victory Park, 400 Edgware Road, London, NW2 6ND Tel: (020) 8450 8944 Fax: (020) 8452 5143 E-mail: csc@timeguard.com

TIME CONTROL SYSTEMS INSTALLATION/RENTAL/SERVICE

Allday Time Systems Ltd, Linchford House, Linchford Lane, Farnborough, Hampshire, GU14 6JD Tel: (01489) 572717 Fax: (020) 7403 2216 E-mail: sales@alldaytime.co.uk

▶ South Wales Time Recorders Sales & Services Ltd, Time House, Regent Street, Barry, South Glamorgan, CF62 8DT Tel: (01446) 721446 Fax: (01446) 744678 E-mail: sales@swtr.co.uk

Time Systems UK Ltd, Systems House, Wavendon, Milton Keynes, MK17 8AA Tel: (01908) 281000 Fax: (01908) 281291 E-mail: sales@timesystemsuk.com

TIME MANAGEMENT SOFTWARE

Data Collection Systems Ltd, 6 Station Court, Station Approach, Borough Green, Sevenoaks, Kent, TN15 8AD Tel: (01732) 780456 Fax: (01732) 780445 E-mail: sales@dcs-sol.com

Elf Productivity, The Stables, Skull House Lane, Appley Bridge, Wigan, Lancashire, WN6 9DJ Tel: (01257) 256000 Fax: (01257) 256010 E-mail: sales@elf.uk.com

TIME RECORDER CARDS

Cotswold Recording Systems, 12 Rodbourne Road, Swindon, SN2 2AG Tel: (01793) 618874 Fax: (01793) 511874 E-mail: rodger@clockingmachine.co.uk

TIME RECORDERS

Addtime Recording Co. Ltd, 2 Eastwell Road, Ashton-in-Makerfield, Wigan, Lancashire, WN4 9QQ Tel: (01942) 272061 Fax: (01942) 274601E-mail: sales@addtimerecording.co.uk

Allday Time Systems Ltd, Linchford House, Linchford Lane, Farnborough, Hampshire, GU14 6JD Tel: (01489) 572717 Fax: (020) 7403 2216 E-mail: sales@alldaytime.co.uk

Anglia Time Recorders Ltd, 3 Cox Close, Kesgrave, Ipswich, IP5 2DW Tel: (01353) 778518 Fax: (01487) 823862 E-mail: sales@angliatime.co.uk

Autoclock Systems Ltd, 93-97 Second Avenue, Newcastle upon Tyne, NE6 5XT Tel: 0191-276 1611 Fax: 0191-265 0586 E-mail: sales@autoclocksystems.co.uk

Birmingham Time Recorder Services Ltd, Rumbow House, Rumbow, Halesowen, West Midlands, B63 3HU Tel: 0121-585 6660 Fax: 0121-585 6661 E-mail: info@ctrn.co.uk

Borer Data Systems Ltd, Gotelee House, Market Place, Wokingham, Berkshire, RG40 1AN Tel: 0118-979 1137 Fax: 0118-977 3526 E-mail: borer@borer.co.uk

Cotswold Recording Systems, 12 Rodbourne Road, Swindon, SN2 2AG Tel: (01793) 618874 Fax: (01793) 511874 E-mail: rodger@clockingmachine.co.uk

Elf Productivity, The Stables, Skull House Lane, Appley Bridge, Wigan, Lancashire, WN6 9DJ Tel: (01257) 256000 Fax: (01257) 256010 E-mail: sales@elf.uk.com

Emefco Time Recorders, 5 The Briars, Harlow, Essex, CM18 7DG Tel: (01279) 419694 Fax: (01279) 419694 E-mail: p.hill@virgin.net

Eurotime Systems Ltd, 101 Blandford Avenue, Birmingham, B36 9JB Tel: 0121-776 6860 Fax: (0871) 9942954 E-mail: sales@eurotime.co.uk

Group 4 Security Systems Ltd, New Challenge House, International Drive, Tewkesbury Business Park, Tewkesbury, Gloucestershire, GL20 8UQ Tel: (01684) 850977 Fax: (01684) 294845 E-mail: sales@g4tec.co.uk

Kronos Systems Ltd, 2 Carey Road, Wokingham, Berkshire, RG40 2NP Tel: 0118-978 9784 Fax: 0118-978 2214 E-mail: ukinfo@kronos.com

▶ Mainbell, Unit 4B, Bridge Farm Industries, Botley Road, Curbridge, Southampton, SO30 2HB Tel: (01489) 799444 Fax: (01445) 821949 E-mail: admin@mainbell.free-online.co.uk

Midland Time Recorder Services Ltd, 324 Hob Moor Road, Small Heath, Birmingham, B10 9HJ Tel: 0121-784 3761 Fax: 0121-784 7461

North West Time Recording Co., 197 Bury Old Road, Prestwich, Manchester, M25 1JF Tel: 0161-798 8002 Fax: 0161-773 2441 E-mail: terry@nwtr.co.uk

Ontime Systems Ltd, Unit 3 Bessemer Crescent, Aylesbury, Buckinghamshire, HP19 8TF Tel: 0800 975 0960 Fax: (01296) 395787 E-mail: ontime-sales@btconnect.com

Rushton Electronic Solutions Ltd, Meadow Mill, Water Street, Stockport, Cheshire, SK1 2BU Tel: (0161) 429 6851 Fax: 0161-480 1855 E-mail: mail@restime.co.uk

Solent Time Recorders, 20 St Johns Road, Locks Heath, Southampton, SO31 6NF Tel: (01489) 572717 Fax: (01489) 572717

▶ South Wales Time Recorders Sales & Services Ltd, Time House, Regent Street, Barry, South Glamorgan, CF62 8DT Tel: (01446) 721446 Fax: (01446) 744678 E-mail: sales@swtr.co.uk

South Wales Time Recorders Sales & Services Ltd, Time House, Regent Street, Barry, South Glamorgan, CF62 8DT Tel: (01446) 721446 Fax: (01446) 744678E-mail: sales@swtr.co.uk

▶ Southern Time Recorders, Westwood House, Thurnham Lane, Bearsted, Maidstone, Kent, ME14 4QZ Tel: (01622) 737177 Fax: (01622) 735424 E-mail: info@southerntime.co.uk

Time Recorder Services, 47 Phillipps Avenue, Exmouth, Devon, EX8 3JE Tel: (01395) 271676 Fax: 01395 271676 E-mail: admin@timerecord.co.uk

Time Recorder Services, 69a Richardshaw Lane, Stanningley, Pudsey, West Yorkshire, LS28 7EL Tel: 0113-257 7920 Fax: 0113-257 7920 E-mail: info@timerecord.co.uk

Time Systems, 210 Broadgate Lane, Horsforth, Leeds, LS18 5BS Tel: 0113-258 7856 Fax: 0113-258 6612 E-mail: salests@aol.com

Time Systems UK Ltd, Systems House, Wavendon, Milton Keynes, MK17 8AA Tel: (01908) 281000 Fax: (01908) 281291 E-mail: sales@timesystemsuk.com

TIME SWITCHES

Danfoss Randall Ltd, Ampthill Road, Bedford, MK42 9ER Tel: (0845) 1217400 Fax: (0845) 1217515 E-mail: danfossrandall@randall.com

Eltime Ltd, 10-14 Hall Road, Heybridge, Maldon, Essex, CM9 4NF Tel: (01621) 859500 Fax: (01621) 855335 E-mail: sales@eltime.co.uk

Grasslin UK Ltd, Tower House, Vale Rise, Tonbridge, Kent, TN9 1TB Tel: (01732) 359888 Fax: (01732) 354445

Horstmann Group Ltd, Roman Farm Road, Bristol, BS4 1UP Tel: 0117-978 8700 Fax: 0117-987 8701 E-mail: reception@horstmann.co.uk

Starkstrom (London) Ltd, 256 Field End Road, Eastcote, Ruislip, Middlesex, HA4 9UW Tel: (020) 8868 3732 Fax: (020) 8868 3736 E-mail: sales@starkstrom.com

Timeguard Ltd, Victory Park, 400 Edgware Road, London, NW2 6ND Tel: (020) 8450 8944 Fax: (020) 8452 5143 E-mail: csc@timeguard.com

TIMERS, *See also headings for particular types*

Thermaco Ltd, Unit 5, Spring Lane North, Malvern, Worcestershire, WR14 1BU Tel: (01684) 566163 Fax: (01684) 892356 E-mail: sales@thermaco.co.uk

TIMERS, CENTRAL HEATING

▶ Curtis Plumbing & Heating, 2 Pollard Court, Pollard Road, Morden, Surrey, SM4 6EH Tel: (07020) 930940 Fax: 020 81506313 E-mail: sales@cphs.co.uk

▶ J & J Rothwell & Son, 156 Parrin Lane, Eccles, Manchester, M30 8BH Tel: (07789) 937405 Fax: 0161-281 0238 E-mail: info@rothwellandson.co.uk

▶ Wolf Heating Uk Ltd, 8 Brunel Court, Rudheath Way, Gadbrook Business Park, Northwich, Cheshire, CW9 7EG Tel: 01606 354371 Fax: 01606 44805 E-mail: info@wolfheatinguk.co.uk

TIMESHARE HOLIDAYS

World Wide Time Share Hypermarket, Woodland Point, Wootton Mount, Bournemouth, BH1 1PJ Tel: (0870) 4431466 Fax: (0870) 4431477 E-mail: sales@timeshare-hypermarket.com

TIMING BELTING

Gould Pulleys & Drives Ltd, Unit 19, Worcester Road Industrial Estate, Chipping Norton, Oxfordshire, OX7 5XW Tel: (01608) 643311 Fax: (01608) 643050 E-mail: sales@gouldpulleys.com

Megadyne U K Ltd, Gildersome Spur, Gildersome, Leeds, LS27 7JZ Tel: 0113-238 2910 Fax: 0113-238 3870 E-mail: sales@megadyne.co.uk

Optibelt UK Ltd, 5 Bishops Court, Winwick Quay, Warrington, WA2 8QY Tel: (0870) 4288800 Fax: (01925) 573751 E-mail: optibelt@optibeltuk.co.uk

TIMING EQUIPMENT

H S Sports Ltd, Unit 5 Radnor Park Industrial Estate, Congleton, Cheshire, CW12 4XN Tel: (01260) 275708 Fax: (01260) 278352 E-mail: info@hssports.co.uk

TIMING PULLEYS

South East Power Transmissions Ltd, Network House, Perry Road, Harlow, Essex, CM18 7ND Tel: (01279) 418300 Fax: (01279) 418100 E-mail: stransltd@aol.com

TIN BOX/CASE/CONTAINER MANUFRS

Ball Packaging Europe UK Ltd, Lakeside, Chester Business Park, Chester, CH4 9QT Tel: (01244) 681155 Fax: (01244) 680320 E-mail: chester_reception@ball-europe.com

Birmingham Tin Box Co., 82 Cliveland Street, Birmingham, B19 3SN Tel: 0121-359 7974 Fax: 0121-359 7975 E-mail: btb@regton.com

Central Tin Containers Ltd, Wilbraham Place, Scotland Road, Liverpool, L5 5BJ Tel: 0151-207 2775 Fax: 0151-298 1487 E-mail: dhunt@centraltincontainers.ltd.co.uk

Container Printers (UK) Ltd, 248 Mackadown Lane, Kitts Green, Birmingham, B33 0JU Tel: 0121-789 7777 Fax: 0121-789 5539 E-mail: info@cprint.co.uk

D K S Packaging Ltd, 62-70 Litherland Road, Bootle, Merseyside, L20 3HZ Tel: 0151-922 2656 Fax: 0151-933 0547 E-mail: reception@dkspackaging.co.uk

Henry Curtis Ltd, 20 Verney Road, London, SE16 3DY Tel: (020) 7237 4500 Fax: (020) 7232 1568

R L M Packaging Ltd, Dairycoates Industrial Estate, Wiltshire Road, Hull, HU4 6PA Tel: (01482) 505585 Fax: (01482) 568115 E-mail: info@rlm-packaging.co.uk

William Say & Co. Ltd, 20-26 Verney Road, London, SE16 3DY Tel: (020) 7237 4500 Fax: (020) 7232 1568 E-mail: sales@pwcon.co.uk

Sure-Can Ltd, Unit 6, 8 & 9 Adam Business Centre, Henson Way, Telford Way Industrial Estate, Kettering, Northamptonshire, NN16 8PX Tel: (01536) 411882 Fax: (01536) 518086 E-mail: sales@sure-can.co.uk

TIN METAL

Cravelon Metal-Pack Ltd, 28 Hayes Street, Bromley, BR2 7LD Tel: (020) 8462 1197 Fax: (020) 8462 5282

Lowden Metals Ltd, 7 Harvey Works Industrial Estate, Shelah Road, Halesowen, West Midlands, B63 3PG Tel: 0121-501 3596 Fax: 0121-585 5162 E-mail: enquiries@metals26.freeserve.co.uk

TIN MINE OPERATORS/TIN PRODUCERS (UK)

▶ Baseresult Holdings Ltd, Dudnance Lane, Pool, Redruth, Cornwall, TR15 3QT Tel: (01209) 715777 Fax: (01209) 716777 E-mail: baseresult@btconnect.com

TIN PLATED STEEL, *See Tinned etc*

TIN PLATING SERVICES

Afon Tinplate Co. Ltd, Afon Works, Llangyfelach, Swansea, SA5 7LN Tel: (01792) 312000 Fax: (01792) 312001 E-mail: sales@afontinplate.co.uk

Thomas Gameson & Sons Ltd, PO Box 1, Cannock, Staffordshire, WS11 0AX Tel: (01543) 504191 Fax: (01543) 462482

Precise Electro Plating Works Ltd, Pitt Road, Southampton, SO15 3FQ Tel: (023) 8022 8014 Fax: (023) 8022 8114

TIN/LEAD ALLOY PRODUCTS

Summit Solder Products, Rail Works, Railway Sidings, Biggleswade, Bedfordshire, SG18 8BD Tel: (01767) 318999 Fax: (01767) 318912 E-mail: summit@mountstar.com

TINNED STEEL STRIPS, *See Tinned etc*

TINNING SERVICES

Thomas Gameson & Sons Ltd, PO Box 1, Cannock, Staffordshire, WS11 0AX Tel: (01543) 504191 Fax: (01543) 462482

TINNING SERVICES – *continued*

Strip Tinning Ltd, Heath Street South, Springhill, Birmingham, B18 7PY Tel: 0121-454 8008 Fax: 0121-454 7600 E-mail: richard@stuk.demon.co.uk

TINPLATE

Afon Tinplate Co. Ltd, Afon Works, Llangyfelach, Swansea, SA5 7LN Tel: (01792) 312000 Fax: (01792) 312001 E-mail: sales@afontinplate.co.uk

▶ William Corbett & Co. Ltd, Pantyffynnon Road, Ammanford, Dyfed, SA18 3HN Tel: (01269) 593215 Fax: (01269) 591929 E-mail: sales@williamcorbett.co.uk

David Matthews Ltd, Clayton Tinplate Works, Pontardulais, Swansea, SA4 8SN Tel: (01792) 882766 Fax: (01792) 885195 E-mail: inquiries@dmlltd.demon.co.uk

Arthur Oakley Transport Ltd, Ramsden Road, Rotherwas Industrial Estate, Hereford, HR2 6LR Tel: (01432) 266662 Fax: (01432) 356660 E-mail: sales@vanoaksteels.co.uk

P W S Ltd, Strawberry Lane, Willenhall, West Midlands, WV13 3SE Tel: (01902) 365200 Fax: (01902) 365201

TINPLATE CANS

▶ Bowler Group Ltd, Bowler House Harvey Road, Burnt Mills Industrial Estate, Basildon, Essex, SS13 1DD Tel: (01268) 470700 Fax: (01268) 477717 E-mail: info@hjbowlerandsons.com

Shirley Jones & Associates Ltd, C The Courtyard, Lonesome Lane, Reigate, Surrey, RH2 7QT Tel: (01737) 244844 Fax: (01737) 243266

Mersey Can Ltd, 12-14 Ebenezer Street, Birkenhead, Merseyside, CH42 1NH Tel: 0151-645 8511 Fax: 0151-644 6749

TINPLATE ELECTROPLATING

East Lancashire Platers Ltd, Oxford Mill, Oxford Road, Burnley, Lancashire, BB11 3BA Tel: (01282) 425621 Fax: (01282) 433618

Robert Stuart plc, 10-11 Edinburgh Wa, Harlow, Essex, CM20 2DH Tel: (01279) 442931 Fax: (01279) 626063 E-mail: sales@robertstuart.plc.uk

TINPLATE FABRICATORS OR WORKERS

Dunnetts Ltd, 170 Kings Road, Tyseley, Birmingham, B11 2AS Tel: 0121-706 9180 Fax: 0121-706 6169 E-mail: dunnetts@dunnetts.co.uk

TINPLATE MERCHANTS (INTERNATIONAL), IMPORTERS, EXPORTERS OR TRADERS

▶ William Corbett & Co. Ltd, Pantyffynnon Road, Ammanford, Dyfed, SA18 3HN Tel: (01269) 593215 Fax: (01269) 591929 E-mail: sales@williamcorbett.co.uk

TINPLATE PRODUCTS, *See headings under Tin*

TINTED TRIACETATE OPTICAL COATINGS

▶ Siltint Ind Ltd, 124 Longley Lane, Sharston, Manchester, M22 4SP Tel: 0161-945 4000 Fax: 0161-945 4040 E-mail: info@siltint.com

TINWARE

Silver Crane Co., 34a Black Moor Road, Ebblake Industrial Estate, Verwood, Dorset, BH31 6BB Tel: (01202) 825155 Fax: (01202) 823300 E-mail: sales@silvercrane.co.uk

TIPPING VEHICLE BODIES

Brade-Leigh Bodies Ltd, Albion Industrial Estate, Oldbury Road, West Bromwich, West Midlands, B70 9EH Tel: 0121-553 4361 Fax: 0121-500 6139 E-mail: sales@brade-leigh.co.uk

▶ Leeward Coachbuilders Ltd, Richards Street, Wednesbury, West Midlands, WS10 8AJ Tel: 0121-526 4709 Fax: 0121-526 4718 E-mail: sales@leewardcoachbuilders.co.uk

SDC Trailers Ltd, Bradder Way, Mansfield, Nottinghamshire, NG18 5DQ Tel: (01623) 625354 Fax: (01623) 626946 E-mail: admin@sdctrailers.com

TISSUE PAPER

Georgia Pacific GB Ltd, Mansell Way, Horwich, Bolton, BL6 6JL Tel: (01204) 673300 Fax: (01204) 673301 E-mail:

Peter Grant Papers Ltd, Caton Road, Lansil Industrial Estate, Lancaster, LA1 3PQ Tel: (01524) 843678 Fax: (01524) 843644

▶ Kiuger Incorparated, Royce Trading Estate, Ashburton Road West, Trafford Park, Manchester, M17 1RY Tel: 0161-874 7300 Fax: 0161-874 7320

Shredhouse Gift Packaging, Salisbury Road Business Park, Salisbury Road, Pewsey, Wiltshire, SN9 5PZ Tel: (01672) 564333 Fax: (01672) 564301

TISSUE PAPER PRODUCTS

A Pollard & Sons Ltd, 51 Aylesbury St, Bletchley, Milton Keynes, MK2 2BQ Tel: (01908) 375221 Fax: (01908) 271552 E-mail: sales@pollards.co.uk

Felber Jucker & Co. Ltd, 48 Minerva Road, Park Royal, London, NW10 6HJ Tel: (020) 8965 9371 Fax: (020) 8961 3732

TITANIUM

Aviation Metals Ltd, Michigan Drive, Tongwell, Milton Keynes, MK15 8JE Tel: (01908) 210012 Fax: (01908) 210066 E-mail: sales@aviationmetals.co.uk

Enpar Special Alloys Ltd, Station Road, Ecclesfield, Sheffield, S35 9YR Tel: 0114-219 3002 Fax: 0114-219 1145 E-mail: sales.esa@firthrixson.com

Gould Alloys Ltd, Carrwood Road, Chesterfield, Derbyshire, S41 9QB Tel: (01246) 263300 Fax: (01246) 260999 E-mail: sales@gouldalloys.co.uk

Rolled Alloys Ltd, Walker Industrial Park, Guide, Blackburn, BB1 2QE Tel: (01254) 582999 Fax: (01254) 582666 E-mail: sales@rolledalloys.co.uk

Timet UK Ltd, Kynoch Works, Witton, Birmingham, B6 7UR Tel: 0121-356 1155 Fax: 0121-356 5413 E-mail: eurosales@timet.com

TITANIUM BARS

Timet UK Ltd, Kynoch Works, Witton, Birmingham, B6 7UR Tel: 0121-356 1155 Fax: 0121-356 5413 E-mail: eurosales@timet.com

TITANIUM COMPONENTS

Aeromet International plc, Eurolink Industrial Centre, Castle Road, Sittingbourne, Kent, ME10 3RN Tel: (01795) 415000 Fax: (01795) 415015 E-mail: andrew.king@aeromet.co.uk

Duckworth & Kent Ltd, Terence House, 7 Marquis Business Centre, Royston Road, Baldock, Hertfordshire, SG7 6XL Tel: (01462) 893254 Fax: (01462) 896288 E-mail: info@duckworth-and-kent.com

Wogen Group Ltd, 4 The Sanctuary, Westminster, London, SW1P 3JS Tel: (020) 7222 2171 Fax: (020) 7222 5862 E-mail: wogen@wogen.co.uk

TITANIUM DIOXIDE

Huntsman Tioxide, Haverton Hill Road, Billingham, Cleveland, TS23 1PS Tel: (01642) 370300 Fax: (01642) 370290

Huntsman Tioxide, Greatham Works, Hartlepool, Cleveland, TS25 2DD Tel: (01642) 545200 Fax: (01642) 546016 E-mail: info@huntsmen.com

Rakem Ltd, Wellington Street, Bury, Lancashire, BL8 2BD Tel: 0161-762 0044 Fax: 0161-762 0033 E-mail: info@rakem.co.uk

Whitchem Ltd, 23 Albert Street, Newcastle, Staffordshire, ST5 1JP Tel: (01782) 711777 Fax: (01782) 717290 E-mail: enquiries@whitchem.co.uk

TITANIUM DIOXIDE PIGMENTS

Rakem Ltd, Wellington Street, Bury, Lancashire, BL8 2BD Tel: 0161-762 0044 Fax: 0161-762 0033 E-mail: info@rakem.co.uk

TITANIUM FABRICATORS

Langfields Ltd, 158 Liverpool Street, Salford, M5 4LJ Tel: 0161-736 4506 Fax: 0161-745 7108 E-mail: sales@langfields.com

TITANIUM FASTENERS

Abbot Fixing Systems Ltd, Manor Farm, Bullington End Road, Hanslope, Milton Keynes, MK19 7BQ Tel: (01908) 511730

Forward Fastners Ltd, 4 Blews Street, Birmingham, B6 4EP Tel: 0121-687 0018 Fax: 0121-687 0024 E-mail: forwardfastenersmfgr@ciscali.co.uk

TITANIUM FOIL

▶ Firebird Metals Ltd, 1 Canal Street, Sheffield, S4 7ZE Tel: (0870) 7622333 Fax: (0870) 7622334 E-mail: neil@firebirdmetals.com

TITANIUM MACHINISTS

Timet UK Ltd, Kynoch Works, Witton, Birmingham, B6 7UR Tel: 0121-356 1155 Fax: 0121-356 5413 E-mail: eurosales@timet.com

TITANIUM RODS

Timet (U K) Ltd, PO Box 57, Swansea, SA1 1XD Tel: (01792) 870330 Fax: (01792) 874569

TITANIUM SPRINGS

Hanson Springs Ltd, Lincoln Street, Rochdale, Lancashire, OL11 1NP Tel: (01706) 522124 Fax: (01706) 640571 E-mail: sales@hanson-springs.co.uk

TITANIUM TURNED PARTS

▶ BST Precision Ltd, Unit D 10, Hortonwood 7, Hortonwood, Telford, Shropshire, TF1 7XU Tel: (01952) 603952 Fax: (01952) 604947 E-mail: tony.edgley@bstprecision.co.uk

TOASTERS, CATERING

Cookcraft Ltd, Welcome House, 21 High Street, Cheslyn Hay, Walsall, WS6 7AB Tel: (01922) 416555 Fax: (01922) 418844

TOASTMASTER SERVICES

▶ Carousel Entertainments, 18 Westbury Lodge Close, Pinner, Middlesex, HA5 3FG Tel: (0870) 7518688 Fax: (0870) 7518668 E-mail: sales@carouselentertainments.co.uk

Peter Moore, 18 College Gardens, London, SW17 7UG Tel: (020) 8767 2103 Fax: (020) 8767 2103 E-mail: peter@toastmasterlondon.com

TOBACCO LEAF PROCESSING MACHINES

Dickinson Legg Ltd, Moorside Road, Winchester, Hampshire, SO23 7SS Tel: (01962) 842222 Fax: (01962) 840567 E-mail: sales@dickinson.com

Griffin Cardwell Ltd, 87 Fleet Road, Fleet, Hampshire, GU51 3PJ Tel: (01252) 365500 Fax: (01252) 612875 E-mail: sales@griffincardwell.com

Hauni London Ltd, Hope House, 45 Great Peter Street, London, SW1P 3LT Tel: (020) 7222 3956 Fax: (020) 7222 8648

Molins Tobacco Machinery Ltd, Haw Lane, Saunderton, High Wycombe, Buckinghamshire, HP14 4JE Tel: (01844) 343211 Fax: (01844) 342410 E-mail: enquiries@molins.co.uk

TOBACCO PIPES

Blakemar Briars, 10 Northampton Road, Litchborough, Towcester, Northamptonshire, NN12 8JB Tel: (01327) 830213 E-mail: mike@blakemar.co.uk

Harwood Bros Ltd, 45 Walker Street, Wirral, Merseyside, CH47 2DY Tel: 0151-632 4327 Fax: 0151-632 4327

Merton & Falcon Ltd, 18 Commercial Road, London, N18 1TU Tel: (020) 8884 2150 Fax: (020) 8803 8887 E-mail: merton@falconltd.freeserve.co.uk

TOBACCO PRODUCT ACCESSORIES

▶ Swedish Match UK Ltd, Sword House, Totteridge Road, High Wycombe, Buckinghamshire, HP13 6DG Tel: (01494) 533300 Fax: (01494) 437459 E-mail: gareth.newton@swedishmatch.co.uk

TOBACCO PRODUCTS

Acetate Products Ltd, 1 Holme Lane, Station Road, Derby, DE21 7BP Tel: (01332) 661422 Fax: (01332) 681786

British American Tobacco (UK) Ltd, Oxford Road, Aylesbury, Buckinghamshire, HP21 8SZ Tel: (01296) 335000 Fax: (01296) 335999

Gallaher Group plc, Members Hill, Brooklands Road, Weybridge, Surrey, KT13 0QU Tel: (01932) 859777 Fax: (01932) 832792 E-mail: info@gallaherltd.com

Gawith Hoggarth & Co., Unit 16 Lake District Business Park, Mint Bridge Road, Kendal, Cumbria, LA9 6NH Tel: (01539) 720047 Fax: (01539) 740556 E-mail: enquiries@gawithhoggarth.co.uk

Imperial Tobacco Ltd, PO Box 244, Bristol, BS99 7UJ Tel: 0117-966 7957 Fax: 0117-966 7405 E-mail: keith.tatham@uk.imptob.com

J F Germain & Son Ltd, 25 Commercial Buildings, St. Helier, Jersey, JE2 3NB Tel: (01534) 724581 Fax: (01534) 767373 E-mail: sales@jfgermain.co.je

Wilsons & Co. (Sharrow) Ltd, Sharrow Mills, Sheffield, S11 8PL Tel: 0114-266 2677 Fax: 0114-267 0504 E-mail: snuff4you@aol.com

TOGGLE CLAMPS

Brauer Limited, Dawson Road, Mount Farm, Milton Keynes, MK1 1JP Tel: (01908) 374022 Fax: (01908) 641628 E-mail: sales@brauer.co.uk

TOGGLE FASTENERS, *See Toggle etc*

TOGGLE LATCH FASTENERS

Southco Europe, Farnham Trading Estate, Farnham, Surrey, GU9 9PL Tel: (01252) 714422 Fax: (01252) 712738 E-mail: info@dzus.com

Wilkes Security Products Ltd, Tipton Road, Tividale, Oldbury, West Midlands, B69 3HY Tel: 0121-520 9666 Fax: 0121-520 9667

TOILET BAGS

Crabtree & Evelyn Trading Ltd, The Oracle Centre, Reading, RG1 2AG Tel: 0118-950 8843

TOILET CUBICLE FITTINGS

A L M Products Ltd, Grindon Way, Heighington Lane Business Park, Newton Aycliffe, County Durham, DL5 6SH Tel: (01325) 313377 Fax: (01325) 315588 E-mail: sales@almproducts.co.uk

Tollgate Products Ltd, Heslop, Halesfield 21, Telford, Shropshire, TF7 4NX Tel: (01952) 520130 Fax: (01952) 586605 E-mail: sales@tollgateproducts.co.uk

TOILET CUBICLE PARTITIONING

GPG Sales Ltd, Unit 6, Luton Street, Liverpool, L5 9XR Tel: 0151-298 1509 Fax: 0151-298 2276 E-mail: sales@gpg-sales.com

Wallis Barfield, 2 Midland Avenue, Netherfield, Nottingham, NG4 2LG Tel: 0115-961 7038 Fax: 0115-961 1482

TOILET PAPER PRODUCTS MANUFRS

Peter Grant Papers Ltd, Stafford Park 12, Telford, Shropshire, TF3 3BJ Tel: (01952) 292200 Fax: (01952) 291108 E-mail: sales@pgpapers.com

Hygiene Warehouse, Unit 6, Ashmead Park, Ashmead Road, Keynsham, Bristol, BS31 1SU Tel: 0117-946 1978 Fax: 0117-946 1959 E-mail: sales@hygienewarehouse.co.uk

TOILETRIES MANUFRS

A M I UK Ltd, Lexus House, Rosslyn Crescent, Harrow, Middlesex, HA1 2RZ Tel: (020) 8863 6868 Fax: (020) 8426 0872 E-mail: harshad@ukaerosols.com

Acol, Castle Hill, Gomersal, Cleckheaton, West Yorkshire, BD19 4HW Tel: (01924) 402061 Fax: (01924) 402061

Alberto-Culver Co. (UK) Ltd, Lime Tree Way, Hampshire International Business Park, Chineham, Basingstoke, Hampshire, RG24 8ER Tel: (01256) 705000 Fax: (01256) 705001

Aslotel Ltd, Aslotel House, Pebble Close, Pebble Coombe, Tadworth, Surrey, KT20 7PA Tel: (01372) 362533 Fax: (01372) 362284 E-mail: asl@aslotel.co.uk

Axis International Ltd, Antry Avenue, White Horse Business Park, Trowbridge, Wiltshire, BA14 0XB Tel: (01225) 768491 Fax: (01225) 716100

▶ Baylis & Harding, Unit 10 The I O Centre, Nash Road, Redditch, Worcestershire, B98 7AS Tel: (01527) 505000 Fax: (01527) 505001 E-mail: post@bayhar.com

Bodycare Toiletries Ltd, A4-A5 Red Scar Industrial Estate, Longridge Road, Ribbleton, Preston, PR2 5NA Tel: (01772) 662400 Fax: (01772) 662401

TOILETRIES MANUFRS – *continued*

Brand Managers Ltd, Ambasidor House, 3rd Floor, Cavendish Avenue, Sudbury Hill, Harrow, Middlesex, HA1 3RW Tel: (020) 8869 4444 Fax: (020) 8869 4455
Broad Oak Toiletries Ltd, Tiverton Way, Tiverton Business Park, Tiverton, Devon, EX16 6TG Tel: (01884) 242626 Fax: (01884) 242602
Cariad, 105 Bancroft, Hitchin, Hertfordshire, SG5 1NB Tel: (01462) 421200 Fax: (01462) 421210 E-mail: shop@cariad.co.uk
Chattem UK Ltd, Ringway Centre, Edison Road, Basingstoke, Hampshire, RG21 6YH Tel: (01256) 844144 Fax: (01256) 844145
Church & Dwight (U K) Ltd, Wear Bay Road, Folkestone, Kent, CT19 6PG Tel: (01303) 850661 Fax: (01303) 858701 E-mail: sales@carterwallace.co.uk
Cosmetochem UK Ltd, Cunningham House, Westfield Lane, Harrow, Middlesex, HA3 9ED Tel: (020) 8907 7779 Fax: (020) 8927 0686 E-mail: cosmetochem@cheshamchemicals.co.uk
Crabtree & Evelyn Trading Ltd, 9 The Podium, Northgate Street, Bath, BA1 5AL Tel: (01225) 481519 Fax: (01225) 329477
Crabtree & Evelyn Trading Ltd, Bentalls Shopping Centre, Wood Street, Kingston upon Thames, Surrey, KT1 1TP Tel: (020) 8974 9610
Crabtree & Evelyn Trading Ltd, 134 Kings Road, London, SW3 4XB Tel: (020) 7589 6263 Fax: (020) 7584 7746
Crabtree & Evelyn Trading Ltd, Kelso Place, London, W8 5QG Tel: (020) 7361 0499 Fax: (020) 7361 0498 E-mail: london@crabtree-evelyn.co.uk
Creightons P.L.C., Lincoln Road, Peterborough, PE4 6ND Tel: (01733) 281000 Fax: (01733) 281028 E-mail: sales@creightons.com
D D D Ltd, 94 Rickmansworth Road, Watford, WD18 7JJ Tel: (01923) 229251 Fax: (01923) 220728
▶ DCS Europe plc, Timothy Bridge Road, Stratford-upon-Avon, Warwickshire, CV37 9YL Tel: (01789) 298000 Fax: (01789) 208030 E-mail: info@dcseurope.com
▶ Deodrant Stone, Caerdelyn, Pencader, Dyfed, SA39 9BX Tel: (01559) 384856 Fax: (01559) 384771 E-mail: info@deodorant-stone.co.uk
Dewhirst Toiletries Ltd, Sunderland Road, Sandy, Bedfordshire, SG19 1QY Tel: (01767) 691990 Fax: (01767) 691908 E-mail: teresa.waller@mellerbeauty.co.uk
Discount Toiletries, 340 Woodstock Road, Belfast, BT6 9DP Tel: (028) 9045 7303
E C De Witt & Co Ltd, Tudor Road, Manor Park, Runcorn, Cheshire, WA7 1SZ Tel: (01928) 756800 Fax: (01928) 579712
Ever Ready Health Care Ltd, 13 Sentinel Square, Hendon, London, NW4 2EL Tel: (020) 8202 3171 Fax: (020) 8203 9083 E-mail: david@everreadyhealthcare.com
F C Paton Southport Ltd, 43a Old Park Lane, Southport, Merseyside, PR9 7PR Tel: (01704) 227717 Fax: (01704) 227717
Fairtrade International Co. Ltd, 12 Cockfosters Parade, Cockfosters Road, Barnet, Hertfordshire, EN4 0BX Tel: (020) 8447 0220 Fax: (020) 8447 0330 E-mail: info@fairtradeint.co.uk
▶ Fake Bake UK Ltd, Unit C Coalburn Road, Fallside Industrial Estate, Bothwell, Glasgow, G71 8DA Tel: (0844) 8565758
Fine English Toiletries Ltd, 15-17 Landsdown Road, Shirley, Southampton, SO15 4HD Tel: (023) 8077 8080 Fax: (023) 8077 5545
Genese International Ltd, The Old Yard, Main Street, Keyingham, Hull, HU12 9RE Tel: (01964) 622251 Fax: (01964) 622525
Gilchrist & Soames, 1210 Lincoln Road, Peterborough, PE4 6LA Tel: (01733) 384100 Fax: (01733) 384101 E-mail: sales@gilchristandsoames.co.uk
Grosvenor Of London plc, International House, 66 Chiltern Street, London, W1U 4JT Tel: (020) 7470 1900 Fax: (020) 7470 1903 E-mail: info@golplc.com
H Bronnley & Co. Ltd, Bronnley Works, Radstone Road, Brackley, Northamptonshire, NN13 5AU Tel: (01280) 702291 Fax: (01280) 703912 E-mail: uksales@bronnley.co.uk
Hampshire Cosmetics Ltd, Brambles House, Waterberry Drive, Waterlooville, Hampshire, PO7 7UW Tel: (023) 9225 7341 Fax: (023) 9226 2003 E-mail: sales@hants-cosmetics.co.uk
Handmade Soap Co. Ltd, Ty'r Waun Bach, Gwernogle, Carmarthen, Dyfed, SA32 7RY Tel: (0870) 0789721 Fax: (01570) 421415
Hanworth Laboratories Ltd, The Grip, Hadstock Road, Linton, Cambridge, CB21 4XN Tel: (01223) 892217 Fax: (01223) 893623 E-mail: sales@hanworthlabs.co.uk
Home Bargains, 22 Moor Street, Ormskirk, Lancashire, L39 2AQ Tel: (01695) 581245
J Floris Holdings Ltd, 89 Jermyn Street, London, SW1Y 6JH Tel: (020) 7930 2885 Fax: (020) 7930 1402 E-mail: fragrance@florestlondon.com
J K J Manufacturing Ltd, Amsterdam Road, Hull, HU7 0XF Tel: (01482) 825868 Fax: (01482) 878659 E-mail: mail@e-pac.co.uk
▶ Janitorial Supplies Huntly Ltd, Bogside Cottage, West Adamston, Drumblade, Huntly, Aberdeenshire, AB54 6AJ Tel: (01466) 740335 Fax: (01466) 740335 E-mail: hall@jslhuntley.fsnet.co.uk
Julius A Meller Holdings plc, Meller House, 42-43 Chagford Street, London, NW1 6EB Tel: (020) 7724 5222 Fax: (020) 7724 3898
Knightsbridge Importers Ltd, 5 Oakwood Road, London, NW11 6QU Tel: (020) 8458 3898 Fax: (020) 8201 9992
Laboratory Facilities Ltd, 24 Britwell Road, Burnham, Slough, SL1 8AG Tel: (01628) 604149 Fax: (01628) 667920 E-mail: officelabfacs@btconnect.com
▶ Lady Care, 67 Main Street, Garforth, Leeds, LS25 1AF Tel: 0113-287 1197
Laleham Healthcare Ltd, Sycamore Park, Mill Lane, Alton, Hampshire, GU34 2PR Tel: (01420) 566500 Fax: (01420) 566566
▶ Lush Hand Made Cosmetics, 73 Broadmead, Bristol, BS1 3DX Tel: 0117-925 7582 Fax: 0117-934 9150
M & S Toiletries Ltd, Express Way, Wakefields, Euro Port, Normanton, West Yorkshire, WF6 2TZ Tel: (01924) 244200 Fax: (01924) 244222
▶ Macks Toiletries, Unit 29 Watford Metro Centre, Dwight Road, Watford, WD18 9SB Tel: (01923) 831931 Fax: (01923) 831932
Medico-Biological Laboratories Ltd, Kingsend House, 44 Kingsend, Ruislip, Middlesex, HA4 7DA Tel: (01895) 632724 Fax: (01895) 622736
Montagne Jeunesse, Astral Court, Central Avenue, Baglan, Port Talbot, West Glamorgan, SA12 7AX Tel: (01639) 861550 Fax: (01639) 861560 E-mail: customerservices@montagnejeunesse.com
▶ Napa Products Ltd, North Main Street, Carronshore, Falkirk, FK2 8HT Tel: (01324) 573472 Fax: (01324) 573401
Norfolk Lavender Ltd, Caley Mill, Lynn Road, Heacham, King's Lynn, Norfolk, PE31 7JE Tel: (01485) 570384 Fax: (01485) 571176 E-mail: admin@norfolk-lavender.co.uk
Nutrimetics International UK Ltd, 3 Garamonde Drive, Wymbush, Milton Keynes, MK8 8DF Tel: (01908) 262020 Fax: (01908) 262021 E-mail: info@nutrimetics.co.uk
P Z Cussons International Ltd, Cussons House, Bird Hall Lane, Stockport, Cheshire, SK3 0XN Tel: 0161-491 8000 Fax: 0161-491 8191
Procter & Gamble Product Supply UK Ltd, Avenue Road, Seaton Delaval, Whitley Bay, Tyne & Wear, NE25 0QJ Tel: 0191-255 6000 Fax: 0191-237 7208
Rose Tissue Converter, Sefton Street, Oldham, OL9 7LT Tel: 0161-682 4447 Fax: 0161-682 7774 E-mail: enquires@rosetissues.co.uk
▶ S P Toiletries Ltd, Appledore Road, Woodchurch, Ashford, Kent, TN26 3TG Tel: (01233) 861120 Fax: (01233) 861140
Sabre Supply Co., 35-37 Brent Street, London, NW4 2EF Tel: (020) 8457 1510 Fax: (020) 8201 7368 E-mail: sabre@sabresupply.co.uk
Sara Lee Household & Body Care UK Ltd, 225 Bath Road, Slough, SL1 4AU Tel: (01753) 523971 Fax: (01753) 570340 E-mail: info@saralee.co.uk
Standard Soap Co. Ltd, Derby Road, Ashby-de-la-Zouch, Leicestershire, LE65 2HG Tel: (01530) 410000 Fax: (01530) 410001 E-mail: sales@standardsoap.co.uk
Statestrong Ltd, Boundary Road, Lytham St. Annes, Lancashire, FY8 5LT Tel: (01253) 741806 Fax: (01253) 794542
Three Pears Ltd, 6 Station Road Industrial Estate, Station Road, Rowley Regis, West Midlands, B65 0JY Tel: 0121-559 5351 Fax: 0121-559 5353 E-mail: edunn@btconnect.com
Topaz Hair Cosmetics Ltd, The House Of Topaz, Guilden Sutton Lane, Guilden Sutton, Chester, CH3 7EX Tel: (01244) 312606 Fax: (01244) 317482 E-mail: glenn@topazhaircosmetics.co.uk
Unilvever, Coal Road, Seacroft, Leeds, LS14 2AR Tel: 0113-222 5000 Fax: 0113-222 5362
Vitality Group Ltd, Garman Road, London, N17 0QN Tel: (020) 8493 1100 Fax: (020) 8885 8203 E-mail: cashandcarry@vitalitygroup.co.uk
Weleda U K Ltd, Heanor Road, Ilkeston, Derbyshire, DE7 8DR Tel: 0115-944 8200 Fax: 0115-944 8210 E-mail: weledauk@compuserve.com
Wigmore Products, 18 Lower Street, Pulborough, West Sussex, RH20 2BL Tel: (01903) 893355 Fax: (01798) 875004
Wordsworth UK Ltd, Grimshaw Lane, Middleton, Manchester, M24 2AE Tel: 0161-653 9006 Fax: 0161-653 2613

TOILETRY CARTONS

Smurfit Cartons UK, Freebournes Road, Witham, Essex, CM8 3DA Tel: (01376) 512501 Fax: (01376) 520442

TOILETS

Aston Matthews Ltd, 141-147a Essex Road, London, N1 2SN Tel: (020) 7226 7220 Fax: (020) 7354 5951 E-mail: sales@astonmatthews.co.uk
Convenience Co., Harvey Road, Basildon, Essex, SS13 1RP Tel: (0845) 1003330 Fax: (01268) 722313 E-mail: enq@luxurytoilethire.com
Rawley Event Toilets, Harvey Road, Basildon, Essex, SS13 1RP Tel: (01268) 722311 Fax: (01268) 722313 E-mail: enq@rawley.co.uk

TOLERANCE RINGS

Rencol Tolerance Rings, Second Way, Bristol, BS11 8DF Tel: 0117-938 1700 Fax: 0117-915 7982 E-mail: sales@rencol.co.uk

TOLL BLENDING

▶ Albion Chemicals Ltd, Union Mills, Oxford Road, Gomersal, Cleckheaton, West Yorkshire, BD19 4JW Tel: (01274) 850300 Fax: (01274) 851252 E-mail: enquiries@albionchemicals.co.uk

TOMBSTONE MONUMENTS

▶ Family Graves Memorials, Thompson Street, Bilston, West Midlands, WV14 0HQ Tel: (01902) 492772 Fax: (01902) 493721

TOMBSTONES

▶ Family Graves Memorials, Thompson Street, Bilston, West Midlands, WV14 0HQ Tel: (01902) 492772 Fax: (01902) 493721

TOOL AND CUTTER GRINDING

A S A P Tooling Ltd, Crondal Road, Exhall, Coventry, CV7 9NH Tel: (024) 7664 4555 Fax: (024) 7636 7019 E-mail: asaptooling@btconnect.com
Alpha Tool Grinding, Unit 6 Stafford Park 4, Telford, Shropshire, TF3 3BA Tel: (01952) 292988 Fax: (01952) 292988
B K Engineering Services, 4 Eye Green Industries, Crowland Road, Eye, Peterborough, PE6 7SZ Tel: (01733) 222711 Fax: (01733) 222711
Balls Grinding Ltd, Unit K, Chosenview Road, Cheltenham, Gloucestershire, GL51 9LT Tel: (01242) 576621 Fax: (01242) 584298 E-mail: ballsgrinding@btconnect.com
Bardek Precision Tools, Britten Street, Redditch, Worcestershire, B97 6HD Tel: (01527) 67358 Fax: (01527) 65145
BHG Grinding Ltd, Unit A Drury Lane, Chadderton, Oldham, OL9 8EU Tel: 0161-682 6519 Fax: 0161-683 4682
Blade & Cutter Ltd, Unit 5 Hattersley Industrial Estate, Stockport Road, Hyde, Cheshire, SK14 3QT Tel: 0161-367 8240 Fax: 0161-367 8785
C & G Cutters & Grinding Ltd, Clarendon Road, Blackburn, BB1 9SS Tel: (01254) 663193 Fax: (01254) 665139 E-mail: sales@cg-grind-eng-serv.co.uk
Canaan Carbides Ltd, Unit 13, 13 Briar Close, Evesham, Worcestershire, WR11 4JQ Tel: (01386) 442818 Fax: (01386) 40564 E-mail: canaancarbides@btconnect.com
Cutter Grinders Birmingham Ltd, Unit 1-2 Armoury Trading Estate, Armoury Road, Birmingham, B11 2RG Tel: 0121-772 6321 Fax: 0121-773 6819 E-mail: cuttergrinders@webleicester.co.uk
Cutter Grinding Services, 22b Guildford Street, Luton, LU1 2NR Tel: (01582) 735626 Fax: (01582) 404164 E-mail: john.malia@tesco.net
Easicut Grinding Co. Ltd, Leestone Road, Sharston Industrial Area, Manchester, M22 4RN Tel: 0161-428 3265 Fax: 0161-428 3267 E-mail: w.kilbride@virgin.net
Falcon Grinding, Unit 1 Anne Street, Willenhall, West Midlands, WV13 1EN Tel: (01902) 601478 Fax: (01902) 606055 E-mail: falcongri@aol.com
Farnworth Grinding Co. Ltd, 20 Gladstone Road, Farnworth, Bolton, BL4 7EH Tel: (01204) 571853 Fax: (01204) 574613
J M Tool & Cutter Ltd, 425 Garstang Road, Broughton, Preston, PR3 5JA Tel: (01772) 866211 Fax: (01772) 865010 E-mail: j.m.tools@breathemail.net
Jones & Clark (Burton-on-Trent) Ltd, 77-80 Waterloo Street, Burton-On-Trent, Staffordshire, DE14 2NE Tel: (01283) 541771 Fax: (01283) 542466 E-mail: sales@jonesandclark.co.uk
London Cutlery Co., 6 Plantagenet Road, Barnet, Hertfordshire, EN5 5JQ Tel: (020) 8441 9505
Micron Precision Grinding, Unit 50 Haydon Industrial Estate, Radstock, BA3 3RD Tel: (01761) 437640 Fax: (01761) 437910
N E C Grinding Services, 61b Shaw Heath, Stockport, Cheshire, SK3 8WH Tel: 0161-480 1899 Fax: 0161-480 1899
P & M Regrinds, Unit 9, Brittania Industrial Park, High Wycombe, Buckinghamshire, HP12 3ES Tel: (01494) 437949 Fax: (01494) 471815 E-mail: pmtools@tiscali.co.uk
Pharon S & R Ltd, 228 Lythalls Lane, Foleshill, Coventry, CV6 6GF Tel: (024) 7668 7235 Fax: (024) 7666 4397 E-mail: skelcher&rowe@pipemedia.co.uk
W.J. Quinn Cutting Tools Ltd, 9 Wainwright Street, Aston, Birmingham, B6 5TH Tel: 0121-328 4640 E-mail: sales@quinntoolsgroup.co.uk
R V J Engineering, Cannock Chase Enterprise Centre, Hednesford, Cannock, Staffordshire, WS12 0QU Tel: (01543) 425264 Fax: (01543) 512451 E-mail: rvj.com@virgin.net
S & B Tools Ltd, Timmis Road, Stourbridge, West Midlands, DY9 7BQ Tel: (01384) 895555 Fax: (01384) 896675
Samwell Tooling Ltd, 29 Benson Road, Nuffield Industrial Estate, Poole, Dorset, BH17 0GB Tel: 01202 687258 Fax: 01202 665698 E-mail: sales@samwell.co.uk
Swemko (UK) Ltd, 29 Bonville Road, Brislington, Bristol, BS4 5QH Tel: (0845) 0760960 Fax: 0117-972 0470 E-mail: sales@swemkoknifes.com
Tornado Cutting Tools, 38a Kenilworth Drive, Oadby, Leicester, LE2 5LG Tel: 0116-271 8686 Fax: 0116-271 8686

TOOL AND CUTTER GRINDING MACHINES

Fein Industrial Power Tools UK Ltd, 4 Badby Park, Heartlands Business Park, Daventry, Northamptonshire, NN11 8YT Tel: (01327) 308730 Fax: (01327) 308739 E-mail: sales@fein-uk.co.uk

TOOL BAGS/ROLLS

Fine Group Son Ltd, 93 Manor Farm Road, London, Wembley, Middlesex, HA0 1XB Tel: (020) 8214 8600 Fax: (020) 8997 8410 E-mail: sales@finegoup.co.uk

TOOL BOXES OR CABINETS OR CASES OR CHESTS, *See also headings for particular materials*

C H Fowler & Co., 32 Bellgrove Road, Welling, Kent, DA16 3PY Tel: (020) 8304 4805 Fax: (020) 8304 7068 E-mail: c.h.fowler@btconnect.com
Jonesco (Preston) Ltd, Pittman Way, Fulwood, Preston, PR2 9ZD Tel: (01772) 704488 Fax: (01772) 702209 E-mail: sales@jonesco-plastics.com
▶ Toms Tool Chest, Foxpit House, Harrington, Workington, Cumbria, CA14 5RX Tel: (01946) 830716 Fax: (01946) 833317 E-mail: TomsToolChest@aol.com
Weatherford (UK), Gapton Hall Road, Gapton Hall Industrial Estate, Great Yarmouth, Norfolk, NR31 0NL Tel: (01493) 441155 Fax: (01493) 657403 E-mail: bdk@eu.wetherford.com

TOOL CLIPS

A B A Clamping & Connecting Products Ltd, 48 Hemming Road, Washford, Redditch, Worcestershire, B98 0EA Tel: (01527) 517100 Fax: (01527) 517300 E-mail: office@abagroup.com

TOOL CONTROL FOAM INSERTS

Polyformes Ltd, Cherrycourt Way, Leighton Buzzard, Bedfordshire, LU7 4UH Tel: (01525) 852444 Fax: (01525) 850484 E-mail: sales@polyformes.co.uk

TOOL DESIGN SERVICES

Ambler Patterns, Riverside Works, Todmerton Rd, Littleborough, Lancs, OL15 9EG Tel: (01706) 378197 Fax: (01706) 377826 E-mail: sales@ambler-patterns.co.uk
Black Gold Oil Tools Ltd, Steven Road, Huntly, Aberdeenshire, AB54 8SX Tel: (01466) 793457 Fax: (01466) 793095
Complete Tooling Solutions Ltd, Kinmel Park, Royal Welch Avenue, Abergele Road, Bodelwyddan, Rhyl, Denbighshire, LL18 5TY Tel: (01745) 583917 Fax: (01745) 584018 E-mail: darren.foster@completetoolingsolutions.com
▶ DJB Tools, Unit 10 Oak Street Industrial Park, Oak Street, Cradley Heath, West Midlands, B64 5JY Tel: (01384) 567292 Fax: (01384) 567292
Exactaform Cutting Tools Ltd, G2 Little Heath Industrial Estate, Old Church Road, Coventry, CV6 7ND Tel: (024) 7666 5823 Fax: (024) 7663 8251 E-mail: sales@exactaform.co.uk
▶ Expertool, Unit 2, Regina Drive, Birmingham, B42 1BZ Tel: 0121-356 2002 Fax: 0121-356 1122 E-mail: expertool@btconnect.com
Gridmaster Ltd, Weekley, Kettering, Northamptonshire, NN16 9UP Tel: (01536) 484948 Fax: (01536) 484948 E-mail: sales@gridmaster.co.uk
Magic Mitre Ltd, 3 Newton Court, Basingstoke, Hampshire, RG24 8GF Tel: 01256 478498
Maltby Punch & Die Ltd, 17a Blyth Road, Maltby, Rotherham, South Yorkshire, S66 8HX Tel: (01709) 816206
North West Design Services, Chartwell, Hundred End Lane, Hundred End, Preston, PR4 6XL Tel: (01772) 814497 Fax: (01772) 815308 E-mail: nwds@btconnect.com
▶ P Johnson Engineering, 16b Mimram Road, Hertford, SG14 1NN Tel: (01992) 552543 Fax: (01992) 552436 E-mail: pjengsvf@aol.com
▶ Paragon Rapid Technologies Ltd, Block 11, Teesside International Airport, Darlington, County Durham, DL2 1PD Tel: 01325 333141

TOOL DESIGN SERVICES – *continued*

▶ R J Caraco, Unit 12 Globe Court, Bentinck Road, West Drayton, Middlesex, UB7 7RQ Tel: (01895) 447509 Fax: (01895) 447611 E-mail: sales@dixontools.com

▶ Swift Micro Products Ltd, 26 Charnwood Road, Shepshed, Loughborough, Leicestershire, LE12 9QF Tel: (01509) 507007 Fax: (01509) 507007

TOOL (HAND) IMPORT/EXPORT MERCHANTS OR AGENTS

Corbin & Frost Ltd, 3 Stepfield, Witham, Essex, CM8 3DP Tel: (01376) 572202 Fax: (01376) 513921 E-mail: corbin.frost@macunlimited.net

Brian Hyde Ltd, Stirling Road, Shirley, Solihull, West Midlands, B90 4LZ Tel: 0121-705 7987 Fax: 0121-711 2465 E-mail: sales@brianhyde.co.uk

Rollins, 1 Parkway, Harlow Business Park, Harlow, Essex, CM19 5QF Tel: (01279) 401570 Fax: (01279) 401581 E-mail: sales@rollins.co.uk

S K S Plant & Equipment Ltd, 11 Redehall Road, Smallfield, Horley, Surrey, RH6 9PY Tel: (01342) 843688 Fax: (01342) 842140 E-mail: export@fks-group.co.uk

Suhner UK Ltd, Pool Road Business Centre, Pool Road, Nuneaton, Warwickshire, CV10 9AQ Tel: (024) 7638 4333 Fax: (024) 7638 4777 E-mail: admin@suhner.com

TOOL HANDLES

Ace Wood Turners & Machinists Ltd, Hazel La, Great Wyrley, Walsall, WS6 6AA Tel: (01922) 416645

Staveley Timber Ltd, Back Lane, Staveley, Kendal, Cumbria, LA8 9LR Tel: (01539) 821234 Fax: (01539) 821898 E-mail: broc@broc.co.uk

TOOL HIRE

▶ Acorn Plant & Tool Hire Ltd, Unit 3-4 Douglas Buildings, Lodge Road, Staplehurst, Tonbridge, Kent, TN12 0QZ Tel: (01580) 891234 Fax: (01580) 891234

▶ A-Plant Ltd, 102 Dalton Avenue, Birchwood Park Birchwood, Warrington, WA3 6YE Tel: (01925) 281030 Fax: (01925) 281005 E-mail: enquiries@aplant.com

▶ Champion Hire Ltd, Craven House, Craven Street South, Hull, HU9 1AP Tel: (0845) 3456905 Fax: (01482) 214840 E-mail: marknorrie@championshire.com

▶ Chesterman & Matthews, 28a Old Parish Lane, Weymouth, Dorset, DT4 0HY Tel: (01305) 781939 Fax: (01305) 781939

▶ Dunloy Tool Hire & Sales, 3 Pulloxhill Business Park, Greenfield Road, Pulloxhill, Bedford, MK45 5EU Tel: (01525) 716715 Fax: (01525) 720795 E-mail: dunloy@btconnect.com

Electro Hire & Supply LLP, The Paddock, Off Wharf Road, Biddulph, Stoke-On-Trent, ST8 6AL Tel: (01782) 518322 Fax: (01782) 515960 E-mail: sales@ehireandsupply.co.uk

▶ H S S Service Hire Group Ltd, 816 Oxford Road, Reading, RG30 1EL Tel: 0118-950 8882 Fax: 0118-975 0841

▶ HSS Hire, Unit 1 Swan Industrial Estate, Gatteridge Street, Banbury, Oxfordshire, OX16 5DH Tel: (01295) 261660 Fax: (01295) 261770

▶ HSS Hire, Wakefield Road, Bradford, West Yorkshire, BD4 7LX Tel: (01274) 308055 Fax: (01274) 724773

▶ HSS Hire, 35-38 Lewes Road, Brighton, BN2 3HQ Tel: (01273) 620588 Fax: (01273) 600656

▶ HSS Hire, Farwig Lane, Bromley, BR1 3RB Tel: (020) 8290 4800 Fax: (020) 8290 1880 E-mail: hire@hss.com

▶ HSS Hire, 5 Admiralty Way, Camberley, Surrey, GU15 3DT Tel: (01276) 32988 Fax: (01276) 35344

▶ HSS Hire, 1a 65-68 Bognor Road, Chichester, West Sussex, PO19 8NS Tel: (01243) 789070 Fax: (01243) 789085

▶ HSS Hire, Manor Royal, Crawley, West Sussex, RH10 9PY Tel: (01293) 551115 Fax: (01293) 527315

▶ HSS Hire, Eastern Avenue Industrial Estate, Eastern Avenue, Dunstable, Bedfordshire, LU5 4JY Tel: (01582) 673256 Fax: (01582) 696294

▶ HSS Hire, Felbridge Forge, London Road, Felbridge, East Grinstead, West Sussex, RH19 2RQ Tel: (01342) 316006 Fax: (01342) 316016

▶ HSS Hire, 403 Seaside, Eastbourne, East Sussex, BN22 7RT Tel: (01323) 410057 Fax: (01323) 431119

▶ HSS Hire, Unit 3 9 High Street, Edgware, Middlesex, HA8 7EE Tel: (020) 8952 8032 Fax: (020) 8952 8042

▶ HSS Hire, 30 Great Cambridge Road, Enfield, Middlesex, EN1 1UT Tel: (020) 8342 1888 Fax: (020) 8342 1777

▶ HSS Hire, 137 Gosport Road, Fareham, Hampshire, PO16 0PZ Tel: (01329) 822488 Fax: (01329) 822988

▶ HSS Hire, Oakland House, Solartron Road, Farnborough, Hampshire, GU14 7QL Tel: (01252) 510241 Fax: (01252) 510273

▶ HSS Hire, 12-14 Cheriton High Street, Folkestone, Kent, CT19 4ER Tel: (01303) 270809 Fax: (01303) 272104

▶ HSS Hire, 119 West Street, Glasgow, G5 8BA Tel: 0141-429 6141 Fax: 0141-429 1342

▶ HSS Hire, Harmony Works, Edinburgh Way, Harlow, Essex, CM20 2DA Tel: (01279) 444997 Fax: (01279) 721422

▶ HSS Hire, 312 Kenton Road, Harrow, Middlesex, HA3 8DF Tel: (020) 8907 3614 Fax: (020) 8907 9776

▶ HSS Hire, 406 Uxbridge Road, Hayes, Middlesex, UB4 0SE Tel: (020) 8561 3846 Fax: (020) 8561 8626

▶ HSS Hire, 7 The Broadway, Haywards Heath, West Sussex, RH16 3AQ Tel: (01444) 451613 Fax: (01444) 458296

▶ HSS Hire, 45 Oxford Road, High Wycombe, Buckinghamshire, HP11 2EB Tel: (01494) 464959 Fax: (01494) 461125

▶ HSS Hire, Unit 1 Haslemere Heathrow Estate, Silver Jubilee Way, Hounslow, TW4 6NF Tel: (020) 8759 9225 Fax: (020) 8759 9226

▶ HSS Hire, 686 London Road, Hounslow, TW3 1PG Tel: (020) 8577 5836 Fax: (020) 8577 7884

▶ HSS Hire, 20 Blatchington Road, Hove, East Sussex, BN3 3YN Tel: (01273) 329838 Fax: (01273) 733472

▶ HSS Hire, 364 High Road, Ilford, Essex, IG1 1QP Tel: (020) 8478 9911 Fax: (020) 8478 9922

▶ HSS Hire, 151 Abbey Lane, Leicester, LE4 5NZ Tel: 0116-268 1441 Fax: 0116-268 1257

▶ HSS Hire, 307-311 Camberwell New Road, London, SE5 0TF Tel: (020) 7701 3838 Fax: (020) 7701 2998

▶ HSS Hire, 11-15 Lillie Road, Earls Court, London, SW6 1TX Tel: (020) 7381 4433 Fax: (020) 7385 5552

▶ HSS Hire, 143 Caledonian Road, London, N1 0SL Tel: (020) 7837 9999 Fax: (020) 7278 1717

▶ HSS Hire, 293 Lewisham High Street, London, SE13 6NL Tel: (020) 8314 5900 Fax: (020) 8314 5714

▶ HSS Hire, 135 Leytonstone Road, London, E15 1LH Tel: (020) 8555 0293 Fax: (020) 8221 0415

▶ HSS Hire, Homebase, 3 Station Road, London, N11 1QJ Tel: (020) 8368 8158 Fax: (020) 8361 6907

▶ HSS Hire, 192 Campden Hill Road, London, W8 7TH Tel: (020) 7727 0897 Fax: (020) 7221 3248

▶ HSS Hire, 14 The Vale, Shepherds Bush, London, W3 7SB Tel: (020) 8743 6300 Fax: (020) 8743 7555

▶ HSS Hire, 340 Clapham Road, London, SW9 9AJ Tel: (020) 7498 8866 Fax: (020) 7720 7421

▶ HSS Hire, 620 Streatham High Road, London, SW16 3QJ Tel: (020) 8679 4948 Fax: (020) 8679 7119

▶ HSS Hire, 451-453 High Road, London, N17 6QH Tel: (020) 8801 3261 Fax: (020) 8493 0145

▶ HSS Hire, 95 Tower Bridge Road, London, SE1 4TW Tel: (020) 7357 9207 Fax: (020) 7357 9208

▶ HSS Hire, Railway Arches, 76-77 Goding Street, London, SE11 5AW Tel: (020) 7735 6500 Fax: (020) 7735 6215

▶ HSS Hire, Point Pleasant Works, 92 Putney Bridge Road, London, SW18 1TU Tel: (020) 8877 3503 Fax: (020) 8877 3532

▶ HSS Hire, 34 Upper Green East, Mitcham, Surrey, CR4 2PB Tel: (020) 8685 9500 Fax: (020) 8685 9600

▶ HSS Hire, 1 Roundtree Way, Norwich, NR7 8SH Tel: (01603) 788556 Fax: (01603) 788539

▶ HSS Hire, 17 Carlton Parade, Orpington, Kent, BR6 0JB Tel: (01689) 834646 Fax: (01689) 830609

▶ HSS Hire, 85 Brighton Road, South Croydon, Surrey, CR2 6EE Tel: (020) 8686 5646 Fax: (020) 8688 8346

▶ HSS Hire, 52 Oxford Road, Denham, Uxbridge, Middlesex, UB9 4DH Tel: (01895) 252727 Fax: (01895) 238638 E-mail: enquiries@touch-stone.co.uk

▶ HSS Hire, 317-319 Lower High Street, Watford, WD17 2JD Tel: (01923) 224253 Fax: (01923) 223347

▶ HSS Hire Shops Ltd, Mace Lane, Ashford, Kent, TN24 8PE Tel: (01233) 610348 Fax: (01233) 622834

▶ HSS Hire Shops Ltd, Chandlers Building Supplies, Timber Yard Lane, Lewes, East Sussex, BN7 2AU Tel: (01273) 471188 Fax: (01273) 478574

▶ HSS Hire Shops Ltd, 128 High Street, Staines, Middlesex, TW18 4BY Tel: (01784) 456349 Fax: (01784) 454413

▶ Speedy Hire Centres Southern Ltd, 6 Broadfields, Aylesbury, Buckinghamshire, HP19 8ZU Tel: (01296) 331007 Fax: (01296) 393930 E-mail: ellesby-southern@speedydepots.co.uk

▶ Speedy Hire Centres Southern Ltd, Dukes Ride, Crowthorne, Berkshire, RG45 6NZ Tel: (01344) 779004 Fax: (01344) 779073

▶ Speedy Hire (Southern) Ltd, Overthorpe Road, Banbury, Oxfordshire, OX16 4SY Tel: (01295) 267977 Fax: (01295) 250045

▶ Wolfe Designs Ltd, 125 Clydesdale Place, Moss Side Industrial Estate, Moss Side, Leyland, PR26 7QS Tel: (01772) 456191 Fax: (01772) 622464 E-mail: daviddesouza@btconnect.com

TOOL HOLDERS, *See also headings for particular types*

E W Equipment, 11 Worcester Road, Cheadle Hulme, Cheadle, Cheshire, SK8 5NW Tel: 0161-485 8730 Fax: 0161-485 6745 E-mail: sales@ewequipment.co.uk

Exe Engineering Co. Ltd, 64 Alphington Road, Exeter, EX2 8HX Tel: (01392) 275186 Fax: (01392) 260336 E-mail: sales@exeengineering.co.uk

I Q T Ltd, 42-44 The Street, Appledore, Ashford, Kent, TN26 2BX Tel: (01233) 758772 Fax: (01233) 758773 E-mail: iqtltd@aol.com

Iscar Tools Ltd, Clapgate Lane, Birmingham, B32 3DE Tel: 0121-422 8585 Fax: 0121-421 8255 E-mail: sales@iscaruk.co.uk

Kennametal UK Ltd, PO Box 29, Kingswinford, West Midlands, DY6 7NP Tel: (01384) 401000 Fax: (01384) 408015 E-mail: kingswinfold.service@kennametal.com

Machine Mart Ltd, Ryhope Road, Sunderland, SR2 9SX Tel: 0191-510 8773 Fax: 0191-514 7389

TOOL REGRINDING

P N Tools, Unit 33 34, Fourways, Carlyon Road Industrial Estate, Atherstone, Warwickshire, CV9 1LH Tel: (01827) 720013 Fax: (01827) 720039

TOOL SECURITY BOXES OR CABINETS OR CASES OR CHESTS

ArmorGard Security Products, Castle Trading Estate, Portchester, FAREHAM, Hants, PO16 9SF Tel: 02392 380280 Fax: 02392 200715 E-mail: sales@armorgardsecurity.com

Birchfield Sheet Metal Sheet Metal, 15 Hadfield Industrial Estate, Waterside, Hadfield, Glossop, Derbyshire, SK13 1BS Tel: (01457) 865536 Fax: (01457) 865536

Scooter Store Ltd, Unit 11 Italstyle Buildings, Cambridge Road, Harlow, Essex, CM20 2HE Tel: (01279) 453565 Fax: (01279) 454030 E-mail: albertwass@site-safe.co.uk

TOOL SHARPENING

Dathan Tool & Gauge Co. Ltd, Mean Lane, Meltham, Holmfirth, HD9 5RU Tel: (01484) 851207 Fax: (01484) 852271 E-mail: sales@dathan.co.uk

N T R Ltd, Unit 372a Thorp Arch Estate, Thorp Arch, Wetherby, West Yorkshire, LS23 7BJ Tel: (01937) 845112 Fax: (01937) 845467 E-mail: info@ntrltd.co.uk

Saw Centre Ltd, 650 Eglinton Street, Glasgow, G5 9RP Tel: (0870) 7280222 Fax: 0141-429 5609 E-mail: sales@thesawcentre.co.uk

TOOL STEEL MANUFRS

B J Special Steels, 14 Burrell Buildings, Chartwell Road, Lancing, West Sussex, BN15 8TZ Tel: (01903) 851059 Fax: (01903) 851037

Finkl UK Ltd, Langley Green Road, Oldbury, West Midlands, B69 4TR Tel: 0121-544 4506 Fax: 0121-544 1706 E-mail: sales@finkl-uk.co.uk

Hillfoot Special Steels Ltd, 16 Hertburn Estate, Hertburn, Washington, Tyne & Wear, NE37 2SF Tel: 0191-417 0185 Fax: 0191-415 4740 E-mail: washington@hillfoot.com

Independent Tool Consultants Ltd, Unit 7, Bamfurlong Industrial Park, Staverton, Cheltenham, Gloucestershire, GL51 6SX Tel: (01452) 712519 Fax: (01452) 714786 E-mail: intoco.extrusion@virgin.net

Intersteel, European Business Pk, Taylors Lane, Oldbury, West Midlands, B69 2BN Tel: 0121-627 9279 Fax: 0121-627 9270 E-mail: sales@intersteel.co.uk

Frank Pickering & Co. Ltd, Beeley Wood Works, Claywheels Lane, Sheffield, S6 1ND Tel: 0114-231 8819 Fax: 0114-285 2564

Peter Stubs Ltd, Causeway Avenue, Warrington, WA4 6QB Tel: (01925) 653939 Fax: (01925) 413870 E-mail: sales@peterstubs.com

Uddeholm Steel Stockholders, European Business Park, Taylors Lane, Oldbury, West Midlands, B69 2BN Tel: 0121-552 5530 Fax: 0121-544 3036 E-mail: sales@uddeholm.co.uk

TOOL STORAGE CABINETS

Sarralle UK UK Ltd, 87 West Street, Oundle, Peterborough, PE8 4EJ Tel: (01832) 270371 Fax: (01430) 473027 E-mail: mail@sarralleuk.fsnet.co.uk

TOOL SUSPENSION BALANCER SYSTEMS

Airtec Filtration Ltd, Manor Street, St. Helens, Merseyside, WA9 3AX Tel: (01744) 733211 Fax: (01744) 730917 E-mail: sales@airtecfiltration.com

Tool Repair Services, Unit 51 The Sir Robert Peel Mill, Mill Lane, Fazeley, Tamworth, Staffordshire, B78 3QD Tel: (01827) 286322 Fax: (01827) 259101 E-mail: toolrepairs@hotmail.com

TOOL TUNGSTEN CARBIDE

J & J Tooling Services, Bridge House, Railway Street, Radcliffe, Manchester, M26 3AA Tel: 0161-724 7799 Fax: 0161-724 0722 E-mail: sales@jjtooling.co.uk

TOOLING, TO SPECIFICATION

DJM Engineering, The Courtyard, Warkworth, Banbury, Oxfordshire, OX17 2AG Tel: (01295) 712424 E-mail: djm.eng@btconnect.com

TOOLMAKERS/TOOLMAKING EQUIPMENT

A R D Tools & Patterns, 1 Roberts Drive, Bridgwater, Somerset, TA6 6BH Tel: (01278) 433177 Fax: (01278) 433160

Atkinson Engineering, Unit 1 Lancaster Close, Sherburn in Elmet, Leeds, LS25 6NS Tel: (01977) 689665 Fax: (01977) 685624 E-mail: sales@atkinsonprecision.co.uk

Cromwell Ltd, Station Road, North Hykeham, Lincoln, LN6 9AL Tel: (01522) 500888 Fax: (01522) 500857 E-mail: sales@cromwell.co.uk

S T Developments, 101 Leigh Road, Wimborne, Dorset, BH21 2AA Tel: (01202) 887048 Fax: (01202) 887048 E-mail: johnstd@globalnet.co.uk

Wentworth Tool & Die, Woodbine House, Wold Newton, Driffield, North Humberside, YO25 3YD Tel: (01262) 470270 Fax: (01262) 470270 E-mail: woodbinehouse@aol.com

▶ Wire Cut Technologies Ltd, 115 Saturn Way, Hemel Hempstead, Hertfordshire, HP2 5PD Tel: (01442) 401856 Fax: (01442) 401856 E-mail: dshew@wire-cut.co.uk

TOOLMAKERS/TOOLMAKING INSTRUMENTS

A Brooks, Revolver House St. Marys Business Park, Albany Road, Great Bowden, Market Harborough, Leicestershire, LE16 7ZH Tel: (01858) 468848 Fax: (01858) 461058 E-mail: andybrooks12@hotmail.com

B L Tooling & Moulding, 7 Hall Road Industrial Estate, Hall Road, Southminster, Essex, CM0 7DA Tel: (01621) 772608 Fax: (01621) 772608

Bridge Abrasives Ltd, Unit E, Ford Road, Totnes Industrial Estate, Totnes, Devon, TQ9 5LQ Tel: (01803) 866667 Fax: (01803) 866001 E-mail: info@bridge-abrasives.co.uk

Burnsall Engineering Co. Ltd, Brandon Road, Binley, Coventry, CV3 2AN Tel: (024) 7644 0444 Fax: (024) 7665 2696 E-mail: info@burnsallengineering.com

Esdale Plastics Ltd, 32 Union Street, Heckmondwike, West Yorkshire, WF16 0HH Tel: (01924) 401921 Fax: (01924) 401923

JJR, 13-15 Ward Street, Willenhall, West Midlands, WV13 1EP Tel: (01902) 637847 Fax: (01902) 637847 E-mail: jan@jjrtoolmakers.co.uk

TOOLMAKERS/TOOLMAKING SERVICES, *See also headings for particular types*

A D S Precision Engineering, 53a Jubilee Road, Waterlooville, Hampshire, PO7 7RE Tel: (023) 9226 7643 Fax: (023) 9226 7743 E-mail: admin@adsprecision.co.uk

A Fawcett Toolmakers 1983 Ltd, James Street, Elland, West Yorkshire, HX5 0HB Tel: (01422) 370966 Fax: (01422) 310068 E-mail: fawcett.toolmakers@ic24.net

A H Engineering North East Ltd, Unit 5 Wagonway Road Industrial Estate, Hebburn, Tyne & Wear, NE31 1SP Tel: 0191-483 9807 Fax: 0191-483 8700 E-mail: aheng@lineone.net

A M H Precision Tools Ltd, Unit 4, Thornsett Trading Estate, Birch Vale, High Peak, Derbyshire, SK22 1AH Tel: 01663 745145 Fax: 01663 745252 E-mail: sales@amhtools.co.uk

A M J Engineering, 38 Towerfield Road, Shoeburyness, Southend-on-Sea, SS3 9QT Tel: (01702) 295331 Fax: (01702) 296862 E-mail: info@amjbuttons.com

Abbey Tool & Dye, Unit 11 Old Canal Wharf, Navigation Road, Stoke-on-Trent, ST6 3BL Tel: (01782) 838137 Fax: (01782) 577372 E-mail: abbeytool@aol.com

TOOLMAKERS/TOOLMAKING SERVICES - *continued*

Abbey Tooling Ltd, Longdon Heath, Upton Upon Severn, Worcester, WR8 0RJ Tel: (01684) 592452 Fax: (01684) 592452

▶ Absolute Tooling, 6 Rookery Road, Barnoldswick, Lancashire, BB18 6YH Tel: (01282) 852997 Fax: (01282) 852997

Altag Tool & Die, 10 3 Wilton Road, Ramsgate, Kent, CT12 5HG Tel: (01843) 588663 Fax: (01843) 853738 E-mail: info@altag.co.uk

Archfact Ltd, 10 Pipers Wood Industrial Park, Waterberry Drive, Waterlooville, Hampshire, PO7 7XU Tel: (023) 9224 0700 Fax: (023) 9223 0157 E-mail: info@archfact.com

Armson-Boult Ltd, 144b George Street, Coventry, CV1 4HE Tel: (024) 7622 6817 Fax: (024) 7622 6817

Astra Precision Engineering Ltd, Mnercian Works, Holyhead Road, Ketley, Telford, Shropshire, TF1 5DY Tel: (01952) 616622 Fax: (01952) 616622

B E L Precision Engineers Ltd, Wyre Street, Padiham, Burnley, Lancashire, BB12 8DF Tel: (01282) 770315 Fax: (01282) 770152

B O P P Precision Engineers Ltd, A Emms Court, Meeting Lane, Brierley Hill, West Midlands, DY5 3LB Tel: (01384) 78646 Fax: (01384) 78646 E-mail: mail@bopppe.fsnet.co.uk

Barden Engineering, Unit 20-21 Joseph Wilson Industrial Estate, Millstrood Road, Whitstable, Kent, CT5 1PP Tel: (01227) 272665 Fax: (01227) 770268

Brennan Tool & Engineering Co. Ltd, Unit 9-11 Brooke Trading Estate, Lyon Road, Romford, RM1 2AT Tel: (01708) 736600 Fax: (01708) 735500 E-mail: david.brennan@brennan-tools.co.uk

Britannia Dynamics, 1 Southside Industrial Park, North Road, Atherton, Manchester, M46 0RE Tel: (01942) 887811 Fax: (01942) 887818 E-mail: sales@britannia-dynamics.com

Bva Tools & Plastics Ltd, Oaks Road, Batley, West Yorkshire, WF17 6LT Tel: (01924) 474455 Fax: (01924) 477566

C & G, 284 North Road, Yate, Bristol, BS37 7LQ Tel: (01454) 228387 Fax: (01454) 228145 E-mail: cgtoolcutter@aol.com

C G P Engineering Ltd, Cross Street, Oadby, Leicester, LE2 4DD Tel: 0116-271 7715 Fax: 0116-272 0701 E-mail: info@cgp-engineering.com

C H E Engineering, Unit 59, Bergen Way, North Lynn Industrial Estate, King's Lynn, Norfolk, PE30 2JL Tel: (01553) 691999 Fax: (01553) 691999

Caine Precision Ltd, Unit 13 Stocklake Park Industrial Estate, Farmborough Cl, Aylesbury, Bucks, HP20 1DQ Tel: (01296) 434586 Fax: (01296) 432683 E-mail: rcaine@nildron.co.uk

Camtool Engineering, 6b Purdy Road, Bilston, West Midlands, WV14 8UB Tel: (01902) 403562 Fax: (01902) 403562 E-mail: camtool.eng@btconnect.com

▶ Capricorn Diesinking Services, Unit 13, Pivington Mill, Pluckley, Ashford, Kent, TN27 0PG Tel: (01233) 840968

Cefn Strain Gauges, Unit E26 Hirwaun Industrial Estate, Hirwaun, Aberdare, Mid Glamorgan, CF44 9UP Tel: (01685) 814451 Fax: (01685) 814342 E-mail: rob@cefn-sg.sfnet.co.uk

Chandu Toolmakers, Church Road, Benfleet, Essex, SS7 4QN Tel: (01268) 565960 Fax: (01268) 757740 E-mail: chandutools@btconnect.com

Clwyd Tool & Die, 35 Greenfield Business Park, Bagillt Road, Greenfield, Holywell, Clwyd, CH8 7HJ Tel: (01352) 715515 Fax: (01352) 715515

Cuffley Tool & Engineering, 6 Spurling Works, Pindar Road, Hoddesdon, Hertfordshire, EN11 0DB Tel: (01992) 478888 Fax: (01992) 478888 E-mail: cuffleytool@tiscali.co.uk

Cutter Services Precision Engineers Ltd, 6 Glebe Road, Letchworth Garden City, Hertfordshire, SG6 1DR Tel: (01462) 671861 Fax: (01462) 670532

CV Precision Engineering, Unit 2 Rea Court, 40 Trent Street, Birmingham, B5 5NL Tel: 0121-643 7144 Fax: 0121-633 3680 E-mail: tomcross@cvprecision.co.uk

Delcam, Talbot Way, Birmingham, B10 0HJ Tel: 0121-766 5544 Fax: 0121-766 5511 E-mail: marketing@delcam.com

E J P Tooling Co. (Coventry) Ltd, Unit 27 Lythalls Lane Industrial Estate, Lythalls Lane, Coventry, CV6 6FL Tel: (024) 7668 6810

Elegant Plaster Mouldings, 1 Talbots La Trading Estate, Talbots Lane, Brierley Hill, West Midlands, DY5 2YX Tel: (01384) 263000 Fax: (01384) 262792 E-mail: die.tech@virgin.net

Eljays Spark Erosion Services Ltd, 6 Kirby Estate, Trout Road, West Drayton, Middlesex, UB7 7RU Tel: (01895) 448380 Fax: (01895) 420977 E-mail: sales@eljays.co.uk

Excel Precision Engineering Services Ltd, Unit 16, Trostra Industrial Estate, Llanelli, Dyfed, SA14 9UU Tel: (01554) 751935 Fax: (01554) 778804 E-mail: debbie@excel-eng.co.uk

F M Instruments, 66A High Street, Oakington, Cambridge, CB4 5AG Tel: (01223) 234141 Fax: (01223) 234141

F T Engineering, Lane End Works, Skipton Road, Earby, Barnoldswick, Lancashire, BB18 6PX Tel: (01282) 844220 Fax: (01282) 843480

F Tooms & Co., Kings Road, Market Harborough, Leicestershire, LE16 7JU Tel: (01858) 462697 Fax: (01858) 431701

Fairfield Tool & Die Co Maesteg Ltd, Cwmdu Institute, Bridgend Road, Maesteg, Mid Glamorgan, CF34 0NW Tel: (01656) 733455 Fax: (01656) 738710 E-mail: ftdtony@btconnect.com

G E M Engineering Services, Unit B9 Tweedale Industrial Estate, Madeley, Telford, Shropshire, TF7 4JR Tel: (01952) 588525 Fax: (01952) 588525

G E Starr Ltd, Dixon Street, Wolverhampton, WV2 2BS Tel: (01902) 576675 Fax: (01902) 350099 E-mail: info@gestarr.co.uk

G Parker Engineering Ltd, Grange Lane, Accrington, Lancashire, BB5 1HX Tel: (01254) 384235 Fax: (01254) 872584 E-mail: info@parkereng.com

A.F. Gaskin Ltd, Downley Road, Naphill, High Wycombe, Buckinghamshire, HP14 4QY Tel: (01494) 563831 Fax: (01494) 562933 E-mail: sales@afgaskin.co.uk

Gauge & Tool Makers Association, 3 Forge House, Summerleys Road, Princes Risborough, Buckinghamshire, HP27 9DT Tel: (01844) 274222 Fax: (01844) 274227 E-mail: gtma@gtma.co.uk

Global Engineering, Eagle Iron Works, Crawford Street, Rochdale, Lancashire, OL16 5NU Tel: (01706) 715757 Fax: (01706) 649969 E-mail: sales@golbaleng.co.uk

Gray Precision Engineering, Units 1-3, Castle Court, Bankside Industrial Estate, Falkirk, FK2 7UU Tel: (01324) 612679 Fax: (01324) 612209 E-mail: stuart.gray@btconnect.com

H J Jennings & Co., St Francis, Silver Street, Shepton Beauchamp, Ilminster, Somerset, TA19 0JZ Tel: (01460) 240499 Fax: (01460) 242179

H L Tool Co Ltd, Gardenvale Mill, Greenfield Road, Colne, Lancashire, BB8 9PD Tel: (01282) 864850 Fax: (01282) 870244 E-mail: sales@hltool.co.uk

Hayes (Plastic) Engineering, Unit 59, Station Road Industrial Estate, Hailsham, East Sussex, BN27 2ES Tel: (01323) 844455 Fax: (01323) 844488 E-mail: info@hayesplastics.com

Hayneswood Engineering UK, Acorn Street, Lees, Oldham, OL4 3DE Tel: 0161-620 5337 Fax: 0161-621 5974 E-mail: engineering@hayneswood.co.uk

Herbert & Criddan, 11 Alliance Close, Attleborough Fields Industrial Estate, Nuneaton, Warwickshire, CV11 6SD Tel: (024) 7638 3400 Fax: (024) 7638 5999 E-mail: ken@herbertandcridan.com

Hi Profile Precision Ltd, Units 1 & 2, Dyson Street, Bradford, West Yorkshire, BD9 4DE Tel: (01274) 482218 Fax: (01274) 482219 E-mail: hpprecisionltd@aol.com

High Speed Hardening Sheffield Ltd, Naseby Street, Sheffield, S9 1BR Tel: 0114-244 1516 Fax: 0114-244 1516

Highbank Tools Ltd, Unit 7 Reliance Trading Estate, Manchester, M40 3AG Tel: 0161-681 2506 Fax: 0161-683 4937

Hildred Engineering Co. Ltd, Units 2 4 & 6, Parkway Court, Nottingham, NG8 4GN Tel: 0115-928 2217 Fax: 0115-985 4998 E-mail: hildredengco@aol.com

I E C Precision Ltd, 3 Daux Road, Billingshurst, West Sussex, RH14 9SJ Tel: (01403) 783629 Fax: (01403) 784792 E-mail: sales@iecprecision.co.uk

Jay Tooling Co., Pindar Road, Hoddesdon, Hertfordshire, EN11 0DA Tel: (01992) 462875 Fax: (01992) 451422 E-mail: jaytool@btinternet.com

Keegal Engineering Ltd, The Link Centre, Unit G Oldmixon CR, Weston-super-Mare, Avon, BS24 9AY Tel: (01934) 419659 Fax: (01934) 641185 E-mail: peter@keegal.co.uk

Kirkby Precision Engineering Ltd, Ashcroft Road, Liverpool, L33 7TW Tel: 0151-549 1007 Fax: 0151-549 2400 E-mail: kirkbyprecision@btclick.com

Lenic Engineering Ltd, Unit 24 Cradle Hill Industrial Estate, Afriston Road, Seaford, East Sussex, BN25 3JE Tel: (01323) 896783 Fax: (01323) 491416 E-mail: info@metalpressings.co.uk

Leopold Grove Engineering Co. Ltd, Amy Johnson Way, Blackpool, FY4 2RP Tel: (01253) 342144 Fax: (01253) 349667 E-mail: office@leopoldeng.co.uk

Lynden Tooling Services, 1 Main Road, Gilberdyke, Brough, North Humberside, HU15 2SW Tel: (01430) 449438 Fax: (01430) 449118 E-mail: sales@lyndentooling.co.uk

Manuel Engineering Co. Ltd, Unit 33 Barking Industrial Park, Alfreds Way, Barking, Essex, IG11 0TJ Tel: (020) 8594 9264 Fax: (020) 8594 5507

▶ Martin Tool Makers, Unit 32 Herons Gate Trading Estate, Paycocke Road, Basildon, Essex, SS14 3EU Tel: (01268) 272240 Fax: (01268) 272097

▶ Mastooplast Tool Design, Westwood Farm, 34 Highcross Road, Southfleet, Gravesend, Kent, DA13 9PH Tel: (01474) 834455 Fax: (01474) 834457E-mail: ne1@mundy-side.prestel.co.uk

Metric Tool & Die Ltd, 10a Havant Road, Horndean, Waterlooville, Hampshire, PO8 0DT Tel: (023) 9257 1544 Fax: (023) 9257 1542

Midland Precision Tool Makers, 3 Cyclo Works, Lifford Lane, Birmingham, B30 3DY Tel: 0121-486 3346 Fax: 0121-486 3346

Minimould Ltd, Units 10A & 10B, Thame Road, Aylesbury, Buckinghamshire, HP17 8LJ Tel: 01844 292880

MJK Specialist Mould Polishers & Polishing Consultants, Pickering, North Yorkshire, Tel: (07946) 714777 E-mail: mjk1@sky.com

Multi Form Machine Tools Ltd, Aviation House, Aviation Way, Southend-on-Sea, SS2 6UN Tel: (0845) 0690290 Fax: (0845) 0690291 E-mail: info@fabricatorsworld.com

North Engineering Works, Block 24 Kilspindie Road, Dunsinane Industrial Estate, Dundee, DD2 3QH Tel: (01382) 889693 Fax: (01382) 889808 E-mail: sales@northeng.co.uk

Orion Precision, 18 Orion Court, Cranes Farm Road, Basildon, Essex, SS14 3DB Tel: (01268) 282445 Fax: (01268) 282445

Timothy Ormerod Ltd, Bryngwyn Manor, Wormelow, Hereford, HR2 8EH Tel: (01981) 540476 Fax: (01981) 540846 E-mail: matormerod@hotmail.com

Precise Engineering Ltd, Cowley Road, Blyth, Northumberland, NE24 5TF Tel: (01670) 363606 Fax: (01670) 352792

▶ Precision International Ltd, Chiltern House, 114 Severalls Avenue, Chesham, Buckinghamshire, HP5 3EL Tel: (01494) 782467 Fax: (01494) 785340

Precision Machining Engineers (Harrow) Ltd, Brember Road, Harrow, Middlesex, HA2 8UN Tel: (020) 8590 5959 Fax: (020) 8422 5077 E-mail: info@cakedecoration.co.uk

Precision Toolmakers & Engineers Rugby Ltd, 19 Somers Road, Rugby, Warwickshire, CV22 7DG Tel: (01788) 543661 Fax: (01788) 565742 E-mail: precisiontmrugby@aol.com

Price & Weston, Orchard St, Worcester, WR5 3DY Tel: (01905) 360463 Fax: (01905) 763040 E-mail: enquiries@price-weston.co.uk

Profile Die Ltd, Unit 32 Knightsbridge Business Centre, Knightsbridge, Cheltenham, Gloucestershire, GL51 9TA Tel: (01242) 680735 Fax: (01242) 680880 E-mail: profiledie.ltd@btinternet.com

Qualitetch Components Ltd, Century Way, March, Cambridgeshire, PE15 8QW Tel: (01354) 658787 Fax: (01354) 650385 E-mail: sales@qualitetch.co.uk

R Lunn Engineering, 2 Vincent Mill, Vincent Street, Macclesfield, Cheshire, SK11 6UJ Tel: (01625) 611682 Fax: (01625) 611682

R S Precision, Unit 30 Hercules Way, Bowerhill, Melksham, Wiltshire, SN12 6TS Tel: (01225) 702738 Fax: (01225) 702583

Regency Mouldings Worcester Ltd, Hylton Road, Worcester, WR2 5JS Tel: (01905) 424909 Fax: (01905) 748310 E-mail: timco@btclick.com

Richard Kell, Blyth Valley Venture Workshops, Plessey Road, Blyth, Northumberland, NE24 4BN Tel: (01670) 363626 Fax: (01670) 363626

Rotometrics International Ltd, Walsall Business Park, Walsall Road, Aldridge, Walsall, WS9 0SW Tel: (01922) 610000 Fax: (01922) 610100

Roxill Engineering & Hydraulics Co. Ltd, 12 Railway Terrace, Nechells, Birmingham, B7 5NG Tel: 0121-328 2189 Fax: 0121-327 7469

S B C Precision Engineering, 2 Kings Court Industrial Estate, Sedgley Road East, Tipton, West Midlands, DY4 8XA Tel: 0121-557 0456 Fax: 0121-557 0457

S Bateman & Sons Ltd, Hart Street, Blackburn, BB1 1HW Tel: (01254) 56153 Fax: (01254) 664416

S Betts & Sons Ltd, 2 Hunsley Street, Sheffield, S4 8DY Tel: 0114-261 9766 Fax: 0114-261 7464 E-mail: sales@betts-tools.co.uk

S G Dieplas Ltd, J8 Dudley Central Trading Estate, Shaw Road, Dudley, West Midlands, DY2 8QX Tel: (01384) 258494 Fax: (01384) 258494 E-mail: gward.inet@court.co.uk

S L M Model Engineers Ltd, Chiltern Road, Prestbury, Cheltenham, Gloucestershire, GL52 5JQ Tel: (01242) 525488 Fax: (01242) 226288 E-mail: mail@slm.uk.com

Sarka Tools, 14 Lodge Road, Atherton, Manchester, M46 9BL Tel: (01942) 894685 Fax: (01942) 894685

Sirch Tool & Design Ltd, 1 Park St Industrial Estate, Osier Way, Aylesbury, Buckinghamshire, HP20 1EB Tel: (01296) 330868 Fax: (01296) 330828

Solent Mould Tools Ltd, 1 Relay Road, Waterlooville, Hampshire, PO7 7XA Tel: (023) 9223 9950 Fax: (023) 9223 9951 E-mail: solentmd@tcp.co.uk

Stour Precision Tools Ltd, George Baylis Road, Berry Hill Industrial Estate, Droitwich, Worcestershire, WR9 9RB Tel: (01905) 773932 Fax: (01905) 776434

Strenco Tools Ltd, 1 Kelston Road, Bristol, BS10 5EP Tel: 0117-950 7447 Fax: 0117-949 6494 E-mail: sales@strencotools.co.uk

T W Engineering Ltd, Angular House, Quarry Hill Road, Ilkeston, Derbyshire, DE7 4DA Tel: 0115-932 3223 Fax: 0115-930 6221 E-mail: tw@tweng.co.uk

Tanoga Ltd, Cradock Rd, Luton, LU4 0JF Tel: (01582) 502882 Fax: (01582) 581781 E-mail: info@tanoga.com

Tarlow Engineering Ltd, Unit 22 Acorn Industrial Park, Crayford Road, Dartford, DA1 4AL Tel: (01322) 550328 Fax: (01322) 522998 E-mail: tarlow@mistral.co.uk

John Taylo Engineering Ltd, Swift Farm, Hensting La, Fishers Pond, Eastleigh, Hants, SO50 7HH Tel: 023 80600012 Fax: 023 80696233

Teal Engineering, Breckland Business Park, Norwich Road, Watton, Thetford, Norfolk, IP25 6UP Tel: (01953) 885312 Fax: (01953) 883666 E-mail: info@tealengineering.co.uk

Technitool Engineers, 5 William Street, Northampton, NN1 3EW Tel: (01604) 626790 Fax: (01604) 233425 E-mail: technitools@talk21.com

Tripos Tools Ltd, Upper Interfields, Malvern, Worcestershire, WR14 1UT Tel: (01886) 833377 Fax: (01886) 833579

Tyne Tools, 17 Deer Park Road, Moulton Park Industrial Estate, Northampton, NN3 6RX Tel: (01604) 647020 Fax: (01604) 790668

Vere Engineering Ltd, 17 Jameson Road, Birmingham, B6 7SJ Tel: 0121-327 3630 Fax: 0121-327 3050

VPM Ltd, Birch House, Fraser Road, Erith, Kent, DA8 1QX Tel: (01322) 430043 Fax: (01322) 430044 E-mail: comptonshaun@aol.com

W R Tooling Ltd, Armytage Road Industrial Estate, Armytage Road, Brighouse, West Yorkshire, HD6 1QF Tel: (01484) 719642 Fax: (01484) 716854 E-mail: info@wrtooling.co.uk

▶ Wessex Tool & Die Ltd, 28 Holton Road, Holton Heath Trading Park, Poole, Dorset, BH16 6LT Tel: (01202) 620242 Fax: (01202) 620252

Witan Pressings Ltd, Unit 3, Alexander Mill, Gibb Street, Long Eaton, Nottingham, NG10 1EE Tel: 0115-946 1545 Fax: 0115-946 0874 E-mail: witan-pressings@btconnect.com

Woodcrafts, 25 Bayton Road Industrial Estate, Bayton Road, Exhall, Coventry, CV7 9EL Tel: (024) 7636 1022 Fax: (024) 7664 4299 E-mail: pdl@btconnect.com

Wroughton Developments, 14 Barcelona Cresent, Wroughton, Swindon, SN4 9EE Tel: (01793) 812292 Fax: (01793) 812292

Wyken Tools Ltd, Unit 3, Bodmin Road, Coventry, CV2 5DZ Tel: (024) 7662 1515 Fax: (024) 7662 1472 E-mail: jezwykentools@aol.com

TOOLMAKING RESINS

Surlyt, 5 The Cross, Dalry, Ayrshire, KA24 5AL Tel: (01294) 832322 Fax: (01294) 832101 E-mail: jim_langlands@1stlam.com

TOOLS

▶ C P A Products, 9 Warrior Business Centre, Fitzherbert Road, Portsmouth, PO6 1TX Tel: (023) 9221 0330 Fax: (023) 9220 1594

▶ T W Patterns, Stoke Row, Coventry, CV2 4JP Tel: (024) 7644 9571

TOOLS, FASTENING, BOLT

Alton Bolt & Tool Co. Ltd, Unit E6 West Ham Industrial Estate, Grafton Way, Basingstoke, Hampshire, RG22 6HY Tel: (01256) 461078 Fax: (01256) 323936

TOOLS, HAND, AUTOMOTIVE

Burwill Moulds, Hillside, London Road, Washington, Pulborough, West Sussex, RH20 3BN Tel: (01903) 892023 Fax: (01903) 892136

Chesterman Marketing Ltd, 3 Kenworthy Road, Stafford, ST16 3DY Tel: (01785) 250341 Fax: (01785) 250345 E-mail: enquiries@chestermanmarketing.com

Snap-On Finance UK Ltd, Telford Way, Industrial Estate, Kettering, Northamptonshire, NN16 8SN Tel: (01536) 516651 Fax: (01536) 413874 E-mail: industrialuk@snapon.com

TOOLS, HAND, COMBINATION SETS

▶ Getme-Tools, 52 Hamilton Rd, Taunton, Somerset, TA1 2ES Tel: 01823 272066 Fax: 01823 272066 E-mail: sales@getme-tools.co.uk

TOOLS, HAND, FIXING

Anglia Fixing Supplies, Anglia House, Grange Avenue, Mayland, Chelmsford, CM3 6BG Tel: (01621) 744490 Fax: (01621) 744821

TOOLS, HAND, PNEUMATIC

F G Lang Grays Ltd, 44 Clarence Road, Grays, Essex, RM17 6QL Tel: (01375) 374901 Fax: (01375) 374216E-mail: info@langs.co.uk

TOOLS, HAND, SOCKETS

▶ Getme-Tools, 52 Hamilton Rd, Taunton, Somerset, TA1 2ES Tel: 01823 272066 Fax: 01823 272066 E-mail: sales@getme-tools.co.uk

TOOLS, HAND, TO SPECIFICATION

A P T, 27 Pant-Y-Fid Road, Aberbargoed, Bargoed, Mid Glamorgan, CF81 9DT Tel: (01443) 835086 Fax: (01443) 835086 E-mail: apt@handtools.org.uk

TOOLS, HAND, TO SPECIFICATION

– continued

Corbin & Frost Ltd, 3 Stepfield, Witham, Essex, CM8 3DP Tel: (01376) 572202 Fax: (01376) 513921 E-mail: corbin.frost@macunlimited.net

M G Tools, 158 Charles Street, Sheffield, S1 2NE Tel: 0114-272 2281 Fax: 0114-278 7157 E-mail: info@mgtools.co.uk

Tool Connection Ltd, Unit 2, Kineton Road, Southam, Warwickshire, CV47 0DR Tel: (01926) 815999 Fax: (01926) 815888 E-mail: lesleyscott@lasertools.co.uk

TOOLS, MECHANICAL ENGINEERS

Stanton-Thompson (Agencies) Ltd, 14 Watcombe Road, Watlington, Oxfordshire, OX49 5QJ Tel: (01491) 613515 Fax: (01491) 613516 E-mail: diana@stanthom.freeserve.co.uk

TOPSIDE OIL WELL INSPECTION

Servtech Ltd, 2 Abbotswell Road, West Tullos, Aberdeen, AB12 3AB Tel: (01224) 878322 Fax: (01224) 895080 E-mail: info@servtech.co.uk

Technology Offshore Onshore Ltd, Woodcroft House, Crow Hill Drive, Mansfield, Nottinghamshire, NG19 7AE Tel: (01623) 654254 Fax: (01623) 420821 E-mail: kcutt@techoffonshore.com

TORCHES

Cape Warwick Ltd, 47 Britannia Way, Britannia Enterprise Park, Lichfield, Staffordshire, WS14 9UY Tel: (01543) 414544 Fax: (01543) 414599E-mail: enquiries@cape-warwick.co.uk

▶ Uni-Lite International Ltd, Unit 7 Colemeadow Road, North Moors Moat, Redditch, Worcestershire, B98 9PB Tel: (01527) 584344 Fax: (01527) 584345 E-mail: sales@uni-lite.com

TORCHES, SUBSEA/ UNDERWATER

Birchley Products, 7 Bush Hay, Church Down, Gloucester, GL3 2QR Tel: (01452) 855312 Fax: (01452) 859245 E-mail: ab@birchleyproducts.co.uk

TOROIDAL COILS

Morite Winding Co. Ltd, Unit 10c Sand Road Industrial Estate, Great Gransden, Sandy, Bedfordshire, SG19 3AH Tel: (01767) 677811 Fax: (01767) 677812 E-mail: sales@morite.co.uk

Wiltan Ltd, Pontnewynydd Industrial Estate, Pontnewynydd, Pontypool, Gwent, NP4 6YW Tel: (01495) 750711 Fax: (01495) 753730 E-mail: sales@wiltan.co.uk

TOROIDAL TRANSFORMERS

A G W Electronics Ltd, Hayford Way, Staveley, Chesterfield, Derbyshire, S43 3JR Tel: (01246) 473086 Fax: (01246) 280082 E-mail: sales@agw.co.uk

Cambridge Transformers Ltd, Quiet Waters, High Street, Earith, Huntingdon, Cambridgeshire, PE28 3PN Tel: (01487) 842154 Fax: (01487) 843445 E-mail: sales@transformers.demon.co.uk

Carnhill Transformers Ltd, 68 Sandford Lane, Kennington, Oxford, OX1 5RW Tel: (01865) 327843 Fax: (01865) 736538 E-mail: sales@carnhill.co.uk

Delta Components, The Courtyard, Sevenacres, Smallfield Road, Horne, Horley, Surrey, RH6 9JP Tel: (01342) 844555 Fax: (01342) 844552 E-mail: sales@deltacomponents.com

Demeter Windings, Beehive Lane, Chelmsford, CM2 9TE Tel: (01245) 344544 Fax: (01245) 265344 E-mail: demeterw@lycos.co.uk

Ingrid West Machinery Ltd, Unit 5L, Delta Drive, Tewkesbury Business Park, Tewkesbury, Gloucestershire, GL20 8HB Tel: (01684) 273164 Fax: (01684) 273171 E-mail: enquiries@ingridwest.co.uk

Isomatic UK Ltd, 9 Pimms Close, Guildford, Surrey, GU4 7YG Tel: (01483) 534634 Fax: (01483) 573624 E-mail: peter.burton@isomatics.biz

Lan Electronics, Unit 5 50, Rother Valley Way, Holbrook, Sheffield, S20 3RW Tel: 0114-251 1066 Fax: 0114-251 1067 E-mail: sales@lanelectronicsltd.co.uk

Morite Winding Co. Ltd, Unit 10c Sand Road Industrial Estate, Great Gransden, Sandy, Bedfordshire, SG19 3AH Tel: (01767) 677811 Fax: (01767) 677812 E-mail: sales@morite.co.uk

Pace Components Ltd, 38 Ballmoor, Buckingham Industrial Estate, Buckingham, MK18 1RQ Tel: (01280) 822733 Fax: (01280) 823839 E-mail: sales@pacecomponents.co.uk

Tam Transformers Ltd, Durban Road, Bognor Regis, West Sussex, PO22 9QT Tel: (01243) 861122 Fax: (01243) 830870 E-mail: tam@tamtransformers.co.uk

TORPEDO PROPULSION UNITS

Sykes Marine Hydromaster Ltd, B6 Fleet House Trading Estate, Motherwell Way, Grays, Essex, RM20 3XD Tel: (01708) 862651 Fax: (01708) 867905 E-mail: sykes.sales@sykeshydromaster.com

TORQUE ANALYSERS

Crane Electronics Ltd, Open House, 3 Watling Drive, Hinckley, Leicestershire, LE10 3EY Tel: (01455) 251488 Fax: (01455) 614717 E-mail: sales@crane-electronics.com

Sensor Technology Ltd, PO Box 36, Banbury, Oxfordshire, OX15 6JB Tel: (01295) 730746 Fax: (01295) 738966 E-mail: info@sensors.co.uk

TORQUE CALIBRATING EQUIPMENT MANUFRS

Crane Electronics Ltd, Open House, 3 Watling Drive, Hinckley, Leicestershire, LE10 3EY Tel: (01455) 251488 Fax: (01455) 614717 E-mail: sales@crane-electronics.com

P D Tools Ltd, 4 Murrills Estate, Fareham, Hampshire, PO16 9RD Tel: (023) 9238 3635 Fax: (023) 9238 3652 E-mail: reception@pdtools.co.uk

Torqueleader, Tannery Lane, Bramley, Guildford, Surrey, GU5 0AJ Tel: (01483) 892772 Fax: (01483) 898536 E-mail: sales@torqueleader.co.uk

Torqueleader, Tannery Lane, Bramley, Guildford, Surrey, GU5 0AJ Tel: (01483) 892772 Fax: (01483) 898536 E-mail: sales@torqueleader.co.uk

TORQUE CONTROL EQUIPMENT MANUFRS

A M C Engineering Ltd, Unit 3, Blackhill Industrial Estate, Findon, Aberdeen, AB12 4RL Tel: (01224) 782232 Fax: (01224) 782480 E-mail: sales@amc-engineering.co.uk

Carel Components, 24 Endeavour Way, London, SW19 8UH Tel: (020) 8946 9882 Fax: (020) 8946 6259 E-mail: ccs@carel.co.uk

Crane Electronics Ltd, Open House, 3 Watling Drive, Hinckley, Leicestershire, LE10 3EY Tel: (01455) 251488 Fax: (01455) 614717 E-mail: sales@crane-electronics.com

K J N Automation Ltd, 5 Peckleton Lane Business Park, Peckleton Common, Peckleton, Leicester, LE9 7RN Tel: (01455) 823304 Fax: (01455) 828186 E-mail: sales@kjnltd.co.uk

K T R Couplings Ltd, Robert House Unit 7, Acorn Business Park, Woodseats Close, Sheffield, S8 0TB Tel: 0114-258 7757 Fax: 0114-258 7740 E-mail: ktr-uk@ktr.com

Torqueleader, Tannery Lane, Bramley, Guildford, Surrey, GU5 0AJ Tel: (01483) 892772 Fax: (01483) 898536 E-mail: sales@torqueleader.co.uk

TORQUE CONVERTERS

J P (Automatic Transmissions) Ltd, Units 4A-4B, Pear Tree Industrial Estate, Bath Road, Upper Langford, Bristol, BS40 5DJ Tel: (01934) 852772 Fax: (01934) 852211 E-mail: info@jpat.co.uk

TORQUE ELECTRIC MOTORS

Coercive Group Ltd, Beta House, Laser Quay, Rochester, Kent, ME2 4HU Tel: (01634) 713053 Fax: (01634) 712541 E-mail: csl@coercive.com

Control Techniques Dynamics Ltd, South Way, Andover, Hampshire, SP10 5AB Tel: (01264) 387600 Fax: (01264) 356561 E-mail: sales@ctdynamics.com

TORQUE EQUIPMENT

Ets UK Ltd, Northside Industrial Park, Whitley Bridge, Goole, North Humberside, DN14 0GH Tel: (01977) 662910 Fax: (01977) 661797 E-mail: sales@ets-uk.co.uk

P D Tools Ltd, 4 Murrills Estate, Fareham, Hampshire, PO16 9RD Tel: (023) 9238 3635 Fax: (023) 9238 3652 E-mail: reception@pdtools.co.uk

TORQUE LIMITING CLUTCHES

L U K A S (Hereford) Ltd, Holme Lacy Road, Rotherwas, Hereford, HR2 6LA Tel: (01432) 265265 Fax: (01432) 275146

TORQUE LIMITING COUPLINGS

British Autogard Ltd, Siddington, Cirencester, Gloucestershire, GL7 6EU Tel: (01285) 640333 Fax: (01285) 659476 E-mail: sales@autogard.co.uk

Renold High Tech Couplings, 112 Parkinson Lane, Halifax, West Yorkshire, HX1 3QH Tel: (01422) 255000 Fax: (01422) 320273 E-mail: sales@hitec.renold.com

TORQUE MEASURING EQUIPMENT MANUFRS

Industrial Measurements, Willow Industrial Park, Willow Road, Castle Donington, Derby, DE74 2NP Tel: (01332) 810240 Fax: (01332) 812440 E-mail: mail@indmeas.co.uk

TORQUE METERS

Astech Electronics Ltd, Forge Industrial Estate, The Street, Binsted, Alton, Hampshire, GU34 4PF Tel: (01420) 22689 Fax: (01420) 22636 E-mail: astech@astech.demon.co.uk

Industrial Measurements, Willow Industrial Park, Willow Road, Castle Donington, Derby, DE74 2NP Tel: (01332) 810240 Fax: (01332) 812440 E-mail: mail@indmeas.co.uk

Torqueleader, Tannery Lane, Bramley, Guildford, Surrey, GU5 0AJ Tel: (01483) 892772 Fax: (01483) 898536 E-mail: sales@torqueleader.co.uk

Torquemeters Ltd, West Haddon Rd, Ravensthorpe, Northampton, NN6 8ET Tel: (01604) 770232 Fax: (01604) 770778 E-mail: info@torquemeters.com

TORQUE SENSORS

Sensor Technology Ltd, PO Box 36, Banbury, Oxfordshire, OX15 6JB Tel: (01295) 730746 Fax: (01295) 738966 E-mail: info@sensors.co.uk

TORQUE TEST EQUIPMENT

Britool Ltd, Churchbridge Works, Walsall Road, Cannock, Staffordshire, WS11 3JR Tel: (01922) 702100 Fax: (01922) 702101 E-mail: uk_sales@britool.co.uk

TORQUE WRENCHES

Norbar Torque Tools Ltd, Beaumont Rd, Banbury, Oxfordshire, OX16 1XJ Tel: (01295) 753600 Fax: (01295) 753609 E-mail: sales@norbar.com

P D Tools Ltd, 4 Murrills Estate, Fareham, Hampshire, PO16 9RD Tel: (023) 9238 3635 Fax: (023) 9238 3652 E-mail: reception@pdtools.co.uk

Torqueleader, Tannery Lane, Bramley, Guildford, Surrey, GU5 0AJ Tel: (01483) 892772 Fax: (01483) 898536 E-mail: sales@torqueleader.co.uk

W Christie (Industrial) Ltd, Christie House, Meadow Bank Road, Rotherham, South Yorkshire, S61 2NF Tel: (01709) 550088 Fax: (01709) 550030 E-mail: sales@wchristie.com

TORSION BARS

▶ ADEPT Precision Ltd, Unit 7 Deacon Trading Estate, 203 Vale Road, Tonbridge, Kent, TN9 1SU Tel: 01732 773777 Fax: 01732 771115 E-mail: sales@adeptprecision.com

TORSION SPRINGS

A S K Springs, Edward Street, Clive Works, Redditch, Worcestershire, B97 6HA Tel: (01527) 63300 Fax: (01527) 63300

TOTAL QUALITY MANAGEMENT CONSULTANCY

▶ Quality Improvements UK Ltd, 26 Queensway Business Centre, Dunlop Way, Queensway Industrial Estate, Scunthorpe, South Humberside, DN16 3RN Tel: (01724) 855125 Fax: (01724) 855749 E-mail: info@quality-improvements.co.uk

TOUCH AND CLOSE FASTENERS

Prym Whitecroft (UK) Ltd, Whitecroft, Lydney, Gloucestershire, GL15 4QG Tel: (01594) 562631 Fax: (01594) 563662 E-mail: sales@whitecroft.co.uk

TOUCH FREE HAND WASHING SYSTEMS

Teal Patents Ltd, 2 Chelmsley Wood Industrial Estate, Waterloo Avenue, Birmingham, B37 6QQ Tel: 0121-770 4017 Fax: 0121-770 0385 E-mail: enquiries@tealwash.com

TOUCH SCREEN EQUIPMENT

3 M Touch Systems, 163 Milton Park, Milton, Abingdon, Oxfordshire, OX14 4SD Tel: (01235) 444400 Fax: (01235) 861603 E-mail: touchsales-uk@mmm.com

Zytronic Displays Ltd, Patterson Street, Blaydon-on-Tyne, Tyne & Wear, NE21 5SG Tel: 0191-414 5511 Fax: 0191-414 0545 E-mail: info@zytronic.co.uk

TOUCH SCREENS

Market Place Merchandising, The Design Building Hewetts Kilns, Tongham Road, Farnham, Surrey, GU10 1PJ Tel: (01252) 781115 Fax: (01252) 781116 E-mail: info@marketplace-merchandising.com

TOUCH SCREENS, KIOSK

3 M Touch Systems, 163 Milton Park, Milton, Abingdon, Oxfordshire, OX14 4SD Tel: (01235) 444400 Fax: (01235) 861603 E-mail: touchsales-uk@mmm.com

Advanced Thinking Systems Ltd, 1 South Lane, Waterlooville, Hampshire, PO8 0RB Tel: (023) 9259 5000 Fax: (023) 9259 5656 E-mail: sales@advanced-thinking.co.uk

Market Place Merchandising, The Design Building Hewetts Kilns, Tongham Road, Farnham, Surrey, GU10 1PJ Tel: (01252) 781115 Fax: (01252) 781116 E-mail: info@marketplace-merchandising.com

Region Services Ltd, Unit 3 Fullwood Close, Aldermans Green Industrial Estate, Coventry, CV2 2SS Tel: (024) 7661 8189 Fax: (024) 7662 2246 E-mail: info@rslkiosks.co.uk

TOUCHSCREEN VISUAL DISPLAY UNITS (VDU)

3 M Touch Systems, 163 Milton Park, Milton, Abingdon, Oxfordshire, OX14 4SD Tel: (01235) 444400 Fax: (01235) 861603 E-mail: touchsales-uk@mmm.com

Brantham Electronics, The Gattinetts, Unit 2b Hadleigh Road, East Bergholt, Colchester, CO7 6QT Tel: (01206) 298951 E-mail: paul.oliver@branthamelectronics.co.uk

TOUGHENED GLASS

A C Yule & Son Ltd, Craigshaw Road, West Tullos Industrial Estate, Aberdeen, AB12 3ZG Tel: (01224) 230000 Fax: (01224) 230011 E-mail: admin@acyule.com

Abbseal (U K) Ltd, Broadway, Broadway, Hyde, Cheshire, SK14 4QW Tel: 0161-368 5711 Fax: 0161-366 8155

B & S Glass Industries Ltd, 47 Sutherland Road, London, E17 6BH Tel: (020) 8527 7575 Fax: (020) 8531 4875 E-mail: colin.tucker4@btopenworld.com

Cab Glazing Services, Unit D3, Button End Industrial Estate, Harston, Cambridge, CB2 5NX Tel: (01223) 872400 Fax: (01223) 872866 E-mail: sales@cabglazing.co.uk

E.N.L Audio Visual, Alfreton Road, Nottingham, NG7 3NR Tel: 0115-924 8305 Fax: 0115-924 8329 E-mail: sales@hotkit.co.uk

J Preedy & Sons Ltd, Lamb Works, North Road, London, N7 9DP Tel: (020) 7700 0377 Fax: (020) 7700 7579 E-mail: sales@preedyglass.com

Pilkington Plyglass, Cotes Park, Somercotes, Alfreton, Derbyshire, DE55 4PL Tel: (01773) 520000 Fax: (01773) 520052

Pilkington UK Ltd, 1 Dunnswood Road, Wardpark South, Cumbernauld, Glasgow, G67 3EN Tel: (01236) 728298 Fax: (01236) 729876 E-mail: cumbernauld@pilkington.com

Piper Toughened Glass Ltd, 29-43 Sydney Road, Watford, WD18 7PZ Tel: (01923) 224047 Fax: (01923) 222741 E-mail: sales@piperglass.co.uk

Saint-Gobain Solaglas, 11 Bridle Way, Bootle, Merseyside, L30 4UA Tel: (0151) 525 7241 Fax: (0151) 523 8212

Schott Industrial Glass Ltd, Ketton Way, Aycliffe Industrial Park, Newton Aycliffe, County Durham, DL5 6SR Tel: (01325) 300111 Fax: (01325) 300354

▶ Sean Timoney & Sons Ltd, 144a Tattygare Road, Mullanaskea, Enniskillen, County Fermanagh, BT74 4JQ Tel: (028) 6632 9252 Fax: (028) 6632 7282 E-mail: seantimoney@yahoo.co.uk

Triwarm Ltd, Unit E, Hamstead Industrial Estate, Austin Way, Great Barr, Birmingham, B42 1DU Tel: 0121-525 0500 Fax: 0121-525 6800 E-mail: sales@tri-warm.co.uk

▶ indicates data change since last edition

TOUR MANAGEMENT

▶ Shaggy Sheep, Cilwen, Abernant, Carmarthen, Dyfed, SA33 5RH Tel: (01267) 281202 E-mail: bookings@shaggysheep.com

TOURISM MARKETING

▶ The Beeches, Boston Road, Heckington, Sleaford, Lincolnshire, NG34 9JQ Tel: (01529) 462059 E-mail: thebeeches@lycos.co.uk

▶ Thomas Doran Parkanaur Trust, 57 Parkanaur Road, Dungannon, County Tyrone, BT70 3AA Tel: (028) 8776 1272 Fax: (028) 8776 1257 E-mail: parkanaurmanorhouse@hotmail.com

▶ Wightcat, 14 Carisbrooke Road, Newport, Isle of Wight, PO30 1BL Tel: (01983) 527525 Fax: (01983) 527579 E-mail: sales@wightcat.com

TOW BARS, TRAILER

▶ A&L TOWBARS, KIRKBURTON, KIRKBURTON, HUDDERSFIELD, HD8 0TJ Tel: 01484 602231 E-mail: andymally@btinternet.com

Mac Farr Engineering Co. Ltd, Garn Road, Blaenavon, Pontypool, Gwent, NP4 9RT Tel: (01495) 790648 Fax: (01495) 790648

▶ Manchester Towbar Trailer & Roofrack Centre Ltd, Baring St (off Fairfield St), Ardwick, Manchester, M12 6HJ Tel: 0161-273 5816 Fax: 0161-273 6678 E-mail: info@manchestertowbars.co.uk

▶ Vanax, 1 Mordaunt Street, Glasgow, G40 3JZ Tel: 0141-550 8881 Fax: 0141-550 8889 E-mail: sales@vanax.co.uk

TOW TRACTOR SPARE PARTS

▶ A M T Logistics Ltd, Hill Business Park, Iddesleigh, Winkleigh, Devon, EX19 8SW Tel: (01837) 811144 Fax: (01837) 811166 E-mail: office@amtlogistics.co.uk

TOWEL CABINETS

Dudley Industries, Preston Road, Lytham St. Annes, Lancashire, FY8 5AT Tel: (01253) 738311 Fax: (01253) 794393 E-mail: dudley@cyberscape.net

TOWEL RAILS

Hampshire Electroplating Co Ltd, 69-75 Empress Road, Southampton, SO14 0JW Tel: (023) 8022 5639 Fax: (023) 8063 9874 E-mail: enquiries@hepcoltd.co.uk

▶ Tivolis Design, Islington Business Centre, 3/5 Islington High Street, London, N1 9LQ Tel: (020) 7745 2375 Fax: (020) 7745 2376 E-mail: sales@tivolisdesign.co.uk

TOWEL SUPPLY SERVICES

The Caterers Linen Supply, 6-8 Jackson Way, Great Western Industrial Park, Southall, Middlesex, UB2 4SF Tel: (020) 8843 5810 Fax: (020) 8843 5865 E-mail: customerservice@catererslinen.co.uk

Cornish Linen Service, Dudnance Lane, Pool, Redruth, Cornwall, TR15 3RA Tel: (01256) 471311 Fax: (01209) 714133 E-mail: sales.camborne@cls-group.co.uk

Initial Textile Services, Unit 10, Eldon Way, Bristol, BS4 3QQ Tel: 0117-971 2387 Fax: 0117-971 6612 E-mail: briscsu@initialtextileservices.co.uk

Johnsons Apparel Master, Cowley Bridge Road, Exeter, EX4 5AA Tel: (01392) 271291 Fax: (01392) 422078

Universal Towel Co. Ltd, 1 Spa Industrial Park, Longfield Road, Tunbridge Wells, Kent, TN2 3EN Tel: (01892) 518822 Fax: (01892) 518118 E-mail: info@u-t-c.co.uk

TOWELS

Advanced Clothing Co., Vantel House, Parkway South, Wheatley, Doncaster, South Yorkshire, DN2 4JR Tel: (01302) 320200

Chortex Ltd, Victoria Mills, Chorley New Road, Horwich, Bolton, BL6 6ER Tel: (01204) 695611 Fax: (01204) 696680 E-mail: mark.tuley@coats-viyella.com

East Lancashire Towel Co. Ltd, Park Mill, Halstead Lane, Barrowford, Nelson, Lancashire, BB9 6HJ Tel: (01282) 612193 Fax: (01282) 697736

Majestic Towels Ltd, 72 Alfred Street, Sparkbrook, Birmingham, B12 8JP Tel: 0121-772 0936 Fax: 0121-766 8029 E-mail: info@majestictowels.co.uk

Midland Linen Services Ltd, 3 Klaxon Tysley Industrial Estate, 751 Warwick Road, Tyseley, Birmingham, B11 2HA Tel: 0121-708 1069 Fax: 0121-707 4686 E-mail: info@midlandlinen.co.uk

TOWER CLOCKS

Gillett & Johnston Croydon Ltd, Unit 9a Twin Bridges Business Park, 232 Selsdon Road, South Croydon, Surrey, CR2 6PL Tel: (020) 8686 2694 Fax: (020) 8681 4028 E-mail: any@gillettjohnston.co.uk

Good Directions Ltd, 8 Bottings Industrial Estate, Hillsons Road, Botley, Southampton, SO30 2DY Tel: 01489 797773 Fax: 01489 796700 E-mail: sales@good-directions.co.uk

J.B. Joyce & Co., Station Road, Whitchurch, Shropshire, SY13 1RD Tel: (01948) 662817 Fax: (01948) 665068 E-mail: sales@jbjoyce.com

William Potts & Sons Ltd, 112 Alfreton Road, Derby, DE21 4AU Tel: (01332) 345569 Fax: (01332) 290642 E-mail: sales@pottsofleeds.com

TOWER CRANE HIRE

Atherstone Crane Hire & Machinery Installation, 166 High Street, Dosthill, Tamworth, Staffordshire, B77 1LR Tel: (01827) 288271 Fax: (01827) 281800 E-mail: enquiries@atherstone-crane.co.uk

W.D. Bennett's Plant & Services Ltd, Burma Road, Sharpness, Gloucestershire, GL13 9UQ Tel: (01453) 811754 Fax: (01453) 811657 E-mail: sales@newsilencers.freeserve.co.uk

City Lifting, Purfleet Industrial Park, Aveley, South Ockendon, Essex, RM15 4YA Tel: (01708) 805550 Fax: (01708) 805558 E-mail: hire@citylifting.co.uk

TOWER CRANES

W.D. Bennett's Plant & Services Ltd, Burma Road, Sharpness, Gloucestershire, GL13 9UQ Tel: (01453) 811754 Fax: (01453) 811657 E-mail: sales@newsilencers.freeserve.co.uk

TOWING BRACKETS

R D F Eurobars, 55 Second Drove, Peterborough, PE1 5XA Tel: (01733) 555263 Fax: (01733) 555913 E-mail: sales@eurobars.co.uk

Tow Bar & Trailer Equipment, 44 Camp Road, Farnborough, Hampshire, GU14 6EP Tel: (01252) 540319

Witter Towbars, 11 Drome Road, Deeside Industrial Park, Deeside, Clwyd, CH5 2NY Tel: (01244) 284500 Fax: (01244) 284577 E-mail: sales@witter-towbars.com

York Tow Bars Ltd, Brokenford Lane, Totton, Southampton, SO40 9DY Tel: (023) 8086 6699 Fax: (023) 8086 2223 E-mail: sales@york-towbars.co.uk

TOWN PLANNING CONSULTANCY OR DESIGN

B Sheldon, Burrs Hill Barn House, Horsmonden Road, Brenchley, Tonbridge, Kent, TN12 7AT Tel: (01892) 723857

Barton Willmore Partnership, Netherton House, 23-29 Marsh Street, Bristol, BS1 4AQ Tel: 0117-929 9677 Fax: 0117-929 4569 E-mail: planning@bartonwillmore.co.uk

Barton Willmore Partnership, 35 Kings Hill Avenue, Kings Hill, West Malling, Kent, ME19 4BW Tel: (01732) 845845 Fax: (01732) 223808 E-mail: architects@eastern.bartonwillmore.co.uk

Broadway Malyan, 3 Weybridge Business Park, Addlestone Road, Addlestone, Surrey, KT15 2BW Tel: (01932) 845599 Fax: (01932) 856206 E-mail: man@broadwaymalyan.com

Cowan Architects Ltd, 9-10 Old Stone Link, Ship Street, East Grinstead, West Sussex, RH19 4EF Tel: (01342) 410242 Fax: (01342) 313493 E-mail: info@cowan-architects.co.uk

Aaron Evans Architects Ltd, 3 Argyle Street, Bath, BA2 4BA Tel: (01225) 466234 Fax: (01225) 444364 E-mail: aea@aearchitects.co.uk

▶ G K A, Unit 1 Bell Business Park, Smeaton Close, Aylesbury, Buckinghamshire, HP19 8JR Tel: (01296) 678300 Fax: (01296) 678301 E-mail: enquiries@gka.co.uk

Hunter & Partners Group Ltd, 26 28 Hammersmith Grove, Hammersmith, London, W6 7HU Tel: (020) 8237 8200 Fax: (020) 8741 2814 E-mail: mail@hunters.co.uk

Planning & Development, The Highland Council, Glenurquhart Road, Inverness, IV3 5NX Tel: (01463) 702250 Fax: (01463) 702298 E-mail: planning@highland.gov.uk

▶ Shire Consulting, The Chapel, Barnsley Hall Road, Bromsgrove, Worcestershire, B61 0SZ Tel: (01527) 579933 Fax: (01527) 579537 E-mail: info@shire-uk.com

▶ Shire Consulting, 8 Spicer Street, St. Albans, Hertfordshire, AL3 4PQ Tel: (01727) 838455 Fax: (01727) 835047 E-mail: enquiries@shire-uk.com

Tacp Landscape Architects, 10 Park Grove, Cardiff, CF10 3BN Tel: (029) 2022 8966 Fax: (029) 2039 4776 E-mail: cardiff@tacp.uk.com

Turley Associates Ltd, 43 Park Place, Leeds, LS1 2RY Tel: 0113-386 3800 Fax: 0113-244 3650 E-mail: leeds@rta.co.uk

Turley Associates Ltd, The Chancery, 58 Spring Gardens, Manchester, M2 1EW Tel: 0161-831 1300 Fax: 0161-831 1301 E-mail: enquiries@turley.co.uk

Urban Initiatives, Adam House, 1 Fitzroy Square, London, W1T 5HE Tel: (020) 7380 4545 Fax: (020) 7380 4546 E-mail: info@urbaninitiatives.co.uk

The W R Davidge Planning Practice, PO Box 463, Peterborough, PE8 6HU Tel: (01780) 763901 Fax: (01733) 235051 E-mail: davidge.planning@virgin.net

Ken Wilson Associates, 52 Union Road, Inverness, IV2 3JY Tel: (01463) 237375 Fax: (01463) 237666 E-mail: enquiries@kwa.uk.net

TOXIC GAS DETECTORS

A T M I (UK), Kingsland House, 512 Wimborne Road East, Ferndown, Dorset, BH22 9NG Tel: (01202) 875753 Fax: (01202) 875763 E-mail: info/europe@atmi.com

Air Quality Assurance, 1 Dunnings Lane, Rochester, Kent, ME1 1YB Tel: (01634) 832895 Fax: (01634) 832882

Honeywell Analytics Ltd, Hatch Pond House, 4 Stinsford Road, Nuffield Estate, Poole, Dorset, BH17 0RZ Tel: (01202) 676161 Fax: (01202) 678011 E-mail: tracy.dawe@honeywell.com

TOXIC WASTE DISPOSAL CONTRACTORS

H A Z Environmental, Bullock Street, West Bromwich, West Midlands, B70 7HE Tel: 0121-580 3055 Fax: 0121-580 3056 E-mail: mail@haz-enviro.co.uk

Phoenix County Metal Ltd, Great Central Way Industrial Estate, Great Central Way, Woodford Halse, Daventry, Northamptonshire, NN11 3PZ Tel: (01327) 260581 Fax: (01327) 260191

TOXICITY TESTING SERVICES

Webs Ltd, Ashborne House Waterperry Court, Middleton Road, Banbury, Oxfordshire, OX16 4QG Tel: (01295) 277272 Fax: (01295) 264070 E-mail: enquiries@websint.com

TOXIN LABORATORY SERVICES

▶ Tranquility, 21 Hartfield Road, Forest Row, East Sussex, RH18 5DY Tel: (01342) 825865 E-mail: linda@l-kernahan.freeserve.co.uk

TOY BALLOONS

A Present World, 6 Elmstead Gardens, Worcester Park, Surrey, KT4 7BD Tel: (020) 8335 3530 Fax: (020) 8335 3530 E-mail: presentworld@hotmail.com

Balloon Art Design Studio, 2 Whitehall Ave, Rumney, Cardiff, CF3 8DQ Tel: (029) 2079 0207

Balloon Buddies, 26 Oxford Street, St. Philips, Bristol, BS2 0QU Tel: 0117-945 1822 E-mail: sales@balloonbuddies.co.uk

Balloon Elegance, 53 Love Street, Paisley, Renfrewshire, PA3 2DZ Tel: 0141-848 6119 Fax: 0141-848 9161 E-mail: jb-promotions@btclick.com

Balloon World, 18 Norfolk Street, King's Lynn, Norfolk, PE30 1AN Tel: (01553) 760909 Fax: (01553) 760909

Balloons Are Taking Off, 390 Gorgie Road, Edinburgh, EH11 2RQ Tel: 0131-346 4446 Fax: 0131-346 2608 E-mail: sales@balloonsaretakingoff.co.uk

Balloons By Post, 1 Audley End, Saffron Walden, Essex, CB11 4JB Tel: (01799) 513335 E-mail: contact@ballonsbypost.com

Balloons & Flora, 53 The Broadway, Loughton, Essex, IG10 3SP Tel: (020) 8508 8977 Fax: (020) 8508 8977

Balloons On Tour, Dart Mills, Old Topnes Road, Buckfastleigh, Devon, TQ11 0NF Tel: (0800) 7834546 Fax: (01364) 642172

Balloons R Us, 25 Military Road, Colchester, CO1 2AD Tel: (01206) 545556 Fax: (01206) 545556

Balloons Worldwide Ltd, London Road, Brown Street, Alderley Edge, Cheshire, SK9 7EQ Tel: (01625) 583168 Fax: (01625) 586098

Bedford Balloons, 165 Castle Road, Bedford, MK40 3RT Tel: (01234) 212232 Fax: (01234) 346289 E-mail: bedfordflorist@amserve.net

Bizarre Balloons, Unit B 43 Foregate Street, Stafford, ST16 2PJ Tel: (01785) 256668 Fax: (01785) 605680 E-mail: sales@bizarreballoons.co.uk

Bizzy Balloons, 4 Old Hall Drive, Dersingham, King's Lynn, Norfolk, PE31 6JT Tel: (01485) 541744

Celebration Balloon Co. Ltd, 90 The Broadway, High Street, Chesham, Buckinghamshire, HP5 1EG Tel: (01494) 791969 Fax: (08700) 526501

Cti Balloons Ltd, 6 Consul Road, Rugby, Warwickshire, CV21 1PB Tel: (01788) 546299 Fax: (01788) 546114 E-mail: ctiballoon@aol.com

It's A Gas, 100 Coventry Road, Market Harborough, Leicestershire, LE16 9DA Tel: (01858) 446216 E-mail: starr@its-a-gas-balloons.co.uk

Louise's Balloon Co, Willow Lodge, Weston Colville Rd, Brinkley, Newmarket, Suffolk, CB8 0SG Tel: 01638 508217 Fax: 01638 508217

▶ Magicboxgifts, Optec House, Westfield Avenue, Wigston, Leicester, LE18 1HY Tel: 0116-229 0232 Fax: 0116-229 0232 E-mail: sales@magicboxgifts.com

Orchardcrown Ltd, 586 Blackpool Road, Ashton, Preston, PR2 1JA Tel: (01772) 728191 Fax: (01772) 727963 E-mail: sales@balloonshot.co.uk

Par Pak Party Time Ltd, 12-14 Gloucester Street, Leamington Spa, Warwickshire, CV31 1EE Tel: (01926) 314699 Fax: (01926) 422122 E-mail: sales@partytimeballoons.co.uk

Party Time, 51 Bransholme Drive, York, YO30 4XN Tel: (01904) 691991 E-mail: yorkhire@tesco.net

R K M Display, 50 Chewton Way, Walkford, Christchurch, Dorset, BH23 5LS Tel: (01425) 274295 Fax: (01425) 274295

Seasonal Reflections Ltd, 30 High Street, Mold, Clwyd, CH7 1BH Tel: (01352) 756070 Fax: (01352) 757011 E-mail: seasonalreflectionsltd@yahoo.co.uk

Smiffy's, Heapham Road South, Caldicott Drive, Heapham Road Industrial Estate, Gainsborough, Lincolnshire, DN21 1FJ Tel: (01427) 616831 Fax: (01427) 617190 E-mail: info@smiffys.com

Special Touch, Ivydene, Whelpley Hill, Chesham, Bucks, HP5 3RN Tel: 01442 831585

Sto-Rose Ltd, Unit 8, Park Farm, Wellham Road, Black Knotley, Braintree, Essex, CM77 8LQ Tel: (01376) 328256 Fax: (01376) 329256 E-mail: sales@fantasiaballoons.com

Surprise Balloons, 82 Newton Rd, Rushden, Northants, NN10 0HQ Tel: 01933 411457

TOY BOXES

▶ Silver Toys & Allsorts, 21 Chapel Lane, Wimblington, March, Cambs, PE15 0QX Tel: 01354 742415 E-mail: paul_silvertoys@btinternet.com

TOY MATERIALS/COMPONENTS

K Toys, Second Avenue, Westfield Industrial Estate, Midsomer Norton, Radstock, BA3 4BH Tel: (01761) 411299 Fax: (01761) 411522 E-mail: mail@ktoys.co.uk

TOY MERCHANTS OR AGENTS

John Adams Trading Co. Ltd, The Barn, 3 Deanes Close, Steventon, Abingdon, Oxfordshire, OX13 6SZ Tel: (01235) 833066 Fax: (01235) 861116 E-mail: trading@johnadams.co.uk

▶ Baby Rug, 61 Pepys Road, London, SW20 8NL Tel: (020) 8944 8674 E-mail: info@babyrug.co.uk

Bandai UK Ltd, Jellicoe House, Grange Drive, Hedge End, Southampton, SO30 2AF Tel: (01489) 790944 Fax: (01489) 790643

Brio Ltd, Sutton House, Bishop Meadow Road, Loughborough, Leicestershire, LE11 5RE Tel: (01509) 231874 Fax: (01509) 234547 E-mail: info@brio.co.uk

Cassidy Brothers plc, Mitcham Road, Marton, Blackpool, FY4 4QW Tel: (01253) 766411 Fax: (01253) 691486 E-mail: toys@casdon.co.uk

▶ D & P Shop, 76 Huddersfield Road, Elland, West Yorkshire, HX5 9AA Tel: (01422) 310552 Fax: (01422) 310552 E-mail: sales@dandpshop.co.uk

Dekkertoys Ltd, 16 Innovation Way, Orton Wistow, Peterborough, PE2 6FL Tel: (01733) 397400 Fax: (01733) 370241 E-mail: sales@dekkertoys.co.uk

▶ Doodlebugz, Marton, Marton cum Grafton, York, YO51 9QE Tel: (01347) 830100 Fax: (01347) 830100 E-mail: info@doodlebugz.co.uk

Dorset Enterprises, Elliott Road, Bournemouth, BH11 8JP Tel: (01202) 577966 Fax: (01202) 570049 E-mail: dorsetenterprises@bournemouth.gov.uk

▶ Father Christmas Letters Ltd, Old School Lane, Whittlesford, Cambridge, CB22 4YS Tel: (0870) 7503159 Fax: (0870) 0941215 E-mail: info@fatherchristmasletters.co.uk

Furrytails, 26-28 Standard Road, London, NW10 6EU Tel: (020) 8965 6836 Fax: (020) 8965 2172E-mail: furrytails@compuserve.com

Hornby Hobbies Ltd, H1-H2 Unit Enterprise Road, Westwood Industrial Estate, Margate, Kent, CT9 4JX Tel: (01843) 233500 Fax: (01843) 233513 E-mail: hornby@btinternet.com

House Of Marbles Ltd, Pottery Road, Bovey Tracey, Newton Abbot, Devon, TQ13 9DS Tel: (01626) 835358 Fax: (01626) 835315 E-mail: sales@houseofmarbles.com

Intersell Agencies Toys Nursery Agents, 8 Nelson Trade Centre, Nelson Street, Belfast, BT15 1BH Tel: (028) 9024 3730 Fax: (028) 9023 8327

TOY MERCHANTS OR AGENTS – *continued*

J A Magson Ltd, Magson House, Kettlestring Lane, York, YO30 4XF Tel: (01904) 690097 Fax: (01904) 691018 E-mail: sales@magson.co.uk

▶ Kulfi Kids, 7 Market place, Camelford, Cornwall, PL32 9PB Tel: 01840 211144 E-mail: orders@kulfikids.co.uk

▶ Lanka Kade, 1 South Folds Road, Corby, Northamptonshire, NN18 9EU Tel: (01536) 461188 Fax: (01536) 461100

Lego Company Ltd, 33 Bath Road, Slough, SL1 3UF Tel: (01753) 495000 Fax: (01753) 495100 E-mail: sales@lego.com

Marshall Group Ltd, Cader House, Cader Avenue, Kinmel Bay, Rhyl, Clwyd, LL18 5HU Tel: (01745) 343131 Fax: (01745) 345223 E-mail: mmar@dialstart.net

Merrythought Ltd, Dale End, Iron Bridge, Telford, Shropshire, TF8 7NJ Tel: (01952) 433116 Fax: (01952) 432054 E-mail: sales@merrythought.co.uk

Otherland Toys, Lee Valley Technopark, Ashley Road, London, N17 9LN Tel: (020) 8880 4919 E-mail: alex@otherlandtoys.co.uk

P E M S Butler Ltd, The Red House, Axminster, Devon, EX13 5SE Tel: (01297) 631435 Fax: (01297) 631437 E-mail: sales@superquick.co.uk

P M S International Group plc, International House, Cricketers Way, Basildon, Essex, SS13 1ST Tel: (01268) 505050 Fax: (01268) 505000 E-mail: sales@pmsinternational.com

▶ Polydron UK Ltd, Old RAF Hangar, Kemble, Cirencester, Gloucestershire, GL7 6BQ Tel: (01285) 770055 Fax: (01285) 770171 E-mail: headoffice@polydron.com

S D L Imports Ltd, 2-18 Windham Road, Bournemouth, BH1 4RW Tel: (01202) 291122 Fax: (01202) 293322 E-mail: sales@sdlimports.co.uk

▶ Silver Toys & Allsorts, 21 Chapel Lane, Wimblington, March, Cambs, PE15 0QX Tel: 01354 742415 E-mail: paul_silvertoys@btinternet.com

▶ Sun Star Models Europe, The Vicarage, Lounts CR, Great Easton, Market Harborough, Leicestershire, LE16 8SX Tel: (01536) 772490 Fax: (01536) 772491 E-mail: sales@sunstartoys.com

T P Activity Toys, Severn Road, Stourport-on-Severn, Worcestershire, DY13 9EX Tel: (01299) 872800 Fax: (01299) 827163 E-mail: enquiries@tptoys.com

Tomy Yujin Europe Ltd, St Nicholas House, St Nicholas Road, Sutton, Surrey, SM1 1EH Tel: (020) 8722 7300 E-mail: office@tomy.co.uk

Toys N Togs, 94 Boundary Road, Hove, East Sussex, BN3 7GB Tel: (01273) 880808 Fax: (01273) 882298 E-mail: zwindle40uk@yahoo.co.uk

Wizard Ltd, Wizard House, Cambridge Road, Teddington, Middlesex, TW11 8DR Tel: (020) 8943 0121 Fax: (020) 8977 9074 E-mail: barry@wizardtoys.com

Worlds Apart Ltd, Unit 4 Union Court, 18-20 Union Road, London, SW4 6JP Tel: (020) 7622 0171 Fax: (020) 7622 7975 E-mail: info@worldsapart.co.uk

▶ www.farmmodels.co.uk, The Old Manor Farmhouse, Lower Road, Edington, Westbury, Wiltshire, BA13 4QW Tel: (01380) 831459 Fax: (01380) 830659 E-mail: office@farmmodels.co.uk

Yaffe Martin International, Arrow Mill, Queensway, Rochdale, Lancashire, OL11 2QN Tel: (01706) 717800 Fax: (01706) 717801 E-mail: info@martinyaffee.com

▶ Your Party By Post, 82 Copthorne Road, Felbridge, East Grinstead, West Sussex, RH19 2NU Tel: (0845) 4084812 E-mail: shop@yourpartybypost.co.uk

TOYS, RADIO CONTROLLED

▶ LYLLOY Co.,LTD, Unit 60, 3-9 Hyde Road, Ardwick Green, Manchester, M12 6BQ Tel: 0773 0383126

TOYS, ROCKING, WOODEN

▶ Class Creations Ltd, The Lippiatt, Cheddar Gorge, Cheddar, Somerset, BS27 3QP Tel: (01934) 740240 Fax: (01934) 740234 E-mail: mail@classcreations.co.uk

▶ Rob Roy Wooden Toys, 81 College Street, Long Eaton, Nottingham, NG10 4NN Tel: 0115-973 3943 E-mail: robroytoy@yahoo.co.uk

▶ Tom's Toys, 22 Manor Road, Newton Longville, Milton Keynes, MK17 0AJ Tel: (01908) 376951

▶ Wooden Choice Ltd, 127 Manchester Road, Worsley, Manchester, M28 3JT Tel: 0161-703 7919 E-mail: info@woodenchoice.co.uk

TRACE HEATING BAG FILTERS

Hertel Services, Sotherby Road, Skippers Lane Idustrial Estate, Middlesbrough, Cleveland, TS6 6LP Tel: (01642) 469532 Fax: (01642) 445614 E-mail: info@hertel.co.uk

TRACEABILITY OR TRACKING SYSTEMS

▶ A M Transport Services, Bay 1 Burnbrae Road, Linwood, Paisley, Renfrewshire, PA3 3BD Tel: (01505) 328906 Fax: (01505) 335120

▶ Meditrax, Group House, Bowling Hill Business Park, Quarry Road, Chipping Sodbury, Bristol, BS37 6JL Tel: (01454) 318373 Fax: (01454) 322792 E-mail: enquiries@meditrax.co.uk

TRACING PAPER

C.D.S Yorks Ltd, Ledgard Way, Reprographic House, Armley, Leeds, LS12 2ND Tel: 0113-263 0601 Fax: 0113-231 0305 E-mail: sales@cds-yorks.com

TRACK ROLL HANDLING SYSTEMS

Rolpex Ltd, Marple, Stockport, Cheshire, SK6 6EF Tel: 0161-449 7707 Fax: 0161-449 7707 E-mail: rolpexuk@aol.com

TRACKED OR CRAWLER EXCAVATORS

▶ City Plant Services Ltd, 12 Craigmore Road, Newry, County Down, BT35 6PL Tel: (028) 3082 5522 Fax: 02830 825533 E-mail: sales@cpsnewry.com

TRACKED VEHICLE CRAWLER SYSTEMS

Strickland Direct Ltd, 5 Main Road, Cropthorne, Pershore, Worcestershire, WR10 3NE Tel: (01386) 860349 Fax: (01386) 860057

TRACKER BALL MANUFRS

▶ Cursor Controls Ltd, Conroi House, Brunel Drive, Newark, Nottinghamshire, NG24 2EG Tel: (01636) 615600 Fax: (01636) 615601 E-mail: sales@cursorcontrols.com

TRACKING SYSTEMS, CELLULAR RADIO TELEPHONE EQUIPMENT

▶ Pda Electronics Ltd, 7 Bevan Hill, Chesham, Buckinghamshire, HP5 2QS Tel: (01494) 794949 Fax: (01494) 791820 E-mail: info@pdaelectronics.com

TRACKSUITS

Ace Sports & Ladyline, 49 Duke Street, Staveley, Staveley, Chesterfield, Derbyshire, S43 3PD Tel: (01246) 470650 Fax: (01246) 280473 E-mail: malc@ace-sports.freeserve.co.uk

Chana Garments Ltd, 169 Booth Street, Birmingham, B21 0NU Tel: 0121-551 1601 Fax: 0121-507 0471

R S Leisurewear, House of Rs, 26 Smith Dorien Road, Leicester, LE5 4BF Tel: 0116-274 0234 Fax: 0116-246 1259 E-mail: rsgroup@webleicester.co.uk

Romus Sportswear, Dixies, High Street, Ashwell, Hertfordshire, SG7 5NT Tel: (01462) 742101 Fax: (01462) 742088 E-mail: johnrbonnett@aol.com

TRACTOR CABS

Alexander Duncan Aberdeen Ltd, Inchbroom, Nigg, Aberdeen, AB12 3GF Tel: (01224) 897278 Fax: (01224) 896954 E-mail: info@duncancabs.co.uk

R S Taylor & Co UK Ltd, 18 Merchant Drive, Mead Lane, Hertford, SG13 7AY Tel: (01992) 551881 Fax: (01992) 500177

TRACTOR SEATS

The Comfy Seat Co., George Baylis Road, Berry Hill Industrial Estate, Droitwich, Worcestershire, WR9 9RB Tel: (01905) 795955 Fax: (01905) 794683 E-mail: sales@comfyseating.co.uk

TRACTOR SPARE PARTS OR WEARING PARTS

▶ AMG Engineering, Wesleyan House, Lode Lane, Alstonefield, Ashbourne, Derbyshire, DE6 2FY Tel: (01335) 310249 Fax: (01335) 310276 E-mail: sales@amg-engineering.co.uk

Bepco UK Ltd, Unit 2, Hatton Gardens Industrial Estate, Kington, Herefordshire, HR5 3RB Tel: (01544) 231144 Fax: (01544) 231484 E-mail: jbrett@bepco.co.uk

International Marketers (London) Ltd, Unit 7, Woolmer Way, Bordon, Hampshire, GU35 9QE Tel: (01420) 482100 Fax: (01420) 482111 E-mail: info@inmalo.co.uk

Kramp UK Ltd, Station Business Park, London Road, Biggleswade, Bedfordshire, SG18 8QB Tel: (01767) 602602 Fax: (01767) 602620 E-mail: info.agri.uk@kramp.com

R C Boreham & Co., Woodfield Farm, Pleshey, Chelmsford, CM3 1HU Tel: (01245) 231320 Fax: (01245) 231435 E-mail: sales@rcboreham.co.uk

Spenco Engineering Co Ltd, Clyst Honiton, Exeter, EX5 2DX Tel: (01392) 369795 Fax: (01392) 364439 E-mail: post@spenco.co.uk

Tractor Spares Ltd, Strawberry Lane, Willenhall, West Midlands, WV13 3RN Tel: (01902) 633614 Fax: (01902) 605685 E-mail: tractorsparesltd@aol.com

Tractormatic Agricultural Services, 61 Waterloo Road, Lisburn, County Antrim, BT27 5NW Tel: (028) 9266 3133 Fax: (028) 9266 3136

Vapormatic Company Limited, P O Box 58, Exeter, EX2 7NB Tel: (01392) 435461 Fax: (01392) 438445 E-mail: sales@vapormatic.com

Whittinghams, 119 Garstang Road, Claughton-on-Brock, Preston, PR3 0PH Tel: (01995) 640302 Fax: (01995) 640790

TRACTORS, INDUSTRIAL

Burdens Distribution Ltd, Spalding Road, Sutterton, Boston, Lincolnshire, PE20 2EX Tel: (01205) 460466 Fax: (01205) 460122 E-mail: sales@burdens.com

Ernest Doe & Sons Ltd, Wilbraham Road, Fulbourn, Cambridge, CB21 5EX Tel: (01223) 880676 Fax: (01223) 880775

Electricars Ltd, 15 Carlyon Road, Atherstone, Warwickshire, CV9 1LQ Tel: (01827) 716888 Fax: (01827) 717841 E-mail: electricars@lineone.net

M S W Machinery (International) Ltd, 84 St James Lane, London, N10 3RD Tel: (020) 8883 0734 Fax: E-mail: michael@mswmc.co.uk

Mark Hellier Tractors Se Ltd, Thousand Acre Farm, Biddenden, Ashford, Kent, TN27 8BF Tel: (01580) 291271 Fax: (01580) 292432 E-mail: mail@markhellier.co.uk

Terex UK Ltd, Central Boulevard, Prologis Park, Coventry, CV6 4BX Tel: (024) 7633 9400 Fax: (024) 7633 9500 E-mail: enquiries@terexce.com

Truck Masters Handling, Norwich Livestock, Hall Road, Norwich, NR4 6EQ Tel: (01603) 458817 Fax: (01603) 452789 E-mail: mail@truckmasters.co.uk

Truckmasters (Handling) Ltd, Boston Road, Wainfleet, Skegness, Lincolnshire, PE24 4HA Tel: (01754) 882182 Fax: (01754) 880197 E-mail: stores@truckmasters.co.uk

Wharfedale Tractors Ltd, Riffa Business Park, Harrogate Road, Otley, West Yorkshire, LS21 2XB Tel: 0113-284 1117 Fax: 0113-284 3110

Whittinghams, 119 Garstang Road, Claughton-on-Brock, Preston, PR3 0PH Tel: (01995) 640302 Fax: (01995) 640790

TRACTORS, UTILITY, COMPACT

▶ Agritrader UK Ltd, 14 Cliftonville, Prescot, Merseyside, L34 2SX Tel: (07919) 471522 Fax: 0151-289 0688 E-mail: dennis@agritrader-uk.com

TRADE ASSOCIATIONS/ ORGANISATIONS/UNIONS, INCLUDING PROFESSIONAL AND INDUSTRIAL

Adhesive Tape Manufacturers Association, Sussex House, 8-10 Homesdale Road, Bromley, BR2 9LZ Tel: (020) 8464 0131 Fax: (020) 8464 6018 E-mail: info@craneandpartners.com

Agency Sector Management UK Ltd, Ashford House, 41-45 Church Road, Ashford, Middlesex, TW15 2TQ Tel: (01784) 242200 Fax: (01784) 242012 E-mail: info@asm.org.uk

Air Conditioning & Refrigeration Industry Board, Kelvin House, 76 Mill Lane, Carshalton, Surrey, SM5 2JR Tel: (020) 8647 7033 Fax: (020) 8773 0165 E-mail: ior@ior.org.uk

Aluminium Extruders Association, Broadway House, Calthorpe Road, Edgbaston, Birmingham, B15 1TN Tel: 0121-456 1103 Fax: 0801389714 E-mail: alfed@alfed.org.uk

Aluminium Rolled Products Manufacturers Association, Broadway House, Calthorpe Road, Edgbaston, Birmingham, B15 1TN Tel: 0121-456 1103 Fax: 0121-456 2274 E-mail: alfed@alfed.org.uk

Amicus, 33-37 Moreland Street, London, EC1V 8HA Tel: (020) 7505 3000 Fax: (020) 7505 3030

Amicus Aeeu, 396-398 Dunstable Road, Luton, LU4 8JT Tel: (01582) 576271 Fax: (01582) 580031

Arca Ltd, 237 Branston Road, Burton-on-Trent, Staffordshire, DE14 3BT Tel: (01283) 531126 Fax: (01283) 568228E-mail: info@arca.org.uk

Architectural Cladding Association, 60 Charles Street, Leicester, LE1 1FB Tel: 0116-253 6161 Fax: 0116-251 4568 E-mail: info@britishprecast.org

Association Of The British Pharmaceutical Industry, 12 Whitehall, London, SW1A 2DY Tel: (020) 7930 3477 Fax: (020) 7747 1411 E-mail: abpi@abpi.org.uk

The Association Of Building Engineers, Jubilee House, Billing Brook Road, Northampton, NN3 8NW Tel: (01604) 404121 Fax: (01604) 784220E-mail: building.engineers@abe.org.uk

Association Of Frozen Food Producers, 6 Catherine Street, London, WC2B 5JJ Tel: (020) 7420 7180 Fax: (020) 7783 6580

Association of Industrial Laser Users (AILU), Oxford House, 100 Ock Street, Abingdon, Oxfordshire, OX14 5DH Tel: (01235) 539595 Fax: (01235) 550499E-mail: mike@ailu.org.uk

Atlas, 4c St. Marys Place, The Lace Market, Nottingham, NG1 1PH Tel: 0115-955 8818 Fax: 0115-941 2238 E-mail: info@atlas-1.org.uk

Autoclaved Aerated Concrete Products Association Ltd, 60 Charles Street, Leicester, LE1 1FB Tel: (0116) 253 6161 Fax: (0116) 251 4568 E-mail: briprecast@aol.com

B C S A Ltd, 4 Whitehall Court, Westminster, London, SW1A 2ES Tel: (020) 7839 8566 Fax: (020) 7976 1634 E-mail: gillian.mitchell@steelconstruction.org

BCCB Trade Organisations, 1 Westminster Palace Gardens, Artillery Row, London, SW1P 1RJ Tel: (020) 7222 3651 Fax: (020) 7222 3664 E-mail: mail@bccb.co.uk

Bicycle Association Of GB Ltd, 3 The Quadrant, Coventry, CV1 2DY Tel: (024) 7655 3838 Fax: (024) 7622 8366 E-mail: info@ba-gb.co.uk

Blackburn With Darwen Borough Council, Town Hall, King William St, Blackburn, BB1 7DY Tel: (01254) 585585 E-mail: regeneration@blackburn.gov.uk

British Adhesives & Sealants Association, 5 Alderson Road, Worksop, Nottinghamshire, S80 1UZ Tel: (01909) 480888 Fax: (01909) 473834 E-mail: sales@basa.uk.com

The British Association For Shooting & Conservation, Marford Mill, Rossett, Wrexham, Clwyd, LL12 0HL Tel: (01244) 573000 Fax: (01244) 573001 E-mail: enquiries@basc.org.uk

▶ British Business Club Ltd, 12 Gatwick Road, Birmingham, B35 6NE Tel: 0121-749 7940 Fax: 08444 844748 E-mail: info@britishbusinessclub.com

British Cables Association, 37a Walton Road, East Molesey, Surrey, KT8 0DH Tel: (020) 8941 4079 Fax: (020) 8783 0104 E-mail: admin@bcauk.org

British Carton Association, 29-35 Farringdon Point, Farrindon Road, London, EC1M 3JF Tel: (020) 7915 8300 Fax: (020) 7405 7784 E-mail: sigs@bpis.org.uk

British Ceramic Confederation, Federation House, Station Road, Stoke-on-Trent, ST4 2SA Tel: (01782) 744631 Fax: (01782) 744102 E-mail: bcc@ceramfed.co.uk

British Dental Trade Association, Mineral Lane, Chesham, Buckinghamshire, HP5 1NL Tel: (01494) 782873 Fax: (01494) 786659 E-mail: admin@bdta.org.uk

British Essential Oil Association Ltd, Flat 15 Exeter Mansions, Exeter Road, London, NW2 3UG Tel: (020) 8450 3713 Fax: (020) 8450 3197 E-mail: beoa@btinternet.com

British Exhibition Contractors Association, Beca House Uplands Business Park, Blackhorse Lane, London, E17 5QJ Tel: (020) 8543 3888 Fax: (020) 8523 5204 E-mail: info@beca.org.uk

British Exporters Association, Broadway House, Tothill Street, London, SW1H 9NQ Tel: (020) 7222 5419 Fax: (020) 7799 2468 E-mail: bexamail@aol.com

British Institute Of Cleaning Science Ltd, Anglia Way, Moulton Park Industrial Estate, Northampton, NN3 6JA Tel: (01604) 678710 Fax: (01604) 645988 E-mail: info@bics.org.uk

British Institute Of Non Destructive Testing, 1 Spencer Parade, Northampton, NN1 5AA Tel: (01604) 630124 Fax: (01604) 231489 E-mail: enquiries@bindt.org

British Jewellery & Giftware Federation Ltd, Federation House, 10 Vyse Street, Hockley, Birmingham, B18 6LT Tel: 0121-236 2657 Fax: 0121-236 3921 E-mail: info@bjgf.org.uk

British Luggage Association, 10 Vyse Street, Hockley, Birmingham, B18 6LT Tel: 0121-237 1107 Fax: 0121-237 1124 E-mail: info@sea.org.uk

British Lymphology Society, 1 Webbs Court, Buckhurst Avenue, Sevenoaks, Kent, TN13 1LZ Tel: (01732) 740850 Fax: (01732) 459225 E-mail: bhta@bhta.com

Britihsh Marine Federation, Marine House, Thorpe Lea Road, Egham, Surrey, TW20 8BF Tel: (01784) 473377 Fax: (01784) 439678 E-mail: enquiries@bmif.co.uk

British Market Research Association, Devonshire House, 60 Goswell Road, London, EC1M 7AD Tel: (020) 7566 3636 Fax: (020) 7689 6220 E-mail: admin@bmra.org.uk

British Metallurgical Plant Constructors Association, c/o EEF, Broadway House, Tothill Street, London, SW1H 9NQ Tel: (0778) 5255218 Fax: (020) 7222 3531 E-mail: enquiries@bmpca.co.uk

TRADE ASSOCIATIONS/ ORGANISATIONS/UNIONS, INCLUDING PROFESSIONAL AND INDUSTRIAL – *continued*

British Office Supplies & Services Federation, Farringdon Point, 29-35 Farringdon Road, London, EC1M 3JF Tel: (0845) 4501565 Fax: (0870) 7706789 E-mail: sales@bossfed.co.uk

British Property Federation, 1 Warwick Row, London, SW1E 5ER Tel: (020) 7828 0111 Fax: (020) 7834 3442 E-mail: info@bpf.org.uk

British Quality Foundation, 32-34 Great Peter Street, London, SW1P 2QX Tel: (020) 7654 5000 Fax: (020) 7654 5001 E-mail: mail@quality-foundation.co.uk

British Safety Council Services, 70 Chancellors Road, London, W6 9RS Tel: (020) 8741 1231 Fax: (020) 8741 4555 E-mail: mail@britsafe.org

British Security Industry Association Ltd, Kirkham House, John Comin Drive, Worcester, WR3 7NS Tel: (0845) 3893889 E-mail: info@bsia.co.uk

The British Turned Parts Manufacturers Association, Heathcote House, 136 Hagley Road, Edgbaston, Birmingham, B16 9PN Tel: 0121-454 4141 Fax: 0121-454 4949 E-mail: heathcotes@btinternet.com

British Water Ltd, 1 Queen Annes Gate, London, SW1H 9BT Tel: (020) 7957 4554 Fax: (020) 7957 4565 E-mail: info@britishwater.co.uk

British Wood Preserving & Damp Proofing Association, 1 Gleneagles House, Vernon Gate, Derby, DE1 1UP Tel: (01332) 225100 Fax: (01332) 225101

Builders Merchants Confederation Ltd, 15 Soho Square, London, W1D 3HL Tel: (020) 7439 1753 Fax: (020) 7734 2766 E-mail: info@bmf.org.uk

Carpet Industry Training Council, C/O 6 Llangorse Close, Stourport-On-Severn, Worcestershire, DY13 8LJ Tel: (01299) 824245 Fax: (01299) 824245 E-mail: jleach.citc@btconnect.com

The Chartered Institute Of Logistics And Transport, 11-12 Buckingham Gate, London, SW1E 6LB Tel: (01536) 740100 Fax: (020) 7592 3111 E-mail: enquiry@iolt.org.uk

Chartered Institute Of Marketing, Moor Hall, The Moor, Cookham, Maidenhead, Berkshire, SL6 9QH Tel: (01628) 427500 Fax: (01628) 427499 E-mail: marketing@cim.co.uk

Chartered Institute Of Purchasing & Supply, Easton House, Church Street, Easton on the Hill, Stamford, Lincolnshire, PE9 3NZ Tel: (01780) 756777 Fax: (01780) 751610 E-mail: sales@cips.org

Chartered Institute Of Taxation, 12 Upper Belgrave Street, London, SW1X 8BB Tel: (020) 7235 9381 Fax: (020) 7838 9958 E-mail: info@att.org.uk

Chartered Management Institute, Management House, Cottingham Road, Corby, Northamptonshire, NN17 1TT Tel: (01536) 204222 Fax: (01536) 201651 E-mail: member@inst-mgt.org.uk

Cima, 26 Chapter Street, London, SW1P 4NP Tel: (020) 7663 5441 Fax: (020) 7663 5442 E-mail: marketing@cimaglobal.com

Civil Aviation Authority, 45-59 Kingsway, London, WC2B 6TE Tel: (020) 7379 7311 Fax: (020) 7453 6028 E-mail: sales@caa.co.uk

Client Services, 66 Portland Place, London, W1B 1AD Tel: (020) 7307 3700 Fax: (020) 7436 9112 E-mail: cs@inst.riba.org

Coffee Trade Federation, 63a Union Street, London, SE1 1SG Tel: (020) 7403 3088 Fax: (020) 7403 7730 E-mail: coffeetradefed@compuserve.com

Confederation Of British Industry, 103 New Oxford Street, London, WC1A 1DU Tel: (020) 7379 7400 Fax: (020) 7240 1578 E-mail: information.centre@cbi.org.uk

Confederation Of British Metal Forming Ltd, 37-47 Birmingham Road, West Bromwich, West Midlands, B70 6PY Tel: 0121-601 6350 Fax: 0121-601 6373 E-mail: info@britishmetalforming.com

Confederation Of British Metal Forming Ltd, 37-47 Birmingham Road, West Bromwich, West Midlands, B70 6PY Tel: 0121-601 6350 Fax: 0121-601 6373 E-mail: info@britishmetalforming.com

Confederation Of Paper Industries, Papermakers House, Rivenhall Road, Westlea, Swindon, SN5 7BD Tel: (01793) 889600 Fax: (01793) 878700 E-mail: fedn@paper.org.uk

Confederation Of Shipbuilding & Engineering Unions, 140 Walworth Road, London, SE17 1JL Tel: (020) 7703 2215 Fax: (020) 7252 7397 E-mail: alanrobson@cseu.org.uk

Construction Confederation, 55 Tufton Street, London, SW1P 3QL Tel: (020) 7227 4500 Fax: (020) 7227 4501 E-mail: bwf@bwf.org.uk

Construction Confederation, 56-64 Leonard Street, London, EC2A 4JX Tel: (020) 7608 5000 Fax: (020) 7631 3872 E-mail: enquiries@thecc.org.uk

Crop Protection Association, Units 20, Culley Court, Bakewell Road, Orton Southgate, Peterborough, PE2 6WA Tel: (01733) 367213 Fax: (01733) 367212 E-mail: info@cropprotection.org.uk

Cutlery & Allied Trades Research Association, Henry Street, Sheffield, S3 7EQ Tel: 0114-276 9736 Fax: 0114-272 2151 E-mail: info@britishtools.com

Dairy Industry Association, 93 Baker Street, London, W1U 6RL Tel: (020) 7486 7244 Fax: (020) 7487 4734 E-mail: mailbox@dif.org.uk

Directory Publishers Association, PO Box 23034, London, W6 0RJ Tel: (020) 8846 9707 E-mail: rosemarypettit@onetel.net

E E F Yorkshire & Humberside, Field Head, Sandhills, Thorner, Leeds, LS14 3DN Tel: 0113-289 2671 Fax: 0113-289 3170 E-mail: mtaylor@eef-yandh.org.uk

▶ Efnarc Building Refurbishment, 99 West Street, Farnham, Surrey, GU9 7EN Tel: (01252) 739147 Fax: (01252) 739140 E-mail: sales@efnarc.org

Energy Industries Council, Newcombe House, 45 Notting Hill Gate, London, W11 3LQ Tel: (020) 7221 2043 Fax: (020) 7221 8813 E-mail: sales@the-eic.com

Energy Institute, 61 New Cavendish Street, London, W1G 7AR Tel: (020) 7467 7100 Fax: (020) 7255 1472 E-mail: info@energyinst.org.uk

Engineering Equipment & Materials Users Association, 20 Long Lane, London, EC1A 9HL Tel: (020) 7796 1293 Fax: (020) 7796 1294 E-mail: sales@eemua.co.uk

The F D A, Boston House, Little Green, Richmond, Surrey, TW9 1QE Tel: (020) 8332 9955 Fax: (020) 8332 2585 E-mail: nicola.breeze@thefda.org.uk

Federation Of Piling Specialists, Forum Court, 83 Copers Cope Road, Beckenham, Kent, BR3 1NR Tel: (020) 8663 0947 Fax: (020) 8663 0949 E-mail: fps@fps.org.uk

Fibre Cement Manufacturers Association Ltd, Station Road East, Stowmarket, Suffolk, IP14 1RQ Tel: (01449) 676053 Fax: (01449) 770028 E-mail: fcma@ghyllhouse.co.uk

Fire Industry Confederation, 55 Eden Street, Kingston Upon Thames, Surrey, KT1 1BW Tel: (020) 8549 8839 Fax: (020) 8547 1564 E-mail: fic@abft.org.uk

Food From Britain Fast Track, Manning House, 22 Carlisle Place, London, SW1P 1JA Tel: (020) 7233 5111 Fax: (020) 7233 9515 E-mail: fasttrack@foodforbritain.co.uk

G A I Ltd, 8 Stepney Green, London, E1 3JU Tel: (020) 7790 3431 Fax: (020) 7790 8517 E-mail: info@gai.org.uk

G M S Marketing Ltd, 44 Albert Street, Newark, Nottinghamshire, NG24 4BQ Tel: (01636) 702961 Fax: (01636) 674876

Galvanizers Association, Wrens Court, 56 Victoria Road, Sutton Coldfield, West Midlands, B72 1SY Tel: 0121-355 8838 Fax: 0121-355 8727 E-mail: ga@hdg.org.uk

Gauge & Tool Makers Association, 3 Forge House, Summerleys Road, Princes Risborough, Buckinghamshire, HP27 9DT Tel: (01844) 274222 Fax: (01844) 274227 E-mail: gtma@gtma.co.uk

Glass & Glazing Federation, 44-48 Borough High Street, London, SE1 1XB Tel: (020) 7403 7177 Fax: (020) 7357 7458 E-mail: info@ggf.org.uk

Grain & Feed Trade Association Ltd, Chapel Court, 6 Chapel Place, London, EC2A 3SH Tel: (020) 7814 9666 Fax: (020) 7814 8383 E-mail: post@gafta.com

Greeting Card Association, United House, North Road, London, N7 9DP Tel: (020) 7619 0396 Fax: (020) 7607 6411

Hairdressing & Beauty Suppliers Association Ltd, Greenleaf House, 128 Darkes Lane, Potters Bar, Hertfordshire, EN6 1AE Tel: (01707) 649499 Fax: (01707) 649497 E-mail: davidmacklin@aol.com

Honeywell Control Systems Ltd, 8 Hill Street Industrial Estate, Cwmbran, Gwent, NP44 7PG Tel: (01633) 872628 Fax: (01633) 860886 E-mail: mandy.wills@honeywell.com

I P 3, 83 Guildford Street, Chertsey, Surrey, KT16 9AS Tel: (0870) 3308625 Fax: (0870) 3308615 E-mail: admin@ip3.org.uk

▶ I R A T A, 99 West Street, Farnham, Surrey, GU9 7EN Tel: (01252) 739150 Fax: (01252) 739140 E-mail: info@irata.org

Independent Footwear Retailers Association, Bank House, 81 St. Judes Road, Englefield Green, Egham, Surrey, TW20 0DF Tel: (0870) 3308623 Fax: (0870) 3308621 E-mail: info@shoeshop.org.uk

Industrial Cleaning Machine Manufacturers Association, Westminster Tower, 3 Albert Embankment, London, SE1 7SL Tel: (020) 7793 3042 Fax: (020) 7793 3003 E-mail: icmma@beama.org.uk

Institute Of, Fanshaws, Brickendon, Hertford, SG13 8PQ Tel: 0131-331 4678 Fax: (01992) 511548 E-mail: imi@motor.org.uk

The Institute Of Brewing & Distilling, 33 Clarges Street, London, W1J 7EE Tel: (020) 7499 8144 Fax: (020) 7499 1156 E-mail: enquiries@iob.org.uk

Institute of Carpenters, 35 Hayworth Road, Sandiacre, Nottingham, NG10 5LL Tel: 0115-949 0641 Fax: 0115-949 1664 E-mail: mail@carpenters-institute.org

Institute of Chartered Accountants-England & Wales, PO Box 433, London, EC2P 2BJ Tel: (020) 7920 8100 Fax: (020) 7920 0547 E-mail: feedback@icaew.co.uk

Institute Of Chartered Secretaries & Administrators, 16 Park Crescent, London, W1B 1AH Tel: (020) 7580 4741 Fax: (020) 7323 1132 E-mail: info@icsa.co.uk

Institute Of Corrosion, Eden Way, Leighton Buzzard, Bedfordshire, LU7 4FY Tel: (01525) 851771 Fax: (01525) 376690 E-mail: admin@icorr.demon.co.uk

Institute Of Export Ltd, Export House, Minerva Business Park, Lynch Wood, Peterborough, PE2 6FT Tel: (01733) 404400 Fax: (01733) 404444 E-mail: institute@export.org.uk

Institute of Food Research, Norwich Research Park, Colney, Norwich, NR4 7UA Tel: (01603) 255000 Fax: (01603) 507723 E-mail: ifr.communications@bbsrc.ac.uk

Institute of Inventors, 19-23 Fosse Way, Ealing, London, W13 0BZ Tel: (020) 8998 3540

Institute Of Marine Engineering Science & Technology, 80 Coleman Street, London, EC2R 5BJ Tel: (020) 7382 2600 Fax: (020) 7382 2670 E-mail: info@imarest.org

Institute of Materials, Minerals & Mining, 1 Carlton House Terrace, London, SW1Y 5DB Tel: (020) 7451 7300 Fax: (020) 7451 7406

Institute of Packaging, IOP Packaging Society, Springfield House, Springfield Road, Grantham, Lincolnshire, NG31 7BG Tel: (01476) 514 590 Fax: (01476) 514591 E-mail: iop@pi2.org.uk

Institute Of Public Relations, 32 St James's Square, London, SW1Y 4JR Tel: (020) 7766 3333 Fax: (020) 7766 3344 E-mail: info@cipr.co.uk

Institute of Quality Assurance, 12 Grosvenor Crescent, London, SW1X 7EE Tel: (020) 7245 6722 Fax: (020) 7245 6788 E-mail: enquiry@iqa.org

Institute Of Sales Promotion, Arena House, 66-68 Pentonville Road, London, N1 9HS Tel: (020) 7837 5340 Fax: (020) 7837 5326 E-mail: enquiries@isp.org.uk

Institute Of Sheet Metal Engineering, 48 Holloway Head, Birmingham, B1 1NG Tel: 0121-622 2860 Fax: 0121-666 6316 E-mail: admin@instituteofmetalfinishing.org

Institute of Transport Administration, Iota House, 7 St. Leonards Road, Horsham, West Sussex, RH13 6EH Tel: (01403) 242412 Fax: (01403) 242413 E-mail: director.iota@btclick.com

Institute Of Vehicle Engineers, 31 Redstone Farm Road, Birmingham, B28 9NU Tel: 0121-778 4354 Fax: 0121-702 2615 E-mail: sales@sae-uk.org

Institution of Agricultural Engineers, Barton Road, Silsoe, MK45 4FH Tel: (01525) 861096 Fax: (01525) 861660 E-mail: crw@iagre.org

Institution Of Civil Engineers, Great George Street, London, SW1P 3AA Tel: (020) 7222 7722 Fax: (020) 7222 7500

Institution Of Diesel & Gas Turbine Engineers, Bedford Heights, Brickhill Drive, Bedford, MK41 7PH Tel: (01234) 214340 Fax: (01234) 355493 E-mail: sales@idgte.org

The Institution Of Engineering & Technology Benevolent Fund, Michael Faraday House, Stevenage, Hertfordshire, SG1 2AY Tel: (01438) 313311 Fax: (01438) 313465 E-mail: postmaster@theiat.org

Institution of Incorporated Engineers, Savoy Hill House, Savoy Hill, London, WC2R 0BS Tel: (020) 7836 3357 E-mail: postmaster@theiet.org.uk

Institution Of Occupational Safety & Health, The Grange, Highfield Drive, Wigston, Leicestershire, LE18 1NN Tel: 0116-257 3100 Fax: 0116-257 3101

International Aluminium Institute Ltd, New Zealand House, 80 Haymarket, London, SW1Y 4TE Tel: (020) 7930 0528 Fax: (020) 7321 0183 E-mail: iai@world-aluminium.org

International Coffee Organisation, 22 Berners Street, London, W1T 3DD Tel: (020) 7612 0600 Fax: (020) 7580 6129 E-mail: info@ico.org

Intras Ltd, Perseus House, Chapel Court Holly Walk, Leamington Spa, Warwickshire, CV32 4YS Tel: (01926) 334137 Fax: (01926) 314755 E-mail: intras@intras.co.uk

Investment Management Association, 65 Kingsway, London, WC2B 6TD Tel: (020) 7831 0898 Fax: (020) 7831 9975

Investors In People UK, 7-10 Chandos Street, London, W1G 9DQ Tel: (020) 7467 1900 Fax: (020) 7636 2386 E-mail: information@iipuk.co.uk

Iron & Steel Trades Confederation, Swinton House, 324 Grays Inn Road, London, WC1X 8DD Tel: (020) 7239 1200 Fax: (020) 7278 8378 E-mail: istc@istc.te.org

Knitting Industries Federation, 12 Beaumanor Road, Leicester, LE4 5QA Tel: 0116-266 3332 Fax: 0116-266 3335 E-mail: directorate@knitfed.co.uk

Lighting Industry Federation Ltd, Swan Ho, 207 Balham High Rd, London, SW17 7BQ Tel: (020) 8675 5432 Fax: (020) 8673 5880 E-mail: info@lif.co.uk

Make It With Lasers, T W I, Granta Park, Great Abington, Cambridge, CB1 6AL Tel: (01223) 891162 Fax: (01223) 890661 E-mail: miwl@twi.co.uk

N F F O Services Ltd, Marsden Road, Grimsby, South Humberside, DN31 3SG Tel: (01472) 349009 Fax: (01472) 242486 E-mail: nffo@nffo.org.uk

National Association Of Shopfitters, 411 Limpsfield Road, Warlingham, Surrey, CR6 9HA Tel: (01883) 624961 Fax: (01883) 626841 E-mail: nas@clara.net

National Bed Federation Ltd, Victoria House, Victoria Street, Taunton, Somerset, TA1 3FA Tel: (01823) 368008 Fax: (01823) 350526 E-mail: sales@bedfed.org.uk

The National Children's Wear Association Of Great Britain & Irela, 5 Portland Place, London, W1B 1PW Tel: (020) 7636 7788 Fax: (020) 7636 7515 E-mail: bita@dial.pipex.com

National Federation Of Meat & Food Traders, 1 Belgrove, Tunbridge Wells, Kent, TN1 1YW Tel: (01892) 541412 Fax: (01892) 535462 E-mail: info@nfmft.co.uk

National Federation Of Retail Newsagents, Yeoman House, Sekforde Street, London, EC1R 0HF Tel: (020) 7253 4225 Fax: (020) 7250 0927 E-mail: info2@nfrn.org

National Federation of Roofing Contractors, 24 Weymouth Street, London, W1G 7LX Tel: (020) 7436 0387 Fax: (020) 7637 5215 E-mail: info@nfrc.co.uk

National Newspaper Mail Order Protection Scheme, 18a King Street, Maidenhead, Berkshire, SL6 1EF Tel: (01628) 641930 Fax: (01628) 637112 E-mail: enquiries@shops-uk.org.uk

National Wool Textile Export Corporation, Lloyds Bank Chambers, 43-45 Hustlergate, Bradford, West Yorkshire, BD1 1PH Tel: (01274) 727877 Fax: (01274) 723124 E-mail: mailbox@bwtec.co.uk

Newspaper Publishers Association Ltd, 34 Southwark Bridge Road, London, SE1 9EU Tel: (020) 7207 2200 Fax: (020) 7928 2067

Nuclear Industry Association, First Floor Whitehall House, 41 Whitehall, London, SW1A 2BY Tel: (020) 7766 6640 Fax: (020) 7839 4695 E-mail: info@niauk.org

Oil & Colour Chemists Association, Priory House, 967 Harrow Road, Wembley, Middlesex, HA0 2SF Tel: (020) 8908 1086 Fax: (020) 8908 1219 E-mail: gensec@occa.org.uk

Oxford Positron Systems Ltd, 5 Landscape Close, Weston-on-the-Green, Bicester, Oxfordshire, OX25 3SX Tel: (01869) 343618 Fax: (01865) 343619

Palletlink Crates & Packing Cases, Clare House, Pinewood Road, High Wycombe, Buckinghamshire, HP12 4DA Tel: (01494) 558282 Fax: (01494) 558383 E-mail: info@palletlink.co.uk

Paper Collect, 83 Guildford Street, Chertsey, Surrey, KT16 9AS Tel: (0870) 3308627 Fax: (0870) 3308617 E-mail: admin@ip3.org

Pet Food Manufacturers Association Ltd, 20 Bedford Street, London, WC2E 9HP Tel: (020) 7379 9009 Fax: (020) 7379 8008 E-mail: sales@pfma.com

Photo Imaging Council, Orbital House, 85-87 Croydon Road, Caterham, Surrey, CR3 6PD Tel: (01883) 334497 Fax: (01883) 334490 E-mail: pipa@admin.co.uk

Picon Ltd, St. Christophers House, Holloway Hill, Godalming, Surrey, GU7 1QZ Tel: (01483) 412000 Fax: (01483) 412001 E-mail: info@picon.co.uk

Pipeline Industries Guild, 14-15 Belgrave Square, London, SW1X 8PS Tel: (020) 7235 7938 Fax: (020) 7235 0074 E-mail: hqsec@pipeguild.co.uk

Plastic Pipe Manufacturers Society, 89 Cornwall Street, Birmingham, B3 3BY Tel: 0121-236 1866 Fax: 0121-200 1389 E-mail: sales@wenhammajor.co.uk

Quality & Business Standards Alliance, Ground Floor, 462 Holdenhurst Road, Bournemouth, BH8 9AF Tel: (01202) 386741 Fax: (01202) 392760 E-mail: info@qbsa.org

Railway Industry Association, 22 Headfort Place, London, SW1X 7RY Tel: (020) 7201 0777 Fax: (020) 7235 5777E-mail: ria@riagb.org.uk

Rics Royal Institute Chartered Surveyors, 12 Great George Street, London, SW1P 3AE Tel: (020) 7222 7000 Fax: (020) 7334 3811 E-mail: contactrics@rics.org

Royal Society For The Prevention Of Accidents Ltd, 353 Bristol Road, Edgbaston, Birmingham, B5 7ST Tel: 0121-248 2000 Fax: 0121-248 2001 E-mail: help@rospa.com

Royal Yachting Association, Ensign Way, Hamble, Southampton, SO31 4RF Tel: (0845) 3450400 Fax: (0845) 3450329 E-mail: admin@rya.org.uk

Scientific Instruments Makers Co., 9 Montague Close, London, SE1 9DD Tel: (020) 7407 4832 Fax: (020) 7407 1565 E-mail: theclark@wcsim.co.uk

Scottish Building, Carrongrange House, Carron Grange, Stenhousemuir, Larbert, Stirlingshire, FK5 3BQ Tel: (01324) 555550 Fax: (01324) 555551 E-mail: sales@scottish-building.co.uk

Sewing Machine Trade Association, 24 Fairlawn Gro, Chiswick, London, W4 5EH Tel: (020) 8995 0411 Fax: (020) 8742 2396 E-mail: smta@netcomuk.co.uk

Society Of British Gas Industries, 36 Holly Walk, Leamington Spa, Warwickshire, CV32 4LY Tel: (01926) 334357 Fax: (01926) 450459 E-mail: sales@sbgi.org.uk

Society Of Consulting Marine Engineers, 202 Lambeth Road, London, SE1 7JW Tel: (020) 7261 0869 Fax: (020) 7261 0871 E-mail: scc@scmshq.org

Society Of Maritime Industries, Great Guildford Business Square, 30 Great Guildford Street, London, SE1 0HS Tel: (020) 7928 9199 Fax: (020) 7928 6599 E-mail: sales@maritimeindustries.org

Society Of Motor Manufacturing & Traders Ltd, Forbes House, Halkin Street, London, SW1X 7DS Tel: (020) 7235 7000 Fax: (020) 7235 7112 E-mail: cford@smmt.co.uk

Society Of Operations Engineers, 22 Greencoat Place, London, SW1P 1PR Tel: (020) 7630 1111 Fax: (020) 7630 6677 E-mail: soe@soe.org.uk

▶ Subsidence Forum, Tournai Hall, Evelyn Woods Road, Aldershot, Hampshire, GU11 2LL Tel: (01252) 357843 Fax: (01252) 357831 E-mail: admin@subsidenceforum.org.uk

Sugar Bureau, Duncan House, Dolphin Square, London, SW1V 3PW Tel: (020) 7828 9465 Fax: (020) 7821 5393 E-mail: info@sugar-bureau.co.uk

TRADE ASSOCIATIONS/ ORGANISATIONS/UNIONS, INCLUDING PROFESSIONAL AND INDUSTRIAL – *continued*

Tac, Gronant Buildings, 14 South Penrallt, Caernarfon, Gwynedd, LL55 1NS Tel: (01286) 671123 Fax: (01286) 678890 E-mail: admin@teledwyr.com

Telecommunications Users' Association, 7 Sylvan Court, Southfields Business Park, Basildon, Essex, SS15 6TD Tel: (0870) 2202071 Fax: (0870) 2202075 E-mail: tua@dial.pipex.com

Textile Services Association Ltd, 7 Churchill Court, 58 Station Road, North Harrow, Harrow, Middlesex, HA2 7SA Tel: (020) 8863 7755 Fax: (020) 8861 2115 E-mail: info@tsa-uk.org

Timber Trade Federation Ltd, Clareville House, 26-27 Oxendon St, London, SW1Y 4EL Tel: (020) 7839 1891 Fax: (020) 7930 0094 E-mail: ttf@ttf.co.uk

Trade Association Management Ltd, Tamesis House, 35 St. Philips Avenue, Worcester Park, Surrey, KT4 8JS Tel: (020) 8330 6446 Fax: (020) 8330 7447 E-mail: mmta@tamgroup.co.uk

The Trading Standards Institute, Suite 3-5 Hadleigh Business Centre, London Road, Hadleigh, Benfleet, Essex, SS7 2BT Tel: (0870) 8729000 Fax: (0870) 8729025 E-mail: institute@tsi.org.uk

Tuc, Congress House, 23-28 Great Russell Street, London, WC1B 3LS Tel: (020) 7636 4030 Fax: (020) 7636 0632 E-mail: info@tuc.org.uk

UK Offshore Operators Association Ltd, 232 Vauxhall Bridge Road, London, SW1V 1AU Tel: (020) 7802 2400 Fax: (020) 7802 2401 E-mail: info@ukooa.co.uk

Water UK Ltd, 1 Queen Annes Gate, London, SW1H 9BT Tel: (020) 7344 1844 Fax: (020) 7344 1866 E-mail: sales@water.org.uk

TRADE EXCHANGES

▶ Chinaventure, 25 Orchard Estate, Twyford, READING, RG10 9JY Tel: 08703 210018 Fax: 08701 383878 E-mail: sally@chinaventure.co.uk

London Metal Exchange Ltd, 56 Leadenhall Street, London, EC3A 2DX Tel: (020) 7264 5555 Fax: (020) 7680 0505 E-mail: info@lme.co.uk

TRADE JOURNALS

▶ Contract Flooring Magazine, 93 Northbank Road, Walthamstow, London, E17 4JY Tel: (020) 8531 4545 E-mail: pstuart40@ntlworld.com

TRADE MARK AGENTS/ ATTORNEYS

A A Thornton & Co., 29 St. Katherines Street, Northampton, NN1 2QZ Tel: (01604) 638242 Fax: (01604) 638164 E-mail: aat@aathornton.com

Abel & Imray, 20 Red Lion Street, London, WC1R 4PQ Tel: (020) 7242 9984 Fax: (020) 7242 9989 E-mail: ai@patentable.co.uk

Anthony Cundy & Co., 39 South Drive, Sutton Coldfield, West Midlands, B75 7TE Tel: 0121-378 4649 Fax: 0121-378 4670 E-mail: cundys@btconnect.com

Appleyard Lees, 15 Clare Road, Halifax, West Yorkshire, HX1 2HY Tel: (01422) 330110 Fax: (01422) 330090 E-mail: ip@appleyardlees.com

Barker Brettell Ltd, 138 Hagley Road, Birmingham, B16 9PW Tel: 0121-456 1364 Fax: 0121-456 1368 E-mail: admin@barkerbrettell.co.uk

Beck Greener, Fulwood House, 12 Fulwood Place, London, WC1V 6HR Tel: (020) 7693 5600 Fax: (020) 7693 5601 E-mail: mail@beckgreener.com

Britter & Co., Enterprise House, 14B White Horse Street, Baldock, Hertfordshire, SG7 6QN Tel: (01462) 894200 Fax: (01462) 893636 E-mail: britterco@aol.com

Bromhead & Co., 37 Great James Street, London, WC1N 3HB Tel: (020) 7405 7010 Fax: (020) 7831 5118 E-mail: mail@bromhead-johnson.com

Bromhead Johnson, Kingsbourne House, 19 Buckingham Street, London, WC2N 6EF Tel: (020) 7839 4935 Fax: (020) 7839 6898 E-mail: mail@bromhead-johnson.com

Brookes Batchellor, 102-108 Clerkenwell Road, London, EC1M 5SA Tel: (020) 7253 1563 Fax: (020) 7253 1214

D Young & Co., 120 Holborn, London, EC1N 2DY Tel: (020) 7269 8550 Fax: (020) 7269 8555 E-mail: mail@dyoung.co.uk

Elkington & Fife, Beacon House, 113 Kingsway, London, WC2B 6PN Tel: (020) 7405 3505 Fax: (020) 7405 1508 E-mail: elkfife@elkfife.co.uk

Elkington & Fife, Prospect House, 8 Pembroke Road, Sevenoaks, Kent, TN13 1XR Tel: (01732) 458881 Fax: (01732) 450346 E-mail: elkfife@elkfife.co.uk

Eric Potter Clarkson LLP, Park View House, 58 The Ropewalk, Nottingham, NG1 5DD Tel: 0115-955 2211 Fax: 0115-955 2201

F J Cleveland & Co., 40-43 Chancery Lane, London, WC2A 1JQ Tel: (020) 7405 5875 Fax: (020) 7831 0749 E-mail: sales@fjcleveland.com

Forrester Ketley & Co., 105 Piccadilly, London, W1J 7NJ Tel: (020) 8889 6622 Fax: (020) 8881 1088 E-mail: fklondon@forresters.co.uk

▶ Frank B Dehn & Co Ltd, 179 Queen Victoria Street, London, EC4V 4EL Tel: (020) 7206 0600 Fax: (020) 7206 0700 E-mail: mail@frankbdehn.com

Franks & Co. Ltd, 15 Jessops Riverside, Brightside Lane, Sheffield, S9 2RX Tel: 0114-256 2677 Fax: 0114-249 9666 E-mail: franksco@franksco.com

G F Redfurn & Co., Lynn House, Ivy Arch Road, Worthing, West Sussex, BN14 8BX Tel: (01903) 820466 Fax: (01903) 820439 E-mail: sueb@gfredfern.com

Gallafent & Co., 9 Staple Inn, London, WC1V 7QH Tel: (020) 7242 3094 Fax: (020) 7539 4999 E-mail: rg@rkallafent.compulink.co.uk

Gill Jennings & Every, 7 Eldon Street, London, EC2M 7LS Tel: (020) 7377 1377 Fax: (020) 7377 1310 E-mail: gje@gje.co.uk

Grant, Spencer, Caisley & Porteous, 16 High Holborn, London, WC1V 6BY Tel: (020) 7216 5888 Fax: (020) 7831 6925 E-mail: grant@gscp.co.uk

Haseltine Lake & Co., West Riding House, 67 Albion Street, Leeds, LS1 5AA Tel: 0113-233 9400 Fax: 0113-233 9401 E-mail: sales@haseltinelake.co.uk

▶ Hindle Lowther, 28 Rutland Square, Edinburgh, EH1 2BW Tel: 0131 2216560 E-mail: mail@hindlelowther.com

▶ HLBB Shaw, 303 Science Park, Milton Road, Cambridge, CB4 0WG Tel: (01223) 425891 Fax: 01223 423701 E-mail: mail@hlbb.com

▶ Hlbbshaw, 10th Floor Metropolitan House, 1 Hagley Road, Birmingham, B16 8TG Tel: 0121-454 4962 Fax: 0121-454 4523 E-mail: enquiries@laurenceshaw.co.uk

I P 21 Ltd, 1 Cornhill, London, EC3V 3ND Tel: (020) 7645 8250 Fax: (020) 7645 8251 E-mail: info@ip21.co.uk

Intellectual Property Office, Patent Office, Concept House, Cardiff Road, Newport, Gwent, NP10 8QQ Tel: (0645) 500505 Fax: (01633) 817777 E-mail: enquiries@ipo.gov.uk

J E Evans Jackson & Co., 13 Northburgh Street, London, EC1V 0JP Tel: (020) 7608 3098 Fax: (020) 7608 2934 E-mail: jeej@markgraaf.co.uk

Jenkins, 26 Caxton Street, London, SW1H 0RJ Tel: (020) 7931 7141 Fax: (020) 7222 4660

Jensen & Son, 366-368 Old Street, London, EC1V 9LT Tel: (020) 7613 0280 Fax: (020) 7613 0267 E-mail: mail@jensens.co.uk

Langner Parry, 52-54 High Holborn, London, WC1V 6RR Tel: (020) 7242 5566 Fax: (020) 7405 1908 E-mail: ip@langnerparry.com

Lloydnorthove Ltd, Pulpit House, 1 The Sqaure, Abingdon, Oxfordshire, OX14 5SZ Tel: (01235) 554499 Fax: (01235) 532878

▶ M F T M, 12 Knightsbridge Avenue, Northwich, Cheshire, CW9 8GE Tel: (01606) 352306 Fax: (0870) 7627906E-mail: mail@mftm.co.uk

Maguire Boss, 24 East Street, St. Ives, Cambridgeshire, PE27 5PD Tel: (01480) 301588 Fax: (01480) 464405 E-mail: tmark@maguires.co.uk

Marks & Clarke, 5 The Quadrant, Coventry, CV1 2EL Tel: (024) 7622 2756 Fax: (024) 7625 6197 E-mail: ip@marks-clarke.com

▶ Marks & Clerk, 19 Royal Exchange Square, Glasgow, G1 3AE Tel: 0141-221 5767 Fax: 0141-221 7739 E-mail: glasgow@marks-clerk.com

Marks & Clerk, 90 Long Acre, London, WC2E 9RA Tel: (020) 7420 0000 Fax: (020) 7836 3339

Marks N Clarke, Cliffords Inn, Fetter Lane, London, EC4A 1BX Tel: (020) 7405 4916 Fax: (020) 7831 0343

Marshall Law, Estate House, 2 Pembroke Road, Sevenoaks, Kent, TN13 1XR Tel: (01732) 458062 Fax: (01732) 458609 E-mail: vpl@marshall-law.co.uk

Masons, 1-4 Portland Square, Bristol, BS2 8RR Tel: 0117-924 5678 Fax: 0117-924 6699 E-mail: enquiries@pinsentmasons.com

▶ Masons, 123 St. Vincent Street, Glasgow, G2 5EA Tel: 0141-248 4858 Fax: 0141-248 6655 E-mail: enquiries@pinsentmasons.com

Mathys & Squire, 120 Holborn, London, EC1N 2SQ Tel: (020) 7830 0000 Fax: (020) 7830 0001 E-mail: sales@mathys-squire.com

Raymond Morris Group Ltd, Invision House, Wilbury Way, Hitchin, Hertfordshire, SG4 0TW Tel: (020) 7729 1234 Fax: (020) 7251 0965 E-mail: infodesk@rmonline.com

Page Hargrave, Manfield House, 1 Southampton Street, London, WC2R 0LR Tel: (020) 7240 6933 Fax: (020) 7379 0268 E-mail: london@pagehargrave.co.uk

▶ Pinsent Masons, 18-22 Melville Street, Edinburgh, EH3 7NS Tel: 0131-225 0000 Fax: 0131-225 0099 E-mail: enquiries@pinsentmasons.com

Pinsent Masons LLP, 1 Park Row, Leeds, LS1 5AB Tel: 0113-244 5000 Fax: 0113-244 8000 E-mail: enquiries@pinsentmasons.com

Raworth Moss & Cook, 36 Sydenham Road, Croydon, CR0 2EF Tel: (020) 8688 8318 Fax: (020) 8760 0055 E-mail: rmc@raworth.co.uk

Reddie & Grose, 16 Theobalds Road, London, WC1X 8PL Tel: (020) 7242 0901 Fax: (020) 7242 3290 E-mail: enquiries@reddie.co.uk

G.F. Redfern & Co., 7 Staple Inn, Holborn, London, WC1V 7QF Tel: (020) 7242 7680 Fax: (020) 7831 7957

Stevens Hewlett & Perkins, 20-23 Holborn, Halton House, London, EC1N 2JD Tel: (020) 7936 2499 Fax: (020) 7404 1844 E-mail: mail@shplondon.co.uk

Swindell & Pearson, 48 Friargate, Derby, DE1 1GY Tel: (01332) 367051 Fax: (01332) 345200 E-mail: sales@patent.co.uk

A.A. Thornton & Co., 235 High Holborn, London, WC1V 7LE Tel: (020) 7405 4044 Fax: (020) 7405 3580 E-mail: aat@aathornton.com

Trade Mark Advice & Service Bureau, Fulwood House, 12 Fulwood Place, London, WC1V 6HR Tel: (020) 7242 2535 Fax: (020) 7405 8113 E-mail: info@beckgreener.com

Trade Mark Advice & Service Bureau, Fulwood House, 12 Fulwood Place, London, WC1V 6HR Tel: (020) 7242 2535 Fax: (020) 7405 8113 E-mail: info@beckgreener.com

Trade Mark Consultants Co. Ltd, 54 Hillbury Avenue, Harrow, Middlesex, HA3 8EW Tel: (020) 8907 6066 Fax: (020) 8907 0743 E-mail: info@trademarkco.co.uk

Urquhart Dykes & Lord, 30 Welbeck Street, London, W1G 8ER Tel: (020) 7487 1550 Fax: (020) 7487 1599E-mail: email@udl.co.uk

Urquhart Dykes & Lord, Amen Corner, St Nicholas Chambers, Newcastle upon Tyne, NE1 1PE Tel: 0191-261 8573 Fax: 0191-222 1604 E-mail: newcastle@udl.co.uk

W P Thompson & Co., Eastcheap House, Central Approach, Letchworth Garden City, Hertfordshire, SG6 3DS Tel: (01462) 682139 Fax: (01462) 676775 E-mail: letchworth@wpt.co.uk

W P Thompson & Co., 55 Drury Lane, London, WC2B 5SQ Tel: (020) 7240 2220 Fax: (020) 7240 8505 E-mail: london@wpt.co.uk

Wildbore & Gibbons, 361 Liverpool Road, London, N1 1NL Tel: (020) 7607 7312 Fax: (020) 7609 9062 E-mail: sales@wildbore.co.uk

Wilson Gunn, Chancery House, 53-64 Chancery Lane, London, WC2A 1QU Tel: (020) 7242 2631 Fax: (020) 7242 0075 E-mail: gee@wilsongunn.com

▶ Wilson Gunn Mccaw, 5th Floor, Blackfriars House, Manchester, M3 2JA Tel: 0161-827 9400 Fax: 0161-832 4905 E-mail: wgm@wilsongunn.com

Withers & Rogers, 75 Colmore Row, Birmingham, B3 2AP Tel: 0121-245 3900 Fax: 0121-245 3930 E-mail: admin@withersrogers.com

Wynne Jones Laine & James, 22 Rodney Road, Cheltenham, Gloucestershire, GL50 1JJ Tel: (01242) 515807 Fax: (01242) 224183 E-mail: patenedagents@wynne-jones.com

TRADE ORGANISATION CONSULTANCY

▶ Chinaventure, 25 Orchard Estate, Twyford, READING, RG10 9JY Tel: 08703 210018 Fax: 08701 383878 E-mail: sally@chinaventure.co.uk

TRADE PROTECTION ASSOCIATIONS

The Association of Suppliers To The British Clothing Industry, Unit 5, 25 Square Road, Halifax, West Yorkshire, HX1 1QG Tel: (01422) 354666 Fax: (01422) 381184

British Association for Chemical Specialities, The Gatehouse, White Cross, Lancaster, LA1 4XQ Tel: (01524) 849606 Fax: (01524) 849194 E-mail: enquiries@bacsnet.org

British Coffee Manufacturers Association, 12 Market Street, Chipping Norton, Oxfordshire, OX7 5UD Tel: (01608) 644995

British Exhibition Contractors Association, Beca House Uplands Business Park, Blackhorse Lane, London, E17 5QJ Tel: (020) 8543 3888 Fax: (020) 8523 5204 E-mail: info@beca.org.uk

British Precast Concrete Federation Ltd, 60 Charles Street, Leicester, LE1 1FB Tel: 0116-253 6161 Fax: 0116-251 4568 E-mail: info@britishprecast.org.uk

British Soft Drinks Association Ltd, 20-22 Stukeley Street, London, WC2B 5LR Tel: (020) 7430 0356 Fax: (020) 7831 6014 E-mail: bsda@britishsoftdrinks.com

Food Service Packaging Association, 64 High Street, Kirkintilloch, Glasgow, G66 1PR Tel: 0141-777 7272 Fax: 0141-777 7747 E-mail: npc@natpack.org.uk

Institute of Carpenters, 35 Hayworth Road, Sandiacre, Nottingham, NG10 5LL Tel: 0115-949 0641 Fax: 0115-949 1664 E-mail: mail@carpenters-institute.org

Plastic Pipe Manufacturers Society, 89 Cornwall Street, Birmingham, B3 3BY Tel: 0121-236 1866 Fax: 0121-200 1389 E-mail: sales@wenhammajor.co.uk

United Fish Products Ltd, Greenwell Place, East Tullos Industrial Estate, Aberdeen, AB12 3AY Tel: (01224) 854444 Fax: (01224) 854333

TRADE WINDOWS

▶ S E A Windows & Doors, Unit 1a North Street, Reading, RG1 7DA Tel: 0118-957 3976 Fax: 0118-939 3610

TRADING ESTATE ADMINISTRATORS OR PROPRIETORS

Ashford Borough Council, Civic Centre, Tannery Lane, Ashford, Kent, TN23 1PL Tel: (01233) 330310 Fax: (01233) 330682

Business In Focus Ltd, Enterprise Centre, Bryn Road, Aberkenfig, Bridgend, Mid Glamorgan, CF32 9BS Tel: (01656) 724414 Fax: (01656) 721163 E-mail: opt@businessinfocus.co.uk

C I S Communications Ltd, 85 Victoria Road, Netherfield, Nottingham, NG4 2NN Tel: 0115-961 3220 Fax: 0115-911 9449 E-mail: paul.tys@ntlworld.com

City of Sunderland, Civic Centre, Sunderland, SR2 7DN Tel: 0191-553 1171 Fax: 0191-553 1180 E-mail: business.investment@sunderland.gov.uk

Colliers Cre, 15-16 Park Row, Leeds, LS1 5HD Tel: 0113-200 1800 Fax: 0113-200 1840 E-mail: leeds@collierscre.co.uk

James Constance & Sons Ltd, The Estate Office Longhope Industrial Estate, Church Road, Longhope, Gloucestershire, GL17 0LB Tel: (01452) 830297

Country Estates Developments Ltd, 17 Albury Close, Loverock Road, Reading, RG30 1BD Tel: 0118-950 8366 Fax: 0118-959 5857 E-mail: sales@countryestates.co.uk

Country Wide Mobility Partners, Copenhagen Court, 32 New Street, Basingstoke, Hampshire, RG21 7DT Tel: (01256) 812700 Fax: (01256) 333420 E-mail: info@countrywidemobility.co.uk

G V A Grimley, Sutherland House, 149 St. Vincent Street, Glasgow, G2 5NW Tel: (0870) 9008990 Fax: 0141-204 1986

Hertel Services, Sotherby Road, Skippers Lane Idustrial Estate, Middlesbrough, Cleveland, TS6 6LP Tel: (01642) 469532 Fax: (01642) 445614 E-mail: info@hertel.co.uk

John Brooke & Sons Ltd, Yorkshire Technology & Office Park, Armitage Bridge, Huddersfield, HD4 7NR Tel: (01484) 340000 Fax: (01484) 340001 E-mail: office@yorkspark.com

Kendal Joinery Co. Ltd, Dockray Hall Road, Kendal, Cumbria, LA9 4RY Tel: (01539) 722629 Fax: (01539) 740891

Letchworth Garden City Heritage Foundation, Suite 401 Spirella Buildings, Bridge Road, Letchworth Garden City, Hertfordshire, SG6 4ET Tel: (01462) 476000 Fax: (01462) 476050 E-mail: info@letchworth.com

Shepway District Council, Civic Centre, Castle Hill Avenue, Folkestone, Kent, CT20 2QY Tel: (01303) 853000 Fax: (01303) 853502 E-mail: jeremy.whittaker@shepway.gov.uk

Swale Borough Council, Swale House, East Street, Sittingbourne, Kent, ME10 3HT Tel: (01795) 417398 Fax: (01795) 417130 E-mail: edu@swale.gov.uk

▶ Tanner Business Centre, Waterside Mill, Chew Valley Road, Greenfield, Oldham, OL3 7NH Tel: (01457) 872273 Fax: (01457) 870133 E-mail: info@tannerbrothers.co.uk

Walsall Metropolitan Borough Council All Enquiries Walsall Boroug, Civic Centre, Walsall, WS1 1DQ Tel: (01922) 654709 Fax: (01922) 615737

TRADITIONAL FINISH NATURAL MINERAL PAINTS

Lime Green Products Ltd, The Coates Kiln, Stretton Road, Much Wenlock, Shropshire, TF13 6DG Tel: (01952) 728611 Fax: (01952) 728361 E-mail: enquire@lime-green.co.uk

TRADITIONAL OR PERIOD LIGHTING

Candela Traditional Lighting Ltd, 319 Long Acre, Birmingham, B7 5JT Tel: 0121-678 6700 Fax: 0121-678 6701 E-mail: sales@candela.co.uk

Classical Lighting, R/O 499 High Rd, Leytonstone, London, E11 4PG Tel: (020) 8556 3056 Fax: (020) 8556 4242 E-mail: sales@classical-lighting.freeserve.co.uk

Noral Ltd, Unit 1 The Oaks, Mill Farm Courtyard, Stratford Road, Beechampton, Milton Keynes, MK19 6DS Tel: (01908) 561818 Fax: (01908) 569785 E-mail: lighting@noral-gb.co.uk

Rochamp Ltd, 5 Shaftesbury Industrial Estate, The Runnings, Cheltenham, Gloucestershire, GL51 9NH Tel: (01242) 525385 Fax: (01242) 227546 E-mail: sales@rochamp.com

Mike Smith Designs Ltd, Unit 10 Fordhouse Road Industrial Estate, Steel Drive, Wolverhampton, WV10 9XE Tel: (01902) 784400 Fax: (01902) 785980 E-mail: sales@mikesmithdesigns.com

Smithbrook Ltd, Unit 10, Manfield Park, Cranleigh, Surrey, GU6 8PT Tel: (01483) 272744 Fax: (01483) 267863 E-mail: smithbrook@smithbrooklighting.co.uk

Sugg Lighting Ltd, Sussex Manor Business Park, Gatwick Road, Crawley, West Sussex, RH10 9GD Tel: (01293) 540111 Fax: (01293) 540114 E-mail: admin@sugglighting.co.uk

TRADITIONAL STYLED ROCKING HORSES

Merrythought Ltd, Dale End, Iron Bridge, Telford, Shropshire, TF8 7NJ Tel: (01952) 433116 Fax: (01952) 432054 E-mail: sales@merrythought.co.uk

▶ Tom's Toys, 22 Manor Road, Newton Longville, Milton Keynes, MK17 0AJ Tel: (01908) 376951

TRAFFIC CONE LAYING MACHINERY

Greentec Industries Ltd, Unit 8 Omni Business Centre, Omega Park, Wilsom Road, Alton, Hampshire, GU34 2QE Tel: (01420) 88088 Fax: (01420) 88099 E-mail: flynn@btconnect.com

TRAFFIC CONTROL OR MANAGEMENT EQUIPMENT

Amber Langis Ltd, Dene Yard, Green Street Green Road, Dartford, DA2 8DH Tel: (01474) 705897 Fax: (01474) 703941 E-mail: info@amberlangis.co.uk

▶ Direct Traffic Management Ltd, Unit 26 Frontier Works, King Edward Road, Thorne, Doncaster, South Yorkshire, DN8 4HU Tel: (01405) 817733 Fax: (01405) 813007 E-mail: info@direct-traffic.co.uk

Peek Traffic Ltd, Centurion Way, Meridian Business Park, Leicester, LE19 1WH Tel: 0116-282 8500 Fax: 0116-282 8528

TRAFFIC CONTROL SYSTEM SOFTWARE

Buchanan Computing, Newcombe House, 45 Notting Hill Gate, London, W11 3PB Tel: (020) 7674 3150 E-mail: sales@buchanancomputing.co.uk

Funkwerk Information Technologies York Ltd, 39 Blossom Street, York, YO24 1AQ Tel: (01904) 639091 Fax: (01904) 639092 E-mail: info@vit-vossloh.com

TRAFFIC CONTROL SYSTEMS

Peek Traffic Ltd, Centurion Way, Meridian Business Park, Leicester, LE19 1WH Tel: 0116-282 8500 Fax: 0116-282 8528

▶ Premier Traffic Management Ltd, Unit 13 Tudhoe Industrial Estate, Spennymoor, County Durham, DL16 6TL Tel: (01388) 815661 Fax: (01388) 420993

TRAFFIC COUNTING SYSTEMS

▶ Crams People Coounting Systems, 6 Lee Road, Marton, Blackpool, FY4 4QS Tel: 01253 769675 E-mail: chris.hirst@candsdesign.co.uk

TRAFFIC MANAGEMENT SPECIALIST SERVICES

A Plant Lux, 16 Missouri Avenue, Salford, M50 2NP Tel: (01925) 281000 Fax: (01925) 281001 E-mail: enquiries@aplant.com

▶ Chevron London Ltd, 9b High Road, Seddington, Sandy, Bedfordshire, SG19 1NU Tel: (01767) 699011 Fax: (01767) 699012 E-mail: sales@chevrontraffic.co.uk

Contraflow Ltd, Unit 2 Stirling Road Industrial Estate, Airdrie, Lanarkshire, ML6 7UD Tel: (01236) 770999 Fax: (01236) 770666

▶ D N Traffic Management Ltd, 21 Waxlow Road, London, NW10 7NU Tel: (020) 8963 0880 Fax: (020) 8963 0996

Fabermaunsell, Beaufort House, 94-96 Newhall Street, Birmingham, B3 1PB Tel: 0121-262 1900 Fax: 0121-262 1999 E-mail: libby.caughtry@fabermaunsell.com

Fleming & Co. (Machinery) Ltd, 60 Woodhead Road, Glasgow, G53 7NX Tel: 0141-881 8155 Fax: 0141-881 8268 E-mail: sales@flemingandcompany.co.uk

Forest Traffic Signals Ltd, Albany Street, Newport, Gwent, NP20 5NJ Tel: (01633) 850222 Fax: (01633) 822000 E-mail: davidwilliams@foresttraffic.co.uk

K.W. Hyde Ltd, 16 Blackthorne Road, Canvey Island, Essex, SS8 7BJ Tel: (07970) 461172 Fax: (07970) 110690 E-mail: kevin@kwhyde.com

King Trailers Ltd, Riverside, Market Harborough, Leicestershire, LE16 7PX Tel: (01858) 467361 Fax: (01858) 467161 E-mail: info@kingtrailers.co.uk

Peek Traffic Ltd, Hazelwood House, Lime Tree Way, Chineham, Basingstoke, Hampshire, RG24 8WZ Tel: (01256) 891800 Fax: (01256) 891870 E-mail: sales@peek-traffic.co.uk

Skyhigh Traffic Data, 28 High Street, Tadcaster, North Yorkshire, LS24 9AT Tel: (01937) 833933 Fax: (01937) 832275 E-mail: mail@skyhightraffic.co.uk

Urban Initiatives, Adam House, 1 Fitzroy Square, London, W1T 5HE Tel: (020) 7380 4545 Fax: (020) 7380 4546 E-mail: info@urbaninitiatives.co.uk

TRAFFIC MANAGEMENT TRAINING

▶ Direct Traffic Management Ltd, Unit 26 Frontier Works, King Edward Road, Thorne, Doncaster, South Yorkshire, DN8 4HU Tel: (01405) 817733 Fax: (01405) 813007 E-mail: info@direct-traffic.co.uk

TRAFFIC OR MOTORWAY BARRIERS

Ashton Plant Hire Dudley Ltd, Dormston Trading Estate, Burton Road, Dudley, West Midlands, DY1 2UF Tel: (01902) 661151 Fax: (01902) 679070 E-mail: rick@safety-fence.co.uk

Hill & Smith Holdings plc, Unit 2 Highlands Court, Cranmore Avenue, Shirley, Solihull, West Midlands, B90 4LE Tel: 0121-704 7430 Fax: 0121-704 7439 E-mail: enquiries@hsholdings.co.uk

Hi-Tec Controls (Bolton) Ltd, Unit 4 Riverside, Waters Meeting Road, The Valley, Bolton, BL1 8TU Tel: (01204) 392172 Fax: (01204) 391660 E-mail: info@hiteccontrols.co.uk

TRAFFIC SIGNAL INSTALLATION OR SERVICING

Banbury Traffic Signals, 1 Overfield, Thorpe Way, Banbury, Oxfordshire, OX16 4XR Tel: (01295) 259922 Fax: (01295) 251478

Forest Traffic Signals Ltd, Albany Street, Newport, Gwent, NP20 5NJ Tel: (01633) 850222 Fax: (01633) 822000 E-mail: davidwilliams@foresttraffic.co.uk

Serco Integrated Services, Building 37, Second Avenue, Pensnett Trading Estate, Kingswinford, West Midlands, DY6 7UL Tel: (01384) 401515 Fax: (01384) 404543

TRAFFIC SIGNALS

Amber Langis Ltd, Dene Yard, Green Street Green Road, Dartford, DA2 8DH Tel: (01474) 705897 Fax: (01474) 703941 E-mail: info@amberlangis.co.uk

Peek Traffic Ltd, Centurion Way, Meridian Business Park, Leicester, LE19 1WH Tel: 0116-282 8500 Fax: 0116-282 8528

Prismo Signs & Systems Ltd, 9 Totman Crescent, Rayleigh, Essex, SS6 7UY Tel: (01268) 745353 Fax: (01268) 745194

Safe Lite (UK) Ltd, 7-11 Phoenix Business Park, Avenue Close, Birmingham, B7 4NU Tel: 0121-359 4034 Fax: 0121-333 3167 E-mail: enquiries@safelite.uk.com

TRAILER AXLES

Avonride Ltd, Spelter Site, Caerau, Maesteg, Mid Glamorgan, CF34 0AQ Tel: (01656) 739111 Fax: (01656) 737677 E-mail: salesmaesteg@knottuk.com

Bradley Doublelock Ltd, Victoria Works, Victoria Street, Bingley, West Yorkshire, BD16 2NH Tel: (01274) 560414 Fax: (01274) 551114 E-mail: larry.lambert@bradleydoublelock.co.uk

Ezze Rise Trailer Solutions Ltd, 5 The Brookside Centre, Red Marsh Drive, Thornton-Cleveleys, Lancashire, FY5 4HG Tel: (01253) 875840 E-mail: info@ezrisetrailersolutions.co.uk

Meredith & Eyre Ltd, Broadway, Hyde, Cheshire, SK14 4QF Tel: 0161-368 6414 Fax: 0161-367 8702 E-mail: sales@meredithandeyre.co.uk

Meritor HVS Ltd, Rackery Lane, Llay, Wrexham, Clwyd, LL12 0PB Tel: (01978) 852141 Fax: (01978) 856173 E-mail: thomas.hughes@arvinmeritor.com

TRAILER BODY BUILDERS

Wigan Trailer Centre Ltd, Cricket St Business Park, Cricket Street, Wigan, Lancashire, WN6 7TP Tel: (01942) 248373 Fax: (01942) 821317 E-mail: info@wtcltd.co.uk

TRAILER CARAVANS

Carnaby Holdings Ltd, Carnaby Industrial Estate, Lancaster Road, Carnaby, Bridlington, North Humberside, YO15 3QY Tel: (01262) 679971 Fax: (01262) 670315 E-mail: info@carnabycaravans.com

Coachman Caravan Co. Ltd, Amsterdam Road, Hull, HU7 0XF Tel: (01482) 839737 Fax: (01482) 878143 E-mail: info@coachman.co.uk

Fleetwood Caravans Ltd, Hall Street, Long Melford, Sudbury, Suffolk, CO10 9JP Tel: (0870) 7740008 Fax: (0870) 7740009 E-mail: fleetwoodcaravans@dial.pipex.com

Gobur Caravans Ltd, Peacock Way, Melton Constable, Norfolk, NR24 2BY Tel: (01263) 860031 Fax: (01263) 861494 E-mail: sales@goburcaravans.co.uk

Harringtons Caravans Ltd, Chester Road, Oakmere, Northwich, Cheshire, CW8 2HB Tel: (01606) 882032 Fax: (01606) 889213 E-mail: sales@harringtonscaravans.co.uk

Michael Jordan Caravans Ltd, Station Approach, Gomshall, Guildford, Surrey, GU5 9NX Tel: (01483) 203335 Fax: (01483) 202780 E-mail: sales@michaeljordancaravans.co.uk

Powrwheel Ltd, 8 Queensway, New Milton, Hampshire, BH25 5NN Tel: (01425) 623123 Fax: (01425) 623111 E-mail: info@powrwheel.com

Swift Holdings Ltd, Dunswell Road, Cottingham, North Humberside, HU16 4JX Tel: (01482) 847332 Fax: (01482) 876335 E-mail: enquire@swiftleisure.co.uk

Willerby Holiday Homes Ltd, Imperial House, 1251 Hedon Road, Hull, HU9 5NA Tel: (01482) 707808 Fax: (01482) 711482 E-mail: sales@willerby.com

TRAILER CHASSIS

A H P Trailers Ltd, Heath Mill Road, Wombourne, Wolverhampton, WV5 8AP Tel: (01902) 895281 Fax: (01902) 894577

Brookside Engineering, Brookside Business Park, Cold Meece, Stone, Staffordshire, ST15 0RZ Tel: (01785) 761000 Fax: (01785) 761361 E-mail: brooksideb@aol.com

Clayton Commercials Ltd, Langley Road, Burscough Industrial Estate, Ormskirk, Lancashire, L40 8JR Tel: (01704) 894244 Fax: (01704) 894226 E-mail: sales@claytoncommercials.com

M & G Trailers Ltd, Hayes Lane, Stourbridge, West Midlands, DY9 8PA Tel: (01384) 424200 Fax: (01384) 424452 E-mail: mandgtrailers@lyeone.net

Meredith & Eyre Ltd, Broadway, Hyde, Cheshire, SK14 4QF Tel: 0161-368 6414 Fax: 0161-367 8702 E-mail: sales@meredithandeyre.co.uk

Wheelbase Engineering Ltd, Lower Eccleshill Road, Darwen, Lancashire, BB3 0RP Tel: (01254) 819399 Fax: (01254) 776920 E-mail: sales@wheelbase.net

TRAILER COMPONENTS/ FITTINGS/ACCESSORIES, *See Trailer Spares etc*

TRAILER COUPLINGS

Avonride Ltd, Spelter Site, Caerau, Maesteg, Mid Glamorgan, CF34 0AQ Tel: (01656) 739111 Fax: (01656) 737677 E-mail: salesmaesteg@knottuk.com

Bradley Doublelock Ltd, Victoria Works, Victoria Street, Bingley, West Yorkshire, BD16 2NH Tel: (01274) 560414 Fax: (01274) 551114 E-mail: larry.lambert@bradleydoublelock.co.uk

Jost Great Britain Ltd, B7, Broadlands, Heywood Distribution Park, Heywood, Lancashire, OL10 2TS Tel: 0161-763 0200 Fax: 0161-763 0234

Meredith & Eyre Ltd, Broadway, Hyde, Cheshire, SK14 4QF Tel: 0161-368 6414 Fax: 0161-367 8702 E-mail: sales@meredithandeyre.co.uk

TRAILER HIRE

Bank Farm Trailers, The Garage, Llangunnor, Carmarthen, Dyfed, SA31 2PG Tel: (01267) 231565 Fax: (01267) 222154 E-mail: sales@bankfarm-trailers.co.uk

Bank Farm Trailers Ltd, Robeston Wathen, Narberth, Dyfed, SA67 8EN Tel: (01834) 860605 Fax: (01834) 861498 E-mail: sales@bankfarm-trailers.co.uk

Bank Farm Trailers, Bank Farm, Spytty Road, Newport, Gwent, NP19 4QW Tel: (01633) 290291 Fax: (01633) 270400

Bank Farm Trailers Ltd, Unit 1 Mill Brook Yard, Landore, Swansea, SA1 2JG Tel: (01792) 795834 Fax: (01792) 799251 E-mail: sales@bankfarm-trailers.co.uk

Bowlea Trailers & Caravan Sales, Bowlea Smithy, Penicuik, Midlothian, EH26 8PX Tel: (01968) 673571 Fax: (01968) 673571

Collease Ltd, Choats Road, Chequers Lane, Dagenham, Essex, RM9 6RJ Tel: (020) 8517 1171 Fax: (020) 8593 0300

Dennett & Parker Ltd, Sydney Nursery, Dover Rd, Sandwich, Kent, CT13 0DA Tel: 01304 613240

East Cheshire Trailers, Sandy Lane Garage, Sandy Lane, Macclesfield, Cheshire, SK10 4RJ Tel: (01625) 611550 Fax: (01625) 611550

Gordon Love Trailers, 192 Bridge St West, Birmingham, B19 2YT Tel: 0121-359 6387 Fax: 0121-359 0317 E-mail: sales@wessex-trailers.co.uk

H F B Trailers (Leek), Horton Head Farm, Horton, Leek, Staffordshire, ST13 8PQ Tel: (01538) 306212 Fax: (01538) 306396 E-mail: nathan@hfbtrailers.com

Hill Hire plc, Wharfedale Road, Euroway Industrial Estate, Bradford, West Yorkshire, BD4 6SG Tel: (0870) 5133423 Fax: (01274) 651347 E-mail: sales@hillhire.co.uk

J W Barrow & Co., Griffiths Road, Lostock Gralam, Northwich, Cheshire, CW9 7NU Tel: (01606) 331222 Fax: (01606) 331333 E-mail: jwbarrow@btinternet.com

Longdon Truck Equipment Ltd, Chapel Street, New Mills, High Peak, Derbyshire, SK22 3JL Tel: (01663) 747101 Fax: (01663) 747561

Purple Trailers, 39-41 High Street, Clay Cross, Chesterfield, Derbyshire, S45 9DX Tel: (0870) 7878687

Reform & Weld, Building A, Gobowen, Oswestry, Shropshire, SY10 7JZ Tel: (01691) 650479 Fax: (01691) 650461

RH Rentals, Lenton Lane, Nottingham, NG7 2NR Tel: 0115-943 8030 Fax: 0115-943 8045 E-mail: daniel.stevenson@rh-freight.co.uk

Trailer & Transport Ltd, Trailer House, West Quay Road, Southampton, SO15 1GZ Tel: (023) 8033 3111 Fax: (023) 8033 3600

Trident Trailers Ltd, 27A Upper Fant Road, Maidstone, Kent, ME16 8BP Tel: (01622) 678811 Fax: (01622) 678262 E-mail: enquiries@trident-trailers.co.uk

TRAILER HIRE, MOTOR VEHICLE

Rent A Merc, 87 Dargan Road, Belfast, BT3 9JU Tel: (028) 9077 9755 Fax: (028) 9077 4374 E-mail: sales@rentamerc.co.uk

TRAILER LANDING GEAR/ SUPPORT LEGS

Jost Great Britain Ltd, B7, Broadlands, Heywood Distribution Park, Heywood, Lancashire, OL10 2TS Tel: 0161-763 0200 Fax: 0161-763 0234

Meritor HVS Ltd, Rackery Lane, Llay, Wrexham, Clwyd, LL12 0PB Tel: (01978) 852141 Fax: (01978) 856173 E-mail: thomas.hughes@arvinmeritor.com

TRAILER MAINTENANCE OR REPAIR SPECIALIST SERVICES

King Trailers Ltd, Riverside, Market Harborough, Leicestershire, LE16 7PX Tel: (01858) 467361 Fax: (01858) 467161 E-mail: info@kingtrailers.co.uk

Panema Trailer Engineering Ltd, Chalk Lane, Snetterton, Norwich, NR16 2JZ Tel: (01953) 887622 Fax: (01953) 888515 E-mail: info@panematrailers.co.uk

R P Towing, Unit 1d Abercromby Avenue, High Wycombe, Buckinghamshire, HP12 3BW Tel: (01494) 528233 Fax: (01494) 638802 E-mail: rp.towing@ntlworld.com

TRAILER SPARE PARTS OR WEARING PARTS

A J Parsons & Sons Ltd, Anglo Trading Estate, Commercial Road, Shepton Mallet, Somerset, BA4 5BY Tel: (01749) 346161 Fax: (01749) 346100 E-mail: sales@parsonsparts.co.uk

Bradley Doublelock Ltd, Victoria Works, Victoria Street, Bingley, West Yorkshire, BD16 2NH Tel: (01274) 560414 Fax: (01274) 551114 E-mail: larry.lambert@bradleydoublelock.co.uk

Eurotruck (Truck Trailer Spares) Ltd, 263 Derby Road, Bramcote, Nottingham, NG9 3JA Tel: 0115-939 7660 Fax: 0115-939 6428

F P S Ltd, Lichfield Road, Tamworth, Staffordshire, B79 7TD Tel: (01827) 52525 Fax: (01827) 52238

Gordon Love Trailers, 192 Bridge St West, Birmingham, B19 2YT Tel: 0121-359 6387 Fax: 0121-359 0317 E-mail: sales@wessex-trailers.co.uk

H G V Truck & Trailer Parts, Marsh Lane, Boston, Lincolnshire, PE21 7SJ Tel: (01205) 365258 Fax: (01205) 355225 E-mail: info@hgvtruckparts.com

Hanford Trailer Spares, 152 Stone Road, Stoke-on-Trent, ST4 8NS Tel: (01782) 658594

Honeyfield Trailers, 279 Bristol Road, Gloucester, GL2 5DD Tel: (01452) 423871 Fax: (01452) 505604 E-mail: darren@honeyfieldtrailers.co.uk

Indespension Ltd, 38a Nimmings Road, Halesowen, West Midlands, B62 9JE Tel: 0121-561 5467 Fax: 0121-561 2180 E-mail: westmids@indespention.com

Jost Great Britain Ltd, B7, Broadlands, Heywood Distribution Park, Heywood, Lancashire, OL10 2TS Tel: 0161-763 0200 Fax: 0161-763 0234

King Trailers Ltd, Riverside, Market Harborough, Leicestershire, LE16 7PX Tel: (01858) 467361 Fax: (01858) 467161 E-mail: info@kingtrailers.co.uk

M & G Trailers Ltd, Hayes Lane, Stourbridge, West Midlands, DY9 8PA Tel: (01384) 424200 Fax: (01384) 424452 E-mail: mandgtrailers@lyeone.net

Maypole Ltd, 54 Kettles Wood Drive, Birmingham, B32 3DB Tel: 0121-423 3011 Fax: 0121-423 3020 E-mail: maypole@maypole.ltd.uk

Meritor HVS Ltd, Rackery Lane, Llay, Wrexham, Clwyd, LL12 0PB Tel: (01978) 852141 Fax: (01978) 856173 E-mail: thomas.hughes@arvinmeritor.com

Site Weld, Manor Farm, Andover, Hampshire, SP11 7DB Tel: (01264) 710194

Truck & Trailer Components Ltd, Unipart House, Garsington Road, Cowley, Oxford, OX4 2PG Tel: (01865) 383999 Fax: (0800) 361677 E-mail: ttc@unipart.co.uk

TRAILER SPARE PARTS OR WEARING PARTS – *continued*

Truck & Trailer Equipment Ltd, 37-39 Hawes Lane, Rowley Regis, Warley, West Midlands, B65 9AL Tel: 0121-559 7711 Fax: 0121-559 5637 E-mail: sales@trucktrailerequip.co.uk
Truckstop Hawkes, Unit 9 Brook Street, Redditch, Worcestershire, B98 8NG Tel: (01527) 68279 Fax: (01527) 60026 E-mail: info@truckstophawkes.co.uk
Western Towing & Alarms, Unit A1 Kingsteignton Industrial Estate, Kingsteignton, Newton Abbot, Devon, TQ12 3BN Tel: (01392) 216336 Fax: (01392) 430415 E-mail: sales@westerntowing.co.uk
Western Truck Ltd, 123 Clydesdale Place, Moss Side Industrial Estate, Leyland, PR26 7QS Tel: (01772) 454124 Fax: (01772) 456075 E-mail: rr@westerntruck.co.uk
Ifor Williams Trailers Ltd, The Smithy, Cynwyd, Corwen, Clwyd, LL21 0LB Tel: (01490) 412527 Fax: (01490) 412770 E-mail: sales@iwt.co.uk
Wilmond Engineering Co. Ltd, 45 Bury Mead Road, Hitchin, Hertfordshire, SG5 1RX Tel: (01462) 459495 Fax: (01462) 420102 E-mail: sales@wilmond.co.uk

TRAILER SUSPENSION UNITS

European Truck Parts Ltd, Junction Two Industrial Estate, Demuth Way, Oldbury, West Midlands, B69 4LT Tel: 0121-544 1222 Fax: 0121-544 9500 E-mail: rob@etp-uk.com

TRAILER UNDERGEARS

Crusely Trailer Engineering Ltd, Beacon Hill Industrial Estate, Botany Way, Purfleet, Essex, RM19 1SR Tel: (01708) 861144 Fax: (01708) 863308

TRAILERS, *See also heading for particular types*

Ace Equipment, Oakley Farm, Croxall, Lichfield, Staffordshire, WS13 8QZ Tel: (01283) 790320 Fax: (01283) 790456 E-mail: sales@aceequip.co.uk
Bank Farm Trailers Ltd, Robeston Wathen, Narberth, Dyfed, SA67 8EN Tel: (01834) 860605 Fax: (01834) 861498 E-mail: sales@bankfarm-trailers.co.uk
Bowlea Trailers & Caravan Sales, Bowlea Smithy, Penicuik, Midlothian, EH26 8PX Tel: (01968) 673571 Fax: (01968) 673571
Crusely Trailer Engineering Ltd, Beacon Hill Industrial Estate, Botany Way, Purfleet, Essex, RM19 1SR Tel: (01708) 861144 Fax: (01708) 863308
H F B Trailers (Leek), Horton Head Farm, Horton, Leek, Staffordshire, ST13 8PQ Tel: (01538) 306212 Fax: (01538) 306396 E-mail: nathan@hfbtrailers.com
Hazlewood Trailers, Bishampton Road, Rous Lench, Evesham, Worcestershire, WR11 4UN Tel: (01386) 792916 Fax: (01386) 793320 E-mail: admin@hazelwoodtrailers.co.uk
Honeyfield Trailers, 279 Bristol Road, Gloucester, GL2 5DD Tel: (01452) 423871 Fax: (01452) 505604 E-mail: darren@honeyfieldtrailers.co.uk
PRG Trailers & Towing Equipment, The Old Wood Yard, Lightwood Green Avenue, Audlem, Crewe, CW3 0EN Tel: (01270) 812402 Fax: (01270) 811293 E-mail: info@prgtrailers.co.uk
R P Towing, Unit 1d Abercromby Avenue, High Wycombe, Buckinghamshire, HP12 3BW Tel: (01494) 528233 Fax: (01494) 638802 E-mail: rp.towing@ntlworld.com
S B S Ltd, Woden Road, Wolverhampton, WV10 0AS Tel: (01902) 455655 Fax: (01902) 453760 E-mail: sales@sbstrailers.co.uk
Site Weld, Manor Farm, Andover, Hampshire, SP11 7DB Tel: (01264) 710194
▶ SWC Trailers & Spares, Manor Farm, Abbotts Ann, Andover, Hampshire, SP11 7DB Tel: (01264) 710610
T A M Leisure Ltd, 180 Kingston Road, New Malden, Surrey, KT3 3RD Tel: (020) 8949 5435 Fax: (020) 8336 1418 E-mail: sales@tamleisure.co.uk
Trident Trailers Ltd, 27A Upper Fant Road, Maidstone, Kent, ME16 8BP Tel: (01622) 678811 Fax: (01622) 678262 E-mail: enquiries@trident-trailers.co.uk
Viking Trailers Ltd, Taylor Holme Industrial Estate, Bacup, Lancashire, OL13 0LE Tel: (01706) 875139 Fax: (01706) 875277 E-mail: sales@vikingtrailers.co.uk
Wesbroom Engineering Ltd, 173 Mersea Road, Colchester, CO2 8PN Tel: (01206) 576959 Fax: (01206) 573788

TRAILERS TO SPECIFICATION

Ace Equipment, Oakley Farm, Croxall, Lichfield, Staffordshire, WS13 8QZ Tel: (01283) 790320 Fax: (01283) 790456 E-mail: sales@aceequip.co.uk
Wesbroom Engineering Ltd, 173 Mersea Road, Colchester, CO2 8PN Tel: (01206) 576959 Fax: (01206) 573788
Western Towing & Alarms, Unit A1 Kingsteignton Industrial Estate, Kingsteignton, Newton Abbot, Devon, TQ12 3BN Tel: (01392) 216336 Fax: (01626) 363111 E-mail: richardsaxton@aol.com

TRAILERS, EXHIBITION/ HOSPITALITY

David Wilson's Trailers, Hillsdown Farm, Birch Grove, Horsted Keynes, Haywards Heath, West Sussex, RH17 7DH Tel: (01825) 740696 Fax: (01825) 740260 E-mail: info@dwt-exhibitions.co.uk

TRAILERS, FIRST AID

▶ Blackburn Trailers Ltd, Whitestone Farm, Main Road, Birdham, Chichester, West Sussex, PO20 7HU Tel: (01243) 513550 Fax: (01243) 513865 E-mail: info@kompak.co.uk

TRAIN DRIVING SIMULATORS

A M S, John Sutcliffe Building, Donibristle Industrial Park, Hillend, Dunfermline, Fife, KY11 9JX Tel: (01383) 821921 Fax: (01383) 824227

TRAINING

▶ Aberdeen Skills & Enterprise Training Ltd, Units 3-9 Minto Operations Training Centre, Minto Avenue, Altens Industrial Estate, Aberdeen, AB12 3JZ Tel: (01224) 859624 Fax: (01224) 859640 E-mail: aset-enquiry@abcol.ac.uk
▶ Achor Limited, 82 Northgate, Beccles, Suffolk, NR34 9AY Tel: (01502) 716870 Fax: (01502) 716587 E-mail: info@achor.co.uk
▶ Activa Solutions Ltd, Activa House, Commerce Way, Edenbridge, Kent, TN8 6ED Tel: (01732) 784300 Fax: (0870) 7544516 E-mail: info@activa.co.uk
▶ AMG People Management, The Springboard Centre, Mantle Lane, Coalville, Leicestershire, LE67 3DW Tel: 01530 510319 E-mail: enquiries@amgpeople.co.uk
▶ Angel Solutions, 30 Faraday Road, Wavertree Technology Park, Liverpool, L13 1EH Tel: (0845) 8330933 Fax: (0845) 8338561 E-mail: info@angelsolutions.co.uk
▶ Arrowhead Training and Consultancy Services, 80 Woolmer Road, Nottingham, NG2 2FB Tel: 0115-952 8603 E-mail: admin@arrowheadtraining.co.uk
Athena Training U K, Suite 3, 13 Sheppey Gardens, Dagenham, Essex, RM9 4LD Tel: (07973) 869163 Fax: (020) 8517 0007 E-mail: enquiries@athenatraininguk.net
▶ AVArcher, Arndean, 4 Maggiewoods Loan, Falkirk, FK1 5SJ Tel: (01324) 621216
▶ Barfil Management Centre, Barfil Farm, Crocketford, Dumfries, DG2 8RW Tel: (01387) 266079 Fax: (01387) 266118
▶ Bead Training, Development House, 24 Heaton Close, Poulton-Le-Fylde, Lancashire, FY6 7TY Tel: 01253 890790 Fax: 01253 890790 E-mail: enquiries@beadtraining.com
Beechbrook Consulting Ltd, 24 Clermont Terrace, Brighton, BN1 6SH Tel: (01273) 561714 Fax: (01273) 561772 E-mail: info@fastrak-consulting.co.uk
▶ Blueprint for Training, Pembroke Cotttage, Vicarage Road, Waresley, Sandy, Bedfordshire, SG19 3DA Tel: 01767 651200 Fax: 01767 654147 E-mail: info@blueprint4all.com
▶ Bourne Training, Bourne House, Sandy Lane, Romsey, Hampshire, SO51 0PD Tel: 01794 523301 Fax: 01794 516720 E-mail: info@bournetraining.co.uk
▶ BSTMS, River Court, 27 Brewhouse Lane, Putney Wharf, London, SW15 2JX Tel: (020) 8780 0805
▶ Caledonia Training & Consultancy Ltd, Silverburn Crescent, Bridge of Don Industrial Estate, Aberdeen, AB23 8EW Tel: (01224) 708141 Fax: (01224) 705718
▶ Career Energy, 4 Staple Inn, London, WC1V 7QH Tel: (020) 7831 2015 E-mail: info@careerenergy.co.uk
▶ Centre For Integrative Medical Training Ltd, 11 North Claremont Street, Glasgow, G3 7NR Tel: 0141-331 0393 Fax: (01383) 417850
▶ Chase International, Dunfermline Business, Learning & Conference Centre, Halbeath, Dunfermline, Fife, KY11 8DY Tel: (01383) 559050 Fax: (01383) 559052
The Composites Centre, Imperial College, Prince Consort Road, London, SW7 2AZ Tel: (020) 7594 5084 Fax: (020) 7594 5083 E-mail: composites@imperial.ac.uk
▶ Coulsons Chartered Accountants, 2 Belgrave Crescent, Scarborough, North Yorkshire, YO11 1UB Tel: (01723) 364141 Fax: (01723) 376010 E-mail: postmaster@coulsons.co.uk
▶ Creative Educationltd, 89 Sanderstead Road, South Croydon, Surrey, CR2 0PF Tel: (020) 8666 0234 Fax: (020) 8666 0414 E-mail: sales@creativeeducation.co.uk
▶ Crossroad Health & Safety Systems, Barn 6 Watsome Farm Development Wotton Road, Kingswood, Wotton-under-Edge, Gloucestershire, GL12 8SP Tel: (01453) 845108 Fax: (08700) 941122 E-mail: info@safetycrossroad.com
▶ Data2Wisdom Ltd t/a Business for Breakfast, 51 Grangeway, Handforth, Wilmslow, Cheshire, SK9 3HY Tel: 0870 742 3090 Fax: 0871 433 5478E-mail: Gez@BforB.co.uk
▶ Denby Training, Sadler Road, Lincoln, LN6 3JR Tel: 01522 503902 Fax: 01522 686372 E-mail: terry.rose@denbytransport.co.uk
LEARN>DO London0" pno ="0000064" corp ="00222477" new="N" rule=" " type="NORM"> Do>Learn>do, 21 Cantelowes Road, London, NW1 9XR Tel: 020 7267 8228 Fax: 020 7267 8228 E-mail: info@do-learn-do.com
▶ Drug & Alcohol Training, 15 Eilean Rise, Ellon, Aberdeenshire, AB41 9NF Tel: (01358) 729547 Fax: (01358) 729547 E-mail: les@datacservices.co.uk
▶ Eskhill & Co., Eskhill House, 15 Inveresk Village, Musselburgh, Midlothian, EH21 7TD Tel: 0131-271 4000 Fax: 0131-271 7000
▶ Export Paperwork Services Ltd, 102 Stansted House, Third Avenue, London Stansted Airport, Stansted, Essex, CM24 1AE Tel: (01279) 680517 Fax: (01279) 680543 E-mail: tim@exportpaperwork.com
▶ F I Training Services, 13 Rubislaw Terrace, Aberdeen, AB10 1XE Tel: (01224) 640891 Fax: (01224) 637982 E-mail: sales@fitraining.com
▶ Feenix E-Learning Ltd, 67 Vancouver Quay, Salford, M50 3TU Tel: 0161-872 5277 Fax: (07092) 115000 E-mail: info2@feenix.co.uk
▶ First Aid Focus, Atrium Business Centrenorth Caldeen Road, Coatbridge, Lanarkshire, ML5 4EF Tel: (01236) 702011 Fax: (01236) 702021
▶ Harris Management Training, Teviotbank Gardens, Denholm, Hawick, Roxburghshire, TD9 8PB Tel: (01450) 870688 Fax: (01450) 870688
Harry Fry Spray Equipment Training Specialist, The Linhay, Manor Road, Stourpaine, Blandford Forum, Dorset, DT11 8TQ Tel: 01258 452364 Fax: 01258 452364 E-mail: spraytrain@btinternet.com
▶ High Edge Consulting Ltd, 115 Musters Road, Ruddington, Nottingham, NG11 6JA Tel: 0115-921 6200 E-mail: info@highedge.co.uk
▶ IDP Safety Services Ltd, 289 Kings Drive, Eastbourne, East Sussex, BN21 2YA Tel: (01323) 507017 Fax: (01323) 507017 E-mail: info@idpsafety.co.uk
▶ J H P Training, Sutherland House, Matlock Road, Coventry, CV1 4JQ Tel: (024) 7666 2096 Fax: (024) 7663 8214 E-mail: enquiries@jhp-group.com
▶ Jigsaw Training & Consultancy Services Ltd, Premier House, 50-52 Cross Lances Road, Hounslow, TW3 2AA Tel: (020) 8572 6388 E-mail: enquiries@outcomes4u.com
▶ John Gilbert Training, Broadfold Road, Bridge of Don, Aberdeen, AB23 8EE Tel: (01224) 825644
▶ John Gilbert Training, 162 Barleyknowe Road, Gorebridge, Midlothian, EH23 4PS Tel: (01875) 823364
▶ Lagta Group Training Ltd, 3 Dryden Place, Loanhead, Midlothian, EH20 9HP Tel: 0131-440 2922 Fax: 0131-440 3933 E-mail: sales@lagta.co.uk
M B W Training, Unit 2-5 Princess Street Enterprise Centre, Princess Street, Blackpool, FY1 5BZ Tel: (01253) 291110 Fax: (01253) 291110
▶ McPhedran Co. UK, 23 Carriage Drive, Kettering, Northamptonshire, NN16 9EN Tel: (07778) 211855
▶ Maxtar Ltd, 14 Chanctonbury View, Henfield, West Sussex, BN5 9TW Tel: (07714) 850950 Fax: (01273) 491848 E-mail: juergen.brinner@maxtar.co.uk
▶ Millennium School Of Motoring Ltd, Unit 111 112, Springvale Industrial Estate, Cwmbran, Gwent, NP44 5BG Tel: (01633) 873022 Fax: (01633) 868181 E-mail: millenniumsom@aol.com
▶ Mullan Training, Amelia Street, Belfast, BT2 7GS Tel: (028) 9032 2228 Fax: (028) 9032 2229 E-mail: enquiries@mullantraining.com
▶ Norland Managed Services, Suite 3G, International House, Stanley Boulevard, Hamilton International Technology Park, Blantyre, Glasgow, G72 0BN Tel: (01698) 404720 Fax: (01698) 404721
▶ OCTG Procter, Peregrine Road, Westhill Business Park, Westhill, Aberdeen, AB32 6JL Tel: (01224) 748600 Fax: (01224) 746676
▶ PANAD Limited, Panad House, Alvaston Business Park, Middlewich Road, Nantwich, Cheshire, CW5 6PF Tel: (01270) 618520 Fax: (01270) 626613 E-mail: info@panadgroup.org
▶ Pro Dive, 247 Hinckley Road, NUNEATON, Warwickshire, CV11 6LL Tel: 0870 199 3099 Fax: 0709 280 8864 E-mail: emea@prodive.com.au
▶ The Projects Group plc, Windsor House, Lodge Place, Sutton, Surrey, SM1 4AU Tel: (020) 8722 8340 Fax: 020 8770 9555 E-mail: Susan.el-zarif@theprojectsgroup.co.uk
Protocol Skills, Aldford House, Lloyd Drive, Ellesmere Port, CH65 9HQ Tel: 0151-373 7700 Fax: 0151-373 7701
QA, QA House, Delta Office Business Park, Welton Road, Swindon, SN5 7WZ Tel: (08709) 060090 Fax: (01793) 696007 E-mail: responsecentre@qa.com
▶ Recruitment Training (Edinburgh) Ltd, 32 & 34 Heriot Hill Terrace, Edinburgh, EH7 4DY Tel: 0131-558 9209 Fax: 0131-558 9187 E-mail: info@rtl-training.com
▶ RSVP Design, Mirren Court Three, 123 Renfrew Road, Paisley, Renfrewshire, PA3 4EA Tel: (0560) 0493245 Fax: 0141-887 3613 E-mail: graham@rsvpdesign.co.uk
▶ Sally Tweddle Training, 6 Ure Bank Terrace, Ripon, North Yorkshire, HG4 1JG Tel: (01765) 608114 E-mail: sally@twed6.freeserve.co.uk
▶ Scottish Training Consultants, 28 Oldmill Crescent, Belmedie, Aberdeen, AB23 8WA Tel: (01358) 742470 Fax: (01358) 742775
Sellsem Training Consultants, 153 Finstall Road, Finstall, Bromsgrove, Worcestershire, B60 3DD Tel: (01527) 835685 Fax: (01527) 575955 E-mail: rmpowell@btinternet.com
▶ Sheppard Moscow Scotland Ltd, 57 Melville Street, Edinburgh, EH3 7HL Tel: 0131-226 3399 Fax: 0131-226 3344
▶ Simulations.co.uk, 11 Colmans Wharf, 45 Morris Road, London, E14 6PA Tel: (020) 7537 2982 E-mail: jeremyhall@simulations.co.uk
▶ Stewart Miller Associates, Na Mara, Innellan, Dunoon, Argyll, PA23 7QN Tel: (01369) 830000
▶ Sunrise Systems, 52 Albany Street, Edinburgh, EH1 3QR Tel: 0131-478 7781 Fax: 0131-478 0239
▶ Sunrise Systems (Scotland), Arbikie Farm, Inverkeilor, Arbroath, Angus, DD11 4UZ Tel: (01241) 830770 Fax: (01241) 830755 E-mail: sales@sunsys.com
▶ Teckchek Europe Ltd, 1a Church Road, Croydon, CR0 1SG Tel: (020) 8401 1188 Fax: (020) 8401 0808 E-mail: dbeer@ikmnet.com
▶ Top Banana Team Ltd, The Old Castle, Farleigh Hungerford, Bath, BA2 7RW Tel: (01225) 752445 E-mail: info@topbananateam.com
Tracs International Ltd, Falcon House, Union Grove Lane, Aberdeen, AB10 6XU Tel: (01224) 321213 Fax: (01224) 321214
▶ Tullos Training Ltd, Craigshaw Drive, West Tullos Industrial Estate, Aberdeen, AB12 3AL Tel: (01224) 872316 Fax: (01224) 894677 E-mail: info@tullostraining.co.uk
▶ Up Front Security Ltd, 307 West George Street, Glasgow, G2 4LF Tel: 0141-221 5448 Fax: 0141-221 5449
▶ Westward Quest Ltd, Ardara, Clachan Seil, Oban, Argyll, PA34 4TL Tel: (01852) 300379 Fax: (01852) 300379 E-mail: rob@westwardquest.co.uk
▶ Woodland Grange, Management Development & Conference Centre, Old Milverton Lane, Leamington Spa, Warwickshire, CV32 6RN Tel: (01926) 336621 Fax: (01926) 450648 E-mail: sales@wgrange.com
▶ www.qrcmodels.co.uk, 18 Conglass Drive, Inverurie, Aberdeenshire, AB51 4LB Tel: (07815) 746035 E-mail: info@qrcmodels.co.uk

TRAINING AIDS/MODELS, TECHNICAL

Audio Visual Machines Ltd, Phoenix House, 2B Upper Teddington Road, Kingston Upon Thames, Surrey, KT1 4DY Tel: (020) 8977 8880 Fax: (020) 8977 8879 E-mail: info@avmachines.com
Laerdal Medical Ltd, Laerdal House, Goodmead Road, Orpington, Kent, BR6 0HX Tel: (01689) 876634 Fax: (01689) 873800 E-mail: customer.service@laerdal.co.uk
Metropolis, Grange Business Centre, Belasis Avenue, Billingham, Cleveland, TS23 1LG Tel: (01642) 361255 Fax: (01642) 365700 E-mail: sales@metropolisdevelopments.co.uk
Tmi, 50 High Street, Henley-in-Arden, West Midlands, B95 5AN Tel: (01527) 851741 Fax: (01527) 851777 E-mail: sales@tmi.co.uk

TRAINING BOTTOMS

▶ Planet Dance, PO Box 233, Leeds, LS16 0AQ Tel: (0870) 1453995 Fax: 0113-226 9295 E-mail: info@planetdancedirect.co.uk

TRAINING CENTRES

Complete Event Solutions, Lymington Bottom Road, Four Marks, Alton, Hampshire, GU34 5DL Tel: (01420) 561105 Fax: (01420) 561105 E-mail: info@completeeventsolutions.com

TRAINING COURSES, CATERING

Royal Society for Public Health, 3rd Floor Market Towers, 1 Nine Elms Lane, London, SW8 5NQ Tel: (020) 3177 1600 Fax: (020) 3177 1601 E-mail: info@rsph.org.uk

TRAINING EQUIPMENT, ELECTRONICS/ COMMUNICATION

Abitec Products, Oak House, 50 Barton Drive, New Milton, Hampshire, BH25 7JJ Tel: (01425) 617852 Fax: (01425) 617852 E-mail: sales@abitec.co.uk

TRAINING EQUIPMENT, ELECTRONICS/COMMUNICATION – *continued*

Intek Europe, 24 Thomas Drive, Newport Pagnell, Buckinghamshire, MK16 8TH Tel: (01908) 610093 E-mail: sales@intek.co.uk
Phone Coach Ltd, Unit 21 Kent House, Old Bexley Business Park, Bexley, Kent, DA5 1LR Tel: (01322) 551170 Fax: (01322) 556680 E-mail: enquiries@phonecoach.com

TRAINING TOPS

▶ Planet Dance, PO Box 233, Leeds, LS16 0AQ Tel: (0870) 1453995 Fax: 0113-226 9295 E-mail: info@planetdancedirect.co.uk

TRAINING VIDEOS, ENGINEERING

▶ Dfire Media Ltd, Shed Studios, 67 Larkhill Road, Abingdon, Oxfordshire, OX14 1BJ Tel: (01235) 559053 E-mail: damian@dfiremedia.com
▶ Small Screen Film & Video, 17 Knole Road, Dartford, DA1 3JN Tel: (01322) 419353 E-mail: sales@smallscreenvideo.com

TRAINING VIDEOS, SAFETY

▶ I-MOTUS, 11 West Mills Yard, Kennet Road, Newbury, Berkshire, RG14 5LP Tel: 0845 430 4448 Fax: 01635 524 449 E-mail: info@i-motus.com

TRAINING, BUSINESS OR SOCIAL DEVELOPMENT

▶ Brookfield, Kent Street, Wigan, Lancashire, WN1 3BB Tel: (07971) 484695
▶ Elaine Scaife Consultancy, Mercury House,, Shipstones Business Centre, Northgate, New Basford, Nottingham, NG7 7FN Tel: 0870 0131700 E-mail: info@elainescaifeconsultancy.co.uk
Gallant 2000 Ltd, 401f The Big Peg, Vyse Street, Hockley, Birmingham, B18 6NF Tel: 0121-212 3410 Fax: 0121-212 3410 E-mail: gallant@netcomuk.co.uk

TRAINING, BUSINESS SKILLS, BENCHMARKING

▶ Elaine Scaife Consultancy, Mercury House,, Shipstones Business Centre, Northgate, New Basford, Nottingham, NG7 7FN Tel: 0870 0131700 E-mail: info@elainescaifeconsultancy.co.uk
Life Coach Associates, 19 Meadow Way, Kinoulton, Nottingham, NG12 3RE Tel: (01949) 81125 E-mail: gerard@life-coach-associates.com
▶ Vocal Coach Studio, Berry Hill, Mansfield, Nottinghamshire, NG18 4HZ Tel: 01623 474464 E-mail: business@vocalcoachstudio.co.uk

TRAINING, CATERING

Ashton-Evans & Associates, PO Box 4, Knaresborough, North Yorkshire, HG5 0AA Tel: (01423) 866125 Fax: (07092) 862117 E-mail: sales@ashtonevans.co.uk
H I T Training Ltd, Minerva Mill Innovation Centre, Station Road, Alcester, Warwickshire, B49 5ET Tel: (0800) 0935892 E-mail: info@hittraining.co.uk
Thomas Danby College, 5 Roundhay Road, Leeds, LS7 3BG Tel: 0113-249 4912 Fax: 0113-240 1967 E-mail: info@thomasdanby.ac.uk

TRAINING, COMMERCIAL/ OFFICE

Communication Skills Europe Ltd, 91 Charterhouse Street, London, EC1M 6HL Tel: (020) 7670 0500 Fax: (020) 7670 0515 E-mail: cse@cseltd.com
Frost & Sullivan Ltd, Sullivan House, 4 Grosvenor Gardens, London, SW1W 0DH Tel: (020) 7730 3438 Fax: (020) 7730 3343
Government Office For London, Riverwalk House, 157-161 Millbank, London, SW1P 4RR Tel: (020) 7217 3222 Fax: (020) 7217 3473
In Comm Business Services Ltd, Unit 12 Hayward Industrial Park, Vigo Place, Walsall, WS9 8UG Tel: (01922) 457686 Fax: (01922) 453211 E-mail: info@in-comm.co.uk
J H P Training, Broadacre House, 16-20 Lowther Street, Carlisle, CA3 8DA Tel: (01228) 536373 Fax: (01228) 591236 E-mail: carlisle.business.centre@jhp-group.com
J H P Training, 9-13 Castle Street, Dumfries, DG1 1DJ Tel: (01387) 279828 Fax: (01387) 266050 E-mail: dumfries.business.centre@jhp-group.com
J H P Training, 25 Frederick Street, Edinburgh, EH2 2ND Tel: 0131-226 1647 Fax: 0131-226 1648 E-mail: edinburgh.business.centre@jhp-group.com
J H P Training, Crown Buildings, Raby Road, Hartlepool, Cleveland, TS24 8AS Tel: (01429) 860211 Fax: (01429) 866598 E-mail: hartlepool.business.centre@jhp-group.com
J H P Training, Abbey House 26 The Parade, High Street, Watford, WD17 1AA Tel: (01923) 238100 Fax: (01923) 238500 E-mail: watford.business.centre@jhp-group.com
JHP Training Wales, Sophia House, 28 Cathedral Road, Cardiff, CF11 9LJ Tel: (029) 2063 6137 Fax: (029) 2063 6138 E-mail: cardiff.business.centre@jhp-group.com
Larne Enterprise Development Co. Ltd, Ledcom Industrial Estate, Bank Road, Larne, County Antrim, BT40 3AW Tel: (028) 2827 0742 Fax: (028) 2827 5653 E-mail: davidgillespie@ledcom.org
Leeds Training Trust, Mitchell House, 139 Richardshaw Lane, Stanningley, Pudsey, West Yorkshire, LS28 6AA Tel: 0113-255 2417 Fax: 0113-236 1004 E-mail: admin@ltt.co.uk
Newport & Gwent Chamber of Commerce & Industry, Unit 30, Enterprise Way, Newport, Gwent, NP20 2AQ Tel: (01633) 222664 Fax: (01633) 222301 E-mail: info@ngb2b.co.uk
Norfolk & Waveney Enterprise Services, Queens Road, Great Yarmouth, Norfolk, NR30 3HT Tel: (01493) 850204 Fax: (01493) 330754 E-mail: enquiries@business-advice.co.uk
Pitman Training Centre Ltd, Portsmouth House, Portsmouth Road, Guildford, Surrey, GU2 4BL Tel: (01483) 572855 Fax: (01483) 300859 E-mail: guildford@pitman-training.net
Plymouth Chamber Of Commerce, 22 Lockyer Street, Plymouth, PL1 2QW Tel: (01752) 220471 Fax: (01752) 600333 E-mail: chamber@plymouth-chamber.co.uk
Prospect Training Organisations Ltd, Kingston House, Myton Street, Hull, HU1 2PS Tel: (01482) 606242 Fax: (01482) 609941 E-mail: info@prospect-training.co.uk
Thames Valley Chamber Of Commerce & Industry Ltd, 467 Malton Avenue, Slough, SL1 4QU Tel: (01753) 870500 Fax: (01753) 870515 E-mail: sales@thamesvalleychamber.co.uk
Tracs International Ltd, Falcon House, Union Grove Lane, Aberdeen, AB10 6XU Tel: (01224) 321213 Fax: (01224) 321214
Training World, 22 Larchwood Close, Romford, RM5 3QX Tel: (01708) 746948 Fax: (01708) 739041 E-mail: info@trainingworld.co.uk
TripleTrack Business Systems Ltd, 25 Market Place, Warminster, Wiltshire, BA12 9BB Tel: (01985) 214260 Fax: (01985) 215806 E-mail: enquiries@tbs-net.com

TRAINING, COMMUNICATIONS

Gustav Kaser Training International Ltd, Essex House, 118 High Street, Ongar, Essex, CM5 9EB Tel: (01277) 365335 Fax: (01277) 365277 E-mail: sales@gustavkaeser.com
Improcom Ltd, Management House, Cottingham Road, Corby, Northamptonshire, NN17 1TD Tel: (01536) 207107 Fax: (01536) 265699 E-mail: admin@improcom.co.uk
Information Transfer, Burleigh House, 15 Newmarket Road, Cambridge, CB5 8EG Tel: (01223) 312227 Fax: (01223) 310200
Ketchum, 35-41 Folgate Street, London, E1 6BX Tel: (020) 7611 3500 Fax: (020) 7611 3501
▶ Lucid Optical Services Ltd, Lucid Training Centre, Garsdale, Sedbergh, Cumbria, LA10 5PE Tel: (01539) 621219 Fax: (01539) 621205 E-mail: annette@lucidos.co.uk

TRAINING, COMPUTER BASED, DISTANCE LEARNING

Ascot Systems (UK) Ltd, Woods Way, Goring-By-Sea, Worthing, West Sussex, BN12 4QY Tel: (01903) 503041 Fax: (01903) 507250 E-mail: sales@ascot-systems.co.uk
▶ Cambridge Online Learning Ltd, Barnsley Business & Innovation Centre, Innovation Way, Barnsley, South Yorkshire, S75 1JL Tel: (01226) 321717 Fax: (01226) 290888 E-mail: info@cambridge-online-learning.co.uk
Charm Managaement Specialists Ltd, 13 High Street, Ruddington, Nottingham, NG11 6DT Tel: 0115-984 7760 Fax: 0115-921 1887 E-mail: resources@charmhrm.co.uk
▶ Sage Training Courses, 41 The Vale, Middlesbrough, Cleveland, TS4 2UE Tel: (01642) 519507 E-mail: info@sage-training-solutions.co.uk
▶ Sage Training Solutions, 183 Bosworth Drive, Chelmsley Wood, Birmingham, B37 5BT Tel: 01642 519507 E-mail: info@sage-training-solutions.co.uk
The Training Foundry, City Campus, Pond Street, Sheffield, S1 1WB Tel: 0114-225 5888 Fax: 0114-225 5889 E-mail: itfoundry@shu.ac.uk

TRAINING, COMPUTER SOFTWARE

1t Solutions, 3 The Crescent, Doncaster Road, Rotherham, South Yorkshire, S65 1NL Tel: (01709) 371441 Fax: (01709) 371440 E-mail: sales@1t-s.com
A K Consultancies Ltd, 141a Prestbury Road, Cheltenham, Gloucestershire, GL52 2DU Tel: (01242) 234123 E-mail: sales@akc.co.uk
Acumen Agencies, 161 Cregagh Road, Belfast, BT6 0LB Tel: (028) 9080 8150 Fax: (028) 9080 8155 E-mail: sales@acumenagencies.com
Ada Computer Systems Ltd, Network House House, Albert Drive, Burgess Hill, West Sussex, RH15 9TN Tel: (01444) 232000 Fax: (01444) 247754E-mail: sales@ada.co.uk
▶ Agile Training Limited, 8 Grafton Court, Canning Circus, Nottingham, NG7 3GH Tel: 07932 696228 E-mail: enquiries@agile-training.co.uk
Blueleaf Ltd, 73 Steventon Road, Drayton, Abingdon, Oxfordshire, OX14 4LA Tel: (01235) 554677 Fax: (01235) 554977
▶ Bristol Computer Training, 92 Egerton Road, Bishopston, Bristol, BS7 8HP Tel: 0117 9247567 E-mail: mail@bristolcomputertraining.co.uk
Broadskill Ltd, Hinderton Grange, Quarry Road, Neston, CH64 7UD Tel: 0151-336 8899 Fax: 0151-336 7799 E-mail: admin@broadskill.com
▶ Business It Central, Sussex College, College Road, Crawley, West Sussex, RH10 1NR Tel: (01293) 442326 Fax: (01293) 453421 E-mail: business1@centralsussex.ac.uk
C G Resources Ltd, 62 Wellington Street West, Broughton, Manchester, M7 2FD Tel: 0161-792 8234 Fax: 0161-792 7080 E-mail: enq@cgresources.com
C G T Ltd, 314 Midsummer Boulevard, Milton Keynes, MK9 2UB Tel: (01908) 690361 Fax: (01908) 669922 E-mail: sales@cgt.co.uk
CBC Ltd, 91C-91D Mora Road, London, NW2 6TB Tel: (020) 8450 9185 Fax: (020) 8450 6090
▶ Centre For Integrative Medical Training Ltd, 11 North Claremont Street, Glasgow, G3 7NR Tel: 0141-331 0393 Fax: (01383) 417850
Cobham Computer Systems Ltd, 56-58 Smithbrook Kiln, Cranleigh, Surrey, GU6 8JJ Tel: (01483) 275515 Fax: (01483) 277067 E-mail: sales@cobhamsystems.co.uk
Computeraid Ltd, Neptune Point, Nettlefold Road, Cardiff, CF24 5JQ Tel: (029) 2066 4285 Fax: (029) 2045 5515 E-mail: training@computeraidwales.com
Computerworld Western, Unit 1 Fernhill Court, Fernhill, Almondsbury, Bristol, BS32 4LX Tel: (01454) 275400 Fax: (01454) 619931 E-mail: enquiries@computerworld.co.uk
Core Estates Ltd, 3 Pendeford Place, Pendeford Industrial Estate, Wolverhampton, WV9 5HD Tel: (0870) 7014343 Fax: (01902) 557701 E-mail: sales@coresystems.co.uk
Cravenplan Computers Ltd, Wilbury Barn, Swallowcliffe, Salisbury, SP3 5QH Tel: (01747) 858000 Fax: (01747) 858010 E-mail: info@cravenplan.co.uk
Daystar, Daystar House, 102 Burnage Lane, Manchester, M19 2NG Tel: 0161-248 8088 Fax: 0161-224 2522
Dotted Eyes Ltd, Hanbury Court Harris Business Park, Hanbury Road, Stoke Prior, Bromsgrove, Worcestershire, B60 4JJ Tel: (01527) 556920 Fax: (01527) 556939 E-mail: info@dottedeyes.com
▶ Dove Computer Solutions, Oak Cottage, Dove Street, Ellastone, Ashbourne, Derbyshire, DE6 2GY Tel: (0845) 2260522 Fax: (01335) 324317 E-mail: info@dovecomputers.com
Ecieurope, Buckingway Business Park, Rowles Way, Swavesey, Cambridge, CB24 4UG Tel: (01954) 278000 Fax: (01954) 278001 E-mail: sales@ipuk.com
Effective Solutions For Business, Acquest Ho, 183 Kingston Rd, London, SW19 1LH Tel: (020) 8395 6472 Fax: (020) 8241 2502 E-mail: sales@effects.co.uk
Experience Payment, Eiger Point Swift Park, Old Leicester Road, Rugby, Warwickshire, CV21 1DZ Tel: (01788) 554800 Fax: (01788) 554900 E-mail: enquiries@eiger.co.uk
F1 Computing Systems Ltd, 3 Kelso Place, Upper Bristol Road, Bath, BA1 3AU Tel: (01225) 427285 Fax: (01225) 444728 E-mail: sales@f1comp.co.uk
▶ F1Group, Kingsley Road, Lincoln Fields, Lincoln, LN6 3TA Tel: (01522) 508080 Fax: (01522) 508085 E-mail: enquiries@f1g.co.uk
Farmplan Computer Systems, Farmplan House, Rank Xerox Business Park, Mitcheldean, Gloucestershire, GL17 0SN Tel: (01594) 545011 Fax: (01594) 545012 E-mail: sales@farmplan.co.uk
Fifth Dimension Computer Solutions Ltd, Park House, Maidenhead Road, Cookham, Maidenhead, Berkshire, SL6 9DS Tel: (01628) 851970
Finmatica Ltd, Finmatica House, Ashted Lock, Aston Science Park, Birmingham, B7 4AZ Tel: 0121-359 5096 Fax: 0121-359 0375 E-mail: enquiries@finmatica.com
▶ Flying Monk Ltd, 4 Twatley Cottages Sherston, Road Malmesbury, Malmesbury, Wiltshire, SN16 0QX Tel: (0845) 056 3989 Fax: (01666) 825773 E-mail: info@flyingmonkgroup.com
G B Direct, The Design Exchange, 34 Peckover Street, Bradford, West Yorkshire, BD1 5BD Tel: (0870) 2007273 E-mail: info@gbdirect.co.uk
▶ Inspark. Intelligent Business Solutions, Grenville Place, 3 Woodfield Lane, Ashtead, Surrey, KT21 2BQ Tel: (07005) 946896 Fax: (07005) 946899 E-mail: stephen.b.symes@newerasolutions.co.uk
Intec Business Colleges, 16 Warwick Street, Rugby, Warwickshire, CV21 3DH Tel: (01788) 575090 Fax: (01788) 575411 E-mail: intec@ibc-rugby.demon.co.uk
▶ Inurface Solutions Ltd, Unit H Anton Studios, 2-8 Anton Street, London, E8 2AD Tel: 0207 241 1200 Fax: 0207 241 2800 E-mail: eion@inurface.co.uk
▶ It Masters, Polhearne Lane, Brixham, Devon, TQ5 9LE Tel: (01803) 855803 Fax: 08716 611198 E-mail: sales@itmasters.co.uk
Jigsaw Consultancy, 272 Bath Street, Glasgow, G2 4JR Tel: 0141-353 9460 Fax: 0141-353 9386 E-mail: dorothy@westfieldtraining.co.uk
▶ JK Assist, Lingley House, Commissioners Road, Rochester, Kent, ME2 4EE Tel: 01634 712171 E-mail: info@jk-assist.co.uk
▶ Learn 247 online, 1 Dawney Drive, Four Oaks, Birmingham, B75 5JA Tel: 0121-323 2224 Fax: 0121-323 2224 E-mail: sales@learn247online.com
Lexicon Lifeline Ltd, Unit 3, 78 Blandford Road, Corfe Mullen, Wimborne, Dorset, BH21 3HQ Tel: (01202) 657252 Fax: (01202) 657252 E-mail: office@lexiconlifeline.co.uk
London College Of Business & Computing, 206 Cambridge Heath Road, London, E2 9NQ Tel: (020) 8983 4193 Fax: (020) 8983 4286 E-mail: lcbc@compuserve.com
M F Business Services, 10 Bodington Road, Sutton Coldfield, West Midlands, B75 5ET Tel: (07973) 639660 Fax: 0121-308 3003 E-mail: enquiries@mfbusiness.co.uk
▶ Mullan Training, Amelia Street, Belfast, BT2 7GS Tel: (028) 9032 2228 Fax: (028) 9032 2229 E-mail: enquiries@mullantraining.com
Newport & Gwent Chamber of Commerce & Industry, Unit 30, Enterprise Way, Newport, Gwent, NP20 2AQ Tel: (01633) 222664 Fax: (01633) 222301 E-mail: info@ngb2b.co.uk
Pageforward Learning, PO Box 230, Diss, Norfolk, IP22 1TA Tel: (01379) 650927 Fax: (01379) 642555 E-mail: info@pageforward.co.uk
Premier E D A Solutions, 1st Floor, Millers House, Roydon Road, Stanstead, Ware, Hertfordshire, SG12 8HN Tel: (01920) 876250 Fax: (01920) 872615E-mail: sales@eda.co.uk
Pyramid Consultancy, Murlain House, Union Street, Chester, CH1 1QP Tel: (01244) 357277 Fax: (01244) 357278 E-mail: sales@pyramidconsultancy.co.uk
Software International Training Ltd, 8 Thorpe Road, Norwich, NR1 1RY Tel: (01603) 667308 Fax: (01603) 761281 E-mail: training@softwareinternational.co.uk
Solstone Plus, 48a Old Steine, Brighton, BN1 1NH Tel: (01273) 206555 Fax: (01273) 387769 E-mail: solestoneplus@solestonegroup.com
Stanford Technologies Ltd, Rayner House, Higher Hillgate, Stockport, Cheshire, SK1 3ER Tel: 0161-480 4051 Fax: 0161-429 0966 E-mail: sales@stanfordtec.co.uk
▶ Sunrise Systems, 52 Albany Street, Edinburgh, EH1 3QR Tel: 0131-478 7781 Fax: 0131-478 0239
▶ Sunrise Systems (Scotland), Arbikie Farm, Inverkeilor, Arbroath, Angus, DD11 4UZ Tel: (01241) 830770 Fax: (01241) 830755 E-mail: sales@sunsys.com
▶ System & Network Training, Robert Denholm House, Bletchingley Road, Nutfield, Redhill, RH1 4HW Tel: (01737) 821590 Fax: (01737) 821590 E-mail: sales@s-nt.co.uk
Touchstone C T A, 89 Barnham Road, Barnham, Bognor Regis, West Sussex, PO22 0EQ Tel: (01243) 553479 E-mail: malcolm@tcta.co.uk
Tribal Asset Management Ltd, Unit E Gillette Close, Staffordshire Technology Park, Stafford, ST18 0LQ Tel: (0870) 0601040 Fax: (0870) 0607040 E-mail: info@tribalassetmanagement.co.uk
Trireme Object Technology International Ltd, Regents House, Heaton Lane, Stockport, Cheshire, SK4 1BS Tel: 0161-225 3240 E-mail: clive@trireme.com
▶ Vantage Training Ltd, 4 Trent Lane, East Bridgford, Nottingham, NG13 8PF Tel: (01949) 21212 Fax: 0870 7406607 E-mail: info@vtl.co.uk

TRAINING, DOCUMENT MANAGEMENT COMPUTER SOFTWARE

Computeraid Ltd, Neptune Point, Nettlefold Road, Cardiff, CF24 5JQ Tel: (029) 2066 4285 Fax: (029) 2045 5515 E-mail: training@computeraidwales.com
▶ Easyfile Ltd, Global House, Shottery Brook Industrial Estate, Timothys Bridge Road, Stratford-upon-Avon, Warwickshire, CV37 9NR Tel: (0870) 2424974 Fax: (0870) 4004799 E-mail: info@easyfile.com

TRAINING, DOCUMENT MANAGEMENT COMPUTER SOFTWARE – *continued*

Intec Business Colleges, 16 Warwick Street, Rugby, Warwickshire, CV21 3DH Tel: (01788) 575090 Fax: (01788) 575411
E-mail: intec@ibc-rugby.demon.co.uk

TRAINING, DRILLING SIMULATION

Drilling Systems UK Ltd, Hurnview House, Bournemouth International Airport, Hurn, Christchurch, Dorset, BH23 6EW Tel: (01202) 582255 Fax: (01202) 582288
E-mail: info@drillingsystems.com

TRAINING, EDUCATION INDUSTRY

T2 Business Solutions, Melrose Hall, Cypress Drive, St. Mellons, Cardiff, CF3 0YZ Tel: (029) 2079 9133 Fax: (029) 2081 9515
E-mail: enquiries@t2business.co.uk

TRAINING, ELEARNING

Internet Consultancy & Management Ltd, 12 Sycamore Avenue, Glapwell, Chesterfield, Derbyshire, S44 5LH Tel: (0800) 0431057 Fax: (0870) 1270965
E-mail: support@icamltd.co.uk

West Of England Friends Housing Society Ltd, PO Box 164, Bristol, BS6 6BH Tel: 0117-989 2020 Fax: 0117-924 4615

TRAINING, EXPORT/IMPORT

▶ Export Paperwork Services Ltd, 102 Stansted House, Third Avenue, London Stansted Airport, Stansted, Essex, CM24 1AE Tel: (01279) 680517 Fax: (01279) 680543
E-mail: tim@exportpaperwork.com

Portsmouth & South East Hampshire Chamber of Commerce & Industry, Regional Business Centre, Harts Farm Way, Havant, Hampshire, PO9 1HR Tel: (023) 9244 9449 Fax: (023) 9244 9444 E-mail: sehants@chamber.org.uk

Wadeworld Trade Ltd, 50 Burnhill Road, Beckenham, Kent, BR3 3LA Tel: (020) 8663 3577 Fax: (020) 8663 3212
E-mail: info@wadetrade.com

TRAINING, FIREFIGHTING, OFFSHORE

Admiral Fire Extinguishers, 19 Flude Road, Coventry, CV7 9AQ Tel: (024) 7636 5157 Fax: (024) 7636 2815
E-mail: admiralfire@btopenworld.com

Humberside Offshore Training Association Ltd, Malmo Road, Hull, HU7 0YF Tel: (01482) 820567 Fax: (01482) 823202
E-mail: bookings@hota.org

Nutec Centre For Safety, Nutec Centre For Safety, Haverton Hill Industrial Estate, Billingham, Cleveland, TS23 1PZ Tel: (01642) 566656 Fax: (01642) 563224
E-mail: enquiries@nutecuk.com

Petans Ltd, Bullocks Hill, Horsham St. Faith, Norwich, NR10 3HT Tel: (01603) 891255 Fax: (01603) 890827
E-mail: michael@petans.co.uk

TRAINING, INSTRUMENTATION AND CONTROL ENGINEERING

▶ Brunswick Instrumentation Ltd, Maritime House, Basin Road North, Portslade, Brighton, BN41 1WR Tel: (01273) 704949 Fax: (01273) 248900 E-mail: info@brun-inst.co.uk

Teeside Tertiary College, Longlands Campus, Douglas St, Middlesbrough, Cleveland, TS4 2JW Tel: (01642) 298942 Fax: (01642) 245313

TRAINING, INVENTORY MANAGEMENT, DEMAND PLANNING OR FORECASTING

▶ Christopher Swann, 408-410 Corn Exchange Building, Fenwick Street, Liverpool, L2 7QS Tel: (0845) 1259010 Fax: (0845) 1259014
E-mail: sales@christopherswann.com

TRAINING, LANGUAGE TUITION

▶ Alpha Anglo College, 3 Dean Street, London, W1D 3TH Tel: (020) 7437 6767
E-mail: info@alphaanglocollege.com

Basil Paterson College, 66 Queen Street, Edinburgh, EH2 4NA Tel: 0131-225 3802 Fax: 0131-226 6701
E-mail: info@basilpaterson.co.uk

Cicero Languages Ltd, 42 Upper Grosvenor Road, Tunbridge Wells, Kent, TN1 2ET Tel: (01892) 547077 Fax: (01892) 522749
E-mail: info@cicero.co.uk

Evendine College, 227 Tottenham Court Road, London, W1T 7QF Tel: (020) 7580 1989 Fax: (020) 7580 1959
E-mail: evendine@evendine.com

Genua Madrigal Ltd, 9 Gillian Park Road, Sutton, Surrey, SM3 9JT Tel: (020) 8286 6589 Fax: (020) 8286 6589
E-mail: info@nineservices.co.uk

International House, 106 Piccadilly, London, W1J 7NL Tel: (020) 7518 6999 Fax: (020) 7495 0284 E-mail: info@ihlondon.co.uk

Kingsway English Centre Language School, 40 Foregate Street, Worcester, WR1 1EE Tel: (01905) 619877 Fax: (01905) 613388
E-mail: info@kingsway-english.com

▶ Lancashire College, Southport Road, Chorley, Lancashire, PR7 1NB Tel: (01257) 276719 Fax: (01257) 241370
E-mail: dawn.shelton@ed.lancscc.gov.uk

▶ The Language Company, The Thistles, 9 Ramblers Close, Colwick, Nottingham, NG4 2DN Tel: 0115 8449369
E-mail: info@thelanguagecompany.co.uk

▶ Lorena Massoni Mico, 4 Croydon Road, Caterham, Surrey, CR3 6QD Tel: (01883) 349205 E-mail: lorena@buylabels4less.com

▶ Only French, 21 Church Street, Maiden Bradley, Warminster, Wiltshire, BA12 7HW Tel: 01985 844659
E-mail: pascale@onlyfrench.com

Oxford House College, 30 Market Place, London, W1W 8AW Tel: (020) 7436 4872 Fax: (020) 7323 4582E-mail: english@oxfordhouse.co.uk

▶ Renaissance Language Services, 51 Auckland Road, Tunbridge Wells, Kent, TN1 2HX Tel: 01892 538932 Fax: 01892 538932
E-mail: info@renaissance-training.co.uk

▶ Spanish Machine, 115 Greenwich South Street, London, SE10 8NX Tel: (020) 8692 3918 E-mail: felipe@thespanishmachine.co.uk

T & I Services UK Ltd, 3 Furtho Manor Farm, Northampton Road, Old Stratford, Milton Keynes, MK19 6NR Tel: (0845) 6008150 Fax: (01908) 265461
E-mail: enquiries@tiservicesuk.com

Training Partnership Ltd, 450 Babbacombe Road, Torquay, TQ1 1HW Tel: (01803) 290222 Fax: (01803) 290333
E-mail: info@thetrainingpartnershipltd.com

Tutor Academy, 19 Marnland Grove, Bolton, BL3 4UJ Tel: (07006) 374147
E-mail: info@tutoracademy.co.uk

▶ Val d'Or Language Tuition, 30 A Dixon Street, Swindon, SN1 3PL Tel: (01793) 514150
E-mail: valou@madasafish.com

TRAINING, LEADERSHIP SKILLS

▶ Arrowhead Training and Consultancy Services, 80 Woolmer Road, Nottingham, NG2 2FB Tel: 0115-952 8603
E-mail: admin@arrowheadtraining.co.uk

C L S Europe, Heritage House, 11 Heritage Court, Chester, CH1 1RD Tel: (01244) 313022 Fax: (01244) 318455
E-mail: sales@clseurope.com

David Lloyd Associates, 35 Victor Road, Harrow, Middlesex, HA2 6PT Tel: (020) 8728 2421 Fax: (020) 8728 2421
E-mail: david_lloyd_a@compuserve.com

The Leadership Trust Training Ltd, Weston Under Penyard, Weston under Penyard, Ross-on-Wye, Herefordshire, HR9 7YH Tel: (01667) 455811 Fax: (01989) 768133
E-mail: enquiries@leadership.co.uk

Teesside Training Enterprise Ltd, Middlesbrough Road East, South Bank, Middlesbrough, Cleveland, TS6 6TZ Tel: (01642) 462266 Fax: (01642) 460873 E-mail: info@tte.co.uk

TRAINING, LEAN MANUFACTURING

Productivity Europe Ltd, Bedford Heights, Manton Lane, Bedford, MK41 7PH Tel: (01234) 215867 Fax: (01234) 218656
E-mail: prodeuro@atlas.co.uk

▶ Scott-Grant Technical Services, Portland Tower, Portland Street, Manchester, M1 3LD Tel: 0161-234 2121 Fax: 0161-234 2125
E-mail: training@scott-grant.co.uk

TRAINING, MARKETING

The Oxford Princeton Program, 1 St Floor, 59 St Aldates, Oxford, OX1 1ST Tel: (01865) 254520 Fax: (01865) 254599
E-mail: info@oxfordprinceton.com

▶ Paramount Learning Ltd, 478 Halifax Road, Bradford, West Yorkshire, BD6 2LH Tel: (01274) 600410
E-mail: info@paramountlearning.co.uk

TRAINING, MOTION CONTROL SYSTEMS

▶ Department of Automatic Control & Systems Engineering, Mappin Street, Sheffield, S1 3JD Tel: 0114-222 5250 Fax: 0114-222 5661
E-mail: z.c.fletcher@shef.ac.uk

TRAINING, NATIONAL VOCATIONAL QUALIFICATION (NVQ), IT

▶ Heart Of England Training, 30 William Street, Rugby, Warwickshire, CV21 3HA Tel: (01788) 553501 Fax: (01788) 552957
E-mail: info@hoet.co.uk

Intec Business Colleges, 16 Warwick Street, Rugby, Warwickshire, CV21 3DH Tel: (01788) 575090 Fax: (01788) 575411
E-mail: intec@ibc-rugby.demon.co.uk

▶ J H P Training, 48-50 Lowgate, Hull, HU1 1YZ Tel: (01482) 224340 Fax: (01482) 587992
E-mail: hull.business.centre@jhp-group.com

▶ J H P Training Manchester, 2nd Floor, Flint Glassworks, 64 Jersey Street, Ancoats Urban Village, Manchester, M4 6JW Tel: 0161-605 0829 Fax: 0161-605 0822
E-mail: manchester.business.centre@jhp-group.com

JHP Training Wales, Sophia House, 28 Cathedral Road, Cardiff, CF11 9LJ Tel: (029) 2063 6137 Fax: (029) 2063 6138
E-mail: cardiff.business.centre@jhp-group.com

▶ JMD It Training, 12 Northcote Road, Twickenham, TW1 1PA Tel: (020) 8892 7497
E-mail: jdonbavand@btinternet.com

TRAINING, NON DESTRUCTIVE TESTING (NDT)

▶ NDT Eagle, Kirkhill Place, Kirkhill Industrial Estate, Dyce, Aberdeen, AB21 0GU Tel: (01224) 722966 Fax: (01224) 773657
E-mail: sales@ndteagle.co.uk

Rope Technical Site Services, Rands Lane, Armthorpe, Doncaster, South Yorkshire, DN3 3DY Tel: (01302) 831987 Fax: (01302) 832559 E-mail: info@ropetech.co.uk

TRAINING, PROCESS PLANT TECHNOLOGY

▶ Department of Automatic Control & Systems Engineering, Mappin Street, Sheffield, S1 3JD Tel: 0114-222 5250 Fax: 0114-222 5661
E-mail: z.c.fletcher@shef.ac.uk

G & A Moulding Technology Ltd, Unit 2, Stonehill, Huntingdon, Cambridgeshire, PE29 6ED Tel: (01480) 414933 Fax: (01480) 414899
E-mail: info@gandamoulding.co.uk

Teeside Tertiary College, Longlands Campus, Douglas St, Middlesbrough, Cleveland, TS4 2JW Tel: (01642) 298942 Fax: (01642) 245313

TRAINING, PROGRAMMABLE LOGIC CONTROL (PLC)

Advanced Control Systems Ltd, 140 Aberford Road, Woodlesford, Leeds, LS26 8LG Tel: 0113-282 7123 Fax: 0113-282 5252

Beta Training Ltd, Thompsons Lane, Hough-on-the-Hill, Grantham, Lincolnshire, NG32 2BB Tel: (01400) 251848 Fax: (01400) 251849 E-mail: info@betatraining.com

▶ Drawtrend Ltd, 95 Mains Lane, Poulton-le-Fylde, Lancashire, FY6 7LD Tel: (01253) 882158 Fax: (01253) 882158
E-mail: sales@drawtrend.com

Global Engineering Services, Yew Tree Cott, Sampford Moor, Wellington, Somerset, TA21 9QL Tel: (0870) 7651508 Fax: (0870) 7652508
E-mail: mauricepinner@compuserve.com

Lingley Control Systems Ltd, Lingley House, Lingley Road, Great Sankey, Warrington, WA5 3ND Tel: (01925) 729933 Fax: (01925) 791331 E-mail: caloffice@cal.uk

▶ Professional Automation Support Services Ltd, Brierley Business Centre, Mirion Street, Crewe, CW1 2AZ Tel: (01270) 211111 Fax: (01270) 258282

TRAINING, QUALITY ASSURANCE

Aberdeen Quality Associates Ltd, 8 Rubislaw Den North, Aberdeen, AB15 4AN Tel: (01224) 315406 E-mail: bill@aqa.co.uk

British Approvals Board Telecommunications Ltd, Claremont House, 34 Molesey Road, Hersham, Walton-on-Thames, Surrey, KT12 4RQ Tel: (01932) 251200 Fax: (01932) 251201 E-mail: m.brain@babt.com

Institute of Quality Assurance, 12 Grosvenor Crescent, London, SW1X 7EE Tel: (020) 7245 6722 Fax: (020) 7245 6788
E-mail: enquiry@iqa.org

Investors In People UK, 7-10 Chandos Street, London, W1G 9DQ Tel: (020) 7467 1900 Fax: (020) 7636 2386
E-mail: information@iipuk.co.uk

▶ Roughtor Training, Roughtor House, 6 Sportsmans, Camelford, Cornwall, PL32 9QU Tel: 01840 211242
E-mail: Ashtonda1@aol.com

TRAINING, QUALITY, INTERNAL AUDITING FOR SMALL BUSINESS

I J Quality Services, 28 Beresford Drive, Sutton Coldfield, West Midlands, B73 5QZ Tel: 0121-355 5159 Fax: 0121-355 5159
E-mail: ivorjones@ijqs.co.uk

TRAINING, RELIEF VALVE MAINTENANCE AND CERTIFICATION

Anderson Greenwood Crosby, Wellheads Terrace, Wellheads Industrial Estate, Aberdeen, AB21 7GF Tel: (01224) 722562 Fax: (01224) 771607
E-mail: cmiln@tyco-valves.com

Tyco Valves & Controls Distribution (UK) Ltd, Wellheads Terr, Wellheads Industrial Estate, Aberdeen, AB22 7GF Tel: (01224) 722562 Fax: (01224) 771607
E-mail: sales_aberdeen@tyco-valves.com

TRAINING, SECURITY ALARM INSTALLATION

Skills For Security Recruitment Ltd, Security House, Barbourne Road, Worcester, WR1 1RS Tel: (01905) 27289 Fax: (01905) 724949 E-mail: info@skillsforsecurity.org.uk

Wilplan Training Ltd, Unit 2, Lake End Court, Taplow Road, Taplow, Maidenhead, Berkshire, SL6 0JQ Tel: (07808) 171295 Fax: (01628) 663740 E-mail: info@wilplantraining.co.uk

TRAINING, SECURITY SERVICES

Insight Consulting, Churchfield House, 3 & 5 The Quintet, Churchfield Road, Walton-On-Thames, Surrey, KT12 2TZ Tel: (01932) 241000 Fax: (01932) 244590
E-mail: insight@insight.co.uk

Lisburn Security Services Ltd, Security House, Lissea Industrial Estate East, Lisburn, County Antrim, BT28 2RD Tel: (028) 9260 5859 Fax: (028) 9262 2423
E-mail: gsmith@lisburnsecurityservices.co.uk

Training World, 22 Larchwood Close, Romford, RM5 3QX Tel: (01708) 746948 Fax: (01708) 739041 E-mail: info@trainingworld.co.uk

Wilplan Training Ltd, Unit 2, Lake End Court, Taplow Road, Taplow, Maidenhead, Berkshire, SL6 0JQ Tel: (07808) 171295 Fax: (01628) 663740 E-mail: info@wilplantraining.co.uk

▶ Xtp international, Adamson House, Towers Business Park, Wilmslow Road, Didsbury, Manchester, M20 2YY Tel: 0161-955 4227 Fax: 0161-445 8225
E-mail: stevew34@hotmail.com

TRAINING, SURVIVAL, OFFSHORE

Humberside Offshore Training Association Ltd, Malmo Road, Hull, HU7 0YF Tel: (01482) 820567 Fax: (01482) 823202
E-mail: bookings@hota.org

Maritime Rescue Institute Lifeboat Station, Old Pier, Stonehaven, Kincardineshire, AB39 2JU Tel: (01569) 765768 Fax: (01569) 764066

Nutec Centre For Safety, Nutec Centre For Safety, Haverton Hill Industrial Estate, Billingham, Cleveland, TS23 1PZ Tel: (01642) 566656 Fax: (01642) 563224
E-mail: enquiries@nutecuk.com

Petans Ltd, Bullocks Hill, Horsham St. Faith, Norwich, NR10 3HT Tel: (01603) 891255 Fax: (01603) 890827
E-mail: michael@petans.co.uk

Soth Tyneside College, Marine Safety Training Centre South Tyneside College, Wapping, South Shields, Tyne & Wear, NE33 1LQ Tel: 0191-427 3664 Fax: 0191-427 3600
E-mail: marine_safety_at_stc@compuserve.com

TRAINING, TELEPHONE CALL CENTRES

Bowman Group Ltd, 1200 Century Way, Thorpe Park Business Park, Leeds, LS15 8ZB Tel: (01422) 322211 Fax: (01325) 151100
E-mail: info@bowman-group.co.uk

▶ Direct Response Ltd, 3 Angel Walk, London, W6 9HX Tel: (0870) 4149000 Fax: (0870) 4149001 E-mail: sales@drltd.com

Endaim, 3rd Floor Phoenix House, Christopher Martin Road, Basildon, Essex, SS14 3HG Tel: (01268) 270022 Fax: (01268) 285050
E-mail: sandie.lorkins@headoffice.endaim.com

Phone Coach Ltd, Unit 21 Kent House, Old Bexley Business Park, Bexley, Kent, DA5 1LR Tel: (01322) 551170 Fax: (01322) 556680
E-mail: enquiries@phonecoach.com

TRAINING, TRANSPORT, DRIVERS HOURS

▶ Accidon'T, 20 East Argyle Street, Helensburgh, Dunbartonshire, G84 7RR Tel: (01436) 678018 Fax: (01436) 678808 E-mail: simon.johnston@accidont.co.uk

▶ Big Rigs LGV Driver Training, Hereford, Hereford, HR4 7SG Tel: 01432 761004 Fax: 01432 769305 E-mail: info@bigrigstraining.com

▶ Driver Development UK Ltd, 3 Euston Close, Forest Park, Lincoln, LN6 0XG Tel: (01522) 839317 E-mail: driverdevelopment@yahoo.co.uk

▶ Steve Robertson Training Services, Peamore Truck Centre, Alphington, Exeter, EX2 9SL Tel: 01392 833369 E-mail: lorrydrivertraining@tiscali.co.uk

TRAINING, TRAVEL PLANNING

A A Appointments, St. Clare House, 30-33 Minories, London, EC3N 1PQ Tel: (01344) 891987 Fax: (020) 7480 5467 E-mail: travel@aaappointments.com

O A G Worldwide, Church Street, Dunstable, Bedfordshire, LU5 4HB Tel: (01582) 600111 Fax: (01582) 695140 E-mail: sales@oag.com

TRAINING, WAREHOUSING AND DISTRIBUTION INDUSTRY

▶ Hudson Haulage, Unit 8 Grove Lane, Elmswell, Bury St. Edmunds, Suffolk, IP30 9HN Tel: (01359) 242777 Fax: (01359) 242567 E-mail: info@hudsonhaulage.com

TRAMPOLINES

▶ All Trampolines, Embassy House, Ledson Road, Manchester, M23 9GP Tel: (0800) 0430437 Fax: (0845) 2571480 E-mail: info@alltrampolines.com

▶ Jumpzone, Maritime House, Basin Road North, Hove, East Sussex, BN41 1WR Tel: 01273 384995E-mail: info@jumpzone.org

Trenchex Garden Machinery, Dove Fields Industrial Estate, Uttoxeter, Staffordshire, ST14 8ER Tel: (01889) 565155 Fax: (01889) 563140 E-mail: enquiries@trenchax.com

TRANSDUCER MANUFRS, *See also headings under Transducers etc*

Knowles Europe, York Road, Burgess Hill, West Sussex, RH15 9TT Tel: (01444) 235432 Fax: (01444) 248724 E-mail: info@knowles.com

R D P Group Ltd, Grove Street, Heath Town, Wolverhampton, WV10 0PY Tel: (01902) 457512 Fax: (01902) 452000 E-mail: sales@rdpelectronics.com

TRANSDUCERS, CERAMIC, ULTRASONIC, AIR

▶ Alba Ultrasound Ltd, Unit 3, Todd Campus, 45 Acre Road, Glasgow, G20 0XA Tel: 0141-946 5000 Fax: 0141-946 5111 E-mail: bwooldridge@albaultrasound.com

TRANSFER PRESSES

Pharos Engineering Ltd, Unit 27 Chess Business Park, Moor Road, Chesham, Buckinghamshire, HP5 1SD Tel: (01494) 775611 Fax: (01494) 784003

TRANSFER PRESSINGS

Clamason Industries Ltd, Gibbons Industrial Park, Dudley Road, Kingswinford, West Midlands, DY6 8XG Tel: (01384) 400000 Fax: (01384) 400588 E-mail: sales@clamason.co.uk

H Hipkiss & Co. Ltd, Park House, Clapgate Lane, Birmingham, B32 3BL Tel: 0121-421 5777 Fax: 0121-421 5333 E-mail: info@hipkiss.co.uk

Jenks & Cattell Engineering Ltd, Neachells Lane, Wolverhampton, WV11 3PU Tel: (01902) 305530 Fax: (01902) 305529 E-mail: sales@jenks-cattell.co.uk

TRANSFER PRINT PAPER

Antalis, 3 Imperial Park Imperial Way, Watford, WD24 4PP Tel: (01923) 636600 Fax: (0870) 6073168 E-mail: contact@antalis.co.uk

Continuous Transfer Paper Printers Ltd, Lotti Works, Two Bridges Road, Newhey, Rochdale, Lancashire, OL16 3SR Tel: (01706) 299015 Fax: (01706) 841159E-mail: sales@ctpp.co.uk

Transfra Graphics Ltd, Stadium Place, Leicester, LE4 0JS Tel: 0116-234 0440 Fax: 0116-235 1881 E-mail: sales@transfragraphics.com

TRANSFERS, *See also headings for particular types under Transfers*

Impressions Design Ltd, Sutherland Works, Beaufort Road, Stoke-on-Trent, ST3 1RH Tel: (01782) 329535 Fax: (01782) 329535 E-mail: info@impressionsdesignltd.co.uk

Presletta Graphics, 66 Kitchener Road, High Wycombe, Buckinghamshire, HP11 2SN Tel: (01494) 526285 E-mail: roy@presletta.com

TRANSFORMER ACCESSORIES

Asco Components, Unit 19 Green Lane Industrial Estate, Bordesley Green, Birmingham, B9 5QP Tel: 0121-773 3090 Fax: 0121-773 3390 E-mail: info@ascocomponents.co.uk

Rosh Engineering Ltd, Newtown Indust Estate, Chester le Street, County Durham, DH3 2QN Tel: 0191-410 6300 Fax: 0191-410 6319 E-mail: info@rosh.co.uk

TRANSFORMER BOBBINS

Asco Components, Unit 19 Green Lane Industrial Estate, Bordesley Green, Birmingham, B9 5QP Tel: 0121-773 3090 Fax: 0121-773 3390 E-mail: info@ascocomponents.co.uk

Miles Platts Ltd, 39 Abbey Park Road, Leicester, LE4 5AN Tel: 0116-262 2593 Fax: 0116-253 7889 E-mail: enquiries@milesplatts.co.uk

▶ Rainer Schneider Ayres, 17 Shirlock Road, London, NW3 2HR Tel: (020) 7267 0812 Fax: (020) 7284 0672 E-mail: rsa_bxt@btinternet.com

Armand Taylor & Co. Ltd, Tuskite Works, Pitsea Hall Lane, Pitsea, Basildon, Essex, SS16 4UL Tel: (01268) 552167

TRANSFORMER BREATHERS

Rosh Engineering Ltd, Newtown Indust Estate, Chester le Street, County Durham, DH3 2QN Tel: 0191-410 6300 Fax: 0191-410 6319 E-mail: info@rosh.co.uk

TRANSFORMER BUSHINGS/ INSULATORS

Trench UK Ltd, South Drive, Hebburn, Tyne & Wear, NE31 1UW Tel: 0191-483 4711 Fax: 0191-430 0633 E-mail: sales@trench-uk.com

TRANSFORMER COMPONENT MANUFRS, *See also specific components*

C D N Windings Ltd, Units 9 & 10 Brockwell Court, Low Willington Industrial Estate, Crook, Co. Durham, DL15 0UT Tel: (01388) 745570 Fax: (01388) 745150 E-mail: cdn.windings@ukf.net

Redlaw Shearing (Lye) Ltd, The White House, Pearson Street, Lye, Stourbridge, West Midlands, DY9 8BB Tel: (01384) 422398 Fax: (01384) 422398

Wound Products Ltd, Brooklands House, Brooklands Approach, North Street, Romford, RM1 1DX Tel: (01708) 729000 Fax: (01708) 733373 E-mail: sales@woundproducts.com

TRANSFORMER CONSULTANTS

C D N Windings Ltd, Units 9 & 10 Brockwell Court, Low Willington Industrial Estate, Crook, Co. Durham, DL15 0UT Tel: (01388) 745570 Fax: (01388) 745150 E-mail: cdn.windings@ukf.net

Dagnall Electronics Ltd, 3 Shuttleworth Road, Elm Farm Industrial Estate, Bedford, MK41 0EP Tel: (01234) 330077 Fax: (01234) 330088 E-mail: sales@dagnall.co.uk

TRANSFORMER CONTROL PANELS

▶ D Electrical, Valley Works, Bacup Road, Todmorden, Lancashire, OL14 7PJ Tel: (01706) 814854 Fax: (01706) 815023

Forrest Transformers Ltd, 349 Haslucks Green Road, Shirley, Solihull, West Midlands, B90 2NQ Tel: 0121-744 2483 Fax: 0121-733 2178E-mail: sales@forrest-transformers.co.uk

▶ Transformer Equipment Ltd, Unit 9 Crystal Business Centre, Sandwich Industrial Estate, Sandwich, Kent, CT13 9QX Tel: (01304) 612551 Fax: (01304) 613630 E-mail: luke@transformers.freeserve.co.uk

TRANSFORMER COOLING RADIATORS

Rosh Engineering Ltd, Newtown Indust Estate, Chester le Street, County Durham, DH3 2QN Tel: 0191-410 6300 Fax: 0191-410 6319 E-mail: info@rosh.co.uk

TRANSFORMER CORE MANUFRS

Permag Ltd, Block 1 Unit 2 Strutherhill Indust Estate, Larkhall, Lanarkshire, ML9 1LR Tel: (01698) 884823 Fax: (01698) 884823 E-mail: sales@permag.freeuk.com

Armand Taylor & Co. Ltd, Tuskite Works, Pitsea Hall Lane, Pitsea, Basildon, Essex, SS16 4UL Tel: (01268) 552167

Unicores Ltd, Unit F Bull Street, Brierley Hill, West Midlands, DY5 3NQ Tel: (01384) 70542 Fax: (01384) 74380

Wiltan Ltd, Pontnewynydd Industrial Estate, Pontnewynydd, Pontypool, Gwent, NP4 6YW Tel: (01495) 750711 Fax: (01495) 753730 E-mail: sales@wiltan.co.uk

TRANSFORMER ENGINEERS, INSTALLATION/MAINTENANCE/ REPAIR SERVICES

Bowers Electricals Ltd, Slack Lane, Heanor, Derbyshire, DE75 7GX Tel: (01773) 531531 Fax: (01773) 716171 E-mail: enquiries@bowerselec.co.uk

Nottingham Transformers Co. Ltd, Unit 37 Little Tennis Street, Nottingham, NG2 4EL Tel: 0115-958 8340 Fax: 0115-958 8341 E-mail: tony_medri@hotmail.com

TRANSFORMER HIRE

FLD Pumps And Power, 2 Ness Road, Erith, Kent, DA8 2LD Tel: (01322) 350088 Fax: (01322) 350066 E-mail: erith@fldpumpspowerpowerent.co.uk

Woodlands Generators, Crab Apple Way, Vale Park, Evesham, Worcestershire, WR11 1GP Tel: (01386) 760256 Fax: (01386) 442740 E-mail: sales@woodlands-generators.com

TRANSFORMER LAMINATIONS

Redlaw Shearing (Lye) Ltd, The White House, Pearson Street, Lye, Stourbridge, West Midlands, DY9 8BB Tel: (01384) 422398 Fax: (01384) 422398

Redlaw Shearing (Lye) Ltd, The White House, Pearson Street, Stourbridge, West Midlands, DY9 8BB Tel: (01384) 422398 Fax: (01384) 422398

TRANSFORMER MANUFRS, *See also headings under Transformers*

A S L Group, 3 Cullwick St, Wolverhampton, WV1 2UL Tel: (01902) 498420 Fax: (01902) 353112 E-mail: sales@birford.co.uk

ABB Limited, East Kingsway, Dundee, DD4 7RP Tel: (01382) 454500 Fax: (01382) 457305

Ace Wound Products Ltd, 1g Skillion Business Park, Thames Road, Barking, Essex, IG11 0JP Tel: (020) 8507 2330 Fax: (020) 8507 8981 E-mail: mac@acewound.com

Adc Electrical Co. Ltd, Burtree Works, Hertburn Estate, Hertburn, Washington, Tyne & Wear, NE37 2SF Tel: 0191-416 5222 Fax: 0191-416 3996 E-mail: info@adc-electrical.co.uk

Aden Electronics Holdings Ltd, Unit 3 Montpelier Business Park, Dencora Way, Ashford, Kent, TN23 4FG Tel: (01233) 664445 Fax: (01233) 664626 E-mail: info@adenelectronics.co.uk

Admagnetics (Manufaturing Division For Solutions) Ltd, Bolton Avenue, Huncoat Industrial Park, Accrington, Lancashire, BB5 6NJ Tel: (01254) 381869 Fax: (01254) 381674 E-mail:

Advanced Power Components plc, Unit 47 Riverside Estate, Sir Thomas Longley Road, Medway City Estate, Rochester, Kent, ME2 4DP Tel: (01634) 290588 Fax: (01634) 290591 E-mail: sales@apc-plc.co.uk

Alstom Power, Kirkton Drive, Pitmedden Industrial Estate, Dyce, Aberdeen, AB21 0BG Tel: (01224) 214500

Amethyst Designs Ltd, 9 Trafalgar Way, Bar Hill, Cambridge, CB3 8SQ Tel: (01954) 789696 Fax: (01954) 789662 E-mail: sales@amethyst-designs.co.uk

Antrim Transformers Ltd, 25 Enkalon Industrial Estate, Randalstown Road, Antrim, BT41 4LD Tel: (028) 9442 8734 Fax: (028) 9446 8745 E-mail: technical@antrimtransformers.com

B E White, Brantwood Road, London, N17 0ED Tel: (020) 8887 1690 Fax: (020) 8884 1865 E-mail: info@bewhite.co.uk

B T L Powertec Ltd, 4 Station Yard, Old Furnace Road, Coniston, Cumbria, LA21 8HU Tel: (01539) 441904 Fax: (01539) 441907

R. Baker (Electrical) Ltd, Evans Road, Speke, Liverpool, L24 9PB Tel: 0151-486 6760 Fax: 0151-448 1225 E-mail: mail@rbaker.co.uk

Best Windings Ltd, Viking Works, Bucklesham Road, Kirton, Ipswich, IP10 0NX Tel: (01394) 448424 Fax: (01394) 448430 E-mail: kevin@bestwindings.co.uk

Birmingham Transformers Ltd, 6 Weston Works, Weston Lane, Birmingham, B11 3RP Tel: 0121-764 5600 Fax: 0121-764 5551 E-mail: sales@birminghamtransformers.co.uk

Bradford Armature Winding Co. Ltd, 429 Bowling Old Lane, Bradford, West Yorkshire, BD5 8HN Tel: (01274) 728379 Fax: (01274) 731518 E-mail: info@bawco.com

C D N Windings Ltd, Units 9 & 10 Brockwell Court, Low Willington Industrial Estate, Crook, Co. Durham, DL15 0UT Tel: (01388) 745570 Fax: (01388) 745150 E-mail: cdn.windings@ukf.net

C R A Manufacturing Ltd, 15a Oglander Road, London, SE15 4EQ Tel: (020) 7635 8201 Fax: (020) 7277 5667

Cambridge Transformers Ltd, Quiet Waters, High Street, Earith, Huntingdon, Cambridgeshire, PE28 3PN Tel: (01487) 842154 Fax: (01487) 843445 E-mail: sales@transformers.demon.co.uk

Carnhill Transformers Ltd, 68 Sandford Lane, Kennington, Oxford, OX1 5RW Tel: (01865) 327843 Fax: (01865) 736538 E-mail: sales@carnhill.co.uk

Carnhill Transformers Ltd, 4 Edison Road, St. Ives, Cambridgeshire, PE27 3LT Tel: (01480) 462978 Fax: (01480) 496196 E-mail: sales@carnhill.co.uk

Castleton Transformers, Unit C14 Fieldhouse Industrial Estate, Fieldhouse Road, Rochdale, Lancashire, OL12 0AA Tel: (01706) 342086 Fax: (01706) 861286

Clairtronic Ltd, Shuttleworth Road, Elm Farm Industrial Estate, Bedford, MK41 0EP Tel: (01234) 330774 Fax: (01234) 330775 E-mail: sales@clairtronic.co.uk

Coilmech Transformer Mnfrs, 1 Barratt Industrial Park, Whittle Avenue, Fareham, Hampshire, PO15 5SL Tel: (01489) 885309 Fax: (01489) 885309

Crawford Hansford & Kimber Ltd, 18 Farnborough Road, Farnborough, Hampshire, GU14 6AY Tel: (01252) 377077 Fax: (01252) 377228 E-mail: admin@crawfordhk.com

Custom Transformers Ltd, Unit 23, Whitewalls, Easton Grey, Malmesbury, Wiltshire, SN16 0RD Tel: (01666) 824411 Fax: (01666) 824413 E-mail: sales@custom-transformers.co.uk

Dagnall Electronics Ltd, 3 Shuttleworth Road, Elm Farm Industrial Estate, Bedford, MK41 0EP Tel: (01234) 330077 Fax: (01234) 330088 E-mail: sales@dagnall.co.uk

Danbury Electronics, 20 Cutlers Road, Saltcoats Industrial Estate, South Woodham Ferrers, Chelmsford, CM3 5XJ Tel: (01245) 328174 Fax: (01245) 328963 E-mail: danburyelectx@aol.com

De Tech, Unit 36e The Lingfield Estate, Mcmullen Road, Darlington, County Durham, DL1 1RW Tel: (01325) 489001 Fax: (01325) 489001 E-mail: sales@detech.fsnet.co.uk

▶ Dee Tech Services Ltd, 5 Jackson Court, Manor Lane, Hawarden, Deeside, Clwyd, CH5 3QP Tel: (01244) 530100 Fax: (01244) 530101

Delta Components, The Courtyard, Sevenacres, Smallfield Road, Horne, Horley, Surrey, RH6 9JP Tel: (01342) 844555 Fax: (01342) 844552 E-mail: sales@deltacomponents.com

▶ East Manufacturing, Pixmore Centre, Pixmore Avenue, Letchworth Garden City, Hertfordshire, SG6 1JG Tel: (01462) 675656 Fax: (01462) 481781

Eastern Transformer Ltd, Overland Industrial Park, Sudbury Road, Little Whelnetham, Bury St. Edmunds, Suffolk, IP30 0UL Tel: (01284) 388033 Fax: (01284) 386969 E-mail: info@ete.co.uk

Electro Wind Scotland Ltd, Units 3, Station Road, Kinghorn, Burntisland, Fife, KY3 9RA Tel: (01592) 890990 Fax: (01592) 891153

Electrosite UK Ltd, Easton Lane, Bozeat, Wellingborough, Northamptonshire, NN29 7NN Tel: (01933) 665022 Fax: (01933) 665520 E-mail: electrosite@kbnet.net

▶ Erea UK Ltd, 6 Carew Court, Dawlish Business Park, Dawlish, Devon, EX7 0NH Tel: (01626) 865551 Fax: (01626) 862434

F I Technology Ltd, Leyden Road, Stevenage, Hertfordshire, SG1 2BW Tel: (01438) 727270 Fax: (01438) 727271

▶ Foreman Electrical Services, B6 Dovers Corner Industrial Estate, New Road, Rainham, Essex, RM13 8QT Tel: (01708) 555381 Fax: (01708) 525897 E-mail: foreman.electric@btconnect.com

Forrest Transformers Ltd, 349 Haslucks Green Road, Shirley, Solihull, West Midlands, B90 2NQ Tel: 0121-744 2483 Fax: 0121-733 2178E-mail: sales@forrest-transformers.co.uk

▶ Glasgow Power Steering, 70 Camelon Street, Glasgow, G32 6AF Tel: 0141-764 1919 Fax: 0141-764 1818

Grand Chain Ltd, Maple House, Laughton Road, Ringmer, Lewes, East Sussex, BN8 5SY Tel: (01273) 813345 Fax: (01273) 814 153 E-mail: sales@grandchain.co.uk

Huco Lightronic Ni Ltd, 3 Aghanloo Industrial Estate, Aghanloo Road, Limavady, County Londonderry, BT49 0HE Tel: (028) 7776 8567 Fax: (028) 7776 8515 E-mail: sales@huco.co.uk

TRANSFORMER MANUFRS – *continued*

International Transformers, Longley Lane, Sharston Industrial Area, Manchester, M22 4RU Tel: 0161-428 9507 Fax: 0161-428 0052 E-mail: info@int-transformers.co.uk
J P S Windings Ltd, 1a Shaftesbury Road, Reading, RG30 2QR Tel: 0118-959 9344
Jades Components Ltd, Derby Road, Kingsbridge, Devon, TQ7 1JL Tel: (01548) 853377 Fax: (01548) 856820 E-mail: jades@jadescomponents.co.uk
Jenstar Ltd, Sturmi Way, Village Farm Industrial Estate, Pyle, Bridgend, Mid Glamorgan, CF33 6BZ Tel: (01656) 745818 Fax: (01656) 745818 E-mail: sales@jenstar.co.uk
Lan Electronics, Unit 5 50, Rother Valley Way, Holbrook, Sheffield, S20 3RW Tel: 0114-251 1066 Fax: 0114-251 1067 E-mail: sales@lanelectronicsltd.co.uk
▶ Lothian Electric Machines Ltd, Hospital Road, Haddington, East Lothian, EH41 3PD Tel: (01620) 828700 Fax: (01620) 828730
Louth Transformer Co. Ltd, Belvoir Way, Fairfield Industrial Estate, Louth, Lincolnshire, LN11 0LQ Tel: (01507) 606436 Fax: (01507) 600168 E-mail: info@louthtransformers.co.uk
Mitchell Transformers Ltd, 12 Allens Lane, Poole, Dorset, BH16 5DA Tel: (01202) 622361 Fax: (01202) 624369
Morite Winding Co. Ltd, Unit 10c Sand Road Industrial Estate, Great Gransden, Sandy, Bedfordshire, SG19 3AH Tel: (01767) 677811 Fax: (01767) 677812 E-mail: sales@morite.co.uk
N E L UK Ltd, 75 Burton Road, Carlton, Nottingham, NG4 3FP Tel: 0115-940 1894 Fax: 0115-987 0878E-mail: tony@nel-uk.co.uk
▶ Norpower & Telecoms Ltd, Muir of Ord Industrial Estate, Great North Road, Muir of Ord, Ross-Shire, IV6 7UA Tel: (01463) 871010 Fax: (01463) 871022
North Devon Electronics Ltd, Velator, Braunton, Devon, EX33 2DX Tel: (01271) 813553 Fax: (01271) 816171E-mail: sales@nde.co.uk
Northern Coil Services, Unit 6 Aston Court, Kingsland Grange, Woolston, Warrington, WA1 4SG Tel: (01925) 819642 Fax: (01925) 825865 E-mail: ncsdeakin@aol.com
Nottingham Transformers Co. Ltd, Unit 37 Little Tennis Street, Nottingham, NG2 4EL Tel: 0115-958 8340 Fax: 0115-958 8341 E-mail: tony_medri@hotmail.com
Pace Components Ltd, 38 Ballmoor, Buckingham Industrial Estate, Buckingham, MK18 1RQ Tel: (01280) 822733 Fax: (01280) 823839 E-mail: sales@pacecomponents.co.uk
Pennine Radio Ltd, 82 Fitzwilliam Street, Huddersfield, HD1 5BE Tel: (01484) 538211 Fax: (01484) 542004 E-mail: info@pr1.co.uk
Pontiac Coil Europe Ltd, PO Box 246, Nottingham, NG2 1NQ Tel: 0115-986 1126 Fax: 0115-986 0563 E-mail: info@pontiaccoil.co.uk
Power & Distribution Transformers Ltd, Westland Works, Westland Square, Leeds, LS11 5SS Tel: 0113-271 7588 Fax: 0113-277 5124 E-mail: sales@wilsonpowersolutions.co.uk
Precision Windings Ltd, Unit J, Durban Road, South Bersted, Bognor Regis, West Sussex, PO22 9QT Tel: (01243) 823311 Fax: (01243) 823318E-mail: sales@precisionwindings.co.uk
R B M Wound Components, The Sanderson Centre, Lees Lane, Gosport, Hampshire, PO12 3UL Tel: (023) 9252 0777 Fax: (023) 9252 4777 E-mail: ron@rbmwoundcomps.co.uk
▶ Rasmi Electronics Ltd, Unit 14a Tanfield Industrial Estate, Tanfield Lea, Stanley, County Durham, DH9 9UU Tel: (01207) 232159 Fax: (01207) 231934 E-mail: sales@rasmi.com
Rafmi Electronics, Morrison Road, Stanley, County Durham, DH9 7RX Tel: (01207) 291300 Fax: (01207) 291304 E-mail: accounts@rasmi.com
Ripley Transformers Ltd, Suite 11, Waterside Centre, North Street, Lewes, East Sussex, BN7 2PE Tel: (01273) 475385 Fax: (01273) 477811 E-mail: sales@grandchain.co.uk
Romarsh Ltd, Clarke Avenue, Portemarsh Industrial Estate, Calne, Wiltshire, SN11 9BS Tel: (01249) 812624 Fax: (01249) 816134 E-mail: sales@romarsh.co.uk
S P Wound Components Ltd, Unit 12 Stanley Green Industrial Estate, Stanley Green Esc, Poole, Dorset, BH15 3TH Tel: (01202) 682828 Fax: (01202) 682828 E-mail: spwoundcomp@boltblue.com
S T L Stewart Transformers Ltd, 1 Townsend Industrial Estate, Waxlow Road, London, NW10 7NU Tel: (020) 8965 9505 Fax: (020) 8961 1499 E-mail: sales@stewart-transformers.co.uk
S T L Transtech Ltd, 64-66 Percy Road, Leicester, LE2 8FN Tel: 0116-283 3321 Fax: 0116-283 0730 E-mail: transtechsales@stlgroup.org
Samsons Transformers, 24 37 Hamilton Road, Twickenham, TW2 6SN Tel: (020) 8893 4053 Fax: (020) 8893 4054 E-mail: enquiries@samsons.co.uk
▶ Semitool (Europe) Ltd, 509 Coldhams Lane, Cambridge, CB1 3JS Tel: (01223) 505000 Fax: (01223) 243026
A.C. Simpson (Transformers) 1981 Ltd, Unit 20, Olds Close, Watford, WD18 9RU Tel: (01923) 777495 Fax: (01923) 771257 E-mail: info@acstx.co.uk
Stadium Power Ltd, 23-29 Owen Road, Vinces Road Industrial Estate, Diss, Norfolk, IP22 4YU Tel: (01379) 644233 Fax: (01379) 650118 E-mail: sales@stadiumpower.co.uk
Sycopel International, Viking Industrial Park, Jarrow, Tyne & Wear, NE32 3DT Tel: 0191-428 5004 Fax: 0191-483 5995 E-mail: sycopelint@aol.co.uk
Tabuchi Electric UK Ltd, Tabuchi House, Robson Avenue, Teesside Industrial Estate, Stockton-on-Tees, Cleveland, TS17 9LS Tel: (01642) 750750 Fax: (01642) 750108
Tam Transformers Ltd, Durban Road, Bognor Regis, West Sussex, PO22 9QT Tel: (01243) 861122 Fax: (01243) 830870 E-mail: tam@tamtransformers.co.uk
Tamura Europe Ltd, Hopton Park, London Road, Devizes, Wiltshire, SN10 2EY Tel: (01380) 731700 Fax: (01380) 731703 E-mail: business@tamura-europe.co.uk
Taylor & Goodman Ltd, 7 Cradock Road, Reading, RG2 0LB Tel: 0118-987 1773 Fax: 0118-931 4945 E-mail: sales@taylorgoodman.co.uk
Tesla Transformers Ltd, Carrington Business Park, Manchester Road, Carrington, Manchester, M31 4ZU Tel: 0161-776 4080 Fax: 0161-776 4446 E-mail: sales@tesla-transformers.com
Tiger Toroids, Unit 5, Pulham Market Hall, Station Road, Pulham Market, Diss, Norfolk, IP21 4XF Tel: (01379) 650580 Fax: (01379) 608871 E-mail: tigertoroids@btinternet.com
▶ Tinto Engineering Ltd, Argyle Crescent, Hillhouse Industrial Estate, Hamilton, Lanarkshire, ML3 9BQ Tel: (01698) 421212
Torr-Tech Ltd, Unit 20 B-C St Helen Industrial Estate, Bishop Auckland, County Durham, DL14 9AZ Tel: (01388) 450005 Fax: (01388) 450039 E-mail: sales@torr-tech.co.uk
Tranilamp Ltd, 69-70 Eastern Way, Bury St. Edmunds, Suffolk, IP32 7AB Tel: (01284) 767055 Fax: (01284) 701921 E-mail: sales@tranilamp.co.uk
Transformer Manufacturing Co. Ltd, Riverside Industrial Estate, Mill Lane, Maldon, Essex, CM9 4LD Tel: (01621) 843322 Fax: (01621) 843355 E-mail: sales@tmc.co.uk
Transmag Power Transformers Ltd, 66-72 Lower Essex Street, Birmingham, B5 6SU Tel: 0121-622 3217 Fax: 0121-622 3217 E-mail: sales@transmag-transformers.co.uk
Transpower Engineering Ltd, 1 Lion Works, Palatine Street, Denton, Manchester, M34 3LY Tel: 0161-336 7111 Fax: 0161-336 5822
Tunewell Transformers, 2 Maple Park, Essex Road, Hoddesdon, Hertfordshire, EN11 0EX Tel: (01992) 801300 Fax: (01992) 801301 E-mail: sales@tunewell.com
▶ Turbine Services Ltd, Phoenix Business Park, Paisley, Renfrewshire, PA1 2BH Tel: 0141-849 6123 Fax: 0141-849 7023 E-mail: info@turbineserviceslimited.com
▶ Tva Transformers Ltd, Unit 20/29, Teesway, North Tees Industrial Estate, Stockton-on-Tees, Cleveland, TS18 2RS Tel: (01642) 612444 Fax: (01642) 633997 E-mail: info@tvatransformers.co.uk
Vector Electronics Ltd, Aco House, Rembrandt Way, Aycliffe Industrial Park, Newton Aycliffe, County Durham, DL5 6BD Tel: (01325) 319182 Fax: (01325) 319182
▶ Vestas-Celtic Wind Technology Ltd, PO Box 9263, Campbeltown, Argyll, PA28 6WA Tel: (01586) 555000 Fax: (01586) 555111
Walsall Transformers Ltd, 246 Green Lane, Walsall, WS2 8HS Tel: (01922) 722933 Fax: (01922) 721222 E-mail: sales@walsall-transformers.co.uk
Walters OEP Ltd, 15 -17 Wroslyn Road Industrial Estate, Wroslyn Road, Freeland, Witney, Oxfordshire, OX29 8SN Tel: (01993) 886200 Fax: (01993) 886210 E-mail: info@oep.co.uk
▶ Wood Group Hit, 9 Deerdykes Court South, Cumbernauld, Glasgow, G68 9HW Tel: (01236) 868180 Fax: (01236) 458872
Wound Products Ltd, Brooklands House, Brooklands Approach, North Street, Romford, RM1 1DX Tel: (01708) 729000 Fax: (01708) 733373 E-mail: sales@woundproducts.com
Zeta Windings Ltd, 416-418 London Road, Isleworth, Middlesex, TW7 5XB Tel: (020) 8568 6875 Fax: (020) 8568 7194 E-mail: chris@zetacool.com

TRANSFORMER OIL/LUBRICANT FILTRATION/RECLAMATION EQUIPMENT

Filterall Ltd, PO Box 29, Daventry, Northamptonshire, NN11 1AQ Tel: (01327) 877624 Fax: (01327) 705749 E-mail: filterall@btconnect.com

TRANSFORMER PRESSINGS

Birmingham Transformers Ltd, 6 Weston Works, Weston Lane, Birmingham, B11 3RP Tel: 0121-764 5600 Fax: 0121-764 5551 E-mail: sales@birminghamtransformers.co.uk

TRANSFORMER RECTIFIERS

T & R Group Ltd, 15-16 Woodbridge Meadows, Guildford, Surrey, GU1 1BJ Tel: (01483) 568281 Fax: (01483) 504961 E-mail: sales@transformers.co.uk

TRANSFORMER TANKS

Eddison & Wanless Ltd, Unit 1, Mallard Industrial Estate, Horbury, Wakefield, West Yorkshire, WF4 5QH Tel: (01924) 271128 Fax: (01924) 271251 E-mail: info@eddisonwanless.co.uk
Euro Tanks, 4 Heritage Way, Corby, Northamptonshire, NN17 5XW Tel: (01536) 201006 Fax: (01536) 400140 E-mail: sales@eurotanks.co.uk

TRANSFORMER TEST SET/ EQUIPMENT MANUFRS

▶ Transformer Equipment Ltd, Unit 9 Crystal Business Centre, Sandwich Industrial Estate, Sandwich, Kent, CT13 9QX Tel: (01304) 612551 Fax: (01304) 613630 E-mail: luke@transformers.freeserve.co.uk

TRANSFORMERS, BARRIER TYPE, FOR DATA MODEMS

Profec Holdings Ltd, 10 Betts Avenue, Martlesham Heath, Ipswich, IP5 3RH Tel: (01473) 611422 Fax: (01473) 611919 E-mail: sales@profec.com

TRANSFORMERS, DISTRIBUTION, UP TO 1 MVA

SDC Industries Ltd, 18 Colvilles Place, Kelvin Industrial Estate, East Kilbride, Glasgow, G75 0PZ Tel: (01355) 265959 Fax: (01355) 265484 E-mail: sales@sdcindustries.co.uk

TRANSFORMERS, HIGH FREQUENCY POWER, OVER 5KVA

Electro Inductors, 19-25 Neville Road, Croydon, CR0 2DS Tel: (020) 8684 6100 Fax: (020) 8684 6109 E-mail: sales@aluminium-inductors.co.uk

TRANSFORMERS, PROTECTIVE, CURRENT TYPE

D K Moriarty Ltd, Eastgates Industrial Estate, Moorside, Colchester, CO1 2TJ Tel: (01206) 867141 Fax: (01206) 867613 E-mail: sales@dk-moriarty.ltd.uk
▶ Tva Transformers Ltd, Unit 20/29, Teesway, North Tees Industrial Estate, Stockton-on-Tees, Cleveland, TS18 2RS Tel: (01642) 612444 Fax: (01642) 633997 E-mail: info@tvatransformers.co.uk

TRANSFORMERS, SINGLE/ THREE PHASE

Leeds Transformer Co. Ltd, Larchfield Road, Leeds, LS10 1QP Tel: 0113-270 5596 Fax: 0113-272 1458 E-mail: sales@leedstransformer.co.uk

TRANSFORMERS, TO SPECIFICATION/CUSTOM BUILT

B T L Powertec Ltd, 4 Station Yard, Old Furnace Road, Coniston, Cumbria, LA21 8HU Tel: (01539) 441904 Fax: (01539) 441907
Cambridge Transformers Ltd, Quiet Waters, High Street, Earith, Huntingdon, Cambridgeshire, PE28 3PN Tel: (01487) 842154 Fax: (01487) 843445 E-mail: sales@transformers.demon.co.uk
Castleton Transformers, Unit C14 Fieldhouse Industrial Estate, Fieldhouse Road, Rochdale, Lancashire, OL12 0AA Tel: (01706) 342086 Fax: (01706) 861286
Coilcraft (U K), 21 Napier Place, Wardpark North, Cumbernauld, Glasgow, G68 0LL Tel: (01236) 730595 Fax: (01236) 730627 E-mail: sales@coilcraft-europe.com
Coilmech Transformer Mnfrs, 1 Barratt Industrial Park, Whittle Avenue, Fareham, Hampshire, PO15 5SL Tel: (01489) 885309 Fax: (01489) 885309
Grand Chain Ltd, Maple House, Laughton Road, Ringmer, Lewes, East Sussex, BN8 5SY Tel: (01273) 813345 Fax: (01273) 814 153 E-mail: sales@grandchain.co.uk
Inphase Transformers Ltd, Kenyon Business Centre, 21 Kenyon Road, Brierfield, Nelson, Lancashire, BB9 5SP Tel: (01282) 614684 Fax: (01282) 695588 E-mail: inphase-tf-ltd@tiscali.co.uk
Louth Transformer Co. Ltd, Belvoir Way, Fairfield Industrial Estate, Louth, Lincolnshire, LN11 0LQ Tel: (01507) 606436 Fax: (01507) 600168 E-mail: info@louthtransformers.co.uk
S P Wound Components Ltd, Unit 12 Stanley Green Industrial Estate, Stanley Green Esc, Poole, Dorset, BH15 3TH Tel: (01202) 682828 Fax: (01202) 682828 E-mail: spwoundcomp@boltblue.com
Tam Transformers Ltd, Durban Road, Bognor Regis, West Sussex, PO22 9QT Tel: (01243) 861122 Fax: (01243) 830870 E-mail: tam@tamtransformers.co.uk

TRANSIENT VOLTAGE PROTECTOR FILTERS

Murata Electronics Ltd, Oak House, Ancells Road, Fleet, Hampshire, GU51 2QW Tel: (01252) 811666 Fax: (01252) 811777 E-mail: enquiry@murata.co.uk

TRANSISTOR MANUFRS, *See also headings under Semiconductor*

Dynex Semi Conductor Ltd, Doddington Road, Lincoln, LN6 3LF Tel: (01522) 500500 Fax: (01522) 500550

TRANSIT CONTAINERS

Protechnic Ltd, Unit 109 Central Park, Petherton Road, Bristol, BS14 9BZ Tel: (01275) 833779 Fax: (01275) 835560 E-mail: sales@protechnic.com
Quentor Ltd, 10 Fitzmaurice Court, Rackheath, Norwich, NR13 6PY Tel: (01603) 721604 Fax: (01603) 721992 E-mail: sales@quentor.com

TRANSITION FITTINGS

Nord Gear Ltd, Riverview House, Friarton Road, Perth, PH2 8DF Tel: (01738) 472023 Fax: (01738) 628855 E-mail: info@nord-uk.com

TRANSLATION CONSULTANTS

▶ B2basics Translations, The Old Smithy, Main Street, Gisburn, Clitheroe, Lancashire, BB7 4HD Tel: (01200) 445749 Fax: (01200) 445576 E-mail: sales@translations-translation.com
▶ Castle Languages, 27 Oakland Drive, Netherton, Wakefield, West Yorkshire, WF4 4LZ Tel: (01924) 262891 Fax: (01924) 262891 E-mail: lisacastillo@castlelanguages.co.uk
▶ FILTRAN Trade & Translation Services, 12 Learmonth Gardens, Edinburgh, EH4 1HB Tel: 0131 3326065 Fax: 0131 3431428 E-mail: sales@filtran.co.uk
Genua Madrigal Ltd, 9 Gillian Park Road, Sutton, Surrey, SM3 9JT Tel: (020) 8286 6589 Fax: (020) 8286 6589 E-mail: info@nineservices.co.uk
▶ Hermann & Associates, 18 St Werburghs Road, Manchester, M21 0TN Tel: 0161-881 3034 Fax: 0161-862 9585 E-mail: sales@nhatranslations.com
▶ Voice Squad, 62 Blenheim Gardens, London, NW2 4NT Tel: (020) 8450 4451 E-mail: voices@voicesquad.com
White Drift Translations Ltd, 2 Stanley Street, Llanelli, Dyfed, SA15 2EU Tel: (01554) 757700 Fax: (01554) 757222 E-mail: info@whitedrift.com

TRANSLATION SERVICES, ON LINE

▶ Wolfestone Translation, Metropole Chambers, Salubrious Passage, Swansea, SA1 3RT Tel: (0845) 0000083 Fax: 0845 000 0083 E-mail: sales@wolfestone.co.uk

TRANSMISSION AND DISTRIBUTION (T AND D) EQUIPMENT

B S H Ltd, 15 Powdrake Road, Grangemouth, Stirlingshire, FK3 9UT Tel: (01324) 474242 Fax: (01324) 665456 E-mail: sales@bshltd.co.uk

TRANSMISSION BELTING TO SPECIFICATION

Transmission Development Co GB Ltd, 26 Dawkins Road, Poole, Dorset, BH15 4HF Tel: (01202) 675555 Fax: (01202) 677466 E-mail: sales@transdev.co.uk

TRANSMISSION CHAINS

James Hesketh & Co. Ltd, New Works, Sion Street, Radcliffe, Manchester, M26 3SB Tel: 0161-723 2789 Fax: 0161-725 9072

TRANSMISSION CHAINS – *continued*

Transtec International, 39, Westbrook Trading Estate, Westbrook Road, Trafford Park, Manchester, M17 1AY Tel: 0161-772 1844 Fax: 0161-772 1845 E-mail: info@transtecinternational.com

TRANSMISSION COMPONENTS/ SPARE PARTS, AUTOMOTIVE

J Judge & Sons, 37 Melbourne Road, Ilford, Essex, IG1 4LF Tel: (020) 8554 3347 Fax: (020) 8554 3347

Newood Transmissions Ltd, 95 Prince Avenue, Southend-on-Sea, SS2 6RL Tel: (01702) 392525 Fax: (01702) 392525 E-mail: sales@newoodtransmissions.co.uk

TRANSMISSION RETARDERS

▶ Telma Retarder Ltd, 25 Clarke Road, Bletchley, Milton Keynes, MK1 1LG Tel: (01908) 642822 Fax: (01908) 641348 E-mail: telma@telma.co.uk

TRANSMISSION SYSTEMS, AUTOMATIC, AUTOMOTIVE

Autoglide Garage Services, Birkett House, Wellington Road, Bollington, Macclesfield, Cheshire, SK10 5HT Tel: (01625) 574126 Fax: (01625) 574126

▶ Automatic Transmissions Ltd, Kebs Road, Todmorden, Lancashire, OL14 8SB Tel: (01706) 812291 E-mail: autotrans@uk2.net

C I Holdings Ltd, 2 Priory Road, Strood, Rochester, Kent, ME2 2EG Tel: (01634) 717747 Fax: (01634) 731115

Denton Engineering Co. Ltd, The Bearing Shop, 194 Talbot Road, Hyde, Cheshire, SK14 4HJ Tel: 0161-368 2097 Fax: 0161-368 0881

J P (Automatic Transmissions) Ltd, Units 4A-4B, Pear Tree Industrial Estate, Bath Road, Upper Langford, Bristol, BS40 5DJ Tel: (01934) 852772 Fax: (01934) 852211 E-mail: info@jpat.co.uk

Nicol Transmission Services, Coppice Trading Estate, Kidderminster, Worcestershire, DY11 7QY Tel: (01562) 752651 Fax: (01562) 823128

Southern Automatic Transmission Services, 2 Avocet Way, Diplocks Way, Hailsham, East Sussex, BN27 3JF Tel: (01323) 843178 Fax: (01323) 843178

Turner Power Train Systems Ltd, Racecourse Road, Wolverhampton, WV6 0QT Tel: (01902) 833000 Fax: (01902) 833750 E-mail: page_kevin_g@cat.com

TRANSMITTER (TEMPERATURE/ PRESSURE) MANUFRS

CMR Controls, 22 Repton Court, Repton Close, Basildon, Essex, SS13 1LN Tel: (01268) 287222 Fax: (01268) 287099 E-mail: sales@cmr.co.uk

Ellison Sensors International Ltd, Sensor House, Wrexham Technology Park, Wrexham, Clwyd, LL13 7YP Tel: (01978) 262255 Fax: (01978) 262233 E-mail: info@esi-tec.com

KDG Instruments, Crompton Way, Crawley, West Sussex, RH10 9YZ Tel: (01293) 525151 Fax: (01293) 533095 E-mail: sales@mobrey.com

Sensing Devices Ltd, 97 Tithebarn Road, Southport, Merseyside, PR8 6AG Tel: (01704) 546161 Fax: (01704) 546231 E-mail: sales@sensing-devices.co.uk

T S M Ltd, Sensor House, Wrexham Technology Park, Wrexham, Clwyd, LL13 7YP Tel: (01978) 291800 Fax: (01978) 291888 E-mail: tsm@esi-tec.com

Trafag UK Ltd, 12 Josselin Court, Josselin Road, Burnt Mills Industrial Estate, Basildon, Essex, SS13 1QF Tel: (01268) 727172 Fax: (01268) 727572 E-mail: sales@trafag.co.uk

Wika Instruments Ltd, 4 Gatton Park Business Centre, Wells Place Merstham, Redhill, RH1 3LG Tel: (01737) 644008 Fax: 01737 644403 E-mail: info@wika.co.uk

TRANSPARENCY VIEWING ACCESSORIES

Verivide, Quartz Close, Enderby, Leicester, LE19 4SG Tel: 0116-284 7790 Fax: 0116-284 7799 E-mail: enquiries@verivide.com

TRANSPARENT BOXES/CASES/ CONTAINERS

Bell Packaging Ltd, Barratt Industrial Park, Airport Way, Luton, LU2 9NH Tel: (01582) 459292 Fax: (01582) 450181 E-mail: info@bellpackaging.com

Transparent Box Co. Ltd, 22 Back Lane, Stonesby, Melton Mowbray, Leicestershire, LE14 4PT Tel: (01664) 464227 Fax: (01664) 464001 E-mail: info@transparentbox.co.uk

TRANSPARENT FILM

C P Films, 13 Acorn Business Centre, Northarbour Road, Cosham, Portsmouth, PO6 3TH Tel: (023) 9221 9112 Fax: (023) 9221 9102 E-mail: marketing.cosham@cpfilms.co.uk

TRANSPARENT FILM NECKTIE SLEEVES

Willeringhaus & Co. Ltd, The Mill, 23 Saunders Copse, Mayford, Woking, Surrey, GU22 0NS Tel: (01483) 723158 Fax: (01483) 723158 E-mail: willeringhaus.co@talk21.com

TRANSPARENT FILM PACKAGING PRODUCTS

Kite Packaging, 2 Crammond Park, Lovet Road, Harlow, Essex, CM19 5TF Tel: (01279) 406160 Fax: (01279) 406161 E-mail: southeast@packwithkite.com

TRANSPARENT FILM PRINTING,

See Flexographic etc

TRANSPARENT WINDOW SAFETY FILM

C P Films, 13 Acorn Business Centre, Northarbour Road, Cosham, Portsmouth, PO6 3TH Tel: (023) 9221 9112 Fax: (023) 9221 9102 E-mail: marketing.cosham@cpfilms.co.uk

Stock Films, PO Box 11, Barnet, Hertfordshire, EN4 8AR Tel: (020) 8441 0449 Fax: (020) 8441 4888

▶ Tinting Express Ltd, New Estate House, Old School Lane, Fremington, Barnstaple, Devon, EX31 3AZ Tel: (01271) 322857 Fax: (01271) 326346 E-mail: sales@tintingexpress.co.uk

Westgate Solar Control, PO Box 21, Stafford, ST16 3YJ Tel: (01785) 242181

TRANSPORT CONSULTANTS/ PLANNING OR ECONOMIC ADVISERS

Astran Cargo Services Ltd, 519, New Hythe Lane, Larkfield, Maidstone, Kent, ME20 6SB Tel: (01622) 716441 Fax: (01622) 791854 E-mail: london@astran-cargo.com

Docklands Light Railway Ltd, PO Box 154, London, E14 0DX Tel: (020) 7363 9898 Fax: (020) 7363 9708

Fabermaunsell, Beaufort House, 94-96 Newhall Street, Birmingham, B3 1PB Tel: 0121-262 1900 Fax: 0121-262 1999 E-mail: libby.caughtry@fabermaunsell.com

Fraikin Ltd, Torwood Place, Westwood Business Park, Coventry, CV4 8HX Tel: (024) 7669 4494 Fax: (024) 7647 0419

Halcrow Asia Partnership Ltd, Vineyard House, 44 Brook Green, London, W6 7BY Tel: (020) 7602 7282 Fax: (020) 7603 0095 E-mail: info@halcrow.com

Logistech Ltd, Exchange House, 494 Midsummer Boulevard, Milton Keynes, MK9 2EA Tel: (01908) 255985 E-mail: info@logistech.co.uk

M V A Consultancy, Sunley Tower, Piccadilly Plaza, Manchester, M1 4BT Tel: 0161-236 0282 Fax: 0161-236 0095

Mini Clipper Ltd, 7 Chartmoor Road, Leighton Buzzard, Bedfordshire, LU7 4WG Tel: (01525) 244700 Fax: (01525) 851445 E-mail: sales@miniclipper.co.uk

Plymouth Citybus Ltd, Milehouse, Milehouse Road, Plymouth, PL3 4AA Tel: (01752) 264207 Fax: (01752) 567209 E-mail: hq@plymouthbus.co.uk

Turley Associates Ltd, 43 Park Place, Leeds, LS1 2RY Tel: 0113-386 3800 Fax: 0113-244 3650 E-mail: leeds@rta.co.uk

Tweedy & Holt, Suite D106, Dean Clough Office Park, Halifax, West Yorkshire, HX3 5AX Tel: (01422) 363161 Fax: (01422) 355290 E-mail: sales@tweedyandholt.co.uk

U T I Worldwide (U K) Ltd, Reading Cargo Centre, Hyperion Way, Rose Kiln Lane, Reading, RG2 0JS Tel: 0118-986 9595 Fax: 0118-987 6074

Ward International Consulting Ltd, Funtley Court, 19 Funtley Hill, Fareham, Hampshire, PO16 7UY Tel: (01329) 280280 Fax: (01329) 221010 E-mail: admin@wardint.co.uk

▶ Wynns Road Haulage Services, 2 High Street, Eccleshall, Stafford, ST21 6BZ Tel: (01785) 850411 Fax: (01785) 851866

TRANSPORT CUSTOMER SERVICES

Northern Ireland Railways Co. Ltd, East Bridge, Belfast, BT1 3PR Tel: (028) 9089 9400 E-mail: feedback@translink.co.uk

TRANSPORT MANAGEMENT

▶ Capital City Cars Ltd, 92 Roan Street, Greenwich, London, SE10 9JT Tel: (08702) 404041 E-mail: colin@capitalcity.info

Chartered Institute of Logistics & Transport (UK), Logistics & Transport Centre, Earlstrees Road, Corby, Northamptonshire, NN17 4AX Tel: (01536) 740100 Fax: (01536) 740101 E-mail: enquiry@ciltuk.org.uk

▶ S E T S, 114 Canterbury Road, Worthing, West Sussex, BN13 1AL Tel: (07711) 674303 Fax: (01903) 523149 E-mail: transport.manager@ntlworld.com

▶ SISTech, Heriot Watt University, Edinburgh, EH14 4AS Tel: 0131-451 8162 Fax: 0131-451 8150

TRANSPORT TURBOCHARGERS

Borgwarner Holdings Ltd, Roydsdale Way, Euroway Industrial Estate, Bradford, West Yorkshire, BD4 6SE Tel: (01274) 684915 Fax: (01274) 689671

Turbo Technics Ltd, 2 Sketty Close, Brackmills, Northampton, NN4 7PL Tel: (01604) 764005 Fax: (01604) 769668 E-mail: enquiries@turbotechnics.com

TRANSPORTATION CONTRACTORS, HEAVY, LOAD-OUT

Abnormal Loads Services International Ltd, 1501 Hedon Road, Hull, HU9 5NX Tel: (01482) 796214 Fax: (01482) 707650 E-mail: info.advertising@abnormal-loads.com

David Gerrard Fisheries Ltd, 4 Mid Shore, Pittenweem, Anstruther, Fife, KY10 2NJ Tel: (01333) 311551 Fax: (01333) 312286

H C Wilson Transport Ltd, Grove Lane, Elmswell, Bury St. Edmunds, Suffolk, IP30 9HN Tel: (01359) 240558 Fax: (01359) 240437 E-mail: traffic@hcwilsontransport.com

Rob Hatfield Ltd, Tower House Lane, Hedon, Hull, HU12 8EE Tel: (01482) 898286 Fax: (01482) 896862

TRANSPORTATION EQUIPMENT

Aberdeen Web Ltd, Unit 5a Wellheads Crescent, Wellheads Indust Estate, Dyce, Aberdeen, AB21 7HG Tel: (01224) 723111 Fax: (01224) 774141

TRANSPORTERS, CAR

▶ Autoporters, 20 Arran Drive, Frodsham, WA6 6AL Tel: (01928) 732846 E-mail: chris.wynne@autoporters.co.uk

▶ Wensley Transport, Green Lane, Castleford, West Yorkshire, WF10 2RY Tel: (01977) 550259 Fax: (01977) 514239 E-mail: wensley@transport76.fsnet.co.uk

TRANSPORTERS, RACING CAR

▶ Autoporters, 20 Arran Drive, Frodsham, WA6 6AL Tel: (01928) 732846 E-mail: chris.wynne@autoporters.co.uk

TRAPS, ANIMAL/VERMIN

John Dee Humane Traps, 4 Russett Cottage, Greendale Barton, Woodbury Salterton, Exeter, EX5 1EW Tel: (01395) 233340 Fax: (01395) 233548 E-mail: desmo1@btopenworld.com

Falcon Works, Hanworth Road, Sunbury-on-Thames, Middlesex, TW16 5DE Tel: (01932) 784225 Fax: (01932) 788175 E-mail: enquiries@falconworks.co.uk

TRAVEL AGENTS

▶ Business Management, 107 Market Street, Manchester, M1 1NN Tel: 0161-832 5647 Fax: 0161-832 5651 E-mail: manchester@btmonline.co.uk

▶ Camberley Travel Centre Ltd, 2a Princess Way, Camberley, Surrey, GU15 3SR Tel: (01276) 28761 Fax: (01276) 692194 E-mail: jo@camberleytravel.co.uk

▶ Never Compromise, 36 London Road, Pulborough, West Sussex, RH20 1AS Tel: (0845) 6449198 Fax: (0871) 2420836 E-mail: sales@never-compromise.com

▶ Transmanche, Passenger Terminal, Beach Road, Newhaven, East Sussex, BN9 0BG Tel: (01273) 612875 Fax: (01273) 612864 E-mail: sales@transmancheferries.com

Vale Of Glamorgan Travel, 53 Coed Mieri, Tyla Garw, Pontyclun, Mid Glamorgan, CF72 9UW Tel: (0870) 0436026 Fax: (0870) 0436127 E-mail: sales@valeofglamtravel.co.uk

▶ Weddings Abroad, 15 High Street, Chasetown, Burntwood, Staffordshire, WS7 3XE Tel: (01543) 686884 Fax: 01543 686884 E-mail: helen@perfect-weddings.net

TRAVEL AGENTS, BUSINESS

▶ Albion Service, 9 Silverwood Way, Up Hatherley, Cheltenham, Gloucestershire, GL51 3TW Tel: (01242) 254771 Fax: (01242) 254771 E-mail: albionservice@btopenworld.com

▶ Ambros Travel, 33 LongBanks, Staple Tye, Harlow, Essex, CM18 7NT Tel: (01279) 639412 Fax: (0870) 7051629 E-mail: travel@ambros.plus.com

▶ Business Management, 107 Market Street, Manchester, M1 1NN Tel: 0161-832 5647 Fax: 0161-832 5651 E-mail: manchester@btmonline.co.uk

▶ Camberley Travel Centre Ltd, 2a Princess Way, Camberley, Surrey, GU15 3SR Tel: (01276) 28761 Fax: (01276) 692194 E-mail: jo@camberleytravel.co.uk

▶ GoCruise South, 46 The Crescent, Eastleigh, Hampshire, SO50 9BR Tel: 02380 392 515 E-mail: karen@gocruisedirect.co.uk

▶ Never Compromise, 36 London Road, Pulborough, West Sussex, RH20 1AS Tel: (0845) 6449198 Fax: (0871) 2420836 E-mail: sales@never-compromise.com

Omega World Travel Ltd, 11 York Road, London, SE1 7NX Tel: (020) 7922 0770 Fax: (020) 7922 0799 E-mail: sales@owt.net

▶ The Travellers' Friend Limited, 3 Barttelot Court, Barttelot Road, Horsham, West Sussex, RH12 1AU Tel: 01403 255977 Fax: 01403 217919 E-mail: sales@travellersfriend.com

▶ Uniglobe Prestige Travel, 28a New Street, St. Neots, Cambridgeshire, PE19 1AJ Tel: (01480) 404680 Fax: (01480) 405656 E-mail: sales@prestigetravel.biz

Vale Of Glamorgan Travel, 53 Coed Mieri, Tyla Garw, Pontyclun, Mid Glamorgan, CF72 9UW Tel: (0870) 0436026 Fax: (0870) 0436127 E-mail: sales@valeofglamtravel.co.uk

▶ Yacht Charters Asia, Halden House, High Halden, Ashford, Kent, TN26 3BT Tel: (0870) 1615098 E-mail: tom@yachtchartersasia.com

▶ Your Tours, 32 Bracken Road, Leigh, Lancashire, WN7 4XA Tel: (0800) 0833213 Fax: (07980) 234871 E-mail: info@your-tours.co.uk

TRAVEL GOODS

▶ Delsey Service Centre, Unit 4, Sharp House, Laindon, Basildon, Essex, SS15 6DR Tel: (01268) 541100 Fax: (01268) 541110

Dewhirst Accessories Ltd, Kitty Brewster Industrial Estate, Blyth, Northumberland, NE24 4RG Tel: (01670) 368587 Fax: (01670) 365773

Gostelow Advertising Ltd, 21-22 Francis Street, Hull, HU2 8DT Tel: (01482) 323459 Fax: (01482) 586325 E-mail: alec@gostelow.karoo.co.uk

Harper- Little Ltd, 50 Brunswick Square, Hove, East Sussex, BN3 1EF Tel: (020) 7993 4087 Fax: (0870) 6220607

Japinda Products Ltd, Constellation Works, Fernhurst Street, Chadderton, Oldham, OL1 2RN Tel: 0161-620 4231 Fax: 0161-627 0914 E-mail: sales@japinda.co.uk

Johnstons Of Elgin Ltd, Newmill, Elgin, Morayshire, IV30 4AF Tel: (01343) 554000 Fax: (01343) 554055 E-mail: elgin@johnstoncashmere.com

Landor Ltd, Riverside House, River Way, Harlow, Essex, CM20 2DW Tel: (01279) 441411 Fax: (01279) 423729 E-mail: paul@landor-hawa.co.uk

Mem's Travel, Unit 27 Market Hall Wood Green Shopping City, High Road, London, N22 6YE Tel: (020) 8889 2631 Fax: (020) 8882 9873

Usel Supported Employment, 182-188 Cambrai Street, Belfast, BT13 3JH Tel: (028) 9035 6600 Fax: (028) 9035 6611 E-mail: sales@usel.co.uk

TRAVEL INFORMATION SERVICES

Accommodations, Lion House, 6 Hawthorn Road, Newcastle upon Tyne, NE3 4DE Tel: 0191-213 2131 Fax: 0191-213 2211 E-mail: sales@accomodationsuk.co.uk

Dancing Octopus Ltd, 2 Millers Gate, Stone, Staffordshire, ST15 8ZF Tel: (01889) 505691 Fax: (01889) 505691 E-mail: webmaster@dancingoctopus.com

▶ Florida Villa Finder, 5, 1 Station Lofts, Strathblane, Glasgow, G63 9BD Tel: (01360) 771856 E-mail: enquiries@florida-villa-finder.com

▶ Guide to International Travel, 3rd Floor Dukeminster House, Church Street, Dunstable, Bedfordshire, LU5 4HU Tel: 01582 676878 Fax: 01582 676893 E-mail: dggtravel@rbi.co.uk

Major Travel plc, Fortress Grove, 28-34 Fortress Road, London, NW5 2HB Tel: (020) 7393 1088 Fax: (020) 7393 1096 E-mail: info@majortravel.co.uk

The Mighty Fine Company Ltd, Quatro House, Lyon Way, Frimley, Surrey, GU16 7ER Tel: 0845 072 0090 E-mail: info@mightyfinecompany.com

O A G Worldwide, Church Street, Dunstable, Bedfordshire, LU5 4HB Tel: (01582) 600111 Fax: (01582) 695140 E-mail: sales@oag.com

TRAVEL INFORMATION SERVICES – *continued*

Pressplan Travel Ltd, 17 Verulam Road, St. Albans, Hertfordshire, AL3 4DA Tel: (01727) 833291 Fax: (01727) 867435
E-mail: info@pressplantravel.com

TRAVEL INSURANCE

▶ Essential Health Ltd, 2-3 Tabernacle Lane, Yeovil, Somerset, BA20 1QA Tel: (0845) 4085444 Fax: (01935) 476668
E-mail: sales@privatesurgery.info

▶ Giles Financial Services, 12 Beresford Terrace, Ayr, KA7 2EG Tel: (01292) 619900 Fax: (01292) 610037

▶ Haydock Finance Ltd, 2 The Cottage, Main Street, Kinnesswood, Kinross, KY13 9HN Tel: (01592) 840480 Fax: (01592) 840480

▶ text2insure, 17th Floor, 30 St Mary Axe, London, EC3A 8BF Tel: (020) 7150 9995
E-mail: linkmaster@text2insure.co.uk

▶ Uniglobe Prestige Travel, 28a New Street, St. Neots, Cambridgeshire, PE19 1AJ Tel: (01480) 404680 Fax: (01480) 405656
E-mail: sales@prestigetravel.biz

TRAVEL MAGAZINES

▶ The Ashford Advertiser, PO Box 1, Ashford, Kent, TN23 4ZU Tel: (01233) 624538 Fax: (01233) 641900
E-mail: theadvertiser@aol.com

TRAVEL PLANNING CONSULTANCY

▶ Albion Service, 9 Silverwood Way, Up Hatherley, Cheltenham, Gloucestershire, GL51 3TW Tel: (01242) 254771 Fax: (01242) 254771
E-mail: albionservice@btopenworld.com

▶ Direct Passport & Visa Company Ltd, 12 Chepstow Road, London, W2 5BD Tel: (029) 1412 2072E-mail: directvisas@e3internet.com

▶ The Travellers' Friend Limited, 3 Barttelot Court, Barttelot Road, Horsham, West Sussex, RH12 1AU Tel: 01403 255977 Fax: 01403 217919 E-mail: sales@travellersfriend.com

TRAVEL RUGS

F & A Hill Ltd, 80 Brewer Street, London, W1F 9TZ Tel: (020) 7734 0652 Fax: (020) 7434 3698

TRAY DRYERS

Powder Systems Ltd, Estuary Business Park, Speke, Liverpool, L24 8RG Tel: 0151-448 7700 Fax: 0151-448 7702
E-mail: sales@p-s-l.com

TRAYS, GLASS FIBRE OR FIBREGLASS

Arnold Designs Ltd, London Rd, Chalford, Stroud, Glos, GL6 8NR Tel: (01453) 882310 Fax: (01453) 886977

Keswick Trays, Forest View Farm, Peckleton Lane, Desford, Leicester, LE9 9JU Tel: (01455) 828990 Fax: (01455) 828999
E-mail: david@keswicktrays.f9.co.uk

TREADMILLS

▶ Auction Fitness, Unit 10 Bakers Park, Cater Road, Bishopsworth, Bristol, BS13 7TW Tel: (0870) 8519419 Fax: 0117-964 9679
E-mail: info@auctionfitness.com

▶ Fitness Equipment Clearance, Boland House, Nottingham South & Wilford Industrial Estate, Nottingham, NG11 7EP Tel: 0115-982 2844 Fax: 0115-982 6775
E-mail: sales@fitness-equipment-clearance.co.uk

▶ Fitness Warehouse, 2b Linton Street, Fulwood, Preston, PR2 3BJ Tel: (01772) 712888 Fax: (01772) 788938
E-mail: sales@gyms4home.com

▶ Powerhouse Retail Ltd, Unit 11 Powerhouse Fitness Business Division, 12 Whitehall Street, Glasgow, G3 8BN Tel: 0141-221 3885

TREE GUARDS

▶ Ashridge Trees, Grove Cross Barn, Castle Cary, Somerset, BA7 7NJ Tel: (01963) 359444 Fax: (01963) 359445
E-mail: julian@ashridgetrees.co.uk

▶ Cheviot Trees Ltd, Newton Brae, Berwick-upon-Tweed, TD15 1UL Tel: (01289) 386755 Fax: (01289) 386750
E-mail: katherine@cheviot-trees.co.uk

TREE PLANTING EQUIPMENT

The Caledonian Tree Company Ltd, Cowbraehill, Tynehead, Pathhead, Midlothian, EH37 5XT Tel: (01875) 835360 Fax: (01875) 835636
E-mail: single@superoots.co.uk

TREE SURGERY

Robin Forestry Surveys Ltd, Coulton House, Tannery Road, Harraby Green Business Park, Carlisle, CA1 2SS Tel: (01228) 409469 Fax: (01228) 540439
E-mail: jaqs@robinsurveys.co.uk

▶ Hawthorn Gardening Services, The Hawthorns, Ewell, Epsom, Surrey, KT17 2QA Tel: 07929 196344
E-mail: jon@hawthorn-gardening.com

▶ Height & Light, 2 Green Lane Bungalows, Woodredon Road, Waltham Abbey, Essex, EN9 3SY Tel: (01992) 653977 Fax: 01992 653977 E-mail: sales@heightandlight.co.uk

▶ Heyes Validator Ltd, Hafan Corwen Road Pontybodkin, Flintshire, Pontybodkin, Mold, Clwyd, CH7 4TG Tel: (01352) 770900

TREES

▶ Ashridge Trees, Grove Cross Barn, Castle Cary, Somerset, BA7 7NJ Tel: (01963) 359444 Fax: (01963) 359445
E-mail: julian@ashridgetrees.co.uk

▶ Mercaston Tree Co., Ednaston, Ednaston, Ashbourne, Derbyshire, DE6 3AE Tel: (01335) 360947 Fax: (01335) 360394
E-mail: enquiries@mercastontreecompany.com

▶ Musgrove Willows, Lakewall, Westonzoyland, Bridgwater, Somerset, TA7 0LP Tel: (01278) 691105 Fax: (01278) 699107
E-mail: info@musgrovewillows.co.uk

▶ www.saundersallotment.co.uk, 88 Dunkeld Road, Gosport, Hampshire, PO12 4NJ Tel: (023) 92 586619
E-mail: berylsau@saundersallotment.co.uk

TRELLIS

Electranets Ltd, 31 Westfield Avenue, Brockworth, Gloucester, GL3 4AU Tel: (01452) 617841 Fax: (01452) 617841
E-mail: roy@electranets.fsnet.co.uk

Forest Garden plc, Unit 291 296, Hartlebury Trading Estate, Hartlebury, Kidderminster, Worcestershire, DY10 4JB Tel: (0870) 1919800 Fax: (0870) 1919898
E-mail: info@forestgarden.co.uk

TRENCH DIGGING EQUIPMENT

A F T Trenchers Ltd, 16-17 Addison Road, Sudbury, Suffolk, CO10 2YW Tel: (01787) 311811 Fax: (01787) 310888
E-mail: info@trenchers.co.uk

TRENCH LINING EQUIPMENT

Jayville Engineering Ltd, Unit A2 Halesfield 24, Telford, Shropshire, TF7 4NS Tel: (01952) 583041 Fax: (01952) 586342

TRENCH SHORING EQUIPMENT

▶ Groundforce, Beckwith Knowle, Otley Road, Beckwithshaw, Harrogate, North Yorkshire, HG3 1UD Tel: (01423) 852295 Fax: (01423) 536731
E-mail: groundforce.northern@vibroplant.co.uk

TRENCHLESS PIPE LAYING CONTRACTORS

▶ Trench Less Installations Ltd, 15 York Street, Wolverhampton, WV1 3RN Tel: (01902) 689110 Fax: (01902) 653478
E-mail: underground@tiltd99.freeserve.co.uk

TRENCHLESS TECHNOLOGY CONTRACTORS

▶ Trench Less Installations Ltd, 15 York Street, Wolverhampton, WV1 3RN Tel: (01902) 689110 Fax: (01902) 653478
E-mail: underground@tiltd99.freeserve.co.uk

TRENCHLESS TECHNOLOGY EQUIPMENT

International Drilling Services Ltd, Carrwood Road, Chesterfield, Derbyshire, S41 9QB Tel: (01246) 269911 Fax: (01246) 269922
E-mail: sales@idsuk.com

T T UK Ltd, Windsor Road, Bedford, MK42 9SU Tel: (01234) 342566 Fax: (01234) 352184
E-mail: info@tt-uk.com

U Mole Ltd, Unit 11 Hardwick Road Industrial Estatepark, Hardwick Road, Great Gransden, Sandy, Bedfordshire, SG19 3BJ Tel: (01767) 677503 Fax: (01767) 677827
E-mail: info@umole.co.uk

Zoomlion Powermole Ltd, 35 Church Road Business Centre, Church Road, Sittingbourne, Kent, ME10 3RS Tel: (01795) 425425 Fax: (01795) 477177
E-mail: allen.kayes@zlpm.com

TREPANNING TOOLS

Linear Tools Ltd, 1 Clock Tower Road, Isleworth, Middlesex, TW7 6DT Tel: (020) 8400 2020 Fax: (020) 8400 2021
E-mail: sales@lineartools.co.uk

TRIMMINGS MANUFRS

A Attenborough & Co Ltd, Nuart Road, Beeston, Nottingham, NG9 2NH Tel: 0115-925 8185 Fax: 0115-922 7445
E-mail: a.attenborough@btinternet.com

A & N Trimmings Ltd, 5-7 Cyril Road, Birmingham, B10 0SS Tel: 0121-771 4040 Fax: 0121-766 6878
E-mail: sales@antrimm.co.uk

Barnett Lawson Trimmings Ltd, 16-17 Little Portland Street, London, W1W 8NE Tel: (020) 7636 8591 Fax: (020) 7580 0669
E-mail: info@bltrimmings.com

Barr Radcliffe Ltd, 97 Grace Road, Leicester, LE2 8AE Tel: 0116-244 0414 Fax: 0116-244 0268 E-mail: info@barr-radcliffe.co.uk

British Trimmings Ltd, Coronation Street, Stockport, Cheshire, SK5 7PJ Tel: 0161-480 6122 Fax: 0161-477 1789
E-mail: uk.sales@btrim.co.uk

Europa Trimmings Ltd, 13-15 Lever Street, London, EC1V 3QU Tel: (020) 7250 1663 Fax: (020) 7253 4309

Frankle Trimmings, 281-285 Bethnal Green Road, London, E2 6AH Tel: (020) 7739 0621 Fax: (020) 7739 0751 E-mail: ftrim@aol.com

G K & Sons Ltd, 235-243 Sussex Way, London, N19 4JD Tel: (020) 7281 3282 Fax: (020) 7272 8992

William Gee Ltd, William Gee House, 520-522 Kingsland Road, London, E8 4AH Tel: (020) 7254 2451 Fax: (020) 7249 8116
E-mail: wmgeetrims@aol.com

Genel 86 Ltd, Kent House, 9 Beech Street, Leicester, LE5 0DF Tel: 0116-251 5156 Fax: 0116-251 5159
E-mail: genel86sales@aol.com

Halicombe Trimmings Ltd, 15-16 Margaret Street, London, W1W 8RW Tel: (020) 7580 5423 Fax: (020) 7323 0245
E-mail: halicombe@aol.com

J Dewalleg Ltd, 361 Amersham Road, Hazlemere, High Wycombe, Buckinghamshire, HP15 7HR Tel: (01494) 711431 Fax: (01494) 711388 E-mail: sales@jdwltd.com

Joseph Hirst Huddersfield Ltd, 29 Byram Street, Huddersfield, HD1 1DY Tel: (01484) 435324 Fax: (01484) 435469

Malhi Trimmings Ltd, Excelda Works, 36 Rookery Road, Handsworth, Birmingham, B21 9NB Tel: (0121) 554 5731 Fax: (0121) 554 5733
E-mail: sales@mahligroup.co.uk

Nottingham Braid Co. Ltd, Gresham Road, Derby, DE24 8AW Tel: (01332) 331314 Fax: (01332) 292977
E-mail: enquiry@nottinghambraid.co.uk

Nottingham Narrow Fabrics, Block A Harrington Mills, Leopold Street, Long Eaton, Nottingham, NG10 4QG Tel: 0115-946 8883 Fax: 0115-946 8652

Nova Trimmings Ltd, 15 Abbey Gate, Leicester, LE4 0AA Tel: 0116-253 1144 Fax: 0116-251 5631 E-mail: nova.trimmings@virgin.net

Pauls Knitwear Co. Ltd, Units 10-14 The Bridge Trading Estate, Bridge St North, Smethwick, West Midlands, B66 2BZ Tel: 0121-525 9595 Fax: 0121-558 7930

Pennine Trims, 5 Rosewood Business Park, St James's Road, Blackburn, BB1 8ET Tel: (01254) 582715 Fax: (01254) 663309

H.A. Percheron Ltd, 202 The Chambers, Chelsea Harbour, London, SW10 0XF Tel: (020) 7349 1590 Fax: (020) 7349 1595
E-mail: info@hapercheron.co.uk

R A L Ltd, 449 Bethnal Green Road, London, E2 9QH Tel: (020) 7739 5149 Fax: (020) 7739 7856 E-mail: sales@ralphswimer.co.uk

Randall Ribbons, 12 Frederick Street, Luton, LU2 7QS Tel: (01582) 721301 Fax: (01582) 720060 E-mail: sales@randallribbons.com

Rayflex Ltd, Unit 6-9, 35 River Road, Barking, Essex, IG11 0DA Tel: (020) 8591 9418 Fax: (020) 8591 9419
E-mail: info@rayflexltd.co.uk

Richards James Weldon, 5-6 The Mews, Hatherley Road, Sidcup, Kent, DA14 4BH Tel: (020) 8300 7878 Fax: (020) 8300 9709

S & T Trimmings Ltd, 56-66 Cambridge Street, Coventry, CV1 5HW Tel: (024) 7622 3366 Fax: (024) 7666 4401
E-mail: info@sttrimmings.com

Sands Fabrics, 27 Gibson Road, High Wycombe, Buckinghamshire, HP12 4QW Tel: (01494) 521939

Schwenk Ltd, 70-71 Wells Street, London, W1T 3HN Tel: (020) 7580 3674 Fax: (020) 7580 2342 E-mail: schwenk.ltd@virgin.net

M.& J. Shapero Ltd, 70 Thomas Street, Aston, Birmingham, B6 4TN Tel: 0121-359 7731 Fax: 0121-353 4557
E-mail: shapero@netcomuk.co.uk

W A Fox Knitting Co Ltd, Unit 12-13 Premier Works, Canal Street, Wigston, Leicestershire, LE18 4PL Tel: 0116-277 2592

W S Robinson & Sons London Ltd, 324a Limpsfield Road, South Croydon, Surrey, CR2 9BX Tel: (020) 8651 2010

TRIMMINGS, COSTUME/ FASHION

▶ Hand & Lock, 86 Margaret Street, London, W1W 8TE Tel: (020) 7580 7488 Fax: (020) 7580 7499
E-mail: enquiries@handembroidery.com

Qasco UK Ltd, 43d Brecknock Road, London, N7 0BT Tel: (020) 7267 3079 Fax: (020) 7267 4212 E-mail: sales@qasco.co.uk

TRIMS, ALUMINIUM/ALLOY

Sapa Pressweld Ltd, Spinnaker Park, Spinnaker Road, Hempsted, Gloucester, GL2 5DG Tel: (01452) 502502 Fax: (01452) 503503
E-mail: sales@pressweld.co.uk

TRIP AMPLIFIERS

Sky Electronic Systems Ltd, Unit D Cavendish Courtyard, Weldon North Industrial Estate, Corby, Northamptonshire, NN17 5DZ Tel: (01536) 267000 Fax: (01536) 267666
E-mail: ian@skyd.fsnet.co.uk

TRITIUM SELF ENERGISED LIGHT SOURCES

SRB Technologies, 6 Portland Business Centre, Manor House Lane, Datchet, Slough, SL3 9EG Tel: (01753) 592492 Fax: (01753) 592692 E-mail: sales@betalight.com

TROLLEY MAINTENANCE/ REPAIR SERVICES

Concorde Wireworking & Cleaning Co. Ltd, 175 Beckenham Road, Beckenham, Kent, BR3 4PT Tel: (020) 8658 8080 Fax: (020) 8658 8282
E-mail: info@concordetrolleys.co.uk

Trolley Maintenance Services Ltd, Chelworth Lodge, Cricklade, Swindon, SN6 6HP Tel: (01793) 759184 Fax: (01793) 759469
E-mail: info@trolleymaintenance.co.uk

TROLLEY REBUILDERS/ REFURBISHMENT SERVICES

Trolley Maintenance Services Ltd, Chelworth Lodge, Cricklade, Swindon, SN6 6HP Tel: (01793) 759184 Fax: (01793) 759469
E-mail: info@trolleymaintenance.co.uk

TROLLEY RETRIEVAL

Symonds Trolley Services Ltd, Wern Trading Estate, Rogerstone, Newport, Gwent, NP10 9XX Tel: (01633) 892362 Fax: (01633) 896618
E-mail: symonds@symondshydroclean.co.uk

TROLLEYS TO SPECIFICATION

Craven & Co. Ltd, Manse Lane, Knaresborough, North Yorkshire, HG5 8ET Tel: (01423) 796208 Fax: (01423) 869189
E-mail: sales@craven-solutions.com

M R P Trucks & Trolleys, 40 Horringer Road, Bury St. Edmunds, Suffolk, IP33 2DR Tel: (01284) 766300 Fax: (01284) 766500
E-mail: sales@mrptruckstrolleys.co.uk

Richardson & Co. Ltd, Smithfold Lane, Worsley, Manchester, M28 0GP Tel: 0161-702 7002

Trolley Watch UK, 18 Alderley Road, Bournemouth, BH8 8SA Tel: (01202) 247111
E-mail: lmoss@cwcom.net

A. & G. Walden Bros Ltd, 34 Wimbledon Avenue, Brandon, Suffolk, IP27 0NZ Tel: (01842) 811776 Fax: (01842) 814603
E-mail: trucks@walden.co.uk

TROLLEYS, AIRPORT BAGGAGE

▶ Airbase GSE (UK) Ltd, Bedfont Trading Estate, Bedfont Road, Feltham, Middlesex, TW14 8EB Tel: (0870) 2405576 Fax: (020) 8751 0952
E-mail: enquiries@airbasegse.co.uk

TROLLEYS, MAILROOM/OFFICE

Alan Stuart, 9-17 Cobden Street, Salford, M6 6NA Tel: 0161-737 4236 Fax: 0161-745 8327 E-mail: sales@alan-stuart.demon.co.uk

TROLLEYS, MAILROOM/OFFICE – *continued*

Ease-E-Load Trolleys Ltd, Saunders House, Moor Lane, Birmingham, B6 7HH Tel: 0121-356 2228 Fax: 0121-356 2220 E-mail: info@ease-e-load.co.uk
MFB Fabrications Ltd, High Street, Clay Cross, Chesterfield, Derbyshire, S45 9DX Tel: (01246) 861700 Fax: (01246) 861777 E-mail: sales@mfbfabs.co.uk

TROPHY ENGRAVERS

▶ Alan Hislop, 32 Holt Road, Horsford, Norwich, NR10 3DD Tel: (01603) 897428 E-mail: sales@ahengraving.co.uk
Avon Trophies, Wharfside, Couch Lane, Devizes, Wiltshire, SN10 1EB Tel: (01380) 724630 Fax: (01380) 720122 E-mail: sales@avontrophies.co.uk
▶ Bazeray, PO Box 3936, Bracknell, Berkshire, RG42 7PX Tel: (01344) 884916 Fax: (01344) 884916 E-mail: info@bazeray.co.uk
▶ Coventry Trophy Centre, 4 Cedars Avenue, Coventry, CV6 1DR Tel: (024) 7659 2022 Fax: (024) 7659 2022 E-mail: coventrytrophies@yahoo.co.uk
Entech Precision Engraving, 4 Old Forge Cottage, Pearson Road, Sonning, Reading, RG4 6UH Tel: 0118-927 2499 Fax: 0118-927 2499 E-mail: ejak@btclick.com
Hallmark Engraving, 116-118 Selsdon Road, South Croydon, Surrey, CR2 6PG Tel: (020) 8686 6649 Fax: (020) 8760 0899 E-mail: sales@hallmarksigns.co.uk
Inverkeithing Trophy & Engraving Centre, 29 Church Street, Inverkeithing, Fife, KY11 1LG Tel: (01383) 411348 Fax: (01383) 411348
M G Engraving, 135 Somerset Road, Coventry, CV1 4EF Tel: (024) 7622 5110 Fax: (024) 7663 2894 E-mail: mg@mgengineering.fsnet.co.uk
▶ Purple Patch Promotions, 3 Gowers Close, Kesgrave, Ipswich, IP5 2XE Tel: (01473) 333388 Fax: (01473) 333388 E-mail: sales@purplepatch.org
Read T, 30 Elmtree Road, Basildon, Essex, SS16 4TN Tel: (01268) 456160
Alan Roberts (Engravers) Ltd, 39A-43A Knight Street, Liverpool, L1 9DT Tel: 0151-709 3404 Fax: 0151-707 8081 E-mail: mail@alanrobertsengravers.co.uk
▶ Stour Valley Trophies, 6 Springfield Terrace, East Street, Sudbury, Suffolk, CO10 2TS Tel: (01787) 377139
▶ Tam O' Shanter Crystal & Awards, 116 Russell Drive, Wallacetown, Ayr, KA8 8JN Tel: (01292) 287765 Fax: E-mail: donald@tamoshanter-crystal.com
▶ V B Trophies, Unit 1 Lumen Road, Royston, Hertfordshire, SG8 7AF Tel: (01763) 244116 Fax: (01763) 250850 E-mail: sales@vbgroup.co.uk

TROPICAL FISH

▶ Murray Aquatics, 1 Houston Place, Glasgow, G5 8SG Tel: 0141-420 1020 Fax: 0141-420 1040 E-mail: sales@murrayaquatics.co.uk
Nicky's Fish, Slade House, 45 Overstone Road, Moulton, Northampton, NN3 7UU Tel: (01604) 644394

TROPICAL FRUIT

▶ Suncrest, Unit B Britannia Trading Estate, Printing House Lane, Hayes, Middlesex, UB3 1AP Tel: (020) 8848 0099 Fax: (020) 8848 4990 E-mail: sales@suncrestdrinks.com

TROUGH BELT CONVEYOR SYSTEMS

Conveyor Belt Systems Ltd, 19 Kewferry Road, Northwood, Middlesex, HA6 2NS Tel: (01923) 820121 Fax: (01923) 835699

TROUSERS

▶ A B Clothing Ltd, 63 Britannia Street, Leicester, LE1 3LE Tel: 0116-251 2518 Fax: 0116-251 2518
▶ Alex Scott & Co Kiltmakers Ltd, 43 Schoolhill, Aberdeen, AB10 1JT Tel: (01224) 643924 Fax: (01224) 626061 E-mail: sales@kiltmakers.co.uk
Baltex Clothing, 63 Hume Street, Smethwick, West Midlands, B66 3PN Tel: (07956) 365202
▶ Blue Star Jeans Ltd, Chesterfield Road, Leicester, LE5 5LF Tel: 0116-273 3533
▶ Caledonia Textiles, Bridgeton Business Centre, 285 Abercromby Street, Glasgow, G40 2DD Tel: 0141-556 2705 Fax: 0141-564 5123
▶ Clan Albanach Kiltmakers, 24 High Street, South Queensferry, West Lothian, EH30 9PP Tel: 0131-331 2221 Fax: 0131-319 2221
▶ Combat Trousers UK, Anchor Street, Tunstead, Norwich, NR12 E-mail: military_kit@btinternet.com
Daks Simpson Ltd, 10 Old Bond Street, London, W1S 4PL Tel: (020) 7409 4000 Fax: (020) 7499 4494
▶ Diadora (UK) Ltd, Sovereign Court, King Edward Street, Macclesfield, Cheshire, SK10 1AA Tel: (01625) 421212
▶ Equi Brief Ltd, Pinmore Mains, Pinmore, Girvan, Ayrshire, KA26 0TD Tel: (01465) 841161 Fax: (01465) 841161
▶ Fabricville Ltd, 83 Mortimer Street, London, W1W 7SL Tel: (020) 7636 2201 Fax: (020) 7631 5399
Falcon Jeanswear, Argyle Works, Alma Street, Smethwick, Warley, West Midlands, B66 2RL Tel: 0121-565 1533 Fax: 0121-565 1533 E-mail: falcon@euroshops.co.uk
Feline Ltd, 48 Lord Street, Cheetham, Manchester, M3 1HN Tel: 0161-819 2717 Fax: 0161-819 2695
Figen Fashions Ltd, 2-4 Tottenham Road, London, N1 4BZ Tel: (020) 7254 1610 Fax: (020) 7249 9772
▶ Finesse Ltd, 7 St. Pancras Commercial Centre, Pratt Street, London, NW1 0BY Tel: (020) 7485 7766 Fax: (020) 7485 7799
▶ Flaxstyle Factory Outlet, Tariff Road, London, N17 0DY Tel: (020) 8808 4088 Fax: (020) 8885 3139 E-mail: info@flaxstyle.co.uk
▶ Fyfe & Allan, 90-96 Dykehead Street, Glasgow, G33 4AQ Tel: 0141-774 5900 Fax: 0141-774 7360
▶ The Gap, 167-201 Argyle Street, Glasgow, G2 8DJ Tel: 0141-221 0629
▶ Gilbey Fashions Ltd, 19-21 Great Portland Street, London, W1W 8QB Tel: (020) 7436 3677 Fax: (020) 7436 7006
G.D. Golding Ltd, 220 Hatfield Road, St. Albans, Hertfordshire, AL1 4LW Tel: (01727) 841321 Fax: (01727) 831462 E-mail: tailors@goldings.co.uk
▶ Gymphlex Ltd, Stamford Buildings, Stamford Street, Leicester, LE1 6NJ Tel: 0116-255 6326 Fax: 0116-247 1215 E-mail: enquiries@gymphlex.co.uk
Hebden Cord Co Ltd, 17 Old Gate, Hebden Bridge, West Yorkshire, HX7 6EW Tel: (01422) 843152 Fax: (01422) 846354 E-mail: hebcord@aol.com
J S Marketing, 7 Wheler Road, Seven Stars Industrial Estate, Coventry, CV3 4LJ Tel: (024) 7651 1155 Fax: (024) 7651 8877 E-mail: sales@jsmarketing.com
▶ Keela (International) Ltd, 53 Nasmyth Road, Glenrothes, Fife, KY6 2SD Tel: (01592) 771241
▶ Lambton Tailoring, Unit 25g Springfield Commercial Centre, Bagley Lane, Farsley, Pudsey, West Yorkshire, LS28 5LY Tel: 0113-257 0841 Fax: 0113-239 4472
Mandair Textiles Ltd, 175 Hockley Hill, Hockley, Birmingham, B18 5AN Tel: 0121-554 9506 Fax: 0121-554 3663 E-mail: mantexltd@hotmail.com
Maple Leaf Design Ltd, 4 Queen Street, Leicester, LE1 1QW Tel: 0116-262 6326 Fax: 0116-222 8919
▶ Mardale Clothing Ltd, Unit 101 Oystons Mill, Strand Road, Preston, PR1 8UR Tel: (01772) 722513 Fax: (01772) 726715 E-mail: sales@mardale.com
Marwaha Textiles Ltd, 7 Brays Lane, Coventry, CV2 4DT Tel: (024) 7644 1216
▶ Moette Leisurewear Ltd, The Old Chapel, Quebec Street, Langley Park, Durham, DH7 9XA Tel: 0191-373 5995 Fax: 0191-373 6318 E-mail: mail@moette.co.uk
▶ New Meuro Design, 99 Bridge Road, Leicester, LE5 3LD Tel: 0116-276 8988 Fax: 0116-276 8988
Norseman (Rainwear) Ltd, Viking Mill, Standish Street, Chorley, Lancs, PR7 3BB Tel: (01257) 262733 Fax: (01257) 261071 E-mail: general@norseman.fsbusiness.co.uk
Northern Mens & Boyswear Ltd, 52 Lower Oxford Street, Castleford, West Yorkshire, WF10 4AF Tel: (01977) 556203 Fax: (01977) 556203
▶ Parmar Clothing, 9 Wanlip Street, Leicester, LE1 2JS Tel: 0116-251 5820
Planet Processing Ltd, 24 Fairfax Road, Heathfield Industrial Estate, Newton Abbot, Devon, TQ12 6UD Tel: (01626) 832229 Fax: (01626) 835559 E-mail: sales@planetprocessing.com
▶ Polaris Apparel Ltd, Business Park, Station Road, Bolsover, Chesterfield, Derbyshire, S44 6BH Tel: (01246) 240218 Fax: (01246) 241560
▶ Positive Clothing London Ltd, 20 Wells Mews, London, W1T 3HQ Tel: (020) 7299 3500 Fax: (020) 7299 3518
R N D Clothing Manufacturers Ltd, 998 Foleshill Road, Coventry, CV6 6EN Tel: (024) 7663 8989 Fax: (024) 7666 6214 E-mail: rdhami@rndclothing.co.uk
▶ R & O Textiles, Unit 1 Frederick Street, Walsall, WS2 9NJ Tel: (01922) 613183 Fax: (01922) 613183
▶ Rair International Ltd, 2 Brougham Street, Leicester, LE1 2BA Tel: 0116-253 3078 Fax: 0116-253 3078
▶ Real Clothing Co. Ltd, Unit 19 Lockwood Industrial Park, Mill Mead Road, London, N17 9QP Tel: (020) 8885 9500 Fax: (020) 8365 1926
▶ Rostrum Sportswear Ltd, Princes Street, Lochmaben, Lockerbie, Dumfriesshire, DG11 1PQ Tel: (01387) 811315 Fax: (01387) 811990 E-mail: info@rostrumsportswear.co.uk
▶ Stewart Christie & Co. Ltd, 63 Queen Street, Edinburgh, EH2 4NA Tel: 0131-225 6639 Fax: 0131-220 2397
▶ Tom James Of London Ltd, 15-17 Christopher Street, London, EC2A 2BS Tel: (020) 7247 5246 Fax: (020) 7247 6153
Uniform World Ltd, 57 Boulton Road, Handsworth, Birmingham, B21 0RB Tel: 0121-523 4538 Fax: 0121-523 4538

TROWELS

Benson Industries Ltd, 5 Norcroft Industrial Estate, Norcroft Street, Bradford, West Yorkshire, BD7 1JA Tel: (01274) 722204 Fax: (01274) 306319 E-mail: enquiries@bensonindustries.co.uk

TROWELS, POINTING

▶ Sealability Concrete Repairing Services, Hirwaun Industrial Estate, Hirwaun, Aberdare, Mid Glamorgan, CF44 9UP Tel: (01685) 814345 E-mail: sales@sealability.co.uk

TRUCK ASSEMBLIES

North West Tippers Ltd, Rockfield Street, Blackburn, BB2 3RG Tel: (01254) 55441 Fax: (01254) 665015 E-mail: stephen@northwesttippers.co.uk

TRUCK BODIES

▶ Leeward Coachbuilders Ltd, Richards Street, Wednesbury, West Midlands, WS10 8AJ Tel: 0121-526 4709 Fax: 0121-526 4718 E-mail: sales@leewardcoachbuilders.co.uk

TRUCK OR TROLLEY HIRE

Hiremech Ltd, 1 Triumph Trading Estate, Tariff Road, London, N17 0EB Tel: (020) 8880 3322 Fax: (020) 8880 3355 E-mail: paul@hiremech.co.uk
▶ Young Excavator Services Ltd, 3 Tornaroy Road, Hannahstown, Belfast, BT17 0ND Tel: (028) 9030 1392 Fax: (028) 9060 0222

TRUCK/TROLLEY MAINTENANCE/REPAIR SERVICES

Essex Pallet Truck Services, 16 Fennel Close, Tiptree, Colchester, CO5 0TF Tel: (07949) 091271 Fax: (01621) 810867 E-mail: essexpallettrucks.services@virgin.net
Hartwell Truck, London Road, Dunstable, Bedfordshire, LU6 3DT Tel: (01582) 597575 Fax: (01582) 582650
Scani GB Ltd, Royds Farm Road, Beeston Royds Industrial Estate, Leeds, LS12 6DX Tel: 0113-231 1411 Fax: 0113-231 1412

TRUCK/TROLLEY MANUFRS, *See also headings for particular types*

Antruck Ltd, 22-24 Southgate Industrial Estate, Cross Street, Heywood, Lancashire, OL10 1PW Tel: (01706) 366636 Fax: (01706) 669989 E-mail: sales@antruck.co.uk
Breg Products Ltd, Tower Works, Birkhouse Lane, Huddersfield, HD1 4SF Tel: (01484) 469944 Fax: (01484) 469955 E-mail: sales@bregproducts.co.uk
▶ Euroquipment Ltd, Mallard House, Avon Way, Newbury Business Park, Newbury, Berkshire, RG14 2RF Tel: (0870) 1630077 Fax: (0870) 1630099 E-mail: sales@euroquipment.co.uk
K. Hertwall Ltd, Flemington Road, Glenrothes, Fife, KY7 5QJ Tel: (01592) 753745 Fax: (01592) 753747
Hooper Knight & Co., St Albans Road, Gloucester, GL2 5FW Tel: (01452) 502888 Fax: (01452) 502960 E-mail: intray@hooperknight.com
Lamb Commercials Ltd, 126 Tamnamore Road, Dungannon, County Tyrone, BT71 6HW Tel: (028) 8772 2111 Fax: (028) 8773 7393 E-mail: lambsales@erf.com
Polymathic Trucks Ltd, Coolie House, Unit 2 Anders, Lichfield Road Industrial Estate, Tamworth, Staffordshire, B79 7TA Tel: (01827) 63441 Fax: (01827) 310765 E-mail: sales@coolie.co.uk
Power Porter, Hill View Industrial Estate, Eastwood End, Wimblington, March, Cambridgeshire, PE15 0PU Tel: (01354) 741133 Fax: (01354) 741833 E-mail: sales@easybarrow.co.uk
Safety Trolley Systems, 41 Praze Road, Leedstown, Hayle, Cornwall, TR27 6DS Tel: 01736 851050 E-mail: sales@sts-trolleys.co.uk
Techniform Sales Ltd, 14 250 Milkwood Road, London, SE24 0HG Tel: (020) 7274 1999 Fax: (020) 7274 0199
Valley Reinforcements Ltd, Endle Street, Southampton, SO14 5FZ Tel: (023) 8022 6126 Fax: (023) 8033 8832 E-mail: andy@vrconstruction.f2s.com
Woodwards of Wigan Ltd, Stephen's Way, Goose Green, Wigan, Lancashire, WN3 6PQ Tel: (01942) 230026 Fax: (01942) 826026

TRUCKS/TROLLEYS, CABLE STORAGE

County Consumables, Lower Common Road, West Wellow, Romsey, Hampshire, SO51 6BT Tel: (01794) 324032 Fax: (01794) 323646 E-mail: sales@countyconsumables.co.uk

TRUCKS/TROLLEYS, ELECTRIC

Adaptatruck, Elm Lodge, North Street, Winkfield, Windsor, Berkshire, SL4 4TE Tel: (01344) 891734 Fax: (01344) 891738 E-mail: derekwine@aol.com
Electricars Ltd, 15 Carlyon Road, Atherstone, Warwickshire, CV9 1LQ Tel: (01827) 716888 Fax: (01827) 717841 E-mail: electricars@lineone.net

TRUCKS/TROLLEYS, ELECTRICAL INDUSTRY

County Consumables, Lower Common Road, West Wellow, Romsey, Hampshire, SO51 6BT Tel: (01794) 324032 Fax: (01794) 323646 E-mail: sales@countyconsumables.co.uk

TRUCKS/TROLLEYS, HAND OPERATED

Ace Equipment, Oakley Farm, Croxall, Lichfield, Staffordshire, WS13 8QZ Tel: (01283) 790320 Fax: (01283) 790456 E-mail: sales@aceequip.co.uk
Alan Stuart, 9-17 Cobden Street, Salford, M6 6NA Tel: 0161-737 4236 Fax: 0161-745 8327 E-mail: sales@alan-stuart.demon.co.uk
Bache Pallets Ltd, Bromley Street, Stourbridge, West Midlands, DY9 8HU Tel: (01384) 897799 Fax: (01384) 891351 E-mail: sales@bache-pallets.co.uk
Brumfitt Factory Equipment Ltd, Foundry Works, Gibson Street, Laisterdyke, Bradford, West Yorkshire, BD3 9TF Tel: (01274) 666760 Fax: (01274) 666760
C H E Coach House Engineering Ltd, 23 Squares Road, Chilton Trinity, Bridgwater, Somerset, TA5 2BW Tel: (01278) 456557 Fax: (01278) 456557
Coningsby Metals Ltd, 47-49 Silver Street, Coningsby, Lincoln, LN4 4SG Tel: (01526) 342141 Fax: (01526) 343382 E-mail: sales@cml-gt.co.uk
Ease-E-Load Trolleys Ltd, Saunders House, Moor Lane, Birmingham, B6 7HH Tel: 0121-356 2228 Fax: 0121-356 2220 E-mail: info@ease-e-load.co.uk
H C Slingsby plc, Otley Road, Shipley, West Yorkshire, BD17 7LW Tel: (01274) 535030 Fax: (01274) 535033 E-mail: sales@slingsby.com
Light Alloy Ltd, 85 Dales Road, Ipswich, IP1 4JR Tel: (01473) 740445 Fax: (01473) 240002 E-mail: sales@lightalloy.co.uk
M R P Trucks & Trolleys, 40 Horringer Road, Bury St. Edmunds, Suffolk, IP33 2DR Tel: (01284) 766300 Fax: (01284) 766500 E-mail: sales@mrptruckstrolleys.co.uk
Redditek Systems Ltd, Unit 53 South Moons Moat Industrial Estate, Padgets Lane, Redditch, Worcestershire, B98 0RD Tel: (01527) 501687 Fax: (01527) 510320 E-mail: sales@redditek.co.uk
Systems Storage, 125 Back Road, Linton, Cambridge, CB1 6UJ Tel: (01223) 892433 Fax: (01223) 893864 E-mail: alfhughes@aol.com
W.J.Horrod Ltd, 1 Leaway, Off Lea Bridge Road, London, E10 7QW Tel: (020) 8539 8746 E-mail: sales@wjhorrod.co.uk
W S Barrett & Son Ltd, Riverside Industrial Estate, Marsh Lane, Boston, Lincolnshire, PE21 7PJ Tel: (01205) 362585 Fax: (01205) 310831 E-mail: info@wsbarrett.co.uk
A. & G. Walden Bros Ltd, 34 Wimbledon Avenue, Brandon, Suffolk, IP27 0NZ Tel: (01842) 811776 Fax: (01842) 814603 E-mail: trucks@walden.co.uk
Wilman Equipment Ltd, Baker Street, Bradford, West Yorkshire, BD2 4NX Tel: (01274) 636977 Fax: (01274) 636714
Wyvern Handling & Storage Equipment Ltd, PO Box 5483, Stourport-on-Severn, Worcestershire, DY13 3BG Tel: (01299) 829300 Fax: (01299) 825799 E-mail: sales@wyvernhandling.co.uk

TRUCKS/TROLLEYS, LIGHT MOTOR

Scani GB Ltd, Royds Farm Road, Beeston Royds Industrial Estate, Leeds, LS12 6DX Tel: 0113-231 1411 Fax: 0113-231 1412

TRUCKS/TROLLEYS, OFFICE EQUIPMENT

MFB Fabrications Ltd, High Street, Clay Cross, Chesterfield, Derbyshire, S45 9DX Tel: (01246) 861700 Fax: (01246) 861777 E-mail: sales@mfbfabs.co.uk

TRUNKING SYSTEMS, *See also headings for particular types*

▶ Falcon Trunking Systems Ltd, Butterworth Street, Littleborough, Lancashire, OL15 8JS Tel: (01706) 372929 Fax: (01706) 371550 E-mail: sales@falcontrunking.co.uk

Uni Trunk Ltd, Altona Road, Lisburn, County Antrim, BT27 5QB Tel: (028) 9262 5100 Fax: (028) 9262 5101 E-mail: lisburn@unitrunk.co.uk

TRUSS SYSTEMS

Boston Retail Products, 10a Lower Guildford Road, Knaphill, Woking, Surrey, GU21 2EW Tel: (0870) 7706680 Fax: (0870) 7706681 E-mail: sales@bostonretail.com

TUBE BENDING

B Saxton & Co. Ltd, Unit 6a Arrow Trading Estate, Corporation Road, Audenshaw, Manchester, M34 5LR Tel: 0161-320 1444 Fax: 0161-320 1555 E-mail: sales@banshaws.com

▶ Fab Serv, Unit 2, Underbank Way, Cars Industrial Estate, Haslingden, Rossendale, Lancashire, BB4 5HH Tel: (01706) 230817 Fax: (01706) 230033 E-mail: enquiries@fabserv.co.uk

▶ G Dalton Engineering Co. Ltd, Enterprise House, 260 Chorley New Road, Horwich, Bolton, BL6 5NY Tel: (01204) 699675 Fax: (01204) 668300

Industrial & Tractor Ltd, Navigation Road, Worcester, WR5 3DF Tel: (01905) 763777 Fax: (01905) 763008 E-mail: sales@intrac.co.uk

Kewtube Ltd, 63 Bideford Avenue, Perivale, Greenford, Middlesex, UB6 7PT Tel: (020) 8991 0062 Fax: (020) 8991 2883 E-mail: info@kewtube.com

Lutley Manufacturing Ltd, Unit H, 100 Dudley Road East, Oldbury, West Midlands, B69 3DY Tel: 0121-552 2456 Fax: 0121-544 3545 E-mail: richardsweeney.lutley@btinternet.com

Phoenix Fabrications Ltd, Unit 11 Meadow Drove, Earith, Huntingdon, Cambridgeshire, PE28 3QF Tel: (01487) 843888 Fax: (01487) 843905

Plant & Automation Ltd, Lord North St, Miles Platting, Manchester, M40 8HT Tel: 0161-205 5756 Fax: 0161-205 0503

Tubetech Ltd, Arundel Road, Uxbridge, Middlesex, UB8 2RP Tel: (01895) 233268 Fax: (01895) 231933

TUBE BENDING MACHINE MANUFRS

Acorn Engineering Services, Units 1-2, Avery Dell Industrial Estate, Lifford Lane, Kings Norton, Birmingham, B30 3DZ Tel: 0121-459 3900 Fax: 0121-459 2600 E-mail: aesbirmingham@aol.com

Addison Mckee, 188 Bradkirk Place, Walton Summit Centre, Bamber Bridge, Preston, PR5 8AJ Tel: (01772) 334511 Fax: (01772) 323227 E-mail: sales@atf.co.uk

Irwin Industial Tool Co. Ltd, Parkway Works, Kettlebridge Road, Sheffield, S9 3BL Tel: 0114-244 9066 Fax: 0114-256 1788 E-mail: nroshier@recordtools.co.uk

P.W. Forming Ltd, Highgrove Close, Willenhall, West Midlands, WV12 5SZ Tel: (01922) 401615 Fax: (01922) 409517

Ridge Tools, Arden Press Way, Pixmore Avenue, Letchworth Garden City, Hertfordshire, SG6 1LH Tel: (01462) 485335 Fax: (01462) 485315 E-mail: sales.uk@ridgid.com

Rothenberger UK Ltd, 2 Kingsthorne Park, Henson Way, Telford Way Industrial Estate, Kettering, Northamptonshire, NN16 8PX Tel: (01536) 310300 Fax: (01536) 310600 E-mail: info@rothenberger.co.uk

W. Veenstra & Co. (UK) Ltd, Unit 1, 57 Bushey Grove Road, Bushey, WD23 2JW Tel: (01923) 637893 Fax: (01923) 248055 E-mail: brandone@btconnect.com

TUBE BENDING MACHINE TOOLING

Acorn Engineering Services, Units 1-2, Avery Dell Industrial Estate, Lifford Lane, Kings Norton, Birmingham, B30 3DZ Tel: 0121-459 3900 Fax: 0121-459 2600 E-mail: aesbirminigham@aol.com

Stockton Engineering Ltd, 84 Barford Street, Birmingham, B5 6AH Tel: 0121-622 7474 Fax: 0121-666 6264 E-mail: peter@stocktonengineering.co.uk

TUBE CLEANING EQUIPMENT

Goodway Service & Safety Ltd, 8 Foundry Court, Daventry, Northamptonshire, NN11 4RH Tel: (01327) 312468 Fax: (01327) 301404 E-mail: goodwaydist@msn.com

Rotatools UK Ltd, Brookfield Drive, Liverpool, L9 7EG Tel: 0151-525 8611 Fax: 0151-525 4868 E-mail: richard_dearn@hotmail.com

Skatoskalo International, 6 Morris Road, Royal Oak Industrial Estate, Daventry, Northamptonshire, NN11 8PD Tel: (01327) 312443 Fax: (01327) 314140 E-mail: sales@skatoskalo.com

Wicksteed Engineering Ltd, Hove Road, Rushden, Northamptonshire, NN10 0JB Tel: (01933) 318555 Fax: (01933) 410103 E-mail: mail@wicksteed.com

TUBE COATING SERVICES

Tube Care Inspection Ltd, Bessemer Way, Harfreys Industrial Estate, Great Yarmouth, Norfolk, NR31 0LX Tel: (01493) 601548 Fax: (01493) 656097 E-mail: sales@tubecare.co.uk

TUBE COUPLINGS

Advance Couplings Ltd, Thwaites Lane, Keighley, West Yorkshire, BD21 4LJ Tel: (01535) 669216 Fax: (01535) 610243 E-mail: sales@advanced-couplings.co.uk

▶ Corus Special Profiles Ltd, Skinningrove, Saltburn-By-The-Sea, Cleveland, TS13 4ET Tel: (01287) 640212 Fax: (01287) 643467

Fernco International Ltd, Newlands Way, Valley Park, Wombwell, Barnsley, South Yorkshire, S73 0UW Tel: (01226) 340209 Fax: (01226) 340400 E-mail: enquiries@fernco.co.uk

▶ Glynwed Pipe Systems Ltd, St. Peters Road, Huntingdon, Cambridgeshire, PE29 7DA Tel: (01480 52121 Fax: (01480) 450430 E-mail: enquiries@gpsuk.com

Pirtek, 5 Stockwell Centre, Stephenson Way, Crawley, West Sussex, RH10 1TN Tel: (01293) 571707 Fax: (01293) 571711 E-mail: pirtekcrawley@fsbdial.co.uk

Rubbernek Fittings Ltd, Hall Lane, Walsall Wood, Walsall, WS9 9AP Tel: (01543) 453533 Fax: (01543) 453531 E-mail: mjones@rubbernek.co.uk

Teconnex Ltd, Bronte Works, Chesham Street, Keighley, West Yorkshire, BD21 4LG Tel: (01535) 691122 Fax: (01535) 691133 E-mail: sales@teconnex.com

Viking Johnson, 46-48 Wilbury Way, Hitchin, Hertfordshire, SG4 0UD Tel: (01462) 443322 Fax: (01462) 443311 E-mail: sales@vikingjohnson.com

TUBE DEBURRING EQUIPMENT

▶ B E W O (UK) Ltd, Unit 3 Bay 2, Eastacre, The Willenhall Estate, Willenhall, West Midlands, WV13 2JZ Tel: (01902) 635027 Fax: (01902) 635843E-mail: info@bewo.co.uk

M O J Machines Ltd, Unit 6-190-192 Beverley Trading Estate, Garth Road, Morden, Surrey, SM4 4LU Tel: 0118-973 7004 Fax: 0118-932 8262

TUBE END FORMING

Hallen Engineering Ltd, PO Box 27, Wednesbury, West Midlands, WS10 7SZ Tel: 0121-556 3324 Fax: 0121-502 0194 E-mail: sales@hallen.co.uk

Industrial & Tractor Ltd, Navigation Road, Worcester, WR5 3DF Tel: (01905) 763777 Fax: (01905) 763008 E-mail: sales@intrac.co.uk

Lutley Manufacturing Ltd, Unit H, 100 Dudley Road East, Oldbury, West Midlands, B69 3DY Tel: 0121-552 2456 Fax: 0121-544 3545 E-mail: richardsweeney.lutley@btinternet.com

TUBE END FORMING/ PREPARATION MACHINES

Ava Matic U K Ltd, 24 Padgets Lane, Redditch, Worcestershire, B98 0RB Tel: (01527) 518520 Fax: (01527) 518526 E-mail: info@avamatic.co.uk

Keihan Systems, Unit 24 Padgets Lane, Redditch, Worcestershire, B98 0RB Tel: (01527) 518525 Fax: (01527) 518526 E-mail: info@keihan.co.uk

M O J Machines Ltd, Unit 6-190-192 Beverley Trading Estate, Garth Road, Morden, Surrey, SM4 4LU Tel: 0118-973 7004 Fax: 0118-932 8262

Williams Machinery, 173 Nine Mile Ride, Finchampstead, Wokingham, Berkshire, RG40 4JD Tel: 0118-973 7004 Fax: 0118-973 7004 E-mail: bdwilliams@tinyworld.co.uk

TUBE END PLUGS

McLaren Plastics Ltd, Pentland Industrial Estate, Loanhead, Midlothian, EH20 9QH Tel: 0131-448 2200 Fax: 0131-448 2221 E-mail: sales@mclaren-plastics.co.uk

TUBE EXPANDER TOOL MANUFRS

Brandone Machine Tool Ltd, Unit 1, 57 Bushey Grove Road, Bushey, WD23 2JW Tel: (01923) 637893 Fax: (01923) 248055 E-mail: brandone@btconnect.com

Wicksteed Engineering Ltd, Hove Road, Rushden, Northamptonshire, NN10 0JB Tel: (01933) 318555 Fax: (01933) 410103 E-mail: mail@wicksteed.com

TUBE FINISHING SERVICES

Alltube Engineering, 3-9 Siddeley Way, Royal Oak Industrial Estate, Daventry, Northamptonshire, NN11 8PA Tel: (01327) 878250 Fax: (01327) 300478 E-mail: cope@wakefind.co.uk

Northpoint Ltd, Globe Lane, Dukinfield, Cheshire, SK16 4UY Tel: 0161-330 4551 Fax: 0161-339 7169 E-mail: sales@northpoint.ltd.uk

TUBE FITTINGS MANUFRS, *See also headings for particular types*

Aberdeen Fluid Systems Technologies Ltd, 1 Stoneywood Park, Stoneywood Road, Dyce, Aberdeen, AB21 7DZ Tel: (01224) 722468 Fax: (01224) 723009 E-mail: info@aberdeen.swagelok.com

Accura Pipe Fitting Ltd, Hickman Avenue, Wolverhampton, WV1 2DW Tel: (01902) 453322 Fax: (01902) 453314 E-mail: pipefittings@accura.co.uk

Advance Couplings Ltd, Thwaites Lane, Keighley, West Yorkshire, BD21 4LJ Tel: (01535) 669216 Fax: (01535) 610243 E-mail: sales@advanced-couplings.co.uk

▶ Allpipe & Valve, 103a Pontefract Road, Ackworth, Pontefract, West Yorkshire, WF7 7EL Tel: (01977) 600606 Fax: (01977) 704215 E-mail: allpipe@aol.com

Azgard Engineering Products, 10 Compton Road, Kinver, Stourbridge, West Midlands, DY7 6DN Tel: (01384) 872286 Fax: (01384) 878203

B M I Engineering Ltd, Vernon Road, Halesowen, West Midlands, B62 8HN Tel: 0121-559 3406 Fax: 0121-561 2603 E-mail: sales@bmi-engineering.co.uk

Bilbeck Ltd, Yorke Street, Mansfield Woodhouse, Mansfield, Nottinghamshire, NG19 9NU Tel: (01623) 651101 Fax: (01623) 653387 E-mail: sales@bilbeck.com

Binney & Son Ltd, Unit H Spring Hill Industrial Park, Steward Street, Birmingham, B18 7AF Tel: 0121-454 4545 Fax: 0121-454 1145 E-mail: binney.eng@btconnect.com

Brassware Sales Ltd, Unit 5 Junction 6 Industrial Park, 66 Electric Avenue, Witton, Birmingham, B6 7JJ Tel: 0121-327 1234 Fax: 0121-327 4066

Burdens, Blackdog Centre, Bridge of Don, Aberdeen, AB23 8BT Tel: (01224) 823664 Fax: (01224) 823667 E-mail: acm@burdens.co.uk

Clesse (UK) Ltd, Unit 8, Planetary Industrial Estate, Wednesfield, Wolverhampton, WV13 3XQ Tel: (01902) 383233 Fax: (01902) 383234 E-mail: sales@clesse.co.uk

Collister & Glover (Pipeline Materials) Ltd, Tenth Avenue, Deeside Industrial Park, Deeside, Clwyd, CH5 2UA Tel: (01244) 288000 Fax: (01244) 289000 E-mail: sales@colglo.co.uk

Crane Building Services & Utilities, Crane House, Epsilon Terrace, West Road, Ipswich, IP3 9FJ Tel: (01473) 277300 Fax: (01473) 270301 E-mail: enquiries@cranebsu.com

D Berry & Co. Ltd, Middlemoor Industrial Estate, Kentish Road, Middlemore Industrial Estate, Birmingham, B21 0AY Tel: 0121-558 4411 Fax: 0121-555 5546 E-mail: enquires@dberryandco.co.uk

Euro Hydraulics Ltd, Unit 4 Park Parade Industrial Estate, Welbeck St South, Ashton-under-Lyne, Lancashire, OL6 7PP Tel: 0161-308 2624 Fax: 0161-343 1926 E-mail: info@eurohydraulics.com

Harrisons Pipeline Engineering Ltd, Curtis Road, Norwich, NR6 6RB Tel: (01603) 426928 Fax: (01603) 414225 E-mail: darren@harrisons-eng.com

Harvard Industries Ltd, Wood Lane, Erdington, Birmingham, B24 9QR Tel: 0121-386 6621 Fax: 0121-386 6721 E-mail: johncauser@aol.com

Hoses Direct, Brighton, BN2 5AW Tel: (0800) 6526038 Fax: (0800) 6526039 E-mail: sales@hoses.co.uk

HYDRAQUIP, Unit 7, Oakhurst Business Park, Wilberforce Way, Southwater, Horsham, West Sussex, RH13 9RT Tel: (01403) 731322 Fax: (01403) 730276 E-mail: salmons@hydraquip.co.uk

J Bown & Co Dukinfield Ltd, Wharf Street, Dukinfield, Cheshire, SK16 4PQ Tel: 0161-339 9888 Fax: 0161-343 1052 E-mail: sale@jbown.com

JD Pipes Ltd, Green Lane, Heywood, Lancashire, OL10 2EU Tel: (01706) 364115 Fax: (01706) 366402 E-mail: heywood@jdpipes.co.uk

John Guest, Horton Road, West Drayton, Middlesex, UB7 8JL Tel: (01895) 449233 Fax: (01895) 420321 E-mail: sales@johnguest.co.uk

Kee Systems Ltd, 11 Thornsett Road, London, SW18 4EW Tel: (020) 8874 6566 Fax: (020) 8874 5726 E-mail: sales@keesystems.com

Marla Tube Fittings Ltd, Units 1-2, Kinwarton Farm Road, Kinwarton, Alcester, Warwickshire, B49 6EH Tel: (01789) 761234 Fax: (01789) 761205 E-mail: alcester@hpf-energy.com

P P S Hydraulics & Pneumatics Ltd, Foxwood Close, Foxwood Industrial Park, Sheepbridge, Chesterfield, Derbyshire, S41 9RN Tel: (01246) 451509 Fax: (01246) 450831 E-mail: ppshydraulics@btconnect.com

Pipeline Centre, 118a Newmarket Road, Bury St. Edmunds, Suffolk, IP33 3TG Tel: (01284) 753046 Fax: (01284) 750042

Pipeline Centre, Kelvin Estate, Long Drive, Greenford, Middlesex, UB6 8PG Tel: (020) 8578 2300 Fax: (020) 8575 3556 E-mail: greenford-pipe@ncenters.co.uk

Pipeline Centre, 2 Hartburn Close, Crow Lane Industrial Estate, Northampton, NN3 9UE Tel: (01604) 410888 Fax: (01604) 410777 E-mail: bv.northhampton@wolsley.co.uk

Pipeline Centre, 4 Deacon Trading Centre, Knight Road, Rochester, Kent, ME2 2AU Tel: (01634) 290469 Fax: (01634) 290128

Pipeline Products Ltd, Units 15-16 Five C Business Centre, Concorde Drive, Clevedon, Avon, BS21 6UH Tel: (01275) 873103 Fax: (01275) 873801 E-mail: info@pipelineproducts.ltd.uk

Pirtek, Moorfield Road, Guildford, Surrey, GU1 1RB Tel: (01483) 454546 Fax: (01483) 454549 E-mail: claire@pirtekportsmouth.co.uk

Premier Pipeline Supplies Ltd, Chatham Street, Halifax, West Yorkshire, HX1 5BU Tel: (01422) 322002 Fax: (01422) 348817 E-mail: info@premierpipeline.co.uk

Proclad International Forging Ltd, Nettlehill Road, Houstoun Industrial Estate, Livingston, West Lothian, EH54 5DL Tel: (01506) 607500 Fax: (01506) 607501 E-mail: info@proclad-int.com

Proteus Fittings Ltd, Unit 6 Stonegravels Lane, Chesterfield, Derbyshire, S41 7LF Tel: (01246) 211303 Fax: (01246) 209700 E-mail: info@proteusfittings.co.uk

S J Andrew & Sons, South Turnpike, Redruth, Cornwall, TR15 2LZ Tel: (01209) 213171 Fax: (01209) 219459 E-mail: nathan@sjandrew.com

Smith Brothers Stores Ltd, Battern Street, Aylestone Road, Leicester, LE2 7PB Tel: 0116-283 3511 Fax: 0116-244 0430 E-mail: sales@sbs-1897.co.uk

South Scotland Valve & Fitting Co Ltd, 9-11 Macadam Place, Irvine, Ayrshire, KA11 4HP Tel: (01294) 213341 Fax: (01294) 213484 E-mail: enquiries@ssvf.co.uk

Specialised Pipe & Services Ltd, F1 Folland Way, Hull, HU9 1NB Tel: (01482) 587060 Fax: (01482) 587099 E-mail: sales@spsworld.com

T P S Technitube UK Ltd, T P S Building, Blatchford Road, Horsham, West Sussex, RH13 5QR Tel: (01403) 269471 Fax: (01403) 265443 E-mail: sales@tpsuk.co.uk

Truflow Hydraulic Components Ltd, Unit F5 Lockside, Anchor Brook Industrial Park, Aldridge, Walsall, WS9 8BZ Tel: (01922) 745488 Fax: (01922) 745399 E-mail: truflow@bt.co.uk

Tube Gear Ltd, Unit B1 Springhead Enterprise Park, Springhead Road, Northfleet, Gravesend, Kent, DA11 8HB Tel: (01474) 321954 Fax: (01474) 321988 E-mail: sales@tube-gear.com

Tubeclamps Ltd, Unit A2, Cradley Business Park, Cradley Heath, West Midlands, B64 7DW Tel: (01384) 565241 Fax: (01384) 410490 E-mail: sales@tubeclamps.co.uk

Tubeclip Ltd, Unit 9-11 British Estate Business Park, 132 Bath Road, Reading, RG30 2EU Tel: 0118-957 2281 Fax: 0118-958 4630 E-mail: tubeclip@btconnect.com

Tubes Fittings Valves Ltd, Bath Lane, Mansfield, Nottinghamshire, NG18 2BZ Tel: (01623) 643235 Fax: (01623) 420920 E-mail: sales@tubefittingsvalves.co.uk

Walker & Howell Ltd, Forge Road, Whaley Bridge, High Peak, Derbyshire, SK23 7HY Tel: (01663) 732471 Fax: (01663) 733927 E-mail: sales@walkerandhowell.co.uk

Westway Pipeline Supplies, 8 Woodward Road, Knowsley Industrial Park North, Liverpool, L33 7UZ Tel: 0151-548 0010 Fax: 0151-549 1545

Yardley Holland Ltd, 154 Stafford Street, Walsall, WS2 8EA Tel: (01922) 633877 Fax: (01922) 634868

Yorkshire Fittings Ltd, P O Box 166, Leeds, LS10 1NA Tel: 0113-270 6945 Fax: 0113-271 5275 E-mail: info@yorkshirefittings.co.uk

TUBE INSPECTION SERVICES

Tube Care Inspection Ltd, Bessemer Way, Harfreys Industrial Estate, Great Yarmouth, Norfolk, NR31 0LX Tel: (01493) 601548 Fax: (01493) 656097 E-mail: sales@tubecare.co.uk

TUBE MANIPULATION MACHINES

Maxpower Automotive Ltd, Bank Street, West Bromwich, West Midlands, B71 1HB Tel: 0121-567 0200 Fax: 0121-588 6828 E-mail: jgarner@maxaut.co.uk

TUBE MANIPULATION/BENDING MACHINERY RECONDITIONING OR MAINTENANCE OR REPAIR

▶ Direct Tube Automation Ltd, 1 Block A, Wednesbury Trading Estate, Wednesbury, West Midlands, WS10 7JN Tel: 0121-505 6388 E-mail: p.mcevoy@dta-ltd.co.uk

TUBE MANIPULATION/BENDING SERVICES OR FABRICATORS

Abaca Engineering, Unit 2, Jackson Road, Holbrooks, Coventry, CV6 4BT Tel: (024) 7666 7390 Fax: (024) 7668 2845 E-mail: sales@abacaengineering.co.uk
Acorn Engineering Services, Units 1-2, Avery Dell Industrial Estate, Lifford Lane, Kings Norton, Birmingham, B30 3DZ Tel: 0121-459 3900 Fax: 0121-459 2600 E-mail: aesbirminigham@aol.com
Alltube Engineering, 3-9 Siddeley Way, Royal Oak Industrial Estate, Daventry, Northamptonshire, NN11 8PA Tel: (01327) 878250 Fax: (01327) 300478 E-mail: cope@wakefind.co.uk
Atlas Tube Bending Ltd, Albert Street, Oldham, OL8 3QP Tel: 0161-683 5556 Fax: 0161-683 5557 E-mail: admin@atlastubebending.co.uk
Barnshaw's Bending Centre Ltd, 2 Arrow Trading Estate, Corporation Road, Audenshaw, Manchester, M34 5LR Tel: 0161-320 9696 Fax: 0161-335 0918
Bernard L Haywood Sales Ltd, 89-91 New Town Row, Birmingham, B6 4HG Tel: 0121-333 6656 Fax: 0121-359 1530 E-mail: sales@hbl.co.uk
▶ Bristol Bending Sanoh Ltd, Quedgeley Court, Shepherd Road, Gloucester, GL2 5EL Tel: (01452) 303062 Fax: (01452) 300575
Coopers Needleworks Ltd, 261-265 Aston Lane, Handsworth, Birmingham, B20 3HS Tel: 0121-356 4719 Fax: 0121-356 3050 E-mail: sales@coopernw.com
Datel Products Ltd, Morgan Rushford Trading Estate, Providence Street, Stourbridge, West Midlands, DY9 8HS Tel: (01384) 893589 Fax: (01384) 893589
Denormo Technics Ltd, 8 Teal Business Pk, Dudwell Bridge, Hinckley, Leics, LE10 3BZ Tel: (01455) 250153 Fax: (01455) 617061
Diametric Metal Fabrications Ltd, The Brookland, Blithbury Road, Rugeley, Staffordshire, WS15 3HQ Tel: (01889) 577243 Fax: (01889) 584672 E-mail: sales@diametricmetalfabrications.co.uk
Exhausts By Design, West Well Farm, West Well Lane, Tingewick, Buckingham, MK18 4BD Tel: (01280) 847756 Fax: (01280) 847759 E-mail: grahamf@ukonline.co.uk
▶ Ferschl Tube Form, 2 Doxford Drive, South West Industrial Estate, Peterlee, County Durham, SR8 2RL Tel: 0191-518 0878 Fax: 0191-518 0938
Finecraft Engineering Ltd, Arundel Road, Uxbridge, Middlesex, UB8 2RP Tel: (01895) 233101 Fax: (01895) 231933
Franklin Silencers Ltd, 1 Grafton Place, Grafton Street Industrial Estate, Northampton, NN1 2PS Tel: (01604) 626266 Fax: (01604) 233757 E-mail: sales@franklinsilencers.co.uk
Garmet Ltd, St. Helens Way, Thetford, Norfolk, IP24 1HG Tel: (01842) 763808 Fax: (01842) 764548
Global Tube Fabrications, Navigation Road, Diglis Trading Estate, Worcester, WR5 3DE Tel: (01905) 764302 Fax: (01905) 764305 E-mail: info@globaltube.biz
H Case & Son Cradley Heath Ltd, Mount Works, Foxoak Street, Cradley Heath, West Midlands, B64 5DQ Tel: (01384) 566358 Fax: (01384) 634601 E-mail: sales@h-caseandson.co.uk
Heathyards Engineering Co. Ltd, Unit 10 Maybrook Industrial Estate, Maybrook Road, Walsall, WS8 7DG Tel: (01543) 376754 Fax: (01543) 452645 E-mail: sales@heathyards.com
Hiflex Powerbend Ltd, Pennywell Industrial Estate, Sunderland, SR4 9EN Tel: 0191-534 0000 Fax: 0191-534 0012 E-mail: tim.dearnley@hiflex-europe.com
Hi-Tech Tubebending, Saunders House, Moor Lane, Witton, Birmingham, B6 7HH Tel: 0121-356 2224 Fax: 0121-356 2220 E-mail: info@scottandbarnett.co.uk
Isleward Ltd, Neptune Industrial Estate, Owen Road, Willenhall, West Midlands, WV13 2PZ Tel: 0121-526 5903 Fax: 0121-568 7421 E-mail: sales@isleward.co.uk
Jara Tube Manipulators Ltd, Unit 4 Block 3, Wednesbury Trading Estate, Wednesbury, West Midlands, WS10 7JN Tel: 0121-556 6141 Fax: 0121-556 6854 E-mail: sales@jaratube.co.uk
K D Engineering Merseyside Ltd, Unit 33b-33c Garston Industrial Estate, Blackburne Street, Liverpool, L19 8JB Tel: 0151-427 8996 Fax: 0151-427 9397 E-mail: kengine@mersinet.co.uk
Kalvex Engineering Ltd, 4A Canal Estate, Station Road, Langley, Slough, SL3 6EG Tel: (01753) 548324 Fax: (01753) 549570
Lander Automotive Ltd, Woodgate Business Park, 174 Clapgate Lane, Birmingham, B32 3ED Tel: 0121-423 1110 Fax: 0121-423 2220 E-mail: enquiries@lander.co.uk
M P Manipulated Tubes Ltd, 40 Bracebridge Street, Aston, Birmingham, B6 4PJ Tel: 0121-359 0478 Fax: 0121-333 3082
Malvern Tubular Components Ltd, Spring Lane, Malvern, Worcestershire, WR14 1DA Tel: (01684) 892600 Fax: (01684) 892337 E-mail: sales@mtc.uk.com
Maniflow Exhaust Centre, Mitchell Road, Salisbury, SP2 7PY Tel: (01722) 335378 Fax: (01722) 320834 E-mail: maniflow@lineone.net
Metallon Ltd, Unit D Lea Road Trading Estate, Lea Road, Waltham Abbey, Essex, EN9 1AE Tel: (01992) 715737 Fax: (01992) 767607 E-mail: sales@metallon.co.uk
▶ Morrison & Macdonald Holdings Ltd, 63 Murray Street, Paisley, Renfrewshire, PA3 1QW Tel: 0141-889 8787 Fax: 0141-889 9760 E-mail: almacdonald@btconnect.com
Newbow Hydraulic Equipment, Benacre Drive, Fazeley Street, Birmingham, B5 5RE Tel: 0121-772 6861 Fax: 0121-643 2637 E-mail: sales@newbow.co.uk
P D Gough Co. Ltd, Old Foundry, Common Lane, Watnall, Nottingham, NG16 1HD Tel: 0115-938 2241 Fax: 0115-945 9162 E-mail: info@pdgough.com
Planet Merchandising Products Ltd, Unit 219b, Aldington Road, London, SE18 5TS Tel: (020) 8855 9594 Fax: (020) 8316 2745 E-mail: sales@planetmerchandising.co.uk
Prescott Powell Ltd, 466 Moseley Road, Birmingham, B12 9AN Tel: 0121-446 4411 Fax: 0121-446 4681 E-mail: liam.duggan@prescottpowell.co.uk
Production Engineering Components Ltd, 104 College Street, Kempston, Bedford, MK42 8LU Tel: (01234) 346587 Fax: (01234) 325385 E-mail: jane@pec.uk.com
R G Ergonomics Ltd, 7 Princewood Road, Earlstrees Industrial Estate, Corby, Northamptonshire, NN17 4AP Tel: (01536) 263691 Fax: (01536) 274988 E-mail: enquires@rgergonomics.co.uk
R M G Fabrications Ltd, 32a Heming Road, Redditch, Worcestershire, B98 0DH Tel: (01527) 525442 Fax: (01527) 527642
Renntec, 69 Woolsbridge Industrial Estate, Three Legged Cross, Wimborne, Dorset, BH21 6SP Tel: (01202) 826722 Fax: (01202) 826747 E-mail: info@renntec.com
Ryeford Engineering Ltd, 49 Arthur Street, Redditch, Worcestershire, B98 8JZ Tel: (01527) 517545
S I T Bray Ltd, Education Road, Meanwood Road, Leeds, LS7 2AN Tel: 0113-281 6700 Fax: 0113-281 6702 E-mail: sit.uk@sitgroup.it
A.L. Starkie Ltd, Wellington Works, Wellington Rd, Ashton-under-Lyne, Lancs, OL6 7EF Tel: 0161-339 4549 Fax: 0161-343 3305 E-mail: sales@superheater.co.uk
Thomson Pettie Chew Products, Unit 37 Trent Valley Trading Estate, Station Road, Rugeley, Staffordshire, WS15 2HQ Tel: (01889) 574274 Fax: (01889) 578193
Toolspec Manufacturing Co. Ltd, Unit E, Sedgwick Road, Luton, LU4 9DT Tel: (01582) 572626 E-mail: toolspec@psilink.co.uk
Tube Form Technology Ltd, Unit D, Waterside Estate, 25-27 Willis Way, Poole, Dorset, BH15 3TD Tel: (01202) 686970 Fax: (01202) 686996
Tubeformers Engineering Ltd, Units 11-15 Strawberry Lane Industrial Estate, Strawberry Lane, Willenhall, West Midlands, WV13 3RS Tel: (01902) 630300 Fax: (01902) 630066
Tubend Manufacturers, Stanley Street, Sowerby Bridge, West Yorkshire, HX6 2AH Tel: (01422) 833461 Fax: (01422) 835319 E-mail: tubenduk@aol.com
Tuberex Exhausts Systems Ltd, Airfield Industrial Estate, Hixon, Stafford, ST18 0PF Tel: (01889) 271212 Fax: (01889) 272112
Unibend Engineering, Kirkdale Works, Spring Place, Whitworth, Rochdale, Lancashire, OL12 8JY Tel: (01706) 853239
Up Country Autoproducts UK Ltd, Norwich Road, Halesworth, Suffolk, IP19 8QJ Tel: (01986) 875171 Fax: (01986) 875260 E-mail: sales@upcountry4x4.co.uk
W Campbell & Son Ltd, Harpings Road, Hull, HU5 4JG Tel: (01482) 444422 Fax: (01482) 444424
Warren Engineering, B4-B5 Unit Northway Trading Estate, Northway Lane, Tewkesbury, Gloucestershire, GL20 8JH Tel: (01684) 298000 Fax: (01684) 295981 E-mail: warrenengineering@aol.com
E.J. Watts Engineering Group, Faldo Road, Barton-le-Clay, Bedford, MK45 4RJ Tel: (01582) 881601 Fax: (01582) 881075 E-mail: info@ejwatts.co.uk
Werneth Manufacturing Co., Unit 2 Dawson Street, Redfern Industrial Estate, Hyde, Cheshire, SK14 1RD Tel: 0161-368 3079 Fax: 0161-368 3079
Willenhall Tube & Forging, Bloxwich Lane Indust Estate, Bloxwich Lane, Walsall, WS2 8TF Tel: (01922) 725505 Fax: (01922) 720131 E-mail: enquiries@willenhalltube.co.uk
Willingale Tubes Ltd, Chilton Industrial Estate, Windham Road, Sudbury, Suffolk, CO10 2XD Tel: (01787) 375300 Fax: (01787) 880108 E-mail: info@willingale-tubes.com

TUBE MILLS

▶ PTC Alliance UK, Gander Lane, Barlborough, Chesterfield, Derbyshire, S43 4PZ Tel: (01246) 573437 Fax: (01246) 573431 E-mail: darren.hunt@ptcalliance.com

TUBE WELDING ENGINEERS OR SERVICES OR SUBCONTRACTORS

Littler Co. Ltd, 2 Greaves Way Industrial Estate, Stanbridge Road, Leighton Buzzard, Bedfordshire, LU7 4UB Tel: (01525) 373310 Fax: (01525) 381371

TUBE WELDING EQUIPMENT

Thermatool Europe Ltd, Thermatool House, Crockford Lane, Basingstoke, Hampshire, RG24 8NA Tel: (01256) 335533 Fax: (01256) 467224 E-mail: thermatooleurope@ttool.co.uk
Y P H Welding Supplies, Unit 1 Stubbins Lane, Claughton-on-Brock, Preston, PR3 0QH Tel: (01995) 604057 Fax: (01995) 604018 E-mail: alan@yphltd.co.uk

TUBES, EXTRUDED PTFE, AUTOMOTIVE INDUSTRY

Goodridge (UK) Ltd, Exeter Airport Business Park, Exeter, EX5 2UP Tel: (01392) 369090 Fax: (01392) 441780

TUBES, FINNED/GILLED, EXTERNAL SURFACE

Tube Fins Ltd, N Riverside Industrial Estate, Atherstone Street, Fazeley, Tamworth, Staffordshire, B78 3SD Tel: (01827) 251234 Fax: (01827) 286612 E-mail: bob@tubefins.co.uk

TUBES, SPIRALLY WOUND, CARDBOARD, NOTCHED

▶ Corespec Ltd, Unit 7 Parkhead, Greencroft Industrial Park, Stanley, County Durham, DH9 7YB Tel: (01207) 529944 Fax: (01207) 529955 E-mail: core.spec@btconnect.com

TUBULAR ELECTRIC MOTORS

Ellard Ltd, Dallimore Road, Roundthorn Industrial Estate, Manchester, M23 9NX Tel: 0161-945 4561 Fax: 0161-945 4566 E-mail: sales@ellard.co.uk

TUBULAR FABRICATORS

A Harvey & Co The Wireworkers Ltd, 2 Stockton End, Sandy, Bedfordshire, SG19 1SB Tel: (01767) 681830 Fax: (01767) 683111 E-mail: sales@harveywire.freeserve.co.uk
Atkinson Vari-Tech Ltd, Unit 4, Sett End Road, Shadsworth, Blackburn, BB1 2PT Tel: (01254) 678777 Fax: (01254) 678782 E-mail: sales@vari-tech.co.uk
Dorset Stainless, 39 Balena Close, Poole, Dorset, BH17 7EB Tel: (01202) 697469 Fax: (01202) 658899 E-mail: solutions@robton.co.uk
Ede Powder Coatings Ltd, Annie Reed Road, Beverley, North Humberside, HU17 0LF Tel: (01482) 865957 Fax: (01482) 864922 E-mail: info@edepc.com
Ernest Gill & Son, Holmfield Industrial Estate, Holmfield, Halifax, West Yorkshire, HX2 9TN Tel: (01422) 246286 Fax: (01422) 240716
Hill Top Fabrications Co 1998 Ltd, Unit 22 Siddons Factory Estate, Howard Street, West Bromwich, West Midlands, B70 0SU Tel: 0121-556 9666 Fax: 0121-556 3777 E-mail: hilltopfab@supanet.com
Jara Tube Manipulators Ltd, Unit 4 Block 3, Wednesbury Trading Estate, Wednesbury, West Midlands, WS10 7JN Tel: 0121-556 6141 Fax: 0121-556 6854 E-mail: sales@jaratube.co.uk
Malvern Tubular Components Ltd, Spring Lane, Malvern, Worcestershire, WR14 1DA Tel: (01684) 892600 Fax: (01684) 892337 E-mail: sales@mtc.uk.com
Parmac Engineers, Broad Street, Long Eaton, Nottingham, NG10 1JH Tel: 0115-972 7679 Fax: 0115-946 8483
Ro Co Engineering Services, Unit 8 Sinclair Court, Great Yarmouth, Norfolk, NR31 0NH Tel: (01493) 602744 Fax: (01493) 658450
Willenhall Tube & Forging, Bloxwich Lane Indust Estate, Bloxwich Lane, Walsall, WS2 8TF Tel: (01922) 725505 Fax: (01922) 720131 E-mail: enquiries@willenhalltube.co.uk

TUBULAR FORGINGS

Heartland Extrusion Forge Ltd, Rocky Lane, Nechells, Birmingham, B7 5EU Tel: 0121-359 6861 Fax: 0121-359 2972 E-mail: enquiries@hef.co.uk

TUBULAR FURNITURE DISTRIBUTORS OR AGENTS, *See Furniture etc*

TUBULAR FURNITURE FRAMES

Tubend Manufacturers, Stanley Street, Sowerby Bridge, West Yorkshire, HX6 2AH Tel: (01422) 833461 Fax: (01422) 835319 E-mail: tubenduk@aol.com
Tubestyle Products Ltd, New John Street, Halesowen, West Midlands, B62 8HT Tel: 0121-561 5522 Fax: 0121-561 5834
Wake Industries Ltd, Basin Lane, Tamworth, Staffordshire, B77 2AH Tel: (01827) 65864 Fax: (01827) 53326 E-mail: info@wakeindustries.co.uk
Watchwise Ltd, 20 North River Road, Great Yarmouth, Norfolk, NR30 1SG Tel: (01493) 842216 Fax: (01493) 857703 E-mail: ngraver@watchwise.co.uk
Zoeftig & Co Ltd, Kings Hill Industrial Estate, Bude, Cornwall, EX23 8QN Tel: (01288) 354512 Fax: (01288) 355954 E-mail: enquires@zoeftig.com

TUBULAR FURNITURE, STEEL

Ards Tubular Furniture Ltd, Unit 24E Blacks Industrial Estate, Mark Street, Newtownards, County Down, BT23 4DT Tel: (028) 9181 3499 Fax: (028) 9181 3499
Gainsthorpe Furniture Ltd, Unit 5 Cromwell Centre, Roebuck Road, Ilford, Essex, IG6 3UG Tel: (020) 8501 3712 Fax: (020) 8501 5448 E-mail: info@gainsthorpe.co.uk
H N D UK Ltd, Unit 15 Shrub Hill Industrial Estate, Worcester, WR4 9EL Tel: (01905) 29294 E-mail: info@hnd-uk.com
Jay Be Ltd, Spen Lane, Gomersal, Cleckheaton, West Yorkshire, BD19 4PN Tel: (01924) 517820 Fax: (01924) 517910 E-mail: sales@jaybe.co.uk
M P Manipulated Tubes Ltd, 40 Bracebridge Street, Aston, Birmingham, B6 4PJ Tel: 0121-359 0478 Fax: 0121-333 3082
Robinson & Liddell Ltd, Redburn Road, Newcastle upon Tyne, NE5 1NB Tel: 0191-286 2049 Fax: 0191-214 0564 E-mail: sales@rlfurniture.co.uk
G.S. Smart & Co. Ltd, Ardath Road, Birmingham, B38 9PN Tel: 0121-459 0983 Fax: 0121-459 8559 E-mail: info@metalrax-group.co.uk
Tecproof Ltd, 266 Dansom Lane North, Hull, HU8 7RS Tel: (01482) 215886 Fax: (01482) 215886
Tubestyle Products Ltd, New John Street, Halesowen, West Midlands, B62 8HT Tel: 0121-561 5522 Fax: 0121-561 5834
Wake Industries Ltd, Basin Lane, Tamworth, Staffordshire, B77 2AH Tel: (01827) 65864 Fax: (01827) 53326 E-mail: info@wakeindustries.co.uk
Washbourn & Garrett Ltd, Ashcroft Road, Knowsley Industrial Park North, Liverpool, L33 7TW Tel: 0151-546 2901 Fax: 0151-548 5562 E-mail: enquiries@washbourngarrett.co.uk

TUBULAR HANDRAILS

Gabriel & Co. Ltd, Abro Works, 10 Hay Hall Road, Tyseley, Birmingham, B11 2AU Tel: 0121-248 3333 Fax: 0121-248 3330 E-mail: sales@gabrielco.com
I M H Birmingham Ltd, Unit 2 Clyde Street, Birmingham, B12 0NY Tel: 0121-773 2240 Fax: 0121-773 2275E-mail: sales@imhltd.com
Stomet Industries Ltd, Thorpe House, Thorpe Way, Banbury, Oxfordshire, OX16 4SP Tel: (01295) 257565 Fax: (01295) 271762 E-mail: sales@oastdeck.com
Waterbury Bathroom Accessories Ltd, 60 Adams Street, Birmingham, B7 4LT Tel: 0121-333 6062 Fax: 0121-333 6459 E-mail: sales@waterbury.co.uk

TUBULAR JOINTING SYSTEMS

Grainger Tubolt Ltd, Unit A, Meyrick Owen Way, Pembroke Dock, Dyfed, SA72 6WS Tel: (01646) 683584 Fax: (01646) 621392 E-mail: sales@grainger-tubolt.co.uk

TUBULAR METAL CLOTHING LINE POSTS

Hills Industries Ltd, Pontygwindy Industrial Estate, Caerphilly, Mid Glamorgan, CF83 3HU Tel: (029) 2088 3951 Fax: (029) 2088 6102 E-mail: info@hills-industries.co.uk
Timber & Tile Products Ltd, Springhill Road, Carnbane Industrial Estate, Newry, County Down, BT35 6EF Tel: (028) 3026 2609 Fax: (028) 3026 4400 E-mail: ejpurdy@timberandtilesproducts.com

TUBULAR OIL WELL SERVICES

Drilltec International Ltd, Margarethe House, Eismann Way, Corby, Northamptonshire, NN17 5ZB Tel: (01536) 262877 Fax: (01536) 200580 E-mail: jane@drilltec-int.co.uk

TUBULAR OILWELL GOODS

Ramco Tubular Services Ltd, Badentoy Road Badentoy Park, Badentoy Industrial Estate, Portlethen, Aberdeen, AB12 4YA Tel: (01224) 782278 Fax: (01224) 783001 E-mail: info@ramco-plc.com

TUBULAR OILWELL GOODS MAINTENANCE/REPAIR SERVICES

Euramco Ltd, The Quadrant, Newark Close, Royston, Hertfordshire, SG8 5HL Tel: (01763) 244490 Fax: (01763) 247733 E-mail: info@euramco.co.uk

M I B International Ltd, Sun Alliance House, Little Park Street, Coventry, CV1 2JZ Tel: (024) 7622 5202 Fax: (024) 7622 1752 E-mail: sales@mibinternational.com

TUBULAR STAINLESS STEEL FABRICATORS

Hogg Engineering Ltd, Lawson Street, North Shields, Tyne & Wear, NE29 6TF Tel: 0191-259 5181 Fax: 0191-296 0641 E-mail: hogg-engineering@talk21.com

TUBULAR STEEL GATES

L.R. Stewart & Sons Ltd, Hampden Road, Hornsey, London, N8 0HG Tel: (020) 8348 5267 Fax: (020) 8340 7774 E-mail: info@lrstewartandsons.co.uk

Thameside Gates & Railings, Coopers Close, Staines, Middlesex, TW18 3JY Tel: (01784) 464655 Fax: (01784) 466417

TUBULAR STEEL STRUCTURE FABRICATORS

A1 Welding & Fabrications, Unit 40 Vale Business Park, Llandow, Cowbridge, South Glamorgan, CF71 7PF Tel: (01446) 773372 Fax: (01446) 773372

▶ Ferschl Tube Form, 2 Doxford Drive, South West Industrial Estate, Peterlee, County Durham, SR8 2RL Tel: 0191-518 0878 Fax: 0191-518 0938

TUFTED CARPETS

Causeway Carpets, Roe Lee Mill, Whalley New Road, Blackburn, BB1 9SU Tel: (01254) 676996 Fax: (01254) 680510 E-mail: info@causewaycarpets.com

Claymore Carpets, 48 Brown Street, Dundee, DD1 5DT Tel: (01382) 229414 Fax: (01382) 229414 E-mail: claymorecarpetscts.co.uk

William Pownall & Sons Ltd, Ensor Mill, Queensway, Rochdale, Lancashire, OL11 2NU Tel: (01706) 716000 Fax: (01706) 649002

TUFTING MACHINES

David Almond Ltd, Union Works, Bacup Road, Rossendale, Lancashire, BB4 7LN Tel: (01706) 214817 Fax: (01706) 214819 E-mail: venor@davidalmond.freeserve.uk

Cobble Blackburn Ltd, Gate Street, Blackburn, BB1 3AH Tel: (01254) 55121 Fax: (01254) 671125 E-mail: info@cobble.co.uk

TUMBLE DRYERS

▶ Masterpart, 4 Grainger Road, Southend-on-Sea, SS2 5BZ Tel: (01702) 310031 Fax: (01702) 312000 E-mail: sales@masterpart.com

TUNGSTEN

Diamond Ground Products Ltd, Blackstone Road, Stukeley Meadows Industrial Estate, Huntingdon, Cambridgeshire, PE29 6EF Tel: (01480) 459706 Fax: (01480) 453649 E-mail: sales@diamondground.co.uk

TUNGSTEN ALLOY PRODUCTS

A & M Tungsten Powders Ltd, 11 Maxted Road, Hemel Hempstead, Hertfordshire, HP2 7DX Tel: (01442) 254691 Fax: (01442) 255503 E-mail: info.amtp@virgin.net

▶ Tungsten Alloys Manufacturing Ltd, Unit C2 Poplar Way, Catcliffe, Rotherham, South Yorkshire, S60 5TR Tel: (01709) 363633 Fax: (01709) 838089 E-mail: sales@tungsten-alloys.co.uk

TUNGSTEN ALLOY STEEL SPRINGS

Hanson Springs Ltd, Lincoln Street, Rochdale, Lancashire, OL11 1NP Tel: (01706) 522124 Fax: (01706) 640571 E-mail: sales@hanson-springs.co.uk

TUNGSTEN ALLOYS

A & M Tungsten Powders Ltd, 11 Maxted Road, Hemel Hempstead, Hertfordshire, HP2 7DX Tel: (01442) 254691 Fax: (01442) 255503 E-mail: info.amtp@virgin.net

▶ Tungsten Alloys Manufacturing Ltd, Unit C2 Poplar Way, Catcliffe, Rotherham, South Yorkshire, S60 5TR Tel: (01709) 363633 Fax: (01709) 838089 E-mail: sales@tungsten-alloys.co.uk

TUNGSTEN CARBIDE

Kerswell Tooling Services Ltd, Britannic Lodge, Britannic Way, Llandarcy, Neath, West Glamorgan, SA10 6EL Tel: (01792) 812101 Fax: (01792) 814575 E-mail: sales@kerswelltoolingservices.com

TUNGSTEN CARBIDE COMPONENTS

Artisan Sintered Products Ltd, Unit 15, Shepley Industrial Estate, Audenshaw, Manchester, M34 5DW Tel: 0161-336 5911 Fax: 0161-3350280 E-mail: sales@artisancarbide.co.uk

Hallamshire Hardmetal Products Ltd, 315 Coleford Road, Sheffield, S9 5NF Tel: 0114-244 1483 Fax: 0114-244 2712 E-mail: sales@halhard.co.uk

Howle Carbides Ltd, Picts Lane, Princes Risborough, Buckinghamshire, HP27 9EA Tel: (01844) 275171 Fax: (01844) 342514 E-mail: info@howlecarbides.com

J W Hill Precision Engineers Ltd, 22-26 Bath Road, Worcester, WR5 3EL Tel: (01905) 356712 Fax: (01905) 763155 E-mail: info@jwhill-engineering.co.uk

TUNGSTEN CARBIDE CUTTERS

Harthill Developments Ltd, Mansfield Road, Aston, Sheffield, S26 5PQ Tel: 0114-287 4522 Fax: 0114-287 6397 E-mail: sales@harthill.com

TUNGSTEN CARBIDE DIES

Carbide Dies (Birmingham) Ltd, 7 Port Hope Road, Birmingham, B11 1JS Tel: 0121-772 0817 Fax: 0121-773 9342 E-mail: jim@ctr-uk.com

Diemaster Associates Ltd, 63 Kenilworth Road, Sale, Cheshire, M33 5DA Tel: 0161-973 1414 Fax: 0161-905 1466

Marshalls Hard Metals Ltd, Windsor Street, Sheffield, S4 7WB Tel: 0114-275 2282 Fax: 0114-273 8499 E-mail: sales@hardmet.com

Tungsten Die Co., 32 Cogan Street, Barrhead, Glasgow, G78 1EJ Tel: 0141-876 1516 Fax: 0141-876 1516

Tungsten Die Services, 54 Ledger La, Wakefield, West Yorkshire, WF1 2PH Tel: 01924 835523 Fax: 01924 835523

Winn Tools Ltd, Kendricks Road, Wednesbury, West Midlands, WS10 8LY Tel: 0121-526 2075 Fax: 0121-526 5095

TUNGSTEN CARBIDE GAUGES

Tungsten Die Co., 32 Cogan Street, Barrhead, Glasgow, G78 1EJ Tel: 0141-876 1516 Fax: 0141-876 1516

TUNGSTEN CARBIDE MILLING CUTTERS

P N Tools, Unit 33 34, Fourways, Carlyon Road Industrial Estate, Atherstone, Warwickshire, CV9 1LH Tel: (01827) 720013 Fax: (01827) 720039

TUNGSTEN CARBIDE ROTARY BURR MANUFRS

Morrisflex Ltd, London Road, Braunston, Daventry, Northamptonshire, NN11 7HX Tel: (01788) 891777 Fax: (01788) 891629 E-mail: sales@morrisflex.co.uk

▶ S G S Carbide Tool UK Ltd, Unit 1 Metro Centre, Toutley Road, Wokingham, Berkshire, RG41 1QW Tel: 0118-979 5200 Fax: 0118-979 5295 E-mail: sales@sgstool.com

TUNGSTEN CARBIDE TIPPED (TCT) CIRCULAR SAWS

Brooke Cutting Tools (UK) Ltd, Denby Way, Hellaby, Rotherham, South Yorkshire, S66 8HU Tel: (01709) 314500 Fax: (01709) 314501 E-mail: info@brooke.co.uk

SNA Europe Ltd, Bahco Thorne, Moorhead Way, Bramley, Rotherham, South Yorkshire, S66 1YY Tel: (01709) 731731 Fax: (01709) 731741 E-mail: uksales@bahco.com

TUNGSTEN CARBIDE TIPPED (TCT) SAWS

C 4 Carbides (International) Ltd, 9 Nuffield Road, Cambridge, CB4 1TF Tel: (01223) 506406 Fax: (01223) 225405 E-mail: janice@c4carbides.com

E Crowley & Son Ltd, Bentalls, Pipps Hill Industrial Estate, Basildon, Essex, SS14 3BY Tel: (01268) 293605 Fax: (01268) 285452 E-mail: sales@crowleysaws.com

F J Cooper, Old Rumbelows Warehouse, Bryant Avenue, Romford, RM3 0AP Tel: (01708) 349036 Fax: (020) 7739 5777

Glendower Cutting Tools Ltd, 21 Pinfold Road, Thurmaston, Leicester, LE4 8AS Tel: 0116-269 5999 Fax: 0116-269 3442 E-mail: sales@glendower.co.uk

Gomex Tools Ltd, Orchard Road, Finedon, Wellingborough, Northamptonshire, NN9 5JF Tel: (01933) 680492 Fax: (01933) 680693 E-mail: sales@gomex.co.uk

N L S Tools, Station Approach, Waltham Cross, Hertfordshire, EN8 7LZ Tel: (01992) 710888 Fax: (01992) 713938 E-mail: sales@nlstools.co.uk

TUNGSTEN CARBIDE TIPS (TCT)

Advanced Carbide Tooling Ltd, Sketchley Meadows Business Park, Hinckley, Hinckley, Leicestershire, LE10 3EZ Tel: (01455) 234000 Fax: (01455) 234022 E-mail: sales@advancedcarbidetooling.co.uk

Annolloy Ltd, 135 Garth Road, Morden, Surrey, SM4 4LF Tel: (020) 8330 2211 Fax: (020) 8330 5599 E-mail: sales@annolloy.co.uk

Artisan Sintered Products Ltd, Unit 15, Shepley Industrial Estate, Audenshaw, Manchester, M34 5DW Tel: 0161-336 5911 Fax: 0161-3350280 E-mail: sales@artisancarbide.co.uk

Brunswick Tooling Ltd, Unit 3, The Tiding Industrial Park, Birds Royd Lane, Brighouse, West Yorkshire, HD6 1LQ Tel: (01484) 719900 Fax: (01484) 404727 E-mail: sales@brunswicktooling.co.uk

Ceratizit UK Ltd, Cliff Lane, Grappenhall, Warrington, WA4 3JX Tel: (01925) 261161 Fax: (01925) 267933

Hallamshire Hardmetal Products Ltd, 315 Coleford Road, Sheffield, S9 5NF Tel: 0114-244 1483 Fax: 0114-244 2712 E-mail: sales@halhard.co.uk

Midland Carbides, Ivanhoe Indust Estate, Smisby Road, Willesley, Ashby-de-la-Zouch, Leicestershire, LE65 2UG Tel: (01530) 414949 Fax: (01530) 417039

Posi-Thread (UK) Ltd, 4-5 Bridgewater Road, Hertburn Industrial Estate, District 11, Washington, Tyne & Wear, NE37 2SG Tel: 0191-417 8178 Fax: 0191-415 3120 E-mail: info@posithread.co.uk

Tungscarb Products Ltd, 5 Bodmin Road, Coventry, CV2 5DB Tel: (024) 7661 4498 Fax: (024) 7660 2173 E-mail: sales@tungscarbproduct.co.uk

TUNGSTEN CARBIDE TOOLS

Advanced Carbide Tooling Ltd, Sketchley Meadows Business Park, Hinckley, Hinckley, Leicestershire, LE10 3EZ Tel: (01455) 234000 Fax: (01455) 234022 E-mail: sales@advancedcarbidetooling.co.uk

Albe (England) Ltd, 51 Bideford Avenue, Perivale, Greenford, Middlesex, UB6 7PR Tel: (020) 8997 7282 Fax: (020) 8998 2932 E-mail: sales@albe.com

Annolloy Ltd, 135 Garth Road, Morden, Surrey, SM4 4LF Tel: (020) 8330 2211 Fax: (020) 8330 5599 E-mail: sales@annolloy.co.uk

Argyle Engineering Ltd, 21-29 Regent Street, Liverpool, L3 7BW Tel: 0151-236 0777 Fax: 0151-236 8073

Brunswick Tooling Ltd, Unit 3, The Tiding Industrial Park, Birds Royd Lane, Brighouse, West Yorkshire, HD6 1LQ Tel: (01484) 719900 Fax: (01484) 404727 E-mail: sales@brunswicktooling.co.uk

Cavat, 7 New Road, Burton Lazars, Melton Mowbray, Leicestershire, LE14 2UU Tel: (01664) 561761 Fax: (01664) 410280 E-mail: cavattools@cavattools.co.uk

Ceratizit UK Ltd, Cliff Lane, Grappenhall, Warrington, WA4 3JX Tel: (01925) 261161 Fax: (01925) 267933

Coventry Carbide Tools Ltd, 1 Telford Road, Bayton Road Industrial Estate, Coventry, CV7 9ES Tel: (024) 7636 5490 Fax: (024) 7636 5465 E-mail: asaptooling@btconnect.com

Depo FHT, Lion House, Welsh Road East, Southam, Warwickshire, CV47 1NE Tel: (01926) 813969 Fax: (01926) 817722 E-mail: sales@fht-uk.com

Diemaster Associates Ltd, 63 Kenilworth Road, Sale, Cheshire, M33 5DA Tel: 0161-973 1414 Fax: 0161-905 1466

F S W Tooling, Brewery Road, Hoddesdon, Hertfordshire, EN11 8HF Tel: (01992) 469538 Fax: (01992) 468996

James D. Gibson & Co. Ltd, 399 Petre Street, Sheffield, S4 8LL Tel: 0114-243 0385 Fax: 0114-242 5490 E-mail: admin@jamesgibson.co.uk

Glendower Cutting Tools Ltd, 21 Pinfold Road, Thurmaston, Leicester, LE4 8AS Tel: 0116-269 5999 Fax: 0116-269 3442 E-mail: sales@glendower.co.uk

H B Tools Ltd, 2 Langley Court, Langley Road, Burscough Industrial Estate, Ormskirk, Lancashire, L40 8JR Tel: (01704) 897722 Fax: (01704) 897303 E-mail: sales@hbtools.co.uk

Howle Carbides Ltd, Picts Lane, Princes Risborough, Buckinghamshire, HP27 9EA Tel: (01844) 275171 Fax: (01844) 342514 E-mail: info@howlecarbides.com

Impact Carbides Ltd, 36 East Bank Road, Sheffield, S2 3PS Tel: 0114-272 7216 Fax: 0114-272 4854 E-mail: sales@impactcarbides.co.uk

Jayess Tools, 11 Star Road, Partridge Green, Horsham, West Sussex, RH13 8RA Tel: (01403) 711006 Fax: (01403) 711345 E-mail: enquiries@jayesstools.co.uk

Marshalls Hard Metals Ltd, Windsor Street, Sheffield, S4 7WB Tel: 0114-275 2282 Fax: 0114-273 8499 E-mail: sales@hardmet.com

Meltham Carbide Precision Co., Bent Ley Mill, Bent Ley Road, Meltham, Holmfirth, HD9 4AP Tel: (01484) 850998 Fax: (01484) 854808 E-mail: mcp.co@btinternet.com

Mitsubishi Carbide, Mitsubishi House, Galena Close, Amington Heights, Tamworth, Staffordshire, B77 4AS Tel: (01827) 312312 Fax: (01827) 312314

Nixon Industrial Diamonds Ltd, Albion Industrial Estate, Endermere Road, Coventry, CV6 5RR Tel: (024) 7668 6069 Fax: (024) 7663 7213 E-mail: sales@nixondiamonds.co.uk

Posi-Thread (UK) Ltd, 4-5 Bridgewater Road, Hertburn Industrial Estate, District 11, Washington, Tyne & Wear, NE37 2SG Tel: 0191-417 8178 Fax: 0191-415 3120 E-mail: info@posithread.co.uk

Precision Carbide Tools Ltd, Unit 23, Stafford Park12, Telford, Shropshire, TF3 3BJ Tel: (01952) 205850 Fax: (01952) 293561 E-mail: sales@precision-carbide.co.uk

Rennie Tool Co. Ltd, 227 Upper Brook Street, Manchester, M13 0HB Tel: 0161-273 3901 Fax: 0161-273 3348 E-mail: rennietool@btconnect.com

Samwell Tooling Ltd, 29 Benson Road, Nuffield Industrial Estate, Poole, Dorset, BH17 0GB Tel: 01202 687258 Fax: 01202 665698 E-mail: sales@samwell.co.uk

Sandvik Coromant UK, Manor Way, Halesowen, West Midlands, B62 8QZ Tel: 0121-504 5400 Fax: 0121-504 5555 E-mail: ukcoromant@sandvik.com

Sandvik Hard Materials Ltd, PO Box 89, Coventry, CV4 0XG Tel: (024) 7647 6000 Fax: (024) 7685 6950

Sorby (UK) Ltd, 7 Orgreave Close, Handsworth, Sheffield, S13 9NP Tel: 0114-269 3803 Fax: 0114-254 0523 E-mail: sales@sorbyuk.co.uk

Stellram, Bowerhill, Melksham, Wiltshire, SN12 6YH Tel: (01225) 897100 Fax: (01225) 897111

Sumitomo Electric Hardmetal Ltd, 50 Summerleys Road, Princes Risborough, Buckinghamshire, HP27 9PW Tel: (01844) 342081 Fax: (01844) 342415 E-mail: enquiries@sumitomo-hardmetal.co.uk

Tekmat Ltd, Ryan House, Trent Lane, Castle Donington, Derby, DE74 2PY Tel: (01332) 853443 Fax: (01332) 853424 E-mail: sales@tekmat.co.uk

Titman Tip Tools Ltd, Valley Road, Clacton-on-Sea, Essex, CO15 6PP Tel: (01255) 220123 Fax: (01255) 221422 E-mail: sales@titman.co.uk

Tooloy (T S) Ltd, Sizers Court Trading Estate, Henshaw Lane, Yeadon, Leeds, LS19 7DP Tel: 0113-250 4717 Fax: 0113-239 1207 E-mail: paul@tooloytsltdco.co.uk

Trio Tools Rainham Ltd, New Road, Rainham, Essex, RM13 8HA Tel: (01708) 555111 Fax: (01708) 555114 E-mail: sales@triotools.fsbusiness.co.uk

U T T Ltd, Ashton Close, Beaumont Leys, Leicester, LE4 2BN Tel: 0116-233 8884 Fax: 0116-233 8885 E-mail: sales@utt-ltd.co.uk

TUNGSTEN CARBIDE WEAR RESISTANT COMPONENTS/ SPARE PARTS

Annolloy Ltd, 135 Garth Road, Morden, Surrey, SM4 4LF Tel: (020) 8330 2211 Fax: (020) 8330 5599 E-mail: sales@annolloy.co.uk

Hallamshire Hardmetal Products Ltd, 315 Coleford Road, Sheffield, S9 5NF Tel: 0114-244 1483 Fax: 0114-244 2712 E-mail: sales@halhard.co.uk

Howle Carbides Ltd, Picts Lane, Princes Risborough, Buckinghamshire, HP27 9EA Tel: (01844) 275171 Fax: (01844) 342514 E-mail: info@howlecarbides.com

J G Markland & Sons, Park Works, Borron Road, Newton-le-Willows, Merseyside, WA12 0EJ Tel: (01925) 220718 Fax: (01925) 220718

Marshalls Hard Metals Ltd, Windsor Street, Sheffield, S4 7WB Tel: 0114-275 2282 Fax: 0114-273 8499 E-mail: sales@hardmet.com

TUNGSTEN CARBIDE WEAR RESISTANT COMPONENTS/SPARE PARTS – *continued*

Midland Carbides, Ivanhoe Indust Estate, Smisby Road, Willesley, Ashby-de-la-Zouch, Leicestershire, LE65 2UG Tel: (01530) 414949 Fax: (01530) 417039
Sandvik Hard Materials Ltd, PO Box 89, Coventry, CV4 0XG Tel: (024) 7647 6000 Fax: (024) 7685 6950
Tungsten Die Co., 32 Cogan Street, Barrhead, Glasgow, G78 1EJ Tel: 0141-876 1516 Fax: 0141-876 1516
Winn Tools Ltd, Kendricks Road, Wednesbury, West Midlands, WS10 8LY Tel: 0121-526 2075 Fax: 0121-526 5095

TUNGSTEN CONTACTS

Ekaton Ltd, Jubilee House, Altcar Road, Formby, Liverpool, L37 8DL Tel: (01704) 870107 Fax: (01704) 831269 E-mail: colinmackay@ekaton.ltd.uk

TUNGSTEN ELECTRODES

Diamond Ground Products Ltd, Blackstone Road, Stukeley Meadows Industrial Estate, Huntingdon, Cambridgeshire, PE29 6EF Tel: (01480) 459706 Fax: (01480) 453649 E-mail: sales@diamondground.co.uk

TUNGSTEN FILAMENTS

Mercatron International Ltd, 15 Johnson Way, Park Royal, London, NW10 7PF Tel: (020) 8961 1973 Fax: (020) 8961 2106 E-mail: info@mercatron.co.uk

TUNGSTEN HALOGEN LAMPS

Intram Barwell Ltd, Barwell Business Park, Leatherhead Road, Chessington, Surrey, KT9 2NY Tel: (020) 8391 7500 Fax: (020) 8974 1629 E-mail: enquiries@ibl.co.uk

TUNGSTEN SCRAP MERCHANTS/PROCESSORS

▶ London Chemicals & Resources Ltd, Studio V, Trinity Buoy Wharf, 64 Orchard Place, London, E14 0JY Tel: (020) 7183 0651 Fax: (020) 7987 7980 E-mail: info@lcrl.net

TUNGSTEN WELDING ELECTRODES

Diamond Ground Products Ltd, Blackstone Road, Stukeley Meadows Industrial Estate, Huntingdon, Cambridgeshire, PE29 6EF Tel: (01480) 459706 Fax: (01480) 453649 E-mail: sales@diamondground.co.uk

TUNING FORKS

H J Fletcher & Newman Ltd, 5 Bourne Enterprise Centre, Wrotham Road, Borough Green, Sevenoaks, Kent, TN15 8DG Tel: (01732) 886555 Fax: (01732) 884789 E-mail: enquiries@fletcher-newman.co.uk

TUNNELLING CONSULTANCY

Amalgamated Construction Co. Ltd, Whaley Road, Barnsley, South Yorkshire, S75 1HT Tel: (01226) 243413 Fax: (01226) 320202 E-mail: info@amco-construction.co.uk
Charles Haswell & Partners Ltd, 3900 Parkside, Birmingham Business Park, Birmingham, B37 7YG Tel: 0121-717 7744 Fax: 0121-717 0902 E-mail: enquiries@severntrent.com

TUNNELLING CONTRACTORS

Bachy Soletanche, Units 2 & 5 Prospect Place, Mill Lane, Alton, Hampshire, GU34 2SX Tel: (01420) 594700 Fax: (01420) 86971 E-mail: geotech@bacsol.co.uk
Burlington Engineers Ltd, Unit 11 Perival Industrial Park, Horsenden Lane South, Perivale, Greenford, Middlesex, UB6 7RL Tel: (020) 8810 7266 Fax: (020) 8998 3517 E-mail: info@burlington-engineers.co.uk
Carillion Mowlems, Foundation House, Eastern Road, Bracknell, Berkshire, RG12 2UZ Tel: (01344) 720001
Coleman Tunnelling & Technology Services Ltd, Old Wolverton Road, Old Wolverton, Milton Keynes, MK12 5NL Tel: (01908) 312744 Fax: (01908) 220676 E-mail: ctil@btconnectaol.com
D C T Civil Engineering Ltd, Prospect House, George Street, Shaw, Oldham, OL2 8DX Tel: (01706) 842929 Fax: (01706) 882158 E-mail: info@dct-civils.co.uk

TUNNELLING MACHINE AND EQUIPMENT CONSULTANCY OR DESIGN

Dosco Overseas Engineering Ltd, Dosco Industrial Estate, Ollerton Road, Tuxford, Newark, Nottinghamshire, NG22 0PQ Tel: (01777) 870621 Fax: (01777) 871580 E-mail: sales@dosco.co.uk
M G Bennett & Associates Ltd, Bennett House, Pleasley Road, Whiston, Rotherham, South Yorkshire, S60 4HQ Tel: (01709) 373782 Fax: (01709) 363730 E-mail: mgb@bennettmg.co.uk

TUNNELLING MACHINES

G D C Steel Fabrications Ltd, Unit H Adamson Industrial Estate, Croft Street, Hyde, Cheshire, SK14 1EE Tel: 0161-367 8990 Fax: 0161-367 8992 E-mail: gdcsteelfab@btconnect.com
Tunnel Engineering Services UK Ltd, Heywood Street, Oldham, OL4 2HA Tel: 0161-626 6005 Fax: 0161-627 0993 E-mail: info@tesuk.co.uk

TUNNELLING SUPPORTS OR LINING SYSTEMS

R O M Ltd, Wheaton Road, Witham, Essex, CM8 3BU Tel: (01376) 533200 Fax: (01376) 533227 E-mail: sales@rom.co.uk

TURBINE ACCESSORIES MAINTENANCE/REPAIR SERVICES, GAS TURBINES

▶ A & I Accessory Ltd, 19 Macadam Place, South Newmoor Industrial Estate, Irvine, Ayrshire, KA11 4HP Tel: (01294) 211555 Fax: (01294) 211114 E-mail: sales@aiaccessory.com

TURBINE BLADES

Alstom Power Ltd, Newbold Road, Rugby, Warwickshire, CV21 2NH Tel: (01788) 577111 Fax: (01788) 531700
Howmet Ltd, Kestrel Way, Sowton Industrial Estate, Exeter, EX2 7LG Tel: (01392) 429700 Fax: (01392) 429701 E-mail: info@howmet.com
Turbine Blading Ltd, Station Road, Shipston-on-Stour, Warwickshire, CV36 4BL Tel: (01608) 661805 Fax: (01608) 662249 E-mail: paul.levitch@ps.ge.com

TURBINE COATING SERVICES

Chromalloy Metal Tectonics Ltd, Bramble Way, Clover Nook Industrial Park, Somercotes, Alfreton, Derbyshire, DE55 4RH Tel: (01773) 521522 Fax: (01773) 521482

TURBINE COMPONENT MAINTENANCE/REPAIR SERVICES

Chromalloy Metal Tectonics Ltd, Bramble Way, Clover Nook Industrial Park, Somercotes, Alfreton, Derbyshire, DE55 4RH Tel: (01773) 521522 Fax: (01773) 521482

TURBINE COMPONENT MAINTENANCE/REPAIR SERVICES, GAS TURBINE

▶ A & I Accessory Ltd, 19 Macadam Place, South Newmoor Industrial Estate, Irvine, Ayrshire, KA11 4HP Tel: (01294) 211555 Fax: (01294) 211114 E-mail: sales@aiaccessory.com
Chromalloy Metal Tectonics Ltd, Bramble Way, Clover Nook Industrial Park, Somercotes, Alfreton, Derbyshire, DE55 4RH Tel: (01773) 521522 Fax: (01773) 521482
Doncaster (Shrewsbury) Ltd, Whitchurch Road, Shrewsbury, SY1 4DP Tel: (01743) 445181 Fax: (01743) 450125 E-mail: mparry@doncasters.com
Skytec Aviation Ltd, Unit 23 Langlands Avenue, Kelvin South Business Park, East Kilbride, Glasgow, G75 0YG Tel: (01355) 279633 Fax: (01355) 279634 E-mail: skytecaviation@btconnect.com
Turbine Support Ltd, 7 Dodnor Park, Newport, Isle of Wight, PO30 5XE Tel: (01983) 826252 Fax: (01983) 826253 E-mail: sales@turbine-support.com
Turbo Power Services Ltd, Unit 2 Waldron Court, Prince William Road, Loughborough, Leicestershire, LE11 5GD Tel: (01509) 240020 Fax: (01509) 240030 E-mail: steve@turbopowerservies.com

TURBINE COMPONENTS

Alstom Power Ltd, Newbold Road, Rugby, Warwickshire, CV21 2NH Tel: (01788) 577111 Fax: (01788) 531700
Russell Benussi Associates, 3 Pebble Close, Tamworth, Staffordshire, B77 4RD Tel: (01827) 68008 Fax: (01827) 69265 E-mail: sales@benussi.com
Howmet Ltd, Kestrel Way, Sowton Industrial Estate, Exeter, EX2 7LG Tel: (01392) 429700 Fax: (01392) 429701 E-mail: info@howmet.com
Sulzer Pumps UK Ltd, Manor Mill Lane, Leeds, LS11 8BR Tel: 0113-270 1244 Fax: 0113-272 4404 E-mail: sales@sulzerpumps.com
Wood Group Accesseries & Components, Unit 22 Wellheads Industrial Centre, Wellheads Crescent, Dyce, Aberdeen, AB21 7GA Tel: (01224) 255810 Fax: (01224) 255818

TURBINE CONSULTANTS, GAS TURBINES

Aetc Ltd, Victoria Avenue, Yeadon, Leeds, LS19 7AW Tel: 0113-250 5151 Fax: 0113-238 6006
G T & G Ltd, 1 Miltons Yard, Petworth Road, Witley, Godalming, Surrey, GU8 5LT Tel: (01428) 683088 Fax: (01428) 680902

TURBINE CONTROL SYSTEMS

Invensys Systems (UK) TLtd, 2 City Place, Beehive Ring Road, London Gatwick Airport, Gatwick, West Sussex, RH6 0PA Tel: (01293) 527777 Fax: (01293) 552640
Turbine Controls Ltd, 52 Kenilworth Drive, Oadby Industrial Estate, Oadby, Leicester, LE2 5LG Tel: 0116-271 7248 Fax: 0116-271 7250 E-mail: mk@turbinecontrolsltd.com

TURBINE INSULATING BLANKETS/JACKETS

Darchem Engineering Ltd, Iron Masters Way, Stillington, Stockton-on-Tees, Cleveland, TS21 1LB Tel: (01740) 630461 Fax: (01740) 630529 E-mail: sales@darchem.co.uk

TURBINE MAINTENANCE/ REPAIR SERVICES

Alstom Power Ltd, Newbold Road, Rugby, Warwickshire, CV21 2NH Tel: (01788) 577111 Fax: (01788) 531700
Atlantic Project Co., 828 Manchester Road, Rochdale, Lancashire, OL11 3AW Tel: (01706) 345661 Fax: (01706) 648243 E-mail: aslack@apcpower.com
Elliott Turbo Machinery Ltd, 120 Thorneycroft Industrial Estste, Worting Road, Basingstoke, Hampshire, RG21 8BJ Tel: (01256) 354334 Fax: (01256) 322464
Gas Turbine Services Ltd, Avon House, Whitwick Business Park, Stenson Road, Coalville, Leicestershire, LE67 4JP Tel: (01530) 814000 Fax: (01530) 812007 E-mail: enquiries@gasturbines.co.uk
Microturbo Ltd, Concorde Way, Fareham, Hampshire, PO15 5RL Tel: (01489) 564848 Fax: (01489) 563905 E-mail: sales@microturbo.co.uk
R J B Engineering, Westminster Industrial Estate, Station Road, North Hykeham, Lincoln, LN6 3QY Tel: (01522) 690491 Fax: (01522) 697543 E-mail: info@sje-engineering.co.uk
Rolls Royce Power Enginering P.L.C., Atlantic Park, Dunnings Bridge Road, Bootle, Merseyside, L30 4UZ Tel: 0151-524 6555 Fax: 0151-524 6557 E-mail: m.morgan@ces.com
Skytec Aviation Ltd, Unit 23 Langlands Avenue, Kelvin South Business Park, East Kilbride, Glasgow, G75 0YG Tel: (01355) 279633 Fax: (01355) 279634 E-mail: skytecaviation@btconnect.com
Solar Turbines Europe Sa, Suite H Centennial Court, Easthampstead Road, Bracknell, Berkshire, RG12 1YQ Tel: (01344) 782920 Fax: (01344) 782930
Turbine Controls Ltd, 52 Kenilworth Drive, Oadby Industrial Estate, Oadby, Leicester, LE2 5LG Tel: 0116-271 7248 Fax: 0116-271 7250 E-mail: mk@turbinecontrolsltd.com
Turbo Power Services Ltd, Unit 2 Waldron Court, Prince William Road, Loughborough, Leicestershire, LE11 5GD Tel: (01509) 240020 Fax: (01509) 240030 E-mail: steve@turbopowerservies.com
Weir Engineering Services, PO Box 4, Barton-upon-Humber, South Humberside, DN18 5BN Tel: (01652) 632702 Fax: (01652) 633112 E-mail: steemturbines@weir.co.uk
Wood Group Accesseries & Components, Unit 22 Wellheads Industrial Centre, Wellheads Crescent, Dyce, Aberdeen, AB21 7GA Tel: (01224) 255810 Fax: (01224) 255818
Wood Group Light Industrial Turbines Ltd, Kirkhill Drive, Kirkhill Industrial Estate, Dyce, Aberdeen, AB21 0EU Tel: (01224) 413000 Fax: (01224) 770008 E-mail: sales@wglit.com

TURBINE SUPPLIES

G T & G Ltd, 1 Miltons Yard, Petworth Road, Witley, Godalming, Surrey, GU8 5LT Tel: (01428) 683088 Fax: (01428) 680902
Gas Turbine Services Ltd, Avon House, Whitwick Business Park, Stenson Road, Coalville, Leicestershire, LE67 4JP Tel: (01530) 814000 Fax: (01530) 812007 E-mail: enquiries@gasturbines.co.uk
Universal Trade Services Ltd, 32 Marylebone High Street, London, W1U 4PR Tel: (020) 7224 5801 Fax: (020) 7935 3237 E-mail: director@utslimited.com

TURBINE WASH/CLEANING PRODUCTS

▶ Rochem Technical Services Europe Ltd, Unit 11 Sun Valley Business Park, Winnall Close, Winchester, Hampshire, SO23 0LB Tel: (01962) 890089 Fax: (01962) 890090

TURBO-EXPANDERS

Dresser-Rand (U K) Ltd, C I Tower St. Georges Square, High Street, New Malden, Surrey, KT3 4DN Tel: (020) 8336 7300 Fax: (020) 8336 0773

TURBOCHARGER ACCESSORIES/COMPONENTS/ SPARE PARTS IMPORT/EXPORT MERCHANTS OR AGENTS

Turbo Force Ltd, Unit 21 Old Mill Industrial Estate, Bamber Bridge, Preston, PR5 6SY Tel: (01772) 697979 Fax: (01772) 697989 E-mail: sales@turboforce.co.uk

TURBOCHARGER MAINTENANCE/REPAIR/ REMANUFACTURING SERVICES

Caterpillar Remanufacturing Services, Lancaster Road, Shrewsbury, SY1 3NX Tel: (01743) 212000 Fax: (01743) 212700
Holderness Ship Repairers Ltd, Wassand Street, Hull, HU3 4AL Tel: (01482) 216055 Fax: (01482) 216056 E-mail: holdernessshiprepairers@compuserve.com
Turbo Force Ltd, Unit 21 Old Mill Industrial Estate, Bamber Bridge, Preston, PR5 6SY Tel: (01772) 697979 Fax: (01772) 697989 E-mail: sales@turboforce.co.uk

TURF

▶ Q Lawns, Corkway Drove, Hockwold, Thetford, Norfolk, IP26 4JR Tel: (01842) 828266 Fax: (01842) 827911 E-mail: sales@qlawns.co.uk
▶ Q Lawns In The Midlands, 41 Grafton Lane, Bidford-on-Avon, Alcester, Warwickshire, B50 4DX Tel: (01789) 772626 Fax: (01789) 772963 E-mail: davidpfisher@btconnect.com

TURF CUTTING MACHINES

▶ Turfmech Machinery Ltd, Hanger 5, New Road, Hixon, Stafford, ST18 0PF Tel: (01889) 271503 Fax: (01889) 271321 E-mail: sales@turfmech.co.uk

TURKEY

▶ Copas Traditional Turkeys Ltd, King Coppice Farm, Grubwood Lane, Cookham, Maidenhead, Berkshire, SL6 9UB Tel: (01628) 474678 Fax: (01628) 474679 E-mail: turkeys@copas.co.uk

TURNED PARTS DISTRIBUTORS/AGENTS/ STOCKHOLDERS

A P T (Leicester) Ltd, Rookery Lane, Groby, Leicester, LE6 0GL Tel: 0116-287 0051 Fax: 0116-287 0053 E-mail: sales@aptleicester.co.uk
Auto Turned Products Northants Ltd, 1 North Portway Close, Round Spinney Industrial Estate, Northampton, NN3 8RD Tel: (01604) 642214 Fax: (01604) 499319 E-mail: info@autoturned.co.uk
B P Engineering Ltd, John Harper Street, Willenhall, West Midlands, WV13 1RE Tel: (01902) 609167 Fax: (01902) 605766
B & P Engineering (Poole) Ltd, Unit 14, Chelwyn Industrial Estate, Parkstone, Poole, Dorset, BH12 4PE Tel: (01202) 743401 Fax: (01202) 730088

▶ indicates data change since last edition

TURNED PARTS DISTRIBUTORS/ AGENTS/STOCKHOLDERS – *continued*

Braefield Precision Engineers Ltd, High Lane, Stanstead, Stansted, Essex, CM24 8LQ Tel: (01279) 815686 Fax: (01279) 815647 E-mail: braefield@tiscali.co.uk
Branberg Machine Tools, Unit 15 Marino Way, Finchampstead, Wokingham, Berkshire, RG40 4RF Tel: 0118-973 4044 Fax: 0118-973 2707
BWS Security Systems Ltd, BWS Security Systems, Unit18 Church Farm Business Park, Corston, Bath, BA2 9AP Tel: (01225) 872385 Fax: (01225) 874565
Cable Access Solutions Ltd, 11 Stanley Street, Luton, LU1 5AL Tel: (01582) 411022 Fax: (01582) 727117 E-mail: sales@zyteklltd.demon.co.uk
A.J. Clarke (Automatic Machinists) Ltd, Unit 7, Wessex Industrial Estate, Bourne End, Buckinghamshire, SL8 5DT Tel: (01628) 521301 Fax: (01628) 819142 E-mail: sales@ajclarke.info
Clint Hill Engineering, Newton Road, Hinckley, Leicestershire, LE10 3DS Tel: (01455) 239239 Fax: (01455) 238559 E-mail: clinthill@wanadoo.co.uk
CNC Precision, Unit 15 Enfield Industrial Estate, Redditch, Worcestershire, B97 6BG Tel: (01527) 596727 Fax: (01527) 585049 E-mail: sales@c-n-c.co.uk
E R I Ltd, Bridge Road, Great Bridge, Tipton, West Midlands, DY4 0HR Tel: 0121-520 8171 Fax: 0121-522 2330 E-mail: sales@eritpltd.fsnet.co.uk
European CNC Turned Parts Ltd, Unit 101 Telsen Industrial Centre, Thomas Street, Birmingham, B6 4TN Tel: 0121-359 2812 Fax: 0121-359 3520 E-mail: mick@europeancnc.com
Farge Engineering Stockport Ltd, 4 Greyhound Industrial Estate, Melford Road, Hazel Grove, Stockport, Cheshire, SK7 6DD Tel: 0161-456 8209 Fax: 0161-483 9738
Foxwood Engineering, 8 Park Trading Estate, Park Road, Hockley, Birmingham, B18 5HB Tel: 0121-554 7567 Fax: 0121-554 3834
H S Rowe & Partners, Building 80, First Avenue, Pensnett Trading Estate, Kingswinford, West Midlands, DY6 7FQ Tel: (01384) 293862 Fax: (01384) 271805 E-mail: sales@buxtonhayes.co.uk
Hamilton Precision Engineering, 7 Hamilton Way, Gore Road Industrial Estate, New Milton, Hampshire, BH25 6TQ Tel: (01425) 613181
Heelman Ltd, Unit 17-18 Sheet Road Indust Estate, Ludlow, Shropshire, SY8 1LR Tel: (01584) 875030 Fax: (01584) 875030
J P Olives Ltd, 31a Heming Road, Redditch, Worcestershire, B98 0DH Tel: (01527) 516600 Fax: (01527) 516611 E-mail: sales@jpolives.co.uk
Kershaw & Co. Ltd, Hixon Industrial Estate, Church Lane, Hixon, Stafford, ST18 0PY Tel: (01889) 270556 Fax: (01889) 271295 E-mail: sales@kershaw-engineering.co.uk
L J Dennison, 94 Leopold Street, Birmingham, B12 0UD Tel: 0121-772 8871 Fax: 0121-772 8871
Lowley Engineering Ltd, Unit B3 Pennygillam Way, Pennygillam Industrial Estate, Launceston, Cornwall, PL15 7ED Tel: (01566) 773998 Fax: (01566) 777137 E-mail: lowleyeng@aol.com
Muller Holdings Ltd, Cleobury Mortimer, Kidderminster, Worcestershire, DY14 8DT Tel: (01299) 270271 Fax: (01299) 270877 E-mail: sales@muller-england.co.uk
Muller Redditch Ltd, Bartleet Road, Washford Industrial Estate, Redditch, Worcestershire, B98 0DG Tel: (01527) 526920 Fax: (01527) 502166 E-mail: sales@muller-redditch.co.uk
N S H Turned Parts, Fordwater Trading Estate, Ford Road, Chertsey, Surrey, KT16 8HG Tel: (01932) 561761 Fax: (01932) 563178
Redditch Production Machining, 47 Padgets Lane, Redditch, Worcestershire, B98 0RD Tel: (01527) 500568 Fax: (01527) 510976
T & J Engineering Ltd, Unit 12a Boston Place, Coventry, CV6 5NN Tel: (024) 7668 8713 Fax: (024) 7668 8713
Techfore Turned Parts Ltd, Unit 32r The Washford Industrial Estate, Heming Road, Redditch, Worcestershire, B98 0DH Tel: (01527) 514218 Fax: (01527) 514200
The Tenable Screw Co. Ltd, Tenable House, Torrington Avenue, Coventry, CV4 9HN Tel: (024) 7669 4422 Fax: (024) 7647 0029 E-mail: sales@tenable.co.uk
The Tenable Screw Co. Ltd, Elcot Lane, Marlborough, Wiltshire, SN8 2AE Tel: (01672) 512900 Fax: (01672) 513915 E-mail: sales@tenable.co.uk
Thomas Engineering, Manning Road, Bourne, Lincolnshire, PE10 9HW Tel: (01778) 422720 Fax: (01778) 425530 E-mail: gecrane@totalise.co.uk
Turnomatic Ltd, Unit C8 Angel Road Works, Advent Way, London, N18 3AH Tel: (020) 8807 0661 Fax: (020) 8807 6134 E-mail: enquiry@turnomaticltd.com
W W Grew & Co. Ltd, Stafford Street, Wednesbury, West Midlands, WS10 7JX Tel: 0121-556 3337 Fax: 0121-556 8171 E-mail: info@wwgrew.com

TURNING SERVICES

A & W Jigboring Ltd, 46 Padgets Lane, Redditch, Worcestershire, B98 0RD Tel: (01527) 522196 Fax: (01527) 517389 E-mail: sales@awjigboring.co.uk
Algernon, Unit 1 Algarnon Industrial Estate, Shiremoor, Newcastle upon Tyne, NE27 0NB Tel: 0191-251 4600 Fax: 0191-297 0360 E-mail: algernoneng@aol.com
Amek Precision Engineers, The Hollies, Campton Road, Meppershall, Shefford, Bedfordshire, SG17 5PB Tel: (01462) 851171 Fax: (01462) 851171
▶ BST Precision Ltd, Unit D 10, Hortonwood 7, Hortonwood, Telford, Shropshire, TF1 7XU Tel: (01952) 603952 Fax: (01952) 604947 E-mail: tony.edgley@bstprecision.co.uk
Chiltern Cam Service Ltd, Unit 2a Watlington Industrial Estate, Cuxham Road, Watlington, Oxfordshire, OX49 5LU Tel: (01491) 614422 Fax: (01491) 613813 E-mail: enquiries@chilterncam.com
Crusherform Grinding Co., 30 Kennington Road, Nuffield Industrial Estate, Poole, Dorset, BH17 0GF Tel: (01202) 679363 Fax: (01202) 682970
Fife Engineering Co. Ltd, Longrigg, Swalwell, Newcastle upon Tyne, NE16 3AW Tel: 0191-496 1133 Fax: 0191-496 5502 E-mail: admin@fife-engineering.com
Greenberry Bros Engineers Ltd, Brunel Drive, Newark, Nottinghamshire, NG24 2EG Tel: (01636) 676694 Fax: (01636) 675830 E-mail: sales@greenberrybros.co.uk
Ims UK, International House, Saltley Trading Estate, Saltley, Birmingham, B8 1BB Tel: 0121-326 3100 Fax: 0121-326 3105
J J Churchill Ltd, Station Road, Market Bosworth, Nuneaton, Warwickshire, CV13 0PF Tel: (01455) 299600 Fax: (01455) 292330 E-mail: sales@jjchurchill.com
Legend Engineering Ltd, Unit B1, Meadow Lane Industrial Estate, Alfreton, Derbyshire, DE55 7EZ Tel: (01773) 520192 Fax: (01773) 830267 E-mail: legend@fsbdial.co.uk
M P Engineering, 7 Locke Place, Birmingham, B7 4HH Tel: 0121-359 5854 Fax: 0121-359 5854
Midland Precision Equipment Co. Ltd, Haslucks Green Road, Shirley, Solihull, West Midlands, B90 2LY Tel: 0121-744 2719 Fax: 0121-733 1296 E-mail: sales@midland-precision.co.uk
F.A. Morris (Sheffield) Ltd, 83 Headford Street, Sheffield, S3 7WA Tel: 0114-276 7327 Fax: 0114-275 3862 E-mail: sales@famorris.co.uk
PJP Precision Engineering Ltd, 5 Berkshire Business Centre, Berkshire Drive, Thatcham, Berkshire, RG19 4EW Tel: (01635) 872792 Fax: (01635) 864390 E-mail: pjpm@msn.com

TURNING TOOLS

S J C Engineering Ltd, 5 Court Industrial Estate, Navigation Road, Chelmsford, CM2 6ND Tel: (01245) 492926 Fax: (01245) 494296 E-mail: enquiries@sjceng.co.uk

TURNKEY AUTOMATION SOLUTIONS

C S L Technical Engineering Services, Office 2 Rainbow Business Centre, Phoenix Way, Swansea Enterprise Park, Swansea, SA7 9EH Tel: 01792 702200 E-mail: sales@csl-ltd.co.uk
Complete Industrial Services Ltd, 63 Cromwell Road, Bushbury Wolverhampton, Wolverhampton, WV10 8UT Tel: (01902) 651795 Fax: (01902) 651795 E-mail: sales@ciservices.worldonline.co.uk

TURNKEY CONTRACTORS ESTIMATING COMPUTER SYSTEMS

▶ LiberRATE Estimating Software, 25B The Borough, Farnham, Surrey, GU9 7NJ Tel: (01252) 725513 Fax: (01252) 727828 E-mail: info@landpro.co.uk

TURNKEY MANUFACTURING SERVICES OR CONTRACTORS

Peter Hall Export Services, Flaunden Lane, Bovingdon, Hemel Hempstead, Hertfordshire, HP3 0QA Tel: (01442) 833241 Fax: (01442) 834142 E-mail: peter@exportservices.co.uk
PGS Engineering Ltd, Quayside Drive, Walsall, WS2 9LA Tel: (01922) 425555 Fax: (01922) 425556
S M S Technologies Ltd, Elizabeth House, Elizabeth Way, Harlow, Essex, CM19 5TL Tel: (01279) 406000 Fax: (01279) 406001 E-mail: admin@smstl.com

TURNSTILES

Broughton Controls Ltd, Shaw Road, Oldham, OL1 4AW Tel: 0161-627 0060 Fax: 0161-627 1362 E-mail: info@broughton-controls.co.uk
Gunnebo Entrance Control Ltd, Optimus, Bell Lane, Bellbrook Industrial Estate, Uckfield, East Sussex, TN22 1QL Tel: (01825) 761022 Fax: (01825) 763835 E-mail: info@gunneboe.co.uk
Heda, Unit D5, Chaucer Business Park, Kemsing, Sevenoaks, Kent, TN15 6YU Tel: (01732) 765474 Fax: (01732) 765478
Turnstile Systems 2000 Ltd, Unit F4 Phoenix Trading Estate, London Road, Thrupp, Stroud, Gloucestershire, GL5 2BX Tel: (01453) 883590 E-mail: bert@turnstile.uk.com
Wanzl Ltd, Europa House, Heathcote Lane, Heathcote, Warwick, CV34 6SP Tel: (01926) 451951 Fax: (01926) 451952
Zeag UK Ltd, Zeag House, 17 Deer Park Road, London, SW19 3XJ Tel: (020) 8543 3281 Fax: (020) 8443 5344 E-mail: sales@zeaguk.com

TURNTABLES, VEHICLE ETC

Car Parking Solutions, St. Peters, Ellachie Mews, Gosport, Hampshire, PO12 2DR Tel: (023) 9252 2017 Fax: (023) 9252 2017 E-mail: infosales@parkingsolutions.co.uk

TURPENTINE

Langley-Smith & Co. Ltd, 36 Spital Square, London, E1 6DY Tel: (020) 7247 7473 Fax: (020) 7375 1470 E-mail: sales@langley-smith.co.uk

TURRET LATHES

H W Ward Service Spares Ltd, Ajax Works, Whitehill Industrial Estate, Stockport, Cheshire, SK4 1NT Tel: 0161-429 6962 Fax: 0161-480 7693 E-mail: ward@bamfordajax.com

TURRET TOOLING

Tower Machine Tools Ltd, Mayflower Close, Chandler's Ford, Eastleigh, Hampshire, SO53 4AR Tel: (023) 8026 0266 Fax: (023) 8026 1012 E-mail: towermctools@compuserve.com

TWEED

Bovey Handloom Weavers, 1 Station Road, Bovey Tracey, Newton Abbot, Devon, TQ13 9AL Tel: (01626) 833424 Fax: (01626) 833424
Cambrian Woollen Mill, Top Floor Weaving Unit, Llanwrtyd Wells, Powys, LD5 4SD Tel: (01591) 610473 Fax: (01591) 610314 E-mail: cambrianwool@tiscali.co.uk
Glenalmond Tweed Co. Ltd, Culnacloich Farm, Glenalmond, Perth, PH1 3SN Tel: (01738) 880322 Fax: (01738) 880431 E-mail: info@glenalmond.com
Islay Woollen Mill Co. Ltd, Islay Woollen Mill, Bridgend, Isle Of Islay, PA44 7PG Tel: (01496) 810563 Fax: (01496) 810677
Trefriw Woollen Mills Ltd, Trefriw, Gwynedd, LL27 0NQ Tel: (01492) 640462 Fax: (01492) 641821 E-mail: info@trefriw-woollen-mills.co.uk

TWEEZERS

Acme United Europe, Estate Office Thorncliffe Park Estate, Newton Chambers Road, Chapeltown, Sheffield, S35 2PH Tel: 0114-220 3709 Fax: 0114-220 3706 E-mail: sales@acmeunited.co.uk

TWINE, *See also headings for particular types*

Colton Packaging Ltd, 60-65 The Warren, East Goscote, Leicester, LE7 3XA Tel: 0116-264 1060 Fax: 0116-264 1066
Daniel Paper & Packaging, 133 Old Lane, Manchester, M11 1DD Tel: 0161-301 4710 Fax: 0161-370 9753
J. Harper Ltd, 32A Temple Street, Wolverhampton, WV2 4AN Tel: (01902) 422865 Fax: (01902) 422865
John Gray Paper & Twine Ltd, 48 Thomas Street, Manchester, M4 1ER Tel: 0161-832 3313 Fax: 0161-839 7068 E-mail: sales@johngray-packaging.co.uk
Kent & Co Twines Ltd, Long Lane, Walton, Liverpool, L9 7DE Tel: 0151-525 1601 Fax: 0151-523 1410 E-mail: kenttwines@aol.com
Nutscene Ltd, Forfar, Angus, DD8 2NS Tel: (01307) 468589 Fax: (01307) 467051 E-mail: sales@nutscene.com
Sicor International Ltd, 3 Murcar Industrial Estate, Denmore Road, Bridge of Don, Aberdeen, AB23 8JW Tel: (01224) 707560 Fax: (01224) 707561 E-mail: sales.sicorabdn@virgin.net

TWIST DRILLS

Guhring Ltd, Castle Bromwich Business Park, Tameside Drive, Castle Vale, Birmingham, B35 7AG Tel: 0121-749 5544 Fax: 0121-776 7224 E-mail: info@guhring.co.uk

TWISTED TUBE HEAT EXCHANGERS

Koch Heat Transfer Company, PO Box 790, Wimborne, Dorset, BH21 5BQ Tel: (01258) 840776 Fax: (01258) 840961 E-mail: bftuk@kochind.com

TWO DIMENSIONAL (2D) PAINTINGS

▶ ChaosArtworks.com, 10 Ambleside Way, Donnington, Telford, Shropshire, TF2 7QE Tel: (01952) 604190 E-mail: info@chaosartworks.com

TWO PART SPRAY EQUIPMENT

Ospray Systems Ltd, 76-80 Sherlock Street, Birmingham, B5 6LT Tel: (0870) 770 7650 Fax: (0870) 770 7651 E-mail: info@eurospraygroup.com

TWO WAY COMMUNICATION RADIO EQUIPMENT

Angila Radio Ltd, Branford House, Valley Road, Tasburgh, Norwich, NR15 1NG Tel: (01508) 470720 Fax: (01508) 471393 E-mail: info@angliaradio.com
Brentwood Communications Ltd, 178 Warley Hill, Warley, Brentwood, Essex, CM14 5HF Tel: (01277) 225254 Fax: (01277) 223089 E-mail: info@bc-ltd.co.uk
Helmsman Electronics Ltd, 31 Faringdon Avenue, Blackpool, FY4 3QQ Tel: (01253) 343056 Fax: (01253) 408004 E-mail: mail@helmsmanuk.co.uk
M R S Communications Ltd, Viaduct Road, Gwaelod Y Garth, Cardiff, CF10 9JN Tel: (029) 2081 0810 Fax: (029) 2081 3755
Radio Links Communications Ltd, Eaton House, Great North Road, Eaton Socon, St. Neots, Cambridgeshire, PE19 8EG Tel: (01480) 217220 Fax: (01480) 406667 E-mail: info@radio-links.co.uk
Rapid Radio Communications, Unit 5 The Acorn Centre, Roebuck Road, Hainault, Ilford, Essex, IG6 3TU Tel: (020) 8500 9999 Fax: (020) 8500 8124 E-mail: mail@rapidradio.com
Stirling Solent Communications, 33 Portsmouth Enterprise Centre, Quartremaine Road, Portsmouth, PO3 5QT Tel: (0870) 7701702 Fax: (023) 9267 3518E-mail: csil@csil-uk.com
Team Simoco Ltd, Field House, Uttoxeter Old Road, Derby, DE1 1NH Tel: (01332) 375500 Fax: (01332) 375501 E-mail: marketing@teamsimoco.com
Mike Weaver Communications Ltd, Unit 6 Fullwood Close, Aldermans Green Industrial Estate, Coventry, CV2 2SS Tel: (024) 7660 2605 Fax: (024) 7660 2609

TWO WAY COMMUNICATION RADIO EQUIPMENT CHARGERS

Consam Communications, 33 Highmeres Road, Leicester, LE4 9LZ Tel: 0116-276 0909 Fax: 0116-276 2141E-mail: info@consam.com
Marlborough Radio Services, 9-11 Kildare Terrace, Leeds, LS12 1DB Tel: 0113-243 1626 Fax: 0113-246 1838 E-mail: andy@marlboroughradio.com

TWO WAY COMMUNICATION RADIO EQUIPMENT INSTALLATION OR MAINTENANCE OR REPAIR

Brentwood Communications Ltd, 178 Warley Hill, Warley, Brentwood, Essex, CM14 5HF Tel: (01277) 225254 Fax: (01277) 223089 E-mail: info@bc-ltd.co.uk
Dee Communications, 453 Brook Lane, Birmingham, B13 0BT Tel: 0121-702 2552 Fax: 0121-778 3633 E-mail: sales@deecomms.co.uk
Moray Instruments, 1 Tyock Industrial Estate, Elgin, Morayshire, IV30 1XY Tel: (01343) 543747 Fax: (01343) 548390
Radio Coms Systems Ltd, 170a Oval Road, Croydon, CR0 6BN Tel: (020) 8680 1585 Fax: (020) 8686 9433 E-mail: info@radiocoms.co.uk
Radio Service, Unit 129 Brookfield Place, Walton Summit Industrial Estate, Bamber Bridge, Preston, PR5 8BF Tel: (01772) 628000 Fax: (01772) 628888 E-mail: ians@rstechnology.co.uk
Radiocoms Systems Ltd, 170a Oval Road, Croydon, ,Hounslow, Hounslow, TW6 2BG Tel: (0870) 4604600 Fax: (020) 8759 1411
Servicom (High Tech) Ltd, Unit 8 The I.O. Centre, Nash Road, Park Farm North, Redditch, Worcestershire, B98 7AS Tel: (01527) 510800 Fax: (01527) 510975 E-mail: sales@servicom.co.uk

TWO WAY COMMUNICATION RADIO EQUIPMENT INSTALLATION OR MAINTENANCE OR REPAIR – *continued*

Sitelink Communications, 14 Collingwood Court, Riverside Park Industrial Esta, Middlesbrough, Cleveland, TS2 1RP Tel: (01642) 232468 Fax: (01642) 226155 E-mail: teeside@sitelink.co.uk
Mike Weaver Communications Ltd, Unit 6 Fullwood Close, Aldermans Green Industrial Estate, Coventry, CV2 2SS Tel: (024) 7660 2605 Fax: (024) 7660 2609

TWO WAY RADIO HIRE

▶ Sitelink Communications Ltd, Radiophone Centre, 179 Hall Street, Stockport, Cheshire, SK1 4JG Tel: 0161-477 9229 Fax: 0161-480 7988 E-mail: manchester@sitelink.co.uk

TYPEFACE DESIGN

▶ Ikographics, 47 Beechy Avenue, Eastbourne, East Sussex, BN20 8NU Tel: (01323) 724461 Fax: (01323) 511418 E-mail: info@ikographics.co.uk

TYPESETTING EQUIPMENT

County Press, County Press Buildings, Station Road, Bala, Gwynedd, LL23 7PG Tel: (01678) 520262 Fax: (01678) 521251 E-mail: budgerigarworld@msn.com
Greenock Telegraph, 2 Crawfurd Street, Greenock, Renfrewshire, PA15 1LH Tel: (01475) 726511 Fax: (01475) 783734 E-mail: advertising@greenocktelegraph.co.uk
I P A Systems Ltd, 4 Liberty Court, 101-103 Bell Street, Reigate, Surrey, RH2 7JB Tel: (01737) 225010 Fax: (01737) 771827 E-mail: sales@ipasystems.co.uk
Tyrone Printing Co., Unit 179, Moygashel Mills, Moygashel, Dungannon, County Tyrone, BT71 7HB Tel: (028) 8772 2274 Fax: (028) 8772 6164

TYPESETTING SERVICES

▶ Ali Alwan DTP, 228 Seaforth Avenue, New Malden, Surrey, KT3 6JW Tel: (020) 8949 6048
B S C Print, B S C House, 48 Weir Road, Wimbledon, London, SW19 8UG Tel: (020) 8947 8571 Fax: (020) 8947 3319 E-mail: sales@bscprint..co.uk
▶ B W W Printers Ltd, Axe Road, Bridgwater, Somerset, TA6 5LW Tel: (01278) 423637 Fax: (01278) 444032
Bedford Typesetters, 36 Woburn Road Industrial Estate Singer Way, Woburn Road Industrial Estate, Kempston, Bedford, MK42 7AF Tel: (01234) 840125 Fax: (01234) 840909
Bookham Print & Design, Homestead, Eastwick Road, Bookham, Leatherhead, Surrey, KT23 4BA Tel: (01372) 454506 Fax: (01372) 452087
Breeze Ltd, Breeze House, Albert Close Trading Estate, Whitefield, Manchester, M45 8EH Tel: 0161-796 3600 Fax: 0161-796 3700 E-mail: info@breez.co.uk
Butler & Tanner Ltd, Cackston Road, Frome, Somerset, BA11 1NF Tel: (01373) 451333 Fax: (01373) 451333
C P Offset Ltd, Kellaw Road, Darlington, County Durham, DL1 4YA Tel: (01325) 462315 Fax: (01325) 462767 E-mail: administrator@banff-buchan.ac.uk
Camberley Printers Ltd, 357 London Road, Camberley, Surrey, GU15 3HQ Tel: (01276) 63048 Fax: (01276) 23477 E-mail: sales@camberleyprinters.co.uk
Chinese Marketing & Communications, 16 Nicholas Street, Manchester, M1 4EJ Tel: (0870) 0181298 Fax: (0870) 0181299 E-mail: support@chinese-marketing.com
Robin Clay Ltd, 31 St. Leonards Road, Bexhill-on-Sea, East Sussex, TN40 1HP Tel: (01424) 730302 Fax: (01424) 730291 E-mail: sarah@ashbuscent.co.uk
Composing Operations Ltd, Sheffield Road, Tunbridge Wells, Kent, TN4 0PD Tel: (01892) 511725 Fax: (01892) 511726 E-mail: compops@btconnect.com
▶ Composing Room, 18 Leather Lane, London, EC1N 7SU Tel: (020) 7430 0861 Fax: (020) 7242 1854 E-mail: sales@thecomposingroom.com
Dalton Printers, Dalton House, Thesiger Street, Cardiff, CF24 4BN Tel: (029) 2023 6832 Fax: (029) 2066 6516 E-mail: daltonprinters@dial.pipex.com
Deltor Communications Ltd, Unit C Long Acre, Saltash, Cornwall, PL12 6LZ Tel: (01752) 841717 Fax: (01752) 850450 E-mail: enquiries@deltor.uk
Design & Media Solutions, Tovil Hill, Maidstone, Kent, ME15 6QS Tel: (01622) 681366 Fax: (01622) 688928 E-mail: craftsmencolour@craftsmencolour.co.uk
The Digital Printed Word Ltd, 19 Briset Street, London, EC1M 5NR Tel: (020) 7250 1404 Fax: (020) 7253 4675 E-mail: printedword@btconnect.com
Dolphin Design, 17 Invincible Road, Farnborough, Hampshire, GU14 7QU Tel: (01252) 518028 Fax: (01252) 518351 E-mail: thomas-frear@btconnect.com
Dorchester Typesetting Group Ltd, Bridport Road, Dorchester, Dorset, DT1 1UA Tel: (01305) 262038 Fax: (01305) 260886 E-mail: dorchtype@btconnect.com
▶ Exe Valley Dataset Ltd, 43 Marsh Green Road West, Marsh Barton Trading Estate, Exeter, EX2 8PN Tel: (01392) 426464 Fax: (01392) 491066 E-mail: sales@evdataset.co.uk
Express Typesetters Ltd, 11 Riverside Park, Dogflud Way, Farnham, Surrey, GU9 7UG Tel: (01252) 724112 Fax: (01252) 721874 E-mail: sales@arrowpress.co.uk
Fericon Press Ltd, 12 Stadium Way, Tilehurst, Reading, RG30 6BX Tel: 0118-945 6100 Fax: 0118-945 4146 E-mail: fericon@dercon.co.uk
Gladstone Press, 701 Gladstone Court Business Centre, London, SW8 4AT Tel: (020) 7498 0071 Fax: (020) 7498 0067 E-mail: nigelmason@spuk.co.uk
Henry Ling Ltd, 23 High East Street, Dorchester, Dorset, DT1 1HD Tel: (01305) 251066 Fax: (01305) 251908 E-mail: production@henryling.co.uk
M F K Group Ltd, 23-25 Gunnels Wood Park, Gunnels Wood Road, Stevenage, Hertfordshire, SG1 2BH Tel: (01438) 312777 Fax: (01438) 317789
P C Graphics, Unit 1, Langley House, Middlegreen Trading Estate, Langley, Slough, SL3 6DF Tel: (01753) 571220 Fax: (01753) 692380 E-mail: sales@pcgraphics.co.uk
Pindar Set Ltd, Newlands House, Caxton Way, Scarborough, North Yorkshire, YO11 3YT Tel: (01723) 502000 Fax: (01723) 502002 E-mail: enquiries@pindarset.com
▶ Refinecatch Ltd, Broad Street, Bungay, Suffolk, NR35 1EF Tel: (01986) 895888 Fax: (01986) 895695
Saltire Graphics, Brook St Studios, 60 Brook Street, Glasgow, G40 2AB Tel: 0141-556 3722 Fax: 0141-554 1621 E-mail: info@saltiregraphics-print.com
Santype International Ltd, Harnham Trading Estate, Netherhampton Road, Salisbury, SP2 8PS Tel: (01722) 334261 Fax: (01722) 333171 E-mail: post@santype.com
Set & Match Ltd, 46 Lower Tower Street, Birmingham, B19 3NH Tel: 0121-333 6329 Fax: 0121-333 6190 E-mail: info@setandmatch.net
Sudak Printers Ltd, Unit 5A, Princess Drive Industrial Estate, Coventry Road, Kenilworth, Warwickshire, CV8 2FD Tel: (01926) 513131 E-mail: info@sudak.co.uk
T A (Printers) Ltd, 43-45 Milford Road, Reading, RG1 8LG Tel: 0118-957 5442 Fax: 0118-958 3899 E-mail: taprinters@i12.com
Tag, 29 Clerkenwell Road, London, EC1M 5TA Tel: (020) 7251 4571 Fax: (020) 7253 5355 E-mail: info@tagmedia.co.uk
Tranex Translation & Typesetting, 10 Barley Mow Passage, London, W4 4PH Tel: (020) 8747 1486 Fax: (020) 8995 0163 E-mail: nagitranex2@aol.com
Word and Page, 45 Lime Grove, Hoole, Chester, CH2 3HW Tel: (01244) 312489 E-mail: edit@wordandpage.co.uk
Word Link Ltd, 121a Godolphin Road, London, W12 8JN Tel: (020) 8749 3388 Fax: (020) 8749 8398 E-mail: sales@wordlink.demon.co.uk

TYPEWRITER MAINTENANCE/ REPAIR SPECIALIST SERVICES

Executive Communications, Hi Tech House, 18 Beresford Avenue, Wembley, Middlesex, HA0 1YP Tel: (020) 8903 3425 Fax: (01784) 431560 E-mail: executivecomm@execs.com
Fax Typewriter Service, Greenlands, Danes Green, Claines, Worcester, WR3 7RU Tel: (01905) 456705 Fax: (01905) 456705
Linconshire Office Friends Ltd, Unit 1 Viking Court, Gilbey Road, Grimsby, North East Lincolnshire, DN31 2UJ Tel: (01472) 341493 Fax: (01472) 341600 E-mail: sales@officefriends.com
Tattersalls, 46 Warner Street, Accrington, Lancashire, BB5 1HN Tel: (01254) 232244 Fax: (01254) 386454

TYPEWRITER RIBBONS

D P I Systems Ltd, L C S House, Ainleys Industrial Estate, Huddesfield Road, Elland, West Yorkshire, HX5 9JP Tel: (01422) 375444 Fax: (01422) 370037 E-mail: elland@dpisystems.co.uk
Typerite Ltd, Upper Dromore Road, Warrenpoint, Newry, County Down, BT34 3PN Tel: (028) 4177 2111 Fax: (028) 4175 2022 E-mail: info@typerite.com

TYPEWRITERS

Brian Green, D B H House, Boundary Street, Liverpool, L5 9YJ Tel: 0151-207 5225 Fax: 0151-207 3300 E-mail: sales@brian-green.co.uk
J D M Office Equipment Services, 66 Harborne Road, Oldbury, West Midlands, B68 9JB Tel: 0121-429 3805 Fax: 0121-554 4627
K T D Colourcraft Ltd, 7 Lowther Street, Carlisle, CA3 8ES Tel: (01228) 528559 Fax: (01228) 819799
Research Micro Systems Ltd, Radclyffe House, 66-68 Hagley Road, Birmingham, B16 8PF Tel: 0121-410 5860
Typewriter & Equipment Co. Ltd, Teco House, High Street, Lye, Stourbridge, West Midlands, DY9 8LU Tel: (01384) 424416 Fax: (01384) 423423 E-mail: info@tecoltd.co.uk

TYPING SERVICES

▶ Arcevia Services, 80 Oakland Avenue, Leicester, LE4 7SF Tel: 0116-220 4655 Fax: (0870) 7625207 E-mail: info@arcevia.com
▶ Birstall Secretarial, 94 Gelderd Road, Birstall, Batley, West Yorkshire, WF17 9LP Tel: (01924) 440291 Fax: (0870) 1334078 E-mail: sales@birstallsecretarial.co.uk
Complus Teltronic Ltd, Sibleys Green, Thaxted, Dunmow, Essex, CM6 2NU Tel: (01371) 830326 Fax: (01371) 831096 E-mail: enquires@complusteltronic.co.uk
Designs To Print, 15 Devonshire Rd, London, W4 2EU Tel: (020) 8995 5155 Fax: (020) 8995 5156
▶ Digital Secretary, Feldwicke Cottage, Ardingly Road, West Hoathly, East Grinstead, West Sussex, RH19 4RA Tel: (01342) 716137 Fax: (01342) 716137 E-mail: info@digital-secretary.co.uk
▶ Havelock Secretarial Services, Havelock Secretarial Services, Enterprise 5, Five Lane Ends, Idle, Bradford, West Yorkshire, BD10 8EW Tel: (01274) 618821 Fax: 01274 612604 E-mail: ltaylor@tayloredwebs.co.uk
▶ SJM Secretarial Services, Nelson Street, Burton-on-Trent, Staffordshire, DE15 0DE Tel: (01283) 509854
▶ Typing For Business, Ridge Mount, Middlewich Road, Wistaston, Nantwich, Cheshire, CW5 6PB Tel: (01270) 252065 E-mail: info@typingforbusiness.co.uk
The Typing Factory Romscot UK, 12 Renfield Street, Glasgow, G2 5AL Tel: 0141-221 1242 Fax: 0141-248 4652 E-mail: christian@typingfactory.com

TYRE CASINGS

Chris Hardy Tyres, The Tyre Station, Hortonwood 8, Telford, Shropshire, TF1 7GR Tel: (01952) 270009 Fax: (01952) 605892

TYRE IMPORT/EXPORT MERCHANTS OR AGENTS

Birmingham Motor Tyre, 11 Washington Street, Birmingham, B1 1JS Tel: (0121) 643 7656 Fax: 0121-643 7606 E-mail: pat@bmtrgroup.com
Carter Horsley (Tyres) Ltd, 10-11 Thurrock Park Way, Thurrock Park Industrial Estate, Tilbury, Essex, RM18 7HZ Tel: (01375) 489509 Fax: (01375) 489501E-mail: info@mswuk.com
Kirkby (Tyres) Ltd, Speke Hall Avenue, Speke, Liverpool, L24 1UU Tel: (07734) 870892 Fax: 0151-486 5391 E-mail: sales@kirkbytyres.co.uk
Tyresales Tyreplus Autoservice, Oxleasow Road, Redditch, Worcestershire, B98 0RE Tel: (01527) 528090 Fax: (01527) 501411
UK Tyre Exporters Ltd, 131 Scrubs Lane, London, NW10 6QY Tel: (020) 8969 7796 Fax: (020) 8960 7863 E-mail: uktyres108@aol.com

TYRE INNER TUBES

Tubeline, 13 Stockwell Drive, Mangotsfield, Bristol, BS16 9DN Tel: 0117-970 2448 Fax: 0117-956 6649 E-mail: sales@tubeline.co.uk

TYRE MOULDS

▶ Aycliffe Engineering Ltd, Beaumont Way, Aycliffe Industrial Park, Newton Aycliffe, County Durham, DL5 6SN Tel: (01325) 300223 Fax: (01325) 300233 E-mail: altringham@aycliffe-engineering.onyxnet.co.uk

TYRE PUNCTURE PREVENTION/ PROOFING MATERIALS

Aromet Group Ltd, 15 Ballinderry Road, Lisburn, County Antrim, BT28 2SA Tel: (028) 9266 5721 Fax: (028) 9260 1611

TYRE REPAIR/MAINTENANCE EQUIPMENT OR MATERIALS

A P Tyres, Wannop Street, Rotherham, South Yorkshire, S62 6ER Tel: (01709) 523827 Fax: (01709) 528242E-mail: aptyres@aol.com
Airvert Ltd, Ghyll Road Industrial Estate, Ghyll Road, Heathfield, East Sussex, TN21 8AW Tel: (01435) 868292 Fax: (01435) 864838 E-mail: mthompson@airvert.co.uk
Apaseal Ltd, Battle Road, Hailsham, East Sussex, BN27 1DX Tel: (01323) 842066 Fax: (01323) 440450 E-mail: sales@apaseal.co.uk
Aromet Group Ltd, 15 Ballinderry Road, Lisburn, County Antrim, BT28 2SA Tel: (028) 9266 5721 Fax: (028) 9260 1611
Auto Tyre & Battery Co., Southern Avenue, Leominster, Herefordshire, HR6 0QF Tel: (01568) 615680
Bush Tyres, 3-5 Bridge Road Industrial Estate, London Road, Long Sutton, Spalding, Lincolnshire, PE12 9EH Tel: (01406) 365930 Fax: (01406) 365933
Central Tyre Ltd, 4 Rashs Green, Dereham, Norfolk, NR19 1JG Tel: (01362) 693901 Fax: (01362) 691502 E-mail: info@centraltyre.net
Linseal International Ltd, 11-13 The Green, Bilton, Rugby, Warwickshire, CV22 7LZ Tel: (01788) 814334 Fax: (01788) 521726 E-mail: sales@linseal.com
Pang UK Ltd, Studlands Park Industrial Estate, Newmarket, Suffolk, CB8 7AU Tel: (01638) 663575 Fax: (01638) 662274
Tyre Maintenance Supplies Ltd, 49 Springvale Industrial Estate, Cwmbran, Gwent, NP44 5BB Tel: (01633) 873512 Fax: (01633) 876096
Tyre Vulcanising Heywood Ltd, 86-90 Chorlton Road, Manchester, M15 4AN Tel: 0161-226 2342 Fax: 0161-226 2342
Tyrework Ltd, 343 Hatton Road, Feltham, Middlesex, TW14 9QS Tel: (020) 8751 3211 Fax: (020) 8884 0189
Walton Tyres, 48 Davenport Drive, Woodley, Stockport, Cheshire, SK6 1PU Tel: 0161-406 6700

TYRE RETREAD REBUILDERS OR SUPPLIERS

Adco Distributors Ni Ltd, Unit 16 Seagoe Industrial Area, Portadown, Craigavon, County Armagh, BT63 5QD Tel: (028) 3835 3121 Fax: (028) 3833 8291 E-mail: tyre@adcoltd.com
Bestway Tyres Ltd, Leopold Street, Pemberton, Wigan, Lancashire, WN5 8DH Tel: (01942) 214827 Fax: (01942) 226311 E-mail: jdc@lancasterhouse.fsnet.co.uk
C Tyres Ltd, Littleburn Industrial Estate, Langley Moor, Durham, DH7 8HJ Tel: 0191-378 0621 Fax: 0191-378 1758 E-mail: info@c-tyres.co.uk
Chris Hardy Tyres, The Tyre Station, Hortonwood 8, Telford, Shropshire, TF1 7GR Tel: (01952) 270009 Fax: (01952) 605892
Kingpin Tyres Ltd, C8 Wem Industrial Estate, Soulton Road, Wem, Shrewsbury, SY4 5SD Tel: (01939) 232156 Fax: (01939) 233889 E-mail: enquiries@kingpin-tyres.com
Tuf Treads Dyfed Ltd, Coalbrook Road, Pontyberem, Llanelli, Dyfed, SA15 5HU Tel: (01269) 870134 Fax: (01269) 870443
UK Tyre Exporters Ltd, 131 Scrubs Lane, London, NW10 6QY Tel: (020) 8969 7796 Fax: (020) 8960 7863 E-mail: uktyres108@aol.com
Ultraseal Birmingham, 64 Maney Hill Road, Sutton Coldfield, West Midlands, B72 1JS Tel: 0121-355 7582 Fax: 0121-355 7582
Vacu Lug Traction Tyres Ltd, Gonerby Hill Foot, Grantham, Lincolnshire, NG31 8HF Tel: (01476) 593095 Fax: (01476) 513809 E-mail: info@vaculug.com

TYRE RETREADING EQUIPMENT

Grumac Ltd, Gonerby Road, Gonerby Hill Foot, Grantham, Lincolnshire, NG31 8HE Tel: (01476) 561873 Fax: (01476) 561873 E-mail: grumac@btclick.com

TYRE SCRAP/WASTE RECYCLING/DISPOSAL/ RECOVERY CONTRACTORS/ PROCESSORS

Charles Lawrence International Ltd, Jessop Way, Newark, Nottinghamshire, NG24 2ER Tel: (01636) 610680 Fax: (01636) 610222 E-mail: sales@clgplc.co.uk

TYRE SERVICING

Abbey Tyres & Tracking Services, 284 Witton Road, Birmingham, B6 6NX Tel: 0121-327 3387 Fax: 0121-327 3387
Midland Fork Lifts Ltd, Orion Way, Kettering Business Park, Kettering, Northamptonshire, NN15 6NL Tel: (01536) 482561 Fax: (01536) 511559 E-mail: sales@midlandforklifts.co.uk
Moss Tyre, Cranswick Industrial Estate, Beverley Road, Cranswick, Driffield, North Humberside, YO25 9QE Tel: (01377) 270790 Fax: (01377) 240042
P K Commercial Tyres Ltd, 4 Forstal Road, Aylesford, Kent, ME20 7AU Tel: (01622) 717277 Fax: (01622) 717377 E-mail: info@commercialtyres.co.uk

TYRE SERVICING – *continued*

Saxon Gate Motorist Centre, London Road Trading Estate, London Road, Biggleswade, Bedfordshire, SG18 8PS Tel: (01767) 314125 Fax: (01767) 314011

Totrax Ltd, Rectory Farm, Mere Booth Road, Langrick, Boston, Lincolnshire, PE22 7AD Tel: (01205) 280578 Fax: (01205) 280520 E-mail: sales@totrax.co.uk

TYRE VULCANISING EQUIPMENT

Installation & Manufacturing Contractors Ltd, Thrifts House, London Road, Ware, Hertfordshire, SG12 9QT Tel: (01920) 468011 Fax: (01920) 460869 E-mail: info@monaflex.com

Treadfast Tyres Ltd, Dudley Road, Halesowen, West Midlands, B62 8EB Tel: 0121-550 2566 Fax: 0121-504 0858

TYRES, *See also headings for particular types*

A T S Euromaster Ltd, Vantage Point, 20 Upper Portland Street, Aston, Birmingham, B6 5TW Tel: 0121-325 7300 Fax: 0121-325 7333 E-mail: info@atseuromaster.co.uk

A T S Exhausts & Tyres (Edenbridge) Ltd, Unit 1 Monza House, Fircroft Way, Edenbridge, Kent, TN8 6EJ Tel: (01732) 867746 Fax: (01732) 868274

A T S North Western Ltd, 74 Oakfield Rd, Altrincham, Cheshire, WA15 8EP Tel: 0161-941 1951 Fax: 0161-942 4623 E-mail: admin@atsnw.co.uk

Abbey Tyres & Tracking Services, 284 Witton Road, Birmingham, B6 6NX Tel: 0121-327 3387 Fax: 0121-327 3387

Allen Bros Southsea Ltd, Albert Road, Southsea, Hampshire, PO5 2SG Tel: (023) 9282 8432 E-mail: sales@allen-bros.co.uk

Anchor Tyres, Unit 6, Oakwood Industrial Park, Gatwick Road, Crawley, West Sussex, RH10 9AZ Tel: (01293) 544577 Fax: (01293) 527477

Ashton Tyre Specialists Ltd, Adlington Industrial Estate, Adlington, Macclesfield, Cheshire, SK10 4NL Tel: (01625) 859123 Fax: (01625) 850181

Aspects Of Beauty, 23 Baldock Street, Ware, Hertfordshire, SG12 9DH Tel: (01920) 466100 Fax: (01920) 822745

Associated Tyre Specialists Ltd, Vantage Point, 20 Upper Portland Street, Aston, Birmingham, B6 5TW Tel: 0121-325 7325 Fax: 0121-325 7333 E-mail: info@ats.euromaster.com

Atlantic Tyre Co. Ltd, 130 Lowfield Street, Dartford, DA1 1JB Tel: (01322) 273031 Fax: (01322) 289054 E-mail: atlantictyres@aol.com

Atlas Alarms, 2-8 Blackburn Road, Darwen, Lancashire, BB3 1QJ Tel: (01254) 873232 Fax: (01254) 761277 E-mail: admin@atlasalarms.co.uk

ATS Euromaster Ltd, 37 Boucher Road, Belfast, BT12 6HR Tel: (028) 9066 3623 Fax: (028) 9066 3894

ATS Euromaster Ltd, 143 Histon Road, Cambridge, CB4 3HZ Tel: (01223) 454631 Fax: (01223) 454654 E-mail: ats@euromaster.com

B.J. Banning Ltd, 501-527 Lichfield Road, Birmingham, B6 7SR Tel: (0121) 327 2741 Fax: (0121) 327 0704

Frank Bather & Son Ltd, 248-258 New Chester Road, Birkenhead, Merseyside, CH41 9BQ Tel: 0151-645 1494 Fax: 0151-644 7171

Birmingham Motor Tyre, 11 Washington Street, Birmingham, B1 1JS Tel: (0121) 643 7656 Fax: 0121-643 7606 E-mail: pat@bmtrgroup.com

Bow Tyre Service, Unit 263A, Carpenters Road, Stratford, London, E15 2DU Tel: (020) 8519 7072 Fax: (020) 8519 7072 E-mail: bowservice@talk21.com

British Rubber Co., Station Road, Baildon, Shipley, West Yorkshire, BD17 6SE Tel: (01274) 585427 Fax: (01274) 532816 E-mail: britishrub@aol.com

Budget Tyre & Auto Service, 95 Orbiston Street, Motherwell, Lanarkshire, ML1 1PY Tel: (01698) 275070 Fax: (01698) 276667

Bush Tyres Ltd, Station Yard, Horncastle, Lincolnshire, LN9 5AQ Tel: (0800) 801054 Fax: (01507) 525439 E-mail: ericcorragan@bushtyres.co.uk

C Tyres Ltd, Littleburn Industrial Estate, Langley Moor, Durham, DH7 8HJ Tel: 0191-378 0621 Fax: 0191-378 1758 E-mail: info@c-tyres.co.uk

Celtic Tyre Services Ltd, Brindley Road, Cardiff, CF11 8TX Tel: (029) 2022 1201 Fax: (029) 2066 4985 E-mail: enquiries@celtictyres.co.uk

Celtic Tyre Services (Bridgend) Ltd, Princes Way, Bridgend Industrial Estate, Bridgend, Mid Glamorgan, CF31 3TT Tel: (01656) 657424 Fax: (01656) 647743 E-mail: enquiries@celtictyres.co.uk

Central Wheel Components Ltd, Station Road Industrial Estate, Station Road, Coleshill, Birmingham, B46 1HT Tel: (01675) 462264 Fax: (01675) 466412 E-mail: info@central-wheel.co.uk

Chessington Tyres Ltd, Unit 19 Beeching Park Industrial Services, Wainwright Road, Bexhill-on-Sea, East Sussex, TN39 3UR Tel: (01424) 223365

Chessington Tyres Ltd, 95 Norman Road, St. Leonards-on-Sea, East Sussex, TN38 0EG Tel: (01424) 437415

Chris Hardy Tyres, The Tyre Station, Hortonwood 8, Telford, Shropshire, TF1 7GR Tel: (01952) 270009 Fax: (01952) 605892

R.H. Claydon Ltd, Saxham Industrial Estate, Saxham, Bury St. Edmunds, Suffolk, IP28 6RZ Tel: (01284) 760748 Fax: (01284) 754833 E-mail: raa@rhc.co.uk

Clives Tyre & Exhaust Co. Ltd, Unit1 Hampers Common, Petworth, West Sussex, GU28 9NN Tel: (01798) 343441 Fax: (01798) 343441

Crockerhill Cars, Unit 10 Quarry Lane, Chichester, West Sussex, PO19 8QA Tel: (01243) 528731 Fax: (01243) 533343 E-mail: rbjervis@aol.com

Duddon Tyres, Hindpool Road, Barrow-in-Furness, Cumbria, LA14 2ND Tel: (01229) 838537 Fax: (01229) 870757

East Grinstead Tyre Service Ltd, 213-217 London Road, East Grinstead, West Sussex, RH19 1HD Tel: (01342) 324127 Fax: (01342) 317582

Eastbourne Tyre Co. Ltd, Fort Road, Eastbourne, East Sussex, BN22 7SE Tel: (01323) 720222 Fax: (01323) 720018

Etb, Cardiff Road, Barry, South Glamorgan, CF63 2QW Tel: (01446) 733167 Fax: (01446) 733167

Eurotek Industrial Tyres Ltd, 313-315 Whapload Road, Lowestoft, Suffolk, NR32 1UL Tel: (01502) 532200 Fax: (01502) 508273 E-mail: colinlong@eurotektyres.com

Exel Wheel & Tyre Services, Unit 18-19, Torrington Avenue, Coventry, CV4 9HB Tel: (024) 7646 8131 Fax: (024) 7646 5260

Feltham Tyres, Green Man Lane, Feltham, Middlesex, TW14 0QD Tel: (020) 8890 7138 Fax: (020) 8751 4428 E-mail: sales@felthamtyre.co.uk

Fossitt & Thorne UK Ltd, 46 Fydell Street, Boston, Lincolnshire, PE21 8LF Tel: (01205) 319960 Fax: (01205) 319972 E-mail: fossitt.thorne@virgin.net

Kings Road Tyres & Repairs Ltd, Pump Lane, Hayes, Middlesex, UB3 3NB Tel: (020) 8561 3737 Fax: (020) 8561 4012 E-mail: info@kingsroadtyres.co.uk

Kipling Motorist Centre, 76 Ifield Road, Crawley, West Sussex, RH11 7BQ Tel: (01293) 612211 Fax: (01293) 612444

Ladybank Tyres Ltd, Commercial Road, Ladybank, Cupar, Fife, KY15 7JS Tel: (01337) 830932 Fax: (01337) 831156 E-mail: ladybank.tyres@virgin.net

▶ Lo Cost Tyre & Exhaust, Unit 6, Wotton Road, Ashford, Kent, TN23 6LL Tel: (01233) 666636

Lodge Tyre Co. Ltd, 25-29 Lord Street, Birmingham, B7 4DE Tel: 0121-380 3206 Fax: 0121-359 0046 E-mail: sales@lodgetyre.com

Mid Sussex Tyres, Wedglen Industrial Estate, Midhurst, West Sussex, GU29 9RE Tel: (01730) 815335 Fax: (01730) 816510

Motokov UK Ltd, Bergen Way, North Lynn Industrial Estate, King's Lynn, Norfolk, PE30 2JG Tel: (01553) 817700 Fax: (01553) 691201

Mr Tyre Ltd, 1 Burton Street, Peterborough, PE1 5HA Tel: (01733) 560484 Fax: (01733) 342613

National Tyre Service Ltd, Regent House, Heaton Lane, Stockport, Cheshire, SK4 1BS Tel: 0161-480 7461 Fax: 0161-475 3540

North Hants Tyre & Remoulding, 2 Christy Estate, Ivy Road, Aldershot, Hampshire, GU12 4TX Tel: (01252) 318666 Fax: (01252) 318777 E-mail: sales@northhantstyres.com

Provincial Motor Factors, William Street, Sunderland, SR1 1TW Tel: 0191-565 8141 Fax: 0191-565 9296 E-mail: sales@provincialtyres.co.uk

Rolls Royce, PO Box 1, Bedford, MK41 7PZ Tel: (01234) 272000 Fax: (01234) 353934

Round Tyres, 4 Grey Friars, Grantham, Lincolnshire, NG31 6PG Tel: (01476) 573273 Fax: (01476) 573273

Ruislip Tyre Service, 75 Park Way, Ruislip, Middlesex, HA4 8NS Tel: (01895) 632652 Fax: (01895) 678971

Runflat International Ltd, Gawne Lane, Cradley Heath, West Midlands, B64 5QY Tel: (01384) 414845 Fax: (01384) 414848 E-mail: info@runflatinternational.com

Southfields Tyre & Battery Service, 288-290 Merton Road, London, SW18 5JN Tel: (020) 8874 5656

Stapletons, 14 Rhodes Way, Watford, WD24 4TJ Tel: (01923) 801039 Fax: (01923) 818416

Stapleton's Commercial & Agricultural Depot, Fourth Avenue, Letchworth Garden City, Hertfordshire, SG6 2TT Tel: (01462) 488844 Fax: (01462) 488845 E-mail: admin@stapletons-tyres.co.uk

Tubeline, 13 Stockwell Drive, Mangotsfield, Bristol, BS16 9DN Tel: 0117-970 2448 Fax: 0117-956 6649 E-mail: sales@tubeline.co.uk

▶ Tumble Tyres & Exhausts, B4 Llannon Road, Upper Tumble, Llanelli, Dyfed, SA14 6BT Tel: (01269) 845022 Fax: (01269) 845022

Tyreways Ltd, Church Street, Uttoxeter, Staffordshire, ST14 8AA Tel: (01889) 564216 Fax: (01889) 564213

Universal Tyres & Spares Ltd, Unit 18 Crown Trading Centre, Clayton Road, Hayes, Middlesex, UB3 1DU Tel: (020) 8569 0090 Fax: (020) 8569 0509

Watts Group Of Companies, Althorpe House, High Street, Lydney, Gloucestershire, GL15 5DD Tel: (01594) 847400 Fax: (01594) 847401 E-mail: info@watts-group.co.uk

Watts Industrial Tyres plc, 9a Brindley Road, Bayton Road Industrial Estate, Coventry, CV7 9EP Tel: (024) 7664 5222 Fax: (024) 7636 7111

Watts Industrial Tyres plc, 9 Spencer Street, Grimsby, South Humberside, DN31 3AA Tel: (01472) 362589 Fax: (01472) 352772

Watts Industrial Tyres plc, Unit 7 Brickfields, Liverpool, L36 6HY Tel: 0151-481 4500 Fax: 0151-481 4501 E-mail: liverpool@watts_tyres.co.uk

Western Tyres Ltd, Alloys House, St.Andrews Road, Avonmouth, Bristol, BS11 9HS Tel: 0117-940 1991 Fax: 0117-923 5099 E-mail: mike@westtyre.demon.co.uk

W.J. Wood & Son Ltd, 1 Fleethall Road, Purdeys Industrial Estate, Rochford, Essex, SS4 1NF Tel: (01702) 544554 Fax: (01702) 530573 E-mail: sales@tyres.uk.com

TYRES, CAR, USED

▶ Car Nation Yaxley, Station Road Garage, Broadway, Yaxley, Peterborough, PE7 3EG Tel: (01733) 243424 E-mail: ishy@carnationcars.com

TYRES, MOTOR CAR/VEHICLE

Bridgestone UK Ltd, Athena Drive, Tachbrook Park, Warwick, CV34 6UX Tel: (01926) 488500 Fax: (01926) 488600 E-mail: bfuk.reception@bridgestone-eu.com

C Tyres Ltd, Littleburn Industrial Estate, Langley Moor, Durham, DH7 8HJ Tel: 0191-378 0621 Fax: 0191-378 1758 E-mail: info@c-tyres.co.uk

Celtic Tyre Services Ltd, Brindley Road, Cardiff, CF11 8TX Tel: (029) 2022 1201 Fax: (029) 2066 4985 E-mail: enquiries@celtictyres.co.uk

Celtic Tyre Services Maesteg Ltd, Talbot Street, Maesteg, Mid Glamorgan, CF34 9BT Tel: (01656) 733514 Fax: (01656) 733514 E-mail: enquiries@celtictyres.co.uk

Continental Tyre Group Ltd, Continental House, 191 High Street, Yiewsley, West Drayton, Middlesex, UB7 7XW Tel: (01895) 425900 Fax: (01895) 425982

Cooper Tyre & Rubber Co UK Ltd, Bath Road, Melksham, Wiltshire, SN12 8AA Tel: (01225) 703101 Fax: (01225) 707880

Etb, Cardiff Road, Barry, South Glamorgan, CF63 2QW Tel: (01446) 733167 Fax: (01446) 733167

Feltham Tyres, Green Man Lane, Feltham, Middlesex, TW14 0QD Tel: (020) 8890 7138 Fax: (020) 8751 4428 E-mail: sales@felthamtyre.co.uk

Fossitt & Thorne UK Ltd, Eastgate, Bourne, Lincolnshire, PE10 9LB Tel: (01778) 424331 Fax: (01778) 424421

▶ Goodyear Dunlop, Tyrefort, 88-98 Wingfoot Way, Erdington, Birmingham, B24 9HY Tel: 0121-306 6166

Goodyear Great Britain Ltd, Bushbury Lane, Bushbury, Wolverhampton, WV10 6DH Tel: (01902) 327000 Fax: (01902) 327060

▶ J J Tyres, 1 Churchill Building, Churchill Road, Doncaster, South Yorkshire, DN1 2TF Tel: (01302) 341200

Kalvin Tyre Co. Ltd, 259 High Road, Broxbourne, Hertfordshire, EN10 6PZ Tel: (01992) 462728

Kumho Tyre (U.K.) Ltd, 6th Floor 9 Sutton Court Road, Sutton, Surrey, SM1 4SZ Tel: (020) 8661 6112 Fax: (020) 8661 2771 E-mail: sales@kumho-euro.com

L B Tyres & Dropshafts, Unit 4a Station Yard, Tolladine Road, Worcester, WR4 9PT Tel: (01905) 612391 Fax: (01905) 612391

▶ Mercury Material Management, Units 14 & 15 Rosevale Road, Parkhouse Industrial Estate West, Newcastle, Staffordshire, ST5 7EF Tel: (01782) 576385 Fax: (01782) 565279

Michelin Tyre Plc, Campbell Road, Stoke-on-Trent, ST4 4EY Tel: (01782) 402000 Fax: (01782) 402253 E-mail: agr@uk.michelin.com

▶ Platinum Nissan, Meridian Motor Park, North Bradley, Trowbridge, Wiltshire, BA14 0BJ Tel: (01225) 759510 Fax: (01225) 759501 E-mail: d17115man@uk.nissan.biz

▶ Platinum Nissan Box, St Martins Garage, Bath Road, Box, Corsham, Wiltshire, SN13 8AE Tel: (01225) 744444 Fax: (01225) 744477 E-mail: sales@platinumnissan.co.uk

▶ Platinum Renault, Meridian Business Park, North Bradley, Trowbridge, Wiltshire, BA14 0BJ Tel: (01225) 759525 Fax: (01225) 759526

▶ Platinum Renault Bath, Lower Bristol Road, Bath, BA2 3DN Tel: (01225) 485410 Fax: (01225) 338653

▶ Platinum Renault Chippenham, London Road, Chippenham, Wiltshire, SN15 3BB Tel: (01249) 651131 Fax: (01249) 658813

▶ Platinum Skoda, Lower Bristol Road, Bath, BA2 3DR Tel: (01225) 324910 Fax: (01225) 324919 E-mail: enquiries@platinumskoda.co.uk

▶ Platinum Toyota, Meridian Motor Park, North Bradley, Trowbridge, Wiltshire, BA14 0BJ Tel: (01225) 759560 Fax: (01225) 759551

▶ Platinum Toyota Bath, Lower Bristol Road, Bath, BA2 3DN Tel: (01225) 486200 Fax: (01225) 420815 E-mail: im-pb@platinum.toyota.co.uk

Top Gear Ltd, 80 Leicester Road, Mountsorrel, Loughborough, Leicestershire, LE12 7AN Tel: 0116-237 6606 E-mail: cars@topgear.uk.com

Toyo Tyre, 4 Express Business Park, Shipton Way, Rushden, Northamptonshire, NN10 6GL Tel: (01933) 411144 Fax: (01933) 410945 E-mail: info@toyo.co.uk

Tyre Team Ltd, Rutherglen, Wycombe Road, Saunderton, Princes Risborough, Buckinghamshire, HP27 9NP Tel: (01844) 273373 Fax: (01844) 273262

▶ Tyre Zone, K Trinity Trading Estate, Tribune Drive, Sittingbourne, Kent, ME10 2PG Tel: (01795) 430043 Fax: (01795) 439740 E-mail: sale@tyrezone.net

United Tyre Ltd, 1 Barkley Square, Clifton, Bristol, BS8 1HL Tel: 0117-929 9291 Fax: 0117-921 4650

Vredestein (UK) Ltd, Unit D, Whittle Close, Park Farm Industrial Estate, Wellingborough, Northamptonshire, NN8 6TY Tel: (01933) 677770 Fax: (01933) 675329 E-mail: customer.uk@vredestein.com

▶ Wellsway BMW, Lower Bristol Road, Bath, BA2 3DR Tel: (01225) 448145 Fax: (01225) 420794

▶ Wellsway Mini, Lower Bristol Road, Bath, BA2 3DR Tel: (01225) 448555 Fax: (01225) 420794 E-mail: sales@wellswaymini.co.uk

U BOLT ISOLATION BRACKETS

Quality Pipe Supports, 1 Dyffryn Industrial Estate, Pool Road, Newtown, Powys, SY16 3BD Tel: (01686) 629898 Fax: (01686) 629797 E-mail: q.p.s@btinternet.com

U BOLTS

Arthur Black General Smiths Ltd, Clay Lane, Oldbury, West Midlands, B69 4TH Tel: 0121-552 4212 Fax: 0121-552 2208 E-mail: info@arthurblack.com

Atlantic Supports Engineering, 3 Llandough Trading Estate, Penarth Road, Cardiff, CF11 8RR Tel: (029) 2070 8461 Fax: (029) 2035 0437 E-mail: sales@atlantic-supports.co.uk

Clark Fixings Ltd, Unit 1, Crescent Works Industrial Estate, Willenhall Road, Darlaston, Wednesbury, West Midlands, WS10 8JJ Tel: 0121-568 6968 Fax: 0121-568 8719 E-mail: clarkfixings@btconnect.com

F J Dyke & Sons, Rear of 27 Dogfield Street, Cardiff, CF24 4QL Tel: (029) 2022 7074

G M E Motor Engineers (Coventry) Ltd, Boston Place, Foleshill, Coventry, CV6 5NN Tel: (024) 7666 4911 Fax: (024) 7666 3020 E-mail: sales@gmesprings.co.uk

Holts, Embankment, London, SW15 1LB Tel: (020) 8789 5557 Fax: (020) 8789 8365 E-mail: sales@holtallen.com

Powell Gee & Co Ltd, PO Box 15, Wednesbury, West Midlands, WS10 0UF Tel: 0121-556 6729 Fax: 0121-556 6729 E-mail: sales@powellgee.co.uk

Quality Pipe Supports, 1 Dyffryn Industrial Estate, Pool Road, Newtown, Powys, SY16 3BD Tel: (01686) 629898 Fax: (01686) 629797 E-mail: q.p.s@btinternet.com

Squires Gear & Engineering Ltd, 98 Swan Lane, Coventry, CV2 4GB Tel: (024) 7623 1110 Fax: (024) 7623 1112 E-mail: djs@squires-gear.co.uk

U GAUGES

Abbirko UK Ltd, 4 Manor Works, Station Road South, Totton, Southampton, SO40 9HP Tel: (023) 8066 8833 Fax: (023) 8066 7777 E-mail: sales@abbirko.co.uk

UKAS ACCREDITED CALIBRATION LABORATORIES

▶ A V Calibration Ltd, 13C Old Bridge Way, Shefford, Bedfordshire, SG17 5HQ Tel: (01462) 638600 Fax: (01462) 638601 E-mail: lab@avcalib.co.uk

Absolute Calibration Ltd, 14 Murrills Estate, Portchester, Fareham, Hampshire, PO16 9RD Tel: (023) 9232 1712 Fax: (023) 9221 0034 E-mail: calit@absolute-cal.co.uk

Aspland Gauge Co Ltd, Broadway, Hyde, Cheshire, SK14 4QF Tel: 0161-368 3432 Fax: 0161-367 8426 E-mail: sales@aspland.co.uk

Bowmonk Ltd, Diamond Road, St. Faiths Industrial Estate, Norwich, NR6 6AW Tel: (01603) 485153 Fax: (01603) 418150 E-mail: info@bowmonk.co.uk

Alan Browne Gauges Ltd, Blackdown Mill, Blackdown, Leamington Spa, Warwickshire, CV32 6QT Tel: (01926) 424278 Fax: (01926) 451865 E-mail: sales@alanbrowne.co.uk

Bruel & Kjaer Ltd, Bedford House, Rutherford Close, Stevenage, Hertfordshire, SG1 2ND Tel: (01438) 739000 Fax: (01438) 739099 E-mail: ukinfo@bksv.com

Calibration Services Ltd, 29 Tennant Avenue, East Kilbride, Glasgow, G74 5NA Tel: (01355) 248102 Fax: (01355) 248102 E-mail: calibriation@dial.pipex.com

Cromwell Tools Ltd, PO Box 14, Wigston, Leicestershire, LE18 1AT Tel: 0116-288 8888 Fax: 0116-288 8222 E-mail: sales@cromwell.co.uk

UKAS ACCREDITED CALIBRATION LABORATORIES – *continued*

Disking International, 5 South Street, Farnham, Surrey, GU9 7QU Tel: (01252) 719719 Fax: (01252) 719819 E-mail: farnhamshop@disking.co.uk

Dowding & Mills Calibration, Fulwood Road South, Sutton-in-Ashfield, Nottinghamshire, NG17 2JZ Tel: (01623) 555110 Fax: (01623) 555022 E-mail: calibration.nottingham@dowdingandmills.com

Dowding & Mills Engineering Services Ltd, 71b Whitecraigs Road, Glenrothes, Fife, KY6 2RX Tel: (01592) 773008 Fax: (01592) 772877 E-mail: calibration.glenrothes@dowdingandmills.com

Electrical Mechanical Instrument Services (UK) Ltd, Central Equipment Base, Greenwell Road, East Tullos Industrial Estate, Aberdeen, AB12 3AX Tel: (01224) 894494 Fax: (01224) 894929 E-mail: info@emis-uk.com

▶ Eley Metrology Ltd, Beaufort House Beaufort Court Industrial Estate, Mansfield Road, Derby, DE21 4FS Tel: (01332) 367475 Fax: (01332) 371435 E-mail: email@eleymet.com

Furness Controls Ltd, Beeching Road, Bexhill-on-Sea, East Sussex, TN39 3LJ Tel: (01424) 730316 Fax: (01424) 730317 E-mail: sales@furness-controls.com

G B Quality Assurance Ltd, 9 Moor Lane Industrial Estate, Chancel Way, Birmingham, B6 7AU Tel: 0121-356 7430 Fax: 0121-344 3837 E-mail: info@gbquality.com

Hitek Ltd, Unit 2, Foundry Court, Foundry Lane, Horsham, West Sussex, RH13 5PY Tel: (01403) 243535 Fax: (01403) 243536 E-mail: sales@hitek.co.uk

Impact Test Equipment Ltd, Building 21, Stevenston Industrial Estate, Stevenston, Ayrshire, KA20 3LR Tel: (01294) 602626 Fax: (01294) 461168 E-mail: sales@impact-test.co.uk

Isothermal Technology Ltd, 42a Pine Grove, Southport, Merseyside, PR9 9AG Tel: (01704) 544611 Fax: (01704) 544799 E-mail: info@isotech.co.uk

Littlebrook Power Services Ltd, Littlebrook Complex, Manor Way, Dartford, DA1 5PU Tel: (01322) 280038 Fax: (01322) 284835 E-mail: general@littlebrookservices.co.uk

Moore & Wright, Unit 15 Bordon Trading Estate, Old Station Way, Bordon, Hampshire, GU35 9HH Tel: 0114-225 0400 Fax: 0114-225 0410 E-mail: sales@moore-and-wright.com

Poulten Selfe & Lee Ltd, Russell House, Burnham Business Park, Burnham-On-Crouch, Essex, CM0 8TE Tel: (01621) 787100 Fax: (01621) 787175 E-mail: info@rheotek.com

Powercut Ltd, Unit 15, Paragon Way, Bayton Road Industrial Estate, Coventry, CV7 9QS Tel: (024) 7664 4224 Fax: (024) 7664 4220 E-mail: sales@calibration-services.co.uk

Premier Calibration Ltd, Unit 3l Lake Enterprise Park, Sandall Stones Road, Kirk Sandall Industrial Estate, Doncaster, South Yorkshire, DN3 1QR Tel: (01302) 888448 Fax: (01302) 881197 E-mail: premcal@btconnect.com

Sercal MTMS Ltd, The Rubicon Centre, Redditch, Worcestershire, B98 8YP Tel: 01527 514015

Servicecal Ltd, 19 Green Lane, Eccles, Manchester, M30 0RP Tel: 0161-789 8990 Fax: 0161-789 8991 E-mail: info@servicecal.co.uk

Southern Calibration Laboratories Ltd, 7 Solent Industrial Estate, Shamblehurst Lane, Hedge End, Southampton, SO30 2FX Tel: (01489) 790296 Fax: (01489) 790294 E-mail: info@southcal.co.uk

T E R Instruments Ltd, 2-6 Peel Lane, Astley, Tyldesley, Manchester, M29 7QX Tel: (01942) 882275 Fax: (01942) 897958 E-mail: info@ter.co.uk

Taylor Hobson, P O Box 36, Leicester, LE4 9JQ Tel: 0116-276 3771 Fax: 0116-274 1350 E-mail: sales@taylor-hobson.com

▶ Tees Valley Measurement, Cannon Street, Middlesbrough, Cleveland, TS1 5JJ Tel: (01642) 223535 Fax: (01642) 210317

UK Accreditation Service Ltd, 21-47 High Street, Feltham, Middlesex, TW13 4UN Tel: (020) 8917 8400 Fax: (020) 8917 8500 E-mail: info@ukas.com

Westco Bilanciai Ltd, Broadgauge House, Westridge Way, Bishops Lydeard, Taunton, Somerset, TA4 3RU Tel: (01823) 433411 Fax: (01823) 433334 E-mail: sales@westcoweigh.co.uk

Wortley Standards Ltd, Forge Lane, Wortley, Sheffield, S35 7DN Tel: 0114-288 2423 Fax: 0114-288 2423 E-mail: wortley@globalnet.co.uk

UL RECOGNISED COMPONENT LABELS

Arc Labels Ltd, The Maltings Industrial Estate, Doncaster Road, Whitley Bridge, Goole, North Humberside, DN14 0HH Tel: (01977) 663063 Fax: (01977) 663064 E-mail: sales@arclabels.com

ULTRA HIGH VACUUM EQUIPMENT

CVT Ltd, 4-6 Carters Lane, Kiln Farm, Milton Keynes, MK11 3ER Tel: (01908) 563267 Fax: (01908) 568354

ULTRAFILTRATION EQUIPMENT/ SYSTEMS

Kalsep UK, Unit 2f Albany Park, Frimley Park, Camberley, Surrey, GU16 7PL Tel: (01276) 675675 Fax: (01276) 676276 E-mail: sales@kalsep.co.uk

ULTRASONIC ANEMOMETERS

Gill Instruments Ltd, Saltmarsh Park, 67 Gosport Street, Lymington, Hampshire, SO41 9EG Tel: (01590) 613500 Fax: (01590) 613501 E-mail: gill@gill.co.uk

ULTRASONIC CLEANING BATHS

Tamark Engineering Ltd, 924 Borough Road, Birkenhead, Merseyside, CH42 6QW Tel: 0151-201 7907 Fax: 0151-334 7407 E-mail: sales@tamarkengineering.co.uk

ULTRASONIC CLEANING CONTRACTORS/SERVICES

Abbey Heat Transfer Ltd, Unit 6 Parham Drive, Eastleigh, Hampshire, SO50 4NU Tel: (023) 8065 3331 Fax: (023) 8065 3332 E-mail: hugh@abbeyheat.co.uk

B&M Longworth (Edgworth) Ltd, Sett End Road North, Shadsworth Business Park, Blackburn, BB1 2QG Tel: (01254) 680501 Fax: (01254) 54041 E-mail: enquiries@bmlongworth.com

Filta Group Ltd, The Locks, Hillmorton, Rugby, Warwickshire, CV21 4PP Tel: (01788) 550100 Fax: (01788) 551839 E-mail: sales@filtagroup.com

Ultrasonic Cleaning Services UK Ltd, 10 Pepper Road, Leeds, LS10 2EU Tel: 0113-271 5807 Fax: 0113-271 5722 E-mail: sales@ucs-uk-ltd.co.uk

ULTRASONIC CLEANING EQUIPMENT MANUFRS

▶ Alphasonics Ultrasonic Equipment Mnfrs, Caddick Road, Knowsley Business Park, Prescot, Merseyside, L34 9HP Tel: 0151-547 3777 Fax: 0151-547 1333 E-mail: alphasonics@alphasonics.co.uk

C T I Ltd, 329 Goodyers End Lane, Bedworth, Warwickshire, CV12 0JA Tel: (024) 7664 4475 Fax: (024) 7636 2259

Crest Ultrasonics Ltd, Units 1 & 4 Italstyle Factory, Cambridge Road, Harlow, Essex, CM20 2HE Tel: (01279) 418942 Fax: (01279) 453926 E-mail: sales@cchydrosonics.com

▶ Kerry Ultrasonics, Snagill Industrial Estate, Keighley Road, Skipton, North Yorkshire, BD23 2QR Tel: (01756) 799911 Fax: (01756) 790213 E-mail: sales@guyson.co.uk

Layton Technologies, Parkhall Business Park, Parkhall Road, Weston Coyney, Stoke-on-Trent, ST3 5XA Tel: (01782) 370400 Fax: (01782) 333202 E-mail: webenquiries@laytontechnologies.com

Medisafe UK Ltd, The Snap Factory, Twyford Road, Bishop's Stortford, Hertfordshire, CM23 3LJ Tel: (01279) 461641 Fax: (01279) 461643 E-mail: info@medisafe.uk.com

Projectworld Ltd, Morvern Works, Church Street, Briton Ferry, Neath, West Glamorgan, SA11 2JP Tel: (01639) 812332 Fax: (01639) 812496 E-mail: info@projectworld.co.uk

S M S Degreasers (Sheet Metal Structures) Ltd, Woodlands, Cliff Road, Salcombe, Devon, TQ8 8LD Tel: (01548) 842454 Fax: (01548) 843380

▶ Vytran UK Ltd, 8 Kew Court Pynes Hill, Rydon Lane, Exeter, EX2 5AZ Tel: (01392) 445777 Fax: (01392) 445009

ULTRASONIC CUTTING MACHINES, CNC

Scan Relation, 2 The Mews, 15a Liverpool Road, Southport, Merseyside, PR8 4AS Tel: (01704) 550500 Fax: (01704) 566958 E-mail: smithage@btinternet.com

ULTRASONIC DESIGN CONSULTANTS

S R A Developments Ltd, Bremridge House, Ashburton, Newton Abbott, Devon, TQ13 7JX Tel: (01364) 652426 Fax: (01364) 653589 E-mail: mail@sra-developments.co.uk

Sonic Technologies Ltd, Ty Coch Farm, Pembrey Rd, Kidwelly, Dyfed, SA17 4TF Tel: (01554) 890612 Fax: (01554) 890612

ULTRASONIC EQUIPMENT DISTRIBUTORS OR AGENTS

Camasonics Ultrasonic Equipment Mnfrs, Unit C2 Fiveways Trading Estate, Westwells Road, Hawthorn, Corsham, Wiltshire, SN13 9RG Tel: (01225) 812223 Fax: (01225) 812223 E-mail: camasonics@hotmail.com

Class Instrumentation Ltd, 837 Garratt Lane, London, SW17 0PG Tel: (020) 8333 2288 Fax: (020) 8944 0141 E-mail: info@classltd.com

Deltex Medical Ltd, Terminus Road, Chichester, West Sussex, PO19 8TX Tel: (01243) 774837 Fax: (01243) 532534 E-mail: info@deltexmedical.com

Fidgeon Ltd, 11 Enterprise Court, Seaham Grange Industrial Estate, Seaham, County Durham, SR7 0PS Tel: 0191-521 1233 Fax: 0191-521 1252 E-mail: sales@fidgeon.co.uk

Merit Lowson & French Ltd, The Barn, Wharfe Bank Terrace, Tadcaster, North Yorkshire, LS24 9AN Tel: (01937) 835225 Fax: (01937) 530225 E-mail: lowson@mlfltd.fsbussines.co.uk

Optimal Technologies Ltd, 3 Marquis Business Centre, Royston Road, Baldock, Hertfordshire, SG7 6XL Tel: (01462) 491616 Fax: (01462) 491600 E-mail: sales@opt-tec.com

Pie Data U K Ltd, 4 Mill Court, Spindle Way, Crawley, West Sussex, RH10 1TT Tel: (01293) 510231 Fax: (01293) 510234 E-mail: sales@piedata.com

Riley Industries Ltd, 152 Wellhead Lane, Birmingham, B42 2SY Tel: 0121-356 2020 Fax: 0121-356 1117 E-mail: sales@rileyindustries.co.uk

Rotajet Systems, Richard Alan House, Shaw Cross Business Park, Dewsbury, West Yorkshire, WF12 7RD Tel: (01924) 468769 Fax: (01924) 485376 E-mail: info@rotajet.co.uk

S R A Developments Ltd, Bremridge House, Ashburton, Newton Abbott, Devon, TQ13 7JX Tel: (01364) 652426 Fax: (01364) 653589 E-mail: mail@sra-developments.co.uk

Sonoscan (Europe) Ltd, The Wincombe Business Centre, Shaftesbury, Dorset, SP7 9QJ Tel: (01747) 855988 Fax: (01747) 855938 E-mail: info@sonoscan.com

Staveley NDT Technologies, 3 Cromwell Park, Banbury Road, Chipping Norton, Oxfordshire, OX7 5SR Tel: (01608) 642001 Fax: (01608) 644752 E-mail: sales@sndt.co.uk

Tamark Engineering Ltd, 924 Borough Road, Birkenhead, Merseyside, CH42 6QW Tel: 0151-201 7907 Fax: 0151-334 7407 E-mail: sales@tamarkengineering.co.uk

Toshiba Medical Systems Ltd, Gatwick Road, Crawley, West Sussex, RH10 9AX Tel: (01293) 653700 Fax: (01293) 653770

▶ Ultronics NDT Ltd, 14 Exeter Close, Chippenham, Wiltshire, SN14 0YG Tel: (01249) 465571 Fax: (01249) 660574 E-mail: davidclark@ultronicsndt.co.uk

ULTRASONIC INSPECTION/TEST EQUIPMENT

Diagnostic Sonar Ltd, Baird Road, Kirkton Campus, Livingston, West Lothian, EH54 7BX Tel: (01506) 411877 Fax: (01506) 412410 E-mail: sales@diagnosticsonar.com

Maltron International Ltd, PO Box 15, Rayleigh, Essex, SS6 9SN Tel: (01268) 778251 Fax: (01268) 745176 E-mail: maltron@msn.com

Meritronics Ltd, Otterden Place, Otterden, Faversham, Kent, ME13 0BT Tel: (01795) 890341 Fax: (01795) 890341 E-mail: contact@meritronics.co.uk

Phoenix Inspection Systems Ltd, 46 Melford Court, Hardwick Grange, Woolston, Warrington, WA1 4RZ Tel: (01925) 826000 Fax: (01925) 838788 E-mail: pryan@phoenixisl.co.uk

Sonatest plc, Dickens Road, Old Wolverton, Milton Keynes, MK12 5QQ Tel: (01908) 316345 Fax: (01908) 321323 E-mail: info@sonatest-plc.com

ULTRASONIC INSPECTION/TEST SERVICES

A W L Inspection & N D T Services Ltd, Unit 34, Royal Industrial Estate, Jarrow, Tyne & Wear, NE32 3HR Tel: 0191-430 0837 Fax: 0191-430 0837 E-mail: awl_ndt@btconnect.com

Capital Inspection Services, 3 Poyle Technical Centre, Willow Road, Colnbrook, Slough, SL3 0DP Tel: (01753) 684896 Fax: (01753) 681739E-mail: cap.inspection@btconnect.com

E M & I (Marine) Ltd, 18 Fairburn Terrace, Dyce, Aberdeen, AB21 7DT Tel: (01224) 771077 Fax: (01224) 771049E-mail: info@emiall.co.uk

Liquitech Ltd, Old Post Office House, East Street, Pembridge, Leominster, Herefordshire, HR6 9HA Tel: (0845) 6449020 Fax: (0845) 6449021 E-mail: andrew@liquitech.co.uk

NDT Services Ltd, 5 Side Ley, Kegworth, Derby, DE74 2FJ Tel: (01509) 680088 Fax: (01509) 680080 E-mail: sales@ndtservices.co.uk

Pudsey Test & Inspection Ltd, Battye Street, Laisterdyke, Bradford, West Yorkshire, BD4 8AG Tel: (01274) 656736 Fax: (01274) 656797 E-mail: darrylatpti@aol.com

Thermal Hire Ltd, Unit A Bedewell Industrial Park, Hebburn, Tyne & Wear, NE31 2HQ Tel: 0191-428 0423 Fax: 0191-428 0061 E-mail: enquiries@thermalhire.com

Ultraspection Ltd, 13 St. Josephs Close, Olney, Buckinghamshire, MK46 5HD Tel: (01234) 714092 Fax: (01234) 714192 E-mail: ultraspection@btinternet.com

ULTRASONIC KNIFE CUTTING MACHINES

Advanced Ultrasonic Technology, Unit C, 127 Parker Drive, Leicester, LE4 0JP Tel: 0116-235 6980 Fax: 0116-236 6066 E-mail: advanced.ultrasonic@virgin.net

ULTRASONIC LEVEL CONTROL EQUIPMENT MANUFRS

Hawker Electronics Ltd, 57 The Avenue, Rubery, Rednal, Birmingham, B45 9AL Tel: 0121-453 8911 Fax: 0121-453 3777 E-mail: info@hawker-electronics.co.uk

Pulsar Process Measurement Ltd, Oak House, Bromyard Road, Worcester, WR2 5HP Tel: (0870) 6039112 Fax: (0870) 6039114 E-mail: info@pulsar-pm.com

ULTRASONIC MEDICAL EQUIPMENT

Diagnostic Sonar Ltd, Baird Road, Kirkton Campus, Livingston, West Lothian, EH54 7BX Tel: (01506) 411877 Fax: (01506) 412410 E-mail: sales@diagnosticsonar.com

Dynamic Imaging Ltd, 9 Cochrane Square, Brucefield Industrial, Livingston, West Lothian, EH54 9DR Tel: (01506) 415282 Fax: (01506) 410603 E-mail: marketing@dynamicimaging.co.uk

S R A Developments Ltd, Bremridge House, Ashburton, Newton Abbott, Devon, TQ13 7JX Tel: (01364) 652426 Fax: (01364) 653589 E-mail: mail@sra-developments.co.uk

ULTRASONIC PROCESSING EQUIPMENT

Apollo, Pond House, Bulmer Lane, Holme-on-Spalding-Moor, York, YO43 4HE Tel: (01430) 860049 Fax: (01430) 861550 E-mail: sales@apolloultrasonics.co.uk

ULTRASONIC PROXIMITY SENSORS

Afriso Eurogauge Ltd, Imberhorne Lane, East Grinstead, West Sussex, RH19 1RF Tel: (01342) 323641 Fax: (01342) 315513 E-mail: sales@eurogauge.co.uk

ULTRASONIC THICKNESS MEASURING INSTRUMENTS

Baugh & Weedon Ltd, Beech Business Park, Tillington Road, Hereford, HR4 9QJ Tel: (01432) 267671 Fax: (01432) 359017 E-mail: sales@bandwndt.co.uk

Merit Lowson & French Ltd, The Barn, Wharfe Bank Terrace, Tadcaster, North Yorkshire, LS24 9AN Tel: (01937) 835225 Fax: (01937) 530225 E-mail: lowson@mlfltd.fsbussines.co.uk

Meritronics Ltd, Otterden Place, Otterden, Faversham, Kent, ME13 0BT Tel: (01795) 890341 Fax: (01795) 890341 E-mail: contact@meritronics.co.uk

Olympus N D T Ltd, 12 Nightingale Court, Nightingale Close, Rotherham, South Yorkshire, S60 2AB Tel: (01709) 836115 Fax: (01709) 835177 E-mail: info.uk@olympusndt.com

Sonatest plc, Dickens Road, Old Wolverton, Milton Keynes, MK12 5QQ Tel: (01908) 316345 Fax: (01908) 321323 E-mail: info@sonatest-plc.com

ULTRASONIC WELDING ENGINEERS/SERVICES/ SUBCONTRACTORS

Dapro Ltd, PO Box 194, Hitchin, Hertfordshire, SG4 0TY Tel: (01462) 432021 E-mail: daprosonics@talktalk.net

DL Plastics Ltd, 9-11 Commerce Way, Lawford, Manningtree, Essex, CO11 1UT Tel: (01206) 396646 Fax: (01206) 396602 E-mail: enquiries@dlplastics.co.uk

Elmlead Services Ltd, Unit 1, Riverside Court, Colne Road, Huddersfield, HD1 3ER Tel: (01484) 425565 Fax: (01484) 425418 E-mail: elmlead@yahoo.co.uk

Needs Ltd, 13 Queensway, Enfield, Middlesex, EN3 4SG Tel: (020) 8804 2281 Fax: (020) 8364 7113 E-mail: sales@needsplastics.co.uk

ULTRASONIC WELDING ENGINEERS/SERVICES/ SUBCONTRACTORS – *continued*

Plan Plastics Ltd, 40 The Warren, Chartridge, Chesham, Buckinghamshire, HP5 2RY Tel: (01494) 772577 Fax: (01494) 772577

Target Plastics Ltd, 138-140 Nathan Way, London, SE28 0AU Tel: (020) 8312 9090 Fax: (020) 8312 9191 E-mail: admin@targetplastics.co.uk

Universal Applications, 2 Clarkes Road, Wigston, Leicestershire, LE18 2BG Tel: 0116-288 8038 Fax: 0116-288 8036

ULTRASONIC WELDING EQUIPMENT MANUFRS

Advanced Ultrasonic Technology, Unit C, 127 Parker Drive, Leicester, LE4 0JP Tel: 0116-235 6980 Fax: 0116-236 6066 E-mail: advanced.ultrasonic@virgin.net

ALS Ultrasonic, Unit 24, Uplands Way, Blandford Forum, Dorset, DT11 7UZ Tel: (01258) 459257 Fax: (01258) 459287 E-mail: als.ultrasonics@virgin.net

Cablespeed, 447 Oakshott Place, Bamber Bridge, Preston, PR5 8AT Tel: (0870) 6098025 Fax: (0870) 6098026 E-mail: sales@cablespeed.co.uk

Phasa Developments, International House, Horsecroft Road, Harlow, Essex, CM19 5SU Tel: (01279) 630200 Fax: (01279) 630222 E-mail: sales@phasa.co.uk

Rainbow Engineering Services, Unit 17 Shaftesbury Industrial Centre, Icknield Way, Letchworth Garden City, Hertfordshire, SG6 1RR Tel: (01462) 480442 Fax: (01462) 480449 E-mail: sales@rainbow-dukane.com

ULTRAVIOLET (UV) CURING EQUIPMENT MANUFRS

G E W Ec Ltd, Kings Mill Lane, South Nutfield, Redhill, RH1 5NB Tel: (01737) 824500 Fax: (01737) 823822 E-mail: sales@gewuv.com

ULTRAVIOLET (UV) DRYERS

G E W Ec Ltd, Kings Mill Lane, South Nutfield, Redhill, RH1 5NB Tel: (01737) 824500 Fax: (01737) 823822 E-mail: sales@gewuv.com

I S T (UK) Ltd, St. Andrew House, Otley Road, Skipton, North Yorkshire, BD23 1EX Tel: (01756) 700741 Fax: (01756) 700734 E-mail: info@uk.ist-uv.com

Primarc Ltd, 816 Leigh Road, Slough, SL1 4BD Tel: (01753) 558001 Fax: (01753) 811678 E-mail: uv@primarc.com

ULTRAVIOLET (UV) INDUSTRIAL EQUIPMENT MANUFRS

Jenton International Ltd, Unit 9 10 Evingar Industrial Estate, Ardglen Road, Whitchurch, Hampshire, RG28 7BB Tel: (01256) 892194 Fax: (01256) 896486 E-mail: sales@jenton.co.uk

Nor Cote International Ltd, 7 Warrior Park, Eagle Close, Chandler's Ford, Eastleigh, Hampshire, SO53 4NF Tel: (023) 8027 0542 Fax: (023) 8027 0543 E-mail: sales@norcote.com

Triogen Ltd, Triogen House, 117 Barfillan Drive, Glasgow, G52 1BD Tel: 0141-810 4861 Fax: 0141-810 5561 E-mail: sales@triogen.com

ULTRAVIOLET (UV) INKS

Fuji Films Sericol UK Ltd, Pysons Road, Broadstairs, Kent, CT10 2LE Tel: (01843) 866668 Fax: (01843) 872184 E-mail: uksales@sericol.com

Sun Chemical Swale, Taylor Road, Urmston, Manchester, M41 7SW Tel: 0161-748 7340 Fax: 0161-748 7685

ULTRAVIOLET (UV) LAMPS

Advanced NDT Ltd, Orchard House, Orchard Close, Severn Stoke, Worcester, WR8 9JJ Tel: (01905) 371460 Fax: (01905) 371477 E-mail: sales@advanced-ndt.co.uk

Covershield Lighting Consultants, 10 Heatons Bridge Road, Scarisbrick, Ormskirk, Lancashire, L40 8JG Tel: (01704) 841073 Fax: (01704) 841362 E-mail: sales@covershield.co.uk

Lightbulb Co. (UK) Ltd, Thomas Edison House, 74-77 Magdalen Road, Oxford, OX4 1RE Tel: (01865) 794500 Fax: (01865) 203996 E-mail: sales@thelightbulb.co.uk

Primarc Ltd, 816 Leigh Road, Slough, SL1 4BD Tel: (01753) 558001 Fax: (01753) 811678 E-mail: uv@primarc.com

Primarc Marketing, Unit 8 Wycombe Road, Wembley, Middlesex, HA0 1RH Tel: (020) 8900 8535 Fax: (020) 8900 2232 E-mail: sales@primarc.co.uk

Trogen UV Technology Ltd, 5 De-Salis Court, Hampton Lovett Industrial Estate, Droitwich, Worcestershire, WR9 0QE Tel: (01905) 771117 Fax: (01905) 772270 E-mail: uksales@trojanuv.com

ULTRAVIOLET (UV) STERILISERS

A T G Willand, Pemberton Business Centre, Richmond Hill, Wigan, Lancashire, WN5 8AA Tel: (01942) 216161 Fax: (01942) 213131 E-mail: sales@atgwilland.com

Hanovia Uv Ltd, 145 Farnham Road, Slough, SL1 4XB Tel: (01753) 515300 Fax: (01753) 534277 E-mail: sales@hanovia.com

Jenton International Ltd, Unit 9 10 Evingar Industrial Estate, Ardglen Road, Whitchurch, Hampshire, RG28 7BB Tel: (01256) 892194 Fax: (01256) 896486 E-mail: sales@jenton.co.uk

UMBILICAL CABLES

Duco Ltd, Nelson Road, Newcastle upon Tyne, NE6 3NL Tel: 0191-295 0303 Fax: 0191-295 0842 E-mail: ducosbd@uk.coflaxip.com

UMBRELLA FRAMES/FITTINGS/ ACCESSORIES

Hoyland Fox Ltd, Manchester Road, Millhouse Green, Sheffield, S36 9NR Tel: (01226) 762244 Fax: (01226) 370022 E-mail: hfsales@hoylandfox.com

Stroud Metal Co. Ltd, Dudbridge, Stroud, Gloucestershire, GL5 3EZ Tel: (01453) 763331 Fax: (01453) 753804 E-mail: enquiries@stroudmetal.co.uk

Walter Phillips Materials Ltd, Unit 3 Ratcliffe Street, Stockport, Cheshire, SK1 3ES Tel: 0161-429 0309 Fax: 0161-477 7884 E-mail: brolly@clara.net

UMBRELLA MANUFRS

Grant Barnett & Co. Ltd, Waterfront House, 55-61 South Street, Bishop's Stortford, Hertfordshire, CM23 3AL Tel: (01279) 758075 Fax: (01279) 758095 E-mail: enquiries@grantbarnett.com

James Smith & Sons Ltd, 53 New Oxford Street, London, WC1A 1BL Tel: (020) 7836 4731 Fax: (020) 7836 4730 E-mail: jsmith.umbrellas@virgin.net

Manchester Umbrella Co. Ltd, Unit 10 Brook St Works, Adcroft Street, Stockport, Cheshire, SK1 3HZ Tel: 0161-480 5328 Fax: 0161-477 7884 E-mail: sales@manchesterumbrellas.co.uk

▶ Simply Umbrellas, 17 Hampstead Gardens, Chadwell Heath, RM6 4FE Tel: (020) 8598 2811E-mail: enquiries@simplyumbrellas.co.uk

Stephens Umbrellas, Sandall Stones Road, Kirk Sandall Industrial Estate, Kirk Sandall, Doncaster, South Yorkshire, DN3 1QR Tel: (01302) 790790 Fax: (01302) 790088 E-mail: sue@oasisleisure.ltd.uk

Swaine Adeney Brigg Ltd, Viking Way, Bar Hill, Cambridge, CB23 8EL Tel: (01799) 530521 Fax: (01799) 530320 E-mail: sales@swaine-adeney-brigg.co.uk

Umbrella Manufacturing & Repairing Co. Ltd, 68h Sapcote Trading Centre, Wyrley Road, Birmingham, B6 7BN Tel: 0121-328 9292 Fax: 0121-328 9292

Walter Phillips Materials Ltd, Unit 3 Ratcliffe Street, Stockport, Cheshire, SK1 3ES Tel: 0161-429 0309 Fax: 0161-477 7884 E-mail: brolly@clara.net

UMBRELLAS, PROMOTIONAL/ ADVERTISING

Harrod Business Promotions Ltd, 3 Goodwood Rise, Marlow BTM, Marlow, Buckinghamshire, SL7 3QE Tel: (01628) 891133 Fax: (01628) 891134 E-mail: sales@harrodpromotions.com

▶ The Promotional Gift Superstore, 79 Villa Road, Stanway, Colchester, CO3 0RN Tel: (0845) 3701022 Fax: (0845) 3701033 E-mail: sales@promogift-superstore.com

UN APPROVED PACKAGING

Packaging Industries Ltd, Beaumont Way, Aycliffe Industrial Pk, Newton Aycliffe, Co. Durham, DL5 6SN Tel: (01325) 313444 Fax: (01325) 300246 E-mail: sales@pi-box.co.uk

UNABLE TO CLASSIFY (INSUFFICIENT INFORMATION)

Hi-Tech Logistics Ltd, Greenford Green Business Park, Rockware Avenue, Greenford, Middlesex, UB6 0RZ Tel: (020) 8566 6060

UNDER CONCRETE VOID FORMING MATERIALS

Polycones Bolt Boxes Ltd, 9 Ashfold Avenue, Findon Valley, Worthing, West Sussex, BN14 0AP Tel: (01903) 526538 Fax: (01903) 526538

UNDERFLOOR ELECTRIC HEATING SYSTEMS

▶ Neoheat, Smallmead Gate, Pingemead Business Centre, Reading, RG30 3UR Tel: (0845) 1080361 Fax: (0845) 1081295 E-mail: infor@neoheat.com

▶ Taipale Automotive UK, New Quay Road, Lancaster, LA1 5QN Tel: (01524) 840804 Fax: (01524) 36450 E-mail: esapirttijarvi@aol.com

▶ Underfloorheatingshop, 66 Rea Street, Birmingham, B5 6LB Tel: 0121-622 4334 Fax: 0121-622 5768 E-mail: manager@underfloorheatingshop.co.k

▶ WarmFloors Ltd, 8 Roundhill Avenue, Cottingley, Bingley, West Yorkshire, BD16 1PH Tel: (01274) 568536 Fax: (01274) 568538 E-mail: sales@warmfloorsonline.com

UNDERFLOOR HEATERS

Beecroft & Co. Ltd, Huddersfield, HD1 9WB Tel: (01422) 374801 Fax: (01422) 370681 E-mail: sales@warmalux.co.uk

Brooks Partners Ltd, The Paddocks, Honey Hill, Wokingham, Berkshire, RG40 3BD Tel: (01344) 772456 Fax: (01344) 776733 E-mail: sales@brookspartners.co.uk

Flexel International Ltd, Queensway Industrial Estate, Flemington Road, Glenrothes, Fife, KY7 5QF Tel: (01592) 757313 Fax: (01592) 754535 E-mail: sales@flexel.co.uk

▶ I M E L, Unit 6, Pages Industrial Park, Eden Way, Leighton Buzzard, Bedfordshire, LU7 4TZ Tel: (01525) 383555 Fax: (01525) 383700 E-mail: info@imel.biz

S A V UK Ltd, Scandia House, Armfield Close, West Molesey, Surrey, KT8 2JR Tel: (020) 8941 4153 Fax: (020) 8783 1132 E-mail: info@savvalvessystems.co.uk

Thermal Dynamics Ltd, Unit 2 Transfer Bridge Indust Estate, County Road, Swindon, SN1 2EG Tel: (01793) 431539 Fax: (01793) 420667

Uponor Housing Solutions Ltd, Snapethorpe, Rugby Road, Lutterworth, Leicestershire, LE17 4HN Tel: (01455) 550355 Fax: (01455) 550366 E-mail: hsenquiries@uponor.co.uk

Warmup P.L.C, Unit 702, Tudor Estate, Abbey Road, London, NW10 7UW Tel: (0845) 3452288 Fax: (0845) 3452299 E-mail: sales@warmup.co.uk

UNDERFLOOR HEATING CABLES

▶ Discount Floor Heating Ltd, Studio 24, Torfaen Business Centre, Gilchrist Thomas Industrial Estate, Blaenavon, Gwent, NP4 9RL Tel: (0845) 6581511 Fax: (0845) 6613557 E-mail: info@discountfloorheating.co.uk

Lagerstedt & Krantz (UK) Ltd, Unit 3, Metana House, Priestley Way, Crawley, West Sussex, RH10 9NT Tel: (0870) 2424873 Fax: (0870) 2424874 E-mail: info@lagerstedt-krantz.co.uk

Nexans Logistics, Llewellyn House, Chesney Wold, Bleak Hall, Milton Keynes, MK6 1NE Tel: (01908) 250850 Fax: (01908) 250851 E-mail: info@nexans.co.uk

▶ WarmFloors Ltd, 8 Roundhill Avenue, Cottingley, Bingley, West Yorkshire, BD16 1PH Tel: (01274) 568536 Fax: (01274) 568538 E-mail: sales@warmfloorsonline.com

UNDERFLOOR HEATING CONTROLS

▶ Anders Heating Co Ltd, Unit G Watcombe Manor Industrial Units, Ingham Lane, Watlington, Oxfordshire, OX49 5EB Tel: (01491) 614694 Fax: (01491) 614489 E-mail: info@andersheating.co.uk

▶ KaMo UK, I-Centre House, Hamilton Way, Oakham Business Park, Mansfield, Nottinghamshire, NG18 5BR Tel: (01623) 422006 Fax: (01623) 422003 E-mail: info@kamouk.com

▶ Neoheat, Smallmead Gate, Pingemead Business Centre, Reading, RG30 3UR Tel: (0845) 1080361 Fax: (0845) 1081295 E-mail: infor@neoheat.com

▶ Underfloorheatingshop, 66 Rea Street, Birmingham, B5 6LB Tel: 0121-622 4334 Fax: 0121-622 5768 E-mail: manager@underfloorheatingshop.co.k

UNDERFLOOR HEATING SYSTEM INSTALLATION

Danfoss Randall Ltd, Ampthill Road, Bedford, MK42 9ER Tel: (0845) 1217400 Fax: (0845) 1217515 E-mail: danfossrandall@randall.com

B.P. Dempsey Ltd, Units 6 & 8, March Street, Sheffield, S9 5DQ Tel: 0114-242 1900 Fax: 0114-243 2232

Dove Heating Ltd, 227 Kingston Road, New Malden, Surrey, KT3 3SZ Tel: (020) 8241 0141 Fax: (020) 8942 9992

▶ Underfloor Heating, Norris House Elton Park Business Centre, Hadleigh Road, Ipswich, IP2 0HU Tel: (01473) 280444 Fax: (01473) 231850

UNDERFLOOR HEATING SYSTEMS

▶ Thermalfloor Underfloor Heating Systems Ltd, School Road, Tnepher Friartor, Perth, PH2 8DF Tel: (08450) 620400 Fax: (01828) 628130

UNDERFLOOR RADIANT HEATING SYSTEMS

▶ Anders Heating Co Ltd, Unit G Watcombe Manor Industrial Units, Ingham Lane, Watlington, Oxfordshire, OX49 5EB Tel: (01491) 614694 Fax: (01491) 614489 E-mail: info@andersheating.co.uk

▶ KaMo UK, I-Centre House, Hamilton Way, Oakham Business Park, Mansfield, Nottinghamshire, NG18 5BR Tel: (01623) 422006 Fax: (01623) 422003 E-mail: info@kamouk.com

UNDERGROUND CABLE ACCESSORIES

▶ Birkett Electric Ltd, Bridge House, Longwick Road, Princes Risborough, Buckinghamshire, HP27 9RS Tel: (01844) 274480 Fax: (01844) 274470 E-mail: info@birkett-electric.com

UNDERGROUND DETECTABLE WARNING TAPES

U K Tapes Ltd, 5 Cooper Drive, Springwood Industrial Estate, Braintree, Essex, CM7 2RF Tel: (01376) 349090 Fax: (01376) 348989 E-mail: sales@uktapes.com

UNDERGROUND LOCATION EQUIPMENT

Underground Location Systems Uls Ltd, 66 Hall Lane, North Walsham, Norfolk, NR28 9DU Tel: (01692) 404494 Fax: (01692) 404494 E-mail: jw@correlators.co.uk

UNDERGROUND PIPELINE INSTALLATION

Chiltern Thrust Bore Ltd, Unit 1 The Barn, Firs Farm, Stagsden, West End, Bedford, MK43 8TB Tel: (01234) 825948 Fax: (01234) 824147 E-mail: chiltern@onweb.co.uk

Molemax International Ltd, Tanglewood House, Murrayfield Loan, Crieff, Perthshire, PH7 3ET Tel: (0870) 4438355 Fax: (0870) 4438356 E-mail: info@molemax.co.uk

UNDERPINNING CONTRACTORS

▶ Abbey Pynford plc, 7 Bridge Works, Woodhead Road, Honley, Holmfirth, HD9 6PW Tel: (01484) 660003 Fax: (01484) 660007 E-mail: admin@abbeypynford.co.uk

Roger Bullivant Ltd, Walton Road, Drakelow, Burton-on-Trent, Staffordshire, DE15 9UA Tel: (01283) 511115 Fax: (01283) 540826 E-mail: marketing@roger-bullivant.co.uk

Morcon Foundations Ltd, 2 Duffield Road Industrial Estate, Duffield Road, Little Eaton, Derby, DE21 5DR Tel: (01332) 834055 Fax: (01332) 834101 E-mail: post@morcon.demon.co.uk

Nolan Davis Contracting Ltd, Devas House, 7A Browning Avenue, Thornhil, Southampton, SO19 6PW Tel: (023) 8046 5000 Fax: (023) 8047 7620 E-mail: info@nd-contracting.co.uk

R E Lay Construction Ltd, 146 West Street, Dunstable, Bedfordshire, LU6 1NX Tel: (01582) 608571 Fax: (01582) 472092 E-mail: admin@r-e-lay.co.uk

Underpin & Makegood (Contracting) Ltd, 37 Millmarsh Lane, Enfield, Middx, EN3 7UY Tel: (020) 8805 4000 Fax: (020) 8805 4222 E-mail: david@underpin.com

UNDERPRESSURE GAS OR WATER MAIN OR PIPELINE DRILLING, *See Underpressure etc*

UNDERWATER CUTTING EQUIPMENT

Goodwin Air Plasma Ltd, Unit 18 Kernan Drive, Loughborough, Leicestershire, LE11 5JF Tel: (01509) 237369 Fax: (01509) 234942 E-mail: goodwinplasma@aol.com

UNDERWATER LIGHTING

Bowtech Products Ltd, Howe Moss Cresent, Kirkhill Industrial Estate, Dyce, Aberdeen, AB21 0GN Tel: (01224) 772345 Fax: (01224) 772900 E-mail: bowtech@bowtech.co.uk

▶ Bridgemary Library, 74 Brewers Lane, Gosport, Hampshire, PO13 0LA Tel: (0845) 6035631 Fax: (01329) 511390 E-mail: bridgemaryaquatics@ntlworld.com

Groove Associates Ltd, Unit 2, Alton Business Centre, Omega Park, Alton, Hampshire, GU34 2YU Tel: (01420) 88776 Fax: (01420) 88777 E-mail: sales@groove-ltd.com

UNDERWATER PHOTOGRAPHY

▶ Pixelate Imaging, 8 Flitcroft Street, London, WC2H 8DL Tel: (020) 7240 9808 Fax: (020) 7240 9188 E-mail: studio@pixelate.biz

▶ Sublime Scuba Photography, PO Box 21524, Stirling, FK8 3YW Tel: 01786 860786

UNDERWATER WELDING

Speciality Welds Ltd, Unit 18, Moorlands Business Centre, Cleckheaton, West Yorkshire, BD19 4EW Tel: (01274) 879867 Fax: (01274) 855975 E-mail: sales@specialwelds.com

UNDERWEAR WHOLESALERS

A & S GB Ltd, 130-132 Taunton Road, Ashton-under-Lyne, Lancashire, OL7 9EE Tel: 0161-330 9131 Fax: 0161-330 9131 E-mail: amjud@aol.com

M. Holt (M/C) Ltd, 159 Cheetham Hill Road, Manchester, M8 8LG Tel: 0161-832 2210 Fax: 0161-839 5217

▶ Hucke Ltd, Berners House, 47-48 Berners Street, London, W1T 3NF Tel: (020) 7580 7890 Fax: (020) 7580 7442 E-mail: sales@hucke.com

Manchester Hosiery Ltd, Queens Road, Hinckley, Leicestershire, LE10 1EE Tel: (01455) 632161 Fax: (01455) 635390 E-mail: sales@palmunderwear.co.uk

Pak Nylon Hosiery Co, 31 Broughton Street, Cheetham Hill, Manchester, M8 8LZ Tel: 0161 832 7371 Fax: 0161 839 5134 E-mail: C_M_Afzal_Khan@hotmail.co.uk

UNDERWEAR, ALL TYPES

Albert Martin & Co. Ltd, Kirkby Road, Sutton-in-Ashfield, Nottinghamshire, NG17 1GP Tel: (01623) 441122 Fax: (01623) 551037

Damartex UK Ltd, Bowling Green Mills, Bingley, West Yorkshire, BD97 1AD Tel: (0870) 8330000 Fax: (01274) 551024 E-mail: infouk@damart.com

G R Bodycote Ltd, Orchard Works, Holliers Walk, Hinckley, Leicestershire, LE10 1QR Tel: (01455) 636271 Fax: (01455) 890025

▶ Glamourbox, Unit 6, 9 St. Johns street, Colchester, CO2 7NN Tel: 01206 570976 E-mail: sales@glamourbox.co.uk

Holt Hosiery Co. Ltd, Deane Road Mill, Bolton, BL3 5AR Tel: (01204) 525611 Fax: (01204) 394620

Jockey, Crown House, Manchester Road, Wilmslow, Cheshire, SK9 1BH Tel: (01625) 419600 Fax: (01625) 419601 E-mail: sales@jockeyuk.com

Manchester Hosiery Ltd, Queens Road, Hinckley, Leicestershire, LE10 1EE Tel: (01455) 632161 Fax: (01455) 635390 E-mail: sales@palmunderwear.co.uk

New Star Fashions Ltd, Arena House, Greenacres Road, Oldham, OL4 1HA Tel: 0161-628 2339 Fax: 0161-628 2337 E-mail: sales@newstarfashions.co.uk

Sihad Textiles Ltd, 3 Camden Street, Leicester, LE1 2AP Tel: 0116-253 9258

Sunspel Menswear Ltd, Cavendish House, Canal Street, Long Eaton, Nottingham, NG10 4HP Tel: 0115-973 5292 Fax: 0115-946 1211 E-mail: sales@sunspel.com

V F Intimates Ltd, Block L Westways Business Park, Porterfield Road, Renfrew, PA4 8DJ Tel: 0141-885 4730 Fax: 0141-885 4731

Wolsey, Abbey Meadows, Leicester, LE4 5AD Tel: 0116-262 6755 Fax: 0116-253 0154 E-mail: sales@wolsey.com

UNDERWRITERS OR UNDERWRITING AGENCIES

Allied Underwriting Agencies Ltd, 14 Fenchurch Avenue, London, EC3M 5AT Tel: (020) 7265 1166 Fax: (020) 7265 1857 E-mail: info@aua-insurance.com

Canopius Management Services Ltd, 36 Gracechurch Street, London, EC3V 0BT Tel: (020) 7369 3000 Fax: (020) 7337 3999

Crownsway Insurance Brokers Ltd, 185 Holyhead Road, Birmingham, B21 0AS Tel: 0121-554 3566 Fax: 0121-523 2992 E-mail: crowns@btconnect.com

Euler Hermes Guarantee plc, Surety House, Lyons Cresent, Tonbridge, Kent, TN9 1EN Tel: (01732) 770311 Fax: (01732) 770361

F M Global (T/U F M Insurance Co. Ltd), 52 Leadenhall St, London, EC3A 2BJ Tel: (020) 7480 4000 Fax: (020) 7265 6738

Riverstone Management Ltd, 66 Mark Lane, London, EC3R 7HS Tel: (020) 7977 1600 Fax: (020) 7977 1610

Robert Malatier, Cigna House, 8 Lime Street, London, EC3M 7AH Tel: (020) 7623 4524 Fax: (020) 7623 3648 E-mail: people@robert-malatier-ltd.com

Towergate Marine Underwritting, 91-92 High Street, Lymington, Hampshire, SO41 9AP Tel: (01590) 671560 Fax: (01590) 679893 E-mail: tmu@towergate.co.uk

UNFINISHED WOOD FLOORING

▶ Mckay Flooring Ltd, 123 Harmony Row, Glasgow, G51 3NB Tel: 0141-440 1586 Fax: 0141-425 1020 E-mail: enquires@mckay.co.uk

UNGROUND SOLID TURNED BEARINGS

Capco Presswork, Bel House, Shady Lane, Birmingham, B44 9ER Tel: 0121-325 1344 Fax: 0121-366 6619

Commercial Bearings Ltd, Plume Street, Birmingham, B6 7RY Tel: 0121-322 2036 Fax: 0121-327 6926 E-mail: sales@commercialbearings.co.uk

UNIFORM ACCESSORIES

Arodix Ltd, Unit 4, 36 Greenford Road, Harrow, Middlesex, HA1 3QH Tel: (020) 8864 2272 Fax: (020) 8423 8870

Badge Design Ltd, Unit 4e Crofts End Industrial Estate, Crofts End Road, Bristol, BS5 7UW Tel: 0117-952 5856 Fax: 0117-952 5857 E-mail: badge.design@btconnect.com

Marvelfairs Ltd, Suite 44-45, Level 7 Westec House, Westgate, Ealing, London, W5 1YY Tel: (020) 8998 9052 Fax: (020) 8991 0995 E-mail: general@marvelfairs.com

N Schahid Ltd, Unit 3 Knoll Business Centre, Old Shoreham Road, Hove, East Sussex, BN3 7GS Tel: (01273) 424200 Fax: (01273) 424204 E-mail: nschahid@aol.com

Premier Workwear Ltd, 24 Friern Watch Avenue, London, N12 9NT Tel: (020) 8445 5115 Fax: (020) 8445 4567 E-mail: info-uk@chefwork.com

UNIFORM CAPS/HATS

Charles Owen & Co (Bow) Ltd, Royal Works, Croesfoel Industrial Estate, Rhostyllen, Wrexham, Clwyd, LL14 4BJ Tel: (01978) 317777 Fax: (01978) 317778 E-mail: charles.owen@ukonline.co.uk

M S Michael & Co. Ltd, 4 Batchelor Street, Chatham, Kent, ME4 4BJ Tel: (01634) 844994 Fax: (01634) 844995

Walter Wright, 29 Albion Road, Luton, LU2 0DS Tel: (01582) 721616 Fax: (01582) 725055 E-mail: enquiries@walterwright.com

UNIFORM CLOTHING MANUFRS, *See also other headings under Uniform*

▶ Ace Embroidery Ltd, 141 Tat Bank Road, Oldbury, West Midlands, B69 4NH Tel: 0121-544 7108 Fax: 0121-544 4965 E-mail: info@ace-embroidery.co.uk

Allen & Douglas Corporate Clothing Ltd, Compton Park, Wildmere Road, Banbury, Oxfordshire, OX16 3EZ Tel: (01295) 272700 Fax: (01295) 270486 E-mail: sales@aandd.co.uk

Armor Products, Cranfield Road, Lostock Industrial Estate, Lostock, Bolton, BL6 4SB Tel: (01204) 664000 Fax: (01204) 664001

▶ Banner & Shields Ltd, Mabgate Mills, Mabgate, Leeds, LS9 7DZ Tel: 0113-243 2860

Fred Bare Ltd, 74 Alexandra National Ho, Seven Sister Rd, London, N4 2PE Tel: (07958) 955707

Blue Jay Of London, 2 Shillingford Street, London, N1 2DP Tel: (020) 7359 4800 Fax: (020) 7704 9654

Blues Clothing Ltd, Brigade House, Parsons Green, London, SW6 4TN Tel: (020) 7371 9900 Fax: (020) 7371 9782 E-mail: marketing@blues-clothing.co.uk

▶ Boyd Cooper Ltd, Bruton House, Stadium Way, Harlow, Essex, CM19 5FT Tel: (01279) 621900 Fax: (01279) 641779 E-mail: enquiries@boydcooper.com

Braidway Ltd, Unit 14 198 Swanston Street, Glasgow, G40 4HH Tel: 0141-550 0333 Fax: 0141-554 3863

Britorion Ltd, PO Box 98, Alton, Hampshire, GU34 4YL Tel: (01420) 22134 Fax: (01420) 520345 E-mail: britorion@aol.com

Chevron Associates Ltd, P O Box 3092, Milton Keynes, MK17 9AN Tel: 01525 290600 Fax: 01525 290600

Classy Clobber, The Croft, Chapel Lane, Lower Withington, Macclesfield, Cheshire, SK11 9DE Tel: (01477) 571999

Corporate CMT Ltd, 59 Featherstone Lane, Featherstone, Pontefract, West Yorkshire, WF7 6LS Tel: (01977) 792226 Fax: (01977) 795536

Corporate Trends, Rotherham Close, Norwood Industrial Estate, Killermarsh, Sheffield, S21 2JU Tel: 0114-251 3511 Fax: 0114-251 3399 E-mail: sales@corporatetrends.co.uk

Corporatewear UK, 98-104 Constitution Hill, Birmingham, B19 3JT Tel: 0121-604 9898 Fax: 0121-604 6868 E-mail: info@corporatewearuk.co.uk

Crossbow Clothing Ltd, 31 Broadway Market, London, E8 4PH Tel: (020) 7923 9313 Fax: (020) 7923 9314 E-mail: sales@crossbowwear.co.uk

▶ David Luke Ltd, 4 Midland Street, Manchester, M12 6LB Tel: 0161-272 7474 Fax: 0161-272 6363 E-mail: sales@davidluke.com

Dewhirst Corporate Clothing, 3 Burdon Drive, North West Industrial Estate, Peterlee, County Durham, SR8 2JH Tel: 0191-518 1888 Fax: 0191-586 3167

Diaward Equipment (UK) Ltd, Firmin House, 82-86 New Town Row, Birmingham, B6 4HU Tel: 0121-359 6666 Fax: 0121-359 3292 E-mail: enquiries@firmin.co.uk

▶ Fashion Mark Retail Ltd, 88 South Road, Southall, Middlesex, UB1 1RD Tel: (020) 8813 8841

Future Garments Ltd, Aqua House, Buttress Way, Smethwick, West Midlands, B66 3DL Tel: 0121-555 7167 Fax: 0121-555 7168 E-mail: sales@future-gmts.com

G B Marketing, 218 Nottingham Road, Burton Joyce, Nottingham, NG14 5BD Tel: 0115-961 9126 Fax: 0115-987 4630

Initial Images, Unit 218, Tedco Business Works, Henry Robson Way, South Shields, Tyne & Wear, NE33 1RL Tel: 0191-455 8128

J B Armstrong & Co. Ltd, Middleton Street, Ilkeston, Derbyshire, DE7 5TT Tel: 0115-932 4913 Fax: 0115-930 0083 E-mail: info@armstrongsmill.co.uk

▶ JM Workwear, Unit 11 Premier Building, Newport Road, Bedwas, Caerphilly, Mid Glamorgan, CF83 8YE Tel: (029) 2086 5530 Fax: (029) 2086 5110 E-mail: sales@jmworkwear.co.uk

John Maden & Sons Ltd, Market Street, Bacup, Lancashire, OL13 0AU Tel: (01706) 873544 Fax: (01706) 879130 E-mail: info@johnmaden.com

Johnsons Apparelmaster Ltd, Rugby Road, Hinckley, Leicestershire, LE10 2NE Tel: (01455) 891191 Fax: (01455) 619056 E-mail: enquiries@johnsonapparemaster.com

Kashket & Partners Ltd, 35 Hoxton Square, London, N1 6NN Tel: (020) 7739 3737 Fax: (020) 7729 0107

▶ Key Wear, 9 Frances Street, Truro, Cornwall, TR1 3DN Tel: (01872) 242233 Fax: (01872) 262390

Linkhill Marketing Ltd, 4 The Linen House, 253 Kilburn Lane, London, W10 4BQ Tel: (020) 8964 3990 Fax: (020) 8964 3910 E-mail: sales@uniformsjohnmarks.com

Maderite Designers, 102 Greenheath Business Centre, Three Colts Lane, London, E2 6JB Tel: (020) 7739 6602 Fax: (020) 7739 6602 E-mail: victorsims@macumltd.net

Nalestar Ltd, Melton House, Melton Place, Leyland, Preston, PR25 4XU Tel: (01772) 431226 Fax: (01772) 622497 E-mail: sales@nalestar.co.uk

Pinnees Clothing Co., 85 Liscard Road, Wallasey, Merseyside, CH44 9AE Tel: 0151-638 1073 Fax: 0151-638 1073 E-mail: sales@pinnees.com

Premier Schoolwear, 688-690 Becontree Avenue, Dagenham, Essex, RM8 3HD Tel: (020) 8592 0141 Fax: (020) 8984 0953

Prima Corporate Wear Ltd, 5 Greenwich View Place, London, E14 9NN Tel: (020) 7515 8877 Fax: (020) 7515 0077 E-mail: sales@primawear.com

Florence Roby, Caddick Road, Knowsley Business Park, Prescot, Merseyside, L34 9HP Tel: 0151-548 2228 Fax: 0151-549 2011 E-mail: froby@uniformcollection.com

School Colours Ltd, Manse Lane, 5 Monkswell Park, Knaresborough, North Yorkshire, HG5 8NQ Tel: (01423) 866906 Fax: (01423) 869319E-mail: enquiries@schoolcolours.co.uk

Uniform Express Ltd, Unit C7 South Way, Bounds Green Industrial Estate, Bounds Green Road, London, N11 2UL Tel: (020) 8368 0114 Fax: (020) 8361 0624 E-mail: mail@uniformexpress.co.uk

▶ Uniform Sportswear Distributors, 35 Ash House Lane, Little Leigh, Northwich, Cheshire, CW8 4RG Tel: (01606) 892783 Fax: (01606) 892549 E-mail: usdltd@enterprise.net

Todd Webb & Co. Ltd, Unit 5 Ryehill Close, Lodge Farm Industrial Estate, Northampton, NN5 7UA Tel: (01604) 581430 Fax: (01604) 586081 E-mail: toddwebb@tiscali.co.uk

Wensum, South Corner, Brighton Road, Lowfield Heath, Crawley, West Sussex, RH11 0PH Tel: (01293) 422700 Fax: (01293) 422701 E-mail: enquiries@wensum.co.uk

Wessex Textiles Ltd, Blake Industrial Park, Colley Lane, Bridgwater, Somerset, TA6 5LT Tel: (01278) 450450 Fax: (01278) 450550 E-mail: sales@wessextextiles.co.uk

Wood Harris, 1 Cleeve Court, Leatherhead, Surrey, KT22 7RJ Tel: (01372) 362990 Fax: (01372) 362920

Wood Harris Ltd, 47-53 Cannon Street, London, EC4M 5SH Tel: (020) 7489 8189 Fax: (020) 7236 7686

UNIFORM FABRICS

Lingcroft Associates Ltd, Park House, Brooke Street, Cleckheaton, West Yorkshire, BD19 3RY Tel: (01274) 876500 Fax: (01274) 876125 E-mail: richard@lingcroft.co.uk

S H Rawnsley Ltd, Birkshead Mill, Wilsden, Bradford, West Yorkshire, BD15 0DH Tel: (01535) 273221 Fax: (01535) 273976

Wallass & Co. Ltd, Lumb Lane Mills, Lumb Lane, Bradford, West Yorkshire, BD8 7GA Tel: (01274) 724215 Fax: (01274) 724839 E-mail: sales@wallass.com

UNINTERRUPTIBLE POWER SUPPLY (UPS) GENERATOR SETS

Arun International (Power) Ltd, Unit F1, Dominion Way, Littlehampton, West Sussex, BN16 3HQ Tel: (01903) 850285 Fax: (01903) 850636 E-mail: sales@arunpower.co.uk

UNINTERRUPTIBLE POWER SUPPLY (UPS) MAINTENANCE

▶ N R G Power Systems Ltd, 10 Westbourne Avenue, Worthing, West Sussex, BN14 8DF Tel: (01903) 200044 Fax: (01903) 200066 E-mail: nigel@nrgpowersystems.com

UNINTERRUPTIBLE POWER SUPPLY (UPS) SWITCHGEARS

Power Systems Warehouse Ltd, Powerguard House, Grimsby Road, Louth, Lincolnshire, LN11 0SX Tel: (01507) 600688 Fax: (01507) 600621 E-mail: sales@powerguard.co.uk

UNIT CONSTRUCTION BRIDGES

Balfour Beatty plc, Fourth Floor, 130 Wilton Road, London, SW1V 1LQ Tel: (020) 7216 6800 Fax: (020) 7216 6950

Fairfield Mabey Ltd, Off Station Road, Chepstow, Gwent, NP16 5YL Tel: (01291) 623801 Fax: (01291) 625453 E-mail: mail@fairfieldmabey.com

▶ Janson Bridging (UK) Ltd, Charles House, Toutley Rd, Wokingham, Berkshire, RG41 1QN Tel: 0845 5262050 Fax: 0118-979 5472 E-mail: sales@jansonbridging.co.uk

Kier Caribbean Ltd, Tempsford Hall, Sandy, Bedfordshire, SG19 2BD Tel: (01767) 640111 Fax: (01767) 641179 E-mail: david.parr@kier.co.uk

UNIVERSAL GRINDING

Easicut Grinding Co. Ltd, Leestone Road, Sharston Industrial Area, Manchester, M22 4RN Tel: 0161-428 3265 Fax: 0161-428 3267 E-mail: w.kilbride@virgin.net

Techni Grind Preston Machining Ltd, Unit 62 Red Scar Industrial Estate, Longridge Road, Ribbleton, Preston, PR2 5ND Tel: (01772) 797589 Fax: (01772) 797682 E-mail: sales@tgmeng.co.uk

UNIVERSAL JOINT KITS

▶ North West Propshafts, Regency Works, Regent Street, Coppull, Chorley, Lancashire, PR7 5AX Tel: (01257) 791681 Fax: (01257) 794232E-mail: info@northwestpropshafts.com

UNIVERSAL JOINT MANUFRS

GKN Driveshafts Ltd, Middlemoor La West, Aldridge, Walsall, WS9 8DT Tel: (01922) 453371 Fax: (01922) 451716 E-mail: martyn.habgood@gkndriveline.com

Spicer Driveshaft UK Ltd, Rutherford Drive, Park Farm Industrial Estate, Wellingborough, Northamptonshire, NN8 6AQ Tel: (01933) 402000 Fax: (01933) 401322

UNIVERSAL SERIAL BUS (USB) CABLES

Suna Supplies Ltd, B 91 Ewell Road, Surbiton, Surrey, KT6 6AH Tel: (020) 8390 8811 Fax: (020) 8390 4331 E-mail: sales@suna.co.uk

UNIVERSAL SERIAL BUS (USB) FLASH DISKS

Faisal, C517 New Providence Wharf, 1 Fairmont Avenue, London, UK, E14 9PF Tel: 07976 289139 Fax: 0870 4586531 E-mail: sales@flashdrive-direct.com

UNIVERSAL TEST EQUIPMENT

Tinius Olsen Ltd, Unit 6, Perrywood Business Park, Honeycrock Lane, Salfords, Redhill, RH1 5DZ Tel: (01737) 765001 Fax: (01737) 764768 E-mail: sales@tiniusolsen.co.uk

UNIVERSITIES, CATERING

University of Derby Buxton, Devonshire Campus, 1 Devonshire Road, Buxton, Derbyshire, SK17 6RY Tel: (01298) 71100 Fax: (01298) 27261 E-mail: enquiriesudb@derby.ac.uk

UNIVERSITY GAS SUPPLY SYSTEMS

Medical Gases Ltd, Aztex House, Perrywood Business Park, Salfords, Redhill, RH1 5DZ Tel: (01737) 378000 Fax: (01737) 378055 E-mail: rsmith@medicalgases.uk.com

UP AND OVER OR SLIDING GARAGE DOORS

Abinger Garage Door Services, Restland, Hoe Lane, Peaslake, Guildford, Surrey, GU5 9SW Tel: (01306) 730801

All Style Door & Gate Services, 25 Woolacombe Lodge Road, Birmingham, B29 6PZ Tel: 0121-472 0675

Avon Manufacturing Ltd, Viande House, Kineton Road, Southam, Warwickshire, CV47 0DR Tel: (01926) 817292 Fax: (01926) 814156 E-mail: sale@avonova.co.uk

▶ Fardoors Garage Doors, 85 Mallory Road, Birkenhead, Merseyside, CH42 6QR Tel: 0151-643 9914 Fax: 0151-643 9914 E-mail: leefardoe@aol.com

G E Garage Doors, 31 Upper Hibbert Lane, Marple, Stockport, Cheshire, SK6 7JQ Tel: 0161-406 7667 E-mail: gegaragedoors@hotmail.co.uk

Garador Enquiries, Bunford Lane, Yeovil, Somerset, BA20 2EJ Tel: (0800) 706670 Fax: (01935) 443744 E-mail: enquiries@garador.co.uk

Garage Doors (London) Ltd, 37 Waterloo Road, London, NW2 7TS Tel: (020) 8452 1233 Fax: (020) 8208 2213

J B Garage Doors London South East Ltd, 74 Swaisland Drive, Crayford, Dartford, DA1 4HY Tel: (01322) 528059 Fax: (01322) 550560 E-mail: enquiries@jbgaragedoors.co.uk

John Teuton Garage Door Specialists, Unit 8, Bankside, Kidlington, Oxfordshire, OX5 1JE Tel: (01865) 373270 Fax: (01865) 842009 E-mail: info@john-teuton.co.uk

Lakeside Security Shutters, Bruce Road, Fforestfach, Swansea, SA5 4HS Tel: (01792) 561117 Fax: (01792) 587046 E-mail: sails@lakesidesecurity.co.uk

Larchbank Supplies, 210 Holbrook Lane, Coventry, CV6 4DD Tel: (024) 7666 7079 Fax: (0560) 0492708 E-mail: larchbankdoors@btconnect.com

M A Kelly, 284 Councillor Lane, Cheadle Hulme, Cheadle, Cheshire, SK8 5PN Tel: 0161-485 2255 Fax: 0161-442 1617

Moffett Thallon & Co. Ltd, 143 Northumberland Street, Belfast, BT13 2JF Tel: (028) 9032 2802 Fax: (028) 9024 1428 E-mail: info@moffett.demon.co.uk

National Door Co., Pyramid House, 52 Guildford Road, Lightwater, Surrey, GU18 5SD Tel: (01276) 451555 Fax: (01276) 453666 E-mail: national4@beeb.net

Nortech Ltd, Unit 14 Terrace Factory, Bassington Industrial Estate, Cramlington, Northumberland, NE23 8AD Tel: (01670) 736811 Fax: (01670) 731252 E-mail: sales@nortechgaragedoors.co.uk

P C Henderson Ltd, Durham Road, Bowburn, Durham, DH6 5NG Tel: 0191-377 0701 Fax: 0191-377 1309 E-mail: sales@pchenderson.com

UPHOLSTERED FURNITURE, *See Upholstery etc*

UPHOLSTERY, *See also headings for particular types*

A & C Furnishings, 3 Reliance Trading Estate, Chestom Road, Bilston, West Midlands, WV14 0RD Tel: (01902) 498293 Fax: (01902) 498293 E-mail: info@aandcfurnishings.co.uk

Albert E Chapman Ltd, 17 Crouch Hill, London, N4 4AP Tel: (020) 7272 2536 Fax: (020) 7263 1033

Amey Cliff & Son, 12 Clive Road, Canton, Cardiff, CF5 1HJ Tel: (029) 2023 3462 Fax: (029) 2023 3462 E-mail: dennis.amey@talk21.com

Art Forma (Furniture) Ltd, Station Road, Castle Donington, Derby, DE74 2NU Tel: (01332) 810474 Fax: (01332) 810277 E-mail: sales@artforma.co.uk

Artistic Upholstery Ltd, Bridge Street, Long Eaton, Nottingham, NG10 4QQ Tel: 0115-973 4481 Fax: 0115-946 1018 E-mail: sales@artisticupholstery.co.uk

Arts & Fashion Co. Ltd, Unit 7 Concorde Business Centre, Concorde Road, Acton, London, W3 0TJ Tel: (020) 8896 2929 Fax: (020) 8814 0735

Ashmoors Headboard Co., 136 Station Road, Broughton Astley, Leicester, LE9 6PW Tel: (01455) 286633 Fax: (01455) 286633

Avent Ltd, Avon Works, Station Street, Walton On The Naze, Essex, CO14 8DA Tel: (01255) 672244 Fax: (01255) 852030 E-mail: Info@aventsltd.co.uk

Bridge Of Weir Leather Co. Ltd, 98 Kilbarchan Road, Bridge of Weir, Renfrewshire, PA11 3RH Tel: (01505) 612132 Fax: (01505) 614964 E-mail: mail@bowleather.co.uk

Brown & Cook Ltd, 77 Allcock Street, Birmingham, B9 4DY Tel: 0121-766 7117 Fax: 0121-753 2155 E-mail: sales@brownandcook.co.uk

Buoyant Upholstery Ltd, Hallam Road, Nelson, Lancashire, BB9 8AJ Tel: (01282) 691631 Fax: (01282) 697298

Angela Burgin Furnishing & Design Ltd, 2a Hazelbury Crescent, Luton, LU1 1DF Tel: (01582) 722563 Fax: (01582) 616131 E-mail: sales@abfd.co.uk

Caddum Design Furniture Products Ltd, Dominion Way, Easting Close, Worthing, West Sussex, BN14 8NW Tel: (01903) 232355 Fax: (01903) 232356 E-mail: sales@caddumdesign.com

▶ Carey B Restoration, Units 2-3, 63A Westcote Road, London, SW16 6BN Tel: (020) 8696 7555 E-mail: info@antiquerestoration.co.uk

Cass Bros, 153 Hastings Road, Bromley, BR2 8NQ Tel: (020) 8462 2387 Fax: (020) 8462 2387

Cavendish Upholstery Ltd, Mayfield Mill, Briercliffe Road, Chorley, Lancashire, PR6 0DA Tel: (01257) 277664 Fax: (01257) 261665 E-mail: suites@cavendish-upholstery.co.uk

Chalford Chairs Ltd, Victoria Works, London Road, Chalford, Stroud, Gloucestershire, GL6 8HN Tel: (01453) 882279 Fax: (01453) 731955

Classic Curtains Blinds & Upholstery, 22 Mercia Dr, Mynydd Isa, Mold, Clwyd, CH7 6UH Tel: 01352 756267

Coach Trimming Coventry, Sutton Stop, Longford, Coventry, CV6 6DF Tel: (024) 7664 5488 Fax: (024) 7636 2545

Collins & Hayes Ltd, Menzies Road, Ponswood, St. Leonards-On-Sea, East Sussex, TN38 9XF Tel: (01424) 720027 Fax: (01424) 720270 E-mail: sales@collinsandhayes.com

Country Upholstery, Unit 1 Kennet Enterprise Centre, Charnham La, Hungerford, Berks, RG17 0EY Tel: (01488) 682226 Fax: (01488) 682226 E-mail: paulcho@btinternet.com

Courtney Contract Furnishers Ltd, J-K Unit Enterprise Centre, Paycocke Road, Basildon, Essex, SS14 3DY Tel: (01268) 531771 Fax: (01268) 271299 E-mail: sales@courtney-contracts.co.uk

Crescent Interiors, Sunnyside Road, Worcester, WR1 1RJ Tel: (01905) 619144 Fax: (01905) 619155 E-mail: sales@crescentinteriors.com

Davison Highley Ltd, Old Oxford Road, Piddington, High Wycombe, Buckinghamshire, HP14 3BE Tel: (01494) 883862 Fax: (01494) 881572 E-mail: magic@davisonhighley.co.uk

Delcor Furniture Ltd, 80-82 Whiteladies Road, Clifton, Bristol, BS8 2QN Tel: 0117-973 0932 Fax: 0191-237 6892

Derwent Upholstery Ltd, Amber Business Centre, Greenhill Lane, Riddings, Alfreton, Derbyshire, DE55 4BR Tel: (01773) 604121 Fax: (01773) 540813 E-mail: sales@derwentupholstery.com

DFS Trading Ltd, 1 Rockingham Way, Adwick-le-Street, Doncaster, South Yorkshire, DN6 7NA Tel: (01302) 330365 Fax: (01302) 330880

Dove Interious, Unit 6, Fairfield Road, Downham Market, Norfolk, PE38 9ET Tel: (01366) 383684 Fax: (01366) 387429 E-mail: simon@doveinteriers.com

Duresta Upholstery Ltd, Fields Farm Road, Long Eaton, Nottingham, NG10 3FZ Tel: 0115-973 2246 Fax: 0115-946 1028

Ereira & Matthews Ltd, 2 13-15 Sunbeam Road, London, NW10 6JP Tel: (020) 8965 8567 Fax: (020) 8965 8567

Euro Fibres Ltd, 76 Forkhill Road, Newry, County Down, BT35 8QY Tel: (028) 3084 8912 Fax: (028) 3084 8179

▶ Glenbery Upholstery Ltd, Walton Street, Long Eaton, Nottingham, NG10 1PB Tel: 0115-946 0625 Fax: 0115-946 0683

Glencraft, 132 Wellington Road, Aberdeen, AB12 3LQ Tel: (01224) 873366 Fax: (01224) 894659 E-mail: sales@glencraft.co.uk

Greensmith Upholstery Ltd, New Tythe Street, Long Eaton, Nottingham, NG10 2DL Tel: 0115-973 3446 Fax: 0115-946 0743

Haywood Upholstery, Kinver Street, Stourbridge, West Midlands, DY8 5AB Tel: (01384) 839454

J E Smith & Son Upholsterers Ltd, 110-110a Langney Road, Eastbourne, East Sussex, BN22 8AQ Tel: (01323) 734206 E-mail: smith-andson@ic24.net

J M Grant, 73 New Road, Rednal, Birmingham, B45 9JT Tel: 0121-453 8783 Fax: 0121-453 8783

Jackson's (Upholsterer's Supplies) Ltd, 359 Argyle Street, Glasgow, G2 8LT Tel: 0141-221 0178 Fax: 0141-204 2792 E-mail: jacksonsltd@tiscali.co.uk

Jeckells & Son Ltd, 128 Bridge Road, Lowestoft, Suffolk, NR33 9JT Tel: (01502) 565007 Fax: (01502) 565606 E-mail: sales@jeckellschandlers.co.uk

Jeckells & Son Ltd, Riverside Road, Hoveton, Norwich, NR12 8UQ Tel: (01603) 784488 Fax: (01603) 783234 E-mail: jeckellstrimmers@ukgateway.net

John Tate & Co. Ltd, 3 Captain Street, Bradford, West Yorkshire, BD1 4HA Tel: (01274) 724426 Fax: (01274) 737117

Joynson Holland Ltd, Abercromby Avenue, High Wycombe, Buckinghamshire, HP12 3AZ Tel: (01494) 530274 Fax: (01494) 473387 E-mail: sales@joynsonholland.co.uk

JP Soft Furnishings, Hitherford Workshop, Hitherford Lane, Over, Cambridge, CB24 5NY Tel: (01954) 230651 E-mail: mje@pjsoftfurnishings.co.uk

Levingstone Manufacturing Ltd, Cranmere House, 196 Upper Chobham Road, Camberley, Surrey, GU15 1HD Tel: (01276) 25915 Fax: (01276) 21251 E-mail: conroy@hendries.freeserve.co.uk

Lewis & Co., Unit 5 Faraday Close, Washington, Tyne & Wear, NE38 8QJ Tel: 0191-419 2234 Fax: 0191-419 0724

Lewis & Co Fabrics Ltd, Sunbury House The Wallows Industrial Estate, Wallows Road, Brierley Hill, West Midlands, DY5 1QA Tel: (01384) 263313 Fax: (01384) 79019

Lewis & Co Fabrics Ltd, Sunbury House, 1 Andrews Road, London, E8 4QL Tel: (020) 7249 4967 Fax: (020) 7241 3163 E-mail: sales@sunburyfabrics.co.uk

Maine Furniture Company Manufacturers, The Goods Yard, Railway Street, Ballymena, County Antrim, BT42 2AF Tel: (028) 2564 7507 Fax: (028) 2564 7507 E-mail: maineupholsterers@irishtrade.net

Meniscus Systems Ltd, Blotts Barn, Brooks Road, Raunds, Wellingborough, Northamptonshire, NN9 6NS Tel: (01933) 625900 Fax: (01933) 625800 E-mail: sales@meniscus.co.uk

Morley Upholstery Works Ltd, Troutbeck, 84-86 Albany Street, London, NW1 4EJ Tel: (020) 7387 3846 Fax: (020) 7388 0651 E-mail: sales@morleyupholstery.co.uk

Nathan Fabrics & Sundries Ltd, 31 Gildart Street, Liverpool, L3 8ET Tel: 0151-207 0777 Fax: 0151-298 1474 E-mail: sales@fabric-crafts.co.uk

New Concept Upholsterer, 70 Thomas Street, Tamworth, Staffordshire, B77 3PR Tel: (01827) 51414

P E C Furniture Ltd, Amble Industrial Estate, Amble, Morpeth, Northumberland, NE65 0PE Tel: (01665) 710593 Fax: (01665) 712735 E-mail: pecfurn@aol.com

P & P Seating, 429 Meadway, Birmingham, B33 0DZ Tel: 0121-784 9441 Fax: 0121-789 7061 E-mail: info@ppseat.co.uk

R D Robins Upholsterers Ltd, The Mews, 39b Church Hill Road, London, E17 9RX Tel: (020) 7704 8182 Fax: (020) 8520 5226 E-mail: rdrobinsuphole@aol.com

R G Collins Ltd, 43 Melton Street, Kettering, Northamptonshire, NN16 9DT Tel: (07753) 627331 Fax: (01536) 514127

Revampsuites, 17 Bonny Brow Street, Middleton, Manchester, M24 4RJ Tel: 0161-654 4262 E-mail: revampsuites@aol.com

Roberts & Chick (Timber Lines) Ltd, 95 St James Mill Road, St James Business Park, Northampton, NN5 5JP Tel: (01604) 753223 Fax: (01604) 586100 E-mail: sales@roberts-chick.co.uk

Ross Fabrics, Manor Mill Lane, Leeds, LS11 8LQ Tel: 0113-385 2200 Fax: 0113-277 8855 E-mail: sales@rossfabrics.co.uk

S M Upholstery Ltd, 212a Whitchurch Road, Cardiff, CF14 3NB Tel: (029) 2061 9813 Fax: (029) 2061 7579 E-mail: sales@smfoam.co.uk

Sands Fabrics, 27 Gibson Road, High Wycombe, Buckinghamshire, HP12 4QW Tel: (01494) 521939

Sarum D I Y Upholstery Supplies, 57 Fisherton Street, Salisbury, SP2 7SU Tel: (01722) 320633 Fax: (01722) 320633

Suite Seat, 12a West Newington Place, Edinburgh, EH9 1QU Tel: 0131- 667 9923 Fax: 0131- 667 9923

Swan Lake Ltd, Harris Way, Sunbury-on-Thames, Middlesex, TW16 7EL Tel: (01932) 783620 Fax: (01932) 772207 E-mail: swanlake@totalise.co.uk

Swan Upholstery, 5-9 George Street, Romford, RM1 2DT Tel: (01708) 740569 Fax: (01708) 740569

Talbot Textiles & Upholstery Supply Co. Ltd, 16-18 Dargan Cresent, Belfast, BT3 9JP Tel: (028) 9078 1521 Fax: (028) 9077 8610 E-mail: ronnie@talbottexile.co.uk

▶ TFC The Furniture Co. Ltd, Swingbridge Road, Grantham, Lincolnshire, NG31 7XT Tel: (01476) 577760 Fax: (01476) 575199

Today Interiors Holdings Ltd, Hollis Road, Grantham, Lincolnshire, NG31 7QH Tel: (01476) 574401 Fax: (01476) 590208 E-mail: info@today-interiors.co.uk

Tokyo Fabric Printing UK Ltd, Overtons Building, Friar Street, Wednesbury, West Midlands, WS10 0RE Tel: 0121-502 2470 Fax: 0121-505 7277 E-mail: j.s.sandhu@tokyofabrics.co.uk

W T Parkes Upholstery, Regency Works, 1a Shakleton Road, Coventry, CV5 6HT Tel: (024) 7669 1199

Wade Upholstery, Bridge Street, Sandy Acre, Nottingham, NG10 5BH Tel: 0115-939 4500 Fax: 0115-949 0465

Welbeck House Ltd, Unit D Long Eaton Industrial Estate, Field Farm Road, Long Eaton, Nottingham, NG10 3FZ Tel: 0115-946 9333 Fax: 0115-983 6322

Wesley-Barrell Ltd, Ducklington Mill, Standlake Road, Ducklington, Witney, Oxfordshire, OX29 7YR Tel: (01993) 893100 Fax: (01993) 702720 E-mail: furniture@wesley-barrell.co.uk

Whiteleaf Ltd, Po Box 2, Princes Risborough, Buckinghamshire, HP27 9DP Tel: (01844) 261199 Fax: (01844) 342337 E-mail: sales@whiteleaffurniture.co.uk

Wimborne Leather Co., Unit 2b, Sunrise Business Park, Blandford Forum, Dorset, DT11 8ST Tel: (01258) 455397 Fax: (01258) 480610

Windmill Sofas, 1 Picks Cottage Factory Unit, Sewardstone Road, London, E4 7RA Tel: (020) 8805 5084 Fax: (020) 8524 2444

Woolnough Ac Ltd, 7 Parmiter Industrial Centre, Parmiter Street, London, E2 9HZ Tel: (020) 8980 9813 Fax: (020) 8980 9814

Wyvern Furniture Ltd, Units 13-15, Hartlebury Trading Estate, Hartlebury, Kidderminster, Worcestershire, DY10 4JB Tel: (01299) 251100 Fax: (01299) 251836

UPHOLSTERY CLEANING EQUIPMENT

Active Chemical Products Ltd, Butts Business Centre, Fowlmere, Royston, Hertfordshire, SG8 7SL Tel: (01763) 208222 Fax: (01763) 208906 E-mail: sales@alltec.co.uk

Broadbent & Co. Ltd, Unit 14a Colwick Business Park, Private Road No 2, Colwick Industrial Estate, Nottingham, NG4 2JR Tel: 0115-940 0777 Fax: 0115-987 3744 E-mail: info@industrialcleaningequipment.co.uk

Host Von Schrader, Unit 6 Capenhurst Technology Park, Capenhurst, Chester, CH1 6EH Tel: 0151-347 1900 Fax: 0151-347 1901 E-mail: host@hostvs.co.uk

Situations Upholsterers, Delvin End, Sible Hedingham, Halstead, Essex, CO9 3LN Tel: (01787) 462141 Fax: (01787) 462141 E-mail: enquiries@situations-uk.com

UPHOLSTERY CLEANING EQUIPMENT HIRE

Rug Doctor Ltd, 29 Decoy Road, Worthing, West Sussex, BN14 8ND Tel: (01903) 235558 Fax: (01903) 209671 E-mail: enquiries@rugdoctor.com

UPHOLSTERY CLEANING PRODUCTS

▶ Olympic Cleaning, 100 Wood Road, Heybridge, Maldon, Essex, CM9 4AU Tel: (01621) 856476 Fax: (01621) 852582 E-mail: sales@olympiccleaning.com

UPHOLSTERY CLEANING SERVICES OR CONTRACTORS

▶ Mattvac Carpet & Upholstery Cleaning, 45 Hallidale Crescent, Renfrew, PA4 0YA Tel: 0141-562 3873 E-mail: sales@mattvac.co.uk

UPHOLSTERY FABRICS, SYNTHETIC LEATHER

▶ David South, 15 High Street, Pateley Bridge, Harrogate, North Yorkshire, HG3 5AP Tel: (01423) 712022 Fax: (01423) 712412 E-mail: sales@davidsouth.co.uk

The London Upholstery Co., 245a Coldharbour Lane, London, SW9 8RR Tel: (0845) 2262178 Fax: (020) 7095 9919 E-mail: info@thelondonupholsterycompany.co.uk

UPHOLSTERY FABRICS, SYNTHETIC LEATHER – *continued*

▶ Upholstery Fabrics UK, 7 Eaton Close, Stockwood, Bristol, BS14 8PR Tel: 01275 830213 E-mail: enquires@upholsteryfabricsuk.co.uk

UPHOLSTERY FILLINGS, *See Fillings etc*

UPHOLSTERY LININGS

Brown & Cook Ltd, 77 Allcock Street, Birmingham, B9 4DY Tel: 0121-766 7117 Fax: 0121-753 2155 E-mail: sales@brownandcook.co.uk
R G Collins Ltd, 43 Melton Street, Kettering, Northamptonshire, NN16 9DT Tel: (07753) 627331 Fax: (01536) 514127

UPHOLSTERY MOQUETTE

Furtex, Hopton Mills, Hopton, Mirfield, West Yorkshire, WF14 8HE Tel: (01924) 490591 Fax: (01924) 495605 E-mail: furtex@eu.interfaceinc.com

UPHOLSTERY REPAIR/ RENOVATION SERVICES

A V Fowlds & Sons Ltd, Progress Works, Addington Square, London, SE5 7JZ Tel: (020) 7703 2686
Barton & Sons (Coach Trimmers), 2 New Town Trading Estate, Chase Street, Luton, LU1 3QZ Tel: (01582) 412932 Fax: (01582) 726867 E-mail: sales@carinteriors.net
Dove Interious, Unit 6, Fairfield Road, Downham Market, Norfolk, PE38 9ET Tel: (01366) 383684 Fax: (01366) 387429 E-mail: simon@doveinteriers.com
Duoflex Ltd, Trimmingham House, 2 Shires Road, Buckingham Road Industrial Estate, Brackley, Northamptonshire, NN13 7EZ Tel: (01280) 701366 Fax: (01280) 704799 E-mail: sales@duoflex.co.uk
Duresta Upholstery Ltd, Fields Farm Road, Long Eaton, Nottingham, NG10 3FZ Tel: 0115-973 2246 Fax: 0115-946 1028
M. Fine & Co., 4 Hoghill Road, Collier Row, Romford, RM5 2DH Tel: (01708) 741489 Fax: (01708) 741489
Finecraft Upholstery, 11 Teesdale Yard, London, E2 6QE Tel: (020) 7739 2000 Fax: (020) 7739 2000
Haywood Upholstery, Kinver Street, Stourbridge, West Midlands, DY8 5AB Tel: (01384) 839454
Henry Moore & Co., 5 The Broadway, London, SW13 0NY Tel: (020) 8878 0656 Fax: (020) 8878 0656
Household Services, Unit 2 Cartlich Street, Stoke-on-Trent, ST6 5PG Tel: (01782) 838058 Fax: (01782) 838058
J E Smith & Son Upholsterers Ltd, 110-110a Langney Road, Eastbourne, East Sussex, BN22 8AQ Tel: (01323) 734206 E-mail: smith-andson@ic24.net
JP Soft Furnishings, Hitherford Workshop, Hitherford Lane, Over, Cambridge, CB24 5NY Tel: (01954) 230651 E-mail: mje@pjsoftfurnishings.co.uk
L G M Ltd, Coppice Trading Estate, Kidderminster, Worcestershire, DY11 7QY Tel: (01562) 823700 Fax: (01562) 68237 E-mail: acook@lgm-ltd.co.uk
Lyn Plan Ltd, 43 Imperial Way, Croydon, CR9 4LP Tel: (020) 8681 1833 Fax: (020) 8680 5727 E-mail: sales@lynplan.com
Michael Figgitt Upholstery Upholstery, Orleans Close, Unit 3, Four Pools Industrial Estate, Evesham, Worcestershire, WR11 2FP Tel: (01386) 45120 Fax: (01386) 45264 E-mail: sales@figgittupholstery.co.uk
Practical Upholsterers Ltd, 35a Pound Farm Road, Chichester, West Sussex, PO19 7PU Tel: (01243) 786090 Fax: (01243) 786090
Profile Seating Ltd, Unit 11A, Fills Road, Willow Farm BusinessPark, Castle Donington, Derby, DE74 2US Tel: (01332) 817888 Fax: (01332) 817899 E-mail: mail@profileuk.com
R D Robins Upholsterers Ltd, The Mews, 39b Church Hill Road, London, E17 9RX Tel: (020) 7704 8182 Fax: (020) 8520 5226 E-mail: rdrobinsuphole@aol.com
R K Leighton, 2 Partridge Court, Price Street, Birmingham, B4 6JZ Tel: 0121-359 0514 Fax: 0121-333 3130 E-mail: sales@rk-leighton.co.uk
R M Upholstery, Rear of, 107 Evesham Road, Redditch, Worcestershire, B97 4JX Tel: (01527) 544490
Swan Upholstery, 5-9 George Street, Romford, RM1 2DT Tel: (01708) 740569 Fax: (01708) 740569
Upholstery Services, 51 Mansfield Road, Sheffield, S12 2AG Tel: 0114-265 4546
Walker Chair Care, 107 Bradford Road, Dewsbury, West Yorkshire, WF13 2ET Tel: (01924) 465588 Fax: (01924) 459688 E-mail: sales@walkerchaircare.co.uk
Windmill Sofas, 1 Picks Cottage Factory Unit, Sewardstone Road, London, E4 7RA Tel: (020) 8805 5084 Fax: (020) 8524 2444

UPHOLSTERY SPRINGS

Charles Blyth & Co. Ltd, Carnival Way, Castle Donington, Derby, DE74 2NJ Tel: (01332) 810283 Fax: (01332) 855810 E-mail: info@charlesblyth-co.co.uk
Cope & Timmins Ltd, Innova House 4 Kinetic Crescent, Enfield, Middlesex, EN3 7XH Tel: (0845) 4588860 Fax: (0800) 0740078 E-mail: customerservice@copes.co.uk
Peter Cook International, Aneal Business Centre, Cross Green Approach, Leeds, LS9 0SG Tel: 0113-235 1111 Fax: 0113-235 0034 E-mail: sales@petercookint.com
▶ Prestwood Interiors, 24 Orchard Lane, Prestwood, Great Missenden, Buckinghamshire, HP16 0NN Tel: (0800) 1694615 Fax: (01494) 890607 E-mail: asheri1234@aol.com
Wade Spring Ltd, Bennett Street, Long Eaton, Nottingham, NG10 4HL Tel: 0115-946 3000 Fax: 0115-946 1361 E-mail: mchiltern@wade-spring.com

UPHOLSTERY SUNDRY FURNITURE COMPONENTS

Conisborough Furniture Components Ltd, Denaby Lane Industrial Estate, Denaby Main, Doncaster, South Yorkshire, DN12 4JS Tel: (01709) 863122 Fax: (01709) 865068 E-mail: components@conisborough.com
Hanes International UK, Unit 11 Trans Pennine Trading Estate, Gorrells Way, Rochdale, Lancashire, OL11 2PX Tel: (01706) 514250 Fax: (01706) 712848 E-mail: sales@hanesindustries.com
The London Upholstery Co., 245a Coldharbour Lane, London, SW9 8RR Tel: (0845) 2262178 Fax: (020) 7095 9919 E-mail: info@thelondonupholsterycompany.co.uk
Ultra Furniture, Churchill House Building 66, Third Avenue, Pensnett Trading Estate, Kingswinford, West Midlands, DY6 7GA Tel: (01384) 400240 Fax: (01384) 405048 E-mail: admin@ultra-furniture.co.uk

UPHOLSTERY TRIMMINGS

Duncan Galliers, Corporation Lane, Shrewsbury, SY1 2PB Tel: (01743) 353981 Fax: (01743) 353981
Hanes International UK, Unit 11 Trans Pennine Trading Estate, Gorrells Way, Rochdale, Lancashire, OL11 2PX Tel: (01706) 514250 Fax: (01706) 712848 E-mail: sales@hanesindustries.com
J M Grant, 73 New Road, Rednal, Birmingham, B45 9JT Tel: 0121-453 8783 Fax: 0121-453 8783
Quality Foam Products, 70-72 Sussex St, Norwich, NR3 3DE Tel: (01603) 622730 Fax: (01603) 622730
Somic plc, PO Box 8, Preston, PR1 5PS Tel: (01772) 790000 Fax: (01772) 795677 E-mail: somic@somic.co.uk
Trim Technology & Services Ltd, 9-14 Colliery Lane, Exhall, Coventry, CV7 9NW Tel: (024) 7664 6000 Fax: (024) 7664 6001 E-mail: sales@trim-technology.com

UPHOLSTERY WEBBING

Amsafe Bridport, The Court, West Street, Bridport, Dorset, DT6 3QU Tel: (01308) 456666 Fax: (01308) 456605 E-mail: david.rumney@amsafe.com
Peter Cook International, Aneal Business Centre, Cross Green Approach, Leeds, LS9 0SG Tel: 0113-235 1111 Fax: 0113-235 0034 E-mail: sales@petercookint.com

UPRIGHT CARPET CLEANERS

▶ Business 2 Home Carpet Care, 37 Thompson Road, uolands, Stroud, Gloucestershire, GL5 1TE Tel: 01453 751409 E-mail: cleancarpetcarpetclean@yahoo.co.uk
▶ Fibrecare, 29 Brooks Road, Street, Somerset, BA16 0PN Tel: (01458) 447460 Fax: (01458) 447491 E-mail: sales@fibrecare.co.uk

UPSET FORGINGS

Commando Fasteners Co. Ltd, 3 Canal Street, Stourbridge, West Midlands, DY8 4LU Tel: (01384) 393949 Fax: (01384) 393933 E-mail: info@comfast.co.uk
Heartland Extrusion Forge Ltd, Rocky Lane, Nechells, Birmingham, B7 5EU Tel: 0121-359 6861 Fax: 0121-359 2972 E-mail: enquiries@hef.co.uk
John Hesketh & Son Ltd, Castlecroft Ironworks, Bury Grounds, Bury, Lancashire, BL9 0HU Tel: 0161-764 1109 Fax: 0161-763 1285
Mettis Aerospace Ltd, Windsor Road, Redditch, Worcestershire, B97 6EF Tel: (01527) 406400 Fax: (01527) 406401 E-mail: info@mettis-aerospace.com
Mills Forgings Ltd, Charterhouse Road, Coventry, CV1 2BJ Tel: (024) 7622 4985 Fax: (024) 7652 5453 E-mail: sales@millsforgings.co.uk
Shellbourne Manufacturing Co. Ltd, Bolton Bus Centre, 44-49 Lower Bridgeman St, Bolton, BL2 1DG Tel: (01204) 546410 Fax: (01925) 740062 E-mail: sales@shellbourne.co.uk
Tensile Forgings, Portersfield Road, Cradley Heath, West Midlands, B64 7BN Tel: (01384) 566758

UREA COMPRESSION MOULDINGS

▶ Cheshire Plastics, 1d Wellington Street, Clayton le Moors, Accrington, Lancashire, BB5 5HU Tel: (01254) 384222 Fax: (01254) 382555 E-mail: geoff@cheshireplastics.co.uk

URINALS

Aqua Free Ltd, 1 Avon Industrial Estate, Butlers Leap, Rugby, Warwickshire, CV21 3UY Tel: (01788) 561221 Fax: (01788) 560663 E-mail: info@aquafree.com

USED BACKHOE LOADERS

▶ Construction Plant Services (SW) Ltd, Nordic House, Longships Road, Cardiff, CF10 4RP Tel: (029) 2048 2002 Fax: (029) 2048 0876 E-mail: info@cpsltd.co.uk

USED CLOTHING WHOLESALE DEALERS

Black Country Rag & Wiper Co. Ltd, Greets Green Road Industrial Estate, Greets Green Road, West Bromwich, West Midlands, B70 9EW Tel: 0121-520 7586 Fax: 0121-522 3340 E-mail: mail@bcrglobaltextiles.co.uk
Lawrence M Barry & Co., Britannia Mill, North Cresent, London, E16 4TG Tel: (020) 7473 2898 Fax: (020) 7473 1381 E-mail: sales@1mb.co.uk
Omega Wipers, 12 Fordrough, Yardley, Birmingham, B25 8DL Tel: 0121-771 2653 Fax: 0121-771 2652 E-mail: omegawipers@aol.com

USED COMMERCIAL VEHICLES

▶ Abbey Group Motors, 32 Abbey Foregate, Shrewsbury, SY2 6BT Tel: 01743 242888
▶ Hopkinsons Fairdeals Ltd, Mayfield Farm, Doncaster Road, East Hardwick, Pontefract, West Yorkshire, WF8 3EQ Tel: (01977) 620418 Fax: (01977) 620419 E-mail: sales@hopdeals.com
▶ North Ayrshire Commercials, 5 Irvine Road, Lugton, Kilmarnock, Ayrshire, KA3 4ED Tel: (01294) 850049 E-mail: enquiries@northayrshirecommercials.co.uk
▶ T A & N White Ltd, Park Road Industrial Estate, Consett, County Durham, DH8 5PY Tel: (01207) 504755 Fax: (01207) 580659 E-mail: info@whitescommercialvehicles.co.uk
▶ W & J Allardyce Commercials Ltd, Hillside Garage, Longridge, Bathgate, West Lothian, EH47 8AN Tel: (01501) 770218 Fax: (01501) 771425 E-mail: william.allardyce@btopenworld.com

USED COMPUTERS

3c Technology Ltd, Network House Pheonix Court, Hawkins Road, Colchester, CO2 8LA Tel: (01206) 790060 Fax: (01206) 790058 E-mail: info@3ctech.co.uk
A M S Systems, 17 The Oval, Bedlington, Northumberland, NE22 5HS Tel: (01670) 531200 Fax: (01670) 797617 E-mail: enquiries@ams-systems.co.uk
Altec Computer Cleaning, 4 Station Road, Belfast, BT4 1RE Tel: (028) 9047 1937 Fax: (028) 9065 0620
Computer Resale, 4 Mill Road, Cambridge, CB1 2AD Tel: (01223) 305007 Fax: (01223) 305008 E-mail: info@computerresale.co.uk
Econocom UK Ltd, Merevale House, Parkshot, Richmond, Surrey, TW9 2RG Tel: (020) 8948 8377 Fax: (020) 8948 8481 E-mail: lisa.dyne@econocom.be
Eurotek HSM, Manor Drive, Aylesbury, Buckinghamshire, HP20 1EW Tel: (01296) 435036 Fax: (01296) 431967 E-mail: james@eurotekhsm.co.uk
Evesham Ltd, 5 Glisson Road, Cambridge, CB1 2HA Tel: (01223) 323898 Fax: (01223) 322883
Genisys Group Ltd, Crockford Lane, Chineham, Basingstoke, Hampshire, RG24 8NA Tel: (01256) 816611 Fax: (01256) 816552 E-mail: sales@genisys.co.uk
Greengage Computer Products, Hilary House, Main Road, Woolverstone, Ipswich, IP9 1BA Tel: (01473) 780080 Fax: (01473) 780077 E-mail: sales@greengage.com
Hi Tec Bradford Ltd, Cliffe House Prospect Road, Otley Road, Bradford, West Yorkshire, BD3 0HT Tel: (01274) 626379 Fax: (01274) 626381 E-mail: sales@hi-tecbradford.co.uk
I S C Networks, Solar House, Blackstone Road, Stukeley Meadows Industrial Es, Huntingdon, Cambridgeshire, PE29 6EF Tel: (01480) 420000 Fax: (01480) 420080 E-mail: enquiries@iscnet.co.uk
I T Trading UK Ltd, Unit 4a Scotts Close, Batten Road, Downton Industrial Estate, Salisbury, SP5 3RA Tel: (01725) 513403 Fax: (01725) 513714 E-mail: info@ittrading.co.uk
J L A Computer Services Ltd, 1 Enterprise Court, Lakes Road, Braintree, Essex, CM7 3QS Tel: (01376) 343456 Fax: (01376) 321277 E-mail: sales@jla-computers.co.uk
Nexpress Ltd, Unit 16, Gelders Hall Road, Shepshed, Loughborough, Leicestershire, LE12 9NH Tel: (01509) 501100 Fax: (01509) 601186 E-mail: sales@nexpress.co.uk
On Line It Ltd, 34 Bedford Road, Hitchin, Hertfordshire, SG5 1HF Tel: (01462) 624624 Fax: (01462) 452452
One Step Beyond Ltd, 9-11 Bedford Street, Norwich, NR2 1AR Tel: (08703) 500252 Fax: (01603) 617378
Technology Services Group, Temple Point, Colton, Leeds, LS15 9JL Tel: 0113-237 5700 Fax: 0113-237 5701 E-mail: sales.north@tsgleeds.co.uk
Unitek Computers, Unitek House, Oxford Road, Tatling End, Gerrards Cross, Buckinghamshire, SL9 7BB Tel: (01753) 890500 Fax: (01753) 891916 E-mail: sales@chilternelectronics.co.uk

USED CONSTRUCTION PLANT OR EQUIPMENT

▶ Nottingham International Construction Equipment Ltd, 22 Hunt Close, Radcliffe-on-Trent, Nottingham, NG12 2EQ Tel: 0115-933 6008 Fax: 0115-933 6009 E-mail: sales@niceuk.co.uk

USED CONTROL SYSTEM SOFTWARE

▶ ControlLoop, 14 St. Davids, Newtongrange, Midlothian, EH22 4LG Tel: (0131) 4540499

USED DISPENSERS

Abtech Europe Ltd, Unit 3 East Quay Mews, East Quay, Bridgwater, Somerset, TA6 4AE Tel: (01278) 447080 Fax: (01278) 447090 E-mail: sales@abtech-europe.com

USED ELECTRONIC EQUIPMENT

Microlease plc, Unit 6 Whitefriars Trading Estate, Tudor Road, Harrow, Middlesex, HA3 5SS Tel: (020) 8420 0200 Fax: (020) 8420 0299 E-mail: info@microlease.com

USED ENVIRONMENTAL CHAMBERS

James Technical Services, 3 Talgarth Business Park, Trefecca Road, Talgarth, Brecon, Powys, LD3 0PQ Tel: (01874) 711209 Fax: (01874) 712010E-mail: sales@jts-test-chambers.co.uk

USED FORKLIFT TRUCKS

Ability Handling Ltd, Mangham Way, Rotherham, South Yorkshire, S61 4RL Tel: (01709) 821821 Fax: (01709) 821421 E-mail: sales@abilityhandlingltd.co.uk
Advanced Handling & Storage Ltd, Staindrop Road, West Auckland, Bishop Auckland, County Durham, DL14 9JY Tel: (01388) 832287 Fax: (01388) 832297 E-mail: advancedracking@aol.com
Bendigo Mitchell Ltd, 104 Windy Arbour, Kenilworth, Warwickshire, CV8 2BH Tel: (01926) 857626 Fax: (01926) 850609 E-mail: sales@bendigomitchell.com
Brindley Lift Truck Services Ltd, Unit 4, Aston Lane, Sharnford, Hinckley, Leicestershire, LE10 3PA Tel: (01455) 272800 Fax: (01455) 274712 E-mail: rhayes@lift-truck.co.uk
Butlins Fork Trucks Ltd, Unit 5 Bourne End, Kineton Road Industrial Estate, Southam, Warwickshire, CV47 0NA Tel: (01926) 812334 Fax: (01926) 811734
▶ D A C Handling Solutions Ltd, Oxford Street Industrial Park, Vulcan Road, Bilston, West Midlands, WV14 7JG Tel: (0845) 6013529 Fax: (0870) 1662904 E-mail: drock@dac-handling.co.uk
East Anglian Tractors Ltd, Arkesden Road, Clavering, Saffron Walden, Essex, CB11 4QU Tel: (01799) 550268 Fax: (01799) 550874 E-mail: sales@eatractors.co.uk
Groundwater Lifttrucks Ltd, Spurryhillock Industrial Estate, Broomhill Road, Stonehaven, Kincardineshire, AB39 2NH Tel: (01569) 763247 Fax: (01569) 766288 E-mail: sales@groundwater.uk.com
Liftruck Liftright, 49 Bankhall Street, Liverpool, L20 8JD Tel: 0151-933 6868 Fax: 0151-922 1110

USED FORKLIFT TRUCKS – *continued*

Mcleman Forklift Services Ltd, 15 Andover Street, Birmingham, B5 5RG Tel: 0121-643 1788 Fax: 0121-631 3725 E-mail: dgillespie@mclemanforklifts.co.uk
Meadows Lift Trucks, Ridley Road, Burnt Mills Industrial Estate, Basildon, Essex, SS13 1EG Tel: (01268) 724422 Fax: (01268) 725282
Newbury Fork Truck Centre Ltd, Unit 12 Bone Lane, Newbury, Berkshire, RG14 5SH Tel: (01635) 41635 Fax: (01635) 35388
Newtown Sideloaders Southern Ltd, 20 Windsor Avenue, Leighton Buzzard, Bedfordshire, LU7 1AP Tel: (01525) 378434 Fax: (01525) 378434
Pareco Fork Trucks Service Ltd, Unit 13 Park Road Industrial Estate, Park Road, Swanley, Kent, BR8 8AH Tel: (01322) 613222 Fax: (01322) 615028 E-mail: sales@pareco.co.uk
R & S Fork Trucks, 6 Ardmore Road, South Ockendon, Essex, RM15 5TH Tel: (01708) 851444 Fax: (01708) 557076 E-mail: randsforklifts@aveley.fsnet.co.uk
Waveney Fork Trucks Ltd, Whapload Road, Lowestoft, Suffolk, NR32 1UL Tel: (01502) 569106 Fax: (01502) 508273 E-mail: info@waveneylifttrucks.co.uk

USED MACHINE TOOLS

A G Machine Tool Technology Ltd, Cranbrooke House, 143a Main Street, Witchford, Ely, Cambridgeshire, CB6 2HP Tel: (01353) 669909 Fax: (01353) 661093 E-mail: sales@ag-machine-tools.com
B W Machine Tools, 4 Lyon Close, Wigston, Leicestershire, LE18 2BJ Tel: 0116-288 6070 Fax: 0116-288 0014 E-mail: toolsbw@aol.com
P. Barraclough & Associates Ltd, 48 Top Lane, Copmanthorpe, York, YO23 3UJ Tel: (01904) 704065 Fax: (01904) 700496
▶ C N C Check Machine Tools Ltd, Kitchener Road, Leicester, LE5 4AT Tel: 0116-274 1044 Fax: 0116-274 1046 E-mail: mail@cnccheckmachinetools.co.uk
Capital Equipment & Machinery Ltd, Mill Mead, Staines, Middlesex, TW18 4UQ Tel: (01784) 456151 Fax: (01784) 466481 E-mail: sales@capital-equipment.com
Clark, Regent Buildings, Tuttle Hill, Nuneaton, Warwickshire, CV10 0HU Tel: (024) 7638 2686 Fax: (024) 7638 8812 E-mail: sales@clarkmachinery.com
▶ Created, Newhouses Road, Broxburn, West Lothian, EH52 5MZ Tel: (01506) 853587 Fax: (01506) 856106
Denis Grimshaw Machinery Ltd, PO Box 64, Droitwich, Worcestershire, WR9 0JR Tel: (01905) 621789 Fax: (01905) 621384 E-mail: sales@grimshaw.co.uk
Emi-Mec, Unit E2 Doulton Road Trading Estate, Doulton Road, Rowley Regis, West Midlands, B65 8JQ Tel: (01384) 633968 Fax: (01384) 633946 E-mail: sales@emi-mec.eu
▶ Ems Ltd, Grimshaw Street, Burnley, Lancashire, BB11 2AZ Tel: (07986) 782978 Fax: (01282) 860638 E-mail: mtools@btinternet.com
Engineering Supplies Peterborough Ltd, Papyrus Road, Peterborough, PE4 5BH Tel: (01733) 577899 Fax: (01733) 321975 E-mail: engsupp@aol.com
Peter Hill Machine Sales, PO Box 3402, Birmingham, B44 8DG Tel: 0121-249 7272 Fax: 0121-244 2378 E-mail: info@peterhillmachinesales.com
Larchwood Machine Tools Ltd, 61 Blue Lake Road, Dorridge, Solihull, West Midlands, B93 8BH Tel: (01564) 776234 Fax: (01564) 779270 E-mail: sales@larchwoodltd.co.uk
Major Machine Tools Ltd, Poyntz House, Harlestone Road, Chapel Brampton, Northampton, NN6 8AW Tel: (01604) 844665 Fax: (01604) 821108 E-mail: sales@majormachinetools.com
Mid-Bucks Machine Tools Ltd, PO Box 15, Chinnor, Oxfordshire, OX39 4AT Tel: (01844) 352329 Fax: (01844) 352348 E-mail: midbucks@nildram.co.uk
Nelson M Green & Sons Ltd, Rippingale Road, Kirkby Underwood, Bourne, Lincolnshire, PE10 0SH Tel: (01778) 440285 Fax: (01778) 440133 E-mail: mail@nelsongreen.com
▶ Oldfield Machine Tools Ltd, 10 Bridge Street, Cambuslang, Glasgow, G72 7ED Tel: 0141-641 0440 Fax: 0141-646 2181 E-mail: mail@oldfield.co.uk
P & H Machine Tool Co. Ltd, 9 Elm Croft, Little Paxton, St. Neots, Cambridgeshire, PE19 6QP Tel: (01480) 212973 Fax: (01480) 474848 E-mail: info@phmachinetools.com
Phoenix Machinery Ltd, Riverside Studios, Mill Lane, Dronfield, Derbyshire, S18 2XL Tel: (01246) 290027 Fax: (01246) 290093
R D Barrett Small Tools, Brow Mills Industrial Estate, Brighouse Road, Hipperholme, Halifax, West Yorkshire, HX3 8DD Tel: (01422) 205828 Fax: (01422) 202358 E-mail: j.n.rushby@supanet.com
Steven Mooney Machinery, Edwards House, Marchants Way, Burgess Hill, West Sussex, RH15 8QY Tel: (01444) 245414 Fax: (01444) 247518 E-mail: stevenmooney@compuserve.com.
Style Machine Tools Ltd, 30a Centurion Industrial Estate, Centurion Way, Farington, Leyland, PR25 4GU Tel: (01772) 624114 Fax: (01722) 624114 E-mail: enquiries@stylemachinetools.co.uk
Tooling Direct Ltd, Salford House, 535 Lichfield Road, Birmingham, B6 7SP Tel: 0121-327 1952 Fax: 0121-327 1954 E-mail: sales@tooling-direct.com
Traktools, Old Buckenham, Old Buckenham, Attleborough, Norfolk, NR17 1PG Tel: (07860) 521375 Fax: (01953) 861126 E-mail: track.tools@virin.net
Uniprize Machine Tools Ltd, A3 Bankfield Industrial Estate, Sandy Lane, Stockport, Cheshire, SK5 7SE Tel: 0161-429 6161 Fax: 0161-429 0606 E-mail: uniprize@uniprize.freeserve.co.uk
Williams Machinery, 173 Nine Mile Ride, Finchampstead, Wokingham, Berkshire, RG40 4JD Tel: 0118-973 7004 Fax: 0118-973 7004 E-mail: bdwilliams@tinyworld.co.uk
YMT Ltd, Brympton Way, Lynx West Trading Estate, Yeovil, Somerset, BA20 2HP Tel: (01935) 428375 Fax: (01935) 432684 E-mail: sales@ymtltd.co.uk

USED MINI EXCAVATORS

▶ Construction Plant Services (SW) Ltd, Nordic House, Longships Road, Cardiff, CF10 4RP Tel: (029) 2048 2002 Fax: (029) 2048 0876 E-mail: info@cpsltd.co.uk
▶ Plant Parts International Ltd, 10 High Street, Pensnett, Kingswinford, West Midlands, DY6 8XD Tel: (01384) 408950 Fax: (01384) 404600 E-mail: sales@dig-dog.com

USED MOTOR VEHICLE COMPONENTS

▶ Ace Motors, Victoria Mill, Alliance Street, Accrington, Lancashire, BB5 2RT Tel: (01254) 232662 E-mail: info@acemotorsbaxenden.co.uk

USED MOTOR VEHICLES

▶ Car Nation Yaxley, Station Road Garage, Broadway, Yaxley, Peterborough, PE7 3EG Tel: (01733) 243424 E-mail: ishy@carnationcars.com
▶ Eddies Autos Ltd, Buckrose Street, Huddersfield, HD1 6HB Tel: 078 76498676 E-mail: edward@eddiesautos.co.uk
▶ Hertz Car Sales, Unit 2 Aire Place Mills, Kirkstall Road, Chipping Warden, Banbury, Oxfordshire, OX17 1LL Tel: (01295) 667000 Fax: (01295) 667017
▶ Hertz Rent A Car Ltd, 34-62 Staines Road, Hounslow, TW3 3LZ Tel: (020) 8570 5000 Fax: (020) 8750 3978

USED OFFICE FURNITURE

▶ Spar, 1 62 Swindon Road, Cheltenham, Gloucestershire, GL50 4AY Tel: (01242) 234323 Fax: (01242) 234323

USED OR RECONDITIONED GENERATOR SETS

Rollo UK Ltd, 2 Balm Road Industrial Estate, Beza Street, Leeds, LS10 2BG Tel: 0113-272 0444 Fax: 0113-272 0499 E-mail: info@rollouk.com

USED OR RECONDITIONED PROCESS PLANT AND MACHINERY

Butler & England Ltd, 20 The Ferns, Larkfield, Aylesford, Kent, ME20 6NE Tel: (01732) 849247 Fax: (020) 8244 9463 E-mail: info@butlerandengland.com

USED OSCILLOSCOPES

Telnet, 1 Stoney Court, Hotchkiss Way, Binley Industrial Estate, Coventry, CV3 2RL Tel: (024) 7665 0702 Fax: (024) 7665 0773 E-mail: sales@telnet.uk.com

USED PLASTIC MACHINERY

Plasplant Ltd, Unit 4 Oakhanger Farm, Oakhanger, Bordon, Hampshire, GU35 9JA Tel: (01420) 473013 Fax: (01420) 475152 E-mail: sales@plasplant.com

USED PRINTED CIRCUIT BOARD (PCB) ASSEMBLY EQUIPMENT

S S U Equipment Ltd, Friars Mount, Friars, Jedburgh, Roxburghshire, TD8 6BN Tel: (01835) 862481 Fax: (01835) 863712 E-mail: davesharman@ssuequipment.co.uk

USED PRINTING MACHINES

S G M, 23 Chelwood Drive, Leeds, LS8 2AT Tel: 0113-393 1999 Fax: 0113-393 1919 E-mail: sales@sgm.co.uk

USED QUAD BIKES

▶ Amazon ATV Ltd (Quad Sales & Hire 6-6yrs), Green Street Industrial Estate, 1 Green Street, Eastbourne, East Sussex, BN21 1QN Tel: (01323) 645564 Fax: (01323) 645564 E-mail: elainechild@tiscali.co.uk

USED ROLLING MILL PLANT AND EQUIPMENT

McMillan Conroy Machinery, PO Box 3081, Walsall, WS2 9SS Tel: (01922) 725444 Fax: (01922) 640336 E-mail: sales@mcmillanconroy.co.uk

USED RUBBER PROCESSING INJECTION MOULDERS

▶ Lock Way Plastics, Highfield Mills, Heaton Street, Cleckheaton, West Yorkshire, BD19 3TN Tel: (01274) 869439 Fax: (01274) 869428 E-mail: sales@lockway.co.uk
Optical Products Ltd, 74-75 Brunner Road, London, E17 7NW Tel: (020) 8520 4047 Fax: (020) 8520 6593 E-mail: sales@ultrasolar.com
▶ R D Engineering, 1130 Melton Road, Syston, Leicester, LE7 2HA Tel: 0116-260 7567

USED SAILING YACHTS

▶ Falmouth School Of Sailing, The Boat Park, Grove Place, Falmouth, Cornwall, TR11 4AU Tel: (01326) 211311 Fax: (01326) 211311 E-mail: sales@falmouthschoolofsailing.com
▶ Mcneil Marine, 1 Tan Y Banc, Graig, Burry Port, Dyfed, SA16 0DT Tel: (01554) 833233 E-mail: surveys@mcneilmarine.com

USED SHEET METALWORKING MACHINERY

Moore Machinery International Ltd, 68 Glover Street, Birmingham, B9 4EL Tel: (0845) 2307040 Fax: (0845) 2307050 E-mail: mooremac@globalnet.co.uk
Phoenix Machinery Ltd, Riverside Studios, Mill Lane, Dronfield, Derbyshire, S18 2XL Tel: (01246) 290027 Fax: (01246) 290093
Sampson International Machine Tools, Keeley Lane, Wootton, Bedford, MK43 9HS Tel: (01234) 851200 Fax: (01234) 851123 E-mail: sales@sampsonmachinetools.com

USED SPARK EROSION MACHINES

Eurospark Cutting Tools, Ashby Road, Stapleton, Leicester, LE9 8JE Tel: (01455) 292002 Fax: (01455) 293002 E-mail: sales@eurospark.co.uk

USED TEST EQUIPMENT

Cooke International, Unit 9 Ford La Business Park, Ford, Arundel, West Sussex, BN18 0UZ Tel: (01243) 555590 Fax: (01243) 551455
Orix Rentec Ltd, 9 Falcon Park Industrial Estate, Neasden Lane, London, NW10 1RZ Tel: (020) 8208 8600 Fax: (020) 8208 8601 E-mail: info@orixrentec.co.uk
Telford Electronics, Hoo Farm, Hoo, Telford, Shropshire, TF6 6DJ Tel: (01952) 605451 Fax: (01952) 677978 E-mail: telfordelectronics@btinternet.com
Telnet, 1 Stoney Court, Hotchkiss Way, Binley Industrial Estate, Coventry, CV3 2RL Tel: (024) 7665 0702 Fax: (024) 7665 0773 E-mail: sales@telnet.uk.com

USED TRAILERS

▶ Dawson's Trailers, Sunny-Vale, Far Westhouse, Ingleton, Carnforth, Lancashire, LA6 3NR Tel: (01524) 241372 E-mail: sydney@dawsonstrailers.f9.co.uk

UTILITIES CONTRACTORS

British Energy Ltd, 3 Redwood Crescent, East Kilbride, Glasgow, G74 5PR Tel: (01355) 262000 Fax: (01355) 262626
E C M (UK) Ltd, The Old Yard, Rectory Lane, Brasted, Westerham, Kent, TN16 1JP Tel: (01959) 569999 Fax: (01959) 563333
J Browne Construction Co. Ltd, Beacon House, North Circular Road, London, NW10 0HF Tel: (020) 8451 4111 Fax: (020) 8459 6879 E-mail: info@jbconstruction.co.uk
▶ Morgan Est plc, Morgan Estate House, Corporation Street, Rugby, Warwickshire, CV21 2DW Tel: (01788) 534500 Fax: (01788) 534579 E-mail: info@morganest.com
Tracerco, Coxwald Way, Belasis Hall Technology Park, Billingham, Cleveland, TS23 1LB Tel: (01642) 370620 Fax: (01642) 370704 E-mail: tracerco@massey.com
Viridian Group Ltd, 120 Malone Road, Belfast, BT9 5HT Tel: (028) 9066 8416 Fax: (028) 9068 9117 E-mail: sales@viridiangroup.co.uk

UTILITIES MAGAZINES

Utility Week, Quadrant House, The Quadrant, Sutton, Surrey, SM2 5AS Tel: (020) 8652 3500

UTILITY COMMERCIAL VEHICLE BODIES

▶ Advanced Body Repairs Ltd, Willow Road, Yaxley, Peterborough, PE7 3HT Tel: (01733) 246970 Fax: (01733) 246979 E-mail: matt.lynn@lawrencedavid.co.uk
▶ LD Trailer Sales Ltd, Munroe House, Ringtail Court, Burscough Industrial Estate, Burscough, Lancashire, L40 8LB Tel: 01704 893009 Fax: 01704 896660 E-mail: sales@ldtrailersales.co.uk

V CLAMPS

Neophix Engineering Co. Ltd, Devonshire House, West Lane, Keighley, West Yorkshire, BD21 2LP Tel: (01535) 667382 Fax: (01535) 680825 E-mail: info@neophix.co.uk
Teconnex Ltd, Bronte Works, Chesham Street, Keighley, West Yorkshire, BD21 4LG Tel: (01535) 691122 Fax: (01535) 691133 E-mail: sales@teconnex.com

V LINK BELTING

Fenner Drives Ltd, Hudson Road, Leeds, LS9 7DF Tel: (0870) 7577007 Fax: 0113-248 9656 E-mail: sales@fennerdrives.com

V PULLEYS

Alldrives Ltd, Unit 6 Mead Park River Way, Harlow, Essex, CM20 2SE Tel: (01279) 445576 Fax: (01279) 425554 E-mail: alldrives@btconnect.co.uk

VACCUM FORMED CERAMIC FIBRE PRODUCTS

Wade Ceramics Ltd, Royal Victoria Pottery, Westport Road, Burslem, Stoke-On-Trent, ST6 4AG Tel: (01782) 577321 Fax: (01782) 575195 E-mail: alan.keenan@wade.co.uk

VACUUM BELLOWS

Palatine Precision Ltd, Airport Industrial Estate, 45 Laker Road, Rochester, Kent, ME1 3QX Tel: (01634) 684571 Fax: (01634) 200836 E-mail: sales@palatineprecision.co.uk

VACUUM BOXES

Brandon Hire P.L.C., 184 New Road, Rainham, Essex, RM13 8RS Tel: (01708) 553541 Fax: (01708) 521010

VACUUM CLEANER BAGS

G. Hunt Filtration Ltd, Portland Mill, Portland Street South, Ashton-Under-Lyne, Lancashire, OL6 7SX Tel: 0161-330 7337 Fax: 0161-343 2365 E-mail: sales@hunt-filtration.co.uk
▶ TML International Ltd, Unit 8 Water Line Estate, Whitby, North Yorkshire, YO21 1UY Tel: (01904) 700500 Fax: (01904) 700600 E-mail: rayw@tregwaremanufacturing.co.uk

VACUUM CLEANER COMPONENTS/SPARE PARTS/ WEARING PARTS MANUFRS

Ashcroft Agencies Ltd, 14a Airfield Road, Christchurch, Dorset, BH23 3TG Tel: (01202) 499945 Fax: (01202) 499207
Gias Services, Brightmet Industrial Estate, Bury Road, Bolton, BL2 6PU Tel: (0870) 5990011 Fax: (01204) 556149
Vacuum Hospital, 4 Mckeown Street, Lisburn, County Antrim, BT28 1BD Tel: (028) 9266 1126

VACUUM CLEANERS, *See also headings for particular types*

Ainsworth's Vacuum Cleaner Sales & Service, Service, 4 Watford Street, Blackburn, BB1 7LD Tel: (01254) 691000
Aqua-Air Ltd, 219 Ashley Road, Hale, Altrincham, Cheshire, WA15 9SZ Tel: 0161-926 9595 Fax: 0161-929 7345 E-mail: sales@aqua-air.co.uk
ARCO West Bromwich, PO Box 2210, West Bromwich, West Midlands, B71 1DQ Tel: 0121-500 4444 Fax: 0121-553 7554 E-mail: westbromwich.branch@arco.co.uk
Ashcroft Agencies Ltd, 14a Airfield Road, Christchurch, Dorset, BH23 3TG Tel: (01202) 499945 Fax: (01202) 499207
▶ C B A Cleaning Solutions, 6-7 Bunting Road, Bury St. Edmunds, Suffolk, IP32 7BX Tel: (01284) 702233 Fax: (01284) 749300
Clandrex Cleaning Ltd, PO Box 14, Grantham, Lincolnshire, NG31 9BL Tel: (01476) 577972 Fax: (01476) 590862
Green & White Ltd, 112 Fortune Green Road, London, NW6 1DH Tel: (020) 7794 7783 Fax: (020) 7433 1143 E-mail: green.white.ltd@lineone.net
J & J Services, 29 Dunville Road, Bedford, MK40 4DY Tel: (01234) 378289 Fax: (01234) 325479 E-mail: lindopjj@aol.com'
London Kbe, 562 Lordship Lane, London, N22 5BY Tel: (020) 8889 9709
Midland Vacum Cleaner Services, 1477-1479 Pershore Road, Stirchley, Birmingham, B30 2JL Tel: 0121-458 7185 Fax: 0121-458 4226 E-mail: enquries@midlandvac.co.uk
Pinnacle Power Equipment Ltd, 235 Berwick Avenue, Slough, SL1 4QT Tel: (01753) 576655
Southwest Service Centre, Unit 2 Merlin Business Park, Fair Oak Close, Clyst Honiton, Exeter, EX5 2UL Tel: (0800) 7839520 Fax: (01392) 445494
Starbrite Chemicals Ltd, X L House, Rutherford Way, Crawley, West Sussex, RH10 9PB Tel: (01293) 434250 Fax: (01293) 434252 E-mail: sales@starbrite.co.uk
Total Home Environment, Swallow House, Cotsworld Business Village, London Road, Moreton-in-Marsh, Gloucestershire, GL56 0JQ Tel: (0845) 2600123 Fax: (01608) 652490 E-mail: info@beamvac.co.uk

VACUUM CLEANERS, COMMERCIAL

▶ Magic Maids, 7 Charmian Avenue, Stanmore, Middlesex, HA7 1LL Tel: (020) 8931 8921 E-mail: sales@magic-maids.co.uk

VACUUM CLEANING SYSTEMS, *See also headings for particular types*

Tecserv, Unit 7, Parsons Green Estate, Boulton Road, Stevenage, Hertfordshire, SG1 4QG Tel: (01438) 750905 Fax: (01438) 315270 E-mail: macserv-fcm@btconnect.com

VACUUM COATING EQUIPMENT

Gencoa Ltd, Physics Road, Liverpool, L24 9HP Tel: 0151-486 4466 Fax: 0151-486 4488 E-mail: sales@gencoa.com
Kurt J Lesker Co. Ltd, Ivyhouse Lane, Hastings, East Sussex, TN35 4NN Tel: (01424) 719101 Fax: (01424) 421160 E-mail: sales@lesker.com
Oxford Instruments Plasma Technology Ltd, North End Road, Yatton, Bristol, BS49 4AP Tel: (01934) 837000 Fax: (01934) 837001 E-mail: plasma.technology@oxinst.co.uk

VACUUM COATING SERVICES

Morplate Ltd, Hammerton Street, Burnley, Lancashire, BB11 1LE Tel: (01282) 428571 Fax: (01282) 413600

VACUUM CONVEYOR SYSTEMS

Dust Control, 1b Pury Business Park, Alderton Road, Paulerspury, Towcester, Northamptonshire, NN12 7LS Tel: (01327) 811510 Fax: (01327) 811413 E-mail: sales@dustcontrol.co.uk

VACUUM COOLANT RECYCLING EQUIPMENT

Freddy Products Ltd, Units 6-7, Goodwood Rd, Pershore, Worcestershire, WR10 2JL Tel: (01386) 561113 Fax: (01386) 556401 E-mail: sales@freddy-products.co.uk

VACUUM CUP MANUFRS

▶ Hamson Engineering, 18 Braefoot Avenue, Milngavie, Glasgow, G62 6JZ Tel: 0141-956 4144 Fax: 0141-956 6946

VACUUM ENGINEERING SERVICES

M G Production Engineering, The Paddocks, Rowley Lane, Barnet, Hertfordshire, EN5 3HW Tel: (020) 8441 3380 Fax: (020) 8441 3432
V_Tech Engineering, Mandy Cottage, Maidenhead Road, Billingbear, Wokingham, Berkshire, RG40 5RT Tel: (01344) 867228 Fax: (01344) 482244 E-mail: v_techuk@yahoo.co.uk

VACUUM EQUIPMENT COMPONENTS

Air Systems Controls Ltd, 51-52 The Bus Development Cour, Stafford Park 4, Telford, Shropshire, TF3 3BA Tel: (01952) 290959 Fax: (01952) 292647 E-mail: sales@airsystemcontrols.com
Vacucom Ltd, Unit 4B, Aspect Court, Cannel Row, Silverdale Enterprise Park, Silverdale, Newcastle, Staffordshire, ST5 6SS Tel: (01782) 660007 Fax: (01782) 660009 E-mail: sales@vacucom.co.uk

VACUUM FILTERS

Piab Ltd, PO Box 43, Loughborough, Leicestershire, LE12 8NY Tel: (01509) 814280 Fax: (01509) 814647E-mail: sales@piab.co.uk
Thermwood Europe Ltd, Unit 3, Evans Business Centre, Belmont Industrial Estate, Durham, DH1 1SE Tel: 0191-383 2883 Fax: 0191-383 2884 E-mail: sales@thermwood.co.uk

VACUUM FLANGES

Instrument Technology Ltd, Menzies Road, Ponswood Industrial Estate, St. Leonards-On-Sea, East Sussex, TN38 9BB Tel: (01424) 442121 Fax: (01424) 719696 E-mail: sales@itl-vacuum.com
V A T Vacuum Products Ltd, Edmund House, Rugby Road, Leamington Spa, Warwickshire, CV32 6EL Tel: (01926) 452753 Fax: (01926) 452758 E-mail: uk@vatvalve.com

VACUUM FLASKS/JUGS

Day Impex Ltd, Station Road, Earls Colne, Colchester, CO6 2ER Tel: (01787) 223232 Fax: (01787) 224171 E-mail: general@day-impex.co.uk

VACUUM FORMED PACKAGING

British Falcon Plastics, Kemmings Close, Paignton, Devon, TQ4 7TW Tel: (01803) 551313 Fax: (01803) 664548

VACUUM FORMED PLASTIC MOULDING ELECTROSTATIC FLOCKING FINISHING

D C A Elect, Unit 3D, Herald Industrial Estate, Hedge End, Southampton, SO30 2JW Tel: (01489) 799927 Fax: (01489) 798770 E-mail: sales@flocking.biz

VACUUM FORMED PLASTIC MOULDING FINISHING

Daro Products Ltd, Churfield Road, Churchfield Industrial Estate, Sudbury, Suffolk, CO10 2YA Tel: (01787) 881191 Fax: (01787) 374291 E-mail: sales@daroproducts.co.uk
Fathomtree Ltd, 5 The Midway, Nottingham, NG7 2TS Tel: 0115-986 0096 Fax: 0115-986 0210 E-mail: sales@fathomtreeltd.com
Hurst Green Plastics Ltd, 1st Floor, Bowland House, The Sidings Business Park, Whalley, Clitheroe, Lancashire, BB7 9SE Tel: 01254 825588 Fax: 01254 824521 E-mail: info@hurstgreenplastics.com

VACUUM FORMED PLASTIC MOULDING TRIMMING

A A C Cyroma Ltd, C P L House, Beaumont Road, Banbury, Oxfordshire, OX16 1RJ Tel: (01295) 759200 Fax: (01295) 270614

VACUUM FORMED PLASTIC PRODUCTS

A A C Spectrum Ltd, Brierley Park Close, Sutton-in-Ashfield, Nottinghamshire, NG17 3FW Tel: (01623) 440111 Fax: (01623) 444670 E-mail: nottingham@aacgroup.co.uk
A C C Plastics, Unit A Peacock View, Fenton Industrial Estate, Stoke-on-Trent, ST4 2XJ Tel: (01782) 201601 Fax: (01782) 201782 E-mail: sales@accplastics.co.uk
A & M Plastic Solutions, Wickham Road, Fareham, Hampshire, PO16 7JB Tel: (01329) 225900 Fax: (01329) 823840 E-mail: sales@amplastic.com
A P Hollings & Sons Ltd, 14 Brook Road Industrial Estate, Sirdar Road, Rayleigh, Essex, SS6 7XF Tel: (01268) 770681 Fax: (01268) 775144 E-mail: andy@aphollings.co.uk
Accuvac Prototypes Ltd, Unit F2 Watlington Industrial Estate, Cuxham Road, Watlington, Oxfordshire, OX49 5LU Tel: (01491) 613161 Fax: (01491) 613161 E-mail: enquiries@accuvac.co.uk
Adept Vacuum Formers & Patterns Ltd, 141 Waterside Road, Hamilton, Leicester, LE5 1TL Tel: 0116-246 0552 Fax: 0116-246 0987 E-mail: enquiries@adeptvp.freeserve.co.uk
Aerovac Ltd, 4 Tetbury Industrial Estate, Cirencester Road, Tetbury, Gloucestershire, GL8 8EZ Tel: (01666) 502546 Fax: (01666) 503009 E-mail: aerovac@saqnet.co.uk
Algram Groups, Eastern Wood Road, Langage Business Park, Plympton, Plymouth, PL7 5ET Tel: (01752) 342388 Fax: (01752) 342482 E-mail: sales@algram.com
Allison Plastics & Paper Ltd, New Pudsey Square, Stanningley, Pudsey, West Yorkshire, LS28 6PX Tel: 0113-256 6435 Fax: 0113-257 5337
Ampco, Unit 4 Prime Buildings, Daux Road, Billingshurst, West Sussex, RH14 9SJ Tel: (01403) 780420 Fax: (01403) 786486 E-mail: sales@ampco.co.uk
Antplace Ltd, Ford Airfield Industrial Estate, Ford, Arundel, West Sussex, BN18 0HY Tel: (01903) 714402 Fax: (01903) 732065
Apollo Plastics, 62 St James Street, Hull, HU3 2DH Tel: (01482) 325394 Fax: (01482) 229826 E-mail: sales@apolloplastics.co.uk
Big Bear Plastic Products Ltd, Fantastic Works, Wassage Way, Hampton Lovett, Droitwich, Worcestershire, WR9 0NX Tel: (01905) 792500 Fax: (01905) 792501 E-mail: louises@big-bear.co.uk
Brisbay Plastics Ltd, Adamsez Industrial Estate, Scotswood Road, Newcastle upon Tyne, NE15 6XA Tel: 0191-274 4774 Fax: 0191-228 0146 E-mail: steve@brisbay.co.uk
Carlon Plastics Leicester Ltd, 128 Fairfax Road, Leicester, LE4 9EL Tel: 0116-276 9562 Fax: 0116-276 1267 E-mail: chris@carlonplastics.co.uk
Cheltec Ltd, Unit B2B, Horsted Keynes Industrial Estate, Horsted Keynes, Haywards Heath, West Sussex, RH17 7BE Tel: (01342) 811303 Fax: (01342) 811802 E-mail: mike@cheltec.co.uk
Daro Products Ltd, Churfield Road, Churchfield Industrial Estate, Sudbury, Suffolk, CO10 2YA Tel: (01787) 881191 Fax: (01787) 374291 E-mail: sales@daroproducts.co.uk
Dimension Development, Komet Works, Sawday Street, Leicester, LE2 7JW Tel: 0116-255 3090 Fax: 0116-255 3092 E-mail: dimensiondev@btconnect.com
E P Packaging Ltd, Queensway Industrial Estate, Queensway, Wrexham, Clwyd, LL13 8YR Tel: (01978) 346600 Fax: (01978) 290259
E & P Plastics Ltd, Gore Road Industrial Estate, New Milton, Hampshire, BH25 6TB Tel: (01425) 611026 Fax: (01425) 615500
E S P Plastics Ltd, Prospect Road, Crook, County Durham, DL15 8JL Tel: (01388) 765400 Fax: (01388) 765300 E-mail: sales@esp-plastics.co.uk
Eyrevac Plastics Ltd, 7-15 Hungerford Road, Bristol, BS4 5HU Tel: 0117-971 5480 Fax: 0117-972 3593 E-mail: mailbox@eyrevac.co.uk
James Fleming Plastics Ltd, 7 Linden Place, Glasgow, G13 1EF Tel: 0141-959 9765 Fax: 0141-954 6693
Focal Plastics Ltd, 34-40 Cutlers Road, South Woodham Ferrers, Chelmsford, CM3 5XJ Tel: (01245) 322788 Fax: (01245) 323194 E-mail: sales@focalplastics.co.uk
Glendale Plastics Ltd, 16 Faraday Road, Glenrothes, Fife, KY6 2RU Tel: (01592) 774888 Fax: (01592) 771680 E-mail: sales@glendaleplastics.co.uk
Global Vacuum Forming Ltd, Vedonis Works, Leicester Road, Lutterworth, Leicestershire, LE17 4HD Tel: (01455) 556891 Fax: (01455) 556099 E-mail: sales@gvf.co.uk
Graphic International Display Ltd, 31-33 Fowler Road, Hainault Industrial Estate, Ilford, Essex, IG6 3UT Tel: (020) 8500 5544 Fax: (020) 8500 7197
Hamilton Plastic Packaging, 18 Galowhill Road, Brackmills Industrial Estate, Northampton, NN4 7EE Tel: (01604) 766329 Fax: (01604) 701790 E-mail: sales@hamiltonpp.com
Holders Ltd, 55-59 Bensham Grove, Thornton Heath, Surrey, CR7 8DD Tel: (07802) 377122 Fax: (020) 8653 3011 E-mail: sales@holders.ltd.uk
J & R Plastics Ltd, 30 Montipilier Rise, Golders Green, London, NW11 9DS Tel: (07957) 627143 E-mail: jrplastics@hotmail.com
Jilks Plastics Ltd, 31 Trowers Way, Redhill, RH1 2LH Tel: (01737) 779799 Fax: (01737) 779800 E-mail: sales@jilksplasticsltd.co.uk
Keyline Associates Ltd, High Meres Road, Leicester, LE4 9LZ Tel: 0116-276 1371 Fax: 0116-274 1570 E-mail: display@keline.co.uk
Kingswood Plastics Ltd, 9 Corbetts Passage, London, SE16 2BD Tel: (020) 7237 6181 Fax: (020) 7252 2842 E-mail: sales@kingswood-plastics.co.uk
Leeds Vacuum Formers Ltd, 4 National Road, Hunslet Business Park, Leeds, LS10 1TD Tel: 0113-277 3800 Fax: 0113-277 5263 E-mail: sales@leedsvacform.com
Leeways Packaging Services Ltd, Lobstock, Churcham, Gloucester, GL2 8AN Tel: (01452) 750487 Fax: (01452) 750653 E-mail: info@leeways.co.uk
Linecross Group Ltd, Station Road, South Luffenham, Oakham, Leicestershire, LE15 8NG Tel: (01780) 720720 Fax: (01780) 722333 E-mail: kgday@linex.uk.com
Mident Trading Co., Remmets House, Lord Street, Bury, Lancashire, BL9 0RE Tel: 0161-761 6060 Fax: 0161-763 1005 E-mail: midentuk@aol.com
T.P. Millen Co. Ltd, 4 Stuart Way, East Grinstead, West Sussex, RH19 4RS Tel: (0787) 6658207 Fax: (01342) 335747 E-mail: tmillen@vodafone.net
Mongoose Plastics Ltd, 57-58 Nasmyth Road, Glenrothes, Fife, KY6 2SD Tel: (01592) 774800 Fax: (01592) 775032 E-mail: george@mongoose-plastics.co.uk
Moorland Plastics Barnsley, Moorland Avenue, Barnsley, South Yorkshire, S70 6PQ Tel: (01226) 242753 Fax: (01226) 293401 E-mail: moorlandplastics@barnsley.gov.uk
Newdev UK, 52-54 Snow Hill, Melton Mowbray, Leicestershire, LE13 1PH Tel: (01664) 569805 Fax: (01664) 481581 E-mail: newdevuk@aol.com
North West Prototypes, The Little Mill, Palatine Street, Denton, Manchester, M34 3LY Tel: 0161-320 5529 Fax: 0161-335 0928
Novo Designs, Church Farm, Eyeworth, Sandy, Bedfordshire, SG19 2HH Tel: (01767) 631117
P 15 Plastics Ltd, 161 Waterside Road, Hamilton, Leicester, LE5 1TL Tel: 0116-276 1495 Fax: 0116-246 0489 E-mail: info@p15plastics.co.uk
P J Packaging Ltd, 20 High Street, Wem, Shrewsbury, SY4 5DL Tel: (01939) 235073 Fax: (01939) 235074 E-mail: sales@pjpackaging.ltd.uk
Pactiv Europe Ltd, 4 Young Square, Brucefield Industrial Estate, Livingston, West Lothian, EH54 9BX Tel: (01506) 462247 Fax: (01506) 415458 E-mail: sales@pactiv.com
Plastic Promotions, Unit 1 Carn Industrial Area, Portadown, Craigavon, County Armagh, BT63 5YY Tel: (028) 3835 6600 Fax: (028) 3835 6601 E-mail: gilbert@plasticpromotion.co.uk
Plastics Manchester Ltd, Plasman Industrial Centre, Peter Moss Way, Manchester, M19 3PX Tel: 0161-257 2929 Fax: 0161-257 3203 E-mail: info@thompson-plastics-group.co.uk
Polyfab & Formings Ltd, Hindley Green Business Park Leigh Road, Hindley, Wigan, Lancashire, WN2 3LL Tel: (01942) 523617 Fax: (01942) 523533 E-mail: sales@polyfab.co.uk
Promotional Forming & Finishing, Moorend House, Highfield Road, Idle, Bradford, West Yorkshire, BD10 8QH Tel: (01274) 620205 Fax: (01274) 620209 E-mail: sales@pff.uk.com
R & R Formings Ltd, Unit 5 Riparian Way, Cross Hills, Keighley, West Yorkshire, BD20 7BW Tel: (01535) 614010 Fax: (01535) 614019 E-mail: richard@rrfoodbox.co.uk
Ridgeway Plastics (Iver) Ltd, Unit 7B Waldeck House, Waldeck Road, Maidenhead, Berkshire, SL6 8BR Tel: (01628) 636621 Fax: (01628) 636621
S.J.M. Eurostat (U.K.) Ltd, Unit 4b, Bramhall Moor Industrial Park, Hazel Grove, Stockport, Cheshire, SK7 5BW Tel: 0161-456 6088 Fax: 0161-456 6089 E-mail: sjm@sjmeurostat.co.uk
Sarik Vacform, Unit 8-9 Pixash Business Centre, Pixash Lane, Keynsham, Bristol, BS31 1TP Tel: 0117-986 0404 Fax: 0117-986 0424 E-mail: info@sarik-vacform.com
Screencraft Publicity Hull, Reservoir Road, Hull, HU6 7QD Tel: (01482) 499999 Fax: (01482) 499994 E-mail: info@screencraft-display.co.uk
Screenprint Plus Ltd, Morton Peto Road, Harfreys Industrial Estate, Great Yarmouth, Norfolk, NR31 0LT Tel: (01493) 440292 Fax: (01493) 440269 E-mail: sales@screenprintplus.co.uk
Show Card, Fontana House, Works Road, Letchworth Garden City, Hertfordshire, SG6 1LD Tel: (01462) 677148 Fax: (01462) 480392 E-mail: sales@showcard.com
Spatz Shop, Unit 9 Brook Street, Redditch, Worcestershire, B98 8NG Tel: (01527) 68168 Fax: (01527) 60026 E-mail: sales@spatz.uk.com
Styleguard Ltd, 7 Long Acre Trading Estate, Long Acre, Birmingham, B7 5JD Tel: 0121-327 3222 Fax: 0121-328 4312
Sundolitt Ltd, 8 Broomfield Road, Montrose, Angus, DD10 8SY Tel: (01674) 676006 Fax: (01674) 676686
T & D Plastics Ltd, 2 Trinity Road North, West Bromwich, West Midlands, B70 6NB Tel: 0121-553 5605 Fax: 0121-553 1897
Tennant PVC, The Midway, Nottingham, NG7 2TS Tel: 0115-988 1300 Fax: 0115-988 5310 E-mail: sales@tennantpvc.co.uk
Theoplastic Ltd, 3 & 45 Barking Industrial Park, Alfreds Way, Barking, Essex, IG11 0TJ Tel: (020) 8591 5534 Fax: (020) 8591 9022 E-mail: theoplastic@aol.com

VACUUM FORMED PLASTIC PRODUCTS – *continued*

Thermovac Plastics Ltd, Unit 1 Low Mill Lane, Ravensthorpe Industrial Estate, Dewsbury, West Yorkshire, WF13 3LN Tel: (01924) 499268 Fax: (01924) 491440 E-mail: sales@thermovacplastics.co.uk
Thompson Plastics Group Ltd, Bridge Works, Hessle, North Humberside, HU13 0TP Tel: (01482) 646464 Fax: (01482) 644446 E-mail: info@thompson-plastics.co.uk
Vacform Group Derbyshire Ltd, Unit B1 Stainsby Close, Holmwood Industrial Estate, Holmewood, Chesterfield, Derbyshire, S42 5UG Tel: (01246) 855811 Fax: (01246) 854963 E-mail: info@vac-form.com
Vacform Group Yorkshire Ltd, Unit 8b Felnex Close, Leeds, LS9 0SR Tel: 0113-248 9994 Fax: 0113-249 1211 E-mail: sales@vacuum-forming-plus.co.uk
Vacuum Formers Ltd, Brunswick Mill, Pickford Street, Macclesfield, Cheshire, SK11 6JN Tel: (01625) 428389 Fax: (01625) 619808 E-mail: info@vacuumformers.co.uk
Westons Development, Pickering Street, Maidstone, Kent, ME15 9RT Tel: 01622 740418 Fax: 01622 743911 E-mail: dbwestons@aol.com
R. Winter Tooling, 7 Stirling Park, Laker Road, Rochester, Kent, ME1 3QR Tel: 01634 666627 Fax: 01634 666637 E-mail: focus@rwintertooling.com
Wrights Plastics Ltd, Brandon Way, West Bromwich, West Midlands, B70 8JH Tel: 0121-580 3080 Fax: 0121-580 3081 E-mail: sales@wrightsplastics.co.uk
Y C Plastics Ltd, Unit 2, Litchard Industrial Estate, Bridgend, Mid Glamorgan, CF31 2AL Tel: (01656) 647774 Fax: (01656) 647323 E-mail: sales@ycplastics.co.uk

VACUUM FORMING, *See also headings for particular types*

Clearex Plastics Ltd, Dubmire Trading Estate, Houghton le Spring, Tyne & Wear, DH4 5RF Tel: 0191-385 2880 Fax: 0191-385 2855
Polyfab & Formings Ltd, Hindley Green Business Park Leigh Road, Hindley, Wigan, Lancashire, WN2 3LL Tel: (01942) 523617 Fax: (01942) 523533 E-mail: sales@polyfab.co.uk
▶ www.caelectrocomps.co.uk, 36 Park Lane, Bishop's Stortford, Hertfordshire, CM23 3NH Tel: (01279) 656051 Fax: (01279) 656051 E-mail: chris@caelectrocomps.co.uk

VACUUM FORMING PLASTIC CUTTERS

Barkby Knives Ltd, 41 Cannock Street, Leicester, LE4 9HR Tel: 0116-276 1101 Fax: 0116-233 2433 E-mail: sales@barkbyknives.co.uk

VACUUM GAUGES

Commercial & Industrial Gauges, Unit 7 Coed Aben Road, Wrexham Industrial Estate, Wrexham Industrial Estate, Wrexham, Clwyd, LL13 9UH Tel: (01978) 661704 Fax: (01978) 660321 E-mail: info@cigltd.co.uk
Nottingham Gauge & Thermometer Co., Unit C, Thornfield Industrial Estate, Off Hooton Street, Carlton, Nottingham, NG3 2NJ Tel: 0115-950 7213 Fax: 0115-950 7227
Piab Ltd, PO Box 43, Loughborough, Leicestershire, LE12 8NY Tel: (01509) 814280 Fax: (01509) 814647E-mail: sales@piab.co.uk
Saunders & Weeks Bristol Ltd, 265-267 Church Road, Redfield, Bristol, BS5 9HU Tel: 0117-955 7142 Fax: 0117-955 6064 E-mail: sales@saundersweeks.co.uk

VACUUM HEAT TREATMENT AND BRAZING SERVICES

Body Coating Treatments Ltd, Cranbourne Road, Gosport, Hampshire, PO12 1RW Tel: (023) 9258 0946 Fax: (023) 9251 0292 E-mail: markdavies@bodycoat.com
Bodycote Heat Treatment Ltd, 11 Bamfurlong Industrial Park, Staverton, Cheltenham, Gloucestershire, GL51 6SX Tel: (01452) 714440 Fax: (01452) 856097 E-mail: sales@bodycote.co.uk
Bodycote Heat Treatment Ltd, Macclesfield Road, Hazel Grove, Stockport, Cheshire, SK7 5EN Tel: 0161-483 0511 Fax: 0161-483 5450 E-mail: sales@bodycote.co.uk
Davis Scientific Treatments Ltd, Delta Drive, Tewkesbury, Gloucestershire, GL20 8HB Tel: (01684) 296601 Fax: (01684) 274239 E-mail: davis.scentific@btconnect.com
Nitram Vacuum Heat Treatments Company Ltd, Pump Lane Industrial Estate, Silverdale Road, Hayes, Middlesex, UB3 3BN Tel: (020) 8573 5111 Fax: (020) 8756 1023 E-mail: enquiries@nitramvacuum.co.uk
Wallwork Heat Treatment Birmingham Ltd, Sydenham Road, New Shires Industrial Estate, Birmingham, B11 1DQ Tel: 0121-771 2467 Fax: 0121-628 1555 E-mail: enquiries@wallworkht.com

VACUUM LIFTING EQUIPMENT

Dalmek Ltd, 2 Ringway Centre, Edisin Road, Basingstoke, Hampshire, RG21 6YH Tel: (01256) 814420 Fax: (01256) 814434 E-mail: info@dalmecltd.co.uk
▶ Danvac Ltd, 3 Jaras Drive, The Bridleways, Baschurch, Shrewsbury, SY4 2DH Tel: (01939) 260403 Fax: (01939) 260403 E-mail: sales@danvac.co.uk
Piab Ltd, PO Box 43, Loughborough, Leicestershire, LE12 8NY Tel: (01509) 814280 Fax: (01509) 814647E-mail: sales@piab.co.uk
Vacuum Lifting, Rowallan, Kilmarnock, Ayrshire, KA3 2LW Tel: (01563) 540400 Fax: (01563) 520139 E-mail: sales@vacuumliftinguk.co.uk
Alan E. Wheeler & Son, Unit 90, Condover Industrial Estate, Condover, Shrewsbury, SY5 7NH Tel: (01743) 718426 Fax: (01743) 718224 E-mail: sales@vacuumlifting.com
Woods Radio Frequency Services Ltd, Bullocks Farm, Bullocks Lane, Takeley, Bishop's Stortford, Hertfordshire, CM22 6TA Tel: (01279) 870432 Fax: (01279) 871689

VACUUM METALLISATION PLASTIC MOULDINGS

Plasmold Plastics Ltd, 8-11 Oak Industrial Park, Chelmsford Road, Dunmow, Essex, CM6 1XN Tel: (01371) 876445 Fax: (01371) 876874 E-mail: lee@plasmoldplastics.co.uk

VACUUM METALLISING LACQUERS

▶ Effpark Limited, Ground Floor Offices, Haverfield House, 4 Union Place, Worthing, West Sussex, BN11 1LG Tel: 01903 601240 Fax: 01903 601239 E-mail: admin@effpark.co.uk
Neogene Paints Ltd, 14 Caxton Way, Watford, WD18 8UJ Tel: (01923) 213737 Fax: (01923) 213617 E-mail: sales@neogenepaints.co.uk

VACUUM METALLISING PLANT

Island Scientific Ltd, Old Station Road, Ventnor, Isle of Wight, PO38 1DX Tel: (01983) 855822 Fax: (01983) 852146 E-mail: enquiries@island-scientific.co.uk
Tungsten Manufacturing Ltd, 22-28 Cambridge Street, Aylesbury, Buckinghamshire, HP20 1RS Tel: (01296) 394566 Fax: (01296) 394566 E-mail: sales@tungsten.co.uk

VACUUM METALLISING SERVICES

Mercatron International Ltd, 15 Johnson Way, Park Royal, London, NW10 7PF Tel: (020) 8961 1973 Fax: (020) 8961 2106 E-mail: info@mercatron.co.uk
Morplate Ltd, Hammerton Street, Burnley, Lancashire, BB11 1LE Tel: (01282) 428571 Fax: (01282) 413600
V M C Ltd, Trafalgar Works, Station Road, Chertsey, Surrey, KT16 8BE Tel: (01932) 563434 Fax: (01932) 566598 E-mail: info@vmclimited.co.uk

VACUUM OILS, *See also High Vacuum etc*

Apiezon Products, Hibernia Way, Trafford Park, Manchester, M32 0ZD Tel: 0161-864 5419 Fax: 0161-864 5444 E-mail: sales@apiezon.com

VACUUM PACKAGING EQUIPMENT/SYSTEMS

▶ Ixia UK, Unit 14 Ridgewood Industrial Estate, New Road, Uckfield, East Sussex, TN22 5SX Tel: (01825) 766800 Fax: (01825) 766500 E-mail: ixiauk@cs.com
Matrix Machinery, Bermar House Unit 38 Rumer Hill Business Estate, Rumer Hill Road, Cannock, Staffordshire, WS11 0ET Tel: (01543) 466256 Fax: (01543) 466320 E-mail: jpl@matrixmachinery.fsnet.co.uk
Swissvac (G B) Ltd, Marish Wharf, St Marys Road, Middlegreen, Slough, SL3 6DA Tel: (01753) 546777 Fax: (01753) 585564 E-mail: mail@swissvac.co.uk

VACUUM PACKAGING POUCHES

Kalle UK Ltd, Perry Road, Industrial Estate East, Witham, Essex, CM8 3YY Tel: (01376) 531800 Fax: (01376) 518522 E-mail: sales@kalle.co.uk

VACUUM PACKAGING SERVICES

Dalziel Packaging, Unit C3 Drumhead Road, Chorley North Business Park, Chorley, Lancashire, PR6 7DE Tel: (01257) 226010 Fax: (01257) 226019 E-mail: chorley@dalziel.co.uk
Fispak Ltd, Marsmount Road, Shawfarm Industrial Estate, Prestwick, Ayrshire, KA9 2TQ Tel: (01292) 474455 Fax: (01292) 474022 E-mail: lehodge@msn.com

VACUUM PICK AND PLACE HANDLING SYSTEMS

▶ Ixia UK, Unit 14 Ridgewood Industrial Estate, New Road, Uckfield, East Sussex, TN22 5SX Tel: (01825) 766800 Fax: (01825) 766500 E-mail: ixiauk@cs.com

VACUUM PRESSES

Aeroform H L M Ltd, Southway, Walworth Industrial Estate, Andover, Hants, SP10 5AF Tel: (01264) 337788 Fax: (01264) 337755 E-mail: hlm@andover.co.uk

VACUUM PUMP HIRE

G.V.E. Ltd, Ashburton House, Trafford Park Road, Trafford Park, Manchester, M17 1BN Tel: 0161-872 0777 Fax: 0161-872 9324 E-mail: info@gvepumps.co.uk
Tuthill Vacuum Systems, Pennine Business Park, Pilsworth Road, Heywood, Lancashire, OL10 2TL Tel: (01706) 362400 Fax: (01706) 362444 E-mail: uksales@tuthill.com

VACUUM PUMP MAINTENANCE/ REPAIR SERVICES

Ace Rewinds Ltd, 25 Ivatt Way, Westwood Industrial Estate, Peterborough, PE3 7PG Tel: (01733) 331464 Fax: (01733) 334075 E-mail: meeksruss@aol.com
▶ Vacflow Pumps, Unit 10 Horbury Bridge Mills, Bridge Road, Horbury, Wakefield, West Yorkshire, WF4 5RW Tel: (01924) 274518 Fax: (01924) 279405
Wilson Air Pneumatics, Unit 1 Southall Enterprise Centre, Bridge Rd, Southall, Middx, UB2 4AE Tel: (020) 8893 5050 Fax: (020) 8893 5011

VACUUM PUMP MANUFRS

Advanced Vacuum Services Ltd, The Fluid Power Centre, Watling Street, Nuneaton, Warwickshire, CV11 6BQ Tel: (024) 7632 0768 Fax: (024) 7635 0842 E-mail: sales@avs-vacuum.co.uk
Airchannel Ltd, Unit 10, Blackburn Industrial Estate, Blackburn, Aberdeen, AB21 0RX Tel: (01224) 790895 Fax: (01224) 790921 E-mail: enquiries@airchannel.co.uk
Airchannel Ltd, Unit 5, Smithies Mill, Bradford Road, Batley, West Yorkshire, WF17 8NS Tel: (01924) 475740 Fax: (01924) 475177 E-mail: enquiries@airchannel.co.uk
Anglo Pumps Ltd, 4a-B Aston Road, Cambridge Road Industrial Estate, Bedford, MK42 0LJ Tel: (01234) 353525 Fax: (01234) 211655 E-mail: sales@anglo-pumps.co.uk
B O C Edwards, Manor Royal, Crawley, West Sussex, RH10 9LW Tel: (01293) 528844 Fax: (01293) 533453 E-mail: admin@edwards.boc.com
Becker U K Ltd, Unit C, Brighton Street Trading Park, Hull, HU3 4XS Tel: (01482) 835280 Fax: (01482) 831275 E-mail: sales@becker.co.uk
Ebara Scotland, 4 Adam Square, Brucefield Industrial Estate, Livingston, West Lothian, EH54 9DE Tel: (01506) 460232 Fax: (01506) 460222
G.V.E. Ltd, Ashburton House, Trafford Park Road, Trafford Park, Manchester, M17 1BN Tel: 0161-872 0777 Fax: 0161-872 9324 E-mail: info@gvepumps.co.uk
▶ Gardner Denver (Alton) Ltd, Unit 1, Waterbrook Estate, Waterbrook Road, Alton, Hampshire, GU34 2UD Tel: (01420) 544184 Fax: (01420) 544183 E-mail: ukinfo@eu.gardnerdenver.com
Genevac Ltd, 6 Farthing Road, Ipswich, IP1 5AP Tel: (01473) 240000 Fax: (01473) 461176 E-mail: sales@genevac.co.uk
Javac UK Ltd, 6 Drake Court, Middlesbrough, Cleveland, TS2 1RS Tel: (01642) 232880 Fax: (01642) 232870E-mail: info@javac.co.uk
Nash Elmo UK Ltd, Road One, Winsford Industrial Estate, Winsford, Cheshire, CW7 3PL Tel: (01606) 542400 Fax: (01606) 542434 E-mail: sales@nasheng.com
T D R Transmissions, 5 Hunsley Street, Sheffield, S4 8DY Tel: 0114-262 6050 Fax: 0114-243 1826 E-mail: sales@tdrtrans.demon.co.uk
VacAir Superstore, Unit 2 Latchmore Industrial Park, Lowfields Road, Leeds, LS12 6dn Tel: 0113-208 8501 Fax: 0113-208 8400 E-mail: sales@vacair-superstore.com
Vacuum Scientific Services Ltd, 44 Ellesmere Street, Manchester, M15 4JY Tel: 0161-833 9108 Fax: 0161-835 1443 E-mail: sales@vacuum-scientific.com
Varian Ltd, 28 Manor Road, Walton-On-Thames, Surrey, KT12 2QF Tel: (01932) 898000 Fax: (01932) 228769

VACUUM PUMP SPARES

▶ A+ Engineering, 45 Broadlands Park, County, CARRICKFERGUS, County Antrim, BT38 7DB Tel: 028 93366516 Fax: 028 93366516 E-mail: info@aplusengineering.co.uk
▶ Marine Representation, Southon House, Station Approach, Edenbridge, Kent, TN8 5LP Tel: (01732) 867722 Fax: (01732) 868222 E-mail: info@activitymarine.com

VACUUM SEALS

Ceramic Seals Ltd, Westwood Industrial Estate, Arkwright Street, Oldham, OL9 9LZ Tel: 0161-627 2353 Fax: 0161-627 2356 E-mail: admin@ceramicseals.co.uk
Ferrotec UK Ltd, Unit 3 I O Centre, Skeffington Street, London, SE18 6SR Tel: (020) 8317 3100 Fax: (020) 8317 9559 E-mail: info@ferrotec.co.uk
V A T Vacuum Products Ltd, Edmund House, Rugby Road, Leamington Spa, Warwickshire, CV32 6EL Tel: (01926) 452753 Fax: (01926) 452758 E-mail: uk@vatvalve.com

VACUUM SYSTEMS, COMPLETE/ PACKAGED

Air Systems Controls Ltd, 51-52 The Bus Development Cour, Stafford Park 4, Telford, Shropshire, TF3 3BA Tel: (01952) 290959 Fax: (01952) 292647 E-mail: sales@airsystemcontrols.com
Nte Vacuum Technology Ltd, 190-192 Stanley Green Road, Poole, Dorset, BH15 3AH Tel: (01202) 677715 Fax: (01202) 677723 E-mail: sales@ntepoole.co.uk
Scientific Vacuum Systems Ltd, 12 Weller Drive, Hogwood Lane Industrial Estate, Wokingham, Berkshire, RG40 4QZ Tel: 0118-973 1946 Fax: 0118-973 1834

VACUUM TANKERS

Eurovac Aegeus Ltd, Unit 6-7 Lee Mills Industrial Estate, Scholes, Holmfirth, HD9 1RT Tel: (01484) 689055 Fax: (01484) 689042 E-mail: sales@csgeurovac.com
Whale Tankers Ltd, Ravenshaw, Solihull, West Midlands, B91 2SU Tel: 0121-704 5700 Fax: 0121-704 5701 E-mail: whalemail@whale.co.uk

VACUUM TURBOCHARGER ACTUATORS

Helical Technology Ltd, Dock Road, Lytham, Lancashire, FY8 5AQ Tel: (01253) 733122 Fax: (01253) 794880 E-mail: sales@helical-technology.co.uk

VACUUM VALVES

V A T Vacuum Products Ltd, Edmund House, Rugby Road, Leamington Spa, Warwickshire, CV32 6EL Tel: (01926) 452753 Fax: (01926) 452758 E-mail: uk@vatvalve.com

VACUUM WASTE REMOVAL SERVICES

Mechanical Cleansing Services Ltd, Unit G, Salford Street Industrial Estate, Aston, Birmingham, B6 7SH Tel: (0845) 5314243 Fax: 0121-327 3105 E-mail: droemcsltd@aol.com

VALIDATION, VERIFICATION AND TEST INFORMATION SERVICES

I C C Information Ltd, First Floor, Rooms 8-10, Scottish Mutual Building, 16 Donegall Square South, Belfast, BT1 5JG Tel: (028) 9055 9559 Fax: (028) 9055 0072 E-mail: reports@iccinformationni.com
▶ Tektonisk (UK) Ltd, Palmerston House, 814 Brighton Road, Purley, Surrey, CR8 2BR Tel: (08707) 606282 Fax: (020) 8655 8501 E-mail: pg@tektonisk.com

VALVE ACCESSORIES

▶ D P Valve Spares Ltd, Unit 51B Port Street, Evesham, Worcestershire, WR11 3LF Tel: (01386) 760033 Fax: (01386) 760099 E-mail: sales@dpvalvespares.co.uk

VALVE ACCESSORIES – *continued*

Furmanite International Ltd, Worldwide Way, Kiln La Trading Estate, Stallingborough, Grimsby, South Humberside, DN41 8DY Tel: (01469) 575143 Fax: (01469) 571074 E-mail: enquiries@furmanite.com

VALVE ACTUATOR ACCESSORIES

Intex Controls Ltd, Tonbridge Road, Hadlow, Tonbridge, Kent, TN11 0AH Tel: (01732) 850360 Fax: (01732) 852133 E-mail: sales@stonel.impex.com

VALVE ACTUATORS, *See also headings for particular types*

A T UK Ltd, Unit A4 Sovereign Park Industrial Estate, Market Harborough, Leicestershire, LE16 9EG Tel: (01858) 468199 Fax: (01858) 468187 E-mail: sales@airtorque.co.uk

Actreg UK Ltd, 2 & 3 Henson Close, Telford Way Industrial Estate, Kettering, Northamptonshire, NN16 8PZ Tel: (01536) 412525 Fax: (01536) 521616 E-mail: sales@actreg.co.uk

Cancarp Ltd, Unit 28 Willan Industrial Estate, Vere Street, Salford, M50 2GR Tel: 0161-736 9026 Fax: 0161-745 8657 E-mail: disc@cancarp.com

Cotswold Valves Ltd, Upper Mills Trading Estate, Stonehouse, Gloucestershire, GL10 2BJ Tel: (01453) 826612 Fax: (01453) 827505 E-mail: info@cotswoldvalves.co.uk

Flowserve, Abex Road, Newbury, Berkshire, RG14 5EY Tel: (01635) 42297 Fax: (01635) 36034 E-mail: jrobinson@flowserve.com

Forac, Unit 8 9 Riverbank Business Centre, Old Shoreham Road, Shoreham-by-Sea, West Sussex, BN43 5FL Tel: (01273) 467100 Fax: (01273) 467101 E-mail: sales@forac.co.uk

H S Pipequipment Ltd, Red Shute Hill Industrial Estate, Hermitage, Thatcham, Berkshire, RG18 9QL Tel: (01635) 201329 Fax: (01635) 201941 E-mail: info@hso.co.uk

Intex Controls Ltd, Tonbridge Road, Hadlow, Tonbridge, Kent, TN11 0AH Tel: (01732) 850360 Fax: (01732) 852133 E-mail: sales@stonel.impex.com

Leengate Valves, Grange Close, Clover Nook Industrial Estate, Somercotes, Alfreton, Derbyshire, DE55 4QT Tel: (01773) 521555 Fax: (01773) 521591 E-mail: info@leengatevalves.co.uk

Opperman Mastergear Ltd, Hambridge Lane, Newbury, Berkshire, RG14 5TS Tel: (01635) 811500 Fax: (01635) 811501 E-mail: sales@opperman-mastergear.co.uk

Tyco Valves & Controls Distribution (UK) Ltd, Crosby Road, Market Harborough, Leicestershire, LE16 9EE Tel: (01858) 467281 Fax: (01858) 434728 E-mail: uk_sales@tyco-valves.com

Valvetech Ltd, Unit 9, Brookside Industrial Estate, Sawtry, Huntingdon, Cambridgeshire, PE28 5SB Tel: (01487) 833080 Fax: (01487) 833081 E-mail: sales@valvetech.co.uk

VALVE AND VALVE SPARE PART DATA MANAGEMENT SERVICES

Anderson Greenwood Crosby, Wellheads Terrace, Wellheads Industrial Estate, Aberdeen, AB21 7GF Tel: (01224) 722562 Fax: (01224) 771607 E-mail: cmiln@tyco-valves.com

Tyco Valves & Controls Distribution (UK) Ltd, Wellheads Terr, Wellheads Industrial Estate, Aberdeen, AB22 7GF Tel: (01224) 722562 Fax: (01224) 771607 E-mail: sales_aberdeen@tyco-valves.com

VALVE BALLS

Sheridan Engineering Hereford, 4 Parkwood Court, Rotherwas Industrial Estate, Hereford, HR2 6NU Tel: (01432) 269683 Fax: (01432) 354410 E-mail: sales@sheridanengineering.co.uk

VALVE COMPONENTS/FITTINGS/ SPARE PARTS

Pipeline Centre, 2 Hartburn Close, Crow Lane Industrial Estate, Northampton, NN3 9UE Tel: (01604) 410888 Fax: (01604) 410777 E-mail: bv.northhampton@wolsley.co.uk

VALVE ENGINEERS, *See also heading for particular types such as Repair/Reconditioning etc*

Specialist On Site Services Ltd, 3 Park Lane, Spalding, Lincolnshire, PE11 1PJ Tel: (01775) 680608 Fax: (01775) 680825

VALVE MANUFRS, *See also headings for particular types under Valves*

A F S Associates, 1 The Paddock, Much Wenlock, Shropshire, TF13 6LT Tel: (01952) 728188 Fax: (01952) 728174 E-mail: sales@afsassociates.co.uk

A J Paveley & Co., 416 Golden Hillock Road, Sparkbrook, Birmingham, B11 2QH Tel: 0121-772 1739 Fax: 0121-771 1386 E-mail: peterpavely@aol.com

Aberdeen Fluid Systems Technologies Ltd, 1 Stoneywood Park, Stoneywood Road, Dyce, Aberdeen, AB21 7DZ Tel: (01224) 722468 Fax: (01224) 723009 E-mail: info@aberdeen.swagelok.com

AC Valves & Controls Ltd, Telford Way, Stephenson Industrial Estate, Coalville, Leicestershire, LE67 3HE Tel: (01530) 832832 Fax: (01530) 838986 E-mail: markc@acvalvealliance.com

▶ Actuation Technology Ltd, Metro House, Northgate, Chichester, West Sussex, PO19 1BE Tel: (01243) 771372 Fax: (01243) 538501 E-mail: mbreen@amgactuators.co.uk

Actuation Valve & Controls, 8 Woodward Road, Knowsley Industrial Park, Liverpool, L33 7UZ Tel: 0151-547 1221 Fax: 0151-547 1222 E-mail: chris@actuation.co.uk

Adanac Valve Specialities Ltd, 14 Windmill Avenue, Woolpit Business Park, Woolpit, Bury St. Edmunds, Suffolk, IP30 9UP Tel: (01359) 240404 Fax: (01359) 240406 E-mail: info@adanac.co.uk

Adaptive Control Solutions Ltd, 1 Ashfield Road, Greetland, Halifax, West Yorkshire, HX4 8HY Tel: (01422) 313456 Fax: (01422) 313567 E-mail: richardarmitage@adaptivecontrol.com

Advanced Valve Technologies Ltd, Millennium Way, Thanet Reach Business Park, Broadstairs, Kent, CT10 2QQ Tel: (01843) 600000 Fax: (01843) 600333 E-mail: avt@advalve.com

Albion Distribution Ltd, Unit 9a Fall Bank Industrial Estate, Dodworth, Barnsley, South Yorkshire, S75 3LS Tel: (01226) 729900 Fax: (01226) 288011 E-mail: dist@albiongroup.co.uk

▶ Allpipe & Valve, 103a Pontefract Road, Ackworth, Pontefract, West Yorkshire, WF7 7EL Tel: (01977) 600606 Fax: (01977) 704215 E-mail: allpipe@aol.com

Anglia Valves Ltd, Unit 12g West Station Industrial Estate West Station Yard, Spital Road, Maldon, Essex, CM9 6TW Tel: (01621) 858861 Fax: (01621) 855942

Aquaflow Ltd, Onneley Works, Newcastle Road, Woore, Crewe, CW3 9RU Tel: (01630) 647111 Fax: (01630) 647734 E-mail: response@aquaflowvalves.com

Bells Engineering Products Ltd, 874 Plymouth Road, Slough, SL1 4LP Tel: (01753) 567788 Fax: (01753) 567799 E-mail: bells.engineering@virgin.net

Russell Benussi Associates, 3 Pebble Close, Tamworth, Staffordshire, B77 4RD Tel: (01827) 68008 Fax: (01827) 69265 E-mail: sales@benussi.com

Besseges Valves Tubes & Fittings Ltd, Jackson House, Turner Lane, Ashton-under-Lyne, Lancashire, OL6 8LP Tel: 0161-343 2225 Fax: 0161-339 0307 E-mail: sales@besseges-vts.co.uk

Bestobell Valves, President Way, Sheffield, S4 7UR Tel: 0114-224 0200 Fax: 0114-278 4974 E-mail: sales@bestobellvalves.com

Binney & Son Ltd, Unit H Spring Hill Industrial Park, Steward Street, Birmingham, B18 7AF Tel: 0121-454 4545 Fax: 0121-454 1145 E-mail: binney.eng@btconnect.com

Boole's Tools & Pipe Fittings Ltd, Haigh Avenue, Whitehill Trading Estate, Stockport, Cheshire, SK4 1NU Tel: 0161-480 7900 Fax: 0161-474 7142 E-mail: enquiries@booles.co.uk

Bosta Agricultural Services, Chapel Pond Hill, Bury St. Edmunds, Suffolk, IP32 7HT Tel: (01284) 716580 Fax: (01284) 716588 E-mail: sales@uk.bosta.com

Broadway Group, 136 Stanwell Road, Ashford, Middlesex, TW15 3QP Tel: (0845) 6019006 Fax: (0845) 6019007 E-mail: ppstechnical@yahoo.co.uk

Capital Valves Ltd, Wembley Point, Harrow Road, Wembley, Middlesex, HA9 6DE Tel: (020) 8900 0471 Fax: (020) 8900 0808 E-mail: sales@capitalvalves.co.uk

▶ Alexander Cardew Ltd, Unit 27 Chelsea Wharf, 15 Lots Road, London, SW10 0QJ Tel: (020) 7235 3785 Fax: (020) 7352 4635 E-mail: sales@cardew.com

Cla-Val (UK) Ltd, Dainton House, Goods Station Road, Tunbridge Wells, Kent, TN1 2DH Tel: (01892) 514400 Fax: (01892) 543423 E-mail: info@cla-val.co.uk

Collister & Glover (Pipeline Materials) Ltd, Tenth Avenue, Deeside Industrial Park, Deeside, Clwyd, CH5 2UA Tel: (01244) 288000 Fax: (01244) 289000 E-mail: sales@colglo.co.uk

Robert Cort Ltd, Elgar Road, Reading, RG2 0DL Tel: 0118-987 4311 Fax: 0118-986 6592 E-mail: mail@robertcort.co.uk

Cotswold Valves Ltd, Upper Mills Trading Estate, Stonehouse, Gloucestershire, GL10 2BJ Tel: (01453) 826612 Fax: (01453) 827505 E-mail: info@cotswoldvalves.co.uk

D R B Power Transmission, First Avenue, Deeside Industrial Park, Deeside, Clwyd, CH5 2QR Tel: (01244) 280280 Fax: (01244) 288367 E-mail: sales@drbgroup.co.uk

D S Controls, Sleekburn Business Centre, Cambois, Blyth, Northumberland, NE24 1QQ Tel: (01670) 520022 Fax: (01670) 520033 E-mail: sales@dscontrolvalves.com

Drainage Center Ltd, 116 London Road, Hailsham, East Sussex, BN27 3AL Tel: (01323) 442333 Fax: (01323) 847488 E-mail: sales@drainagecenter.co.uk

▶ E S I Process Ltd, 2 Hill Street, Ty Coch Industrial Estate, Cwmbran, Gwent, NP44 7PG Tel: (01633) 877505 Fax: (01633) 877605 E-mail: sales@esitechnologies.co.uk

Ebtrade Ltd, Albion Dockside Works, Bristol, BS1 6UT Tel: 0117-927 9204 Fax: 0117-929 8193 E-mail: enquiries@seetru.com

Emmerson Process Management Ltd, Heath Place, Bognor Regis, West Sussex, PO22 9SH Tel: (01243) 867554 Fax: (01243) 867554

F E L Valves Ltd, Pickmere Lane, Wincham, Northwich, Cheshire, CW9 6EB Tel: (01565) 733137 Fax: (01565) 733841 E-mail: fel.valves@virgin.net

▶ Flow Control Solutions Ltd, Unit D Knowl Street, Stalybridge, Cheshire, SK15 3AL Tel: 0161-303 9777 Fax: 0161-303 9888 E-mail: rob@flowcontrolsolutions.com

Flucon Pumps Ltd, 1 High Street, St. Asaph, Clwyd, LL17 0RG Tel: (01745) 584772 Fax: (01745) 582096 E-mail: info@flucon.co.uk

G J Johnson & Sons Ltd, 7 Trinity Court, Brunel Road, Totton, Southampton, SO40 3WX Tel: (023) 8066 9666 Fax: (023) 8066 9606 E-mail: sales@johnsonvalves.com

G S Hydro UK Ltd, Unit 47 Howe Moss Avenue, Kirkhill Industrial Estate, Dyce, Aberdeen, AB21 0GP Tel: (01224) 772111 Fax: (01224) 772054 E-mail: info@gshydro.co.uk

Gowing Technical Services, 21 Norris Way, Rushden, Northamptonshire, NN10 6BP Tel: (01933) 350350 Fax: (01933) 350222

Grange Controls Ltd, Unit 3 Midland Way, Thornbury, Bristol, BS35 2BS Tel: (01454) 418256 Fax: (01454) 415214 E-mail: sales@grangecontrols.co.uk

H S Pipequipment Ltd, Red Shute Hill Industrial Estate, Hermitage, Thatcham, Berkshire, RG18 9QL Tel: (01635) 201329 Fax: (01635) 201941 E-mail: info@hso.co.uk

H S Pipequipment (Aberdeen) Ltd, Unit 2 Hillview Road, East Tullos Industrial Estate, Aberdeen, AB12 3HB Tel: (01224) 249900 Fax: (01224) 249222

Holdfast Radiator Valves Ltd, Bagnall Road, Bagnall, Stoke-on-Trent, ST9 9JY Tel: (01782) 544982 Fax: (01782) 544983

Hoses Direct, Brighton, BN2 5AW Tel: (0800) 6526038 Fax: (0800) 6526039 E-mail: sales@hoses.co.uk

▶ Howford Hydraulics, Old Howford Road, Catrine, Ayrshire, KA5 5JX Tel: (01290) 551428 Fax: (01290) 550549 E-mail: sales@howford.demon.co.uk

HYDRAQUIP, Unit 7, Oakhurst Business Park, Wilberforce Way, Southwater, Horsham, West Sussex, RH13 9RT Tel: (01403) 731322 Fax: (01403) 730276 E-mail: salmons@hydraquip.co.uk

Indachem Process Valves Ltd, The Valve Centre Calder Road, Ravensthorpe, Dewsbury, West Yorkshire, WF13 3JS Tel: (01924) 438353 Fax: (01924) 438373

Induchem, Unit 1 Greenfield Farm Industrial Estate, Congleton, Cheshire, CW12 4TR Tel: (01260) 277234 Fax: (01260) 277649 E-mail: sales@induchem.ie

International Pipeline Supplies Ltd, 3 Cookson House, River Drive, South Shields, Tyne & Wear, NE33 1TL Tel: 0191-455 9648 Fax: 0191-454 0505 E-mail: office@internationalgroup.fsbusiness.co.uk

Isis Fluid Control Ltd, Station Yard The Leys, Chipping Norton, Oxfordshire, OX7 5HZ Tel: (01608) 645755 Fax: (01608) 645532 E-mail: sales@isis-fluid.com

Jetseal Ballvalves Manufacturers, Unit 71, Cobham Road, Ferndown Industrial Estate, Wimborne, Dorset, BH21 7QE Tel: (01202) 897427 Fax: (01202) 890292 E-mail: office@jetseal.co.uk

▶ John Clark Ltd, Portrack Grange Road, Stockton-on-Tees, Cleveland, TS18 2PH Tel: (01642) 602288 Fax: (01642) 603388

John Clark Ltd, Portrack Grange Road, Stockton-on-Tees, Cleveland, TS18 2PH Tel: (01642) 602288 Fax: (01642) 603388 E-mail: sales@jcvltd.com

Lamberts.Co.Uk Industrial Distributor, Whiffler Road, Norwich, NR3 2AY Tel: (01603) 422100 Fax: (01603) 422130 E-mail: nr.sales@lamberts.co.uk

Leengate Valves, Grange Close, Clover Nook Industrial Estate, Somercotes, Alfreton, Derbyshire, DE55 4QT Tel: (01773) 521555 Fax: (01773) 521591 E-mail: info@leengatevalves.co.uk

London Fluid Systems Technologies Ltd, Unit 11, Kingley Park, Station Road, Kings Langley, Hertfordshire, WD4 8GW Tel: (01923) 272000 Fax: (01923) 272027 E-mail: info@london.swagelok.com

Machineair Engineering Ltd, 70 Colliers Water Lane, Thornton Heath, Surrey, CR7 7LB Tel: (020) 8684 4849 Fax: (020) 8683 4635

Marflow Engineering Ltd, Austin Way, Hampstead Industrial Estate, Birmingham, B42 1DU Tel: 0121-358 1555 Fax: 0121-358 1444 E-mail: sales@marflow.co.uk

Marshall Engineering Services, Kendrick House, Mere View Industrial Estate, Yaxley, Peterborough, PE7 3HS Tel: (01733) 240045 Fax: (01733) 241821

Mechtech Valves Services, The Stenders, Mitcheldean, Gloucestershire, GL17 0ZE Tel: (01594) 541717 Fax: (01594) 541716

Midland Brass Fittings Ltd, Wynford Industrial Trading Estate, Wynford Road, Birmingham, B27 6JT Tel: 0121-707 6666 Fax: 0121-708 1270 E-mail: sales@midbras.co.uk

Midland Pipeline Supplies Ltd, 92 Old Eaton Road, Rugeley, Staffordshire, WS15 2HA Tel: (01889) 585054 Fax: (01889) 585194

Modern Valves & Fittings, Unit 13A, Victoris Industrial Estate, Voctoris Road West, Hebburn, Tyne & Wear, NE31 1UP Tel: 0191-250 2384 Fax: 0191-250 2247

Mokveld, Unit 2 Butts Courtyard, The Butts, Poulton, Cirencester, Gloucestershire, GL7 5HY Tel: (01285) 851225 Fax: (01285) 851342 E-mail: uk@mokveld.com

Multi Process, Unit 8 Stroud Enterprise Centre, Lightpill, Stroud, Gloucestershire, GL5 3NL Tel: (01453) 750002 Fax: (01453) 758271

Nevesco Ltd, 3 Walton Road, Pattinson North, Washington, Tyne & Wear, NE38 8QA Tel: 0191-415 0037 Fax: 0191-415 3532 E-mail: nevescoltd@eol.com

Ogley Bros Ltd, Smithfield, Sheffield, S3 7AS Tel: 0114-276 8948 Fax: 0114-275 5105 E-mail: ogleybrothers@btconnect.com

Oppenheimer Engineering Services, 20 Vanguard Way, Shoeburyness, Southend-on-Sea, SS3 9RA Tel: (0870) 8722752 Fax: (0870) 8722750 E-mail: oes@oppenheimers.co.uk

P J Valves Ltd, 8 Merchant Drive, Mead Lane, Hertford, SG13 7BH Tel: (01992) 587878 Fax: (01992) 550132 E-mail: scharles@pjvalves.co.uk

Pipeline Centre Ltd, Leads Road, Hull, HU7 0BY Tel: (01482) 838880 Fax: (01482) 878827 E-mail: sales@piplinecenter.co.uk

Pipeline Centre, 4 Deacon Trading Centre, Knight Road, Rochester, Kent, ME2 2AU Tel: (01634) 290469 Fax: (01634) 290128

Pipemore, 3 Crompton Road, Glenrothes, Fife, KY6 2SF Tel: (01592) 630633 Fax: (01592) 630623E-mail: sales@pipemorescotland.co.uk

Poynton Valves Ltd, 81a Coppice Road, Poynton, Stockport, Cheshire, SK12 1SL Tel: (01625) 871014 Fax: (01625) 879814 E-mail: sales@poyntonvalves.com

Premier Pipeline Supplies Ltd, Chatham Street, Halifax, West Yorkshire, HX1 5BU Tel: (01422) 322002 Fax: (01422) 348817 E-mail: info@premierpipeline.co.uk

Presreg Valve, 18 Bakewell Road, Loughborough, Leicestershire, LE11 5QY Tel: (01509) 264242 Fax: (01509) 263308

Process Equipment Parts (UK) Ltd, Kershaw House, 449 Great West Road, Hounslow, TW5 0BU Tel: (020) 8754 3999 Fax: (020) 8754 3990 E-mail: mail@process-equipment.co.uk

Process & Instrumentation Valves Ltd, Stewart House, Stewart Road, Falkirk, FK2 7AS Tel: (01324) 630030 Fax: (01324) 629112 E-mail: sales@piv-online.com

Process Valve Supplies Ltd, 2 Ringtail Industrial Estate, Tollgate Road, Burscough, Ormskirk, Lancashire, L40 8RT Tel: (01704) 894403 Fax: (01704) 897046 E-mail: sales@processvalve.co.uk

Q Controls, Waterton House, Stoneywood, Bucksburn, Aberdeen, AB21 9HX Tel: (01224) 715464 Fax: (01224) 716079 E-mail: sales@jbpipeline.co.uk

Radlett Valve & Engineering Co. Ltd, 38 Watling Street, Radlett, Hertfordshire, WD7 7NN Tel: (01923) 852131 Fax: (01923) 854484 E-mail: sales@radlettvalve.co.uk

S A V UK Ltd, Scandia House, Armfield Close, West Molesey, Surrey, KT8 2JR Tel: (020) 8941 4153 Fax: (020) 8783 1132 E-mail: info@savvalvessystems.co.uk

Sabre Instrument Valves Ltd, Golf Road, Hale, Altrincham, Cheshire, WA15 8AH Tel: 0161-925 4000 Fax: 0161-925 4001 E-mail: info@sabre-valves.com

SAFI Ltd, 35 Holton Road, Holton Heath Trading Park, Poole, Dorset, BH16 6LT Tel: (01202) 624618 Fax: (01202) 628500 E-mail: sales@safi-limited.com

Score Europe Ltd, Glenugie Engineering Works, Burnhaven, Peterhead, Aberdeenshire, AB42 0YX Tel: (01779) 480000 Fax: (01779) 481111 E-mail: adm@score-group.com

Sealpump Engineering Ltd, Innovation Centre, Kirkleatham Business Park, Redcar, Cleveland, TS10 5SH Tel: (01642) 777720 Fax: (01642) 777730 E-mail: sales@sealpump.com

Serto UK Ltd, Unit 3 West Court, Buntsford Park Road, Bromsgrove, Worcestershire, B60 3DX Tel: (01527) 573960 Fax: (01527) 870291 E-mail: sales@serto.co.uk

Simm Engineering Group, Gilbertson Works, Jessell Street, Sheffield, S9 3HY Tel: 0114-244 0764 Fax: 0114-244 2725 E-mail: sales@simmengineeringgroup.co.uk

Smith Brothers Stores Ltd, Battern Street, Aylestone Road, Leicester, LE2 7PB Tel: 0116-283 3511 Fax: 0116-244 0430 E-mail: sales@sbs-1897.co.uk

Specialised Pipe & Services Ltd, F1 Folland Way, Hull, HU9 1NB Tel: (01482) 587060 Fax: (01482) 587099 E-mail: sales@spsworld.com

Stauff Scotland, Unit 3-4 Altens Trade Centre, Hareness Circle, Altens Industrial Estate, Aberdeen, AB12 3LY Tel: (01224) 238518 Fax: (01224) 238500 E-mail: sales@stauffscotland.co.uk

Stoneleigh Engineering Services Ltd, Unit 10 Lansdowne Workshops, Lansdowne Mews, London, SE7 8AZ Tel: (020) 8305 0792 Fax: (020) 8858 6665

VALVE MANUFRS – *continued*

T P S Technitube UK Ltd, T P S Building, Blatchford Road, Horsham, West Sussex, RH13 5QR Tel: (01403) 269471 Fax: (01403) 265443 E-mail: sales@tpsuk.co.uk
T R W Systems Ltd, Rainhill Road, Washington, Tyne & Wear, NE37 3HP Tel: 0191-419 4477 Fax: 0191-419 4191
Tamo Ltd, 195 Horton Road, West Drayton, Middlesex, UB7 8HP Tel: (01895) 859700 Fax: (01895) 859888 E-mail: info@tamo.co.uk
Tanks & Vessels Industries, Bankwood Lane Industrial Estate, Bankwood Lane, New Rossington, Doncaster, South Yorkshire, DN11 0PS Tel: (01302) 866003 Fax: (01302) 864990 E-mail: sales@tanksandvessels.com
Transmac Valves Ltd, Unit 4 Building 26, First Avenue, Pensnett Trading Estate, Kingswinford, West Midlands, DY6 7TB Tel: (01384) 288265 Fax: (01384) 288096
Transmark FCX Ltd, Heaton House, Riverside Drive, Hunsworth Lane, Bradford, West Yorkshire, BD19 4DH Tel: (01274) 700000 Fax: (01274) 700152 E-mail: jhill@heaton-valves.co.uk
Trimline Valves Ltd, 6 Dales Park Drive Worsley Road, Swinton, Manchester, M27 0FP Tel: 0161-727 8128 Fax: 0161-727 9060 E-mail: harrycope@trimlinevalveslimited.co.uk
Trouvay & Cauvin Ltd, Broadgate, Oldham Broadway Business Park, Chadderton, Oldham, OL9 9XA Tel: 0161-684 7488 Fax: 0161-684 7487 E-mail: sales@trouvay-cauvin.co.uk
▶ Valve & Process Solutions, Unit 11 Pottery La West, Chesterfield, Derbyshire, S41 9BN Tel: (01246) 220070 Fax: (0870) 220969 E-mail: sales@vandpsolutions.com
Valve Solutions Ltd, Units 6-7, Enterprise Court, Micklefield, Leeds, LS25 4BU Tel: 0113-287 6888 Fax: 0113-287 6999
Valvelink UK Ltd, 17 Cotswold Green, Stonehouse, Gloucestershire, GL10 2ES Tel: (01453) 822222 Fax: (01453) 821111
Valvestock, 2 Fielder Drive, Fareham, Hampshire, PO14 1JG Tel: (01329) 283425 Fax: (01329) 822741 E-mail: enquiries@valvestock.co.uk
W T Armatur UK Ltd, Singleton Court Business Centre, Wonastow Road Industrial Estate (West), Monmouth, Gwent, NP25 5JA Tel: (01600) 712178 Fax: (01600) 712179
Watts Industries UK Ltd, Grosvenor Business Centre, Enterprise Way, Vale Park, Evesham, Worcestershire, WR11 1GA Tel: (01386) 446997 Fax: (01386) 41923 E-mail: sales@wattsindustries.com
Western Automation Ivac, 5 Colemans Bridge, Witham, Essex, CM8 3HP Tel: (01376) 511808 Fax: (01376) 500862 E-mail: sales@waivac.co.uk
Western Tooling Ltd, 55-57 Sterte Avenue, Poole, Dorset, BH15 2AJ Tel: (01202) 677654 Fax: (01202) 677876 E-mail: sales@westerntooling.co.uk
Wilson UK Ltd, Unit 3 Bloxwich Lane Industrial Estate, Bloxwich Lane, Walsall, WS2 8TF Tel: (01922) 725800 Fax: (01922) 649888 E-mail: uksales@wilsononline.com
Wood Group Pressure Control Ltd, Blackhouse Circle, Blackhouse Industrial Estate, Peterhead, Aberdeenshire, AB42 1BN Tel: (01779) 474293 Fax: (01779) 474298
Yardley Holland Ltd, 154 Stafford Street, Walsall, WS2 8EA Tel: (01922) 633877 Fax: (01922) 634868

VALVE MODIFICATION

Adanac Valve Specialities Ltd, 14 Windmill Avenue, Woolpit Business Park, Woolpit, Bury St. Edmunds, Suffolk, IP30 9UP Tel: (01359) 240404 Fax: (01359) 240406 E-mail: info@adanac.co.uk
Nuthall Pump & Engineering Services, Queen Street, Langley Mill, Nottingham, NG16 4EJ Tel: (01773) 530630 Fax: (01773) 531532

VALVE MONITORING EQUIPMENT/SYSTEMS

Westlock Controls Ltd, 22 Chapman Way, Tunbridge Wells, Kent, TN2 3EF Tel: (01892) 516277 Fax: (01892) 516279 E-mail: info@westlockcontrols.com

VALVE MOUNTING KITS

Kits & Bits, Reform Street, Sutton-in-Ashfield, Nottinghamshire, NG17 5DB Tel: (01623) 442524 Fax: (01623) 442545 E-mail: kitsandbitsltd@aol.com

VALVE REPAIR/ RECONDITIONING/ REFURBISHMENT SERVICES, (INCLUDING ON SITE)

Anderson Greenwood Crosby, Wellheads Terrace, Wellheads Industrial Estate, Aberdeen, AB21 7GF Tel: (01224) 722562 Fax: (01224) 771607 E-mail: cmiln@tyco-valves.com
Chemtrol Valve Manufacturers, Clerk Green Street, Batley, West Yorkshire, WF17 7SE Tel: (01924) 475481 Fax: (01924) 475879
Clapham & Woolley Ltd, 3 Mandale, South Street, Keighley, West Yorkshire, BD21 1DB Tel: (01535) 665143 Fax: (01535) 691893
Comid Engineering Ltd, Greenacres Road, Oldham, OL4 2AB Tel: 0161-624 9592 Fax: 0161-627 1620 E-mail: sales@comid.co.uk
Compressor Valve Engineering Ltd, 4 Burnell Road, Ellesmere Port, CH65 5EX Tel: 0151-355 5937 Fax: 0151-357 1098 E-mail: sales@compvalve.co.uk
Control Valve Maintenance (Staines) Ltd, 874 Plymouth Road, Slough Trading Estate, Slough, SL1 4LP Tel: (01753) 567744 Fax: (01753) 567799 E-mail: controlvalves@cvml.demon.co.uk
Controlled Repair Instruments Ltd, Controlled Repair Institute Ltd, 1-5 Dock Tavern Lane, Gorleston, Great Yarmouth, Norfolk, NR31 6PY Tel: (01493) 602060 Fax: (01493) 441782 E-mail: sales@controlvalverepairs.co.uk
County Engineering Southern Ltd, Unit 9, Annington Commercial Centre, Annington Road, Bramber, Steyning, West Sussex, BN44 3WA Tel: (01903) 879428 Fax: (01903) 815077 E-mail: ces@countyeng.demon.co.uk
CSB Engineering Services Ltd, 56 Roman Bank, Saracens Head, Spalding, Lincolnshire, PE12 8BB Tel: (01406) 425201 E-mail: csbeng@valves66.fsnet.co.uk
D R B Power Transmission, First Avenue, Deeside Industrial Park, Deeside, Clwyd, CH5 2QR Tel: (01244) 280280 Fax: (01244) 288367 E-mail: sales@drbgroup.co.uk
Essex Valves Engineering Services, Unit 13 Newlands End, Basildon, Essex, SS15 6DU Tel: (020) 8595 8749 Fax: (020) 8595 8749
Furmanite Engineering Ltd, 7 Colville Court, Winwick Quay, Warrington, WA2 8QT Tel: (01925) 418858 Fax: (01925) 418863 E-mail: enquiries@furmanite.com
Furmanite International Ltd, Owens Road, Skippers Lane Industrial Estate, Middlesbrough, Cleveland, TS6 6HE Tel: (01642) 455111 Fax: (01642) 465692
Hodgson Engineering Ltd, Unit 8 Metcalfe Road, Skippers Lane Industrial Estate, Middlesbrough, Cleveland, TS6 6PT Tel: (01642) 440888 Fax: (01642) 440888 E-mail: dene@hodgson-engineering.com
Hoerbiger UK Ltd, 1649 Pershore Road, Stirchley, Birmingham, B30 3DR Tel: 0121-433 3636 Fax: 0121-433 3854 E-mail: info.huk@hoerbiger.com
Marshall Engineering Services, Kendrick House, Mere View Industrial Estate, Yaxley, Peterborough, PE7 3HS Tel: (01733) 240045 Fax: (01733) 241821
Neath Valve & Engineering Co. Ltd, Tank Farm Road, Llandarcy, Neath, West Glamorgan, SA10 6EN Tel: (01792) 817418 Fax: (01792) 817418
New Forest Instrument Control Ltd, 84 Cobham Road, Ferndown Industrial Estate, Wimborne, Dorset, BH21 7RW Tel: (01202) 875308 Fax: (01202) 893462 E-mail: info@newforestinstruments.co.uk
Nuthall Pump & Engineering Services, Queen Street, Langley Mill, Nottingham, NG16 4EJ Tel: (01773) 530630 Fax: (01773) 531532
Redmayne Engineering Ltd, Romsey Indust Estate, Greatbridge Road, Romsey, Hampshire, SO51 0HR Tel: (01794) 830832 Fax: (01794) 830123
S P P Pumps Ltd, Greg St, Reddish, Stockport, Cheshire, SK5 7BU Tel: 0161-480 4955 Fax: 0161-476 2193
Specialist On Site Services Ltd, 3 Park Lane, Spalding, Lincolnshire, PE11 1PJ Tel: (01775) 680608 Fax: (01775) 680825
Steadvale Air Systems Ltd, Boston Road, Glenrothes, Fife, KY6 2RE Tel: (01592) 771891 Fax: (01592) 772759 E-mail: sales@steadvale.co.uk
Stoneleigh Engineering Services Ltd, Unit 10 Lansdowne Workshops, Lansdowne Mews, London, SE7 8AZ Tel: (020) 8305 0792 Fax: (020) 8858 6665
Suff Marine (Europe) Ltd, 15 Allanfield Drive, Newton Stewart, Wigtownshire, DG8 6BP Tel: (01671) 401216 Fax: (01671) 401216 E-mail: sales@suffmarine.com
Turbine Controls Ltd, 52 Kenilworth Drive, Oadby Industrial Estate, Oadby, Leicester, LE2 5LG Tel: 0116-271 7248 Fax: 0116-271 7250 E-mail: mk@turbinecontrolsltd.com
Tyco Valves & Controls Distribution (UK) Ltd, Wellheads Terr, Wellheads Industrial Estate, Aberdeen, AB22 7GF Tel: (01224) 722562 Fax: (01224) 771607 E-mail: sales_aberdeen@tyco-valves.com
V C E Ltd, Unit 3 Hamilton Street, Carluke, Lanarkshire, ML8 4HA Tel: (01555) 772567 Fax: (01555) 770530
Valve Services Ltd, Station Road, South Shields, Tyne & Wear, NE33 1ED Tel: 0191-454 6185 Fax: 0191-454 6185
Valvekits Ltd, Brookside Way, Huthwaite, Sutton-in-Ashfield, Nottinghamshire, NG17 2NL Tel: (01623) 446700 Fax: (01623) 440214 E-mail: valvekits@valvekits.co.uk
Vesco Services Ltd, 6B Middlefield Road, Falkirk, FK2 9AG Tel: (01324) 611166 Fax: (01324) 621166 E-mail: sales@vescovalves.co.uk
Whittle Valve Repairs Ltd, Unit 3 Tower Enterprise Park, Great George Street, Wigan, Lancashire, WN3 4DP Tel: (01942) 493495 E-mail: sales@whittle-valves.co.uk

VALVE SACKS

Korsnas Packaging Ltd, Priory Road, Rochester, Kent, ME2 2BD Tel: (01634) 716701 Fax: (01634) 717468

VALVE TESTING SERVICES

Adanac Valve Specialities Ltd, 14 Windmill Avenue, Woolpit Business Park, Woolpit, Bury St. Edmunds, Suffolk, IP30 9UP Tel: (01359) 240404 Fax: (01359) 240406 E-mail: info@adanac.co.uk
A-Valvetech Services Ltd, 4 The Courtyard, D'Arcy Business Park, Llandarcy, Neath, West Glamorgan, SA10 6EJ Tel: (01792) 817708 Fax: (01792) 815298 E-mail: valtec3@hotmail.com
Y P S Valves Ltd, Richardshaw Road, Grangefield Industrial Estate, Pudsey, West Yorkshire, LS28 6QW Tel: 0113-256 7725 Fax: 0113-236 1987 E-mail: info@yps-valves.co.uk

VALVES, CHECK, DOUBLE FLAPPER

▶ Ham Baker Hartley, Garner Street, Etruria, Stoke-on-Trent, ST4 7BH Tel: (01782) 202300 Fax: (01782) 203639 E-mail: sale@hambaker.co.uk

VALVES, CHOKE, SUBSEA

Masterflo Valve Co (U K) Ltd, Blackness Road, Altens Industrial Estate, Altens, Aberdeen, AB12 3LH Tel: (01224) 878999 Fax: (01224) 878989 E-mail: info@masterflo.co.uk

VALVES, CONTROL, SUBSEA, CHOKE

Circor Instrumentation Ltd, Frays Mill Works, Cowley Road, Uxbridge, Middlesex, UB8 2AF Tel: (01895) 206780 Fax: (020) 8423 5933 E-mail: aratna@circor.co.uk
Cooper Energy Services, Mondial House, 5 Mondial Way, Hayes, Middlesex, UB3 5AR Tel: (020) 8990 1900 Fax: (020) 8990 1911
Koso Kent Introl Ltd, Armytage Road, Brighouse, West Yorkshire, HD6 1QF Tel: (01484) 710311 Fax: (01484) 407407 E-mail: control.valve@kentintrol.com

VALVES, FIRE EXTINGUISHER

Fire Protection Centre, Atkinsons Way, Foxhills Industrial Estate, Scunthorpe, South Humberside, DN15 8QJ Tel: (01724) 854199 Fax: 01724 854213 E-mail: bthloden@fireprotectioncentre.com

VALVES, GAS/AIR

Bemasan Ltd, Owen Road, Wolverhampton, WV3 0BB Tel: (01902) 772975 Fax: (01902) 424374 E-mail: nevasales@bemasan.com
British Metallic Packings Co 1933 Ltd, 15 Invicta Road, Dartford, DA2 6AY Tel: (01322) 224514
Fort Vale Engineering Ltd, Parkfield Works, Brunswick Street, Nelson, Lancashire, BB9 0SG Tel: (01282) 440000 Fax: (01282) 440046 E-mail: sales@fortvale.com
Leafield Engineering Ltd, Leafield Industrial Estate, Corsham, Wiltshire, SN13 9SS Tel: (01225) 810771 Fax: (01225) 810614 E-mail: lel@leafield.co.uk
Zoedale P.L.C., Stannard Way, Priory Business Park, Bedford, MK44 3WG Tel: (01234) 832832 Fax: (01234) 832800 E-mail: enquiries@zoedale.co.uk

VALVES, PRESSURE REDUCING/CONTROL

Dynamic Controls Ltd, Union Street, Royton, Oldham, OL2 5JD Tel: 0161-633 3933 Fax: 0161-633 4113 E-mail: sales@dynamiccontrols.co.uk
Fuller Water Systems, Cyder Works, High Street, Ixworth, Bury St. Edmunds, Suffolk, IP31 2HT Tel: (01359) 231481 Fax: (01359) 232345 E-mail: enq@fullerwatersys.co.uk
Husco International Ltd, 6 Rivington Road, Whitehouse Industrial Estate, Runcorn, Cheshire, WA7 3DT Tel: (01928) 701888 Fax: (01928) 710813 E-mail: uksales@huscointl.com
Nord Hydraulic Ltd, Unit Lkr3 L & M Business Park, Norman Road, Altrincham, Cheshire, WA14 4ES Tel: 0161-928 1199 Fax: 0161-941 5667 E-mail: david@nordhydraulic.co.uk
Premium Bermad UK Ltd, Newbury Crash Repair Centre, Arnhem Road, Newbury, Berkshire, RG14 5RU Tel: (01635) 528717 Fax: (01635) 528642 E-mail: chris.elliott@2bermad.co.uk
Safety Systems UK Ltd, Sharp Street, Worsley, Manchester, M28 3NA Tel: (01925) 820281 Fax: 0161-799 4335 E-mail: support@safetysystemsuk.com
Tecnica Europe Ltd, Suite 2 Baxall Business Centre, Adswood, Stockport, Cheshire, SK3 8LF Tel: 0161 480 5700 Fax: 0161 447 4476

VALVES, PUMP PROTECTION

▶ Control Valve Systems, Lower Coilentowie, Callander, Perthshire, FK17 8LW Tel: (01786) 841228

VALVES, SPECIAL PURPOSE/TO SPECIFICATION

Besseges Valves Tubes & Fittings Ltd, Jackson House, Turner Lane, Ashton-under-Lyne, Lancashire, OL6 8LP Tel: 0161-343 2225 Fax: 0161-339 0307 E-mail: sales@besseges-vts.co.uk
DMI Young & Cunningham Ltd, West Chirton Industrial Estate, Gloucester Road, North Shields, Tyne & Wear, NE29 8RQ Tel: 0191-270 4690 Fax: 0191-270 4691 E-mail: newcastle@yandc.co.uk
Radlett Valve & Engineering Co. Ltd, 38 Watling Street, Radlett, Hertfordshire, WD7 7NN Tel: (01923) 852131 Fax: (01923) 854484 E-mail: sales@radlettvalve.co.uk

VALVES, SUBSEA

MSCM, Unit 8 First Avenue, Marlow, Buckinghamshire, SL7 1YA Tel: (01628) 488361 Fax: (01628) 478760 E-mail: sales@mscmltd.co.uk
Oliver Valves Ltd, Haig Road, Parkgate Industrial Estate, Knutsford, Cheshire, WA16 8DX Tel: (01565) 632636 Fax: (01565) 654089 E-mail: cornwell@valves.co.uk

VALVES, TUBELESS TYRE

▶ DM Tyre Supplies, In2Connect house, Acton Road, Nottingham, NG10 1NJ Tel: 07779 765614 Fax: 0115 9284912 E-mail: dmtyrsupplies@btopenworld.com

VAN TRAILERS

Wilkinson Mobile Catering Systems Ltd, Unit 1, Global Way,, Lower Eccleshill Road,, Darwen, Lancashire, BB3 0RP Tel: 01254 706348 Fax: 01254 701335 E-mail: sales@wilkinsoncatering.co.uk

VANDAL RESISTANT LIGHTING

Designplan Lighting Ltd, 6 Wealdstone Road, Sutton, Surrey, SM3 9RW Tel: (020) 8254 2000 Fax: (020) 8644 4253 E-mail: info@designplan.co.uk
Maelor-Trafflex Ltd, Wrexham Industrial Estate, Abbey Road, Wrexham, Clwyd, LL13 9RF Tel: (01978) 661040 Fax: (01978) 661450 E-mail: orders@maelortraflex.co.uk

VANITY TOPS AND WASH BASINS

Oyster Products Ltd, Unit 3 Stonestile Farm, Stone Stile Farm, Selling, Faversham, Kent, ME13 9SD Tel: (01227) 732345 Fax: (01227) 738850 E-mail: oysterproducts@hotmail.com
Versital Ltd, Victoria Mill, Bradford Road, Bolton, BL3 2HF Tel: (01204) 380780 Fax: (01204) 392831 E-mail: np@langnp.demon.co.uk

VANITY UNITS

Armitage Venesta Washroom Systems Ltd, Imperial Business Estate, West Mill, Gravesend, Kent, DA11 0DL Tel: (01474) 353333 Fax: (01474) 533558 E-mail: info@armitage-venesta.co.uk
Dunhams Of Norwich, Hellesdon Park Road, Drayton High Road, Norwich, NR6 5DR Tel: (01603) 424855 Fax: (01603) 413336
Mermaid Panels Ltd, DBC House, Grimsby Road, Laceby, Grimsby, South Humberside, DN37 7DP Tel: (01472) 279940 Fax: (01472) 752575 E-mail: sales@mermaidpanels.com

VANS, *See Commercial Vehicle etc*

VAPOUR DEGREASING EQUIPMENT

S M S Degreasers (Sheet Metal Structures) Ltd, Woodlands, Cliff Road, Salcombe, Devon, TQ8 8LD Tel: (01548) 842454 Fax: (01548) 843380

VAPOUR RECOVERY SYSTEMS MANUFRS

Roplex Engineering Ltd, Roplex House, Church Road, Shedfield, Southampton, SO32 2HW Tel: (01329) 835772 Fax: (01329) 834480

VAPOURISERS, STEAM/ ELECTRIC

Chemtec UK Ltd, PO Box 3, Beith, Ayrshire, KA15 1JQ Tel: (01505) 502206 Fax: (01505) 502545 E-mail: sales@chemtecuklimted.co.uk

VARIABLE BORE RAMS

Stallion Hydraulic Services Ltd, Wharf Road, Gravesend, Kent, DA12 2RU Tel: (01474) 564707 Fax: (01474) 564752 E-mail: sales@stallion-group.com

VARIABLE HYDRAULIC PUMPS

C-Tronix UK Ltd, 185a Lower Blandford Road, Broadstone, Dorset, BH18 8DH Tel: (01202) 695500 E-mail: ap9000mart@aol.com

VARIABLE RESISTORS

Reo UK Ltd, Unit 8-9 Long Lane Industrial Estate, Long Lane, Craven Arms, Shropshire, SY7 8DU Tel: (01588) 673411 Fax: (01588) 672718 E-mail: sales@reo.co.uk

VARIABLE SPEED AIR COMPRESSORS

Air Response Ltd, Unit 8b Camp Industrial Estate, Rycote Lane, Milton Common, Thame, Oxfordshire, OX9 2NP Tel: (01844) 279870 Fax: (01844) 278669

VARIABLE SPEED DRIVE MANUFRS

Axiom Transmissions Ltd, 18 Manor Road, Folksworth, Peterborough, PE7 3SU Tel: (01733) 241234 Fax: (01733) 242435

Bennett Electrical Co, 6-8 Reginald St, Burslem, Stoke-on-Trent, ST6 1DU Tel: (01782) 825281 Fax: (01782) 575120 E-mail: motors@bennettelectrical.com

Berges UK Ltd, 3 Nelson Business Centre, Nelson Street, Denton, Manchester, M34 3ET Tel: (0161) 335 0995 Fax: 0161-335 0935

Chalwyn Estates Ltd, Chalwyn Industrial Estate, St Clement Road, Poole, Dorset, BH12 4PF Tel: (01202) 715400 Fax: (01202) 715600 E-mail: sales@chalwyn.co.uk

Control Techniques, Business Development Centre, Stafford Park 4, Telford, Shropshire, TF3 3BA Tel: (01952) 213727 Fax: (01952) 213701 E-mail: uksales@controltechniques.com

Controlled Speed Engineering Ltd, St Pegs House, Thornhills Beck Lane, Brighouse, West Yorkshire, HD6 4AH Tel: (01484) 721981 Fax: (01484) 721984 E-mail: info@controlledspeed.co.uk

Robert Cupitt Ltd, 4 Joplin Court, Sovereign Business Park, Crownhill, Milton Keynes, MK8 0JP Tel: (01908) 563063 Fax: (01908) 562910 E-mail: sales@robertcupitt.co.uk

Disco Drives (Kings Lynn) Ltd, Oldmedow Road, Hardwick Trading Estate, King's Lynn, Norfolk, PE30 4LE Tel: (01553) 761331 Fax: (01553) 692137 E-mail: enquiries@discodrives.co.uk

Electro Control Systems, Backlands, Church Way, Guilsborough, Northampton, NN6 8QF Tel: (01604) 740305 Fax: (01604) 740305

Hagglund Drives, Foxbridge Way, Normanton Industrial Estate, Normanton, West Yorkshire, WF6 1TN Tel: (01924) 220100 Fax: (01924) 890111 E-mail: sales@hagglund.com

▶ Newton Tesla (Electric Drives) Ltd, Unit G18 Warrington Business Park, Long Lane, Warrington, WA2 8TX Tel: (01925) 444773 Fax: (01925) 241477 E-mail: info@newton-tesla.com

Radway Control Systems, Business & Technology Centre, Radway Grn, Crewe, CW2 5PR Tel: (01270) 886176 Fax: (01270) 886275 E-mail: pjtomkinson@radway.co.uk

Sheppee International Ltd, Airfield Industrial Park, York Road, Elvington, York, YO41 4AU Tel: (01904) 608999 Fax: (01904) 608777 E-mail: sales@sheppee.com

Slater Drive Systems Ltd, 6a Dukesway, Prudhoe, Northumberland, NE42 6PQ Tel: (01661) 835566 Fax: (01661) 833868 E-mail: sales@slater-drives.com

Sprint Electric Ltd, Unit C2 Rudford Industrial Estate, Ford Road, Ford, Arundel, West Sussex, BN18 0BD Tel: (01903) 730000 Fax: (01903) 730893 E-mail: sales@sprint-electric.com

STM Power Transmission Ltd, Unit 10 Hartford Business Centre, Chester Road, Hartford, Northwich, Cheshire, CW8 2AB Tel: (01606) 557200 Fax: (01606) 301260 E-mail: info@stmuk.co.uk

Stock Electronics Ltd, 10 Edison Road, Salisbury, SP2 7NU Tel: (01722) 321758 Fax: (01722) 413079 E-mail: enquiries@stockelectronics.co.uk

Teco Electric Europe Ltd, Teco Building Centrepoint, Marshall Stevens Way, Trafford Park, Manchester, M17 1PP Tel: 0161-877 8025 Fax: 0161-877 8030 E-mail: enquiries@teco.co.uk

VARIABLE SPEED DRIVE SYSTEMS

I C P Projects Ltd, Cwm Cynon Business Park, Mountain Ash, Mid Glamorgan, CF45 4ER Tel: (01443) 477970 Fax: (01443) 476707 E-mail: sales@icpprojects.co.uk

VARIABLE SPEED ELECTRIC MOTORS

A S K Rewinds Ltd, Unit 5 Laneside, Metcalf Drive, Altham Industrial Estate, Accrington, Lancashire, BB5 5TU Tel: (01282) 776475 Fax: (01282) 779438 E-mail: sales@ask-rewinds-ltd.co.uk

C J Controls Ltd, Crofty Industrial Estate, Penclawdd, Swansea, SA4 3RS Tel: (01792) 851083 Fax: (01792) 850442 E-mail: sales@cjcontrols.co.uk

Mondside Ltd, Unit 22 Jubilee Trade Centre, Jubilee Road, Letchworth Garden City, Hertfordshire, SG6 1SP Tel: (01462) 682875 Fax: (01462) 686698 E-mail: mail@monside.com

VARIABLE SPEED GEARS

Allspeeds Ltd, Royal Works, Atlas Street, Clayton le Moors, Accrington, Lancashire, BB5 5LP Tel: (01254) 615100 Fax: (01254) 615199 E-mail: sales@allspeeds.co.uk

Combidrive Ltd, Unit 6, Parc Menter, Meadows Bridge, Cross Hands, Llanelli, Carmarthenshire, SA14 6RA Tel: (01269) 834848 Fax: (01269) 834850 E-mail: sales@combidrive.com

Compact Orbitial Gears Ltd, Unit A Brynberth Industrial Estate, Rhayader, Powys, LD6 5EW Tel: (01597) 811676 Fax: (01597) 811677 E-mail: info@compactorbitalgears.com

Motovario Ltd, Rushock Trading Estate, Rushock, Droitwich, Worcestershire, WR9 0NR Tel: (01299) 250859 Fax: (01299) 251493 E-mail: sales@motovario.co.uk

Opperman Mastergear Ltd, Hambridge Lane, Newbury, Berkshire, RG14 5TS Tel: (01635) 811500 Fax: (01635) 811501 E-mail: sales@opperman-mastergear.co.uk

VARIABLE SPEED PUMPING SETS

Allan Aqua-Systems Ltd, Allan Aqua House, Sedgwick Rd, Luton, LU4 9DT Tel: (01582) 574048 Fax: (01582) 574293 E-mail: info@allanaqua.co.uk

VARIABLE VOLTAGE TRANSFORMERS

Harrocell Ltd, 15e Wintersells Road, Byfleet, West Byfleet, Surrey, KT14 7LF Tel: (01932) 356347 Fax: (01932) 356347 E-mail: harrocell@btconnect.com

Reo UK Ltd, Unit 8-9 Long Lane Industrial Estate, Long Lane, Craven Arms, Shropshire, SY7 8DU Tel: (01588) 673411 Fax: (01588) 672718 E-mail: sales@reo.co.uk

VARNISHES, *See also headings for particular types*

Akzo Nobel Industrial Coatings Ltd, Crown House, Hollins Road, Darwen, Lancashire, BB3 0BG Tel: (01254) 760760 Fax: (01254) 701092 E-mail:

Akzo Nobel Woodcare, Meadow Lane, St. Ives, Cambridgeshire, PE27 4UY Tel: (01480) 496868 Fax: (01480) 496801 E-mail: woodcare@sis.akzonobel.com

Coo Var, Ellenshaw Works, Lockwood St, Hull, HU2 0HN Tel: (01482) 328053 Fax: (01482) 219266 E-mail: sales@coo-var.co.uk

N W E Paints Ltd, 66-70 Ffordd Las, Rhyl, Clwyd, LL18 2EA Tel: (01745) 342342 Fax: (01745) 334746 E-mail: admin@nwepaints.co.uk

Osmose Ltd, Timber Treatments Division, Fieldhouse Lane, Marlow, Buckinghamshire, SL7 1LS Tel: (01628) 486644 Fax: (01628) 476757 E-mail: info@protimsolignum.com

V I L Resins Ltd, Union Road, Bolton, BL2 2DT Tel: (01204) 388800 Fax: (01204) 362775 E-mail: enquiries@vilresins.com

The Valspar UK Holding Corporation Ltd, Unit 2-3 Avenue One, Witney, Oxfordshire, OX28 4XR Tel: (01993) 707400 Fax: (01993) 775579

VASES

▶ Rod Page Woodturning, 11 Southmead Crescent, Crewkerne, Somerset, TA18 8DH Tel: (01460) 271426 Fax: E-mail: rod@rodpage-woodturner.co.uk

VECTOR NETWORK ANALYSERS (VNA)

▶ Alternative Test Equipment, PO Box 3470, Wokingham, Berkshire, RG40 9AH Tel: (0845) 3457791 Fax: (0845) 3457792 E-mail: sales@AlternativeTest.co.uk

VEGETABLE HANDLING EQUIPMENT

Peter Cox Marketing Ltd, High Street, Wrestlingworth, Sandy, Bedfordshire, SG19 2EN Tel: (01767) 631733 Fax: (01767) 631722 E-mail: info@petercoxmarketing.co.uk

VEGETABLE PREPARATION

▶ Fresh Peeled Produce Ltd, Sutton Road, Walpole Cross Keys, King's Lynn, Norfolk, PE34 4HD Tel: (01553) 829481 Fax: (01553) 827095

VEGETABLE PREPARING MACHINES

Kiremko Food Processing Equipment UK Ltd, Armstrong House, First Avenue, Doncaster Finningley Airport, Doncaster, South Yorkshire, DN9 3GA Tel: (01302) 772929 Fax: (01302) 770548 E-mail: sales@kiremko.com

Nalco, Unit 5a Springside, Howard Road, Park Farm Industrial Estate, Redditch, Worcestershire, B98 7SE Tel: (01527) 453200 Fax: (01527) 520717

VEGETABLE WASH SOLUTIONS, FRESH PRODUCE

Del Monte Europe Ltd, Del Monte House, London Road, Staines, Middlesex, TW18 4JD Tel: (01784) 447400 Fax: (01784) 465301

VEGETABLES

▶ Fruit Sallad, 1 Blue Slates Close, Wheldrake, York, YO19 6NB Tel: (01904) 448080 E-mail: fruitsaladcom@btinternet.com

▶ Gowrie Growers, Longforgan, Dundee, DD2 5HJ Tel: (01382) 360620

▶ Namayasai LLP, Fair Hall, Southover High Street, Lewes, East Sussex, BN7 1HX Tel: (01273) 470667 Fax: (01273) 488816 E-mail: info@namayasai.co.uk

Pauleys Ltd, Sondes Road, Willowbrook East Industrial Estate, Corby, Northamptonshire, NN17 5XP Tel: (01536) 207200 Fax: (01536) 207201 E-mail: sales@pauleys.co.uk

VEHICLE ACCESS CONTROL SYSTEMS

Auto Audio Leeds Ltd, 35 Wakefield Road, Swillington, Leeds, LS26 8DT Tel: 0113-286 2970 Fax: 0113-287 0222 E-mail: autoaudiosales@aol.com

Broughton Controls Ltd, Shaw Road, Oldham, OL1 4AW Tel: 0161-627 0060 Fax: 0161-627 1362 E-mail: info@broughton-controls.co.uk

Came Automation Ltd, Design House, 27 Salt Hill Way, Slough, SL1 3TR Tel: (01753) 550660 Fax: (01753) 552424 E-mail: info@atlasgroup.co.uk

Clover Systems, 7 Endsleigh Gardens, Long Ditton, Surbiton, Surrey, KT6 5JL Tel: (020) 8399 1822 Fax: (020) 8770 0556 E-mail: cloversystems@btconnect.com

Electra Controls Ltd, 20 Acorn Close, Enfield, Middlesex, EN2 8LX Tel: (020) 8366 1433

Fleet Factors Ltd, 1b Beels Road, Stallingborough, Grimsby, South Humberside, DN41 8DN Tel: (01469) 577888 Fax: (01469) 578003

Identicar, Rushland Farm, Knowle Lane, Wookey, Wells, Somerset, BA5 1LD Tel: (01749) 677381

Vehicle Security Systems, 292-294 St. Helens Road, Bolton, BL3 3RP Tel: (01204) 660822 Fax: (01204) 660820 E-mail: info@vehiclesecuritysystems.co.uk

VEHICLE ACCESS RAMPS

▶ Robin Ramps, The Courtyard, Durham Way North, Aycliffe Industrial Park, Newton Aycliffe, County Durham, DL5 6HP Tel: (01325) 304070 Fax: (01325) 304088 E-mail: info@robinproducts.com

VEHICLE ACCESSORIES, ELECTRICAL

▶ Cartel Uk Ltd, 20 Colwell Road, Leicester, LE3 9AX Tel: (07977) 777742 Fax: 0116-223 9702 E-mail: cartel_uk@hotmail.co.uk

VEHICLE (BROADCAST/CINE/ VIDEO) MOBILE UNIT HIRE

Dales Broadcast Ltd, Unit 4, Oaks Industrial Estate, Coventry Road, Narborough, LE19 2GF Tel: 0116-272 5190 Fax: 0116-272 5196 E-mail: sales@dalesbroadcast.co.uk

Network Car, Unit 6 The Willows, 80 Willow Walk, London, SE1 5SY Tel: (020) 7231 1122 Fax: (020) 7231 2082

Scanners Television Outside Broadcast Ltd, 3 Chrysalis Way, Langley Bridge, Eastwood, Nottingham, NG16 3RY Tel: (01773) 718111 Fax: (01773) 716004

VEHICLE (BROADCAST/CINE/ VIDEO) MOBILE UNITS

C P S-Lanmear Ltd, 158 Little Hardwick Rd, Aldridge, Walsall, WS9 0SF Tel: 0121-353 5705 Fax: 0121-353 5705 E-mail: csiddell@compuserve.com

Clyde Broadcast Products Ltd, 2 Rutherford Court, 15 North Avenue, Clydebank Business Park, Clydebank, Dunbartonshire, G81 2QP Tel: 0141-952 7950 Fax: 0141-941 1224 E-mail: mail@clydebroadcast.com

D E G A Broadcast Systems, 1 Newton Court, Rankine Road, Basingstoke, Hampshire, RG24 8GF Tel: (01256) 816220 Fax: (01256) 843952 E-mail: david@dega.co.uk

S T V Videos, PO Box 299, Bromley, BR2 9EE Tel: (020) 8464 4287 E-mail: sales@stvvideos.co.uk

VEHICLE CHASSIS

A B T Products Ltd, Ashburton Industrial Estate, Ross-on-Wye, Herefordshire, HR9 7BW Tel: (01989) 563656 Fax: (01989) 566824 E-mail: abtproducts@clara.net

VEHICLE CHASSIS LUBRICATING SYSTEMS

Engineering & General Equipment Ltd, Eley Estate, Edmonton, London, N18 3BB Tel: (020) 8807 4567 Fax: (020) 8884 2229 E-mail: sales@centralube.com

Filtakleen (Manufacturing) Ltd, Forelle Centre, 30 Black Moor Road, Ebblake Industrial Estate, Verwood, Dorset, BH31 6BB Tel: (01202) 826280 Fax: (01202) 813207 E-mail: sales@filtakleen.com

VEHICLE (CROSS COUNTRY/ ROUGH TERRAIN/OFF-ROAD) MAINTENANCE AND REPAIR SERVICES

Continental Service Station Ltd, Brecon Road, Caerbont, Abercrave, Swansea, SA9 1SW Tel: (01639) 730279 Fax: (01639) 730282 E-mail: continentalss@aol.com

VEHICLE DEMOUNTABLE BODIES

Adcliffe Drawdeal Ltd, Rempstone Road, Coleorton, Coalville, Leicestershire, LE67 8HR Tel: (01530) 222010 Fax: (01530) 222589 E-mail: sales@adcliffe.co.uk

Ray Smith Group plc, Fengate, Peterborough, PE1 5XG Tel: (01733) 563936 Fax: (01733) 377090

S P S Ltd, Unit 9, Buildwas Road, Clayhill Light Industrial Park, Neston, CH64 3TU Tel: 0151-353 1775 Fax: 0151-353 1775 E-mail: pyeinc@supanet.com

VEHICLE EXHAUST EXTRACTION SYSTEMS, GARAGE/WORKSHOP ETC

Garage Equipment Services, Unit 2100, The Crescent, Solihull Parkway, Birmingham Business Park, Birmingham, B37 7YE Tel: 0121-329 1154 Fax: 0121-329 1190 E-mail: ges@unipart.co.uk

VEHICLE EXTERIOR CLEANING SYSTEMS

Ceetek Chemicals Ltd, Firs Industrial Estate, Kidderminster, Worcestershire, DY11 7QN Tel: (01562) 755337 Fax: (01562) 865660 E-mail: ceetek@aol.com

P G & C Nottingham Ltd, Main Road, Tallington, Stamford, Lincolnshire, PE9 4RN Tel: (01778) 380666 Fax: (01778) 381707 E-mail: enquiries@pgcnottingham.co.uk

Smith Bros & Webb Ltd, 22 Tything Road East, Kinwarton, Alcester, Warwickshire, B49 6EX Tel: (01789) 400096 Fax: (01789) 400231 E-mail: sales@vehicle-washing-systems.co.uk

▶ Tec UK, Royal Oak Way North Unit A, Daventry Distribution Centre, Royal Oak Industrial Estate, Daventry, Northamptonshire, NN11 8LR Tel: (01327) 300400 Fax: (01327) 879679 E-mail: tecuk@aol.com

Under Pressure, Unit 8 Eastlands, Coal Park Lane, Southampton, SO31 7GW Tel: (01489) 589891 Fax: (01489) 589785 E-mail: info@underpressure.uk.com

▶ Washtec UK Ltd, 14a Oak Industrial Park, Chelmsford Road, Dunmow, Essex, CM6 1XN Tel: (01371) 878800 Fax: (01371) 878810 E-mail: sales@washtec-uk.com

VEHICLE FLEET MANAGEMENT SOFTWARE

C F C Sollutions, 1310 Solihull Parkway, Birmingham Business Park, Birmingham, B37 7YB Tel: 0121-717 7040 Fax: 0121-717 7011 E-mail: enquiries@cfcsolutions.co.uk

Cartek Vehicle Solutions, Craven House Lansbury Estate, 102 Lower Guildford Road, Knaphill, Woking, Surrey, GU21 2EP Tel: (01483) 799499 Fax: (01483) 487400 E-mail: sales@cartek.co.uk

▶ Intelligent Fleet Ltd, Eden House, 101A Marsland Road, Sale, Cheshire, M33 3HS Tel: (0870) 2856125 Fax: (0870) 2856126 E-mail: mail@intelligentfleet.co.uk

Thermeon Europe Ltd, Russ Hill Farm, Russ Hill, Charlwood, Horley, Surrey, RH6 0EL Tel: (01293) 864300 E-mail: sales@thermeoneurope.com

V T Software Solutions, Unit 4Thornbury Office Park, Midland Way, Thornbury, Bristol, BS35 2BS Tel: (01454) 874002 Fax: (01454) 874001 E-mail: enquire@vtsoftwaresolutions.com

VEHICLE FLOOR RUGS

Easirider Co. Ltd, S2 Nene Centre, Freehold Street, Northampton, NN2 6EF Tel: (01604) 714103 Fax: (01604) 714106 E-mail: info@easirider.com

VEHICLE GRAPHICS

Art All, 34 Britannia Way, Britannia Enterprise Park, Lichfield, Staffordshire, WS14 9UY Tel: (01543) 258222 Fax: (01543) 258444 E-mail: signs@artall.co.uk

▶ Design Works, 18 High Street, Swindon, SN1 3EP Tel: (01793) 421900 Fax: (01793) 421901E-mail: enquiries@designswindon.com

Girdwood Display, 44 St. Marys Street, Edinburgh, EH1 1SZ Tel: 0131-556 7024 Fax: 0131-557 8288 E-mail: girdwooddisplay@aol.com

▶ Hot Dog Screenprint, Liddicoat Road, Lostwithiel, Cornwall, PL22 0YY Tel: (01208) 873839 Fax: (01208) 873839 E-mail: enquiries@hotdog-decals.com

▶ Ingenious, 16 Jackdaw Close, Stevenage, Hertfordshire, SG2 9DA Tel: (0845) 345 2576 Fax: (01438) 860359 E-mail: chris@ingeniousdisplays.co.uk

▶ Just William UK, Unit 31, 19b Moor Road, Broadstone, Dorset, BH18 8AZ Tel: (07775) 658148 Fax: (0871) 6614691 E-mail: sales@jwuk.com

Signline, Wayside House, Chapel Road, Meppershall, Shefford, Bedfordshire, SG17 5NQ Tel: (01462) 850718 Fax: (01462) 851212 E-mail: sales@signline.co.uk

C.J. Strain & Son Ltd, Lugton Road, Shillford, Hamlet, Glasgow, G78 3BA Tel: (01505) 850950 Fax: (01505) 850951 E-mail: cjstrain@btconnect.com

VEHICLE HIRE OR LEASING

▶ All Action American & English Taxicabs, Salop Street Garage, 2 Salop Street, Bolton, BL2 1DZ Tel: (01204) 361462 Fax: (01204) 531426 E-mail: julie@raytomkinson.demon.co.uk

Artcom Tradebridge Ltd, Unit 2E, South Bridgend, Crieff, Perthshire, PH7 4DJ Tel: (01764) 654666 Fax: (0560) 1163109 E-mail: enquiries@scot-track.co.uk

▶ Commercial Leasing Quote, 65 High Street, Hemel Hempstead, Hertfordshire, HP1 3AF Tel: (0800) 0198836 E-mail: inbox@commercialleasingquote.co.uk

▶ H & S Roe & Sons Ltd, Roe House, Boundry Lane, South Hykeham, Lincoln, LN6 9NQ Tel: (01522) 681542 Fax: (01522) 680199

▶ Hackfield Leasing Ltd, 121 High Street, Cranfield, Bedford, MK43 0BS Tel: (01234) 756152 Fax: (01234) 750850 E-mail: rex.holton@hacfield.com

Key Vehicle Solutions, 80a Main Street, Cherry Burton, Beverley, North Humberside, HU17 7RF Tel: (0845) 1662405 Fax: (0845) 1662406 E-mail: sales@key-vehicle-solutions.co.uk

▶ Lowestoft Electrical Co. Ltd, Service House, Wildes Street, Lowestoft, Suffolk, NR32 1XH Tel: (01502) 565484 Fax: (01502) 588933 E-mail: enquiries@lowestoftelectricalgroup.co.uk

▶ Mach Vehicle & Finance Ltd, 12 High Street, Madeley, Telford, Shropshire, TF7 5AQ Tel: (01952) 277700 Fax: (01952) 277703 E-mail: terry.mvf@virgin.net

Neva Consultants Leeds, Unit 41, Unity Business Centre, 26 Roundhay Road, Leeds, LS7 1AB Tel: (0845) 2062277 Fax: (0845) 2072277 E-mail: howard.mostyn@nevaplc.co.uk

▶ Vehicle Consulting - (S&B), 17 Menzies Avenue, Basildon, Essex, SS15 6SX Tel: 0845 0535719 Fax: 0845 0535720 E-mail: brian@vehicleconsulting.com

West Midlands Hire & Haulage, Dartmouth Road, Smethwick, West Midlands, B66 1BG Tel: 0121-555 5558 Fax: 0121-555 4939 E-mail: roylangford@wmhh.co.uk

VEHICLE HIRE, VINTAGE CAR

▶ Niall Johnston, 22 Berens Road, Shrivenham, Swindon, SN6 8EG Tel: (08709) 502012 Fax: (01793) 783769 E-mail: info@stretched4u.com

VEHICLE HIRE, WEDDING CAR

▶ Cameo Chauffeur Services, 43 Claremont Crescent, Croxley Green, Rickmansworth, Hertfordshire, WD3 3Qp Tel: 01923 238397 E-mail: enquiry@cameoservices.co.uk

▶ Niall Johnston, 22 Berens Road, Shrivenham, Swindon, SN6 8EG Tel: (08709) 502012 Fax: (01793) 783769 E-mail: info@stretched4u.com

▶ Mark One Limousines, 75 Merrivale Road, Portsmouth, PO2 0TH Tel: (023) 9266 9062 Fax: (023) 9267 7755 E-mail: markone.limousines@ntlworld.com

▶ The Marriage Carriage Co., 85 Hay Green Road South, Terrington St. Clement, King's Lynn, Norfolk, PE34 4PU Tel: (01553) 827198 Fax: (01553) 829758 E-mail: tony@themarriagecarriagecompany.co.uk

North Wales Trophies & Engravers, 34 Tan-Y-Bryn Road, Llandudno, Gwynedd, LL30 1UU Tel: (01492) 860363

▶ Platinum Chauffeurs, 42 Church Street, Needingworth, St. Ives, Cambridgeshire, PE27 4TB Tel: (01480) 463777 E-mail: info@platinumdrive.co.uk

▶ R J Poots & Co, 22 Bridge Street, Dromore, County Down, BT25 1AN Tel: (028) 9269 2349 E-mail: enquiries@rjpoots.co.uk

▶ SMJ Classic Cadillac Hire, Unit C1, Cromer House, Caxton Way, Stevenage, Hertfordshire, SG1 2DF Tel: 01438 356925 Fax: 01438 236023 E-mail: smjclassiccad64@aol.com

▶ Topclass Executive Private Hire, 1st Floor Co-op Stores, The Street, Woolpit, Bury St. Edmunds, Suffolk, IP30 9RU Tel: (07949) 372949 E-mail: info@topclass-executive.co.uk

VEHICLE IGNITION SYSTEMS

Boyer Bransden Electronics Ltd, Frinsbury House, Cox Street, Detling, Maidstone, Kent, ME14 3HE Tel: (01622) 730939 Fax: (01622) 730930 E-mail: sales@boyerbransden.com

Rex Caunt, 6 Kings Court, Kingsfield Road, Barwell, Leicester, LE9 8NZ Tel: (01455) 846963 Fax: (01455) 846963 E-mail: rex@rexcauntracing.com

VEHICLE IMMOBILISER SYSTEMS

Immobiliser UK, PO Box 223, Borehamwood, Hertfordshire, WD6 1AH Tel: (020) 8953 9803 Fax: (020) 8905 1541

Kosran ECV (UK) Ltd, No. 6 The Glenmore Centre, Grove Technology Park, Wantage, Oxfordshire, OX12 9FA Tel: (0870) 7875687 Fax: (0870) 7875633 E-mail: sales@kosran.com

Manx Security, 27 Regent Square, Belvedere, Kent, DA17 6EP Tel: (01322) 439333 Fax: (01322) 408331 E-mail: brian.manx@ntlworld.com

MBM, Unit 7 Gibson Square, Talbot Street, Golborne, Warrington, WA3 3NN Tel: (01942) 721126 Fax: (01942) 276410

Precision Alarms, Pauls Court, 12b Meppel Avenue, Canvey Island, Essex, SS8 9RZ Tel: (01268) 696787 Fax: (01268) 696922 E-mail: sales@precisionalarms.co.uk

Retrofit Alarmacar, 652 Chester Road, Sutton Coldfield, West Midlands, B73 5JR Tel: 0121-382 8933 Fax: 0121-682 7720 E-mail: sales@retrofit.co.uk

VEHICLE LIVERY SIGNS

Allsteed Signs & Graphics Ltd, Unit 4 & 5 Palmerston Business Park, New Gate Lane, Fareham, Hampshire, PO14 1DJ Tel: (01329) 234224 Fax: 01329 317659 E-mail: sales@allspeedsigns.co.uk

Badgemans Recognition Express, 8 Hillside Industrial Estate, London Road, Horndean, Waterlooville, Hampshire, PO8 0BL Tel: (023) 9259 5509 Fax: (023) 9259 5528 E-mail: sales@re-southern.co.uk

Baker Ward Ltd, 1137 Yardley Wood Road, Birmingham, B14 4LS Tel: 0121-474 3185 Fax: 0121-474 6291 E-mail: sales@bakerward.co.uk

Burkett Quicksign, Unit 19 Carbrook Hall Industrial Estate, Dunlop Street, Sheffield, S9 2HR Tel: 0114-256 0720 Fax: 0114-256 0192 E-mail: sales@burkettquicksign.co.uk

Car & Business Cosmetics, 1 Maxwell Street, South Shields, Tyne & Wear, NE33 4PU Tel: 0191-456 3795 Fax: 0191-454 4078

Caractor Graphics, 330 Moorhey Road, Liverpool, L31 5LR Tel: 0151-520 0500 Fax: 0151-520 0900 E-mail: caractorgraphics@yahoo.co.uk

Contrast Signs, 135 Roxeth Green Avenue, Harrow, Middlesex, HA2 0QJ Tel: (020) 8864 9242

Cotswold Graphics Ltd, 10 Draycott Business Village, Draycott, Moreton-in-Marsh, Gloucestershire, GL56 9JY Tel: (01386) 701222 Fax: (01386) 701228 E-mail: johnl@cotswold-graphics.co.uk

D E Signs, Cartref, Chelmsford Road, Barnston, Dunmow, Essex, CM6 1LS Tel: (01371) 874011 Fax: (01371) 874011 E-mail: tim@de-signs.co.uk

Euro Signs UK Ltd, 92 Cato Street, Hartlands, Birmingham, B7 4TS Tel: 0121-359 5566 Fax: 0121-359 5354 E-mail: sales@europlate.com

Eventsigns Sign Makers, Unit 6 Poplar Drive, Witton, Birmingham, B6 7AD Tel: 0121-344 3141 Fax: 0121-344 3181 E-mail: eventsignsgb@aol.com

Hazchem Signs, The Old Rectory, Main Street, Shalstone, Buckingham, MK18 5LT Tel: (01280) 841400 Fax: (01280) 840599

Henley Sign People, Unit 1b Vines Farm, Reading Road, Cane End, Reading, RG4 9HE Tel: 0118-972 4567 Fax: 0118-972 3205 E-mail: sales@signpeople.com

Imagination Signs, 43 Birdham Road, Chichester, West Sussex, PO19 8TB Tel: (01243) 783569 Fax: (01243) 785011 E-mail: sales@imaginationsigns.co.uk

Jupiter Signs, 20 Singer Way, Kempston, Bedford, MK42 7AE Tel: (01234) 854577 Fax: (01234) 841401 E-mail: sales@jupitersigns.com

Letters & Logos Ltd, Crow La Bus Park, Crow, Ringwood, Hampshire, BH24 3EA Tel: (01425) 477281 Fax: (01425) 480094 E-mail: team@lettersandlogos.co.uk

Lyons, 206 Lylehill Road, Belfast, BT14 8SN Tel: (028) 9082 5688 Fax: (028) 9082 5688

Mcquillan Signs, Cleves, Keymer Road, Burgess Hill, West Sussex, RH15 0AP Tel: (01444) 471847 Fax: (01444) 248592 E-mail: johntmcquillan@fsnet.co.uk

Motor Mode, The Art Works, 53 Butchers Lane, Mereworth, Maidstone, Kent, ME18 5QA Tel: (01622) 817400 Fax: (01732) 868167 E-mail: office@motormode.com

Steve Petrek Signs, Unit 5 Ladford Trading Park, Seighford, Stafford, ST18 9QL Tel: (01785) 282497 Fax: (01785) 282497

R M H Refinishing, 2 Rutland Court, Manners Avenue, Manners Industrial Estate, Ilkeston, Derbyshire, DE7 8EF Tel: 0115-944 1528 Fax: 0115-944 1526

Ram Signs, 4 Brighton Road, Lower Kingswood, Tadworth, Surrey, KT20 6SY Tel: (01737) 833444 Fax: (01737) 833432 E-mail: rsgsales@aol.com

Sigma Signs Ltd, Unit 4B, Arun Buildings, Arundel Road, Uxbridge, Middlesex, UB8 2RP Tel: (01895) 273268 Fax: (01895) 271614 E-mail: signs@sigmasigns.com

Sign & Display Centre, 253 Barlow Moor Road, Manchester, M21 7GJ Tel: 0161-861 7311 Fax: 0161-861 7306 E-mail: sales@signanddisplay.co.uk

The Sign Shop (Horsham) Ltd, 55a Park Terrace East, Horsham, West Sussex, RH13 5DJ Tel: (01403) 268988 Fax: (01403) 253085 E-mail: enquiries@thesignshop.co.uk

Sign Workshop, 8 The Ridgeway, Hitchin, Hertfordshire, SG5 2BT Tel: (01462) 442440 Fax: (01462) 442440 E-mail: sales@thesignworkshop.co.uk

Signage Ltd, Units 31-32 Bloomfield Commercial Centre, 5 Factory Street, Belfast, BT5 5AW Tel: (028) 9045 0145 Fax: (028) 9073 2533 E-mail: signageltd@btconnect.com

Signam Ltd, Harris Road, Warwick, CV34 5FY Tel: (01926) 417300 Fax: (01926) 417333 E-mail: sales@signam.co.uk

Solihull Signs, 270 Lode Lane, Solihull, West Midlands, B91 2HY Tel: 0121-704 1624 Fax: 0121-704 1624 E-mail: sales@solihullsigns.co.uk

Spa Display Ltd, 23 North Street Industrial Estate, Droitwich, Worcestershire, WR9 8JB Tel: (01905) 775428 Fax: (01905) 795417 E-mail: signs@spa-display.sagehost.co.uk

Spectrum Signs, 290 Northholt Road, South Harrow, Harrow, Middlesex, HA2 8EB Tel: (020) 8422 1168 Fax: (020) 8864 4220 E-mail: spectrumsigns@webtribe.net

Technosign Ltd, Unit 3 35a Stanbridge Road, Leighton Buzzard, Bedfordshire, LU7 4PZ Tel: (01525) 382111 Fax: (01525) 382382

Treble Nine Signs, 8 Whittingham Road, Halesowen, West Midlands, B63 3TE Tel: 0121-550 1581 Fax: 0121-550 1581 E-mail: russ@treble-nine-signs.freeserve.co.uk

Vision Visual Solutions Ltd, 1 Solent Industrial Estate, Shamblehurst Lane, Hedge End, Southampton, SO30 2FX Tel: (01489) 781000 Fax: (01489) 781100 E-mail: sales@vvsltd.co.uk

Wolverhampton Plastics Holdings Ltd, Sharrocks Street, Wolverhampton, WV1 3RP Tel: (01902) 455116 Fax: (01902) 455200 E-mail: wton.plastics@virgin.net

VEHICLE LOADING CONVEYOR SYSTEMS

Caljan Rite Hite Ltd, Moorbridge Road, Bingham, Nottingham, NG13 8GG Tel: (01949) 838850 Fax: (01949) 836953 E-mail: caljanritehite@caljanritehite.co.uk

Owens Conveyor, Westgate House, Westgate, Aldridge, Walsall, WS9 8EX Tel: (01922) 452333 Fax: (01922) 458777 E-mail: msullivan@ocon.co.uk

Rolamat Ltd, Unit 5 Bunas Park, Hollow Down Road, Lopcombe, Salisbury, SP5 1BP Tel: (01264) 782143 Fax: (01264) 782580 E-mail: info@rolamat.co.uk

VEHICLE LOCATING OR TRACKING SYSTEMS

▶ Internal Communications Installations Ltd, 24 A Progress Business Park, Orders Lane, Kirkham, Preston, PR4 2TZ Tel: (0845) 6340085 Fax: (01772) 687529 E-mail: info@4pm.uk.com

Siemens V D O Trading Ltd, Wiltshire House County Park, Shrivenham Road, Swindon, SN1 2NR Tel: (01793) 500100 Fax: (01793) 500101E-mail: sales@siemens-datatrack.com

Terrafix Ltd, Unit 23c Newfields Industrial Estate, High Street, Stoke-on-Trent, ST6 5PD Tel: (01782) 577015 Fax: (01782) 835667 E-mail: sales@terrafix.co.uk

VEHICLE LOCATION TRACKING EQUIPMENT

▶ Digicore, Sage House, 319 Pinner Road, Harrow, Middlesex, HA1 4HF Tel: (020) 8515 2900 Fax: (020) 8861 3888 E-mail: mark.naldrett@digicore.co.uk

▶ Mobile Tracking Systems, 1-2 Kingdom Close, Fareham, Hampshire, PO15 5TJ Tel: (01489) 571600 E-mail: admin@mtsgroup.co.uk

Transcomm UK Ltd, Heathrow Boulevard, 280 Bath Road, West Drayton, Middlesex, UB7 0DQ Tel: (020) 8990 9090 Fax: (020) 8990 9110 E-mail: customer.services@transcomm.uk.com

VEHICLE MIRRORS

Ashtree Glass Ltd, Ashtree Works, Brownroyd Street, Bradford, West Yorkshire, BD8 9AF Tel: (01274) 546732 Fax: (01274) 548525 E-mail: sales@ashtree.yorks.com

Bradley Glass Ltd, 19 Ham Bridge Trading Estate, Willowbrook Road, Worthing, West Sussex, BN14 8NA Tel: (01903) 205411 Fax: (01903) 214395 E-mail: enquiries@bradleyglass.co.uk

D C Carter Ltd, Meadow Farm, Packards Lane, Wormingford, Colchester, CO6 3AH Tel: (01206) 243309 Fax: (01206) 242161 E-mail: dccarter@onetel.com

Schefenacker Vision Systems UK Ltd, Portchester 2, Castle Trading Estate, Fareham, Hampshire, PO16 9SD Tel: (023) 9221 0022 Fax: (023) 9253 9522

Spafax International Ltd, Kingsland Industrial Park, Stroudley Road, Basingstoke, Hampshire, RG24 8UG Tel: (01256) 814400 Fax: (01256) 814141 E-mail: sales@spafaxmirrors.com

Truck-Lite Co. Ltd, Waterfall Lane, Cradley Heath, West Midlands, B64 6QB Tel: 0121-561 7000 Fax: 0121-561 1415 E-mail: birminghamsales@truck-lite.com

VEHICLE MOUNTED BEACONS

Delta Design, 1 Kings Park Industrial Estate, Primrose Hill, Kings Langley, Hertfordshire, WD4 8ST Tel: (01923) 269522 Fax: (01923) 260167 E-mail: sales@deltadesign.co.uk

VEHICLE MOUNTED CRANES

Fassi UK Ltd, 26 Blick Road, Heathcote Industrial Estate, Warwick, CV34 6TA Tel: (01926) 889779 Fax: (01926) 885777 E-mail: mail@fassi.co.uk

VEHICLE MOUNTED SKIP LOADERS

Trio Skips & Hooks Ltd, Ashville Road, Gloucester, GL2 5DA Tel: (01452) 331022 Fax: (01452) 331566 E-mail: info@trio-waste.co.uk

VEHICLE MOUNTED WORKING PLATFORMS

Niftylift Ltd, Fingle Drive, Stonebridge, Milton Keynes, MK13 0ER Tel: (01908) 223456 Fax: (01908) 312733E-mail: info@niftylift.com

VEHICLE MOVING LIFTS

Rod Brown Engineering Ltd, Western Villa 58 The Dean, Alresford, Hampshire, SO24 9BD Tel: (01962) 735220 Fax: (01962) 735239 E-mail: sales@rodbrowneng.co.uk

VEHICLE NAVIGATION SYSTEMS

▶ M R D The Ice Zone, MRD House, Glasgow Road, Bathgate, West Lothian, EH48 2QW Tel: (01506) 630575 Fax: (01506) 630575 E-mail: sales@mrdbathgate.com

Oxford Technical Solutions, 77 Heyford Park, Camp Road, Upper Heyford, Bicester, Oxfordshire, OX25 5HD Tel: (01869) 238015 Fax: (01869) 238016

VEHICLE REFRIGERATION EQUIPMENT

B S Panel Van Conversions, 1 Carloggas Industrial Units, St. Columb Major Industrial Estate, St. Columb, Cornwall, TR9 6SF Tel: (01637) 880700 Fax: (01637) 880056 E-mail: enquiries@bspanelvanconversions.gbr.fm

Carrier Transicold UK Ltd, 260 Cygnet Court, Centre Park, Warrington, WA1 1RR Tel: (01925) 401200 Fax: (01925) 401222

Cold Start Ltd, Little Tennis St South, Nottingham, NG2 4EU Tel: 0115-950 5095 Fax: 0115-950 5096 E-mail: sue@coldstart.freeserve.co.uk

VEHICLE SEAT HEATERS

Denso Manufacturing UK Ltd, Queensway Campus, Hortonwood, Telford, Shropshire, TF1 7FS Tel: (01952) 608400 Fax: (01952) 675222

Foursome Vehicle Heaters Ltd, Brockhill Works, Windsor Road, Redditch, Worcestershire, B97 6DJ Tel: (01527) 64126 Fax: (01527) 584611 E-mail: info@vehicleheaters.co.uk

VEHICLE SOUNDPROOFING SERVICES

Stewart Energy Insulation Ltd, Connect House, 21 Willow Lane, Mitcham, Surrey, CR4 4NA Tel: (020) 8648 6601 Fax: (020) 8648 6602 E-mail: info@stewart-energy.com

VEHICLE STEAM CLEANING CONTRACTORS

A T Jones, 109 Woodfield Road, Balsall Heath, Birmingham, B12 8TE Tel: (07947) 501791 Fax: 0121-440 2653

VEHICLE TILT COVERS

C J Covers Ltd, 30 Williamson Street, Hull, HU9 1EP Tel: (01482) 226970 Fax: (01482) 327218

G. Mudford & Sons Ltd, Aurillac Way, Hallcroft Road, Retford, Nottinghamshire, DN22 7PX Tel: (01777) 703489 Fax: (01777) 704743 E-mail: info@mudfordmarquees.co.uk

Roland Tilts UK Ltd, Unit 1 Usher Street, Bradford, West Yorkshire, BD4 7DS Tel: (01274) 391645 Fax: (01274) 305156

Stronghold International, Nicholson Court, Geddings Road, Hoddesdon, Hertfordshire, EN11 0NE Tel: (01992) 460274 Fax: (01992) 479471 E-mail: sales@stronghold.co.uk

VEHICLE TIPPING GEAR

Harsh Ltd, The Industrial Estate, Full Sutton, York, YO41 1HS Tel: (01759) 372100 Fax: (01759) 371414 E-mail: sales@harshuk.com

Jespro 2000 Ltd, Central Mills, Raymond Street, Bradford, West Yorkshire, BD5 8DT Tel: (01274) 735446 Fax: (01274) 394909 E-mail: sales@jespro.com

VEHICLE TOWING EQUIPMENT

Nimbus Products (Sheffield) Ltd, Julian Way, Tyler Street Industrial Estate, Sheffield, S9 1GD Tel: 0114-243 2362 Fax: 0114-243 5046 E-mail: sales@nimbusproducts.co.uk

R D F Eurobars, 55 Second Drove, Peterborough, PE1 5XA Tel: (01733) 555263 Fax: (01733) 555913 E-mail: sales@eurobars.co.uk

Tanfield Towbars, Blatchford Road, Horsham, West Sussex, RH13 5QR Tel: (01403) 269100 Fax: (01403) 251199

Western Towing & Alarms, Unit A1 Kingsteignton Industrial Estate, Kingsteignton, Newton Abbot, Devon, TQ12 3BN Tel: (01392) 216336 Fax: (01626) 363111 E-mail: richarddsaxton@aol.com

Witter Towbars, 11 Drome Road, Deeside Industrial Park, Deeside, Clwyd, CH5 2NY Tel: (01244) 284500 Fax: (01244) 284577 E-mail: sales@witter-towbars.com

York Tow Bars Ltd, Brokenford Lane, Totton, Southampton, SO40 9DY Tel: (023) 8086 6699 Fax: (023) 8086 2223 E-mail: sales@york-towbars.co.uk

VEHICLE TRACKING NIGHT VISION EQUIPMENT

▶ DIY Tracking Ltd, Brooklands House, 3 Kingdom Close, Fareham, Hampshire, PO15 5TJ Tel: (01489) 571600 Fax: (01489) 571010 E-mail: sales@diytracking.com

Vistar Night Vision Ltd, 24 Doman Road, Camberley, Surrey, GU15 3DF Tel: (01276) 708800 Fax: (01276) 708807 E-mail: info@vistar.co.uk

VEHICLE TRACKING PERSONAL PROTECTION ALARM SYSTEMS

▶ Astrata Group Ltd, Astrata, 112-113 The Chambers, Chelsea Harbour, London, SW10 0XF Tel: (07841) 213759 E-mail: sales@astratagroup.com

Big Brother UK, 23 Castalia Square, London, E14 3NG Tel: (0800) 0186315 Fax: (0871) 8713816 E-mail: bigbrotheruk@hotmail.com

▶ Car Communications, 33 London Road, Blackburn, BB1 7HA Tel: (0845) 2266454 E-mail: info@carcommunications.co.uk

▶ Digicore, Sage House, 319 Pinner Road, Harrow, Middlesex, HA1 4HF Tel: (020) 8515 2900 Fax: (020) 8861 3888 E-mail: mark.naldrett@digicore.co.uk

▶ DIY Tracking Ltd, Brooklands House, 3 Kingdom Close, Fareham, Hampshire, PO15 5TJ Tel: (01489) 571600 Fax: (01489) 571010 E-mail: sales@diytracking.com

▶ Mobile Tracking Systems, 1-2 Kingdom Close, Fareham, Hampshire, PO15 5TJ Tel: (01489) 571600 E-mail: admin@mtsgroup.co.uk

North London Car Sounds Vhcle Security Systems, PO Box 302, Welwyn Garden City, Hertfordshire, AL8 7NQ Tel: (01707) 371681 E-mail: info@piranha-alarms.co.uk

Siemens V D O Trading Ltd, Wiltshire House County Park, Shrivenham Road, Swindon, SN1 2NR Tel: (01793) 500100 Fax: (01793) 500101E-mail: sales@siemens-datatrack.com

VEHICLE TRANSPORTER OPERATORS

Duggan Transport Ltd, Church Road, Shilton, Coventry, CV7 9HX Tel: (024) 7661 2871 Fax: (024) 7661 2871

Mainland Car Deliveries Ltd, Mainland House, Bootle, Merseyside, L20 3EF Tel: 0151-933 9612 Fax: 0151-933 4751 E-mail: contactus@mcd-ltd.co.uk

Vehicle Movements (North East) Ltd, Sandy Lane, North Gosforth, Newcastle Upon Tyne, NE3 5HE Tel: 0191-236 1101 Fax: 0191-236 1143 E-mail: vehiclemovements@murrayhogg.co.uk

VEHICLE WEIGHING SYSTEMS, ON-BOARD

R D S Technology Ltd, Cirencester Road, Minchinhampton, Stroud, Gloucestershire, GL6 9BH Tel: (01453) 733300 Fax: (01453) 733311 E-mail: info@rdstec.com

VEHICLE WRAPPING FILM

Burkett Quicksign, Unit 19 Carbrook Hall Industrial Estate, Dunlop Street, Sheffield, S9 2HR Tel: 0114-256 0720 Fax: 0114-256 0192 E-mail: sales@burkettquicksign.co.uk

VEHICLES, DIY/KIT/REPLICA

Best International Equipment Ltd, Unit 5 Centre One, Old Sarum Park Lysander Way, Old Sarum, Salisbury, SP4 6BU Tel: 01722 410203 Fax: 01722 320831

D J Sportscars International Ltd, 2 Edinburgh Place, Harlow, Essex, CM20 2DJ Tel: (01279) 442661 Fax: (01279) 434956 E-mail: post@daxcars.co.uk

Dakar Cars Ltd, Stanhill Farm, Birchwood Road, Dartford, DA2 7HD Tel: (01322) 614044 Fax: (01322) 668500 E-mail: sales@dakar.co.uk

Pilgrim Cars (U K) Ltd, Unit 14 Mackley Industrial Estate, Henfield Road, Small Dole, Henfield, West Sussex, BN5 9XR Tel: (01273) 493860 Fax: (01273) 494889 E-mail: sales@pilgrimcars.com

Westfield Sports Cars Ltd, 1 Gibbons Industrial Park, Dudley Road, Kingswinford, West Midlands, DY6 8XF Tel: (01384) 400077 Fax: (01384) 288781 E-mail: info@westfield-sportscars.co.uk

VELVET

British Velvets Ltd, Wyre Street, Padiham, Burnley, Lancashire, BB12 8DQ Tel: (01282) 778134 Fax: (01282) 772168 E-mail: sales@britishvelvets.co.uk

Furtex, Hopton Mills, Hopton, Mirfield, West Yorkshire, WF14 8HE Tel: (01924) 490591 Fax: (01924) 495605 E-mail: furtex@eu.interfaceinc.com

VENDING CUP AND LID PRINTING MACHINES

Pentex Sales Ltd, Hamilton House Broadfields, Bicester Road, Aylesbury, Buckinghamshire, HP19 3BG Tel: (01296) 318220 Fax: (01296) 339973 E-mail: sales@pentex.co.uk

VENDING MACHINE COMPONENTS

England Worthside Ltd, Hope Mills, South Street, Keighley, West Yorkshire, BD21 1AG Tel: (01535) 682222 Fax: (01535) 682223 E-mail: enquiries@worthside.co.uk

I J G Machines, 59 The Promenade, Portstewart, County Londonderry, BT55 7AF Tel: (028) 7083 3154

Nebrak Ltd, 1 Ipplepen Business Park, Edgelands Lane, Ipplepen, Newton Abbot, Devon, TQ12 5UG Tel: (01803) 813900 Fax: (01803) 812300 E-mail: sales@nebrak.com

▶ R P C Tedeco-Gizeh UK Ltd, Kenfig Industrial Estate, Margam, Port Talbot, West Glamorgan, SA13 2PG Tel: (01656) 746655 Fax: (01656) 743074 E-mail: sales@rpc-tedeco-gizeh.com

VENDING MACHINE DESIGN

▶ Safer Systems UK Ltd, Units 7 & 8, Molyneux Business Park, Matlock, Derbyshire, DE4 2HJ Tel: (01629) 735577 Fax: (01629) 735588 E-mail: sales@safetysystems.co.uk

VENDING MACHINE INGREDIENTS

Betttavend Ltd, 5 Speedwell Close, Chandlers Ford Industrial Estate, Eastleigh, Hampshire, SO53 4BT Tel: (023) 8025 5222 Fax: (023) 8027 6644 E-mail: enquiries@bettavend.co.uk

Jede North East, Unit B4, Benfield Business Park, Benfield Road, Newcastle Upon Tyne, NE6 4NQ Tel: 0191-238 8000 Fax: 0191-238 8001 E-mail: jede.uk@jede.com

▶ P M Vending Ltd, Unit 25 Clearview Business Park, Loughborough Road, Quorn, Loughborough, Leicestershire, LE12 8DU Tel: (01509) 415333 Fax: (01509) 211650 E-mail: pmvending@btopenworld.com

The Red Pelican Coffee Company Ltd, Little Horwood Road, Great Horwood, Milton Keynes, MK17 0NZ Tel: (01296) 713280 Fax: (01296) 714961

VENDING MACHINE MANAGEMENT SERVICES

Bundz Vending Services Ltd, Southern Messsenger Close, Loughborough, Leicestershire, LE11 5SR Tel: (01509) 230481 Fax: (01509) 233572

Selecta UK Ltd, Unit 7 Stockton Close, Minworth Industrial Park, Minworth, Sutton Coldfield, West Midlands, B76 1DH Tel: 0121-313 2442 Fax: 0121-313 5037

VENDING MACHINE MANUFRS,

See also headings for particular types

Alba Beverage Co. Ltd, Unit 4, Sauchiebank, Edinburgh, EH11 2NN Tel: 0131-539 2755 Fax: 0131-346 8008 E-mail: albabeverageco@msn.com

▶ Allied Machine Sales, 23 Saxton Lane, Saxton, Tadcaster, North Yorkshire, LS24 9QD Tel: (01937) 558560 Fax: (01937) 558642 E-mail: info@alliedmachines.co.uk

Aramark Ltd, Caledonia House Lawnswood Business Park, Redvers Close, Leeds, LS16 6QY Tel: 0113-230 5300 Fax: (0870) 1118199 E-mail: client-care@aramark.co.uk

Armadale Vending Services Ltd, Armadale House, Bury Road Industrial Estate, Ramsey, Huntingdon, Cambridgeshire, PE26 1NF Tel: (01487) 813892 Fax: (01487) 813021 E-mail: info@armadale-vending-services.co.uk

▶ Automatic Retailing (Scotland LTD), Barrmill Road, Galston, Ayrshire, KA4 8HH Tel: (01563) 821900 Fax: (01563) 820329 E-mail: enquires@automaticretail.co.uk

Bundz Vending Services Ltd, Southern Messsenger Close, Loughborough, Leicestershire, LE11 5SR Tel: (01509) 230481 Fax: (01509) 233572

Bunzl Vending Services Ltd, 7 Sandpiper Way, Strathclyde Business Park, Bellshill, Lanarkshire, ML4 3NG Tel: (01698) 574580 Fax: (01698) 841517 E-mail: sales.glasgow@bunzlvend.com

C P V Watercoolers, 90 Cannon Lane, Pinner, Middlesex, HA5 1HR Tel: (020) 8866 1585 Fax: (020) 8558 6780 E-mail: sales@c-p-v.co.uk

Coinage (Bristol) Ltd, 91 Mayflower Street, Plymouth, PL1 1SB Tel: (0870) 1600992 Fax: (01364) 73799 E-mail: sales@coinage.co.uk

▶ Dass Manufacturing Ltd, Sutton Business Centre, Restmor Way, Wallington, Surrey, SM6 7AH Tel: (020) 8669 8012 Fax: (020) 8669 9529

Drinkmaster Holdings Ltd, Plymouth Road, Liskeard, Cornwall, PL14 3PG Tel: (01579) 342082 Fax: (01579) 342591 E-mail: info@drinkmaster.co.uk

Elite Vending Services Ltd, East Street, Grantham, Lincolnshire, NG31 6QW Tel: (01476) 591703 Fax: (01476) 576422 E-mail: neville@elitevending.freeserve.co.uk

Free Enterprise (Technical) Ltd, Swale Marina, Conyer, Sittingbourne, Kent, ME9 9HM Tel: (07810) 391393

Golden Valley Supplies Ltd, N2b Unit Inchbrook Trading Estate, Bath Road, Woodchester, Stroud, Gloucestershire, GL5 5EY Tel: (01453) 832976 Fax: (01453) 836976 E-mail: sales@gvend.f9.co.uk

Grange Total Solutions Ltd, The Grange, Grange Lane, Downham, Billericay, Essex, CM11 1LE Tel: (01268) 710209 Fax: (01268) 710095 E-mail: info@grangetotalsolutionsfsnet.co.uk

Hillday Leasing & Supplies Ltd, 1a Haverscroft Industrial Estate, New Road, Attleborough, Norfolk, NR17 1YE Tel: (01953) 454014 Fax: (01953) 454014 E-mail: hillday@btinternet.com

Jede North East, Unit B4, Benfield Business Park, Benfield Road, Newcastle Upon Tyne, NE6 4NQ Tel: 0191-238 8000 Fax: 0191-238 8001 E-mail: jede.uk@jede.com

Kent & Sussex Vending, K S V Business Park, Nan Tucks Lane, Buxted, Uckfield, East Sussex, TN22 4PN Tel: (01825) 732772 Fax: (01825) 732696 E-mail: info@ksv.co.uk

Locwil Ltd, Unit 17 Spring Road Industrial Estate, Lanesfield Drive, Wolverhampton, WV4 6UB Tel: (01902) 404093 Fax: (01902) 497561 E-mail: info@locwil.com

Matrix Catering Systems Ltd, Victoria Court, Hurricane Way, Wickford, Essex, SS11 8YY Tel: (01268) 574001 Fax: (01268) 574004

Millsons Vending, 89 Pembury Road, Tonbridge, Kent, TN9 2JF Tel: (01732) 500599 Fax: (01732) 363318 E-mail: info@millsons.co.uk

N & W Global Vending, PO Box 25, Bilston, West Midlands, WV14 0LF Tel: 01902 355000 Fax: 01902 402272 E-mail: sales@nwglobalvending.co.uk

D. Pelosi & Son Ltd, 38 Nithsdale Road, Glasgow, G41 2AN Tel: 0141-423 5944 Fax: 0141-423 5945 E-mail: enquiries@pvend.com

Precision Vending Machines Ltd, Unit 2, Avonside Industrial Estate, Feeder Road, St. Philips, Bristol, BS2 0UB Tel: 0117-972 3232 Fax: 0117-972 3887

▶ RefreshU, 1 Scotts Close, Downtown Business Centre, Salisbury, SP5 3HU Tel: 0800 389 3461 Fax: (01725) 513135 E-mail: vending@refreshu.com

Selecta Ltd, 28 Duncrue Road, Belfast, BT3 9BP Tel: (028) 9077 1177 Fax: (028) 9037 0051 E-mail: sales@uk.slecta.com

Simply Drinks Ltd, 17 Rufus Business Centre, Ravensbury Terrace, London, SW18 4RL Tel: (020) 8879 8300 Fax: (020) 8879 8301 E-mail: sales@simplydrinks.co.uk

Stradway Vending Ltd, Stradway Buildings, Hume St, Kidderminster, Worcestershire, DY11 6RD Tel: (01562) 822272

Strong Vend Ltd, 8 St Marks Industrial Estate, 439 North Woolwich Road, London, E16 2BS Tel: (020) 7511 3511 Fax: (020) 7473 0573 E-mail: info@strongvend.co.uk

Tege Fresh Fries Ltd, Central Business Exchange, 90 Midsummer Boulevard, Milton Keynes, MK9 2RJ Tel: 01908 843627

▶ Tommy Tucker Vending, 5c Dunslow Road, Eastfield, Scarborough, North Yorkshire, YO11 3UT Tel: (01723) 584390 Fax: (01723) 582350 E-mail: info@tommytuckervending.co.uk

Unicorn Containers Ltd, 5 Ferguson Drive, Lisburn, County Antrim, BT28 2EX Tel: (028) 9266 7264 Fax: (028) 9262 5616 E-mail: sales@unicorn-containers.com

Upton Vending Ltd, Vivars Way, Canal Road, Selby, North Yorkshire, YO8 8BE Tel: (01757) 291515 Fax: (01757) 294600 E-mail: sales@uptonvending.co.uk

VENDING MACHINE MANUFRS – *continued*

Venda Valet Ltd, Unit 3-4 Neville Street Industrial Estate, Neville Street, Chadderton, Oldham, OL9 6LD Tel: 0161-633 3793 Fax: 0161-628 3805
Vendingworld Services Ltd, Court Lodge Farm, Warren Road, Chelsfield, Orpington, Kent, BR6 6ER Tel: (01689) 873107 Fax: (01689) 835787 E-mail: info@vendingworld.co.uk
Westomatic Vending Systems Ltd, Shaldon Road, Newton Abbot, Devon, TQ12 4TZ Tel: (01626) 323100 Fax: (01626) 332828 E-mail: mailbox@westomatic.com

VENDING MACHINE OPERATING SERVICES

Compass Group plc, Compass House, Guilford Street, Chertsey, Surrey, KT16 9BQ Tel: 0121-457 5555 Fax: (01932) 569956

VENDING MACHINE REPAIR SERVICES

▶ Border Vending Group, Unit 4 Willow Court, West Quay Road, Winwick, Warrington, WA2 8UF Tel: 01925 423900 Fax: 01925 423902
▶ Technical Vending Services, T V S House, Nash Road, Beachampton, Milton Keynes, MK19 6EA Tel: (01908) 263600 Fax: (01908) 263600 E-mail: info@technicalvendingsupport.com

VENDING MACHINES, COIN OPERATED

▶ Border Vending Group, Unit 4 Willow Court, West Quay Road, Winwick, Warrington, WA2 8UF Tel: 01925 423900 Fax: 01925 423902
▶ Chiltern Coffee, 18 Shenley Hill Road, Leighton Buzzard, Bedfordshire, LU7 3BT Tel: (01525) 853691 Fax: (01525) 853691 E-mail: info@chilterncoffee.co.uk
▶ Eurocup, 7 Paddock Road, Skelmersdale, Lancashire, WN8 9PL Tel: (01695) 550820 Fax: (01695) 558550 E-mail: sales@eurocup.co.uk

VENEER LOGS, BEECH

Europace Ltd, 3 London Road, Stanmore, Middlesex, HA7 4PA Tel: (020) 8958 9333 Fax: (020) 8958 9333 E-mail: warshawron@aol.com

VENEER LOGS, CHERRY

Europace Ltd, 3 London Road, Stanmore, Middlesex, HA7 4PA Tel: (020) 8958 9333 Fax: (020) 8958 9333 E-mail: warshawron@aol.com

VENEER LOGS, OAK

Europace Ltd, 3 London Road, Stanmore, Middlesex, HA7 4PA Tel: (020) 8958 9333 Fax: (020) 8958 9333 E-mail: warshawron@aol.com

VENEERED PANELS

Bespoke Services (Manchester) Ltd, Whitehill Industrial Estate, Whitehill Street, Reddish, Stockport, Cheshire, SK5 7LW Tel: 0161-476 3522 Fax: 0161-476 0522 E-mail: info@bespoke-services.co.uk
Beverley Veneers Ltd, Grovehill Road, Beverley, North Humberside, HU17 0JJ Tel: (01482) 882537 Fax: (01482) 869520
BLP UK Ltd, B L P House, Sandall Stones Road, Kirk Sandall Industrial Estate, Doncaster, South Yorkshire, DN3 1QR Tel: (01302) 890555 Fax: (01302) 886724 E-mail: mail@blpuk.com
C B Veneers Ltd, Progress Rd, Sands Industrial Estate, High Wycombe, Bucks, HP12 4JD Tel: (01494) 471959 Fax: (01494) 471961 E-mail: cbveneers@msn.com
Erste Technik Ltd, 1 Grange Close, Clover Nook Industrial Park, Somercotes, Alfreton, Derbyshire, DE55 4QT Tel: (01773) 521180 Fax: (01773) 521190 E-mail: info@erste-technik.co.uk
F.R. Shadbolt & Sons, Ltd, 7 Springwood Drive, Braintree, Essex, CM7 2YN Tel: (01376) 333376 Fax: (020) 8523 2774 E-mail: sales@shadbolt.co.uk
H Shawyer & Sons Ltd, 1-3 Redburn Industrial Estate, Woodall Road, Enfield, Middlesex, EN3 4LF Tel: (020) 8805 7080 Fax: (020) 8804 3883 E-mail: sales@hshawyer.demon.co.uk
▶ Lawcris Panel Products Ltd, Unit C Cross Green Close, Leeds, LS9 0RY Tel: 0113-217 7177 Fax: 0113-240 5588 E-mail: sales@lawcris.co.uk
Midland Veneers Ltd, 3 The Hayes Trading Estate, Folkes Road, Stourbridge, West Midlands, DY9 8RG Tel: (01384) 424924 Fax: (01384) 424929 E-mail: sales@mid-ven.co.uk
Plastics & Veneers Sales Ltd, Stronghold House, 43 Fourth Street, Kirkdale, Liverpool, L20 8NL Tel: 0151-944 7150 Fax: 0151-944 7157 E-mail: sales@plasticsandveneers.co.uk
Ruddy Joinery Ltd, Enterprise Way, Flitwick, Bedford, MK45 5BS Tel: (01525) 716603 Fax: (01525) 718595 E-mail: enquiries@ruddy.co.uk
▶ Spa Laminates Limited, 59 Pepper Road, Leeds, LS10 2TH Tel: 0113-271 8311 Fax: 0113-270 3968 E-mail: info@spalaminates.co.uk
Thornell Veneers Ltd, Rushey Lane, Birmingham, B11 2BL Tel: 0121-707 7077 Fax: 0121-706 6165
W Button & Co. Ltd, Larchfield Works, Larchfield Road, Leeds, LS10 1QP Tel: 0113-270 4287 Fax: 0113-277 6975 E-mail: wbuttonco@aol.com
Wooster & Williams Ltd, Jubilee Road, High Wycombe, Buckinghamshire, HP11 2PG Tel: (01494) 525372 Fax: (01494) 463469
Wycombe Panels Ltd, Coronation Road, Cressex Business Park, High Wycombe, Buckinghamshire, HP12 3RP Tel: (01494) 530473 Fax: (01494) 461815 E-mail: sales@wycombepanels.co.uk

VENEERING SERVICES

▶ Spa Laminates Limited, 59 Pepper Road, Leeds, LS10 2TH Tel: 0113-271 8311 Fax: 0113-270 3968 E-mail: info@spalaminates.co.uk

VENEERS

Aaronson Veneers, 56 Dennis Lane, Stanmore, Middlesex, HA7 4JW Tel: (020) 8954 1555 Fax: (020) 8954 1555
Amerind Holdings Ltd, Bilsten House, Blackbushe Business Park, Yateley, Hampshire, GU46 6GE Tel: (01252) 861800 Fax: (01252) 861801 E-mail: admin@amerind.co.uk
Atkinson & Kirby Ltd, 2 Burscough Road, Ormskirk, Lancashire, L39 2XG Tel: (01695) 573234 Fax: (01695) 586902 E-mail: sales@akirby.co.uk
C B North Ltd, 65 Hedon Road, Hull, HU9 1LW Tel: (01482) 329847 Fax: (01482) 215048
C B Veneers Ltd, Progress Rd, Sands Industrial Estate, High Wycombe, Bucks, HP12 4JD Tel: (01494) 471959 Fax: (01494) 471961 E-mail: cbveneers@msn.com
Constructional Veneers Ltd, 2 Timberwharf Road, Stamford Hill, London, N16 6DB Tel: (020) 8802 1166 Fax: (020) 8802 4222 E-mail: veneers@talk21.com
Derwent Stone Products Ltd, Unit 16 Greencroft Industrial Estate, Stanley, County Durham, DH9 7XP Tel: (01207) 521482 Fax: (01207) 521455 E-mail: derwentstone@aol.com
Dobsons, 104-106 Stoke Road, Slough, SL2 5AP Tel: (01753) 520978 Fax: (01753) 823821 E-mail: dobsons@hotmail.com
Eden AngloFrench Ltd, 26 Uplands Business Park, Blackhorse Lane, London, E17 5QJ Tel: (020) 8503 2121 Fax: (020) 8503 2122 E-mail: sales@eaf.demon.co.uk
Exotic Veneer Co. Ltd, Uplands Trading Estate, Blackhorse Lane, London, E17 5QJ Tel: (020) 8531 3327 Fax: (020) 8531 2820 E-mail: andy@exotic-veneer.co.uk
Nantwich Veneers Ltd, Unit 3, Barony Employment Park, Beam Heath Way, Nantwich, Cheshire, CW5 6PQ Tel: (01270) 625361 Fax: (01270) 625597 E-mail: info@nantwichveneers.com
Reif & Son Ltd, 8 Blue Chip Business Park, Atlantic Street, Broadheath, Altrincham, Cheshire, WA14 5DD Tel: 0161-927 9192 Fax: 0161-927 9193 E-mail: reif@btconnect.com
Robbins Timber, 8-18 Brookgate, Bristol, BS3 2UN Tel: 0117-963 3136 Fax: 0117-963 7927 E-mail: sales@robbins.co.uk
Sajemay Ltd, PO Box 528, York, YO24 2YH Tel: (01904) 778704 Fax: (01904) 778705
Union Veneers, 20 Rigg Approach, London, E10 7QN Tel: (020) 8556 8866 Fax: (020) 8539 1382
▶ Vale Veneers, 29 Poplar Road, Aylesbury, Buckinghamshire, HP20 1XN Tel: (01296) 433151 E-mail: info@valeveneers.co.uk

VENETIAN BLINDS

Allan Blinds, 2 Senacre Square, Maidstone, Kent, ME15 8QF Tel: (01622) 677574 Fax: (01622) 677574
▶ Apollo Blinds Ltd, 64 Main Street, Rutherglen, Glasgow, G73 2HY Tel: 0141-647 0341 Fax: 0141-647 0341
Apollo Blinds Ltd, 102 BMK Industrial Estate, Wakefield Road, Liversedge, West Yorkshire, WF15 6BS Tel: (01924) 413010 Fax: (01924) 410170 E-mail: sales@apollo-blinds.co.uk
Baileys Blinds Ltd, Unit 15 Bellway Industrial Estate, Whitley Road, Newcastle Upon Tyne, NE12 9SW Tel: 0191-270 0501 Fax: 0191-266 8993 E-mail: info@baileys-blinds.co.uk
Barnett Window Blinds, 66 Dunmore Road, Ballynahinch, County Down, BT24 8PR Tel: (028) 9756 2635 Fax: (028) 9756 1174
Bill Blind Spot, 904 Shettleston Road, Glasgow, G32 7XN Tel: 0141-778 1866 Fax: 0141-778 2759
Hillary's Blinds (Northern) Ltd, Glover Industrial Estate, Spire Road, Washington, Tyne & Wear, NE37 3ES Tel: 0191-416 2354 Fax: 0191-416 2369
Bradrail Blinds & Awnings, 7-15 Main Street, Bulwell, Nottingham, NG6 8QH Tel: 0115-927 5251 Fax: 0115-977 0274 E-mail: enquiries@bradrail.co.uk
Brightview Blinds, 91 Charlock Way, Watford, WD18 6JT Tel: (01923) 243392 Fax: (01923) 231092
Centurion Blinds Ltd, Oakdale Trading Estate, Ham Lane, Kingswinford, West Midlands, DY6 7JH Tel: (01384) 279797 Fax: (01384) 292354 E-mail: paulmorris@centruionblinds.com
Charles Bell 1963 Ltd, 344 Oldpark Road, Belfast, BT14 6QE Tel: (028) 9074 7244 Fax: (028) 9074 7248
CS Blinds, 11 Merlin Court, Newton Industrial Estate, Carlisle, CA2 7NY Tel: (01228) 598646
Discount Blind Centre, 11 Centurion Street, Belfast, BT13 3AS Tel: (028) 9033 3606 Fax: (028) 9024 5724
Faber Blinds UK Ltd, Kilvey Road, Brackmills Industrial Estate, Northampton, NN4 7BQ Tel: (01604) 766251 Fax: (01604) 768802 E-mail: sales@faberblinds.co.uk
▶ Flamingo Blinds & Signs, 12 Chaseville Parade, Chaseville Park Road, London, N21 1PG Tel: (020) 8881 0751 Fax: (020) 8881 0771 E-mail: admin@flamingoblinds.co.uk
Hannan Blinds & Window Fashions, 72-74 Plungington Road, Preston, PR1 7RA Tel: (01772) 254140 Fax: (01772) 202198
Hillarys Blinds Ltd, Private Road 2, Colwick Industrial Estate, Nottingham, NG4 2JR Tel: 0115-961 7420 Fax: 0115-852 2525 E-mail: enquiries@hillarys.co.uk
Hunter Douglas Ltd, Unit 8a Swanscombe Business Centre, London Road, Swanscombe, Kent, DA10 0LH Tel: (01322) 624580 Fax: (01322) 624558 E-mail: info.contract@luxaflex-sunway.co.uk
J Harrison, 2 Gorsey Brow, Billinge, Wigan, Lancashire, WN5 7NX Tel: (01744) 892349 Fax: (01744) 892349
Levolux Ltd, 1 Forward Drive, Harrow, Middlesex, HA3 8NT Tel: (020) 8863 9111 Fax: (020) 8863 8760 E-mail: info@levolux.com
Milton Keynes Blind Co. Ltd, 12 Wolseley Road Woburn Industrial Estate, Woburn Road Industrial Estate, Kempston, Bedford, MK42 7TN Tel: (01234) 841515 Fax: (01234) 840682 E-mail: sales@concordeblinds.com
Radiant Blinds Ltd, 101 Ewell Road, Surbiton, Surrey, KT6 6AH Tel: (020) 8390 8755 Fax: (020) 8390 2005 E-mail: info@radiantblinds.co.uk
Rol Lite Blinds Ltd, St Pauls Trading Estate, Demesne Drive, Stalybridge, Cheshire, SK15 2QF Tel: 0161-338 2681 Fax: 0161-338 4193 E-mail: rol-lite@ben.co.uk
T.F. Sampson Ltd, Creeting Road, Stowmarket, Suffolk, IP14 5BA Tel: (01449) 613535 Fax: (01449) 678381 E-mail: sales@t-f-sampson.co.uk
Saxon Blinds Ltd, 7 Magee Street, Northampton, NN1 4JT Tel: (01604) 601888 Fax: (01604) 631212 E-mail: saxonblinds@hotmail.com
See More Blinds, 24 Church Square, Midsomer Norton, Radstock, BA3 2HX Tel: (01761) 411063 Fax: (01761) 411063 E-mail: seemoreblinds@yahoo.com
Sheraton Blinds Ltd, Unit 3 High Cross Centre, Fountayne Road, London, N15 4QN Tel: (020) 8885 5518 Fax: (020) 8365 1108 E-mail: barry@sheraton-blinds.co.uk
Solaris Sunblinds Ltd, 48 Victoria Road, Woolston, Southampton, SO19 9DX Tel: (023) 8043 1739 Fax: (023) 8043 7531 E-mail: info@solarissunblinds.co.uk
Solo Manufacturing Ltd, 18 South Nelson Road, South Nelson Industrial Estate, Cramlington, Northumberland, NE23 1WF Tel: (01670) 733788 Fax: (01670) 590555
Sunset Blinds, Rugby House, Hinckley Road, Sapcote, Leicester, LE9 4FS Tel: (01455) 274927 Fax: (01455) 274948
Sunshade Blinds, 592 Kingstanding Road, Birmingham, B44 9SH Tel: 0121-373 1919 Fax: 0121-373 1919
Turner Sunblinds, Forrest Street, Blackburn, BB1 3BB Tel: (01254) 57763 Fax: (01254) 272101
Vertical Tec, Unit 14 Ash Industrial Estate, Flex Meadow, Harlow, Essex, CM19 5TJ Tel: (020) 7383 3388 Fax: (01279) 413388 E-mail: sales@verticaltec.co.uk
W M Herdman Manufacturing Co. Ltd, Orchard Road, Finedon, Wellingborough, Northamptonshire, NN9 5JG Tel: (01933) 680416 Fax: (01933) 681369
W & P Blinds, Unit M2 The Paddocks, 347 Cherry Hinton Road, Cambridge, CB1 8DH Tel: (01223) 243030 Fax: (01223) 243030 E-mail: info@wandpblinds.co.uk
Window World Wholesale, Marl Road, Knowsley Industrial Park, Liverpool, L33 7UH Tel: 0151-546 0333 Fax: 0151-546 0333

VENISON

▶ Border County Foods, The Old Vicarage, Crosby-On-Eden, Carlisle, CA6 4QZ Tel: (01228) 573500 Fax: (01228) 672021 E-mail: info@cumberland-sausage.net

VENTILATED CEILINGS

Wimbock U K, Aspen Way, Yalberton Industrial Estate, Paignton, Devon, TQ4 7QR Tel: (01803) 407006 Fax: (01803) 407006 E-mail: wimbockuk@btconnect.com

VENTILATED SOFFIT BOARD

B H W Glass, The Gables, Church Road, Partridge Green, Horsham, West Sussex, RH13 8JS Tel: (01403) 713757 Fax: (01403) 864932 E-mail: enquiries@bhwglass.co.uk

VENTILATING FANS

A R Ellis Ltd, The Green, Horton Road, Horton, Slough, SL3 9NU Tel: (01753) 685333 Fax: (01753) 680749E-mail: tony@arellis.com
Air Vent Technology Ltd, Unit 1 Regents Court, Walworth Industrial Estate, Andover, Hampshire, SP10 5NX Tel: (01264) 356415 Fax: (01264) 337854 E-mail: avtltd@btopenworld.com
Baxi Heating Ltd, Brook House, Coventry Road, Warwick, CV34 4LL Tel: (01772) 693700 Fax: (01926) 410006 E-mail: service@heatteam.co.uk
▶ Cadamp Ltd, Wharfedale House, Great Pasture Lane, Burley in Wharfedale, Ilkley, West Yorkshire, LS29 7DB Tel: (01943) 863884 Fax: (01943) 862630 E-mail: info@cadamp.co.uk
E H S International Ltd, E H S House, Lyons Road, Trafford Park, Manchester, M17 1RN Tel: 0161-872 4541 Fax: 0161-872 5491 E-mail: enquiries@ehs-intl.co.uk
Fans & Spares Ltd, 1 Midas Business Centre, Wantz Road, Dagenham, Essex, RM10 8PS Tel: (020) 8595 5226 Fax: (020) 8593 4257 E-mail: info@fansandspares.co.uk
Fans & Spares Ltd, Unit 25 Whitemoor Court Industrial Estate, Whitemoor Court, Nottingham, NG8 5BY Tel: 0115-929 4104 Fax: 0115-929 2710 E-mail: nottingham@fansandspares.co.uk
Key Electronic Components, 4 Kitwood Drive, Lower Earley, Reading, RG6 3TA Tel: 0118-935 1546 Fax: 0118-966 0294 E-mail: sales@keyelectronic.com
London Fan Co. Ltd, 75-81 Stirling Road, London, W3 8DJ Tel: (020) 8992 6923 Fax: (020) 8992 6928 E-mail: sales@londonfan.co.uk
Manrose Manufacturing Ltd, Albion House, Albion Close, Slough, SL2 5DT Tel: (01753) 691399 Fax: (01753) 692294 E-mail: sales@manrose.com
Rapid Climate Control Ltd, 423 Becontree Avenue, Dagenham, Essex, RM8 3UH Tel: 0121-543 6211 Fax: (020) 8590 8303 E-mail: info@rapidclimatecontrol.com
Silavent Ltd, 60 High Street, Sandhurst, Berkshire, GU47 8DY Tel: (01252) 878282 Fax: (01252) 871212 E-mail: admin@silavent.co.uk
Strathclyde Fans Ltd, Unit B4 Somervell Trading Estate, Somervell Street, Cambuslang, Glasgow, G72 7EB Tel: 0141-641 0224 Fax: 0141-641 7796
Vent Axia Ltd, Fleming Way, Crawley, West Sussex, RH10 9YX Tel: (01293) 526062 Fax: (01293) 551188 E-mail: info@vent-axia.com

VENTILATION CONSULTANCY OR DESIGN

A S Contracts Ltd, Warstock Road, Birmingham, B14 4RS Tel: 0121-436 7969 Fax: 0121-436 7970
Airducts Design, Unit 45 Wassage Way, Hampton Lovett, Droitwich, Worcestershire, WR9 0NX Tel: (01905) 775454 Fax: (01905) 775656
▶ Airtech Environmental Services, 3 Hampton Court Road, East Molesey, Surrey, KT8 9BN Tel: (020) 8979 2158 Fax: (020) 8941 9623 E-mail: airtechlondon@mcmail.com
B T U (Heating) Ltd, 38 Weyside Road, Guildford, Surrey, GU1 1JB Tel: (01483) 590600 Fax: (01483) 590601 E-mail: enquiries@btu-heating.com
C H Lindsey & Son Ltd, Brunel Way, Severalls Industrial Park, Colchester, CO4 9QW Tel: (01206) 844567 Fax: (01206) 844483 E-mail: info@lindsey-aircon.com
Doublescale, Beili Glas Uchaf, Gwaun Cae Gurwen, Ammanford, Dyfed, SA18 1PR Tel: (01269) 822440 Fax: (01269) 822440 E-mail: sales@doublescale.ltd.uk
Ellesmere Engineering Co. Ltd, Pennington Street, Worsley, Manchester, M28 3LR Tel: 0161-799 7626 Fax: 0161-703 8254 E-mail: marion@ellesmereeng.com
Emberheat, 295 Aylestone Road, Leicester, LE2 7PB Tel: 0116-287 8300
▶ Flexadux Plastics Ltd, Middlefield Lane, Gainsborough, Lincolnshire, DN21 1UU Tel: (01427) 617547 Fax: (01427) 810128 E-mail: sales@flexadux.co.uk
Haynes Manufacturing UK, Marlowe House, Stewkins, Stourbridge, West Midlands, DY8 4YW Tel: (01384) 371416 Fax: (01384) 371416 E-mail: info@haynes-uk.co.uk
Lucas & Steen Ltd, Castle Works, 88 Hill Street, Ardrossan, Ayrshire, KA22 8HE Tel: (01294) 468671 Fax: (01294) 604018

VENTILATION CONSULTANCY OR DESIGN – *continued*

M S Air Movement, Unit 2a Hexton Manor Stables, Hexton, Hitchin, Hertfordshire, SG5 3JH Tel: (01582) 883662 Fax: (01582) 881009 E-mail: info@msairmovement.co.uk

Mcveigh Technical Solutions Ltd, PO Box 407, Leicester, LE3 8ZA Tel: 0116-232 1181 Fax: 0116-232 1186

Marime Ltd, 47 Ryhill Way, Lower Earley, Reading, RG6 4AZ Tel: 0118-986 9685 Fax: 0118-975 6196

Mytchett Engineering Services, Sunnyhaven, Salisbury Terrace, Mytchett, Camberley, Surrey, GU16 6DB Tel: (01252) 511397 Fax: (01252) 377460

Pro-Duct (Fife) Ltd, 3 Church Wynd, Kingskettle, Cupar, Fife, KY15 7PS Tel: (01337) 831862 Fax: (01337) 831832

Ventilation Services Co., 6 Callender Place, Stoke-on-Trent, ST6 1JL Tel: (01782) 575140 Fax: (01782) 832796

VENTILATION DUCT SYSTEMS

▶ Air Diffusion Technology, 52 London Road, Oadby, Leicester, LE2 5DH Tel: 0116-272 1231 Fax: 0116-271 4441 E-mail: info@euro-air.co.uk

VENTILATION DUCTING OR DUCTS

Air Heating & Manufacturing, Seaton Lane, St. Helier, Jersey, JE2 3QJ Tel: (01534) 734830 Fax: (01534) 767681 E-mail: airheating@hotmail.com

Airducts Design, Unit 45 Wassage Way, Hampton Lovett, Droitwich, Worcestershire, WR9 0NX Tel: (01905) 775454 Fax: (01905) 775656

Alkie Ltd, Millwood View, Stalybridge, Cheshire, SK15 3AU Tel: 0161-338 8070 Fax: 0161-338 3191 E-mail: alkie.ltd@virgin.net

Alter Air, 6 Holly Grove, Basildon, Essex, SS16 6SB Tel: (01268) 540862 Fax: (01268) 540862

Alvent Heating Contractors, Units 5-6 Alexandra Industrial Estate, Locarno Road, Tipton, West Midlands, DY4 9SJ Tel: 0121-557 6727 Fax: 0121-520 8717

Anchor Ventilation Co Britair Ltd, Malt Lane, Stoke-on-Trent, ST3 1RR Tel: (01782) 312809 Fax: (01782) 311138

Asm Engineering Ltd, 74 Wilbury Way, Hitchin, Hertfordshire, SG4 0TP Tel: 01462 477360 Fax: 01582 454772 E-mail: office@asmeng.co.uk

B G Ventilation, Lynton Industrial Estate, Stanley, Perth, PH1 4QQ Tel: (01738) 828800 Fax: (01383) 420216 E-mail: bgvent@aol.com

B & L Sheetmetal (2003) Ltd, Ramsden Road, Rotherwas Industrial Estate, Hereford, HR2 6LR Tel: (01432) 355040 Fax: (01432) 343844 E-mail: bandl2003@btconnect.com

B T M Services, Unit 16 The Lays Farm Trading Estate, Charlton Road, Keynsham, Bristol, BS31 2SE Tel: 0117-986 8390 Fax: 0117-986 1031 E-mail: btmservs@yahoo.co.uk

B W Fabrications Ltd, 3 Market Side, Albert Road, St. Philips, Bristol, BS2 0XS Tel: 0117-972 4002 Fax: 0117-972 3094 E-mail: bwfabrications@hotmail.com

Blazon Fabrication, Unit 31 125-127 London Road, Stone, Dartford, DA2 6BH Tel: (01322) 280561 Fax: (01322) 228825 E-mail: blazon@btconnect.com

Borahurst Ltd, Devonshire House, 31 Holmesdale Road, Reigate, Surrey, RH2 0BJ Tel: (01737) 221733 Fax: (01737) 223512 E-mail: info@borahurst.com

Boyd & Co (Metalworkers) Ltd, Chainbridge Road, Blaydon-on-Tyne, Tyne & Wear, NE21 5SW Tel: 0191-414 3331 Fax: 0191-414 0340 E-mail: info@boydduct.co.uk

C C L Veloduct Ltd, Unit 3 Eleventh Avenue, Team Valley Trading Estate, Gateshead, Tyne & Wear, NE11 0JY Tel: 0191-414 0888 Fax: 0191-487 4260

Centravent Ltd, Churchbridge, Oldbury, West Midlands, B69 2AX Tel: 0121-543 6878

Cityarch Ltd, 3 Potters Lane, Kiln Farm, Milton Keynes, MK11 3HE Tel: (01908) 265557 Fax: (01908) 265400 E-mail: cityarch.limited@virgin.net

Contract Components, Unit 37 Pitcliffe Way, Bradford, West Yorkshire, BD5 7SG Tel: (01274) 721982 Fax: (01274) 306876 E-mail: sales@cclveloduct.co.uk

Croydon Ductwork Ltd, 312 Lower Addiscombe Road, Croydon, CR0 7AF Tel: (020) 8654 7813 Fax: (020) 8654 9527 E-mail: richardwood@croydenductwork1td.co.uk

D M C Ltd, 7 Sherwood Court, Thurston Road, Lewisham, London, SE13 7SD Tel: (020) 8297 1001 Fax: (020) 8297 1002

Ductwork By Design Ltd, Unit 7, 193 Garth Rd, Morden, Surrey, SM4 4LZ Tel: (020) 8330 0091 Fax: (020) 8330 0103 E-mail: info@dbdltd.com

Ductwork Projects Ltd, Unit 303-305 Woolsbridge Industrial Park, Woolsbridge Industrial Estate, Three Legged Cross, Wimborne, Dorset, BH21 6SX Tel: (01202) 823621 Fax: (01202) 823744 E-mail: enquiries@dpl-kvd.co.uk

Eventemp (Midlands) Ltd, Carrwood Road, Chesterfield Trading Estate, Sheepbridge, Chesterfield, Derbyshire, S41 9QB Tel: (01246) 453685 Fax: (01246) 260359 E-mail: enquiries@eventempmidland.ltd.uk

Fabricair Systems Ltd, 5 Burbidge Road, Birmingham, B9 4US Tel: 0121-766 7707 Fax: 0121-766 8356 E-mail: sales@fabricairsystems.co.uk

Fan Maintenance Ltd, Eastern Works 4 Eastern Road, Walthamstow, London, E17 9DU Tel: (020) 8521 1856 Fax: (020) 8521 9421

Filtex Filters, 4 7 Union Park, Navigation Way, West Bromwich, West Midlands, B70 9DF Tel: 0121-553 1283 Fax: 0121-500 5289 E-mail: sales@ioi.co.uk

Firth Sheet Metal Ltd, Barrys Lane, Scarborough, North Yorkshire, YO12 4HA Tel: (01723) 376771 Fax: (01723) 351325 E-mail: info@firmac.co.uk

▶ Flexadux Plastics Ltd, Middlefield Lane, Gainsborough, Lincolnshire, DN21 1UU Tel: (01427) 617547 Fax: (01427) 810128 E-mail: sales@flexadux.co.uk

Frixos Metal Works Ltd, Unit 4, 30 Aden Road, Brimsdown, Enfield, Middlesex, EN3 7SY Tel: (020) 8443 1050 Fax: (020) 8440 1233 E-mail: jimmy@frixosmetalworks.co.uk

▶ Gallaway Group Northern, Low Mill Lane, Ravensthorpe Industrial Estate, Dewsbury, West Yorkshire, WF13 3LN Tel: (01924) 490056 Fax: (01924) 490763 E-mail: sales.dewsbury@gallowaygroup.co.uk

M.G. Godfrey & Co. Ltd, 174a Perry Vale, London, Greater London, SE23 2LR Tel: 020 82914168

Harrison Industrial Ltd, Rodney Road, Southsea, Hampshire, PO4 8SY Tel: (023) 9275 1687 Fax: (023) 9281 8564 E-mail: harrison.indl@btclick.com

Heasman & Sadler Ltd, 29 Park Road, Faringdon, Oxfordshire, SN7 7BP Tel: (01367) 240286 Fax: (01367) 242056

Hotchkiss Air Supply (HAS), Heath Mill Road, Wombourne, Wolverhampton, WV5 8AP Tel: (01902) 895161 Fax: (01902) 892045 E-mail: info@hotchkissairsupply.co.uk

J D W Engineering Ltd, Tameside Mill, Park Road, Dukinfield, Cheshire, SK16 5LP Tel: 0161-330 1989 Fax: 0161-343 1905 E-mail: sales@jdwengineering.com

James French, Balloo Avenue, Bangor, County Down, BT19 7QT Tel: (028) 9147 3436 Fax: (028) 9145 1793 E-mail: info@french-eng.co.uk

Lewis Ductwork, 450 Rathgar Road, London, SW9 7EP Tel: (020) 7737 4435 Fax: (020) 7737 4435

Lucas & Steen Ltd, Castle Works, 88 Hill Street, Ardrossan, Ayrshire, KA22 8HE Tel: (01294) 468671 Fax: (01294) 604018

Mackley & Co. Ltd, Chatham Street, Sheffield, S3 8EJ Tel: 0114-272 3991 Fax: 0114-272 1004

Macklow Industrial Ltd, The Mill, Station Road, Salhouse, Norwich, NR13 6NY Tel: (01603) 720950 Fax: (01603) 720033 E-mail: info@macklow.co.uk

Major Air Systems Ltd, Union Works, Andover Street, Birmingham, B5 5RG Tel: 0121-634 1580 Fax: 0121-643 2320

Mastervent Ventilation Systems, 2 Engine Street, Smethwick, West Midlands, B66 3DT Tel: 0121-558 1559 Fax: 0121-565 4047 E-mail: home@masterventltd.go-plus.net

Mechanical Air Supplies Ltd, Crouch Indust Estate, Barnett Wood Lane, Leatherhead, Surrey, KT22 7DG Tel: (01372) 370084 Fax: (01372) 370085

Merseyside Metalwork Ltd, Cotton Street, Liverpool, L3 7DY Tel: 0151-236 7349 Fax: 0151-236 6397

Middleton Sheet Metal Co. Ltd, Spring Vale, Middleton, Manchester, M24 2HS Tel: 0161-643 2462 Fax: 0161-643 3490 E-mail: info@msmgroup.org

Millwrights Liverpool Ltd, 31-33 Naylor Street, Liverpool, L3 6DR Tel: 0151-236 0479 Fax: 0151-255 0198

Mitrechoice Ltd, Haynes Garage, The Knoll, Sherington, Newport Pagnell, Buckinghamshire, MK16 9NZ Tel: (01908) 611054 Fax: (01908) 611054

Nobles Engineering Solutions Ltd, 11 Mallard Close, Earls Barton, Northampton, NN6 0JF Tel: (01604) 810695 Fax: (01604) 812586

P J S Mechanical & Electrical Building Services, Barn House, Folly Farm, Basingstoke, Hampshire, RG25 2BS Tel: (01256) 397544 Fax: (01256) 398304

Prompt Profiles Ltd, Liberator House, Bidwell Road, Norwich, NR13 6PT Tel: (01603) 720090 Fax: (01603) 720202

R A Green (Mechanical Servises) Ltd, Southdown, Western Road, Crowborough, East Sussex, TN6 3EW Tel: (01892) 652177 Fax: (01892) 667225 E-mail: ragreen@btinternet.com

R & B Fabrications, 4 Vulcan Road, Solihull, West Midlands, B91 2JY Tel: 0121-711 3279 Fax: 0121-711 3279

Refrigeration Mitton Ltd, Polar House, East Norfolk Street, Carlisle, CA2 5JL Tel: (01228) 522481 Fax: (01228) 514897

Sansome Construction, Bond Street, Southampton, SO14 5AN Tel: (023) 8022 2349

Senior Hargreaves Ltd, Lord Street, Bury, Lancashire, BL9 0RG Tel: 0161-764 5082 Fax: 0161-762 2333 E-mail: postbox@senior-hargreaves.co.uk

Serco, Unit 63 Hillgrove Business Park, Nazeing Road, Nazeing, Waltham Abbey, Essex, EN9 2HB Tel: (01992) 893917 Fax: (01992) 893759

Severn Environmental Engineering Ltd, Scan Buildings, Oldbury Road, Cwmbran, Gwent, NP44 3JU Tel: (01633) 866241 Fax: (01633) 874664

Charles Smethurst Ltd, Castlemill Street, Oldham, OL1 3HL Tel: 0161-624 4505 Fax: 0161-628 4282 E-mail: info@charlessmethurst.co.uk

Tayside Sheet Metal Ltd, 8 Angus Works, Neish Street, Dundee, DD3 7JN Tel: (01382) 828822 Fax: (01382) 828833 E-mail: vent@taysidesheetmetal.freeserve.co.uk

Thermafabrications Ltd, New Craven Gate, Leeds, LS11 5NF Tel: 0113-245 7510 Fax: 0113-244 9430

Thistle Vent Ltd, 7 Strathclyde Street, Glasgow, G40 4JR Tel: 0141-554 6669 Fax: 0141-554 6669

Universal Sheetmetal Works, 317 Blucher Road, London, SE5 0LH Tel: (020) 7703 4575

V & C Installation Ltd, 24 Severnside Industrial Estate, Sudmeadow Road, Gloucester, GL2 5HS Tel: (01452) 415236 Fax: (01452) 309324 E-mail: paulvye@btconnect.com

Vent Duct, The Hollies, Campton Road, Meppershall, Shefford, Bedfordshire, SG17 5PB Tel: (01462) 815018 Fax: (01462) 817045

Ventilate Ltd, Solent Industrial Estate, Shamblehurst Lane, Hedge End, Southampton, SO30 2FX Tel: (01489) 782262 Fax: (01489) 781822 E-mail: info@peelfabs.co.uk

West Mercia Air Conditioning Ltd, 29a Tarsmill Court, Rotherwas Industrial Estate, Hereford, HR2 6JZ Tel: (01432) 358489 Fax: (01432) 358489 E-mail: sales@wmaircon.com

Woodford Sheet Metal Ltd, 14 Wham Street, Heywood, Lancashire, OL10 4QU Tel: (01706) 364295 Fax: (01706) 621996 E-mail: woodford-sm@lineone-net.co.uk

Worcester Ventilation Systems Ltd, PO Box 190, Droitwich, Worcestershire, WR9 7DE Tel: (01905) 794422 Fax: (01905) 794488 E-mail: mail@worcester-vent.co.uk

Worthside Engineering, Dalton Lane, Keighley, West Yorkshire, BD21 4JU Tel: (01535) 605698 Fax: (01535) 610302

Zephyr Ducts & Fittings Ltd, 8 Commerce Way, Leighton Buzzard, Bedfordshire, LU7 4RW Tel: 01525 376446

VENTILATION EQUIPMENT OR FITTINGS

A C S, Unit 74 Standard Way, Gravelly Industrial Park, Birmingham, B24 8TL Tel: 0121-326 8484 Fax: 0121-326 8585 E-mail: paul.kirkup@venductacs.co.uk

Ab Services, 14 Carmyle Avenue, Glasgow, G32 8HJ Tel: 0141-764 1130 Fax: 0141-764 1131 E-mail: enquires@thefanman.co.uk

Air Controlled Environmental Systems Ltd, 6 Gazelle Buildings, Wallingford Road, Uxbridge, Middlesex, UB8 2SX Tel: (01895) 813312 Fax: (01895) 813443 E-mail: gary@aces-ductwork.co.uk

Airforce Ventilation Products, 3 Brunel Gate, West Portway Industrial Estate, Andover, Hampshire, SP10 3SL Tel: (01264) 358101 Fax: (01264) 358404 E-mail: enquiries@airforcevp.com

Alan Williams & Co Bristol Ltd, 4 Bonville Business Centre, Dixon Road, Bristol, BS4 5QQ Tel: 0117-971 7606 Fax: 0117-971 7366 E-mail: bristol@alanwilliams.co.uk

B & G Ventilation Ltd, Coppice Trading Estate, Kidderminster, Worcestershire, DY11 7QY Tel: (01562) 740815 Fax: (01562) 751123 E-mail: office@bgvent.co.uk

B P Air Ventilation, 284 Coulsdon Road, Coulsdon, Surrey, CR5 1EB Tel: (01737) 556499 Fax: (01737) 552955 E-mail: brian.knightingale@britishlibrary.net

Building Product Design Ltd, 6 Tonbridge Chambers, Pembury Road, Tonbridge, Kent, TN9 2HZ Tel: (01732) 355519 Fax: (01732) 355536 E-mail: info@bpd.com

C F Airflow, Tameside Works, Dukinfield, Cheshire, SK16 5PT Tel: 0161-339 0707 Fax: 0161-339 0808

CCL Veloduct, 1-3 Dean Road, Lincoln, LN2 4DR Tel: (01522) 567087 Fax: (01522) 563525

▶ Droitwich Fabrication & Installation Services Ltd, 10 North St Industrial Estate, Droitwich, Worcestershire, WR9 8JB Tel: (01905) 775096 Fax: (01905) 775880 E-mail: droitwich.fabs@virgin.net

▶ Euro Air, 118 Claverham Road, Yatton, Bristol, BS49 4LE Tel: (01934) 835662 Fax: (01934) 835662

Fans & Spares Ltd, 10 Low Mills Road, Leeds, LS12 4UY Tel: 0113-279 0501 Fax: 0113-231 0969 E-mail: sales@fansandspares.co.uk

▶ Flexadux Plastics Ltd, Middlefield Lane, Gainsborough, Lincolnshire, DN21 1UU Tel: (01427) 617547 Fax: (01427) 810128 E-mail: sales@flexadux.co.uk

▶ Freshair, Newport Road, Market Drayton, Shropshire, TF9 2AA Tel: (01630) 657606 Fax: (01630) 655545

▶ Fume Extraction Services, 1 Mowbray Street, Sheffield, S3 8EN Tel: 0114-278 7570 Fax: 0114-278 7600 E-mail: sales@fumeextraction.net

▶ J.A. Glover, Unit 701B, Tudor Estate, Abbey Road, London, NW10 7UY Tel: (020) 8961 1666 Fax: (020) 8961 7666

Graham Taylor Sales Ltd, Camps Farm, Hoe Lane, Nazeing, Waltham Abbey, Essex, EN9 2RG Tel: (01279) 635651 Fax: (01992) 892907

▶ Indusvent Engineering Northern Ltd, Smallbridge Industrial Park, Riverside Drive, Rochdale, Lancashire, OL16 2SH Tel: (0870) 7583280 Fax: (0870) 7583299 E-mail: mail@indusvent.com

J A Glover Ltd, 23 Lordswood Industrial Estate, Revenge Road, Chatham, Kent, ME5 8UD Tel: (01634) 684419 Fax: (01634) 200423 E-mail: chatham@jagglover.demon.co.uk

J A Glover Ltd, A Pioneers Industrial Park, Beddington Farm Road, Croydon, CR0 4XY Tel: (020) 8665 7055 Fax: (020) 8665 5108

▶ Kair Ventilation, Unit 6, Chiltonian Industrial Estate, Manor Lane, London, SE12 0TX Tel: (0845) 1662240 Fax: (0845) 1662250

▶ Konvekta Ltd, Knowsley Road Industrial Estate, Haslingden, Rossendale, Lancashire, BB4 4RR Tel: (01706) 227018 Fax: (01706) 831124

Lindab Ltd, 98 Roding Road, London, E6 6LS Tel: (020) 7474 5102 Fax: (020) 7476 8001

Lindab Ltd, 8 Deans Road Industrial Estate, Deans Road, Swinton, Manchester, M27 0RD Tel: 0161-727 5200 Fax: 0161-727 5201

Marshalls Sheetmetal Blackrow Barns, Short Thorn Road, Blackrow Barns, Felthorpe, Norwich, NR10 4DE Tel: (01603) 755473 Fax: (01603) 754040 E-mail: enquiries@marshallssheetmetal.co.uk

Mechanical Air Supplies Ltd, Crouch Indust Estate, Barnett Wood Lane, Leatherhead, Surrey, KT22 7DG Tel: (01372) 370084 Fax: (01372) 370085

Morison & Miller Engineering Ltd, 249 Glasgow Road, Rutherglen, Glasgow, G73 1SU Tel: 0141-647 0825 Fax: 0141-647 3133 E-mail: sales@morisonandmiller.co.uk

▶ O'Brien Commisioning, Bridge Street, Pendlebury, Swinton, Manchester, M27 4DU Tel: 0161-728 3444 Fax: 0161-728 3555 E-mail: job.commissioning@ukonline.co.uk

Price Technical Ltd, 27 Melbourne Terrace, Clevedon, Avon, BS21 6HQ Tel: (01275) 879811 Fax: (01275) 873052 E-mail: sales@pricetec.co.uk

Rytons Building Products Ltd, Design House, Orion Way, Kettering Business Park, Kettering, Northamptonshire, NN15 6NL Tel: (01536) 511874 Fax: (01536) 310455 E-mail: vents@rytons.com

S K (Sales) Ltd, Unit C1, Sapphire Way, Rhombus Business Park, Norwich, NR6 6NN Tel: (01603) 417522 Fax: (01603) 417524 E-mail: orders@sksales.co.uk

Swan Enviro Freshmesh Systems, 10 Engine Road, Loanhead, Midlothian, EH20 9RF Tel: 0131-440 3812 Fax: 0131-448 2119 E-mail: sales@swanenviro.com

Trade Supplies, Unit 208, The Commercial Centre, Picket Piece, Andover, Hampshire, SP11 6LU Tel: (01264) 334108 Fax: (01264) 337727

Trade Supplies, Trade House, Freestone Road, Bristol, BS2 0QN Tel: 0117-972 8230 Fax: 0117-972 8231

United Air Systems, 32 Alexandra Road, Clevedon, Avon, BS21 7QH Tel: 01275 341322

Ventco Fan Stockists, 1 Bull Lane, Pill, Bristol, BS20 0EF Tel: (01275) 372340 Fax: (01275) 372340

Ventilation & Heating Sales, Unit 5 Whitequarries Industrial Estate, Winchburgh, Broxburn, West Lothian, EH52 6PZ Tel: (01506) 830033 Fax: (01506) 830022

Volume Ventalation Ltd, The Old Quarry, Springwell Lane, Rickmansworth, Hertfordshire, WD3 8UX Tel: (01923) 770331 Fax: (01923) 290313 E-mail: sales@volvent.com

VENTILATION FLEXIBLE DUCTING

▶ Air Diffusion Technology, 52 London Road, Oadby, Leicester, LE2 5DH Tel: 0116-272 1231 Fax: 0116-271 4441 E-mail: info@euro-air.co.uk

VENTILATION INSTALLATION OR SERVICING, *See also Heating & Ventilation Engineers etc*

A B S Ltd, New House, Christchurch Road, Ringwood, Hampshire, BH24 3AP Tel: (01425) 477777 Fax: (01425) 474400 E-mail: first@absme.co.uk

A C J Industrial Ltd, Longbeck Trading Estate, Marske-By-The-Sea, Redcar, Cleveland, TS11 6HB Tel: (01642) 483045 Fax: (01642) 487588 E-mail: garbut@globalnet.co.uk

A C Mechanical Services Ltd, 16 Kingdom Close, Fareham, Hampshire, PO15 5TJ Tel: (01489) 579016 Fax: (01489) 579018 E-mail: info@acms.co.uk

Adm, Ling Fields, Skipton, North Yorkshire, BD23 1UX Tel: (01756) 701051 Fax: (01756) 701076 E-mail: info@admsystems.co.uk

Advent Engineering Ltd, 9 Sherwood Road, Bromsgrove, Worcestershire, B60 3DR Tel: (01527) 874414 Fax: (01527) 831603 E-mail: info@adventmanchester.co.uk

VENTILATION INSTALLATION OR SERVICING – *continued*

Air & Ventilation Services, Birds Cottage, Crabtree Hill, Lambourne End, Romford, RM4 1ND Tel: (020) 8500 8834 Fax: (020) 8500 3932 E-mail: sarahcresswell@aol.com

Airflow Engineering Services Heating Ventilation Air Conditioning, Drift Road, Kymba House, Whitehill, Bordon, Hampshire, GU35 9DZ Tel: (01420) 473401 Fax: (01420) 489955

Airomet Ltd, Unit 4 Millenium Court, Bunsford Park Road, Bromsgrove, Worcestershire, B60 3DX Tel: (01527) 837500 Fax: (01527) 833818

Andrew Engineering Ltd, Unit 4, Cobnar Wood Close, Chesterfield, Derbyshire, S41 9RQ Tel: (0845) 1267873 Fax: (0845) 1267874 E-mail: sales@andrew-eng.co.uk

Anglia Air Conditioning Ltd, 7 Fletcher Way, Weston Road, Norwich, NR3 3ST Tel: (01603) 787383 Fax: (01603) 403480 E-mail: sales@anglia-aircon.co.uk

Aqua Mechanical Services Ltd, Aqua House, Rose & Crown Road, Swavesey, Cambridge, CB4 5RB Tel: (01954) 230948 Fax: (01954) 230593 E-mail: group@aqua.co.uk

Arun Environmental, Batten Street, Aylestone Road, Leicester, LE2 7PB Tel: 0116-283 0020 Fax: 0116-244 0430 E-mail: tomwhalley@arunenvironmental.co.uk

B M S Ltd, 1 Dalzells Lane, Burwell, Cambridge, CB5 0GA Tel: (01638) 741275 Fax: (01638) 742236 E-mail: reception@burmech.co.uk

B T U (Heating) Ltd, 38 Weyside Road, Guildford, Surrey, GU1 1JB Tel: (01483) 590600 Fax: (01483) 590601 E-mail: enquiries@btu-heating.com

William Bailey Ltd, Merlin Court, Ripley Road, Ambergate, Belper, Derbyshire, DE56 2EP Tel: (01773) 853703 Fax: (01773) 856930 E-mail: enquiries@williambailey.co.uk

Beaver Co. Ltd, 968 North Circular Road, London, NW2 7JR Tel: (020) 8208 1839 Fax: (020) 8452 4610 E-mail: bopco@aol.com

Brunswick Engineering, 27 Sterling Road, Enfield, Middlesex, EN2 0LN Tel: (020) 8882 1877 Fax: (020) 8886 7933 E-mail: brunswick@wwmail.co.uk

Building Product Design Ltd, 2 Brooklands Road, Sale, Cheshire, M33 3SS Tel: 0161-905 5700 Fax: 0161-905 2085 E-mail: postmaster@buildingproductdesign.com

C D Stone Dunstable Ltd, Fairway Works, Southfields Road, Dunstable, Bedfordshire, LU6 3EP Tel: (01582) 605353 Fax: (01582) 660103

Caterfab UK, Haleys Yard, Leeds, LS13 3LA Tel: 0113-228 9101 Fax: 0113-228 9201

Charlestown Engineering Services Ltd, Rayner House, Bayley Street, Stalybridge, Cheshire, SK15 1PZ Tel: 0161-338 7300 Fax: 0161-338 4884 E-mail: sales@charlestown1.com

City Air Conditioning Ltd, 6 Palace Industrial Estate, Bircholt Road, Maidstone, Kent, ME15 9XU Tel: (01622) 692338 Fax: (01622) 672377 E-mail: cityair@cityairltd.co.uk

Control Design, Unit Z Paddock Wood Distribution Centre, Paddock Wood, Tonbridge, Kent, TN12 6UU Tel: (01892) 836350 Fax: (01892) 837292 E-mail: controldesign@btconnect.com

Crosskill Ventilation Ltd, Spar Road, Norwich, NR6 6BX Tel: (01603) 423028 Fax: (01603) 401136 E-mail: crosskill@btconnect.com

Darnells Ltd, Oakfield Industrial Estate, Eynsham, Witney, Oxfordshire, OX29 4TH Tel: (01865) 883996 Fax: (01865) 883986 E-mail: mail@darnells.ltd.uk

Ducatt Heating Co. Ltd, Platts Road, Stourbridge, West Midlands, DY8 4YT Tel: (01384) 394641 Fax: (01384) 440455 E-mail: info@ducattheating.co.uk

Duct Com Ltd, 94 Shrewsbury Lane, London, Greater London, SE18 3JL Tel: 0208 3172563 Fax: 0208 3174554E-mail: info@ductcom.com

E Poppleton & Son Ltd, Conway Road, Mochdre, Colwyn Bay, Clwyd, LL28 5HL Tel: (01492) 546061 Fax: (01492) 544076 E-mail: sales@poppleton.co.uk

Emberheat, 295 Aylestone Road, Leicester, LE2 7PB Tel: 0116-287 8300

Envirovent Fife, Strathore Road, Thornton, Kirkcaldy, Fife, KY1 4DF Tel: (01592) 774301 Fax: (01592) 630853

Erskine Environmental Engineering Ltd., 16 Lady Lane, Paisley, Renfrewshire, PA1 2LJ Tel: 0141-887 7784 Fax: 0141-889 4338

Essex Electric Ltd, 46 Hanbury Road, Chelmsford, CM1 3TL Tel: (01245) 251291 Fax: (01245) 354051

Extracair Services, 250 Bournemouth Road, Poole, Dorset, BH14 9HZ Tel: (01202) 736999 Fax: (01202) 736777 E-mail: sales@extracair.co.uk

Fabricair Systems Ltd, 5 Burbidge Road, Birmingham, B9 4US Tel: 0121-766 7707 Fax: 0121-766 8356 E-mail: sales@fabricairsystems.co.uk

▶ FLC Property Services, Granitehill Enterprise Centre, Unit4 Granitehill Road, Aberdeen, AB16 7AX Tel: (01224) 662030 Fax: (01224) 662010 E-mail: flowclean1@aol.com

Force Heating & Cooling Services, 80 Rawmarsh Hill, Parkgate, Rotherham, South Yorkshire, S62 6EX Tel: (01709) 527920 Fax: (01709) 526290 E-mail: force.heating@virgin.net

Fred G Alden Ltd, Langford Locks, Kidlington, Oxfordshire, OX5 1LJ Tel: (01865) 855000 Fax: (01865) 855008

G F Cross & Sons, Unit 10 Kings Meadow, Ferry Hinksey Road, Oxford, OX2 0DP Tel: (01865) 242358 Fax: (01865) 241648 E-mail: info@gfcrossandsons.co.uk

▶ Gallaway Group Northern, Low Mill Lane, Ravensthorpe Industrial Estate, Dewsbury, West Yorkshire, WF13 3LN Tel: (01924) 490056 Fax: (01924) 490763 E-mail: sales.dewsbury@gallowaygroup.co.uk

Glenair Ltd, 171-177 Hessle Road, Hull, HU3 4AA Tel: (01482) 223313 Fax: (01482) 229962 E-mail: info@glenair.ltd.uk

Gradwood Ltd, Lansdown House, 85 Buxton Road, Stockport, Cheshire, SK2 6LR Tel: 0161-480 9629 Fax: 0161-474 7433 E-mail: sales@gradwood.co.uk

Heating & Pipework Installations Leeds Ltd, 353 Tong Road, Leeds, LS12 4QG Tel: 0113-263 0318 Fax: 0113-231 0687 E-mail: drawings@hpileeds.co.uk

Heating & Ventilating Services Ltd, 50 Park Lane, Basford, Nottingham, NG6 0DT Tel: 0115-978 1445 Fax: 0115-978 1596

Heronridge Services (Nottingham) Ltd, Units 2, Palm Court, Palm Street, New Basford, Nottingham, NG7 7HU Tel: 0115-979 0644 Fax: 0115-979 0438 E-mail: sales@heronridge.co.uk

▶ Industrial & Commercial Environment Ltd, Bowdens, Broad Oak, Sturminster Newton, Dorset, DT10 2HG Tel: (01258) 471954 Fax: (01258) 471904 E-mail: office@ice-uk.eu.com

Invensys Building Systems, Unit 3 Earls Court, Fifth Avenue, Team Valley Trading Estate, Gateshead, Tyne & Wear, NE11 0HF Tel: 0191-499 4500 Fax: 0191-499 4501 E-mail: andrew.kingston@invensys.com

Iona Ventilation Co. Ltd, 320 Pinkston Road, Glasgow, G4 0LP Tel: 0141-331 2606 Fax: 0141-333 1055

▶ Kershaw Mechanical Services Ltd, Beadle Trading Estate, Ditton Walk, Cambridge, CB5 8PD Tel: (01223) 715800 Fax: (01223) 411061 E-mail: enquiries@kershaw-grp.co.uk

A. Longworth & Sons Ltd, 55 Waverley Road, Sale, Cheshire, M33 7AY Tel: 0161-973 8398 Fax: 0161-905 1095

M Bielby Ltd, 4 Cave Street, Hull, HU5 2TZ Tel: (01482) 342653 Fax: (01482) 447366 E-mail: info@mbielby.com

M T Buxton Industrial Services Ltd, 237 Station Road, Langley Mill, Nottingham, NG16 4AD Tel: (01773) 714339 Fax: (01773) 535251 E-mail: enquiries@mtbuxton.com

Mansfield, Pollard & Co. Ltd, Edward House, Parry Lane, Bradford, West Yorkshire, BD4 8TL Tel: (01274) 774050 Fax: (01274) 775424 E-mail: admin@manpo.co.uk

Marshalls Sheetmetal Blackrow Barns, Short Thorn Road, Blackrow Barns, Felthorpe, Norwich, NR10 4DE Tel: (01603) 755473 Fax: (01603) 754040 E-mail: enquiries@marshallssheetmetal.co.uk

Metal Fabrication Co (Cardiff) Ltd, East Moors Road, Cardiff, CF24 5EE Tel: (029) 2048 9767 Fax: (029) 2048 0407 E-mail: sales@metal-fab.co.uk

Midland Air Conditioning Ltd, 253 Walsall Road, Perry Barr, Birmingham, B42 1TY Tel: 0121-356 1809 Fax: 0121-356 9478 E-mail: midlandaircon@btclick.com

Modus Air Ltd, 75 Lifford Lane, Birmingham, B30 3JH Tel: 0121-459 3060 Fax: 0121-459 6417 E-mail: modusair@btinternet.com

Nu Star Fabricators Ltd, 15 Baltic Lane, Glasgow, G40 4UB Tel: 0141-550 8823 Fax: 0141-550 8824

P & D Installation Services, 16 Badger Way, Prenton, Merseyside, CH43 3HQ Tel: 0151-608 0672 Fax: 0151-608 0672

▶ P & P Duct Services Ltd, Zagale House, Kelpatrick Road, Slough, SL1 6BW Tel: (01628) 666616 Fax: (01628) 666604

P S I (Resources) Ltd, Unit 3, Barlow Street, Walkden, Manchester, M28 3BQ Tel: 0161-703 8911 Fax: 0161-703 8995 E-mail: sales@p-s-i.co.uk

Paul Dentish, Unit E, Roe Cross Industrial Park, Mottram, Hyde, Cheshire, SK14 6NB Tel: (01457) 766304 Fax: (01457) 766305

Pidra Environments Ltd, 23 Avebury Avenue, Sherbourne Park Estate, Choppington, Northumberland, NE62 5HE Tel: 0191-267 7111 Fax: 0191-267 7222 E-mail: david@pidra.ltd.uk

Premi-air Systems, Newbattle Road, Dalkeith, Midlothian, EH22 3LL Tel: 0131-654 1565 Fax: 0131-654 1565

R A Green (Mechanical Servises) Ltd, Southdown, Western Road, Crowborough, East Sussex, TN6 3EW Tel: (01892) 652177 Fax: (01892) 667225 E-mail: ragreen@btinternet.com

R M F Ventilation Ltd, Stoneholme Business Centre, 42 High Street, Bury, Lancashire, BL8 3AN Tel: 0161-761 6099 Fax: 0161-764 1699 E-mail: rmf.ventilation@btinternet.com

R T Refrigaration & Air Conditioning, 1a Rowan Trade Park, Neville Road, Bradford, West Yorkshire, BD4 8TQ Tel: (01274) 737248 Fax: (01274) 309767

R T S Engineering (Somerset) Ltd, Unit 6, Sedgemount Industrial Park, Bristol Road, Bridgwater, Somerset, TA6 4AR Tel: (01278) 457294 Fax: (01278) 453772

Rowley & Hall Ventilation Ltd, 4 Canal Lane, Tunstall, Stoke-on-Trent, ST6 4NZ Tel: (01782) 837592 Fax: (01782) 833810

S A Ductwork, 1 Parc Y Nant, Nantgarw, Cardiff, CF15 7TJ Tel: (01443) 844210

S I A S Building Services Ltd, Unit 4 Knowle Spring Industrial Estate, South Street, Keighley, West Yorkshire, BD21 1AQ Tel: (01535) 611336 Fax: (01535) 611361 E-mail: consultants@siasbuildingservices.co.uk

S P E Ltd, 27 Dinghouse Wood, Buckley, Clwyd, CH7 3DH Tel: (01244) 549790 Fax: (01244) 549790 E-mail: s.mogridge@btinternet.com

Sayes & Co. Ltd, Richardshaw Road, Grangefield Industrial Estate, Stanningley, Pudsey, West Yorkshire, LS28 6BR Tel: 0113-257 8411 Fax: 0113-256 9275 E-mail: contact@sayesandcoltd.co.uk

Seaflame Co. Ltd, Cameron House, 839-841 London Road, Sutton, Surrey, SM3 9DR Tel: (020) 8330 6055 Fax: (020) 8335 3052 E-mail: info@seaflame.co.uk

Sheet Metal Products, St. Michaels Road, Newcastle upon Tyne, NE6 1QS Tel: 0191-276 3028 Fax: 0191-276 3028

Skinner Board & Co. Ltd, Sussex Street, Bristol, BS2 0RE Tel: 0117-955 1592 Fax: 0117-935 1408

Slidaway, 5 Gardener Industrial Estate, Kent House Lane, Beckenham, Kent, BR3 1QZ Tel: (020) 8778 7566 Fax: (020) 7778 1839

J.E. Smith (Higham Ferrers) Ltd., 24 Saffron Road, Higham Ferrers, Rushden, Northamptonshire, NN10 8ED Tel: (01933) 312495 Fax: (01933) 410424 E-mail: aircon@jesmith.sagehost.co.uk

Tac Satchwell, Europa House, 310 Europa Boulevard, Westbrook, Warrington, WA5 7XR Tel: (01925) 401000 Fax: (01925) 401166

Thermafabrications Ltd, New Craven Gate, Leeds, LS11 5NF Tel: 0113-245 7510 Fax: 0113-244 9430

Thermal Transfer (Northern) Ltd, Thermal Transfer House, 2 Railway Street, Glossop, Derbyshire, SK13 7AG Tel: (01457) 854341 Fax: (01457) 868357 E-mail: ttglossop@compuserve.co.uk

Thermal Transfer (U K) Ltd, Scottish Enterprise Technology Park, Rankine Avenue, East Kilbride, Glasgow, G75 0QF Tel: (01355) 234567 Fax: (01355) 266466

Thermatic Maintenance Ltd, 3 Sovereign Enterprise Park, King William Street, Salford, M50 3UP Tel: 0161-872 3724 Fax: 0161-848 0516 E-mail: dave.oakley@thermatic.co.uk

Townley Hughes & Co. Ltd, Unit 7 Meadow La Industrial Park, Ellesmere Port, CH65 4TY Tel: 0151-357 1800 Fax: 0151-357 2117 E-mail: townleyhughes@aol.com

Vaughan Mechanical Services (Scotland) Ltd, Aercon Works, East Mains Industrial Estate, Broxburn, West Lothian, EH52 5ND Tel: (01506) 853506 Fax: (01506) 854006 E-mail: vel@vaughan-group.co.uk

Vent Services Ltd, 4 Old Airfield Industrial Estate, Cheddington Lane, Long Marston, Tring, Hertfordshire, HP23 4QR Tel: (01296) 660000 Fax: (01296) 660111

Vented Services Telford Ltd, Unit A6 Hortonwood 10, Telford, Shropshire, TF1 7ES Tel: (01952) 677788 Fax: (01952) 677789 E-mail: addessee@vented-services.co.uk

Ventek Ltd, Unit 5, Starcrest Industrial Estate, Talbots Lane, Brierley Hill, West Midlands, DY5 2YT Tel: (01384) 79414 Fax: (01384) 79434 E-mail: sales@ventek.co.uk

W & H Fabrications Ltd, Scatcherd Works, Morley, Leeds, LS27 9BE Tel: 0113 2534633

West Mercia Air Conditioning Ltd, 29a Tarsmill Court, Rotherwas Industrial Estate, Hereford, HR2 6JZ Tel: (01432) 358489 Fax: (01432) 358489 E-mail: sales@wmaircon.com

Wright Bros Partnership Ltd, Waverley Road, Sheffield, S9 4PL Tel: 0114-244 1807 Fax: 0114-243 9277

VENTILATION OR AIR BRICKS

R J Donaghy & Sons, 71b Lissan Road, Cookstown, County Tyrone, BT80 8QX Tel: (028) 8676 3202 Fax: (028) 8676 2835

Red Bank Manufacturing Co. Ltd, Atherstone Road, Measham, Swadlincote, Derbyshire, DE12 7EL Tel: (01530) 270333 Fax: (01530) 270542 E-mail: info@redbank-manufacturing.co.uk

VENTILATION SYSTEMS, INDUSTRIAL

Fan Installation Services Ltd, PO Box 182, Twickenham, TW1 4WR Tel: (020) 8893 3316 Fax: (07946) 689758 E-mail: colin@fanservices.co.uk

VENTING EXPLOSION PROTECTION EQUIPMENT

BS&B Safety Systems (UK) Ltd, Adamson House, Tower Business Pk, Wilmslow Rd, Didsbury, Manchester, M20 2YY Tel: 0161-955 4202 Fax: 0161-955 4282 E-mail: sales@bsb-systems.co.uk

Stuvex Safety Systems Ltd, 48 Church Street, Weybridge, Surrey, KT13 8DP Tel: (01932) 849602 Fax: (01932) 852171 E-mail: sales@stuvex.com

VENTURE CAPITAL

▶ Business Angel Finance, 21 Dapps Hill, Keynsham, Bristol, BS31 1ES Tel: (0845) 8380936 E-mail: info@businessangelfinance.co.uk

Cambridge Venture Management Ltd, Unit 54, St. Johns Innovation Centre, Cowley Road, Cambridge, CB4 0WS Tel: (01223) 423828 Fax: (01223) 420418 E-mail: cvm@dial.pipex.com

Charterhouse Development Capital Ltd, 5 Paternoster Square, London, EC4M 7DX Tel: (020) 7334 5300 Fax: (020) 7334 5333 E-mail: recept@charterhouse.co.uk

E C I Ventures, Brettenham House, Lancaster Place, London, WC2E 7EN Tel: (020) 7606 1000 Fax: (020) 7240 5050

Newchurch Computer Systems, Causeway House, 13 The Causeway, Teddington, Middlesex, TW11 0JR Tel: (020) 8783 3300 Fax: (020) 8977 8198 E-mail: info@newchurch.co.uk

Prelude Technology Investment Holdings Ltd, Sycamore Studios, New Road Over, Cambridge, CB24 5PJ Tel: (01954) 288090 Fax: (01954) 288099 E-mail: prelude@prelude-ventures.com

Top Technology Benches Ltd, 20-21 Tooks Court, Cursitor Street, London, EC4A 1LB Tel: (020) 7242 9900 Fax: (020) 7405 2863 E-mail: ttv@toptechnology.co.uk

VERMIN DESTROYER OR REPELLENT PREPARATIONS

Bayles & Wylie Ltd, Forge Mill, Bestwood, Nottingham, NG6 8SX Tel: 0115-927 8227 Fax: 0115-977 0281

Modern Maintenance Products International, Brunel Close, Park Farm Industrial Estate, Wellingborough, Northamptonshire, NN8 6QX Tel: (01933) 670870 Fax: (01933) 670800 E-mail: info@mmp-international.co.uk

Ratatak Pest & Vermin Control, Osbourne House, 5 Massingham Road, Grimston, King's Lynn, Norfolk, PE32 1BD Tel: (01485) 600368

Scaringbirds.com Ltd, Lower Upton, Ludlow, Shropshire, SY8 4BB Tel: (01584) 711701 Fax: (01584) 711478 E-mail: info@scaringbirds.com

V E S Pest Control, Netherside, Bradwell, Hope Valley, Derbyshire, S33 9JL Tel: (01433) 621199 Fax: (01433) 621714 E-mail: ves@legend.co.uk

VERTICAL BLINDS

▶ Finavon Fabrics, 128 Murray Street, Montrose, Angus, DD10 8JG Tel: (01674) 676141

VERTICAL BORING

Ajax Minerva Ltd, Edderthorpe Street, Bradford, West Yorkshire, BD3 9JX Tel: (01274) 735910 Fax: (01274) 307706 E-mail: ajax_minerva@hotmail.com

Bridgeforth Engineering, Unit 13-14, Belleknowes Industrial Estate, Inverkeithing, Fife, KY11 1HZ Tel: (01383) 413441 Fax: (01383) 418391 E-mail: sales@bridgeforthl.co.uk

Crowther Engineering Ltd, 52 Hutton Close, Crowther, Washington, Tyne & Wear, NE38 0AH Tel: 0191-417 9916 Fax: 0191-415 5136 E-mail: nick@crowthereng.co.uk

Dawton Engineers Ltd, Unit 11-12, Waleswood Road, Wales Bar, Sheffield, S26 5PY Tel: (01909) 515313 Fax: (01909) 515499 E-mail: enquiries@dawton.co.uk

Maple Worcester Ltd, Stanier Road, Warndon, Worcester, WR4 9FE Tel: (01905) 754567 Fax: (01905) 756334 E-mail: sales@mapleworcester.com

VERTICAL BROACHING MACHINES

Forst UK Ltd, 14 Dartford Road, Leicester, LE2 7PR Tel: 0116-245 2000 Fax: 0116-245 2037 E-mail: sales@forst.co.uk

VERTICAL DRILLING MACHINES

H M Machinery UK Ltd, 41 Scholey Close, Halling, Rochester, Kent, ME2 1JZ Tel: (01634) 244600 Fax: (01634) 244599

Meddings Machine Tools, Kingsley Close, Lee Mill Industrial Estate, Ivybridge, Devon, PL21 9LL Tel: (01752) 313323 Fax: (01752) 313333 E-mail: sales@meddings.co.uk

O'Brian Manufacturing Ltd, Robian Way, Swadlincote, Derbyshire, DE11 9DH Tel: (01283) 217588 Fax: (01283) 215613

VERTICAL FORM FILLING/ SEALING MACHINERY

Gainsborough Engineering Co., Corringham Road Industrial Estate, Corringham Road, Gainsborough, Lincolnshire, DN21 1QB Tel: (01427) 617677 Fax: (01427) 810443 E-mail: info@gains-eng.co.uk

VERTICAL HONING MACHINES

Engis UK Ltd, Unit 9 Centenary Business Park, Station Road, Henley-on-Thames, Oxfordshire, RG9 1DS Tel: (01491) 411117 Fax: (01491) 412252 E-mail: sales@engis.uk.com

Equipment For You, PO Box 6, Cheltenham, Gloucestershire, GL51 9NJ Tel: (01242) 241822 Fax: (01242) 222994 E-mail: sales@3dsports.co.uk

Sunnen Products Ltd, Enterprise House, Maxted Road Hemel Hempstead Industrial Estate, Hemel Hempstead Industrial Estate, Hemel Hempstead, Hertfordshire, HP2 7BT Tel: (01442) 393939 Fax: (01442) 391212 E-mail: sales@sunnen.com

VERTICAL LOUVRE BLIND PRODUCTION MACHINERY

North East Secure Electronics Ltd, North East Innovation Centre, Neilson Road, Gateshead, Tyne & Wear, NE10 0EW Tel: 0191-477 9235 Fax: 0191-478 3639 E-mail: g.ord@neic.co.uk

VERTICAL LOUVRE BLINDS

A1 Blinds, Unit 17 Bridge Street Industrial Estate, Tredegar, Gwent, NP22 4LA Tel: (01495) 717545

Aaron Blinds, B 8 Chester Road, Whitby, Ellesmere Port, CH65 6RU Tel: 0151-355 2704 Fax: 0151-355 2704

Albany Blind Co., The Albany Boat House, Lower Ham Road, Kingston upon Thames, Surrey, KT2 5BB Tel: (020) 8549 5436 Fax: (020) 8549 5332 E-mail: peter@albany-blind.co.uk

Allan Blinds, 2 Senacre Square, Maidstone, Kent, ME15 8QF Tel: (01622) 677574 Fax: (01622) 677574

Arcadia Blinds & Coverings, 47 Main Street, Kilwinning, Ayrshire, KA13 6AN Tel: (01294) 554441 Fax: (01294) 559991

B J's Blinds, Hillend Bridge, Pudford Lane, Worcester, WR6 6QL Tel: (01886) 888966 Fax: (01886) 888481

Bath Blind Co., Lower Bristol Road, Bath, BA2 7DL Tel: (01225) 837517 Fax: (01225) 837517E-mail: stewart.davies@ukonline.co.uk

Beverleyblinds, 93 Nunts Park Avenue, Holbrooks, Coventry, CV6 4GX Tel: (024) 7664 4727 Fax: (024) 7666 6232

Hillary's Blinds (Northern) Ltd, Glover Industrial Estate, Spire Road, Washington, Tyne & Wear, NE37 3ES Tel: 0191-416 2354 Fax: 0191-416 2369

Bradrail Blinds & Awnings, 7-15 Main Street, Bulwell, Nottingham, NG6 8QH Tel: 0115-927 5251 Fax: 0115-977 0274 E-mail: enquiries@bradrail.co.uk

Brightview Blinds, 91 Charlock Way, Watford, WD18 6JT Tel: (01923) 243392 Fax: (01923) 231092

Butterfly Blinds, Cambridge Road, Milton, Cambridge, CB24 6AT Tel: (0500) 011363 Fax: (01223) 425355 E-mail: butterflyblinds@tiscali.co.uk

Centurion Blinds Ltd, Oakdale Trading Estate, Ham Lane, Kingswinford, West Midlands, DY6 7JH Tel: (01384) 279797 Fax: (01384) 292354 E-mail: paulmorris@centruionblinds.com

Claxton Blinds Ltd, Beaumont Works, Sutton Road, St. Albans, Hertfordshire, AL1 5HH Tel: (01727) 840001 Fax: (01727) 840004 E-mail: claxton-blinds@btconnect.com

Cottage Blinds Of Sedgley Ltd, Old Nail Works, Brick Street, Dudley, West Midlands, DY3 1NT Tel: (01902) 661267 Fax: (01902) 884312 E-mail: info@cottageblinds.co.uk

Coverlite Blinds & Awnings, 9-11 Hanover Street, Bolton, BL1 4TG Tel: (01204) 364444 Fax: (01204) 397232

CS Blinds, 11 Merlin Court, Newton Industrial Estate, Carlisle, CA2 7NY Tel: (01228) 598646

Cumbria Blinds North West, 111 Corporation Road, Workington, Cumbria, CA14 2PN Tel: (01900) 605070 Fax: (01900) 605070

Dixons Blinds Manufacturers Ltd, Customes House, Ridley Street, Blyth, Northumberland, NE24 3AG Tel: (01670) 355011 Fax: (01670) 355011

European Blinds, 10 Oakdale Avenue, Peterborough, PE2 8TA Tel: (01733) 347978

Faber Blinds UK Ltd, Kilvey Road, Brackmills Industrial Estate, Northampton, NN4 7BQ Tel: (01604) 766251 Fax: (01604) 768802 E-mail: sales@faberblinds.co.uk

▶ Flamingo Blinds & Signs, 12 Chaseville Parade, Chaseville Park Road, London, N21 1PG Tel: (020) 8881 0751 Fax: (020) 8881 0771 E-mail: admin@flamingoblinds.co.uk

Homefair Blinds (U K), Dundas Street, Middlesbrough, Cleveland, TS1 1HT Tel: (01642) 217181 Fax: 0191-521 4446

Levolux A T Ltd, Levolux House 24 Eastville Close, Eastern Avenue, Gloucester, GL4 3SJ Tel: (01452) 500007 Fax: (01452) 527496 E-mail: info@levolux.com

Malvern Blinds, The Old Fire Station, Howsell Road, Malvern, Worcestershire, WR14 1TF Tel: (01684) 574047 Fax: (01684) 892729 E-mail: info@malvernblinds.co.uk

Olympic Blinds Ltd, Olympic House Bilton Court, Bilton Way, Luton, LU1 1LX Tel: (01582) 737878 Fax: (01582) 402182 E-mail: sales@olympicblindsltd.co.uk

R N Contract Blinds, 57 Dyott Avenue, Whittington, Lichfield, Staffordshire, WS14 9NF Tel: (01543) 433433 Fax: (01543) 304047

Radiant Blinds Ltd, 101 Ewell Road, Surbiton, Surrey, KT6 6AH Tel: (020) 8390 8755 Fax: (020) 8390 2005 E-mail: info@radiantblinds.co.uk

Reflex-Rol, Ryeford Hall, Ryeford, Ross-on-Wye, Herefordshire, HR9 7PU Tel: (01989) 750704 Fax: (01989) 750768 E-mail: reflexrol@btinternet.com

Riverside Blinds, 284 Park Road, Toxteth, Liverpool, L8 4UE Tel: 0151-283 5600 Fax: 0151-283 0998

James Robertshaw & Sons (1954) Ltd, Albion Works, Lark Hill, Farnworth, Bolton, BL4 9LB Tel: (01204) 574764 Fax: (01204) 705424 E-mail: sales@jamesrobertshaw.co.uk

Rol Lite Blinds Ltd, St Pauls Trading Estate, Demesne Drive, Stalybridge, Cheshire, SK15 2QF Tel: 0161-338 2681 Fax: 0161-338 4193 E-mail: rol-lite@ben.co.uk

Sheraton Blinds Ltd, Unit 3 High Cross Centre, Fountayne Road, London, N15 4QN Tel: (020) 8885 5518 Fax: (020) 8365 1108 E-mail: barry@sheraton-blinds.co.uk

Solaris Sunblinds Ltd, 48 Victoria Road, Woolston, Southampton, SO19 9DX Tel: (023) 8043 1739 Fax: (023) 8043 7531 E-mail: info@solarissunblinds.co.uk

Solihull Blinds Ltd, A 85, Skelcher Road, Shirley, Solihull, West Midlands, B90 2EY Tel: 0121-733 1001 Fax: 0121-733 3062 E-mail: solihullblinds@blueyonder.co.uk

Solo Manufacturing Ltd, 18 South Nelson Road, South Nelson Industrial Estate, Cramlington, Northumberland, NE23 1WF Tel: (01670) 733788 Fax: (01670) 590555

Sunbright Blinds, 56 Gloucester Road, Urmston, Manchester, M41 9AE Tel: 0161-881 8181 Fax: 0161-748 2227 E-mail: ged.sunbright@virgin.net

Sunrite Blinds Ltd, 4 Newhailes Industrial Estate, Musselburgh, Edinburgh, EH21 6SY Tel: 0131-669 2345 Fax: 0131-665 7711 E-mail: info@sunrite.co.uk

Sunshade Blinds, 592 Kingstanding Road, Birmingham, B44 9SH Tel: 0121-373 1919 Fax: 0121-373 1919

SW Blinds & Interiors Ltd, Unit 60-61 Faraday Mill Business Park, Faraday Road, Plymouth, PL4 0ST Tel: (01752) 663517 Fax: (01752) 226150 E-mail: info@swblinds.com

Vertical Tec, Unit 14 Ash Industrial Estate, Flex Meadow, Harlow, Essex, CM19 5TJ Tel: (020) 7383 3388 Fax: (01279) 413388 E-mail: sales@verticaltec.co.uk

W M Herdman Manufacturing Co. Ltd, Orchard Road, Finedon, Wellingborough, Northamptonshire, NN9 5JG Tel: (01933) 680416 Fax: (01933) 681369

W & P Blinds, Unit M2 The Paddocks, 347 Cherry Hinton Road, Cambridge, CB1 8DH Tel: (01223) 243030 Fax: (01223) 243030 E-mail: info@wandpblinds.co.uk

Window World Wholesale, Marl Road, Knowsley Industrial Park, Liverpool, L33 7UH Tel: 0151-546 0333 Fax: 0151-546 0333

VERTICAL MACHINING CENTRE MACHINE TOOLS

▶ Millbrook Machine Tools, Park Road, Holmewood, Chesterfield, Derbyshire, S42 5UY Tel: (01246) 859999 Fax: (01246) 856069 E-mail: info@millbrookgroup.co.uk

VERTICAL MILLING MACHINES

Rowan Engineering, Garland Works, Desborough Avenue, High Wycombe, Buckinghamshire, HP11 2RN Tel: (01494) 531213 Fax: (01494) 465226 E-mail: enquiries@drjeng.fsnet.co.uk

VERTICAL TURNING LATHES

Charter Engineering Services, 6 Sycamore Centre, Sycamore Road, Eastwood Trading Estate, Rotherham, South Yorkshire, S65 1EN Tel: (01709) 836822 Fax: (01709) 836955 E-mail: sales@chartmach.co.uk

▶ D S Technology Ltd, 43-45 Phoenix Park, Avenue Close, Nechells, Birmingham, B7 4NU Tel: 0121-359 3637 Fax: 0121-359 1135 E-mail: info@ds-technology.co.uk

MS Pollard Ltd, St. Saviours Rd, Leicester, LE5 4HP Tel: 0116-276 7534 Fax: 0116-274 1547 E-mail: finn@mspollard.com

Somerset Machine Tools, 29 Brimbleworth Lane, St. Georges, Weston-super-Mare, Avon, BS22 7XS Tel: (01934) 510686 Fax: (01934) 522279 E-mail: smtcnc@aol.com

VESSEL ENTRY EQUIPMENT

Scottish Fisheries Protection Agency, Old Harbour Buildings, Scrabster, Thurso, Caithness, KW14 7UJ Tel: (01847) 895074 Fax: (01847) 894377

VETERAN VEHICLE WELDING REPAIRS

Light Engineering Services, 28 Rampton End, Willingham, Cambridge, CB4 5JB Tel: (01954) 260804 Fax: (01954) 260804 E-mail: lightengservices@lineone.net

VETERINARY AUXILIARY EQUIPMENT

▶ Electronic Design Associates, 20 Greenock Road, Streatham, London, SW16 5XG Tel: 020 86796355 Fax: 020 86796355 E-mail: bill@electronicdesignassociates.co.uk

VETERINARY GROOMING SERVICES

▶ Watt A Dog Grooming, 5 Hasman Terrace, Cove Bay, Aberdeen, AB12 3GD Tel: (01224) 874841 E-mail: jenifer@watt-a-dog.co.uk

VETERINARY INSTRUMENTS

Animalcare Ltd, Common Road, Dunnington, York, YO19 5RU Tel: (01904) 487687 Fax: (01904) 487611

B C F Technology Ltd, 3 Rutherford Square, Brucefield Industrial Estate, Livingston, West Lothian, EH54 9BU Tel: (01506) 460023 Fax: (01506) 460045 E-mail: office@bcftech.demon.co.uk

Bar Knight Precision Engineers Ltd, 588-588a Glasgow Road, Clydebank, Dunbartonshire, G81 1NH Tel: 0141-952 4000 Fax: 0141-952 1157 E-mail: sales@barknight.co.uk

Brookwick Ward, Fearby Road, Masham, Ripon, North Yorkshire, HG4 4ES Tel: (0870) 1118610 Fax: (0870) 1118609 E-mail: sales@brookwickward.com

Kaycee Veterinary Products, Unit 14 Lindfield Enterprise Park, Lewes Road, Lindfield, Haywards Heath, West Sussex, RH16 2LH Tel: (01444) 482888 Fax: (01444) 483383 E-mail: tds@kaycee.co.uk

Medivance Instrumnets Ltd, Barretts Green Road, London, NW10 7AP Tel: (020) 8965 2913 Fax: (020) 8963 1270 E-mail: enquiries@velopex.com

Scala Surgical Ltd, 200 Church Road, London, NW10 9NP Tel: (020) 8459 1816 Fax: (020) 8459 3416 E-mail: scala_impex@yahoo.co.uk

Surgical Holdings Ltd, 8 Parkside Centre, Potters Way, Southend-on-Sea, SS2 5SJ Tel: (01702) 602050 Fax: (01702) 460006 E-mail: office@surgicalholdings.co.uk

Veterinary Instrumentation, Broadfield Road, Sheffield, S8 0XL Tel: (0845) 1309596 Fax: (0845) 1308687 E-mail: info@vetinst.co.uk

Wellington Pharmacy, 39 Knightsbridge, London, SW1X 7NL Tel: (020) 7235 2653 Fax: (020) 7235 0158E-mail: wellington1@btconnect.com

Y D T Medical Ltd, 92 Hartley Down, Purley, Surrey, CR8 4EB Tel: (020) 8763 9777 Fax: (020) 8763 9444 E-mail: ydtlimited@aol.com

VETERINARY MEDICINE/ PHARMACEUTICAL MANUFRS

▶ Alstoe Ltd, The Industrial Estate, York Road, Sheriff Hutton, York, YO60 6RZ Tel: (01347) 878606 Fax: (01347) 878333 E-mail: info@alstoe.co.uk

Anglian Nutrition Products Co., Lady Lane Industrial Estate, Crocatt Road, Hadleigh, Ipswich, IP7 6RD Tel: (01473) 822121 Fax: (01473) 822156 E-mail: mail@anupco.com

Aquaculture Holdings Ltd, 24 26 Gold Street, Saffron Walden, Essex, CB10 1EJ Tel: (01799) 28167 Fax: (01799) 25546 E-mail: spaquaculture@spcorp.com

Aviform Ltd, Unit 4, G-K Wellesley Road, Tharston Industrial Estate, Long Stratton, Norwich, NR15 2PD Tel: (01508) 530813 Fax: (01508) 530873 E-mail: sales@aviform.co.uk

Battle Hayward & Bower Ltd, Crofton Drive, Lincoln, LN3 4NP Tel: (01522) 529206 Fax: (01522) 538960 E-mail: bhb@battles.co.uk

Biochek UK Ltd, Unit 11 Mill Farm Business Park, Millfield Road, Hounslow, TW4 5PY Tel: (020) 8893 3000 Fax: (020) 8893 3101 E-mail: admin@biochek.com

▶ Cliffe Veterinary Group, 70 Springett Avenue, Ringmer, Lewes, East Sussex, BN8 5QX Tel: (01273) 814590 Fax: (01273) 815310

Cross Vetpharm Group UK Ltd, Unit 2 Bryn Cefni Industrial Park, Llangefni, Gwynedd, LL77 7XA Tel: (01248) 725400 Fax: (01248) 725416 E-mail: sales@bimeda.co.uk

Francis Cupiss Ltd, The Wilderness, The Entry, Diss, Norfolk, IP22 4NT Tel: (01379) 642045 Fax: (01379) 642045 E-mail: mail@franciscupiss.co.uk

Farm 2000 - Teisen Products Ltd, Bradley Green, Redditch, Worcestershire, B96 6RP Tel: (01527) 821621 Fax: (01527) 821665 E-mail: heat@farm2000.co.uk

Frank A Mccaughan, 27 Ann Street, Ballycastle, County Antrim, BT54 6AA Tel: (028) 2076 2480 Fax: (028) 2076 3225

Gabriel Veterinary Supplies & Services, 452 Shaw Road, Royton, Oldham, OL2 6PG Tel: (01706) 881619 Fax: (01706) 881619

The Hatchwell Co. Ltd, Unit G1 Riverside Industrial Estate, Hermitage Street, Rishton, Blackburn, BB1 4NF Tel: (01254) 888479 Fax: (01254) 883822 E-mail: sales@hatchwell.co.uk

Intervet UK Ltd, Walton Manor, Walton, Milton Keynes, MK7 7AJ Tel: (01908) 665050 Fax: (01908) 664778 E-mail: info@intervet.com

Johnsons Veterinary Products Ltd, 5 Reddicap Trading Estate, Sutton Coldfield, West Midlands, B75 7DF Tel: 0121-378 1684 Fax: 0121-311 1758 E-mail: info@johnsons-vet.com

Kingwood Stud, Lambourn Woodlands, Lambourn Woodlands, Hungerford, Berkshire, RG17 7RS Tel: (01488) 71657 Fax: (01488) 73434

Laycocks Agricultural Chemists, Gargrave Road, Skipton, North Yorkshire, BD23 1UD Tel: (01756) 792166 Fax: (01756) 701008 E-mail: info@laycocks.co.uk

Mccaskie Farm Supplies Ltd, 4 Munro Road, Springkerse Industrial Estate, Stirling, FK7 7UU Tel: (01786) 474481 Fax: (01786) 464099 E-mail: admin@mccaskie.co.uk

Meditech Veterinary Pharmacies, 2 Upper Russell Street, Wednesbury, West Midlands, WS10 7AR Tel: 0121-505 6370 Fax: 0121-505 3564

Norbrook Exports Ltd, Camlough Road, Newry, County Down, BT35 6JP Tel: (028) 3026 4435 Fax: (028) 3025 1141 E-mail: enquiries@norbrook.co.uk

H. & C. Pearce & Sons Ltd, Farndon Road, Market Harborough, Leicestershire, LE16 9NP Tel: (01858) 432704 Fax: (01858) 466026 E-mail: info@hcpearce.co.uk

Stockcare Ltd, 83 West Street, Leven, Beverley, North Humberside, HU17 5LR Tel: (01964) 543924 Fax: (01964) 542750 E-mail: sales@goldlabeluk.com

Veterinary Immunogenics, Carleton Hill, Carleton, Penrith, Cumbria, CA11 8TZ Tel: (01768) 863881 Fax: (01768) 891389

Vetoquinol Ltd, Buckingham Industrial Park, Great Slade, Buckingham, MK18 1UA Tel: (01280) 814500 Fax: (01280) 825462 E-mail: sales@vetoquinol.co.uk

W & J Dunlop, College Mains Road, Dumfries, DG2 0NU Tel: (01387) 263733 Fax: (01387) 254326 E-mail: admin@dunlops.com

Wellington Pharmacy, 39 Knightsbridge, London, SW1X 7NL Tel: (020) 7235 2653 Fax: (020) 7235 0158E-mail: wellington1@btconnect.com

William Daniels UK Ltd, Unit 1c Beacon Industrial Estate, Hull Road, Withernsea, North Humberside, HU19 2EG Tel: (01964) 614081 Fax: (01964) 614341 E-mail: sales@williamdaniels.co.uk

VETERINARY OPERATING TABLES

Poltec Ltd, 1 Old Stafford Road, Slade Heath, Wolverhampton, WV10 7PH Tel: (01902) 790238 E-mail: sales@poltec.co.uk

VETERINARY SCALES

▶ 1 Stop Scale Shop, 47 Market Place, Henley-on-Thames, Oxfordshire, RG9 2AN Tel: (0845) 1307330 Fax: (0845) 1307440 E-mail: sales@1stopscaleshop.co.uk

Marsden Weighing Machine Group, 47 Market Place, Henley-on-Thames, Oxfordshire, RG9 2AD Tel: (0845) 1307330 Fax: (0845) 1307440 E-mail: sales@marsdengroup.demon.co.uk

VETERINARY TUB TABLES

Poltec Ltd, 1 Old Stafford Road, Slade Heath, Wolverhampton, WV10 7PH Tel: (01902) 790238 E-mail: sales@poltec.co.uk

VG OR DIN SPECIFICATION CONNECTORS

Panduit Europe Ltd, West World, Westgate, London, W5 1UD Tel: (020) 8601 7200 Fax: (020) 8601 7319

VIA INTERNET PRINTED STATIONERY

▶ Sussex Internet Ltd, Enterprise Works Ltd, Beach Road, Newhaven, East Sussex, BN9 0BX Tel: (01273) 514710 E-mail: info@sussex-internet.net

VIALS/PHIALS, GLASS

F B G Trident, Unit 1, Humber Road, Cricklewood, London, NW2 6DN Tel: (020) 8830 8000 Fax: (020) 8830 5347

Labco, Brow Works, Copyground Lane, High Wycombe, Buckinghamshire, HP12 3HE Tel: (01494) 459741 Fax: (01494) 465101 E-mail: sales@labco.co.uk

VIBRATING ROLLERS

▶ FarmEquip.co.uk, Strichen, Fraserburgh, Aberdeenshire, AB43 6NY Tel: (01771) 637413

▶ FarmEquip.co.uk, 16 Camperdown Road, Boathpark, Nairn, IV12 5AR Tel: (01667) 456842

VIBRATION ANALYSIS SERVICES, MACHINE/ STRUCTURE

Anstee & Ware Group Ltd, Unit 1 St Georges Industrial Estate, St Andrews Road, Bristol, BS11 9HS Tel: 0117-982 0081 Fax: 0117-982 3501 E-mail: admin@ansteeware.co.uk

R M S Vibration Test Laboratory, 26 Coder Road, Ludlow Business Park, Ludlow, Shropshire, SY8 1XE Tel: (01584) 861395 Fax: (01584) 861395 E-mail: rms.vibes@avignon.enta.net

Universal Balancing Ltd, Unit 12 Douglas Road Industrial Estate, Douglas Road, Kingswood, Bristol, BS15 8PD Tel: 0117-907 7403 Fax: 0117-907 7402 E-mail: sales@unibal.co.uk

VIBRATION CONTROL CONSULTANCY

C M T Dynamics, PO Box 36, Cradley Heath, West Midlands, B64 7DQ Tel: (01384) 563220 Fax: (01384) 563225 E-mail: sales@cmt-dynamics.co.uk

Eurovib Acoustic Products Ltd, Goodwood House, 86 Holmethorpe Avenue, Redhill, RH1 2NL Tel: (01737) 779577 Fax: (01737) 779537 E-mail: sales@eurovib.co.uk

Noise & Vibration Engineering Ltd, 1 Rothesay Avenue, London, SW20 8JU Tel: (020) 8542 9226 Fax: (020) 8540 8481 E-mail: enquiries@noise-vibration.co.uk

▶ Peninsular Acoustics, 114 Shrewsbury Road, Prenton, Merseyside, CH43 8SP Tel: 0151-652 6270 Fax: 0151-652 6270 E-mail: noise@btconnect.com

Vibronoise Ltd, 62 Talbot Rd, Old Trafford, Manchester, M16 0PN Tel: 0161-428 3100 Fax: 0161-428 1198 E-mail: info@virbronoise.co.uk

VIBRATION CONTROL EQUIPMENT

Data Physics (UK) Ltd, South Rd, Hailsham, East Sussex, BN27 3JJ Tel: (01323) 846464 Fax: (01323) 847550 E-mail: sales@dataphysics.com

Eurovib Acoustic Products Ltd, Goodwood House, 86 Holmethorpe Avenue, Redhill, RH1 2NL Tel: (01737) 779577 Fax: (01737) 779537 E-mail: sales@eurovib.co.uk

VIBRATION FREE CONCRETE SURFACE PREPARATION

Hydro Pumps Ltd, 19 High Mead, Fareham, Hampshire, PO15 6BL Tel: (01329) 823420 Fax: (01329) 823425 E-mail: sales@hydro-pumps.co.uk

VIBRATION MEASURE/ MONITOR/ANALYSIS/METER SYSTEMS MANUFRS

Prosig Ltd, 44a High Street, Fareham, Hampshire, PO16 7BQ Tel: (01329) 239925 Fax: (01329) 239159 E-mail: info@prosig.com

Schmitt Europe Ltd, Sir William Lyons Road, University of Warwick Science Park, Coventry, CV4 7EZ Tel: (024) 7669 7192 Fax: (024) 7641 2697 E-mail: enquiries@schmitt.co.uk

VIBRATION MEASURING/ MONITORING/ANALYSIS/ METERING SERVICES

Denis R Robinson & Associates, 169 Sherwood Avenue, Northampton, NN2 8TB Tel: (01604) 843807 Fax: (01604) 843807 E-mail: denis-rr@skynet.co.uk

R M S Vibration Test Laboratory, 26 Coder Road, Ludlow Business Park, Ludlow, Shropshire, SY8 1XE Tel: (01584) 861395 Fax: (01584) 861395 E-mail: rms.vibes@avignon.enta.net

VIBRATION PROOF FASTENERS

W T I Fasteners Ltd, Unit 10 Huntingdon Court, Westminster Industrial Estate, Measham, Swadlincote, Derbyshire, DE12 7DS Tel: (01530) 273100 Fax: (01530) 273007 E-mail: admin@wireinserts.com

VIBRATION SENSORS

Diagnostic Solutions Ltd, Unit 1, Rossett Business Village, Rossett, Chester, LL12 0AY Tel: (01244) 571411 Fax: (01244) 571977 E-mail: office@diagnosticsolutions.co.uk

VIBRATION TEST EQUIPMENT

Dynamic Test Systems, 1 High Street, Puckeridge, Ware, Hertfordshire, SG11 1RN Tel: (01920) 821095 Fax: (01920) 822797 E-mail: dtsinfo98@aol.com

Environmental Equipments Ltd, 12, Eleanor House, Kingsclere Park, Kingsclere, Newbury, Berkshire, RG20 4SW Tel: (01635) 298502 Fax: (01635) 296499 E-mail: sales@e-equipments.com

Gearing & Watson Electronics Ltd, South Road, Hailsham, East Sussex, BN27 3JJ Tel: (01323) 846464 Fax: (01323) 847550 E-mail: sales@dataphysics.com

L D S Test & Measurement Ltd, Heath Works, Baldock Road, Royston, Hertfordshire, SG8 5BQ Tel: (01763) 242424 Fax: (01763) 249711 E-mail: sales@lds-group.com

Servotest Testing Systems Ltd, Unit 1 Beta Way, Thorpe Industrial Estate, Egham, Surrey, TW20 8RE Tel: (01784) 274410 Fax: (01784) 274438 E-mail: info@servotestsystems.com

Spectral Dynamics UK Ltd, Fulling Mill, Fulling Mill Lane, Welwyn, Hertfordshire, AL6 9NP Tel: (01438) 716626 Fax: (01438) 716628 E-mail: sales@spectraldynamics.co.uk

Team Corporation UK Ltd, 11 Old Ladies Court, High Street, Battle, East Sussex, TN33 0AH Tel: (01424) 777004 Fax: (01424) 777005 E-mail: sales@teamcorporation.co.uk

V S R Co., Unit 13A, Shrub Hill Industrial Estate, Worcester, WR4 9EL Tel: (01905) 452800 Fax: (01905) 731811E-mail: sales@v-s-r.co.uk

VIBRATION TRANSDUCERS

IGE Energy Services (UK) Ltd, 2 Kelvin Close, Science Park North, Birchwood, Warrington, WA3 7BL Tel: (01925) 818504 Fax: (01925) 817819

Sensonics Ltd, North Bridge Road, Berkhamsted, Hertfordshire, HP4 1EF Tel: (01442) 876833 Fax: (01442) 876477 E-mail: sales@sensonics.co.uk

Spectral Dynamics UK Ltd, Fulling Mill, Fulling Mill Lane, Welwyn, Hertfordshire, AL6 9NP Tel: (01438) 716626 Fax: (01438) 716628 E-mail: sales@spectraldynamics.co.uk

VIBRATORY BOWL FEEDER EQUIPMENT

Alphamation Ltd, Bassett Road, Halesowen, West Midlands, B63 2RE Tel: (01384) 412255 Fax: (01384) 413191 E-mail: info@alphamation.co.uk

Aylesbury Automation Ltd, Unit 2 Farmbrough Cl, Stocklake Industrial Pk, Aylesbury, Buckinghamshire, HP20 1DQ Tel: (01296) 314300 Fax: (01296) 482424 E-mail: enquiry@aylesbury-automation.co.uk

Performance Feeders, Lavender House, Station Road, Hammerwich, Burntwood, Staffordshire, WS7 0JZ Tel: (01543) 454055 Fax: (01543) 454047 E-mail: enquiries@performancefeeders.co.uk

Tribal Automation Ltd, 6 Lodge Forge Trading Estate, Cradley Road, Cradley Heath, West Midlands, B64 7RW Tel: (01384) 562563 Fax: (01384) 562563

Vibro Automation Ltd, Acton Av, Long Eaton, Nottingham, NG10 1GA Tel: 0115-946 8361 Fax: 0115-946 8362

VIBRATORY CONVEYOR SYSTEMS

Alphamation Ltd, Bassett Road, Halesowen, West Midlands, B63 2RE Tel: (01384) 412255 Fax: (01384) 413191 E-mail: info@alphamation.co.uk

Cox & Plant Products Ltd, Monument Works, Balds Lane, Stourbridge, West Midlands, DY9 8SE Tel: (01384) 895121 Fax: (01384) 893611 E-mail: convey@cox-plant.com

General Kinematics Ltd, Dawley Brook Works, Kingswinford, West Midlands, DY6 7BB Tel: (01384) 273303 Fax: (01384) 273404 E-mail: mail@generalkinematics.co.uk

K M G Systems Ltd, Station Road, Gamlingay, Sandy, Bedfordshire, SG19 3HE Tel: (01767) 650760 Fax: (01767) 651622 E-mail: admin@kmgsystems.com

Wright Machinery Ltd, Stonefield Way, Ruislip, Middlesex, HA4 0JU Tel: (020) 8842 2244 Fax: (020) 8842 1113 E-mail: sales@wright.co.uk

VIBRATORY FEEDERS, CONVEYOR/ELEVATOR

A C Automation, Hartland Avenue, Tattenhoe, Milton Keynes, MK4 3DN Tel: (01908) 501796 Fax: (01908) 501796 E-mail: sales@ac-automation.co.uk

K F Alliance Engineering Ltd, Units 28-29, Enfield Industrial Estate, Redditch, Worcestershire, B97 6BY Tel: (01527) 63331 Fax: (01527) 591191 E-mail: kfa@btconnect.com

Mogensen, Harlaxton Road, Grantham, Lincolnshire, NG31 7SF Tel: (01476) 566301 Fax: (01476) 590145 E-mail: sales@mogensen.co.uk

Process Link Ltd, Tilemans Lane, Shipston-on-Stour, Warwickshire, CV36 4QZ Tel: (01608) 662878 Fax: (01608) 662968 E-mail: info@processlink.co.uk

Rotex Europe Ltd, Whitehouse Vale, Aston La North, Runcorn, Cheshire, WA7 3FA Tel: (01928) 706100 Fax: (0870) 7529920

Towerip Ltd, Unit 1-2 162 Leabrook Road, Tipton, West Midlands, DY4 0DY Tel: 0121 5020469

VIBRATORY SCREENS

Filter Screen Supply Ltd, 2 Paynes Place Farm, Cuckfield Road, Burgess Hill, West Sussex, RH15 8RG Tel: (01444) 244406 Fax: (01444) 230303E-mail: sales@filterscreensupply.co.uk

H R International Crushing & Screening Ltd, Huntingdon Court, Huntingdon Way, Measham, Swadlincote, Derbyshire, DE12 7NQ Tel: (01530) 272799 Fax: (01530) 272787 E-mail: hril@lineone.net

Kason Corporation Europe, Unit 12-13 Parkhall Business Village, Parkhall Road, Stoke-on-Trent, ST3 5XA Tel: (01782) 597540 Fax: (01782) 597549 E-mail: sales@kasoneurope.co.uk

Mogensen, Harlaxton Road, Grantham, Lincolnshire, NG31 7SF Tel: (01476) 566301 Fax: (01476) 590145 E-mail: sales@mogensen.co.uk

Rotex Europe Ltd, Whitehouse Vale, Aston La North, Runcorn, Cheshire, WA7 3FA Tel: (01928) 706100 Fax: (0870) 7529920

VIBRO/VIBRATORY FINISHING/ POLISHING EQUIPMENT

Crauford Technology Ltd, 135B Edinburgh Avenue Trading Estate, Slough, SL1 4SW Tel: (01753) 531462 Fax: (01753) 552580 E-mail: davidd@craufurd.com

Norfinish Engineering Ltd, Sleekburn Business Centre, West Sleekburn, Bedlington, Northumberland, NE22 7DD Tel: (01670) 855087 Fax: (01670) 855079 E-mail: info@norfinish.co.uk

Sharmic Engineering Ltd, Baldwin Road, Stourport-on-Severn, Worcestershire, DY13 9AX Tel: (01299) 878123 Fax: (01299) 879409 E-mail: info@sharmic.co.uk

VIDEO BROADCASTING EQUIPMENT

B Tech International Ltd, Vulcan House, Vulcan Way, New Addington, Croydon, CR0 9UG Tel: (01689) 848535 Fax: (01689) 841073 E-mail: info@b-tech-int.com

▶ Broadcast Services, The Coach House, Ruxbury Road, Chertsey, Surrey, KT16 9EP Tel: (01932) 570001 Fax: (01932) 570443 E-mail: hire@broadcast-services.co.uk

Contour Video Productions, 164 Ellerdine Road, Hounslow, TW3 2PX Tel: (020) 8737 6557 Fax: (020) 8737 6557

Libra Professional Broadcast, Chester House, 91-95 Alcester Road, Studley, Warwickshire, B80 7NJ Tel: (01527) 853305 Fax: (01527) 852086 E-mail: andy@libraproinfo.co.uk

Mosses & Mitchell Ltd, Unit 5, Bath Road Business Centre, Devizes, Wiltshire, SN10 1XA Tel: (01380) 722993 Fax: (01380) 728422 E-mail: sales@mosses-mitchel.com

Northern Visions, 23 Donegall Street, Belfast, BT1 2FF Tel: (028) 9024 5495 Fax: (028) 9032 6608 E-mail: info@northanvisions.org

Star Quality Video Productions, 36 Mount Ephraim Lane, London, SW16 1JD Tel: (020) 8769 6425 Fax: (020) 8769 6425 E-mail: starqualityvideo@aol.com

Video House Productions, 32 Ash Street, Fleetwood, Lancashire, FY7 6TH Tel: (01253) 770510 Fax: (01253) 776729 E-mail: gilly@slater.co.uk

VIDEO CAMERA HIRE

▶ hdvcameraman, 4 Salt Lane, Hydestile, Godalming, Surrey, GU8 4DG Tel: (01483) 202206 E-mail: paul@hdvcameraman.co.uk

VIDEO CASSETTES

▶ Discount DVDs & Videos, 16 Craighead Drive, Huntly, Aberdeenshire, AB54 8LG Tel: (01466) 799142 E-mail: cheapstock@tiscali.co.uk

VIDEO CONFERENCING SERVICES

Congress Centre, Congress House, 23-28 Great Russell Street, London, WC1B 3LS Tel: (020) 7467 1200 Fax: (020) 7467 1313 E-mail: congress.centre@tuc.org.uk

Image Business Systems UK Ltd, 455 Maxwell Avenue, Harwell Intnl Business Centre, Didcot, Oxfordshire, OX11 0PY Tel: (01235) 865500 Fax: (01235) 865511 E-mail: sales@imagebusinesssystems.co.uk

Internet Video Communication, Alexander House Mere Park, Dedmere Road, Marlow, Buckinghamshire, SL7 1FX Tel: (01628) 484446 Fax: (01628) 475708

J B Communications Group Ltd, 15 Brackenbury Road, London, W6 0BE Tel: (020) 8749 6036 Fax: (020) 8749 9676 E-mail: interest@jbcommunications.co.uk

Prescience Communications Ltd, Haymarket House, 8 Clifton Terrace, Edinburgh, EH12 5DR Tel: 0131-313 3599 Fax: 0131-346 1294

VIDEO CONFERENCING SYSTEMS

Cameron Communications (Aberdeen) Ltd, Suite B Colts Business Centre, Station Road, Colts, Aberdeen, AB15 9NP Tel: (01224) 865005 Fax: (01224) 865205 E-mail: camcomabdn@aol.com

Mach Agencies International UK Ltd, 265 Fullwell Avenue, Barkingside, Ilford, Essex, IG5 0RD Tel: (020) 8550 8177

▶ Multisense Communications Ltd, Red Lion House, 600 London Road, High Wycombe, Buckinghamshire, HP11 1EX Tel: (01494) 461949 Fax: (01494) 536261 E-mail: sales@multisense.co.uk

VIDEO CONFERENCING SYSTEMS, ROOM AND DESK TOP

F V C Com, Bridge View House, Ray Mead Road, Maidenhead, Berkshire, SL6 8NJ Tel: (01628) 687700

VIDEO CONSULTANTS OR DESIGNERS

▶ JBP Royalty Free, 40 Rempstone Drive, Chesterfield, Derbyshire, S41 0YB Tel: 01246 540341

S T V S, Unit 8, 2 Perry Way, Witham, Essex, CM8 3SX Tel: (01376) 517333 Fax: (01376) 517333

VIDEO DATA COMMUNICATION SYSTEMS

Av Niche Recording Systems, 5 Heron Court, Cranes Farm Road, Basildon, Essex, SS14 3DF Tel: (01268) 474608 Fax: (01268) 531482 E-mail: avniche@btconnect.com

VIDEO DATA PROJECTORS

Comm-Tec Ltd, 6 Danbury Court, Sunrise Parkway, Linford Wood East, Milton Keynes, MK14 6PL Tel: (01908) 550039 Fax: (01908) 696120 E-mail: sales@comm-tec.co.uk

VIDEO DISPLAYS, PORTABLE

▶ Able Schott Production, Moon Cottage Studio, Higher Eype, Bridport, Dorset, DT6 6AS Tel: 01308 423095 E-mail: info@ableschott.co.uk

VIDEO DOOR BELLS

▶ Empire, 4 Rose Cottages, Station Road, Claygate, Esher, Surrey, KT10 9DJ Tel: (07010) 714766 Fax: (01372) 466158

VIDEO EDITING CARDS

System Enterprises Ltd, Unit 21, Hartley Fold, Hartley, Kirkby Stephen, Cumbria, CA17 4JA Tel: (0845) 6430556 E-mail: info@systementerprises.com

VIDEO FILM PRODUCTION, COMMERCIAL/INDUSTRIAL/ TRAINING/EDUCATIONAL

A V Sightline, Dylan House, Town End Street, Godalming, Surrey, GU7 1BQ Tel: (01483) 861555 Fax: (01483) 861516 E-mail: action@sightline.co.uk
▶ Activity Media Ltd, 7 Conway Drive, Flitwick, Bedford, MK45 1DE Tel: (01525) 759047
▶ Ambient Light Productions Ltd, 6 Shipquay Street, Londonderry, BT48 6DN Tel: (028) 7136 3525 E-mail: info@ambient-light.co.uk
Ardath Video, 56 Ardath Road, Birmingham, B38 9PH Tel: 0121-451 3332 Fax: 0121-459 5127 E-mail: sales@ardathvideo.co.uk
Atmosphere Productions Ltd, 6 Lothair Road, Leicester, LE2 7QB Tel: 0116-244 0041 E-mail: info@atmospheres.co.uk
▶ Bop TV (E-Video Productions), Alexander House, Foxlands Drive, Wolverhampton, WV4 5NB Tel: (01902) 344844 Fax: (01902) 340544 E-mail: sara_longman@fish.co.uk
▶ Casual Productions, Unit 52, Stafford Business Village, Staffordshire Technology Park, Stafford, ST18 0TW Tel: 01785 887979 Fax: 01785 887825 E-mail: info@casualproductions.com
▶ Eon Media, Thomas Street, Hull, HU9 1EH Tel: (01482) 339650 Fax: (01482) 339701 E-mail: tevison@eon-media.com
Generation Software, 59 Victoria Road, Tilehurst, Reading, RG31 5AB Tel: 0118-948 2468 Fax: 0118-948 2470 E-mail: office@generationsoftware.com
▶ Grasshopper Films Ltd, 3rd Floor 14 Bacon Street, London, E1 6LF Tel: (020) 7739 7154 Fax: (020) 7739 6359 E-mail: info@grasshopperfilms.com
▶ Harliquin.co.uk, Dover Street, Totton, Southampton, SO14 6GL Tel: (07050) 196660 E-mail: ian@harliquin.co.uk
▶ i2i Television Ltd, The Studio, Bankhead Farm Road, Strathaven, Lanarkshire, ML10 6TR Tel: (01698) 794100 E-mail: crews@i2itv.com
▶ I-MOTUS, 11 West Mills Yard, Kennet Road, Newbury, Berkshire, RG14 5LP Tel: 0845 430 4448 Fax: 01635 524 449 E-mail: info@i-motus.com
▶ Mindset Communications, Nelson Close, Farnham, Surrey, GU9 9AR Tel: (07771) 870868 Fax: (01252) 316881 E-mail: info@mindsetcomms.co.uk
▶ On The River Film & Video Production, 2/1 5 McIntyre Place, Paisley, Renfrewshire, PA2 6EE Tel: 0141-889 2411 Fax: 0141-889 2411 E-mail: info@concepttoscreen.com
One To One Productions, Glasshoughton Cultural Industries Centre, Redhill Avenue, Castleford, West Yorkshire, WF10 4QH Tel: (01977) 603431 Fax: (01977) 735000 E-mail: sales@one2one-connected.com
Picture Palace Films Ltd, 13 Egbert Street, London, NW1 8LJ Tel: (020) 7586 8763 Fax: (020) 7586 9048 E-mail: info@picturepalace.com
▶ Retina Productions Ltd, 6 Mount Pleasant Crescent, London, N4 4HP Tel: (020) 7272 4448 Fax: (020) 7272 5756 E-mail: nisrine@retina-productions.co.uk
S T V Videos, PO Box 299, Bromley, BR2 9EE Tel: (020) 8464 4287 E-mail: sales@stvvideos.co.uk
Video Arts Group Ltd, 6-7 St. Cross Street, London, EC1N 8UA Tel: (020) 7400 4800 Fax: (020) 7400 4900 E-mail: sales@videoarts.co.uk
▶ Western Eye, Kinley House, 43 The Crescent, Bristol, BS9 4RP Tel: (07803) 593833 E-mail: mail@western-eye.com
▶ WV Entertainment Limited, C/O The Suite, 3 Goldthorn Avenue, Wolverhampton, WV4 5AA Tel: 07939 930781

VIDEO FILTERS

Faraday Technology Ltd, Units 22-26 Croft Road Indust Estate, Newcastle, Staffordshire, ST5 0TW Tel: (01782) 661501 Fax: (01782) 630101 E-mail: sales@faradaytech.co.uk

VIDEO FRAME GRABBING EQUIPMENT

Matrox Vite Ltd, C Sefton Park, Bells Hill, Stoke Poges, Slough, SL2 4JS Tel: (01753) 665500 Fax: (01753) 665599

VIDEO INFORMATION SYSTEMS

Acord Electronics Ltd, Madeira Road, West Byfleet, Surrey, KT14 6DN Tel: (01932) 354565 Fax: (01932) 350140 E-mail: sales@acord.co.uk

VIDEO LINK EQUIPMENT

F V C Com, Bridge View House, Ray Mead Road, Maidenhead, Berkshire, SL6 8NJ Tel: (01628) 687700

VIDEO MAINTENANCE/REPAIR SERVICES, INDUSTRIAL/ PROFESSIONAL

A T L Televisions Ltd, 200 Cauldwell Hall Rd, Ipswich, IP4 5DB Tel: (01473) 720445 Fax: (01473) 720445
Armstrong Hi-Fi & Video Service Ltd, 32a Blackhorse Lane, London, E17 6HJ Tel: (020) 8523 0051 Fax: (020) 8523 4395 E-mail: ahvsltd@aol.com
Avery Electronic Services, Unit 4 Wren Industrial Estate, Coldred Road, Parkwood, Maidstone, Kent, ME15 9XN Tel: (01622) 682138 Fax: (01622) 691232
Clicks Media Studios, Amp House, Grove Road, Strood, Rochester, Kent, ME2 4BX Tel: (01634) 723838 E-mail: pjstv@blueyonder.co.uk
Jai Electronics, 155 High Street, London, NW10 4TR Tel: (020) 8965 5080 Fax: (020) 8961 2924 E-mail: jai@beeb.net
Kingsway TV & Video, 28 Greenheys Road, Wallasey, Merseyside, CH44 5UP Tel: 0151-630 4071

VIDEO PRODUCTION GRAPHIC DESIGN

▶ Benben, 5 Trafalgar Road, Cambridge, CB4 1EU Tel: (07771) 902020 E-mail: benben@benben.co.uk
Deeva Productions, 174 Singlewell Road, Gravesend, Kent, DA11 7RB Tel: (01474) 350300 Fax: (01474) 353931
▶ Eon Media, Thomas Street, Hull, HU9 1EH Tel: (01482) 339650 Fax: (01482) 339701 E-mail: tevison@eon-media.com
▶ Just Film, 7 Barnsway, Kings Langley, Hertfordshire, WD4 9PW Tel: (01923) 269599 E-mail: info@justfilm.co.uk
▶ Mole Productions, Old Lion Court, High Street, Marlborough, Wiltshire, SN8 1HQ Tel: (0845) 1235725 E-mail: enquiries@moleproductions.com
▶ Wooden House Design & Media, Upton House, Baldock Street, Royston, Hertfordshire, SG8 5AY Tel: 01763 247288 E-mail: kelly@woodenhouse.com

VIDEO PROJECTION EQUIPMENT SERVICES

Big Screen, Church Lane, Gorleston, Great Yarmouth, Norfolk, NR31 7BG Tel: (01493) 662913 Fax: (01493) 440677 E-mail: sales@bigscreenonline.co.uk
Genius Sound & Vision, Unit 8 Anchorage Point, 90 Anchor & Hope Lane, London, SE7 7SQ Tel: (020) 8472 9011 Fax: (020) 8472 9012 E-mail: info@genius.uk.com
LCI Ltd, 55 Merthyr Terrace, Barnes, London, SW13 8DL Tel: (020) 8741 5747 Fax: (020) 8748 9879 E-mail: contact@lci-uk.com

VIDEO RECORDER SECURITY DEVICES

Electronic Modular Solutions Ltd, Kendal House, 20 Blaby Road, Wigston, Leicestershire, LE18 4SB Tel: 0116-277 5730 Fax: 0116-277 4973 E-mail: sales@video-captures.com
Ovation Systems Ltd, Springfield Barn, Milton Common, Thame, Oxfordshire, OX9 2JY Tel: (01844) 279638 Fax: (01844) 279071 E-mail: sales@ovation.co.uk
Quadrant Research & Development Ltd, 3a Attenborough Lane, Beeston, Nottingham, NG9 5JN Tel: 0115-925 2521 Fax: 0115-943 1561 E-mail: sales@quadrantcctv.com

VIDEO RECORDERS

Bang & Olufsen, Unit 630 Wharfdale Road, Winnersh Triangle, Wokingham, Berkshire, RG41 5TP Tel: 0118-969 2288 Fax: 0118-969 3388
HCVF Video Production Companies, 67-69 Kenneth Street, Inverness, IV3 5QF Tel: (01463) 224788 Fax: (01463) 711460 E-mail: info@hcvf.co.uk
J V C Forex UK Ltd, JVC House, JVC Business Park, London, NW2 7BA Tel: (020) 8450 3282 Fax: (020) 8208 4385
J V C UK Ltd, Gelderd Lane, Leeds, LS12 6AL Tel: 0113-279 5741 Fax: 0113-263 3987

VIDEO RECORDERS, DIGITAL

MyVideoTalk, 2 Glebe Meadows, Chester, Cheshire, Mickle Trafford, Chester, CH2 4QX Tel: 01244 303253 Fax: 08700 513684 E-mail: post@videotalk4all.com

VIDEO SURVEILLANCE EQUIPMENT

Electronic Modular Solutions Ltd, Kendal House, 20 Blaby Road, Wigston, Leicestershire, LE18 4SB Tel: 0116-277 5730 Fax: 0116-277 4973 E-mail: sales@video-captures.com
L M W Electronics Ltd, L M W House Merrylees Industrial Estate, Lee Side, Desford, Leicester, LE9 9FS Tel: (01530) 231141 Fax: (01530) 231143 E-mail: sales@lmw.co.uk
Octec Ltd, Unit 12-13 The Western Centre, Western Road, Bracknell, Berkshire, RG12 1RW Tel: (01344) 465200 Fax: (01344) 465201 E-mail: sales@octec.co.uk
Ovation Systems Ltd, Springfield Barn, Milton Common, Thame, Oxfordshire, OX9 2JY Tel: (01844) 279638 Fax: (01844) 279071 E-mail: sales@ovation.co.uk
Security Enforcement Services, 66 Lone Valley, Waterlooville, Hampshire, PO7 5EB Tel: (023) 9220 0924 Fax: (023) 9221 5154 E-mail: robert@security-enforcement.fsnet.co.uk
SMD Hydrovision Ltd, Davy Banks, Wallsend, Tyne & Wear, NE28 6UZ Tel: +44 (0) 1224 772150 Fax: +44 (0) 1224 772166 E-mail: smd@smdhydrovision.com

VIDEO SYSTEM DESIGN

Octec Ltd, Unit 12-13 The Western Centre, Western Road, Bracknell, Berkshire, RG12 1RW Tel: (01344) 465200 Fax: (01344) 465201 E-mail: sales@octec.co.uk

VIDEO TAPE DUPLICATING SERVICES TO THE TRADE

Ascent Media, Film House, 142 Wardour Street, London, W1F 8DD Tel: (020) 7878 0000 Fax: (020) 7878 7800
Colour Film Services Ltd, 10 Wadsworth Road, Perivale, Greenford, Middlesex, UB6 7JX Tel: (020) 8998 2731 Fax: (020) 8997 8738 E-mail: johnward@colourfilmservices.co.uk
De Luxe Media Services Ltd, Phoenix Park, Great West Road, Brentford, Middlesex, TW8 9PL Tel: (020) 8232 7600 Fax: (020) 8232 7601
Humphries Video Services Ltd, Unit 2 Willow Business Centre, 17 Willow Lane, Mitcham, Surrey, CR4 4NX Tel: (020) 8648 6111 Fax: (020) 8648 5261E-mail: sales@hvs.co.uk
Intervideo Video Filming Equipment, 87 Boundary Road, London, NW8 0RG Tel: (020) 7624 1711 Fax: (020) 7624 2683 E-mail: admin@intervideo.co.uk

VIDEO TAPE DUPLICATING SYSTEMS

S T V Videos, PO Box 299, Bromley, BR2 9EE Tel: (020) 8464 4287 E-mail: sales@stvvideos.co.uk

VIDEO TAPE EDITING (VTE)/ CUTTING/POST-PRODUCTION SERVICES

Ascent Media, Film House, 142 Wardour Street, London, W1F 8DD Tel: (020) 7878 0000 Fax: (020) 7878 7800
Ascent Media Camden, 13 Hawley Cresent, London, NW1 8NP Tel: (020) 7284 7900 Fax: (020) 7284 1018
Central Video Studios, 70 Main Street, Shieldhill, Falkirk, FK1 2DT Tel: (01324) 631317
Classic Video Productions Ltd, 19 Waterloo Street, Glasgow, G2 6BT Tel: 0141-248 3882 Fax: 0141-204 1535
The Club, 35 Bedfordbury, London, WC2N 4DU Tel: (020) 7759 7100 Fax: (020) 7379 5210 E-mail: bill@theclubpc.co.uk
▶ Eon Media, Thomas Street, Hull, HU9 1EH Tel: (01482) 339650 Fax: (01482) 339701 E-mail: tevison@eon-media.com
Holmes Corporation Ltd, 38-42 Whitfield Street, London, W1T 4HJ Tel: (020) 7813 4333 Fax: (0870) 1245242 E-mail: holmesassociate@blueyonder.co.uk
▶ i2i Television Ltd, The Studio, Bankhead Farm Road, Strathaven, Lanarkshire, ML10 6TR Tel: (01698) 794100 E-mail: crews@i2itv.com
▶ Retina Productions Ltd, 6 Mount Pleasant Crescent, London, N4 4HP Tel: (020) 7272 4448 Fax: (020) 7272 5756 E-mail: nisrine@retina-productions.co.uk
Teddington Studios Ltd, Broom Road, Teddington, Middlesex, TW11 9NT Tel: (020) 8977 3252 Fax: (020) 8943 4050 E-mail: sales@pinewoodgroup.com
Wild Strawberry Interactive Multimedia Ltd, 1 Cartland Avenue, Shrewsbury, SY2 5UW Tel: (01743) 354386 Fax: (01743) 354386

VIDEO TAPE ENHANCEMENT SERVICES

Classic Video Productions Ltd, 19 Waterloo Street, Glasgow, G2 6BT Tel: 0141-248 3882 Fax: 0141-204 1535
De Luxe Media Services Ltd, Phoenix Park, Great West Road, Brentford, Middlesex, TW8 9PL Tel: (020) 8232 7600 Fax: (020) 8232 7601
▶ Omega Red Group Ltd, Dabell Avenue, Blenheim Industrial Estate, Bulwell, Nottingham, NG6 8WA Tel: 0115-877 6666 Fax: 0115-876 7766 E-mail: aimiga@redgroup.co.uk

VIDEO TAPE STANDARDS CONVERSION SERVICES

Ardath Video, 56 Ardath Road, Birmingham, B38 9PH Tel: 0121-451 3332 Fax: 0121-459 5127 E-mail: sales@ardathvideo.co.uk
Humphries Video Services Ltd, Unit 2 Willow Business Centre, 17 Willow Lane, Mitcham, Surrey, CR4 4NX Tel: (020) 8648 6111 Fax: (020) 8648 5261E-mail: sales@hvs.co.uk

VIDEO TELEPHONE EQUIPMENT

Motion Media Technology Ltd, Motion Media Technology Centre, Severn Bridge, Aust, Bristol, BS35 4BL Tel: (01454) 635400 Fax: (01454) 635401

VIDEO WEB INSPECTION SYSTEMS

Fife Tidland Ltd, 70-72 Manchester Road, Denton, Manchester, M34 3PR Tel: 0161-320 2000 Fax: 0161-320 4513 E-mail: sales_uk@maxcess.de

VIDEO WHOLESALE DISTRIBUTORS OR AGENTS

Focal Point Audio Visual Ltd, 1-3 Kew Place, Cheltenham, Gloucestershire, GL53 7NQ Tel: (01242) 693118 Fax: (01242) 693118
Fox Pathe Home Entertainment, 20th Century House, 31-32 Soho Square, London, W1D 3AP Tel: (020) 7753 0015 Fax: (020) 7434 1435
Harris & Russell, 124 East Road, London, N1 6AF Tel: (0870) 7277551 Fax: (020) 7608 2970 E-mail: harrisrussell@msn.com
P E C Video Ltd, 65-66 Dean Street, London, W1D 4PL Tel: (020) 7437 4633 Fax: (020) 7025 1320 E-mail: sales@pec.co.uk
Videotron Ltd, 441-443 Cranbrook Road, Ilford, Essex, IG2 6EW Tel: (020) 8554 7617 Fax: (020) 8554 0110 E-mail: phobbs@videotronltd.freeserve.co.uk
Wansbeck Teaching Tapes, 3 Bankside, Morpeth, Northd, NE61 1XD Tel: (01670) 505455 Fax: (01670) 518011 E-mail: wansbeck@btinternet.com
▶ Wild Insight Ltd, 5 Cambridge Road, Ely, Cambridgeshire, CB7 4HJ Tel: (01353) 665304 Fax: (01353) 610466 E-mail: enquiries@wildinsight.co.uk

VIEWDATA COMPUTER SYSTEMS

Adare Ltd, Vantage House, 1 Weir Road, London, SW19 8UX Tel: (020) 8946 7537 Fax: (020) 8947 2740

VIEWPORT INSPECTION EQUIPMENT

Suncombe Ltd, Jade House, Lockfield Avenue, Brimsdown, Enfield, Middlesex, EN3 7JY Tel: (020) 8443 3454 Fax: (020) 8443 3969 E-mail: sales@suncombe.com

VINEGAR

Aspall, The Cider House, Aspall Hall, Debenham, Stowmarket, Suffolk, IP14 6PD Tel: (01728) 860510 Fax: (01728) 861031 E-mail: barry@aspall.co.uk

VINTAGE/CLASSIC CAR RESTORATION SERVICES

Fiennes Restoration Ltd, Clanfield Mill, Little Clanfield, Bampton, Oxfordshire, OX18 2RX Tel: (01367) 810438 Fax: (01367) 810532 E-mail: enquiries@fiennes.co.uk
The Hutson Motor Company Ltd, Pawson Street, Bradford, West Yorkshire, BD4 8DF Tel: (01274) 669052 Fax: (01274) 669685 E-mail: hutsonmc@talk21.com

VINYL COMMERCIAL VEHICLE SIGNS

Dynamic Graphix, 8 Quarry Street, Hamilton, Lanarkshire, ML3 7AR Tel: (01698) 891172 Fax: (01698) 337449 E-mail: dynamicgrafix@btconnect.com

▶ Freestyle Sign & Print, 8 Sheeplands Farm, Twyford Road, Wargrave, Reading, RG10 8DL Tel: 0118-940 4000 Fax: 0118-940 6275 E-mail: freestyle@provider.co.uk

Impress Express, Unit 10 Merlin Park, Fred Dannatt Road, Mildenhall, Bury St. Edmunds, Suffolk, IP28 7RD Tel: (01638) 718878 Fax: (01638) 711887 E-mail: info@impressexpress.co.uk

▶ M R L Signs, 23 Finkle Hill, Sherburn in Elmet, Leeds, LS25 6EB Tel: (01977) 682168 E-mail: enquiries@mrlsigns.com

Prescott Graphics Services, Unit 17M, Westside Ind Est, St. Helens, Merseyside, WA9 3AT Tel: (0800) 9546172 E-mail: enquiries@precottgraphics.co.uk

▶ Sign Impact, 1 High House Cottage, Woodham Road, Battlesbridge, Wickford, Essex, SS11 7QL Tel: (01268) 761116 E-mail: sales@sign-impact.co.uk

▶ Signs Express Ltd, Unit 16 Anglo Business Park, Smeaton Close, Aylesbury, Buckinghamshire, HP19 8UP Tel: (01296) 339998 Fax: (01296) 331118 E-mail: aylesbury@signsexpress.co.uk

Signs Express Ltd, 257b Dukesway, Team Valley Trading Estate, Gateshead, Tyne & Wear, NE11 0PZ Tel: 0191-487 4900 Fax: 0191-487 5900 E-mail: gateshead@signsexpress.co.uk

Signtech Sign Makers, 18-19 Lion Hill, Stourport-on-Severn, Worcestershire, DY13 9HG Tel: (01299) 827309 Fax: (01299) 877086 E-mail: sales@signtech.co.uk

▶ Wackygraphics.Com, 1 Jays Close, Basingstoke, Hampshire, RG22 4BS Tel: (01256) 346794 E-mail: sales@wackygraphics.com

VINYL DECKING

Hy Clad, Avonbridge, Falkirk, FK1 2LF Tel: (01324) 861307 Fax: (01324) 861307

VINYL FENCING

Hy Clad, Avonbridge, Falkirk, FK1 2LF Tel: (01324) 861307 Fax: (01324) 861307

VINYL FLOOR COVERINGS

C. Abbott Ltd, Dane Place, 470-480 Roman Road, Bow, London, E3 5LU Tel: (020) 8980 4158 Fax: (020) 8981 3852 E-mail: info@abbottscarpets.co.uk

Armstrong UK Investments, Armstrong House, 38 Market Square, Uxbridge, Middlesex, UB8 1NG Tel: (01895) 251122 Fax: (01895) 231571

Carpetright plc, Amberley House, New Road, Rainham, Essex, RM13 8QN Tel: (01708) 525522 Fax: (01708) 559361 E-mail: enquiries@carpetright.co.uk

G W Brooks Flooring Ltd, Unit 19 Waterside Industrial Estate, Ettingshall Road, Wolverhampton, WV2 2RH Tel: (01902) 498213 Fax: (01902) 495707 E-mail: sales@brooksflooring.co.uk

P M N Aviation Ltd, Unit B, Crawford Street, Rochdale, Lancashire, OL16 5NU Tel: (01706) 655134 Fax: (01706) 631561 E-mail: info@pegasusaviation.co.uk

Polyflor Ltd, P O Box 3965, Manchester, M45 7NR Tel: 0161-767 1111 Fax: 0161-767 1100 E-mail: info@polyflor.com

Tarkett Ltd, Dickley Lane, Lenham, Maidstone, Kent, ME17 2QX Tel: (01622) 854000 Fax: (01622) 854500 E-mail: uksales@tarkett.com

Westco Group Ltd, Penarth Road, Cardiff, CF11 8YN Tel: (029) 2037 6700 Fax: (029) 2038 3573 E-mail: westco@westcodiy.co.uk

VINYL FLOOR TILES

▶ Bradbury Flooring Ltd, 39-41 Carlisle Street, Leicester, LE3 6AH Tel: 0116-254 2655 Fax: 0116-254 2656 E-mail: sales@bradburyflooring.co.uk

C P Flooring Services Ltd, The Heysoms, 163 Chester Road, Northwich, Cheshire, CW8 4AQ Tel: 0161-432 9688 Fax: 0161-432 4042 E-mail: sales@cpflooringservices.co.uk

VINYL SELF ADHESIVE DECORATIVE FLOOR COVERINGS

Allprint Ltd, Llantrisant Business Park, Llantrisant, Pontyclun, Mid Glamorgan, CF72 8LF Tel: (01443) 228555 Fax: (01443) 237477 E-mail: sales@allprint2000.com

VINYL SIGN MAKING MATERIALS

A P A UK Ltd, Unit 10 Capital Industrial Estate, Crabtree Manorway South, Belvedere, Kent, DA17 6BJ Tel: (020) 8311 4400 Fax: (020) 8312 4777 E-mail: apauk@apaspa.com

Allstick Decals, 133 Ridge Road, Kingswinford, West Midlands, DY6 9RG Tel: (01384) 271505 Fax: (01384) 271505 E-mail: enquiries@allstickdecals.co.uk

Andersons Ltd, Powells Farm, Berkham Lane, Bentworth, Alton, Hampshire, GU34 5RP Tel: (01420) 563646 Fax: (01420) 561897 E-mail: sales@andersons-uk.net

Classic Graphics, Standard Way Industrial Estate, Standard Way Industrial Estate, Northallerton, North Yorkshire, DL6 2XA Tel: (01609) 761060 Fax: (01609) 761060

Craft Signs, 1 Hermitage Lane, Mansfield, Nottinghamshire, NG18 5HA Tel: (01623) 626166 Fax: (01623) 420977

Graffiti Signs, Parrs Corner Shopping Centre, Stanley Road, Bootle, Merseyside, L20 3EX Tel: 0151-933 2906 Fax: 0151-933 2506 E-mail: sales@graffitisignworks.co.uk

▶ Graphica Plus Ltd, Bentworth, Alton, Hampshire, GU34 5RP Tel: (01420) 563646 Fax: (01420) 561897 E-mail: sales@andersons.uk.net

Midland Graphics Sign Depot, 14 Victoria Terrace, Leamington Spa, Warwickshire, CV31 3AB Tel: (01926) 452009 Fax: (01926) 470767

Midway Designs Ltd, Unit A1 Pear Mill Industrial Estate, Stockport Road West, Bredbury, Stockport, Cheshire, SK6 2BP Tel: 0161-430 7810 Fax: 0161-430 1714 E-mail: sales@midwaydesigns.co.uk

Neon & Signmakers, Unit 1 Durham Yard, London, E2 6QF Tel: (020) 7729 5959 Fax: (020) 7772 9772

Peterborough Signs, 17-18 Leofric Square, Peterborough, PE1 5TU Tel: (01733) 555060 Fax: (01733) 344293 E-mail: info@peterbourgh-signs.co.uk

The Sign Co., 16 Parmington Close, Callow Hill, Redditch, Worcestershire, B97 5YL Tel: (01527) 550962 Fax: (01527) 402777

Sign Centre, 1 Farrier Road, Lincoln, LN6 3RU Tel: (01522) 500024 Fax: (01522) 500054 E-mail: enquires@signcentre-uk.com

Sign Design, Unit 2 Pottery La West, Chesterfield, Derbyshire, S41 9BN Tel: (01246) 554334 Fax: (01246) 554334 E-mail: sign-design@btconnect.com

Signs Of The Times, 324 Smithdown Road, Liverpool, L15 5AJ Tel: 0151-734 4616 Fax: 0151-734 4616

Southpark Signs, 258 Green Lane, Ilford, Essex, IG1 1YF Tel: (020) 8553 1123 Fax: (020) 8553 0789

Subak Signs, 9a Stocks Street, Manchester, M8 8GW Tel: 0161-835 9993 Fax: 0161-835 9994 E-mail: info@subaksigns.co.uk

VINYL SIGNS

A1 Signs, 7 Woodspring Court, Sheffield, S4 8FP Tel: 0114-243 6964 Fax: 0114-243 6964

Andersons Ltd, Powells Farm, Berkham Lane, Bentworth, Alton, Hampshire, GU34 5RP Tel: (01420) 563646 Fax: (01420) 561897 E-mail: sales@andersons-uk.net

Apollo Signs & Engraving, Wigwam Lane Unit E1, Imex Enterprise Park, Hucknall, Nottingham, NG15 7SZ Tel: 0115-963 1366 Fax: 0115-961 1355 E-mail: dexterapolo@aol.com

Avia Signs & Labels, Shore Head, Stonehaven, Kincardineshire, AB39 2JY Tel: (01569) 767290 Fax: (01569) 767290 E-mail: david@aviasigns.freeserve.co.uk

Boston Signs & Displays, Unit 1, Spalding Road, Boston, Lincolnshire, PE21 8XL Tel: (01205) 363849 Fax: (01205) 367725 E-mail: boston_signs@yahoo.co.uk

Branch Signs, 7 Dalmeny Road, Worcester Park, Surrey, KT4 8UU Tel: (020) 3277 1060 Fax: (020) 8949 3690 E-mail: michaelbranch@freenet.co.uk

Brighton Sign Co., Foredown House, 2-4 Foredown Drive, Portslade, Brighton, BN41 2BB Tel: (01273) 424900 Fax: (01273) 412006 E-mail: sales@brightonsigns.co.uk

Butterfield Signs Ltd, 174 Sunbridge Road, Bradford, West Yorkshire, BD1 2RZ Tel: (01274) 722244 Fax: (01274) 848998 E-mail: general@butterfield-signs.co.uk

Certa Ceto Sandbach, 45 Hightown, Crewe, CW1 3BZ Tel: (01270) 251333 Fax: (01270) 251444 E-mail: mellorremstar@aol.com

Cobal Sign Systems Ltd, Brookway Industrial Estate, Brookway, Hambridge Lane, Newbury, Berkshire, RG14 5PE Tel: (01635) 570600 Fax: (01635) 32432 E-mail: info@cobal.co.uk

Combined Signs, 4 Carpenters Place, London, SW4 7TD Tel: (020) 7720 5797 Fax: (020) 7720 2318 E-mail: signs@combinedsigns.co.uk

Computerised Engraving, 10 Waterloo Road, Widnes, Cheshire, WA8 0PY Tel: 0151-420 4590 Fax: 0151-495 1132 E-mail: info@computerisedengraving.com

County Engravers & Signs, Unit 5 Trentview Court, Nottingham, NG2 3FX Tel: 0115-985 1171 Fax: 0115-986 1007 E-mail: sales@countyengravers-signs.co.uk

E Signs, 118 Piccadilly, Mayfair, London, W1J 7NW Tel: (0800) 7312259 Fax: (0845) 0042259 E-mail: info@e-signs.co.uk

Gee Tee Signs Ltd, Bestwood Road, Nottingham, NG6 8SS Tel: 0115-976 1188 Fax: 0115-976 1213 E-mail: sales@geeteesigns.com

Gem Engraving, 33 Hayes Close, Wimborne, Dorset, BH21 2JJ Tel: (01202) 881907 Fax: (01202) 887691 E-mail: sales@gemengraving.co.uk

Hallmark Engraving, 116-118 Selsdon Road, South Croydon, Surrey, CR2 6PG Tel: (020) 8686 6649 Fax: (020) 8760 0899 E-mail: sales@hallmarksigns.co.uk

Northallerton Sign Co., The Units, Morton On Swale, Northallerton, N. Yorkshire, DL7 9RJ Tel: (01609) 777687 Fax: (01609) 777687 E-mail: sales@allertonsigns.co.uk

Riverway Building & Signage Ltd, Riverway, Trowbridge, Wiltshire, BA14 8LL Tel: (01225) 760131 Fax: (01225) 777207 E-mail: mail@riverwaywilts.co.uk

▶ Sign Impact, 1 High House Cottage, Woodham Road, Battlesbridge, Wickford, Essex, SS11 7QL Tel: (01268) 761116 E-mail: sales@sign-impact.co.uk

Signs Express Ltd, 257b Dukesway, Team Valley Trading Estate, Gateshead, Tyne & Wear, NE11 0PZ Tel: 0191-487 4900 Fax: 0191-487 5900 E-mail: gateshead@signsexpress.co.uk

Signtech Sign Makers, 18-19 Lion Hill, Stourport-on-Severn, Worcestershire, DY13 9HG Tel: (01299) 827309 Fax: (01299) 877086 E-mail: sales@signtech.co.uk

Taylor & Pickles Ltd, Bushell St Mills, Bushell Street, Preston, PR1 2SP Tel: (01772) 251520 Fax: (01772) 561610 E-mail: info@taylorandpickles.co.uk

Touch Print Ltd, 49 Maple Avenue, Bulwark, Chepstow, Gwent, NP16 5RG Tel: (01291) 621401 Fax: (01291) 621403 E-mail: sales@touchprint.co.uk

P.J. Wilkes Plastics Ltd, Unit 12A Izons Industrial Estate, Oldbury Road, West Bromwich, West Midlands, B70 9BS Tel: 0121-525 4224 Fax: 0121-525 2242 E-mail: pjw@pjwsigns.freeserve.co.uk

VINYL UPHOLSTERY FABRICS

▶ Upholstery Fabrics UK, 7 Eaton Close, Stockwood, Bristol, BS14 8PR Tel: 01275 830213 E-mail: enquires@upholsteryfabricsuk.co.uk

VINYL WALLCOVERINGS

Harlequin Fabric & Wallcoverings Ltd, Ladybird House, Beeches Road, Loughborough, Leicestershire, LE11 2HA Tel: (0870) 8300355 Fax: (0870) 8300359 E-mail: sales@harlequin.uk.com

Muraspec, Tonbridge Road, East Peckham, Tonbridge, Kent, TN12 5JX Tel: (01622) 871384 Fax: (01622) 871011 E-mail: customerservices@muraspec.com

Newmor Group Ltd, Madoc Works, Henfaes Lane, Welshpool, Powys, SY21 7BE Tel: (01938) 552671 Fax: (01938) 554285 E-mail: enquiries@newmor.com

Speciality Coatings Darwen Ltd, Dewhurst Street, Darwen, Lancashire, BB3 2EN Tel: (01254) 706026 Fax: (01254) 777132 E-mail: sales@sclgroup.com

Tektura Wallcoverings, One Heron Quay, London, E14 4JA Tel: (020) 7536 3300 Fax: (020) 7536 3322 E-mail: sales@tektura.com

VIOLINS

▶ Guitar Spares & Repairs, 89 Old Snow Hill, Next to Sound Control, Birmingham, B4 6HW Tel: 0121 2455867 E-mail: info@guitarsparesandrepairs.com

VIP/EXECUTIVE PROTECTION SERVICES

▶ Platinum Chauffeurs, 42 Church Street, Needingworth, St. Ives, Cambridgeshire, PE27 4TB Tel: (01480) 463777 E-mail: info@platinumdrive.co.uk

VIRAL MARKETING

Leith Agency Ltd, 37 The Shore, Edinburgh, EH6 6QU Tel: 0131-561 8600 Fax: 0131-561 8601

VIRGIN POLYSTYRENE (PS) BEADS

▶ Bean Bag Refill, Beanbag Filling, 11 Belgrave Court, Blackwater, Camberley, Surrey, GU17 9JE Tel: 0 870 285 1593 E-mail: info@bean-bag.co.uk

VIRTUAL ASSISTANT SERVICES

▶ A Virtual Solution, 11 Langley Close, Louth, Lincolnshire, LN11 8YP Tel: (01507) 609043 Fax: (01507) 609043 E-mail: sales@avirtualsolution.co.uk

▶ Beserved Virtual Offices Ltd, Newlands, 13 The Green, Tuddenham, Bury St. Edmunds, Suffolk, IP28 6SD Tel: (0845) 2268064 E-mail: bev@beserved.co.uk

Busy Life, 5 Abingdon Road, Leicester, LE2 1HA Tel: (07729) 288515 E-mail: busy.life@ntlworld.com

▶ Easy Typing, 16 Burn View, Bude, Cornwall, EX23 8BZ Tel: 01288 355587 E-mail: easytyping@hotmail.co.uk

▶ Girl Friday Solutions, 13 Lower Icknield Way, Marsworth, Tring, Hertfordshire, HP23 4LW Tel: (07921) 770516 E-mail: girlfridaysolutions@hotmail.co.uk

▶ MK Virtual PA, 64 Trueman Place, Oldbrook, Milton Keynes, MK6 2HJ Tel: 07712 353957 E-mail: info@mkvirtualpa.co.uk

▶ N & S OFFICE SOLUTIONS LTD, 25 PRINCES STREET, TUNBRIDGE WELLS, KENT, TN2 4SL Tel: 01892 514643 E-mail: nsoffice@btinternet.com

▶ NG Office Solutions, 19 Regency Green, Colchester, CO3 4TD Tel: 01206 369 530 Fax: 01206 369 530 E-mail: enquiries@ngofficesolutions.com

▶ Office Assist, 2a Cowper Road, Bedford, MK40 2AS Tel: (07771) 995545 E-mail: mail@office-assist.co.uk

▶ SpiderWeb Business Admin, 16 Allerton Close, Coventry, CV2 5DH Tel: (07981) 785717 Fax: E-mail: info@spideradmin.co.uk

VIRTUAL OFFICE ACCOMMODATION ADDRESSES

4business, 72 New Bond Street, London, W1S 1RR Tel: (020) 7514 9901 E-mail: sales@base4business.com

▶ Gainsborough Business Centres, 100 Pall Mall, St. James's, London, SW1Y 5HP Tel: (0800) 3282668 E-mail: sales@gainsbc.co.uk

Kendlebell, 236 Nantwich Road, Crewe, CW2 6BP Tel: (01270) 219500 Fax: (01270) 219500 E-mail: heleng@kendlebell.co.uk

▶ MLS Business Centres South West, 66 Queen Square, Bristol, BS1 4JP Tel: 0117-987 6200 Fax: 0117-987 6201 E-mail: tom.endacott@mlsbusinesscentres.com

▶ myHotDesk, 27 John Player Building, Stirling Enterprise Park, Stirling, Stirling, FK7 7RP Tel: 01786 450022 E-mail: advice@www.myhotdesk.com

▶ Saturn Facilities Ltd, Bedford Heights, Brickhill Drive, Bedford, MK41 7PH Tel: (01234) 244500 Fax: (01234) 244511 E-mail: tjordan@saturnfacilities.com

▶ Saturn Facilities, Saturn Centre, Spring Road, Ettingshall, Wolverhampton, WV4 6JX Tel: (01902) 493192 Fax: (01902) 402553 E-mail: tjordan@saturnfacilities.com

▶ Saturn Facilities Birmingham, Ephraim Phillips House, Bissell Street, Birmingham, B5 7UP Tel: 0121 6221366 E-mail: tjordan@saturnfacilities.com

▶ Saturn Facilities Mayfair, 5-6 Carlos Place, Mayfair, London, W1K 3AP Tel: (020) 7907 9700 E-mail: tjordan@saturnfacilities.com

▶ Saturn Facilities Worthing, Columbia House, Columbia Drive, Worthing, West Sussex, BN13 3hd Tel: (01903) 262663 E-mail: tjordan@saturnfacilities.com

▶ Totally Inbound, European Communication Centre, Vicarage Farm Road, Fengate, Peterborough, PE1 5TX Tel: 0845 117 7000 Fax: 01733 704080 E-mail: info@totallyinbound.co.uk

▶ Whitchurch Business Centre, Green End, Whitchurch, Shropshire, SY13 1AD Tel: (01948) 660550 Fax: (01948) 660560 E-mail: james.archer@whitchurchbc.co.uk

VIRTUAL PROTOTYPING SIMULATION SOFTWARE

▶ Virtio, Alba Centre, Alba Campus, Livingston, West Lothian, EH54 7EG Tel: (01506) 402410

VIRTUAL RECEPTION TELEPHONE CALL CENTRES

▶ Ansaback, Melford Court 2 The Havens, Ransomes Europark, Ipswich, IP3 9SJ Tel: (01473) 322900 Fax: (01473) 321801 E-mail: mtaylor@ansaback.co.uk

▶ City Office - Virtual Office Services, 12 St. James Square, St. James's, London, SW1Y 4RB Tel: (020) 7692 0608 Fax: (020) 7692 0607 E-mail: Sales@YourCityOffice.com

Kendlebell, 236 Nantwich Road, Crewe, CW2 6BP Tel: (01270) 219500 Fax: (01270) 219500 E-mail: heleng@kendlebell.co.uk

▶ Saturn Facilities Ltd, Bedford Heights, Brickhill Drive, Bedford, MK41 7PH Tel: (01234) 244500 Fax: (01234) 244511 E-mail: tjordan@saturnfacilities.com

VIRTUAL RECEPTION TELEPHONE CALL CENTRES – *continued*

▶ Taw Valley Telecoms Ltd, 63 High Street, Barnstaple, Devon, EX31 1JB Tel: (01271) 336336 Fax: 0870 4607798 E-mail: martin@tawvalleytelecoms.co.uk
▶ Totally Inbound, European Communication Centre, Vicarage Farm Road, Fengate, Peterborough, PE1 5TX Tel: 0845 117 7000 Fax: 01733 704080 E-mail: info@totallyinbound.co.uk

VISCOMETERS

▶ Anderson Instruments, East Lodge, Drum, Drumoak, Banchory, Kincardineshire, AB31 5AN Tel: (01224) 733835 Fax: (01224) 733835 E-mail: ian@anderson-instruments.co.uk
Benson Viscometers Ltd, Croft Quarry, West Williamston, Kilgetty, Dyfed, SA68 0TN Tel: (01646) 650065
Brookfield Viscometers Ltd, 1 Whitehall Estate Flex Meadow, Pinnacles West, Harlow, Essex, CM19 5TP Tel: (01279) 451774 Fax: (01279) 451775 E-mail: sales@brookfield.co.uk
C R S Solutions Ltd, Provincial House, 6 High Street, Southampton, SO14 2DH Tel: (023) 8063 2440 Fax: (023) 8063 2550
Hydramotion Ltd, Unit 1a, York Road Business Park, Malton, North Yorkshire, YO17 6YA Tel: (01653) 600294 Fax: (01653) 693446 E-mail: sales@hydramotion.com
Melecular Control Systems Ltd, 1 Greetby Place, Skelmersdale, Lancashire, WN8 9UL Tel: (01695) 566700 Fax: (01695) 50329 E-mail: sales@porpoise.co.uk
Poulten Selfe & Lee Ltd, Russell House, Burnham Business Park, Burnham-On-Crouch, Essex, CM0 8TE Tel: (01621) 787100 Fax: (01621) 787175 E-mail: info@rheotek.com
Ravenfield Designs Ltd, Russell Street, Heywood, Lancashire, OL10 1NX Tel: (01706) 369307 Fax: (01706) 360472 E-mail: post@ravenfield.com
Research Equipment London Ltd, 72 Wellington Road, Twickenham, TW2 5NX Tel: (020) 8977 5529 Fax: (020) 8943 2219 E-mail: info@research-equipment.com

VISCOUS FOOD FORM FILL AND SEAL MACHINES

▶ Food Forming Machines Ltd, 15 Gosditch Street, Cirencester, Gloucestershire, GL7 2AG Tel: (01285) 658995 Fax: (01285) 659099 E-mail: mail@foodformingmachines.com

VISCOUS LIQUID PUMPS

Albany Standard Pumps, Richter Works, Garnett Street, Bradford, West Yorkshire, BD3 9HB Tel: (01274) 725351 Fax: (01274) 742467 E-mail: sales@albany-pumps.co.uk
Centrilift, Howe Moss Place, Kirkhill Industrial Estate, Dyce, Aberdeen, AB21 0ES Tel: (01224) 772233 Fax: (01224) 771021 E-mail: sales@centrilift.com
Grundfos Manufacturing Ltd, Ferryboat Lane, Castletown, Sunderland, SR5 3JL Tel: 0191-549 5555 Fax: 0191-516 0067

VISITOR ATTRACTION MARKETING

▶ Thomas Doran Parkanaur Trust, 57 Parkanaur Road, Dungannon, County Tyrone, BT70 3AA Tel: (028) 8776 1272 Fax: (028) 8776 1257 E-mail: parkanaurmanorhouse@hotmail.com

VISOR COVERS, REPLACEMENT, RESPIRATORY PROTECTION, SPRAY PAINTING

▶ Piccadilly Secretarial Services, Piccadilly, Manchester, M1 2AQ Tel: 0161-228 1721 Fax: 0161-228 6542

VISORS, FULL FACE, AIR FED, SPRAY PAINTING

▶ Piccadilly Secretarial Services, Piccadilly, Manchester, M1 2AQ Tel: 0161-228 1721 Fax: 0161-228 6542

VISUAL AID PRODUCTION SERVICES, EDUCATIONAL/ INSTRUCTIONAL

Drake Educational Associates Ltd, 89 St. Fagans Road, Fairwater, Cardiff, CF5 3AE Tel: (029) 2056 0333 Fax: (029) 2055 4909 E-mail: info@drakeav.com
Magiboards Ltd, Unit F, Stafford Park 12, Telford, Shropshire, TF3 3BJ Tel: (01952) 292111 Fax: (01952) 292280 E-mail: sales@magiboards.co.uk
Metro Plan Ltd, Lake District Business Park, Mint Bridge Road, Kendal, Cumbria, LA9 6NH Tel: (01539) 730103 Fax: (01539) 730765 E-mail: sales@metroplan.co.uk
▶ Touch The Sky Ltd, Mulberry Business Centre, 323 Goring Road, Goring-by-Sea, Worthing, West Sussex, BN12 4NX Tel: 01903 507744 E-mail: lucienne.sharpe@touchthesky.uk.com

VISUAL AID SUPPLIERS, EDUCATIONAL/INSTRUCTIONAL

▶ Touch The Sky Ltd, Mulberry Business Centre, 323 Goring Road, Goring-by-Sea, Worthing, West Sussex, BN12 4NX Tel: 01903 507744 E-mail: lucienne.sharpe@touchthesky.uk.com

VISUAL DISPLAY (VDU) OR VIDEO MONITOR UNIT MAINTENANCE OR REPAIR

Avery Electronic Services, Unit 4 Wren Industrial Estate, Coldred Road, Parkwood, Maidstone, Kent, ME15 9XN Tel: (01622) 682138 Fax: (01622) 691232
Nova Electronics, 700-702 Attercliffe Road, Sheffield, S9 3RP Tel: 0114-244 7257 Fax: 0114-261 7721 E-mail: info@nova-electronics.co.uk
S E G Digital Ltd, Unit 1 Willow Court, Bracewell Avenue, Poulton-le-Fylde, Lancashire, FY6 8JF Tel: (01253) 893688 Fax: (01253) 899226 E-mail: sales@sege.com

VISUAL DISPLAY (VDU) OR VIDEO MONITOR UNITS

Lynx Technology Ltd, 3 Midland Way, Barlborough, Chesterfield, Derbyshire, S43 4XA Tel: (01246) 574000 Fax: (01246) 819401 E-mail: enquiries@lynxtec.com
Y S L Videowall Hire Ltd, Unit 11 Concorde Park, Amy Johnson Way, York, YO30 4WT Tel: (01904) 693535 Fax: (01904) 691114 E-mail: info@yslvideowallhire.co.uk

VISUAL PLANNING SYSTEMS

Signal Business Systems Ltd, Swan Corner, Pewsey, Wiltshire, SN9 5HL Tel: (01672) 563333 Fax: (01672) 562391 E-mail: signalbusiness.systems@virgin.net

VISUAL PLANNING/CHARTING SYSTEMS

GBC UK Holdings Ltd, Rutherford Road, Basingstoke, Hampshire, RG24 8PD Tel: (01256) 842828 Fax: (01256) 842581 E-mail: sales@gbcuk.co.uk
Metro Plan Ltd, Lake District Business Park, Mint Bridge Road, Kendal, Cumbria, LA9 6NH Tel: (01539) 730103 Fax: (01539) 730765 E-mail: sales@metroplan.co.uk

VISUALISATION SOFTWARE

Exitech Computers Ltd, Units 2-3, Sovereign Business Centre, Stockingswater Lane, Enfield, Middlesex, EN3 7JX Tel: (020) 8804 9942 Fax: (0845) 3701400
▶ Thumbprint Animation, 120 Whitelands Avenue, Chorleywood, Rickmansworth, Hertfordshire, WD3 5RG Tel: (01923) 285754 Fax: (01923) 283903 E-mail: info@thumbprintanimation.co.uk
Virtalis, Chester House, 79 Dane Road, Sale, Cheshire, M33 7BP Tel: 0161-969 1155 Fax: 0161-969 1166 E-mail: info@vrweb.com
▶ Visualisation Services, 18 Hodder Avenue, Liverpool, L31 9PQ Tel: 0151-520 1128 E-mail: simon@manning65.freeserve.co.uk
Windowlink Ltd, Station Road, Minety, Malmesbury, Wilts, SN16 9QY Tel: (0870) 7701640 Fax: (01666) 860889

VITAMIN B COMPLEX

▶ Dennis Regan, Suites 2 & 4, Beauford House, Serpentine Road, Cleckheaton, West Yorkshire, BD19 3HU Tel: (01274) 850940 Fax: (01274) 850940 E-mail: sales@therapyexpressltd.co.uk

VITAMIN EXTRACTS/ SUPPLEMENTS/PREPARATIONS

Aphrodite, 1a Priory Lane, Penwortham, Preston, PR1 0AR Tel: (01772) 746555
Countryworld Ltd, Common Lane, Culcheth, Warrington, WA3 4EH Tel: (01925) 765448
Cultech Ltd, Unit 2/3, Christchurch Road, Baglan Industrial Park, Port Talbot, West Glamorgan, SA12 7BZ Tel: (01639) 825101 Fax: (01639) 825100 E-mail: sales@cultech.co.uk
G R Lane Health Products Ltd, Sisson Road, Gloucester, GL2 0GR Tel: (01452) 524012 Fax: (01452) 300105 E-mail: export@laneshealth.com
Merc Serono, Bedfont Cross, Bedfont, Feltham, Middlesex, TW14 8NX Tel: (01895) 452200 Fax: (01895) 420605 E-mail: info@merckpharma.co.uk
Nature's Own Ltd, Unit 8, Hanley Workshops, Hanley Road, Hanley Swan, Worcester, WR8 0DX Tel: (01684) 310022 Fax: (01684) 312022 E-mail: peter@well-being.co.uk
Nutec Holdings Ltd, Eastern Avenue, Lichfield, Staffordshire, WS13 7SE Tel: (01543) 306312 Fax: (01543) 306307
Perrigo UK, William Nadin Way, Swadlincote, Derbyshire, DE11 0BB Tel: (01283) 228300 Fax: (01283) 228328 E-mail: info@perrigouk.com
Portobello Wholefoods, 266 Portobello Road, London, W10 5TY Tel: (020) 8968 9133 Fax: (020) 8560 1840
Premier Health Products, Wolfe Road, Coventry, CV4 9UP Tel: (024) 7642 2050 Fax: (024) 7647 3577E-mail: sales@premier-health.co.uk
Roche Vitamins UK Ltd, Drakemyre, Dalry, Ayrshire, KA24 5JJ Tel: (01294) 832345 Fax: (01294) 832700 E-mail:
Seaford Laboratories Ltd, Cradle Hill Industrial Estate, Seaford, East Sussex, BN25 3JE Tel: (01323) 896779 Fax: (01323) 490452
Seven Seas Ltd, Hedon Road, Hull, HU9 5NJ Tel: (01482) 375234 Fax: (01482) 374345 E-mail: terry.simpson@sseas.com
Vega Nutritionals Ltd, 41 Central Avenue, West Molesey, Surrey, KT8 2QZ Tel: (020) 8939 3480 Fax: (0845) 2267400 E-mail: sales@vegavitamins.co.uk
Vitabiotics Health Foods, 1 Apsley Way, London, NW2 7HF Tel: (020) 8955 2600 Fax: (020) 8955 2601
Wassen International Ltd, Unit 14 Mole Business Park, Randalls Road, Leatherhead, Surrey, KT22 7BA Tel: (01372) 379828 Fax: (01372) 376599 E-mail: info@wassen.com
▶ www.Nutritionzone.co.uk, Unit 5, Mill Road Industrial Estate, Linlithgow Bridge, Linlithgow, West Lothian, EH49 7QY Tel: (01506) 848968 E-mail: admin@nutrtionzone.co.uk

VITREOUS CHINA DOMESTIC SINKS, *See Sanitary Ware etc*

VITREOUS CHINA SANITARY WARE

Porcelanosa Yorkshire Ltd, Unit 15 Shaw Lane Industrial E, Ogden Rd, Doncaster, South Yorkshire, DN2 4SQ Tel: (01302) 341029 Fax: (01302) 739273
Shires Bathrooms Ltd, Beckside Road, Bradford, West Yorkshire, BD7 2JE Tel: (01274) 521199 Fax: (01274) 521583 E-mail: marketing@shires-bathrooms.co.uk
Twyford Bathrooms Ltd, Lawton Road, Alsager, Stoke-on-Trent, ST7 2DF Tel: (01270) 879777 Fax: (01270) 873864

VITREOUS ENAMEL MANUFRS

Escol Products Ltd, Windover Road, Huntingdon, Cambridgeshire, PE29 7EB Tel: (01480) 454631 Fax: (01480) 411626 E-mail: info@escolproducts.co.uk
Trico VE Ltd, 76 Windmill Hill, Colley Gate, Halesowen, West Midlands, B63 2BZ Tel: (01384) 569555 Fax: (01384) 565777 E-mail: anjella@trico-ve.co.uk

VITREOUS ENAMEL OXIDES

Escol Products Ltd, Windover Road, Huntingdon, Cambridgeshire, PE29 7EB Tel: (01480) 454631 Fax: (01480) 411626 E-mail: info@escolproducts.co.uk

VITREOUS ENAMELLED PRODUCTS

Mark Davis Engineering Co. Ltd, Hayes Lane, Lye, Stourbridge, West Midlands, DY9 8RA Tel: (01384) 424404 Fax: (01384) 424707 E-mail: enquiries@markdavis.co.uk

VITREOUS ENAMELLED SIGNS

Burnham Signs Ltd, Burnham Way, London, SE26 5AG Tel: (020) 8659 1525 Fax: (020) 8659 4707 E-mail: sales@burnhamsigns.com

VITREOUS ENAMELLING

Protect Enamel Ltd, G K Davies Industrial Estate, Hayes Lane, Stourbridge, West Midlands, DY9 8QX Tel: (01384) 898844 Fax: (01384) 424483 E-mail: sales@protecenamel.co.uk
Reliable Stamping, 38 New John St West, Birmingham, B19 3NB Tel: 0121-359 6918 Fax: 0121-333 4691 E-mail: sales@reliable-stamping.co.uk
▶ Unique Enamelling Services, Bee Mill, Preston Road, Ribchester, Preston, PR3 3XJ Tel: (01254) 878265 Fax: (01524) 792299 E-mail: enqiuries@ues-ltd.co.uk

VITRIFIED CLAY DRAIN OR SANITARY PIPES

Hepworth Building Products Holdings Ltd, Hazlehead, Crow Edge, Sheffield, S36 4HG Tel: (01226) 763561 Fax: (01226) 764827 E-mail: info@hepworth.co.uk
Naylor Concrete Products Ltd, Clough Green, Cawthorne, Barnsley, South Yorkshire, S75 4AD Tel: (01226) 790591 Fax: (01226) 790531 E-mail: info@naylor.co.uk
W T Knowles & Sons Ltd, Ash Grove Sanitary Pipe Works, Elland Road, Elland, West Yorkshire, HX5 9JA Tel: (01422) 372833 Fax: (01422) 370900 E-mail: martin@wtknowles.co.uk

VOICE ALARM SYSTEMS

Audix Systems Ltd, Station Road, Wendens Ambo, Saffron Walden, Essex, CB11 4LG Tel: (01799) 540888 Fax: (01799) 541618 E-mail: sales@tepg.com
B L Acoustics Ltd, 152 Enterprise Court, Eastways, Witham, Essex, CM8 3YS Tel: (01376) 521525 Fax: (01376) 521526 E-mail: male@blacoustics.net
Baldwin Boxall Communications Ltd, Wealden Industrial Estate, Farningham Road, Crowborough, East Sussex, TN6 2JR Tel: (01892) 664422 Fax: (01892) 663146 E-mail: mail@baldwinboxall.co.uk
Cameo Systems Ltd, 29 Haviland Road, Ferndown Industrial Estate, Wimborne, Dorset, BH21 7SA Tel: (01202) 892088 Fax: (01202) 861449 E-mail: rob@cameosystems.co.uk
Millbank, Westmorland Business Centre, 41-43 Westmorland Road, Newcastle Upon Tyne, NE1 4EH Tel: 0191-232 1301 Fax: 0191-232 1302 E-mail: enquiries@ampekko.com
Tyco Fire & Integrated Solutions, Molly Avenue, Mapperley, Nottingham, NG3 5FW Tel: 0115-955 1199 Fax: 0115-955 1919 E-mail: spectorlumunex.uk@tycoint.com
Vision Fire & Security, Vision House Focus 31, Mark Road, Hemel Hempstead Industrial Estate, Hemel Hempstead, Hertfordshire, HP2 7BW Tel: (01442) 242330 Fax: (01442) 249327

VOICE COMMUNICATION MANAGED NETWORK SERVICES

I C C Communications Ltd, 14A Boxer Place, Mosside Industrial Estate, Leyland, PR26 7QL Tel: (01772) 622621 Fax: (01772) 622300 E-mail: networks@icc-comms.co.uk

VOICE COMMUNICATION SYSTEMS DESIGN

▶ Milestone Technologies Ltd, 6 Jardine Cottages, Templewood Lane, Stoke Poges, Slough, SL2 4BQ Tel: 01753 662182 Fax: 0870 134 1924 E-mail: enquiries@milestonetechnologies.co.uk

VOICE COMMUNICATION SYSTEMS INSTALLATION

C I M Systems Ltd, 1st Floor, Ross House, Kempson Way, Suffolk Business Park, Bury St. Edmunds, Suffolk, IP32 7AR Tel: (01284) 727200 Fax: (01284) 706602 E-mail: info@cimsystems.co.uk
Commercial Software Management Ltd, Devereux House, Church Hill, Coleshill, Birmingham, B46 3AA Tel: (01675) 466731 Fax: (01675) 466734 E-mail: sales@csmltd.co.uk
Crown House Technologies, Peal House, 50 Waterloo Road, Wolverhampton, WV1 4RU Tel: (01902) 428666 Fax: (01902) 428774
Nectar, Artemis Court, St. Johns Road, Meadowfield Industrial Estate, Durham, DH7 8TZ Tel: 0191-378 1946 Fax: 0191-378 1469 E-mail: sales@nectar.uk.com
Worth Installations Ltd, Bramwell House, Park Lane, Keighley, West Yorkshire, BD21 4QX Tel: (01535) 210510 Fax: (01535) 691508 E-mail: sales@worthcomms.co.uk

VOICE DATA COMMUNICATION SYSTEMS

Applinet, Unit 14 Thatcham Business Village, Colthrop Way, Thatcham, Berkshire, RG19 4LW Tel: (01635) 848900 Fax: (01635) 848920 E-mail: sales@applinet.co.uk

VOICE DATA COMMUNICATION SYSTEMS – *continued*

B D C, Unit 4 Redfields Industrial Estate, Redfields Lane, Church Crookham, Fleet, Hampshire, GU52 0RD Tel: (01252) 851688 Fax: (01252) 850577
County Communications, Yew Tree, Walls Quarry, Brimscombe, Stroud, Gloucestershire, GL5 2PA Tel: (01453) 887594 Fax: (01453) 883428
Du Pre plc, Unit 3-4 The Vo-Tec Centre, Hambridge Lane, Newbury, Berkshire, RG14 5TN Tel: (01635) 555555 Fax: (01635) 555533 E-mail: sales@dupre.co.uk
E C I Telecom, Isis House, Gastons Wood, Chineham, Basingstoke, Hampshire, RG24 8TW Tel: (01256) 388000 Fax: (01256) 388143
Ensign Communications Ltd, Unit 20-21 Sandford La Industrial Estate, Sandford Lane, Wareham, Dorset, BH20 4DY Tel: (01929) 556553 Fax: (01929) 554516 E-mail: call@ensign-net.co.uk
Internal Communications Network Ltd, 268 Hackney Road, London, E2 7SJ Tel: (020) 7613 0000 Fax: (020) 7723 7300 E-mail: icm@talk21.com
Intervoice, Brite Court, Park Road, Gatley, Cheadle, Cheshire, SK8 4HZ Tel: 0161-495 1000 Fax: 0161-495 1001 E-mail: sales@intervoice-brite.com
P D Systems, 20 West Craigs Crescent, Edinburgh, EH12 8NB Tel: 0131-339 4171 Fax: 0131-538 7713 E-mail: pdsystems@blueyonder.co.uk
Tailor Made Telecom Ltd, Bridge House, 7 & 9 Church Road, Bristol, BS5 9JJ Tel: 0117-955 9830 Fax: 0117-955 9840 E-mail: info@tmtelecom.co.uk
Ian Tofte Voice & Data Communications, 32 Bronte Close, Aylesbury, Buckinghamshire, HP19 8LF Tel: (01296) 487982 Fax: (01296) 488050 E-mail: itofte@tiscalli.co.uk
Vitec Group Communications Ltd, 7400 Beach Drive, Cambridge Research Park, Cambridge, CB25 9TP Tel: (01223) 815000 Fax: (01223) 815001 E-mail: vgc.uk@vitecgroup.com
Voice Products Ltd, Innovation House, Alexander Bell Centre, Hopkinson Way, Andover, Hampshire, SP10 3UR Tel: (0870) 0503870 Fax: (0870) 0503872 E-mail: info@voiceproducts.co.uk

VOICE MAIL SYSTEMS

Dataflex Design Communications Ltd, 2Nd Floor Chancery House, St. Nicholas Way, Sutton, Surrey, SM1 1JB Tel: (020) 8710 1700 Fax: (020) 8710 1705
Du Pre plc, Unit 3-4 The Vo-Tec Centre, Hambridge Lane, Newbury, Berkshire, RG14 5TN Tel: (01635) 555555 Fax: (01635) 555533 E-mail: sales@dupre.co.uk
Oak Telecom Ltd, 7 Albany Park, Cabot Lane, Poole, Dorset, BH17 7BX Tel: (01202) 607000 Fax: (01202) 607001
Telequip Ltd, 5 Acorn Business Centre, Northarbour Road, Portsmouth, PO6 3TH Tel: (023) 9221 5215 Fax: (08707) 770778 E-mail: postmaster@telequip.co.uk

VOICE OVER SERVICES, RADIO/ TELEVISION

▶ Broadcast Services, The Coach House, Ruxbury Road, Chertsey, Surrey, KT16 9EP Tel: (01932) 570001 Fax: (01932) 570443 E-mail: hire@broadcast-services.co.uk
▶ Celebrity Voices Ltd, 23 Springfeilds, Waltham Abbey, Essex, EN9 1UD Tel: (01992) 611097 E-mail: stuart@celebrityvoices.co.uk
▶ Christine Elcombe Voice Over Artist, 3 Elizabeth Drive, Capel-le-Ferne, Folkestone, Kent, CT18 7NA Tel: 0207 558 8269 Fax: 0870 137 8050 E-mail: webmaster@moneyspiderwebdesign.co.uk
Creative Audio Design, 12 Harold Road, Hawley, Dartford, DA2 7SA Tel: (01322) 224998 E-mail: jbthecad@homecall.co.uk

VOICE RECOGNITION SYSTEMS

Fluency Voice Technology Ltd, Block 6, 1St Floor Westbrook Centre, Cambridge, CB4 1YG Tel: (01223) 300101 Fax: (01223) 326701 E-mail: enquires@vocalis.com

VOICE RECORDING EQUIPMENT

▶ Direct Response Ltd, 3 Angel Walk, London, W6 9HX Tel: (0870) 4149000 Fax: (0870) 4149001 E-mail: sales@drltd.com
Precision Applications Ltd, Unit 19 Lodge Hill Industrial Estate, Station Road, Westbury sub Mendip, Wells, Somerset, BA5 1EY Tel: (01749) 870525 Fax: (01749) 870525 E-mail: sales@precisionapplications.co.uk
Speech Machines Ltd, Merebrook Business Park, Hanley Road, Welland, Malvern, Worcestershire, WR13 6NP Tel: (01684) 312300 Fax: (01684) 312301

VOILE CURTAINS

▶ H D Chadwick & Sons, Gorton Road, Manchester, M11 2DZ Tel: 0161-223 1701 Fax: 0161-231 6752 E-mail: roger.chadwick@tesco.net
▶ Net Curtains Direct, 14 Alder Close, Dibden Purlieu, Southampton, SO45 5SJ Tel: (023) 8084 6946

VOLLEYBALLS, BEACH

▶ H4 Sports, 2 Cudsdens Court, Chesham Road, Great Missenden, Buckinghamshire, HP16 0QX Tel: (01494) 862370 Fax: (01494) 862730 E-mail: info@h4sports.com

VOLTAGE CONTROLLED CRYSTAL OSCILLATORS (VCO)

Onspec Oscillators Ltd, Unit 10, Alliance Close, Attleborough Fields Industrial Estate, Nuneaton, Warwickshire, CV11 6SD Tel: (024) 7664 2024 Fax: (024) 7664 2073 E-mail: sales@onspec.co.uk

VOLTAGE REGULATORS

Linear Technology Ltd, 3 The Listons, Liston Road, Marlow, Buckinghamshire, SL7 1FD Tel: (01628) 477066 Fax: (01628) 478153
Marathon Electric, 6 Thistleton Road, Market Overton, Oakham, Leicestershire, LE15 7PP Tel: (01572) 768206 Fax: (01572) 768217 E-mail: meuk@btinternet.com
Sollatek (UK) Ltd, Units 10 Poyle, 14 Industrial Estate, Newlands Drive, Poyle, Slough, SL3 0DX Tel: (01753) 688300 Fax: (01753) 685306 E-mail: sales@sollatek.com

VOLTAGE STABILISERS

Sollatek (UK) Ltd, Units 10 Poyle, 14 Industrial Estate, Newlands Drive, Poyle, Slough, SL3 0DX Tel: (01753) 688300 Fax: (01753) 685306 E-mail: sales@sollatek.com

VOUCHER INCENTIVE SCHEME PROVIDERS

The Grass Roots Group UK Ltd, Pennyroyal, Station Road, Tring, Hertfordshire, HP23 5QY Tel: (01442) 829400 Fax: (01442) 829405 E-mail: contactus@grg.com

VULCANISED FIBRE COIL OR SHEET

Multi Engineering Components Co., E3 Seedbed Centre, Avenue Road, Nechells, Birmingham, B7 4NT Tel: 0121-359 6022 Fax: 0121-359 0137 E-mail: sales@multiengineering.co.uk

VULCANISED FIBRE WASHERS

Godfrey Insulations Ltd, Siddons Factory Estate, Howard Street, West Bromwich, West Midlands, B70 0SZ Tel: 0121-556 0011 Fax: 0121-556 9553

VULCANISING AUTOCLAVES

▶ LBBC Ltd, Beechwood Street, Pudsey, West Yorkshire, LS28 6PT Tel: 0113-205 7400 Fax: 0113-256 3509 E-mail: sales@lbbc.co.uk

VULCANISING PLANT AND EQUIPMENT

Installation & Manufacturing Contractors Ltd, Thrifts House, London Road, Ware, Hertfordshire, SG12 9QT Tel: (01920) 468011 Fax: (01920) 460869 E-mail: info@monaflex.com

VULCANISING SERVICES

Ammeraal Beltech Ltd, John Tate Road, Foxholes Business Park, Hertford, SG13 7QE Tel: (01992) 500550 Fax: (01992) 553010 E-mail: sales@ammeraalbeltech.co.uk
Apex Belting Co. Ltd, 9 Boldero Road, Bury St. Edmunds, Suffolk, IP32 7BS Tel: (01284) 752486 Fax: (01284) 750542 E-mail: sales@apex-belting.co.uk
Brec Ltd, Moor Park Court, St. Georges Road, Preston, PR1 6AQ Tel: (01772) 555000 Fax: (01772) 555422 E-mail: info@brec-ltd.com
Jason Industrial Ltd, Unit 29 Normanby Park Workshops, Normanby Road, Scunthorpe, North Lincolnshire, DN15 8QZ Tel: (01724) 861006 Fax: (01724) 869846
Press & Fab Ltd, Unit 1 Boathouse Lane, Stockton-on-Tees, Cleveland, TS18 3AW Tel: (01642) 616114 Fax: (01642) 605598
Swift Vulcanising Services, Unit 10 Littleton Business Park, Littleton Drive, Cannock, Staffordshire, WS12 4TR Tel: (01543) 468018 Fax: (01543) 468018 E-mail: petrasedgley@btconnect.com
Transbelt Ltd, 46 The Acorn Centre, Barry Street, Oldham, OL1 3NE Tel: 0161-620 0493 Fax: 0161-627 0084 E-mail: sales@transbelt.co.uk

WADDING, MAN-MADE/ SYNTHETIC FIBRE

Cowens Ltd, Ellers Mill, Dalston, Carlisle, CA5 7QJ Tel: (01228) 710205 Fax: (01228) 710331 E-mail: info@cowens.co.uk
Platt & Hill Ltd, Belgrave Mill, Fitton Hill Road, Oldham, OL8 2LZ Tel: 0161-621 4400 Fax: 0161-621 4408 E-mail: sales@phfillings.co.uk

WADDING, MEDICAL/SURGICAL

Fourstones Paper Mill Co. Ltd, South Tyne Mill, Hexham, Northumberland, NE46 3SD Tel: (01434) 602444 Fax: (01434) 607046 E-mail: team@fourstonespapermill.co.uk

WAFER CHECK VALVES

Goodwin International Ltd, Ivy House Foundry, Hanley, Stoke-on-Trent, ST1 3NR Tel: (01782) 220000 Fax: (01782) 208060 E-mail: goodwinplc@goodwin.co.uk
W T Armatur UK Ltd, Singleton Court Business Centre, Wonastow Road Industrial Estate (West), Monmouth, Gwent, NP25 5JA Tel: (01600) 712178 Fax: (01600) 712179

WAISTBANDS, TROUSER ETC

The Locke Group Ltd, Unit 2, Millshaw, Leeds, LS11 8EG Tel: 0113-237 9400 Fax: 0113-237 9419 E-mail: sales@lockeuk.com
Profit Manufacturing Ltd, Unit 36 Albion Mills, Albion Road, Bradford, West Yorkshire, BD10 9TF Tel: (01274) 610590 Fax: (01274) 610541 E-mail: sales@pro-fit-int.com

WAITERS KNIVES

Gilberts Food Equipment Ltd, Gilbert House, 1 Warwick Place, Borehamwood, Hertfordshire, WD6 1UA Tel: (0845) 2300681 Fax: (0845) 2300682 E-mail: info@topgourmet.co.uk

WALKING STICKS

All Handling Ltd, Mobility House, 492 Kingston Road, London, SW20 8DX Tel: (020) 8542 1021 Fax: (020) 8395 4410
▶ e-craft, info@e-craft.co.uk, Irthlingborough, Wellingborough, Northants, NN9 5EP Tel: 07905 759109 E-mail: info@e-craft.co.uk
James Smith & Sons Ltd, 53 New Oxford Street, London, WC1A 1BL Tel: (020) 7836 4731 Fax: (020) 7836 4730 E-mail: jsmith.umbrellas@virgin.net
Phoenix Walking Stick Co. Ltd, Unit 6a-6c Nailsworth Mills, Avening Road, Nailsworth, Stroud, Gloucestershire, GL6 0BS Tel: (01453) 835816 Fax: (01453) 835819 E-mail: jf@sticks.org
Somerwood Ltd, 52a Summerhill Road, Saffron Walden, Essex, CB11 4AJ Tel: (01799) 500180

WALL CLADDING, *See also headings for particular materials*

A C Bacon Engineering Ltd, Norwich Road, Hingham, Norwich, NR9 4LS Tel: (01953) 850611 Fax: (01953) 851445 E-mail: steel@acbacon.co.uk
Campbell-lee Contracts, 84 Greasby Road, Greasby, Wirral, Merseyside, CH49 3NG Tel: 0151-606 8779 Fax: 0151-678 1640 E-mail: sales@campbelllee.co.uk
Panel Systems Ltd, Unit 3-9 Welland Close, Sheffield, S3 9QY Tel: 0114-275 2881 Fax: 0114-276 8807 E-mail: mail@panelsystems.co.uk
Seal Service Ltd, 1 & 2 Kingfisher Court, Kestrel Close, Quarry Hill Industrial Estate, Ilkeston, Derbyshire, DE7 4RD Tel: 0115-932 4308 Fax: 0115-944 0279

WALL CLADDING CONTRACTORS OR FIXING SERVICES

Construction Profiles Ltd, Carriage House, Little Broom Street, Birmingham, B12 0EU Tel: 0121-766 6633 Fax: 0121-766 7792 E-mail: accounts@construction-profiles.co.uk
Northwich Industrial Roofing Ltd, 4 Bridge Street, Northwich, Cheshire, CW9 7NR Tel: (01606) 43884 Fax: (01606) 43884
Pinnacle Structures, Unit 7 Westwood Industrial Estate, Ewyas Harold, Hereford, HR2 0EL Tel: (01981) 241414 Fax: (01981) 241195 E-mail: mail@pinnaclestructures.co.uk

WALL CLADDING INSULATED COMPOSITE PANELS

A M E, 5 Glebe Road, Skelmersdale, Lancashire, WN8 9JP Tel: (01695) 50658 Fax: (01695) 50652 E-mail: info@amefacades.com
Colamet Manufacturing Ltd, 870 South St, Whiteinch, Glasgow, G14 0SY Tel: 0141-959 1183 Fax: 0141-958 1173 E-mail: info@booth-muirie.co.uk
Gilmour Ecometal, 245 Govan Road, Glasgow, G51 2SQ Tel: 0141-427 1264 Fax: 0141-427 2205 E-mail: info@gilmour-ecometal.co.uk
▶ Laminated Supplies Ltd, Valletta House, Valletta Street, Hedon Road, Hull, HU9 5NP Tel: (01482) 781111 Fax: (01482) 701185 E-mail: sales@laminatedsupplies.com
Mercury Panel Products Ltd, 132 Sculcoates Lane, Hull, HU5 1DP Tel: (01482) 441400 Fax: (01482) 441500
Panel Systems Ltd, Unit 3-9 Welland Close, Sheffield, S3 9QY Tel: 0114-275 2881 Fax: 0114-276 8807 E-mail: mail@panelsystems.co.uk
Panels & Profiles, Tewksbury Business Park, Severn Drive, Tewkesbury Business Park, Tewkesbury, Gloucestershire, GL20 8TX Tel: (01684) 856600 Fax: (01684) 856601 E-mail: sales@coruspanelsandprofiles.co.uk
Supaclad Ltd, Timmis Road, Stourbridge, West Midlands, DY9 7BQ Tel: (01384) 896647 Fax: (01384) 892457
Vulcan Plastics Ltd, Hosey Hill, Westerham, Kent, TN16 1TZ Tel: (01959) 562304

WALL COPINGS

Alifabs Woking Ltd, 4 Kernel Court, Walnut Tree Close, Guildford, Surrey, GU1 4UD Tel: (01483) 546547 Fax: (01483) 546548 E-mail: sales@alifabs.com
George Farrar (Quarries) Ltd, Bradford Street, Keighley, West Yorkshire, BD21 3EB Tel: (01535) 602344 Fax: (01535) 606247 E-mail: sales@farrar.co.uk

WALL FINISH OR COATING CONTRACTORS

Ltd Anti-Corrosion Services, Carrington Business Park, Carrington, Manchester, M31 4QW Tel: 0161-776 4019 Fax: 0161-775 8995
Cement Glaze Decorators Ltd, 5 Barry Parade, Barry Road, London, SE22 0JA Tel: (020) 8299 2553 Fax: (020) 8299 2346
Firthglow Ltd, 1 Papyrus Road, Werrington, Peterborough, PE4 5BH Tel: (01733) 570345 Fax: (01733) 576115

WALL OR FLOOR HYGIENE FINISHING, FOOD INDUSTRY

▶ Filon Products, Unit 3 Ring Road Zone 2, Burntwood Business Park, Burntwood, Staffordshire, WS7 3JQ Tel: (01543) 687300 Fax: (01543) 687303 E-mail: admin@filon.co.uk

WALL OR FLOOR TILING CONTRACTORS

A E S Roofing Contractors Ltd, Lingens Bungalow, Sledgemoor, Broadwas, Worcester, WR6 5NR Tel: (01905) 333697 Fax: (01905) 333650 E-mail: info@aesroofing.co.uk
A G Ceramics, The Coach House, 4 Bradford Street, Braintree, Essex, CM7 9AS Tel: (0870) 4862912 Fax: (0870) 4862913 E-mail: agceramics@angeljaz21.co.uk
Ace Kitchens, 47-57 Feeder Road, Bristol, BS2 0SE Tel: 0117-971 3682 Fax: 0117-977 7004
Alan Cox & Son, 19 Craigweil Crescent, Stockton-on-Tees, Cleveland, TS19 0DU Tel: (01642) 611672 Fax: (01642) 651349 E-mail: andrewcoxdec@hotmail.com
Andrews Bros Plastering Ltd, Bridge House, Clyst St. Mary, Exeter, EX5 1BR Tel: (01392) 875755 Fax: (01392) 876617
Ltd Anti-Corrosion Services, Carrington Business Park, Carrington, Manchester, M31 4QW Tel: 0161-776 4019 Fax: 0161-775 8995
Birmingham Tile & Mosaic Co. Ltd, Ceramic House, 198 Kings Road, Tyseley, Birmingham, B11 2AP Tel: 0121-707 4505 Fax: 0121-707 5585 E-mail: mail@btandm.co.uk
▶ Carrara-Tiling, 17 Lytham Close, Doncaster, South Yorkshire, DN4 6UT Tel: (01302) 370352 Fax: (01302) 370352 E-mail: carrara-tiling@tiscali.co.uk
▶ Ceramic Art, 41 Whitehouse Meadows, Leigh-on-Sea, Essex, SS9 5TY Tel: (01702) 526348 E-mail: ceramicart_uk@msn.com

WALL OR FLOOR TILING CONTRACTORS – *continued*

Ceramic Design & Installations, 3 St Pauls Close, Farington Moss, Leyland, PR26 6RT Tel: (01772) 311902 Fax: (01772) 311992
Cladding Components Ltd, 17 Trinity Street, Leamington Spa, Warwickshire, CV32 5RH Tel: (01926) 420825 Fax: (01926) 313927 E-mail: clad.comp@ic24.net
D Kelleher Flooring Ltd, Unit 1 B Alexandria Park 1, Penner Road, Havant, Hampshire, PO9 1QY Tel: (023) 9247 1029 Fax: (023) 9245 3288E-mail: mail@kelleherflooring.co.uk
Dave Prior Tiling Co., 40 Kingsley Road, London, E17 4AU Tel: (020) 8531 7221 Fax: 020 85317221
Easifloor Ltd, Cranes Close, Basildon, Essex, SS14 3JB Tel: (01268) 288744 Fax: (01268) 532305 E-mail: tiles@easifloor.fsnet.co.uk
G & M Floorlayers Derby Ltd, Sandown Road, Derby, DE24 8SR Tel: (01332) 344282 Fax: (01332) 298491
Gateway Ceramics Ltd, School Lane, Chandler's Ford, Eastleigh, Hampshire, SO53 4DG Tel: (023) 8026 0290 Fax: (023) 8025 1049
▶ Impermia, 1 shaftesbury Gdns, London, NW10 6LP Tel: (020) 8961 5259 Fax: (020) 8961 5359 E-mail: info@impermia.co.uk
Plunkett Tiling Ltd, Dukes Way, Low Prudhoe Industrial Estate, Prudhoe, Northumberland, NE42 6PQ Tel: (01661) 836960 Fax: (01661) 836847 E-mail: personnel@plunketttiling.co.uk
Resilient Tile & Flooring Co. (Ealing) Ltd, 2 Replingham Rd, London, SW18 5LS Tel: (020) 8874 6655 Fax: (020) 8874 6656
▶ S D Flooring, 30 Guildford Road, Worthing, West Sussex, BN14 7LL Tel: (01903) 538201 E-mail: sales@sdflooring.co.uk
▶ Selwood Ceramics Floor and Wall Tiling, 15 Havelock Road, Maidenhead, Berkshire, SL6 5BJ Tel: (01628) 782393 E-mail: sales@selwoodceramics.co.uk
Spot On Ceramics Ltd, 1 Moorview Court, Estover Close, Plymouth, PL6 7PL Tel: (01752) 692170 Fax: (01752) 788785 E-mail: enquiries@spotonceramics.co.uk
T P Tiling, 36 Draper Way, Leighton Buzzard, Bedfordshire, LU7 4UD Tel: (07821) 894855 E-mail: tpickup@tiscali.co.uk
Tilecraft Services Ltd, 11 Scotts Road, Paisley, Renfrewshire, PA2 7AN Tel: 0141-887 4051 Fax: 0141-889 5247 E-mail: info@tilecraftservices.co.uk
Tiling Co., Unit 1, Hampson Mill Lane, Bury, Lancashire, BL9 9TZ Tel: 0161-766 4710 Fax: 0161-796 3190 E-mail: ttc.northwest@thetilingcompany.co.uk
▶ Tiling For UK, 9 Meadwell Road, Leicester, LE3 1SU Tel: 0116-255 1863 Fax: 0116-255 1863 E-mail: tilingforuk@tiscali.co.uk

WALL PANEL FIXING SYSTEMS

▶ Commercial Systems (Fabrication) Ltd, 1 Queensway, Rochdale, Lancashire, OL11 2LA Tel: (01706) 644223 Fax: (01706) 644188 E-mail: atonyarmstrong@aol.com

WALL PANELLING, *See Wall Panelling etc*

WALL PLAQUES

Tryst, Kippen Station, Kippen, Stirling, FK8 3JA Tel: (01786) 870295

WALL PROTECTION SYSTEMS

▶ Mccue International, Mount House, Bond Avenue, Bletchley, Milton Keynes, MK1 1SF Tel: (01908) 365511 Fax: (01908) 365527 E-mail: sales@mccuecorp.co.uk

WALL TIE INSTALLATION OR REPLACEMENT

Anchor Building Services, 14 Ivy Street, Burnley, Lancashire, BB10 1TD Tel: (01254) 394137 Fax: (01254) 394137
Brick Lock Ltd, 8 Brexdale Avenue, Kippax, Leeds, LS25 7EJ Tel: 0113-232 0800
Homeguard (South East) Ltd, 19 Broadmead Road, Folkestone, Kent, CT19 5AN Tel: (01702) 471666 Fax: (0845) 3703883 E-mail: linda@dwcuk.com
Poulton Remedial Services Ltd, 86-88 Church Street, Old Town, Eastbourne, East Sussex, BN21 1QJ Tel: (01424) 422122 Fax: (01323) 734596 E-mail: enquiries@structuralrepairs.com
South East Ties Ltd, The Old Forge House, Manston Road, Manston, Ramsgate, Kent, CT12 5HG Tel: (0845) 8387442 Fax: (0845) 8387443
Timberwise UK plc, 1 Drake Mews, Gadbrook Park, Northwich, Cheshire, CW9 7XF Tel: (01606) 333636 Fax: (01606) 334664 E-mail: hq@timberwise.co.uk
Well Tied Ltd, 6 Llwynderw Drive, West Cross, Swansea, SA3 5AP Tel: (01792) 405151

WALL TIES, *See also headings for particular types*

C F P Supplies, Unit 6-7 Building, 53b Third Avenue, Pensnett Trading Estate, Kingswinford, West Midlands, DY6 7XG Tel: (01384) 400220 Fax: (01384) 400160
C R S Specialised Building Services Ltd, 45a Stoke Road, Gosport, Hampshire, PO12 1LS Tel: (023) 9258 3084 Fax: (023) 9258 3084 E-mail: enq@crsbuilders.co.uk
Helifix Ltd, Unit B2 First Avenue, Tyne Tunnel Trading Estate, North Shields, Tyne & Wear, NE29 7SU Tel: 0191-257 4577 Fax: 0191-257 0426 E-mail: brian.breeze@helifix.co.uk
Perma-Tie, 20 South Street, Havant, Hampshire, PO9 1DA Tel: (023) 9266 8116 Fax: (023) 9245 5785
Regent Systems Ltd, Unit D11c, Dower House Farm, Blackboys, Uckfield, East Sussex, TN22 5HJ Tel: (01435) 864424 Fax: (01435) 868102
Shaped Wires Ltd, Prospect Mills, Scholes, Cleckheaton, West Yorkshire, BD19 6NJ Tel: (01274) 855635 Fax: (01274) 851116 E-mail: sales@shapedwires.com
Tackburn Ltd, Unit 11A Imex Business Centre, Oxleason Road, East Moons Moat, Redditch, Worcestershire, B98 8LG Tel: (01527) 68559 Fax: (01527) 68559
Trafford Timber & Damp-Proofing Specialists Ltd, 1086 Chester Road, Stretford, Manchester, M32 0HL Tel: 0161-972 5777 Fax: 0161-972 5888 E-mail: admin@traffordtds.fsworld.co.uk
▶ Vista Engineering, 16 Baronald Street, Rutherglen, Glasgow, G73 1AH Tel: 0141-613 3144 Fax: 0141-613 3031

WALLBOARD

Arnold Laver Birmingham Board Timberworld, Dudley Road, Oldbury, West Midlands, B69 3DA Tel: 0121-552 7788 Fax: 0121-544 7186 E-mail: sales@birminghamtimberworld.co.uk
Midland Wallboards Ltd, Severn House, Western Road, Oldbury, West Midlands, B69 4LY Tel: 0121-552 9333 Fax: 0121-552 9330 E-mail: sales@midlandwallboards.co.uk
Minster Composite Products, Minster House, Private Road 2, Colwick Industrial Estate, Nottingham, NG4 2JR Tel: 0115-940 0644 Fax: 0115-940 0655 E-mail: minster@btclick.com
N R Burnett Ltd, West Carr Lane, Hull, HU7 0AW Tel: (01482) 838800 Fax: (01482) 822110
Panel Systems Ltd, Unit 3-9 Welland Close, Sheffield, S3 9QY Tel: 0114-275 2881 Fax: 0114-276 8807 E-mail: mail@panelsystems.co.uk
Porters, George Cayley Drive, Clifton Moore, York, YO30 4XE Tel: (01904) 690023 Fax: (01904) 692045

WALLCOVERING CONTRACTORS OR FIXING SERVICES

Collins Contractors Ltd, 31 Gillian Street, London, SE13 7AJ Tel: (020) 8690 0077 Fax: (020) 8690 4077 E-mail: info@collins-contractors.co.uk

WALLCOVERINGS, *See also headings for particular materials*

▶ Amy Nicholas Interior Design, Rose Cottage, Main Street, Grindleton, Clitheroe, Lancashire, BB7 4QT Tel: 01200 441854 Fax: 01200 441854 E-mail: info@amynicholas.co.uk
B N International, Metro Centre, Dwight Road, Watford, WD18 9YD Tel: (01923) 219132 Fax: (01923) 219134
Cwv Group Ltd, 1 The Beehive, Lions Drive, Shadworth Business Park, Blackburn, BB1 2QS Tel: (01254) 222800 Fax: (01254) 222960
Id Wall, The Mill, 150 Penistone Road, Shelley, Huddersfield, HD8 8JQ Tel: (01484) 603020 E-mail: info@id-wall.com
Irving Little & Co. Ltd, 213 Cleveland Street, Birkenhead, Merseyside, CH41 3QE Tel: 0151-666 1004 Fax: 0151-666 1013
Newmor Group Ltd, Madoc Works, Henfaes Lane, Welshpool, Powys, SY21 7BE Tel: (01938) 552671 Fax: (01938) 554285 E-mail: enquiries@newmor.com
Oaktree Interiors Ltd, Frederick House, 498 Reading Road, Winnersh, Wokingham, Berkshire, RG41 5EX Tel: 0118-979 6600 Fax: 0118-979 4044 E-mail: sales@oaktreeoffice.com
▶ Pat Oliver Designs, 7-8 Park Gate, Skelmanthorpe, Huddersfield, HD8 9BB Tel: (01484) 864263 E-mail: patoliver@bbmax.co.uk
▶ Property Network Services Ltd., 29 Woodlands Crescent, Johnstone, Renfrewshire, PA5 0AZ Tel: 01505 320281
R M D (U K) Ltd, Thornham Works, Oozewood Road, Royton, Oldham, OL2 5SQ Tel: 0161-620 4418
Simpson's Paints Ltd, 122-124 Broadley Street, London, NW8 8BB Tel: (020) 7723 6657 Fax: (020) 7706 4662
Tektura Wallcoverings, One Heron Quay, London, E14 4JA Tel: (020) 7536 3300 Fax: (020) 7536 3322 E-mail: sales@tektura.com
Today Interiors Holdings Ltd, Hollis Road, Grantham, Lincolnshire, NG31 7QH Tel: (01476) 574401 Fax: (01476) 590208 E-mail: info@today-interiors.co.uk

WALLPAPER PASTE

C Brewer & Sons Ltd, Albany House, Ashford Road, Eastbourne, East Sussex, BN21 3TR Tel: (01323) 437801 Fax: (01323) 721435 E-mail: decorating@brewers.co.uk
Cliff Madden Angling, 5 Church Street, Staveley, Chesterfield, Derbyshire, S43 3TL Tel: (01246) 472410
Unibond, Apollo Court, 2 Bishops Square Business Park, Hatfield, Hertfordshire, AL10 9EY Tel: (01707) 289041 Fax: (01707) 289099

WALLPAPER PRODUCTION MACHINERY

Emerson & Renwick Ltd, Peel Bank Works, Peel Bank, Church, Accrington, Lancashire, BB5 4EF Tel: (01254) 872727 Fax: (01254) 871109 E-mail: sales@eandr.com
Eurograv Ltd, Sprint Industrial Estate, Chertsey Road, Byfleet, West Byfleet, Surrey, KT14 7BD Tel: (01932) 336262 Fax: (01932) 336271 E-mail: sales@eurograv.co.uk

WALLPAPER STRIPPING MACHINE HIRE

Wallwik UK, 86 Sulivan Court, Peterborough Road, London, SW6 3DB Tel: 0845 094 0501 Fax: 0845 094 0801 E-mail: paul.rydzyk@wallwik-uk.com

WALLPAPER STRIPPING MACHINES

Earlex Ltd, Opus Park Moorfield Road, Slyfield Industrial Estate, Guildford, Surrey, GU1 1SZ Tel: (01483) 454666 Fax: (01483) 454548 E-mail: enquiries@earlex.co.uk
Hire Technicians Group, Chalk Hill House, 8 Chalk Hill, Watford, WD19 4BH Tel: (0845) 2303340 Fax: (0845) 2303345 E-mail: sales@hiretech.biz
Wallwik UK, 86 Sulivan Court, Peterborough Road, London, SW6 3DB Tel: 0845 094 0501 Fax: 0845 094 0801 E-mail: paul.rydzyk@wallwik-uk.com

WALLPAPERS

Colefax Group plc, 39 Brook Street, Mayfair, London, W1K 4JE Tel: (020) 7493 2231 Fax: (020) 7355 4037
Cwv Group Ltd, 1 The Beehive, Lions Drive, Shadworth Business Park, Blackburn, BB1 2QS Tel: (01254) 222800 Fax: (01254) 222960
Dulux Ltd, Manchester Road, West Timperley, Altrincham, Cheshire, WA14 5PG Tel: 0161-968 3000 Fax: 0161-973 4202
Dulux Ltd, 66 Burleys Way, Leicester, LE1 3BD Tel: 0116-262 9471 Fax: 0116-251 2985
Anna French Ltd, 36 Hinton Road, London, SE24 0HJ Tel: (020) 7737 6555 E-mail: info@annafrench.co.uk
Glyn Webb Group Ltd, Old Darby House, Derker Street, Oldham, OL1 3XF Tel: 0161-6214500 Fax: 0161-621 4501 E-mail: contactus@glynwebb.co.uk
Graham & Brown Ltd, Harwood Street, Blackburn, BB1 3BD Tel: (01254) 691321 Fax: (01254) 582208 E-mail: customer.services@grahambrown.com
Harlequin Fabric & Wallcoverings Ltd, Ladybird House, Beeches Road, Loughborough, Leicestershire, LE11 2HA Tel: (0870) 8300355 Fax: (0870) 8300359 E-mail: sales@harlequin.uk.com
Milton Keynes Blind Co. Ltd, 12 Wolseley Road Woburn Industrial Estate, Woburn Road Industrial Estate, Kempston, Bedford, MK42 7TN Tel: (01234) 841515 Fax: (01234) 840682 E-mail: sales@concordeblinds.com
Retford Wall Coverings, 1c Birkdale Road, Scunthorpe, South Humberside, DN17 2AU Tel: (01724) 281154 Fax: (01724) 875151 E-mail: admin@retwall.co.uk
Robinson & Neal Ltd, 129 Sefton Street, Toxteth, Liverpool, L8 5SN Tel: 0151-709 9481 Fax: 0151-707 1377
S. J. Dixon International Ltd, Dixon House, Old Heath Road, Wolverhampton, WV1 2RR Tel: (01902) 455114 Fax: (01902) 452602
SigmaKalon, 16D 16F Kilroot Business Park, Larne Road, Carrickfergus, County Antrim, BT38 7PR Tel: (028) 9335 1567 Fax: (028) 9335 1569
Thos Kelly & Co., Dromore Street, Ballynahinch, County Down, BT24 8AG Tel: (028) 9756 2380 Fax: (028) 9756 1564

WAR BASED GAMES

▶ Role'N'Play Model Shops, 174 Stafford Street, Wolverhampton, WV1 1NA Tel: (01902) 310027 E-mail: info@role-n-play.co.uk

WARDROBES

▶ Britannia Wardrobes Ltd, Ebberns Road, Hemel Hempstead, Hertfordshire, HP3 9QS Tel: (01442) 239900 Fax: (01442) 244121
▶ The Fitted Wardrobe Site, 3 Salvington Road, Crawley, West Sussex, RH11 8XE Tel: 01293 223398
▶ Interior Door Systems Ltd, Hopton House 3 & 4 Rivington Court, Hardwick Grange, Woolston, Warrington, WA1 4RT Tel: (01925) 813100 E-mail: sales@interiordoorsystems.co.uk

WAREHOUSE AGENTS

C Steinweg London Ltd, 106 Leadenhall Street, London, EC3A 4AA Tel: (020) 7626 4769 Fax: (020) 7929 1451
▶ Cert plc, Hellaby Lane, Hellaby, Rotherham, South Yorkshire, S66 8HN Tel: (01709) 544822 Fax: (01709) 531365
Crown Records Management Ltd, Marshgate Business Centre, 10-12 Marshgate Lane, London, E15 2NH Tel: (020) 8555 1880 Fax: (020) 8555 2110
▶ D H L, Western Avenue, Western Docks, Southampton, SO15 0HH Tel: (023) 8077 2200 Fax: (023) 8078 1111
Alan Firmin Ltd, Mid Kent Business Park, Sortmill Road, Snodland, Kent, ME6 5GP Tel: (01634) 241200 Fax: (01622) 820823 E-mail: transport@alanfirmin.co.uk
Firmin Coates Ltd, Wares Farm, Redwall Lane, Linton, Maidstone, Kent, ME17 4BB Tel: (01622) 820273 Fax: (01622) 820823 E-mail: afl@alanfirmin.co.uk
Fowler Welch Coolchain P.L.C., West Marsh Road, Spalding, Lincolnshire, PE11 2BB Tel: (01795) 580056 Fax: (01795) 980307
▶ Great Bear Distribution Ltd, Moulton Park Business Centre, Redhouse Road, Moulton Park Industrial Estate, Northampton, NN3 6AQ Tel: (01604) 643648 Fax: (01604) 643649
Kimberley Distribution Ltd, Wanlip Road, Syston, Leicester, LE7 1PD Tel: 0116-260 2224
Logistics Simulation Ltd, The Capstan House, Middlewood Road, Poynton, Stockport, Cheshire, SK12 1SH Tel: (01625) 850919 Fax: (01625) 850377 E-mail: info@logsim.co.uk
Salvesen Consumer Logistics, Parkhouse Industrial Estate We, Newcastle, Staffordshire, ST5 7DU Tel: (01782) 566099 Fax: (01782) 561184
Saturn Facilities Ltd, 8-10 Grosvenor Gardens, London, SW1W 0DH Tel: (020) 7861 0550 Fax: (020) 7861 0551 E-mail: enquiries@saturnfacilities.com
TDG UK Ltd, Knockmore Industrial Estate, Moira Road, Lisburn, County Antrim, BT28 2EJ Tel: (028) 9260 2133 Fax: (028) 9260 2786
▶ W K T Global Logistics Ltd, Unit 2 & 8, Capitol Industrial Centre, Fulmar Way, Wickford, Essex, SS11 8YW Tel: (01268) 560843
Wincanton Group Ltd, Middle Bank, Doncaster, South Yorkshire, DN4 5JJ Tel: (01302) 507100 Fax: (01302) 507114

WAREHOUSE DESIGN CONSULTANCY

Inline Logistics Ltd, The Grange, Brixworth, Northampton, NN6 9DL Tel: (01604) 882200 Fax: (01604) 882323

WAREHOUSE MANAGEMENT SYSTEM SOFTWARE

1t Solutions, 3 The Crescent, Doncaster Road, Rotherham, South Yorkshire, S65 1NL Tel: (01709) 371441 Fax: (01709) 371440 E-mail: sales@1t-s.com
Catalyst International Ltd, Capital Court, 30 Windsor Street, Uxbridge, Middlesex, UB8 1AB Tel: (01895) 450400 Fax: (01895) 450401 E-mail: europe@catalystinternational.com
Chess Logistics Technology, Commerce Way, Trafford Park, Manchester, M17 1HW Tel: 0161-888 2580 Fax: 0161-888 2590 E-mail: info@chess.uk.com
Cpio Ltd, Arden House The Courtyard, Gorsey Lane, Coleshill, Birmingham, B46 1JA Tel: (01675) 467046 Fax: (01675) 467682 E-mail: rcf@cpio.co.uk
Delta Software Ltd, Whitwood Lodge, Whitwood Lane, Whitwood, Wakefield, West Yorkshire, WF10 5QD Tel: (01204) 529171 Fax: (01977) 668378 E-mail: info@deltasoftware.co.uk
Excel Computer Systems, Bothe Hall, Tamworth Road, Long Eaton, Nottingham, NG10 3XL Tel: 0115-946 0101 Fax: 0115-946 0606 E-mail: sales@exel.co.uk
Fossoft, Newstead House, Lake View Drive, Annesley, NG15 0DT Tel: (01623) 720012 Fax: (01623) 720006

WAREHOUSE MANAGEMENT SYSTEM SOFTWARE – *continued*

H C M Systems Ltd, 3 Church Street, Leamington Spa, Warwickshire, CV31 1EG Tel: (01926) 451551 Fax: (01926) 451556 E-mail: sales@hccm.co.uk

Infor Global Solutions Frimley Ltd, 1 Lakeside Road, Farnborough, Hampshire, GU14 6XP Tel: (01276) 417200 Fax: (01276) 417201

Interchain UK Ltd, 44 Shenley Pavilions, Chalkdell Drive, Shenley Wood, Milton Keynes, MK5 6LB Tel: (01908) 521000 Fax: (01908) 522000 E-mail: pbz@interchain.co.uk

Kuehne + Nagel Ltd, Hays House, Sunrise Parkway, Linford Wood, Milton Keynes, MK14 6BW Tel: (01908) 255000 Fax: (01908) 255200

Logistics Business, 17 The Crescent, Bromsgrove, Worcestershire, B60 2DF Tel: (01527) 889060 Fax: (01527) 559192 E-mail: info@logistics.co.uk

Newmind Ltd, Yarburgh House, King Street, Yarburgh, Louth, Lincolnshire, LN11 0PN Tel: (01507) 363636 Fax: (01507) 363764 E-mail: sales@newmind.ltd.uk

X K S Ltd, Unit 19 St. Asaph Business Park, Glascoed Road, St. Asaph, Clwyd, LL17 0LJ Tel: (01745) 584953 Fax: (01745) 583047

WAREHOUSE MANAGEMENT SYSTEMS

▶ Bar Code Systems (London) Ltd, Lakeside House, 1 Furzeground Way, Stockley Park, Uxbridge, Middlesex, UB11 1BD Tel: (0870) 3516496 Fax: (020) 8622 3249 E-mail: robertmoorman@barcode-systems.com

Catalyst International Ltd, Capital Court, 30 Windsor Street, Uxbridge, Middlesex, UB8 1AB Tel: (01895) 450400 Fax: (01895) 450401 E-mail: europe@catalystinternational.com

▶ First Concepts Ltd, Concept House, 7 Holly Grove, Tabley, Knutsford, Cheshire, WA16 0HR Tel: (0845) 4567684 Fax: (0845) 4567694 E-mail: info@firstconcepts.co.uk

Len Lothian U Store, 11 Bankhead Broadway, Edinburgh, EH11 4DB Tel: 0131-538 8200 Fax: 0131-538 8210 E-mail: info@lenlothain.com

WAREHOUSE MANAGEMENT SYSTEMS FOR AUTOMATED SYSTEMS

▶ Redprairie, Beacon House, Ibstone Road, Stokenchurch, High Wycombe, Buckinghamshire, HP14 3AQ Tel: (01494) 486500 Fax: (01494) 485465 E-mail: sales@online-internet.co.uk

Supply Chain & Logistics Consulting Ltd, The Chimes, 1 Park Road, Congleton, Cheshire, CW12 1DS Tel: (01260) 276469 E-mail: info@supplychainlogistics-consulting.co.uk

WAREHOUSING AND DISTRIBUTION

▶ Alacer, Unit 2 Acorn Way, Mansfield, Nottinghamshire, NG18 3HD Tel: (01623) 635070 Fax: (01623) 643245 E-mail: sean@alacer.net

▶ Combined Book Services Ltd, Units I-K, Paddock Wood Distribution Centre, Paddock Wood, Tonbridge, Kent, TN12 6UU Tel: (01892) 837171 Fax: (01892) 837272 E-mail: info@combook.co.uk

▶ F Lloyd Penley Ltd, Bridge Road, Wrexham Industrial Estate, Wrexham, Clwyd, LL13 9SQ Tel: (01978) 661751 Fax: (01978) 664408

▶ Great Bear Distribution Ltd, Moulton Park Business Centre, Redhouse Road, Moulton Park Industrial Estate, Northampton, NN3 6AQ Tel: (01604) 643648 Fax: (01604) 643649

▶ Norish Ltd, P O Box 255, Dartford, DA1 9AL Tel: (0870) 7351318 Fax: (01322) 303470 E-mail: sales@norish.com

▶ Rollstore, Chatsworth Avenue, Long Eaton, Nottingham, NG10 2FL Tel: 0115-946 3524 E-mail: sales@rollstore.co.uk

▶ Smallwood Storage Ltd, Moss End Farm, Moss End, Smallwood, Sandbach, Cheshire, CW11 2XQ Tel: (01477) 500376 Fax: (01477) 500444 E-mail: info@smallwoodstorage.co.uk

▶ Tenkey Ltd, Elgan House, Ashfield Road Norton, Bury St. Edmunds, Suffolk, IP31 3NJ Tel: (01359) 244250 Fax: (01359) 244250 E-mail: stewart@tenkey.co.uk

▶ Unipart Logistics, Unipart House, Garsington Road, Cowley, Oxford, OX4 2PG Tel: (01865) 383793 Fax: (01865) 383669 E-mail: lyn_mcdowell@unipart.co.uk

▶ Viamaster International Ltd, Valley Farm Way, Leeds, LS10 1SE Tel: 0113-270 0033 Fax: 0113 2707723 E-mail: hroberts@viamaster.co.uk

WAREHOUSING SERVICES, STORAGE

▶ 1st Storage Centres, Stoneygate Close, Gateshead, Tyne & Wear, NE10 0AZ Tel: 0191-469 7777 Fax: 0191-469 7999 E-mail: gateshead@storagecentres.co.uk

A E Parker Ltd, Terminus Road, Chichester, West Sussex, PO19 8TX Tel: (01243) 783319 Fax: (01243) 532617 E-mail: transport@parkerltd.co.uk

A Wilkins & Sons, Unit 1 3 The Elms Centre, Glaziers Lane, Normandy, Guildford, Surrey, GU3 2DF Tel: (01483) 575919 Fax: (01483) 570140

A1 Freight Ltd, Maybells Commercial Estate, Ripple Road, Barking, Essex, IG11 0TP Tel: (020) 8592 1202 Fax: (020) 8593 0291 E-mail: hgrent@onetel.net

Abbey Self Storage, Abbey Business Centre, Ingate Place, London, SW8 3NS Tel: (020) 7627 8000 Fax: (020) 7720 6633

Adams & Adams Ltd, Adams House, Dickerage Lane, New Malden, Surrey, KT3 3SF Tel: (020) 8949 1121 Fax: (020) 8336 1126 E-mail: adamsnewmalden@aol.com

Alpine Storage Ltd, West Road, Old Hooton Airfield, Hooton, Ellesmere Port, CH65 1BR Tel: 0151-327 5651 Fax: 0151-327 7870 E-mail: alpine@mersinet.co.uk

▶ Amh Direct Ltd, Units 3-4 Tannock Street, Kilmarnock, Ayrshire, KA1 4DN Tel: (01563) 522000

Archbold Logistics Ltd, Albert Road, Morley, Leeds, LS27 8TT Tel: 0113-252 2333 Fax: 0113-252 7915 E-mail: enq@archbold.co.uk

▶ Archive & Data Storage Ltd, 7 Northumberland Court, Chelmsford, CM2 6UW Tel: (01245) 461000 Fax: (01245) 467000

Arrowpak Transport & Warehousing Ltd, Norwood Road, Brandon, Suffolk, IP27 0PB Tel: (01842) 812165 Fax: (01842) 813051 E-mail: sales@arrowpak.co.uk

Associated Cold Stores & Transport Ltd, South Humberside Industrial Estate, Grimsby, South Humberside, DN31 2WR Tel: (01472) 240269 Fax: (01472) 240269 E-mail: acoldnsn@acst.co.uk

▶ Autrans (Europe) Ltd, Cherry Blossom Way, Sunderland, SR5 3QZ Tel: 0191-416 1133 E-mail: info@autrans.co.uk

B Vaughan & Partners, 14 Northbourne Avenue, Shanklin, Isle of Wight, PO37 7LT Tel: (01983) 864175 E-mail: mark.harrison@tiscali.co.uk

Baird Lends A Hand Ltd, 75 Beardmore Way, Clydebank, Dunbartonshire, G81 4HT Tel: 0141-952 0962 Fax: 0141-941 2205 E-mail: jb@baird-uk.com

Barnes Of Lincoln Ltd, Fort Barnes, Freeman Road, North Hykeham, Lincoln, LN6 9AP Tel: (01522) 686404 Fax: (01522) 681000

Baylis Distribution Ltd, Billington Road, Leighton Buzzard, Bedfordshire, LU7 9HH Tel: (01525) 375550 Fax: (01525) 850149 E-mail: email@baylislogistics.com

▶ Bemis Associates, 5 Turnpike Close, Grantham, Lincolnshire, NG31 7XU Tel: (01476) 594000 Fax: (01476) 576922

Bishops Move, 1-5 Kelvin Way, Crawley, West Sussex, RH10 9SP Tel: (01293) 512646 Fax: (01293) 550105 E-mail: crawley@bishopsmove.com

Bishops Move (Guildford) Ltd, Unit 3 Riverway Industrial Estate, Portsmouth Road, Peasmarsh, Guildford, Surrey, GU3 1LZ Tel: (01483) 722207 Fax: (01483) 302454 E-mail: gillford@bishopsmove.com

Bishop's Move Industrial & Household, South Road, Brighton, BN1 6SB Tel: (01273) 557423 Fax: (01273) 501295 E-mail: brighton@bishops-move.co.uk

Bishops Move Maidstone, 14 Spa Industrial Park, Longfield Road, Tunbridge Wells, Kent, TN2 3EN Tel: (01892) 530191 Fax: (01892) 540201 E-mail: tunbridgewells@bishopsmove.com

Bower Green Ltd, Dryden Street, Bradford, West Yorkshire, BD1 5ND Tel: (01274) 733537 Fax: (01274) 393511 E-mail: info@bowergreen.co.uk

Bower Green Ltd, Station Road, Norwood Green, Halifax, West Yorkshire, HX3 8QD Tel: (01274) 672450 Fax: (01274) 693136 E-mail: norwood@bowergreen.co.uk

Bridgwater Warehousing Co. Ltd, Colley Lane Industrial Estate, Bridgwater, Somerset, TA6 5LN Tel: (01278) 424921 Fax: (01278) 431168

▶ Bristol Oil Storage Ltd, Royal Edward Dock, Bristol, BS11 9BT Tel: 0117-923 5868 Fax: 0117-923 5854

Britania Leatherbarrows, Building, 105 Aviation Park West, Hurn, Christchurch, Dorset, BH23 6NW Tel: (01202) 495600 Fax: (01202) 581639 E-mail: admin@1eatherbarrows.co.uk

T.H. Brown Ltd, Estate Road No. 1, South Humberside Industal Estate, Grimsby, North East Lincolnshire, DN31 2TA Tel: (01472) 362603 Fax: (01472) 360112 E-mail: admin@thbrown.co.uk

▶ Butchers Removals & Storage Co., 6b Quarry Wood Industrial Estate, Mills Road, Aylesford, Kent, ME20 7NA Tel: (01622) 725888 Fax: (01622) 725219 E-mail: info@butchersremovals.co.uk

C S M Archives Storage & Distribution, Chequers Lane, Dagenham, Essex, RM9 6PR Tel: (020) 8596 0088 Fax: (020) 8596 0099

▶ Charles Tennant & Co., Craighead, Whistleberry Road, Blantyre, Glasgow, G72 0TH Tel: (01698) 717900 Fax: (01698) 717910 E-mail: tennants.scot@dial.pipex.com

Christian Salvessen Industrial Division, Swift House, Lodge Way Industrial Estate, Duston, Northampton, NN5 7TU Tel: (01604) 759900 Fax: (01604) 584101 E-mail: sales@salvesen.com

Clearway Distribution, Triumph Road, Nottingham, NG7 2GA Tel: 0115-924 8484 Fax: 0115-942 3148

Clugston Distribution Services, Brigg Road, Scunthorpe, South Humberside, DN16 1BB Tel: (01724) 855029 Fax: (01724) 270240 E-mail: andrew.hansed@clugston.co.uk

Colin E J Bennett, Bridgend Works, Bridgend, Stonehouse, Gloucestershire, GL10 2BA Tel: (01453) 825090 Fax: (01453) 825868

Con-Lloyd Ltd, Chapter Street, Manchester, M40 2AY Tel: 0161-203 4660 Fax: 0161-205 4518 E-mail: info@con-lloyd.com

Conquest Joinery Co. Ltd, Hacken Lane, Bolton, BL3 1SD Tel: (01204) 520201 Fax: (01204) 361484

Convoys Chatham Ltd Head Office, No 3 Basin, Chatham Docks, Chatham, Kent, ME4 4SR Tel: (01634) 892099 Fax: (01634) 895235 E-mail: enquiries@convoys.co.uk

Cooperative Retail Logistics Ltd, Unit 24, Raleigh Hall Industrial Estate, Eccleshall, Stafford, ST21 6JL Tel: (01785) 850831 Fax: (01785) 851850

Cory Logistics Ltd, 90 Giles Street, Leith, Edinburgh, EH6 6BZ Tel: 0131-554 6631 Fax: 0131-554 8504 E-mail: info@cory.co.uk

D L Packing Ltd, Unit 4 Lawrence Trading Estate, Blackwell Lane, Greenwich, London, SE10 0AR Tel: (020) 8858 3713 Fax: (020) 8293 4578 E-mail: dlpacking@btconnect.com

▶ Darlington Group plc, Bankfields Drive, Wirral, Merseyside, CH62 0AZ Tel: 0151-328 5600 Fax: 0151-328 5605 E-mail: martin@darlingtons-group.co.uk

▶ David Hathaway Ltd, Westerleigh Business Park, 30 Woodward Avenue, Yate, Bristol, BS37 5YS Tel: (01454) 334500 Fax: (01454) 334550 E-mail: contact@davidhathaway.co.uk

▶ Debach Enterprises Ltd, Blue Stem Road, Ransomes Industrial Estate, Ipswich, IP3 9RR Tel: (01473) 270207 Fax: (01473) 719939 E-mail: sales@debach.co.uk

Deltamove Ltd, Clare Terrace, Carterton, Oxfordshire, OX18 3ES Tel: (01993) 845020 Fax: (01993) 843023 E-mail: andy@deltamove.co.uk

Denmans Of Whitchurch, Highgate, Whitchurch, Shropshire, SY13 1SD Tel: (01948) 666611 Fax: (01948) 667723 E-mail: denmanmovers@aol.com

Direct Security Systems Midlands Ltd, 7 Doctors Piece, Willenhall, West Midlands, WV13 1PZ Tel: (01902) 602042 Fax: (01902) 602888 E-mail: service@direct-security.co.uk

E C Logistics, Swallowfield Way, Hayes, Middlesex, UB3 1DQ Tel: (020) 8569 1918 Fax: (020) 8813 6564 E-mail: helpdesk@eclogistics.co.uk

▶ E & S J Walpole Ltd, 64 Causeway Road, Earlstrees Industrial Estate, Corby, Northamptonshire, NN17 4DU Tel: (01536) 201221 Fax: (01536) 406098

▶ E & W Fullertons, Stephenson Street, Hillington Industrial Estate, Glasgow, G52 4NX Tel: 0141-810 1588

E W Taylor & Co Forwarding Ltd, Dunbar House Eurolink Industrial Centre, Castle Road, Sittingbourne, Kent, ME10 3RN Tel: (01795) 410110 Fax: (01795) 410111 E-mail: sharonlambert@ewtaylorgroup.com

Eclipse Motor Transport Co. Ltd, Clay Street, Hull, HU8 8HD Tel: (01482) 320066 Fax: (01482) 586617

▶ Eldencross Ltd, Park Bridge, Ashton-under-Lyne, Lancashire, OL6 8AW Tel: 0161-330 3446 E-mail: info@eldencross.co.uk

▶ Elmbank Logistics, Lodge Road, Sandbach, Cheshire, CW11 3HP Tel: (01270) 758840 Fax: (01270) 758848

ETS Distribution Services, Logistics House, 175 Meadow Lane, Loughborough, Leicestershire, LE11 1NF Tel: (01509) 615050 Fax: (01509) 615067 E-mail: info@etsltd.co.uk

▶ European Van Lines International Ltd, Unit 3 100 Church Street, Staines, Middlesex, TW18 4YA Tel: (01784) 466117 Fax: (01784) 464484 E-mail: info@evl.co.uk

Exel Freight Management UK Ltd, Great South West Road, Feltham, Middlesex, TW14 8NE Tel: (020) 8750 7000 Fax: (020) 8890 8444

Fergusons (Blyth) Ltd, Ennerdale Road, Kitty Brewster Estate, Blyth, Northumberland, NE24 4RD Tel: (01670) 353761 Fax: (01670) 357401 E-mail: sales@fergusonsremovals.co.uk

Ferris Stevedores Ltd, 2 Corry Place, Belfast Harbour Estate, Belfast, BT3 9HY Tel: (028) 9074 8371 Fax: (028) 9074 6500 E-mail: robert@ferris-belfast.freeuk.com

▶ Finspa Storage Handling Ltd, 3 Dewing Road, Rackheath Industrial Estate, Rackheath, Norwich, NR13 6PS Tel: (01603) 722002 Fax: (01603) 720322 E-mail: info@finspa.com

Firmin Coates Ltd, Wares Farm, Redwall Lane, Linton, Maidstone, Kent, ME17 4BB Tel: (01622) 820273 Fax: (01622) 820823 E-mail: afl@alanfirmin.co.uk

Firmin Coates Ltd, The Pines, Fordham Road, Newmarket, Suffolk, CB8 7LG Tel: (01638) 720481 Fax: (01638) 721240 E-mail: i.murfitt@firmincoates.co.uk

Fitzmaurice Carriers Ltd, Avian Way, Salhouse Road, Norwich, NR7 9AJ Tel: (01603) 429277 Fax: (01603) 788562

Flixborough Wharf Ltd, Trent Port House, Flixborough, Scunthorpe, North Lincolnshire, DN15 8RS Tel: (01724) 867691 Fax: (01724) 851207 E-mail: info@flixboroughwharf.co.uk

Fowler Welch Coolchain P.L.C., West Marsh Road, Spalding, Lincolnshire, PE11 2BB Tel: (01795) 580056 Fax: (01795) 980307

Fox Moving & Storage, Block C, Stourbridge Industrial Estate, Mill Race Lane, Stourbridge, West Midlands, DY8 1YL Tel: (01384) 395072 Fax: (01384) 440520 E-mail: stourbridge@fox-moving.com

Francis Willey British Wools 1935 Ltd, Ravenscliff Mills, Ravenscliffe Road, Calverley, Pudsey, West Yorkshire, LS28 5RY Tel: (01274) 612541 Fax: (01274) 613012 E-mail: fw@francis-willey.freeserve.co.uk

▶ Freight Control Services Ltd, Unit 10 Cambrian Industrial Estate East Side, Coedcae Lane, Pontyclun, Mid Glamorgan, CF72 9EW Tel: (01443) 222796 Fax: (01443) 223006

Fuller & Sons Warehouse Ltd, Kelvin Way, West Bromwich, West Midlands, B70 7LH Tel: 0121-553 6211 Fax: 0121-525 9085 E-mail: fullerandsonsltd@aol.com

▶ Furness Logistics UK Ltd, 1 Maidstone Road, Kingston, Milton Keynes, MK10 0BD Tel: (01908) 282870 Fax: (01908) 282872

G Abbott & Co. Ltd, Brenda Road, Hartlepool, Cleveland, TS25 2BJ Tel: (01429) 234841 Fax: (01429) 234445

G B Nationwide Crate Hire Ltd, Heritage House, 345 Southbury Road, Enfield, Middlesex, EN1 1UP Tel: (020) 8219 8180 Fax: (020) 8219 8181 E-mail: moreinfo@gbnationwide.com

G & C Johnson Claxby Ltd, Crosby Grange, Crosby Grange Road, Scunthorpe, South Humberside, DN15 8UH Tel: (01724) 856262 Fax: (01724) 854626 E-mail: gc.johnson@btconnect.com

G & J Ping Ltd, 63 Coates Road, Eastrea, Whittlesey, Peterborough, PE7 2BA Tel: (01733) 203383 Fax: (01733) 351204

G R Warehousing Ltd, Old Station Road, Mendlesham, Stowmarket, Suffolk, IP14 5RT Tel: (01449) 768009 Fax: (01449) 766823 E-mail: mike@grwarehousing.fsnet.co.uk

Gent Transport, Unit 5, Badminton Road, Yate, Bristol, BS37 5NS Tel: (01454) 881000 Fax: (01454) 881122

Gibbs & Ball Ltd, St Margarets Road, South Darenth, Dartford, DA4 9LB Tel: (01322) 862232 Fax: (01322) 864954

▶ Gibson Taylor Tranzol Ltd, Bent Ley Farm, Bent Ley Road, Meltham, Holmfirth, HD9 4AP Tel: (01484) 859293 Fax: (01484) 859339 E-mail: zoltan.gibsontaylor@btconnect.com

Goddard Warehousing Ltd, Compton House, Furnace Lane, Finedon, Wellingborough, Northamptonshire, NN9 5NY Tel: (01536) 726060 Fax: (01536) 726006 E-mail: admin@goddardwarehousing.com

Graysons Freight Services Ltd, Border Freight Terminal, 4 Hollands Road, Haverhill, Suffolk, CB9 8PP Tel: (01440) 762558 Fax: (01440) 707119 E-mail: sales@graysons.net

Great Bear Distribution Ltd, 6 Glendale Park Glendale Avenue, Sandycroft Industrial Estate, Sandycroft, Deeside, Clwyd, CH5 2QP Tel: (01244) 520020 Fax: (01244) 537716

▶ Great Yarmouth Port Co., 20-21 South Quay, Great Yarmouth, Norfolk, NR30 2RE Tel: (01493) 335500 Fax: (01493) 852480 E-mail: gypa@gypa.co.uk

Gregory Distribution Ltd, 118-124 London Road, Amesbury, Salisbury, SP4 7ZS Tel: (01980) 590100 Fax: (01980) 624355 E-mail: amesburytransport@compuserve.com

Gunness Wharf Ltd, Gunness Wharf, Gunness, Scunthorpe, South Humberside, DN15 8SY Tel: (01724) 867691 Fax: (01724) 851207 E-mail: info@flixboroughwharf.co.uk

H W Coates Ltd, Main Street, Cosby, Leicester, LE9 1UW Tel: 0116-284 8403 Fax: 0116-275 0417

H Whittaker & Son Ltd, Heapy Street, Macclesfield, Cheshire, SK11 7JD Tel: (01625) 424637 Fax: (01625) 613470

Harman Warehousing Ltd, Old Aerodrome, Crabtree Lane, High Ercall, Telford, Shropshire, TF6 6AP Tel: (01952) 770266 Fax: (01952) 770116

Haven Warehousing & Distribution Ltd, Sixth Avenue, Flixborough, Scunthorpe, South Humberside, DN15 8SH Tel: (01724) 854735 Fax: (01724) 281687 E-mail: havendst@aol.com

Hoults Removals Ltd, Crown House, Earlsway, Team Valley Trading Estate, Gateshead, Tyne & Wear, NE11 0RQ Tel: 0191-265 3696 Fax: 0191-482 4259 E-mail: houltsremovals@hoults.co.uk

Howard Tenens Andover Ltd, Unit 2c Macadam Way, West Portway, Andover, Hampshire, SP10 3LF Tel: (01264) 324449 Fax: (01264) 332253 E-mail: boston@tenens.com

Howard Tenens Associates Ltd, Kingfisher Business Park, London Road, Thrupp, Stroud, Gloucestershire, GL5 2BY Tel: (01453) 885087 Fax: (01453) 886145 E-mail: enquiries@tenens.com

Howard Tenens Boston Ltd, Riverside Industrial Estate, Marsh Lane, Boston, Lincolnshire, PE21 7SZ Tel: (01205) 311808 Fax: (01205) 354086 E-mail: sales@tenens.com

Howarth Bros Haulage Ltd, Unit 3 Moss Lane, Royton, Oldham, OL2 6HR Tel: (01706) 847514 Fax: (01706) 882607 E-mail: howarth.bros@btinternet.com

WAREHOUSING SERVICES, STORAGE - *continued*

Immingham Railfreight Terminals Ltd, Netherlands Way, Stallingborough, Grimsby, North East Lincolnshire, DN41 8DF Tel: (01469) 576363 Fax: (01469) 571934 E-mail: peterdibdin@tpdibdin.com

Imorex, Dooley Road, Felixstowe, Suffolk, IP11 3HG Tel: (01394) 607743 Fax: (01394) 607767 E-mail: info@imorex.co.uk

Innovative Marketing International Ltd, 21 Dorset Square, London, NW1 6QE Tel: (020) 7723 7228 Fax: (020) 7723 1192 E-mail: enquiries@innovativemarketing.co.uk

The International Moving Co., Unit B1, Stewart Road, Altrincham, Cheshire, WA14 5GR Tel: 0161-876 8844 Fax: 0161-929 8765 E-mail: sthelens@int-moving.com

J B Wheaton & Sons Ltd, Chard Junction, Chard, Somerset, TA20 4QN Tel: (01460) 220531 Fax: (01460) 221456 E-mail: mark.wheaton@jbwheaton.co.uk

J H Davies Haulage Ltd, Foundry Lane, Ditton, Widnes, Cheshire, WA8 8TZ Tel: 0151-420 8877 Fax: 0151-495 1994 E-mail: admin@jhdavies.com

John Evans & Sons Llanelli Ltd, Sandy Road, Llanelli, Dyfed, SA15 4DP Tel: (01554) 773332 Fax: (01554) 759215

▶ John Lewis plc, 2 Mercury Drive, Brackmills Industrial Estate, Northampton, NN4 7PN Tel: (01604) 767676 Fax: (01604) 767775

K L M Storage Ltd, Rushock Trading Estate, Droitwich, Worcestershire, WR9 0NR Tel: (01299) 250885 Fax: (01299) 251450 E-mail: info@klmstorage.com

K & M Hauliers Ltd, The Aerodrome, Watnall Road, Hucknall, Nottingham, NG15 6EN Tel: 0115-963 0630 Fax: 0115-968 0126 E-mail: traffic@kmhauliers.co.uk

Kelly Freight, C Cedars Transport Depot, Church Manorway, Erith, Kent, DA8 1DE Tel: (01322) 430231 Fax: (01322) 463446 E-mail: upn55scott@aol.com

Kent Link Transport & Storage, Unit 18 Henwood Business Centre, Henwood, Ashford, Kent, TN24 8DH Tel: (01233) 638889 Fax: (01233) 635869 E-mail: sales@kentlink.com

Kimberley Distribution Ltd, Wanlip Road, Syston, Leicester, LE7 1PD Tel: 0116-260 2224

Kirkpatrick Holdings Ltd, 88 Arthur Street, Redditch, Worcestershire, B98 8JY Tel: (01527) 522384 Fax: (01527) 517065 E-mail: sales@kirkpatrickcarriers.com

Knowles Transport Ltd, New Road, Wimblington, March, Cambridgeshire, PE15 0RG Tel: (01354) 740233 Fax: (01354) 741333 E-mail: sales@knowles-transport.co.uk

Kuehne & Nagel Ltd, B6 Broadlands, Heywood Distribution Park, Heywood, Lancashire, OL10 2TS Tel: 0161-761 8000 Fax: 0161-761 8001

Kuehne & Nagel UK Ltd, Old Bath Road, Colnbrook, Slough, SL3 0NW Tel: (01895) 552000 Fax: (01753) 762401

L C P Developments Ltd, L C P House, The Pensnett Estate, Kingswinford, West Midlands, DY6 7NA Tel: (01384) 400123 Fax: (01384) 400862

Laceys I O W Ltd, 42 High Street, Bembridge, Isle of Wight, PO35 5SF Tel: (01983) 872663 Fax: (01983) 872575 E-mail: sales@laceysremovals.co.uk

Lambert Brothers Holdings Ltd, Woodside Avenue, Boyatt Wood Industrial Estate, Eastleigh, Hampshire, SO50 4ZR Tel: (023) 8061 7331 Fax: (023) 8062 9261 E-mail: info@lambro.co.uk

Larne Harbour Ltd, 9 Olderfleet Road, Larne, County Antrim, BT40 1AS Tel: (028) 2887 2100 Fax: (028) 2887 2209 E-mail: info@portoflarne.co.uk

Len Lothian U Store, 11 Bankhead Broadway, Edinburgh, EH11 4DB Tel: 0131-538 8200 Fax: 0131-538 8210 E-mail: info@lenlothain.com

Lenham Storage Ltd, Ham Lane, Lenham, Maidstone, Kent, ME17 2LH Tel: (01622) 858441 Fax: (01622) 850469 E-mail: info@lenhamstorage.co.uk

Lenham Storage Southern Ltd, Fyfield Road, Weyhill, Andover, Hampshire, SP11 8DL Tel: (01264) 772166 Fax: (01264) 773431 E-mail: administration@lenhamstoragesouthern.co.uk

The Little Packaging Company Ltd, Unit 10, Athena Avenue, Elgin Industrial Estate, Swindon, SN2 8HH Tel: (01793) 693179 Fax: (01793) 693945 E-mail: littlepackagingco@unidsl.co.uk

Losberger Walter UK, 27 High Street, Collingham, Collingham, Newark, Nottinghamshire, NG23 7LA Tel: (01636) 893776 Fax: (01636) 893774 E-mail: losbergeruk@losberger.com

Lowe Paddock Wood Paddock Wood Cold Storage Ltd, Transfesa Road, Paddock Wood, Tonbridge, Kent, TN12 6UT Tel: (01892) 832436 Fax: (01892) 835028 E-mail: lowepaddockwood@btconnect.com

M & G Express, M & G House, Head Road, Douglas, Isle Of Man, IM1 5BF Tel: (01624) 623841 Fax: (01624) 623004 E-mail: postmaster@mcb.net

▶ Maersk Logistics UK Ltd, Blowfield Road, Felixstowe, Suffolk, IP11 4XQ Tel: (01394) 613206 Fax: (01394) 613207 E-mail: gbrlogsal@maersk-logistics.com

Marshall's Transport (Evesham) Ltd, Long Lane, Throckmorton, Pershore, Worcestershire, WR10 2JH Tel: (01386) 556808 Fax: (01386) 556760 E-mail: brian@marshallsofevesham.co.uk

Maxi Haulage Ltd, Macadam Way, West Portway Industrial Estate, Andover, Hampshire, SP10 3LF Tel: (01264) 361888 Fax: (01264) 332206

Maxi Haulage Ltd, Hawkes Drive, Heathcote Industrial Estate, Warwick, CV34 6LX Tel: (01926) 881192 Fax: (01926) 881937 E-mail: action@maxihaulage.co.uk

Mayer Cohen Industries Ltd, Newtown Industrial Estate, Cross Keys, Newport, Gwent, NP11 7PZ Tel: (01495) 272777 Fax: (01495) 271270

Moonbridge Air Project S A Freight Ltd, Unit 9, Ascot Road, Bedfont, Feltham, Middlesex, TW14 8QH Tel: (01784) 259555 Fax: (01784) 259599 E-mail: administrator@moonbridge.co.uk

Murray Hogg Ltd, Sandy Lane, North Gosforth, North Gosforth, Newcastle Upon Tyne, NE3 5HE Tel: 0191-236 4211 Fax: 0191-236 3189 E-mail: sales@murrayhogg.co.uk

▶ N E M S Ltd, North Moor St, South Dock, Sunderland, SR1 2BQ Tel: 0191-514 5037 Fax: 0191 510 8108 E-mail: sales@nems.uk.com

▶ Naylors Transport (Leyland) Ltd, Comet Road, Moss Side Industrial Estate, Leyland, PR26 7PF Tel: (01772) 424731 Fax: (01772) 621065

Nelsons Transport Keighley Ltd, Bocking Farm, Keighley, West Yorkshire, BD22 9BG Tel: (01535) 642097 Fax: (01535) 647015 E-mail: nelsonstransport@btinternet.com

Norfolk Line, Transit 3, Westbank Road, Belfast, BT3 9JL Tel: (028) 9077 1122 Fax: (028) 9077 2645 E-mail: belfast@norfolkline.com

▶ Norish Plc, Block C, Walton Avenue, Felixstowe, Suffolk, IP11 3HH Tel: (01394) 675700 Fax: 01394 675440 E-mail: sales@norish.com

▶ Norish Ltd, Station Lane, Shipton By Beningbrough, York, YO30 1BS Tel: (01904) 470523 Fax: (01904) 470580 E-mail: sales@norish.com

Oakfield Rubber Co., 480 Hawthorne Road, Bootle, Merseyside, L20 9PP Tel: 0151-933 6266 Fax: 0151-922 8743

Arthur Oakley Transport Ltd, Ramsden Road, Rotherwas Industrial Estate, Hereford, HR2 6LR Tel: (01432) 266662 Fax: (01432) 356660 E-mail: sales@vanoaksteels.co.uk

▶ Octavian Ltd, Eastlays Warehouse, Gastard, Corsham, Wiltshire, SN13 9PP Tel: (01225) 810735 Fax: (01225) 811369

P C Howard Ltd, West Hay, Kings Cliffe, Peterborough, PE8 6XX Tel: (01780) 444444 Fax: (01780) 444744

P F Couriers Ltd, Unit 2, Lowfield Heath Industrial Estate, Crawley, West Sussex, RH11 0PQ Tel: (01293) 515661 Fax: (01293) 547045 E-mail: reception@pfcouriers.co.uk

Parker International Ltd, Globe Lane Industrial Estate, Globe Lane, Dukinfield, Cheshire, SK16 4RE Tel: 0161-330 7421 Fax: 0161-339 2653 E-mail: info@parkerinternational.co.uk

Parkside Warehousing & Transport Co. Ltd, Parkside House, Tomo Industrial Estate, Creeting Road, Stowmarket, Suffolk, IP14 5AY Tel: (01449) 676551 Fax: (01449) 672954

Payne Pallet Inverters Ltd, Dereham Road, Beeston, King's Lynn, Norfolk, PE32 2NQ Tel: (01328) 700138 Fax: (01328) 701879 E-mail: david@paynepalletinverters.co.uk

Pennine Parcels Ltd, Listers Road, Shibden, Halifax, West Yorkshire, HX3 7XA Tel: (01422) 330215 Fax: (01422) 330187 E-mail: robert.rushworth@penparcels.co.uk

Peter D Stirling Ltd, Reema Road, Bellshill, Lanarkshire, ML4 1RR Tel: (01698) 749555 Fax: (01698) 740569

▶ Peters & May Ltd, Prysmian House, Dew Lane, Eastleigh, Hampshire, SO50 9PX Tel: (023) 8048 0501 Fax: (01752) 775699 E-mail: enquiriesplh@petersandmay.com

Porters Of Woking, 5 North Road, Woking, Surrey, GU21 5DS Tel: (01483) 765432 Fax: (01483) 756432 E-mail: sales@portersremovals.co.uk

R Collett & Sons Transport Ltd, Albert Road, Halifax, West Yorkshire, HX2 0DF Tel: (01422) 255233 Fax: (01422) 255244 E-mail: sales@collett.co.uk

Railstore Ltd, Childerditch Lane, West Horndon, Brentwood, Essex, CM13 3ED Tel: (01277) 814600 Fax: (01277) 814609 E-mail: sales@railstore.co.uk

Read & Sutcliffe Ltd, St. Johns Road, Boston, Lincolnshire, PE21 6HG Tel: (01205) 310444 Fax: (01205) 310500 E-mail: info@rsboston.com

Revells Warehousing & Transport, Eastlands Industrial Estate, Leiston, Suffolk, IP16 4LL Tel: (01728) 830849 Fax: (01728) 830849 E-mail: revellsremovals@aol.com

Richman Ring Ltd, Eurolink Way, Sittingbourne, Kent, ME10 3HH Tel: (01795) 427365 Fax: (01795) 428804 E-mail: info@richman-rwg.com

Ripponden Carriers Ltd, Oldham Road, Ripponden, Sowerby Bridge, West Yorkshire, HX6 4ED Tel: (01422) 822266 Fax: (01422) 823882 E-mail: info@rippondencarriers.co.uk

Roadways Container Logistics Ltd, Gartsherrie Road, Coatbridge, Lanarkshire, ML5 2DS Tel: (01236) 504700 Fax: (01236) 504730

▶ Robinsons International Removals, 5 Aquarius Business Park, Priestley Way, London, NW2 7AJ Tel: (020) 8208 8480 Fax: (020) 8208 8488

▶ Ross Chemicals & Storage Co. Ltd, Grange Dock, Grangemouth, Stirlingshire, FK3 8UD Tel: (01324) 474774 Fax: (01324) 485476

Round Oak Rail Terminal Ltd, Round Oak Terminal, Pedmore Road, Brierley Hill, West Midlands, DY5 1LJ Tel: (01384) 263109 Fax: (01384) 265428

RSF Commercial Services Ltd, Unit 24 Walkers Road, Moons Moat North Industrial Estate, Redditch, Worcestershire, B98 9HE Tel: (01527) 598777 Fax: (01527) 598538 E-mail: office@rsfonline.co.uk

Rycon Shipping & Forwarding Ltd, Rycon Warehouse, Rye Harbour Road, Rye, East Sussex, TN31 7TE Tel: (01797) 222747 Fax: (01797) 224535 E-mail: ryecon@btconnect.com

S C C Transport (Devizes) Ltd, London Road, Hopton Estate, Devizes, Wiltshire, SN10 2EU Tel: (01380) 723324 Fax: (01380) 724850

S H S Freight Services Ltd, Unit 20 Riverside Development, Chesterton Road, Eastwood Trading Estate, Rotherham, South Yorkshire, S65 1SU Tel: (01709) 377071 Fax: (01709) 820959 E-mail: davidmaw@aol.com

S & S Distribution, 400 Vale Road, Tonbridge, Kent, TN9 1SW Tel: (01732) 358800 Fax: (01732) 770772 E-mail: traffic@ssdistribution.co.uk

▶ S T Services Ltd, Imperial Dock, Leith, Edinburgh, EH6 7DR Tel: 0131-553 2827

Salvesen Consumer Logistics, Parkhouse Industrial Estate We, Newcastle, Staffordshire, ST5 7DU Tel: (01782) 566099 Fax: (01782) 561184

▶ Seabrook Warehousing Ltd, Unit 2-5 Heath Park Industrial Estate, Freshwater Road, Dagenham, Essex, RM8 1RX Tel: (020) 8548 3540 Fax: (0870) 9901921

Seaham Harbour Dock Co., Cargo Durham Distribution Centre, Seaham, County Durham, SR7 7NZ Tel: 0191-516 1700 Fax: 0191-516 1701 E-mail: info@seahamharbour.com

▶ Select London, 131a Weedington Road, London, NW5 4PQ Tel: (020) 7428 0505 Fax: (020) 7267 0232

▶ Severn Valley Storage Ltd, Alveley Industrial Estate, Alveley, Bridgnorth, Shropshire, WV15 6HG Tel: (01746) 780123 Fax: (01746) 781234E-mail: info@severnvalleystorage.com

Solihull Storage Ltd, Beresford House, Highlands Road, Shirley, Solihull, West Midlands, B90 4ND Tel: 0121-705 2323 Fax: 0121-705 7683 E-mail: sales@storage-removals.co.uk

▶ Spring Distribution Ltd, 14a Blackburn Road, Bathgate, West Lothian, EH48 2EY Tel: (01506) 631875 Fax: (01506) 652245

▶ Stanford Logistics Ltd, Blantyre Industrial Estate, Blantyre, Glasgow, G72 0XB Tel: (01698) 712504 Fax: (01698) 712877 E-mail: sales@stanford-logistics.com

Star Transport & Warehousing Ltd, Brunel Way, Thetford, Norfolk, IP24 1HP Tel: (01842) 752603 Fax: (01842) 765085 E-mail: traffic@star-transport.co.uk

Stiller Group, Boeing Way, Preston Farm Industrial Estate, Stockton-on-Tees, Cleveland, TS18 3TE Tel: (01642) 607777 Fax: (01642) 607711 E-mail: enquiries@stiller.co.uk

Sutch & Searle Shipping Ltd, Highwood Road, Writtle, Chelmsford, CM1 3PT Tel: (01245) 421770 Fax: (01245) 422734 E-mail: keith.davis@sutchanddsearle.com

R. Swain & Sons Ltd, Medway Freight Terminal, Corys Road, Rochester, Kent, ME1 1PZ Tel: (01634) 830531 Fax: (01634) 829318 E-mail: davidmorton@rswain.com

T B Group Ltd, The Arch, Walney Road, Barrow-in-Furness, Cumbria, LA14 5UT Tel: (01229) 870077 Fax: (01229) 811101 E-mail: brady@brady.furness.co.uk

T D G European Chemical Division, Picow Farm Road, Runcorn, Cheshire, WA7 4UW Tel: (01928) 580588 Fax: (01928) 565968

T M Logistics, Edgar House, Berrow Green Road, Martley, Worcester, WR6 6PQ Tel: (01886) 888241 Fax: (01886) 888196

T W Logistics Ltd, The Old Ship Yard, Gainsborough, Lincolnshire, DN21 1NQ Tel: (01427) 614551 Fax: (01427) 613770

Tab Logix Ltd, 200 Milton Park, Abingdon, Oxfordshire, OX14 4TF Tel: (01235) 864818 Fax: (01235) 861275

TDG UK Ltd, High Street, Coleshill, Birmingham, B46 3BP Tel: (01675) 467447 Fax: (01675) 467585

TDG UK Ltd, West Carr Lane, Hull, HU7 0BS Tel: (01482) 839839 Fax: (01482) 839565

Teamsped Ltd, Unit 4 Waterfall La Trading Estate, Cradley Heath, West Midlands, B64 6PU Tel: 0121-561 3886 Fax: 0121-561 3959 E-mail: john@teamsped.co.uk

▶ Teccon Ltd, Dexion House, Attleborough Fields Industrial Estate, Attleborough Fields, Nuneaton, Warwickshire, CV11 6RX Tel: 02476 322880 Fax: 02476 328425 E-mail: sales@tecconltd.co.uk

Teesside Warehousing Ltd, Fleck Way, Teesside Industrial Estate, Stockton-on-Tees, Cleveland, TS17 9JZ Tel: (01642) 762534 Fax: (01642) 765777 E-mail: lisa.pluves@vectoris.co.uk

Tibbett & Britten Group P.L.C., Laverstoke Road, Allington, Maidstone, Kent, ME16 0LE Tel: (01622) 671400 Fax: (01622) 692495

TNT Freight Management, Unit 5 & 6 Park Way Trading Estate, Cranford Lane, Hounslow, TW5 9QA Tel: (020) 8814 7000 Fax: (020) 8814 7078 E-mail: info@uk.tntfreight.com

Tomhead Ltd, 2a Ramsden Road, Rotherwas Industrial Estate, Hereford, HR2 6NP Tel: (01432) 358420 Fax: (01432) 354448 E-mail: info@tomhead.co.uk

Tomsetts Distribution Ltd, North Quay Road, Newhaven, East Sussex, BN9 0AB Tel: (01273) 513347 Fax: (01273) 516042 E-mail: enquiries@tomsetts.com

Total Logistics, Leigh Park, Fulflood Road, Havant, Hampshire, PO9 5AX Tel: (023) 9247 4123 Fax: (023) 9247 0467 E-mail: sales@appliedlogistics.co.uk

Trade Counter Ltd, Unit D Trading Estate Road, London, NW10 7LU Tel: (020) 8385 2753 Fax: (020) 8965 9765 E-mail: ptc@netcomuk.co.uk

Uniex Freight Services, Lodge Way, Thetford, Norfolk, IP24 1HE Tel: (01842) 751751 Fax: (01842) 751665 E-mail: freight@uniex.co.uk

▶ United Distillers & Vintners, Menstrie Bond, Menstrie, Clackmannanshire, FK11 7EP Tel: (01259) 761351

United Supplies Ltd, United House, 6 Regent Road, Aberdeen, AB11 5NS Tel: (01224) 581321 Fax: (01224) 573141

Universal Express Ltd, 139-141 Hamilton Road, Felixstowe, Suffolk, IP11 7BL Tel: (01394) 282867 Fax: (01394) 286767 E-mail: info@universalexpress.co.uk

▶ Viamaster International Ltd, Valley Farm Way, Leeds, LS10 1SE Tel: 0113-270 0033 Fax: 0113 2707723 E-mail: hroberts@viamaster.co.uk

Viking Shipping Services Ltd, Ousegate, Selby, North Yorkshire, YO8 8BL Tel: (01757) 702688 Fax: (01757) 701601 E-mail: sales@vikingshipping.co.uk

▶ W A Humphreys International Transport Ltd, Unit 8 Ely Valley Industrial Estate, Pontyclun, Mid Glamorgan, CF72 9DZ Tel: (01443) 226582 Fax: (01443) 237647

W H Bowker Ltd, Holme Road, Bamber Bridge, Preston, PR5 6BP Tel: (01772) 628800 Fax: (01772) 628801 E-mail: enquiries@bowker.co.uk

▶ Walkden Warehousing Ltd, 3 Orion Trading Estate, Tenax Road, Trafford Park, Manchester, M17 1JT Tel: 0161-848 7684 Fax: 0161-877 5373

J. & W. Watt Ltd, London Road, Carlisle, CA1 2NN Tel: (01228) 522311 Fax: (01228) 511926 E-mail: office@wattstorage.com

We 'R' Storage Ltd, Richmond Street, West Bromwich, West Midlands, B70 0DD Tel: 0121-520 3532 Fax: 0121-522 3862 E-mail: johnlee@werstorage.freeserve.co.uk

Whittall Warehouses Ltd, The Old Court House, Back Lane, Hereford, HR4 8SG Tel: (01544) 318788 Fax: (01544) 318165 E-mail: whittall@wwlgroup.co.uk

▶ Wincanton Logistics Ltd, Wellington Parkway, Magna Park, Lutterworth, Leicestershire, LE17 4XW Tel: (01455) 550444 Fax: (01455) 559060

▶ Wincanton Logistics Ltd, Aston Lane North, Preston Brook, Runcorn, Cheshire, WA7 3GA Tel: (01928) 703500 Fax: (01928) 703555

Woodrush Distribution, Unit 6 Greenfield Road, Pulloxhill, Bedford, MK45 5EY Tel: (01525) 717199 Fax: (01525) 717606 E-mail: sales@woodrush.co.uk

▶ World Freight Centre Ltd, 26 Bond, Europa Way, Trafford Park, Manchester, M17 1WF Tel: 0161-848 0066 Fax: 0161-848 0055 E-mail: sales@worldfreightcentre.com

Wrefords Transport, Ransome Road, Northampton, NN4 8AD Tel: (01604) 761429 Fax: (01604) 768764 E-mail: sales@swwreford.co.uk

WARM AIR CENTRAL HEATING SYSTEMS

Carmen Plumbing & Heating, 20 The Borough, Aldreth, ELY, Cambs, CB6 3PJ Tel: 01223 655367 Fax: 01223 280298 E-mail: carmenltd@msn.com

▶ Classic Heating Services, 103 Station Road, Sutton Coldfield, West Midlands, B73 5LA Tel: 0121-355 1782 E-mail: ian@walklett.freeserve.co.uk

▶ The Gasworks Company UK Ltd, 24 Baycliff Drive, Dalton-in-Furness, Cumbria, LA15 8XE Tel: (07841) 342298 Fax: (01229) 768266 E-mail: support@thegasworkscompany.co.uk

WARP DRESSERS/SIZERS, TEXTILE

Howorths Nelson, Manor Mill, Hallam Road, Nelson, Lancashire, BB9 8DN Tel: (01282) 612382 Fax: (01282) 695130 E-mail: howorthsnelson@btconnect.com

WARP KNITTED FABRICS

Frederick Beardsley & Co. Ltd, 1 Cotmanhay Road, Ilkeston, Derbyshire, DE7 8HR Tel: 0115-932 4502 Fax: 0115-944 1298 E-mail: sales@frederickbeardsley.com

Clarkson Knitting Ltd, Western Industrial Estate, Lon-Y-Llyn, Caerphilly, Mid Glamorgan, CF83 1XJ Tel: (029) 2086 1411 Fax: (029) 2086 0127 E-mail: paulslevin@clarksonknitting.com

Simplex Knitting Ltd, Bye Pass Road, Beeston, Nottingham, NG9 5HN Tel: 0115-925 4980 Fax: 0115-943 0772 E-mail: enquiries@simplexknittingcompany.ltd.uk

Small & Tidmas Ltd, Vicarage Street, Barnstaple, Devon, EX32 7HA Tel: (01271) 375972 Fax: (01271) 379753 E-mail: info@smallandtidmas.co.uk

WARP KNITTED FABRICS – *continued*

W Ball & Son Holdings Ltd, Albion Works, Burr Lane, Ilkeston, Derbyshire, DE7 5JD Tel: 0115-932 2403 Fax: 0115-944 0630 E-mail: sales@baltex.co.uk

WASHABLE KITCHEN GREASE AIR FILTERS

C P L Filters, Unit 1-2 Alma Industrial Estate, Regent Street, Rochdale, Lancashire, OL12 0HQ Tel: (01706) 642823 Fax: (01706) 642537 E-mail: dorothy.clarke@pure-filters.com

Vianen Ventilation Systems, Coten House, 59-63 Coten End, Warwick, CV34 4NU Tel: (01926) 496644 Fax: (01926) 493977 E-mail: info@vianen.co.uk

WASHERS, *See also headings for particular types*

A & J Fasteners, 19 Manor Trading Estate, Brunel Road, Benfleet, Essex, SS7 4PS Tel: (01268) 566422 Fax: (01268) 566422

A1 Survey Ltd, 1 Cefn Graig, Rhiwbina, Cardiff, CF14 6SW Tel: (029) 2091 5858 Fax: (029) 2091 5858 E-mail: sales@a1survey.net

Allfix Ltd, 2 Leyland Road, Poole, Dorset, BH12 5HB Tel: (01202) 519066 Fax: (01202) 518353 E-mail: sales@allfix.co.uk

Bluemay Weston, Cooks Cross, South Molton, Devon, EX36 4AW Tel: (01769) 574574 Fax: (01769) 512944 E-mail: sales@bluemayweston.co.uk

Buckinghamshire Fastener Co. Ltd, 14 Wilverley Road, Christchurch, Dorset, BH23 3RU Tel: (01202) 488202 Fax: (01202) 474442 E-mail: sales@buckfastener.co.uk

Fasteners & Engineering Supplies Ltd, 5 Westgate, South Cowbridge, South Glamorgan, CF71 7AQ Tel: (01446) 774888 Fax: (01446) 773778 E-mail: sales@f-e-s.co.uk

Industrial Trading Co. Ltd, PO Box 51, Worcester, WR1 1QE Tel: (01905) 20373 Fax: (01905) 27158

J G Ross & Co Components Ltd, 19b Pershore Trading Estate, Station Road, Pershore, Worcestershire, WR10 2DD Tel: (01386) 552140 Fax: (01386) 555628 E-mail: info@jgross.co.uk

Rafseal Ltd, Millers Avenue, Brynmenyn Industrial Estate, Brynmenyn, Bridgend, Mid Glamorgan, CF32 9TD Tel: (01656) 725118 Fax: (01656) 724520 E-mail: rafseal@btclick.com

Stones Bros, Garratt Street, Brierley Hill, West Midlands, DY5 1JU Tel: (01384) 79888 Fax: (01384) 77966

Universal Manufacturing Supplies, 25 Whitehorse Street, Baldock, Hertfordshire, SG7 6QB Tel: (01462) 892277 Fax: (01462) 892277

J.J. Williams (Gaskets) Ltd, 1 Beresford Road, Whitstable, Kent, CT5 1JP Tel: (01227) 265522 Fax: (01227) 770146 E-mail: enquiries@jjwilliams.co.uk

WASHING MACHINE COMPONENTS, SPARE PARTS OR WEARING PARTS

Alton Electrical Services, 25-27 Southview Rise, Alton, Hampshire, GU34 2AB Tel: (01420) 86194 Fax: (01420) 86194

Bargain Buys, 35 Shafto Way, Newton Aycliffe, County Durham, DL5 5QN Tel: (01325) 321678

Brassware Sales Ltd, Unit 5 Junction 6 Industrial Park, 66 Electric Avenue, Witton, Birmingham, B6 7JJ Tel: 0121-327 1234 Fax: 0121-327 4066

▶ Dave Quirk Washing Machine, Unit 4 St. Michaels Industrial Estate, Widnes, Cheshire, WA8 8TL Tel: 0151-424 0539 E-mail: info@davequirkwashingmachines.com

M D Phillips Appliances, 44 Hackenden Close, East Grinstead, West Sussex, RH19 3DS Tel: (01342) 314670 Fax: (01342) 325445

▶ Masterpart, 4 Grainger Road, Southend-on-Sea, SS2 5BZ Tel: (01702) 310031 Fax: (01702) 312000 E-mail: sales@masterpart.com

WASHING MACHINES, BAR/ HOTEL/CATERING GLASSWARE

Clenal Ware Systems, Farnham Trading Estate, Farnham, Surrey, GU9 9NN Tel: (01252) 712789 Fax: (01252) 723719 E-mail: info@clenalware.com

▶ Magnetron Catering Equipment, 5-21 Carrock Road, Croft Business Park, Bromborough, Wirral, Merseyside, CH62 3RA Tel: (0870) 8400720 Fax: (08708) 740721 E-mail: sales@catmag.fsnet.co.uk

WASHING MACHINES, BOX/ CRATE/TRAY

FJS Services, Westfield Road, Manea, March, Cambridgeshire, PE15 0LN Tel: (01354) 680752 Fax: (01354) 680176

Gimson Ltd, 30 Boston Road, Leicester, LE4 1AU Tel: 0116-236 8688 Fax: 0116-236 3663 E-mail: a_sims@gimsoneng.co.uk

WASHING MACHINES, FOOD/ BEVERAGE INDUSTRY

Haith-Tickhill Group, Cowhouse Lane, Armthorpe, Doncaster, South Yorkshire, DN3 3EE Tel: (01302) 831911 Fax: (01302) 300173 E-mail: sales@haith.co.uk

Microdat Automation Co Uk Ltd, Unit2, Benyon Park Way, Leeds, LS12 6DP Tel: 0113-244 5225 Fax: 0113-244 5226 E-mail: info@microdat.co.uk

WASHING SODAS

East Lancashire Chemical Co. Ltd, Edge Lane, Droylsden, Manchester, M43 6AU Tel: 0161-371 5585 Fax: 0161-301 1990 E-mail: info@eastlancschemical.com

WASHROOM AIR FRESHENER INSTALLATION

▶ Cibshygiene.com, 211 Picadilly, London, W1J 9HF Tel: (0800) 0757890 Fax: (0870) 3452511 E-mail: sales@ci-bs.com

▶ Swisher (Bath), Unit Mill Road Ind Estate, Radstock, BA3 5TX Tel: 01761 436791 E-mail: contact@swisherbath.co.uk

WASHROOM EQUIPMENT

Armitage Venesta Washroom Systems Ltd, Imperial Business Estate, West Mill, Gravesend, Kent, DA11 0DL Tel: (01474) 353333 Fax: (01474) 533558 E-mail: info@armitage-venesta.co.uk

Central Hygiene Ltd, Unit 4e Brymau Three Trading Estate, River Lane, Saltney, Chester, CH4 8RQ Tel: (01244) 675066 Fax: (01244) 680129 E-mail: sales@central-hygiene.co.uk

▶ Cibshygiene.com, 211 Picadilly, London, W1J 9HF Tel: (0800) 0757890 Fax: (0870) 3452511 E-mail: sales@ci-bs.com

Colmart Marketing Ltd, Vulcan Rd, Lode Lane Industrial Estate, Solihull, W. Midlands, B91 2JY Tel: 0121-705 4645 Fax: 0121-711 2051 E-mail: sales@lslmarketing.co.uk

F C Frost Ltd, 7 Benfield Way, Braintree, Essex, CM7 3YS Tel: (01376) 329111 Fax: (01376) 347002 E-mail: sales@fcfrost.com

FOCUS Washrooms, Unit 9, Fieldings Road, Cheshunt, Waltham Cross, Hertfordshire, EN8 9TL Tel: (01992) 625990

Maxwood, Bodmin Road, Wyken, Coventry, CV2 5DB Tel: (024) 7662 1122

Ophardt Product UK Ltd, 18 Shaftesbury St South, Derby, DE23 8YH Tel: (01332) 297666 Fax: (01332) 343354 E-mail: sales@ophardt.com

Petal Postforming Ltd, Drumharvey, Irvinestown, Enniskillen, County Fermanagh, BT94 1ET Tel: (028) 6862 1766 Fax: (028) 6862 1004 E-mail: sales@petalgroup.com

Protech Fabrications Ltd, Rushden Road, Milton Ernest, Bedford, MK44 1RU Tel: (01234) 826233 Fax: (01234) 822762 E-mail: info@protech-food-systems.co.uk

Teal Patents Ltd, 2 Chelmsley Wood Industrial Estate, Waterloo Avenue, Birmingham, B37 6QQ Tel: 0121-770 4017 Fax: 0121-770 0385 E-mail: enquiries@tealwash.com

WASHROOM EQUIPMENT, HAND CLEANER PUMP

▶ Millennium Hygiene Services, Unit 20 Longton Business Park, Station Road, Little Hoole, Preston, PR4 5LE Tel: (0870) 7669119 Fax: (0870) 7665119 E-mail: office@mhsuk.com

WASHROOM HYGIENE SERVICES

Brooks Bourne Venture, Manning Road, Bourne, Lincolnshire, PE10 9EU Tel: (01778) 394900 Fax: (01778) 394218

Initial, Botany Brow, Chorley, Lancashire, PR6 0HX Tel: (01257) 272311 Fax: (01257) 233575

Intersplash Ltd, 14 London House, Canons Corner, Edgware, Middlesex, HA8 8AX Tel: (020) 8958 2002 Fax: (020) 8958 1810

Personalised Services, 18-20 Boundaries Road, Balham, London, SW12 8HU Tel: (020) 8675 3313 Fax: (020) 8675 7042

Principal Hygine System, Unit B4 Hilton Trading Estate, Hilton Road, Lanesfield, Wolverhampton, WV4 6DW Tel: (01902) 404550 Fax: (01902) 353455 E-mail: sales@principalhygiene.com

Vacman Specialist Cleaning, Budmhor, Portree, Isle of Skye, IV51 9DJ Tel: (01478) 613111 Fax: (01478) 613321 E-mail: info@vacman.co.uk

WASHROOM LIQUID SOAP DISPENSERS

Appor Ltd, Duffield Road Industrial Estate, Little Eaton, Derby, DE21 5EG Tel: (01332) 832455 Fax: (01332) 834427 E-mail: info@appor.com

Diversey Lever Equipment Ltd, 4 Finway, Dallow Road, Luton, LU1 1TR Tel: (01582) 702100 Fax: (01582) 702171

KWC UK Ltd, 149 Balham Hill, London, SW12 9DJ Tel: (020) 8675 9335 Fax: (020) 8675 8568 E-mail: kwcuk@globalnet.co.uk

Ophardt Product UK Ltd, 18 Shaftesbury St South, Derby, DE23 8YH Tel: (01332) 297666 Fax: (01332) 343354 E-mail: sales@ophardt.com

WASHROOM SOAP DISPENSERS

Diversey Lever Equipment Ltd, 4 Finway, Dallow Road, Luton, LU1 1TR Tel: (01582) 702100 Fax: (01582) 702171

Johnson Service Group, Johnson House, Monks Way, Preston Brook, Runcorn, Cheshire, WA7 3GH Tel: 0151-933 6161 Fax: (01928) 704620

WASHROOMS

FOCUS Washrooms, Unit 9, Fieldings Road, Cheshunt, Waltham Cross, Hertfordshire, EN8 9TL Tel: (01992) 625990

WASTE AND ENVIRONMENTAL LAW TRAINING

Key Consultancy Ltd, 277 Birmingham Road, Bromsgrove, Worcestershire, B61 0EP Tel: (01527) 575182 Fax: (01527) 576288 E-mail: sales@thekeyconsultancy.co.uk

WASTE COLLECTION, CONFIDENTIAL

▶ Premier Shredding Ltd, Unit 3J, North Road, Marchwood Industrial Park, Marchwood, Southampton, SO40 4BL Tel: (023) 8086 8888 Fax: (023) 8086 7475 E-mail: sales@premiershredding.co.uk

WASTE DISPOSAL CONTAINERS

Chad Containers Ltd, Burrell Way, Thetford, Norfolk, IP24 3QS Tel: (01842) 763583 Fax: (01842) 750055

Chemsafe Containers Ltd, Higher Merley Lane, Corfe Mullen, Wimborne, Dorset, BH21 3EG Tel: (01202) 881502 Fax: (01202) 841282 E-mail: chemsafe@iswgroup.co.uk

Marshall Cooke Ltd, Burrell Way, Thetford, Norfolk, IP24 3RW Tel: (01842) 764312 Fax: (01842) 761033 E-mail: sales@marshallcooke.com

Egbert H Taylor & Co. Ltd, Oak Park, Rylands Lane, Elmley Lovett, Droitwich, Worcestershire, WR9 0QZ Tel: (01299) 251333 Fax: (01299) 254142 E-mail: custserv@taylor-ch.co.uk

Empteezy Ltd, Alpha House, 4 Muir Road, Houstoun Industrial Estate, Livingston, West Lothian, EH54 5DR Tel: (01506) 430309 Fax: (01506) 441466 E-mail: sales@empteezy.co.uk

▶ Envirogreen Special Waste Services, 765 Henley Road, Slough, SL1 4JW Tel: (0845) 7125398 Fax: (01753) 537314 E-mail: info@envirogreen.co.uk

Firber Engineering Ltd, Sidings Road, Lowmoor Business Park, Kirkby-in-Ashfield, Nottingham, NG17 7JZ Tel: (01623) 757794 Fax: (01623) 688990 E-mail: sales@firber.co.uk

Nu Mac Steel Ltd, Temple Hill Road, Newry, County Down, BT34 2LR Tel: (028) 3026 8332 Fax: (028) 3025 2828 E-mail: sales@numac.co.uk

Sellers Engineering Ltd, Sellers Way, Chadderton, Oldham, OL9 8EY Tel: 0161-681 5846 Fax: 0161-683 5621

Skip Units Ltd, Industrial Estate, Sinfin Lane, Derby, DE24 9GL Tel: (01332) 761361 Fax: (01332) 270013 E-mail: sales@skipunits.co.uk

Tweeny, Kingfisher House, Wheel Park, Westfield, Hastings, East Sussex, TN35 4SE Tel: (07004) 893369 Fax: (01424) 751444 E-mail: sales@tweeny.co.uk

WASTE DISPOSAL SYSTEMS/ PLANT, COMPLETE

Bollegraaf UK Ltd, 93-96 William Street, West Bromwich, West Midlands, B70 0BG Tel: 0121-557 9700 Fax: 0121-557 9800 E-mail: info@bollegraaf.co.uk

▶ Hardall International Ltd, Fairway Works, Southfields Road, Dunstable, Bedfordshire, LU6 3EP Tel: (01582) 500860 Fax: (01582) 690975 E-mail: sales@hardall.co.uk

Hydro Dynamic Products Ltd, Unit 2-3, Harbour Way, Shoreham-by-Sea, West Sussex, BN43 5HZ Tel: (01273) 464881 Fax: (01273) 464626 E-mail: sales@hdp.co.uk

Integrated Recycling Systems Ltd, Burnt Meadow Road, North Moons Moat, Redditch, Worcestershire, B98 9PA Tel: (01527) 65432 Fax: (01527) 65868 E-mail: info@mastermagnets.co.uk

WASTE DISPOSAL UNIT ENGINEERS, INSTALLATION OR SERVICE, ELECTRIC

F A Saunders & Son, 32 Franklyn Road, Canterbury, Kent, CT2 8PS Tel: (01227) 457241 Fax: (01227) 768136 E-mail: roberttwymp@aol.com

F R C Services, Coxby House, Bottom Street, Northend, Southam, Warwickshire, CV47 2TH Tel: (01295) 770027 Fax: (01295) 770048 E-mail: richard.bracewell@ukonline.co.uk

▶ Halton Container Services, 6 Waterloo Centre, Waterloo Road, Widnes, Cheshire, WA8 0PR Tel: 0151-420 0092 Fax: 0151-420 0092 E-mail: hcsl@merseymail.com

Q Mac, 13 Bencroft, Cheshunt, Waltham Cross, Hertfordshire, EN7 6BE Tel: (020) 8804 6666 Fax: (020) 8804 1313 E-mail: qmac@btinternet.com

WASTE DISPOSAL, PAINT

▶ BCB Environmental Management Ltd, Liverpool Road, Eccles, Manchester, M30 7HZ Tel: (0870) 2432341 Fax: 08702 432389 E-mail: sales@bcbenvironmental.co.uk

WASTE DISPOSAL/RECOVERY/ RECYCLING CONTRACTOR/ PROCESSORS, INDUSTRIAL, *See also specialist services*

A M G, Lower Trinity Street, Birmingham, B9 4AG Tel: 0121-772 3551 Fax: 0121-455 9301

A1 Waste Disposal Co. Ltd, Eastways, Witham, Essex, CM8 3YU Tel: (01376) 515615 Fax: (01376) 515616 E-mail: admin@a1demolition.co.uk

Adas Gleadthorpe Grange, Gleadthorpe, Meden Vale, Mansfield, Nottinghamshire, NG20 9PF Tel: (01623) 844331 Fax: (01623) 844472

▶ Advanced Recycling Solutions Ltd, The Factory Boswithian Road, Tolvaddon, Camborne, Cornwall, TR14 0EJ Tel: (01209) 611898 Fax: (01209) 712888 E-mail: sales@ars-chs.co.uk

Ahern Waste Management Services Ltd, 10-11 Heron Court, Cranes Farm Road, Basildon, Essex, SS14 3DF Tel: (01268) 533535 Fax: (01268) 293141 E-mail: enquiries@ahern.co.uk

Alco Waste Management Ltd, Joseph Noble Road, Lillyhall Industrial Estate, Lillyhall, Workington, Cumbria, CA14 4JH Tel: (01900) 602205 Fax: (01900) 601886

ASM Metal Recycling Ltd, Griffin Lane, Aylesbury, Buckinghamshire, HP19 8BB Tel: (01296) 337711 Fax: (01296) 337751 E-mail: asm@asm-recycling.co.uk

Barnes E A & Sons Ltd, Unit 5, Vulcan Road, Lichfield, Staffordshire, WS13 6RW Tel: (01543) 250480 Fax: (01543) 250480 E-mail: sales@eabarnes.co.uk

Beolia Enviromental Services plc, 154a Pentonville Road, London, N1 9PE Tel: (020) 7812 5000 Fax: (020) 7812 5026 E-mail: edward.demaslatrie@veolia.co.uk

Biffa Holdings Ltd, Coronation Road, Cressex, High Wycombe, Buckinghamshire, HP12 3TZ Tel: (0800) 307307 E-mail: marketing@biffa.co.uk

Biffa Waste Services Ltd, Gavell Road, Twechar, Kilsyth, Glasgow, G65 9LP Tel: (01236) 821607 Fax: (01236) 822007

Biffa Waste Services Ltd, Boiling Plant, Stoneferry Road, Hull, HU8 8BZ Tel: (01482) 322311 Fax: (01482) 322321

Biffa Waste Services Ltd, Private Road 2, Colwick Industrial Estate, Nottingham, NG4 2JR Tel: 0115-961 6424 Fax: 0115-940 0102

Biffa Waste Services Ltd, Potters Lane, Wednesbury, West Midlands, WS10 7NR Tel: 0121-502 5500 Fax: 0121-505 2120 E-mail: wednesbury@biffa.co.uk

Big John Rubbish Removals, 25 Lister Road, Dudley, West Midlands, DY2 8JR Tel: (01384) 232359

W.M. Briers & Son (Tamworth) Ltd, Anchor Siding, Glascote Road, Tamworth, Staffordshire, B77 2AN Tel: (01827) 62668 Fax: (01827) 53721 E-mail: equiries@wmbriers.co.uk

Brisco Waste Disposal Ltd, 87 Ystrad Road, Fforestfach, Swansea, SA5 4BU Tel: (01792) 584585 Fax: (01792) 586811

Brook Street Metal Co. Ltd, Bridge Street, Bury, Lancashire, BL9 6HH Tel: 0161-764 4950 Fax: 0161-764 4619

C H C Waste Facilities Management, Blackwell, Bromsgrove, Worcestershire, B60 1BE Tel: 0121-445 3344 Fax: 0121-445 3245 E-mail: infodesk@chcwastemgt.co.uk

WASTE DISPOSAL/RECOVERY/ RECYCLING CONTRACTOR/ PROCESSORS, INDUSTRIAL – continued

C H Middleton Ltd, 65-71 Sprotbrough Road, Doncaster, South Yorkshire, DN5 8BW Tel: (01302) 783731 Fax: (01302) 390024 E-mail: c.h.middleton@btconnect.com

C T Composites, 2 Industrial Estate, Kempshott Park, Beggarwood, Basingstoke, Hampshire, RG23 7LP Tel: (01256) 396400 Fax: (01256) 397664 E-mail: sales@ctcomposites.co.uk

L. Capstick, Middlegate, White Lund Industrial Estate, Morecambe, Lancashire, LA3 3BN Tel: (01524) 63141 Fax: (01524) 846173

Central Waste Oil Collections Ltd, 143 Queen Street, Walsall, WS2 9NT Tel: (01922) 725966 Fax: (01922) 721966

Chad Containers Ltd, Burrell Way, Thetford, Norfolk, IP24 3QS Tel: (01842) 763583 Fax: (01842) 750055

Collier Industrial Waste Ltd, Nash Road, Trafford Park, Manchester, M17 1SX Tel: 0161-848 7722 Fax: 0161-872 9906

Colt Industrial Services Ltd, Colt Business Park, Witty Street, Hull, HU3 4TT Tel: (01482) 214244 Fax: (01482) 215037 E-mail: sales@colt.co.uk

▶ Computer Salvage Specialist Ltd, 5 Abex Road, Newbury, Berkshire, RG14 5EY Tel: (01635) 552666 Fax: (01635) 582990 E-mail: enquiries@computersalvagespecialists.com

D B I Ailsa, 33-35 McFarlane Street, Paisley, Renfrewshire, PA3 1FE Tel: 0141-887 0666 Fax: 0141-889 8765 E-mail: into@dbigroup.co.uk

Dunstable Waste Group Ltd, Townsend Farm Indust Estate, Blackburn Road, Houghton Regis, Dunstable, Bedfordshire, LU5 5DD Tel: (01582) 476600 Fax: (01582) 664117 E-mail: admin@dwg.uk.com

Envirosol Ltd, Unit 28 Thornleigh Trading Estate, Dudley, West Midlands, DY2 8UB Tel: (01384) 241808 Fax: (01384) 237519 E-mail: sales@envirosol.co.uk

Evans Skip Hire, Park Lane, Halesowen, West Midlands, B63 2RA Tel: (01384) 412289 Fax: (01384) 412289 E-mail: sales@evansskips.com

F & R Cawley Ltd, 1 Covent Garden Close, Luton, LU4 8QB Tel: (01582) 492694 Fax: (01582) 847453 E-mail: sales@frcawley.co.uk

George Blackett Skip Hire, Brunswick Industrial Estate, Brunswick Village, Newcastle upon Tyne, NE13 7BA Tel: 0191-236 7509 Fax: 0191-217 0176

Grundon Waste Ltd, Lakeside Industrial Estate, Colnbrook By Passage, Colnbrook, Slough, SL3 0EG Tel: (01753) 686777 Fax: (01753) 686002

H A Z Environmental, Bullock Street, West Bromwich, West Midlands, B70 7HE Tel: 0121-580 3055 Fax: 0121-580 3056 E-mail: mail@haz-enviro.co.uk

H Wicks Lindel, Park Road, Sowerby Woods Industrial Estat, Barrow-in-Furness, Cumbria, LA14 4QR Tel: (01229) 432114 Fax: (01229) 432056 E-mail: sales@wicksgroup.co.uk

Alan Hadley Ltd, Colthrop Lacolthrop Business Park, Thatcham, Berkshire, RG19 4NB Tel: 0118-988 3266 Fax: 0118-988 4538 E-mail: waste@hadleys.co.uk

Hales Waste Control Ltd, Coronation Road, Cressex Business Park, High Wycombe, Buckinghamshire, HP12 3TZ Tel: (01494) 521221 Fax: (01992) 640212 E-mail: marketing@biffa.co.uk

Hamworthy P.L.C., Fleets Corner, Poole, Dorset, BH17 0JT Tel: (01202) 662600 Fax: (01202) 662636 E-mail: info@hamworthy.com

Hereford Metal Recycling, Units 109-110 Holmer Trading Estate, College Road, Hereford, HR1 1JS Tel: (01432) 269154

Hills Waste Sollutions Ltd, Ailesbury Court, High Street, Marlborough, Wiltshire, SN8 1AA Tel: (01672) 516999 Fax: (01672) 516699

Holden Environmental Ltd, Shore Road, Perth, PH2 8BH Tel: (01738) 634747 Fax: (01738) 637150 E-mail: sales@holden-enviro.com

Robert Hopkins & Son Ltd, Bullock Street, West Bromwich, West Midlands, B70 7HE Tel: 0121-553 0403 Fax: 0121-525 6448

Hurn Waste Oil Ltd, 20 Winkham Business Park, Shaftesbury, Dorset, SP7 9QJ Tel: (01747) 858561 Fax: (01747) 858562 E-mail: oilwaterltd@hotmail.com

I V S International Ltd, 715 New Hey Road, Huddersfield, HD3 3YL Tel: (01422) 310333 Fax: (01422) 310332 E-mail: sales@ivsinternational.co.uk

Interserve Site Services, Brickyard Road, Aldridge, Walsall, WS9 8YP Tel: (01922) 749000 Fax: (01922) 745973 E-mail: siteservices@interserveprojects.com

Irish Waste Services Ltd, 94-96 Hillsborough Road, Carryduff, Belfast, BT8 8HT Tel: (028) 9081 0000 Fax: (028) 9081 0001 E-mail: info@irishwaste.net

J F Lloyd & Son, Nottingham Road, Ashby-de-la-Zouch, Leicestershire, LE65 1DR Tel: (01530) 413347 Fax: (01530) 560264

Kappa Paper Recycling, Private Road 2, Colwick Industrial Estate, Nottingham, NG4 2JR Tel: 0115-961 1753 Fax: 0115-940 0102

D.P. Kelly (Holdings) Ltd, Nether Handley, Sheffield, S21 5RP Tel: (01246) 451167 Fax: (01246) 451167

E.H. Lee Ltd, Holly House, New Road, Woodston, Peterborough, PE2 9HB Tel: (01733) 554853 Fax: (01733) 897024 E-mail: info@ehlee.co.uk

Mil Tek Environmental Ltd, 3 Queens Close, Oswestry, Shropshire, SY11 2JA Tel: (01691) 670891E-mail: sales@pressingsolutions.co.uk

J. & M. Murdoch & Son Ltd, Crofthead Industrial Estate, Lochlibo Road, Neilston, Glasgow, G78 3NE Tel: 0141-580 6322 Fax: 0141-580 6323 E-mail: info@jmmurdoch.com

Mustdestroy.Com, Unit 1 Invicta Centre, Alfreds Way, Barking, Essex, IG11 0BA Tel: (020) 8591 7900 Fax: (020) 8591 7901

North Sea Compactors, 7 Logman Centre, Greenbank Cresent, East Tullos Industrial Estate, Aberdeen, AB12 3BG Tel: (01224) 248455 Fax: (01224) 248454 E-mail: nscompac@netcomuk.co.uk

Onyx Ltd, Unit 10a Greenway, Bedwas House Industrial Estate, Bedwas, Caerphilly, Mid Glamorgan, CF83 8DW Tel: (029) 2088 5897 Fax: (029) 2086 0228

Onyx Environmental Group P.L.C., 154A Pentonville Road, London, N1 9PE Tel: (020) 7812 5000 Fax: (020) 7812 5001

Owen Skip Hire, Lingard Lane, Bredbury Park Industrial Estate, Bredbury, Stockport, Cheshire, SK6 2RN Tel: 0161-430 5650 Fax: 0161-430 5650 E-mail: owenskiphire@tiscalli.co.uk

P & R Disposal Services, 117 Clydesdale Place, Leyland, PR26 7QS Tel: (01772) 454129 Fax: (01772) 622258 E-mail: sales@distillex.xo.uk

Colin Parsons & Sons Ltd, Heywood Bridge, Mucklow Hill, Halesowen, West Midlands, B62 8DL Tel: 0121-550 7531 Fax: 0121-585 5341

Porthmadog Skip Hire, Penamser Industrial Estate, Porthmadog, Gwynedd, LL49 9NZ Tel: (07979) 506624 Fax: (01766) 515217 E-mail: welshskips@supanet.com

Premier Waste Management Ltd, Prospect House, Aykley Heads, Durham, DH1 5TS Tel: 0191-384 4000 Fax: 0191-384 5869

Roy E Wheeler, Holly House, High Street, Moorsholm, Saltburn-by-the-Sea, Cleveland, TS12 3JH Tel: (01287) 660625 Fax: (01287) 660625 E-mail: roycatwheeler@telco4u.net

S I T A Ltd, D12 Red Scar Industrial Estate, Longridge Road, Ribbleton, Preston, PR2 5NQ Tel: (01772) 703100 Fax: (01772) 703111

S W S Ltd, Thomlinson Road, Hartlepool, Cleveland, TS25 1NS Tel: (01429) 864320 Fax: (01429) 864320 E-mail: sws.waste@themail.co.uk

Safety Kleen UK Ltd, 2 Broughton Industrial Estate, Broughton Mills Road, Bretton, Chester, CH4 0BY Tel: (01244) 660184 Fax: (01244) 661338

Shanks Waste Solutions, Loughborough Road, Bunny, Nottingham, NG11 6QN Tel: 0115-945 6069 Fax: 0115-940 5170

Sims Metal Management, Long Marston, Stratford-upon-Avon, Warwickshire, CV37 8AQ Tel: (01789) 720431 Fax: (01789) 720940 E-mail: info.uk@simsmm.com

Sita, Wallsend Road, North Shields, Tyne & Wear, NE29 7SH Tel: 0191-257 8426 Fax: 0191-296 3402

Sita Security Shredding, Sinon House, The Hyde, Lower Bevendean, Brighton, BN2 4JE Tel: (01273) 699969 Fax: (01273) 690999

Solvents With Safety Ltd, Plumtree Road, Bircotes, Doncaster, South Yorkshire, DN11 8EW Tel: (01302) 711733 Fax: (01302) 711744 E-mail: sales@solventswithsafety.co.uk

South Herts Waste Management Ltd, 12 Barbers Road, Stratford, London, E15 2PH Tel: (020) 8519 5622 Fax: (020) 8519 8269 E-mail: info@shwm.co.uk

Stutley Bros Ltd, Elms Depot, Stevenage Road, Little Wymondley, Hitchin, Hertfordshire, SG4 7HZ Tel: (01438) 354495 Fax: (01438) 354495 E-mail: stutleybros@aol.com

T P M Services, 39 Downland Drive, Crawley, West Sussex, RH11 8QZ Tel: (07836) 795835 Fax: (01293) 413084

Terra Eco Systems, Bracknell Sewage Treatment, Hazelwood Lane, Binfield, Bracknell, Berkshire, RG42 5NE Tel: 0118-964 0301 Fax: 0118-964 0333

UK Oils Birmingham Ltd, 115-119 Wainwright Street, Birmingham, B6 5TG Tel: 0121-328 8770 Fax: 0121-326 9770 E-mail: uk.oils@btconnect.com

Uxbridge Skip Hire Ltd, Harvil Road, Harefield, Uxbridge, Middlesex, UB9 6JW Tel: (01895) 257639 Fax: (01895) 810329 E-mail: sales@uxbridgeskiphire.co.uk

Valve Grove, Unit 15 16 Withy Road Industrial Estate, Withy Road, Bilston, West Midlands, WV14 0RX Tel: (01902) 498560 Fax: (01902) 498474

Viridor Waste Management Ltd, Great Western House, Station Approach, Taunton, Somerset, TA1 1QW Tel: (01823) 721400 Fax: (01823) 334027

▶ Viridor Waste Management Ltd, 42 Kings Hill Avenue, Kings Hill, West Malling, Kent, ME19 4AJ Tel: (01732) 229200

Walter Roofing Contractors Ltd, Paper Mill End, Aldridge Road, Great Barr, Birmingham, B44 8NH Tel: 0121-331 4441 Fax: 0121-356 8271

Donald Ward Ltd, Moira Road, Woodville, Swadlincote, Derbyshire, DE11 8DG Tel: (01283) 217192 Fax: (01283) 212515

White Reclamation Ltd, New Hall Farm, Liverpool Road, Eccles, Manchester, M30 7LJ Tel: 0161-789 3268 Fax: 0161-707 5909 E-mail: mail@thewhitegroup.co.uk

Worlds End Waste, Pensbury Place, London, SW8 4TP Tel: (020) 8874 8130 Fax: (020) 7720 9159

WASTE DRUM OR TANK DISPOSAL

Clear Wise, 41 Cresswell Road, Newbury, Berkshire, RG14 2PQ Tel: (01635) 48196 Fax: (01635) 48196

▶ Envirogreen Special Waste Services, 765 Henley Road, Slough, SL1 4JW Tel: (0845) 7125398 Fax: (01753) 537314 E-mail: info@envirogreen.co.uk

Soptralentz UK Ltd, Ravell Drum Works, Gelderd Road, Leeds, LS12 6DL Tel: 0113-263 8573 Fax: 0113-263 7842 E-mail: ken@peaserecycling.co.uk

WASTE EXTRACTION SYSTEMS OR PLANT

▶ Delta Neu Ltd, Newby Road Industrial Estate, Newby Road, Hazel Grove, Stockport, Cheshire, SK7 5DR Tel: 0161-456 5511 Fax: 0161-456 2460

WASTE EXTRACTION SYSTEMS/ PLANT, COMPLETE

M & Y Air Systems Ltd, Twickenham Trading Centre, Rugby Road, Twickenham, TW1 1DN Tel: (020) 8892 8893 Fax: (020) 8891 6175 E-mail: sales@myairsystems.fsnet.co.uk

WASTE FIRED COMBUSTION/ ENERGY CONSERVATION EQUIPMENT

Flare Products Ltd, 14 Broadmead Business Park, Broadmead Road, Stewartby, Bedford, MK43 9NX Tel: (01234) 767755 Fax: (01234) 768624 E-mail: stuartalansimpson@btopenworld.com

WASTE HANDLING MACHINERY

K.K. Balers Ltd, Victory House, Victory Park Road, Addlestone, Surrey, KT15 2AX Tel: (01932) 852423 Fax: (01932) 847170 E-mail: sales@kkbalers.com

Bernard Mccartney Ltd, Unit 2 National Trading Estate, Bramhall Moor Lane, Hazel Grove, Stockport, Cheshire, SK7 5AA Tel: 0161-456 0102 Fax: 0161-483 5399 E-mail: mccartney@macpactor.co.uk

The Boughton Group, Graycar Business Park, Barton Turn, Barton under Needwood, Burton-on-Trent, Staffordshire, DE13 8EN Tel: (01283) 711771 Fax: (01283) 711669 E-mail: enquiries@reynoldsboughton.com

▶ Holt JCB Ltd, Third Way, Avonmouth, Bristol, BS11 9ZG Tel: 0117-982 7921 Fax: 0117-982 1028 E-mail: becky.selby@holtjcb.co.uk

L J H Group Ltd, Leigh Road, Chantry, Frome, Somerset, BA11 3LR Tel: (01373) 836451 Fax: (01373) 836879 E-mail: sales@ljhgroup.co.uk

Meiller Maintenance Service Ltd, 99 Saffron Drive, Oakwood, Derby, DE21 2SW Tel: (01332) 678334 Fax: (01332) 727736 E-mail: meiller@oakwood.fs.business.co.uk

O Kay Engineering Services Ltd, Valley Way, Market Harborough, Leicestershire, LE16 7PS Tel: (01858) 435500 Fax: (01858) 435511 E-mail: sales@okay.co.uk

WASTE MANAGEMENT, INTEGRATED

▶ Total Waste Management, Vatster, Gott, Shetland, ZE2 9SG Tel: (01595) 840431 Fax: (01595) 840703

WASTE MANAGEMENT, OFFICE

▶ Wastecycle Ltd, Private Road 4, Colwick Industrial Estate, Nottingham, NG4 2JT Tel: 0115-940 3111 Fax: 0115-940 4141 E-mail: sales@wastecycle.co.uk

WASTE OIL COLLECTION

▶ Pelican Fine Foods, 6 St. Johns Lane, Bewdley, Worcestershire, DY12 2QZ Tel: (01299) 400598 Fax: (01299) 404090 E-mail: pelican@wasteoil.co.uk

WASTE PAPER COLLECTION SERVICES

▶ Prima Recycling, 7 D2 Trading Estate, Castle Road, Sittingbourne, Kent, ME10 3RH Tel: (01795) 439307 Fax: (01795) 437344 E-mail: webhouse@primapaper.co.uk

WASTE PAPER EXPORT MERCHANTS OR AGENTS

A P G Atlantic Paper Ltd, 7 Earls Court Square, London, SW5 9BY Tel: (020) 7373 3132 Fax: (020) 7373 3880 E-mail: bruce@wastepaper.com

▶ WPT (UK) Ltd., One Canada Square, 28th Floor, Canary Wharf, London, E14 5DY Tel: 020 7956 8697 Fax: 020 7956 8666 E-mail: info@wpt-uk.com

WASTE PAPER HANDLING EQUIPMENT

▶ Rovert Equipment Co. Ltd, Rovert House, Water Tower Road, Clayhill Light Industrial Park, Neston, CH64 3US Tel: 0151-336 2122 Fax: 0151-336 8997 E-mail: david@rovert.co.uk

WASTE PAPER MANAGEMENT

▶ Bradford Skip Hire, Cottingley Moor Road, Bingley, West Yorkshire, BD16 1UU Tel: (01274) 733999 Fax: (01274) 546343

▶ Prima Recycling, 7 D2 Trading Estate, Castle Road, Sittingbourne, Kent, ME10 3RH Tel: (01795) 439307 Fax: (01795) 437344 E-mail: webhouse@primapaper.co.uk

▶ Wastecycle Ltd, Private Road 4, Colwick Industrial Estate, Nottingham, NG4 2JT Tel: 0115-940 3111 Fax: 0115-940 4141 E-mail: sales@wastecycle.co.uk

WASTE PAPER MERCHANTS/ PROCESSORS/RECYCLERS

A J Thompson, Studlands Park Industrial Estate, Newmarket, Suffolk, CB8 7AU Tel: (01638) 664517 Fax: (01638) 664517

Alibone Recycling Ltd, Sandy Hill Lane, Moulton, Northampton, NN3 7JB Tel: (01604) 644963 Fax: (01604) 492685 E-mail: info@paperwaste.co.uk

Anglia Recycling Ltd, Crow Hall Farm, Northfield Road, Soham, Ely, Cambridgeshire, CB7 5UF Tel: (01353) 624004 Fax: (01353) 723888 E-mail: sales@angliarecycling.co.uk

C & J Blackburn, West End Mills, Watergate Road, Dewsbury, West Yorkshire, WF12 9QB Tel: (01924) 465958 Fax: (01924) 454155 E-mail: carol@cjblackburn.co.uk

Capital Waste Paper Ltd, Dayton Drive, Darent Industrial Park, Erith, Kent, DA8 2LE Tel: (01322) 350555 Fax: (01322) 351758 E-mail: capitalwastepaper@tiscali.co.uk

L. Capstick, Middlegate, White Lund Industrial Estate, Morecambe, Lancashire, LA3 3BN Tel: (01524) 63141 Fax: (01524) 846173

Elsa Waste Paper Ltd, Unit 1 Station Road, Reddish, Stockport, Cheshire, SK5 6YZ Tel: 0161-432 3984 Fax: 0161-442 3105

John W. Hannay & Co. Ltd, Linwood Avenue, East Kilbride, Glasgow, G74 5NE Tel: (01355) 225455 Fax: (01355) 231463 E-mail: sales@hannay.co.uk

Holborn Waste Ltd, Massie Works, 305 A -335 Lichfield Road, Aston, Birmingham, B6 7ST Tel: 0121-327 1046 Fax: 0121-327 3968 E-mail: hwsales@btconnect.com

Hollands Recycling Ltd, 1 Holland Park, Bentley Road South, Wednesbury, West Midlands, WS10 8LN Tel: 0121-526 2454 Fax: 0121-568 6148 E-mail: enquiries@hollands-recycling.co.uk

Keeble Paper Recycling Ltd, Paper Recycling Centre, Ferry Lane, Rainham, Essex, RM13 9DB Tel: (01708) 528000 Fax: (01708) 521991 E-mail: recycle@kpr.co.uk

M & B Haulage & Waste Paper Co. Ltd, Low Mill Lane, Dewsbury, West Yorkshire, WF13 3LX Tel: (01924) 494240 Fax: (01924) 480574

M W White Ltd, Station Lane, Hethersett, Norwich, NR9 3AZ Tel: (01603) 812898 Fax: (01603) 812838 E-mail: enquiries@mwwhite.co.uk

Martock Waste Paper Co. Ltd, Great Western Road, Martock, Somerset, TA12 6HB Tel: (01935) 823101 Fax: (01935) 826612 E-mail: martockwp@aol.com

Perrys Recycling, Rimpton Road, Marston Magna, Yeovil, Somerset, BA22 8DL Tel: (01935) 850111 Fax: (01935) 851555 E-mail: sam@perrys-recycling.co.uk

Robert Hough (Fibres) Ltd, 50-52 Thomas Road, London, E14 7BJ Tel: (07976) 558234 Fax: (020) 7537 2838 E-mail: enquiries@robert-hough.u-net.com

S C A Recycling UK Ltd, Lakeside Wharf, South Heighton, Newhaven, East Sussex, BN9 0HW Tel: (01273) 513863 Fax: (01273) 512030

Sca Recycling UK, Sca Packaging House, 543 New Hythe Lane, Aylesford, Kent, ME20 7PE Tel: (01622) 883000 Fax: (01622) 790905

Severnside Recycling, The Pines, Heol-Y-Forlan, Cardiff, CF14 1AX Tel: (029) 2061 5871 Fax: (029) 2069 2120 E-mail: enquire@severnside.com

Severnside Recycling, Unit 6 Bamfurlong Industrial Park, Staverton, Cheltenham, Gloucestershire, GL51 6SX Tel: (01452) 855767 Fax: (01452) 713197 E-mail: justin@severnside.com

WASTE PAPER MERCHANTS/ PROCESSORS/RECYCLERS – *continued*

Severnside Recycling UK, Folds Road, Bolton, BL1 2SW Tel: (01204) 372700 Fax: (01204) 372707 E-mail: bpbrecyclinguk@msn.com

Shirleys Ltd, Canterbury Street, Blackburn, BB2 2HP Tel: (01254) 59361 Fax: (01254) 697600

Sita Recycling Services Ltd, Unit 34 Coneygre Industrial Estate, Tipton, West Midlands, DY4 8XP Tel: 0121-522 2216 Fax: 0121-522 2942

Sivyer Waste Management, Unit D2 Kent Kraft Industrial Estate, Lower Road, Northfleet, Gravesend, Kent, DA11 9SR Tel: (01322) 386265

Charles Storer Ltd, Coopers Lane, Northaw, Potters Bar, Hertfordshire, EN6 4NE Tel: (01707) 656261 Fax: (01707) 652919 E-mail: chasstorer@freeuk.com

WASTE RECLAMATION OR DISPOSAL OR MANAGEMENT CONSULTANCY, *See also Specialised Services and Waste Products*

Bernard Mccartney Ltd, Unit 2 National Trading Estate, Bramhall Moor Lane, Hazel Grove, Stockport, Cheshire, SK7 5AA Tel: 0161-456 0102 Fax: 0161-483 5399 E-mail: mccartney@macpactor.co.uk

Biffa Waste Services Ltd, Rixton Old Hall, Manchester Road, Rixton, Warrington, WA3 6EW Tel: 0161-775 1011 Fax: 0161-775 7291

Bristol Tank Ltd, Princess House, Princess Street, St Philips, Bristol, BS2 0RR Tel: 0117-954 0838 Fax: 0117-954 0839 E-mail: bristoltank@aol.com

Clearway Disposals Ltd, 41 Dobbin Road, Portadown, Craigavon, County Armagh, BT62 4EY Tel: (028) 3833 7333 Fax: (028) 3833 6716 E-mail: info@clearwaypordesign.ffs.uk

Collier Industrial Waste Ltd, Nash Road, Trafford Park, Manchester, M17 1SX Tel: 0161-848 7722 Fax: 0161-872 9906

European Metals Recycling Ltd, Willows, Station Road, East Tilbury, Tilbury, Essex, RM18 8QR Tel: (01375) 856902 Fax: (01375) 843880

Evans Skip Hire, Park Lane, Halesowen, West Midlands, B63 2RA Tel: (01384) 412289 Fax: (01384) 412289 E-mail: sales@evansskips.com

Grundon Waste Ltd, Lakeside Industrial Estate, Colnbrook By Passage, Colnbrook, Slough, SL3 0EG Tel: (01753) 686777 Fax: (01753) 686002

▶ Hazwaste Environmental Ltd, 30 Minster Drive, Urmston, Manchester, M41 5HA Tel: 0161-748 4750 Fax: 0161-748 4750 E-mail: sales@hazwaste.co.uk

J Doyle Ltd, PO Box 33, Bolton, BL1 2QS Tel: (01204) 527008 Fax: (01204) 364002 E-mail: j.doyle@hargreaveshamilton.co.uk

C. Porter Ltd, Britannia Road, Waltham Cross, Hertfordshire, EN8 7PE Tel: (01992) 713565 Fax: (01992) 712980

Raw Chemical Distribution, Morton Peto Road, Harfreys Industrial Estate, Great Yarmouth, Norfolk, NR31 0LT Tel: (01493) 443223 Fax: (01493) 443177 E-mail: sales@rawchem.co.uk

Safety Kleen UK Ltd, 9-10 Arkwright Road Industrial Estate, Arkwright Road, Bedford, MK42 0LQ Tel: (01234) 341292 Fax: (01234) 349200

Sita South Gloucestershire Ltd, Grenfell Road, Maidenhead, Berkshire, SL6 1ES Tel: (01628) 513100 Fax: (01628) 513101

Solvwaste Environmental Ltd, Cogdean Elms Industrial Estate, Higher Merley Lane, Corfe Mullen, Wimborne, Dorset, BH21 3EG Tel: (01202) 840084 Fax: (01202) 841282 E-mail: sales@iswgroup.co.uk

Veolia Enviromental Services plc, Norwood Industrial Estate, Ellisons Road, Killamarsh, Sheffield, S21 2DR Tel: 0114-247 9000 Fax: 0114-247 9018 E-mail: info@onyxgroup.co.uk

Wastefile UK, Radford House, Stafford Park 7, Telford, Shropshire, TF3 3BQ Tel: (01952) 292000 Fax: (01952) 299984 E-mail: admin@wastefile.com

Yph Waste Management Ltd, Lufton Park, Lufton Way, Lufton Trading Estate, Lufton, Yeovil, Somerset, BA22 8HP Tel: (01935) 412211 Fax: (01935) 411963

WASTE RECYCLING OR PROCESSING PLANT AND EQUIPMENT

B J D Crushers Ltd, B B I Centre, Innovation Way, Wilthorpe, Barnsley, South Yorkshire, S75 1JL Tel: (01226) 241425 Fax: (01226) 296713 E-mail: sales@bjdcrushers.co.uk

Blackburn Products Co. Ltd, Whalley Banks, King Street, Blackburn, BB2 1NU Tel: (01254) 51655 Fax: (01254) 51740

▶ Brown & Mason Ltd, New Loom House, 101 Back Church Lane, London, E1 1LU Tel: (020) 7264 1120 Fax: (020) 7481 8244 E-mail: b&m@brownandmason.ltd.uk

Copa Ltd, Copa House, Crest Industrial Estate, Pattenden Lane, Marden, Tonbridge, Kent, TN12 9QJ Tel: (01622) 833900 Fax: (01622) 831466 E-mail: enquiries@copa.co.uk

▶ DJB Recycling Machinery Ltd, 37 Cotswold Road, Sheffield, S6 4QY Tel: 0114-233 3058 Fax: 01142 333058

E C T Commercial Ltd, 112 Burcott Road, Severnside Trading Estate, Avonmouth, Bristol, BS11 8AF Tel: 0117-982 3825 Fax: 0117-982 4666 E-mail: commercial@ectrecycling.co.uk

East Riding Sacks Ltd, Full Sutton Industrial Estate, Stamford Bridge, Full Sutton, York, YO41 1HS Tel: (01759) 371366 Fax: (01759) 372125 E-mail: sales@eastridingsacks.co.uk

▶ enviro-pc.com, Unit2 Duncote Mill, Walcot, Telford, Shropshire, TF6 5ER Tel: (01952) 740200

Eurogreen Machinery, The Tythe Barn, North Barn Farm, Titnore Lane, Worthing, West Sussex, BN12 6NZ Tel: (01903) 700678 Fax: (01903) 247585 E-mail: admin@eurogreenuk.com

Finlay Hydrascreens, 6 Gillygooly Road, Omagh, County Tyrone, BT78 5PN Tel: (028) 8224 5127 Fax: (028) 8224 4294 E-mail: sales@terexfinlay.com

Freedmans Ltd, 7-8 Ashburton Terrace, London, E13 0JB Tel: (020) 8472 1357 Fax: (020) 8472 1303 E-mail: freedmanbalers@talk21.com

General Bridge & Engineering Ltd, Fleming Road, Earlstrees Industrial Estate, Corby, Northamptonshire, NN17 4SW Tel: (01536) 205744 Fax: (01536) 402456 E-mail: email@genbridge.fsnet.co.uk

Integrated Recycling Systems Ltd, Burnt Meadow Road, North Moons Moat, Redditch, Worcestershire, B98 9PA Tel: (01527) 65432 Fax: (01527) 65868 E-mail: info@mastermagnets.co.uk

Javah Ltd, Warwick Mills, Howard Street, Batley, West Yorkshire, WF17 6JH Tel: (01924) 452156 Fax: (01924) 455015 E-mail: sales@javah.com

Lennox House Holdings Ltd, Beeding Close, Southern Cross Trading Estate, Bognor Regis, West Sussex, PO22 9TS Tel: (01243) 866565 Fax: (01243) 868301 E-mail: enquiries@ggcompacters.co.uk

Clusky McCloskey International Ltd, 47 Moor Road, Coalisland, Dungannon, County Tyrone, BT71 4QB Tel: (028) 8774 0926 Fax: (028) 8774 7242

Mil Tek Scotland Ltd, 16 Monreith Road, Glasgow, G43 2NX Tel: 0141-571 3100 Fax: 0141-571 3200

Miracle Mills Ltd, Knightsdale Road, Ipswich, IP1 4LE Tel: (01473) 742325 Fax: (01473) 462773 E-mail: info@cristy-turner.com

▶ Mountain Skip Hire, The Recycling Centre, Whitley Way, Northfields Industrial Estate, Market Deeping, Peterborough, PE6 8AR Tel: (0800) 0263699 Fax: (0845) 0908112 E-mail: sales@greenmountains.co.uk

▶ Oxplas Ltd, 104 Wycombe Road, Princes Risborough, Buckinghamshire, HP27 0EY Tel: (01844) 342184 Fax: (020) 8181 6050 E-mail: info@oxplas.co.uk

P P S Recovery Systems Ltd, 9 Metrocentre, Welbeck Way, Peterborough, PE2 7WH Tel: (01733) 390029 Fax: (01733) 390031 E-mail: enquiry@pps-ltd.com

Talbotts Biomass Energy Ltd, Tollgate drive, Tollgate Industrial Estate, Stafford, ST16 3HS Tel: (01785) 213366 Fax: (01785) 256418 E-mail: sales@talbotts.co.uk

WASTE RECYCLING SYSTEMS

▶ JMC Recycling Systems, Harrimans Lane, Lenton Lane Industrial Estate, Nottingham, NG7 2SD Tel: 0115-940 9630 Fax: 0115-979 1478 E-mail: neil@jmcrecycling.com

WASTE WATER AERATION SYSTEMS

Environmental Performance Technologies, Clarendon House, 52 Cornmarket Street, Oxford, OX1 3EJ Tel: (01865) 304060 Fax: (01865) 304001 E-mail: st@eptuk.com

WASTE WATER CONSULTANTS

Biffa Waste Services Ltd, Potters Lane, Wednesbury, West Midlands, WS10 7NR Tel: 0121-502 5500 Fax: 0121-505 2120 E-mail: wednesbury@biffa.co.uk

Ellaway Bros, Mill House, Hawford, Worcester, WR3 7SE Tel: (01905) 458704 Fax: (01905) 754143

Environmental Performance Technologies, Clarendon House, 52 Cornmarket Street, Oxford, OX1 3EJ Tel: (01865) 304060 Fax: (01865) 304001 E-mail: st@eptuk.com

WRC plc, Frankland Road, Blagrove, Swindon, SN5 8YF Tel: (01793) 865000 Fax: (01793) 865001 E-mail: solutions@wrcplc.co.uk

WASTE WATER MONITORING EQUIPMENT

Hughes Environmental Services Ltd, 8 High Street, West Molesey, Surrey, KT8 2NA Tel: (020) 8979 7352 Fax: (020) 8979 9400

MD Instruments Ltd, 31 Yarmouth Close, Toothill, Swindon, SN5 8LL Tel: (01793) 433595 Fax: (01793) 644244 E-mail: sales@mdinstruments.co.uk

▶ Precise Solutions, Cote House, Wetheral, Carlisle, CA4 8HZ Tel: (01228) 562234 Fax: (01228) 501923 E-mail: derekjohnston@precise-solutions.co.uk

Rivertrace Engineering Ltd, P Kingsfield Business Centre, Philanthropic Road, Redhill, RH1 4DP Tel: (0870) 7702721 Fax: (0870) 7702722 E-mail: info@rivertrace.com

Suprafilt Ltd, Units 2 Rochdale Industrial Estate, Albion Road, Rochdale, Lancashire, OL11 4JB Tel: (01706) 640909 Fax: (01706) 640683 E-mail: sales@suprafilt.com

WASTE WATER RECOVERY/ TREATMENT PLANT

Copa Ltd, Copa House, Crest Industrial Estate, Pattenden Lane, Marden, Tonbridge, Kent, TN12 9QJ Tel: (01622) 833900 Fax: (01622) 831466 E-mail: enquiries@copa.co.uk

Environmental Performance Technologies, Clarendon House, 52 Cornmarket Street, Oxford, OX1 3EJ Tel: (01865) 304060 Fax: (01865) 304001 E-mail: st@eptuk.com

Hytec Industrie, PO Box 642, Guildford, Surrey, GU2 7WE Tel: (01483) 827065 Fax: (01483) 827075 E-mail: uk@hytec-industrie.com

WASTE WATER RECOVERY/ TREATMENT PLANT CONTRACTORS OR DESIGNERS

Beckart Environmental International Ltd, 62 Upper Way, Upper Longdon, Rugeley, Staffordshire, WS15 1QA Tel: (01543) 493189 Fax: (0870) 3835292 E-mail: beckart.uk@virgin.net

Hytech Water Ltd, Unit 36 Southfield Road Trading Estate, Southfield Road, Nailsea, Bristol, BS48 1JE Tel: (01275) 858386 Fax: (01275) 858387 E-mail: sales@hytech-water.co.uk

WASTE WATER SAMPLING/ RESEARCH SERVICES

Aquamatic Ltd, Mayfield Industrial Park, Liverpool Road, Irlam, Manchester, M44 6GD Tel: 0161-777 6607 Fax: 0161-777 6617 E-mail: admin@aquamatic.ltd.uk

Crowther Clayton Associates, 31 Tennyson Road, London, NW7 4AB Tel: (020) 8959 7376 Fax: (020) 8959 6880 E-mail: info@crowther-clayton.com

Dpus Plus Ltd, Flotta Oil Terminal, Flotta, Stromness, Orkney, KW16 3NP Tel: (01856) 702000 Fax: (01856) 701473 E-mail: admin@opusplus.co.uk

WASTE WATER TREATMENT SYSTEMS, BIOLOGICAL

▶ P I P S, Waterside House, Falmouth Road, Penryn, Cornwall, TR10 8BE Tel: (01326) 372500 Fax: (0871) 9898823

WASTEWATER TREATMENT CHEMICALS

▶ Airmec H2o Ltd, 1360 Aztec West, Almondsbury, Bristol, BS32 4RX Tel: (01454) 275050 Fax: (01454) 275051 E-mail: enquiries@airmec.co.uk

WATCH AND CLOCK CALIBRATING EQUIPMENT

Time Products UK Ltd, Chartwell Drive, Wigston, Leicestershire, LE18 2EZ Tel: (0870) 8508200 Fax: (0870) 8508201 E-mail: info@sekonda.co.uk

WATCH AND CLOCK GLASS

Harrow Watch & Jewellery Clinic, Unit 4 St. Anns Shopping Centre, St. Anns Road, Harrow, Middlesex, HA1 1AS Tel: (020) 8424 2601 Fax: (020) 8424 2601

Lethenian Enterprises, Barnsurges, Mincombe Post, Sidbury, Sidmouth, Devon, EX10 0QP Tel: (01395) 597666 Fax: (01395) 222894

WATCH AND CLOCK MATERIALS OR TOOLS

Gleave & Co., 111-113 St. John Street, London, EC1V 4JA Tel: (020) 7253 1345 Fax: (020) 7253 0447 E-mail: gleaveandco@aol.com

H M Temple & Co. Ltd, 111 Broughton Street, Edinburgh, EH1 3RZ Tel: 0131-556 4791 Fax: 0131-556 3609

Shesto Ltd, 2 Sapcote Trading Centre, 374 High Road, London, NW10 2DH Tel: (020) 8451 6188 Fax: (020) 8451 5450 E-mail: sales@shesto.co.uk

E. Vanner, 63 Radnor Drive, Southport, Merseyside, PR9 9RS Tel: (01704) 226384

WATCH AND CLOCK REPAIRERS TO THE TRADE

Cheltenham Clocks, 16a Lansdown Place Lane, Cheltenham, Gloucestershire, GL50 2LB Tel: (01242) 516022

F W W Brown & Son, 39 Queen Street, Horbury, Wakefield, West Yorkshire, WF4 6LP Tel: (01924) 271696

Frosts Of Clerkenwell Ltd, 60-62 Clerkenwell Road, London, EC1M 5PX Tel: (020) 7253 0315 Fax: (020) 7253 7454

▶ Hubert's Clocks, 9-10 Beatrice Street, Swindon, SN2 1BB Tel: 01793 335752

▶ Oban Precision Instruments, 47 Combie Street, Oban, Argyll, PA34 4HS Tel: (01631) 564330

Topical Time Ltd, 5 Bleeding Heart Yard, London, EC1N 8SJ Tel: (020) 7405 2439 Fax: (020) 7831 4254E-mail: topicaltime@btconnect.com

▶ Topsham Clocks, 28 Fore Street, Topsham, Exeter, EX3 0HD Tel: (01392) 876694

W Haycock, Leys Bank, North Leys, Ashbourne, Derbyshire, DE6 1DQ Tel: (01335) 342395 Fax: (01335) 342395

WATCH BOXES

Arbutus, Unit 14 The Bridgeway Centre, Bridge Road, Wrexham Industrial Estate, Wrexham, Clwyd, LL13 9QS Tel: (01978) 661572 Fax: (01978) 661572 E-mail: jon@arbutus-watch.co.uk

WATCH BRACELETS

J.A. Main Ltd, 20 Portway Road, Oldbury, West Midlands, B69 2BY Tel: 0121-552 2941 Fax: 0121-511 1401E-mail: info@jamain.co.uk

W H Wilmot Ltd, 62 Albion Street, Birmingham, B1 3EA Tel: 0121-236 1729 Fax: 0121-233 4957 E-mail: sales@whwilmot.com

WATCH CASES

Arbutus, Unit 14 The Bridgeway Centre, Bridge Road, Wrexham Industrial Estate, Wrexham, Clwyd, LL13 9QS Tel: (01978) 661572 Fax: (01978) 661572 E-mail: jon@arbutus-watch.co.uk

W H Wilmot Ltd, 62 Albion Street, Birmingham, B1 3EA Tel: 0121-236 1729 Fax: 0121-233 4957 E-mail: sales@whwilmot.com

WATCH CLEANING FLUIDS

Time Products UK Ltd, Chartwell Drive, Wigston, Leicestershire, LE18 2EZ Tel: (0870) 8508200 Fax: (0870) 8508201 E-mail: info@sekonda.co.uk

WATCH DIALS

Time Products UK Ltd, Chartwell Drive, Wigston, Leicestershire, LE18 2EZ Tel: (0870) 8508200 Fax: (0870) 8508201 E-mail: info@sekonda.co.uk

WATCH IMPORT/EXPORT MERCHANTS OR AGENTS

Ablex International Ltd, 113 Warstone Lane, Birmingham, B18 6NZ Tel: 0121-233 1313 Fax: 0121-233 1115 E-mail: admin@ablexuk.com

Peers Hardy (U K) Ltd, Tompion House, 25 Birmingham Road, West Bromwich, West Midlands, B70 6RR Tel: 0121-525 8577 Fax: 0121-500 5276 E-mail: nbaker@peershardy.co.uk

Premier Watch Co. Ltd, 107 The Street, Capel St. Mary, Ipswich, IP9 2EH Tel: (01473) 312123

Rolex Watch Ltd, 19 St. James's Square, London, SW1Y 4JE Tel: (020) 7024 7300 Fax: (020) 7024 7317

Santima International, Globe House, 20-22 Cobb Street, London, E1 7LB Tel: (020) 7377 0166 Fax: (020) 7375 1906 E-mail: info@sanglobe.com

Topical Time Ltd, 5 Bleeding Heart Yard, London, EC1N 8SJ Tel: (020) 7405 2439 Fax: (020) 7831 4254E-mail: topicaltime@btconnect.com

WATCH IMPORT/EXPORT MERCHANTS OR AGENTS – *continued*

Verity Time Co. Ltd, PO Box 188, Tring, Hertfordshire, HP23 6YU Tel: (01442) 828585 Fax: (01442) 826945 E-mail: info@veritytime.co.uk

WATCH MANUFRS, *See also headings under Watches*

Ablex International Ltd, 113 Warstone Lane, Birmingham, B18 6NZ Tel: 0121-233 1313 Fax: 0121-233 1115 E-mail: admin@ablexuk.com

Accurist Watches, Asher House, Blackburn Road, London, NW6 1AW Tel: (020) 7447 3900 Fax: (020) 7447 3946 E-mail: sales@accurist.co.uk

Arbutus, Unit 14 The Bridgeway Centre, Bridge Road, Wrexham Industrial Estate, Wrexham, Clwyd, LL13 9QS Tel: (01978) 661572 Fax: (01978) 661572 E-mail: jon@arbutus-watch.co.uk

▶ Avant Garde, 28 Tadmarton, Downhead Park, Milton Keynes, MK15 9BD Tel: (01908) 675977 Fax: (01908) 675890 E-mail: page@ag-gifts.co.uk

▶ Designer Time, High Street, Bridgnorth, Shropshire, WV16 4DX Tel: (01746) 768444 Fax: (01746) 780870 E-mail: info@Designer-Time.Com

Frederick Allen Ltd, 24 Winchcombe Street, Cheltenham, Gloucestershire, GL52 2LX Tel: (01242) 514869 Fax: (01242) 514869

Frosts Of Clerkenwell Ltd, 60-62 Clerkenwell Road, London, EC1M 5PX Tel: (020) 7253 0315 Fax: (020) 7253 7454

Gill Enterprises, 6 Cobb Street, London, E1 7LB Tel: (020) 7247 1191 Fax: (020) 7247 1077 E-mail: gillent@tinyworld.co.uk

R. Hancocks Watch And Clocks Ltd, 17 Warstone Mews, Warstone Lane, Birmingham, B18 6JB Tel: 0121-236 9368 Fax: 0121-233 1358

F.W. Needham Ltd, 84 Great Hampton Street, Birmingham, B18 6EP Tel: 0121-554 5453 Fax: 0121-554 9859 E-mail: fw-needham@btconnect.com

Optimum Time, PO Box 39, Peterborough, PE6 8BS Tel: (01733) 333324 Fax: (01733) 333324 E-mail: sales@optimumtime.co.uk

Phoenix Straps Ltd, 30 Springfield Gardens, Morganstown, Cardiff, CF15 8LQ Tel: (029) 2084 3677 Fax: (029) 2084 3677 E-mail: phoenixstraps@aol.com

Rolex Watch Ltd, 19 St. James's Square, London, SW1Y 4JE Tel: (020) 7024 7300 Fax: (020) 7024 7317

Rotary Watches, Adia House 84-86 Regent Street, London, W1B 5RR Tel: (020) 7434 5500 Fax: (020) 7434 5548 E-mail: time@rotarywatches.com

Santima International, Globe House, 20-22 Cobb Street, London, E1 7LB Tel: (020) 7377 0166 Fax: (020) 7375 1906 E-mail: info@sanglobe.com

Seiko UK Ltd, S C House, Vanwall Road, Maidenhead, Berkshire, SL6 4UW Tel: (01628) 770001 Fax: (01628) 770655 E-mail: services@seiko.co.uk

Sovereign UK Ltd, 38 Smith Street, Birmingham, B19 3ER Tel: 0121-551 4124 Fax: 0121-445 8413

Time Products UK Ltd, 23 Grosvenor Street, London, W1K 4QL Tel: (020) 7416 4160 Fax: (020) 7416 4161

UK Time Ltd, 1000 Great West Road, Brentford, Middlesex, TW8 9DW Tel: (020) 8326 6900 Fax: (020) 8326 6999 E-mail: sales@timex.com

WATCH STRAPS/BANDS/ BRACELETS

Condor Group Ltd, 700 Great Cambridge Road, Enfield, Middlesex, EN1 3EA Tel: (020) 8370 4300 Fax: (020) 8370 4321 E-mail: sales@condorgrp.com

▶ K Danks, 3 St. Aidans Terrace, Prenton, Merseyside, CH43 8ST Tel: 0151-653 6598 E-mail: ken@thestrapshop.co.uk

J.A. Main Ltd, 20 Portway Road, Oldbury, West Midlands, B69 2BY Tel: 0121-552 2941 Fax: 0121-511 1401E-mail: info@jamain.co.uk

Perfect Leather Sales Ltd, Carmel Works, Chapel Street, Porth, Mid Glamorgan, CF39 0PU Tel: (01443) 757150 Fax: (01443) 757150 E-mail: petervalek@petervalek.worldonline.co.uk

WATCHMAKERS EYEGLASSES

▶ Babla's Jewellers, 517 High Road, Wembley, Middlesex, HA0 2DH Tel: (020) 8900 9229 Fax: (020) 8900 9229 E-mail: info@bablas.co.uk

WATCHMAKERS SCREWDRIVERS

▶ Babla's Jewellers, 517 High Road, Wembley, Middlesex, HA0 2DH Tel: (020) 8900 9229 Fax: (020) 8900 9229 E-mail: info@bablas.co.uk

WATER ANALYSIS/RESEARCH CONSULTANTS/SERVICES

Bristol Scientific Services, 7 Redcross Street, Bristol, BS2 0BA Tel: 0117-903 8666 Fax: 0117-903 8667 E-mail: labmail@sciserv.demon.co.uk

Chiltern Water Management Services, 1 Inkerman Drive, Hazlemere, High Wycombe, Buckinghamshire, HP15 7JJ Tel: (01494) 712831 Fax: (01494) 712831 E-mail: rh@chilternwater.co.uk

Crowther Clayton Associates, 31 Tennyson Road, London, NW7 4AB Tel: (020) 8959 7376 Fax: (020) 8959 6880 E-mail: info@crowther-clayton.com

Global Analysis, Tappers Building, Huddersfield Road, Mirfield, West Yorkshire, WF14 9DQ Tel: (01924) 499776 Fax: (01924) 499325 E-mail: user@globalanalysis.co.uk

Ionics UK Ltd, 3 Mercury Park, Mercury Way, Urmston, Manchester, M41 7LY Tel: 0161-866 9337 Fax: 0161-866 9630

Phoenix Analytical, The Laboratory, 270 London Road, Wallington, Surrey, SM6 7DJ Tel: (020) 8647 0003 Fax: (020) 8647 0004

Proton Water Services Ltd, Knaptoft Hall Farm, Knaptoft, Lutterworth, Leicestershire, LE17 6PA Tel: 0116-279 9030 Fax: 0116-279 9082 E-mail: info@protonwater.com

Seres UK Ltd, 178 Dukes Ride, Crowthorne, Berkshire, RG45 6DS Tel: (01344) 762211 Fax: (01344) 761255

▶ Stansted Laboratories, Unit 9, Riverside Industrial Estate, 27, Thames Road, Barking, Essex, IG11 0ND Tel: (020) 8594 5104 Fax: (020) 8591 8762 E-mail: sales@stanstedlabs.co.uk

UK Technology, 2 Hillside Cottages, Shirenewton, Chepstow, Gwent, NP16 6RU Tel: (01291) 641477

W C S Environmental Ltd, Home Close Stables, Station Road, Iron Acton, Bristol, BS37 9TA Tel: (01454) 227122 Fax: (01454) 227190

WRC plc, Frankland Road, Blagrove, Swindon, SN5 8YF Tel: (01793) 865000 Fax: (01793) 865001 E-mail: solutions@wrcplc.co.uk

WATER BASED PROTECTIVE COATINGS

Teknos (UK) Ltd, Unit E1 Heath Farm, Banbury Road, Swerford, Chipping Norton, Oxfordshire, OX7 4BN Tel: (01608) 683494 Fax: (01608) 683487 E-mail: sales@teknos.co.uk

WATER BOOSTER PUMPS, *See Water Booster etc*

WATER BOOSTER SETS

▶ Albion Water Management Ltd, 30/31 Station Close, Potters Bar, Hertfordshire, EN6 1TL Tel: (01707) 607230 Fax: (01707) 607235 E-mail: water@albiongroup.co.uk

Allan Aqua-Systems Ltd, Allan Aqua House, Sedgwick Rd, Luton, LU4 9DT Tel: (01582) 574048 Fax: (01582) 574293 E-mail: info@allanaqua.co.uk

▶ Pumpac Pump Mnfrs, Unit 16 Pentood Industrial Estate, Cardigan, Dyfed, SA43 3AG Tel: (01239) 621308 Fax: (01239) 614942 E-mail: sales@pumpac.co.uk

Wilo Salmson Pumps Ltd, Centrum 100, Burton-on-Trent, Staffordshire, DE14 2WJ Tel: (01283) 523000 Fax: (01283) 523099 E-mail: sales@wilo.co.uk

WATER CHILLERS

Real Mackay Water Bottling Co., Penyffin, Nantgaredig, Carmarthen, Dyfed, SA32 7LJ Tel: (01267) 290655 Fax: (01267) 290960

Watercoolers (UK) Ltd, Unit 4 Brickfields Industrial Estate, Finway Road, Hemel Hempstead, Hertfordshire, HP2 7QA Tel: (01442) 211121 Fax: (01442) 211171 E-mail: sales@mainlinewater.co.uk

WATER CHLORINATION

Active Water Systems, 122 Newport Road, Caldicot, Monmouthshire, NP26 4BT Tel: (01291) 420012 Fax: (0870) 4294048 E-mail: us@ActiveWater.co.uk

▶ Allied Industrial Services, 1 Withensfield, Wallasey, Merseyside, CH45 7NP Tel: 0151-734 4242 Fax: 0151-734 4242

WATER COMPANIES OR MANAGEMENT SERVICES

Anglian Water, Hendeson House, Lancaster Way, Ermine Business Park, Huntingdon, Cambridgeshire, PE29 6XQ Tel: (01480) 323900 Fax: (01480) 326981

Bristol Water Holdings plc, Bridgwater Road, Bridgwater Road, Bristol, BS99 7AU Tel: 0117-966 5881 Fax: 0117-963 3755 E-mail: corporate.affaires@bristolwater.co.uk

Cambridge Water plc, 90 Fulbourn Road, Cherry Hinton, Cambridge, CB1 9JN Tel: (01223) 706050 Fax: (01223) 214052 E-mail: info@cambridge-water.co.uk

Cinque Ports Water Ltd, 4 Walton Road, Folkestone, Kent, CT19 5QR Tel: (01303) 223773 Fax: (01303) 221675

Dee Valley Water plc, Packsaddle, Wrexham Road, Rhostyllen, Wrexham, Clwyd, LL14 4EH Tel: (01978) 846946 Fax: (01978) 846888 E-mail: contact@deevallygroup.com

Hendry, Glenlatterach Cottage, Birnie, Elgin, Morayshire, IV30 8RR Tel: (01343) 860217 Fax: (01343) 860217

Paul Strachan Consulting Ltd, 30 Turfbeg Drive, Forfar, Angus, DD8 3LH Tel: (01307) 460667 Fax: (0870) 420 3597 E-mail: info@strachanconsulting.co.uk

Severn Trent Water Ltd, 2297 Coventry Road, Birmingham, B26 3PU Tel: 0121-722 4000 Fax: 0121-722 4800 E-mail: customer.relations@severntrent.co.uk

Sutton & East Surrey Water, London Road, Redhill, RH1 1LJ Tel: (01737) 772000 Fax: (01737) 766807 E-mail: sesw@waterplc.com

Tendring Hundred Water Services Ltd, Mill Hill, Manningtree, Essex, CO11 2AZ Tel: (01206) 399200 Fax: (01206) 399212 E-mail: info@thws.co.uk

Three Valleys Water plc, PO Box 48, Hatfield, Hertfordshire, AL10 9HL Tel: (01707) 268111 Fax: (01707) 277333

United Utilities Operational Services Highland Ltd, Dawson House, Great Sankey, Warrington, WA5 3LW Tel: (01925) 234000 Fax: (01925) 233360 E-mail: enquiries@unitedutilities.com

WATER CONSERVATION EQUIPMENT

Aqualogic, Brighton Street, Wallasey, Merseyside, CH44 6QJ Tel: 0151-638 6111 Fax: 0151-638 6777 E-mail: info@aqualogic-wc.com

Marnic Technology Ltd, Station Road, Reddish, Stockport, Cheshire, SK5 6ND Tel: 0161-431 3662 E-mail: sales@marnict.demon.co.uk

Rainharvesting Systems Ltd, Cheltenham Road, Bisley, Stroud, Gloucestershire, GL6 7BX Tel: (01452) 772000 Fax: (01452) 770115 E-mail: sales@rainharvesting.co.uk

WATER COOLED ROLLMAKERS

A T Roberts Ltd, 9-13 Aldenham Road, Watford, WD19 4AB Tel: (01923) 223969 Fax: (01923) 244497 E-mail: info@atroberts.fsnet.co.uk

WATER COOLED TRANSFORMERS UP TO 1.5 MVA

Mitchell Transformers Ltd, 12 Allens Lane, Poole, Dorset, BH16 5DA Tel: (01202) 622361 Fax: (01202) 624369

WATER COOLER (DRINKING) MANUFRS

Acme Refrigeration Ltd, Cunliffe Road, Whitebirk Industrial Estate, Blackburn, BB1 5ST Tel: (01254) 277999 Fax: (01254) 277988 E-mail: email@acmerefrigeration.co.uk

Aquaid, 22 New Lane, Burscough, Ormskirk, Lancashire, L40 8JA Tel: (01704) 891344 Fax: (01704) 891599

▶ Aquaid Liverpool, Bridle Way, Bootle, Merseyside, L30 4UJ Tel: 0151-525 6006 Fax: 0151-525 6116 E-mail: aquaid.liverpool@btconnect.com

▶ Aquaid North London, Unit 9a Rosebery Industrial Park, Rosebery Avenue, London, N17 9SR Tel: (020) 8801 9789 Fax: (020) 8801 9678

Aquaid South Kent, Eythorne Courtshepherdswell Roadeythorne, Eythorne, Dover, Kent, CT15 4AD Tel: (01304) 831122 Fax: (01304) 832244

▶ Aquator Water Coolers, Unit 8, Packhorse Place, Watling Street, Kensworth, Dunstable, Bedfordshire, LU6 3QL Tel: (01582) 842828 Fax: (01582) 842727

Blue Spring, Hanney Road, Steventon, Abingdon, Oxfordshire, OX13 6DJ Tel: (01235) 861000 Fax: (01235) 861999

Cameron Water Ltd, 6 Belgrave Street, Bellshill Industrial Estate, Bellshill, Lanarkshire, ML4 3NP Tel: (01698) 845050 Fax: (01698) 748368

Cascade Springs Water Co, High Furze Farm, St. Breock, Wadebridge, Cornwall, PL27 7LF Tel: (01208) 814544 Fax: (01208) 813064

Chilburne Spring Ltd, Acre House, Kilburn, York, YO61 4AL Tel: (01347) 868181 Fax: (01347) 868151

The Coffee Exchange (Birmingham) Ltd, 654 Holly Lane, Erdington, Birmingham, B24 9PD Tel: 0121-682 2093 Fax: 0121-682 0008

Coolwater (Essex) Ltd, Unit 9,Thurrock Business Centre, Breach Road, West Thurrock, Grays, Essex, RM20 3NR Tel: (01708) 252522 Fax: (01708) 862423 E-mail: info@coolwateressex.co.uk

Crystal Spring Water Co. Ltd, 4050 Chander Court, Oxford Business Park South, Garsington Road, Oxford, OX4 2JY Tel: (01865) 848848 Fax: (01865) 847847 E-mail: customerservice@powwowwaters.com

Culligan International Ltd, Culligan House, Outwood Lane, Coulsdon, Surrey, CR5 3NA Tel: (01737) 550087 Fax: (01737) 550092 E-mail: slcs@culligan.co.uk

▶ Forest Edge Water, Mill Cottage, Beaulieu, Hampshire, SO42 7YG Tel: (01590) 611227 Fax: (01590) 611487

▶ Freshflow Water Coolers, 6 Churchlands Farm Industrial Estate, Bascote Road, Ufton, Leamington Spa, Warwickshire, CV33 9PL Tel: (01926) 613906 Fax: (01926) 614215

▶ Koolatron International, Unit C3 Knights Park, Knight Road Strood, Rochester, Kent, ME2 2LS Tel: (01634) 297383 Fax: (01634) 297374

Maestro International Ltd, 11-17 Powerscroft Road, Sidcup, Kent, DA14 5NH Tel: (020) 8302 4035 Fax: (020) 8302 8933 E-mail: info@maestrointl.co.uk

Mainline (Water Solutions) Ltd, Unit 4 Brickfields Indust Est, Finway Rd, Hemel Hempstead, Hertfordshire, HP2 7QA Tel: (01442) 211121 Fax: (01442) 211171 E-mail: sales@mainlinewater.co.uk

Nestle Waters Pow Wow, Unit 7 Matrix Park, Talbot Road, Segensworth South, Fareham, Hampshire, PO15 5AP Tel: (01329) 849248

Nestle Waters Pow Wow, Unit 6 Circle South, Wharside Way, Trafford, Manchester, M17 1NS Tel: (0845) 6013030 Fax: 0161-877 5258

Nestles Water Powwow, Units D9-D10, Cross Green Industrial Estate, Leeds, LS9 0PF Tel: 0113-380 7050 Fax: 0113-380 7068

Norscot Cooling Services Ltd, 50 Flixton Road, Urmston, Manchester, M41 5AB Tel: 0161-747 0863 Fax: 0161-747 8883 E-mail: sales@norscot-cooling.co.uk

Rydon Springwater UK Ltd, Higher Mills, Crossley Moor Road, Kingsteignton, Newton Abbot, Devon, TQ12 3LE Tel: (01626) 367033 Fax: (01626) 203205

Sparkling Spring Water UK Ltd, Unit M, Progress Road, High Wycombe, Buckinghamshire, HP12 4JD Tel: (01494) 473111 Fax: (01494) 539356

Speedwater Ltd, Silverdale, Glynleigh Road, Hankham, Pevensey, East Sussex, BN24 5BJ Tel: (01323) 761475 Fax: (01323) 760020 E-mail: sales@speedwater.co.uk

Springwater Direct Ltd, 152 Park Road, Kirkcaldy, Fife, KY1 3EP Tel: (01592) 650022 Fax: (01592) 653664

Swithland Spring Water Ltd, Hall Farmmain Streetswithland, Swithland, Loughborough, Leicestershire, LE12 8TQ Tel: (01509) 891189 Fax: (01509) 891189 E-mail: spring.water@btconnect.com

Tasteful Vending (Southern) Ltd, Unit 2, Shirley, Solihull, West Midlands, B90 4FZ Tel: (08707) 517519 Fax: (08707) 517716 E-mail: sales@tasteful-vending.co.uk

Water Systems, 3 Sunnylaw Road, Bridge of Allan, Stirling, FK9 4QD Tel: (01786) 834676 Fax: (01786) 833988

Water Waiter Ltd, Telford Way, Telford Way Industrial Estate, Kettering, Northamptonshire, NN16 8UN Tel: (01536) 310444

WATER COOLER FILTERS

▶ Aquator Water Coolers, Unit 8, Packhorse Place, Watling Street, Kensworth, Dunstable, Bedfordshire, LU6 3QL Tel: (01582) 842828 Fax: (01582) 842727

WATER COOLER INTAKE FILTER SCREENS

Taprogge U K Ltd, Unit 6, Hurlbutt Road, Heathcote Industrial Estate, Warwick, CV34 6TD Tel: (01926) 336614 Fax: (01926) 336617 E-mail: taprogge@taprogge.co.uk

WATER COOLERS

▶ Aquapoint Ltd, 9 Rye Close, York Road Business Park, Malton, North Yorkshire, YO17 6YD Tel: (08700) 555333 Fax: (08700) 555600 E-mail: sales@aquapoint.co.uk

▶ Automatic Retailing (Scotland LTD), Barrmill Road, Galston, Ayrshire, KA4 8HH Tel: (01563) 821900 Fax: (01563) 820329 E-mail: enquires@automaticretail.co.uk

Coolwater (Essex) Ltd, Unit 9,Thurrock Business Centre, Breach Road, West Thurrock, Grays, Essex, RM20 3NR Tel: (01708) 252522 Fax: (01708) 862423 E-mail: info@coolwateressex.co.uk

▶ Crystal Clear Products 2000 Ltd, Grove Cottages, Wormingford Grove, Wormingford, Colchester, CO6 3AJ Tel: (01206) 243700 Fax: (01206) 241806 E-mail: sales@pure-watercoolers.co.uk

▶ Premier Watercoolers Ltd, 17 Ash, Kembrey Park, Swindon, SN2 8UN Tel: (0800) 1955740

▶ indicates data change since last edition

WATER COOLERS – *continued*

▶ Water Smart (NW) Ltd, Unit 5 Imex Spaces, Glenfield Business Park, Philips Road, Blackburn, BB1 5PF Tel: (0845) 4506984 Fax: (01257) 793366 E-mail: watersmart@btinterent.com

WATER COST REDUCTION OR CONSERVATION CONSULTANCY

▶ Lion Consultancy Services, Woodpecker Cottage, Talwrn Road, Legacy, Wrexham, LL14 4ES Tel: (01978) 844397 Fax: (01978) 844397 E-mail: mike@lionconsultancy.com
Nus Consulting Group, Regent House, Queensway, Redhill, RH1 1QT Tel: (01737) 781200 Fax: (01737) 766799 E-mail: service@nusconsulting.co.uk
Rainharvesting Systems Ltd, Cheltenham Road, Bisley, Stroud, Gloucestershire, GL6 7BX Tel: (01452) 772000 Fax: (01452) 770115 E-mail: sales@rainharvesting.co.uk

WATER DAMAGE RESTORATION

▶ Brown's French Polishers, Unit A2 Pixmore Estate, Pixmore Avenue, Letchworth Garden City, Hertfordshire, SG6 1JJ Tel: (01462) 680241 Fax: (01462) 482999 E-mail: info@brownsfrenchpolishing.co.uk
▶ David Price Property Services, Meadow View, Low Cotehill, Carlisle, CA4 0EL Tel: 01228 562632 E-mail: david@priceps.wanadoo.co.uk
▶ Exact Property Services, Unit B10 Moss Industrial Estate, St. Helens Road, Leigh, Lancashire, WN7 3PT Tel: (01942) 684466 Fax: (01942) 671918

WATER DEIONISING EQUIPMENT

Capital Water Treatment Ltd, 79a Lansdowne Road, Croydon, CR0 2BF Tel: (020) 8649 9503 Fax: (020) 8649 9504 E-mail: sales@capitalwater.co.uk

WATER DEMINERALISATION PLANT

A W E Anderson Water Equipment Ltd, R04-R05 Unit Cardiff Bay Business Centre, Titan Road, Cardiff, CF24 5EL Tel: (029) 2049 2848 Fax: (029) 2049 1369 E-mail: sales@aweltd.co.uk
Hydro-X Water Treatment Ltd, Unit 3a Eden Place, Outgang Lane Dinnington, Dinnington, Sheffield, S25 3QT Tel: (01909) 565133 Fax: (01909) 564301 E-mail: office@hydro-x.co.uk
Kinetico UK Ltd, Bridge House, Park Gate Business Centre, Park Gate, Southampton, SO31 1FQ Tel: (01489) 566970 Fax: (01489) 566976 E-mail: info@kinetico.co.uk
Veoilawater Solutions & Technologys, Marlow International, Parkway, Marlow, Buckinghamshire, SL7 1YL Tel: (01494) 887700 Fax: (01628) 897001 E-mail: sales.uk@veoliawater.com

WATER DISTILLATION SYSTEMS

Aquapure Water Treatment Equipment, 9 Richmond Mansions, Denton Road, Twickenham, TW1 2HH Tel: (020) 8892 9010 Fax: (020) 8892 9010 E-mail: info@aquapure.co.uk

WATER ENGINEERS CONSULTANCY OR DESIGN

Aqua Engineering Systems, Unit 4 Whitefield Place, Morecambe, Lancashire, LA3 3EA Tel: (01524) 66512 Fax: (01524) 846397
Beeney & Co. Ltd, Oakville Farm, Easons Green, Blackboys, Uckfield, East Sussex, TN22 5JH Tel: (01825) 840276 Fax: (01825) 840276
Bowen Water Systems, Pasture House, Main Street, Kirkby Malzeard, Ripon, North Yorkshire, HG4 3SD Tel: (01765) 658293 Fax: (01765) 658830
Charles Haswell & Partners Ltd, 3900 Parkside, Birmingham Business Park, Birmingham, B37 7YG Tel: 0121-717 7744 Fax: 0121-717 0902 E-mail: enquiries@severntrent.com
M & B Brick Cutting Services, Old Canal Yard, 52 Reuben Street, Stockport, Cheshire, SK4 1PS Tel: 0161-476 6939 Fax: 0161-429 7896

WATER ENGINEERS INSTALLATION OR SERVICING

Aqua Engineering Systems, Unit 4 Whitefield Place, Morecambe, Lancashire, LA3 3EA Tel: (01524) 66512 Fax: (01524) 846397
Barr + Wray Ltd, 324 Drumoyne Road, Glasgow, G51 4DY Tel: 0141-882 5757 Fax: 0141-882 3690 E-mail: sales@barrandwray.com
Capital Water Treatment Ltd, 79a Lansdowne Road, Croydon, CR0 2BF Tel: (020) 8649 9503 Fax: (020) 8649 9504 E-mail: sales@capitalwater.co.uk
Frazer, Station Road, Hebburn, Tyne & Wear, NE31 1BD Tel: 0191-428 7801 Fax: 0191-483 3628 E-mail: sales.northern@ashworth-frazer.co.uk
G Stow plc, Heathercroft Industrial Estate, Lupton Road, Wallingford, Oxfordshire, OX10 9BS Tel: (01491) 834444 Fax: (01491) 827640 E-mail: gstowplc@btinternet.com
H & H Services, Unit 1 Straw House Farm, Kirkby Road, Ripon, North Yorkshire, HG4 3JU Tel: (01765) 600144 Fax: (01765) 600144
H R Holfeld Belfast Ltd, Altona Road, Lisburn, County Antrim, BT27 5RU Tel: (028) 9267 7523 Fax: (028) 9266 0263
Harpers Weybridge, 135 Stubbington Lane, Fareham, Hampshire, PO14 2NF Tel: (01329) 662293 Fax: (01329) 665518
Hollinger Trenching, Hollinger, Wheatsheaf Road, Henfield, West Sussex, BN5 9AX Tel: (01273) 492220 Fax: (01273) 492220
▶ Mac Mole, East Sutton Road, Headcorn, Ashford, Kent, TN27 9PS Tel: (01622) 891366 Fax: (07836) 250549 mobile
Simon Moore Water Services, Unit 2, Poundbury West Industrial Estate, Dorchester, Dorset, DT1 2PG Tel: (01305) 251551 Fax: (01305) 257107
Mountjoy Water Supplies, Parkhurst, Boyton, Launceston, Cornwall, PL15 8NS Tel: (01566) 785733 Fax: (01566) 785733
Panks Engineers, 8 Heigham Street, Norwich, NR2 4TE Tel: (01603) 620297 Fax: (01603) 762679 E-mail: sales@panks.co.uk
John Wallis Titt & Co. Ltd, Manor Road, Frome, Somerset, BA11 4BQ Tel: (01373) 463594 Fax: (01373) 451382
Tolta Pumps Ltd, Unit 10, Bangors Road, Pennygillam Way, Launceston, Cornwall, PL15 7ED Tel: (01566) 773310 Fax: (01566) 779165 E-mail: sales@harburro.co.uk
W J Hatt Ltd, Foxcovert Farm, Goring Heath, Reading, RG8 7SL Tel: (01491) 680424 Fax: (01491) 680425 E-mail: wjhatt@aol.com
Whatley & Co (Pewsley) Ltd, Avonside Works, Pewsey, Wiltshire, SN9 5AS Tel: (01672) 562404 Fax: (01672) 563091 E-mail: whatley.pewsey@lineone.net

WATER FEATURE DESIGN

▶ David Harber, Valley Farm, Turville, Henley-on-Thames, Oxfordshire, RG9 6QU Tel: (01491) 576956 Fax: (01491) 413524 E-mail: sales@davidharbersundials.com
▶ Garden Options Ltd, 3 The Wynd, Melrose, Roxburghshire, TD6 9LD Tel: (01896) 820630 E-mail: enquiries@gardenoptions.co.uk
▶ Kinsman Water Features & Fountains, 56a Priory Road, Reigate, Surrey, RH2 8JB Tel: (01737) 222040 Fax: (01737) 222040 E-mail: mark@moesmoulds.co.uk
▶ SPECTRUM PRODUCTS LTD, The Workshop, 8 Church Street, Little Lever, Bolton, BL3 1BE Tel: 01204 452731 Fax: 01204 452731 E-mail: spectrummail@aol.com
▶ WonderFalls, Manderley, Auldgirth, Dumfries, DG2 0SA Tel: 01387 740685 Fax: 01387 740697 E-mail: ian@wonderfalls.co.uk

WATER FEATURE EQUIPMENT SUPPLIES OR INSTALLATION AND MAINTENANCE

Bath Patio Slab Centre, Whiteway Road, Bath, BA2 2RG Tel: (01225) 319334 Fax: (01225) 319334 E-mail: info@bathslabs.com

WATER FILTER/FILTRATION SYSTEMS ENGINEERS, INSTALLATION OR SERVICE

A E Freshwater Ltd, Old Court House, Town Hall CR, Haltwhistle, Northumberland, NE49 0DQ Tel: (01434) 321931 Fax: (01434) 321798 E-mail: info@ae-freshwater.fsnet.co.uk
Watercoolers (UK) Ltd, Unit 4 Brickfields Industrial Estate, Finway Road, Hemel Hempstead, Hertfordshire, HP2 7QA Tel: (01442) 211121 Fax: (01442) 211171 E-mail: sales@mainlinewater.co.uk

WATER FILTER/FILTRATION SYSTEMS MANUFRS

3M Water Filtration, 3M Centre, Cain Road, Bracknell, Berkshire, RG12 8HT Tel: (01344) 858000 Fax: (01344) 858559 E-mail: foodservice-europe@mmm.com
Albany International Ltd, Pilsworth Road, Bury, Lancashire, BL9 8QE Tel: 0161-767 7531 Fax: 0161-766 2993
Aqua Cure P.L.C, Aqua Cure House, Hall Street, Southport, Merseyside, PR9 0SE Tel: (01704) 501616 Fax: (01704) 544916 E-mail: sales@aquacure.plc.uk
Barr + Wray Ltd, 324 Drumoyne Road, Glasgow, G51 4DY Tel: 0141-882 5757 Fax: 0141-882 3690 E-mail: sales@barrandwray.com
▶ Calmag Ltd, Unit 3-6, Crown Works, Bradford Road, Sandbeds, Keighley, West Yorkshire, BD20 5LN Tel: (01535) 210320 Fax: (01535) 210321 E-mail: sales@calmagltd.com
Clearflow Southern, 10 Laxton Gardens, Redhill, RH1 3NJ Tel: (01737) 644625
Dorset Water Centre Ltd, 9 Pomeroy Buildings, Grove Trading Estate, Dorchester, Dorset, DT1 1ST Tel: (01305) 265548 Fax: (01305) 269404 E-mail: tim@dorset-water.co.uk
▶ Eastern Counties Pumps, 3 Burrell Road, Ipswich, IP2 8AD Tel: (01473) 400101 Fax: (01473) 400103 E-mail: sales@ecpgroup.com
Freshtec Ltd, PO Box 18, Dawlish, Devon, EX7 9YL Tel: (01626) 867090 Fax: (01626) 867199 E-mail: sales@freshtec.co.uk
Lacron UK Ltd, Radfield, London Road, Teynham, Sittingbourne, Kent, ME9 9PS Tel: (01795) 521733 Fax: (01795) 522085 E-mail: info@lacron.co.uk
Premium Bermad UK Ltd, Newbury Crash Repair Centre, Arnhem Road, Newbury, Berkshire, RG14 5RU Tel: (01635) 528717 Fax: (01635) 528642 E-mail: chris.elliott@2bermad.co.uk
The Pure Group, 10 Mead Court, Cooper Road, Thornbury, Bristol, BS35 3UW Tel: (01454) 411888 Fax: (01454) 411117 E-mail: puregroup@puregroup.co.uk
Servebrow Ltd, Bay 11 Central Works, Peartree Lane, Dudley, West Midlands, DY2 0XG Tel: (01384) 351453 Fax: (01384) 74948
Unipools Leisure Construction Ltd, 621 Watford Way, Mill Hill, London, NW7 3JN Tel: (020) 8959 8686 Fax: (020) 8959 2037 E-mail: info@unipools.com

WATER FILTERS, *See Water etc*

WATER FILTERS, DOMESTIC

▶ Ontap Home Water Filter Systems, Westfield Road, Berkhamsted, Hertfordshire, HP4 3PW Tel: (01442) 876583 E-mail: sales@ontapsystems.co.uk

WATER FILTRATION EQUIPMENT

▶ Eau Coolers Ltd, Unit 6 Woolmer Way, Bordon, Hampshire, GU35 9QF Tel: (01420) 488600 Fax: (01420) 488691 E-mail: eaucoolers@drinkingwater.co.uk

WATER FLOW BALANCING CONTROL SYSTEMS

Flowco Mariflo Ltd, 19 Auriol Park Road, Worcester Park, Surrey, KT4 7DP Tel: (020) 8330 2487 Fax: (020) 8330 2487 E-mail: mariflo@flowco.co.uk

WATER JET CUTTING MACHINERY

▶ K M T Waterjet Systems, Alexander House, Foxlands Drive, Wolverhampton, WV4 5NB Tel: (01902) 340140 Fax: (01902) 340544 E-mail: peter_longman@kmt-waterjet.co.uk
Mechtronic Industries Ltd, Innovation Centre, Kirton Lane, Stainforth, Doncaster, South Yorkshire, DN7 5DA Tel: (01302) 845000 Fax: (01302) 844440 E-mail: mechtro@aol.com

WATER JET CUTTING SERVICES

County Fabrications Leicester Ltd, B1 Valley Way, Market Harborough, Leicestershire, LE16 7PS Tel: (01858) 433958 Fax: (01858) 410463 E-mail: contact@countyfabs.co.uk
Fabcon Projects Ltd, Delta Close, Norwich, NR6 6BG Tel: (01603) 482338 Fax: (01603) 484064 E-mail: andrew@fabcon.co.uk
J C Jetting, 84 Bonnington Walk, Bristol, BS7 9XD Tel: 0117-904 1638 Fax: 0117-904 1638 E-mail: rachod@ukonline.co.uk
Leicester Water Jet Ltd, Unit B6 Troon Way Business Centre, Humberstone Lane, Leicester, LE4 9HA Tel: 0116-274 2551 Fax: 0116-274 2551 E-mail: info@leicesterwaterjet.co.uk
Prestige Marble Co., Armoury Works, Armoury Way, London, SW18 1EZ Tel: (020) 8874 7100 Fax: (020) 8870 0025 E-mail: prestigemarble@aol.com
Profile & Fabrication Services, P O Box 1002, Yateley, Hampshire, GU46 6ZA Tel: (01252) 875739 Fax: (01252) 664124
▶ Responsive Engineering Group, Kingsway South, Team Valley, Gateshead, Tyne & Wear, NE11 0SH Tel: 0191-497 3400 Fax: 0191-497 3401 E-mail: sales@responsive-engineering.com
Sciss Ltd, Unit 9 Larkstore Park, Lodge Road, Staplehurst, Tonbridge, Kent, TN12 0QY Tel: (01580) 890582 Fax: (01580) 890583 E-mail: sales@sciss.co.uk
Sparta Ltd, Victoria Works, Hill End Lane, Rossendale, Lancashire, BB4 7AG Tel: (01706) 221111 Fax: (01706) 222309 E-mail: enquiries@sparta.co.uk
Streamline Waterjet & Laser Cutters Ltd, Kingsway South, Team Valley Trading Estate, Gateshead, Tyne & Wear, NE11 0JL Tel: 0191-491 4422 Fax: 0191-497 3421 E-mail: streamline@responsive-engineering.com
Tech Mat Convertors Ltd, Alder Court, Springwood Way, Tytherington Business Park, Macclesfield, Cheshire, SK10 2XG Tel: (01625) 610441 Fax: (01625) 613199 E-mail: nigels@techmat.co.uk
Watercut Profiles Ltd, Unit 3, Murdock Road, Bicester, Oxon, OX26 4PP Tel: (01869) 327888 Fax: (01869) 249410 E-mail: sales@watercut.co.uk

WATER JET CUTTING SERVICES, STEEL

Leicester Water Jet Ltd, Unit B6 Troon Way Business Centre, Humberstone Lane, Leicester, LE4 9HA Tel: 0116-274 2551 Fax: 0116-274 2551 E-mail: info@leicesterwaterjet.co.uk

WATER JET (HIGH PRESSURE) CHEMICAL CLEANING PRODUCTS

Quadralene Ltd, Bateman Street, Derby, DE23 8JL Tel: (01332) 292500 Fax: (01332) 295941 E-mail: info@quadralene.co.uk

WATER JET (HIGH PRESSURE) CLEANING EQUIPMENT, ENGINE DRIVEN

▶ Zero Gum, Foxgloves, ByPass Road, Chester, CH3 8EF Tel: (01829) 741309 E-mail: jim@zerogum.org.uk

WATER JET HIGH PRESSURE CLEANING OR WASHING EQUIPMENT

Air Services, Redgate Road South Lancashire Industrial Estate, South Lancashire Industrial Es, Ashton-in-Makerfield, Wigan, Lancashire, WN4 8DT Tel: (01942) 722333 Fax: (01942) 725716 E-mail: sales@air-serv.co.uk
Checo 2000, Brailwood Road, Bilsthorpe, Newark, Nottinghamshire, NG22 8UA Tel: (01623) 871976 Fax: (01623) 871964 E-mail: info@checo200.co.uk
Cleanwell High Pressure Washers Ltd, Unit 12a Apsley Industrial Estate, Kents Avenue, Hemel Hempstead, Hertfordshire, HP3 9XH Tel: (01442) 263552 Fax: (01442) 266871 E-mail: sales@cleanwell.co.uk
Compressors & Washers Ltd, James David Building, 134 Widemarsh Street, Hereford, HR4 9HN Tel: (01432) 268799 Fax: (01432) 279922 E-mail: sales@compressorsandwashers.co.uk
Cymac Damon, 3 West Bawtry Road, Canklow, Rotherham, South Yorkshire, S60 2XG Tel: (01709) 370213 Fax: (01709) 367705
Hoselines Ltd, 25 Longfields Road, Carlton, Barnsley, South Yorkshire, S71 3HT Tel: (01226) 240838 Fax: (01226) 204315
Nilfisk-ALTO, Bowerbank Way, Penrith, Cumbria, CA11 9BQ Tel: (01768) 868995 Fax: (01768) 864713 E-mail: sales.uk@nilfisk-alto.com
Phillard Pump Co., Unit B, Holmes Court, Horncastle, Lincolnshire, LN9 6AS Tel: (01507) 523281 Fax: (01507) 527437
Power Clean Services, 3 Regent Business Centre, Pump Lane, Hayes, Middlesex, UB3 3NP Tel: (020) 8573 9893 Fax: (020) 8573 7765
Scotkleen Warwick Power Washers, 149a Glasgow Road, Wishaw, Lanarkshire, ML2 7QJ Tel: (0870) 8600600 Fax: (01698) 356697 E-mail: info@scotkleen.co.uk
Shorflow Engineering Co. Ltd, Unit 11, Step Bridge Road, Coleford, Gloucestershire, GL16 8PJ Tel: (01594) 839393 Fax: (01594) 839394
Starbrite Chemicals Ltd, X L House, Rutherford Way, Crawley, West Sussex, RH10 9PB Tel: (01293) 434250 Fax: (01293) 434252 E-mail: sales@starbrite.co.uk
Sterling Products Ltd, Richmond Street, West Bromwich, West Midlands, B70 0DD Tel: 0121-557 0022 Fax: 0121-557 0222
Andreas Stihl Ltd, Stihl House, Stanhope Road, Camberley, Surrey, GU15 3YT Tel: (01276) 20202 Fax: (01276) 670510 E-mail: postmaster@stihl.co.uk
T D C Services, T D C House, Ferry Hill, Ewloe, Deeside, Clwyd, CH5 3AW Tel: (01244) 534521 Fax: (01244) 533562 E-mail: sales@tdcservices.co.uk
Taybur Power Washes, 33 Craven Street, Bury, Lancashire, BL9 7PP Tel: 0161-763 6219 Fax: 0161-763 6219
Viking Services, Glenfoot, Abernethy, Perth, PH2 9LS Tel: 01738 850631

WATER JET HIGH PRESSURE CLEANING OR WASHING EQUIPMENT – *continued*

Ward's Flexible Rod Co. Ltd, 22 James Carter Road, Mildenhall, Bury St. Edmunds, Suffolk, IP28 7DE Tel: (01638) 713800 Fax: (01638) 716863 E-mail: sales@wardsflex.co.uk

Wickham Auto Wash Ltd, Norton Road, Stevenage, Hertfordshire, SG1 2BB Tel: (01438) 314041 Fax: (01438) 740140 E-mail: all@wickham-autowash.co.uk

WATER JET HIGH PRESSURE CLEANING OR WASHING EQUIPMENT HIRE

Rentajet Ltd, Paultons Park, Ower, Romsey, Hampshire, SO51 6AL Tel: (023) 8081 2921 Fax: (023) 8081 4016 E-mail: sales@rentajet.co.uk

Simpsons, Trowbridge Road, Westbury, Wiltshire, BA13 3AY Tel: (01373) 826578 Fax: (01373) 865315 E-mail: simpson1979@aol.com

WATER JET HIGH PRESSURE CLEANING OR WASHING EQUIPMENT SPARE PARTS

Exchange Engineering Ltd, Ruston Road, Grantham, Lincolnshire, NG31 9SW Tel: (01476) 578505 Fax: (01476) 590908 E-mail: admin@exchange-engineering.co.uk

WATER JET (HIGH PRESSURE) PROFILING MACHINERY MANUFRS

▶ K M T Waterjet Systems, Alexander House, Foxlands Drive, Wolverhampton, WV4 5NB Tel: (01902) 340140 Fax: (01902) 340544 E-mail: peter_longman@kmt-waterjet.co.uk

WATER JETTING UNITS

Earl Road Sweepers Ltd, Shardlowes Farm, Hedingham Road, Gosfield, Halstead, Essex, CO9 1PL Tel: (01787) 273777 Fax: (01787) 273777 E-mail: office@ersweepers.wanadoo.co.uk

WATER LEAKAGE DETECTION OR CONTROL SERVICES

Radiodetection Ltd, Western Drive, Bristol, BS14 0AF Tel: 0117-988 6232 Fax: (01275) 550004 E-mail: sales@radiodetection.com

WATER METER INSTALLATION CONTRACTORS

Bristol Water Holdings plc, Bridgwater Road, Bridgwater Road, Bristol, BS99 7AU Tel: 0117-966 5881 Fax: 0117-963 3755 E-mail: corporate.affaires@bristolwater.co.uk

WATER METERS

Actaris Metering Systems Ltd, Langer Road, Felixstowe, Suffolk, IP11 2ER Tel: (01394) 694000 Fax: (01394) 276030 E-mail: csaunders@actaris.co.uk

Cambridge Water plc, 90 Fulbourn Road, Cherry Hinton, Cambridge, CB1 9JN Tel: (01223) 706050 Fax: (01223) 214052 E-mail: info@cambridge-water.co.uk

G J Johnson & Sons Ltd, 7 Trinity Court, Brunel Road, Totton, Southampton, SO40 3WX Tel: (023) 8066 9666 Fax: (023) 8066 9606 E-mail: sales@johnsonvalves.com

Nation Water Treatments Ltd, Unit 1 Shawlands Court, Newchapel Road, Lingfield, Surrey, RH7 6BL Tel: (01342) 833693 Fax: (01342) 833787 E-mail: nwt@nationwatertreatments.co.uk

NDL Bends, Unit 3 Littleton Drive, Cannock, Staffordshire, WS12 4TR Tel: (01543) 579900 Fax: (01543) 577772

WATER OR ARTESIAN WELL DRILLING

G Stow plc, Heathercroft Industrial Estate, Lupton Road, Wallingford, Oxfordshire, OX10 9BS Tel: (01491) 834444 Fax: (01491) 827640 E-mail: gstowplc@btinternet.com

T W Page & Son Ltd, 7 Buxton Road, Frettenham, Norwich, NR12 7NQ Tel: (01603) 898071 Fax: (01603) 898049 E-mail: admin@twpage.co.uk

W J Groundwater Ltd, 9 Park Road, Bushey, WD23 3EE Tel: (020) 8950 7256 Fax: (020) 8950 5207 E-mail: info@wjgl.com

Windsor House Natural Water Co Ltd, Park Road, Emsworth, Hampshire, PO10 8NY Tel: (01243) 376156 Fax: (01243) 379100

WATER PLAYGROUND EQUIPMENT

▶ Tawny Wood Outdoor Play, The Owls, Clayford Road, Kilgetty, Dyfed, SA68 0RR Tel: (01834) 813227 Fax: (01834) 813227 E-mail: tawnywood@yahoo.co.uk

WATER PUMP MAINTENANCE OR REPAIR

▶ W.H. Shoebridge & Sons Ltd, 90 South Street, Stanground, Peterborough, PE2 8EZ Tel: (01733) 340281 Fax: (01733) 897002 E-mail: whshoebridge.pet@btconnect.com

WATER PUMPS

Assured Performance Group Ltd, Kenlis Road, Barnacre, Preston, PR3 1GD Tel: (01995) 604600 Fax: (01995) 606651 E-mail: info@apgroup.uk.com

Barber Pumps Ltd, Jacksons Yard, Douglas Road North, Fulwood, Preston, PR2 3QH Tel: (01772) 715502 Fax: (01772) 712716 E-mail: barberpumps@aol.com

Barnaby Climax Ltd, White Ladies Close, Little London, Worcester, WR1 1PZ Tel: (01905) 22014 Fax: (01905) 723828 E-mail: wildon@sweepaxpumps.co.uk

Blandford Engineering, Unit 7 Littletowns Estate, Blandford Heights, Blandford Forum, Dorset, DT11 7UR Tel: (01258) 454222 Fax: (01258) 480433 E-mail: blandfordpumps@btinternet.com

Bradshaws Direct Ltd, James Nicolson Link, Clifton Moore, York, YO30 4XX Tel: (01904) 691169 Fax: (01904) 691133 E-mail: ferrey@aol.com

Briggs & Stratton Power Products Group, Road Four, Winsford Industrial Estate, Winsford, Cheshire, CW7 3QN Tel: (01606) 862182 Fax: (01606) 862201

▶ Calder Ltd, Gregory's Bank, Worcester, WR3 8AB Tel: (01905) 723255 Fax: (01905) 723904 E-mail: pumps@calder.co.uk

Centrilift, Howe Moss Place, Kirkhill Industrial Estate, Dyce, Aberdeen, AB21 0ES Tel: (01224) 772233 Fax: (01224) 771021 E-mail: sales@centrilift.com

Concentric Pumps Ltd, Unit 10 Gravelly Park, Tyburn Road, Birmingham, B24 8HW Tel: 0121-327 2081 Fax: 0121-327 6187 E-mail: general@concentric-pumps.co.uk

Dab Pumps Ltd, 4 Stortford Hall Industrial Park, Dunmow Road, Bishop's Stortford, Hertfordshire, CM23 5GZ Tel: (01279) 652776 Fax: (01279) 655147 E-mail: info@dabpumps.com

Alan Dale Pumps Ltd, 75 Clockhouse Lane, Ashford, Middlesex, TW15 2HA Tel: (01784) 421114 Fax: (01784) 421092 E-mail: info@alandalepumps.wanadoo.co.uk

E P Services, Unit 1, Central Industrial Estate, Cable Street, Wolverhampton, WV2 2RJ Tel: (01902) 452914 Fax: (01902) 871547 E-mail: enquiries@ep-services.co.uk

Hurst Plant Sales Ltd, Station Yard Station Road, Haxey Junction, Doncaster, South Yorkshire, DN9 2NL Tel: (01427) 753030 Fax: (01427) 752030 E-mail: sales@hurstplantsales.co.uk

P & B Electrical Company, 1a St Dunstans Road, London, SE25 6EU Tel: (020) 8771 6555 Fax: (020) 8771 9867

▶ Sabar UK Ltd, 17 Duckworth Street, Darwen, Lancashire, BB3 1AR Tel: (01254) 702456 Fax: (01254) 702456 E-mail: sabaruk@ntlworld.com

Sparrow Quality Water Solutions, The Abbey, Preston Road, Yeovil, Somerset, BA20 2EN Tel: (01935) 479395 Fax: (01935) 848523

▶ Stuart Group Ltd, Stuart House, Crowshall Lane, Attleborough, Norfolk, NR17 1AD Tel: (01953) 454540 Fax: (01953) 456968 E-mail: info@stuartpumps.co.uk

Stuart Pumps Ltd, Stuart House, Crowshall Lane, Attleborough, Norfolk, NR17 1AD Tel: (01953) 454540 Fax: (01953) 456968 E-mail: info@stuartpumps.co.uk

W Robinson & Sons Ec Ltd, 35-41 Fowler Road, Hainault Industrial Estate, Ilford, Essex, IG6 3WR Tel: (020) 8559 6000 Fax: (020) 8559 6001 E-mail: info@pump.co.uk

Watermill Products Ltd, Fairview Industrial Estate, Hurst Green, Oxted, Surrey, RH8 9BD Tel: 01883 715425

WATER PURIFICATION ENGINEERS, INSTALLATION OR SERVICE

DSI International Ltd, Unit 6, Abbey Road Enterprise Park, Neath, West Glamorgan, SA10 7DN Tel: (01639) 645400 Fax: (01639) 644664 E-mail: sales@aquapur950.com

H R Holfeld Belfast Ltd, Altona Road, Lisburn, County Antrim, BT27 5RU Tel: (028) 9267 7523 Fax: (028) 9266 0263

Real Water, 29 Albion Street, Kenilworth, Warwickshire, CV8 2FX Tel: (01926) 851100 Fax: (01926) 511893 E-mail: sales@realwater.co.uk

WATER PURIFICATION EQUIPMENT, POTABLE WATER

DSI International Ltd, Unit 6, Abbey Road Enterprise Park, Neath, West Glamorgan, SA10 7DN Tel: (01639) 645400 Fax: (01639) 644664 E-mail: sales@aquapur950.com

WATER PURIFICATION SYSTEMS OR EQUIPMENT

3M Water Filtration, 3M Centre, Cain Road, Bracknell, Berkshire, RG12 8HT Tel: (01344) 858000 Fax: (01344) 858559 E-mail: foodservice-europe@mmm.com

A W E Anderson Water Equipment Ltd, R04-R05 Unit Cardiff Bay Business Centre, Titan Road, Cardiff, CF24 5EL Tel: (029) 2049 2848 Fax: (029) 2049 1369 E-mail: sales@aweltd.co.uk

Contactus Water Treatment Equipment, 227 Walsall Road, Sutton Coldfield, West Midlands, B74 4QA Tel: 0121-353 7208 Fax: 0121-352 0117 E-mail: contactus@fsmail.net

Dorset Water Centre Ltd, 9 Pomeroy Buildings, Grove Trading Estate, Dorchester, Dorset, DT1 1ST Tel: (01305) 265548 Fax: (01305) 269404 E-mail: tim@dorset-water.co.uk

East Midland Water Co., 3 Cannock Street, Leicester, LE4 9HR Tel: 0116-276 3334 Fax: 0116-276 3335 E-mail: sales@emwc.uk.com

Ecowater Systems Ltd, 1 Independent Business Park, Mill Road, Stokenchurch, High Wycombe, Buckinghamshire, HP14 3TP Tel: (01494) 484000 Fax: (01494) 484396 E-mail: sales@ecowater.co.uk

G R I Ltd, Gene House, Queenborough Lane, Rayne, Braintree, Essex, CM77 6TZ Tel: (01376) 332900 Fax: (01376) 344724 E-mail: gri@gri.co.uk

Industrial Purification Systems Ltd, Unit 10 Lea Green Business Park, St. Helens, Merseyside, WA9 4TR Tel: (01744) 811652 Fax: (01744) 833687 E-mail: info@industrial-purification.co.uk

Kinetico UK Ltd, Bridge House, Park Gate Business Centre, Park Gate, Southampton, SO31 1FQ Tel: (01489) 566970 Fax: (01489) 566976 E-mail: info@kinetico.co.uk

Lakeway Filtration Ltd, 7 North Street, North Tawton, Devon, EX20 2DE Tel: (01837) 82777 Fax: (01837) 82777

Lubron UK Ltd, 14 Commerce Way, Colchester, CO2 8HH Tel: (01206) 866444 Fax: (01206) 866800 E-mail: joe.austin@lubron.co.uk

Millipore (UK) Ltd, Units 3-5 The Court Yard, Hattes Lane, Watford, WD18 8YH Tel: (0870) 9004645 Fax: (0870) 9004646 E-mail: csr_uk@millipore.com

Pre Mac International Ltd, Unit 5 Morewood Close, Sevenoaks, Kent, TN13 2HU Tel: (01732) 460333 Fax: (01732) 460222 E-mail: office@pre-mac.com

The Pure Group, 10 Mead Court, Cooper Road, Thornbury, Bristol, BS35 3UW Tel: (01454) 411888 Fax: (01454) 411117 E-mail: puregroup@puregroup.co.uk

Purite Ltd, Bandet Way, Thame Industrial Estate, Thame, Oxfordshire, OX9 3SJ Tel: (01844) 217141

Salamander (Engineering) Ltd, The Heath Business & Technical Park, Runcorn, Cheshire, WA7 4QX Tel: (01928) 583280 Fax: (01928) 562890 E-mail: enquiries@salamander-engineering.co.uk

Sussex Water Treatment Systems, 17 Harefield Road, Bognor Regis, West Sussex, PO22 6EE Tel: (01243) 587928 Fax: (01243) 587928

Tarn Pure, 2-4 Copyground Lane, High Wycombe, Buckinghamshire, HP12 3HE Tel: (01494) 535576 Fax: (01494) 464175 E-mail: info@tarn-pure.com

Veoilawater Solutions & Technologys, Marlow International, Parkway, Marlow, Buckinghamshire, SL7 1YL Tel: (01494) 887700 Fax: (01628) 897001 E-mail: sales.uk@veoliawater.com

WATER PURITY MONITORING SYSTEMS

Marine Ventures Ltd, Marven House, 1 Field Road, Reading, RG1 6AP Tel: 0118-950 3707 Fax: 0118-950 4066 E-mail: info@marineventures.co.uk

WATER QUALITY ADVISERS OR MONITORING AND MANAGEMENT CONSULTANCY

Chiltern Water Management Services, 1 Inkerman Drive, Hazlemere, High Wycombe, Buckinghamshire, HP15 7JJ Tel: (01494) 712831 Fax: (01494) 712831 E-mail: rh@chilternwater.co.uk

Westfield Caledonian Ltd, 4 Mollins Court, Cumbernauld, Glasgow, G68 9HP Tel: (01236) 786300 Fax: (01236) 786301 E-mail: info@west-cal.co.uk

WATER QUALITY MONITORING EQUIPMENT

▶ Achromatic Limited, Grangemouth Enterprise & Technology Centre, Falkirk Road, Grangemouth, Stirlingshire, FK3 8XS Tel: (01324) 619360 Fax: (01324) 622399 E-mail: info@achromatic.co.uk

Enviro Technology Services plc, Unit B1 Kingfisher Business Park, London Road, Thrupp, Stroud, Gloucestershire, GL5 2BY Tel: (01453) 733200 Fax: (01453) 733201 E-mail: sales@et.co.uk

Lovibond Water Testing, Waterloo Road, Salisbury, SP1 2JY Tel: (01722) 327242 Fax: (01722) 412322 E-mail: sales@tintometer.com

MD Instruments Ltd, 31 Yarmouth Close, Toothill, Swindon, SN5 8LL Tel: (01793) 433595 Fax: (01793) 644244 E-mail: sales@mdinstruments.co.uk

Partech Electronics Ltd, Charlestown Road, St. Austell, Cornwall, PL25 3NN Tel: (01726) 879800 Fax: (01726) 879801 E-mail: sales@partech.co.uk

Robin Instruments Ltd, PO Box 541, Bagshot, Surrey, GU19 5XB Tel: (01276) 451365 Fax: (01276) 474103 E-mail: sales@robin-instruments.co.uk

WATER QUALITY RISK ASSESSMENT

City Water Pre-Com Ltd, Maidenhead Yard, The Wash, Hertford, SG14 1PX Tel: (01992) 505353 Fax: (01992) 554852 E-mail: enquiries@city-water.com

WATER RECYCLING SYSTEMS, WASH WATER ETC

Atlantis International Ltd T/A Karcher Vehicle Wash, Lion court, Staunton Harold Hall, Melbourne Road, Staunton Road, Ashby-de-la-Zouch, Leicestershire, LE65 1RT Tel: (01332) 695035 Fax: (01332) 695036 E-mail: jodieburgess@atlantisint.co.uk

WATER REPELLENTS

Kingfisher Building Products Ltd, Cooper Lane, Bardsea, Ulverston, Cumbria, LA12 9RA Tel: (01229) 869100 Fax: (01229) 869101 E-mail: sales@kingfisherchem.com

Wd-40 Co. Ltd, PO Box 440, Milton Keynes, MK11 3LJ Tel: (01908) 555400 Fax: (01908) 266900 E-mail: sales@wd40.co.uk

WATER SAVING EQUIPMENT

Rainharvesting Systems Ltd, Cheltenham Road, Bisley, Stroud, Gloucestershire, GL6 7BX Tel: (01452) 772000 Fax: (01452) 770115 E-mail: sales@rainharvesting.co.uk

Sensaflow Ltd, P O Box 61, Bridgwater, Somerset, TA5 1YY Tel: (01278) 732620 Fax: (01278) 732647

WATER SEALING PRODUCTS

Hadham Water Ltd, Church End, Little Hadham, Ware, Hertfordshire, SG11 2DY Tel: (01279) 771248 Fax: (01279) 771057 E-mail: sales@hadham.co.uk

WATER SOFTENERS

E P Laboratories Ltd, Amersham Road, Chesham, Buckinghamshire, HP5 1NE Tel: (01494) 791585 Fax: (01494) 771853 E-mail: sales@eplabs.com

New Cheshire Salt Works Ltd, Wincham Lane, Wincham, Northwich, Cheshire, CW9 6DD Tel: (01606) 42361 Fax: (01606) 48333 E-mail: general@ncsw.co.uk

Rodol Ltd, Richmond Row, Liverpool, L3 3BP Tel: 0151-207 3161 Fax: 0151-207 3727

WATER SOFTENING

D A Baldwin & Son, Head Office Pasford House, Chesterton Road, Pattingham, Wolverhampton, WV6 7DZ Tel: (01902) 700456 Fax: (01902) 700492 E-mail: watersoft@aol.com

Euro Water Systems, 26 Hartwell Gardens, Harpenden, Hertfordshire, AL5 2RW Tel: (01582) 766062 Fax: (01582) 621756 E-mail: sales@clemsoft.co.uk

Flowsoft Watercare, Baytrees, Pluckley Road, Charing, Ashford, Kent, TN27 0AQ Tel: (01233) 712610 Fax: (01233) 712610 E-mail: flowsoftwatercare@intamail.com

▶ indicates data change since last edition

WATER SOFTENING – *continued*

Life Science Products Ltd, 185l Milton Park, Milton, Abingdon, Oxfordshire, OX14 4SR Tel: (01235) 832111 Fax: (01235) 832129 E-mail: sales@lifescience.co.uk

Oxford Water Softeners, 6 Bertie Road, Cumnor, Oxford, OX2 9PS Tel: (01865) 862795 Fax: (01865) 862795

Softflow Water Treatment Equipment, Wantz Stores, Main Road, Woodham Ferrers, Chelmsford, CM3 8RP Tel: (01245) 322816 Fax: (01245) 320008 E-mail: info@softflowsofteners.co.uk

Water Softening Services, Meadows End House, 22 Bridge Meadow, Denton, Northampton, NN7 1DA Tel: (01604) 890805

Zephyr Water Treatment Ltd, 23 Brass Mill Enterprise Centre, Brass Mill Lane, Bath, BA1 3JN Tel: (01225) 334838 Fax: (01225) 442028 E-mail: service@zephyrwater.co.uk

WATER SOFTENING EQUIPMENT

B & G Softwater Services, Barnside, Wrotham Road, Meopham, Gravesend, Kent, DA13 0AU Tel: (01474) 812005 E-mail: contact@softwaterservices.co.uk

Dorset Water Centre Ltd, 9 Pomeroy Buildings, Grove Trading Estate, Dorchester, Dorset, DT1 1ST Tel: (01305) 265548 Fax: (01305) 269404 E-mail: tim@dorset-water.co.uk

Life Science Products Ltd, 185l Milton Park, Milton, Abingdon, Oxfordshire, OX14 4SR Tel: (01235) 832111 Fax: (01235) 832129 E-mail: sales@lifescience.co.uk

Sussex Water Treatment Systems, 17 Harefield Road, Bognor Regis, West Sussex, PO22 6EE Tel: (01243) 587928 Fax: (01243) 587928

WATER SOLUBLE CUTTING OIL

▶ J B Lubes & Tools, Hillborough Business Park, Sweechbridge Road, Herne Bay, Kent, CT6 6TE Tel: (0787) 6025560 Fax: (01227) 740475 E-mail: jblubes@yahoo.co.uk

WATER SOLUBLE PLASTIC FILM

▶ Clarisol, 1 Holme Lane, Spondon, Derby, DE21 7BP Tel: (01332) 681210 Fax: (01332) 660178 E-mail: info@clarifoil.com

WATER SUPPLY INSTALLATION CONTRACTORS OR ENGINEERS

Folkestone & Dover, The Cherry Garden, Cherry Garden Lane, Folkestone, Kent, CT19 4QB Tel: (01303) 298888 Fax: (01303) 276712 E-mail: enquiries@fdws.co.uk

WATER SUPPLY INSTALLATION DESIGN CONSULTANCY OR SERVICES

Anglian Water, Hendeson House, Lancaster Way, Ermine Business Park, Huntingdon, Cambridgeshire, PE29 6XQ Tel: (01480) 323900 Fax: (01480) 326981

Everton Water Gardens, Newlands Manor, Everton, Lymington, Hampshire, SO41 0JH Tel: (01590) 644405 Fax: (01590) 642343 E-mail: sales@water-garden-workshop.com

WATER SYSTEMS RUST/SCALE PREVENTION PRODUCTS

Aquachemix Ltd, PO Box 1, Dunstable, Bedfordshire, LU5 6HX Tel: (01525) 872432 Fax: (01525) 872210

WATER TANK CLEANING/ RELINING SERVICES

Freeston Water Treatment Ltd, West Quay Road, Southampton, SO15 1GZ Tel: (023) 8022 0738 Fax: (023) 8063 9853 E-mail: info@freeston.co.uk

Intergrated Water Services Ltd, Vincients Road, Bumpers Farm Industrial Estate, Chippenham, Wiltshire, SN14 6NQ Tel: (01249) 461744 Fax: (01249) 461766

Liquitech Ltd, Old Post Office House, East Street, Pembridge, Leominster, Herefordshire, HR6 9HA Tel: (0845) 6449020 Fax: (0845) 6449021 E-mail: andrew@liquitech.co.uk

Tankline Water Treatment Equipment, 16 Babington Road, Hornchurch, Essex, RM12 4AR Tel: (01708) 450234 Fax: (07971) 113276 E-mail: sales@tank-line.co.uk

WATER TANK REFURBISHMENT

Aquatreat Group Ltd, Stanley House, 9 Bunting Close, Mitcham, Surrey, CR4 4ND Tel: (020) 8401 8391 Fax: (020) 8401 8392 E-mail: mailbox@aquatreat.uk.com

K T Tank Lining Services, Building 43, Kingsnorth Industrial Estate, Kingsnorth, Hoo, Rochester, Kent, ME3 9ND Tel: (01634) 846824 Fax: (01634) 845441

Liquitech Ltd, Old Post Office House, East Street, Pembridge, Leominster, Herefordshire, HR6 9HA Tel: (0845) 6449020 Fax: (0845) 6449021 E-mail: andrew@liquitech.co.uk

Precision Pipework Ltd, Horn Hill, Lowestoft, Suffolk, NR33 0PX Tel: (01502) 500646 Fax: (01502) 566957 E-mail: sales@pumps4all.com

WATER TANKS

Boil Irrigation Ltd, 46 Montford Road, Sunbury-on-Thames, Middlesex, TW16 6EJ Tel: (01932) 788301 Fax: (01932) 780437 E-mail: davidjones@boilirrigation.co.uk

▶ Brice-Baker Group, Rookery Road, The Lane, Wyboston, Bedford, MK44 3AX Tel: (01480) 216618 Fax: (01480) 406226 E-mail: info@bricebaker.co.uk

Gledhill Water Storage Ltd, Unit 22, Corngreves Trading Estate, Charlton Dive, Cradley Heath, West Midlands, B64 7BJ Tel: (01384) 636245 Fax: (01384) 413700

Lochinvar Ltd, 7 Lombard Way, Banbury, Oxfordshire, OX16 4TJ Tel: (01295) 269981 Fax: (01295) 271640 E-mail: sales@lochinvar.ltd.uk

WATER TESTING PRODUCTS

Bio Seekers Ltd, 7 Notley Farm, Chearsley Road, Long Crendon, Aylesbury, Buckinghamshire, HP18 9ER Tel: (01844) 201745 Fax: (01844) 201963 E-mail: bioseekers@aol.com

▶ Casp Products Ltd, W.H.S. Building, Harcourt Road, Harrogate, North Yorkshire, HG1 5NL Tel: (01423) 525206 Fax: (01423) 536500 E-mail: sales@casp-products.com

Dimanco Ltd, 24 Henlow Industrial Estate, Henlow, Bedfordshire, SG16 6DS Tel: (01462) 813933 Fax: (01462) 817407 E-mail: dimanco@ltdhenlow.fsbusiness.co.uk

Lovibond Water Testing, Waterloo Road, Salisbury, SP1 2JY Tel: (01722) 327242 Fax: (01722) 412322 E-mail: sales@tintometer.com

Palintest Ltd, Kingsway, Team Valley Trading Estate, Gateshead, Tyne & Wear, NE11 0NS Tel: 0191-491 0808 Fax: 0191-482 5372 E-mail: sales@palintest.com

Professional Test Systems, Summer Court, Manafon, Welshpool, Powys, SY21 8BJ Tel: (01686) 650160 Fax: (01686) 650170 E-mail: sales@proftest.com

WATER TREATMENT CHEMICAL PRODUCTS

Aqua Marine Chemicals Ltd, Unit 6 Strensham Business Park, Strensham, Worcester, WR8 9JZ Tel: (01684) 290077 Fax: (01684) 290608 E-mail: laura@bayer-wood.co.uk

Aquadition Ltd, 220 Copnor Road, Copnor, Portsmouth, PO3 5DA Tel: (023) 9269 1035 Fax: (023) 9261 8200 E-mail: sales@aquadition.co.uk

Aquatec Consultancy Services Ltd, Pocket Nook Lane, Lowton, Warrington, WA3 1AB Tel: (01942) 603268 Fax: (01942) 261521 E-mail: info@aquatecchemicalservices.com

Aquatreat Group Ltd, Stanley House, 9 Bunting Close, Mitcham, Surrey, CR4 4ND Tel: (020) 8401 8391 Fax: (020) 8401 8392 E-mail: mailbox@aquatreat.uk.com

Ashland UK, Wimsey Way, Somercotes, Alfreton, Derbyshire, DE55 4LR Tel: (01773) 604321 Fax: (01773) 606901

Baker Petrolite, Howe Moss Avenue, Kirkhill Industrial Estate, Dyce, Aberdeen, AB21 0GP Tel: (01224) 405700 Fax: (01224) 405705

Cayley Chemical Corporation Ltd, 10 Manor Park Business Centre, Mackenzie Way, Swindon Village, Cheltenham, Gloucestershire, GL51 9TX Tel: (01242) 222971 Fax: (01242) 227634 E-mail: cayley@btinternet.com

Central Cooling Services Ltd, Garrison House, Garrison Street, Bordesley, Birmingham, B9 4BN Tel: 0121-766 7227 Fax: 0121-766 6156 E-mail: centralcoolingservices@btinternet.com

E C Gulbrandsen Ltd, Water Lane, Ancaster, Grantham, Lincolnshire, NG32 3QS Tel: (01400) 230700 Fax: (01400) 230601

Eaton Environmental Services Ltd, Bradley Farm, Cumnor, Oxford, OX2 9QU Tel: (01865) 864488 Fax: (01865) 865855 E-mail: info@eatonenvironmental.co.uk

Freeston Water Treatment Ltd, West Quay Road, Southampton, SO15 1GZ Tel: (023) 8022 0738 Fax: (023) 8063 9853 E-mail: info@freeston.co.uk

G E Water & Process Technologies Ltd, Foundry Lane, Widnes, Cheshire, WA8 8UD Tel: 0151-424 5351 Fax: 0151-423 2722

Hydro-X Water Treatment Ltd, Unit 3a Eden Place, Outgang Lane Dinnington, Dinnington, Sheffield, S25 3QT Tel: (01909) 565133 Fax: (01909) 564301 E-mail: office@hydro-x.co.uk

Nalco, Wilton International, Wilton, Redcar, Cleveland, TS10 4RG Tel: (01642) 430105 Fax: (01642) 459390

Nation Water Treatments Ltd, Unit 1 Shawlands Court, Newchapel Road, Lingfield, Surrey, RH7 6BL Tel: (01342) 833693 Fax: (01342) 833787 E-mail: nwt@nationwatertreatments.co.uk

Norit UK Ltd, Clydesmill Place, Cambuslang Industrial Estate, Clydesmill Industrial Estate, Glasgow, G32 8RF Tel: 0141-641 8841 Fax: 0141-641 8411 E-mail: fisher.martin.nl@norit.com

Omex Environmental Ltd, Riverside Industrial Estate, King's Lynn, Norfolk, PE30 2HH Tel: (01553) 770092 Fax: (01553) 776547 E-mail: enquire@omex.com

Process Technology Associates Ltd, 8 Waverton Business Park, Saighton Lane, Waverton, Chester, CH3 7PD Tel: (01244) 332441 Fax: (01244) 332325 E-mail: mail@processtech.co.uk

Water Technology Ltd, Powke Lane Industrial Estate, Blackheath, Rowley Regis, West Midlands, B65 0AH Tel: 0121-561 3144 Fax: 0121-561 3329 E-mail: water.tech@virgin.net

Watercare Specialists Ltd, Unit 2 Beech Tree Park, Bidford-on-Avon, Alcester, Warwickshire, B50 4JF Tel: (01789) 778177 Fax: (01789) 490001

Waterchem Ltd, Unit 2c, Derwent Close, Worcester, WR4 9TY Tel: (01905) 23669 Fax: (01905) 729959 E-mail: info@waterchem.co.uk

Watermarc Chemical Services, Unit 38 Nine Mile Point Industrial Estate, Cwmfelinfach, Ynysddu, Newport, Gwent, NP11 7HZ Tel: (01495) 200005 Fax: (01495) 200844

Zephyr Water Treatment Ltd, 23 Brass Mill Enterprise Centre, Brass Mill Lane, Bath, BA1 3JN Tel: (01225) 334838 Fax: (01225) 442028 E-mail: service@zephyrwater.co.uk

WATER TREATMENT MONITORING EQUIPMENT

Aquamix Water Purification, 20 Orville St, St. Helens, Merseyside, WA9 3JJ Tel: (01744) 816990 Fax: (01744) 816990

Bio Seekers Ltd, 7 Notley Farm, Chearsley Road, Long Crendon, Aylesbury, Buckinghamshire, HP18 9ER Tel: (01844) 201745 Fax: (01844) 201963 E-mail: bioseekers@aol.com

Clear Brook Water Treatment, 8 Hollow Hill Road, Ditchingham, Bungay, Suffolk, NR35 2QZ Tel: (01986) 893076 Fax: (01986) 893076

Rivertrace Engineering Ltd, P Kingsfield Business Centre, Philanthropic Road, Redhill, RH1 4DP Tel: (0870) 7702721 Fax: (0870) 7702722 E-mail: info@rivertrace.com

Water Support Services, 18a High West Street, Dorchester, Dorset, DT1 1UW Tel: (01305) 266614 Fax: (01305) 267017 E-mail: info@water-support.co.uk

WATER TREATMENT PLANT AND EQUIPMENT MANUFRS

▶ A W P Enviromental, Unit 10, Campbells Yard, 75 Bellfast Road, Newry, County Down, BT34 1QH Tel: (028) 3083 5533 Fax: (028) 3082 5523 E-mail: sales@awpenviromental.net

Alpha Bio Systems Ltd, Harlaw Way, Hawlaw Road Industrial Estate, Harlaw Road Industrial Estate, Inverurie, Aberdeenshire, AB51 4SG Tel: (01467) 620266 Fax: (01467) 620265

▶ Aqua Bio UK Ltd, Fenpark Industrial Estate, Park Lane, Stoke-on-Trent, ST4 3JP Tel: (01782) 593263 Fax: (01782) 593263

▶ Aqua & Effluence Systems, Witham Friary, Frome, Somerset, BA11 5HA Tel: (01373) 836403 Fax: (01373) 836404

▶ Aqua Serve, 13 Pinewood, Somerton, Somerset, TA11 6JW Tel: (01458) 272444 Fax: (01458) 272444 E-mail: clive@aqua-serve.co.uk

Aqua Spring Ltd, 177 Kingston Road, Leatherhead, Surrey, KT22 7NX Tel: (01372) 373023 Fax: (01372) 360003 E-mail: sales@aquaspring.co.uk

Aquachemix Ltd, PO Box 1, Dunstable, Bedfordshire, LU5 6HX Tel: (01525) 872432 Fax: (01525) 872210

Arbour Tech Ltd, Kingsland, Leominster, Herefordshire, HR6 9SF Tel: (01568) 708840 Fax: (01568) 708974 E-mail: enquiries@arbourtech.com

Bio Seekers Ltd, 7 Notley Farm, Chearsley Road, Long Crendon, Aylesbury, Buckinghamshire, HP18 9ER Tel: (01844) 201745 Fax: (01844) 201963 E-mail: bioseekers@aol.com

Culligan International UK Ltd, Culligan House, Coronation Road, High Wycombe, Buckinghamshire, HP12 3SU Tel: (01494) 436484 Fax: (01494) 523833 E-mail: enquires@culligan.co.uk

Direct Water Services UK Ltd, 2 Woodford Road, Barnby Dun, Doncaster, South Yorkshire, DN3 1BN Tel: (01302) 883838 Fax: (01302) 883838

▶ Dolphin Enviromental Services, Unit 1, Dolphin Business Park, 58D Arthur Street, Redditch, Worcestershire, B98 8JY Tel: (01527) 525505 Fax: (01527) 527622

Dunham Water Treatment, 17 Bracken Road, Long Eaton, Nottingham, NG10 4DA Tel: 0115-972 7812 Fax: 0115-877 6238 E-mail: bob@dunhamwater.co.uk

▶ Ewan Group plc, Canterbury House Stephensons Way, Wyvern Business Park, Chaddesden, Derby, DE21 6LY Tel: (01332) 680066 Fax: (01332) 680080

Excel Water, Unit 441a Thorp Arch Trading Estate, Thorp Arch, Wetherby, West Yorkshire, LS23 7BJ Tel: (01937) 844211 Fax: (01937) 844101 E-mail: sales@excelwater.co.uk

Graham Ash Plumbing & Heating Installations, Highways, Station Hill, Lynton, Devon, EX35 6LB Tel: (01598) 753592

▶ Guardian, 9-10 Capricorn Centre, Cranes Farm Road, Basildon, Essex, SS14 3JJ Tel: (01268) 287477 Fax: (01268) 287156 E-mail: info@gwtltd.com

Inflow UK Ltd, Unit 5a+6 Mount Industrial Estate, Mount Road, Stone, Staffordshire, ST15 8LL Tel: (01785) 812150 Fax: (01785) 812031 E-mail: sales@inflowuk.co.uk

Invent Water Treatment Ltd, 2 Hurst Street, Rochdale, Lancashire, OL11 1BH Tel: (01706) 359155 Fax: (01706) 653598 E-mail: sales@inventwater.com

J C Phillips & Son Ltd, 162a South Street, Bridport, Dorset, DT6 3NP Tel: (01308) 422179 Fax: (01308) 421956

K J Water Treatments Ltd, 19 Hardings La, London, SE20 7JJ Tel: 020 86597216 Fax: 0208 6760138

Kalsep UK, Unit 2f Albany Park, Frimley Park, Camberley, Surrey, GU16 7PL Tel: (01276) 675675 Fax: (01276) 676276 E-mail: sales@kalsep.co.uk

▶ Lakeside Water & Building Services, Unit 2 St. Marys Road Industrial Estate, Ramsey, Huntingdon, Cambridgeshire, PE26 2SW Tel: (01487) 815914 Fax: (01487) 815070 E-mail: elaine@lakesidewater.co.uk

▶ Lifetime Water, North East Suffolk Business Centre, Pinbush Road, Lowestoft, Suffolk, NR33 7NQ Tel: (01502) 515200

Lubron UK Ltd, 14 Commerce Way, Colchester, CO2 8HH Tel: (01206) 866444 Fax: (01206) 866800 E-mail: joe.austin@lubron.co.uk

MD Instruments Ltd, 31 Yarmouth Close, Toothill, Swindon, SN5 8LL Tel: (01793) 433595 Fax: (01793) 644244 E-mail: sales@mdinstruments.co.uk

Nalco, 5 Riverside Business Park, Dogflud Way, Farnham, Surrey, GU9 7SS Tel: (01252) 735454 Fax: (01252) 734430 E-mail: enquiries@ondeo-nalco.com

Nalco, 20-22 Albion Way, Kelvin Industrial Estate, East Kilbride, Glasgow, G75 0YN Tel: (01355) 573900 Fax: (01355) 263660

Nalco Ltd, Weavergate Works, P O Box 11, Winnington Avenue, Northwich, Cheshire, CW8 4DX Tel: (01606) 74488 Fax: 01606 79557

▶ Nemco Utilities Ltd, Hillside Business Park, 12 Kimpson Way, Bury St. Edmunds, Suffolk, IP32 7EA Tel: (01284) 724503 Fax: (01284) 724826

Partech Electronics Ltd, Charlestown Road, St. Austell, Cornwall, PL25 3NN Tel: (01726) 879800 Fax: (01726) 879801 E-mail: sales@partech.co.uk

Partners In Water, Old Forge, Rochford, Tenbury Wells, Worcestershire, WR15 8SP Tel: (01584) 781782 Fax: (01584) 781783

▶ Phoenix Instrumentation Ltd, Ivel Road, Shefford, Bedfordshire, SG17 5JU Tel: (01462) 851747 Fax: (01462) 815382 E-mail: sales@phoenixinstrumentation.ltd.uk

Purifio Ltd, 44 Holton Road, Holton Heath Trading Park, Poole, Dorset, BH16 6LT Tel: (01202) 625656 Fax: (01202) 621002 E-mail: sales@rhe-purifio.co.uk

Rodol Ltd, Richmond Row, Liverpool, L3 3BP Tel: 0151-207 3161 Fax: 0151-207 3727

▶ Seko Ltd, Blackminster Business Park, Old Birmingham Road, Badsey, Evesham, Worcestershire, WR11 7RE Tel: (01386) 839010 Fax: (01386) 839011 E-mail: seko.uk@seko.com

Shaw Water, Bristol House, 15 Ridge Way, Hillend, Dunfermline, Fife, KY11 9JH Tel: (01383) 820595 Fax: (01383) 820979 E-mail: shawwater@aol.com

Trade Effluent Monitoring Equipment, 2a Croft Street, Cheltenham, Gloucestershire, GL53 0EE Tel: (01242) 228745 Fax: (01242) 228745

Trogen UV Technology Ltd, 5 De-Salis Court, Hampton Lovett Industrial Estate, Droitwich, Worcestershire, WR9 0QE Tel: (01905) 771117 Fax: (01905) 772270 E-mail: uksales@trojanuv.com

Trojan Mixers, 1191 Stratford Road, Hall Green, Birmingham, B28 8BX Tel: 0121-777 5555 Fax: 0121-777 5555 E-mail: trojanmixers@hotmail.com

Vine Water Services, 96 Chichester Rd, Seaford, E. Sussex, BN25 2DT Tel: 01323 894967 Fax: 01323 892535

VWS Westgarth Ltd, Orbital House, 3 Redwood Crescent, East Kilbride, Glasgow, G74 5PR Tel: (01355) 588038 Fax: (01355) 588001

▶ Wallace & Tiernan, Priory Works, Five Oak Green Road, Tonbridge, Kent, TN11 0QL Tel: (01732) 771777 Fax: (01732) 771800 E-mail: sales@wallace-tieman.com

Water Soft Ltd, 35 Meadow Rise, Blackmore, Essex, CM4 0QY Tel: (01277) 822771 Fax: (01277) 822771

WATER TREATMENT PLANT AND EQUIPMENT MANUFRS – *continued*

Wci Pollution Control Ltd, Unit 1 Old Brewery Road, Wiveliscombe, Taunton, Somerset, TA4 2PW Tel: (01984) 623404 Fax: (01984) 624449 E-mail: wcipc@aol.com

Weldon Engineering Ltd, Unit 4B Climpy Industrial Park, Climpy Road, Forth, Lanark, ML11 8EW Tel: (01555) 812233 Fax: (01555) 812454 E-mail: sales@weldon-engineering.com

▶ Zenon Environmental UK Ltd, Bullhouse Mill, Lee Lane, Millhouse Green, Sheffield, S36 9NN Tel: (01226) 760600 Fax: (01226) 370714 E-mail: info@zenon.com

WATER TREATMENT PLANT AND EQUIPMENT ULTRAVIOLET (UV) SYSTEMS

A T G Willand, Pemberton Business Centre, Richmond Hill, Wigan, Lancashire, WN5 8AA Tel: (01942) 216161 Fax: (01942) 213131 E-mail: sales@atgwilland.com

Hanovia Uv Ltd, 145 Farnham Road, Slough, SL1 4XB Tel: (01753) 515300 Fax: (01753) 534277 E-mail: sales@hanovia.com

Trogen UV Technology Ltd, 5 De-Salis Court, Hampton Lovett Industrial Estate, Droitwich, Worcestershire, WR9 0QE Tel: (01905) 771117 Fax: (01905) 772270 E-mail: uksales@trojanuv.com

WATER TREATMENT PLANT CONTRACTORS OR DESIGNERS

Ashland UK, Wimsey Way, Somercotes, Alfreton, Derbyshire, DE55 4LR Tel: (01773) 604321 Fax: (01773) 606901

Barr + Wray Ltd, 324 Drumoyne Road, Glasgow, G51 4DY Tel: 0141-882 5757 Fax: 0141-882 3690 E-mail: sales@barrandwray.com

Bellpumps & Pollution Control, La Petite Fosse, St. Ouen, Jersey, JE3 2GN Tel: (01534) 485555 Fax: (01534) 482245 E-mail: enquiries@bellpumps.com

Direct Water Services UK Ltd, 2 Woodford Road, Barnby Dun, Doncaster, South Yorkshire, DN3 1BN Tel: (01302) 883838 Fax: (01302) 883838

Esmil Process Systems Ltd, 30 Abbey Barn Road, High Wycombe, Buckinghamshire, HP11 1RW Tel: (01494) 474515 Fax: (01494) 474515 E-mail: info@esmil.co.uk

Goodwater Ltd, 23-24 Ivanhoe Road, Hogwood Industrial Estate, Finchampstead, Wokingham, Berkshire, RG40 4QQ Tel: 0118-973 5003 Fax: 0118-973 5004 E-mail: info@goodwater.co.uk

Hytech Water Ltd, Unit 36 Southfield Road Trading Estate, Southfield Road, Nailsea, Bristol, BS48 1JE Tel: (01275) 858386 Fax: (01275) 858387 E-mail: sales@hytech-water.co.uk

Inflow UK Ltd, Unit 5a+6 Mount Industrial Estate, Mount Road, Stone, Staffordshire, ST15 8LL Tel: (01785) 812150 Fax: (01785) 812031 E-mail: sales@inflowuk.co.uk

Interserve Project Service Ltd, Crabtree Manorway South, Belvedere, Kent, DA17 6BH Tel: (020) 8311 5500 Fax: (020) 8311 1701 E-mail: belvedere.office@interserveprojects.com

Interserve Project Services Ltd, 395 George Road, Erdington, Birmingham, B23 7RZ Tel: 0121-344 4888 Fax: 0121-344 4801 E-mail: information@interserveprojects.com

Interserve Project Services Ltd, Tilbury House, Hermitage Lane, Mansfield, Nottinghamshire, NG18 5HE Tel: (01623) 633216 Fax: (01623) 659438 E-mail: mansfield.office@interserveprojects.com

Interserve Projects Ltd, Edwinstowe House, High Street, Edwinstowe, Mansfield, Nottinghamshire, NG21 9PR Tel: (01623) 827840 Fax: (01623) 827841 E-mail: edwinstowe.office@interserveprojects.com

Itsc Ltd, 9 Northfields Prospect, Northfields, London, SW18 1PE Tel: (020) 8874 7282 Fax: (020) 8874 7539 E-mail: itscuk@aol.com

Kennicott Water Systems Ltd, Kennicott House, Well Lane, Wolverhampton, WV11 1XR Tel: (01902) 721212 Fax: (01902) 721333 E-mail: sales@kennicott.co.uk

Sandess Water Treatment Co. Ltd, 70-72 Fearnley Street, Watford, WD18 0RD Tel: (01923) 236395 Fax: (01923) 818693 E-mail: sandess.@btconnect.co.uk

WATER TREATMENT SERVICES

Aquatreat Group Ltd, Stanley House, 9 Bunting Close, Mitcham, Surrey, CR4 4ND Tel: (020) 8401 8391 Fax: (020) 8401 8392 E-mail: mailbox@aquatreat.uk.com

Bristol Water Holdings plc, Bridgwater Road, Bridgwater Road, Bristol, BS99 7AU Tel: 0117-966 5881 Fax: 0117-963 3755 E-mail: corporate.affaires@bristolwater.co.uk

Carillion Regional Civil Engineering, Port Causeway, Bromborough, Wirral, Merseyside, CH62 3PS Tel: 0151-482 3502 Fax: 0151-482 3584 E-mail: martin.c.smith@carillionplc.com

City Water Pre-Com Ltd, Maidenhead Yard, The Wash, Hertford, SG14 1PX Tel: (01992) 505353 Fax: (01992) 554852 E-mail: enquiries@city-water.com

Culligan International UK Ltd, Culligan House, Coronation Road, High Wycombe, Buckinghamshire, HP12 3SU Tel: (01494) 436484 Fax: (01494) 523833 E-mail: enquires@culligan.co.uk

G E Water, Hydro House, Newcombe Way, Olrton Southgate, Peterborough, PE2 6SE Tel: (01733) 394555 Fax: (01733) 390179

G E Water & Process Technologies Ltd, Foundry Lane, Widnes, Cheshire, WA8 8UD Tel: 0151-424 5351 Fax: 0151-423 2722

I N I Environmental Services Ltd, 77 Westwood Glen, Tilehurst, Reading, RG31 5NW Tel: 0118-942 7314 Fax: 0118-942 7313 E-mail: inienviro@aol.com

Moorland Ltd, 1 Snells Wood Court, Cokes Lane, Amersham, Buckinghamshire, HP7 9QT Tel: (01494) 763965 Fax: (07890) 138190 E-mail: moorland.limited@btinternet.com

Nalco, 20-22 Albion Way, Kelvin Industrial Estate, East Kilbride, Glasgow, G75 0YN Tel: (01355) 573900 Fax: (01355) 263660

Nalco Ltd, Weavergate Works, P O Box 11, Winnington Avenue, Northwich, Cheshire, CW8 4DX Tel: (01606) 74488 Fax: 01606 79557

Nalco, Unit 5a Springside, Howard Road, Park Farm Industrial Estate, Redditch, Worcestershire, B98 7SE Tel: (01527) 453200 Fax: (01527) 520717

Portsmouth Water P.L.C., 8 West Street, Havant, Hampshire, PO9 1LG Tel: (023) 9249 9888 Fax: (023) 9245 3632

Purolite International Ltd, Unit D, Llantrisant, Rct Walescf, Pontyclun, Mid Glamorgan, CF72 8LF Tel: (01443) 229334 Fax: (01443) 231113 E-mail: sales@purolite.com

T W Page & Son Ltd, 7 Buxton Road, Frettenham, Norwich, NR12 7NQ Tel: (01603) 898071 Fax: (01603) 898049 E-mail: admin@twpage.co.uk

Three Valleys Water plc, PO Box 48, Hatfield, Hertfordshire, AL10 9HL Tel: (01707) 268111 Fax: (01707) 277333

WATER TREATMENT SERVICES, LEGIONELLA CONTROL

▶ Achromatic Limited, Grangemouth Enterprise & Technology Centre, Falkirk Road, Grangemouth, Stirlingshire, FK3 8XS Tel: (01324) 619360 Fax: (01324) 622399 E-mail: info@achromatic.co.uk

Beacon Water Treatments Ltd, 4 Parsons Hall, High Street, Irchester, Wellingborough, Northamptonshire, NN29 7AB Tel: (01933) 410066 Fax: (01933) 410077 E-mail: beaconwt@ukf.net

Chiltern Water Management Services, 1 Inkerman Drive, Hazlemere, High Wycombe, Buckinghamshire, HP15 7JJ Tel: (01494) 712831 Fax: (01494) 712831 E-mail: rh@chilternwater.co.uk

Dimanco Ltd, 24 Henlow Industrial Estate, Henlow, Bedfordshire, SG16 6DS Tel: (01462) 813933 Fax: (01462) 817407 E-mail: dimanco@ltdhenlow.fsbusiness.co.uk

Nation Water Treatments Ltd, Unit 1 Shawlands Court, Newchapel Road, Lingfield, Surrey, RH7 6BL Tel: (01342) 833693 Fax: (01342) 833787 E-mail: nwt@nationwatertreatments.co.uk

Sas Safe & Secure, Birchwoodmoor House, Roston, Ashbourne, Derbyshire, DE6 2EH Tel: (01889) 591595 Fax: (01889) 591595 E-mail: sales@legionnairesdisease.co.uk

Towerite Environmental Consultants, Old Road, Lamport, Northampton, NN6 9HF Tel: (01604) 686772 Fax: (01604) 686773 E-mail: info@towerite.co.uk

Water Treatment Technology, PO Box 2333, Sudbury, Suffolk, CO10 7HW Tel: (01787) 313993 Fax: (01787) 311693 E-mail: sales@h2owtt.com

Watermarc Chemical Services, Unit 38 Nine Mile Point Industrial Estate, Cwmfelinfach, Ynysddu, Newport, Gwent, NP11 7HZ Tel: (01495) 200005 Fax: (01495) 200844

WATER TREATMENT SPECIALIST PIPEWORK

Inflow UK Ltd, Unit 5a+6 Mount Industrial Estate, Mount Road, Stone, Staffordshire, ST15 8LL Tel: (01785) 812150 Fax: (01785) 812031 E-mail: sales@inflowuk.co.uk

WATER TREATMENT SPECIALIST PIPEWORK INSTALLATION CONTRACTORS

A M T Systems, West Stockwith Park, Stockwith Road, Misterton, Doncaster, South Yorkshire, DN10 4ES Tel: (01427) 890022 Fax: (01427) 890063 E-mail: graham@amt-systems.co.uk

Statham Engineering Services Ltd, Warrington Lane, Lymm, Cheshire, WA13 0SW Tel: (01925) 754965 Fax: (01925) 754127 E-mail: info@stathameng.co.uk

WATER TREATMENT STERILISATION SERVICES, CHLORINE DIOXIDE

Green & Carter, Vulcan Works, Rectory Road, Ashbrittle, Wellington, Somerset, TA21 0LQ Tel: (01823) 672365 Fax: (01823) 672950 E-mail: general@greenandcarter.com

M M R International Ltd, 32 Station Approch, West Byfleet, Surrey, KT14 6NF Tel: (01932) 351733 Fax: (020) 7482 3518

MSM Water Services, Landing Lane, Haxby, York, YO32 2NB Tel: (01904) 766878 Fax: (01904) 766878

WATER TREATMENT STERILISATION SERVICES, ULTRAVIOLET (UV)

Warkworth Treatment Works, Warkworth, Morpeth, Northd, NE65 0UB Tel: (01665) 711386 Fax: (01665) 713309 E-mail: david.richardson@mwl.co.uk

WATER TREATMENT TANNIN

Roy Dickson Wilson, Alrewas House, Main Street, Alrewas, Burton-on-Trent, Staffordshire, DE13 7ED Tel: (01283) 792255 Fax: (01283) 792041

WATER TREATMENT TECHNICAL SERVICES

Altek Chemical Engineering 2000 Ltd, Cuckoo Hill, Bures, Suffolk, CO8 5JH Tel: (01787) 242007 Fax: (01787) 227000

Aqua Soft Services, Downland, The Vale, Chalfont St. Peter, Gerrards Cross, Buckinghamshire, SL9 9SD Tel: (01753) 885551 Fax: (01753) 885551

Aquamatic, PO Box 117, Godalming, Surrey, GU8 4FF Tel: (01483) 861598

Aquastat West, Hillgate House, Bridgwater Road, Bleadon, Weston-super-Mare, Avon, BS24 0BA Tel: (01934) 811264 Fax: (01934) 811394

Aquatide Ltd, 26 Hewell Road, Redditch, Worcestershire, B97 6AN Tel: (01527) 592777 Fax: (01527) 592888

Bailey & Partners Ltd, 30 South Park Road, Gatley, Cheadle, Cheshire, SK8 4AN Tel: 0161-428 8212 Fax: 0161-428 8212

Cascade Water Systems Ltd, Cascade House, 35a King Street, Hoyland, Barnsley, South Yorkshire, S74 9JU Tel: (01226) 361665 Fax: (01226) 361671 E-mail: mail@cascade-water-filters.co.uk

Chisnall Environmental Services, 63 Vernon Road, Poynton, Stockport, Cheshire, SK12 1YS Tel: (01625) 858567 Fax: (01625) 858856

Earthly Goods, 8 Field Close, Grafham, Huntingdon, Cambridgeshire, PE28 0AY Tel: (01480) 812004 Fax: 01480 812004 E-mail: timbers85@hotmail.com

Ems Ltd, Sentinal House, 11a High Street, Long Buckby, Northampton, NN6 7RE Tel: (01327) 844848 Fax: (01327) 844849 E-mail: duncan@environmental-mechanical-services.co.uk

Excel Water, Unit 441a Thorp Arch Trading Estate, Thorp Arch, Wetherby, West Yorkshire, LS23 7BJ Tel: (01937) 844211 Fax: (01937) 844101 E-mail: sales@excelwater.co.uk

Guardian Water Engineering Ltd, Woodland Croft, Orchard Road, Matlock Bath, Matlock, Derbyshire, DE4 3PF Tel: (01629) 55655 Fax: (01629) 55655

Hydrotec UK Ltd, 5 Manor Courtyard, Hughenden Avenue, High Wycombe, Buckinghamshire, HP13 5RE Tel: (01494) 796040 Fax: (01494) 796049 E-mail: sales@hydrotec.co.uk

Hytech Water Ltd, Unit 36 Southfield Road Trading Estate, Southfield Road, Nailsea, Bristol, BS48 1JE Tel: (01275) 858386 Fax: (01275) 858387 E-mail: sales@hytech-water.co.uk

I N I Environmental Services Ltd, 77 Westwood Glen, Tilehurst, Reading, RG31 5NW Tel: 0118-942 7314 Fax: 0118-942 7313 E-mail: inienviro@aol.com

Lime Guard UK, PO Box 2796, Calne, Wiltshire, SN11 9ZY Tel: (01249) 816749 Fax: (01249) 816838 E-mail: enquiries@limeguard.com

Orchard Environmental Ltd, 6 Newford Close, Hemel Hempstead, Hertfordshire, HP2 4QZ Tel: (01442) 253610 Fax: (01442) 253610 E-mail: info@orchard-environmental.co.uk

Soft Waterworks Co. Ltd, Chorlton House, 149 Bridgnorth Road, Stourton, Stourbridge, West Midlands, DY7 6RY Tel: (01384) 872548 Fax: (01384) 878105 E-mail: ipayton@softwaterworks.fsbusiness.co.uk

Towerite Environmental Consultants, Old Road, Lamport, Northampton, NN6 9HF Tel: (01604) 686772 Fax: (01604) 686773 E-mail: info@towerite.co.uk

Whitewater UK Ltd, 2 Beech Road, Purley on Thames, Reading, RG8 8DS Tel: 0118-984 5565 Fax: 0118-961 5626 E-mail: tech@whitewater.net

WATER TREATMENT/ DESALINATION SYSTEMS

Salt Separation Services, Grosvenor House, Gorrell Street, Rochdale, Lancashire, OL11 1AP Tel: (01706) 655522 Fax: (01706) 654475 E-mail: sss@saltsep.co.uk

WATER TURBINES

G E Energy UK Ltd, Kvaerner House, Ten Pound Walk, Doncaster, South Yorkshire, DN4 5HW Tel: (01302) 761761 Fax: (01302) 760230

Gilbert Gilkes & Gordon Ltd, Canal Iron Works, Kendal, Cumbria, LA9 7BZ Tel: (01539) 720028 Fax: (01539) 732110 E-mail: sales@gilkes.com

WATER VALVES

Aqua-Gas Avk Ltd, P O Box 143, Northampton, NN4 7ZU Tel: (01604) 601188 Fax: (01604) 604818 E-mail: info@aquagas.co.uk

Aqua-Gas Manufacturing Ltd, Arnsley Road, Weldon North Industrial Estate, Corby, Northamptonshire, NN17 5QW Tel: (01536) 275910 Fax: (01536) 204256 E-mail: fran.brody@agmc.co.uk

Arrow Valves Ltd, 68 High Street, Tring, Hertfordshire, HP23 4AG Tel: (01442) 823123 Fax: (01442) 823234 E-mail: info@arrowvalves.co.uk

Bemasan Ltd, Owen Road, Wolverhampton, WV3 0BB Tel: (01902) 772975 Fax: (01902) 424374 E-mail: nevasales@bemasan.com

Crane Building Services & Utilities, Crane House, Epsilon Terrace, West Road, Ipswich, IP3 9FJ Tel: (01473) 277300 Fax: (01473) 270301 E-mail: enquiries@cranebsu.com

Drain Centre, Heron Works, Heron Road, Sowton Industrial Estate, Exeter, EX2 7LL Tel: (01392) 445588 Fax: (01392) 445599

Dynafluid Ltd, Units D1-D2, Halesfield 21, Telford, Shropshire, TF7 4NX Tel: (01952) 580946 Fax: (01952) 582546 E-mail: enquiries@dynafluid.com

Pipeline Centre, Millmarsh Lane, Enfield, Middlesex, EN3 7QG Tel: (020) 8805 9588 Fax: (020) 8805 2297

WATER WEIGHTED BAGS FOR CRANE TESTING

I M E S Ltd, Tern Place, Denmore Road, Bridge of Don, Aberdeen, AB23 8JX Tel: (01224) 705777 Fax: (01224) 824808 E-mail: marketing@imes-group.com

WATER WELL DRILLING EQUIPMENT

Archway Engineering (UK) Ltd, Ainleys Industrial Estate, Elland, West Yorkshire, HX5 9JP Tel: (01422) 373101 Fax: (01422) 374847 E-mail: sales@archway-engineering.com

D C M Drillquip Ltd, Hazel Way, Bermuda Road, Nuneaton, Warwickshire, CV10 7QG Tel: (024) 7634 8328 Fax: (024) 7634 8329 E-mail: sales@drillquip.co.uk

Drill Supply Ltd, 41 Green Lane, Lower Kingswood, Tadworth, Surrey, KT20 6TJ Tel: (01737) 832820 Fax: (01737) 833025 E-mail: drillsupply@onetel.com

International Drilling Services Ltd, Carrwood Road, Chesterfield, Derbyshire, S41 9QB Tel: (01246) 269911 Fax: (01246) 269922 E-mail: sales@idsuk.com

Marton Geotechnical Services Ltd, Heyford Close, Aldermans Green Industrial Estate, Coventry, CV2 2QB Tel: (024) 7660 2323 Fax: (024) 7660 2116 E-mail: sales@mgf.co.uk

Southern Drilling Services Ltd, The Factory, Ford Airfield Industrial Estate, Ford, Arundel, West Sussex, BN18 0HY Tel: (01903) 732359 Fax: (01903) 732476 E-mail: info@southern-drilling.co.uk

Stuart Pumps Ltd, Stuart House, Crowshall Lane, Attleborough, Norfolk, NR17 1AD Tel: (01953) 454540 Fax: (01953) 456968 E-mail: info@stuartpumps.co.uk

Terex Halco, PO Box 25, Halifax, West Yorkshire, HX3 9TW Tel: (01422) 399900 Fax: (01422) 330186 E-mail: halco@halcodrilling.com

WATERBED CONDITIONERS

▶ Waterbeds Direct, 7 Talbot Row, Euxton, Chorley, Lancashire, PR7 6HS Tel: (0808) 1001419 E-mail: sales@waterbedsdirect.co.uk

WATERING CAN ROSE

Haws Watering Cans, 120 Beakes Road, Smethwick, West Midlands, B67 5AB Tel: 0121-420 2494 Fax: 0121-429 1668 E-mail: sales@haws.demon.co.uk

WATERPROOF BREATHABLE CHILDRENS TROUSERS

▶ Waterproof World, 113 Cowper Road, Hemel Hempstead, Hertfordshire, HP1 1PF Tel: (01442) 401300 Fax: 0114-240 1301 E-mail: info@waterproofworld.co.uk

WATERPROOF BREATHABLE FABRICS

Lingcroft Associates Ltd, Park House, Brooke Street, Cleckheaton, West Yorkshire, BD19 3RY Tel: (01274) 876500 Fax: (01274) 876125 E-mail: richard@lingcroft.co.uk

WATERPROOF ELECTRIC HEATERS

▶ Hyco Manufacturing Ltd, Units 1 & 2, Calder Works, Methley Road, Castleford, West Yorkshire, WF10 1NX Tel: (01977) 517555 Fax: (01977) 517666 E-mail: sales@hycomanufacturing.co.uk

WATERPROOF MATERIALS, *See also headings for particular types*

G D Textile Manufacturing Co., 3 Stocks Mill, Legh Street, Eccles, Manchester, M30 0UT Tel: 0161-788 2100 Fax: 0161-788 2109 E-mail: gd.textstyle@btinternet.com

WATERPROOF MEMBRANE ROOFING CONTRACTORS

▶ Building Diagnostic & Assessment Services Ltd, Liberator House, Glasgow Prestwick International, Glasgow Prestwick Intnl Airpor, Prestwick, Ayrshire, KA9 2PL Tel: (0800) 7314364 Fax: (01292) 471146

Granflex (Roofing) Ltd, Brick Kiln Lane, Basford, Stoke-On-Trent, ST4 7BT Tel: (01782) 202208 Fax: (01782) 273601 E-mail: sales@granflexroofing.co.uk

Hyflex Roofing, Halfords Lane, Smethwick, West Midlands, B66 1BJ Tel: 0121-555 6464 Fax: 0121-555 5862 E-mail: smethwick@hyflex.co.uk

▶ Impermia, 1 shaftesbury Gdns, London, NW10 6LP Tel: (020) 8961 5259 Fax: (020) 8961 5359 E-mail: info@impermia.co.uk

Independent Roofing Systems Ltd, 118 Eastbourne Road, Darlington, County Durham, DL1 4ER Tel: (01325) 466423 Fax: (01325) 466493 E-mail: irsltd@globalnet.co.uk

Lambert Contracts & Coatings Ltd, Hamilton House, Blackhall Lane, Paisley, Renfrewshire, PA1 1TA Tel: 0141-840 1444 Fax: 0141-848 9593 E-mail: sales@lambertcontracts.co.uk

▶ Lane Roofing, Walsall House, 167 Walsall Road, Perry Barr, Birmingham, B42 1TX Tel: 0121-331 4407 Fax: 0121-344 3782 E-mail: info@laneroofing.co.uk

Midland Properties, Reeves Street, Walsall, WS3 2DL Tel: (01922) 404148 Fax: (01922) 400212

Pallard Contracts Ltd, 84 Court Lane, Cosham, Portsmouth, PO6 2LR Tel: (023) 9221 0075 Fax: (023) 9232 5716 E-mail: enquiries@pallard.co.uk

Robseal Roofing Ltd, Unit 3 Nimrod Way, Elgar Road South, Reading, RG2 0EB Tel: 0118-975 4800 Fax: 0118-975 4854 E-mail: mail@robseal.co.uk

Springvale Weatherproofing Ltd, 5 Broad Street, Newport, Gwent, NP20 2DQ Tel: (01633) 213433 Fax: (01633) 212005

Wheatley & Sons Ltd, 25a Arnison Road, East Molesey, Surrey, KT8 9JQ Tel: (020) 8979 5762 Fax: (020) 8941 7388

WATERPROOF OR SPLASH PROOF CONNECTORS

A E R C O Ltd, Units 16-17 Lawson Hunt Industrial Park, Broadbridge Heath, Horsham, West Sussex, RH12 3JR Tel: (01403) 260206 Fax: (01403) 259760 E-mail: sales@aerco.co.uk

Custom Design Mouldings Ltd, Unit 212-215, Springvale Industrial Estate, Cwmbran, Gwent, NP44 5BJ Tel: (01633) 861441 Fax: (01633) 876412 E-mail: sales@cdg-uk.com

WATERPROOF PORTABLE RADIO CASES

J & B Leathers, 37 Orford Road, London, E17 9NL Tel: (020) 8923 7720 Fax: (020) 8923 7720 E-mail: sales@jbleathers.co.uk

WATERPROOF PVC COATED CHILDRENS TROUSERS

▶ Waterproof World, 113 Cowper Road, Hemel Hempstead, Hertfordshire, HP1 1PF Tel: (01442) 401300 Fax: 0114-240 1301 E-mail: info@waterproofworld.co.uk

WATERPROOF SPORTS JACKETS

▶ Air Assault Kiteboarding, Air Assault Ltd, Horley, Surrey, RH6 7JX Tel: 07739 733600 E-mail: info@air-assault.com

WATERPROOFED CANVAS

The British Millerain Company Ltd, Melloroid Works, Belfield Road, Rochdale, Lancashire, OL16 2XA Tel: (01706) 649242 Fax: (01706) 527611 E-mail: sales@britishmillerain.com

J.T. Inglis & Sons Ltd, Riverside Works, Carolina Port, Dundee, DD1 3LU Tel: (01382) 462131 Fax: (01382) 462846

WATERPROOFED CLOTHING

Bolton Metropolitan Borough Council Commercial Services Bolmoor I, St Helens Road, Bolton, BL3 3NS Tel: (01204) 336855 Fax: (01204) 658072 E-mail: sales@bolmoor.co.uk

Central Safety Ltd, 30 North Street Industrial Estate, Droitwich, Worcestershire, WR9 8JB Tel: (01905) 774737 Fax: (01905) 796356

Guy Cotton Ltd, Unit 1 Heathlands Road Industrial Estate, Station Road, Liskeard, Cornwall, PL14 4DH Tel: (01579) 347115

Globe Weatherwear, 59 Waterloo Road, Smethwick, West Midlands, B66 4JS Tel: 0121-558 7483 Fax: 0121-558 7483

Hebden Cord Co Ltd, 17 Old Gate, Hebden Bridge, West Yorkshire, HX7 6EW Tel: (01422) 843152 Fax: (01422) 846354 E-mail: hebcord@aol.com

Henri Lloyd International Ltd, Smithfold Lane, Worsley, Manchester, M28 0GP Tel: 0161-799 1212 Fax: 0161-975 2500 E-mail: information@henrilloyd.co.uk

Hike & Bike, 1 North Street, Alfriston, Polegate, East Sussex, BN26 5UG Tel: (01323) 871861 Fax: (01323) 871861 E-mail: mike@hikeandbike.co.uk

Lavenham Leisure Ltd, 24-25 Churchfield Road, Sudbury, Suffolk, CO10 2YA Tel: (01787) 379535 Fax: (01787) 880096 E-mail: info@lavenhamhorserugs.com

M B Products Ltd, Parkgate Works, Coleman Street, Parkgate, Rotherham, South Yorkshire, S62 6EL Tel: (01709) 528215 Fax: (01709) 710796 E-mail: roger@mbpgroup.freeserve.co.uk

Macintosh Ltd, Unit 10a Blairlinn Industrial Estate, Cumbernauld, Glasgow, G67 2TW Tel: (01422) 846953 Fax: (01236) 723924 E-mail: sales@mackintosh-scotland.com

Mountain Man Supplies, 133 South Street, Perth, PH2 8PA Tel: (01738) 632368 Fax: (01738) 580284 E-mail: enquiries@mountainsupplies.co.uk

Portsmouth Gun Centre, 295 London Road, Portsmouth, PO2 9HF Tel: (023) 9266 0574 Fax: (023) 9264 4666

Premier Rainwear, 46 Stanley Street, Manchester, M8 8SH Tel: 0161-834 9481

Peter Stunt, Beam Wireless Station, North Petherton, Bridgwater, Somerset, TA7 0DX Tel: (01278) 663344 Fax: (01278) 663343 E-mail: sales@peterstunt.co.uk

Togged-Up, 2 Wellgate, Clitheroe, Lancashire, BB7 2DP Tel: (01200) 427630 Fax: (01200) 424873 E-mail: linda@tusport.co.uk

S. Yaffy Protective Clothing, 310 Main Street, Glasgow, G40 1LW Tel: 0141-554 2202 Fax: 0141-556 4347 E-mail: admin@yaffy.co.uk

WATERPROOFED COVERS

F Waites & Sons, Harper Street, Driffield, North Humberside, YO25 6LY Tel: (01377) 253310 Fax: (01377) 253310

Fine Group Son Ltd, 93 Manor Farm Road, London, Wembley, Middlesex, HA0 1XB Tel: (020) 8214 8600 Fax: (020) 8997 8410 E-mail: sales@hfine.co.uk

Fisher Tarpaulins, Unit 5-6 The Maltings, Navigation Drive, Hurst Business Park, Brierley Hill, West Midlands, DY5 1UT Tel: (01384) 571313 Fax: (01384) 261666

▶ Selective Covers Ltd, G Lumley Close, Thirsk Industrial Park, Thirsk, North Yorkshire, YO7 3TD Tel: (01845) 522856 Fax: (01845) 574227

T & C Robinson, Tattershall Road, Billinghay, Lincoln, LN4 4BN Tel: (01526) 860436 Fax: (01526) 861352 E-mail: sales@saddleforce9.co.uk

WATERPROOFED FABRICS

Farnbeck Ltd, 32 Swanfield, Edinburgh, EH6 5RX Tel: 0131-553 5353 Fax: 0131-553 3979 E-mail: dm001@post.almac.co.uk

Mansam Products Ltd, 49-51 Broughton Lane, Manchester, M8 9UE Tel: 0161-834 1356 Fax: 0161-835 1024 E-mail: sales@mansam.co.uk

Sealproof Ltd, Dan Lane Mill, Tyldesley Road, Atherton, Manchester, M46 9DA Tel: (01942) 878012 Fax: (01942) 878298

WATERPROOFED PAPER

Packaging Products Ltd, Collyhurst Road, Manchester, M40 7RT Tel: 0161-205 4181 Fax: 0161-203 4678 E-mail: sales@packagingproducts.co.uk

WATERPROOFING BUILDING MEMBRANES

Cinque Products Ltd, Harbour Road, Rye, East Sussex, TN31 7TE Tel: (01797) 223561 Fax: (01797) 224530 E-mail: longproducts@aol.com

John Newton & Co. Ltd, 12 Verney Road, London, SE16 3DH Tel: (020) 7237 1217 Fax: (020) 7252 2769 E-mail: sales@newton-membranes.co.uk

Premier Coatings Ltd, Marley Farm, Headcorn Road, Smarden, Ashford, Kent, TN27 8PJ Tel: (01233) 770663 Fax: (01233) 770633 E-mail: premiercoating@aol.com

Support Site P.L.C., Pedmore Road, Dudley, West Midlands, DY2 0RN Tel: (01384) 472250 Fax: (01384) 472251 E-mail: birmingham@supportsite.co.uk

Triton Chemical Manufacturing Co. Ltd, Unit 5 Lyndean Industrial Estate, 129 Felixstowe Road, London, SE2 9SG Tel: (020) 8310 3929 Fax: (020) 8312 0349 E-mail: info@triton-chemicals.com

Vandex (UK) Ltd, PO Box 200, Guildford, Surrey, GU2 4WD Tel: (0870) 2416264 Fax: (0870) 2416274 E-mail: info@vandex.co.uk

WATERPROOFING OR WEATHERPROOFING ROOFING MATERIALS, *See also Asphalt; Bitumen; Bituminous etc*

Isothane Ltd, Newhouse Road, Huncoat Industrial Estate, Accrington, Lancashire, BB5 6NT Tel: (01254) 872555 Fax: (01254) 871522 E-mail: enquiries@isothane.com

Sarnafil Ltd, 11 Robberds Way, Bowthorpe Employment Area, Norwich, NR5 9JF Tel: (01603) 748985 Fax: (01603) 743054 E-mail: sales@sarnafil.com

WATERSPORTS GOODS

A S Watersports, 1-3 Waterside, Exeter, EX2 8GU Tel: (01392) 421831 Fax: (01392) 421831 E-mail: sales@aswatersports.co.uk

▶ Ocean Leisure, 11-14 Northumberland Avenue, London, WC2N 5AQ Tel: (020) 7930 5050 Fax: (020) 7930 3032 E-mail: info@oceanleisure.co.uk

Splashsports Services, 5 8 Meadow Road, Glasgow, G11 6HX Tel: 0141-337 2828 Fax: 0141-339 7788 E-mail: sales@splashsports.co.uk

Tiki International (Plastics) Ltd, Velator Industrial Estate, Braunton, Devon, EX33 2DX Tel: (01271) 812442 Fax: (01271) 816570 E-mail: tiki@tikisurf.force9.co.uk

West Bay Water Sports Ltd, 10A West Bay, Bridport, Dorset, DT6 4EL Tel: (01308) 421800 Fax: (01308) 421800 E-mail: steve@anglianmailorder.com

WATTMETERS

Taylor Bros Oldham Ltd, Lee Street, Oldham, OL8 1EE Tel: 0161-652 3221 Fax: 0161-626 1736 E-mail: karen.taylorbrs@btinternet.com

WAVEGUIDE COMPONENTS

Alroy Microwaves & Electronics Ltd, Boulton Road, Stevenage, Hertfordshire, SG1 4QX Tel: (01438) 314753 Fax: (01483) 367430 E-mail: sales@alroymicrowave.co.uk

WAVEGUIDE SYSTEMS

Alroy Microwaves & Electronics Ltd, Boulton Road, Stevenage, Hertfordshire, SG1 4QX Tel: (01438) 314753 Fax: (01483) 367430 E-mail: sales@alroymicrowave.co.uk

WAX FILLETS, GLASS FIBRE OR FIBREGLASS MOULDING

Phillips (1969) Ltd, Unit 3, Stambermill Industrial Estate, Lye, Stourbridge, West Midlands, DY9 7BJ Tel: (01384) 897324 Fax: (01384) 895435 E-mail: phillips@bradleeboilers.com

WAX MELTING EQUIPMENT

Controlled Equipment, 17 The Mead Business Centre, Mead Lane, Hertford, SG13 7BJ Tel: (01992) 584404 Fax: (01992) 500177 E-mail: sales@meltingtank.com

WAX POLISH

Myland's Paints & Woodfinishes, 80 Norwood High Street, London, SE27 9NW Tel: (020) 8761 5197 Fax: (020) 8761 5700 E-mail: sales@mylands.co.uk

WAXED CHEESE

Ashley Chase Estate Ltd, Parks Farm, Litton Cheney, Dorchester, Dorset, DT2 9AZ Tel: (01308) 482580 Fax: (01308) 482662 E-mail: cheese@fordfarm.com

WAXED COTTON CLOTHING

Carrington Novare, Calder Works, Thornhill Road, Dewsbury, West Yorkshire, WF12 9QQ Tel: (01924) 465161 Fax: (01924) 457596 E-mail: enquiries@cpf.co.uk

R K Clothing Manufacturers Ltd, 300-306 Park Road, Hockley, Birmingham, B18 5HE Tel: 0121-551 1379 Fax: 0121-551 1379

WAXED PAPER

Interflex Group, Peggys Mill, Mayfield Industrial Estate, Dalkeith, Midlothian, EH22 4AE Tel: 0131-654 2626 Fax: 0131-654 2606

▶ Riverside Packaging Printers Ltd, Roughmoor, Williton Industrial Estate, Taunton, Somerset, TA4 4RF Tel: (01984) 631757 Fax: (01984) 635910 E-mail: sales@rppl.co.uk

WAXES, *See also headings for particular types*

Associated Dental Products Ltd, Kemdent Works, Cricklade Road, Purton, Swindon, SN5 4HT Tel: (01793) 770256 Fax: (01793) 772256 E-mail: sales@kemdent.co.uk

Darent Wax Co., Horton Road, South Darenth, Dartford, DA4 9AA Tel: (01322) 865892 Fax: (01322) 864598 E-mail: mail@darentwax.com

Liberon, Mountfield Industrial Estate, Learoyd Road, New Romney, Kent, TN28 8XU Tel: (01797) 367555 Fax: (01797) 367575

Poth Hille & Co. Ltd, 37 High Street, London, E15 2QD Tel: (020) 8534 7091 Fax: (020) 8534 2291 E-mail: enquiries@poth-hille.co.uk

Thew, Arnott & Co. Ltd, Newman Works, 270 London Road, Wallington, Surrey, SM6 7DJ Tel: (020) 8669 3131 Fax: (020) 8669 7747 E-mail: sales@thewarnott.co.uk

Valan Wax Products Ltd, Unit 14 Alfred Court Saxon Business Park, Hanbury Road, Stoke Prior, Bromsgrove, Worcestershire, B60 4AD Tel: (01527) 876541 Fax: (01527) 570054

WEAPON DESIGN/ DEVELOPMENT ENGINEERS

Bae Systems Defence Systems Ltd, Warwick House, P O Box 87, Farnborough, Hampshire, GU14 6YU Tel: (01252) 373232 Fax: (01252) 383000

M S I Defence Systems Ltd, Salhouse Road, Norwich, NR7 9AY Tel: (01603) 484065 Fax: (01603) 415649 E-mail: contact@msi-dsl.com

WEAR RESISTANT CASTINGS

Britcast Plant & Machinery Dealer, Green Acres, Shere Road, West Clandon, Guildford, Surrey, GU4 8SG Tel: (01483) 223696 Fax: (01483) 223696 E-mail: britcast@lineone.net

Caddy Castings Ltd, Springfield Road, Grantham, Lincolnshire, NG31 7BQ Tel: (01476) 566667 Fax: (01476) 570220 E-mail: caddycastings@btinternet.com

WEAR RESISTANT COATING/ LINING PROCESSORS OR SERVICES

▶ 3 J Lining Systems Ltd, Unit 2g Lake Enterprise Park, Sandall Stones Road, Kirk Sandall Industrial Estate, Doncaster, South Yorkshire, DN3 1QR Tel: (01302) 880800 Fax: (01302) 880900 E-mail: jeff@3jlinings.co.uk

Armoloy UK Ltd, Mammoth Drive, Wolverhampton Science Park, Wolverhampton, WV10 9TF Tel: (01902) 310375 Fax: (01902) 310075 E-mail: armoloyuk@aol.com

WEAR RESISTANT COATING/LINING PROCESSORS OR SERVICES –

continued

Kingfisher Industrial, Rushock Trading Estate, Droitwich, Worcestershire, WR9 0NR Tel: (01299) 251121 Fax: (01299) 251021 E-mail: enquiries@kingfisher-industrial.co.uk
Triten International Ltd, Shawfield Road, Barnsley, South Yorkshire, S71 3HS Tel: (01226) 702300 Fax: (01226) 702311 E-mail: triten@triten.co.uk

WEAR RESISTANT COATINGS/ LININGS

▶ 3 J Lining Systems Ltd, Unit 2g Lake Enterprise Park, Sandall Stones Road, Kirk Sandall Industrial Estate, Doncaster, South Yorkshire, DN3 1QR Tel: (01302) 880800 Fax: (01302) 880900 E-mail: jeff@3jlinings.co.uk
Praxair Surface Technologies Ltd, Westfield Road, Kineton Road Industrial Estate, Southam, Warwickshire, CV47 0JH Tel: (01926) 812348 Fax: (01926) 817775

WEAR RESISTANT STEEL

Hoganas GB Ltd, Munday Works, Morley Road, Tonbridge, Kent, TN9 1RP Tel: (01732) 362243 Fax: (01732) 770262 E-mail: sales@powdrex.com

WEATHER SEALS OR STRIPS

A & S Rubber & Plastics, Unit 10c Old Park Industrial Estate, Old Park Road, Wednesbury, West Midlands, WS10 9LR Tel: 0121-556 4415 Fax: 0121-556 2414 E-mail: info@asrubber.com
Norsound, Unit 5, Regents Drive, Prudhoe, Northumberland, NE42 6PX Tel: 0 1661 831 311 Fax: 0 1661 830 099 E-mail: sales@norsound.co.uk

WEATHER STATIONS

Environmental Measurements Ltd, Business & Innovation Centre, Wearfield, Sunderland Enterprise Park, Sunderland, SR5 2TA Tel: 0191-501 0064 Fax: 0191-501 0065 E-mail: sales@emltd.net

WEAVING PICKING STICKS

Crossley's Shuttles Ltd, Woodbottom Mill, Hollins Road, Walsden, Todmorden, Lancashire, OL14 6PG Tel: (01706) 812152 Fax: (01706) 813767 E-mail: sales@crossleysshuttles.co.uk

WEAVING SHUTTLES

Crossley's Shuttles Ltd, Woodbottom Mill, Hollins Road, Walsden, Todmorden, Lancashire, OL14 6PG Tel: (01706) 812152 Fax: (01706) 813767 E-mail: sales@crossleysshuttles.co.uk
Pilkingtons Ltd, Belgrave Court, Caxton Road, Fulwood, Preston, PR2 9PL Tel: (01772) 705566 Fax: (01772) 705599 E-mail: info@pilkingtonsltd.com

WEB HANDLING SYSTEMS

▶ Marknine Networks, 19 Crabtree Walk, Broxbourne, Hertfordshire, EN10 7NH Tel: (07075) 055577 Fax: (07075) 055577 E-mail: tonym@marknine.net

WEB INSPECTION SYSTEMS

Another Dimension Ltd, 167 Ardleigh Green Road, Hornchurch, Essex, RM11 2LF Tel: (01708) 701511 Fax: (01708) 701994 E-mail: info@anotherdimension.co.uk

WEB MANAGEMENT/CONTROL SYSTEMS

Carino Communications, 143 Boundary Road, Wooburn Green, High Wycombe, Buckinghamshire, HP10 0DL Tel: (01628) 526005 Fax: (01628) 851205 E-mail: andy@carino.co.uk
Ci-Net, Langford Locks, Kidlington, Oxfordshire, OX5 1GA Tel: (01865) 856000 Fax: (01865) 856001 E-mail: info@ci-net.com
Flynet Ltd, King William House, The Causeway, Burwell, Cambridge, CB5 0DU Tel: (01638) 611111 Fax: (01638) 611115 E-mail: info@flynet.co.uk
Marven Ltd, 3 Farm La, London, SW6 1PU Tel: (020) 7386 9445 Fax: (020) 7386 9775
Neonstream Ltd, 23 Woodcote, Maidenhead, Berkshire, SL6 4DU Tel: (01628) 622022 Fax: (01628) 785458 E-mail: rws@neonstream.net
Pershore Leisure Centre, PO Box 2000, Pershore, Worcestershire, WR10 1QU Tel: (01386) 552346 Fax: (01386) 556559 E-mail: post@c2000.com
Wick Hill Ltd, Rivercourt, Albert Drive, Woking, Surrey, GU21 5RP Tel: (01483) 227600 Fax: (01483) 227700 E-mail: info@wickhill.co.uk

WEB OFFSET PRINTING

A Mcclay & Co. Ltd, Longwood Drive, Cardiff, CF14 7ZB Tel: (029) 2054 4100 Fax: (029) 2054 4123 E-mail: 106740.3652@compuserve.com
▶ Artisan Press Ltd, 4 Boston Road, Leicester, LE4 1AQ Tel: 0116-235 5221 Fax: 0116-236 6222 E-mail: sales@artisanpress.co.uk
▶ B G P Bicester, Chaucer Business Park, Launton Road, Bicester, Oxfordshire, OX26 4QZ Tel: (01869) 363333 Fax: (01869) 363306 E-mail: marketing@bgprint.co.uk
▶ Eclipse Colour Print Ltd, Riley Road, Telford Way Industrial Estate, Kettering, Northamptonshire, NN16 8NN Tel: (01536) 483401 Fax: (01536) 481102 E-mail: sales@eclipsecolourprint.co.uk
Graphoprint Ltd, 1 North House, Bond Avenue, Mount Farm, Milton Keynes, MK1 1AY Tel: (01908) 371110 Fax: (01908) 371130
Tom Gutherless Ltd, 34 & 34a St James Street, Hull, HU3 2DH Tel: (01482) 214184 Fax: (01482) 215211 E-mail: print@tom-guther.co.uk
Jarrold & Sons Ltd, Whitefriars, Norwich, NR3 1SH Tel: (01603) 660211 Fax: (01603) 630162 E-mail: info@njp.co.uk
Polestar Chromoworks Ltd, Wigman Road, Nottingham, NG8 3JA Tel: 0115-900 8300 Fax: 0115-900 8320
The Print Factory Ltd, South Portway Close, Round Spinney, Northampton, NN3 8RH Tel: (01604) 790079 Fax: (01604) 492515 E-mail: info@theprintfactory.co.uk
Quebecor World UK Holdings plc, 15 Saxon Way East, Oakley Hay Industrial Park, Corby, Northamptonshire, NN18 9EX Tel: (01536) 747474 Fax: (01536) 742042 E-mail: kspencer@quebecorworldplc.com
Special Occasions, 105 High Street, Rowley Regis, West Midlands, B65 0EG Tel: 0121-559 2573 Fax: 0121-559 2878
Strachan & Livingston, 23-25 Kirk Wynd, Kirkcaldy, Fife, KY1 1EP Tel: (01592) 261451 Fax: (01592) 204180
Wyndeham Heron & Co. Ltd, The Bentalls Complex, Colchester Road, Heybridge, Maldon, Essex, CM9 4NW Tel: (01621) 877777 Fax: (01621) 877776
Wyndeham Impact Ltd, Units L1-L3, Impact House, Grafton Way, West Ham Industrial Estate, Basingstoke, Hampshire, RG22 6HY Tel: (01256) 479816 Fax: (01256) 324671 E-mail: impact@wyndeham.co.uk

WEB TENSION CONTROL SPECIALIST SERVICES

C M C Controls Ltd, Chaucer Business Park, Watery Lane, Kemsing, Sevenoaks, Kent, TN15 6PL Tel: (01732) 763278 Fax: (01732) 763279 E-mail: sales@cmccontrols.co.uk
▶ Erhardt & Leimer, Russell Court, 9 Wool Gate, Cottingley, Bingley, West Yorkshire, BD16 1PE Tel: (08707) 559773 Fax: (08707) 559774 E-mail: info-uk@erhardt-leimer.com

WEBBING AND STRAP ASSEMBLIES

Apb Products, Unit 30 Tweedale Court Industrial Estate, Madeley, Telford, Shropshire, TF7 4JZ Tel: (01952) 681940 Fax: (01952) 681945 E-mail: malcolm.harris@apbproducts.co.uk
Auto-Med Technologies Ltd, 127 North Gate, Nottingham, NG7 7FZ Tel: 0115-919 1234 Fax: 0115-919 1236 E-mail: sales@auto-med.com

WEBBING EQUIPMENT

William Birch Engineers Ltd, Milton Street, Salford, M7 1UX Tel: 0161-834 9675 Fax: 0161-833 2268 E-mail: sales@william-birch.co.uk

WEBBING MANUFRS, *See also headings for particular types*

Intercontinental Mercantile Ltd, 23 Dollis Hill Estate, 105 Brook Road, London, NW2 7BZ Tel: (020) 8830 7388 Fax: (020) 8830 7388

WEBBING PROCESSORS TO THE TRADE

William Birch Engineers Ltd, Milton Street, Salford, M7 1UX Tel: 0161-834 9675 Fax: 0161-833 2268 E-mail: sales@william-birch.co.uk

WEBBING SLINGS

Beeweb Lifting Equipment, Ambrose Street, Rochdale, Lancashire, OL11 1QX Tel: (01706) 648717 Fax: (01706) 653012 E-mail: beeweb@btconnect.com
Bradley Thallon Industries Ltd, Kiltonga Industrial Estate, Belfast Road, Newtownards, County Down, BT23 4TJ Tel: (028) 9181 5403 Fax: (028) 9181 5409 E-mail: terence@bradleythallon.co.uk
DSM, Riverside Works, Huddersfield Road, Mirfield, West Yorkshire, WF14 9DL Tel: (01924) 490781 Fax: (01924) 491128 E-mail: sales@dsm-group.co.uk
Metcalf Leenside Ltd, 139-143 Canal Street, Nottingham, NG1 7HD Tel: 0115-958 0865 Fax: 0115-959 8934 E-mail: sales@metcalf.co.uk
Ollard Westcombe, Bridge Street, Downpatrick, County Down, BT30 6HD Tel: (028) 4461 7557 Fax: (028) 4461 3580 E-mail: office@dthomason.freeserve.com
▶ Super Slitters, 7-8 Lessarna Court, Bowling Back Lane, Bradford, West Yorkshire, BD4 8ST Tel: (01274) 735290 Fax: (01274) 740193 E-mail: superslitters@hotmail.com

WEBBING STRAPS

Apb Products, Unit 30 Tweedale Court Industrial Estate, Madeley, Telford, Shropshire, TF7 4JZ Tel: (01952) 681940 Fax: (01952) 681945 E-mail: malcolm.harris@apbproducts.co.uk
DSM, Riverside Works, Huddersfield Road, Mirfield, West Yorkshire, WF14 9DL Tel: (01924) 490781 Fax: (01924) 491128 E-mail: sales@dsm-group.co.uk
Fine Group Son Ltd, 93 Manor Farm Road, London, Wembley, Middlesex, HA0 1XB Tel: (020) 8214 8600 Fax: (020) 8997 8410 E-mail: sales@finegoup.co.uk
Package Control (U.K.) Ltd, Unit 5 Bunas Business Park, Hollom Down Road, Lopcombe, Salisbury, SP5 1BP Tel: (01264) 782143 Fax: (0844) 8800384 E-mail: sales@package-control.co.uk
Trans-Web Ltd, Manchester Street, Oldham, OL9 6EF Tel: 0161 6270022

WEBSITE CONSULTANCY

▶ 3w Designs Ltd, 2 Cowslip Close, Tilehurst, Reading, RG31 4EY Tel: (0870) 0175050 E-mail: dave@3w-designs.co.uk
▶ A F D, 28 Belgravia Gardens, Bromley, BR1 4TB Tel: (020) 8464 3823 Fax: (07092) 277379 E-mail: info@afd.net
▶ A Web Whisper, 103 Lower End, Leafield, Witney, Oxfordshire, OX29 9QG Tel: (01993) 878356 E-mail: info@webwhisper.co.uk
▶ Ah Copy, 137 Nightingale Road, Hitchin, Hertfordshire, SG5 1RG Tel: (0845) 0090944 E-mail: enquiries@ahcopy.co.uk
▶ And Then There Was Light, The Digital World Centre, The Quays, Manchester, M50 3UB Tel: 0870 2407507 E-mail: enquiries@andlight.co.uk
▶ Artlines Media Ltd, 54 Cressex Buissness Park, Lincoln Road, High Wycombe, Buckinghamshire, HP12 3RL Tel: (01494) 614600 Fax: (01494) 614601 E-mail: tom@artlines.co.uk
▶ Assertis Ltd, 22 Warwick Park, Tunbridge Wells, Kent, TN2 5TB Tel: (01892) 513688 E-mail: info@assertis.co.uk
▶ Captain Seo, 3 The Croft, Park Hill, London, W5 2NB Tel: (020) 8816 8877 Fax: (0870) 1258147 E-mail: info@captainseo.com
▶ Coreware Ltd, Gosden Common, Tannery Lane, Bramley, Guildford, Surrey, GU5 0AB Tel: (01483) 894158 Fax: (01483) 898932 E-mail: debs@russellsharpe.com
▶ CRM4Business Limited, Huntington House Business Centre, 278 - 290 Huntington Street, Nottingham, NG7 7FN Tel: (0870) 3501808 E-mail: james.bogue@crm4business.co.uk
▶ Currier Co.Ltd, 48 Park Street, Shifnal, Shropshire, TF11 9BL Tel: (01952) 462200 E-mail: info@currier.co.uk
▶ DVH Design, 75 Bedells Avenue, Black Notley, Braintree, Essex, CM77 8NA Tel: 01376 322782 E-mail: request@dvhdesign.co.uk
▶ Emergence Communications, Commercial Centre, Exchange Street, Colne, Lancashire, BB8 0SQ Tel: 0845 8381401 Fax: 0870 1342929 E-mail: info@emergence.biz
fast-trak.net, 110 Front Street, Cockfield, Bishop Auckland, County Durham, DL13 5AA Tel: (01388) 710833 Fax: (01388) 710755
▶ hostukdomain.com, Flat 1, 23 Acock Grove, Northolt, Middlesex, UB5 4RT Tel: (0800) 0409695 E-mail: sales@hostukdomain.com
▶ Jojet Ltd, Ashley House,, 2, Lower Park Terrace, Pontypool, Torfaen, NP4 6LB Tel: (07183) 944621
▶ Kilo75 Ltd, Round Foundry Media Centre, Foundry Street, Leeds, LS11 5QP Tel: 0113 394 4606 E-mail: info@kilo75.com
▶ Limegreentangerine, 57 Cowbridge Road East, Cardiff, CF11 9AE Tel: (029) 2046 2544 E-mail: info@limegreentangerine.co.uk
▶ Mojo Creation = Marketing & Graphic Design, 85 Boundary Crescent, Stony Stratford, Milton Keynes, MK11 1DH Tel: 01908 263023 Fax: 01908 263023 E-mail: info@mojocreation.com
▶ Net Commerce Solutions Ltd, 6 Bramble Close, Harpenden, Hertfordshire, AL5 4AN Tel: (0870) 2467642 Fax: (0871) 4337349 E-mail: info@net-commerce-solutions.co.uk
▶ North Square, Hardwick, Wellingborough, Northamptonshire, NN9 5AL Tel: (01933) 401501 Fax: (01933) 402403 E-mail: info@north-square.com
▶ Northstar Marketing & Design, Northstar House, 5 Ferns Mead, Farnham, Surrey, GU9 7XP Tel: (01252) 734070 Fax: (01252) 734071 E-mail: info@northstarmarketing.co.uk
▶ Oceanic Design, Highview, Little Staughton, Bedford, MK44 2BH Tel: (01234) 378171 E-mail: sales@oceanicdesign.com
Oppo Consulting Ltd, 38 Stoke Fields, Guildford, Surrey, GU1 4LS Tel: (01483) 563502 Fax: (01483) 453773 E-mail: sales@oppo-consulting.co.uk
▶ Oxford Internet Marketing, 10 Manor Farm Close, Kingham, Chipping Norton, Oxfordshire, OX7 6YX Tel: (01608) 658803 Fax: (0870) 1275668 E-mail: stephen@oxfordinternetmarketing.co.uk
P S Consultants, Hockham Hill House, Spring Elms Lane, Little Baddom, Chelmsford, CM3 4SD Tel: (01245) 222065 Fax: (01245) 287057 E-mail: info@ps-consultants.co.uk
▶ PELICAN Solutions Ltd, 5 Westbrook Court, Sharrow Vale Road, SHEFFIELD, S11 8YZ Tel: 0114 233 5200
▶ Pink Pigeon Ltd, 34-35 Berwick Street, London, W1F 8RP Tel: (020) 7439 3266 Fax: (020) 7439 3277 E-mail: info@pinkpigeon.net
▶ Quality Business Promotions, 11 Arundel Close, Dronfield Woodhouse, Dronfield, Derbyshire, S18 8QS Tel: (01246) 414250 E-mail: enquiries@qbpromotions.co.uk
Redweb Ltd, Quay House, 7 The Quay, Poole, Dorset, BH15 1HA Tel: (01202) 779944 Fax: (01202) 773643 E-mail: stuart@redweb.co.uk
▶ S E Marketing, 6 Hallas Grove, Manchester, M23 0GZ Tel: 0161-946 1116 E-mail: semarketing@postmaster.co.uk
▶ Software Consulting Ltd, 10 Lime Kiln Road, Mannings Heath, Horsham, West Sussex, RH13 6JH Tel: (01403) 263269 E-mail: sales@scss.co.uk
▶ Toile Solutions, 1 Starr Road, Henham, Bishop's Stortford, Hertfordshire, CM22 6AW Tel: (01279) 850277 Fax: (0870) 1635365 E-mail: sales@toilesolutions.com
▶ Webcredible Ltd, 99 Mansell Street, London, E1 8AX Tel: (020) 7423 6320 Fax: 0207 481 2569 E-mail: info@webcredible.co.uk
▶ Xecore Ltd, 59 Highbury Gardens, Seven Kings Ilford, Ilford, Essex, IG3 8AF Tel: (07800) 590908 E-mail: sales@xecore.co.uk
▶ Xyligo Softwares, 7 Roebuck Court, Didcot, Oxfordshire, OX11 8UT Tel: 01235 519500 E-mail: dgallacher@xyligo.com

WEBSITE CREATION, MULTIPLE WEB PAGES, OWN DOMAIN NAME

▶ 3w Designs Ltd, 2 Cowslip Close, Tilehurst, Reading, RG31 4EY Tel: (0870) 0175050 E-mail: dave@3w-designs.co.uk
▶ AcornDomains.co.uk, Lewis Close, Addlestone, Surrey, KT15 2XG Tel: (01932) 841869
▶ And Then There Was Light, The Digital World Centre, The Quays, Manchester, M50 3UB Tel: 0870 2407507 E-mail: enquiries@andlight.co.uk
▶ Choicedomains.Co.Uk, 30a Wings Road, Farnham, Surrey, GU9 0HW Tel: (01252) 820863 Fax: (01252) 821001 E-mail: admin@choicedomains.co.uk
▶ Cymitric, 5 The Brache, Maulden, Bedford, MK45 2DZ Tel: (01525) 404434 Fax: (0871) 4335545 E-mail: info@cymitric.net
▶ Dream Designs, 11 Cove Way, Cove Bay, Aberdeen, AB12 3DW Tel: (07971) 522186 E-mail: sales@dream-designs.co.uk
Ellipse Design, 45 Marsh Lane, Crosspool, Sheffield, S10 5NN Tel: 0114-268 2961 Fax: 0114-268 2961 E-mail: enquiries@ellipsedesign.co.uk
Kaydee Web Design, 2 Meadow Close, Shipton-under-Wychwood, Chipping Norton, Oxfordshire, OX7 6BY Tel: 07769 970021 Fax: 01993 831072 E-mail: design@kaydee.net
▶ Oneuponedown Creative Solutions Ltd, 413a Chingford Road, London, E17 5AF Tel: (020) 8527 4440 Fax: (020) 8527 4527 E-mail: info@lupldown.com
▶ SAC Consultancy & Design, 55 Olympia Close, Northampton, NN4 0RU Tel: (07733) 177743 E-mail: sacharlton@sac-consult-design.com
▶ Web Alive (UK) Ltd, 25 Chalk Farm Road, London, NW1 8AG Tel: (0871) 4346400 Fax: (0871) 4346401 E-mail: fraser.henderson@webalive.co.uk
▶ Websites For You, 38 Howard Road, Portsmouth, PO2 9PS Tel: (023) 9271 0311 Fax: (023) 9271 0311 E-mail: trevor@websitesforyou.co.uk

WEBSITE DESIGN AND DEVELOPMENT

11 Out Of 10 Ltd, 84 Polefield Road, Prestwich, Manchester, M25 2QW Tel: 0161-798 7977 E-mail: info@11outof10.com

121webconsultancy, 8 Comer Gardens, Worcester, WR2 6JH Tel: 01905 422256 E-mail: steve@121webconsultancy.co.uk

▶ 2f3 Internet, 103 Malbet Park, Edinburgh, EH16 6WB Tel: 0131-666 2555 E-mail: info@2f3.com

▶ 4VisMedia, 18 Alderwood, Chineham, Basingstoke, Hampshire, RG24 8TU Tel: (01256) 320733 E-mail: enquiries@4vismedia.co.uk

▶ A F D, 28 Belgravia Gardens, Bromley, BR1 4TB Tel: (020) 8464 3823 Fax: (07092) 277379 E-mail: info@afd.net

A K Consultancies Ltd, 141a Prestbury Road, Cheltenham, Gloucestershire, GL52 2DU Tel: (01242) 234123 E-mail: sales@akc.co.uk

▶ ADH WebCreations, 55 Chaucer Road, Gillingham, Kent, ME7 5LX Tel: 01634 566138 E-mail: info@adhwebcreations.co.uk

▶ Amazing Internet Ltd, 82 Heath Road, Twickenham, TW1 4BW Tel: (020) 8607 9535 Fax: (020) 8607 9536 E-mail: contact@amazinginternet.com

▶ Amber Web Designs, 16 High Street, Baldock, Hertfordshire, SG7 6AS Tel: (01462) 895018

▶ Ashridge New Media, 131-151 Great Titchfield Street, London, W1W 5BB Tel: (0845) 2305105

▶ Auxilior Ltd, 6 Steventon Road, Southampton, SO18 5HA Tel: (023) 8047 3441 E-mail: kevin.haynes@auxilior.co.uk

▶ Beanwebs and Beandesigns, Georgian House, Orchard lane, East Hendred, Wantage, Oxfordshire, OX12 8JW Tel: 01235 832192 E-mail: enquiries@beanwebs.co.uk

▶ Bewebsmart Web Design Solutions, 24 Canolblas Avenue, Bodelwyddan, Rhyl, Denbighshire, LL18 5TW Tel: (01745) 583418 E-mail: mail@bewebsmart.co.uk

▶ Blueclaw, 21 Denton Avenue, Leeds, LS8 1LE Tel: 0113-226 2760 E-mail: info@blueclaw.co.uk

▶ Branches Design Ltd, Unit 4, Shawbridge Sawmill, Taylor Street, Clitheroe, Lancashire, BB7 1LY Tel: (01200) 444443 E-mail: info@branchesdesign.co.uk

▶ Brand 5, 19 Portico Road, Derby, DE23 3NJ Tel: 0845 2261883

▶ Brand Attention Ltd, 30A Bridge Street, Hitchin, Hertfordshire, SG5 2DF Tel: (01462) 435330 E-mail: info@brandattention.com

▶ Bright Star, 4 Barra Close, Hull, HU8 9JB Tel: (0845) 2578501 Fax: (0845) 2578501 E-mail: info@brightstarwebdesign.co.uk

▶ C Q M, 3 Westbrook Court, Sharrow Vale Road, Sheffield, S11 8YZ Tel: 0114-281 5781 Fax: 0114-281 5785 E-mail: enquireies@cqmltd.co.uk

▶ CanCreative, 16 The Mallards, Silsden, West Yorkshire, BD20 0NT Tel: 01535 652600 E-mail: candie@dataconline.co.uk

Cedalion Ltd, Great Michael House, 14 Links Place, Edinburgh, EH6 7EZ Tel: 0131-477 7741 Fax: 0131-477 7742 E-mail: info@cedalion.co.uk

▶ Clearpeople Ltd, 17 Heathmans Road, London, SW6 4TJ Tel: (0870) 1999910 Fax: (0709) 2163189 E-mail: info@clearpeople.com

▶ Comcraft Computer Consultants, 57 Old Tye Avenue, Biggin Hill, Westerham, Kent, TN16 3NA Tel: (01959) 570798 Fax: (01959) 540047 E-mail: sales@comcraft.freeserve.co.uk

▶ Coreware Ltd, Gosden Common, Tannery Lane, Bramley, Guildford, Surrey, GU5 0AB Tel: (01483) 894158 Fax: (01483) 898932 E-mail: debs@russellsharpe.com

▶ Cutting Edge Consulting, 16 Holford Way, Barton Hills, Luton, LU3 4EB Tel: (07973) 721097 E-mail: gian@cec08.com

▶ Cymitric, 5 The Brache, Maulden, Bedford, MK45 2DZ Tel: (01525) 404434 Fax: (0871) 4335545 E-mail: info@cymitric.net

D J Consultants, The Leas, Elsworth Road, Conington, Cambridge, CB3 8LW Tel: (01954) 267441 Fax: (01954) 267441 E-mail: enquiries@djinter.net

▶ D W M Productions, 83 Stonelaw Drive, Rutherglen, Glasgow, G73 3PA Tel: 0141-647 4221 E-mail: webdesign@dwmproductions.co.uk

▶ Da Media Ltd, 8 Fallowfield, Sittingbourne, Kent, ME10 4UT Tel: (01795) 559456 E-mail: info@da-media.co.uk

Datasouth UK, 5 Chevron Business Park, Limekiln Lane, Holbury, Southampton, SO45 2QL Tel: (023) 8089 0800 Fax: (023) 8089 0875 E-mail: info@datasouth.co.uk

▶ Datatec Online, Market House, 2 Marlborough Road, Swindon, SN3 1QY Tel: 01793 694777 E-mail: doug@datateconline.com

▶ Desworx Ltd, 2 Allan Close, Stourbridge, West Midlands, DY8 4BB Tel: (01384) 832832 E-mail: info@desworx.com

Diam Software Ltd, 4 Lincoln Avenue, Canterbury, Kent, CT1 3YD Tel: (01227) 479333 E-mail: enquiries@diam.co.uk

▶ Digits Industries Ltd, Office 4 Universal Marina, Crableck Lne, Sarisbury Green, Southampton, SO31 7ZN Tel: (01489) 564845 Fax: (01489) 564846 E-mail: sales@digits.co.uk

▶ Martin Dixon, 5B Julien Road, Ealing, London, W5 4XA Tel: (020) 8354 0510 E-mail: martin@m-dixon.com

▶ Dream Designs, 11 Cove Way, Cove Bay, Aberdeen, AB12 3DW Tel: (07971) 522186 E-mail: sales@dream-designs.co.uk

▶ Duck - Feet, Elm Cottagewinchester Rdkings Somborne, Kings Somborne, Stockbridge, Hampshire, SO20 6NZ Tel: (01794) 388672 E-mail: andrea@duck-feet.com

Easiserv.Com, Suite C70 The Business Centre, Chapel Place, Northampton, NN1 4AQ Tel: (01604) 467930 Fax: (01604) 259749 E-mail: neil@easiserv.com

Edge Designs Ltd, Enterprise House, Courtaulds Way, Coventry, CV6 5NX Tel: (024) 7666 7337 Fax: (024) 7666 7657 E-mail: sales@edgedesigns.co.uk

Edge9 Design and Image Solutions, Liverpool Road, Eccles, Manchester, M30 Tel: 0161-707 1311

Effective Multimedia, 1107 Evesham Road, Astwood Bank, Redditch, Worcestershire, B96 6EB Tel: (01527) 892394 E-mail: sales@effectivemultimedia.co.uk

▶ Entropy Internet Designs, 35A Britania Row, London, N1 8QH Tel: (07815) 141091 E-mail: info@entropyid.com

Excel Marketing, Excel House, 6 The Crescent, Abbots Langley, Hertfordshire, WD5 0DS Tel: (01923) 261003 Fax: (01923) 266899 E-mail: adrianclarke@excelmarketing.co.uk

▶ Firedup Marketing Communications, Unit 2, Lakeside, Festival Way, Stoke-on-Trent, ST1 5RY Tel: (01782) 207336 E-mail: studio@getfiredup.co.uk

▶ Fluid Creativity Ltd, 5 Fifth Avenue, Dukinfield, Cheshire, SK16 4PP Tel: (0845) 6588373 Fax: 0161-343 5577 E-mail: lee@fluidcreativity.co.uk

▶ FourSquare Innovations LLP, 6 Hawksworth Grove, Leeds, LS5 3NB Tel: (0870) 3930044 Fax: (0870) 1326527 E-mail: info@foursquareinnovations.co.uk

Frog Networking Solutions Ltd, 1 Lion Works, Cambridge, CB2 4NL Tel: (01223) 493500 Fax: (0870) 4446772 E-mail: system@frog.co.uk

Gallery Partnership Ltd, 53-55 The Hop Exchange, 24 Southwark Street, London, SE1 1TY Tel: (020) 7096 2800 Fax: (020) 7096 2810 E-mail: mkemp@gallerypartnership.co.uk

▶ Genie Studios, Henson Road, Bedworth, Warwickshire, CV12 0DL Tel: (08700) 272501

▶ Genner (Web Site) Construction, PO Box 653, Telford, Shropshire, TF3 1ZN Tel: (01952) 411902 E-mail: kevin@genner.co.uk

▶ Gibbs Business Solutions Ltd, 10 Strathearn Road, North Berwick, East Lothian, EH39 5BZ Tel: (01620) 892736 E-mail: charles.gibbs@gbsl.co.uk

▶ Hayes Computing Solutions, 2 Central Close, Hethersett, Norwich, NR9 3ER Tel: (01603) 811367 E-mail: info@hcoms.co.uk

HCL Technologies Europe Ltd, Network House, Norreys Drive, Maidenhead, Berkshire, SL6 4FJ Tel: (01628) 778555 Fax: (01628) 777566 E-mail: semipractice@hcltech.com

Heartfield Technologies Ltd, Bromley, BR2 0WL Tel: (020) 8313 3088 Fax: (020) 8313 3002 E-mail: info@heartfield.co.uk

▶ Heathfield Studios, Heathfield, Heathlands Road, Wokingham, Berkshire, RG40 3AR Tel: (01344) 751125 E-mail: info@heathfield-studios.co.uk

Icm Computer Group plc, 3 Phoenix Place, Nottingham, NG8 6BA Tel: 0115-870 1000 Fax: (0870) 1218354 E-mail: sales@icm-computer.co.uk

Icode Systems Ltd, Icode System Ltd Grange Business Park, Sandy Lane, Shedfield, Southampton, SO32 2HQ Tel: (01329) 835335 Fax: (01329) 835338 E-mail: sales@icode.co.uk

▶ ICOM International Ltd, Norwood House, 53 Brighton Grove, Manchester, M14 5JT Tel: 0161-259 0100 E-mail: info@internetcommunication.co.uk

▶ ID Pages Ltd, 9 Cornfield Lane, Eastbourne, East Sussex, BN21 4NE Tel: 01323 479728 Fax: 01323 439485 E-mail: sales@idpages.co.uk

▶ Id76 Creative, 4 Whitley Park Lane, Reading, RG2 7BE Tel: (07946) 881875 Fax: (07092) 864176 E-mail: info@id76.com

▶ Ideka Ltd, 57 Barleyfields Road, Wetherby, West Yorkshire, LS22 7PT Tel: (01937) 582942 Fax: (01937) 582942 E-mail: sales@ideka.co.uk

▶ Image Website Design, 10 Hereford Close, Exmouth, Devon, EX8 5QT Tel: (01395) 223255 Fax: (01395) 223255 E-mail: sales@imagewebsitedesign.co.uk

▶ Imaginit, Shaw House, Pegler Way, Crawley, West Sussex, RH11 7AF Tel: 0845 6027397 E-mail: solutions@imaginit.net

▶ INCO Software Solutions, 11 Pendeford Place, Pendeford Business Park, Wobaston Road, Wolverhampton, WV9 5HD Tel: (0870) 0460060 Fax: (0870) 0460061

▶ Initiative2 Web Site Design, Rosewood, Hareburn Road, Bridge of Don, Aberdeen, AB23 8AR Tel: (01224) 820960 E-mail: sales@initiative2.com

Instant Business, 8-10 Colston Avenue, Bristol, BS1 4ST Tel: 0117-915 5175 Fax: 0117-915 5185 E-mail: info@ibltd.com

Intec Systems Ltd, Intec House, St. Nicholas Close, Fleet, Hampshire, GU51 4JA Tel: (01252) 775400 Fax: (01252) 775444 E-mail: info@intec.co.uk

▶ It Is It, 8 Beechwood Drive, Cobham, Surrey, KT11 2DX Tel: (01372) 841439 E-mail: info@it-is-it.co.uk

▶ It Pros Ltd, 15 Strathyre Gardens, Bearsden, Glasgow, G61 2BD Tel: 0141-563 7215 E-mail: dj@it-pros.co.uk

▶ JMCWD.com, 8 Dunevly Road, Portaferry, Newtownards, County Down, BT22 1NB Tel: (028) 4272 9738 E-mail: misc@jmcwd.com

▶ KJH Digital, Forest Hill, Yeovil, Somerset, BA20 2PE Tel: 07955 154433 E-mail: production@kjhdigital.com

Knibbs Computer Services Ltd, Suite 1 Falmer Court, London Road, Uckfield, East Sussex, TN22 1HN Tel: (01825) 749416 Fax: (0870) 7051341 E-mail: info@knibbs.com

▶ Labrys Multimedia, 179 Meltham Road, Huddersfield, HD4 7BG Tel: (01484) 662448 E-mail: jane@labrysmm.co.uk

▶ M8 Design, 102 Bath Street, Glasgow, G2 2EN Tel: (0870) 7460424 Fax: (0870) 7420745

▶ Machine Networks, PO Box 69, Immingham, South Humberside, DN40 1PL Tel: (0870) 7607750 Fax: (0870) 7607750 E-mail: info@machinenetworks.co.uk

Malbrook, C.S. Ltd, 8 Millbank Court, Millbank Way, Bracknell, Berkshire, RG12 1RP Tel: (01344) 424458 Fax: (01344) 424459 E-mail: support@csmb.co.uk

▶ Marmic Solutions, 6 Pathfields Road, Clacton-on-Sea, Essex, CO15 3JH Tel: (01255) 425676

Matcom, 140 Windsor Road, Maidenhead, Berkshire, SL6 2DW Tel: (01628) 626352 Fax: (01628) 631757 E-mail: postbox@matcom.co.uk

▶ MMS Almac Print Ltd, Unit 4 Tyock Industrial Estate, Elgin, Morayshire, IV30 1XY Tel: (01343) 551353 Fax: (01343) 551962 E-mail: sales@mms-almac.co.uk

▶ My Modern Art, 81 Beveley Road, Oakengates, Telford, Shropshire, TF2 6SD Tel: (07740) 338778 E-mail: sales@mymodernart.co.uk

▶ Nivek Design Ltd, 7 Kingston Avenue, Shoeburyness, Southend-on-Sea, SS3 8TS Tel: (01702) 292400 E-mail: kevin@nivekdesign.com

▶ Online Design Media Ltd, Caversham House, 4 Gosbrook Road, Caversham, Reading, RG4 8BS Tel: 0118-947 6644 Fax: 0118-947 6690 E-mail: sales@online-design.co.uk

▶ Online Secretarial Services, 31 Derwent Drive, Ferry Fryston, Castleford, West Yorkshire, WF10 3SX Tel: 0771 8320166 E-mail: onlinesecretarialservices@hotmail.co.uk

▶ P R Systems, 22 Leyshade Court, DUNDEE, DD4 8XN Tel: 01382 522467 Fax: 01382 522467 E-mail: sales@prsystems.net

▶ Paradigm Web Solutions Ltd, Building 188 First Street, New Greenham Park, Newbury, Berkshire, RG19 6HW Tel: (01635) 277499 Fax: (01635) 277497 E-mail: info@parawebsol.co.uk

▶ Pathfinder Technologies UK Ltd, Lancaster Street, Birmingham, B4 7AR Tel: 0121-333 7000 E-mail: sales@pftec.co.uk

▶ Pawprintz, Barnsley BIC, Innovation Way, Barnsley, South Yorkshire, S75 1JL Tel: (01226) 249590 Fax: (01226) 731867 E-mail: info@pawprintz.co.uk

▶ PELICAN Solutions Ltd, 5 Westbrook Court, Sharrow Vale Road, SHEFFIELD, S11 8YZ Tel: 0114 233 5200

Pier Design, 1 Browning Road, Poole, Dorset, BH12 2JU Tel: (01202) 734400 E-mail: sales@pierdesign.co.uk

▶ Pipedream Design, Durham House, Durham House Street, London, WC2N 6HG Tel: (0870) 8032293 E-mail: andy@pipedreamdesign.co.uk

Prion Associates, Branscombe, Chart Road, Sutton Valence, Maidstone, Kent, ME17 3AW Tel: (01622) 844595 Fax: (01622) 844595 E-mail: aq02@dial.pipex.com

▶ Q R 8 Design, Arundel Street, Sheffield, S1 2NS Tel: 0114-221 1818 Fax: (0870) 1338957 E-mail: enquiries@miswebdesign.com

Qurius UK Ltd, Waterfall Business Park, Bury, Lancashire, BL9 7BR Tel: 0161-705 6000 Fax: 0161-705 6001 E-mail: mike.dickson@cedilla.co.uk

R & A Software Systems Ltd, Bank Chambers, 244 Fulwood Road, Sheffield, S10 3BB Tel: 0114-267 9669 Fax: 0114-267 9670 E-mail: info@rasoft.co.uk

▶ Reach New Media Ltd, Clayton House, Tummock Road, Ballymoney, County Antrim, BT53 8NR Tel: (028) 2766 7987 Fax: (028) 2544 6130 E-mail: info@reach-newmedia.com

▶ The Red Word, 15 Heath Drive, Binfield Heath, Henley-on-Thames, Oxfordshire, RG9 4LX Tel: 0118-947 1181 E-mail: info@theredword.co.uk

▶ Refreshed Media Ltd, Homelife House Business Centre, Bournemouth, BH8 8EZ Tel: (01202) 242200 Fax: 08701 315094 E-mail: sarah@refreshedmedia.com

▶ Rubber Dragon Limited, 19 Juno Way, Swindon, SN5 9ZD Tel: (07879) 637159

▶ S H O Design, 57 Farringdon Road, London, EC1M 3JB Tel: (020) 7993 5472 E-mail: adam@sho-mail.com

▶ Scott Britten, 16 Pheonix House, Hyssop Close, Cannock, Staffordshire, WS11 7GA Tel: (01543) 579977 Fax: 01543 467260 E-mail: info@scottbritten.co.uk

▶ Site Wizard, Ascot House, 22-24 Albion Place, Maidstone, Kent, ME14 5DZ Tel: (01622) 200045 Fax: (01622) 206700 E-mail: info@sitewizard.co.uk

▶ Sliced Ltd, 91 Western Road, Brighton, BN1 2NW Tel: (01273) 776373 Fax: (01273) 706030 E-mail: info@slicedcreative.co.uk

▶ Software Consulting Ltd, 10 Lime Kiln Road, Mannings Heath, Horsham, West Sussex, RH13 6JH Tel: (01403) 263269 E-mail: sales@scss.co.uk

▶ Sparta Database Development, 17 Cyncoed Close, Dunvant, Swansea, SA2 7RS Tel: 01792 425730 E-mail: enquiries@sparta-development-db.co.uk

Spina, 8 Hillside Road, Pannal, Pannal, Harrogate, North Yorkshire, HG3 1JP Tel: (07780) 734797 Fax: (01423) 870392 E-mail: tracy@spina.co.uk

Studio Digital Media Ltd, Windsor Park, Trent Valley Road, Lichfield, Staffordshire, WS13 6EU Tel: (01543) 416912 Fax: (01543) 416914 E-mail: info@studiodm.co.uk

▶ Studio Emergence, PO Box 139, Thornton-Cleveleys, Lancashire, FY5 4WU Tel: (07834) 986958 E-mail: interest@studioemergence.net

▶ Sussex Internet Ltd, Enterprise Works Ltd, Beach Road, Newhaven, East Sussex, BN9 0BX Tel: (01273) 514710 E-mail: info@sussex-internet.net

Technol 2000 Ltd, 5-7 Chester Road, Northwich, Cheshire, CW8 1EZ Tel: (01606) 784044 Fax: (01606) 784055 E-mail: info@technol.co.uk

Telecetera Computer Consultants, Carden Close, Worcester, WR1 2AR Tel: (01905) 612220 Fax: (01905) 612226 E-mail: info@telecetera.co.uk

▶ Time for Design, 8 Lichfield Road, Stone, Staffordshire, ST15 8PY Tel: (01785) 819764 E-mail: dme@timefordesign.co.uk

▶ Tippabush Ltd, 5 Rookery Close, Louth, Lincolnshire, LN11 0GF Tel: (01507) 608331 E-mail: info@tippabush.co.uk

Trend U K, Unit 75 Questor, Powder Mill Lane, Dartford, DA1 1JA Tel: (0870) 1218326 Fax: (0870) 1218328

▶ V H S Holdings Ltd, 7 College Park Drive, Westbury-On-Trym, Bristol, BS10 7AN Tel: 0117- 950 0202 Fax: 0117- 377 7842 E-mail: vgr@vhsholdings.com

▶ Virtual Tapestry Ltd, Dulcote, Dulcote, Wells, Somerset, BA5 3NU Tel: (0870) 7456334 Fax: (0870) 7456334 E-mail: linda@virtualtapestry.co.uk

W S I Expert Net Solutions, 54 Gleneagles Road, Bloxwich, Walsall, WS3 3UJ Tel: (07855) 413370 Fax: (07813) 964997 E-mail: jon@wsiexpertnetsolutions.com

▶ Webease, The Old Fountain, 12 Dennis Green, Gamlingay, Sandy, Bedfordshire, SG19 3LQ Tel: (01767) 650730 E-mail: ricsale@webeaseuk.co.uk

▶ Webfresh Design, 40 Castlegate Drive, Bradford, West Yorkshire, BD10 8BW Tel: 0845 8382527 E-mail: info@webfreshdesign.co.uk

▶ The WebsiteGirl, Chester House, Chester Road, gillingham, Kent, ME7 4AF Tel: 01634 322819 E-mail: info@thewebsitegirl.co.uk

▶ Websites For You, 38 Howard Road, Portsmouth, PO2 9PS Tel: (023) 9271 0311 Fax: (023) 9271 0311 E-mail: trevor@websitesforyou.co.uk

▶ Who Media Ltd, 18 Bircham Tofts, Bircham Tofts, King's Lynn, Norfolk, PE31 6QT Tel: (01904) 781526

Wida Group, 2 Brookside Road, Ruddington, Nottingham, NG11 6AT Tel: 0115-921 4797 Fax: 0115-984 5097 E-mail: info@widagroup.com

▶ Wide Blue Yonder, 20 Purbrook Road, Tadley, Hampshire, RG26 4PR Tel: (07976) 274018 E-mail: info@wideblueyonderweb.co.uk

Yelrom Designs, 6 Oundle Drive, Ilkeston, Derbyshire, DE7 5DX Tel: (07976) 068235 E-mail: info@evolution-media.co.uk

WEBSITE DESIGN OR CREATION SERVICES

1 Websearch Marketing, 104 Dyke Rd, Brighton, BN1 3JD Tel: (08703) 219679 Fax: (01273) 771785

121webconsultancy, 8 Comer Gardens, Worcester, WR2 6JH Tel: 01905 422256 E-mail: steve@121webconsultancy.co.uk

▶ 2k Business Services Ltd, 2 Laburnum Cottages, Caerleon Road, Ponthir, Newport, Gwent, NP18 1HE Tel: (01633) 430166 Fax: (01633) 421014 E-mail: enquiry@2kbs.co.uk

3l1t3 Ltd, 43 Beckfield Road, Bingley, West Yorkshire, BD16 1QR Tel: (01274) 820102 Fax: (01274) 825558 E-mail: admin@3l1t3.com

▶ 4VisMedia, 18 Alderwood, Chineham, Basingstoke, Hampshire, RG24 8TU Tel: (01256) 320733 E-mail: enquiries@4vismedia.co.uk

▶ A F D, 28 Belgravia Gardens, Bromley, BR1 4TB Tel: (020) 8464 3823 Fax: (07092) 277379 E-mail: info@afd.net

▶ A & H Commercial Printers, 153-155 Ley Street, Ilford, Essex, IG1 4BL Tel: (020) 8478 2558 Fax: (020) 8514 5366 E-mail: info@ahprinters.com

▶ A M S Web Design, Hillcrest, 42 Station Road, Dunure, Ayr, KA7 4LL Tel: (01292) 500499 E-mail: info@amswebdesign.co.uk

WEBSITE DESIGN OR CREATION SERVICES – *continued*

A N Q, The Manor House, 14 Market Street, Lutterworth, Leicestershire, LE17 4EH Tel: (01455) 559446 Fax: (01455) 558523 E-mail: lgibson@anq.com

A R M Direct, 1 Bentinck Mews, London, W1U 2AF Tel: (020) 7317 3230 Fax: (020) 7224 3041 E-mail: info@arm-direct.co.uk

A1 Netservices, 23 Tudor Road, Wheathampstead, St. Albans, Hertfordshire, AL4 8NW Tel: (01582) 834208 Fax: (0871) 7501428 E-mail: info@a1-netservices.co.uk

Abel Internet, Pentland View House Damhead, Lothianburn, Edinburgh, EH10 7DZ Tel: 0131-445 5555 Fax: (0871) 7173452

Ace Works, 216 Chorley New Rd, Horwich, Bolton, BL6 5NP Tel: (01204) 668667 Fax: (0870) 845 9049 E-mail: info@aceworks.com

Action Group, Garston Business Park, Blackburne Street, Liverpool, L19 8JB Tel: 0151-427 1084 Fax: 0151-427 7130 E-mail: dkeen@theactiongroup.co.uk

Activity Domain Ltd, Moulton Park Business Centre, Redhouse Road, Moulton Park, Northampton, NN3 6AQ Tel: (0845) 3100811 E-mail: victor@activitydomain.com

Advanced Network, 12 Primrose Gdns, London, NW3 4TN Tel: (020) 7586 3232

▶ Alderdesigns, 79 Forrestal Street, Edzell, Brechin, Angus, DD9 7XG Tel: (01356) 648069 E-mail: phil.alder@alderdesigns.co.uk

▶ Amber Web Designs, 16 High Street, Baldock, Hertfordshire, SG7 6AS Tel: (01462) 895018

Applied Interactive Ltd, Cranfield Innovation Centre, University Way, Cranfield, Bedford, MK43 0BT Tel: (01234) 756050 Fax: (01234) 756138 E-mail: sales@applied-interactive.co.uk

▶ Apricot Studio, 11 Charles CR, Drymen, Glasgow, G63 0BU Tel: (01360) 661028 E-mail: info@apricot-studios.com

▶ Assistpoint Limited, 40 Allendale Road, Barnsley, South Yorkshire, S75 1BJ Tel: 0114 2387569 E-mail: sales@assistpoint.co.uk

Astec Computing UK Ltd, Astec House, 10-12 Sedlescombe Road South, St. Leonards-on-Sea, East Sussex, TN38 0TA Tel: (01424) 460721 Fax: (01424) 430888 E-mail: enquiries@asteccomputing.com

▶ Auger Productions, Suite F16, Scope House, Weston Road, Crewe, CW1 6DD Tel: (01270) 258111 Fax: (01270) 258161 E-mail: info@auger-productions.com

Ballard Chalmers Ltd, 1 Christopher Road, East Grinstead, West Sussex, RH19 3BT Tel: (01342) 410223 Fax: (01342) 410225 E-mail: info@ballardchalmers.com

Blenheim Systems, 31 Blenheim Gardens, Wembley, Middlesex, HA9 7NP Tel: (020) 8904 9317 Fax: (07092) 215433 E-mail: enq@blenheim-systems.com

▶ Blue Earth Web Solutions, Globe House, 17 Vale Walk, Worthing, West Sussex, BN14 0BS Tel: (0845) 3311396 E-mail: info@blueearthsolutions.co.uk

Brainsmead Ltd, Tangley Brainsmead Close, Cuckfield, Haywards Heath, West Sussex, RH17 5EZ Tel: (01444) 441951 E-mail: richard@brainsmead.co.uk

▶ Brand 5, 19 Portico Road, Derby, DE23 3NJ Tel: 0845 2261883

▶ Bright Star, 4 Barra Close, Hull, HU8 9JB Tel: (0845) 2578501 Fax: (0845) 2578501 E-mail: info@brightstarwebdesign.co.uk

British Publishing Co., Messenger House, 33 St Michaels Square, Gloucester, GL1 1HX Tel: (01452) 418191 Fax: (01452) 300069 E-mail: info@british-publishing.com

Brittan Design Partnership, 7 The Old Fire Station Annexe, Fairfield Road, Market Harborough, Leicestershire, LE16 9QJ Tel: (01858) 466950 Fax: (01858) 434632 E-mail: enquiry@goto-bdp.co.uk

▶ Brown Ink, 309 St. Michaels Avenue, Yeovil, Somerset, BA21 4ND Tel: (01935) 424607 E-mail: info@brown-ink.co.uk

Business-ip Ltd, 60 High Street, Measham, Swadlincote, Derbyshire, DE12 7HZ Tel: (01530) 272229 Fax: (01530) 272229 E-mail: info@business-ip.co.uk

Bytecraft Ltd, 5 The Quad, Mercury Court, Chester, CH1 4QP Tel: (01244) 390109 Fax: (01244) 390051 E-mail: sales@bytecraft.co.uk

C G T Ltd, 314 Midsummer Boulevard, Milton Keynes, MK9 2UB Tel: (01908) 690361 Fax: (01908) 669922 E-mail: sales@cgt.co.uk

▶ CanCreative, 16 The Mallards, Silsden, West Yorkshire, BD20 0NT Tel: 01535 652600 E-mail: candie@cancreative.co.uk

▶ CD Web Design, Forester's Cottage, Kilmaron Estate, Cupar, Fife, KY15 4NE Tel: (07715) 707953 Fax: (01334) 650908

Ci-Net, Langford Locks, Kidlington, Oxfordshire, OX5 1GA Tel: (01865) 856000 Fax: (01865) 856001 E-mail: info@ci-net.com

Cloud Ten, Tadlow, Royston, Hertfordshire, SG8 0EP Tel: (01767) 631810 Fax: (01767) 631811 E-mail: office@cloud-ten.co.uk

CMS International Ltd, Crowborough, East Sussex, TN6 1XU Tel: (01892) 669966 Fax: (01892) 669977 E-mail: info@cmsinternational.com

Comtech Telecommunications Ltd, 30 Bradford Road, Stanningley, Pudsey, West Yorkshire, LS28 6DD Tel: 0113-255 3927 Fax: 0113-205 7567 E-mail: info@comtech-telecom.co.uk

▶ Conception Design, 83 Alder Close, Leyland, PR26 7TU Tel: (01772) 434464 Fax: (0870) 6618883 E-mail: info@conceptiondesign.co.uk

Connaught Lithoservices Ltd, 129 Munster Road, London, SW6 6DD Tel: (020) 7731 0900 Fax: (020) 7731 0066 E-mail: info@connaught.net

▶ Coreware Ltd, Gosden Common, Tannery Lane, Bramley, Guildford, Surrey, GU5 0AB Tel: (01483) 894158 Fax: (01483) 898932 E-mail: debs@russellsharpe.com

▶ Creative Fusion, 1 Church Close, Todber, Sturminster Newton, Dorset, DT10 1JH Tel: (01258) 820702 Fax: 01258 820702 E-mail: hannah@creative-fusion.co.uk

Creative Store Ltd, Studio House, 142 Merton Hall Road, London, SW19 3PZ Tel: (020) 8543 3855 Fax: (020) 8540 7367 E-mail: sales@thecreativestore.co.uk

Custom Software Systems, 2 Undercliff Rd, Wemyss Bay, Renfrewshire, PA18 6AQ Tel: 01475 522541 Fax: 01475 522572

▶ Cyberzia Ltd, PO Box 555, Stoke-on-Trent, ST11 9DY Tel: (01782) 631112 E-mail: mail@cyberzia.net

▶ Cymitric, 5 The Brache, Maulden, Bedford, MK45 2DZ Tel: (01525) 404434 Fax: (0871) 4335545 E-mail: info@cymitric.net

▶ Datatec Online, Market House, 2 Marlborough Road, Swindon, SN3 1QY Tel: 01793 694777 E-mail: doug@datateconline.com

▶ DBSconsultants ltd, 44 osborne rd, Palmers Green, London, UK, N13 5PS Tel: 07940 379 935 E-mail: kingsley_ijomah@yahoo.com

▶ Design Distillery Ltd, 12 Northgate, Chichester, West Sussex, PO19 1BA Tel: (01243) 537837 Fax: (01243) 839448 E-mail: leslie@design-distillery.co.uk

▶ Billy Devine, PO Box 16272, Glasgow, G13 9AW Tel: (07903) 303307 E-mail: info@thedevinesite.com

Diafade Ltd, 4 Norfolk Road, Buntingford, Hertfordshire, SG9 9AN Tel: (01763) 273379 E-mail: mailroom@diafade.co.uk

▶ Martin Dixon, 5B Julien Road, Ealing, London, W5 4XA Tel: (020) 8354 0510 E-mail: martin@m-dixon.com

▶ Doepud Web Design, PO Box 16263, Glasgow, G13 9AJ Tel: 0141-954 8671 E-mail: info@doepud.co.uk

Dome Products Ltd, Burnside Business Centre, Burnside Road, Boddam, Peterhead, Aberdeenshire, AB42 3AW Tel: (01779) 481964 Fax: (01779) 481965

Dorset Merc, 851 Wimborne Road, Bournemouth, BH9 2BG Tel: (01202) 775566 E-mail: david.bridgewater@dorset-merc.net

DPI 21 Ltd, 10 Heaton Street, Blackburn, BB2 2EF Tel: (07903) 243666 Fax: (01254) 694485 E-mail: studio@dpi21.com

▶ Dream Designs, 11 Cove Way, Cove Bay, Aberdeen, AB12 3DW Tel: (07971) 522186 E-mail: sales@dream-designs.co.uk

▶ Duck - Feet, Elm Cottagewinchester Rdkings Somborne, Kings Somborne, Stockbridge, Hampshire, SO20 6NZ Tel: (01794) 388672 E-mail: andrea@duck-feet.com

Easiserv.Com, Suite C70 The Business Centre, Chapel Place, Northampton, NN1 4AQ Tel: (01604) 467930 Fax: (01604) 259749 E-mail: neil@easiserv.com

Easy Web, 10 St Andrews Cresent, Cardiff, CF10 3DD Tel: (029) 2034 4006 Fax: (029) 2034 4008 E-mail: enquiries@eazyweb.co.uk

▶ Easysoft Webdesign, 27 Holbeck Avenue, Scarborough, North Yorkshire, YO11 2XH Tel: (01723) 374713

Ecotec Research & Consulting Ltd, 12-26 Albert Street, Birmingham, B4 7UD Tel: 0121-616 3600 Fax: 0121-616 3699 E-mail: welcome@ecotec.co.uk

The Edge, 3 Wolseley Terrrence, Cheltenham, Gloucestershire, GL50 1TH Tel: (01242) 580365 Fax: (01242) 261816 E-mail: design@theedge.co.uk

Edge9 Design and Image Solutions, Liverpool Road, Eccles, Manchester, M30 Tel: 0161-707 1311

Effective Multimedia, 1107 Evesham Road, Astwood Bank, Redditch, Worcestershire, B96 6EB Tel: (01527) 892394 E-mail: sales@effectivemultimedia.co.uk

Electronic Business Solutions, Business Centre West Letchworth Business Centre, Avenue One, Letchworth Garden City, Hertfordshire, SG6 2HB Tel: (01462) 483868

▶ Emergence Communications, Commercial Centre, Exchange Street, Colne, Lancashire, BB8 0SQ Tel: 0845 8381401 Fax: 0870 1342929 E-mail: info@emergence.biz

Entee Global Services Ltd, 2morrow Court, Appleford Road, Sutton Courtenay, Abingdon, Oxfordshire, OX14 4FH Tel: (01235) 845100 Fax: (01235) 845108 E-mail: mail@entee.co.uk

Enterprise A B Ltd, 9 St. Albans Enterprise Centre, Long Spring, Porters Wood, St. Albans, Hertfordshire, AL3 6EN Tel: (01727) 751445 Fax: (01727) 759507 E-mail: admin@eab.co.uk

▶ The First Web, 91 Augusta Drive, Macclesfield, Cheshire, SK10 2UR Tel: (01625) 430379 E-mail: admin@thefirstweb.com

Flare Imaging Ltd, 200 Brook Drive, Greenpark, Reading, RG2 6UB Tel: 0118-922 2999 Fax: 0118-986 7999 E-mail: nick@flareimaging.com

Forest Software Ltd, 9 Pembroke Grove, Glinton, Peterborough, PE6 7LG Tel: (01733) 253332 Fax: (0870) 7474942 E-mail: sales@forestsoftware.co.uk

Freerange Design, 521 Royal Exchange, Manchester, M2 7EN Tel: 0161-835 2312 Fax: 0161-835 3121 E-mail: paulb@freerangedesign.com

▶ Fruity Websites, PO Box 7143, Kettering, Northamptonshire, NN16 6BT Tel: 01536 738198 E-mail: hello@fruitywebsites.co.uk

▶ Fusionxs, 7 Wisley Close, West Bridgford, Nottingham, NG2 7NY Tel: 0115-878 7003 Fax: (0845) 8688485 E-mail: info@fusionxs.co.uk

▶ Gempro Website Design and Development Services, 249 Beaver Lane, Ashford, Kent, TN23 5PA Tel: 01233 334069 E-mail: info@gempro.co.uk

Geotechnix Computer Services Ltd, 39 West Hill Road, London, SW18 1LL Tel: (020) 8871 1497 Fax: (020) 8333 6714

GGH Marketing Communications, 1 West Street, Titchfield, Fareham, Hampshire, PO14 4DH Tel: (01329) 846166 Fax: (01329) 512063 E-mail: geoff@ggh.co.uk

Go Internet Ltd, 36 Gloucester Avenue, London, NW1 7BB Tel: (020) 7419 0001 E-mail: jerry@go.co.uk

Graham Bell Design Ltd, 43, Halnaker, Chichester, West Sussex, PO18 0NQ Tel: (01243) 755910 Fax: (01243) 755911 E-mail: john@gbd.co.uk

▶ Hareslade Webs, 32 Hareslade, Bishopston, Swansea, SA3 3DX Tel: (01792) 234782 E-mail: p.hailey@virgin.net

▶ Hocking Marketing Partnership, 22 Armstrong Close, Crownhill, Milton Keynes, MK8 0AU Tel: (01908) 563883E-mail: info@hmpltd.co.uk

▶ Home & Business Computer Service, 12 David Close, Braunton, Devon, EX33 2AT Tel: (01271) 815262 E-mail: info@handbcs.co.uk

▶ I F A Systems Ltd, 27 New Street, Charfield, Wotton-under-Edge, Gloucestershire, GL12 8ES Tel: (01453) 521855 Fax: (0870) 4208391 E-mail: sales@ifa-systems.co.uk

▶ ID Pages Ltd, 9 Cornfield Lane, Eastbourne, East Sussex, BN21 4NE Tel: 01323 479728 Fax: 01323 439485 E-mail: sales@idpages.co.uk

▶ Id76 Creative, 4 Whitley Park Lane, Reading, RG2 7BE Tel: (07946) 881875 Fax: (07092) 864176 E-mail: info@id76.com

▶ Ideal Web Solutions, PO Box 487, Wigan, Lancashire, WN2 4WP Tel: (0789) 1989138

▶ Imaginit, Shaw House, Pegler Way, Crawley, West Sussex, RH11 7AF Tel: 0845 6027397 E-mail: solutions@imaginit.net

Imtex Computer Consultants, Stratford Arcade, 75 High Street, Stony Stratford, Milton Keynes, MK11 1AY Tel: (01908) 261216 Fax: (01908) 261216

▶ Indrum Website & Graphic Design, 2c Bennett Road, Brighton, BN2 5JL Tel: (01273) 530275 E-mail: indrum@indrum.com

▶ Infinite Distance Secretarial Services, 35 Nursery Road, Edgbaston, Birmingham, B15 3JX Tel: 0121-244 3633 E-mail: infinitedistance@blueyonder.co.uk

▶ Initiative2 Web Site Design, Rosewood, Hareburn Road, Bridge of Don, Aberdeen, AB23 8AR Tel: (01224) 820960 E-mail: sales@initiative2.com

▶ INTECH, Nant Yr Ynys, Llanpumsaint, Carmarthen, SA33 6LJ Tel: (07092) 872570 Fax: (07092) 872733 E-mail: admin@insteptechnology.net

Internet Marketing Kent, 70c High Street, Whitstable, Kent, CT5 1BB Tel: (01227) 281611 Fax: (01227) 264727 E-mail: mark.smith@i-m-k.co.uk

▶ It Is It, 8 Beechwood Drive, Cobham, Surrey, KT11 2DX Tel: (01372) 841439 E-mail: info@it-is-it.co.uk

▶ It Pros Ltd, 15 Strathyre Gardens, Bearsden, Glasgow, G61 2BD Tel: 0141-563 7215 E-mail: dj@it-pros.co.uk

IT Service Link Ltd, The Black Barn, The Folley, Layer De La Haye, Colchester, CO2 0HZ Tel: (01206) 235000 Fax: (01206) 235001 E-mail: danielle@hi-tech-sales.co.uk

▶ J.C Design, 35 Gainsborough Avenue, Maghull, Liverpool, L31 7AT Tel: 0151-526 5127 E-mail: john@jcdesign.me.com

J L Fearnley, Manor Farm, Manor Farm Road, Denton, Harleston, Norfolk, IP20 0AX Tel: (01986) 788630 Fax: (01986) 788637 E-mail: sales@fcs.uk.com

Jordan IT Services, 28 Carter Ave, Broughton, Kettering, Northants, NN14 1LZ Tel: (01536) 790425 Fax: (08701) 367829 E-mail: info@jordanitservices.com

Kindways.Com, 4 Trinity Avenue, Llandudno, Gwynedd, LL30 2NQ Tel: (01492) 879312 Fax: (01492) 873811

▶ KJH Digital, Forest Hill, Yeovil, Somerset, BA20 2PE Tel: 07955 154433 E-mail: production@kjhdigital.com

Kubiak Creative Ltd, 1 Farleigh Court, Old Weston Road, Flax Bourton, Bristol, BS48 1UR Tel: (01275) 464836 Fax: (01275) 461295 E-mail: sales@kubiakcreative.com

Kudos Visions Ltd, The White House, Main Road, Gwaelod-y-Garth, Cardiff, CF15 9HJ Tel: (08707) 605325 E-mail: info@kudosvisions.com

▶ L X R Web Design, Po Box 601, Altrincham, Cheshire, WA14 1WE Tel: (01925) 753629 E-mail: studio@lxrwebdesign.co.uk

Lion Bridge, Copthall Terrace, Coventry, CV1 2FP Tel: (024) 7622 2844 Fax: (024) 7625 8892

Looking Glass Design Ltd, 95 High Street, Crowthorne, Berkshire, RG45 7AD Tel: (020) 7384 1322 E-mail: info@lookinglassdesign.com

▶ Loyal E, 39 Stonewell Park Road, Congresbury, Bristol, BS49 5DP Tel: (01934) 832143 Fax: (01934) 832143 E-mail: enquiries@loyal-e.com

M B A Systems Ltd, Staple House, Staple Gardens, Winchester, Hampshire, SO23 8SR Tel: (01962) 841494 Fax: (01962) 864770

M F Business Services, 10 Bodington Road, Sutton Coldfield, West Midlands, B75 5ET Tel: (07973) 639660 Fax: 0121-308 3003 E-mail: enquiries@mfbusiness.co.uk

▶ M L I T C, 40 Roman Way, Felixstowe, Suffolk, IP11 9NP Tel: (01394) 671579 E-mail: mark@mlconsultancy.co.uk

M P S Group, 207 Desborough Road, High Wycombe, Buckinghamshire, HP11 2QL Tel: (01494) 452600 Fax: (01494) 449122 E-mail: bbi@bbi.co.uk

Marketing for Profits Ltd, Top Floor, 33 Southbourne Grove, Southbourne, Bournemouth, BH6 3QT Tel: 01202 257423 Fax: 01202 257423 E-mail: accounts@consultancymarketing.co.uk

Markland Advertising & Marketing Ltd, The Old Chapel, 13 Victoria Road, Chester, CH2 2AX Tel: (01244) 651951 Fax: (01244) 651952

▶ Marmic Solutions, 6 Pathfields Road, Clacton-on-Sea, Essex, CO15 3JH Tel: (01255) 425676

Marriott Design, St James House, 3 Lower St. James Street, Newport, Isle of Wight, PO30 5HE Tel: (01983) 529039 Fax: (01983) 821544 E-mail: studio@marriott-design.co.uk

Matcom, 140 Windsor Road, Maidenhead, Berkshire, SL6 2DW Tel: (01628) 626352 Fax: (01628) 631757 E-mail: postbox@matcom.co.uk

Media Magic Computers, Media House, 196a Abbey Road, Leeds, LS5 3NG Tel: 0113-228 9911 Fax: 0113-228 9933

▶ Metro Research Ltd, 118 The Chandlery, 50 Westminster Bridge Road, London, SE1 7QY Tel: (0870) 9979777 Fax: (020) 7953 7450 E-mail: vinesh@metroresearch.com

Micro-Fix, Hemlock Place, Hyssop Close, Cannock, Staffordshire, WS11 7GA Tel: (01543) 467579 Fax: (01543) 469624 E-mail: info@on2net.co.uk

Micro-HELP (Scotland), 47 Parkhill Circle, Dyce, Aberdeen, AB21 7FN Tel: (01224) 773438 Fax: (01224) 773438E-mail: dwh@mh-s.co.uk

Midpoint Ltd, 18 Leeds Road, Harrogate, North Yorkshire, HG2 8AA Tel: (01423) 528520 Fax: (01423) 529484 E-mail: enquiries@midpoint.co.uk

▶ Milo Web Designs, 34 Lifestyle House, 2 Melbourne Avenue, Sheffield, S10 2QH Tel: 0114 2678414 E-mail: miloweb@btinternet.com

N M Design, The Foundry, Unit 5, Albert Street, Brigg, South Humberside, DN20 8HU Tel: (01652) 658559 Fax: (01652) 651758 E-mail: info@nmdesign.co.uk

Net Formation Ltd, Godstone Green, Godstone, Surrey, RH9 8DZ Tel: (01883) 740000 Fax: (01883) 744465 E-mail: info@forfront.net

Net Resources Ltd, 26a Palmerston Place, Edinburgh, EH12 5AL Tel: 0131-477 7127 Fax: 0131-477 7126 E-mail: info@netresources.co.uk

▶ Nick Sutcliffe, 74 High Ridge Park, Rothwell, Leeds, LS26 0NN Tel: (07717) 754441 E-mail: info@sutcliffevs.co.uk

NPS Media, Ayrton Buildings, Forty Foot Road, Middlesbrough, Cleveland, TS2 1HG Tel: (01642) 231231 Fax: (01642) 256565 E-mail: sales@npsmedia.com

▶ Online Secretarial Services, 31 Derwent Drive, Ferry Fryston, Castleford, West Yorkshire, WF10 3SX Tel: 0771 8320166 E-mail: onlinesecretarialservices@hotmail.co.uk

Oppo Consulting Ltd, 38 Stoke Fields, Guildford, Surrey, GU1 4LS Tel: (01483) 563502 Fax: (01483) 453773 E-mail: sales@oppo-consulting.co.uk

▶ Orbital Design Ltd, 2 33 Palmerston Road, Bournemouth, BH1 4HN Tel: (01202) 304455 Fax: (01202) 304466 E-mail: justin@orbital.co.uk

Output Ltd, 1 Amptronic Industrial Estate, Heath Mill Road, Wombourne, Wolverhampton, WV5 8AP Tel: (01902) 895107 Fax: (01902) 895113 E-mail: sales@outputdigital.com

▶ Pawprintz, Barnsley BIC, Innovation Way, Barnsley, South Yorkshire, S75 1JL Tel: (01226) 249590 Fax: (01226) 731867 E-mail: info@pawprintz.co.uk

▶ Phase 2, 1 Wheeler Grove, Wells, Somerset, BA5 2GB Tel: (01749) 674458 Fax: (01749) 671319 E-mail: info@phase2.org.uk

▶ Pinebank Design, 30 Pine Bank, Hindhead, Surrey, GU26 6SS Tel: 020 88168613 E-mail: contact@pinebankdesign.com

Piranha Corporation, 35 Olivine Close, Walderslade Woods, Chatham, Kent, ME5 9NQ Tel: (01634) 869889 Fax: (01634) 869889

Pixel Image Ltd, 100 Constitution Street, Edinburgh, EH6 6AW Tel: 0131-555 3003 Fax: 0131-555 5927 E-mail: ssmith@pixelimage.co.uk

Pollen Recording Studios, 97 Main Street, Bishop Wilton, York, YO42 1SP Tel: (01759) 368223 E-mail: enquiries@pollenstudio.co.uk

Prion Associates, Branscombe, Chart Road, Sutton Valence, Maidstone, Kent, ME17 3AW Tel: (01622) 844595 Fax: (01622) 844595 E-mail: aq02@dial.pipex.com

▶ Q R 8 Design, Arundel Street, Sheffield, S1 2NS Tel: 0114-221 1818 Fax: (0870) 1338957 E-mail: enquiries@miswebdesign.com

▶ Quality Business Promotions, 11 Arundel Close, Dronfield Woodhouse, Dronfield, Derbyshire, S18 8QS Tel: (01246) 414250 E-mail: enquiries@qbpromotions.co.uk

WEBSITE DESIGN OR CREATION SERVICES – *continued*

▶ Queue Solutions Ltd, 5 Ellie Close, Stanford-le-Hope, Essex, SS17 0GZ Tel: (01375) 671349 E-mail: stevenf@queuesolutions.co.uk
Raphael Creative Design, Raphael Court, Upper St. John Street, Lichfield, Staffordshire, WS14 9DX Tel: (01543) 261220 Fax: (01543) 261221 E-mail: info@raphaeldesign.co.uk
▶ Reach New Media Ltd, Clayton House, Tummock Road, Ballymoney, County Antrim, BT53 8NR Tel: (028) 2766 7987 Fax: (028) 2544 6130 E-mail: info@reach-newmedia.com
Redweb Ltd, Quay House, 7 The Quay, Poole, Dorset, BH15 1HA Tel: (01202) 779944 Fax: (01202) 773643 E-mail: stuart@redweb.co.uk
Saqqara Technology Ltd, 47 Sandfield Road, Headington, Oxford, OX3 7RW Tel: (01865) 744505 Fax: (01865) 744505
Seven Internet Ltd, 35 Blanquettes Avenue, Worcester, WR3 8DA Tel: (01905) 745339 E-mail: sales@seveninternet.co.uk
▶ Signature Image Consultants Ltd, Boughton Monchelsea, Maidstone, Kent, ME17 4XQ Tel: (01622) 744659 E-mail: results@signature.gb.com
▶ Silvercoast Media, 12 Chainwalk Drive, Kenwyn, Truro, Cornwall, TR1 3ST Tel: 01872 271696 E-mail: mail@silvercoast.co.uk
▶ Silverfish Solutions, Bullrushes, Main Street, Peasmarsh, Rye, East Sussex, TN31 6UL Tel: (01797) 230976 Fax: (01797) 230976 E-mail: info@silverfishsolutions.co.uk
▶ Simmetrics Ltd, 59 Cambridge Road, Carshalton, Surrey, SM5 3QR Tel: (020) 8642 8672 E-mail: hello@simmetrics.co.uk
▶ sitewriters.co.uk, 42 North Street, Haworth, Keighley, West Yorkshire, BD22 8EP Tel: (01535) 210472 Fax: (01535) 210472 E-mail: john@sitewriters.co.uk
SKTS, 451 Bushey Mill Lane, Bushey, WD23 2AT Tel: (01923) 223657 Fax: (01923) 333731 E-mail: enquiries@shkata.com
Small Back Room, 88 Camberwell Road, London, SE5 0EG Tel: (020) 7701 4227 Fax: (020) 7703 3474 E-mail: sbr@smallbackroom.co.uk
Studio Digital Media Ltd, Windsor Park, Trent Valley Road, Lichfield, Staffordshire, WS13 6EU Tel: (01543) 416912 Fax: (01543) 416914 E-mail: info@studiodm.co.uk
Styleware Ltd, 28 Wittering Road, Hayling Island, Hampshire, PO11 9SP Tel: (023) 9246 1561 Fax: (023) 9246 1501 E-mail: sales@styleware.co.uk
▶ Sumari Business Systems Ltd, Branston Court, Branston Street, Birmingham, B18 6BA Tel: 0121-244 8111 Fax: 0121-244 8811 E-mail: sumari@sumari.co.uk
▶ Synergis Group, Rutherglen, Glasgow, G73 1NP Tel: 0141-613 1333
Co U Help Ltd, 32 Beech Hill, Haywards Heath, West Sussex, RH16 3RX Tel: (01444) 440551 Fax: (01444) 441698 E-mail: info@compuhelp.co.uk
UK Landscape, 88 Moring Road, London, SW17 8DL Tel: (020) 8682 0624 E-mail: sales@uklandscape.net
▶ Virtual Tapestry Ltd, Dulcote, Dulcote, Wells, Somerset, BA5 3NU Tel: (0870) 7456334 Fax: (0870) 7456334 E-mail: linda@virtualtapestry.co.uk
Vivitext Designers, The Old School, Old Hunstanton Road, Hunstanton, Norfolk, PE36 6HZ Tel: (01485) 534566 Fax: (01485) 534828 E-mail: viv@vivitext.co.uk
▶ Viziononline, 1 Red Place, London, W1K 6PL Tel: 0207 6478699 Fax: 0207 6478699 E-mail: henry@viziononline.co.uk
Volume Design Associates, The Studio, 22 Kings Road, High Wycombe, Buckinghamshire, HP11 1SA Tel: (01494) 459989 Fax: (01494) 459089 E-mail: info@vda.co.uk
▶ Webaddons, Ardlyn, Linton Bank Drive, West Linton, Peeblesshire, EH46 7DT Tel: (07817) 156829
Websight Solutions, 254 Kingsley Avenue, Kettering, Northamptonshire, NN16 9EZ Tel: (01536) 518587 Fax: (0870) 1224871 E-mail: sales@websight-solutions.com
▶ WebsynergiDesign, Suite 23, 57 Frederick Street, Birmingham, B1 3HS Tel: 0121 2706505E-mail: info@websynergidesign.co.uk
▶ Webtones, 17 Main Street, Saxelby, Melton Mowbray, Leicestershire, LE14 3PQ Tel: (0845) 6443089 Fax: (0870) 7625228
▶ Duncan Weddell Web Services, Duncanlaw, Gifford, Haddington, East Lothian, EH41 4PQ Tel: (01620) 810343 E-mail: info@duncanweddell.co.uk
▶ Who Media Ltd, 18 Bircham Tofts, Bircham Tofts, King's Lynn, Norfolk, PE31 6QT Tel: (01904) 781526
William Martin Ltd, The Studio, Tubney Warren Barn, Tubney, Abingdon, Oxfordshire, OX13 5QJ Tel: (01865) 390258 Fax: (01865) 390234 E-mail: info@wmproductions.co.uk
Wired Media Ltd, Broad Plain, Bristol, BS2 0JP Tel: 0117-930 4365 Fax: 0870-169 7625 E-mail: info@wiredmedia.co.uk
Woodstock Computer Solutions Ltd, Malvern, Oakhanger, Bordon, Hampshire, GU35 9JJ Tel: (01420) 474722 E-mail: roly@wcsweb.co.uk
Yelrom Designs, 6 Oundle Drive, Ilkeston, Derbyshire, DE7 5DX Tel: (07976) 068235 E-mail: info@evolution-media.co.uk
Zadeh Designs, 5 Ashurst Crescent, Corby, Northamptonshire, NN18 0JF Tel: (01536) 443738 Fax: E-mail: support@zadehdesigns.com

WEBSITE HOSTING

1 Websearch Marketing, 104 Dyke Rd, Brighton, BN1 3JD Tel: (08703) 219679 Fax: (01273) 771785
▶ 121 Technology Ltd, Kincora House, 143 Deganwy Road, Llandudno, Gwynedd, LL30 1NE Tel: (0870) 7747121
▶ 2f3 Internet, 103 Malbet Park, Edinburgh, EH16 6WB Tel: 0131-666 2555 E-mail: info@2f3.com
▶ 3B Designs, 32 Eaglewood Close, Torquay, TQ2 7SS Tel: (01803) 615903
A W C, 97 Commercial Road, Bournemouth, BH2 5RT Tel: (01202) 789269 Fax: (01202) 789277 E-mail: sales@awc.co.uk
Ace Works, 216 Chorley New Rd, Horwich, Bolton, BL6 5NP Tel: (01204) 668667 Fax: (0870) 845 9049 E-mail: info@aceworks.com
▶ David Anderson Associates, Unit 3 Saffron Walden Business Centre, Elizabeth Cl, Saffron Walden, Essex, CB10 2BL Tel: (0797) 3227402 Fax: (0870) 0527516 E-mail: sales@anderson.ath.cx
▶ Ash Internet Services, 3 Punch Croft, New Ash Green, Longfield, Kent, DA3 8HP Tel: 0870 1996484 E-mail: admin@ashinternet.com
Baniftec Ltd, Farley Edge, Farley Common, Westerham, Kent, TN16 1UB Tel: (01959) 564526 E-mail: enquiries@baniftec.com
▶ BB Online UK Ltd, PO Box 2162, Luton, LU3 2JL Tel: (01582) 572148 Fax: (01582) 585057 E-mail: info@bb-online.co.uk
▶ Broadland Hosting, 11 Mill Crescent, Acle, Norwich, NR13 3BL Tel: (01493) 750428
▶ Broxden Ltd, 8 Algo Business Centre, Glenearn Road, Perth, PH2 0NJ Tel: (01738) 450422 Fax: (01738) 783685 E-mail: sales@broxden.co.uk
▶ Businets Web Design Ltd, 19 Spencers Way, Harrogate, North Yorkshire, HG1 3DN Tel: (0845) 3457849 Fax: (0870) 0119435 E-mail: help@businets.co.uk
Bytecraft Ltd, 5 The Quad, Mercury Court, Chester, CH1 4QP Tel: (01244) 390109 Fax: (01244) 390051 E-mail: sales@bytecraft.co.uk
Cad Capture Ltd, Greenbank Technology Park, Challenge Way, Blackburn, BB1 5RR Tel: (01254) 504400 Fax: (01254) 504401 E-mail: info@cadcap.co.uk
▶ CD Web Design, Forester's Cottage, Kilmaron Estate, Cupar, Fife, KY15 4NE Tel: (07715) 707953 Fax: (01334) 650908
Clik Ltd, The Tobacco Factory, Raleigh Road, Bristol, BS3 1TF Tel: 0117-902 2012 Fax: 0117-902 2010
Cloud Ten, Tadlow, Royston, Hertfordshire, SG8 0EP Tel: (01767) 631810 Fax: (01767) 631811 E-mail: office@cloud-ten.co.uk
Computer Sciences Corporation, Euxton House, Euxton Lane, Chorley, Lancashire, PR7 6FE Tel: (01257) 265507 Fax: (01257) 242609
▶ Digital Freedom Ltd, 109 Trent Road Shaw, Oldham, OL2 7QH Tel: (01706) 847772
Easy Web, 10 St Andrews Cresent, Cardiff, CF10 3DD Tel: (029) 2034 4006 Fax: (029) 2034 4008 E-mail: enquiries@eazyweb.co.uk
Empresa Ltd, 160 Northumberland Street, Norwich, NR2 4EE Tel: (01603) 623030 Fax: (01603) 623525 E-mail: sales@empresa.co.uk
Enterprise A B Ltd, 9 St. Albans Enterprise Centre, Long Spring, Porters Wood, St. Albans, Hertfordshire, AL3 6EN Tel: (01727) 751445 Fax: (01727) 759507 E-mail: admin@eab.co.uk
First 4 It, Sceptre House, 1 Hornbeam Square North, Harrogate, North Yorkshire, HG2 8PB Tel: (01423) 859370 Fax: (01423) 859371 E-mail: sales@first4it.co.uk
Forest Software Ltd, 9 Pembroke Grove, Glinton, Peterborough, PE6 7LG Tel: (01733) 253332 Fax: (0870) 7474942 E-mail: sales@forestsoftware.co.uk
Frontline Consultancy Business Services Ltd, Frontline House, Epsom Avenue, Handforth, Wilmslow, Cheshire, SK9 3PW Tel: (0870) 2410715 Fax: (0870) 6067300 E-mail: sales@frontline-consultancy.co.uk
▶ Fusionxs, 7 Wisley Close, West Bridgford, Nottingham, NG2 7NY Tel: 0115-878 7003 Fax: (0845) 8688485 E-mail: info@fusionxs.co.uk
▶ Giantpea Limited, PO Box 232, Romsey, Hampshire, SO51 8GE Tel: (01794) 230035 E-mail: hello@giantpea.com
Graham Bell Design Ltd, 43, Halnaker, Chichester, West Sussex, PO18 0NQ Tel: (01243) 755910 Fax: (01243) 755911 E-mail: john@gbd.co.uk
▶ Hocking Marketing Partnership, 22 Armstrong Close, Crownhill, Milton Keynes, MK8 0AU Tel: (01908) 563883E-mail: info@hmpltd.co.uk
IT Service Link Ltd, The Black Barn, The Folley, Layer De La Haye, Colchester, CO2 0HZ Tel: (01206) 235000 Fax: (01206) 235001 E-mail: danielle@hi-tech-sales.co.uk
▶ Iweave Ltd, 4 Brentham Crescent, Stirling, FK8 2AZ Tel: (01786) 450606 Fax: (01786) 462876
▶ J K Computer Solutions, The Dairy, Lynn Road, Hillington, King's Lynn, Norfolk, PE31 6BJ Tel: (07775) 941121 E-mail: john@jkcomputersolutions.com
▶ JAB Web Solutions, Suite 145, Cardiff, CF24 3DG Tel: (0777) 9633038 E-mail: andrew@jabwebsolutions.co.uk
▶ L & M Hosting, Internet House, 64 Haig Street, Grangemouth, Stirlingshire, FK3 8QF Tel: (0845) 3312898 Fax: (0845) 6443809
Manumit Computers Ltd, Scope House, Weston Road, Crewe, CW1 6DD Tel: (01270) 250022 Fax: (01270) 250033 E-mail: contact@manumit-computers.com
Net Formation Ltd, Godstone Green, Godstone, Surrey, RH9 8DZ Tel: (01883) 740000 Fax: (01883) 744465 E-mail: info@forfront.net
Paul Schoeller U K, Unit 2 70 Partridge Way, Cirencester, Gloucestershire, GL7 1BQ Tel: (01285) 657521 Fax: (01285) 657521 E-mail: sales@schoeller.co.uk
▶ Red Create, 145-157 St. John Street, London, EC1V 4PY Tel: (020) 7060 5004 Fax: 0871 4330485 E-mail: Info@redcreate.com
Savannah Web Design, Gatcombe Court, Dexter Close, St. Albans, Hertfordshire, AL1 5WA Tel: (01727) 763737
Services Online, 42 Kirby Drive, Luton, LU3 4AW Tel: (01582) 583823 Fax: (01582) 491384 E-mail: webmaster@services-online.co.uk
Styleware Ltd, 28 Wittering Road, Hayling Island, Hampshire, PO11 9SP Tel: (023) 9246 1561 Fax: (023) 9246 1501 E-mail: sales@styleware.co.uk
▶ Sumari Business Systems Ltd, Branston Court, Branston Street, Birmingham, B18 6BA Tel: 0121-244 8111 Fax: 0121-244 8811 E-mail: sumari@sumari.co.uk
▶ Sussex Internet Ltd, Enterprise Works Ltd, Beach Road, Newhaven, East Sussex, BN9 0BX Tel: (01273) 514710 E-mail: info@sussex-internet.net
▶ TWD Hosting Limited, 76 Oak Street, Shaw, Oldham, OL2 8EJ Tel: 01706 881126 E-mail: sales@twdhosting.co.uk
▶ Vizion online, 1 Red Place, London, W1K 6PL Tel: 0207 6478699 Fax: 0207 6478699 E-mail: henry@viziononline.co.uk
▶ Web Age Ltd, The Walled Garden, Sundrum, Ayr, KA6 5LA Tel: (01292) 571460 Fax: (01292) 571470
Wida Group, 2 Brookside Road, Ruddington, Nottingham, NG11 6AT Tel: 0115-921 4797 Fax: 0115-984 5097 E-mail: info@widagroup.com
▶ www.webmozaic.com, 16 Moss Lane, Elworth, Sandbach, Cheshire, CW11 3JN Tel: 01270 750180 E-mail: info@webmozaic.com

WEBSITE HOSTING RESELLING

▶ Easily .Co.Uk, Prospero House, 241 Borough High Street, London, SE1 1GA Tel: (020) 7015 9241 E-mail: helpdesk@easily.co.uk
▶ Isc Computer Consultants, 16 Holford Way, Luton, LU3 4EB Tel: (01582) 585807 E-mail: gian@gianmahil.com
▶ JAB Web Solutions, Suite 145, Cardiff, CF24 3DG Tel: (0777) 9633038 E-mail: andrew@jabwebsolutions.co.uk
▶ Onebighost, 106 Drumaney Road, Coagh, Cookstown, County Tyrone, BT80 0HN Tel: (07050) 382091 Fax: (028) 8673 5871 E-mail: admin@onebighost.com

WEBSITE HOSTING, ELECTRONIC COMMERCE (ECOMMERCE)

4business, 72 New Bond Street, London, W1S 1RR Tel: (020) 7514 9901 E-mail: sales@base4business.com

WEBSITE PROMOTION

▶ The Adworks, No. 9 Cork Place, Bletchley, Milton Keynes, MK3 7WH Tel: 08707 447404 Fax: 08707 447405 E-mail: dbartlett@the-adworks.com
▶ Amber Green, 135 George Street, Edinburgh, EH2 4JS Tel: 0131-514 4000 Fax: 0131-514 4001 E-mail: info@ambergreen.co.uk
▶ Auger Productions, Suite F16, Scope House, Weston Road, Crewe, CW1 6DD Tel: (01270) 258111 Fax: (01270) 258161 E-mail: info@auger-productions.com
▶ Best Web Site Design, 13 Larkspur Close, Bishop's Stortford, Hertfordshire, CM23 4LL Tel: (01279) 303878 Fax: (0870) 7058397
▶ Captain Seo, 3 The Croft, Park Hill, London, W5 2NB Tel: (020) 8816 8877 Fax: (0870) 1258147 E-mail: info@captainseo.com
Guaranteed Website Promotion, 30 Duke Street, Windsor, Berkshire, SL4 1SA Tel: (01753) 852888 Fax: (01753) 855599 E-mail: george@ guaranteed-website-promotion.co.uk
▶ ICOM International Ltd, Norwood House, 53 Brighton Grove, Manchester, M14 5JT Tel: 0161-259 0100 E-mail: info@internetcommunication.co.uk
▶ Oxford Internet Marketing, 10 Manor Farm Close, Kingham, Chipping Norton, Oxfordshire, OX7 6YX Tel: (01608) 658803 Fax: (0870) 1275668 E-mail: stephen@oxfordinternetmarketing.co.uk
▶ Smartways Technology Ltd, 1 Scirocco Close, Northampton, NN3 6AP Tel: (01604) 670500 Fax: (01604) 670567 E-mail: admin@a-i-t.co.uk
▶ Toucan Graphics, 20 Calderhall Avenue, East Calder, Livingston, West Lothian, EH53 0DJ Tel: (01506) 204700 Fax: (01506) 204700 E-mail: info@toucangraphics.com
▶ Vnet Web Solutions, 46 Clensmore Street, Kidderminster, Worcestershire, DY10 2JS Tel: (01562) 66610 Fax: (01562) 829026 E-mail: vnet@veldonn.co.uk
▶ WSI Core Solutions, 65 Hendon Way, London, NW2 2LX Tel: (020) 8458 2928 Fax: (0871) 6616581 E-mail: sally@wsicoresolutions.com

WEBSITE SERVICES, MANAGED

▶ Mosketo, 1 Webster Street, Preston, PR2 1BY Tel: (07723) 042246 E-mail: enquiries@mosketo.net

WEDDING ACCESSORIES

▶ Heavenly Halos (UK), Churston, Paignton, Devon, TQ4 Tel: 0845 833 0938 E-mail: sales@heavenlyhalos.co.uk

WEDDING BALLOONS

Balloons Galore, 61 Leedham Avenue, Tamworth, Staffordshire, B77 3LZ Tel: (01827) 62995

WEDDING CAKE STANDS

▶ Alice's Cake Store, C/o Latteridge House, Latteridge Green, Iron Acton, Bristol, BS37 9TS Tel: (0870) 1995481
Fire & Iron Ltd, Rowhurst Forge, Oxshott Road, Leatherhead, Surrey, KT22 0EN Tel: (01372) 386453 Fax: (01372) 386516 E-mail: sales@fireandiron.co.uk
▶ Olive Tree Coffee and Chocolate Shop, Greenfields, Lhanbryde, Elgin, Morayshire, IV30 8LN Tel: (07817) 430635 E-mail: shop@olivetreeofelgin.co.uk

WEDDING CAKES

▶ Chocolate Fountains from Hot Chocolate Lunch Ltd, St Hilda Close, Deepcar, Sheffield, S36 2TH Tel: 0784 0685595 E-mail: info@hotchocolatelunch.com

WEDDING CATERING

▶ Badger Bars, The Post Office, Firsby Road, Great Steeping, Spilsby, Lincolnshire, PE23 5PT Tel: 07731 576864
▶ Bites to Banquets, 6 Park Avenue, Sleaford, Lincolnshire, NG34 7JQ Tel: 01529 410522 E-mail: bites@mprl.co.uk
▶ Create a Cake, Unit H, Maesteg Market Area, Maesteg, CF34 9DA Tel: (07976) 518649 E-mail: helen@createacake.co.uk
▶ David Tyrrell Catering & Hospitality, 481 Chessington Road, Epsom, Surrey, KT19 9JH Tel: (020) 8397 3030 Fax: (020) 8397 4747 E-mail: davidtyrrell@btconnect.com
▶ Kensingtons Ltd, 2 Dixon Place, College Milton, East Kilbride, Glasgow, G74 5JF Tel: (0845) 2722845 Fax: E-mail: enquiry@kensingtons-catering.co.uk
▶ Midsummer House, Midsummer Common, Cambridge, CB4 1HA Tel: (01223) 369299 Fax: (01223) 302672 E-mail: reservations@midsummerhouse.co.uk
▶ Olive Tree Coffee and Chocolate Shop, Greenfields, Lhanbryde, Elgin, Morayshire, IV30 8LN Tel: (07817) 430635 E-mail: shop@olivetreeofelgin.co.uk
▶ Perfect Banqueting, PO BOX 2104, Leigh-on-Sea, Essex, SS9 3WW Tel: 01702 476360E-mail: perfectbanqueting@uwclub.net
Southwest Sumo Hire, Lower Brexworthy, Bradworthy, Holsworthy, Devon, EX22 7TR Tel: (07779) 782716 E-mail: Budesumo@hotmail.co.uk
▶ Tony Patti Entertainments, Sunrise Radio, Merrick Road, Southall, Middlesex, UB2 4AU Tel: 07961 908650 E-mail: tonypatti@sunriseradio.com

WEDDING DECORATIONS

Draytords Silk Wedding Flowers, 198, Derby Road, Chesterfield, Derbyshire, S40 2EP Tel: (01246) 205914
▶ Hot Chocolates - Chocolate Fountain Hire, 83 Findon Road, Elson, Gosport, Hampshire, PO12 4ER Tel: (023) 9250 1416 E-mail: enquiries@hotchocolates.co.uk
▶ Jessica Claire Designs, 133 Unicorn Avenue, Coventry, CV5 7FB Tel: (024) 7646 5577 E-mail: k.stewardson@btinternet.com
▶ MTS Occasions by Design, Inglenook House, 125 Mottram Old Road, Stalybridge, Cheshire, SK15 2SZ Tel: 01457 766088 E-mail: enquiries@mts-occasionsbydesign.co.uk
▶ Olive Tree Coffee and Chocolate Shop, Greenfields, Lhanbryde, Elgin, Morayshire, IV30 8LN Tel: (07817) 430635 E-mail: shop@olivetreeofelgin.co.uk
▶ Organza Events, 72 Clarence Road, London, E12 5BH Tel: (020) 8553 5523 Fax: 0208 553 5523 E-mail: info@organzaevents.com
▶ Pollen Palace, 39 Snowsfields, London, SE1 3SU Tel: (0800) 0437901 Fax: (020) 7378 1058 E-mail: enquiries@pollenpalace.com

WEDDING DECORATIONS – *continued*

▶ Pretty Chairs, 32 St. Matthews Close, Renishaw, Sheffield, S21 3WT Tel: (01246) 430883 E-mail: sales@prettychairs.co.uk

▶ Tony Patti Entertainments, Sunrise Radio, Merrick Road, Southall, Middlesex, UB2 4AU Tel: 07961 908650 E-mail: tonypatti@sunriseradio.com

WEDDING DRESSES

Anderson Apparel Ltd, Unit 4-5 Village Workshops, Pandy Road, Llanbrynmair, Powys, SY19 7AA Tel: (01650) 521880 Fax: (01650) 521880

▶ Dreamweaver Weddings, 113 Cleethorpe Road, Grimsby, South Humberside, DN31 3ES Tel: (01472) 355001 Fax: (01472) 238742 E-mail: shirley@dreamweaverweddings.co.uk

▶ Eshenda Moda Ltd, Unit 23, Cygnus Business Centre,, Dalmeyer Road, London, NW10 2XA Tel: (020) 8200 3560 Fax: (020) 8200 6623 E-mail: shinyi_j@yahoo.co.uk

▶ John Frost Designer Bridalwear, 44 Smawthorne Lane, Castleford, West Yorkshire, WF10 4EW Tel: (01977) 552913 Fax: (01977) 604646

▶ Topclass Wedding Gowns, 1st Floor Co-op Stores, The Street, Woolpit, Bury St. Edmunds, Suffolk, IP30 9RU Tel: (01359) 241422 E-mail: topclassgowns@aol.com

▶ Trousseau Ltd, 284a North Road, Gabalfa, Cardiff, CF14 3BN Tel: 029 20610099 E-mail: admin@trousseaultd.co.uk

▶ Truly Scrumptious, 85 New Road, Porthcawl, Mid Glamorgan, CF36 5DH Tel: (01656) 788080 Fax: 01656 788080 E-mail: lorraine@trulyscrumptiousonline.co.uk

WEDDING FLORAL SUPPLIES

▶ claire gray floral designs, 57 Clement Way, Upminster, Essex, RM14 2NX Tel: 07800 918615 E-mail: claire.gray57@ntlworld.com

Creative Flowers, 28 Highwalls Avenue, Dinas Powys, South Glamorgan, CF64 4AP Tel: (029) 2051 4754 Fax: (029) 2051 4754 E-mail: creflow@aol.com

Draÿfords Silk Wedding Flowers, 198, Derby Road, Chesterfield, Derbyshire, S40 2EP Tel: (01246) 205914

▶ Florabundance.Co.Uk, 73 London Road, East Grinstead, West Sussex, RH19 1EQ Tel: (01342) 311478 Fax: (01342) 311542 E-mail: sales@florabundance.co.uk

▶ Mayhew Flowers, 6 Cockpit Hill, Cullompton, Devon, EX15 1DF Tel: (01884) 839826 Fax: 01884 839826 E-mail: info@mayhewflowers.co.uk

▶ Oak Floral Design, Manor Farm, Main Street, Shangton, Leicester, LE8 0PG Tel: (07754) 07122

WEDDING GIFTWARE

▶ A Rosy Marriage Balloon & Party Megastore, 14 Barn Way, Hednesford, Cannock, Staffordshire, WS12 0FP Tel: (07795) 102050 E-mail: sales@arosymarriage.co.uk

▶ Amazing Days, 78 Gallaghers Mead, Andover, Hants, SP10 3BW Tel: 01264 395081

▶ Anastasia Flowers, 131 Easterly Road, Leeds, LS8 2TP Tel: 0113-235 1010 Fax: 0113-235 1010 E-mail: lana@anastasiaflowers.co.uk

▶ Butterfly Occasions Ltd, 56 Foxholes Road, Chelmsford, CM2 7HS Tel: (01245) 472529 E-mail: info@butterflyoccasions.co.uk

▶ Carnmeal Cottage Flowers, Carnmeal Cottage, Carnmeal, Breage, Helston, Cornwall, TR13 9NL Tel: (01326) 572901 Fax: (01326) 565698 E-mail: sales@carnmeal.com

▶ French Flavour Ltd, PO Box 2192, Wrexham, Clwyd, LL14 2TB Tel: (01978) 844378 Fax: (01978) 844378 E-mail: info@frenchflavour.co.uk

▶ Hands On, 23 Seldon Road, Worthing, West Sussex, BN11 2LN Tel: 07731 522290 E-mail: info@five-minute-massage-company.com

heirlooms.uk.com, 11 Fontaine Road, London, SW16 3PB Tel: 02086 792196 Fax: 020 7738 9787 E-mail: info@heirlooms.uk.com

▶ Inspirit Interiors, Repton Road, Nottingham, NG6 9GE Tel: 0115-877 6959 Fax: 0115-877 6959 E-mail: enquiries@inspirit-interiors.co.uk

▶ The Mulberry Bush, Limberlost Farm, Swife Lane, nr. Broad Oak, Heathfield, East Sussex, TN21 8YA Tel: (01435) 882014

▶ Sharemymemory.com, P.O. Box 3756, Sheffield, S6 9AB Tel: 08707 202 686 Fax: 08707 202 687 E-mail: mail@sharemymemory.com

▶ The Silverware shop, 50a Tenby Street North, Hockley, Birmingham, B1 3EG Tel: 0121-248 7702 Fax: 0121-248 7701 E-mail: silverwareshop@aol.com

▶ Swarovski Store Guilford, 10 White Lion Walk, Guildford, Surrey, GU1 3DN Tel: (01483) 568200 E-mail: swarovskiguildford@ntlworld.com

WEDDING NAPKINS

▶ Amazing Days, 78 Gallaghers Mead, Andover, Hants, SP10 3BW Tel: 01264 395081

▶ Butterfly Occasions Ltd, 56 Foxholes Road, Chelmsford, CM2 7HS Tel: (01245) 472529 E-mail: info@butterflyoccasions.co.uk

▶ Carnmeal Cottage Flowers, Carnmeal Cottage, Carnmeal, Breage, Helston, Cornwall, TR13 9NL Tel: (01326) 572901 Fax: (01326) 565698 E-mail: sales@carnmeal.com

▶ MTS Occasions by Design, Inglenook House, 125 Mottram Old Road, Stalybridge, Cheshire, SK15 2SZ Tel: 01457 766088 E-mail: enquiries@mts-occasionsbydesign.co.uk

▶ The Silverware shop, 50a Tenby Street North, Hockley, Birmingham, B1 3EG Tel: 0121-248 7702 Fax: 0121-248 7701 E-mail: silverwareshop@aol.com

WEDDING STATIONERY

▶ A Wedding to Talk About, 1 Brennan Close, Barrow-in-Furness, Cumbria, LA13 0TD Tel: (01229) 812921

▶ Bespoke Cards, 9B Higham Road, Woodford Green, Essex, IG8 9JN Tel: (0845) 270 1410 Fax: (0845) 270 1411 E-mail: theteam@bespokecards.net

▶ Caricature/Cartoon Portrait Wedding Invitations, 5 Hillview Cottages (Off Plough Hill), Basted, Borough Green, Sevenoaks, Kent, TN15 8PS Tel: (01732) 883555 E-mail: weddings@christmanncreative.co.uk

▶ Carnmeal Cottage Flowers, Carnmeal Cottage, Carnmeal, Breage, Helston, Cornwall, TR13 9NL Tel: (01326) 572901 Fax: (01326) 565698 E-mail: sales@carnmeal.com

▶ Celebration Stationery, Unit 1, The Caxton Centre, Porters Wood, St. Albans, Hertfordshire, AL3 6XT Tel: (01727) 868237 Fax: (01727) 847883 E-mail: chris@celebrationstationery.co.uk

▶ Charming Invitations, 170 Erskinefauld Road, Linwood, Paisley, Renfrewshire, PA3 3QH Tel: (01505) 353353 E-mail: charminginvitations@yahoo.co.uk

▶ Dreamweaver Weddings, 113 Cleethorpe Road, Grimsby, South Humberside, DN31 3ES Tel: (01472) 355001 Fax: (01472) 238742 E-mail: shirley@dreamweaverweddings.co.uk

▶ Handmade Wedding Invitations & Stationery By Datz Creationz, 5 Alwin Road, Rowley Regis, West Midlands, B65 8BN Tel: (07759) 820406 E-mail: datzcreationz@blueyonder.co.uk

▶ Katrina's Cards, Unit 20 Century Business Centre, Century Park, Manvers, Rotherham, South Yorkshire, S63 5DA Tel: (01709) 300206 Fax: (01709) 300201 E-mail: contact@katrinascards.co.uk

▶ Linda Abrahams, 27 Chelwood Drive, Leeds, LS8 2AT Tel: 0113-295 0098 Fax: 0113-295 6697 E-mail: Linda@lindaabrahams.co.uk

▶ Lolly's Loft, Sale, Cheshire, M33 Tel: 0161-976 6071 E-mail: lollysloft@btinternet.com

▶ MTS Occasions by Design, Inglenook House, 125 Mottram Old Road, Stalybridge, Cheshire, SK15 2SZ Tel: 01457 766088 E-mail: enquiries@mts-occasionsbydesign.co.uk

▶ Porosol Ltd, Tennis House, 249-251 Belper Road, Stanley Common, Ilkeston, Derbyshire, DE7 6FY Tel: 0115-930 7977 Fax: 0115-944 2147 E-mail: t.shaw@porosol.fsnet.co.uk

▶ Postpots Ltd, 108 Titan House, Cardiff Bay Business Centre, Cardiff, CF24 5BS Tel: (02920) 472002 Fax: (02920) 472003

▶ Wightcat Wedding Services, Medina Avenue, Newport, Isle of Wight, PO30 1EL Tel: (01983) 248214 E-mail: weddings@wightcat.com

▶ YCARTwedding Stationary, 1B Union Street, Greenock, Renfrewshire, PA16 8JH Tel: (07951) 145871E-mail: tracy@ycart.co.uk

WEDDING TABLEWARE

Catering Linen Hire, Unit E7 Aladdin Centre, Long Drive, Greenford, Middlesex, UB6 8UH Tel: (020) 8575 1844 Fax: (020) 8575 9025 E-mail: maureen.cooper@ukonline.co.uk

▶ Pretty Chairs, 32 St. Matthews Close, Renishaw, Sheffield, S21 3WT Tel: (01246) 430883 E-mail: sales@prettychairs.co.uk

WEDGE WIRE

Screen Systems Ltd, PO Box 237, Warrington, WA5 0JZ Tel: (01925) 659906 Fax: (01925) 571060 E-mail: info@screensystems.com

WEIGH SCALES, DIGITAL

▶ WarehouseEquipment.co.uk, 58 Gleneagles Ave, Leicester, LE4 7GB Tel: 0116-266 4478 Fax: 0116-266 4478 E-mail: sales@warehouseequipment.co.uk

WEIGH/COUNT (COMBINED) MACHINE MANUFRS

A D F Scale Co., Unit 6 Key Point, Keys Park Road, Hednesford, Cannock, Staffordshire, WS12 2FN Tel: (01543) 572165 Fax: (01543) 459005 E-mail: enquiries@adfscale.co.uk

Abacus Weighing Services, Unit 3B, Barlow Street, Walkden, Manchester, M28 3BQ Tel: 0161-799 7131 Fax: 0161-799 7140 E-mail: info@abacusweighing.co.uk

Bizerba UK Ltd, Eastman Way, Hemel Hempstead Industrial Estate, Hemel Hempstead, Hertfordshire, HP2 7DU Tel: (01442) 240751 Fax: (01442) 231328 E-mail: info@bizerba.co.uk

Howard Scale Co. Ltd, 14 Oughton Road, Birmingham, B12 0DF Tel: 0121-446 5190 Fax: 0121-446 5191 E-mail: sale@howardscale.com

St Turier, Unit 7 Block 5 Shenstone Trading Estate, Bromsgrove Road, Halesowen, West Midlands, B63 3XB Tel: 0121-501 6880 Fax: 0121-501 6881 E-mail: sales@turierscales.co.uk

Stevens Group Ltd, Challenge Way, Blackburn, BB1 5QB Tel: (01254) 685200 Fax: (01254) 685202 E-mail: sales@stevensgroup.com

Trent Scales Ltd, Eagle Road, Ilkeston, Derbyshire, DE7 4RB Tel: 0115-944 1141

Weighwell Engineering, 23 Orgreave Place, Sheffield, S13 9LU Tel: 0114-269 9955 Fax: 0114-269 9256 E-mail: sales@weighwell.co.uk

Weighwright Weighing Equipment, 55a Putnoe Lane, Bedford, MK41 9AE Tel: (01234) 313883 Fax: (01234) 313883 E-mail: info@scalemart.co.uk

WEIGHBRIDGES

A W M Ltd, 17/18 Mercers Hill Road, Chapel Pond HL, Bury St. Edmunds, Suffolk, IP32 7HX Tel: (01284) 701222 Fax: (01284) 703559 E-mail: brian@awmlimited.co.uk

Abacus Weighing Services, Unit 3B, Barlow Street, Walkden, Manchester, M28 3BQ Tel: 0161-799 7131 Fax: 0161-799 7140 E-mail: info@abacusweighing.co.uk

▶ Avery Weigh Tronix Ltd, 13-14 Monckton Road Industrial Estate, Wakefield, West Yorkshire, WF2 7BP Tel: (0870) 9050041 Fax: (0870) 9050042 E-mail: hiredivisionuk@awtxglobal.com

Golden River Traffic Ltd, Talisman Road, Bicester, Oxfordshire, OX26 6HR Tel: (01869) 362800 Fax: (01869) 246858 E-mail: sales@goldenriver.com

Parkerfarm Weighing Systems, Titan Works, Bridge Way, Broombank Road, Chesterfield, Derbyshire, S41 9QJ Tel: (01246) 456729 Fax: (01246) 260844 E-mail: sales@parkerfarm.com

Precia-Molen UK, Unit 30 Walkers Road, Moons Moat North Industrial Es, Redditch, Worcestershire, B98 9HE Tel: (01527) 590320 Fax: (01527) 590301 E-mail: sales@preciamolen.co.uk

Shering Weighing Group Ltd, Pitreavie Business Park, Queensferry Road, Dunfermline, Fife, KY11 8UL Tel: (01383) 621505 Fax: (01383) 620262 E-mail: sales@shering.com

▶ Top Weigh Ltd, Scale House, Jeffrey Estate, Rockcliffe, Carlisle, CA6 4BH Tel: (01228) 672400 Fax: (01228) 672402

Trent Scales Ltd, Eagle Road, Ilkeston, Derbyshire, DE7 4RB Tel: 0115-944 1141

Weighfab Ltd, Unit 3, 35 Catley Rd, Sheffield, S9 5JF Tel: 0114-261 1132 Fax: 0114-261 1132

Weightron (U K) Ltd, Weightron House, Brimington Road North, Chesterfield, Derbyshire, S41 9AN Tel: (01246) 260062 Fax: (01246) 260844 E-mail: info@weightroncb.co.uk

Weighwell Engineering, 23 Orgreave Place, Sheffield, S13 9LU Tel: 0114-269 9955 Fax: 0114-269 9256 E-mail: sales@weighwell.co.uk

WEIGHER/WEIGHING SYSTEMS,

See also headings for particular types

Accurate Weight Co. Ltd, 5 Bridle Way, Bootle, Merseyside, L30 4UA Tel: 0151-524 3341 Fax: 0151-525 5864 E-mail: sales@accurateweight.co.uk

Allprep Weighing Equipment, 26 Church Lane, Caythorpe, Grantham, Lincolnshire, NG32 3DU Tel: (01400) 273877 Fax: (01400) 273877

Autoweigh Scales UK Ltd, James Street, Elland, West Yorkshire, HX5 0HB Tel: (01422) 376965 Fax: (01422) 378109 E-mail: autoweigh.sales@virgin.net

Ayrshire Service, 7 Campsie Avenue, Bourtreehill South, Irvine, Ayrshire, KA11 1JF Tel: (01294) 212410 Fax: (01294) 312223

Cornwall Scale & Equipment Co., Wallasey, 29 Mount Ambrose, Redruth, Cornwall, TR15 1NX Tel: (01209) 213413 Fax: (01209) 213413 E-mail: martin.jsanders@virgin.net

Digi Europe Ltd, Digi House, Rookwood Way, Haverhill, Suffolk, CB9 8DG Tel: (01440) 712176 Fax: (01440) 712173

Easiweigh Ltd, Unit 1b Shrub Hill Industrial Estate, Worcester, WR4 9EL Tel: (01905) 28075 Fax: (01905) 22229 E-mail: sales@easiweigh.co.uk

Epelsa UK Ltd, Unit 10, Wroslyn Road Industrial Estate, Freeland, Witney, Oxfordshire, OX29 8HZ Tel: (01993) 882786 Fax: (01993) 883594 E-mail: epelsauk@bulkblue.com

Ian Fellows Ltd, 37 Lower Keyford, Frome, Somerset, BA11 4AR Tel: (01373) 473161 Fax: (01373) 451609 E-mail: sales@ianfellows.co.uk

Mersey Weigh Ltd, Unit 48 Canal Bridge Enterprise Centre, Meadow Lane, Ellesmere Port, CH65 4EH Tel: 0151-356 5274 Fax: 0151-356 5274

Minsterport Weighing Equipment, Baildon Mills, Northgate, Baildon, Shipley, West Yorkshire, BD17 6JX Tel: (01274) 580028 Fax: (01274) 583800

Northern Data Machines, 35 The Square, Grantown-on-Spey, Morayshire, PH26 3HF Tel: (01479) 873777 Fax: (01479) 87377 E-mail: enquiries@northerndata.co.uk

Precision Balance Services, 3 Atlas Court, Coalville, Leicestershire, LE67 3FL Tel: (01530) 834650 Fax: (01530) 834650 E-mail: sales@precisionbalance.co.uk

Scalesmart Ltd, Unit 37, The Warren, East Goscote, Leicester, LE7 3XA Tel: (0800) 9154201 Fax: (0800) 9154202 E-mail: scales@scalesmart.com

Select Scales Ltd, 36 Skinner Street, Creswell, Worksop, Nottinghamshire, S80 4JH Tel: (01909) 725043 Fax: (01909) 724057

Stevens Group Ltd, Challenge Way, Blackburn, BB1 5QB Tel: (01254) 685200 Fax: (01254) 685202 E-mail: sales@stevensgroup.com

Surrey Scales Co, 2 The Parade, Philanthropic Road, Redhill, RH1 4DN Tel: (01737) 769745 Fax: (01737) 760390

T Cole & Son, 18 Meadowbank Road, Carrickfergus, County Antrim, BT38 8YF Tel: (028) 9336 0844 Fax: (028) 9336 0855 E-mail: sales@tcoleandson.co.uk

Weigh Control Systems Ltd, 2 Felton Mill, Felton, Morpeth, Northumberland, NE65 9HL Tel: (01670) 787177 Fax: (01670) 787179

Weighing Technology Services Ltd, 4 Selbury Drive, Oadby Induast Estate, Oadby, Leicester, LE2 5NG Tel: 0116-271 3228 Fax: 0116-271 3229 E-mail: enquires@wts-ltd.co.uk

WEIGHER/WEIGHING SYSTEMS HIRE

Abacus Weighing Services, Unit 3B, Barlow Street, Walkden, Manchester, M28 3BQ Tel: 0161-799 7131 Fax: 0161-799 7140 E-mail: info@abacusweighing.co.uk

Autoweigh Scales UK Ltd, James Street, Elland, West Yorkshire, HX5 0HB Tel: (01422) 376965 Fax: (01422) 378109 E-mail: autoweigh.sales@virgin.net

Evans Peter Light Engineering, Bromyard Road Industrial Estate, Unit 12, Ledbury, Herefordshire, HR8 1NS Tel: (01531) 634177 Fax: (01531) 634177

J A Lorrimar & Co., Lorrimar House Hatfield Hi-Tech Park, Goulton Street, Hull, HU3 4DD Tel: (01482) 228173 Fax: (01482) 214106 E-mail: info@lorrimar.co.uk

WEIGHER/WEIGHING SYSTEMS MAINTENANCE/REPAIR SERVICES

Accurate Weight Co. Ltd, 5 Bridle Way, Bootle, Merseyside, L30 4UA Tel: 0151-524 3341 Fax: 0151-525 5864 E-mail: sales@accurateweight.co.uk

County Scales Ltd, Langley Business Park, Station Road, Langley Mill, NG16 4DG Tel: (0800) 7311774 Fax: (01773) 763222

Industrial Scales UK Ltd, B2-B3 Hilton Trading Estate, Hilton Road, Lanesfield, Wolverhampton, WV4 6DW Tel: (01902) 354141 Fax: (01902) 402252

Mersey Weigh Ltd, Unit 48 Canal Bridge Enterprise Centre, Meadow Lane, Ellesmere Port, CH65 4EH Tel: 0151-356 5274 Fax: 0151-356 5274

Metropolitan Weighing Machine Co. Ltd, Metro Weighing Machines, Foxton Road, Grays, Essex, RM20 4XX Tel: (01375) 390140 Fax: (01375) 390140 E-mail: enquiries@metroweigh.com

Newtec Odense UK Ltd, 1 Park View, Arrow, Alcester, Warwickshire, B49 5PN Tel: (01789) 764590 Fax: (01789) 763836 E-mail: p.crouch@newtecuk.com

Rowecon Systems Ltd, Treeton Centre, Rother Cresent, Treeton, Rotherham, South Yorkshire, S60 5QY Tel: 0114-254 0660 Fax: 0114-254 0661 E-mail: sales@rowecon.co.uk

S & S Electronics, Canal Works, Cadman Street, Sheffield, S4 7ZG Tel: 0114-275 8593 Fax: 0114-275 8593

Scaleways Leicester Ltd, 35 Carlisle Street, Leicester, LE3 6AH Tel: 0116-255 5092 Fax: 0116-255 5143 E-mail: sales@scaleways.co.uk

Surrey Scales Co, 2 The Parade, Philanthropic Road, Redhill, RH1 4DN Tel: (01737) 769745 Fax: (01737) 760390

Talent Weighing S & S Ltd, 3j Anchor Bridge Way, Dewsbury, West Yorkshire, WF12 9QS Tel: (01924) 438127 Fax: (01924) 438129 E-mail: info@talentweighing.co.uk

Team Weighing Co., 12 Rowley Avenue, Sidcup, Kent, DA15 9LA Tel: (020) 8302 9965 Fax: (01322) 286515 E-mail: mike@teamweighing.fsnet.co.uk

Yorkshire Scientific Instruments, Garth House, 3 Garth Avenue, Leeds, LS17 5BH Tel: 0113-268 3206 Fax: 0113-269 6047 E-mail: yorkinsts@aol.com

WEIGHER/WEIGHING SYSTEMS, AUTOMATIC

Chronos Richardson Ltd, Unit 1 Centurion Business Centre, Dabell Avenue, Nottingham, NG6 8WN Tel: 0115-935 1351 Fax: 0115-935 1353 E-mail: info@chronos-richardson.com
Comcount Ltd, Unit 16 Cranham Estate, Shipston Close, Worcester, WR4 9XN Tel: (01905) 454710 Fax: (01905) 455849 E-mail: mail@comcount.co.uk
Easiweigh Ltd, Unit 1b Shrub Hill Industrial Estate, Worcester, WR4 9EL Tel: (01905) 28075 Fax: (01905) 22229 E-mail: sales@easiweigh.co.uk
Estera Scales Ltd, Europa House, Dorking Business Park, Dorking, Surrey, RH4 1HJ Tel: (01306) 740785 Fax: (01306) 740786
Evans Peter Light Engineering, Bromyard Road Industrial Estate, Unit 12, Ledbury, Herefordshire, HR8 1NS Tel: (01531) 634177 Fax: (01531) 634177
Kliklok Woodman International Ltd, Western Drive, Bristol, BS14 0AY Tel: (01275) 836131 Fax: (01275) 891754 E-mail: sales@kliklok-woodman-int.com
M P M Scales & Fabrications, Unit 3 Millbuck Way, Sandbach, Cheshire, CW11 3HT Tel: (01270) 768470 Fax: (01270) 762992 E-mail: info@mpmscales.co.uk
Mass Measuring Systems, 149 Holland Street, Denton, Manchester, M34 3GE Tel: 0161-304 5700 Fax: 0161-336 4383 E-mail: enquiries@mass-measuring.com
▶ Qualipack (U K), 50 Kinnersley, Severn Stoke, Worcester, WR8 9JR Tel: (01905) 371226 Fax: (01905) 371529 E-mail: sales@qualipack.co.uk
Team Weighing Co., 12 Rowley Avenue, Sidcup, Kent, DA15 9LA Tel: (020) 8302 9965 Fax: (01322) 286515 E-mail: mike@teamweighing.fsnet.co.uk
Ward Bekker Ltd, Three Winds, Madge Hill, Kinnersley, Severn Stoke, Worcester, WR8 9JN Tel: (01905) 371200 Fax: (01905) 371049

WEIGHER/WEIGHING SYSTEMS, BATCH

Electronic Products & Industrial Control Systems Ltd, Unit 2 Bailey Drive, Sheffield, S21 2JF Tel: 0114-251 0801 Fax: 0114-248 8197 E-mail: epicsystemsltd@btinternet.com
Kingswinford Engineering Co. Ltd, Shaw Road, Dudley, West Midlands, DY2 8TS Tel: (01384) 253411 Fax: (01384) 258107 E-mail: kfordengcoltd@aol.com
Nova Weigh Ltd, Unit 30 Walkers Road, Moons Moat North Indust Estate, Redditch, Worcestershire, B98 9HE Tel: (01527) 67557 Fax: (01527) 60213 E-mail: sales@novaweigh.co.uk
Precia-Molen UK, Unit 30 Walkers Road, Moons Moat North Industrial Es, Redditch, Worcestershire, B98 9HE Tel: (01527) 590320 Fax: (01527) 590301 E-mail: sales@preciamolen.co.uk
Promtek Ltd, Fisher Street, Brindley Ford, Stoke-on-Trent, ST8 7QJ Tel: (01782) 375600 Fax: (01782) 375605 E-mail: sales@promtek.com
Rospen Industries Ltd, Oldends Lane Industrial Estate, Oldends Lane, Stonehouse, Gloucestershire, GL10 3RQ Tel: (01453) 825212 Fax: (01453) 828279 E-mail: enquiries@rospen.com
Trent Scales Ltd, Eagle Road, Ilkeston, Derbyshire, DE7 4RB Tel: 0115-944 1141

WEIGHER/WEIGHING SYSTEMS, COMPUTERISED

A.E.W. Delford, Main Road, Dovercourt, Harwich, Essex, CO12 4LP Tel: (01255) 241000 Fax: (01255) 241155 E-mail: sales@delford.co.uk
DEM Industrial Weighing Systems, 3 Hill Rise, Measham, Swadlincote, Derbyshire, DE12 7NZ Tel: (01530) 272704 Fax: (01530) 272704 E-mail: sales@demmachines.co.uk
Palway Ltd, 6 Macadam Close, Drayton Fields Industrial Estate, Daventry, Northamptonshire, NN11 8RX Tel: (01327) 876387 Fax: (01327) 872615 E-mail: sales@palway.com
Shering Weighing Group Ltd, Pitreavie Business Park, Queensferry Road, Dunfermline, Fife, KY11 8UL Tel: (01383) 621505 Fax: (01383) 620262 E-mail: sales@shering.com

WEIGHER/WEIGHING SYSTEMS, CONTINUOUS

A.E.W. Delford, Main Road, Dovercourt, Harwich, Essex, CO12 4LP Tel: (01255) 241000 Fax: (01255) 241155 E-mail: sales@delford.co.uk
Rospen Industries Ltd, Oldends Lane Industrial Estate, Oldends Lane, Stonehouse, Gloucestershire, GL10 3RQ Tel: (01453) 825212 Fax: (01453) 828279 E-mail: enquiries@rospen.com
Team Weighing Co., 12 Rowley Avenue, Sidcup, Kent, DA15 9LA Tel: (020) 8302 9965 Fax: (01322) 286515 E-mail: mike@teamweighing.fsnet.co.uk

WEIGHER/WEIGHING SYSTEMS, COUNTER COMBINED, *See Weigh/Count etc*

WEIGHER/WEIGHING SYSTEMS, ELECTRICAL

Applied Weighing International Ltd, Unit 5 Southview Park, Caversham, Reading, RG4 5AF Tel: 0118-946 1900 Fax: 0118-946 1862 E-mail: info@appliedweighing.co.uk

WEIGHER/WEIGHING SYSTEMS, ELECTRONIC

A D F Scale Co., Unit 6 Key Point, Keys Park Road, Hednesford, Cannock, Staffordshire, WS12 2FN Tel: (01543) 572165 Fax: (01543) 459005 E-mail: enquiries@adfscale.co.uk
A & D Instruments Ltd, 24-26 Blacklands Way, Abingdon, Oxfordshire, OX14 1DY Tel: (01235) 550420 Fax: (01235) 550485 E-mail: sales@aandd-eu.net
Abacus Automation, Seaview House, The Parade, Parkgate, Neston, CH64 6SB Tel: 0151-336 7754 Fax: 0151-336 7548 E-mail: mail@abacusautomation.co.uk
Avon Scale Co. Ltd, 1 Claremont Street, London, N18 2RP Tel: (020) 8807 2254 Fax: (020) 8803 6653 E-mail: accounts@avonscale.freeserve.co.uk
Cherlyn Electronics Ltd, Brookmount Court, Kirkwood Road, Cambridge, CB4 2QH Tel: (01223) 424169 Fax: (01223) 426543 E-mail: mail@cherlyn.co.uk
Design Initiative Ltd, The Old Granary, The Street, Glynde, Lewes, East Sussex, BN8 6SX Tel: (01273) 858525 Fax: (01273) 858531 E-mail: info@designit.eu.com
Ian Fellows Ltd, 37 Lower Keyford, Frome, Somerset, BA11 4AR Tel: (01373) 473161 Fax: (01373) 451609 E-mail: sales@ianfellows.co.uk
Howard Scale Co. Ltd, 14 Oughton Road, Birmingham, B12 0DF Tel: 0121-446 5190 Fax: 0121-446 5191 E-mail: sale@howardscale.com
M P M Scales & Fabrications, Unit 3 Millbuck Way, Sandbach, Cheshire, CW11 3HT Tel: (01270) 768470 Fax: (01270) 762992 E-mail: info@mpmscales.co.uk
Nova Weigh Ltd, Unit 30 Walkers Road, Moons Moat North Indust Estate, Redditch, Worcestershire, B98 9HE Tel: (01527) 67557 Fax: (01527) 60213 E-mail: sales@novaweigh.co.uk
Palway Ltd, 6 Macadam Close, Drayton Fields Industrial Estate, Daventry, Northamptonshire, NN11 8RX Tel: (01327) 876387 Fax: (01327) 872615 E-mail: sales@palway.com
Promtek Ltd, Fisher Street, Brindley Ford, Stoke-on-Trent, ST8 7QJ Tel: (01782) 375600 Fax: (01782) 375605 E-mail: sales@promtek.com
Rowecon Systems Ltd, Treeton Centre, Rother Cresent, Treeton, Rotherham, South Yorkshire, S60 5QY Tel: 0114-254 0660 Fax: 0114-254 0661 E-mail: sales@rowecon.co.uk
St Turier, Unit 7 Block 5 Shenstone Trading Estate, Bromsgrove Road, Halesowen, West Midlands, B63 3XB Tel: 0121-501 6880 Fax: 0121-501 6881 E-mail: sales@turierscales.co.uk
Talent Weighing S & S Ltd, 3j Anchor Bridge Way, Dewsbury, West Yorkshire, WF12 9QS Tel: (01924) 438127 Fax: (01924) 438129 E-mail: info@talentweighing.co.uk
▶ Top Weigh Ltd, Scale House, Jeffrey Estate, Rockcliffe, Carlisle, CA6 4BH Tel: (01228) 672400 Fax: (01228) 672402
Toshiba TEC Europe UK Operations, 1 Siskin House, Marlins Meadow, Croxley Business Park, Watford, WD18 8TY Tel: (01923) 233688 Fax: (01923) 233698 E-mail: administrator@toshibatec-eu.co.uk
Waymatic Ltd, 15 Bridgewater Way, Windsor, Berkshire, SL4 1RD Tel: (01753) 869218 Fax: (01753) 830519 E-mail: waymatic@btconnect.com
Wellgates, Unit 6 Junction 7 Business Park, Blackburn Road, Clayton Le Moors, Lancashire, BB5 5JW Tel: (01254) 395379 Fax: (01254) 395379

WEIGHER/WEIGHING SYSTEMS, INDUSTRIAL

A W M Ltd, 17/18 Mercers Hill Road, Chapel Pond HL, Bury St. Edmunds, Suffolk, IP32 7HX Tel: (01284) 701222 Fax: (01284) 703559 E-mail: brian@awmlimited.co.uk
Autoscales & Service Co. Ltd, Truweigh House, Ordnance Street, Blackburn, BB1 3AE Tel: (01254) 676938 Fax: (01254) 682374 E-mail: info@autoscales.co.uk
Calibra Weighing Systems Ltd, Calibra House, Sandy La Industrial Estate, Stourport-on-Severn, Worcestershire, DY13 9QB Tel: (01299) 879944 Fax: (01299) 871188 E-mail: enquiries@calibraweighingsystems.co.uk
D Brash & Sons Ltd, 37 Stamperland Crescent, Clarkston, Glasgow, G76 8LH Tel: 0141-638 2284 Fax: 0141-620 1842 E-mail: sales@dbrash.co.uk
Estera Scales Ltd, Europa House, Dorking Business Park, Dorking, Surrey, RH4 1HJ Tel: (01306) 740785 Fax: (01306) 740786
Euroscales Holdings Ltd, Queens Court, Queens Avenue, Macclesfield, Cheshire, SK10 2BN Tel: (01625) 619554 Fax: (01625) 613295 E-mail: sales@euroscales.com
Ian Fellows Ltd, 37 Lower Keyford, Frome, Somerset, BA11 4AR Tel: (01373) 473161 Fax: (01373) 451609 E-mail: sales@ianfellows.co.uk
Globeweigh UK Ltd, Market Street, Tandragee, Craigavon, County Armagh, BT62 2BP Tel: (028) 3884 0714 Fax: (028) 3884 0420 E-mail: sales@globeweigh.com
Halifax Scale Co., Brighouse Road, Hipperholme, Halifax, West Yorkshire, HX3 8EF Tel: (01422) 201016 Fax: (01422) 203775 E-mail: info@halifaxscale.co.uk
K F C Co., PO Box 55, Gloucester, GL14 3YB Tel: (01594) 822025 Fax: (01594) 822195 E-mail: info@kfcco.com
Load Monitor (U K) Ltd, The Marchioness Building, Commercial Rd, Bristol, BS1 6TG Tel: 0117-925 2300 Fax: 0117-925 2300 E-mail: sales@loadmonitor.com
M P M Scales & Fabrications, Unit 3 Millbuck Way, Sandbach, Cheshire, CW11 3HT Tel: (01270) 768470 Fax: (01270) 762992 E-mail: info@mpmscales.co.uk
Nesco Weighing Ltd, 89-91 Lambert Street, Hull, HU5 2SH Tel: (01482) 346865 Fax: (01482) 445483 E-mail: info@nesco-weighing.co.uk
Nova Weigh Ltd, Unit 30 Walkers Road, Moons Moat North Indust Estate, Redditch, Worcestershire, B98 9HE Tel: (01527) 67557 Fax: (01527) 60213 E-mail: sales@novaweigh.co.uk
Parkerfarm Weighing Systems, Titan Works, Bridge Way, Broombank Road, Chesterfield, Derbyshire, S41 9QJ Tel: (01246) 456729 Fax: (01246) 260844 E-mail: sales@parkerfarm.com
Precia-Molen UK, Unit 30 Walkers Road, Moons Moat North Industrial Es, Redditch, Worcestershire, B98 9HE Tel: (01527) 590320 Fax: (01527) 590301 E-mail: sales@preciamolen.co.uk
Prolec Ltd, Unit 5, Link 35, Nuffield Industrial Estate, Poole, Dorset, BH17 0GB Tel: (01202) 681190 Fax: (01202) 677909 E-mail: sales@prolec.co.uk
Promtek Ltd, Fisher Street, Brindley Ford, Stoke-on-Trent, ST8 7QJ Tel: (01782) 375600 Fax: (01782) 375605 E-mail: sales@promtek.com
Scales Plus, 25 Roundtree Close, Norwich, NR7 8SX Tel: (01603) 416569 Fax: (01603) 788045 E-mail: sales@scalesplus.co.uk
Shering Weighing Group Ltd, Pitreavie Business Park, Queensferry Road, Dunfermline, Fife, KY11 8UL Tel: (01383) 621505 Fax: (01383) 620262 E-mail: sales@shering.com
Southern Weighing Group, Calibra House, Splott Industrial Estate, Splott, Cardiff, CF24 5FF Tel: (029) 2048 8124 Fax: (029) 2048 1115 E-mail: sales@calibraweighing.co.uk
Spectrum Weighing Technology Industrial Weighing Equipement, Newbigging Road, Carnock, Dunfermline, Fife, KY12 9GD Tel: (01383) 851600 Fax: (01383) 851600
Thames Side Mayward Ltd, Unit 17 Stadium Way, Tilehurst, Reading, RG30 6BX Tel: 0118-945 8200 Fax: 0118-945 8225 E-mail: sales@thames-side.co.uk
Waymatic Ltd, 15 Bridgewater Way, Windsor, Berkshire, SL4 1RD Tel: (01753) 869218 Fax: (01753) 830519 E-mail: waymatic@btconnect.com
Weightron (U K) Ltd, Weightron House, Brimington Road North, Chesterfield, Derbyshire, S41 9AN Tel: (01246) 260062 Fax: (01246) 260844 E-mail: info@weightroncb.co.uk
Weighwell Engineering, 23 Orgreave Place, Sheffield, S13 9LU Tel: 0114-269 9955 Fax: 0114-269 9256 E-mail: sales@weighwell.co.uk
John White & Son (Weighing Machines) Ltd, 6 Back Dykes, Auchtermuchty, Cupar, Fife, KY14 7DW Tel: (01337) 827600 Fax: (01337) 827444 E-mail: enquiries@johnwhiteandson.com

WEIGHER/WEIGHING SYSTEMS, MOBILE, BAGGING/CONVEYING ETC

Ken Mills Engineering Ltd, New Street Works, Shawclough, Rochdale, Lancashire, OL12 6NS Tel: (01706) 644698 Fax: (01706) 649285 E-mail: ken.mills@zen.co.uk

WEIGHER/WEIGHING SYSTEMS, MULTIHEAD

Multipond Ltd, 20 St. Johns Road, Penn, High Wycombe, Buckinghamshire, HP10 8HW Tel: (01494) 816644 Fax: (01494) 816206 E-mail: multipond_uk@btconnect.com

WEIGHER/WEIGHING SYSTEMS, PACKER COMBINED

W J Morray Engineering Ltd, Anglia Way, Braintree, Essex, CM7 3RG Tel: (01376) 322722 Fax: (01376) 323277 E-mail: sales@morray.com

WEIGHER/WEIGHING SYSTEMS, PALLET TRUCK

Euroscales Holdings Ltd, Queens Court, Queens Avenue, Macclesfield, Cheshire, SK10 2BN Tel: (01625) 619554 Fax: (01625) 613295 E-mail: sales@euroscales.com

WEIGHER/WEIGHING SYSTEMS, RAILWAY ROLLING STOCK

Railweight, Hurstfield Industrial Estate, Hurst Street, Stockport, Cheshire, SK5 7BB Tel: 0161-431 5155 Fax: 0161-443 1356 E-mail: sales@railweight.co.uk

WEIGHER/WEIGHING SYSTEMS, RECONDITIONED

Betterweigh Leicester, 48 The Half Croft, Syston, Leicester, LE7 1LD Tel: (0845) 2602602 Fax: 0116-269 7767 E-mail: enquiries@betterweighleicester.com

WEIGHER/WEIGHING SYSTEMS, STATIC/DYNAMIC

Railweight, Hurstfield Industrial Estate, Hurst Street, Stockport, Cheshire, SK5 7BB Tel: 0161-431 5155 Fax: 0161-443 1356 E-mail: sales@railweight.co.uk

WEIGHER/WEIGHING SYSTEMS, VEHICLE AXLE/SELF WEIGHING/ PAYLOAD

Red Forge Ltd, 5 Palmers Road, Redditch, Worcestershire, B98 0RF Tel: (01527) 526112 Fax: (01527) 523862 E-mail: sales@redforge.co.uk

WEIGHT RECORDING SYSTEMS

Proweight Ltd, 131 Beech Avenue, New Basford, Nottingham, NG7 7LS Tel: 0115-970 3778 Fax: 0115-979 0142 E-mail: roulstone@btconnect.com

WEIGHTS

Barr & Grosvenor Ltd, Jenner Street, Wolverhampton, WV2 2AE Tel: (01902) 352390 Fax: (01902) 871342 E-mail: sales@bargrosvenorwannado.co.uk
Delta Scales, Kalena Cottage, Higher Tremar, Liskeard, Cornwall, PL14 5HP Tel: (01579) 344832 Fax: (01579) 344832
Hereford Scale Co., 1 Vaga Street, Hereford, HR2 7AT Tel: (01432) 356472 Fax: (01432) 352646

WEIGHTS, BALANCING, STATIC/ DYNAMIC

▶ Balancing, Unit 12, Logan Road, Birkenhead, Merseyside, CH41 1JJ Tel: 0151-639 9898 Fax: 0151-639 9898 E-mail: enquiries@dp-engineering.co.uk

WELD BOLT/STUD/NUT MANUFRS

Nelson Stud Welding UK, Rabans Lane Industrial Area, 47-49 Edison Road, Aylesbury, Buckinghamshire, HP19 8TE Tel: (01296) 433500 Fax: (01296) 487930 E-mail: enquiries@nelson-europe.co.uk

WELD MONITORING/ANALYSING EQUIPMENT/SYSTEMS

Stockall Electronics Ltd, Bond House, Howsell Road, Malvern, Worcestershire, WR14 1TF Tel: (01684) 574977 Fax: (01684) 574977 E-mail: enquiries@stockallelectronics.com

WELD OVERLAY CLADDING SERVICES

Arc Energy Resources Ltd, Unit 12 Eastington Industrial Estate, Meadow Mill, Eastington, Stonehouse, Gloucestershire, GL10 3RZ Tel: (01453) 823523 Fax: (01453) 823623 E-mail: sales@arcenergy.co.uk

IODS Ltd, 3 Langlands Court, Kelvin South Business Park, East Kilbride, Glasgow, G75 0YG Tel: (01355) 249224 Fax: (01355) 248836 E-mail: ff@iodsltd.com

WELDED ASSEMBLIES

S W S Alloys & Metals Ltd, Progress Drive, Cannock, Staffordshire, WS11 0JE Tel: (01543) 572149 Fax: (01543) 573834

WELDED FABRICATIONS

A Stanley Engineering, Gee House, Holborn Hill, Birmingham, B7 5JR Tel: 0121-326 0014 Fax: 0121-326 1779

A & W Fabrications & Structural Services, Old Bush Street, Brierley Hill, West Midlands, DY5 1UB Tel: (01384) 573676 Fax: (01384) 573676

Air Stream Engineering, Charfleets Close, Canvey Island, Essex, SS8 0PW Tel: (01268) 681400 Fax: (01268) 681412

Amenco (Poole) Ltd, Units 14-18, Willis Way, Fleets Industrial Estate, Poole, Dorset, BH15 3ST Tel: 0845 1306660 Fax: (01202) 671436 E-mail: office@amenco.co.uk

J.F. Appelbe & Co. Ltd, Littlefair Road, Hedon Road, Hull, HU9 5LN Tel: (01482) 781191 Fax: (01482) 781235 E-mail: enquiries@applebes.com

Arch Motor & Manufacturing Co Co. Ltd, Redwongs Way, Huntingdon Trading Estate, Huntingdon, Cambridgeshire, PE29 7HD Tel: (01480) 459661 Fax: (01480) 450923 E-mail: info@archmotor.co.uk

▶ Arcwell Mobile Welding, 64 Tansey Green Road, Brierley Hill, West Midlands, DY5 4TE Tel: (07860) 419626 Fax: (01384) 78009 E-mail: patricia@hopton8339fsnet.co.uk

B H L Manufacturing Ltd, Llewellyns Quay, Port Talbot, West Glamorgan, SA13 1RG Tel: (01639) 884878 Fax: (01639) 890317

Beejay Welding Engineers, 5 Newlyn Road, Cradley Heath, West Midlands, B64 6BE Tel: (01384) 566205 Fax: (01384) 565245

BenweldSecure, Unit 14a Hartlebury Trading Estate, Hartlebury, Kidderminster, Worcestershire, DY10 4JB Tel: (01299) 251750 Fax: (01299) 253576 E-mail: info@benweld.co.uk

Bonlea Engineering, 4 Ajax Works, Hertford Road, Barking, Essex, IG11 8DY Tel: (020) 8591 2183 Fax: (020) 8594 3605

R. Bristoll Ltd, Timothy Bridge Road, Stratford-upon-Avon, Warwickshire, CV37 9NQ Tel: (01789) 204881 Fax: (01789) 204883

Bush Welding & Engineering, 6 Grainger Road Industrial Estate, Southend-on-Sea, SS2 5DD Tel: (01702) 610871 Fax: (01702) 610871

Clayton Engineering Co., Church Street, Belper, Derbyshire, DE56 1EY Tel: (01773) 828955 Fax: (01773) 828243 E-mail: claytonenguk@aol.com

Ron Cook Engineers, 48-50 Oxford Street, Hull, HU2 0QP Tel: (01482) 327187 Fax: (01482) 213658

Creighton & Son Ltd, 2 Parr Road, Stanmore, Middlesex, HA7 1QA Tel: (020) 8952 8252 Fax: (020) 8951 1434 E-mail: metalman@btconnect.com

D V R Fabrications, Unit 10 Winster Grove Industrial Estate, Winster Grove, Birmingham, B44 9EG Tel: 0121-325 0087 Fax: 0121-325 0087

Daro Engineering Stafford Ltd, Unit 7a & 7b Dewick Depot, Cannock Road, Brocton, Stafford, ST17 0SU Tel: (01785) 660391 Fax: (01785) 665347 E-mail: office@daroengineering.co.uk

Easiflo Fabrications, 4 Building 64, Third Avenue, Pensnett Trading Estate, Kingswinford, West Midlands, DY6 7XX Tel: (01384) 279245 Fax: (01384) 400030

Elecon Sheet Metal, Ravensfield Industrial Estate, Charles Street, Dukinfield, Cheshire, SK16 4SD Tel: 0161-339 6210 Fax: 0161-343 1006

The Forge, 2a Watson Road, Worksop, Nottinghamshire, S80 2BB Tel: (01909) 501745 Fax: (01909) 501745

G B Metal Spinnings Ltd, 68a Glover Street, Birmingham, B9 4EL Tel: 0121-773 5444 Fax: 0121-773 5666 E-mail: lee@gb-metalspinnings.com

Grantham Welding Ltd, Unit3 & 4 North Bank, Berry Hill Industrial Estate, Droitwich, Worcestershire, WR9 9AU Tel: (01905) 773335 Fax: (01905) 773335

Hadee Engineering Co. Ltd, New Street, Holbrook Industrial Estate, Holbrook, Sheffield, S20 3GH Tel: 0114-248 3711 Fax: 0114-247 7858 E-mail: peterlowe@hadee.co.uk

Harrier Engineering Ltd, 20a Kendale Road, Scunthorpe, South Humberside, DN16 1DT Tel: (01724) 872935 Fax: (01724) 271218

Hawkes Metalmex, Holbrook Trading Estate, Old Lane, Halfway, Sheffield, S20 3GZ Tel: 0114-251 0251 Fax: 0114-251 0151 E-mail: sales@pct-automotive.co.uk

William Hawkes Ltd, 183 & 184 High St, Deritend, Birmingham, B12 0LH Tel: 0121-772 2694 Fax: 0121-772 2694

Hawkesley Engineering Ltd, Unit 3, Avery Dell Industrial Estate, Birmingham, B30 3DZ Tel: 0121-433 4277 Fax: 0121-433 4280 E-mail: enquiries@hawkesley.co.uk

J B Place & Son Welders Ltd, Unit 25 Sapcote Industrial Estate, 20 James Road, Tyseley, Birmingham, B11 2BA Tel: 0121-707 8021 Fax: 0121-707 8021

J Harper & Sons Welding Fabrications Ltd, Willenhall La Industrial Estate, Willenhall Lane, Bloxwich, Walsall, WS3 2XN Tel: (01922) 478419 Fax: (01922) 409553

J.N.J. Fabrications Ltd, Ambrose Street, Gorton, Manchester, M12 5DD Tel: 0161-223 7277 Fax: 0161-223 7277 E-mail: sales@jnjfabs.co.uk

J O & R H Baird Ltd, Industry Road, Newcastle upon Tyne, NE6 5XF Tel: 0191-265 5538 Fax: 0191-265 5833

▶ J R R Engineering Ltd, 37 Highmeres Road, Leicester, LE4 9LZ Tel: 0116-276 8801 Fax: 0116-246 0015

John Eccles & Co Blackheath Ltd, Holt Road, Halesowen, West Midlands, B62 9HQ Tel: 0121-559 1753 Fax: 0121-559 1753

Brian Jones Engineering (Fabrications), Heulwen, Penrhyndeudraeth, Gwynedd, LL48 6AH Tel: (01766) 770731 Fax: (01766) 770731

Kastle Engineering Ltd, Longbeck Trading Estate, Marske By The Sea, Redcar, Cleveland, TS11 6HR Tel: (01642) 485506 Fax: (01642) 488601 E-mail: kastle10@btinternet.com

L D Engineering Ltd, Great Northern Works, Hartham Lane, Hertford, SG14 1QW Tel: (01992) 584049 Fax: (01992) 584927 E-mail: ldeng@tiscali.co.uk

Lake & Nicholls Engineering, 4 Cornish Way, North Walsham, Norfolk, NR28 0AW Tel: (01692) 404602 Fax: (01692) 406723 E-mail: enquiries@lakeandnicholls.co.uk

Luxomation Ltd, 5 Worton Hall Industrial Estate, Worton Road, Isleworth, Middlesex, TW7 6ER Tel: (020) 8568 6373 Fax: (020) 8847 2603

Lycett Fabrications Ltd, Mariner, Lichfield Road Industrial Estate, Tamworth, Staffordshire, B79 7UL Tel: (01827) 53231 Fax: (01827) 69650 E-mail: mckd@lycettfab13.freeserve.co.uk

M R M Engineering Ltd, Units 15-16, Enterprise Drive, Westhill Industrial Estate, Westhill, Aberdeenshire, AB32 6TQ Tel: (01224) 742383 Fax: (01224) 742326 E-mail: sales@mrmengineering.co.uk

Morgans UK Ltd, Roma Road, Birmingham, B11 2JH Tel: 0121-706 3216 Fax: 0121-765 4177

Nelson Sheetmetal Fabricators Ltd, Walton St Works, Walton St, Colne, Lancashire, BB8 0EW Tel: (01282) 866966 Fax: (01282) 866990 E-mail: nsc@fsmail.net

Nelson Unit Ltd, Victoria Works, Lodge Lane, Dukinfield, Cheshire, SK16 5HY Tel: 0161-330 1007 Fax: 0161-343 1346 E-mail: info@nelsonunit.co.uk

P J Welding & Fabricating, Unit 12, Summerhill Industrial Estate, Goodman Street, Birmingham, B1 2SS Tel: 0121-236 8152 Fax: 0121-212 1705

Patera Engineering Ltd, Unit 2a Galveston Grove, Oldfields Business Park, Stoke-on-Trent, ST4 3ES Tel: (01782) 318822 Fax: (01782) 318822 E-mail: pateraeng@cs.com

Perfab Engineering Ltd, Unit 3 Northway Lane, Tewkesbury, Gloucestershire, GL20 8HA Tel: (01684) 298423 Fax: (01684) 850427

Peterborough Sheet Metal Ltd, Unit 12 Towermead Business Centre, High Street, Peterborough, PE2 9DY Tel: (01733) 344880 Fax: (01733) 898421

Philrae Fabrications Ltd, 53 Circular Road, Storforth Lane Trading Estate, Chesterfield, Derbyshire, S41 0QR Tel: (01246) 279234 Fax: (01246) 234862

Pierce Engineering Services Ltd, Horton Close, West Drayton, Middlesex, UB7 8EB Tel: (01895) 447689 Fax: (01895) 447689

Plant Welding & Engineering Ltd, Private Road 7, Colwick Industrial Estate, Nottingham, NG4 2AB Tel: 0115-987 0702 Fax: 0115-940 0375

Primary Designs Ltd, Unit 4 International House, Station Yard, Thame, Oxfordshire, OX9 3UH Tel: (01844) 216057 Fax: (01844) 216058 E-mail: patbarrett@primarydesigns.co.uk

R J Kingston Engineering Ltd, Timothys Bridge Road, Stratford-upon-Avon, Warwickshire, CV37 9NQ Tel: (01789) 205008 Fax: (01789) 415645

R M G Fabrications Ltd, 32a Heming Road, Redditch, Worcestershire, B98 0DH Tel: (01527) 525442 Fax: (01527) 527642

Rolls Royce plc, Watnall Road, Hucknall, Nottingham, NG15 6EU Tel: 0115-963 3111 Fax: 0115-964 2345

S Willetts (Fabrications) Ltd, Pleasant Street, Lyng, West Bromwich, West Midlands, B70 7DT Tel: 0121-553 2705 Fax: 0121-525 0581

Sertec Birmingham Ltd, Gorsey Lane, Coleshill, Birmingham, B46 1JU Tel: (01675) 463361 Fax: (01675) 465539 E-mail: sertecgroup@sertec.co.uk

Skyglass Ltd, Morgans Yard, Arundel Road Industrial Estate, Uxbridge, Middlesex, UB8 2RP Tel: (01895) 234432 Fax: (01895) 271118

Starweld Engineering Ltd, 46 Harleston Street, Sheffield, S4 7QB Tel: 0114-272 0283 Fax: 0114-275 0383 E-mail: sales@starweld.com

Steel Engineering Services Ltd, Unit 7f Block Westway, Porterfield Road, Renfrew, PA4 8DJ Tel: 0141-885 0885 Fax: 0141-886 3322 E-mail: info@steeleng.com

Supercraft Ltd, Canada Road, Byfleet, West Byfleet, Surrey, KT14 7JL Tel: (01932) 351941 Fax: (01932) 340807 E-mail: sales@supercraft.co.uk

T A B Sheet Fabrications Ltd, Unit 3 Galliford Road Industrial Estate, Heybridge, Maldon, Essex, CM9 4XX Tel: (01621) 858848 Fax: (01621) 583847 E-mail: info@tabfab.co.uk

Task Welding Ltd, 8a Culverin Square, Limberline Road, Hilsea, Portsmouth, PO3 5BU Tel: (023) 9269 0868

A. Taylor & Son (Leeds) Ltd, Weaver Street, Leeds, LS4 2AY Tel: 0113-263 9036 Fax: 0113-231 0286 E-mail: sales@ataylor.co.uk

Technical Welding Services, Corporation Road, Rochdale, Lancashire, OL11 4HJ Tel: (01706) 655402 Fax: (01706) 657735 E-mail: sales@technicalwelding.co.uk

Thomson Lockhart (Engineering) Ltd, 5 Simonsburn Road, Loreny Industrial Estate, Kilmarnock, Ayrshire, KA1 5LE Tel: (01563) 527398 Fax: (01563) 522710 E-mail: info@thomsonlockhart.com

Tilewind Ltd, Carcroft Industrial Estate, Adwick Le St, Doncaster, South Yorkshire, DN6 7BD Tel: 01302 721205

D.H. Townsend & Co. Ltd, Unit 1, St Andrews Industrial Estate, Bridport, Dorset, DT6 3DL Tel: (01308) 423305 Fax: (01308) 427913 E-mail: dhtownsendeng@aol.com

Tulgrove Ltd, Jameson Road, Aston, Birmingham, B6 7SJ Tel: 0121-327 2296 Fax: 0121-328 5612 E-mail: tulgrove@tulgrove.co.uk

W Campbell & Son Ltd, Harpings Road, Hull, HU5 4JG Tel: (01482) 444422 Fax: (01482) 444424

W R R Pedley & Co. Ltd, Ann Street, Willenhall, West Midlands, WV13 1EW Tel: (01902) 366060 Fax: (01902) 603411

Wayside Engineering Services Limited, Rhosddigre, Llandegla, Wrexham, Clwyd, LL11 3AU Tel: (01978) 790269 Fax: (01978) 790478 E-mail: graham.dillon@btinternet.com

Webgibb Welding & Fabrications, Unit 11 Bluebird Industrial Estate, Park Lane, Wolverhampton, WV10 9QQ Tel: (01902) 722040 Fax: (01902) 722040 E-mail: shane@webgibb.u-net.com

Weldex Ltd, Kingsway South, Team Valley Trading Estate, Gateshead, Tyne & Wear, NE11 0JL Tel: 0191-497 3410 Fax: 0191-497 3411 E-mail: weldex@responsive-engineering.com

Welding Fabrication Services, Unit 10 Rollingmill Business Park, Rollingmill Street, Walsall, WS2 9EQ Tel: (07875) 405253 Fax: (01922) 474686

West Cumberland Engineering Ltd, Joseph Noble Road, Lillyhall Industrial Estate, Lillyhall, Workington, Cumbria, CA14 4JX Tel: (01900) 872787 Fax: (01900) 872789 E-mail: wcel@wcel.vhe.co.uk

WELDED NICKEL ALLOY TUBES

S W S Alloys & Metals Ltd, Progress Drive, Cannock, Staffordshire, WS11 0JE Tel: (01543) 572149 Fax: (01543) 573834

WELDED SEAM STEEL TUBES

Broson Ltd, Church Hill Road, Thurmaston, Leicester, LE4 8DJ Tel: 0116-269 8899 Fax: 0116-269 8898 E-mail: sales@broson.co.uk

Corus Tubes plc, PO Box 101, Corby, Northamptonshire, NN17 5UA Tel: (01536) 402121 Fax: (01536) 404111

Metal Sections Ltd, Broadwell Road, Oldbury, West Midlands, B69 4HE Tel: 0121-601 6000 Fax: 0121-601 6121 E-mail: metsecplc@metsec.com

Star Tubes (Southern) Ltd, Lilliput Road, Brackmills, Northampton, NN4 7DT Tel: (01908) 311777 Fax: (01908) 321874 E-mail: sales@startubes-southern.co.uk

WELDED TUBES, *See also Steel Tubes, Welded etc: also other headings for particular types*

Voest Alpine Stahl Ltd, Albion Place, London, W6 0QT Tel: (020) 8600 5800 Fax: (020) 8741 3099 E-mail: officelondon@vosetalpine.com

WELDED WIRE MESH

Dale Engineering Co. Ltd, Wolverhampton Road, Wedges Mills, Cannock, Staffordshire, WS11 1SN Tel: (01543) 503265 Fax: (01543) 505475

General Steel Services, 45 Sydenham Road, Belfast, BT3 9DH Tel: (028) 9045 6327 Fax: (028) 9045 8096 E-mail: gss@metsteel.co.uk

Weldgrip, 2d Redbrook Business Park, Wilthorpe Road, Barnsley, South Yorkshire, S75 1JN Tel: (01226) 785553 Fax: (01226) 731563 E-mail: info@weldgrip.com

WELDING, *See also headings for specialist services*

A A Sheet Metals, 1 Fletcher Way, Weston Road, Norwich, NR3 3ST Tel: (01603) 417030 Fax: (01603) 417128 E-mail: alan.harrowing@aasheetmetalnorwich.fsnet.co.uk

A & D Scrivens, 5 Allens Lane, Poole, Dorset, BH16 5DA Tel: (01202) 621585 Fax: (01202) 621584 E-mail: scrivenss@aol.com

A J Sosbe, Factory 6, Maidstone Road, Leicester, LE2 0BA Tel: 0116-262 6492 Fax: 0116-262 6492

A & R Welding, Carpenters Road, St. Helens, Ryde, Isle of Wight, PO33 1YW Tel: (01983) 872965 Fax: (01983) 611924

A V Birch Ltd, Aldenham Mill, Muckley Cross, Acton Round, Bridgnorth, Shropshire, WV16 4RR Tel: (01746) 714418 Fax: (01746) 714419 E-mail: enquiries@avbirch.co.uk

A W Jeffreys Southampton Ltd, 91-97 Dukes Road, Southampton, SO14 0ST Tel: (023) 8055 3730 Fax: (023) 8067 1345 E-mail: awj@awjefferys.co.uk

Ace Welding (Edensbridge), Merle Common Road, Oxted, Surrey, RH8 0RP Tel: (01883) 712668 Fax: (01883) 717524

Advanced Sheet Metal Ltd, 6-8 Albany Road, Granby Industrial Estate, Weymouth, Dorset, DT4 9TH Tel: (01305) 771061 Fax: (01305) 752829 E-mail: info@asm-ltd.com

Albion Welding & Fabrication, Unit 27 North Pontypool Industrial Park, Pontnewynydd, Pontypool, Gwent, NP4 6PB Tel: (01495) 750180 Fax: (01495) 769819 E-mail: arsamins@btconnect.com

Alex Morton, 43 Killysorrell Road, Dromore, County Down, BT25 1LB Tel: (028) 9269 3651 Fax: (028) 9269 3951 E-mail: amorton@domora43.fsnet.co.uk

Altech Services, 1 Cemetery Road, Houghton Regis, Dunstable, Bedfordshire, LU5 5BZ Tel: (01582) 472882 Fax: (01582) 471887

Ambrose Wood & Son, Ovenhouse Farm Depot, Henshall Road, Bollington, Macclesfield, Cheshire, SK10 5DN Tel: (01625) 573291

Anglo-Swedish Engineering & Welding (Southern) Ltd, Unit 12, Lansdowne Workshops, Lansdowne Mews, Charlton, London, SE7 8AZ Tel: (020) 8858 2024 Fax: (020) 8858 7301 E-mail: info@metboilerrepairs.co.uk

Apollo Fabrications Ltd, Unit 20 Canalside Industrial Estate, Brettell Lane, Brierley Hill, West Midlands, DY5 3JU Tel: (01384) 484603 Fax: (01384) 484603 E-mail: ralph-apollo@supanet.com

Araywelds Mobile Services, 6 Flanders Road, London, E6 6DU Tel: (07885) 431727 Fax: (020) 8507 7056

Arnway Ltd, 24 Burtonwood Industrial Centre, Phipps Lane, Burtonwood, Warrington, WA5 4HX Tel: (01925) 229479 Fax: (01925) 220865 E-mail: steve@arnway.co.uk

Ashby Welding, 13 Potters Industrial Park, Church Crookham, Fleet, Hampshire, GU52 6EU Tel: (01252) 815811

Axestone Engineering, North Cresent, London, E16 4TQ Tel: (020) 7473 3737 Fax: (020) 7473 3738

BenweldSecure, Unit 14a Hartlebury Trading Estate, Hartlebury, Kidderminster, Worcestershire, DY10 4JB Tel: (01299) 251750 Fax: (01299) 253576 E-mail: info@benweld.co.uk

Blaker Specialised Welding Repairs Ltd, Worthing Road, Dial Post, Horsham, West Sussex, RH13 8NJ Tel: (01403) 710333 Fax: (01403) 711234 E-mail: simon@blaker.co.uk

Bradford Welding & Sheet Metal Co. Ltd, 340b Thornton Road, Bradford, West Yorkshire, BD8 8LD Tel: (01274) 480288 Fax: (01274) 480284

Bragman Flett Ltd, 34 Holmethorpe Avenue, Redhill, RH1 2NL Tel: (01737) 779200 Fax: (01737) 779600 E-mail: bragman.flett@btopenworld.com

Browse Engineering Services, 34b Cowleigh Road, Malvern, Worcestershire, WR14 1QD Tel: (01684) 567125 Fax: (01684) 568240 E-mail: sales@ibrowse2.com

Bunns Lane Welding, Bunns Lane Works, Bunns Lane, London, NW7 2AJ Tel: (020) 8959 8046

Burgess Marine Services, Channel View Road, Dover, Kent, CT17 9TJ Tel: (01304) 207707 Fax: (01304) 207727 E-mail: info@burgessengineering.co.uk

C Hargreaves, Stockfield Mill, Melbourne Street, Chadderton, Oldham, OL9 9ES Tel: 0161-633 5330 Fax: 0161-633 5330

Caletrim Fabrications Ltd, 7a Bowes Road, Middlesbrough, Cleveland, TS2 1LU Tel: (01642) 224121 Fax: (01642) 224121

Clwyd Precision Engineering, Bridge Road, Wrexham Industrial Estate, Wrexham, Clwyd, LL13 9PS Tel: (01978) 660259 Fax: (01978) 661069 E-mail: cpe@bytecraft.net

Coles, Steam Mill Lane, Great Yarmouth, Norfolk, NR31 0HP Tel: (01493) 602100 Fax: (01493) 602100

Creighton & Son Ltd, 2 Parr Road, Stanmore, Middlesex, HA7 1QA Tel: (020) 8952 8252 Fax: (020) 8951 1434 E-mail: metalman@btconnect.com

D F Barber, Bunwell Road, Besthorpe, Attleborough, Norfolk, NR17 2NZ Tel: (01953) 452422 Fax: (01953) 452422

D Mcinnes, Clayslap, Kilmarnock, Ayrshire, KA1 5LN Tel: (01563) 522774 Fax: (01563) 571530 E-mail: enquires@duncanmcinnes.com

▶ indicates data change since last edition

WELDING – *continued*

D Tobias Ltd, 50 Rogart Street, Glasgow, G40 2AA Tel: 0141-554 2348 Fax: 0141-550 1090

Dart Mobile Welding, 1 Pembroke Road, Paignton, Devon, TQ3 3UR Tel: (01803) 522877

Delta Pipework Services Ltd, 17 Hazel Road, Southampton, SO19 7GA Tel: (023) 8068 5411 Fax: (023) 8042 2435

Deplynn Engineering Ltd, 3 Thornham Grove, London, E15 1DN Tel: (020) 8519 6028 Fax: (020) 8519 6028

Dielife Actheron, 30 Commercial Street, Middlesbrough, Cleveland, TS2 1JW Tel: (01642) 241516 Fax: (01642) 245171

Domic Welding & Sheetmetal Ltd, Unit 8 Victor Business Centre, Arthur Street, Redditch, Worcestershire, B98 8JY Tel: (01527) 515445 Fax: (01527) 510403 E-mail: touv@domic-pjwelding.fsnet.co.uk

E Bacon & Co. Ltd, Hutton Road, Grimsby, South Humberside, DN31 3PS Tel: (01472) 350267 Fax: (01472) 250987 E-mail: info@baconengineering.com

Eddison & Wanless Ltd, Unit 1, Mallard Industrial Estate, Horbury, Wakefield, West Yorkshire, WF4 5QH Tel: (01924) 271128 Fax: (01924) 271251 E-mail: info@eddisonwanless.co.uk

Elite Engineering, Enterprise Road, Mablethorpe, Lincolnshire, LN12 1NB Tel: (07931) 404413 E-mail: colin@eliteengineering.org.uk

Ellis Welding & Fabrications, Ollershaw Lane, Marston, Northwich, Cheshire, CW9 6ES Tel: (01606) 45405 Fax: (01606) 40237 E-mail: sales@e-w-l.com

Elnor Engineering, Checkley, Nantwich, Cheshire, CW5 7QA Tel: (01270) 520282

Elston Manufacturing Wolverhampton Co., 30 Mander Street, Wolverhampton, WV3 0JZ Tel: (01902) 422159 Fax: (01902) 429465

Exact Weld (GB) Ltd, Unit 8E, Charlwoods Road, East Grinstead, West Sussex, RH19 2HG Tel: (01342) 311595 Fax: (01342) 326526

Fenweld Steel Fabricators, Bramley Road, St. Ives, Cambridgeshire, PE27 3WS Tel: (01480) 300877 Fax: (01480) 492120

Flexbore, Pontygwindy Industrial Estate, Caerphilly, Mid Glamorgan, CF83 3HU Tel: (029) 2088 3552 Fax: (029) 2086 6410

Freeman & Proctor, PO Box 22, Nuneaton, Warwickshire, CV11 4XY Tel: (024) 7638 2032 Fax: (024) 7637 4353 E-mail: info@freemanandproctor.co.uk

G B Welding Services Rutland Ltd, Unit 8 Pillings Road Industrial Estate, Oakham, Leicestershire, LE15 6QF Tel: (01572) 722764 Fax: (01572) 724347 E-mail: admin@gbwelding.co.uk

A.A. Gates Ltd, Culver Garden Centre, Cattlegate Road, Crews Hill, Enfield, Middlesex, EN2 9DS Tel: (020) 8367 3500 Fax: (020) 8342 1115 E-mail: argonarc@aol.com

Lionel W. Gibbs (Horton) Ltd, Horley Road, Hornton, Banbury, Oxfordshire, OX15 6BW Tel: (01295) 670310 Fax: (01295) 670732

Gravesend Engineering Co. Ltd, East Crescent Road, Gravesend, Kent, DA12 2AR Tel: (01474) 365475 Fax: (01474) 365475

Great Bridge Welding Co., Bagnall Street, Golds Hill, West Bromwich, West Midlands, B70 0TS Tel: 0121-557 2325

Haigh & Ellis, St Andrews Road, Huddersfield, HD1 6SB Tel: (01484) 421647 Fax: (01484) 428324 E-mail: mark@haighandellis.fsbusiness.co.uk

Hallcalm UK, Redworth Street, Hartlepool, Cleveland, TS24 7LG Tel: (01429) 891011 Fax: (01429) 236746 E-mail: engineering@hallcalm.co.uk

Handsworth Welding Co., 110 Handsworth New Road, Birmingham, B18 4QE Tel: 0121-554 0137

Harbour Welding Services Ltd, 91-93 Sterte Avenue West, Poole, Dorset, BH15 2AL Tel: (01202) 668692 Fax: (01202) 666158 E-mail: harbourwelding@btopenworld.com

Hart Brothers Engineering Ltd, Sothall Works, Sothall, Oldham, OL4 2AD Tel: 0161-737 6791 Fax: 0161-633 5316 E-mail: xk220@aol.com

Harwoods For Steel Ltd, Whitegate Farm, Waterlooville, Hampshire, PO8 0TG Tel: (023) 9259 3442 Fax: (023) 9259 6010

Dennis Hawkins Welding, Westside Farm, High Street, Stoke Goldington, Newport Pagnell, Buckinghamshire, MK16 8NP Tel: (01908) 551400

Hawthorne Engineering Ltd, Unit 5 Hexthorpe Trading Park, Littlewood Street, Hexthorpe, Doncaster, South Yorkshire, DN4 0EJ Tel: (01302) 321990 Fax: (01302) 349939 E-mail: sales@hawthorneengineeringltd.co.uk

▶ Hoperole Ltd, 4 Norman Way Indust Estate, Over, Cambridge, CB24 5LY Tel: (01954) 230900 Fax: (01954) 230990

Howard Fabrications, Swainshill, Hereford, HR4 7QA Tel: (01432) 353100 Fax: (01432) 353100

I E P Gardening Products, Unit 3 Budds Lane, Romsey, Hampshire, SO51 0HA Tel: (01794) 830899 Fax: (01794) 830923 E-mail: iepgp@btinternet.com

Imperial, 65 North Acton Road, London, NW10 6PJ Tel: (020) 8965 8596 Fax: (020) 8961 9352 E-mail: info@iwsm.co.uk

Ivanhoe Forge Ltd, Station Road, Seaton Delaval, Whitley Bay, Tyne & Wear, NE25 0QB Tel: 0191-237 0676 Fax: 0191-237 6887

J B Place & Son Welders Ltd, Unit 25 Sapcote Industrial Estate, 20 James Road, Tyseley, Birmingham, B11 2BA Tel: 0121-707 8021 Fax: 0121-707 8021

J & J Engineering, 10 Misson Mill, Bawtry Road, Misson, Doncaster, South Yorkshire, DN10 6DP Tel: (01302) 719531 Fax: (01302) 719531

J M Fabweld Ltd, Llewellyns Quay, Port Talbot, West Glamorgan, SA13 1RF Tel: (01639) 884550 Fax: (01639) 891015 E-mail: jmfabwellltd@btconnect.com

J O & R H Baird Ltd, Industry Road, Newcastle upon Tyne, NE6 5XF Tel: 0191-265 5538 Fax: 0191-265 5833

J R Hill & Sons Ltd, Broad Platt Croft, Broad Platt, Rotherfield Greys, Henley-on-Thames, Oxfordshire, RG9 4PD Tel: (01491) 628533 Fax: (01491) 628770 E-mail: jrhillwelding@aol.com

J T Blythe Ltd, Kings Mill Lane, Redhill, RH1 5JY Tel: (01737) 823314 Fax: (01737) 822937 E-mail: harry@jtblythe.co.uk

Johnson's Engineering & Electrical Co., 61 High Street, Standlake, Witney, Oxfordshire, OX29 7RH Tel: (01865) 300270 Fax: (01865) 300911

Kilmarnock Engineers, Spittalhill Works, Ayr Road, Kilmarnock, Ayrshire, KA1 5NX Tel: (01563) 830198 Fax: (01563) 830692

Kirmell Ltd, Eyre Street, Birmingham, B18 7AA Tel: 0121-456 3141 Fax: 0121-456 3151 E-mail: sales@kirmell.co.uk

W.G. Knight & Son, 18 Main Ridge, Boston, Lincolnshire, PE21 6SS Tel: 01205 363084

Knights Design & Manufacturer, Trident Business Park, 6 Park Street, Nuneaton, Warwickshire, CV11 4NS Tel: (024) 7634 4822 Fax: (024) 7634 4822

L D Engineering Ltd, Great Northern Works, Hartham Lane, Hertford, SG14 1QW Tel: (01992) 584049 Fax: (01992) 584927 E-mail: ldeng@tiscali.co.uk

Lander Automotive Ltd, Woodgate Business Park, 174 Clapgate Lane, Birmingham, B32 3ED Tel: 0121-423 1110 Fax: 0121-423 2220 E-mail: enquiries@lander.co.uk

Liftech Engineering, 12d Tower Workshops, Riley Road, London, SE1 3DG Tel: (020) 7237 6580 Fax: (020) 7252 3785

Liverpool Auto Service, Unit 12b Weaver Industrial Estate, Blackburne Street, Liverpool, L19 8JA Tel: 0151-427 5707 Fax: 0151-427 5707

Longhope Welding Engineers, Church Road, Longhope, Gloucestershire, GL17 0LA Tel: (01452) 830572 Fax: (01452) 830983

M L (UK) Ltd, Kettering Terrace, Mile End, Portsmouth, PO2 7AE Tel: (023) 9281 9114 Fax: (023) 9282 3386 E-mail: martin@mluk.co.uk

The M O T Welding Service (Auto Weld) Of Worthing, Unit 14 Ivy Arch Road, Worthing, West Sussex, BN14 8BX Tel: (01903) 230634

M R K Services, Unit 97 Northwick Business Centre, Northwick Park, Blockley, Moreton-in-Marsh, Gloucestershire, GL56 9RF Tel: (01386) 700912 Fax: (01386) 700922 E-mail: sales@mrkservices.co.uk

M T Perry Ltd, 5 Rawcliffe House, Howarth Road, Maidenhead, Berkshire, SL6 1AP Tel: (01628) 630330 Fax: (01628) 630330 E-mail: enquiries@perryfabs.co.uk

▶ Mcevoy Engineering Ltd, 5b Harbour Industrial Estate, Montgomerie Street, Ardrossan, Ayrshire, KA22 8EG Tel: (01294) 467677 Fax: (01294) 467677 E-mail: chris@mcevoyengineering.co.uk

Matann Metal Fabrication Ltd, 5 Blatchford Road, Horsham, West Sussex, RH13 5QR Tel: (01403) 249994 Fax: (01403) 249355

Meakins Transport Ltd, The Garage, Back Lane, Spencers Wood, Reading, RG7 1JB Tel: 0118-988 2134 Fax: 0118-988 4150

Metalock Engineering, Hamilton, Glasgow, Tel: 0141-641 3368 E-mail: sales@metalock.co.uk

Metalock Engineering UK Ltd, Paragon Way, Bayton Road Industrial Estate, Coventry, CV7 9QS Tel: (01322) 290090 Fax: (01322) 290088 E-mail: sales@metalock.co.uk

MGL Van Hire, Unit 8, Trench Lock Industrial Estate, Telford, Shropshire, TF1 5SW Tel: (01952) 252396

Millbrook Engineering, Wesley Road, Cinderford, Gloucestershire, GL14 2JN Tel: (01594) 823822 Fax: (01594) 823222

Mudd Farm Equipment, Park View, Marthwaite, Sedbergh, Cumbria, LA10 5HS Tel: (01539) 620704 Fax: (01539) 621573

N K F Metal Services, Unit 5 East Thamesmead Business Park, Kencot Close, Erith, Kent, DA18 4AB Tel: (020) 8310 2199 Fax: (020) 8310 2204 E-mail: john.oshea60@virgin.net

Northern Arc Electric Welding Co Leicester Ltd, 161 Scudamore Road, Leicester, LE3 1UQ Tel: 0116-287 4949 Fax: 0116-287 5153

Olympic Welding Ltd, Station Road, Acle, Norwich, NR13 3BZ Tel: (01493) 750496 Fax: (01493) 751968

On Site Welding Solutions Ltd, 6b Sweetmans Yard, Plough Lane, Hereford, HR4 0EE Tel: (01432) 276639 Fax: (01432) 276639 E-mail: andrew-skinner@tiscaly.co.uk

Oxford Welding, Unit 1 Wharf Farm Buildings, Eynsham Road, Cassington, Witney, Oxfordshire, OX29 4DB Tel: (01865) 884366 Fax: (01865) 884366

P Gillan & Sons, 1 Blezard Court, Transbritannia Enterprise Park, Blaydon-on-Tyne, Tyne & Wear, NE21 5NH Tel: 0191-499 0294 Fax: 0191-414 5353

P H Welding Services, Freehold Mill, Market Street, Shawforth, Rochdale, Lancashire, OL12 8HJ Tel: (01706) 854320

Perry Pearson Engineering Co. Ltd, Unit 6 219 Torrington Avenue, Coventry, CV4 9HN Tel: 024 76460339

Philton Fire & Security Ltd, 61 Lower Road, Harrow, Middlesex, HA2 0DE Tel: (020) 8864 7534 Fax: (020) 8864 8631

Pioneer Finishers, Pioneer Business Park, Princess Road, Ramsgate, Kent, CT11 7RX Tel: (01843) 596615 Fax: (01843) 580933 E-mail: pioneer.paul@talk21.com

Plymol Tubes Ltd, 6 Ravells Yard, Carr Lane, Hoylake, Wirral, Merseyside, CH47 4AZ Tel: 0151-632 1354 Fax: 0151-632 4912 E-mail: sales@flagstaffs.co.uk

Portobello Engineering Ltd, Milton Works, Bowden Lane, Chapel-en-le-Frith, High Peak, Derbyshire, SK23 0QG Tel: (01298) 812309 Fax: (01298) 812336 E-mail: hal@portobelloltd.co.uk

Professional Welding Services Ltd, 80-82 Cobham Road, Ferndown Industrial Estate, Wimborne, Dorset, BH21 7RW Tel: (01202) 895080 Fax: (01202) 861463 E-mail: sales@prowelding.co.uk

Projexe Engineering, 7 Merriott House, Hennock Road, Marsh Barton Trading Estate, Exeter, EX2 8NJ Tel: (01392) 258441 Fax: (01392) 498441

Q A Weldtech Ltd, 1a Bowes Road, Middlesbrough, Cleveland, TS2 1LU Tel: (01642) 222831 Fax: (01642) 242003 E-mail: quality@qaweldtech.co.uk

Q Mac Engineering, 161 Ballymaguire Road, Stewartstown, Dungannon, County Tyrone, BT71 5NN Tel: (028) 8673 7312

R Fawcett & Sons, Woodhall Park, Woodhall, Askrigg, Leyburn, North Yorkshire, DL8 3LB Tel: (01969) 663255 Fax: (01969) 663114

R Thompson & Co., 12 Manderston Street, Edinburgh, EH6 8LY Tel: 0131-554 6501

Rainbow Engineering Services, Unit 17 Shaftesbury Industrial Centre, Icknield Way, Letchworth Garden City, Hertfordshire, SG6 1RR Tel: (01462) 480442 Fax: (01462) 480449 E-mail: sales@rainbow-dukane.com

Rainham Welding Works Ltd, 152 New Road, Rainham, Essex, RM13 8RS Tel: (01708) 554107 Fax: (01708) 554107

Ray Weld, Dayton Drive, Darent Industrial Park, Erith, Kent, DA8 2LE Tel: (01322) 334499

Reardon Engineering Co., Unit 6 9, 35 River Road, Barking, Essex, IG11 0DA Tel: (01708) 748253 Fax: (020) 8594 7398

Pat Regan Mobile Welding, 7 Copland Close, Broomfield, Chelmsford, CM1 7DT Tel: (01245) 440951 Fax: (01245) 440951

Riber Engineering Ltd, Brindley Way, Speedwell Industrial Estate, Staveley, Chesterfield, Derbyshire, S43 3JF Tel: (01246) 471244 Fax: (01246) 471233 E-mail: ribereng@aol.com

Round Green Engineering Ltd, 199 Camford Way, Luton, LU3 3AN Tel: (01582) 503808 Fax: (01582) 503898 E-mail: barrie@roundgreen.com

S & D Fabricators Ltd, Greenbank CR, East Tullos Industrial Estate, Aberdeen, AB12 3BG Tel: (01224) 895564 Fax: (01224) 899065

S & S Engineering Ltd, Blackwell Industrial Estate, Station Road, Tilbrook, Huntingdon, Cambridgeshire, PE28 0JY Tel: (01480) 860426 Fax: (01480) 860355

S & S Engineering, Unit 21 Such Close, Letchworth Garden City, Hertfordshire, SG6 1JF Tel: (01462) 675983 Fax: (01462) 675983

Sharand Ltd, Churnetside Business Park, Station Road, Cheddleton, Leek, Staffordshire, ST13 7EE Tel: (01538) 360178 Fax: (01538) 360111

Site Weld, Manor Farm, Andover, Hampshire, SP11 7DB Tel: (01264) 710194

Smillie & Cuthbertson Ltd, 17 James Little St, Kilmarnock, Ayrshire, KA1 4AU Tel: 01563 521819

Solent Manufacturing Ltd, Unit 4-5 Pipers Wood Industrial Park, Waterberry Drive, Waterlooville, Hampshire, PO7 7XU Tel: (023) 9223 2348 Fax: (023) 9223 2358 E-mail: pam.a@solentmanufacturing.co.uk

Starweld Engineering Ltd, 46 Harleston Street, Sheffield, S4 7QB Tel: 0114-272 0283 Fax: 0114-275 0383 E-mail: sales@starweld.com

Strand Engineering North West Ltd, Ironworks Road, Barrow-in-Furness, Cumbria, LA14 2PH Tel: (01229) 821991 Fax: (01229) 811104 E-mail: strandeng@yahoo.co.uk

T Bland, Sandars Road, Heapham Road Industrial Estate, Gainsborough, Lincolnshire, DN21 1RZ Tel: (01427) 610116 Fax: (01427) 810287 E-mail: t.bland@virgin.net

T G Welding Ltd, Unit 4 Stone La Industrial Estate, Wimborne, Dorset, BH21 1HB Tel: (01202) 881267 Fax: (01202) 849523 E-mail: tgwelding@yahoo.com

T Hendry, 40 Benedict Square, Peterborough, PE4 6GD Tel: (01733) 577617

Tanker & General Ltd, Hedley Avenue, West Thurrock, Grays, Essex, RM20 4EL Tel: (01375) 370660 Fax: (0870) 8723134 E-mail: mgeary@tankergeneral.com

Task Welding Ltd, 8a Culverin Square, Limberline Road, Hilsea, Portsmouth, PO3 5BU Tel: (023) 9269 0868

Technical Fabrications, Unit 28 Rowfant Business Centre, Wallage Lane, Rowfant, Crawley, West Sussex, RH10 4NQ Tel: (01342) 717523 Fax: (01342) 715392

Thompson Friction Welding Ltd, Hereward Rise, Halesowen, West Midlands, B62 8AN Tel: 0121-585 0888 Fax: 0121-585 0810 E-mail: sales@thompson-friction-welding.co.uk

Thurston Engineering Ltd, Hallsford Bridge Industrial Estate, Stondon Road, Ongar, Essex, CM5 9RB Tel: (01277) 362135 Fax: (01277) 365076 E-mail: sales@thurstonengineering.co.uk

Triad Fabrications, Globe Works, Queensway, Rochdale, Lancashire, OL11 2QY Tel: (01706) 655099 Fax: (01706) 658712 E-mail: admin@triadfabs.com

Truturn Precision Engineering (Charfield) Ltd, Units L2-L3, Bath Road Trading Estate, Lightpill, Stroud, Gloucestershire, GL5 3QF Tel: (01453) 752888 Fax: (01453) 753888 E-mail: truturn@truturn.co.uk

Universal Fabrications North West Ltd, Star Iron Works, Taurus Street, Oldham, OL4 2BN Tel: 0161-620 0550 Fax: 0161-620 0247 E-mail: sales@universal-fabrications.co.uk

Venture Oilfield Services Ltd, 11 Faraday Road, Southfields, Glenrothes, Fife, KY6 2RU Tel: (01592) 772176 Fax: (01592) 775455 E-mail: mail@ventureoil.com

Viper Metal Products Ltd, Oldmixon Cresent, Weston-super-Mare, Avon, BS24 9AX Tel: (01934) 621912 Fax: (01934) 614347 E-mail: tony@viparmetal.co.uk

W H Hannaford, 100 Chester Road, Watford, WD18 0RE Tel: (01923) 223669 Fax: (01923) 223669

Walkerworld Steel Fabricators, 451 Stanton Road, Burton-on-Trent, Staffordshire, DE15 9RS Tel: (01283) 515439 Fax: (01283) 517554

Wallace Sheetmetal & Fabrication Ltd, Old Jam Works Lane, Station Road, Wigton, Cumbria, CA7 9AX Tel: (01697) 342918 Fax: (01697) 344617E-mail: mail@wallacesheetmetal.co.uk

Watties Welders & Fabricators, New Cottage Rosemill, Bridgefoot, Dundee, DD3 0PW Tel: (01382) 812794 Fax: (01382) 884114 E-mail: info@wattieswelders.com

Webgibb Welding & Fabrications, Unit 11 Bluebird Industrial Estate, Park Lane, Wolverhampton, WV10 9QQ Tel: (01902) 722040 Fax: (01902) 722040 E-mail: shane@webgibb.u-net.com

Weldex Ltd, Kingsway South, Team Valley Trading Estate, Gateshead, Tyne & Wear, NE11 0JL Tel: 0191-497 3410 Fax: 0191-497 3411 E-mail: weldex@responsive-engineering.com

Welding Services (Weldon) Ltd, Trevithick Road, Willowbrook South Industrial E, Corby, Northamptonshire, NN17 5XY Tel: (01536) 266623 Fax: (01536) 403159 E-mail: weldingservices@aol.com

Weldtec Welding Services, Mackleys Industrial Estate, Henfield Road, Small Dole, Henfield, West Sussex, BN5 9XE Tel: (01273) 493493 Fax: (01273) 493493 E-mail: weldtecwelding@aol.com

West Bromwich Pressings Ltd, Pleasant Street, Lyng, West Bromwich, West Midlands, B70 7DT Tel: 0121-525 5540 Fax: 0121-525 0581

Whites Material Handling Ltd, 10-12 Dixon Road, Bristol, BS4 5QW Tel: 0117-972 0006 Fax: 0117-972 3296 E-mail: enquiries@whitesmh.co.uk

Wimborne Welding Supplies Ltd, Unit 16J Chalwyn Industrial Estate, Old Wareham Road, Parkstone, Poole, Dorset, BH12 4PE Tel: (01202) 722606 Fax: (01202) 722606

Wooler Ltd, North Way, Andover, Hampshire, SP10 5AZ Tel: (01264) 324181 Fax: (01264) 333554

WRES Ltd, 25 Whitney Road, Nuffield Industrial Estate, Poole, Dorset, BH17 0GL Tel: (01202) 674480 Fax: (01202) 660776

Wright Air Systems Ltd, 11 Regent Street, Rochdale, Lancashire, OL12 0HQ Tel: (01706) 343980 Fax: (01706) 525771 E-mail: was@ame-services.co.uk

WELDING ACCESSORIES

Caswells, Lagonda Road, Cowpen Lane Industrial Estate, Billingham, Cleveland, TS23 4JA Tel: (01642) 379600 Fax: (01642) 562978 E-mail: sales@caswellsgroup.com

Cledwyn Saunders & Son Ltd, Rhigos Road, Rhigos, Aberdare, Mid Glamorgan, CF44 9YR Tel: (01685) 813613

Exact Weld (GB) Ltd, Unit 8E, Charlwoods Road, East Grinstead, West Sussex, RH19 2HG Tel: (01342) 311595 Fax: (01342) 326526

Fowlmere Engineering Ltd, Rectory Lane, Fowlmere, Royston, Hertfordshire, SG8 7TJ Tel: (01763) 208265 Fax: (01763) 208515

Gullco International (UK) Ltd, 5 Stonecrop, North Quarry Business Park, Appley Bridge, Wigan, Lancashire, WN6 9DB Tel: (01257) 253579 Fax: (01257) 254629 E-mail: sales@gullco.co.uk

Jaymig Engineering, Unit 6 Redland Close, Aldermans Green Industrial Estate, Coventry, CV2 2NP Tel: (024) 7661 8630 Fax: (024) 7661 4412

Murex Welding Products Ltd, Hanover House, Queensgate, Britania Road, Waltham Cross, Hertfordshire, EN8 7TF Tel: (01992) 710000 Fax: (01992) 715803 E-mail: info@murexwelding.co.uk

Parweld Ltd, Alton Works, Long Bank, Bewdley, Worcestershire, DY12 2UJ Tel: (01299) 266800 Fax: (01299) 266900 E-mail: info@parweld.co.uk

Rapide Tankers, The Airfield, Full Sutton, York, YO41 1HS Tel: (01759) 372224 Fax: (01759) 372231

WELDING ACCESSORIES – *continued*

Shropshire Welding Supplies Ltd, Unit A10, Stafford Park 15, Telford, Shropshire, TF3 3BB Tel: (01952) 290610 Fax: (01952) 211960 E-mail: swsltd@compuserve.com

Weldspares-OKI Ltd, Unit 50 Melford Court, Hardwick Grange, Warrington, WA1 4RZ Tel: (01925) 813288 Fax: (01925) 817223 E-mail: sales@weldspares-oki.com

WELDING AND CUTTING TORCHES

Esab Group UK Ltd, Hanover House Britannia Road, Queens Gate, Waltham Cross, Hertfordshire, EN8 7TF Tel: (01992) 768515 Fax: (01992) 715803 E-mail: info@esab.co.uk

Parweld Ltd, Alton Works, Long Bank, Bewdley, Worcestershire, DY12 2UJ Tel: (01299) 266800 Fax: (01299) 266900 E-mail: info@parweld.co.uk

T & B Welding Products (UK) Ltd, Unit 1B, Ravenstor Road, Wirksworth Industrial Estate, Wirksworth, Matlock, Derbyshire, DE4 4FY Tel: (01629) 823779 Fax: (01629) 824961

WELDING AUTOMATED SYSTEMS

Obara UK, 1 Tomlinson Industrial Estate, Alfreton Road, Derby, DE21 4ED Tel: (01332) 297868 Fax: E-mail: sales@obara.co.uk

Power Electronics & Controls Ltd, 1 Kingsthorne Park, Henson Way, Telford Way Industrial Estate, Kettering, Northamptonshire, NN16 8PX Tel: (01536) 310070 Fax: (01536) 525466 E-mail: sales@powerelectronics.co.uk

Pyramid Engineering Services Co. Ltd, 4 Orchard Business Centre, Kangley Bridge Road, London, SE26 5AQ Tel: (020) 8776 5545 Fax: (020) 8768 7650 E-mail: enquiries@pyramideng.com

Redman Controls & Electronics Ltd, Brick Kiln Industrial Estate, Malders Lane, Maidenhead, Berkshire, SL6 6NQ Tel: (01628) 630514 Fax: (01628) 625254 E-mail: sales@redmancontrols.com

Sciaky Electric Welding Machines Ltd, 212 Bedford Avenue, Slough, SL1 4RH Tel: (01753) 525551 Fax: (01753) 821416 E-mail: sales@sciaky.co.uk

Yajima UK Ltd, Unit 17, Rassau Industrial Estate, Rassau, Ebbw Vale, Gwent, NP23 5SD Tel: (01495) 307190 Fax: (01495) 308677 E-mail: adams@yajima-uk.co.uk

WELDING CABLE MANUFRS

Total Welding Supplies Ltd, Unit 12-13, St. Johns Road, Kirkdale, Liverpool, L20 8PR Tel: 0151-933 7213 Fax: 0151-944 1177 E-mail: totalwelding@btconnect.com

WELDING COMPOUNDS/FLUXES

Bohler Thyssen Welding (UK) Ltd, European Business Park, Taylors Lane, Oldbury, West Midlands, B69 2BN Tel: 0121-569 7700 Fax: 0121-544 2876 E-mail: info@btwuk.co.uk

Eutectic Co. Ltd, Moons Moat North Industrial Estate, Redditch, Worcestershire, B98 9HL Tel: (01527) 582200 Fax: (01527) 582201 E-mail: sales@eutectic.com

WELDING CONSULTANCY

Bunns Lane Welding, Bunns Lane Works, Bunns Lane, London, NW7 2AJ Tel: (020) 8959 8046

▶ C D Welding & Inspection Services, Crofton Road, Stockton-on-Tees, Cleveland, TS18 2QZ Tel: (01642) 616987 Fax: (01642) 607799

Code-A-Weld, 2nd Avenue, Westfield Trading Estate, Midsomer Norton, Radstock, BA3 4BE Tel: (01761) 410410 Fax: (01761) 418388 E-mail: info@codeaweld.com

Exact Weld (GB) Ltd, Unit 8E, Charlwoods Road, East Grinstead, West Sussex, RH19 2HG Tel: (01342) 311595 Fax: (01342) 326526

T. Pretty Engineers, Unit 1 Homestead Farm, Queniborough, Leicester, LE7 3FP Tel: 0116-260 6362 Fax: 0116-260 6362

W V H Welding Services, 6 Midas Industrial Estate, Longbridge Way, Cowley, Uxbridge, Middlesex, UB8 2YT Tel: (01895) 233501

WELDING CONSUMABLES/ SUPPLIES

Adlington Welding Supplies Ltd, Highfield Industrial Estate, North Street, Chorley, Lancashire, PR7 1QD Tel: (01257) 279364 Fax: (01257) 241352 E-mail: adweld@easynet.co.uk

Arc Welding Supplies & Repairs, 6 Palmbourne Industrial Park, Castle Street, Stafford, ST16 2TB Tel: (01785) 281007 Fax: (01785) 240688

B D Welding Supplies, 203 Halesowen Road, Netherton, Dudley, West Midlands, DY2 9PU Tel: (01384) 214577 Fax: (01384) 214577

Bohler Thyssen Welding (UK) Ltd, European Business Park, Taylors Lane, Oldbury, West Midlands, B69 2BN Tel: 0121-569 7700 Fax: 0121-544 2876 E-mail: info@btwuk.co.uk

Elga Welding Consumables, Unit 102 Rivington House, Horwich Business Park, Chorley New Road, Horwich, Bolton, BL6 5UE Tel: (01204) 473020 Fax: (01204) 473039 E-mail: sales@itw-welding.co.uk

Eltham Welding Supplies Ltd, 7 Mill Road, Portslade, Brighton, BN41 1PD Tel: (01273) 414381 Fax: (01273) 424603 E-mail: ews.sussex@dial.pipex.com

Luvaca Wolverhampton Ltd, Unit B, Smeston Bridge Industrial Estate, Bridgnorth Road, Wombourne, Wolverhampton, WV5 8AY Tel: (01902) 324747 Fax: (01902) 324501 E-mail: sales@thatcher-alloys.com

Mercury Welding Supplies, 6-7 Jubilee Estate, Horsham, West Sussex, RH13 5UE Tel: (01403) 260200 Fax: (01403) 217544 E-mail: sales@mercurywelding.com

Murex Welding Products Ltd, Hanover House, Queensgate, Britania Road, Waltham Cross, Hertfordshire, EN8 7TF Tel: (01992) 710000 Fax: (01992) 715803 E-mail: info@murexwelding.co.uk

Rock Welding Supplies Ltd, Princes Dr Industrial Estate, Coventry Road, Kenilworth, Warwickshire, CV8 2FD Tel: (01926) 851430 Fax: (01926) 851562

S K S Welding & Fasteners Supplies Ltd, Unit 33 Parkhouse Road East, Parkhouse Industrial Estate Ea, Newcastle, Staffordshire, ST5 7RB Tel: (01782) 566911 Fax: (01782) 561964 E-mail: sks.enquiries@btconnect.com

Sifbronze Ltd, Prentice Road, Stowmarket, Suffolk, IP14 1RD Tel: (01449) 771443 Fax: (01449) 771945 E-mail: sif@sifbronze.co.uk

Special Metal Welding Products, Waterloo Road, Bidford-on-Avon, Alcester, Warwickshire, B50 4JN Tel: (01789) 491780 Fax: (01789) 491781 E-mail: sales.uk@iaiwpc.com

Thermit Welding GB Ltd, 87 Ferry Lane, Rainham, Essex, RM13 9YH Tel: (01708) 522626 Fax: (01708) 553806

WELDING CURTAINS/DRAPES, PVC

Ductwork Accessories Ltd, Haldon House, 385 Brettell Lane, Brierley Hill, West Midlands, DY5 3LQ Tel: (01384) 571767 Fax: (01384) 571767

Seabrook Welding Supplies Ltd, 4-6 Cannock Street, Leicester, LE4 9HR Tel: 0116-276 4091 Fax: 0116-246 0492

WELDING ELECTRODES, *See also headings for particular types*

Eutectic Co. Ltd, Moons Moat North Industrial Estate, Redditch, Worcestershire, B98 9HL Tel: (01527) 582200 Fax: (01527) 582201 E-mail: sales@eutectic.com

M W A International Ltd, PO Box 17, Wednesbury, West Midlands, WS10 0AB Tel: 0121-556 6366 Fax: 0121-556 5566 E-mail: info@mwa-international.com

Metrode Products Ltd, Hanworth Lane, Chertsey, Surrey, KT16 9LL Tel: (01932) 566721 Fax: (01932) 565168 E-mail: info@metrode.com

Obara UK, 1 Tomlinson Industrial Estate, Alfreton Road, Derby, DE21 4ED Tel: (01332) 297868 Fax: E-mail: sales@obara.co.uk

R W Cushway & Co. Ltd, 180 Brooker Road, Waltham Abbey, Essex, EN9 1HT Tel: (01992) 713749 Fax: (01992) 788367 E-mail: info@cushways.co.uk

R.W.M. Mandrian Ltd, PO Box 517, Reading, RG30 6WF Tel: 0118-972 4455 Fax: 0118-972 4477

S K S Welding & Fasteners Supplies Ltd, Unit 33 Parkhouse Road East, Parkhouse Industrial Estate Ea, Newcastle, Staffordshire, ST5 7RB Tel: (01782) 566911 Fax: (01782) 561964 E-mail: sks.enquiries@btconnect.com

WELDING ENGINES

P C T Group Ltd, 45 Regent Street, Rochdale, Lancashire, OL12 0HQ Tel: (01706) 649321 Fax: (01706) 657452 E-mail: matterson@pctgroup.co.uk

WELDING EQUIPMENT, *See also headings for particular types*

▶ A.I. Welders, Unit 16, Dalcross Industrial Estate, Inverness, IV2 7XB Tel: (01667) 461383 Fax: (01667) 462520 E-mail: sales@ai-welders.co.uk

A & N Plant, St. James House, 46 High Street, Amersham, Buckinghamshire, HP7 0DJ Tel: (01494) 722820 Fax: (01494) 729240 E-mail: info@anplant.com

Advanced Welding & Design Ltd, PO Box 131, Bury St. Edmunds, Suffolk, IP32 7LS Tel: (01284) 705256 Fax: (01284) 705256

Cromwell Tools Ltd, Gibraltar Island Road, Old Mill Business Park, Leeds, LS10 1RJ Tel: 0113-277 7730 Fax: 0113-277 7724 E-mail: leeds@cromwell.co.uk

Gas Control Equipment Ltd, Yew Tree Way, Golborne, Warrington, WA3 3JD Tel: (01942) 292950 Fax: (01942) 292951 E-mail: sales@gceuk.com

L R Engineering, Milton Farm Workshop, West End Gardens, Fairford, Gloucestershire, GL7 4JB Tel: (01285) 713163 Fax: (01285) 713632 E-mail: lrengineering@btconnect.com

Migatronic Welding Equipment Ltd, 21 Jubilee Drive, Loughborough, Leicestershire, LE11 5XS Tel: (01509) 211492 Fax: (01509) 231959 E-mail: sales@migatronic.co.uk

Murex Welding Products Ltd, Hanover House, Queensgate, Britania Road, Waltham Cross, Hertfordshire, EN8 7TF Tel: (01992) 710000 Fax: (01992) 715803 E-mail: info@murexwelding.co.uk

Newgate Welding Supplies, Heritage Business Park, Heritage Way, Gosport, Hampshire, PO12 4BG Tel: (023) 9260 4555 Fax: (023) 9260 4554 E-mail: newgate@specfabs.co.uk

Obara UK, 1 Tomlinson Industrial Estate, Alfreton Road, Derby, DE21 4ED Tel: (01332) 297868 Fax: E-mail: sales@obara.co.uk

Pressure Welding Machines Ltd, Belmont Farm Business Centre, Snoad Hill, Bethersden, Ashford, Kent, TN26 3DY Tel: (01233) 820817 Fax: (01233) 820591 E-mail: sales@pwmltd.co.uk

Safety Welding & Lifting (International) Ltd, Site 4 Inverbreakie Industrial Estate, Invergordon, Ross-Shire, IV18 0QR Tel: (01349) 852187 Fax: (01349) 853585 E-mail: info@safetyweldinglifting.co.uk

Stewart Scott Fabrications Ltd, 16 East Cromwell Street, Edinburgh, EH6 6HD Tel: 0131-555 0375 Fax: 0131-553 7958

Weld-AC Supplies Ltd, Unit 3 Arden Works, Fenton Road, Kings Cross, Halifax, West Yorkshire, HX1 3PP Tel: (01422) 346536 Fax: (01422) 364994 E-mail: sales@weldac.co.uk

Welding Alloys Ltd, The Way, Fowlmere, Royston, Hertfordshire, SG8 7QS Tel: (01763) 207500 Fax: (01763) 207501 E-mail: sales@welding-alloys.com

Weldspares-OKI Ltd, Unit 50 Melford Court, Hardwick Grange, Warrington, WA1 4RZ Tel: (01925) 813288 Fax: (01925) 817223 E-mail: sales@weldspares-oki.com

Wescol Ltd, PO Box 41, Wolverhampton, WV1 2RZ Tel: (01902) 351283 Fax: (01902) 871937 E-mail: sales@wescol.com

WELDING EQUIPMENT HIRE

A76 Plant & Tool Hire Ltd, 203-205 Etruria Road, Stoke-on-Trent, ST1 5NS Tel: (01782) 858998 Fax: (01782) 858999

Arc Welding Services, 17 Sandy Lane, Aston, Birmingham, B6 5TP Tel: 0121-327 2249 Fax: 0121-327 4797 E-mail: service@arcweld.freeserve.co.uk

Banson Tool Hire Ltd, 125 Pellon Lane, Halifax, West Yorkshire, HX1 5QN Tel: (01422) 254999 Fax: (01422) 254778

Brandon Hire plc, 151 Bute Street, Cardiff, CF10 5HQ Tel: (029) 2048 9898 Fax: (029) 2048 0772 E-mail: cardiff23@brandonhire.plc.uk

Electro Cal Ltd, 4 Bridge End Business Park, Park Road, Milnthorpe, Cumbria, LA7 7RH Tel: (01539) 564202 Fax: (01539) 564203 E-mail: sales@electro-cal.co.uk

Eltham Welding Supplies Ltd, 2-12 Parry Place, London, SE18 6AN Tel: (020) 8854 1226 Fax: (020) 8854 2720 E-mail: sales.woolwich@elthamweldingsupplies.co.uk

Gauge & Welding Equipment Repairs Ltd, PO Box 48, Dartford, DA1 1YA Tel: (01322) 270036 Fax: (01322) 288625 E-mail: mail@gwer.co.uk

Geartrodes South Wales Ltd, DC Griffiths Way, Neath, West Glamorgan, SA11 1BT Tel: (01639) 630081 Fax: (01639) 644394 E-mail: info@geartrodesweldingsupplies.co.uk

Genweld Supplies Ltd, 41 Unit 2, Wolverhampton, WV1 2RZ Tel: (01902) 351438 Fax: (01902) 351475 E-mail: sales@genweld.com

Hember Plant Hire Ltd, Lilford Street, Warrington, WA5 0LA Tel: (01925) 656023 Fax: (01925) 653104 E-mail: hire@hemberplant.co.uk

M H Spencer Ltd, Charter Avenue, Coventry, CV4 8AF Tel: (024) 7646 4044 Fax: (024) 7669 4011 E-mail: james.evans@mhspencer.co.uk

▶ Philpott & Cowlin Ltd, Unit 12 Liberty Industrial Park, South Liberty Lane, Bristol, BS3 2SU Tel: 0117-966 8431 Fax: 0117-966 0129 E-mail: philpottcowlin@pcweldmetals.co.uk

Plant Hire Ltd, Unit 3, Aquarius Business Park, Priestley Way, London, NW2 7AN Tel: (020) 8208 3838 Fax: (020) 8450 3716

Shropshire Welding Supplies Ltd, Unit A10, Stafford Park 15, Telford, Shropshire, TF3 3BB Tel: (01952) 290610 Fax: (01952) 211960 E-mail: swsltd@compuserve.com

Six Hills Welding Supplies Ltd, 7 Pate Road, Melton Mowbray, Leicestershire, LE13 0RG Tel: (01664) 480801 Fax: (01664) 481833

Specialized & General Welding, Unit 35 The Wallows Industrial Estate, Brierley Hill, West Midlands, DY5 1QA Tel: (01384) 480408 Fax: (01384) 480828

T P S Fronius, 1 The Omni Business Centre, Omega Park, Alton, Hampshire, GU34 2QD Tel: (01420) 546855 Fax: (01420) 546856 E-mail: alton@tps-fronius.co.uk

Telford Group Ltd, Enterprise House, Stafford Park 1, Telford, Shropshire, TF3 3BD Tel: (01952) 290800 Fax: (01952) 291303 E-mail: info@telfordgroup.co.uk

TPS Fronius, 108 Highfields Road, Bilston, West Midlands, WV14 0LD Tel: (01902) 495686 Fax: (01902) 496461

TPS Fronius Ltd, 5 Simonsburn Road, Kilmarnock, Ayrshire, KA1 5LE Tel: (01563) 529435 Fax: (01563) 523510 E-mail: sales@tps-fronius.co.uk

Weldmet Ltd, Unit 8, 55 Weir Road, Wimbledon, London, SW19 8UG Tel: (020) 8947 1244 Fax: (020) 8947 6080 E-mail: sales@weldmet.co.uk

West Country Welding Supplies Ltd, 4 Ashmead Business Centre, Ashmead Road, Keynsham, Bristol, BS31 1SX Tel: 0117-986 6006 Fax: 0117-986 1892 E-mail: sales@westcoweld.co.uk

WELDING EQUIPMENT MAINTENANCE/REPAIR SERVICES

Allis Welding Services, Unit 6 Bath Street, Newcastle upon Tyne, NE6 3PH Tel: 0191-295 0041 Fax: 0191-263 0614 E-mail: awswelding@ukonline.co.uk

Andrew Beattie & Co., Ilkley House, Brighton Road, Tadworth, Surrey, KT20 6SU Tel: (0845) 3301373 Fax: (0845) 3301373

Arc Welding Supplies & Repairs, 6 Palmbourne Industrial Park, Castle Street, Stafford, ST16 2TB Tel: (01785) 281007 Fax: (01785) 240688

Chiltern Electrical Services, 1 Shenstone Drive, Burnham, Slough, SL1 7HJ Tel: (01628) 665090 Fax: (01628) 665090 E-mail: miketerry@chilelecserv.freeserve.co.uk

Electro Cal Ltd, 4 Bridge End Business Park, Park Road, Milnthorpe, Cumbria, LA7 7RH Tel: (01539) 564202 Fax: (01539) 564203 E-mail: sales@electro-cal.co.uk

Gauge & Welding Equipment Repairs Ltd, PO Box 48, Dartford, DA1 1YA Tel: (01322) 270036 Fax: (01322) 288625 E-mail: mail@gwer.co.uk

M I H Welding Supplies Ltd, Unit E Rio Works, Polesdon Lane, Ripley, Woking, Surrey, GU23 6JX Tel: (01483) 225409 Fax: (01483) 224242

M J P Ltd, 9 Alpha Business Park, Travellers Close, North Mymms, Hatfield, Hertfordshire, AL9 7NT Tel: (01707) 261179 Fax: (01707) 272470 E-mail: mike.player@virgin.net

Meopham Welding Supplies, Railway Sidings, Station Approach, Meopham, Gravesend, Kent, DA13 0LT Tel: (01474) 812050 Fax: (01474) 813714

Mercury Welding Supplies, 6-7 Jubilee Estate, Horsham, West Sussex, RH13 5UE Tel: (01403) 260200 Fax: (01403) 217544 E-mail: sales@mercurywelding.com

North Catering Equipment Ltd, St. Georges Road Industrial Estate, Donnington, Telford, Shropshire, TF2 7QZ Tel: (01952) 616655 Fax: (01952) 417799

Sphinx Welding Repair & Supplies, 37B Broad Street, Coventry, CV6 5AX Tel: (024) 7666 3365 Fax: (024) 6666 3365 E-mail: joefletch@tiscali.co.uk

Starmaker Welding Services, 16 Pembroke Avenue, Waterbeach, Cambridge, CB25 9QR Tel: (01223) 860662 Fax: (01223) 440009 E-mail: sales@starmake-rwelding.fsnet.co.uk

Tipton Welding Service, Brick Kiln Street, Tipton, West Midlands, DY4 9BP Tel: 0121-557 1282 Fax: 0121-557 1282

United Welding Supplies Ltd, Unit 32, The Cam Centre, Wilbury Way, Hitchin, Hertfordshire, SG4 0TW Tel: (01462) 437991 Fax: (01462) 421274 E-mail: sales@unitedwelding.co.uk

Welding Repairs & Supplies Co. Ltd, Brandon Way, West Bromwich, West Midlands, B70 8JW Tel: 0121-553 6581 Fax: 0121-553 2953 E-mail: weldingrepair@aol.com

Weldmet Ltd, Unit 8, 55 Weir Road, Wimbledon, London, SW19 8UG Tel: (020) 8947 1244 Fax: (020) 8947 6080 E-mail: sales@weldmet.co.uk

WELDING EQUIPMENT, MIG/TIG

Stewart Scott Fabrications Ltd, 16 East Cromwell Street, Edinburgh, EH6 6HD Tel: 0131-555 0375 Fax: 0131-553 7958

T & B Welding Products (UK) Ltd, Unit 1B, Ravenstor Road, Wirksworth Industrial Estate, Wirksworth, Matlock, Derbyshire, DE4 4FY Tel: (01629) 823779 Fax: (01629) 824961

WELDING EQUIPMENT, MULTIPLE PROCESS

Wildcat Taconic, School Close, Burgess Hill, West Sussex, RH15 9RD Tel: (01444) 247756 Fax: (01444) 248416 E-mail: sales@wildcat-taconic.com

WELDING EQUIPMENT, SPECIAL PURPOSE/CUSTOM BUILDERS

Advanced Welding & Design Ltd, PO Box 131, Bury St. Edmunds, Suffolk, IP32 7LS Tel: (01284) 705256 Fax: (01284) 705256

Corewire Ltd, Poplars Farm, Station Road West, Ash Vale, Aldershot, Hampshire, GU12 5QD Tel: (01252) 517766 Fax: (01252) 515833 E-mail: info@corewire.com

Electro Mechanical Services Ltd, 24B Portman Road, Reading, RG30 1EA Tel: 0118-956 1222 Fax: 0118-956 1220 E-mail: info@emssolutions.co.uk

Fusion, 9 Fishwicks Industrial Estate, Kilbuck Lane, Haydock, St. Helens, Merseyside, WA11 9SZ Tel: (01942) 271517 Fax: (01942) 716187 E-mail: northwest@fusiongroup.co.uk

Redman Controls & Electronics Ltd, Brick Kiln Industrial Estate, Malders Lane, Maidenhead, Berkshire, SL6 6NQ Tel: (01628) 630514 Fax: (01628) 625254 E-mail: sales@redmancontrols.com

Swiftool Precision Engineering Ltd, Unit 1, Brierley Indust Park, Stanton Hill, Sutton-in-Ashfield, Nottinghamshire, NG17 3FW Tel: (01623) 515544 Fax: (01623) 442166 E-mail: sales@swiftool.co.uk

Y P H Welding Supplies, Unit 1 Stubbins Lane, Claughton-on-Brock, Preston, PR3 0QH Tel: (01995) 604057 Fax: (01995) 604018 E-mail: alan@yphltd.co.uk

WELDING EQUIPMENT, SUBSEA/UNDERWATER

Hydroweld Divers, 46 Bedford Drive, Sutton Coldfield, West Midlands, B75 6AX Tel: 0121-378 1230 Fax: 0121-378 1281 E-mail: info@hydroweld.com

Speciality Welds Ltd, Unit 18, Moorlands Business Centre, Cleckheaton, West Yorkshire, BD19 4EW Tel: (01274) 879867 Fax: (01274) 855975 E-mail: sales@specialwelds.com

WELDING FABRICATION AND MACHINING

A Weld Ltd, Tank Farm Road, Llandarcy, Neath, West Glamorgan, SA10 6EN Tel: (01792) 816132 Fax: (01792) 812913 E-mail: info@aweldlimited.co.uk

Aarcweld Scotland Ltd, 7 Rennie Place, East Kilbride, Glasgow, G74 5HD Tel: (01355) 244545 Fax: (01355) 244589 E-mail: sales@aarcweld.co.uk

Acorn Fabrications, Unit 4a, 179 Cardiff Road, Reading, RG1 8HD Tel: 0118-958 7466 Fax: 0118-958 7466 E-mail: dinoacornfabs@live.co.uk

Arc Energy Resources Ltd, Unit 12 Eastington Industrial Estate, Meadow Mill, Eastington, Stonehouse, Gloucestershire, GL10 3RZ Tel: (01453) 823523 Fax: (01453) 823623 E-mail: sales@arcenergy.co.uk

Arc Services Ltd, Unit 1-2 Andrews Road Industrial Estate, Andrews Road, Cardiff, CF14 2JP Tel: (029) 2055 1919 Fax: (029) 2055 2777

Arc-Tec, Unit 4 Bound Oak, Eversley Road, Arborfield, Reading, RG2 9PN Tel: 0118-976 1777 Fax: 0118-976 1444

Ashby Welding, 13 Potters Industrial Park, Church Crookham, Fleet, Hampshire, GU52 6EU Tel: (01252) 815811

A-Tech Fabrications Ltd, Woodham Road, Aycliffe Industrial Park, Newton Aycliffe, County Durham, DL5 6HT Tel: (01325) 304033 Fax: (01325) 304044

Avon Welding & Marine, 50 Grace Drive, Kingswood, Bristol, BS15 4JU Tel: 0117-975 4443

Axon Welding & Fabrication, Green Lane, Challock, Ashford, Kent, TN25 4BL Tel: (01233) 740691 Fax: (01233) 740691

B & R Welding Fabrications, Unit 1a Ribble Business Park, Challenge Way, Blackburn, BB1 5QB Tel: (01254) 670503 Fax: (01254) 670503

Bartek Engineering Ltd, 24 Industrial Estate, Cornwall Road, Smethwick, West Midlands, B66 2JS Tel: 0121-555 8885 Fax: 0121-555 8885

Boweld Engineering, Pentre Halkyn, Rhes-y-Cae, Holywell, Clwyd, CH8 8JP Tel: (01352) 781566 Fax: (01352) 781141

Bymax Ltd, Glengarnock Workshops, Glengarnock, Beith, Ayrshire, KA14 3DA Tel: (01505) 683242 Fax: (01505) 683242

C O'Connor Engineers Ltd, Halberton Street, Smethwick, West Midlands, B66 2QP Tel: 0121-555 5992 Fax: 0121-555 6007

Castle Gates, Castlelaurie Works, Falkirk, FK2 7XF Tel: (01324) 633510

Cook Fabrications Ltd, Broomfield Works, Fernfield Lane, Hawkinge, Folkestone, Kent, CT18 7AW Tel: (01303) 893011 Fax: (01303) 893407 E-mail: info@cookfabrications.co.uk

D Mcinnes, Clayslap, Kilmarnock, Ayrshire, KA1 5LN Tel: (01563) 522774 Fax: (01563) 571530 E-mail: enquires@duncanmcinnes.com

D O J Pipe Welding Services, 6 Pear Tree Close, Little Billing, Northampton, NN3 9TH Tel: (01604) 404010 Fax: (01604) 408636 E-mail: welding@pipewelding.co.uk

Das Fabrications Ltd, Ajax Works, Whitehill Street, Stockport, Cheshire, SK4 1NT Tel: 0161-476 1222 Fax: 0161-476 1333 E-mail: dave@dasfabs.fsbusiness.co.uk

Datona Ltd, Unit 1A, Lawton Rd, Rushden, Northants, NN10 0DX Tel: (01933) 411616 Fax: (01933) 411873

Dehavilland, 10 Stonehouse Commercial Centre, Bristol Road, Stonehouse, Gloucestershire, GL10 3RD Tel: (01453) 828272 Fax: (01453) 821945

Dockdale Ltd, 30 Lower Dartmouth Street, Birmingham, B9 4LG Tel: 0121-771 4681 Fax: 0121-773 7783

E & G Engineering, The Street, Gooderstone, King's Lynn, Norfolk, PE33 9BS Tel: (01366) 328424 Fax: (01366) 328424 E-mail: mariko@supanet.com

G A Fabrications Ltd, 8 1 St. Annes Road, Willenhall, West Midlands, WV13 1DY Tel: (01902) 603892 Fax: 01902 603027 E-mail: gafabs@talk21.com

G D W Engineering & Plant Services Ltd, Low Mill, Town Lane, Whittle-le-Woods, Chorley, Lancashire, PR6 7DJ Tel: (01257) 262491 Fax: (01257) 241174 E-mail: graham.watkinson@gdwengineeriring.co.uk

Gibbs (General Engineering) Ltd, 7 High Street, Prestatyn, Clwyd, LL19 9AF Tel: (01745) 853759 Fax: (01745) 854360 E-mail: office@gibbsge.com

Harbour Welding Services Ltd, 91-93 Sterte Avenue West, Poole, Dorset, BH15 2AL Tel: (01202) 668692 Fax: (01202) 666158 E-mail: harbourwelding@btopenworld.com

Dennis Hawkins Welding, Westside Farm, High Street, Stoke Goldington, Newport Pagnell, Buckinghamshire, MK16 8NP Tel: (01908) 551400

Heatherside Engineering Ltd, Old Oak Close Industrial Estate, Old Oak Close, Arlesey, Bedfordshire, SG15 6XD Tel: (01462) 731575 Fax: (01462) 731575 E-mail: heatherside@btconnect.com

High Pressure Welding Ltd, Sundon Business Park, Dencora Way, Luton, LU3 3HP Tel: (01582) 565400 Fax: (01582) 565500 E-mail: hpweldingltd@aol.com

▶ Howard Berkin, Victoria Road, Ripley, Derbyshire, DE5 3FX Tel: (01773) 513800 Fax: (01773) 513600 E-mail: howardberkin@tiscali.co.uk

Hubert Davies & Sons, The Green, Neath, West Glamorgan, SA11 1SE Tel: (01639) 643022

I M Products Ltd, 2 London Hill Farm, London Road, Stockbridge, Hampshire, SO20 6EN Tel: (01264) 810261 Fax: (01264) 810642

J & D Services, Highhouse Indust Estate, Barony Road, Auchinleck, Cumnock, Ayrshire, KA18 2LL Tel: (01290) 423752 Fax: 01290 421587

J J Welding Fabrication Ltd, Greenbank Road, East Tullos Industrial Estate, Aberdeen, AB12 3BQ Tel: (01224) 898889 Fax: (01224) 873139 E-mail: njohnston@twma.co.uk

J Pratley & Sons Ltd, Pingemead Farm, Pingewood, Reading, RG30 3UR Tel: 0118-975 7500 Fax: 0118-975 6787 E-mail: sales@j.pratleysons.co.uk

R.E. & P. Kettle Ltd, 11 Ruston Road, Grantham, Lincolnshire, NG31 9SW Tel: 01476 563473

M C Engineering Services, Unit 3b The Lays Farm, Charlton Road, Keynsham, Bristol, BS31 2SE Tel: 0117-986 4196 Fax: 0117-986 4196 E-mail: info@kagemforge.co.uk

Mobile M I G, Unit 4 Arnold Street, Lowestoft, Suffolk, NR32 1PU Tel: (01502) 512970 Fax: (01502) 512971 E-mail: sales@mobilemig.co.uk

Mobile Welding & Fabrications Ltd, Unit 220 Alexandra Business Park, Sunderland, SR4 6UG Tel: 0191 5147985

Nci, 2 Nelsons Lane, Hurst, Reading, RG10 0RR Tel: 0118-934 5316 Fax: 0118-934 2010 E-mail: info@nciservices.co.uk

P Quinton, 2 Northern Court, Nottingham, NG6 0BJ Tel: 0115-975 5837 Fax: 0115-975 5837 E-mail: paul@paul-quinton.freeserve.co.uk

Phillips Welding, Sedgedale Cottage, Killingworth Village, Newcastle upon Tyne, NE12 6BL Tel: 0191-268 6741 Fax: 0191-268 6741

M. Pickering (Scarborough) Ltd, 66 Londesborough Road, Scarborough, North Yorkshire, YO12 5AF Tel: 01723 373852

Precision Fabrications Ltd, Units 8-9 Sea Vixen Industrial Estate, 3 Wilverley Road, Christchurch, Dorset, BH23 3RU Tel: (01202) 474406 Fax: (01202) 473821 E-mail: enquiries@precisionfabricationsltd.co.uk

R & R Development, Llewellyns Quay, The Docks, Port Talbot, West Glamorgan, SA13 1SD Tel: (01639) 870330 Fax: (01639) 890317

S & S Engineering Ltd, Blackwell Industrial Estate, Station Road, Tilbrook, Huntingdon, Cambridgeshire, PE28 0JY Tel: (01480) 860426 Fax: (01480) 860355

S W S Alloys & Metals Ltd, Progress Drive, Cannock, Staffordshire, WS11 0JE Tel: (01543) 572149 Fax: (01543) 573834

Schofield Fabrications Bromsgrove Ltd, Sugarbrook Road, Bromsgrove, Worcestershire, B60 3DN Tel: (01527) 870220 Fax: (01527) 575409 E-mail: schofab@aol.com

Sherborne Metal Masters, Ash Lane, Little London, Tadley, Hampshire, RG26 5EL Tel: (01256) 880096 Fax: (01256) 880096

Steel Engineering Services Ltd, Unit 7f Block Westway, Porterfield Road, Renfrew, PA4 8DJ Tel: 0141-885 0885 Fax: 0141-886 3322 E-mail: info@steeleng.com

Structures (Cordell) Ltd, Sotherby Road, Skippers Lane Industrial Estate, South Bank, Middlesbrough, Cleveland, TS6 6LP Tel: (01642) 452406 Fax: (01642) 464118 E-mail: structures@cordellgroup.com

T M Fabrications, Unit 2, Dale St, Accrington, Lancashire, BB5 0AP Tel: 01254 351668

T R W Fabrication & Welding, 1 Milnthorpe Road, Holme, Carnforth, Lancashire, LA6 1PS Tel: (01524) 782647

T T C Engineering Ltd, Unit 13, Chalwyn Industrial Estate, Old Wareham Road, Poole, Dorset, BH12 4PE Tel: (01202) 738181

Tombi, Unit 20, Limberline Industrial Estate, Limberline Spur, Hilsea, Portsmouth, PO3 5DY Tel: (023) 9269 0215 Fax: (023) 9269 1095

Trifab Steel Fabrication Co. Ltd, Unit 2 Lakeland Business Centre, Parish Lane, Pease Pottage, Crawley, West Sussex, RH10 5NY Tel: (01293) 511263 Fax: (01293) 512899 E-mail: a7bsl@aol.co.uk

Twelco Fabrications Ltd, Old Airfield, Belton Road, Sandtoft, Doncaster, South Yorkshire, DN8 5SX Tel: (01724) 710844 Fax: (01724) 710188 E-mail: twelcofabltd@aol.com

Universal Applications, 2 Clarkes Road, Wigston, Leicestershire, LE18 2BG Tel: 0116-288 8038 Fax: 0116-288 8036

Up Country Autoproducts UK Ltd, Norwich Road, Halesworth, Suffolk, IP19 8QJ Tel: (01986) 875171 Fax: (01986) 875260 E-mail: sales@upcountry4x4.co.uk

V P Welding Ltd, VP Square, Storeys Bar Road, Peterborough, PE1 5YS Tel: (01733) 552888 Fax: (01733) 311972

Ventfix Fabrications Ltd, Unit 54-55 Youngs Industrial Estate, Aldermaston, Reading, RG7 4PW Tel: 0118 9816246

Whites Material Handling Ltd, 10-12 Dixon Road, Bristol, BS4 5QW Tel: 0117-972 0006 Fax: 0117-972 3296 E-mail: enquiries@whitesmh.co.uk

Winfield Engineering Ltd, Alma Park Road, Grantham, Lincolnshire, NG31 9SE Tel: (01476) 567105 Fax: (01476) 566505

WELDING FABRICATION MACHINERY

▶ A.I. Welders, Unit 16, Dalcross Industrial Estate, Inverness, IV2 7XB Tel: (01667) 461383 Fax: (01667) 462520 E-mail: sales@ai-welders.co.uk

Bonlea Engineering, 4 Ajax Works, Hertford Road, Barking, Essex, IG11 8DY Tel: (020) 8591 2183 Fax: (020) 8594 3605

Chelmer Precision Welding, Marks Hall, Marks Hall Lane, Margaret Roding, Dunmow, Essex, CM6 1QT Tel: (01245) 231269 Fax: (01245) 231842 E-mail: cpweld@aol.com

WELDING FIXTURES, SPOT WELDING

▶ Pentangle Engineering Services Ltd, Isaac Newton Way, Grantham, Lincolnshire, NG31 9RT Tel: (01476) 572354 Fax: (01476) 590356 E-mail: nigel.rivers@pentangle-eng.co.uk

WELDING FLANGES

Park Lane Flanges & Fittings Ltd, Unit 12A Bluebird Industrial Estate, Park Lane, Wolverhampton, WV10 9QG Tel: (01902) 728400 Fax: (01902) 728600 E-mail: parklaneltd@hotmail.com

WELDING FUME EXTRACTION EQUIPMENT

Fumex Ltd, 411 Effingham Rd, Sheffield, S9 3QD Tel: 0114-243 0538 Fax: 0114-243 2394 E-mail: enquiries@fumex.co.uk

Seabrook Welding Supplies Ltd, 4-6 Cannock Street, Leicester, LE4 9HR Tel: 0116-276 4091 Fax: 0116-246 0492

WELDING HELMETS/FACE SHIELDS

▶ Auto Dark Helmet, 43 Long Hassocks, Rugby, Warwickshire, CV23 0JS Tel: (01788) 573056 Fax: (01788) 573057 E-mail: sales@autodarkhelmet.co.uk

WELDING INSPECTION ENGINEERS/SERVICES

Evans Ltd, 11 St James Industrial Estate, Westhampnett Road, Chichester, West Sussex, PO19 7JU Tel: (07976) 444316 Fax: (01243) 530828 E-mail: john@evanswelding.com

WELDING NOZZLES

▶ Flame-Equip Ltd, 8 Mandervelle Road, Oadby, Leicester, LE2 5LQ Tel: 0116-271 3364 Fax: 0116-272 0126 E-mail: sales@flame-equip.demon.co.uk

Jaymig Engineering, Unit 6 Redland Close, Aldermans Green Industrial Estate, Coventry, CV2 2NP Tel: (024) 7661 8630 Fax: (024) 7661 4412

WELDING POSITIONERS

F Bode & Sons Ltd, 1 Street Cottages, Stubbins Lane, Claughton-on-Brock, Preston, PR3 0QH Tel: (01995) 643210 Fax: (01995) 643211 E-mail: sales@bode.co.uk

WELDING PROTECTIVE CLOTHING

Birmingham Safety Wear, Unit 14 Mount Street Business Centre, Mount Street, Nechells, Birmingham, B7 5RD Tel: 0121-327 0873 Fax: 0121-327 0873 E-mail: sales@birminghamsafetywear.co.uk

WELDING REPAIR

▶ Arcwell Mobile Welding, 64 Tansey Green Road, Brierley Hill, West Midlands, DY5 4TE Tel: (07860) 419626 Fax: (01384) 78009 E-mail: patricia@hopton8339fsnet.co.uk

▶ J Little, Norfolk Street, Nelson, Lancashire, BB9 7SY Tel: (01282) 698777 E-mail: johnlittle@yahoo.co.uk

Thermsave Welding, 9 Wavertree Park Gardens, Low Moor, Bradford, West Yorkshire, BD12 0UY Tel: (01274) 424478 Fax: (01274) 424479 E-mail: thermsavewelding@blueyonder.co.uk

WELDING RODS

Eutectic Co. Ltd, Moons Moat North Industrial Estate, Redditch, Worcestershire, B98 9HL Tel: (01527) 582200 Fax: (01527) 582201 E-mail: sales@eutectic.com

Special Metal Welding Products, Waterloo Road, Bidford-on-Avon, Alcester, Warwickshire, B50 4JN Tel: (01789) 491780 Fax: (01789) 491781 E-mail: sales.uk@iaiwpc.com

W B Alloy Products Ltd, 37 Dalsetter Avenue, Glasgow, G15 8TE Tel: 0141-944 5500 Fax: 0141-944 9000

WELDING STUDS

Components & Technology, Unit M Valley Way, Market Harborough, Leicestershire, LE16 7PS Tel: (01858) 439503 Fax: (01858) 466536 E-mail: sales@coldform.co.uk

Studweldpro UK Ltd, Ollerton Road, Tuxford, Newark, Nottinghamshire, NG22 0PQ Tel: (01777) 874500 Fax: (01777) 874555 E-mail: sales@swpuk.com

WELDING SUPPLIES

A P O Flame Equipment Ltd, 605 Main Street, Bellshill, Lanarkshire, ML4 1DX Tel: (01698) 747630 Fax: (01698) 749465

A S K For Service, 16 Tollpark Road, Cumbernauld, Glasgow, G68 0LN Tel: (01236) 739245 Fax: (01236) 735429 E-mail: sales@askforservice.co.uk

Adlington Welding Supplies Ltd, Highfield Industrial Estate, North Street, Chorley, Lancashire, PR7 1QD Tel: (01257) 279364 Fax: (01257) 241352 E-mail: adweld@easynet.co.uk

Allis Welding Services, Unit 6 Bath Street, Newcastle upon Tyne, NE6 3PH Tel: 0191-295 0041 Fax: 0191-263 0614 E-mail: awswelding@ukonline.co.uk

Andrew Beattie & Co, 332 Chipstead Valley Road, Coulsdon, Surrey, CR5 3BE Tel: (01737) 557811

Andrew Beattie & Co., Ilkley House, Brighton Road, Tadworth, Surrey, KT20 6SU Tel: (0845) 3301373 Fax: (0845) 3301373

Arb Sales, 13 School Street, Hazel Grove, Stockport, Cheshire, SK7 4RA Tel: 0161-483 9661 Fax: 0161-483 6160 E-mail: sales.arb@ntlworld.com

Arc Welding Products Ltd, 5 Charlestown Industrial Estate, Robinson Street, Ashton-under-Lyne, Lancashire, OL6 8NS Tel: 0161-330 1671 Fax: 0161-330 1714

Arc Welding Services, 17 Sandy Lane, Aston, Birmingham, B6 5TP Tel: 0121-327 2249 Fax: 0121-327 4797 E-mail: service@arcweld.freeserve.co.uk

Arc Welding Supplies & Repairs, 6 Palmbourne Industrial Park, Castle Street, Stafford, ST16 2TB Tel: (01785) 281007 Fax: (01785) 240688

Arun Welding Supplies Ltd, Block B, Rudford Industrial Estate, Ford, Arundel, West Sussex, BN18 0BS Tel: (01903) 717606 Fax: (01903) 730214 E-mail: enquiry@arunwelding.com

WELDING SUPPLIES – *continued*

Bergas, 35 Keithleigh Gardens, Pitmedden, Ellon, Aberdeenshire, AB41 7GF Tel: (0771) 1205998 Fax: (01651) 842793 E-mail: bergas.scotland@talk21.com

Bohler Thyssen Welding (UK) Ltd, European Business Park, Taylors Lane, Oldbury, West Midlands, B69 2BN Tel: 0121-569 7700 Fax: 0121-544 2876 E-mail: info@btwuk.co.uk

Bryant Welding Supplies, PO Box 100, Southampton, SO40 9LA Tel: (023) 8086 7789 Fax: (023) 8066 3688 E-mail: sales@bryantwelding.co.uk

▶ Buck & Hickman Ltd, C2 Waterside Road, Hamilton, Leicester, LE5 1TL Tel: 0116-299 2990 Fax: 0116-299 3301 E-mail: leicester@buckhickmaninone.com

Central Fasteners (Staffs) Ltd, Airfield Trading Estate, Hixon, Stafford, ST18 0PY Tel: (01889) 270163 Fax: (01889) 271270 E-mail: centralfasteners@aol.com

Clwyd Welding Services Ltd, Clwyd Close, Hawarden Industrial Park, Hawarden, Deeside, Clwyd, CH5 3PZ Tel: (01244) 531667 Fax: (01244) 531842 E-mail: clwydweld@aol.com

Comainwells Ltd, Harfreys Road, Great Yarmouth, Norfolk, NR31 0LS Tel: (01493) 656444 Fax: (01493) 656444 E-mail: comwell@hotmail.co.uk

Cotswold Industrial & Welding Supplies, B Staverton Connection, Gloucester Road, Staverton, Cheltenham, Gloucestershire, GL51 0TF Tel: (01452) 855507 Fax: (01452) 859006

Crawley Welding Supplies Ltd, Royce Road, Crawley, West Sussex, RH10 9NX Tel: (01293) 529761 Fax: (01293) 545081 E-mail: crawleywelding@btclick.co.uk

D G Jackson Industrial Supplies Ltd, Dukeries Way, Worksop, Nottinghamshire, S81 7DW Tel: (01909) 474085 Fax: (01909) 477201

D & V Engineering, 17 Browning Avenue, Sutton, Surrey, SM1 3QU Tel: (020) 8642 5127 Fax: (020) 8770 1992

Deltawaite Ltd, Old Dairy, Roose Road, Barrow-in-Furness, Cumbria, LA13 0EP Tel: (01229) 821959 Fax: (01229) 820377 E-mail: sales@deltawaite.co.uk

E M S Euroweld Ltd, 203 Strathmartine Road, Dundee, DD3 8PH Tel: (01382) 858947 Fax: (01382) 832359

East Midland Welding Supply Co. Ltd, Baker Brook Industrial Estate, Wigwam Lane, Hucknall, Nottingham, NG15 7SZ Tel: 0115-964 2000 Fax: 0115-964 1651 E-mail: sales@eastmidwelding.freeserve.co.uk

Electraweld Ltd, Unit 1, Lowlands Bus Estate, Rochester, Kent, ME2 4AZ Tel: (01634) 291000 Fax: (01634) 291004 E-mail: dale@theweld.fsnet.co.uk

Electro Cal Ltd, 4 Bridge End Business Park, Park Road, Milnthorpe, Cumbria, LA7 7RH Tel: (01539) 564202 Fax: (01539) 564203 E-mail: sales@electro-cal.co.uk

Ellis (Faull), Kemys Way, Swansea Enterprise Park, Swansea, SA6 6QA Tel: (01792) 797722 Fax: (01792) 792974

Elmdale Welding & Engineering Supplies Ltd, 100b Lady Lane Industrial Estate, Hadleigh, Ipswich, IP7 6BQ Tel: (01473) 827722 Fax: (01473) 828080 E-mail: hadleighsales@btconnect.com

Elmdale Welding & Engineering Supplies Ltd, 25-27 Brook Road, Rayleigh, Essex, SS6 7XR Tel: (01268) 779011 Fax: (01268) 745192 E-mail: barry.cecil@elmdale.co.uk

Elmer Wallace Plansee, 30 Nasmyth Road South, Hillington Industrial Estate, Glasgow, G52 4RE Tel: 0141-810 5530 Fax: 0141-810 5539 E-mail: alex@elmerwallace.co.uk

Eltham Export Ltd, Crown House, Home Gardens, Dartford, DA1 1DZ Tel: (01322) 424600 Fax: (01322) 424601 E-mail: sales@elthamexport.com

Eltham Welding Supplies Ltd, 7 Mill Road, Portslade, Brighton, BN41 1PD Tel: (01273) 414381 Fax: (01273) 424603 E-mail: ews.sussex@dial.pipex.com

Eltham Welding Supplies Ltd, 2-12 Parry Place, London, SE18 6AN Tel: (020) 8854 1226 Fax: (020) 8854 2720 E-mail: sales.woolwich@elthamweldingsupplies.co.uk

Energas Ltd, Soho Street, Smethwick, West Midlands, B66 2RH Tel: 0121-555 5050 Fax: 0121-565 3830 E-mail: engweld@smethwick.fslife.co.uk

Esab Group UK Ltd, Hanover House Britannia Road, Queens Gate, Waltham Cross, Hertfordshire, EN8 7TF Tel: (01992) 768515 Fax: (01992) 715803 E-mail: info@esab.co.uk

Express Cutting & Welding Services Ltd, 245 Dawson Place, Walton Summit Centre, Bamber Bridge, Preston, PR5 8AL Tel: (01772) 334071 Fax: (01772) 628895 E-mail: sales@expressweld.co.uk

Express Welding Suppliers Ltd, Express House, Wilmington Commercial Park, Bedford St, Hull, HU8 8AR Tel: (01482) 223745 Fax: (01482) 210350 E-mail: paul.woodgate@brc.com

Express Welding Supplies Ltd, Unit B3 Empress Park, Empress Road, Southampton, SO14 0JX Tel: (023) 8022 8668 Fax: (023) 8063 9697

Joseph Firth, 10 Pepper Road, Leeds, LS10 2EU Tel: 0113-271 1148 Fax: 0113-270 3101 E-mail: sales@josephfirth.co.uk

Foster Industrial, Church Street, Lenton, Lenton, Nottingham, NG7 2FH Tel: 0115-970 0598 Fax: 0115-942 3388 E-mail: richard@fosterindustrial.co.uk

Fowlmere Engineering Ltd, Rectory Lane, Fowlmere, Royston, Hertfordshire, SG8 7TJ Tel: (01763) 208265 Fax: (01763) 208515

Future Industrial Welding Supplies, 21-23 Cotton Street, Aberdeen, AB11 5EG Tel: (01224) 212288 Fax: (01224) 212164

G M Equipment, 106 Morgans Hill Road, Cookstown, County Tyrone, BT80 8BW Tel: (028) 8676 3810 Fax: (028) 8675 8558

G T Central Welding & Gasses Supply Co., Hunters Lane, Rugby, Warwickshire, CV21 1EA Tel: (01788) 547212 Fax: (01788) 541589 E-mail: sales@gtcentralwelding.co.uk

Gaffney Gas Welding Supplies Ltd, 32-33 Brewsdale Road, Middlesbrough, Cleveland, TS3 6LJ Tel: (01642) 223466 Fax: (01642) 230224

Gauge & Welding Equipment Repairs Ltd, PO Box 48, Dartford, DA1 1YA Tel: (01322) 270036 Fax: (01322) 288625 E-mail: mail@gwer.co.uk

Genweld Supplies Ltd, 41 Unit 2, Wolverhampton, WV1 2RZ Tel: (01902) 351438 Fax: (01902) 351475 E-mail: sales@genweld.com

Grahams Machinery Sales Ltd, Deva House, Knutsford Way, Sealand Industrial Estate, Chester, CH1 4NX Tel: (01244) 376764 Fax: (01244) 377177 E-mail: sales@grahams-machinery.co.uk

H & J Howells, Ardenmore, Marros, Pendine, Carmarthen, Dyfed, SA33 4PN Tel: (01994) 453609 Fax: (01994) 453786

Heathcol Welding Supplies Ltd, 257a Dukesway, Team Valley Trading Estate, Gateshead, Tyne & Wear, NE11 0PZ Tel: 0191-487 2922 Fax: 0191-487 2924

House of Welding Ltd, 18 Wildwood Drive, Wildwood, Stafford, ST17 4PY Tel: (01785) 661890 Fax: (01785) 661890

Industrial & Welding Systems Ltd, Fallons Road, Wardley Industrial Estate, Worsley, Manchester, M28 2NY Tel: 0161-728 3366 Fax: 0161-728 5878 E-mail: paul.rushton@boc.com

J E Marchant, Theobalds Bungalow, Theobalds Green, Heathfield, East Sussex, TN21 8BU Tel: (07973) 430836 Fax: (01435) 865321

Jaymig Engineering, Unit 6 Redland Close, Aldermans Green Industrial Estate, Coventry, CV2 2NP Tel: (024) 7661 8630 Fax: (024) 7661 4412

Frank Langfield Ltd, Hollins Mill Lane, Sowerby Bridge, West Yorkshire, HX6 2RF Tel: (01422) 835388 Fax: (01422) 834452 E-mail: sales@langfieldwelding.com

Lindsey Welding Supply Co., Warwick Road, Fairfield Industrial Estate, Louth, Lincolnshire, LN11 0YB Tel: (01507) 604083 Fax: (01507) 604083 E-mail: sales@lindseyweldings.sagehost.co.uk

M I H Welding Supplies Ltd, Unit E Rio Works, Polesdon Lane, Ripley, Woking, Surrey, GU23 6JX Tel: (01483) 225409 Fax: (01483) 224242

M J P Ltd, 9 Alpha Business Park, Travellers Close, North Mymms, Hatfield, Hertfordshire, AL9 7NT Tel: (01707) 261179 Fax: (01707) 272470 E-mail: mike.player@virgin.net

M W A International Ltd, PO Box 17, Wednesbury, West Midlands, WS10 0AB Tel: 0121-556 6366 Fax: 0121-556 5566 E-mail: info@mwa-international.com

Meopham Welding Supplies, Railway Sidings, Station Approach, Meopham, Gravesend, Kent, DA13 0LT Tel: (01474) 812050 Fax: (01474) 813714

Mercury Welding Supplies, 6-7 Jubilee Estate, Horsham, West Sussex, RH13 5UE Tel: (01403) 260200 Fax: (01403) 217544 E-mail: sales@mercurywelding.com

Mersey Equipment Co. Ltd, Arcade Housed, 82-90 Taylor Street, Birkenhead, Merseyside, CH41 1BQ Tel: 0151-647 9751 Fax: 0151-647 3343 E-mail: admin@merseq.fssbusiness.co.uk

Metalpoint Ltd, Factory D, Western Approach, South Shields, Tyne & Wear, NE33 5NN Tel: 0191-455 6086 Fax: 0191-455 2447 E-mail: sales@arndale.co.uk

Midland Welding Supply Co. Ltd, Starley Way, Birmingham, B37 7HF Tel: 0121-782 1977 Fax: 0121-782 1921

Morse Welding Supplies Ltd, Watercombe Lane, Lynx West Trading Estate, Yeovil, Somerset, BA20 2SU Tel: (01935) 426390 Fax: (01935) 420451 E-mail: info@morsewelding.com

North Catering Equipment Ltd, Unit 12, St. Georges Road Industrial Estate, Donnington, Telford, Shropshire, TF2 7QZ Tel: (01952) 616655 Fax: (01952) 417799

Northants Welding Supplies Ltd, 8-9 Vaux Road, Finedon Road Industrial Estate, Wellingborough, Northamptonshire, NN8 4TG Tel: (01933) 224614 Fax: (01933) 441045

Parkins Industrial Supplies, Blundells Road, Tiverton, Devon, EX16 4DA Tel: (01884) 254444 Fax: (01884) 258142

▶ Philpott & Cowlin Ltd, Unit 12 Liberty Industrial Park, South Liberty Lane, Bristol, BS3 2SU Tel: 0117-966 8431 Fax: 0117-966 0129 E-mail: philpottcowlin@pcweldmetals.co.uk

Planet Welding Supplies Ltd, Unit 4 Artesian Close, London, NW10 8RW Tel: (020) 8451 5553 Fax: (020) 8451 1079 E-mail: info@planetwelding.fsnet.co.uk

Premier Welding Services (North) Ltd, 8 Atlas Way, Atlas North Industrial Estate, Sheffield, S4 7QQ Tel: 0114-243 0555 Fax: 0114-243 0777 E-mail: premierwelding@btconnect.com

▶ Rapid Weldings & Industrial Supplies Ltd, Unit 1 C, Hamilton Road, Portchester Park, Portsmouth, PO6 4QE Tel: (023) 9221 4214 Fax: (023) 9220 1505 E-mail: sales@rapidwelding.co.uk

Rightweld Welding Equipment, Unit 6 Ebbsfleet Industrial Estate, Northfleet, Gravesend, Kent, DA11 9DZ Tel: (01474) 320575 Fax: (01474) 536768

Sealey UK Ltd, Kempson Way, Bury St. Edmunds, Suffolk, IP32 7AR Tel: (01284) 757500 Fax: (01284) 703534 E-mail: sales@sealey.co.uk

Shipley Fabrications Ltd, Willoughby Road, Ancaster, Grantham, Lincolnshire, NG32 3RT Tel: (01400) 231115 Fax: (01400) 231220

Shropshire Welding Supplies Ltd, Unit A10, Stafford Park 15, Telford, Shropshire, TF3 3BB Tel: (01952) 290610 Fax: (01952) 211960 E-mail: swsltd@compuserve.com

Six Hills Welding Supplies Ltd, 7 Pate Road, Melton Mowbray, Leicestershire, LE13 0RG Tel: (01664) 480801 Fax: (01664) 481833

Specialized & General Welding, Unit 35 The Wallows Industrial Estate, Brierley Hill, West Midlands, DY5 1QA Tel: (01384) 480408 Fax: (01384) 480828

Spectrum Welding Supplies Ltd, Spectrum House, Chesterfield, Derbyshire, S40 2WB Tel: 01246 205267

Sphinx Welding Repair & Supplies, 37B Broad Street, Coventry, CV6 5AX Tel: (024) 7666 3365 Fax: (024) 7666 3365 E-mail: joefletch@tiscali.co.uk

Starmaker Welding Services, 16 Pembroke Avenue, Waterbeach, Cambridge, CB25 9QR Tel: (01223) 860662 Fax: (01223) 440009 E-mail: sales@starmake-rwelding.fsnet.co.uk

Steveweld Ltd, 3 Hillview Road, East Tullos Industrial Estate, Aberdeen, AB12 3HB Tel: (01224) 899944 Fax: (01224) 898998 E-mail: sales@steveweld.co.uk

Toolpak plc, Rhosddu Industrial Estate, Old Rhosrobin, Rhosrobin, Wrexham, Clwyd, LL11 4YL Tel: (01978) 291771 Fax: (01978) 290068 E-mail: sales@toolpak.co.uk

Total Welding Supplies Ltd, Unit 12-13, St. Johns Road, Kirkdale, Liverpool, L20 8PR Tel: 0151-933 7213 Fax: 0151-944 1177 E-mail: totalwelding@btconnect.com

Tower Welding Alloys Ltd, 5 Malham Road Industrial Estate, London, Greater London, SE23 1AH Tel: 020 82915533

United Welding Supplies Ltd, Unit 32, The Cam Centre, Wilbury Way, Hitchin, Hertfordshire, SG4 0TW Tel: (01462) 437991 Fax: (01462) 421274 E-mail: sales@unitedwelding.co.uk

Weld-AC Supplies Ltd, Unit 3 Arden Works, Fenton Road, Kings Cross, Halifax, West Yorkshire, HX1 3PP Tel: (01422) 346536 Fax: (01422) 364994 E-mail: sales@weldac.co.uk

Welding Alloys N W, Station Road, Sandycroft, Deeside, Clwyd, CH5 2PT Tel: (01244) 520588 Fax: (01244) 535635

Welding Engineering Services Ltd, Unit 2, Barking Industrial Park, Alfreds Way, Barking, Essex, IG11 0TJ Tel: (020) 8591 5777 Fax: (020) 8594 0622

Welding Repairs & Supplies Co. Ltd, Brandon Way, West Bromwich, West Midlands, B70 8JW Tel: 0121-553 6581 Fax: 0121-553 2953 E-mail: weldingrepair@aol.com

Welding Supplies UK Ltd, 7a Sketchley Meadows, Hinckley, Leicestershire, LE10 3EN Tel: (01543) 572544 Fax: (01543) 466156 E-mail: sales@weldingsupplies-uk.co.uk

Welding Tool Supplies, Cromer House, Caxton Way, Stevenage, Hertfordshire, SG1 2DF Tel: (01438) 726991 Fax: (01438) 350022

Weldmet Ltd, Unit 8, 55 Weir Road, Wimbledon, London, SW19 8UG Tel: (020) 8947 1244 Fax: (020) 8947 6080 E-mail: sales@weldmet.co.uk

Weldsafe, New Albion Estate, Yoker, Glasgow, G13 4DJ Tel: 0141-952 2200 Fax: 0141-941 3777 E-mail: weldsafeltd@btconnect.com

Weldspares-OKI Ltd, Unit 50 Melford Court, Hardwick Grange, Warrington, WA1 4RZ Tel: (01925) 813288 Fax: (01925) 817223 E-mail: sales@weldspares-oki.com

Weldspeed Ltd, Protea Way, Pixmore Avenue, Letchworth Garden City, Hertfordshire, SG6 1JT Tel: (01462) 481616 Fax: (01462) 482202 E-mail: sales@weldspeed.co.uk

Wellington Welding Supplies Ltd, Pottington Road, Barnstaple, Devon, EX31 1JH Tel: (01271) 325333 Fax: (01271) 325334

West Country Welding Supplies Ltd, 4 Ashmead Business Centre, Ashmead Road, Keynsham, Bristol, BS31 1SX Tel: 0117-986 6006 Fax: 0117-986 1892 E-mail: sales@westcoweld.co.uk

West Mercia Welding Services Ltd, Mercia House, Wednesfield Road, Willenhall, West Midlands, WV13 1AN Tel: (01902) 608620 Fax: (01902) 606905 E-mail: wmws@cwcom.net

J. Weston & Partners Ltd, Cudgamoor Farm, East Putford, Holsworthy, Devon, EX22 7XR Tel: (01237) 451838 Fax: (01237) 451553 E-mail: nigel.moulder@hotmail.co.uk

Wholesale Welding Supplies Ltd, 1 The Orbital Centre, Icknield Way, Letchworth Garden City, Hertfordshire, SG6 1ET Tel: (01462) 482200 Fax: (01462) 482202 E-mail: wws@wholeweld.co.uk

Wirs Ltd, Church Lane, Wolverhampton, WV2 4AL Tel: (01902) 712525 Fax: (01902) 429016 E-mail: sales@wirs.co.uk

World Welding Alloys Ltd, Unit 18 Shrivenham Hundred Business Park, Majors Road, Watchfield, Swindon, SN6 8TZ Tel: (01793) 783880 Fax: (01793) 782977 E-mail: info@welding.fsnet.co.uk

WELDING SUPPLIES IMPORT/ EXPORT MERCHANTS OR AGENTS

Eltham Export Ltd, Crown House, Home Gardens, Dartford, DA1 1DZ Tel: (01322) 424600 Fax: (01322) 424601 E-mail: sales@elthamexport.com

WELDING TEST SERVICES

Argos Inspection Co. Ltd, Tower Road, Washington, Tyne & Wear, NE37 2SH Tel: 0191-417 7707 Fax: 0191-415 4979 E-mail: ndt@argosinspection.com

P T S - Total Quality Management, Verulam Road, Stafford, ST16 3EA Tel: (01785) 250706 Fax: (01785) 250906

Tracey John Welding Ltd, Block 12, 5 Clydesmill Drive, Clydesmill Industrial Estate, Glasgow, G32 8RG Tel: 0141-641 7500 Fax: 0141-641 9738 E-mail: john@john-tracey-welding.co.uk

WELDING TO SPECIFICATION

Acorn Fabrications, Unit 4a, 179 Cardiff Road, Reading, RG1 8HD Tel: 0118-958 7466 Fax: 0118-958 7466 E-mail: dinoacornfabs@live.co.uk

Hussey & Greenhow Ltd, Unit 4 Hercules Way, Bowerhill, Melksham, Wiltshire, SN12 6TS Tel: (01225) 707888 Fax: (01225) 790523 E-mail: judy@husseygreenhow.co.uk

WELDING TRAINING

Code-A-Weld, 2nd Avenue, Westfield Trading Estate, Midsomer Norton, Radstock, BA3 4BE Tel: (01761) 410410 Fax: (01761) 418388 E-mail: info@codeaweld.com

Speciality Welds Ltd, Unit 18, Moorlands Business Centre, Cleckheaton, West Yorkshire, BD19 4EW Tel: (01274) 879867 Fax: (01274) 855975 E-mail: sales@specialwelds.com

Thermit Welding GB Ltd, 87 Ferry Lane, Rainham, Essex, RM13 9YH Tel: (01708) 522626 Fax: (01708) 553806

Tracey John Welding Ltd, Block 12, 5 Clydesmill Drive, Clydesmill Industrial Estate, Glasgow, G32 8RG Tel: 0141-641 7500 Fax: 0141-641 9738 E-mail: john@john-tracey-welding.co.uk

WELDING WIRES, *See also headings for particular types*

Corewire Ltd, Poplars Farm, Station Road West, Ash Vale, Aldershot, Hampshire, GU12 5QD Tel: (01252) 517766 Fax: (01252) 515833 E-mail: info@corewire.com

Special Metal Welding Products, Waterloo Road, Bidford-on-Avon, Alcester, Warwickshire, B50 4JN Tel: (01789) 491780 Fax: (01789) 491781 E-mail: sales.uk@iaiwpc.com

Welding Alloys Ltd, The Way, Fowlmere, Royston, Hertfordshire, SG8 7QS Tel: (01763) 207500 Fax: (01763) 207501 E-mail: sales@welding-alloys.com

WELDING WIRES, STAINLESS STEEL, MIG/TIG

Metrode Products Ltd, Hanworth Lane, Chertsey, Surrey, KT16 9LL Tel: (01932) 566721 Fax: (01932) 565168 E-mail: info@metrode.com

Premier Welding Services (North) Ltd, 8 Atlas Way, Atlas North Industrial Estate, Sheffield, S4 7QQ Tel: 0114-243 0555 Fax: 0114-243 0777 E-mail: premierwelding@btconnect.com

Westbrook Welding Alloy Ltd, 5 Melford Court, Hardwick Grange, Woolston, Warrington, WA1 4RZ Tel: (01925) 839983 Fax: (01925) 839990E-mail: sales@westbrookwelding.co.uk

WELDING, ELECTRIC, ARC, *See Welding, Arc, etc*

WELL CONTROL ENGINEERING

Norwell Oil & Gas Exploration, Norwell House, 78 Queens Road, Aberdeen, AB15 4YE Tel: (01224) 498400 Fax: (01224) 208300 E-mail: samantha@norwellengineering.com

WELL DRILLING DRILLING MUDS OR FLUIDS

International Drilling Services Ltd, Carrwood Road, Chesterfield, Derbyshire, S41 9QB Tel: (01246) 269911 Fax: (01246) 269922 E-mail: sales@idsuk.com

WELL LOGGING CONSULTANTS

Robertson Geologging Ltd, York Road, Deganwy, Conwy, Gwynedd, LL31 9PX Tel: (01492) 582323 Fax: (01492) 582322 E-mail: sales@geologging.com

WELL LOGGING EQUIPMENT

Energy Systems Ltd, Unit 5 Nevis Business Park, Balgownie Road, Aberdeen, AB22 8NT Tel: (01224) 822580 Fax: (01224) 707153 E-mail: sales@nangall.co.uk

Read Well Services Ltd, Viking House, 1 Claymore Avenue, Bridge of Don, Aberdeen, AB23 8GW Tel: (01224) 336600 Fax: (01224) 336611 E-mail: sales@readgroupuk.com

Schlumberger Evaluation & Production Services UK Ltd, Unit 46 Howe Moss Terrace, Kirkhill Industrial Estate, Dyce, Aberdeen, AB21 0GR Tel: (01224) 406000 Fax: (01224) 723257

Sondex Ltd, Ford Lane, Bramshill, Hook, Hampshire, RG27 0RH Tel: 0118-932 6755 Fax: 0118-932 6704 E-mail: sondex@sondex.com

Weatherford, Crawpeel Road, Altens Industrial Estate, Aberdeen, AB12 3LG Tel: (01224) 380280 Fax: (01224) 380088

WELL SERVICING CONTRACTORS

Expro North Sea Ltd, Unit B2, Kirkhill Place, Kirkhill Industrial Estate, Dyce, Aberdeen, AB21 0GU Tel: (01224) 214600 Fax: (01224) 770295 E-mail: marketing.enquiries@exprogroup.com

Weatherford, Crawpeel Road, Altens Industrial Estate, Aberdeen, AB12 3LG Tel: (01224) 380280 Fax: (01224) 380088

WELL STIMULATION

B J Services Co (U K) Ltd, Marine Base, Southtown Road, Great Yarmouth, Norfolk, NR31 0JJ Tel: (01493) 680680 Fax: (01493) 680780

WELLHEAD CONTROL SYSTEMS

Tyco, Jarrold Way, Bowthorpe Employment Area, Norwich, NR5 9JD Tel: (01603) 201201 Fax: (01603) 201333 E-mail: tycocontrolsystems.uk@tycoint.com

Vetco Grey, 2 High Street, Nailsea, Bristol, BS48 1BS Tel: (01275) 810100 Fax: (01275) 851467 E-mail: paul.roberts@vetco.com

WELLHEAD EQUIPMENT

Abb Vetco Gray UK Ltd, Gapton Hall Road, Great Yarmouth, Norfolk, NR31 0NL Tel: (01493) 444777 Fax: (01493) 414221 E-mail: shaun.bradley@vetco.com

WELSH TRANSLATION SERVICES

▶ Translation Agency TGV24, Crimond Croft, Whitehouse, Alford, Aberdeenshire, AB33 8DL Tel: (01577) 862702 E-mail: tgv24@e3internet.com

WENDY HOUSES

▶ Anchor Woodworking, 3 Mid Row, Croftouterly, Leslie, Glenrothes, Fife, KY6 3DR Tel: (01592) 748900 Fax: (01592) 748900 E-mail: info@anchorwoodworking.co.uk

▶ Burtenshaw Garden Buildings Ltd, c/o Notcutts Garden Centre, Tonbridge Road, Pembury, Tunbridge Wells, Kent, TN2 4QN Tel: (01892) 825338 E-mail: enquiries@burtenshawgardenbuildings.co.uk

▶ Shed Express, Roberts Yard, Off Crompton Road, Ilkeston, Derbyshire, DE7 4BG Tel: 0115-877 6696 Fax: 0115-930 8500 E-mail: terry@shedexpress.com

▶ Sheds & Chalets, Llanelli Enterprise Workshops, Lower Trostre Road, Llanelli, Dyfed, SA15 2EA Tel: (01554) 759472 Fax: (01554) 775022 E-mail: sales@shedsnchalets.co.uk

Summer Garden & Leisure Buildings, High Street, Horningsea, Cambridge, CB25 9JG Tel: (0800) 9777828 Fax: (01223) 441141 E-mail: enquiries@summergardenbuildings.co.uk

WET DUST SUPPRESSION SYSTEMS

Connectomatic Ltd, 31 Bretton Street, Dewsbury, West Yorkshire, WF12 9BJ Tel: (01924) 452444 Fax: (01924) 430607 E-mail: sales@connectomatic.co.uk

Quarry Plant & Roadsprays (Q P R), Ivy Mill, Longton Road, Stone, Staffordshire, ST15 8TB Tel: (01785) 812706 Fax: (01785) 811747 E-mail: nsirrigation@aol.com

WET MATEABLE CONNECTORS

Remote Marine Systems, Derwent Road, York Road Business Park, Malton, North Yorkshire, YO17 6YB Tel: (01653) 690001 Fax: (01653) 690002 E-mail: sales@rmsltd.com

WET SPRAY FINISHING

▶ Icom Spray Paint Systems, Penn Road, Hazlemere, High Wycombe, Buckinghamshire, HP15 7PB Tel: (01494) 812733 E-mail: mail@icomsps.freeserve.co.uk

WET/DRY VACUUM CLEANERS

Broadbent & Co. Ltd, Unit 14a Colwick Business Park, Private Road No 2, Colwick Industrial Estate, Nottingham, NG4 2JR Tel: 0115-940 0777 Fax: 0115-987 3744 E-mail: info@industrialcleaningequipment.co.uk

Starvac, 13 Thornhill Park Road, Bitterne, Southampton, SO18 5TP Tel: (023) 8036 6848 Fax: (023) 8036 7684 E-mail: sales@starmix.co.uk

WETLAND CONSULTANCY

▶ Tayreed Co., Airfield Industrial Estate, Errol, PH2 7TB Tel: (01821) 642466 Fax: (01821) 642827

WETSUITS

Diamond Wildwater, Northolt Drive, Bolton, BL3 6RE Tel: (01204) 528225 Fax: (01204) 361549 E-mail: diamondwild-water@mikar.co.uk

GUL International Ltd, Callywith Gate Industrial Estate, Bodmin, Cornwall, PL31 2RQ Tel: (01208) 262400 Fax: (01208) 262474 E-mail: gul@gul.com

Sola Wet Suits & Leisure Wear Ltd, Saltash Industrial Estate, Saltash, Cornwall, PL12 6LF Tel: (01752) 854418 Fax: (01752) 854401 E-mail: info@sola.co.uk

Tiki International (Plastics) Ltd, Velator Industrial Estate, Braunton, Devon, EX33 2DX Tel: (01271) 812442 Fax: (01271) 816570 E-mail: tiki@tikisurf.force9.co.uk

▶ The Wetsuit Factory, 24 Bay Tree Hill, Liskeard, Cornwall, PL14 4BG Tel: (01579) 343573 Fax: (01579) 342062 E-mail: sales@thewetsuitfactory.com

WHEEL BALANCING EQUIPMENT MANUFRS

Apaseal Ltd, Battle Road, Hailsham, East Sussex, BN27 1DX Tel: (01323) 842066 Fax: (01323) 440450 E-mail: sales@apaseal.co.uk

Haweka UK Ltd, Unit No 5 Beta, Orchard Industrial Estate, Toddington, Cheltenham, Gloucestershire, GL54 5EB Tel: (01242) 621001 Fax: (01242) 620558 E-mail: John.Pullin@haweka.co.uk

WHEEL BALANCING WEIGHTS

Airvert Ltd, Ghyll Road Industrial Estate, Ghyll Road, Heathfield, East Sussex, TN21 8AW Tel: (01435) 868292 Fax: (01435) 864838 E-mail: mthompson@airvert.co.uk

Apaseal Ltd, Battle Road, Hailsham, East Sussex, BN27 1DX Tel: (01323) 842066 Fax: (01323) 440450 E-mail: sales@apaseal.co.uk

Trax, Unit 1a Severn Farm Industrial Estate, Welshpool, Powys, SY21 7DF Tel: (01938) 554297 Fax: (01938) 554597 E-mail: sales@traxjh.com

U K Equipment Ltd, 48 Suttons Park Avenue, Reading, RG6 1AZ Tel: 0118-966 9121 Fax: 0118-966 4369

WHEEL CLAMPS

▶ Euro Seals & Gaskets Limited, PO BOX 1139, Luton, LU2 0WU Tel: (01582) 895459 Fax: (01582) 895469 E-mail: sales@eurosealsandgaskets.co.uk

WHEEL MAINTENANCE/REPAIR SPECIALIST SERVICES

Pristine Alloy Wheel Refurbishers Ltd, Newport Road, Woburn Sands, Milton Keynes, MK17 8UD Tel: (01908) 282628 Fax: (01908) 281093 E-mail: sales@pristinealloywheels.co.uk

WHEEL RIM ALIGNMENT SERVICES

▶ Steertrak Commercial Vehicle Servicing, Commercial House Station Road Business Park, Station Road, Tewkesbury, Gloucestershire, GL20 5DR Tel: (01684) 276900 Fax: (01684) 276500 E-mail: sales@steertrak.co.uk

WHEEL RIMS

Totrax Ltd, Rectory Farm, Mere Booth Road, Langrick, Boston, Lincolnshire, PE22 7AD Tel: (01205) 280578 Fax: (01205) 280520 E-mail: sales@totrax.co.uk

WHEEL SPOKES

V H M Systems Ltd, 80-86 Chapel Street, Thatcham, Berks, RG18 4QN Tel: (01635) 861707

WHEEL WASHING EQUIPMENT

▶ Hippowash, Poplar Grove, Crewe, CW1 4AZ Tel: 01270 252669 Fax: 01270 252670 E-mail: info@hippowash.com

Quarry Plant & Roadsprays (Q P R), Ivy Mill, Longton Road, Stone, Staffordshire, ST15 8TB Tel: (01785) 812706 Fax: (01785) 811747 E-mail: nsirrigation@aol.com

Wheelwash Ltd, Leslie Road, Woodford Park Industrial Estate, Winsford, Cheshire, CW7 2RB Tel: (01606) 592044 Fax: (01606) 592045 E-mail: sales@wheelwash.com

Wickham Auto Wash Ltd, Norton Road, Stevenage, Hertfordshire, SG1 2BB Tel: (01438) 314041 Fax: (01438) 740140 E-mail: all@wickham-autowash.co.uk

WHEELBARROWS, TRAILER/ TOWING

Central Spares Ltd, Units 3-7, Brook Road, Wimborne, Dorset, BH21 2BH Tel: (01202) 882000 Fax: (01202) 881783 E-mail: sales@the-trolley-shop.co.uk

WHEELCHAIR RAMPS

Portaramp, Roudham Road, Harling Road, Norwich, NR16 2QN Tel: (01953) 714599 Fax: (01842) 714598 E-mail: sales@portaramps.co.uk

Powerguards Ramping Systems, Bennetts Mead, Southgate Road, Wincanton, Somerset, BA9 9EB Tel: (01963) 31206 Fax: (01963) 31904 E-mail: powerguardsinc@beeb.net

WHEELCHAIRS, *See also Disabled/Handicapped Person etc*

Bromakin Wheelchairs, 12 Prince William Road, Loughborough, Leicestershire, LE11 5GU Tel: (01509) 217569 Fax: (01509) 233954 E-mail: sales@bromakin.co.uk

Lomax Mobility Ltd, Chalmers Building, Charles Bowman Avenue, Claverhouse Industrial Park, Dundee, DD4 9UB Tel: (01382) 503000 Fax: (01382) 503550 E-mail: sales@lomaxmobility.com

Sunrise Medical Ltd, Sunrise Business Park, High Street, Wollaston, Stourbridge, West Midlands, DY8 4PS Tel: (01384) 446688 Fax: (01384) 446699 E-mail: sunmail@sunmed.co.uk

WHEELED LOADERS

R Savage Plant Hire Co. Ltd, 222 St Margarets Road, Ward End, Birmingham, B8 2BG Tel: 0121-328 1100 Fax: 0121-327 3548 E-mail: enquiries@savageplanthire.co.uk

WHEELS, *See also headings for particular types*

Cardiff Castor Co. Ltd, The Handling Centre, Penarth Road, Cardiff, CF11 8TW Tel: (029) 2071 1171 Fax: (029) 2070 6464 E-mail: sandadirect@ukonline.co.uk

CMS Industries, Downsview Road, Wantage, Oxfordshire, OX12 9FF Tel: (01235) 773370 Fax: (01235) 773371 E-mail: sales@cmsindustries.com

K Toys, Second Avenue, Westfield Industrial Estate, Midsomer Norton, Radstock, BA3 4BH Tel: (01761) 411299 Fax: (01761) 411522 E-mail: mail@ktoys.co.uk

Kings Cross Truck, 41 Leighlands, Crawley, West Sussex, RH10 3DN Tel: (01293) 873767 Fax: (01293) 873767 E-mail: sales@kingscrosstruck.co.uk

Magnetto Topy Wheels UK Ltd, Holbrook Lane, Coventry, CV6 4QZ Tel: (024) 7666 7738 Fax: (024) 7666 7401

North Hants Tyre & Remoulding, 2 Christy Estate, Ivy Road, Aldershot, Hampshire, GU12 4TX Tel: (01252) 318666 Fax: (01252) 318777 E-mail: sales@northhantstyres.com

P & L Industrial Equipment Ltd, Lind Street, Manchester, M40 7ES Tel: 0161-273 2626 Fax: 0161-274 3633 E-mail: sales@plcastors.co.uk

Transmission & Engineering Services, Unit 17 Springfield Road, Grantham, Lincolnshire, NG31 7BL Tel: (01476) 591500 Fax: (01476) 590336

H. Varley Ltd, Unit 82, The Wenta Business Centre, Colne Way, Watford, WD24 7ND Tel: (01923) 249334 Fax: (01923) 245513 E-mail: sales@varley.co.uk

▶ The Wheel Surgery, 67, Nutfield Road, Merstham, Redhill, RH1 3ER Tel: (01737) 644123 Fax: (01737) 644123

WHEELS, CYCLE

▶ Ride Low Ltd, 27-29 Church Street, Manchester, M4 1PE Tel: 0161-834 5788 E-mail: george@ridelow.co.uk

WHISKY

▶ Dillon's Ltd, Hardres Court, Canterbury, Kent, CT4 6EN Tel: (01227) 700236 E-mail: info@dillonsspirits.com

WHITE METAL BEARINGS

▶ Coleherne Laser, Newton Moor Industrial Estate, Lodge Street, Hyde, Cheshire, SK14 4LE Tel: 0161-366 6603 Fax: 0161-367 8239 E-mail: brian@coleherneuk.com

L V W Auto Motive Components Ltd, 118 Cleveland Street, Birkenhead, Merseyside, CH41 3QP Tel: 0151-666 2000 Fax: 0151-647 7220 E-mail: precision@senareng.demon.co.uk

Michell Bearings, Scotswood Road, Newcastle upon Tyne, NE15 6LL Tel: 0191-273 0291 Fax: 0191-272 2787 E-mail: sales@michellbearings.com

Osborne Engineering, Unit 19 Atley Way, North Nelson Industrial Estate, Cramlington, Northumberland, NE23 1WA Tel: (01670) 737077 Fax: (01670) 736127 E-mail: info@osborne-engineering.com

WHITE OIL, *See also headings for particular types*

▶ Magenta Chemicals, Golf Course Road, Southampton, SO16 7LE Tel: (023) 8076 8842 Fax: (023) 8076 6460 E-mail: magentachemicals@btclick.com

WHITENERS AND BRIGHTENERS

Ciba Specialty Chemicals P.L.C., Ashton New Road, Clayton, Manchester, M11 4AP Tel: 0161-223 1391 Fax: 0161-223 4315

WHOLESALE DISTRIBUTION INDUSTRY SOFTWARE

Acc-Sys Software Ltd, 11-13 Philip Road, Ipswich, IP2 8BH Tel: (01473) 400161 Fax: (01473) 400163 E-mail: enquiries@accsys.uk

The Clearance Store Ltd, 74 Oakfield Road, London, E17 5RP Tel: (0800) 7312689 Fax: (020) 8503 2600

G B D Ltd, 9 Geilston Park, Cardross, Dumbarton, G82 5ND Tel: (01389) 842021 Fax: (01389) 841751

International Business Systems Ltd, IBS House, Elstree Way, Borehamwood, Hertfordshire, WD6 1FE Tel: (020) 8207 5655 Fax: (020) 8207 6770 E-mail: marketing@ibsuk.com

P W S Ltd, 132 Fairway, Keyworth, Nottingham, NG12 5DL Tel: 0115-937 4723 Fax: 0115-937 6842

Prime Computer Systems Ltd, 2 Medlar Close, Bredgar, Sittingbourne, Kent, ME9 8EL Tel: (01622) 884641 Fax: (01622) 884322

Quantum Peripheral Products Ltd, Quantum House 3 Bracknell Beeches, Old Bracknell La West, Bracknell, Berkshire, RG12 7BW Tel: (01344) 353500 Fax: (01344) 353510

WHOLESALE IRONMONGERY

A & A Metalcraft, 169 Whittingham Lane, Goosnargh, Preston, PR3 2JJ Tel: (01772) 866133 Fax: (01772) 864656

A Pollard & Sons Ltd, 51 Aylesbury St, Bletchley, Milton Keynes, MK2 2BQ Tel: (01908) 375221 Fax: (01908) 271552 E-mail: sales@pollards.co.uk

Abbey Architectural Ironmongery Co Ltd, Unit 12 Linguard Business Park, Wood Street, Rochdale, Lancashire, OL16 5QN Tel: (01706) 644880 Fax: (01706) 711122 E-mail: sales@abbeyarchitectural.co.uk

Adams Ironmongers Sutton Coldfield Ltd, 112 Holland Road, Sutton Coldfield, West Midlands, B72 1RE Tel: 0121-354 4822 Fax: 0121-355 6968 E-mail: sales@adamsindustrial.co.uk

All Bees Ltd, A B L House, Bashley Road, London, NW10 6SL Tel: (020) 8961 4321 Fax: (020) 8961 1597

Bell Donaldson Steele, 17 Westfield Street, Edinburgh, EH11 2QQ Tel: 0131-337 6303 Fax: 0131-313 5328 E-mail: sales@belldonaldsonsteele.fsnet.co.uk

Robert Bernard & Son Ltd, 26 Oxton Road, Birkenhead, Merseyside, CH41 2QJ Tel: 0151-652 3136 Fax: 0151-652 7552 E-mail: sales@bernards.co.uk

Brookers Builders Merchants Ltd, 43-53 Norman Road, St. Leonards-on-Sea, East Sussex, TN38 0EQ Tel: (01424) 423107 Fax: (01424) 718341

Calder Trade Supplies Ltd, Unit 11-12 Halifax Industrial Centre, Marshway, Halifax, West Yorkshire, HX1 5RW Tel: (01422) 330008 Fax: (01422) 349437 E-mail: sales@caldertrade.co.uk

Cooper Kitchen, 48 Southgate, Elland, West Yorkshire, HX5 0DQ Tel: (01422) 372577 Fax: (01422) 372577

Coopers Great Yarmouth Ltd, New Road, Fritton, Great Yarmouth, Norfolk, NR31 9HR Tel: (01493) 602204 Fax: (01493) 655620 E-mail: enquiries@supercoopers.co.uk

Cusden's, 104 Arlington Road, London, NW1 7HP Tel: (020) 7424 0349 Fax: (020) 7324 0352 E-mail: cusdens@aol.com

Daniel Lewis & Son Ltd, 493-495 Hackney Road, London, E2 9ED Tel: (020) 7739 8881 Fax: (020) 7739 2136 E-mail: daniellewis@ad.com

Driffield Hardware Centre, Cranwell Road, Driffield, North Humberside, YO25 6UH Tel: (01377) 241399 Fax: (01377) 241252

Evans Bros, 6 High Street, Menai Bridge, Gwynedd, LL59 5ED Tel: (01248) 712388 Fax: (01248) 712388

George Boyd & Graham Ltd, Bothwell St, Easter Road, Edinburgh, EH7 5SQ Tel: 0131-661 6144 Fax: 0131-661 2887

I R Laidlaw, The Building Centre, 26 Store Street, London, WC1E 7BT Tel: (020) 7436 0779 Fax: (020) 7436 0740 E-mail: infolondon@laidlaw.net

Interhire Power Tool Services Ltd, Park Road, Ilkeston, Derbyshire, DE7 5DA Tel: 0115-930 6382 Fax: 0115-944 0407

J Headridge & Co., 1 Shearer Street, Glasgow, G5 8TA Tel: 0141-429 8911 Fax: 0141-420 1602

Jewson Ltd, Orchard Road, Royston, Hertfordshire, SG8 5HA Tel: (01763) 241561 Fax: (01763) 247759

K C C, 20-21A Harbour Court, Heron Road, Sydenham Business Park, Belfast, BT3 9LE Tel: (028) 9046 9914 Fax: (028) 9046 9915 E-mail: sales@kcchardware.com

Laidlaw Architectural Hardware, 7 Dakota Avenue, Salford, M50 2PU Tel: 0161-848 1700 Fax: 0161-872 9313 E-mail: info@laidlaw.net

Laidlaw Solutions Ltd, T Y Cefnfar, Ocean Way, Cardiff, CF24 5PE Tel: (029) 2047 1808 Fax: (029) 2049 0250

Laidlaw Solutions Ltd, PO Box 15, Perth, PH1 3DU Tel: (01738) 620581 Fax: (01738) 633262

Lugg Facilities Ltd, 99-107 Hill Top, West Bromwich, West Midlands, B70 0RY Tel: 0121-556 1551 Fax: 0121-556 1552 E-mail: sales@lugg-tools.co.uk

M W Partridge & Co. Ltd, 60 High Street, Hadleigh, Ipswich, IP7 5EE Tel: (01473) 822333 Fax: (01473) 828009 E-mail: sales@partridgemw.co.uk

Malletts Home Hardware, 6-7 Victoria Square, Truro, Cornwall, TR1 2RT Tel: (01872) 274441 Fax: (01872) 240664 E-mail: sales@mallettshomehardware.co.uk

Mercer & Sons Ltd, Pump Street Warehouses, Blackburn, BB2 1PG Tel: (01254) 587000 Fax: (01254) 680875 E-mail: info@mercer-sons.co.uk

Merton Timber Ltd, 65-71 Grove Vale, London, SE22 8EQ Tel: (020) 8299 4131 Fax: (020) 8693 4136 E-mail: sales@mertontimber.co.uk

Merton Timber, 28 Goat Road, Mitcham, Surrey, CR4 4HU Tel: (020) 8687 0055 Fax: (020) 8648 5663 E-mail: sales@merton-timber.co.uk

Merton Timber, Central House, Murray Road, Orpington, Kent, BR5 3QY Tel: (01689) 890044 Fax: (01689) 890066 E-mail: sales@merton-timber.co.uk

Midland Fixing Services Ltd, Unit 20 Bordesley Trading Estate, Bordesley Green Road, Birmingham, B8 1BZ Tel: 0121-327 5713 Fax: 0121-328 1842

O & D Williams, 8 Larkhill Lane, Clubmoor, Liverpool, L13 9BR Tel: 0151-226 5654 Fax: 0151-270 2549

Price & Oliver Ltd, 254 Lozells Road, Birmingham, B19 1NR Tel: 0121-554 8491 Fax: 0121-554 8989

R E Thorns & Co., 22 Exchange Street, Norwich, NR2 1AT Tel: (01603) 622891 Fax: (01603) 622952 E-mail: mail@thornsdiy.com

R H Bruce Co Ltd, 4 The Idas, Pontefract Road, Leeds, LS10 1SP Tel: 0113-271 5533 Fax: 0113-271 8833

T.F. Sampson Ltd, Creeting Road, Stowmarket, Suffolk, IP14 5BA Tel: (01449) 613535 Fax: (01449) 678381 E-mail: sales@t-f-sampson.co.uk

James Sime & Co. Ltd, 29 Cow Wynd, Falkirk, FK1 1PT Tel: (01324) 622592 Fax: (01324) 612522

George Spence & Sons Ltd, 105 Wellington Road, Leeds, LS12 1DX Tel: 0113-279 0507 Fax: 0113-263 6817 E-mail: sales@geospence.co.uk

Spiller & Webber Ltd, Viney Court, Victoria Street, Taunton, Somerset, TA1 3JA Tel: (01823) 337333 Fax: (01823) 321364

T D Ladd & Son, Belle Vue, Clynderwen, Dyfed, SA66 7NQ Tel: (01437) 563217 Fax: (01437) 563217

Towy Works Ltd, The Quay, Carmarthen, Dyfed, SA31 3JR Tel: (01267) 236601 Fax: (01267) 238189

Travis Perkins plc, Livsey Street, Rochdale, Lancashire, OL16 1SS Tel: (01706) 657325 Fax: (01706) 648026 E-mail: rochdale@travisperkins.co.uk

Watt & Dewar, 62-68 New Row, Dunfermline, Fife, KY12 7EF Tel: (01383) 724146 Fax: (01383) 622966

Westward Building Services Ltd, Burraton Road, Saltash, Cornwall, PL12 6LU Tel: (01752) 844600 Fax: (01752) 854254 E-mail: sales@westwoodbuildingservices.com

Wolseley (U K) Ltd, Overton Road, Kirkcaldy, Fife, KY1 2DU Tel: (01592) 653555 Fax: (01592) 650228 E-mail: kirkcaldytsb@woolsely.co.uk

Woodcraft Industries & DIY, 191 London Road, Glasgow, G40 1PA Tel: 0141-552 1437 Fax: 0141-552 1437

WIDE AREA NETWORK (WAN) SYSTEM INSTALLATION

Adax Europe Ltd, Reada Court, Vachel Road, Reading, RG1 1NY Tel: 0118-952 2800 Fax: 0118-957 1530 E-mail: info@adax.co.uk

Adder Technology Ltd, Technology House, Trafalgar Way, Bar Hill, Cambridge, CB3 8SQ Tel: (01954) 780044 Fax: (01954) 780081 E-mail: sales@addertec.com

CNS Computer Networks Ltd, Transport Hall, Gloucester Road, Avonmouth, Bristol, BS11 9AQ Tel: (0870) 7771650 Fax: (0870) 7771655 E-mail: sales@c-n-s.co.uk

Comp-Connection, 4 Park Grove, Belhelvie, Belhelvie, Aberdeen, AB23 8YG Tel: (07713) 508201 Fax: (01358) 743666 E-mail: sales@comp-connection.co.uk

Dacoll Ltd, Gardners Lane, Bathgate, West Lothian, EH48 1TP Tel: (01506) 815000 Fax: (01506) 656012 E-mail: sales@dacoll.co.uk

Discovery Computer Services Ltd, Burnham Business Park, Springfield Road, Burnham-on-Crouch, Essex, CM0 8TE Tel: (01621) 786860 Fax: (01621) 786861 E-mail: info@buy-it-back.com

Doncaster Computer Exchange, 250 Great North Road, Woodlands, Doncaster, South Yorkshire, DN6 7HP Tel: (01302) 728737 Fax: (01302) 725129 E-mail: dceexchange@aol.com

Itech Quality Business Solutions Ltd, Lion Court Storten Harolrd, Whitick Business Park, Stenson Road, Coalville, Leicestershire, LE65 1RT Tel: (0870) 2249295 Fax: (0870) 8519295 E-mail: info@itechqbs.co.uk

J T S Datacom Ltd, 2 Crossfields Close, Shinfield, Reading, RG2 9AY Tel: (0845) 6443193 Fax: (0845) 6448195 E-mail: info@jtsdata.com

Metrodata Ltd, Blenheim House Crabtree Office Village, Eversley Way, Egham, Surrey, TW20 8RY Tel: (01784) 744700 Fax: (01784) 477423 E-mail: sales@metrodata.co.uk

Nectar, Artemis Court, St. Johns Road, Meadowfield Industrial Estate, Durham, DH7 8TZ Tel: 0191-378 1946 Fax: 0191-378 1469 E-mail: sales@nectar.uk.com

S M T Network Solutions Ltd, 20 Park Street, Princes Risborough, Buckinghamshire, HP27 9AH Tel: (01844) 275100 Fax: (01844) 275111 E-mail: info@smtnet.co.uk

Silicon City Distribution, 50 Temple Avenue, London, N20 9EH Tel: (020) 8445 5251 Fax: (0870) 7052314E-mail: sales@silcity.com

Supportive Ltd, Old Studios, Hyde Park Road, Leeds, LS6 1RU Tel: 0113-245 7302 Fax: 0113-245 7304 E-mail: post@supportive.co.uk

WIDE FORMAT DIGITAL PRINTERS

Allprint Ltd, Llantrisant Business Park, Llantrisant, Pontyclun, Mid Glamorgan, CF72 8LF Tel: (01443) 228555 Fax: (01443) 237477 E-mail: sales@allprint2000.com

C D T Signs, 9 Woodlands Road, Cirencester, Gloucestershire, GL7 1SP Tel: (01285) 640680 Fax: (01285) 652346

City Digital East Midlands Ltd, Samson House, Samson Road, Coalville, Leicestershire, LE67 3FP Tel: (01530) 815581 Fax: (01530) 815262

▶ Creative Place Ltd, 4 Millfield House, Woodshots Meadow, Watford, WD18 8SS Tel: (01923) 227272 Fax: (01923) 246556 E-mail: sales@thecreativeplace.co.uk

▶ D P I Ltd, Printing House, Church Lane, Norton, Worcester, WR5 2PS Tel: (0845) 0700750 Fax: (0845) 0700751 E-mail: dclover@dpi4xerox.co.uk

▶ Impress Repro By Design, 2 A1 Parkway, Southgate Way, Orton Southgate, Peterborough, PE2 6YN Tel: (01733) 397350 Fax: (01733) 397351

▶ Links Screens Ltd, 36 Parker Road, Hastings, East Sussex, TN34 3TT Tel: (01424) 729444 Fax: (01424) 729555 E-mail: info@linksscreens.co.uk

▶ PhotoBloc, Leorific House, Binley Road, Coventry, CV3 1JN Tel: (024) 7667 1076 E-mail: submit@photobloc.com

Showprint Photographics Ltd, 29 High Street, Hampton Wick, Kingston Upon Thames, Surrey, KT1 4DA Tel: (020) 8943 9572 Fax: (020) 8943 5372

Spectrum Signs, 22 Bladon Road, Southampton, SO16 6QD Tel: (023) 8077 2264 Fax: (023) 8032 2264 E-mail: sales@spectrum-signs.co.uk

Tracks Cad Systems Ltd, London Road, Wokingham, Berkshire, RG40 1PD Tel: (01344) 455046 Fax: (01344) 860547 E-mail: sales@trackscad.co.uk

WILD BIRD SEED

Harris Tobias Ltd, 3 Station Road, Stansted, Essex, CM24 8BE Tel: (01279) 647164 Fax: (01279) 647038 E-mail: info@harristobias.com

WILDLIFE PHOTOGRAPHERS

▶ Inspired Photography Ltd, 27 Kirkdale Mount, Leeds, LS12 6AZ Tel: 0113 2109653 E-mail: timlawton1981@yahoo.co.uk

WILL LEGAL SERVICES

Classic Legal Services Ltd, Suite 3a & 3b, Britannia House, Cowbridge, South Glamorgan, CF71 7EG Tel: (0800) 389 4137 Fax: (01446) 774000 E-mail: alun@weeks4444.fslife.co.uk

▶ Colin Tyzack / National Legal Services, 14 Cleveland Road, Aylesbury, Buckinghamshire, HP20 2 AZ Tel: (01296) 581300 E-mail: colin@colin-tyzack.co.uk

▶ Elite Estate Planning, West Midlands House, Gipsy Lane, Willenhall, West Midlands, WV13 2HA Tel: (0800) 4589188 E-mail: jon@eliteestateplanning.co.uk

▶ GWG Legal Services Ltd, 12 Ainley Close Birchencliffe, Huddersfield, HD3 3RJ Tel: (01422) 440058 E-mail: info@gwgls.co.uk

▶ Lee Associates, Denmark House, 3b High Street, Willingham, Cambridge, CB24 5ES Tel: (01954) 262120 Fax: (01954) 262129 E-mail: info@willwriting-services.co.uk

▶ Randle Thomas, 2 Wendron St, Helston, Cornwall, TR13 8PP Tel: (01326) 572951 Fax: 01326 563122 E-mail: rt@randlethomas.co.uk

▶ Webster Richard & Co., 30 Leigh Road, Eastleigh, Hampshire, SO50 9DT Tel: (023) 8032 2312 Fax: (023) 8061 1698 E-mail: mail@rwco.co.uk

▶ Whiteford Crocker Ltd, Park House, 28 Outland Road, Plymouth, PL2 3DE Tel: (01752) 550711 Fax: (01752) 560029 E-mail: mail@whitefordcrocker.com

WILL WRITING

▶ Elite Estate Planning, West Midlands House, Gipsy Lane, Willenhall, West Midlands, WV13 2HA Tel: (0800) 4589188 E-mail: jon@eliteestateplanning.co.uk

▶ Emenex (Financial) Ltd, Fen Drayton House, Park Lane, Fen Drayton, Cambridge, CB4 5SW Tel: (01954) 232078 E-mail: julianredman@emenex.com

▶ Grant Saw, Norman House, 110-114 Norman Road, London, SE10 9EH Tel: (020) 8858 6971 Fax: (020) 8858 5796 E-mail: enquiries@grantsaw.co.uk

▶ GWG Legal Services Ltd, 12 Ainley Close Birchencliffe, Huddersfield, HD3 3RJ Tel: (01422) 440058 E-mail: info@gwgls.co.uk

▶ Heritage Law, Wellfield House, Springfield Road, Woolacombe, Devon, EX34 7BX Tel: (01271) 870506 E-mail: kevinderham@btopenworld.com

▶ Lee Associates, Denmark House, 3b High Street, Willingham, Cambridge, CB24 5ES Tel: (01954) 262120 Fax: (01954) 262129 E-mail: info@willwriting-services.co.uk

▶ Lee Associates, Denmark House, 3b High Street, Willingham, Cambridge, CB24 5ES Tel: (01954) 262120 Fax: (01954) 262129 E-mail: info@lee-associates.co.uk

▶ Webster Richard & Co., 30 Leigh Road, Eastleigh, Hampshire, SO50 9DT Tel: (023) 8032 2312 Fax: (023) 8061 1698 E-mail: mail@rwco.co.uk

▶ Whiteford Crocker Ltd, Park House, 28 Outland Road, Plymouth, PL2 3DE Tel: (01752) 550711 Fax: (01752) 560029 E-mail: mail@whitefordcrocker.com

WILLOW

R.R. Hector, 18 Windmill Hill, North Curry, Taunton, Somerset, TA3 6NA Tel: (01823) 490236

WILTON CARPETS

Avena Carpets Ltd, Bankfield Mills, Haley Hill, Halifax, West Yorkshire, HX3 6ED Tel: (01422) 330261 Fax: (01422) 348399 E-mail: avena@btconnect.com

Brintons Carpets (U S A) Ltd, PO Box 16, Kidderminster, Worcestershire, DY10 1AG Tel: (01562) 820000 Fax: (01562) 634540 E-mail: solutions@brintons.co.uk

WINCHES

Aquamarine, 216 Fair Oak Road, Eastleigh, Hampshire, SO50 8HU Tel: (023) 8060 0473 Fax: (023) 8060 1381 E-mail: admin@aqua-marine.co.uk

Fisher Offshore, North Meadows, Oldmeldrum, Inverurie, Aberdeenshire, AB51 0GQ Tel: (01651) 873932 Fax: (01651) 873939 E-mail: info@fisheroffshore.com

▶ Goodwinch Lifting Equipment, Eastfoldhay, Zeal Monachorum, Crediton, Devon, EX17 6DH Tel: (01363) 82666 Fax: (01363) 82782 E-mail: sales@davidbowyer.com

Koppen & Lethem Ltd, 6 Glenholm Park, Brunel Drive, Newark, Nottinghamshire, NG24 2EG Tel: (01636) 676794 Fax: (01636) 671055 E-mail: sales@koppen-lethem.co.uk

Manitowoc Potain Ltd, Unit 2c Tomo Industrial Estate, Packet Boat Lane, Uxbridge, Middlesex, UB8 2JP Tel: (01895) 430053 Fax: (01895) 459500

Rotrex Winches, Gryphon Works, Wimsey Way, Alfreton Trading Estate, Alfreton, Derbyshire, DE55 4LS Tel: (01773) 603997 Fax: (01773) 540566 E-mail: sales@rotrexwinches.co.uk

Slingtak Hoists Ltd, Quarry Road, Westgate, Cleckheaton, West Yorkshire, BD19 5HP Tel: (01274) 851724 Fax: (01274) 851724 E-mail: info@slingtak.co.uk

Speed Engineering, Station Yard, Broome, Aston-on-Clun, Craven Arms, Shropshire, SY7 0NT Tel: (01588) 660427 Fax: (01588) 660771

Superwinch Ltd, Union Mine Road, Pitts Cleave, Tavistock, Devon, PL19 0PW Tel: (01822) 614101 Fax: (01822) 615204 E-mail: sales@superwinch.net

WINCHES, RIGGING

▶ Chaos Lighting, 36 Hollicondane Road, Ramsgate, Kent, CT11 7PH Tel: 01843 596997 Fax: 01843 596997 E-mail: russell@chaoslighting.co.uk

WIND DRIVEN GENERATORS

Ampair, Park Farm, West End Lane, Warfield, Bracknell, Berkshire, RG42 5RH Tel: (01344) 303311 Fax: (01344) 303312 E-mail: sales@ampair.com

▶ Bright Green Energy, 26 Woodmere Way, Beckenham, Kent, BR3 6SL Tel: (020) 8663 3273 Fax: (020) 8650 9037 E-mail: sales@brightgreenenergy.co.uk

Secure Power Systems Ltd, 2A Watermoor Road, Cirencester, Gloucestershire, GL7 1JW Tel: (01285) 651768 Fax: (01285) 657053 E-mail: wknight756@aol.com

Solar Energy Alliance, 8 Battery Green Road, Lowestoft, Suffolk, NR32 1DE Tel: (01502) 515532 Fax: (01502) 589159 E-mail: info@solarenergyalliance.com

WIND ENERGY CONSULTANCY

▶ RH2 Renewable Energy, 2nd Floor, 145-157 St. John Street, LONDON, EC1V 4PY Tel: 0870 446 7424 E-mail: info@rh-2.co.uk

▶ West Coast Energy Ltd, 18d Liberton Brae, Edinburgh, EH16 6AE Tel: 0131-672 1888 Fax: 0131-672 1999 E-mail: mail@westcoastenergy.co.uk

WIND MUSICAL INSTRUMENTS

Generation Music Ltd, Grays Inn House, Unit 14 Mile Oak Industrial Estate, Oswestry, Shropshire, SY10 8GA Tel: (01691) 653970 Fax: (01691) 679403 E-mail: sales@generationmusic.co.uk

Gillanders & McLeod Ltd, 25 Brougham Place, Edinburgh, EH3 9JU Tel: 0131-228 5535 Fax: 0131-228 2775 E-mail: mail@gandmbagpipes.co.uk

T W Howarth & Co. Ltd, 31-35 Chiltern Street, London, W1U 7PN Tel: (020) 7935 2407 Fax: (020) 7224 2564 E-mail: sales@howarth.uk.com

WIND POWERED ELECTRICITY SUPPLY SYSTEMS MANUFRS

Proven Engineering Products Ltd, Wardhead Park, Stewarton, Kilmarnock, Ayrshire, KA3 5LH Tel: (01560) 485570
E-mail: info@provenenergy.com
Solar Energy Alliance, 8 Battery Green Road, Lowestoft, Suffolk, NR32 1DE Tel: (01502) 515532 Fax: (01502) 589159
E-mail: info@solarenergyalliance.com

WIND TUNNEL EQUIPMENT

Aerotech A T E Ltd, Crown Technical Centre, Burwash Road, Heathfield, East Sussex, TN21 8QZ Tel: (01435) 865245 Fax: (01435) 865588
C & B Consultants Ltd, 194 Stanley Green Road, Poole, Dorset, BH15 3AH Tel: (01202) 673666 Fax: (01202) 671776
E-mail: candbaero@candbconsultants.com
Northwest Aero Dynamic Models Ltd, 206 Longhurst Lane, Mellor, Stockport, Cheshire, SK6 5PN Tel: 0161-427 8474 Fax: 0161-427 7027

WIND TUNNEL TESTING FACILITIES/SERVICES

Enstec Services, 141 Queen Ediths Way, Cambridge, CB1 8PT Tel: (01223) 566471 Fax: (01223) 413800
E-mail: ss_ens@netcomuk.co.uk

WIND TURBINES

▶ Ampliflaire Ltd, Off The Square Trade Centre, Bowmont Street, Kelso, Roxburghshire, TD5 7JH Tel: (01573) 225209 Fax: (01573) 225886
▶ Renewable Devices Energy Solutions, Bush Estate, Penicuik, Midlothian, EH26 0PH Tel: 0131-535 3403 Fax: 0131-535 3303
E-mail: info@renewabledevices.com

WINDING MACHINE FILAMENTS

Pultrex Ltd, Century House, North Station Road, Colchester, CO1 1PD Tel: (01206) 369555 Fax: (01206) 576554
E-mail: sales@pultrex.com

WINDING MACHINES

C M Machinery, 50 Seagoe Industrial Area, Portadown, Craigavon, County Armagh, BT63 5QE Tel: (028) 3833 3341 Fax: (028) 3833 0915 E-mail: info@cmmachinery.co.uk

WINDING WIRE

Essex Nexans UK Ltd, Ellis Ashton Street, Liverpool, L36 6BW Tel: 0151-443 6000 Fax: 0151-443 6025
E-mail: sales@essexgroup.co.uk

WINDMILL DRIVEN PUMPS

Abachem Engineering Ltd, Jessop Way, Newark, Nottinghamshire, NG24 2ER Tel: (01636) 676483 Fax: (01636) 708632

WINDOW CLEANING CLOTHS

▶ Clearview Window Cleaning Services, PO Box 4117, Hornchurch, Essex, RM12 4ER Tel: (0800) 7311332 Fax: (01708) 502899
E-mail: mail@clearviewwindowcleaners.co.uk

WINDOW CLEANING CONTRACTORS/SERVICES

Action Industrial Cleaning Services UK Ltd, Bridge House, 1 Bridge Close, Romford, RM7 0AU Tel: (01708) 725356 Fax: (01708) 737117
▶ AQC, 9 Hartfield Road, Eastbourne, East Sussex, BN21 2AP Tel: 01323 720659
E-mail: info@a-q-c.co.uk
▶ As new, 33 Walnut Avenue, Mansbridge, Southampton, SO18 2HT Tel: (023) 8057 2324
E-mail: as_new@msn.com
Aztec Cleaning Services Ltd, 10 Birkbeck Road, Sidcup, Kent, DA14 4DE Tel: (020) 8300 6571 Fax: (020) 8308 0502
E-mail: ray@aztec-cleaning.prestel.co.uk
Blue Sparkle Cleaning Contractors, 2 Clarenden Place, Dartford, DA2 7HL Tel: (01322) 669494
▶ Bright Window Cleaning, 53 Hurdford Drive, Thatcham, Berkshire, RG19 4WA Tel: 07818 403736
E-mail: Info@brightwindowcleaning.co.uk
▶ C&K CLEANING SERVICES, 18 SEVERN WALK, CORBY, NORTHANTS, NN17 2HZ Tel: 01536 391460
▶ Clearview Window Cleaning Services, PO Box 4117, Hornchurch, Essex, RM12 4ER Tel: (0800) 7311332 Fax: (01708) 502899
E-mail: mail@clearviewwindowcleaners.co.uk
▶ Crystal Clear Contractors, 3 Earlston Road, Wallasey, Merseyside, CH45 5DX Tel: 0151-630 3339
E-mail: crystalclear007@hotmail.co.uk
D & R Services, 36 Eastfield Road, Wellingborough, Northamptonshire, NN8 1QU Tel: (01933) 278921 Fax: (01933) 278921
Dalzell Window Cleaning Service, 23 Polwarth Gardens, Edinburgh, EH11 1JT Tel: 0131-229 3874
E-mail: dpark@window-cleaning-in-edinburgh.com
Design & Care Cleaning Services Ltd, 89 Walcot Square, London, SE11 4UB Tel: (020) 7261 1502 Fax: (020) 7820 0032
E-mail: design.care@virgin.net
English Cleaning Co., 272 Latimer Industrial Estate, Latimer Road, London, W10 6RQ Tel: (020) 8960 0000 Fax: (020) 8969 7077
E-mail: info@english-cleaning.co.uk
Ezy-Clean Windows Ltd, Parsonage Oast, East Sutton Hill, East Sutton, Maidstone, Kent, ME17 3DG Tel: (01622) 842727 Fax: (01622) 843827
E-mail: businesscentre@ezy-clean.co.uk
▶ GECS Cleaning, 3 Church View, Wyverstone, Stowmarket, Suffolk, IP14 4SQ Tel: 01449 781603
E-mail: glenn@gecomputerservices.co.uk
General & Industrial Window Cleaning Co. Ltd, 203-209 Gateford Road, Worksop, Nottinghamshire, S81 7BB Tel: (01909) 472967 Fax: (01909) 472967
Harwoods Cleaning Contractors Ltd, Unit 3 Block 13 Whiteside Industrial Estate, Bathgate, West Lothian, EH48 2RX Tel: (01506) 633584 Fax: (01506) 636868 E-mail: harcc@aol.com
Hugh Evans HDR Window Cleaning Services, 25 Trent Valley Rd, Lichfield, Staffs, WS13 6EZ Tel: 01543 258339
E-mail: Randa@tadelevenone.fsnet.co.uk
Jason Hunt, 57 Shelton Street, Wilnecote, Tamworth, Staffordshire, B77 5DB Tel: (01827) 282892
Imperial Cleaning, Unit 7 Springwood, Cheshunt, Waltham Cross, Hertfordshire, EN7 6AZ Tel: (01992) 628342 Fax: (01992) 628342
E-mail: imperialenquiries@btinternet.com
Initial Window Cleaning, Solecast House, 13-27 Brunswick Place, London, N1 6DX Tel: (020) 7466 7776 Fax: (020) 7466 7775
▶ J V Price Ltd, Unit 2 Tower Hill, Chipperfield, Kings Langley, Hertfordshire, WD4 9LH Tel: (01442) 831777 Fax: (01442) 831888
E-mail: enquiries@jvprice.co.uk
▶ Jay, 59 Grove Gardens, Southampton, SO19 9QZ Tel: (07840) 183969
E-mail: graftersinfo@hotmail.co.uk
Kilbey Cleaning & Maintenance Services, 104 Mansfield Road, London, NW3 2HX Tel: (020) 7267 8829 Fax: (020) 7284 4525
L & M Window Cleaning Co. Ltd, 7-9 Summer Hill Terrace, Birmingham, B1 3RA Tel: 0121-236 1448 Fax: 0121-233 0037
E-mail: info@londonandmidland.co.uk
Lawrence & Tester Ltd, Property Services House, George Summers Close, Medway City Estate, Rochester, Kent, ME2 4NS Tel: (01306) 886313 Fax: (01634) 290777
E-mail: reception@lawrenceandtester.co.uk
The Mayfair Cleaning Company Ltd, 374 Wandsworth Road, London, SW8 4TD Tel: (020) 7720 6447 Fax: (020) 7498 8246
E-mail: info@mayfaircleaning.co.uk
▶ Mes High Access, 22 Dale Drive, Brighton, BN1 8LD Tel: (01273) 557711 Fax: (01273) 557711
E-mail: mark@mes-window-cleaning.co.uk
N J M Cleaning Ltd, 137 Essex Road, Romford, RM7 8BD Tel: (01708) 742127
E-mail: sales@njmcleaning.co.uk
O C S Group, Servia Road, Leeds, LS7 1NJ Tel: 0113-246 1281 Fax: 0113-234 1682
E-mail: ecleaning@ocs.co.uk
P & H Cleaning Co. Ltd, 72-74 Gipsy Hill, London, SE19 1PD Tel: (020) 8761 5324 Fax: (020) 8761 7306
E-mail: admin@pandhcleaning.co.uk
▶ Pristine Cleaning, 4 Woodside Grove, Bristol, BS10 7RF Tel: 0117-950 1772
E-mail: pristine@marketable.co.uk
R P C Cleaning Services Ltd, 201 Acton Lane, London, W4 5DA Tel: (020) 8994 4778 Fax: (020) 8994 4178
Sawston Cleaning Services Ltd, 25 Brookfield Road, Sawston, Cambridge, CB22 3EH Tel: (01223) 832922 Fax: (01223) 830031
E-mail: enquiries@sawstoncleaning.co.uk
▶ Stephen Kinsella, 200 Garston Old Road, Garston, Liverpool, L19 1QL Tel: 0151-427 4698 E-mail: ste.kinsella@ntlworld.com
Supacleen Ltd, 1 Bessemer Close, Cardiff, CF11 8DL Tel: (029) 2066 6663 Fax: (029) 2066 6663 E-mail: supacleen@onetel.net.uk
▶ Super Clean Commercial, 45 Phipps Road, Oxford, OX4 3HJ Tel: (01865) 712169 Fax: (01865) 712169
E-mail: superclean_oxford@hotmail.com
▶ Superior Cleaning Services, 111 George Street, Edinburgh, EH2 4JN Tel: 0131-624 7169 Fax: 0131-624 7168
E-mail: info@superiorcs.co.uk
▶ The UPVC Cleaning Company Ltd, PO BOX 559, Edgware, Middlesex, HA8 4BM Tel: 0800 1973033
E-mail: enquiries@upvc-cleaning.co.uk
Victoria Medical & General Cleaning Services Ltd, Victoria House, Skeltons Lane, London, E10 5BZ Tel: (020) 8556 0141 Fax: (020) 8558 9437
Wesco Access Ltd, 1 Struan Place, Douglas Water, Lanark, ML11 9LW Tel: (01555) 880808 Fax: (01555) 880901
E-mail: neil@wescoaccess.com
▶ Wind-O-Kleen, 3 Queens Avenue, Glazebury, Warrington, WA3 5NE Tel: (01925) 765092 Fax: (01925) 479173
E-mail: manager@wind-o-kleen.com
The Window Cleaning Co., 57 Shelton Street, Wilnecote, Tamworth, Staffordshire, B77 5DB Tel: (01827) 282892
E-mail: thewincleaningco@aol.com

WINDOW CLEANING EQUIPMENT

A L Maugham & Co. Ltd, 5-9 Fazakerley Street, Liverpool, L3 9DN Tel: 0151-236 1872 Fax: 0151-236 1872
Brodex Ltd, Unit 4, 76 Stevenson Way, Formby, L37 8EG Tel: (01704) 834477 Fax: (01704) 833104 E-mail: brodex@ukonline.co.uk
▶ Clearview Window Cleaning Services, PO Box 4117, Hornchurch, Essex, RM12 4ER Tel: (0800) 7311332 Fax: (01708) 502899
E-mail: mail@clearviewwindowcleaners.co.uk
F Moxham & Son, 43 Higher Market Street, Farnworth, Bolton, BL4 8HQ Tel: (01204) 573342 Fax: (01204) 573342
▶ J V Price Ltd, Unit 2 Tower Hill, Chipperfield, Kings Langley, Hertfordshire, WD4 9LH Tel: (01442) 831777 Fax: (01442) 831888
E-mail: enquiries@jvprice.co.uk
Omnipole UK Ltd, 281 Addiscombe Road, Croydon, CR0 7HZ Tel: (020) 8654 4188 Fax: (020) 8407 0439
▶ Reach & Clean, 18 Veronica Gardens, Streatham Vale, London, SW16 5JS Tel: (0870) 1993533 Fax: (0709) 2809786
E-mail: info@reachandclean.co.uk

WINDOW CONSULTANCY OR DESIGN

Bartell Contract Furnishings Ltd, Bartell House, 733 Oldham Road, Manchester, M40 5AP Tel: 0161-205 0222 Fax: 0161-205 0444
E-mail: info@bar-tell.co.uk
Kellett Engineering Co. Ltd, Hill Top Road, Leeds, LS12 3PX Tel: 0113-263 9041 Fax: 0113-231 0717 E-mail: klt@btconnect.co.uk
Provincial Windows Ltd, Unit 3c Birches Industrial Estate, East Grinstead, West Sussex, RH19 1XZ Tel: (01342) 313767 Fax: (01342) 311407
Structura UK Ltd, Phoenix Works, Davis Road, Chessington, Surrey, KT9 1TH Tel: (020) 8397 4361 Fax: (020) 8391 5805
E-mail: sales@structura-uk.com

WINDOW CONTROL SYSTEMS CONTRACTORS OR INSTALLATION OR SERVICE OR SUPPLIERS

Rka Services Ltd, Unit 25, Stevenage Enterprise Centre Orc, Stevenage, Hertfordshire, SG1 3HH Tel: (01438) 361888
Rob Installations Ltd, 25 Chesterford Green, Basildon, Essex, SS14 3PR Tel: (01268) 522471 Fax: (01268) 286657
Sash Window Workshop, 4 Kiln Lane, Bracknell, Berkshire, RG12 1NA Tel: (01344) 868668 Fax: (01344) 868858
Windor Controls Ltd, Unit 58 Hillgrove Business Park, Nazeing, Waltham Abbey, Essex, EN9 2HB Tel: (01992) 893737 Fax: (01992) 893130
E-mail: barryrichards@windorcontrols.co.uk
▶ Windowworld Ltd, Unit G, Belgrave Industrial Centre, Ross Walk, Leicester, LE4 5HH Tel: 0116-261 0078

WINDOW ENDLESS CORDS

James Lever & Sons Ltd, Unit 26 Orient Works Morris Green, Business Park Prescott, Bolton, BL3 3PE Tel: (01204) 658154 Fax: (01204) 658154 E-mail: sales@jameslever.co.uk

WINDOW FILM, *See also headings for particular types*

▶ Apollo Blinds Ltd, 4 Mallard Buildings, Station Road, New Milton, Hampshire, BH25 6HY Tel: (01425) 623624 Fax: (01425) 629709
E-mail: apolloblinds1@btconnect.com
Johnson Window Films UK Ltd, 3 Mitchell Point, Ensign Way, Hamble, Southampton, SO31 4RF Tel: (023) 8045 4593 Fax: (023) 8045 4594 E-mail: jwsinstall@btconnect.co.uk

WINDOW FILMS, AUTOMOTIVE

▶ Image Tint, 31 Snowdon Avenue, Maidstone, Kent, ME14 5NW Tel: (01622) 672272
E-mail: info@imagetint.co.uk

WINDOW FITTINGS

All Trim Plastics, Unit 1-2, Spring Lane, Willenhall, West Midlands, WV12 4HL Tel: (0845) 6099922 Fax: (01422) 370953
E-mail: sales@dqs.co.uk
Ashton Industrial Sales Ltd, 4 Anderson Road, Woodford Green, Essex, IG8 8ET Tel: (020) 8551 4046 Fax: (020) 8551 1433
E-mail: ashton@ashton-industrial.com
J. Banks & Co. Ltd, Excelsior Works, Wood Street, Willenhall, West Midlands, WV13 1JY Tel: (01902) 605084 Fax: (01902) 603248
E-mail: contact@jbanks.co.uk
Bilanco Ltd, Units 3-4, Powdrake Road, Grangemouth, Stirlingshire, FK3 9OT Tel: (01324) 473707 Fax: (01324) 471926
Building Profiles Ltd, Timothys Bridge Road, Stratford-upon-Avon, Warwickshire, CV37 9NQ Tel: (01789) 414044 Fax: (01789) 415273
E-mail: info@building-profiles.co.uk
Carlton Industries Ltd, Units 1-4, Progress Business Park, Progress Way, Croydon, CR0 4XD Tel: (020) 8686 9898 Fax: (020) 8686 9848
Cavendish Hardware, 8 242 Tithe Street, Leicester, LE5 4BN Tel: 0116-274 1746 Fax: 0116-246 1545
E-mail: sales@cavendish-hardware.co.uk
Cotswold Architectural Products Ltd, Manor Park Industrial Estate, Manor Road, Cheltenham, Gloucestershire, GL51 9SQ Tel: (01242) 246624 Fax: (01242) 221146
E-mail: info@cotswold-windows.co.uk
Direct Commissioning Services, 8 Ashfields, Loughton, Essex, IG10 1SB Tel: (020) 8418 9996 Fax: (020) 8418 9914
E-mail: directcommissioning@btinternet.com
Dorma UK Ltd, Unit 3 Cala Trading Estate, Ashton Vale Road, Ashton, Bristol, BS3 2HA Tel: 0117-963 9014 Fax: 0117-953 3462
Dortrend International Ltd, Riverside Business Centre, Worcester Road, Stourport-on-Severn, Worcestershire, DY13 9BZ Tel: (01299) 827837 Fax: (01299) 827094
E-mail: sales@dortrend.co.uk
Double Glazing Supplies Group plc, Sycamore Road, Castle Donington, Derby, DE74 2NW Tel: (01332) 811611 Fax: (01332) 812650
E-mail: reception@dgsgroup.co.uk
Groupco Ltd, 18 Tresham Road, Orton Southgate, Peterborough, PE2 6SG Tel: (01733) 234750 Fax: (01733) 235246
E-mail: sales@groupcoltd.co.uk
Hoppe UK Ltd, Gailey Park, Gravelly Way, Standeford, Wolverhampton, WV10 7GW Tel: (01902) 484400 Fax: (01902) 484406
IFI Scotland Ltd, Rennie Place, East Kilbride, Glasgow, G74 5HD Tel: (01355) 598440 Fax: (0800) 6520780 E-mail: sales@ifiltd.net
Lightfoot Windows Ltd, 31 Crouch Hill, London, N4 4AS Tel: (020) 7272 1622 Fax: (020) 7281 1404
M B Distribution Cleveland Ltd, Wallis Road, Skippers Lane Industrial Estate, Middlesbrough, Cleveland, TS6 6JB Tel: (01642) 455945 Fax: (01642) 455504
E-mail: sales@mb-distribution.co.uk
Reddiplex Group Logistics, Unit 33 The Furlong, Berry Hill Industrial Estate, Droitwich, Worcestershire, WR9 9BG Tel: (01905) 774400 Fax: (01905) 791866
E-mail: reddiplex@reddiplex.com
Rugby Windows Mant Ltd, Rugby House, Hinckley Road, Sapcote, Leicester, LE9 4FU Tel: (01455) 274747 Fax: (01455) 274686
Titon Hardware Ltd, International House, Peartree Road, Stanway, Colchester, CO3 0JL Tel: (01206) 713800 Fax: (01206) 543126
E-mail: sales@titon.co.uk
Titon Hardware, 11 Piperell Way, Haverhill, Suffolk, CB9 8PH Tel: (01440) 762223 Fax: (01440) 706808
Urolite Ltd, 4 Northwold Road, London, N16 7HR Tel: (020) 7241 6093
E-mail: info@urolite.co.uk
Windows Direct Merseyside Ltd, Hastings House, Sandford Street, Birkenhead, Merseyside, CH41 1AR Tel: 0151-666 1414 Fax: 0151-666 1515 E-mail: sales@windowsdirect.org

WINDOW FRAME MAINTENANCE OR REPAIR

Plastal Commercial Ltd, Alders Way, Paignton, Devon, TQ4 7QE Tel: (01803) 697111 Fax: (01803) 559619
Technol Window Repairs, 100 Braeside Road, Greenock, Renfrewshire, PA16 0QX Tel: (01475) 639989 Fax: (01475) 635301

WINDOW FRAMES, *See also other headings under Window(s)*

▶ Abbey Southern Ltd, 4 Warren Way, Holton Heath Trading Park, Poole, Dorset, BH16 6NJ Tel: (01202) 622226 Fax: (01202) 622866
▶ Accurate Windows, 163 Moston Lane, Manchester, M9 4HR Tel: 0161-202 4000 Fax: 0161-202 4001
▶ Advance Window & Home Improvements, Unit 22A, Bonlea Industrial Estate, Thornaby, Stockton-On-Tees, Cleveland, TS17 7AQ Tel: (0800) 0528400 Fax: (01642) 614851
▶ Advanced Glass & Window Systems Ltd, Stafford Park 15, Telford, Shropshire, TF3 3BB Tel: (01952) 210210 Fax: (01952) 210210

WINDOW FRAMES – *continued*

▶ Advanced Window Systems, Leamore Lane, Walsall, WS2 7DQ Tel: (01922) 710044 Fax: (01922) 712255
▶ Altro Window Frame Mnfrs, Unit 51 Barns Court, Turners Hill Road, Crawley Down, Crawley, West Sussex, RH10 4HQ Tel: (01342) 718702 Fax: (01342) 718942
Arden Windows Ltd, Arden House, Sparkbrook St, Coventry, CV1 5ST Tel: (024) 7663 2423 Fax: (0870) 7890161 E-mail: enquiries@ardenwindows.net
▶ Bespoke Timber Design, Harrier House, Unit 2C Rossbank Road, Ellesmere Port, CH65 3AN Tel: 0151-355 8183
▶ Big Window Co., Smallwood Street, Redditch, Worcestershire, B98 7AZ Tel: (01527) 585258 Fax: (01527) 585258
Cambrian Windows Ltd, Units 11-13 Thomas Court, London Road Industrial Estate, Pembroke Dock, Dyfed, SA72 4RZ Tel: (01646) 687455
▶ Cardine Windows & Doors, 10b Barleyfield, Hinckley, Leicestershire, LE10 1YE Tel: (01455) 890555 Fax: (01455) 891888
▶ Classic Trade Frames Ltd, Unit 7 Priestley Road, Worsley, Manchester, M28 2LY Tel: 0161-793 1166 Fax: 0161-793 1177
▶ Climitize Upvc Windows, Shady Lane, Birmingham, B44 9ER Tel: 0121-325 1792 Fax: 0121-325 1799
▶ Diamond Glaze Ltd, Fen Road, Ruskington, Sleaford, Lincolnshire, NG34 9TH Tel: (01526) 832228 Fax: (01526) 832228
Door Stop, 1 Park Lane, St. Clement, Truro, Cornwall, TR1 1SX Tel: (01872) 261260 Fax: (01872) 262260
Dunster House, Caxton Road, Bedford, MK41 0LF Tel: (01234) 272445 Fax: (01234) 272588 E-mail: enquiries@garden-buildings-uk.co.uk
Engels, 1 Kingley Centre, Downs Road, West Stoke, Chichester, West Sussex, PO18 9HJ Tel: (01243) 576644 Fax: (01243) 576644 E-mail: sales@engels.co.uk
▶ Five Star Windows, 385 Tong Street, Bradford, West Yorkshire, BD4 9RU Tel: (01274) 680476 Fax: (01274) 680476
▶ G & T Trade Windows, Oswin Avenue, Balby, Doncaster, South Yorkshire, DN4 0NR Tel: (01302) 857555
▶ H W Plastics, Britannia House Stanley Matthews Way, Trentham Lakes South, Stoke-on-Trent, ST4 8GR Tel: (01782) 645700 Fax: (01782) 645727
▶ J B Window Fabrication, Unit 8D International House, Battle Road, Heathfield Industrial Estate, Newton Abbot, Devon, TQ12 6RY Tel: (01626) 830030
▶ Jay Dee Windows, Unit 32a Westminster Industrial Park, Rossfield Road, Ellesmere Port, CH65 3DU Tel: 0151-357 2112 Fax: 0151-357 2122
Kitson Trade Windows Ltd, South Road, Alnwick, Northumberland, NE66 2PD Tel: (01665) 606150 Fax: (01665) 606382 E-mail: enquiries@kitson.co.uk
▶ Krystal Upvc Windows, Newton Place, Bradford, West Yorkshire, BD5 7JW Tel: (01274) 683622 Fax: (01274) 681228
▶ Ledan Windows Ltd, 25-27 Concorde Road, Norwich, NR6 6BJ Tel: (01603) 482428 Fax: (01603) 488428 E-mail: sales@ledan.co.uk
▶ Leonardo Windows Ltd, Turncroft House Unit 3b, Turncroft Lane, Stockport, Cheshire, SK1 4AR Tel: 0161-480 5885 Fax: 0161-480 6005
▶ M D P Windows Ltd, 9 Hattersley Industrial Estate, Stockport Road, Hyde, Cheshire, SK14 3QT Tel: 0161-367 9265 Fax: 0161-367 9802
▶ M1 Trade Frames, Units 1 & 2 Intake Road Intake Industrial Estate, Bolsover, Chesterfield, Derbyshire, S44 6BD Tel: (01246) 240225 Fax: (01246) 240230
▶ Mount Pleasant Windows, 13 Bartleet Road, Redditch, Worcestershire, B98 0DQ Tel: (01527) 510400 Fax: (01527) 526700
▶ Nce Windows & Conservatories, Unit 10 Reginald Road Industrial Estate, Brindley Road, Reginald Road Industrial Estat, St. Helens, Merseyside, WA9 4HY Tel: (01744) 811111 Fax: (01744) 811111
Northdown Windows, 326 Northdown Road, Margate, Kent, CT9 3PW Tel: (01843) 232081 Fax: (01843) 224211 E-mail: info@northdown-windows.co.uk
▶ The Oak Window Co. Ltd, Unit 4, Manton Industrial Estate, Manton, Rutland, Oakham, Leicestershire, LE15 8SZ Tel: (01780) 460621 Fax: (0800) 5424300
▶ Offley Timber Structures Ltd, Unit 3, Raleigh Hall Industrial Estate, Eccleshall, Stafford, ST21 6JL Tel: (01785) 851333 Fax: (01785) 851933 E-mail: sales@offleytimber.com
Olympic Of Waterhouses Ltd, Manifold Works, Leek Road, Waterhouses, Stoke-on-Trent, ST10 3HN Tel: (01538) 308486 Fax: (01538) 308185
P Mcquaid, Hill Street, Milford, Armagh, BT60 3PB Tel: (028) 3751 0057
Panoramic Ltd, 534 London Road, North Cheam, Sutton, Surrey, SM3 9QE Tel: (020) 8641 4488 Fax: (020) 8641 5900 E-mail: sales@panoramic-products.co.uk
▶ Paradise Windows, Unit 14 Block 15 Amber Business Centre, Greenhill Lane, Riddings, Alfreton, Derbyshire, DE55 4BR Tel: (01773) 606333 Fax: (01773) 606444
Prescot Door & Window Centre, Squires House, Cyprus Street, Prescot, Merseyside, L34 5RY Tel: 0151-430 9601 Fax: 0151-426 2212
Preston Joinery, Walton Avenue, North Shields, Tyne & Wear, NE29 9NQ Tel: 0191-257 0776 Fax: 0191-257 2002
Shaw Bros, Viaduct Works, Clay Lane, Linthwaite, Huddersfield, HD7 5BG Tel: (01484) 846442 Fax: (01484) 847774 E-mail: carole@shawbros.fsnet.co.uk
▶ Skaala Windows & Doors, Diss Business Centre, Dark Lane, Scole, Diss, Norfolk, IP21 4HD Tel: (01379) 640580 Fax: (01379) 640590 E-mail: sales@skaala.com
▶ Taylor Made Windows London, Unit 22 Roxwell Trading Park, Argall Avenue, London, E10 7QY Tel: (020) 8558 6688
Trident Windows & Blinds, 193 South Farm Road, Worthing, West Sussex, BN14 7TW Tel: (01903) 202022 Fax: (01903) 200199
▶ Weatherbreak, Unit 27 Scott Road Industrial Estate, Luton, LU3 3BF Tel: (01582) 585500 Fax: (01582) 580994 E-mail: info@weatherbreak.co.uk
▶ Window Widget, Unit 1, Venture Business Centre Madleaze Road, Gloucester, GL1 5SJ Tel: (01452) 300912 Fax: (01452) 300912
Windows & Doors U Fit, Manor Way, Kinmel Bay, Rhyl, Clwyd, LL18 5BE Tel: (01745) 354540 Fax: (01745) 354540 E-mail: sales@conservatories-northwales.co.uk
Woodstock Joinery Co., 9A Windermere Road, London, N19 5SG Tel: (020) 7281 4866 Fax: (020) 7263 4888

WINDOW GRAPHIC WINDOW FILM

City Screen Print Ltd, Unit 2 Sextant Park Neptune Close, Medway City Estate, Rochester, Kent, ME2 4LU Tel: (01634) 297779 Fax: (01634) 294264 E-mail: info@cityscreenprint.co.uk
Contra Vision Ltd, Victoria House, 19-21 Ack Lane East, Bramhall, Stockport, Cheshire, SK7 2BE Tel: 0161-439 9307 Fax: 0161-440 7934 E-mail: sales@contravision.com
▶ Durable, 1 498 Reading Road, Winnersh, Wokingham, Berkshire, RG41 5EX Tel: (0870) 2402480 Fax: 0118-989 5209 E-mail: mail@durable.co.uk
North Western Lead Co Hyde Ltd, Mill Street, Newton Moor Industrial Estate, Hyde, Cheshire, SK14 4LJ Tel: 0161-368 4491 Fax: 0161-366 5103 E-mail: sales@decraled.co.uk

WINDOW GRILLES

Brook Design Hardware Ltd, Brook House, Dunmurry Industrial Estate, Dunmurry, Belfast, BT17 9HU Tel: (028) 9061 6505 Fax: (028) 9061 6518 E-mail: sales@brookvent.co.uk
High Wood Security, 2-4 Slaters Road, Stanningley, Pudsey, West Yorkshire, LS28 6EY Tel: 0113-257 7707 Fax: 0113-257 4051
Neil Jordan Grills & Doors, 8E, 8E Sweechbridge Rd, Herne Bay, Kent, CT6 6TE Tel: (01227) 749991 Fax: (01227) 749991
Portman Doors Ltd, Unit 3 Bradshaw Works, Printers Lane, Bolton, BL2 3DW Tel: (01204) 699521 Fax: (01204) 669094 E-mail: info@portmandoors.co.uk
Romford Blinds & Shutters Ltd, Danes Road, Romford, RM7 0HL Tel: (01708) 754754 Fax: (01708) 733128
Trellidor Ltd, Unit 20 Bloomfield Park, Bloomfield Road, Tipton, West Midlands, DY4 9AH Tel: 0121-557 0303 Fax: 0121-557 0353 E-mail: sales@trellidor.co.uk

WINDOW GUARDS

Bri-Stor Systems Ltd, Church Lane, Hixon, Stafford, ST18 0PS Tel: (01889) 271202 Fax: (01889) 271178 E-mail: systems@bristor.co.uk
C Aiano & Sons Ltd, 64-70 Chrisp Street, London, E14 6LR Tel: (020) 7987 1184 Fax: (020) 7538 2786 E-mail: caianoandson@aol.com

WINDOW HINGES

Cotswold Architectural Products Ltd, Manor Park Industrial Estate, Manor Road, Cheltenham, Gloucestershire, GL51 9SQ Tel: (01242) 246624 Fax: (01242) 221146 E-mail: info@cotswold-windows.co.uk
Laird Security Hardware, Bloomfield Park, Bloomfield Road, Tipton, West Midlands, DY4 9AP Tel: 0121-224 6131 Fax: 0121-520 1039 E-mail: sales@saracen-secure.co.uk

WINDOW INSTALLATION

Olympic Of Waterhouses Ltd, Manifold Works, Leek Road, Waterhouses, Stoke-on-Trent, ST10 3HN Tel: (01538) 308486 Fax: (01538) 308185
Ringwood Glass, 14 Lions Wood, St. Leonards, Ringwood, Hampshire, BH24 2LU Tel: (01425) 478445 Fax: (01425) 478484

WINDOW LEAD

Mannings, 347 Footscray Road, London, SE9 2EH Tel: (020) 8859 3908 Fax: (020) 8859 3908
North Western Lead Co Hyde Ltd, Mill Street, Newton Moor Industrial Estate, Hyde, Cheshire, SK14 4LJ Tel: 0161-368 4491 Fax: 0161-366 5103 E-mail: sales@decraled.co.uk

WINDOW LOCKS

Davenport Burgess, 47 Wednesfield Road, Willenhall, West Midlands, WV13 1AL Tel: (01902) 366448 Fax: (01902) 602472 E-mail: sales@davenport-burgess.com

WINDOW MACHINE/ FABRICATING SYSTEMS, ENGINEERS, INSTALLATION OR SERVICE

▶ Amex Holdings, 5 Cherrywood, Stag Oak Lane, Chineham, Basingstoke, Hampshire, RG24 8WF Tel: (01256) 471000 Fax: (01256) 708989
Kall Kwik UK Ltd, Heaton Mersey Industrial Estate, Battersea Road, Stockport, Cheshire, SK4 3EA Tel: 0161-486 1911 Fax: 0161-431 8069 E-mail: sales@kallkwik.uk.com
Specialized Door & Window Services, Unit 5-6 Merlin Way, Hillend Industrial Park, Hillend, Dunfermline, Fife, KY11 9JY Tel: (01383) 829912 Fax: (01383) 825372

WINDOW PRODUCTION CONSUMABLES

Ashton Industrial Sales Ltd, 4 Anderson Road, Woodford Green, Essex, IG8 8ET Tel: (020) 8551 4046 Fax: (020) 8551 1433 E-mail: ashton@ashton-industrial.com
Prime Time Innovations, 22 Austin Way, Royal Oak Industrial Estate, Daventry, Northamptonshire, NN11 8QY Tel: (01327) 300761 Fax: (01327) 878743

WINDOW REPLACEMENT CONSULTANCY OR SERVICES

Advanced Windows, Unit 21 Ariane, Tamworth, Staffordshire, B79 7XF Tel: (01827) 66991 Fax: (01827) 56453 E-mail: pam@advancedwindowsuk.co.uk
Allard Windows & Doors, Unit 3b Conners Yard, Crowborough Hill, Crowborough, East Sussex, TN6 2DA Tel: (01892) 665224 Fax: (01892) 669545 E-mail: john.allard@btclick.com
Alliance Group (Bristol) Ltd, Unit 303 Central Park, Petherton Road, Hengrove, Bristol, BS14 9BZ Tel: (01275) 892882 Fax: (01275) 892766 E-mail: general@alliancegroupbristol.co.uk
Bridgewater Glass, 44-52 Vicarage Road, Watford, WD18 0EN Tel: (01923) 237533 Fax: (01923) 817118 E-mail: bridgewaterglass@aol.com
Carters, 19a Belper Road, Luton, LU4 8RG Tel: (01582) 571477 Fax: (01582) 480980
Cavendish Hardware, 8 242 Tithe Street, Leicester, LE5 4BN Tel: 0116-274 1746 Fax: 0116-246 1545 E-mail: sales@cavendish-hardware.co.uk
Churchill Windows, Unit 18 Northbrook Trading Estate, Northbrook Road, Worthing, West Sussex, BN14 8PN Tel: (01903) 230918 Fax: (01903) 823091 E-mail: sales@churchill-windows.co.uk
Corinthian Windows, Oak Street, Quarry Bank, Brierley Hill, West Midlands, DY5 2JQ Tel: (01384) 411033
County Windows, 22 Stephenson Road, St. Ives, Cambridgeshire, PE27 3WJ Tel: (01480) 461505 Fax: (01480) 494407 E-mail: enquiries@countywindows.com
DNS Windows Ltd, Daniels Way, Hucknall, Nottingham, NG15 7LL Tel: 0115-963 6361 Fax: 0115-968 0183
Four Seasons Ltd, Unit 14, Papermill End, Aldridge Road, Great Barr, Birmingham, B44 8NH Tel: 0121-356 0909 Fax: 0121-356 0513
Great Yarmouth Glass, 113 Nelson Road Central, Great Yarmouth, Norfolk, NR30 2NJ Tel: (01493) 842323 Fax: (01493) 850913 E-mail: info@gyglass.co.uk
James Pearson & Co West Bromwich Ltd, Mount Pleasant Street, West Bromwich, West Midlands, B70 7DL Tel: 0121-553 3580 Fax: 0121-553 7903
K J M Replacement Windows Ltd, 4 Sterling Park, Andover, Hampshire, SP10 3TZ Tel: (01264) 359355 Fax: (01264) 353441 E-mail: sales@kjmgroup.com
Marathon Window Co. Ltd, 35 Upper High Street, Epsom, Surrey, KT17 4RA Tel: (01372) 740706 Fax: (01372) 722857
Olivand Metal Windows Ltd, 43a Chesley Gardens, London, E6 3LN Tel: (020) 8471 8111 Fax: (020) 8552 7015
Perfecta Windows, Unit 11, Longton Trading Estate, Winterstoke Road, Weston-super-Mare, Avon, BS23 3YB Tel: (01934) 624632 Fax: (01934) 636631
Pinner Metal Window Services, 102-104 Church Road, Teddington, Middlesex, TW11 8PY Tel: (020) 8943 2335 Fax: (020) 8943 3151
R Walker & Sons Preston Ltd, 103 Market St West, Preston, PR1 2HB Tel: (01772) 254176 Fax: (01772) 202246
Simplas, Unit 8 Horcott Industrial Estate, Horcott Road, Fairford, Gloucestershire, GL7 4BX Tel: (01285) 713175 Fax: (01285) 713175
Solaglas Ltd, Treefield Industrial Estate, Gelderd Road, Morley, Leeds, LS27 7JU Tel: 0113-253 8030 Fax: 0113-253 7659 E-mail: solaglas.gpd@saint-gobain-glass.com
Staybrite Windows, Weston Road, Norwich, NR3 3TP Tel: (0800) 0832656 Fax: (01603) 406185 E-mail: mike.holmes@zsltd.co.uk
Steel Windows Service & Supplies Ltd, 30 Oxford Road, London, N4 3EY Tel: (020) 7272 2294 Fax: (020) 7281 2309 E-mail: post@steelwindows.co.uk
Thermoshield Window Services Ltd, 11 Purdeys Way, Rochford, Essex, SS4 1ND Tel: (01702) 541841 Fax: (01702) 541729 E-mail: sales@thermoshield.co.uk
West Midland Glazing Co. Ltd, 123-125 Grove Lane, Birmingham, B17 0QT Tel: 0121-426 1275 Fax: 0121-428 1625

WINDOW VENTILATORS

Brook Design Hardware Ltd, Brook House, Dunmurry Industrial Estate, Dunmurry, Belfast, BT17 9HU Tel: (028) 9061 6505 Fax: (028) 9061 6518 E-mail: sales@brookvent.co.uk
Powrmatic Ltd, Hort Bridge, Ilminster, Somerset, TA19 9PS Tel: (01460) 53535 Fax: (01460) 52341 E-mail: info@powrmatic.co.uk
R W Simon Ltd, Hatchmoor Industrial Estate, Torrington, Devon, EX38 7HP Tel: (01805) 623721 Fax: (01805) 624578 E-mail: info@rwsimon.co.uk
Ruskin Air Management Ltd, Stourbridge Road, Bridgnorth, Shropshire, WV15 5BB Tel: (01746) 761921 Fax: (01746) 766450 E-mail: sales@naco.co.uk
Titon Hardware Ltd, International House, Peartree Road, Stanway, Colchester, CO3 0JL Tel: (01206) 713800 Fax: (01206) 543126 E-mail: sales@titon.co.uk

WINDSCREEN/WINDOW REPLACEMENT SPECIALIST SERVICES

Auto Shield, 465 Barlow Moor Road, Manchester, M21 8AU Tel: 0161-881 3463 Fax: 0161-881 3463
Autoglass Ltd, 1 Priory Business Park, Cardington, Bedford, MK44 3US Tel: (01234) 273636 Fax: (01234) 831100 E-mail: postmaster@autoglass.co.uk
Bristol & West Windscreens, 5 Chardstock Avenue, Bristol, BS9 2RY Tel: 0117-908 2256 Fax: 0117-908 2256 E-mail: sales@bristolwindscreens.com
Car Glass Replacement, Norwich Road, Cardiff, CF23 9AB Tel: (029) 2049 0151 Fax: (029) 2049 9431
▶ Crystal Windscreens Ltd, Springvale Industrial Park, Bilston, West Midlands, WV14 0QL Tel: (01902) 405040 Fax: (01902) 405474 E-mail: sales@crystal-windscreens.com
National Windscreens Ltd, F Cottage Industrial Estate, Forstal Road, Aylesford, Kent, ME20 7AD Tel: (01622) 715696 Fax: (01622) 715738
Walford E A Chelmsford, Navigation Road, Chelmsford, CM2 6HD Tel: (01245) 262426 Fax: (01245) 352301

WINDSCREEN/WINDOW WIPERS, COMMERCIAL VEHICLE

Britax P S V Wypers Ltd, Navigation Road, Diglis, Worcester, WR5 3DE Tel: (01905) 350500 Fax: (01905) 763928 E-mail: sales@psvwypers.com
Hepworth Marine, Hepworth House, Brook Street, Redditch, Worcestershire, B98 8NF Tel: (01527) 61243 Fax: (01527) 66836 E-mail: bhepworth@b-hepworth.com
Matador Co. Ltd, Unit 6, Top Angel, Buckingham Industrial Park, Buckingham, MK18 1TH Tel: (01280) 823824 Fax: (01280) 817717 E-mail: wipers@matador.co.uk
Trico Ltd, Skewfields, Pontypool, Gwent, NP4 0XZ Tel: (01495) 767700 Fax: (01495) 767877 E-mail: sales@tricoproducts.com

WINDSCREEN/WINDOW WIPERS, LOCOMOTIVE

Britax P S V Wypers Ltd, Navigation Road, Diglis, Worcester, WR5 3DE Tel: (01905) 350500 Fax: (01905) 763928 E-mail: sales@psvwypers.com

WINDSCREEN/WINDOW WIPERS, LOCOMOTIVE – *continued*

Hepworth Marine, Hepworth House, Brook Street, Redditch, Worcestershire, B98 8NF Tel: (01527) 61243 Fax: (01527) 66836 E-mail: bhepworth@b-hepworth.com

Matador Co. Ltd, Unit 6, Top Angel, Buckingham Industrial Park, Buckingham, MK18 1TH Tel: (01280) 823824 Fax: (01280) 817717 E-mail: wipers@matador.co.uk

WINDSCREEN/WINDOW WIPERS, MARINE

Hepworth Marine, Hepworth House, Brook Street, Redditch, Worcestershire, B98 8NF Tel: (01527) 61243 Fax: (01527) 66836 E-mail: bhepworth@b-hepworth.com

Wynnstruments Ltd, Wynn House, Lansdown Estate, Cheltenham, Gloucestershire, GL51 8PL Tel: (01242) 232266 Fax: (01242) 231131 E-mail: sales@wynn.co.uk

WINDSCREEN/WINDOW WIPERS, MOTOR VEHICLE

Britax P S V Wypers Ltd, Navigation Road, Diglis, Worcester, WR5 3DE Tel: (01905) 350500 Fax: (01905) 763928 E-mail: sales@psvwypers.com

Matador Co. Ltd, Unit 6, Top Angel, Buckingham Industrial Park, Buckingham, MK18 1TH Tel: (01280) 823824 Fax: (01280) 817717 E-mail: wipers@matador.co.uk

Trico Ltd, Skewfields, Pontypool, Gwent, NP4 0XZ Tel: (01495) 767700 Fax: (01495) 767877 E-mail: sales@tricoproducts.com

WINDSCREENS/WINDOWS

Auto Asylum, 78 Portlock Road, Maidenhead, Berkshire, SL6 6DZ Tel: (01628) 782782 Fax: (01628) 784541

Autoglass Ltd, 1 Priory Business Park, Cardington, Bedford, MK44 3US Tel: (01234) 273636 Fax: (01234) 831100 E-mail: postmaster@autoglass.co.uk

Car Glass Replacement, Norwich Road, Cardiff, CF23 9AB Tel: (029) 2049 0151 Fax: (029) 2049 9431

Charles Pugh, Millmarsh Lane, Enfield, Middlesex, EN3 7QG Tel: (020) 8805 5222 Fax: (020) 8805 2251 E-mail: sales@pughs.co.uk

D A K International, Unit 12 Ashmead Business Centre, Ashmead Road, Keynsham, Bristol, BS31 1SX Tel: 0117-986 6198 Fax: 0117-986 6704

▶ Glass Technics, Church Lane, Hartley Wespall, Basingstoke, Hampshire, RG27 0BB Tel: (01256) 882339 E-mail: tony@glasstechnics.co.uk

Motor Sport (Glass) Ltd, 11 Claymore, Tame Valley Industrial Estate, Wilnecote, Tamworth, Staffordshire, B77 5DQ Tel: (01827) 283688 Fax: (01827) 283689 E-mail: sales@heatedwindscreen.com

▶ Old School Windscreens, The Old School Cafe, Longcross Road, Longcross, Chertsey, Surrey, KT16 0DP Tel: (01932) 873506 Fax: (01932) 872933 E-mail: enquiries@oldschoolwindscreens.co.uk

▶ Optic Kleer, 20 Datchet Close, Hemel Hempstead, Hertfordshire, HP2 7JX Tel: (01442) 407716 Fax: (01442) 407716 E-mail: optickleer_hemel@hotmail.com

▶ UK Windscreens, 44 Grassington Crescent, Liverpool, L25 9RU Tel: 0151 2844471 E-mail: info@ukwindscreens.co.uk

WINDSCREENS/WINDOWS, MOTOR VEHICLE

A G C Automotives UK Ltd, Unit B, Edgemead Close, Round Spinney, Northampton, NN3 8RG Tel: (01604) 671150 Fax: (01604) 671140

Auto Glass York Ltd, Layerthorpe, York, YO31 7YW Tel: (01904) 644723 Fax: (01904) 611624

National Mobile Windscreens, 36 Queens Road, Newbury, Berkshire, RG14 7NE Tel: (01635) 49494 Fax: (01635) 521661 E-mail: enquiries@nationalwindscreens.co.uk

▶ Old School Windscreens, The Old School Cafe, Longcross Road, Longcross, Chertsey, Surrey, KT16 0DP Tel: (01932) 873506 Fax: (01932) 872933 E-mail: enquiries@oldschoolwindscreens.co.uk

Pilkington Automotives, Triplex House, Eckersall Road, Birmingham, B38 8SR Tel: 0121-254 3000 Fax: 0121-254 3188

WINE BOTTLE OPENERS

▶ Hawk P O S Ltd, 7 Church Road, Flamstead, St. Albans, Hertfordshire, AL3 8BN Tel: (01582) 849313 Fax: (01582) 840144 E-mail: sales@hawkpos.co.uk

WINE CELLAR AIR CONDITIONING (AC) EQUIPMENT

Wine Corner Ltd, Unit 4, British Coal Enterprise Park, Brunel Close, Harworth, Doncaster, South Yorkshire, DN11 8SG Tel: (01302) 744916 Fax: (01302) 751233 E-mail: info@winecorner.co.uk

WINE CELLARS

Wine Corner Ltd, Unit 4, British Coal Enterprise Park, Brunel Close, Harworth, Doncaster, South Yorkshire, DN11 8SG Tel: (01302) 744916 Fax: (01302) 751233 E-mail: info@winecorner.co.uk

WINE DISPENSERS

A W H Consultants, Chadburn House, Weighbridge Road, Mansfield, Nottinghamshire, NG18 1AH Tel: (01623) 465207 Fax: (01623) 400196 E-mail: enquiries@ynotwine.co.uk

Charles Hawkins, The Offices, Glaston Road, Uppingham, Oakham, Leicestershire, LE15 9EU Tel: (01572) 823030 Fax: (01572) 823040 E-mail: info@charleshawkinsandpartners.com

Kingsland, The Winery, Fairhills Road, Irlam, Manchester, M44 6BD Tel: 0161-333 4300 Fax: 0161-333 4301 E-mail: info@kingsland-wines.com

WINE IMPORT

Donatel Freres Ltd, The Vintage House, 42 Old Compton Street, London, W1D 4LR Tel: (020) 7437 2592 Fax: (020) 7734 1174 E-mail: vintagehouse.co@virgin.net

▶ SullyVin, 19 Birchwood Avenue, Hutton, Preston, PR4 5EE Tel: (01772) 612152 E-mail: enquiries@sullyvin.com

WINE PRESERVATION SYSTEMS

Vintellect Ltd, Fetcham Park House, Lower Road, Fetcham, Leatherhead, Surrey, KT22 9HD Tel: (01372) 371093 E-mail: info@vintellect.co.uk

WINE RACKS

Rta Wine Rack Co. Ltd, Station Road, Great Ryburgh, Fakenham, Norfolk, NR21 0DX Tel: (01328) 829666 Fax: (01328) 829667 E-mail: rtawr@globalnet.co.uk

▶ VintageView UK, 16 Lower Park Road, New Southgate, London, N11 1QD Tel: (0870) 7659225 Fax: (0870) 7052939 E-mail: info@vintageview.co.uk

WINE SERVICE PRODUCTS

Kingsland, The Winery, Fairhills Road, Irlam, Manchester, M44 6BD Tel: 0161-333 4300 Fax: 0161-333 4301 E-mail: info@kingsland-wines.com

WIPE SUPPLY SERVICES

Acorn Cleaning Service, 2a Lothair Road, London, W5 4TA Tel: (020) 8579 1177 Fax: (020) 8840 7545

Castlewest Ltd, 6 Greenwood Court, Ramridge Road, Luton, LU2 0TN Tel: (01582) 455757 Fax: (01582) 413114 E-mail: info@castlewest.co.uk

Chello Chemicals, Homme Castle, Shelsley Walsh, Worcester, WR6 6RR Tel: (01886) 812877 Fax: (01886) 812899 E-mail: sales@chellochemicals.co.uk

Cleaning Rag Supply Co. Ltd, 28 Brearley Street, Hockley, Birmingham, B19 3NR Tel: 0121-333 4446 Fax: 0121-333 4442 E-mail: enquiries@cleaningragsupply.co.uk

Easiclean Products, 10 East House Farm, Atherstone Lane, Merevale, Atherstone, Warwickshire, CV9 2HT Tel: (01827) 874787 Fax: (01827) 874745 E-mail: info@easicleanwipersl.com

Icp Hygiene, 14 Ronald Close, Woburn Road Industrial Estate, Kempston, Bedford, MK42 7SH Tel: (01234) 843666 Fax: (01234) 843636 E-mail: icpsales@jangro.net

J Williams, Unit 2 Freeman Street, Birkenhead, Merseyside, CH41 1BR Tel: 0151-647 6532 Fax: 0151-647 6532

Johnsons Apparelmaster, 150 Stoney Rock Lane, Leeds, LS9 7BL Tel: 0113-249 5755 Fax: 0113-249 7036

Le Vigneron, 26 Lion Road, Bexleyheath, Kent, DA6 8NR Tel: (020) 8303 3534 Fax: (020) 8303 3534 E-mail: sales@levigneron.co.uk

PJ's Workwear, 42 The Tything, Worcester, WR1 1JT Tel: (01905) 22051 Fax: (01905) 617476

WIPES, FABRIC/FIBRE

Britannia Wiper Co., Tidal Basin Road, London, E16 1AD Tel: (020) 7476 6888 Fax: (020) 7476 9888E-mail: sales@britannia-wiper.co.uk

Colletex Ltd, Whitebirk Road, Blackburn, BB1 3JA Tel: (01254) 261768 Fax: (01254) 665425 E-mail: sales@colletex.co.uk

Coppermill, 118-122 Cheshire Street, London, E2 6EJ Tel: (020) 7739 6102 Fax: (020) 7739 9400 E-mail: info@coppermill.ltd.uk

D W Begal & Son, Vulcan Works, Malta Street, Manchester, M4 7AP Tel: 0161-273 3296 Fax: 0161-273 3293

Easiclean Products, 10 East House Farm, Atherstone Lane, Merevale, Atherstone, Warwickshire, CV9 2HT Tel: (01827) 874787 Fax: (01827) 874745 E-mail: info@easicleanwipersl.com

Omega Wipers, 12 Fordrough, Yardley, Birmingham, B25 8DL Tel: 0121-771 2653 Fax: 0121-771 2652 E-mail: omegawipers@aol.com

WIRE BASKETS

▶ Eurowire Containers Ltd, Maypole Fields, Cradley, Halesowen, West Midlands, B63 2QB Tel: (01384) 561786 Fax: (01384) 564044 E-mail: support@eurowirecontainers.com

▶ R V Rugg Ltd, Station Lane, Featherstone, Pontefract, West Yorkshire, WF7 5BA Tel: (01977) 791944 Fax: (01977) 707468

Wirex Metal Baskets, Marston Road, Hoddesdon, Hertfordshire, EN11 0AD Tel: (01992) 469585 Fax: (01992) 441940

WIRE BELTING

Davies Woven Wire Ltd, Unit 38 Cradley Heath Factory Centre, Woods Lane, Cradley Heath, West Midlands, B64 7AQ Tel: (01384) 411991 Fax: (01384) 410999 E-mail: sales@davieswovenwire.co.uk

George Lane & Sons Ltd, Bannerley Road, Birmingham, B33 0SL Tel: 0121-784 5525 Fax: 0121-783 6988 E-mail: info@georgelane.co.uk

WIRE BENDING MACHINES

Pave Automation Design & Development Ltd, Padholme Road East, Peterborough, PE1 5XL Tel: (01733) 342519 Fax: (01733) 563500 E-mail: pave@enterprise.net

▶ Ultimation Machines Ltd, Laundry Way, Capel, Dorking, Surrey, RH5 5LG Tel: (01306) 712205 Fax: (01306) 713182

WIRE BINDING SYSTEMS

Joto Ltd, 1c North Cresent, London, E16 4TG Tel: (020) 7511 4411 Fax: (020) 7511 5266

WIRE BRAIDING MACHINES

▶ Oma UK Ltd, Unit 3-4 Greenfield Farm Industrial Estate, Hopkins Lane, Congleton, Cheshire, CW12 4TR Tel: (01260) 278585 Fax: (01260) 278590 E-mail: omauk@aol.com

WIRE BRUSHES

Buckleys Brushes, Lowland Works, Hurst Lane, Mirfield, West Yorkshire, WF14 8LY Tel: (01924) 498214 Fax: (01924) 480632 E-mail: brit.bung@telincon.co.uk

K T S Wire Industries Ltd, Park Mills, South Street, Morley, Leeds, LS27 8AT Tel: 0113-253 2421 Fax: 0113-307 6868 E-mail: mail@ktswire.com

P M R Industrial Services, 13-21 Liverpool Road, Kidsgrove, Stoke-on-Trent, ST7 1EA Tel: (01782) 776325 Fax: (01782) 771912

Progress Shaving Brush Ltd, 24 Spring Valley Industrial Estate, Douglas, Isle of Man, IM2 2QR Tel: (01624) 676030 Fax: (01624) 662056E-mail: enquiries@progress-vulfix.com

Howard Richard Sales Ltd, 10 Holkham Road, Orton Southgate, Peterborough, PE2 6TE Tel: (01733) 237779 Fax: (01733) 230027 E-mail: sales@hrsales.co.uk

WIRE CUTTING BLADES

CGB Engineering Services Ltd, 2 Britannia House, Gorton Road, Manchester, M11 2DA Tel: 0161-231 7347 Fax: 0161-231 7077 E-mail: cgbservices@aol.com

WIRE DRAWERS, *See Wire, Steel etc; also other headings for particular metal or usage*

WIRE DRAWING ACCESSORIES

Locton Ltd, Unit 6a Alfred Court Saxon Business Park, Hanbury Road, Stoke Prior, Bromsgrove, Worcestershire, B60 4AD Tel: (01527) 570977 Fax: (01527) 878990 E-mail: locton@spring-tooling.co.uk

WIRE DRAWING DIES

J G Markland & Sons, Park Works, Borron Road, Newton-le-Willows, Merseyside, WA12 0EJ Tel: (01925) 220718 Fax: (01925) 220718

WIRE DRAWING MACHINERY

Pentre Overseas Holdings Ltd, Neills Road, Bold Industrial Park, Bold, St. Helens, Merseyside, WA9 4TJ Tel: (01744) 811820 Fax: (01744) 819994 E-mail: sales@pentre.co.uk

WIRE (ENAMELLED) MANUFRS

Essex Nexans UK Ltd, Ellis Ashton Street, Liverpool, L36 6BW Tel: 0151-443 6000 Fax: 0151-443 6025 E-mail: sales@essexgroup.co.uk

Reyton Metals Ltd, 1 Malvern View Business Park, Stella Way, Cheltenham, Gloucestershire, GL52 7DQ Tel: (01242) 631000 Fax: (01242) 631110

Von Roll UK Ltd, Unit 6, Lawrence Way, Dunstable, Bedfordshire, LU6 1BD Tel: (01582) 500500 Fax: (01582) 476456 E-mail: wire@vonroll.com

WIRE EROSION ELECTRICAL DISCHARGE MACHINING (EDM) MACHINE TOOLS

A Form Tooling Ltd, 542 Aylestone Road, Leicester, LE2 8JB Tel: 0116-283 5936 Fax: 0116-244 0277 E-mail: aform.tooling@ntlworld.com

Gibtool Engineers, 1 Whitehall Mill, Whitehall Street, Darwen, Lancashire, BB3 2LP Tel: (01254) 705909 Fax: (01254) 705909

WIRE EROSION MACHINERY

Ells Machinery (Spark Erosion), 49 The Rise, Partridge Green, Horsham, West Sussex, RH13 8JB Tel: (01403) 710609 Fax: (01403) 710609

WIRE EROSION MACHINING SERVICES (INCLUDING ON SITE)

Ash Tool Co. Ltd, Lord Street, Ashton-under-Lyne, Lancashire, OL6 6HZ Tel: 0161-330 2325 Fax: 0161-343 2229 E-mail: ash.tool@zen.co.uk

Bevan, 53a Frederick Street, Birmingham, B1 3HS Tel: 0121-236 9263 Fax: 0121-236 9263

Clifton Precision Tools Ltd, Cakemore Road, Rowley Regis, West Midlands, B65 0QW Tel: 0121-559 3096 Fax: 0121-561 5661 E-mail: p.clifton@cliftonprecision.com

Comcir Radio Communications, 66 Goldstone Villas, Hove, East Sussex, BN3 3RU Tel: (01273) 779828 Fax: (01273) 204900 E-mail: info@comcir.co.uk

D R Case & Son, 5 Lady Bee Marina Industrial Units, Albion Street, Southwick, Brighton, BN42 4EG Tel: (01273) 870850 Fax: (01273) 870855 E-mail: colin.case@btconnect.com

Di-Spark Ltd, Unit 3B Wessex Gate, Portsmouth Road, Horndean, Waterlooville, Hampshire, PO8 9LP Tel: (023) 9259 6338 Fax: (023) 9259 4077 E-mail: sales@dispsrks.co.uk

G K Precision 96, 4 Sidings Road, Lowmoor Industrial Estate, Kirkby-in-Ashfield, Nottingham, NG17 7JZ Tel: (01623) 721919 Fax: (01623) 751616

▶ Hardmetal Engineering Cornwall Ltd, Treleigh Industrial Estate, Jon Davey Drive, Redruth, Cornwall, TR16 4AX Tel: (01209) 202809 Fax: (01209) 202819 E-mail: sales@tungsten-carbide.com

Hi Tech E D M Services Ltd, 18 Bayton Road, Bayton Road Industrial Estate, Exhall, Coventry, CV7 9EJ Tel: (024) 7664 4404 Fax: (024) 7636 3777 E-mail: sales@hitechaerospace.com

K F C Engineering Ltd, Unit 6 Little Forge Road, Redditch, Worcestershire, B98 7SF Tel: (01527) 520371 Fax: (01527) 520346 E-mail: kevin@kfcengineering.co.uk

WIRE EROSION MACHINING SERVICES (INCLUDING ON SITE) –

continued

K Pilcher Engineering, Unit D1 Guy Motors Industrial Park, Park Lane, Wolverhampton, WV10 9QF Tel: (01902) 728820 Fax: (01902) 304769 E-mail: kpeng@waverider.co.uk

Karson 2002 Engineering Ltd, Tram Way, Oldbury Road, Smethwick, West Midlands, B66 1NR Tel: 0121-558 4852 Fax: 0121-558 4852 E-mail: sales@karson.co.uk

Le Craft Products, Unit 10-11 Ebblake Industrial Estate, Forest Close, Ebblake Industrial Estate, Verwood, Dorset, BH31 6DE Tel: (01202) 827171 Fax: (01202) 813020

M P M Presstools, 1 Chancel Way Industrial Estate, Chancel Way, Birmingham, B6 7AU Tel: 0121-356 7600 Fax: 0121-356 9766 E-mail: mpm.presstools@btconnect.com

Meridian Tooling Co. Ltd, Unit 6, Exis Court, Veasey Close, Attleborough Fields Industrial Estate, Nuneaton, Warwickshire, CV11 6RT Tel: (024) 7634 0187 Fax: (024) 7664 1301 E-mail: meridian@netcomuk.co.uk

Multispark Erosion Ltd, 145 Camford Way, Luton, LU3 3AN Tel: (01582) 502015 Fax: (01582) 507836 E-mail: sales@multispark.co.uk

Pascoe Engineering Ltd, 127 Nitshill Road, Glasgow, G53 7TD Tel: 0141-880 6444 Fax: 0141-881 4832 E-mail: info@pascoelimited.com

Penico Systems Ltd, Albion Works, Keighley Road, Bingley, West Yorkshire, BD16 2RD Tel: (01274) 511044 Fax: (01274) 510770

PT Wire & Spark Erosion, Short Acre Street, Walsall, WS2 8HW Tel: (01922) 633708 Fax: (01922) 643072

R S T Spark Erosion Ltd, 7 Firbank Court, Leighton Buzzard, Bedfordshire, LU7 4YJ Tel: 01525 850797

Ryeland Toolmakers, Units 17-18 Barton Road, Water Eaton Industrial Estate, Milton Keynes, MK2 3JJ Tel: (01908) 647746 Fax: (01908) 270236 E-mail: info@ryelandtoolmakers.co.uk

S L S Precision Engineers Ltd, 1 Hermitage Way, Mansfield, Nottinghamshire, NG18 5ES Tel: (01623) 456601 Fax: (01623) 456602 E-mail: slsprec@aol.com

Sertrix Tools Ltd, Clayton Road, Hayes, Middlesex, UB3 1BQ Tel: (020) 8848 9545 Fax: (020) 8561 7077

Sheen Spark Ltd, 1 Ewhurst Avenue, Birmingham, B29 6EY Tel: 0121-472 6241 Fax: 0121-472 5396

Springfield Tools Ltd, Unit 14B, 54 College Road, Perry Barr, Birmingham, B44 8BS Tel: 0121-356 3403 Fax: 0121-356 2155 E-mail: andrewregan@btconnect.com

Sutton Tooling Ltd, Reservoir Road, Hull, HU6 7QD Tel: (01482) 342879 Fax: (01482) 446911 E-mail: suttontool@aol.com

T & G Engineering Co. Ltd, Unit 14 Camphill Industrial Estate, Camphill Road, West Byfleet, Surrey, KT14 6EW Tel: (01932) 353228 Fax: (01932) 349692 E-mail: sales@tgengineering.co.uk

Tarpey-Harris Ltd, Flamstead House, Denby Hall Business Park, Denby, Ripley, Derbyshire, DE5 8NN Tel: (01332) 883950 Fax: (01332) 883951 E-mail: steve.jones@tarpey-harris.co.uk

Tecform Engineering, 34 Soho Mills, Wooburn Green, High Wycombe, Buckinghamshire, HP10 0PF Tel: (01628) 524989 Fax: (01628) 524989 E-mail: sales@tecform.co.uk

Thistle Tools Ltd, Unit 6a, Sandwich Industrial Estate, Sandwich, Kent, CT13 9LN Tel: (01304) 612696 Fax: (01304) 619207

Thornpark Ltd, B1-B2 Pegasus Court, Ardglen Road, Whitchurch, Hampshire, RG28 7BP Tel: (01256) 896161 Fax: (01256) 896162 E-mail: sales@thornpark.co.uk

V & P Engineering, Wakefield Road, Brighouse, West Yorkshire, HD6 1PE Tel: (01484) 719360 Fax: (01484) 400093

Wines Precision Engineers, The Old Dairy, Egg Pie Lane, Weald, Sevenoaks, Kent, TN14 6NP Tel: (01732) 740542 Fax: (01732) 464440 E-mail: sales@winesweb.com

Winn Tools Ltd, Kendricks Road, Wednesbury, West Midlands, WS10 8LY Tel: 0121-526 2075 Fax: 0121-526 5095

Wire Erosion Co. Ltd, Units 8-9, Springfield Business Centre, Oldends Lane, Stonehouse, Gloucestershire, GL10 3SX Tel: (01453) 827771 Fax: (01453) 827761

WIRE FENCING

Hampton Steel & Wire, London Road, Wellingborough, Northamptonshire, NN8 2DJ Tel: (01933) 233333 Fax: (01933) 442701 E-mail: sales@hamptonsteel.co.uk

Lanlee Supplies Ltd, Red Scar Works, Burnley Road, Colne, Lancashire, BB8 8ED Tel: (01282) 868204 Fax: (01282) 870116 E-mail: sales@lanleesupplies.co.uk

Rom Group Ltd, Eastern Avenue, Trent Valley, Lichfield, Staffordshire, WS13 6RN Tel: (01543) 414111 Fax: (01543) 421605 E-mail: sales@rom.co.uk

WIRE FENCING PRODUCTION MACHINERY

C L D Fencing Systems Suppliers, Unit 11, Springvale Business Centre, Millbuck Way, Sandbach, Cheshire, CW11 3HY Tel: (01270) 764751

WIRE FORMED/SHAPED COMPONENTS/PRODUCTS

A S K Springs, Edward Street, Clive Works, Redditch, Worcestershire, B97 6HA Tel: (01527) 63300 Fax: (01527) 63300

The Active Spring Company Ltd, Sibleys Green, Sibleys Lane, Thaxted, Dunmow, Essex, CM6 2NU Tel: (01371) 830557 Fax: (01371) 831151 E-mail: sales@tascuk.com

Alton Wire Products, Pennypot Industrial Estate, Hythe, Kent, CT21 6PE Tel: (01303) 266061 Fax: (01303) 261080 E-mail: finance@delphinware.co.uk

Bevans Holdings Leicester Ltd, Gloucester Cresent, Wigston, Leicestershire, LE18 4YR Tel: 0116-278 2331 Fax: 0116-277 8307 E-mail: sales@bevanscomponents.co.uk

CDP Ltd, Old Popplewell Lane, Scholes, Cleckheaton, West Yorkshire, BD19 6DW Tel: (01274) 697697 Fax: (01274) 697797 E-mail: webtech@cdpltd.co.uk

Central Wheel Components Ltd, Station Road Industrial Estate, Station Road, Coleshill, Birmingham, B46 1HT Tel: (01675) 462264 Fax: (01675) 466412 E-mail: info@central-wheel.co.uk

D B Springs Ltd, 1 Double Century Works, High Street, Astwood Bank, Redditch, Worcestershire, B96 6AR Tel: (01527) 893220 Fax: (01527) 893220

Doig Springs, Unit 1 Fairview Estate, Beech Road, Wycombe Marsh, High Wycombe, Buckinghamshire, HP11 1RY Tel: 01494 556700 Fax: 01494 511002 E-mail: enquiries@springs.co.uk

F B A Spring Engineers, 4 Howard Road, Park Farm Industrial Estate, Redditch, Worcestershire, B98 7SE Tel: (01527) 523524 Fax: (01527) 523524

Farm Harned Ltd, 56 Magdalen Road, Tilney St. Lawrence, King's Lynn, Norfolk, PE34 4RG Tel: (01945) 880582 Fax: (01945) 881511 E-mail: sales@farmharnedsolutions.com

A. & J. Green Engineering Ltd, Units 12-13, Enfield Industrial Estate, Redditch, Worcestershire, B97 6BG Tel: (01527) 62666 Fax: (01527) 584298 E-mail: ddptools@aol.com

H A Light Multiforms, Woods Lane, Cradley Heath, West Midlands, B64 7AL Tel: (01384) 569283 Fax: (01384) 633712

Hamster Baskets, Ayhill, Aylton, Ledbury, Herefordshire, HR8 2QJ Tel: (01531) 670209 Fax: (01531) 670630 E-mail: richard@hamsterbaskets.co.uk

Innovative Springs & Wireforms, Unit 17 Millard Industrial Estate, Cornwallis Road, Lyng, West Bromwich, West Midlands, B70 7JF Tel: 0121-553 3373 Fax: 0121-553 3375

Jourdans Sheet Metal Work, Marsh End, Lords Meadow Industrial Estate, Crediton, Devon, EX17 1DN Tel: (01363) 773562 Fax: (01363) 773365 E-mail: pluxton@jourdansmetal.co.uk

K D Engineering Merseyside Ltd, Unit 33b-33c Garston Industrial Estate, Blackburne Street, Liverpool, L19 8JB Tel: 0151-427 8996 Fax: 0151-427 9397 E-mail: kengine@mersinet.co.uk

Lander Automotive Ltd, Woodgate Business Park, 174 Clapgate Lane, Birmingham, B32 3ED Tel: 0121-423 1110 Fax: 0121-423 2220 E-mail: enquiries@lander.co.uk

Oakham Engineering, Newtown, Evesham, Worcestershire, WR11 8RZ Tel: (01386) 446513

▶ Oswald Springs, 76 Arthur Street, Redditch, Worcestershire, B98 8LJ Tel: (01527) 527777 Fax: (01527) 527785 E-mail: oswald@oswaldsprings.co.uk

Peterson Spring Europe Ltd, Unit 21, Trescott Road, Trafford Park, Redditch, Worcestershire, B98 7AH Tel: (01527) 585657 Fax: (01527) 588317 E-mail: sales@peterson.co.uk

▶ R V Rugg Ltd, Station Lane, Featherstone, Pontefract, West Yorkshire, WF7 5BA Tel: (01977) 791944 Fax: (01977) 707468

Spring Developments Ltd, Lyng Lane, West Bromwich, West Midlands, B70 7RP Tel: 0121-553 6543 Fax: 0121-553 7552

Spring & Press Developments Ltd, Unit 49 Enfield Industrial Estate, Redditch, Worcestershire, B97 6DE Tel: (01527) 67602 Fax: (01527) 60183 E-mail: sales@kn-products.co.uk

Springmakers Redditch Ltd, Unit 2b Ipsley Street, Redditch, Worcestershire, B98 7BU Tel: (01527) 65300 Fax: (01527) 65300

Stockton Engineering Ltd, 84 Barford Street, Birmingham, B5 6AH Tel: 0121-622 7474 Fax: 0121-666 6264 E-mail: peter@stocktonengineering.co.uk

Tomkins Buckle, Brockhurst CR, Walsall, WS5 4QG Tel: (01922) 723003 Fax: (01922) 723149 E-mail: sales@fhtomkins.com

United Springs Ltd, Mandale Park, Norman Road, Rochdale, Lancashire, OL11 4HP Tel: 01706 644551 Fax: 01706 630516 E-mail: amay@united-springs.co.uk

Whitmarley Engineering Co. Ltd, Ivy Road, Stirchley, Birmingham, B30 2NX Tel: 0121-458 7491 Fax: 0121-433 4137 E-mail: enquiries@whitmarley.fsnet.co.uk

WIRE FORMING AND BENDING

▶ Anglia Springs Ltd, Unit N Loddon Industrial Estate, Little Money Road, Loddon, Norwich, NR14 6JD Tel: (01508) 528396 Fax: (01508) 528240 E-mail: info@angliasprings.com

Crane Spring Co., Frederick Street, Walsall, WS2 9NJ Tel: (01922) 625313 Fax: (01922) 723561 E-mail: sales@cranesp.co.uk

Vanguard Wire Products, Victoria Wire Works, Raglan Street, Halifax, West Yorkshire, HX1 5QY Tel: (01422) 353339 Fax: (01422) 364532 E-mail: info@thinkg.co.uk

WIRE FORMING/MULTIPLE SLIDE MACHINE/PRESS MANUFRS

Clwyd Tool & Die, 35 Greenfield Business Park, Bagillt Road, Greenfield, Holywell, Clwyd, CH8 7HJ Tel: (01352) 715515 Fax: (01352) 715515

John H. Smith (Engineers) Ltd, Birds Royd Lane, Brighouse, West Yorkshire, HD6 1LQ Tel: (01484) 715295 Fax: (01484) 710253

Pave Automation Design & Development Ltd, Padholme Road East, Peterborough, PE1 5XL Tel: (01733) 342519 Fax: (01733) 563500 E-mail: pave@enterprise.net

WIRE GAUZE/CLOTH MANUFRS

Caldwell Filtration Ltd, Unit 3d, Lyncastle Way, Barley Castle Trading Estate, Warrington, WA4 4ST Tel: (01925) 267111 Fax: (01925) 267744 E-mail: info@caldwellfiltration.co.uk

Dale Engineering Co. Ltd, Wolverhampton Road, Wedges Mills, Cannock, Staffordshire, WS11 1SN Tel: (01543) 503265 Fax: (01543) 505475

East Anglian Wire Works, Wright Road, Ipswich, IP3 9RN Tel: (01473) 270820

▶ Graepel Perforators Ltd, Unit 5 Burtonwood Industrial Centre, Phipps Lane, Burtonwood, Warrington, WA5 4HX Tel: 0845 4941749 Fax: (01925) 228069 E-mail: sales@graepeluk.com

Midland Wire Mesh Ltd, Lodgefield Road, Halesowen, West Midlands, B62 8AX Tel: 0121-559 4020 Fax: 0121-561 4030 E-mail: waltmesh@aol.co.uk

▶ R & J Mesh, 2 The Wallows Industrial Estate, Fens Pool Avenue, Brierley Hill, West Midlands, DY5 1QA Tel: (01384) 70488 Fax: (01384) 265663 E-mail: sales@rjmesh.co.uk

Robinson Wire Cloth Ltd, 1 Rebecca Street, Stoke-On-Trent, ST4 1AG Tel: (01782) 412521 Fax: (01782) 412766 E-mail: info@wirecloth.uk.com

WIRE GAUZE/CLOTH, NON FERROUS

▶ Graepel Perforators Ltd, Unit 5 Burtonwood Industrial Centre, Phipps Lane, Burtonwood, Warrington, WA5 4HX Tel: 0845 4941749 Fax: (01925) 228069 E-mail: sales@graepeluk.com

WIRE GOODS/PRODUCTS, AUTOMOTIVE

Vanguard Wire Products, Victoria Wire Works, Raglan Street, Halifax, West Yorkshire, HX1 5QY Tel: (01422) 353339 Fax: (01422) 364532 E-mail: info@thinkg.co.uk

WIRE GOODS/PRODUCTS, DOMESTIC

A Harvey & Co The Wireworkers Ltd, 2 Stockton End, Sandy, Bedfordshire, SG19 1SB Tel: (01767) 681830 Fax: (01767) 683111 E-mail: sales@harveywire.freeserve.co.uk

Delfinware, Pennypot Industrial Estate, Pennypot, Hythe, Kent, CT21 6PE Tel: (01303) 266061 Fax: (01303) 261080 E-mail: sampsonwwp@aol.com

Farm Harned Ltd, 56 Magdalen Road, Tilney St. Lawrence, King's Lynn, Norfolk, PE34 4RG Tel: (01945) 880582 Fax: (01945) 881511 E-mail: sales@farmharnedsolutions.com

Gardman Ltd, High Street, Moulton, Spalding, Lincolnshire, PE12 6QD Tel: (01406) 372222 Fax: (01406) 372233 E-mail: sales@gardman.co.uk

Hill & Sons, Ringstones, Bridgemont, Whaley Bridge, High Peak, Derbyshire, SK23 7PD Tel: (01663) 732607 Fax: (01663) 734913 E-mail: hillsriddles@btinternet.com

J & C R Wood, 66 Clough Road, Hull, HU5 1SR Tel: (01482) 345067 Fax: (01482) 441141 E-mail: info@jandcrwood.co.uk

J W Lister Ltd, Clifton Road, Brighouse, West Yorkshire, HD6 1SL Tel: (01484) 712925 Fax: (01484) 715314 E-mail: sales@jwlister.co.uk

Moss Lighting Ltd, Unit 2a Bordesley Street, Birmingham, B5 5PG Tel: 0121-643 0529 Fax: 0121-633 4576

Newco Wire Products Ltd, Unit 1, 257 Dalmarnock Road, Glasgow, G40 4LX Tel: 0141 5547732

▶ R V Rugg Ltd, Station Lane, Featherstone, Pontefract, West Yorkshire, WF7 5BA Tel: (01977) 791944 Fax: (01977) 707468

WIRE GOODS/PRODUCTS, INDUSTRIAL

Arkinstall Ltd, 6 Buntsford Park Road, Bromsgrove, Worcestershire, B60 3DX Tel: (01527) 872962 Fax: (01527) 837127 E-mail: info@arkinstall.co.uk

Buchanan Wire Mesh Ltd, 21b Drapersfield Road, Cookstown, County Tyrone, BT80 8RS Tel: (028) 8675 8644 Fax: (028) 8676 5764 E-mail: info@buchananwire.com

Craven & Co. Ltd, Manse Lane, Knaresborough, North Yorkshire, HG5 8ET Tel: (01423) 796208 Fax: (01423) 869189 E-mail: sales@craven-solutions.com

Diaploy Ltd, Manners Avenue, Manners Industrial Estate, Ilkeston, Derbyshire, DE7 8EF Tel: 0115-944 2272 Fax: 0115-944 2272

East Anglian Wire Works, Wright Road, Ipswich, IP3 9RN Tel: (01473) 270820

Farm Harned Ltd, 56 Magdalen Road, Tilney St. Lawrence, King's Lynn, Norfolk, PE34 4RG Tel: (01945) 880582 Fax: (01945) 881511 E-mail: sales@farmharnedsolutions.com

Gold Bros Ltd, Arches Abc, 408 Ellingfort Road, London, E8 3PA Tel: (020) 8985 7926 Fax: (020) 9898 5729 E-mail: info@goldbros.co.uk

Henry Lewis & Son Ltd, 7 Bolling Road, Bradford, West Yorkshire, BD4 7HN Tel: (01274) 307359 Fax: (01274) 370784

J W Lister Ltd, Clifton Road, Brighouse, West Yorkshire, HD6 1SL Tel: (01484) 712925 Fax: (01484) 715314 E-mail: sales@jwlister.co.uk

James Gilbert & Son Ltd, 129 The Vale, London, W3 7RQ Tel: (020) 8743 1566 Fax: (020) 8746 1393 E-mail: metalforest@hotmail.com

James Murphey Of Falkirk Ltd, Lochlands Industrial Estate, Unit 45, Larbert, Stirlingshire, FK5 3NS Tel: (01324) 562029 Fax: (01324) 621245 E-mail: sales@jamesmurphy-falkirk.co.uk

Metalcote Wire Products Mnfrs, Unit 14 Bromyard Road Industrial Estate, Ledbury, Herefordshire, HR8 1NS Tel: (01531) 633704 Fax: (01531) 635085 E-mail: enquiries@metalcote.co.uk

Newco Wire Products Ltd, Unit 1, 257 Dalmarnock Road, Glasgow, G40 4LX Tel: 0141 5547732

Norfolk Industries For The Blind, Oak Street, Norwich, NR3 3BP Tel: (01603) 667957 Fax: (01603) 624265 E-mail: sales@norfolk-industries.co.uk

R Worsdall & Co., 17-19 Reform Street, Hull, HU2 8EF Tel: (01482) 320383 Fax: (01482) 320383

Reid Wire Ltd, 162 Glenpark Street, Glasgow, G31 1PG Tel: 0141-554 7081 Fax: 0141-556 4483 E-mail: sales@reidwire.com

Roycott Ltd, Royston Road, Byfleet, West Byfleet, Surrey, KT14 7NY Tel: (01932) 343515 Fax: (01932) 351285 E-mail: info@charlesausten.com

Speedwell Reinforcement Ltd, White Lane, Chapeltown, Sheffield, S35 2YG Tel: 0114-246 7551 Fax: 0114-240 2519 E-mail: enquiries@speedwellreinforcement.co.uk

Stoke On Trent Workshops For The Blind, 211 City Road, Stoke-on-Trent, ST4 2PN Tel: (01782) 233900 Fax: (01782) 234900 E-mail: sales@stokeworkshops.co.uk

Thomas Shaw & Son (M/C) Ltd, Star Works, Holt Town, Manchester, M40 7FQ Tel: 0161-273 7686 Fax: 0161-274 3699 E-mail: tommy.shaw@virgin.net

W J Gowar & Co. Ltd, Rheidol Mews, London, N1 8NU Tel: (020) 7226 3644 Fax: (020) 7226 2969

Wirex Metal Baskets, Marston Road, Hoddesdon, Hertfordshire, EN11 0AD Tel: (01992) 469585 Fax: (01992) 441940

WIRE GOODS/PRODUCTS, TO SPECIFICATION

Carclo Engineering Group, PO Box 14, Ossett, West Yorkshire, WF5 9LR Tel: (01924) 268040 Fax: (01924) 283226 E-mail: investor.relations@carclo-plc.com

Suffolk Wire, River Hill, Bramford, Ipswich, IP8 4BB Tel: (01473) 748713 Fax: (01473) 748713

WIRE MANUFRS, *See also Wire, Steel etc; also other headings for particular metal or usage*

Amodil Supplies Ltd, Enterprise Trading Estate, Guinness Road, Trafford Park, Manchester, M17 1SG Tel: 0161-877 4539 Fax: 0161-877 4541 E-mail: mcl@amodilmanchester.demon.co.uk

WIRE MANUFRS – *continued*

Barnfather Wire Ltd, Willenhall Road, Wednesbury, West Midlands, WS10 8JG Tel: 0121-526 2880 Fax: 0121-526 3130 E-mail: sales@barnfatherwire.co.uk

Bridon Wire Special Steels Division, Sheephouse Wood, Stocksbridge, Sheffield, S36 4GS Tel: 0114-288 4207 Fax: 0114-288 4874

Carrington Binns Ltd, Lowfields Way, Lowfields Business Park, Elland, West Yorkshire, HX5 9DA Tel: (01422) 372372 Fax: (01422) 315100 E-mail: sales@carringtonwire.com

Draka Wire, Coastal Link Road, Llanelli, Dyfed, SA15 2NH Tel: (01554) 750121 Fax: (01554) 783808 E-mail: wiresales@draka.com

James Smith & Son Redditch Ltd, 22-24 Bromsgrove Road, Redditch, Worcestershire, B97 4QY Tel: (01527) 62034 Fax: (01527) 68826

Jourdans Sheet Metal Work, Marsh End, Lords Meadow Industrial Estate, Crediton, Devon, EX17 1DN Tel: (01363) 773562 Fax: (01363) 773365 E-mail: pluxton@jourdansmetal.co.uk

R & S Wire Ltd, Grove Street, Kirklees Steel Works, Brighouse, West Yorkshire, HD6 1PL Tel: (01484) 715120 Fax: (01484) 711882

John Riddel & Son Ltd, 1A Dagger Road, Lisburn, County Antrim, BT28 2TJ Tel: (028) 9262 0810 Fax: (028) 9262 0811 E-mail: sales@riddel.co.uk

Temple Taunton Co Ltd, 55 Lockfield Avenue, Enfield, Middlesex, EN3 7JJ Tel: (020) 8344 9840 Fax: (020) 8344 9850

Tri Wire Ltd, Good Hope Close, Normanton, West Yorkshire, WF6 1TR Tel: (01924) 223744 Fax: (01924) 220098 E-mail: sales@nexanstriwire.com

Webster & Horsfall Ltd, Fordrough, Birmingham, B25 8DW Tel: 0121-772 2555 Fax: 0121-772 0762 E-mail: sales@websterandhorsfall.co.uk

WIRE MARKERS, *See also headings for particular types*

Grafoplast, PO Box 159, Stevenage, Hertfordshire, SG2 7QA Tel: (01438) 861166 Fax: (01438) 861123 E-mail: sales@grafoplasteurope.com

WIRE MESH, *See also headings for particular types*

Caldwell Filtration Ltd, Unit 3d, Lyncastle Way, Barley Castle Trading Estate, Warrington, WA4 4ST Tel: (01925) 267111 Fax: (01925) 267744 E-mail: info@caldwellfiltration.co.uk

Davtex UK Ltd, Link House, Bute Street, Fenton, Stoke-on-Trent, ST4 3PR Tel: (01782) 318000 Fax: (01782) 319000 E-mail: davtexuk@netscapeonline.co.uk

▶ Graepel Perforators Ltd, Unit 5 Burtonwood Industrial Centre, Phipps Lane, Burtonwood, Warrington, WA5 4HX Tel: 0845 4941749 Fax: (01925) 228069 E-mail: sales@graepeluk.com

Maccaferri Ltd, 7600 The Quorum, Oxford Business Park North, Garsington Road, Oxford, OX4 2JZ Tel: (01865) 770555 Fax: (01865) 774550 E-mail: oxford@maccaferri.co.uk

Midland Wire Mesh Ltd, Lodgefield Road, Halesowen, West Midlands, B62 8AX Tel: 0121-559 4020 Fax: 0121-561 4030 E-mail: waltmesh@aol.co.uk

▶ R & J Mesh, 2 The Wallows Industrial Estate, Fens Pool Avenue, Brierley Hill, West Midlands, DY5 1QA Tel: (01384) 70488 Fax: (01384) 265663 E-mail: sales@rjmesh.co.uk

Rigby Wireworks & Co. (1982) Ltd, Cross Smithfields, Sheffield, S3 7AU Tel: 0114-272 4615 Fax: 0114-276 6840

Robinson Wire Cloth Ltd, 1 Rebecca Street, Stoke-On-Trent, ST4 1AG Tel: (01782) 412521 Fax: (01782) 412766 E-mail: info@wirecloth.uk.com

Thames Wire Production Ltd, Unit 11A Worton Hall, Worton Road, Isleworth, Middlesex, TW7 6ER Tel: (020) 8560 4936 Fax: (020) 8569 8145 E-mail: thameswire@btconnect.com

Wirecloth Sales & Development Ltd, 11a East View, Grappenhall, Warrington, WA4 2QH Tel: (01925) 268417 Fax: (01925) 604861 E-mail: wireclothsales@aol.com

WIRE MESH PRODUCTS

Catalytic Support Systems Ltd, Thelwall New Road Industrial Estate, Thelwall, Warrington, WA4 2LY Tel: (01928) 566344 Fax: (01925) 264995 E-mail: adrian_wood@knitwire.com

Dewric Ltd, St Lawrence Street, Great Harwood, Blackburn, BB6 7QZ Tel: (01254) 884855 Fax: (01254) 884855 E-mail: neil.dewhurst@tesco.net

Essex Wirework Company Ltd, PO Box 1, Hockley, Essex, SS5 5LD Tel: (01702) 205022 Fax: (01702) 207678

Maccaferri Ltd, 7600 The Quorum, Oxford Business Park North, Garsington Road, Oxford, OX4 2JZ Tel: (01865) 770555 Fax: (01865) 774550 E-mail: oxford@maccaferri.co.uk

▶ Metalmesh Ltd, PO Box 138, Marlborough, Wiltshire, SN8 1XE Tel: (01672) 841404 Fax: (01672) 841484 E-mail: sales@meshpartitions.com

Rigby Wireworks & Co. (1982) Ltd, Cross Smithfields, Sheffield, S3 7AU Tel: 0114-272 4615 Fax: 0114-276 6840

Wireguard Ltd, Crabtree Manorway South, Belvedere, Kent, DA17 6AW Tel: (020) 8320 6181 Fax: (020) 8311 6435

WIRE MESH, GALVANISED STEEL

BRC Welded Mesh, Whaley Road, Barugh, Barnsley, South Yorkshire, S75 1HT Tel: 01226 283438 Fax: 01226 248738 E-mail: industrialmesh@brc.ltd.uk

WIRE OR FIBRE ROPE NETS

Sicor International Ltd, 3 Murcar Industrial Estate, Denmore Road, Bridge of Don, Aberdeen, AB23 8JW Tel: (01224) 707560 Fax: (01224) 707561 E-mail: sales.sicorabdn@virgin.net

WIRE OR STRIP ELECTROPLATING

Leoni Temco Ltd, Whimsey Industrial Estate, Cinderford, Gloucestershire, GL14 3HZ Tel: (01594) 820100 Fax: (01594) 823691 E-mail: general@leonitemco.com

E. Williams Plating Ltd, Unit 3, The Dean, Alresford, Hampshire, SO24 9BQ Tel: (01962) 733199 Fax: (01962) 735146 E-mail: enquiries@ewp-hants.co.uk

WIRE PREPARATION

Croydon Cut & Strip, 105 Shirley Church Road, Croydon, CR0 5AG Tel: (020) 8656 4416 Fax: (020) 8656 6319 E-mail: ccs.stratford@virgin.net

WIRE RACE BEARINGS

Healy Bearings International Ltd, 4 Earls Close Industrial Estate, Earls Close, Thurmaston, Leicester, LE4 8FZ Tel: 0116-260 0849 Fax: 0116-260 0867 E-mail: healybearings@aol.com

Intake Engineering Ltd, Wingham Industrial Estate, Goodnestone Road, Wingham, Canterbury, Kent, CT3 1AR Tel: (01227) 720282 Fax: (01227) 728398 E-mail: contact@intakeengineering.co.uk

WIRE RINGS

Oakham Engineering, Newtown, Evesham, Worcestershire, WR11 8RZ Tel: (01386) 446513

WIRE ROPE ASSEMBLIES

Hamble Ropes & Rigging Ltd, 65-69 Bernard Street, Southampton, SO14 3BA Tel: (023) 8033 8286 Fax: (023) 8033 8288 E-mail: info@hrrlcovercraft.fsnet.co.uk

Imperial Wire Products Ltd, 78 Wharfdale Road, Tyseley, Birmingham, B11 2DE Tel: 0121-706 3802 Fax: 0121-706 8202

▶ Latch & Batchelor, Hay Mills, Birmingham, B25 8DW Tel: 0121-772 1386 Fax: 0121-772 0762 E-mail: sales@latchandbatchelor.co.uk

Matek Business Media Ltd, 4 Field Place Estate, Field Place, Broadbridge Heath, Horsham, West Sussex, RH12 3PB Tel: (01403) 276300 Fax: (01403) 276311E-mail: sales@matek.net

Midland Wire Cordage Co. Ltd, 2a Eagle Road, Moons Moat North Industrial Estate, Redditch, Worcestershire, B98 9HF Tel: (01527) 594150 Fax: (01527) 64322 E-mail: info@mid-cord.co.uk

R & G Marine & Industrial Services, Units 1a-2a Brickmakers Industrial Estate, Castle Road, Sittingbourne, Kent, ME10 3RL Tel: (01795) 470430 Fax: (01795) 429722 E-mail: sales@randgmarine.co.uk

▶ Rope Assemblies Ltd, Aurillac Way, Retford, Nottinghamshire, DN22 7PX Tel: (01777) 700714 Fax: (01777) 860719 E-mail: siobhan@ropeasseblies.co.uk

Tayco Engineering, Unit 6 Sherwood Industrial Estate, Bonnyrigg, Midlothian, EH19 3LW Tel: 0131-654 9655 Fax: 0131-654 9656 E-mail: graham@tayco.co.uk

WIRE ROPE ASSEMBLIES TO SPECIFICATION

▶ Rope Assemblies Ltd, Aurillac Way, Retford, Nottinghamshire, DN22 7PX Tel: (01777) 700714 Fax: (01777) 860719 E-mail: siobhan@ropeasseblies.co.uk

WIRE ROPE ATTACHMENTS OR FITTINGS

Imperial Wire Products Ltd, 78 Wharfdale Road, Tyseley, Birmingham, B11 2DE Tel: 0121-706 3802 Fax: 0121-706 8202

Reliance Barker Davies, Cheapside, Bridgend Industrial Estate, Bridgend, Mid Glamorgan, CF31 3UN Tel: (01656) 656381 Fax: (01656) 663869 E-mail: info@reliancebarkerdavies.com

WIRE ROPE LASHINGS

J W O'Pray & Sons Ltd, Gillane Works, Wassand Street, Hull, HU3 4AL Tel: (01482) 323014 Fax: (01482) 215944 E-mail: sales@oprays.com

WIRE ROPE OR CHAIN HOISTS

Lifting Gear Hire Ltd, Avon Trading Estate, 20A Albert Road, Bristol, BS2 0XA Tel: 0117-977 9514 Fax: 0117-972 3076

Slingtak Hoists Ltd, Quarry Road, Westgate, Cleckheaton, West Yorkshire, BD19 5HP Tel: (01274) 851724 Fax: (01274) 851724 E-mail: info@slingtak.co.uk

WIRE ROPE SLINGS

Gunnebo Ltd, Woolaston Road, Park Farm North, Redditch, Worcestershire, B98 7SG Tel: (01527) 522560 Fax: (01527) 510185 E-mail: sales@gunnebo.co.uk

J W O'Pray & Sons Ltd, Gillane Works, Wassand Street, Hull, HU3 4AL Tel: (01482) 323014 Fax: (01482) 215944 E-mail: sales@oprays.com

Onecall, 50 Avenue Road, Aston, Birmingham, B6 4DY Tel: (0800) 6524646 Fax: 0121-333 3996

Pfeifer Drako Ltd, Marshfield Bank, Crewe, CW2 8UY Tel: (01270) 587728 Fax: (01270) 587913 E-mail: admin@pfeiferdrako.co.uk

RSS Group, Unit 32A/32B Village Farm Industrial Estate, Pyle, Bridgend, Mid Glamorgan, CF33 6BL Tel: (01656) 740074 Fax: (01656) 747057 E-mail: steve@rssgroup.co.uk

Tayco Engineering, Unit 6 Sherwood Industrial Estate, Bonnyrigg, Midlothian, EH19 3LW Tel: 0131-654 9655 Fax: 0131-654 9656 E-mail: graham@tayco.co.uk

WIRE ROPES

A P Lifting Gear Co., Unit 7 Yarra Industrial Park, Ecclesfield, Sheffield, S35 9YA Tel: 0114-246 2422 Fax: 0114-246 2522 E-mail: peter.vernon@aplifting.com

Cotesi Ltd, 5-7 Mill Fold, Sowerby Bridge, West Yorkshire, HX6 4DJ Tel: (01422) 821000 Fax: (01422) 821007 E-mail: enquiries@cotesi.co.uk

Crosby Europe (U K) Ltd, Unit 10, Fallbank Industrial Estate, Dodworth, Barnsley, South Yorkshire, S75 3LS Tel: (01226) 290516 Fax: (01226) 240118 E-mail: sales@crosbyeurope.co.uk

▶ Latch & Batchelor, Hay Mills, Birmingham, B25 8DW Tel: 0121-772 1386 Fax: 0121-772 0762 E-mail: sales@latchandbatchelor.co.uk

Midland Wire Cordage Co. Ltd, 2a Eagle Road, Moons Moat North Industrial Estate, Redditch, Worcestershire, B98 9HF Tel: (01527) 594150 Fax: (01527) 64322 E-mail: info@mid-cord.co.uk

Pfeifer Drako Ltd, Marshfield Bank, Crewe, CW2 8UY Tel: (01270) 587728 Fax: (01270) 587913 E-mail: admin@pfeiferdrako.co.uk

Rope Services Tipton Ltd, St Georges Works, Bradleys Lane, Tipton, West Midlands, DY4 9EZ Tel: 0121-557 7521 Fax: 0121-557 8921

Ropetek Ltd, Unit 2 Caerphilly Business Park, Caerphilly, Mid Glamorgan, CF83 3ED Tel: (029) 2086 2688 Fax: (029) 2086 2767

S M W Engineering Ltd, Unit 2c Durham Road Industrial Estate, Wolsingham, Bishop Auckland, County Durham, DL13 3JW Tel: (01388) 528930

Tayco Engineering, Unit 6 Sherwood Industrial Estate, Bonnyrigg, Midlothian, EH19 3LW Tel: 0131-654 9655 Fax: 0131-654 9656 E-mail: graham@tayco.co.uk

WIRE SCREENS

Dale Engineering Co. Ltd, Wolverhampton Road, Wedges Mills, Cannock, Staffordshire, WS11 1SN Tel: (01543) 503265 Fax: (01543) 505475

Potter & Soar Ltd, Beaumont Road, Banbury, Oxfordshire, OX16 1SD Tel: (01295) 253344 Fax: (01295) 272132 E-mail: potter.soar@btinternet.com

Screen Manufacturing Co Scotland Ltd, Old Station Yard, Friockheim, Arbroath, Angus, DD11 4SJ Tel: (01241) 828697 Fax: (01241) 828690 E-mail: sales.enquiries@screenmanufacturing.co.uk

Screen Systems Ltd, PO Box 237, Warrington, WA5 0JZ Tel: (01925) 659906 Fax: (01925) 571060 E-mail: info@screensystems.com

WIRE SHELVING

▶ Bridledene Steel Fabricators, Little Marsh Quarter, Sandhurst, Cranbrook, Kent, TN18 5NY Tel: (01580) 850860 Fax: (01580) 850870 E-mail: info@bridledene.com

WIRE STRAIGHTENING/ CUTTING MACHINE MANUFRS

John H. Smith (Engineers) Ltd, Birds Royd Lane, Brighouse, West Yorkshire, HD6 1LQ Tel: (01484) 715295 Fax: (01484) 710253

▶ Thompson & Hudson Wire Machinery, Atlas Mill Road, Brighouse, West Yorkshire, HD6 1ES Tel: (01484) 715129 Fax: (01484) 717026 E-mail: info@thompsonandhudson.co.uk

WIRE STRAIGHTENING/ CUTTING SERVICES

Barnfather Wire Ltd, Willenhall Road, Wednesbury, West Midlands, WS10 8JG Tel: 0121-526 2880 Fax: 0121-526 3130 E-mail: sales@barnfatherwire.co.uk

Boswell Rod & Wire Ltd, 4 The Wallows Industrial Estate, Wallows Road, Brierley Hill, West Midlands, DY5 1QB Tel: (01384) 263238 Fax: (01384) 480223 E-mail: sales@boswellrod.co.uk

Carrington Binns Ltd, Lowfields Way, Lowfields Business Park, Elland, West Yorkshire, HX5 9DA Tel: (01422) 372372 Fax: (01422) 315100 E-mail: sales@carringtonwire.com

Croydon Cut & Strip, 105 Shirley Church Road, Croydon, CR0 5AG Tel: (020) 8656 4416 Fax: (020) 8656 6319 E-mail: ccs.stratford@virgin.net

Cutform Holdings Ltd, 6 Phoenix Industrial Estate, North Street, Lewes, East Sussex, BN7 2PQ Tel: (01273) 480420 Fax: (01273) 483089 E-mail: sales@cutform.co.uk

F B A Spring Engineers, 4 Howard Road, Park Farm Industrial Estate, Redditch, Worcestershire, B98 7SE Tel: (01527) 523524 Fax: (01527) 523524

Stride Supplies Ltd, 33 Monkspath Business Park, Highlands Road, Shirley, Solihull, West Midlands, B90 4NZ Tel: 0121-733 3010 Fax: 0121-733 3360 E-mail: sales@stride-technical.co.uk

WIRE STRIPPING

Croydon Cut & Strip, 105 Shirley Church Road, Croydon, CR0 5AG Tel: (020) 8656 4416 Fax: (020) 8656 6319 E-mail: ccs.stratford@virgin.net

WIRE STRIPPING MACHINES

Series 4 Ltd, 9 Westwood Court, Caomoor Industrial Estate, Totton, Southampton, SO40 3WX Tel: (023) 8086 6377 Fax: (023) 8086 6323 E-mail: sales@series4.co.uk

WIRE WORKING MACHINES

Cable & Wire Technical Services Ltd, 12 Tudor Grove, Gillingham, Kent, ME8 9AF Tel: (01634) 234786 Fax: (01634) 370980

Edscha (U K) Manufacturing Ltd, Middlemarch Business Park, Coventry, CV3 4FJ Tel: (024) 7651 6900 Fax: (024) 7630 2299 E-mail: enquiries@edscha.co.uk

John H. Smith (Engineers) Ltd, Birds Royd Lane, Brighouse, West Yorkshire, HD6 1LQ Tel: (01484) 715295 Fax: (01484) 710253

▶ Thompson & Hudson Wire Machinery, Atlas Mill Road, Brighouse, West Yorkshire, HD6 1ES Tel: (01484) 715129 Fax: (01484) 717026 E-mail: info@thompsonandhudson.co.uk

WIRE WOUND COMPONENTS

Carter Services, 12A The Butts, Belper, Derbyshire, DE56 1HX Tel: (01773) 821235 Fax: (01773) 821235 E-mail: carterservices@ndcarter.freeserve.co.uk

Catenate Consulting Ltd, Beech Leigh, Rectory Hill, Berrynarbor, Ilfracombe, Devon, EX34 9SE Tel: (01271) 882460 Fax: (01271) 882460 E-mail: sales@catenate-consulting.co.uk

WIRE, BED/SEAT

Carrington Binns Ltd, Lowfields Way, Lowfields Business Park, Elland, West Yorkshire, HX5 9DA Tel: (01422) 372372 Fax: (01422) 315100 E-mail: sales@carringtonwire.com

▶ indicates data change since last edition

WIRE, NON-FERROUS METAL,
See Copper Wire etc; also other headings for particular metal or usage

WIRED TELEVISION DISTRIBUTION SYSTEMS

F W Patterson Television Ltd, 21C1 Ben Nevis Estate, Claggan, Fort William, Inverness-Shire, PH33 6RU Tel: (01397) 702612 Fax: (01397) 701054 E-mail: fwpatterson@btconnect.com
Videor Technical GmbH, 14 Campbell Court, Bramley, Tadley, Hampshire, RG26 5EG Tel: (0870) 7749944 Fax: (0870) 7749955 E-mail: info@videortechnical.com

WIRELESS DOOR BELLS

▶ Empire, 4 Rose Cottages, Station Road, Claygate, Esher, Surrey, KT10 9DJ Tel: (07010) 714766 Fax: (01372) 466158

WIRELESS EQUIPMENT

Remploy Ltd, 63a Effra Road, London, SW2 1BZ Tel: (020) 7274 6681 Fax: (020) 7274 0715

WIRELESS FIRE ALARM SYSTEMS

▶ Cook Facilities Ltd, Technology Centre, 20 Westgate, Morecambe, Lancashire, LA3 3LN Tel: (01524) 402090 Fax: (01524) 418269 E-mail: sales@cookfire.co.uk
▶ Elektrek Services Ltd, 19 Manning Road, Felixstowe, Suffolk, IP11 2AY Tel: (01394) 270777 Fax: 01394 670189 E-mail: mail@elektrek.com

WIRELESS INTRUDER ALARMS

▶ 1st Step Security, 164 Malpas Road, Lewisham, London, SE4 1DH Tel: (0845) 0092879 E-mail: sales@firststepsecurity.co.uk
A Solo Security Ltd, 22a Horseshoe Park, Pangbourne, Reading, RG8 7JW Tel: 0118-984 4083 Fax: 0118-984 4204 E-mail: sales@asolosecurity.co.uk
▶ Allied Electronic Security Ltd, 10 Town End, Caterham, Surrey, CR3 5UG Tel: (01883) 381382 Fax: (01883) 340267 E-mail: info@allied-security.co.uk
▶ Anglo American Security Ltd, 160 Bridport Way, Braintree, Essex, CM7 9FF Tel: 01376 333631 Fax: 01376 333640 E-mail: info@anglo-american-security.com
▶ Better Environment & Security Technologies B E S T Ltd, Glen Rose, The Hollow, West Hoathly, East Grinstead, West Sussex, RH19 4QE Tel: (01342) 811990 Fax: 01342 811990 E-mail: britsectec@aol.com
▶ I F S Electronic Security Division, 20 St. Johns Road, Bootle, Merseyside, L20 8NJ Tel: 0151-955 4200 Fax: 0151-955 4240 E-mail: phill.ashton@ifscontractors.com
▶ Initial Electronic Security Systems Ltd, 19 Castle Park Road, Whiddon Valley Industrial Estate, Barnstaple, Devon, EX32 8PA Tel: (01271) 371309 Fax: (01271) 321115
▶ Intruder Protection Services Ltd, 2 Wenban Road, Worthing, West Sussex, BN11 1HY Tel: (01903) 204845
▶ Secure Solutions, 37 New Road, Burton Lazars, Melton Mowbray, Leicestershire, LE14 2UU Tel: 01664 568155 Fax: 01664 561990
▶ Wessex Fire & Security Ltd, Wessex House, Wincombe Lane, Shaftesbury, Dorset, SP7 8PJ Tel: (01747) 851661 Fax: (01747) 858860 E-mail: fire@wessex.org

WIRELESS LOCAL AREA NETWORK (WLAN) SOLUTIONS

▶ London Property Management Services Ltd, 2 Hall Place, Sutton Square, London, E9 6EG Tel: (0800) 1078760 Fax: (020) 8533 7756 E-mail: wireless@additional-knowledge.com

WIRELESS LOOP SYSTEMS

▶ Actuate S C R, Manor Barn, Thurloxton, Taunton, Somerset, TA2 8RH Tel: (07971) 682097 Fax: (0870) 1336615 E-mail: info@actuate.eu.com

WIRELESS NETWORK SYSTEMS, BROADBAND, FIXED

▶ Actuate S C R, Manor Barn, Thurloxton, Taunton, Somerset, TA2 8RH Tel: (07971) 682097 Fax: (0870) 1336615 E-mail: info@actuate.eu.com
▶ Tecnia, 63 Cromwell Road, Norwich, NR7 8XJ Tel: (01603) 488434 Fax: (0870) 1211941 E-mail: info@TECNiA.co.uk
▶ www.broadbandbuyer.co.uk, Unit 8, Cromwell Business Centre, Howard Way, Interchange Park, Newport Pagnell, Buckinghamshire, MK16 9QS Tel: (01908) 888327 Fax: (01908) 614521 E-mail: sales@broadbandbuyer.co.uk

WIRELESS NETWORKING

▶ A E C P.L.C., 25 Southampton Row, Holborn, London, WC1B 5HJ Tel: (0845) 0506296 Fax: (0870) 4199001 E-mail: info@aec.com
Infomatrix Ltd, The Old School, High Street, Fen Drayton, Cambridge, CB24 4SJ Tel: (01954) 232010 Fax: (01954) 230031 E-mail: chris.jones@infomatrix.com
▶ London Property Management Services Ltd, 2 Hall Place, Sutton Square, London, E9 6EG Tel: (0800) 1078760 Fax: (020) 8533 7756 E-mail: wireless@additional-knowledge.com
▶ No Wires Networks, 4 Laxton Close, Luton, LU2 8SJ Tel: (0845) 0093781 Fax: (0870) 1162823 E-mail: info@nowiresnetworks.co.uk
▶ Protocol Data Services Ltd, Wyndburgh, Lincoln Crescent, Wrockwardine Wood, Telford, Shropshire, TF2 6LU Tel: (01952) 412312 Fax: (0871) 2640312 E-mail: support@pdsnet.co.uk
Sitecom UK Ltd, Falcon House, 16 Fernhill Road, Farnborough, Hampshire, GU14 9RX Tel: (01252) 551050 Fax: (01252) 511333 E-mail: sales@sitecom.com
T D C I, Sopwith Close, Drayton Fields Industrial Esta, Daventry, Northamptonshire, NN11 8EA Tel: (01327) 312570 Fax: (01327) 312721 E-mail: info@tdci.eu.com
T D K Systems Europe Ltd, 126 Colindale Avenue, London, NW9 5HD Tel: (020) 8938) 1000 Fax: (020) 8905 8606 E-mail: info@tdksys.com
▶ Tecnia, 63 Cromwell Road, Norwich, NR7 8XJ Tel: (01603) 488434 Fax: (0870) 1211941 E-mail: info@TECNiA.co.uk
▶ XP Computers, Rivendell, 46A Queens Road, Hertford, SG13 8AZ Tel: (07801) 142365 Fax: (0870) 7058640 E-mail: enquiry@xpcomputers.co.uk

WIRELESS TEST EQUIPMENT

C S W Erlang Ltd, Unit 10, Green Farm, Fritwell, Bicester, Oxfordshire, OX27 7QU Tel: (01869) 345050 Fax: (01869) 345954 E-mail: mandy.jenkins@erlangcsw.co.uk

WIRELINE EQUIPMENT

E M Cable Service North Sea Ltd, Unit 4c Wellheads Terrace, Wellheads Industrial Estate, Aberdeen, AB21 7GF Tel: (01224) 771791 Fax: (01224) 724335 E-mail: em.cables@virgin.net
Elmar Services Ltd, Westhill Industrial Estate, Westhill, Aberdeenshire, AB32 6TQ Tel: (01224) 740261 Fax: (01224) 743138 E-mail: sales@elmar.co.uk

WIRELINE OPERATORS

Schlumberger Completions, Kirkton Avenue, Pitnedden Road Industrial Estate, Pitnedden Road Industrial Estate, Dyce, Aberdeen, AB21 0BF Tel: (01224) 723970 Fax: (01224) 770432
Wetherford Wellserv, Crawpeel Road, Altens Industrial Estate, Aberdeen, AB12 3LG Tel: (01224) 410000 Fax: (01224) 380060

WIRELINE TOOLS

Bowen Tools Div I R I International, Kirkton Avenue, Pitmedden Road Industrial Estate, Dyce, Aberdeen, AB21 0BF Tel: (01224) 771339 Fax: (01224) 723034
Wood Group Production Technology Ltd, Maersk House, Greenbank Road, East Tullos Industrial Estate, Aberdeen, AB21 3BR Tel: (01224) 840000 Fax: (01224) 216775

WIRELINE UNITS, OILWELL

Hunting Energy Services, Silverburn Place, Bridge of Don Industrial Estate, Aberdeen, AB23 8EG Tel: (01224) 820909 Fax: (01224) 823123 E-mail: cromar@cromar.com
Zone Power Ltd, High Road, Bressingham, Diss, Norfolk, IP22 2AT Tel: (01379) 687796 Fax: (01379) 687437 E-mail: sales@zonepower.com

WIRING ACCESSORIES

Elliott Electrical Supplies, 39 Margetts Road, Kempston, Bedford, MK42 8DT Tel: (01234) 857800 Fax: (01234) 857800
FOCUS Sb Ltd, Napier Road, St. Leonards-on-Sea, East Sussex, TN38 9NY Tel: (01424) 440734 Fax: (01424) 853862 E-mail: sales@fucussb.co.uk
Legrand Electric Ltd, Great King Street North, Birmingham, B19 2LF Tel: 0121-515 0515 Fax: 0121-515 0516 E-mail: legrand.sales@legrand.co.uk
M L Accessories Ltd, 5A-5B Kings Street, Houghton Regis, Bedfordshire, LU5 5DF Tel: (01582) 868903 Fax: (01582) 868830
Yazaki (Europe) Ltd, Second Floor St. Katherines House, St. Marys Wharf, Mansfield Road, Derby, DE1 3TC Tel: (01332) 202023 Fax: (01332) 204023

WIRING HARNESSES

A B Cable & Wiring, 8 Walworth Enterprise Centre Duke Close, West Way, Andover, Hampshire, SP10 5AP Tel: (01264) 334076 Fax: (01264) 337721 E-mail: sales@abcableandwiring.com
Airfawn Consultants Ltd, New Haden Works, Draycott Cross Road, Cheadle, Stoke-on-Trent, ST10 2NW Tel: (01538) 750788 Fax: (01538) 751511 E-mail: aiirfawnltd@btconnect.com
Higar Engineering Ltd, Gore Road Industrial Estate, New Milton, Hampshire, BH25 6TH Tel: (01425) 617511 Fax: (01425) 629463 E-mail: sales@higar.com
J K Control Systems Ltd, Unit 14 Kernick Industrial Estate, Penryn, Cornwall, TR10 9EP Tel: (01326) 378432 Fax: (01326) 378423 E-mail: info@jkcontrolsystems.co.uk
▶ Wiring Solutions Ltd, 21 High Street, Glinton, Peterborough, PE6 7LS Tel: (01733) 253910
Yazaki (Europe) Ltd, Second Floor St. Katherines House, St. Marys Wharf, Mansfield Road, Derby, DE1 3TC Tel: (01332) 202023 Fax: (01332) 204023

WIRING PREFABRICATED/ PREFORMED SYSTEMS

▶ Rise Advanced Cable Systems, Conway House, Tenterfields, Thornhill Road, Dewsbury, West Yorkshire, WF12 9QW Tel: 01924 464343 Fax: 01924 438388 E-mail: sales@rise-uk.com

WIRING PROTOTYPE SYSTEMS

LAM Electronics Ltd, Unit 6/A, Mercury House, Calleva Park, Aldermaston, Reading, RG7 8PN Tel: 0118-981 1717 Fax: 0118-981 7475 E-mail: almelecinfo@almelec.co.uk
Time 24 Ltd, Robimatic House, 19 Victoria Gardens, Burgess Hill, West Sussex, RH15 9NB Tel: (01444) 257655 Fax: (01444) 259000 E-mail: sales@time24.co.uk

WIRING SYSTEMS

▶ Rise Advanced Cable Systems, Conway House, Tenterfields, Thornhill Road, Dewsbury, West Yorkshire, WF12 9QW Tel: 01924 464343 Fax: 01924 438388 E-mail: sales@rise-uk.com

WOK GAS BURNERS

J P Burners Ltd, 14 Monks Crescent, Leicester, LE4 2WA Tel: 0116-246 0400 Fax: 0116-235 8411 E-mail: sales@jpburners.co.uk

WOOD ANTIQUE REPRODUCTION, *See Furniture, Reproduction etc*

WOOD BED FRAMES

Allen Malpass, 3 Pottery Road, Bovey Tracey, Newton Abbot, Devon, TQ13 9DS Tel: (01626) 835200 Fax: (01626) 835200 E-mail: allen.malpass@hotmail.co.uk
Blairgowrie Bedding Centre, 67 Perth Street, Blairgowrie, Perthshire, PH10 6DL Tel: (01250) 873148 Fax: (01250) 873148
Friendship Mill Beds Ltd, Unit 22 Friendship Mill, Whalley Road, Read, Burnley, Lancashire, BB12 7PN Tel: (01282) 772662 Fax: (01282) 772662
Futon Co Ltd, 72-74 Upper Parliament Street, Nottingham, NG1 6LF Tel: 0115-959 9616 Fax: 0115-950 7511
Inpine Ltd, Anglia Way Industrial Estate, Anglia Way, Mansfield, Nottinghamshire, NG18 4LP Tel: (01623) 625468
Laywell Beds Ltd, Cordingley Street, Bradford, West Yorkshire, BD4 0PP Tel: (01274) 681000 Fax: (01274) 681666
Peacock & Chandler Ltd, 134 Villiers Road, London, NW2 5PU Tel: (020) 8459 0519 Fax: (020) 8451 1049 E-mail: sales@peacockandchandler.com

WOOD BEDSTEADS

Allen Malpass, 3 Pottery Road, Bovey Tracey, Newton Abbot, Devon, TQ13 9DS Tel: (01626) 835200 Fax: (01626) 835200 E-mail: allen.malpass@hotmail.co.uk
The Bedroom, 61 Market Place, Shaw, Oldham, OL2 8NN Tel: (01706) 299522 Fax: (01706) 299522
Simmons Bedding Group P.L.C., Knight Road, Strood, Kent, ME2 2BP Tel: (01634) 723557 Fax: (01634) 290257
Sweet Dreams Bed Centre, 55-57 New Road, Skewen, Neath, West Glamorgan, SA10 6EP Tel: (01792) 815080 Fax: (01792) 324177

WOOD BOATS

Moss David Boat Builders, Wyre Road, Skippool Creek, Thornton-Cleveleys, Lancashire, FY5 5LF Tel: (01253) 893830 Fax: (01253) 893830 E-mail: mr.davidmoss@virgin.net
▶ Seawing Boats, 18 Darrowby Close, Thirsk, North Yorkshire, YO7 1FJ Tel: (01845) 527397 E-mail: info@seawingboats.co.uk

WOOD BORING OR DRILLING TOOLS

Chadburns Fence Suppliers, 22 Wortley View, Blacker Hill, Barnsley, South Yorkshire, S74 0RD Tel: (01226) 744028
J E Morrison & Sons Ltd, Burton Weir Works, Warren Street, Sheffield, S4 7WT Tel: 0114-270 1525 Fax: 0114-243 4158
K W O Tools (UK) Ltd, 4 Strawberry Vale, Vale Road, Tonbridge, Kent, TN9 1SJ Tel: (01732) 364444 Fax: (01732) 351144 E-mail: sales@kwo.co.uk

WOOD BOXES

Leonard Gould & Co. Ltd, Union Park, Bircholt Road, Maidstone, Kent, ME15 9XT Tel: (01622) 623400 Fax: (01622) 686695 E-mail: sales@leonardgould.co.uk
Pearsons Packages Ltd, Benington Road, Butterwick, Boston, Lincolnshire, PE22 0EX Tel: (01205) 760755 Fax: (01205) 761080
Powell's of Sherborne, Middlemarsh, Sherborne, Dorset, DT9 5QW Tel: (01300) 345255 Fax: (01300) 345367 E-mail: pow@connect-2.co.uk
▶ The Routing & Packaging Company Ltd, Unit 1 Walk Mill Green Road, Colne, Lancashire, BB8 8AL Tel: (01282) 864629 Fax: (01282) 864661 E-mail: nigel@trppackaging.co.uk
▶ Stadium, Hannington Works, Longrigg, Swalwell, Newcastle upon Tyne, NE16 3AS Tel: 0191-496 1321 Fax: 0191-488 4127 E-mail: sales-gh@stadium-packing.co.uk
Unirose Ltd, Mount Ephraim Farm, Freight Lane, Cranbrook, Kent, TN17 3PG Tel: (01580) 714477 Fax: (01580) 713534
Valleys Woodcraft Ltd, Unit 1-2 Cwmdraw Industrial Estate, Newtown, Ebbw Vale, Gwent, NP23 5AE Tel: (01495) 350758 Fax: (01495) 307054 E-mail: sales@valleyswoodcraft.com

WOOD BURNING STOVES

▶ Ablaze Stoves & Fireplaces, 1 Pickhill Farm, Smallhythe Road, Tenterden, Kent, TN30 7LZ Tel: (01580) 761316 Fax: (01580) 761316 E-mail: ablazestoves@aol.com
Almondsbury Forge Works Ltd, Sundays Hill, Almondsbury, Bristol, BS32 4DS Tel: (01454) 613315 Fax: (01454) 613303 E-mail: sales@almondsburyforge.co.uk
Chase Heating Ltd, Somerfield Stores, Racecourse Road, Pinvin, Pershore, Worcestershire, WR10 2EY Tel: (01386) 553542 Fax: (01386) 552269 E-mail: chasehtg@gxn.co.uk
▶ Chase Of Milford, The White House, Main Road, Milford, Stafford, ST17 0UW Tel: (01785) 660939 Fax: (01785) 660914 E-mail: caseofmillford@aol.com
Clearview Stoves, More Works, Bishops Castle, Shropshire, SY9 5HH Tel: (01588) 650401 Fax: (01588) 650493
Dingley Dell Enterprises, Kidderminster, Worcestershire, DY14 9ZE Tel: (01905) 621636 Fax: (01905) 620311
Dowling Stoves, 3 Bladnoch Bridge Industrial Estate, Bladnoch, Wigtown, Newton Stewart, Wigtownshire, DG8 9AB Tel: (01988) 402666 Fax: (01988) 402666 E-mail: enquiries@dowlingstoves.com
Fotheringhay Forge & Woodburners, The Old Forge, Fotheringhay, Peterborough, PE8 5HZ Tel: (01832) 226323 Fax: (01832) 226323 E-mail: enquiries@woodburnersat fotheringhay.co.uk
Heta UK, The Stove Shop, The Street, Hatfield Peverel, Chelmsford, CM3 2DY Tel: (01245) 381247 Fax: (01245) 381606
Log Onto Fires.Com, Colston Cross, Colston, Axminster, Devon, EX13 7NF Tel: (01297) 631669 Fax: (01297) 33007
Metal Developments Ltd, The Workshop, Wheatcroft Farm, Cullompton, Devon, EX15 1RA Tel: (01884) 35806 Fax: (01884) 35505

WOOD BURNING STOVES – *continued*

Moldow Ltd, Unit 31 Britannia Way, Britannia Enterprise Park, Lichfield, Staffordshire, WS14 9UY Tel: (01543) 258844 Fax: (01543) 416311

Projexe Engineering, 7 Merriott House, Hennock Road, Marsh Barton Trading Estate, Exeter, EX2 8NJ Tel: (01392) 258441 Fax: (01392) 498441

Rye Fires & Stoves, 20 Landgate, Rye, East Sussex, TN31 7LH Tel: (01797) 222041 Fax: (01797) 222041 E-mail: sales@ryefiresandstoves.co.uk

▶ Shire Stoves, 71 High Street, Chobham, Woking, Surrey, GU24 8AF Tel: 01276 857879

Stovax Ltd, Falcon Road, Sowton Industrial Estate, Exeter, EX2 7LF Tel: (01392) 474011 Fax: (01392) 219932E-mail: info@stovax.com

The Stove Gallery, 41-43 High Street, Starbeck, Harrogate, North Yorkshire, HG2 7LQ Tel: (01423) 887799 Fax: (01423) 889416 E-mail: sales@thestovegallery.com

Taltrees Stoves, Taltrees Centre, Worcester Road, Newnham Bridge, Tenbury Wells, Worcestershire, WR15 8JA Tel: (01584) 781361 Fax: (01584) 781363

WOOD CARVING TOOLS

Bristol Design (Tools) Ltd, 14 Perry Road, Bristol, BS1 5BG Tel: 0117-929 1740

Henry Taylor Tools Ltd, Peacock Estate, Liversey Street, Sheffield, S6 2BL Tel: 0114-234 0282 Fax: 0114-285 2015 E-mail: sales@henrytaylortools.co.uk

WOOD CHAIR FRAMES

John K. Bone, 404 Cremer Business Centre, Cremer Street, London, E2 8HD Tel: (020) 7739 2470 Fax: (020) 7739 2470 E-mail: terryberry321@hotmail.com

Breaston Chair Frames Co. Ltd, Unit 21b Merlin Way, Quarry Hill Industrial Estate, Ilkeston, Derbyshire, DE7 4RA Tel: 0115-944 0626

Simon Butler, Unit 10E, Wincombe Park Business Centre, Shaftesbury, Dorset, SP7 9QJ Tel: (01747) 850150 Fax: (01747) 850250 E-mail: info@comptonsmith.co.uk

F E Shaw Ltd, Acton Close, Long Eaton, Nottingham, NG10 1FZ Tel: 0115-973 3816 Fax: 0115-973 0708

Formston Evans Ltd, Kent Street, Bolton, BL1 2LN Tel: (01204) 523424 Fax: (01204) 529644 E-mail: pat@formstonevans.co.uk

Frames & Fabric Ltd, Unit D1 West End Mills, Leopold Street, Long Eaton, Nottingham, NG10 4QD Tel: 0115-972 6282 Fax: 0115-946 1697

Gravell & Jones Ltd, 12 Heron Court, Cranes Farm Road, Basildon, Essex, SS14 3DF Tel: (01268) 522611 Fax: (01268) 281188

H Vaughan Ltd, 26 Naval Row, London, E14 9PS Tel: (020) 7515 4551 Fax: (020) 7515 4551

Umney Brothers, Midland Structures Estate, Ampthill Road, Bedford, MK42 9JJ Tel: (01234) 348671 Fax: (01234) 348671

WOOD CHIPS

Longleat Forestry, Picket Post, Warminster, Wiltshire, BA12 7JS Tel: (01985) 213507 Fax: (01985) 847438

M I Edwards Engineers, Mundford Road, Weeting, Brandon, Suffolk, IP27 0PL Tel: (01842) 813555 Fax: (01842) 811595

WOOD CONSERVATORIES

Atrium, 6 The Old Foundry, Victoria Road, Kington, Herefordshire, HR5 3DA Tel: (01544) 231769 Fax: (01544) 231008 E-mail: atrium@srump.fsnet.co.uk

Aurora Conservatories, The Old Station, Naburn, York, YO19 4RW Tel: (01904) 631234 Fax: (01904) 610318 E-mail: info@btconnect.com

C M Joinery, Coggeshall Road, Bradwell, Braintree, Essex, CM77 8EU Tel: (01376) 331666 Fax: (01376) 331444 E-mail: info@wood-work.demon.co.uk

Chardstock Joinery, Chubbs Yard, Chardstock, Axminster, Devon, EX13 7BT Tel: (01460) 221148 Fax: (01460) 221148

Charisma Blinds, 3 Manitoba Place, Chapel Allerton, Leeds, LS7 4LU Tel: 0113-228 7193 Fax: 0113-262 1626 E-mail: charismablindswetherby@yahoo.co.uk

Classic Joinery, 324 Guildford Road, Bisley, Woking, Surrey, GU24 9AE Tel: (01932) 354333 Fax: (01483) 797713 E-mail: john@classicjoinery.co.uk

▶ Durabuild Glazed Structures Ltd, Carlton Road, Coventry, CV6 7FL Tel: (024) 7666 9169 Fax: (024) 7666 9170 E-mail: enquiries@durabuild.co.uk

J W Cooper Joinery, 6 Sea Lane, Rustington, Littlehampton, West Sussex, BN16 2RB Tel: (01903) 776941 Fax: (01903) 776941 E-mail: sales@cooperjoinery.co.uk

▶ Sherlock & Neal Ltd, Ashmores Yard, Horsham Road, Rusper, Horsham, West Sussex, RH12 4PR Tel: (01293) 871343 Fax: (01293) 871298 E-mail: shirlock.neil@tiscali.co.uk

▶ U C M Timber Speciality Ltd, Roylance Buildings, 90-92 Waters Green, Macclesfield, Cheshire, SK11 6LH Tel: (01625) 616433 Fax: (01625) 511015 E-mail: sales@mercantile.uk.com

Valtone Woodcraft, 2 Goodly Hill, Pershore, Worcestershire, WR10 3HE Tel: (01386) 554759 Fax: (01386) 553686 E-mail: valtonewoodcraft@btconnect.com

WOOD CRATES

Bradley Thallon Industries Ltd, Kiltonga Industrial Estate, Belfast Road, Newtownards, County Down, BT23 4TJ Tel: (028) 9181 5403 Fax: (028) 9181 5409 E-mail: terence@bradleythallon.co.uk

Commercial Trading, Bridge Road, Kingswood, Bristol, BS15 4PT Tel: 0117-961 0710 Fax: 0117-960 2933 E-mail: commercial.trading@btinternet.com

Factory Reconstruction Co. (Manchester) Ltd, Paradise Mill, Bell Street, Oldham, OL1 3PY Tel: 0161-624 5988 Fax: 0161-665 1994 E-mail: ukpallets@aol.com

Norbury (Pallets) Ltd, Unit 28, Marshgate Drive, Hertford, SG13 7AJ Tel: (01992) 504236 Fax: (01992) 584978 E-mail: sales@norburypallets.com

Powell's of Sherborne, Middlemarsh, Sherborne, Dorset, DT9 5QW Tel: (01300) 345255 Fax: (01300) 345367 E-mail: pow@connect-2.co.uk

WOOD CURTAIN RAILS OR POLES OR FITTINGS

H. Brettell & Sons Ltd, 20 Chestnut Ave, Forest Gate, London, E7 0JH Tel: (020) 8555 4037 Fax: (020) 8555 2106 E-mail: sales@brettells.co.uk

▶ Fit-ex.com, 36 Hobhouse Close, Great Barr, Birmingham, B42 1HB Tel: 0121 2411164 E-mail: steve.burns@fit-ex.com

▶ Fit-Ex.Com, 30 Hans Apel Drive, Brackley, Northamptonshire, NN13 6HD Tel: (01280) 701090 Fax: (01280) 701090 E-mail: fitex@btinternet.com

WOOD CURTAIN RINGS

Grooms House Turnery, Grooms House, Stanshawes Court, Yate, Bristol, BS37 4DZ Tel: (01454) 325525 Fax: (01454) 325525 E-mail: info@grooms-house-turnery.co.uk

WOOD DANCE FLOORING

▶ Atkinson Sanding, 97 Replingham Road, Southfields, London, SW18 5LU Tel: (0770) 4571080E-mail: tom@atkinsondsanding.co.uk

WOOD DECKING

▶ Acorn Timber Decking, 158 Werrington Road, Stoke-on-Trent, ST2 9AW Tel: (01782) 869805 Fax: (07786) 001962 E-mail: simon.kearns@ntlworld.com

Arnold Laver, Manningham Sawmills, Canal Road, Bradford, West Yorkshire, BD2 1AR Tel: (01274) 732861 Fax: (01274) 737060 E-mail: sales@bradford.timberworld.co.uk

▶ DIYdeals.com, 6 The Shaw, Glossop, Derbyshire, SK13 6DE Tel: (01457) 855259 E-mail: timber@diydeals.com

Far Landscapes, 2 Cedar Avenue, Methil, Leven, Fife, KY8 2AY Tel: (01333) 421506 E-mail: a.a.ritchie@homecall.co.uk

H J Cooper Timber Ltd, Thornleigh Trading Estate, Dudley, West Midlands, DY2 8UB Tel: (01384) 254591 Fax: (01384) 237119 E-mail: info@cooperstimber.co.uk

▶ HGM Landscapes Ltd, 90 Harrowby Road, Grantham, Lincolnshire, NG31 9DS Tel: (01476) 573345 Fax: (01476) 573345 E-mail: enquiries@hgmlandscapes.co.uk

▶ Sharps World Of Wood, York Road Garage, York Road, Barmby Moor, York, YO42 4HS Tel: (01759) 305566 Fax: (01759) 306699 E-mail: paul@sharpsworldofwood.com

▶ Timber To Go, Newport Road, Coventry, CV6 4BQ Tel: (024) 7668 8886 Fax: (024) 7668 8869 E-mail: sales@timbertogo.com

WOOD DECKING FASTENING CLIPS

▶ DIYdeals.com, 6 The Shaw, Glossop, Derbyshire, SK13 6DE Tel: (01457) 855259 E-mail: timber@diydeals.com

WOOD DOORS

Adorable Doors, 580 Pershore Road, Selly Oak, Birmingham, B29 7EN Tel: 0121-471 2414 Fax: 0121-471 2414 E-mail: enquiries@adorabledoors.co.uk

All Doors Of Bromsgrove, 1 All Saints Road, Bromsgrove, Worcestershire, B61 0AG Tel: (01527) 579901

Ambass-A-Door Windows & Doors Ltd, 18 Bidwell Road, Rackheath Industrial Estate, Norwich, NR13 6PT Tel: (01603) 720332 Fax: (01603) 721245 E-mail: sales@ambassadoor.fsnet.co.uk

▶ Apex Enterprises, Kern House, Corporation Road, Birkenhead, Merseyside, CH41 1HB Tel: 0151-647 9323 Fax: 0151-647 9324

Balham Glass & Joinery, 260-262 Cavendish Road, London, SW12 0BT Tel: (020) 8675 1640 Fax: (020) 8657 6784 E-mail: balhamglass@btclick.com

Burbidge & Son Ltd, Burnsall Road, Coventry, CV5 6BS Tel: (024) 7667 1600 Fax: (024) 7669 1010 E-mail: sales@burbidge.co.uk

C & B Joinery, 8 Dowding Mews, Lincoln, LN3 4PN Tel: (01522) 568868 Fax: (01522) 568868

Castle Point Hand Looms, Unit 32 Brittania Court, Basildon, Essex, SS13 1EU Tel: (01268) 729707 Fax: (01268) 728330

Chichester Joinery Ltd, Unit 12 Quarry Lane Industrial Estate, Gravel Lane, Chichester, West Sussex, PO19 8PQ Tel: (01243) 784723 Fax: (01243) 533382 E-mail: michaelcarter3@btconnect.com

Chindwell Co. Ltd, Hyde House, The Hyde, London, NW9 6JT Tel: (020) 8208 0808 Fax: (020) 8205 8800 E-mail: chindwell_co_ltd@compuserve.com

Cox Long Ltd, Airfield Industrial Estate, Hixon, Stafford, ST18 0PA Tel: (01889) 270166 Fax: (01889) 271041 E-mail: info@coxlong.com

Elvet Structures Ltd, Low Willington Industrial Estate, Willington, Crook, County Durham, DL15 0UH Tel: (01388) 747120 Fax: (01388) 745861 E-mail: gordan.pearson@elvetstructures.co.uk

Emanuel Whittaker Ltd, 400 Rochdale Road, Oldham, OL1 2LW Tel: 0161-624 6222 Fax: 0161-785 5510 E-mail: mail@emanuel-whittaker.co.uk

Glyngary Joinery Ltd, Unit H2, Risley, Warrington, WA3 6BL Tel: (01925) 763836 Fax: (01925) 762388 E-mail: sales@glyngary.co.uk

H Shawyer & Sons Ltd, 1-3 Redburn Industrial Estate, Woodall Road, Enfield, Middlesex, EN3 4LF Tel: (020) 8805 7080 Fax: (020) 8804 3883 E-mail: sales@hshawyer.demon.co.uk

Howarth Timber and Building Merchants Ltd, Medlock Sawmills, Shaw Road, Oldham, OL1 3LJ Tel: 0161-620 2128 Fax: 0161-620 9527 E-mail: htoldh@plp.howarth-timber.co.uk

Howarth Windows & Doors Ltd, The Dock, New Holland, Barrow-upon-Humber, North Lincolnshire, DN19 7RT Tel: (01469) 530577 Fax: (01469) 531559 E-mail: windows&doors@howarth-timber.co.uk

Humphrey & Stretton (Properties) Ltd, Stretton House, 20 Pindar Road, Hoddesdon, Hertfordshire, EN11 0EU Tel: (01992) 462965 Fax: (01992) 463996 E-mail: sales@humphreystretton.com

Neil Jordan Grills & Doors, 8E, 8E Sweechbridge Rd, Herne Bay, Kent, CT6 6TE Tel: (01227) 749991 Fax: (01227) 749991

M A Products Ltd, 36 Hirst Lane, Malthouse Road, Tipton, West Midlands, DY4 9AE Tel: 0121-520 7077 Fax: 0121-520 9677

Manor Doors Ltd, Manor House, 6-8 Creek Road, Barking, Essex, IG11 0TA Tel: (020) 8591 3300 Fax: (020) 8591 3338 E-mail: enquiries@manordoors.com

Meridian Technology Ltd, Unit 24 Park Gate Business Centre Chandlers Way, Park Gate, Southampton, SO31 1FQ Tel: (01489) 577599 Fax: (01489) 579472 E-mail: sales@19inchracks.com

Merton Timber, Rowfant Sawmills, Wallage Lane, Rowfant, Crawley, West Sussex, RH10 4NQ Tel: (01342) 716633 Fax: (01342) 716655 E-mail: sales@merton-timber.co.uk

Noberne Doors Ltd, Lupton Street, Leeds, LS10 2QP Tel: 0113-277 8577 Fax: 0113-277 2049 E-mail: nobernedoors@cs.com

Premdor Crosby Ltd, Huddersfield Road, Darton, Barnsley, South Yorkshire, S75 5JS Tel: (01226) 383434 Fax: (01226) 388808 E-mail: ukmarketing@premdor.com

R B D Builders Norfolk Ltd, 32 Southgates Road, Great Yarmouth, Norfolk, NR30 3LL Tel: (01493) 855891 Fax: (01493) 331615

Riverside Joinery Co. Ltd, Barker Street, Norwich, NR2 4TN Tel: (01603) 624858 Fax: (01603) 614924

S T P Distribution, C Kelbrook Road, Manchester, M11 2QA Tel: 0161-223 8232 Fax: 0161-230 7814

S T P Group Ltd, Watford Bridge Road, New Mills, High Peak, Derbyshire, SK22 4HJ Tel: (01663) 744030 Fax: (01663) 745295 E-mail: stpgroupltd@btinternet.com

▶ Scottish Prison Service, SPS HQ Industries, Central Store, Main Street, Fauldhouse, Bathgate, West Lothian, EH47 9DJ Tel: (01501) 773980 Fax: (01501) 771835 E-mail: anthony.apperley@sps.gov.uk

▶ Standards Group, Bentley Hall Barn, Alkmonton, Ashbourne, Derbyshire, DE6 3DJ Tel: (01335) 330263 Fax: (01335) 330922 E-mail: uk@standardsgroup.co.uk

▶ Sunflex, Sapphire Way, Rhombus Business Park, Norwich, NR6 6NN Tel: (01603) 424434 Fax: (01603) 408839

Tower Doors Ltd, 107 Coltness Lane Queenslie Indust Estate, Glasgow, G33 4DR Tel: 0141-774 6162 Fax: 0141-774 6163

▶ U C M Timber Speciality Ltd, Roylance Buildings, 90-92 Waters Green, Macclesfield, Cheshire, SK11 6LH Tel: (01625) 616433 Fax: (01625) 511015 E-mail: sales@mercantile.uk.com

Veneer Workshop Ltd, 37a South Street, Portslade, Brighton, BN41 2LE Tel: (01273) 422332 Fax: (01273) 418220 E-mail: mail@veneerworkshop.co.uk

WOOD DOWELS

A G Evans & Sons, Joinery Works, Industrial Estate, Bala, Gwynedd, LL23 7NL Tel: (01678) 520660 Fax: (01678) 520660

B & P Joiners Ltd, Thomas Street, Crewe, CW1 2BD Tel: (01270) 250969 Fax: (01270) 250969

Bainbridge Joinery, Faraday Road, Kirkby Stephen, Cumbria, CA17 4QL Tel: (01768) 372100 Fax: (01768) 372303

Bristol & West Joinery & Turnings, 56-58 Park Rd, Stapleton, Bristol, BS16 1AU Tel: 0117-965 8662 Fax: 0117-965 8662

Charmans Joinery, Dean Lane, Bristol, BS3 1DD Tel: 0117-966 2781 Fax: 0117-966 2781 E-mail: sales@charmansjoinery.co.uk

Cherry Woodworkers Ltd, Village Road, Denham, Uxbridge, Middlesex, UB9 5BH Tel: (01895) 832056 Fax: (01895) 834219

Grange Joinery, Trent Business Centre, Canal Street, Long Eaton, Nottingham, NG10 4HN Tel: 0115-946 3433

Arthur Heath & Co. Ltd, Hall Road, Aylesford, Kent, ME20 7QZ Tel: (01622) 717507 Fax: (01622) 710551 E-mail: admin@arthurheath.com

L & S Schofield Ltd, Unit 11-13, Haigh Avenue, Stockport, Cheshire, SK4 1NU Tel: 0161-480 3570 Fax: 0161-480 0836 E-mail: steve@dowelpins.fsnet.co.uk

M J Sherwin, Unit 16 Lord Nelson Industrial Estate, Commercial Road, Stoke-on-Trent, ST1 3QF Tel: (01782) 213289 Fax: (01782) 204587

Midleton Joinery, Midleton Industrial Estate, Guildford, Surrey, GU2 8XW Tel: (01483) 451994 Fax: (01483) 452110 E-mail: enquiries@midletonjoinery.co.uk

Shield Woodworking Ltd, Station Road, Kingham, Chipping Norton, Oxfordshire, OX7 6SX Tel: (01608) 658698 Fax: (01608) 658404 E-mail: shieldwood@btconnect.com

Wilkinson Joinery Ltd, Market Hill, Wigton, Cumbria, CA7 9EY Tel: (01697) 342344 Fax: (01697) 342718

WOOD DRYING KILNS

▶ Kiln Services Ltd, Burnham Business Park, Springfield Road, Burnham-on-Crouch, Essex, CM0 8TE Tel: (01621) 785935 Fax: (01621) 785937

WOOD FENCING

A & B Fencing & Roofing Ltd, Love Lane Industrial Estate, Love Lane, Cirencester, Gloucestershire, GL7 1YG Tel: (01285) 651330 Fax: (01285) 651330

Alltype Fencing Co. Ltd, Howgare Road, Broad Chalke, Salisbury, SP5 5DR Tel: (01722) 780563 Fax: (01722) 780138 E-mail: sales@alltypefencing.fsnet.co.uk

Ashvale Timber Industries, 62-68 Birling Road, Ashford, Kent, TN24 8BB Tel: (01233) 623592 Fax: (01233) 712611

Barrowmore Industries, Barrowmore Enterprise Estate, Barnhouse Lane, Great Barrow, Chester, CH3 7JA Tel: (01829) 742590 Fax: (01829) 742571 E-mail: kat@barrowmore.org.uk

Blakes Sheds & Fencing, Salop Street, Dudley, West Midlands, DY1 3AT Tel: (01384) 456800 Fax: (01384) 459585

British Gates & Timber Ltd, Biddenden, Ashford, Kent, TN27 8DN Tel: (01580) 291555 Fax: (01580) 292011 E-mail: sales@britishgates.co.uk

Bruno Timber Products, Weston Court, Holton Road, Barry, South Glamorgan, CF63 4JD Tel: (01446) 732693 Fax: (01446) 732693

C A Palmer & Sons, Clayford Cottages, Clayford, Wimborne, Dorset, BH21 7BJ Tel: (01202) 893467 Fax: (01202) 893467

Chase Timber Products Ltd, Twickenham Avenue, Brandon, Suffolk, IP27 0PD Tel: (01842) 810690 Fax: (01842) 812987 E-mail: mail@chasetimberproducts.co.uk

Cheltenham Fencing & Landscaping Supplies, Hayden Road, Cheltenham, Gloucestershire, GL51 0SN Tel: (01242) 526946 Fax: (01242) 526480E-mail: info@cheltenhamfencing.co.uk

D N S Fencing, Station Road, West Hallam, Ilkeston, Derbyshire, DE7 6HB Tel: 0115-944 4280 Fax: 0115-944 4280

Demo Fences, 4 Garden Close, London, SW15 3TH Tel: (020) 8785 1078

Drayton Fencing, 93 Park View Road, Uxbridge, Middlesex, UB8 3LN Tel: (01895) 444727 Fax: (01895) 431054

E T C Sawmills Ltd, Elson, Ellesmere, Shropshire, SY12 9EU Tel: (01691) 622441 Fax: (01691) 623468 E-mail: info@etcsawmills.co.uk

East Ferry Timber Co., Shoemaker Lodge, 3 Brigg Road, Scotter, Gainsborough, Lincolnshire, DN21 3HU Tel: (01724) 762626 Fax: (01724) 762629

Eaton Berry Ltd, Bridge Farm, Reading Road, Arborfield, Reading, RG2 9HT Tel: 0118-976 1076 Fax: 0118-976 0479 E-mail: info@eatonberry.com

WOOD FENCING – *continued*

F J Campion Ltd, Thames View, Upper Sunbury Road, Hampton, Middlesex, TW12 2DL Tel: (020) 8979 2351 Fax: (020) 8979 2351
Fellwood Products, Cherryfields, Fullers Road, Rowledge, Farnham, Surrey, GU10 4DF Tel: (01252) 793807
Fencing Products Ltd, 10 King Street Lane, Winnersh, Wokingham, Berkshire, RG41 5AS Tel: 0118-978 5162 Fax: 0118-977 6422 E-mail: j.a.o.@btinternet.com
Fernden Construction Winchester Ltd, Barfield Close, Winchester, Hampshire, SO23 9SQ Tel: (01962) 866400 Fax: (01962) 864139 E-mail: sales@ferndenwin.co.uk
Forest Garden plc, Unit 291 296, Hartlebury Trading Estate, Hartlebury, Kidderminster, Worcestershire, DY10 4JB Tel: (0870) 1919800 Fax: (0870) 1919898 E-mail: info@forestgarden.co.uk
Goodwood Fencing & Co., Spencer Courtyard, Rear of 266 Regents Park Road, London, N3 3HN Tel: (020) 8346 0827 Fax: (020) 8346 6430 E-mail: sales@jwc-gwf.com
H G Froud & Son, 24 Newtown Road, Verwood, Dorset, BH31 6EJ Tel: (01202) 822444
Hailey Wood Sawmill Ltd, Stroud Road, Coates, Cirencester, Gloucestershire, GL7 6LA Tel: (01285) 652191 Fax: (01285) 654649
Hardman & Cain Fencing Ltd, Stotts Pit Yard, Church Street, Westhoughton, Bolton, BL5 3QW Tel: (01942) 815312 Fax: (01942) 815312 E-mail: enquiries@hardmancainfencing.co.uk
J Bradnam & Sons, Melbourne Bridge, Withersfield, Haverhill, Suffolk, CB9 7RR Tel: (01440) 702110 Fax: (01440) 704463
J E Homewood & Son, 20 Weyhill, Haslemere, Surrey, GU27 1BX Tel: (01428) 643819 Fax: (01428) 645419 E-mail: steve@homewoodfencing.co.uk
J R Concrete, Harcourt Street, Worsley, Manchester, M28 3GN Tel: (01204) 571004
Jewson, St. Peg Works, St. Peg Lane, Cleckheaton, West Yorkshire, BD19 3SH Tel: (01274) 872549 Fax: (01274) 864532
Job Earnshaw & Bros.Limited, Main Offices Stocksmoor Road, Midgley, Wakefield, West Yorkshire, WF4 4JG Tel: (01924) 830099 Fax: (01924) 830080 E-mail: john@job-earnshaw.co.uk
KDM International plc, The Havens, Ransomes Europark, Ipswich, IP3 9SJ Tel: (01473) 276900 Fax: (01473) 276911 E-mail: sales@kdm.co.uk
Landworth Product Ltd, 555 London Road, Hadleigh, Benfleet, Essex, SS7 2EA Tel: (01702) 558373
Leigh Timber Co. Ltd, 1388-1416 London Road, Leigh-on-Sea, Essex, SS9 2UJ Tel: (01702) 711366 Fax: (01702) 470993
McArthur Fencing Ltd, Udimore Road, Broad Oak, Brede, Rye, East Sussex, TN31 6BX Tel: (01424) 882888 Fax: (01424) 882559
Matthews Of Keynsham Ltd, Keynsham Road, Keynsham, Bristol, BS31 2DE Tel: 0117-986 4356 Fax: 0117-986 7491 E-mail: sales@matthewsofkeynsham.com
P & A Group of Companies, Mold Industrial Estate, Wrexham Road, Mold, Flintshire, CH7 4HE Tel: (01352) 752555 Fax: (01352) 755200 E-mail: sales@p-a-group.com
Pat'Erns Network UK Ltd, Stephenson Road, Clacton-on-Sea, Essex, CO15 4XA Tel: (01255) 427654 Fax: (01255) 420535
Robert Ballantine & Son, East End, Star, Glenrothes, Fife, KY7 6LQ Tel: (01592) 758542 Fax: (01592) 610707
Roc Fencing Ltd, Firs Indust Estate, Kidderminster, Worcestershire, DY11 7QN Tel: (01562) 69440 Fax: (01562) 823718 E-mail: sales@rocfencing.co.uk
The Scotia Fencing Company Ltd, Howe Road, Kilsyth, Glasgow, G65 0TA Tel: (01236) 823339 Fax: (01236) 826434
▶ Sharps World Of Wood, York Road Garage, York Road, Barmby Moor, York, YO42 4HS Tel: (01759) 305566 Fax: (01759) 306699 E-mail: paul@sharpsworldofwood.com
W.H. Wesson (Fencing) Ltd, 126 Connaught Road, Brookwood, Woking, Surrey, GU24 0AS Tel: (01483) 472124 Fax: (01483) 472115
Westwood Fencing, Bathpool, Taunton, Somerset, TA1 2DX Tel: (01823) 337150 Fax: (01823) 351991
Woodland Timber Products, Haughmond Hill Upton Magna, Haughmond, Uffington, Shrewsbury, SY4 4RW Tel: (01743) 709383 Fax: (01743) 709366

WOOD FILES

Delivery Service Ltd, Stoke Hall Road, Ipswich, IP2 8EJ Tel: (01473) 601564 Fax: (01473) 602789 E-mail: sales@ipswichdeliveryservice.co.uk

WOOD FINISHES, *See also headings for particular types*

A & G Toseland Ltd, St. Michael Road, Kettering, Northamptonshire, NN15 6AU Tel: (01536) 414401 Fax: (01536) 414402 E-mail: premierfinishes_uk@yahoo.co.uk
Becker Acroma Ltd, Rookwood Way, Haverhill, Suffolk, CB9 8PF Tel: (01440) 703611 Fax: (01440) 761091 E-mail: frar@beckeracroma.com
Fairleys Paint Stripping, Unit 14 Byron House, Hall Dene Way, Seaham Grange Industrial Estat, Seaham, County Durham, SR7 0PY Tel: 0191-510 0051 Fax: 0191-510 0051
Foxell & James, 57 Farringdon Road, London, EC1M 3JB Tel: (020) 7405 0152 Fax: (020) 7405 3631 E-mail: sales@foxellandjames.co.uk
▶ Waxall Wood Finishes, Unit 1 Kilroot Park, Carrickfergus, County Antrim, BT38 7PR Tel: (028) 9336 5690 Fax: (028) 9336 5690 E-mail: enquiries@waxall.co.uk

WOOD FINISHING

▶ Aquarius Paint & Lacquer, Granary Buildings, Eastgate Street, North Elmham, Dereham, Norfolk, NR20 5HF Tel: (07752) 602789 Fax: (01362) 860793 E-mail: aquariuspaintandlacquer@yahoo.co.uk
C S Surface Coating Ltd, 2 Mackay Transport, Colonial Way, Watford, WD24 4JU Tel: (01923) 246982 Fax: (01923) 237841 E-mail: mail@cs-surface-coating.co.uk
Morells, 99 Mabgate, Leeds, LS9 7DR Tel: 0113-245 0371 Fax: (0845) 4501717 E-mail: leeds@morrells-woodfinishes.com
Page Lacquer Co. Ltd, 3 Ferrier Industrial Estate, Ferrier Street, London, SW18 1SN Tel: (020) 8871 1235 Fax: (020) 8874 8167 E-mail: info@pagelacquer.co.uk
▶ Waxall Wood Finishes, Unit 1 Kilroot Park, Carrickfergus, County Antrim, BT38 7PR Tel: (028) 9336 5690 Fax: (028) 9336 5690 E-mail: enquiries@waxall.co.uk

WOOD FIRE DOORS

Acorn Timber & Joinery Ltd, Britannia Works, Upper Cyrus Street, Manchester, M40 7FD Tel: 0161-273 3871 Fax: 0161-274 3203 E-mail: sales@acorntimber.com
▶ North West Timber Products Ltd, Unit 11B, Newhaven Business Park, Barton Lane, Eccles, Manchester, M30 0HH Tel: 0161-7073797 Fax: 0161-7079717 E-mail: sales@nwtimberproducts.co.uk

WOOD FLOORING

▶ KBC Wood Floors Ltd, 135 Banbury Road, Brackley, Northamptonshire, NN13 6AX Tel: (01280) 700305 Fax: (01280) 700305 E-mail: kev@kbcwoodfloors.com
▶ Rover's Flooring Ltd, 2 Woodside Industrial Park, Works Road, Letchworth Garden City, Hertfordshire, SG6 1LA Tel: (01462) 486586 Fax: (01462) 486584 E-mail: info@rovers.nl

WOOD FLOORING SPECIALIST SERVICES

▶ 1926 Trading Co. Ltd, 2 Daimler Close, Royal Oak Industrial Estate, Daventry, Northamptonshire, NN11 8QJ Tel: (01327) 312200 Fax: (01327) 310123 E-mail: sales@1926trading.co.uk
▶ Allwood Floors, 28 Faraday Road, Rugby, Warwickshire, CV22 5ND Tel: (01788) 569980 Fax: (01788) 569978 E-mail: info@allwood-floors.co.uk
▶ Elba Flooring & Bed Centre, 23-24 Mill Street, Gowerton, Swansea, SA4 3ED Tel: (01792) 879555 Fax: (01792) 879555
▶ G D Floors Ltd, 8 Broomhill Court, Kilwinning, Ayrshire, KA13 6UL Tel: (01294) 559745 E-mail: info@gdfloors.co.uk
▶ Kinv Property Maintenance, 6 High Street, Princes Risborough, Buckinghamshire, HP27 0AX Tel: (01844) 274876 Fax: (01844) 274876 E-mail: info@kinv.co.uk
▶ Naturally Wood Ltd, 44 Forest Road, Loughton, Essex, IG10 1DX Tel: (020) 8508 2555 Fax: (020) 8508 6261 E-mail: info@naturallywood.net
Online-Flooring.co.uk, Willoughby Coachworks, Coxes Farm Road, Billericay, Essex, CM11 2UB Tel: (01277) 633053 E-mail: sales@online-flooring.co.uk
Woodline Floors Ltd, Unit 3, Brook Farm, Horsham Road, Cowfold, Horsham, West Sussex, RH13 8AH Tel: (01403) 860000 Fax: (0870) 8400040 E-mail: sales@woodlinefloors.co.uk

WOOD FRAMED BUILDINGS

Tony Graham & Co, 33-35 Whistley Road, Potterne, Devizes, Wiltshire, SN10 5QY Tel: (01380) 729445 Fax: (07005) 802576 E-mail: tony@tonygraham.co.uk

WOOD FRAMED WINDOWS

B M Prickett, Unit 1 Dodwell Trading Estate, Dodwell, Stratford-upon-Avon, Warwickshire, CV37 9ST Tel: (01789) 204930 Fax: (01789) 204930
George Barnsdale & Sons Ltd, 24 High Street, Donington, Spalding, Lincolnshire, PE11 4TA Tel: (01775) 823000 Fax: (01775) 823010 E-mail: lnewell@gbstp.com
Black Millwork Co Incorporated, Anderson House, Dallow St, Burton-on-Trent, Staffordshire, DE14 2PQ Tel: (01283) 511122 Fax: (01283) 510863 E-mail: enquiries@andersenwindows.com
Boyland Joinery Ltd, Stony Lane, Christchurch, Dorset, BH23 1EZ Tel: (01202) 499499 Fax: (01202) 499037 E-mail: enquires@boylandjoinery.co.uk
Bristol Woodtech Ltd, 208 South Liberty Lane, Bristol, BS3 2TY Tel: 0117-953 2592 Fax: 0117-953 2595
C & B Joinery, 8 Dowding Mews, Lincoln, LN3 4PN Tel: (01522) 568868 Fax: (01522) 568868
D J Gardner (Joinery) Ltd, Forest Vale Industrial Estate, Cinderford, Gloucestershire, GL14 2YA Tel: (01594) 823030 Fax: (01594) 823030
David Davies & Sons, 1 Waylands Upper Church Street, Oswestry, Shropshire, SY11 2AA Tel: (01691) 653116 Fax: (01691) 650702 E-mail: hugh@daviddaviesandsons.co.uk
Fairmitre Ltd, Village Way, Trafford Park, Manchester, M17 1AD Tel: 0161-872 1841 Fax: 0161-872 2501 E-mail: sales@fairmitre.uk
Glyngary Joinery Ltd, Unit H2, Risley, Warrington, WA3 6BL Tel: (01925) 763836 Fax: (01925) 762388 E-mail: sales@glyngary.co.uk
Howarth Windows & Doors Ltd, The Dock, New Holland, Barrow-upon-Humber, North Lincolnshire, DN19 7RT Tel: (01469) 530577 Fax: (01469) 531559 E-mail: windows&doors@howarth-timber.co.uk
Inwido UK Ltd, Po Box 10, Droitwich, Worcestershire, WR9 8ES Tel: (01527) 881060 Fax: (01527) 881061 E-mail: mail@inwido.co.uk
J & R Hateley Ltd, Lockside Tat Bank Road, Oldbury, West Midlands, B69 4NS Tel: 0121-544 6327 Fax: 0121-552 1150
Keyline Brick & Builders Merchant, Beaufort Road, Plasmarl, Swansea, SA6 8HR Tel: (01792) 792264 Fax: (01792) 796279 E-mail: swanseavea@keyline.co.uk
M A Products Ltd, 36 Hirst Lane, Malthouse Road, Tipton, West Midlands, DY4 9AE Tel: 0121-520 7077 Fax: 0121-520 9677
M & D Joinery Ltd, 56 Stanworth Street, London, SE1 3NY Tel: (020) 7231 2965 Fax: (020) 7231 2965
Mumford & Wood Ltd, Tower Business Park, Kelvedon Road, Tiptree, Colchester, CO5 0LX Tel: (01621) 818155 Fax: (01621) 818175 E-mail: chrisw@mumfordwood.com
Premdor Crosby Ltd, Huddersfield Road, Darton, Barnsley, South Yorkshire, S75 5JS Tel: (01226) 383434 Fax: (01226) 388808 E-mail: ukmarketing@premdor.com
R B D Builders Norfolk Ltd, 32 Southgates Road, Great Yarmouth, Norfolk, NR30 3LL Tel: (01493) 855891 Fax: (01493) 331615
Real Wooden Window Co., Unit 7-8 Alms Close, Stukeley Meadows Industrial Estate, Huntingdon, Cambridgeshire, PE29 6DY Tel: (01480) 356463 E-mail: info@realwoodenwindows.co.uk
S T P Group Ltd, Watford Bridge Road, New Mills, High Peak, Derbyshire, SK22 4HJ Tel: (01663) 744030 Fax: (01663) 745295 E-mail: stpgroupltd@btinternet.com
▶ South Yorkshire Home Improvements, Hoyle Mill Lane, Thurlstone, Sheffield, S36 9PZ Tel: (01226) 370270 Fax: (01226) 370377 E-mail: sales@syhi.co.uk
Walker Timber Ltd, Carriden Sawmills, Bo'Ness, West Lothian, EH51 9SN Tel: (01506) 823331 Fax: (01506) 822590 E-mail: mail@walkertimber.com
West Midland Glazing Co. Ltd, 123-125 Grove Lane, Birmingham, B17 0QT Tel: 0121-426 1275 Fax: 0121-428 1625
Whitaker & Co Denholme Ltd, Denholme Gate, Bradford, West Yorkshire, BD13 4EW Tel: (01274) 833611 Fax: (01274) 833782
Woodcraft Windows, 104 Hull Road, Hessle, North Humberside, HU13 9NB Tel: (01482) 644315

WOOD FRENCH DOORS

Acorn Timber & Joinery Ltd, Britannia Works, Upper Cyrus Street, Manchester, M40 7FD Tel: 0161-273 3871 Fax: 0161-274 3203 E-mail: sales@acorntimber.com
▶ Bygones Reclaimation Canterbury, Merton Lane, Canterbury, Kent, CT4 7BA Tel: (01227) 767453 Fax: (01227) 762153 E-mail: bob@bygones.net
▶ J B Joinery, Unit 7 Skelmanthorpe Business Park, Elm Street, Skelmanthorpe, Huddersfield, HD8 9DZ Tel: (01484) 860601 Fax: (01484) 860601
▶ North West Timber Products Ltd, Unit 11B, Newhaven Business Park, Barton Lane, Eccles, Manchester, M30 0HH Tel: 0161-7073797 Fax: 0161-7079717 E-mail: sales@nwtimberproducts.co.uk
Real Wooden Window Co., Unit 7-8 Alms Close, Stukeley Meadows Industrial Estate, Huntingdon, Cambridgeshire, PE29 6DY Tel: (01480) 356463 E-mail: info@realwoodenwindows.co.uk
▶ Valley Windows Ltd, The Old Spray Shop, Woodside Trading Estate, Usk, Monmouthshire, NP15 1SS Tel: (01291) 675470 Fax: (01291) 675472 E-mail: ian@valleywindows.co.uk

WOOD FURNITURE

A Woodcock & Son, 8a Asfordby Street, Leicester, LE5 3QG Tel: 0116-262 2176
Acorn Industries, Brandsby, York, YO61 4RG Tel: (01347) 888217 Fax: (01347) 888382
Anbercraft Furniture, 315 Princes Road, Stoke-on-Trent, ST4 7JS Tel: (01782) 413719 Fax: (01782) 749156
Andrena Direct Furniture, Auction House, Geddings Road, Hoddesdon, Hertfordshire, EN11 0NT Tel: (01992) 451722 Fax: (01992) 466024 E-mail: enquiries@anrenda.co.uk
Anthony Barkworth, Dorchester Road, Lytchett Minster, Poole, Dorset, BH16 6HS Tel: (01202) 632838 Fax: (01202) 632838
Barlis Pine Ltd, 5-6 Tentercroft Street Industrial Estate, Lincoln, LN5 7ED Tel: (01522) 567745 Fax: (01522) 544336 E-mail: barlispine@hotmail.com
Bartholomew Joinery Ltd, The Workshop Great Hidden Farm, Wantage Road, Eddington, Hungerford, Berkshire, RG17 0PW Tel: (01488) 685407 Fax: (01488) 681624 E-mail: bart.joinery@amserve.net
Beech Dene Craft Centre, Beechdene, Carr Lane, Hambleton, Poulton-le-Fylde, Lancashire, FY6 9DW Tel: (01253) 701371 Fax: (01253) 701848
Colinton Manufacturing Ltd, 2 Lochend Road South, Musselburgh, Midlothian, EH21 6BD Tel: 0131-665 0371 Fax: 0131-665 9993 E-mail: sales@colintonfurniture.co.uk
Combined Frame Makers Ltd, Hopes Lane, Ramsgate, Kent, CT12 6RN Tel: (01843) 595846 Fax: (01843) 851831
Countryside Cabinet Maker, 8 Wellsway Works, Wells Road, Radstock, BA3 3RZ Tel: (0781) 2688101 Fax: (01225) 840864 E-mail: scott.joyce@virgin.net
Dartmoor Hardwoods, Duchy Yard, Station Road, Princetown, Yelverton, Devon, PL20 6QX Tel: (01822) 890559 Fax: (01822) 890559
Eye Of The Heart Woodworking, Friday Street, Bridge Farm, Brandeston, Woodbridge, Suffolk, IP13 7BP Tel: (01728) 685890
Farrell Furniture, West Harwood Farm, West Calder, West Lothian, EH55 8LF Tel: (01506) 873990
Feasibility Ltd, Weston Green, Hampton Court Way, Thames Ditton, Surrey, KT7 0JP Tel: (020) 8398 8088 Fax: (020) 8398 1547 E-mail: feasibility@btconnsct.com
Fray Design Ltd, Ghyll Way Airedale Business Centre, Keighley Road, Skipton, North Yorkshire, BD23 2TZ Tel: (01756) 704040 Fax: (01756) 704041 E-mail: sales@fraydesign.co.uk
H B Pine Products, Herrington Burn, Houghton Le Spring, Tyne & Wear, DH4 4JW Tel: 0191-385 2822 Fax: 0191-385 2267
H Postill, The Old Chapel, Fangfoss, York, YO41 5QP Tel: (01759) 368209
Hill-Rom UK Ltd, Clinitron House, Ashby Park, Ashby-de-la-Zouch, Leicestershire, LE65 1JG Tel: (01530) 411000 Fax: (01530) 411555 E-mail: name@hill-rom.co.uk
John F White Cabinet Makers, Unit 6 Veasey Close, Attleborough Fields Industrial Estate, Nuneaton, Warwickshire, CV11 6RT Tel: (024) 7634 7347 Fax: (024) 7638 2077 E-mail: enquiries@jfw-cabinet.com
Latham Jenkins Ltd, Brown Street, Wigan, Lancashire, WN3 4DH Tel: (01942) 821414 Fax: (01942) 821432
Lauriston Pine, 319 Torquay Road, Paignton, Devon, TQ3 2EY Tel: (01803) 664077 Fax: (01803) 664077
Libraco Library Accessories, Filston Farm, Filston Lane, Sevenoaks, Kent, TN14 5JU Tel: (01959) 524074 Fax: (01959) 525218 E-mail: sales@1ibraco.uk.com
Luke Jones, Greinan Farm, Tower Hill, Chipperfield, Kings Langley, Hertfordshire, WD4 9LU Tel: (01442) 832891 Fax: (01442) 831115
Martin & Frost, Kinnaird Park, Newcraighall Road, Edinburgh, EH15 3HP Tel: 0131-657 0820 Fax: 0131-657 0821
Norfolk Cabinet Makers Ltd, Park Farm Workshops, Beeston Lane, Beeston St. Andrew, Norwich, NR12 7BP Tel: (01603) 408904 Fax: (01603) 488718 E-mail: info@norfolkcabinetmakers.co.uk
Oblique, Stamford Works, Gillett Street, London, N16 8JH Tel: (020) 7503 2100 Fax: (020) 7275 7495
P Bastow, Silver Street, Reeth, Richmond, North Yorkshire, DL11 6SP Tel: (01748) 884555 Fax: (01748) 884181
Pine Stable, 78 Carroway Head, Canwell, Sutton Coldfield, West Midlands, B75 5RZ Tel: 0121-308 0231 Fax: 0121-308 1100 E-mail: aagadar@aol.com
Reel Furniture, 37 St. Stephens Square, Norwich, NR1 3SS Tel: (01603) 629356 E-mail: info@reelfurniture.co.uk
Remploy Ltd, Railway Road, Wrexham, Clwyd, LL11 2DN Tel: (01978) 291465 Fax: (01978) 290017 E-mail: gerrard.newrick@remploy.co.uk
Sauvagnat UK Ltd, Unit 12 Weights Farm Business Park, Weights Lane, Redditch, Worcestershire, B97 6RG Tel: (0845) 0536000 Fax: (0845) 0536001 E-mail: sales@edencontractfurniture.co.uk
Sitting Firm Ltd, The Old Saw Mill, Harvest Hill Lane, Allesley, Coventry, CV5 9DD Tel: (024) 7640 7930 Fax: (024) 7640 7940 E-mail: info@sittingfirm.co.uk

WOOD FURNITURE – *continued*

Stuart Interiors Ltd, Barrington Court, Barrington, Ilminster, Somerset, TA19 0NQ Tel: (01460) 240349 Fax: (01460) 242069 E-mail: design@stuartinteriors.com

Ternex Ltd, Ayot Green Sawmill, 27 Ayot Green, Ayot St. Peter, Welwyn, Hertfordshire, AL6 9BA Tel: (01707) 324606 Fax: (01707) 334371 E-mail: sales@ternex.co.uk

Tough Furniture, Stokewood Road, Craven Arms Business Park, Craven Arms, Shropshire, SY7 8NR Tel: (01588) 674340 Fax: (01588) 674341

Turnercraft Cabinet Makers, 5 Furlong Parade, Stoke-on-Trent, ST6 3AX Tel: (01782) 837618 Fax: (01782) 837618

John Warren Furniture Ltd, 4-6 New Inn, Broadway, London, EC2A 3PZ Tel: (020) 8986 3366 Fax: (020) 7729 8770 E-mail: sales@jwfltd.co.uk

Waywood Cabinet Makers, Butts Green, East End, Chadlington, Chipping Norton, Oxfordshire, OX7 3LT Tel: (01608) 676433 Fax: (01608) 676291 E-mail: sales@waywood.co.uk

Woodfurn, Unit 6 Easter Court, Woodward Avenue, Yate, Bristol, BS37 5YS Tel: (01454) 313684 Fax: (01454) 313731

Working Wood Ltd, Unit 1 New Cut, Wellington Street, Newmarket, Suffolk, CB8 0HT Tel: (01638) 669256

WOOD FURNITURE COMPONENTS

B A Jones & Co., 27 Padgets Lane, Redditch, Worcestershire, B98 0RB Tel: (01527) 523377 Fax: (01527) 523377 E-mail: stevethewoodturner@blueyonder.co.uk

Braintree Pine Centre, Spring Wood Industrial Estate, Warner Drive, Braintree, Essex, CM7 2YW Tel: (01376) 349493 Fax: (01376) 349553

Brown & Wakelin Sales Ltd, The Croft, Marsh Gibbon, Bicester, Oxfordshire, OX27 0EU Tel: (01869) 277337 Fax: (01869) 278844 E-mail: sales@brownandwakling.co.uk

J.J. Bunker & Son Ltd, 73 Common Road, Chandlers Ford, Eastleigh, Southampton, SO53 1HE Tel: (023) 8026 8176 Fax: (023) 8027 0668

Burbidge & Son Ltd, Burnsall Road, Coventry, CV5 6BS Tel: (024) 7667 1600 Fax: (024) 7669 1010 E-mail: sales@burbidge.co.uk

Cerrig Furniture, Cae Bryn, Cerrigydrudion, Corwen, Clwyd, LL21 9SW Tel: (01490) 420372

Country Corner, 25-27 High Street, Swanage, Dorset, BH19 2LS Tel: (01929) 421198 Fax: (01929) 421198

Country Furniture, 36london Rd, Nantwich, Cheshire, CW5 7JR Tel: 01270 610543 Fax: 01270 610543

Forest Products, 2 Ridgeway Farm, Evesham Road, Weethley, Alcester, Warwickshire, B49 5LZ Tel: (01789) 400206 Fax: (01789) 400204 E-mail: roderick@globalnet.co.uk

Good Wood Cellars, 16-17 The Quay, Exeter, EX2 4AP Tel: (01392) 498030 Fax: (01392) 202252

Haldane (U K) Ltd, 7 Blackwood Way, Bankhead Industrial Estate, Glenrothes, Fife, KY7 6JF Tel: (01592) 775656 Fax: (01592) 775757 E-mail: sales@haldaneuk.com

Arthur Heath & Co. Ltd, Hall Road, Aylesford, Kent, ME20 7QZ Tel: (01622) 717507 Fax: (01622) 710551 E-mail: admin@arthurheath.com

Mansells Ltd, 20 Vanguard Way, Shoeburyness, Southend-on-Sea, SS3 9RA Tel: (01702) 294222 Fax: (08708) 722750 E-mail: man@oppenheimers.co.uk

Mauve Furniture Ltd, Arnlie, 79 Edinburgh Road, Dumfries, DG1 1JX Tel: (01387) 248889 Fax: (01387) 248889 E-mail: info@mauvefurniture.co.uk

▶ Mitchell Veneers & Components Ltd, 170 Folly Lane, St. Albans, Hertfordshire, AL3 5JG Tel: (01727) 763705 Fax: (01727) 867974 E-mail: paul.mitchell.com@ntlworld.com

Nycholwood Ltd, 17 Brindley Road, Hinckley, Leicestershire, LE10 3BY Tel: 01455 610300

Panararmer Furniture, Bank House, Leasgill, Milnthorpe, Cumbria, LA7 7FG Tel: (01539) 563523 Fax: (01539) 563466

S C F Hardware Ltd, 3 Brook Park Estate, 27 Brook Road, Wimborne, Dorset, BH21 2BH Tel: (01202) 857140 Fax: (01202) 884419 E-mail: sales@scfhardware.com

Shaw Timber Ltd, Bridge Street, Slaithwaite, Huddersfield, HD7 5JN Tel: (01484) 848484 Fax: (01484) 848494 E-mail: sales@shawtimber.com

Somerdell Furniture, 98 Radstock Road, Midsomer Norton, Radstock, BA3 2AU Tel: (01761) 418969 Fax: (01761) 418969 E-mail: somerdell@aol.com

Thorpes Of Great Glen Ltd, Church Road, Great Glen, Leicester, LE8 9FE Tel: 0116-259 3888 Fax: 0116-259 2016 E-mail: thorpes@bespoke-joinery.co.uk

The World of Wood, Ganol Bldgs, Sarn, Pwllheli, Gwynedd, LL53 8HG Tel: (01758) 730544 Fax: (01758) 730544

Wup Doodle, The Street, Hepworth, Diss, Norfolk, IP22 2PS Tel: (01359) 254001 Fax: (01953) 688378 E-mail: info@wupdoodle.com

WOOD FURNITURE FITTINGS

▶ Bicester Furniture Studio, 24 Church Street, Bicester, Oxfordshire, OX26 6AZ Tel: (01869) 325669 Fax: (01869) 323164 E-mail: sezzybfs@tesco.net

Deacon & Sandys, Apple Pie Farm, Cranbrook Road, Benenden, Cranbrook, Kent, TN17 4EU Tel: (01580) 243331 Fax: (01580) 243301 E-mail: sales@deaconandsandys.co.uk

Erste Technik Ltd, 1 Grange Close, Clover Nook Industrial Park, Somercotes, Alfreton, Derbyshire, DE55 4QT Tel: (01773) 521180 Fax: (01773) 521190 E-mail: info@erste-technik.co.uk

Stewart Paton, Croftnacreich North Kessock, Inverness, IV1 3ZE Tel: (01463) 731204 Fax: (01463) 731204

Sharps Bedrooms Ltd, Homebase, Kingsway, Derby, DE22 3NF Tel: (01332) 383538

Somerdell Furniture, 98 Radstock Road, Midsomer Norton, Radstock, BA3 2AU Tel: (01761) 418969 Fax: (01761) 418969 E-mail: somerdell@aol.com

WOOD FURNITURE TO SPECIFICATION

▶ Bamber's Special Projects, 5 Challenge Court, Love La Industrial Estate, Bishops Castle, Shropshire, SY9 5DW Tel: (01588) 638111 Fax: (01588) 638111 E-mail: info@specialprojects.co.uk

▶ Bingham Pine Furniture, Grantham Road, Radcliffe-on-Trent, Nottingham, NG12 2JP Tel: 0115-933 2555 Fax: 0115-933 2555 E-mail: binghampine@aol.com

▶ Stephen J. Davies, 43 Curtis Avenue, Abingdon, Oxfordshire, OX14 3UL Tel: (01235) 200869

▶ Dimension Furniture, Church Lane, OXTED, Surrey, RH8 9LH Tel: 07860 809104 E-mail: martin.parsons@dimensionfurniture.co.uk

K Johnstone, Rear of, 351 Loxley Road, Sheffield, S6 4TH Tel: 0114-234 2131 Fax: 0114-234 2131

▶ MosleyDonaldson, Chimneys, Stretton on Fosse, Moreton-in-Marsh, Gloucestershire, GL56 9QU Tel: (01452) 547879 E-mail: enquiries@mosleydonaldson.co.uk

WOOD GARDEN STRUCTURES

1st Aid 4 Fencing, 2 Cornbrash Rise, Hilperton, Trowbridge, Wiltshire, BA14 7TT Tel: 0800 611 8344 E-mail: info@1staid4fencing.com

▶ Mercury Architectural Projects Ltd, 2 Shrike Close Clayton Heights, Bradford, West Yorkshire, BD6 3YG Tel: (0800) 695 7595 E-mail: info@mercurygardens.co.uk

WOOD GATES

A & B Fencing & Roofing Ltd, Love Lane Industrial Estate, Love Lane, Cirencester, Gloucestershire, GL7 1YG Tel: (01285) 651330 Fax: (01285) 651330

B G Petchell Ltd, Church Farm, Langar, Nottingham, NG13 9HH Tel: (01949) 860509 Fax: (01949) 861156

Bendrey Bros, Bath Road, Bridgeyate, Bristol, BS30 5JW Tel: 0117-967 4382 Fax: 0117-967 4383

C A Palmer & Sons, Clayford Cottages, Clayford, Wimborne, Dorset, BH21 7BJ Tel: (01202) 893467 Fax: (01202) 893467

Challenge Fencing Contractors Ltd, The Sawyard, Downside Road, Downside, Cobham, Surrey, KT11 3LY Tel: (01932) 860101 Fax: (01932) 866445 E-mail: sales@challengefencing.com

Chapman Woodcraft Ltd, Gravelly Bottom Road, Kingswood, Maidstone, Kent, ME17 3NU Tel: (01622) 844599 Fax: (01622) 844818 E-mail: chapmangates@hormail.co.uk

Cheltenham Fencing & Landscaping Supplies, Hayden Road, Cheltenham, Gloucestershire, GL51 0SN Tel: (01242) 526946 Fax: (01242) 526480E-mail: info@cheltenhamfencing.co.uk

Clemmitt Nick Joinery Contracts, Ghyll Crest, Over Silton, Thirsk, North Yorkshire, YO7 2LJ Tel: (01609) 883636 Fax: (01609) 883111 E-mail: sales@timbergates.co.uk

Fletcher Joinery, 261 Whessoe Road, Darlington, County Durham, DL3 0YL Tel: (01325) 357347 Fax: (01325) 357347 E-mail: enquiries@fletcherjoinery.co.uk

Gate Makers, Petford Lea, Buckland, Aylesbury, Buckinghamshire, HP22 5HU Tel: (01296) 630798 Fax: (01296) 631373 E-mail: admin@thegatemakers.co.uk

H G Froud & Son, 24 Newtown Road, Verwood, Dorset, BH31 6EJ Tel: (01202) 822444

Harleston Firs Saw Mill, Harlestone Road, Northampton, NN5 6UJ Tel: (01604) 581444 Fax: (01604) 759611 E-mail: sales@hfstimber.co.uk

J G S Metalwork, Unit 6 Broomstick Estate, High Street, Edlesborough, Dunstable, Bedfordshire, LU6 2HS Tel: (01525) 220360 Fax: (01525) 222786 E-mail: enquiries@weathervanes.org.uk

Kingsland Saw Mills Ltd, Kingsland, Leominster, Herefordshire, HR6 9SF Tel: (01568) 708206 Fax: (01568) 708258 E-mail: info@kingslandstabling.com

Morgan & Co Strood Ltd, Knight Road, Rochester, Kent, ME2 2BA Tel: (01634) 290909 Fax: (01634) 290800 E-mail: info@morgantimber.co.uk

Nicholas Soper & Co, 225 Citadel Road East, Plymouth, PL1 2NG Tel: (01752) 695748 Fax: (01752) 696740

Sawmill UK Ltd, Ward Lane, Stanley, Wakefield, West Yorkshire, WF3 4LU Tel: (01924) 374953 Fax: (01924) 378294

Sparkford Sawmills Ltd, Sparkford, Yeovil, Somerset, BA22 7LH Tel: (01963) 440414 Fax: (01963) 440982 E-mail: enquiries@sparkford.com

Stately Gates Inc 'Urswick Engineering, Long Lane, Barrow-in-Furness, Cumbria, LA13 0PF Tel: (01229) 462646 Fax: (01229) 462646

Trew Gates Ltd, Unit 4 Trefor Work Shops, Trefor, Caernarfon, Gwynedd, LL54 5LD Tel: (01286) 660418 Fax: (01286) 660687 E-mail: sales@trewgates.com

W A Skinner & Co UK Ltd, Dorset Way, Byfleet, West Byfleet, Surrey, KT14 7LB Tel: (01932) 344228 Fax: (01932) 348517

W Howkins & Co., 65-67 Newnham Avenue, Bedford, MK41 9QJ Tel: (01234) 261143 E-mail: sales@whowkins.co.uk

Wyckham Blackwell Group Ltd, Old Station Road, Hampton-In-Arden, Solihull, West Midlands, B92 0HB Tel: (01675) 442233 Fax: (01675) 442227E-mail: info@wyckham-blackwell.co.uk

WOOD HANDLES

Ace Wood Turners & Machinists Ltd, Hazel La, Great Wyrley, Walsall, WS6 6AA Tel: (01922) 416645

James Constance & Sons Ltd, The Estate Office Longhope Industrial Estate, Church Road, Longhope, Gloucestershire, GL17 0LB Tel: (01452) 830297

Lloyd Ltd, Vale Business Park, Llandow, Cowbridge, South Glamorgan, CF71 7PF Tel: (01446) 773231 Fax: (01446) 771039 E-mail: enquiries@plmortgages.co.uk

Pilkingtons Ltd, Belgrave Court, Caxton Road, Fulwood, Preston, PR2 9PL Tel: (01772) 705566 Fax: (01772) 705599 E-mail: info@pilkingtonsltd.com

Staveley Timber Ltd, Back Lane, Staveley, Kendal, Cumbria, LA8 9LR Tel: (01539) 821234 Fax: (01539) 821898 E-mail: broc@broc.co.uk

WOOD HANDRAILS

H. Brettell & Sons Ltd, 20 Chestnut Ave, Forest Gate, London, E7 0JH Tel: (020) 8555 4037 Fax: (020) 8555 2106 E-mail: sales@brettells.co.uk

Bristol Woodtech Ltd, 208 South Liberty Lane, Bristol, BS3 2TY Tel: 0117-953 2592 Fax: 0117-953 2595

Haldane (U K) Ltd, 7 Blackwood Way, Bankhead Industrial Estate, Glenrothes, Fife, KY7 6JF Tel: (01592) 775656 Fax: (01592) 775757 E-mail: sales@haldaneuk.com

WOOD HOSPITAL FURNITURE

Will Beck Ltd, Kitchener Road, High Wycombe, Buckinghamshire, HP11 2SW Tel: (0845) 4500444 Fax: (0845) 4500445 E-mail: sales@wil.co.uk

Huntleigh Renray, Huntleigh Renray Ltd, Road Five, Winsford Industrial Estate, Winsford, Cheshire, CW7 3RB Tel: (01606) 593456 Fax: (01606) 861354 E-mail: sales@renraydavidbaker.co.uk

M A P Woodcraft (Caerphilly) Ltd, The Rhos, Bedwas Road, Caerphilly, Mid Glamorgan, CF83 3AU Tel: (029) 2088 2339 Fax: (029) 2086 8315

WOOD JEWELLERY

Grooms House Turnery, Grooms House, Stanshawes Court, Yate, Bristol, BS37 4DZ Tel: (01454) 325525 Fax: (01454) 325525 E-mail: info@grooms-house-turnery.co.uk

WOOD KITCHEN UNIT DOORS

Real Wooden Window Co., Unit 7-8 Alms Close, Stukeley Meadows Industrial Estate, Huntingdon, Cambridgeshire, PE29 6DY Tel: (01480) 356463 E-mail: info@realwoodenwindows.co.uk

WOOD KITCHEN UNITS

Dove Furniture, 1 Nursery Buildings, York Road, Riccall, York, YO19 6QQ Tel: (01757) 249171 Fax: (01757) 249278 E-mail: craigandkim@btinternet.com

Eglinton Wood Turners, Mid Lodge Cottage, Eglinton, Irvine, Ayrshire, KA12 8TA Tel: (01294) 558145 Fax: (01294) 558145

Heritage Cabinet Makers, 1 Mushroom Farm, Bottesford Lane, Orston, Nottingham, NG13 9NX Tel: (01949) 851505

WOOD LADDERS

A Bratt & Son Ltd, Abbeyfield Road, Nottingham, NG7 2SZ Tel: 0115-986 6851 Fax: 0115-986 1991 E-mail: sales@brattsladders.com

C A Brown, 5 Young Street Industrial Estate, Young Street, Bradford, West Yorkshire, BD8 9RE Tel: (01274) 488099 Fax: (01274) 498868 E-mail: sales@castortruckladder.co.uk

Clow Group Ltd, 185 Broad Street, Glasgow, G40 2QR Tel: 0141-554 1739 Fax: 0141-551 0813 E-mail: clow@ladders-direct.co.uk

Roger Haydock & Co. Ltd, Mersey View Road, Widnes, Cheshire, WA8 8LN Tel: 0151-425 2525 Fax: 0151-425 4141 E-mail: rdh@haydockwidnes.demon.co.uk

Hewitt Ladders Ltd, 37 Melrose Street, Leicester, LE4 6FD Tel: 0116-266 3304 Fax: 0116-261 3033 E-mail: hewittladdersltd@btconnect.com

The Ladder Man, City Ladder Works, Victoria Road, Fenton, Stoke-On-Trent, ST4 2HS Tel: 0800 197 3839 Fax: (01782) 410172 E-mail: info@theladderman.co.uk

T J Dobson, Tattersall Street, Oldham, OL9 6EY Tel: 0161-624 1958 Fax: 0161-624 1958

W H Hulley, 26 Ebenezer Street, Sheffield, S3 8SR Tel: 0114-272 1205 Fax: 0114-276 5621 E-mail: sales@hulley-ladders.co.uk

WOOD LAMP STANDARDS

▶ Coconut House Ltd, Hall Street, Long Melford, Sudbury, Suffolk, CO10 9JQ Tel: (01787) 312922 E-mail: chrisandgina@coconuthouse.co.uk

Russell Lowe Ltd, Unit 37, Broomhills Industrial Estate, Braintree, Essex, CM7 2RW Tel: (01245) 351599 Fax: (01376) 345825

WOOD MACHINISTS, *See Woodwork, Repetition etc*

WOOD MIRROR FRAMES

▶ Frames, 6 Ladbroke Park, Millers Road, Warwick, CV34 5AN Tel: (01926) 419784 Fax: (01926) 419784 E-mail: info@framesuk.co.uk

▶ Framework, 5 Station Parade, Ashford, Middlesex, TW15 2RX Tel: (01784) 258800 Fax: (01784) 250503 E-mail: sales@jandmframework.com

Gray & Mcdonnell, Unit 3 4 City Cross Business Park, Salutation Road, London, SE10 0AT Tel: (020) 8858 8050 Fax: (020) 8269 1513 E-mail: mirrors@graymcdonnell.co.uk

Ruralcraft Furniture Ltd, Kimberley Road, Clevedon, Avon, BS21 6QJ Tel: (01275) 873869 Fax: (01275) 340969

WOOD MOULDINGS

Richard Burbidge Ltd, Whittington Road, Oswestry, Shropshire, SY11 1HZ Tel: (01691) 655131 Fax: (01691) 657694 E-mail: info@richardburbidge.co.uk

D W Mouldings Ltd, 58 Sunderland Road, Sandy, Bedfordshire, SG19 1QY Tel: (01767) 683400 Fax: (01767) 692296 E-mail: info@dwmouldings.co.uk

Drysdale Timber & Mouldings Ltd, 36-38 River Road, Barking, Essex, IG11 0DN Tel: (020) 8594 6004 Fax: (020) 8594 1089 E-mail: sales@blumsom.co.uk

L & S Schofield Ltd, Unit 11-13, Haigh Avenue, Stockport, Cheshire, SK4 1NU Tel: 0161-480 3570 Fax: 0161-480 0836 E-mail: steve@dowelpins.fsnet.co.uk

T.W. Parker Ltd, 90-118 Green Lane, London, N13 5UP Tel: (020) 8888 3477 Fax: (020) 8888 2273

M.W. Sales Ltd, 33-37 The Oval, Hackney Road, London, E2 0AS Tel: (020) 7739 5185 Fax: (020) 7729 3138

Veneer Workshop Ltd, 37a South Street, Portslade, Brighton, BN41 2LE Tel: (01273) 422332 Fax: (01273) 418220 E-mail: mail@veneerworkshop.co.uk

Winther,Browne & Company Ltd, 75 Bilton Way, Enfield, Middlesex, EN3 7ER Tel: (020) 8344 9050 Fax: (020) 8344 9051 E-mail: sales@wintherbrowne.co.uk

WOOD OFFICE FURNITURE

A F I Ltd, Unit 17-20, Greenfield, Royston, Hertfordshire, SG8 5HN Tel: (01763) 241007 Fax: (01763) 241040 E-mail: sales@phase.co.uk

Acorn Partition & Storage Systems, Kingsley Road, Lincoln, LN6 3TA Tel: (01522) 688771 Fax: (01522) 680404 E-mail: sales@apss.co.uk

Advanced Computer Furniture, Unit 2 Masons Road Industrial Estate, Masons Road, Stratford-upon-Avon, Warwickshire, CV37 9NF Tel: (01789) 414449 Fax: (01789) 415553

▶ Apple Display Systems Ltd, Units 1-9, Nelson Business Centre, Nelson Street, Manchester, M34 3ET Tel: 0161-335 0660

Arenson Group Ltd, Arenson Centre, Arenson Way, Dunstable, Bedfordshire, LU5 5UL Tel: (01582) 678300 Fax: (01582) 678111

WOOD OFFICE FURNITURE - *continued*

B & B Business Equipment, 137 Lovibonds Avenue, Orpington, Kent, BR6 8EN Tel: (01689) 853821 Fax: (01689) 851114 E-mail: info@ukofficeshop.com
▶ Beck Interiors Ltd, Victory House, Cox Lane, Chessington, Surrey, KT9 1SG Tel: (020) 8974 0500 Fax: (020) 8974 0555 E-mail: mail@beckinteriors.com
▶ Blevins Ltd, 189 Old Shettleston Road, Glasgow, G32 7HN Tel: 0141-764 3733 Fax: 0141-764 3734
Blue Line Office Furniture, Endeavour House, London Stansted Airport, Stansted, Essex, CM24 1SJ Tel: (01279) 669470 Fax: (01279) 669471 E-mail: sales@blueline.uk.com
▶ Bulmer Interior Contracts Ltd, Lauren House, 164 Brinkburn Street, Newcastle upon Tyne, NE6 2AR Tel: 0191-276 4781 Fax: 0191-276 2663
▶ Carlton Screens Ltd, 1 Real Workshops, Westfield Road, Parkgate, Rotherham, South Yorkshire, S62 6EY Tel: (01709) 525414 Fax: (01709) 710158
▶ Carlton Shopfitting Ltd, Carlton House, Carlton Road, Dewsbury, West Yorkshire, WF13 2AT Tel: (01924) 454612 Fax: (01924) 460042
▶ Central Shopfitters Ltd, Palm Street, New Basford, Nottingham, NG7 7HS Tel: 0115-942 2671 Fax: 0115-919 1993
Computing Needs Ltd, 9-11 Manor Road, Felixstowe, Suffolk, IP11 2EJ Tel: (01394) 278067 Fax: (01394) 458140 E-mail: sales@computingneeds.co.uk
▶ Peter Craig, Wallyford Industrial Estate, Wallyford, Musselburgh, Midlothian, EH21 8QJ Tel: 0131-665 4517 Fax: 0131-653 1969
▶ Dixon Timber Products Ltd, Roberts Road, Balby, Doncaster, South Yorkshire, DN4 0JT Tel: (01302) 341833 Fax: (01302) 341839 E-mail: dixontimber@btconnect.com
▶ Eastlake Group Ltd, Unit 1, Philipshill Industrial Estate, East Kilbride, Glasgow, G74 5PG Tel: (01355) 593200 Fax: (01355) 593201 E-mail: info@eastlakegroup.com
Eborcraft Ltd, 11-12 Chessingham Park Common Road, Dunnington, York, YO19 5SE Tel: (01904) 481020 Fax: (01904) 481022 E-mail: sales@eborcraft.co.uk
Edwards Office Furniture, Twentypence Road, Cottenham, Cambridge, CB4 8PS Tel: (01954) 250949 Fax: (01954) 250949
Evertaut, Lions Drive, Shadsworth Business Park, Blackburn, BB1 2QS Tel: (01254) 297880 Fax: (01254) 274859 E-mail: sales@evertaut.co.uk
Flexiform Business Furniture Ltd, The Office Furniture Centre, 1392 Leeds Road, Bradford, West Yorkshire, BD3 7AE Tel: (01274) 656013 Fax: (01274) 665760 E-mail: sales@flexiform.co.uk
G H UK Distribution Ltd, 13 York House, Langston Road, Loughton, Essex, IG10 3TQ Tel: (020) 8502 0100 Fax: (020) 8508 2114 E-mail: ghukdistribution@btconnect.com
Ernest Gill & Son, Holmfield Industrial Estate, Holmfield, Halifax, West Yorkshire, HX2 9TN Tel: (01422) 246286 Fax: (01422) 240716
▶ Gresham Office Furniture, Lynstock Way, Lostock, Bolton, BL6 4SA Tel: (01204) 664400 Fax: (01204) 664433 E-mail: info@gof.co.uk
Hands Of Wycombe, 36 Dashwood Avenue, High Wycombe, Buckinghamshire, HP12 3DX Tel: (01494) 524222 Fax: (01494) 526508
▶ I R W (Enclosures) Ltd, Unit 7, Liskeard Enterprise Centre, Station Road, Liskeard, Cornwall, PL14 4DA Tel: (01579) 344334
▶ K M Furniture Ltd, Newton House, Pottery La West, Chesterfield, Derbyshire, S41 9BN Tel: (01246) 260123 Fax: (01246) 260221
Komfort, 96 Hopewell Drive, Chatham, Kent, ME5 7PY Tel: (01634) 829290 Fax: (01634) 831213
▶ Logic Office Interiors Ltd, 748 London Road, Hounslow, TW3 1PD Tel: (020) 8572 7474
Lowe Of Loughborough, 37-40 Churchgate, Loughborough, Leicestershire, LE11 1UE Tel: (01509) 217876
▶ Martins Shop & Bar Fitters Ltd, 2-8 West Bowling Green Street, Edinburgh, EH6 5PQ Tel: 0131-553 4777
E.F.G. Matthews Ltd, Northfield Drive, Milton Keynes, MK15 0DQ Tel: (01908) 665643 Fax: (01908) 609948
▶ Midas Contract Systems, 1 Airth Drive, Glasgow, G52 1JU Tel: 0141-849 1001 Fax: 0141-840 2112
Milton Joinery, Unit 9 Ridge Way, Drakes Drive, Long Crendon, Aylesbury, Buckinghamshire, HP18 9BF Tel: (01844) 203630 Fax: (01844) 203635
Moffett & Sons Ltd, Seymour Hill Industrial Estate, Dunmurry, Belfast, BT17 9PW Tel: (028) 9030 1411 Fax: (028) 9061 0785 E-mail: enquiries@moffett.co.uk
▶ Monks Maberly Ltd, Gibson St Works, Gibson St, Nelson, Lancashire, BB9 8RR Tel: (01282) 614974 Fax: (01282) 614977 E-mail: sales@interform-furniture.co.uk
H. Morris & Co. Ltd, 24 Rosyth Road, Glasgow, G5 0YD Tel: 0141-300 7200 Fax: 0141-300 7240
▶ Ollerton Ltd, Samlesbury Mill, Goosefoot Lane, Samlesbury Bottoms, Preston, PR5 0RN Tel: (01254) 852127
Pentos Office Furniture Ltd, Asher Lane, Pentrich, Ripley, Derbyshire, DE5 3RE Tel: (01773) 570700 Fax: (01773) 570160 E-mail: email@pentos-plc.co.uk
▶ Plan It Contracts Ltd, 37 Colquhoun Avenue, Glasgow, G52 4PL Tel: 0141-883 8741 Fax: 0141-882 7071
Premier Seating International Ltd, Parkside Mill, Walter Street, Blackburn, BB1 1TL Tel: (01254) 673400 Fax: (01254) 665571 E-mail: sales@premierseating.co.uk
▶ Prestige Shop Fitting Installations, 79 Carron Place, East Kilbride, Glasgow, G75 0YL Tel: (01355) 244540 Fax: (01355) 235080 E-mail: lindadesign@prestigeinstalations.net
John Pulsford Associates Ltd, 4 Sphere Industrial Estate, Campfield Road, St. Albans, Hertfordshire, AL1 5HT Tel: (01727) 840800 Fax: (01727) 840083 E-mail: info@jpa-furniture.com
▶ Queensbury Shelters Ltd, Fitzherbert Road, Portsmouth, PO6 1SE Tel: (023) 9221 0052 Fax: (023) 9221 0059
Of Quest Ltd, Irton House, Tower Estate, Warpsgrove Lane, Chalgrove, Oxford, OX44 7TH Tel: (01865) 891444 Fax: (01865) 893722 E-mail: customerservice@ofquest.co.uk
▶ R A P Industries Ltd (Sheet Metal), Welbeck Way, Peterborough, PE2 7WH Tel: (01733) 394841 Fax: (01733) 391825
Roc Furniture Ltd, Austin Way, Birmingham, B42 1DF Tel: 0121-358 2436 Fax: 0121-358 6016 E-mail: sales@roc-office.co.uk
▶ Roebuck & Holmes Ltd, 1-6 Farnley Mill, Farnley Road, Farnley Tyas, Huddersfield, HD4 6UN Tel: (01484) 665553 Fax: (01484) 664828 E-mail: admin@roebuckandholmes.co.uk
Royal Strathclyde Blindcraft Industries Beds Mattresses Office Re, 12 Edgefauld Avenue, Glasgow, G21 4BB Tel: 0141-287 0800 Fax: 0141-287 0880
▶ Ryan, Sandars Road, Heapham Road Industrial Estate, Gainsborough, Lincolnshire, DN21 1RZ Tel: (01427) 677556 Fax: (01427) 617773 E-mail: info@martinryan.co.uk
▶ S Barber & Co Shopfitters Ltd, Bangor Terrace, Leeds, LS12 5PS Tel: 0113-263 9996 Fax: 0113-279 0158 E-mail: info@sbarber.co.uk
Samuel Bruce, 1-7 Corstorphine Road, Edinburgh, EH12 6DD Tel: 0131-313 3760 Fax: 0131-313 3721
Screen Solutions Ltd, Beaufort House, Newton Road, Peacehaven, East Sussex, BN10 8JQ Tel: (01273) 589922 Fax: (01273) 589921 E-mail: sales@screensolutions.co.uk
Smiths Office & Commercial Furniture, Windsor Road, Redditch, Worcestershire, B97 6DJ Tel: (01527) 66663 Fax: (01527) 69333 E-mail: info@smithseating.co.uk
Sven Christiansen plc, Riverway Industrial Estate, Portsmouth Road, Peasmarsh, Guildford, Surrey, GU3 1LZ Tel: (01483) 302728 Fax: (01483) 569903 E-mail: info@sven.co.uk
Talbot Office Products Equipment Ltd, 5 Gunnery Terrace, The Royal Arsnal, Woolwich, London, SE18 6SW Tel: (020) 7231 7020 Fax: (020) 7231 8087
Tower Systems Furniture Ltd, 45 Garman Road, London, N17 0UR Tel: (020) 8885 4422 Fax: (020) 8801 9822
Tract Ltd, Mckay Trading Estate, Station Approach, Bicester, Oxfordshire, OX26 6BF Tel: (01869) 326300 Fax: (01869) 323430 E-mail: info@tract.ltd.uk
Trojan Woodworking, Bourne Road, Pode Hole, Spalding, Lincolnshire, PE11 3LW Tel: (01775) 767786 Fax: (01775) 767786
▶ Tube & Wire Display Ltd, Middle Mill, Oxford Street East, Ashton-under-Lyne, Lancashire, OL7 0NE Tel: 0161-339 4877 Fax: 0161-343 2596
Verco Office Furniture Ltd, Chapel Lane, High Wycombe, Buckinghamshire, HP12 4BG Tel: (01494) 448000 Fax: (01494) 464216 E-mail: sales@verco.co.uk
▶ Woodcraft Designs, 121 The Pannier Market, South Street, Torrington, Devon, EX38 8HD Tel: (01805) 625444 E-mail: info@woodcraftdesigns.co.uk
Woodland Furniture Co., Woodlands, Gwersyllt, Wrexham, Clwyd, LL11 4NW Tel: (01978) 755666 Fax: (01978) 758222 E-mail: john@bostock55.freeserve.co.uk

WOOD OFFICE FURNITURE COMPONENTS

▶ Mitchell Veneers & Components Ltd, 170 Folly Lane, St. Albans, Hertfordshire, AL3 5JG Tel: (01727) 763705 Fax: (01727) 867974 E-mail: paul.mitchell@ntlworld.com

WOOD OR PLYWOOD OR CHIPBOARD WALL PANELLING

Bruynzeel Multipanel, 8 High Street, Southminster, Essex, CM0 7DE Tel: (01621) 774728 Fax: (01621) 773825 E-mail: lbundy@bruynzeelmultipanel.com
Egger UK Holdings Ltd, Anick Grange Road, Hexham, Northumberland, NE46 4JS Tel: (01434) 602191 Fax: (01434) 605103 E-mail: info@egger.co.uk
Gariff Construction Ltd, Village House, Eleventh Street, Trafford Park, Manchester, M17 1JF Tel: 0161-848 9983 Fax: 0161-848 9984 E-mail: leeunsworth@gariff.co.uk
International Decorative Services, Dukesway, Team Valley Trading Estate, Gateshead, Tyne & Wear, NE11 0PZ Tel: 0191-491 7000 Fax: 0191-491 7007
Mermaid Panels Ltd, DBC House, Grimsby Road, Laceby, Grimsby, South Humberside, DN37 7DP Tel: (01472) 279940 Fax: (01472) 752575 E-mail: sales@mermaidpanels.com

WOOD PAINT SPRAYING

▶ Brown's French Polishers, Unit A2 Pixmore Estate, Pixmore Avenue, Letchworth Garden City, Hertfordshire, SG6 1JJ Tel: (01462) 680241 Fax: (01462) 482999 E-mail: info@brownsfrenchpolishing.co.uk
▶ Fire Place, Clarence Road, Worksop, Nottinghamshire, S80 1QA Tel: (01909) 530626 E-mail: sales@fireplacegallery.co.uk
▶ Repolishing.Co.Uk, Connors Yard, Crowborough Hill, Crowborough, East Sussex, TN6 2DA Tel: (01892) 668001 Fax: (01892) 861301 E-mail: gavin.mason@repolishing.co.uk
▶ Woodspray Timber Preservation Services, 21 Hillhead Road, Toomebridge, Antrim, BT41 3SF Tel: (028) 7965 1794 Fax: (028) 7965 1795 E-mail: info@woodsprayltd.com

WOOD PALLET OR STILLAGES

A Gordon & Co. Ltd, 14 Barrasgate Road, Fraserburgh, Aberdeenshire, AB43 9DQ Tel: (01346) 513297 Fax: (01346) 516003
A.M Pallet Services Ltd, Goods Yard, Bryanstone Road, Waltham Cross, Hertfordshire, EN8 7PJ Tel: (01992) 652700 Fax: (01992) 651185 E-mail: sales@prpallets.com
▶ Abacus Pallet Distribution, Fruit Market, A1 Blochairn Road, Glasgow, G21 2DU Tel: 0141-552 6123 Fax: 0141-552 6123
Askern UK Ltd, High Street, Askern, Doncaster, South Yorkshire, DN6 0AA Tel: (01302) 703065 Fax: (01302) 701992 E-mail: info@askern.com
Berkshire Pallets Ltd, Unit 2 Membury Business Park, Lambourn Woodlands, Hungerford, Berkshire, RG17 7TJ Tel: (01488) 73700 Fax: (01488) 73701
Bolam & Shaw Ltd, Red Doles Works, Red Doles Lane, Huddersfield, HD2 1YF Tel: (01484) 425705 Fax: (01484) 430480 E-mail: sales@bolamandshaw.co.uk
Bradley Thallon Industries Ltd, Kiltonga Industrial Estate, Belfast Road, Newtownards, County Down, BT23 4TJ Tel: (028) 9181 5403 Fax: (028) 9181 5409 E-mail: terence@bradleythallon.co.uk
Breydon Enterprises Ltd, Fenner Road, Unit 1, Great Yarmouth, Norfolk, NR30 3PS Tel: (01493) 331411 Fax: (01493) 331411 E-mail: breydonenterprises@fsmail.net
Bripak UK Ltd, Delta Works, Devonshire Road, Eccles, Manchester, M30 0WX Tel: 0161-787 8770 Fax: 0161-707 0009
Bruno Timber Products, Weston Court, Holton Road, Barry, South Glamorgan, CF63 4JD Tel: (01446) 732693 Fax: (01446) 732693
Cargo Pallets Ltd, West Lane, Grangetown, Middlesbrough, Cleveland, TS6 7AA Tel: (01642) 468878 Fax: (01642) 461868 E-mail: cargopallets@btconnect.com
Central Pallet Company Ltd, 36-51 Lower Dartmouth Street, Bordesley, Birmingham, B9 4LG Tel: 0121-772 5620 Fax: 0121-766 5778
Clanville Sawmills Ltd, Clanville, Castle Cary, Somerset, BA7 7PQ Tel: (01963) 350881 Fax: (01963) 351562 E-mail: admin@clanvillsawmills.co.uk
▶ Combine Pallets, Grove Road, Northfleet, Gravesend, Kent, DA11 9AX Tel: (01474) 363421 Fax: (01474) 353031 E-mail: ian@pallet.co.uk
Copeplan Co., Neath Road, Landore, Swansea, SA1 2JG Tel: (01792) 799895 Fax: (01792) 776670
E S Harverson & Son Transport Ltd, Unit 3 Abbey Industrial Estate, Mitcham, Surrey, CR4 4NA Tel: (020) 8648 5553 Fax: (020) 8646 7009 E-mail: bharverson@aol.com
E W Turner & Co. Ltd, Tame Street, West Bromwich, West Midlands, B70 0QP Tel: 0121-556 1141 Fax: 0121-556 3911 E-mail: accounts@ewturner.co.uk
East Bros Holdings Ltd, The Sawmills, West Dean, Salisbury, SP5 1JA Tel: (01794) 340270 Fax: (01794) 341317 E-mail: mail@eastbros.co.uk
Factory Reconstruction Co. (Manchester) Ltd, Paradise Mill, Bell Street, Oldham, OL1 3PY Tel: 0161-624 5988 Fax: 0161-665 1994 E-mail: ukpallets@aol.com
▶ Fortune, North Western Street, Manchester, M12 6DX Tel: 0161-273 5257
Geddes Packaging, Dumbledeny Lane, Walsall, WS9 0DH Tel: (01922) 455988 Fax: (01922) 454988E-mail: sales@geddespackaging.co.uk
T. Ginder (Packaging) Ltd, Upper Brook Street, Walsall, WS2 9PE Tel: (01922) 622251 Fax: (01922) 643265
H G Timber Ltd, Three Ways Wharf, Rigby Lane, Hayes, Middlesex, UB3 1ET Tel: (020) 8561 3311 Fax: (020) 8569 2122 E-mail: sales@hgtimber.co.uk
H L C (Wood Products) Ltd, High Road, Needham, Harleston, Norfolk, IP20 9LB Tel: (01379) 852873 Fax: (01379) 852761 E-mail: sales@hlcwood.demon.co.uk
Hambrook Pallets Ltd, Ironchurch Road, Avonmouth, Bristol, BS11 9AF Tel: 0117-982 1236 Fax: 0117-982 2252
George Hill Ltd, Biddings Lane, Bilston, West Midlands, WV14 9NW Tel: (01902) 403631 Fax: (01902) 492308 E-mail: sales@g-hill2000.co.uk
Hilton Industrial Services Ltd, The Old Cheese Factory, Stone Road, Hill Chorlton, Newcastle, Staffordshire, ST5 5DR Tel: (01782) 680680 Fax: (01782) 680546
I P S Fencing Supplies, 65 Toms Lane, Kings Langley, Hertfordshire, WD4 8NJ Tel: (01923) 268431 Fax: (01923) 261459 E-mail: info@ipsfencing.com
Industrial Pallet & Transport Services, Kirkhaw Lane, Knottingley, West Yorkshire, WF11 8RD Tel: (01977) 671886 Fax: (01977) 671995
J B J Pallets Ltd, Hedingham Road, Wethersfield, Braintree, Essex, CM7 4EQ Tel: (01371) 850035 Fax: (01371) 850420
J K Francis & Son Ltd, 16 Fortnum Close, Birmingham, B33 0JY Tel: 0121-783 7568 Fax: 0121-789 7140
J Nicklin & Sons Ltd, 36 Erskine Street, Birmingham, B7 4LL Tel: 0121-359 8101 Fax: 0121-359 6673 E-mail: sales@nicklin.co.uk
J & R Hall Joinery Ltd, Deanroyd Works, Deanroyd Road, Todmorden, Lancashire, OL14 6TX Tel: (01706) 810300 Fax: (01706) 810400 E-mail: jrhalljoinery@zen.co.uk
▶ Killeavy Wood Products, 25 Ballintemple Road, Killeavy, Newry, County Down, BT35 8LQ Tel: (028) 3084 9374 Fax: (028) 3084 9375 E-mail: technatab@fsmail.net
J.B. Kind Ltd, Shobnall Street, Burton-On-Trent, Staffordshire, DE14 2HP Tel: (01283) 564631 Fax: (01283) 511132
Larner Pallets Recycling Ltd, Jute Lane, Brimsdown, Enfield, Middlesex, EN3 7PJ Tel: (020) 8804 1494 Fax: (020) 8804 1164 E-mail: admin@larnerpallets.com
Edwin Lawton Ltd, Old Quarry, Uttoxeter Road, Blythe Bridge, Stoke-on-Trent, ST11 9ND Tel: (01782) 393631 Fax: (01782) 388221 E-mail: pallets@edwinlawton.com
M & J Enterprises, Cuckoo Lane, Winterbourne Down, Bristol, BS36 1AG Tel: 0117-957 2440 Fax: (01454) 318710
M S Shirts Box Ltd, 45 Finchwell Road, Sheffield, S13 9AS Tel: 0114-244 2591 Fax: 0114-244 3909 E-mail: msshirtsbox@ssbdial.co.uk
Monmouthshire Timber Supplies Ltd, PO Box 20, Newport, Gwent, NP20 2YQ Tel: (01633) 213268 Fax: (01633) 257088 E-mail: mts@montimber.co.uk
Musson Wood Products Ltd, Common La Industrial Estate, Kenilworth, Warwickshire, CV8 2EL Tel: (01926) 859616 Fax: (01926) 850844
N & R Manufacturing Ltd, Lawrence House Apollo, Lichfield Road Industrial Estate, Tamworth, Staffordshire, B79 7TA Tel: (01827) 57218 Fax: (01827) 60289
Newfields Timber Yard Co. Ltd, 420 High Street, Stoke-on-Trent, ST6 5ES Tel: (01782) 834057 Fax: (01782) 839772
Norbury (Pallets) Ltd, Unit 28, Marshgate Drive, Hertford, SG13 7AJ Tel: (01992) 504236 Fax: (01992) 584978 E-mail: sales@norburypallets.com
P & A Group of Companies, Mold Industrial Estate, Wrexham Road, Mold, Flintshire, CH7 4HE Tel: (01352) 752555 Fax: (01352) 755200 E-mail: sales@p-a-group.com
P R Pallet Services, Macdermott Road, Widnes, Cheshire, WA8 0PF Tel: 0151-495 1422 Fax: 0151-495 1123
P & R Pallets & Cases, 2 Bridge Industrial Estate, Hot Lane, Stoke-on-Trent, ST6 2DL Tel: (01782) 822555 Fax: (01782) 822555
Palick (Wolverhampton) Ltd, Hilton Main Industrial Estate, Bognop Road, Essinton, Wolverhampton, WV11 2BE Tel: (01902) 727691 E-mail: sales@palick.co.uk
Pallet Handling Ltd, Chiddingstone Causeway, Tonbridge, Kent, TN11 8JD Tel: (01892) 870655 Fax: (01892) 870746
Palletforce Crates & Packing Cases, Waterton Industrial Estate, Bridgend, Mid Glamorgan, CF31 3WT Tel: (01656) 662600 Fax: (01656) 661190 E-mail: palletforce67@owens-logistics.com
Pallets Unlimited, Barley Croft End, Furneux Pelham, Buntingford, Hertfordshire, SG9 0LL Tel: (01279) 777715 Fax: (01279) 777736 E-mail: janborltd@aol.com
Pine Products Ltd, 1 Hope Carr Way, Leigh, Lancashire, WN7 3DE Tel: (01942) 604999 Fax: (01942) 260734 E-mail: info@pine-products.net
Poskitt Painters Ltd, Empire Works, Holywell Lane, Castleford, West Yorkshire, WF10 3HJ Tel: (01977) 553089 Fax: (01977) 555765 E-mail: plastics@hotmail.com
Powell's of Sherborne, Middlemarsh, Sherborne, Dorset, DT9 5QW Tel: (01300) 345255 Fax: (01300) 345367 E-mail: pow@connect-2.co.uk
R Elliott & Sons Ltd, 21 Bridge Street, Uttoxeter, Staffordshire, ST14 8AR Tel: (01889) 565241 Fax: (01889) 563203
Red Joinery Ltd, Aquaduct Wharf, Hurst Lane, Bollington, Macclesfield, Cheshire, SK10 5LP Tel: (01625) 572128
Robert Birkbeck & Son Ltd, Thurcroft Industrial Estate, New Orchard Road, Thurcroft, Rotherham, South Yorkshire, S66 9HY Tel: (01709) 546459 Fax: (01709) 546780 E-mail: robertbirkbeckandson@hotmail.com
Rowlinson Packaging Ltd, Unit 1 Green Lane, Wardle, Nantwich, Cheshire, CW5 6BN Tel: (01829) 260571 Fax: (01829) 260718 E-mail: packaging@rowlinson.co.uk

WOOD PALLET OR STILLAGES – *continued*

Stanlow Pallets Ltd, Indigo Road, Ellesmere Port, CH65 4AJ Tel: 0151-356 3932 Fax: 0151-357 2667

Star Pallets, Shawlands Farm, Newchapel Road, Lingfield, Surrey, RH7 6BL Tel: (01342) 833704 Fax: (01342) 833704

T R Price & Son, Unit F3 Dudley Central Trading Estate, Hope Street, Dudley, West Midlands, DY2 8RS Tel: (01384) 237629

Timber Seventy Three Ltd, Stourvale Trading Estate, Banners Lane, Halesowen, West Midlands, B63 2AX Tel: (01384) 410799 Fax: (01384) 411080

Raymond Tisdale & Co. Ltd, Common Lane, Kenilworth, Warwickshire, CV8 2EL Tel: (01926) 852227 Fax: (01926) 850844

▶ United Pallet Repairs, Unit 11, Black Rock Mills, Waingate, Linthwaite, Huddersfield, HD7 5NS Tel: (01484) 847363 Fax: (01484) 847363

Whirlowdale Trading Co. Ltd, Canklow Meadows Industrial Estate, West Bawtry Road, Rotherham, South Yorkshire, S60 2XL Tel: (01709) 829061 Fax: (01709) 378947 E-mail: sales@whirlowdale.com

Wrexham Pallet Services, Rhosddu Industrial Estate, Main Road, Rhosrobin, Wrexham, Clwyd, LL11 4YL Tel: (01978) 261043 Fax: (01978) 312695

WOOD PANEL FENCING

▶ Fast Fences Ltd, 44 Fountain Court, Waterside, Evesham, Worcestershire, WR11 1JX Tel: (0800) 0193019 E-mail: nigelrb@nigelrb.com

Jacksons Garden Centre, 426-430 Stockfield Road, Yardley, Birmingham, B25 8JJ Tel: 0121-707 5066 Fax: 0121-707 5028 E-mail: martin@jacksons20.fsnet.co.uk

▶ Solid Timber Products, Heathfield Way, Gladstone Industry, Northampton, NN5 7QP Tel: (0845) 1297171 Fax: (0845) 1249499 E-mail: adam@solidonline.co.uk

▶ Sunny Aspects Ltd, 36 Udney Park Road, Teddington, Middlesex, TW11 9BG Tel: (020) 8977 4149 E-mail: info@sunnyaspects.co.uk

WOOD PARTITIONING

Alco Beldan Ltd, Accordial House, 35 Watford Metro Centre, Watford, WD18 9XN Tel: (01923) 246600 Fax: (01923) 245654 E-mail: enquiries@alcobeldan.com

C & M Partitioning Ltd, 10-12 Stirling Road, London, E17 6BT Tel: (020) 8531 3834 Fax: (020) 8531 3837

WOOD PATTERNS FOR PLASTIC

Seymour Patterns & Castings, Oak St Trading Estate, Oak Street, Quarry Bank, Brierley Hill, West Midlands, DY5 2JQ Tel: (01384) 78768 Fax: (01384) 79138 E-mail: john.elwell@yesit.co.uk

WOOD PICTURE FRAME MOULDINGS

Arqadia Ltd, 2 Wolseley Road, Woburn Road Industrial Estate, Bedford, MK42 7AD Tel: (01234) 857488 Fax: (01234) 840190 E-mail: sales@arqadia.co.uk

Ashworth & Thompson Ltd, Freestone Drive, Bulwell, Nottingham, NG6 8UZ Tel: 0115-927 8504 Fax: 0115-977 0152 E-mail: sales@ashworthandthompson.co.uk

D J Simons & Sons Ltd, 122-150 Hackney Road, London, E2 7QL Tel: (020) 7739 3744 Fax: (020) 7739 4452 E-mail: dsimons@djsimons.co.uk

M G Framing, Unit 8 Islwyn Workshops, Pontymister Industrial Estate, Risca, Newport, Gwent, NP11 6NP Tel: (01633) 612034 Fax: (01633) 612034 E-mail: mgframing@btinternet.com

Nottingham Moulding Co., Daleside Road, Nottingham, NG2 3GG Tel: 0115-986 6839 Fax: 0115-986 3709

WOOD PIPEWORK INSULATION BLOCKS

Support Systems Nottingham Ltd, Nottingham Road, Beeston, Nottingham, NG9 6DP Tel: 0115-922 9067 Fax: 0115-925 5555

WOOD PLAYGROUND EQUIPMENT

▶ The Children's Playground Co. Ltd, 1 George Street, Wolverhampton, WV2 4DG Tel: (01902) 422515 Fax: (028) 9032 7614 E-mail: sales@thechildrensplayground.com

▶ Tawny Wood Outdoor Play, The Owls, Clayford Road, Kilgetty, Dyfed, SA68 0RR Tel: (01834) 813227 Fax: (01834) 813227 E-mail: tawnywood@yahoo.co.uk

WOOD PLUGS

Moorland Woodturning Co. Ltd, Woodlands Mill, Luke Lane, Thongsbridge, Holmfirth, HD9 7TB Tel: (01484) 683126

WOOD PRESERVATION PRODUCTS

Akzo Nobel Woodcare, Meadow Lane, St. Ives, Cambridgeshire, PE27 4UY Tel: (01480) 496868 Fax: (01480) 496801 E-mail: woodcare@sis.akzonobel.com

Clam-Brummer Ltd, London Road, Spellbrook, Bishop's Stortford, Hertfordshire, CM23 4BA Tel: (020) 7476 3171 Fax: (020) 7474 0098 E-mail: sales@brummer.co.uk

Haynes Manufacturing UK, Marlowe House, Stewkins, Stourbridge, West Midlands, DY8 4YW Tel: (01384) 371416 Fax: (01384) 371416 E-mail: info@haynes-uk.co.uk

Hobstar Ltd, Palace Chemicals Ltd, Speke Hall Industrial Estate, Liverpool, L24 4AB Tel: 0151-486 6101 Fax: 0151-448 1982 E-mail: sales@palacechemicals.co.uk

Kingfisher Building Products Ltd, Cooper Lane, Bardsea, Ulverston, Cumbria, LA12 9RA Tel: (01229) 869100 Fax: (01229) 869101 E-mail: sales@kingfisherchem.com

Liver Grease Oil & Chemical Company Ltd, 11 Norfolk Street, Liverpool, L1 0BE Tel: 0151-709 7494 Fax: 0151-709 3774 E-mail: sales@livergrease.co.uk

N W E Paints Ltd, 66-70 Ffordd Las, Rhyl, Clwyd, LL18 2EA Tel: (01745) 342342 Fax: (01745) 334746 E-mail: admin@nwepaints.co.uk

Oakmere Technical Services Ltd, Unit 9, Pool Bank Business Park, High St, Chester, CH3 8JH Tel: (01829) 742100 Fax: (01829) 742109 E-mail: sales@oakmerets.com

Osmose Ltd, Timber Treatments Division, Fieldhouse Lane, Marlow, Buckinghamshire, SL7 1LS Tel: (01628) 486644 Fax: (01628) 476757 E-mail: info@protimsolignum.com

Triton Chemical Manufacturing Co. Ltd, Unit 5 Lyndean Industrial Estate, 129 Felixstowe Road, London, SE2 9SG Tel: (020) 8310 3929 Fax: (020) 8312 0349 E-mail: info@triton-chemicals.com

WOOD PRESERVATION SERVICES

▶ Richardson & Starling Northern Ltd, 3 Block 1 Maxwelltown Industrial Estate, Glasgow Road, Dumfries, DG2 0NW Tel: (01387) 269681 Fax: (01387) 264667

WOOD PROTECTION PAINTS

Osmose Ltd, Timber Treatments Division, Fieldhouse Lane, Marlow, Buckinghamshire, SL7 1LS Tel: (01628) 486644 Fax: (01628) 476757 E-mail: info@protimsolignum.com

WOOD PULP

Euroforest Ltd, Mead House, Bentley, Farnham, Surrey, GU10 5HY Tel: (01420) 23030 Fax: (01420) 23774

Paperun Group Of Companies, 1 East Barnet Road, Barnet, Hertfordshire, EN4 8RR Tel: (020) 8447 4141 Fax: (020) 8447 4241 E-mail: paper4u@paperun.com

Robert Horne, Huntsman House, Woodside Road, Eastleigh, Hampshire, SO50 4ET Tel: (023) 8061 8811 Fax: (023) 8061 0005

S C A Graphic Paper UK Ltd, 54 New Hythe Lane, Larkfield, Aylesford, Kent, ME20 7PE Tel: (01622) 883000 Fax: (01622) 883895

WOOD PUZZLES AND GAMES

▶ Faze 3, 23 Abergele Road, Colwyn Bay, Clwyd, LL29 7RS Tel: (01492) 534294 Fax: (01492) 534294 E-mail: alan@faze3.co.uk

▶ Sri Toy Europe, P. O Box 36957, London, SE6 4WT Tel: 020 8690 6995 Fax: 020 8690 8990 E-mail: sales@sritoyseurope.com

WOOD RECLAMATION/ RECYCLING SERVICES

▶ Giffords Recycling, Kelvin Way, West Bromwich, West Midlands, B70 7JR Tel: 0121-553 1910 Fax: 0121-500 4919 E-mail: info@giffords.biz

Hollands Recycling Ltd, 1 Holland Park, Bentley Road South, Wednesbury, West Midlands, WS10 8LN Tel: 0121-526 2454 Fax: 0121-568 6148 E-mail: enquiries@hollands-recycling.co.uk

Pallets Unlimited, Barley Croft End, Furneux Pelham, Buntingford, Hertfordshire, SG9 0LL Tel: (01279) 777715 Fax: (01279) 777736 E-mail: janborltd@aol.com

WOOD ROLLERS

Lind Wood Components Ltd, River Mill, Park Road, Dukinfield, Cheshire, SK16 5LR Tel: 0161-330 2624 Fax: 0161-343 1094 E-mail: info@lindwood.co.uk

WOOD SCAFFOLDING

▶ Brent Scaffold Boards Ltd, The Airfield, Breighton, Selby, North Yorkshire, YO8 6DJ Tel: (01757) 289199 Fax: (01757) 289105

WOOD SCREWS

Armstrong Fastenings Ltd, PO Box 6, Wednesbury, West Midlands, WS10 8UL Tel: 0121-224 2000 Fax: 0121-224 2007 E-mail: info@armfast.com

Carn Fasteners Ltd, 29 Garvagh Road, Swatragh, Maghera, County Londonderry, BT46 5QE Tel: (028) 7940 1248 Fax: (028) 7940 1533 E-mail: info@carnfasteners.com

Corroy Products Ltd, 25 Queen Street, Premier Business Park, Walsall, WS2 9NT Tel: (01922) 644884 Fax: (01922) 471370 E-mail: sales@corroy.co.uk

Don Industrial Supplies Ltd, Unit 17 Guildhall Industrial Estate, Sandall Stones Road, Kirk Sandall Industrial Estate, Doncaster, South Yorkshire, DN3 1QR Tel: (01302) 884086 Fax: (01302) 887458 E-mail: donindust@aol.com

Fosseway Technical Tapes, 8 Ladywood Works, Leicester Road, Lutterworth, Leicestershire, LE17 4HD Tel: (01455) 550515 Fax: (01455) 550122 E-mail: sales@fossewaytapes.co.uk

Herting & Son plc, Frederick House, 25 Armstrong Way, Southall, Middlesex, UB2 4SD Tel: (020) 8606 7000 Fax: (020) 8606 7010 E-mail: sales@fpherting.co.uk

C.J.D. Mayers & Co. Ltd, Unit 6, Speedwell Close Industrial Estate, Speedwell Road, Yardley, Birmingham, B25 8HT Tel: 0121-773 0101 Fax: 0121-773 0104 E-mail: mayers@madasafish.com

Midland Fixing Services Ltd, Unit 20 Bordesley Trading Estate, Bordesley Green Road, Birmingham, B8 1BZ Tel: 0121-327 5713 Fax: 0121-328 1842

P & D Fasteners Ltd, Mapplewell BSNS Park, Blacker Road, Staincross, Barnsley, South Yorkshire, S75 6BP Tel: (01226) 388899

WOOD SHAVINGS CONTRACTORS

H Eggleston Junior & Son Ltd, Lanchester, Durham, DH7 0TP Tel: (01207) 520869 Fax: (01207) 521941 E-mail: h.eggleston@onyxnet.co.uk

Snowflake Animal Bedding Ltd, Riverside Industrial Estate, Marsh Lane, Boston, Lincolnshire, PE21 7ST Tel: (0870) 3003355 Fax: (01205) 310298 E-mail: snowflakesales@plevin.co.uk

Snowflake Animal Bedding Ltd, Slimbridge Crossroads, Bristol Road, Slimbridge, Gloucester, GL2 7DW Tel: (0870) 3003355 Fax: (01453) 890047 E-mail: snowflakesales@plevin.co.uk

Whitfire Shavings & Sawdust Supplies Ltd, Heatherfield Works, Church Lane, Farington Moss, Leyland, PR26 6RD Tel: (01772) 335178 Fax: (01772) 629843

Woodflakes Of Daventry Ltd, Unit 1, Hollandstone Farm, High Street, Flore, Northamptonshire, NN7 4LP Tel: (01327) 343344 Fax: (01327) 342470 E-mail: woodflakes@interface99.fsbusiness.co.uk

WOOD SHELVING

E J Herok Ltd, Charlton Mead Lane, Hoddesdon, Hertfordshire, EN11 0DJ Tel: (01992) 462943 Fax: (01992) 464792 E-mail: info@herok.com

H G Timber Ltd, Three Ways Wharf, Rigby Lane, Hayes, Middlesex, UB3 1ET Tel: (020) 8561 3311 Fax: (020) 8569 2122 E-mail: sales@hgtimber.co.uk

Shaw Timber Ltd, Bridge Street, Slaithwaite, Huddersfield, HD7 5JN Tel: (01484) 848484 Fax: (01484) 848494 E-mail: sales@shawtimber.com

WOOD SIGNS

Ashford Signmakers Ltd, Unit 11q Godinton Way Industrial Estate, Godinton Way, Ashford, Kent, TN23 1JB Tel: (01233) 621447 Fax: (01233) 624327 E-mail: coneysigns@aol.com

Brewer Sign Services, 24 Meredith Road, Portsmouth, PO2 9NN Tel: (023) 9266 8602 Fax: (023) 9266 8602

Elmtree Signs, 62 Empress Road, Southampton, SO14 0JU Tel: (023) 8023 0903 Fax: (023) 8023 0904 E-mail: rod@elmtreesigns.co.uk

Forest Enterprise Signs Workshop, Coed Y Brenin Centre, Ganllwyd, Dolgellau, Gwynedd, LL40 2HY Tel: (01341) 440215 Fax: (01341) 440622 E-mail: sales@signworkshop.co.uk

▶ Signs & Design Ltd, 22-23 King Street Trading Estate, Middlewich, Cheshire, CW10 9LF Tel: (01606) 738833 Fax: (01606) 738547 E-mail: info@golfcoursesigns.co.uk

Sirocco Signs, 5 Strathpeffer Road, Dingwall, Ross-Shire, IV15 9QF Tel: (01349) 866726 Fax: (01349) 866727 E-mail: info@siroccosigns.com

W R Advertising Ltd, Black Lake, West Bromwich, West Midlands, B70 0PL Tel: 0121-525 2626 Fax: 0121-525 2955 E-mail: sales@wradvertising.co.uk

WOOD STAINS

Ag Woodcare Products, 3a Waterloo Industrial Estate, Waterloo Road, Bidford-on-Avon, Alcester, Warwickshire, B50 4JH Tel: (01789) 778628 Fax: (01789) 490296 E-mail: email@agwoodcare.co.uk

Akzo Nobel Woodcare, Meadow Lane, St. Ives, Cambridgeshire, PE27 4UY Tel: (01480) 496868 Fax: (01480) 496801 E-mail: woodcare@sis.akzonobel.com

Marrs Cross & Wilfrid Fairbairns Ltd, Hardwood House, 1 Oglander Road, London, SE15 4EH Tel: (020) 7639 5106 Fax: (020) 7639 5106 E-mail: mxf@ukgateway.net

WOOD STAIRCASES

George Barnsdale & Sons Ltd, 24 High Street, Donington, Spalding, Lincolnshire, PE11 4TA Tel: (01775) 823000 Fax: (01775) 823010 E-mail: lnewell@gbstp.com

Boyland Joinery Ltd, Stony Lane, Christchurch, Dorset, BH23 1EZ Tel: (01202) 499499 Fax: (01202) 499037 E-mail: enquires@boylandjoinery.co.uk

Brank Brook, Bescot Crescent, Walsall, WS1 4ND Tel: (01922) 728600 Fax: (01922) 728644

Bristol Woodtech Ltd, 208 South Liberty Lane, Bristol, BS3 2TY Tel: 0117-953 2592 Fax: 0117-953 2595

C & M Joinery, Unit 1, Plot 7 Claymore, Tame Valley Industrial Estate, Wilnecote, Tamworth, Staffs, B77 5DQ Tel: (01827) 250849 Fax: (01827) 287913

Chardstock Joinery, Chubbs Yard, Chardstock, Axminster, Devon, EX13 7BT Tel: (01460) 221148 Fax: (01460) 221148

Chichester Joinery Ltd, Unit 12 Quarry Lane Industrial Estate, Gravel Lane, Chichester, West Sussex, PO19 8PQ Tel: (01243) 784723 Fax: (01243) 533382 E-mail: michaelcarter3@btconnect.com

D J Gardner (Joinery) Ltd, Forest Vale Industrial Estate, Cinderford, Gloucestershire, GL14 2YA Tel: (01594) 823030 Fax: (01594) 823030

Essex Stairs & Joinery, Holmewood Farm, Brookhall Road, Fingringhoe, Colchester, CO5 7DG Tel: (01206) 728716 Fax: (01206) 729587

H & K Joinery Ltd, Moravian Road, Bristol, BS15 8ND Tel: 0117-960 2849 Fax: 0117-961 8250

Jarrett & Lawson Ltd, 5 The Old Quarry, Nene Valley Business Park, Oundle, Peterborough, PE8 4HN Tel: (01832) 275551 Fax: (01832) 275553 E-mail: jarrettlawson@pgrconstructions.co.uk

▶ Keating & King, Unit 13-14, The Bridge, Narberth, Dyfed, SA67 8QZ Tel: (01834) 861676 Fax: (01834) 861858 E-mail: keatingjoinery@aol.com

London Woodturners, 45 Hackney Road, London, E2 7NX Tel: (020) 7739 2296 Fax: (020) 7729 7270 E-mail: lwt@blueyonder.co.uk

M & D Joinery Ltd, 56 Stanworth Street, London, SE1 3NY Tel: (020) 7231 2965 Fax: (020) 7231 2965

N B Stairways Ltd, 2A Milton Road, London, E17 4SR Tel: (020) 8520 3566 Fax: (020) 8520 9673E-mail: nicholsbros@btinternet.com

Northern Joinery, Daniel Street, Whitworth, Rochdale, Lancashire, OL12 8DA Tel: (01706) 852345 Fax: (01706) 853114 E-mail: northern-joinery@compuserve.com

Riverside Joinery Co. Ltd, Barker Street, Norwich, NR2 4TN Tel: (01603) 624858 Fax: (01603) 614924

Sandiford Son & Bannister Ltd, 153 Croydon Road, Caterham, Surrey, CR3 6PF Tel: (01883) 343545 Fax: (01883) 346808

Stair Well Ltd, Olympic Industrial Estate, 3 Watkin Road, Wembley, Middlesex, HA9 0YG Tel: (020) 8902 7885

Stairway Projects, Unit 16 Taylors, Gravel Lane, Chigwell, Essex, IG7 6DQ Tel: (020) 8559 9226 Fax: (020) 8559 9226

Winther,Browne & Company Ltd, 75 Bilton Way, Enfield, Middlesex, EN3 7ER Tel: (020) 8344 9050 Fax: (020) 8344 9051 E-mail: sales@wintherbrowne.co.uk

WOOD TOOL BOXES OR CABINETS OR CASES OR CHESTS

Clanville Sawmills Ltd, Clanville, Castle Cary, Somerset, BA7 7PQ Tel: (01963) 350881 Fax: (01963) 351562 E-mail: admin@clanvillsawmills.co.uk

Charles Kirkby & Sons Ltd, 84 Sidney Street, Sheffield, S1 4RH Tel: 0114-272 1327 Fax: 0114-275 6506

WOOD TOYS

Brio Ltd, Sutton House, Bishop Meadow Road, Loughborough, Leicestershire, LE11 5RE Tel: (01509) 231874 Fax: (01509) 234547 E-mail: info@brio.co.uk
Escor Toys, Elliott Road, Bournemouth, BH11 8JP Tel: (01202) 591081 Fax: (01202) 570049 E-mail: escortoys@bournemouth.gov.uk
James Galt & Co. Ltd, Sovereign House, Stockport Road, Cheadle, Cheshire, SK8 2EA Tel: 0161-428 9111 Fax: 0161-428 6597 E-mail: sales@galt.co.uk
▶ Rob Roy Wooden Toys, 81 College Street, Long Eaton, Nottingham, NG10 4NN Tel: 0115-973 3943 E-mail: robroytoy@yahoo.co.uk
▶ Silver Toys & Allsorts, 21 Chapel Lane, Wimblington, March, Cambs, PE15 0QX Tel: 01354 742415 E-mail: paul_silvertoys@btinternet.com
▶ Sri Toy Europe, P. O Box 36957, London, SE6 4WT Tel: 020 8690 6995 Fax: 020 8690 8990 E-mail: sales@sritoyseurope.com
▶ Tom's Toys, 22 Manor Road, Newton Longville, Milton Keynes, MK17 0AJ Tel: (01908) 376951
▶ Wooden Choice Ltd, 127 Manchester Road, Worsley, Manchester, M28 3JT Tel: 0161-703 7919 E-mail: info@woodenchoice.co.uk

WOOD TRAYS

Pimpernel (Holdings) Ltd, 26-32 Derwent Street, Consett, County Durham, DH8 8LY Tel: 01207 588402 Fax: (01207) 507873 E-mail: sales@pimpernelinternational.com
Take One Ltd, Unit 1, Moor Barn, Sheldon Lane, Bakewell, Derbyshire, DE45 1QR Tel: (01629) 814610 Fax: (01629) 814610 E-mail: info@takeoneltd.com

WOOD TURNERY

Amos Swift Co. Ltd, Boathouse Lane, Stockton-on-Tees, Cleveland, TS18 3AW Tel: (01642) 675241 Fax: (01642) 675241 E-mail: john.hingley@ntlworld.com
B A Jones & Co., 27 Padgets Lane, Redditch, Worcestershire, B98 0RB Tel: (01527) 523377 Fax: (01527) 523377 E-mail: stevethewoodturner@blueyonder.co.uk
Birmingham Woodcrafts, Units 9-10 All Saints Industrial Estate, Hockley, Birmingham, B18 7RJ Tel: 0121-523 8007 Fax: 0121-507 0685
Breaston Chair Frames Co. Ltd, Unit 21b Merlin Way, Quarry Hill Industrial Estate, Ilkeston, Derbyshire, DE7 4RA Tel: 0115-944 0626
Briggs Trading Co Southern Ltd, Ebblake Industrial Estate, 21 Blackmoor Road, Verwood, Dorset, BH31 6AX Tel: (01202) 825555 Fax: (01202) 823980 E-mail: enquiries@briggsproducts.com
Brown & Wakelin Sales Ltd, The Croft, Marsh Gibbon, Bicester, Oxfordshire, OX27 0EU Tel: (01869) 277337 Fax: (01869) 278844 E-mail: sales@brownandwakling.co.uk
C & M Joinery, Unit 1, Plot 7 Claymore, Tame Valley Industrial Estate, Wilnecote, Tamworth, Staffs, B77 5DQ Tel: (01827) 250849 Fax: (01827) 287913
Cole & Mason Ltd, Bridge House, Eelmoor Road, Farnborough, Hampshire, GU14 7UE Tel: (01252) 522322 Fax: (01252) 522542 E-mail: customer.service@coleandmason.co.uk
Eglinton Wood Turners, Mid Lodge Cottage, Eglinton, Irvine, Ayrshire, KA12 8TA Tel: (01294) 558145 Fax: (01294) 558145
Haldane (U K) Ltd, 7 Blackwood Way, Bankhead Industrial Estate, Glenrothes, Fife, KY7 6JF Tel: (01592) 775656 Fax: (01592) 775757 E-mail: sales@haldaneuk.com
Lind Wood Components Ltd, River Mill, Park Road, Dukinfield, Cheshire, SK16 5LR Tel: 0161-330 2624 Fax: 0161-343 1094 E-mail: info@lindwood.co.uk
London Woodturners, 45 Hackney Road, London, E2 7NX Tel: (020) 7739 2296 Fax: (020) 7729 7270 E-mail: lwt@blueyonder.co.uk
Russell Lowe Ltd, Unit 37, Broomhills Industrial Estate, Braintree, Essex, CM7 2RW Tel: (01245) 351599 Fax: (01376) 345825
N B Stairways Ltd, 2A Milton Road, London, E17 4SR Tel: (020) 8520 3566 Fax: (020) 8520 9673E-mail: nicholsbros@btinternet.com
Nichols & Nichols, Stour Wharf, 10 Stour Road, London, E3 2NT Tel: (020) 8986 3392 Fax: (020) 8986 3392
Pilkingtons Ltd, Belgrave Court, Caxton Road, Fulwood, Preston, PR2 9PL Tel: (01772) 705566 Fax: (01772) 705599 E-mail: info@pilkingtonsltd.com
Prickett's Wood Products, 73 Bredgar Rd, London, N19 5BS Tel: (020) 7272 3931 Fax: (020) 7272 3931
R L Trim, 9 Acreman Street, Cerne Abbas, Dorchester, Dorset, DT2 7LD Tel: (01300) 341209 Fax: (01300) 341815
Rooksmoor Timber Co. Ltd, Vatch Lane, Eastcombe, Stroud, Gloucestershire, GL6 7DY Tel: (01453) 882240 Fax: (01453) 731112 E-mail: enquiries@rooksmoor.com
Staveley Timber Ltd, Back Lane, Staveley, Kendal, Cumbria, LA8 9LR Tel: (01539) 821234 Fax: (01539) 821898 E-mail: broc@broc.co.uk
T J Dobson, Tattersall Street, Oldham, OL9 6EY Tel: 0161-624 1958 Fax: 0161-624 1958
Henry Taylor Tools Ltd, Peacock Estate, Livesey Street, Sheffield, S6 2BL Tel: 0114-234 0282 Fax: 0114-285 2015 E-mail: sales@henrytaylortools.co.uk
Thornwood Designs, 6 Top Factory, Cringle Lane, Stoke Rochford, Grantham, Lincolnshire, NG33 5EF Tel: (01476) 530600 Fax: (01476) 577544 E-mail: info@lampstyle.com
Turnstyle Wood Turners, Leicester Street, Melton Mowbray, Leicestershire, LE13 0PP Tel: (01664) 562460 Fax: (01664) 562460
W Hanson Silsden Ltd, Hainsworth Road, Silsden, Keighley, West Yorkshire, BD20 0LY Tel: (01535) 652347 Fax: (01535) 652347 E-mail: woodturners@btinternet.com
▶ Woodware Repetitions Ltd, 47 Mowbray Street, Sheffield, S3 8EN Tel: 0114-272 6060 Fax: 0114-279 7475

WOOD TURNING LATHES

Hegner, 8 North Cresent, Diplocks Way, Hailsham, East Sussex, BN27 3JF Tel: (01323) 442440 Fax: (01323) 840696 E-mail: sales@hegner.co.uk

WOOD TURNING TOOLS AND ACCESSORIES

G & M Tools, Mill Lane, Ashington, Pulborough, West Sussex, RH20 3BX Tel: (01903) 892510 Fax: (01903) 892221 E-mail: sales@gandmtools.co.uk
Hegner, 8 North Cresent, Diplocks Way, Hailsham, East Sussex, BN27 3JF Tel: (01323) 442440 Fax: (01323) 840696 E-mail: sales@hegner.co.uk

WOOD TURNING WOODWORK TRAINING

Craft Supplies Ltd, Newburgh Works, Netherside, Bradwell, Hope Valley, Derbyshire, S33 9NT Tel: (01433) 622550 Fax: (01433) 622552 E-mail: sales@craft-supplies.co.uk

WOOD WASTE EXTRACTION PLANT

Dust Control Systems Ltd, Churwell Vale, Shaw Cross Business Park, Dewsbury, West Yorkshire, WF12 7RD Tel: (01924) 482500 Fax: (01924) 482530 E-mail: sales@dcslimited.co.uk

WOODCUTTING BANDSAW BLADES

Harrison Saw & Tool Ltd, Underbank Way, Carrs Industrial Estate, Haslingden, Rossendale, Lancashire, BB4 5HR Tel: (01706) 225221 Fax: (01706) 831409 E-mail: sales@harrisonsaw.co.uk

WOODEN ANTIQUE RESTORATION

▶ Lenten Hall Antiques, Lenten Hall, Lenten Pool, Llansannan, Denbigh, LL16 3LG Tel: (01745) 870283 Fax: (01745) 870283 E-mail: sales@lentenhallantiques.com
▶ Michael Eeley & Son, Hose Street Works, Hose Street, Stoke-on-Trent, ST6 5AL Tel: (01782) 813383 Fax: (01782) 813383
▶ Thomas Edwards, Heavers House, Chapel Street, Ryarsh, West Malling, Kent, ME19 5JU Tel: (01732) 875771 Fax: (01732) 841043 E-mail: t1jce@aol.com

WOODEN CONCRETE FORMWORK

Woodtec, 38 Festival Drive, Loughborough, Leicestershire, LE11 5XJ Tel: (01509) 219246 Fax: (01509) 260117 E-mail: sales@woodtec2.co.uk

WOODEN DOUBLE GLAZED WINDOWS

▶ Westport Manufacturing Ltd, Unit 15 Solway Trading Estate, Maryport, Cumbria, CA15 8NF Tel: (01900) 814225 Fax: (01900) 818581

WOODEN GARDEN FURNITURE

A & E Leisure Ltd, 9 Craddock Road, Reading, RG2 0JT Tel: 0118-923 0300 Fax: 0118-923 0349 E-mail: sales@aelsolutions.com
Anglesey Wood Products, 101 Gerwin Uchaf, Gaerwen, Gwynedd, LL60 6HN Tel: (01248) 421086 Fax: (01248) 421086 E-mail: heather@angleseywoodproducts.co.uk
Ashwood Garden Services & Crafts, Blendworth, Waterlooville, Hampshire, PO8 0QG Tel: (07071) 229946 Fax: (023) 9257 1700
B S Sectional Buildings, Stapleford Road, Trowell, Nottingham, NG9 3PS Tel: 0115-932 3280 Fax: 0115-932 3290 E-mail: sales@bssectional.co.uk
Barlow Tyrie Ltd, Springwood Industrial Estate, Braintree, Essex, CM7 2RN Tel: (01376) 557600 Fax: (01376) 557610 E-mail: sales.uk@teak.com
Britannic Garden Furniture Ltd, Costers Close, Alveston, Bristol, BS35 3HZ Tel: (01454) 411601 Fax: (01454) 417941
Cadbury Garden & Leisure, Smallway, Congresbury, Bristol, BS49 5AA Tel: (01934) 876464 Fax: (01934) 875701 E-mail: info@cadbury.g-l.co.uk
Cathedral Garden Furniture, Unit 9 Hetton Lane Industrial Estate, Colliery Lane, Hetton-le-Holey, Houghton Le Spring, Tyne & Wear, DH5 0BD Tel: 0191-517 1700 Fax: 0191-517 1700 E-mail: sales@cathedralgardenfurniture.co.uk
Country Boarding Kennels, Pitt Farm, Swettenham Lane, Swettenham, Congleton, Cheshire, CW12 2JY Tel: (01260) 224270 Fax: (01260) 224769
▶ Custom Creations, 1 Plot 120 Village Farm Road, Village Farm Industrial Estate, Pyle, Bridgend, Mid Glamorgan, CF33 6BL Tel: (01656) 749855 Fax: (01656) 749855 E-mail: customc@tiscali.co.uk
Dandf Garden Products Ltd, Unit 6, Onward Business Park, Wakefield Road, Ackworth, Pontefract, West Yorkshire, WF7 7BE Tel: (01977) 624200 Fax: (01977) 624201 E-mail: sales@dandf.co.uk
Dorset Enterprises, Elliott Road, Bournemouth, BH11 8JP Tel: (01202) 577966 Fax: (01202) 570049 E-mail: dorsetenterprises@bournemouth.gov.uk
English Hurdle, Curload, Stoke St. Gregory, Taunton, Somerset, TA3 6JD Tel: (01823) 698418 Fax: (01823) 698859 E-mail: hurdle@enterprise.net
Fantails Garden & Patio Furniture Distributors, 64 Ulwell, Swanage, Dorset, BH19 3DG Tel: (01929) 427676 Fax: (01929) 421509 E-mail: fantails@freenetname.co.uk
Forsham Cottage Arks Ltd, Gorseside, Great Chart, Ashford, Kent, TN26 1JU Tel: (01233) 820229 Fax: (01233) 820157 E-mail: office@foreshamcottagearks.com
Garden Buildings Services, 60 Dalton Street, Hartlepool, Cleveland, TS26 9EL Tel: (01429) 861169 Fax: (01429) 861169 E-mail: sales@gardenbuildingservices.co.uk
Garden Crafts, Workshop Showroom, Forden, Welshpool, Powys, SY21 8NE Tel: (01938) 580401
The Garden Furniture Centre Ltd, Yew Tree Farm, Stratford Road, Wootton Wawen, Henley-in-Arden, West Midlands, B95 6BY Tel: (01564) 793652 Fax: (01564) 793652 E-mail: sales@gardenfurniturecentre.co.uk
Garstone Garden Ornament Wholesalers, 8 New Quay Street, Teignmouth, Devon, TQ14 8DA Tel: (01626) 775925 Fax: (01626) 891745
Harvington Lesiure, Kimberley Cottage, Worcester Road, Harvington, Kidderminster, Worcestershire, DY10 4LJ Tel: (01562) 777255
Horley Garden Centre, Station Approach, Horley, Surrey, RH6 9HQ Tel: (07866) 433473
Indian Ocean Trading Co., Castle Grounds, Hawarden, Deeside, Clwyd, CH5 3NY Tel: (01244) 537906 Fax: (01244) 537737
J & W Milligan, Galston Road, Hurlford, Kilmarnock, Ayrshire, KA1 5HS Tel: (01563) 527572 Fax: (01563) 536758 E-mail: sales@millicabin.com
Jacobs Young & Westbury, Bridge Road, Haywards Heath, West Sussex, RH16 1UA Tel: (01444) 412411 Fax: (01444) 457662 E-mail: sales@jyw-uk.com
Lister Lutyens Co. Ltd, 6 Alder Close, Eastbourne, East Sussex, BN23 6QF Tel: (01323) 431177 Fax: (01323) 639314 E-mail: sales@listerteak.com
Loxford Timber Supplies, 332 Ilford Lane, Ilford, Essex, IG1 2LT Tel: (020) 8553 0362 Fax: (020) 8594 7956
N Gosling, Occupation Lane, New Bolingbroke, Boston, Lincolnshire, PE22 7JZ Tel: (01205) 480691 Fax: (01205) 480691
Nova Garden Furniture Ltd, Graveney Road, Faversham, Kent, ME13 8UN Tel: (01795) 535511 Fax: (01795) 539215 E-mail: sales@novagardenfurniture.co.uk
Phoenix Fencing Supplies, The Chalk Hole, Harbour Farm, Molash, Canterbury, Kent, CT4 8HN Tel: (01233) 740004
Rain Or Shine, Ashfield House, Common Platt, Purton, Swindon, SN5 5JZ Tel: (01793) 541134 Fax: (01793) 541134
Rusticraft Garden Furniture, 312a Brant Road, Lincoln, LN5 9AF Tel: (01522) 721014 Fax: (01522) 729122
▶ Scottish Prison Service, SPS HQ Industries, Central Store, Main Street, Fauldhouse, Bathgate, West Lothian, EH47 9DJ Tel: (01501) 773980 Fax: (01501) 771835 E-mail: anthony.apperley@sps.gov.uk
▶ Sharps World Of Wood, York Road Garage, York Road, Barmby Moor, York, YO42 4HS Tel: (01759) 305566 Fax: (01759) 306699 E-mail: paul@sharpsworldofwood.com
▶ Smartwood Lesiure Products, Belle Vue Barn, Mansergh, Carnforth, Lancashire, LA6 2EJ Tel: (01524) 273333 Fax: (01524) 273303
Teesdale Garden Crafts, Unit 5 Industrial Estate, Stainton Grove, Barnard Castle, County Durham, DL12 8UJ Tel: (01833) 631772
Trojan Woodworking, Bourne Road, Pode Hole, Spalding, Lincolnshire, PE11 3LW Tel: (01775) 767786 Fax: (01775) 767786
▶ Wooden Garden, 9 Moffathill, Airdrie, Lanarkshire, ML6 8PY Tel: (01236) 602715
Ye Old Court Yard, 29 South Street, Newtownards, County Down, BT23 4JT Tel: (028) 9182 0044

WOODEN PAPER REEL CORE PLUGS

Moorland Woodturning Co. Ltd, Woodlands Mill, Luke Lane, Thongsbridge, Holmfirth, HD9 7TB Tel: (01484) 683126

WOODEN SIGN CARVING MACHINES

Fine Signs, Lower Road, Cookham, Maidenhead, Berkshire, SL6 9EH Tel: (01628) 522023 Fax: (01628) 528731 E-mail: signs@finesigns.co.uk
Micom Engineering Ltd, 7 Industrial Estate, The St, Heybridge, Maldon, Essex, CM9 4XB Tel: (01621) 856324 Fax: (01621) 858778 E-mail: sales@micomltd.co.uk

WOODGRAIN PAPER

▶ Momentum Packaging Ltd, Enterprise Way, Lowton, Warrington, WA3 2BP Tel: (01942) 267211 Fax: (01942) 267200 E-mail: info@foilco.co.uk

WOODWARE

Dalescraft Art & Craft Materials, 26a Bondgate Green, Ripon, North Yorkshire, HG4 1QW Tel: (01765) 692053 Fax: (01765) 692053 E-mail: colin@dalescraft.com
Philbar & Co. Ltd, 254 Kilburn High Road, London, NW6 2BX Tel: (020) 7624 8681 Fax: (020) 7624 8683

WOODWOOL

Wood Wool, 22 Broach Road, Sandy Lane Industrial Estate, Stourport-on-Severn, Worcestershire, DY13 9QB Tel: (01299) 828059 Fax: (01299) 826975

WOODWORK TO SPECIFICATION

Acorn Joinery, Floodgates Farm, Castle Lane, West Grinstead, Horsham, West Sussex, RH13 8LH Tel: (01403) 711330 Fax: (01403) 711330 E-mail: acornjoinery@resource24.net
Badman & Badman Ltd, The Drill Hall, Langford Road, Weston-super-Mare, Avon, BS23 3PQ Tel: (01934) 644122 Fax: (01934) 628189 E-mail: sales@badman.co.uk
Brockwood Collection, Brockwood Hill Farm, Park Lane, Audley, Stoke-On-Trent, ST7 8HR Tel: (01782) 722569 Fax: (01782) 722569 E-mail: louise@brockwood.freeserve.co.uk
N. Carpenter Custom Made Joinery & Furniture, Unit 7, Parklands Farm, Parklands, Shere, Guildford, Surrey, GU5 9JQ Tel: (01483) 203759 Fax: (01483) 203759
Croxfords Joinery Manufacturers, Meltham Joinery Works, New Street, Meltham, Holmfirth, HD9 5NT Tel: (01484) 850892 Fax: (01484) 850969 E-mail: ralph@croxfords.demon.co.uk
E C Hopkins, Unit 34 Stretford Motorway Estate, Stretford, Manchester, M32 0ZH Tel: 0161-866 9122 Fax: 0161-866 9121 E-mail: sales@echopkins.com
The Mad Cow Puzzles Ltd, 2 Weycroft Avenue, Axminster, Devon, EX13 5HU Tel: (01297) 35577 Fax: (01297) 33883 E-mail: info@madcowpuzzles.co.uk
Park Way Joinery Ltd, Nicholson Road, Ryde, Isle of Wight, PO33 1BE Tel: (01983) 567812 Fax: (01983) 611775 E-mail: parkwayjoinery@btconnect.com
Pitman Joinery Works, Limington, Yeovil, Somerset, BA22 8EG Tel: (01935) 840431 Fax: (01935) 841100
▶ Keith Preston Joinery Co. Ltd, 20 Brest Road, Plymouth, PL6 5XP Tel: (01752) 781700 Fax: (01752) 777423 E-mail: sales@keithprestonjoinery.co.uk
R E H Kennedy Ltd, Whitehouse Road, Ipswich, IP1 5LT Tel: (01473) 240044 Fax: (01473) 240098 E-mail: sales@rehkennedy.co.uk
R T A Joinery Ltd, 5 Birling Road, Tunbridge Wells, Kent, TN2 5LX Tel: (01892) 543897 Fax: (01892) 545345 E-mail: rtajoinery@btconnect.com
Reflection Art Furniture, Tresparrett, Camelford, Cornwall, PL32 9ST Tel: (01840) 261212 Fax: (01840) 261212 E-mail: cornishfunky@aol.com

WOODWORK TO SPECIFICATION – *continued*

Rudd Joinery, Treowen Road, Pembroke Dock, Dyfed, SA72 6NY Tel: (01646) 685712 Fax: (0871) 7334946 E-mail: ray@ruddjoinery.com

UK Contracts Warwick Ltd, Thorn Way, Long Itchington, Southam, Warwickshire, CV47 9PF Tel: (01926) 813308 Fax: (01926) 813349 E-mail: ukcontracts@connectfree.co.uk

WOODWORK, ELECTRICAL/ ELECTRONIC TRADE

Moray Timber Ltd, 11 Perimeter Road, Elgin, Morayshire, IV30 6AF Tel: (01343) 545151 Fax: (01343) 549518 E-mail: roncameron@btconnect.com

WOODWORKING ADHESIVES

▶ Aldcroft Adhesives Ltd, Unit 13A Horwich Loco Industrial Estate, Chorley New Road, Horwich, Bolton, BL6 5UE Tel: (01204) 668282 Fax: (01204) 668780 E-mail: info@aldcroftadhesives.com

Gluegunsdirect.Com Ltd, Regent House, Regent Street, Oldham, OL1 3TZ Tel: 0161-627 1001 Fax: 0161-627 5072 E-mail: sales@gluegunsdirect.com

WOODWORKING CHISELS

Bristol Design (Tools) Ltd, 14 Perry Road, Bristol, BS1 5BG Tel: 0117-929 1740

WOODWORKING MACHINE BLADES

J C Tool Hire, Valley St North, Darlington, County Durham, DL1 1QE Tel: (01325) 382038 Fax: (01325) 468539 E-mail: sales@joegreeners.co.uk

David Price Woodworking Machinery Ltd, 21 Cae Garw, Thornhill, Cardiff, CF14 9DX Tel: (029) 2061 6977 Fax: (029) 2061 6977 E-mail: info@dpmachines.co.uk

WOODWORKING MACHINE INSTALLATION OR SERVICING

Elliot Technology Ltd, Unit 35 Earith Business Park, Meadow Drove, Earith, Cambridgeshire, PE28 3QF Tel: (01487) 841626 Fax: (01487) 841553 E-mail: ipcroft@hotmail.com

Michael Weinig UK Ltd, 5 Blacklands Way, Abingdon, Oxfordshire, OX14 1DY Tel: (01235) 557600 Fax: (01235) 538070 E-mail: sales@weinig.co.uk

Norfolk Saw Services, Dog Lane, Horsford, Norwich, NR10 3DH Tel: (01603) 898695 Fax: (01603) 898695 E-mail: sales@norfolksawservices.co.uk

WOODWORKING MACHINE KNIVES OR CUTTERS

Fernite Of Sheffield Ltd, Fernite Works, Coleford Road, Sheffield, S9 5NJ Tel: 0114-244 0527 Fax: 0114-244 5922 E-mail: sales@fernite.co.uk

WOODWORKING MACHINE MAINTENANCE OR REPAIR

Blundell Woodworking Machinery Ltd, Park Drive, Braintree, Essex, CM7 1AP Tel: (01376) 346565 Fax: (01376) 551230 E-mail: blundell@btconnect.com

Blyth Woodmachinery Ltd, 15 Ashville Way, Cambridge Road Industrial Estate, Whetstone, Leicester, LE8 6NU Tel: 0116-286 1617 Fax: 0116-286 1618 E-mail: jonathan@blythmachinery.co.uk

J W Machinery Services, Claytile Workshop, Fairy Hall Lane, Rayne, Braintree, Essex, CM77 6SZ Tel: (01376) 328034 Fax: (01376) 551676 E-mail: info@jwmservices.co.uk

M S L Woodworking Machinery Ltd, Burnley Road, Mytholmroyd, Hebden Bridge, West Yorkshire, HX7 5QL Tel: (01422) 886542 Fax: (01422) 886542

Timberman Woodworking Machinery, Gelli Garage, Bronwydd Arms, Carmarthen, Dyfed, SA33 6BE Tel: (01267) 232621 Fax: (01267) 222616 E-mail: sales@timberman.co.uk

Woodworking Machinery Services & Repairs, 35 Merlewood, Dickleburgh, Diss, Norfolk, IP21 4PL Tel: (01379) 741412 Fax: (01379) 741412

WOODWORKING MACHINE TOOLING

Carbide (UK) Ltd, 8 Park Street, Anlaby Road, Hull, HU3 2JF Tel: (01482) 227234 Fax: (01482) 212902 E-mail: carbideuk@carbideuk.com

Colton Tooling Ltd, 4 Highmeres Road, Leicester, LE4 9LZ Tel: 0116-276 6225 Fax: 0116-276 6226 E-mail: colton@talk21.com

Datum Tools Ltd, Mardens Hill, Crowborough, East Sussex, TN6 1XL Tel: (01892) 667800 Fax: (01892) 667900

W.R. Doe Engineering, The Boat House, Timsway, Staines, Middlesex, TW18 3JY Tel: (01784) 461408 Fax: (01784) 461408

Gerry Lynch, 29 Kingsland Bridge Mansions, Murivance, Shrewsbury, SY1 1JF Tel: (01743) 353254 Fax: (01743) 248296 E-mail: gerry.lynch@talk21.com

Bob Richardson Tools & Fasteners Ltd, Pedmore Road, Dudley, West Midlands, DY2 0RL Tel: (01384) 482789 Fax: (01384) 481888 E-mail: sales@toolstoday.co.uk

Scott & Sargeant Wood Working Machinery Ltd, 1 Blatchford Road, Horsham, West Sussex, RH13 5QR Tel: (01403) 273000 Fax: (01403) 274444 E-mail: sales@machines4wood.com

South Eastern Saws (Industrial) Ltd, Unit 6 Spectrum, Parkwood Industrial Estate, Maidstone, Kent, ME15 9XZ Tel: (01622) 750177 Fax: (01622) 688112

WOODWORKING MACHINERY COMPONENTS

W S Wood Machinery, 9 36 Hornock Road, Coatbridge, Lanarkshire, ML5 2QA Tel: (01236) 432700 Fax: (01236) 432909

WOODWORKING MACHINES

Advantage Automation Ltd, 21 Broadway, Maidenhead, Berkshire, SL6 1NJ Tel: (01628) 777759 Fax: (01628) 778681

Appleford Woodworking Machinery, 49 Derham Park, Yatton, Bristol, BS49 4EA Tel: (01934) 838025E-mail: applewood.machine@virgin.net

Applied Drilling Systems Ltd, 18 Concorde Drive, Five C Business Centre, Clevedon, Avon, BS21 6UH Tel: (01275) 340763 Fax: (01275) 340765

▶ Arborplant Ltd, The Log House, Kiln Lane, Henley-on-Thames, Oxfordshire, RG9 4EN Tel: 0118-940 4739 Fax: 0118-940 4739

Arrow Tool & Cutter Co Ltd, 13 Ireton Avenue, Leicester, LE4 9EU Tel: 0116-276 1633

Blundell Woodworking Machinery Ltd, Park Drive, Braintree, Essex, CM7 1AP Tel: (01376) 346565 Fax: (01376) 551230 E-mail: blundell@btconnect.com

▶ Calderbrook Woodworking Machinery, Unit 7 New Line Industrial Estate, The Sidings, Bacup, Lancashire, OL13 9RW Tel: (01706) 873344 Fax: (01706) 873388

Cannon Electronics & Automation Ltd, White Gates Factory, Dunmow Road, Hatfield Heath, Bishop's Stortford, Hertfordshire, CM22 7ED Tel: (01279) 730709

Cecil W Tyzack, 79-81 Kingsland Road, London, E2 8AH Tel: (020) 7739 2630 Fax: (020) 7729 3373

Central c.n.c. Machinery Ltd, Unit 12B, Scar La, Milnsbridge, Huddersfield, HD3 4PE Tel: 0845 4941645 Fax: (01484) 460101 E-mail: enquiries@centralcnc.co.uk

Charnwood, Cedar Court, Walker Road, Bardon Hill, Coalville, Leicestershire, LE67 1TU Tel: (01530) 516925 Fax: (01530) 516929 E-mail: sales@charnwood.net

Contract Services, Madera House, 25 Brindley Road Hertburn Industrial Estate, Hertburn, Washington, Tyne & Wear, NE37 2SB Tel: 0191-416 2230 Fax: 0191-416 2366

D B Keighley Machinery Ltd, Vickers Place, Stanningley, Pudsey, West Yorkshire, LS28 6LZ Tel: 0113-257 4736 Fax: 0113-257 4293 E-mail: sales@dbkeighley.co.uk

Discount Tool Supplies Ltd, 66 St. Johns Lane, Bristol, BS3 5AF Tel: 0117-977 8076 Fax: 0117-971 7991 E-mail: info@harryneill.com

W.R. Doe Engineering, The Boat House, Timsway, Staines, Middlesex, TW18 3JY Tel: (01784) 461408 Fax: (01784) 461408

A.M. Ede Technical Services Ltd, Conger Cottage, Market Square, Dunstable, Bedfordshire, LU5 6BP Tel: (01525) 873890 Fax: (01525) 873890

G B Engineering, 111 Wilsons Lane, Longford, Coventry, CV6 6AB Tel: (024) 7636 3634 Fax: (024) 7636 3634 E-mail: gb.eng@talk21.com

▶ J & C O'Meara Ltd, Ringtail Industrial Estate, Tollgate Road, Burscough, Ormskirk, Lancashire, L40 8LD Tel: (01704) 893109 Fax: (01704) 232445 E-mail: sale@jcomeara.fs.nt.co.uk

J J Smith Technical Services Ltd, Moorgate Point, Moorgate Road, Knowsley Industrial Park, Liverpool, L33 7DR Tel: 0151-546 1308 Fax: 0151-549 1771 E-mail: sales@jjsmith.co.uk

J L Woodworking Machinery, 40 Sketchley Road, Burbage, Hinckley, Leicestershire, LE10 2DZ Tel: (01455) 251557 Fax: (01455) 251557 E-mail: j.l.wood40@gmail.com

Lancashire Saw Co. Ltd, Imperial Mill, Gorse Street, Blackburn, BB1 3EU Tel: (01254) 51116 Fax: (01254) 672046 E-mail: info@lancashiresaw.co.uk

Leicester Wood Technique Ltd, Main Steet, Theddingworth, Lutterworth, Leicestershire, LE17 6QY Tel: (01858) 880643

M H C Industrials Ltd, Wetmore Road, Burton-On-Trent, Staffordshire, DE14 1QN Tel: (01283) 564651 Fax: (01283) 511526 E-mail: sales@mhcind.co.uk

M Sedgwick & Co. Ltd, Swinnow Lane, Leeds, LS13 4QG Tel: 0113-257 0637 Fax: 0113-239 3412 E-mail: sales@sedgewicks.co.uk

Machine Sales & Services Ltd, 23 Cowley Road, Nuffield Industrial Estate, Poole, Dorset, BH17 0UJ Tel: (01202) 686238 Fax: (01202) 686661 E-mail: enquiries@machinesalesandservices.co.uk

Masterwood UK Ltd, St Andrews, 13 East Abercromby Street, Helensburgh, Dunbartonshire, G84 7SP Tel: (01436) 675000 Fax: (01436) 678999

Mayer Services (UK) Ltd, The Springboard Centre, Mandle Lane, Coalville, Leicestershire, LE67 3DW Tel: (0845) 0093542 Fax: (0871) 5972419

Michael Weinig UK Ltd, 5 Blacklands Way, Abingdon, Oxfordshire, OX14 1DY Tel: (01235) 557600 Fax: (01235) 538070 E-mail: sales@weinig.co.uk

Ney Ltd, Middlemarch Business Park Coventry Trading Estate, Siskin Drive, Middlemarch Business Park, Coventry, CV3 4FJ Tel: (024) 7630 8100 Fax: (024) 7630 8102 E-mail: info@ney.co.uk

Orteguil (UK) Ltd, PO Box 2, Stockport, Cheshire, SK12 2NN Tel: (01663) 762187 Fax: (01663) 766721 E-mail: info@orteguil.com

R W Woodmachines Ltd, 25-27 Murdock Road, Bicester, Oxfordshire, OX26 4PP Tel: (01869) 244943 Fax: (01869) 253498 E-mail: sales@rw-machines.co.uk

S C Woodworking Machines (Kent) Ltd, Fairview Garage, 161 Fairview Avenue, Gillingham, Kent, ME8 0PX Tel: (01634) 386012 Fax: (01795) 558469 E-mail: info@sbwoodworkingmachinery.co.uk

Savecrest Machines Ltd, Stepney Grove, Bridlington, North Humberside, YO16 7PD Tel: 01262 671921

Smeaton Hanscomb & Co. Ltd, Lisle Road, Hughenden Avenue, High Wycombe, Buckinghamshire, HP13 5SQ Tel: (01494) 521051 Fax: (01494) 461176 E-mail: sales@smeathans.plus.com

▶ Triton Workshop Systems, Pontygwindy Industrial Estate, Caerphilly, Mid Glamorgan, CF83 3HU Tel: (02920) 888815

Wadkin Ltd, Franks Road, Hilltop Industrial Estate, Bardon, Coalville, Leicestershire, LE67 1TT Tel: (01530) 513500 Fax: (01530) 513513 E-mail: info@wadkin.com

Wood Mac Ltd, Vale Street, Todmorden, Lancashire, OL14 5HG Tel: 01706 814224

Woodworking Machinery Ireland, 72-74 Waterloo Road, Lisburn, County Antrim, BT27 5NW Tel: (028) 9266 0034 Fax: (028) 9266 0979

WOODWORKING SAW BLADES

N L S Tools, Station Approach, Waltham Cross, Hertfordshire, EN8 7LZ Tel: (01992) 710888 Fax: (01992) 713938 E-mail: sales@nlstools.co.uk

WOODWORM CONTROL SERVICES

Bacogold (1965) Ltd, 18a Malyons Rd, London, SE13 7XG Tel: (020) 8690 4665

Complete Preservation Service Ltd, 4-5 Wyvern House, Harriers Trading Estate, Stadium Close, Kidderminster, Worcestershire, DY10 1NJ Tel: (01562) 69945 Fax: (01562) 69945 E-mail: complete.preservation@ukonline.co.uk

Dampco (U.K.) Ltd, 21 Lythalls Lane, Coventry, CV6 6FN Tel: (0800) 626925 Fax: (024) 7668 7683 E-mail: info@dampco.org

Essex & Anglia Preservation Ltd, 24 Church End Lane, Runwell, Wickford, Essex, SS11 7JQ Tel: (0800) 0851695 Fax: (0800) 0851695 E-mail: info@essexandanglia.co.uk

Gulliver Timber Treatments Ltd, Bank Buildings, Station Road, Sevenoaks, Kent, TN14 5QX Tel: (01959) 524966 Fax: (01959) 525176 E-mail: enquiries@gullivertt.co.uk

J H Garlick Ltd, 180 Park View Road, Welling, Kent, DA16 1ST Tel: (020) 8303 2941 Fax: (020) 8303 0951 E-mail: surveyors@jhgarlickltd.fsnet.co.uk

▶ Lifecote Damp Proofing, 5 Higher Beacon, Ilminster, Somerset, TA19 9AJ Tel: (01460) 52669 Fax: (01460) 52669 E-mail: info@lifecote.net

R H Smith Worthing Ltd, Southdownview Way, Worthing, West Sussex, BN14 8NL Tel: (01903) 238316 E-mail: rhsmith1956@tiscali.co.uk

Tapco Homecare Services, Commercial Unit, Pool House Estate, Bancroft Road, Reigate, Surrey, RH2 7RP Tel: (020) 8398 6663 Fax: (01737) 247265 E-mail: info@tapco.uk

WOOL

▶ Ryte Lynes Upholstery Co., 4 Shaftesbury Road, Leicester, LE3 0QN Tel: 0116-254 1063 Fax: 0116-255 2902 E-mail: robert-fenn@lineone.net

WOOL BROKERS

Chantry Simonard (Bradford) Ltd, The Granary, Bleach Mill Lane, Menston, Ilkley, West Yorkshire, LS29 6AW Tel: (01943) 878882 Fax: (01943) 872999

Stewart & Ramsden Ltd, North Wheatlands Mill, Wheatlands Road, Galashiels, Selkirkshire, TD1 2HQ Tel: (01896) 754898 Fax: (01896) 758767

WOOL COMBS, *See Textile Combs etc*

WOOL DYERS, *See Dyers/Finishers to Textile Trades*

WOOL EXPORT MERCHANTS OR AGENTS

Walbrad Wool Trading Co., White Rose Mill, Holdsworth Road, Halifax, West Yorkshire, HX3 6SN Tel: (01422) 241001 Fax: (01422) 246331 E-mail: info@cashmere-fibre.co.uk

WOOL IMPORT MERCHANTS OR AGENTS

Chantry Simonard (Bradford) Ltd, The Granary, Bleach Mill Lane, Menston, Ilkley, West Yorkshire, LS29 6AW Tel: (01943) 878882 Fax: (01943) 872999

WOOL TESTING SERVICES/ WOOL TEST HOUSES

Wool Testing Authority Europe Ltd, Oakwood Warehouse, City Road, Bradford, West Yorkshire, BD8 8JY Tel: (01274) 732396 Fax: (01274) 760419

WOOL TOPS/NOIL

Bulmer & Lumb, Royds Hall Lane, Buttershaw, Bradford, West Yorkshire, BD6 2NE Tel: (01274) 676321 Fax: (01274) 691239 E-mail: sales@bulmerandlumb.com

Laycock International Ltd, Stanley Mills, Whitley Street, Bingley, West Yorkshire, BD16 4JH Tel: (01274) 562563 Fax: (01274) 562823 E-mail: mohair@legend.co.uk

WOOL WASTE MERCHANTS OR PROCESSORS

Chantry Simonard (Bradford) Ltd, The Granary, Bleach Mill Lane, Menston, Ilkley, West Yorkshire, LS29 6AW Tel: (01943) 878882 Fax: (01943) 872999

Walbrad Wool Trading Co., White Rose Mill, Holdsworth Road, Halifax, West Yorkshire, HX3 6SN Tel: (01422) 241001 Fax: (01422) 246331 E-mail: info@cashmere-fibre.co.uk

WOOLLEN AGENTS/ REPRESENTATIVES

Wheeler, Hickson & Co., 10-11 Lower John Street, London, W1F 9EB Tel: (020) 7437 0186 Fax: (020) 7439 4994 E-mail: info@wheelerhickson.co.uk

WOOLLEN FABRICS AND WORSTED CLOTH

W.F.B. Baird & Co, Ltd, 72 Shankbridge Road, Kells, Ballymena, County Antrim, BT42 3DL Tel: (028) 2589 8144 Fax: (028) 2589 8153

Beazley's (Savile Row) Ltd, 9-10 Savile Row, London, W1S 3PF Tel: (020) 7437 1831 Fax: (020) 7439 2166

Cambrian Woollen Mill, Top Floor Weaving Unit, Llanwrtyd Wells, Powys, LD5 4SD Tel: (01591) 610473 Fax: (01591) 610314 E-mail: cambrianwool@tiscali.co.uk

Dawson International plc, Lochleven Mills, Kinross, KY13 8GL Tel: (01577) 867000 Fax: (01577) 867010 E-mail: enquiries@dawson-international.co.uk

William Edleston, Moorbrook Mills, New Mill, Holmfirth, HD9 1JZ Tel: (01484) 690600 Fax: (01484) 690601 E-mail: email@william-edleston.co.uk

WOOLLEN FABRICS AND WORSTED CLOTH – *continued*

Ellis Joshua & Co., Grange Valley Road, Grange Road, Batley, West Yorkshire, WF17 6LW Tel: (01924) 350070 Fax: (01924) 350071 E-mail: genoffice@joshuaellis.co.uk

J.W. Ellison & Co. Ltd, 677-681 Little Horton Lane, Bradford, West Yorkshire, BD5 9DQ Tel: (01274) 571943 Fax: (01274) 571943

Fine Woollen Company Ltd, Savile House, Glendale Mills Sheffield Road, New Mill, Holmfirth, HD9 7EN Tel: (01484) 688848 Fax: (01484) 683469 E-mail: wainshiell@compuserve.com

Fox Brothers & Co., Milverton Road, Wellington, Somerset, TA21 0BA Tel: (01823) 662271 Fax: (01823) 666963 E-mail: enquiries@foxflannel.com

Greenwood & Walsh Ltd, Melbourne Street, Morley, Leeds, LS27 8BG Tel: 0113-253 8611 Fax: 0113-252 6849

H Lesser & Sons London Ltd, 43-53 Markfield Road, London, N15 4QA Tel: (020) 8275 6400 Fax: (020) 8275 6401 E-mail: info@hlesser.co.uk

Harrisons Burley Ltd, Sandylands, Anderton Street, Cross Hills, Keighley, West Yorkshire, BD20 7ED Tel: (01535) 637410 Fax: (01535) 637498 E-mail: sales@harrisonsburley.co.uk

Holland & Sherry (Furnishing) Ltd, 5th Floor, C/O Holland & Sherry Limited, London, W1S 3PF Tel: (020) 7437 0404 Fax: (020) 7734 6110 E-mail: enquiries@hollandandsherry.com

J & S Taylor Ltd, Corporation Mill, Corporation Street, Sowerby Bridge, West Yorkshire, HX6 2QQ Tel: (01422) 832616 Fax: (01422) 833686 E-mail: jands.taylor@btinternet.com

Kenneth Mackenzie Holdings Ltd, Sandwick Road, Stornoway, Isle of Lewis, HS1 2SJ Tel: (01851) 702772 Fax: (01851) 705271 E-mail: sales.kennethmckenzie@fsmail.net

Leigh Knight Ltd, 82 Arnos Grove, London, N14 7AR Tel: (020) 8886 9806 Fax: (020) 8447 8332 E-mail: sales@leighknight.com

Lear Browne & Dunsford, Waterbridge Court, Matford Park Road, Marsh Barton Trading Estate, Exeter, EX2 8FD Tel: (01392) 822510 Fax: (01392) 823270 E-mail: sales@lbd-harrisons.com

Linton Tweeds Ltd, Shaddon Mills, Shaddongate, Carlisle, CA2 5TZ Tel: (01228) 527569 Fax: (01228) 512062 E-mail: info@lintontweeds.co.uk

Loch Carron, Waverley Mill, Huddersfield Street, Galashiels, Selkirkshire, TD1 3AY Tel: (01896) 752091 Fax: (01896) 758833 E-mail: sales@1ochcarron.com

Lochcarron Weavers, Lochcarron, Strathcarron, Ross-Shire, IV54 8YH Tel: (01520) 722212 Fax: (01520) 722634

Mallalieu's Of Delph Ltd, Valley Mill, Millgate, Delph, Oldham, OL3 5DG Tel: (01457) 874811 Fax: (01457) 870231 E-mail: sales@mallalieus.com

Abraham Moon & Sons Ltd, Netherfield Mills, Guiseley, Leeds, LS20 9PA Tel: (01943) 873181 Fax: (01943) 870182 E-mail: sales@moons.co.uk

Robert Noble Ltd, March Street, Peebles, EH45 8ER Tel: (01721) 724311 Fax: (01721) 721893 E-mail: enquiries@robert-noble.co.uk

Otterburn Mill Ltd, Otterburn, Newcastle Upon Tyne, NE19 1JT Tel: (01830) 520225 Fax: (01830) 520032 E-mail: enquiries@otterburnmill.co.uk

P H B Textiles Ltd, PO Box 35586, London, NW4 1XG Tel: (07958) 492545 Fax: (020) 8203 5388

Ramsden Bros Huddersfield Ltd, Crosland Moor Mills, Blackmoorfoot Road, Huddersfield, HD4 5AH Tel: (01484) 421042 Fax: (01484) 559236

Riverstone Spinning Ltd, Ravensthorpe Mill, Huddersfield Road, Ravensthorpe, Dewsbury, West Yorkshire, WF13 3NA Tel: (01924) 462182 Fax: (01924) 461626

St. Georges Woollen Mills Ltd, Glen Road, Laxey, Isle Of Man, IM4 7AR Tel: (01624) 861395

Scabal UK Ltd, 12 Savile Row, London, W1S 3PQ Tel: (020) 7734 1867 Fax: (020) 7439 0093 E-mail: info@scabaluk.com

Sydney H. Shaw & Co. Ltd, Green Grove Mills, Kirkburton, Huddersfield, HD8 0QY Tel: (01484) 602614 Fax: (01484) 608459 E-mail: sydshaw.cloth@dial.pipex.com

Simportex, 452a Finchley Road, London, NW11 8DG Tel: (020) 8457 8770 Fax: (020) 8457 7484 E-mail: sales@simportex.com

Smith & Co Woollen Ltd, 16a Dufours Place, London, W1F 7SP Tel: (020) 7437 6226 Fax: (020) 7287 5324

Smiths Of Peterhead Ltd, Kirkburn Mills, Wevers Lane, Peterhead, Aberdeenshire, AB42 1SA Tel: (01779) 871400 Fax: (01779) 478989 E-mail: smithsofpeterhead@btconnect.com

Trefriw Woollen Mills Ltd, Trefriw, Gwynedd, LL27 0NQ Tel: (01492) 640462 Fax: (01492) 641821 E-mail: info@trefriw-woollen-mills.co.uk

Wain Shiell & Son Ltd, 12 Saville Row, London, W1S 3PQ Tel: (020) 7734 1464 Fax: (020) 7439 0093

Woolexpo Ltd, 19 Bruton Place, London, W1J 6LZ Tel: (020) 8274 0565 Fax: (020) 7629 2513 E-mail: chris@woolexpo.biz

WOOLLEN GOODS, MADE-UP, *See also headings for particular products*

Bovey Handloom Weavers, 1 Station Road, Bovey Tracey, Newton Abbot, Devon, TQ13 9AL Tel: (01626) 833424 Fax: (01626) 833424

Brynkir Woollen Mill Ltd, Brynkir Woollen Factory, Golan, Garndolbenmaen, Gwynedd, LL51 9YU Tel: (01766) 530236

WOOLLEN YARN

Joseph Barraclough Ltd, Bankfield Mills, Mirfield, West Yorkshire, WF14 9DD Tel: (01924) 493147 Fax: (01924) 490702 E-mail: info@barrayarn.co.uk

Brierley Bros Ltd, Albert Mills, Albert Street, Huddersfield, HD1 3PZ Tel: (01484) 426511 Fax: (01484) 430244 E-mail: office@brierleybrothers.com

King Cole Ltd, Merrie Mills, Old Souls Way, Crossflatts, Bingley, West Yorkshire, BD16 2AX Tel: (01274) 561331 Fax: (01274) 551095 E-mail: enquiries@kingcole.co.uk

Fred Lawton & Son Ltd, Meltham Mills, Meltham, Holmfirth, HD9 4AY Tel: (01484) 852573 Fax: (01484) 852737 E-mail: enquiries@fredlawton.com

McAndrews Textiles Ltd, West Scholes Mill, West Scholes, Queensbury, Bradford, West Yorkshire, BD13 1NQ Tel: (01274) 881111 Fax: (01274) 883311 E-mail: info@mcandrewtextiles.co.uk

R Gledhill Ltd, Pingle Mill, Pingle Lane, Delph, Oldham, OL3 5EX Tel: (01457) 874651 Fax: (01457) 872428 E-mail: general@rgledhill.co.uk

Stork Bros Ltd, Bay Hall Mills, Bay Hall Common Road, Huddersfield, HD1 5EP Tel: (01484) 424283 Fax: (01484) 542876

WORD PROCESSING EQUIPMENT OR SYSTEMS

Brother (U K) Ltd, Shepley St, Guide Bridge, Manchester, M34 5JD Tel: 0161-330 6531 Fax: 0161-308 3281 E-mail: sales@brother-uk.com

Danter Automatics, 11a Copse Cross Street, Ross-on-Wye, Herefordshire, HR9 5PD Tel: (01989) 563604 Fax: (01989) 563604

Delta Business Equipment, Unit G3 Meadow Mill, Water Street, Stockport, Cheshire, SK1 2BY Tel: 0161-480 1222 Fax: 0161-480 0022 E-mail: sales@deltaoffice.co.uk

Arthur C. Smith Ltd, Oldmedow Road, Hardwick Industrial Estate, King's Lynn, Norfolk, PE30 4LD Tel: (01553) 817220 Fax: (0845) 0500864 E-mail: sales@acssupplies.com

WORD PROCESSING PERSONNEL RECRUITMENT AGENCIES/CONSULTANTS/ SERVICES

Aarron Personnel, Unit 12 Hollins Business Centre, Rowley Street, Stafford, ST16 2RH Tel: (0870) 7456587 Fax: (0870) 7456588 E-mail: lisa@kcen.co.uk

BSC Sales Specialists, BSC House, 16 Blackfriars Street, Salford, M3 5BQ Tel: 0161-834 6234 Fax: 0161-835 3114

WORD PROCESSING SERVICES/ BUREAU SERVICES

1 2 3 Express Mailing, 67-69 Chancery Lane, London, WC2A 1RF Tel: (020) 7405 7547 Fax: (020) 7831 0878

Bond Street Business Base, 3 Bond Street, St. Helier, Jersey, JE2 3NP Tel: (01534) 724100 Fax: (01534) 759662 E-mail: info@bondbase.info

Business Services Bureau, 11 Greenland Road, Barnet, Hertfordshire, EN5 2AL Tel: (020) 8440 3474 Fax: (020) 8440 3676 E-mail: bsb@busybee.demon.co.uk

▶ OnLine Office Services, 15 Knocklands Court, Ballymoney, County Antrim, BT53 6LN Tel: (028) 2766 9566 Fax: (028) 2766 9566 E-mail: info@onlineofficeservices.co.uk

▶ Purple Creature, 6 Rosemount Square, Aberdeen, AB25 2UB Tel: (01224) 643673 E-mail: info@purplecreature.co.uk

▶ SJM Secretarial Services, Nelson Street, Burton-on-Trent, Staffordshire, DE15 0DE Tel: (01283) 509854

Torplan Ltd, 216 Heaton Moor Road, Stockport, Cheshire, SK4 4DU Tel: 0161-443 1881 Fax: 0161-431 0786 E-mail: sales@torplan.co.uk

▶ Typing For Business, Ridge Mount, Middlewich Road, Wistaston, Nantwich, Cheshire, CW5 6PB Tel: (01270) 252065 E-mail: info@typingforbusiness.co.uk

The Typing Factory Romscot UK, 12 Renfield Street, Glasgow, G2 5AL Tel: 0141-221 1242 Fax: 0141-248 4652 E-mail: christian@typingfactory.com

Word Processing Services, 107 Dashwood Avenue, High Wycombe, Buckinghamshire, HP12 3EB Tel: (01494) 538090 Fax: (01494) 538088 E-mail: info@wordproc.co.uk

WORK BOATS

▶ Izax Offshore Marine Services, 2 Littlemoor Lane, Newton, Alfreton, Derbyshire, DE55 5TY Tel: (01773) 875986 Fax: (01773) 875986 E-mail: matt_izax@hotmail.com

Kiwi Canoes, 72 Hartley Rd, Radford, Nottingham, NG7 3AD Tel: 0115-978 4149

Steelkit, Abberleri Boatyard, Ynyslas, Borth, Dyfed, SY24 5JU Tel: (01970) 871713 Fax: (01970) 871879E-mail: info@steelkit.com

WORK MEASUREMENT

▶ Edison Consultancy, PO Box 6479, Brackley, Northamptonshire, NN13 5YU Tel: 01280 841500E-mail: work@edison-consultancy.com

WORKBENCHES

A M Designs Powergrip, 45 Tyler Hill Road, Blean, Canterbury, Kent, CT2 9HU Tel: (01227) 472203 Fax: (01227) 454749 E-mail: am@powergrip.co.uk

Benchmaster Ltd, Glover Centre, Egmont Street, Mossley, Ashton-under-Lyne, Lancashire, OL5 9PY Tel: (01457) 837146 Fax: (01457) 837981 E-mail: sales@benchmaster.co.uk

Emmerich (Berlon) Ltd, Kingsnorth Industrial Estate, Wotton Road, Ashford, Kent, TN23 6JY Tel: (01233) 622684 Fax: (01233) 645801 E-mail: emmerick@emir.co.uk

Lista (UK) Ltd, 17 Alston Drive, Bradwell Abbey, Milton Keynes, MK13 9HA Tel: (01908) 222333 Fax: (01908) 222433 E-mail: info.uk@lista.com

▶ P A F Systems Ltd, Brunel Close, Park Farm Industrial Estate, Wellingborough, Northamptonshire, NN8 6QX Tel: (01933) 403555 Fax: (01933) 403888 E-mail: sales@pafsystem.com

Pinder Versatool Ltd, Padholme Road East, Peterborough, PE1 5XL Tel: (01733) 552727 Fax: (01733) 552717 E-mail: malcolm.bayes@pinder-versatool.co.uk

QMP, Timmis Road, Stourbridge, West Midlands, DY9 7BQ Tel: (01384) 899800 Fax: (01384) 899801 E-mail: qmp@qmp.uk.com

Sono UK Ltd, Enterprise House, Murdock Road, Dorcan, Swindon, SN3 5HY Tel: (01793) 488488 Fax: (01793) 522868 E-mail: info@sono-uk.com

Static Safe, 6 Timmis Road, Stourbridge, West Midlands, DY9 7BQ Tel: (01384) 898599 Fax: (01384) 898577 E-mail: sse@static-safe.demon.co.uk

Treston Ltd, 5b Bone Lane, Newbury, Berkshire, RG14 5SH Tel: (01635) 521521 Fax: (01635) 37452 E-mail: salesuk@treston.com

Tudor, 3 Ellesmere Business Park, Oswestry Road, Ellesmere, Shropshire, SY12 0EW Tel: (01691) 623424 Fax: (01691) 624479 E-mail: nevilletudor@virgin.net

WORKHOLDING EQUIPMENT

Craftsman Tools Ltd, Side Copse, Otley, West Yorkshire, LS21 1JE Tel: (01943) 466788 Fax: (01943) 850144 E-mail: r.johnson@craftsmantools.com

WORKHOLDING SYSTEMS MANUFRS

Coburg Engineering Ltd, Unit 22F, Wincombe Business Park, Shaftesbury, Dorset, SP7 9QJ Tel: (01747) 855022 Fax: (01747) 854744 E-mail: info@coburg.co.uk

Rem Systems Ltd, Unit 24 26, Sabre Close, Quedgeley, Gloucester, GL2 4NZ Tel: (01452) 314100 Fax: (01452) 314101 E-mail: sales@remsystems.co.uk

Standaparts Ltd, 7A South Bank, Thames Ditton, Surrey, KT7 0UD Tel: (020) 8398 7812 Fax: (020) 8398 7813 E-mail: standaparts@btclick.com

Stocdon Ltd, 2 Mackenzie Way, Swindon Village, Cheltenham, Gloucestershire, GL51 9TX Tel: (01242) 241123 Fax: (01242) 241133 E-mail: info@stocdon.co.uk

T D T Technology Ltd, Unit 20 Woodside Park, Rugby, Warwickshire, CV21 2NP Tel: (01788) 570411 Fax: (01788) 567632 E-mail: sales@tdt-technology.co.uk

Thame Engineering Co. Ltd, Field End, Thame Road, Long Crendon, Aylesbury, Buckinghamshire, HP18 9EJ Tel: (01844) 208050 Fax: (01844) 201699 E-mail: sales@thame-eng.com

W D S Watford, Hagden Lane, Watford, WD18 7DJ Tel: (01923) 226606 Fax: (01923) 242799 E-mail: sales@wdsltd.co.uk

John Walton Machine Tools Ltd, Smithy Carr Lane, Brighouse, West Yorkshire, HD6 2HL Tel: (01484) 712507 Fax: (01484) 710549 E-mail: cyoung@chucks.co.uk

WORKING PLATFORMS

Max Access Ltd, Unit 17 Bankside, Station Approach, Kidlington, Oxfordshire, OX5 1JE Tel: (01865) 373566 Fax: (01865) 378021 E-mail: info@maxaccess.co.uk

Upright International, Unit F1, Halesfield 4, Telford, Shropshire, TF7 4AP Tel: (01952) 685200 Fax: (01952) 685255 E-mail: mdavey@uprighteuro.com

WORKSHOP GRINDERS

Goodwood Engineering, Enterprise Way, King's Lynn, Norfolk, PE30 4LJ Tel: (01553) 766574 Fax: (01553) 766574 E-mail: andy@goodwoodeng.co.uk

WORKSTATION COMPUTERS

Computers For Schools & Education, 21 Bramble Bank, Frimley Green, Camberley, Surrey, GU16 6PN Tel: (01252) 836463 E-mail: james.findlay@lineone.net

WORKSTATIONS, *See also headings for particular types*

Lista (UK) Ltd, 17 Alston Drive, Bradwell Abbey, Milton Keynes, MK13 9HA Tel: (01908) 222333 Fax: (01908) 222433 E-mail: info.uk@lista.com

WORKTOPS

▶ The Oriental Stone Co. Ltd, Ashfarm, Leysters, Leominster, Herefordshire, HR6 0HP Tel: (01568) 750550 Fax: (01568) 750586 E-mail: info@orientalstone.co.uk

WORKWEAR, *See also headings for particular types*

▶ 1st Coverall, Tovil Green Business Park, Burial Ground Lane, Tovil, Maidstone, Kent, ME15 6TA Tel: (01622) 664427 Fax: (01622) 664427

A C E Atlas Commission Embroidery, Block 2 Phoenix Works Industrial Estate, Richards Street, Wednesbury, West Midlands, WS10 8BZ Tel: 0121-568 7117 Fax: 0121-526 3909 E-mail: aceembroidery2001@yahoo.co.uk

A & E Russell Ltd, Baird Avenue, Dryburgh Industrial Estate, Dundee, DD2 3TN Tel: (01382) 811566 Fax: (01382) 833455 E-mail: enquiries@aerussell.com

A & E Russell Ltd, 33 Tennant Street, Edinburgh, EH6 5NA Tel: 0131-555 0577 Fax: 0131-553 4722 E-mail: enquiries@aerussell.co.uk

A & E Russell Ltd, 7-9 Chetham Court, Winwick Quay, Warrington, WA2 8RF Tel: (01925) 643700 Fax: (01925) 643707 E-mail: warrington@aerussell.co.uk

▶ Body Talk, 48-57, Market Hall, Derby, DE1 2DB Tel: (01332) 298989 Fax: (01332) 296661

Broadweave, Hayhill Industrial Estate, Barrow Upon Soar, Loughborough, Leicestershire, LE12 8LD Tel: (01509) 816123 Fax: (01509) 814867 E-mail: sales@broadweaveltd.co.uk

C I C Co Ltd, 95-97 Palmerston Road, Bournemouth, BH1 4HP Tel: (01202) 301033 Fax: (01202) 300006

Camouflage Protective Equipment, 82 High Street, Boston, Lincolnshire, PE21 8SX Tel: (01205) 353514 Fax: (01205) 353514

Crest Identity Ltd, Crest House, Stockton Road, Hartlepool, Cleveland, TS25 1TY Tel: (01429) 233533 Fax: (01429) 272400

Culm Industrial Clothing, Saunders Way, Cullompton, Devon, EX15 1BS Tel: (01884) 32302 Fax: (01884) 38482

Engel Workwear, Carters Yard, 30 Carters Lane, Kiln Farm, Milton Keynes, MK11 3HL Tel: (01908) 561560 Fax: (01908) 563805 E-mail: sales@f-engel.co.uk

Felford Industrial Clothing & Supplies, Riverside, Market Harborough, Leicestershire, LE16 7PT Tel: (01858) 434218 Fax: (01858) 410706 E-mail: felfordsupplies@btconnect.com

H Q Industrial Supplies Ltd, 44a Masters Lane, Halesowen, West Midlands, B62 9HL Tel: 0121-559 3776 Fax: 0121-559 3777

▶ Halkon Hunt Designer, Unit 1 14-20 Gunhills Lane, Armthorpe, Doncaster, South Yorkshire, DN3 3EB Tel: (01302) 834145 Fax: (01302) 833274

▶ Harris's Sports, 22a Griffin Road, Clevedon, Avon, BS21 6HH Tel: (01275) 874351 Fax: (01275) 349806 E-mail: ddavies@harrissports.co.uk

D.R. Hunt, 29 Alexandra Road, Margate, Kent, CT9 5SP Tel: (01843) 209800

Jay Stores, 130 Lower Road, London, SE16 2UG Tel: (020) 7237 2410 Fax: (020) 7237 2410

Manufacturers Supplies Acton Ltd, 2 Langley Wharf, Railway Terrace, Kings Langley, Hertfordshire, WD4 8JE Tel: (01923) 260845 Fax: (01923) 260847 E-mail: manusupplies@aol.com

Parflo Ltd, Huxley Street, Broadheath, Altrincham, Cheshire, WA14 5EL Tel: 0161-928 3579 Fax: 0161-926 8140

WORKWEAR – *continued*

Redgold Fashions Ltd, 219-221 Bow Road, London, E3 2SJ Tel: (020) 8980 9745 Fax: (020) 8980 4979

▶ Safety Solutions Ni, Rathdown Close, Lissue Industrial Estate, Lisburn, County Antrim, BT28 2RB Tel: (028) 9262 2444 Fax: (028) 9262 2333

Spectrum Signs, 22 Bladon Road, Southampton, SO16 6QD Tel: (023) 8077 2264 Fax: (023) 8032 2264 E-mail: sales@spectrum-signs.co.uk

▶ Storrm Industrial, 7 Axis Way, Eaton Socon, St. Neots, Cambridgeshire, PE19 8QE Tel: (01480) 216056 Fax: (01480) 352332

Stronghold Safety Workwear, Cocklebury Road, Chippenham, Wiltshire, SN15 3NT Tel: (01249) 655976 Fax: (01249) 460623

Sutcliffe Farrar & Co. Ltd, Banksfield Works, Mytholmroyd, Hebden Bridge, West Yorkshire, HX7 5LT Tel: (01422) 883363 Fax: (01422) 885479 E-mail: sales@fieldclassics.com

Tag, Unit 1 Derby Road Business Park, Burton-on-Trent, Staffordshire, DE14 1RW Tel: (01283) 531855 Fax: (01283) 741411 E-mail: sales@taglesuire.co.uk

▶ The Work Wear Department, 4, 93 West Main Street, Broxburn, West Lothian, EH52 5LE Tel: (01506) 859333 Fax: (01506) 859333

Work-Kit Ltd, Unit 18c Rovex Business Park, Hay Hall Road Tyseley, Birmingham, B11 2AG Tel: 0121-706 4341 Fax: 0121-707 4831 E-mail: mail@work-kit.fsnet.co.uk

Workwear Express Ltd, The Image Centre, Wesley Place, Coxhoe, Durham, DH6 4LG Tel: 0191-377 9318 Fax: 0191-377 9001 E-mail: info@workwearexpress.com

WORKWEAR CLOTHING

▶ Acti Stitch, Unit 13 Lufton Heights Commerce Park, Boundary Way, Lufton, Yeovil, Somerset, BA22 8UY Tel: (01935) 420820 Fax: (01935) 428850 E-mail: info@actistitch.com

Avalon and Lynwood, PO Box 608, Altrincham, Cheshire, WA15 7ZP Tel: 0161-904 8642 E-mail: sales@avalonandlynwood.com

Bolton Metropolitan Borough Council Commercial Services Bolmoor I, St Helens Road, Bolton, BL3 3NS Tel: (01204) 336855 Fax: (01204) 658072 E-mail: sales@bolmoor.co.uk

Busy Embroidery, 3 Village Farm Industrial Estate, Pyle, Bridgend, Mid Glamorgan, CF33 6ZR Tel: (01656) 741274 Fax: (01656) 741274 E-mail: sales@fusionembroidery.co.uk

C M Supplies, 8 Brothock Bridge, Arbroath, Angus, DD11 1NG Tel: (01241) 434800 Fax: (01241) 434800 E-mail: cmsupplies1@aol.com

▶ Cheerful Promotions Ltd, 38 Ferncroft Avenue, London, NW3 7PE Tel: (020) 7431 6293 Fax: (020) 7431 2060 E-mail: sales@cheerfulpromotions.co.uk

Cosalt Ballyclare Ltd, Banner House, Greg Street, Stockport, Cheshire, SK5 7BT Tel: 0161-429 1100 Fax: (0870) 8502376 E-mail: info@cosalt-ballyclare.com

Debaer Incorperating Rimac, 7 Langley Business Centre, Station Road, Langley, Slough, SL3 8DS Tel: (01753) 710071 Fax: (01753) 572772 E-mail: sales@rimac.co.uk

Engel Workwear, Carters Yard, 30 Carters Lane, Kiln Farm, Milton Keynes, MK11 3HL Tel: (01908) 561560 Fax: (01908) 563805 E-mail: sales@f-engel.co.uk

▶ Grantham Clothing Co., Unit 1a Partnership House, Withambrook Park Industrial Estate, Grantham, Lincolnshire, NG31 9ST Tel: (01476) 594330 Fax: (01476) 593863 E-mail: granthamclothing@btclick.com

▶ Jami-Q's T-Shirt Printers, Unit 6, Wrexham Indust Estate, Wrexham, Clwyd, LL13 9RF Tel: (01978) 660220 Fax: (01978) 664604 E-mail: sales@jamiqs.co.uk

Kaotic Design, Unit 8, Priest Court, Springfield Business Park, Grantham, Lincolnshire, NG31 7BG Tel: (0870) 0633015 Fax: (0870) 0633017 E-mail: sales@kaoticdesigns.co.uk

▶ Meltemi Co Clothing Ltd, Barnard Road, Bowthorpe Employment Area, Norwich, NR5 9JB Tel: (01603) 731330 Fax: (0870) 7871759 E-mail: sales@meltemi.co.uk

MyWorkwear.co.uk, Unit 1-2, Kingsland Tradeing Estate, Telford, Shropshire, TF7 4QW Tel: (0870) 3503150 Fax: (01952) 585991 E-mail: orders@myworkwear.co.uk

▶ Safely Workwear, Church Road, Worcester Park, Surrey, KT4 7RJ Tel: (020) 8337 5558 E-mail: sales@safelyworkwear.co.uk

Trading Style, Unit 2, Pemberton Business Centre, Richmond Hill, Pemberton, Wigan, Lancashire, WN5 8AA Tel: (01942) 621942 Fax: (01942) 620909 E-mail: info@tradingstyle.co.uk

▶ Tryline Rugbywear, Unit 101, Greenwich Commercial Centre,, 49, Greenwich High Road, London, SE10 8JL Tel: (020) 8694 6888 Fax: (020) 8694 6888 E-mail: trylinerugbywear@aol.com

▶ Ultimate Cleaners (Industrial) Ltd, Unit 9, Cousin Street, Dudley Road, Wolverhampton, WV2 3DG Tel: (01902) 451451 E-mail: sales@ultimateindustrial.co.uk

Wenaas UK Ltd, Wenaas Buildings, Hareness Circle, Altens Industrial Estate, Aberdeen, AB12 3LY Tel: (01224) 894000 Fax: (01224) 878789 E-mail: sales@wenaas.co.uk

Winnard Workwear, 129 Edenfield Road, Rochdale, Lancashire, OL11 5AE Tel: (01706) 352947 E-mail: slocw@yahoo.co.uk

▶ Work Wear Warehouse, Duncrue CR, Belfast, BT3 9BW Tel: (028) 9077 7114 Fax: (028) 9077 3115 E-mail: sales@garmentgraphixs.co.uk

Work-Kit Ltd, Unit 18c Rovex Business Park, Hay Hall Road Tyseley, Birmingham, B11 2AG Tel: 0121-706 4341 Fax: 0121-707 4831 E-mail: mail@work-kit.fsnet.co.uk

WORKWEAR FABRICS

Cosalt Workwear Ltd, Banner House, Greg Street, Stockport, Cheshire, SK5 7BT Tel: (0800) 0188110 Fax: (0870) 8502378 E-mail: info@cosalt-workwear.com

Debonair, Anchor House, 4 Bridgeman Street, Walsall, WS2 9NW Tel: (01922) 649399 Fax: (01922) 648091 E-mail: salesdebonair@aol.com

Engel Workwear, Carters Yard, 30 Carters Lane, Kiln Farm, Milton Keynes, MK11 3HL Tel: (01908) 561560 Fax: (01908) 563805 E-mail: sales@f-engel.co.uk

Morleys Leisurewear Centres Ltd, 25 Hereward Cross, Peterborough, PE1 1TE Tel: (01733) 562834

Overall Workwear, 3 Alexander Square, Clayton, Bradford, West Yorkshire, BD14 6QU Tel: (01274) 814649 Fax: (01274) 814649

Stockbridge Workwear, 6 House O'Hill Avenue, Edinburgh, EH4 5DD Tel: 0131-343 1039 Fax: 0131-332 6766 E-mail: richie.pearson@virgin.net

WORKWEAR SUPPLY SERVICES

A & E Russell Ltd, 5 Brown Street, Coatbridge, Lanarkshire, ML5 4AS Tel: (01236) 433511 Fax: (01236) 440070 E-mail: sales@aerussell.co.uk

A & E Russell Ltd, Unit 18 Crystal Drive, Smethwick, West Midlands, B66 1QG Tel: 0121-543 4850 Fax: 0121-543 4855 E-mail: birmingham@aerussell.co.uk

Allsafe Protection Ltd, 120 Moorfield Road, Widnes, Cheshire, WA8 3HX Tel: 0151-424 7299 Fax: 0151-424 2040

Arcs N Sparks Ltd, The Long House, Villiers Street, Willenhall, West Midlands, WV13 1DF Tel: (01902) 636133 Fax: (01902) 636122 E-mail: sales@arcsnsparks.co.uk

Brooks Bourne Venture, Manning Road, Bourne, Lincolnshire, PE10 9EU Tel: (01778) 394900 Fax: (01778) 394218

Brooks Textile Rentals P.L.C., 400 Centenary Way, Batley, West Yorkshire, WF17 8JY Tel: (01924) 444964 Fax: (01924) 477487

Buckler Ltd, 3 Angus Works, North Isla Street, Dundee, DD3 7JQ Tel: (01382) 828200 Fax: (01382) 828882 E-mail: info@bucklerboots.com

C L S, 71 Bankhouse Road, Bury, Lancashire, BL8 1DY Tel: 0161-764 9898 Fax: 0161-764 9898

The Caterers Linen Supply, 6-8 Jackson Way, Great Western Industrial Park, Southall, Middlesex, UB2 4SF Tel: (020) 8843 5810 Fax: (020) 8843 5865 E-mail: customerservice@catererslinen.co.uk

Cornish Linen Service, Dudnance Lane, Pool, Redruth, Cornwall, TR15 3RA Tel: (01256) 471311 Fax: (01209) 714133 E-mail: sales.camborne@cls-group.co.uk

Cradley Heath Army Stores, 1 Upper High Street, Cradley Heath, West Midlands, B64 5HX Tel: (01384) 560796 Fax: (01384) 560796

Davmar Workwear, 1 Centenary Court, Earlsway, Team Valley Trading Estate, Gateshead, Tyne & Wear, NE11 0RQ Tel: 0191-487 2249 Fax: 0191-491 4237 E-mail: contact@davmarworkwear.com

Essential Hygiene & Workwear Services Ltd, 14 The Rowans, Leeds, LS13 1BD Tel: 0113-257 4411 Fax: 0113-256 2151

Fenland Laundries Ltd, Roman Bank, Skegness, Lincolnshire, PE25 1SQ Tel: (01754) 767171 Fax: (01754) 610344

Initial, Botany Brow, Chorley, Lancashire, PR6 0HX Tel: (01257) 272311 Fax: (01257) 233575

Initial Garment Services, PO Box 392, Bradford, West Yorkshire, BD7 2YY Tel: (01274) 575656 Fax: (01274) 504960

Initial Textile Services, Unit 10, Eldon Way, Bristol, BS4 3QQ Tel: 0117-971 2387 Fax: 0117-971 6612 E-mail: briscsu@initialtextileservices.co.uk

Johnson Cleaners UK Ltd, Ruthvenfield Road, Perth, PH1 3SW Tel: (01738) 623456 Fax: (01738) 635160

Johnsons Apparel Master Ltd, Mill Road, Fishersgate, Portslade, Brighton, BN41 1PX Tel: (01273) 412111 Fax: (01273) 414056

Johnsons Apparel Master, Cowley Bridge Road, Exeter, EX4 5AA Tel: (01392) 271291 Fax: (01392) 422078

Johnsons Apparelmaster P.L.C., Aldridge Road, Perry Barr, Birmingham, B42 2EU Tel: 0121-356 4512 Fax: 0121-344 3520

Johnsons Apparelmaster, 150 Stoney Rock Lane, Leeds, LS9 7BL Tel: 0113-249 5755 Fax: 0113-249 7036

Orna Met Co., 337 Leysdown Road, Leysdown-on-Sea, Sheerness, Kent, ME12 4AR Tel: (01795) 510630

Quartermasters Protective Equipment, 248 City Road, Cardiff, CF24 3JJ Tel: (029) 2049 1059

Rana Textiles Ltd, 914-918 Stratford Road, Sparkhill, Birmingham, B11 4BT Tel: 0121-777 3986 Fax: 0121-247 2255

Slater Safety Supplies, 238 Woodplumpton Road, Woodplumpton, Preston, PR4 0TA Tel: (01772) 691000 Fax: (01772) 691436

The Sunlight Service Group Ltd, Shap Road, Kendal, Cumbria, LA9 6DQ Tel: (01539) 723378 Fax: (01539) 740921 E-mail: kendal@sunlight.co.uk

Texicare Ltd, Unit 6, Lansil Industrial Estate, Caton Road, Lancaster, LA1 3PQ Tel: (01524) 39666 Fax: (01524) 841963 E-mail: stevenh@texicare.co.uk

Tibard Laundry Services Ltd, Holden Street, Ashton-under-Lyne, Lancashire, OL6 9JB Tel: 0161-330 5106 Fax: 0161-339 9995

Victory Workwear Ltd, 5 Holder Road, Aldershot, Hampshire, GU12 4RH Tel: (01252) 352800 Fax: (01252) 352805

W I S, Kings Castle Business Parke, The Drove, Bridgwater, Somerset, TA6 4AG Tel: (01278) 439128 Fax: (01278) 439129

Wellfast Industrial Supplies Ltd, 157-159 New John Street, Halesowen, West Midlands, B62 8HT Tel: 0121-559 3805 Fax: 0121-559 9836E-mail: david@page6745.freeserve.co.uk

Workware & Business Casuals, Unit 26 Snedshill Industrial Estate, Snedshill, Telford, Shropshire, TF2 9NH Tel: (01952) 615976 Fax: (01952) 614440 E-mail: enquiries@myworkwear.co.uk

WORM GEAR OR SCREW OPERATED JACKS

Metallifacture Ltd, Mansfield Road, Redhill, Nottingham, NG5 8PY Tel: 0115-966 0200 Fax: 0115-967 0133 E-mail: mail@metallifacture.co.uk

Motovario Ltd, Rushock Trading Estate, Rushock, Droitwich, Worcestershire, WR9 0NR Tel: (01299) 250859 Fax: (01299) 251493 E-mail: sales@motovario.co.uk

P A R Communications (Leeds) Ltd, Mile End Road, Colwick Industrial Estate, Colwick, Nottingham, NG4 2BU Tel: 0115-961 4744 Fax: 0115-940 0714 E-mail: parcom@btconnect.com

Pfaff-Silberblau Ltd, Prenton Way, North Cheshire Trading Estate, Prenton, Merseyside, CH43 3DU Tel: 0151-609 0099 Fax: 0151-609 0852 E-mail: anyone@pfaff-silberblau.co.uk

WORM GEARBOXES

Gudel Lineartec (U.K.) Ltd, Unit 5 Wickmans Drive, Banner Lane, Coventry, CV4 9XA Tel: (024) 7669 5444 Fax: (024) 7669 5666 E-mail: info@uk.gudel.com

Nottingham Electrical Transmissions, Northern Court, Nottingham, NG6 0BJ Tel: 0115-975 3655 Fax: 0115-977 0366 E-mail: info@net-eng.co.uk

WORM GEARS

Fraser & Macdonald Electric Motors Ltd, 176 Woodville Street, Glasgow, G51 2RN Tel: 0141-445 3874 Fax: 0141-425 1135 E-mail: frasmcd@aol.com

Hunter Gears Ltd, Addison Works, Haugh Lane, Blaydon-on-Tyne, Tyne & Wear, NE21 4SB Tel: 0191-414 4545 Fax: 0191-414 0135

Kelston Precisions Gears Ltd, Crews Hole Road, Bristol, BS5 8BB Tel: 0117-955 8671 Fax: 0117-935 0023 E-mail: sales@kelstongears.co.uk

Unigears Ashford Ltd, Unit 8 Henwood Business Centre, Henwood Industrial Estate, Ashford, Kent, TN24 8DH Tel: (01233) 642798 Fax: (01233) 650725 E-mail: sales@unigears.co.uk

WORSTED CLOTH, *See also Woollen Fabric/Worsted Cloth etc*

Alfred Brown Worsted Mills Ltd, Empire Mills, Mill Lane, Leeds, LS13 3HG Tel: 0113-256 0666 Fax: 0113-257 2315 E-mail: sales@alfredbrown.co.uk

Anglia Textile Manufacturers Ltd, Holly Park Mills, Calverley, Pudsey, West Yorkshire, LS28 5QS Tel: 0113-257 0861 Fax: 0113-257 2391 E-mail: fabrics@angliat.free.online.co.uk

Batley & Robinson (Worsteds) Ltd, 7-9 Valley Road Business Park, Keighley, West Yorkshire, BD21 4LZ Tel: (0845) 1235516 Fax: (01535) 610047 E-mail: sales@batleyandrobinson.com

Bower Roebuck & Co. Ltd, Glendale Mills, New Mill, Holmfirth, HD9 7EN Tel: (01484) 682181 Fax: (01484) 683469 E-mail: info@bowerroebucks.com

Bulmer & Lumb Group Ltd, Albert Street, Lockwood, Huddersfield, HD1 3PE Tel: (01484) 423231 Fax: (01484) 435313 E-mail: headoffice@taylor-and-lodge.co.uk

Drummond Parkland Of England, Park Valley Mills, Meltham Road, Huddersfield, HD4 7BH Tel: (01484) 668400 Fax: (01484) 668570

Edwin Woodhouse & Co. Ltd, Unit 2a Sunnybank Mills, 83-85 Town Street, Farsley, Pudsey, West Yorkshire, LS28 5UJ Tel: 0113-257 4331 Fax: 0113-239 3228 E-mail: sales@edwin-woodhouse.co.uk

J.W. Ellison & Co. Ltd, 677-681 Little Horton Lane, Bradford, West Yorkshire, BD5 9DQ Tel: (01274) 571943 Fax: (01274) 571943

Fox Brothers & Co., Milverton Road, Wellington, Somerset, TA21 0BA Tel: (01823) 662271 Fax: (01823) 666963 E-mail: enquiries@foxflannel.com

Gamma Beta Holdings Ltd, Briggella Mills, Bradford, West Yorkshire, BD5 0QA Tel: (01274) 525508 Fax: (01274) 521157 E-mail: furnishing@hield.co.uk

Harrisons Burley Ltd, Sandylands, Anderton Street, Cross Hills, Keighley, West Yorkshire, BD20 7ED Tel: (01535) 637410 Fax: (01535) 637498 E-mail: sales@harrisonsburley.co.uk

Huddersfield Fine Worsteds, Kirkheaton Mills, Huddersfield, HD5 0NS Tel: (01484) 420377 Fax: (01484) 429156

Kaye & Stewart, Rashcliffe Mills, Albert Street, Lockwood, Huddersfield, HD1 3PE Tel: (01484) 423231 Fax: (01484) 435313 E-mail: headoffice@taylor-and-lodge.co.uk

Kelwood Exports, 70 Blover Road, Lindley, Huddersfield, HD3 3HR Tel: (01484) 653053 Fax: (01484) 658934

Linton Tweeds Ltd, Shaddon Mills, Shaddongate, Carlisle, CA2 5TZ Tel: (01228) 527569 Fax: (01228) 512062 E-mail: info@lintontweeds.co.uk

Moxon, Yew Tree Mills, Holmbridge, Holmfirth, HD9 2NN Tel: (01484) 691500 Fax: (01484) 691505 E-mail: sales@moxon.co.uk

Robert Noble Ltd, March Street, Peebles, EH45 8ER Tel: (01721) 724311 Fax: (01721) 721893 E-mail: enquiries@robert-noble.co.uk

P H B Textiles Ltd, PO Box 35586, London, NW4 1XG Tel: (07958) 492545 Fax: (020) 8203 5388

Ramsden Bros Huddersfield Ltd, Crosland Moor Mills, Blackmoorfoot Road, Huddersfield, HD4 5AH Tel: (01484) 421042 Fax: (01484) 559236

Schofield & Smith Huddersfield Ltd, Clough Road Mills, Slaithwaite, Huddersfield, HD7 5DB Tel: (01484) 842471 Fax: (01484) 842684 E-mail: sales@schofieldandsmith.co.uk

William Halstead & Co Dudley Hill Ltd, Stanley Mills, Edward Street, Bradford, West Yorkshire, BD4 9RS Tel: (01274) 682921 Fax: (01274) 685698 E-mail: sales@williamhalstead.co.uk

WORSTED YARN

Coats Crafts U.K, Lingfield, McMullen Road, Darlington, County Durham, DL1 1YQ Tel: (01325) 394394 Fax: (01325) 394200 E-mail: consumer.services@coats.com

Craven Yarn Services, Milton House, Cononly, Keighley, West Yorkshire, BD20 8LL Tel: (01535) 630683 Fax: (01535) 630683 E-mail: john@cravenyarns.fsnet.co.uk

E Mesrie & Sons Ltd, 3 Brazil Street, Manchester, M1 3PJ Tel: 0161-236 6274 Fax: 0161-236 8086 E-mail: yarns@mdmresourcing.com

Joseph Horsfall & Sons Ltd, Pellon Lane, Halifax, West Yorkshire, HX1 4AA Tel: (01422) 360213 Fax: (01422) 321579 E-mail: info@jhorsfall.com

King Cole Ltd, Merrie Mills, Old Souls Way, Crossflatts, Bingley, West Yorkshire, BD16 2AX Tel: (01274) 561331 Fax: (01274) 551095 E-mail: enquiries@kingcole.co.uk

West Yorkshire Spinners Ltd, Lowertown Mills, Lowertown, Oxenhope, Keighley, West Yorkshire, BD22 9JQ Tel: (01535) 642824 Fax: (01535) 642655

WOUND ELECTRONIC COMPONENTS

A G W Electronics Ltd, Hayford Way, Staveley, Chesterfield, Derbyshire, S43 3JR Tel: (01246) 473086 Fax: (01246) 280082 E-mail: sales@agw.co.uk

Ace Wound Products Ltd, 1g Skillion Business Park, Thames Road, Barking, Essex, IG11 0JP Tel: (020) 8507 2330 Fax: (020) 8507 8981 E-mail: mac@acewound.com

E M R Windings Ltd, Units 5 & 6, Kiln Park Industrial Park, Searle Crescent, Weston-super-Mare, Somerset, BS23 3XP Tel: (01934) 631374 Fax: (01934) 622698 E-mail: lee.graham@emrelectronics.co.uk

Zeal Electronics Ltd, Vanguard Trading Estate, Britannia Road, Chesterfield, Derbyshire, S40 2TZ Tel: (01246) 209009 Fax: (01246) 232994 E-mail: sales@zeal-electronics.co.uk

WOVEN BADGES

Bell Woven Brake, New Market Street, Colne, Lancashire, BB8 9DA Tel: (01282) 864000 Fax: (01282) 864325 E-mail: info@bellwoven.co.uk

Cash's, Torrington Avenue, Coventry, CV4 9UZ Tel: (024) 7646 6466 Fax: (024) 7646 2525 E-mail: sales@jjcash.co.uk

▶ Delta Labelling, Unit A Apollo Park Apollo, Litchfield Road Industrial, Lichfield Road Industrial Estate, Tamworth, Staffordshire, B79 7TA Tel: (01827) 302862 Fax: (01827) 300891E-mail: enquiries@delta-labelling.co.uk

WOVEN BOOKBINDING CLOTHS

F J Ratchford Ltd, Kennedy Way, Green Lane, Stockport, Cheshire, SK4 2JX Tel: 0161-480 8484 Fax: 0161-480 3679 E-mail: sales@fjratchford.co.uk

WOVEN BOOKBINDING CLOTHS – *continued*

Fibermark Red Bridge International Ltd, Ainsworth, Ainsworth, Bolton, BL2 5PD Tel: (01204) 522254 Fax: (01204) 384754 E-mail: sales@redbridge.co.uk

A. Holt & Sons Ltd, 115 Whitecross Street, London, EC1Y 8JQ Tel: (020) 7256 2222 Fax: (020) 7638 3578 E-mail: sales@aholt.co.uk

Polyone Acrol, Unit G 3, Newton Business Park, Talbot Road, Hyde, Cheshire, SK14 4UQ Tel: 0161-367 8773 Fax: 0161-367 8281

WOVEN CABLE TAPES

Scapa, Manchester Road, Ashton-under-Lyne, Lancashire, OL7 0ED Tel: 0161-301 7400 Fax: 0161-301 7445E-mail: sales@scapa.com

WOVEN OR KNITTED FABRIC GLOVES

Dents, Fairfield Road, Warminster, Wiltshire, BA12 9DL Tel: (01985) 212291 Fax: (01985) 216435 E-mail: dents@dents.co.uk

Eskimo Knitwear, Vinola Ho, Bruin St, Leicester, LE4 5AB Tel: 0116-266 3895 Fax: 0116-266 5280

Robert Mackie & Co. Ltd, Holm Mill, Stewarton, Kilmarnock, Ayrshire, KA3 5HT Tel: (01560) 482124 Fax: (01560) 485213 E-mail: mackies@dial.pipex.com

Sudburys Gloves Ltd, Calvesford Road, Greenbank, Torrington, Devon, EX38 7DP Tel: (01805) 622006 Fax: (0870) 4100089 E-mail: sales@sudburys-gloves.co.uk

WOVEN POLYPROPYLENE (PP) BAGS

Allan Austin Ltd, Crystal Drive, Smethwick, West Midlands, B66 1QG Tel: 0121-552 8513 Fax: 0121-552 1480 E-mail: allan@austinltd.freeserve.co.uk

WOVEN SACKS

James Glennon Packaging Ltd, Upper Dunmurry Lane, 14 Kilwee Business Park, Dunmurry, Belfast, BT17 0HD Tel: (028) 9061 6677 Fax: (028) 9062 6477

J & H M Dickson Ltd, Seath Road, Rutherglen, Glasgow, G73 1RW Tel: 0141-643 0244 Fax: 0141-643 0219 E-mail: sales@dicksonforsacks.co.uk

J R Parkin Ltd, Whiteheads Mill, Young St, Bradford, West Yorkshire, BD8 9RQ Tel: (01274) 498567 Fax: (01274) 482023 E-mail: ian@jrparkin.wanadoo.co.uk

J W Martin Ltd, Prince Regent Road, Belfast, BT5 6QR Tel: (028) 9070 2021 Fax: (028) 9070 5566 E-mail: mail@jwmartin.co.uk

South Wales Sack & Bag, 4 Rhymney River Bridge Road, Cardiff, CF23 9AF Tel: (029) 2049 5060 Fax: (029) 2049 5055 E-mail: andrew_manuel@amserve.net

Storsack UK Ltd, Dalton Airfield, Dalton, Thirsk, North Yorkshire, YO7 3HE Tel: (01845) 577464 Fax: (01845) 578175 E-mail: info@storsack.co.uk

Whaleys Bradford Ltd, Harris Court, Bradford, West Yorkshire, BD7 4EQ Tel: (01274) 576718 Fax: (01274) 521309 E-mail: whaleys@btinternet.com

WOVEN TEXTILE BELTING

Marathon Belting Ltd, Healey Mill, Whitworth Road, Rochdale, Lancashire, OL12 0TF Tel: (01706) 657052 Fax: (01706) 525143 E-mail: sales@marathonbelting.co.uk

WOVEN THROWS OR COVERS

Bovey Handloom Weavers, 1 Station Road, Bovey Tracey, Newton Abbot, Devon, TQ13 9AL Tel: (01626) 833424 Fax: (01626) 833424

F & A Hill Ltd, 80 Brewer Street, London, W1F 9TZ Tel: (020) 7734 0652 Fax: (020) 7434 3698

WOVEN UPHOLSTERY FABRICS

A Shufflebotham & Son, 8 Gunco Lane, Macclesfield, Cheshire, SK11 7JX Tel: (01625) 423304 Fax: (01625) 423304

Duresta Upholstery Ltd, Fields Farm Road, Long Eaton, Nottingham, NG10 3FZ Tel: 0115-973 2246 Fax: 0115-946 1028

Guilford (Europe) Ltd, Cotes Park Lane, Somercotes, Alfreton, Derbyshire, DE55 4NJ Tel: (01773) 841200 Fax: (01773) 547315

Replin Fabrics, March Street Mills, March Street, Peebles, EH45 8ER Tel: (01721) 724310 Fax: (01721) 721893 E-mail: enquiries@replin-fabrics.co.uk

▶ Upholstery Fabrics UK, 7 Eaton Close, Stockwood, Bristol, BS14 8PR Tel: 01275 830213 E-mail: enquires@upholsteryfabricsuk.co.uk

WOVEN WIRE MACHINE GUARDS

Wireguard Ltd, Crabtree Manorway South, Belvedere, Kent, DA17 6AW Tel: (020) 8320 6181 Fax: (020) 8311 6435

WOVEN WIRE MESH, *See also Wire Gauze/Cloth etc*

W J Gowar & Co. Ltd, Rheidol Mews, London, N1 8NU Tel: (020) 7226 3644 Fax: (020) 7226 2969

WRAPPING MACHINES

Bramigk & Co. Ltd, Chelmsford, CM2 7WG Tel: (01245) 477616 Fax: (01245) 477498 E-mail: info@bramigk.co.uk

Fischbein-Saxon, 274 Alma Road, Enfield, Middlesex, EN3 7RS Tel: (020) 8805 6111 Fax: (020) 8344 6625 E-mail: sales@fischbein-saxon.co.uk

GD Automatic Machinery Ltd, Grove Park Industrial Estate, Waltham Road, White Waltham, Maidenhead, Berkshire, SL6 3LW Tel: (01628) 823123 Fax: (01628) 829123

It's A Wrap Northeast Ltd, Unit 24 Grasmere Way, Kitty Brewster Industrial Estate, Blyth, Northumberland, NE24 4RR Tel: (01670) 543663 Fax: (01670) 543663 E-mail: sales@itsawrap.org.uk

Marden Edwards Ltd, 2 East Dorset Trade Park, Nimrod Way, Wimborne, Dorset, BH21 7SH Tel: (01202) 861200 Fax: (01202) 861400 E-mail: sales@mardenedwards.com

▶ Newrap, 11 Castle Clough, Hapton, Burnley, Lancashire, BB12 7LN Tel: (01282) 777953 Fax: (01282) 778558 E-mail: info@newrap.co.uk

Wrap Film Systems Ltd, Hortonwood 45, Telford, Shropshire, TF1 7FA Tel: (01952) 678800 Fax: (01952) 678801 E-mail: sales@wrapfilm.com

Wrapid Holdings Ltd, 250 Thornton Road, Bradford, West Yorkshire, BD1 2LB Tel: (01274) 220220 Fax: (01274) 736195 E-mail: mail@wrapid.co.uk

WRIST BANDS

▶ Fashion-4U, 87 Woolston Avenue, Congleton, Cheshire, CW12 3ED Tel: (07708) 731770 E-mail: sales@fashion-4u.co.uk

WRITING INKS

Manuscript Pen Co. Ltd, New Road, Highley, Bridgnorth, Shropshire, WV16 6NN Tel: (01746) 861236 Fax: (01746) 862737 E-mail: manuscript@calligraphy.co.uk

▶ Zoom Business Services Ltd, Suite 2, 131 Friargate, Preston, PR1 2EF Tel: 07888 813931 E-mail: info@editmywork.co.uk

WRITING INSTRUMENTS, *See also headings for particular types*

▶ Traditional Values Ltd, 10-14 West Street, Southend-on-Sea, SS2 6HJ Tel: (01702) 300087 Fax: (01702) 390766 E-mail: info@traditional-values.co.uk

WROUGHT IRON ARTWORK

▶ Ferretteria, Culberry Nursery, Dappers Lane, Angmering, Littlehampton, West Sussex, BN16 4EW Tel: (07733) 142726 E-mail: sales@ferretteria.co.uk

WROUGHT IRON DECORATIONS

W H Tinsley & Sons Ltd, Wem Industrial Estate, Soulton Road, Wem, Shrewsbury, SY4 5SD Tel: (01939) 232301 Fax: (01939) 235110

WROUGHT IRON ESTATE GATES

ALL SEASONS WROUGHT IRON UK LTD, UNIT 15 PARKWAY COURT, GLAISDALE PARKWAY, BILBOROUGH, NOTTINGHAM, NG8 4GN Tel: 0115 928 6688 E-mail: jimbrowne701@hotmail.com

WROUGHT IRON FORGINGS

Chris Topp & Company Ltd, Lyndhurst, Carlton Husthwaite, Thirsk, North Yorkshire, YO7 2BJ Tel: (01845) 501415 Fax: (01845) 501072 E-mail: enquiry@realwroughtiron.com

Metal Art Co., Cadgerhill, Glendaveny, Peterhead, Aberdeenshire, AB42 3DY Tel: (01779) 838888 Fax: (01779) 838333 E-mail: info@classicmetalart.co.uk

WROUGHT IRON FURNITURE

▶ Artistry In Iron Ltd, Unit D2 Commercial Avenue, Cheadle Hulme, Cheadle, Cheshire, SK8 6QH Tel: 0161-482 8022 Fax: 0161-482 8023 E-mail: sales@artistryuk.com

▶ Ferretteria, Culberry Nursery, Dappers Lane, Angmering, Littlehampton, West Sussex, BN16 4EW Tel: (07733) 142726 E-mail: sales@ferretteria.co.uk

▶ Treehouse Furniture Ltd, 174 Penarth Road, Cardiff, CF11 6NL Tel: (029) 2023 0796 Fax: (029) 2023 0796 E-mail: ralph@intothewoods.co.uk

WROUGHT IRON LIGHTING

Falcon Forge, 428 Limpsfield Road, Warlingham, Surrey, CR6 9LA Tel: (01883) 623377 Fax: (01883) 624477 E-mail: sales@falconforge.co.uk

WROUGHT IRON SECTIONS/ SHEETS

A & D Gates & Railings, 44 Rice Lane, Liverpool, L9 1DD Tel: 0151-287 1003

Grow & Show Ltd, The Weld Arms Barn, East Lulworth, Wareham, Dorset, BH20 5QQ Tel: (01929) 400293 Fax: (01372) 469445

J B Ironworks, Heys Lane, Great Harwood, Blackburn, BB6 7UA Tel: (01254) 889920 Fax: (01254) 889920

Regency Products, 101-107 Broughton Lane, Sheffield, S9 2DE Tel: 0114-244 1205

WROUGHT IRONWORKERS OR IRONWORK

▶ A C Welding & Fabrication, 23 Mountbatten Road, Tiverton, Devon, EX16 6SW Tel: (01884) 244900

A Findlay, Old Forge, Clenchers Mill Lane, Eastnor, Ledbury, Herefordshire, HR8 1RR Tel: (01531) 634999 Fax: (01531) 635980

A J B Wrought Iron & Welding Service, 65 Slades Road, St. Austell, Cornwall, PL25 4HA Tel: (01726) 61697

Absolute Security, Unit 18 Westerhope Small Business Park, Redburn Road, Newcastle upon Tyne, NE5 1NF Tel: 0191-214 5555

Allweld Wrought Ironwork, 3 300 Archer Road, Sheffield, S8 0LA Tel: 0114-236 8239 Fax: 0114-236 8239 E-mail: sales@allweld.com

Architectural Metal Fixing Services, 18 Penshurst Way, Sutton, Surrey, SM2 6HR Tel: (020) 8643 7469

B Rourke & Co. Ltd, Accrington Road, Burnley, Lancashire, BB11 5QD Tel: (01282) 422841 Fax: (01282) 458901 E-mail: info@rourkes.co.uk

Ballinliss Forge Works, 17 Tamnaghbane Road, Newry, County Down, BT35 8RF Tel: (028) 3084 8694 Fax: (028) 3084 8694 E-mail: info@ballinliss.co.uk

Barking Engineering, Barking Forge, Barking, Ipswich, IP6 8HJ Tel: (01449) 720087 Fax: (01449) 723131

Barry Wheatley & Sons, King Street, Hodthorpe, Worksop, Nottinghamshire, S80 4XA Tel: (01909) 720692

Bentleys Fabrications, Gatesland, Stafford Road, Huntington, Cannock, Staffordshire, WS12 4NQ Tel: (01543) 570911 Fax: (01543) 570911

Brettell Bros, Hungary Hill, Stourbridge, West Midlands, DY9 7NH Tel: (01384) 395711 Fax: (01384) 372948 E-mail: sales@brettellbrothersgates.co.uk

Calmels Design Ltd, 3-7 Southville, London, SW8 2PR Tel: (020) 7622 6181 Fax: (020) 7498 2889 E-mail: lois@calmels.co.uk

▶ Cheshire Metalcraft, 17 Atterburys Park Estate, Attenburys Lane, Timperley, Altrincham, Cheshire, WA14 5QE Tel: 0161-962 3838 Fax: 0161-962 3838

Chris Topp & Company Ltd, Lyndhurst, Carlton Husthwaite, Thirsk, North Yorkshire, YO7 2BJ Tel: (01845) 501415 Fax: (01845) 501072 E-mail: enquiry@realwroughtiron.com

City Wrought Iron Centre, 2 Erskine Street, Liverpool, L6 1AL Tel: 0151-260 0550 Fax: 0151-260 0550

Colourcode Cable Colouring Services, 243C Watford Road, Croxley Green, Rickmansworth, Hertfordshire, WD3 3RX Tel: (01923) 250767 Fax: (01923) 234772

Colston Forge, Colston Yard, Colston Street, Bristol, BS1 5BD Tel: 0117-927 3660 Fax: 0117-927 3660

Country Forge, Kidderminster Road, Dodford, Bromsgrove, Worcestershire, B61 9DU Tel: (01527) 575765 Fax: (01527) 575761 E-mail: sales@metalartproducts.co.uk

Cransons, 55 Sherburn Terrace, Consett, County Durham, DH8 6ND Tel: (01207) 505621

Custom & Ornamental Iron Work, Glan Moelyn, Llanrug, Caernarfon, Gwynedd, LL55 4PG Tel: (01286) 677725 Fax: (01286) 677725

D F Barber, Bunwell Road, Besthorpe, Attleborough, Norfolk, NR17 2NZ Tel: (01953) 452422 Fax: (01953) 452422

▶ Davis Ornamental Ironwork, Hoghton Road Business Centre, Hoghton Road, St. Helens, Merseyside, WA9 3HS Tel: (01744) 821400 Fax: (01744) 821400 E-mail: daviesornamental@merseymail.com

▶ Distinctive Design, Oldmill Street, Stoke-on-Trent, ST4 2RP Tel: (01782) 844629 Fax: (01782) 849334

Dorset Weather Vanes, 284 Bournemouth Road, Charlton Marshall, Blandford Forum, Dorset, DT11 9NG Tel: (01258) 453374 Fax: (01258) 453374 E-mail: enquiries@weathervanes-direct.co.uk

E J Collins & Son, 57 Addington Village Road, Croydon, CR0 5AS Tel: (01689) 843059

▶ Exmore Metalcraft, Unit 1b Barns Close Industrial Estate, Barns Close, Dulverton, Somerset, TA22 9DZ Tel: (07779) 062850

F Kitchen Lancaster Ltd, Unit 6 Forestgate, Whiteland Industrial Estate, Morecambe, Lancashire, LA3 3PD Tel: (01524) 63835 Fax: 01524 63835 E-mail: sales@fkitchen.co.uk

Fenland Ironworks Ltd, Unit 18a-18b Highlode Industrial Estate, Stocking Fen Road, Ramsey, Huntingdon, Cambridgeshire, PE26 2RB Tel: (01487) 814049 Fax: (01487) 814049 E-mail: fenlandiron@boltblue.net

Fire & Iron Ltd, Rowhurst Forge, Oxshott Road, Leatherhead, Surrey, KT22 0EN Tel: (01372) 386453 Fax: (01372) 386516 E-mail: sales@fireandiron.co.uk

▶ Flairmet, Unit 1 2, Ladfordfields Industrial Park, Seighford, Stafford, ST18 9QE Tel: (01785) 282301 Fax: (01785) 282626 E-mail: flairmet@weathervane.uk.com

Fontley Wrought Iron, Fontley Road, Titchfield, Fareham, Hampshire, PO15 6QZ Tel: (01329) 847700

The Forge, 2a Watson Road, Worksop, Nottinghamshire, S80 2BB Tel: (01909) 501745 Fax: (01909) 501745

Forge Fabrications, 8 South Street, Crowland, Peterborough, PE6 0AJ Tel: (01733) 211441 Fax: (01733) 211258 E-mail: justin@forgefabrications.co.uk

Forge Group, Holbrook Commerce Park, Holbrook Close Holbrook Indust Estate, Holbrook, Sheffield, S20 3FJ Tel: 0114-248 2222 Fax: 0114-248 2222

Fotheringhay Forge & Woodburners, The Old Forge, Fotheringhay, Peterborough, PE8 5HZ Tel: (01832) 226323 Fax: (01832) 226323 E-mail: enquiries@woodburnersat fotheringhay.co.uk

Frank Whitfield & Co., 126 English Street, Hull, HU3 2BT Tel: (01482) 227376 Fax: (01482) 227376

G G Fabrications, St. James Place, Baildon, Shipley, West Yorkshire, BD17 7LD Tel: (01274) 414657 Fax: (01274) 420422

G T Engineering, Enkalon Industrial Estate, Randalstown Road, Antrim, BT41 4LD Tel: (028) 9446 3882 Fax: (028) 9442 8819

G W Day & Co., East Chiltington Forge, Highbridge Lane, East Chiltington, Lewes, East Sussex, BN7 3QY Tel: (01273) 890398 Fax: (01273) 891410 E-mail: peterniccicronin@cs.com

V. Garcia & Son, Malakoff Works, Malakoff Street, Stalybridge, Cheshire, SK15 1TD Tel: 0161-303 7383 Fax: 0161-338 2151 E-mail: bill-garcia@btconnect.com

Gate Place, 16 Boston Road, Leicester, LE4 1AU Tel: 0116-236 6525 Fax: 0116-236 6525

▶ The Gates & Railings Co., 4 Lea Farm Crescent, Leeds, LS5 3QQ Tel: 0113-217 8901

Gaytsmaid Wrought Ironwork, Unit 1 St. Johns Lane, Bewdley, Worcestershire, DY12 2QY Tel: (01299) 405153 Fax: (01299) 405153 E-mail: enquiries@gaytsmaid.co.uk

Lionel W. Gibbs (Horton) Ltd, Horley Road, Hornton, Banbury, Oxfordshire, OX15 6BW Tel: (01295) 670310 Fax: (01295) 670732

Grange Welding Services, Earl Street, Sheffield, S1 4PY Tel: 0114-272 7606 Fax: 0114-272 7606

Haddoncraft Forge, Forge House, Church Lane, East Haddon, Northampton, NN6 8DB Tel: (01604) 772027 Fax: (01604) 772027 E-mail: info@haddoncraft.co.uk

Halifax Ironworks Ltd, Walker Lane, Sowerby Bridge, West Yorkshire, HX6 2AR Tel: (01422) 836470 Fax: (01422) 834490

Hall Farm Nursery, Hall Farm, Harpswell, Gainsborough, Lincolnshire, DN21 5UU Tel: (01427) 668412 Fax: (01427) 667478 E-mail: products@hall-farm.co.uk

Happy Hedgehog Wrought Ironsmiths Ltd, Pascall House, 51 Gatwick Road, Crawley, West Sussex, RH10 9RD Tel: (01293) 611611 Fax: (01293) 510333 E-mail: happyhedgehog@tiscali.co.uk

A.J. Hutt & Co., Unit 18, Peerglow Industrial Estate, Olf Approach, Tolpits Lane, Watford, WD18 9SR Tel: (01923) 718777 Fax: (01923) 718933

Inmart Steel Ltd, 2 Bolton Road Workshops, Bolton Road, Wath-upon-Dearne, Rotherham, South Yorkshire, S63 7JY Tel: (01709) 760389 Fax: (01709) 760389 E-mail: info@iron-components.co.uk

Iron Art, Unit 1, Birch Industrial Estate, Eastbourne, East Sussex, BN23 6PH Tel: (01323) 722784 Fax: (01323) 722784 E-mail: info@iron-art.co.uk

Iron Awe, Unit 24 Lansil Walk, Lansil Industrial Estate, Lancaster, LA1 3PQ Tel: (01524) 845511 Fax: (01524) 845511 E-mail: petersmalley@ironawe.com

WROUGHT IRONWORKERS OR IRONWORK – *continued*

▶ Iron Designs, Unit 51 Bowers Mill, Branch Road, Barkisland, Halifax, West Yorkshire, HX4 0AD Tel: (01422) 377555 Fax: (01422) 377555

Ironage Wrought Ironwork, Standalone Farm, Wilbury Road, Letchworth Garden City, Hertfordshire, SG6 4JN Tel: (01462) 485395 Fax: (01462) 484542

Ironcraft, 92 High Street, Earl Shilton, Leicester, LE9 7DG Tel: (01455) 847548 Fax: (01455) 842422 E-mail: office@ironcraft.co.uk

▶ Ironcrafts Stroud Ltd, Inchbrook Trading Estate, Bath Road, Woodchester, Stroud, Gloucestershire, GL5 5EY Tel: (01453) 836581 Fax: (01453) 836581 E-mail: martinphill@onetel.com

▶ Iron-Sides, 67d Dukesway, Teesside Industrial Estate, Stockton-on-Tees, Cleveland, TS17 9LT Tel: (07976) 265331 E-mail: colin@iron-sides.com

Ironworx, Springfield Farm, Springfield Avenue, Morley, Leeds, LS27 9PW Tel: 0113-252 0040 Fax: 0113 252 0040

J A Roskelly & Son, The Forge, 19 Penmare Terrace, Hayle, Cornwall, TR27 4PH Tel: (01736) 753160

J A Smith, Harrowgate Road, London, E9 5ED Tel: (020) 8525 9842 Fax: (020) 8525 9842

J Lawrence, Scotland Street, Stoke by Nayland, Colchester, CO6 4QG Tel: (01206) 263459 Fax: (01206) 262166 E-mail: sales@jim-lawrence.co.uk

J W Barrett Steel Fabrications, 55 High Street, Feckenham, Redditch, Worcestershire, B96 6HU Tel: (01527) 893866 Fax: (01527) 893866 E-mail: james@artmetal.co.uk

John H Place Steels Ltd, 44 Black Park Road, Toomebridge, Antrim, BT41 3SL Tel: (028) 7965 0481 Fax: (028) 7965 0175 E-mail: sales@johnhplace.com

Kington Forge, 2 The Old Foundry, Victoria Road, Kington, Herefordshire, HR5 3DA Tel: (01544) 231690 Fax: (01544) 231690

Lake, Muckley & Co. Ltd, The Stable, Lillyfee Farm, Lillyfee Farm Lane, Wooburn Green, High Wycombe, Buckinghamshire, HP10 0LL Tel: (01494) 673632 Fax: (01494) 673632

Leicester Wrought Iron Co., 25-27 Thurcaston Road, Leicester, LE4 5PG Tel: 0116-266 3566 Fax: 0116-266 3566

Lincoln Metalcraft, 2 Branston Business Park, Lincoln Road, Branston, Lincoln, LN4 1NT Tel: (01522) 795000 Fax: (01522) 794444

Lloyds Fabrications, Unit 7, Star Trading Estate, Ponthir, Newport, Gwent, NP18 1PQ Tel: (01633) 430378 Fax: (01633) 430378 E-mail: sales@lloydsfabrications.co.uk

Madewell Products Ltd, Sandy Way, Tamworth, Staffordshire, B77 4DS Tel: (01827) 67721 Fax: (01827) 67721 E-mail: sales@madewellproducts.co.uk

Martin Works, 271 Lynn Road, Wisbech, Cambridgeshire, PE13 3DZ Tel: (01945) 589005 Fax: (01945) 474694

Marton Gateway Engineers, 96 Vicarage Lane, Blackpool, FY4 4EL Tel: 01253 692611

Metalcrafts 1991 Ltd, 22 St Helens Road, Prescot, Merseyside, L34 6HR Tel: 0151-430 6078 Fax: 0151-430 6078

Metallic Construction Co. Ltd, Alfreton Road, Derby, DE21 4AQ Tel: (01332) 831296 Fax: (01332) 833712

Modern Ornate Steel & Iron Crafts Mosaic, 19-25 Nelson Street, Nottingham, NG1 1DR Tel: 0115-910 0115 Fax: 0115 9100156

Moorside Wrought Iron, Piercy End, Kirkbymoorside, York, YO62 6DQ Tel: (01751) 432244

▶ N J Metals, Unit 2, Hawksworth Road, Horsforth, Leeds, LS18 4JP Tel: 0113-258 2611 Fax: 0113-274 8465

N J Metals, R/O 10 Vesper Road, Leeds, LS5 3NX Tel: 0113-230 4818

Newtown Gate & Welding, Arundel Street, Newtown, Wigan, Lancashire, WN5 9BQ Tel: (01942) 238057 Fax: (01942) 238057 E-mail: newtowngatesandwelding@blueyonder.co.uk

▶ Nigel Tyas Hand Crafted Ironwork, Bullhouse Mill, Lee Lane, Millhouse Green, Sheffield, S36 9NN Tel: (01226) 761300

Northern Creative Metal Arts, Lock Street, Dewsbury, West Yorkshire, WF12 9BZ Tel: (01924) 469944 Fax: (01924) 469944

▶ Nowak Art Metal Co. (Krupa), 14 Brook Street, Bury, Lancashire, BL9 6AH Tel: 0161-792 3890 Fax: 0161-764 8722 E-mail: chris@krupabros-son.freeserve.co.uk

Ornamental Iron Works & Forge, Unit2, Pinfold La Industrial Estate, Bridlington, North Humberside, YO16 6XS Tel: (01262) 401498 Fax: (01262) 401498 E-mail: ornamental-ironwork@bridlington.net

Ovenden Engineers, 2 Radnor Street, Folkestone, Kent, CT19 6AQ Tel: (01303) 254387 Fax: (01303) 254387

P Brockwell, Pocklington Industrial Estate, Pocklington, York, YO42 1NP Tel: (01759) 304742 Fax: (01759) 304742 E-mail: enquiries@brockwellfabrications.co.uk

▶ P Warren, The Forge, Higher Mill Lane, Cullompton, Devon, EX15 1AG Tel: (07860) 285481 E-mail: sales@peterwarrenkitchens.co.uk

G. Potter, The Forge, Village Road, Bonchurch, Ventnor, Isle Of Wight, PO38 1RG Tel: (01983) 855233

Premier Fabrications, Unit 1, Tainton Park Gelderd Road, Leeds, LS12 6HD Tel: 0113-244 2356 Fax: 0113-244 2356

Richard Quinnell Ltd, Rowhurst Forge, Oxshott Road, Leatherhead, Surrey, KT22 0EN Tel: (01372) 375148 Fax: (01372) 386516 E-mail: rjquinnell@aol.com

R G Clark & Sons, Hemnall Street, Epping, Essex, CM16 4LW Tel: (01992) 572081

R Ovenden & Son, 29 Oxford Road, Littlemore, Oxford, OX4 4PF Tel: (01865) 779357 Fax: (01865) 779357

R Thompson & Co., 12 Manderston Street, Edinburgh, EH6 8LY Tel: 0131-554 6501

▶ Rai Lea Fabrications Ltd, Units 8-9 Woods Farm, Britwell Salome, Watlington, Oxfordshire, OX49 5HD Tel: (01491) 613300 Fax: (01491) 613300

Ramsay Fabrications, Baden-Powell Road, Kirkton Industrial Estate, Arbroath, Angus, DD11 3LS Tel: (01241) 870314 Fax: (01241) 870314

Red Rose Iron Work, The Old Press House, Irwell Vale Road, Rossendale, Lancashire, BB4 6LF Tel: (01706) 830506 Fax: (01706) 830506

Reddick Forge, Crawley Down Road, Felbridge, East Grinstead, West Sussex, RH19 2PS Tel: (01342) 302055 Fax: (01342) 302055 E-mail: sales@reddickforge.co.uk

S Buck, 36 Stanley Road, Warmley, Bristol, BS15 4NX Tel: 0117-967 4740 Fax: 0117-961 8050

S Burvill & Son Ltd, The Forge Cossins Farm, Downside Road, Downside, Cobham, Surrey, KT11 3LZ Tel: (01932) 589666 Fax: (01932) 589669

Saxon Forge, Silver Snaffles, Verwood Road, Three Legged Cross, Wimborne, Dorset, BH21 6RR Tel: (01202) 826375 Fax: (01202) 826375

Serpell BC Engineering, New England Bungalow, Plympton, Plymouth, PL7 5BA Tel: (01752) 881060 Fax: (01752) 880060

Slatter & Sons, 61a Spencer Bridge Road, Northampton, NN5 7DP Tel: (01604) 753333 Fax: (01604) 753333

Stackwell Forge, Front Road, Parson Drove, Wisbech, Cambridgeshire, PE13 4JQ Tel: (01945) 700666 Fax: (01945) 701242 E-mail: sales@stackwellforge.com

▶ Stretton Gates & Automation, Unit 11 Manor Industrial Estate, Lower Wash Lane, Warrington, WA4 1PL Tel: (01925) 268414

Suburban Ironcraft, Heavy Metal House, Rolling Mill Road, Bettys Lane Norton Canes, Cannock, Staffordshire, WS11 3UH Tel: (01543) 495250 Fax: (01543) 495251 E-mail: subironcraft@aol.com

T E Hirst, Unit 1-2 Norristhorpe Lane, Liversedge, West Yorkshire, WF15 7AZ Tel: (01924) 401852 Fax: (01924) 412181

Taylor Forge Ltd, Unit 3 Lime Grove, Balsall Heath, Birmingham, B12 8SY Tel: 0121-446 4196 Fax: 0121-446 4793

Thames Forge Ltd, Fullers Yard, Sheephouse Road, Maidenhead, Berkshire, SL6 8HA Tel: (01628) 622423 Fax: (01628) 622423

Town & Country Gates & Railings, Unit 6e Waterloo Industrial Estate, Gorsey Mount Street, Stockport, Cheshire, SK1 3BU Tel: 0161-429 7325 Fax: 0161-480 4388 E-mail: philbohen@aol.com

Tryst, Kippen Station, Kippen, Stirling, FK8 3JA Tel: (01786) 870295

W Farthing & Sons, Fulton Road, Benfleet, Essex, SS7 4PZ Tel: (01268) 794103 Fax: (01268) 756094

▶ T. Wassell, Unit 5 Field Road Industrial Estate, Bloxwich, Walsall, WS3 3JW Tel: 01922 408883

Weldcraft Engineering, Hayeswood Farm, Hayeswood Road, Timsbury, Bath, BA2 0FQ Tel: (01761) 472722 Fax: (01761) 479062

Woking Forge Ltd, 126A High Street, Old Woking, Woking, Surrey, GU22 9JN Tel: (01483) 760313 Fax: (01483) 756332

Wrights Engineering, 7 Tardygate Mill, Coote Lane, Lostock Hall, Preston, PR5 5JD Tel: (01772) 337070 Fax: (01772) 337070

Wrought Iron Shop, 136 Prescot Road, Fairfield, Liverpool, L7 0JB Tel: 0151-252 0460 Fax: 0151-252 0460

X RAY FLUORESCENCE (XRF) SPECTROMETERS

Spectro Analytical UK Ltd, Fountain House, Great Cornbow, Halesowen, West Midlands, B63 3BL Tel: 0121-550 8997 Fax: 0121-550 5165 E-mail: sales@spectro.co.uk

X-RAY ACCESSORIES

Everything X-Ray Ltd, Mill End Road, High Wycombe, Buckinghamshire, HP12 4JN Tel: (01494) 510911 Fax: (01494) 510914 E-mail: office@evexray.co.uk

Fidgeon Ltd, 11 Enterprise Court, Seaham Grange Industrial Estate, Seaham, County Durham, SR7 0PS Tel: 0191-521 1233 Fax: 0191-521 1252 E-mail: sales@fidgeon.co.uk

Kenex Electro Medical Ltd, 24 Burnt Mill Industrial Estate, Elizabeth Way, Harlow, Essex, CM20 2HS Tel: (01279) 417241 Fax: (01279) 443749 E-mail: kenex@kenex.co.uk

Wardray Premise Ltd, 3 Hampton Court Estate, Summer Road, Thames Ditton, Surrey, KT7 0SP Tel: (020) 8398 9911 Fax: (020) 8398 8032 E-mail: sales@wardray-premise.com

Wolverson X-Ray & Electro-Medical Ltd, Walsall Street, Willenhall, West Midlands, WV13 2DY Tel: (01902) 637333 Fax: (01902) 605482 E-mail: enquiries@wolversonx-ray.co.uk

X Ray Accessories Ltd, 16 Rudolph Road, Bushey, WD23 3DY Tel: (020) 8950 2223 Fax: (020) 8950 5015

X-RAY COMPONENTS

McKinlay Electrical Manufacturing Co. Ltd, 62 Weir Rd, Wimbledon, London, SW19 8UG Tel: (020) 8879 1141 Fax: (020) 8946 3047 E-mail: mckinlayelec@aol.com

X-RAY FILM

Hospital Engineering Ltd, 6 Mercury Park, Mercury Way, Urmston, Manchester, M41 7HS Tel: 0161-866 9066 Fax: 0161-865 3378 E-mail: simonmcde@heis.co.uk

X-RAY INDUSTRIAL EQUIPMENT

Celtic S M R Ltd, Unit 9-10, Dolphin Court, Brunel Quay, Neyland, Milford Haven, Dyfed, SA73 1PY Tel: (01646) 603150 Fax: (01646) 603159 E-mail: gmacphail@celticsmr.co.uk

Constant Instruments, Unit 8 Minster Court, Courtwick Lane, Wick, Littlehampton, West Sussex, BN17 7RN Tel: (01903) 739333 Fax: (01903) 739222 E-mail: sales@constant-ceia.com

▶ Electron-X Ltd, 20 Burners Lane, Kiln Farm, Milton Keynes, MK11 3HB Tel: (01908) 566794 Fax: 01908 305062 E-mail: sales@electron-x.co.uk

J M E Ltd, Electron House, Old Nelson St, Lowestoft, Suffolk, NR32 1EQ Tel: (01502) 500969 Fax: (01502) 511932 E-mail: sales@jme.co.uk

X Tek Systems Ltd, Unit 5 Icknield Way Industrial Estate, Icknield Way, Tring, Hertfordshire, HP23 4JX Tel: (01442) 828700 Fax: (01442) 828118 E-mail: sales@xtek.co.uk

X-RAY INSPECTION EQUIPMENT, BAGGAGE

L3 Comunnications Ltd, Astro House, Brants Bridge, Bracknell, Berkshire, RG12 9HW Tel: (01344) 477900 Fax: (01344) 477901 E-mail: matthew.woodman@l-3.com

Todd Research Ltd, Robjohns Road, Chelmsford, CM1 3DP Tel: (01245) 262233 Fax: (01245) 269409 E-mail: xray@toddresearch.co.uk

X-RAY INSPECTION EQUIPMENT, REAL TIME

A & D Group of Companies, Commerce Way, Lancing, West Sussex, BN15 8TA Tel: (01903) 763940 Fax: (01903) 763905 E-mail: sales@adauto.co.uk

X Tek Systems Ltd, Unit 5 Icknield Way Industrial Estate, Icknield Way, Tring, Hertfordshire, HP23 4JX Tel: (01442) 828700 Fax: (01442) 828118 E-mail: sales@xtek.co.uk

X-Innovation Ltd, Unit 5 Springwater Business Park, Crews Hole Road, Bristol, BS5 8AN Tel: 0117-941 2291 Fax: 0117-941 2292 E-mail: nickt@x-innovations.demon.co.uk

X-RAY INSPECTION SERVICES

X Tek Systems Ltd, Unit 5 Icknield Way Industrial Estate, Icknield Way, Tring, Hertfordshire, HP23 4JX Tel: (01442) 828700 Fax: (01442) 828118 E-mail: sales@xtek.co.uk

X-RAY MEDICAL DIAGNOSIS EQUIPMENT MANUFRS

Kenex Electro Medical Ltd, 24 Burnt Mill Industrial Estate, Elizabeth Way, Harlow, Essex, CM20 2HS Tel: (01279) 417241 Fax: (01279) 443749 E-mail: kenex@kenex.co.uk

Philips Medical Systems, PO Box 263, Reigate, Surrey, RH2 0FY Tel: (01737) 230400 Fax: (01737) 230401 E-mail: claire.daynes@philips.com

Toshiba Medical Systems Ltd, Gatwick Road, Crawley, West Sussex, RH10 9AX Tel: (01293) 653700 Fax: (01293) 653770

Wolverson X-Ray & Electro-Medical Ltd, Walsall Street, Willenhall, West Midlands, WV13 2DY Tel: (01902) 637333 Fax: (01902) 605482 E-mail: enquiries@wolversonx-ray.co.uk

X-RAY MEDICAL TREATMENT EQUIPMENT

Philips Medical Systems, PO Box 263, Reigate, Surrey, RH2 0FY Tel: (01737) 230400 Fax: (01737) 230401 E-mail: claire.daynes@philips.com

Todd Research Ltd, Robjohns Road, Chelmsford, CM1 3DP Tel: (01245) 262233 Fax: (01245) 269409 E-mail: xray@toddresearch.co.uk

X-RAY PHOTOGRAPHIC FILM

Technical Photo Systems Ltd, 22-28 Napier Place, Wardpark North, Cumbernauld, Glasgow, G68 0LL Tel: (01236) 739668 Fax: (01236) 738376 E-mail: alan@tpsmedical.co.uk

X-RAY PROTECTION EQUIPMENT

Kenex Electro Medical Ltd, 24 Burnt Mill Industrial Estate, Elizabeth Way, Harlow, Essex, CM20 2HS Tel: (01279) 417241 Fax: (01279) 443749 E-mail: kenex@kenex.co.uk

▶ Raybloc Ltd, 32 Bilston Lane, Willenhall, West Midlands, WV13 2QD Tel: (01902) 633383 Fax: (01902) 609453 E-mail: raybloc@btconnect.com

Wardray Premise Ltd, 3 Hampton Court Estate, Summer Road, Thames Ditton, Surrey, KT7 0SP Tel: (020) 8398 9911 Fax: (020) 8398 8032 E-mail: sales@wardray-premise.com

X-RAY TEST SERVICES, INDUSTRIAL

Cobalt NDT Ltd, 2 Eccleston Park Trade Centre, Prescot Road, St. Helens, Merseyside, WA10 3BZ Tel: (01744) 734321 Fax: (01744) 734321

Format Quality Assurance Services Ltd, 25-27 Brindley Road, Reginald Road Industrial Estate, St. Helens, Merseyside, WA9 4HY Tel: (01744) 816225 Fax: (01744) 820161 E-mail: bjjformat@msn.com

Gammax Independent Inspection Services Ltd, The Grove, The Green, Depten, Bury St. Edmunds, Suffolk, IP29 4BY Tel: (01284) 850888 Fax: (01284) 850808

N D T Electronics, 30 Royal Industrial Estate, Jarrow, Tyne & Wear, NE32 3HR Tel: 0191-428 0962 Fax: 0191-428 0904 E-mail: ian.armson@ndtelectronicservices.com

Pudsey Test & Inspection Ltd, Battye Street, Laisterdyke, Bradford, West Yorkshire, BD4 8AG Tel: (01274) 656736 Fax: (01274) 656797 E-mail: darrylatpti@aol.com

Wardray Premise Ltd, 3 Hampton Court Estate, Summer Road, Thames Ditton, Surrey, KT7 0SP Tel: (020) 8398 9911 Fax: (020) 8398 8032 E-mail: sales@wardray-premise.com

X.25 PROTOCOL DATA COMMUNICATION SYSTEMS

Farsite Communications Ltd, Tempus Business Centre, 60 Kingsclere Road, Basingstoke, Hampshire, RG21 6XG Tel: (01256) 330461 Fax: (01256) 854931 E-mail: sales@farsite.co.uk

XANTHAN GUM

C P Kelco UK Ltd, Cleeve Court, Cleeve Road, Leatherhead, Surrey, KT22 7UD Tel: (01372) 369400 Fax: (01372) 369401

YACHT BUILDERS

Bangor Yacht Services, 98 Warren Road, Donaghadee, County Down, BT21 0PQ Tel: (028) 9188 8600 Fax: (028) 9188 8481

Bay Class Yachts Ltd, Conyer Wharf, Teynham, Sittingbourne, Kent, ME9 9HN Tel: (01795) 520787 Fax: (01795) 520788

Buckie Shipyard Ltd, Commercial Road, Buckie, Banffshire, AB56 1UR Tel: (01542) 832727 Fax: (01542) 831825 E-mail: office@buckieshipyard.com

Camper & Nicholsons (Yachting) Ltd, 229 West Street, Fareham, Hampshire, PO16 0HZ Tel: (023) 9258 0221

Clare Lallow, 3 Medina Road, Cowes, Isle of Wight, PO31 7BU Tel: (01983) 292112 Fax: (01983) 281180 E-mail: lallows@lallowsboatyard.com

Exe Boat Store Marine Ltd, 6 Camperdown Terrace, Exmouth, Devon, EX8 1EJ Tel: (01395) 263095 Fax: (01395) 263095

Fairline Boats plc, Barnwell Road, Oundle, Peterborough, PE8 5PA Tel: (01832) 273661 Fax: (01832) 273432 E-mail: sales@fairline.com

Frank Halls & Son, Mill Lane, Walton on the Naze, Essex, CO14 8PF Tel: (01255) 675596 Fax: (01255) 677772

David Hillyard Ltd, Rope Walk, Littlehampton, West Sussex, BN17 5DG Tel: (01903) 713327 Fax: (01903) 722787 E-mail: info@hillyards.co.uk

Jackson Yacht Services Ltd, Le Boulevard, St. Aubin, Jersey, JE3 8AB Tel: (01534) 743819 Fax: (01534) 745952 E-mail: sales@jacksonyatch.com

YACHT BUILDERS – *continued*

Princess Yachts International plc, Newport Street, Plymouth, PL1 3QG Tel: (01752) 203888 Fax: (01752) 203777 E-mail: info@princess-yachts.com

Smr Marine Limited, Unit 1A East Lockside, East Lockside, Brighton Marina, Brighton, BN2 5UG Tel: (01273) 668900 Fax: (01273) 668905 E-mail: boatsales@smrmarine.co.uk

Tough Surveys Ltd, 27 Ferry Road, Teddington, Middlesex, TW11 9NN Tel: (020) 8977 4494 Fax: (020) 8977 7546 E-mail: johntough@ctinternet.com

Traditional Shipwright Services Ltd, Westons Point Boat Yard, Turks Lane, Sandbanks Road, Parkstone, Poole, Dorset, BH14 8EW Tel: (01202) 748029 E-mail: paulk0611@aol.com

YACHT CHANDLERS/BOAT CHANDLERS

▶ ARGONAUTIC TRANSPORT, 77 Albany Road, Kensington, Liverpool, L7 8RQ Tel: (0845) 1307133 E-mail: aahbtrans@yahoo.co.uk

Arthur Beale Ltd, 194 Shaftesbury Avenue, London, WC2H 8JP Tel: (020) 7836 9034 Fax: (020) 7836 5807

Boat Store, Falmouth Yacht Marina, North Parade, Falmouth, Cornwall, TR11 2TD Tel: (01326) 318314 Fax: (01326) 318314

Bosuns Locker, 10 Military Road, Ramsgate, Kent, CT11 9LG Tel: (01843) 597158 Fax: (01843) 597158

John Bridger Marine, Haven Road, Exeter, EX2 8DP Tel: (01392) 250970 Fax: (01392) 410955E-mail: bridgermarine@btconnect.com

Chertsey Marine Ltd, Penton Hook Marina, Mixnams Lane, Chertsey, Surrey, KT16 8QR Tel: (01932) 565195 Fax: (01932) 571668

Davey & Co London Ltd, 1 Commerce Way, Colchester, CO2 8HR Tel: (01206) 500945 Fax: (01206) 500949 E-mail: chandlery@davey.co.uk

The Dinghy Store, Sea Wall, Whitstable, Kent, CT5 1BX Tel: (01227) 274168 Fax: (01227) 772750 E-mail: sales@thedinghystore.co.uk

Jamison & Green Ltd, 102-108 Ann Street, Belfast, BT1 3HU Tel: (028) 9032 2444 Fax: (028) 9033 0491 E-mail: sales@jamisonandgreen.co.uk

Jeckells & Son Ltd, 128 Bridge Road, Lowestoft, Suffolk, NR33 9JT Tel: (01502) 565007 Fax: (01502) 565606 E-mail: sales@jeckellschandlers.co.uk

K J Howells, Cobbs Quay, Poole, Dorset, BH15 4EL Tel: (01202) 665724 Fax: (01202) 665724 E-mail: sales@kjhowells.com

Kelpie Boats, Hobbs Point, Pembroke Dock, Dyfed, SA72 6TR Tel: (01646) 683661 Fax: (01646) 621398 E-mail: martin@kelpieboats.com

L D C Racing Sail Boats, Trafalgar Close, Chandler's Ford, Eastleigh, Hampshire, SO53 4BW Tel: (023) 8027 4500 Fax: (023) 8027 4800 E-mail: info@ldcracingsailboats.co.uk

L H Jones & Son Ltd, Low Road, St. Ives, Cambridgeshire, PE27 5ET Tel: (01480) 494040 Fax: (01480) 495280 E-mail: info@jonesboatyard.co.uk

Maldon Chandlery Ltd, North Street, Maldon, Essex, CM9 5HL Tel: (01621) 854280 Fax: (01621) 843849 E-mail: chandlers@marinestore.co.uk

Mid-thames Chandlery, Mill Green, Caversham, Reading, RG4 8EX Tel: 0118-948 4226 Fax: 0118-946 1371

Mike's Boatyard Ltd, 17 High Street, Old Leigh, Leigh-On-Sea, Essex, SS9 2EN Tel: (01702) 713151 Fax: (01702) 480092

Piplers Chandlers, The Quay, Poole, Dorset, BH15 1HF Tel: (01202) 673056 Fax: (01202) 683065 E-mail: sales@piplers.co.uk

S Roberts Marine Ltd, Coburg Wharf, Liverpool, L3 4BP Tel: 0151-707 8300 Fax: 0151-707 8300E-mail: stephen@robmar.freeserve.co.uk

Sand Point Marina, Woodyard Road, Dumbarton, G82 4BG Tel: (01389) 762396 Fax: (01389) 732605E-mail: sales@sandpoint-marina.co.uk

Scarborough Marine Engineers Ltd, 35-36 Sandside, Scarborough, North Yorkshire, YO11 1PQ Tel: (01723) 375199 Fax: (01723) 379734E-mail: info@scarboroughmarine.co.uk

Sea Cruisers Of Rye, 28 Winchelsea Road, Rye, East Sussex, TN31 7EL Tel: (01797) 222070 E-mail: info@sea-cruisers.co.uk

Seamark Nunn & Co., 400 High Road, Trimley St. Martin, Felixstowe, Suffolk, IP11 0SG Tel: (01394) 275327 Fax: (01394) 670329 E-mail: sales@seamarknunn.com

Solent Marine Chandlery Ltd, Mumby Road, Gosport, Hampshire, PO12 1AQ Tel: (023) 9258 4622 Fax: (023) 9258 2325 E-mail: info@solentmarine.co.uk

South Ferriby Marina Ltd, South Ferriby Marina, Red Lane, South Ferriby, Barton-Upon-Humber, South Humberside, DN18 6JH Tel: (01652) 635620 Fax: (01652) 660517 E-mail: tferguson_ie@yahoo.co.uk

Staniland Marina, Staniland Marina, Lock Hill, Thorne, Doncaster, South Yorkshire, DN8 5EP Tel: (01405) 813150 Fax: (01405) 740592 E-mail: sales@staniland-marina.co.uk

Stone Boat Building Co. Ltd, Newcastle Road, Stone, Staffordshire, ST15 8JZ Tel: (01785) 812688 Fax: (01785) 811317 E-mail: sales@stoneboatbuilding.co.uk

Tewkesbury Marina Ltd, Bredon Road, Tewkesbury, Gloucestershire, GL20 5BY Tel: (01684) 293737 Fax: (01684) 293076 E-mail: sales@tewkesbury-marina.co.uk

W L Bussell & Co. Ltd, 30 Hope Street, Weymouth, Dorset, DT4 8TU Tel: (01305) 785633 Fax: (01305) 768657 E-mail: sales@bussells.co.uk

Walkers Yacht Chandlery, 1 Brunel Road, Leigh-on-Sea, Essex, SS9 5JL Tel: (01702) 421321 Fax: (01702) 421321

Captain O.M. Watts, 7 Dover Street, London, W1S 4LD Tel: (020) 7493 4633 Fax: (020) 7495 0755 E-mail: captianwatts@marineforce.com

YACHT CHARTERING

▶ Hurst Point Yacht Charters Ltd, Little Howdens, Rhinefield Close, Brockenhurst, Hampshire, SO42 7SU Tel: (01590) 623765 E-mail: info@hurstpointyachts.co.uk

▶ Mec Sail Ltd, Mount Lee Lodge, Egham, Surrey, TW20 0EU Tel: (01784) 436113 Fax: (01784) 436945 E-mail: davidmccarthy@mec-sail.com

▶ New Horizon Sailing, Troon Yacht Haven, Harbour Road, Troon, Ayrshire, KA10 6DJ Tel: (01844) 260854 Fax: (01844) 260854 E-mail: info@newhorizonsailing.com

▶ PFAMetals.com, 2 Stone Circle Road, Northampton, NN3 8RF Tel: (01604) 671536 Fax: (01604) 670831 E-mail: sales@pfametals.com

▶ R & E Yachting Ltd, 2 Pretoria Villas Main Road, Colden Common, Winchester, Hampshire, SO21 1RR Tel: (01962) 712545 E-mail: info@reyachtcharter.co.uk

Scotia Marine, Clyde Marina, The Harbour, Ardrossan, Ayrshire, KA22 8DB Tel: (01294) 469584 Fax: (01294) 469584 E-mail: enquiries@scotiamarine.com

YACHT CRADLES

Yacht Shipping Ltd, Bowling Green House, 1 Orchard Place, Southampton, SO14 3PX Tel: (023) 8022 3671 Fax: (023) 8033 0880 E-mail: info@ysl.wainwrightgroup.com

YACHT FITTINGS AND HARDWARE

Allen Bros Fittings Ltd, Hallmark Industrial Estate, Hall Road, Southminster, Essex, CM0 7EH Tel: (01621) 774689 Fax: (01621) 774536 E-mail: liz.adams@allenbrothers.co.uk

Barton Marine Equipment Ltd, Marine House, Tyler Way, Whitstable, Kent, CT5 2RS Tel: (01227) 792979 Fax: (01227) 793555 E-mail: sales@bartonmarine.com

Bosuns Locker, 10 Military Road, Ramsgate, Kent, CT11 9LG Tel: (01843) 597158 Fax: (01843) 597158

▶ Defence Estates, Building Moss, HMNB Devonport, Plymouth, PL2 2BG Tel: (01752) 554952 Fax: (01752) 554740 E-mail: plymouth@gdpmod.co.uk

Dickies, Garth Road, Bangor, Gwynedd, LL57 2SE Tel: (01248) 363414 Fax: (01248) 354169 E-mail: info@dickies.co.uk

▶ Freewing Masts, Clachnaharry Works Lock, Clachnaharry Road, Inverness, IV3 8RA Tel: (01463) 243161 Fax: (01463) 794506

Holts, Embankment, London, SW15 1LB Tel: (020) 8789 5557 Fax: (020) 8789 8365 E-mail: sales@holtallen.com

Lewmar Ltd, Southmoor Lane, Havant, Hampshire, PO9 1JJ Tel: (023) 9247 1841 Fax: (023) 9248 5720 E-mail: info@lewmar.com

Navtec North Europe Ltd, South Moore Lane, Havant, Hampshire, PO9 1JJ Tel: (023) 9248 5777 Fax: (023) 9248 5770 E-mail: navnor@navtec.net

Spinlock Ltd, 41 Birmingham Road, Cowes, Isle of Wight, PO31 7BH Tel: (01983) 295555 Fax: (01983) 295542 E-mail: prosupport@spinlock.co.uk

YACHT KEELS

Irons Bros Ltd, Factory, St. Breock, Wadebridge, Cornwall, PL27 7JP Tel: (01208) 812635 Fax: (01208) 814884 E-mail: sales@ironsbrothers.com

YACHT REPAIR SERVICES

Alto Digital, Sommerville House, Leathley Road, Leeds, LS10 1BG Tel: 0113-244 3016 Fax: 0113-242 4765

Burnham Yacht Harbour, Foundry Lane, Burnham-on-Crouch, Essex, CM0 8BL Tel: (01621) 782150 Fax: (01621) 785848 E-mail: admin@burnhamyachtharbour.co.uk

Dickies, Garth Road, Bangor, Gwynedd, LL57 2SE Tel: (01248) 363414 Fax: (01248) 354169 E-mail: info@dickies.co.uk

Falmouth Boat Construction Ltd, Little Falmouth, Flushing, Falmouth, Cornwall, TR11 5TJ Tel: (01326) 374309 Fax: (01326) 377689 E-mail: bernie@fal-boat.demon.co.uk

Hayling Pontoons Ltd, Mill Rithe, Hayling Island, Hampshire, PO11 0QQ Tel: (023) 9246 3592 Fax: (023) 9246 4432 E-mail: haylingyacht@mcmail.com

David Hillyard Ltd, Rope Walk, Littlehampton, West Sussex, BN17 5DG Tel: (01903) 713327 Fax: (01903) 722787 E-mail: info@hillyards.co.uk

Hythe Marine Services, Prospect Place, Hythe, Southampton, SO45 6AU Tel: (023) 8084 8782 Fax: (023) 8084 6760 E-mail: raymithchener@btconnect.com

Mashford Bros Ltd, Shipbuilding Yard, Cremyll, Torpoint, Cornwall, PL10 1HY Tel: (01752) 822232 Fax: (01752) 823059 E-mail: mashfords@btconnect.com

Penrose, 50 Church Street, Falmouth, Cornwall, TR11 3DS Tel: (01326) 312705 Fax: (01326) 312033 E-mail: robbie@penrosesales.freeserve.co.uk

Sand Point Marina, Woodyard Road, Dumbarton, G82 4BG Tel: (01389) 762396 Fax: (01389) 732605E-mail: sales@sandpoint-marina.co.uk

YACHT SHIPPING AND TRANSPORTATION

Yacht Shipping Ltd, Bowling Green House, 1 Orchard Place, Southampton, SO14 3PX Tel: (023) 8022 3671 Fax: (023) 8033 0880 E-mail: info@ysl.wainwrightgroup.com

YACHTSMANS KNIVES

F E & J R Hopkinson Ltd, 124 Scotland Street, Sheffield, S3 7DE Tel: 0114-272 7486 Fax: 0114-275 0290 E-mail: sales@sheffieldknives.co.uk

Stephenson & Wilson Ltd, Louvic Works, 44 Garden Street, Sheffield, S1 3HL Tel: 0114-249 3889 Fax: 0114-249 3891 E-mail: stephenson@wilsonltd.freeserve.co.uk

YARD SCRAPERS, AGRICULTURAL

▶ Yardscrapers UK, 82 Cheetham Meadow, Leyland, PR26 7UA Tel: (01772) 434484 Fax: (01772) 434484 E-mail: maxiscrape@aol.com

YARN DYERS

A T C Dyers, Royds Hall Lane, Buttershaw, Bradford, West Yorkshire, BD6 2NE Tel: (01274) 691169 Fax: (01274) 690016 E-mail: atcdyers@legend.co.uk

Blackburn Yarn Dyers Ltd, Grimshaw Park Dye Works, Haslingden Road, Blackburn, BB2 3HN Tel: (01254) 53051 Fax: (01254) 672233 E-mail: info@bydltd.co.uk

Bulmer & Lumb, Royds Hall Lane, Buttershaw, Bradford, West Yorkshire, BD6 2NE Tel: (01274) 676321 Fax: (01274) 691239 E-mail: sales@bulmerandlumb.com

Pennine Yarn Dyeing Ltd, Bridge End Works, Saddleworth Road, Elland, West Yorkshire, HX5 0RY Tel: (01422) 372401 Fax: (01422) 373735 E-mail: info@pyd.com

Todd & Duncan, Lochleven Mills, Kinross, KY13 8DH Tel: (01577) 863521 Fax: (01577) 864533 E-mail: sales@todd-duncan.com

YARN MERCHANTS OR AGENTS

A Orme & Co., Long Lea Mills, Halifax Road, Elland, West Yorkshire, HX5 0SH Tel: (01422) 374848 Fax: (01422) 312824

Alan Appleton Oldham Ltd, Jowett Street, Oldham, OL1 4JQ Tel: 0161-652 0327 Fax: 0161-633 0019 E-mail: sales@alanappleton.freeserve.co.uk

Butedean Ltd, Springfield Mill, Sherborne Street West, Salford, M3 7LT Tel: 0161-832 4724 Fax: 0161-832 2746

Cheshire Textiles Ltd, 11 Ruskin Way, Knutsford, Cheshire, WA16 6TJ Tel: (01565) 633535 Fax: (01565) 653152 E-mail: cheshiretex@aol.com

Empress Mills (1927) Ltd, Glen Mill, North Valley Road, Colne, Lancashire, BB8 9DT Tel: (01282) 863181 Fax: (01282) 870935 E-mail: chris@empressmill.co.uk

F W Bramwell & Co Ltd, Old Empress Mills, King Street, Colne, Lancashire, BB8 9HU Tel: (01282) 860388 Fax: (01282) 860389 E-mail: info@bramwellcrafts.co.uk

Fabrics & Yarns Macclesfield Ltd, Hulley Road, Macclesfield, Cheshire, SK10 2LP Tel: (01625) 427311 Fax: (01625) 424769

G D Yarns Ltd, 200 Gorton Road, Manchester, M12 5DX Tel: 0161-231 0055 Fax: 0161-231 0066 E-mail: gdyarns@btinternet.com

H E Textiles, 20b The Nook, Cosby, Leicester, LE9 1RQ Tel: 0116-275 3353 Fax: 0116-275 3389 E-mail: nicola.pollock@pgen.net

Howorths Nelson, Manor Mill, Hallam Road, Nelson, Lancashire, BB9 8DN Tel: (01282) 612382 Fax: (01282) 695130 E-mail: howorthsnelson@btconnect.com

John Preston & Co Belfast Ltd, Blaris Industrial Estate, Altona Road, Lisburn, County Antrim, BT27 5QB Tel: (028) 9267 7077 Fax: (028) 9267 7099 E-mail: info@jphealthcare.co.uk

Geoffrey E. Macpherson Ltd, Unit 8, The Midway, Lenton, Nottingham, NG7 2TS Tel: 0115-986 8701 Fax: 0115-986 4430 E-mail: gem@macphersons.co.uk

Samuel S. Mee Ltd, 5 Museum Square, Leicester, LE1 6UF Tel: 0116-255 2756 Fax: 0116-247 1083 E-mail: samuel.mee@btconnect.com

Norland Burgess, 93-105 St. James Boulevard, Newcastle upon Tyne, NE1 4BW Tel: 0191-232 9722 Fax: 0191-232 9722

Premier Textiles Ltd, 61 Bloom Street, Manchester, M1 3LY Tel: 0161-236 2212 Fax: 0161-236 9786 E-mail: info@premier-textiles.com

R P Textiles, Castley Lane, Castley, Otley, West Yorkshire, LS21 2PY Tel: (01423) 734682 Fax: (01423) 734687 E-mail: ronpattex72@tiscali.co.uk

Rex H Perkins Ltd, Hucknall Aerodrome, Watnall Rd, Hucknall, Nottingham, NG15 6EQ Tel: 0115-963 5712 Fax: 0115-963 0129 E-mail: sales@rhperkins.co.uk

Rogerson Yarns Ltd, Heathside, 1 Clifton Road, Halifax, West Yorkshire, HX3 0BT Tel: (01422) 364088 Fax: (01422) 348709 E-mail: jonathan@rogersonyarnsltd.co.uk

Shaw Moor Yarns Ltd, Bryom Mill, Knowl Street, Stalybridge, Cheshire, SK15 3AW Tel: 0161-303 1770 Fax: 0161-303 1069 E-mail: 100436.327@compuserve.com

Sillaford Ltd, Martin House, 2 Martin Street, Brighouse, West Yorkshire, HD6 1DA Tel: (01484) 710231 Fax: (01484) 714607 E-mail: sales@sillaford.com

Swiscot Textiles Ltd, Canada House, 3 Chepstow Street, Manchester, M1 5FW Tel: 0161-236 1025 Fax: 0161-236 6635 E-mail: info@swiscot.com

T F & S L Textiles Ltd, 114 Raleigh Street, Nottingham, NG7 4DJ Tel: 0115-978 0515 Fax: 0115-978 5825

Texere Yarns, College Mill, Barkerend Road, Bradford, West Yorkshire, BD1 4AU Tel: (01274) 722191 Fax: (01274) 393500 E-mail: info@texereyarns.co.uk

Thornton Kelley & Co. Ltd, Spring Place Mills, Northorpe, Mirfield, West Yorkshire, WF14 0QT Tel: (01924) 493128 Fax: (01924) 495119 E-mail: david@thorntonkelley.co.uk

YARN PROCESSING MACHINES

Cel International, Cel House Westwood Way, Westwood Business Park, Coventry, CV4 8HS Tel: (024) 7686 2000 Fax: (024) 7686 2200 E-mail: info@cel-international.com

S P T Machines Ltd, Brookside Ave, Rustington, Littlehampton, W. Sussex, BN16 3LF Tel: (01903) 784212 Fax: (01903) 770288 E-mail: info@sptmachines.co.uk

YARN SPINNERS AND DOUBLERS, *See also headings for individual yarns*

Joseph Barraclough Ltd, Bankfield Mills, Mirfield, West Yorkshire, WF14 9DD Tel: (01924) 493147 Fax: (01924) 490702 E-mail: info@barrayarn.co.uk

Cheshire Textiles Ltd, 11 Ruskin Way, Knutsford, Cheshire, WA16 6TJ Tel: (01565) 633535 Fax: (01565) 653152 E-mail: cheshiretex@aol.com

Joseph Horsfall & Sons Ltd, Pellon Lane, Halifax, West Yorkshire, HX1 4AA Tel: (01422) 360213 Fax: (01422) 321579 E-mail: info@jhorsfall.com

Lightowlers Yarns Ltd, Brigg House Mills, 7 The Cobbles, Meltham, Holmfirth, HD9 5QQ Tel: (01484) 850908 Fax: (01484) 850424 E-mail: lighthowlersyarns@aol.com

Norfolk Textured Yarns Cromer Ltd, Holt Road, Cromer, Norfolk, NR27 9JW Tel: (01263) 513188 Fax: (01263) 515347

S Lyles & Sons Co, Calder Bank Mills, Calder Bank Road, Dewsbury, West Yorkshire, WF12 9QW Tel: (01924) 436500 Fax: (01924) 436511

Todd & Duncan, Lochleven Mills, Kinross, KY13 8DH Tel: (01577) 863521 Fax: (01577) 864533 E-mail: sales@todd-duncan.com

Z Hinchliffe & Sons Ltd, Hartcliffe Mills, Denby Dale, Huddersfield, HD8 8QL Tel: (01484) 862207 Fax: (01484) 865227 E-mail: office@zhinchliffe.co.uk

Zhincliffe Ltd, Dobroyd Mills, Jackson Bridge, New Mill, Holmfirth, HD9 1AF Tel: (01484) 684155 Fax: (01484) 684158

YARN SPINNING MACHINES

Alfred Briggs Sons & Co. Ltd, 108 Church Lane, Gomersal, Cleckheaton, West Yorkshire, BD19 4QL Tel: (01274) 873272 Fax: (01274) 869999 E-mail: sales@alfred-briggs.ltd.uk

Texkimp Ltd, Manchester Road, Northwich, Cheshire, CW9 7NN Tel: (01606) 40345 Fax: (01606) 40366 E-mail: info@texkimp.co.uk

YARN WINDERS/SLIVERERS, COMMISSION

Maxilusta Ltd, 24A Main Road, Radcliffe-On-Trent, Nottingham, NG12 2FH Tel: 0115-933 4966 Fax: 0115-933 5974

YARNS, SYNTHETIC/ CONTINUOUS FILAMENT

Craven Yarn Services, Milton House, Cononly, Keighley, West Yorkshire, BD20 8LL Tel: (01535) 630683 Fax: (01535) 630683 E-mail: john@cravenyarns.fsnet.co.uk

McAndrews Textiles Ltd, West Scholes Mill, West Scholes, Queensbury, Bradford, West Yorkshire, BD13 1NQ Tel: (01274) 881111 Fax: (01274) 883311 E-mail: info@mcandrewtextiles.co.uk

Shakespeare International Ltd, Enterprise Way, Off Venture Road, Fleetwood, Lancashire, FY7 8RY Tel: (01253) 858787 Fax: (01253) 859595

Woodrow Universal Ltd, Junction Mills, Skipton Road, Cross Hills, Keighley, West Yorkshire, BD20 7SE Tel: (01535) 633364 Fax: (01535) 634439 E-mail: sales@woodrowuniversal.co.uk

YEAR PLANNERS

Claire Clifford Stationery & Office Products, 48 Watt Road, Hillington Park, Hillington Industrial Estate, Glasgow, G52 4RY Tel: 0141-882 6789 Fax: 0141-882 7777 E-mail: mail@claire-clifford.co.uk

YIELD MANAGEMENT SOFTWARE

Easy (Ez) Revenue Management Solutions Ltd, 2nd Floor, New Liverpool House, 15 Eldon Street, London, EC2M 7LD Tel: (020) 7495 0773 Fax: (020) 7495 7725 E-mail: hdq@easyrms.com

YOGA MATS

▶ Equilibrium Complementary Health Centre, 16 Station Street, Lewes, East Sussex, BN7 2DB Tel: (01273) 470955 E-mail: info@equilibrium-clinic.com

▶ Life Foundation School of Therapeutics, Maristowe House, Dover Street, Bilston, West Midlands, WV14 6AL Tel: (01902) 409164 Fax: (01902) 497362 E-mail: chrision2000@yahoo.co.uk

▶ Triyoga UK Ltd, 6 Erskine Road, London, NW3 3AJ Tel: (020) 7483 3344 Fax: (020) 7483 3346 E-mail: info@triyoga.co.uk

ZINC ALLOY CASTINGS

Mazak, Willenhall La Industrial Estate, Willenhall Lane, Bloxwich, Walsall, WS3 2XN Tel: (01922) 714430 Fax: (01922) 714433 E-mail: sales@mazak-limited.co.uk

Penhall Ltd, 9 Enterprise Court, Newton Close, Park Farm Industrial Estate, Wellingborough, Northamptonshire, NN8 6UW Tel: (01933) 678851 Fax: (01933) 674204

ZINC ALLOY PRESSURE CASTINGS

Cronite Precision Castings Ltd, Blacknell Lane, Crewkerne, Somerset, TA18 7YA Tel: (01460) 270300 Fax: (01460) 72643 E-mail: cpc@cronite.co.uk

ZINC BASE ALLOY PRESSURE DIE CASTINGS

Alzin Engineering Ltd, Century Works, Briggate, Elland, West Yorkshire, HX5 9HG Tel: (01422) 373456 Fax: (01422) 373813 E-mail: info@alzin.co.uk

B S C (Diecasting) Ltd, Fryers Close, Walsall, WS3 2XQ Tel: (01922) 710070 Fax: (01922) 408008 E-mail: tech@bscdiecasting.co.uk

Etma Engineering Ltd, Victoria Road, Halesowen, West Midlands, B62 8HY Tel: 0121-559 5333 Fax: 0121-559 2236E-mail: sales@etma.co.uk

▶ G T Group Ltd, 8 Faraday Road, Peterlee, County Durham, SR8 5AP Tel: 0191-586 2366 Fax: 0191-587 2111 E-mail: info@gtgroup.co.uk

JC Trophies, The Business Centre, 21 James Road, Tyseley, Birmingham, B11 2BA Tel: 0121-707 0606 Fax: 0121-707 0609 E-mail: jdcmanufacturing@blueyonder.co.uk

K G Diecasting Weston Ltd, Tudor Centre, 264 Milton Road, Weston-super-Mare, Avon, BS22 8EN Tel: (01934) 412665 Fax: (01934) 412886 E-mail: kgdiecasting@btclick.com

McDonald Diecasting Ltd, Unit 21a Coneygre Industrial Estate, Birmingham New Rd, Tipton, West Midlands, DY4 8XP Tel: 0121-520 1177 Fax: 0121-557 0677 E-mail: info@mcdonald-diecasting.co.uk

Taylor Group, 25 St. Marys Road, Dundee, DD3 9DL Tel: (01382) 826763 Fax: (01382) 832238 E-mail: info@tgdiecasting.co.uk

W Hallam Castings Ltd, Coulman Road Industrial Estate, Thorne, Doncaster, South Yorkshire, DN8 5JU Tel: (01405) 813006 Fax: (01405) 813786 E-mail: sales@hallamcastings.co.uk

West Alloy Ltd, Garth Road, Morden, Surrey, SM4 4LN Tel: (020) 8337 2211 Fax: (020) 8330 7640 E-mail: sales@westalloy.com

ZINC CASTINGS

A & D Diecasters Ltd, Westgate, Aldridge, Walsall, WS9 8DD Tel: (01922) 451212 Fax: (01922) 743048

A M E Pressure Die Casting Ltd, Unit 59c Siddons Factory Estate, Howard Street, West Bromwich, West Midlands, B70 0SU Tel: 0121-505 5222 Fax: 0121-505 5444 E-mail: amediecasting@aol.com

Kenwell Precision Die Casting Ltd, 1 Smallbridge Industrial Park, Riverside Drive, Rochdale, Lancashire, OL16 2SH Tel: (01706) 640412 Fax: (01706) 711894 E-mail: sales@kenwellprecisiondiecastings.co.uk

ZINC DIE CASTINGS

A & D Diecasters Ltd, Westgate, Aldridge, Walsall, WS9 8DD Tel: (01922) 451212 Fax: (01922) 743048

A G S (Zinc Alloys) Ltd, Adams Street, Walsall, WS2 8ND Tel: (01922) 647520 Fax: (01922) 720133

Hyde Die Casting & Manufactring Ltd, 1 Providence Mill, Alexandra Street, Hyde, Cheshire, SK14 1DX Tel: 0161-368 0996 Fax: 0161-368 6022 E-mail: hydediecasting@aol.com

L C L Castings Ltd, Showfield Lane, Malton, North Yorkshire, YO17 6BT Tel: (01653) 694436 Fax: (01653) 600224 E-mail: sales@lcl-castings.co.uk

Norfran Products Ltd, Alveley Industrial Estate, Alveley, Bridgnorth, Shropshire, WV15 6HG Tel: (01746) 780919 Fax: (01746) 780297 E-mail: mail@norfran.com

P M S Diecasting, Unit 11 Braithwell Way, Hellaby, Rotherham, South Yorkshire, S66 8QY Tel: (01709) 701901 Fax: (01709) 700833 E-mail: gpanter@pmsdiecasting.co.uk

Pressure Cast Products Ltd, Fairacres Industrial Estate, Dedworth Road, Windsor, Berkshire, SL4 4LE Tel: (01753) 868969 Fax: (01753) 840475 E-mail: info@pressurecast.co.uk

ZINC OXIDES

James M Brown Ltd, Boving Works, Napier Street, Stoke-on-Trent, ST4 4NX Tel: (01782) 744171 Fax: (01782) 744473 E-mail: sales@jamesmbrown.co.uk

ZINC PHOSPHATES

James M Brown Ltd, Boving Works, Napier Street, Stoke-on-Trent, ST4 4NX Tel: (01782) 744171 Fax: (01782) 744473 E-mail: sales@jamesmbrown.co.uk

ZINC PLATERS/PLATING SERVICES

A1 Plating, 36 Padgets Lane, Redditch, Worcestershire, B98 0RB Tel: (01527) 528852 Fax: (01527) 528852 E-mail: office@a1-plating.co.uk

Beacon Metal Finishers Ltd, Unit 10 Sirhowy Industrial Estate, Thomas Ellis Way, Sirhowy, Tredegar, Gwent, NP22 4QZ Tel: (01495) 711383 Fax: (01495) 711383

Brinksway Electro Plating Ltd, Unit 17 Latham Close, Bredbury Park Industrial Estate, Bredbury, Stockport, Cheshire, SK6 2SD Tel: 0161-494 6161 Fax: 0161-406 6447

C S M Plating Ltd, Progress Works, Heath Mill La, Birmingham, B9 4AP Tel: 0121-772 2084 Fax: 0121-772 5190

D F King Electroplating, 5-7 Sandhurst Close, Kings Road, Canvey Island, Essex, SS8 0QY Tel: (01268) 695672 Fax: (01268) 511014

E C Williams Ltd, 17 Spencer Street, Birmingham, B18 6DN Tel: 0121-236 2524 Fax: 0121-233 4931 E-mail: plating@ecwilliams.co.uk

Electrolytic Plating Co. Ltd, Crown Works, Wednesbury Road, Walsall, WS1 4JJ Tel: (01922) 627466 Fax: (01922) 723844 E-mail: sales@electrolytic.co.uk

Hastings Metal Finishers, Unit 7-8 Prince Consort Industrial Estate, Hebburn, Tyne & Wear, NE31 1EH Tel: 0191-483 9213 Fax: 0191-483 9213 E-mail: hmf.sales@tiscali.co.uk

M D Plating Ltd, 21 Wedgewood Gate Industrial Estate, Wedgewood Way, Stevenage, Hertfordshire, SG1 4SU Tel: (01438) 350527

Merthyr Electroplating Co. Ltd, Unit 23a Merthyr Tydfil Industrial Estate, Dowlais, Merthyr Tydfil, CF48 2SR Tel: (01685) 723677 Fax: (01685) 379343 E-mail: martin.sullivan@merthyrelectroplating.com

Miller Plating Co., Unit 15 All Saints Industrial Estate, All Saints Street, Birmingham, B18 7RJ Tel: 0121-523 3348 Fax: 0121-515 3187

Niphos Metal Finishing Co. Ltd, 25 Hope Street, Crewe, CW2 7DR Tel: (01270) 214081 Fax: (01270) 214089

P A R Communications (Leeds) Ltd, Mile End Road, Colwick Industrial Estate, Colwick, Nottingham, NG4 2BU Tel: 0115-961 4744 Fax: 0115-940 0714 E-mail: parcom@btconnect.com

Plating Company Ltd, The, Curriers Cl, Canley, Coventry, CV4 8AW Tel: (024) 7647 0545 Fax: (024) 7669 4120 E-mail: crplating@btconnect.com

Processed Light Alloys Ltd, 2 Astra Centre, Royle Barn Road, Rochdale, Lancashire, OL11 3DT Tel: (01706) 345551

Roundcroft Metal Finishing, Unit 1 Roundcroft, Willenhall, West Midlands, WV13 2PN Tel: (01902) 606962 Fax: (01902) 606962

Verichrome Plating Services Ltd, Larkhall Industrial Estate, Larkhall, Lanarkshire, ML9 2PG Tel: (01698) 886060 Fax: (01698) 886060 E-mail: may@verichrome.com

Willochrome Ltd, Westside, Jackson Street, St. Helens, Merseyside, WA9 3AT Tel: (01744) 738488 Fax: (01744) 23039

ZINC ROOFING CONTRACTORS

J.H. Brill & Son Ltd, 1A Merivale Rd, Putney, London, United Kingdom, SW15 2NW Tel: (020) 8788 2217 Fax: (020) 8788 5800 E-mail: info@brillandson.co.uk

ZINC ROOFING MATERIALS

Metra Non-Ferrous Metals Ltd, Pindar Road, Hoddesdon, Hertfordshire, EN11 0DE Tel: (01992) 460455 Fax: (01992) 451207 E-mail: enquiries@metra-metals.co.uk

ZINC SCRAP MERCHANTS OR PROCESSORS

Mason Metals Ltd, Two Woods Lane, Mill Street, Brierley Hill, West Midlands, DY5 1TA Tel: (01384) 79841 Fax: (01384) 76414 E-mail: info@masonmetals.co.uk

ZINC SHEETS

Metra Non-Ferrous Metals Ltd, Pindar Road, Hoddesdon, Hertfordshire, EN11 0DE Tel: (01992) 460455 Fax: (01992) 451207 E-mail: enquiries@metra-metals.co.uk

ZINC/ALLOY BARS

Mazak, Willenhall La Industrial Estate, Willenhall Lane, Bloxwich, Walsall, WS3 2XN Tel: (01922) 714430 Fax: (01922) 714433 E-mail: sales@mazak-limited.co.uk

ZINC/ALLOY PRODUCERS/ REFINERS/SMELTERS

A G S (Zinc Alloys) Ltd, Adams Street, Walsall, WS2 8ND Tel: (01922) 647520 Fax: (01922) 720133

B & B Zinc Alloys Ltd, 233 Station Road, Knowle, Solihull, West Midlands, B93 0PU Tel: (01564) 773062 Fax: (01564) 778907

Brock Metal Co., Walsall Road, Norton Canes, Cannock, Staffordshire, WS11 9NR Tel: (01543) 276666 Fax: (01543) 276418 E-mail: brock@brock-metal.co.uk

Impalloy Ltd, Alloys House, Willenhall Lane, Bloxwich, Walsall, WS3 2XN Tel: (01922) 714400 Fax: (01922) 714411 E-mail: sales@impalloy.com

▶ The Powdertech Group, 108 Churchill Road, Bicester, Oxfordshire, OX26 4XD Tel: (01869) 320600 Fax: (01869) 246330 E-mail: lisa.r@powdertech.co.uk

ZIP FASTENER MANUFRS

A & N Trimmings Ltd, 5-7 Cyril Road, Birmingham, B10 0SS Tel: 0121-771 4040 Fax: 0121-766 6878 E-mail: sales@antrimm.co.uk

Barr Radcliffe Ltd, 97 Grace Road, Leicester, LE2 8AE Tel: 0116-244 0414 Fax: 0116-244 0268 E-mail: info@barr-radcliffe.co.uk

Butonia, 260-264 Kingsland Road, London, E8 4DG Tel: (020) 7249 5141 Fax: (020) 7249 8859 E-mail: bltd@butonia-group.com

Europa Trimmings Ltd, 13-15 Lever Street, London, EC1V 3QU Tel: (020) 7250 1663 Fax: (020) 7253 4309

Alan McCormick & Co. Wholesale, 84A Locking Road, Weston-super-Mare, Somerset, BS23 3ET Tel: (01934) 626635 Fax: (01934) 645042 E-mail: alanmccormickco@aol.com

Slik Fasteners Ltd, Units B2-B3 The Dresser Centre, Whitworth Street, Openshaw, Manchester, M11 2NE Tel: 0161-230 6878 Fax: 0161-230 7636 E-mail: info@slik.co.uk

▶ Zipex UK Ltd, 15 Abbey Gate, Leicester, LE4 0AA Tel: 0116-262 4988 Fax: 0116-251 3745 E-mail: sales@zipex.co.uk

ZIP FASTENER SLIDERS

C L P Holding Co. Ltd, Tudor Works, Windmill Lane, Smethwick, West Midlands, B66 3EU Tel: 0121-558 2618 Fax: 0121-558 8825 E-mail: sales@clpzips.co.uk

ZIRCONIA LASER CUTTING

Laser Cutting Ceramics Ltd, Wide Range Works, Catley Road, Sheffield, S9 5JF Tel: 0114-249 4005 Fax: 0114-242 5194 E-mail: info@lasercutting-ceramics.co.uk

ZIRCONIA OXYGEN ANALYSERS

Cambridge Sensotec Ltd, Unit 8, Royce Court, Burrel Road, St. Ives, Cambridgeshire, PE27 3NE Tel: 0845 5314235 Fax: (01480) 466032 E-mail: sales@cambridge-sensotec.co.uk

▶ Enotec UK Ltd, PO Box 9026, Dumfries, DG1 3YH Tel: (0870) 3500102 Fax: (0870) 3500302 E-mail: enotec.uk@enotec.com

ZIRCONIUM

Alembic Ltd, Unit 6, Wimbourne Buildings, Atlantic Way, Barry, South Glamorgan, CF63 3RA Tel: (01446) 733174 Fax: (01446) 733184E-mail: david@alembic.freeserve.co.uk

Hines Milling & Processing Ltd, Scott Lidgett Industrial Estate, Scott Lidgett Road, Longport, Stoke-On-Trent, ST6 4NQ Tel: (01782) 819616 Fax: (01782) 837174 E-mail: hines@iclwebkite.co.uk

M E L Chemicals, PO Box 6, Manchester, M27 8LS Tel: 0161-911 1066 Fax: 0161-911 1090 E-mail: melchemsales@melchemicals.com

ZIRCONIUM POWDER

Alembic Ltd, Unit 6, Wimbourne Buildings, Atlantic Way, Barry, South Glamorgan, CF63 3RA Tel: (01446) 733174 Fax: (01446) 733184E-mail: david@alembic.freeserve.co.uk

ZONE ONE AND TWO HAZARDOUS AREA LIGHTING

Chalmit Lighting, 388 Hillington Road, Hillington Industrial Estate, Glasgow, G52 4BL Tel: 0141-882 5555 Fax: 0141-883 3704 E-mail: sales@chalmit.com

Medc Ltd, Colliery Road, Pinxton, Nottingham, NG16 6JF Tel: (01773) 864111 Fax: (01773) 582800 E-mail: sales@medc.com

Voltek Automation, Churchill Way, Nelson, Lancashire, BB9 6RT Tel: (0870) 7454971 Fax: (0870) 7454972 E-mail: sales@voltek.co.uk

Section 2 Company Information

@Pcproblem Co UK Ltd, Hillside House 215 Ashby Road, Burton On Trent, Burton-on-Trent, Staffordshire, DE15 0LA Tel: (0870) 1994812 E-mail: sales@pcproblem.co.uk

▶ @UK PLC, 5 Jupiter House, Calleva Park, Aldermaston, RG7 8NN Tel: (0870) 4866006 E-mail: info@ukplc.net *Same day UK company formation and company registration, for just £24.99 with free Companies House search by leading online company formation agent and company registration agent @UK PLC*

001 Mobile Car Audio & Security, 1 Esher Road, Walton-on-Thames, Surrey, KT12 4JZ Tel: (01932) 253001 E-mail: sales@001mobile.com *Car audio & alarm manufrs*

02 UK, 260 Bath Road, Slough, SL1 4DX Tel: (01753) 565000 Fax: (01753) 565010 *Air time providers*

▶ 020 Locksmiths Ltd, 19 Third Avenue, London, E17 9QJ Tel: (020) 8223 0396 Fax: (020) 8521 5470 E-mail: info@020locksmiths.com *Burglary Prevention/Repair.*Access Control.*Door Entry Systems.*Non-Destructive Door Opening.*UPVc Lock Specialist.*Chubb, ERA, Union, Banham, Yale & Mul-T-Lock Stockist.*Bars, Grilles & Gates.*

1 2 1 Security, 17 Henley Fields, St. Michaels, Tenterden, Kent, TN30 6EL Tel: (01580) 762588 Fax: (0704) 4066150 *Security Systems*

1 2 3 Express Mailing, 67-69 Chancery Lane, London, WC2A 1RF Tel: (020) 7405 7547 Fax: (020) 7831 0878 *Word processing & direct mailing services*

▶ 1 A Emergency Services, Ashley House, 1f Ashley Terrace, Edinburgh, EH11 1RF Tel: 0131-477 7901 Fax: 0131-477 7902

1 Can Help P C Problem Solving & Training Services, 60 Springwood Road, Heathfield, East Sussex, TN21 8JX Tel: (01435) 866575 E-mail: gordon@1canhelp.com *Computer consultants*

1 Communication Ltd, 4 Clearway Court, 139-141 Croydon Road, Caterham, Surrey, CR3 6PF Tel: (01883) 333880 Fax: (01883) 333881 E-mail: marketing@tisl.com *Telecommunication equipment suppliers*

1 Entity Software Ltd, Thames Acre, Hamm Court, Weybridge, Surrey, KT13 8YD Tel: (01932) 847784 Fax: (0870) 2203896 *Computer consultants*

▶ 1 Onion Ltd, 20 Abbeville Mews, London, SW4 7BX Tel: (07004) 166466 E-mail: info@1onion.com *Management consultancy*

1 Solutions, 15 Royston Road, St. Albans, Hertfordshire, AL1 5NF Tel: (01727) 869020 E-mail: 101@another.com *1 provide media and sales solutions - from planning and buying to training your sales force in how to negotiate more effectively with media owners.*

▶ 1 Stop Ltd, Boardman Industrial Estate, Boardman Road, Swadlincote, Derbyshire, DE11 9DL Tel: (01283) 819933 Fax: (01283) 819947 E-mail: martin@rosehouse.co.uk *Hairdressing accessory suppliers*

1 Stop Data Ltd, 46 High Street, Ewell, Epsom, Surrey, KT17 1RW Tel: (020) 8786 9111 Fax: (020) 8786 9115 E-mail: sales@1stopdata.com *List managers*

▶ 1 Stop Scale Shop, 47 Market Place, Henley-on-Thames, Oxfordshire, RG9 2AN Tel: (0845) 1307330 Fax: (0845) 1307440 E-mail: sales@1stopscaleshop.co.uk *The 1 Stop Scale Shop offers a huge range of scales and health monitors for the home and gym. From Body Fat Monitors to Kitchen scales we offer competitive prices on all the top brands. All deliveries to within the mainland UK are free.*

1 T O 1 Lionheart, Trump House, 15 Edison Street, Hillington Industrial Estate, Glasgow, G52 4JW Tel: 0141-810 5353

1 Websearch Marketing, 104 Dyke Rd, Brighton, BN1 3JD Tel: (08703) 219679 Fax: (01273) 771785 *Search engine positioning*

▶ 1:50, 15 Silver Birch Close, Sholing, Southampton, SO19 8FY Tel: (0845) 2262817 E-mail: info@1-50.co.uk *1:50, a Southampton based interior design company, provide a bespoke range of services including room restyling, homestaging (house doctoring), interior design and project management.*

▶ 1000's of Business Centres, 302 Regent Street, London, W1B 3HH Tel: (0800) 3899707 Fax: (0870) 4205206 E-mail: info@fofltd.com *Excellent free search & advice for people looking to rent office space. Access to 1000's of Business Centres across London and the UK. Register or call to search for space. No fees.*

101 Furniture Solutions Ltd, 59 Burton Road, Carlton, Nottingham, NG4 3DQ Tel: 0115-987 9631 Fax: 0115-940 0931 E-mail: info@101fs.co.uk *Cabinet manufrs*

1066 Design T O Print, 7 St James Road, Bexhill-On-Sea, East Sussex, TN40 2DE Tel: (01424) 810033

11 Out Of 10 Ltd, 84 Polefield Road, Prestwich, Manchester, M25 2QW Tel: 0161-798 7977 E-mail: info@11outof10.com *Highly professional web design agency*

▶ 111 A Roofleaks, 88 Dumpton Park Drive, Ramsgate, Kent, CT11 8BA Tel: (01843) 580359 E-mail: biggtara@aol.com *Roofing services*

12 VoltZ Ltd, 5 Fleetwood St, Preston, PR2 2PT Tel: (0871) 2500555 Fax: (0871) 2500554 E-mail: help@12voltz.com *Remote Power Solutions through Renewable Energy, from remote road signs/cameras to remote home power. Wind Power, Solar Power & small scale water generators, solar panels, DC-AC inverters, battery chargers, batteries, towers, and accessories. Full Energy Saving Consultancy.*

▶ 121 Accounts, 139 Monreith Road East, Glasgow, G44 3DF Tel: (07790) 180916 E-mail: enquiries@121accounts.co.uk *Book keeping & payroll services for small sole trader businesses*

▶ 121 Technology Ltd, Kincora House, 143 Deganwy Road, Llandudno, Gwynedd, LL30 1NE Tel: (0870) 7747121 *Web design & hosting, specialising in database-driven web sites*

121webconsultancy, 8 Comer Gardens, Worcester, WR2 6JH Tel: 01905 422256 E-mail: steve@121webconsultancy.co.uk

▶ 123 Bounce Croydon, 14 Waldorf Close, Croydon, CR2 6DY Tel: 0208 6456719 Fax: 07736 315888 *Bouncy Castles, Inflatable Slides, Themed Castles for Hire: Croydon, Purley, Couldsdon, Selsdon, Waddon & Wallington*

▶ 123iceni Ltd, The Studio, Long Lane, Fradley, Lichfield, Staffordshire, WS13 8NX Tel: (01283) 792990 Fax: (01283) 792993 E-mail: dvd@123iceni.co.uk *DVD & CD replication services*

▶ 18records Ltd, 16 Folly Terrace, Pity Me, Durham, DH1 5DS Tel: 0191-384 3415

▶ 1926 Trading Co. Ltd, 2 Daimler Close, Royal Oak Industrial Estate, Daventry, Northamptonshire, NN11 8QJ Tel: (01327) 312200 Fax: (01327) 310123 E-mail: sales@1926trading.co.uk *Distributors of high quality hardwood flooring*

▶ 1A Enclosures, Unit 2 Highmoor Park, Clitheroe, Lancashire, BB7 1NP Tel: (07790) 633624 Fax: (07790) 633624 E-mail: grahamgallagher@environmentalenclosure.com *We design and manufacture protective PC, laptop and printer enclosures for all industries. We also supply wash down units for the food industry.*

1a Productions Ltd, Langshot, Torrance, Glasgow, G64 4DL Tel: (01360) 620855 Fax: (01360) 620788 *Television*

▶ 1aaa Torquay Roofing, 43 Hoxton Road, Torquay, TQ1 1NY Tel: (01803) 290549 Fax: (01803) 290549 E-mail: sales@torquayroofing.co.uk *Complete roofing specialist services*

▶ 1car1.com, 15 / Walter Street, Kirkstall, Leeds, LS4 2BB Tel: 0113 387 5559 Fax: 0113 387 5561 E-mail: sales@1car1.com *Largest independant car rental company in the UK, over 90 locations throughout the UK and over 12500 cars on fleet. Car rental from £99 per week.*

1ccormick, 8 John Street, Stratford-upon-Avon, Warwickshire, CV37 6UB Tel: (01789) 264098 Fax: (01789) 264101

▶ 1Coast-2-Coast, 54 Foads Lane, Cliffsend, Ramsgate, Kent, CT12 5JJ Tel: (07921) 355318 Fax: (01843) 581045 E-mail: c2ccouriers@aol.com *Urgent sameday or nextday deliveries nationwide.From a letter to pallet distribution.*visit our website. c2ccouriers.co.uk*

▶ 1Gift4All, PO Box 172, Pudsey, West Yorkshire, LS28 5XT Tel: (0789) 9067059 E-mail: sales@1gift4all.com *Thousands of presents and gifts for all the family. Unique gifts and unusual birthday presents to suit all tastes, from metal animals to incense and household items.*

1spatial Group Ltd, Unit 6 Cambridge Business Park, Cowley Road, Cambridge, CB4 0WZ Tel: (01223) 420414 Fax: (01223) 420044 E-mail: info@1spatial.com *Mapping & charting software developers*

▶ 1st 4 Recruitment, 1 Gurney Lane, Norwich, NR4 7SB Tel: (01603) 456231 E-mail: welcome@1st4jobs.com *recruitment*

1st Aid 4 Fencing, 2 Cornbrash Rise, Hilperton, Trowbridge, Wiltshire, BA14 7TT Tel: 0800 611 8344 E-mail: info@1staid4fencing.com *We supply and erect Timber Fencing for commercial and residential customers. We believe that we offer the most competitive prices in the area. Call now for a free no obligation quote. Garden Structures also supplied and erected.*

▶ 1st Airports Express Cars, 104 Gloucester Road, London, SW7 4RH Tel: (020) 7244 6556 *Taxi company*

1st Alert Alarm Systems, 44a Rhone Road, Dungannon, County Tyrone, BT71 7EN Tel: (028) 8778 9669 Fax: (028) 8778 9703 E-mail: info@1st-alertalarms.co.uk *Commercial & residential intruder alarm systems installation*

▶ 1st APS Conservatory Roof Repairs, Crawford Place, New Road, Staines, Middlesex, TW18 3DH Tel: (01784) 464613 Fax: (01784) 464663 *conservatory roof refurbishment specialists*double glazing repairs*

▶ 1st Bounce Croydon, 60 Pawsons Road, Croydon, CR0 2QF Tel: (020) 8689 4997 Fax: 07932 999569 E-mail: info_1stbounce@hotmail.co.uk *Bouncy castle hire company*

▶ 1st Byte, Cade Road, Ashford, Kent, TN23 6JE Tel: (01233) 637056

▶ 1st call aacronite, po box 16255, London, N19 5WF Tel: (07939) 484677 E-mail: mail@aacronite.com

▶ 1st Call Changing Group, Monton House, Monton Green, Eccles, Manchester, M30 9LE Tel: 0161-281 7007 Fax: 0161-281 6006 E-mail: sales@1stcallbuildingservices.co.uk

▶ 1st Call Environmental Services Ltd, 61 Derby Road, Melbourne, Derby, DE73 8FE Tel: (01332) 862737 Fax: (01332) 862832 *Pest control services*

▶ 1st Call Lockouts Ltd, 9 Beaumont Road, Bournville Birmingham, Birmingham, B30 2EA Tel: 0121-459 8772 Fax: 0121-451 1315 E-mail: enquiries@1stcalllockouts.co.uk *All locks opened (non destructive methods employed), replaced and installed. **One of the UKs No1 locksmith training centres. Delivering a 5 day intensive 'hands-on' programme for those new to the industry. Call today for further details.*

1st Call Mercury Signs, Highfield View, Park Lane, Stokenchurch, Buckinghamshire, HP14 3TQ Tel: (01494) 482288 Fax: (01494) 483152 E-mail: mcgillsign@aol.com *Sign contractors, plastic printing & full colour digital print services*

▶ 1st Call ProWeigh (Yorkshire) Ltd (Scales), 8 The Sycamores, Doncaster, South Yorkshire, DN5 7UH Tel: 01302 787176 Fax: 01302 787176 E-mail: info@proweigh.co.uk *We supply a full quality package. Scheduled Servicing, Calibration, Hire of all makes of scales. Sales Distributors for Mettler, Toledo and Ohaus. 24Hr Callout Availability. Suppliers of Balances, Bench Scales, Counting Scales, Floor Platforms, Reconditioned Scales (inc Atex)& Weighbridges. Industrial and Retail scales, Electronic or Mechanical. It Pays To ProWeigh.*

1st Call Rotosign Ltd, Pressmetal House, St Augustines Business Park, Whitstable, Kent, CT5 2QJ Tel: (01227) 794490 Fax: (01227) 794488 E-mail: sales@amp-uk.co.uk *Sign manufrs*

1st Choice, Stileway Business Park, Lower Strode Road, Clevedon, Avon, BS21 6UU Tel: (01275) 871131 Fax: (01275) 871115 E-mail: fcgbristol@aol.com *Audio visual retailers*

1st Choice, 6 St. Ives Crescent, Sale, Cheshire, M33 3RU Tel: (07840) 344464 E-mail: firstchoicecvservices@ntlworld.com *CV Services.*Covering Letters.*Acess to various Job Sector Databas Contacts and Companies.*Help with Employment Applications.*

1st Choice Asbestos Removals Ltd, 21c Hellesdon Park Road, Drayton High Road, Norwich, NR6 5DR Tel: (01603) 426217 Fax: (01603) 417382 E-mail: sales@1stchoiceasbestos.co.uk *Asbestos removal consultants services*

1st Choice Blinds, 11 Mander Grove, Warwick, CV34 6RY Tel: 01926 740593 E-mail: sales@1stchoiceblinds.com Purchasing Contact: M. Nwangwa Sales Contact: M. Nwangwa *Online vertical window blinds retailer*

▶ 1st Choice Fitted Bedrooms, Unit A, Springvale Business Park, Darwen, Lancashire, BB3 2EP Tel: (01254) 873173 Fax: (01254) 873787 E-mail: 1stchoicebedrooms@tiscali.co.uk *Quality bespoke fitted bedroom furniture*

▶ 1st Choice Kitchens, 6 The Dell, Yateley, Hampshire, GU46 6EL Tel: 01252 860661 Fax: 01252 665237 *Providing off the shelf & bespoke kitchens nationwide*

▶ 1st Choice Plastics, 1 Halcyon Court, Muxton, Telford, Shropshire, TF2 8RX Tel: (01952) 676644 Fax: (01952) 676644 E-mail: belinda@residentalsline.co.uk *uPVC Fascia, Soffits & guttering replacement*

1st Choice Plumbing Services Nw, 2 Buxton Street, Accrington, Lancashire, BB5 0SF Tel: (07947) 355964 E-mail: john23zx@aol.com *Commercial & domestic plumbing contractors*

1st Choice Publishing Ltd, 355 Aylsham Road, Norwich, NR3 2RX Tel: (01603) 404001 Fax: (01603) 404410 E-mail: jan@0800service.com *Publishers*

1st Choice Security Services Ltd, Unit 4 Hall Court, Bridge Street, Polesworth, Tamworth, Staffordshire, B78 1DT Tel: (01827) 899972 Fax: (01827) 899953 E-mail: pgrace@1stcss.co.uk *Security services*

1st Choice Superseal Ltd, 688 Aldridge Road, Great Barr, Birmingham, B44 8NJ Tel: 0121-366 6782 Fax: 0121-366 6624 *Specialist group flat roofing*

1st Class, 13 Osbert Rd, Rotherham, South Yorkshire, S60 3LD Tel: 01709 531782 Fax: 01709 518458 *Fork lift trucks repair, service & sales*

1st Class Catering Equipment Hire, 29 Flash Lane, Mirfield, West Yorkshire, WF14 0PJ Tel: (01924) 496592 Fax: (01924) 496592 *Crockery Hirer*

▶ 1st Class Corporate Entertainment, 4 Porchester Court, Bournemouth, BH8 8JE Tel: (01202) 467970 E-mail: funcasino@msn.com *Corporate entertainment services*

▶ 1st Class Drivers, Queen Street, Morley, Leeds, LS27 9BR Tel: 0161-615 1311 Fax: 0113-252 3534 *1st Class Drivers a quality specialist driving agency. Employing 95% of drivers on full time permanent employment contracts. They provide HGV drivers to transport companies in Manchester, Leeds, Sheffield, Bradford, Barnsley, Wakefield & Doncaster areas. **

1st Class Fork Truck Services, Unit 1, Oaks Green, Sheffield, S9 3WR Tel: 0114-261 9495 *Fork lift trucks service & repairers*

▶ 1st Class Post Ltd, 3 Silver Royd Business Park, Silver Royd Hill, Leeds, LS12 4QQ Tel: 0113-263 8684 Fax: 0113-263 7347 *Envelope over printers*

▶ 1st Class Secretarial Services, 34 New Hunterfield, Gorebridge, Midlothian, EH23 4BD Tel: (01875) 823215 Fax: (01875) 823215 E-mail: dawn.lawson@1stclass.uk.com *Providing a 1st class digital transcription services. All file types transcribed. Competative rates, accurate and professional presentation. Confidentiality guaranteed. Audio transcription service also available. We can meet all your administrative requirements. We work weekends to meet customer demand.*

1st Class Transport, 60 Birchen Grove, London, NW9 8SA Tel: (020) 8205 2244 Fax: (020) 8838 1515 *Removal contractors*

1st Computer Consultancy, 55 Argarmeols Road, Liverpool, L37 7BY Tel: (01704) 833588 Fax: (01704) 833588 *Computer consultancy*

▶ 1st Computer Systems, 539 Moseley Road, Birmingham, B12 9BU Tel: 0121-446 4646

1st Contact, Clydesdale Bank House, 33 Regent Street, London, SW1Y 4ZT Tel: (0800) 0393082 Fax: (020) 7494 4334 E-mail: info@1st-contact.co.uk *Company formation agents*

▶ 1st Coverall, Tovil Green Business Park, Burial Ground Lane, Tovil, Maidstone, Kent, ME15 6TA Tel: (01622) 664427 Fax: (01622) 664427 *Manufacture work wear*

▶ 1st Dirt Busters, 20 Clarendon Road, Southsea, Hampshire, PO5 2EE Tel: (023) 9282 9429 E-mail: dirt.busters@virgin.net *Mobile Car Valet aiming to provide professional services to the public and motor industry. Carpet & Upholstery Cleaning from a full house clean to single rooms.*

1st Engravers & Trophies, Wimbledon Station, London, SW19 7NL Tel: (020) 8946 9037 Fax: (020) 8949 3330 *Trophies, medals & rosettes*

▶ 1st Fix Systems, Hobson Industrial Estate, Hobson, Newcastle upon Tyne, NE16 6EA Tel: (01207) 271777 Fax: (01207) 271777 *Suppliers to building trade*

Trojan, 3 Lyon Road, Hersham Trading Estate, Walton-On-Thames, Surrey, KT12 3PU Tel: (01932) 232400 Fax: (01932) 267987 E-mail: info@trojansigns.com *Sign makers*

▶ 1st For Furniture Ltd, Fairclough Hall Farm, Halls Green, Weston, Hitchin, Hertfordshire, SG4 7DP Tel: (01462) 790990 Fax: (01462) 790995 E-mail: info@1st-for-furniture.co.uk *Internet company*

1st Galaxy Fireworks Ltd, The Pyro Plot, Nottingham Road, Ravenshead, Nottingham, NG15 9HP Tel: (01623) 792121 Fax: (0870) 4430211 E-mail: sales@1stgalaxy.co.uk *Firework retailers & wholesalers*

▶ 1st Hygiene Solutions, 12 Mount Road, Southdown, Bath, BA2 1LD Tel: (0870) 7773867 Fax: (01225) 319601 E-mail: enqiuries@1sthygienesolutions.co.uk *Washroom services*

▶ 1st Insulation Partners Ltd, Insulation House, Shaw Road, Eastwood Trading Estate, Rotherham, South Yorkshire, S65 1SG Tel: (01709) 365785 Fax: 01709 365786 E-mail: office@firstinsulation.com *Suppliers of parts & materials to the insulation trade*

▶ 1st Kensington Riders Cars, 180-186 Cromwell Road, Kensington And Chelsea, London, SW5 0SS Tel: (020) 7244 7744 *Taxi cab & airport transfer inbound outbound*

▶ 1st Office Equipment, Victoria Orchards, Kennford, Exeter, EX6 7TH Tel: (01392) 833373 Fax: (01934) 713843 E-mail: sales@1st-office.com

▶ 1st Port, Allen House, The Maltings, Station Road, Sawbridgeworth, Hertfordshire, CM21 9JX Tel: (01279) 602150 Fax: (01279) 723957

1st Quote Fire, 49 Forthview Walk, Tranent, East Lothian, EH33 1FE Tel: 0131-448 0723 Fax: 0131-448 0723 *Fire extinguishers*

▶ 1st Response Medical Services, Units 1-48, Beacon Lane, Exeter, EX4 8LJ Tel: (01392) 499951 E-mail: enquiries@1st-response-services.com *Providers of special care services*

▶ 1st Security Concepts, 796 London Road, Larkfield, Aylesford, Kent, ME20 6HJ Tel: (01732) 321695 E-mail: thecoppings@msn.com *Supply & fitting of alarms*

▶ 1st South East Aerials, 43 Old Mead, Southend-on-Sea, SS2 6SW Tel: (01702) 526555 Fax: (01702) 524622

▶ 1st Step Security, 164 Malpas Road, Lewisham, London, SE4 1DH Tel: (0845) 0092879 E-mail: sales@firststepsecurity.co.uk *We Install, Service and Repair Intruder Alarms, CCTV and Access control.*We specialize at installing various types of home and business security alarm systems to detect emergencies and alert the proper authorities. Statistically we know that security alarm systems work at preventing greater loss and damage to both persons and property and that is why we are committed to the task of educating others*

1st Stop Door Shop, 13 Tavistock Close, Northampton, NN3 5DQ Tel: (0800) 0435341 E-mail: info@1ststopdoorshop.co.uk *Supply & installation of garage doors*

▶ 1st Storage Centres, Stoneygate Close, Gateshead, Tyne & Wear, NE10 0AZ Tel: 0191-469 7777 Fax: 0191-469 7999 E-mail: gateshead@storagecentres.co.uk *Self storage business services*

1st Vinyl Demand Signs, 80-82 Beckenham Lane, Bromley, BR2 0DW Tel: (020) 8313 9199 Fax: (020) 8313 9979 *Sign manufrs*

▶ 1stautobulbs, Randstad House, Crowhall Road, Nelson Park, Cramlington, Northumberland, NE23 1WH Tel: 01670 706985 Fax: 01670 730820 E-mail: chrisclark@randstadltd.co.uk *distributor of high quality upgrade auto bulbs xenon halgen HID LED types from Philips, Osram, Bosch & G.E.*

▶ 1stUniversal Trading Ltd, 86 Victoria Road, Stoke-on-Trent, ST4 2JX Tel: (01782) 763700 Fax: (01782) 763636 E-mail: universalfirst@hotmail.co.uk *General trading company. Specializing in Business to business trading, in a wide variety of goods to include pharmaceutical, optical equipment, sports & leisure products within the global markets.*

▶ 1swim.com, Beauchamp Road, East Molesey, Surrey, KT8 0PA Tel: (0870) 1283186 E-mail: info@1swim.com *Swimming pool equipment suppliers*

1t Solutions, 3 The Crescent, Doncaster Road, Rotherham, South Yorkshire, S65 1NL Tel: (01709) 371441 Fax: (01709) 371440 E-mail: sales@1t-s.com *Software developers & it services*

▶ 1TeK Computer Services, Tor Close, Purbrook, Waterlooville, Hampshire, PO7 8SU Tel: (07963) 873799 Fax: (07092) 034359 E-mail: seocontact@1tek.net *Computer services*

2 Aim Productions, 17 Clare Court, 829 Hertford Road, Enfield, Middlesex, EN3 6UJ Tel: (07958) 678583 E-mail: info@2aimproductions.com *2 Aim productions supplie on line marketing solutions to small to medium sized companies in the UK and Ghana*

▶ 2 C F Communications Ltd, 42c Barrack Square, Martlesham Heath, Ipswich, IP5 3RF Tel: (01473) 622263 Fax: (01473) 622515 E-mail: info@2cf.com *Design & marketing agency*

2 Cousins Access Ltd, Shell House, Watlington Road, Cowley, Oxford, OX4 6NF Tel: (01865) 779778 Fax: (01865) 401041 E-mail: keith@2cousins.co.uk *Access platform hire/leasing/rental*

2 E (UK) Ltd, Heyes Farm House, Grimshaw Road, Skelmersdale, Lancashire, WN8 6BH Tel: (01695) 50300 Fax: (01695) 50338 E-mail: sales@2euk.com *Cable accessory distributors*

▶ 2 Evolve UK, 2a Cunningham Road, Stirling, FK7 7SW Tel: (0870) 3501795 Fax: (0870) 3507096 E-mail: sales@2e-volve.com *IT software suppliers, system support*

2 M Power Systems Ltd, Howe Moss Drive, Kirkhill Industrial Estate, Dyce, Aberdeen, AB21 0GL Tel: (01224) 725506 Fax: (01224) 723717 E-mail: 2mpowerltd@btconnect.com *Diesel engine suppliers*

2 R Systems Ltd, Unit 5 Collec Depot, Billington Road, Leighton Buzzard, Bedfordshire, LU7 9HH Tel: (01525) 852151 Fax: (01525) 852149 *Photocopier supplier service & maintenance*

2 U Computers, Stambourne Road, Hawkes Farm, Little Sampford, Saffron Walden, Essex, CB10 2QS Tel: (01799) 586300 Fax: (01799) 586210 E-mail: admin@2ucomputers.co.uk *Computer systems & software sales*

20 20 Presentations Ltd, 11 Jersey Close, Congleton, Cheshire, CW12 3TW Tel: (01260) 280308 Fax: (01260) 208309 E-mail: enquiries@20-20presentations.co.uk *Audio visual rental services*

20 Twenty Graphics Ltd, Unit 2, Parkfield Industrial Estate, London, SW11 5BA Tel: (020) 8541 4526 Fax: (020) 7819 9922 E-mail: graphics@20twentygraphics.co.uk *Sign manufr*

20/20 Telecom, 102 High Street, Canvey Island, Essex, SS8 7SQ Tel: (01268) 511700 Fax: (01268) 696151 *Business telephone systems sales*

20-20 Direct Mail, Unit 49 The Washford Industrial Estate, Heming Road, Redditch, Worcestershire, B98 0EA Tel: (01527) 510444 Fax: (01527) 510006 E-mail: sales@2020dml.com *Data processing, direct mail & transaction processing service bureau*

▶ 20five eight Lifestyle Management, 8 Rubislaw Terrace, Aberdeen, AB10 1XE Tel: 01224 611555 E-mail: sherida@20five8.co.uk *Lifestyle and concierge services covering Aberdeen and NE Scotland. *Individual and corporate packages available to help busy people attain their desired and deserved work/life balance*Also offer bespoke wedding coordination and design.*

▶ 21 Colour Ltd, 21 Summerlee Street, Glasgow, G33 4DB Tel: 0141-774 4455 Fax: 0141-774 3739

2112 Systems Ltd, The Old Telephone Exchange, Longcross Road, Longcross, Chertsey, Surrey, KT16 0DP Tel: (01932) 873111 Fax: (01932) 874340 E-mail: enquiries@2112hire.com *Audio visual hire services*

21st Century, Security House, 65 Canterbury Street, Blackburn, BB2 2HT Tel: (01254) 661199 Fax: (01254) 699969 E-mail: sales@cctv-uk.com *CCTV suppliers*

▶ 21st Century Lifts Ltd, Unit 28 Metro Business Centre, Kangley Bridge Road, London, SE26 5BW Tel: (020) 8676 5700 Fax: (020) 8676 5701

21st Century Security, PO Box 60, Heathfield, East Sussex, TN21 8ZJ Tel: (01435) 868245 Fax: (01435) 868245 *Security*

▶ 21st Century Transport Ltd, Unit G2-G3 G6 H5-H6 Hastingwood Trading Estate, 35 Harbet Road, London, N18 3HT Tel: (020) 8887 0796 Fax: (020) 8807 7624

▶ 24 7 CCTV Security Ltd, 33 Kingswood Road, Basildon, Essex, SS16 5UP Tel: (0870) 2242247 Fax: (0870) 4215949 E-mail: info@247cctv.co.uk *Installers of high quality CCTV, door entry systems and Security Bollards and posts...*

▶ 24 7 Staff Luton, 25 Upper George Street, Luton, LU1 2RD Tel: (01582) 722336 E-mail: luton@247staff.net *Staffing solutions to the industrial & commercial sectors*

24 Acoustics, 24 Bell Street, Romsey, Hampshire, SO51 8GW Tel: 01794 515999 Fax: (0871) 2420156 E-mail: info@24acoustics.co.uk *Acoustic consultants*Noise and Vibration consultants*

▶ 24 Hour Plumbing Services, Brand Street, Glasgow, G51 1DG Tel: 0141-427 3320 Fax: 0141-427 5639

▶ 24 HR Rugby Locksmith Ltd, 3 St. Matthews Street, Rugby, Warwickshire, CV21 3BY Tel: (01788) 544111 Fax: (01788) 544222 E-mail: emergencylocksmiths@tiscali.co.uk *Locksmiths, safe engineers*

▶ 24-7 Electrical Ltd, 167 Townfields Road, Winsford, Cheshire, CW7 4AX Tel: (01625) 266309 Fax: (01625) 266309 E-mail: mail@24-7group.co.uk *24-7 Electrical Ltd and elecbits.com are both a labour management company and suppliers of major electrical components, Power tools, circular saws, halogen lamps/lights, cable ties, tie mounts, cable glands, hammer drills, drills, safety work wear, safety glasses and more.*

▶ 247 Finance Services, Regent Street, London, W1B 2QD Tel: 0560 0029542 E-mail: contact@247-services.co.uk *Offers personal loans, mortgages and other financial services to the UK homeowners and tenants. APR 6.4%*

▶ 24-7 Weighing Solutions Ltd, 63 Blenheim Place, Stenhousemuir, Larbert, Stirlingshire, FK5 4PW Tel: (01324) 878569 Fax: (01324) 878816 E-mail: sales@weighingsolutions.co.uk *Weighing equipment service providers & suppliers*

24hourdrains.Com, 26 Colwyn Avenue, Morecambe, Lancashire, LA4 6EH Tel: (01524) 410410 Fax: (01524) 411880 *# Drain and Pipe Cleaning*# Clearance*# Water Jetting*# CCTV Surveys*# Rodding*# Plunging*# Sewer Cleaning*# Pressure Washing*# Drain Repairs*# Drain Excavation*# Root Cutting*# Free Estimates*# Insurance Reports*# High pressure Water Jetting*

▶ 24hr Recruitment Ltd, Pendle Innovation Centre, Brook Street, Nelson, Lancashire, BB9 9PS Tel: (01282) 878353 Fax: (01282) 877147 E-mail: info@24hrrecruitment.com *Recruitment service*

24Store Ltd, Siberia House, Church Street, Basingstoke, Hampshire, RG21 7QN Tel: (01256) 867700 Fax: (01256) 867701 E-mail: sales@24store.com *Computer dealers*

28 Black London, Unit 3A, Trafalgar Business Park, Broughton Lane, Manchester, M8 9TZ Tel: 0161-839 2224 Fax: 0161-839 6661 *Casual wear jackets & tracksuits distributors*

▶ 2as Ltd, Logic House, Marsh Lane, Easton-in-Gordano, Bristol, BS20 0NH Tel: (01275) 374524 Fax: (01275) 373820

2canvas Limited, 155 Stockwell Street, Glasgow, G1 4LR Tel: 0141-552 0005 E-mail: design@2canvas.co.uk *Take your photo images, printed, slides or digital and use them to produce an original work of art! Images printed on Water resistant art canvas,photo papers, acid free archival papers, banners and posters with pigmented ink which is UV resistant for 70+ years and stretched on quality kiln dried pine or hardwood frames.**Original art work is costly and difficult to find, let us produce a canvas which is personal and unique to you, no one else will have your art on their walls. **All you have to do is search your albums for suitable images and we will preserve your images and memories on a beautiful canvas.**We also provide stock images to decorate any home. *Our corporate division can also help businesses reinforce their corporate image by producing canvases of their products, mission statement or logo"""'s.**Check out our website and then contact us by phone or e-mail and let us provide you with a quote.*

2CL Communications Ltd, Unit 3 The Crosshouse Centre, Crosshouse Road, Southampton, SO14 5GZ Tel: (023) 8033 6411 Fax: (023) 8072 0038 E-mail: sales@2cl.co.uk *Communications equipment retailers*

▶ 2CTV.co.uk, PO Box 2011, Preston, PR5 8WU Tel: 07929 610498 E-mail: sales@2ctv.co.uk *An Internet based distributor of low tech day to day consumable products for the security industry*

▶ 2Dmedia Web Site Design Essex Ltd, PO Box 7881, Braintree, Essex, CM7 3BT Tel: (0845) 6580115 E-mail: ksales@2dmedia.co.uk *2Dmedia provide professional affordable web site design*

▶ 2f3 Internet, 103 Malbet Park, Edinburgh, EH16 6WB Tel: 0131-666 2555 E-mail: info@2f3.com *Website designs*

▶ 2-home-business.com Ltd, 501 International House, 223 Regent Street, London, UK, W1B 2QD Tel: 01743 284757 E-mail: enquiries@2-home-business.com *Business Start Up Help & Support Through An Integrated Learning Program Of Ongoing Mentoring & Support, Creative Workshops, Proven Business Ideas And Professional Consultation*

▶ 2-Inspire, 8 Old School Close, Netheravon, Salisbury, SP4 9QJ Tel: (01980) 671182 *Computer and laptop repairs, upgrades and installation. Custom PC"s. Home and small business security advice and setup and more.*

▶ 2k Business Services Ltd, 2 Laburnum Cottages, Caerleon Road, Ponthir, Newport, Gwent, NP18 1HE Tel: (01633) 430166 Fax: (01633) 421014 E-mail: enquiry@2kbs.co.uk *Business Consultancy*

2K Polymer Systems Limited, PO Box 7, Alfreton, Derbyshire, DE55 7RA Tel: (01773) 540440 Fax: (01773) 607638 E-mail: info@2kps.net *Manufacturers of high performance two-part adhesive bonded anchor systems and repair compounds, that are exclusively supplied labelled with your brand name to fit along side your current product range.*

2KM UK Ltd, 11 Sherwood House, Sherwood Road, Aston Fields Trading Estate, Bromsgrove, Worcestershire, B60 3DR Tel: (01527) 834720 Fax: (01527) 834729 E-mail: sales@2km.co.uk Principal Export Areas: Worldwide *Manufacturer of Epoxy resin mixing machines, Adhesive, polyurethane, urethane or resin dispensing, mixing and coating equipment.Dispensing guns, pumps, systems.Gasketing, foam in place. Silicone rubber machinery. Airless paint spraying equipment manufacturers. WORLDWIDE SUPPLIER. Epoxy Resin Mixing Machines, Adhesive Dispensing Equipment, Urethane or Synthetic Rubber Mixing or Dispensing Machines, Polyurethane (PU) Mixing or Dispensing Machines, Paint Spraying Equipment, Airless, Adhesive Dispensing or Mixing Equipment, Adhesive Application or Coating Equipment, Liquid Dispensing Equipment, Meter and Mix, adhesive Applications, Robotic, dispensing Systems*

▶ 2nd 2 None Ltd, 235 Beehive Lane, Chelmsford, CM2 9SH Tel: (07815) 290214 Fax: (01245) 602046 E-mail: info@2nd2noneltd.com *We are a family run courier company that specialises in 2 man deliveries, retail distribution and light removals. We also provide a sameday delivery service, multidrop delivery service and a european delivery service.*

2nd Chance Ltd, Basepoint Business & Innovation Centre, East Portway, Caxton Close, Andover, Hampshire, SP10 5HS Tel: 0800 0112164 Fax: 01264 353124 E-mail: info@2ndchance.co.uk *Web Design Company offers website design, flash design, web development, e-commerce, hosting, open source customisation, logo, search engines and promotional services from Andover, Hampshire, UK. Whether you need to build a personalised e-commerce system or scalable Intranet portal, customise a database system, or develop web animation or custom graphic design, we can help reduce your overhead development, design and maintenance costs.*

2nd To None Rubbish Removals, Penarth Road, Deane, Bolton, BL3 5RJ Tel: (01204) 665569 E-mail: darren@2ndtonone.co.uk *Rubbish removal & cleaning contractors*

▶ 2NITY Machine Operatives, 37 Ripley Road, Canning Town, London, E16 3EA Tel: (020) 7366 4408 Fax: (020) 7366 4408 E-mail: info@2nitypersonnel.co.uk *We provide CITB/CPCS certified machine operativesfor construction machines like the telehandler forklift, 360 digger, Dump Trucks, counter balance forklift, site labour amongst other services*

▶ 2u phones, 5 Avon House,, York Close,, Northam,, Southampton, SO14 5SE Tel: 02380 943371 E-mail: im_with_cheryl@yahoo.com *We sell new phones, insurance, and iPOD insurance, fascias.*

▶ 2XL: Business Solutions, 22 Lenten Grove, Heywood, Lancashire, OL10 2LR Tel: (01706) 620998 E-mail: info@2xlbusinesssolutions.com *Management consultancy providing integrated solutions for the developing business*

▶ 3 County Locksmiths, 1 Tudor Court, Gillingham, Dorset, SP8 4TF Tel: (01747) 826311 Fax: (01747) 826311 E-mail: mark@3countylocksmiths.co.uk *Specialists in security & provide a 24hr call out*

3 D Engineering Midlands Ltd, Unit 15, The Wallows Industrial Estate, Fens Pool Avenue, Brierley Hill, Dudley, West Midlands, DY5 1QA Tel: (01384) 480604 Fax: (01384) 480604 E-mail: 3dengineering@btconnect.com *Press tool manufrs*

▶ 3 D Tooling, 2 Slade Street, Little Lever, Bolton, BL3 1BD Tel: (01204) 701000 Fax: (01204) 701001 E-mail: info@3dtooling.co.uk *Saw doctor*

3 Dimensional Print Ltd, Unit 37 Acorn Industrial Park, Crayford Road, Dartford, DA1 4AL Tel: (01322) 555942 Fax: (01322) 528973 E-mail: sales@3dp.co.uk *Lithographic printers*

3 Dimensions Ltd, Maple House, 6 Sherbourne Close, Cambridge, CB4 1RT Tel: (01223) 693097 Fax: (01223) 693097 E-mail: info@3dimensions.ltd.uk *Suspended Ceiling installers Partitioning installers. Interior Refurbishment specialists. Office Refurbishment. Office fitters.*

3 I Plc, 3 The Embankment, Sovereign St, Leeds, LS1 4BJ Tel: 0113-243 0511 Fax: 0113-244 5800 E-mail: leeds@3i.com *Venture capitalists*

▶ 3 J Lining Systems Ltd, Unit 2g Lake Enterprise Park, Sandall Stones Road, Kirk Sandall Industrial Estate, Doncaster, South Yorkshire, DN3 1QR Tel: (01302) 880800 Fax: (01302) 880900 E-mail: jeff@3jlinings.co.uk *Low friction & abrasive resistant lining systems suppliers & manufrs*

3 J's, 70 Llandaff Road, Cardiff, CF11 9NL Tel: (029) 2022 6262 Fax: (029) 2022 6268 *Joinery manufrs*

3 M Touch Systems, 163 Milton Park, Milton, Abingdon, Oxfordshire, OX14 4SD Tel: (01235) 444400 Fax: (01235) 861603 E-mail: touchsales-uk@mmm.com Principal Export Areas: Worldwide *3M Touch Systems provides 3M's world-renown technological innovation, product reliability, and customer service to touch device manufacturers, touch systems integrators and resellers, around the world.*

3 T H Ltd, 9 Hinksey Business Centre, North Hinksey Lane, Oxford, OX2 0NR Tel: (01865) 791452 Fax: (01865) 794267 E-mail: sales@3th.co.uk *System integrators service*

3 Thinking, 34 Windermere, Swindon, SN3 6JZ Tel: (0870) 1283075 Fax: (01793) 474522 E-mail: sales@3thinking.com *Computer consultant programming*

321 Systems Ltd, 6 Maryon Mews, London, NW3 2PU Tel: (020) 7794 3236 Fax: (020) 7431 3213 E-mail: info@321systems.com *Computer systems & software suppliers*

360 Solutions, Unit 1, Nobles Gate Yard, Bell Yews Green, Tunbridge Wells, Kent, TN3 9AT Tel: (0870) 7606404 Fax: (0870) 7606404 E-mail: info@360ss.com *Computer consultants & web design*

▶ 360red Productions, LCB Depot, 31 Rutland Street, Leicester, LE1 1RE Tel: 0116-253 3420 E-mail: info@360red.co.uk *Multimedia production*

▶ 365 Payroll Services Ltd, Kyama House, 5 Ingle Dell, Camberley, Surrey, GU15 2LP Tel: (0845) 0573598 Fax: (01276) 22732 E-mail: jhealy@365payroll.co.uk *Payroll bureau, payroll administration services*

▶ 3B Designs, 32 Eaglewood Close, Torquay, TQ2 7SS Tel: (01803) 615903 *Low cost web site design for small businesses based in Torbay, design, hosting & email all included.*

3b Systems Ltd, The Technology Centre, Carr Road, Nelson, Lancashire, BB9 7JS Tel: (01282) 619534 Fax: (0870) 7705152 E-mail: sales@3bsystems.co.uk *PC components peritherals & systems suppliers*

▶ 3b Waste Solutions, Unit C Scotch Park Trading Estate, Forge Lane, Leeds, LS12 2PY Tel: 0113-279 2348 Fax: (0870) 7520745 E-mail: info@3bwaste.co.uk *Waste management*

▶ 3c Technology Ltd, 29-33 Lower Kings Road, Berkhamsted, Hertfordshire, HP4 2AB Tel: (01442) 863388 Fax: (01442) 863444 E-mail: sales@3ctech.co.uk *Computer systems consultancy, services, software*

3c Technology Ltd, Network House Pheonix Court, Hawkins Road, Colchester, CO2 8LA Tel: (01206) 790060 Fax: (01206) 790058 E-mail: info@3ctech.co.uk *Computer resellers*

3C Test Ltd, Technology Park, Silverstone Circuit, Silverstone, Towcester, Northamptonshire, NN12 8GX Tel: (01327) 857500 Fax: (01327) 857747 E-mail: sales@3ctest.co.uk *EMC test house*

3CL, Stafford Park 16, Telford, Shropshire, TF3 3BS Tel: (01952) 290941 Fax: (01952) 290943 E-mail: info@3cl.com *Industrial refrigeration engineers*

▶ 3D Air Sales Ltd Scotland, McGregor House, South Bank Business Park, Kirkintilloch, Glasgow, G66 1XF Tel: 0141-777 5007 Fax: 0141-777 5009 *Refrigeration services*

3d Computer Systems Ltd, Albany House, 11 New Road, Chippenham, Wiltshire, SN15 1HJ Tel: (01249) 460766 Fax: (01249) 460583 E-mail: sales@3d-computers.co.uk *Computer supplier*

▶ 3d Courier Services, 71 Furnace Lane, Sheffield, S13 9XD Tel: (07817) 708363 E-mail: info@3dcourier.com *Dedicated Direct Deliveries Nationwide*

3d Displays Ltd, Upper Brents, Faversham, Kent, ME13 7DR Tel: (01795) 532947 Fax: (01795) 539934 E-mail: info@3ddisplays.co.uk *Shop fitters*

▶ 3D Group, 3D Group, 165 Westdale Lane, Mapperley, Nottingham, NG3 6DH Tel: 0115-952 2772 E-mail: ddkeypro@hotmail.com *Locksmiths*

▶ 3D Illustration - Digital Illustration Specialists, South View, 43 Queens Road, Accrington, Lancashire, BB5 6AR Tel: (01254) 381027 E-mail: team@3dillustration.co.uk *Design*

3-D Labs, Meadlake Place, Thorpe Lea Road, Egham, Surrey, TW20 8HE Tel: (01784) 470555 Fax: (01784) 470699 E-mail: info@3dlabs.co.uk *Microchip manufacturers & leading suppliers high performance graphics*

3d Machine Shop Engineering Ltd, 23 The Business Centre, 20 James Road, Tyseley, Birmingham, B11 2BA Tel: 0121-628 6628 Fax: 0121-628 2008 E-mail: cliffdavies1@btconnect.com *Special fastener manufrs*

▶ 3D Me, 55 Roman Road, Bearsden, Glasgow, G61 2SG Tel: 0141-530 9553 Fax: 0141-530 9554 E-mail: 3dme@hillsoft.co.uk *3D Me is a trading style of Hillside Software Publishing Ltd.*

3D Mouding Ltd, Unit 55-59, Broton Drive, Halstead, Essex, CO9 1HB Tel: (01787) 476864 Fax: (01787) 475856 E-mail: asmith@3dmouding.co.uk *Injection moulders manufrs*

3D Security Systems Ltd, 66A Market Street, Watford, WD18 0PX Tel: (01923) 219141 Fax: (01923) 219142 *Security installers*

3d Services Ltd, The Studio, 142 Main Street, Yaxley, Peterborough, PE7 3LB Tel: (01733) 243552 Fax: (01733) 243182 *Commercial & architectural model makers*

▶ 3D Space Ltd, Warwick Way, Pimlico, London, SW1V 1QT Tel: (020) 7840 8130 E-mail: enquiries@3dspacestorage.co.uk *3D Space specialise in offering storage solutions in the very heart of London. We currently have sites in Pimlico and Queensway. 24 /7 access means full flexibility, with state of the art security.*

▶ 3D Structural Fabrications, Bull Street, Gornal Wood, Dudley, West Midlands, DY3 2NQ Tel: (01902) 656263 Fax: (01902) 656036 E-mail: structuralservices@blueyonder.co.uk *Structural steelwork fabrication company.*

▶ 3D Structural Services, 35 Humphrey Street, Lower Gornal, Dudley, West Midlands, DY3 2AW Tel: (01902) 656263 Fax: (01902) 656263 E-mail: structuralservices@blueyonder.co.uk *Structural steelwork civil detailing services*

3d Systems Europe Ltd, Mark House, Mark Road, Hemel Hempstead, Hertfordshire, HP2 7UA Tel: (01442) 282600 Fax: (01442) 282601 *Rapid prototyping machine systems*

3d Transmissions, 5 Blackwater Trading Estate, Blackwater Way, Aldershot, Hampshire, GU12 4DJ Tel: (01252) 310413 Fax: (01252) 350572 E-mail: sales@3dtransmissions.com *Reconditioned gear box & unit rebuilders*

▶ 3DAV - video by numbers, Studio 2-11, Parkers House, 48 Regents Street, Cambridge, CB2 1FD Tel: 01223 505600 E-mail: jamie@3dav.com *Conference videos, events, filming*

3DD, 3 Marlow Workshops, Arnold Circus, London, E2 7JN Tel: (020) 7739 7933 Fax: (020) 7739 7195 E-mail: sales@3dd.co.uk *Model makers*

3di International, Brighton Road, Shoreham-by-Sea, West Sussex, BN43 6RE Tel: (01273) 464883 Fax: (01273) 454238 E-mail: sussex@3dillc.com *Aerial survey & mapping service*

▶ 3ds Pallets, 7 Stanley Road, Barnsley, South Yorkshire, S70 3PG Tel: (01226) 292211 Fax: (01226) 292211

▶ 3dtp Ltd, Cardrew Industrial Estate, Redruth, Cornwall, TR15 1SS Tel: (01209) 314458 *Technical graphic designers*

▶ 3E's Multimedia, Cooks Lane, Kingshurst, Birmingham, B37 6NZ Tel: 0121 329 8366 Fax: 0121 779 1317 E-mail: jan.richards@3es.com *E learning curriculum supplier*

3form Design, Unit 63 Basepoint Business & Innovation Centre, Caxton Close, Andover, Hampshire, SP10 3FG Tel: (01264) 326306 Fax: (01264) 326308 E-mail: info@3formdesign.com *3form Design (3fD) are a leading Product & Engineering Design Consultancy cased in the South UK.*With our manufacturing facilities we can take a product from Concept to Manufacture.*

▶ 3G Creative Graphic Design Glasgow Scotland, Design House, 7 Woodside Crescent, Glasgow, GL3 7UL Tel: 0141-332 3892 Fax: 0141-332 2233 E-mail: g3creative@tiscali.co.uk *we have just completed organic soup label designs for Antony Worrall Thompson, we have design a range of packs for weightwatchers our clients include: the Largest Tourist Board in scotland, The Red Cross and DMAS the worlds largest supplier of offshore cabins - call: 0141 332 3892 or visit our web site www.g3creative.co.uk*

▶ 3g Distribution, Marshalls Court, Shrewsbury, SY1 2HX Tel: (01743) 270470 Fax: (01743) 270470 *Motorcycle distributors*

▶ 3gdesign Studio, 251 Kingsway, Manchester, M19 1AL Tel: (0870) 0638370 Fax: 0161-610 6018 E-mail: sales@3Gdesignstudio.co.uk *Complete graphic design solutions,*innovate, create, exhibit*

▶ 3k Make-up, Showroom & Studio, 84, Queens Road, North Camp, Farnborough, Hampshire, GU14 6JR Tel: (01252) 371123 Fax: (01252) 377110 E-mail: info@3kmake-up.com *Family run business range of make-up & training, professionals*

3l1t3 Ltd, 43 Beckfield Road, Bingley, West Yorkshire, BD16 1QR Tel: (01274) 820102 Fax: (01274) 825558 E-mail: admin@3l1t3.com *Computer consultancy*

3M Abrasive Systems, 3 M Centre, Cain Road, Bracknell, Berkshire, RG12 8HT Tel: (01344) 858974 Fax: (01344) 858195 E-mail: abrasives.uk@mmm.com *Manufacturers of abrasive belts*

3M Health Care Ltd, 3M House, Morley Street, Loughborough, Leicestershire, LE11 1EP Tel: (01509) 611611 Fax: (01509) 613061 E-mail: jsmith123@mmm.com *3M, a global technology company is continuously finding new ways to make amazing things happen. 3M completed its acquisition of Biotrace International PLC, a manufacturer and supplier of industrial microbiology products used in food processing safety, health care, industrial hygiene and defence applications in November 2006.*

▶ 3m Hillington, Johnstone Avenue, Hillington Industrial Estate, Glasgow, G52 4NZ Tel: 0141-891 4300

3M Neotechnic Ltd, UpBrooks, Clitheroe, Lancashire, BB7 1NX Tel: (01200) 422251 Fax: (01200) 428993 E-mail: neotechnic@mmm.com *Aerosol can & valve manufacturers. Also deep drawing specialist services*

3M Tapes & Adhesives Group, 3M Centre, Cain Road, Bracknell, Berkshire, RG12 8HT Tel: (01344) 858000 Fax: (01344) 858278 *Adhesive tapes, industrial, packaging & double sided*

3m UK plc, Gorseinon Road, Penllergaer, Swansea, SA4 9GD Tel: (01792) 893021 Fax: (01792) 890427 *Adhesive tape manufrs*

3M Water Filtration, 3M Centre, Cain Road, Bracknell, Berkshire, RG12 8HT Tel: (01344) 858000 Fax: (01344) 858559 E-mail: foodservice-europe@mmm.com *Total solutions for commercial and domestic water filtration and treatment needs. 3M Water Filtration based in Bracknell, Berkshire offers a total solution for water filtration and treatment needs in the home, in foodservice and vending and for caravans and boats. They also provide reverse osmosis systems for various applications notably steamers and combi ovens.*

3p Paint Co Stockport Ltd, Hallam Mill, Hallam Street, Stockport, Cheshire, SK2 6PT Tel: 0161-477 4202 Fax: 0161-477 4202 E-mail: 3ppaintcompany@tiscali.co.uk *Industrial & general purpose paints*

▶ 3rd Way Communications Ltd, 5 Woodhouse Court, Mansfield Woodhouse, Mansfield, Nottinghamshire, NG19 9LQ Tel: (0870) 2486001 Fax: 0871 2425703 E-mail: info@3rdwaycomms.com

3S Balloon Printers, Unit 9, Hortonwood 33, Telford, Shropshire, TF1 7EX Tel: (01952) 677506 Fax: (01952) 677464 E-mail: sales@3sballons.com *Balloon, t-shirt & sign printers*

3t Productions, Hill House, 8 Warwick Road, Southam, Warwickshire, CV47 0HN Tel: (01926) 811822 Fax: (01926) 811823 E-mail: 3t@inovates.it *Design consultants*

3tech Systems Ltd, Whitwick Business Park, Stenson Road, Coalville, Leicestershire, LE67 4JP Tel: (01530) 276500 Fax: (01530) 813526 E-mail: info@3techsystems.co.uk *IT consultants*

3-Towns Courier Services, 1 New England Road, Saltcoats, Ayrshire, KA21 6JT Tel: (07890) 981 974 Fax: (01294) 471 294 E-mail: sean.docherty@3-townscourierservices.co.uk *Same day courier service*

▶ 3TYUK (uk), 7 The Brent, Dartford, DA1 1YD Tel: (01322) 311899 E-mail: makinfe@yahoo.com *Printing internet access & stationary*

▶ 3w Designs Ltd, 2 Cowslip Close, Tilehurst, Reading, RG31 4EY Tel: (0870) 0175050 E-mail: dave@3w-designs.co.uk *We offer a flexible and comprehensive web design service that meets the needs of all types and sizes of companies. From a single page site to a full e-commerce solution, we have the knowledge and experience to offer you a value for money web site that you can be proud of.*

3y2k Computer Maintenance, The Coach House, Trewyn, Pandy, Abergavenny, Gwent, NP7 7PG Tel: (01873) 890002 E-mail: threey2k@hotmail.com *Commercial computer systems supply &support*

▶ 4 Advantage Metering Solutions Ltd, Westside House, Old Great North Road, Sutton-On-Trent, Newark, Nottinghamshire, NG23 6QS Tel: (01636) 822860 Fax: (01636) 823066 E-mail: juliec@4advantage.co.uk *Metering, monitoring & controls suppliers*

▶ 4 Conveyor Solutions Ltd, PO Box 87, Batley, West Yorkshire, WF17 9YB Tel: (01924) 422110 Fax: (01924) 422009 E-mail: enquiries@nuwavesystems.plus.com *Materials handling including all types of conveyors & turnkey systems*

4 D Model Shop Ltd, 120 Leman Street, London, E1 8EU Tel: (020) 7264 1288 Fax: (020) 7264 1299 E-mail: info@modelshop.co.uk *Model retailer*

▶ 4 Dimensions, Tall Pines, London Road, Crowborough, East Sussex, TN6 1TA Tel: 01892 663534 E-mail: handy@4dimensions.co.uk *Property maintenance and general handyman service*

▶ 4 Homes Abroad, 6 Henley Close, Chardstock, Axminster, Devon, EX13 7SX Tel: (01454) 777686 E-mail: sales@4homesabroad.com *International property sales company, offering the largest range of property from many countries around the world.*Visit our website and contact us to open the door on this great selection of homes and services.*

4 Imprint Group, Broadway House, Trafford Wharf Road, Trafford Park, Manchester, M17 1DD Tel: 0161-872 9527 Fax: (0870) 2413441 E-mail: sales@4imprint.co.uk *Incentive gift designers & manufrs*

4 Kids, 74 High St, Hanham, Bristol, BS15 3DS Tel: 0117-961 6808 *Baby & nursery equipment*

4 Mat Systems Ltd, 69 High Street, Swadlincote, Derbyshire, DE11 8JA Tel: (01283) 512333 Fax: (01283) 229905 *Computer resellers*

4 Q D Motor Control, 30 Reach Road, Burwell, Cambridge, CB25 0AH Tel: (01638) 741930 Fax: (01638) 744080 E-mail: sales@4qd.co.uk *Motor controllers*

4 S Informations Systems Ltd, 4 The Square, Milnthorpe, Cumbria, LA7 7QJ Tel: (01539) 563091 Fax: (01539) 562475 E-mail: sales@4s-dawn.com *Software developers*

▶ 4 Sight Consulting, 20 Watt Road, Bridge of Weir, Renfrewshire, PA11 3DL Tel: (01505) 615119 Fax: (01505) 615119 E-mail: enquiries@4-sightconsulting.co.uk *Safety engineering consultancy*

4 Web UK Ltd, 12 Maycroft Avenue, Withington, Manchester, M20 4XX Tel: 0161-291 8082 E-mail: ross@4webuk.com *E commerce & website design development promotion & hosting*

▶ 400 Co. Ltd, Unit A1-A2 Askew Crescent Workshops, 2 Askew Cresent, London, W12 9DP Tel: (020) 8746 1400 Fax: (020) 8746 0847 E-mail: christian@the400.co.uk *The 400 Company provide the best in Digi cameras, crewing & Avid Post-Production for the broadcast industry.*

476 Sprowston Road, 277 Aylsham, Norwich, NR3 2RE Tel: (01603) 400757 Fax: (01603) 406927 E-mail: info@anglingdirect.co.uk *Fishing tackle retailers*

4business, 72 New Bond Street, London, W1S 1RR Tel: (020) 7514 9901 E-mail: sales@base4business.com *4 BUSINESS provides a range of company formation and business services that aim to support your business in the UK*

4c Electronics Ltd, Diamond Court Douglas Close, Preston Farm Business Park, Preston Farm Industrial Estate, Stockton-on-Tees, Cleveland, TS18 3SB Tel: (01642) 616449 Fax: (01642) 605772 E-mail: sales@4celectronics.co.uk *Control system & electronic design consultants*

4c Security Systems Ltd, 7 Fern Hill, Benllech, Tyn-y-Gongl, Gwynedd, LL74 8UE Tel: (01248) 853525 Fax: (01248) 853525 E-mail: sales@4csecurity.co.uk *Burglar alarm systems fitters*

▶ 4Consultancy Ltd, 45 Grange Avenue, Highbridge, Somerset, TA9 3AJ Tel: (01278) 785919 E-mail: Brad@4consultancy.net *4C, a South West UK based agency. We do the things companies keep meaning to get around to. Sales - Marketing - Creative - New Media (Web design). Approachable and creative. For more information visit www.4consultancy.net*

4d Engineering Ltd, Phoenix House, Phoenix Way, Cirencester, Gloucestershire, GL7 1QG Tel: (01285) 650111 Fax: (01285) 650150 E-mail: sales@mastercam.co.uk *CAD software consultants*

4d Signs, The Old Dairy, Wonston, Hazelbury Bryan, Sturminster Newton, Dorset, DT10 2EE Tel: (01258) 817878 Fax: (01258) 817879 E-mail: info@4dsigns.co.uk *Sign makers & digital printers*

▶ 4Designs, 1 Gables Close, Maidenhead, Berkshire, SL6 8QD Tel: (01628) 675269 E-mail: info@4Designs.co.uk *Electronics design consultancy*

▶ 4discussion, Crown House, Manchester Road, Wilmslow, Cheshire, SK9 1BH Tel: 01625 543711 Fax: 01625 521432 E-mail: research@fastforwardresearch.com

▶ 4ja Transport Ltd, Welton Industrial Estate, Railway Road, Blairgowrie, Perthshire, PH10 6EP Tel: (01250) 872233 Fax: (01250) 872299

▶ 4Leisure Recruitment, PO Box 845, Uxbridge, Middlesex, UB8 9BJ Tel: (0870) 2423339 Fax: (01895) 235581 E-mail: info@4leisurerecruitment.co.uk *A UK recruitment and training company specialising in jobs in the health, leisure and fitness industry. Candidates can search for jobs and apply online*

4m Flooring UK Ltd, House The Wharf, Thomas Street, Crewe, CW1 2BD Tel: (01270) 251244 Fax: (01270) 251344 E-mail: sales@4m-flooring.co.uk *Specialist industrial flooring manufrs*

▶ 4mags, 30B Grosvenor Road, Caversham, Reading, RG4 5EN Tel: 07939 084481 E-mail: sales@4mags.co.uk *Sells Playboy magazine back issues from 1950s to present day.*

▶ 4Max Visual Impact, The Stables, Claverdon Oaks, Henley Road, Claverdon, Warwick, CV35 8PS Tel: (0870) 2364163 Fax: (0870) 2364164 E-mail: john.blakey@4max.co.uk *Large format Digital printing including Exhibition stands and graphics, panels, posters, banners, pop up and banner stands, canvas prints. All traditional litho printing also undertaken.*

▶ 4plas Ltd, 7 Aldin Way, Hinckley, Leicestershire, LE10 0GE Tel: (01455) 612601 Fax: (01455) 613853 E-mail: enquiries@4plas.com *Technical sales, plastic raw materials & distributors*

▶ 4point2 media, Hampton, Peterborough, PE7 8BQ Tel: (01733) 890360 Fax: (01733) 890360 E-mail: answers@4point2.co.uk *Web Design, Web Development, Content Management Systems, E-Commerce Sites, Database Development, Hosting, Dedicated & CoLocation Consultancy*

4productions, 1-3 Lime Hill Road, Tunbridge Wells, Kent, TN1 1LJ Tel: (01892) 524428 Fax: 01892 614811 E-mail: info@4productions.co.uk *4Productions is a leading supplier of sms bulk messaging technologies. Being a flexible dynamic company with no red tape, we can provide a solution to your wildest communication needs. We are one of the UK's leading SMS software integrators providing VOIP, two way sms messaging, reverse bill sms, bulk messaging, contract sims and an sms gateway with direct contact to airtime providers. Contact your customers in the most efficient and cost effective way directly from your software. We are here to help!*

4th Hospitality Ltd, Unit 3 Des Roches Square, Witney, Oxfordshire, OX28 4LQ Tel: (01993) 899200 Fax: (01993) 775081 E-mail: info@abs-ltd.com *E-business provider*

▶ 4VisMedia, 18 Alderwood, Chineham, Basingstoke, Hampshire, RG24 8TU Tel: (01256) 320733 E-mail: enquiries@4vismedia.co.uk *Web design services*

▶ 4xCM Ltd, Craigleith Road, Edinburgh, EH4 2EB Tel: 0131-477 7775 Fax: 0131-332 7467 E-mail: info@4xcm.co.uk *Specialists in CRM Products and services, for sales, marketing and customer service teams. Customer Relationship Management experience and know how to ensure effective implementations for companies of all sizes.*

5 Fifteen Ltd, 180 Bedford Avenue, Slough, SL1 4RA Tel: (01753) 440515 Fax: (01753) 440567 E-mail: info@5fifteen.com *Computer software & systems suppliers*

▶ 5 Star Adhesives, P O Box 96, Liverpool, L17 3BY Tel: 0151-733 7182 Fax: 0151-733 7182 E-mail: info@glue-shop.com *Adhesive manufacturers including industrial & cyanoacrylate. In addition, automotive chemical product manufrs*

5 Star Catering Equipment Hire, 20 Greys Court, Kingsland Grange, Woolston, Warrington, WA1 4SH Tel: 0161-835 4040 Fax: (01925) 820179 E-mail: sales@5starhire.co.uk *Barbeques: Authentic Mediterranean barbeque - cooked from charcoal grills for Events, Fun days and Corporate Functions. Events Catering: Anything from a single unit to a complete catering and ice cream package from an ISO registered family run Company with over thirty years experience. Outside Catering: Catering at permanent sites with static or mobile units. All types of modern catering units available for Events. Caterers Contract: Short or long term catering options at construction sites etc. Many years experience of Stadium Catering, Park Cafe's and Mobile catering contracts.*

5 Star Homes Ltd, 104 Corkill Road, Omagh, County Tyrone, BT78 1UX Tel: (028) 8284 0900 Fax: (028) 8284 0281 E-mail: sales@5starhomes.co.uk *Property developers & timber frame house manufrs*

5 Star Meats, 95 Redlam, Blackburn, BB2 1UN Tel: (01254) 698781 Fax: (01254) 698781 *Butchers*

5 Star Windows & Conservatories Ltd, The Old Stores, Stanklyn Lane, Summerfield, Kidderminster, Worcestershire, DY11 7RY Tel: (01562) 66955 Fax: (01562) 66955 E-mail: sales@5star-online.co.uk *Suppliers and installers of fine quality Windows,Doors,Porches,Conservatories and Orangeries. Main agents for Sunflex bi-folding doors,Pilkington energikare glass, fitrite decking & fencing.Large Showroom open 7 days...NEW..Trade Counter now open..*

▶ 50plus Handyman, 11 Sycamore Dene, Chesham, Buckinghamshire, HP5 3JT Tel: (0845) 2250495 Fax: (01494) 791609 E-mail: enquiries@the50plus.co.uk *50plus Handyman provides a reliable & guaranteed handyman, plumbing, electrical & repair service for businesses & householders.*

52nd Street, Unit 11 Oakwell Business Centre, Oakwell View, Barnsley, South Yorkshire, S71 1HX Tel: (01226) 200900 Fax: (01226) 200222 E-mail: shaun@52ndstreet.co.uk *Sound & light installers & distributors*

▶ 533 Software, Arable Centre, Winterbourne Monkton, Swindon, SN4 9NW Tel: (01672) 539000 Fax: (01672) 539111 *Computer consumables*

▶ 5750 Components Ltd, 1 Overbrook Lane, Villiers Court, Knowsley Business Pk, Prescot, Merseyside, L34 9FB Tel: 0151-548 5750 Fax: 0151-548 1222 E-mail: am@5750components.co.uk Sales Contact: A. Murphy *Laser cutting & profiling cutting services. Also CNC engineering services or machinists & sheet metalwork engineers & fabricators*

▶ 5th of 4th Business Development, 57 Kennedy Way, Airth, Falkirk, FK2 8GB Tel: 01324 831789 E-mail: enquiries@5th-of-4th.com *Business Development and research consultancy based in and working throughout Scotland.**Specialising in, but not restricted to work with not-for-profit organisations, and the social sector (public or voluntary).**Can lead or assist with business planning, market research, independent reviews and grant applications.*

▶ 6 Nations, 12 South Bridge, Edinburgh, EH1 1DD Tel: (0870) 3500890 Fax: 0870 350 0891 E-mail: sales@6-nations-hospitality.com *6 Nations Hospitality are delighted to offer OFFICIAL packages at all venues.* *Our product range enables you to decide which packages most suit your budget*

60 Plus Textiles Services Ltd, Ingsend Farm, Barley, Nelson, Lancashire, BB9 6LJ Tel: (01282) 614442 Fax: (01282) 694620 *Textiles*

600 Centre, Unit 18-19 Loughborough Motorway Trading Estate, Gelders Hall Road, Shepshed, Loughborough, Leicestershire, LE12 9NH Tel: (01509) 600600 Fax: (01509) 600159 E-mail: sales@600centre.co.uk Purchasing Contact: R. Grocock Sales Contact: R. Grocock *The 600 Centre is a focal point for customers to appreciate demonstrations of some of the most sought after international machine tool products covering turning, milling, grinding, wire and die sink EDM. Application engineering and turnkey cells and systems for production and toolmaking sectors are carried out at the 30,000 sq ft permanent exhibition centre at Shepshed a well as nationwide support for sales, service and spares.*International machine tool names include Fanuc Vertical Machining Centres, Fanuc EDM Wirecut Machines, Toyoda Mitsui Seiki Horizontal and Vertical Machining Centres, Toyoda Mitsui Seiki Cylindrical Grinding Machines, Thread Grinding Machines, Okamoto Grinding Machines, Richmond Vertical Machining Centres, Perfect Grinding Machines, Colchester and Harrison Turning Centres and Lathes.*

600 Group Plc, 600 House, Landmark Court, Revie Road, Leeds, LS11 8JT Tel: 0113-277 6100 Fax: 0113-276 5600 E-mail: sales@600group.com *Machine tool manufrs*

600 Lathes, Union Street, Heckmondwike, West Yorkshire, WF16 0HL Tel: (01924) 415000 Fax: (01924) 415017 E-mail: sales@600lathes.co.uk *Standard centre lathe manufrs*

6th Degree Ltd, Suite 6, Bank Chambers, 29 High Street, Ewell, Epsom, Surrey, KT17 1SB Tel: 020 8786 3664 Fax: 020 8786 3665 *6th degree ltd - brand driven web and print communications agency. We are an experienced team of professionals who are able to provide you with the tools required to help your business grow. We are experts in the fields of corporate identity and logo design, brochure and leaflet design and print, website design and web programming, website banner adverts, marketing communications materials design and production. We are able to offer your company a wide range of services and can provide as little or as much support as you require. Email or call us today to discuss how we can help your business grow.*

▶ 7 Safe Ltd, Unit L, South Cambridge Business Park, Babraham Road, Sawston, Cambridge, CB22 3JH Tel: (0870) 6001667 Fax: (0870) 6001668 E-mail: kris.raven@7safe.com *Computer security system services*

▶ 7 Valley Transport Ltd, Unit 29 Shifnal Industrial Estate, Lamledge Lane, Shifnal, Shropshire, TF11 8SD Tel: (01952) 461991 Fax: (01952) 461950 E-mail: sales@7valleytransport.com

▶ 75 Ltd, Studio 52, The Truman Brewery, 91 Brick Lane, London, E1 6QL Tel: 0845 2221075 E-mail: info@ten75.com

777 Waste Management, 158 Beddington Lane, Croydon, CR0 4TE Tel: (020) 8689 6861 Fax: (020) 8689 7176 E-mail: maxine.grew@777group.co.uk *Skip & bin hire, waste removal & recycling centre*

▶ 8el, Sovereign House, Vastern Road, Reading, RG1 8BT Tel: 0845 3300093 Fax: 0845 3300093 E-mail: info@8el.com *Telecoms service providers*

8over8 Ltd, T S I C, University Of Ulster, Northland Road, Londonderry, BT48 7TW Tel: (028) 7137 5655 Fax: (028) 7137 5652 E-mail: jobs@8over8.com *Procon is a web based lifecycle contract management system designed with the needs of the energy sector in mind, an information management tool*

925 Ltd, Unit 46-47 Monument Business Park, Warpsgrove Lane, Chalgrove, Oxford, OX44 7RW Tel: (01865) 891925 Fax: (01865) 891929 E-mail: enquiries@925ltd.co.uk *Office furniture designers and manufacturers.*

939 Engineering Co., Lodgefield Road, Halesowen, West Midlands, B62 8AX Tel: 0121-559 1133 Fax: 0121-559 0321 *Machinists & electrical engineers*

▶ 999print, 251 Kingsway, Manchester, M19 1AL Tel: 0161-610 8032 Fax: 0161-610 6015 E-mail: sales@999print.com *Premium full colour print fast*

▶ 9SKY, 135 High Street, Parade House, Watford, WD17 1NS Tel: 01923 630877 E-mail: admin@9sky.org.uk *Based in India and the UK we supply incense and incense burners, Vapourising oils, soapstone burners , handicrafts, glass pipes, herb grinders, organic masalas,india travel*

A 1 Dynamic Balancing Ltd, 7-9 Hagley Road, Hayley Green, Halesowen, West Midlands, B63 1DG Tel: 0121-501 3705 Fax: 0121-501 3615 E-mail: sales@wdbltd.co.uk *Dynamic & static balancing services*

A.1. Electronics, Warren Avenue, Koloma, Fakenham, Norfolk, NR21 8NP Tel: (01328) 856226 Fax: (0845) 1665227 E-mail: enquiries@a1electronics.co.uk *Electronic repair centre services*

▶ A 1 Hire & Sales Ltd, 76 Old Wareham Road, Poole, Dorset, BH12 4QR Tel: (01202) 736899 Fax: (01202) 732726 E-mail: sales@a1hire.co.uk *Tool hire & sales, powered access machines, operators available*

▶ A 1 Monitor Repairs Ltd, D Spring Hill Industrial Park, 110 Steward Street, Birmingham, B18 7AF Tel: 0121-454 6396 *Computer maintenance & repair services*

A 1 Sheetmetal Flues Ltd, Maun Way, Boughton Industrial Estate, Newark, Nottinghamshire, NG22 9ZD Tel: (01623) 860578 Fax: (0870) 1602281 E-mail: info@a1flues.co.uk *Metal chimney & flue manufrs*

▶ A 2 B Removals, 64 Longtown Road, Dundee, DD4 8JS Tel: (01382) 860830

A 4 Engineering Ltd, 7 Manor Park, 35 Willis Way, Poole, Dorset, BH15 3SZ Tel: (01202) 676047 Fax: (01202) 684675 E-mail: a4eng@a4eng.com *Precision engineers*

▶ A A A Carpetcare, 45 Kinmundy Drive, Westhill, Aberdeenshire, AB32 6SU Tel: (01224) 740992 E-mail: info@aaacarpetcare.co.uk *CARPET CLEANING IN ABERDEEN, ABERDEENSHIRE, CARPET CLEANING SPECIALISTS FOR DOMESTIC AND COMMERCIAL PREMISES. CONTRACT WELCOME*

▶ A A A Conservatory Roof Repairs & Replacement, 8 Birchwood Drive, Lightwater, Surrey, GU18 5RX Tel: (01276) 453654 Fax: E-mail: timhayesaaa@msn.com *Conservatory repairs refurbishment & replacement also double glazing*

A A A Stationery, 15-19 Benwell Road, London, N7 7BL Tel: (020) 7700 4246 Fax: (020) 7700 3150 E-mail: info@galaxywholesalers.com *Stationery suppliers*

A A A www.3d-imaging.co.uk, 4 George Street, Whalley, Clitheroe, Lancashire, BB7 9TH Tel: (0870) 7409016 Fax: (0870) 1315997 *3D computer animation rendering, architecture & illustrations*

▶ A A Aardvark Locksmiths, Dane Road, Coventry, CV2 4JW Tel: (0845) 0710126 E-mail: ray@raygibbins.wanadoo.co.uk *24 HOUR LOCKSMITH SERVICES.*All types of locks opened and replaced.*Upvc specialist.Wooden door locks, patio, garage and window locks.*All work guaranteed.*Senior citizen discount.*

A A Apointments, St. Clare House, 30-33 Minories, London, EC3N 1PQ Tel: (01344) 891987 Fax: (020) 7480 5467 E-mail: travel@aaappointments.com

continued

Employment agency Also at: Bracknell, Crawley & Salford

A A Automatics, Unit E1 Gadd Street, Nottingham, NG7 4BJ Tel: 0115-978 0965 Fax: 0115-978 0965 *Amusement machine operators & repairers*

A & A Bodies, Morbec Farm, Arterial Road, Wickford, Essex, SS12 9JF Tel: (01268) 590446 Fax: (01268) 414416 *Commercial vehicle manufrs*

A A Brown & Sons, 1 Snake Lane, Alvechurch, Birmingham, B48 7NT Tel: 0121-445 5395 Fax: 0121-445 2113 E-mail: sales@aabrownandsons.com *Fine quality sporting gun makers & repairers*

A & A Building Maintenance Ltd, 22 Tannoch Drive, Cumbernauld, Glasgow, G67 2XX Tel: (01236) 456027 Fax: (01236) 456027 *Joinery manufrs*

A A C, Unit 24, AK Business Park, Russell Road, Southport, Merseyside, PR9 7SA Tel: (01704) 505213 Fax: (01704) 506480 E-mail: info@allairconditioning.net *Air conditioning installers*

▶ A A C C Ltd, 32 Beaumaris Grove, Shenley Church End, Milton Keynes, MK5 6EN Tel: (01908) 330800 *Computer software consultants*

A A C Cyroma Ltd, C P L House, Beaumont Road, Banbury, Oxfordshire, OX16 1RJ Tel: (01295) 759200 Fax: (01295) 270614 *Plastic injection moulding & vacuum forming*

A A C Spectrum Ltd, Brierley Park Close, Sutton-in-Ashfield, Nottinghamshire, NG17 3FW Tel: (01623) 440111 Fax: (01623) 444670 E-mail: nottingham@aacgroup.co.uk *Plastics injection moulders*

▶ A A Carriers Ltd, Oaks Lane, Barnsley, South Yorkshire, S71 1HT Tel: (01226) 285222 Fax: (01226) 285222

A A Computer Services, The Old Smithy, Henllan Amgoed, Whitland, Dyfed, SA34 0SN Tel: 01994 240832 Fax: 01994 240786 *Computer sales & services*

▶ A A Contractors, 1 Somerton Green, Bognor Regis, West Sussex, PO22 8EZ Tel: (01243) 863209 Fax: (01243) 863025

A A Duncan Biggar Ltd, 16a Broughton Road, Biggar, Lanarkshire, ML12 6HA Tel: (01899) 220170 Fax: (01899) 220170 *Electrical plumbers & heating engineers*

A A Electric UK Ltd, Witty Street, Hull, HU3 4TT Tel: (01482) 229880 Fax: (01482) 589644 E-mail: sales@aaelectric.co.uk *Electrical component distributors*

A A Electronique Services Ltd, Unit 5, Gtrove Park Business Estate, Waltham Road, White Waltham, Maidenhead, Berkshire, SL6 3LW Tel: (020) 8893 1907 Fax: (020) 8893 1908 *Sub-contracting repair service*

A A Engineering Industrial Doors, The Garage Doors Showroom, Seven Brethren Bank, Sticklepath, Barnstaple, Devon, EX31 2AS Tel: (01271) 375531 Fax: (01271) 375577 E-mail: info@aaengineering.co.uk *Garage & industrial roller shutter doors manufrs*

▶ A & A Fabrications, Unit 2 Athertons Quay, Warrington, WA5 1AH Tel: (01925) 419357 Fax: (01925) 419357 *Steel fabricators*

▶ A A Fabrications South West Ltd, Unit 10 Deverill Road Trading Estate, Deverill Road, Sutton Veny, Warminster, Wiltshire, BA12 7BZ Tel: (01985) 841441 Fax: (01985) 841441 *Steel fabricators*

A A Fire Security, 69 Rawson Road, Bolton, BL1 4JQ Tel: (01204) 497305 Fax: (01294) 849181 *Fire extinguisher suppliers*

A A F-Mcquay UK Ltd, Bassington Lane, Cramlington, Northumberland, NE23 8AF Tel: (01670) 713477 Fax: (01670) 714370 *Air conditioning, filtration & clean room manufrs*

A A Fork Truck & Engineering Ltd, 98-104 Vauxhall Road, Liverpool, L3 6EZ Tel: 0151-236 7421 Fax: 0151-236 2767 E-mail: sales@evcuk.com *Fork lift truck manufrs*

A & A Furnishings Ltd, Farington, Leyland, PR25 4GU Tel: (01772) 457836 Fax: (01772) 436188 *Furniture frames manufrs*

▶ A A Glanville Ltd, 53 Ashford Road, Plymouth, PL4 7BL Tel: (01752) 660906

▶ A A Gliderobes, Stour Valley Industrial Estate, Ashford Road, Chartham, Canterbury, Kent, CT4 7HF Tel: (01227) 731746 Fax: (01227) 733745 *Sliding wardrobe systems manufrs*

A A H Pharmaceuticals Ltd, Sapphire Court, Walsgrave Triangle, Coventry, CV2 2TX Tel: (024) 7643 2000 Fax: (024) 7643 2001 E-mail: info@aah.co.uk *Pharmaceutical distributors* Also at: Branches throughout the U.K.

A A H Pharmaceuticals Ltd, 120 Lobley Hill Road, Gateshead, Tyne & Wear, NE8 4YR Tel: (024) 7643 2000 Fax: 0191-461 0175 *Pharmacy sales*

A A H Pharmaceuticals Ltd, 204 Polmadie Road, Glasgow, G42 0PH Tel: 0141-423 5888 Fax: 0141-423 7662 *Pharmaceutical products wholesalers*

A A H Pharmaceuticals Ltd, Faringdon Avenue, Romford, RM3 8LG Tel: (01708) 349311 Fax: (01708) 370353 *Pharmaceuticals suppliers*

A A H Pharmaceuticals Ltd, Stonefield Way, Ruislip, Middlesex, HA4 0JP Tel: (020) 8841 6010 Fax: (020) 8842 1108 *Pharmaceuticals services*

▶ A A Industrial Door, Canklow Meadows Industrial Estate, West Bawtry Road, Rotherham, South Yorkshire, S60 2XL Tel: (01709) 830090 Fax: (01709) 830990 E-mail: aadoors@btinternet.com *Established in 1991 we are the norths leading force in the manufacture, repair and service of all types of Roller Shutter Doors.*

A A Insurance Services, St. Patricks House, 17 Pennarth Road, Cardiff, CF10 5ZA Tel: (0870) 5332211 Fax: (029) 2072 5516 *Insurance brokers*

A A Interior Design Ltd, 187 Downs Road, Walmer, Deal, Kent, CT14 7TL Tel: (01304) 373205 Fax: (01304) 373205 E-mail: info@aadesign.uk.com *Independent kitchen, bathroom, design & supply*

A & A Lampkin, Greengate, Silsden, Keighley, West Yorkshire, BD20 9LA Tel: (01535) 652328 Fax: (01535) 657866 *Subcontract precision engineers*

▶ A A Material Handling Ltd, 5 Telford Place, South Newmoor Industrial Estate, Irvine, Ayrshire, KA11 4HW Tel: (01294) 221133 Fax: (01294) 221136 E-mail: enquiries@aamaterialhandlingltd.co.uk *Fork lift truck dealers*

A & A Metalcraft, 169 Whittingham Lane, Goosnargh, Preston, PR3 2JJ Tel: (01772) 866133 Fax: (01772) 864656 *Metal wrought iron manufrs*

A A Packaging Ltd, The Light Industrial Estate, Hesketh Bank, Preston, PR4 6SP Tel: (01772) 617481 Fax: (01772) 614856 E-mail: info@aapackaging.co.uk *Plastic film converters*

A & A Packaging Company Unlimited, 16B Westfield Industrial Estate, Off Portsmouth Road, Horndean, Waterlooville, Hampshire, PO8 9JX Tel: (023) 9259 7792 Fax: (023) 9259 0049 E-mail: sales@aandapackaging.co.uk *General packaging suppliers*

A A Pest Controler, 12 Crossley Crescent, Ashton-under-Lyne, Lancashire, OL6 9EJ Tel: (07835) 423786 Fax: 0161-339 8576 E-mail: info@pestcontroler.co.uk *Pest Control Services including rats, wasps, mice, fleas, rabbit, cockroach, fox, squirrel to name just a few*

A A R Ltd, Unit 12 Langley Wharf, Railway Terrace, Kings Langley, Hertfordshire, WD4 8JE Tel: (01923) 260043 Fax: (01923) 260478 E-mail: info@aar.co.uk *Asbestos waste removal & survey services*

A A R K Electrical Ltd, 4 Dolphin Square, Station Road, Bovey Tracey, Newton Abbot, Devon, TQ13 9AL Tel: (01626) 833703 Fax: (01626) 833475 E-mail: kevinmeldrum@aark-electrical.co.uk *Electrical contractors*

A & A Scaffolding Plus 8 2003 Ltd, Garner Street, Stoke-on-Trent, ST4 7AX Tel: (01782) 202474 Fax: (01782) 201354 E-mail: info@scaffoldingstaffordshire.co.uk *Scaffolding contractors*

▶ A & A Security, 17-25 Devon Place, Glasgow, G41 1RB Tel: 0141-778 6388

A & A Services, 22 Laycock Avenue, Aston, Sheffield, S26 2FU Tel: 0114-287 2787 *Security alarms installation services*

A A Sheet Metals, 1 Fletcher Way, Weston Road, Norwich, NR3 3ST Tel: (01603) 417030 Fax: (01603) 417128 E-mail: alan.harrowing@aasheetmetalnorwich. fsnet.co.uk *Sheet metalwork engineers*

A A Smith Ltd, Pontefract, West Yorkshire, WF7 6WZ Tel: (0845) 3303805 Fax: (0845) 3303806 E-mail: sales@aasmith.co.uk *Blade suppliers & saw doctors*

A A T Computer Services, 57 High Street, Donaghadee, County Down, BT21 0AQ Tel: (028) 9188 8114 Fax: (028) 9188 8370 E-mail: andrew@aatcs.co.uk *Computer services*

A A Telecom Ltd, 38 Thames Street, Sunbury-on-Thames, Middlesex, TW16 6AF Tel: (01932) 788256 Fax: (01932) 781368 E-mail: aatelecom@aol.com *Telecommunications services*

A A Thornton & Co., 29 St. Katherines Street, Northampton, NN1 2QZ Tel: (01604) 638242 Fax: (01604) 638164 E-mail: aat@aathornton.com *Patent, trade mark agents & lawyers*

A & A Time Ltd, 13 Rutherford Road, Maghull, Liverpool, L31 3DD Tel: 0151-531 6913 Fax: 0151-531 7353 E-mail: sales@aandatime.co.uk *Time clocks suppliers*

A & A Traders, 11 Devonshire Mews, Chiswick, London, W4 2HA Tel: (020) 8994 1333 Fax: (020) 8994 5291 E-mail: aat1@aol.com *Medical equipment distributors & suppliers*

A A V Plastic Design, Gore Cross Business Park, Corbin Way, Bradpole, Bridport, Dorset, DT6 3UX Tel: (01308) 427000 Fax: (01308) 420088 E-mail: office@aavplastics.com *Plastic mouldings, toolmaking product design*

A A W Control Systems Ltd, Unit 1, The Firs Farm, Leckhampstead, Newbury, Berkshire, RG20 8RD Tel: (01488) 638928 Fax: (01488) 638947 E-mail: aaw@aawcs.co.uk *Monitoring control*

A A Z Aluminium & uPVC Centre, Satya-Niwas, 53 Hencroft Street South, Slough, SL1 1RF Tel: (01753) 539248 Fax: (01753) 539248 *Insulation specialists*

A Adamson Ltd, Reeki House, Aberdeen Road, Laurencekirk, Kincardineshire, AB30 1AJ Tel: (01561) 377332 Fax: (01561) 378024

▶ A Andrews & Co. Ltd, Unit 1 Kimberley House, Stockport, Cheshire, SK6 3JG Tel: 0161-430 3996

A Andrews & Sons Ltd, 324-330 Meanwood Road, Leeds, LS7 2JE Tel: 0113-262 4751 Fax: 0113-262 3337 E-mail: contracts@andrews-tiles.co.uk *Tile, marble & terrazzo contractors*

A Anthony, Rose Hill House, Pygons Hill Lane, Liverpool, L31 4JF Tel: 0151-526 4008 Fax: 0151-526 1673 *Mergers & acquisitions service to the private company sector*

▶ A Anthony Art, 4 Stanhope Road, Horncastle, Lincolnshire, LN9 5DG Tel: (01507) 526487 Fax: (01507) 526487 E-mail: tonyfield@btinternet.com *Renowned Artist using different forms of media including Sculpting and Fine Art. Hire or Sales of artwork plus also commission work taken. Art Workshops to Schools, Colleges, Hospitals, Prisons and other services. Ring now for a brochure.*

A Attenborough & Co Ltd, Nuart Road, Beeston, Nottingham, NG9 2NH Tel: 0115-925 8185 Fax: 0115-922 7445 E-mail: a.attenborough@btinternet.com *Braid & fringe trimming manufrs*

A B A Alite Ltd, 4 Fen End, Stotfold, Hitchin, Hertfordshire, SG5 4BA Tel: (01462) 732777 Fax: (01462) 732999 *Filling machine manufrs*

A B A Clamping & Connecting Products Ltd, 48 Hemming Road, Washford, Redditch, Worcestershire, B98 0EA Tel: (01527) 517100 Fax: (01527) 517300 E-mail: office@abagroup.com Principal Export Areas: Worldwide *Hose clip & clamp & tool clip manufrs*

A. B. A. Courier Services, Suite F, 2nd Floor, 10-14 West Street, Southend-on-Sea, SS2 6HJ Tel: (01702) 435855 Fax: (01702) 347837 E-mail: sales@abacouriers.co.uk *Courier services, specialising in immediate collection & direct delivery nationwide*

▶ A B Aerials, 38 Old Farm Road, Poole, Dorset, BH15 3LW Tel: (01202) 250550 Fax: (01202) 680626 E-mail: sales@abaerials.co.uk *Suppliers and Installers of Satellite and Terrestrial TV equipment*

A & B Air Systems Ltd, Unit 41 Abenbury Way, Wrexham Industrial Estate, Wrexham, Clwyd, LL13 9UZ Tel: (01978) 661999 Fax: (01978) 664330 E-mail: sales@ab-airsystems.co.uk *Compressed air equipment suppliers*

A & B Auto Electrical Services Ltd, Unit 4 Regal Road Industrial Estate, Weasenham Lane, Wisbech, Cambridgeshire, PE13 2RQ Tel: (01945) 587022 Fax: (01945) 585300 *Auto electrical services*

A B B Ltd, Deben House, 1 Selsdon Way, City Harbour, London, NW10 6DH Tel: (020) 7515 5551 Fax: (020) 7515 5551 E-mail: abb.buildingtechnology@gb.abb.com *Mechanical & electrical*

A B B Ltd, Howard Road, St. Neots, Cambridgeshire, PE19 8EU Tel: (01480) 475321 Fax: (01480) 217948 E-mail: automationltd.sales@gb.abb.com *Industrial instrumentation manufrs* Also at: Luton & Stonehouse

A B B Ltd, Hanover Place, Sunderland, SR4 6BY Tel: 0191-514 4555 Fax: 0191-514 5505 *Control panel manufrs*

A B B Ltd, Hortonwood 37, Telford, Shropshire, TF1 7XT Tel: (01952) 670477 Fax: (01952) 670455 *Process analytical Equipment*

A B B Power Ltd, Stonefield Works, Oulton Road, Stone, Staffordshire, ST15 0RS Tel: (01785) 825050 Fax: (01785) 819019 *Global technology solutions group*

▶ A & B Builders, 8 York Road South, Wigan, Lancashire, WN4 9DT Tel: (01942) 720968 Fax: (01942) 272388 E-mail: abconstruction@abtec.net *Civil engineering services*

A B C Catering Equipment, 196 Edgeware Bury Lane, Edgware, Middlesex, HA8 8QW Tel: (020) 8958 1958 Fax: (020) 8958 1958 E-mail: sales@abccatering.co.uk *A B C Catering Equipment based in Edgware, Middlesex are catering equipment suppliers. Their products include refrigeration, cooking equipment and glass and dishwashers.*

A B C Chemical Co, Woodhouse Road, Todmorden, Lancashire, OL14 5TD Tel: (01200) 420180 Fax: (01706) 819554 E-mail: info@abcchem.co.uk *Printing chemicals manufrs*

A B C Conveyor Belting Ltd, Northfield Rd, Soham, Ely, Cambs, CB7 5UF Tel: (01353) 624322 Fax: (01353) 723859 *Conveyor belt manufacturers, 24 hour service. Site vulcanising*

A B C Enamelling & Fabrications Ltd, High Street, Nailsea, Bristol, BS48 1BW Tel: (01275) 810454 Fax: (01275) 810535 *Metal spraying services*

A B C Fire Ltd, Unit 14 Heath Hill Industrial Estate, Dawley, Telford, Shropshire, TF4 2RH Tel: (01952) 505098 Fax: (01952) 505098 *Closed circuit TV fire & intruder alarm consultants & installers*

A B C Graphics Ltd, 12 Ossory Road, London, SE1 5AN Tel: (020) 7231 5588 Fax: (020) 7231 6128 *Exhibition stands manufrs*

▶ A B C Grimsby Ltd, Lancaster Approach, North Killingholme, Immingham, South Humberside, DN40 3JZ Tel: (01469) 540966 Fax: (01469) 540908

▶ A B C Hygiene Ltd, 39 The Rise, Loudwater, Buckinghamshire, HP13 7BD Tel: (0800) 3286452 Fax: (01494) 816750 E-mail: sales@abchygiene.co.uk *Specialists in washroom hygiene & janitorial products*

▶ A B C Inflatables, 40 Parker Street, Barnsley, South Yorkshire, S70 6EG Tel: (01226) 241314 E-mail: carol@abc-inflatables.org.uk *We hire bouncy castles in the barnsley area , we also cater for fairs with our disco dome*

A B C Insulation Co. Ltd, Alexandra Docks, Newport, Gwent, NP20 2NP Tel: (01633) 211473 Fax: (01633) 843212 *Asbestos removal & thermal insulation*

▶ A B C Lasers, Unit 4, Breaks House, Mill Court, Great Shelford, Cambridge, CB2 5LD Tel: (01223) 210244 Fax: (01223) 846471 E-mail: info@a-b-c-uk.com *Medical laser services*

A B C Net Internet Services, 386 Kenton Road, Harrow, Middlesex, HA3 9DP Tel: (020) 8909 1933 Fax: (020) 8909 2918 E-mail: info@abcnet.co.uk *Internet solution providers*

▶ A B C Removals & Storage, High Peaks, Church Lane, Bledlow Ridge, High Wycombe, Buckinghamshire, HP14 4AX Tel: (01494) 481277 E-mail: info@abcremovalsandstorage.com *Domestic & Commercial Removals, Storage and Packing.**Single items, full or part loads, Optional complete packing service, clean dry secure storage, fully insured. **Please visit our website for more information or to obtain a free no-obligation quote.**

A B C Saddlery Ltd, 31 Hasse Road, Soham, Ely, Cambridgeshire, CB7 5UW Tel: (01353) 721673 Fax: (01353) 721673 *Saddlery product suppliers & exporters*

A B C Signs & Engraving, 17 Whitehall, Christchurch, Dorset, BH23 1DE Tel: (01202) 488444 Fax: (01202) 488822 E-mail: info@florassecret.co.uk *Sign manufr*

▶ A B C Sound & Lighting, 36 Stepfield, Witham, Essex, CM8 3TH Tel: (01376) 511335 Fax: (01376) 511335 *Disco equipment & lighting distributors*

A B C Stainless Ltd, Empson Road, Peterborough, PE1 5UP Tel: (01733) 314515 Fax: (01733) 315273 E-mail: abcstainless@aol.com *Stainless steel fabricator*

A B C Transport Ltd, Plot U Unswood Industrial Estate, Theaklen Drive, St. Leonards-on-Sea, East Sussex, TN38 9AZ Tel: (01424) 755059 Fax: (01424) 722234 *Road transport & haulage*

A B Cable & Wiring, 8 Walworth Enterprise Centre Duke Close, West Way, Andover, Hampshire, SP10 5AP Tel: (01264) 334076 Fax: (01264) 337721 E-mail: sales@abcableandwiring.com *Electrical contractors*

▶ A B Clothing Ltd, 63 Britannia Street, Leicester, LE1 3LE Tel: 0116-251 2518 Fax: 0116-251 2518

▶ A B Computer Repairs, 1 Miramar Way, Hornchurch, Essex, RM12 6LP Tel: (01708) 455192 E-mail: sales@abcomputerrepairs.co.uk *Computer maintenance & repair services*

A B Computers, 12 Union Street, Andover, Hampshire, SP10 1PA Tel: (01264) 406406 Fax: (01264) 395880 E-mail: support@andover.co.uk *Internet service provider & computer manufrs*

A & B Containers Ltd, Windsor Street, Salford, M5 4DG Tel: 0161-736 0716 Fax: 0161-743 8445 E-mail: info@aandbcontainers.co.uk *Pallets & plastic containers*

A & B Contractors Devon Ltd, Porte Farm Kentisbury, Kentisbury, Barnstaple, Devon, EX31 4NL Tel: (01271) 882006 Fax: (01271) 882006 E-mail: info@aandbcontractors.co.uk *Agricultural contractors*

A B Controls & Technology Ltd, Sanderson Street, Lower Don Valley, Sheffield, S9 2UA Tel: 0114-244 2424 Fax: 0114-243 4312 E-mail: info@ab-tech.co.uk Principal Export Areas: Worldwide *Electrical & electronic equipment suppliers*

A & B Converters, 8a Common Lane, Sawston, Cambridge, CB22 3HW Tel: (01223) 830026 Fax: (01223) 830026 E-mail: ab_converters@hotmail.com *Adhesive tape printers*

A B Copyright Ltd, Whitehall Chambers, Halifax Road, Hipperholme, Halifax, West Yorkshire, HX3 8EN Tel: (01422) 200200 Fax: (01422) 200150 E-mail: enquiries@abcopyright.co.uk *Computer consumables & general stationery*

A & B Crane & Electrical Services Ltd, Prince Consort Road, Hebburn, Tyne & Wear, NE31 1EH Tel: 0191-483 6767 Fax: 0191-428 0317 *Crane repair maintenance & manufrs*

A B Creasy & Sons, Scotter Common, Gainsborough, Lincolnshire, DN21 3JF Tel: (01724) 762664 Fax: (01724) 762664 *Sectional building manufrs*

A B D I Machine Tool Co., 67 Camden Street, Birmingham, B1 3DD Tel: 0121-236 1517 Fax: 0121-236 9342 E-mail: dereckcornock@abditools.fsnet.co.uk *Machine tool rebuild & reconditioning of wick man profile grinders*

A B Dust Control Ltd, 79-81 High Street, Albrighton, Wolverhampton, WV7 3JA Tel: (01902) 373155 Fax: (01902) 373133 E-mail: abdustconltd@aol.com Principal Export Areas: Worldwide *Dust collecting equipment manufrs*

A B E (Ledbury) Ltd, Bromyard Road, Ledbury, Herefordshire, HR8 1LG Tel: (01531) 633195 Fax: (01531) 633192

▶ A B E Solutions, Mile-End Avenue, Aberdeen, AB15 5LR Tel: (01224) 622239 Fax: (01224) 622240 E-mail: sales@abesolutions.co.uk *Cash register equipment manufrs*

A B E Specialist Products, Haymoor Hall, Wybunbury Lane, Wybunbury, Nantwich, Cheshire, CW5 7HD Tel: (01270) 841174 Fax: (01270) 841128 E-mail: enquiries@haymoorleisure.co.uk *Convert coated fabrics into products*

▶ A B Electrical & Security Co. Ltd, 6 Haywood Way, Ivyhouse Lane Industrial Estate, Hastings, East Sussex, TN35 4PL Tel: (01424) 436385 Fax: (01424) 461538 E-mail: enquiries@abelec.co.uk

A B Electronic Ltd, Colbern House, Spring Gardens, Romford, RM7 9LP Tel: (01708) 762222 Fax: (01708) 762981 E-mail: info@abelectronic.com *Electronic component parts manufrs*

A B Equipment, Unit 13a Owen O'Cork Mills, 288 Beersbridge Road, Belfast, BT5 5DX Tel: (028) 9045 5520 Fax: (028) 9045 5520 E-mail: ab_equipment@yahoo.co.uk *Fork lift truck sales*

A & B Fabrications, 12 Cherrywood Road, Birmingham, B9 4UD Tel: 0121-771 3143 Fax: 0121-771 3143 *Steel welders & fabricators services*

A & B Fabrications, 1 Morrell Street, Maltby, Rotherham, South Yorkshire, S66 7LL Tel: (01709) 816402 *Steel fabricators*

A & B Fencing & Roofing Ltd, Love Lane Industrial Estate, Love Lane, Cirencester, Gloucestershire, GL7 1YG Tel: (01285) 651330 Fax: (01285) 651330 *Wood fencing erectors*

A & B Fire Prevention Wales, Mayfield, Chester Road, Buckley, Clwyd, CH7 3AH Tel: (01244) 543171 Fax: (01244) 544310 *Fire alarm installers*

▶ A B Fire Safety Training Services, 16 Buttermere Drive, Millom, Cumbria, LA18 4PL Tel: (01229) 772653 Fax: (01229) 772653 E-mail: steve@abfire.co.uk *Provider of Health and Safety training. Speacilising in Fire Safety solutions. Providng following training courses: Fire Warden, Fire Safety, Manual Handling, First Aid and others. *Other services: Fire Risk Assessments and Portable Appliance Testing.*

A B G Fabrications, Old Tin Plate Works, Old Tin Works Road, Pontypridd, Mid Glamorgan, CF37 1UD Tel: (01443) 402085 Fax: (01443) 491664 *Steel fabricators & erectors*

▶ A B Glass Doors & Windows Ltd, Clifford House, Felinfach, Fforestfach, Swansea, SA5 4HF Tel: (01792) 584440 Fax: (01792) 588440 *PVC manufrs*

A & B Glassworks, 124 Stoke Newington High Street, London, N16 7NY Tel: (020) 7254 4541 Fax: (020) 7254 4541 *Glass merchants*

A B H Services, 11 Ash Court, Maltby, Rotherham, South Yorkshire, S66 8RQ Tel: (01709) 819621 Fax: (01709) 769825 *Catering equipment engineers*

A B Hobley Ltd, Victoria Road, Bradford, West Yorkshire, BD2 2DD Tel: (01274) 639619 Fax: (01274) 641877 E-mail: paulhobley@abhobley.co.uk *Special purpose machine building*

A B Hoses & Fittings Ltd, Units 6-7 Warwick Street Industrial Estate, Storforth Lane, Chesterfield, Derbyshire, S40 2TT Tel: (01246) 208831 Fax: (01246) 209302 E-mail: sales@ab-hoses.org.uk *Hose & hydraulic solutions*

▶ A B Humbercraft Ltd, Unit 6b Kingston Way, Stockholm Road, Hull, HU7 0XW Tel: (01482) 370223 Fax: (01482) 823673 *Property maintenance services*

A B I Electronics Ltd, Dodworth Business Park, Dodworth, Barnsley, South Yorkshire, S75 3SP Tel: (01226) 207420 Fax: (01226) 207620 E-mail: post@abielectronics.co.uk *Test equipment manufacturers & contract electronic manufrs*

A B J Precision Engineering, Unit 22 Central City Industrial Estate, Red Lane, Coventry, CV6 5RY Tel: (024) 7658 1877 Fax: (024) 7658 1717 *Precision engineers*

A B K Group Finance Ltd, Lower Meadow Road Brooke Park, Steadings House, Handforth, Wilmslow, Cheshire, SK9 3LP Tel: 0161-486 6721 Fax: 0161-482 6301 E-mail: sales@abkplc.com *Electrical equipment hire services*

A B L Perpack 1985 Ltd, 7 Baron Avenue, Telford Way Industrial Estate, Kettering, Northamptonshire, NN16 8UW Tel: (01536) 412744 Fax: (01536) 412752 E-mail: sales@ablperpack.co.uk *Packaging distributors*

▶ A B Linear Services Ltd, Glebe Farm Charles, Brayford, Barnstaple, Devon, EX32 7PT Tel: (01598) 710952 Fax: (01598) 710813 E-mail: info@ablservicesltd.com *Service & repair machine tool parts*

A B Lockers Ltd, Alvis Court, Alvis Close, Cowpen Lane Industrial Estate, Billingham, Cleveland, TS23 4JG Tel: (01642) 560170 Fax: (01642) 566784 *Steel storage equipment manufrs*

A B M Ltd, Pitt Street, Widnes, Cheshire, WA8 0TG Tel: 0151-420 2829 Fax: 0151-495 1689 E-mail: sales@abm-ltd.co.uk *Automation brewing, food, chemical & water service*

A B M Computer Services, 356 York Road, Leeds, LS9 9DN Tel: 0113-240 5543 Fax: 0113-235 0541 *Pc manufrs*

▶ A B M I T Solutions Ltd, 79 Lee High Road, London, SE13 5NS Tel: (020) 8297 4450 Fax: (020) 8297 0052 E-mail: b.chakarto@abm-itsolutions.co.uk *Computer maintenance services*

A B M Interthene Ltd, 37 Stopgate Lane, Walton, Liverpool, L9 6DX Tel: 0151-525 7775 Fax: 0151-525 7776 E-mail: sales@abminterthene.co.uk *Embossed film manufrs*

A B M Motor Factors Ltd, 65 Plumstead High Street, London, SE18 1SB Tel: (020) 8316 0400 Fax: (020) 8317 2621 E-mail: sales@abmmotorspares.co.uk *Motor vehicle spares & accessories*

A B M Precisions Nuneaton Ltd, Ansley Common, Nuneaton, Warwickshire, CV10 0QN Tel: (024) 7639 2866 Fax: (024) 7639 7283 E-mail: enquiries@abmprecisions.co.uk *Precision engineers*

A B M Security Systems Ltd, 20 Warrington Road, Prescot, Merseyside, L34 5RB Tel: 0151-426 0233 Fax: 0151-430 7962 E-mail: info@abmsecurity.co.uk *Intruder alarm & cctv installers & distributors*

A & B M Suffield & Sons, Homelea Farm, Bearley Road, Aston Cantlow, Henley-in-Arden, West Midlands, B95 6LD Tel: (01789) 488040 Fax: (01789) 488971 *Agricultural contractors & engineers*

▶ A B Maritime Ltd, 106 Church Road, Wembury, Plymouth, PL9 0LA Tel: (01752) 862089 Fax: (01752) 862089 E-mail: andybrown@abmaritime.freeserve.co.uk *Hydrographic survey consultants*

A B N Ltd, 160 Moira Road, Lisburn, County Antrim, BT28 1JB Tel: (028) 9266 2611 Fax: (028) 9267 7202 E-mail: bibby@psilink.co.uk *Manufacturer of animal feed binders*

A B O S Wedding Services, 43 Grove Gdns, Enfield, Middx, EN3 5PG Tel: 020 88051706 *Balloons, flowers & decorations suppliers*

A & B Office Furnishers, 4 Charlton Mead Lane, Hoddesdon, Hertfordshire, EN11 0DJ Tel: (0870) 0502040 *Equipment, material & office furnishers suppliers*

A B P H, Manby Road, Immingham, South Humberside, DN40 3EG Tel: (01469) 551308 Fax: (01469) 571588 *Shipping & transportation*

A B P I Ltd, Waterside House, Waltham Business Park, Brickyard Road, Southampton, SO32 2SA Tel: (01489) 897700 Fax: (01489) 897707 *Pipework*

A B P Scotland Ltd, Whitburn Road, Bathgate, West Lothian, EH48 2HR Tel: (01506) 632722 Fax: (01506) 632802 *Meat processing plant abattoir*

A B Parker & Sons, 7 Franklyn Street, Bristol, BS2 9LA Tel: 0117-955 6544 Fax: 0117-955 6544 *Wholesale stationers*

A B Pharos Marine Ltd, Steyning Way, Hounslow, TW4 6DL Tel: (020) 8538 1100 Fax: (020) 8577 4170 E-mail: sales@pharosmarine.com *Navigational aid manufrs*

A B Plumbing Supplies Ltd, Savoy Works, Pershore Road, Kingsnorton, Birmingham, B30 3DR Tel: 0121-433 3099 Fax: 0121-458 5698 E-mail: sales@abplumbing.co.uk *Plumbing & heating merchants*

A & B Pneumatics, 117 Halftown Road, Lisburn, County Antrim, BT27 5RF Tel: (028) 9268 3440 Fax: (028) 9268 3440 E-mail: abpneumaticsltd@hotmail.com Principal Export Areas: Central/East Europe & West Europe *Air & suspension spring manufrs*

▶ A B Polymers, Ynysboeth Factory Estate, Abercynon, Mountain Ash, Mid Glamorgan, CF45 4SF Tel: (01443) 743930 Fax: (01443) 743939 *Plastic injection moulding for the automotive & medical industry*

A B Powles, Porters Lodge, Coughton, Ross-on-Wye, Herefordshire, HR9 5ST Tel: (01989) 565137 Fax: (01989) 565139 *Haulage company*

▶ A B Prattis & Sons, 15 Main Street, Hillend, Dunfermline, Fife, KY11 9ND Tel: (01383) 414793

A B Precision Poole Ltd, 1 Fleets Lane, Poole, Dorset, BH15 3BZ Tel: (01202) 665000 Fax: (01202) 675965 E-mail: automation@abprecision.co.uk *ABP design & build bespoke systems for automated manufacture, assembly & test, from individual workstations to complete assembly systems, incorporating rotary, linear & robotic handling*

A B R Specialists Welding Ltd, 2 Haines Street, West Bromwich, West Midlands, B70 7DS Tel: 0121-525 1319 Fax: 0121-525 1311 E-mail: enquiries@abrspecialistwelding.co.uk *Precision welding, plastic mould, pressure die casting & press tools*

A B Rooms & Son Ltd, 4 Field Street, Hull, HU9 1HS Tel: (01482) 320260 Fax: (01482) 219384 E-mail: enquiries@abrooms.co.uk *Locksmiths & security engineers*

A B S Ltd, New House, Christchurch Road, Ringwood, Hampshire, BH24 3AP Tel: (01425) 477777 Fax: (01425) 474400 E-mail: first@absme.co.uk *Heating & air conditioning engineers*

A B S Cases, 2 Pylon Trading Estate, Cody Road, London, E16 4SP Tel: (020) 7474 0333 Fax: (020) 7473 2548 E-mail: sales@abscases.co.uk *Flight cases manufrs*

A B S (Electrical Engineering & Supplies) Ltd, Unit F, Northbrook Trading Estate, Northbrook Road, Worthing, West Sussex, BN14 8PN Tel: (01903) 235636 Fax: (01903) 232512 E-mail: sales@abs-electrical.co.uk *Electrical wholesalers*

A B S Hovercraft Ltd, Coopers House, The Horsefair, Romsey, Hampshire, SO51 8JZ Tel: (01794) 526300 Fax: (01794) 526301 E-mail: info@abs-hovercraft.com *Patrol boat builders & hovercraft manufrs*

A.B.S. International Ltd, Persia House, 27 Aughton Road, Southport, Merseyside, PR8 2AG Tel: (01704) 564386 Fax: (01704) 550091 E-mail: abs@provider.co.uk *Tile distributors, importers & exporters*

A B S Photocopiers, 26 Atherstone Street, Fazeley, Tamworth, Staffordshire, B78 3RF Tel: (01827) 281515 Fax: (01827) 281515 *Photocopier sales & service*

A B S Pumps Ltd, Astral Towers, 5TH Floor, Betts Way, Crawley, West Sussex, RH10 9UY Tel: (01293) 558140 Fax: (01293) 527972 *Pump manufrs*

A B & S Taysom, The Parks, Canon Pyon, Hereford, HR4 8NP Tel: (01432) 830282 Fax: (01432) 830282 *Agricultural contractors*

A B S Waste Water Treatment Technology, Unit 1 Bridges Industrial Estate, Bridge Road, Horshay, Telford, Shropshire, TF4 3EE Tel: (01952) 632030 Fax: (01952) 632040 E-mail: roger.youngman@absgroup.com *Axial & submersible pumps* Also at: Birmingham, Croydon & Horley

A B Seals, Unit 15 Canal Industrial Park, Canal Road, Gravesend, Kent, DA12 2PA Tel: (01474) 350777 Fax: (01474) 533314 E-mail: sales@abseals.com *Seal & bearing distributors or agents*

▶ A B T International Ltd, Westwood Farm, Westwood, Peterborough, PE3 9UW Tel: (01733) 333322

A B T Products Ltd, Ashburton Industrial Estate, Ross-on-Wye, Herefordshire, HR9 7BW Tel: (01989) 563656 Fax: (01989) 566824 E-mail: abtproducts@clara.net *Material handling product manufrs*

A B Terratec Ltd, Units 2-2a, Phoebe La Industrial Estate, Halifax, West Yorkshire, HX3 9EX Tel: (01422) 354469 Fax: (01422) 354460 E-mail: sales@plantpots.co.uk *Plant pot suppliers*

A B Textiles, 191 Wigston Lane, Leicester, LE2 8DJ Tel: 0116-283 3585 Fax: 0116-283 3533 *Textiles*

A B Tools, Marsh Way, Rainham, Essex, RM13 8UP Tel: (01708) 526644 Fax: (01708) 526655 *Press tool manufrs*

A B Trade Supplies, South Denes Road, Great Yarmouth, Norfolk, NR30 3PF Tel: (01493) 859475 Fax: (01493) 330544 E-mail: sales@abtradesupplies.co.uk *Industrial & hydraulic hose distribs*

A & B Welding Services Ltd, 1a Woodside Road, Bridge of Don Industrial Estate, Aberdeen, AB23 8EF Tel: (01224) 823444 Fax: (01224) 825079 E-mail: sales@abweld.com Principal Export Areas: Worldwide *Steel fabricators*

▶ A B Wholesale Flowers Ltd, Unit 11 Maun Valley Industrial Estate, Junction Road, Sutton-in-Ashfield, Nottinghamshire, NG17 5GS Tel: (01623) 437602 E-mail: anne@abwholesaleflowers.co.uk *Suppliers of wholesale flowers, florists sundries and bridal accessories to the floristry trade.*

A & B Window Blinds Ltd, 111 Neilston Road, Paisley, Renfrewshire, PA2 6ER Tel: 0141-848 5565 Fax: 0141-842 1066 E-mail: info@ab-windowblinds.co.uk *Blinds manufrs*

A Baillie Hygiene & Co., Water Street, Kettering, Northamptonshire, NN16 0JR Tel: (01536) 519048 Fax: (01536) 417892 *Cleaning materials suppliers*

▶ A Barn Full Of Brass Beds, Main Road, Conisholme, Louth, Lincolnshire, LN11 7LS Tel: (01507) 358092 E-mail: brassbeds@clara.co.uk *Sales of brass & iron beds*

A Barraclough, 72 Tyler Street, Sheffield, S9 1DH Tel: 0114-243 1683 Fax: 0114-243 2804 E-mail: sales@abarraclough.co.uk *Sheet metalwork fabricators*

A Beasley, Lanesfield Drive Industrial Estate, Wolverhampton, WV4 6UB Tel: (01902) 353820 Fax: (01902) 354264 *Road transport/haulage/ freight agents*

A Bedingfield, Island Road, Hersden, Canterbury, Kent, CT3 4HD Tel: (0845) 2300970 Fax: (0845) 2300971 E-mail: bedcrane@btconnet.com *Crane hire services*

A Bennett Hosiery Ltd, North End Mills, North End, Wirksworth, Matlock, Derbyshire, DE4 4FG Tel: (01629) 822677 Fax: (01629) 824731 *Hosiery manufrs*

A Bertram Edwards Ltd, Old Coleham, Shrewsbury, SY3 7BU Tel: (01743) 357071 Fax: (01743) 357073 E-mail: info@bertram-edwards.co.uk *Building timber materials merchants*

A Beswetherick, Venn Farm, Launcells, Bude, Cornwall, EX23 9LL Tel: (01288) 321472 *Kitchen designers & manufrs*

A Bet A Technology Ltd, Suite 9, 5 Lenten Street, Alton, Hampshire, GU34 1HG Tel: (01420) 549988 Fax: (01420) 546710 E-mail: info@abeta.co.uk *Software for betting machines*

▶ A Black, Hangar 3, Drem Airfield, North Berwick, East Lothian, EH39 5AW Tel: (01620) 850263 Fax: (01620) 850517

A Bleakley & Co., Winters Bridge, Portsmouth Road, Thames Ditton, Surrey, KT7 0ST Tel: (020) 8398 8137 Fax: (020) 8398 7877 E-mail: peter@ableakley.freeserve.co.uk *Ceramic tile distributors*

A Bliss, 5 Bakers Yard, London, EC1R 3HF Tel: (020) 7837 4959 Fax: (020) 7837 8244 E-mail: sales@abliss.co.uk *Dry mounting sealing & framing services*

A Blundell Jewel Bearings Ltd, 203 Torrington Avenue, Coventry, CV4 9UT Tel: (024) 7647 3625 Fax: (024) 7646 6399 *Sapphire products manufrs*

A Boyall Ltd, 187 High Street, Hampton Hill, Hampton, Middlesex, TW12 1NL Tel: (020) 8941 0880 Fax: (020) 8941 3718 E-mail: boyalls@ukonline.co.uk *Architectural ironmongers*

▶ A Bradley Ltd, 213 Shore Road, Ballyronan, Magherafelt, County Londonderry, BT45 6LW Tel: (028) 7941 8421 Fax: (028) 7941 8383 E-mail: abradleyltd@tiscali.co.uk

A Bratt & Son Ltd, Abbeyfield Road, Nottingham, NG7 2SZ Tel: 0115-986 6851 Fax: 0115-986 1991 E-mail: sales@brattsladders.com *Ladder makers*

A Brooks, Revolver House St. Marys Business Park, Albany Road, Great Bowden, Market Harborough, Leicestershire, LE16 7ZH Tel: (01858) 468848 Fax: (01858) 461058 E-mail: andybrooks12@hotmail.com *Tool makers*

A Brown & Co., 2a Everton Road, Croydon, CR0 6LA Tel: (020) 8654 7310 Fax: (020) 8654 7316 E-mail: buttons@buttonhouse.fsnet.co.uk *Button merchants*

▶ A Brown & Co. (Chair Frames) Ltd, 37 Garturk Street, Glasgow, G42 8JG Tel: 0141-423 3467 *Sofas*

▶ A Burgoyne Electrical Contractors Ltd, 80 Fulbar Street, Renfrew, PA4 8PA Tel: 0141-886 5917 Fax: 0141-885 2558

A Bush Engineering Services Ltd, 16-18 Manor Road, Leeds, LS11 9AH Tel: 0113-246 0581 Fax: 0113-246 0043 E-mail: info@abush.co.uk *Refractory anchor manufrs*

A C 2000 Ltd, 224 Blackbird Road, Leicester, LE4 0AG Tel: 0116-224 2425 Fax: 0116-224 2426 E-mail: acleicester@ac2000.co.uk *Air-conditioning & mechanical services suppliers*

A C 2000, North Bridge Place, Frog Island, Leicester, LE3 5BG Tel: 0116-262 0411 Fax: 0116-251 8967 E-mail: aircon@ac2000.co.uk *Air conditioning ventilation services* Also at: Leeds & Romford

A C A Cable Distributors, Unit 7 Coegnant Close, Brackla Industrial Estate, Bridgend, Mid Glamorgan, CF31 2AY Tel: (01656) 766060 Fax: (01656) 664123 E-mail: sales@acacables.co.uk *Electrical cable & accessory distributors*

A C A S Pneumatic Controls, D1 Broadway Industrial Estate, King William Street, Salford, M50 3UQ Tel: 0161-876 0096 Fax: 0161-876 0134 *Pneumatic equipment distributors*

▶ A C Air Systems, Newburgh Building, Selby Place, Stanley Industrial Estate, Skelmersdale, Lancashire, WN8 8EF Tel: (01695) 722066 Fax: (01695) 722933

A C Automation, Hartland Avenue, Tattenhoe, Milton Keynes, MK4 3DN Tel: (01908) 501796 Fax: (01908) 501796 E-mail: sales@ac-automation.co.uk *Feed & feeder systems & automation special purpose equipment manufrs*

▶ A C B Office Services, 137-139 St Marychurch Road, Torquay, TQ1 3HW Tel: (01803) 328332 Fax: (01803) 311707 E-mail: acb.officeservices@virgin.net *Payroll & bookkeeping services*

A C Bacon Engineering Ltd, Norwich Road, Hingham, Norwich, NR9 4LS Tel: (01953) 850611 Fax: (01953) 851445 E-mail: steel@acbacon.co.uk *Structural steelwork engineers*

A C Baker & Son Ltd, Wood Cottage, The Green, Sarratt, Rickmansworth, Hertfordshire, WD3 6AT Tel: (01923) 269190 Fax: (01923) 269190 *Ground work contractors*

A & C Black Publishers Ltd, 38 Soho Square, London, W1D 3HB Tel: (020) 7758 0200 Fax: (020) 7758 0222 E-mail: enquiries@acblack.com *Publishers*

▶ A C Body Repairs, Unit 2 Yattendon Road, Upper Basildon, Reading, RG8 8NW Tel: (01491) 671800

A C Burn Ltd, Mounthooly, Jedburgh, Roxburghshire, TD8 6TJ Tel: (01835) 850250 Fax: (01835) 850250 *Agricultural merchants*

A C C Automatic Transmission, 24 The Fairways, New River Trading Estate, Cheshunt, Waltham Cross, Hertfordshire, EN8 0NL Tel: (01992) 639678 Fax: (01992) 634544 *Automotive transmission specialists*

▶ A C C Distribution Ltd, Distribution Depot, Mossburn Avenue, Harthill, Shotts, Lanarkshire, ML7 5NF Tel: (01501) 753333

A C C Flooring Ltd, Unit 1a Woodvale Workshops, Thornhill Beck Lane, Brighouse, West Yorkshire, HD6 4AH Tel: (01484) 715400 Fax: (01484) 716001 E-mail: nick@accflooring.co.uk *ACC Flooring Ltd, based in West Yorkshire, has over 20 years experience within the Resin Flooring Industry, specialising in the installation of flooring & drainage systems in some of the most hostile of industrial environments.We work on a national*

continued

Company Information

continuation
basis, covering the UK, we offer free on site surveys to ensure you receive the optimum solution. We are FeRFA's only Contractor to be Highly Commended. Due to our experience the leading material manufacturers have us on their approved contractor listings, but as independent contractors we are able to offer an unbiased approach to solving any flooring problem or maintenance issue you may have. We are active full contractor members of the resin flooring federation FeRFA, & have helped in the development of many resin systems & modern installation techniques. We have a proven track record direct for large corporate organisations within the food, printing, electrical & engineering industries & have worked closely with large construction companies.

A C C Plastics, Unit A Peacock View, Fenton Industrial Estate, Stoke-on-Trent, ST4 2XJ Tel: (01782) 201601 Fax: (01782) 201782 E-mail: sales@accplastics.co.uk *Plastic fabricators & vacuum formers manufrs*

A C & C Service Centre, 15 Herbert Road, London, NW9 6AJ Tel: (020) 8203 4555 Fax: (020) 8203 6444 *Computer maintenance*

▶ A C C Silicones, Amber House, Showground Road, Bridgwater, Somerset, TA6 6AJ Tel: (01278) 411400 Fax: (01278) 411444 E-mail: info@acc-silicones.com *Silicone adhesives manufrs*

A C C Systems Ltd, 6 Vulcan Court, Vulcan Way, Coalville, Leicestershire, LE67 3FW Tel: (01530) 814151 Fax: (01530) 814152 E-mail: sales@accsystems.co.uk *Special purpose machinery designers*

A C Canoe Products Chester Ltd, Unit 102 Tenth Avenue, Deeside Industrial Park, Deeside, Clwyd, CH5 2UA Tel: (01244) 280416 Fax: (01244) 288190 E-mail: ac.canoe@btinternet.com Principal Export Areas: Worldwide *We are Rotational Moulders - of 26 years standing- of large sized - up to 5.1 M length x 1.6 M width and 200 kg - products in polyethylene to the trade with 7 independent machines. A specialism is 3 layer sandwich foam products in polyethylene which we have been carrying out for 15 years. We also manufacture and sell worldwide out own range of polyethylene kayaks and paddles."*

A C Carey, 142 Wycombe Lane, Wooburn Green, High Wycombe, Buckinghamshire, HP10 0HH Tel: (01628) 524994 Fax: (01628) 524755 *Concrete distributors*

A C Components Ltd, A1 Springmeadow Road, Springmeadow Business Park, Rumney, Cardiff, CF3 2GA Tel: (029) 2077 6200 Fax: (029) 2077 6111 *High voltage power suppliers*

▶ A C Controls Ltd, 45-46 Clarendon Court, Winwick Quay, Warrington, WA2 8QP Tel: (01925) 242245 Fax: (01925) 411562 E-mail: info@accontrols.co.uk *Access control equipment, traffic control suppliers*

A C Copiers, Westward House, Bury Road, Hatfield, Hertfordshire, AL10 8BJ Tel: (01707) 259060 Fax: (01707) 259070 E-mail: sales@accopiers.com *Suppliers of new & used photocopiers*

A C Cossor & Son Surgical Ltd, Accoson Works, Vale Road, London, N4 1PS Tel: (020) 8800 1172 Fax: (020) 8809 5170 E-mail: accoson@accoson.com *Surgical instrument manufrs*

A C D C Automated Systems Ltd, Unit 1 Horizon Park, Valley Way, Swansea Enterprise Park, Swansea, SA6 8RG Tel: (01792) 771440 Fax: (01792) 796916 E-mail: enquiries@automatedsystems.co.uk *Control panels manufrs*

A C D C Lighting Systems Ltd, Pasture Lane Works, Pasture Lane, Barrowford, Nelson, Lancashire, BB9 6ES Tel: (01282) 608400 Fax: (01282) 608401 E-mail: sales@acdclighting.co.uk *Cold cathode lighting product manufrs*

A C D C Signs, 1 Hill Street, Milford, Armagh, BT60 3NZ Tel: (028) 3752 4755 Fax: (028) 3752 4755 E-mail: enquiries@acdcsigns.co.uk *Sign makers*

A C D Engineering Ltd, Unit 17 Central City Industrial Estate, Red Lane, Coventry, CV6 5RY Tel: (024) 7666 7555 Fax: (024) 7666 8282 *Precision engineers*

A C D Plant, Unit 20 Slingsby Close, Attleborough Fields Ind Estate, Nuneaton, Warwickshire, CV11 6RP Tel: (024) 7638 1503 Fax: (024) 7635 4445 *Power tool hire & sales*

A C Dare & Partners, Higher Knapp Farm, Knapp, North Curry, Taunton, Somerset, TA3 6AY Tel: (01823) 490747 Fax: (01823) 490747 *Agricultural contractors*

A C E Atlas Commission Embroidery, Block 2 Phoenix Works Industrial Estate, Richards Street, Wednesbury, West Midlands, WS10 8BZ Tel: 0121-568 7117 Fax: 0121-526 3909 E-mail: aceembroidery2001@yahoo.co.uk *Embroiders of work wear*

A C E Metalworks Ltd, 14 Stacey Avenue, London, N18 3PL Tel: (020) 8807 6533 Fax: (020) 8807 7145 E-mail: sales@acemetalworks.freeserve.co.uk *Fabricate structural steel*

A C E Security Ltd, Hole Farm, Lye Garden, Crowborough, East Sussex, TN6 1UU Tel: (01892) 603800 Fax: (01892) 603808 E-mail: onwatch@onwatch.com *CCTV security installation, monitoring & maintenance services*

A C Electrical Contractors, 7 Lynwood Avenue, Exeter, EX4 1EF Tel: (01392) 211109 Fax: (01392) 439494 *Electrical contractors*

▶ A C Electrical & Data Ltd, Ellerbeck House, Stokesley Industrial Estate, Stokesley, Middlesbrough, Cleveland, TS9 5JZ Tel: (01642) 712979

A C Electrical Wholesale Ltd, 2 Parkway Industrial Estate, Heneage Street, Birmingham, B7 4LY Tel: 0121-333 4959 Fax: 0121-333 4403 E-mail: birmingham@ac-electrical.co.uk *Electrical, data & communication wholesalers* Also at: Branches throughout the U.K.

A C Electrical Wholesale Ltd, 2 Royal Buildings, Marlborough Road, Lancing, West Sussex, BN15 8SJ Tel: (01903) 765813 Fax: (01903) 753467 E-mail: lancing@ac-electrical.co.uk *Electric suppliers*

A C Engineers Ltd, Unit 7, Mill Industrial Estate, Kings Coughton, Alcester, Warwickshire, B49 5QG Tel: (01789) 763956 Fax: (01789) 400565 E-mail: ace@acegroup.co.uk *Air conditioning engineers*

▶ A C Engineers & Fabricators, 9 Beacon Trading Estate, Middlemore Lane, Aldridge, Walsall, WS9 8DU Tel: (01922) 453494 *Steel fabricators*

A C Environmental Refrigeration Ltd, Evergreen Venture Park, Barton Road, Wisbech, Cambridgeshire, PE13 4TP Tel: (01945) 419081 Fax: (01945) 419082 *Industrial & commercial refrigeration engineers*

A C F Office Seating Collection, Wellington Street, Bury, Lancashire, BL8 2BD Tel: 0161-761 6889 Fax: 0161-761 6853 *Office seating manufrs*

A C Fixings, 10 Montrose Road, Chelmsford, CM2 6TX Tel: (01245) 451234 Fax: (01245) 451701 E-mail: acfixingsltd@blueyonder.com *Construction fixing systems & fasteners distributors*

▶ A C Forge, 12 Roseberry Grove, Tranmere, Birkenhead, Merseyside, CH42 9PR Tel: 0151-652 7033

A & C Furnishings, 3 Reliance Trading Estate, Chestom Road, Bilston, West Midlands, WV14 0RD Tel: (01902) 498293 Fax: (01902) 498293 E-mail: info@aandcfurnishings.co.uk *Hotel & bar seating upholstery*

▶ A C G Installations Ltd, Elisabeth House, Willows Road, Walsall, WS1 2DR Tel: (01922) 648509 Fax: (01922) 648509

A C H Access Control Ltd, High Point, South Hanningfield Road, Wickford, Essex, SS11 7PF Tel: (01268) 710636 Fax: (01268) 710556 E-mail: markwetton@ach.demon.co.uk *Gate automations wholesalers*

▶ A C I Ltd, 3, Verulam Buildings, Gray's Inn, London, WC1R 5NT Tel: (020) 7404 1000 Fax: (020) 7404 2000 E-mail: admin@aci-adr.com *Professional Mediation and Arbitration services throughout UK and International commercial dispute resolution.*

A C I C International Ltd, Blacknest Road, Blacknest, Alton, Hampshire, GU34 4PX Tel: (01420) 23930 Fax: (01420) 23921 E-mail: sales@acic.co.uk *Data acquisition measurement control systems suppliers*

A C I Europe Ltd, 16 Plover Close, Interchange Park, Newport Pagnell, Buckinghamshire, MK16 9PS Tel: (01908) 514500 Fax: (01908) 610111 E-mail: sales@aciuk.co.uk *Digital readout systems manufrs*

A C J Industrial Ltd, Longbeck Trading Estate, Marske-By-The-Sea, Redcar, Cleveland, TS11 6HB Tel: (01642) 483045 Fax: (01642) 487588 E-mail: garbut@globalnet.co.uk *Heating & ventilation engineers*

A C Jigs, 10 Porters Way, Birmingham, B9 5RR Tel: 0121-753 0304 Fax: 0121-753 0304 *Plating, powder coating & electroplating jig manufrs*

A C K Ltd, 35 Grosvenor Road, Caversham, Reading, RG4 5EN Tel: 0118-948 2588 Fax: 0118-946 5984 E-mail: sales@ackltd.co.uk *Credit card authorisation agents*

▶ A C L Advanced Consulting Ltd, 55 Dublin Street, Edinburgh, EH3 6NL Tel: 0131-478 0976

A C L Camcom Ltd, Unit 1 The Hamiltons, Torquay Road, Shaldon, Teignmouth, Devon, TQ14 0AY Tel: (01626) 871043 *CCTV servicing & installers*

A C L Engineering Ltd, Anglia House, Sandown Road Industrial Estate, Watford, WD24 7UA Tel: (01923) 249444 Fax: (01923) 242368 E-mail: sales@aclengineering.co.uk *Building services & air compressors*

A C L Structures Ltd, Holland Way, Blandford Forum, Dorset, DT11 7TA Tel: (01258) 456051 Fax: (01258) 450566 E-mail: enquiries@aclstructures.co.uk *Steel framed building manufrs*

A C Labels Ltd, 3 Centurion Way Business Park, Alfreton Road, Derby, DE21 4AY Tel: (01332) 366117 Fax: (01332) 291292 E-mail: d.clouston@aclabels.co.uk *Printing services*

A C Lighting Ltd, Centauri House, Hillbottom Road, High Wycombe, Buckinghamshire, HP12 4HQ Tel: (01494) 446000 Fax: (01494) 461024 E-mail: sales@aclighting.com *Stage lighting wholesaler & installer*

A C M Bearings Ltd, 2 Wath West Industrial Estate, Derwent Way, Wath-upon-Dearne, Rotherham, South Yorkshire, S63 6EX Tel: (01709) 874951 Fax: (01709) 878818 E-mail: sales@acmbearings.co.uk Principal Export Areas: Worldwide *Bearing brushes, wear rings & bridge, marine bearings*

▶ A & C Maintenance Ltd, C Thurcroft Industrial Estate, Kingsforth Road, Thurcroft, Rotherham, South Yorkshire, S66 9HU Tel: (01709) 700840 Fax: (01709) 545341

▶ A & C Management Consultants Ltd, 13a Harben Parade, Finchley Road, London, NW3 6LH Tel: (020) 7564 7050 Fax: (020) 7564 8764 E-mail: acmanagement@tiscali.co.uk *Management Consultants and Marketing and Import experts specialising in , "The Timber Industry, Textile & Clothing Industries"The Professions*

A C Mechanical Services Ltd, 16 Kingdom Close, Fareham, Hampshire, PO15 5TJ Tel: (01489) 579016 Fax: (01489) 579018 E-mail: info@acms.co.uk *Air conditioning & ventilation installers*

A C Midas, 102-104 Rockingham Road, Corby, Northamptonshire, NN17 1AE Tel: (01536) 267711 Fax: (01536) 262214 *Stationery & business machines suppliers*

A C Moxom Ltd, Chalk Pit Lane, Litton Cheney, Dorchester, Dorset, DT2 9AN Tel: (01308) 482242 Fax: (01308) 482584 E-mail: alan@acmoxom.com *General engineers*

▶ A C Nelson & Associates, 11 Branson Park, Grenofen, Tavistock, Devon, PL19 9EN Tel: (01822) 616775 E-mail: morse.nelson@virgin.net *Covering the South West, Wales and the Midlands, A. C. Nelson and Associates offer a professional, cost*

continued

effective service that is able to respond to all employers requirements in respect of their duties and responsibilities under current and pending safety and environmental legislation.

A C Nicholas Ltd, Nicon House, 45 Silver St, Enfield, Middlesex, EN1 3EF Tel: (020) 8363 8366 Fax: (020) 8367 7841 *Building contractors & developers*

A C Nielsen Ltd, Nielsen House, London Road, Headington, Oxford, OX3 9RX Tel: (01865) 742742 Fax: (01865) 742222 E-mail: graham.northfield@acnielsen.co.uk *Oxford-based A.C. Nielsen is the leading global provider of marketing research information services, analytical systems and tools, and professional client services that help clients win in the marketplace.*

▶ A C P, T1 The Maltings, Roydon Road, Stanstead Abbotts, Ware, Hertfordshire, SG12 8HG Tel: (01920) 870355 Fax: (01920) 870355 E-mail: admin@acprinting.co.uk *Graphic designers*

▶ A C P Construction, Runkerry, Maidstone Road, Sutton Valence, Maidstone, Kent, ME17 3LS Tel: (01622) 840216 Fax: (01622) 840216 E-mail: dave1pros@aol.com *Bricklaying services*

▶ A C Panel Services Ltd, 7C-7D Weston Way Industrial Estate, Lower Road, Stoke Mandeville, Aylesbury, Buckinghamshire, HP22 5GT Tel: (01296) 614005 Fax: (01296) 614005

A C Plastic Industries Ltd, Armstrong Road, Basingstoke, Hampshire, RG24 8NU Tel: (01256) 329334 Fax: (01256) 817862 E-mail: sales@ac-plastics.com *Sectional tank manufrs*

A C R C Ltd, The Courtyard, North Street, Wigston, Leicestershire, LE18 1PS Tel: 0116-257 0066 Fax: 0116-257 0099 E-mail: info@acrcltd.co.uk *Air conditioning engineers*

A C R Cash Register Systems, 570 Pollokshaws Road, Glasgow, G41 2PF Tel: 0141-424 0558 Fax: 0141-424 0655 *Cash registers & check-out equipment*

A C R Heat Transfer Ltd, Rollesby Road, King's Lynn, Norfolk, PE30 4LN Tel: (01553) 763371 Fax: (01553) 771322 E-mail: acrheat@msn.com *Heat exchanger designers & manufrs*

A C R Logistics, 2300 Park Avenue, Dove Valley Park, Foston, Derby, DE65 5BY Tel: (01283) 586200 Fax: (01283) 586419 *Storage distribution & warehousing services*

A & C R Patchitt, The Pencil Works, Lenton Street, Sandiacre, Nottingham, NG10 5DX Tel: 0115-939 0011 Fax: 0115-939 0044 *Joinery manufrs*

A C Refinish, Westgate Mills, White Lund Industrial Estate, Morecambe, Lancashire, LA3 3BS Tel: (01524) 60682 Fax: (01524) 39098 E-mail: sales@acrefinish.com *Automotive paints, coatings, tools*

A C S, Unit 74 Standard Way, Gravelly Industrial Park, Birmingham, B24 8TL Tel: 0121-326 8484 Fax: 0121-326 8585 E-mail: paul.kirkup@venductacs.co.uk *Ventilation service*

A C S Ltd, Victoria Court, Kent Street, Nottingham, NG1 3LZ Tel: 0115-958 3100 Fax: 0115-958 3199 E-mail: aspeckcooling@hotmail.com *Air conditioning systems*

A C S, 33 Vernon Walk, Tadworth, Surrey, KT20 5QP Tel: (01737) 371286 *Ceilings services*

▶ A C S, Oakleigh, Smithy Lane, Pentre Bychan, Wrexham, Clwyd, LL14 4EN Tel: (01978) 846173 Fax: (01978) 846262 *Installation & maintenance of air cooling systems for offices, shops, surgeries, conservatories & showrooms*

A C S Air Conditioning Services, 153 Peperharow Road, Godalming, Surrey, GU7 2PR Tel: (01483) 415935 Fax: (01483) 860549 E-mail: sales@acsairconsvs.co.uk *Air conditioning*

A C S Environmental UK Ltd, Caxton Point, Caxton Way, Stevenage, Hertfordshire, SG1 2XU Tel: (01438) 353415 Fax: (01438) 362973

A C S Industries Ltd, Huffwood Trading Estate, Billingshurst, West Sussex, RH14 9UR Tel: (01403) 784225 Fax: (01403) 784046 E-mail: frontend@acsind.co.uk *Printed circuit services*

A C S Office Solutions Ltd, 11 The Spinney, Bradwell, Milton Keynes, MK13 9BX Tel: (01604) 704000 Fax: (01604) 704001 *Computer & office furniture suppliers*

A C S & T Wolverhampton Ltd, Park Lane, Wolverhampton, WV10 9QD Tel: (01902) 731611 Fax: (01902) 862947 E-mail: adodd@acst.co.uk *Cold storage services & packing* Also at: Grimsby & Tewkesbury

A C S Thermal Engineers Ltd, 264 Trafford Road, Eccles, Manchester, M30 0JJ Tel: 0161-787 9084 Fax: 0161-787 9116 E-mail: a.c.s.@thermal.com *Industrial furnish liners*

▶ A C S Wade Ltd, Unit B6, Pinfold Industrial Estate, Rhyl, Clwyd, LL18 2YR Tel: (01745) 342998 Fax: (01745) 336006 E-mail: mail@acswade.co.uk *Air conditioning, close control systems, installation and maintenance dust/fume extraction installation and design. Laboratory fume cupboard manufacture and service. Kitchen canopies, gas ventilation interlocks. Gas installation and service, natural gas, LPG, medical gases, compressed air lines. COSHH testing and biological testing of ventilation systems. Corgi Reg. No. 5829*

A C Sissling Specialist Ironmongers Ltd, 20 Fitzwilliam Street, Bradford, West Yorkshire, BD4 7BL Tel: (01274) 200320 Fax: (01274) 220330 E-mail: sales@sissling-group.co.uk *Architectural ironmongers*

▶ A C Site Construction Services Ltd, Construction House, Fourth Way, Wembley, Middlesex, HA9 0LH Tel: (020) 8900 2737

A & C Steels Ltd, 7 Brookvale Trading Estate, Moor Lane, Birmingham, B6 7AQ Tel: 0121-356 1080 Fax: 0121-344 3731 *Steel shearers & stockholders*

A C Supply Ltd, St. Christopher House, 126 Ridge Road, Letchworth Garden City, Hertfordshire, SG6 1PT Tel: (01462) 481808 Fax: (01462) 481806 E-mail: sales@acsupply.co.uk *Power tools, accessories & industrial fasteners distributors*

▶ A C Systems, 42 St. James Road, Torquay, TQ1 4AY Tel: (0870) 4448995 Fax: (08704) 448996 E-mail: sales@acsystems.co.uk *Installation of telephone systems, cctv, door entry, sound & lighting*

▶ A C T Comms Ltd, Hexagon House, 71 Lower Road, Kenley, Caterham, Surrey, CR8 5NH Tel: (0870) 7747576 Fax: (0870) 1600094 E-mail: sales@actcomms.co.uk *Telecommunication system installers*

A C T (Devon) Ltd, Barton Farmhouse, Dartington Hall, Dartington, Totnes, Devon, TQ9 6ED Tel: (01803) 864432 Fax: (01803) 868188 E-mail: actcon@btconnect.com *Management & business consultants*

A C T (Fasteners & Components) Ltd, Units 13 & 16, Four Ashes Industrial Estate, Station Road, Four Ashes, Wolverhampton, WV10 7DB Tel: (01902) 791880 Fax: (01902) 791884 E-mail: info@actfasteners.co.uk *Fastener & screw distributors.*

A C T Teleconferencing, Queens House, Kymberley Road, Harrow, Middlesex, HA1 1US Tel: (020) 8901 5401 Fax: (020) 8901 5492 E-mail: marketing@europe.acttel.com *Audio video web conferencing service*

A C Tonks Orthopaedics Ltd, 5 Riverside Industrial Estate, Meir Road, Redditch, Worcestershire, B98 7SY Tel: (01527) 518611 Fax: (01527) 518612 E-mail: office@actonks.co.uk *Made to measure appliances*

A C V Engineers, Units A-B, Camp Street, Bury, Lancashire, BL8 1FE Tel: 0161-764 0644 Fax: 0161-761 7202 *General engineers*

A C W Engineering Services Ltd, The Sanderson Centre, Lees Lane, Gosport, Hampshire, PO12 3UL Tel: (023) 9250 2854 Fax: (023) 9250 2854 E-mail: acwesl@tinyonline.co.uk *Precision engineers*

A C W Technology Ltd, Comines Way, Hedge End, Southampton, SO30 4XX Tel: (023) 8048 6000 Fax: (023) 8048 6001 E-mail: welcome@acw.co.uk *Electronic equipment manufrs*

A C Webb Electrical, Mill Rise, Old Bury Road, Stanton, Bury St. Edmunds, Suffolk, IP31 2BX Tel: (01359) 250039 Fax: (01359) 250592 E-mail: acwebbelec@msn.com *Electrical contractors*

▶ A C Welding & Fabrication, 23 Mountbatten Road, Tiverton, Devon, EX16 6SW Tel: (01884) 244900 *Wrought ironworkers*

A C Yule & Son Ltd, Craigshaw Road, West Tullos Industrial Estate, Aberdeen, AB12 3ZG Tel: (01224) 230000 Fax: (01224) 230011 E-mail: admin@acyule.com *Glass, glazing & architectural supply* Also at: Elgin & Glasgow

A C Yule & Son Ltd, 1 Pinefield Parade, Elgin, Morayshire, IV30 6AG Tel: (01343) 545222 Fax: (01343) 542246 E-mail: elgin@acyule.com *Pul frames & flat glass products*

▶ A Campbell, Fernhurst Road, Milland, Liphook, Hampshire, GU30 7LU Tel: (01428) 741646 Fax: (01428) 741648 *Work wear manufrs*

▶ A Carpenter & Son (Builders) Ltd, Landguard Manor, Landguard Manor Road, Shanklin, Isle Of Wight, PO37 7JB Tel: (01983) 862014 Fax: (01983) 864797

A Cars Express Despatch Ltd, Unit 14 Langley Terrace Industrial Park, Latimer Road, Luton, LU1 3XQ Tel: (01582) 731900 Fax: (0870) 2330612 E-mail: acars@acars.co.uk *Road transport, haulage & freight services*

A Chard & Son Ltd, Unit 1 Small Street, St. Philips, Bristol, BS2 0SQ Tel: 0117-977 7876 Fax: 0117-977 7876 *Commercial body repairers*

A Clarke & Co Smethwick Ltd, Union Road, Oldbury, West Midlands, B69 3ER Tel: 0121-552 2854 Fax: 0121-552 6385 E-mail: barry@clarketransport.co.uk *Road transport, haulage & freight services*

▶ A Clarke & Co Smethwick Ltd, Unit 6 Kenfig Industrial Estate, Margam, Port Talbot, West Glamorgan, SA13 2PE Tel: (01656) 745767 Fax: (01656) 741518

▶ A Clarke & Co Smethwick Ltd, Pickering Works, Netherton Road, Wishaw, Lanarkshire, ML2 0EQ Tel: (01698) 350088 Fax: (01698) 358400

A Cohen, 10 Palace Gate, London, W8 5NF Tel: (020) 7225 0022 Fax: (020) 7584 9520 *Textile waste importer & exporters*

▶ A Coupland Surfacing Ltd, Pudding Lane, Off Warden Tree Lane, Pinchbeck, Spalding, Lincolnshire, PE11 3TJ Tel: (01775) 767110 Fax: (01775) 711246

A Coventry Locksmith, 58 Beake Avenue, Coventry, CV6 3AR Tel: (024) 7660 1222 Fax: (024) 7660 1222 E-mail: coventrylockmiths@live.co.uk *24hour 7 day emergency service*

A Cuthbertson, Unit F Burnfoot Industrial Estate, Hawick, Roxburghshire, TD9 8SL Tel: (01450) 378188 Fax: (01450) 378188 *Joinery manufrs*

A D 2000 Strathallan Electronics, 7 Bay Terrace, Girvan, Ayrshire, KA26 0AS Tel: (01465) 715200 Fax: (01465) 712575 *Computer maintenance & repairs*

▶ A D A Fastfix Ltd, 5 Parkhouse Business Centre, Desborough Park Road, Parkhouse Business Centre, High Wycombe, Buckinghamshire, HP12 3DJ Tel: (0870) 7207100 Fax: (0870) 7207120 E-mail: alan@adafastfix.co.uk *Suppliers of fixings*

▶ A D Allen Pharma Ltd, Bower Hill Industrial Estate, Epping, Essex, CM16 7BN Tel: (01992) 566366 Fax: (01992) 577582 E-mail: amanda@adallenpharma.com *Drugs, crude, botanical or medicinal suppliers*

A & D Billiards & Pool Services Ltd, 1421 Pershore Road, Stirchley, Birmingham, B30 2JL Tel: 0121-689 9988 Fax: 0121-451 3261 E-mail: andy@aanddbilliards.co.uk *Billiard pool & snooker requisites*

A D Billington, Greenbank Farm, Limes Lane, Whitley, Warrington, WA4 4DU Tel: (01925) 730285 *Agricultural contractors*

▶ A D Bly, Unit 4d Nup End Business Centre, Old Knebworth, Knebworth, Hertfordshire, SG3 6QJ Tel: (01438) 821779 Fax: (01438) 821870

▶ A D Broughton Ltd, 17 Harefield Road, Bognor Regis, West Sussex, PO22 6EE Tel: (01243) 584114 Fax: (01243) 583657 E-mail: enquiries@adbroughton.co.uk

▶ A & D Builders Ltd, Thorne House, Eastville, Yeovil, Somerset, BA21 4JD Tel: (01935) 411334

▶ A & D Building Services Ltd, 106-108 Salamander Street, Edinburgh, EH6 7LA Tel: 0131-467 7170

A D Buildings Ltd, 2A Crown Street, Redbourn, St. Albans, Hertfordshire, AL3 7JU Tel: (01582) 794842 Fax: (01582) 793889 E-mail: adbuildings@connectfree.co.uk *Building & air conditioning contractors*

A.D. Burs, 9 Madleaze Trading Estate, Bristol Road, Gloucester, GL1 5SG Tel: (01452) 307171 Fax: (01452) 307187 E-mail: sales@sswhite.com Principal Export Areas: Worldwide *Dental & industrial burs*

A D & C Ltd, 80 Wrentham Street, Birmingham, B5 6QL Tel: 0121-666 6070 Fax: 0121-666 7585 E-mail: davidaustin@btconnect.com *Aluminium & alloy gravity die-casting services*

A D C Marketing Ltd, Unit 4, Richardson Way, Crosspoint Business Park, Coventry, CV2 2TY Tel: (0870) 7525252 Fax: (0870) 7525251 E-mail: enquiries@adc-uk.com *Direct mail services*

A D C Systems, 110 Station Road, Llandaff North, Cardiff, CF14 2FH Tel: (029) 2057 8476 Fax: (029) 2057 8477 E-mail: adcsystems@hotmail.co.uk *Specialist fire alarms installation*

A D C Technology Ltd, A D C Ho, Broomfield Place, Coventry, CV5 6GY Tel: (024) 7671 5858 Fax: (024) 7671 4462 *Computer distributors & installation services*

A D Cragg, Whisperings, Osborne Road, Pitsea, Basildon, Essex, SS13 2LG Tel: (01268) 726737 Fax: (01268) 727668 *Forklift hire & maintainers*

A D Developments Ltd, 5a London Road, Loughton, Milton Keynes, MK5 8AB Tel: (01908) 222606 E-mail: enquiries@addevelopments.com *Computer software developers*

A & D Diecasters Ltd, Westgate, Aldridge, Walsall, WS9 8DD Tel: (01922) 451212 Fax: (01922) 743048 *Diecasting manufrs*

A D E Engineering Ltd, Prospect Close, Lowmoor Business Park, Kirkby-In-Ashfield, Nottingham, NG17 7LF Tel: (01623) 753888 Fax: (01623) 750543 *Sheet metal fabricators*

A D Engineering Co., Edward Street, Redditch, Worcestershire, B97 6HA Tel: (01527) 60355 Fax: (01527) 63639 *Pressings & strapping clip manufrs*

A D F Scale Co., Unit 6 Key Point, Keys Park Road, Hednesford, Cannock, Staffordshire, WS12 2FN Tel: (01543) 572165 Fax: (01543) 459005 E-mail: enquiries@adfscale.co.uk *Electronic & mechanical industrial weighing equipment manufrs*

A D Fabrications Telford Ltd, Unit B5 Dawley Bank Industrial Estate, Cemetery Road, Dawley Bank, Telford, Shropshire, TF4 2BS Tel: (01952) 505525 Fax: (01952) 505489 *Sheet metalwork engineers & fabricators*

A D Flooring Ltd, 23 Ebbisham Road, Worcester Park, Surrey, KT4 8ND Tel: (020) 8330 5419 Fax: (020) 8330 1180 E-mail: adflooring@fsmail.net *Hardwood flooring specialists*

▶ A D Garrie & Sons, 141 High Street, Auchterarder, Perthshire, PH3 1AD Tel: (01764) 662481

A & D Gates & Railings, 44 Rice Lane, Liverpool, L9 1DD Tel: 0151-287 1003 *Wrought iron manufrs*

A & D Group of Companies, Commerce Way, Lancing, West Sussex, BN15 8TA Tel: (01903) 763940 Fax: (01903) 763905 E-mail: sales@adauto.co.uk *Electronic engineers*

▶ A.D.H Flooring Ltd, 1a Shepherds Avenue, Worksop, Nottinghamshire, S81 0JD Tel: (01909) 489915 Fax: 01909 470094 E-mail: antonyharper@btinternet.com *Domestic & commercial floor screeding services*

▶ A D Hamilton Ltd, 1227-1235 Cumbernauld Road, Glasgow, G33 1AW Tel: 0141-770 5031

▶ A & D Haulage (Telford) Ltd, Unit B3, Court Works Industrial Estate, Bridgnorth Road, Telford, Shropshire, TF7 4JB Tel: (01952) 582800 Fax: (01952) 585467 E-mail: andhaulage@tiscali.co.uk

A & D Hope Ltd, Evelyn House, 3 Elstree Way, Borehamwood, Hertfordshire, WD6 1RN Tel: (020) 8953 7278 Fax: (020) 8953 7279 E-mail: admin@adhope.com *Leather clothing & ladies outerwear manufrs* Also at: Manchester

A D I American Distributors Inc, Units 3-4 Peckworth Industrial Estate, Bedford Road, Lower Standon, Henlow, Bedfordshire, SG16 6EE Tel: (01462) 850804 Fax: (01462) 819596 E-mail: sales@americandistr.com *Distributors & agents of electronic components*

A D I Supplies & Services, Block 2, Rosendale Way, Blantyre, Glasgow, G72 0NJ Tel: (01698) 829991 Fax: (01698) 829992 E-mail: sales@adi-supplies.co.uk *Non destructive testing equipment supplier*

A D I Treatments Ltd, Doranda Way Industrial Park, Doranda Way, West Bromwich, West Midlands, B71 4LE Tel: 0121-525 0303 Fax: 0121-525 0404 E-mail: aaron.rimmer@aditreatments.com *-ADI Treatments Ltd provides heat treatment services to iron foundries and steel parts manufacturers. The business carries out unique Austempering and annealing processes. - We are an expert source for Austempered Ductile Iron (ADI), which is used increasingly in automotive, earth moving and renewable energy markets. - Working alongside castings producers and users, we exploit design and materials know-how to engineer new component solutions with enhanced performance and cost savings. - We operate the largest commercially available batch Austempering furnaces with sealed quench salt baths accommodating parts up to 1800mm dimensions and maximum weight 2500kg. - Our people have long experience in the industry; they include qualified engineers and metallurgists specifically trained in ADI alloys, furnaces and production. We actively promote our technology and will visit to deliver seminars at customers' works. - Located near Birmingham, ADI Treatments Ltd operates with ISO 9001:2000 approval and supports customers throughout Europe*

A D Installation, 14 North Road, Dartford, DA1 3NA Tel: (01322) 223648 Fax: (01322) 419501 *Refrigeration & air conditioning engineers*

A & D Instruments Ltd, 24-26 Blacklands Way, Abingdon, Oxfordshire, OX14 1DY Tel: (01235) 550420 Fax: (01235) 550485 E-mail: sales@aandd-eu.net *Weighing machine manufrs*

A D J Fabrications Ltd, Unit 8a Bowes Road, Riverside Park Industrial Estate, Middlesbrough, Cleveland, TS2 1LU Tel: (01642) 225726 Fax: (01642) 242738 *Steel sheet metalworkers & laser cutters manufrs*

▶ A & D Joinery Ltd, Unit 14, Bolton Road Mill, Bolton Road, Bolton, BL5 3JG Tel: (01942) 814501 Fax: (01942) 810468 E-mail: john@aanddjoinery *Windows conservatory's doors, porches & roof products installations & manufrs*

▶ A & D Joinery, Premier Partnership Estate, Leys Road, Brierley Hill, West Midlands, DY5 3UP Tel: (01384) 265165 Fax: (01384) 265464

▶ A D K Environmental Management, 2 Foldside, Freckleton, Preston, PR4 1JX Tel: (01772) 493215 Fax: (01772) 467094 E-mail: adk@adk-environmental.co.uk *Environmental advisors service for the construction industry*

A D K (Northwest) Ltd, 215 Accrington Road, Blackburn, BB1 2AQ Tel: (01254) 278999 Fax: (01254) 278970 E-mail: jemimah@london.com *Security wholesalers*

▶ A D L Building Plastics, Unit, Russell Town Avenue Industrial Centre, Lawrence Hill, Bristol, BS5 9LT Tel: 0117-955 2660 Fax: 0117-939 5521 E-mail: adl-info@blueyonder.co.uk *Suppliers of upvc building materials. Underground Drainage & Soil Pipe Systems. Gutter & Rainwater pipes. Fascias, Claddings, Hygiene Claddings. Polycarbonate Roof Systems.Corrugated Roof Sheets. Manhole Covers. Channel Drain. Land Drain, perforated & unperforated.Waste pipe, mains water pipes & fittings & traps.Plumbing- copper & plastic & UFCH.*

A D Litho, Unit 3 Wycombe Industrial Mall, West End Street, High Wycombe, Buckinghamshire, HP11 2QY Tel: (01494) 536117 Fax: (01494) 531298 E-mail: adlitho@aol.com *Commercial & colour printers*

A & D Lock & Key Co. Ltd, 6-7 Hockley Hill, Birmingham, B18 5AA Tel: 0121-554 7894 Fax: 0121-554 8220 E-mail: reconditionedsafes@btconnect.com *Safe dealers & locksmiths*

▶ A & D Logistics, Gas Street, Johnstone, Renfrewshire, PA5 8BJ Tel: (01505) 329539 Fax: (01505) 327486

A D M Automation, Nest Road, Gateshead, Tyne & Wear, NE10 0ES Tel: 0191-438 7888 Fax: 0191-438 7899 E-mail: sales@adm-automation.co.uk Principal Export Areas: Worldwide *Manufacturers & distributors of automated systems*

A D M Imaging, 59-61 Summer Lane, Birmingham, B19 3TH Tel: 0121-359 5424 Fax: 0121-359 7038 E-mail: info@abmimaging.co.uk *Digital, litho, large format printing services & graphic design*

▶ A D M Joinery, 51 Hawthorn Avenue, Batley, West Yorkshire, WF17 7BZ Tel: (01924) 505220 Fax: (01924) 505220 E-mail: a.karani@btinternet.com *Building contractors, joinery*

▶ A D M Millings Ltd, Seaforth Flour Mill, Seaforth Dock, Seaforth, Liverpool, L21 4PG Tel: 0151-922 8911 *Flour manufrs*

▶ A D M Office Supplies Ltd, PO Box 1, Yateley, Hampshire, GU46 6WY Tel: (01252) 876494 Fax: (01252) 879505 E-mail: admin@admoffice.co.uk *Creative artwork, 3D modelling, Presentations, Copywriting and proofchecking, All print including BIG posters, Business incentives*

▶ A D M Precision Engineering Ltd, 31 Chartwell Drive, Wigston, Leicestershire, LE18 2FL Tel: 0116-257 0704 Fax: 0116-257 1647

▶ A D M Seafoods, 1 Bedale Walk, Dartford, DA2 6HS Tel: (0871) 2447305 Fax: (0871) 2113186 E-mail: sales@admseafoods.com *Wholesalers & retailers of fresh frozen & smoked fish*

A D M UK Ltd, Pondswood Industrial Estate, Drury Lane, St. Leonards-on-Sea, East Sussex, TN38 9XL Tel: (01424) 456900 Fax: (01424) 426483 *Frozen food processors & products manufrs*

A D Milburn, Brookside, Whitbeck, Millom, Cumbria, LA19 5UP Tel: (01229) 718638 *Agricultural contractors*

▶ A.D.Moore & Son Kitchen Installations, Bryn Hafod, Aberhafesp, Newtown, Powys, SY16 3JJ Tel: (01686) 688967 E-mail: adrianmoore0@lycos.com *Kitchen planning & installation services*

A D Morton Ltd, New Line Industrial Estate, The Sidings, Bacup, Lancashire, OL13 9RW Tel: (01706) 878358 Fax: (01706) 878380 *Steel fabricators*

▶ A D P, 29 Invincible Drive, Armstrong Industrial Park, Newcastle upon Tyne, NE4 7HX Tel: 0191-256 8071 Fax: 0191-256 8072 E-mail: adpengineering@aol.com *Sub contracting engineering service*

▶ A D P Diamond Cutting Solutions Ltd, Unit 29, Dunmere Road, Bodmin, Cornwall, PL31 2QN Tel: (01208) 269898 Fax: (01208) 264818 E-mail: sales@adpdiamex.co.uk *Tele-sales diamond cutting tool manufrs*

A D P (Lancashire) Ltd, Unit 1, Apian Way Industrial Estate, Salford, M7 4WZ Tel: 0161-792 1034 Fax: 0161-792 6811 E-mail: adppaints@aol.com *Paints & powders*

A D P Marketing Services, Unit 5 Carr Mills, 919 Bradford Road, Birstall, Batley, West Yorkshire, WF17 9JY Tel: (01924) 470490 Fax: (01924) 471644 E-mail: mail@adpservices.net *Graphic designers & printers*

A D P Supplies Ltd, 65 Peach Street, Wokingham, Berkshire, RG40 1XP Tel: 0118-978 5525 *Business to business computer supplies*

▶ A D Precision Engineering Ltd, Unit 3a-C, Rink Road Indust Estate, Ryde, Isle of Wight, PO33 1LP Tel: (01983) 810708 Fax: (01983) 613987 E-mail: adprecision@btconnect.com

▶ A D Profiles, 534 Attercliffe Road, Sheffield, S9 3QP Tel: 0114-244 7184 Fax: 0114-244 7184 *Steel fabricators*

A D R Art Metalwork, 109 Railway Arches, Cannon Street Road, London, E1 2LY Tel: (020) 7488 3776 Fax: (020) 7488 3776 *Steel fabricators*

A.D.S Fasteners, Blackburn Road, Rotherham, South Yorkshire, S61 2DR Tel: (01709) 559856 *PVC windows & doors manufrs*

▶ A D S Plumbing Services, 27 Tarrareoch Court, Armadale, Bathgate, West Lothian, EH48 2TF Tel: (01501) 734504 Fax: (01501) 734504 E-mail: adsplumbers@aol.com *fast efficent services*all aspects of plumbing work undertaken*no call out fee*24 hour emergency service *specialist bathroom installers*lead pipe removal *water tanks replaced*radiators moved*leaking taps *shower replacments*level access/flush floor/wetroom*Covering the whole of Central Scotland, Edinburgh, Glasgow, Lothian, Stirling,*All work guaranteed, done to Local and Model Water Bylaws*

A D S Precision Engineering, 53a Jubilee Road, Waterlooville, Hampshire, PO7 7RE Tel: (023) 9226 7643 Fax: (023) 9226 7743 E-mail: admin@adsprecision.co.uk *Special purpose machines manufrs*

▶ A D S Sign & Light Ltd, 248 Seaward Street, Kinning Park, Glasgow, G41 1NG Tel: 0141-429 1110

A D S Worldwide Ltd, West Carr Lane, Sutton Fields, Hull, HU7 0BW Tel: (01482) 820219 Fax: (01482) 831596 E-mail: sales@ads-worldwide.com *Lithographic printing company*

A & D Scrivens, 5 Allens Lane, Poole, Dorset, BH16 5DA Tel: (01202) 621585 Fax: (01202) 621584 E-mail: scrivenss@aol.com *Welding, fabrication, seismic & geophysical services*

A D Signs & Engraving Ltd, Unit 3 Webner Industrial Estate, Alltingshaw Road, Wolverhampton, WV2 2LD Tel: (01902) 353535 Fax: (01902) 496775 E-mail: sales@ad-signs.co.uk *Industrial engravers & sign manufrs*

▶ A D Stretch Wrap Ltd, 1 Hermitage Way, Mansfield, Nottinghamshire, NG18 5ES Tel: (01623) 648845 Fax: (01623) 608846 *Polythene converters packaging material suppliers*

▶ A & D Sutherland Ltd, Spittal Mains Quarry, Spittal, Wick, Caithness, KW1 5XR Tel: (01847) 841329 Fax: (01847) 841321

A D T Fire & Security P.L.C., Security House, The Summit, Hanworth Road, Sunbury-on-Thames, Middlesex, TW16 5DB Tel: (0800) 0111111 *Security & fire systems, manufacture, install, service & distributor*

A D T Joinery, Joinery Works, Llynfi St, Bridgend, Mid Glamorgan, CF31 1SY Tel: (01656) 653644 Fax: (01656) 653644 E-mail: arby.richard@virgin.net *Joinery & construction*

A D Tech, 4 Bowmont Place, East Kilbride, Glasgow, G75 8YG Tel: (01355) 242432 Fax: (01355) 242432 *Fork lift training services*

▶ A D V Audio Visual Installations Ltd, 12 York Place, Leeds, LS1 2DS Tel: (0870) 1995755 Fax: (0709) 2100142 E-mail: shaun@adv-installs.co.uk *Installers of home cinema systems, surround sound systems*

A D V Transport, 42 Mill Hill, Shoreham-by-Sea, West Sussex, BN43 5TH Tel: (01273) 462696 Fax: (01273) 462697 E-mail: advtransport@btinternet.net *Road transport, haulage & freight services*

A & D Webb Metal Polishing Specialists, 3 Standard Works, Orchard Place, Stonehouse, Gloucestershire, GL10 2PL Tel: (01453) 825573 Fax: (01453) 825573 E-mail: sales@adwebbmetalpolishers.co.uk *Metal polishing services*

A D X Precision Engineering, The Sanderson Centre, Lees Lane, Gosport, Hampshire, PO12 3UL Tel: (023) 9252 0027 Fax: (023) 9252 0027 E-mail: dave@adxprecision.freeserve.co.uk *Precision engineers*

▶ A D Young, Greenacre Court Ruffet Road, Kendleshire, Winterbourne, Bristol, BS36 1AN Tel: (01454) 252910 Fax: (01454) 252911 E-mail: admin@adyoung.com *Repair & service of plotters & printers, including*

A Davenport Trimmings Ltd, 1 Snell Street, Manchester, M4 7EL Tel: 0161-273 6539 Fax: 0161-273 6295 E-mail: info@adtrimmings.co.uk *Furnishing accessories manufrs*

▶ A Davie, East Happas Farm, Forfar, Angus, DD8 2JW Tel: (01307) 820264 Fax: (01307) 463353

A.Davies & Co.(Shopfitters)Limited, Chiswick Studios, Power Road, London, W4 5PY Tel: (020) 8987 4100 Fax: (020) 8987 2647 E-mail: info@daviesshopfitters.com *Shop fitters*

A Davies & Sons Sales Ltd, Alpha Works, Old Moor Road, Bredbury, Stockport, Cheshire, SK6 2QF Tel: 0161-430 5297 Fax: 0161-494 2758 *Electrical enclosure distributors*

▶ A Dee Kay Joinery Ltd, Unit 25 Sapcote Trading Centre, Small Heath Highway, Birmingham, B10 0HR Tel: 0121-766 6036 Fax: 0121-771 1367

A Diamond & Son Timber Ltd, 35 New Mills Road, Coleraine, County Londonderry, BT52 2JB Tel: (028) 7034 3452 Fax: (028) 7034 3279 E-mail: sales@adiamondandson.co.uk *Timber merchants*

A Different Calibre Ltd, 16 The Wynd, Letchworth Garden City, Hertfordshire, SG6 3EL Tel: (01462) 674861 *Sports & shooting equipment retailers*

A Docker, The Windmill, Edlesborough, Dunstable, Bedfordshire, LU6 1RU Tel: (01525) 229321 *Glass fibre moulding services*

A E A Technology plc, Harwell Intnl Business Centre, Didcot, Oxfordshire, OX11 0QJ Tel: (0870) 1901900 Fax: (0870) 1908261 E-mail: enquiry@aeat.co.uk *Process engineering services*

A E Blanchard, 144 Station Road, Ratby, Leicester, LE6 0JP Tel: 0116-239 3831 Fax: 0116-239 3831 *Model manufrs*

A E Burgess & Sons Ltd, Ulverscroft Road, Leicester, LE4 6BY Tel: 0116-262 0065 Fax: 0116-251 0501 *Scrap iron merchants*

▶ A E C P.L.C., 25 Southampton Row, Holborn, London, WC1B 5HJ Tel: (0845) 0506296 Fax: (0870) 4199001 E-mail: info@aec.com *IT consultants*

A E C Engineering, Unit 1a Conway Morfa Indust Estate, Aberconwy, Conwy, Gwynedd, LL32 8HB Tel: (01492) 584139 Fax: (01492) 584139 *Plastic thermoset moulding & precision machining services*

A E Chapman & Son Ltd, Timbermill Way, Gauden Road, London, SW4 6LY Tel: (020) 7622 4414 Fax: (020) 7720 0189 E-mail: aecsonltd@aol.com *Wholesale glass bottle merchants*

A E Corkill Removals Ltd, Removal House, Finch Road, Douglas, Isle of Man, IM1 2PW Tel: (01624) 675495 Fax: (01624) 661095

▶ A E Costin Ltd, Unit 3 Morgan Close, Willenhall, West Midlands, WV12 4LH Tel: (01902) 635939 Fax: (01902) 608556

A E Cox & Sons, Caretakers Caravan, North Street, Winterton, Scunthorpe, South Humberside, DN15 9QN Tel: (01724) 732676 Fax: (01724) 732676 *Garden furniture, fencing & shed manufrs*

A E Davidson & Son Ltd, 3 Alton Road Industrial Estate, Ross-on-Wye, Herefordshire, HR9 5NB Tel: (01989) 764850 Fax: (01989) 768291 E-mail: aedties@btinternet.com *Tie interlining suppliers & cutters*

A E Dennett & Son Ltd, 28 Boston Road, Spilsby, Lincolnshire, PE23 5HG Tel: (01790) 752573 Fax: (01790) 752598 E-mail: dennetts@mod-comp.co.uk *Ice cream manufrs*

▶ A & E Edm Ltd, 25 Mornington Road, Smethwick, West Midlands, B66 2JE Tel: 0121-558 8352 Fax: 0121-558 8350 E-mail: info@amedm.co.uk *Wire & spark eroding, wire erosion,*

A & E Elkins Ltd, 6 Insulcrete Works, Yeoman Street, London, SE8 5DT Tel: (020) 7231 8808 Fax: (020) 7252 3758 E-mail: sales@roofingspecialistuk.com *Roofing contractors*

A E Engineering Services, 8 Eye Green Industries, Crowland Road, Eye, Peterborough, PE6 7SZ Tel: (01733) 223355 Fax: (01733) 222330 E-mail: tony@aeengineering.co.uk *Printing engineering & installation services*

▶ A E F Ltd, Unit K6 Liners Industrial Estate, Pitt Road, Southampton, SO15 3FQ Tel: (023) 8033 9305 Fax: (023) 8033 9260 E-mail: enquiries@aeflooring.co.uk

A E F Solutions Ltd, Units 33-34, Mitchell Point, Ensign Way, Hamble, Southampton, SO31 4RF Tel: (023) 8045 5050 Fax: (023) 8045 5022 E-mail: enquiries@aefsolutions.com *Electro magnetic interference*

A E Felgate Ltd, 59 George Street, Reading, RG1 7NP Tel: 0118-961 4141 Fax: 0118-967 7717 E-mail: aefelgate@piscarli.co.uk *Electrical contractors*

A E Freshwater Ltd, Old Court House, Town Hall CR, Haltwhistle, Northumberland, NE49 0DQ Tel: (01434) 321931 Fax: (01434) 321798 E-mail: info@ae-freshwater.fsnet.co.uk *Water filtration installation*

▶ A & E Gauges, 6-7 Redbourn Industrial Centre, High Street, Redbourn, St. Albans, Hertfordshire, AL3 7LG Tel: (01582) 793527 Fax: (01582) 794463

A E Griffin & Son, 10 North Street, Bere Regis, Wareham, Dorset, BH20 7LA Tel: (01929) 471253 Fax: (01929) 472208 E-mail: aegriffinandson@aol.com *Specialist builders*

A E Hadley Ltd, Limberline Spur, Portsmouth, PO3 5JR Tel: (023) 9266 4341 Fax: (023) 9266 4940 E-mail: info@aehadley.com *Shop fitters, joinery, furnishing & carpets*

A E Harris & Co Birmingham Ltd, 109-138 Northwood Street, Birmingham, B3 1SZ Tel: 0121-233 2386 Fax: 0121-200 3702 E-mail: sales@aeharris.co.uk *Presswork & press tool manufrs*

A E Harrison Plant Hire London Ltd, 219 Horn Lane, London, W3 9ED Tel: (020) 8993 5981 Fax: (020) 8752 1211 *Contractors' plant hire*

A E Hawkins, Oak Lane, Kingswinford, West Midlands, DY6 7JS Tel: (01384) 294949 Fax: (01384) 400069 *Road transport, haulage & freight services*

▶ A E Howlett Ltd, Claybury Hall Farm, Roding Lane North, Woodford Green, Essex, IG8 8ND Tel: (020) 8550 2395 Fax: (020) 8551 6261

A E Huddleston, Mardale, Quernmore, Lancaster, LA2 9EG Tel: (01524) 66914 Fax: (01524) 66914 *Agricultural contractors*

A E Hughes & Sons Contracts Ltd, Plough Industrial Estate, Kingston Road, Leatherhead, Surrey, KT22 7LF Tel: (01372) 373851 Fax: (01372) 373557 *Roofing contractors*

A E I Compounds Ltd, Crete Hall Road, Gravesend, Kent, DA11 9AF Tel: (01474) 566736 Fax: (01474) 564386 E-mail: sales@aeicompounds.co.uk *Manufacturers of plastic compounds*

A E I Systems Ltd, 1 Kings Ride Park, Kings Ride, Ascot, Berkshire, SL5 8AP Tel: (01344) 636200 Fax: (01344) 636205 E-mail: info@airequip.co.uk *Aircraft weapon system manufrs*

A E Industrial & Air Equipment Ltd, Burma Road, Blidworth, Mansfield, Nottinghamshire, NG21 0RT Tel: (01623) 797897 Fax: (01623) 796318 *Compressed air equipment distributors* Also at: Chesterfield, Hull, Huntingdon, Leeds, Nottingham & Stoke

A.E.Jennings Ltd, 5 Bellingham Trading Estate, Franthorne Way, London, SE6 3BX Tel: (020) 8695 8950 Fax: (020) 8698 0556 E-mail: studio@aejennings *Printers*

A E Jones, 11 Mortimer Street, Cleckheaton, West Yorkshire, BD19 5AR Tel: (01274) 851126 Fax: (01274) 870155 E-mail: sales@aejones.co.uk *Manufacturers of pharmaceutical sampling equipment*

▶ A E Kenwell & Sons, 44 Main Street, Dromore, Omagh, County Tyrone, BT78 3AB Tel: (028) 8289 8205 Fax: (028) 8289 8209 E-mail: kenwelld@hotmail.com *General merchants*

A & E Leisure Ltd, 9 Craddock Road, Reading, RG2 0JT Tel: 0118-923 0300 Fax: 0118-923 0349 E-mail: sales@aelsolutions.com *Garden furniture manufrs*

▶ A E M Ltd, 31 Risborough Lane, Folkestone, Kent, CT19 4JH Tel: (01303) 275862 Fax: (01303) 270766

A E M Ltd, Unit 6001, Taylors End, Long Border Road, Stansted Airport, Stansted, Essex, CM24 1RB Tel: (01279) 680030 Fax: (01279) 680040 E-mail: info@aem.co.uk *Aircraft accessory repair & overhaul services*

A E M Products Ltd, Unit 141 Leyland Estate, Irthlingborough Road, Wellingborough, Northamptonshire, NN8 1RA Tel: (01933) 442861 Fax: (01933) 225527 E-mail: enquiry@aem-products.co.uk *Precision engineers*

A E Mccandless & Co. Ltd, 23 Bishop Street, Londonderry, BT48 6PR Tel: (028) 7136 2071 Fax: (028) 7126 8996 *Shirt & blouse, sports wear manufrs*

A & E Marketing Electronics Ltd, 9 Nicol Street, Kirkcaldy, Fife, KY1 1NY Tel: (01592) 261222 Fax: (01592) 261333 E-mail: sales@aemarketing.info Principal Export Areas: Worldwide *Display designers & manufrs*

▶ A E Monsen, West End Industrial Estate, West End, Penryn, Cornwall, TR10 8RT Tel: (01326) 373581 Fax: (01326) 377213 E-mail: falmouth@aemonsen.com *Ships stores ships chandlers*

A E Oscroft & Sons, 49d Pipers Road, Park Farm Industrial Estate, Redditch, Worcestershire, B98 0HU Tel: (01527) 502203 Fax: (01527) 510378 E-mail: info@aeoscroft.co.uk *Presswork manufrs*

▶ A E P, Unit J Rich Industrial Estate, Avis Way, Newhaven, East Sussex, BN9 0DS Tel: (01273) 612777 Fax: (01273) 515959 E-mail: peter.aep@dsl.pytex.com *CNC lathes, milling, turning & sub machining service*

A E Parker Ltd, Terminus Road, Chichester, West Sussex, PO19 8TX Tel: (01243) 783319 Fax: (01243) 532617 E-mail: transport@parkerltd.co.uk *Commercial warehouse keepers & road haulage distribution*

▶ A E Partridge & Sons, The Laurels, Morchard Bishop, Crediton, Devon, EX17 6PL Tel: (01363) 877266

A & E Plastic Fabrications Ltd, 40 St. Peters Street, Radford, Nottingham, NG7 3FF Tel: 0115-978 0048 Fax: 0115-979 1351 E-mail: info@aaep.co.uk *Plastic fabricators & sign manufrs*

A E Procter Ltd, 22 Park Road, Feltham, Middlesex, TW13 6PU Tel: (020) 8898 0214 Fax: (020) 8898 4965 E-mail: info@bmf.org.uk *Builders' merchants*

A E R Ltd, Wotton Road, Kingsnorth Industrial Estate, Ashford, Kent, TN23 6LN Tel: (01233) 632777 Fax: (01233) 661673 E-mail: sales@aer.co.uk *Electric motor & pump suppliers*

A E R C O Ltd, Units 16-17 Lawson Hunt Industrial Park, Broadbridge Heath, Horsham, West Sussex, RH12 3JR Tel: (01403) 260206 Fax: (01403) 259760 E-mail: sales@aerco.co.uk *Connectors & electronic components distributors*

A E R Cooling Ltd, 21 Woburn St, Ampthill, Bedford, MK45 2HP Tel: (01525) 403221 Fax: (01525) 406060 *Refrigeration & air conditioning contractors & installers*

▶ A E Rumens, Upper Crowbourne, Blind Lane, Goudhurst, Cranbrook, Kent, TN17 1JD Tel: (01580) 211413

A & E Russell Ltd, 5 Brown Street, Coatbridge, Lanarkshire, ML5 4AS Tel: (01236) 433511 Fax: (01236) 440070 E-mail: sales@aerussell.co.uk *Suppliers of safetywear & tools*

A & E Russell Ltd, Baird Avenue, Dryburgh Industrial Estate, Dundee, DD2 3TN Tel: (01382) 811566 Fax: (01382) 833455 E-mail: enquiries@aerussell.com *Suppliers of personal safety equipment*

A & E Russell Ltd, 33 Tennant Street, Edinburgh, EH6 5NA Tel: 0131-555 0577 Fax: 0131-553 4722 E-mail: enquiries@aerussell.co.uk *Suppliers of personal safety equipment*

A & E Russell Ltd, 3 19 Henderson Road, Inverness, IV1 1SN Tel: (01463) 717687 Fax: (01463) 717750 E-mail: enquiries@aerussell.co.uk *Suppliers of personal safety tools & equipment*

A & E Russell Ltd, 22 Mcgowan Street, Paisley, Renfrewshire, PA3 1QJ Tel: 0141-887 4411 Fax: 0141-889 9431 *Contractor tools & protective clothing suppliers*

A & E Russell Ltd, Unit 18 Crystal Drive, Smethwick, West Midlands, B66 1QG Tel: 0121-543 4850 Fax: 0121-543 4855 E-mail: birmingham@aerussell.co.uk *Suppliers of tools, equipment, workwear*

A & E Russell Ltd, 7-9 Chetham Court, Winwick Quay, Warrington, WA2 8RF Tel: (01925) 643700 Fax: (01925) 643707 E-mail: warrington@aerussell.co.uk *Protective clothing, tools & work wear suppliers*

▶ A E S Associates, 48a Edith Avenue, Peacehaven, East Sussex, BN10 8JB Fax: (01342) 332102

A E S (Birmingham) Ltd, Unit 39 Rovex Business Park, Hayhall Road, Tyseley, Birmingham, B11 2AG Tel: 0121-706 8251 Fax: 0121-706 5080 E-mail: bernard@aesltd63freeserve.co.uk *Electric mechanical repairs*

A E S Engraving Co. Ltd, Unit 19, Boulton Industrial Centre, Hockley, Birmingham, B18 5AU Tel: 0121-551 9525 Fax: 0121-551 9535 E-mail: enquiries@aes-signs.com *Screen printers & engravers*

A E S Enterprises Ltd, Nuffield Industrial Estate, 40 Banbury Road, Poole, Dorset, BH17 0GA Tel: (01202) 683875 Fax: (01202) 683875 *Machine tool maintenance*

A E S Industries Ltd, Unit 3 Appleby Glade Industrial Estate, Ryder Close, Swadlincote, Derbyshire, DE11 9EU Tel: (01283) 210033 Fax: (01283) 229330 *Engineering & hydraulic services*

A E S Roofing Contractors Ltd, Lingens Bungalow, Sledgemoor, Broadwas, Worcester, WR6 5NR Tel: (01905) 333697 Fax: (01905) 333650 E-mail: info@aesroofing.co.uk *Roofing contractors services*

A E Simmons Ltd, Bilton Road, Chelmsford, CM1 2UJ Tel: (01245) 352480 Fax: (01245) 359733 E-mail: sales@simmonsprint.co.uk *Printers*

A E Spink Ltd, Kelham Street, Doncaster, South Yorkshire, DN1 3RA Tel: (01302) 321514 Fax: (01302) 327543 *Builders & plumbers merchants*

A E T Transport Services Ltd, 8 Allens Lane, Poole, Dorset, BH16 5DA Tel: (01202) 632221 Fax: (01202) 632380 E-mail: aet-transport@btconnect.com *Machinery removal contractors*

A E Taylor & Co. Ltd, 44 Borough Road, Sunderland, SR1 1PW Tel: 0191-567 5078 Fax: 0191-510 2268 *Polyethylene & polythene product manufrs*

A E Westwood Ltd, Tything Road, Kinwarton, Alcester, Warwickshire, B49 6ES Tel: (01789) 765777 Fax: (01789) 765727 E-mail: aewestwood@thesjgroup.com *Oilcans, grease guns & lubricating systems manufrs*

▶ A & E White Bakers Ltd, Charles Street, Worsbrough, Barnsley, South Yorkshire, S70 5AF Tel: (01226) 203457

A E Williams, 6 Well Lane, Birmingham, B5 5TE Tel: 0121-643 4756 Fax: 0121-643 2977 E-mail: admin@pewtergiftware.com *Antique pewter ware manufrs*

▶ A E Wilson Commercials Ltd, Belton Road, Sandtoft, Doncaster, South Yorkshire, DN8 5SX Tel: (01724) 710373 Fax: (01724) 711178

A Elfes Ltd, 155-157 Green Lane, Ilford, Essex, IG1 1XW Tel: (020) 7788 3290 Fax: (020) 8478 7979 *Monumental masons*

A Evans Builders, 7 Langham Green, Sutton Coldfield, West Midlands, B74 3PS Tel: 0121-353 3661 Fax: 0121-353 3661 E-mail: albert.evans@btinternet.com *Building maintenance services*

A Evans & Son Ltd, 35 Wyle Cop, Shrewsbury, SY1 1XF Tel: (01743) 343078 Fax: (01743) 357141 *Flooring covering specialists*

A F Aerospace Ltd, Unit 2 Chariot Way, Glebe Farm Industrial Estate, Rugby, Warwickshire, CV21 1DA Tel: (01788) 578431 Fax: (01788) 540268 E-mail: sales@lentern.co.uk *Aircraft industry fasteners manufrs*

A F Blakemore & Son Ltd, Arden Industrial Estate, Arden Road, Saltley, Birmingham, B8 1DL Tel: 0121-328 2111 Fax: 0121-327 7366 *Shop fittings manufrs*

A F C Linear Products, Unit 45, Llantarnam Industrial Park, Cwmbran, Gwent, NP44 3AW Tel: (01633) 861414 Fax: (01633) 872039 E-mail: afc-cwmbran@fsmail.net *Linear motion equipment suppliers*

▶ A F Consulting, 19 Waylands, Cricklade, Swindon, SN6 6BT Tel: (01793) 751398 Fax: (01793) 751398 E-mail: info@afcons.co.uk *Health & safety consultants, asbestos surveys & consultants, fire risk assessors, planning supervisors*

▶ A F Crudden Associates, 209 High Street, Elgin, Morayshire, IV30 1DJ Tel: (01343) 550500 Fax: (01343) 550886

▶ A F D, 28 Belgravia Gardens, Bromley, BR1 4TB Tel: (020) 8464 3823 Fax: (07092) 277379 E-mail: info@afd.net *Graphic design, printing & signmaking, website design & hosting, hotfoil printing, logo design*

A F Dobbie, A Pitreavie Business Park, Queensferry Road, Dunfermline, Fife, KY11 8PU Tel: (01383) 723111 *Wholesale paper merchants*

A F Drew Construction Ltd, 38 Mill Lane, Frampton Cotterell, Bristol, BS36 2AA Tel: (01454) 850004 Fax: (01454) 850061 *Steel fabricators*

A F E Comber, 2-2a Brownlow Street, Comber, Newtownards, County Down, BT23 5ER Tel: (028) 9187 8088 Fax: (028) 9187 3290 *Fire extinguisher services*

A F Electrics, Millbank Street, Stoke-on-Trent, ST3 1AE Tel: (01782) 332276 Fax: (01782) 341036 E-mail: arnot@audemex.co.uk *Audio demonstration & exhibition stand manufrs*

A F G Electronics, Fairfield House, Goose Hill, Headley, Thatcham, Berkshire, RG19 8AU Tel: (01635) 268496 Fax: (01635) 268020 E-mail: sales@afg.pins.co.uk *Electronic equipment manufrs*

A F Goose Services Ltd, 41 Southwold Drive, Nottingham, NG8 1PA Tel: 0115-928 2999 Fax: 0115-928 8831 *Refrigeration & air conditioning repairers*

▶ A & F Grant, Georgetown Farm, Ballindalloch, Banffshire, AB37 9BA Tel: (01807) 500211 Fax: (01807) 500364

A F Hussey London Ltd, Unit B10 Down Bounds Green Industrial Estate, Ringway, London, N11 2UD Tel: (020) 8368 3680 Fax: (020) 8361 2992 *Sheet metalworkers & electric welding specialists*

A F I Ltd, Unit 17-20, Greenfield, Royston, Hertfordshire, SG8 5HN Tel: (01763) 241007 Fax: (01763) 241040 E-mail: sales@phase.co.uk *Office furniture manufrs*

A F Joinery, 75 Seacoast Road, Limavady, County Londonderry, BT49 9DW Tel: (028) 7772 2202 Fax: (028) 7772 2202 *Joinery manufrs*

A F L Trucks Ltd, 8 Factory Road, Poole, Dorset, BH16 5HT Tel: (01202) 621212 Fax: (01202) 621111 E-mail: sales@afltrucks.co.uk *Fork lift truck repair, hire & sales*

A F Litho Ltd, Grenaby Works, Grenaby Road, Croydon, CR0 2EJ Tel: (020) 8689 7849 Fax: (020) 8689 0479 E-mail: sales@aflitho.co.uk *General printers*

A F M Precision Die & Tool Co. Ltd, Froysell St, Willenhall, West Midlands, WV13 1QH Tel: (01902) 607640 Fax: (01902) 634505 *Forging dies*

▶ A F McPherson & Co., 84-90 Holmscroft Street, Greenock, Renfrewshire, PA15 4DG Tel: (01475) 720881

A F R Refrigeration Ltd, Units 5-6 Delta Business Park, 10 Smugglers Way, London, SW18 1EG Tel: (020) 8875 1999 Fax: (020) 8875 0125 E-mail: sales@afr.co.uk *Refrigeration equipment distributors*

A F S, Shelwick Farm, Shelwick, Hereford, HR1 3AL Tel: (01432) 341131 Fax: (01432) 264190 *Food consultants*

A F S Associates, 1 The Paddock, Much Wenlock, Shropshire, TF13 6LT Tel: (01952) 728188 Fax: (01952) 728174 E-mail: sales@afsassociates.co.uk *Safety disc (bursting) manufacturers, valve distributors/ agents/stockholders; valves, check & valves, line blind*

A F S Engineering Co., 41 Great Lister Street, Birmingham, B7 4LW Tel: 0121-359 5048 Fax: 0121-359 4562 *Precision engineers*

A F S Fire & Security, Unit 5d Mullacott Cross Indust Estate, Two Potts, Ilfracombe, Devon, EX34 8PL Tel: (01271) 864754 Fax: (01271) 864754 *Firefighting equipment services*

A F S Rotel Ltd, Unit E Central Industrial Estate, St Marks Street, Bolton, BL3 6NR Tel: (01204) 388077 Fax: (01204) 386309 E-mail: info@pump-spares.co.uk *Centrifugal pump spare part manufrs*

▶ A F S Security Ltd, 582-584 Barking Road, London, E13 9JU Tel: (020) 8471 9000 Fax: (020) 8475 0877 E-mail: afssecurity@btconnect.com *Locksmiths master key suite specialists*

A F S Systems Ltd, 9 Tamworth Road, Lichfield, Staffordshire, WS14 9EY Tel: (01543) 264034 Fax: (01543) 414367 E-mail: enquiries@arrowfire.co.uk *Complete fire protection*

A F Smith & Son, Fengate, Peterborough, PE1 5XB Tel: (01733) 319595 Fax: (01733) 898370 *Motor vehicle re-trimming*

A & F Sprinklers Ltd, Atrium House, 574 Manchester Road, Bury, Lancashire, BL9 9SW Tel: 0161-796 5397 Fax: 0161-796 6057 E-mail: lhill@afsprinklers.co.uk *design & supply automatic sprinkler systems*servicing & maintenance*

A & F Supplies, Railway Road, Adlington, Chorley, Lancashire, PR6 9RF Tel: (01257) 480500 Fax: (01257) 483338 E-mail: sales@a-f-supplies.co.uk *Expanded metal & wire goods manufrs*

A F Switchgear & Control Panels Ltd, Nunn Brook Road, Huthwaite, Sutton-in-Ashfield, Nottinghamshire, NG17 2HU Tel: (01623) 555600 Fax: (01623) 555800 E-mail: e-mail@afswitchgear.co.uk *Switchgear & control panel manufrs*

A F T Trenchers Ltd, 16-17 Addison Road, Sudbury, Suffolk, CO10 2YW Tel: (01787) 311811 Fax: (01787) 310888 E-mail: info@trenchers.co.uk *Trenching machines*

A F T UK Ltd, Industrial Estate, Hallcroft Road, Retford, Nottinghamshire, DN22 7SS Tel: (01777) 700722 Fax: (01777) 860335 E-mail: sales@aft-glass.co.uk *Glass production furnaces & machinery*

▶ A F Training, 4 Middleton Road, Clipstone Village, Mansfield, Nottinghamshire, NG21 9AU Tel: (01623) 632999 Fax: (01623) 425849 E-mail: info@aftraining.co.uk *All aspects of First Aid Training for the work place, Schools, Lesiure and Child Care Courses, both in house and sheduled courses in our training venues.*As well as providing a comprehensive programme of training courses, we also supply a wide range of first aid materials. We supply a wide range of products from complete kits to replenishing stock items for use within the workplace, in a leisure setting, within groups and care settings.*

A F Whiteley & Co. Ltd, Bingswood Road, Whaley Bridge, High Peak, Derbyshire, SK23 7NB Tel: (01663) 732288 Fax: (01663) 734180 E-mail: sales@whiteley-knives.com *Hardened & tipped steel knife & blade manufrs*

A Fawcett Toolmakers 1983 Ltd, James Street, Elland, West Yorkshire, HX5 0HB Tel: (01422) 370966 Fax: (01422) 310068 E-mail: fawcett.toolmakers@ic24.net *Toolmaking services & contractors*

A Fax Ltd, Drakes Industrial Estate, Shay Lane, Ovenden, Halifax, West Yorkshire, HX3 6RL Tel: (01422) 331133 Fax: (01422) 323533 E-mail: sales@a-fax.com *Plastic core extruder & pallet manufrs*

A Finch & Co., 1-21 Bedminster Down Road, Bristol, BS13 7AB Tel: 0117-963 2763 Fax: 0117-963 2826 *Electrical contractors, sign manufacturing & installation*

A Findlay, Old Forge, Clenchers Mill Lane, Eastnor, Ledbury, Herefordshire, HR8 1RR Tel: (01531) 634999 Fax: (01531) 635980 *Wrought ironwork*

▶ A Fleming, 19 Laurel Braes, Bridge of Don, Aberdeen, AB22 8XY Tel: (01224) 820333 E-mail: info@aflemingcarpetclean.com *Carpet & Upholstery Cleaning*

▶ A Flett, St Marys, Holm, Orkney, KW17 2RU Tel: (01856) 781209 Fax: (01856) 781219

A Form Tooling Ltd, 542 Aylestone Road, Leicester, LE2 8JB Tel: 0116-283 5936 Fax: 0116-244 0277 E-mail: aform.tooling@ntlworld.com *Wire & spark erosion toolmakers*

A Foster, Unit 4 Dove Court, Aylesbury Road, Aston Clinton, Aylesbury, Buckinghamshire, HP22 5AQ Tel: (01296) 631616 Fax: (01296) 631616 *Dental laboratory*

A Four Business Equipment Ltd, 61 Follingsby Drive, Gateshead, Tyne & Wear, NE10 8YH Tel: 0191-442 0957 Fax: 0191-442 3299 E-mail: enquiries@afourbusiness.co.uk *Photocopiers & fax machines & laser printers*

A French & Sons, Huntingdon Road, Cambridge, CB3 0DL Tel: (01223) 276638 *Animal feed & pet suppliers*

▶ A French Touch, 20 Lewis Street, Eccles, Manchester, M30 0PX Tel: 0774 2641509 Fax: 0161 7079145 E-mail: sales@finestfrench.com

A G A Group, Crawfold Farm, Balls Cross, Petworth, West Sussex, GU28 9JT Tel: (01403) 820999 Fax: (01403) 820011 E-mail: info@agagroup.org.uk *Soil erosion control specialists*

A G B Diesels Ltd, 20 Blaris Industrial Estate, Altona Road, Lisburn, County Antrim, BT27 5QB Tel: (028) 9266 1010 Fax: (028) 9266 7711 E-mail: enquiries@aves.co.uk *Forklift truck supplier*

A G B Narib Ltd, Fen End, Stotfold, Hitchin, Hertfordshire, SG5 4BA Tel: (01462) 730488 Fax: (01462) 835282 *Joinery manufrs*

A G Beech, Purdy Road, Batmans Hill Trading Estate, Bilston, West Midlands, WV14 8UB Tel: (01902) 491728 Fax: (01902) 491728 *Haulage contractors*

A G Block Ltd, 87 Church Road, Kessingland, Lowestoft, Suffolk, NR33 7SJ Tel: (01502) 741894 Fax: (01502) 742003 *Engineerss general engineering*

A G Bracey Paint Division, P O Box 8, Bristol, BS30 5NE Tel: 0117-937 4376 Fax: 0117-937 4326 *Coach bodies spraying*

▶ A G Brown Ltd, 42 Ramsden Road, Glenrothes, Fife, KY6 2SN Tel: (01592) 630003 Fax: (01592) 630975

A G Budget Discount Swimming Pools & Spas, Aqua Garden House, East Molesey, Surrey, KT8 0PA Tel: (0870) 1283185 Fax: (0870) 1283188 E-mail: info@agbudget.co.uk *In ground & above ground swimming pools, spas & saunas manufrs*

A G C Automotives UK Ltd, Unit B, Edgemead Close, Round Spinney, Northampton, NN3 8RG Tel: (01604) 671150 Fax: (01604) 671140 *Automotive glass assemblers*

A G C Engineering Co. Ltd, London Road, Apsley, Hemel Hempstead, Hertfordshire, HP3 9ST Tel: (01442) 253694 Fax: (01442) 233332 *Production engineers*

A G C Gasket Co., 1 30 Albert Road, St. Philips, Bristol, BS2 0XA Tel: 0117-972 1410 Fax: 0117-972 3896 E-mail: agcgaskets@onetel.com *Gasket manufrs*

A G Ceramics, The Coach House, 4 Bradford Street, Braintree, Essex, CM7 9AS Tel: (0870) 4862912 Fax: (0870) 4862913 E-mail: agceramics@angeljaz21.co.uk *Wall & floor, ceramic & stone tiler, over 25 yrs experience with all types of tiling including victorian geometric/encaustic floors. All work carried out to extremely high standards.*

A G Duck & Sons Ltd, Charlton Mead Lane, Hoddesdon, Hertfordshire, EN11 0DJ Tel: (01992) 462188 Fax: (01992) 450991 *Purpose-made joinery manufrs*

A G Evans & Sons, Joinery Works, Industrial Estate, Bala, Gwynedd, LL23 7NL Tel: (01678) 520660 Fax: (01678) 520660 *Joinery specialist & funeral directors services*

A G F Circuits, Unit 2, Comet Way, Southend-on-Sea, SS2 6GD Tel: (01702) 420153 *Printed circuit boards*

A G & G C Gibson, Forge House, Old Forge Lane, West Rasen, Market Rasen, Lincolnshire, LN8 3LS Tel: (01673) 842891 Fax: (01673) 842891 *Agricultural engineers*

A G Hydraulics Ltd, Unit 40 Plume Street Industrial Estate, Plume Street, Birmingham, B6 7RT Tel: 0121-326 6395 Fax: 0121-328 2923 E-mail: sales@aghydraulics.com *Hydraulic equipment, valve & pump distributors*

A G I S Telecom Ltd, Blairs Business Centre, South Deeside Road, Blairs, Aberdeen, AB12 5LF Tel: (01224) 864864 Fax: (0870) 1645149 E-mail: sales@agis-telecom.com *Telecommunications*

▶ A G International Freight Ltd, Claybrook Drive, Washford Industrial Estate, Redditch, Worcestershire, B98 0DT Tel: (01527) 838520 Fax: (01527) 838529 E-mail: stevec@avon-groupage.co.uk *Freight and groupage operators to and from Italy. Spain, France. own depots in Paris, Barcelona, Brescia, Italy*

A & G Joinery, Wheal Chance, Radnor Road, Redruth, Cornwall, TR16 5EQ Tel: (01209) 820144 Fax: (01209) 820144 *Joinery manufrs*

▶ A & G King Timber Ltd, Terregles Sawmill, Terregles, Dumfries, DG2 9RU Tel: (01387) 720210 Fax: (01387) 720145

A G Lester & Sons Ltd, Unit 1 Erskine Street, Birmingham, B7 4RU Tel: 0121-359 1018 Fax: 0121-359 1018 E-mail: info@aglesterandsons.sagenet.co.uk *Manufatcturers of bespoke sheet metal products according to our customer requirements. **Here at A. G. Lester you can be assured that we have the skill, knowledge and expertise which enables us to see your project through from the design stage to manufacture.**We supply a wide range of products manufactured in tin, brass, galvanized steel, copper and stainless steel.**If your product is not listed, please call us to discuss your requirements.***

▶ A G M Builders, 46 Headingley Road, Norton, Doncaster, South Yorkshire, DN6 9EN Tel: (01302) 708374 Fax: 01302 708374 E-mail: alan@agmbuilders.co.uk *F.M.B REGISTERED &fully qualified craftsmen who fit kitchens , bathrooms , tiling , roofing , paving , brickwork , blockwork , extensions , fencing , joinery , plastering , rendering , pointing , drainage , garages plumbing , all types of general repairs*

A.G.M. (Distributors) Ltd, 40b Ravenhill Road, Belfast, BT6 8EB Tel: (028) 9045 2613 Fax: (028) 9045 0023 E-mail: sales@agmbuckley.demon.co.uk *Bathroom & sanitary ware distributors*

A G M Media Group, 212-214 Hylton Road, Sunderland, SR4 7UZ Tel: 0191-565 6776 Fax: 0191-565 5604 *Computer rebuilding & consulting*

A G M Plastics, 3-4 The Drove, West Wilts Trading Estate, Bratton, Westbury, Wiltshire, BA13 4JE Tel: (01373) 827771 Fax: (01373) 827772 E-mail: alan@agmplastics.co.uk *Plastic injection moulding*

A G Machine Tool Technology Ltd, Cranbrooke House, 143a Main Street, Witchford, Ely, Cambridgeshire, CB6 2HP Tel: (01353) 669909 Fax: (01353) 661093

continued

continuation
E-mail: sales@ag-machine-tools.com *CNC machine tool purchasers & suppliers*

▶ A G P Printers, 7 Colvend Street, Glasgow, G40 4DU Tel: 0141-556 4900 Fax: 0141-556 6090

A & G Precision Engineers Ltd, 1 Hythe Works, Diplocks Way, Hailsham, East Sussex, BN27 3JF Tel: (01323) 847718 Fax: (01323) 440138 *Precision engineers & subcontractors*

A G Precision Huntingdon Ltd, 2 Windover Road, Huntingdon, Cambridgeshire, PE29 7EA Tel: (01480) 52334 Fax: (01480) 456055 E-mail: agprecision@tiscali.co.uk *General precision engineering*

A G Precision Sheet Metal Ltd, Unit 2-3 Bay Close, Progress Way, Luton, LU4 9UP Tel: (01582) 570391 Fax: (01582) 583339 E-mail: rgovier@agpsm.com *Established in 1982,AG Precision have over 25 years experience in fine limit sheet metalwork. ISO9001 accredited Suppliers to the marine, aerospace and refrigeration industries, we can offer a comprehensive product design service and fast turn around of high quality steel and aluminium fabrications. Our CNC are linked to off-line CAD/CAM workstations. Facilities include laser cutting, punching, folding, TIG & MIG welding, graining and assembly. With our onsite painting facility we can offer a comprehensive service to our customers. For more details call 01582 579239 or email rgovier@agpsm.com*

A G Products, 4-5 North Bar Street, Banbury, Oxfordshire, OX16 0TB Tel: (01295) 259608 Fax: (01295) 271787 E-mail: steve@agproducts.co.uk *Advertising & business gift distributors*

A G R Automation Ltd, Elliot Industrial Estate, Arbroath, Angus, DD11 2NJ Tel: (01241) 872961 Fax: (01241) 871723 E-mail: agr@agr-automation.com *Special purpose machinery manufrs*

A G & R L Cornes, Hollins Farm, Station Road, Halmer End, Stoke-on-Trent, ST7 8AR Tel: (01782) 722804 Fax: (01782) 721445 *Agricultural contractors*

A G Rutter Ltd, Fitzherbert Road, Portsmouth, PO6 1RU Tel: (023) 9278 9300 Fax: (023) 9278 9500 E-mail: sales@dtw-tiles.co.uk *Kitchen & bathroom ceramic tiles*

▶ A G S Computers Ltd, 29 Queen Elizabeth Avenue, East Tilbury, Tilbury, Essex, RM18 8SP Tel: (01375) 844478

A G S Environmental Maintenance, The Oaks, Boxhill Road, Tadworth, Surrey, KT20 7JT Tel: (01737) 843656 Fax: (01737) 842883 E-mail: sales@agsmaintenance.co.uk *Industrial boiler cleaning & maintenance, refractory repairs, chemical & mechanical descaling of boilers & calorifiers, water tanks cleaned & chlorinated to HS(G)70 & BS 6700 requirements, waste oil removal & hygiene & deep cleaning of kitchen & duct systems*

A G S Noise Control Ltd, 16 Digby Drive, Melton Mowbray, Leicestershire, LE13 0RQ Tel: (01664) 568728 Fax: (01664) 481190 E-mail: sales@agsnoisecontrol.co.uk Principal Export Areas: Central/East Europe & West Europe *Acoustic engineers & noise control equipment manufrs*

A G S Security Systems Ltd, Field Way, Denbigh Road, Mold, Flintshire, CH7 1BP Tel: (01244) 812222 Fax: (01352) 707889 E-mail: info@ags-security.co.uk *Security system installers*

A G S (Zinc Alloys) Ltd, Adams Street, Walsall, WS2 8ND Tel: (01922) 647520 Fax: (01922) 720133 *Zinc alloy suppliers*

▶ A G Servicing Ltd, 68 Wychall Drive, Bushbury, Wolverhampton, WV10 8UX Tel: (01902) 787121 Fax: (01902) 787121 E-mail: sales@agservicing.co.uk *Electrostatic powder coating equipment sales, service & hire services*

A G Shepherd Machinery Ltd, Toledo Works, Neepsend Lane, Sheffield, S3 8AW Tel: 0114-270 6146 Fax: 0114-270 6147 E-mail: sales@agshepherd.com *Machinery merchants*

A G Site Services, Carrington Business Park, Manchester Road, Carrington, Manchester, M31 4QW Tel: 0161-775 8001 Fax: 0161-775 8090 E-mail: sales@agsiteservices.co.uk *Portable building hire & suppliers*

A G Stuart Holdings Ltd, Old Rayne, Insch, Aberdeenshire, AB52 6RX Tel: (01464) 851208 Fax: (01464) 851202 E-mail: sales@sylvanstuart.com *Timber engineering services*

▶ A G Thomson & Sons, Spott Road, Dunbar, East Lothian, EH42 1RR Tel: (01368) 862315 Fax: (01368) 863000

A & G Toseland Ltd, St. Michael Road, Kettering, Northamptonshire, NN15 6AU Tel: (01536) 414401 Fax: (01536) 414402 E-mail: premierfinishes_uk@yahoo.co.uk *Wood coatings & anti bacterial finishing service*

A G W Electronics Ltd, Hayford Way, Staveley, Chesterfield, Derbyshire, S43 3JR Tel: (01246) 473086 Fax: (01246) 280082 E-mail: sales@agw.co.uk *Wound component manufrs*

A Gammie & Sons, Croftcrunie Farm, Tore, Muir of Ord, Ross-Shire, IV6 7SB Tel: (01463) 811240 Fax: (01463) 811240 *Dairy farming*

A Gordon & Co. Ltd, 14 Barrasgate Road, Fraserburgh, Aberdeenshire, AB43 9DQ Tel: (01346) 513297 Fax: (01346) 516003 *Box saw millers*

▶ A Gordon & Co. Ltd, Bridgend Sawmill, Longside, Peterhead, Aberdeenshire, AB42 4XE Tel: (01779) 821295

A Grade Division, Block 40, North Harbour, Ayr, KA8 8AH Tel: (01292) 289718 Fax: (01292) 289939 E-mail: info@hipg.co.uk *Machine sub-contractors*

A H Allen Ltd, Downing Road, West Meadows Industrial Estate, Derby, DE21 6HA Tel: (01332) 346400 Fax: (01332) 291023 E-mail: sales@aha-steel-derby.co.uk *Steel stockholders*

A H Allen Steel Services Ltd, Liliput Road, Brackmills Industrial Estate, Northampton, NN4 7DT Tel: (01604) 762211 Fax: (01604) 765525 E-mail: sales@aha-steel.co.uk *Steel stockholders & processors* Also at: Branches throughout the U.K.

A & H Ashby, Wakes Colne Mills, Colchester Road, Wakes Colne, Colchester, CO6 2BY Tel: (01787) 222259 *Solid fuel merchants.*

A & H Brass, 209 Edgware Road, London, W2 1ES Tel: (020) 7706 2262 Fax: (020) 7402 0110 E-mail: sales@aandhbrass.co.uk *Architectural ironmongers & lighting retailer*

A H C Camberley Ltd, 415-417 London Road, Camberley, Surrey, GU15 3HZ Tel: (01252) 735176 Fax: (01276) 709068 E-mail: oliver@ahc-camberley.co.uk *Tools, fasteners & fixings retailers*

▶ A H C (Warehousing) Ltd, Foundry Lane, Widnes, Cheshire, WA8 8UF Tel: 0151-424 7100 Fax: 0151-495 1990

▶ A H Callus Ltd, 48 Hall Drive, Hardwick, Cambridge, CB23 7QN Tel: (07740) 620543 E-mail: tony@ahcallus.com *Wooden flooring manufacturers & installation*

▶ A & H Commercial Printers, 153-155 Ley Street, Ilford, Essex, IG1 4BL Tel: (020) 8478 2558 Fax: (020) 8514 5366 E-mail: info@ahprinters.com *Design & print business stationery, posters, leaflets, business cards, letterheads, compliment slips, invoices, delivery notes, colour brochures & books, banners, labels, boxes, POS materials*

A H Designs, Mountain Ash, Rhydyfoel Road, Llanddulas, Abergele, Clwyd, LL22 8EG Tel: (01492) 512765 Fax: (01492) 512662 *Model airplanes accessories mail order & manufrs*

A H Distributors, 53 Donaldson Street, Kirkintilloch, Glasgow, G66 1XG Tel: 0141-776 2844 Fax: 0141-776 6099 *Household furniture distributor*

A H Electrical Services Ltd, 21 Manshead Court, Galley Hill, Milton Keynes, MK11 1NR Tel: (01908) 569754 Fax: (01908) 569754 E-mail: alanholland2000@yahoo.com *Electrical design & cad services*

A H Engineering North East Ltd, Unit 5 Wagonway Road Industrial Estate, Hebburn, Tyne & Wear, NE31 1SP Tel: 0191-483 9807 Fax: 0191-483 8700 E-mail: aheng@lineone.net *Precision tool & mould manufrs*

A & H Europe Ltd, Unit 24 B, Star Road, Partridge Green, Horsham, West Sussex, RH13 8RA Tel: (01403) 710055 Fax: (01403) 711082 E-mail: sale@aandheurope.com *Display packaging for ladies & mens jewellery*

A H Fabrication, Thorn Office Centre, Thorn Business Park, Rotherwas, Hereford, HR2 6JT Tel: (01432) 354704 Fax: (01432) 359762 E-mail: alexahfabs@fairadsl.co.uk *Racing, rally car engineering services*

▶ A H Fabrications, 1 Brean Farm, Warren Road, Brean, Burnham-on-Sea, Somerset, TA8 2RR Tel: (01278) 751930 Fax: (01278) 751930 *Steel fabricators*

A & H Fabrications, Unit 2-3 Rawreth Industrial Estate, Rawreth Lane, Rayleigh, Essex, SS6 9RL Tel: (01268) 781118 Fax: (01268) 781118 *Steel fabricators*

▶ A & H Fine Foods, 2 Limbrick Building, Crosse Hall Street, Chorley, Lancashire, PR6 0UH Tel: (01257) 241332 Fax: (01257) 261333 E-mail: sales@finefoods.co.uk *Fine foods suppliers*

A H Fire Prevention, 233a Golders Green Road, London, NW11 9ES Tel: (020) 8458 0448 Fax: (020) 8458 0338 *Fire protection engineers & services*

A.H. French Polishers, 4 Hunters Grove, Orpington, Kent, BR6 7TW Tel: (01689) 859853 Fax: (01689) 859853 *French polishing services*

A H Garner Ltd, Harrimans Lane, Lenton Lane Industrial Estate, Nottingham, NG7 2SD Tel: 0115-978 5161 Fax: 0115-924 4704 E-mail: sales@ahgarner.co.uk *Precision & hydraulic engineers*

▶ A H Hales Ltd, 35 Northampton Road, Scunthorpe, South Humberside, DN16 1UJ Tel: (01724) 843703 Fax: (01724) 271863

A H Hanson Ltd, Marley Street, Keighley, West Yorkshire, BD21 5JX Tel: (01535) 604112 Fax: (01535) 610085 E-mail: sales@wheel-clamp.com *General presswork & motor vehicle wheel clamp manufrs*

A H Hiller & Son Ltd, Dunnington Heath Farm, Alcester, Warwickshire, B49 5PD Tel: (01789) 772771 Fax: (01789) 490439 *Fruit growers & importers*

▶ A & H Interiors Ltd, Unit 40 Minerva Works, Crossley Lane, Huddersfield, HD5 9SA Tel: (01484) 432422 Fax: (01484) 426228 *Fireplace manufrs*

A H L Industrial Pipework Specialists Ltd, Unit 22 Royal Industrial Estate, Blackett Street, Jarrow, Tyne & Wear, NE32 3HR Tel: 0191-428 0282 Fax: 0191-483 8893 E-mail: info@ahlpipework.co.uk *Processed pipe work contractors*

▶ A H Lewis Contractors, 50 Cradge Bank, Spalding, Lincolnshire, PE11 3AB Tel: (01775) 411570

A H Marks & Co. Ltd, Wyke Lane, Wyke, Bradford, West Yorkshire, BD12 9EJ Tel: (01274) 691234 Fax: (01274) 691176 E-mail: info@ahmarks.com *Chemical manufrs*

A H P Trailers Ltd, Heath Mill Road, Wombourne, Wolverhampton, WV5 8AP Tel: (01902) 895281 Fax: (01902) 894577 *Road trailer manufrs*

A H Shaw & Partner, Phoenix Works, Manor Road, Ossett, West Yorkshire, WF5 0LF Tel: (01924) 273474 Fax: (01924) 273474 *Surgical appliances manufrs*

▶ A & H Wrought Iron Work, 14b Smeaton Industrial Estate, Hayfield Road, Kirkcaldy, Fife, KY1 2HE Tel: (07949) 501853 E-mail: adam.guthrie@sky.com *fabrications , gates, railings security grills, stair railings.memorial fences*

A Hallworth & Sons, 2 Dale Mill, Roch Street, Rochdale, Lancashire, OL16 2UH Tel: (01706) 648768 *Powder coatings*

A Handley & Partners, Townsditch, Rossett, Wrexham, LL12 0AN Tel: (01978) 760341 Fax: (01978) 760341 *Agricultural contractors & farmers*

A Hartrodt UK Ltd, Unit 2 Pump Lane Industrial Estate, Hayes, Middlesex, UB3 3NB Tel: (020) 8848 3545 Fax: (020) 8561 0940 E-mail: london@hartrodt.co.uk *International freight forwarders* Also at: Liverpool & Rugeley

A Harvey & Co The Wireworkers Ltd, 2 Stockton End, Sandy, Bedfordshire, SG19 1SB Tel: (01767) 681830 Fax: (01767) 683111 E-mail: sales@harveywire.freeserve.co.uk *Wire products & tubular fabricators*

A Healey Office Equipment Ltd, The Meadows, 2 Waterberry Drive, Waterlooville, Hampshire, PO7 7XX Tel: (023) 9226 9711 Fax: (023) 9226 9722 E-mail: sales@ahealey.co.uk *Photocopier & faxes dealers*

A Hingley Transport Ltd, Talbots La Trading Estate, Talbots Lane, Brierley Hill, West Midlands, DY5 2YX Tel: (01384) 262221 Fax: (01384) 573286

A Hodgson Engineers & Smiths Ltd, 54 Guest Street, Leigh, Lancashire, WN7 2HD Tel: (01942) 673038 Fax: (01942) 673038 E-mail: hodgsoneng@fsnet.co.uk *Steel fabricators & welding specialists*

A Hodgson & Sons, Church Bank, Terrington St. Clement, King's Lynn, Norfolk, PE34 4NA Tel: (01553) 828361 Fax: (01553) 827262 E-mail: info@ajhodgesoneng.co.uk *Metal fabricators, structural & general engineers*

▶ A Hoggarth & Sons, Selly Hill, Guisborough Road, Whitby, North Yorkshire, YO21 1SG Tel: (01947) 604777 Fax: (01947) 829829

▶ A Houghton & Co. Ltd, 630 Cranbrook Road, Ilford, Essex, IG6 1HJ Tel: (020) 8554 5716 Fax: (020) 8518 5327

A Howe Light Engineering, 1 Priory Works, Priory Cresent, Southend-on-Sea, SS2 6LD Tel: (01702) 611451 Fax: (01702) 469078 E-mail: david.knight@steelfabricators1.co.uk *Steel fabricators & general engineers*

▶ A & I Accessory Ltd, 19 Macadam Place, South Newmoor Industrial Estate, Irvine, Ayrshire, KA11 4HP Tel: (01294) 211555 Fax: (01294) 211114 E-mail: sales@aiaccessory.com *Accessory components repair & overhaul*

A I C (Automotive & Industrial Consumables) Ltd, 1 Kingsfield Close, Northampton, NN5 7QS Tel: (01604) 586500 Fax: (01604) 586576 *Janitorial suppliers*

A & I Composites Ltd, Mile End Road, Colwick, Nottingham, NG4 2DW Tel: 0115-940 2228 Fax: 0115-940 2228 *GRP mouldings*

A I Electronics Ltd, Bothwell Road, Hamilton, Lanarkshire, ML3 0DW Tel: (01698) 285225 Fax: (01698) 285944 E-mail: aielec@aol.com *Precision engineers*

A & I Engineering Ltd, 49 Depot Road, Cwmavon, Port Talbot, West Glamorgan, SA12 9BA Tel: (01639) 896141 Fax: (01639) 896141 *Sheet metalworkers*

▶ A I G Engineering Ltd, 33 Copenhagen Road, Hull, HU7 0XQ Tel: (01482) 823306 Fax: (01482) 835543

A I G Europe UK Ltd, The Aig Building, 58 Fenchurch Street, London, EC3M 4AB Tel: (020) 7954 7000 Fax: (020) 7954 7001 *Insurance company* Also at: Branches throughout the UK

A & I Holmes & Co. Ltd, Unit 8c Kayley Industrial Estate, Richmond Street, Ashton-under-Lyne, Lancashire, OL7 0AU Tel: 0161-343 1911 Fax: 0161-343 2959 E-mail: aiholmes@btconnect.com *Dairy & cheese textile manufacturers*

A I M Ltd, Victoria House, Derringham Street, Hull, HU3 1EL Tel: (01482) 326971 Fax: (01482) 228465 E-mail: aim@aim.co.uk *Legal computer systems supplier* Also at: Leeds & St. Albans

A I M Group plc, 16 Carlton Cresent, Southampton, SO15 2ES Tel: (023) 8033 5111 Fax: (023) 8022 9733 *Aircraft interior designers*

A I M S Ltd, Unit 3, Parkwater Industrial Estate, Forest Road, Newport, Isle Of Wight, PO30 4LY Tel: (01983) 520526 Fax: (01983) 520298 E-mail: aims@forklifttrucks.eu.com *Fork lift truck suppliers*

▶ A I M S Accountants For Business, 23 Fender Way, Wirral, Merseyside, CH61 9NP Tel: 0151-648 4506 Fax: 0151-648 4506 E-mail: timc@aims.co.uk

A I M S Elmbridge, 12 Rushett Road, Thames Ditton, Surrey, KT7 0UX Tel: (020) 8224 8107 Fax: (020) 8224 8107 E-mail: ianw@aims.co.uk *Management & business consultants*

▶ A I Materials, Otter Street, Sheffield, S9 3WL Tel: 0114-243 1206 Fax: 0114-261 1419 E-mail: sales@ai-materials.co.uk *Supply of titanium ingots*

A & I (Peco) Acoustics Ltd, 100 Sandford Street, Birkenhead, Merseyside, CH41 1AZ Tel: 0151-647 9015 Fax: 0151-666 1805 E-mail: sales@peco.co.uk *Automotive & industrial silencers suppliers*

A & I Plastics Ltd, Unit 5, Boundary Road, Buckingham Road Industrial Estate, Brackley, Northamptonshire, NN13 7ES Tel: (01280) 840050 E-mail: sales@aiplastics.co.uk *Plastics extrusions, assembly & press workers*

A I R Engineering, 4 Tyn Y Bonau Road, Pontarddulais, Swansea, SA4 8SG Tel: (01792) 881112 Fax: (01792) 881113 E-mail: aireng@freenet.com *Precision engineers*

A I S Alarms, Wharton House, 9 Wharton Avenue, Manchester, M21 7SQ Tel: 0161-881 4700 Fax: 0161-881 5203 *Burglar alarms installers*

A I S Countdown, 8 Carronshore Road, Carron, Falkirk, FK2 8DZ Tel: (01324) 570627 Fax: (01324) 562535 E-mail: admin@aisltd.co.uk *Cleaning products merchants*

A I S Countdown Ltd, Unit 33 Riverside, Medway City Estate, Sir Thomas Longley Road, Rochester, Kent, ME2 4DP Tel: (01634) 719422 Fax: (01634) 290269 E-mail: sales@aiscountdown.com *Cleanroom contamination control products*

A I S Sheet Metal Ltd, Hoo Farm Industrial Estate, Worcester Road, Kidderminster, Worcestershire, DY11 7RA Tel: (01562) 820700 Fax: (01562) 829401 E-mail: sales@aissheetmetal.co.uk *Shearing & press brake workers*

A I Systems, 548 Scott Hall Road, Leeds, LS7 3RA Tel: 0113-237 0626 *System builders*

A I T London Technologies, 2 25 Downham Road, London, N1 5AA Tel: (020) 7923 1011 Fax: (020) 7275 8344 *Computer maintenance & repairers*

▶ A.I. Welders, Unit 16, Dalcross Industrial Estate, Inverness, IV2 7XB Tel: (01667) 461383 Fax: (01667) 462520 E-mail: sales@ai-welders.co.uk *Welding machines*

A Ii D Solutions Ltd, 2 Wyvern Avenue, Stockport, Cheshire, SK5 7DD Tel: 0161-480 3163 Fax: 0161-480 3043 E-mail: info@aiid.co.uk *Data acquisition manufrs*

A J A Associates, 4 Portchester Court, Great Holm, Milton Keynes, MK8 9DU Tel: (01908) 569617 Fax: (01908) 569617 E-mail: aja.associates@virgin.net *Quantity surveyors & cost engineers*

A J Adams Engineering, Hassall Road, Skegness, Lincolnshire, PE25 3TB Tel: (01754) 765421 Fax: (01754) 765435 E-mail: dave@adamsengineering.ffsnet.co.uk *General & precision engineers*

A J Alder & Son Ltd, Unit 7 108 Nathan Way, London, SE28 0AU Tel: (020) 8854 8375 Fax: (020) 8855 1918 *Structural engineers, fabrication & installing*

A. J. B. Floor Coverings Ltd, Unit 1 Bulay Commercial Park, St Thomas Road Longroyd Bridge, Huddersfield, HD1 3LG Tel: (01484) 537255 Fax: (01484) 549328 E-mail: info@ajbflooring.co.uk *Industrial floor covering contractors carpets wood suppliers*

A J B Joinery, Little Merebrook, Hanley Swan, Worcester, WR8 0EH Tel: (01684) 310610 Fax: (01684) 311917 *Joinery manufrs*

A J B Partitioning & Ceiling, 13 Long Lane, Billesdon, Leicester, LE7 9AL Tel: 0116-259 6347 E-mail: ajb@billesdon.fsbusiness.co.uk *Partitioning & suspended ceilings manufrs*

A J B Wrought Iron & Welding Service, 65 Slades Road, St. Austell, Cornwall, PL25 4HA Tel: (01726) 61697 *Wrought iron & welding service*

A J Bernasconi, 15 Mill Green, Warboys, Huntingdon, Cambridgeshire, PE28 2SA Tel: (01487) 822660 Fax: (0870) 1413038 *Cast iron restoration specialists services*

A & J Brooks, 37-39 North Acton Road, London, NW10 6PF Tel: (020) 8965 1440 Fax: (020) 8965 1440 *Packaging materials*

A J Buckle Joinery, Hawthorn Farm, Willis Lane, Four Marks, Alton, Hampshire, GU34 5AP Tel: (01420) 588689 Fax: (01420) 588689 E-mail: andybuckle@hotmail.co.uk *Joinery manufrs*

▶ A & J Butterworth Ltd, Road End Garage, Off Chew Valley Road, Greenfield, Oldham, OL3 7JL Tel: (01457) 872098 Fax: (01457) 870760

A J Carlier & Sons Ltd, Mansfield Road, Derby, DE21 4AW Tel: (01332) 380615 *Road transport, haulage & freight services*

▶ A J Catering, Concorde House, Concorde Way, Preston Farm Industrial Estate, Stockton-on-Tees, Cleveland, TS18 3RB Tel: (01642) 617948 Fax: (01642) 607906 *Family run professional catering business. Long established in Teesside area. Catering for your business's everyday refreshments, special occasions, functions and parties. Meals to suit, free delivery, personal service. Also catering for private functions 7 days a week.*

A & J Civil Engineering, 25 Croyland Road, Edmonton Green, London, N9 7BA Tel: 078 1649 2523 Fax: (020) 8807 9553 E-mail: joegallagher25@hotmail.com *Specialising in all types of shuttering formwork/ steel fixing & labour hire*

▶ A J Clark Construction Ltd, 19 Bentinck Street, Kilmarnock, Ayrshire, KA1 4AW Tel: (01563) 539993

▶ A J Computer Services, 1 Grasmere, Sunderland, SR6 7QF Tel: 0191-537 2094 Fax: 0191-537 2094 *Computer maintenance consultants*

▶ A & J Computers, 50 Tamworth Road, Long Eaton, Nottingham, NG10 3LW Tel: 0115-946 2020 Fax: 0115 9462020 E-mail: enquiries@aj-computers.co.uk *Quality Computers and Laptops for Long Eaton, Beeston, Nottingham, Derby and surrounding areas. Full workshop facilities available*

▶ A J Computing, 12 Church Lane, Little Bytham, Grantham, Lincolnshire, NG33 4QP Tel: (01780) 410998 E-mail: alex@aj-computing.co.uk *Manufacturer of custom computers. Supply of computer hardware/software and related services*

▶ A J Contracts Whitstable, Unit 181 John Wilson Business Park, Harvey Drive, Chestfield, Whitstable, Kent, CT5 3RB Tel: (01227) 280009 Fax: (01227) 275683 E-mail: sales@ajcontracts.co.uk

A J Cope & Son Ltd, 11-12 The Oval, London, E2 9DU Tel: (020) 7729 2405 Fax: (020) 7729 2657 E-mail: marketing@ajcope.co.uk *Laboratory equipment retailers*

A J D Engineering Ltd, Moat Farm, Church Road, Milden, Ipswich, IP7 7AF Tel: (01449) 740544 Fax: (01449) 741584 *Aircraft restoration services*

A J D Instruments, 9 Lindfield Enterprise Park, Lewes Road, Lindfield, Haywards Heath, West Sussex, RH16 2LX Tel: (01444) 484055 Fax: (01444) 484042 E-mail: sales@ajdinstruments.co.uk *Storage tank gauge manufrs*

A J D Security Shutters, 106 Leeds Road, Wakefield, West Yorkshire, WF1 2QD Tel: (01924) 381385 Fax: (01924) 381385 *Security shutters & grills*

▶ A J Electrical, Unit 7, Back Grantley Street, Wakefield, West Yorkshire, WF1 4LG Tel: (01924) 362944 Fax: (01924) 362955

A J F Projects, 480 Earlham Road, Norwich, NR4 7HP Tel: (01603) 453226 Fax: (01603) 453226 E-mail: adam@ajfprojects.co.uk *Pallet repair & pallet handling*

▶ A J F Transport, Trinidad Works, Wanstrow, Shepton Mallet, Somerset, BA4 4SL Tel: (01749) 880554 Fax: (01749) 880288

A & J Fab Tech Ltd, Walkley Works, Walkley Lane, Heckmondwike, West Yorkshire, WF16 0PH Tel: (01924) 402151 Fax: (01924) 412966 *Fabricating engineers*

A J Fabrications, 28A Somerset Street, Northampton, NN1 3LW Tel: (01604) 628070 Fax: (01604) 627929 *Sheet metal light engineering services*

A & J Fasteners, 19 Manor Trading Estate, Brunel Road, Benfleet, Essex, SS7 4PS Tel: (01268) 566422 Fax: (01268) 566422 *Fasteners & fixing devices*

A J Finishers Ltd, 45 Barton Road, Bletchley, Milton Keynes, MK2 3BA Tel: (01908) 648437 Fax: (01908) 645016 *Industrial stove enamellers*

▶ A J Framemaker, 3 Alrewas Road, Kings Bromley, Burton-on-Trent, Staffordshire, DE13 7HW Tel: (01543) 473791 Fax: (01543) 473932 E-mail: sales@ajframemaker.co.uk *Insulation stockists & distributor of thermal insulation*

▶ A J Glass Fibre Ltd, Carr Wood Industrial Estate, Carr Wood Road, Castleford, West Yorkshire, WF10 4SB Tel: (01977) 603651 Fax: (01977) 603650 E-mail: lynn.kenney@haglassfibre.co.uk *Glass fibre moulders*

▶ A & J Glass & Glazing Ltd, 3 West Harbour Road, Edinburgh, EH5 1PH Tel: 0131-552 0001 Fax: 0131-552 0055

▶ A & J Gough Ltd, 370 Portland Road, Hove, East Sussex, BN3 5SD Tel: (01273) 417638 Fax: (01273) 418488

A & J Gummers Ltd, Unit H Redfern Park Way, Birmingham, B11 2DN Tel: 0121-706 2241 Fax: 0121-706 2960 E-mail: sales@gummers.co.uk *Boiler & water fittings & shower manufrs*

A J H Pump Supply & Repair, The Warehouse, Church Street, Wakefield, West Yorkshire, WF1 5QY Tel: (01924) 368773 Fax: (01924) 382229 E-mail: john@ajhpumpsupply.co.uk *Pump supply & repairers*

▶ A J Hawkridge & Sons, The Old Passenger Station, Milby, Boroughbridge, York, YO51 9BW Tel: (01423) 322506 Fax: (01423) 326752

A J Higginson Press Tools Ltd, 19 Industrial Estate, Cornwall Road, Smethwick, West Midlands, B66 2JS Tel: 0121-558 9413 Fax: 0121-558 6489 E-mail: johnking@ajhpresstools.freeserve.co.uk *Press toolmakers*

A & J Hobby Ceramics, 876 Wimborne Road, Bournemouth, BH9 2DR Tel: (01202) 516160 Fax: (01202) 523971 E-mail: sales@ajhobbyceramics.co.uk *Hobby ceramics - bisque ware - pergamano stockiest - card crafting suppliers*

▶ A J Homecrafts, Coppins Rest, 25 Saxhorn Road, Lane End, High Wycombe, Bucks, HP14 3JN Tel: 01494 883138 Fax: 01494 883138 E-mail: ajhomecrafts@fsmail.net *Hand and machine-knitted & crocheted clothing, tableware and bedcovers.**Machined table linen (placemats, coasters etc)***

A & J Installations, 1 The Chestnuts, Codicote, Hitchin, Hertfordshire, SG4 8XR Tel: (01438) 821058 Fax: (01438) 821970 *Lightning protection*

▶ A J K Services, Unit 3, Ordnance Road, Tidworth, Hampshire, SP9 7QD Tel: (01980) 846127 Fax: (01980) 846255

A J Kane, Castlelaurie Industrial Estate, Falkirk, FK2 7XF Tel: (01324) 620827 Fax: (01324) 620827 *Manual transmission repairs*

A J Kirby & Son, Whitchurch, Ross-on-Wye, Herefordshire, HR9 6DJ Tel: (01600) 890295 Fax: (01600) 890556 *Agricultural equipment manufrs*

▶ A J Kramer, 77 Colvend Street, Glasgow, G40 4DU Tel: 0141-551 9333 Fax: 0141-551 9944

A J & L M Perrett, 19a Cotton End, Northampton, NN4 8BS Tel: (01604) 761249 Fax: (01604) 767095 *Scrap metal merchants*

▶ A & J Locksmiths, 346 Lansbury Drive, Hayes, Middlesex, UB4 8SW Tel: (0800) 6951221 E-mail: john@a-jlocksmiths.com *We are a locksmith company offering a 24 hour emergency service. We open all types of locks & safes, we can cut keys on site from our mobile workshops, burglary repairs and door replacement*

▶ A & J Locksmiths, 34 Iveagh Close, Northwood, Middlesex, HA6 2TE Tel: (0800) 6951771 E-mail: john@a-jlocksmiths.com *Locksmiths*

A J Lockwood, Lynn Road, West Winch, King's Lynn, Norfolk, PE33 0PD Tel: (01553) 842188 Fax: (01553) 842170 *Refrigerated road haulage services*

A J M Consultants, Bradstones, Hewshott Lane, Liphook, Hampshire, GU30 7SU Tel: (01428) 723030 Fax: (01428) 727232 E-mail: ajm.consultants@farmline.com *Agricultural business management*

A J M Engineering Ltd, Park Lane, Park Lane Trading Estate, Corsham, Wiltshire, SN13 9LG Tel: (01249) 712620 Fax: (01249) 714932 E-mail: sales@ajmay.co.uk *Rubber mould tool manufrs*

▶ A J M Systems, 30 Khandala Gardens, Waterlooville, Hampshire, PO7 5UA Tel: (023) 9223 2134 Fax: 02392 232133 E-mail: info@ajm-systems.co.uk

▶ A J Maiden & Son Ltd, Cross Green, Allscott, Telford, Shropshire, TF6 5EG Tel: (01952) 255877 Fax: (01952) 222289 E-mail: info@maidensoftelford.co.uk

A J Mare Instruments, 110 Church Road, Perry Barr, Birmingham, B42 2LF Tel: 0121-356 8511 Fax: 0121-344 3644 E-mail: pimmy-21@hotmail.com *Calibration instrument suppliers*

A J Mechanical Handling Services Ltd, Bridge Works, 2 North End Road, Yatton, Bristol, BS49 4AL Tel: (01934) 835835 Fax: (01934) 838999 *Mechanical handling equipment suppliers*

A J Metal Fabrications Ltd, 21 Walthamstow Business Centre, Clifford Road, London, E17 4SX Tel: (020) 8527 4860 Fax: (020) 8527 4870 E-mail: steve@ajmetalfabs.co.uk *General sheet metal fabrication*

A J Metal Products Ltd, Cookley Wharf Industrial Estate, Bay 11, Leys Rd, Brierley Hill, West Midlands, DY5 3UP Tel: (01384) 74301 Fax: (01384) 485772 E-mail: sales@ajmetals.co.uk Principal Export Areas: Central/East Europe *Manufacturers of air receivers*

A J Middleton & Co. Ltd, 45 York Road, Ilford, Essex, IG1 3AD Tel: (020) 8514 1123 Fax: (020) 8478 1501 *Tool merchants & power tool repairers*

A J Mobility Ltd, Unit 17 Diplocks Way, Hailsham, East Sussex, BN27 3JF Tel: (01323) 847250 Fax: (01323) 849707 E-mail: sales@ajmobility.co.uk *Disabled wheelchairs suppliers*

▶ A J Morrisroe & Sons Ltd, 114 Elms Lane, Wembley, Middlesex, HA0 2NP Tel: (020) 8908 5411 Fax: (020) 8904 0041

▶ A & J Nelson Ltd, Great North Road, Kelty, Fife, KY4 0HE Tel: (01383) 830359 Fax: (01383) 831685

A & J Nightingale, Big House Farm, Breach Oak Lane, Fillongley, Coventry, CV7 8DE Tel: (01676) 540252 Fax: (01676) 540252 *Agricultural contractors*

A J Parsons & Sons Ltd, Anglo Trading Estate, Commercial Road, Shepton Mallet, Somerset, BA4 5BY Tel: (01749) 346161 Fax: (01749) 346100 E-mail: sales@parsonsparts.co.uk *Brake component distributors* Also at: Launceston

A J Paveley & Co., 416 Golden Hillock Road, Sparkbrook, Birmingham, B11 2QH Tel: 0121-772 1739 Fax: 0121-771 1386 E-mail: peterpavely@aol.com *Plumbers merchants*

A J Philpott & Sons Ltd, Fountain Street, Stoke-on-Trent, ST4 2HA Tel: (01782) 848603 Fax: (01782) 410726 E-mail: ajphilpott@email.com *General & builders merchants*

A J Pledger & Co Metals Ltd, West Street, Stamford, Lincolnshire, PE9 2PN Tel: (01780) 762245 Fax: (01780) 754531 E-mail: sales@pledger.co.uk *Farriers equipment hire & retailers*

A J Plumbing Supplies Ltd, Greenbank Industrial Estate, Rampart Road, Newry, County Down, BT34 2QU Tel: (028) 3026 3348 Fax: (028) 3026 3263 E-mail: info@ajplumbing.co.uk *Plumbing & bathroom supplies & distribution*

A & J Precision Engineering, 3 Fenland Business Centre, Longhill Road, March, Cambridgeshire, PE15 0BL Tel: (01354) 652203 Fax: (01354) 652203 E-mail: anjprecision@tiscali.co.uk *Precision engineers*

A J Pressings Ltd, 95 Reddings Lane, Tyseley, Birmingham, B11 3EY Tel: 0121-706 9886 Fax: 0121-706 9887 E-mail: tony@ajwilliams.co.uk *Presswork tool making crook lock branded products*

A & J Print Services, 330 London Road, Westcliff-on-Sea, Essex, SS0 7JJ Tel: (01702) 348456 Fax: (01702) 348456 *Rubber stamp printers & manufrs*

A J R Elsworth Ltd, Firwood Works, Firwood Industrial Estate, Thicketford Road, Firwood Fold, Bolton, BL2 3TR Tel: (01204) 595710 Fax: (01204) 302096 *Timber merchants & machinists*

A J R Precision Plastics Ltd, Unit 13 Calthorpe Industrial Park, Regina Drive, Perry Barr, Birmingham, B42 1BZ Tel: 0121-356 1763 Fax: 0121-356 9680 *Moulded plastics product suppliers*

▶ A J Rennie Ltd, Inverboyndie Industrial Estate, Banff, AB45 2JJ Tel: (01261) 818666 Fax: (01261) 818777

A J Restoration Co Ltd, Restoration House, Second Avenue, Greasley St, Nottingham, NG6 8NE Tel: 0115-927 7044 Fax: 0115-976 3476 E-mail: ajrestoration.co@btconnect.com *Specialist contractors*

A J Roberts Ltd, 12 Methley Road, Castleford, West Yorkshire, WF10 1LX Tel: (01977) 553027 Fax: (01977) 513613 *Building contractors*

A & J Robertson Granite Ltd, Church Street, Irvine, Ayrshire, KA12 8PE Tel: (01294) 279558 Fax: (01294) 279558 *Monumental memorial manufrs*

A J Rowe Bakers, 46 Haybridge Road, Hadley, Telford, Shropshire, TF1 6LT Tel: (01952) 242029 Fax: (01952) 242029 *Bakery*

A J S Contracts Ltd, Unit 3, Craggs Industrial Park, Morven St, Worksop, Nottinghamshire, S80 4AJ Tel: (01909) 722239 Fax: (01909) 724411 E-mail: ajscontracts@aol.com *Steel fabricators mechanical engineering*

A J S Electrical Ltd, 14A Brewery Street, Aston, Birmingham, B6 4JB Tel: 0121-685 9991 Fax: 0121-685 9992 *Electric motor rewind*

A J S Fasteners Ltd, 9 Maple Business Park, Walter Street, Birmingham, B7 5ET Tel: 0121-327 0660 Fax: 0121-327 3553 E-mail: sales@ajsfasteners.co.uk *Rivet & fastener distributors*

A J S Group, Unit 8 Cairnhall Industrial Estate, Cairnhall Industrial Estate, Inverurie, Aberdeenshire, AB51 0YQ Tel: (01467) 633301 Fax: (01467) 633302 *Liquid storage tanks & generators suppliers*

A J S Machine Sales & Spares Ltd, 22 Exeter Road, Urmston, Manchester, M41 0RE Tel: 0161-747 7436 Fax: 0161-718 0952 *Tractor spares suppliers*

▶ A J S Packaging Ltd, Unit 23 Queens Court Trading Estate, Greets Green Road, Greets Green, West Bromwich, West Midlands, B70 9EL Tel: 0121-520 2738 Fax: 0121-557 1406 E-mail: boxes@ajspackaging.co.uk *Packaging manufrs*

A J S Tarpaulin Services, Mariner Way, Felnex Industrial Estate, Newport, Gwent, NP19 4PQ Tel: (01633) 290387 Fax: (01633) 277317 E-mail: ajstarpaulins@tinyworld.co.uk *Tarpaulin manufrs*

A J S Theatre Lighting & Stage Supplies Ltd, 25-26 Hightown Industrial Estate, Crow Arch Lane, Ringwood, Hampshire, BH24 1ND Tel: (01425) 481100 Fax: (01425) 471398 E-mail: enquiries@ajs.co.uk *Theatre lighting sound & stage suppliers*

A J S Tools, 39 Mill Road, Waterlooville, Hampshire, PO7 7DH Tel: (023) 9223 1800 Fax: (023) 923 2221E-mail: ajs-tools@virgin.net *Tools sales & service*

A.J. Signs Ltd, No 2 Foundation House, Westfield Road, Slyfield Industrial Estate, Guildford, Surrey, GU1 1SF Tel: (01483) 300500 Fax: (01483) 535050 E-mail: sales@ajsigns.co.uk *Sign contractors, installers, signwriting & lettering services*

A J Smith & Son Benfleet Ltd, 242 High Road, Benfleet, Essex, SS7 5LA Tel: (01268) 792771 Fax: (01268) 750780 E-mail: info@ajsmith.uk.com *Timber importers & merchants. Ipe decking specialists. Hardwood and softwood decking merchants. Cedar cladding suppliers. Cedar shingles stockists.*

A J Sosbe, Factory 6, Maidstone Road, Leicester, LE2 0BA Tel: 0116-262 6492 Fax: 0116-262 6492 *Welding & engineering services*

A J Sparkes, Luke Street, Berwick St. John, Shaftesbury, Dorset, SP7 0HQ Tel: (01747) 828496 Fax: (01747) 828496 *Farriers & blacksmiths*

A & J Stead Ltd, 31 Derwent Road, York Road Business Park, Malton, North Yorkshire, YO17 6YB Tel: (01653) 693742 Fax: (01653) 691594 E-mail: admin@steadandson.co.uk *Steelwork & cladding specialist suppliers*

A J Thompson, Studlands Park Industrial Estate, Newmarket, Suffolk, CB8 7AU Tel: (01638) 664517 Fax: (01638) 664517 *Waste paper merchants*

▶ A J Transmissions, 4 Stanhope Close, Wilmslow, Cheshire, SK9 2NN Tel: (01625) 533466 Fax: (01625) 533466 E-mail: tomatajt@aol.co.uk *Mechanical power transmission equipment supplies*

A J Way & Co. Ltd, Sunters End, Hillbottom Road, Sands Industrial Estate, High Wycombe, Buckinghamshire, HP12 4HS Tel: (01494) 471821 Fax: (01494) 450597 E-mail: sales@ajway.co.uk *Chair manufrs*

A J Williams & Son Ltd, Wisloe Road, Cambridge, Gloucester, GL2 7AF Tel: (01453) 899099 Fax: (01453) 890642 E-mail: ajwilliamsltd@aol.com *Precision engineers*

▶ A & J Window Cleaners, 33 Auckland Avenue, Ramsgate, Kent, CT12 6HZ Tel: (01843) 597808 E-mail: ukgb_net@yahoo.co.uk *A and J are, based in Ramsgate, Kent, UK and are domestic and commercial window cleaners with over 20 years experience.**A and J's customers can rest assured that if their windows don't sparkle when the've finished cleaning them, it's on the inside! http://home.green-day.co.uk*

A J Wright Agricultural Services, Mickleton, Chipping Campden, Gloucestershire, GL55 6PS Tel: (01386) 438536 Fax: (01386) 438536 *Farm & agricultural contractors*

A J Wyatt Animal Feeds & Supplies, Stowey House Farm, Stowey, Bishop Sutton, Bristol, BS39 5TQ Tel: (01275) 333312 Fax: (01275) 332013 *Agricultural merchants*

A Jardine & Sons, Northgate, White Lund Industrial Estate, Morecambe, Lancashire, LA3 3PA Tel: (01524) 33113 Fax: (01524) 843262 *Crane & transport hire* Also at: Kendall & Lancaster

▶ A K A Pest Control, 104a Gorgie Road, Edinburgh, EH11 2NP Tel: (0800) 0737380 Fax: 0131-623 6227

A K Carcasses, 4B Priory Street, Dover, Kent, CT17 9AA Tel: (01304) 216190 Fax: (01304) 216190 *Built-in & fitted furniture*

A & K Clothing (Derby) Ltd, 110A Porter Road, Derby, DE23 6RA Tel: (01332) 772795 Fax: (01332) 772794 E-mail: info@akclothing.com *Leisurewear manufrs*

A K Consultancies Ltd, 141a Prestbury Road, Cheltenham, Gloucestershire, GL52 2DU Tel: (01242) 234123 E-mail: sales@akc.co.uk *IT consultants*

A K Controls, Unit 17 Fleetsbridge Business Park, Upton Road, Poole, Dorset, BH17 7AF Tel: (01202) 660061 Fax: (01202) 660200 E-mail: office@akcontrols.com *Control panel designers & manufrs*

▶ A K D Systems Ltd, 69 Peffer Place, Edinburgh, EH16 4BB Tel: 0131-621 6000 Fax: 0131-621 8200 E-mail: info@akdsystems.co.uk *Data voice & electrical supplier*

A & K Fashions, 1 Stonehouse Street, Middlesbrough, Cleveland, TS5 6HR Tel: (01642) 850574 Fax: (01642) 850584 *Clothing manufrs*

A K I T Solutions (UK) Ltd, 110-114 Grafton Road, London, NW5 4BA Tel: (020) 7482 0304 Fax: (020) 7482 3852 *Retailers of computers & accessories*

A K Industries Ltd, Foxwood Court, Rotherwas Industrial Estate, Rotherwas, Hereford, HR2 6JQ Tel: (01432) 375100 Fax: (01432) 263532 E-mail: sales@aki.co.uk *Injection mouldings (plastic) manufrs*

A K Knitwear Manufacturing Co., 2 Springmill Street, Bradford, West Yorkshire, BD5 7HF Tel: (01274) 742287 *Knitwear manufrs*

A K & L F Hutchings, The Barton, Thornbury, Holsworthy, Devon, EX22 7DD Tel: (01409) 261373 *Beef & sheep farmers*

A K L Sheet Metal Co., 7 Embassy Industrial Estate, Attwood Street, Stourbridge, West Midlands, DY9 8RY Tel: (01384) 892361 Fax: (01384) 892361 *Ductwork & ducting (sheet metal) contractors*

A & K Metal Polishing, Bourne Mills, London Road, Brimscombe, Stroud, Gloucestershire, GL5 2TA Tel: (01453) 883747 Fax: (01453) 883747 *Expert polishers*

A & K Office Products Ltd, 7 Crraftsman Square, Temple Farm Industrial Estate, Southend-on-Sea, SS2 6RH Tel: (01702) 313233 Fax: (0800) 614051 *Commercial stationers*

A & K Partners, Hill House, 20 Hill House Road, Norwich, NR1 4AA Tel: (01603) 667142 Fax: (01603) 667159 *Duct work*

▶ A K Plastic Mouldings Ltd, Unit 32 Herons Gate Trading Estate, Paycocke Road, Basildon, Essex, SS14 3EU Tel: (01268) 272241 Fax: (01268) 272097 *Plastic injection moulders*

A K Plastics, Unit 8 Reindeer Close, Horncastle, Lincolnshire, LN9 5AA Tel: (01507) 523883 Fax: (01507) 523883 *Fibre glass manufrs*

A K S Air Conditioning Ltd, 4 Edinburgh Road, Formby, Liverpool, L37 6EP Tel: (01704) 833755 Fax: (01704) 833422 *Air conditioning installation maintenance & service*

A K S Hairdressing Supplies, 3 H C M Industrial Estate, Wetmore Road, Burton-on-Trent, Staffordshire, DE14 1QR Tel: (01283) 535408 Fax: (01283) 535409 *Hair & beauty product wholesalers*

A K S Ward Ltd, 1 West Midfield, London, EC1A 9JU Tel: (020) 7236 0161 Fax: (020) 7236 3239 E-mail: consult@aksward.com *Consulting engineers*

▶ A.K.S Ward, West Way, Botley, Oxford, OX2 0JJ Tel: (01865) 240071 Fax: (01865) 248006

A K Security, 12 Hailsham Close, Mickleover, Derby, DE3 0PE Tel: (01332) 518070 *Electrical security*

A & K Services Co., 807 Lea Bridge Road, London, E17 9DS Tel: (020) 8509 2600 Fax: (020) 8520 9678 E-mail: a.kservices@btconnect.com *Plumbing & heating contractors*

A K Steel (Stainless Steel Stockholders), Lloyds Bank Chmbrs, 3 High St, Baldock, Hertfordshire, SG7 6BB Tel: (01462) 499400 Fax: (01462) 896763 E-mail: sales@aksteel.co.uk *Suppliers of Armco grades 17-4PH, 15-5PH, Nitronic 50 and Nitronic 60 plus Armco ingot iron (pure iron) in bars. Also flat rolled stainless steels for automotive and electrical steels for transformer applications.*

A K Supplies, 5 Regent Road, Handsworth, Birmingham, B21 8AB Tel: 0121-554 7107 Fax: 0121-682 3958 *Industrial skin care suppliers & paper disposables*

▶ A K Transport Ltd, Blenheim Road, Airfield Industrial Estate, Ashbourne, Derbyshire, DE6 1HA Tel: (01335) 342958 Fax: (01335) 345103

A K Waugh Ltd, 49 Dalsetter Avenue, Glasgow, G15 8TE Tel: 0141-944 3303 Fax: 0141-944 4750 E-mail: sales@akwaugh.com *A.K. Waugh Ltd. manufactures Industrial Process Heaters for a wide variety of fluid heating applications. With 65 years of experience we can offer solutions for virtually any fluid heating problem.*

A K Williams & Sons Ltd, Queen Street, Madeley, Telford, Shropshire, TF7 4BH Tel: (01952) 585740 Fax: (01952) 582021 *Timber & builders merchants*

A Kelly Ltd, Mita House, Wester Gourdie Industrial Estate, West Gourdie Industrial Estate, Dundee, DD2 4UH Tel: (01382) 623311 Fax: (01382) 611910 E-mail: admin@kellyscopiers.co.uk *Office furniture & equipment suppliers*

A Kidman Engineering, Atlas Mill Road, Brighouse, West Yorkshire, HD6 1ES Tel: (01484) 720520 Fax: (01484) 401051 *Precision & sub-contract engineers*

A K-IT Solutions (UK) Ltd, 205-207 City Road, London, EC1V 1JN Tel: (020) 7684 6543 Fax: (020) 7684 8807 *IT suppliers*

A L A Rail Ltd, Byass Works, The Docks, Port Talbot, West Glamorgan, SA13 1RS Tel: (01639) 885435 Fax: (01639) 899842 E-mail: sales@ala-rail.com *Railway maintenance service*

A L Atack Ltd, Church Street, Ossett, West Yorkshire, WF5 9DG Tel: (01924) 263358 Fax: (01924) 281546 *Promotional keyrings & banner sales*

▶ A L B Accountancy, 4 Brighton Road, Horsham, West Sussex, RH13 5BA Tel: (01403) 255788 Fax: (01403) 255704 E-mail: info@franaccounts.co.uk *ALB Accountancy provides accounting solutions for businesses of all sizes. Fixed fees and professional nationwide service.*

▶ A & L Computers, 8 High Street, Rhyl, Clwyd, LL18 1ES Tel: (01745) 338200 Fax: (01745) 356682 E-mail: sales@al-computers.co.uk *Computer maintenance consultants*

A L D Engineering (UK) Ltd, Les Searle Plant Yard, Parsonage Way, Horsham, West Sussex, RH12 4AL Tel: (01403) 271964 Fax: (01403) 271965 *Diesel engineers*

A.L.D. Lighting, Unit 6E Southbourne Business Park, Courtlands Road, Eastbourne, East Sussex, BN22 8UY Tel: (01323) 729337 Fax: (01323) 732356 E-mail: sales@aldlighting.com *Manufacturers of light fittings*

A L F Plant Hire, Lyndon Lodge, Kilby Road, Fleckney, Leicester, LE8 8BQ Tel: 0116-240 3749

A L Gordon Engineering, Abbotshaugh Works, Abbots Road, Bankside Industrial Estate, Falkirk, FK2 7UU Tel: (01324) 622055 Fax: (01324) 613383 E-mail: info@al-gordon.co.uk *Sheet metalworkers*

A L I C O, Alico House, 22 Addiscombe Road, Croydon, CR9 5AZ Tel: (020) 8680 6000 Fax: (020) 8680 7217 *Personal accidents & investment bond services*

▶ A L K Technologies Ltd, 4 Bloomsbury Square, London, WC1A 2RP Tel: (020) 7404 4222 Fax: (020) 7404 7778 *Computer software consultants*

▶ A L M Ltd, Enterprise Unit 1 Maes Y Clawdd, Maesbury Road Industrial Estate, Oswestry, Shropshire, SY10 8NN Tel: (01691) 655940 Fax: (01691) 655940 *Clothing manufrs*

A L M Partitioning, 9 East End, Langtoft, Peterborough, PE6 9LP Tel: (01733) 266333 Fax: (01733) 266333 *Ceiling & partition contractor & supplier*

A L M Products Ltd, Grindon Way, Heighington Lane Business Park, Newton Aycliffe, County Durham, DL5 6SH Tel: (01325) 313377 Fax: (01325) 315588 E-mail: sales@almproducts.co.uk *Cubicle hardware manufrs*

A L Maugham & Co. Ltd, 5-9 Fazakerley Street, Liverpool, L3 9DN Tel: 0151-236 1872 Fax: 0151-236 1872 *Light leather merchants*

▶ A & L Mechanical Installations, 35 Portree Avenue, Kilmarnock, Ayrshire, KA3 2GA Tel: (01563) 525425 Fax: (01563) 525952

▶ A & L Movers, 87 Burnell Avenue, Welling, Kent, DA16 3HP Tel: (020) 8309 8005 E-mail: sales@aandlmovers.co.uk *International removal company*

A L Musselwhite Ltd, Budds Lane, Romsey, Hampshire, SO51 0HA Tel: (01794) 516222 Fax: (01794) 830224 E-mail: almusselwhite@virgin.net *Commercial vehicle builders*

A L P Electrical Ltd, 70 St. Marks Road, Maidenhead, Berkshire, SL6 6DW Tel: (01628) 633998 Fax: (01628) 760981 E-mail: alp@alpelectrical.com *Electrical contractors/control panel manufrs*

▶ A L P Plants, Unit 26b Central Industrial Estate, Cable Street, Wolverhampton, WV2 2RJ Tel: (01902) 455592 Fax: (01902) 455586 *Metal finishing equipment distributors*

A L Povey, The Forge, Owslebury Bottom, Winchester, Hampshire, SO21 1LY Tel: (01962) 777473 Fax: (01962) 777473 E-mail: alan.povey@tesco.net *Farriers*

▶ A L S Cleaning Services, 12 The Close, Great Holland, Frinton-on-Sea, Essex, CO13 0JR Tel: (01255) 852781 E-mail: info@als-cleaning.co.uk *Hi ALS-Cleaning carry out daily weekley and monthly contracts to Window, Office & Common-way cleaning areas covered: Essex - suffolk - London. We are accredited by the Safe-Contractor scheme and members of the Federation of Master Window cleaners. We carry out ladderless window cleaning to heights of 60feet working within the new Working at Height Directive.*Gutter Cleaning, PVC Cleaning & Pressure Washing.*

A & L Services Ltd, Millcraig Farm Cottages, Alness, Ross-Shire, IV17 0YA Tel: (01349) 882344 Fax: (01349) 884800 E-mail: sales@software-scotland.co.uk *Computer consultants*

A L Spinnings - CNC Punch Weld, Unit 499-101 Newhall Street, Willenhall, West Midlands, WV13 1LQ Tel: (01902) 601318 Fax: (01902) 601318 E-mail: adacncpunch@aol.com *Sheet metalworking,*

A & L Stronach, Unit 16 17 Camiestone Road, Kemnay, Inverurie, Aberdeenshire, AB51 5GT Tel: (01467) 624655 Fax: (01467) 624629 *Forklift hire services*

A L Technical Ltd, 2 Woodston Business Centre, Shrewsbury Avenue, Peterborough, PE2 7EF Tel: (01733) 390123 Fax: (01733) 394933 E-mail: altechnical@yahoo.co.uk *Installation & maintenance engineers*

▶ A La Maison, 119 Norman Road, West Malling, Kent, ME19 6RW Tel: (01732) 844129

A Lewis & Sons Willenhall Ltd, 47 Church Street, Willenhall, West Midlands, WV13 1QW Tel: (01902) 605428 Fax: (01902) 601181 E-mail: lewislocksltd@aol.com *We are A. LEWIS & SONS (WILLENHALL) LTD. We were founded in 1920 by Master Locksmith Arthur Lewis, and became a Limited Company in 1947. We are now proud to have the fourth generation in the Company ensuring the same high quality of service that can only come from a family business. *Our Products: We stock a wide range of Camlocks, Handles and Furniture Locks from the Lowe & Fletcher range and other leading Lock Manufacturers. We also manufacture High Quality Brass Cabinet Locks and Drug Cupboard Locks. Brass Lever Locks , Cam Locks ,Locks, Metal, Handles & Knobs ,Radial Pin Tumbler Locks ,Budget Locks ,Mortice Locks ,and much more. Come to A. LEWIS & SONS for the type of Quality and personal service that can only come from four generations experience in the Lock Industry. No order too large or small and advice is free! We are now approved stockists of Croft high quality English Architectural hardware.*

▶ A Licensed Security Co., Derwen Deg, Llansilin, Oswestry, Shropshire, SY10 7PU Tel: (01691) 791491 E-mail: pat@vallysecurit.co.uk *Security services*

A Lloyd & Son, Urban Road, Kirkby-in-Ashfield, Nottingham, NG17 8AP Tel: (01623) 752965 Fax: (01623) 752965 *Commercial vehicle body builders*

A M A Carpentry Services Ltd, Unit 2 Caerbont Enterprise Park, Ystradgynlais, Swansea, SA9 1SW Tel: (01639) 730538 Fax: (01639) 730165 E-mail: ama-carpentry@fsmail.net *Structure at all stages of manufrs*

A M A Fabrications Ltd, Low Mill Lane, Ravensthorpe Industrial Estate, Dewsbury, West Yorkshire, WF13 3LN Tel: (01924) 507217 Fax: (01924) 507216 E-mail: sales@ama-fabs.co.uk *Metal display specialists*

A M A Plastics, Unit 1 Moreton Park Industrial Estate, Moreton Road South, Luton, LU2 0TL Tel: (01582) 734630 Fax: (01582) 419260 *AMA Plastics Lts based in Luton, Bedfordshire offer high volume plastic injection moulding services to industries across the UK including the manufacturing, automotive and leisure sectors.*

A.M. Agencies, 81 Bargery Road, London, SE6 2LP Tel: (020) 8698 8896 Fax: (020) 8461 3627 *Flexible packaging material agents*

A & M Associates, Unit 2, Stuart Street, Off Fishwick Street, Rochdale, Lancashire, OL16 5NB Tel: (01706) 710747 Fax: (01706) 710746 E-mail: amasso@zen.co.uk *Catering disposable products janitorial & hygiene products, plastic & paper packaging*

A M B Products Ltd, Marriott Road, Swinton, Mexborough, South Yorkshire, S64 8AG Tel: (01709) 583132 Fax: (01709) 587252 E-mail: amb@walterblack.co.uk *Bleach & detergent distributors*

A M B Technical Expertise Ltd, 20 Falsgrave Road, Scarborough, North Yorkshire, YO12 5AT Tel: (01723) 363477 Fax: (01723) 363477 E-mail: sales@it-department.co.uk *Computer services*

A M C Engineering Ltd, Unit 3, Blackhill Industrial Estate, Findon, Aberdeen, AB12 4RL Tel: (01224) 782232 Fax: (01224) 782480 E-mail: sales@amc-engineering.co.uk *Torque equipment manufrs*

A M C Food Machinery Ltd, 55-57 Waverley Road, Yate, Bristol, BS37 5QR Tel: (01454) 322315 Fax: (01454) 323144 E-mail: sales@amcfoodmachinery.com *Meat processing equipment distributors*

A M C O, Tresham House, 166 High Street, Deal, Kent, CT14 6BQ Tel: (01304) 239185 Fax: (01304) 239185 E-mail: ajm@emec.co.uk *Light fittings importer*

A M C (Projects) Ltd, Unit 3B Pincents Kiln Industrial Park, Pincents Kiln, Reading, RG31 7SD Tel: 0118-932 3313 Fax: 0118-930 6163 E-mail: admin@amc.uk.net *Architect metal workers*

A M Cleaning Services, West Lodge, Beckenham Place Park, Beckenham, Kent, BR3 5BP Tel: (020) 8658 8181 E-mail: info@amcleaning.info *Office & commercial carpet cleaners*

A & M Cleaning Supplies, 3-7 Orbital Crescent, Watford, WD25 0HB Tel: (01923) 671587 Fax: (01923) 671889 E-mail: sales@aandmcs.co.uk *Cleaning products distribution*

A & M Curtains, Ray Street, Huddersfield, HD1 6BL Tel: (01484) 307507 Fax: (01484) 307507 *Curtain manufrs*

A M Designs Powergrip, 45 Tyler Hill Road, Blean, Canterbury, Kent, CT2 9HU Tel: (01227) 472203 Fax: (01227) 454769 E-mail: am@powergrip.co.uk *Hand tool & engineers clamp manufrs*

A M Doors Ltd, Unit 11 Borough Close, Paignton, Devon, TQ4 7EP Tel: (01803) 520344 Fax: (01803) 558510 *Industrial doors*

A & M Drive Systems, 16 Bayfield Avenue, Frimley, Camberley, Surrey, GU16 8TU Tel: (01276) 26651 Fax: (01276) 685193 *Power transmission equipment*

A M E, 5 Glebe Road, Skelmersdale, Lancashire, WN8 9JP Tel: (01695) 50658 Fax: (01695) 50652 E-mail: info@amefacades.com *Wall cladding panels manufrs*

A M E C Design & Management Ltd, Amec House, Timothy's Bridge Road, Stratford-Upon-Avon, Warwickshire, CV37 9NJ Tel: (01789) 204288 Fax: (01789) 299135 Principal Export Areas: Worldwide *Design & management of construction project services*

A M E C Group Ltd, Church Street, Adlington, Chorley, Lancashire, PR7 4LB Tel: (01257) 484400 Fax: (01257) 484405 *Civil engineers*

A M E Pressure Die Casting Ltd, Unit 59c Siddons Factory Estate, Howard Street, West Bromwich, West Midlands, B70 0SU Tel: 0121-505 5222 Fax: 0121-505 5444 E-mail: amediecasting@aol.com *Specialists in zinc alloy pressure diecasting*

▶ A M E Product Development Solutions, Momentun House, Carrera Court, Dinnington, Sheffield, S25 2RG Tel: (01909) 550999 Fax: (01909) 550888 E-mail: ian.johannessen@ame-solutions.com *Prototyping bureau & design consultancy*

A & M Electrical Services, 30 Radcliffe Lane, Pudsey, West Yorkshire, LS28 8BE Tel: 0113-255 7903 Fax: 0113-256 6030 *Electrical contracting & testing services*

A & M Energy Fires, Pool House, Main Road, Huntley, Gloucester, GL19 3DZ Tel: (01452) 830662 Fax: (01452) 830891 E-mail: am@energy fires.co.uk *Suppliers of glass fireplace doors and mesh spark curtains made-to-measure. Fireplace Doors, Fire Guards, Chainmail curtains, Fire place enclosures. Througout the UK. Measuring and fitting service direct from Manufacturer.*

A & M Engineering, Briercliffe Business Centre, Burnley Road, Briercliffe, Burnley, Lancashire, BB10 2HG Tel: (01282) 412706 Fax: (01282) 424880 *Engineering & fabrication*

A M Engineering, Old Forge, 206 Woodrow Rd, Forest, Melksham, Wilts, SN12 7RD Tel: (01225) 704230 *General blacksmiths*

A & M Engineering, Merlins Cross, Pembroke, Dyfed, SA71 4AG Tel: (01646) 685169 Fax: (01646) 622060 *Agricultural engineers*

A & M Engineering Hull Ltd, Unit 30 B, Foster Street, Hull, HU8 8BT Tel: (01482) 820806 Fax: (01482) 824614 E-mail: sales@am-engineering.co.uk *Manufacturers of conveying & mechanical handling equipment*

A M F Business Systems Ltd, New Malden, Surrey, KT3 5NW Tel: (020) 8605 1111 Fax: (020) 8605 1105 *Copying machine agents*

A M F Polymers Ltd, Avondale Way, Avondale Industrial Estate, Pontrhydyrun, Cwmbran, Gwent, NP44 1TS Tel: (01633) 873229 Fax: (01633) 866600 *Plastic reclamation & granulation*

A M Fabrications, Unit 2 Block 2, Newlands Avenue, Brackla Industrial Estate, Bridgend, Mid Glamorgan, CF31 2AG Tel: (01656) 658874 Fax: (01656) 658874 *General steel fabricators*

A M Fabrics, 15 Sulgrave Road, Leicester, LE5 0LH Tel: 0116-274 2128 Fax: 0116-274 2790 *Fabric manufrs*

A M Farm Supplies, Unit 6, 154 Newlands, Witney, Oxfordshire, OX28 3JH Tel: (01993) 772574 Fax: (01993) 706499 *Dairy farm suppliers*

A M G, Lower Trinity Street, Birmingham, B9 4AG Tel: 0121-772 3551 Fax: 0121-455 9301 Principal Export Areas: Worldwide *Metal recyclers* Also at: Hartlepool & Llanelli

▶ A M G Electronics Ltd, Unit 1 & 5, Stephenson Court, Brindley Road, Stephenson Industrial Estate, Coalville, Leicestershire, LE67 3HG Tel: (01530) 836877 Fax: (01530) 836878 *Electronic contract assemblers*

A M G Outdoor Ltd, Kelburn Business Park, Port Glasgow, Renfrewshire, PA14 6TD Tel: (01475) 744122 Fax: (01475) 742333 E-mail: info@amg-outdoor.co.uk *Camping, skiing equipment & clothing manufrs*

A M G Roofing Services, 1 Trent Rise, Spondon, Derby, DE21 7PE Tel: (01332) 677163 *Roofing contractors*

▶ A & M Gearboxes Automatic & Manual, Lorien, The Shrave, Four Marks, Alton, Hampshire, GU34 5BH Tel: (07901) 661065

A M Glazing (Contractors) Ltd, 440a Hornsey Road, London, N19 4EB Tel: (020) 7263 7796 Fax: (020) 7281 7112 E-mail: sales@amglazing.com *Glazing contractors*

A M H Precision Tools Ltd, Unit 4, Thornsett Trading Estate, Birch Vale, High Peak, Derbyshire, SK22 1AH Tel: (01663) 745145 Fax: 01663 745252 E-mail: sales@amhtools.co.uk *AMH Precision Tools Ltd based in Stockport, Cheshire is a specialist toolmaker for the plastic and injection mould industry. Our in house design department uses 3D CAD-CAM software and whether the job is large or small we can handle even the more complicated design in house cutting down on costs and time. AMH machines include ... Bridgeport turret millers, Lathes (max swing 700 mm) Jig-Borers, Cincinnati Millers (bed size 4 ft x 1 ft) Surface Grinders, Universal Grinders, Honing, Charmilles EDM machines, CNC Milling, Hurco Knee Mill, Two Hurco Machining Centres , 4 axis wire. We provide a local service for the Greater Manchester area, however we do cover the whole of the UK including Scotland & Wales. We provide tools for plastic and injection moulders for all industries including a leader blind manufacturer and also for medical equipment. Other services include wire erosion, spark erosion, Charmilles EDM, CNC machining, CNC press tools and much more.*

A M Handling Ltd, Burneston, Bedale, North Yorkshire, DL8 2JW Tel: (01845) 567233 Fax: (01845) 567360 *Agricultural machinery*

A M Hobbs Ltd, The Island, Midsomer Norton, Radstock, BA3 2HQ Tel: (01761) 413961 Fax: (01761) 413961 E-mail: sales@amhobbsfirearms.co.uk *Fishing tackle retailer*

A M Hydraulics, Unit 4 Hockley Brook Trading Estate, South Road Avenue, Birmingham, B18 5JR Tel: 0121-554 7576 Fax: 0121-554 4640 E-mail: info@amhydraulics.com *Hydraulic cylinder manufrs*

A M I Exchangers Ltd, Apex Workshops, Graythorp Industrial Estate, Hartlepool, Cleveland, TS25 2DF Tel: (01429) 860187 Fax: (01429) 860673 E-mail: sales@ami-exchangers.co.uk *We offer innovative solutions to Marine and Industrial hot spots. AMI Exchangers is one of Europe's largest producers of new and replacement heat exchangers to many different market sectors.*

A M I Supplies Ltd, 2 Centre 2000, St. Michaels Road, Sittingbourne, Kent, ME10 3DZ Tel: (01795) 420430 Fax: (01795) 426817 E-mail: sales@amigroup.co.uk *Printers' services & supplies*

A M I Systems Ltd, 1159-1163 New Chester Road, Wirral, Merseyside, CH62 0BY Tel: 0151-200 2121 Fax: 0151-200 2122 *Computer re-sellers*

A M I UK Ltd, Lexus House, Rosslyn Crescent, Harrow, Middlesex, HA1 2RZ Tel: (020) 8863 6868 Fax: (020) 8426 0872 E-mail: harshad@ukaerosols.com *Manufactures of household toiletries*

▶ A & M IT Solutions, 93 Lever Street, London, EC1V 3RQ Tel: (020) 7253 6123 *Computer consultants*

A M J Engineering, 38 Towerfield Road, Shoeburyness, Southend-on-Sea, SS3 9QT Tel: (01702) 295331 Fax: (01702) 296862 E-mail: info@amjbuttons.com *Precision engineers*

A M J Fencing, Unit 7 Arden Street, Swindles Yard, Stockport, Cheshire, SK12 4NS Tel: (01663) 744560 Fax: (01663) 744560 *Fencing manufrs*

A M J Pneumatics '99' Ltd, Rossfield Road, Ellesmere Port, CH65 3AW Tel: 0151-355 8978 Fax: 0151-357 1431 *Pneumatic & hydraulic equipment distributors*

A & M Mclellan Ltd, 94-96 Moorside Road, Swinton, Manchester, M27 0HJ Tel: 0161-794 1169 Fax: 0161-794 3733 E-mail: sales@mclellan-sport.co.uk *Embroided sportswear manufrs*

▶ A & M Marquees, 11 Stanley Road, Knutsford, Cheshire, WA16 0DE Tel: (07866) 580529 Fax: (01565) 633977 E-mail: info@ammarquees.com *Marquee hire, corporate events, weddings, traditional marquees*

▶ A & M Metal Services Ltd, Horbury Wagon Works, Charles Roberts Street, Horbury, Wakefield, West Yorkshire, WF4 5QH Tel: (01924) 266333 Fax: (01924) 266600 *Steel fabricators*

▶ A M Mouldings, Lower Copy, Allerton Road, Allerton, Bradford, West Yorkshire, BD15 7QQ Tel: (01274) 547844 Fax: (01274) 483350 E-mail: j.barraclough@btinternet.com *Manufacturers of post boxes & general glassfibre products*

▶ A M Norris Ltd, Brunel Way, Stephenson Industrial Estate, Coalville, Leicestershire, LE67 3HF Tel: (01530) 831451 Fax: (01530) 813767

A M P Electrical Wholesalers, 28 Amhurst Road, London, E8 1JN Tel: (020) 8985 3013 Fax: (020) 8986 7971 E-mail: enquiries@ampelectrical.co.uk *Electrical wholesalers & lighting distributors*

A M P L Ltd, Prospect House, Deva Industrial Park, Factory Road, Sandycroft, Deeside, Flintshire, CH5 2QJ Tel: (01244) 527600 Fax: (01244) 527601 E-mail: nicholas.learoyd@ampl.co.uk *Plant & equipment services*

▶ A M P M Office Equipment Ltd, 12 South Street, Braunton, Devon, EX33 2AA Tel: (01271) 815859 Fax: (01271) 815858 E-mail: darren@ampmofficeequipment.co.uk *Office equipment*

▶ A M P M Transport, 35 Underwood Road, Paisley, Renfrewshire, PA3 1TH Tel: 0141-889 7754

A M P Metalworks, 837-839 Consort Road, London, SE15 2PR Tel: (020) 7277 5569 Fax: (020) 7635 6001 E-mail: sales@apmetalworks.co.uk *Architectural metalworkers*

A M P Rose, Heapham Road, Gainsborough, Lincolnshire, DN21 1QU Tel: (01427) 611969 Fax: (01427) 616854 E-mail: admin@amp-rose.com *New*

continued

confectionery, chocolate processing & wrapping machinery manufrs

A M P S Fabrications Ltd, Arch 36 Miles Street, London, SW8 1RY Tel: (020) 7587 1444 Fax: (020) 7587 5141 E-mail: ampsfabs@aol.com *Steel fabricators*

A M P Scaffold Co. Ltd, 39A Deakin Road, Erdington, Birmingham, B24 9AJ Tel: 0121-373 3863 Fax: 0121-377 8588 E-mail: sales@ampscaffold.co.uk *Scaffolding contractors*

A M P Wire Ltd, Sun Iron Works, Ward Street, Chadderton, Oldham, OL9 9EX Tel: 0161-620 7250 Fax: 0161-688 5566 E-mail: pam@ampwire.co.uk *Metal fabricators*

A.M Pallet Services Ltd, Goods Yard, Bryanstone Road, Waltham Cross, Hertfordshire, EN8 7PJ Tel: (01992) 652700 Fax: (01992) 651185 E-mail: sales@prpallets.com *Pallet manufacturers & secondhand*

A M Phillip Ltd, Ardlaw Garage, Fraserburgh, Aberdeenshire, AB43 7DA Tel: (01346) 541351 Fax: (01346) 541703 *Agricultural engineers*

A M Phillip Trucktech, Muiryfaulds, Forfar, Angus, DD8 1XP Tel: (01307) 820255 Fax: (01307) 820417 E-mail: agritech@amphillip.co.uk *Commercial & agricultural vehicles manufrs*

A M Photographic, St. Johns Innovation Centre, Cowley Road, Cambridge, CB4 0WS Tel: (0870) 1635192 E-mail: tony@amphotographic.co.uk *Industrial photographic services*

A & M Plastic Solutions, Wickham Road, Fareham, Hampshire, PO16 7JB Tel: (01329) 225900 Fax: (01329) 823840 E-mail: sales@amplastic.com Purchasing Contact: J. Cripps Sales Contact: I. Ward *Plastics vacuum formed products & plastics mouldings manufrs*

A M Print, Lemsford Road, Hatfield, Hertfordshire, AL10 0DE Tel: (01707) 271512 Fax: (01707) 271512 E-mail: enquiries@amprint.co.uk *Commercial printers*

A M Profiles Ltd, Hardwick View Road, Homewood Industrial Estate, Holmewood, Chesterfield, Derbyshire, S42 5SA Tel: (01246) 856000 Fax: (01246) 855105 E-mail: sales@amprofiles.com *Manufactures & suppliers of aluminium windows,, curtain walling*

A M Pumps & Spares Ltd, 429 Jockey Road, Sutton Coldfield, West Midlands, B73 5XH Tel: 0121-321 3488 Fax: 0121-321 3499 E-mail: ampumpsltd@aol.com *Pumps & pumping system distributors*

▶ A M R (Burnley) Ltd, Unit 3, Gannow Business Park, Gannow Lane, Burnley, Lancashire, BB12 6JJ Tel: (01282) 448008 Fax: (01282) 448419 E-mail: sales@lasercutters.co.uk *Laser & profile cutting services*

A M R Cabinet Makers & French Polishers, Unit 3 Millie Street, Kirkcaldy, Fife, KY1 2NL Tel: (01592) 640941 Fax: 0159 2640 941 *Cabinet manufrs*

▶ A M Reid Plumbing & Heating Ltd, 16 Christie Street, Dunfermline, Fife, KY12 0AQ Tel: (01383) 730293 Fax: (01383) 730293

A & M Rotary, Wheatear, Perry Road, Witham, Essex, CM8 3YY Tel: (01376) 515600 Fax: (01376) 513502 *Rotary cutter die manufrs*

A M S, John Sutcliffe Building, Donibristle Industrial Park, Hillend, Dunfermline, Fife, KY11 9JX Tel: (01383) 821921 Fax: (01383) 824227 *Simulators manufrs*

▶ A M S 2000 Ltd, Ladywell, Barnstaple, Devon, EX31 1QS Tel: (01271) 328663 Fax: (01271) 375436 E-mail: asbestos@ams-2000.co.uk *Specialists in asbestos removal*

A M S A Ltd, 2 Great Marlborough Street, London, W1F 7HQ Tel: (020) 7734 0532 Fax: (020) 7494 1509 E-mail: recruit@amsa.co.uk *Architectural employment recruitment*

A M S Acoustics, Rayleigh House, 21 Queen Annes Place, Enfield, Middlesex, EN1 2QB Tel: (020) 8886 4060 Fax: (020) 8360 2640 E-mail: info@amsacoustics.co.uk *Acoustic designers or consultants*

A M S (Burnham) Fluid Sealing, 30-32 Dropmore Road, Burnham, Slough, SL1 8BE Tel: (01628) 603311 Fax: (01628) 660040 *Pump seals packing & gasket manufrs*

A M S Connections Ltd, 14 Highmeres Road, Leicester, LE4 9LZ Tel: 0116-224 0070 Fax: 0116-224 0073 E-mail: astrid@amsconnections.co.uk *Fasteners & steel strip distributors*

A M S Corporation Ltd, 58-59 Haampton St, Birmingham, B19 3LU Tel: 0121-200 1633 Fax: 0121-200 1685 *Metal spinning services*

A M S Educational, 38 Parkside Road, Leeds, LS6 4QG Tel: 0113-275 9900 Fax: 0113-275 7799 E-mail: admin@amseducational.co.uk *Miltary & local history publishers & library security consultants*

A M S Engineering, Units C & D Stratton Park, Biggleswade, Bedfordshire, SG18 8QS Tel: (01767) 600888 Fax: (01767) 600668 *Precision engineers*

A M S Fabric Ltd, 53 Rolleston Street, Leicester, LE5 3SD Tel: 0116-274 0253 Fax: 0116-251 6865 *Clothing manufrs*

A M S Glaswall Ltd, Shielhill Works, Loch Thom Road, Inverkip, Greenock, Renfrewshire, PA16 9NB Tel: (01475) 520170 Fax: (01475) 521653 E-mail: enquiries@glaswall.pluf.com *Agricultural merchants*

▶ A M S Manchester, 27 Honey Street, Manchester, M8 8RG Tel: 0161-819 2540 Fax: 0161-819 2541 E-mail: enquiries@ams-steam-eng.co.uk *Textile machinery, parts & maintenance*

A M S Neve Ltd, Billington Road, Burnley, Lancashire, BB11 5UB Tel: (01282) 457011 Fax: (01282) 417282 E-mail: info@ams-neve.com *Audio equipment distributors & manufrs*

A M S Systems, 17 The Oval, Bedlington, Northumberland, NE22 5HS Tel: (01670) 531200 Fax: (01670) 797617 E-mail: enquiries@ams-systems.co.uk *New & corporate computer building & selling*

▶ A M S Web Design, Hillcrest, 42 Station Road, Dunure, Ayr, KA7 4LL Tel: (01292) 500499 E-mail: info@amswebdesign.co.uk *Web design & low cost web hosting & search engine optimisation*

A M Screen Print, 5 Millsborough House, Millsborough Road, Redditch, Worcestershire, B98 7BU Tel: (01527) 62323 Fax: (01527) 62401 E-mail: amscreenprint@btconnect.com *Textile printing contract services*

▶ A M Securities, Shore Road, Perth, PH2 8BD Tel: (01382) 623485 Fax: (01738) 639704

A M Security Group Ltd, Unit 7 English Business Park, Hove, East Sussex, BN3 7ET Tel: (01273) 740400 Fax: (01273) 740401 *Intruder alarm systems*

A & M Supplies (Catering) Ltd, 8-10 Hallsteads, Dove Holes, Buxton, Derbyshire, SK17 8BJ Tel: (01298) 816023 Fax: (01298) 816153 E-mail: sales@a-mcateringsupplies.co.uk *Catering equipment suppliers*

▶ A M T Logistics Ltd, Hill Business Park, Iddesleigh, Winkleigh, Devon, EX19 8SW Tel: (01837) 811144 Fax: (01837) 811166 E-mail: office@amtlogistics.co.uk *Airport equipment suppliers & engineers*

A M T Systems, West Stockwith Park, Stockwith Road, Misterton, Doncaster, South Yorkshire, DN10 4ES Tel: (01427) 890022 Fax: (01427) 890063 E-mail: graham@amt-systems.co.uk *Water industry contractors*

A M Time Services, 8 Ivyside Close, Killamarsh, Sheffield, S21 1JT Tel: 0114-248 5855 Fax: 0114-248 5855 E-mail: info@amtime.co.uk *Time & attendance systems sales & service*

A M Transport (Liverpool) Ltd, Unit 12 B, Candy Park, Plantation Road, Bromborough, Wirral, Merseyside, CH62 3QS Tel: 0151-346 1780 Fax: 0151-346 1781 *Haulage services*

▶ A M Transport Services, Bay 1 Burnbrae Road, Linwood, Paisley, Renfrewshire, PA3 3BD Tel: (01505) 328906 Fax: (01505) 335120

A & M Tungsten Powders Ltd, 11 Maxted Road, Hemel Hempstead, Hertfordshire, HP2 7DX Tel: (01442) 254691 Fax: (01442) 255503 E-mail: info.amtp@virgin.net *Tungsten powder & heavy metals*

▶ A M V Construction, Tepna Wharf, Twyford Avenue, Portsmouth, PO2 8QA Tel: (023) 9266 7887 Fax: (023) 9266 7895 E-mail: amvconstrustion@btconnect.com *Plant hirers*

▶ A M V Supplies, Laser Quay, Culpeper Close, Medway City Estate, Rochester, Kent, ME2 4HU Tel: (01634) 296900 Fax: (01634) 296990

▶ A M W Ltd, 18-20 Lindsay Street, Kilmarnock, Ayrshire, KA1 2BB Tel: (01563) 533086

A M Warkup Ltd, Aerodrome Works, Lissett, Driffield, North Humberside, YO25 8PT Tel: (01262) 468666 Fax: (01262) 468656 E-mail: amwarkup@amwarkup.co.uk *Pig housing specialists*

▶ A M White, Daytona, Whittington Hill, Whittington, King's Lynn, Norfolk, PE33 9TE Tel: (01366) 500212 Fax: (01366) 500880

A Mcclay & Co. Ltd, Longwood Drive, Cardiff, CF14 7ZB Tel: (029) 2054 4100 Fax: (029) 2054 4123 E-mail: 106740.3652@compuserve.com *Printers*

A Mcpherson Blacksmiths Ltd, West Fulton Smithy, Craigends Road, Houston, Johnstone, Renfrewshire, PA6 7EH Tel: (01505) 321282 Fax: (01505) 331662 *Structural steel work*

A Maffei & Sons, Pollard Street East, Manchester, M40 7FS Tel: 0161-273 4029 *Grinding equipment & services*

A Markham & Sons Ltd, London Road, Bowers Gifford, Basildon, Essex, SS13 2DT Tel: (01268) 553748 Fax: (01268) 584502 E-mail: info@markhams.co.uk *Automatic gates & barriers manufrs*

▶ A Melville Ltd, Beechwood Garage, Glamis Road, Kirriemuir, Angus, DD8 5DF Tel: (01575) 572635 Fax: (01575) 572912

▶ A Models, 56 Shoreditch High Street, London, E1 6JJ Tel: (020) 7613 0424 Fax: (020) 7613 2955 *Model manufrs*

▶ A Moretti P.L.C., 44 Liverpool Road, Southport, Merseyside, PR8 4AY Tel: (01704) 566424 *Bakery*

A Morris & Sons Ltd, The Iron Mills, Dunsford, Exeter, EX6 7EE Tel: (01647) 252352 *Billhook & grass hook manufrs*

▶ A Morrison, 1 Rigs Road, Stornoway, Isle of Lewis, HS1 2RF Tel: (01851) 705700 Fax: (01851) 706700

A N Audio, 34 Huntingdon Street, St. Neots, Huntingdon, Cambridgeshire, PE19 1BB Tel: (01480) 472071 Fax: (01480) 386456 E-mail: sales@anaudio.co.uk *Electrical retailers*

▶ A N C Aylesbury, 1-4 Smeaton Close, Rabans Lane Industrial Area, Aylesbury, Buckinghamshire, HP19 8SU Tel: (01296) 427484 Fax: (01296) 489130

▶ A N C Ayrshire, Block 5, Moorfield Industrial Estate, Kilmarnock, Ayrshire, KA2 0AG Tel: (01563) 571363 Fax: (01563) 522700

A N C Harlow Ltd, 5 Edinburgh Place, Edinburgh Way, Harlow, Essex, CM20 2DJ Tel: (01279) 442031 Fax: (01279) 428753 E-mail: operations0023@anc.co.uk *Express parcel delivery services*

▶ A N C Holdings, 7-9 Finch Drive, Braintree, Essex, CM7 2SF Tel: (01376) 341708 Fax: (01376) 341708

▶ A N C Kent Ltd, Gateway Centre, Castle Road, Sittingbourne, Kent, ME10 3RN Tel: (01795) 413620 Fax: (01795) 413610 E-mail: sales0008@anc.co.uk *UK Express, Timed, Sameday Parcel & Pallet Couriers.*

▶ A N C London West, 9 Central Way, London, NW10 7XQ Tel: (020) 8453 3500 Fax: (020) 8453 3501

A N C Nottingham Ltd, Unit 2 Finch Close, Nottingham, NG7 2NN Tel: 0115-985 0800 Fax: 0115-985 0900 E-mail: customerservices0139@anc.co.uk *Road transport, haulage & freight services*

▶ A N C Parcels, 2 Babbage Road, Engineer Park, Sandycroft, Deeside, Clwyd, CH5 2QD Tel: (01244) 530562 Fax: (01244) 530563

A N D & Group, Tanners Bank, North Shields, Tyne & Wear, NE30 1JH Tel: (01233) 635278 Fax: (0870) 4449680 E-mail: info@and-group.net *Marine safety systems & marine electronics*

A & N Engineering, 2 Emsworth Road, Southampton, SO15 3LX Tel: (023) 8031 5193 Fax: (023) 8070 4033 *Precision engineering services*

A & N Engineering Services Ltd, 4 Adam Business Centre, Henson Way, Telford Way Industrial Estate, Kettering, Northamptonshire, NN16 8PX Tel: (01536) 411182 Fax: (01536) 523317 *Engineering subcontract services*

A N Fabrication, The Old Airfield, Town Lane, Brockford, Stowmarket, Suffolk, IP14 5NF Tel: (01449) 767821 Fax: (01449) 766606 *Steel fabrication*

A N Hydraulics, Sandlow Green Farm, Marsh Lane, Holmes Chapel, Crewe, CW4 8AS Tel: (01477) 533522 Fax: (01477) 533522 *New & reconditioned hydraulic units*

A N I Ltd, Suite 1, 98A Castle Lane West, Bournemouth, BH9 3JU Tel: (01202) 598737 Fax: (01202) 598722 E-mail: info@ani-ltd.co.uk *Design & installation of structured cabling*

▶ A N K Logistics, Warwick Mill, Oldham Road, Middleton, Manchester, M24 1AZ Tel: 0161-643 1871

▶ A N Logistics, 18 Canal Side, Beeston, Nottingham, NG9 1NG Tel: (0800) 8818167 Fax: 0845 4660167 E-mail: alan@anlogistics.co.uk *Freephone 0800 8818167**Light Haulage & Couriers**UK and Europe*

A N Pecision Ltd, Salisbury Road, Hoddesdon, Hertfordshire, EN11 0HU Tel: (01992) 463666 Fax: (01992) 441730 E-mail: derek.heard@lineone.net *CNC precision engineers*

A & N Plant, St. James House, 46 High Street, Amersham, Buckinghamshire, HP7 0DJ Tel: (01494) 722820 Fax: (01494) 729240 E-mail: info@anplant.com *Welding equipment manufrs*

A N Q, The Manor House, 14 Market Street, Lutterworth, Leicestershire, LE17 4EH Tel: (01455) 559446 Fax: (01455) 558523 E-mail: lgibson@anq.com *New media development & web development services*

A & N Resources Ltd, 8a Rowsley Avenue, West Didsbury, Manchester, M20 2XD Tel: 0161-438 0784 Fax: 0161-438 0784 *Lingerie*

▶ A N S Brass Ltd, 56 Standard Road, Park Royal, London, NW10 6EU Tel: (020) 8453 1017 Fax: (020) 8961 2791 *Wholesalers of architectural brass & ironmongery*

▶ A N T Welding Ltd, Collington Works, Collington, Bromyard, Herefordshire, HR7 4ND Tel: (01885) 410607 Fax: (01885) 410607 E-mail: ANTwelding@AOL.COM *MANUFACTURERS OF STEEL MANHOLE COVERS & FRAMES*

A N Tools Ltd, Carlyon Road, Atherstone, Warwickshire, CV9 1LQ Tel: (01827) 716878 Fax: (01827) 717859 E-mail: ant@antools.co.uk *Precision toolmakers & engineers*

A & N Trimmings Ltd, 5-7 Cyril Road, Birmingham, B10 0SS Tel: 0121-771 4040 Fax: 0121-766 6878 E-mail: sales@antrimm.co.uk *Trimmings wholesalers*

A N Wallis, Greasley Street, Nottingham, NG6 8NG Tel: 0115-927 1721 Fax: 0115-875 6630 E-mail: info@an-wallis.com *Manufacturers of electrical earthing equipment*

A Neaverson & Sons Ltd, St Pegas Road, Peakirk, Peterborough, PE6 7NN Tel: (01733) 252225 Fax: (01733) 252121 *Garden sheds, kennels, catteries & garages manufrs*

▶ A New Solution Ltd, 59 Elmfield Way, South Croydon, Surrey, CR2 0EJ Tel: (020) 8657 7441 Fax: (0870) 7060376 E-mail: sales@anewsolution.co.uk *Software licensing specialists*

A Nichols Cowmills Ltd, Station Road, Yate, Bristol, BS37 4AD Tel: (01454) 313788 Fax: (01454) 326692 E-mail: general@anichols.co.uk *Agricultural animal feeds*

A Nielson & Co. Ltd, Kings Dock, Swansea, SA1 1RJ Tel: (01792) 652421 Fax: (01792) 476466 E-mail: a_nielsen@talk21.com *Ships agents export services*

A Norman Tate & Co. Ltd, Caddick Road, Knowsley Business Park, Prescot, Merseyside, L34 9HP Tel: 0151-922 3064 Fax: 0151-922 4460 *Analytical chemists & consultants*

A & O Consultancy Ltd, 92A The Maltings, Roydon Road, Stanstead Abbotts, Ware, Hertfordshire, SG12 8UU Tel: (01920) 872321 E-mail: *Software & database consultants*

A O N Converters Ltd, Unit 2 Holmes Lane, Liverpool, L21 6PL Tel: 0151-920 7329 Fax: 0151-949 0483 E-mail: aonfoam@aol.com *Foam converters for the packaging industry*

▶ A O Roberts Ltd, Gaerwen Industrial Estate, Gaerwen, Gwynedd, LL60 6HR Tel: (01248) 422101 Fax: (01248) 422141 E-mail: enquiries@aoroberts.co.uk

A O Smith Electrical Products Ltd, Heapham Road Industrial Estate, Gainsborough, Lincolnshire, DN21 1XU Tel: (01427) 614141 Fax: (01427) 617513 E-mail: d.heatlie@aosmith.net *Fractional horse power motor manufrs*

A One, Unit 3 Central Park Estate, Staines Road, Hounslow, TW4 5DJ Tel: (020) 8607 4412 Fax: (020) 8607 4413 E-mail: aoneprec@aol.com *Precision engineers*

A One Feed Supplements Ltd, North Hill, Dishforth Airfield, Thirsk, North Yorkshire, YO7 3DH Tel: (01423) 322706 Fax: (01423) 323260 E-mail: sales@a-one.co.uk *Animal feed supplement manufrs*

A Orme & Co., Long Lea Mills, Halifax Road, Elland, West Yorkshire, HX5 0SH Tel: (01422) 374848 Fax: (01422) 312824 *Yarn merchants*

▶ A P, 3 Godfrey Avenue, Gosberton, Spalding, Lincolnshire, PE11 4HF Tel: (01775) 841819 Fax: (01775) 841819 E-mail: shazza@freeserve.co.uk *Crane hire*

A P A UK Ltd, Unit 10 Capital Industrial Estate, Crabtree Manorway South, Belvedere, Kent, DA17 6BJ Tel: (020) 8311 4400 Fax: (020) 8312 4777 E-mail: apauk@apaspa.com *Sign making material distributors*

▶ A P C Glasgow Ltd, 1 239 Blairtummock Road, Glasgow, G33 4ED Tel: 0141-771 6888 Fax: 0141-771 7888

A P C (Scotland) Ltd, Po Box 14554, Kinross, KY13 9ZJ Tel: (01577) 864231 Fax: (01577) 865677 *Specialist chemical manufrs*

A P C Solutions (UK) Ltd, Unit 18 The Old Cinema, Allshots Industrial Estate, Kelvedon, Colchester, CO5 9DF Tel: (01376) 585554 Fax: (01376) 585727 E-mail: info@apcsolutionuk.com *IT network & maintenance*

▶ A P Chant Ltd, Gore Cross Business Park, Corbin Way, Bridport, Dorset, DT6 3UX Tel: (01308) 420170

▶ A P Computing, Unit 2, Bentinck Street, Birkenhead, Merseyside, CH41 4DY Tel: 0151-647 6789 *Pc repair*

A P D Screen Process Ltd, 39A Albert Street, Syston, Leicester, LE7 2JA Tel: 0116-260 2606 Fax: 0116-264 0105 *Silk screen printers*

▶ A P Development Products Ne Ltd, 28-29 Front Street, Pelton, Chester le Street, County Durham, DH2 1LU Tel: 0191-370 1968 Fax: 0191-370 0750 E-mail: apdevs@gotadsl.co.uk *Specialist manufacturers of rfi suppression devices*

A P Diesel Ltd, 25 Victoria Street, Englefield Green, Egham, Surrey, TW20 0QY Tel: (01784) 433832 Fax: (01784) 430690 E-mail: apdiesel@mcmail.com *Equipment repairs & manufrs*

▶ A P Distribution, 8 Block 6, Myregormie Place, Mitchelston Industrial Estate, Kirkcaldy, Fife, KY1 3NA Tel: (01592) 650222 Fax: (01592) 650222

A P E L Contractors, 1 Station Road, Methley, Leeds, LS26 9ER Tel: (01977) 603890 Fax: (01977) 603890 *Building contractors*

A & P Engineering Ltd, 2 Bilston Key Industrial Estate, Oxford Street, Bilston, West Midlands, WV14 7DW Tel: (01902) 408087 Fax: (01902) 408311 *Precision & general engineers*

A P Engineering (Portsmouth) Ltd, 6a Fitzherbert Spur, Farlington, Portsmouth, PO6 1TT Tel: (023) 9238 4012 Fax: (023) 9237 9454 E-mail: sales@apeng.co.uk *Tubular fabrications, display equipment stands*

A & P Falmouth Ltd, The Docks, Falmouth, Cornwall, TR11 4NR Tel: (01326) 212100 Fax: (01326) 211635 E-mail: falmouth@ap-group.co.uk Principal Export Areas: Worldwide *Ship repair conversion & engineering*

A P G Atlantic Paper Ltd, 7 Earls Court Square, London, SW5 9BY Tel: (020) 7373 3132 Fax: (020) 7373 3880 E-mail: bruce@wastepaper.com *Waste paper recycle fibres & exporters*

A P G Screenprint Ltd, Unit 2 Fullwood Close, Aldermans Green Industrial Estate, Coventry, CV2 2SS Tel: (024) 7660 2060 Fax: (024) 7660 2003 E-mail: apg.screenprint@btinternet.com *Screen printers*

A P G Technology, Units 13-14 Raleigh Court, Priestley Way, Crawley, West Sussex, RH10 9PD Tel: (01293) 428565 Fax: (01293) 428566 E-mail: andrew.bause@apgtechnology.co.uk *Computer manufrs*

A P G Visual Colour Ltd, 5 Gregson Road, South Reddish, Stockport, Cheshire, SK5 7SS Tel: 0161-477 0166 Fax: 0161-476 5431 E-mail: apg@apgvisualcolour.co.uk *Lithographic plate printing & manufrs*

A P Grieveson, 8 Middlesex Road, Stockport, Cheshire, SK5 8HT Tel: 0161-355 9051 Fax: (07855) 913417 E-mail: p_grieveson@hotmail.com *Quality Paving and Landscaping with over 12 years experience providing all your garden needs including, Natural stone paving,Cobble Sett Laying, Block paving, Concrete, Paving slabs, Patios, Paths, Driveways, Fencing, Walling, Turf, Garden makeovers & conversions, Installation of all types of Drainage foul, surface water, Lawn drains and Soak aways.(Commercial or domestic)*

A P H Signs, 4 The Nurseries, Cymau, Wrexham, Clwyd, LL11 5LE Tel: (01978) 761487 Fax: (01978) 856568 *Signs makers*

A & P Hill Fruit Ltd, Oakleigh, Thorn Road, Marden, Tonbridge, Kent, TN12 9EJ Tel: (01622) 728404 Fax: (01622) 832492 E-mail: graham@aphillfruit.co.uk *Apple merchants & irrigation consultants*

A P Hollings & Sons Ltd, 14 Brook Road Industrial Estate, Sirdar Road, Rayleigh, Essex, SS6 7XF Tel: (01268) 770681 Fax: (01268) 775144 E-mail: andy@aphollings.co.uk *Rapid prototype development engineers*

▶ A P Hollingworth Ltd, 71 Barnsley Road, Upper Cumberworth, Huddersfield, HD8 8NS Tel: (01484) 606282 Fax: (01484) 607762

A P I, Unit 21-22, Britannia Park Industrial Estate North Road, Stoke-on-Trent, ST6 2PZ Tel: (01782) 206995 Fax: (01782) 206826 *Pneumatic control systems distributors*

A P I C Plastics Ltd, 28 Plantation Road, Amersham, Buckinghamshire, HP6 6HJ Tel: (01494) 431066 Fax: (01494) 726309 E-mail: apicplastics@lineone.net *Injection moulders*

A P I Coated Products Ltd, The Vineyards, Gloucester Road, Cheltenham, Gloucestershire, GL51 8NH Tel: (01242) 512345 Fax: (01242) 576633 E-mail: enquiries@adcoat.co.uk *Paper coatings*

▶ A P I Fire & Safety Ltd, Unit 7, Vulcan Way, Eaton Socon, St. Neots, Cambridgeshire, PE19 8TS Tel: (01480) 217774 Fax: (01480) 217775 *Fire alarm manufrs*

A P I Foils Ltd, Loughborough University, Ashby Road, Loughborough, Leicester, LE11 3TU Tel: (01509) 265232 Fax: (01509) 232772 *Holograms design, origination & mass production*

A P I Foils Ltd, Astor Road, Salford, M50 1BB Tel: 0161-789 8131 Fax: 0161-707 5315 E-mail: marketing@apigroup.com *Hot foil manufrs*

▶ A P I Group plc, Second Avenue, Poynton, Stockport, Cheshire, SK12 1ND Tel: (01625) 858700 Fax: (01625) 858701 E-mail: enquiries@apilaminates.com *At Henry & Leigh Slater we are committed to providing innovative solutions that focus on added value & product differentiation*

A P Information Services Ltd, Marlborough House, 298 Regents Park Road, London, N3 2UU Tel: (020) 8349 9988 Fax: (020) 8349 9797 E-mail: info@apinfo.co.uk *Directory publishers*

A P L Industrial Ltd, 14 Carlisle Road, London, NW9 0HL Tel: (020) 8205 2444 Fax: (020) 8200 8037 E-mail: info@apl-industrial.co.uk *Nameplate & labels manufrs*

▶ A P Lane, 257 Lampits, Hoddesdon, Hertfordshire, EN11 8EE Tel: 01992 445886 E-mail: antpatlane@yahoo.co.uk *Painters & Decorators*All Maintenance & Refurbishment Works undertaken.*Roof repairs, New Roofs*All areas of Carpentry*(ie: fitted Wardrobes, Kitchens)*Bathroom Installations*and much more......*

A P Lewis & Sons Ltd, Orion Way, Kettering Business Park, Kettering, Northamptonshire, NN15 6NL Tel: (01536) 525295 Fax: (01536) 525296 *Building contractors*

A P Lifting Gear, Northfield Road, Dudley, West Midlands, DY2 9JQ Tel: (01384) 250552 Fax: (01384) 250282 E-mail: apliftingsales@btconnect.com *Lifting gear manufrs*

A P Lifting Gear Co., Unit 7 Yarra Industrial Park, Ecclesfield, Sheffield, S35 9YA Tel: 0114-246 2422 Fax: 0114-246 2522 E-mail: peter.vernon@aplifting.com *Steel wire rope & lifting gear manufrs*

A P Litho Ltd, Units 9-10 Bourne Road Industrial Park, Bourne Road, Dartford, DA1 4BZ Tel: (01322) 523289 Fax: (01322) 527343 E-mail: alan@printapl.fsnet.co.uk *Printing services*

A P Metalising, Dunsford Road, Meadow Lane Industrial Estate, Alfreton, Derbyshire, DE55 7RH Tel: (01773) 835398 Fax: (01773) 521229 *Metallising processors & services*

A P N Polishing, Unit 9, 54 Shernall Street, London, E17 9HP Tel: (020) 8520 3538 Fax: (020) 8520 3538 *Metal finishing services*

A P O Flame Equipment Ltd, 605 Main Street, Bellshill, Lanarkshire, ML4 1DX Tel: (01698) 747630 Fax: (01698) 749465 *Welding suppliers*

A P P Lifting Services Ltd, Wrights Business Park, Stevens Road, Doncaster, South Yorkshire, DN4 0LT Tel: (01302) 367755 Fax: (01302) 855222 E-mail: sales@applifting.co.uk Principal Export Areas: Worldwide *Manufacture, hire, repair and supply of all forms of lifting, pulling and materials handling equipment from standard chain hoists to custom designed lifting solutions for the railway, power generation, mining, petro-chemical, steel and construction industries. Light Engineering and fabrication.*

A.P.P.S, 26 Thurnham Street, Lancaster, LA1 1XU Tel: (01524) 841286 Fax: (01524) 842330 E-mail: sales@promotional-goods.org.uk *Promotional goods, printed garments, & stationery retailers*

A P Patterns Ltd, Unit 7-8 Clarendon Industrial Estate, Hyde, Cheshire, SK14 2EW Tel: 0161-368 6389 Fax: 0161-367 9669 E-mail: appatterns@btconnect.com *Engineers pattern manufrs*

▶ A P Precision Engineering, Hopton Industrial Estate, Devizes, Wiltshire, SN10 2EU Tel: (01380) 725710 Fax: (01380) 720565 E-mail: alan-pocock@btconnect.com *Precision Engineers.*

▶ A P Press Tools, 239 Heneage Street, Birmingham, B7 4LY Tel: 0121-359 2161 Fax: 0121-333 7418 *Manufacturers of press tools*

A P R Photography Ltd, Robeson Way, Gatley, Manchester, M22 4SX Tel: (01625) 610999 Fax: (01625) 610055 E-mail: tim@aprphoto.co.uk *Studio & location photography*

A P R Telecoms Maintenance, Appointment House, Philip Ford Way, Silfield, Wymondham, Norfolk, NR18 9AQ Tel: (01953) 713333 Fax: (01953) 713345 *Telephone systems install & maintenance*

A P Robinson Ltd, 6c Fitzherbert Spur, Farlington, Portsmouth, PO6 1TT Tel: (023) 9238 3427 Fax: (023) 9222 1238 E-mail: aprobinson@btnet.com *Powder coating services*

▶ A P S, 50 Kings Road, Beith, Ayrshire, KA15 2BJ Tel: (01505) 500066 Fax: (01505) 500077 E-mail: brian@apsstationery.co.uk *Graphic design & stationery suppliers*

A P S Ltd, Sea King Road, Lynx Trading Estate, Yeovil, Somerset, BA20 2NZ Tel: (01935) 410710 Fax: (01935) 410888 E-mail: aps@rtv2.co.uk *Silicone distributors & manufrs*

▶ A P S Engineering Ltd, Mountford House, Grafton Street, High Wycombe, Buckinghamshire, HP12 3AJ Tel: (01494) 511533 Fax: (01494) 511566 E-mail: sales@apsworldwide.com

A P S Freight Ltd, Lord Warden House, Lord Warden Square, Dover, Kent, CT17 9EQ Tel: (01304) 225600 Fax: (01304) 225601 E-mail: office@apsfreight.com *Import/export services to and from Eastern Europe. Full Customs Clearance and Intrastat services.*

A P S Recruitment Ltd, 7 Wellington Court, Wellington Street, Cambridge, CB1 1HZ Tel: (01223) 464040 Fax: (01223) 309002 E-mail: kevin@aps-recruitment.co.uk *Recruitment agency services*

▶ A P S Security, 18 Jubilee Avenue, Crewe, CW2 7PR Tel: (01270) 663553 Fax: (01270) 650044 E-mail: contact@apssecurity.co.uk *Security installation services*

A.P. Sachets Ltd, Stafford Park 6, Telford, Shropshire, TF3 3AT Tel: (01952) 234100 Fax: (01952) 234111 E-mail: sales@sachets.co.uk *A Specialist sachet manufacturer that offers a comprehensive & flexible service, including design, printing & packing, across a very broad range of sachets products*

A P Smith & Son Metal Pressing Ltd, 8 Kings St, Birmingham, B19 3AR Tel: 0121-523 0011 Fax: 0121-554 7244 E-mail: sales@apsmith.co.uk *Metal pressing agents*

A P Systems, 16 Grant Street, Cullen, Buckie, Banffshire, AB56 4RS Tel: (01542) 841121 Fax: (01542) 841334 *Computer services*

A P T, 27 Pant-Y-Fid Road, Aberbargoed, Bargoed, Mid Glamorgan, CF81 9DT Tel: (01443) 835086 Fax: (01443) 835086 E-mail: apt@handtools.org.uk *Hand tools including point master & pro-staff manufrs*

▶ A P T Fixing Ltd, Unit C1 Doulton Trading Estate, Doulton Road, Rowley Regis, West Midlands, B65 8JQ Tel: (01384) 560059 Fax: (01384) 560059 *Shop fitting manufrs*

A P T (Leicester) Ltd, Rookery Lane, Groby, Leicester, LE6 0GL Tel: 0116-287 0051 Fax: 0116-287 0053 E-mail: sales@aptleicester.co.uk *CNC precision turned parts manufrs*

▶ A P T Ski Data Ltd, The Power House, Chantry Place, Harrow, Middlesex, HA3 6NY Tel: (020) 8421 2211 Fax: (020) 8428 6622 E-mail: info@skidata.com *Bespoke access & controls equipment for all sizes of car parks*

A P T T Ltd, Ty-Bach, Mount Bradford, St. Martins, Oswestry, Shropshire, SY11 3EY Tel: (01691) 773732 Fax: (01691) 773732 E-mail: enquiries@rmbtrainingsevices.co.uk *Fork lift training services*

▶ A P Training, Green Lane, Tadworth, Surrey, KT20 6TB Tel: (01737) 832111 Fax: (01737) 832111 E-mail: aptandhrltd@btconnect.com *Management & inter personal skill consultants service*

A & P Tyne, Wagonway Road, Hebburn, Tyne & Wear, NE31 1SP Tel: 0191-430 8600 Fax: 0191-428 6228 E-mail: tyne@ap-group.co.uk *Ship repairers* Also at: Wallsend

A P Tyres, Wannop Street, Rotherham, South Yorkshire, S62 6ER Tel: (01709) 523827 Fax: (01709) 528242 E-mail: aptyres@aol.com *Tyre distributors*

A P V Products, 3 Earlsfield Close, Lincoln, LN6 3RT Tel: (01522) 690774 Fax: (01522) 690723 *Sheet metal engineers*

A P W Ltd, Unit 12 Deacon Trading Estate, Earle Street, Newton-le-Willows, Merseyside, WA12 9XD Tel: (01925) 295577 Fax: (01925) 295588 E-mail: sales@apw.co.uk *Sheet metal perforators*

▶ A P W Transport Ltd, Hownsgill Drive, Consett, County Durham, DH8 9HU Tel: (01207) 581019 Fax: (01207) 503920

A P Woolrich, Canalside, Huntworth, Bridgwater, Somerset, TA7 0AJ Tel: (01278) 663020 Fax: (01278) 663913 E-mail: sales@ap-woolrich.co.uk *Museum model manufrs*

▶ A Pank & Son Ltd, 29 St Giles Street, Norwich, NR2 1JW Tel: (01603) 621501

▶ a Partydisco, 85 Watlands View, Porthill, Newcastle, Staffordshire, ST5 8AG Tel: (01782) 861481 E-mail: enquiries@partydisco.co.uk *Mobile Discos for all ages. We do childrens parties right upto golden Wedding Anniversaries. We try and cater for all.... Please contact for a competitive quote.*

A Pile & Son Ltd, St Vincents Road, Dartford, DA1 1UU Tel: (01322) 224346 Fax: (01322) 277321 *Motor vehicle repairers*

A Pinder Ltd, 16 Moore Street, Sheffield, S3 7US Tel: 0114-272 7574 Fax: 0114-275 1071 E-mail: sales@pindersofsheffield.co.uk *Reprographics*

▶ A Plant Ltd, Poole Lane, Bournemouth, BH11 9DU Tel: (01202) 582580 Fax: (01202) 582581

A Plant Accommodation, 659 Eccles New Road, Salford, M50 1AY Tel: 0161-787 9041 Fax: 0161-787 8291 E-mail: manchesteraccomm@aplants.com *Portable cabin hire*

▶ A Plant Groundcare, Cootham Lea Workshop, Pulborough Road, Cootham, Pulborough, West Sussex, RH20 4JN Tel: (01903) 742348 Fax: (01903) 742351

A Plant Lux, 16 Missouri Avenue, Salford, M50 2NP Tel: (01925) 281000 Fax: (01925) 281001 E-mail: enquiries@aplant.com *Plant hire*

▶ A Plus Driving School Ltd, 441 Dudley Road, Wolverhampton, WV2 3AQ Tel: (0845) 1308880 E-mail: info@thedrivingschool.co.uk *Free Online Driving Theory Test, Driving lessons, Training Aids, Step By Step guide to your Driving Test and much much more! All from A+ Driving Schools*

A Plus Office Furniture & Interiors, 363 Dunstable Road, Luton, LU4 8BY Tel: (01582) 707272 E-mail: sales@aplusoffice.co.uk *Office interior solutions and office furniture suppliers. One stop shop for all your office needs from partitioning to new desks! We cover from Birmingham to London.*

A Pollard & Sons Ltd, 51 Aylesbury St, Bletchley, Milton Keynes, MK2 2BQ Tel: (01908) 375221 Fax: (01908) 271552 E-mail: sales@pollards.co.uk *Tool contractors & maintenance & janitorial supplies*

A Poole & Son Ltd, Hewell Road, Redditch, Worcestershire, B97 6AY Tel: (01527) 63676 Fax: (01527) 60136 *Aerospace spring manufrs*

A Present World, 6 Elmstead Gardens, Worcester Park, Surrey, KT4 7BD Tel: (020) 8335 3530 Fax: (020) 8335 3530 E-mail: presentworld@hotmail.com *Balloon decorators*

A Print Finishing Co Ltd, 26-27 Sittingbourne Industrial Park, Crown Quay Lane, Sittingbourne, Kent, ME10 3JG Tel: (01795) 430050 Fax: (01795) 430495 *All aspects of print fulfillment*

▶ A Purchase Ltd, Level Street, Brierley Hill, West Midlands, DY5 1UA Tel: (01384) 78725 Fax: (01384) 78386

▶ A Purkiss Ltd, 2A Limberline Road, Portsmouth, PO3 5JS Tel: (023) 9269 8668

A Quick Kill Pest Control Ltd, 28 Lonsdale Road, Bilston, Bilston, West Midlands, WV14 7AF Tel: (0800) 1957056 Fax: (01902) 403373 *Pest control*

A R Adams & Son Ltd, Pill Bank Works, Coomassie Street, Newport, Gwent, NP20 2US Tel: (01633) 262060 Fax: (01633) 258295 *Industrial boiler repair services*

▶ A R Aspinall & Sons Ltd, 2 Station Road, Willingham, Cambridge, CB4 5HF Tel: (01954) 260391

A R B Audio & Visual Hire Ltd, Unit 4, Building G, Tingewick Road Industrial Park, Tingewick Road, Buckingham, MK18 1SU Tel: (01295) 262000 Fax: (01280) 817948 E-mail: info@arb-teamwork.com *Event technical services*

A R B Bearings & Industrial Products, 3 Honywood Road, Basildon, Essex, SS14 3DS Tel: (01268) 286633 Fax: (01268) 286655 E-mail: sales@arbbearings.com *Bearings, V Belts, Lubricants, Pulleys, Motors, Gearboxes, Sprokets, Oil Seals, O Rings, Full Fittings and After Care Service*

A R B Contractors, Pepper Hill Farm, Pepper Hill, Halifax, West Yorkshire, HX3 7TH Tel: (01274) 674055 Fax: (01274) 693506 E-mail: sales@arbcontractors.co.uk *Contractors specialising in excavation, groundwork, drainage,*landscaping, plant hire and winter maintenance/gritting.*

▶ A R B Mechanical Ltd, Winchester Road, Waltham Chase, Southampton, SO32 2LL Tel: (01489) 896611

A R B Precision Engineers Ltd, Unit 69 Station Road Industrial Estate, Hailsham, East Sussex, BN27 2ES Tel: (01323) 846935 Fax: (01323) 846937 E-mail: keith@arbprecision.freeserve.co.uk *Sub-contract precision engineers*

A R Business Systems & Software Ltd, Wrang Beck House, Leyburn Road, Middleham, Leyburn, North Yorkshire, DL8 4PN Tel: (01325) 481647 Fax: (01325) 369744 E-mail: office@arbs.net *Business management systems & software developers*

A R C, Ripley Drive, Normanton Business Park, Normanton Industrial Estate, Normanton, West Yorkshire, WF6 1QT Tel: (01924) 223333 Fax: (0871) 4330708 E-mail: sales@arccomputers.co.uk *Computer networking consultants*

A R C, Silver Springs, Church Lane, Tydd St Giles, Wisbech, Cambridgeshire, PE13 5LG Tel: (01945) 871081 Fax: (01945) 871081 *Refrigeration suppliers*

▶ A R C Entertainments, 10 Church Lane, Redmarshall, Stockton-on-Tees, Cleveland, TS21 1EP Tel: (01740) 631292 E-mail: arcents@aol.com *Entertainments Agency Supplying Entertainers, Face painters, Jugglers, Stilt Walkers, Caricaturists, etc*

A R C O Ltd, PO Box 7, Ossett, West Yorkshire, WF5 9JG Tel: (01482) 222522 Fax: (01924) 280262 E-mail: ossett.branch@arco.co.uk *Protective clothing distributors*

A R C S Ltd, Unit 3 Cwmtawe Business Park, Pontardawe, Swansea, SA8 4EZ Tel: (01792) 869660 Fax: (01792) 869550 E-mail: arcsltd@btconnect.com *Air conditioning contractors*

A R C Technical Services, 8a Watersedge, Frodsham, WA6 7NQ Tel: (01928) 731106 Fax: (01928) 732066 *Air conditioning service & install ation*

A R C Welding Services, Lapthorne, Totnes Road, Ipplepen, Newton Abbot, Devon, TQ12 5TN Tel: (01803) 813092 Fax: (01803) 813091 *Steel fabricators*

A R Cartwright Ltd, 4 Berrington Road, Nuneaton, Warwickshire, CV10 0LA Tel: (024) 7639 2901 Fax: (024) 7639 6471 *Joinery services*

A R Clay, Low Farm, Littlebeck, Whitby, North Yorkshire, YO22 5EY Tel: (01947) 893574 Fax: (01947) 893574 *Agricultural contractors*

▶ A & R Courier & Delivery Service Ltd, CWM Tawel Pontardulais Road, Cross Hands, Llanelli, Dyfed, SA14 6PG Tel: (01269) 845194 Fax: (01269) 845194 E-mail: enqs@swansea-couriers.co.uk *Sameday courier company covering South and West Wales for delivery throughout the UK. Able to collect from most areas withing the hour. Transport urgent goods from a letter to 1400kgs in dedicated vehicles. Fully insured.*

A R Craig Engineering Ltd, 6 Vale Lane, Bristol, BS3 5RU Tel: 0117-966 7735 Fax: 0117-966 0604 *Precision & general engineers*

A R D Tools & Patterns, 1 Roberts Drive, Bridgwater, Somerset, TA6 6BH Tel: (01278) 433177 Fax: (01278) 433160 *Tool makers*

▶ A & R Designs Ltd, Unit 21, Stevenston Industrial Estate, Stevenston, Ayrshire, KA20 3LR Tel: (01294) 601042 Fax: (01294) 601400 E-mail: ardgas@aol.com *Electronics specialists*

A R Dixon Display Ltd, 7a Waterloo Industrial Estate, Waterloo Road, Bidford-on-Avon, Alcester, Warwickshire, B50 4JH Tel: (01789) 772233 Fax: (01789) 490928 *Signs & displays manufrs*

A R E Refrigeration & Air Conditioning, 1 Elcho Place, Port Seton, Prestonpans, East Lothian, EH32 0DL Tel: (01875) 813947 Fax: (01875) 813947 *Refrigerator & air conditioning services*

A R Ellis Ltd, The Green, Horton Road, Horton, Slough, SL3 9NU Tel: (01753) 685333 Fax: (01753) 680749 E-mail: tony@arellis.com *Heating & ventilation supplies*

A R F Polythene, Unit 5 Building C, Ramsden Road, Rotherwas Industrial Estate, Hereford, HR2 6NP Tel: (01432) 355643 Fax: (01432) 355643 *Polythene bag converters & manufrs*

A R F Trading Co., 104A Durham St, Rochdale, Lancashire, OL11 1LS Tel: (01706) 352144 Fax: (01706) 352144 *Clothing manufrs*

A R Fabb Bros Ltd, 29-31 Risborough Road, Maidenhead, Berkshire, SL6 7BJ Tel: (01628) 623533 Fax: (01628) 622705 E-mail: sales@fabb.co.uk *Masonic regalia & badges manufrs*

A R Facer Ltd, Kerry St, Horsforth, Leeds, LS18 4AW Tel: 0113-258 2551 Fax: 0113-259 0868 E-mail: sales@facerprinters.demon.co.uk *Colour & general printers*

A & R Fencing Ltd, Paxton Street, Stoke-on-Trent, ST1 3SD Tel: (01782) 215419 Fax: (01782) 208516 E-mail: ian@aandrfencing.co.uk *Fencing contractors*

A R G Electrodesign Ltd, Querns Business Centre, Whitworth Road, Cirencester, Gloucestershire, GL7 1RT Tel: (01285) 658501 Fax: (01285) 885376 E-mail: info@arg.co.uk *Broadcast & telecom equipment manufrs*

A R G Europe Ltd, Unit 2, 58A Alexandra Road, Ponders End, Enfield, Middlesex, EN3 7EH Tel: (020) 8804 8008 Fax: (020) 8805 7600 E-mail: argeurope@aol.com *Asbestos removal services*

A R G Tools Ltd, Harrier Road, Humber Bridge Industrial Estate, Barton-upon-Humber, South Humberside, DN18 5RP Tel: (01652) 660382 Fax: (01652) 660382 *Injection mould toolmakers*

A R Gane & Sons, West Lydford, Somerton, Somerset, TA11 7DL Tel: (01963) 240501 Fax: (01963) 240502 *Agricultural animal feed & agricultural haulage services*

A R Gurteen Ltd, Kingsley House, Freezemoor Road, Houghton le Spring, Tyne & Wear, DH4 7BH Tel: 0191-584 4555 Fax: 0191-512 0222

A R K S Tool Hire Ltd, Dawley Brook Road, Kingswinford, West Midlands, DY6 7BD Tel: (01384) 274050 Fax: (01384) 400459 E-mail: sales@arkstoolhire.co.uk *Tool hire builders service*

A R M Ltd, 110 Fulbourn Road, Cherry Hinton, Cambridge, CB1 9NJ Tel: (01223) 400400 Fax: (01223) 400410 E-mail: info@arm.com *Research & development services*

A R M Direct, 1 Bentinck Mews, London, W1U 2AF Tel: (020) 7317 3230 Fax: (020) 7224 3041 E-mail: info@arm-direct.co.uk *Creative design consultants*

A R M Electronics Ltd, 14 Kempson Cl, Gatehouse Way, Aylesbury, Bucks, HP19 8UQ Tel: (01296) 437021 Fax: (01296) 483463 E-mail: a2470580@infotrade.co.uk *Electronic design & manufacture*

A R M Holdings, Moorbridge Road, Maidenhead, Berkshire, SL6 8LT Tel: (01628) 427700 Fax: (01628) 427701 E-mail: enquiries@arm.com *Design & licence IP*

A R Manley & Son Ltd, Rodington, Shrewsbury, SY4 4RF Tel: (01952) 770278 Fax: (01952) 770976 E-mail: sales@armanley.co.uk *Joinery manufrs*

A & R Metal Finishers, Streetbridge Works, Royton, Oldham, OL2 5ZY Tel: 0161-627 0177 Fax: 0161-627 0177 *Anodises & metal finishers*

A & R Milton, Arable View, Udny Green, Ellon, Aberdeenshire, AB41 7RS Tel: (01651) 843123 Fax: (01651) 842501 *Agricultural contractors*

A R P Co. Ltd, Unit 2 Jubilee Way, Avonmouth, Bristol, BS11 9HU Tel: 0117-982 6301 Fax: 0117-923 5487 E-mail: sales@avonmouth-rubber.co.uk *Industrial hose & fittings manufrs*

A R P Electrical, 31 Edwards Road, Halifax, West Yorkshire, HX2 7DG Tel: (01422) 353778 Fax: (01422) 353778 *Security installers*

A R Paper Convertors Ltd, 20 River Road, Barking, Essex, IG11 0DG Tel: (020) 8591 7868 Fax: (020) 8591 7083 E-mail: sales@arpaper.co.uk *Paper converters*

A & R Pest Control, Nant Y Cynog, Tywyn, Gwynedd, LL36 9HY Tel: (01654) 710556 *Pest control service providers*

▶ A R Plant Hire Ltd, Tanglewood Derritt Lane, Bransgore, Christchurch, Dorset, BH23 8AR Tel: (01425) 673388 Fax: (01425) 674485 E-mail: mail@ar-planthire.co.uk *Plant hire & groundwork contractors*

A & R Printing, The Gables, 160A London Road, Brandon, Suffolk, IP27 0LP Tel: (01842) 811331 Fax: (01842) 811375 E-mail: ray.boreham@btinternet.com *Reprographic printing trade supplies*

A & R Refrigeration & Fabrication, 102 Soho Street, Liverpool, L3 8AS Tel: 0151-207 0344 Fax: 0151-207 0344 *Refrigeration installation*

A R S Anglian Diesels Ltd, Unit 9c Headway Business Park, Denby Dale Road, Wakefield, West Yorkshire, WF2 7AZ Tel: (01924) 332492 Fax: (01924) 332493 E-mail: enquiries@arsangliandiesels.co.uk *Hydraulic power packs supplies & manufrs*

A & R Sheet Metal Ltd, 68-70 College Street, Kempston, Bedford, MK42 8LU Tel: (01234) 348841 Fax: (01234) 262784 E-mail: sales@arsheetmetal.co.uk *Ups & battery cubicles manufrs*

A R Tackle, 8 Castle Street, Hastings, East Sussex, TN34 3DY Tel: (01424) 422094 *Fishing equipment*

A & R Transmissions, Pridham Lane, Plymouth, PL2 3PH Tel: (01752) 770777 Fax: (01752) 777716 *General gear box repair*

A & R Vehicle Services Ltd, Darlaston Road, Wednesbury, West Midlands, WS10 7TZ Tel: 0121-526 6611 Fax: 0121-526 2848 E-mail: admin@aandrvehicleservices.co.uk *Commercial vehicle repairs & refurbishment*

▶ A & R Way Boatbuilding, 5 Creag Ghlas, Cairnbaan, Lochgilphead, Argyll, PA31 8UE Tel: (01546) 606657 Fax: (01546) 606326 E-mail: arway@tiscali.co.uk *Wooden boat repair & manufrs*

A & R Welding, Carpenters Road, St. Helens, Ryde, Isle of Wight, PO33 1YW Tel: (01983) 872965 Fax: (01983) 611924 *Wrought ironmongers*

A R Wentworth Ltd, Monarch Works, Catley Road, Darnall, Sheffield, S9 5JF Tel: 0114-244 7693 Fax: 0114-242 3159 E-mail: sales@wentworth-pewter.com *Pewter ware manufrs*

A R Wilson Packaging, 151 Nottingham Road, Nottingham, NG6 0FU Tel: 0115-978 1047 Fax: 0115-942 2302 E-mail: arwilson@proweb.co.uk *Ice cream packaging supplier*

▶ A Richardson, Unit 5 Bridge Street Industrial Estate, Potters Lane, Wednesbury, West Midlands, WS10 0AS Tel: 0121-502 2005 Fax: 0121-505 5126 E-mail: andy@abrichardson.fsnet.co.uk *Die & tool manufrs*

A Ring-A-Till Ltd, 129 Stanningley Road, Armley, Leeds, LS12 3PJ Tel: (0800) 0189713 Fax: 0113-203 8282 *Till & scale suppliers*

A Roberts, 67 Hatton Garden, London, EC1N 8JY Tel: (020) 7405 4987 *Diamond merchants*

A Robinson, Gelt Hall Farm, Castle Carrock, Brampton, Cumbria, CA8 9LT Tel: (01228) 670260 Fax: (01228) 670260 *Agricultural contractors & bed & breakfast*

A Robinson & Son, 14 Main Street, Annalong, Newry, County Down, BT34 4TR Tel: (028) 4376 8213 Fax: (028) 4376 8872 E-mail: enquiries@arobinson.co.uk *Natural stone specialists*

A Romanes & Son Ltd, Pitreavie Business Park, Dunfermline, Fife, KY11 8QS Tel: (01383) 728201 Fax: (01383) 737040 E-mail: advertising@dunfermlinepress.co.uk *Printers, publications & publishers*

▶ A Ross, Kendal Crescent Yard, Kendal Cresent, Alness, Ross-Shire, IV17 0UG Tel: (01349) 882250 Fax: (01349) 882266

▶ A Rosy Marriage Balloon & Party Megastore, 14 Barn Way, Hednesford, Cannock, Staffordshire, WS12 0FP Tel: (07795) 102050 E-mail: sales@arosymarriage.co.uk *Balloon decorations suppliers for all occasions*

A Rowe Ltd, Unit 24 Newhaven Business Park, Barton Lane, Eccles, Manchester, M30 0HH Tel: 0161-787 8150 Fax: 0161-787 8140 E-mail: sales@arowe.co.uk *Knitted fabric retailers & manufrs*

▶ A Ryall & Son (Contractors) Ltd, 83 Victoria Road, Mexborough, South Yorkshire, S64 9BX Tel: (01709) 583248

A S A, 12-18 Paul Street, London, EC2A 4JH Tel: (020) 7669 5200 Fax: (020) 7669 5208 E-mail: group@asagroup.co.uk *Recuitment agency*

A S A Hydraulik, 22 Brewers Lane, Badsey, Evesham, Worcestershire, WR11 7EU Tel: 01386 833400 Fax: 01386 833555 E-mail: support@asahydraulik.com *Oil coolers, heat exchangers & butterfly valves*

A S A International Ltd, 6 Coates Crescent, Edinburgh, EH3 7AL Tel: 0131-226 6222 Fax: 0131-226 5110 E-mail: edincoates@asainternational.co.uk *Recruitment consultancy*

A S A Law, Glade House, 52 Carter Lane, London, EC4V 5JL Tel: (020) 7236 2395 Fax: (020) 7246 4746 *Employment agency*

A S A M S Ltd, Marine Building Owen Road, Harfreys Industrial Estate, Great Yarmouth, Norfolk, NR31 0NA Tel: (01493) 653535 Fax: (01493) 653254 E-mail: sales@asams.co.uk *Materials testing & inspecting equipment service*

A S A P Pest Control, 3 White Cottage, Baldock Road, Royston, Hertfordshire, SG8 9NR Tel: (01763) 853872 *Pest control services to trade & domestic*

▶ A S A P Same Day Delivery Service, 30 Clarendon Court, Winwick Quay, Warrington, WA2 8QP Tel: (01925) 637453 E-mail: pete@asapsameday.com *A.S.A.P. Same-day Delivery Services, Warrington""'s leading independent same day courier service can provide courier services for simple documents or consignments up to tons, 24 hours a day 7 days a week from it""'s base in Warrington Cheshire, to local,national,european and most worldwide destinations*

A S A P Sign Services, 9 Bradley Road, Wrexham, Clwyd, LL13 7TG Tel: (01978) 353265 Fax: (01978) 354689 E-mail: asap.sign-services@dail.pipex.com *Screen print & design services*

A S A P Tooling Ltd, Crondal Road, Exhall, Coventry, CV7 9NH Tel: (024) 7664 4555 Fax: (024) 7636 7019 E-mail: asaptooling@btconnect.com *Special purpose cutting tool manufrs*

A & S Alarms, 25 Rothbury Gardens, Plymouth, PL6 8TU Tel: (01752) 700284 *Security alarms installation*

A S Allman Ltd, Newmarket Drive, Ascot Drive Indust Estate, Derby, DE24 8HT Tel: (01332) 753167 Fax: (01332) 296250 *General engineers*

▶ A S Bairds, 15 Michelin Road, Newtownabbey, County Antrim, BT36 4PT Tel: (028) 9083 5333 Fax: (028) 9083 5015 E-mail: bairds@btconnect.com

A S Ball, Pennti Lowarn, Mount, Bodmin, Cornwall, PL30 4ET Tel: (01208) 821381 Fax: (01208) 821381 *Farrier*

▶ A S Ballantine Ltd, 214 Lisnaragh Road, Dunamanagh, Strabane, County Tyrone, BT82 0SB Tel: (028) 7139 8276 Fax: (028) 7139 8189 E-mail: asballantine@btconnect.com *Quarrying industry*

A S Belting Products, Headland House, Severn Road, Cardiff, CF11 9XH Tel: (029) 2022 6301 Fax: (029) 2023 7441 E-mail: asbeltings@aol.com *Belting distributors*

A S C Cartons Ltd, Hillside Works, Leeds Road, Shipley, West Yorkshire, BD18 1DZ Tel: (01274) 599842 Fax: (01274) 592225 E-mail: sales@asc-cartons.co.uk *Cardboard cartons manufrs*

A S C Materials Handling Ltd, 67 Europa Business Park, Bird Hall Lane, Stockport, Cheshire, SK3 0XA Tel: 0161-428 8600 Fax: 0161-428 1112 E-mail: sales@as-c.co.uk *Dry bulk materials handling engineers*

A S C Metals Ltd, 3 Jackdaw Close, Crow Lane Industrial Estate, Northampton, NN3 9ER Tel: (01604) 415036 Fax: (01604) 415019 *Aluminium & stainless steel stockholders*

A S C Metals Ltd, 20a Maxwell Road, Peterborough, PE2 7JD Tel: (01733) 370626 Fax: (01733) 370392 *Aluminium & stainless steel stockholders*

A S C Metals Ltd, Shaw Road, Bushbury, Wolverhampton, WV10 9LA Tel: (01902) 371700 Fax: (01902) 424324 *Complete stockholders & aluminium*

A S C Partnership plc, 3 Park Road, London, NW1 6AS Tel: (020) 7616 6628 Fax: (020) 7616 6634 E-mail: central@asc.co.uk *Commercial mortgage brokers*

A S Clothing, 3 Bayswater Crescent, Leeds, LS8 5QG Tel: 0113-240 4085 *Clothing & fabric manufrs*

A & S Clothing Manufacturers Ltd, 7 Mott Street, Birmingham, B19 3HD Tel: 0121-233 3625 Fax: 0121-236 2730 *Casual wear, rally coats, rainwear & anoraks suppliers*

Company Information

A S Contracts Ltd, Warstock Road, Birmingham, B14 4RS Tel: 0121-436 7969 Fax: 0121-436 7970 Purchasing Contact: A. Stanley Sales Contact: A. Stanley *Ventilation & air condition engineers*

▶ A & S Crushing Services Ltd, Theedhams Farm, Steeple Road, Southminster, Essex, CM0 7BD Tel: 01621 772620 *A & S Crushing Services Ltd provide a singular service for your building or demolition project. Our crusher can break even the hardiest of site materials to type one. We are happy to transport our Guidetti MF450 directly to wherever is required by our client. We also sell crushed concrete.*

A S D Anderson Brown, 24 South Gyle Crescent, South Gyle Industrial Estate, Edinburgh, EH12 9EB Tel: 0131-459 3200 Fax: 0131-459 3266 E-mail: customer.care@asdplc.co.uk *Steel stockholders*

A S D Coil Processing, Tipton Road, Tividale, Oldbury, West Midlands, B69 3HU Tel: 0121-522 2215 Fax: 0121-522 2293 E-mail: customer.care@asdplc.co.uk *Steel stockholders*

A S D Fire Protection, Fisher Street, Newcastle upon Tyne, NE6 4LT Tel: (01698) 356444 Fax: (01698) 356678 E-mail: asdfire@btconnect.com *Fire fighting equipment distributors*

A S D International, PO Box 54, Bridgend, Mid Glamorgan, CF31 4YP Tel: (01656) 880013 Fax: (01656) 880865 *Agents & distributors to the food industry*

A S D Metal Services, Unit 6-8 Vernon House Walker Industrial Estate, Walker Road, Guide, Blackburn, BB1 2QE Tel: (01254) 696969 Fax: (01254) 696988 E-mail: sales@asdmetalservices.co.uk *Stainless steel stockholders*

A S D Metal Services, Suit 107, 1111 Parkway, Whiteley, Fareham, Hampshire, PO15 7AB Tel: (01489) 611660 Fax: (01489) 611750 *Stainless steel & aluminium stockholders* Also at: Cambridge, Dudley, Middlesbrough & Newport

A S D Metal Services Ltd, Gibson Lane, Melton, North Ferriby, East Yorkshire, HU14 3HX Tel: (01482) 633360 Fax: (01482) 633370 E-mail: hull@asdmetalservices.co.uk *Steel stockholders*

A S D Metal Services, Tunstall Road, Biddulph, Stoke-on-Trent, ST8 6JZ Tel: (01782) 515152 Fax: (01782) 522240 E-mail: asdmetalservices@asdplc.co.uk *Steel stockholders & processors*

A S D Metal Services Ltd, PO Box 5, Stoke-on-Trent, ST4 2NQ Tel: (01782) 202118 Fax: (01782) 283220 E-mail: stoke@asdmetalservices.co.uk *Steel stockholders processors*

A S D Metal Services Cardiff, East Moors Road, Cardiff, CF24 5SP Tel: (029) 2046 0622 Fax: (029) 2049 0105 E-mail: cardiff@asdmetalservices.co.uk *Steel stockholders & processors*

A S D Metal Services Carlisle, Unit C Earls Way, Kingmoor Park Central, Carlisle, CA6 4SE Tel: (01228) 674766 Fax: (01228) 674197 E-mail: carlisle@asdmetalservices.co.uk *Steel stockholders*

A S D Motor Services, Drum Industrial Estate, Drum Industrial Estate, Chester le Street, County Durham, DH2 1ST Tel: 0191-492 2322 Fax: 0191-410 0126 *Steel coil/plate/sheet stockholders*

A & S Electrical Services, 1 Carisbrooke Drive, Halesowen, West Midlands, B62 8SL Tel: 0121-550 2228 Fax: 0121-550 2228 E-mail: admin@niceic.org.uk *Electrical installations & breakdowns*

A & S Fabrications Nottingham, Unit E1 County Business Park, Eastcroft, Nottingham, NG2 3HS Tel: 0115-986 8382 Fax: 0115-986 9238 *Sheet work fabricators*

▶ A S Fashions Ltd, Imperial Typewriter Buildings, East Park Road, Leicester, LE5 4QD Tel: 0116-276 2780 Fax: 0116-276 2780

A S G, 15 Wharfside, Bletchley, Milton Keynes, MK2 2AZ Tel: (01908) 375020 Fax: (01908) 375145 E-mail: sales@asgoffice.co.uk *Office furniture distribs*

▶ A S G I Systems 2000, 14a Cambridge Street, Wellingborough, Northamptonshire, NN8 1DJ Tel: (01933) 223005 Fax: (01933) 223005 *Computer maintenance & repair services*

A S G Services Ltd, 8 Easter Court, Europa Boulevard, Westbrook, Warrington, WA5 7ZB Tel: (01925) 710923 Fax: (01925) 712966 E-mail: info@asgservices.co.uk *Warehouse labels, barcodes, signs and floor marking products. Manufactured and installed by our own team and operation.*

A S Garments Ltd, 16 Sycamore Road, Handsworth, Birmingham, B21 0QL Tel: 0121-551 6158 Fax: 0121-551 6158 *Leisure wear manufrs*

A & S GB Ltd, 130-132 Taunton Road, Ashton-under-Lyne, Lancashire, OL7 9EE Tel: 0161-330 9131 Fax: 0161-330 9131 E-mail: amjud@aol.com *Underwear importers*

▶ A & S Glazing, Greets Green Road, West Bromwich, West Midlands, B70 9EG Tel: 0121-557 3150 Fax: 0121-557 3150 *Fabricators*

A S I (Auto Systems Industries) Ltd, PO Box 463, Maidstone, Kent, ME14 5PU Tel: (01622) 735781 Fax: (01622) 734686 E-mail: sales@asi.gb.com *Automation systems manufrs*

▶ A S International Enterprise, 4 Redgarth Court, Furze Lane, East Grinstead, West Sussex, RH19 2SF Fax: (01342) 332102

A & S Joinery, Coldwell Street, Linthwaite, Huddersfield, HD7 5QN Tel: (01484) 842782 *Joinery manufrs*

▶ A & S Joinery Manufacturers Ltd, Unit 1 Imperial Road, Bulwell, Nottingham, NG6 9GB Tel: 0115-927 9927 Fax: 0115-927 9947 *Joinery manufrs*

A S K Electrical Ltd, 10-14 Victoria Road, Bangor, County Down, BT20 5EX Tel: (028) 9127 0308 Fax: (028) 9145 8196 E-mail: info@askelectrical.com *Electrical engineers*

A S K Europe plc, Trent House University Way, Cranfield Technology Park, Cranfield, Bedford, MK43 0AN Tel: (01234) 757575 Fax: (01234) 757576 E-mail: mail@askeurope.com *Management development & training services*

A S K Mcgowan Ltd, Coombs Wood Business Park, Steelpark Road, Halesowen, West Midlands, B62 8HD Tel: 0121-561 6800 Fax: 0121-561 6803 E-mail: central@askmcgowan.co.uk *Steel stockholders & processors*

A S K Rewinds Ltd, Unit 5 Laneside, Metcalf Drive, Altham Industrial Estate, Accrington, Lancashire, BB5 5TU Tel: (01282) 776475 Fax: (01282) 779438 E-mail: sales@ask-rewinds-ltd.co.uk *Rewind services & electric motors sales*

A S K For Service, 16 Tollpark Road, Cumbernauld, Glasgow, G68 0LN Tel: (01236) 739245 Fax: (01236) 735429 E-mail: sales@askforservice.co.uk *Welding supplies & distributors*

A S K Springs, Edward Street, Clive Works, Redditch, Worcestershire, B97 6HA Tel: (01527) 63300 Fax: (01527) 63300 *Spring & wire shape manufrs*

A S K UK, Herschel Street, Slough, SL1 1XS Tel: (01753) 701050 Fax: (01753) 701001 *Supply LCD & data projectors*

A S L Group, 3 Cullwick St, Wolverhampton, WV1 2UL Tel: (01902) 498420 Fax: (01902) 353112 E-mail: sales@birford.co.uk Principal Export Areas: Worldwide *Manufacturers of electrical transformers*

A S L R Fabrication Services Ltd, Opal Way, Stone Business Park, Stone, Staffordshire, ST15 0SS Tel: (01785) 286060 Fax: (01785) 818728 E-mail: sales@aslr.co.uk *Pipework fabricators*

A S M Facilities Ltd, Form House, York Way, Lancaster Road, High Wycombe, Buckinghamshire, HP12 3PY Tel: 01494 464684 Fax: 01494 464683 E-mail: info@asm-facililites.co.uk *ASM Facilities Limited specialise in all aspects of commercial premises maintenance, including the repair and servicing of mechanical, electrical and life-safety systems*

A S Mechanical Engineering Ltd, Unit 16, Depot Road, Middlesbrough, Cleveland, TS2 1LE Tel: (01642) 250180 Fax: (01642) 250180 *General engineers*

▶ A & S Nevin, Oakcroft, Guildford Road, Normandy, Guildford, Surrey, GU3 2DA Tel: (01344) 777019 E-mail: asnevin@asnevin.co.uk *A family run building company boasting three generations in the business. We work mostly around Surrey, Berkshire and Hampshire, but do consider work further a field.*

▶ A S O Glass Blowing Ltd, Unit 1 The Old Power Station, Ardington, Wantage, Oxfordshire, OX12 8QJ Tel: (01235) 834477 Fax: (01235) 834477 E-mail: enq@asoglass.demon.co.uk *Scientific glassblowing, prototype, production, repairs, & design*

A S P Electronic Design Ltd, 3a Warren House Road, Wokingham, Berkshire, RG40 5PN Tel: 0118-979 0825 Fax: 0118-977 1749 E-mail: enquiries@asp.uk.com *Computer aided design systems manufrs*

A & S Plastics, Unit 138 Harbour Road Trading Estate, Lydney, Gloucestershire, GL15 4EJ Tel: (01594) 843000 Fax: (01594) 843000 *Polyurethane products manufrs*

A S Plastics, Unit 3, Harvey Court Harvey Lane, Golborne, Warrington, WA3 3QN Tel: (01942) 271271 Fax: (01942) 271271 *Plastic fabricator specialists*

A & S Print Finishers, Unit 1 Northgate Industrial Pk, Collier Row, Romford, RM5 2BG Tel: (020) 8548 7200 Fax: (020) 8548 7201 *Print trade finishing services*

▶ A S R Shutters, 2 Woodseats Road, Woodseats, Sheffield, S8 0PJ Tel: (0800) 9230016 *service installation and repair of all types of industrial commercial and domestic doors roller shutters rapid roll sectional overhead fire doors security grills and pvc strip curtains*

A & S Rubber & Plastics, Unit 10c Old Park Industrial Estate, Old Park Road, Wednesbury, West Midlands, WS10 9LR Tel: 0121-556 4415 Fax: 0121-556 2414 E-mail: info@asrubber.com *Adhesive coated cellular foam*

A S Russell, Craigowmill Farm Cottage, Kinross, KY13 0RR Tel: (01577) 865111 Fax: (01577) 865111 *House builders*

Assaabloy Hospitality Ltd, Unit 21 Stadium Way, Tilehurst, Reading, RG30 6BX Tel: 0118-945 2200 Fax: 0118-945 1375 E-mail: uk@vcegroup.com *Reading-based ASSA Abloy Hospitality Ltd offer a complete range of electronic locking systems and hotel door locks, electronic hotel safes and minibars.*

A S S Stephens, Long Meadow, Stoke Orchard, Cheltenham, Gloucestershire, GL52 7RY Tel: (01242) 680629 *Agricultural contractors*

A S Security Alarms Ltd, Springclose House Post Office Lane, South Chard, Chard, Somerset, TA20 2PL Tel: (01460) 221137 Fax: (01460) 221137 E-mail: assecurityalarms@btconnect.com *Security systems installations*

A & S Security Systems, 8 Woodcroft Rise, Ballymena, County Antrim, BT42 1TA Tel: (028) 2565 8969 Fax: (028) 2565 8969 *Security systems installation*

▶ A & S Signs, 240 Holliday Street, Birmingham, B1 1SJ Tel: 0121-632 6222 Fax: 0121-632 6222 E-mail: designwithsigns@btinternet.com *Sign making*

A S T Distribution Ltd, Unit 16, Berkshire House, Swindon, SN1 2NR Tel: (01793) 541890 Fax: (01793) 541891 E-mail: sales@astcables.co.uk *Electrical/ electronic cable assembly/harness manufrs*

▶ A S T Express, Preston Street, Manchester, M18 8DB Tel: 0161-223 7878 Fax: 0161-230 7745

A S T Fork Truck Training Ltd, PO Box 2218, Redditch, Worcestershire, B98 8SZ Tel: (01527) 595946 Fax: (01527) 595931 *Fork lift truck training services*

A S T Networks Ltd, Temple Court, Cathedral Road, Cardiff, CF11 9HA Tel: (0870) 1160110 Fax: (0870) 1160611 E-mail: enquiries@astnetworks.co.uk *Telecommunications installation maintenance & suppliers*

continued

▶ A S T Print Group Ltd, Ipswich Road, Cardiff, CF23 9AQ Tel: (029) 2049 7901 Fax: (029) 2045 0189

A S Transport, 359a Staines Road, Hounslow, TW4 5AP Tel: (020) 8577 5888 Fax: (020) 8577 1588 E-mail: clairecooley@hotmail.com *Crane hire*

▶ A S W Marquees Ltd, 26 Glendevon Road, Woodley, Reading, RG5 4PL Tel: 0118-969 5568 Fax: 0118-969 5568 E-mail: aswmarquees@btconnect.com *Marquees & furniture hire*

▶ A S Walter, 42 Chapel Avenue, Long Stratton, Norwich, NR15 2TE Tel: (01508) 532528 Fax: (01508) 532528 E-mail: enquiries@aswalter.co.uk *Electrical contractor, lighting specialists & installations*

A S Watersports, 1-3 Waterside, Exeter, EX2 8GU Tel: (01392) 421831 Fax: (01392) 421831 E-mail: sales@aswatersports.co.uk *Water sports retailers*

▶ A S Wellington, 58-59 Village Farm Road, Village Farm Industrial Estate, Pyle, Bridgend, Mid Glamorgan, CF33 6BN Tel: (01656) 748020 Fax: (01656) 748029

A S Whitaker & Sons, Stephenson Avenue, Pinchbeck, Spalding, Lincolnshire, PE11 3SW Tel: (01775) 722789 Fax: (01775) 710519 E-mail: phil@whitakers-bodyshop.co.uk *Motor car body repairers*

A Schulman Inc Ltd, Croespenmaen Industrial Estate, Crumlin, Newport, Gwent, NP11 3AG Tel: (01495) 244090 Fax: (01495) 249277 *Plastic compound manufrs*

A Searle, Unit 24 Bourne Road Industrial Park, Bourne Road, Dartford, DA1 4BZ Tel: (01322) 529119 Fax: (01322) 528528 E-mail: sales@asearle.co.uk Principal Export Areas: Worldwide *Distributors of aviation fuel test & aircraft ground support equipment*

A Shade Above The Rest, 22 Lamb House, Elmington Estate, London, SE5 7JF Tel: 07956 459892 Fax: (020) 7701 5404 E-mail: enquiries@snookerman.co.uk *Billiard, snooker & pool table repairers*

▶ A Sharman & Sons Ltd, 22 Lynn Road, Southery, Downham Market, Norfolk, PE38 0HU Tel: (01366) 377571

A Shores & Co Leather & Canvas Products Ltd, Byron St Mills, Millwright Street, Leeds, LS2 7QG Tel: 0113-245 6062 *Canvas goods manufrs*

A Shufflebotham & Son, 8 Gunco Lane, Macclesfield, Cheshire, SK11 7JX Tel: (01625) 423304 Fax: (01625) 423304 *Textile merchants*

A Small Firms Loan, 21 Dapps Hill, Keynsham, Bristol, BS31 1ES Tel: (08458) 386917 Fax: (08701) 369549 E-mail: strategy@nildram.co.uk *The Small Firms Loan Guarantee scheme - SFLG -has been in existence to enable small businesses with a viable business plan, but lacking security, to borrow money from approved lenders. The Small Firms Loan Guarantee scheme (SFLG) is a joint venture between the DTI and the approved lenders. *The scheme will provide loans between ·5000 and ·100,000 for companies with a trading record of less than 2 years and this amount is increased to ·250,000 for the older businesses. The DTI do not lend the money as they leave the commercial decision to the bankers. **

▶ A Smith Sandwell Ltd, Union Road, Oldbury, West Midlands, B69 3EU Tel: 0121-544 6575 Fax: 0121-552 1537 E-mail: asmithsandwell@btconnect.com *Steel coil stockholders*

A Solicitor Information Service, 4 Charles Lane, London, NW8 7SB Tel: (020) 7483 4833 *Legal information services & publishers*

A Solo Security Ltd, 22a Horseshoe Park, Pangbourne, Reading, RG8 7JW Tel: 0118-984 4083 Fax: 0118-984 4204 E-mail: sales@asolosecurity.co.uk *Security installation*

▶ A Spriggs Courier Services, 46 Garth Avenue, Normanton, West Yorkshire, WF6 1DJ Tel: (01924) 782005 E-mail: andy@aspriggs.com *24/7 Local and long distance courier service, Competitive rates for that same day delivery your customer is screaming for*

A Stanley Engineering, Gee House, Holborn Hill, Birmingham, B7 5JR Tel: 0121-326 0014 Fax: 0121-326 1779 *Fabricators of steel & stainless steel & welded fabrication manufrs*

A Stewart & Sons, 5 Redford Road, Padanaram, Forfar, Angus, DD8 1PZ Tel: (01307) 463135 *Joinery manufrs*

A Stone, Unit 11 Camp Industrial Estate, Rycote Lane, Milton Common, Thame, Oxfordshire, OX9 2NP Tel: (01844) 278966 *Agricultural engineers*

A Storage Solution Ltd, Riverside House, Leaside Road, London, E5 9LU Tel: (020) 8806 3155 Fax: (020) 8806 7265 E-mail: storsol@aol.com *Storage contractors*

A Sturrock & Son Ltd, Whigstreet, Kirkbuddo, Forfar, Angus, DD8 2NN Tel: (01307) 820209 Fax: (01307) 820289 E-mail: info@asturrock.co.uk *Joinery manufrs*

A T A Engineering Processes, Unit 2 Saracen Industrial Estate, Mark Road, Hemel Hempstead, Hertfordshire, HP2 7BJ Tel: (01442) 264411 Fax: (01442) 231383 E-mail: sales@ataeng.com *Aerospace tooling, wood work, plastics machinery & accessories*

▶ A T A Grinding Processes Ltd, 37 Dalsetter Avenue, Drumchapel, Glasgow, G15 8TE Tel: 0141-940 4720 Fax: 0141-940 4721 E-mail: ata@atagrinding.co.uk *Pneumatic tools manufrs*

A & T A Payne, Stretch Hill, Fittleworth, Pulborough, West Sussex, RH20 1JJ Tel: (01798) 865642 *Fencing manufrs*

▶ A T A Scaffolding, Langdale Street, Bootle, Merseyside, L20 3BX Tel: 0151-933 1616 Fax: 0151-922 1919

▶ A T A Security Solutions Ltd, Amon House, Station Road, Heckington, Sleaford, Lincolnshire, NG34 9JH Tel: (01529) 461789 E-mail: info@ata4security.co.uk *COMPLETE SECURITY PRODUCTS *FORENSIC CODING SYSTEM*ALARMS*LOCKS*GPS/GPRS LOCATING SYSTEMS*NUMEROUS OTHER PRODUCTS*

continued

A T Alarms, 4 Hazelwood, Chadderton, Oldham, OL9 9TB Tel: 0161-626 3106 *Security installations & services*

A T Best Handlers Ltd, 114 Main Street, Chapelhall, Airdrie, Lanarkshire, ML6 8SB Tel: (01236) 607077 Fax: (01236) 607079 E-mail: info@atbesthandlers.co.uk *Manitou telescopic handlers & forklifts specialist suppliers*

A T C Ltd, 2 Thomas Holden Street, Bolton, BL1 2QG Tel: (01204) 550600 Fax: (01204) 381702 E-mail: enquiries@atc.co.uk *Telecommunications distributors*

A T C Ltd, Greenway House, Greenway Business Centre, Harlow, Essex, CM19 5QD Tel: 0161-406 1000 Fax: (0870) 0558081 E-mail: sales@atc.co.uk *Radio telephone distributors*

A T C, Holmethorpe Avenue, Redhill, RH1 2NG Tel: (01737) 765686 Fax: (01737) 764048 E-mail: sales@atcltd.co.uk *High accuracy machined components*

A T C Colours Ltd, Vale Works, New Haden Road, Cheadle, Stoke-on-Trent, ST10 1UF Tel: (01538) 754400 Fax: (01538) 751212 E-mail: mail@atccolours.co.uk *Ceramics distributor & manufrs*

A T C Dyers, Royds Hall Lane, Buttershaw, Bradford, West Yorkshire, BD6 2NE Tel: (01274) 691169 Fax: (01274) 690016 E-mail: atcdyers@legend.co.uk *Package yarn dyer suppliers*

A T Communications, Canon House, Thame Road, Haddenham, Aylesbury, Buckinghamshire, HP17 8LH Tel: (01844) 266266 Fax: (01844) 266262 *Telephone systems*

A T Communications, 13-19 Gate Lane, Boldmere, Sutton Coldfield, West Midlands, B73 5TR Tel: 0121-354 7582 Fax: 0121-354 7669 E-mail: atc@atcomms.co.uk *Audio visual supplies & hire*

A & T Computer Rentals Ltd, Robert Cort Industrial Estate, Britten Road, Reading, RG2 0AU Tel: 0118-986 4666 Fax: 0118-986 4777 E-mail: admin@aandt.co.uk *Computer rentals*

A T Computers (Applemac), Unit E2 Green La Business Park, Green Lane, Tewkesbury, Gloucestershire, GL20 8SJ Tel: (01684) 291112 Fax: (01684) 274829 *Apple mac service providers, resellers & training*

A T Cross Ltd, Windmill Trading Estate, Thistle Road, Luton, LU1 3XJ Tel: (01582) 422793 Fax: (01582) 456097 E-mail: crossuk@cross.com *Warehouse distribution*

▶ A & T Distribution, 19 Wainman Road, Peterborough, PE2 7BU Tel: (01733) 231005

A T E Technology Ltd, ATE House, 48 Green Meadows, Westhoughton, Bolton, BL5 2BN Tel: (01942) 815603 Fax: (01942) 815321 E-mail: info@ate-technology.com *Suppliers of business test solutions & support*

▶ A & T Engineering Ltd, 9 Carr Lane Industrial Estate, Carr Lane, Hoylake, Wirral, Merseyside, CH47 4AX Tel: 0151-632 1308 Fax: 0151-632 6383

A T Engineering Supplies Ltd, Garstang Road, Claughton-on-Brock, Preston, PR3 0RB Tel: (01995) 640058 Fax: (01995) 640031 *Fastener stockists & engineers merchants*

A T F Services, 60 Brick Kiln Lane, Parkhouse Industrial Estate West, Newcastle, Staffordshire, ST5 7AS Tel: (01782) 561095 Fax: (01782) 566444 *Commercial vehicle servicing & repairers*

▶ A T & F Solutions Ltd, The Great Barn, Dunstall, Earls Croome, Worcester, WR8 9DF Tel: (0870) 1657321 Fax: (0870) 1657421 E-mail: sales@atfsolutions.com *Developers & suppliers of health & safety training courses*

A T Free & Co. Ltd, Jackson Street, St. Helens, Merseyside, WA9 1AH Tel: (01744) 22252 Fax: (01744) 453036 *Glazing contractors & stained glass manufrs*

A T G Willand, Pemberton Business Centre, Richmond Hill, Wigan, Lancashire, WN5 8AA Tel: (01942) 216161 Fax: (01942) 213131 E-mail: sales@atgwilland.com *Engineers*

▶ A T Garage Equipment Services Ltd, Unit 5-8 Swan La Industrial Estate, Swan Lane, West Bromwich, West Midlands, B70 0NU Tel: 0121-553 2278 Fax: (01902) 338339 *Garage equipment manufrs*

▶ A T Goodyear & Son Ltd, Weston Hills, Spalding, Lincolnshire, PE12 6BX Tel: (01775) 722281

▶ A & T Group, 183 Manor Road North, Southampton, SO19 2DZ Tel: (023) 8044 3127 E-mail: andie@chessun.fsnet.co.uk *Concrete formwork solutions services*

A T H Alden Ltd, Sutherland Road, London, E17 6BU Tel: (020) 8531 3358 Fax: (020) 8527 9105 E-mail: simon@aldens.fsbusiness.co.uk *Metal fittings for leather goods*

A T Hunter, Blacksness, Scalloway, Shetland, ZE1 0TQ Tel: (01595) 880388 Fax: (01595) 880733 E-mail: hgibbie@aol.com *Fish merchants*

A T Jones, 109 Woodfield Road, Balsall Heath, Birmingham, B12 8TE Tel: (07947) 501791 Fax: 0121-440 2653 *Vehicle steam cleaning*

A T Juniper Liverpool Ltd, Marshalls Works, 5-17 Bleasdale Road, Liverpool, L18 5JB Tel: 0151-733 1553 Fax: 0151-734 3166 E-mail: sales@juniper-liverpool.com *Aircraft ground support equipment manufrs*

A T Kearney Ltd, Lansdowne House, Berkeley Square, London, W1J 6ER Tel: (020) 7468 8000 Fax: (020) 7468 8001 *Management consultants*

▶ A T Kinetics Ltd, 5 Townend Farm, Audley Road, Alsager, Stoke-on-Trent, ST7 2QR Tel: (01270) 877771 Fax: (01270) 878333 E-mail: sales@atkinetics.com *Industrial Motion Control Suppliers*

▶ A T Knott & Sons, Cornelian Cottages, 76a Manor Road, Wallington, Surrey, SM6 0AB Tel: (020) 8669 5208 Fax: (020) 8669 5150

A T L Telecommunications Ltd, Cypress Drive, St Mellons, Cardiff, CF3 0EG Tel: (029) 2050 0700 Fax: (029) 2050 0701 E-mail: sales@atltelecom.com Principal Export Areas: Worldwide *Telecommunication equipment manufrs*

A T L Televisions Ltd, 200 Cauldwell Hall Rd, Ipswich, IP4 5DB Tel: (01473) 720445 Fax: (01473) 720445 *T V sales & repairs*

A T Landquip, Lonmay, Fraserburgh, Aberdeenshire, AB43 8RN Tel: (01346) 532492 Fax: (01346) 532547 E-mail: sales@atlandquip.com *Agricultural machinery retailers*

A T Laser Dies, Unit 1B Elizabeth Trading Estate, Juno Way, London, SE14 5RW Tel: (020) 8691 7843 Fax: (020) 8692 8720 E-mail: sales@atlaser.co.uk *Laser & tool manufrs*

A T London Ltd, 28 Hornsey Road, London, N7 7LL Tel: (020) 7607 3512 Fax: (020) 7607 3522 E-mail: sales@atlondonltd.co.uk *We are a specialist Adhesive Coating company, who apply adhesive to prints and other materials for universal display.*

A T M Ltd, Knaves Beech Industrial Estate, Knaves Beech Way, Loudwater, High Wycombe, Buckinghamshire, HP10 9QY Tel: (01628) 642200 Fax: (01628) 642226 *Computer systems (for home & business)*

A T M Automation Ltd, Winchester Avenue, Blaby Industrial Park, Blaby, Leicester, LE8 4GZ Tel: 0116-277 3607 Fax: 0116-277 9800 E-mail: sales@atmautomation.com *Industrial robot systems manufrs*

A T M I (UK), Kingsland House, 512 Wimborne Road East, Ferndown, Dorset, BH22 9NG Tel: (01202) 875753 Fax: (01202) 875763 E-mail: info/europe@atmi.com *Gas & toxic gas detection equipment manufrs*

A T Office Services, 15 Spence Avenue, Byfleet, West Byfleet, Surrey, KT14 7TG Tel: (01932) 344833 Fax: (01932) 344833 E-mail: enquiries@atofficeservices.co.uk *Proof reading, copy editing, secretarial services & virtual office assistants*

A T Oliver & Sons Ltd, Home Park Works, Station Road, Kings Langley, Hertfordshire, WD4 8LW Tel: (01923) 265211 Fax: (01923) 261759 *Agriculture & horticulture machine repair & sales services*

A T Oliver & Sons Ltd, Wandon End Works, Wandon End, Luton, LU2 8NY Tel: (01582) 727111 Fax: (01582) 729763 E-mail: ato@atoliver.co.uk *Agricultural engineers* Also at: King's Langley & Shefford

A T Osborne Ltd, Wytchwood, Shelley Lane, Ower, Romsey, Hampshire, SO51 6ZL Tel: (023) 8081 4340 Fax: (023) 8081 2941 *Agricultural & forestry engineers*

A T Palmer Ltd, Unit G Smarden Business Estate, Smarden, Ashford, Kent, TN27 8QL Tel: (01233) 770077 Fax: (01233) 770030

A T Refractories, Ryandel Business Park, Brookhouse Way, Cheadle, Stoke-on-Trent, ST10 1SR Tel: (01538) 750461 Fax: (01538) 750461 *Refractory services*

A T Roberts Ltd, 9-13 Aldenham Road, Watford, WD19 4AB Tel: (01923) 223969 Fax: (01923) 244497 E-mail: info@atroberts.fsnet.co.uk *Printing roller manufrs*

▶ A T S Business Machines, Brithdir House, Brithdir Street, Cardiff, CF24 4LE Tel: (029) 2037 7455 Fax: (029) 2037 7455 E-mail: sales@atsbm.co.uk *Suppliers & service providers of office equipment*

A T S Electro Lube UK Ltd, Unit 383l, Jedburgh Court, Team Valley Trading Estate, Gateshead, Tyne & Wear, NE11 0BQ Tel: 0191-491 4212 Fax: 0191-491 4224 E-mail: info@ats-electro-lube.co.uk *Electro-lube automatic electronic lube dispensers*

A T S Euromaster Ltd, Vantage Point, 20 Upper Portland Street, Aston, Birmingham, B6 5TW Tel: 0121-325 7300 Fax: 0121-325 7333 E-mail: info@atseuromaster.co.uk *Tyres & batteries* Also at: Branches throughout the U.K.

A T S Exhausts & Tyres (Edenbridge) Ltd, Unit 1 Monza House, Fircroft Way, Edenbridge, Kent, TN8 6EJ Tel: (01732) 867746 Fax: (01732) 868274 *Tyre, battery & exhaust fitters suppliers*

A T S North Western Ltd, 74 Oakfield Rd, Altrincham, Cheshire, WA15 8EP Tel: 0161-941 1951 Fax: 0161-942 4623 E-mail: admin@atsnw.co.uk *Tyre retailers & distribs* Also at: Branches throughout the U.K.

A T S Panels Ltd, Unit B, Lammas Courtyard, Weldon Industrial Estate, Corby, Northamptonshire, NN17 5EZ Tel: (01536) 407474 Fax: (01536) 409443 *Generator control panels manufrs*

A T S S (East Anglia) Ltd, Station Road East, Stowmarket, Suffolk, IP14 1RQ Tel: (01449) 674944 Fax: (01449) 678678 E-mail: sales@atssea.co.uk *Computer services*

A T Sack Fillers, Unit 26 Highlode Industrial Estate, Stocking Fen Road, Ramsey, Huntingdon, Cambridgeshire, PE26 2RB Tel: (01487) 814002 Fax: (01487) 814002 E-mail: sales@simplafillsystems.co.uk *Sack filling machine manufrs*

▶ A & T Services Ltd, 7 Industrial Estate, St. Columb, Cornwall, TR9 6SF Tel: (01637) 881430 Fax: (01637) 881433 E-mail: andybaigent@atservices.demon.co.uk *Mechanical & electrical contractors*

A.T.T.A.C. Aberdeen Technology Transfer & Consultancy, 26 Albert Terrace, Aberdeen, AB10 1XY Tel: (01224) 641953 Fax: (01224) 643651 E-mail: bill@aqa.co.uk *Technology transfer consultants*

A T T & C, Tudor House, Catherine Road, Benfleet, Essex, SS7 1HY Tel: (01268) 759398 Fax: (01268) 565102 *Computer training & consultants*

A T Tool Centre Ltd, 26-27 Buckingham Trade Park, Buckingham Avenue, Slough, SL1 4QA Tel: 01753 536811 Fax: 01753 532709 E-mail: slough@at-toolcentre.co.uk *A.T. Toolcentre is an Industrial Supplies Company covering a radius of 40+ miles from each of our branch locations. We offer a daily delivery service through our own fleet of vehicles. All branches carry an extensive range of quality industrial products supported by the Group Central Warehouse in Northampton. We are able to to supply any brand of product and to any specification required.**Our specialist divisions are:*Hand Tools, Power Tools and Accessories, Welding, Fasteners and Fixings, Pipeline, Precision Measurement, Cutting Tools, Carbide Cutting Tools, VMIS, Oils and Lubricants, Adhesives, Abrasives, Paints and Industrial Coatings, Janitorial and Hygiene, First Aid, Safety Flooring, Workwear and PPE, Laundry, Signs and Labels, Storage and Handling, Packaging.*

A T UK Ltd, Unit A4 Sovereign Park Industrial Estate, Market Harborough, Leicestershire, LE16 9EG Tel: (01858) 468199 Fax: (01858) 468187 E-mail: sales@airtorque.co.uk *Actuator manufrs*

A T Warping, Unit W8 Legrams Mill, Legrams Lane, Bradford, West Yorkshire, BD7 1NH Tel: (01274) 724836 Fax: (01274) 722846 *Textiles manufrs*

▶ A T X Computers, 114 Bancroft Road, Widnes, Cheshire, WA8 3LL Tel: 0151-422 0088 *Computer maintenance services*

▶ A Tait & Sons, Dounby, Orkney, KW17 2HT Tel: (01856) 771236 Fax: (01856) 771762

▶ A - Tanks, The Cottage Back Lane, Northwick Tanks, Mark Moor, Highbridge, Somerset, TA9 4PQ Tel: 01278 641410 Fax: 01278 641410 E-mail: natasha@a-tanks.co.uk *Water treatment & sewage*

A Taylor & Sons, 77 High Street, Morton, Bourne, Lincolnshire, PE10 0NR Tel: (01778) 570445 *Agricultural contractors*

A Tec Group, Units 6-9 Buckley Road Industrial Estate, Buckley Road, Rochdale, Lancashire, OL12 9EF Tel: (01706) 643050 Fax: (01706) 632767 E-mail: info@atecgroup.co.uk *Stationery supplies manufrs*

A Tec International Ltd, 109-111 St. Johns Hill, Sevenoaks, Kent, TN13 3PE Tel: (01732) 743737 Fax: (01732) 743838 E-mail: vic@a-tecuk.com *Electronic component distributors*

▶ A To Z Glass & Glazing Company Ltd, 186 Feenan Highway, Tilbury, Essex, RM18 8HD Tel: (01375) 844153 E-mail: linda.atozglazing@blueyonder.co.uk *Glass, Glazing, Polycarbonate, Double Glazed Units, Stainless Steel Mirrors, 180 degree half hemispheres, 360 degree ceiling domes, Carpentry. Doors & Security Grilles. Roller Shutters*

▶ A To Z Logistics, 9 Law Place, Nerston Industrial Estate, East Kilbride, Glasgow, G74 4QL Tel: (01355) 224480 Fax: (01355) 265230

▶ A Top Bounce, Unit 9a Rosebery Industrial Park, Rosebery Avenue, London, N17 9SR Tel: (020) 8365 1793 *Inflatable bouncy castle manufrs*

A Touch of Brass Ltd, 210 Fulham Road, London, SW10 9PJ Tel: (020) 7351 2255 Fax: (020) 7352 4682 *Brassware manufrs*

A Touch Of Pine, 150-152 Buckingham Road, Aylesbury, Buckinghamshire, HP19 9QN Tel: (01296) 433883 Fax: (01296) 334822 *Pine wood*

A Touch Of Pine Shop, Telford Road, Bicester, Oxfordshire, OX26 4LD Tel: (01869) 357100 Fax: (01869) 248867 E-mail: info@atouchofpine.co.uk *Pine furniture manufrs*

A Touch Of Taste, Unit 15 Monument Business Park, Warpsgrove Lane, Chalgrove, Oxford, OX44 7RW Tel: (01865) 400968 Fax: (01865) 400970 E-mail: admin@atouchoftaste.co.uk *Event organiser & caterer.*

A U Computers, 20 Glebe Road, Bedlington, Northumberland, NE22 6JT Tel: (01670) 829763 Fax: (01670) 823454 E-mail: joe@aucomputers.com *Computer maintenance*

A U S A (UK) Ltd, Unit 6-7 Alma Industrial Estate, Regent Street, Rochdale, Lancashire, OL12 0HQ Tel: (01706) 649691 Fax: (01706) 649720 E-mail: ausa@comel.demon.co.uk *Construction equipment manufrs*

A U T (Wheels & Castors) Co. Ltd, The Wheel House, Egmont Street, Mossley, Ashton-under-Lyne, Lancashire, OL5 9NB Tel: (01457) 837772 Fax: (01457) 832472 E-mail: sales@aut.co.uk *Castor & wheel distributors & agents*

A V Birch Ltd, Aldenham Mill, Muckley Cross, Acton Round, Bridgnorth, Shropshire, WV16 4RR Tel: (01746) 714418 Fax: (01746) 714419 E-mail: enquiries@avbirch.co.uk Principal Export Areas: Worldwide *Mechanical & general engineering contractors*

▶ A V Calibration Ltd, 13C Old Bridge Way, Shefford, Bedfordshire, SG17 5HQ Tel: (01462) 638600 Fax: (01462) 638601 E-mail: lab@avcalib.co.uk *Acoustic & vibration calibration*

A V Communication Solutions Ltd, Boston Buildings, 14-16 Yellow House Lane, Southport, Merseyside, PR8 1ER Tel: (01704) 531469 Fax: (01704) 539326 E-mail: av_comm_sols@btinternet.com *Security designers*

▶ A V Custom, 42 Winslow Road, Wingrave, Aylesbury, Buckinghamshire, HP22 4PS Tel: (01296) 682381 Fax: (01296) 682676 *Audio visual suppliers & installation*

▶ A V Dawson Ltd, Riverside Park Road, Middlesbrough, Cleveland, TS2 1QW Tel: (01642) 219271 Fax: (01642) 256828

A V E Composites, Compstall Mill, Compstall, Stockport, Cheshire, SK6 5HN Tel: 0161-427 1552 Fax: 0161-426 0016 E-mail: sales@avecomposites.co.uk *Glass fibre custom moulders*

A V Engineering Services Ltd, Saxon Way, Melbourn, Royston, Hertfordshire, SG8 6DN Tel: (01763) 261818 Fax: (01763) 262622 E-mail: sales@aveng.co.uk *Precision fabricating & forming in plastics*

A V F Group Ltd, Road 30, Hortonwood Industrial Estate, Telford, Shropshire, TF1 7YE Tel: (01952) 670009 Fax: (01952) 606205 E-mail: sales@avf.co.uk *Video appliances*

A V Fowlds & Sons Ltd, Progress Works, Addington Square, London, SE5 7JZ Tel: (020) 7703 2686 *Upholstery repair & renovation services*

A V Group Ltd, Hall Road, Langley Mill, Nottingham, NG16 4HP Tel: (01773) 711079 Fax: (01773) 711246 E-mail: sales@avgroup.co.uk *Portable accommodation suppliers*

A V Hire Shop, Unit 11, Concorde Park, Amy Johnson Way, York, YO30 4WT Tel: (01904) 693000 Fax: (01904) 691114 *Audio visual hire equipment*

▶ A V Interactive Ltd, Minerva Mill Innovation Centre, Station Road, Alcester, Warwickshire, B49 5ET Tel: (01789) 761331 E-mail: enquiry@avi.co.uk *Corporate video production. Services Include:- DVD & CD-Rom Authoring*Encoding *DVD/CD Duplication & Replication*Video Production editing filming programme making encoding web streaming*

A V L United Kingdom Ltd, Avon House, Hartlebury Trading Estate, Hartlebury, Kidderminster, Worcestershire, DY10 4JB Tel: (01299) 254600 Fax: (01299) 253734 E-mail: uk.sales@avl.com *Internal Combustion Engine Test Equipment and Instrumentation. Engineering Design, Manufacture, Installation and Calibration of Automotive Test Equipment and Systems. After Sales Maintenance, Upgrade and Spare Parts supply - Automotive Test Equipment Instrumentation and Systems.*

A V M Air Spring Ltd, Unit 2A, Brook Lane Industrial Estate, Westbury, Wiltshire, BA13 4EP Tel: (01373) 858223 Fax: (01373) 858224 E-mail: info@avmspring.com *Anti-vibration mounting manufrs*

A V O Systems Ltd, Unit 3 Dodnor Lane, Newport, Isle Of Wight, PO30 5XA Tel: (01983) 526527 Fax: (01983) 526524 E-mail: sales@avosystems.com Principal Export Areas: Worldwide *Marine electronic manufrs*

A V Plastics, Unit 1 Chiddingstone Causeway, Tonbridge, Kent, TN11 8JU Tel: (01892) 870461 Fax: (01892) 871262 E-mail: sales@avplastics.co.uk *Plastics injection mouldings manufrs*

A V Q Ltd, Unit 26d Bull Commercial Centre, Stockton Lane, Stockton on the Forest, York, YO32 9LE Tel: (01904) 400121 Fax: (01904) 400565 E-mail: info@avq.co.uk *Audiovisual support services*

▶ A V Services, Unit 17 Avenue Industrial Estate, Southend Arterial Road, Harold Wood, Romford, RM3 0BY Tel: (01708) 376221 Fax: (01708) 376224

▶ A V Shopper, S1 St. James House, Vicar Lane, Sheffield, S1 2EX Tel: (0870) 7532295 Fax: 0114-223 6333 E-mail: info@avshopper.co.uk *Audio visual equipment & accessory retailers*

A V Sightline, Dylan House, Town End Street, Godalming, Surrey, GU7 1BQ Tel: (01483) 861555 Fax: (01483) 861516 E-mail: action@sightline.co.uk *Multimedia & video production*

▶ A V Steel Laser Services Ltd, 20a Mandervell Road, Oadby, Leicester, LE2 5LQ Tel: 0116-271 8080 Fax: 0116-271 1551 E-mail: sales@avsteel.co.uk *Manufactures of specialist and bespoke fabrication products.*

▶ A V Trading Co., 22 St Lukes Terrace, Sunderland, SR4 6NQ Tel: 0191-565 6136 Fax: 0191-565 6136 E-mail: avtrad@yahoo.co.uk *Socks, nightwear, underwear, thermal wear import & distribution*

A V X Ltd, Admiral House, Harlington Way, Fleet, Hampshire, GU51 4BB Tel: (01252) 770000 Fax: (01252) 770001 E-mail: sales@flt.avxeur.com *Electronic component manufrs* Also at: Coleraine, Larne & Paignton

▶ A Virtual Solution, 11 Langley Close, Louth, Lincolnshire, LN11 8YP Tel: (01507) 609043 Fax: (01507) 609043 E-mail: sales@avirtualsolution.co.uk *Freelance Virtual assistant working with micro and small businesses providing 'as and when' secretarial services*

A W A Refiners Ltd, 10 Mead Industrial Park, Riverway, Harlow, Essex, CM20 2SE Tel: (01279) 423743 Fax: (01279) 422243 E-mail: sales@awarefiners.com *Precious metal refiners & electronic scrap recyclers*

▶ A W Angus & Co. Ltd, 24 Croydon Street, Leeds, LS11 9RT Tel: 0113-245 3246 Fax: 0113-234 1322

A W B S Ltd, Wyevale Garden Centre, South Hinksey, Oxford, OX1 5AR Tel: (01865) 327111 Fax: (01865) 327333 *Landscaping products suppliers*

A W Bag Manufacturers, 84 Silk Street, Manchester, M4 6BJ Tel: 0161-205 6661 Fax: 0161-205 6661 *Sports bags & hold alls manufrs*

▶ A W Bathrooms, 80 Buttershaw Lane, Bradford, West Yorkshire, BD6 2DA Tel: (07979) 300252 E-mail: awbathrooms@hotmail.com *Bathroom installation*

A W C, 97 Commercial Road, Bournemouth, BH2 5RT Tel: (01202) 789269 Fax: (01202) 789277 E-mail: sales@awc.co.uk *Computer hardware, software & internet*

A W Champion Ltd, 2 Hartfield Cresent, London, SW19 3SD Tel: (020) 8542 1606 Fax: (020) 8540 7237 *Timber merchants*

A W Champion Properties Ltd, Champion House, Burlington Road, New Malden, Surrey, KT3 4NB Tel: (020) 8949 1621 Fax: (020) 8949 0271 E-mail: marketing@championtimber.com *Timber merchants & importers* Also at: Bromley, Claygate, Dorking, Edenbridge, Epsom, Sutton & Wimbledon

A W Computer Solutions Ltd, 8e Port Road, Carlisle, CA2 7AF Tel: (01228) 594682 Fax: (01228) 594683 E-mail: info@armstrongwatson.co.uk *Computer systems, software & training*

A.W. Construction Ltd, Old House, Gorsey Lane, Coleshill, Birmingham, B46 1JU Tel: (01675) 432102 Fax: (01675) 432112 E-mail: info@awconstruction.plc.uk *Civil engineers & building contractors*

A & W Cushion Ltd, St Benedicts Sawmills, Barn Road, Norwich, NR2 4PW Tel: (01603) 628527 Fax: (01603) 765071 E-mail: cushion@kimbernorwich.demon.co.uk *Timber merchants* Also at: Great Yarmouth

A W D Chase De Vere Ltd, 10 Paternoster Square, London, EC4M 7DY Tel: (020) 7618 0207 Fax: (020) 7248 7741 *Independent financial advisors*

A W D Chase Devere P.L.C., 10 Paternoster Square, London, EC4M 7DY Tel: (020) 7828 9297 Fax: (020) 7248 7742 E-mail: enquiries@awdplc.com *Finance planning & benefit consultants* Also at: Leeds, Llandudno & Manchester

A W E Anderson Water Equipment Ltd, R04-R05 Unit Cardiff Bay Business Centre, Titan Road, Cardiff, CF24 5EL Tel: (029) 2049 2848 Fax: (029) 2049 1369 E-mail: sales@aweltd.co.uk Principal Export Areas: Worldwide *Water treatment specialists*

▶ A W E Europe Ltd, Unit BI, Longmead Business Centre, Blenheim Road, Epsom, Surrey, KT19 9QQ Tel: (01372) 729777 Fax: (01372) 729767 E-mail: info@awe-europe.co.uk *Audio visual equipment & accessory suppliers*

▶ A W Electronic, 2 Sandford Dairy, Shanklin Road, Sandford, Ventnor, Isle of Wight, PO38 3EX Tel: (01983) 840211 Fax: (01983) 840211 *Electronic manufrs*

A W Engraving, 11 Lifford Way, Binley Industrial Estate, Coventry, CV3 2RN Tel: (024) 7663 5453 Fax: (024) 7663 5486 *Industrial & promotional engravers*

A W Fabrications Ltd, Unit 3 Parsons Hall, High Street, Irchester, Wellingborough, Northamptonshire, NN29 7AB Tel: (01933) 357163 Fax: (01933) 410021 *Sheet metalwork fabricators*

A & W Fabrications & Structural Services, Old Bush Street, Brierley Hill, West Midlands, DY5 1UB Tel: (01384) 573676 Fax: (01384) 573676 *Fabrications & welding*

A W Framing Ltd, PO Box 844, Cardiff, CF10 4YF Tel: (029) 2045 4515 Fax: (029) 2045 4514 E-mail: info@awframing.co.uk *Engineers*

A W G Utility Services, Hampden House, Hitchin Road, Arlesey, Bedfordshire, SG15 6RT Tel: (01462) 731133 Fax: (01462) 834829 *Utility, plant & facility services*

A W Green Agricultural Engineers, Stable Works, Climpsetts Farm, Robertsbridge, East Sussex, TN32 5SP Tel: (01580) 860630 Fax: (01580) 860630 *Agricultural engineers*

A W H Consultants, Chadburn House, Weighbridge Road, Mansfield, Nottinghamshire, NG18 1AH Tel: (01623) 465207 Fax: (01623) 400196 E-mail: enquiries@ynotwine.co.uk *Wine suppliers*

A W H Joinery, The Old Workshop, Hyde Home Farmllower Luton Road, The Hyde, Luton, LU2 9PS Tel: (01582) 713255 Fax: (01582) 713255 *Joiners*

A W Hardy & Co. Ltd, Stock Road, Southend-on-Sea, SS2 5QG Tel: (01702) 462721 Fax: (01702) 469062 E-mail: enqs@hardygroup.demon.co.uk *Builders & civil engineers*

A W Interiors Ltd, 4 Streetgate Park, Sunniside, Newcastle upon Tyne, NE16 5LD Tel: 0191-488 9910 Fax: 0191-488 9920 E-mail: bill@awinteriors.freeserve.co.uk *Suppliers of office & works partitions*

A W Intruder Alarms, Wycherley, Llanvihangel Crucorney, Abergavenny, Gwent, NP7 7LB Tel: (01873) 890272 Fax: (01873) 890272 *Alarm systems*

A W Jeffreys Southampton Ltd, 91-97 Dukes Road, Southampton, SO14 0ST Tel: (023) 8055 3730 Fax: (023) 8067 1345 E-mail: awj@awjefferys.co.uk *Architectural art & general metal workers services*

A & W Jigboring Ltd, 46 Padgets Lane, Redditch, Worcestershire, B98 0RD Tel: (01527) 522196 Fax: (01527) 517389 E-mail: sales@awjigboring.co.uk *General machine manufrs*

A W L Inspection & N D T Services Ltd, Unit 34, Royal Industrial Estate, Jarrow, Tyne & Wear, NE32 3HR Tel: 0191-430 0837 Fax: 0191-430 0837 E-mail: awl_ndt@btconnect.com *Radiographic, ultrasonic test & inspection services*

▶ A W Lithgow Ltd, 2 Edinburgh Road, Cleghorn, Lanark, ML11 7RW Tel: (01555) 665066

A W M Ltd, 17/18 Mercers Hill Road, Chapel Pond HL, Bury St. Edmunds, Suffolk, IP32 7HX Tel: (01284) 701222 Fax: (01284) 703559 E-mail: brian@awmlimited.co.uk *Scales & weighbridges distributors*

▶ A W Mackintosh Electrical Contractors, Shore Road, Perth, PH2 8BD Tel: (01738) 627172 Fax: (01738) 639704 E-mail: info@amsecurities.co.uk

A W Midgley & Son Ltd, 13 Cheddar Business Park, Wedmore Road, Cheddar, Somerset, BS27 3EB Tel: (01934) 741741 Fax: (01934) 741555 E-mail: sales@awmidgley.co.uk *Leather skins distributors*

▶ A W Morris Ltd, Unit 4 6 & 7 West Mews, West Road Tottenham, London, N17 0QT Tel: (020) 8880 9191 Fax: (020) 8801 8736 E-mail: sales@morrismirrors.com *Mirrors manufrs*

▶ A W P Enviromental, Unit 10, Campbells Yard, 75 Bellfast Road, Newry, County Down, BT34 1QH Tel: (028) 3083 5533 Fax: (028) 3082 5523 E-mail: sales@awpenviromental.net *Sewage treatment services*

▶ A W Parry, 1 Ashmead Business Park, Ashmead Road, Keynsham, Bristol, BS31 1SX Tel: 0117-986 9020 Fax: 0117-986 9040 E-mail: dparry@awparrylistf.co.uk *Lift installation & maintenance*

A W Perry Electrical Co. Ltd, 35 Stroud Road, London, SE25 5DR Tel: (020) 8654 3122 Fax: (020) 8656 8806 E-mail: mail@perryelectrical.co.uk *Data communications & office refurbishments*

A W Phillips Awp Ltd, 47-51 Plashet Grove, London, E6 1AD Tel: (020) 8472 6656 Fax: (020) 8471 8317 *Plant hire & tool merchants*

A W Plant Services Ltd, Eurocentre, North River Road, Great Yarmouth, Norfolk, NR30 1TE Tel: (01493) 330209 Fax: (01493) 843470 *Mobile crane hire*

A W Precision Ltd, Cosford Lane, Rugby, Warwickshire, CV21 1QN Tel: (01788) 542271 Fax: (01788) 561256 E-mail: sales@awp-ltd.com *Punches, dies & die sets manufrs*

Company Information

A & W Precision Tools Ltd, Unit 2 Brookside Industrial Pk, Crankhall La, Wednesbury, W. Midlands, WS10 0QZ Tel: 0121-505 1359 Fax: 0121-505 1359 *Precision*

A W R Ceilings & Partitions, Jack O Watton Industrial Estate, Lichfield Road, Water Orton, Birmingham, B46 1NU Tel: 0121-748 2608 Fax: 0121-776 7561 E-mail: triciaharris@eidosnet.co.uk *Ceiling & flooring contractors*

A W R Instruments Ltd, 1 Northpoint Business Estate, Enterprise Close, Rochester, Kent, ME2 4LX Tel: (01634) 290751 Fax: (01634) 290295 E-mail: info@awr-instruments.com *Instrument & system manufrs*

A W Raybould Ltd, Barons Court, Newhouse Lane, Upton Warren, Bromsgrove, Worcestershire, B61 9ET Tel: (01527) 861006 Fax: (01527) 861292 E-mail: info@academypewter.co.uk *Pewter ware manufrs*

A W S, Nelsons Wharf, Sandy Lane Industrial Estate, Stourport-on-Severn, Worcestershire, DY13 9QB Tel: (01299) 829202 Fax: (01299) 829203 E-mail: sales@aws-services.co.uk *Steel sections, cold rolled. Also manufacturers of cold rolled products, non-ferrous metal sections & rolled steel products*

▶ A W S Electrical Services, 30 Glenwood Place, Glasgow, G45 9UH Tel: 0141-631 2222 Fax: 0141-631 4400

A W S Engineering, Unit F1, Shaw Road, Dudley, West Midlands, DY2 8TP Tel: (01384) 236488 Fax: (01384) 236489 E-mail: tony@steel-fabrications.co.uk *Steel fabricators*

A W S Group Plc, Systems House, Hoo Farm Industrial Estate, Worcester Road, Kidderminster, Worcestershire, DY11 7RA Tel: (01562) 743700 Fax: (01562) 829775 E-mail: info@awsgroupplc.co.uk *Aluminium, upvc doors & windows* Also at: Greenford

A W S Metal Finishers, 79 Baltimore Road, Birmingham, B42 1DG Tel: 0121-357 3127 Fax: 0121-357 3127 E-mail: airbrush12@aol.com *Sign manufrs*

A W S Turner-Fain Ltd, Roman Acre House, West Bank, Berry Hill Industrial Estate, Droitwich, Worcestershire, WR9 9AE Tel: (01905) 774267 Fax: (01905) 775565 E-mail: aws@turnerfainltd.co.uk *Aluminium window manufrs*

A W Technology, West Street, Earl Shilton, Leicester, LE9 7EJ Tel: (01455) 841116 E-mail: hello@awtechnology.com *Technology developers*

A W V Turner & Co. Ltd, Rex Works, Harvest Lane, Sheffield, S3 8EB Tel: 0114-272 4162 Fax: 0114-276 9284 E-mail: awvturner@awvturner.f9.co.uk *Engineering supplies, power tool leasing, lubricants & abrasives*

A W W Computers, South Road, Harlow, Essex, CM20 2AS Tel: (01279) 626354 Fax: (01279) 444800 E-mail: admin@wenham.co.uk *Computer dealership services*

A W Warner & Sons Ltd, Guilton Lodge, Guilton, Ash, Canterbury, Kent, CT3 2HS Tel: (01304) 812396 Fax: (01304) 813635 *Agricultural engineers*

▶ A Wade Tax Consultancy, 2 Plough Cottages, Great Munden, Ware, Hertfordshire, SG11 1HS Tel: (01920) 438010 Fax: (01920) 438998 E-mail: amanda@tax-consultancy.co.uk

A Walter, Stones Tenement, Croford, Wiveliscombe, Taunton, Somerset, TA4 2TS Tel: (01984) 623624 Fax: (01984) 624768 *Horse transport*

A Wardle & Co., 51 Albion Street, Birmingham, B1 3EA Tel: 0121-236 2733 Fax: 0121-200 3056 E-mail: info@awardle.co.uk *Jewellery casting processors*

A Warne & Co. Ltd, Nelson Trading Estate, 11 The Path, London, SW19 3BL Tel: (020) 8543 3045 Fax: (020) 8543 6089 E-mail: sales@awarne.com *Paper, plastic & film converters*

A Warren & Sons Ltd, Stamford Works, Constantine Street, Oldham, OL4 3AD Tel: 0161-624 4621 Fax: 0161-627 5163 E-mail: warrens@zen.co.uk *Plumbing & heating merchants*

▶ A Watson (Hauliers) Ltd, Thorpe Lane Garage, Thorpe Lane, Leeds, LS10 4EP Tel: 0113-270 1871

▶ A Web Whisper, 103 Lower End, Leafield, Witney, Oxfordshire, OX29 9QG Tel: (01993) 878356 E-mail: info@webwhisper.co.uk *Internet marketing, search engine optimisation & copywriting*

▶ A Wedding to Talk About, 1 Brennan Close, Barrow-in-Furness, Cumbria, LA13 0TD Tel: (01229) 812921 *Service in wedding, christening*

A Weld Ltd, Tank Farm Road, Llandarcy, Neath, West Glamorgan, SA10 6EN Tel: (01792) 816132 Fax: (01792) 812913 E-mail: info@aweldlimited.co.uk *Welding & fabricators*

A Weston, 23 Marsh St South, Stoke-on-Trent, ST1 1JA Tel: (01782) 214580 Fax: (01782) 214581 *Sign manufrs*

A White, 18 Sunrise Crescent, Hemel Hempstead, Hertfordshire, HP3 9NR Tel: (07843) 192574 E-mail: info@a-white-plumbing-service.co.uk *Watford plumbing service offering all your plumbing needs. 24/7 Call out service at no extra charge.*

A Wilkins & Sons, Unit 1 3 The Elms Centre, Glaziers Lane, Normandy, Guildford, Surrey, GU3 2DF Tel: (01483) 575919 Fax: (01483) 570140 *Road transport, haulage & freight services*

A Williamson & Son, 34 Main Street, Milton of Balgonie, Glenrothes, Fife, KY7 6PX Tel: (01592) 758307 Fax: (01592) 610570 *Cable drum manufrs*

A Winston & Sons, 461 Paisley Road, Glasgow, G5 8RJ Tel: 0141-429 4278 Fax: 0141-429 0577 E-mail: bryanwinston@hotmail.co.uk *Engineering & industrial suppliers*

A Woodcock & Son, 8a Asfordby Street, Leicester, LE5 3QG Tel: 0116-262 2176 *Carpenters & joiners*

A Woods Agricultural Engineers, Pipwell Gate, Holbeach, Spalding, Lincolnshire, PE12 8BA Tel: (01406) 426108 Fax: (01406) 490101 E-mail: woodsagri@tiscali.co.uk *Agricultural repairs, fabrications & classic tractor sales*

A World Of Ceramics, 82 Priory Road, Kenilworth, Warwickshire, CV8 1LQ Tel: (01926) 854500 Fax: (01926) 856660 *Tile distributors*

▶ A World of Digital, 104 Walton Road, Chesterfield, Derbyshire, S40 3BY Tel: (01246) 229585 E-mail: aworldofdigital@aol.com *Digital aerials & satellite systems installers & maintenance services*

▶ A World of Old, The Barns, Wingrave Road, Aston Abbotts, Aylesbury, Buckinghamshire, HP22 4LU Tel: (01296) 680406 Fax: (01296) 680437 *Pine & antique furniture manufrs*

A World Of Pine, 2 The Wyndham Centre, Dairy Meadow L, Salisbury, SP1 2TJ Tel: (01722) 413532 Fax: (01722) 413532 E-mail: info@worldofpine.co.uk *Pine, oak & leather distributors*

▶ A X L Security, 2 Nidd Valley Trading Estate, Market Flat Lane, Scotton, Knaresborough, North Yorkshire, HG5 9JA Tel: (01423) 860300 Fax: (01423) 869779 E-mail: sales@axlsecurity.co.uk

A Y Agencies, Millbank, 3 Cargill Avenue, Maybole, Ayrshire, KA19 8AD Tel: (01655) 883041 Fax: (01655) 883981 *Textile agency*

A Z Sunroof Services, 21 Lilley Lane, Birmingham, B31 3JU Tel: 0121-411 1222 Fax: 0121-608 6008 *Roof & car alarms & tow bar fittings services*

A&D, 3 44 Colville Road, London, W3 8BL Tel: (020) 8992 6721 Fax: (020) 8992 4677 *Bolt & nut, fastener & screw distributors*

▶ A&D Surveillance and Security Consultants, 15, Chester Close, Dorking, Surrey, RH4 1PP Tel: 01306 885717 Fax: 01306 885717 E-mail: info@adssc.co.uk *Private Investigators*

▶ A&E Consulting, 1 Westbrae Road, Newton Mearns, Glasgow, G77 6EQ Tel: (01355) 268088

▶ A&L TOWBARS, KIRKBURTON, KIRKBURTON, HUDDERSFIELD, HD8 0TJ Tel: 01484 602231 E-mail: andymally@btinternet.com *MOBILE TOWBAR FITTING SERVICE*AND DIY TOW BAR SUPPLIES IN WEST YORKSHIRE*

▶ A&S Design Services, 19 Cornlands, Sampford Peverell, Tiverton, Devon, EX16 7UA Tel: 01884 829285 Fax: 01884 829285 E-mail: ascad@aol.com *Provision of Computer Aided Design and draughting services to the architectural, building industry including building services. Qualified energy assement consultants*

▶ A&T, Fairview, Agraria Road, Guildford, Surrey, GU2 4LE Tel: (01483) 568181 Fax: (01483) 855187 E-mail: info@atbuilders.com *A&T Builders undertake a variety of general building projects both large and small. We are a member of Checkatrade and registered with Surrey Trading Standards - Buy with Confidence - scheme.*

▶ A+ Engineering, 45 Broadlands Park, County, CARRICKFERGUS, County Antrim, BT38 7DB Tel: 028 93366516 Fax: 028 93366516 E-mail: info@aplusengineering.co.uk *We are suppliers of all things Vacuum. We can supply parts for all makes of vacuum pumps including Busch, Rietschle, Becker and many more. Process pumping equipment supplied, fitted and we are your complete service provider.*

▶ A1 Access, Unit 8c Hybris Business Park, Warmwell Road, Crossways, Dorchester, Dorset, DT2 8BF Tel: (01305) 854990 Fax: (01305) 851983 E-mail: terry@a1access.org.uk *Door automation systems suppliers*

A1 Accommodation, Hunts Plant Yard, Great North Road, Buckden, St. Neots, Cambridgeshire, PE19 5UL Tel: (01480) 810013 Fax: (01480) 810868 E-mail: sales@a1-accommodation.co.uk *Portable accommodation sales*

A1 Aerials Ltd, 14 Arden Oak Road, Sheldon, Birmingham, B26 3LX Tel: 0121-742 0026 Fax: 0121-742 7360 E-mail: a1aerials@btconnect.com

▶ A1 Air Systems, Unit 4, 111-117 Sydenham Road, Birmingham, B11 1DG Tel: 0121-773 2525

▶ A1 Blast Services, 26 Camborne Close, Northampton, NN4 8PH Tel: (07901) 972536 *Shot blasting*

A1 Blasting Cleaning & Painting, Riverside House Wallerscote Island, Winnington Lane, Northwich, Cheshire, CW8 4YF Tel: (01606) 783203 Fax: (01606) 781581 *Industrial blasting, cleaning & painting*

A1 Blinds, Unit 17 Bridge Street Industrial Estate, Tredegar, Gwent, NP22 4LA Tel: (01495) 717545 *Blind manufrs*

▶ A1 Bouncy Castle, 13 Northfield Road, Princes Risborough, Buckinghamshire, HP27 0HY Tel: (01844) 274300 E-mail: farooqchappar@btconnect.com *Bouncy castle hire*

▶ A1 Bouncy Castles, Green Leys, Downley, High Wycombe, Buckinghamshire, HP13 5UH Tel: (01494) 464902 *Supply a wide range of quality bouncy castles*

▶ A1 Building & Roofing, 4 Grasmere Road, Purley, Surrey, CR8 1DU Tel: (020) 8407 0202 E-mail: tom@a-onebuildingandroofingltd.co.uk *South London Builder specialising in all aspects of Building, Roofing and Home Improvements.*Loft Conversions, Home Extensions,Refurbishment, Painting and Decorating.*New Roofs, Slating and Tiling, Flat Roofs, Roof Repairs, Lead Flashings, Guttering.*Members of The Federation of Master Builders.*

A1 Business Service Centre, 94 University Avenue, Belfast, BT7 1GY Tel: (028) 9032 3334 Fax: (028) 9023 8601 E-mail: a1businessservicecentre@hotmail.com *Digital printing disc duplicating services*

A1 Cable Express Ltd, Unit 27 Hailey Road Business Park, Hailey Road, Erith, Kent, DA18 4AA Tel: (020) 8312 4006 Fax: (020) 8312 4883 *Electric cable distributors*

▶ A1 Cad, 19 Totnes Close, Poulton-le-Fylde, Lancashire, FY6 7TP Tel: (01253) 882812 Fax: (01253) 882812

A1 Copying Systems & Supplies Ltd, 36 Church Street, Leighton Buzzard, Bedfordshire, LU7 1BT Tel: (01525) 371333 Fax: (01525) 371339 E-mail: a1copyingsys@btclick.com *Photocopying machines supplies & services*

▶ A1 Corporate Gifts, 10 Oldhill, Dunstable, Bedfordshire, LU6 3ER Tel: (01582) 660465 Fax: (01582) 601759 E-mail: sales@a1cg.co.uk *Promotional merchandise suppliers*

A1 Cutting Formes, 117 Whitehouse Lane, Bedminster, Bristol, BS3 4DN Tel: 0117-963 7897 Fax: 0117-953 8101 E-mail: info@a1cuttingformes.co.uk *Cutting formes*

A1 Electrical Installations Ltd, 120-122 Becontree Avenue, Dagenham, Essex, RM8 2TS Tel: (020) 8597 0953 Fax: (020) 8597 2556 E-mail: info@a1electrical.co.uk *Electrical contractors*

A1 Exterminators Pest Control Services, 76 Dormington Road, Birmingham, B44 9LG Tel: 0121-360 1477 Fax: 0121-360 1477 *Pest control services*

A1 Extraction Ltd, Wentworth Road, Heathfield Industrial Estate, Newton Abbot, Devon, TQ12 6TL Tel: (01626) 832007 Fax: (01626) 834590 Principal Export Areas: Worldwide *Dust extraction engineers*

A1 Fasteners Ltd, Unit 5/6, Brookwood Insutrial Estate, Eastleigh, Southampton, SO50 9EY Tel: (023) 8065 0666 Fax: (023) 8065 0601 E-mail: sales@a1-fasteners.co.uk *Trading since 1987, A1 Fasteners has emerged as a leading supplier of fasteners and associated products and can point to an unusually strong track record in the fastener industry. We believe that real customer service can only be achieved through a careful balance of people, product knowledge and quality systems. With this in mind, we continually invest in all three. Our product knowledge and support systems are another reason for competitive advantage. So, if sourcing the right fasteners from the right supplier is a challenge, put us to the test. We also provide Bolts and Nuts*

A1 Fitting, 36 Oxgangs Crescent, Edinburgh, EH13 9HL Tel: 0131-441 4404 Fax: 0131-441 4404 *Curtain fitting*

A1 Freight Ltd, Maybells Commercial Estate, Ripple Road, Barking, Essex, IG11 0TP Tel: (020) 8592 1202 Fax: (020) 8593 0291 E-mail: hgrent@onetel.net *Warehousing & transport services*

▶ A1 Fruit, 12 Berrington Road, Leamington Spa, Warwickshire, CV31 1NB Tel: (01926) 312222 *Fruit juice suppliers*

▶ A1 Glazing Services, Factory Complex, Southchurch Drive, Nottingham, NG11 8AQ Tel: 0115-921 2617 Fax: 0115-914 8777 *Double glazing manufrs*

▶ A1 Grafters, 83 Ermine Road, Lewisham, London, SE13 7JJ Tel: (020) 8690 6635 E-mail: advice@a1grafters.com *Emergency plumbers*

A1 Graphics, Mk: Two Business Centre Barton Road Water Eaton, Barton Road, Bletchley, Milton Keynes, MK2 3HU Tel: 01908 821110 Fax: 01429 278444 E-mail: mksales@a1-graphics.co.uk *Commercial & Industrial Engravers in brass, steel, aluminium and plastic. Full range of signage products and rubber stamps.*

A1 Marsden Recovery Specialists Ltd, Musgrave Park Industrial Estate, Stockmans Way, Belfast, BT9 7ET Tel: (028) 9068 2892 Fax: (028) 9038 1319 E-mail: linda@a1marsden.com *Breakdown & recovery vehicle services*

A1 Metal Fabrications, 22 Boston Road, Leicester, LE4 1AU Tel: 0116-235 0444 Fax: 0116-235 0444 *General sheet metal engineers*

A1 Metal Spinners Ltd, Clovelly Road, Southbourne, Emsworth, Hampshire, PO10 8PF Tel: (01243) 378401 Fax: (01243) 374219 E-mail: info@metalspinners-in.co.uk *We are one of the few Specialist Metal Spinning Companies in the UK that have the knowledge and wealth of expertise and technical knowhow in the art of Metal Spinning. We are equipped with the latest state of the art PNC Liefeld programmable Automatic Spinning Machines that enable us to manufacture precision spun Aerospace components in most materials - hastelloy, nimonic, inconel, titanium, mu-metal, tantalum and aerospace alloys and steels etc - max. diameter 1100mm x 12mm thick. In addition to our Power Forming Division we have one of the most experienced assembled team of time served manual craftsmen who between them cover the whole spectrum from engineering precision spinning to general commercial components -max. diameter 2100mm x 4mm thick etc. We design and manufacture Tooling up to 3 tons. We carry many Company Approvals such as Rolls Royce Approval No. 90130 and we are also fully ISO 9001-2000 Accredited. We offer a full manufacturing service*

▶ A1 Mini Mix Concrete Ltd, Bestwood Road, Nottingham, NG6 8SS Tel: 0115-976 2255 Fax: 0115-976 2255 *Supply ready mix concrete*

A1 Moulders Ltd, Smeckley Wood Close, Chesterfield, Derbyshire, S41 9PZ Tel: (01246) 455705 Fax: (01246) 454895 E-mail: a1moulders@bt.com *Technical & industrial plastic moulding manufrs*

A1 Netservices, 23 Tudor Road, Wheathampstead, St. Albans, Hertfordshire, AL4 8NW Tel: (01582) 834208 Fax: (0871) 7501428 E-mail: info@a1-netservices.co.uk *Computer services*

▶ A1 Outsource Ltd, 32 St. Ives Road, Coventry, CV2 5FZ Tel: (07903) 857799 E-mail: mitin@a1outsource.co.uk *Project management & engineering components*

A1 Paper P.L.C., Roebuck Street, West Bromwich, West Midlands, B70 6RB Tel: 0121-553 7131 Fax: 0121-553 5040 E-mail: sales@a1paper.co.uk *Paper merchants*

A1 Partitions, Fairview, Vicarage Close, Ravensden, Bedford, MK44 2RW Tel: (01234) 771144 Fax: (01234) 772080 E-mail: info@a1-partitions.co.uk *Refurbishment contractors*

▶ A1 Pat Testing, 65 Welldeck Road, Hartlepool, Cleveland, TS26 8JS Tel: 01429 421679 E-mail: info@a1pat-testing.co.uk *PORTABLE APPLIANCE TESTING SPECIALISTS(PAT)FOR THE TEESSIDE/DURHAM AND SURROUNDING AREA.FOR A PROFESSIONAL AND RELIABLE SERVICE AT A FAIR PRICE CONTACT US FOR YOUR FREE NO OBLIGATION ESTIMATE.ALL TESTING CARRIED OUT BY CITY&GUILDS TRAINED ENGINEERS USING THE LATEST EQUIPMENT.*

A1 Patios, The Old Bakehouse Yard, Maesteg Road, Sarn, Bridgend, Mid Glamorgan, CF32 9UH Tel: (01656) 720428 *Patio & ornaments manufrs*

▶ A1 PC Support, 39 Stirling Road, Bournemouth, BH3 7JQ Tel: (01202) 386292 *A1 PC Support is Bournemouth''s premier computer repair centre. We perform PC upgrades, fault diagnosis, virus removal, data recover, operating system installation and more. We provide a 24 hour call-out service with quick turnaround time at very reasonable prices.*

▶ A1 perfect placement uk ltd, 58 Thorpe Road, Norwich, NR1 1RY Tel: 08450 212123 *Motor Trade Recruitment Automotive Industry Recruitment Consultants and agency for Vehicle Technicians Mechanics Service Advisors Sales Managers General Managers Receptionists HGV fitters Dealer Principle Paint Sprayer Body work Workshop Controller*

A1 Plant Sales Ltd, Stephenson Street, Queensway Meadows Industrial E, Newport, Gwent, NP19 4XB Tel: (01633) 676800 Fax: (01633) 274974 E-mail: reeves.wilfred@ntlworld.com *Plant parts spares & service*

A1 Plating, 36 Padgets Lane, Redditch, Worcestershire, B98 0RB Tel: (01527) 528852 Fax: (01527) 528852 E-mail: office@a1-plating.co.uk *Electroplating services & Zinc Plating Specialists Capacity for Small to medium size quantity's, offering a mayday service for the just in time scenario, and advice on the complicated issues with metal finishing problems.*

A1 Plymol Flagstaff Co., Unit 6 Carr Lane Business Park, Carr Lane, Hoylake, Wirral, Merseyside, CH47 4AZ Tel: 0151-632 1354 Fax: 0151-632 4912 E-mail: sales@flagstaffs.co.uk *Flag pole contractors & engineering*

A1 Powder Coatings Ltd, Unit 5 Beta Buildings Willments Industrial Estate, Hazel Road, Southampton, SO19 7HS Tel: (023) 8044 6874 Fax: (023) 8044 6879 E-mail: enquiries@a1powdercoatings.co.uk *Powder Coating Specialist. Long life anti-corrosion coatings, large and small batch runs, 7 metre oven, shot blasting, metal spraying, wet spray painting and painting contractors.*

A1 Promotional Pens, 2-4 Mount Pleasant Road, Aldershot, Hampshire, GU12 4NL Tel: (01252) 320571 Fax: (01252) 403635 E-mail: sales@pens.co.uk *Promotional pens & pencils*

A1 Rentals Ltd, A1 House 22b Navigation Drive, Hurst Business Park, Brierley Hill, West Midlands, DY5 1UT Tel: (01384) 486200 Fax: (01384) 486204 E-mail: admin1@a1rentals.entadsl.com *Tool & plant hire*

▶ A1 Repair, Lower Church House, Flyford Flavell, Worcester, WR7 4BX Tel: (07789) 746645 E-mail: sam_munro@hotmail.com

A1 Results Ltd, Jervaulx House, Station Road, Newton le Willows, Bedale, North Yorkshire, DL8 1TB Tel: (01677) 450665 Fax: (01677) 450665 *Industrial electronic systems*

A1 Roper Ltd, Crown Works, Worth Way, Keighley, West Yorkshire, BD21 5LR Tel: (01535) 604215 Fax: (01535) 602689 E-mail: a1-roper@compuserve.com *Foundry equipment suppliers*

A1 Ropes & Rigging Ltd, Rope House, 39a Wheatash Road, Addlestone, Surrey, KT15 2ES Tel: (01932) 561355 Fax: (01932) 561433 E-mail: info@a1ropesandrigging.ltd.uk *Lifting gear distributors, agents & stockholders*

A1 Sandblasting, Reeds Farm, Cow Watering Lane, Writtle, Chelmsford, CM1 3SB Tel: (01245) 422188 *Blast cleaning contractors & services*

▶ A1 Secure Fabrications, Unit 4 Clifton Avenue, Long Eaton, Nottingham, NG10 2GA Tel: 0115-946 1777 Fax: 0115-946 1777 E-mail: a1securefabs@aol.com *Sheet metal fabricators*

A1 Security Systems, 4 Viceroy Court, Bedford Road, Petersfield, Hampshire, GU32 3LJ Tel: (01730) 266811 Fax: (01730) 262652 E-mail: admin@a1securitysystems.co.uk *Security suppliers*

A1 Service From Wynnstay Fuels, Saighton Lane, Waverton, Chester, CH3 7PD Tel: (01244) 332055 Fax: (01244) 355482 E-mail: wynnstayfuels@btconnect.com *Fuel oil distribution*

A1 Signs, 7 Woodspring Court, Sheffield, S4 8FP Tel: 0114-243 6964 Fax: 0114-243 6964 *Sign & nameplate manufrs*

▶ A1 Stainless Steel Fabrications, Redhill Works, 200 Prospect Row, Dudley, West Midlands, DY2 8SG Tel: (01384) 253738 Fax: (01384) 256157 E-mail: info@a1stainless.co.uk *Specialist stainless steel fabricators,*

▶ A1 Supplies, The Acorns, Willisham Road, Barking, Ipswich, IP6 8HY Tel: (01473) 657227 Fax: (01473) 657229 *Nuts, bolts & power tool suppliers*

A1 Supreme Sales Signs, 24 Nuneaton Way, Newcastle upon Tyne, NE5 1QN Tel: 0191-267 9333 Fax: 0191-229 0759 *Electronic signs distributors*

A1 Survey Ltd, 1 Cefn Graig, Rhiwbina, Cardiff, CF14 6SW Tel: (029) 2091 5858 Fax: (029) 2091 5858 E-mail: sales@a1survey.net *Measuring equipment including spirit levels & binoculars manufrs*

A1 T S Security Systems, 65 Woodchurch Lane, Birkenhead, Merseyside, CH42 9PL Tel: 0151-608 0935 Fax: 0151-608 9741 *Supply CCTV to commercial property*

▶ indicates data change since last edition

A1 Top Spares, 15 Walton Way, Brandon, Suffolk, IP27 0HP Tel: 01842 814524 Fax: 01842 811666 *Hydraulic spare parts*

A1 Trophies, PO Box 200, Sutton Coldfield, West Midlands, B75 7TR Tel: 0121-378 2828 Fax: 0121 378 0500 *Trophy manufrs*

▶ A1 Trophies & Engraving, Whitworth Road, South West Industrial Estate, Peterlee, County Durham, SR8 2LY Tel: 0191-586 1159 Fax: 0191-587 2970 E-mail: info@a1trophiesandengraving.com *Sports trophies engravers*

A1 Turning, 7 Holbrook Lane, Coventry, CV6 4AD Tel: (024) 7668 6333 Fax: (024) 7668 6222 E-mail: salesa1turning@btconnect.com *Precision engineers & special fasteners manufrs*

A1 Vision, Vision House, 25 Bradford Road, Riddlesden, Keighley, West Yorkshire, BD21 4ET Tel: (01535) 607080 Fax: (01535) 603010 E-mail: sales@a1vision.com *Repairs & sales of televisions, videos & computers*

A1 Wasp Control, Hurn Honey Farm, Barrack Road, West Parley, Ferndown, Dorset, BH22 8UB Tel: (01202) 593040 *Bee & wasp controllers*

A1 Waste Disposal Co. Ltd, Eastways, Witham, Essex, CM8 3YU Tel: (01376) 515615 Fax: (01376) 515616 E-mail: admin@a1demolition.co.uk *Waste disposal contractors*

A1 Welding & Fabrications, Unit 40 Vale Business Park, Llandow, Cowbridge, South Glamorgan, CF71 7PF Tel: (01446) 773372 Fax: (01446) 773372 *Tubular steel manufrs*

▶ A10 Security, 78 Windmill Hill, Enfield, Middlesex, EN2 7AY Tel: (0800) 8496769 E-mail: Georgina@acornsecurity.co.uk *Emergency locksmith services, 24 hours each & everyday*

▶ A19 Duplication, PO Box 428, Middlesbrough, Cleveland, TS1 9AF Tel: (01642) 225283 E-mail: sales@a19duplication.co.uk

▶ a1shoppingchannel.com, Koloma House, Warren Avenue, Fakenham, Norfolk, NR21 8NP Tel: 0845 1665226 Fax: 0845 1665227 E-mail: sales@a1shoppingchannel.com *Shopping on line everything under one roof.*

A2a Fabrications, Hill Farm, Tunnel Road, Galley Common, Ansley, Nuneaton, Warwickshire, CV10 9PE Tel: (024) 7639 7888 Fax: (024) 7639 7888 E-mail: a2afabrications@tiscali.co.uk *we are Manufactures of Security Roller Shutter,Bar Gates,Collapible Grilles,Gates Fences & Railings,You can also find our advert in the Yellow pages under Roller Shutters.*

▶ A2b Direct Transport & Removals, 8a Mill Walk, Maidstone, Kent, ME16 9LE Tel: (07855) 428428 Fax: (01622) 721790 E-mail: quotes@a2bdirect.co.uk *Household and office removals company based in Maidstone Kent. Specialising in domestic removals both locally and nationwide. Also road haulage up to 1.5 tonnes*

A2B Plastics Ltd, Swan Road, Mochdre Business Park, Mochdre, Colwyn Bay, Clwyd, LL28 5HB Tel: (01492) 544332 Fax: (01492) 543794 E-mail: james@a2bplastics.co.uk *Plastic injection mouldings*

▶ A2e Ltd, Adaptive House, Quarrywood Court, Livingston, West Lothian, EH54 6AX Tel: (01506) 463393 Fax: (01506) 461257 *Electronic design services*

▶ A2n Management Ltd, Sunnyside, Howle Hill, Ross-on-Wye, Herefordshire, HR9 5SP Tel: (01989) 561093 Fax: 01989 561093 E-mail: linda@a2n.co.uk

A2z, 139 Lillie Road, London, SW6 7SX Tel: (07957) 586656 E-mail: a2zcounselling@yahoo.com *Management consultancy, interpersonal training, counseling & therapy services*

▶ A2Z Disco Roadshow, Grove Street, Stoke-on-Trent, ST6 2JA Tel: (07734) 699095 E-mail: leigh@leighs.org *Well established Mobile disco and DJ based in Stoke on Trent and the North Staffordshire area.*Why not book us today to entertain you tomorrow?*

▶ A2Z Electrical Ltd, Parkers Avenue, Wick, Bristol, BS30 5QX Tel: 0117-900 3450 *Domestic and Commercial Electrical Services. Part P registered.*

▶ A3 Light Haulage, Suite 8 Enterprise Centre, Bowen Industrial Estate, Aberbargoed, Bargoed, Mid Glamorgan, CF81 9EP Tel: (01443) 839622 Fax: (01443) 839622 E-mail: info@a3lighthaulage.co.uk *Collection, delivery in UK /Europe. Sameday /Nextday. Guaranteed service. Small/midi /lwb vans. Fully serviced /insured & available at short notice. Secure storage.*

A30 Interiors, 167 Cannon Workshops, 3 Cannon Drive, London, E14 4AS Tel: (0800) 3161000 Fax: (0207) 719 844 E-mail: enq@a30interiors.com *Suspended ceilings, partition contractors & suppliers*

A4 Computers, 2nd Floor, 32 B Church Road, Ashford, Middlesex, TW15 2UY Tel: (0870) 0634283 Fax: (0870) 0632106 E-mail: info@a4it.co.uk *Computer services*

A4 Cryogenics, 10 Carlisle Road, Templepatrick, Ballyclare, County Antrim, BT39 0AW Tel: (028) 9443 3408 Fax: (028) 9443 3408 *Gas distributors*

A4 Pest Control, 19 Audley Road, Chippenham, Wiltshire, SN14 0DY Tel: (07966) 527538 Fax: (01249) 447378 *Pest controllers*

A4 Plus Drawing Services Ltd, 11a Park Street, Chatteris, Cambridgeshire, PE16 6AB Tel: (01354) 691820 Fax: (01354) 691821 E-mail: enquiries@a4plus.co.uk *Systems designers*

A5 Hydraulics Ltd, 46a Alliance Industrial Estate, Dodsworth Street, Darlington, County Durham, DL1 2NG Tel: (01325) 464354 Fax: (01325) 464356 E-mail: sales@a5hydraulics.co.uk *Hydraulic engineers*

A50 Office Furniture, Unit 4, The Old Boatyard, Church Broughton Road, Foston, Derby, DE65 5PW Tel: (01283) 810015 Fax: (01283) 814474 E-mail: sales@a50officefurniture.co.uk *Specialising in new furniture and good quality second hand office furniture. Experts in supplying chairs for back pain sufferers, with prices to suit most budgets. Family owned and*

continued

run business with its own delivery and installation service.

A6 Gates, Unit 1, Causeway Mill Longcauseway, Farnworth, Bolton, BL4 9BQ Tel: 01204 701690 Fax: 01204 701690 *Gate manufrs*

A76 Plant & Tool Hire Ltd, 203-205 Etruria Road, Stoke-on-Trent, ST1 5NS Tel: (01782) 858998 Fax: (01782) 858999 *Tool & plant hire services*

▶ Aa Computer Hardware, 975 Lincoln Road, Peterborough, PE4 6AF Tel: (01733) 326444 Fax: (01733) 326444 *Computer systems & hardware suppliers*

Aa Computer Maintenance Ltd, 4 Edge Business Centre, Humber Road, London, NW2 6EW Tel: (020) 8452 8033 Fax: (020) 8450 6360 *Computer maintenance service providers*

Aa Computer Repair Centre, 1 Bridle Road, Bootle, Merseyside, L30 4XR Tel: 0151-524 2524 Fax: 0151-524 1010 *Computer services*

▶ AA Computer Solutions, 173 Northview, Swanley, Kent, BR8 7TB Tel: (01322) 664774 *Computer maintenance & repair services*

AA Removals, 64 Ridge Road, Crouch End, London, N8 9LH Tel: (07845) 783589 E-mail: rachel_taylor_007@hotmail.com *Moving flat? moving stuff? want something collected and delivered? Transit Van (Hi Top) and driver based in North London. £30 for the first hour £15 per hour after that. Plus £1 per mile. *Reliable, punctual, efficient,friendly service. **Longer distances covered. **

AAA Aardvark Locksmiths, Unit 9, Solihull Road, Shirley, Solihull, West Midlands, B90 3HB Tel: (0845) 0710128 E-mail: aardvark@raygibbins.wanadoo.co.uk *24 hour locksmith services.No callout charge.Lockouts.Burglaries.Lost keys.Lock fitting.Upvc specialists.Oap and student discounts.Fast,friendly 1 hour service.*

▶ AAA Aardvark Locksmiths, Unit 8, Station Road, Studley, West Midlands, B80 7HS Tel: (0845) 0760710 E-mail: molly@raygibbins.wanadoo.co.uk *24 HOUR EMERGENCY LOCKSMITHS.No callout charge.Local engineers.Senior and student discounts.Upvc specialists.Yale and mortice locks fitted.1 hour service.Fast, friendly service.Lockouts.Security surveys.*

Aaa Badges Of Quality, Tumble Weed House, Hamsterley, Bishop Auckland, County Durham, DL13 3RA Tel: (01388) 488733 Fax: (01388) 488048 E-mail: sales@aaabadgesofquality.co.uk *Enamel badge suppliers*

Aaa Fabrication, 1 Pottery Demolition SD, Burnham Street, Stoke-on-Trent, ST4 3EZ Tel: (01782) 332493 Fax: (01782) 327091 E-mail: aaafabricationukltd@hotmail.co.uk *We have the skilled experience, the machinery and more so the skilled work force to manufacture your sheet metal work, from proto-types through to production runs. Your requirements will be handled professionally from the minute of contact with unbeatable price and quality. We have now installed state of the art JET-CAM computer controlled sheet metal working machinery to enable us to offer you the very best quality, service and reliability.*

Aaa Training Co., East Anglian Training Centre, 9 Churchfield Road, Sudbury, Suffolk, CO10 2YA Tel: (0800) 5878063 Fax: (01787) 313113 E-mail: sales@aaa-training.com *Training company*

▶ Aaa V Systems Ltd, Unit 28 City Industrial Units, Crafton St West, Leicester, LE1 2DE Tel: 0116-262 7818 Fax: 0116-262 7818 E-mail: sales@aaavsystems.co.uk *Design, program, commissioning & servicing of control & audio visual systems*

Aaaa Aardvark, 24 School Lane, Solihull, West Midlands, B91 2QQ Tel: (0845) 0710125 E-mail: spud@raygibbins.wanadoo.co.uk *24 Hour Emergency Locksmiths.Lockouts.Mortice and yale locks fitted.Vehicle opening.Senior and student discounts.local engineers.Fast, friendly serviceUPVC specialists.*

▶ AAAA Pest Control, 9 Glorat Avenue, Lennoxtown, Glasgow, G66 7DP Tel: (01360) 310977 E-mail: rogie87@fsmail.net *Environmental services including rodent vermin and insect pest control.**ADAS accredited.*

Aaask Innobative Solutions, The Gap, Hafod Moor, Gwernaffield, Mold, Clwyd, CH7 5ET Tel: 0141-616 3333 Fax: 0141-639 5895 E-mail: sales@aaask.com *Banner & flag manufrs*

Aable Roller Shutters, Barnes Street, Barrhead, Glasgow, G78 1QN Tel: 0141-881 8216 Fax: 0141-880 5088 E-mail: sales@aable-shutters.co.uk *Roller shutter manufrs*

Aacorn Engineering, Earlswood Trading Estate, Poolhead Lane, Earlswood, Solihull, West Midlands, B94 5EW Tel: (01564) 703545 Fax: (01564) 703511 E-mail: mail@aacorn-engineering.freeserve.co.uk *Zinc die toolmakers*

▶ Aacorn Joinery & Design Ltd, 2 Balaclava Place, Bridport, Dorset, DT6 3PE Tel: (01308) 456217 Fax: (01308) 424511 E-mail: sales@aacornjoinery.co.uk *Joiners*

Aad Logistics Ltd, Unit 49b Atcham Industrial Estate, Upton Magna, Shrewsbury, SY4 4UG Tel: (01743) 761992 Fax: (01743) 761993

Aadvark, 242 Gosport Road, Fareham, Hampshire, PO16 0SS Tel: (01329) 822515 Fax: (01329) 823630 *Industrial cleaning services*

▶ Aaf, Unit D1 Royal Pennine Trading Estate, Lynroyle Way, Rochdale, Lancashire, OL11 3EX Tel: (01706) 869238 Fax: (01706) 860059

Aah Pharmaceuticals Ltd, Woburn Road, Warrington, WA2 8UH Tel: (01925) 240444 Fax: (01925) 230255 *Pharmaceutical distributors or agents*

Aairecool Technical Services Ltd, 3 Eastfield Farm Road, Penicuik, Midlothian, EH26 8EZ Tel: (01968) 679365 Fax: (01968) 679316 E-mail: aairecool@btconnect.com *Air conditioning & refrigeration system suppliers*

Aalmar Surveys Ltd, 32-38 Dukes Place, London, EC3A 7LP Tel: (020) 7929 1401 Fax: (020) 7626 3775 E-mail: info@aalmar.com *Marine surveyors*

Aalpha Solutions (North West) Ltd, 169 Cross Green Lane, Cross Green, Leeds, LS9 0BD Tel: 0113-249 6900 Fax: 0113-249 6906 E-mail: info@aalphasolutions.co.uk *With our dedicated, industry specialist consultants dealing with every new candidate, we are one step away from getting you the job that you truly feel will benefit you, progress your experiences and offer the career fullfillment you are seeking.*

▶ AAMdesign.co.uk, 80 Heath Road, Locks Heath, Southampton, SO31 6PJ Tel: 01489 605337 E-mail: andy.moore@aamdesign.co.uk *Corporate Literature, Technical Publications, Graphic Design, Web Design and Photo Retouching*

▶ Aanco Glass Windows & Conservatories Ltd, Lustrum Avenue, Portrack Lane, Stockton-On-Tees, Cleveland, TS18 2RB Tel: (01642) 612204 *Double glazing*

Aar Dee Locks & Shutters Ltd, 16 Boswell Square, Hillington, Hillington Industrial Estate, Glasgow, G52 4BQ Tel: 0141-810 3444 Fax: 0141-810 3777 E-mail: sales@aaree.co.uk *Security engineers*

▶ Aaran Sheet Metal Ltd, Unit 6 Crossley Hall Works, York Street, Bradford, West Yorkshire, BD8 0HR Tel: (01274) 549100 Fax: (01274) 549300 E-mail: aaranmetal@aol.com *Sheet metal fabrication*

Aarchive Film Productions, 26 St. Johns Drive, Plymouth, PL9 9SB Tel: (01752) 404296 E-mail: enquiries@aarchive.co.uk *Video producers*

Aarcweld Scotland Ltd, 7 Rennie Place, East Kilbride, Glasgow, G74 5HD Tel: (01355) 244545 Fax: (01355) 244589 E-mail: sales@aarcweld.co.uk *Mezzanine floor platform constructors*

Aardvark Couriers, 206 Thornbridge Avenue, Birmingham, B42 2AH Tel: 0121-360 5253 *Courier services*

Aardvark Electrical Repairs, 22 Commercial Street, Pontnewydd, Cwmbran, Gwent, NP44 1DZ Tel: (01633) 875381 Fax: (01633) 873101 E-mail: simon.ardvark@virgin.net *Electrical repairs services*

▶ Aardvark Locksmiths, 604a Bristol Road, Selly Oak, Birmingham, B29 6BQ Tel: (0845) 0760724 E-mail: buddy@raygibbins.wanadoo.co.uk *24 Hour Emergency Locksmiths.No callout charge.1 Hour service.Lockouts.Upvc specialists,Yale and mortice locks fitted and replaced.LOCAL ENGINEERS.Fast, friendly service.Vehicle opening.Senior and student discounts.**

▶ Aardvark Locksmiths, Unit 19 Pochard Close, Kidderminster, Worcestershire, DY10 4UB Tel: (01562) 750077 E-mail: ray@raygibbins.wanadoo.co.uk *24 hour locksmith services*

Aardvark Pest Control Services, 25 Wheatley Close, Welwyn Garden City, Hertfordshire, AL7 3LJ Tel: (01707) 339183 Fax: (01707) 895886 *Pest control services*

Aardvark Roofing, 80 Swain House Road, Bradford, West Yorkshire, BD2 1JW Tel: (0800) 0193769 E-mail: info@aardvark-roofing.co.uk *Roofing contractors & repair, EPDM rubber roof specialist 20yr guarantee FREE quotes/estimates*

▶ Aardvark Site Investigations Ltd, Unit 7C Smallford Works, Smallford Lane, St. Albans, Hertfordshire, AL4 0SA Tel: (01727) 827375 Fax: (01727) 828098 E-mail: info@aardvarksi.com *Site investigation*

▶ Aardvark Sre Ltd, 18 Cherington Drive Tyldesley, Tyldesley, Manchester, M29 8WE Tel: (01942) 882397 E-mail: info@aardvarksre.ltd.uk *Safety risk environment specialising in high hazard industries*

Aardvark Transatlantic Ltd, 106 New Road, Ascot, Berkshire, SL5 8QH Tel: (01344) 882314 Fax: (01344) 884506 E-mail: atlmonoglass@aol.com *Thermal & acoustic insulation material manufrs*

▶ Aardvark Wisdom, 126 Station Road, Tempsford, Sandy, Bedfordshire, SG19 2AY Tel: (0870) 3500880 Fax: (0870) 3500881

Aarison Packaging, Townfoot Industrial Estate, Brampton, Cumbria, CA8 1SW Tel: (0845) 1301864 Fax: (0845) 1301864 E-mail: enq@aarison.co.uk *Manufacturers of polyethylene bags*

Aaron, Waltham Business Park, Brickyard Road, Swanmore, Southampton, SO32 2SA Tel: (01489) 892111 Fax: (01489) 892117 *Office furniture manufrs*

Aaron Blinds, B 8 Chester Road, Whitby, Ellesmere Port, CH65 6RU Tel: 0151-355 2704 Fax: 0151-355 2704 *Blind manufrs*

Aaron Manufacturing Ltd, Unit K-L Waterside, 25-27 Willis Way, Poole, Dorset, BH15 3TD Tel: (01202) 670071 Fax: (01202) 682952 E-mail: enquiries@aaronmanufacturing.co.uk *Precision engineers*

Aaron Packaging Machinery, Leeds 12 Business Park, Barras Garth Road, Leeds, LS12 4JY Tel: (07802) 886250 E-mail: sales@aaron-pack-mart.co.uk *Suppliers of new, used or fully refurbished shrink-wrapping machines*

Aaron Precision Turned Parts Ltd, 433 Thurmaston Boulevard, Leicester, LE4 9LA Tel: 0116-253 6353 Fax: 0116-251 5237 E-mail: kaby@kaby.co.uk *Precision turned parts*

Aaron Printing Ltd, Aaron House, Island Farm Avenue, West Molesey, Surrey, KT8 2RG Tel: (020) 8224 1122 Fax: (020) 8224 8624 E-mail: gary@aaronprintingltd.com *Printing services*

Aaron Roller Shutters, Unit 3 Northburn Road Industrial Estate, Coatbridge, Lanarkshire, ML5 2HY Tel: (01236) 423445 Fax: (01236) 606673 E-mail: info@aaronrollershutters.co.uk *All types of roller shutters, commercial, domestic, industrial*

Aaron White Ltd, 20 Bland Street, Sheffield, S4 8DG Tel: 0114-261 9519 Fax: 0114-261 9348 *Demolition & excavation contractors*

Aaronson Veneers, 56 Dennis Lane, Stanmore, Middlesex, HA7 4JW Tel: (020) 8954 1555 Fax: (020) 8954 1555 *Veneer merchants*

Aarron Personnel, Unit 12 Hollins Business Centre, Rowley Street, Stafford, ST16 2RH Tel: (0870) 7456587 Fax: (0870) 7456588 E-mail: lisa@kcen.co.uk *Personnel specialising in recruitment & training*

Aashish Motors, 374 High Road, London, N17 9HY Tel: (020) 8808 2407 Fax: (020) 8885 3127 *Motor spare parts suppliers*

▶ Aask Us, 1 Murdock Road, Bicester, Oxfordshire, OX26 4PP Tel: (01869) 322771 Fax: (01869) 322772 *Suspended ceiling systems contractors*

▶ Aautoclean Car Valet Services, 30 Oakdale Road, Oldbury, West Midlands, B68 8AY Tel: (07776) 194420 Fax: 0121-544 3276 E-mail: aautoclean@blueyonder.co.uk *Mobile car valeting & pressure wash services*

Aavf Co. Ltd, Clovelly Road, Bideford, Devon, EX39 3EX Tel: (01237) 475501 Fax: (01237) 479879 E-mail: sales@aavf.co.uk *Composite tubes & rods, thermoplastic, thermoset mouldings, precision machined components & insulation product manufacturers*

Aavid Thermalloy Ltd, Cheney Manor, Swindon, SN2 2QN Tel: (01793) 401400 Fax: (01793) 615396 E-mail: sales@uk.aavid.com Principal Export Areas: Worldwide *Thermal heat suppliers*

Aaxico Europe, 84 Station Road, Petersfield, Hampshire, GU31 4AH Tel: (01730) 268641 Fax: (01730) 268701 E-mail: sales@aaxico.com *Aircraft spares distributors*

A-B Accessories, 93 Ilchester Rd, Yeovil, Somerset, BA21 3BJ Tel: (08707) 450976 Fax: (01935) 434100 E-mail: andy@abaccessories.co.uk *Sales of mobile phones & accessories*

▶ AB Aerial ,Satellite & Security, 45 School Lane, Herne Bay, Kent, CT6 7AL Tel: (01227) 360489 E-mail: info@abaerials.com *Antenna security communication service*

▶ Ab CD Solutions, 7 Bower Road, Wrecclesham, Farnham, Surrey, GU10 4ST Tel: (01252) 793577 Fax: (01252) 795146 E-mail: sales@ab-cd.co.uk *CD & DVD duplication & printing services*

▶ AB Clearspan Marquees, Chapel House, Chapel Road, Plumpton Green, Lewes, East Sussex, BN7 3DD Tel: (01273) 891511 E-mail: info@abcmarquees.co.uk *ABC Marquees near Brighton, Sussex: quality marquee hire for weddings, parties & corporate events in Sussex, Kent, Surrey & Berkshire.*

Ab Graphic International, Carnaby Industrial Estate, Lancaster Road, Carnaby, Bridlington, North Humberside, YO15 3QY Tel: (01262) 671138 Fax: (01262) 606359 E-mail: info@abgint.com *Label printing machinery suppliers.*

Ab Light Engineering, Hollygrove Farm, Upper Northam Drive, Hedge End, Southampton, SO30 4BG Tel: (023) 8046 6657 Fax: (023) 8046 6657 *Welding & fabrication services*

Ab Services, 14 Carmyle Avenue, Glasgow, G32 8HJ Tel: 0141-764 1130 Fax: 0141-764 1131 E-mail: enquires@thefanman.co.uk *Ventilation equipment*

▶ Ab Welding, 13 Mode Wheel Road South, Salford, M50 1DG Tel: 0161-877 5757 E-mail: sales@abweld.co.uk *STEEL FABRICATION*CONTRACTORS*

▶ Aba Foods, 6 Morrison Yard, 551a High Road, London, N17 6SB Tel: (020) 8885 2710 Fax: (020) 8959 6062 *Manufacturers of food products*

Aba Key Ltd, 5 Spring Garden Lane, Gosport, Hampshire, PO12 1HY Tel: (023) 9251 1617 Fax: (023) 9251 1416 E-mail: abakey@dhbaccountants.co.uk *Computerised book-keeping & trainers*

▶ ABA Training Ltd, South Suffolk Business Centre, Alexandra Road, Sudbury, Suffolk, CO10 2ZX Tel: 01787 377988 Fax: 01787 377988 E-mail: info@aba-training.com *Tailor-made training to meet your business needs, with effective follow up, to ensure it makes a difference:-**Management Development Programmes**Team Building Courses**Coaching for senior managers**Motivation and Delegation Skills**Dealing with Dificult People**Appraisal Skills**Creative Problem Solving**Customer Service Skills*and much more....**

Abaca Engineering, Unit 2, Jackson Road, Holbrooks, Coventry, CV6 4BT Tel: (024) 7666 7390 Fax: (024) 7668 2845 E-mail: sales@abacaengineering.co.uk *Tube manipulators, metal fabricators, general engineers*

▶ Abacab Sound, Cambridge Road, Whetstone, Leicester, LE8 6LH Tel: 0116-286 7123 Fax: 0116-286 7123 E-mail: rockflightcases@aol.com *Manufacturers of flight cases*

Abacas Electrical Supplies Ltd, Unit 3 Anthonys Way, Medway City Estate, Rochester, Kent, ME2 4NW Tel: (01634) 714468 Fax: (01634) 714480 E-mail: sales@abacuselectricalsupplies.co.uk *Electrical wholesalers & suppliers*

Abachem Engineering Ltd, Jessop Way, Newark, Nottinghamshire, NG24 2ER Tel: (01636) 676483 Fax: (01636) 708632 *Abattoir & wind pump equipment suppliers*

Abaco Industrial Tapes, Marnic House, 37 Shooters Hill Road, Blackheath, London, SE3 7HS Tel: (020) 8858 8100 Fax: (020) 8305 1401 E-mail: tapes@marnic.com *Adhesive tape & scrim distributors*

Abacon Ltd, 2 Atlas Way, Sheffield, S4 7QQ Tel: 0114-256 2266 Fax: 0114-256 2268 E-mail: sales@abacon.co.uk *Abrasive products manufrs*

Abacus, 93 Woodfield Road, Hadleigh, Benfleet, Essex, SS7 2ES Tel: (01702) 552354 Fax: 01702 551658 *Blinds*

Abacus, Unit 29, Ardent Way, Mountheath Industrial Park, Prestwich, Manchester, M25 9WE Tel: 0161-773 7594 Fax: 0161-773 0093 E-mail: info@abacusweighing.com *Weighing services*

Abacus, Omnicom House, 2 Alexandra Road, Reading, RG1 5PE Tel: 0118-376 6664 Fax: 0118-376 6660 E-mail: sales@abacus-billing.com *Telecommunications software*

▶ Abacus Agents Ltd, Faraday Street, Dryburgh Industrial Estate, Dundee, DD2 3UG Tel: (01382) 884000 Fax: (01382) 818881 E-mail: enquiries@abacusagents.co.uk *Glass & glazing industry distributors*

Abacus Aquameter Ltd, 8 Woodlands Drive, Hoddesdon, Hertfordshire, EN11 8AZ Tel: (01992) 442861 Fax: (01992) 467919 E-mail: info@abacusaquameter.com *Food processing equipment manufrs*

Abacus Automation, Seaview House, The Parade, Parkgate, Neston, CH64 6SB Tel: 0151-336 7754 Fax: 0151-336 7548 E-mail: mail@abacusautomation.co.uk *Automation system manufrs*

Abacus Building Components, Manor House, Rise Road, Skirlaugh, Hull, HU11 5QH Tel: (01964) 533720 Fax: (01964) 535958 E-mail: abacuscomp@aol.com *Cloakroom equipment & sliding partitions manufrs*

abacus Careerwear Ltd, Unit D6 Newton Business Park, Cartwright Street, Hyde, Cheshire, SK14 4EH Tel: 0161-351 1211 Fax: 0161-367 8819 E-mail: alan@abacus-careerwear.co.uk *Blouse & shirt manufrs*

Abacus Choice, Rooks Street, Cottenham, Cambridge, CB24 8QZ Tel: (01954) 287070 Fax: (01954) 252078 *Electronic component distributors*

Abacus Computer Systems, 97 Bryant Road, Rochester, Kent, ME2 3ES Tel: (01634) 291310 Fax: (01634) 717569 E-mail: sales@abacusjb.co.uk *Computer retailers*

Abacus Crime Prevention, 17 Staverton Close, Bracknell, Berkshire, RG42 2HH Tel: (01344) 303606 Fax: (01344) 648765 *Security installation & repair*

Abacus Data Management Ltd, PO Box 67, Teddington, Middlesex, TW11 8QR Tel: (020) 8977 6367 Fax: (020) 8943 9473 *Computer consultants*

Abacus Dc Ltd, 1 Russell Rd, Lee-on-the-Solent, Hants, PO13 9HR Tel: (023) 9255 2159 *Computer consultants*

Abacus Deltron, Deltron Emcon House, Hargreaves Way, Sawcliffe Industrial Park, Scunthorpe, South Humberside, DN15 8RF Tel: (01724) 273200 Fax: (01724) 270230 E-mail: info@abacus-deltron.co.uk *As part of the Abacus Group, Abacus Deltron is one of the leading distributors of electronic components in Europe. With over 180 franchises from leading manufacturers and extensive technical expertise across our portfolio of electromechanical, semiconductor and passive components, Abacus Deltron is able to meet almost any customer requirement. Well known as emech specialists for more than 25 years, our electromechanical solutions include: alarms and microphones, connectors, circuit protection, consumable items, enclosures, filters, potentiometers and encoders, positioning controls, resistors, switches and relays, thermal protection, unwound cores and accessories, wound products and transformers. As part of the Abacus Group, we can also provide access to specialist products including wired and wireless communications, displays and embedded computing products.*

▶ Abacus Developments Ltd, 1 Abacus Park, Forth Avenue Industrial Estate, Kirkcaldy, Fife, KY2 5NZ Tel: (01592) 268408 Fax: (01592) 640740

Abacus Eiger Northeast, Hall Mews, Clifford Road, Boston Spa, Wetherby, West Yorkshire, LS23 6DT Tel: (01937) 841312 Fax: (01937) 841062 *Electronic component distributors*

▶ Abacus Electrical Services Ltd, 6 High Street, Winterbourne, Bristol, BS36 1JN Tel: 0117-970 1688 Fax: (01454) 777567 E-mail: sales@abacuselectrical.co.uk

Abacus entertainment, PO Box 6213, Basildon, Essex, SS14 0AJ Tel: (01268) 412516 E-mail: fun@bouncycastle-hire.co.uk *Bouncy castle hire services*

Abacus E-Solutions Ltd, Albany House, Concorde Street, Luton, LU2 0JD Tel: (01582) 702702 Fax: (01582) 452106 E-mail: sales@abacusuk.com *Data processing services*

▶ Abacus Fire & Security, 33 Clermiston Drive, Edinburgh, EH4 7PP Tel: 0131-476 0084

▶ Abacus Gas, 35 Fordel Road, Catford, London, SE6 1XS Tel: 020 8461 3300 Fax: 020 8461 3300 E-mail: help@abacusgas.com *Central heating & gas engineers*

▶ Abacus Handling Ltd, Unit 25, Romsey Industrial Estate, Greatbridge Road, Romsey, Hants, SO51 0HR Tel: 01794 522722 Fax: 01794 519915 E-mail: abacushandling@btconnect.com *Suppliers of quality used and refurbished fork lift trucks. National servicing, hire contracts, short & long term, driver training, competitive finance arrangements with no deposit.*

▶ Abacus Healthcare Services Ltd, Radway Green Venture Park, Radway Green Road, Crewe, CW2 5PR Tel: (01270) 844260

Abacus Holdings Ltd, Oddicroft Lane, Sutton-in-Ashfield, Nottinghamshire, NG17 5FT Tel: (01623) 511111 Fax: (01623) 552133 E-mail: sales@abacuslighting.com *Exterior lighting & street furniture*

▶ Abacus Joinery, Finnimore Indust Estate, Alansways, Venn Ottery, Ottery St. Mary, Devon, EX11 1RE Tel: (01404) 811700 Fax: (01404) 811700

Abacus Leewell, 30b High Street, Langford, Biggleswade, Bedfordshire, SG18 9RR Tel: (01462) 700229 Fax: (01462) 701291 E-mail: sales@abacus-leewell.co.uk *Office machine distributors*

Abacus Lithographic Printers Ltd, 34-38 Gloucester Way, London, EC1R 0BN Tel: (020) 7278 4637 Fax: (020) 7278 8535 E-mail: sales@abacusprinting.com *General printers*

Abacus Neon Sign Maker, 30 Greenfield Road, Atherton, Manchester, M46 9LW Tel: (01942) 883622 *Neon sign manufrs*

▶ Abacus Pallet Distribution, Fruit Market, A1 Blochairn Road, Glasgow, G21 2DU Tel: 0141-552 6123 Fax: 0141-552 6123 *Reconditioners of wooden pallets*

Abacus Pine, 34 Rawmarsh Hill, Parkgate, Rotherham, South Yorkshire, S62 6EU Tel: (01709) 719509 *Pine furniture manufrs*

Abacus Plant Hire Ltd, 273 Willesden Lane, London, NW2 5JG Tel: (020) 8459 7744 *Contractors' plant hirers*

Abacus Polar plc, Cherrycourt Way, Leighton Buzzard, Bedfordshire, LU7 4YY Tel: (01525) 858000 Fax: (01525) 858102 E-mail: sales@abacus.co.uk *Electronic component distributors*

▶ Abacus Presentation Services, Unit 5 Hermitage Road, London, N4 1LZ Tel: (020) 8211 1600 Fax: (020) 8211 1600 E-mail: info@abacuspresentationservices.co.uk *Hot foil printing services*

▶ Abacus Safety Training, 7 Pennywort Grove, Harrogate, North Yorkshire, HG3 2XJ Tel: (01423) 550413 Fax: (01423) 552355 E-mail: info@abacussafetytraining.com *Forklift truck, plant operator, abrasive wheels,manual handling training*

Abacus Security Systems, 1a Bowdon Avenue, Barlborough, Chesterfield, Derbyshire, S43 4JE Tel: (01246) 813800 Fax: (01246) 813800 *Security systems installation & repairs*

Abacus Security Systems, 38 Randall Road, Kenilworth, Warwickshire, CV8 1JY Tel: (01926) 851322 *Intruder alarms installation*

Abacus Services, 1 Strand, Torquay, TQ1 2AA Tel: (01803) 211187 Fax: (01803) 290648 *Accountants*

Abacus Signs, L4a Unit Colchester Estate, Colchester Avenue, Penylan, Cardiff, CF23 9AP Tel: (029) 2046 5030 Fax: (029) 2048 7376 E-mail: sales@abucussigns.co.uk *Silk screen printers & sign makers*

Abacus Software Ltd, 6-14 Underwood Street, London, N1 7JQ Tel: (020) 7549 2500 Fax: (020) 7549 2501 E-mail: info@abacusemedia.com *Software house*

Abacus Weighing Services, Unit 3B, Barlow Street, Walkden, Manchester, M28 3BQ Tel: 0161-799 7131 Fax: 0161-799 7140 E-mail: info@abacusweighing.co.uk *Weighing systems distributors*

Abakhan Fabrics, Llanerch-y-Mor, Holywell, Clwyd, CH8 9DX Tel: (01745) 562101 Fax: (01745) 562101 E-mail: enquiries@abakhan-fabricsfirst.co.uk *Textile merchants* Also at: Birkenhead, Liverpool & Manchester

Abaloid Plastics Ltd, 165 Scudamore Road, Leicester, LE3 1UQ Tel: 0116-232 0212 Fax: 0116-232 0569 E-mail: enquiries@abaloidplastics.co.uk *Injection mould toolmakers*

Abas Rope Co., Eldorado Works, Drake Avenue, Gresham Road, Staines, Middlesex, TW18 2AP Tel: (01784) 464447 Fax: (01784) 454788 E-mail: sales@splicingallied.com *Lifting equipment manufrs*

Abastra Asbestos Removal Service Ltd, 19 Leigham Ave, London, SW16 2PT Tel: (020) 8677 4455 Fax: (020) 8677 4222 E-mail: eharrington@abastra.co.uk *Asbestoes removal contractors/surveys/consultancy*

▶ Abate, Caydon Cottage, Kingsteignton, Newton Abbot, Devon, TQ12 3QD Tel: (0800) 0286689 E-mail: nathanhill@blueyonder.co.uk *Pest controllers*

▶ Abate Ltd, Mill House, Browick Road, Wymondham, Norfolk, NR18 0QW Tel: (01953) 603390 Fax: (01603) 852533 E-mail: abatelimited@tiscali.co.uk *Pest control services*

Abatec Staff Consultants plc, Abatec House, Old Mixon Cresent, Weston-super-Mare, Avon, BS24 9AX Tel: (01934) 635025 Fax: (01934) 419999 E-mail: mail@abatec.co.uk *Engineering employment agency*

Abatron Ltd, 24 Chapel Street, Potton, Sandy, Bedfordshire, SG19 2PT Tel: (01767) 261333 Fax: (01767) 262205 *Contact lens care distributor & manufrs*

ABB Ltd, 21-25 Commerce Street, Maritime Centre, Aberdeen, AB11 5FE Tel: (01224) 592123 Fax: (01224) 592690 E-mail: lynn.boyne@gb.abb.com Principal Export Areas: Worldwide *Marine electrical contractors, equipment suppliers & distributors*

ABB Ltd, Grovelands House, Longford Road, Coventry, CV7 9ND Tel: (024) 7636 8500 Fax: (024) 7636 4499 E-mail: info@gb.abb.com *ABB is a leader in power and automation technologies that enable utility and industry customers to improve performance while lowering environmental impacts.*

ABB Limited, East Kingsway, Dundee, DD4 7RP Tel: (01382) 454500 Fax: (01382) 457305 *Fusegear (industrial) & transformer manufrs*

Abb, Rossmore Road East, Ellesmere Port, CH65 3DD Tel: 0151-357 8400 Fax: 0151-355 9137 *Power factor correction equipment manufrs*

Abb Vetco Gray UK Ltd, Gapton Hall Road, Great Yarmouth, Norfolk, NR31 0NL Tel: (01493) 444777 Fax: (01493) 414221 E-mail: shaun.bradley@vetco.com *Suppliers of jack-up drilling equipment*

Abba Blinds Ltd, Unit 8 Old Mill Park, Kirkintilloch, Glasgow, G66 1SP Tel: 0141-777 7598 Fax: 0141-775 2500 *Blind manufrs*

Abba Consultants, Calamare, Holly Close, Woking, Surrey, GU21 7QZ Tel: (01483) 833021 Fax: (01483) 833022 *Computer consultancy*

▶ Abba Hire, Delbro House, Factory Road, Sealand, Deeside, Clwyd, CH5 2QJ Tel: (01244) 531986 Fax: (01244) 531986 E-mail: info@abbahire.co.uk *Tool hire & sales*

Abba Loos, Brynolwg, Bontgoch, Talybont, Dyfed, SY24 5DP Tel: (01970) 832960 Fax: (01970) 832081 *Portable toilet hirers*

Abba Party Land, 1a Greenford Avenue, Southall, Middlesex, UB1 2AA Tel: (020) 8574 8275 Fax: (020) 8574 6036 *Catering equipment hire services*

▶ Abbaballoons, 122 Forester Road, Crawley, West Sussex, RH10 6EF Tel: (01293) 611260 Fax: *Balloons & party decorations*

Abbas Cabins, 30 Crow Lane, Crow, Ringwood, Hampshire, BH24 3DZ Tel: (01202) 590008 Fax: (01202) 331963 E-mail: enquiries@abbascabins.co.uk *Chemical toilets & port a cabin hire services*

▶ abbasco., 255 PRINGLE ST., QUEENS PARK, Blackburn, BB1 1TR Tel: (07949) 617654 E-mail: abbasco@hotmail.co.uk *Maketing & Management Consultants promoting products & services through the U.K.*

▶ Abberley Ltd, Unit 7, Roach View, Millhead Way, Rochford, Essex, SS4 1LB Tel: (01702) 533761 Fax: (01702) 533760 *Memory foam mattresses & mattress toppers manufrs*

▶ Abberley Foam Products Ltd, Unit 7 Roach View, Millhead Way, Purdeys Industrial Estate, Rochford, Essex, SS4 1LB Tel: (01702) 533761 Fax: (01702) 533760 E-mail: mailbox@abberley-limited.co.uk *Foam Conversion* Manufacturer of Electric Beds* Mattress Maker**

Abbeville Instrument Control Ltd, Bridge Street, Derby, DE1 3LA Tel: (01332) 371138 Fax: (01332) 291668 E-mail: sales@aicderby.co.uk *Instrument & combustion engineers*

Abbey Angling & Aquatic Centre, 54b High Street, Hanham, Bristol, BS15 3DR Tel: 0117-985 5448 Fax: 0117-908 1130 *Angling & aquatic centre*

Abbey Architectural Ironmongery Co Ltd, Unit 12 Linguard Business Park, Wood Street, Rochdale, Lancashire, OL16 5QN Tel: (01706) 644880 Fax: (01706) 711122 E-mail: sales@abbeyarchitectural.co.uk *Architectural ironmongery wholesalers*

▶ Abbey Attachments Ltd, Unit 7, Croft Lane Industrial Estate, Pilsworth, Bury, Lancashire, BL9 8QG Tel: 0161-766 8885 Fax: 0161-767 9017 E-mail: sales@abbey-attachments.co.uk *Specialists in Forklift Truck Attachments. Abbey Attachments is one of the UK"s leading specialists in the supply of new and reconditioned lift truck attachments. Hire, Sales & Service, all under one roof. Carton clamps, Bale clamps, Pulp clamps, Paper Roll clamps, Double Pallet handlers, Push pull units, Rotators, Fork calmps, Pallet inverters, Keg clamps, Foam clamps, Reach & Roller forks, Camera Systems,*

Abbey Blinds, 31 St Nicholas Street, Ipswich, IP1 1TW Tel: (01473) 254591 Fax: (01359) 271340 *Blinds manufrs*

▶ Abbey Blinds & Shading, 6 Chandler Court, Tolworth Rise South, Surbiton, Surrey, KT5 9NN Tel: (020) 8330 4558 Fax: (020) 8335 3908 *Manufacturers & retailers of blinds, curtains & film*

Abbey Board, Cromwell House, Altendiez Way, Burton Latimer, Kettering, Northamptonshire, NN15 5YZ Tel: (01536) 420055 Fax: (01536) 421726 E-mail: sales@abbeyboard.co.uk *Corrugated cardboard sheet manufrs*

Abbey Business Machines, 13-15 Oakford, Kingsteignton, Newton Abbot, Devon, TQ12 3EQ Tel: (01626) 202502 Fax: (01626) 202503 E-mail: sales@abbeybusinessmachines.co.uk *Business machines suppliers*

▶ Abbey Cakes Ltd, 29 Alston Drive, Bradwell Abbey, Milton Keynes, MK13 9HA Tel: (01908) 311622 Fax: (01908) 226128 *Produce gingerbread & chocolate products*

Abbey Case Co. Ltd, Britannia Road, Waltham Cross, Hertfordshire, EN8 7NZ Tel: (01992) 715996 Fax: (01992) 719852 E-mail: sales@abbeycase.co.uk *Packing case makers*

Abbey Central, 90 Croydon Road, Beckenham, Kent, BR3 4DF Tel: (020) 8650 2456 Fax: (020) 8650 2456 *Second-hand office furniture sales*

▶ Abbey Chauffeur Services, 299 Southwell Road East, Rainworth, Mansfield, Nottinghamshire, NG21 0BL Tel: (01623) 794406 Fax: E-mail: sales@abbey-chauffeurs.co.uk *Chauffeur services*

▶ Abbey Contractors Ltd, Haydock Park Road, Derby, DE24 8HT Tel: (01332) 291646

Abbey Craftsmen, 127 Haslemere Road, Liphook, Hampshire, GU30 7BX Tel: (01428) 727187 Fax: (0800) 0561362 E-mail: terry@abbey.go-plus.net *Plastic & metal nameplate manufrs*

▶ Abbey Dental Laboratory, 56 Orford Lane, Warrington, WA2 7AF Tel: (01925) 232032 Fax: (01925) 629558 *Medical & surgical supplies*

Abbey Design, Unit 4/5, Glen Trading Estate, Wellyhole Street, Oldham, OL4 3BF Tel: 0161-620 8295 Fax: 0161-785 0130 E-mail: sales@abbeydesign.cc *Coating & laminating machinery designers & manufrs*

Abbey Design Ltd, Lakeside Trading Centre, Beoley Road East, Redditch, Worcestershire, B98 8PE Tel: (01527) 585888 Fax: (01527) 596334 E-mail: sales@systematicdisplays.co.uk *Exhibition design & manufrs*

Abbey Developments Ltd, Abbey House, 2 Southgate Road, Potters Bar, Hertfordshire, EN6 5DU Tel: (01707) 651266 Fax: (01707) 646836 *Building contractors & maintenance services*

Abbey Die & Tool Ltd, Bentley Mill Close, Walsall, WS2 0BN Tel: (01922) 626545 Fax: (01922) 721717 E-mail: sales@abbeydieandtool.co.uk *Manufacture of pressure dies, gravity dies*

▶ Abbey Direct Print, B2 Manor Way Business Park, Manor Way, Swanscombe, Kent, DA10 0PP Tel: (01322) 380191 Fax: (01322) 382066 E-mail: sales@abbeygroup.co.uk

Abbey Electronic Controls, 21 Fleet Street, Wigan, Lancashire, WN5 0DU Tel: (01942) 227652 Fax: (01942) 227653 E-mail: enquiries@abbeyltd.com *Sensors, controllers & filters*

▶ Abbey Electronics, Unit 11 Whalley Industrial Park, Clitheroe Road, Barrow, Clitheroe, Lancashire, BB7 9WP Tel: (01254) 825759 Fax: (0870) 0558951 E-mail: admin@abbeyeectronics.com *Designers & builders of special purpose machinery*

Abbey Engraving, Unit 15 New Horizon Business Centre, Barrows Road, Harlow, Essex, CM19 5FN Tel: (01279) 626277 Fax: (01279) 626277 E-mail: info@abbeyengraving.co.uk *Engravers*

Abbey Extrusions Ltd, 2 Ivanhoe Industrial Estate, Tournament Way, Ashby-de-la-Zouch, Leicestershire, LE65 2UU Tel: (01530) 416177 Fax: (01530) 417230 E-mail: sales@abbeyextrusions.co.uk Principal Export Areas: Worldwide *Manufacturers of PVC extrusions, plastic extrusions & plastic hoses*

Abbey Fencing, 4 Foxholes Road, Leicester, LE3 1TH Tel: 0116-287 7795 *Fencing distributors*

Abbey Fire, 22 Willow Court, West Quay Road, Winwick, Warrington, WA2 8UF Tel: (0870) 2099920 Fax: (01925) 423735 E-mail: sales@abbeyfireuk.co.uk *Fire equipment suppliers & maintenance services*

Abbey Forwarding Ltd, 50 Purland Road, Nathan Way, London, SE28 0AT Tel: (020) 8311 4222 Fax: (020) 8310 1859 E-mail: admin@abbeyforwarding.co.uk *Freight forwarders*

Abbey Furnishing Ltd, Unit 1a The Distribution Centre, Stoke Road, Stoke Orchard, Cheltenham, Gloucestershire, GL52 7RS Tel: (01242) 673555 Fax: (01242) 673666 E-mail: info@abbey-furnishings.co.uk *Contract furniture suppliers & manufactures.*

Abbey Gauge Co. Ltd, 139-141 Becontree Avenue, Dagenham, Essex, RM8 2UL Tel: (020) 8590 3233 Fax: (020) 8590 5082 E-mail: sales@abbeygauge.co.uk *Pressure gauge & thermometer repairs & manufrs*

▶ Abbey Grit Blasting Services, Unit 13 Clopton Commercial Park, Woodbridge, Suffolk, IP13 6QT Tel: (01473) 737788 Fax: (01473) 737788 E-mail: abbeygrit@aol.com *Blast Cleaning,BeadBlasting, Sandblasting,gritblasting, shotblasting,Hydro blasting, commercial paint spraying,epoxy coatings, structural steel preparation ,plant & machinery , pressure washing.*We undertaken jobs large or small, free quotations given. Est 1984*

▶ Abbey Group Motors, 32 Abbey Foregate, Shrewsbury, SY2 6BT Tel: 01743 242888 *Used car dealers*

Abbey Heat Transfer Ltd, Unit 6 Parham Drive, Eastleigh, Hampshire, SO50 4NU Tel: (023) 8065 3331 Fax: (023) 8065 3332 E-mail: hugh@abbeyheat.co.uk *Heat exchanger repair & manufrs*

▶ Abbey Interior Systems Ltd, 82a High Street, Cosham, Portsmouth, PO6 3AJ Tel: 023 92325355 Fax: 023 92325355 E-mail: abbeyinterior@hotmail.com

▶ Abbey IT Consultants, Lafone House, 11-13 Leathermarket Street, London, SE1 3HN Tel: (020) 7378 6616 *IT consultants*

Abbey Janitorial, Abbey House, Derry Street, Wolverhampton, WV2 1EY Tel: (01902) 838700 Fax: (01902) 835202 *Contract cleaners*

▶ Abbey Joinery, Swingbridge Yard, Wincolmlee, Hull, HU5 1RH Tel: (01482) 586008 Fax: (01482) 581606 E-mail: rita@wrshull.com

Abbey Life Assurance Co. Ltd, 80 Holdenhurst Road, Bournemouth, BH8 8ZQ Tel: (01202) 292373 Fax: (01202) 293159 *Life assurance, mortgages & investmets*

▶ Abbey Locksmiths, 54 Halsey Park, London Colney, St. Albans, Hertfordshire, AL2 1BH Tel: (01727) 828048 Fax: (07092) 003147 E-mail: service@abbeylocks.co.uk *British locksmith association approved company, police registered*

Abbey Lodge Hotel, 38 Belfast Road, Downpatrick, County Down, BT30 9AU Tel: (028) 4461 4511 Fax: (028) 4461 6415 *Hotel*

▶ ABBEY MANUFACTURING, UNIT 2 TATES, AVIS WAY, NEWHAVEN, EAST SUSSEX, BN9 0DH Tel: 01273 513100 Fax: 01273 513100 E-mail: info.abbey@btconnect.com *Manufacturer of medical, industrial and mobile weighing systems.*

Abbey Mews Builders Ltd, 618 Harrow Road, London, W10 4NJ Tel: (020) 8969 2449 Fax: (020) 8960 5090 *Building contractors*

ABBEY PLANT HIRE, Great Frenchstone, South Molton, DEVON, EX36 4JH Tel: (01769) 579460 E-mail: admin@graysplanthire.co.uk *Mini digger hire all sizes.*Dumpers from 1 ton hi tip to 3 tons Great rates*

Abbey Plastics Ltd, Unit 4 Orbital Centre, Southend Road, Woodford Green, Essex, IG8 8HD Tel: (020) 8551 8000 Fax: (020) 8551 8453 E-mail: sales@abbeyplastics.com *PVC binders & folders manufrs*

Abbey Plastics & Tooling Ltd, Unit 8, 108 Nathan Way, London, SE28 0AQ Tel: (020) 8316 4333 Fax: (020) 8316 4333 *Injection mould toolmaking & plastic injection*

Abbey Polymers Ltd, Innovation Centre, Staffordshire Technology Park, Stafford, ST18 0AR Tel: (01785) 241343 Fax: (01785) 241340 *Plastic raw material distributors*

Abbey Precision Ltd, 72 Alston Drive, Bradwell Abbey, Milton Keynes, MK13 9HG Tel: (01908) 225858 Fax: (01908) 225848 E-mail: sales@abbeyprecision.com *Precision engineers*

▶ Abbey Printers Of Bradford Ltd, Robin Mills, Leeds Road, Idle, Bradford, West Yorkshire, BD10 9TE Tel: (01274) 620238 Fax: (01274) 612964 E-mail: sales@abbeyprinters.co.uk *Print agents*

Abbey Products Norfolk Ltd, Ayton Road, Wymondham, Norfolk, NR18 0QH Tel: (01953) 602627 Fax: (01953) 601428 E-mail: info@abbey4pu.com *Engineer pattern manufrs*

Abbey Products Toolmakers, 14 Ashville Way, Whetstone, Leicester, LE8 6NU Tel: 0116-286 1862 Fax: 0116-286 1864 E-mail: info@abbey-products.net *Vacuum forming toolmakers*

▶ Abbey Pynford plc, 7 Bridge Works, Woodhead Road, Honley, Holmfirth, HD9 6PW Tel: (01484) 660003 Fax: (01484) 660007 E-mail: admin@abbeypynford.co.uk

Abbey Racking, 1-7 Ruby Mews, Ruby Road, London, E17 4RB Tel: (020) 8521 6176 Fax: (020) 8521 2214 E-mail: sales@usedshelving.co.uk *Storage equipment & systems distributors*

▶ Abbey Roadtanks Ltd, 2 Littlefair Road, Hull, HU9 5LP Tel: (01482) 798177 Fax: (01482) 797713 E-mail: sales@abbeyroadtanks.com

Abbey Roller Shutters & Doors, Unit A-B Caxton St North, London, E16 1JL Tel: (020) 7476 4422 Fax: (020) 7476 4433 *Industrial door repairs & manufrs*

Abbey Rose Buildbase, Blackpool Road, Peckham, London, SE15 3SU Tel: (020) 7639 0138 Fax: (020) 7732 5150 E-mail: peckham@buildbase.co.uk *Buildbase is one of the UK's fastest growing builders merchants. All of our branches are long*

continued

▶ indicates data change since last edition

continuation
established companies which have been serving local trades people for many years, with knowledge and experience to match. We believe strongly in understanding the needs of trades professional and our business has been developed specifically to meet those demands. Massive stocks, top quality products, competitive pricing, reliable delivery, specialist staff and exceptional customer service.

Abbey Saddlery Ltd, Camden Street, Walsall, WS4 2AX Tel: (01565) 650343 Fax: (01565) 633825 *Britain's leading wholesale supplier of British hardware, leather & textiles for equestrian, country sports & manufacturing industries. Includes buckles, tools, webbings, tapes, rivets & dyes.*

▶ Abbey Safety Solutions Ltd, 17 Honeypot Road, Brompton on Swale, Richmond, North Yorkshire, DL10 7HT Tel: (01748) 810813 E-mail: info@assluk.com *Health, Safety and Environmental (HSE)Consultancy. Consulting on all aspects HSE - Risk Management - Policies and Procedures - Manual Handling - Dispaly Screen Equipment - Fire Risk Assessment - Legal Compliance Audits + Inspections - Accident Investigation*

Abbey Self Storage, Abbey Business Centre, Ingate Place, London, SW8 3NS Tel: (020) 7627 8000 Fax: (020) 7720 6633 *Storage contractors*

Abbey Sheetmetal Ltd, Unit 3 Apex Pk, Diplocks Way, Hailsham, East Sussex, BN27 3JF Tel: (01323) 848454 Fax: (01323) 848456 E-mail: post@abbeysheetmetal.co.uk *Manufacture & installation of air-conditioning & ventilation*

Abbey Signs, 6-8 Glentanar Place, Glasgow, G22 7XT Tel: 0141-336 3610 Fax: 0141-336 4629 E-mail: sales@abbeysigns.fsnet.co.uk *Sign manufrs*

Abbey Signs, Unit 1, The Yarn Barn, Upper Manor Road, Preston, Paignton, Devon, TQ3 2TP Tel: (01803) 559029 Fax: (01803) 666010 E-mail: sales@abbey4signs.com *Sign manufrs*

▶ Abbey Southern Ltd, 4 Warren Way, Holton Heath Trading Park, Poole, Dorset, BH16 6NJ Tel: (01202) 622226 Fax: (01202) 622866 *Upvc & aluminium window frame manufrs*

Abbey Spares & Supplies, 16g Top Barn Business Centre, Worcester Road, Holt Heath, Worcester, WR6 6NH Tel: (01905) 621666 *Testing equipment manufrs*

Abbey Stainless Steel Co Ltd, Admiral Steel Works, Sedgley Road, Sheffield, S6 2DN Tel: 0114-231 2271 Fax: 0114-232 4983 E-mail: info@abbeystainless.co.uk *Stainless steel forging stockholders & manufrs*

Abbey Steel & Shearing Co. Ltd, 5 Cartwright Road, Pin Green Industrial Area, Stevenage, Hertfordshire, SG1 4QJ Tel: (01438) 741888 Fax: (01438) 740980 E-mail: sales@abbeysteel.co.uk *Steel stockholders & sharing*

Abbey Storage & Office Systems Ltd, International House, 30 Villa Road, Benfleet, Essex, SS7 5QL Tel: (01268) 794070 Fax: (01268) 566141 E-mail: doug@abbeystorage.freeserve.co.uk *Shelving & racking distributors or agents*

Abbey Supply Co. Ltd, 8 Balena Close, Poole, Dorset, BH17 7DB Tel: (01202) 603067 Fax: (01202) 601966 *Care products manufrs*

Abbey Surgical Repairs, Silver Wing Industrial Estate, Horatius Way, Croydon, CR0 4RU Tel: (020) 8688 8555 Fax: (020) 8688 8557 E-mail: info@abbeysurgical.com *Surgical instrument repairs & suppliers of suction equipment*

Abbey Tablet, 1 High Street, Coupar Angus, Blairgowrie, Perthshire, PH13 9DB Tel: (01828) 627695 Fax: (01828) 627695 *Confectionery manufrs*

Abbey Telecom, Logic House, Ordnance Street, Blackburn, BB1 3AE Tel: (01254) 272000 Fax: (01254) 272001 E-mail: sales@abbeytelecom.co.uk *Telecommunications suppliers & installers*

Abbey Tool & Dye, Unit 11 Old Canal Wharf, Navigation Road, Stoke-on-Trent, ST6 3BL Tel: (01782) 838137 Fax: (01782) 577372 E-mail: abbeytool@aol.com *Specialist manufacturers to diecasting industry*

Abbey Tooling Ltd, Longdon Heath, Upton Upon Severn, Worcester, WR8 0RJ Tel: (01684) 592452 Fax: (01684) 592452 *Tool makers*

▶ Abbey Trading Co., 252 Seven Mile Straight, Nutts Corner, Crumlin, County Antrim, BT29 4YT Tel: (028) 9082 5000

Abbey Transmission Services Ltd, Unit 15 Sidings Industrial Estate, Hainault Road, London, E11 1HD Tel: (020) 8558 4028 Fax: (020) 8539 0312 *Gearbox repairers & rebuilders*

Abbey Transport Ltd, Concorde Road, Norwich, NR6 6BH Tel: (01603) 425928 Fax: (01603) 413333 *Machinery installations & abnormal loads*

Abbey Tyres & Tracking Services, 284 Witton Road, Birmingham, B6 6NX Tel: 0121-327 3387 Fax: 0121-327 3387 *Tyres new & part worn, supplied, fitted*

Abbey Upholsterers Ltd, 8 Abbeyville Place, Newtownabbey, County Antrim, BT37 0AQ Tel: (028) 9086 9345 Fax: (028) 9036 5034 E-mail: info@abbeyupholsterers.com *Furniture manufrs*

▶ Abbey Wedding Services, Lye Head, Bewdley, Worcestershire, DY12 2UZ Tel: (01299) 269055 Fax: (01299) 269055 E-mail: loml@lakes.wanadoo.co.uk *Lift installation, service & repair*

▶ Abbeygate, 39 Shaftesbury Crescent, Staines, Middlesex, TW18 1QL Tel: (01784) 423405 Fax: (01784) 423405

Abbeygate Diaries & Gifts, 28 Northern Way, Bury St. Edmunds, Suffolk, IP32 6NL Tel: (01284) 760044 Fax: (01284) 750077 *Promotional items manufrs*

▶ Abbeygrey Ltd, 331 Nottingham Road, Eastwood, Nottingham, NG16 2AP Tel: (01773) 769245 Fax: (01773) 533127

▶ AbbeyHill Associates, 40 Tunbridge, Emersons Green, Bristol, BS16 7EX Tel: 0117 3730098 E-mail: info@abbeyhillassociates.co.uk *Accountancy firm specialising in outsource finance services.*

▶ Abbeylite Ltd, 3 Longmead, Shaftesbury, Dorset, SP7 8PL Tel: (01747) 852583 Fax: (01747) 851169 *Light fittings*

Abbeylocks Suffolk Locksmiths, 12 Waveney Road, Bury St. Edmunds, Suffolk, IP32 6JX Tel: (01284) 700104 E-mail: abbeylocks@chason.fsnet.co.uk *Locksmith services*

Abbeystone Stone Merchants, Harbury Lane, Heathcote, Warwick, CV34 6SL Tel: (01926) 450111 Fax: (01926) 336354 *Mould making & caste stone manufrs*

Abbfab Services Ltd, Windley Street, Bolton, BL2 2AH Tel: (01204) 523441 Fax: (01204) 557930 E-mail: admin@abbfab.co.uk *General fabricators*

Abbirko UK Ltd, 4 Manor Works, Station Road South, Totton, Southampton, SO40 9HP Tel: (023) 8066 8833 Fax: (023) 8066 7777 E-mail: sales@abbirko.co.uk *Manufacturers of pressure test equipment*

Abbot Fixing Systems Ltd, Manor Farm, Bullington End Road, Hanslope, Milton Keynes, MK19 7BQ Tel: (01908) 511730 *Fixing suppliers & manufrs*

Abbot Security, Unit 4, The Courtyard, Fore Street, Saltash, Cornwall, PL12 6JR Tel: (01752) 841007 *Security systems installation*

Abbots Mead Builders, Unit 18 Bumpers Lane, Sealand Industrial Estate, Chester, CH1 4LT Tel: (01244) 374987 Fax: (01244) 375544 *Building maintenance*

Abbotsfield Metals, Abbotsfield Road, Reginald Road Industrial Estate, St. Helens, Merseyside, WA9 4HU Tel: (01744) 817474 Fax: (01744) 817474 *Scrap metal dealers*

Abbotsgate Printers, Lincoln Street, Hull, HU2 0PB Tel: (01482) 225257 Fax: (01482) 225559 E-mail: abbotsgateprint@aol.com *Printers*

▶ Abbotshall Homes Ltd, 5 Oswald Road, Kirkcaldy, Fife, KY1 3JE Tel: (01592) 653653 Fax: (01592) 653353

C. Abbott Ltd, Dane Place, 470-480 Roman Road, Bow, London, E3 5LU Tel: (020) 8980 4158 Fax: (020) 8981 3852 E-mail: info@abbottscarpets.co.uk *Carpet & flooring retailers Also at: London E3*

Abbott Diabetes Care, Abbott House, Norden Road, Maidenhead, Berkshire, SL6 4XE Tel: (01628) 773355 Fax: (01628) 644305 *Pharmaceutical company manufrs*

Abbott Fabrications Ltd, Unit 1b Woodleys Yard, Newton Road, Higham Ferrers, Rushden, Northamptonshire, NN10 8HW Tel: (01933) 419942 Fax: (01933) 411619 E-mail: enquiries@abbott-fabrications.co.uk *Sheet metal & fabrication engineers*

Abbott Group Ltd, Golden Cross, Hailsham, East Sussex, BN27 4AH Tel: (01825) 872567 Fax: (01825) 872033 E-mail: sales@abbott-group.co.uk *UPVC window & door makers*

Abbott Holliday Partnership, 9 Greens Court, Lansdowne Mews, London, W11 3AP Tel: (020) 7792 1147 Fax: (01233) 820755 E-mail: enquiries@peter-holliday.co.uk Sales Contact: P. Holliday *Structural & civil engineering consultants, consulting engineers/designers & surveyors*

Abbott Laboratories Ltd, North Road, Queenborough, Kent, ME11 5EL Tel: (01795) 580099 Fax: (01795) 593335 *Pharmaceutical chemical manufrs Also at: Maidenhead*

Abbott Mead Vickers Bbdo Ltd, 151 Marylebone Road, London, NW1 5QE Tel: (020) 7616 3500 Fax: (020) 7616 3600 E-mail: malona.a@amvbbdo.com *Holding company for an international advertising company*

Abbott Signs, 29 Victoria Road, Northampton, NN1 5ED Tel: (01604) 636793 Fax: (01604) 632302 E-mail: info@abbottsigns.co.uk *Sign manufacturers, screen printing & digital signs specialists*

Abbott Signs, Unit 12 Kendal Court, Hurricane Way, Wickford, Essex, SS11 8YB Tel: (01268) 572626 Fax: (01268) 574626 E-mail: abbotsignltd@btconnect.com *Sign manufrs*

Abbott & Co Wessex Ltd, Abberley House, Park Street, Cirencester, Gloucestershire, GL7 2BX Tel: (01285) 653738 Fax: (01285) 885134 E-mail: sales@air-receivers.co.uk *Hay & straw merchants*

Abbotts Creative Print Ltd, Turnpike Close, Bilton Way, Lutterworth, Leicestershire, LE17 4YB Tel: (01455) 552636 Fax: (01455) 551699 E-mail: info@abbottsuk.net *Lithographers creative & printers*

Abbotts Office Solutions, Station Yard, Thame, Oxfordshire, OX9 3UH Tel: (01844) 268360 Fax: (01844) 268370 E-mail: abbott@officesolutions.co.uk *Commercial stationery, computer suppliers & furniture*

Abbozzo, 24 Sandyford Place, Glasgow, G3 7NG Tel: 0141-221 5110 Fax: 0141-248 7632 E-mail: info@abbozzo.co.uk *abbozzo architects, offers bespoke architectural solutions.*contemporary architects, services include individual houses for clients*

Abbra Security, 127 Charlemont Road, London, E6 6HD Tel: (020) 8552 7160 *Security services*

Abbseal (U K) Ltd, Broadway, Broadway, Hyde, Cheshire, SK14 4QW Tel: 0161-368 5711 Fax: 0161-366 8155 *Glass processors*

Abbtex Sports, 215 Galton Road, Smethwick, West Midlands, B67 5JH Tel: 0121-429 8830 Fax: 0121-247 5772 E-mail: admin@abbtexsports.co.uk *Sports & corporate uniforms manufrs*

▶ Abc, 15 Goulburn Road, Norwich, NR7 9UX Tel: (01603) 438491 Fax: (01603) 466710 *Emergency locksmith services*

Abc Axworthy's Ltd, Cotswold House, Kingsland Trading Estate, St Phillips Road, Bristol, BS2 0JZ Tel: 0117-927 2700 Fax: 0117-927 3345 E-mail: abc@axworthys.co.uk *Office equipment suppliers*

Abc Blinds Ltd, 120 High Street, Staple Hill, Bristol, BS16 5HH Tel: 0117-957 1067 Fax: 0117-957 1067 E-mail: info@abcblinds.co.uk *Blinds, awnings & canopies retailers & manufrs*

▶ Abc Computer, Whitfield Buildings, 192-200 Pensby Road, Heswall, Wirral, Merseyside, CH60 7RJ Tel: 0151-342 2791

▶ Abc Computer Services, Highview, 5a King Edward Road, Stanford-le-Hope, Essex, SS17 0EF Tel: (01375) 404495 E-mail: sales@mitefixit.com *Computer Services, Mobile to Business/Home, Same Day Service, No Local Callout Charge, Internet Services, Friendly and Professional Service, Tuition, Advice and Guidance, Repairs to PC/Laptops*

Abc Lifting Equipment Ltd, 4 Alliance Business Park, Corporation Street, Accrington, Lancashire, BB5 0RR Tel: (01254) 233349 Fax: (01254) 233533 E-mail: sales@abclifting.co.uk *Lifting gear suppliers*

▶ Abc Macintosh Ltd, Bleak Hall Farm Bleak Lane, Hoscar Moss, Lathom, Ormskirk, Lancashire, L40 4BP Tel: (01704) 896677 E-mail: enquires@abcmacintosh.com *Firefighting chemicals manufrs*

Abcas Cleaning Services, 8 Coningham Gardens, Aberdeen, AB24 2TS Tel: (01224) 485592 *Industrial cleaning contractors*

ABCO Computer Services Ltd, Airways House, First Avenue, London Stansted Airport North, Stansted, Essex, CM24 1RY Tel: (01279) 680000 Fax: (01279) 661371 E-mail: abcopay@ndirect.co.uk **Secure, comprehensive payrolls for small to medium size companies *We can use your terms on the payslips & reports *Revenue & BACS approved *Turnaround 24 hrs *Always cost effective*

Abco Engineering Hydraulics, Mill Park, Station Road, Southwell, Nottinghamshire, NG25 0Et Tel: (01636) 812674 Fax: 01636 815448 E-mail: sales@abcohydraulics.com *Hydraulic Couplings, Hydraulic Hose Fittings, Hydraulic Components & Fittings, Hydraulic Cylinders or Rams, Hydraulic Equipment or Systems, Hydraulic Pumps, Motors & Valves, Hydraulic Oil, Hydraulic Hand Pumps, 12 & 20 Ton Commercial Pit Jacks optional 8 Ton Spreader Beam & a full range of Garage & Workshop Equipment from Bottle Jacks to M.O.T Bays available from ABCO Engineering Hydraulics based in Sothwell near Newark. Click the link below to visit our website or contact us via our profile page.*

Abco Industrial Fastners, Unit 5 The Gloucesters, Crompton Close, Basildon, Essex, SS14 3AY Tel: (01268) 520561 Fax: (01268) 534321 *Bolt, nut & fastener distributors*

Abco Janitorial Supplies, 78-90 Cheshire Street, London, E2 6EH Tel: (020) 7729 6465 Fax: (020) 7739 9400 *Janitorial supplies*

▶ Abco Lifting Equipment Ltd, Unit 11, Mundells Industrial Centre, Welwyn Garden City, Hertfordshire, AL7 1EW Tel: (01707) 328847 E-mail: liambullough@hotmail.com *Lifting gear & hoist distributors*

ABCO-Anderson Beverage Co. Ltd, Unit 6B, Chevychase Court, Seaham Grange Estate, Seaham, County Durham, SR7 0PR Tel: 0191-521 3366 Fax: 0191-521 3377 E-mail: info@abcosoftdrinks.co.uk *Suppliers of branded post mix syrups cola, food service & on-trade sites*

Abdex Hose & Couplings Ltd, Unit 3 Commerce Way, Leighton Buzzard, Bedfordshire, LU7 4RW Tel: (01525) 377770 Fax: (01525) 851990 E-mail: enquiries@abdexhose.com *Ultra high pressure hose & couplings manufrs*

▶ Abdullah Musa & Sons Ltd., Head Office: Musa House, 262 Deepdale Road, Preston, PR1 6QB Tel: 01772 700005 Fax: 01772 705550 E-mail: info@musagroup.co.uk *Wholesalers of prime quality halal meat and beef*

Abec Fixings Ltd, Unit 22 Small Heath Trading Estate, Armoury Road, Birmingham, B11 2RJ Tel: 0121-683 0061 Fax: 0121-683 0064 E-mail: sales@abecfixings.co.uk *Bolt, nut & fastener manufrs*

Abec Industrial & Engineering Ltd, Unit 10 Firsland Park Estate, Henfield Road, Albourne, Hassocks, West Sussex, BN6 9JJ Tel: (01273) 494960 Fax: (01273) 494960 E-mail: abeclimited@aol.com *Distributor of power transmission equipment*

Abee Signs London Ltd, 435 Lordship Lane, London, N22 5DH Tel: (020) 8889 6126 Fax: (020) 8888 9009 E-mail: sales@abeesigns.co.uk *Cutting self adhesive vinyl logos & lettering services*

Abel Alarm Co. Ltd, 370 West Road, Newcastle upon Tyne, NE4 9JY Tel: 0191-275 0130 Fax: 0191-274 6067 E-mail: info.newcastle@abelarm.co.uk *Installation of burglar alarms*

Abel Alarm Co. Ltd, 1a Albert Street, Oldham, OL8 3QP Tel: 0161-682 3689 Fax: 0161-684 8986 E-mail: info.manchester@abelalarm.co.uk *Alarm installers*

Abel Alarm Co. Ltd, 17 Slader Business Park, Witney Road, Nuffield Industrial Estate, Poole, Dorset, BH17 0GP Tel: (01202) 677144 Fax: (01202) 677944 E-mail: info.bournemouth@abelalarm.co.uk *Security alarm installers*

Abel Alarm Co. Ltd, 98 Addington Road, Reading, RG1 5PX Tel: 0118-935 2218 Fax: 0118-966 7277 E-mail: info.reading@abelalarm.co.uk *Alarm installation & manufrs*

Abel Alarm Co. Ltd, Unit 9 Woodside Road, South Marston Park, Swindon, SN3 4WA Tel: 01793 829312 Fax: 01793 825452 E-mail: info.swindon@abelalarm.co.uk *Install security alarms*

Abel Alarm Co Ltd, 2 Discovery House, Cook Way, Taunton, Somerset, TA2 6BJ Tel: (01823) 333868 Fax: (01823) 337852 E-mail: info.taunton@abelalarm.co.uk *Security alarm supplier & locksmith*

Abel Alarm Co. Ltd, 84 Barden Road, Tonbridge, Kent, TN9 1UB Tel: (01732) 355592 Fax: (01732) 365241 E-mail: info.tonbridge@abelalarm.co.uk *Security system installation services*

▶ Abel Building & Roofing Services, Station Road, Rowlands Gill, Tyne & Wear, NE39 1QD Tel: (01207) 544633

▶ Abel Drew Printhaus Ltd, 31 Heathfield, Stacey Bushes, Milton Keynes, MK12 6HR Tel: (01908) 227321 Fax: (01908) 227322

▶ Abel Engineering Fabrications Ltd, Unit 8 Borthwick View, Pentland Industrial Estate, Loanhead, Midlothian, EH20 9QH Tel: 0131-448 2226 Fax: 0131-440 1119 E-mail: admin@abelengineering.co.uk *Steel fabrication, steel staircases, architectural steel*

Abel Fasteners, 25 Albion Street, Rugeley, Staffordshire, WS15 2BY Tel: (01889) 586675 Fax: (01889) 586676 *Nut & bolt stockholders*

Abel Foxall Lifting Gear Ltd, Wood Street, Liverpool, L1 4LA Tel: 0151-709 6882 Fax: 0151-707 0723 E-mail: allanmolloy@rossendalegroup.co.uk *Lifting gear inspection, maintenance & repairers*

Abel & Imray, 20 Red Lion Street, London, WC1R 4PQ Tel: (020) 7242 9984 Fax: (020) 7242 9989 E-mail: ai@patentable.co.uk Principal Export Areas: Worldwide *Abel & Imray is a leading firm of Patent Attorneys and Trade Mark Attorneys with offices in London as well as Cardiff, Bath and Munich (near to the European Patent Office).**We can help you obtain (register), license, and enforce intellectual property rights, such as patents, registered trade marks, registered designs and other related rights.**Our clients range from multinationals to SMEs including well-known international clients, many of whom have been our clients for over half a century. This loyalty reflects our policy of providing high-quality service, at acceptable cost, to all clients. Our emphasis on quality has been rewarded by an excellent track record of success in even the most difficult cases. **All our Patent Agents have specialist knowledge and experience in one or more technical fields, and our patent work covers all areas of technology. We also have a strong team of trademark agents and registered design specialists.*

Abel Internet, Pentland View House Damhead, Lothianburn, Edinburgh, EH10 7DZ Tel: 0131-445 5555 Fax: (0871) 7173452 *Internet access & web design*

▶ Abela Secretarial Services, 26 Campbell Road, Maidstone, Kent, ME15 6QA Tel: 01622 210552 Fax: 01622 210552 E-mail: info@abelasecretarial.com *Virtual Assistant providing professional, remote secretarial and office support to sole traders, and small to medium sized businesses. Services offered include word processing, audio transcription, telephone answering in own company name, bookkeeping, travel, diary management, mail forwarding etc. We offer a very professional, reliable and flexible service at all times.*

A-Belco Property Ltd, Jubilee Industrial Estate, Ashington, Northumberland, NE63 8UG Tel: (01670) 813275 Fax: (01670) 851141 E-mail: sscullion@a-belco.co.uk *Manufacturer of Low voltage electrical accessories, switchgear and EMU units. Also Supply Cubicles, transformers and Points Heating for the Rail industry.*

Abell Fasteners, Unit 337 Rushock Trading Estate, Rushock, Droitwich, Worcestershire, WR9 0NR Tel: (01299) 251533 Fax: (01299) 251533 *Bolts, nuts & fasteners distributors*

Abels Moving Services Ltd, Wimbledon Avenue, Brandon, Suffolk, IP27 0NZ Tel: (01842) 816600 Fax: (01842) 813613 E-mail: enquiries@abels.co.uk *Storage & worldwide removal specialists Also at: Colchester, Darlington, Deptford, Draycott, Huntingdon & St. Albans*

Aber Instruments Ltd, Unit 5, Science Park, Aberystwyth, Dyfed, SY23 3AH Tel: (01970) 636300 Fax: (01970) 615455 E-mail: sales@abercominstruments.com *Yeast monitoring instrument manufrs*

Abercarn Constitutional Club Ltd, Bridge Street, Abercarn, Newport, Gwent, NP11 4SE Tel: (01495) 243047 Fax: (01495) 244538 *Concrete products manufrs*

Abercolwyn Fire & Security, Fron Deg, Gilfach Road, Penmaenmawr, Gwynedd, LL34 6EY Tel: (01492) 623650 Fax: (01492) 623650 *Fire alarm installers & maintainers*

Abercorn Engineering Ltd, 49 New Sneddon Street, Paisley, Renfrewshire, PA3 2AZ Tel: 0141-840 1606 Fax: 0141-840 1607 *General engineers*

Abercorn Heating Ltd, 105 Abercorn Street, Paisley, Renfrewshire, PA3 4AT Tel: 0141-887 0308 Fax: 0141-887 6823 E-mail: markbrooks@abercorn-heating.co.uk *Industrial heater distributors*

Aberdare Demolition, Cwmbach New Road, Aberdare, Mid Glamorgan, CF44 0PN Tel: (01685) 882744 Fax: (01685) 882744 *Demolition & plant hire*

Aberdeen Appointments Agency Ltd, 461 Union Street, Aberdeen, AB11 6DB Tel: (01224) 211211 Fax: (01224) 211411 E-mail: info@aaa.uk.com *Recruitment agency*

Aberdeen Asset Management plc, 123 St. Vincent Street, Glasgow, G2 5EA Tel: 0141-306 7400 Fax: 0141-306 7401 E-mail: customer.services@aberdeen-asset.com *Investment management*

Aberdeen Blast Cleaning Services Ltd, Hillview Road, East Tullos Industrial Estate, Aberdeen, AB12 3HB Tel: (01224) 896565 Fax: (01224) 894989 *Shot blasting contractors*

Aberdeen Catering, 38 Upperkirkgate, Aberdeen, AB10 1BA Tel: (01224) 658588 Fax: (01224) 658588 *We currently operate an O"Briens franchise and our Office Catering Services division provides delivered buffets to offices around Aberdeen.*

Aberdeen City Libraries, Rosemount Viaduct, Aberdeen, AB25 1GW Tel: (01224) 634622 Fax: (01224) 636811 E-mail: bustech@-rec.aberdeen.net.uk *Business & technical information agents*

Aberdeen Computer Services Ltd, 24 Balnagask Road, Aberdeen, AB11 8HR Tel: (01224) 875867 Fax: (01224) 879247 E-mail: sales@acsltd.co.uk *Integrated computer systems suppliers*

Aberdeen Control Ltd, Unit 1 Union Glen, Aberdeen, AB11 6ER Tel: (01224) 211133 Fax: (01224) 211177 E-mail: gcraig@rsc.co.uk *Hazardous control equipment manufrs*

Aberdeen Drilling Consultants Ltd, 58 Queens Road, Aberdeen, AB15 4YE Tel: (01224) 209123 Fax: (01224) 209579 E-mail: adcltd@msn.com *Training including trade, vocational, safety & first aid services*

▶ Aberdeen Electrical Services Ltd, Unit 26 Frederick St Business Centre, Frederick Street, Aberdeen, AB24 5HY Tel: (01224) 649111 Fax: (01224) 649123

Aberdeen Exhibition & Conference Centre, Exhibition Avenue, Bridge of Don, Aberdeen, AB23 8BL Tel: (01224) 824824 Fax: (01224) 825276 E-mail: aecc@aecc.co.uk *Conference & exhibition centre*

Aberdeen Fabrication Ltd, Links Place, Aberdeen, AB11 5DY Tel: (01224) 588321 Fax: (01224) 583898 E-mail: sales@afab.co.uk *Design, fabrication & welding of heavy structural steel*

Aberdeen Fluid Systems Technologies Ltd, 1 Stoneywood Park, Stoneywood Road, Dyce, Aberdeen, AB21 7DZ Tel: (01224) 722468 Fax: (01224) 723009 E-mail: info@aberdeen.swagelok.com *Stock holders*

▶ Aberdeen Foundries, 23-41 Willowdale Place, Aberdeen, AB24 5AQ Tel: (01224) 635435 Fax: (01224) 633919 E-mail: sales@aberdeenfoundries.co.uk

Aberdeen Glass Fibre Ltd, Lethenty, Inverurie, Aberdeenshire, AB51 0HQ Tel: (01467) 623564 Fax: (01467) 623564 E-mail: ab.glassfibre@btopenworld.com *Glass fibre manufrs*

▶ Aberdeen & Grampian Chamber Of Commerce, 213 George Street, Aberdeen, AB25 1HY Tel: (01224) 620621 Fax: (01224) 645777 E-mail: info@agcc.co.uk *Comprehensive portfolio of services & support encompassing policy & representation, information & advice, networking & events, business development & training, & international trade*

Aberdeen Harbour Board, 16 Regent Quay, Aberdeen, AB11 5SS Tel: (01224) 597000 Fax: (01224) 571507 E-mail: info@aberdeen-harbour.co.uk *Port authorities*

Aberdeen Inshore Fish Selling Co., 154 North Esplanade East, Aberdeen, AB11 5QD Tel: (01224) 573317 Fax: (01224) 583568 *Fishing vessel managers*

▶ Aberdeen Joinery, 43 Thistle Lane, Aberdeen, AB10 1TZ Tel: (01224) 644148 *Joinery*

Aberdeen Journals Ltd, Lang Stracht, Aberdeen, AB15 6DF Tel: (01224) 690222 Fax: (01224) 699575 E-mail: pj.editor@ajl.co.uk *Publishers of books & magazines*

▶ Aberdeen Label Centre, 78 Great Western Road, Aberdeen, AB10 6QF Tel: (01224) 213313 Fax: (01224) 213316 *Label manufrs*

▶ Aberdeen Mechanical Services Ltd, 39 Fraser Place, Aberdeen, AB25 3TY Tel: (01224) 620330 Fax: (01224) 620331

Aberdeen Medical Services, 6 Rubislaw Terrace, Aberdeen, AB10 1XE Tel: (01224) 625766 Fax: (01224) 646612 *Medical consultant services*

Aberdeen Mineral Water Co. Ltd, Greyhope Road, Aberdeen, AB11 9RD Tel: (01224) 876888 Fax: (01224) 876676 *Soft drink manufrs*

Aberdeen Pressure Washer Centre, 22-26 Duff Street, Turriff, Aberdeenshire, AB53 4AX Tel: (01888) 563050 Fax: (01888) 563841 E-mail: info@tapltd.co.uk *Pressure washer equipment maintenance*

▶ Aberdeen Projector Hire, 8 Albert Place, Aberdeen, AB25 1RG Tel: (01224) 261303 Fax: (01224) 261302 *We hire XGA & SVGA data /video projectors and accessories which are suitable for use with a wide variety of input sources such as laptop computers, video or dvd players, games consoles, etc.*

Aberdeen Quality Associates Ltd, 8 Rubislaw Den North, Aberdeen, AB15 4AN Tel: (01224) 315406 E-mail: bill@aqa.co.uk *Quality assurance consultants & trainers*Health & Safety consultants and trainers*Environmental consultants and trainers*www.happyatwork.co.uk*

Aberdeen Radiators Ltd, 53 Wellington Street, Aberdeen, AB11 5BX Tel: (01224) 575692 Fax: (01224) 211023 E-mail: len.hubert@aberdeen-radiators.co.uk *Heat transfer specialists*

▶ Aberdeen Self Storage, PO Box 10114, Aberdeen, AB21 9YB Tel: (01224) 774682

Aberdeen Sign & Engraving Co. Ltd, 93 Victoria Road, Aberdeen, AB11 9LU Tel: (01224) 898984 Fax: (01224) 898954 E-mail: sales@absign.co.uk *Sign manufrs*

▶ Aberdeen Skills & Enterprise Training Ltd, Units 3-9 Minto Operations Training Centre, Minto Avenue, Altens Industrial Estate, Aberdeen, AB12 3JZ Tel: (01224) 859624 Fax: (01224) 859640 E-mail: aset-enquiry@abcol.ac.uk *Training provider for Oil & Gas, Electrical & Ex, Marine, Health & Safety, Computing and People & Business Management courses*

Aberdeen Tarpaulins, 42a Seaforth Road, Aberdeen, AB24 5PU Tel: (01224) 631915 Fax: (01224) 631012 *Tarpaulin manufrs*

Aberdeen Time Recorder Co., 66 Morningside Road, Aberdeen, AB10 7NT Tel: (01224) 322400 Fax: (01224) 322400 E-mail: sales@aberdeentimerecorder.co.uk *Staff time recorders & systems suppliers*

▶ Aberdeen Trailers, Crichney Lade Croft, Fyvie, Turriff, Aberdeenshire, AB53 8QY Tel: (01651) 891538 Fax: (01651) 891538

Aberdeen Web Ltd, Unit 5a Wellheads Crescent, Wellheads Indust Estate, Dyce, Aberdeen, AB21 7HG Tel: (01224) 723111 Fax: (01224) 774141 *Lifting sling manufrs*

▶ Aberfeldy Construction Equipment, 9 Market Square, Aberfeldy, Perthshire, PH15 2RB Tel: (01887) 829536 E-mail: sinclairderek@hotmail.com *Mechanical equipment suppliers*

▶ Abergavenny Consultancy Ltd, Elephant House, Clifton Road, Abergavenny, Gwent, NP7 6AG Tel: (01873) 850534 Fax: (01873) 850534 E-mail: info@aberfood.com *Process & engineering consultancy with expertise in food & manufacturing industries. Trained expert witness.*

▶ Abergele Mobility, Glanrafon House, Bridge Street, Abergele, Clwyd, LL22 7HA Tel: (01745) 827990 Fax: (01745) 827990 E-mail: mobilitysales@freeola.com *Mobility equipment suppliers*

Abergwili Concrete Products Ltd, Abergwili, Carmarthen, Dyfed, SA32 7EP Tel: (01267) 236461 Fax: (01267) 237792 *Pre cast concrete products*

Aberlink Ltd, Avening Mill, High Street, Avening, Tetbury, Gloucestershire, GL8 8LU Tel: (01453) 835737 Fax: (01453) 832574 E-mail: sales@aberlink.co.uk *Measuring machines manufrs*

Abernant Lake Hotel, Station Road, Llanwrtyd Wells, Powys, LD5 4RR Tel: (01591) 610250 Fax: (01591) 610684 *Hotel services*

William Abernethy Ltd, 10-14 Erskine Square, Glasgow, G52 4PE Tel: 0141-882 2289 Fax: 0141-883 7582 E-mail: enquiries@abernethy-eng.co.uk *General engineers*

Abertec Ltd, Cledwyn Building, Penglais, Aberystwyth, Dyfed, SY23 3DD Tel: (01970) 622385 Fax: (01970) 622959 E-mail: dkc@aber.ac.uk *Scientific consultants*

Abex Ltd, Abex House, 93 Cato Street, Birmingham, B7 4TS Tel: 0121-359 2623 Fax: 0121-359 7277 E-mail: enquiries@abexltd.co.uk *Material handling equipment hire, service & sales*

ABG Rubber & Plastics Ltd, Galowhill Rd, Brackmills Industrial Estate, Northampton, NN4 7EE Tel: (01604) 700880 Fax: (01604) 766113 E-mail: sales@abgrp.co.uk *Rubber & plastic components. Also plastic machinists. In addition plastic bearings, industrial cutting board, plastic material, high performance & industrial rubber product manufrs*

Abic Engineering Associates Ltd, 4 Lyon Close, Woburn Road Industrial Estate, Kempston, Bedford, MK42 7SB Tel: (01234) 852900 Fax: (01234) 304010 E-mail: info@abicengineering.co.uk *Engineering services*

Ability Handling Ltd, Mangham Way, Rotherham, South Yorkshire, S61 4RL Tel: (01709) 821821 Fax: (01709) 821421 E-mail: sales@abilityhandlingltd.co.uk *Fork lift truck & side loader services*

Ability Plus Software (UK) Ltd, 4 King Charles Terr, Sovereign Court, London, E1W 3HL Tel: (020) 7231 1004 Fax: (020) 7231 6310 E-mail: info@ability.com *Software publishers*

Ability Security Systems Ltd, Eton House, 156 High Street, Ruislip, Middlesex, HA4 8LJ Tel: (01895) 677070 Fax: (01895) 677055 E-mail: info@ability-security.co.uk *Security systems installation services*

Abingdon Freight Fowarding, Park 34, Collett, Didcot, Oxfordshire, OX11 7WB Tel: (01235) 813471 Fax: (01235) 750040 E-mail: info@affa.co.uk *Freight forwarders & export packers*

Abingdon King Dick, Unit 11 Roman Way, Coleshill, Birmingham, B46 1HG Tel: (01675) 467776 Fax: (01675) 464277 E-mail: sales@kingdicktools.co.uk *Hand tool manufrs*

Abinger Garage Door Services, Restland, Hoe Lane, Peaslake, Guildford, Surrey, GU5 9SW Tel: (01306) 730801 *Garage doors suppliers*

Abington Business Systems, 121 The Drive, Northampton, NN1 4SW Tel: (01604) 714241 Fax: (01604) 714847 *Bespoke software*

Abird Ltd, Ramsgate Road, Sandwich, Kent, CT13 9ND Tel: (01304) 613221 Fax: (01304) 614833 E-mail: info@abird.co.uk *Generator hire & rental, 10 KVA to 1000 KVA*

Abishot Mouldings, 6 Rushton Road, Rothwell, Kettering, Northamptonshire, NN14 6HF Tel: (01536) 712380 Fax: (01536) 418110 *Trade moulding*

Abitec Products, Oak House, 50 Barton Drive, New Milton, Hampshire, BH25 7JJ Tel: (01425) 617852 Fax: (01425) 617852 E-mail: sales@abitec.co.uk *Electronic equipment manufrs*

Abitech Systems, 13 Main Street, Keyworth, Nottingham, NG12 5AA Tel: 0115-937 4549 Fax: 0115-937 3662 E-mail: sales@abitech.co.uk *Computer services*

▶ Ablaze Building Solutions Ltd, Wesley House, 24 Grosvenor Road, Aldershot, Hampshire, GU11 1DP Tel: (01252) 401030 Fax: (01252) 310864 E-mail: sales@ablaze.co.uk *Fire alarms*

▶ Ablaze Stoves & Fireplaces, 1 Pickhill Farm, Smallhythe Road, Tenterden, Kent, TN30 7LZ Tel: (01580) 761316 Fax: (01580) 761316 E-mail: ablazestoves@aol.com *Retailers fireplaces & stoves*

▶ Able, 10 Moretons Close, Whittlesey, Peterborough, PE7 1XP Tel: (01733) 208992 Fax: (01733) 208992 E-mail: ableroofing44@tiscali.co.uk *WE ARE A FAMILY RUN BUSINESS FOR OVER 40 YEARS.WE PRIDE OURSELVES ON GOOD QUALITY WORKMANSHIP AND EXCELIENT SERVICE. WE DEAL IN ALL ASPECTS OF FLAT ROOFING BOTH DOMESTIC AND COMMERCIAL.WE ARE A MEMBER OF THE NATIONAL ROOFING FEDERATION AND WE ARE HOLDERS OF FULL PUBLIC LIABILITY INSURANCE.FOR PROMPT ATTENTION AND FREE NO OBLIGATION ESTIMATE RING 01733 208992/mobile 07973847442*

Able Cleaning Services Ltd, Kemp House, 152-160 City Road, London, EC1V 2NP Tel: (020) 7250 3722 Fax: (020) 7608 3424 *Office cleaners*

Able Doorspring & Metal Window Co., Unit 29 Oakwood Hill Industrial Estate, Oakwood Hill, Loughton, Essex, IG10 3TZ Tel: (020) 8508 9703 Fax: (01277) 375141 *Door operation equipment repairers*

▶ Able Engineering, PO Box 13321, Roslin, Midlothian, EH25 9RT Tel: 0131-448 2226

Able Engineering, Dunslow Road, Eastfield, Scarborough, North Yorkshire, YO11 3UT Tel: (01723) 585639 Fax: (01723) 581605 E-mail: admin@nswinches.co.uk *Engineering services*

Able Engineering, Cadley Hill Road, Swadlincote, Derbyshire, DE11 9EQ Tel: (01283) 227160 Fax: (01283) 222375 E-mail: dave@able-engineering.co.uk *Turnkey, project management, design, manufacture and installation of stainless steel pressure vessels, pipework and plant installation, for all industries.*

Able Engineering Design, 8 Macaulay Road, Rugby, Warwickshire, CV22 6HE Tel: (01788) 817010 E-mail: danny@200300.co.uk *Mechanical engineering design*

Able Instruments & Controls Ltd, Danehill, Lower Earley, Reading, RG6 4UT Tel: 0118-931 1188 Fax: 0118-931 2161 E-mail: sales@able.co.uk *Process instrumentation suppliers*

Able Instruments & Controls Ltd, Danehill, Lower Earley, Reading, RG6 4UT Tel: 0118-931 1188 Fax: 0118-931 2161 E-mail: sales@able.co.uk *Float & temperature switches*

Able Lifting Gear Swansea Ltd, Unit 4 Clarion Close, Swansea Enterprise Park, Swansea, SA6 8QZ Tel: (01792) 771965 Fax: (01792) 773645 E-mail: sales@ableliftinggear.co.uk *Specialists in mechanical handling*

▶ Able Packaging Designs Ltd, 23 Buckland Road, Penmill Trading Estate, Pen Mill Trading Estate, Yeovil, Somerset, BA21 5HA Tel: (01935) 470070 Fax: (01935) 477706 E-mail: sales@ablebox.com *Manufacture paperboard, cardboard boxes, cases & containers*

▶ Able Packaging Group Ltd, Firmin Coates Indust Estate, Middlewich Road, Byley, Middlewich, Cheshire, CW10 9NT Tel: (01606) 836161 Fax: (01606) 836970 E-mail: info@ablepackaging.co.uk *Manufacturers of antistatic materials*

Able Pest Control, 6 Hemplands, Chedworth, Cheltenham, Gloucestershire, GL54 4NH Tel: (01285) 720651 Fax: (01285) 720651 *Pest control*

▶ Able Plastering, 14 Wilson Avenue, Wigan, Lancashire, WN6 7HD Tel: 07838 251505 E-mail: enquiries@getplastered.biz *Based in Wigan, Greater Manchester we generally operate in a 30 mile radius covering Preston, Chorley, Warrington and outlying areas. We are happy to carry out all types of interior plastering work, dry lining, coving and tiling.*

Able Production, 77 Arthur Street, Redditch, Worcestershire, B98 8JY Tel: (01527) 510899 Fax: (01527) 514234 *Press & assembly work*

▶ Able Removal Services, 6 K9 Industrial Estate, Ferry Lane, Rainham, Essex, RM13 9YH Tel: (01708) 555665 Fax: (01708) 555778

▶ Able Schott Production, Moon Cottage Studio, Higher Eype, Bridport, Dorset, DT6 6AS Tel: 01308 423095 E-mail: info@ableschott.co.uk *ABLE SCHOTT PRODUCTION provide a fully digital video filming service mainly for the corporate sector. Training, Commercial, Promotional material filmed, edited and delivered on a variety of media including web streaming all at very affordable rates. In addition special events covered: conferences, sports events etc..*

▶ Able Services, Ayton Smiddy House, Newburgh, Cupar, Fife, KY14 6JQ Tel: (0800) 9178539

▶ Able Services (Scotland) Ltd, The Conifers, Station Road, Springfield, Cupar, Fife, KY15 5RU Tel: (01334) 652538

Able Shutter Services Ltd, Unit 3, 46 Chalgrove Road, London, N17 0JB Tel: (020) 8885 5332 Fax: (020) 8885 6786 E-mail: admin@able-shutters.co.uk *Shutter manufrs*

Able Signs, Unit 5, 1-2 Davey Road, Clacton-On-Sea, Essex, CO15 4XD Tel: (01255) 427350 Fax: (01255) 221658 *Sign makers*

Able Steel Fabrications Ltd, Unit 1 Park Street, Gosport, Hampshire, PO12 4UH Tel: (023) 9242 5425 Fax: (023) 9242 5444 E-mail: ablesteelfab@btconnect.com *Steel fabricators & stainless steel fabricators*

Able Steel Fabrications Ltd, Unit 1 Park Street, Gosport, Hampshire, PO12 4UH Tel: (023) 9242 5425 Fax: (023) 9242 5444 *General fabrication, pipework & ship repair*

Able Systems Ltd, Denton Drive, Northwich, Cheshire, CW9 7TU Tel: (01606) 48621 Fax: (01606) 44903 E-mail: sales@able-systems.com *Electronic mini-printer manufrs*

▶ Able Telecom, 70C Berrow Road, Burnham-on-Sea, Somerset, TA8 2EZ Tel: (07971) 519572

Able (U K) Ltd, Able House, Billingham Reach Industrial Estate, Haverton Hill, Billingham, Cleveland, TS23 1PX Tel: (01642) 806080 Fax: (01642) 655655 E-mail: info@ableuk.com *Industrial property developers*

▶ Able Window Gates, Able House, Chalgrove Road, Tottenham, London, N17 0JJ Tel: (020) 8885 5332 E-mail: info@able-window-gates.co.uk *Suppliers of commercial and domestic window security gates, security folding gates for patio doors and windows.*

▶ Ableit, Swan Court, Waterhouse Street, Hemel Hempstead, Hertfordshire, HP1 1DS Tel: 0845 3312987 Fax: 0845 3312687 E-mail: letstalk@ableit.co.uk *Ableit offer website design, development, integration and optimisation services to clients nationwide.*

Ablemail Electronics Ltd, Unit 17 Christie St Industrial Estate, Christie Street, Stockport, Cheshire, SK1 4LR Tel: 0161-480 6910 Fax: 0161-480 8686 E-mail: info@ablemail.co.uk *Direct current converters vehicles auto electrical equipment manufrs*

Ablemix Concrete, Gibbet Lane, Shawell, Lutterworth, Leicestershire, LE17 6AA Tel: (01788) 860100 Fax: (01788) 860937 *Ready mixed concrete distributors & manufrs*

▶ Ableworld, 39 Beam Street, Nantwich, Cheshire, CW5 5NF Tel: (01270) 626971 Fax: (01270) 626971 *Mobility equipment sales*

Ablex International Ltd, 113 Warstone Lane, Birmingham, B18 6NZ Tel: 0121-233 1313 Fax: 0121-233 1115 E-mail: admin@ablexuk.com *Clock & watch distributors*

▶ Ablib, 1 Foresters Cottages, Mead Road, Edenbridge, Kent, TN8 5DE Tel: (01732) 867879 E-mail: ablibcleaners@hotmail.co.uk *builders cleans, show home cleans, one off cleans, pre/ after party cleans, spring cleans, tenancy cleans, weekly cleans. Domestic & commercial cleaners*

▶ Ably Resources Ltd, 1 Cumbernauld Road, Buchanan Business Park, Stepps, Glasgow, G33 6HZ Tel: 0141-565 1270 Fax: 0141-779 1616 E-mail: enquiries@ablyresource.com *Oil & gas, engineering, technical & construction recruitment*

Ably Shelters Ltd, 1700 Blueprint, Dundas Spur, Portsmouth, PO3 5RW Tel: (023) 9244 8040 Fax: (023) 9244 8049 E-mail: sales@ablyshelters.co.uk Principal Export Areas: Africa *Scaffolding & shelter manufrs*

Abm Labels & Print, Blaenant Industrial Estate, Blaenavon Road, Brynmawr, Ebbw Vale, Gwent, NP23 4BX Tel: (01495) 312835 Fax: (01495) 312819 E-mail: info@abmlabels.co.uk *Manufacturer picture frame backs*

Abm Trucks, 16 Roudham Park Industrial Estate, Harling Road, Norwich, NR16 2SN Tel: (01953) 718572 Fax: (01953) 718572 *Commercial vehicle spraying*

▶ Abmas Engineering, Crichiebank Business Centre, Mill Road, Inverurie, Aberdeenshire, AB51 5NQ Tel: (01467) 625970 Fax: 01467 894031 E-mail: mason@abmas.fsnet.co.uk *Electrical engineering and offshore services*

Abnormal Loads Services International Ltd, 1501 Hedon Road, Hull, HU9 5NX Tel: (01482) 796214 Fax: (01482) 707650 E-mail: info.advertising@abnormal-loads.com Principal Export Areas: Worldwide *With over 25 years of specialist transport knowledge and expertise, ALS (Freight Management Group) Limited incorporating Abnormal Load Services (International) Limited, Hull, UK offers a complete range of logistics services for abnormal and out of gauge loads by: road, air, sea, rail and canal, including: IT/Tracking and Tracing, Inventory Management, Warehousing and Operations Management. ALS are heavy lift project specialists in the global transportation of oversized cargo for sectors including; mining, energy, oil and gas, construction & plant, engineering, paper, marine and offshore. ALS has 15 offices in: Belgium, Germany, Hong Kong, Italy, Netherlands, Romania, Singapore and UK and partners worldwide to deal with your logistics requirements. ALS are equipped to handle any enquiry no matter how large or small: from air freighting the smallest components to shipping and distributing the largest machines, picking and packing operations, bonded warehousing, to machine modifications; ALS will consider supply chain requirements all over the world.*

▶ Abode Interior Design, Oxbow Farm, Avon Dassett, Southam, Warwickshire, CV47 2AQ Tel: (01295) 690196 Fax: (01295) 690194 E-mail: info@uk-designer.com *A professional interior design company specialising in interior renovation using our own team of tradespeople and highly recommended builders. Commercial and domestic projects undertaken.*Member of The British Interior Design Association*

Abode Security, 155 Moor Lane, Salford, M7 3QE Tel: 0161-792 4223 *Alarm & CCTV installers*

Abolish Pest & Vermin Control, 11 Cheatham Street, Birmingham, B7 5PS Tel: 0121-326 7904 *Commercial & domestic pest control*

▶ About Engineering Ltd, Thistleton Road Industrial Estate, Market Overton, Rutland, Oakham, Leicestershire, LE15 7PP Tel: (01572) 768007

▶ About Turn Creative, Somerford Business Court, Holmes Chapel Road, Somerford, Congleton, Cheshire, CW12 4SN Tel: (01260) 281431 Fax: (01260) 289362 E-mail: info@aboutturncreative.co.uk *Advertising, marketing & design specialising in business to business*

▶ Aboutalluneed, Fletcher House, 4 Betley Court, Main Road, Betley, Crewe, CW3 9BH Tel: (01270) 820344 Fax: (01270) 820344 E-mail: thisis@aboutalluneed.co.uk *Computer Services, repairs, upgrades, training, advice*

Aboval & Co. Ltd, 24 Firtrees Close, Rotherhide, London, SE16 5NG Tel: (07774) 852505 Fax: (020) 7252 3793 *Steeplejacks flagstaff & pole manufrs*

Above All, 178 High Road, Chilwell, Beeston, Nottingham, NG9 5BB Tel: 0115-925 1959 Fax: 0115-943 1408 E-mail: service@aboveall.co.uk *Suspended ceiling cleaning*

Above Average Computers, 21 William Avenue, Blythe Bridge, Stoke-on-Trent, ST3 6HN Tel: (07909) 547211 E-mail: info@aacomps.co.uk *Comuters Systems Software Components Upgrades*

▶ Aboyne Fire & Stoves Ltd, Bourtreebush Smithy, Bruntland Road, Portlethen, Aberdeen, AB12 4QN Tel: (01224) 781150

Abpac, Wessex Way, Wincanton Business Park, Wincanton, Somerset, BA9 9RR Tel: (01963) 32913 Fax: (01963) 34358 E-mail: sales@abpac.co.uk *Catering & food industry suppliers*

Abra Systems, 37 Crossall Street, Macclesfield, Cheshire, SK11 6QF Tel: (01625) 503448 Fax: (01625) 503448 *Computer repairers & maintenance*

Abracadabra Discotheques, 314 Nelson Road, Twickenham, TW2 7AH Tel: (020) 8893 3313 Fax: (020) 8893 8813 E-mail: sales@abra.co.uk *Disco sales & hire*

Abrae Technology Ltd, Park Hill Street, Bolton, BL1 4AR Tel: (01204) 361400 Fax: (0870) 3000693 *Design & production of electronic equipment*

Abrahams & Carlisle Ltd, Carlham Works, Newman Street, Bradford, West Yorkshire, BD4 9NT Tel: (01274) 651555 Fax: (01274) 686135 E-mail: sales@abrahams-and-carlisle.co.uk *Specialist joiners*

Abrahone Engineering, Unit 4 Thornes Trading Estate, Wakefield, West Yorkshire, WF1 5QN Tel: (01924) 378733 Fax: (01924) 200014 E-mail: abrahone@btconnect.com *supplier of*

continued

continuation
*honing equipment,abrasive sticks,tooling,*honed bore tube,sub contract honing.*

Abram Fencing, 59 Old Park Lane, Southport, Merseyside, PR9 7BQ Tel: (01704) 224923 Fax: (01704) 224923 E-mail: john@abramfencing.co.uk *Fencing contractors, distributors & manufrs*

Henry Abram & Sons Ltd, 17 Sandyford Place, Glasgow, G3 7NB Tel: 0141-221 3075 Fax: 0141-226 5501 E-mail: shipping@henryabram.co.uk *Shipping agents & heavy lift shipping contractors*

Abramsons Kosher Food Products, 61 Bury Old Road, Prestwich, Manchester, M25 0FG Tel: 0161-773 2020 Fax: 0161-798 6550 *Butchers*

▶ Abraqsys Business Systems, 13 Duncan Close, Moulton Park Industrial Estate, Northampton, NN3 6WL Tel: (01604) 797950 Fax: (01604) 797951 E-mail: sales@abraqsys.co.uk *Computer software packages, development & support*

Abrasive Blades Ltd, 4 Greenhill Crescent, Watford Business Park, Watford, WD18 8RE Tel: (01923) 223248 Fax: (01923) 210234 *Abrasive wheel manufrs*

Abrasive Chasers Drilling & Sawing LLP, 96 Broom Road, Stanford, Biggleswade, Bedfordshire, SG18 9JE Tel: (01462) 813666 Fax: (01462) 813351 E-mail: abrasive.chasers@btconnect.com

Abrasive Services & Stockists, 18 Baldock Road, Stotfold, Hitchin, Hertfordshire, SG5 4NZ Tel: (01462) 730886 Fax: (01462) 733354 *Abrasive distributors*

Abrasive Technology Ltd, Roxby Place, London, SW6 1RT Tel: (020) 7471 0200 Fax: (020) 7471 0202 E-mail: info@abrasive-tech.com *Manufacturer of natural & polycrystalline diamond tooling*

Abrasives & Screw Products Ltd, Cropton House, Three Tuns Lane, Liverpool, L37 4AQ Tel: (01704) 879311 Fax: (01704) 870158 E-mail: sales@aspltd.co.uk *Industrial fastener distributors*

Abraxas plc, 47 Eastcastle Street, London, W1W 8DY Tel: (020) 7255 5555 Fax: (020) 7636 0333 E-mail: corporate@abraxas.com *IT recruitment agents*

Abraxas Catering Ltd, Ricketts Place, Firs Lane Industrial Estate, Kidderminster, Worcestershire, DY11 7QN Tel: (01562) 863222 Fax: (01562) 863133 E-mail: info@abraxascatering.co.uk *Supply and installation of new and reconditioned catering equipment. Design and installation of commercial kitchens. Fabrication and installation of extraction and supply air systems. Supply and installation of cladding systems including s/steel etc. Fabrication of bespoke stainless steel equipment.*

Abreption Leather Products, Unit 14 Turnpike Close, Grantham, Lincolnshire, NG31 7XU Tel: (01476) 569020 Fax: (01476) 569020 E-mail: email@abreption.co.uk *Leather goods*

Abrichem Composite Ltd, Unit 20 Heath Farm Estate, Iron Mould Lane Brislington, Bristol, BS4 4FZ Tel: 0117-977 1213 Fax: 0117-971 7623 *GRP fibre glass moulding manufrs*

Abron Refinishers, Berryleys, Grange, Keith, Banffshire, AB55 6LN Tel: (01542) 870354 Fax: (01542) 870354 E-mail: info@abronrefinishers.co.uk *Commercial refinishers*

Abru Ltd, Derwentside Industrial Park, Derby Road, Belper, Derbyshire, DE56 1WE Tel: (01773) 525700 Fax: (01773) 828059 E-mail: sales@abru.co.uk *Ladder manufrs*

Abs Ltd, 1 Ridge Close, Hatch Warren, Basingstoke, Hampshire, RG22 4RN Tel: (01256) 357270 Fax: (01256) 301521 E-mail: admin@ABSuk.com *Computer consultancy*

Abs Brymar Floor's Ltd, Dane Road Industrial Estate, Sale, Cheshire, M33 7BH Tel: 0161-972 5000 Fax: 0161-972 5001 E-mail: sales@absbrymarfloors.co.uk *Concrete industrial floors*

Abs Technology plc, Technology House, Church Road, Shottermill, Haslemere, Surrey, GU27 1NU Tel: (01428) 664900 Fax: (01428) 664901 *IT equipment suppliers*

Absoft Ltd, Units B3-B4 Aberdeen Science & Technology Park, Balgownie Road, Bridge of Don, Aberdeen, AB22 8GT Tel: (01224) 707088 Fax: (01224) 707099 E-mail: info@absoft.co.uk *Computer solutions & accessories*

▶ Absoloute Bathrooms Aim, 3 Warrington Road, Ashton-in-Makerfield, Wigan, Lancashire, WN4 9PL Tel: (01942) 271557 Sales Contact: R Ingram

▶ Absolut Form Ltd, Gilbert House 1 Warwick Place, Warwick Road, Borehamwood, Hertfordshire, WD6 1UA Tel: (020) 8731 3700 Fax: (020) 8731 3737 E-mail: sales@absolutform.co.uk *Promotional items & weather instruments manufrs*

Absolute, Convent Drive, Waterbeach, Cambridge, CB25 9QT Tel: (01223) 440022 Fax: (01223) 440033 E-mail: mail.winborn_products@virgin.net *Sheet metal engineers*

▶ Absolute, Unit 11 Viewpoint, Boxley Road, Penenden Heath, Maidstone, Kent, ME14 2DZ Tel: (01622) 663345 Fax: (01622) 890419 E-mail: info@absoluteaudiosystemsltd.co.uk *Audio visual equipment & accessories suppliers & installers*

Absolute Action Ltd, 6 Tonbridge Road, Maidstone, Kent, ME16 8RP Tel: (01622) 351000 Fax: (01622) 351001 E-mail: enquiries@absolute-action.com *Fibre optics lighting manufrs*

▶ Absolute Audio Visual Solutions, Cheney Lodge, 81 Station Road, Odsey, Baldock, Hertfordshire, SG7 5RP Tel: (01462) 743003 E-mail: enquiry@absoluteavs.co.uk *Audio visual equipment sales, rental, installations & repairs*

Absolute Battery UK Ltd, Darrell House, Darrell Road, Felixstowe, Suffolk, IP11 3UU Tel: (01394) 674949 Fax: (01394) 279005 *Power solutions computer systems*

▶ Absolute Business Services Ltd, 33 Suffolk Drive, Guildford, Surrey, GU4 7FD Tel: (01483) 826377 E-mail: info@absolutebusinessservices.com *Absolute Business Services has been established to provide a 'one-stop-shop' for all IT and business related services and solutions. We deal with businesses, from sole traders to large national and multinational corporations. **We provide excellent service in the following business areas: **consultancy, internet, recruitment, networks and training.**

Absolute Calibration Ltd, 14 Murrills Estate, Portchester, Fareham, Hampshire, PO16 9RD Tel: (023) 9232 1712 Fax: (023) 9221 0034 E-mail: calit@absolute-cal.co.uk *Calibrating services, electronic & temperature equipment & humidity & pressure. Also calibration laboratory, UKAS accredited*

▶ Absolute Coldroom, 22 Victoria Terrace, Guiseley, Leeds, LS20 9EX Tel: (07980) 789223 Fax: (01943) 879679 E-mail: info@absolutecoldroom.co.uk *Cold room repairers, installers & suppliers*

▶ Absolute Comfort Plc, Unit 7 Roach View, Millhead Way, Purdeys Industrial Estate, Rochford, Essex, SS4 1LB Tel: (01702) 533764 Fax: (01702) 533760 *Visco elastic products,*memory foam mattresses, mattress toppers & pillows*

Absolute Computers Ltd, 19 Old High Street, Headington, Oxford, OX3 9HS Tel: (01865) 744115 Fax: (01865) 744155 E-mail: admin@absolute.co.uk *Computer resellers*

Absolute Insulations, 21 Wanstead Road, Leicester, LE3 1TR Tel: 0116-287 8958 Fax: 0116-231 4002 *Absolute Insulation Ltd of Leicester UK, was established in 1992 Absolute Insulation continues to invest in the latest technology and highly qualified staff to establish our reputation as one of the foremost insulation companies in the region. Absolute Insulation offers services for individual domestic consumers as well as builders, architects, local authorities and government agencies. Cavity Wall Insulation, Loft Insulation, Timber Framed Insulation (new build only). Experienced surveyors are pleased to offer a free no-obligation quote.*

▶ Absolute It Solutions Ltd, 1 Lon Pobty, Bangor, Gwynedd, LL57 1HR Tel: (01248) 360047 *Computer software suppliers*

▶ Absolute It Solutions, 22 St. Michaels Road, Woking, Surrey, GU21 5PY Tel: (01483) 834887

▶ Absolute It Solutions Ltd, Fodol Cottage, Y Felinheli, Gwynedd, LL56 4QD Tel: (01248) 671007 Fax: (01248) 671099

▶ Absolute Marketing, 115 Elmdon Lane, Marston Green, Birmingham, B37 7DN Tel: 0121 688 7686 Fax: 0121 688 7686 E-mail: absolutemarketing@blueyonder.co.uk *Creative Marketing Solutions Company*

Absolute Museum & Gallery Products, 66 Leonard Street, London, EC2A 4LW Tel: (020) 7729 5817 Fax: (020) 7613 4224 E-mail: info@absoluteproduct.com *Museum & gallery products*

▶ Absolute Packaging Solutions Ltd, Unit 7, 400 Cromwell Road, Grimsby, North East Lincolnshire, DN31 2BN Tel: (01472) 233324 Fax: (01472) 233326 E-mail: apackaging_solutions@hotmail.com *Specialists in supplying reconditioned multihead/ linear weighers and form fill seal bagging machines. Bespoke packaging lines built to specification and budget*

▶ Absolute PC Support, 21 Highbury Road, Hitchin, Hertfordshire, SG4 9SA Tel: (01462) 621658 E-mail: tech@absolutepcsupport.co.uk *APCS offer timely, reliable computer repairs and a wide range of other IT services and solutions for home users and small to medium sized businesses at very competitive prices.*

Absolute Proof, 7 The Hatchingtan, Worplesdon, Guildford, Surrey, GU3 3SB Tel: (0800) 0680409 *Pest control services*

Absolute Security, Unit 18 Westerhope Small Business Park, Redburn Road, Newcastle upon Tyne, NE5 1NF Tel: 0191-214 5555 *Wrought ironworkers*

Absolute Software, Mount Pleasant, Chapel Hill, Porthtowan, Truro, Cornwall, TR4 8AS Tel: (01209) 891320 E-mail: info@absolute-software.co.uk *Absolute Software provides embedded programming and PC programming solutions. From simple drivers to complete multiprocessor systems, we are just what you need.*We will agree a specification with you, and then give you a fixed price quotation, making budgeting easy for you. We have considerable experience in many areas, visit our portfolio for a taster.**At Absolute Software, we are aware that our clients have a wide range of requirements, and depending on your available in-house skills and budget, different levels of service might be needed from us. Visit our website to see the 3 levels of service available.**In 2005, Absolute Software received Microchip Certified Consultancy status for our PIC programming skills.*

Absolute Sounds Ltd, 58 Durham Road, London, SW20 0TW Tel: (020) 8971 3909 Fax: (020) 8879 7962 E-mail: info@absolutesounds.com *Audio visual retailers*

▶ Absolute Tooling, 6 Rookery Road, Barnoldswick, Lancashire, BB18 6YH Tel: (01282) 852997 Fax: (01282) 852997

▶ Absolute Windows Ltd, Unit 7 Priestley Road, Wardley Industrial Estate, Worsley, Manchester, M28 2LY Tel: (01204) 394006 *Manufacture plastic products*

Absolutely Fabulous Fireworks, 4 Park Parade, Gunnersbury Avenue, London, W3 9BD Tel: (01753) 524648 E-mail: info@fireworks-uk.com *Fireworks, firework display wholesalers & retailers*

▶ Absolutely Lights, Shedfield House Dairy, Sandy Lane, Shedfield, Southampton, SO32 2HQ Tel: (01329) 835999 Fax: (01329) 835999

▶ Absolutely PC Ltd, 11 Bradley Road, Patchway, Bristol, BS34 5LF Tel: 0117-975 9523 E-mail: Sales@AbsolutelyPC.co.uk *Brake fix repair & networking*

Absolutely Splashing Aquatic Consultants, 15 Salkeld Avenue, Ashton-in-Makerfield, Wigan, Lancashire, WN4 9NH Tel: (01942) 511947 *Aquarium displays*

Absorbent Dripmats Ltd, Aero Mill, Kershaw Street, Church, Accrington, Lancashire, BB5 4JS Tel: (01254) 234247 Fax: (01254) 383996 E-mail: info@naylergroup.co.uk *General printers & beer mats producer*

Absorbopak Ltd, Wilson Road, South Wigston, Leicester, LE18 4TQ Tel: 0116-258 1160 E-mail: patc@absorbopak.com *Moisture damage & condensation damage repairs*

Abstract Office Interiors Ltd, 3 Forest Industrial Park, Forest Road, Hainault, Ilford, Essex, IG6 3HL Tel: (020) 8501 6633 Fax: (020) 8501 6634 *Office refurbishers*

Abstract Signs & Graphics Ltd, Unit 4 High Hazels Court, Coombe Road, Nottingham, NG16 3SU Tel: (01773) 711611 Fax: 0115-963 3711 E-mail: info@abstractsigns.co.uk *Sign manufrs*

Abstrakt Services Ltd, 58 Chester Street, Aston, Birmingham, B6 4LW Tel: 0121-380 2600 Fax: 0121-333 6537 E-mail: mail@abstrakt.co.uk *Direct marketing services*

▶ Abt Engineering Ltd, Unit 1, Cargo Terminal Campsie Drive, Abbotsinch, Paisley, Renfrewshire, PA3 2SG Tel: 0141-887 4404 *Engineering*

▶ Abtap, 326B St Albans Road, Watford, WD24 6PQ Tel: (01923) 630022 Fax: (01923) 630011 E-mail: abtap@btconnect.com *Plumbing & heating distributors*

Abtec Engineering Ltd, Rowhurst Close, Rowhurst Indust Estate, Newcstle Stfs, Newcastle, Staffordshire, ST5 6BD Tel: (01782) 565658 Fax: (01782) 565688 *Steel fabricators*

▶ AbTec Industries Ltd, Unit 4, Venture Court, Boleness Road, Wisbech, Cambridgeshire, PE13 2XQ Tel: (01945) 585500 Fax: (01945) 585052 E-mail: sales@abrasivetechnology.net *Abrasive products*

Abtech Europe Ltd, Unit 3 East Quay Mews, East Quay, Bridgwater, Somerset, TA6 4AE Tel: (01278) 447080 Fax: (01278) 447090 E-mail: sales@abtech-europe.com *Electronic manufrs*

Abtech Precision Ltd, 95 Alston Drive, Bradwell Abbey, Milton Keynes, MK13 9HF Tel: (01908) 318218 Fax: (01908) 318308 E-mail: enquiries@abtech-precision.co.uk *Toolmakers & precision engineers*

Abtek Ltd, Unit 10, Camperdown Industrial Estate, Newcastle upon Tyne, NE12 5UJ Tel: 0191-268 8555 Fax: 0191-268 8777 E-mail: sales@abtekltd.co.uk *Sheet metal & general fabricators*

Abtek (Biologicals) Ltd, Unit 4, Taylor Street, Liverpool, L5 5AD Tel: 0151-298 1501 Fax: 0151-298 1758 E-mail: info@abtekbio.com *Laboratory diagnostic product suppliers*

▶ Abucon Ltd, 21a Vincent Square, London, SW1P 2NA Tel: (020) 7834 1066 Fax: (020) 7828 1828 E-mail: info@abucon.co.uk *Public relations & marketing consultants*

Aburnet Ltd, Walter Street, Draycott, Derby, DE72 3NU Tel: (01332) 874797 Fax: (01332) 875284 E-mail: info@aburnet.co.uk *Hair net manufrs.*

▶ Abvleisure, 44 Satis Avenue, Sittingbourne, Kent, ME10 2LF Tel: (01795) 410459 E-mail: info@abvleisure.co.uk *Bouncy castle & party tent hire*

Abwood Machine Tools, 615 Princes Road, Dartford, DA2 6EF Tel: (01322) 225271 Fax: (01322) 291862 E-mail: sales@abwoodcnc.co.uk *Machine tool manufrs*

▶ Abysss Audio & Lighting Sales, 24 Burton Road, Overseal, Swadlincote, Derbyshire, DE12 6LQ Tel: (07960) 953489 E-mail: sales@abyssaudiolighting.co.uk *CD players, disc jockey, dual suppliers*

▶ AC DECORATING SERVICES, 35 Milton Road, Croydon, CR0 2BG Tel: (07973) 273541 E-mail: admin@acdecoratingservices.co.uk

AC Valves & Controls Ltd, Telford Way, Stephenson Industrial Estate, Coalville, Leicestershire, LE67 3HE Tel: (01530) 832832 Fax: (01530) 838986 E-mail: markc@acvalvealliance.com *Valve distributors*

▶ Aca Security, 9 Redlees Close, Isleworth, Middlesex, TW7 7HE Tel: (07876) 355611 E-mail: sales@aca-security.co.uk *Installation, maintenance & repairs of all security systems*

Aca Systems Ltd, Sovereign House, Ellen Terrace, Washington, Tyne & Wear, NE37 3AS Tel: 0191-417 3166 Fax: 0191-417 3288 *Software providers*

Acacia, 37 Shoebury Avenue, Shoeburyness, Southend-on-Sea, SS3 9BH Tel: (01702) 297555 Fax: (01702) 298015 *Packaging distributors*

Acacia Joinery Ltd, Old Carpenters Shop, Old Gee, Bridgend, Mid Glamorgan, CF31 3AP Tel: (01656) 649639 Fax: (01656) 649639 *Joinery manufrs*

Acacia Studio, PO Box 400, Crewe, CW3 9FL Tel: (01782) 752575 Fax: (01782) 752575 *Ceramic transfer manufrs*

▶ Acacia Works, 20 Gayal Croft, Shenley Brook End, Milton Keynes, MK5 7HX Tel: (01908) 501268 E-mail: sales@acaciaworks.co.uk *Picture framing*

Academy Guards Limited, 36a Church Hill, Loughton, Essex, IG10 1LA Tel: 0870 0847010 Fax: 0870 0847011 E-mail: info@academyguards.co.uk *We are a London based security company specialising in offering our security guards, security reception and cleaning personnel. **

▶ Academy Hair & Beauty UK Ltd, 4 Kent Street Industrial Estate, 26 Kent Street, Leicester, LE5 3BD Tel: 0116-262 4946 Fax: 0116-251 6489 E-mail: mail@academy-beauty.com *Manufacturers & distributors of hair & beauty products*

Academy Pest Control, 46 Star Post Road, Camberley, Surrey, GU15 4DF Tel: (01276) 501911 Fax: (01276) 784493 *Pest controllers*

Academy Solutions Ltd, 46 Brasenose Drive, Kidlington, Oxfordshire, OX5 2EQ Tel: (01865) 371012 Fax: (01865) 847276 E-mail: paul.guest@acadsol.co.uk *Computer consultants*

Academy Windows & Conservatories Ltd, 21 Denmark Street, Wokingham, Berkshire, RG40 2AY Tel: 0118-977 1144 Fax: 0118-989 1268 E-mail: academy.gordon@btconnect.com *PVC windows, doors & conservatory manufrs*

Acal Technologies Ltd, 3 The Business Centre, Molly Millars Lane, Wokingham, Berkshire, RG41 2EY Tel: 0118-978 8878 Fax: 0118-977 6095 E-mail: *Microprocessor systems distribs*

Acal Technology Ltd, 3 The Business Centre, Molly Millers Lane, Wokingham, Berkshire, RG41 2EY Tel: 0118-902 9702 Fax: 0118-902 9614 E-mail: admin@amega-group.com *Electronic components distributors*

Acam Instrumentation Ltd, 23 Thomas Street, Northampton, NN1 3EN Tel: (01604) 628700 Fax: (01604) 628700 E-mail: tom@acamltd.co.uk *We are a leading supplier of strain gauge bonding services with in house technology for ceramic, semiconductors and foil gauges. We supply state of the art transducers and sensors for pressure, temperature, load and torque*

▶ Acamology, 74 Retallick Meadows, St. Austell, Cornwall, PL25 3BY Tel: (01726) 69001 Fax: (0870) 0519348 *Computer systems consultants*

▶ Acanthus, Unit 2-4 Sandon Industrial Estate, Sandon Way, Liverpool, L5 9YN Tel: 0151-207 1057 Fax: 0151-207 3537 E-mail: sales@acanthusfurniture.co.uk *Furniture makers*

▶ Acanthus Press Ltd, Sylvan Road Trading Estate, Wellington, Somerset, TA21 8ST Tel: (01823) 663339 Fax: (01823) 665531

Acardia, Venture House 2 Arlington Square, Downshire Way, Bracknell, Berkshire, RG12 1WA Tel: (0845) 2301055 Fax: (01344) 868333 E-mail: admin@acardia.co.uk *Sun microsystems resellers*

Acaster Carpets, Brockett Industrial Estate, The Airfield, Acaster Malbis, York, YO23 2PT Tel: (01904) 702343 Fax: (01904) 702343 *Carpet suppliers*

▶ Accappella, Nightingale Farm, Whiteacre Lane, Waltham, Canterbury, Kent, CT4 5SR Tel: (01227) 700725 E-mail: emma@accappellastudio.co.uk *Quality custom picture framing*

Accel, 5 Chickney Rd, Henham, Bishop's Stortford, Herts, CM22 6BE Tel: (01279) 850547 *Computer consultants*

▶ Accelerate Consultancy Ltd, Bryn Tirion Brynford Road, Pentre Halkyn, Holywell, Clwyd, CH8 8AW Tel: (0845) 1259573 E-mail: information@accelerate-consultancy.co.uk *Accelerate Consultancy Limited, under the TAMS brand, provide intelligent IT infrastructure and service management software, ranging from Desktop Audit and Inventory, to advanced SLA monitoring and reporting solutions. Accelerate provide very cost effective solutions that contain all the features of far more expensive alternatives.*

▶ Accelerated Drain Services Ltd, 47 Suffolk Road, Barking, Essex, IG11 7QP Tel: (020) 8594 7171 E-mail: info@accelerated-drains.co.uk *Emergency Drainage Services, CCTV Drain Surveys London, Drain Unblocking London, Drain Cleaning London, Drain Descaling London*

Accelerated Mailing & Marketing, The Penny Black, Marchants Way, Burgess Hill, West Sussex, RH15 8QY Tel: (01444) 245917 Fax: (01444) 870960 E-mail: info@accelerated-mail.co.uk *Mailing house*

▶ Accelerated Weathering Laboratory Ltd, Berkeley House, Hunts Rise, South Marston Industrial Estat, Swindon, SN3 4TG Tel: (01793) 834211 Fax: (01793) 721212 E-mail: info@awlltd.co.uk *Test & evaluation laboratory services*

Accellent, Unit E3 Brookside Business Park, Greengate, Middleton, Manchester, M24 1GS Tel: 0161-643 0018 Fax: 0161-643 0019 E-mail: susan.ward@accellent.com *Accellent in Manchester is a division of large American medical device manufacturing and outsourcing organisation providing contract manufacturing and design services to medical and non-medical product manufacturers. The facility at Manchester was set up in 1993 to service the growing UK and European market. Accellent's core strengths is precision engineering expertise and applying this to cutting, forming, laser welding, machining, stamping and finishing of precision tubular and machined components manufactured from tube, strip and solid, in volumes from 1 to 100 million per year. Accellent specializes in the medical device field, but also applies this expertise to aerospace, automotive, electrical, electronics and industrial sectors where precision and repeatability is key. We are currently certified to ISO 9001:2000 and have recently completed the work required for ISO 13485:2003.*

▶ Accelrys Ltd, 334 Science Park, Milton Road, Cambridge, CB4 0WN Tel: (01223) 228500 Fax: (01223) 228501 E-mail: admin@accelrys.com *Research & development of software for the pharmaceutical industry*

▶ Accenan Ltd, 2 Chirton Dene Way, North Shields, Tyne & Wear, NE29 6XL Tel: 0191-258 3633 Fax: 0191-258 3633 E-mail: enquiries@accenan.co.uk *Accenan Ltd is a mechanical design consultancy located on North Tyneside, serving the North of England. We offer a full mechanical design service for all aspects of machine requirements: from jig and fixture design through to complete assembly and test machines.*

Accent Business Solutions Ltd, 6 Upper Stone Street, Maidstone, Kent, ME15 6EX Tel: (01732) 841794 Fax: (01622) 671477 E-mail: accentsolu@aol.com *Computer maintenance & sales*

Accent Fuels Ltd, Barracks Road, Sandy La Industrial Estate, Stourport-on-Severn, Worcestershire, DY13 9QB Tel: (01299) 822690 Fax: (01299) 877351 *Fuel & oil distribs*

Accent Hansen, Greengate Industrial Estate, Greenside Way, Middleton, Manchester, M24 1SW Tel: 0161-284 4100 Fax: 0161-655 3119 E-mail: operations@accenthansen.co.uk *Steel door manufrs*

Accent Lighting Ltd, 3 Candidus Court, Werrington, Peterborough, PE4 5DB Tel: (01733) 574524 Fax: (01733) 574524 E-mail: sales@accent-lighting.co.uk *Lighting designers*

▶ Accent Office Interiors, 53-55 Cardiff Road, Luton, LU1 1PP Tel: (01582) 722211 *Office designers, fitters, planners & refurbishment*

Accent On Ceilings & Partitioning Ltd, Long Acre, Biddenfield Lane, Wickham, Fareham, Hampshire, PO17 5NU Tel: (023) 9266 9803 Fax: (023) 9265 5779 E-mail: sales@accent-on.co.uk *Office partitions & suspended ceilings*

Accent Optical Technologies (U K) Ltd, Haxby Road, York, YO31 8SD Tel: (01904) 715500 Fax: (01904) 645624 E-mail: admin@accentopto.com *Distributors & manufacturers in optical technologies*

▶ Accent Print & Design, 28-29 Maxwell Road, Woodston Industry, Peterborough, PE2 7JE Tel: (01733) 233238 Fax: (01733) 246519 E-mail: sales@accentprint.net *Business printed products eg. invoices, business cards, ncr sets, letterheads, booklets, note pads, compliment slips, flyers, brochures, invitations, laminating, small books, if it's printed and you need it, the chances are we do it!*

Accent Services Air Conditioning Ltd, 4 Brooklands Close, Sunbury-on-Thames, Middlesex, TW16 7DX Tel: (01932) 765648 Fax: (01932) 788706 E-mail: info@accent.ac.co.uk *Air conditioning engineers*

Accent Steel Ltd, 164 West Wycombe Road, High Wycombe, Buckinghamshire, HP12 3AE Tel: (01494) 465421 Fax: (01494) 524044 E-mail: accentsteel@ukonline.co.uk *Steel sheet stockholders*

Accent Textiles, Cambridge Industrial Estate, Dickinson Street, Salford, M3 7LW Tel: 0161-832 3003 Fax: 0161-832 9129 E-mail: info@accent-textiles.com *Household textile goods manufrs*

Accenture, 60 Queen Victoria Street, London, EC4N 4TW Tel: (020) 7844 4000 Fax: (020) 7844 4444 *Management consultants*

▶ Acceptus Ingredients & Blends, 109 St. Helens Road, Westcliff-on-Sea, Essex, SS0 7LF Tel: 07979 243025

Access, Silkmoor, New Street, Shrewsbury, SY3 8LN Tel: (01743) 360607 Fax: (01743) 340706 E-mail: admin@access-taxis.co.uk *Taxi company*

▶ Access 24, 3 Stadhampton Road, Drayton St. Leonard, Wallingford, Oxfordshire, OX10 7AR Tel: (01865) 400928 E-mail: admin@access24.co.uk *Locksmith*

Access Accounting (Scotland) Ltd, The Business Centre, Denside School, Glenogil, Forfar, Angus, DD8 3SQ Tel: (01356) 650222 Fax: (01356) 650322 E-mail: info@access-scotland.co.uk *Software accounts & supplies services*

▶ Access Appraisals Ltd, White Cottage, Stourton, Shipston-on-Stour, Warwickshire, CV36 5HG Tel: (01608) 685039 E-mail: md@wheelchair-ramps.co.uk *Online retailer and affiliate*

▶ Access Audio Ltd, Unit 32-35,, Hardengreen Business Park, Dalhousie Road, Eskbank, Dalkeith, Midlothian, EH22 3NX Tel: 0131-663 0777 Fax: 0131-660 9777 E-mail: info@accessaudio.co.uk *Provider of safety equipment for the disabled*

▶ Access CCTV & Securities, 119 Hoyle Street, Warrington, WA5 0LP Tel: (01925) 632000 Fax: (01925) 632777 E-mail: accesscctvsec@yahoo.co.uk *Installation services of security equipment, cctv*

Access Chemicals Ltd, Hedging Lane, Wilnecote, Tamworth, Staffordshire, B77 5EX Tel: (01827) 289000 Fax: (01827) 289080 E-mail: sales@accesschemicals.co.uk *Industrial chemicals & metal finishing suppliers*

Access Cleaning Solutions, 321 Blythswood Court, Glasgow, G2 7PH Tel: 0141-221 7355 E-mail: info@accesscleaningsolutions.co.uk *Glasgow carpet & upholstery cleaning specialists*

Access Computers, 411 Bearwood Road, Smethwick, West Midlands, B66 4DF Tel: 0121-429 5558 Fax: 0121-429 5558 *Computer maintenance, services & manufrs*

Access Computing Solutions Ltd, Optima House, Wharf BSNS Centre, Bourne End, Buckinghamshire, SL8 5RU Tel: (01628) 819500 Fax: (01628) 819508 E-mail: sales@acstech.co.uk *IT maintenance, networking & computer hardwear supplies*

▶ Access consulting, 5 Errwood Crescent, Burnage, Manchester, M19 2NX Tel: 0161 2257342 Fax: 07896 344014 E-mail: jimthomas007@ntlworld.com *We are able to offer development, regulatory affairs,Microbiology,QA consultancy services primarily for the personal care & household products sectors. We can offer DGSA services for any sector.**Finally we can source a range of consumer durables from China*

Access Control Automation Ltd, Arun Business Park, Bognor Regis, West Sussex, PO22 9SX Tel: (01243) 830641 Fax: (01243) 830738 E-mail: sales@accesscontrolautomation.com *Electronic automatic operated gates suppliers*

Access Control Services, 20-26 High Street, Greenhithe, Kent, DA9 9NN Tel: (01322) 370777 Fax: (01322) 370076 E-mail: admin@xplan.com *Security system manufrs*

Access Controls UK Ltd, 62 Ocean Close, Fareham, Hampshire, PO15 6QP Tel: (01329) 513222 Fax: (01329) 513221 E-mail: enquiries@accesscontrols.co.uk *Access control engineers*

▶ Access Copiers, 58 Ashton Road, Failsworth, Manchester, M35 9WL Tel: 0161-684 8655 E-mail: access.copiers@virgin.net *Photocopiers, fax machines & printer retailers*

▶ Access Design & Engineering, Halesfield 18, Telford, Shropshire, TF7 4JS Tel: (01952) 588788 Fax: (01952) 685139 E-mail: sales@access-design.co.uk *Steel fabricators*

▶ Access Diamond Drilling Ltd, Elm View, 2 Longley Road, Croydon, CR0 3LH Tel: (020) 8239 1486 Fax: (020) 8239 1486 E-mail: davidhann@blueyonder.co.uk *Diamond core drilling contractors*

▶ Access Disability Ltd, 55 Coronation Street, Blackpool, FY1 4NY Tel: (01253) 753300 Fax: 01253 733402 E-mail: Keith@accessdisability.co.uk *Mobility hire shop*

Access Door Services, Unit 6-7 Trent South Industrial Park, Nottingham, NG2 4EQ Tel: 0115-958 0768 Fax: 0115-985 9240 *Industrial door suppliers, repairs & manufrs*

Access Fire & Security Ltd, Henley House, 1293-1295 Warick Road, Acocks Green, Birmingham, B27 6PU Tel: 0121-765 4900 Fax: 0121-765 4901 E-mail: michael@accessfire.co.uk *Close circuit television installers*

Access Company Formations Ltd, 31 Church Rd, Hendon, London, NW4 4EB Tel: (020) 8202 2220 Fax: (020) 8202 2202 E-mail: graham@offshorecos.freeserve.com *Company formations UK & international*

Access Gates & Shutters, Suite 2-3 Banters La Ecf Complex, Main Road, Great Leighs, Chelmsford, CM3 1QX Tel: (01245) 360366 Fax: (01245) 361401 *Rolling shutter installers*

▶ Access Hardware Ltd, Jewsons Ltd, The Slough, Spernal, Studley, Warwickshire, B80 7EN Tel: (01527) 852948 Fax: (01527) 854192 E-mail: sales@accesshardware.co.uk *Manufacturers & distributors of architectural stainless steel*

Access Industrial Door Co Midlands Ltd, 148a Crankhall Lane, Wednesbury, West Midlands, WS10 0ED Tel: 0121-505 1435 Fax: 0121-505 3318 E-mail: neelsangha@aol.com *Industrial doors*

Access Instrumentation Ltd, Reading Road, Eversley, Hook, Hampshire, RG27 0RP Tel: 0118-973 4702 Fax: 0118-973 1177 E-mail: sales@accessinstrumentation.co.uk *Process instruments*

Access Interiors Ltd, 140 Science Park Milton Road, Cambridge, CB4 0GF Tel: (01223) 506441 Fax: 01223 506441 *Office refurbishment*

Access It Ltd, The Old Grain Store, Brenley Lane, Boughton-under-Blean, Faversham, Kent, ME13 9LY Tel: (01227) 750555 Fax: (01227) 750070 E-mail: sales@accessit.co.uk *Network reseller*

▶ Access Job Boards Ltd, BioCity, Pennyfoot Street, Nottingham, NG1 1GF Tel: 0845 644 5481 Fax: 0845 644 5482 E-mail: info@access-sciencejobs.co.uk *The specialist online recruitment job board for the UK science industry.*

▶ Access Law, 14-24 Cannon Street, Southampton, SO15 5PQ Tel: (023) 8087 8600 Fax: 023 80878611 E-mail: law@accesslaw.co.uk *Southampton based family law practice Solicitors undertaking both Legal Aid and private work including Family and Divorce, Mental Health, Conveyancing and Wills and Probate. We hold Legal Services Commission contracts in both Family and Mental Health Law. Our partners are accredited specialists with the Law Society Family Law, Children and Mental Health Review Tribunal Panels and with Resolution. We provide free legal advice and information on our website and by email*

Access Mechanical Handling Ltd, 11 Sholto Cresent, Righead Industrial Estate, Bellshill, Lanarkshire, ML4 3LX Tel: (01698) 745859 Fax: (01698) 740869 E-mail: sales@forktrucks-scotland.co.uk *Fork lift truck services*

▶ Access Sales International, 9 Kings Lodge Drive, Mansfield, Nottinghamshire, NG18 5GZ Tel: (01623) 624411 Fax: (01623) 624415 E-mail: sales@asionline.co.uk *Providers of access equipment*

Access Scaffold Systems Ltd, Unit 5, Duchess Industrial Estate, Sievewright Street, Rutherglen, Glasgow, G73 1LL Tel: 0141-613 0000 Fax: 0141-613 0011 *Scaffold hire*

▶ Access Scaffolding Contractors, Marston Hall Depot, Marston Jabbett, Bedworth, Warwickshire, CV12 9SD Tel: (024) 7649 4433 Fax: (024) 7649 4477

Access & Security 24Hr Locksmiths, Key House Coombe Rise, Oadby, Leicester, LE2 5TT Tel: 0116-271 9003 Fax: 0116-271 9229 E-mail: info@leicesterlocksmith.com *Master locksmiths*

Access & Security Systems Ltd, 7 Bacchus House, Calleva Park, Aldermaston, Reading, RG7 8EN Tel: 0118-981 7300 Fax: 0118-982 0455 E-mail: info@securityrollershutters.co.uk *Security shutters manufrs*

Access Self Storage Ltd, 93 Park Lane, London, W1K 7TB Tel: (020) 7297 4000 E-mail: enquiries@accessstorage.com *Access Self Storage - your local self storage facility for London and throughout the UK.**We provide great value self storage at 45 stores across the country. Visit our website to find your nearest one. **Store excess stock & paperwork; *Free unlimited access, 7 days a week;*No-deposit option & prepayment discounts;*Store from as little as a week;*Specialist archiving facilities available;*Serviced office space, meeting rooms & showrooms available;*Cost-effective, secure parking in gated compounds;*24 hour CCTV monitoring; *Free trolley use;*Fork lift facilities & pallet trucks;*Undercover loading bays;*Storing & packing materials available;*Deliveries & collections can be overseen;*Waste disposal service available.*

Access Company Services Ltd, 103-106 Chadwick Road, Astmoor Industrial Estate, Runcorn, Cheshire, WA7 1PW Tel: (01928) 590880 Fax: (01928) 590877 *Aluminium tower hire & scaffold manufrs*

▶ Access Services, 7 Renfrew Green, Strensall, York, YO32 5PF Tel: (01904) 490156 Fax: (01904) 490142 E-mail: nh@access-services.net *Access database developer with a wealth of experience and the business acumen to deliver systems that are easy to use and importantly, really do work*

Access Shipping Ltd, Rainham House Rainham Trading Estate, New Road, Rainham, Essex, RM13 8RA Tel: (01708) 521113 Fax: (01708) 521151 E-mail: access-shipping@cnsmail.co.uk *Freight forwarders*

Access Storage, Shentonfield Road, Leestone Road Sharston Industrial Estate, Sharston Industrial Area, Manchester, M22 4RW Tel: 0161-428 1348 Fax: 0161-495 2100 E-mail: sharston@accessstorage.com *Storage rooms rented all sizes also stock a range of packing materials*

Access To Data Solutions Ltd, 3 Beech Lees, Farsley, Pudsey, W. Yorkshire, LS28 5JY Tel: 0113-236 1134 *Computer consultants*

Access Training Services Ltd, Unit 4, 45 Mowbray Street, Sheffield, S3 8EN Tel: 0114-273 1333 Fax: 0114-280 2010 E-mail: info@the-access-group.com *Training services*

AC-CESS Co. UK Ltd, Tyrebagger Works, Kinellar, Aberdeen, AB21 0TT Tel: (01224) 790100 Fax: (01224) 790111 E-mail: info@ac-cess.com *The AC-ROV mini submersible, the smallest and most portable ROV on the market, setting new standards in the Hand Carry Class. Applications include underwater inspection, diver support, and homeland security.*

Access Unlimited, 20 George Street, Alderley Edge, Cheshire, SK9 7EJ Tel: (01625) 584130 Fax: (01625) 584623 E-mail: info@accessunlimited.co.uk *Computer support*IT support*Database software development*Software development*PC support*Server support*

▶ Access2cash Ltd, The Grange, Porcupine Lane, Par, Cornwall, PL24 2RP Tel: (0870) 4584666 Fax: (01726) 813100 E-mail: info@access2cash.co.uk *Access2cash limited are a UK distributer of Dash ATM outdoor ATM pods. We also are the franchise arm of Astracomm ATM Limited within the UK for franchise operations in ATM cash machines.*

Accessible Hire & Refrigeration Ltd, Masters House, 46 Bridgnorth Road, Wollaston, Stourbridge, West Midlands, DY8 3QG Tel: (01384) 446000 Fax: (01384) 375242 E-mail: hire@ahrltd.co.uk *Refrigerated units hire services*

Accessible I T Ltd, 9 Rees Drive, Coventry, CV3 6QF Tel: (024) 7669 3901 E-mail: rbs@accessibleit.co.uk *Computer consultants*

▶ Accessory Store, 1617 London Road, Leigh-on-Sea, Essex, SS9 2SQ Tel: (01702) 480537 Fax: (01702) 480537 *Bathroom fittings retailers*

▶ Accident Advice Helpline, Accident Advice House, Merrion Avenue, Stanmore, Middlesex, HA7 4RP Tel: (0800) 1804400 E-mail: info@accidentadvicehelpline.com *Leading no win no fee personal injury compensation specialist*

▶ Accidents Revisited, 12 Kariba Close, Chesterfield, Derbyshire, S41 0FP Tel: (01246) 207285 Fax: (0871) 242 9547 E-mail: accidents.revisited@tiscali.co.uk *Personal injury accident claims & investigation*

▶ Accidon'T, 20 East Argyle Street, Helensburgh, Dunbartonshire, G84 7RR Tel: (01436) 678018 Fax: (01436) 678808 E-mail: simon.johnston@accidont.co.uk *Fleet driver training, bespoke packages to reduce the risk of accidents*

Acclaim Carpet Cleaners, 20 Graydon Avenue, Chichester, West Sussex, PO19 8RF Tel: (01243) 780381 Fax: (01243) 780381 E-mail: info@1aacclaim.co.uk *Carpet & upholstery cleaning services*

Acclaim Fabrications, 7b Meadow Road, Reading, RG1 8LB Tel: 0118-939 3413 Fax: 0118-939 3413 *Sheet metalworkers & ironworkers*

Acclaim Fasteners & Turned Parts, Unit 17 Premier Park Estate, Leys Road, Brierley Hill, West Midlands, DY5 3UP Tel: (01384) 76263 Fax: (01384) 76268 *Fasteners & turned parts distributors*

Acclaim Pest & Environmental Services, 25 Granville Street, Market Harborough, Leicestershire, LE16 9EU Tel: (01858) 432797 Fax: (01858) 445085 E-mail: acclaimpest@hotmail.com *Pest control services*

Accles & Shelvoke Ltd, Selco Way Off First Avenue, Minworth Industrial Estate, Minworth, Sutton Coldfield, West Midlands, B76 1BA Tel: 0121-313 4567 Fax: 0121-313 4569 E-mail: sales@eley.co.uk *Humane slaughtering equipment manufrs*

Acco Eastlight Ltd, Ashton Road, Denton, Manchester, M34 3LR Tel: 0161-336 9431 Fax: 0161-320 8012 E-mail: mark.winstanley@acco-eastlight.co.uk *Filing systems manufrs*

Acco UK Ltd, Gatehouse Road, Aylesbury, Buckinghamshire, HP19 8DT Tel: (01296) 397444 Fax: (01296) 311000 E-mail: info@acco-uk.co.uk *Office product distributors & manufrs*

Acco UK Ltd, Bretton Way, Bretton, Peterborough, PE3 8YE Tel: (01733) 264711 Fax: (01733) 269910 *Office equipment manufrs*

▶ Accolade Food Manufacturers Ltd, North Wall, Grimsby, South Humberside, DN31 3SY Tel: (01472) 349762 Fax: (01472) 349769 *Food processors*

Accolade Photography, Cannybrow Barn, Gatebeck, Kendal, Cumbria, LA8 0HS Tel: (01539) 567030 Fax: (01539) 567030 E-mail: sales@thebestphotography.co.uk *Industrial photographers*

Accom Ltd, 1 Cliffside Industrial Estate, Askew Farm Lane, Grays, Essex, RM17 5XR Tel: (01375) 396262 Fax: (01375) 396363

▶ Accommadata Cabins Direct, Unit 1, Crowland Street Industrial Estate, Russell Road, Blowick, Southport, Merseyside, PR9 7AS Tel: (01704) 540956 Fax: (01704) 220247 E-mail: accommadata@churchtown.co.uk *Portable jackleg cabins & modular office buildings*

▶ Accommodation Services Management Ltd, Greenhole Park, Greenhole Place, Bridge of Don Industrial Estate, Aberdeen, AB23 8EU Tel: (01224) 826100 Fax: (01224) 826101 E-mail: info@asm.co.uk *Property services*

Accommodations, Lion House, 6 Hawthorn Road, Newcastle upon Tyne, NE3 4DE Tel: 0191-213 2131 Fax: 0191-213 2211 E-mail: sales@accomodationsuk.co.uk *Hotel & conference booking agents*

▶ Accor Electrical Engineering Services Ltd, 63 Montonfields Rd, Monton, Eccles, Manchester, M30 8AW Tel: 0161-707 3692 E-mail: enquiries@accorgroup.co.uk *We undertake Domestic, Commercial and Industrial work ranging from replacing a single light fitting to overhauling a factory"s power distribution system. We offer a wide range of services including Domestic Installation, Inspection & Testing, Commercial Portable Appliance Testing and Industrial maintenance, Design and Installation.*

Accord Air Systems, Lawmans Centre, 28-32 Beddington Lane, Croydon, CR0 4TB Tel: (020) 8401 2058 Fax: (020) 8401 2059 E-mail: accordair@lineone.net *Air con, ventilation & heating*

Accord Computer Systems Ltd, 7-9 Union Street, Stratford-upon-Avon, Warwickshire, CV37 6QT Tel: (01789) 415541 Fax: (01789) 414410 E-mail: info@accordltd.co.uk *Software & hardware house*

Accord Lift Services Ltd, Unit 5A Beechcroft Farm Industries, Chapel Wood Road, Ash, Sevenoaks, Kent, TN15 7HX Tel: (01474) 879858 Fax: (01474) 874143 E-mail: info@accordlifts.co.uk *Lift engineers*

Accord Office Supplies Ltd, Unit 22 Bridge Mead, Westmead Industrial Estate, Westlea, Swindon, SN5 7TL Tel: (0800) 7311133 Fax: (0800) 7311133 E-mail: sales@accordoffice.co.uk *Stationery & office furniture suppliers*

▶ Accountancy & Business Cartoons, 4 Auckland Way, Hartburn, Stockton-on-Tees, Cleveland, TS18 5LG Tel: (01642) 581847 Fax: (01642) 581847 E-mail: vh2@businesscartoons.co.uk *Cartoon agency*

Accountancy Divisions, 37 George Street, Croydon, CR0 1LB Tel: (020) 8686 5353 Fax: (020) 8686 2666 E-mail: croydon@hays.com *Employment agency* Also at: Branches throughout the U.K.

Accountancy & General Ltd, 37 South Molton St, London, W1K 5RJ Tel: (020) 7495 3840 Fax: (020) 7491 0023 E-mail: hr@puddledock.ltd.uk *Employment agency*

▶ Accountancy Services, 16 Grosvenor Avenue, Newquay, Cornwall, TR7 1BQ Tel: (01637) 876795 Fax: (01637) 876795 E-mail: info@accountancyservices.uk.net *Accountancy*

Accountancy Support Reading Ltd, 8 Hencroft St North, Slough, SL1 1RD Tel: (01753) 533006 Fax: (01753) 533002 E-mail: andy@accountancysupport.co.uk *Employment agencies*

Accountancy Systems & Training Ltd, 35 Church Walk, Denny, Stirlingshire, FK6 6DF Tel: (01324) 822222 E-mail: info@astl.co.uk *Training & support specialist in accounting systems*

▶ Accounting Products Ltd, 16 Lynton Road, New Malden, Surrey, KT3 5EE Tel: (020) 7043 2777 Fax: (0870) 1373744 E-mail: sarah.seddon@accountingproducts.co.uk *Free software for GL, AP, AR, supply chain management, light manufacturing, warehouse management, call centre management, voicemail, voicemail to e-mail, remote worker support, CMS and VoIP. We also offer our own paperless office/document management systems, bank reconciliation, cash forecasting and control, as well as consulting.*

▶ Accounting Taxation & Business Services, 58 Queen Elizabeth Drive, Beccles, Suffolk, NR34 9LP Tel: (01502) 713362 Fax: (01502) 714366 E-mail: mail@atbs1.co.uk *Our clients range from the self employed, small businesses to limited companies. We advise clients on things like their tax affairs, accounting, P.A.Y.E and a wide variety of other services. We are fully computerised*

▶ Accounting Technology Ltd, Europe House, 10 Bancroft Road, Reigate, Surrey, RH2 7RP Tel: (01737) 222261 Fax: (01737) 225585 *Business solutions*

▶ Accounts Plus, 25 Elm Tree Road, Cosby, Leicester, LE9 1SR Tel: 0116-286 7874 Fax: 0116-286 7874 *Accountants, limited company, partnerships, sole traders, bookeeping, VAT, PAYE etc.*

▶ Account-Wryte Ltd, Suite 105, York House, 2-4 York Road, Felixstowe, Suffolk, IP11 7QG Tel: (01394) 277888 Fax: (0871) 2771548 E-mail: accountwryteltd@yahoo.co.uk *Modern, prompt & cost effective accountancy practice*

▶ Accranut Co. Ltd, 1 Closers Business Centre, Avenue Road, Nuneaton, Warwickshire, CV11 4ND Tel: (024) 7638 4062 Fax: (024) 7638 7889

Accrapak Systems Ltd, Burtonwood Industrial Centre, Burtonwood, Warrington, WA5 4HX Tel: (01925) 222926 Fax: (01925) 220137 E-mail: enquiries@accrapak.co.uk *Bag & sack filling machine manufrs*

Accredited Roofing, 21 River Court, Minster Road, Coventry, CV1 3AT Tel: (024) 7625 6325 E-mail: enquires@accreditedroofing.co.uk *Roofing contractors covering coventry, Kenilworth, Leamington, Warwick & local areas, felting, tiling, flat roofs, pointing, ridge tiles, guttering, lead flashings, plastering etc*

Accrington Brush Co. Ltd, Lower Grange Mill, Church Street, Accrington, Lancashire, BB5 2ES Tel: (01254) 871414 Fax: (01254) 872064 E-mail: info@a-brush.co.uk *Manufacture brushes to customer specification*

Accrington Non Ferrous Metals, Argyle Street, Accrington, Lancashire, BB5 1DQ Tel: (01254) 234550 Fax: (01254) 234550 *Non ferrous metal merchants*

Accrofab Ltd, 11 Stoney Gate Road, Station Road, Spondon, Derby, DE21 7RX Tel: (01332) 666878 Fax: (01332) 666245 Principal Export Areas: Central/East Europe *Precision engineers*

Accrol Papers Ltd, Roman Road Indust Estate, Blackburn, BB1 2LU Tel: (01254) 278844 Fax: (01254) 278855 E-mail: info@accrol.co.uk *Paper converters*

▶ The Accruals Bureau & Credithouse P.L.C., Spectrum House, Dunstable Road, Redbourn, St. Albans, Hertfordshire, AL3 7PR Tel: (0870) 4441753 Fax: (01582) 791203 E-mail: info@abandc.co.uk *Financial solutions for business.*

Acc-Sys Software Ltd, 11-13 Philip Road, Ipswich, IP2 8BH Tel: (01473) 400161 Fax: (01473) 400163 E-mail: enquiries@accsys.uk *Software & computer suppliers*

Accuma Plastics Ltd, Princewood Road, Earlstrees Industrial Estate, Corby, Northamptonshire, NN17 4AP Tel: (01536) 263461 Fax: (01536) 263516 E-mail: sales@accuma.co.uk *Plastic battery container manufrs*

Accura Holdings, Hickman Avenue, Wolverhampton, WV1 2DW Tel: (01902) 454460 Fax: (01902) 451840 E-mail: enquiries@accura.co.uk *Special support services*

Accura Pipe Fitting Ltd, Hickman Avenue, Wolverhampton, WV1 2DW Tel: (01902) 453322 Fax: (01902) 453314 E-mail: pipefittings@accura.co.uk *Pipe fittings manufrs*

▶ Accura Surveys Ltd, The Granary, Breadstone, Berkeley, Glos, GL13 9HG Tel: 01453 511998 E-mail: info@accura-surveys.com *Dimensional control survey consultancy for the petrochemical and nuclear industries. **Surveys carried out for first time fit of pipework and structures, quality audits, shimming analysis, procedure compilation and offshore platform installations.*

Accuramatic Laboratory Equipment, 42 Windsor Road, King's Lynn, Norfolk, PE30 5PL Tel: (01553) 777253 Fax: (01553) 777253 E-mail: info@accuramatic.co.uk *Laboratory equipment manufrs*

Accurate Business Solutions Ltd, 80 Peach Street, Wokingham, Berkshire, RG40 1XH Tel: 0118-977 3880 Fax: 0118-977 1260 E-mail: info@accurate.co.uk *IT consultants*

Accurate Controls, 25 Cowley Road, Nuffield Industrial Estate, Poole, Dorset, BH17 0UJ Tel: (01202) 678108 Fax: (01202) 670161 E-mail: info@accurate-controls.ltd.uk *Temperature control gauges & systems manufrs*

Accurate Grinding, Unit 6 Dawsons Lane, Barwell, Leicester, LE9 8BE Tel: (01455) 840888 Fax: (01455) 840888 *Grinding services*

▶ Accurate Mechanical Services, Unit 18 Pegasus Court, North Lane, Aldershot, Hampshire, GU12 4QP Tel: (01252) 315000 Fax: (01252) 315252

Accurate Section Benders Ltd, Dawley Brook Road, Kingswinford, West Midlands, DY6 7AU Tel: (01384) 402402 Fax: (01384) 402462 E-mail: sales@accuratesectionbenders.co.uk *Metal bending & forming services*

Accurate Weight Co. Ltd, 5 Bridle Way, Bootle, Merseyside, L30 4UA Tel: 0151-524 3341 Fax: 0151-525 5864 E-mail: sales@accurateweight.co.uk *Industrial scales supplier & repairers*

▶ Accurate Windows, 163 Moston Lane, Manchester, M9 4HR Tel: 0161-202 4000 Fax: 0161-202 4001 *Window frames manufrs*

Accure Geneva Ltd, 1-5 Goodwood Road, Pershore, Worcestershire, WR10 2JL Tel: (01386) 555335 Fax: (01386) 556739 E-mail: enquiries@geneva.accura.co.uk *Deep hole boring services*

Accuride International Ltd, Liliput Road, Brackmills Industrial Estate, Northampton, NN4 7AS Tel: (01604) 761111 Fax: (01604) 767190 E-mail: saleseurope@accuride-europe.com *Drawer slides*

▶ Accurist Fabrications Ltd, Wharf Foundry, Well Street, Bolton, BL1 1TZ Tel: (01204) 529383 Fax: (01204) 362896 E-mail: sales@accfabs.co.uk

Accurist Watches, Asher House, Blackburn Road, London, NW6 1AW Tel: (020) 7447 3900 Fax: (020) 7447 3946 E-mail: sales@accurist.co.uk *Watch & clock importers* Also at: London W1

Accurite Industries, Cumbria, Haws Bank, Coniston, Cumbria, LA21 8AP Tel: (01539) 441313 Fax: (01539) 441225 *Stonework machinery suppliers*

▶ Accurite Industries, Low Mill Business Park, Morecambe Road, Ulverston, Cumbria, LA12 9EE Tel: (01229) 480800 Fax: (01229) 480801 E-mail: mark@accurite.co.uk

Accuromm UK Ltd, 20 Welsh Road, Garden City, Deeside, Clwyd, CH5 2RA Tel: (01244) 836385 Fax: (01244) 241100 E-mail: info@accurommuk.com *Plastics injection moulding manufrs*

Accu-Rout Ltd, Maltings Lane, Castleton, Rochdale, Lancashire, OL11 2UY Tel: (01706) 631277 Fax: (01706) 646207 *Engraving machine services*

Accurus Ltd, Giles Road, Oldbury, West Midlands, B68 8JG Tel: 0121-544 5335 Fax: 0121-544 5339 E-mail: admin@accurus.co.uk *Engineering/ presswork*

▶ Accuscene, Unit 1, St Davids Drive, St Davids Business Park, Dalgety Bay, Dunfermline, Fife, KY11 9PF Tel: (01383) 828880

Accused, Ark Lane, Deal, Kent, CT14 6PU Tel: (01304) 360626 Fax: (01304) 364600 E-mail: accused@accused.co.uk *Sports clothing & fashion manufrs*

Accutec Design Ltd, Unit C3 Haysbridge Business Centre, Brickhouse Lane, South Godstone, Godstone, Surrey, RH9 8JW Tel: (01342) 842129 Fax: (01342) 844027 *Clock manufactures, importers & distributors of innovative gadgets*

Accutest Ltd, Wren Nest Road, Glossop, Derbyshire, SK13 8HB Tel: (01457) 866613 Fax: (01457) 856789 E-mail: sales@accutest.co.uk *Communication systems*

Accuvac Prototypes Ltd, Unit F2 Watlington Industrial Estate, Cuxham Road, Watlington, Oxfordshire, OX49 5LU Tel: (01491) 613161 Fax: (01491) 613161 E-mail: enquiries@accuvac.co.uk *Engineering prototype production engineers*

Accuweigh, Unit 14, East Riding Business Centre, Annie Reed Road, Beverley, North Humberside, HU17 0LS Tel: (01482) 475650 *Repair of weighing equipment*

ACDOCO Ltd, Mallison Street, Bolton, BL1 8PP Tel: (01204) 600500 Fax: (01204) 600501 E-mail: specialist@acdo.co.uk *Manufacture soap powder & laundry aids*

▶ Ace, Esdralon, Les Varendes, St. Andrew, Guernsey, GY6 8TG Tel: (07781) 154152 E-mail: sales@aceproperty.co.uk

Ace, Farleigh Cottage, Ricketts Hill Road, Tatsfield, Westerham, Kent, TN16 2NA Tel: (01959) 577139 Fax: (01959) 577283 E-mail: aceukaircon@btinternet.com *Air conditioning installation services*

Ace Adhesives Ltd, Shenstone Drive, Walsall, WS9 8TP Tel: (01922) 459393 Fax: (01922) 743417 E-mail: sales@aceadhesives.com *Adhesive suppliers & manufrs*

Ace Appointments, 4 Market Square, Northampton, NN1 2DL Tel: (01604) 630781 Fax: (01604) 620495 E-mail: recruit@aceappsnorth.co.uk *Employment agency*

Ace Body Builders Ltd, Albert Road, Leeds, LS27 8LD Tel: 0113-253 2562 Fax: 0113-252 8673 E-mail: info@acebodybuilders.fsbusiness.co.uk *Commercial motor body builders*

Ace Business Machines, 21 Clarendon Road, Kenilworth, Warwickshire, CV8 1HZ Tel: (024) 7667 0715 Fax: (024) 7667 0715 *Catering equipment distributors*

Ace Business Machines, 1 Lacre Way, Letchworth Garden City, Hertfordshire, SG6 1NR Tel: (01462) 676002 Fax: (01462) 484315 E-mail: sales@acetills.co.uk *Cash register distributors*

Ace Catering Hire, 115 Nursery Gardens, Staines, Middlesex, TW18 1EL Tel: (01784) 455243 Fax: (01784) 455243 E-mail: jmansell_507@hotmail.com *Catering & refrigeration equipment suppliers*

Ace Cleaning Service, Corner Road, Pillowell, Lydney, Gloucestershire, GL15 4QU Tel: (01594) 562688 Fax: (01594) 563722 E-mail: acecleaning@lydney24.fsbusiness.co.uk *Contract cleaners*

Ace Cleaning Services Ltd, 72-74 High Street, Dawlish, Devon, EX7 9HF Tel: (01626) 889500 Fax: (01626) 889500 E-mail: david@acecleaning.co.uk *Industrial cleaning products*

Ace Components Ltd, 4 Priory Gardens, Scorton, Preston, PR3 1AQ Tel: (01524) 793893 Fax: (01524) 793894 E-mail: colinbabbs.ace@ukonline.co.uk Principal Export Areas: Worldwide *Suppliers of semiconductors & semiconductor components*

Ace Computer Co. Ltd, 13 Queens Road, London, N11 2QJ Tel: (020) 8889 3622 Fax: (020) 8889 9566 *Computer manufrs*

Ace Computer Services Ltd, 19 Westerby Lane, Smeeton Westerby, Leicester, LE8 0RA Tel: 0116-279 3673 *Computer resellers*

Ace Contracts, 1 Frontier Works, 33 Queen Street, London, N17 8JA Tel: (020) 8801 9011 Fax: (020) 8801 9933 E-mail: acecontracts@btconnect.com *Blind manufrs*

Ace Controls International, 1 Belvedere Road, Newton-le-Willows, Merseyside, WA12 0JJ Tel: (01925) 227171 Fax: (01925) 229323 E-mail: sales@ace-controls.co.uk *Industrial shock absorbers manufrs*

▶ Ace Conveyor Equipment Ltd, Plumtree Farm Industrial Estate, Plumtree Road, Bircotes, Doncaster, South Yorkshire, DN11 8EW Tel: (01302) 718800 Fax: (01302) 711998 E-mail: info@ace247.com *Belt conveyor products & services*

Ace Copying Equipment Ltd, Unit 9 Union Close, Tamworth, Staffordshire, B77 1BB Tel: (01827) 63374 Fax: (01827) 69749 E-mail: info@ace-copying.com *Sales & services of new & used photocopiers faxes & printers*

▶ Ace Courier Services, 13 Ullswater Road, Tyldesley, Manchester, M29 7AQ Tel: (01942) 873990 Fax: (01942) 709137 E-mail: al63@blueyonder.co.uk *Courier services*

Ace Cutters London Ltd, Unit 10 Lewisham Way Industrial Estate, 151-163 Lewisham Way, London, SE14 6QP Tel: (020) 8692 4671 Fax: (020) 8692 0433 E-mail: sales@acecutters.co.uk *Trade die makers*

▶ Ace Design & Development Ltd, 10 Goldington Crescent, Billericay, Essex, CM12 0QJ Tel: (01277) 627240 Fax: 01277 659617 E-mail: ace.design@btconnect.com *Ace Design & Developments aim to provide a complete design and cad service specifically for the construction and shopfitting industry.*We are fully capable of overseeing a project from prototype to mass production.*

Ace Electroplating Ltd, Wordsworth Road, Leicester, LE2 6EE Tel: 0116-270 8651 Fax: 0116-270 2593 *Electroplating services*

Ace Elevators Ltd, Galven House, Bakewell Road, Loughborough, Leicestershire, LE11 5QY Tel: (01509) 265383 Fax: (01509) 269275 E-mail: midlands@ace-elevators.co.uk *Passenger, goods lifts, bespoke designers*

Ace Elevators Southern Ltd, Millennium House, 74 South Street, Keighley, West Yorkshire, BD21 1DQ Tel: (01535) 602239 Fax: (01535) 661268 E-mail: sales@ace-elevators.co.uk *Lift repair service & manufrs*

▶ Ace Embroidery Ltd, 141 Tat Bank Road, Oldbury, West Midlands, B69 4NH Tel: 0121-544 7108 Fax: 0121-544 4965 E-mail: info@ace-embroidery.co.uk *Suppliers of embroidered clothing of all types*

Ace Engineers Ltd, Albert Road, Morley, Leeds, LS27 8LD Tel: 0113-252 2611 Fax: 0113-238 0274 E-mail: sales@ace-engineers.co.uk *Aluminium stockholders & fabricators*

Ace Engraving Ltd, 12 Vulcan House, Vulcan Road North, Norwich, NR6 6AQ Tel: (01603) 485667 Fax: (01603) 485667 E-mail: sales@aceengraving.co.uk *Industrial engraving services, signs, labels, control panels*

Ace Envelopes Ltd, Hillside House, 2-6 Friern Park, London, N12 9BT Tel: (020) 8445 0123 Fax: (020) 8446 9423 E-mail: sales@ace-envelopes.co.uk *Envelope print brokers*

Ace Equipment, Oakley Farm, Croxall, Lichfield, Staffordshire, WS13 8QZ Tel: (01283) 790320 Fax: (01283) 790456 E-mail: sales@aceequip.co.uk *Trolley manufrs*

Ace European Group, The Ace Building, 100 Leadenhall Street, London, EC3A 3BP Tel: (020) 7173 7000 Fax: (020) 7173 7800 E-mail: info@ace-ina.com *Insurance company*

▶ Ace Fabrications Ltd, 31 Dalmarnock Road, Rutherglen, Glasgow, G73 1AE Tel: 0141-613 0111 Fax: 0141-613 1199 *Metal fabrication specialists*

▶ Ace of Face, 5 Manstead Gardens, Rainham, Essex, RM13 9HL Tel: 01708 738802 E-mail: sarahjane.mcdonald@aon.co.uk *Fabulous face painting, mini-makeovers and temporary tattoo service for childrens parties, corporate events and private functions. Catering for the Essex and London areas. Face painting courses also provided and face painting products for sale - all top brands. Bouncy castles coming soon.*

Ace Fibreglass Mouldings Repairs, Castletown Way, Sherborne, Dorset, DT9 4EA Tel: (01935) 816437 E-mail: sales@fibreglass.com *Light industrial grip manufrs*

Ace Fire Ltd, 14 Concorde Road, Norwich, NR6 6BW Tel: (01603) 787333 Fax: (01603) 787332 E-mail: info@acefire.co.uk *Installers of fire extinguishers*

Ace Fire Midlands Ltd, 15 Lichfield Lane, Mansfield, Nottinghamshire, NG18 4RA Tel: (01623) 662805 *Maintain fire equipment*

Ace Fixings, 69 Sydenham Road, Belfast, BT3 9DJ Tel: (028) 9073 8900 Fax: (028) 9073 8903 *Fasteners, fixings & power tools suppliers*

▶ Ace Flooring UK Ltd, 6 Warden Mill Close, Wateringbury, Maidstone, Kent, ME18 5DJ Tel: (01622) 815544 E-mail: aceflooring@btinternet.com *Laminate, engineered & solid wood flooring manufrs*

Ace Freight, Penshaw Way, Portobello Industrial Estate, Birtley, Chester Le Street, County Durham, DH3 2SA Tel: 0191-410 5511 Fax: 0191-410 6344 *Road transport, haulage & freight services*

▶ Ace Garage Doors UK Ltd, Unit 12 Salamanca Road, Tharston Industrial Estate, Norwich, NR15 2PF Tel: (01603) 490119 Fax: (01508) 536094 E-mail: info@acegaragedoors.com *Suppliers & installers of remote control roller shutter garage doors*

Ace Garage Services, 34 Railway Approach, Worthing, West Sussex, BN11 1UR Tel: (01903) 233823 E-mail: cars@acecarhire.com *Courier services & car hire*

Ace General Engineering Cornwall Ltd, Quarry Park Road, Newquay, Cornwall, TR7 2NY Tel: (01637) 873324 Fax: (01637) 876904 *Catering equipment manufrs & distributors*

▶ Ace Heating Ltd, 24 Camaultmuir, Camault Muir, Kiltarlity, Beauly, Inverness-Shire, IV4 7JH Tel: (01463) 741300 Fax: (01463) 741224

▶ Ace Home Heating, 14 Seafield Road, Inverness, IV1 1SG Tel: (01463) 718300 Fax: (01463) 718800

Ace Industrial Boiler Cleaners, 10 Rollscourt Avenue, London, SE24 0EA Tel: (020) 7733 1676 *Boiler cleaning & servicing*

Ace Inflatables, 23 Alexandra Road, Uckfield, East Sussex, TN22 5BB Tel: (01825) 769951 *Inflatable castle hire*

Ace Interactive Ltd, Roe Garage, Charlton Road, Andover, Hampshire, SP10 3JZ Tel: (01264) 350424 Fax: (01264) 356281 *Mechanical spare parts distributors*

Ace International, Wedge Street, Walsall, WS1 2HQ Tel: (01922) 746454 Fax: (01922) 638484 E-mail: ace@aceinternationaluk.com *International traders*

▶ Ace Internet, Business & Arts Centre Houldsworth Mill, Houldsworth Street, Stockport, Cheshire, SK5 6DA Tel: (0870) 7407555 Fax: (0870) 7405335 E-mail: sales@ace-internet.co.uk *Internet services provider*

Ace Kitchens, 47-57 Feeder Road, Bristol, BS2 0SE Tel: 0117-971 3682 Fax: 0117-977 7004 *Kitchen unit planners*

Ace Lamps, Unit 30, New Forest Enterprise Centre, Chapel Lane, Totton, Southampton, SO40 9LA Tel: 02380 866728 E-mail: acelamps@deslamps.co.uk *SPECIALIST MEDICAL LAMP SUPPLIER*

▶ Ace Maintenance, Unit 4 & 5, Coatbank Business Centre, Coatbridge, Lanarkshire, ML5 3AG Tel: (01236) 440858

Ace Marine, Bankside, Thorpe Lane, Trimley St. Martin, Felixstowe, Suffolk, IP11 0RY Tel: (01394) 273357 Fax: (01394) 276828 *Sign contractors & installers*

Ace Metal, 10 Morgan Way, Bowthorpe Employment Area, Norwich, NR5 9JJ Tel: (01603) 731935 Fax: (01603) 748421 E-mail: acemetalsupplies@aol.com *Suppliers of non-ferrous metals*

Ace Minimix Ltd, Stancombe Lane, Flax Bourton, Bristol, BS48 3QD Tel: (01275) 465846 Fax: (01275) 465876 *Ready mix concrete distributors*

Ace Minimix Ltd, Saucepan Industrial Estate, Babraham Road, Sawston, Cambridge, CB22 3LH Tel: (01223) 301436 *Ready-mixed concrete manufacturers & distributors*

Ace Minimix, Rover Way, Cardiff, CF24 2RX Tel: (029) 2045 3894 Fax: (029) 2045 3894 *Concrete distributors*

Ace Minimix Ltd, Bellhouse Pit, Warren Lane, Stanway, Colchester, CO3 0NN Tel: (01206) 330178 Fax: (020) 8555 2612 E-mail: easten.amix@tarmac.co.uk *Ready mixed concrete supplier*

Ace Minimix Ltd, Sharpstones Lane, Bayston Hill, Shrewsbury, SY3 0AN Tel: (01743) 874083 Fax: (01544) 232185 *Ready mixed concrete suppliers*

▶ Ace Minimix, Warne Road, Weston-super-Mare, Avon, BS23 3UU Tel: (01934) 615470 Fax: (01275) 465876

▶ Ace Motors, Victoria Mill, Alliance Street, Accrington, Lancashire, BB5 2RT Tel: (01254) 232662 E-mail: info@acemotorsbaxenden.co.uk *Vehicles bought & sold, removed, new & used car parts supplied, fitted*

Ace Plantline, 10 Aghaginduff Road, Dungannon, County Tyrone, BT70 3AX Tel: (028) 8776 1433 Fax: (028) 8776 7017 E-mail: ace.plantline@btclick.com *Powder handling equipment distribs*

▶ Ace Plumbing, 78 Spring Road, Bournemouth, BH1 4PT Tel: (01202) 669171 Fax: (01202) 399751

Ace Precision Engineers, 5 Tait Road, Croydon, CR0 2DT Tel: (020) 8683 0487 Fax: (020) 8684 4583 E-mail: l.povada-ace@fsbdial.co.uk *Precision engineers*

Ace Refrigeration, 21 Mayhall Rd, Portsmouth, PO3 5AU Tel: 023 92696322 *Refrigeration & air conditioning installation*

Ace Rewinds Ltd, 25 Ivatt Way, Westwood Industrial Estate, Peterborough, PE3 7PG Tel: (01733) 331464 Fax: (01733) 334075 E-mail: meeksruss@aol.com *Motor rewind services*

Ace Safe Co. Ltd, Forest Corner Farm, Hangersley Hill, Hangersley, Ringwood, Hampshire, BH24 3JW Tel: (01425) 489860 Fax: (01425) 478780 E-mail: sales@acesafes.co.uk *New & reconditioned safe suppliers*

Ace Safety Services, The Court, Holywell Business Park, Kineton Road Industrial Estate, Southam, Warwickshire, CV47 0FS Tel: (01926) 813356 Fax: (01926) 817311 E-mail: enquiries@theacegroup.co.uk *Health & safety trainers*

▶ Ace Scaffolding Manchester Ltd, Weymouth Road, Eccles, Manchester, M30 8BT Tel: 0161-787 7872 Fax: 0161-787 7565

Ace Scale & Cash Systems, Whisperdale Farm, Silpho, Scarborough, North Yorkshire, YO13 0JT Tel: 01723 381579 Fax: 01723 381579 *Cash system repair services*

Ace Security, Security House, 248 Pellon Lane, Halifax, West Yorkshire, HX1 4PZ Tel: (01422) 342444 E-mail: sales@acesecurity.com *Security equipment installers*

Ace Security & Electrical Ltd, 150-152 Loughton Way, Buckhurst Hill, Essex, IG9 6AR Tel: (020) 8506 1421 Fax: (020) 8506 6666 *Installation of security systems*

▶ Ace Security Systems Ltd, 12 Triumph Way, Kempston, Bedford, MK42 7QB Tel: (01234) 854455 Fax: (01234) 855345 E-mail: sales@acesecurity.co.uk *Ace Security Systems Ltd are a family owned Security Installations Company who can cater for your every security need. *We are able to carry out installations, takeover and upgrades to Intruder Alarms, CCTV systems, Access Control Systems, Fire Systems, Locks and Safes. *We also carry out maintenance to these systems on a fully comprehensive contract basis. This is supported by our fully qualified team of 15.*

▶ Ace Security Systems Ltd, 12 Triumph Way, Kempston, Bedford, MK42 7QB Tel: (01234) 854455 Fax: (01234) 855345 E-mail: sales@acesecurity.co.uk *Ace Security Systems Ltd are a family owned Security Installations Company who can cater for your every security need. **We are able to carry out installations, takeover and upgrades to Intruder Alarms, CCTV systems, Access Control Systems, Fire Systems, Locks and Safes. *We also carry out maintenance to these systems on a fully comprehensive contract basis.*

Ace Signs Group, 1 Bentalls, Basildon, Essex, SS14 3BS Tel: (01268) 706800 Fax: (01702) 294325 E-mail: enquiries@asg.co.uk *Sign manufacturers & shop display fittings*

Ace Signs Group, Oak Tree Road, Binley, Coventry, CV3 2RR Tel: (024) 7660 8200 Fax: (024) 7660 8201 E-mail: info@asg.co.uk *Sign manufacturers & corporate identity specialists*

▶ Ace Software Engineering, High Street, Berkhamsted, Herts, HP4 2DJ Tel: (01442) 875910

Ace Specialist Hire Ltd, PO Box 498, Folkestone, Kent, CT18 7GG Tel: (01797) 369222 Fax: (01797) 369333 E-mail: sales@ashclean.co.uk *Cleaning machines hire & sales*

Ace Sports & Ladyline, 49 Duke Street, Staveley, Staveley, Chesterfield, Derbyshire, S43 3PD Tel: (01246) 470650 Fax: (01246) 280473 E-mail: malc@ace-sports.freeserve.co.uk *Sport & school clothes, in-house print embroidery company logos manufrs*

Ace Systems Ltd, Rose Green Road, Bristol, BS5 7XE Tel: 0117-952 0624 Fax: 0117-935 4255 E-mail: sales@acestorage.co.uk *Shelving, partitioning & ceilings manufrs*

Ace Systems, 72 Albert Road, Carrickfergus, County Antrim, BT38 8AE Tel: (028) 9336 2266 Fax: (028) 9336 2422 E-mail: info@ace-systems.co.uk *Computer consultants*

▶ Ace Systems Installations Ltd, 103 Elsenham Street, London, SW18 5NY Tel: (020) 8874 8966 Fax: (020) 8265 6050 E-mail: sales@fire-alarms.uk.com *We have been installing top quality fire alarm and emergency lighting systems since 1981 and offer competative prices within the M25 area and in Surrey.*

Ace Tarpaulins, Dovecot Street, Stockton-on-Tees, Cleveland, TS18 1HG Tel: (01642) 886216 Fax: (01642) 886244 E-mail: enquiries@acetarpaulinsltd.co.uk *Tarpaulin manufrs*

Ace Townsend Coaters, Two Woods Lane, Brierley Hill, West Midlands, DY5 1TA Tel: (01384) 70331 Fax: (01384) 78981 *Plastic coatings services*

Ace Training Services, Glebe Farm, Church Lane, Winterbourne, Bristol, BS36 1SG Tel: (01454) 250073 Fax: (01454) 250073 E-mail: sue@ace-training-services.freeserve.co.uk *Fork lift truck training*

Ace Visual & Sound Systems Ltd, Field House, Fieldside, Thorne, Doncaster, South Yorkshire, DN8 4BE Tel: (01405) 740393 Fax: (01405) 814807 E-mail: kevin@showmagic.com *Show control systems designers & suppliers*

Ace Webmasters, 34-40 Wormgate, Boston, Lincolnshire, PE21 6NR Tel: (07050) 224352 E-mail: firstatboston@yahoo.co.uk *Software engineers*

Ace Welding (Edensbridge), Merle Common Road, Oxted, Surrey, RH8 0RP Tel: (01883) 712668 Fax: (01883) 717524 *Welders & fabricators*

Ace Wood Turners & Machinists Ltd, Hazel La, Great Wyrley, Walsall, WS6 6AA Tel: (01922) 416645 *Wood handles & general woodwork machinists*

Ace Works, 216 Chorley New Rd, Horwich, Bolton, BL6 5NP Tel: (01204) 668667 Fax: (0870) 845 9049 E-mail: info@aceworks.com *Business internet services*

Ace Wound Products Ltd, 1g Skillion Business Park, Thames Road, Barking, Essex, IG11 0JP Tel: (020) 8507 2330 Fax: (020) 8507 8981 E-mail: mac@acewound.com *Transformers manufrs*

Acecutter Engineers Ltd, Unit 3 The Acre, Dappers Lane, Angmering, West Sussex, BN16 4EN Tel: (01903) 779977 Fax: (01903) 779966 E-mail: eng@seivad.co.uk Principal Export Areas: West Europe *Machinery reconditioning services*

Acedes Gear Tools, 2-4 Fleming Road, Newbury, Berkshire, RG14 2DE Tel: (01635) 524252 Fax: (01635) 521085 E-mail: sales@acedes.co.uk *Gear hob & shaper cutter manufrs*

Acemaster Products Ltd, 1 Julius Way, Lydfield Green, Lydney, Gloucestershire, GL15 5QS Tel: (01594) 842442 Fax: (01594) 843033 *Diamond tool suppliers*

▶ Acer Motorcycle Training, 18 Severn Oaks, Quedgeley, Gloucester, GL2 4YX Tel: (01452) 720975 E-mail: sales@acermotorcycles.com *Motorcycle Training CBT Motorcycle Test Gloucester Cheltenham Dursley Tewkesbury*

Acergy Ltd, Bucksburn House, Howes Road, Aberdeen, AB16 7QU Tel: (01224) 718200 Fax: (01224) 715129 E-mail: uk-hr@acergy-group.com *Underwater engineering contractors* Also at: London SE1

Aces Ltd, Unit 10 Manor Farm, Peppard Common, Henley-on-Thames, Oxfordshire, RG9 5LA Tel: (01491) 629671 Fax: (01491) 629621 E-mail: sales@acescomp.co.uk *Refrigeration compressor re-manufacturers*

Aces Dust Control Ltd, Unit 3 Fossil Bank, Upper Colwall, Malvern, Worcestershire, WR13 6PL Tel: (01684) 576573 Fax: (01684) 576583 *Dust control equipment distributors*

Aces Fans Ltd, 6 Ryefield Crescent, Northwood, Middlesex, HA6 1LR Tel: (01923) 827533 Fax: (01923) 835514 E-mail: sales@fixings-diy.co.uk *Fixings & fastener distributors*

Acetarc Welding & Engineering Co. Ltd, Atley Works, Dalton Lane, Keighley, West Yorkshire, BD21 4HT Tel: (01535) 607323 Fax: (01535) 602522 E-mail: sales@acetarc.co.uk Principal Export Areas: Worldwide *Manufacturers of foundry & plant equipment*

Acetate Products Ltd, 1 Holme Lane, Station Road, Derby, DE21 7BP Tel: (01332) 661422 Fax: (01332) 681786 *Acetate products manufrs*

▶ Acg Nutri Snacks, Unit 10 Elmfield Business Park, Lotherton Way, Garforth, Leeds, LS25 2JY Tel: 0113-287 7819 Fax: 0113-287 7434 E-mail: acgnutri@hotmail.com *Health food manufrs*

Achason & Glover Ltd, Lisdoonan, Belfast Road, Saintfield, Ballynahinch, County Down, BT24 7EP Tel: (028) 9081 3848 Fax: (028) 9081 4505 *Manufacture concrete products*

Acheson & Glover Ltd, 60 Creagh Road, Toomebridge, Antrim, BT41 3SE Tel: (028) 7965 0631 Fax: (028) 7965 0751 E-mail: info@acheson-glover.co.uk *Brick manufrs* Also at: Clumlin

Acheson & Glover Ltd, Creenagho, Belcoo, Enniskillen, County Fermanagh, BT93 5HA Tel: (028) 6638 6555 Fax: (028) 6638 6554 *Quarrying specialists*

Acheson Industries Europe Ltd, Cattewater Road, Plymouth, PL4 0SP Tel: (01752) 218788 Fax: (01752) 207133 E-mail: acheson.plymouth@nstarch.com *Lubricants, die casting, graphite manufrs* Also at: Birmingham & Reading

Acheson Industries Europe Ltd, Sun Life House, 85 Queens Road, Reading, RG1 4LP Tel: 0118-958 8844 Fax: 0118-957 4897 *Manufacturers of lubricants & coatings*

▶ Achieve UK, 10 Hubbard Close, Twyford, Reading, RG10 0XU Tel: 0118-934 4119 *Specialists in New Business Development, Telemarketing, Sales Lead Generation, Appointment Setting & Sales Training.*

Achieveglobal, Spencer House, 23 Sheen Road, Richmond, Surrey, TW9 1BN Tel: (020) 8322 4000 Fax: (020) 8322 4001 E-mail: service@achieveglobal.co.uk *Consultancy & training services*

Achiever Business Solutions, Cross Pillory House, Cross & Pillory Lane, Alton, Hampshire, GU34 1HL Tel: (01420) 547507 Fax: (01420) 547501 E-mail: jinny.groome@goachiever.com *Quality, health & safety & environmental software specialists*

Achiever Software, Ashted Lock Way, Birmingham, B7 4AZ Tel: 0121-380 1010 Fax: 0121-380 1011 E-mail: sales@achiever.co.uk *Software house manufrs*

▶ Achor Limited, 82 Northgate, Beccles, Suffolk, NR34 9AY Tel: (01502) 716870 Fax: (01502) 716587 E-mail: info@achor.co.uk

▶ Achromatic Limited, Grangemouth Enterprise & Technology Centre, Falkirk Road, Grangemouth, Stirlingshire, FK3 8XS Tel: (01324) 619360 Fax: (01324) 622399 E-mail: info@achromatic.co.uk *Water Analysers, Water Treatment, Automatic Coagulation & Flocculation Control Systems, Polymer Dosing Control, Polymer Analysers, Coagulation Analysers, Spectrophotometers*

Aci Solutions (Europe) Ltd, Boundary Road, Sturmer, Haverhill, Suffolk, CB9 7YH Tel: (01440) 712525 Fax: (01440) 718801 E-mail: sales@aci-solutions.net *Fibre optic cable assembly equipment manufrs*

▶ ACI Watford Ltd Air Conditioning, 1st Floor, 462-464 St Albans Road, Watford, WD24 6SR Tel: 01923 440265 Fax: 01923 440999 E-mail: Aciwatford@hotmail.com

ACI Worldwide Ltd, 27-33 Cookridge Street, Leeds, LS2 3AG Tel: 0113-394 0100 Fax: 0113-394 0129 *Computer software developers*

Acia Engineering, 39 Garners Lane, Stockport, Cheshire, SK3 8SD Tel: 0161-487 2225 Fax: (0871) 9941778 E-mail: ian@acia-acoustics.co.uk *Acoustical consulting engineers*

Ackerman Engineering Ltd, Corbin Way, Gore Cross Business Park, Bradpole, Bridport, Dorset, DT6 3UX Tel: (01308) 422185 Fax: (01308) 458276 E-mail: sales@ackerman-eng.com *Precision Sheet Metal Work Laser Cutting & Powder Coating*

Ackland Automatics, Unit 2 Lower Union Road, Kingsbridge, Devon, TQ7 1EF Tel: (01548) 852668 Fax: (01548) 852668 *Automatic distributors service*

Ackroyd & Abbott, 2 Rotherham Road, Sheffield, S13 9LL Tel: 0114-269 3201 Fax: 0114-254 0272 *Builders merchant*

Acksen Ltd, 42 University Road, Belfast, BT7 1NJ Tel: (028) 9020 1050 Fax: (028) 9020 1060 E-mail: sales@acksen.com *Software development services*

Acl Packaging Solutions, Unit F Argent Court, Hook Rise South, Surbiton, Surrey, KT6 7NL Tel: (020) 8391 4660 Fax: (020) 8391 4514 E-mail: sales@aclps.com *Transparent packaging*

Aclaim Handling Ltd, Woodbastwick, Norwich, NR13 6AG Tel: (01603) 721208 Fax: (01603) 721235 *Forklift truck hire/sales/service*

Acle Stove Centre, Beaconsfield Barn, The Street, Acle, Norwich, NR13 3DX Tel: (01493) 751575 *Wood burning stove suppliers & installation*

Acm Air Conditioning, Unit 10 Armley Workshops, Pickering Street, Leeds, LS12 2QG Tel: 0113-203 8240 Fax: 0113-279 7088 *Air conditioning engineers*

Acme Appointments, 122 Middlesex Street, London, E1 7HY Tel: (020) 7377 9923 Fax: (020) 7375 2948 *Recruitment*

Acme Appointments, 315 Oxford Street, London, W1C 2HH Tel: (020) 7493 4000 Fax: (020) 7493 4383 *Recruitment consultants*

Acme Electrical Manufacturing Tottenham Ltd, Tariff Road, Tottenham, London, N17 0EP Tel: (020) 8808 2702 Fax: (020) 8801 9017 *AC & DC control geal mnfg*

Acme Model Products, 48 Highgate Road, Sileby, Loughborough, Leicestershire, LE12 7PP Tel: (01509) 812177 Fax: (01509) 812177 E-mail: sales@acmemodels.co.uk *Model railway retailers*

Acme Neon, Fitzroy Terrace, Grafton Street, Northampton, NN1 2NU Tel: (01604) 631068 Fax: (01604) 631068 E-mail: sales@acmeneon.co.uk *Sign manufrs*

▶ Acme Printing Co. Ltd, 37 Aston Road, Waterlooville, Hampshire, PO7 7XF Tel: (023) 9282 5036 Fax: (023) 9225 9521

Acme Refrigeration Ltd, Cunliffe Road, Whitebirk Industrial Estate, Blackburn, BB1 5ST Tel: (01254) 277999 Fax: (01254) 277988 E-mail: email@acmerefrigeratiop.co.uk *Refrigeration engineers*

Acme Spinning Co. Ltd, Garratts Lane, Cradley Heath, West Midlands, B64 5RE Tel: 0121-559 1648 Fax: 0121-559 1299 E-mail: info@acmespinning.com Principal Export Areas: West Europe *Metal spinners & general presswork.*

Acme United Europe, Estate Office Thorncliffe Park Estate, Newton Chambers Road, Chapeltown, Sheffield, S35 2PH Tel: 0114-220 3709 Fax: 0114-220 3706 E-mail: sales@acmeunited.co.uk *Scissors & manicure requisites manufrs*

ACO Buildings Drainage, Hitchin Road, Shefford, Bedfordshire, SG17 5TE Tel: (01462) 816666 Fax: (01462) 851490 E-mail: buildingdrainage@aco.co.uk *Manufacturers of drainage products*

▶ ACO Contracting Services, 2 Newmin Way, Clavering Park Estate, Whickham, Newcastle upon Tyne, NE16 5RE Tel: 0191-488 4871 E-mail: andrewoliver1975@hotmail.com *We are Construction and Civil Engineering management consultants. We have worked on a diversity of projects within the core areas of legal, commercial and production management.*

Aco Electronics Ltd, Unit 3 Manor Farm Business Park, Shingay cum Wendy, Royston, Hertfordshire, SG8 0HW Tel: (01223) 208222 Fax: (01223) 208150 E-mail: sales@acoelectronics.com *Forgery detection equipment manufacturing services*

Aco Technologies Plc, Hitchin Road, Meppershall, Shefford, Bedfordshire, SG17 5TE Tel: (01462) 816666 Fax: (01462) 815895 E-mail: customersupport@aco.co.uk *ACO is a design, manufacturing and marketing company at the forefront of material technology, providing a number of highly advanced products for the construction, processing, rail and environmental industries.*

Acol, Castle Hill, Gomersal, Cleckheaton, West Yorkshire, BD19 4HW Tel: (01924) 402061 Fax: (01924) 402061 *Toiletries*

Acomb Engineering Ltd, Catfoss, Hull, HU11 5SP Tel: (01964) 542724 Fax: (01964) 543939 *General engineers*

Acompany P.L.C., Elsley House, 24-30 Great Titchfield Street, London, W1W 8BF Tel: (020) 8443 1236 Fax: (020) 7631 1163 E-mail: info@acompany.co.uk *Handbag & small leather goods manufrs*

Acon Equipment Ltd, Constance Road, Leicester, LE5 5DD Tel: 0116-273 9823 Fax: 0116-249 0802 E-mail: cadaconequip@aol.com *Press tool manufrs*

Aconia Jewellery Casters Ltd, 43 Northampton Street, Birmingham, B18 6DU Tel: 0121-236 9838 Fax: 0121-212 1840 *Jewellery casting*

▶ Aconsultingmk Business Transfer Agents, 24 Iron Duke Close, Daventry, Northamptonshire, NN11 9LN Tel: (01327) 705100 Fax: (01327) 705100 E-mail: brian@amicia.co.uk *aconsultingMK is an independent Business Sales Consultancy offering a discreet and confidential service to owners who are planning an exit strategy from their business.**Covering an area from Birmingham to Peterborough and down to London from our office in Daventry, we work with our colleagues in the Axis Partnership to provide a nationwide presence.**Our website and other marketing media generate a steady stream of enquiries from companies and individuals who are looking to buy going concerns.**Initial consultations are free of charge and without obligation.**A good referral for me today would be an owner/director of a business with a turnover between £¼M and £6M who is thinking about his exit strategy and planning to sell his business over the next couple of years.**

Acord Electronics Ltd, Madeira Road, West Byfleet, Surrey, KT14 6DN Tel: (01932) 354565 Fax: (01932) 350140 E-mail: sales@acord.co.uk *Electronic control system design services*

Acord Fluid Power Ltd, Unit 21, Llantarnam Industrial Estate, Cwmbran, Gwent, NP44 3AX Tel: (01633) 838181 Fax: (01633) 867711 *Hydraulic engineers & pneumatic equipment distributors*

▶ Acordia, 46-48 Alfreton Road, Nottingham, NG7 3NN Tel: 0115-978 4513 Fax: 0115-847 5212 *Training organisation*

Acordis Services Ltd, Po Box 111, Coventry, CV6 5RS Tel: (024) 7658 2288 Fax: (024) 7668 2737 E-mail: enquiries@acordisservices.com *Acordis Services Ltd, formerly Acordis Speciality Fibres, has led the way in the production of specialist materials for over 20 years. We have been committed to the development and manufacture of revolutionary new fibres and the application of customised solutions since the early 1980s. Services include wet spinning, melt spinning, chemical modification, non woven fabrics, FMP/clean room production facilities, Alginate & Micropake*

Acorn, Raleigh House, 152-156 Hedon Road, Hull, HU9 1NJ Tel: (01482) 223447 Fax: (01482) 375089 E-mail: simpson6@simpson6.crew.co.uk *Pallet company*

▶ Acorn Building Services Ltd, Sefton St, Leigh, Lancashire, WN7 1LX Tel: (01942) 609966 Fax: (01942) 262444 E-mail: reception@acornbuilders.com

Acorn Business Machines, Unit 4 Crossley Mills, New Mill Road, Honley, Holmfirth, HD9 6QB Tel: (0800) 5429405 Fax: (01484) 660076 E-mail: mark@acornbuisnessmachines.co.uk *Sales*

Acorn Business Supplies Ltd, Acorn House Motorway Industrial Estate, Forstal, Aylesford, Kent, ME20 7AF Tel: (01622) 882233 Fax: (01622) 882101 E-mail: sales@acorn-business-supplies.co.uk *Office equipment suppliers*

Acorn Catering Equipment Co., George Baylis Road, Berry Hill Industrial Estate, Droitwich, Worcestershire, WR9 9RB Tel: (01905) 798080 Fax: (01905) 797745 E-mail: sales@acorncateringequipment.co.uk *Catering equipment suppliers*

▶ Acorn Chemical Services, Unit 16-17, Milland Road Industrial Estate, Neath, West Glamorgan, SA11 1NJ Tel: (01639) 641222 Fax: (01639) 632255 E-mail: admin@equilibrium.net *Chemical manufrs*

Acorn Cleaning Service, 2a Lothair Road, London, W5 4TA Tel: (020) 8579 1177 Fax: (020) 8840 7545 *Cleaning cloth suppliers*

Acorn Design, 96 Appletree Lane, Brockhill, Redditch, Worcestershire, B97 6TS Tel: (01527) 62189 *Digital & lithographic printers service*

Acorn Doors, 2 Abbas Business Centre, Main Road, Itchen Abbas, Winchester, Hampshire, SO21 1BQ Tel: (01962) 791111 Fax: (01962) 791111 *Traditional door manufrs*

Acorn Engineering, 6 Kingscroft Court, Ridgway, Havant, Hampshire, PO9 1LS Tel: (023) 9249 2040 Fax: (023) 9247 0377 E-mail: mail@acorn-engineering.co.uk *Custom built machinery manufrs*

Acorn Engineering Services, Units 1-2, Avery Dell Industrial Estate, Lifford Lane, Kings Norton, Birmingham, B30 3DZ Tel: 0121-459 3900 Fax: 0121-459 2600 E-mail: aesbirminigham@aol.com *Tube manipulation & bending services*

Acorn Engraving Co., 4 Pump Lane, Regent Business Centre, Hayes, Middlesex, UB3 3NP Tel: (020) 8848 7367 Fax: (020) 8756 1028 *Engravers*

Acorn Environmental, Windsor Terrace, East Herrington, Sunderland, SR3 3SF Tel: 0191-528 2444 Fax: 0191-520 2201 *Pest control services*

Acorn Fabrications, Unit 4a, 179 Cardiff Road, Reading, RG1 8HD Tel: 0118-958 7466 Fax: 0118-958 7466 E-mail: dinoacornfabs@live.co.uk *Steel Fabricators*

Acorn Fasteners Ltd, Unit W4 Lambs Business Park, Tilburstow Hill Road, South Godstone, Godstone, Surrey, RH9 8LJ Tel: (01342) 893500 Fax: (01342) 892820 E-mail: sales@acornfastenersltd.co.uk *Fastener distributors*

Acorn Feed Products Ltd, The Old Chapel, Loddon Bridge Road, Woodleyd, Reading, RG5 4BG Tel: 0118-944 0144 Fax: 0118-944 0357 E-mail: chris@acornfeeds.co.uk *Animal feed merchants*

Acorn Graphics, Mercia Way, Foxhills Industrial Estate, Scunthorpe, South Humberside, DN15 8RE Tel: (01724) 280368 Fax: (01724) 271988 E-mail: sales@acorn-graphics.co.uk *Flexographic Printing Plates, for the corrugated, label and polythene industries.*

Acorn Hip Flasks Ltd, Reliance Works, 62 Northwood Street, Birmingham, B3 1TT Tel: (0777) 9724408 Fax: 0121-233 4336 E-mail: peter@hipflasks.co.uk *Hipflasks, nipcup sets, coinholders, money clips, cufflinks, keyrings, credit card cases, hip flasks, spirit flasks, whiskey flasks, tot cup sets, numbered cup sets, shooters cups, business gifts*

Acorn Ice Cubes, 66A Waldeck Road, London, W4 3NU Tel: (020) 8994 9339 *Ice merchants*

Acorn Industrial Developments, 3 Wallbrook Court, Netherwood Road, Rotherwas Industrial Estate, Hereford, HR2 6JG Tel: (01432) 276600 Fax: (01432) 341268 *Precision engineering, machining & sheet metalwork*

Acorn Industrial Services Ltd (Midlands), Units 17-21, Bloomfield Park, Bloomfield Road, Tipton, West Midlands, DY4 9AH Tel: 0121-521 5999 Fax: 0121-521 5888 E-mail: midlands@acorn-ind.co.uk *Acorn are one of the UK"s largest independent stockist and best-known suppliers of all types of bearings, seals and power transmission products. With twenty-five years experience in the engineering industry, Acorn have built an unrivalled reputation for outstanding customer service, product choice and customer solutions. *Authorised distributors for many of the worlds leading manufacturers including SKF, Megadyne belts, Optibelt, Goodyear, NB Linear systems, RBC Bearings, NICE, Diamond Chain, MarelliMotori Motors and many more.**

Acorn Industries, Brandsby, York, YO61 4RG Tel: (01347) 888217 Fax: (01347) 888382 *Hand made furniture manufrs*

Acorn Joinery, Floodgates Farm, Castle Lane, West Grinstead, Horsham, West Sussex, RH13 8LH Tel: (01403) 711330 Fax: (01403) 711330 E-mail: acornjoinery@resource24.net *Joiners*

Acorn Leisure, The Paddock, Tenby, Dyfed, SA70 8DJ Tel: (01834) 842931 Fax: (01834) 845174 *Leisure & amusement machines*

Acorn Lifting Services Ltd, Northern Court, Off Vernon Road, Nottingham, NG6 0BJ Tel: 0115-976 2862 Fax: 0115-976 1406 E-mail: als@acorn-lifting.co.uk *Crane repairers*

Acorn Mailing Services, Chaucer Business Park, Watery Lane, Kemsing, Sevenoaks, Kent, TN15 6HU Tel: (01732) 760042 Fax: (01732) 760043 E-mail: info@acornmailingservices.co.uk *Direct mail services*

Acorn Maintenance Systems, 33 Brayford Avenue, Brierley Hill, West Midlands, DY5 3PW Tel: (01384) 423351 Fax: (01384) 423351 *Chemical cleaning product retailer*

▶ Acorn Mechanical Pipework Services Ltd, Suite F Lancaster House Grange Business Park, Enderby Road, Whetstone, Leicester, LE8 6EP Tel: 0116-277 8687 Fax: 0116-277 8106

▶ Acorn Packaging Services Ltd, Joinery Works, Butts Road, Stanford-le-Hope, Essex, SS17 0JH Tel: (01375) 643277 Fax: (01375) 643277 E-mail: sales@acornpackaging.co.uk *Manufacturers of timber & plywood export packaging*

Acorn Partition & Storage Systems, Kingsley Road, Lincoln, LN6 3TA Tel: (01522) 688771 Fax: (01522) 680404 E-mail: sales@apss.co.uk

▶ Acorn Petroleum Services Ltd, 36 Lodge Field Road, Whitstable, Kent, CT5 3RF Tel: please use e-mail E-mail: gh56@acorn-ps.com *Reservoir Engineering Consultancy for the upstream oil & gas industry*

▶ Acorn Plant & Tool Hire Ltd, Unit 3-4 Douglas Buildings, Lodge Road, Staplehurst, Tonbridge, Kent, TN12 0QZ Tel: (01580) 891234 Fax: (01580) 891234

Acorn Precision, 19 Stairbridge Lane, Bolney, Haywards Heath, West Sussex, RH17 5PA Tel: (01444) 248160 Fax: (01444) 246354 *Precision sheet metalworkers & general fabrication*

▶ Acorn Press Swindon Ltd, Westmead Industrial Estate, Westlea, Swindon, SN5 7UU Tel: (01793) 608900 Fax: (01793) 608901 E-mail: sales@acornpress.co.uk

Acorn Print, 5 Vale Road, Spilsby, Lincolnshire, PE23 5HE Tel: (01790) 754575 Fax: (01790) 754575 *Self-adhesive labels manufrs*

Acorn Print (North Space), 60 Hampton Street, Birmingham, B19 3LU Tel: (01902) 630733 Fax: (01902) 608540 E-mail: sales@acornprint.uk.com *Commercial printers*

Acorn Screen Products Ltd, Meadow Lane, Loughborough, Leicestershire, LE11 1JX Tel: (01509) 610665 Fax: (01509) 212972 E-mail: enquiries@acornscreenproducts.co.uk *Ink manufrs*

Acorn Security Alarms Ltd, Swan House, Bonds Mill, Stonehouse, Gloucestershire, GL10 3RF Tel: (01453) 794050 Fax: (01453) 794051 E-mail: info@acornsecurityalarms.co.uk *Security alarm suppliers & fitters*

Acorn Security Systems, Royal Insurance Building, 6 The Strand, Derby, DE1 1BA Tel: (01332) 370561 *Alarm systems*

▶ Acorn Services, 242 Portobello High Street, Edinburgh, EH15 2AT Tel: 0131-669 8444 Fax: 0131-669 8444

Acorn Services, Unit 3 Access Point, Willenhall Industrial Centre, Bloxwich, Walsall, WS3 2XN Tel: (01922) 491676 Fax: (01922) 710305 E-mail: jane@acornservices.wannado.co.uk *Powder coating services*

Acorn Signs, 16 Church Street, Hadfield, Glossop, Derbyshire, SK13 2AD Tel: (01457) 861211 E-mail: acorn@signs95.fsnet.co.uk *Sign manufrs*

Acorn Signs, Unit 3, 42 Harbour Road, Inverness, IV1 1UF Tel: (01463) 713708 Fax: (01463) 710332 E-mail: sales@acornsigns.co.uk *Sign manufrs*

Acorn Signs, Oaktree Business Park, Oakwood Road, Mansfield, Nottinghamshire, NG18 3HQ Tel: (01623) 414004 Fax: (01623) 414005 E-mail: signsfromacorn@btconnect.com *Sign manufrs*

Acorn Signs, 203 London Road, Stoke-on-Trent, ST4 5RW Tel: (01782) 412020 Fax: (01782) 412259 *Sign manufrs*

▶ Acorn Soft Furnishings, 12 Almond Drive, Burtonwood, Warrington, WA5 4QE Tel: 01925 291237 Fax: 01925 293255 E-mail: bev@acorn-soft-furnishings.co.uk *We are a soft furnishings business specialising in made to measure curtains, pelmets, cushion covers, tiebacks etc.*We also make embroidered goods for that special occasion*

▶ Acorn Timber Decking, 158 Werrington Road, Stoke-on-Trent, ST2 9AW Tel: (01782) 869805 Fax: (07786) 001962 E-mail: simon.kearns@ntlworld.com *Staffordshire. Cheshire. Derbyshire. Profesional installation company.*New hidden fastening system with 15year guarantee.*multi level specialists.Deck builders for the last seven years.*

Acorn Timber & Joinery Ltd, Britannia Works, Upper Cyrus Street, Manchester, M40 7FD Tel: 0161-273 3871 Fax: 0161-274 3203 E-mail: sales@acorntimber.com *Timber and Joinery Merchants. Suppliers of Arbordeck garden decking, OSMO natural woodfinishes, timber, mouldings, hardwood, softwood, sheet materials, stairs and stair parts, timber flooring, log cabins*

Acorn Trading Co., 101 Shakespeare Road, London, W3 6SA Tel: (020) 8992 6366 Fax: (020) 8992 9660 *Packaging material distributors*

Acorn Woodcraft, Northcote Workshop, Burrington, Umberleigh, Devon, EX37 9NF Tel: (01769) 560108 Fax: (01769) 560555 *Garden furniture supplier*

▶ AcornDomains.co.uk, Lewis Close, Addlestone, Surrey, KT15 2XG Tel: (01932) 841869 *Domain business & selling*

▶ Acornley Decorating, 38 Chalk Hill, Watford, WD19 4BX Tel: (07956) 150093 E-mail: macornley@hotmail.com *Assessed and approved by Dulux - free 12 month Dulux guarantee. Now offering you natural paints: eco-friendly, no harmful chemicals, no toxic fumes.*

Acorns Lettings and Property Management, High Street, Stanwell Village, Staines, Middlesex, TW19 7JS Tel: 01784 254596 E-mail: info@acorns-lettings.co.uk *Sales & Lettings Estate Agents*

Acorus Agricultural Services, 10 Risbygate Street, Bury St. Edmunds, Suffolk, IP33 3AA Tel: (01284) 753271 Fax: (01284) 748750 *Rural property services*

Acota Ltd, Unit B1 Centrepoint Stafford Drive, Battlefield, Shrewsbury, SY1 3BF Tel: (01743) 466392 Fax: (01743) 466555 E-mail: admin@acota.co.uk *Printed circuit conformal coating specialists*

Acoustafoam Ltd, Unit D, Halesfield 10, Telford, Shropshire, TF7 4QP Tel: (01952) 581340 Fax: (01952) 581455 E-mail: mike@acoustafoam.com *Manufacturers of foam (plastic) converters products*

▶ Acousteel, Naylor Court, Patterson Street, Blaydon-on-Tyne, Tyne & Wear, NE21 5SD Tel: (0870) 7072000 Fax: (0870) 7072001 E-mail: info@acousteel.com *Specialists suppliers in sound dead steel*

Acoustic Arrangements, York Farm, Fenn Lane, Upton, Nuneaton, Warwickshire, CV13 6BL Tel: (01455) 213373 Fax: (01455) 213581 E-mail: mail@a-a.uk.com *Audio visual installations & suppliers*

Acoustic Arts, The Old Laundry, Kingswood Foundation Est Britannia Rd, Kingswood, Bristol, BS15 8DB Tel: 0117-935 2034 Fax: 0117-935 2034 *Children's musical activities workshop*

Acoustic Ceilings Ltd, Unit 16-18, Loftus Street, Cardiff, CF5 1HL Tel: (029) 2034 2918 Fax: (029) 2034 2919 *Suspended ceiling suppliers*

Acoustic Consultancy Services, 2 Belhaven Terrace Lane, Glasgow, G12 9LZ Tel: 0141-339 7536 Fax: 0141-339 7536 E-mail: andywatson@talk21.com *Acoustic consultants*

Acoustic Control Systems, 64 Cromley Road, High Lane, Stockport, Cheshire, SK6 8BU Tel: (01663) 764409 Fax: (01663) 764409 E-mail: sales@acousticcontrol.co.uk Principal Export Areas: Worldwide *Acoustic consultants*

Acoustic Design Consultancy, Aldham House, Lady La Industrial Estate, Hadleigh, Ipswich, IP7 6BQ Tel: (01473) 824452 Fax: (01473) 824408 E-mail: adc@acoustic.co.uk *Noise & vibration consultants*

Acoustic Enclosures Co. Ltd, Unit 3 Waldergraves Business Park, Waldergraves Lane, West Mersey, Colchester, CO5 8SE Tel: (01206) 384377 Fax: (01206) 384611 E-mail: acoustic.enclosures@btinternet.com *Noise & acoustic engineers*

Acoustic & Engineer Consultants Ltd, 1 Stockport Road, Marple, Stockport, Cheshire, SK6 6BD Tel: 0161-449 5900 Fax: 0161-449 5901 E-mail: kaw@aecltd.co.uk *Industrial noise control & acoustic consultants*

Acoustic Engineering Services (UK) Ltd, PO Box 322, West Byfleet, Surrey, KT14 6YN Tel: (01932) 352733 Fax: (01932) 355265 E-mail: sales@aesuk.co.uk *Noise vibration control engineers*

Acoustic & Noise Partnership, Penburn House, 25a Upper Dock Street, Newport, Gwent, NP20 1DL Tel: (01633) 252957 Fax: (01633) 252958 E-mail: paul@acoustics-and-noise.co.uk *Noise consultants*

Acoustic Products Ltd, 167 Tankerton Road, Whitstable, Kent, CT5 2AR Tel: (01227) 281140 Fax: (01227) 281141 E-mail: admin@acoustic-products.co.uk *Partition & door suppliers*

▶ Acousticabs Industrial Noise Control Ltd, Unit 52, Pocklington Industrial Estate, Pocklington, York, YO42 1NR Tel: (01759) 305266 Fax: (01759) 305268 E-mail: info@acousticabs.com *Design, supply & installation of acoustic treatments & equipment for: Architectural Applications Acoustic wall panels/linings with coloured fabric facings (CP Wall Panels; Stretch Acoustic System). Acoustic* continued *ceiling panels - 24 different colours - up to 80mm thick for enhanced performance (TBS; TBS/I). Specially reinforced panels for sports halls & areas with high demands (Acoustishock). Acoustic baffles suspended vertically in the roof space. Available in several sizes and thicknesses - coloured or perforated faces - up to 3m long for specialist applications. (TBS Baffle; Perfbaffle). Industrial Applications Standard acoustic panels for easy assembly into acoustic enclosures/refuges/screens (SP). Specially designed acoustic enclosures (TP). Environmental Applications Acoustic louvres in a range of performance levels for incorporating into buildings or enclosing plant. Fixed external acoustic screens such as SPS & Profiled Screen System (e.g. for night time delivery areas).*

Acoustical Investigation & Research Organisation Ltd, Duxons Turn, Hemel Hempstead, Hertfordshire, HP2 4SB Tel: (01442) 247146 Fax: (01442) 256749 E-mail: airo@bcs.org.uk *Acoustic consultants & test laboratory*

Acousticar Car Entertainment Systems, 4 Kingsley Industrial Park, New Road, Kibworth, Leicester, LE8 0LE Tel: 0116-279 3113 Fax: 0116-279 3224 E-mail: sales@acousticar.co.uk *Car stereo security*

Acoustics Noise & Vibration, Hastings House, Auckland Park, Bletchley, Milton Keynes, MK1 1BU Tel: (01908) 642811 Fax: (01908) 642800 E-mail: info@anv.uk.com *Acoustic consultants*

Acoustilux Suspended Ceilings, 4a Old Lodge Lane, Purley, Surrey, CR8 4DE Tel: (020) 8660 3300 Fax: (020) 8660 6644 *Suspended ceilings & partitions installation*

▶ Acp Woodwork, 37a Newington Road, Ramsgate, Kent, CT12 6EJ Tel: (01843) 590957

▶ ACPR, 18 Spencer Mews, Lansdowne Way, London, SW8 1HF Tel: (020) 7820 7768 E-mail: antonia@acpr.co.uk *Help to promote your small business.*

▶ Acquatech Plumbing, Heating & Electrical, 301 Amersham Road, Hazlemere, Bucks, HP15 7PX Tel: 01494 717777 E-mail: info@acquatech.co.uk *Domestic plumbing heating and electrical services*

▶ Acra Screed Ltd, Pendle View Farm, Tosside, Skipton, North Yorkshire, BD23 4SJ Tel: (01729) 840000 E-mail: acrascreed@yahoo.co.uk *ACRA SCREED and Accessories systems, a revolutionary screed chair system. Tolerance of +/- 1/50th" - 1/2mm. Power/hand screeds can run on it. Base block, reinforcement support with 4 different cover heights,sturdy and strong,no interference with structural steel.Any height,fast and easy to set up. Economically competitive.*

▶ Acre House Equestrian, 2 Spencer Trading Estate, Rhyl Road, Denbigh, Clwyd, LL16 5TQ Tel: (01745) 816628 Fax: (01745) 816628 *Equestrian suppliers*

Acre Investments Ltd, Short Acre Street, Walsall, WS2 8HW Tel: (01922) 623360 Fax: (01922) 623360 *Property investment & rental*

Acre Joinery Ltd, 2 The Waterings, St Martins Road, Norwich, NR3 3EU Tel: (01603) 628602 Fax: (01603) 762483 *Joinery manufrs*

Acre Metals Ltd, Unit 6 Claremont Way Industrial Estate, Cricklewood, London, NW2 1BG Tel: (020) 8458 0581 Fax: (020) 8201 9807 *Scrap metal merchants*

Acre Packaging Supplies Ltd, 15 Kepler, Lichfield Road Industrial Estate,, Tamworth, Staffordshire, B79 7XE Tel: (01827) 310330 Fax: (01827) 310337 E-mail: sales@acrepackaging.co.uk *Packaging supplies & Strapping Machines.*

Acrelane Builders Merchants Ltd, 53 Acre Lane, London, SW2 5TN Tel: (020) 7738 3777 Fax: (020) 7738 6842 E-mail: info@diamond-merchants.co.uk *Heating & plumbing merchants*

Acrivarn Ltd, South Park Mills, Hare Lane, Pudsey, West Yorkshire, LS28 8DR Tel: 0113-257 8875 Fax: 0113-257 7564 E-mail: sales@acrivarn.co.uk *Bakery equipment manufrs*

Acro Security Engineers, 43 Compton Close, London, NW1 3QS Tel: (020) 7388 6300 Fax: (020) 7388 6400 *Locksmiths & lock opening services*

Acrogen Ltd, 14A Cambridge Road, Granby Industrial Estate, Weymouth, Dorset, DT4 9TJ Tel: (01305) 769754 Fax: (01305) 784555 E-mail: acrogen@acrogen.com *Designers & manufacturers of electronic power supplies*

Acrokool Ltd, 1 Veerman Park, Thaxted Road, Saffron Walden, Essex, CB10 2UP Tel: (01799) 513631 Fax: (01799) 513635 E-mail: sales@acrokool.co.uk *Manufacturers of cooler/cooling (industrial) systems, fountain (drinking), water cooler (drinking), water cooler (industrial) & refrigeration engineers. Also fountain (drinking) & water cooler distributors or agents*

Acrol Air Conditioning Co. Ltd, Salt Meadows Road, East Gateshead Industrial Estate, Gateshead, Tyne & Wear, NE8 3AH Tel: 0191-477 7999 Fax: 0191-477 7222 E-mail: sales@acrolairconditioningco.co.uk *Air conditioning design, installation & service*

Acrol Air Conditioning Services Ltd, Unit 49b, Leechmare East Industrial Estate, Sunderland, SR2 9TE Tel: 0191-523 6441 Fax: 0191-523 6425 E-mail: mail@aacs.demon.co.uk *Refrigeration, air conditioning & electrical services*

Acrona Engineering, Unit 1, Woodview Estate, Church Hanborough, Witney, Oxfordshire, OX29 8AA Tel: (01993) 880588 Fax: (01993) 880590 E-mail: sales@acrona-engineering.co.uk *CNC & precision engineering services*

Acropolis Computers Ltd, 2D Dolphin Way, Stapleford, Cambridge, CB2 5DW Tel: (01223) 841700 Fax: (01223) 841802 E-mail: info@biosoft.com *Software publishers*

Acrow Galvanising Ltd, 4 Commercial Centre, Ashdon Road, Saffron Walden, Essex, CB10 2NH Tel: (01799) 522219 Fax: (01799) 522447 E-mail: acrow@wedge-galv.co.uk *Hot dip galvanising organisation*

▶ acrylic aquarium co (UK), 3 Fitzstephen Road, Dagenham, Essex, RM8 2YP Tel: 020 8593 3305 E-mail: info@aquariummasters.freeserve.co.uk *Large Acrylic aquarium,suppliers,installers for Business and Commercial installations.One-offs,custom work a speciality,including Acrylic tubes,odd shapes etc.*World-wide coverage !!!!!!*

▶ Acrylicon Installations North East Ltd, North Speed House, Moor View, Leeds, LS11 9NF Tel: 0113-245 2707 Fax: 0113-245 2649 E-mail: acrylicon@hotmail.co.uk *Specialised flooring installation service*

Acrylicon UK, Unit 11/12, Brook Road, Bicton Industrial Park, Kimbolton, Huntingdon, Cambridgeshire, PE28 0LR Tel: (01480) 861034 *Flooring contractors*

Acrylube Technical Services, Clegg Street, Brierfield, Nelson, Lancashire, BB9 5JQ Tel: (01282) 698595 Fax: (01282) 611244 E-mail: sales@lubricantsuk.co.uk *Lubricants & equipment suppliers*

▶ Acs Air Conditioning Solutions, 3 Law Close, Littleport, Ely, Cambridgeshire, CB6 1TS Tel: (01353) 860360 Fax: (01353) 860360 E-mail: www.info@qualityacs.co.uk *We offer a design,sales,lease,hire,installation,maintenance & repair service in the E/Anglia area or nation wide. Our engineers are all certified by C.I.T.B & we are a member of the Federation of small businesses.*

ACS Cabins, Midlands Farm, Mill Lane, Headley, Bordon, Hampshire, GU35 0PB Tel: (01428) 714900 *Relocatable buildings hirers & suppliers*

▶ Acs Computers Ltd, 2f South Hams Business Park, Churchstow, Kingsbridge, Devon, TQ7 3QH Tel: (01548) 853358 Fax: (01548) 856540 *Computer maintenance*

Acs Dobfar UK Ltd, Cambois, Bedlington, Northumberland, NE22 7DB Tel: (01670) 565656 Fax: (01670) 850571 E-mail: mike.fitzgerald@acsdobfar.co.uk *Researchers & developers*

ACS Engineering, 2 Cairndubh Cottages, Cairnbaan, Lochgilphead, Argyll, PA31 8SQ Tel: (01546) 603849 E-mail: acs-engineering@wargyll.fsnet.co.uk *Manufacturers of model steam engines, boilers & steam accessories*

▶ ACS Ergonomics, 1-2 Redbrick Cottages, Main Street, Southwick, Peterborough, PE8 5BL Tel: 01832 272958 *Welcome to ACS Ergonomics. We are an Ergonomics Consultancy specialising in the design of accessible and usable products, without compromising on the aesthetics. We can assist in designing products that are attractive, accessible, easy to use and affordable. ** **With a background in Occupational Therapy and Ergonomics we also have extensive experience in carrying out workstation assessments and providing preventative training. We can help increase personal comfort, minimise the chance of ill health and increase efficiency and a happier/healthier work force.**

▶ ACS Mobile Valeting, Wilthorpe, Barnsley, South Yorkshire, S75 1JW Tel: 07913 504999 E-mail: valeting@acsmobile.co.uk *Mobile valeting service providing competitive rates for contract, private and fleet vehicles at your home or place of work.*

ACS (UK) Ltd, Park View House, 6 Woodside Place, Glasgow, G3 7QF Tel: 0141- 572 3020 Fax: 0141- 572 4020 *Software consultants services*

Acsl Precision Engineering, 3 Cartwright Road, Stevenage, Hertfordshire, SG1 4QJ Tel: (01438) 359123 Fax: (01438) 741819 E-mail: acsl@btinternet.com *CNC Precision Engineering*

Acsoft Ltd, Unit 8B, Wingbury Courtyard, Leighton Road, Wingrave, Aylesbury, Buckinghamshire, HP22 4LW Tel: (01296) 682686 Fax: (01296) 682860 E-mail: sales@acsoft.co.uk *Sales of noise & vibration equipment*

Acson International, Hansard Gate, West Meadows, Derby, DE21 6JN Tel: 0845 601 2015 Fax: (01332) 371061 E-mail: marketing@jehall.co.uk *Acson International is a leading brand of air-conditioning, made in Malaysia, exported to more than 50 countries in 5 continents. Launched in the UK in 2002 Acson International goes from strength to strength. Acson's continuing growth is due to the company's commitment to quality, product development as well as the dedication and professionalism of its management and staff. Our dedicated product support team is designed to ensure and encourage continuous improvement in productivity and customer confidence in Acson's products and services.*

▶ ACT, F1 Capital Point, Capital Business Park, Parkway, Cardiff, CF3 2PY Tel: (0845) 074 0100 Fax: (0845) 074 0120 E-mail: ian@actrepro.co.uk *Large format displays, simple posters to giant building wraps*

Act Consultant Services, The Old Wood Mill, Church Lane Madingley, Sawston, Cambridge, CB22 3JR Tel: (01954) 210766 Fax: (01954) 211466 *Theatre planning & designers* Also at: Seaford

Actaris Metering Systems Ltd, Langer Road, Felixstowe, Suffolk, IP11 2ER Tel: (01394) 694000 Fax: (01394) 276030 E-mail: csaunders@actaris.co.uk *Electric meter manufrs*

Actaris Metering Systems Ltd, PO Box 3, Manchester, M32 0XX Tel: 0161-865 1181 Fax: 0161-954 4902 E-mail: watersales@manchester.com *Offers a complete range of water meters & communication modules*

Actem UK Ltd, 2 Sea View Industrial Estate, Peterlee, County Durham, SR8 4TQ Tel: 0191-518 0235 Fax: 0191-586 1139 E-mail: paula.w@btclick.com *Steel fabricators*

Actemium, Meteor Business Park, Cheltenham Road East, Gloucester, GL2 9QL Tel: (01452) 713222 Fax: (01452) 713444 E-mail: actemium@actemium.co.uk *Generator control panels & MCC specialists*

▶ Acti Stitch, Unit 13 Lufton Heights Commerce Park, Boundary Way, Lufton, Yeovil, Somerset, BA22 8UY Tel: (01935) 420820 Fax: (01935) 428850 E-mail: info@actistitch.com *Suppliers of quality work wear embroidery & screen-print services*

Actia UK Ltd, Unit 81, Mochdre Industrial Estate, Newtown, Powys, SY16 4LE Tel: (01686) 611150 Fax: (01686) 621068 E-mail: mail@actia.co.uk *Automotive electronics systems & diagnostics*

▶ Actikem Ltd, Ravensdale, Stoke-on-Trent, ST6 4NU Tel: (01782) 577002 Fax: (01782) 577008 E-mail: andrew.mooney@actikem.com *Chemical manufrs*

▶ Actinic Holdings Ltd, Globe House, Lavender Park Road, West Byfleet, Surrey, KT14 6ND Tel: (01932) 358340 Fax: (01932) 358341 E-mail: enquiries@actinic.co.uk *E-commerce & epos solutions providers*

▶ Actinic PCB Design, 67 Elm Grove, Brighton, BN2 3ET Tel: (01273) 705525 E-mail: mail@actinicpcb.com *Circuit board design*

Action Apparal Ltd, 62-63 Hemming Road, Washford, Redditch, Worcestershire, B98 0EA Tel: (01527) 510545 Fax: (01527) 510678 E-mail: alans@actionapparal.co.uk *Fashion clothing designers & distributors*

▶ Action Bikes Ltd, 15 West Street, Reading, RG1 1TT Tel: 0118-951 1345 Fax: 0118-951 1456 *Bicycle retailers*

Action Business Systems, 8 The Broadway, Hampton Court Way, Thames Ditton, Surrey, KT7 0LX Tel: (0870) 1607911 Fax: (0870) 1607933 E-mail: customercare@action-plc.co.uk *Office equipment suppliers*

▶ Action Drive Ltd, 15 Grove Market Place, Court Yard, London, SE9 5PU Tel: (020) 8850 3763 Fax: (020) 8850 4113 E-mail: actiondrive@hotmail.com *Employment agency*

Action EPC Ltd, Unit 14 Adam Business Centre, Cranes Farm Road, Basildon, Essex, SS14 3JF Tel: (01268) 288387 Fax: (01268) 288956 E-mail: actionplating@fsmail.net *Electroplating*

Action Graphics (Birmingham) Ltd, Units 3 & 5 Phoenix Park Industrial Estate, Avenue Close, Aston, Birmingham, B7 4NU Tel: 0121-242 4000 Fax: 0121-242 4030 E-mail: info@action-graphics.co.uk *Sign writing & graphic designers*

Action Group, Garston Business Park, Blackburne Street, Liverpool, L19 8JB Tel: 0151-427 1084 Fax: 0151-427 7130 E-mail: dkeen@theactiongroup.co.uk *Manufacturers & installers of aggregates, security fencing & gates*

Action Handling Equipment Ltd, Maltings Industrial Estate, Station Road, Sawbridgeworth, Hertfordshire, CM21 9JY Tel: (01279) 724989 Fax: (01279) 600224 E-mail: sales@actionhandling.co.uk *To supply all types of material handling equipment including lifting equipment, access equipment, cranes, hoists trolleys and scissor tables*

Action Hire Centres, 90 Cotmandene Crescent, St Pauls Cray, Orpington, Kent, BR5 2RG Tel: (020) 8300 2359 Fax: (020) 8302 7422 *Tool & equipment hire*

Action Indusrial Cleaning Services UK Ltd, Bridge House, 1 Bridge Close, Romford, RM7 0AU Tel: (01708) 725356 Fax: (01708) 737117 *Office cleaning contractors*

Action Information Technologies Ltd, 1 Butler Road, Shrewsbury, SY3 7AJ Tel: (01743) 244377 Fax: (01743) 244367 E-mail: sales@actionit.demon.co.uk *Software developers*

▶ Action International, 6 New James Street, Blaenavon, Pontypool, Torfaen, NP4 9JU Tel: (01495) 790008 Fax: (08701) 333796 E-mail: gitenkapdee@action-international.com *We are a Business Coaching practice, we coach business owners to improve their business through guidance, support and encouragement. We help the owners of SME businesses with their sales, marketing, management, team building and so much more.*

Action Jacket Co., PO Box 1180, Stourbridge, West Midlands, DY9 0ZF Tel: (01562) 887096 Fax: (01562) 882010 E-mail: info@actionjacket.co.uk *Promotional jacket & clothing manufrs*

▶ Action Mobility, 48 Lower Kings Road, Berkhamsted, Hertfordshire, HP4 2AA Tel: (01442) 877433 E-mail: mail@bettermobility.co.uk *Mobility aids suppliers & maintenance services*

▶ Action Optics, 16 Butts Ash Gardens, Hythe, Southampton, SO45 3BL Tel: (023) 8084 2801 Fax: (023) 8084 2801 E-mail: richard@actionoptics.co.uk *Optical instrument repair workshop that also sells new & pre-owned binoculars, telescopes & rifle sights & new night vision equipment*

Action P C's, 20 Canford Av, Bournemouth, BH11 8RX Tel: 01202 538141 *Computer systems & software*

Action Refrigeration, 18-22 North Street, Jarrow, Tyne & Wear, NE32 3PG Tel: 0191-483 3579 Fax: 0191-428 5615 *Refrigeration*

▶ Action Seals Ltd, Westfield Road, Wallasey, Merseyside, CH44 7JA Tel: 0151-652 6661 Fax: 0151-653 4994 E-mail: sales@actionseals.co.uk *Rotary shaft oil seal stockist*

Action Shutters Midlands Ltd, 2 Garretts Green Trading Estate, Valepits Road, Birmingham, B33 0TD Tel: 0121-605 6005 Fax: 0121-605 7050 *Manufacturers & installers of roller shutter doors*

Action Staff Bureau Ltd, 47a High St, Tunbridge Wells, Kent, TN1 1XL Tel: (01892) 542822 Fax: (01892) 542827 E-mail: sales@asbrecruitment.com *Employment agency*

Action Tapes Ltd, Red Scar Industrial Estate, Longridge Road, Ribbleton, Preston, PR2 5NE Tel: (01280) 700591 Fax: (01280) 700590 E-mail: sales@prestec.co.uk *Cover ting adhesive video tapes service*

Company Information

Action Team For Jobs, Belasis Business Centre, Coxwold Way, Belasis Hall Technology Park, Billingham, Cleveland, TS23 4EA Tel: (01642) 343434 Fax: (01642) 370328
E-mail: lynn.hitchin@dbh-officers.com *Business centre*

Action Vulcanising Services, 37 Stretton Close, Doncaster, South Yorkshire, DN4 6UE
Tel: (01302) 530510 Fax: (01302) 530510
Conveyor belt suppliers

Actionpoint Packaging Materials, The Old Brickfields, Otterham Quay Lane, Rainham, Gillingham, Kent, ME8 8NA Tel: (01634) 373736 *Promotional items & business gift suppliers*

Actionwest, 5 Orchard Industrial Estate South, Union Road, Kingsbridge, Devon, TQ7 1EG
Tel: (01548) 856696 Fax: (01548) 856616
E-mail: sales@actionwest.co.uk *Business equipment suppliers & servicing*

Activ Computer Services, PO Box 15, York, YO26 9YE Tel: (01423) 331646 Fax: (01423) 331647 E-mail: links@activ.co.uk *Computer services*

Activ8, 56 Rabans Close, Rabans Lane Industrial Area, Aylesbury, Buckinghamshire, HP19 8RS
Tel: (01296) 436378 Fax: (01296) 393401 *Pest control*

▶ Activa, 7 Montpellier Terrace, Cheltenham, Gloucestershire, GL50 1US Tel: (01242) 230555 Fax: (01242) 231333

▶ Activa Solutions Ltd, Activa House, Commerce Way, Edenbridge, Kent, TN8 6ED Tel: (01732) 784300 Fax: (0870) 7544516
E-mail: info@activa.co.uk *Activa Solutions, formerly ASC telecom Ltd, specialises in providing call recording (voice, VoIP and data), quality monitoring, live agent coaching, automated customer surveys and telephone infrastructure solutions to contact centres, financial institutions, public safety operations and government organisations.*

Active Aerials & Systems, 53 Rugeley Road, Armitage, Rugeley, Staffordshire, WS15 4AR
Tel: 01543 307072
E-mail: active.systems@ntlworld.com *Digital tv aerial & satellite services*

▶ Active Air Conditioning Ltd, Braehead Centre, Blackness Avenue, Altens Industrial Estate, Aberdeen, AB12 3PG Tel: (01224) 870777 Fax: (01224) 870888
E-mail: info@active-aircon.co.uk *Air conditioning specialists*

▶ Active Alarms Ltd, 3 Fayland Avenue, London, SW16 1TB Tel: (020) 8769 5003
E-mail: sales@active-alarms.com *Supply & install burglar alarms cctv access control redcare monitoring*

Active Alarms Plymouth Ltd, 42 Aylesbury Crescent, Whitleigh, Plymouth, PL5 4HX
Tel: (01752) 774424 Fax: (01752) 774424
Installing burglar alarms

Active Appliances, 13 Orchard Road, South Croydon, Surrey, CR2 9LY Tel: (020) 8657 0493 *Domestic appliance sales*

Active Asian Suits, 420 Katherine Road, London, E7 8NP Tel: (020) 8471 1894 Fax: (020) 8470 0022 E-mail: activeasiansuits@aol.com *Asian clothing*

▶ Active Breaks, Haland House, 66 York Road, Weybridge, Surrey, KT13 9DY Tel: (0845) 3308584

Active Chemical Products Ltd, Butts Business Centre, Fowlmere, Royston, Hertfordshire, SG8 7SL Tel: (01763) 208222 Fax: (01763) 208906 E-mail: sales@alltec.co.uk *Carpet & upholstery cleaning equipment manufrs*

Active Circuits, 14 North Street, Melton Mowbray, Leicestershire, LE13 1NL Tel: (01664) 562968 Fax: (01664) 562968 *Electronic circuit manufrs*

▶ Active Communications, 10 Unicorn Avenue, Eastern Green, Coventry, CV5 7GH Tel: (024) 7647 4124 E-mail: sales@activecomms.com *Telecommunication services*

Active Computer Graphics, Robin Lodge, Heynes West End, Haynes, Bedford, MK45 3RB
Tel: 01234 740257 *Computer graphics presentations*

Active Computing & Telecoms Ltd, 3 Larks Way, Tree Beech Enterprise Park Gunn, Goodleigh, Barnstaple, Devon, EX32 7NZ Tel: (01271) 831325 Fax: (01271) 830987
E-mail: sales@activecomputing.co.uk *Telephone systems specialists consultants*

▶ Active Content, 65 Ditton Fields, Cambridge, CB5 8QQ Tel: (01223) 570536 Fax: (08716) 618553 E-mail: info@activecontent.co.uk *Managing and building websites: that's what Active Content does **We provide a complete service, from specification, design and build through to hosting, content management and internet marketing.**Most importantly we provide our clients with the peace of mind that they are working with people who are in it for the long term. We will take over the management of your website on an ongoing basis, and make sure that your website is always up-to-date and is meeting its business objectives.*

Active Controls, 6 Court Yard Workshops, Bath Street, Market Harborough, Leicestershire, LE16 9EW Tel: (01858) 466504 Fax: (01858) 463650 E-mail: activecontrols@ukonline.co.uk *Control panel manufrs*

Active Data Management, West Malvern Road, Mathon, Malvern, Worcestershire, WR13 5NZ
Tel: (01684) 576022 Fax: (01684) 576026
E-mail: info@activedatamanagement.co.uk *Data base management software*

Active Electronics Plc, Albion House, Gordon Road, High Wycombe, Buckinghamshire, HP13 6ET
Tel: (01494) 441414 Fax: (01494) 524674
E-mail: pool@active-electronics.co.uk *Electronic component distributors*

Active Environmental Services, 12 Cover Green, Home Meadow, Worcester, WR4 0JF
Tel: (01905) 723129 Fax: (01905) 330158 *Pest controllers*

Active Groundworks, C Polglaze Barton Farm, Liskey Hill, Perranporth, Cornwall, TR6 0BB
Tel: (01872) 573222 *Excavation contractors & garden services*

Active Handling (Sales) Ltd, Unit 10, Pipers Lane Trading Estate, Pipers Lane, Thatcham, Berkshire, RG19 4NA Tel: (01635) 872972 Fax: (01635) 872909

continued

E-mail: sales@stacatruc.co.uk *Fork lift truck hire & distributors*

▶ The Active Hands Co., 12 Rothwell Gardens, Woodley, Reading, RG5 4TJ Tel: 0118 9618481
E-mail: info@activehands.co.uk *The Active Hands Company is a manufacturer of gripping aids for people with weak grip or limited hand function. Active Hands aids enable individuals to hold and use everyday items such as DIY tools and gardening implements, and to take part in pursuits like skiing for the disabled, weightlifting or using other gym equipment, e.g. rowing machines.*

Active Health Ltd, Unit 12 Lakeside Business Park, Swan Lane, Sandhurst, Berkshire, GU47 9DN
Tel: (01252) 861666 Fax: (01252) 861455 *Health food supplements by mail order*

Active Information Systems, Unit 3 Brooks Green Road, Coolham, Horsham, West Sussex, RH13 8GR Tel: (01403) 740400 Fax: (01403) 741125 E-mail: active@activegrp.co.uk *IT support & network installation*

Active International Movements Ltd, 380 Ringwood Road, Poole, Dorset, BH12 3LT Tel: (01202) 307349 Fax: (01202) 743707
E-mail: sales@activefreight.co.uk *Freight forwarding specialists*

▶ Active Learning Ltd, Hartley Business Centre, 28 Hucknall Road, Nottingham, NG5 1FD
Tel: 0115-960 6111 Fax: 0115-960 6111
E-mail: sales@activelearning-uk.com *Nursery equipment manufrs*

Active Logic Ltd, 46 Victoria Road, Penarth, South Glamorgan, CF64 3HY Tel: (029) 2070 2100
E-mail: enquiries@active-logic.co.uk *Software consultants*

Active Media Technology Ltd, Golden Gate Lodge, Weston Road, Crewe, CW2 5XN Tel: (01270) 580400 Fax: (01270) 589800
E-mail: info@active-media-online.com *Software developers*

Active Metals, Unit F Holbrook Green, Holbrook Industrial Estate, Holbrook, Sheffield, S20 3FE
Tel: 0114-247 3662 Fax: 0114-247 8372
E-mail: mlee@active-metals.freeserve.co.uk *Metal powder manufrs*

Active Network Systems Ltd, 5 Coneygear Road, Hartford, Huntingdon, Cambridgeshire, PE29 1QL Tel: (01480) 437997 Fax: (01480) 436031 E-mail: sales@ans-ltd.co.uk *Computer storage system integrator & value-added reseller*

▶ Active Networks Ltd, Copperfield, Coppice Drive, Wraysbury, Staines, Middlesex, TW19 5JG
Tel: (01784) 488420 *Computer systems consultants*

▶ Active Plumbing & Heating UK Ltd, 33 Thurloe Walk, Grays, Essex, RM17 5AN Tel: (01375) 369347 Fax: (01708) 349380 *Plumbing, heating, drainage, maintenance, corgi registered*

Active Pump Service Ltd, Unit G17 Rudford Industrial Estate, Ford Road, Ford, Arundel, West Sussex, BN18 0BD Tel: (01903) 734030 Fax: (01903) 733640
E-mail: nigel@activepumpservices.co.uk *Pump maintenance & repair services*

▶ Active Safety Associates, 39 Tindale Close, Sanderstead, South Croydon, Surrey, CR2 0RT
Tel: 020 8651 6601 Fax: 020 8651 6601
E-mail: rmeech@activesafetyassociates.co.uk *Health & safety consultants*

▶ Active Seating, 1 35 Brook Road, Rayleigh, Essex, SS6 7XJ Tel: (01268) 779991 Fax: (01268) 773289
E-mail: info@arrowoffice.co.uk *Office furniture distributors*

Active Security Group Ltd, Horsecroft Place, Harlow, Essex, CM19 5BT Tel: (01279) 420016 Fax: (01279) 444491 *Burglar alarm installers*

Active Security Systems, 25 Engaine Drive, Shenley Church End, Milton Keynes, MK5 6BA
Tel: (01908) 508998 *Security alarms installers*

Active Security UK Ltd, 7 Little Hereford Street, Bromyard, Herefordshire, HR7 4DE Tel: (01885) 488994 Fax: (01885) 482194
E-mail: sales@activesecurityuk.com *Metal fabricators*

Active Sensors Ltd, Unit 12 Sea Vixen Industrial Estate, 3 Wilverley Road, Christchurch, Dorset, BH23 3RU Tel: (01202) 480620 Fax: (01202) 480664 E-mail: sales@activesensors.com *Control & measurement sensors*

Active Signs Ltd, 24 Leigh Road, Haine Industrial Estate, Ramsgate, Kent, CT12 5EU Tel: (01843) 850800 Fax: (01843) 852830 *Sign manufrs*

Active Signs Maintenance, 24 Leigh Road, Ramsgate, Kent, CT12 5EU Tel: (01843) 580801 Fax: (01843) 852830
E-mail: sales@activevehicles.co.uk *Contract hire car leasing*

Active Software Solutions Ltd, Jaywick Enterprise Centre, Lotus Way, Clacton-on-Sea, Essex, CO15 2LU Tel: (01255) 688286 Fax: (01255) 436205 *Software, customer relations*

The Active Spring Company Ltd, Sibleys Green, Sibleys Lane, Thaxted, Dunmow, Essex, CM6 2NU Tel: (01371) 830557 Fax: (01371) 831151 E-mail: sales@tascuk.com *Wire shapes & spring manufrs*

Active Springs, Redditch Road, Studley, Warwickshire, B80 7AY Tel: (01527) 854932 Fax: (01527) 854969
E-mail: robert@active-springs.co.uk *Springs, wire shapers & pressings manufrs*

Active Training, 2 Fair Oaks, Slitting Mill, Rugeley, Staffs, WS15 2UU Tel: (07973) 482002 Fax: (01889) 574939
E-mail: yvonneclarke@activetraining.fsnet.co.uk *Active training for professional people*

▶ Active Voice & Data Ltd, Unit 14 Kendray Business Centre, Thornton Road, Barnsley, South Yorkshire, S70 3NA Tel: (01226) 704610
E-mail: sales@active-voicedata.co.uk *Telecommunications*

Active Water Systems, 122 Newport Road, Caldicot, Monmouthshire, NP26 4BT
Tel: (01291) 420012 Fax: (0870) 4294048
E-mail: us@ActiveWater.co.uk *Water treatment equipment and service. Pool, potable water, cooling towers, industrial waste/efflient and horticulture industries specialised.*

▶ Active Workwear, 56 Bradford Road, Stanningley, Pudsey, West Yorkshire, LS28 6EF
Tel: 0113-256 7021 Fax: 0113-256 6600
E-mail: info@workwearshop.co.uk *Work & safety clothing supplies boots & full range of ppe*

▶ Active-PCB Solutions Ltd, Unit 4, Acre Road, Reading, RG2 0SU Tel: 0118-931 0292 Fax: 0118-931 2975
E-mail: sales@active-pcb.com *Sub contract electronic manufrs*

▶ Activia Training, 268 Bath Road, Slough, SL1 4DX Tel: (0870) 3500131 Fax: 0870 3500151 E-mail: sales@activia.co.uk *Activia are specialists in providing quality, flexible training for Microsoft, Lotus, Sage and Personal Development, with standard or bespoke courses delivered on your premises or ours*

Activity Domain Ltd, Moulton Park Business Centre, Redhouse Road, Moulton Park, Northampton, NN3 6AQ Tel: (0845) 3100811
E-mail: victor@activitydomain.com *We are an Information and Communications Technology company (ICT) based in Northampton. We provide website design, website hosting, electronic marketing, remote email and wireless networking services to companies both large and small.*

▶ Activity Media Ltd, 7 Conway Drive, Flitwick, Bedford, MK45 1DE Tel: (01525) 759047

▶ Activnet Biz, Little Gaddesden, Berkhamsted, Hertfordshire, HP4 1PA Tel: (01442) 843516 Fax: (0870) 7060164
E-mail: marika.woods@activnet.biz *E-commerce specialists*

Acton Bright Steel Ltd, Gordon Road, Staines, Middlesex, TW18 3BG Tel: (01784) 463595 Fax: (01784) 451748
E-mail: sales@actonbrightsteel.co.uk *Engineering steels and non ferrous metals.*

Acton Delta Ltd, Wombrook Business Centre, Giggetty Lane, Wombourne, Wolverhampton, WV5 8LZ Tel: (01902) 326563 Fax: (01902) 326564 E-mail: mail@actondelta.co.uk *Control panel manufrs*

J.M. Acton RSS, Horse Shoe Farm, Creake Road, Fakenham, Norfolk, NR21 9JA Tel: (01328) 823561 *Blacksmiths welding & fabrication service*

Acton's Made To Measure Bed Linen, Hamer Lane, Rochdale, Lancashire, OL16 2UL Tel: (01706) 642361 Fax: (01706) 860544
E-mail: sales@actonandactonltd.co.uk *Bed linen manufrs*

Actreg UK Ltd, 2 & 3 Henson Close, Telford Way Industrial Estate, Kettering, Northamptonshire, NN16 8PZ Tel: (01536) 412525 Fax: (01536) 521616 E-mail: sales@actreg.co.uk *Valve actuator manufrs*

▶ Acts And Events, Slough, SL1 3UD Tel: (01753) 572047 Fax: (07870) 854910
E-mail: enquiries@acts-and-events.com *OUR AIM is to provide the best acts for your event - or to produce a complete event tailored to your requirements - exceeding client expectation!*

Actual Reality, Stainton Moor View, Matlock, Derbyshire, DE4 3NE Tel: (01629) 760801 Fax: (08702) 201805
E-mail: admin@ar-computers.co.uk *Computer system*

Actual Systems UK, 9 Bankhead Drive, Edinburgh, EH11 4EJ Tel: 0131-538 8538 Fax: 0131-538 8539 *Software house*

▶ Actuate S C R, Manor Barn, Thurloxton, Taunton, Somerset, TA2 8RH Tel: (07971) 682097 Fax: (0870) 1336615
E-mail: info@actuate.eu.com *Geographic info systems & data analysis*

▶ Actuation Technology Ltd, Metro House, Northgate, Chichester, West Sussex, PO19 1BE
Tel: (01243) 771372 Fax: (01243) 538501
E-mail: mbreen@amgactuators.co.uk *Pneumatic actuators & switch boxes*

Actuation Valve & Controls, 8 Woodward Road, Knowsley Industrial Park, Liverpool, L33 7UZ
Tel: 0151-547 1221 Fax: 0151-547 1222
E-mail: chris@actuation.co.uk *Valve distributors*

Acuity Contact Lenses, Plumpton Road, Hoddesdon, Hertfordshire, EN11 0LB
Tel: (01992) 445035 Fax: (01992) 451223
E-mail: enquiries@acuity-lenses.co.uk *Keratoconus lens/specialist contact lens manufrs*

▶ Acuityflooring, 32 Henry Street, Rhostyllen, Wrexham, Clwyd, LL14 4DA Tel: (01978) 266302 Fax: (01978) 266302
E-mail: dianeandacuity@tiscali.co.uk *Epoxy screeds, coatings & cementation pump screeds manufrs*

Aculab plc, Lakeside Bramley Road, Mount Farm, Bletchley, Milton Keynes, MK1 1PT Tel: (01908) 273800 Fax: (01908) 273801 *Computer & telecom equipment manufrs*

▶ Acuma Solutions Ltd, Waterside Court, 1 Crewe Road, Manchester, M23 9BE Tel: (0870) 7894321 Fax: (0870) 7894002
E-mail: enquiries@acuma.co.uk *Computer maintenance & repair services*

▶ Acumen Ltd, Unit 2, Harrison & Macklin Road, Foley Trading Estate, Hereford, HR1 2SF
Tel: (01432) 344466 Fax: (01432) 379168
E-mail: high-care@btconnect.com *Fabrications of stainless mild steel & alloys*

▶ Acumen Accountants & Advisors Ltd, Bon Accord House, Riverside Drive, Aberdeen, AB11 7SL Tel: (01224) 573904 Fax: (01224) 572721 E-mail: enquiries@acumen.info *IT Support For SME"s, PC, Network & Server Solutions, Virus & Spyware Protection, Consultancy, Hardware & Software Supply, Email & Internet Solutions*

Acumen Agencies, 161 Cregagh Road, Belfast, BT6 0LB Tel: (028) 9080 8150 Fax: (028) 9080 8155 E-mail: sales@acumenagencies.com *Computer systems & software distributors*

Acumen Seales, Wharton House, Wharton Lane, Little Hulton, Manchester, M38 9XF
Tel: 0161-703 9999 Fax: 0161-703 9988
E-mail: office@acumenseals.co.uk *Mechanical seals refurbishment & manufrs*

Acumon Services UK, 27 The Oaks, Chorley, Lancashire, PR7 3QT Tel: (01257) 241624 Fax: (01257) 241624 E-mail: info@acmon.co.uk *Acoustic conditioning monitoring & thermal imaging*

Acutech, Unit 5 York House, Langston Road, Loughton, Essex, IG10 3TQ Tel: (020) 8502 2155 Fax: (020) 8508 8562
E-mail: sales@acuutech.com *Computer services*

▶ Acutest Ltd, Blackwell House, Guildhall Yard, London, EC2V 5AE Tel: (020) 7917 2838
E-mail: enquiries@acutest.co.uk *UK software testing company providing a full range of testing services such as performance testing, UAT, test improvement, non functional testing, automated testing, usability testing, compatability testing, DR and business continuity testing and security testing. Particularly effective on large programmes.*

Acv UK Ltd, St. Davids Drive, St. Davids Business Park, Dalgety Bay, Dunfermline, Fife, KY11 9PF
Tel: (01383) 820100 Fax: (01383) 820180
E-mail: information@acv-uk.com *Distributors of water heaters*

Acxiom, Counting House, 53 Tooley Street, London, SE1 2QN Tel: (020) 7526 5100 Fax: (020) 7526 5200 *Direct marketing agents*

Acxiom, Park House, Station Road, Teddington, Middlesex, TW11 9AD Tel: (020) 8213 5500 Fax: (020) 8213 5588
E-mail: info-uk@claritaseu.com *Database marketing & direct mail services*

▶ Ad Draughting & Design, Victoria House, 5 East Blackhall Street, Greenock, Renfrewshire, PA15 1HD Tel: (01475) 807155 Fax: (01475) 807145 *Draught services*

Ad Plastics, 13 Willow Road, Poyle Trading Estate, Colnbrook, Slough, SL3 0BS Tel: (01753) 684777 Fax: (01753) 683139
E-mail: adplasticsltd@hotmail.com *Specialise in plastic injection moulding. Have machines ranging from 80 tons to 360 tonnes. Offer assemblies, sonic welding, and silk screening*

▶ The Ad Studio, 23 Martlet Close, Cherque Farm, Lee on the Solent, Gosport, Hampshire, PO13 8FP Tel: 02392 553442 Fax: 08715 227697 E-mail: info@theadstudio.co.uk *We provide a bespoke advertising and graphic design service to businesses who want to look the business.*

Ad Tek Products Ltd, 35 Broton Drive, Halstead, Essex, CO9 1HB Tel: (01787) 474470 Fax: (01787) 475880
E-mail: ad-tek@lineone.net *Sheet metal fine limit manufrs*

▶ Ad Wraps Europe, 2 Marshall Street, London, W1F 9BB Tel: (020) 7534 5490 Fax: (020) 7534 5401 E-mail: info@ad-wraps.co.uk *Vehicle wrapping and Fleet Livery specialists. Adwraps undertake all aspects of Fleet Branding including Design, Large Format Digital Print, vehicle graphics and vehicle wrapping.*

▶ Ad3 Envelope Printers Ltd, Unit 143 Aireplace Mills, Kirkstall Road, Leeds, LS3 1JL
Tel: 0113-244 3700 Fax: 0113-244 9400
E-mail: andy.martin@ad3envelope.co.uk *Envelope printers & suppliers*

Ada Computer Systems Ltd, Network House, House, Albert Drive, Burgess Hill, West Sussex, RH15 9TN Tel: (01444) 232000 Fax: (01444) 247754 E-mail: sales@ada.co.uk *Networking & computer engineers*

Ada Machining Services Ltd, Kayley Industrial Estate, Richmond Street, Ashton-under-Lyne, Lancashire, OL7 0AU Tel: 0161-339 3221 Fax: 0161-339 3981
E-mail: mail@ada-ms.co.uk *Sub contract engineers*

Adaero Precision Components Ltd, Unit 6 Down End, Lords Meadow Industrial Estate, Crediton, Devon, EX17 1HN Tel: (01363) 778660 Fax: (01363) 773977
E-mail: enquiries@adaero.co.uk *Precision engineers*

Adage Co. Ltd, 1c Bridge Road, Camberley, Surrey, GU15 2QR Tel: (01276) 684922 Fax: (01276) 692025 E-mail: adage@eur-isp.com *CNC manual milling, turning & welding, sheet metal work fabrication & fixtures manufrs*

Adair & Milliken Ltd, 1 Parkside Gardens, Belfast, BT15 3AW Tel: (028) 9074 8271 Fax: (028) 9075 1064
E-mail: adairandmilliken@btconnect.com *Electrical contractors*

Adam & Co. P.L.C., 22 Kings Street, London, SW1Y 6QY Tel: (020) 7839 4615 Fax: (020) 7839 5994 E-mail: london@adambank.com *Private bank services* Also at: Edinburgh & Glasgow

Adam Adams Ltd, 1 Chapel Road, Portslade, Brighton, BN41 1PF Tel: (01273) 431100 Fax: (01273) 431110
E-mail: adam-adams@cwcom.net *Packaging merchants* Also at: Chichester

Adam Beeny Halson, 4 Sudley Road, Bognor Regis, West Sussex, PO21 1EU Tel: (01243) 865661 Fax: (01243) 841533
E-mail: info@adamsbeeny.com *Accountants*

Adam Cleaning Service, 29 Somersby Close, Gregg Hall, Lincoln, LN6 8AF Tel: (01522) 530467 *Host dry carpet cleaning & distributors*

Adam Dyeing Ltd, Greenhill Industrial Estate, Birmingham Road, Kidderminster, Worcestershire, DY10 2SH Tel: (01562) 821525 Fax: (01562) 827916
E-mail: aac@adamcarpets.com *Carpet yarn dyers*

Adam Engineering Fabrication, Acton Hall Enterprise Park, Station Lane, Featherstone, Pontefract, West Yorkshire, WF7 6EQ
Tel: (01977) 600280 Fax: (01977) 602196 *Steel fabricators*

▶ Adam & Co Financial Management, 1 Edmund Street, Bradford, West Yorkshire, BD5 0BH
Tel: (01274) 744877 Fax: (01274) 741966
E-mail: barrysmith@adam-co.com *Accountancy*

▶ Adam & Co Financial Management, 1 Edmund Street, Bradford, West Yorkshire, BD5 0BH
Tel: (01274) 744877 Fax: (01274) 741966
E-mail: Profit@Advice.Tv *Be "in the Know" With Adam & Co.....**Professionals Online: All The Time.....**Safe Tax Havens From Business Mavens.....**You'll Recieve Good Advice & Solid Solutions.....**Guaranteed To Make Or Save You Money.....**Business Advice & Solutions For The Small To Medium Sized Business.....**Weekend And Evening Appointments Are Always A Pleasure.....**For Your Initial Free Consultation Please Contact.....**Barry Smith FCA or Shahbaz*

continued

continuation
*Munir FCCA....**To Gain Free Expert Financial & Business Training For Your Valued Work Force That Is Sponsored By The Learning Skills Council And Business Link....Please Contact David Hartley ACIS At Our Sister Company HKR Limited....Good Training & Education Is The Foundation And The Zenith Our Firm....**Remember: It Takes More Wisdom To Profit From Good Advice Than To Give IT....**Providing You Financial Products And Training To Enhance And Secure The Future Of Your Buinsess, Your Work Force And Your Family.*

▶ Adam Phones Ltd, 2-3 Dolphin Square, Edensor Road, London, W4 2ST Tel: (0800) 123000 Fax: (0500) 001230 E-mail: info@fonehire.com *Adam Phones were pioneers of short-term mobile phone hire, renting out our first cellular telephone in 1988. **

R.P. Adam Ltd, Arpal Works, Riverside Road, Selkirk, TD7 5DU Tel: (01750) 21586 Fax: (01750) 21506 E-mail: salesinfo@rpadam.co.uk *Industrial chemical manufrs*

Adam Stark Ltd, 83 Cairnhill Road, Airdrie, Lanarkshire, ML6 9HA Tel: (01236) 761322

Adam & Co Textiles Ltd, 52 London Street, Leicester, LE5 3RU Tel: 0116-276 8693 Fax: 0116-246 0955 E-mail: adamandco@mribiz.net *Knitted jersey fabrics manufrs*

▶ Adamant Safe & Lock Co. Ltd, Adamant House Unit 1, Princeville Road Industrial Estate, Duncombe Street, Bradford, West Yorkshire, BD8 9AJ Tel: (01274) 726698 Fax: (01274) 543358 *Locksmith*

Adamas GB Ltd, Unit W3 Littlemoor Business Centre, Littlemoor, Eckington, Sheffield, S21 4EF Tel: (01246) 433965 Fax: (01246) 436895 *Industrial diamond products*

Adament Refractory Settings Ltd, 54 Bolton Road, Kearsley, Bolton, BL4 9BT Tel: (01204) 573197 Fax: (01204) 571517 *Refractory contractors & repairers*

▶ Adams, Vale House, 19 Hainge Road, Tividale, Oldbury, West Midlands, B69 2NR Tel: 0121-522 0560 Fax: 0121-522 0570

Adams & Adams Ltd, Adams House, Dickerage Lane, New Malden, Surrey, KT3 3SF Tel: (020) 8949 1121 Fax: (020) 8336 1126 E-mail: adamsnewmalden@aol.com *Storage warehousing office & industrial units*

Adams & Associates UK Ltd, 14 Barclay Road, Croydon, CR0 1JN Tel: (020) 8680 0766 Fax: (020) 8680 0066 E-mail: info@adamsandassocs.com *Recruitment*

Adams Aviation Supply Co. Ltd, Hunter House Churchill Way, Biggin Hill Airport, Biggin Hill, Westerham, Kent, TN16 3BN Tel: (01959) 576129 Fax: (01959) 576660 E-mail: mail@adamsaviation.com *Aircraft parts & avionics distributors*

Adams Bristow Ltd, The Old Mill, Old Malden Lane, Worcester Park, Surrey, KT4 7QS Tel: (020) 8330 3366 Fax: (020) 8330 3368 *Machinery removal contractors*

▶ Adams Castles, 54 Grittleton Road, Bristol, BS7 0UZ Tel: 0117-983 4280 Fax: 0117-983 4280 *Bouncy castle equipment hire*

Adams Cundell Engineers Ltd, The Coach House, Wicken, Milton Keynes, MK19 6DH Tel: (01908) 562191 Fax: (01908) 260461 E-mail: info@aceplant.co.uk *Tractor sales & services*

Adams Engineering, Unit 3c Innsworth Technology Park, Innsworth Lane, Gloucester, GL3 1DL Tel: (01452) 730385 Fax: (01452) 736146 *Precision engineers*

Adams Exhibitions, 6 Rose Green Road, Bristol, BS5 7XE Tel: 0117-952 1000 Fax: 0117-952 2000 E-mail: joe@adams-exhibitions.co.uk *Adams Exhibitions Ltd Specialise in the design and build of all types of exhibition stands, from modular kits and custom built projects to pop ups, banners and graphics.*

▶ Adams Fireplaces, 117 London Road, King's Lynn, Norfolk, PE30 5ES Tel: (01553) 760541 *Fireplace supplier*

Adams Food Ingredients Ltd, Prince St, Leek, Staffordshire, ST13 6DB Tel: (01538) 399686 Fax: 01538 399476 E-mail: sales@adams-food-ingredients.co.uk *Ingredient supplier for food manufrs*

Adams Food Ingredients Ltd, Prince St, Leek, Staffordshire, ST13 6DB Tel: (01538) 399686 Fax: (01538) 399766 E-mail: sales@adams-food-ingredients.co.uk *Milk powdered & processed products manufrs*

▶ Adams Franklin, 4 Adelaid Terrace, Northampton, NN2 6AH Tel: (01604) 633000 E-mail: cv@adamsfranklin.com *Sales & marketing recruitment specialists*

▶ Adams Glass, St George St, Leicester, LE1 1QG Tel: 0116-251 1715

Adams Hydraulics Ltd, PO Box 15, York, YO30 4XE Tel: (01904) 695695 Fax: (01904) 695600 E-mail: sales@adamshydraulics.co.uk Principal Export Areas: Worldwide *Design, supply, manufacture &installation of water & wastewater treatment equipment*

Adams Ironmongers Sutton Coldfield Ltd, 112 Holland Road, Sutton Coldfield, West Midlands, B72 1RE Tel: 0121-354 4822 Fax: 0121-355 6968 E-mail: sales@adamsindustrial.co.uk *General ironmongers*

J.R. Adams (Newcastle) Ltd, Hannington Works, Longrigg, Swalwell, Newcastle Upon Tyne, NE16 3AS Tel: 0191-488 7911 Fax: 0191-488 3101 *Road haulage & storage contractors*

John Adams Trading Co. Ltd, The Barn, 3 Deanes Close, Steventon, Abingdon, Oxfordshire, OX13 6SZ Tel: (01235) 833066 Fax: (01235) 861116 E-mail: trading@johnadams.co.uk *Toy manufrs*

Adams Lube Tech Ltd, Unit 6 Binns Close, Coventry, CV4 9TB Tel: (024) 7646 7941 Fax: (024) 7669 4002 E-mail: info@adamslube.com *Lubrication equipment manufacturers*

Adams Morey Ltd, Yeomans Industrial Park, Yeomans Way, Bournemouth, BH8 0BJ Tel: (01202) 524422 Fax: (01202) 524448 E-mail: enquiries@adamsmorey.com

continued

Commercial vehicle distributors Also at: Southampton

Adams Morey, Unit A 1-2 River Way Industrial Estate, Newport, Isle of Wight, PO30 5UY Tel: (01983) 522552 Fax: (01983) 821169 *Vehicle distributors & maintenance services*

Adams Packaging Ltd, Timberlaine Estate, Quarry Lane, Chichester, West Sussex, PO19 8PP Tel: (01243) 783474 Fax: (01243) 815960 E-mail: adams-adams@cwcom.net *Specialist packaging suppliers*

Adams Pork Products Ltd, 1 Viscount Way, Woodley, Reading, RG5 4DZ Tel: 0118-921 9227 Fax: 0118-944 8756 *Pork product distributors*

Adams Pork Products Ltd, Sleaford Road, Ruskington, Sleaford, Lincolnshire, NG34 9BL Tel: (01526) 832216 Fax: (01526) 833439 *Sausage & pork pie manufrs*

Adams Pork Products Ltd, Crescent House, Fulney Lane, Spalding, Lincolnshire, PE12 6EZ Tel: (01775) 766161 Fax: (01775) 710717 E-mail: sales@geo-adams.co.uk *Pork product suppliers*

Adams PR & Marketing, 78 Woodside Avenue North, Coventry, CV3 6BD Tel: (024) 7669 0700 Fax: (024) 7669 0700 *Advertising & public relations services*

Adams Ricardo Ltd, Millbrook Road, Yate, Bristol, BS37 5PB Tel: (01454) 311646 Fax: (01454) 324114 E-mail: sales@adamsricardo.com *Blower repairers & manufrs*

Adams Rite Europe Ltd, 6 Moreton Industrial Estate, London Road, Swanley, Kent, BR8 8TZ Tel: (01322) 668024 Fax: (01322) 660996 E-mail: info@adamsrite.co.uk *Architectural hardware*

Russell Adams Ltd, Beechwood House, Tanners Lane, Berkswell, Coventry, CV7 7DA Tel: (024) 7685 6400 Fax: (024) 7685 6401 E-mail: sales@russelladams.com *Software development services*

Adams Of Rye Ltd, 8 High Street, Rye, East Sussex, TN31 7JH Tel: (01797) 223136 Fax: (01797) 223380 E-mail: adamsrye@aol.com *Printers, stationers & department store*

Adams Sandy Engng, Fordoun Aerodrome, Fordoun, Laurencekirk, Kincardineshire, AB30 1JR Tel: (01561) 320800 Fax: (01561) 320811 E-mail: info@sandyadamsengineering.co.uk *Engineering services & ornamental gates*

Adams Sheet Metal Ltd, Mill Street, Wibsey, Bradford, West Yorkshire, BD6 3BQ Tel: (01274) 693630 Fax: (01274) 693631 E-mail: sales@a-s-m.co.uk *Ducting components*

Adams Tarpaulins, The Old Bakery, Ford Road, Wiveliscombe, Taunton, Somerset, TA4 2RE Tel: (01984) 623315 Fax: (01984) 623602 *Tarpaulin manufrs*

Adamsez Ltd, 766 Upper Newtownards Road, Dundonald, Belfast, BT16 1TQ Tel: (028) 9048 0465 Fax: (028) 9048 0485 E-mail: mail@adamsez.com *Bath tubs manufrs*

A. Adamson, 81 Iona Way, Tirainttilloch, Glasgow, G66 3PU Tel: (0141) 552 5749 Fax: (0141) 552 4917 *Marine & cargo surveyors* Also at: Leith

Adamson Fabrications (Dundee) Ltd, 360 Strathmore Avenue, Dundee, DD3 6RU Tel: (01382) 812101 Fax: (01382) 832189 E-mail: sales@adamsonfabrications.co.uk *Sheet metalwork engineers & fabricators*

Adamson J.F Bakers Confectioners, 29 High Street, Pittenweem, Anstruther, Fife, KY10 2LA Tel: (01333) 311336 *Bakery*

▶ Adamson Laboratory Services, 49 Lampits Hill, Corringham, Stanford-le-Hope, Essex, SS17 9AA Tel: (01375) 673279 Fax: (01375) 678059 E-mail: sales@alsltd.co.uk *We are a health, safety and environmental consultancy. Provision of health & safety consultants, health & safety training. Asbestos management and surveys.*

Adamson & Partners Ltd, 10 Lisbon Square, Leeds, LS1 4LY Tel: 0113-245 1212 Fax: 0113-242 0802 E-mail: stuart.adamson@adamsons.com *Executive search & selection services*

Adan Ltd, Nursery Road Industrial Estate, Boston, Lincolnshire, PE21 7TN Tel: (01205) 311500 Fax: (01205) 358013

▶ E-mail: sales@adanltd.co.uk *Hydraulic engineers*

▶ Adana Construction Ltd, Europa Business Park, Bird Hall Lane, Stockport, Cheshire, SK3 0XA Tel: 0161-428 1613

Adanac Valve Specialities Ltd, 14 Windmill Avenue, Woolpit Business Park, Woolpit, Bury St. Edmunds, Suffolk, IP30 9UP Tel: (01359) 240404 Fax: (01359) 240406 E-mail: info@adanac.co.uk Principal Export Areas: Asia Pacific, Middle East, Central/East Europe, West Europe & North America *Industrial valve modification*

Adapt Technology Ltd, 11a Green Lane, London, NW4 2NL Tel: (020) 8203 2222 Fax: (020) 8203 2259 E-mail: info@adapt-technology.com *Network support & suppliers*

Adaptaflex Ltd, Station Road Industrial Estate, Station Road, Coleshill, Birmingham, B46 1HT Tel: (01675) 468200 Fax: (01675) 462090 E-mail: sales@adaptaflex.co.uk Principal Export Areas: Worldwide *Conduit manufrs*

Adaptatruck, Elm Lodge, North Street, Winkfield, Windsor, Berkshire, SL4 4TE Tel: (01344) 891734 Fax: (01344) 891738 E-mail: derekwine@aol.com *Heavy lifting equipment & industrial electric vehicles manufrs*

▶ Adapted Eye Design Ltd, 9 Stamford House, 23 Westside Common, Wimbledon Village, London, SW19 4UF Tel: 020 8946 0782 Fax: 020 8944 0353 E-mail: info@adaptedeyedesign.com *Adapted Eye Design are a top design agency based in Wimbledon Village. We specialise in web design, web site marketing and online branding.*

Adaptive Computing Co., Crabtree Farm, Wisborough Green, Billingshurst, West Sussex, RH14 0AD Tel: (01403) 753333 Fax: (01403) 753386 E-mail: info@adaptive-instruments.com *Data acquisition systems manufrs*

Adaptive Control Solutions Ltd, 1 Ashfield Road, Greetland, Halifax, West Yorkshire, HX4 8HY Tel: (01422) 313456 Fax: (01422) 313567 E-mail: richardarmitage@adaptivecontrol.com *Process controller & control system manufrs*

Adare Ltd, Vantage House, 1 Weir Road, London, SW19 8UX Tel: (020) 8946 7537 Fax: (020) 8947 2740 *Direct mail computer bureau*

▶ Adare Ltd, Bankside, Dockfield Road, Shipley, West Yorkshire, BD17 7BJ Tel: (01274) 771111 Fax: (01274) 208308 E-mail: info@adare.com *Mailing house*

Adare Carwin, Unit B Wellington Gate, Silverthorne Way, Waterlooville, Hampshire, PO7 7XY Tel: (023) 9224 5000 Fax: (023) 9224 5060 E-mail: info@adare.com *Print management*

Adare Halcyon Ltd, Park Mill, Clayton West, Huddersfield, HD8 9QQ Tel: (01484) 863411 Fax: (01484) 862355 E-mail: info@adare.com *Stationery design & manufrs*

Adare Label Converters Ltd, Falconer Road, Haverhill, Suffolk, CB9 7XU Tel: (01440) 714996 Fax: (01440) 766501 E-mail: sales@labelconverters.co.uk *Multilayer & promotional labels* Also at: Dublin

Adare Pillings Ltd, Elland Lane, Elland, West Yorkshire, HX5 9DZ Tel: (01422) 379711 Fax: (01422) 377503 E-mail: info@adarepillings.com *Printers & creative designers*

Adas Gleadthorpe Grange, Gleadthorpe, Meden Vale, Mansfield, Nottinghamshire, NG20 9PF Tel: (01623) 844331 Fax: (01623) 844472 *Environmental & research land base consultancy*

Adas International Ltd, Woodthorne, Wergs Road, Wolverhampton, WV6 8TQ Tel: (01902) 754190 Fax: (01902) 693465 E-mail: enquiries@adas.co.uk *Land-based consultants, environmental & rural consultants*

Adastra Label Marketing Co. Ltd, 42 Gloucester Way, London, EC1R 0BR Tel: (020) 7278 8020 Fax: (020) 7837 3770 E-mail: sales@adastralabels.com *Textile labels distribtors & manufrs*

Adax Europe Ltd, Reada Court, Vachel Road, Reading, RG1 1NY Tel: 0118-952 2800 Fax: 0118-957 1530 E-mail: info@adax.co.uk *Network communications*

Adbeck Fabrications Ltd, Loomer Road Industrial Estate, Loomer Road, Chesterton, Newcastle, Staffordshire, ST5 7LB Tel: (01782) 565774 Fax: (01782) 565774 E-mail: adbeckfabs@aol.com *Adbeck Fabrications is a small to medium steel fabrication company based in Newcastle Under Lyme in Staffordshire. We specialise in the following areas: automotive; architectural; water industry and general fabrications in mild and stainless steel. We will consider contracts up to £30,000. We have 2000 feet of fabrication space available with maximum cranage of 2.5 tons. We pride ourselves on the quality of our work and due to our size can offer an excellent and flexible service. For a no obligation competitive quote please contact Cliff on 01782 565774.*

Adbruf Ltd, Gibbs Marsh Trading Estate, Stalbridge, Sturminster Newton, Dorset, DT10 2RX Tel: (01963) 362640 Fax: (01963) 363762 E-mail: sales@adbruf.com *Road marking & safety material manufrs*

▶ Adby Interiors Ltd, 19 Alford Road, High Wycombe, Buckinghamshire, HP12 4PT Tel: (01494) 441507 Fax: (01494) 474330 E-mail: info@adbyinteriors.co.uk *Interior designers*

ADC Communications (UK) Ltd, Runnings Road, Kingsditch Trading Estate, Cheltenham, Gloucestershire, GL51 9NQ Tel: (01242) 264400 Fax: (01242) 264488 E-mail: christianname.surname@adckrone.com *Manufacturers of computer installation local area network systems*

Adc Electrical Co. Ltd, Burtree Works, Hertburn Estate, Hertburn, Washington, Tyne & Wear, NE37 2SF Tel: 0191-416 5222 Fax: 0191-416 3996 E-mail: info@adc-electrical.co.uk *Electric motor repair services*

Adc Gas Analysis Ltd, Hoddesdon Industrial Centre, Pindar Road, Hoddesdon, Hertfordshire, EN11 0FF Tel: (01992) 478600 Fax: (01992) 478938 E-mail: sales@adc-analysers.com *Gas detection & analysis services*

Adcal Labels Ltd, Jayem Works, Gomm Road, High Wycombe, Buckinghamshire, HP13 7DJ Tel: (01494) 530761 Fax: (01494) 461651 E-mail: sales@adcal-labels.co.uk *Laminate, print rolls, window stickers, suppliers of trade work*

Adcas 1997 Ltd, Unit 12a Parkview East Industrial Estate, Parkview Road East, Hartlepool, Cleveland, TS25 1PG Tel: (01429) 283212 Fax: (01429) 420900 E-mail: sales@adcas1997.co.uk *Architectural door manufrs*

Adcliffe Drawdeal Ltd, Rempstone Road, Coleorton, Coalville, Leicestershire, LE67 8HR Tel: (01530) 222010 Fax: (01530) 222589 E-mail: sales@adcliffe.co.uk *Commercial vehicle body builders*

Adco Distributors Ni Ltd, Unit 16 Seagoe Industrial Area, Portadown, Craigavon, County Armagh, BT63 5QD Tel: (028) 3835 3121 Fax: (028) 3833 8291 E-mail: tyre@adcoltd.com *Truck tyre retreads*

Adco Industrial Wear Ltd, 61 Court Road, Kingswood, Bristol, BS15 9QG Tel: 0117-967 7656 Fax: 0117-935 2546 *Industrial clothing suppliers*

Adco Signs, 15 Cleggs Buildings, Bolton, BL1 4AN Tel: (01204) 529167 Fax: (01204) 399214 E-mail: adcoinfo.signs@virgin.net *Sign manufrs*

▶ Adcock Group Ltd, Midland House, Vicarage Farm Road, Peterborough, PE1 5UH Tel: (01733) 344300 Fax: (01733) 312919 E-mail: mail25@adcock.co.uk *Air conditioning & refrigeration systems*

Adcock Refrigeration & Air Conditioning Ltd, 5 Industrial Estate, London Road, Pampisford, Cambridge, CB22 3XX Tel: (01223) 834189 Fax: (01223) 837116 E-mail: enquiries@adcock.co.uk *Refrigeration & air conditioning installers*

Adcock Refrigeration & Air Conditioning Ltd, 152 London Road, Copford, Colchester, CO6 1BQ Tel: (01206) 212502 Fax: (01206) 212080 E-mail: mail20@adcock.co.uk *Refrigeration & air conditioning engineers*

▶ Adcock Refrigeration & Air Conditioning Ltd, Unit E5 Premier Business Centre, Speedfields Park, Fareham, Hampshire, PO14 1TY Tel: (01329) 235800 Fax: (01329) 233216 *Refrigeration & air conditioning supply & repair*

Adcock Refrigeration & Air Conditioning Ltd, Unit 15, Business Science Park, Nunns Corner, Grimsby, South Humberside, DN34 5FQ Tel: (01472) 870559 Fax: (01472) 751966 E-mail: julianlloyd@adcock.co.uk *Refrigeration & air conditioning installators*

Adcock Refrigeration & Air Conditioning Ltd, 35 Key Street, Ipswich, IP4 1BZ Tel: (01473) 258090 Fax: (01473) 232160 *Refrigeration & air conditioning installation services*

Adcock Refrigeration & Air Conditioning Ltd, 22 Mason Road, Norwich, NR6 6RF Tel: (01603) 786900 Fax: (01603) 418147 *Air conditioning & refrigeration designers & installers* Also at: Cambridge

▶ Adcraft Ltd, Block 10, Moorfield Industrial Estate, Kilmarnock, Ayrshire, KA2 0BA Tel: (01563) 530130 Fax: (01563) 534390

Add Plant Ltd, Grovehill Road, Beverley, East Yorkshire, HU17 0JN Tel: (01482) 867227 Fax: (01482) 872868 E-mail: hire@addplant.karoo.co.uk *Plant transport vehicle hire & repairs*

Addacabin Ltd, Southend, Thornton, Kirkcaldy, Fife, KY1 4ED Tel: (01592) 774387 Fax: (01592) 779474 E-mail: info@addacabin.co.uk *Portable building suppliers*

Addaction Scotland, Nethergate Business Centre, Dundee, DD1 4ER Tel: (01382) 206888 Fax: (01382) 229870 E-mail: salt@salts.co.uk *Surgical suppliers*

Addagrip Surface Treatments UK Ltd, Addagrip House, Bell Lane Industrial Estate, Uckfield, East Sussex, TN22 1QL Tel: (01825) 761333 Fax: (01825) 768566 E-mail: sales@addagrip.co.uk *Addagrip are manufacturers, formulators and suppliers of a complete range of resin based surfacing and repair systems. These include the market leading Addastone® resin bonded aggregate surfacing system, Addaset resin bound (trowelled) aggregate surfacing system, flooring epoxy resins, 2 pack epoxy resins, solvent and water dispersed epoxy floor coatings, polyurethane systems. All producing durable surfaces and in a variety of specifications from roller coats to self levelling, with a wide choice of formulations, colours and mechanical properties for exterior and interior solutions for domestic, retail industrial and landscaping projects.*

▶ K. Addams Industrial Roofing Contractors Limited, ARC House, Sundon Road, Chalton, Luton, LU4 9UA Tel: (01525) 877740 Fax: (01525) 877118 E-mail: k.addams@btinternet.com *We undertake all types of roof related work to factories and commercial premises, including: Valleys, gullies, asbestos sheeting, skylight cleaning, solar reflective coating & new roofs.*

▶ Addaphone Telecommunication Services, 6 Cotswold Green, Aylesbury, Buckinghamshire, HP20 2HB Tel: (01296) 397322 E-mail: dj@addaphone.co.uk *Fitting & updating internal telephone extension sockets*

Addax Signs & Display Ltd, 22 Eastmuir Street, Annick Industrial Estate, Glasgow, G32 0HS Tel: 0141-778 8881 Fax: 0141-778 5490 *Signs manufrs*

Added Value Software, 2-4 York Road, Felixstowe, Suffolk, IP11 7HX Tel: (01394) 286828 Fax: (0870) 0941003 E-mail: angus@a-v-s.co.uk *Software house*

Adder Technology Ltd, Technology House, Trafalgar Way, Bar Hill, Cambridge, CB3 8SQ Tel: (01954) 780044 Fax: (01954) 780081 E-mail: sales@addertec.com *Keyboard, monitor, mouse & video switches*

▶ Addicott Electrics Ltd, Quay Road, Teignmouth, Devon, TQ14 8EL Tel: (01626) 774087 Fax: (01626) 778463 E-mail: addicott@netcomuk.co.uk *Manufacturers of generators*

▶ Adding Value Solutions Ltd, Unit 66, Alloa Business Centre, Whins Road, Alloa, Clackmannanshire, FK10 3SA Tel: (07768) 653017 E-mail: info@addingvaluesolutions.co.uk *Full range of marketing and promotional services including :** Design, staffing and management of promotional campaigns** Design and production of promotional communication** Promotion and presenting staff** Logistics*

Addis, Zone 3 Waterton Point, Brocastle Avenue, Waterton Industrial Estate, Bridgend, Mid Glamorgan, CF31 3US Tel: (01656) 664455 Fax: (01656) 664456 E-mail: e.marketing@addis.co.uk *Industrial cleaning equipment*

▶ Addis Locksmiths, 36 lawrence close, Andover, Hampshire, SP10 3SY Tel: 01264 350980 E-mail: info@addislocksmiths.co.uk *we are a small independent company that offer the full range of locksmith services. At a very competetive rate, All our work is Fully garentead, and completed to insurence standards.*

Cliff Addison Drainage, Far End Cottage, Worsall Road, Kirklevington, Yarm, Cleveland, TS15 9PE Tel: (01642) 782702 Fax: (01642) 790038 E-mail: sales@cliffaddisondrainage.co.uk *Drainage contractors & plant hire*

Addison Corporate Marketing Ltd, 2 Cathedral Street, London, SE1 9DE Tel: (020) 7403 7444 Fax: (020) 7403 1243 E-mail: peter.chodel@addison.co.uk *Corporate marketing agents*

▶ Addison Electrical Ltd, 18 Silverhillock, Cornhill, Banff, AB45 2AY Tel: (01466) 751607 Fax: (01466) 751414

▶ Addison Electrical, Hopetown, Boyndie, Banff, AB45 2LR Tel: (01261) 843870 Fax: (01261) 843870

Addison Glass Works Ltd, 175 Walnut Tree Close, Guildford, Surrey, GU1 4TX Tel: (01483) 538480 Fax: (01483) 531273 E-mail: addisons@cix.compulink.co.uk *Glazing contractors*

Company Information

Addison Mckee, 188 Bradkirk Place, Walton Summit Centre, Bamber Bridge, Preston, PR5 8AJ Tel: (01772) 334511 Fax: (01772) 323227 E-mail: sales@atf.co.uk *Tube bending machines manufrs*

▶ Addison Ross, Berwick Road, Wooler, Northumberland, NE71 6AH Tel: (01668) 281872 Fax: (01668) 281613

Addison Signs, Unit 16 Links Business Centre, Raynham Road, Bishop's Stortford, Hertfordshire, CM23 5NZ Tel: (01279) 507407 Fax: (01279) 507477 E-mail: enquiries@addisonsigns.co.uk *Sign manufrs*

Addisons, North Holme, Main Street, Bonby, Brigg, South Humberside, DN20 0PY Tel: (01652) 618661 Fax: (01652) 618575 *Agricultural machinery parts suppliers*

Addlestone Electronics, Kistadan, Church Lane, Bisley, Woking, Surrey, GU24 9EA Tel: (01483) 480969 Fax: (01483) 797268 E-mail: sales@addlestone-electronics.co.uk *Closed circuit television transmission equipment, specialist in telemetry systems*

Addmore Engineering, Unit 18 Broadmead Business Park, Broadmead Road, Stewartby, Bedford, MK43 9NX Tel: (01234) 766957 Fax: (01234) 766951 E-mail: sales@addmoreengineering.co.uk *Sliding heads, CNC; CNC precision turned parts & turned parts manufrs*

▶ Addsales Software Ltd, 40 Solar Court, Etchin Park Road, London, N3 2DZ Tel: (020) 8343 3042 Fax: 020 834 3495 E-mail: addsales@add-sales.co.uk *Very, very simple to use Sales Contact, Order Booking and Management Software.*

Addscan Hire Centre, 221 Edleston Road, Crewe, CW2 7HT Tel: (01270) 211061 Fax: (01270) 211353 E-mail: lynne_smith@btconnect.com *Contractors of plant & vehicle hire*

Addspace Furniture Ltd, Lowfield Road, Bolton-upon-Dearne, Rotherham, South Yorkshire, S63 8JF Tel: (01709) 899400 Fax: (01709) 897369 E-mail: paul.hakes@addspacefl.co.uk *Self-assembly furniture manufrs*

Addtime Recording Co. Ltd, 2 Eastwell Road, Ashton-in-Makerfield, Wigan, Lancashire, WN4 9QQ Tel: (01942) 272061 Fax: (01942) 274601 E-mail: sales@addtimerecording.co.uk *Time recorder & attendance systems distributors & agents.*

▶ ADE International Corp, 24 Scott Street, Hamilton, Lanarkshire, ML3 6SH Tel: (01698) 200025

▶ Ade Sims, 23 Heathfield, Chippenham, Wiltshire, SN15 1BQ Tel: 01249 461295 E-mail: adesims@supanet.com *Qualified Computer support, Upgrades, Repairs, Internet Connections, Networks set up, Tutorials. Home visits by appointment.**

Adecco UK Ltd, 44 Shenley Road, Borehamwood, Hertfordshire, WD6 1DR Tel: (020) 8953 6700 Fax: (020) 8207 4686 E-mail: info@adecco.co.uk *Employment agency* Also at: Branches throughout the U.K.

Adecco UK Ltd, Mayflower House, 178 Armada Way, Plymouth, PL1 1LD Tel: (01752) 262526 Fax: (01752) 220481 E-mail: 638.plymouth@adecco.co.uk *Recruitment consultants*

Adecco UK Ltd, 13-15 Blagrave Street, Reading, RG1 1PJ Tel: 0118-950 0321 Fax: 0118-959 1920 E-mail: first.last@adecco.co.uk *Recruitment solution agency & service providers*

Adecs Ltd, 1 Mercia Business Village, Torwood Close, Westwood Business Park, Coventry, CV4 8HX Tel: (024) 7646 4753 Fax: (08453) 109600 E-mail: services@adecs.co.uk *Computer consultants*

Adel Rootstein, 9 Beaumont Avenue, London, W14 9LP Tel: (020) 7381 1447 Fax: (020) 7381 3263 E-mail: sales@adelrootstein.co.uk *Mannequin manufrs*

Adelaide Sash Windows Ltd, 145 Islingword Road, Brighton, BN2 9SH Tel: (01273) 602329 Fax: (01273) 602222 *Renovation draft proofing, double glazed, suppliers*

Adelard Computer Consultants, 10 Northampton Square, London, EC1V 0HB Tel: (020) 7490 9450 Fax: (020) 7490 9451 E-mail: sales@adelard.co.uk *Computer consultants*

Adelco Screen Process Ltd, 16 18 Highview, High Street, Bordon, Hampshire, GU35 0AX Tel: (01420) 488388 Fax: (01420) 476445 E-mail: sales@adelco.co.uk *Screen printers*

▶ Adele Addams Accociates, 71 Keighley Road, Skipton, North Yorkshire, BD23 2LX Tel: (01756) 797444 Fax: (01756) 799506

Adelphi Coin Ltd, Adelphi House, Freeholdland Road, Pontnewynydd, Pontypool, Gwent, NP4 8LN Tel: (01495) 751933 Fax: (01495) 752872 E-mail: sales@carmarketwales.co.uk *Motor bikes & quad wholesalers*

▶ Adelphi Engineering & Construction, Unit 1 Imex Business Centre, Lugar, Cumnock, Ayrshire, KA18 3JG Tel: (01290) 426677 Fax: (01290) 425588 *Structural steel engineers*

Adelphi Plant Hire Centres Ltd, Rear of Service Station 7-9 Tudor Parade, Well Hall Road, London, SE9 6SX Tel: (020) 8850 2430 Fax: (020) 8294 1817 *Portable toilet hire*

Adelphi Precision Ltd, Sawpit Industrial Estate, Tibshelf, Derbyshire, DE55 5NH Tel: (01773) 872351 Fax: (01773) 875067 E-mail: adelphiprecision@ic24.net *CNC engineering services*

Adem Ltd, Unit 15 Metro Business Centre, Kangley Bridge Road, London, SE26 5BW Tel: (020) 8676 8092 Fax: (020) 8659 0354 E-mail: mail@adem.co.uk *Microfilming maintenance & services*

Aden Electronics Holdings Ltd, Unit 3 Montpelier Business Park, Dencora Way, Ashford, Kent, TN23 4FG Tel: (01233) 664445 Fax: (01233) 664626 E-mail: info@adenelectronics.co.uk *Coil winders & electrical coils manufrs*

▶ Adept Building Contractors, 367-369 Croydon Road, Wallington, Surrey, SM6 7NY Tel: (020) 8254 9785 Fax: (020) 8254 9786

Adept Cleaning Services Ltd, 5 Gainsborough Drive, Mile Oak, Tamworth, Staffordshire, B78 3PJ Tel: (01827) 287100 Fax: (01827) 287666 *Commercial & industrial contract cleaners*

▶ Adept Communications Ltd, 140 The Broadway, Tolworth, Surbiton, Surrey, KT6 7JE Tel: (0845) 4561025 Fax: (0845) 4561029 E-mail: ianw@adeptcom.net *Telephone systems installation, maintenance & support*

Adept Design & Construction Ltd, Unit D7 Cowdray Centre, Cowdray Avenue, Colchester, CO1 1BW Tel: (01206) 762126 Fax: (01206) 763557 *Furniture manufrs*

Adept Engineering & Design, 7-2 Halas Industrial Estate, Forge Lane, Halesowen, West Midlands, B62 8EB Tel: 0121-602 5060 Fax: 0121-602 5080 E-mail: aedrollers@tiscali.co.uk *Principal Export Areas: Central/East Europe, West Europe & North America Conveyor rollers/belt systems manufacturers*

Adept Heating & Mechanical Services Ltd, Raidons, Nutbourne Lane, Nutbourne, Pulborough, West Sussex, RH20 2HS Tel: (01798) 875239 Fax: (01798) 875239 E-mail: daveblaber@aol.com *Suppliers boilers, heating equipment, commercial, industrial, domestic*

Adept Packaging Co. Ltd, 78-82 Nightingale Grove, Hither Green, London, SE13 6DZ Tel: (020) 8318 7511 Fax: (020) 8852 9120 E-mail: sales@adeptpack.co.uk *Polyethylene manufrs*

▶ ADEPT Precision Ltd, Unit 7 Deacon Trading Estate, 203 Vale Road, Tonbridge, Kent, TN9 1SU Tel: 01732 773777 Fax: 01732 771115 E-mail: sales@adeptprecision.com *Precision Engineers making components for the Automotive, Aerospace and Hydraulic Industries. Fine Grinding, Spline Rolling, CNC Turning, Centreless Grinding etc.*

Adept Precision Sheet Metal Ltd, Ardglen Trading Estate, Whitchurch, Hampshire, RG28 7BB Tel: (01256) 893177 Fax: (01256) 893904 E-mail: info@adept-sheetmetal.co.uk *Sheet metalwork engineers*

Adept Scientific plc, Amor Way, Letchworth Garden City, Hertfordshire, SG6 1ZA Tel: (01462) 480055 Fax: (01462) 480213 E-mail: info@adeptscience.co.uk *Computer systems services*

Adept Tooling Ltd, 25b Tir Llwyd Industrial Estate, Kinmel Bay, Rhyl, Clwyd, LL18 5JA Tel: (01745) 345050 Fax: (01745) 345060 *Diamond tool manufrs*

Adept Vacuum Formers & Patterns Ltd, 141 Waterside Road, Hamilton, Leicester, LE5 1TL Tel: 0116-246 0552 Fax: 0116-246 0987 E-mail: enquiries@adeptvp.freeserve.co.uk *Plastic vacuum formed products manufrs*

▶ Adeptias Ltd, 37 Beauchamp Avenue, Leamington Spa, Warwickshire, CV32 5TD Tel: (01926) 831555 Fax: 01926 422600 *Designers of computers & desks*

Adeptstar Shipping Ltd, Estate House, Marsh Way, Fairview Industrial Park, Rainham, Essex, RM13 8UH Tel: (01708) 550909 Fax: (01708) 551945 E-mail: adeptstar@shipping-ltd.fsnet.co.uk *Freight forwarders*

▶ Adeptus Marketing & Design, 20 Station Road, Parkstone, Poole, Dorset, BH14 8UB Tel: 01202 711416 Fax: 07092 236937 E-mail: info@adeptusdesign.com *Marketing Consultancy offering Design, Advertising and Web Development Services.*

▶ Adestra, Hollywell House, Osney Mead, Oxford, OX2 0EN Tel: (01865) 242425 Fax: (01865) 255241 E-mail: Sales@adestra.com *Adestra Ltd are a digital marketing agency that specialise in inbound and outbound email marketing broadcast services, fax marketing broadcasting and SMS broadcast solutions.*

Adex Interiors For Industry Ltd, 5 Avebury Court, Hemel Hempstead, Hertfordshire, HP2 7TA Tel: (01442) 232327 Fax: (01442) 262713 E-mail: adex@msn.com *Ceiling, partition & mezzanine floor contractors*

Adex Technical Ltd, Unit 4 Canal Ironworks, Hope Mill Lane, London Road, Stroud, Gloucestershire, GL5 2SH Tel: (01453) 889202 Fax: (01453) 889203 E-mail: sales@adexltd.co.uk *Capacitor distributors*

Adey Steel, Meadow Lane, Loughborough, Leicestershire, LE11 1JU Tel: (01509) 556677 Fax: (01509) 828622 E-mail: admin@adey-steel.co.uk *Construction Steel suppliers & installers - Steel fabricators & steel stockholders*

Adfield-Harvey Ltd, The Granary, Beckbury, Shifnal, Shropshire, TF11 9DG Tel: (01952) 752500 Fax: (01952) 752510 E-mail: info@adfield.co.uk *Marketing & business consultants*

Adford CNC Ltd, 96 Smirrells Road, Birmingham, B28 0LB Tel: 0121-622 2232 Fax: 0121-622 2242 E-mail: sales@adfordcnc.co.uk *Machine tool repair*

AdGiftsOnline, 17 The Barracks, Barracks Road, Newcastle, Staffordshire, ST5 1LG Tel: (01782) 713177 Fax: (01782) 715431 E-mail: sales@adgiftsonline.com *Business gifts & promotional item distributors & sourcing specialists*

Adglow plc, Ledbury House, Alexandra Way, Ashchurch, Tewkesbury, Gloucestershire, GL20 8NB Tel: (01684) 850650 Fax: (01684) 850729 E-mail: mail@adglow.co.uk *Display designers, producers or suppliers & point of sale*

▶ ADH WebCreations, 55 Chaucer Road, Gillingham, Kent, ME7 5LX Tel: 01634 566138 E-mail: info@adhwebcreations.co.uk **ADH WebCreations is a small business - aimed at small businesses * *We will enable your company to achieve a simple yet effective web presence, whether it""s 1 page or , a new site or redesign, we""ll help you get on the web and in public view 24 hours a day - 7 days a week. *From start-up to initial trading and beyond, however small or large you may be, an effective website shouldn""t be out of reach.** *We deliver a professional service to help you gain a web presence that complies with the Disabilities Discriminations Act and keep you informed every* continued *step of the way.*Simply supply us with any logos, product & service information and company details and we""ll do the rest. We""ll design, register and host your site without you having to lift a finger.**It""s that easy!** **

Adhere Industrial Tapes Ltd, Unit 1 Whitehall Road, Whitehall Industrial Estate, Colchester, CO2 8WA Tel: (01206) 871999 Fax: (01206) 871998 E-mail: sales@adhere.co.uk *Adhesive tape distributors/agents (required worldwide). Building, glass/glazing construction, print finishing & point of sale commercial body building*

The Adhesive Co., 51 Church Walk South, Swindon, SN2 2JE Tel: (01793) 537816 Fax: (01793) 537816 E-mail: sales@theadhesivecompany.co.uk *Adhesives distributors*

▶ Adhesive Applications, 2 Richmond Drive, Lichfield, Staffordshire, WS14 9SZ Tel: (01543) 255149 Fax: 01543 255149 E-mail: dancerpw@aol.com *Our aim is to ensure the correct adhesive for your application in your production environment, matched to efficient application equipment, at the right price*

Adhesive & Coating Supplies, Sherborne St West, Salford, M3 7LF Tel: 0161-835 1420 Fax: 0161-839 3543 E-mail: sales@chemipat.co.uk *Industrial adhesives & coatings*

▶ Adhesive Coatings, Eagle Technology Park, Queensway, Rochdale, Lancashire, OL11 1TQ Tel: (01706) 356125 Fax: (01706) 524853 E-mail: postbox@adhesive-coatings.co.uk *We produce self-adhesive film & paper*

Adhesive Developments Ltd, John Lee Fold, Middleton, Manchester, M24 2LR Tel: 0161-643 3965 Fax: 0161-643 7889 E-mail: gluee@supanet.com *Industrial adhesive manufrs*

Adhesive Tape Manufacturers Association, Sussex House, 8-10 Homesdale Road, Bromley, BR2 9LZ Tel: (020) 8464 0131 Fax: (020) 8464 6018 E-mail: info@craneandpartners.com *Accountants*

Adhesive Tape Manufacturing Co Ltd, 2 Bilston Industrial Estate, Oxford Street, Bilston, West Midlands, WV14 7EG Tel: (01902) 409598 Fax: (01902) 409599 E-mail: sales@atmuk.co.uk *Adhesive tape manufrs*

Adhesive Technical Services Ltd, Beacon Hill Industrial Estate, Botany Way, Purfleet, Essex, RM19 1SR Tel: (01708) 867355 Fax: (01708) 869804 E-mail: sales@adhtechnical.com *Adhesive consultants manufrs*

Adhesives International Ltd, Northleigh Business Park, Woodstock Road, North Leigh, Witney, Oxfordshire, OX29 6RN Tel: (01993) 882749 Fax: (01993) 883887 E-mail: info@adhesivesintnl.com *Industrial hot melt adhesive & coating equipment specialists*

ADI UK Ltd, Pittman Court, Pittman Way, Fulwood, Preston, PR2 9ZG Tel: (0800) 592346 Fax: (01772) 708201 E-mail: sales@theadigroup.com *Audio visual systems integrators*

▶ Adis Scaffolding Ltd, M1 Commerce Park, Markham Lane, Duckmanton, Chesterfield, Derbyshire, S44 5HS Tel: (01246) 827997 Fax: (01246) 827998 E-mail: adisscaffolding@tiscali.co.uk *Scaffolding services*

Adit Ltd, Tyn Rardd, Dwyran, Llanfairpwllgwyngyll, Gwynedd, LL61 6AJ Tel: (01248) 430075 Fax: (01248) 430771 E-mail: sales@adit.co.uk *Software house*

▶ Aditech Ltd, 3 Midshires Business Park, Smeaton Close, Aylesbury, Buckinghamshire, HP19 8HL Tel: (01296) 398085 Fax: (01296) 337755 E-mail: sales@aditech.co.uk *Security software, hardware development services*

▶ Adjayi Secretarial, 3 Maple Leaf Cottages, Blackboys, Uckfield, East Sussex, TN22 5LJ Tel: 01825 890955 Fax: 01825 890955 E-mail: sue@adjayi-secretarial.co.uk *Professional, flexible, reliable, yet cost effect, admin/secretarial services. Including typing, filing, database creation/maintenance, internet research, mailshots and much more.....*

▶ Adjusting Solutions, 1 Alie Street, London, E1 8DE Tel: (020) 7488 3066 E-mail: support@iss-web.co.uk *Web designers, software development*

▶ Adjuvant Recruitment Ltd, P.O. Box 65, Tenterden, Kent, TN30 7WD Tel: 0845 33 12395 E-mail: info@adjuvantrecruitment.com *"ADJUVANT" specialises in the recruitment of Pharmacists, Technicians and associated professionals. We recruit for the Community sector, Hospitals and Industry throughout the UK.*

Adlam & Beadle, Unit 5, North Lane, Newhaven, East Sussex, BN9 9BF Tel: (01273) 611091 Fax: (01273) 612989 E-mail: info@adlambeadle.co.uk *Kitchen furniture manufrs*

Adler & Allan Ltd, 22-42 Livingstone Road, London, E15 2LJ Tel: (020) 8555 7111 Fax: (020) 8519 3090 E-mail: sales@adlerandallan.co.uk *Oil & environmental services*

Adler Recruitment Ltd, 71 Friar Street, Droitwich, Worcestershire, WR9 8EQ Tel: (01905) 795008 Fax: (01905) 795009 E-mail: info@adler-recruitment.co.uk *Recruitment agents*

Adlib Cleaning Materials, Willesley Road, Willesley, Ashby-de-la-Zouch, Leicestershire, LE65 2UN Tel: (01530) 274444 Fax: (01530) 274999 *Cleaning products suppliers*

Adline Personalised Products, Sterling House, 20 Renfield Street, Glasgow, G2 5AP Tel: 0141-248 4411 Fax: 0141-248 4411 E-mail: sales@adlinepersonalised.com *Personalised & promotional products distributors*

Adline Press, 5 Bear Court, Basingstoke, Hampshire, RG24 8QT Tel: (01256) 463779 Fax: (01256) 840591 E-mail: design@adline-group.com *Printers & designers*

Adlington Paper & Board Supplies Ltd, Unit 1 Adlington Industrial Estate, Adlington, Macclesfield, Cheshire, SK10 4NL Tel: (01625) 850885 Fax: (01625) 850882 continued E-mail: adlingtonpaper@btconnect.com *Paper & board distributors*

Adlington Welding Supplies Ltd, Highfield Industrial Estate, North Street, Chorley, Lancashire, PR7 1QD Tel: (01257) 279364 Fax: (01257) 241352 E-mail: adweld@easynet.co.uk *Distributors of welding supplies*

▶ Adlink UK Ltd, Nagi House, Alperton Lane, Wembley, Middlesex, HA0 1DX Tel: (020) 8991 5017 Fax: (020) 8991 9496 E-mail: sales@adlinkuk.com *Plumbing, heating, bathroom, electrical & spares stockists*

Adlor Garage Door Services, 8 Brittania Business Park, Mills Road, Quarry Wood, Aylesford, Kent, ME20 7NT Tel: (01622) 882370 Fax: (01622) 882313 *Industrial doors, security grilles & shutters*

▶ Adm, South End Mills, Mill Street, Liverpool, L8 6QZ Tel: 0151-552 5100 Fax: 0151-552 5150

Adm, Ling Fields, Skipton, North Yorkshire, BD23 1UX Tel: (01756) 701051 Fax: (01756) 701076 E-mail: info@admsystems.co.uk *Ventilation systems suppliers & installers*

Adm Milling Ltd, 1 King Edward Road, Brentwood, Essex, CM14 4HG Tel: (01277) 262525 Fax: (01277) 694358 *Flour millers, processors & factors*

ADM Pura Foods Ltd, Erith Oil Works, Church Manorway, Erith, Kent, DA8 1DL Tel: (01322) 443000 Fax: (01322) 443027 *Margarine, fats & oils manufrs*

Admagnetics (Manufaturing Division For Solutions) Ltd, Bolton Avenue, Huncoat Industrial Park, Accrington, Lancashire, BB5 6NJ Tel: (01254) 381869 Fax: (01254) 381674 E-mail: *Principal Export Areas: Worldwide Transformer manufacturers & standby power systems*

▶ Admart Promotions, Saracens House Business Centre, 25 St. Margarets Green, Ipswich, IP4 2BN Tel: (01473) 735094 Fax: (01473) 735121 E-mail: sales@admartpromotions.co.uk *Promotional merchandise suppliers*

Admicra Computer Systems, Unit 5b Factory Lane, Beeston, Nottingham, NG9 4AA Tel: 0115-925 2627 Fax: 0115-925 2626 E-mail: info@admicra.co.uk *Computer consultants*

Adminglade Ltd, Caxton House, Stoke Street, Sheffield, S9 3QH Tel: 0114-244 1932 Fax: 0114-244 1932 *General engineering & piston ring manufrs*

▶ Admiral Business Centre, Suite F1-2 Venture Tower, Fratton Road, Portsmouth, PO1 5DL Tel: (023) 9275 4002 Fax: (023) 9275 4002

Admiral Cleaning Supplies Ltd, Admiral House Whitwick Business Park, Stenson Road, Coalville, Leicestershire, LE67 4JP Tel: (01530) 278920 Fax: (01530) 278930 E-mail: info@admiral-cleaning-supplies.co.uk *Cleaning supplies distributors*

Admiral Display, 18 Seas End Road, Surfleet, Spalding, Lincolnshire, PE11 4DQ Tel: (01775) 680410 Fax: (01775) 680921 E-mail: admiraldisplay@aol.com *We specialise in the design and manufacture of wooden point-of-sale display units, both flat pack and fully assembled. Working primarily in timber, our designs also incorporate other materials to give striking, practical, economical results.*

Admiral Fire Extinguishers, 19 Flude Road, Coventry, CV7 9AQ Tel: (024) 7636 5157 Fax: (024) 7636 2815 E-mail: admiralfire@btopenworld.com *Service & supply fire fighting equipment*

Admiral Labels & Print Ltd, Unit 16 Caldershaw Business Centre, Ings Lane, Rochdale, Lancashire, OL12 7LQ Tel: (01706) 527111 Fax: (01706) 350660 E-mail: sales@admiral-labels.co.uk *Labelling printers*

Admiral Security Systems Ltd, 4 Endsleigh Road, Merstham, Redhill, RH1 3LX Tel: (01737) 645650 Fax: (01737) 645253 E-mail: admiralsecurity@totalise.co.uk *Security systems installation & service*

Admiral Signs Ltd, 121 Oak Street, Norwich, NR3 3BP Tel: (01603) 627573 Fax: (01603) 619954 E-mail: info@admiral-signs.co.uk *Sign manufrs*

Admiral Signs & Graphics, Clough Street, Stoke-on-Trent, ST1 4BA Tel: (01782) 206065 Fax: (01782) 264200 E-mail: admiral.sings@btinternet.com *Sign manufrs*

Admiral Signs Of Hull Ltd, Sainsbury Way, Hessle, North Humberside, HU13 9NX Tel: (01482) 575007 Fax: (01482) 219098 E-mail: info@admiral-signs-hull.co.uk *Sign manufrs*

▶ Admiral Signs London, 71 Penenden, New Ash Green, Longfield, Kent, DA3 8LS Tel: 01474 874412 Fax: 01474 874412 E-mail: info@admiralsignslondon.co.uk *Signs, manufacturers and installers*

Admiral Welding Ltd, Aston Bury Farm, Aston, Stevenage, Hertfordshire, SG2 7EG Tel: (01438) 880309 Fax: (01438) 880174 E-mail: info@admiralwelding.co.uk *Steel fabricators*

▶ Admor Ltd, Jubilee Works, Kings Close, Yapton, Arundel, West Sussex, BN18 0EX Tel: (01243) 553078 Fax: (01243) 555017

Admor Services, Foxes Retreat, Worlds End, Beedon, Newbury, Berkshire, RG20 8SE Tel: (01635) 248088 Fax: (01635) 247877 E-mail: terry@admorservices.co.uk *Power washer specialists*

Adms, 151 Albury Road, Redhill, RH1 3LW Tel: (01737) 645319 Fax: (01737) 219640 E-mail: adms@ntlworld.com *Electrical air conditioning repair & installation*

Adnan UK Ltd, 25 Friar Mews, West Norwood, London, SE27 0PU Tel: (020) 8766 0262 Fax: (020) 8766 6260 *International import & export merchants*

Adnet Precision Engineering Ltd, Nexus Court Unit B1 Gloucester Business Park, Hurricane Road, Brockworth, Gloucester, GL3 4AQ Tel: (01452) 611826 Fax: (01452) 623929 E-mail: info.adnetprecision@virgin.net *Component manufrs*

▶ Adnett, Butcher Close, Staplehurst, Kent, TN12 0TJ Tel: (01580) 892682 E-mail: sales@adnett.co.uk *Computer consultants*

Adnor Ltd, Mill Place, Kingston upon Thames, Surrey, KT1 2RL Tel: (020) 8549 4728 Fax: (020) 8549 8989 E-mail: sales@adnor.co.uk *Sheet metal workers & fabricators*

Ado UK Ltd, Abex Road, Newbury, Berkshire, RG14 5EY Tel: (01635) 521261 Fax: (01635) 529005 *Net curtain suppliers*

Adobe Systems (U K) Ltd, 3 Roundwood Avenue, Stockley Park, Uxbridge, Middlesex, UB11 1AY Tel: (020) 8606 4000 Fax: (020) 8606 4004 E-mail: jobs@adobe.co.uk *Computer software development services*

Adodo, Howitt Buildings, Lenton Boulevard, Nottingham, NG7 2BG Tel: 0115-970 1471 Fax: 0115-970 1671 E-mail: solutions@adodo.co.uk *Business communication consultants*

Adoorable Doors, 580 Pershore Road, Selly Oak, Birmingham, B29 7EN Tel: 0121-471 2414 Fax: 0121-471 2414 E-mail: enquiries@adoorabledoors.co.uk *Wooden door distributors*

▶ Adoremus Contemporary Church Textiles, 14 Beamont Drive, Preston, PR1 8UN Tel: 01772 889111 E-mail: information@adoremus.co.uk *We specialise in providing beautiful and affordable vestments and banners to the church worldwide both modern and traditional.*

▶ ADP, Phoenix House, Phoenix Crescent, Strathclyde Business Park, Bellshill, Lanarkshire, ML4 3NJ Tel: (01488) 662662 Fax: (01698) 501061 *Computer hardware & systems provider*

Adp, 40-48 Pyrcroft Road, Chertsey, Surrey, KT16 9JT Tel: (0845) 2300237 Fax: (0845) 2302371 E-mail: sales@adp-es.co.uk *Supplier of payroll*

Adpac Packaging Supplies, 63d Milton Park, Milton, Abingdon, Oxfordshire, OX14 4RX Tel: (01553) 612130 Fax: (01235) 832821 E-mail: enquiries@adpac.co.uk *Tape dispenser wholesalers*

Adpak Machinery Systems Ltd, 3 Pendleside, Lomeshaye Industrial Estate, Nelson, Lancashire, BB9 6RY Tel: (01282) 601444 Fax: (01282) 612201 E-mail: info@adpak.co.uk *Shrink wrap machinery manufrs*

Adpro Securities, 28a Highgate, Cherry Burton, Beverley, North Humberside, HU17 7RR Tel: (01964) 550555 Fax: (01964) 551954 *Alarm installers*

Ad-Qual Group, 28 Mirfield Road, Solihull, West Midlands, B91 1JD Tel: 0121- 711 8785 Fax: 0121- 711 8785 E-mail: castech@blueyonder.co.uk Sales Contact: M. Cowley *Specialist consultants/ advisory services on all aspects of industrial paints, powders and other surface coatings, including training, testing & analysis facilities. Environmental emission monitoring; Development of Health & Safety risk assessment, policy & safe systems of work.*

▶ Adr Engineering, Unit 3 Foxley Court Farm, Ascot Road, Maidenhead, Berkshire, SL6 3LA Tel: (01628) 783030 Fax: (01628) 776851 E-mail: sales@adr-engineering.co.uk *ADR engineering, manufacturers of motor sport*

Adr Forktruck Components, Leeds Road, Wakefield, West Yorkshire, WF1 2DT Tel: (01924) 873101 Fax: (01924) 873103 E-mail: adrian@forktruckcomopents.com *Fork lift truck spare part sales*

Adr International Ltd, 82 High Street, Wallingford, Oxfordshire, OX10 0BT Tel: (01491) 825666 Fax: (01491) 825688 E-mail: info@adr-international.com *Purchasing consultants*

▶ ADR Qwik-Trak Couriers, Park Road, Hagley, Stourbridge, West Midlands, DY9 0NS Tel: (07812) 126717 Fax: (01562) 884234 E-mail: despatch@qwik-trak.co.uk *A dedicated ADR Courier and Express Light Haulage business, with polite, uniformed and responsible drivers, offering realistic rates for secure transport solutions.*

Adray Plastics Ltd, James Scott Road, Halesowen, West Midlands, B63 2QT Tel: (01384) 569864 Fax: (01384) 411833 E-mail: sales@adrayplastics.co.uk *Plastics fabricators & machinists*

Adreco Ltd, Bilton Rd, Bletchley, Milton Keynes, MK1 1HW Tel: (01908) 374144 Fax: (01908) 643270 E-mail: sales@adreco.co.uk *Plastics mould toolmakers*

▶ Adrecotech Ltd, 4 Sandy Lane, Woodbridge, Suffolk, IP12 4DH Tel: (01394) 382325 Fax: 01394 382325 E-mail: info@adrecotech.co.uk *Official UK & Ireland distributor of Simsite structural composite components. Impellers, wear rings, bearings, shafts, pumps, butterfly valve parts etc for a wide variety of applications. Reverse engineered to suit your needs. US, German & Australian Navy approved.*

Adrem Engineering Ltd, Unit 3, Murdock Rd, Bicester, Oxon, OX26 4PP Tel: (01869) 321365 Fax: (01869) 241764 *Engineering subcontractors*

Adrem Recruitment Ltd, 1-3 Dufferin Street, London, EC1Y 8NA Tel: (020) 7562 8282 Fax: (020) 7562 8283 E-mail: registration@adrum.uk.com *Specialist recruitment consultants for architects, interior designers*

▶ Adremit Ltd, Unit 2, Whalley Industrial Park, Barrow, Clitheroe, Lancashire, BB7 1QA Tel: (01254) 822021 Fax: (01254) 825720 E-mail: info@adremit.co.uk *Air purifications, heating & cooling service*

Adrian Armstrong Medical Equipment, 46 Newbolt Avenue, Sutton, Surrey, SM3 8EE Tel: (020) 8641 0099 Fax: (020) 8641 0031 *Surgical foam goods suppliers*

▶ Adrian Dale Potatoes Ltd, Three Boundries Farm, Coventry Road, Croft, Leicester, LE9 3GP Tel: (01455) 285577 Fax: (01455) 284785 *Potato merchants*

Adrian Essential Oils Ltd, 1 Essence House, Crabtree Road, Thorpe Industrial Estate, Egham, Surrey, TW20 8RN Tel: (01784) 485600 Fax: (01784) 472255 E-mail: uksales@adrian.fr *Essential oil distillers*

Adrian March, 5 The Paddock, Kings Worthy, Winchester, Hampshire, SO23 7QR Tel: (01962) 882277 E-mail: adrian@adrianmarch.com *Equipment and aids for swimming & water aerobics: aquatics teaching and teacher training: equipment storage and transport products for leisure centres, clubs, and teachers.*

Adrian Stanley, Unit 95, Imperial Trading Estate Lambs La North, Rainham, Essex, RM13 9XL Tel: (020) 8986 8232 Fax: (020) 8985 6755 *Lithographic printers*

▶ Adrio Communications Ltd, 5 Meadway, Staines, Middlesex, TW18 2PW Tel: (01784) 455511 E-mail: info@adrio-communications.com *Electronic consultancy*

Adris Ltd, Riverise House Brunel Road, Totton, Southampton, SO40 3WX Tel: (023) 8086 8947 Fax: (023) 8086 1618E-mail: sales@adris.co.uk *Computer software & hardware resellers*

Adroit, 1 Townsend Centre Blackburn Road, Townsend Industrial Estate, Houghton Regis, Dunstable, Bedfordshire, LU5 5BQ Tel: (01582) 672141 Fax: (01582) 672140 E-mail: mick.haron@btconnect.com *Precision engineers & sub contractors*

Adroit Accessories Ltd, Henry Street, Walsall, WS2 9XU Tel: (01922) 632839 Fax: (01922) 629154 E-mail: sales@adroit-accessories.co.uk *Auto electrical accessories suppliers & manufrs*

Adroit Group Ltd, Trow Way, Worcester, WR5 3BX Tel: (01905) 356443 Fax: (01905) 351868 E-mail: sales@adroitgroup.co.uk *Property investment*

▶ Adroit Technologies Ltd, PO Box 19, Nantwich, Cheshire, CW5 6FF Tel: (01270) 627072 Fax: (01270) 629399 E-mail: sales@adroit-europe.com *Software suppliers*

▶ ADRS Ltd, 7, Charlton Road, London, N9 8HN Tel: 020 8805 7000 E-mail: info@adrs.ltd.uk *Nationwide electrical testing, including Portable Appliance Testing (PAT) and Landlords" 16th edition. Training services and equipment also available.*

▶ Ads, Unit 6 7 Phoenix Industrial Estate, Loxdale Street, Bilston, West Midlands, WV14 0PR Tel: (01902) 409453 Fax: (01902) 409215 E-mail: www.geraldine@advanceddeliveryservices.co.uk *Courier service*

▶ ADS Precision Ltd, 716 Penistone Road, Hillsbough, Sheffield, S6 2DF Tel: 0114-234 7352 Fax: 0114-234 7362 E-mail: sales@adprecision.com *Engineer fabricators*

Adscom UK, Thurston Lodge, Thedwastre Rd, Thurston, Bury St. Edmunds, Suffolk, IP31 3SD Tel: (01359) 232661 Fax: (01359) 232549 *Computer supplies & hardware manufr*

Adseal, 2 Charnwood Park, Foreshore Road, Cardiff, CF10 4LZ Tel: (029) 2047 1200 Fax: (029) 2047 1230 E-mail: adsealltd@btconnect.com *Adhesive & sealant distributors & manufrs*

ADSEC Booke Keeping Services, PO Box 88, Cardiff, CF72 0AE Tel: 0845 230 1423 E-mail: email@adsec.co.uk *ADSEC Book Keeping Services is a professional book keeping and payroll service. We operate on a freelance basis at your premises or by uplifting necessary files and processing and reconciling the paperwork before returning the information to you.*We also provide monthly management accounts so that you can monitor your business" progress. We also prepare your accounts ready for Audit by your chartered accountant for limited companies and/or self assessment for your tax accountant. **Services include:*General Book Keeping: including sales and purchase ledger operation and reconciliation, bank reconciliation and supplier payments, etc. *VAT return preparation and reconciliation. *Payroll. *Additional tasks relevant to book keeping. *A wide range of services and structures to suit your particular requirements. Ask for a FREE quote. **

Adshead Ratcliffe, Derby Road, Belper, Derbyshire, DE56 1WJ Tel: (01773) 596300 Fax: (01773) 821215 E-mail: admin@arbo.co.uk Principal Export Areas: Worldwide *Concrete repair product manufrs*

Adshead Ratcliffe & Co. Ltd, 4 Woodford Trading Estate, Southend Road, Woodford Green, Essex, IG8 8HG Tel: (020) 8551 0031 Fax: (020) 8550 2142 *Silicon sealant manufacturers & suppliers* Also at: Bristol, Glasgow & Manchester

Ad-Stik Enterprise, Bromley, BR1 2WN Tel: (020) 8468 7924 Fax: (020) 8468 7924 *Screen and label printers*

Adstone Construction, Wassage Way, Hampton Lovett, Droitwich, Worcestershire, WR9 0NX Tel: (01905) 794561 Fax: (01905) 794040 E-mail: mail@adstone.org.uk *Structural steelworkers*

Adsyst (Automation) Ltd, Unit 1 Ferranti Court, Staffordshire Technology Park, Stafford, ST18 0AR Tel: (01785) 212400 Fax: (01785) 212500 E-mail: info@adsyst.co.uk *Automation control systems*

Adsyst (Automation) Ltd, White Lodge Court, Reading Road, Yateley, Hampshire, GU46 7RX Tel: (01252) 860600 Fax: (01252) 872015 E-mail: info@adsyst.co.uk *Systems Integrators*

ADT Fire & Security plc, Adt House, Kilmartin Place, Uddingston, Glasgow, G71 5PH Tel: (01698) 486000 Fax: (01698) 486100 E-mail: info@adtfireandsecurity.co.uk *CCTV fire protection & electronic article surveillance manufrs*

Adtech Ltd, 6 East Street, Braintree, Essex, CM7 3JJ Tel: (01376) 346511 Fax: (01376) 349871 E-mail: sales@adtechltd.co.uk *Distribute tape & packaging materials*

▶ Adtech D S N Ltd, Dryburgh House, Meikle Road, Livingston, West Lothian, EH54 7DE Tel: (01506) 498546 Fax: (01506) 498547

▶ Adur Bath Tubs, 5 St. Marys Road, Shoreham-by-Sea, West Sussex, BN43 5ZA Tel: (01273) 441788 Fax: (01273) 441769 E-mail: adurbathtubs@btconnect.com *Bathroom fitters*

Adur Packaging Ltd, 1 Brook Farm, Horsham Road, Cowfold, Horsham, West Sussex, RH13 8AH Tel: (01403) 864994 Fax: (01403) 864774 E-mail: adurpackaging@aol.com *Polystyrene packaging suppliers*

Adv Lighting Ltd, 22 Electric Avenue, Harrogate, North Yorkshire, HG1 2BB Tel: (01423) 545493 Fax: (0845) 2801640 E-mail: advlighting@advlighting.co.uk *Lighting manufacturer specialising in low energy*

Advance, 18 Overbury Cres, Croydon, CR0 0LL Tel: 020 8123 0389 E-mail: info@advancestudio.co.uk *Specialist in PDF creation from Microsoft packages and all popular printing applications. Flight checked and rip ready PDFS. We also design for web and print.*

Advance, 3 Wootton Road, King's Lynn, Norfolk, PE30 4EZ Tel: (01553) 691587

Advance Bunzl Ltd, West Point, New Hive Lane, Larkfield, Kent, ME20 6XJ Tel: (01622) 764504 Fax: (01622) 208157 E-mail: sales@advancebunzl.com *Self adhesive labels manufrs*

Advance Cash Registers Ltd, 9 Ashbourne Parade, London, W5 3QS Tel: (020) 8997 8070 Fax: (020) 8997 2265 E-mail: advancedcr@aol.com *Cash register distributors*

▶ Advance Ceilings Ltd, Foundation House, Lodge Lane, Grays, Essex, RM17 5RZ Tel: (01375) 396311 Fax: (01375) 392759 E-mail: sales@advancedceilings.co.uk *Aluminium suspended ceiling components manufrs*

▶ Advance Cleaning, 43 Cork Lane, Glen Parva, Leicester, LE2 9JS Tel: 0116-277 4482 Fax: (0870) 1394795 E-mail: info@advancecleaning.co.uk *Advance Cleaning provides a Commercial Cleaning Service that specializes in the cleaning & maintenance of Hi Tech Environments including antistatic treatments for floors, carpets, and IT rooms as well as PC & equipment cleaning. Tel: 0116 2774482 for a Free Survey.*

Advance Cleaning & Supplies, 4 Station Road, Ystradgynlais, Swansea, SA9 1NT Tel: (01639) 841444 *Cleaning materials supplier*

Advance Communications, Business Development Centre, Main Avenue, Treforest Indust Estate, Pontypridd, Mid Glamorgan, CF37 5UR Tel: (01443) 843555 Fax: (01443) 841449 *Optical fibre & copper cable installation*

Advance Communications & Rentals, 111 Kingsley Crescent, Stonebroom, Alfreton, Derbyshire, DE55 6HZ Tel: (01773) 874887 Fax: (01773) 874888 *Telecommunications sales & rental*

▶ Advance Construction Group Ltd, Caldergrove House Caldergrove, Hamilton Road, Blantyre, Glasgow, G72 8YA Tel: (01698) 824442 Fax: (01698) 820050 E-mail: thomasdignall@btconnect.com *Groundworks for roads & housing construction*

Advance Couplings Ltd, Thwaites Lane, Keighley, West Yorkshire, BD21 4LJ Tel: (01535) 669216 Fax: (01535) 610243 E-mail: sales@advanced-couplings.co.uk *Stainless steel couplings manufrs*

Advance Cryo Refrigeration Services, 37 St Catherines Avenue, Luton, LU3 1QG Tel: (01582) 416036 Fax: (01582) 454782 E-mail: ade@advanecryo1945.fsnet.co.uk *Refrigeration machinery repairers*

Advance Despatch Ltd, Station Road Business Park, 1 Station Road, Auchtermuchty, Cupar, Fife, KY14 7DP Tel: (01337) 827333 Fax: (01337) 828080

Advance Display Cabinets Ltd, 29 Sugarbrook Road, Bromsgrove, Worcestershire, B60 3DN Tel: (01527) 579744 Fax: (01527) 579744 *Point of sale display producers*

Advance Display Solutions Ltd, 10 Mount Avenue, Bletchley, Milton Keynes, MK1 1LS Tel: (01908) 641008 Fax: (01908) 640579 E-mail: info@advancedisplay.co.uk *Point of sale equipment*

▶ Advance Door Engineering Ltd, Malthouse Road, Tipton, West Midlands, DY4 9AE Tel: 0121-557 0611 Fax: 0121-520 1233 E-mail: sales@advancedooreng.com *Doors: insulating curtain & automatic*

Advance Door Services, 227 Bolton Road, Turton, Bolton, BL7 0HY Tel: (01204) 853199 Fax: (01204) 853994 *Door & gate installation & sales*

Advance Engineering HX Ltd, Park Road Buildings, Park Road, Elland, West Yorkshire, HX5 9HP Tel: (01422) 375228 Fax: (01422) 310433 E-mail: phillgibson@advanceengineering.fsbusiness.co.uk *Precision engineers*

Advance Engineering Services Ltd, Unit 1, Farley Bank, Hastings, East Sussex, TN35 5QA Tel: (01424) 424720 Fax: (01424) 442924 E-mail: sales@advance-eng.co.uk *Precision engineers & subcontract services*

Advance Fabrications Ltd, 1 Harrow Garage, Newbury Road, Headley, Thatcham, Berkshire, RG19 8LG Tel: (01635) 268234 Fax: (01635) 268704 *Steel fabricators*

Advance Fire Services, 21-23 Lawrence Street, York, YO10 3BP Tel: (01904) 634036 Fax: (01904) 634036 E-mail: sales@advancefireyork.co.uk *We are a fire safety company based in York established in 1976. We maintain and install Fire Alarm Systems, Emergency Lighting and Fire Fighting Equipment.**The distances we cover are as far north as Newcastle down to Nottingham and from East Coast to just past Leeds /Bradford area.**We also do not perform discharge testing as BS states it is only a recommendation and not a requirement, and a lot of companies use this test to generate more income for themselves.**As I mentioned earlier we also maintain fire alarm systems and offer an emergency after hours call out service if needed.**We custom make our own fire safety signs keeping our customers compliant.**Should*

continued

you require any further details or information, please do not hesitate to contact us.

Advance Foam Converters Ltd, Maitland Road, London, E15 4EL Tel: (020) 8534 9643 Fax: (020) 8519 0211 *Foam converters*

Advance Group plc, Ockley Road, Bognor Regis, West Sussex, PO21 2HW Tel: (01243) 829100 Fax: (01243) 866822 E-mail: sales@advancegroup.plc.uk *Business machines suppliers*

▶ Advance Hygiene, Unit 1 Cadzow Industrial Estate, Hamilton, Lanarkshire, ML3 7QU Tel: (01698) 284319 Fax: (01698) 283163 *Cleaning product suppliers*

▶ Advance Intergrated Systems, Unit 1A, Spa Fields Industrial Estate, New Street, Slaithwaite, Huddersfield, HD7 5BB Tel: (01484) 844433 Fax: (01484) 845533 *CCTV intruder & fire alarms installers*

▶ Advance Joinery Ltd, Old Brickyard, Pontrilas, Hereford, HR2 0DJ Tel: (01981) 241071 Fax: (01981) 241072

Advance Metal Components Ltd, Units 12-14, Minters Industrial Estate, Southwall Road, Deal, Kent, CT14 9PZ Tel: (01304) 380574 Fax: (01304) 380619 E-mail: sales@amc-uk.com *CNC engineering services*

Advance Networks Ltd, 43 Cork Lane, Glen Parva, Leicester, LE2 9JS Tel: 0116-277 4482 Fax: (0870) 1394795 E-mail: info@advance-networks.co.uk *Business communications*

Advance Onsite Training, 10 Knutsford Road, Holmes Chapel, Crewe, CW4 7DE Tel: 07929 575197 Fax: 01297 631671 E-mail: andrew@advance-onsite-training.co.uk *Andrew Bentham has had 15 years experience as an instructor, training large and small groups across a wide variety of industries. Andrews training experience and people skills combine to offer unique, thorough and enjoyable courses. Advance Training is an RTITB Accredited organisation so all our courses are backed up with RTIYB Certification. All courses are carried out on site with the clients equipment to a timescale which suits the busiest of work schedules.*

▶ Advance Packaging Technology Of America, Howard Street, North Shields, Tyne & Wear, NE30 1AR Tel: 0191-258 6912 Fax: 0191-258 4554 *Suppliers of semi-conductive devices*

▶ Advance Products Ltd, Meadow Mills, Carlton Road, Dewsbury, West Yorkshire, WF13 2BA Tel: (01924) 486000 Fax: (01924) 486001 E-mail: sales@advance-products.co.uk Principal Export Areas: Worldwide *Nationwide janitorial and hygiene distributor established in 1929. Over 3000 products in stock including: textile wipes, rags, wipers, non-woven wipes, Tufall, paper wipes, floor rolls, centrefeed rolls, hygiene rolls, Jobwipe, Bosswipe, impregnated wipes, wet wipes, Handies, heavy-duty wipes, all-purpose wipes, graffiti wipes, disinfectant wipes, latex disposable gloves, polythene gloves, nitrile disposable gloves, PVC gloves, welders gauntlet, yellow rubber gloves, nitrile gloves, green nitrile gloves, rigger gloves, stockinette gloves, microbiological cleaning products, odour removal products, Zybax, Meleco, magic sponge, melamine foam, yellow dusters, mops, stockinette, mutton cloth, floor cloths, dust sheets, nylon scourers, car sponge, detergents, disinfectants, multi-purpose cleaner, kitchen degreaser, anti-bacterial spray, glass cleaner, air freshener, bleach, cream cleaner, toilet rolls, jumbo toilet rolls, mini-jumbo toilet rolls, hand towels, soap and C-fold towels.* Also at: Dewsbury

▶ Advance Removals Ltd, 1 Station Road, Auchtermuchty, Cupar, Fife, KY14 7DP Tel: (0800) 7819397 E-mail: sales@advancedremovals.co.uk

▶ Advance Reprographic Printers Ltd, Olympic House, 317 Latimer Road, London, W10 6RA Tel: (020) 8969 6055

Advance Security Detection, 4 Falcon Road, Dewsbury, West Yorkshire, WF12 9NH Tel: (01924) 438844 Fax: (01924) 438844 *Alarm system installers*

▶ Advance Supplies Eastern Ltd, Victoria Stables, South Road, Bourne, Lincolnshire, PE10 9JZ Tel: (01778) 426633 Fax: (01778) 426899 E-mail: sales@advancesupplies.co.uk *Fencing sales & installation*

Advance Tools (Oxford), 7 Links Road, Kennington, Oxford, OX1 5RU Tel: (01865) 739739 Fax: (01865) 739755 E-mail: advancetools@ic24.net *Garage equipment specialists*

Advance Trade Signs, Unit 18, Moorside Maltings, Burton Row, Leeds, LS11 5NX Tel: 0113-276 5621 Fax: 0113-276 5621 *Sign manufrs*

Advance Training & Consultancy Ltd, Unit 10, 225 Putney Bridge Road, London, SW15 2PX Tel: (020) 8871 9886 Fax: (020) 8871 9781 *Web design trainers*

▶ Advance U K, 73 Chapel Street, Leigh, Lancashire, WN7 2DA Tel: (01942) 609996 Fax: (01942) 269508 E-mail: sales@advanceuk.com *Computer sales services*

▶ Advance Vacuum & Lift, 4 Beverley Avenue, Newtownards, County Down, BT23 7UE Tel: (028) 9181 8095 Fax: (028) 9182 7523 E-mail: sales@avlift.com *Vacuum lifting, hoists, crane systems & vacuum lifting devices*

▶ Advance Window & Home Improvements, Unit 22A, Bonlea Industrial Estate, Thornaby, Stockton-On-Tees, Cleveland, TS17 7AQ Tel: (0800) 0528400 Fax: (01642) 614851 *Window retailers*

Advance Workwear & Disposables Ltd, Unit 12a South Leicester Industrial Estate, Ellistown, Coalville, Leicestershire, LE67 1EU Tel: (01530) 263321 Fax: (01530) 262623 E-mail: info@advanceworkwear.com *Disposable protective headwear & clothes manufrs*

Advance Yacht Systems Ltd, Unit 3, Saxon Wharf, Lower York Street, Southampton, SO14 5QF Tel: (023) 8033 7722 Fax: (023) 8033 7622 E-mail: info@advanceyacht.co.uk *Yacht engineering, sales repair & installation services*

Advanced, PO Box 6433, Birmingham, B30 3HG Tel: 0121-459 3838 Fax: 0121-459 1415 *Air conditioning installers*

Advanced 24, 40 Potton Road, St. Neots, Cambridgeshire, PE19 2NP Tel: (01480) 381632 Fax: 01480 381632 *Computer Consultancy & Services*

▶ Advanced Access Ltd, Unit 1b Spinney View, Stone Circle Road, Round Spinney Industrial Estat, Northampton, NN3 8RF Tel: (01604) 647555 Fax: (01604) 647333

Advanced Admixtures Ltd, 147 Park Road, Timperley, Altrincham, Cheshire, WA15 6QQ Tel: 0161-962 6267 Fax: 0161-962 6267 *Manufacturers & suppliers of construction chemicals*

Advanced Air (UK) Ltd, Burrell Way, Thetford, Norfolk, IP24 3WB Tel: (01842) 765657

Advanced Alarm Systems, 7 Fettercairn Gardens, Bishopbriggs, Glasgow, G64 1AY Tel: 0141-762 0040 Fax: 0141-563 9026 *Security alarms*

Advanced Alarms Lincs Ltd, 44 Richmond Road, Cleethorpes, South Humberside, DN35 8PE Tel: (01472) 236749 Fax: (01472) 315848 E-mail: sales@advancedalarms.co.uk *Security installation*

Advanced Alloys Ltd, Unit 17 Parham Drive, Eastleigh, Hampshire, SO50 4NU Tel: (023) 8061 8891 Fax: (023) 8061 1481 E-mail: sales@advancedalloysltd.co.uk *Advanced Alloys were established in 1988 as specialist stockists of copper alloys in tube, bar and sheet. We hold one of the largest ranges of engineering copper tube stocked in the UK*

Advanced Analysis & Integration Ltd, Riverpark Road, Manchester, M40 2XP Tel: 0161-231 1800 Fax: 0161-231 0509 E-mail: sales@aail.co.uk *Bespoke software & custom test system services*

▶ Advanced Barcoding Solutions Ltd, 10-12 High Street, Burnham, Slough, SL1 7JH Tel: (0845) 1305975 Fax: (01628) 669530 E-mail: elliott.jones@abarcode.co.uk *Thermal transfer printers*

Advanced Battery Care Ltd, Whittonditch Works, Whittonditch, Ramsbury, Marlborough, Wiltshire, SN8 2XB Tel: (01672) 520572 Fax: (01672) 520717 E-mail: sales@batterycare.co.uk *Battery maintenance or testing services*

▶ Advanced Beauty Cosmetics Ltd, 4 Shelford Bottom, Cambridge, CB22 3AA Tel: (01223) 210244 E-mail: info@a-b-c-uk.com *Laser equipment and Ipl*Hair Removal * Skin Rejuvenation * Vascular Lesions *Pigmentated Lesions * Acne Clearance * Tattoo Removal *The world leading Laser the Superior*Line of skin Care products* Accent - Aesthetic RF for Body and Facial reshaping* Cellulite Clearance* Fat Reduction* Skin Rejuvenation Lift ,firm and younger looking skin*

▶ Advanced Body Repairs Ltd, Willow Road, Yaxley, Peterborough, PE7 3HT Tel: (01733) 246970 Fax: (01733) 246979 E-mail: matt.lynn@lawrencedavid.co.uk *Commercial vehicle repairs, sand blasting & painting*

Advanced Boiler Services Limited, 1 Newlands Road, Corsham, Wiltshire, SN13 0BH Tel: 01761 453407 E-mail: info@advancedboilerservices.co.uk *Industrial steam and hot water boiler inspection and ndt preparations*Pipe work,Complete boiler installations, spares and service coded welders steam boiler services, insurance boiler inspections,*

▶ Advanced Car Audio & Security, Unit 36 Vulcan Road South, Norwich, NR6 6AF Tel: (01603) 789896 Fax: (01603) 789467 *Car audio suppliers & installers*

Advanced Carbide Tooling Ltd, Sketchley Meadows Business Park, Hinckley, Hinckley, Leicestershire, LE10 3EZ Tel: (01455) 234000 Fax: (01455) 234022 E-mail: sales@advancedcarbidetooling.co.uk *Manufacturers & Importers of Carbide cutting tool products*

Advanced Care Products Ltd, Unit 6 Chalfont Square, Old Foundry Road, Ipswich, IP4 2AJ Tel: (01473) 219220 Fax: (01473) 219049 E-mail: sales@advancedcareproducts.co.uk *Medical & cosmetic suppliers*

▶ Advanced Carpet Care Services, 4 Elmanoak Grove, Llay, Wrexham, Clwyd, LL12 0LZ Tel: (01978) 855846 E-mail: brian@advancecarpetcare.co.uk *Commercial & domestic carpet & upholstery cleaning services*

▶ Advanced Cctv Mounting Equipment, Philips Road, Whitebirk Industrial Estate, Blackburn, BB1 5PG Tel: (01254) 676632 Fax: (01254) 677627

Advanced Ceramics, Fenton Barns Retail Village, North Berwick, East Lothian, EH39 5BW Tel: (01620) 850435 Fax: (01620) 850435 *Ceramic tile suppliers & fitters*

Advanced Ceramics Ltd, Castle Works, Stafford, ST16 2ET Tel: (01785) 241000 Fax: (01785) 214073 E-mail: mail@aclstafford.co.uk *Advanced ceramics & glass ceramics manufrs*

▶ Advanced Cleaning Services, 81 Parkfield Drive, Castle Bromwich, Birmingham, B36 9TJ Tel: 0121-749 3013 E-mail: leewitten@advanced-cleaning.co.uk *Kitchen deep cleaning, hospital & operating theatre infection control service*

▶ Advanced Cleaning Services, Chapel Street, Exning, Newmarket, Suffolk, CB8 7HA Tel: (01638) 578444 Fax: (01638) 578542 E-mail: adrian@actltd.co.uk

Advanced Clothing Co., Vantel House, Parkway South, Wheatley, Doncaster, South Yorkshire, DN2 4JR Tel: (01302) 320200 *Medical, catering, health & beauty uniforms*

▶ Advanced Coldstore Technology Ltd, Unit 25C, Anniesland Industrial Estate, Glasgow, G13 1EU Tel: 0141-959 9200 Fax: 0141-959 9400 E-mail: sales@advancedcoldstores.co.uk *Cold storage contractors*

Advanced Colour Coatings Ltd, Bannerley Road, Garretts Green, Birmingham, B33 0SL Tel: +44 (0) 121-789 6991 Fax: +44 (0) 121-789 6992 E-mail: enquiry@accoatings.co.uk *Located in Birmingham, ACC specialises in the application of quality surface finishing ,including powder coating and wetspray, to components supplied into various blue chip sectors on a wide range of substrates, where quality & process control is paramount & ensures total compliance to demanding customer specifications. Accredited to ISO9001, TS16949,ISO 14001 and Investors In People, ACC provides technical expertise & a dedicated customer service.*

Advanced Combustion Engineering Ltd, Carrs Industrial Estate, Commerce Street, Haslingden, Rossendale, Lancashire, BB4 5JT Tel: (01706) 212218 Fax: (01706) 228735 E-mail: enq@aceburners.co.uk *Heating component distributors*

▶ Advanced Communciction Solution Advanced, Unit 22-23, Beaumont Close, Banbury, Oxfordshire, OX16 1TG Tel: (01295) 257485 Fax: (01295) 259093 E-mail: info@hearingprotection.co.uk *Manufacturers of custom hearing protection & communication products*

Advanced Computer Centre Ltd, 59 George Lane, London, E18 1JJ Tel: (020) 8518 8353 Fax: (020) 8518 8056 E-mail: info@accldn.co.uk *Computer maintenance, repair, networking & sales services*

Advanced Computer Furniture, Unit 2 Masons Road Industrial Estate, Masons Road, Stratford-upon-Avon, Warwickshire, CV37 9NF Tel: (01789) 414449 Fax: (01789) 415553 *Office equipment & furniture manufrs*

Advanced Computer Group, The Pentagon Centre, 36 Washington Street, Glasgow, G3 8AZ Tel: 0141-248 4000 Fax: 0141-248 4001 *Computer consultancy*

Advanced Computer Installations Ltd, Unit W8 141 Charles Street, Glasgow, G21 2QA Tel: 0141-552 6366 Fax: 0141-552 6388 *Computer consultants*

Advanced Computer Installations Ltd, Unit 7 Salford Enterprise Centre, 5 Guide St, Salford, M50 1EW Tel: 0161-737 5654 Fax: 0161-737 5227 E-mail: veronica@acimanchester.co.uk *Data cabling services*

▶ Advanced Computer Solutions Ltd, Dolphin House, 41 Seldown Lane, Poole, Dorset, BH15 1UA Tel: (01202) 675005 Fax: (01202) 675009 E-mail: enquiries@advanced-computers.biz *Advanced Computers are specialists in I.T. for small to medium sized businesses. We realise that most small businesses cannot justify a full time I.T. Manager or paying high rates for I.T. engineering. At Advanced Computers we provide Dorset based businesses a local I.T. support Service. So if you have a small to medium sized I.T. system and cannot justify a full time IT Manager but, would like independent and professional guidance at a reasonable cost then we can help.*

Advanced Computer Solutions Europe Ltd, 1 Home Farm, Cople Road, Cardington, Bedford, MK44 3SN Tel: (01234) 834920 Fax: (01234) 832601 E-mail: mailbox@caddie.co.uk *Development of cad systems*

Advanced Concrete Ltd, 154 Beddington Lane, Croydon, CR9 4QD Tel: (020) 8689 3342 Fax: (020) 8684 3012 *Concrete ready mix suppliers*

Advanced Control Electronics, 98 Ashby Road, Loughborough, Leicestershire, LE11 3AF Tel: (01509) 211333 Fax: (01509) 211333 E-mail: ac.electronics@lycos.co.uk *Electronic repair services*

▶ Advanced Control Systems Ltd, 140 Aberford Road, Woodlesford, Leeds, LS26 8LG Tel: 0113-282 7123 Fax: 0113-282 5252 E-mail: office@xcl.co.uk *Business process consultancy*

Advanced Control Systems Ltd, 140 Aberford Road, Woodlesford, Leeds, LS26 8LG Tel: 0113-282 7123 Fax: 0113-282 5252 *Process control systems manufrs*

Advanced Cooling Systems U.K Ltd, Highfield Industrial Estate, Warren Road, Folkestone, Kent, CT19 6DD Tel: (01303) 255465 Fax: (01303) 246186 E-mail: info@atsuk.com *Mould tool & tooling manufrs*

Advanced Cutting Systems, Unit 23 Station Lane Industrial Estate, Old Whittington, Chesterfield, Derbyshire, S41 9QX Tel: (01246) 454536 Fax: (01246) 454536 E-mail: sales@advancedcutting.co.uk *Cutting machine manufrs*

Advanced Data Management, 1 Candelan Way, High Legh, Knutsford, Cheshire, WA16 6TP Tel: (01925) 758543 Fax: (01925) 757950 E-mail: enquiries@adm-partnership.co.uk *Computer consultants*

Advanced Diesel Engineering, Unit 14, Langthwaite Road, Langthwaite Business Park, South Kirkby, Pontefract, West Yorkshire, WF9 3AP Tel: (01977) 658100 Fax: (01977) 608111 E-mail: r.brown@adeltd.co.uk *Generator supply, installation & manufrs*

Advanced Digital Security, 6 Vicarage Road, Woking, Surrey, GU22 9BP Tel: (01483) 828233 Fax: (01483) 590905 E-mail: ads.co@virgin.net *Security systems*

Advanced Digital Technology UK Ltd, Unit 10 Lord Wilmot House, Bristol Road, Bumpers Farm, Chippenham, Wiltshire, SN14 6LH Tel: (01249) 653654 Fax: (01249) 659258 *Computer systems consultants*

Advanced Door Controls Ltd, 1c Bonchurch Road, Brighton, BN2 3PJ Tel: (01273) 693393 Fax: (01273) 693393 E-mail: sales@advanceddoorcontrols.co.uk *Designers & manufacturers of door controls & automated doors*

Advanced Dynamics Ltd, 250 Thornton Road, Bradford, West Yorkshire, BD1 2LB Tel: (01274) 220300 Fax: (01274) 308953 E-mail: info@advanceddynamics.co.uk *Packaging machine manufrs*

▶ Advanced Electrical Services, 1 Water Works Cottages, Pildacre Lane, Ossett, West Yorkshire, WF5 8HN Tel: (01924) 283737 Fax: (01924) 283737 E-mail: info@aesyksltd.co.uk *Industrial & commercial electrical engineers & contractors*

▶ Advanced Electrics Ltd, Arden House, Glentauchers, Mulben, Keith, Banffshire, AB55 6YL Tel: (01542) 860371 Fax: (01542) 860283 *Electrical contractors*

▶ Advanced Electronics, Unit 34 Moorland Way, Nelson Park, Cramlington, Northumberland, NE23 1WE Tel: (01670) 707111 Fax: (01670) 707222 *Manufacturers of fire & emergency lighting control panels*

Advanced Energy Industries UK Ltd, 5 Minton Place, Victoria Road, Bicester, Oxfordshire, OX26 6QB Tel: (01869) 320022 Fax: (01869) 325004 *Plasma generator manufrs*

Advanced Energy Monitoring Systems Ltd, The Energy Centre, Finnimore Industrial Estate, Ottery St. Mary, Devon, EX11 1NR Tel: (01404) 812294 Fax: (01404) 812603 E-mail: info@yatesmeter.co.uk *Energy & environmental management*

Advanced Engineering Middleton Ltd, Unit 5D, Transpennine Trading Estate, Gorells way, Rochdale, Lancashire, OL11 2PX Tel: (01706) 759003 Fax: (01706) 759004 E-mail: info@aemixers.com *HIGH SHEAR MIXERS & HIGH SPEED MIXING EQUIPMENT* Advanced Engineering design and manufacture a range of High Shear Mixers & High Speed Mixing Equipment:* High Shear Mixers Batch Mixers Bottom Entry Mixers Side Entry Mixers Single and Multi-Stage Mixers* These are used extensively in the following industries:* Chemical Pharmaceutical Food Paint and Inks* We also offer a full range of Fluid Mixers, Propellers and Turbine Paddle Mixers; these mixers can be manufactured to your specific requirements.* Advanced offer a full technical mixing service to both existing and potential new customers. Our aim is not only to supply new equipment, but to provide a repair and maintenance service. We carry spares for all machines at our Rochdale works, therefore providing a fast service to our customers. Field Service Engineers are also available. Our engineering works is equipped to a high standard; along with the mixing machines we also manufacture precision components.*

Advanced Engineering Techniques Ltd, 9-15 Holbrook Avenue, Holbrook Industrial Estate, Holbrook, Sheffield, S20 3FF Tel: 0114-247 5725 Fax: 0114-247 5726 E-mail: sales@aetuk.com *Laser & profile cutting services*

Advanced Environmental Ltd, 31 Ermine St, Thundridge, Ware, Hertfordshire, SG12 0SY Tel: (01920) 487450 *Air conditioning equipment*

▶ Advanced Ergonomic Technologies Ltd, 201-203 London Road, East Grinstead, West Sussex, RH19 1HA Tel: (01342) 310400 Fax: (01342) 310401 E-mail: aet@flexiblespace.com *Under floor air conditioning systems suppliers*

Advanced Expert Systems Ltd, Woburn House, Vernon Gate, Derby, DE1 1UL Tel: (01332) 383521 Fax: (01332) 383532 *Software developers*

Advanced Finishing Technologies Ltd, 8 Dudley Road, Stourbridge, West Midlands, DY9 8EL Tel: (01384) 898765 Fax: (01384) 898766 E-mail: sales@asp-uk.com *Powder coating services*

▶ Advanced Fire & Security Services Ltd, 18 Acorn Industrial Park, Crayford Road, Dartford, DA1 4AL Tel: (01322) 557755 Fax: (01322) 557507

▶ Advanced Food Equipment, Unit 18 20, Priory Road Industrial Estate, Beverley, North Humberside, HU17 0EW Tel: (01482) 679637 Fax: (01482) 679657 E-mail: info@afeuk.co.uk *Sales and service of new and used bakery equipment. UK agents for Sottoriva and Tecnomac.*

Advanced Food Technology, 3a Wenman Road, Thame, Oxfordshire, OX9 3UF Tel: (01844) 217303 Fax: (01844) 212341 E-mail: info@appliedfood.co.uk Principal Export Areas: Worldwide *Food processors*

Advanced Fork Lift Service Midlands Ltd, Chapel Street, Handsworth, Birmingham, B21 0PA Tel: 0121-554 8811 Fax: 0121-554 4812 E-mail: info@advancedforklift.co.uk *Fork lift hire, sales & services*

Advanced Furnace Technology Ltd, 65 Church End, Cambridge, CB1 3LF Tel: (01223) 245033 Fax: (01223) 410267 *Furnace manufrs*

Advanced Furnace Technology, 18 Cheddars Lane, Cambridge, CB5 8LD Tel: (01223) 461321 Fax: (01223) 362318 *Furnace repairers & specialised cleaners*

Advanced Gas, 40 Station Road, Erdington, Birmingham, B23 6UE Tel: 0121-377 7387 *Gas appliances services & maintenance*

▶ Advanced Glass Products, Site 7, Kidderminster Road, Rushock, Droitwich, Worcestershire, WR9 0NS Tel: (01299) 851525 Fax: (01299) 851544 *Specialist glass products*

▶ Advanced Glass & Window Systems Ltd, Stafford Park 15, Telford, Shropshire, TF3 3BB Tel: (01952) 210210 Fax: (01952) 210210

Advanced Handling & Storage Ltd, Staindrop Road, West Auckland, Bishop Auckland, County Durham, DL14 9JY Tel: (01388) 832287 Fax: (01388) 832297 E-mail: advancedracking@aol.com *Shelving & partitioning distributors*

Advanced Healthcare Ltd, Dukes Factory, Chiddingstone Causeway, Tonbridge, Kent, TN11 8JU Tel: (01892) 870500 Fax: (01892) 870482 E-mail: sales@ahl.uk.com *Medical device manufrs*

▶ Advanced Illustrations Ltd, 2-4, Moody Street, Congleton, Cheshire, CW12 4AP Tel: (01260) 280568 Fax: (01260) 298171 E-mail: info@advancedillustration.co.uk *Illustration & cartography services*

▶ Advanced Images Ltd, Clydeway Skypark, 8 Elliot Place, Glasgow, G3 8EP Tel: 0141-221 4898 Fax: 0141-226 3602

Advanced Industries Ltd, 4 Avocet Trading Estate, Richardson Street, High Wycombe, Buckinghamshire, HP11 2SB Tel: (01494) 450722 Fax: (01494) 448998 E-mail: sales@office-refurbishment.com *Interior fit out & design*

Advanced Infra Red Systems, 3 Galliford Road, Heybridge, Maldon, Essex, CM9 4XD Tel: (01621) 855000 Fax: (01621) 853847 E-mail: info@h-v2000.co.uk *Manufacturers of infrared ovens & infrared heating, drying & process equipment - see TAB Fabrications Ltd*

Advanced Inspection Services (AIS) Ltd, 43 Booth Drive, Park Farm South, Wellingborough, Northamptonshire, NN8 6GR Tel: (01933) 674030 Fax: (01933) 674858 E-mail: sales@aisxray.co.uk *AIS (Advanced Inspection Services) x-ray inspection & product recovery services including contamination detection services for food products, pharmaceuticals, electricals and toys. AIS is the largest and most established x-ray product recovery provider in Europe.*

Advanced Interconnection Technology Ltd, Business & Technology Centre, Green Lane, Eccles, Manchester, M30 0RJ Tel: 0161-787 3143 Fax: 0161-787 3144 E-mail: sales@ait-ltd.com *Specialised ceramic printed circuit board manufrs*

Advanced Lifting Equipment, Goosens Workshop, Broadclyst, Exeter, EX5 3JQ Tel: (01392) 461393 Fax: (01392) 462393 *Crane repairers & manufrs*

Advanced Lighting Technology Ltd, Admail 3614, Oxford, OX1 1XZ Tel: (01706) 713240 E-mail: sales@advancedlighting.co.uk *Lighting designers*

Advanced Machining Technology, Unit 16 Colomendy Business Park, Rhyl Road, Denbigh, Clwyd, LL16 5TA Tel: (01745) 815888 Fax: (01745) 813222 E-mail: ben@oelheldgroup.co.uk *Service machines for the tool industry*

▶ Advanced Mailing Solutions, 2 Howard Court, Nerston Industrial Estate, East Kilbride, Glasgow, G74 4QZ Tel: (01355) 522839 Fax: (01355) 524839 E-mail: enquiries@amsnet.co.uk *Mailing house*

Advanced Main Drain, 109 High Street, Edenbridge, Kent, TN8 5AX Tel: (01732) 863607 Fax: (01732) 866931 *Property maintenance services/drainage repairs*

Advanced Maintenance Services Ltd, Alchorne Place, The Airport, Portsmouth, PO3 5QL Tel: (023) 9267 3333 Fax: (023) 9269 3319 E-mail: ams@zoom.co.uk *Industrial service contractors*

Advanced Manufacturing Management, Wentworth House, 3 Lichfield Road, Burntwood, Staffordshire, WS7 0HQ Tel: (01543) 677635 Fax: (0870) 0547750 *Software company*

▶ Advanced Media Engineering Ltd, Sannerville Chase, Main Road, Exminster, Exeter, EX6 8AT Tel: (01392) 824022 Fax: (01392) 824838 E-mail: sales@amesolutions.co.uk *IT consultant services*

▶ Advanced Medical Products, 10 Brindley Road, Clacton-on-Sea, Essex, CO15 4XL Tel: (01255) 421634 Fax: (01255) 432149

Advanced Medical Supplies Ltd, Freemantle House, Kingsclere Park, Kingsclere, Newbury, Berkshire, RG20 4SW Tel: (01635) 299857 Fax: (01635) 297546 E-mail: sales@ams-med.com *Medical equipment service & sales*

Advanced Metal Engineering Ltd, 200 Rickmansworth Road, Watford, WD18 7JS Tel: (01923) 211133 Fax: (01923) 241124 E-mail: ameltd@btconnect.com *Sheet metalwork precision engineers*

Advanced Metals International Ltd, Odhams Trading Estate, St.Albans Road, Watford, WD24 7RT Tel: (01923) 205599 Fax: (01923) 205588 E-mail: sales@advancedmetals.com Purchasing Contact: Lawrence *Stockholders of aircraft metal, aluminium/alloy bar/section, american specification metal, magnesium alloy, nickel alloy, stainless steel, titanium. Also distributors of fasteners (aircraft/aerospace industry), Wire & steel special or speciality, racing car supply services, stainless steel (duplex type) stockholders & stainless steel (duplex type) sheet & plate stockholders. In addition metallurgical analysts/assayers/ metallurgists*

Advanced Micro Devices UK Ltd, Amd House, Frimley Business Park, Frimley, Camberley, Surrey, GU16 7SL Tel: (01276) 803100 Fax: (01276) 803102 E-mail: info@amd.com *PC processors manufrs*

▶ Advanced Micropower Ltd, 2a Loughaghrey Road, Annahilt, Hillsborough, County Down, BT26 6DB Tel: (028) 9263 8225 Fax: (028) 9263 8225 E-mail: sales@advancedmicropower.co.uk *Design and Manufacture of Electronic Weighing Systems, Recipe Systems, Batch Control Systems, Checkweighing,Poultry Weighers, Marine Scales, Combination Weighers, Bespoke Systems*

Advanced Modular Computers Ltd, Union House Deseronto Estate, St. Marys Road, Slough, SL3 7EW Tel: (01753) 580660 Fax: (01753) 580653 E-mail: moreinfo@amcuk.com *Computer hardware suppliers & systems integrated*

Advanced Mouldings, The Broyle, Ringmer, Lewes, East Sussex, BN8 5NP Tel: (01273) 813456 Fax: (01273) 813456 *Fibre glass mouldings manufrs*

Advanced NDT Ltd, Orchard House, Orchard Close, Severn Stoke, Worcester, WR8 9JJ Tel: (01905) 371460 Fax: (01905) 371477 E-mail: sales@advanced-ndt.co.uk Principal Export Areas: Worldwide *Manufacturers of corrosion control*

Advanced Netting, 157 St Osyth Road, Clacton-on-Sea, Essex, CO15 3HD Tel: (01255) 428988 Fax: (01255) 220668 E-mail: sales@advancednetting.co.uk *Fishing, industrial & sports netting manufacturers*

Advanced Network, 12 Primrose Gdns, London, NW3 4TN Tel: (020) 7586 3232 *Telecommunication systems equipment distributors & agents*

▶ Advanced Noise Solutions Ltd, 13 Boissy Close, St Albans, St. Albans, Hertfordshire, AL4 0UE Tel: (01727) 864667 *Noise control solutions that use advanced technology to achieve high noise reductions at considerably lower cost than common solutions*

Advanced Panels & Products, Grosvenor Road, Gillingham Business Park, Gillingham, Kent, ME8 0SA Tel: (01634) 378880 Fax: (01634) 378381 *Door manufrs*

▶ Advanced Perimeter Systems, 16 Cunningham Road, Springkerse Industrial Estate, Stirling, FK7 7TP Tel: (01786) 479862 Fax: (01786) 470331

continued

continuation
E-mail: sales@aps-perimeter-security.com *Manufacturer of perimeter security systems*

Advanced Plastics & Composites Ltd, 31 Bergen Way, Sutton Fields Industrial Estate, Hull, HU7 0YQ Tel: (01482) 823038 Fax: (01482) 822945 E-mail: info@advanced-plastics.co.uk *Plastic injection moulding manufrs*

Advanced Power Components plc, Unit 47 Riverside Estate, Sir Thomas Longley Road, Medway City Estate, Rochester, Kent, ME2 4DP Tel: (01634) 290588 Fax: (01634) 290591 E-mail: sales@apc-plc.co.uk *Capacitors & electronic distributors*

Advanced Process Engineering & Simulation Services, 6 Milford Street, Cambridge, CB1 2LP Tel: (01223) 521149 E-mail: martin.sneesby@apess.co.uk *Specialist simulation & expert process engineering services*

Advanced Process Fabrications Ltd, Unit 19 Worton Hall Industrial Estate, Worton Road, Isleworth, Middlesex, TW7 6ER Tel: (020) 8568 2964 Fax: (020) 8569 7034 *Fabricating engineers*

Advanced Products (Seals & Gaskets) Ltd, Unit 25C, Number One Industrial Estate, Consett, Co. Durham, DH8 6SR Tel: (01207) 500317 Fax: (01207) 501210 E-mail: gc@advancedproducts.co.uk *Manufacturers of seals for extreme environments, metal & PTFE seals*

Advanced Property Solutions, 38 Riverside Steps, St. Annes Park, Bristol, BS4 4RH Tel: (07775) 671339 E-mail: anything@advancedpropertysolutions.co.uk *APS is a Britol based company specialising in Kitchen Fitting, Bathroom Fitting, Ceramic Tiling, Plastering, Plumbing, Laminate Flooring and Painting & Decorating. Our Kitchen Fitters and Bathroom Fitters are trained to a high standard, providing a high quality and reliable service. Please consult our web page for more information on our services.*

Advanced Protective Packaging Ltd, Unit 58 Pioneer Mill, Milltown Street, Radcliffe, Manchester, M26 1WN Tel: 0161-724 8080 Fax: 0161-725 9074 E-mail: brian@advanced-pp.co.uk *Manufacturers of plastic & polyethylene foam products*

Advanced Protective Packaging Ltd, 25 Towerfield Road, Shoeburyness, Southend-on-Sea, SS3 9QT Tel: (01702) 293312 Fax: (01702) 298556 E-mail: salessouth@advanced-pp.co.uk *Packaging polystyrene cut piece manufrs, foam*

Advanced Radiators Ltd, Unit 6 Bells Close Industrial Estate, Newcastle upon Tyne, NE15 6UF Tel: 0191-267 3312 Fax: 0191-264 2707 E-mail: info@adrad.co.uk *Car radiator repairers & reconditioners*

▶ Advanced Recycling Solutions Ltd, The Factory Boswithian Road, Tolvaddon, Camborne, Cornwall, TR14 0EJ Tel: (01209) 611898 Fax: (01209) 712888 E-mail: sales@ars-chs.co.uk Sales Contact: J. Williams *The Advanced Recycling Solutions range of equipment is designed and manufactured in the UK by the Engineering led CHS Engineering Group at Tolvaddon in Cornwall, whose history can be traced back to 1976. The range of recycling equipment includes: can sorters, can crushers, paper balers, card balers, paper shredders, card shredders, plastic bottle balers, drum crushers, textile shredders, tyre shredders, vertical balers, rear feed vertical balers and horizontal balers which are supplied to a wide range of organisations. The Advanced Recycling Solutions range of equipment is easily expandable. Advanced Recycling Solutions can also design and build MRF's to suit customers individual specifications. All Advanced Recycling Solutions equipment comes with full service cover and as an optional extra, can be fitted with modems to enable diagnostics to be carried out remotely. As the equipment is made within the UK, any modifications required to standard products can be easily carried out.*

▶ Advanced Refrigeration, Millcroft, Monteach Road, Methlick, Ellon, Aberdeenshire, AB41 7JT Tel: (01224) 773774 Fax: (0845) 2805554 E-mail: info@advanced-refrigeration.co.uk *Refrigeration & air conditioning engineers industrial & commercial*

Advanced Remedial Treatments Ltd, 5 Stoke Road, Gosport, Hampshire, PO12 1LT Tel: (023) 9252 5244 Fax: (023) 9251 0750 *Wood preservation services, remedial treatments*

▶ Advanced Research Associates Ltd, 65 Mill Lane, Attleborough, Norfolk, NR17 2NW Tel: (01953) 452751 Fax: 01953 452751 E-mail: ARAltd@aol.com *Business Development consultant specialising in the Automotive Sector. Provides sales support and strategic advice to tier 1 suppliers. Market Research and business strategy provided for industrial & engineering sectors.*

Advanced Safety Communications, 26b Brookfield Road, Arnold, Nottingham, NG5 7ER Tel: 0115-967 9067 Fax: 0115-956 1585 E-mail: sales@ascaudio.co.uk *Advanced Safety Communications was established in 1993 to design and manufacture Voice Alarm, Public Address and General Alarm systems primarily intended for service in: Shopping Malls Offshore and Hazardous Area Locations Sports and Lesuire Complexes Office Buildings Industrial Plant Theatres Hotels Educational Establishments*

▶ Advanced Screen Technology Ltd, 5 Enterprise Close, Croydon, CR0 3RZ Tel: (020) 8665 9887 E-mail: info@astluk.com *Printing screen manufrs*

Advanced Seals & Gaskets, Polymer Works, Hope Street, Dudley, West Midlands, DY2 8RS Tel: (01384) 252555 Fax: (01384) 252373 E-mail: kate@advancedseals.co.uk *Adhesive tape, foam, plastic gasket & rubber extrusion manufrs*

▶ Advanced Security, Chevron House, 346 Long Lane, Hillingdon, Uxbridge, Middlesex, UB10 9PF Tel: (01895) 201800 Fax: (01895) 201801 E-mail: info@securiplan.co.uk *Security guard services providers*

Advanced Security Data Electrical, 26 West Street, Bognor Regis, West Sussex, PO21 1XE Tel: (01243) 841626 Fax: (01243) 820372 E-mail: info@advancedelectricaluk.com *Electrical contracting & security installation*

Advanced Security Systems, 932 Ashton Road, Oldham, OL8 3JS Tel: 0161-785 8000 Fax: 0161-785 8888 *Electronic security equipment maintenance & installation*

Advanced Sheet Metal Ltd, 6-8 Albany Road, Granby Industrial Estate, Weymouth, Dorset, DT4 9TH Tel: (01305) 771061 Fax: (01305) 752829 E-mail: info@asm-ltd.com *Sheet metalworkers & welding services*

Advanced Sheet Metal Engineering Ltd, 4 Lisle Road, High Wycombe, Buckinghamshire, HP13 5SH Tel: (01494) 451251 Fax: (01494) 535274 *Sheet metalwork fabricators*

Advanced Signs, Unit 1 Langhaugh Industrial Estate, Galashiels, Selkirkshire, TD1 2AJ Tel: (01896) 757203 Fax: (01896) 758521 E-mail: advanced-signs@hotmail.com *Sign manufrs*

▶ Advanced Solutions International Europe, The Old Pump House, The Stables, Pettaugh Road, Stonham Aspal, Stowmarket, Suffolk, IP14 6AU Tel: 08705 887700 Fax: 01473 892032 E-mail: info-eu@advsol.com *Computer software developers*

Advanced Structures Ltd, 227 Bristol Road, Birmingham, B5 7UB Tel: 0121-446 4809 Fax: 0121-446 4986 E-mail: advanced@freeuk.com *Structural consulting engineers*

▶ Advanced Supplies Ltd, Suite 113 The Standish Centre, Cross Street, Standish, Wigan, Lancashire, WN6 0HQ Tel: (01257) 424231 Fax: (01257) 424232 E-mail: sales@advancedsupplies.co.uk *Printing engineering services*

Advanced Surface Treatments Ltd, Unit 11, Alpha Business Park, Deedmore Road, Coventry, CV2 1EQ Tel: (024) 7660 3232 Fax: (024) 7661 1776 E-mail: sales@astec-uk.com *Electroplating services*

Advanced Systems UK Ltd, Smarden BSNS Estate, Monks Hill, Smarden, Ashford, Kent, TN27 8QJ Tel: (01233) 770000 Fax: (01233) 770000 E-mail: admin@advancedsystemsltd.co.uk *Coach building*

Advanced Technology Machines Ltd, 4 Molly Millars Bridge, Wokingham, Berkshire, RG41 2WY Tel: 0118-977 0099 Fax: 0118-989 2288 E-mail: sales@atmmt.com *CNC machine tools & tooling manufrs*

Advanced Technology Systems Ltd, 1 Russetts, Basildon, Essex, SS16 6SH Tel: (01268) 491900 E-mail: sales@atsweb.co.uk *Office equipment sales & service*

Advanced Telephone Systems, Willoughby House, Willoughby Road, Harpenden, Hertfordshire, AL5 4PS Tel: (01582) 767799 Fax: (01582) 762266 *Telephone system distributors*

▶ Advanced Tempered & Insulating Glass Ltd, Ynyshir Industrial Estate, Llanwonno Road, Porth, Mid Glamorgan, CF39 0HU Tel: (01443) 681681 Fax: (01443) 681814

▶ Advanced Testing & Control Systems Ltd, 2 Wheatstone Place, Southfield Industrial Estate, Glenrothes, Fife, KY6 2SW Tel: (01592) 777520 *Electronics manufrs*

Advanced Thinking Systems Ltd, 1 South Lane, Waterlooville, Hampshire, PO8 0RB Tel: (023) 9259 5000 Fax: (023) 9259 5656 E-mail: sales@advanced-thinking.co.uk *Museum & heritage industry services*

▶ Advanced Ticket Systems Ltd, 10 Barley Mow Passage, London, W4 4PH Tel: (0870) 3506071

▶ Advanced Tool Manufacture Ltd, 29 James Watt Place, East Kilbride, Glasgow, G74 5HG Tel: (01355) 264141 Fax: (01355) 235890

Advanced Topograhic Development & Images Ltd, 4-7 Kingsland Court, Three Bridges Road, Crawley, West Sussex, RH10 1HL Tel: (01293) 522052 Fax: (01293) 522521 E-mail: enquiries@atdi.co.uk *Radio network planning*

Advanced Ultrasonic Technology, Unit C, 127 Parker Drive, Leicester, LE4 0JP Tel: 0116-235 6980 Fax: 0116-236 6066 E-mail: advanced.ultrasonic@virgin.net *Plastic welding equipment manufrs*

Advanced Vacuum Services Ltd, The Fluid Power Centre, Watling Street, Nuneaton, Warwickshire, CV11 6BQ Tel: (024) 7632 0768 Fax: (024) 7635 0842 E-mail: sales@avs-vacuum.co.uk *Vacuum pump manufrs*

Advanced Valve Technologies Ltd, Millennium Way, Thanet Reach Business Park, Broadstairs, Kent, CT10 2QQ Tel: (01843) 600000 Fax: (01843) 600333 E-mail: avt@advalve.com *Composite valve manufrs*

Advanced Vehicle Builders Ltd, Bridge Street Industrial Estate, Bridge Street, Clay Cross, Chesterfield, Derbyshire, S45 9NU Tel: (01246) 250022 Fax: (01246) 250016 E-mail: info@minibus.co.uk *Manufacturer of minibuses*

Advanced Vehicle Security of Bath, 5 Gabrial Crescent, Swindon, SN25 2AT Tel: (0800) 328 4082 *Vehicle security supply & installation*

Advanced Welding & Design Ltd, PO Box 131, Bury St. Edmunds, Suffolk, IP32 7LS Tel: (01284) 705256 Fax: (01284) 705256 *Specialized welding & engineering equipment*

▶ Advanced Window Systems, Leamore Lane, Walsall, WS2 7DQ Tel: (01922) 710044 Fax: (01922) 712255 *UPVC manufacturing & installers*

Advanced Windows, Unit 21 Ariane, Tamworth, Staffordshire, B79 7XF Tel: (01827) 66991 Fax: (01827) 56453 E-mail: pam@advancedwindowsuk.co.uk *PVC replacement window consultants*

▶ Advanced Windows & Conservatories, 5 Law Place, Nerston Industrial Estate, East Kilbride, Glasgow, G74 4QL Tel: (01355) 266889 Fax: (01355) 260888 E-mail: sales@advancedwins.co.uk *Double glazing suppliers*

Advanced Woodford Glazing, Maybank Industrial Estate, Unit 10 Maybank Road, London, E18 1EJ Tel: (020) 8559 0900 Fax: (020) 8559 0933 *Glazing contractors*

Advanta Marketing Ltd, 190 Cromwell Road, Newport, Gwent, NP19 0HP Tel: (01633) 292939 Fax: (01633) 292938 E-mail: sales@advantamarketing.co.uk *Manufactures & Printers of Tax Disc Holders, keyrings, bookmarks, coasters, mouse-mats, badges etc. Personalised & customised products, diaries, business gifts & fundraising etc. Specialising in bespoke items. One to full colour + photo print finish & hot foil blocking (print) to specifications.*

Advantage Automation Ltd, 21 Broadway, Maidenhead, Berkshire, SL6 1NJ Tel: (01628) 777759 Fax: (01628) 778681 *Woodworking machinery distributors*

Advantage Blinds, Fisher's Brook, Calne, Wiltshire, SN11 9HB Tel: (01249) 813254 Fax: (01249) 811511 E-mail: sales@advantageblinds.com *Blind manufrs*

▶ Advantage Business Gifts Ltd, PO Box 35, Mablethorpe, Lincolnshire, LN12 9AA Tel: (01507) 440510 Fax: (01507) 440168 E-mail: info@advantagebg.co.uk *Promotional products manufrs*

Advantage Business Group Ltd, East St, Farnham, Surrey, GU9 7TB Tel: (01252) 738500 Fax: (01252) 717065 E-mail: enquiries@advantage-business.co.uk Principal Export Areas: Worldwide *Technical consultants*

Advantage Business Systems, 97-101 Cleveland Street, London, W1T 6PW Tel: (020) 7663 1234 Fax: (020) 7663 1200 E-mail: info@advantage.co.uk *IT consultants*

▶ Advantage Computer Training Ltd, 83-85 Bridge Road, East Molesey, Surrey, KT8 9HH Tel: (020) 8979 8977 *IT training consultancy service*

Advantage Technologies Ltd, Nether Hall, Nether Row, Thetford, Norfolk, IP24 2EG Tel: (01842) 763131 Fax: (01842) 766778 *Computer network cabling design & maintenance*

▶ Advantage Travel, 6 The Parade, High Sstreet, Swanscombe, Kent, DA10 0LT Tel: 01322 383861 Fax: 01322 383055 E-mail: tony.duke@adcosol.com *Club LaBourse Vacance - your access to thousands of weeks of highly discounted apartments/condos in Europe, Africa, Asia, Oceania, North America, Central/Latin America, the Caribbean and the Pacific Islands.*

Advantec Systems Ltd, 39 Westfield Close, Dorridge, Solihull, West Midlands, B93 8DY Tel: (01564) 739134 *Computer consultants*

▶ Advantech Ltd, 5 Clarence Road, Grays, Essex, RM17 6QA Tel: (01375) 392822 Fax: (01375) 392399 E-mail: enquiries@advantechltd.co.uk *IT consultancy*

Advantech, Edison Road, St. Ives, Cambridgeshire, PE27 3LF Tel: (01480) 357600 Fax: (01480) 357601 E-mail: sales.europe@advantechamt.com *Satellite communications & defence*

Advantech Controls Ltd, Hoggs Park House, Chilsworthy, Holsworthy, Devon, EX22 7BL Tel: (01409) 259254 Fax: (01409) 259253 E-mail: jorge@advantech-controls.co.uk *Electrical & electronic engineering services*

Advantis Laboratories Ltd, Unit 13, Lawson Hunt Industrial Park, Guildford Road, Broadbridge Heath, Horsham, West Sussex, RH12 3JR Tel: (01403) 263100 Fax: (01403) 254493 *Cosmetics manufrs*

▶ Advantiv Ltd, 46-47 Centerprise House, New Greenham Park, Greenham, Newbury, Berkshire, RG19 6HP Tel: (01635) 817371 Fax: (01635) 817471 E-mail: sales@advantiv.co.uk *Suppliers of industrial parts & equipment*

Advartex Ltd, Pickforde Lane, Ticehurst, Wadhurst, East Sussex, TN5 7BL Tel: (01580) 200120 Fax: (01580) 201001 E-mail: andy@advartex.co.uk *Textile printers*

Advasign, Gelli Industrial Estate, Gelli, Pentre, Mid Glamorgan, CF41 7UW Tel: (01443) 441112 E-mail: info@advasign.co.uk *Sign making*

Advensys Computer Systems, 63a Borough Street, Castle Donington, Derby, DE74 2LB Tel: (01332) 853113 Fax: (01332) 853949 E-mail: info@advensys.co.uk *Software developers*

Advent Communications, Preston Hill House, Preston Hill, Chesham, Buckinghamshire, HP5 3HE Tel: (01494) 774400 Fax: (01494) 791127 E-mail: sales@vislink.com *Satellite communication services*

Advent Electronics Ltd, 4 Forward Drive, Pennington, Lymington, Hampshire, SO41 8GA Tel: (023) 8028 2703 Fax: (023) 8028 3275 E-mail: mail@advent-elect.co.uk *Electronic component distributors service*

Advent Engineering Ltd, 9 Sherwood Road, Bromsgrove, Worcestershire, B60 3DR Tel: (01527) 874414 Fax: (01527) 831603 E-mail: info@adventmanchester.co.uk *Ventilation & dust control engineers*

Advent Publishing Systems, 3b2 House, 12 Bath Road, Swindon, SN1 4BA Tel: (01793) 511432 Fax: (01793) 536616 E-mail: info@3b2.com Principal Export Areas: Worldwide *Electronic publishing solutions*

▶ Adventi, 10 James Street, Righead Industrial Estate, Bellshill, Lanarkshire, ML4 3LU Tel: (0845) 6582080 Fax: 0131-623 7279 E-mail: info@scotsys.co.uk *Computer maintenance & repair services*

▶ Adventure Electronics, 46 Back Lane, Baxenden, Accrington, Lancashire, BB5 2RE Tel: 01254 399731 Fax: 01254 399731 E-mail: info@adventureelectronics.co.uk *Great deals on marine electronics from leading manufrs*

▶ Adventure Motorcycle Holidays, Bryn Alyn, Denbigh Road, Rhydymwyn, Mold, Flintshire, CH7 5HF Tel: (01352) 742122 E-mail: sales@amch.co.uk *We are a motorcycle activity centre, where you can choose from greenlaning,trials,roadriding and quad treking*

Adventure Playgrounds Ltd, Old Hall Farm, Hall Road, Carleton Rode, Norwich, NR16 1ND Tel: (01953) 788991 Fax: (01953) 788992 *Children's play equipment manufrs*

▶ Adverteyes, 109 Tennyson Avenue, Harrogate, North Yorkshire, HG1 3LE Tel: (01423) 508430 E-mail: adverteyes@adverteyes.biz *advertising lines and trademarks online database. advertising lines and trademarks research.*

Advertime Ltd, 752 C Finchley Road, London, NW11 7TH Tel: (020) 8201 9222 Fax: (020) 8201 9111 E-mail: sales@advertime.co.uk *Printed promotional gift supplier*

Advertising Constructions Ltd, Engineering Centre, Brick Kiln Lane, Stoke-on-Trent, ST4 7BS Tel: (01782) 213444 Fax: (01782) 266555 E-mail: adcons@adcons.co.uk *Exhibition contractors design & construction*

Advertising Design & Photography, 16-20 Little Patrick Street, Belfast, BT15 1BA Tel: (028) 9032 2605 Fax: (028) 9023 1235 E-mail: adesphot@yahoo.co.uk *Advertising & design agents*

Advertising Management, 4 Church Farm Close, Lofthouse, Wakefield, West Yorkshire, WF3 3SA Tel: (01924) 822558 Fax: (01924) 825793 E-mail: sales@advertisingmanagement.co.uk *Advertising specialists*

Advertising Signs, 11 Teal Court, Strathclyde Business Park, Bellshill, Lanarkshire, ML4 3NN Tel: (01698) 844114 Fax: (01698) 844377 *Sign manufrs*

Advice By Telephone Ltd, 306 St. Marys Lane, Upminster, Essex, RM14 3HL Tel: (01708) 640110 Fax: (01708) 224802 E-mail: admin@advice.uk.com *Computer consultants*

Advision Advertising, Vision House, Main Cross Road, Great Yarmouth, Norfolk, NR30 3NZ Tel: (01493) 854000 Fax: (01493) 330016 E-mail: advision@btconnect.com *Advertising agency*

Advisory Data, 20 Butt Haw Close, Hoo, Rochester, Kent, ME3 9BA Tel: (01634) 251906 Fax: (01634) 256823 E-mail: ifor@advisorydata.co.uk *Computer programmers & consultants*

▶ Adwebtiser, 300 Bradford Road, Batley, West Yorkshire, WF17 5PW Tel: (01924) 420712 E-mail: info@adwebtiser.com *Advertising & promotion services*

Adwel International Ltd, Park House, 15-19 Greenhill CR, Watford, WD18 8PH Tel: (01923) 254433 Fax: (01923) 218278 E-mail: sales@adwel.co.uk *Generator set test equipment manufrs*

▶ The Adworks, No. 9 Cork Place, Bletchley, Milton Keynes, MK3 7WH Tel: 08707 447404 Fax: 08707 447405 E-mail: dbartlett@the-adworks.com *Website services including, building, optimisation, search engine submission, marketing and hosting. We also offer great website products like shopping carts and e-classifieds.**

Ady, Antrim Road, Warrington, WA2 8JT Tel: (01925) 419933 Fax: (01925) 419944 E-mail: sales@bulkbags.co.uk *Manufacturers of polypropylene bags*

AE Carbide Ltd, Cheltenham, GL53 8RA Tel: (01242) 539707 E-mail: a.emberson@btinternet.com *Providers of bespoke tungsten carbide wear solutions.*

▶ Aea Technology Battery Systems, Denchi House, Thurso Enterprise Park, Thurso, Caithness, KW14 7XW Tel: (01847) 808060

Aedean Chemical Industrial Ltd, 73A Old Woking Road, West Byfleet, Surrey, KT14 6LF Tel: (01932) 336171 Fax: (01932) 336758 E-mail: info@aedean.co.uk *Flooring, acid/corrosion resistant &jointless resin/cementitious based*

▶ Aegis Alarm Systems Ltd, 19 Bennetts Gate, Hemel Hempstead, Hertfordshire, HP3 8EW Tel: (01442) 240140 E-mail: admin@aegisalarms.co.uk

Aegis Precision Engineering, Bolney Grange Indust Estate, Stairbridge Lane, Bolney, Haywards Heath, West Sussex, RH17 5PA Tel: (01444) 244720 Fax: (01444) 248327 E-mail: info@aegis-rubber-eng.co.uk *Rubber engineers*

▶ AEGIS Risk and Safety Solutions Ltd, Unit, 15 Tenlands, Middleton Cheney, Banbury, Oxfordshire, OX17 2NL Tel: 01295 713532 E-mail: info@aegisrss.co.uk

Aegis Rubber Engineering Ltd, 15 Stairbridge Lane, Bolney, Haywards Heath, West Sussex, RH17 5PA Tel: (01444) 871116 Fax: (01444) 248327 E-mail: are-ape.sales@netmail.co.uk *Rubber bonded products & anti-vibration mountings manufrs*

Aegis Security, Dane Road, Bletchley, Milton Keynes, MK1 1JQ Tel: (01908) 375451 Fax: (01908) 375044 E-mail: info@kemco-aegis.com *Computer security container systems*

▶ Aegis Security Solutions, 7 Allenby Business Park, Crofton Road, Lincoln, LN3 4NL Tel: (01522) 529321 Fax: (01522) 539039 *Security services*

Aegis Survey Consultants Ltd, Ongar Road, Abridge, Romford, RM4 1AA Tel: (01708) 688050 Fax: (01708) 688045 E-mail: nt@aegissurveyconsultants.com *Mapping of buried services*

▶ Aegis Verity Yorkshire, 7 Willow Glade, Clifford, Wetherby, West Yorkshire, LS23 6ST Tel: (01937) 541325 Fax: (01937) 841057 E-mail: yorkshire@aegis-verity.com *Certification services to ISO9001, ISO14001 and other standards.*

▶ Aels Ltd, 19 Queensbury Road, Seaham, County Durham, SR7 8AY Tel: 0191-581 2512 Fax: 0191-581 8419 *Asbestos surveys*

Aerborn Equestrian Ltd, 198 Sneinton Dale, Nottingham, NG2 4HJ Tel: 0115-941 4040 Fax: 0115-948 3273 E-mail: sales@aerborn.co.uk *Equestrian textile manufrs*

▶ Aercomp Precision, 27 Factory Road, Poole, Dorset, BH16 5SL Tel: (01202) 620053 Fax: (01202) 620054 *Aero space engineering*

Aerial Close-Up Ltd, 70 Northampton Road, Denton, Northampton, NN7 1DL Tel: (01604) 899499 Fax: (08708) 318491 E-mail: info@aerialcloseup.com *Low level aerial photographers*

▶ Aerial Services (Edinburgh) Ltd, 86 Dalry Road, Edinburgh, EH11 2AX Tel: 0131-337 4421

Aerial Splendour, St. Giles Farm, Blendworth, Waterlooville, Hampshire, PO8 0AG Tel: (07709) 955294 Fax: (023) 9225 6111 E-mail: aerialsplendour@aol.com *Balloon decoration & deliveries*

Aerialect Ltd, 34 High Street, Kelvedon, Colchester, CO5 9AG Tel: (01376) 570135 Fax: (01376) 571545 *Television aerials & satellite systems*

▶ Aerialek, 42-44 Ulverston Road, Dalton-In-Furness, Cumbria, LA15 8EF Tel: (01229) 463168

Aerials For Industry, Diamond House, Thornes Moor Road, Wakefield, West Yorkshire, WF2 8PT Tel: (0870) 7871513 Fax: (01924) 374545 E-mail: info@afi-platforms.co.uk *Access equipment hire services*

Aero Dart Ltd, 5 Brook Road, Benfleet, Essex, SS7 5JB Tel: (01268) 566111 Fax: (01268) 565222 E-mail: direct@aerodart.ndirect.co.uk *Electronic component distributors & export agents*

▶ Aero Fasteners Co. Ltd, Unit 2, Block 4 Northherbour, Ayr, KA1 8BN Tel: (0870) 0509005 Fax: (0870) 0509006 E-mail: aerofastuk@btconnect.com *Aerospace fasteners suppliers*

▶ Aero Inventory, 30 Lancaster Road, Barnet, Hertfordshire, EN4 8AP Tel: (020) 8449 9263 Fax: (020) 8449 3555

Aero Metals International, 53 Furze Hill Court, Furze Hill, Hove, East Sussex, BN3 1PG Tel: (01273) 383000 Fax: (01273) 387387 E-mail: info@aerometals.co.uk *International metal merchants, importers & exporters*

Aero Quality Sales Ltd, 8 Airlinks Estate, Spitfire Way, Heston, Hounslow, TW5 9NR Tel: (020) 8561 4211 Fax: (020) 8848 1568 E-mail: kgreene@mckaero.com *Battery & battery charger distribs*

Aero Stanrew Ltd, Gratton Way, Roundswell Business Park, Barnstaple, Devon, EX31 3AR Tel: (01271) 341300 Fax: (01271) 341301 E-mail: sales@aerostanrew.co.uk *Electronic engineering & assembly*

Aerocan (UK) Ltd, Folly Road, Roundway, Devizes, Wiltshire, SN10 2HT Tel: (01380) 727006 Fax: (01380) 732440 *Aluminium can manufrs*

Aerocom Tools, Green Zone Aviation Park West, Bournemouth International Airpor, Hurn, Christchurch, Dorset, BH23 6NW Tel: (01202) 580333 Fax: (01202) 580333 *Compressed air tools repairs*

Aerocrete Ltd, 1001 Shore Road, Belfast, BT36 7DE Tel: (028) 9078 2755 Fax: (028) 9078 2766 E-mail: info@jpcorry.co.uk *Builders & plumbers merchants*

Aerodex Floyd Ltd, Aerodex Floyd, Tinge Wick Road Industrial Park, Buckingham, MK18 1FY Tel: (01280) 813095 Fax: (01280) 813095 E-mail: aerodex.floyd@talk21.com *Stationery manufrs*

Aerodyne Services, 10 Hydepark Close, Newtownabbey, County Antrim, BT36 4WS Tel: (028) 9083 6333 Fax: (028) 9084 1525 *Consultants & commercial vehicle component makers*

Aerofab Restorations, Bourne Park Estate, Hurstbourne Tarrant, Andover, Hampshire, SP11 0DG Tel: (01264) 736635 Fax: (01264) 736636 *Aircraft restoration services*

▶ Aerofill, 33-35 Clayton Road, Hayes, Middlesex, UB3 1RU Tel: (020) 8848 4501 Fax: (020) 8561 3308 E-mail: sales@aerofill.com *Aerosol & liquid filling equipment manufrs*

Aeroflex Ltd, 480 Bath Road, Slough, SL1 6BE Tel: (01628) 604455 Fax: (01628) 662017 E-mail: riws@aeroflex.com *Electronic instrument manufrs*

Aeroflex Co. Ltd, Long Acres House, 6 Hills Way, Stevenage, Hertfordshire, SG1 2AN Tel: (01438) 742200 Fax: (01438) 727601 E-mail: deb.stockman@ifrsys.com *Manufacturers of electronic measuring instrument & systems* Also at: Donibristle, Luton & Stevenage

Aeroflex, Burnham, 1 Progress House, Progress Business Centre, Whittle Parkway, Slough, SL1 6DQ Tel: (01628) 604455 Fax: (01628) 662017 Principal Export Areas: Worldwide *Electronic instrument & test equipment manufrs*

Aeroflex International, Ramsey Building Donibristle Industrial Estate, Muirton Way, Hillend, Dunfermline, Fife, KY11 9FZ Tel: (01383) 646464 Fax: (01383) 646468

Aeroflot Russian International Airlines, 70 Piccadilly, London, W1J 8SB Tel: (020) 7355 2233 Fax: (020) 7355 2323 E-mail: infres@aeroflot.co.uk *Airline company*

Aerofoam Ltd, 30 Dalston Gardens, Stanmore, Middlesex, HA7 1BY Tel: (020) 8204 8411 Fax: (020) 8204 7072 *Foam converters*

▶ Aeroform Ltd, Dawkins Road Industrial Estate, Hamworthy, Poole, Dorset, BH15 4JW Tel: (01202) 683496 Fax: (01202) 622033 E-mail: sales@aeroform.co.uk Principal Export Areas: Worldwide *Manufacturers of autoclaves, composite component moulding systems, composite material curing ovens, composite material repair systems & process controller & control systems. Composite component development services & process controller instrumentation & systems engineering*

Aeroform H L M Ltd, Southway, Walworth Industrial Estate, Andover, Hants, SP10 5AF Tel: (01264) 337788 Fax: (01264) 337755 E-mail: hlm@andover.co.uk *Manufacturers of adhesive application/coating equipment, vacuum presss*

Aerogo UK Ltd, 11a Orchard Road, Royston, Hertfordshire, SG8 6HL Tel: (01763) 249349 Fax: (0870) 4014546 E-mail: sales@aerogo-uk.co.uk *Air skate & air jack sales*

Aeromaritime UK Ltd, Thruxton Airport, Andover, Hampshire, SP11 8PN Tel: (01264) 771700 Fax: (01264) 774630 E-mail: info@aeromaritime.co.uk *Helicopter repairers*

Aeromatic Fielder Ltd, PO Box 15, Eastleigh, Hampshire, SO53 4ZD Tel: (023) 8026 7131 Fax: (023) 8025 3381 E-mail: sales-uk@aeromatic-fielder.com *continued* *Pharmaceutical granulation & drying equipment manufrs*

Aeromatix Ltd, Denby Works, Ripley, Derbyshire, DE5 8JH Tel: (01773) 744925 Fax: (01773) 570170 E-mail: info@aeromatix.com *Gas burner manufrs*

Aeromega Ltd, Hanger 1, Stapleford Aerodrome, Stapleford Tawney, Romford, RM4 1SJ Tel: (01708) 688361 Fax: (01708) 688566 E-mail: enquiries@aeromega.com *Helicopter charter operators*

Aeromet International plc, Eurolink Industrial Centre, Castle Road, Sittingbourne, Kent, ME10 3RN Tel: (01795) 415000 Fax: (01795) 415015 E-mail: andrew.king@aeromet.co.uk *Aircraft component manufrs*

Aeron Automation Ltd, 44-48 Wilson Place, East Kilbride, Glasgow, G74 4QD Tel: (01355) 226022 Fax: (01355) 235077 E-mail: alan@aeron.co.uk *Precision & production engineers*

Aeron Bacon Supplies, Unit 1 Felin Fach Industrial Estate, Felinfach, Lampeter, Dyfed, SA48 8AE Tel: (01570) 471065 *Bacon & ham curers & merchants*

Aeron Valley Supplies, Perthi Yard, Llanrhystud, Dyfed, SY23 5ED Tel: (01974) 272585 Fax: (01974) 272585 *Dairy produce wholesalers*

Aeropak Chemical Products, Viking Road, Great Yarmouth, Norfolk, NR31 0NU Tel: (01493) 660820 Fax: (01493) 660848 *Pharmaceutical manufrs*

Aeroparts International Ltd, 2 George House, Beam Heath Way, Nantwich, Cheshire, CW5 6GD Tel: (01270) 620260 Fax: (01270) 620261 E-mail: sales@aeroparts-international.com *Tool (hand) distributors*

Aeroplas UK Ltd, Great Western Park, Great Bridge, Tipton, West Midlands, DY4 7AB Tel: 0121-522 3000 Fax: 0121-522 3333 E-mail: mail@aeroplas.net *Plastics injection mouldings*

Aero-Print Securities Ltd, Gatehouse Way, Aylesbury, Buckinghamshire, HP19 8DD Tel: (01296) 485131 Fax: (01296) 485097 E-mail: sales@aero-print.co.uk *Printers of air line tickets*

▶ Aeroprinting, Unit 54B, Aidan Court, Bede Industrial Estate, Jarrow, Tyne & Wear, NE32 3EF Tel: 0191 4282428 Fax: 0191 4837266 E-mail: info@aeroprinting.co.uk *attention to detail**At Aeroprinting we pride ourselves on the highest level of quality print. We understand fully the level of detail we put into every print reflects on you, our customer just as much as us.**excellence in service**"Focused on quality, Aeroprinting pride themselves on providing an efficient and reliable print service, offering dependability and speedy turnarounds on any job. Their experienced and trustworthy team will meet your business needs with satisfaction guaranteed..." Mark Fraser**respond to needs**Your needs for today and the future are important to us and we are constantly evaluating our business to ensure that your needs can be met. Utilising bespoke software that allows us to manage your workflow from quotation to the final delivery note, matched with proven press technology. We use the latest G5 apple mac¿s, and a team of staff to ensure that communication is concise and effective.*

Aerosol Products Ltd, West Carr Lane, Hull, HU7 0BU Tel: (01482) 836222 Fax: (01482) 839856 *Aerosol sales & contracting*

Aerospace Bestobell, Ashby Road, Shepshed, Loughborough, Leicestershire, LE12 9EQ Tel: (01509) 500000 Fax: (01509) 500150 *Amour systems manufrs*

Aerospace Composite Technologies Ltd, Percival Way, London Luton Airport, Luton, LU2 9PQ Tel: (01582) 731441 Fax: (01582) 423456 E-mail: gkn@ts.aero.gknplc.com *Aircraft windows & canopy manufrs*

▶ Aerospace Machining Technology Ltd, 20 West Shore Road, Edinburgh, EH5 1QD Tel: 0131-552 4271 Fax: 0131-552 2552 *Sheet metalwork engineers & fabricators*

Aerospace Systems & Technologies Group Ltd, Unit 24 Number One Industrial Estate, Consett, County Durham, DH8 6SR Tel: (01207) 582811 Fax: (01207) 582812 E-mail: enquiries@cav-aerospace.net *Aerospace structures components manufrs*

▶ Aerospace & Technical Engineering, Units 5-6, Station Road, Leatherhead, Surrey, KT22 7AG Tel: (01372) 379929 Fax: (01372) 386973 E-mail: sales@at-engineering.co.uk

Aerospheres (UK) Ltd, Aerospace House, 2A Tudor Road, Harrow, Middlesex, HA3 5PE Tel: (020) 8863 8578 Fax: (020) 8427 1005 E-mail: sales@aerospheres.com *Aircraft repair materials distributors*

Aerostill Insulation Co. Ltd, Gainsborough Road, London, E11 1HT Tel: (020) 8539 7587 Fax: (020) 8556 9140 E-mail: info@aerostill.co.uk *Insulation contractors*

▶ Aerostructures Business Consultancy Ltd, 2 Hornchurch Court, Heritage Place, Heywood, Lancashire, OL10 2WL Tel: (01706) 360548 Fax: 01706 360548 E-mail: rob.lundy@virgin.net *Consultancy for Aerospace and Manufacturing companies. Business development an area of expertise*

Aerosystems International Ltd, Turing House, Grovewood Road, Malvern, Worcestershire, WR14 1GD Tel: (01684) 585700 Fax: (01684) 585711 *Computer software developers*

Aerotech A T E Ltd, Crown Technical Centre, Burwash Road, Heathfield, East Sussex, TN21 8QZ Tel: (01435) 865245 Fax: (01435) 865588 *Wind tunnel equipment manufrs*

Aerotech Precision Manufacturing Ltd, 1 Stone Lane, Wimborne, Dorset, BH21 1HB Tel: (01202) 848484 Fax: (01202) 848989 E-mail: sales@aero-tech.co.uk *Precision manufrs*

Aerovac Ltd, 4 Tetbury Industrial Estate, Cirencester Road, Tetbury, Gloucestershire, GL8 8EZ Tel: (01666) 502546 Fax: (01666) 503009 E-mail: aerovac@saqnet.co.uk *Plastics vacuum forming services*

▶ Aes, 8 Eden Court, Eden Way, Leighton Buzzard, Bedfordshire, LU7 4FY Tel: (01525) 217191 Fax: (01525) 381136

▶ AES, Northumberland Dock Road, Wallsend, Tyne & Wear, NE28 0QD Tel: 0191-296 8500 Fax: 0191-296 8560 E-mail: enquiry@aes-services.co.uk *Health & safety training specialists*

AES Science Ltd, The Old Laundry, 15 Barratt Street, Easton, Bristol, BS5 6DE Tel: 0117-951 0234 Fax: 0117-952 0234 E-mail: aes@aessigns.co.uk *Acid etchers & signs manufrs*

▶ AES Training Services, 1 Lower Bar, Newport, Shropshire, TF10 7BE Tel: (01952) 812535 Fax: (01952) 272233 E-mail: safety@aes-training.com *Fork truck operator training to RTITB accredited standards on site anywhere in the UK. Risk assessment courses, crane operator and manual handling.*

▶ AES UK Ltd, Old Exchange, South Cadbury, Yeovil, Somerset, BA22 7ET Tel: (01963) 441311 Fax: (01963) 441312 E-mail: sales@aes-clever.co.uk *Software development*

▶ Aesthetic Dental Services Ltd, 201 Bristol Avenue, Blackpool, FY2 0JF Tel: (01253) 594245 Fax: (01253) 500592 E-mail: andypheland@firstdental.co.uk *Dental technician*

▶ Aesthetic Dental Services Ltd, 112 Wetherby Road, Harrogate, North Yorkshire, HG2 7AB Tel: (01423) 885268 Fax: (01423) 880036

▶ Aesthetic Frames & Pictures, 33 Northfield Crescent, Driffield, East Yorkshire, YO25 5ES Tel: (01377) 256243 E-mail: mick@pictureframing-uk.com *DIY picture framing & courses, pictures for sale*

Aestus Ltd, Unit 5, Strawberry Lane, Willenhall, West Midlands, WV13 3RF Tel: (01902) 632256 Fax: (01902) 635800 E-mail: sales@aestus-radiators.com *Radiator suppliers & manufrs*

Aetc Ltd, Victoria Avenue, Yeadon, Leeds, LS19 7AW Tel: 0113-250 5151 Fax: 0113-238 6006 *Aerospace gas path components manufrs*

Aetee Ltd, Unit 11 Spring Mill Industrial Estate, Avening Road, Nailsworth, Stroud, Gloucestershire, GL6 0BS Tel: (01453) 835857 Fax: (01453) 836009 E-mail: admin@aetee.com *AeTee Limited is an import and trading company, sourcing a variety of products from Asia. Our main items are for jewellery and products for interior design.*

▶ AEYE, 1 Glencairn House, 70 Ridgway, London, London, SW19 4RA Tel: (020) 8879 9832 Fax: (020) 9212 9079 E-mail: info@aeye.biz *Web Applications and Software Development using C#, C++, Java, ASP, PHP, HTML, Flash, SQL.*

AF Associates, Chantry House, Askrigg, Leyburn, North Yorkshire, DL8 3BW Tel: 01592 882550 Fax: 0871 6613347 E-mail: office@foodsafety-training.co.uk *Food Safety, Nutrition, Health & Safety and First Aid Training and Consultancy. Specialists in Food Safety Management Systems (HACCP), helping organisations meet their legal requirements and those of the private quality assurance schemes such as BRC and EFSIS.*

Af Engineering Services Ltd, 121 Downs Road, Istead Rise, Gravesend, Kent, DA13 9HD Tel: (01474) 832041 Fax: (01474) 834736 E-mail: sales@afengineering.co.uk *Engineering consultancy to the biotechnology, pharmaceutical and food industries, specialising in engineering project management.*

▶ Afan Card Crafts, 6a High Street, Cwmavon, Port Talbot, SA12 9BH Tel: (01639) 761025 E-mail: lesleyfitzgerald@ntlworld.com

▶ Afan Digital Photography, 6A High Street, Cwmavon, Port Talbot, SA12 9LE Tel: (01639) 761025 E-mail: info@afandigital.co.uk *Photographic services Port Talbot, Neath, Bridgend and Swansea area. Wedings, Portraits, Commercial, Advertising, PR, Events and other photographic assignments.*

Afay Ltd, 6 Stoddart Street, South Shields, Tyne & Wear, NE34 0JT Tel: 0191-456 1253 Fax: 0191-454 2808 *Clothing & fabric manufrs*

Afb Farm Supplies, Sheriff House, Nantwich Road, Stanthorne, Middlewich, Cheshire, CW10 0LH Tel: (01606) 836464 Fax: (01606) 837676 *Agricultural suppliers*

Afe Online, Unit 20 Centurion Way, Meridian Business Park, Leicester, LE19 1WJ Tel: (01827) 309190 Fax: (0800) 525829 E-mail: sales@afeonline.net *Catering equipment wholesalers*

AFF Fabrication Services Ltd, Abbey Fruit Pk, Grange Rd, Butlocks Heath, Southampton, SO31 5FF Tel: 023 80454100 Fax: 023 80454260 *Steel fabrication*

▶ Affiliated Building Contracts, The Cottage, Draycote, Rugby, Warwickshire, CV23 9RB Tel: (01926) 634710 Fax: (01926) 632029

Affinis LBD Ltd, Cavil Head, Acklington, Morpeth, Northumberland, NE65 9DF Tel: (01670) 761966 Fax: (01670) 761966 E-mail: sales@affinislbd.com *Business Training that delivers the Business - helping you equip your workforce with the skills to meet your company's Business Plan objectives. Performance Management Training; Personnel Training; Personal and Management Development Training; Human Resources Training. Ring or email us to cut the jargon and find out how we can help you maximise your workforce's genuine potential.*

Affinite Europe, 32 Station Road, Burley in Wharfedale, Ilkley, West Yorkshire, LS29 7JL Tel: (01943) 864124 Fax: (01943) 864917 E-mail: office@affinite.co.uk *Software resellers & developers*

Affiniti, Unit 2630, Kings Court, Birmingham, B37 7YE Tel: 0121-770 4141 Fax: 0121-779 7222 E-mail: info@affiniti.com *Enterprise solutions provider*

▶ Affinity Consultancy Services Ltd, Innovation House, Turnhams Green Park, Pincents Lane, Tilehurst, RG31 4UH Tel: 0845 601 4565 Fax: 0118 972 8459 E-mail: sriches@arcsuk.com *Affinity Consultancy Services specialise in the provision of outsourced Human Resource and Business Consultancy Services to SME companies nationwide. As all employers are aware, there is* *continued* *an ever increasing amount of Employment Legislation that is affecting and exposing employers. **Did you know that 459 companies get taken to Employment Tribunal a day?**Did you know that 11 Directors went to jail last year?**Don't become another statistic.... Contact Affinity Consultancy and we will be happy to discuss any concerns you may have.****************************

Affirm Ltd, The Barn, Upton-upon-Severn, Worcester, WR8 0ST Tel: (01684) 291710 Fax: (01684) 291712 E-mail: sales@screenjet.com *Software consultants*

▶ Affleck Electrical, Unit 10 Oppenheimer Centre, Greenbridge Indust Estate, Greenbridge Industrial Estate, Swindon, SN3 3LS Tel: (01793) 533222 Fax: (01793) 533215

▶ AffordaBand, 275 Rotherhithe Street, London, SE16 5EY Tel: (020) 7237 7886

▶ Affordable Cranite & Marble Ltd, Stoney Ley Sawmills, Main Road, Stanton-in-the-Peak, Matlock, Derbyshire, DE4 2LW Tel: (01629) 630022 Fax: (01629) 630041 E-mail: info@ukaffordablegranite.com *Wholesale, trade and retail supply of granite and travertine tiles and granite worktops. Available as material only or processed for kitchens, bathrooms and vanity units. Large stocks and budget prices.*

▶ Affordable Digital Solutions Ltd, Tong Hall Tong Village, Tong Lane, Bradford, West Yorkshire, BD4 0RR Tel: 0113-285 4882 Fax: (0870) 4443895 E-mail: sales@affordabledigitalsolutions.co.uk *Telecommunication systems & equipment manufrs*

▶ Affordable Flood Solutions Ltd, 16 Birch Green, Staines, Middlesex, TW18 4HA Tel: (01784) 460874 Fax: (01784) 460894 E-mail: info@a-f-s.biz *Inconspicuous and affordable door flood shields to protect your property from the devastating effects of flooding.*

Affordable Franking Machines Q P S Ltd, Wellesbourne, Warwick, CV35 9TQ Tel: (01789) 470250 Fax: (01789) 470255 *Franking machinery suppliers*

▶ Afford-Able Locksmiths, 116 Albert Road, Epsom, Surrey, KT17 4EL Tel: 01372 725916 Fax: 07970 093934 E-mail: nick.palladino@ntlworld.com *For all your locksmith and key needs 24 hours.*

Affordable Machines, 185 Hoylake Road, Wirral, Merseyside, CH46 9QA Tel: 0151-677 7755 Fax: 0151-677 7755 *Sewing machines & accessories retailers*

▶ Afirm Ltd, 10 Windsor Road, Lindford, Bordon, Hampshire, GU35 0RY Tel: (01420) 473573 Fax: (01420) 473573 E-mail: afirm@freenet.co.uk *Mediation is a way for couples to resolve issues or disputes following the breakdown of their relationship by negotiating with each other with the assistance of a skilled and fully trained mediator.*

Aflex Hose Ltd, Spring Bank Industrial Estate, Watson Mill Lane, Sowerby Bridge, West Yorkshire, HX6 3BW Tel: (01422) 317200 Fax: (01422) 836000 E-mail: sales@aflex-hose.co.uk Principal Export Areas: Worldwide *PTFE hose, PTFE hose manufacturers; flexible metallic hose/tubing manufacturers; flexible tubing/hose/conduit manufacturers; hose coupling manufrs*

Afon Tinplate Co. Ltd, Afon Works, Llangyfelach, Swansea, SA5 7LN Tel: (01792) 312000 Fax: (01792) 312001 E-mail: sales@afontinplate.co.uk *Tinplate service centre*

AFOS (NSE) Ltd, Kingston House,, Saxon Way, Priory Park West, Hessle, East Yorkshire, HU13 9PB Tel: (01482) 372100 Fax: (01482) 372150 E-mail: info@afosgroup.com *Fish & meat process equipment*Smoking Kilns*Defrosters*

African Cloth Co., 7 Hurstmere Close, Grayshott, Hindhead, Surrey, GU26 6TR Tel: (01428) 607516 Fax: (01428) 607164 *Import African cloth*

African Dream Ltd, 31-33 East Street, London, SE17 2DJ Tel: (020) 7701 3886 Fax: (020) 7701 3886 *African cosmetic manufrs*

Afriso Eurogauge Ltd, Imberhorne Lane, East Grinstead, West Sussex, RH19 1RF Tel: (01342) 323641 Fax: (01342) 315513 E-mail: sales@eurogauge.co.uk *Level control equipment manufrs*

▶ Afrobest, 310 Foleshill Road, Coventry, CV6 5AJ Tel: (024) 7666 5508 E-mail: info@afrobest.co.uk *Hair, cosmetic & music product retailers*

AFS Redhill Ltd, Perrywood Business Park, Honeycrock Lane, Salfords, Redhill, RH1 5JQ Tel: (01737) 771929 Fax: (01737) 764434 E-mail: peter@afsredhill.co.uk *Servicing & repair centre, diagnostics, tyre fitting centre*

Aftercrete Constructional Engineering Co. Ltd, 5 Nursery Road, Luton, LU3 2RG Tel: (01582) 507270 Fax: (01582) 493878 E-mail: neill@aftercrete.co.uk *Civil engineering contractors, external works contractors*

Afterglow Lighting Ltd, Unit 4 Q, Saxby Road Industrial Estate, Melton Mowbray, Leicestershire, LE13 1BS Tel: (01664) 566377 Fax: (01664) 482139 *Lampshade wire frames & gimbals suppliers & manufrs*

Afton Bakery, 26 Afton Bridgend, New Cumnock, Cumnock, Ayrshire, KA18 4AU Tel: (01290) 332519 *Baking suppliers*

Afton Chemical, London Road, Bracknell, Berkshire, RG12 2UW Tel: (01344) 304141 Fax: (01344) 420666 E-mail: ethyleurope@ethyl.com *Lubricating oil & petroleum additives*

Ag Con Products Ltd, 45 Newtown Road, Rostrevor, Newry, County Down, BT34 3BZ Tel: (028) 4173 8963 Fax: (028) 4173 8971 E-mail: brian@ag.con.fsnet.co.uk *Agricultural construction contractors*

▶ AG Transport Services, 26 Mill Acre Close, Ilkeston, Derbyshire, DE7 9JQ Tel: 0115-876 9368 E-mail: t.garbett@ntlworld.com *A G Transport Services offers a Nationwide Same Day courier service for anything from a envelope to multi pallet loads. We are available 24/7 and* *continued*

continuation
all our vehicles are equipped with Satelite Navigation to ensure the direct delivery for your goods. Minimum Goods In Transit insurance of £15,000, this can be increased upon request, and we also have full courier Insurance.

▶ AG Visible Projects Ltd, Locks Heath, Southampton, SO31 6ZE Tel: (0870) 7661085 Fax: (0871) 9906323E-mail: studio@agvp.co.uk *Design & advertising*

Ag Woodcare Products, 3a Waterloo Industrial Estate, Waterloo Road, Bidford-on-Avon, Alcester, Warwickshire, B50 4JH Tel: (01789) 778628 Fax: (01789) 490296 E-mail: email@agwoodcare.co.uk *Wood finishing supplies*

Aga Factory Shop, Station Road, Ketley, Telford, Shropshire, TF1 5AQ Tel: (01952) 642024 Fax: (01952) 243138 E-mail: info@aga-web.co.uk *Suppliers of multi-fuel cooking*

Aga Print Finishing Ltd, 76 Cato Street North, Birmingham, B7 5AN Tel: 0121-359 1414 Fax: 0121-333 4388 *Print finishers*

Aga Rayburn Reconditioned Ranges, Crowan, Praze, Camborne, Cornwall, TR14 9ND Tel: (01209) 718531 Fax: (01209) 718531 E-mail: sales@agarayburn.freeserve.co.uk *Aga sales & repair*

Aga Shop, 12 Widcombe Parade, Bath, BA2 4JT Tel: (01225) 335237 Fax: (01225) 443302 *Aga cookers*

Aga Shop, 23 Queen Street, Derby, DE1 3DS Tel: (01332) 340057 Fax: (01332) 204256 E-mail: derby@aga-web.co.uk *Cooker sales & service*

Aga Shop, 66-68 Princes Street, Perth, PH2 8LJ Tel: (01738) 443642 Fax: (01738) 443641 *Cooker sales & service*

Aga Shop, 10 Upper High Street, Thame, Oxfordshire, OX9 3ER Tel: (01844) 214214 Fax: (01844) 218445 *Aga cookers sellers & repairers*

Agamik Ltd, Cathlaw House, Bathgate, West Lothian, EH48 4NW Tel: (01506) 650163 Fax: (01506) 630216 E-mail: info@agamik.co.uk *Bar code software manufrs*

Aganto Ltd, Unit 5, Saw Mill Road, Hermitage, Thatcham, Berkshire, RG18 9QL Tel: (01635) 202979 Fax: (01635) 202467 E-mail: info@aganto.co.uk *We are the UK's leading independent supplier of aluminium framed temporary & prefabricated building solutions for industry, waste, public sector & education.**We supply a vast range of temporary buildings & storage buildings for hire or sale; from emergency next day solutions & budget structures for weather protection, through to Part L2A complaint buildings.**Our prefabricated buildings are transported, installed & dismantled by the Aganto Site Management Teams who are amongst the most professional & experienced in the temporary buildings industry.**Buildings range from 10m to 60m spans & up to 17m height & can provide rapid effective solutions for temporary warehouses, logistics, workshops, recycling, retail, leisure, classrooms & public services.**As a compact, efficient & highly professional team we take pride in offering superior engineered modular buildings at competitive market prices. This quality guarantee, together with our friendly, down-to-earth approach makes Aganto the ideal choice.*

▶ Agar Ltd, Unit F2 Blackpole Trading Estate East, Blackpole Road, Worcester, WR3 8SG Tel: (01905) 452717 Fax: (01905) 458589 *Steel fabricators*

▶ George Agar, Church Road, Ravenscar, Scarborough, North Yorkshire, YO13 0LZ Tel: (01723) 870966 Fax: (01723) 870771

Agar Scientific Ltd, 66a Cambridge Road, Stansted, Essex, CM24 8DA Tel: (01279) 813519 Fax: (01279) 815106 E-mail: sales@agarscientific.com *Microscope accessories manufrs*

Agars Ltd, Port Hall Mews, Dyke Road, Brighton, BN1 5PB Tel: (01273) 540330 Fax: (01273) 540330 *Pearl restringing*

Agarwal Associates, Clockhouse, Partridge Lane, Newdigate, Dorking, Surrey, RH5 5EE Tel: (01306) 631888 Fax: (01306) 631011 E-mail: alokagarwal@nch.it *Computer consultants*

Agatha, 4 South Molton Street, London, W1K 5QD Tel: (020) 7495 2779 Fax: (020) 7495 3699 *Jewellers*

▶ Agb Decorators, 6 Burdon Terrace, Newcastle upon Tyne, NE2 3AE Tel: 0191-281 9108 E-mail: sales@agb-decorators.co.uk *An interior decorating and supplies specialist based in newcastle upon tyne. designing, planning and undertaking the final concept. supplying hand made papers and unique fabrics and soft furnishings. serving tweedside to teeside with bespoke and niche products.*

Ag-Bag Systems, Cleaveanger, Coldridge, Crediton, Devon, EX17 6BE Tel: (01363) 83996 *Agricultural contractors*

Agco International Ltd, PO Box 62, Coventry, CV4 0GF Tel: (024) 7669 4400 Fax: (024) 7685 2495 *Agricultural machinery manufrs*

Age Communications, 20 Upper Ground, London, SE1 9PF Tel: (020) 7805 5590 Fax: (020) 7805 5910 E-mail: iln@ilng.co.uk *Publishers*

Agema Ltd, G4-G6 Little Heath Industrial Estate, Old Church Road, Coventry, CV6 7ND Tel: (024) 7663 7699 Fax: (024) 7663 8014 E-mail: sales@agema-ind.com *Plastic injection mould toolmakers*

Agency Sector Management UK Ltd, Ashford House, 41-45 Church Road, Ashford, Middlesex, TW15 2TQ Tel: (01784) 242200 Fax: (01784) 242012 E-mail: info@asm.org.uk *Air freight computer software developers*

▶ Agency Staff Ltd, PO Box 8315, Birmingham, B31 2AL Tel: 0121-476 8337 Fax: 0121-476 8337 E-mail: agency.staff@virgin.net *We are an agency that places teaching staff in schools for teaching posts, supply cover and as teaching assistants.*

Agenda Vehicle Specialists, Drayton Garage, Barton Stacey, Winchester, Hampshire, SO21 3NF Tel: (01264) 720612 Fax: (01264) 720612 *Commercial vehicle bodybuilders & repairers*

Agentdraw Ltd, 42 Great Central Street, Leicester, LE1 4JT Tel: 0116-251 9990 Fax: 0116-251 9997 E-mail: kevin@agentdraw.co.uk *Injection moulding plastics & tool making*

▶ AgentPhone Ltd, P.O.Box 5064, Leighton Buzzard, Bedfordshire, LU7 3FT Tel: 01525 243000 Fax: 01525 379180 E-mail: mail@agentphone.com *24 hours call answering service, virtual P.A. Virtual Office.*

Charles Ager Ltd, 20-26 Corporation Street, Coventry, CV1 1GF Tel: (024) 7622 1619 Fax: (024) 7663 2684 E-mail: sales@charlesager.co.uk *Stockiest of branded footwear*

▶ Agetur Ltd, St. Davids Court, Top Station Road, Brackley, Northamptonshire, NN13 7UG Tel: (01280) 702121 Fax: (01280) 703088

AGFA-Gevaert Ltd, 27 Great West Road, Brentford, Middlesex, TW8 9AX Tel: (020) 8231 4301 Fax: (020) 8231 4315 E-mail: agfauk@agfa.com *Digital imaging systems photo plates, inkjet material manufrs Also at: Birmingham, Bristol, Dunstable, Glasgow & Manchester*

Agglomeration Technology Ltd, 7 Manse Lane, Monkswell Park, Knaresborough, North Yorkshire, HG5 8NQ Tel: (01423) 868411 Fax: (01423) 868410 E-mail: sales@aggtech.co.uk *ATL is the leading provider of speciality powder manufacturing services to the food and nutrition industries.*

AGGORA (Technical) Ltd, Centech House, Centech Park, Fringe Meadow Road, Redditch, Worcestershire, B98 9NR Tel: (0845) 1177999 Fax: (0845) 1177222 E-mail: solutions@aggora.co.uk

▶ Aggregate Industries Ltd, Old Station Yard, Beauly, Inverness-Shire, IV4 7BG Tel: (01463) 782868 Fax: (01463) 782873 *Quarry*

Aggregate Industries Ltd, Old Station Yard, Beauly, Inverness-Shire, IV4 7BG Tel: (01463) 782868 Fax: (01463) 782873 *Quarry operators*

Aggregate Industries Ltd, Sand Pit Road, Calne, Wiltshire, SN11 8TJ Tel: (01249) 811818 Fax: (01249) 821528 *Concrete products manufrs*

Aggregate Industries Ltd, Bardon Hill, Coalville, Leicestershire, LE67 1TL Tel: (01530) 510066 Fax: (01530) 510123 E-mail: ukenquiries@ukaggregate.com *Aggregates & building materials producer*

Aggregate Industries Plc, Uffculme Works, The Downs, Uffculme, Cullompton, Devon, EX15 3BL Tel: (01884) 841140 Fax: (01884) 841919 *Block paving manufrs*

▶ Aggregate Industries Ltd, Auchengeich Road, Chryston, Glasgow, G69 0JL Tel: 0141-776 8410 Fax: 0141-776 2464 *Manufacture concrete products*

▶ Aggregate Industries Ltd, Croy Quarry Constarry Road, Kilsyth, Glasgow, G65 9HY Tel: (01236) 823274 Fax: (01236) 825311 *Quarry specialists*

Aggregate Industries, Kemnay Quarry, Aquithie Road, Kemnay, Inverurie, Aberdeenshire, AB51 5PD Tel: (01467) 643861

Aggregate Industries Ltd, Toms Forest Quarry, Kintore, Inverurie, Aberdeenshire, AB51 0YU Tel: (01467) 644200 Fax: (01467) 644250 E-mail: enquiries@aggregates.com *Construction services*

▶ Aggregate Industries Ltd, Marybank, Isle of Lewis, HS2 0DD Tel: (01851) 703342 Fax: (01851) 705282 *Civil engineering & quarry works*

Aggregate Industries P.L.C., Garside Sands, Eastern Way, Heath & Reach, Leighton Buzzard, Bedfordshire, LU7 9LF Tel: (01525) 237911 Fax: (01525) 237991 E-mail: emma.george@aggregate.com *Sand producers & processors*

▶ Aggregate Industries Ltd, Melbur Works, Summercourt, Newquay, Cornwall, TR8 5UA Tel: (01726) 862233 Fax: (01726) 862240 *Quarrying*

▶ Aggregate Industries, Duntilland Quarry, Salsburgh, Shotts, Lanarkshire, ML7 4NZ Tel: (01698) 870811 *Quarry*

▶ Aggregate Industries Ltd, North End Farm Works, Ashton Keynes, Swindon, SN6 6QX Tel: (01285) 646800 Fax: (01285) 646897

Aggregate Industries UK Ltd, Hulland Ward, Ashbourne, Derbyshire, DE6 3ET Tel: (01335) 372222 Fax: (01335) 370074 *Suppliers of specialist aggregates*

Aggregate Processing & Recycling Ltd, Unit 9, Hedging Lane Industrial Estate, Wilnecote, Tamworth, Staffordshire, B77 5HH Tel: (01827) 260290 Fax: (01827) 287770 *Crushers & waste disposal*

Aggregates Industries, Whitworth Quarry, Tong Lane, Whitworth, Rochdale, Lancashire, OL12 8BE Tel: (01706) 853296 Fax: (01706) 854286 *Quarrying stone*

Aggreko UK Ltd, Exchange House, Watling Street, Bridgtown, Cannock, Staffordshire, WS11 0BN Tel: (01543) 437777 Fax: (01543) 437788 E-mail: doncaster@aggreko.co.uk *Generator hire, lease & rental*

Aggreko UK Ltd, Birch Road, Dumbarton, G82 2RF Tel: (01389) 742214 Fax: (01389) 742554 *Principal Export Areas: Worldwide Generator*

Aghabridge Ltd, Unit 1-4 Sheldon Business Centre, Maritime Close, Medway City Estate, Rochester, Kent, ME2 4AF Tel: (01634) 294944 Fax: (01634) 294577 E-mail: ahgabridge@aol.com *Hydraulic engineers & motor factors services*

Agie Charmilles Ltd, North View, Coventry Walsgrave Triangle, Coventry, CV2 2SJ Tel: (024) 7653 8666 Fax: (024) 7653 0023 *Suppliers of EDM machine consumables & spare parts*

Agil Chemicals Products, Hercules 2, Calleva Park, Aldermaston, Reading, RG7 8DN Tel: 0118-981 3333 Fax: 0118-981 0909 E-mail: sales@agil.com *Animal feed additives manufrs*

▶ Agile Projects, 13 Stourvale Gardens, Chandler's Ford, Eastleigh, Hampshire, SO53 3NE Tel: (023) 8025 1010 Fax: 02380 251010 E-mail: enquiries@agileprojects.co.uk *Agile*

continued

*Projects Limited is an International Project Management company, providing interim project staff, project management and service management training and consultancy services.**Agile Projects Limited works with a range of accredited consultancy and training organisations to offer the widest range of project, programme and service management training solutions worldwide. Our mission is to provide individuals and organisations with a flexible and personal approach to training, whether you're a new comer or in senior management we can create the right personal development plan to meet your needs.*

▶ Agile Training Limited, 8 Grafton Court, Canning Circus, Nottingham, NG7 3GH Tel: 07932 696228 E-mail: enquiries@agile-training.co.uk *Computer Software Training Company. Training provided on the most popular software packages including Microsoft Office, Adobe Graphics Suite, CorelDraw, QuarkXpress, Macromedia Suite. Access, Excel, Word, PowerPoint, Project, PhotoShop, InDesign, Dreamweaver etc...*

▶ Agilent Technologies U K Ltd, Agilent Technologies UK Ltd, South Queensferry, West Lothian, EH30 9TG Tel: 0131-331 1000 Fax: 0131-331 3000

▶ Agilent Technologies U K Ltd, Agilent Technologies UK Ltd, South Queensferry, West Lothian, EH30 9TG Tel: 0131-331 1000 Fax: 0131-331 3000

Agilent Technologies UK Ltd, Eskdale Road, Winnersh, Wokingham, Berkshire, RG41 5DZ Tel: (07004) 666666 Fax: (07004) 444555 E-mail: contactcenter_uk@agilent.com *Test & measurement, digital design products, in circuit test products manufrs*

▶ AGIS Business Communications, Blairs Business Centre, South Deeside Road, Aberdeen, AB12 5LF Tel: (01224) 860335 Fax: (0870) 1645149 E-mail: johnw@agis.uk.com *IT consultants*

Agm, 32 Teesdale Road, Ridgeway, Sheffield, S12 3XH Tel: 0114-248 9198 Fax: 0114-247 2551 E-mail: agm1ac@aol.com *Air conditioning distributors*

Agma Ltd, Gemini Works, Haltwhistle, Northumberland, NE49 9HA Tel: (01434) 320598 Fax: (01434) 321650 E-mail: enquiries@agma.co.uk *Specialist chemical compound sterile wipes cleaning for hospitals*

▶ Agora Business Improvements Ltd, 5 Montgomery Mews, Leegomery, Telford, Shropshire, TF1 6YU Tel: 08454 089429 E-mail: neil.thomas@a-b-i.co.uk *Business Improvements Service that concentrates on the Operational area of the business.*Procurement, Warehousing, Production Planning, Production, Quality, Despatch, KPI implementation, Lean manufacturing.*

Agora Metals Ltd, Millfields Road, Wolverhampton, WV4 6JQ Tel: (01902) 402134 Fax: (01902) 403737 E-mail: mark@parkrow-alloys.co.uk *Aluminium stockholders*

Agostino Ferrari UK Ltd, Units H & L Strawberry Street Industrial Estate, Strawberry Street, Hull, HU9 1EN Tel: (01482) 594450 Fax: (01482) 594455 E-mail: info@aferrariuk.com *Furniture fittings*

Agp, Mussons Path, Luton, LU2 7RQ Tel: (01582) 735446 Fax: (01582) 400875 E-mail: alanwithy@hotmail.com *General engineering services*

Agp Blinds & Curtains, 1 Exhibition Way, Pinhoe Trading Estate, Exeter, EX4 8JD Tel: (01392) 462767 Fax: (01392) 205147 E-mail: agp.astrablinds@hotmail.co.uk *Sun blinds manufrs*

Agra Heat Treatment, 15 Ure Street, Dundee, DD1 5JD Tel: (01382) 201600 Fax: (01382) 226918 *Heat treatment services*

Agra Informa Ltd, 80 Calverley Road, Tunbridge Wells, Kent, TN1 2UN Tel: (020) 7017 7500 Fax: (01892) 544895 E-mail: marketing@agra-europe.com *Publishers book & magazine & conference organiser*

Agra (Precision Engineering) Co. Ltd, 15 Ure Street, Dundee, DD1 5JD Tel: (01382) 229333 Fax: (01382) 226918 E-mail: info@agra-eng.co.uk *Precision engineers*

▶ A-Grade Laboratory Fume Cupboards, Unit 8, Premier Business Development Centre, Whitehouse Enterprise Centre, Whitehouse Road, Newcastle upon Tyne, NE15 6EP Tel: 0191-259 6903 Fax: 0191-258 5061 E-mail: enquiry@fumeextraction.co.uk

Agramkow Fluid Systems Ltd, Windmill House Industrial Estate, Sutton Road, Wigginton, York, YO32 2RA Tel: (01904) 750320 Fax: (01904) 750321 E-mail: agramkow@agramkow.co.uk *Automotive & refrigeration fluid distributors*

Agremimpex Trading House Ltd, Trafalgar House, 11 Waterloo Place, London, SW1Y 4AU Tel: (020) 7839 2887 Fax: (020) 7930 0465 E-mail: isclon@msn.com *Export consultants*

Agri - Hire Ltd, Fidgeons Farm, Bullen Lane, Bramford, Ipswich, IP8 4JJ Tel: (01473) 744088 Fax: (01473) 240740 E-mail: agrihire@agrihire.co.uk *Agricultural plant hire*

Agri Products, Finchley Road, London, NW3 6JG Tel: (020) 7483 2737 Fax: (020) 7586 7338 E-mail: gtitchener@agriproducts.com *Gum acacia (arabic) suppliers*

Agri Products, Finchley Road, London, NW3 6JG Tel: (020) 7483 2737 Fax: (020) 7586 7338 *Gum arabic producers & international traders*

▶ Agri Tech Services, Shefford Hardwicke Farm, Bedford Road, Shefford, Bedfordshire, SG17 5NU Tel: (01462) 813303 Fax: (01462) 815684 *Agri-tech services*

Agri Web, Enterprise House, 2-4 Balloo Avenue, Bangor, County Down, BT19 7QT Tel: (028) 9127 5913 Fax: (028) 9127 5563 *Grating screen manufrs*

Agri Weld Services, Willow Bridge Mills, Dalton, Thirsk, North Yorkshire, YO7 3BN Tel: (01845) 577963 Fax: (01845) 577963 *Steel engineering fabricators*

▶ Agribulk Ltd, Milner Road, Chilton Road Industrial Estate, Sudbury, Suffolk, CO10 2XG Tel: (01787) 375533 Fax: (01787) 374004

Agricar Ltd, 6 Lochside Road, Forfar, Angus, DD8 3JE Tel: (01307) 462281 Fax: (01307) 467199 E-mail: derek.johnston@agricar.co.uk Principal Export Areas: Worldwide *Agricultural engineers*

Agricar Ltd, Station Road, Laurencekirk, Kincardineshire, AB30 1BE Tel: (01561) 378888 Fax: (01561) 378032 E-mail: admin@agricar-laurencekirk.co.uk *Agricultural engineers*

Agricar Ltd, West Huntingtower, Almondbank, Perth, PH1 3NP Tel: (01738) 583249 Fax: (01738) 583869 E-mail: admin@agricar.co.uk *Agricultural engineer services*

▶ Agri-Care Engineering Ltd, 25 Summerhouse View, Yeovil, Somerset, BA21 4DJ Tel: (07708) 863282 E-mail: agricare276@hotmail.com *Agricultural tractor & machinery servicing, maintenance repairs & welding services*

Agricentre, Redhill, Bristol, BS40 5TG Tel: (01934) 863123 Fax: (01934) 862891 E-mail: redhill@agricentre.net *Agricultural merchants*

Agricentre, Castle Gate Business Park, Old Sarum, Salisbury, SP4 6QX Tel: (01722) 320316 Fax: (01722) 325613 *Agricultural merchants*

Agricon Engineers Ltd, Station Road, Kirk Hammerton, York, YO26 8DN Tel: (01423) 330014 Fax: (01423) 331347 *Agricultural engineers*

Agricultral & Cross Country Vehicle, Drayton Mount Farm, Barrow Hill, Belbroughton, Stourbridge, West Midlands, DY9 0BL Tel: (01562) 730404 *Landrover sales*

Agricultural Brokerage Company Ltd, 18 Camp Hill Close, Dallamires Industrial Estate, Ripon, North Yorkshire, HG4 1QY Tel: (01765) 608522 Fax: (01765) 608040 E-mail: agricsupply@agriculturalsupply.co.uk *Agricultural merchants*

Agricultural Brokerage Company Ltd, 18 Camp Hill Close, Dallamires Industrial Estate, Ripon, North Yorkshire, HG4 1QY Tel: (01765) 608522 Fax: (01765) 608040 *Agricultural services*

Agricultural Bulk Services Bristol Ltd, Royal Portbury Dock, Portbury, Bristol, BS20 7XL Tel: (01275) 375777 Fax: (01275) 374932 *Storage & distribution of feeding stuffs*

Agricultural & Commercial Supplies Ltd, 2 Healey Lane Mill, Healey Lane, Batley, West Yorkshire, WF17 7SH Tel: (01924) 420354 Fax: (01924) 420357 *Agricultural engineers*

Agricultural Contracting Services Ltd, Buddington Farm, Buddington La, Easebourne, Midhurst, W. Sussex, GU29 0QP Tel: 01730 812441 Fax: 01730 812441 *Agricultural contractors*

Agricultural Credit Bureau, Suite 413, The Cotton Exchange Buildings, Old Hall Street, Liverpool, L3 9LQ Tel: 0151-236 6463 Fax: 0151-236 0922 E-mail: mail@lltps.co.uk *Debt recovery & credit information services*

Agricultural Machinery Nantwich Ltd, Millstone Lane, Nantwich, Cheshire, CW5 5PJ Tel: (01270) 624141 Fax: (01270) 624140 E-mail: sales@ag-mac.co.uk *Agricultural machinery services & sales*

Agricultural Machinery & Repairs, Station Yard, Bootle Station, Bootle, Millom, Cumbria, LA19 5XB Tel: (01229) 718364 *Agricultural machinery suppliers*

Agricultural & Mobile Air Conditioning Ltd, Avening Road, Nailsworth, Stroud, Gloucestershire, GL6 0BS Tel: (01453) 832884 Fax: (01453) 832040 E-mail: sales@ama-airconditioning.co.uk *Vehicle air conditioning manufrs*

Agricultural Mortgage Corporation Plc, Charlton Place, Charlton Road, Andover, Hampshire, SP10 1RE Tel: (01264) 334747 Fax: (01264) 334614 E-mail: info@amconline.co.uk *Finance company*

Agricultural Timber Supplies & Forestry Products, Side House, Burneside, Kendal, Cumbria, LA8 9AA Tel: (01539) 822089 Fax: 01539 822089 *Joinery*

Agrie Mach Ltd, Wayfarers, Domewood, Copthorne, Crawley, West Sussex, RH10 3HD Tel: (01342) 713743 Fax: (01342) 719181 E-mail: info@agriemach.com Principal Export Areas: Worldwide *Distributors for specialist heat control products for vehicle*

▶ Agrifit, 4 Craig Terrace, Innerleithen, Peeblesshire, EH44 6LU Tel: (01896) 831997 Fax: (01896) 831997 E-mail: neil@agrifit.co.uk *agrifit is a small business based in the scottish borders,*agricultural contract fitters working with the poultry industry*nests,flooring,belt welding,augers,nipple lines,pans,ramps,lighting,nest box problems,limit switches etc*

Agrihire, Moors Farm, Moors Lane, Bourton-on-the-Water, Cheltenham, Gloucestershire, GL54 2HA Tel: (01451) 821292 Fax: (01451) 821292 E-mail: sales@agrihire.co.uk *Agricultural engineers*

Agrimark Europe Agricultural Merchants, Folly Lane, Bell Royd Farm, Thurlstone, Sheffield, S36 7QF Tel: (01226) 370013 Fax: (01226) 370178 *Fertiliser & graphite manufrs*

Agrimech Farming Ltd, Willow Farm, Common Lane, Church Fenton, Tadcaster, North Yorkshire, LS24 9QR Tel: (01937) 557779 Fax: (01937) 557093 *Agricultural sales & repairers*

Agripower Ltd, Broomfield Farm, Rignall Road, Great Missenden, Buckinghamshire, HP16 9PE Tel: (01494) 866776 Fax: (01494) 866779 E-mail: sales@agripower.co.uk *Land drainage & sports turf contractors*

Agrisense BCS Ltd, Unit 1 3, Taffs Mead Road, Treforest Industrial Estate, Pontypridd, Mid Glamorgan, CF37 5SU Tel: (01443) 841155 Fax: (01443) 841152 E-mail: sales@agrisense.co.uk *Pest control equipment distributors & agents*

Agriservices, Unit N3 Blackpole Trading Estate East, Blackpole Road, Worcester, WR3 8SG Tel: (01905) 754929 Fax: (01905) 754929 E-mail: agriservices@bitsmail.co.uk *Agricultural machinery engineers*

Agrispares, 116 Haven Road, Haverfordwest, Dyfed, SA61 1DP Tel: (01437) 764863 *Agricultural spares*

Agrispares, 62 Gortin Road, Omagh, County Tyrone, BT79 7HT Tel: (028) 8224 3793 Fax: (028) 8224 6050 *Agricultural merchants*

Agrispares Ni Ltd, 701 Feeny Road, Feeny, Londonderry, BT47 4SU Tel: (028) 7778 1522 Fax: (028) 7778 1631 *Agriculture merchants*

Agritask Construction Ltd, Tanhouse Farm, Rusper Road, Newdigate, Dorking, Surrey, RH5 5BX Tel: (01306) 631334 Fax: (01306) 631891 E-mail: info@agritask.co.uk *Agricultural farm constructors & civil engineers*

Agritek Sales & Service Ltd, Upgate Road, Seething, Norwich, NR15 1EL Tel: (01508) 483200 Fax: (01508) 483201 E-mail: info@agritek.co.uk *Suppliers of bowsers & tanks also fertiliser manufrs*

► Agritrader UK Ltd, 14 Cliftonville, Prescot, Merseyside, L34 2SX Tel: (07919) 471522 Fax: 0151-289 0688 E-mail: dennis@agritrader-uk.com *We sell quality used Japanese Kubota, Iseki, Yanmar and Mitsubishi compact tractors.*

Agriwise, Lower Hutcherleigh, Blackawton, Totnes, Devon, TQ9 7AD Tel: (01548) 521404 Fax: (01548) 521581 *Animal feed supplements*

Agronomy Services, 31 Mortimer Dr, Orleton, Ludlow, Shropshire, SY8 4JW Tel: 01568 780990 Fax: 01568 780990 *Agricultural services*

Agropharm Ltd, Buckingham House, Church Road, Penn, High Wycombe, Buckinghamshire, HP10 8LN Tel: (01494) 816575 Fax: (01494) 816578 E-mail: sales@agropharm.co.uk *Pharmaceutical chemical & insecticide manufrs*

Agrovista UK Ltd, Broadway Drive, Halesworth, Suffolk, IP19 8QR Tel: (01986) 875181 Fax: (01986) 875483 *Distributors of agricultural chemical products*

Agrovista UK Ltd, Unit 2f Heathlands Industrial Estate, Liskeard, Cornwall, PL14 4DH Tel: (01579) 343142 Fax: (01579) 340258 *Agricultural supplies*

► AGs GPS and Land Surveys, 205 Overndale Road, Downend, Bristol, BS16 2RQ Tel: 0117 9394336 E-mail: andreas@AGSurveys.co.uk *Land-, Engeneering-, Building-, GPS- and all other forms of measured Surveys. Survey and Geomatics Consultancy. General Mapping.*

Agustawestland Aircraft Services, Lysander Road, Yeovil, Somerset, BA20 2YB Tel: (01935) 475222 Fax: (01935) 702131 E-mail: info@gkn-whl.co.uk *Helicopter designers & builders* Also at: London SW1

Agut Control Gear Ltd, Mosley Street Works, Mosley Street, Blackburn, BB2 3SU Tel: (01254) 683714 Fax: (01254) 663630 E-mail: sales@agut.co.uk *Electric motor control gear*

► Ah Copy, 137 Nightingale Road, Hitchin, Hertfordshire, SG5 1RG Tel: (0845) 0090944 E-mail: enquiries@ahcopy.co.uk *Copywriting, editing & proof-reading services*

Ahandah Blinds, Honeymeade, Sawbridgeworth, Hertfordshire, CM21 0AR Tel: (01279) 422855 Fax: (01279) 423222 *Blind cleaning services & manufrs*

► Ahead4, 11 Trinity Square, South Woodham Ferrers, Chelmsford, CM3 5JX Tel: (0845) 4584192 E-mail: info@ahead4.com *Computer maintenance & website repair services*

Ahern Waste Management Services Ltd, 10-11 Heron Court, Cranes Farm Road, Basildon, Essex, SS14 3DF Tel: (01268) 533535 Fax: (01268) 293141 E-mail: enquiries@ahern.co.uk *Waste disposal skip hire*

► Ahika Ltd, Unit 13, 2 Lansdowne Drive, London, E8 3EZ Tel: (0870) 4440650 E-mail: info@ahikaflame.com *Ahika sell a range of gel burners, candles and oil lamps. We sell gel fire refills for all gel burners from £3 per litre.*

Ahli United Bank (UK) P.L.C., 7 Baker Street, London, W1U 8EG Tel: (020) 7487 6500 Fax: (020) 7487 6808 E-mail: helpdesk@ahliunitedbank.com *Commercial & investment bankers*

► Ahlstrom Chirnside Ltd, Chirnside, Duns, Berwickshire, TD11 3JW Tel: (01890) 818303 Fax: (01890) 818256 E-mail: karen.renton@ahlstrom.com *Manufacturers of filter paper, hospital disposable products & non-woven fabric. Also automotive/ interior trim manufrs.*

Ahmad Textiles, Ahmad House, Downham Street, Bradford, West Yorkshire, BD3 9QY Tel: (01274) 727069 Fax: (01274) 390407 E-mail: info@ahmadtextiles.co.uk *Textile merchants*

► Ahrend Holdings Ltd, Hogarth Buiness Park, Burlington Lane, London, W4 2TX Tel: (020) 8747 8383 Fax: (020) 8747 0025 E-mail: furnishing.uk.info@ahrend.com *Supply & installation of office furniture**Desking: Mehes, Essa, A500*Chairs: A350, A430, A220, Centennial*Cabinets & Screens**

Ai International Couriers Ltd, 17 Vicarage Lane, Horley, Surrey, RH6 8AR Tel: (01293) 776875 Fax: (01293) 820950 E-mail: ailgw@clara.net *Courier services*

Aichess Print, Hoo Farm Industrial Estate, Worcester Road, Kidderminster, Worcestershire, DY11 7RA Tel: (01562) 744517 Fax: (01562) 746067 *Printers & stationers*

► Aid Building Company Ltd, 18 Camborne Avenue, Romford, RM3 8QP Tel: (07718) 757762 Fax: 01708 38442 E-mail: info@aidbuilding.com *specialists in disabled adaptations*

Aided Design & Draughting Supplies, 14-16 West Street, Exeter, EX1 1BA Tel: (01392) 445580 Fax: (01392) 444126 *Drawing office suppliers*

Aided Design & Draughting Supplies, Spreadeagle Court, Northgate Street, Gloucester, GL1 1SL Tel: (01452) 505040 Fax: (01452) 505040 *Design office equipment suppliers*

► Alex Aiken & Son Ltd, Dales Industrial Estate, Peterhead, Aberdeenshire, AB42 3GY Tel: (01779) 475121

James Aiken (Offshore) Ltd, Horizons Ho, 81 Waterloo Quay, Aberdeen, AB11 5DE Tel: (01224) 573322 Fax: (01224) 572666 E-mail: sales@aikenoffshore.com *Engineering Project Management.*

James Aiken (Sheetmetal) Ltd, 10 Wellington Street, Aberdeen, AB11 5BT Tel: (01224) 572555 Fax: (01224) 571214 E-mail: enquiries@jasm.com *Sheet metalwork engineers*

Aikona, Leigh Road, Chichester, West Sussex, PO19 8TT Tel: (01243) 771790 Fax: (01243) 532226 E-mail: info@aikona.co.uk *Flooring company producing vinyl, wood effect flooring manufrs*

► Aileen's Cards, 5 Finlay Avenue, East Calder, Livingston, West Lothian, EH53 0RP Tel: (01506) 881760 E-mail: info@aileens-cards.co.uk *Handmade cards & wedding stationery retailers*

► Ailsa Building Ltd, 251 Dundyvan Road, Coatbridge, Lanarkshire, ML5 4AU Tel: (01236) 422615 Fax: (01236) 602623

► Aim, 17 Warleigh Drive, Bath, BA1 7PT Tel: (0845) 8381843 Fax: (01225) 581158 E-mail: info@aimbusiness.co.uk *It support services*

Aim, 20 Coales Gardens, Market Harborough, Leicestershire, LE16 7NY Tel: (01858) 434177 Fax: (01858) 466699

Aim Aviation Ltd, Building 138, Bournemouth International, Airport, Christchurch, Dorset, BH23 6NW Tel: (01202) 599666 Fax: (01202) 599677 E-mail: enquiries@aim-aviation.co.uk *Aircraft paint sprayers & avionics*

Aim Aviation Henshalls Ltd, Abbot Close, Byfleet, West Byfleet, Surrey, KT14 7JT Tel: (01932) 351011 Fax: (01932) 352792 E-mail: c.herrington@aim-henshalls.co.uk *Aircraft galley systems manufrs* Also at: Southampton

AIM Composites Ltd, Pembroke Avenue, Waterbeach, Cambridge, CB5 9QR Tel: (01223) 441000 Fax: (01223) 862336 E-mail: sales@aimcomposites.com Principal Export Areas: Worldwide *Manufacturers of honeycomb core board & aircraft components*

Aim Engineering Ltd, Melandra Road, Brookfield, Glossop, Derbyshire, SK13 6JE Tel: (01457) 862505 Fax: (01457) 861753 E-mail: sdada@aimeng.co.uk *Subcontract engineers*

► AIM Technologies Europe Ltd, 12 Ferry Row, Fairlie, Largs, Ayrshire, KA29 0AJ Tel: (01475) 568423 Fax: (01475) 568808 E-mail: powerquality@aimeurope.com *Electrical power quality*

Aim UK Ltd, 21 Lincoln Road, Cressex Business Park, High Wycombe, Buckinghamshire, HP12 3RB Tel: (01494) 446844 Fax: (01494) 449324 E-mail: salesuk@aim-online.com *Avionics databus solutions*

Aims, Unit 15C Compton Place Business Centre, Surrey Avenue, Camberley, Surrey, GU15 3DX Tel: (01276) 691366 Fax: (01276) 61488 *Health & safety consultant*

► Aims, 29 Meadowcroft, Higher Kinnerton, Chester, CH4 9AY Tel: (01244) 661859 E-mail: craig.wynne@aims.co.uk *Accountants in construction*

► Aims Accountants For Business, 44 Dale Lee, Westhoughton, Bolton, BL5 3YE Tel: (01942) 842345 E-mail: jean.lawson@aims.co.uk *Accountancy and taxation services for business people provided at a competitive fee agreed in advance by a local professionally qualified accountant supported by a London-based Services Team*

► AIMS - Accountants for Business, 16 Jacaranda Close, Chelmsford, CM1 6NN Tel: 01245 463859 Fax: 01245 463860 E-mail: philip.manson@aims.co.uk

► AIMS - Accountants for Business, 33 Isis House, Bridge Wharf, Chertsey, Surrey, KT16 8LB Tel: 01932 561936 Fax: 01932 561936 E-mail: andrewm@aims.co.uk

► Aims Engineering, Unit H, Ditchling Common Industrial Estate, Ditchling, Hassocks, West Sussex, BN6 8SG Tel: (01444) 870221 Fax: (01444) 244860 E-mail: mail@aimsengineering.co.uk *Precision machined parts, small & large batch*

► Aimteq Services Ltd, 9 Wilkinson Road, Love Lane Industrial Estate, Cirencester, Gloucestershire, GL7 1YT Tel: (01285) 655772 Fax: (01285) 655782 E-mail: info@aimteq.co.uk

Ainscough Ltd, Col Industrial Estate, Old Bath Road, Slough, SL3 0NJ Tel: (01753) 684811 Fax: (01753) 684005 *Contract lifting & crane hire*

Ainscough Building Supplies Ltd, Mossy Lea Road, Wrightington, Wigan, Lancashire, WN6 9RS Tel: (01257) 421000 Fax: (01257) 426848 E-mail: ainscoughbuildingsupplies@hotmail.com *Builders merchants*

Ainscough Crane Hire Ltd, Old Mill Lane, Aylesford, Kent, ME20 7DT Tel: (01622) 716500 Fax: (01622) 716066 E-mail: maidstone@ainscough.co.uk *Mobile crane hire services*

Ainscough Crane Hire Ltd, Ipswich Road, Cardiff, CF23 9AQ Tel: (029) 2049 5455 Fax: (029) 2049 3967 E-mail: cardiff@inc.co.uk *Crane hire & contract lifting services*

Ainscough Crane Hire Ltd, Stanlow Refinery, PO Box 3, Ellesmere Port, CH65 4HB Tel: 0151-355 8812

► Ainscough Crane Hire Ltd, Langmuir Way, Baillieston, Glasgow, G69 7RW Tel: 0141-773 0500 Fax: 0141-781 1010 E-mail: general@ainscough.co.uk

Ainscough Crane Hire Ltd, Kings Road, Immingham, South Humberside, DN40 1AL Tel: (01469) 576266 Fax: (01469) 576351 E-mail: immingham@ainscough.co.uk *Crane hire & contract lifting services* Also at: Branches throughout the U K

► Ainscough Crane Hire Ltd, Scott Lane, Morley, Leeds, LS27 0NQ Tel: 0113-253 4366 Fax: 0113-253 2321

► Ainscough Crane Hire Ltd, Rugby Road, Princethorpe, Rugby, Warwickshire, CV23 9PN Tel: (01926) 634786 Fax: (01926) 634763 E-mail: coventry@ainscough.co.uk *Crane hire* Also at: Bristol

Ainscough Crane Hire Ltd, Harewood Works, Middlesbrough Road, Thornaby, Stockton-on-Tees, Cleveland, TS17 7BN Tel: (01642) 661111 Fax: (01642) 612422 E-mail: general@ainscough.co.uk *Crane hire & contract lifting services* Also at: Branches throughout the U.K.

Ainscough Engineering Services Ltd, Farington Business Park, Leyland, PR25 3GG Tel: (01772) 622116 Fax: (01772) 622210 E-mail: a.keith@ainscoughengineering.co.uk *Crane engineering, repair & testing services*

► Ainscough Training Services Ltd, Farington Business Park, Golden Hill Lane, Leyland, PR25 3GG Tel: (01772) 623591 Fax: (01772) 622654 E-mail: ianfisher@ainscoughtraining.co.uk *Construction plant training*

Ainscough Vanguard, William Thorpe Industrial Park, Park Road, Holmwood, Chesterfield, Derbyshire, S42 5UY Tel: (01246) 854644 Fax: (01246) 854161 *Factory relocations*

Ainsdale Computer Consultants Ltd, Goodyear Business Park, New Street, Mawdesley, Ormskirk, Lancashire, L40 2QP Tel: (01704) 823430 Fax: (01704) 823232 E-mail: post@ainsdale-computers.co.uk *Computer consultants*

Ainsworth, Frenches Works, Chew Valley Road, Greenfield, Oldham, OL3 7AE Tel: (01457) 879000 Fax: (01457) 873279 E-mail: diyshop@ainsworthdiy.co.uk *DIY retailers*

Ainsworth & Burgess Ltd, The Forstal, Lenham Heath, Maidstone, Kent, ME17 2JB Tel: (01622) 858343 Fax: (01622) 850664 E-mail: mail@ainsworthburgess.plus.com *Frozen fruit processors & products manufrs*

► Ainsworth & Martin Preston Ltd, Crossley House, Leyland Road, Penwortham, Preston, PR1 9QP Tel: (01772) 744396 Fax: (01772) 744461

Ainsworth's Vacuum Cleaner Sales & Service, Service, 4 Watford Street, Blackburn, BB1 7LD Tel: (01254) 691000 *Vacuum cleaner sales & service*

Aintree Concrete Pumping, 21 Aintree Close, Gravesend, Kent, DA12 5AS Tel: (01474) 333616 Fax: (01474) 333616 E-mail: info@aintreeconcretepumping.co.uk *Commercial & domestic concrete pumping services*

► Aipex Engineering Ltd, Units 1-3 Stream Farm, Chiddingly, Lewes, East Sussex, BN8 6HG Tel: (01825) 873600 Fax: (01825) 873601 E-mail: barry@aipex-sussex.com *Precision gauging & control equipment manufacturers for plastics industry*

Air Algerie, 10 Baker Street, London, W1U 3BT Tel: (020) 7486 8068 Fax: (020) 7487 5709 *Airline*

Air America (Rugby) Ltd, Midland Trading Estate, Consul Road, Rugby, Warwickshire, CV21 1PB Tel: (01788) 574555 Fax: (01788) 547997 E-mail: air.america@wyko.co.uk *Engineers & power transmission distributors*

Air And Water Centre.Com, Artex Avenue, Rustington, Littlehampton, West Sussex, BN16 3LN Tel: (01903) 858657 Fax: (01903) 850345 E-mail: sales@airandwatercentre.com *Air conditioning distributors or agents*

► Air Assault Kiteboarding, Air Assault Ltd, Horley, Surrey, RH6 7JX Tel: 07739 733600 E-mail: info@air-assault.com *Air Assault is a 'New Skool' Kiteboarding company that manufactures some of the most advanced boards, accessories and apparel on the market.*

► Air Business Communication Ltd, Riverside Business Centre, Riverside Road, Lowestoft, Suffolk, NR33 0TQ Tel: 08700 420675 E-mail: sales@airmobiles.co.uk *AiR Business Communication Ltd specialise in B2B mobile phone solutions. We can connect to all the major UK networks and save you time and money by finding the best solution for your business.*

► Air Care, 125 New Bridge Street, Newcastle upon Tyne, NE1 2SW Tel: 0191-261 1144 Fax: 0191-261 1188 E-mail: info@aircare-services.co.uk *Air conditioning ventilation repair*

Air Care Mechanical Services Ltd, 297 Avenue Road Extension, Clarendon Park, Leicester, LE2 3ER Tel: 0116-270 9707 Fax: 0116-270 5737 E-mail: sales@aircaremechanical.co.uk *Heating & air conditioning contractors*

► Air Care Products, Gosbecks Road, Colchester, CO2 9JT Tel: (01206) 564443 Fax: (01206) 564462

Air Cargo Transport Ltd, 4 Ladygate, Diseworth, Derby, DE74 2QF Tel: (01332) 811464 Fax: (01332) 812223 E-mail: admin@air-cargo.uk.com *Road transport, haulage & freight services*

► Air Charter Connections Ltd, 40-44 Church Street, Reigate, Surrey, RH2 0AJ Tel: (0870) 382 0767 Fax: (0870) 382 0787 E-mail: info@aircharterconnections.com *Air Charter Connections is a U.K. based aviation group serving clients across the globe, in all aspects of aircraft charter, leasing, flight management, consulting, aircraft sales and re-marketing. **From scheduled fleet support and emergency response, to executive and group travel, we provide comprehensive solutions through our global resources, delivering flight operations of the highest standard on behalf of our clients and airline partners. ***

► Air Chilled Solutions, 40 Stoneleigh Court, Westcroft, Milton Keynes, MK4 4BT Tel: 01908 526585 Fax: 01908 526585 E-mail: info@airchilledsolutions.co.uk *Air Chilled Solutions provide a turn key, commercial and domestic service for Air conditioning and refrigeration needs.*

Air Con, 30 Woodbrook Road, Springhead, Oldham, OL4 4BS Tel: 0161-678 8862 Fax: 0161-678 8862 *Air conditioning installation*

Air Conditioning Accessories, 105 Ash Road, Sutton, Surrey, SM3 9LA Tel: (020) 8288 1181 Fax: (020) 8288 1185 *Air conditioning distributors*

Air Conditioning Agency, 7 Tabernacle Walk, Blandford Forum, Dorset, DT11 7DL Tel: (01258) 455522 Fax: (01258) 455622 E-mail: info@airconagency.co.uk *Air conditioning distributors*

► Air Conditioning Corporation (Midlands) Ltd, Unit G11, Roden Street, Nottingham, NG3 1JH Tel: (0800) 2343506 E-mail: enquiries@airconcorp.co.uk *Supplying services to design, install, maintain, breakdown support*

Air Conditioning Design Ltd, Unit 6, Manchester Road, Haslingden, Rossendale, Lancashire, BB4 6LB Tel: (01706) 219101 Fax: (01706) 219190 *Air conditioning designers & contractors*

Air Conditioning Distribution Ltd, Clarence Street, Cleckheaton, West Yorkshire, BD19 5HJ Tel: (01274) 862804 Fax: (01274) 862807 E-mail: sales@acd.co.uk *Air conditioning distributors*

Air Conditioning (Jersey), 9 New Street, St Helier, Jersey, JE2 3RA Tel: (01534) 870022 Fax: (01534) 870044 *Air conditioning installers*

Air Conditioning Refrigeration and Environmental, 56 Moathouse Lane East, Wednesfield, Wolverhampton, WV11 3DD Tel: (01902) 733503 Fax: (01902) 307899 *Air conditioning equipment suppliers & maintenance*

Air Conditioning & Refrigeration Industry Board, Kelvin House, 76 Mill Lane, Carshalton, Surrey, SM5 2JR Tel: (020) 8647 7033 Fax: (020) 8773 0165 E-mail: ior@ior.org.uk *Learned society*

Air Conditioning & Refrigeration Services Ltd, 16 Brunel Street, Newcastle upon Tyne, NE4 7AH Tel: 0191-273 7700 Fax: 0191-256 8700 E-mail: acr@16brunel.sfnet.co.uk *Air conditioning sales, design & installation*

Air Conditioning & Refrigeration Services, Lynfelde, 14 East Street, Long Buckby, Northampton, NN6 7RA Tel: (01327) 843192 Fax: (01327) 843192 E-mail: aircon1@supanet.com *Air conditioning & refrigeration services*

Air Conditioning Services, 15 Torland Road, Plymouth, PL3 5TS Tel: (01752) 778985 Fax: (01752) 778985 *Air conditioning installation & services*

► The Air Conditioning Showroom, 28 Brookley Road, Brockenhurst, Hampshire, SO42 7RR Tel: (01590) 623244 Fax: (01590) 623756

► Air Conditioning Solutions, Dipmans Lodge, Brinkton Road, East Haddon, Northampton, NN6 8DS Tel: (01604) 770660 Fax: (01604) 770036

► Air Conditioning Solutions UK Ltd, Concept Park, Watling Street, Towcester, Northamptonshire, NN12 7YD Tel: (01327) 810510 Fax: (01327) 811529 E-mail: info@airconsolutions.co.uk *Installation & servicing of air conditioning systems*

Air Contractors, Ema Cargo West, East Midland Int Airport, Castle Donington, Derby, DE74 2TR Tel: (01332) 857850 Fax: (01332) 857859 E-mail: info@aircontractors.com *Cargo airline*

Air Control & Development Ltd, Unit 5 ABS Business Park, Northgate, Aldridge, Walsall, WS9 8TH Tel: (01922) 455523 Fax: (01922) 455528 E-mail: simon.r@aircontrol.co.uk *Air conditioning & ventilation services*

Air Controlled Environmental Systems Ltd, 6 Gazelle Buildings, Wallingford Road, Uxbridge, Middlesex, UB8 2SX Tel: (01895) 813312 Fax: (01895) 813443 E-mail: gary@aces-ductwork.co.uk *Duct work & ventilation manufrs*

Air Controls Ltd, Garden Close, Langage Business Park, Plympton, Plymouth, PL7 5EU Tel: (01752) 344443 Fax: (01752) 346789 E-mail: aircontrols@eur-isp.com *Automation special purpose equipment*

Air Controls & Compressors Ltd, 9 Trafalgar Court, Widnes, Cheshire, WA8 0SZ Tel: 0151-423 1750 Fax: 0151-495 2079 E-mail: sales@accltd.com *Air compressor distributors*

Air Cool Engineering Ltd, Unit G, Aghanloo Industrial Estate, Aghanloo Road, Limavady, County Londonderry, BT49 0HE Tel: (028) 7776 7114 Fax: (028) 7776 7115 E-mail: sales@ni.aircool.co.uk *Air conditioning equipment installers*

Air Cool Engineering Midlands Ltd, Fairway House, Vulcan Road, Solihull, West Midlands, B91 2JY Tel: 0121-711 4700 Fax: 0121-711 4757 E-mail: dsteele@aircoolmidlands.co.uk *Air conditioning engineers & contractors*

Air Curtain Engineering Ltd, 15-29 Air Street Hill, London, EC1R 5LB Tel: (020) 7833 2940 Fax: (020) 7833 8299 *Manufacturers & installers of air curtains*

Air Design Developments Ltd, Unit 37 Westley Grange, Chartwell Drive, Wigston, Leics, LE18 2FL Tel: 0116-281 3491 Fax: 0116-288 5428 *Air handling equipment manufrs*

Air Diffusion Ltd, 164 Great North Road, Hatfield, Hertfordshire, AL9 5JN Tel: (01707) 272601 Fax: (01707) 274951 E-mail: hatfield@air-diffusion.co.uk *Air conditioning grill manufrs*

Air Diffusion Sales Northern Ltd, Unit 39 Sefton La Industrial Estate, Liverpool, L31 8BX Tel: 0151-527 2525 Fax: 0151-527 2717 *Air diffusion equipment suppliers*

► Air Diffusion Technology, 52 London Road, Oadby, Leicester, LE2 5DH Tel: 0116-272 1231 Fax: 0116-271 4441 E-mail: info@euro-air.co.uk *Supplier of air socks /fabric ducting /textile ventilation.***

Air Displays (International) Ltd, Building 509, Churchill Way, Biggin Hill Airport, Westerham, Kent, TN16 3BN Tel: (01959) 572277 Fax: (01959) 575969 E-mail: sales@airdisplaysint.co.uk *Air display & exhibition organisers*

Air Domestique Ltd, Unit 4b Benbridge Industrial Estate, Holloway Road, Heybridge, Maldon, Essex, CM9 4ER Tel: (01621) 852994 Fax: (01621) 850643 E-mail: mail@ad-manufacturing.fsnet.co.uk *Sheet metalwork engineers*

► Air Duct Systems (Southern) Ltd, 5 Oxford Road, Pen Mill Trading Estate, Yeovil, Somerset, BA21 5HR Tel: (01935) 431809 *Air duct manufacturers & controllers*

Air Engineering Controls Ltd, Unit 4, Forest Row Business Park, Station Road, Forest Row, East Sussex, RH18 5DW Tel: (01342) 826488 Fax: (01342) 826489 E-mail: conrtrols@airengineering.co.uk *Engineering services*

▶ Air Environmental Technology Ltd, 52 Springvale Industrial Estate, Cwmbran, Gwent, NP44 5BB Tel: (01633) 875520 Fax: (01633) 875540

Air Equipment, 5 Kings Road, Flitwick, Bedford, MK45 1ED Tel: (01525) 723700 Fax: (01525) 723737 E-mail: info@air-equipment.co.uk *Air compressor distributors*

Air & Finishing Systems Ltd, 7 Blaenau Enterprise Centre, Rising Sun Industrial Estate, Blaina, Abertillery, Gwent, NP13 3JW Tel: (01495) 292880 Fax: (01495) 292800 *Air conditioning manufrs*

Air Flow Measurements Ltd, 72 Manchester Road, Kearsley, Bolton, BL4 8NZ Tel: (01204) 571499 Fax: (01204) 571734 E-mail: info@airflowmeasurements.com *Airflow & electrical measurement engineers consultants*

Air & Gas Blowers, 22 Hitch Lowes, Chelford, Macclesfield, Cheshire, SK11 9SR Tel: (01625) 860146 Fax: (01625) 860147 Sales Contact: A. Woodcock *'Rotron' & 'Continental' blowers & gas booster manufacturers, air blowers & air blowers, ionising; blowers, blowers, air; sewage industry, blowers, air, water industry; blowers combustion air; blowers, gas; blowers, gas boosting, blowers, ionised air: blowers, side channel; exhausters; gas boosters; gas boosters, breathing air; gas boosters, carbon dioxide (CO2); gas boosters, carbon monoxide (CO); gas boosters, methane; gas boosters, neon; gas boosters, nitrogen; gas boosters, nitrous oxide; gas boosters, oxygen*

Air & General Finance Ltd, Tolworth Tower, Ewell Road, Surbiton, Surrey, KT6 7EL Tel: (020) 8390 9444 Fax: (020) 8390 8211 E-mail: office@airandgeneral.com *Aircraft finance*

▶ Air & Ground Aviation Ltd, Aviation House, London Road, Shirleywich, Stafford, ST18 0PN Tel: (01889) 271777 Fax: (01889) 270756 E-mail: office@airandground.com *Aircraft supplies parts*

Air Handlers Northern Ltd, Bute Street, Salford, M50 1DU Tel: 0161-745 8888 Fax: 0161-745 9900 E-mail: sales@airhandlers.com *Air handling & air cooling equipment suppliers*

Air Handling Equipment Ltd, 23 Cotton Street, Liverpool, L3 7DY Tel: 0151-236 2910 Fax: 0151-236 2910 E-mail: sales@ahe.co.uk *Air handling equipment manufrs*

Air Handling Systems Ltd, Unit 3-5 Furnace Industrial Estate, Shildon, County Durham, DL4 1QB Tel: (01388) 776287 Fax: (01388) 775494 E-mail: general@ahs.uk.com *Air conditioning equipment manufrs*

Air Heating & Manufacturing, Seaton Lane, St. Helier, Jersey, JE2 3QJ Tel: (01534) 734830 Fax: (01534) 767681 E-mail: airheating@hotmail.com *Ventilation ductwork fabricators*

Air For Hire Ltd, Frederick House, Anchor Lane, Bilston, West Midlands, WV14 9NE Tel: (01902) 887262 Fax: (01902) 884632 *Hire and contract rental specialists for compressed air equipment, using HPC screw compressors, air receivers, dryers and filtration systems to all types of industrial applications. 24-hour after-sales service, routine maintenance and repairs, installations and hire.*

Air Improve Ltd, Unit 4 City Business Centre, Hyde Street, Winchester, Hampshire, SO23 7TA Tel: (01962) 841366 Fax: (01962) 840185 E-mail: enquiries@airimprove.ltd.uk *Air conditioning design & installation*

Air Industrial Developments Ltd, Union Street, Kencrick Way, West Bromwich, West Midlands, B70 6DB Tel: 0121-553 4446 Fax: 0121-525 5983 E-mail: paint.sales@airind.co.uk *Paint spray engineers*

▶ Air Jump, 65 Totterdown Road, Weston-Super-Mare, Avon, BS23 4LJ Tel: (07900) 481550 E-mail: lindsaylawence@btconnect.com *Bouncy castle hire services*

Air Linen Laundry, 4 Shentonfield Road, Sharston Industrial Area, Manchester, M22 4RW Tel: 0161-428 8099 Fax: 0161-428 8116 *Linen laundry & hire services*

Air Liquide Ltd, Johnsons Bridge Road, West Bromwich, West Midlands, B71 1LG Tel: 0121-500 1000 Fax: 0121-500 1111 E-mail: trevor.longley@uk.linde-gas.com *Gas producers & suppliers & nitrogen production plant*

Air Liquide UK Ltd, Cedar House, 39 London Road, Reigate, Surrey, RH2 9QE Tel: (01737) 241133 Fax: (01737) 241842 E-mail: geneng.aluk@airliquide.com Purchasing Contact: C. Kemp Sales Contact: T. Bonnett *Industrial gas products*

Air Marks Systems Ltd, A3-A4 Salcombe Road, Alfreton, Derbyshire, DE55 7RG Tel: (01773) 832228 Fax: (01773) 830186 E-mail: sales@airmarkssystems.ltd.uk *Sheet metal fabricators*

Air Mauritius, 49 Conduit Street, London, W1S 2YS Tel: (020) 7434 4375 Fax: (020) 7439 4101 E-mail: reservations@airmauritiusuk.com *Airline*

▶ Air Mechanical Contractors, 14 Hemming Street, Kidderminster, Worcestershire, DY11 6NA Tel: (07917) 324325 Fax: (01562) 634303 E-mail: info@airuk.biz *Air conditioning specialists*

Air Menzies International Ltd, 5 The Enterprise Centre, Kelvin Lane, Crawley, West Sussex, RH10 9PT Tel: (01293) 658000 Fax: (01293) 551114 E-mail: info@airmenzies.com *Airfreight wholesalers*

Air Methods Ltd, Frederick House, Anchor Lane, Bilston, West Midlands, WV14 9NE Tel: (01902) 884466 Fax: (01902) 884632 E-mail: sales@airmethods.co.uk *Compressed air specialists with over 50 years experience supplying HPC screw compressors, air receivers, dryers and filtration systems to all types of industrial applications. 24-hour after-sales service, routine maintenance and repairs, installations and hire.*

Air Partner Insurance Consultants Ltd, Platinum House Gatwick Road, Crawley, West Sussex, RH10 9RP Tel: (01293) 549555 Fax: (01293) 536810 E-mail: france@airpartner.com *Aircraft charter brokers*

Air Plants Environmental Control Systems, 295 Aylestone Road, Leicester, LE2 7PB Tel: 0116-283 7800 Fax: 0116-283 7311 E-mail: sales@airplants.co.uk *Dust extraction equipment designers*

▶ Air Plants Environmental Control Systems, 295 Aylestone Road, Leicester, LE2 7PB Tel: 0116-283 7800 Fax: 0116-283 7311 E-mail: sales@airplants.co.uk *Installation & Service*Warm Air Heating*Radiant Tube Heating**

Air Pollution Services, Suite 6 Chiltern House, Leys Road, Brierley Hill, West Midlands, DY5 3UP Tel: (01384) 78094 Fax: (01384) 480940 E-mail: martinwil@msn.com *Environmental control systems*

Air Power Centre, Unit B4 Anchorage Business Park, Chain Caul Way, Ashton-on-Ribble, Preston, PR2 2YL Tel: (01772) 728513 Fax: (01772) 736506 E-mail: apcpreston@airpowercentre.com *Air compressors & spraying equipment suppliers*

Air Power & Hydraulics Ltd, 15 Watt Rd, Hillington Park, Glasgow, G52 4PQ Tel: 0141-810 4511 Fax: 0141-883 3825 E-mail: hydraulics@aph.co.uk *Air Power & Hydraulics Ltd is a leading specialist designer and manufacturer of custom hydraulic cylinders, actuators and power units. Our experience in hydraulic problem-solving has been applied in contracts in the general engineering sector and process industries and the rail, nuclear, offshore and defence industries.*Hydraulic Cylinders There are four ranges of hydraulic cylinder: the C10 standard industrial cylinders and CEPAC cylinders for subsea and hostile environments. K10 high pressure cylinders use high alloy steels for working pressures of 700 bar. PENCYL stainless steel cylinders for bore sizes from 10mm. A full CYLINDER REFURBISHMENT service is available. *Rotary Actuators A range of semi-rotary rack and pinion actuators in carbon, stainless steel and alloy materials for industrial, marine and subsea use. *Hydraulic Power Units Standard and customised power units up to 75kW for industrial and marine use.*

Air Products plc, Enterprise Drive, Westhill Industrial Estate, Westhill, Aberdeenshire, AB32 6TQ Tel: (0845) 6015163 Fax: (01224) 749065 *Industrial gas producers*

▶ Air Products (B R) Ltd, Hersham Place, Molesey Road, Walton-on-Thames, Surrey, KT12 4RZ Tel: (0800) 3890202 Fax: (01932) 249565

Air Products (Chemicals) P.L.C., Clayton Lane, Clayton, Manchester, M11 4SR Tel: 0161-230 4230 Fax: 0161-223 5488 E-mail: epoxybox@airproducts.com *Epoxy additives manufrs*

Air Quality Assurance, 1 Dunnings Lane, Rochester, Kent, ME1 1YB Tel: (01634) 832895 Fax: (01634) 832882 *Health & safety*

Air Quality Control Ltd, Ground Floor, 339 Hollinwood Avenue, Manchester, M40 0JA Tel: 0161-688 6880 Fax: 0161-682 6864 E-mail: admin@aqc-ltd.co.uk *Air conditioning & heating installators*

Air Response Ltd, Unit 8b Camp Industrial Estate, Rycote Lane, Milton Common, Thame, Oxfordshire, OX9 2NP Tel: (01844) 279870 Fax: (01844) 278669 *Distributors of air compressors including breathing, high performance air compressor maintenance, repair & reconditioning services. Air compressor pipework installation services, compressed air/ gas condensate management systems, air filtration equipment installation, inspection, maintenance and refurbishment services. Air quality testing.*

Air Safety Ltd, Vickers Industrial Estate, Mellishaw Lane, Morecambe, Lancashire, LA3 3EN Tel: (01524) 388696 Fax: (01524) 33386 E-mail: sales@airsafetymedical.com *Medical filter manufrs*

▶ Air Science Technologies Ltd, Suite 8, Jubilee House, Altcar Road, Formby, Liverpool, L37 8DL Tel: (01704) 833338 Fax: (01704) 833500 E-mail: info@airscienceuk.com *Manufacturers of clean air equipment & fume cupboards*

Air Sea Packing Group Ltd, Air Sea House, Third Cross Road, Twickenham, TW2 5EB Tel: (020) 8893 3303 Fax: (020) 8893 3068 E-mail: sales@airseapacking.com *Antique fine art export packers & shippers*

Air Seal Products, Unit 8e, Greenham Business Park, Greenham, Wellington, Somerset, TA21 0LR Tel: (01823) 674411 Fax: (01823) 674486 E-mail: info@air-sealproducts.com *Industrial tyre product manufrs*

Air Services, Redgate Road South Lancashire Industrial Estate, South Lancashire Industrial Es, Ashton-in-Makerfield, Wigan, Lancashire, WN4 8DT Tel: (01942) 722333 Fax: (01942) 725716 E-mail: sales@air-serv.co.uk *Forecourt equipment suppliers*

▶ Air South West 2000, Unit 20 Bell Park, Bell Close, Plympton, Plymouth, PL7 4TA Tel: (01752) 344010 Fax: (01752) 344011 E-mail: air2000plymouth@eidosnet.co.uk *Air compressor sales, service, repair & hire*

Air Steel Ltd, Furnace Hill, Halesowen, West Midlands, B63 3LZ Tel: 0121-550 2968 Fax: 0121-520 1346 *Sheet metalwork engineers*

Air Stream Engineering, Charfleets Close, Canvey Island, Essex, SS8 0PW Tel: (01268) 681400 Fax: (01268) 681412 *Sheet metalwork fabricators*

Air Supply, 7 Steatite Way, Stourport-On-Severn, Worcestershire, DY13 8PQ Tel: (01299) 825336 Fax: (01299) 825336 *Air conditioning services*

Air Supply Aviation Store Ltd, 97 High Street, Yeadon, Leeds, LS19 7TA Tel: 0113-250 9581 Fax: 0113-250 0119 *Aviation supplies*

Air Supply Systems Ltd, 8 Harmony Square, Glasgow, G51 3LW Tel: 0141-440 2121 Fax: 0141-440 0330 *Air conditioning engineers*

Air System Controls, Units 51-52, Business Development Centre, Stafford Park 4, Telford, Shropshire, TF3 3BA Tel: (01952) 290959 Fax: (01952) 292647 E-mail: sales@aircontrol-uk.com *Pneumatic, process controls & related ancillary products suppliers*

Air Systems Ltd, 20-22 Grafton Road, Sparkbrook, Birmingham, B11 1JP Tel: 0121-772 1561 Fax: 0121-766 8727 *Air compressor suppliers*

Air Systems Controls Ltd, 51-52 The Bus Development Cour, Stafford Park 4, Telford, Shropshire, TF3 3BA Tel: (01952) 290959 Fax: (01952) 292647 E-mail: sales@airsystemcontrols.com *Suppliers of pneumatic & process control equipment offering an extensive choice of top quality products, also providing professional technical advice with products direct from stock coupled with total commitment to customers and quality satisfaction*

Air Technique Ltd, Eagle Centre, 1 Progress Way, Luton, LU4 9TR Tel: (01582) 495151 Fax: (01582) 495152 E-mail: sales@air-technique.co.uk *Air compressor distributors*

Air Technology, Unit 1 Oaks Industrial Estate, Festival Drive, Loughborough, Leicestershire, LE11 5XN Tel: (01509) 264900 Fax: (01509) 264800 E-mail: office@airtechnology.co.uk *Measurement based engineering consultants*

Air Technology & Acoustics Ltd, 1451 Stratford Road, Hall Green, Birmingham, B28 9HT Tel: 0121-777 1847 Fax: 0121-777 3468 *Acoustic consultants*

▶ Air Tek Analytical, Unit 1-5 Meadow Mill, Water Street, Stockport, Cheshire, SK1 2BY Tel: 0161-477 3777 *Life support equipment supplier & services*

Air Terminal Ltd, 80 Deansgate Lane, Timperley, Altrincham, Cheshire, WA14 1SP Tel: 0161-928 8918 Fax: 0161-926 8234 *Air conditioning products manufrs*

Air Tube Carrier Systems, 79 Turnberry, Bracknell, Berkshire, RG12 8ZH Tel: (01344) 423659 Fax: (01344) 423659 *Pneumatic tube carrier systems*

Air Vehicles Design & Engineering Ltd, Unit 4 Three Gates Road, Cowes, Isle of Wight, PO31 7UT Tel: (01983) 293194 Fax: (01983) 291987 E-mail: info@airvehicles.co.uk *Air marine equipment manufrs*

Air Vent Technology Ltd, Unit 1 Regents Court, Walworth Industrial Estate, Andover, Hampshire, SP10 5NX Tel: (01264) 356415 Fax: (01264) 337854 E-mail: avtltd@btopenworld.com *Manufacturers of air handling units*

Air & Ventilation Services, Birds Cottage, Crabtree Hill, Lambourne End, Romford, RM4 1ND Tel: (020) 8500 8834 Fax: (020) 8500 3932 E-mail: sarahcresswell@aol.com *Heating & ventilation engineers*

Air Views, Old Buckenham Airfield, Abbey Road, Old Buckenham, Attleborough, Norfolk, NR17 1PU Tel: (01953) 861111 Fax: (01953) 861031 E-mail: admin@airviews.co.uk *Air photography*

▶ Air-2-There.Co.Uk, 55 Leighswood Avenue, Walsall, WS9 8AT Tel: (01922) 864248 E-mail: enquires@air-2-there.co.uk *Minibus & taxi's hire*

Airbags International Ltd, Viking Way, Congleton, Cheshire, CW12 1TT Tel: (01260) 294300 Fax: (01260) 294301 *Car safety component manufrs*

▶ Airbase GSE (UK) Ltd, Bedfont Trading Estate, Bedfont Road, Feltham, Middlesex, TW14 8EB Tel: (0870) 2405576 Fax: (020) 8751 0952 E-mail: enquiries@airbasegse.co.uk *Airline repair services*

Airbase Interiors (U K) Ltd, Vincent Street, Crewe, CW1 4AA Tel: (01270) 581556 Fax: (01270) 251407 E-mail: sales@airbaseservices.co.uk *Aircraft seat cover manufrs*

Airbase Services UK Ltd, Gatwick Gate Industrial Estate, Lowfield Heath, Crawley, West Sussex, RH11 0TG Tel: (01293) 553337 Fax: (01293) 530600 E-mail: reception@airbase-interiors.com *Airline seats manufrs*

Airborne Industrial Access Ltd, Pegasus House 15 Irwin Road, Guildford, Surrey, GU2 7PW Tel: (01483) 451610 Fax: (01483) 533009 E-mail: ringway@btinternet.com *Scaffold*

Airborne Packaging Ltd, Pegasus House, Beatrice Road, Leicester, LE3 9FH Tel: 0116-253 6136 Fax: 0116-251 4485 E-mail: sales@airbornebags.co.uk Sales Contact: M. Taylor *Promotional carrier bags*

Airbridge Networks Ltd, Blackburn Technology Management Centre, Blackburn, BB1 5QB Tel: (01254) 667900 Fax: (01254) 663907 E-mail: info@airbridge-networks.com *Implementation of wireless technology & it disposal solutions*

Airbrush Co Ltd, 7 Marlborough Road, Lancing, West Sussex, BN15 8UF Tel: (0870) 0660445 Fax: (08700) 660817 E-mail: sales@airbrushes.com *The Airbrush Company is the UK distributor of Iwata airbrushes, Iwata Studio Series compressors, Medea Beauty Products, Com Art water-based acrylic colours, Artool stencils, making film, frisket film, cutting rails and cutting mats, Life Color model paint and Airbrush Action instructional DVD videos and books. We also supply Premi-Air, Paasche and Badger air brushes, Createx colours and Auto Air paint. We offer a complete range of airbrush accessories, fittings, spare parts and a repair service. We supply spray equipment and Training Courses for all airbrush markets including Spray Tanning, Airbrush Nail Art, Airbrush Body Art, Airbrush Makeup, Art and Graphics, Custom Automotive Graphics, Radio Controlled and Plastic Scale Modelling, Textiles, Leather and T-Shirt Airbrushing, Sign Painting, Ceramics, Wood Crafts, Paper Crafts and Cake Decorating.*

Airbus, Chester Road, Broughton, Chester, CH4 0DR Tel: (01244) 520444 Fax: (01244) 523000 *Airbus wing manufrs*

Aircare, PO Box 2425, Slough, SL2 1WF Tel: (020) 8566 7000 Fax: (01753) 518167 *Air purification equipment*

▶ Aircare Compressor Services Ltd, 5 B Crucible Road, Corby, Northamptonshire, NN17 5TS Tel: (01536) 403808 Fax: (01536) 403860 *Air compressor suppliers*

Aircare Europe Ltd, Unit 27 Tatton Court, Kingsland Grange, Woolston, Warrington, WA1 4RR Tel: (08707) 445588 Fax: (01925) 850325 E-mail: info@aircareeurope.com *Air cleaning, air conditioning & purification equipment suppliers*

Aircare Ventilation Engineers Ltd, Unit 3d Newbattle Abbey Annexe, Newbattle Road, Newbattle, Dalkeith, Midlothian, EH22 3LJ Tel: 0131-660 9555 Fax: 0131-660 9666 E-mail: aircare@fsbdial.co.uk *Ventilation engineers*

Aircargo & Container Services Ltd, Unit H President Way, Luton, LU2 9NL Tel: (01582) 456700 Fax: (01582) 401646 E-mail: chris@accs.co.uk *Freight agency*

Aircat Ltd, Unit A1, Milestone Business Park, Oslo Road, Sutton Fields Industrial Estate, Hull, HU7 0YN Tel: (01482) 878878 Fax: (01482) 878801 E-mail: sales@aircat.karoo.co.uk *Pneumatic component distributors*

Airchannel Ltd, Unit 10, Blackburn Industrial Estate, Blackburn, Aberdeen, AB21 0RX Tel: (01224) 790895 Fax: (01224) 790921 E-mail: enquiries@airchannel.co.uk *Airchannel specialises in the selection of high quality compressed air equipment to meet our customers' requirements. Our relationships with some of the worlds best compressed air equipment suppliers and our many years of experience help us to find the best solution to our customer.*Airchannel prides itself on its expertise in this field and keeping up to date with any new innovations in service techniques or product development is a major part of that expertise.*

Airchannel Ltd, Unit 5, Smithies Mill, Bradford Road, Batley, West Yorkshire, WF17 8NS Tel: (01924) 475740 Fax: (01924) 475177 E-mail: enquiries@airchannel.co.uk *Airchannel specialises in the selection of high quality compressed air equipment to meet our customers' requirements. Our relationships with some of the worlds best compressed air equipment suppliers and our many years of experience help us to find the best solution to our customer.*Airchannel prides itself on its expertise in this field and keeping up to date with any new innovations in service techniques or product development is a major part of that expertise. **

Airchannel, 115 Burrell Road, Ipswich, IP2 8AE Tel: (01473) 690000 Fax: (01473) 685058 E-mail: enquiries@anglair.co.uk *Compressed air & pneumatic equipment*

Airchannel, Unit 16, Hurworth Road, Aycliffe Industrial Park, Aycliffe, Newton Aycliffe, County Durham, DL5 6UD Tel: (01325) 321237 Fax: (01325) 318397 E-mail: aycliife@woodsidecompressors.co.uk *Air compressor agents & distributors* Also at: Washington

Airclean Ltd, PO Box 147, Maidstone, Kent, ME14 2LA Tel: (01622) 832777 Fax: (01622) 832507 E-mail: info@airclean.co.uk *Air filter manufrs*

▶ Airco Air Conditioning, 120 Stoneferry Road, Hull, HU8 8DA Tel: (01482) 587038 Fax: (01482) 229997

Airco Pneumatics Ltd, Malmesbury Road, Kingsditch Trading Estate, Cheltenham, Gloucestershire, GL51 9PL Tel: (01242) 690480 Fax: (01242) 690490 E-mail: info@aircopneumatics.co.uk *Distributors & agents of air compressors*

▶ Airco UK Ltd, Unit G Argent Court, Hook Rise South, Surbiton, Surrey, KT6 7NL Tel: (0800) 3284510 E-mail: info@airways.ac *Sole UK Distributors of Aisin Toyota Gas Engine Heat Pumps air conditioners.VRF/VRV style air conditioning systems running on natural gas or lpg and ranging in size from 14kW upwards.Use very little electricity so ideal for buildings with limited electrical supplies.Please call for further inbformation or free survey.**

Aircogen CHP Solutions, Werrington Parkway, Peterborough, PE4 5HG Tel: (01733) 292450 Fax: (01733) 292460 E-mail: info@aircogen.co.uk *Combined heat & power solutions*

Aircon Refrigeration Ltd, 35e Dukesway, Teesside Industrial Estate, Stockton-on-Tees, Cleveland, TS17 9LT Tel: (01642) 760565 Fax: (01642) 764011 E-mail: aircon.refrigeration@btinternet.com *Air conditioning sales & services*

Airconaire Ltd, Unit 6 Deacon Trading Centre, Knight Road, Rochester, Kent, ME2 2AU Tel: (01634) 711264 Fax: (01634) 717100 E-mail: info@airconaire.co.uk *Building service contractors*

▶ Airconditioning Birmingham, 8 Turton Gardens, Redditch, Worcestershire, B96 6JB Tel: 01527 892823 Fax: 01527 892823 E-mail: sales@airconditioningbirmingham.co.uk *Air-conditioning installation, hire, maintenance & sales*

▶ Airconditioning & Chiller Co. Ltd, The Corner House, Northfield Avenue, Pleasley Vale, Mansfield, Nottinghamshire, NG19 8SG Tel: 01623 658580 Fax: 01623 659506 E-mail: sales@airconditioning-chiller.co.uk *Air conditioning services & installation*

Air-Conditioning & Refrigeration Concerns, 5 Mingarry, Birtley, Chester Le Street, County Durham, DH3 2JB Tel: 0191-410 3594 Fax: 0191-410 8504 *Refrigerator maintenance & installation*

Airconstruct Midlands Ltd, Littleton Drive, Cannock, Staffordshire, WS12 4TS Tel: (01543) 572300 Fax: (01543) 574090 E-mail: sales@airconstruct.co.uk *Heat ventilation & air conditioning contractors & ductwork manufrs*

▶ Aircool Building Services Ltd, 244 Shenley Road, Borehamwood, Hertfordshire, WD6 1TJ Tel: (0845) 1658071

▶ Aircraft Braking Systems Europe Ltd, 683-685 Stirling Road, Slough, SL1 4ST Tel: (01753) 696006 Fax: (01753) 696012 E-mail: awitney@absel.co.uk *Aircraft wheel & brake maintenance specialists*

continued

▶ indicates data change since last edition

Aircraft & Commercial Tools (Sheffield) Ltd, Bowling Green Street, Shalesmoor, Sheffield, S3 8SU Tel: 0114-272 8112 Fax: 0114-275 9273 E-mail: aircraft@globalnet.co.uk *Press tools, jigs & fixtures*

Aircraft Components Equipment & Supplies Ltd, 171 Upper Halliford Road, Shepperton, Middlesex, TW17 8SN Tel: (01932) 701417 Fax: (01932) 701419 E-mail: neil@acraftcomponants.co.uk Principal Export Areas: Worldwide *Aircraft components importers & distributors*

Aircraft Ground Equipment Supply Ltd, 4 Sheepcoft Lane, Whitemoor, Holt, Wimborne, Dorset, BH21 7DA Tel: (01202) 848511 Fax: (01202) 848522 E-mail: tim@aircraftaccess.com *Aircraft ground maintenance equipment manufrs*

Aircraft Maintenance Ltd, Eagle House, Village Farm Industrial Estate, Pyle, Bridgend, Mid Glamorgan, CF33 6NU Tel: (01656) 743700 Fax: (01656) 744265 E-mail: office@amssgse.co.uk *Aircraft ground support equipment suppliers*

Aircraft Materials Ltd, Llangeinor, Bridgend, Mid Glamorgan, CF32 8PL Tel: (01656) 727000 Fax: (01656) 721100 *Precision engineers - aeronautical*

▶ Aircraft Replicas Ltd, Unit 4E, Industrial Estate, Sinfin Lane, Derby, DE24 9GL Tel: (01332) 271600 Fax: (01332) 271600

Aircraft Spares and Materials Ltd, 6 Armstrong Road, Manor Trading Estate, Benfleet, Essex, SS7 4PW Tel: (01268) 792681 Fax: (01268) 795375 E-mail: spares@airsam.clara.net *Aircraft component stockists*

Aircraft Unit Engineering Co. Ltd, 10 Horatius Way, Silver Wing Industrial Estate, Croydon, CR0 4RU Tel: (020) 8686 7755 Fax: (020) 8681 3837 E-mail: office@aircraftunit.com *Light engineering, mechanical & tool making services*

John Aird & Co. Ltd, Greenbank Mills, East Main Street, Darvel, Ayrshire, KA17 0JB Tel: (01560) 323600 Fax: (01560) 323601 E-mail: johnaird@compuserve.com *Net curtain manufrs*

Aird, Walker & Ralston Ltd, 12F Lawson Street, Kilmarnock, Ayrshire, KA1 3JP Tel: (01563) 522236 Fax: (01563) 521304 E-mail: sales@airdwalker.co.uk *Electrical engineers*

Airdrie Grain & Health Foods, 37 Hallcraig Street, Airdrie, Lanarkshire, ML6 6AH Tel: (01236) 754291 *Health food retailers*

▶ Airdrie Print Services, 24-26 Flowerhill Street, Airdrie, Lanarkshire, ML6 6AP Tel: (01236) 751833 Fax: (01236) 748134

Airduct Ltd, Raywell Street, Hull, HU2 8EP Tel: (01482) 326868 Fax: (01482) 589991 E-mail: airduct@hull92.freeserve.co.uk *Heating & ventilation contractors*

Airducts Design, Unit 45 Wassage Way, Hampton Lovett, Droitwich, Worcestershire, WR9 0NX Tel: (01905) 775454 Fax: (01905) 775656 *Industrial ventilation engineers*

Aire Bearings, 34 Bradford Road, Stanningley, Pudsey, West Yorkshire, LS28 6DD Tel: 0113-256 5676 Fax: 0113-255 4894 E-mail: sales@airebearings.co.uk *Power transmission equipment*

Aire Sales Scotland, The Mews, 19 Sandyford Place Lane, Glasgow, G3 7HS Tel: 0141-204 4750 Fax: 0141-204 4755 *Air conditioning distributors*

Aire Truck Bodies Ltd, Lennerton Lane, Sherburn in Elmet, Leeds, LS25 6JE Tel: (01977) 684541 Fax: (01977) 683351 E-mail: post@aire-trucks.com *Commercial vehicle body builders*

Aire Truck Bodies Ltd Shipley, Wharncliffe Road, Shipley, West Yorkshire, BD18 2AW Tel: (01274) 585250 Fax: (01274) 532398 E-mail: shipley@aire-trucks.com *Commercial vehicle body building specialists*

▶ Aire Valley Architectural, 1 Parkwood Street, Keighley, West Yorkshire, BD21 4QH Tel: (01535) 683290 Fax: (01535) 683299 *Aluminium fabricators*

Aire Valley Metal Products Ltd, Shaw House, Goulbourne Street, Keighley, West Yorkshire, BD21 1PG Tel: (01535) 600162 Fax: (01535) 600162 E-mail: aire@valleymetals.fsnet.co.uk *Sheet metalwork engineers & fabricators*

▶ Aireco Airconditioning Ltd, 59 Burnhams Close, Andover, Hampshire, SP10 4NJ Tel: (0870) 4320920 Fax: (0870) 4320634 *Air Conditioning equipment suppliers*

Airedale Blinds & Shutters, 10 Wellington Street, Laisterdyke, Bradford, West Yorkshire, BD4 8BW Tel: (01274) 661266 Fax: (01274) 661222 E-mail: abs@fallers.co.uk *Blind & shutter manufrs*

Airedale Catering Equipment Ltd, Airedale House, Victoria Road, Eccleshill, Bradford, West Yorkshire, BD2 2BN Tel: (01274) 626666 Fax: (01274) 626750 E-mail: design@airedale-group.co.uk *Catering equipment manufrs*

Airedale Computer Centre, 33 Station Road, Baildon, Shipley, West Yorkshire, BD17 6HS Tel: (01274) 581777 Fax: (01274) 581777 E-mail: royston.moore@btinternet.com *Computer consultants*

Airedale Cooling Services Ltd, Airedale Building, East Parade, Keighley, West Yorkshire, BD21 5HZ Tel: (01535) 602202 Fax: (01535) 610772 E-mail: info@airedalecooling.com *Refrigeration & air conditioning engineers*

Airedale Fire Protection Services, Howden Grange, Holden Lane, Silsden, Keighley, West Yorkshire, BD20 0LS Tel: (01535) 652069 Fax: (01535) 652069 *Fire protection consultants*

▶ Airedale International Air Conditioning Ltd, Leeds Road, Rawdon, Leeds, LS19 6JY Tel: 0113-239 1000 Fax: 0113-250 7219 E-mail: enquiries@airedale.com Principal Export Areas: Worldwide *Air conditioning & process cooling equipment manufrs*

Airedale Stainless Fabrications Ltd, Unit 2a, Crosshills Enterprise Centre, Keighley, West Yorkshire, BD20 7BX Tel: (01535) 636831 Fax: (01535) 636831 *Engineering*

Airedale Tubes & Fittings Ltd, Royds Farm Road, Leeds, LS12 6DX Tel: 0113-231 1227 Fax: 0113-231 1866 E-mail: airedaleinfo@btconnect.com *Hose, hydraulic equipment systems & tubing fittings distributors*

Aireserve Air Conditioning, Airrex House, Hambledon Road, Hambledon, Waterlooville, Hampshire, PO7 4QX Tel: (023) 9223 3300 Fax: (023) 9223 8555 E-mail: dfarr@mail.aireserv.com *Need air conditioning or refrigeration? Aire Serv is a national air conditioning and refrigeration contractor. We supply, install, service and maintain all types of commercial, and retail refrigeration and air conditioning systems and products. We are well respected and count a number of well known blue chip companies in our portfolio. We can supply references from all manner of clients for all manner of projects.*

Aireworth Ltd, Parson Street, Keighley, West Yorkshire, BD21 3HD Tel: (01535) 662545 Fax: (01535) 611149 E-mail: aireworth@appelbe.com *General engineering*

J. Airey, Scott Laithe Farm, Gisburn Road, Bolton By Bowland, Clitheroe, Lancashire, BB7 4LT Tel: (01200) 447616 *Agricultural engineers*

Airfawn Consultants Ltd, New Haden Works, Draycott Cross Road, Cheadle, Stoke-on-Trent, ST10 2NW Tel: (01538) 750788 Fax: (01538) 751511 E-mail: aiirfawnltd@btconnect.com *Cable harness manufrs*

Airfeso Ltd, 16-18 Main Street, Bolton by Bowland, Clitheroe, Lancashire, BB7 4NW Tel: (01200) 447206 Fax: (01200) 447443 E-mail: airfeso@aol.com *Clean air systems manufrs*

Airflare Bouncy Castle Hire, Quarry Cottage, 94 Worlebury Hill Road, Weston-super-Mare, Avon, BS22 9TG Tel: (01934) 414286 Fax: (01934) 414286 *Bouncy castle hire*

▶ Airflo Distribution Ltd, Unit 16, Norton Enterprise Park, Whittle Road, Salisbury, SP2 7YS Tel: (01722) 415535 Fax: (01722) 415390 *Air conditioning distributors*

Airflo Envirorental, Kelham Street, Doncaster, South Yorkshire, DN1 3TA Tel: (01302) 730000 Fax: (01302) 321222 *Hire, leasing & rental of industrial air conditioning, heating, ventilation equipment. Also dehumidifiers* Also at: Cuffley (Herts)

▶ Airflow Air Conditioning Ltd, St. Sidwells, Canworthy Water, Launceston, Cornwall, PL15 8UA Tel: (01566) 781777 Fax: (01566) 781777 E-mail: sales@airflowaircon.co.uk *Air conditioning consultants & designers*

Airflow Compressors & Pneumatics Ltd, 100 Lord Street, Leigh, Lancashire, WN7 1BY Tel: (01942) 673529 Fax: (01942) 604672 E-mail: mail@airflow-compressors.co.uk *Air compressors, pneumatic valves & cylinders*

Airflow Engineering Services Heating Ventilation Air Conditioning, Drift Road, Kymba House, Whitehill, Bordon, Hampshire, GU35 9DZ Tel: (01420) 473401 Fax: (01420) 489955 *Industrial heating engineers*

▶ Airflow Instrumentation, 7 West Vale, Neston, CH64 9SE Tel: 0151-336 1899 Fax: 0151-336 8705 E-mail: airflowinstrumentation@hotmail.co.uk *Instrumentation Engineers,DCS, UCP,Entronic commissioning & maintenance,calibration equipment hire, Cold blast cupola measurements and control systems.*

Airflow (Nicoll Ventilators) Ltd, Queensway, New Milton, Hampshire, BH25 5NN Tel: (01425) 611547 Fax: (01425) 638912 E-mail: sales@airflow-vent.co.uk *Plastic building product manufrs*

Airflow Ventilation Supplies, Shackleton Rd, Cressex Business Pk, High Wycombe, Bucks, HP12 3RH Tel: (01494) 463490 Fax: (01494) 471507 E-mail: info@avs.co.uk *Electric fan distributors*

Airfluid Hydraulics & Pneumatics Ltd, Tong Road, Bishops Wood, Stafford, ST19 9AB Tel: (01952) 850246 Fax: (01952) 850246 E-mail: hydraulicbjr@aol.com *Hydraulic systems equipment manufrs*

Airforce Ventilation Products, 3 Brunel Gate, West Portway Industrial Estate, Andover, Hampshire, SP10 3SL Tel: (01264) 358101 Fax: (01264) 358404 E-mail: enquiries@airforcevp.com *Ventilation equipment manufrs*

Airfotos Ltd, 37 Belsay Gardens, Newcastle upon Tyne, NE3 2AU Tel: 0191-285 4625 Fax: 0191-285 4625 *Commercial ariel photographers*

Airgun Centre, 107 London Road, Rayleigh, Essex, SS6 9AX Tel: (01268) 780730 Fax: (01268) 783102 E-mail: sales@theairguncentre.co.uk *Air gun retailers*

▶ AirisQ Ltd, 36 Hillydeal Road, Otford, Sevenoaks, Kent, TN14 5RU Tel: (01959) 525937 Fax: (01959) 525889 E-mail: admin@airisq.co.uk *Ventilation & indoor air quality consultants*

Airite Compressor Supplies & Services, Unit 1 Petersfield Works, 1357B Stratford Rd, Hall Green, Birmingham, B28 9HW Tel: 0121-778 5772 Fax: 0121-778 5773 *Air compressor distributors*

Airite Southern Ltd, 1 Milners Upper Street, Leeds Village, Maidstone, Kent, ME17 1GZ Tel: (01622) 861411 Fax: (01622) 861415 E-mail: airiteec@btconnect.com *Air conditioning*

Airkool Projects Ltd, 10 Rotterdam Road, Hull, HU7 0XD Tel: (01482) 371888 Fax: (01482) 371889 E-mail: info@airkool.co.uk *Refrigeration & electrical engineers*

Airlec Truck & Bus Parts, Unit 24 Tomlinson Business Park, Tomlinson Road, Leyland, PR25 2DY Tel: (01772) 433564 Fax: (01772) 433568 E-mail: sales@airlec.co.uk *Commercial vehicle components suppliers*

Airlift & Tilt Ltd, BDC Business Park, Fountain Street, Morley, Leeds, LS27 0AA Tel: 0113 2959450 Fax: 0113 2197201 E-mail: enquiries@airliftandtilt.com *Manufactors of Materials Handling Equipment. Airbags, Airbag Powered Scissor Lifts, Airbag lift & Tilt units, Airskates, Airskate platforms and Turntables. All units ATEX compliant*

Airline Business, Quadrant House, The Quadrant, Brighton Road, Sutton, Surrey, SM2 5AS Tel: (020) 8652 3500 *Airline Business is a monthly international magazine for senior airline management*

▶ Airline Cars & Coaches, Drumshoreland Road, Fernlea, Broxburn, West Lothian, EH52 5PF Tel: (01506) 852473 Fax: (01506) 857274 E-mail: aircab1@aol.com *Taxis & minibus hire*

Airline Services Ltd, Canberra House, Robeson Way, Sharston Green Business Park, Manchester, M22 4SX Tel: 0161-495 6900 Fax: 0161-495 6969 E-mail: enquiries@airline-services.com *Aircraft cleaning & presentation service*

AIRLINK, 15 Masefield Avenue, Portsmouth, PO6 4PD Tel: 02392 851396 Fax: 02392 376662 E-mail: airlink@elite.co.uk *We supply, repair, and service every type of air compressor and all associated equipment to over 3000 businesses across the UK and are very proud of our unrivalled commitment to our customers.**Please take a look at our extensive range of products available at the cheapest prices on the net!!.*

▶ Airman Engineering Services Ltd, 10 Boleyn Court, Manor Park, Runcorn, Cheshire, WA7 1SR Tel: (01928) 571945 Fax: (01928) 571946 E-mail: sales@airman-otd.co.uk *Air compressor distributors*

Airmark, 6 Becket Road, London, N18 3PN Tel: (020) 8807 7891 Fax: (020) 8884 3898 E-mail: airmarkcom@aol.com *Air compressor manufrs*

Airmaster, 49A High Street, Beighton, Sheffield, S20 1EE Tel: 0114-288 9911 Fax: 0114-288 9922 E-mail: team@airmaster.uk.com *Air conditioning installers*

Airmat Machinery Ltd, 43 Bridgeman Terrace, Wigan, Lancashire, WN1 1TT Tel: (01942) 493563 Fax: (01942) 496276 E-mail: info@airmat-machinery.co.uk *Air expanding shafts & chucks*

▶ Airmec H2o Ltd, 1360 Aztec West, Almondsbury, Bristol, BS32 4RX Tel: (01454) 275050 Fax: (01454) 275051 E-mail: enquiries@airmec.co.uk *Risk assessment ductwork services*

Airmech Engineering Services Ltd, Littleburn Lane, Langley Moor, Durham, DH7 8HA Tel: 0191-378 0045 Fax: 0191-378 0854 E-mail: airmechplant@hotmail.co.uk *Plant machinery wholesalers*

Airmed Medical Equipment Mnfrs, Southfield House, 99 Barry Road, London, SE22 0HR Tel: (020) 8693 0594 Fax: (020) 8693 0342 E-mail: info@airmedltd.com *Medical ventilators & masks*

Airnesco Group Ltd, Unit 2, Bredgar Industrial Estate, Bredgar Road, Gillingham, Kent, ME8 6PL Tel: (01634) 267070 Fax: (01634) 267079 E-mail: info@airnesco.com *Barrel cleaning equipment manufacturers & services*

Airocean Freight Ltd, 6-9 Spring Road, Smethwick, West Midlands, B66 1PE Tel: 0121-580 6730 Fax: 0121-525 5296 E-mail: info@airoceanfreight.co.uk *Shipping & forwarding agents*

Air-O-Ducts Contracts Ltd, Unit 10, 865 Ringwood Road, Bournemouth, BH11 8LL Tel: (01202) 576511 Fax: (01202) 570511 *HVAC engineers*

Airology Systems Ltd, Brickyard Lane, Studley, Warwickshire, B80 7EE Tel: (01527) 850717 Fax: (01527) 850737 E-mail: aircon@airology.freeserve.co.uk *Air conditioning design & installation*

Airomatic Tools Ltd, Coleham Green Farm, Woodchurch, Ashford, Kent, TN26 3PP Tel: (01233) 861400 Fax: (01233) 860040 *Pneumatic equipment distributors*

Airomet Ltd, Unit 4 Millenium Court, Bunsford Park Road, Bromsgrove, Worcestershire, B60 3DX Tel: (01527) 837500 Fax: (01527) 833818 *Ducting contractors & ventilation engineers*

Airops Ltd, Fairoaks Airport, Chobham, Woking, Surrey, GU24 8HU Tel: (0870) 7655100 Fax: (01276) 858485 *Computer system manufrs*

Airow Safe, Unit 14e Eleventh Avenue North, Team Valley Trading Estate, Gateshead, Tyne & Wear, NE11 0NJ Tel: 0191-491 4271 Fax: 0191-491 4272 E-mail: info@airowsafe.co.uk *Electrical contractors*

Air-o-wear, Aydon South Farm, Corbridge, Northumberland, NE45 5PL Tel: (01434) 632816 Fax: (01434) 632849 *Equestrian protection wear manufrs*

▶ Airpac Air Compressors, Mugiemoss Road, Bucksburn, Aberdeen, AB21 9NP Tel: (01224) 715008 Fax: (01224) 714290 E-mail: airpac.rentals@vpplc.com *Air compression, on-site steam & nitrogen generation equipment hire*

▶ Airpel Filtration, Hambridge Road, Newbury, Berkshire, RG14 5TR Tel: +44 (0) 1635 263915 Fax: +44 (0) 1635 36006 E-mail: airpel@spx.com *Industrial strainers, coatings, liquid & paint filter manufrs*

▶ Airport 24 7, 152-154 Coles Green Road, London, NW2 7HD Tel: (020) 8208 4880 Fax: (020) 8452 0701 E-mail: renata@exclusiveairports.com *Airport transfer services*

Airport Bearing Co. Ltd, 4/5 Bennerly Court, Blenheim Industrial Estate, Bulwell, Nottingham, NG6 8UT Tel: 0115-975 7571 Fax: 0115-927 3778 E-mail: sales@abco-online.co.uk *Distributors for Bearings, Power transmission equipment, sealing technologies and allied products*

▶ Airport Cars, Synegis House, Crockhamwell Road, Woodley, Reading, RG5 3LE Tel: 0118-967 0252 Fax: E-mail: sales@airportcarswokingham.co.uk *Airport shuttle service & chauffer driven car hire*

▶ Airport Couriers, Unit A Golden CR, Hayes, Middlesex, UB3 1AQ Tel: (020) 8569 2759 Fax: (020) 8569 2760

Airport Engineering Co., 1 Harold Court Road, Romford, RM3 0YU Tel: (01708) 342358 Fax: (01708) 304598 E-mail: sales@propshafts.sagehost.co.uk *Cylinder borers engineering*

Airpro Systems, 265 Holton Road, Barry, South Glamorgan, CF63 4HT Tel: (01446) 729900 Fax: (01446) 729909 *Ductwork contractors*

▶ Airquee Ltd, Unit 2a Barton Hill, Trading Estate, Bristol, BS5 9RD Tel: 0117-941 4918 Fax: 0117-941 4919 *Bouncy castle hire manufrs*

Airquick Newark Ltd, Northern Road, Newark, Nottinghamshire, NG24 2EU Tel: (01636) 640480 Fax: (01636) 701216 E-mail: info@airquick.co.uk *Air compressor distributors & railway engineers*

Airscrew Ltd, 111 Windmill Road, Sunbury-on-Thames, Middlesex, TW16 7EF Tel: (01932) 765822 Fax: (01932) 761098 E-mail: airscrew@ametek.co.uk Principal Export Areas: Asia Pacific, Central Asia, Africa, Central/East Europe & West Europe *YFans, motors & generators designers & manufrs*

Airspace Avionics Ltd, 7-8 New Road Avenue, Chatham, Kent, ME4 6BB Tel: (01634) 843878 Fax: (01634) 401361 E-mail: peterfarrer@airspaceavionics.co.uk *Design, supply & manufacture of wiring harnesses to military/civil aircraft, communications & motor sport industries. cable assembly/harness (electrical/electronic)*

Airsprung Furniture Group plc, Canal Road Industrial Estate, Canal Road, Trowbridge, Wiltshire, BA14 8RQ Tel: (01225) 754411 Fax: (01225) 763256 E-mail: sales@airsprungbeds.co.uk *Bed manufrs*

Airtec Filtration Ltd, Manor Street, St. Helens, Merseyside, WA9 3AX Tel: (01744) 733211 Fax: (01744) 730917 E-mail: sales@airtecfiltration.com *Dust & fume extraction manufrs*

Airtech Air Conditioning Services Ltd, Devon House, Eastbourne Road, Lingfield, Surrey, RH7 6JJ Tel: (01342) 836000 Fax: (01342) 835930 E-mail: ac@airtech.uk.com *Air conditioning engineers*

Airtech Analysis Ltd, 6 Sopwith CR, Hurricane Way, Wickford, Essex, SS11 8YU Tel: (01268) 562645 Fax: (01268) 570198 E-mail: airtech@dsl.pipex.com *Asbestos consultants*

▶ Airtech Environmental Services, 3 Hampton Court Road, East Molesey, Surrey, KT8 9BN Tel: (020) 8979 2158 Fax: (020) 8941 9623 E-mail: airtechlondon@mcmail.com *Heating ventilation & air conditioning*

▶ Airtek Air Conditioning & Technical Services Ltd, Designer House, 44 Lorraine Road, Timperley, Altrincham, Cheshire, WA15 7NB Tel: 0161-904 9333 Fax: 0161-904 8558

Airtek Fan Solutions Ltd, 2 Ventura Centre, Upton Industrial Estate, Poole, Dorset, BH16 5SW Tel: (01202) 623333 Fax: (01202) 632576 E-mail: enquiries@airtekfs.co.uk *UK manufacturers of cross flow (tangential) fans & heaters*

Airtemp A.C. Ltd, 18 Theaklen Drive, Ponswood Industrial Estate, St. Leonards-on-Sea, East Sussex, TN38 9AZ Tel: (0845) 8725657 Fax: (0845) 8725658 E-mail: sales@airtempac.co.uk *Air conditioning contractors*

Airtex Products Ltd, Hanworth Trading Estate, Hampton Road West, Feltham, Middlesex, TW13 6EH Tel: (020) 8755 4400 Fax: (020) 8894 3026 E-mail: info@airtex.co.uk *Automotive component manufrs*

Airtight Ductwork Ltd, New Town, Kington Magna, Gillingham, Dorset, SP8 5EU Tel: (01747) 838777 Fax: (01747) 838999 E-mail: info@airtightductwork.co.uk *Ventilation & air conditioning suppliers*

▶ Airtime Charters, Hanger, 266 Aviation Park West, Hurn, Christchurch, Dorset, BH23 6NW Tel: (01202) 579949 Fax: (01202) 572907 E-mail: info@airtimecharters.com *Airtime Charters offer high quality air charter and air taxi services for business travel and leisure.*

Airtronics Ltd, Victoria Works, 14A Albert Road, Belvedere, Kent, DA17 5LJ Tel: (01322) 431638 Fax: (01322) 430413 E-mail: sales@airtronics.co.uk *Wound component manufrs*

Airvert Ltd, Ghyll Road Industrial Estate, Ghyll Road, Heathfield, East Sussex, TN21 8AW Tel: (01435) 868292 Fax: (01435) 864838 E-mail: mthompson@airvert.co.uk *Wheel balance weight manufrs*

Airwair International Ltd, Cobbs Lane, Wollaston, Wellingborough, Northamptonshire, NN29 7SW Tel: (01933) 663281 Fax: (01933) 663848 *Footwear & protective footwear*

▶ Airware, Unit 5c Arrow Trading Estate, Corporation Road, Audenshaw, Manchester, M34 5LR Tel: 0161-320 4777 Fax: 0161-320 7829

Airway Solutions, Unit 18 Uveco Business Centre, Dock Road, Birkenhead, Merseyside, CH41 1FD Tel: 0151-630 0650 Fax: 0151-630 4050 E-mail: sunhill@airwaysolutions.co.uk *Air conditioning & ventilation suppliers*

▶ Air-Weigh Inc Ltd, Fleet Villa, Godnow Road, Crowle, Scunthorpe, East Yorkshire, DN17 4DU Tel: (01724) 712000 Fax: (01724) 712111 E-mail: airweighinc@hotmail.com *Suppliers of onboard weighing equipment*

▶ Airwell Air Conditioning Equipment, Unit 5 Hurtmore Heights Commercial Centre, Hurtmore Road, Hurtmore, Godalming, Surrey, GU7 2FD Tel: (01483) 418282 Fax: (01483) 425826 *Air conditioning designers*

Airworld International, 2 The Faraday Centre, Faraday Road, Crawley, West Sussex, RH10 9PX Tel: (01293) 510007 Fax: (01293) 521361 E-mail: airsales@allport.co.uk *Freight forwarding agents*

AIS Fire Tech Tech, Unit 12 Riverside Business Park, 33 River Road, Barking, Essex, IG11 0DA Tel: (020) 8591 3433 Fax: (020) 8594 1226 E-mail: enquiries@firetech.co.uk *Fire extinguisher distributors*

Aish Electro, Unit 2b Cowley Road, Nuffield Industrial Estate, Poole, Dorset, BH17 0UJ Tel: (01202) 677100 Fax: (01202) 677233 E-mail: serbite@aishem.co.uk *Specialised pump breakdown, installation, maintenance & repair service*

Aish Technologies Ltd, Broom Road, Poole, Dorset, BH12 4NL Tel: (01202) 307007 Fax: (01202) 307000 E-mail: sales@aishtechnologies.com Principal Export Areas: Central/East Europe, West Europe, North America, Central America & South America *Electro-mechanical systems design services & manufrs*

▶ Aitchee Engineering, Orchard Cottage Farm, Red Lane, Oxted, Surrey, RH8 0RT Tel: (01883) 723334 Fax: (01883) 723334 E-mail: aitchee@hotmail.co.uk *Engineering services*

▶ Aitken Building Contractors, 5 Wych Elm, Harlow, Essex, CM20 1QP Tel: (01279) 419422 Fax: (01279) 413199

▶ Aitkens Bakery, 39-43 Glenbervie Road, Aberdeen, AB11 9JE Tel: (01224) 877768 Fax: (01224) 877756 *Bakery*

▶ Aiveen Daly Upholstery & Design, 2 Letchford Gardens, London, NW10 6AS Tel: 0208 962 0044 E-mail: info@aiveendaly.com *Furniture upholstery service*

Aizlewoods Buildbase, Hermitage Mill, Hermitage Lane, Mansfield, Nottinghamshire, NG18 5HA Tel: (01623) 420121 Fax: (01623) 420384 E-mail: mansfield@buildbase.co.uk *Buildbase is one of the UK's fastest growing builders merchants. All of our branches are long established companies which have been serving local trades people for many years, with knowledge and experience to match. We believe strongly in understanding the needs of trades professional and our business has been developed specifically to meet those demands. Massive stocks, top quality products, competitive pricing, reliable delivery, specialist staff and exceptional customer service.*

▶ Aj Civil Engineering Ltd, Nantllan, Clarach, Aberystwyth, Dyfed, SY23 3DT Tel: (01970) 828316 Fax: (01970) 820446

▶ Aj Fabrications, Touch Wood, Dirty Lane, Fishlake, Doncaster, South Yorkshire, DN7 5LS Tel: (07855) 760620 Fax: (01302) 849769 E-mail: info@ajfabrications.net *we offer a design and build service where we are able to come on to site take the relevant measurments and design your project in CAD and then take care of the other aspects for you also we produce portal frame buildings,staircases,handrail,security fencing and armco barriers and also we offer a number of services including mig,tig and arc method and using a number of ferrous and non ferrous materials*

Aj Freezer Water Services Ltd, Lynn Road, Swaffham, Norfolk, PE37 7PY Tel: (01760) 723400 Fax: (01760) 336199 E-mail: info@ajfreezer.co.uk *Irrigation services*

▶ Aj New Media, Holgate Villa, 22 Holgate Road, York, YO24 4AB Tel: (01759) 368100 Fax: (01757) 282255 E-mail: info@ajnewmedia.co.uk *Advertising, web design, print, marketing, branding*

Aja Ltd, 6 Heathlands Close, Twickenham, TW1 4BP Tel: (020) 8892 8900 Fax: (020) 8892 8901 *Weighing machines*

▶ Aja Services, 32 Talbot Street, Church Gresley, Swadlincote, Derbyshire, DE11 9PG Tel: (01283) 214204 Fax: (01283) 214204 *Agricultural consultants*

Ajax Minerva Ltd, Edderthorpe Street, Bradford, West Yorkshire, BD3 9JX Tel: (01274) 735910 Fax: (01274) 307706 E-mail: ajax_minerva@hotmail.com *Precision engineers*

▶ Ajay Autoparts, 3 St. Johns Court Foster Road, Ashford Business Park, Sevington, Ashford, Kent, TN24 0SJ Tel: (01233) 501000 Fax: (01233) 501111

Ajay Electronics Ltd, 4 Kimpton Trade Business Centre, 40 Kimpton Road, Sutton, Surrey, SM3 9QP Tel: (020) 8644 0534 Fax: (020) 8641 6558 *Electronic sub-contractors*

Ajay Patterns, 236 Berwick Avenue, Slough, SL1 4QT Tel: (01753) 525505 Fax: (01753) 825411 *Pattern makers*

▶ Ajb Landscapes, 18 West Way, Rossett, Wrexham, LL12 0DX Tel: (01244) 579333 *Garden designers*

Ajec Racing, Unit 3 Vernon Court, Meteor Business Park, Cheltenham Road East, Staverton, Gloucester, GL2 9QL Tel: (01452) 615333 Fax: (01452) 615777 E-mail: ajecracing@btconnect.com *BMW & performance car specialist services*

Ajl, 5-6 Bankside, Kidlington, Oxfordshire, OX5 1JE Tel: (01865) 375262 Fax: (01865) 370839 *Vehicle repairers*

Ajot UK Ltd, Hurricane Close, Sherburn in Elmet, Leeds, LS25 6PB Tel: (01977) 687040 Fax: (01977) 687041 E-mail: sales@ejot.co.uk *Industrial fastener manufrs*

▶ AJRB Systems, 188 Birkenhead Road, Meols, Wirral, Merseyside, CH47 0NF Tel: 0151-632 3505 E-mail: andy@andy-barrett.co.uk *Small industrial PCB electronic repairs, fault finding, small scale electronic solutions*

Ajs Profiles, Unit 12a Parkrose Industrial Estate, Middlemore Road, Smethwick, West Midlands, B66 2DZ Tel: 0121-565 5379 Fax: 0121-565 5379 E-mail: ajsprofiles.ltd@virgin.net *Profile cutting & grinding services*

Ajt Computing, The Westbrook Centre, Grassmere Way, Waterlooville, Hampshire, PO7 8SE Tel: (023) 9224 0080 Fax: (023) 9224 0080 E-mail: ajt@ajtcomputing.co.uk *Computer suppliers*

Ajt Engineering Ltd, Craigshaw Crescent, West Tullos Industrial Estate, Aberdeen, AB12 3TB Tel: (01224) 871791 Fax: (01224) 890251 E-mail: info@ajt-engineering.co.uk *Subsea oilfield equipment repairs & manufrs*

Ak Developments, 5 Station Road, Isleham, Ely, Cambridgeshire, CB7 5QT Tel: (01638) 720727 Fax: (01638) 720724 E-mail: cse@akd.co.uk *Special purpose custom built machinery constructors & manufrs*

▶ Akaray, North Circular Road, London, NW2 7AX Tel: (020) 8438 8222

Akcros Chemicals, PO Box 1, Manchester, M30 0BH Tel: 0161-785 1111 Fax: 0161-788 7886 E-mail: info.eccles@akcros.com *Chemical manufrs Also at: Birtley & Burnley*

Akd Engineering, Horn Hill, Lowestoft, Suffolk, NR33 0PX Tel: (01502) 527800 Fax: (01502) 527848 E-mail: info@akd-engineering.co.uk *Engineering & fabrication sub-contract services*

Ake Scaffolding, Unit 1, Hereford Way, King's Lynn, Norfolk, PE30 4JD Tel: (01553) 775326 Fax: (01553) 773262 E-mail: akescaff@aol.com *AKE Qualified Scaffolding Specialists. AKE Norfolk Based Scaffolding Contractors. Scaffolding Installation in Norfolk, Scaffolding Erection services, Scaffolders, Scaffolding Services, All Major Contracts Taken welcome, Scaffolding Contractors Based in East Anglia, Supplying Scaffolding Services to East Anglia, AKE Scaffolding are based in Kings Lynn and provide the highest quality scaffolding services to a wide range of clients throughout Norfolk and surrounding counties. AKE Scaffolders will ensure that all scaffolding is properly erected and they always put safety as their first priority. Scaffolding Contractors, Mobile Scaffolding erectors, Special Purpose Scaffolding contractors, Access Scaffolding erection, Steel Scaffolding services, Scaffolding Construction, Weather Protection Scaffolding.*

Akehurst & Sons Ltd, 4 Railway Street, Gillingham, Kent, ME7 1YF Tel: (01634) 851526 Fax: (01634) 580996 *Builders merchants & road transport*

Akeister & Faulkner, 65 Market Street, Hoyland, Barnsley, South Yorkshire, S74 0ET Tel: (01226) 746347 Fax: (01226) 740252 *Bar & shopfittings joinery manufrs*

▶ Akela Construction Contractors, 55 Hawbank Road, East Kilbride, Glasgow, G74 5EG Tel: (01355) 267744 Fax: (01355) 235656

Aker Kvaerner, Wellesley Road, Methil, Leven, Fife, KY8 3RA Tel: (01592) 268181 Fax: (01592) 715574 E-mail: peter.holt@akerkvaerner.com *Offshore construction engineers*

Aker Kvaerner Engineering Services Ltd, Phoenix House, 3 Surtees Way, Surtees Business Park, Stockton-on-Tees, Cleveland, TS18 3HR Tel: (01642) 334000 Fax: (01642) 334001 *Aker Kvaerner Engineering Services is a leading provider of both turnkey and reimbursable engineering solutions and life cycle services to the nuclear, water, metals, energy and process industries in the UK and worldwide. ***

Aker Kvaerner Subsea Ltd, Unit 59, Clivemont Road, Cordwallis Industrial Estate, Maidenhead, Berkshire, SL6 7BZ Tel: (01628) 506560 Fax: (01628) 506501 E-mail: info@kvaerner.com *Design subsea equipment*

Aker Maritime, McNulty Quay, Commercial Rd, South Shields, Tyne & Wear, NE33 1RZ Tel: 0191-401 5977 Fax: 0191-401 5958 *Offshore fabricators*

Akers UK Ltd, Suite 14, Shire Hall Complex, Pentonville, Newport, Gwent, NP20 5HB Tel: (01633) 265544 E-mail: sales@akersuk.com *Rolls for steel & non-ferrous industries*

Akhter Group Holdings P.L.C., Akhter House, Perry Road, Harlow, Essex, CM18 7PN Tel: (01279) 443521 Fax: (01279) 821300 *Computer repair services*

▶ Akiko Design, Suite 4 Jeffries House, 1-5 Jeffries Passage, Guildford, Surrey, GU1 4AP Tel: (01483) 510510 Fax: (01483) 510519 E-mail: admin@akikodesign.com *Website & graphic design*

▶ Akita, 16 Dalrymple Street, Girvan, Ayrshire, KA26 9AE Tel: (01465) 712930 *Furniture retailers*

Akki Aviation Services Ltd, Turweston Aerodrome, Biddlesden Road, Westbury, Brackley, Northamptonshire, NN13 5YD Tel: (01280) 706616 Fax: (01280) 840033 E-mail: akki@globalnet.co.uk *Light aircraft maintenance services*

Akramatic Engineering Co. Ltd, Keys Road, Nix's Hill Industrial Estate, Alfreton, Derbyshire, DE55 7FQ Tel: (01773) 833223 Fax: (01773) 520595 E-mail: info@akramatic.com *Sheet metal goods fabricators*

Akro Valves Co., 2 Chaucer Industrial Estate, Dittons Road, Polegate, East Sussex, BN26 6JF Tel: (01323) 485272 Fax: (01323) 485273 E-mail: info@akrovalve.co.uk *Valve, pipe & fitting distributors & manufrs*

▶ Akromultihire, Unit 6 Naysmyth Place, Houston Industrial Estate, Livingston, West Lothian, EH54 5EG Tel: (01506) 441991 Fax: (01506) 441856 *Power tools & accessories*

Akron, Building 107b Aviation Park West, Bournemouth International Air, Hurn, Christchurch, Dorset, BH23 6NW Tel: (01202) 580800 Fax: (01202) 593010 E-mail: office@akron.demon.co.uk *Plastic machinery manufacturers & plastics machinery (reconditioned) rebuilders & suppliers*

Akron Construction, Unit 2 Baxter Street, Aberdeen, AB11 9QA Tel: (01224) 896959 Fax: (01224) 896875 *Joiners*

▶ Akros Print Ltd, 8 Wilson Place, East Kilbride, Glasgow, G74 4QD Tel: (01355) 226184 Fax: (01355) 248364

Aks Hair & Beauty Ltd, 8 Peter Baines Industrial Estate, Woods Lane, Derby, DE22 3UD Tel: (01332) 380028 Fax: (01332) 380073 *Hairdressing products wholesalers*

▶ AKS Heat Transfer Services, Sheffield Road, Woodhouse Mill, Sheffield, S13 9WH Tel: 0114-269 4002 Fax: 0114-293 9164 E-mail: tech@aksheattransfer.com *Spares, repairs, refurbishment & new heat exchangers*

Aks Machining Ltd, 5 Wistaston Road Business Centre, Wistaston Road, Crewe, CW2 7RP Tel: (01270) 585554 Fax: (01270) 586606 *Machinists & precision engineering services*

Aktec, Office 3 78-86 Pennywell Road, Old Market, Bristol, BS5 0TG Tel: 0117-935 1999 Fax: 0117-935 1950 E-mail: info@aktecltd.com *Importers & exporters of communication & rfid equipment*

Aktion Automotive Ltd, Unit N3 Cardiff Bay Business Centre, Titan Road, Cardiff, CF24 5EJ Tel: (029) 2046 4668 Fax: (029) 2046 4669 E-mail: sales@aktionautomotive.co.uk *Automotive component distributors specialising in Deutz Hatz Kubota Yanmar Bosch Donaldson. Suppliers to all mkt sectors, locally and nationaly, involving Plant Equipment*

Aktiv Kapital (UK) Ltd, Merchants House, Crook Street, Chester, CH1 2BE Tel: (01244) 319912 Fax: (01244) 314635 E-mail: collect@aktivkapital.co.uk *Credit information & debt recovery services*

▶ Aktron Ltd, 8 Greenlea Park, Prince Georges Road, London, SW19 2JD Tel: (020) 8685 9461 Fax: (020) 8640 8688

Akwil Projects Ltd, 493-495 Chester Road, Manchester, M16 9HF Tel: 0161-872 7337 Fax: (08712) 205338 E-mail: sales@akwil.com *Lighting & sound distributors*

Akzo Nobel Coatings Holdings Ltd, 136 Milton Park, Abingdon, Oxfordshire, OX14 4SB Tel: (01235) 862226 Fax: (01235) 862236 E-mail: cr@akzonobel.com *Paint & car paint manufrs Also at: Glasgow, Hull & Warrington*

Akzo Nobel Industrial Coatings Ltd, Crown House, Hollins Road, Darwen, Lancashire, BB3 0BG Tel: (01254) 760760 Fax: (01254) 701092 E-mail: *Varnish, paint & adhesive manufrs*

Akzo Nobel Woodcare, Meadow Lane, St. Ives, Cambridgeshire, PE27 4UY Tel: (01480) 496868 Fax: (01480) 496801 E-mail: woodcare@sis.akzonobel.com *Timber stain distributors*

▶ AL Global 4 Phones Ltd, Deemouth Centre, South Esplanade East, Aberdeen, AB11 9PB Tel: (01224) 245000

Al Tools Ltd, Sidings Road, Lowmoor Road Business Park, Kirkby-in-Ashfield, Nottingham, NG17 7JZ Tel: (01623) 751577 Fax: (01623) 755590 E-mail: alanlockyear@altoolsltd.co.uk *Mould toolmakers & diecastings*

Ala Metal Fabrications, 2 Roe Farm, Station Road, Cogenhoe, Northampton, NN7 1NH Tel: (01604) 891170 Fax: (01604) 890557 *Metal fabrications*

▶ Alacer, Unit 2 Acorn Way, Mansfield, Nottinghamshire, NG18 3HD Tel: (01623) 635070 Fax: (01623) 643245 E-mail: sean@alacer.net *Contract packing, fulfilment & pre retail services*

Alacrity Signs, Woodrolfe Road, Tollesbury, Maldon, Essex, CM9 8SE Tel: (01621) 860579 Fax: (01621) 868522 *Metal work & sign manufrs*

▶ Aladdins Lighting, The Street, Long Stratton, Norwich, NR15 2XJ Tel: (01508) 536895 Fax: (01508) 532538 E-mail: orders@aladdins-lighting.co.uk *Lighting retailers*

Alami International Ltd, 7 Dace Road, London, E3 2NG Tel: (020) 8533 7800 Fax: (020) 8533 0026 E-mail: sales@alami.co.uk *Leather goods import merchants*

▶ Alamo Security Services, Channelsea House, Canning Road, Stratford, London, E15 3ND Tel: (020) 8519 8866 Fax: (020) 8519 1191 E-mail: info@alamosecurity.co.uk *Security services, manned guarding, key holding & mobile patrol*

Alamode Engraving & Sign Co. Ltd, 3 Reform Street, Hull, HU2 8EF Tel: (01482) 323704 Fax: (01482) 216403 E-mail: sales@alamode.freeserve.co.uk *Engraved labels & nameplate manufrs*

Alan Appleton Oldham Ltd, Jowett Street, Oldham, OL1 4JQ Tel: 0161-652 0327 Fax: 0161-633 0019 E-mail: sales@alanappleton.freeserve.co.uk *Yarn & stockinet manufrs*

▶ Alan Benfield Ltd, Sunny Bank Gardens, Belper, Derbyshire, DE56 1WD Tel: (01773) 821474 Fax: (01773) 828257

Alan Bettin Holdings Ltd, Seale Lane, Seale, Farnham, Surrey, GU10 1LD Tel: (01252) 782022 Fax: (01252) 782283 E-mail: sales@abpools.co.uk *Swimming pool contractors*

▶ Alan Bishop & Sons Builders Ltd, 34 Wedderburn Crescent, Dunfermline, Fife, KY11 4SE Tel: 01383 738072 E-mail: alan.bishop.bldrs@btinternet.com *New house building, attic conversions, extensions."42 years" experience.*

▶ Alan Boddy & Co. Ltd, Damer House, Meadoway, Wickford, Essex, SS12 9HA Tel: (01268) 571466 Fax: (01268) 570638 E-mail: alan@albodd.freeserve.co.uk *Provision of accountancy, taxation, book-keeping, payroll, and VAT services to sole traders, partnerships, and limited companies.*

▶ Alan Boon Ltd, Unit 2, Stoneylands Road, Egham, Surrey, TW20 9QR Tel: (01784) 437999

▶ Alan Boswell, High Street, Attleborough, Norfolk, NR17 2EH Tel: (01953) 455600 Fax: (01953) 456400 E-mail: insurance@alanboswell.co.uk *Business & personal insurance services*

▶ Alan Boswell Insurance Brokers, Harbour House, 126 Thorpe Road, Norwich, NR1 1UL Tel: (01603) 218000 Fax: (01603) 762862 E-mail: info@alanboswell.com *Independent brokers & financial advisors*

Alan C Cowan, Hartburn, Morpeth, Northumberland, NE61 4EN Tel: (01670) 772555 Fax: (01670) 772655 *Agricultural contractor*

Alan Cox & Son, 19 Craigweil Crescent, Stockton-on-Tees, Cleveland, TS19 0DU Tel: (01642) 611672 Fax: (01642) 651349 E-mail: andrewcoxdec@hotmail.com *Painters & decorators*

Alan Davies Stainless Ltd, 62 Westhoughton Road, Adlington, Chorley, Lancashire, PR7 4ET Tel: (01257) 481652 Fax: (01257) 483110 E-mail: ads@stainless316.fsnet.co.uk *Stainless steel fabricators*

Alan Davis Ltd, Woodland Close, Torquay, TQ2 7BD Tel: (01803) 612261 Fax: (01803) 615201 E-mail: adaamusements@hotmail.com *Amusement machine operators*

Alan Dawson Associates Ltd, Joseph Noble Road, Lillyhall Industrial Estate, Lillyhall, Workington, Cumbria, CA14 4JX Tel: (01900) 64433 Fax: (01900) 605911 E-mail: mail@adawson.co.uk *Architectural metalworkers & fabricators manufrs*

▶ Alan Electrical Ltd, Porters Wood, Valley Rd, St. Albans, Hertfordshire, AL3 6PE Tel: (01727) 841344

Alan Englefield, Owl Cottage, High Street, Netheravon, Salisbury, SP4 9PJ Tel: (01980) 670396 Fax: (01980) 670396 *Cabinets manufrs*

▶ Alan Gallagher Driveways, 12 Hillocks Place, Troon, Ayrshire, KA10 6TU Tel: (01292) 314449

Alan Godrich, 17-20 Charter Street, Leicester, LE1 3UD Tel: 0116-253 2322 Fax: 0116-262 9887 E-mail: sales@alan-godrich.com *Sewing machine specialists service Also at: Birmingham*

Alan Gordon, George Street, Chorley, Lancashire, PR7 2BE Tel: (01257) 274723 Fax: (01257) 241342 E-mail: sales@alangordoneng.co.uk *Engineers' toolmakers*

Alan Graham, Unit 7 Ayr Street, Nottingham, NG7 4FX Tel: 0115-970 1677 Fax: 0115-970 1677 E-mail: alan@agmodelmakers.co.uk *Model manufrs*

Alan Grant Grampian Ltd, 59 Main Street, Alford, Aberdeenshire, AB33 8PX Tel: (01975) 562573 Fax: (01975) 563631

Alan Griffiths, Fawley Green, Fawley, Henley-on-Thames, Oxfordshire, RG9 6JF Tel: (01491) 414169 Fax: (01491) 414179 *Plastic consultants*

▶ Alan Hislop, 32 Holt Road, Horsford, Norwich, NR10 3DD Tel: (01603) 897428 E-mail: sales@ahengraving.co.uk *Specialist hand engraving, sand blasting & restoration*

Alan Howard, Unit 6 Healey Wood Road Industrial Estate, Burnley, Lancashire, BB11 2LZ Tel: (01282) 433444 Fax: (01282) 433444 E-mail: info@salonlink.co.uk *Hair & beauty suppliers*

Alan J I & M D James, Tegfan, Cilrhedyn, Llanfyrnach, Dyfed, SA35 0AB Tel: (01239) 698373 Fax: (01239) 698473 *Agricultural contractors & plant hirers*

Alan Johnson Cabinet Maker, Kingsgate Workshops, 110-116 Kingsgate Road, London, NW6 2JG Tel: (020) 7372 6736 Fax: (020) 7328 7878 *Bespoke fitted furniture design manufacture & installation*

Alan Litman plc, Damad House, 490 Radford Road, Nottingham, NG7 7EE Tel: 0115-970 8992 Fax: 0115-942 0546 E-mail: alanlitman.plc@virgin.net *Lace manufrs*

▶ Martin Alan Construction Ltd, Limemount, 5 Dudhope Terrace, Dundee, DD3 6HG Tel: (01382) 206330 Fax: (01382) 206331

Alan Mead, Severn House, 30 Ombersley St West, Droitwich, Worcestershire, WR9 8QZ Tel: (01905) 791050 Fax: (01905) 773226 E-mail: alan.mead@alanmeadrecruitment.co.uk *Recruitment agency for estate agents*

▶ Alan Megaw, 64 Mount Merrion Avenue, Belfast, BT6 0FR Tel: (028) 9058 2233

Alan Myerscough, The Ellers, Ulverston, Cumbria, LA12 0AA Tel: (01229) 584444 Fax: (01229) 581213 E-mail: alanmyerscoughford@ic24.net *Ford accident repair services*

Alan Pharmaceuticals, 2 Kingsgate Avenue, London, N3 3BH Tel: (020) 8346 4311 Fax: (020) 8346 5218 E-mail: enquiries@alanpharmaceuticals.com *Manufacturers & world distributors of pharmaceutical products*

▶ Alan Price & Sons (Bargoed) Ltd, End-Y-Deri, Deri, Bargoed, Mid Glamorgan, CF81 9JA Tel: (01443) 831639

▶ Alan R Cross & Son Ltd, 22a Station Road, Wymondham, Norfolk, NR18 0JX Tel: (01953) 603637 Fax: (01953) 602321 E-mail: enquiries@arcrosselectrical.co.uk

Alan Roberts Midlands Ltd, Alan Roberts Midlands Ltd, Barton Dock Road, Stretford, Manchester, M32 0YL Tel: (01384) 263266 Fax: (01384) 265830 E-mail: jaspemal@aol.com *Building & packaging sheeting*

▶ Alan S Dickson, 11-13 Erskine Square, Hillington Industrial Estate, Glasgow, G52 4BJ Tel: 0141-883 3622 Fax: 0141-883 2129

Alan Stuart, 9-17 Cobden Street, Salford, M6 6NA Tel: 0161-737 4236 Fax: 0161-745 8327 E-mail: sales@alan-stuart.demon.co.uk *Truck & trolley manufrs*

Alan Walter (Timber), 7-23 Louisa St, Midland Road, Bristol, BS2 0LE Tel: 0117-926 8370 Fax: 0117-926 8370 *Timber merchants*

Alan White, Woodside House, 20-23 Woodside Place, Glasgow, G3 7QF Tel: 0141-582 1419 Fax: 0141-582 1484 E-mail: alan@alanwhitedesign.com *Engineering design consultancy*

▶ Alan Whiteford Contracts Ltd, Moulandale, Burnhervie, Fetternear, Inverurie, Aberdeenshire, AB51 5JU Tel: (01467) 642151 Fax: (01467) 643770

Alan Williams & Co Bristol Ltd, 4 Bonville Business Centre, Dixon Road, Bristol, BS4 5QQ Tel: 0117-971 7606 Fax: 0117-971 7366 E-mail: bristol@alanwilliams.co.uk *Fans & ventilating equipment distributors*

Alan Yorke Ltd, 4 Midland Business Centre, Bury Close, Higham Ferrers, Rushden, Northamptonshire, NN10 8BE Tel: (01933) 358219 Fax: (01933) 410546 E-mail: sales@alanyorke.co.uk *Manufacturers of rotational moulding machines*

▶ Alanco Motor Services Ltd, Goldmartin Garage, Sampys Mill, Mawnan Smith, Falmouth, Cornwall, TR11 5EW Tel: (01326) 250394 Fax: (01326) 250394 E-mail: info@alanco.co.uk *Car & van servicing, mechanical repairs & breakdown recovery service*

Alanders Hindson Ltd, Merlin Way, New York Business Park, Newcastle upon Tyne, NE27 0YT Tel: 0191-280 0400 Fax: 0191-280 0401 E-mail: info@elandershindson.co.uk *Commercial printers*

▶ Alandola Design, Midton House, By Alloway, Ayr, KA7 4EG Tel: (01292) 442226 Fax: (01292) 442226 E-mail: adrienne@alandola-design.fsworld.co.uk *Hand made quality soft furnishings, curtains, cushions, pelmets*

Alanod Ltd, Chippenham Drive, Kingston, Milton Keynes, MK10 0AN Tel: (01908) 282044 Fax: (01908) 282033 E-mail: alanod@alanod.co.uk *Manufacturers of anodised aluminium coil & sheet.*

▶ Alan-Peters Group, 38 Newton Road, Isleworth, Middlesex, TW7 6QD Tel: 020 8569 9006 Fax: 020 8569 7789 E-mail: info@alan-petersgroup.co.uk *Vehicle collection and delivery UK wide. A long established company we specalise in one trip deliveries using experienced drivers. Vehicles*

continued

Company Information

continuation
are inspected on collection and delivery. Fully comprehensive insurance and breakdown cover. Prompt, reliable, professional and respected service backed up by extremely competative rates.

Alan's Autos, Chapel La, Anslow, Burton-on-Trent, Staffs, DE13 9QA Tel: (01283) 567000 *Repair services*

Alan's Home Care, 22 Upper Wickham Lane, Welling, Kent, DA16 3HE Tel: (020) 8304 0903 *Household products store retailer*

Alansons Industrial Supplies, 7 Flowers Hill, Bristol, BS4 5JJ Tel: 0117-971 1364 Fax: (0870) 7773272 Purchasing Contact: A. Nunn Sales Contact: R. Nunn *Distributors of abrasive/ abrasive products & adhesives. Also adhesive consultants/advisory services & adhesives, industrial*

Alara Health Foods, 58-60 Marchmont Street, London, WC1N 1AB Tel: (020) 7837 1172 Fax: (020) 7833 8089 *Health food shop*

▶ Alard Electrical, Unit 7, Cromwell Road, Bredbury, Stockport, Cheshire, SK6 2RF Tel: 0161-406 6600 Fax: 0161-430 8022

Alaric Systems Ltd, 22-24 Devonshire Street, Keighley, West Yorkshire, BD21 2AU Tel: (01535) 680000 Fax: (01535) 610223 E-mail: sales@alaric.co.uk *Software services*

Alarm Communication Ltd, 1 Westfield Road, Woking, Surrey, GU22 9LZ Tel: (01483) 771186 Fax: (01483) 771861 E-mail: office@alarmcommunication.co.uk *CCTV installation*

Alarm Communications & Electronic Systems Ltd, 121 Stokes Croft, Bristol, BS1 3RW Tel: 0117-924 1344 Fax: 0117-942 0319 *Security systems installation & maintenance*

Alarm Doctor Ltd, 59 Hempstalls Lane, Newcastle, Staffordshire, ST5 0SN Tel: (01782) 633532 *Alarms & closed circuit television suppliers*

▶ Alarm Guard, PO Box 156, Plymouth, PL1 4WY Tel: (0845) 6123130 Fax: (0871) 4332264 E-mail: paul@alarmguard.co.uk *Intruder alarms, cctv & fire alarms*

Alarm Installations, Unit 11 Moorside Maltings, Burton Row, Leeds, LS11 5NX Tel: 0113-271 1944 Fax: 0113-271 1902 *Alarm installation*

▶ Alarm it, 26 Kennett Dr, Leyland, PR25 3QX Tel: 07734 822279 E-mail: Sales@leylec.co.uk *Security systems installed and maintained*

Alarm It Northern UK, Lamport Street, Middlesbrough, Cleveland, TS1 5QL Tel: (01642) 244634 Fax: (01642) 242033 E-mail: autotune@btconnect.com *Garage services*

Alarm Line Security Systems, Bozon Hall, Wash Road, Kirton, Boston, Lincolnshire, PE20 1QJ Tel: (01205) 722838 Fax: (01205) 366755 E-mail: info@alarmline.co.uk *Alarm systems installers*

Alarm Radio Monitoring Ltd, Southern Avenue, Leominster, Herefordshire, HR6 0QF Tel: (01568) 610016 Fax: (01568) 615511 *Radio alarm manufrs*

Alarm Security, 150 Hunter Dr, Bletchley, Milton Keynes, MK2 3NF Tel: 01908 642653 Fax: 01908 642653 *Alarm security installation*

Alarm Shop, 110 Balls Pond Road, London, N1 4AG Tel: (020) 7275 9990 *Vehicle alarm systems installation & service*

Alarm Tech 2000, 42 Edinburgh Drive, Holton-le-Clay, Grimsby, South Humberside, DN36 5DF Tel: (01472) 825555 Fax: (01472) 595044 E-mail: alarm_tech_2000@yahoo.com *Security device installers*

▶ Alarmfast Supervision Security Systems Ltd, 56 Ingram Street, Glasgow, G1 1EX Tel: 0141-564 4400 Fax: 0141-564 4409

Alarmguard Security, 9 Cromwell Centre, Roebuck Road, Ilford, Essex, IG6 3UG Tel: (020) 8559 8989 Fax: (020) 8559 8425 E-mail: srb1625@aol.co.uk *Coin collection security case manufrs*

Alarms For All Premises, Little Adelaide, Lower Road, East Farleigh, Maidstone, Kent, ME15 0JN Tel: (01622) 729439 Fax: 01622 729439 *Security & vinyl signs*

▶ Alarmstrong Security Systems Ltd, 16 Adelaide Road, St. Leonards-on-Sea, East Sussex, TN38 9DA Tel: (01424) 442366 E-mail: info@alarmstrongsecurity.co.uk *Installation of security services*

Alarmtec Ltd, 49 Fore Street, Bradninch, Exeter, EX5 4NN Tel: (01392) 881620 Fax: (01392) 882016 E-mail: alarmtec@alarmtec.co.uk *Fire alarm & extinguishers installation & service*

Alarmwise Burglar Alarm Systems, 37 Littlebeck Drive, Darlington, County Durham, DL1 2TN Tel: (01325) 480254 Fax: (01325) 266804 *Burglar alarm installation & service*

Alasdair Grigor, Albion Works, Fortrose, Ross-Shire, IV10 8SS Tel: (01381) 620571 Fax: (01381) 620571 *Agricultural engineers*

Alasdair W Woods Ltd, Largs, Ayrshire, KA30 8WA Tel: (01475) 673300 Fax: (01475) 673355 *Ice cream manufacturing machinery & refrigeration*

▶ Alaska Estates Ltd, Sitka Drive, Shrewsbury Business Park, Shrewsbury, SY2 6LG Tel: (01743) 343322 Fax: (01743) 343399 E-mail: rita@alaskagroup.com *Property Developers, letting/freehold offices on Shrewsbury Business Park*

Alba plc, Bush House The Waterfront, Elstree Road, Elstree, Borehamwood, Hertfordshire, WD6 3BS Tel: (020) 8238 7660 Fax: (020) 8953 8465 E-mail: albaplc@netcomuk.co.uk *Holding company*

Alba Beverage Co. Ltd, Unit 4, Sauchiebank, Edinburgh, EH11 2NN Tel: 0131-539 2755 Fax: 0131-346 8008 E-mail: albabeverageco@msn.com *Coffee suppliers*

Alba Diagnostics Ltd, Unit 1 Bankhead Avenue, Glenrothes, Fife, KY7 6JG Tel: (01592) 774333 Fax: (01592) 774777 E-mail: marketing@brakefluidtester.com *Manufacturers of garage diagnostic equipment*

▶ Alba Engineering, 2 Camlachie Street, Glasgow, G31 4JH Tel: 0141-554 5831 Fax: 0141-556 4947

▶ Alba Hire & Sales, 5 Broughton Industrial Estate, Broughton Mills Road, Bretton, Chester, CH4 0BY Tel: (01244) 661820 Fax: (01244) 661763

Alba Hydraflow Ltd, Unit 7, Block 4, Woodend Industrial Estate, Cowdenbeath, Fife, KY4 8HW Tel: (01383) 514543 Fax: (01383) 510324 E-mail: sales@albahydraflow.co.uk *Hydraulic hose distributors*

▶ Alba Photography, 54 Milndavie Crescent, Strathblane, Glasgow, G63 9DF Tel: (01360) 770349

▶ Alba Safety Ltd, Unit 6, Mercian Buildings, Shore Road, Perth, PH2 8BD Tel: 01738 629457 Fax: 01738 629543 *A new business providing Head-to-Toe Protective and Safety Clothing, Safety Equipment, Safety Signs, Janitorial Supplies and Leisurewear with complete embroidery and logo service.*

▶ Alba Sailing, Dunbeg, Oban, Argyll, PA37 1PX Tel: (01631) 565630 Fax: (01631) 565620

Alba Self Adhesive Tape Supply Co. Ltd, 10 Rhynie Road, Broughty Ferry, Dundee, DD5 1RH Tel: (01382) 731100 Fax: (01382) 731100 E-mail: frank@albatapes.co.uk *Distributors of self adhesive tapes*

▶ Alba Ultrasound Ltd, Unit 3, Todd Campus, 45 Acre Road, Glasgow, G20 0XA Tel: 0141-946 5000 Fax: 0141-946 5111 E-mail: bwooldridge@albaultrasound.com *Design & manufacture of ultrasonic transducers*

Albacom, George Buckman Drive, Camperdown Industrial Estate, Dundee, DD2 3SP Tel: (01382) 889311 Fax: (01382) 810171 E-mail: sales@albacom.co.uk *Microwave power supplies & electronic component manufrs*

Alban Engineering Services Ltd, Wood Street Passage, Wood Street, Kettering, Northamptonshire, NN16 9SQ Tel: (01536) 513225 Fax: (01536) 513225 *Metal fabricators*

▶ Alban Telecom, Apsley Mill Cottage, London Road, Hemel Hempstead, Hertfordshire, HP3 9QU Tel: (01442) 249900 E-mail: sales@albantelecom.co.uk *Telecommication equipment suppliers*

Albanian Press Ltd, 107 Camp Road, St. Albans, Hertfordshire, AL1 5HL Tel: (01727) 853495 Fax: (01727) 846690 E-mail: info@albanian-press.co.uk *Commercial printers*

Albann Ltd, Unit 69 Third Avenue, Heatherhouse Industrial Estate, Irvine, Ayrshire, KA12 8HN Tel: (01294) 272311 Fax: (01294) 276677 E-mail: sales@albann.co.uk *Aluminium window & door manufrs*

Albann Mckinney Window Co Ltd, Hyde Park, Mallusk, Newtownabbey, County Antrim, BT36 4PX Tel: (028) 9084 2611 Fax: (028) 9034 2317 E-mail: mailbox@mcneill-mcmanus.com *Window manufrs*

Albany Appliances, 16 Albany Road, Cardiff, CF24 3RP Tel: (029) 2048 3168 *Kitchen appliances reconditioning & repairs*

Albany Belt Co., 31-33 Beler Way, Leicester Road Industrial Estate, Melton Mowbray, Leicestershire, LE13 0DG Tel: (01664) 566055 Fax: (01664) 410205 E-mail: albany.belt@btinternet.com *Quality Leather belts, Handbags & Wallets manufacturers made to clients own designs from the best components*

Albany Blind Co., The Albany Boat House, Lower Ham Road, Kingston upon Thames, Surrey, KT2 5BB Tel: (020) 8549 5436 Fax: (020) 8549 5332 E-mail: peter@albany-blind.co.uk *Blinds & canopie suppliers*

Albany Blinds, 1 Murieston Valley, Murieston, Livingston, West Lothian, EH54 9HB Tel: (01506) 420000 Fax: (01506) 420000 *Blinds manufrs*

Albany Fine China Ltd, 75 Water Works Road, Worcester, WR1 3EZ Tel: (01905) 726320 Fax: (01905) 726360 *Ornamental china manufrs*

Albany International Ltd, Pilsworth Road, Bury, Lancashire, BL9 8QE Tel: 0161-767 7531 Fax: 0161-766 2993 *Paper & felt manufrs* Also at: Slough

▶ Albany Investigations Ltd, Albany House, Gannel Road, Newquay, Cornwall, TR7 2AD Tel: 08700 114314 E-mail: albanymc@hotmail.com *Northern Office*Albany House*Cobden Road*Chesterfield*Derbyshire*S40 4TD**We are a well established Company of Private investigators originally established in 1993. Our staff are all ex-police or Military (British) and have relevant experience.*We act for Solicitors, Insurance companies and Council authorities.*Our services include;*Tracing;*Process Serving;*Asset Tracing;*General investigation.**

Albany Lighting, Albany House, New Street, Congleton, Cheshire, CW12 3AH Tel: (01260) 281551 Fax: (01260) 281561 *Lampshade manufrs*

Albany Metal Spinners, 18 Stirling Close, Washington, Tyne & Wear, NE38 8QD Tel: 0191-419 4588 Fax: 0191-416 3700 E-mail: sales@albanymetalspinners.co.uk *Metal spinning services to the industry*

Albany Standard Pumps, Richter Works, Garnett Street, Bradford, West Yorkshire, BD3 9HB Tel: (01274) 725351 Fax: (01274) 742467 E-mail: sales@albany-pumps.co.uk Principal Export Areas: Worldwide *Pump manufacturers including gear & viscous liquid*

Albar Associates, Meridian House, Road One, Winsford, Cheshire, CW7 3QG Tel: (01606) 861351 Fax: (01606) 861643 E-mail: albar@albar-energy.co.uk *Energy monitoring equipment*

Albar Construction Ltd, 115 Burys Bank Road, Crookham Common, Thatcham, Berkshire, RG19 8DE Tel: (01635) 867713 Fax: (01635) 867730 *Steel frame buildings*

▶ Albatops Kitchen Worktops, 47 Accademy Street, Inveerness, Dingwall, Ross-Shire, IV15 1LP Tel: (01463) 663348 Fax: (01463) 711481 E-mail: sales@alarisavenue.co.uk *Kitchen worktops manufrs*

Albatross, 63 Orchard Way, Croydon, CR0 7NQ Tel: (020) 8777 2665 E-mail: albatrossremoval@aol.com *Removals & storage contractors*

Albatross Commercial & Industrial Cleaning Co. Ltd, Marlborough Business Centre, Marlborough Road, London, E18 1AH Tel: (020) 8530 5888 Fax: (020) 8530 4747 E-mail: alb@btconnect.com *Industrial cleaning contractors*

▶ Albatross Models, The Coach House, St. Pauls Walden, Hitchin, Hertfordshire, SG4 8BP Tel: (01438) 871688 Fax: (01438) 871874 E-mail: enquiries@albatrossmodels.co.uk *Models sets & model effects suppliers*

Albe (England) Ltd, 51 Bideford Avenue, Perivale, Greenford, Middlesex, UB6 7PR Tel: (020) 8997 7282 Fax: (020) 8998 2932 E-mail: sales@albe.com *Tungsten carbide tool manufrs*

▶ Albemarle Graphics Ltd, 35 Astbury Road, London, SE15 2NL Tel: (020) 7639 3249 Fax: (020) 7358 0754 E-mail: info@ag-online.co.uk *Sign makers & printers*

Albemarle Interim Management P.L.C., 26-28 Great Portland Street, London, W1W 8QT Tel: (020) 7079 3737 Fax: (020) 7631 1881 E-mail: managers@albemarle.co.uk *Interim management services*

Albemarle UK Ltd, Teesport, Middlesbrough, Cleveland, TS6 7SA Tel: (01642) 463314 Fax: (01642) 463315 *Chemical manufrs* Also at: Bude

Albert E Chapman Ltd, 17 Crouch Hill, London, N4 4AP Tel: (020) 7272 2536 Fax: (020) 7263 1033 *Upholsterers & curtain manufrs*

Albert Harrison Company Ltd, Queens Road, Accrington, Lancashire, BB5 6DS Tel: (01254) 306840 Fax: (01254) 872174 E-mail: sales@albert-harrison.co.uk *Supply over 5000 products to the retail trade. Online ordering of World Cup,toys, health & beauty, gifts, Stationery & non prescription medicines. FREE DELIVERY on orders over £0 UK TRADE ONLY*

Albert Hartley Ltd, Crownest Mill, Skipton Road, Barnoldswick, Lancashire, BB18 5RH Tel: (01282) 666000 Fax: (01282) 666002 E-mail: ssmith@alberthartley.co.uk *Textile printing services*

Albert Jones Textiles Ltd, 51-53 Richmond Street, Manchester, M1 3WB Tel: 0161-236 4043 Fax: 0161-236 0434 *Furnishing fabrics & textile merchants*

Albert Looms Ltd, Megaloughton Lane, Spondon, Derby, DE21 7ND Tel: (01332) 673663 Fax: (01332) 660430 *Scrap iron & steel merchants*

Albert Martin & Co. Ltd, Kirkby Road, Sutton-in-Ashfield, Nottinghamshire, NG17 1GP Tel: (01623) 441122 Fax: (01623) 551037 *Underwear & leisurewear manufrs*

▶ Albert & Son Ltd, 9 Whitechapel Road, London, E1 1DU Tel: (020) 7247 3948 Fax: 0207 2476303 *Ladies Clothing Wholesale and*manufacture*

Albert Taylor & Sons,Limited, Thames House, Thames Street, Rotherham, South Yorkshire, S60 1LU Tel: (01709) 515131 Fax: (01709) 515135 E-mail: info@taylorsprint.com *Continuous stationery printers*

▶ Alberti Ltd, Allenbrook Road, Rosehill Industrial Estate, Carlisle, CA1 2UT Tel: (01228) 533965 Fax: (01228) 514983

Alberto-Culver Co. (UK) Ltd, Lime Tree Way, Hampshire International Business Park, Chineham, Basingstoke, Hampshire, RG24 8ER Tel: (01256) 705000 Fax: (01256) 705001 *Hair care & toiletries products*

▶ Albertronic, Unit 305 Vale Enterprise Centre, Hayes Road, Sully, Penarth, South Glamorgan, CF64 5SY Tel: (01446) 709000 Fax: (01446) 709002 *Telecommunication systems & equipment manufrs*

The Albion, Station Road, Caythorpe, Grantham, Lincolnshire, NG32 3EW Tel: (01400) 272726 Fax: (01400) 273508 E-mail: caythorpe@albionwaterheaters.com *Hot water units manufrs*

Albion Architectural Concrete Ltd, Newbrook Works, Pound Lane, Upper Beeding, Steyning, West Sussex, BN44 3JD Tel: (01903) 815262 Fax: (01903) 815619 E-mail: mike@albionart.co.uk *Manufactures of pre-cast architectural concrete*

Albion Automotive Ltd, Lancashire Enterprises Business Park, Centurian Way, Leyland, PR26 6TZ Tel: (01772) 831400 Fax: (01772) 831401 Principal Export Areas: Worldwide *Precision metal heat treatment service & specialist crankshaft manufrs*

Albion Chemicals Ltd, 46-50 Sydney Street West, Belfast, BT13 3GX Tel: (028) 9078 7450 Fax: (028) 9075 2500 E-mail: sales@albionchemicals.co.uk *Industrial chemicals suppliers*

Albion Chemicals Ltd, Bristol Road, Portishead, Bristol, BS20 6QG Tel: (01275) 844518 Fax: (01275) 818041 *Industrial chemical distributors*

▶ Albion Chemicals Ltd, Union Mills, Oxford Road, Gomersal, Cleckheaton, West Yorkshire, BD19 4JW Tel: (01274) 850300 Fax: (01274) 851252 E-mail: enquiries@albionchemicals.co.uk

▶ Albion Chemicals Ltd, Union Mills, Oxford Road, Gomersal, Cleckheaton, West Yorkshire, BD19 4JW Tel: (01274) 850300 Fax: (01274) 851252 E-mail: enquiries@albionchemicals.co.uk *Chemical distributors*

Albion Chemicals, Pensnett House, Second Avenue, Pensnett Trading Estate, Kingswinford, West Midlands, DY6 7PP Tel: (01384) 400222 Fax: (01384) 400020 E-mail: sales@brenntag.co.uk *Chemical merchants*

▶ Albion Chemicals Ltd, Albion House Warden Park, Green Lane, Yeadon, Leeds, LS19 7XX Tel: 0113-387 9200 Fax: 0113-387 9280 E-mail: enquiries@albionchemicals.co.uk *Chemical distributors*

Albion Chemicals Ltd, Albion House Warden Park, Green Lane, Yeadon, Leeds, LS19 7XX Tel: 0113-387 9200 E-mail: comm@hayschem.co.uk *Chemical manufrs* Also at: Branches throughout the U.K.

Albion Colours Ltd, High Level Way, Halifax, West Yorkshire, HX1 4PN Tel: (01422) 358431 Fax: (01422) 330867 E-mail: colours.sales@albionchemicals.co.uk *Textile & paper colours manufrs* Also at: Branches throughout the U.K.

Albion Computers P.L.C., 112 Strand, London, WC2R 0AG Tel: (020) 7212 9090 Fax: (020) 7212 9091 E-mail: sales@albion.co.uk *Microcomputers & computer software agents*

Albion Cooling Systems Ltd, 33 Albion Road, Westcliff-on-Sea, Essex, SS0 7DP Tel: (01702) 392361 Fax: (01702) 392361 E-mail: info@albioncoolingsystems.com *Evaporative cooling equipment suppliers*

Albion Design of Cambridge Ltd, 131 Mereside, Soham, Ely, Cambridgeshire, CB7 5EG Tel: (01223) 836128 Fax: (01353) 722567 E-mail: sales@albionspirals.co.uk *Spiral staircase manufrs*

Albion Distribution Ltd, Unit 9a Fall Bank Industrial Estate, Dodworth, Barnsley, South Yorkshire, S75 3LS Tel: (01226) 729900 Fax: (01226) 288011 E-mail: dist@albiongroup.co.uk *Gas, ball valve & pipe distributors*

Albion Dyestuffs Ltd, Rook Lane Mills, Law Street, Bradford, West Yorkshire, BD4 9NF Tel: (01274) 652907 Fax: (01274) 689359 E-mail: albiondyestuffs@aol.com *Dyestuff manufrs*

Albion Electric Stores Ltd, South Accommodation Road, Leeds, LS10 1PR Tel: 0113-245 0196 Fax: 0113-234 1408 E-mail: sales@albionelectric.co.uk *Electrical wholesalers*

▶ Albion Electrical & Mechanical Engineering, 15, Parkfield Avenue, Warrington, WA4 1NY Tel: (01925) 636010 Fax: (01925) 575777 E-mail: albioneng@btconnect.com *Refrigeration engineers*

Albion Extrusions Ltd, Penrose Works, Penrose Street, Bolton, BL2 6DX Tel: (01204) 385803 Fax: (01204) 385816 E-mail: info@albionextrusions.co.uk *Kitchen furniture & plastic extrusions*

Albion Fencing Ltd, 2239 London Road, Glasgow, G32 8XL Tel: 0141-778 1672 Fax: 0141-778 6688 E-mail: info@albionfencing.co.uk *Fencing contractors*

▶ Albion Homefinders Yorkshire Ltd, 31 Moor Lane, Addingham, Ilkley, West Yorkshire, LS29 0PS Tel: (01943) 831807 E-mail: info@albionhomefinders.co.uk *Albion Homefinders provides property search and related relocation services to corporate and private clients wishing to buy or let a home in Yorkshire.*We specialise in the areas of Leeds, Harrogate, York, Ilkley Otley, Thirsk, Ripon, Bradford, Skipton, Malton, Pickering, Whitby, Scarborough and the Yorkshire Dales.*

Albion Hose Ltd, Albion Works, Alma Street, Smethwick, West Midlands, B66 2RL Tel: 0121-565 4103 Fax: 0121-558 7220 E-mail: sales@albionhose.co.uk *Hydraulic hose distributors*

Albion Joinery, Albion Works, 23 Rectory Gro, Croydon, CR0 4JA Tel: (020) 8667 0067 Fax: (020) 8667 1267 *Joinery manufrs*

▶ Albion Machinery Ltd, Unit 57a The Washford Industrial Estate, Heming Road, Redditch, Worcestershire, B98 0DH Tel: (01527) 517928 Fax: (01527) 517912 E-mail: info@albionmac.co.uk *Printing press manufrs*

Albion Manufacturing Ltd, The Granary, Silfield Road, Wymondham, Norfolk, NR18 9AU Tel: (01953) 605983 Fax: (01953) 606764 E-mail: sales@albionmanufacturing.com *LIVE CATCH TRAPS - FOR EVERYTHING-MANUFACTURERS*

▶ Albion Preservation, 10 Carlton Grange, 20 Alness Road, Whalley Range, Manchester, M16 8FX Tel: 0161-232 9304 Fax: 0161-232 9304 E-mail: frank2329304@aol.com *damp proof course rot and woodworm lateral strapping and lintels*

Albion Press, 41a Justice Street, Aberdeen, AB11 5HS Tel: (01224) 644242 Fax: (01224) 644060 E-mail: info@albionpress.fsnet.co.uk *Printers*

Albion Printers, 3 Bearsted Green Business Centre, The Green, Bearsted, Maidstone, Kent, ME14 4DF Tel: (01622) 631666 *Lithographic printers*

▶ Albion Robotics Ltd, 6 Castletown, Portland, Dorset, DT5 1BD Tel: (01305) 826384 Fax: (01305) 826056 E-mail: shipping@albiongroup.org *Shipping agents*

Albion Saddlemakers, 17-21 Bridgeman Street, Walsall, WS2 9PG Tel: (01922) 646210 Fax: (01922) 643777 E-mail: sales@albionsaddlemakers.co.uk *Saddlery manufrs*

Albion Section Ltd, Albion Road, West Bromwich, West Midlands, B70 8BD Tel: 0121-553 1877 Fax: 0121-553 5507 E-mail: albionsections@enterprise.net Principal Export Areas: Worldwide *Cold rolled steel sections manufrs*

▶ Albion Service, 9 Silverwood Way, Up Hatherley, Cheltenham, Gloucestershire, GL51 3TW Tel: (01242) 254771 Fax: (01242) 254771 E-mail: albionservice@btopenworld.com

Albion Spring Co Ltd, Oldbury Road, West Bromwich, West Midlands, B70 9EE Tel: 0121-557 3081 Fax: 0121-520 4983 E-mail: sales@albionspring.co.uk *Springs, pressings & wire forms manufrs*

Albion Tower Properties Ltd, 177 Greets Green Road, West Bromwich, West Midlands, B70 9ET Tel: 0121-557 4000 Fax: 0121-522 2703 *Building access equipment & scaffold hire services*

Albion Transmission, Unit 5 Industry Road, Carlton, Barnsley, South Yorkshire, S71 3PQ Tel: (01226) 726200 Fax: (01226) 726979 *Bearing distributors, agents & stockholders*

Albion Water Heaters, Shelah Road, Halesowen, West Midlands, B63 3PG Tel: 0121-585 5151 Fax: 0121-501 3826 E-mail: sales@albionwaterheaters.com *Copper cylinder manufrs*

▶ Albion Water Management Ltd, 30/31 Station Close, Potters Bar, Hertfordshire, EN6 1TL Tel: (01707) 607230 Fax: (01707) 607235 E-mail: water@albiongroup.co.uk *Manufacturers of pressurisation units & oxygen analysers*

Albion Welding & Fabrication, Unit 27 North Pontypool Industrial Park, Pontnewynydd, Pontypool, Gwent, NP4 6PB Tel: (01495) 750180 Fax: (01495) 769819 E-mail: arsamins@btconnect.com *Steel fabricators & welders*

Albol Electronic & Mechanical Products Ltd, Crown Buildings, Crown Street, London, SE5 0UR Tel: (020) 7703 2311 Fax: (020) 7703 3282 E-mail: sales@albol.co.uk *Thermal circuit breakers*

Albon Engineering & Munfacturing plc, Roche Hall Way, Rochford, Essex, SS4 1JU Tel: (01702) 530500 Fax: (01702) 547618 E-mail: malcolm-webster@albonplc.com *Engineers*

ALBRI FASHION ACCESSORIES, 69 Thornham Street, Greenwich, London, SE10 9SB Tel: (07957) 254825 Fax: (0870) 242 0473 E-mail: info@albrifashion.com *Fashion accessories, handbags, hats, shoes & sea shell jewellery*

Albright Engineers Ltd, 125 Red Lion Road, Surbiton, Surrey, KT6 7QS Tel: (020) 8390 5357 Fax: (020) 8390 1927 E-mail: sales@albright.co.uk *Switchgear manufrs* Also at: Whitchurch

Albro Dyco Gravfil, Henwood Industrial Estate, Ashford, Kent, TN24 8DH Tel: (01233) 629161 Fax: (01233) 639560 E-mail: ashfordsales@bradmanlake.com *Liquid & powder filling machinery manufrs*

Albro Windows, Albro House, 59 Palmerston Road, Harrow, Middlesex, HA3 7RR Tel: (020) 8863 7383 Fax: (020) 8427 6248 *Aluminium framed windows & doors upvc manufrs*

Albroco Ltd, Unit C28 Ashmount Enterprise Park, Aber Road, Flint, Clwyd, CH6 5YL Tel: (01352) 734182 Fax: (01352) 734159 E-mail: sales@albrocos.co.uk *Hydraulic motor distributors*

Albury Lodge Ltd, 5 Fieldings Road, Cheshunt, Waltham Cross, Hertfordshire, EN8 9TR Tel: (01992) 620107 Fax: (01992) 621879 E-mail: alburylodgeltd@btconnect.com *Albury Lodge based in Cheshunt, Hertfordshire are manufacturers of pre-cast concrete and artificial stone products. Albury Lodge can manufacture a wide range of products in pre-cast concrete or artificial stone to customer specification. Some of the products Albury Lodge can manufacture include: Pre-cast concrete columns, natural stone columns, architectural columns, concrete balustrades, stone balustrades, concrete balconies, concrete lintels, architectural stonework, ornamental stonework, ornamental concrete products, artificial stone products and a wide range of other pre-cast concrete products. Albury Lodge work throughout Hertfordshire, Essex, Middlesex, Bedfordshire, London, Buckinghamshire, Cambridgeshire, Kent and surrounding areas. To discuss your requirements please contact us and quote "Kellysearch"*

Albury S I Ltd, Miltons Yard, Petworth Road, Witley, Godalming, Surrey, GU8 5LH Tel: (01428) 684836 Fax: (01428) 685261 E-mail: info@alburysi.co.uk *Geotechnical site & contamination surveyors services*

▶ Albyn of Stonehaven Ltd, Davidson House, Campus 1, Aberdeen Science And Technology Park, Bridge Of Don, Aberdeen, AB22 8GT Tel: (01224) 335800 Fax: (01224) 335801 E-mail: info@albyn-int.com *New product development services*

Alcad, 1st Floor Unit 5 Astra Centre, Edinburgh Way, Harlow, Essex, CM20 2BN Tel: (01279) 772555 Fax: (01279) 420696 E-mail: carter.sarah@alcad.com

Alcan Packaging, 83 Tower Road North, Warmley, Bristol, BS30 8XP Tel: 0117-958 2200 Fax: 0117-958 2206 E-mail: sarah.harriman@alcan.com *Printing & packaging manufrs*

Alcan Packaging Corby Ltd, 5 Adderlade House, Corby Gate Business Park, Corby, Northamptonshire, NN17 5JG Tel: (01536) 400500 Fax: (01536) 400333 *Plastic, aluminium & laminated tubes manufrs*

Alcan Packaging (Cumbria), Salterbeck Trading Estate, Salterbeck, Workington, Cumbria, CA14 5DX Tel: (01946) 839600 Fax: (01946) 830199 E-mail: sales@alcanpackaging.com *Flexible packaging manufrs* Also at: Workington

Alcan Packaging Materials, The Sawmill, Eridge Road, Eridge Green, Tunbridge Wells, Kent, TN3 9JR Tel: (01892) 509100 Fax: (01892) 509190 *Aluminum foil & flexible packaging suppliers*

Alcan Primary Europe, Lochaber Smelter, Fort William, Inverness-Shire, PH33 6TH Tel: (01397) 902233 Fax: (01397) 902200 *Aluminium smelter suppliers*

Alcan Smelting & Power (UK), Lynemouth Smelter, Ashington, Northumberland, NE63 9YH Tel: (01670) 393811 Fax: (01670) 393956 *Aluminium smelting*

▶ Alcatel Electronics, Starlaw Park, Starlaw Road, Livingston, West Lothian, EH54 8SF Tel: (01506) 426000 *Manufacture devices for broadband*

▶ Alcatel Optronics UK Ltd, Starlaw Park, Livingston, West Lothian, EH54 9SF Tel: (01506) 426000

Alcatel Submarine Networks Ltd, Christchurch Way, London, SE10 0AG Tel: (020) 8293 2000 Fax: (020) 8293 2433 *Underwater cable systems manufrs*

Alcatel Telecom Ltd, Bulding N140, Christchurch Way, London, SE10 0AG Tel: (0870) 9033600 Fax: (020) 8293 2433 Principal Export Areas: Worldwide *Communication services*

Alcester Broach & Tool Co. Ltd, Pipers Road, Park Farm Industrial Estate, Redditch, Worcestershire, B98 0HU Tel: (01527) 523107 Fax: (01527) 526137 E-mail: sales@alcesterbroach.com *Broach Tool Design, Manufacture, and Service. Sub-Contract Broaching Services.*

Alchemie Ltd, Warwick Road, Kineton, Warwick, CV35 0HU Tel: (01926) 640600 Fax: (01926) 641698 E-mail: sales@alchemie.com *Alchemie Limited, based in Kineton UK distributes a full product range of materials designed for the automotive, ceramics, model making, electrical encapsulation and rapid prototyping industries. Our product range consists of epoxy resins, polyurethane resins, silicones, modelboards, sheet wax and vacuum casting materials.*

Alchemy Lettering Co. Ltd, 11-15 Wade Street, Bristol, BS2 9DR Tel: 0117-941 1800 Fax: 0117-941 2800 E-mail: alchemyltd@btconnect.com *Sign makers*

Alchemy Plus, Halliday House, Dingwall Business Park, Dingwall, Ross-Shire, IV15 9XL Tel: (01349) 865000 Fax: (01349) 865111 E-mail: info@alchemyplus.com *Computer consultants & networking*

Alcina Engineering, Wetherby Road, Ascot Drive, Derby, DE24 8HL Tel: (01332) 343435 Fax: (01332) 385722 *Precision engineers*

Alco Beldan Ltd, Accordial House, 35 Watford Metro Centre, Watford, WD18 9XN Tel: (01923) 246600 Fax: (01923) 245654 E-mail: enquiries@alcobeldan.com *Acoustic movable wall system manufrs*

Alco Builders World, Midhill Road, Sheffield, S2 3GW Tel: 0114-255 0021 Fax: 0114-255 6681 E-mail: email-sales@sheffield.timberworld.co.uk *Builders merchants*

Alco Electric Hairdryer Repairs, Fernhill Road, Solihull, West Midlands, B92 7RU Tel: 0121-706 1404 Fax: 0121-706 1404 *Hair dryer equipment repairs*

Alco Engineering (Sheet Metal) Co.Ltd, High Bullen, St. Giles, Torrington, Devon, EX38 7JA Tel: (01805) 622461 Fax: (01805) 624011 E-mail: sales@alcoeng.co.uk *Sheet metalworkers*

Alco Leather Ltd, Crank Mills, Station Road, Morley, Leeds, LS27 8JR Tel: 0113-252 4644 Fax: 0113-238 3205 *Leather goods manufrs*

▶ Alco Valves Ltd, Mission Works, Birds Royd Lane, Brighouse, West Yorkshire, HD6 1LQ Tel: 01484 710511 Fax: 01484 713009 E-mail: uk@alco-valves.com *Suppliers and Manufacturers of a complete range of Industrial valves,(Ball, Needle, Check etc etc),with a long history of supplying the petrochemical industry. Alco Valves operate under ISO9001, plus appear on the Lloyds register. Alco Valves are able to supply valves which are CE marked and comply with the Pressure Equipment Requirements PED 97/23/EC & PER (Si1999 No. 2001). Alco Valves also subscribe to Achilles and 1stPoint Assessment.*

Alco Waste Management Ltd, Joseph Noble Road, Lillyhall Industrial Estate, Lillyhall, Workington, Cumbria, CA14 4JH Tel: (01900) 602205 Fax: (01900) 601886 *Waste disposal contractors*

Alcoa C S I (UK) Ltd, Kelvin Way, West Bromwich, West Midlands, B70 7LB Tel: 0121-532 5000 Fax: 0121-553 3710 E-mail: ciaran.martin@alcoa.com *Soft drink & spirit closure manufrs*

Alcoa (Europe), Southam Road, Banbury, Oxfordshire, OX16 2SN Tel: (01295) 454444 Fax: (01295) 454454 Principal Export Areas: Worldwide *Aluminium alloy tube & extrusion scaffolding stockholders & manufrs*

Alcoa Europe Flat Rolled Products, Clark Street, Dolgarrog, Conwy, Gwynedd, LL32 8JH Tel: (01492) 614200 Fax: (01492) 614294 E-mail: info@dolgarrog.com *Non-ferrous rolled metal products*

Alcoa Fastening Systems Ltd, Stafford Park 7, Telford, Shropshire, TF3 3BQ Tel: (01952) 290011 Fax: (01952) 290459 E-mail: info@huck.co.uk *Industrial fasteners for industrial industry*

Alcom Computing, 84 The Broadway, High Street, Chesham, Buckinghamshire, HP5 1EG Tel: (01494) 784784 Fax: (01494) 778424 E-mail: sales@alcomcomputing.com *Computer maintenance & repair services*

Alcon Components Ltd, Concentric Park, Apollo, Tamworth, Staffordshire, B79 7TN Tel: (01827) 723700 Fax: (01827) 723701 E-mail: info@alcon.co.uk *Specialist brakes & clutches manufrs*

Alda Plastics, Unit 13 Monks Brook Indust P, School Close, Chandler's Ford, Eastleigh, Hampshire, SO53 4RA Tel: (023) 8027 3396 Fax: (023) 8027 3496 *Specialist in plastic fabrication*

Alda Production Services Ltd, 14 Deanfield Court, Links 59 Business Park, Clitherhall, Rossendale, Lancashire, BB7 1QS Tel: (01200) 444354 Fax: (01200) 444359 E-mail: alda@alda.co.uk *Electrical assembly services*

▶ Aldanca Wine, 19 Mountbatten Court, Raleigh Close, New Milton, Hampshire, BH25 5LB Tel: 01425 621733 Fax: 01425 618440 E-mail: marketing@aldanca-wine.co.uk *We at Aldanca Wine are a company dedicated to offering you the unique pleasure of tasting and enjoying the Portuguese Wines. Portugal is one of the best wine regions in the world, full of history and amazing wines.**Aldanca Wine want you to get pleasure from drinking our wines. Therefore we pride ourselves on providing Portugal"s best wines.**Aldanca Wine are an independent and innovating company, trading only in Portuguese wines, combining high technology with a high product level.**We aim to provide you the highest levels of satisfaction in our products.**We are confident that we have the products and prices to fully satisfy your requirements.*

Aldas Trophies & Glass Engraving, 72 High Street, Ringwood, Hampshire, BH24 1AQ Tel: (01425) 479822 Fax: (01425) 479822 E-mail: mail@aldaglassengraving.com *Trophies, medals & rosette manufrs & glass engraving*

▶ Aldcroft Adhesives Ltd, Unit 13A Horwich Loco Industrial Estate, Chorley New Road, Horwich, Bolton, BL6 5UE Tel: (01204) 668282 Fax: (01204) 668780 E-mail: info@aldcroftadhesives.com *Adhesive manufacturers including hot melt & woodworking*

Aldebaran Print & Design, 1 Ariane, Tamworth, Staffordshire, B79 7XF Tel: (01827) 50417 Fax: (01827) 63773 E-mail: info@myprinters.co.uk *General printers*

Aldebaran Systems Ltd, Unit 47 Cressex Enterprise Centre, Lincoln Road, High Wycombe, Buckinghamshire, HP12 3RL Tel: (01494) 614630 E-mail: info@aldebaran.co.uk *Computer software developers*

Aldeburgh Boatyard Co. Ltd, Fort Green, Aldeburgh, Suffolk, IP15 5DE Tel: (01728) 452019 Fax: (01728) 452019 *Boat builders & repairers*

Aldeby Painting Services Ltd, Britannia Way, Thurmaston, Leicester, LE4 8JY Tel: 0116-269 5699 Fax: 0116-260 2887 E-mail: kevin.aldeby@virgin.net *Shot blasters & painters*

Alden Cabinet Designs, 6 Marlborough Business Centre, Marlborough Road, Lancing, West Sussex, BN15 8TP Tel: (01903) 765521 Fax: (01903) 851087 *Cabinet makers*

Aldenham Gearbox Services, 85-87 Sydney Road, Watford, WD18 7XZ Tel: (01923) 254273 Fax: (01923) 460251 E-mail: iagsgearboxes@btclick.com *Gear box repairs & services*

Alder Sportswear Ltd, Alder, Lewdown, Okehampton, Devon, EX20 4PJ Tel: (01566) 783444 Fax: (01566) 783483 *Manufacturers of sportswear*

▶ Alder Timber, Tsitika, 9 Torgormack, Beauly, Inverness-Shire, IV4 7AQ Tel: (01463) 783355 Fax: (01463) 783366

Alderbury Forge, Old Road, Alderbury, Salisbury, SP5 3AR Tel: (01722) 711027 Fax: (01722) 711026 *Blacksmiths*

▶ Aldercote Ltd, The Embankment, Woodhouse Street, Hull, HU9 1RJ Tel: (01482) 222377 Fax: (020) 7681 3117 E-mail: sales@aldercote.com *Commercial coach builders special vehicle engineers & servicing*

Alderdale Fixing Systems, New John Street, Halesowen, West Midlands, B62 8HT Tel: 0121-561 5500 Fax: 0121-561 3535 E-mail: sales@alderdale.com *Designers & manufacturers of masonry support services*

▶ Alderdesigns, 79 Forrestal Street, Edzell, Brechin, Angus, DD9 7XG Tel: (01356) 648069 E-mail: phil.alder@alderdesigns.co.uk *Web design & solutions*

▶ Alderglade Picture Framers, The Alderglade, Harefield Road, Uxbridge, Middlesex, UB8 1PN Tel: (01895) 231205 E-mail: john@alderglade.com *We manufacture all types of picture frames and have a mobile service within a 15 mile radius of our workshop in Uxbridge.*Our prices are competitive.*

▶ Alderley P.L.C., Alderley House, Arnolds Field Estate,, The Downs,, Wickwar,, Wotton-Under-Edge, Gloucestershire, GL12 8JD Tel: (01454) 294556 Fax: (01454) 299272 E-mail: marketing@alderley.com *Design & manufacturers of oil & gas metering systems*

Alderley plc, Alderley House, Arnolds Field Estate, Wotton-under-Edge, Gloucestershire, GL12 8JD Tel: (01454) 299888 Fax: (01454) 299720 E-mail: marketing@alderley.com *Engineering services & skid mounted process equipment to the oil and gas, energy, chemical & process industries*

▶ Alderley Materials Ltd, Station Road, Berkeley, Gloucestershire, GL13 9RL Tel: (01453) 511600 Fax: (01453) 810108 E-mail: marketing@alderley.com *Fire protective material manufrs*

Aldermaston Signs, Unit 24 Youngs Industrial Estate, Paices Hill, Aldermaston, Reading, RG7 4PW Tel: 0118-981 1170 Fax: 0118-981 7690 E-mail: info@aldermastonsigns.co.uk *Sign makers*

Alderney Plating Ltd, Thrush Road, Poole, Dorset, BH12 4NP Tel: (01202) 744664 Fax: (01202) 733577 *Anodising, electroplating & polishing agents*

▶ Alders of Corsham, 61 Northleaze, Bradford Road, Corsham, Wiltshire, SN13 0QP Tel: (01249) 713939 Fax: (01249) 701845 E-mail: bookings@aldersofcorsham.co.uk *Courier service*

Aldersbrook Engineering, B Ajax Works, Hertford Road, Barking, Essex, IG11 8DY Tel: (020) 8591 0685 Fax: (020) 8591 9388 E-mail: enquiries@aldersbrook-engineering.com *Machining services sub-contract & CNC milling & turning services CNC*

Aldersgate Technical Mouldings, Ebblake Industrial Estate, Verwood, Dorset, BH31 6AU Tel: (01202) 825454 Fax: (01202) 827516 E-mail: paul@aldersgateplastics.com *Manufacturers of plastic injection mouldings*

▶ Alderside Engineering, Biggar Road, Cleland, Motherwell, Lanarkshire, ML1 5PB Tel: (01698) 860157 Fax: (01698) 861966 *Engineering manufactures & repairs*

▶ Aldersley Battery Chairs Ltd, New Cross Street, Wednesbury, West Midlands, WS10 7ST Tel: 0121-568 8999

▶ Alderson Building Services, Whitehouse Lane, Ushaw Moor, Durham, DH7 7PG Tel: 0191-373 0393 Fax: 0191-373 6762

Aldersons (Northampton) Ltd, 4 William St, Northampton, NN1 3EW Tel: (01604) 639346 Fax: (01604) 638542 E-mail: aldersonsltd@aol.com *Aldersons are manufacturers of industrial leather components & leather strapping. Our product range includes: Leather belting, Leather cutting services, Leather Elbow patches, Industrial leather components, Leather luggage tags, Leather Straps, Leather shoulder straps. We can also provide Bespoke leather services.*

Albert Alderton, Town Cross Avenue, Bognor Regis, West Sussex, PO21 2DP Tel: (01243) 824700 Fax: (01243) 821482 *Recycling metal merchant*

Alderwicks Ltd, Clay Lane, Haverfordwest, Dyfed, SA61 1UH Tel: (01437) 762298 Fax: (01437) 765195 *Soft drink manufrs*

▶ Aldex Software Ltd, 6 High Street, Sutton, Ely, Cambridgeshire, CB6 2RB Tel: (01353) 778012 Fax: (01353) 776055 E-mail: devlabs@aldex.co.uk *Computer software manufrs*

Aldon Automotive Ltd, Breener Industrial Estate, Station Drive, Brierley Hill, West Midlands, DY5 3JZ Tel: (01384) 572553 Fax: (01384) 480418 E-mail: alden@yesit.co.uk *Motor vehicle tuning & spares* Also at: Hartlebury & Worcester

Aldon Brearley Print, The Engine House, Ashley Lane, Shipley, West Yorkshire, BD17 7DB Tel: (01274) 583192 Fax: (01274) 532862 E-mail: aldon.brearley@btconnet.co.uk *Wholesale printers & stationers*

Aldona Seals, 1 Brindley Road, South West Industrial Estate, Peterlee, County Durham, SR8 2LT Tel: 0191-518 1555 Fax: 0191-518 0555 E-mail: gtsm@gtgroup.co.uk *Rubber Mouldings*Hydraulic & Pneumatic Seals*Rubber to Metal Bonded Products*Offshore seals - up to 1.5m dia*GRP Offshore Light Canopies*GRP Lighting Canopies*GRP HiFi Speaker Baffles*

▶ Aldous Associates, 4 Aldous Way, Sheffield, S26 6SH Tel: (01909) 515414 E-mail: aldousmail@tesco.net *Friendly, professional consultancy offering practical guidance and assistance in areas of quality health & safety and environmental management. Services include (but not limited to) policy, systems and procedure development, risk assessment work, auditing/inspections, employee training and advisor service.*

Fred Aldous Ltd, Handicraft Centre, 37 Lever Street, Manchester, M1 1LW Tel: 0161-236 2477 Fax: 0161-236 6075 E-mail: aldous@btinternet.com Principal Export Areas: Worldwide *Hobby craft & hobby materials suppliers*

Aldridge Bros Sheetmetal Ltd, Balfour Road, Altrincham, Cheshire, WA14 5LS Tel: 0161-928 4810 Fax: 0161-941 7765 *Steel fabricators & sheet metalwork*

▶ Aldridge Fabrications Ltd, Mount Road, Burntwood, Staffordshire, WS7 0AX Tel: (01543) 682121 Fax: (01543) 674680 E-mail: davidneville@aldridge-fabrications.co.uk *Steel fabrications*

Aldridge Holdings Ltd, Silca House, 32-34 Eagle Wharf Road, London, N1 7EG Tel: (020) 7253 5665 Fax: (020) 7251 2601 E-mail: sales@e-aldridge.co.uk *Wholesale locksmiths* Also at: Manchester

Aldridge Mechanical Services, 244 Goldcroft, Yeovil, Somerset, BA21 4DA Tel: (01935) 420162 Fax: (01935) 420162 *Air conditioning & central heating contractors*

Aldridge Piling Equipment Hire Co. Ltd, Conduit Road, Norton Canes, Cannock, Staffordshire, WS11 9TJ Tel: (01543) 277680 Fax: (01543) 270090 E-mail: info@miniape.com *Piling plant hirers & manufacturers of piling equipment*

Aldridge & Son Wholesale Ltd, 50 Queen Street, Salford, M3 7DQ Tel: 0161-828 0828 Fax: 0161-828 0838 E-mail: sales@e-aldridge.co.uk *Wholesale lock factors*

Aldridge & Trillwood Ltd, 12 Railway Approach, East Grinstead, West Sussex, RH19 1BP Tel: (01342) 322519 Fax: (01342) 322519 *Decorators merchants* Also at: Edenbridge & Hastings

Aldrington Body Care, 8 Basin Road North, Portslade, Brighton, BN41 1WA Tel: (01273) 411312 Fax: (01273) 430836 E-mail: juliagraeme@aol.com *Car body repairers*

Aldruscilla, 8 Deer Park Road, London, SW19 3UU Tel: (020) 8543 8710 Fax: (020) 8543 0605 E-mail: metal@aldruscilla.co.uk *Aldruscilla Ltd are the nation's leading specialist non ferrous metal & ferrous metal stockholding company supplying materials nation and worldwide. We are based in Merton, London, England specializing in supply of non standard metals, obsolete metals and unusual specifications of metals. We also provide fabrication and machining services for "one offs" to multiple quantities. Aldruscilla Ltd provides an excellent service in both the technical advice given and the supply of the correct products, for your specific needs.*

Aldwick Doors & Windows, 59 Sunnymead Drive, Selsey, Chichester, West Sussex, PO20 0DG Tel: (01243) 778557 Fax: (01243) 778557 E-mail: sales@aldwickdoorsandwindows.co.uk *Joiners*

Alec Williams, Forden, Welshpool, Powys, SY21 8TS Tel: (01938) 580329 Fax: (01938) 580329 *Farming contractors*

Aleck J Shone, 16 High Street, Saltney, Chester, CH4 8SE Tel: (01244) 683531 Fax: (01244) 659770 *Electrical contractors & security system installers*

Aleena Pool & Snooker Services, 1 Golden Triangle Industrial Estate, Hale Road, Widnes, Cheshire, WA8 8TN Tel: 0151-420 8071 Fax: 0151-420 8071 *Pool & snooker table repairs & sales*

Alembic Ltd, Unit 6, Wimbourne Buildings, Atlantic Way, Barry, South Glamorgan, CF63 3RA Tel: (01446) 733174 Fax: (01446) 733184 E-mail: david@alembic.freeserve.co.uk *Aluminium chlorohydrate producers*

▶ Alert 24 Hour Plumbing Services Ltd, 11 Dumgoyne Drive, Bearsden, Glasgow, G61 3AP Tel: 0141-942 0103

Alert Alarms, 16 Church Parade, Canvey Island, Essex, SS8 9RQ Tel: (01268) 696534 Fax: (01268) 680785 E-mail: alertalarms@blueyonder.co.uk *Security systems*

Alert Electrical Wholesalers Ltd, Unit 2/3, Clarendon Court, Manners Industrial Estate, Ilkeston, Derbyshire, DE7 8EF Tel: 0115 944 4664 Fax: 0115 944 4345 E-mail: martin@alertelectrical.com *UK wholesalers, distributors and suppliers to trade and retail of discounted electrical supplies, burglar alarms, lighting, switches, cctv, wiring accessories Alert Electrical supplies online*

▶ Alert Fire Ltd, Unit 18, Britannia Court, Burnt Mills Industrial Estate, Basildon, Essex, SS13 3EU Tel: (01268) 726999 Fax: (01268) 725292 E-mail: info@alert-fire.co.uk *Fire protection and safety company specialising in the supply and service of portable fire extinguishers, fire blankets, safety signs and posters.*FETA certified engineers.*

Company Information

Alert Products, Hollins Lane, Tilstock, Whitchurch, Shropshire, SY13 3NU Tel: (01948) 880627 Fax: (01948) 880339 E-mail: graham.dewson@ukonline.co.uk *Cleanroom equipment manufrs*

▶ Alerts Security/Installations Ltd, 1a Jubilee Terrace, Ryton, Tyne & Wear, NE40 4HL Tel: 0191-413 9090 Fax: 0191-413 9090 *Security system installations*

Alex Bonar & Co. Ltd, Pennybridge Industrial Estate, Ballymena, County Antrim, BT42 3HB Tel: (028) 2565 2449 Fax: (028) 2564 1838 E-mail: info@alexanderbonar.com *Electrical engineers*

▶ Alex Brewster, 32 Maxwell Place, Stirling, FK8 1JU Tel: (01786) 473851 Fax: (01786) 474825

Alex J Cheetham Ltd, Morton Street, Failsworth, Manchester, M35 0BP Tel: 0161-681 1115 Fax: 0161-681 0339 E-mail: mark@alexjcheetham.co.uk *Architectural, sheet metalwork & stainless steel fabricators*

▶ Alex Lovie & Son, 41 Main Street, New Deer, Turriff, Aberdeenshire, AB53 6TA Tel: (01771) 644295 Fax: (01771) 644787

Alex Morrison Ltd, 56 Gilwilly Road, Gilwilly Industrial Estate, Penrith, Cumbria, CA11 9BL Tel: (01768) 863037 Fax: (01768) 890950 *Motor body repairers*

Alex Morton, 43 Killysorrell Road, Dromore, County Down, BT25 1LB Tel: (028) 9269 3651 Fax: (028) 9269 3951 E-mail: amorton@domora43.fsnet.co.uk *Engineering & welding sub-contract services*

Alex Nangle Electrical Ltd, Unit 3 Oakbank Park Way, Mid Calder, Livingston, West Lothian, EH53 0TH Tel: (01506) 449400 Fax: (01506) 449404 E-mail: info@nangle.co.uk Principal Export Areas: Worldwide *Fuse & gear distributors or agents*

▶ Alex Parker & Co. Ltd, 11 Eagle Brow, Lymm, Cheshire, WA13 0LP Tel: (01925) 758889 Fax: (01925) 758894 E-mail: info@alexparker.co.uk *Charted accountants*

Alex R Ross & Son, 44 Chapel Street, Aberdeen, AB10 1SP Tel: (01224) 643527 Fax: (01224) 643527 *Bakery wholesale manufrs*

▶ Alex Ross & Sons Ltd, 21 Henderson Drive, Inverness, IV1 1TR Tel: (01463) 232061 Fax: (01463) 713740 *Quarrying*

▶ Alex Scott & Co Kiltmakers Ltd, 43 Schoolhill, Aberdeen, AB10 1JT Tel: (01224) 643924 Fax: (01224) 626061 E-mail: sales@kiltmakers.co.uk *Kilt makers*

▶ Alex Stewart Assayers Ltd, Caddick Road, Knowsley Business Park, Prescot, Merseyside, L34 9HP Tel: 0151-548 7777 Fax: 0151-548 0714 E-mail: info@alexstewart.com *Samplers assayers & metallurgical analysts*

▶ Alex Tomlinson Photography, Alington House, Ledbury Road, Ross-on-Wye, Herefordshire, HR9 7BG Tel: 01989 563430 E-mail: enquiry@the-photographer.eclipse.co.uk *The Ross-on-Wye wedding and portrait photographer specialising in naturally posed stunning photographs.*We give you an extra personal touch which makes your day truly supreme.*

▶ Alexander Anderson Ltd, 30-32 Byron Street, Glasgow, G11 6LS Tel: 0141-334 9354 Fax: 0141-357 4542

▶ Alexander Arthur & Sons (Scotland) Ltd, 4 Novar Drive, Glasgow, G12 9PU Tel: 0141-339 8595

Alexander Associates, 21 Hillward Close, Orton Longueville, Peterborough, PE2 7AB Tel: (01733) 371770 Fax: (01733) 371770 E-mail: david.thorpe8@ntlworld.com *Press & public relations consultancy*

Alexander Buchan Ltd, East Quay, Peterhead, Aberdeenshire, AB42 1JF Tel: 0131-554 9400 Fax: (01779) 471910 *Fish processors*

Alexander Chapel, Orchard Lea, Winkfield Lane, Windsor, Berkshire, SL4 4RU Tel: (0870) 1609610 Fax: 0117-985 9986 E-mail: windsor@alexanderchapel.co.uk *Sales recruitment consultancy*

Alexander & Duncan Ltd, Southern Avenue, Leominster, Herefordshire, HR6 0QB Tel: (01568) 613434 Fax: (01568) 613736 E-mail: simon@alexanderandduncan.co.uk *Agricultural machinery agents*

Alexander Duncan Aberdeen Ltd, Inchbroom, Nigg, Aberdeen, AB12 3GF Tel: (01224) 897278 Fax: (01224) 896954 E-mail: info@duncancabs.co.uk *Tractor cab spare part suppliers*

▶ Alexander Duthie & Sons Ltd, 103 Berryden Road, Aberdeen, AB25 3SJ Tel: (01224) 639983 Fax: (01224) 639983

▶ Alexander Duthie & Sons Ltd, 2 St. Andrew Street, Peterhead, Aberdeenshire, AB42 1DS Tel: (01779) 472628 Fax: (01779) 492628

Alexander Fitted Furniture, 25 Beech Grove, Bedlington, Northumberland, NE22 5DA Tel: (01670) 820200 Fax: (01670) 820200 *Furniture showroom*

Alexander Higgins & Sons 1987 Ltd, The Hayes, Stourbridge, West Midlands, DY9 8NH Tel: (01384) 422304 *Engineers & general engineers*

Alexander Industrial Supplies Essex Ltd, Unit D Eastways, Witham, Essex, CM8 3YQ Tel: (01376) 500303 Fax: (01376) 502090 E-mail: sales@alexander-industrial.co.uk Principal Export Areas: Worldwide *Castor, hand wheel & plastic tube end cap fasteners distributors*

▶ Alexander James Executive Search Ltd, Winslow House, 16 Rumford Court, Rumford Place, Liverpool, L3 9DG Tel: 0151 236 1875 Fax: 0151 258 2018 E-mail: info@alexanderjamesltd.co.uk *Alexander James provide a refreshing and dynamic approach to executive recruitment. We provide executive search and advertised selection services for Based in the North West, the team at Alexander James Executive Search has more than twelve years' experience in the executive recruitment sector, having worked extensively across the UK, and internationally.**We work across all sectors of industry and practice and specialise in financial roles from Tax Partner to FD's to Finance Managers, typically in the £40-0k salary range. Our clients range from FTSE 0 companies to regional practices and SME's.**We are proud of our professional approach and outstanding reputation, which have enabled us to cultivate a strong network of contacts with some of the UK's largest and most prestigious companies and organizations. **By commanding such confidence and trust, we are able to use our contacts in assisting both clients and candidates within any industry, at the highest level**

▶ Alexander Johnston Plasterers Ltd, 4 Urquhart Lane, Aberdeen, AB24 5LQ Tel: (01224) 626838

Alexander Mills, 43 Main Street, Benburb, Dungannon, County Tyrone, BT71 7JY Tel: (028) 3754 8971 Fax: (028) 3754 8691 E-mail: sales@alexander-mills.co.uk *Agricultural machinery manufrs*

▶ Alexander Morton Homes Scotland Ltd, Kilmaurs, Kilmarnock, Ayrshire, KA3 2PG Tel: (0845) 230 0204

Alexander Newall Machine Tool Co. Ltd, Unit A, Brook Road, Waltham Cross, Hertfordshire, EN8 7LR Tel: (01992) 651122 Fax: (01992) 651123 E-mail: newall-london@supanet.com *Machine & cutting tool distributors*

▶ Alexander Plant Hire, Office 3A, 7 York Street, Ayr, KA8 8AN Tel: (01292) 265335

▶ Alexander Removals Ltd, 7 Nobel Road, West Gourdie Industrial Estate, Dundee, DD2 4UH Tel: (01382) 401403 Fax: (01382) 401402

▶ Alexander Ritchie & Son Ltd, 163 Bonnington Road, Pilrig Industrial Estate, Edinburgh, EH6 5RE Tel: 0131-554 0431

Alexander Stirling & Co., Meadowforth Road, Stirling, FK7 7SA Tel: (01786) 473333 Fax: (01786) 450408 E-mail: sales@alexanderstirling.co.uk *Steel stockholders*

Alexander Technologies (Europe) Ltd, 4 Doxford Drive, South West Industrial Estate, Peterlee, County Durham, SR8 2RL Tel: 0191-587 2787 Fax: 0191-587 2587 E-mail: mail@alexenergy.co.uk *Rechargeable batteries for portable equipment manufrs*

Theodore Alexander Ltd, Chapel Hill, Kingsclere Road, Basingstoke, Hampshire, RG21 5UQ Tel: (01256) 406200 Fax: (01256) 406205 *Fine furniture designers & makers*

Alexander Trading Co., Oakmere Training Centre, Cherry Lane, Liverpool, L4 6UG Tel: 0151-286 0061 Fax: 0151-284 4380 *Merchants & agents for cardboard boxes & packaging*

▶ Alexanders, 342 Shirley Road, Southampton, SO15 3HJ Tel: (023) 8070 4321 Fax: (023) 8077 8784 E-mail: alex@alexandersestateagency.com *International Estate Agents selling property in mainland Spain, Canary Islands, Cyprus, Turkey, Bulgaria, Dubai, Portugal and Florida*

Alexanders Sawmills Ltd, Heathfield Road, Ayr, KA8 9SS Tel: (01292) 267842 Fax: (01292) 610707 *Timber importers & merchants*

▶ Alexander's Woodworks, Whitebridge Garage, Old Bath Road, Charvil, Reading, RG10 9QJ Tel: 0118-932 1966 Fax: 0118-944 0517 E-mail: alexwoodltd@onetel.com *Cabinet makers*

▶ Alexandra Locksmiths, 11 Palace Court Gardens, London, N10 2LB Tel: (020) 8883 1555 E-mail: pau.@alexandralocksmiths.co.uk *Locksmiths & intercom services*

Alexandra Palace, Alexandra Palace Way, London, N22 7AY Tel: (020) 8365 2121 Fax: (020) 8883 3999 E-mail: sales@alexandrapalace.com *Exhibition & conference centre facilities*

Alexandra Saw Mills Ltd, Byron Street, Carlisle, CA2 5TB Tel: (01228) 525368 Fax: (01228) 590282 *Timber merchants*

Alexandrer, Unit B, Barrows Road, Harlow, Essex, CM19 5FD Tel: (01920) 462383 Fax: (01279) 419744 *Bus & coach repairers*

▶ Alexandria Associates, 4a, Leyland Road, Penwortham, Preston, PR1 9XR Tel: (01772) 742224 Fax: (01772) 751124

Alexco Emblems, 94 Guildford Road, Croydon, CR0 2HJ Tel: (020) 8683 0546 Fax: (020) 8689 4749 E-mail: alexco@btconnect.com *T-shirts, badges & promotional goods manufrs*

Alexes Jewels, 214-215 Straitmile Road, Rotherwas, Hereford, HR2 6JP Tel: (01432) 354959 Fax: (01432) 352767 *Jewellery manufacturer & repairs*

Alexican Ltd, 177 King Street, Dukinfield, Cheshire, SK16 4LG Tel: 0161-339 1999 Fax: 0161-330 1555 E-mail: info@alexican.co.uk *Photocopiers & faxes, sales & service specialists*

Alexir Packaging Ltd, Faraday Road, Crawley, West Sussex, RH10 9UR Tel: (01293) 544644 Fax: (01293) 544744 E-mail: enquiries@alexir.co.uk *Carton manufrs*

Alexon Group plc, 40-48 Guildford Street, Luton, LU1 2PB Tel: (01582) 723131 Fax: (01582) 724158 *Ladies clothing manufrs* Also at: London W1 & Milton Keynes

Alexsys Communications, Manor Farm, High Street, Chewton Mendip, Radstock, BA3 4LL Tel: (01761) 241695 Fax: (01761) 241696 E-mail: enquiries@alexsys.co.uk *Computer consultants services*

Alf Arrowsmith & Son Ltd, Church View, Cheswardine, Market Drayton, Shropshire, TF9 2RW Tel: (01630) 661208 Fax: (01630) 661334 *Road transport & haulage service*

▶ Alf Kitching & Sons Ltd, Double Rivers, Crowle, Scunthorpe, South Humberside, DN17 4DD Tel: (01724) 710286 Fax: (01724) 710477

Alf Wright Ltd, 31 Saffron Road, Wigston, Leicestershire, LE18 4UR Tel: 0116-278 1005 Fax: 0116-278 1006 E-mail: headoffice@alfwright.co.uk *Joinery construction & maintainance*

Alfa, Rockwood, Keldholme, York, YO62 6NB Tel: (01751) 432953 Fax: (01751) 432518 *Investment castings in steel & ferrous alloys*

▶ Alfa Aesar, Shore Road, Port Of Heysham Industrial Park, Heysham, Morecambe, Lancashire, LA3 2XY Tel: (01524) 850506 Fax: (01524) 850608 E-mail: uksales@alfa.com *Research chemicals, metals & materials*

Alfa Aggregates Products Ltd, Kingsley Works, Kingsley, Stoke-on-Trent, ST10 2DG Tel: (01538) 754773 Fax: (01538) 750280 E-mail: alpha.aggregates@btopenworld.com *Refractory materials*

▶ Alfa Chemicals Ltd, Arc House, Terrace Road South, Binfield, Bracknell, Berkshire, RG42 4PZ Tel: (01344) 861800 Fax: (01344) 451400 E-mail: info@alfa-chemicals.co.uk *Speciality chemical distributors*

▶ Alfa Construction Services Ltd, Coleshill Road, Atherstone, Warwickshire, CV9 1BW Tel: (01827) 713000 Fax: (01827) 714444

Alfa Display & Design Ltd, Unit 4 Sandleheath Industrial Estate, Sandleheath, Fordingbridge, Hampshire, SP6 1PA Tel: (01425) 653943 Fax: (01425) 657075 E-mail: info@alfadisplay.co.uk *Exhibition display designers & contractors*

Alfa Electric Ltd, 14 Burgess Road, Ivyhouse Industrial Estate, Hastings, East Sussex, TN35 4NR Tel: (01424) 440240 Fax: (01424) 424040 E-mail: sales@alfaelectric.co.uk *Commercial & industrial electrical contractors*

Alfa Fans Ltd, Unit 7, Green Lane, Bridgtown, Cannock, Staffordshire, WS11 0JJ Tel: (01543) 466420 Fax: (01543) 462393 E-mail: sales@alfafans.co.uk *Manufacturers of blowers, axial & centrifugal fans*

Alfa Gomma UK Ltd, 3 Cranford Court, Hardwick Grange, Woolston, Warrington, WA1 4RX Tel: (01925) 820800 Fax: (01925) 810926 *Hydraulic hose & fittings manufrs*

Alfa Laval Ltd, Castle Vale Industrial Estate, Maybrook Road, Minworth, Sutton Coldfield, West Midlands, B76 1AL Tel: 0121-351 3131 Fax: 0121-351 7888 E-mail: admin@alfalaval.com *Pharmaceutical pumps & valves manufrs*

Alfa Laval 2000, 7 Doman Road, Camberley, Surrey, GU15 3DN Tel: (01276) 663383 Fax: (01276) 413603 E-mail: *Service repair sales pumps engineering equipment*

Alfa Laval Eastbourne Ltd, Birch Road, Eastbourne, East Sussex, BN23 6PQ Tel: (01323) 412555 Fax: (01323) 414515 *Pump manufrs*

Alfa Precision & General Engineering Co. Ltd, Solway Trading Estate, Maryport, Cumbria, CA15 8NF Tel: (01900) 815678 Fax: (01900) 814191 E-mail: alfaprecision@btclick.com *Precision machinists*

Alfabet Screenprint Ltd, 9 Sargeant Turner Trading Estate, Bromley Street, Stourbridge, West Midlands, DY9 8HZ Tel: (01384) 897355 Fax: (01384) 893414 E-mail: info@alfabet.com *Screen printers*

Alfalaval Ltd, Salvesen Tower, Blaikies Quay, Aberdeen, AB11 5PW Tel: (01224) 424300 Fax: (01224) 424315 *Sales of high speed centrifuges*

Alfast Engineering Supplies Ltd, 2 Gloucester Road, Luton, LU1 3HX Tel: (01582) 418498 Fax: (01582) 418833 E-mail: sales@alfast.co.uk *Industrial fastener specialists*

Alfatronix Ltd, 29 Newtown Business Park, Albion Close, Poole, Dorset, BH12 3LL Tel: (01202) 715517 Fax: (01202) 715122 E-mail: sales@alfatronix.co.uk *Radio communication accessories manufrs*

Alfing Kessler Engineering Ltd, 56a Bramhall Lane South, Bramhall, Stockport, Cheshire, SK7 1AH Tel: 0161-440 0104 Fax: 0161-440 0115 E-mail: alfingkessler@btconnect.com *Crankshaft importers*

Alford Engineering, Fen Lane, Maltby le Marsh, Alford, Lincolnshire, LN13 0JT Tel: (01507) 450566 Fax: (01507) 450327 *Turning, milling & drilling engineers*

Alframes Holdings Ltd, 1A Arnold Road, London, SW17 9HU Tel: (020) 8648 9394 Fax: (020) 8648 4985 *Double glazing manufrs*

Alfran Fasteners Ltd, Central Ironworks, Parson Street, Keighley, West Yorkshire, BD21 3HD Tel: (01535) 664993 Fax: (01535) 664994 E-mail: sales@alfranfasteners.co.uk *Alfran Fasteners was formed a decade ago to supply quality home produced fasteners, utilising our sister companies forging facilities to offer a fastener service which leads the field, we stock a comprehensive range of fasteners including HSFG PT1, PT2 and CSK, grades 8.8/10.9/12.9, high tensile bolts and sets, metric and imperial, we also offer turned parts made to order and all plating types are available, we service an enviable list of prestige clients within the distribution industries, structural bolting, railways, tunneling, wind power, automotive, motorway barrier and water and marine outlets, a product service backed up by a highly capable sales team always on hand to discuss your individual requirements, and because every customer is important to us you will always receive excellent friendly service.*

Alfred Bagnall & Sons London Ltd, 4 Udney Park Road, Teddington, Middlesex, TW11 9BG Tel: (020) 8977 4474 Fax: (020) 8943 5389 *Commercial painting & decorators* Also at: Belvedere, Bristol, Cardiff, Ellesmere Port, Shipley & Wolverhampton

Alfred Bagnall & Sons Restoration Ltd, St Thomas Road, Belvedere, Kent, DA17 6AG Tel: (020) 8311 3910 Fax: (020) 8311 3833 *Protective coatings & concrete repairers*

Alfred Briggs Sons & Co. Ltd, 108 Church Lane, Gomersal, Cleckheaton, West Yorkshire, BD19 4QL Tel: (01274) 873272 Fax: (01274) 869999 E-mail: sales@alfred-briggs.ltd.uk *Reconditioned woollen machinery*

Alfred Brown Worsted Mills Ltd, Empire Mills, Mill Lane, Leeds, LS13 3HG Tel: 0113-256 0666 Fax: 0113-257 2315 E-mail: sales@alfredbrown.co.uk *Worsted cloth manufrs* Also at: London W1

▶ Alfred Cox & Sons Brighton Ltd, 28a Brigden Street, Brighton, BN1 5DP Tel: (01273) 552762 Fax: (01273) 552012

▶ Alfred Groves & Sons Ltd, Shipton Road, Milton-under-Wychwood, Chipping Norton, Oxfordshire, OX7 6JP Tel: (01993) 830302 Fax: (01993) 831752

Alfred Harrold Containers Ltd, Sandyland, Wisbech, Cambridgeshire, PE13 1TF Tel: (01945) 583776 Fax: (01945) 585577 E-mail: elaine@harrolds.co.uk *Packaging merchants & suppliers*

Alfred J Hurst, Unit 2 Duncrue Cresent, Belfast, BT3 9BW Tel: (028) 9077 0037 Fax: (028) 9077 9749 E-mail: sales@ajhurst.com *Electrical lighting suppliers*

Alfred J Parker Ltd, Armoury Works, 348 Moseley Road, Birmingham, B12 9AZ Tel: 0121-440 1480 Fax: 0121-446 4194 E-mail: alfredjparker@yahoo.co.uk *Guns, rifles & shooting accessory manufrs*

Alfred Mcalpine plc, Kinnaird House, 1 Pall Mall East, London, SW1Y 5AZ Tel: (020) 7930 6255 Fax: (020) 7839 6902 *Civil engineering & public works contractors*

▶ Alfred Mcalpine plc, Trafford Park, Manchester, M17 1JJ Tel: 0161-848 7666 Fax: 0161-872 6887

Alfred Mcalpine plc, West Carr Road, Retford, Nottinghamshire, DN22 7SW Tel: (01777) 714200 Fax: (01777) 714233 E-mail: sales@alfred-mcalpine.com *Civil engineering contractors*

▶ Alfred Mcalpine Business Services Ltd, 1a Newquay Road, St. Columb Road, St. Columb, Cornwall, TR9 6PZ Tel: (01726) 860059 Fax: (01726) 860455

▶ Alfred Mcalpine Infrastructure Servicess, 1 Lilybank Street, Hamilton, Lanarkshire, ML3 6NN Tel: (01698) 281319 Fax: (01698) 286547

▶ Alfred Ramsay, 299 Martindale Road, Hounslow, TW4 7HG Tel: (07951) 477347 Fax: (01932) 770943 E-mail: info@alfredramsay.co.uk *General carpentry & tiling*

Alfred Wood & Sons Ltd, 32 Eveline Road, Mitcham, Surrey, CR4 3LE Tel: (020) 8648 3528 Fax: (020) 8640 8707 E-mail: roger.felstead@virgin.net *Repetition component manufrs*

▶ Alfresco Mini Marquee Hire, 12 Valley Road, Newbury, Berkshire, RG14 6ER Tel: (0800) 9706753 E-mail: info@alfrescomarqueehire.co.uk *mini marquee hire, marquee hire uk, tent marquee hire, in Berkshire, South East England*

Alfreton Fabrications Ltd, Unit 5b Wimsey Way, Somercotes, Alfreton, Derbyshire, DE55 4LS Tel: (01773) 608163 Fax: (01773) 608163 E-mail: sales@alfertonfabs.co.uk *Steel fabricators & general engineers*

Alfreton Joinery Co., Old Swanwick Colliery Road, Derby Road, Swanwick, Alfreton, Derbyshire, DE55 1BH Tel: (01773) 832022 Fax: (01773) 836014 *Joinery manufrs*

Alfreton Transport, Wimsey Way, Somercotes, Alfreton, Derbyshire, DE55 4LS Tel: (01773) 604347 Fax: (01773) 603834 *Road transport, haulage & freight services*

Alg Enterprise, 312 Wandsworth Bridge Road, London, SW6 2UA Tel: (020) 7736 7714 Fax: (020) 7384 1329 E-mail: enquiries@algcomputers.co.uk *PC repairers*

Algernon, Unit 1 Algarnon Industrial Estate, Shiremoor, Newcastle upon Tyne, NE27 0NB Tel: 0191-251 4600 Fax: 0191-297 0360 E-mail: algernoneng@aol.com *Precision engineers*

Algo Business Centre, Glenearn Road, Perth, PH2 0NJ Tel: (01738) 450450 Fax: (01738) 450460 E-mail: pa@algo.co.uk *Steelwork engineers design & build industrial buildings*

Algo Schetronics Ltd, Crinacontt Farm, Pyworthy, Holsworthy, Devon, EX22 6LJ Tel: (01409) 254595 E-mail: info@algo-sales.co.uk *Precision electronic measuring instrument repairs service*

Algram Groups, Eastern Wood Road, Langage Business Park, Plympton, Plymouth, PL7 5ET Tel: (01752) 342388 Fax: (01752) 342482 E-mail: sales@algram.com *Plastic vacuum formed products*

▶ Alhco Sewer Rehabilitation Ltd, 114 Station Road, Westbury, Wiltshire, BA13 4TW Tel: (01373) 823814 E-mail: richard.jemmett@alhco.co.uk *Gas installation, maintenance & service provider*

▶ Alhpa Nursing Agency, Bentham house, 97 Heaton Street, Standish, Wigan, Lancs, WN6 0DA Tel: 01257 473455 E-mail: enquires@agency-nurses.co.uk *Domiciliary Care, Nursing staff, Care staff, domestic duties, cleaning, ironing, shopping, collecting pension collection, dressing, personbal hygene, meal preperation, feeding, respite, post-operation, social, disabled assistance, 24 hours live in care, moving, handling, basic life support, first aid, health, safety, nvqs, prep, food, staff development, new mothers, nursing homes, holiday, sickness, cover, staffing, training courses, clinics, Wigan and Southport*

▶ Ali Alwan DTP, 228 Seaforth Avenue, New Malden, Surrey, KT3 6JW Tel: (020) 8949 6048 *London based company specialising in Arabic Typesetting.*

Alias Ltd, Stuart Road, Manor Park, Runcorn, Cheshire, WA7 1TS Tel: (01928) 579311 Fax: (01928) 579389 E-mail: info@alias.ltd.uk *Industrial software products*

▶ Aliathon Engineers, Pitreavie Business Park, Queensferry Road, Dunfermline, Fife, KY11 8UU Tel: (01383) 737736 Fax: (01383) 749501

Aliblast Services, 5a Greenpark, Edinburgh Road, Linlithgow, West Lothian, EH49 6AA Tel: (01506) 671844 Fax: (01506) 671844 *Glass & grit contractors*

Alibone Recycling Ltd, Sandy Hill Lane, Moulton, Northampton, NN3 7JB Tel: (01604) 644963 Fax: (01604) 492685 E-mail: info@paperwaste.co.uk *Waste paper merchants*

Alice Soundtech Ltd, Unit 34d Hobbs Industrial Estate, Newchapel, Lingfield, Surrey, RH7 6HN Tel: (01342) 833500 Fax: (01342) 833350 E-mail: sales@alice.co.uk *Broadcast solutions radio broadcasting equipment ,mixing desks suppliers*

▶ Alice's Cake Store, C/o Latteridge House, Latteridge Green, Iron Acton, Bristol, BS37 9TS Tel: (0870) 1995481 *Stockists of Fmm, Pme, Jem, and Orchard, essential cakemaking equipment including cutters, sugarflair colours,*

continued

continuation
cake stands, books and videos. *We also have a cake decorating forum & chatroom.*

Alif UK Ltd, 33 Parker Drive, Leicester, LE4 0JP Tel: 0116-235 5050 Fax: 0116-235 5500 E-mail: sales@alifuk.co.uk *Fashion fabric importers & exporters*

Alifab, New Hall Mills, Milton Road, Stoke-on-Trent, ST1 6LE Tel: (01782) 544844 Fax: (01782) 544866 E-mail: sales@alifab.co.uk *Welding & fabricating engineers*

Alifabs Woking Ltd, 4 Kernel Court, Walnut Tree Close, Guildford, Surrey, GU1 4UD Tel: (01483) 546547 Fax: (01483) 546548 E-mail: sales@alifabs.com *Aluminum fabricators*

Alimak Hek Ltd, Northampton Road, Rushden, Northamptonshire, NN10 6BW Tel: (01933) 354700 Fax: (01933) 410600 E-mail: ukinfo@alimakhek.com *Supply lifts*

▶ Alimex UK Possion In Aluminium Ltd, 6 Fingle Drive, Stonebridge, Milton Keynes, MK13 0AB Tel: (01908) 224240 Fax: (01908) 224241 E-mail: info@alimex.uk.com Principal Export Areas: Worldwide *Manufacturers of quality precision aluminium plate*

Alinco Ltd, 22 Albert Drive, Burgess Hill, West Sussex, RH15 9TN Tel: (01444) 232719 Fax: (01444) 871680 E-mail: alinco@btinternet.com *Sheet metalworkers & machinists*

▶ A-Line Audio Visual Services, Parkhill, Bucksburn, Aberdeen, AB21 7AT Tel: (01224) 723377 Fax: (01224) 723399 E-mail: sales@a-line.co.uk *PA system installers*

▶ A-LINE OCEANA LTD, P O BOX 322, RAMSGATE, KENT, CT12 6GL Tel: 01843 570791 Fax: 01843 570791 E-mail: LOISBRIAN8@AOL.COM

Gordon Alison Ltd, 16 Jordan Street, Liverpool, L1 0BP Tel: 0151-709 4687 Fax: 0151-709 4723 E-mail: edwards@gordon-alison.fsnet.co.uk *Ship repairers & general engineers*

▶ Alison Handling, Freckleton Road, Kirkham, Preston, PR4 3RB Tel: (01772) 687940 Fax: (01772) 685400 E-mail: enquiries@alison-handling.co.uk *Alison Handling Ltd are the UK's largest stockist of new and used plastic handling equipment. Our large warehouses in Kirkham Lancashire stock over 300,000 plastic boxes as well as plastic pallets and plastic pallet boxes. Our range includes: Plastic containers, plastic pallet boxes, plastic boxes, plastic storage boxes, plastic trays, plastic distribution containers, plastic mobiles, plastic bins, plastic pallets, plastic trucks.*

Alison Hodge Associates, 12 Heathfield Gardens, London, W4 4JY Tel: (020) 8995 5485 Fax: (020) 8995 4341 E-mail: alisonhodge@dial.pipex.com *Organisational training & consulting*

Alistair Clark Associates, Rait, Perth, PH2 7RT Tel: (01821) 670570 Fax: (01821) 670570 *Computer consultants & software developers*

Alitalia, 2a Cains Lane, Feltham, Middlesex, TW14 9RL Tel: (020) 8745 8200 Fax: (020) 8745 8299 E-mail: sales@alitalia.co.uk *Airline*

Aljac Fuelling Components, Pitfield House, Station Approach, Shepperton, Middlesex, TW17 8AN Tel: (01932) 269869 Fax: (01932) 269230 E-mail: sales@aljac.com *Aviation refuelling equipment distributors*

Aljon Engineering, Lancaster House, 234-236 Fields New Road, Chadderton, Oldham, OL9 8NZ Tel: 0161-628 7800 Fax: 0161-628 7072 E-mail: atjoneng@zen.co.uk *Precision engineering & rope access work*

Alkal Leisure, Unit 24, Lyon Road, Walton-on-Thames, Surrey, KT12 3PU Tel: (0845) 2305656 Fax: (0845) 2305676 E-mail: info@akc-uk.com *Janitorial & leisure equipment supplies*

Alkemi M F Technologies, Clwyd Close, Manor Lane, Hawarden, Deeside, Clwyd, CH5 3PZ Tel: (01244) 536299 Fax: (01244) 520363 E-mail: simonn@alkemimetalfinishing.co.uk *Electroplating services & powder coating painters*

Alkemi M F Technology, 15 Central Trade Park, Marley Way, Saltney, Chester, CH4 8SX Tel: (01244) 674800 Fax: (01244) 681063 *Electroplating services, powder coating & shot blasting*

Alken Construction Ltd, Redmoss Business Centre, Greenbank Road, East Tullos Industrial Estate, Aberdeen, AB12 3BQ Tel: (01224) 875265 Fax: (01224) 879023 *Joiners & shop fitters*

Alker Optical Equipment Ltd, Alker House, 190 North Gate, New Basford, Nottingham, NG7 7FT Tel: 0115-942 0290 Fax: 0115-978 8190 E-mail: sales@alker.co.uk *Distributors of fibre optic cable*

Alkie Ltd, Millwood View, Stalybridge, Cheshire, SK15 3AU Tel: 0161-338 8070 Fax: 0161-338 3191 E-mail: alkie.ltd@virgin.net *Ventilation ductwork & metalwork*

▶ All Inc, 30 Brambles Enterprise Centre, Waterberry Drive, Waterlooville, Hampshire, PO7 7TH Tel: (023) 9224 3101 Fax: (023) 9226 2729 E-mail: info@allinc.co.uk

All About Signs Ltd, 19 Ordnance Court, Ackworth Road Hilsea, Portsmouth, PO3 5RZ Tel: (023) 9265 4720 Fax: (023) 9265 4721 E-mail: admin@allaboutsigns.co.uk *Sign makers & digital printers*

▶ All Action American & English Taxicabs, Salop Street Garage, 2 Salop Street, Bolton, BL2 1DZ Tel: (01204) 361462 Fax: (01204) 531426 E-mail: julie@raytomkinson.demon.co.uk *Vehicles & wedding car hire supplier, taxis imported*

All Bees Ltd, A B L House, Bashley Road, London, NW10 6SL Tel: (020) 8961 4321 Fax: (020) 8961 1597 *Ironmongers*

▶ All Blinds Ltd, 1 Century Park, Garrison Lane, Birmingham, B9 4NZ Tel: 0121-771 3000 Fax: 0121-771 3000 E-mail: sales@imageblinds.co.uk *Suppliers of Window Blinds, Conservatory Blinds, Awnings, Plantation Shutters, Curtains, Internal/External Security, PVC Strip Curtains, & Associated Coverings. We supply mainly to the demanding and fiercely competitive commercial /contract market. Our customer base includes many large nationally known commercial organisations, as*

continued

well as schools, colleges, universities, local authorities, government departments, hospitals, Gas, Water and Electric Companies. We are members of the British Blind and Shutters Association which represents the leading manufacturers of blinds and shutters in the UK. All members of the Association must undergo a selection procedure which ensures they are capable of providing a quality product and full back up service. All members are bound to abide by the Association's code of practice which is YOUR guarantee of work to the highest standards. Trade enquiries welcome.

All Bright & Seeds, Holyhead Road, Whiston, Albrighton, Wolverhampton, WV7 3BX Tel: (01902) 372266 Fax: (01902) 372266 E-mail: sales@equestrianessentrials.com *Equestrian essentials retailer for all your horse & rider clothing*

All Care Cleaning Services, 16 Brondesbury Villas, London, NW6 6AA Tel: (020) 7625 2225 *Carpet & upholstery cleaners*

▶ The All Clean Group Ltd, 1 Southview Parade, New Road, Rainham, Essex, RM13 8HH Tel: (01708) 554400 Fax: (01708) 554499 E-mail: info@allcleangroup.com *Sale & hire of cleaning machines*

▶ The All Clear Co., 15 Rigg Approach, London, E10 7QN Tel: (0800) 1693633 Fax: (020) 8539 9462 E-mail: enquiries@theallclearcompany.co.uk *professional rubbish clearance in london and essex. house, office and garden cleared and recycled. an easy alternative to skip hire. one call junk removal.*

▶ All Digital, Rear of, 198 Howard Road, Sheffield, S6 3RX Tel: 0114-231 5050 *Computer software services*

All Doors Of Bromsgrove, 1 All Saints Road, Bromsgrove, Worcestershire, B61 0AG Tel: (01527) 579901 *Suppliers of doors*

All Electrical Services Ltd, North Mace House, Viaduct Road, Cardiff, CF15 9XF Tel: (029) 2081 0274 Fax: (029) 2081 0282 E-mail: info@allelectricalserviceswales.com *Electrical contractors*

All Fill Ltd, 5 Gateshead Close, Sandy, Bedfordshire, SG19 1RS Tel: (01767) 691100 Fax: (01767) 681406 E-mail: info@allfill.co.uk *Powder granule & paste filling machine suppliers*

▶ All Floors 'N' Rugs, 14 Limes Walk, Oakengates, Telford, Shropshire, TF2 6EP Tel: (01952) 618191 Fax: (01952) 222151 E-mail: sales@floorsnrugs.co.uk *Contract & domestic floor covering services*

▶ All Foundations Ltd, PO Box 2146, Watford, WD18 1AS Tel: (0870) 3503050 Fax: (0870) 3503060 E-mail: mail@allfoundations.co.uk *All Foundations has created a reputation for providing a fast, friendly, "no hassle" approach to providing its Contracting Partners /Engineers / Architects /Developers /Home Owners with a "One Stop Shop" for all their foundation needs.**Our range of services that we are able to offer include:*> Piling from 0mm to 750mm diameter, restricted and unrestricted, in any ground conditions.*> Associated excavation, reinforced concrete works, ground beams, slabs, walls.*> Excavated and piled underpinning.*>Basement construction.*

▶ All French Translators, 407-409 Oxford Street, London, W1C 2PB Tel: 020 79079400 Fax: 020 79079427 E-mail: info@allfrenchtranslators.com *Translation and Interpreting Agency*

All Fresh, ABC House, Lakeside Industrial Park, Cotswold Dene, Standlake, Witney, Oxfordshire, OX29 7PJ Tel: (01865) 300900 Fax: (01865) 300879 *Foods manufrs*

All Gear Services 1990 Ltd, 8 Hogwood Farm, Sheerlands Road, Finchampstead, Wokingham, Berkshire, RG40 4QY Tel: 0118-973 0053 Fax: 0118-973 4722 E-mail: linda.rapley@btinternet.com *Gear manufacturers & cutters*

All Gear Tools, The Weighbridge Office, The Wharf, Carlton-on-Trent, Newark, Nottinghamshire, NG23 6NR Tel: (01636) 821100 Fax: (01636) 821100 E-mail: sales@allgeartools.co.uk *Gear cutting tool retailers*

All Guard, 2 Glan Yr Afon, Berriew, Welshpool, Powys, SY21 8PN Tel: (01686) 640235 Fax: (01686) 640693 E-mail: creaven@freenet.co.uk *Insect screen manufrs*

All Handling Ltd, Mobility House, 492 Kingston Road, London, SW20 8DX Tel: (020) 8542 1021 Fax: (020) 8395 4410 *Distributors of equipment for disabled people* Also at: Aldershot

All Hose & Hydraulics Norwich Ltd, 2 Javelin Road, Norwich, NR6 6HX Tel: (01603) 788686 Fax: (01603) 483081 E-mail: allhosesales@btinternet.com *Rubber hose suppliers*

▶ All Ict Ltd, Fairgate House, 205 Kings Road, Tyseley, Birmingham, B11 2AA Tel: 0121-708 5454 Fax: 0121-708 5455 E-mail: sales@allict.com *ICT solutions & infrastructure for business's*

All In One Leisure Buildings, Rochdale Road, Middleton, Manchester, M24 2RB Tel: (01706) 717427 Fax: (01706) 759759 E-mail: sales@allinone.co.uk *Garden builders*

▶ All Ink Ltd, 30 Brambles Enterprise Centre, Waterberry Drive, Waterlooville, Hampshire, PO7 7TH Tel: (023) 9226 2715

All Languages Ltd, 362-364 Old Street, London, EC1V 9LT Tel: (020) 7739 6641 Fax: (020) 7739 6542 E-mail: info@alllanguages.co.uk *Language school, translation & interpreting services*

All Management Services Ltd, PO Box 8098, Birmingham, B38 9SP Tel: 0121-680 1981 Fax: 0121-243 8717 E-mail: amslimited@aol.com *Management consultants*

All Marque, Unit 5 Block F, St. Michaels Industrial Estate, Widnes, Cheshire, WA8 8TL Tel: 0151-424 1984 Fax: 0151-420 3144 E-mail: sales@allmarque.co.uk *Fibre, copper & metallic washers*

All Metal Fabrications Services Ltd, Thundridge Business Park, Great Cambridge Road, Thundridge, Ware, Hertfordshire, SG12 0SS Tel: (01920) 485200 Fax: (01920) 485055 *Metalwork manufrs*

All Metal Polishers, Unit 41 65 Caroline Street, Birmingham, B3 1UG Tel: 0121-236 1162 *Metal finishers & polishers*

All Metal Services Ltd, 6 Horton Industrial Park, Horton Road, West Drayton, Middlesex, UB7 8JD Tel: (01895) 444066 Fax: (01895) 420963 E-mail: london@allmetal.co.uk *Metal stockholders*

▶ All Natural, 61e-61f Gorse Industrial Estate, Barnham, Thetford, Norfolk, IP24 2PH Tel: (01842) 890891 Fax: (01842) 890891 E-mail: michael@allnaturalbakery.co.uk *Organic and Biodynamic Sourdough Breads with emphasis on special dietary needs such as : low carb, no Baker's yeast, dairy free, no modern wheat, vegan, gluten free, low sodium. All Natural supplies independent health food shops, wholefood stores, delicatessen and farm shops throughout East Anglia and in London. Also mail order.*

▶ All Oceans Engineering Ltd, Tyrebagger Works, Kinellar, Aberdeen, AB21 0TT Tel: (01224) 791001 Fax: (01224) 791002 E-mail: admin@alloceans.co.uk *Design, Manufacture, Winches, Launch and Recovery, Underwater Winches, Tether Management, ROV Tools, Torque Tools, Mini ROV, Pressure compensatory, load latches, swivels, diver meteorology, cable reels, submersible housings and junction boxes.*

All Phone Communications, 18 Glendale, Orton Wistow, Peterborough, PE2 6YL Tel: (01733) 233386 E-mail: steveallpress@supanet.com *Telecommunications services*

All Pine, 97 Dymchurch Road, Hythe, Kent, CT21 6JN Tel: (01303) 262373 Fax: (01303) 262373 *Restoration & pine furniture manufrs*

▶ All Points Marine Services, 232 - 5 Charter House, Lord Montgomery Way, Portsmouth, PO1 2SN Tel: (07854) 454826 Fax: (01983) 249576 E-mail: marineboatsurveyor@yahoo.co.uk *A Portsmouth (Cowes), Hampshire, UK based company experienced in Pre-Purchase,*Re-Insurance, Valuation, and Claims Surveys, as well as Offshore Vessel Inspection,*Investigation Consulting Services, for Power and Sailing Craft and Transport Canada Approved Vessel Tonnage Measurement and Yacht Management Contracts.**

▶ All Property Care, 7 Highfield Close, Danbury, Chelmsford, CM3 4EG Tel: (01245) 222320 E-mail: admin@allpropertycare.co.uk *Service providers of estate management, cleaning, ground maintenance.*

All Regions, B 2 Miller Road, Bedford, MK42 9NY Tel: (01234) 355388 Fax: (01234) 355504 E-mail: all.regions@ntlworld.com *Glaziers services*

▶ All Role Solutions, Unit 1 Bridge Farm, Holme Drove, Wyton, Huntingdon, Cambridgeshire, PE28 2AD Tel: (01487) 843255 Fax: (01487) 843003 E-mail: sales@allrol.co.uk *Suppliers of thermal paper rolls*

▶ All Round Engineering Ltd, 498-499 Ipswich Road, Slough, SL1 4EP Tel: (01753) 516996 Fax: (01753) 692746 E-mail: sales@allroundengineering.co.uk *Metal fabrication services*

▶ All Saints, 18 Syston Mill, Mill Lane, Syston, Leicester, LE7 1NS Tel: 0116-269 2909 *Engineers*

All Seasons, The Hermitage, Alders Avenue, Baldwins Hill, East Grinstead, West Sussex, RH19 2BX Tel: (0844) 8005827 Fax: (01342) 321162 *Cabinet manufrs*

All Seasons, Malpas Road, Northwich, Cheshire, CW9 7BJ Tel:

All Seasons Angling Centre, 8 Dunton Street, Wigston, Leicestershire, LE18 4PU Tel: 0116-278 2440 *Angling services retailer*

ALL SEASONS WROUGHT IRON UK LTD, UNIT 15 PARKWAY COURT, GLAISDALE PARKWAY, BILBOROUGH, NOTTINGHAM, NG8 4GN Tel: 0115 928 6688 E-mail: jimbrowne701@hotmail.com

All Secure Roller Shutters, The Office, 103 Rockbank Road, Liverpool, L13 7BG Tel: 0151-220 6000 Fax: 0151-228 1609 E-mail: info@shuttersandgrilles.co.uk *Roller shutter manufrs*

All Security Ltd, 1a Colston Avenue, Carshalton, Surrey, SM5 2PH Tel: (020) 8643 2151 Fax: (020) 8770 0038 *Security services*

▶ All Services Management Ltd, 9 Tennyson Road, High Wycombe, Buckinghamshire, HP11 2XA Tel: (07968) 740788 Fax: (01494) 534279 E-mail: robert@services-management.co.uk *Co-ordination & management of electrical & mechanical contractors & services on new developments & refurbishments*

▶ All Signs & Design Ltd, Unit 24 Knightcott Industrial Estate, Banwell, Avon, BS29 6JN Tel: (01934) 822800 Fax: (01934) 822800 *Sign manufacturers & installers*

All Solution Products Ltd, 4 Skylark Rise, Whitchurch, Hampshire, RG28 7SY Tel: (01256) 893863 Fax: (01256) 893863 E-mail: sales@allsolutionproducts.com *Swiss made deburring chamfering & routing equipment*

▶ All Solutions, 1 Merton Court, 54 Christchurch Road, Bournemouth, BH1 3PF Tel: (01202) 551862 *Hardware, software & pc's av products suppliers*

All Spring Ltd, C/O Multistroke Ltd, King Street, Old Hill, Cradley Heath, West Midlands, B64 6JJ Tel: (01384) 567773 Fax: (01304) 566589 E-mail: allspringltd@btconnect.com *Spring manufrs*

All Stainless Ltd, 21 Camford Way, Luton, LU3 3AN Tel: (01582) 584075 Fax: (01582) 585234 E-mail: info@stainlesssteelsupplies.com *Stainless steel stockholders*

All Stainless Ltd, 21 Camford Way, Luton, LU3 3AN Tel: (01582) 584075 Fax: (01582) 585234 E-mail: info@allstainlessltd.co.uk *Stainless steel tube stockholders*

▶ All Stars Fireworks, 379c Gloucester Road, Horfield, Bristol, BS7 8TN Tel: 0117-944 4880 E-mail: sales@allstarsfireworks.co.uk *All year round suppliers of retail fireworks and display team for weddings, corporate events, and private parties.*

All Style Door & Gate Services, 25 Woolacombe Lodge Road, Birmingham, B29 6PZ Tel: 0121-472 0675 *Garage door suppliers*

All Swim, Link Trade Park, Cardiff, CF11 8TT Tel: (029) 20 705059 Fax: (029) 2071 3340 E-mail: sales@allswimltd.com *All Swim - A UK supplier of DIY swimming pools, spas, above ground pools, saunas, steam rooms & all chemicals and accessories. All Swim"s pool and spa warehouse for all your swimming pool and spa needs from automatic pool cleaners, pool heaters, pumps & covers. buy on line or visit our showroom in Cardiff*

▶ All Technicut Ltd, Colwall St, Attercliffe, Sheffield, S9 3WP Tel: 0114-256 0093 *High performance wear & cutting solutions*

▶ All Test Ltd, 12 Hall Lane, Elsham, Brigg, North Lincolnshire, DN20 0QY Tel: (01652) 680404 Fax: (01652) 680404 E-mail: gerald@alltest.co.uk *Portable appliance testing service*

▶ All That Bounce, 83 Hay Leaze, Yate, Bristol, BS37 7YL Tel: (07766) 087783 E-mail: sales@allthatbounce.co.uk

All Tools Tool Shop, 181 Alder Road, Poole, Dorset, BH12 4AN Tel: (01202) 730376 Fax: (01202) 733145 *Power tools distributors*

▶ All Top Books, 30 Marischal Road, London, SE13 5LG Tel: (0845) 0542730 E-mail: contact@alltopbooks.co.uk *Book distributors*

All Tracks Ltd, 231 Brunswick Park Rd, London, N11 1EL Tel: 020 83610211 *Curtain track makers & fitters*

▶ All Trampolines, Embassy House, Ledson Road, Manchester, M23 9GP Tel: (0800) 0430437 Fax: (0845) 2571480 E-mail: info@alltrampolines.com *UK based supplier of trampolines*

All Trim Plastics, Unit 1-2, Spring Lane, Willenhall, West Midlands, WV12 4HL Tel: (0845) 6099922 Fax: (01422) 370953 E-mail: sales@dqs.co.uk *Component window distributors*

▶ All Way Surfacing & Construction Ltd, 1 Fermoy, Frome, Somerset, BA11 2EP Tel: (01373) 473641 Fax: (01373) 452532

▶ All Wrapped Up, 53 Liverpool Road, Kidsgrove, Stoke-on-Trent, ST7 1EA Tel: (01782) 771007 *Party balloons distributors*

▶ All Year Security, 1 Peall Road, Croydon, CR0 3EX Tel: (0845) 9000707 Fax: (0845) 9000808 E-mail: info@allyearsecurity.co.uk *Manned security guard solutions for offices, retail, warehouse*

▶ Allafricamarket.com, London, SW2 3LR Tel: 08701 997859 E-mail: enquiries@allafricamarket.com

Allam Marine Ltd, 10-12 Lime Street, Hull, HU8 7AB Tel: (01482) 224861 Fax: (01482) 226680 *Manufacturers of generators*

Allan Aqua-Systems Ltd, Allan Aqua House, Sedgwick Rd, Luton, LU4 9DT Tel: (01582) 574048 Fax: (01582) 574293 E-mail: info@allanaqua.co.uk Purchasing Contact: J. Doman Sales Contact: B. Burke *Specialist designer and manufacturer of packaged water booster sets to meet customer requirements. All our booster pump packages are designed to meet the individual requirements on each project and include the all new 'next generation' PCU600 pump controller designed and developed in-house by Allan Aqua-Systems Limited. The controller can handle up to 6 pumps on either a fixed or variable speed basis. The controller has a host of advanced control features such as the low pressure start up facility where the performance of the pumps is limited on start up to prevent pressure surge in the system. We also design and manufacture Category 5 pump set packages with WRAS approved break tank assemblies for use on high risk installations such as washdown, irrigation and laboratories.*

Allan & Bertram Ltd, Cuffley Gate, Sopers Road, Cuffley, Hertfordshire, EN6 4RY Tel: (01707) 876677 Fax: (01707) 877960 *High quality calendar, diary & advertising gift designers & producers*

Allan Blinds, 2 Senacre Square, Maidstone, Kent, ME15 8QF Tel: (01622) 677574 Fax: (01622) 677574 *Blind manufrs*

Allan Cartons, Unit 1d Langley House Middlegreen Trading Estate, Middlegreen Road, Slough, SL3 6DF Tel: (01753) 577900 Fax: (01753) 577900 *Corrugated cardboard box manufrs*

▶ Allan Dyson Asbestos Services Ltd, Cagex House, Leyden Road, Stevenage, Hertfordshire, SG1 2BP Tel: (01438) 360656 Fax: 01438 721973 E-mail: mailbox@adas.co.uk *Asbestos specialist services*

▶ Allan Environmental Solutions, Hewitt House, Winstanley Road, Billinge, Wigan, Lancashire, WN5 7XA Tel: (01695) 682010 Fax: (01695) 682011 E-mail: info@cleantechuk.com *UK Supplier of floor cleaning equipment,cleaning chemicals and janitorial supplies. Available to hire buy or lease.We have a nationwide fleet of service engineers to carry out repairs on all leading brand of equipment*

Ian Allan Publishing Ltd, Riverdene Business Park, Molesey Road, Walton-On-Thames, Surrey, KT12 4RG Tel: (01780) 484630 Fax: (01932) 266601 E-mail: sales@ianallanpub.co.uk *Publishers & printers*

Allan Ian Travel, Terminal House, Station Approach, Shepperton, Middlesex, TW17 8AS Tel: (01932) 255676 Fax: (01932) 252748 *Publishing, printing & business organic gardening services*

Allan Industrial Products Ltd, Suite 3, 30 Bancroft, Hitchin, Hertfordshire, SG5 1LE Tel: (01462) 454021 Fax: (01462) 421312 E-mail: sales@allanindustrial.co.uk *Steel merchants*

▶ Allan W J Wilson Ltd, Office, 1 Balnagore, Fearn, Tain, Ross-Shire, IV20 1RP Tel: (01862) 832840 Fax: (01862) 832840

Allans, Chapel Walk, Rotherham, South Yorkshire, S60 1EP Tel: (01709) 377530 Fax: (01709) 837672 E-mail: allanscarpets@btinternet.com *Carpet contract specialists*

▶ Allarburn Holdings Ltd, Edgar Road, Elgin, Morayshire, IV30 6XQ Tel: (01343) 547455 Fax: (01343) 552297

Company Information

▶ indicates data change since last edition

Allard Windows & Doors, Unit 3b Conners Yard, Crowborough Hill, Crowborough, East Sussex, TN6 2DA Tel: (01892) 665224 Fax: (01892) 669545 E-mail: john.allard@btclick.com *Double glazing installation services*

Allards Lifts, 3a Vectis Business Centre, Coombe Road, Paignton, Devon, TQ3 2QT Tel: (01803) 855136 Fax: (01803) 851082 E-mail: allardlifts@btconnect.com *Lift maintenance & distribution*

▶ Allards Staffs Ltd, Ephraim Street, Stoke-on-Trent, ST1 3SH Tel: (01782) 266441 Fax: (01782) 273856 *Engineers*

Allardyce Engineers, 28 Telford Road, Dryburgh Industrial Estate, Dundee, DD2 3QW Tel: (01382) 832045 Fax: (01382) 832045 E-mail: allardyceengs@ukonline.co.uk *Pipework & plant installation & fabrication*

▶ All-Around Handyman Services, Benedicts, Bosham Lane, Bosham, West Sussex, PO18 8HG Tel: 01243 572127 E-mail: office@all-around.co.uk *Home to the all-around handyman & home services franchise providing proven business opportunities at low cost.*

▶ Allaston Grove Fencing, Allaston Road, Lydney, Gloucestershire, GL15 4EX Tel: (01594) 842365 *Fencing supplies & erectors*

Allaway Acoustics Ltd, 1 Queens Road, Hertford, SG14 1EN Tel: (01992) 550825 Fax: (01992) 554982 E-mail: enquiries@allawayacoustics.co.uk *Noise & vibration control engineers*

Allbatteries UK Ltd, 34 The Metro Centre, Dwight Road, Watford, WD18 9SB Tel: (01923) 241500 Fax: (01923) 245700 E-mail: sales@allbatteries.com *Battery distributors & agents*

▶ Allbits Plumbing Supplies Romney Ltd, Cinque Ports Road, New Romney, Kent, TN28 8LJ Tel: (01797) 363623 Fax: (01797) 363625 E-mail: sales@allbitsupplies.co.uk *Suppliers of plumbing heating & bathroom equipment*

Allbrite Cleaning Services Ltd, Darleydale Road, Corby, Northamptonshire, NN17 2DF Tel: (01536) 202295 Fax: (01536) 266246 *Cleaning equipment retailers*

Allbrite Metal Polishers, 13 Shelah Road, Halesowen, West Midlands, B63 3PG Tel: 0121-550 3819 Fax: 0121-550 4747 *Metal finishing & polishing services*

Allbrook Printers, 12 Fulmar Crescent, Hemel Hempstead, Hertfordshire, HP1 1SG Tel: (01442) 240748 Fax: (01442) 240748 E-mail: steve@allbrookprinters.co.uk *Printers*

Allcap Ltd, Unit 24c Morelands Trading Estate, Bristol Road, Gloucester, GL1 5RZ Tel: (01452) 525800 Fax: (01452) 331125 E-mail: sales@allcap.co.uk *Engineering tool & fasteners distributors*

▶ Allcare Facilities Management Ltd, 49 High Street, St. Mary Cray, Orpington, Kent, BR5 3NJ Tel: (01689) 820146

Allchem (International) Ltd, Broadway House, 21 Broadway, Maidenhead, Berkshire, SL6 1NJ Tel: (01753) 443331 Fax: (01753) 443323 E-mail: info@allchem.co.uk *Chemical import merchants*

Allchem Midlands Ltd, Wingate Close, Nottingham, NG8 4LP Tel: 0115-929 5258 Fax: 0115-929 2379 *Paper disposables & cleaning products services*

▶ Allclean & Safety, Garston Industrial Estate, Blackburne Street, Liverpool, L19 8JB Tel: 0151-494 2929 Fax: 0151-494 2206 E-mail: sales@allclean.net *Safety & cleaning equipment suppliers*

J. Allcock & Sons Ltd, Textile Street, West Gorton, Manchester, M12 5DL Tel: 0161-223 7181 Fax: 0161-223 0173 E-mail: ja@allcocks.co.uk *Rubber recycling & chemical distributors*

▶ Allcomm Communications Ltd, 44 Mount Road, Tettenhall Wood, Wolverhampton, WV6 8HW Tel: (01902) 743000 Fax: (01902) 744665 E-mail: cburgwinn@allcomm.co.uk *ISP computer suppliers*

Allcontrols Ltd, 20 Halifax Road, Cambridge, CB4 3PX Tel: (01223) 366164 Fax: (0870) 4580314 E-mail: info@allcontrols.co.uk *Sole distributors of monitoring & measuring equipment*

Allcord Ltd, Ilford Road, Newcastle upon Tyne, NE2 3NX Tel: 0191-284 8444 Fax: 0191-284 1550 E-mail: enquiries@allcord.co.uk *Safety equipment distributors*

Allcraft Metals, 69 Fleet Road, Fleet, Hampshire, GU51 3PJ Tel: (01252) 811901 *Steel rack manufrs.*

Allcut Machine Tool Ltd, Unit 12 Triangle Business Park, Quilters Way, Stoke Mandeville, Aylesbury, Buckinghamshire, HP22 5BL Tel: (01296) 615368 Fax: (01296) 615369 E-mail: dave@allcut.freeserve.co.uk *Machine tool merchants*

Alldales Drive Systems Ltd, Little Cross, Church Street, Warnham, Horsham, West Sussex, RH12 3QR Tel: (01403) 218787 Fax: (01403) 218833 E-mail: sales@alldales.co.uk *Variable speed appliances servicing & suppliers*

Nick Allday, Broadley Works, Stoke Gabriel, Totnes, Devon, TQ9 6PU Tel: (01803) 782742 Fax: (01803) 782742 *Agricultural engineers manufacture & service*

Allday Time Systems Ltd, Linchford House, Linchford Lane, Farnborough, Hampshire, GU14 6JD Tel: (01489) 572717 Fax: (01252) 544463 E-mail: sales@alldaytime.co.uk *Allday Time Systems are based in Farnborough, Hampshire. During their long history they have had the pleasure of providing many solutions for their clients in the public sector, these include flexible working time systems for local authorities, fixed working hour systems for County Councils with both clock card and PC-linked badge swipe solutions. Allday also supply clocks for driving attendance boards for rapid viewing of who is in or out and their range includes business systems, access control systems, payroll link info, time and attendance system info and much more.*

Allday Time Systems Ltd, Linchford House, Linchford Lane, Farnborough, Hampshire, GU14 6JD Tel: (01489) 572717 Fax: (020) 7403 2216 E-mail: sales@alldaytime.co.uk *Specialists*

continued

in standard & computerised time recording systems

Alldays Peacock & Co., First Floor, 7 Morston Court, Aise Combe, Weston-Super-Mare, Avon, BS22 8NA Tel: (01422) 313351 Fax: (01934) 623727 E-mail: apco@alldays-peacock-co.com *Industrial fan manufrs*

Alldoors Security Systems, Church Lane, Old Basing, Basingstoke, Hampshire, RG24 7DJ Tel: (01256) 359932 Fax: (01256) 352703 *Door & gate operating equipment*

Alldos Ltd, 82 Gravelly Industrial Park, Birmingham, B24 8TL Tel: 0121-328 3336 Fax: 0121-328 4332 E-mail: alldos.uk@alldos.com Principal Export Areas: Worldwide *Manufacturers of chemical injection equipment*

Alldrives Ltd, Unit 6 Mead Park River Way, Harlow, Essex, CM20 2SE Tel: (01279) 445576 Fax: (01279) 425554 E-mail: alldrives@btconnect.co.uk *Conveyor belting distributors*

▶ Allectra Ltd, Network House, Quarry Road, Newhaven, East Sussex, BN9 9DB Tel: (01273) 517957 Fax: (01273) 512503 E-mail: uksales@allectra.com *UHV & high vacuum components, manipulators, motorized stages, valves manufrs*

▶ Allegiance Finance, 12 Royal Cresent, Cheltenham, Gloucestershire, GL50 3DA Tel: (01242) 260557 Fax: (01242) 269874 E-mail: enquiries@allegiance-developments.co.uk *Specialists in locating and arranging the purchases of overseas properties for investment, retirement or second home purchases. We deal in over 16 countries around the world in off plan and re-sale properties.*

▶ Allegiance Finance, 12 Royal Cresent, Cheltenham, Gloucestershire, GL50 3DA Tel: (01242) 260557 Fax: (01242) 269874 E-mail: enquiries@allegiance-finance.co.uk *Specialist brokers in the secured and un-secured loans market including commercial loans, bridging loans, second charge loans, adverse loans and self certified loans.*

Allegro Bags, 110 Huttoft Road, Sutton-On-Sea, Mablethorpe, Lincolnshire, LN12 2RU Tel: (01507) 440192 E-mail: allegrobags@btconnect.com *Promotional bag manufrs*

▶ Allegro Transport Ltd, Birchwood Way, Somercotes, Alfreton, Derbyshire, DE55 4QQ Tel: (01773) 541771 Fax: (01773) 541774

▶ Allelecmech Ltd, 3 Breckland Business Park, Norwich Road, Watton, Thetford, Norfolk, IP25 6UP Tel: (01953) 884451 Fax: (01953) 883038 *Electrical wholesaler*

▶ Allelys Heavy Haulage Ltd, The Slough, Studley, Warwickshire, B80 7EN Tel: (01527) 852408 Fax: (01527) 857623 E-mail: enquiries@allelys.co.uk

▶ Allelys Heavy Haulage Ltd, The Slough, Studley, Warwickshire, B80 7EN Tel: (01527) 852408 Fax: (01527) 857623

A.B. Allen Engineering Ltd, Phoenix House, 20 Duncrue Crescent, Belfast, BT3 9BW Tel: (028) 9037 0269 Fax: (028) 9077 7817 E-mail: sales@allen-engineering.co.uk *Shelving & stainless steel chimney distributors*

▶ Chris Allen Architects, 22 The Brook, Enniskillen, County Fermanagh, BT74 7EU Tel: (028) 6632 4059 Fax: (028) 6634 0057 E-mail: mail@chrisallenarchitects.com *Registered architectural practice established by a Chartered Architect. Practice provides full range of architectural and extensive 3D visualisation/animation services.*

Allen Bros Fittings Ltd, Hallmark Industrial Estate, Hall Road, Southminster, Essex, CM0 7EH Tel: (01621) 774689 Fax: (01621) 774536 E-mail: liz.adams@allenbrothers.co.uk *Yacht masts & fitting, yacht parts fittings products manufrs*

Allen Bros Southsea Ltd, Albert Road, Southsea, Hampshire, PO5 2SG Tel: (023) 9282 8432 E-mail: sales@allen-bros.co.uk *Tyre & battery distributors*

Allen Concrete Ltd, 38 Willow Lane, Mitcham, Surrey, CR4 4NA Tel: (020) 8687 2222 Fax: (020) 8687 5400 *Concrete product manufrs*

Allen Concrete Ltd, 35-37 Rixon Road, Wellingborough, Northamptonshire, NN8 4BA Tel: (01933) 276848 Fax: (01933) 442013 E-mail: info@allenconcrete.co.uk *Concrete manufrs*

Allen & Douglas Corporate Clothing Ltd, Compton Park, Wildmere Road, Banbury, Oxfordshire, OX16 3EZ Tel: (01295) 272700 Fax: (01295) 270486 E-mail: sales@aandd.co.uk *Corporate clothing suppliers* Also at: Bedworth

Edgar Allen Ltd, Whitburn Road, Bathgate, West Lothian, EH48 2RB Tel: (01506) 652341 Fax: (01506) 631331 *Track rail manufrs*

Allen Engineering Ltd, Narlow Works, Thorpe, Ashbourne, Derbyshire, DE6 2AT Tel: (01335) 350419 Fax: (01335) 350533 E-mail: sales@allenandhunt.co.uk *Construction engineers*

Allen Engineering, 34 Great Western Industrial Estate, Great Western Close, Birmingham, B18 4QF Tel: 0121-551 5487 Fax: 0121-551 5487 *Precision engineers & jig grinders*

Allen Engineering Rotherham Ltd, North Street, Rotherham, South Yorkshire, S60 1LG Tel: (01709) 836800 Fax: (01709) 830300 E-mail: sales@alleneng.co.uk *Welding engineers*

Allen Fabrications Ltd, Davies Road, Four Pools Industrial Estate, Evesham, Worcestershire, WR11 1DR Tel: (01386) 47277 Fax: (01386) 765450 E-mail: info@allenfabs.co.uk *Structural steel fabricators*

Allen & Feldhaus Ltd, Hathaway House, Fermor Road, Crowborough, East Sussex, TN6 3AN Tel: (0800) 781 9885 Fax: (01892) 762 3882 E-mail: dan.f@orange.net *For all your Commercial and Domestic Security Access Gates, Barriers and CCTV requirements just call 01892 667070 for some friendly advice. We supply all types of Automatic Barriers, Wooden or Iron Gates, Access Control and Intercom Entry Systems to the entire South East region. From the initial design through to supply and installation, Allen & Feldhaus will provide a high quality and reliable service.*

Fred Allen Products Ltd, Number 16, Balena Close, Creekmoore Trading Estate, Poole, Dorset, BH17 7DB Tel: (01202) 657740 Fax: (01202) 667778 E-mail: sales@fredallenproducts.com Purchasing Contact: F. Allen Sales Contact: F. Allen *Fred Allen Products (FAP): Plastic injection moulding & plastic mouldings manufacturers. Also precision engineers & injection mould & plastic mould toolmakers*

G.A. Allen & Co., 131 Grovehill Road, Banbridge, County Down, BT32 5AB Tel: (028) 4065 1303 Fax: (028) 4065 1370 *Agricultural engineering services*

Allen Gears, Atlas Works, Station Road, Pershore, Worcestershire, WR10 2BZ Tel: (01386) 552211 Fax: (01386) 554491 E-mail: sales@allengears.com *Differential epicyclical & reduction gears*

Allen Groundcare Ltd, 3 Home Close, Greens Norton, Towcester, Northamptonshire, NN12 8AY Tel: (01327) 354789 Fax: (01327) 354053 E-mail: steve@allengroundcare.co.uk *Public,Commercial & Domestic Groundcare and Tree Surgery.*

Howard Allen Seeds, 42 Calvertstown Road, Portadown, Craigavon, County Armagh, BT63 5NY Tel: (028) 3832 3213 Fax: (028) 3834 5583 E-mail: info@howardallen-seeds.com *Agricultural contractors*

Allen Howard Stockport, Thornley Avenue, Blackburn, BB1 3HJ Tel: (01254) 664113 Fax: (01254) 664113 *Hair dressing wholesalers*

Allen Industrial, Phoenix House, Kinmel Park Industrial Estate, Bodelwyddan, Rhyl, Clwyd, LL18 5TY Tel: (01745) 586300 Fax: (01745) 586301 E-mail: mail@allen-industrial.co.uk *Nylon tubing manufrs*

James Allen & Associates, PO Box 8, York, YO41 4YE Tel: (01904) 607227 Fax: (01904) 607337 E-mail: james_allen.associates@lineone.net *Executive selection services*

Allen Lyman Office Equipment Ltd, 213 Wellingborough Road, Northampton, NN1 4EF Tel: (01604) 639586 Fax: (01604) 231249 E-mail: allen.lyman@virgin.net *Office equipment*

Allen Malpass, 3 Pottery Road, Bovey Tracey, Newton Abbot, Devon, TQ13 9DS Tel: (01626) 835200 Fax: (01626) 835200 E-mail: allen.malpass@hotmail.co.uk *Exclusive designer of bespoke hardwood furniture fitted and free standing, in any hardwoods, home grown or imported. Commissioned high quality furniture to enhance your home or office.*

Allen Martin Conservation Ltd, 504 Dudley Road, Wolverhampton, WV2 3AA Tel: (01902) 560065 Fax: (01902) 560066 E-mail: support@allen-martin.co.uk *Energy saving control switches manufrs*

Allen Mezzanines, 42 Croft Lane, Letchworth Garden City, Hertfordshire, SG6 1AP Tel: (01462) 484022 Fax: (01462) 484022 E-mail: allenmezzanines@ntlworld.com *Mezzanines construction*

Allen Mouldings Ltd, 5 Boscombe Mews, Boscombe Road, Southend-on-Sea, SS2 5JD Tel: (01702) 617461 Fax: (01702) 617461 *Purpose made joinery*

Allen Newport Ltd, 31 New Path, Walton House, Fordham, Ely, Cambridgeshire, CB7 5JZ Tel: (01638) 720228 Fax: (01638) 721332 E-mail: info@allen-newport.co.uk *Sand, gravel & concrete producers*

Allen & Orr Ltd, The Albion Sawmills, Union Walk, Chesterfield, Derbyshire, S40 4SA Tel: (01246) 232426 Fax: (01246) 559099 *Saw millers & timber merchants* Also at: Doncaster

Allen & Page Ltd, Norfolk Mill, Shipdham, Thetford, Norfolk, IP25 7SD Tel: (01362) 822900 Fax: (01362) 822910 E-mail: sales@allenandpage.co.uk *Animal food manufrs*

Allen Production Services, Unit 6b Tractor Spares Industrial Estate, Strawberry Lane, Willenhall, West Midlands, WV13 3RN Tel: (01902) 366035 Fax: (01902) 601221 *Engineers*

Allen Signs Ltd, Waddington House, Whisby Way, Lincoln, LN6 3LQ Tel: (01522) 501500 Fax: (01522) 501600 E-mail: enquiries@allensigns.co.uk *Sign manufrs*

▶ Terry Allen Education, Lower Bramblewood, Mill Hill Lane, Brockham, Betchworth, Surrey, RH3 7LR Tel: (01737) 843212 Fax: (01737) 843212 E-mail: contacts@terryalleneducation.co.uk *We offer teaching products that teaches people how to invest in property and shares with return of 59% p.a. on average in renting out shares(whist risk free). You will be provided with a list of properties undermarket value which you can purchase and with the equity of the existing amount you can use it to rent out shares*

W. Allen, 176 Milton Road, Gillingham, Kent, ME7 5LR Tel: (07748) 474957 *Building plaster & decorating services*

▶ Allen Wilson Joinery Ltd, Unit 12, Trident Close, Rochester, Kent, ME2 4ER Tel: (01634) 290560 E-mail: all@allenwilson.co.uk

▶ Allen & Youngs, Marsh Farm, Marsh Road, Hilperton Marsh, Trowbridge, Wiltshire, BA14 7PJ Tel: (01225) 776858 Fax: (01225) 776858

▶ Allenbuild Ltd, Unit 4b Interchange 25 Business Park, Bostocks Lane, Sandiacre, Nottingham, NG10 5QG Tel: 0115-921 0150 Fax: 0115-921 0199 E-mail: mailbox@allenbuild.co.uk

Allenbuild Ltd, Jubilee House, Waterside Drive, Wigan, Lancashire, WN3 5AZ Tel: (01942) 246265 Fax: (01942) 821573 E-mail: north.west@allenbuild.co.uk *Building contractors*

Allenchrome Electroplating Ltd, Pocklington Industrial Estate, Pocklington, York, YO42 1NP Tel: (01759) 303788 Fax: (01759) 305776 E-mail: sales@allenchrome.co.uk *Electroplaters & metal finishing services*

Allendale Components, 28 Allendale Tee, New Marske, Redcar, Cleveland, TS11 8HN Tel: (01642) 478738 Fax: (01642) 272683 E-mail: p.wall@ntlworld.com *CNC production machiners*

Allendor Products Ltd, Bentinck Street, Ashton-under-Lyne, Lancashire, OL7 0PT Tel: 0161-330 6839 Fax: 0161-344 0741 *Door protection plates manufrs*

Allenfield Precision Engineering Ltd, Richs Sidings, Broadway, Didcot, Oxfordshire, OX11 8AG Tel: (01235) 816880 Fax: (01235) 811848 E-mail: trina@allenfield.co.uk *Precision machinists*

▶ Allens Catering Hire, Middlesex Business Centre, Bridge Road, Southall, Middlesex, UB2 4AB Tel: (020) 8574 9600 Fax: (020) 8574 1385 E-mail: sales@allenshire.co.uk *Catering equipment & furniture hire*

Allens (Disinfectants) Ltd, 462 Cleveland St, Birkenhead, Merseyside, CH41 8EQ Tel: 0151-652 4877 Fax: 0151-652 3800 *Soap manufrs*

Allens Group Ltd, Beaumont House, Allens Business Park Saxilby, Saxilby, Lincoln, LN1 2LR Tel: (01522) 705111 E-mail: sales@cncxl.com

Allens Hairdressers Wholesalers, 31 Somerset Avenue, Leicester, LE4 0JX Tel: 0116-235 6855 Fax: 0116-234 1996 *Hairdressers wholesalers*

Allens Removals, 161 Jackmans Place, Letchworth Garden City, Hertfordshire, SG6 1RG Tel: (07850) 872308 Fax: (01462) 621701 *Cardboard & corrugated boxes*

▶ Allens Stourbridge Transport Ltd, 4 Old Wharf Road, Stourbridge, West Midlands, DY8 4LS Tel: (01384) 370721 Fax: (01384) 371741

Allenvale Tools & Productions Ltd, Riverside Works, Thanet Way, Whitstable, Kent, CT5 3JQ Tel: (01227) 277777 Fax: (01227) 277788 E-mail: allenvale@aol.com *Press tool manufrs*

Allenwest Wallacetown Ltd, 66 Third Avenue, Heatherhouse Industrial Estate, Irvine, Ayrshire, KA12 8HN Tel: (01294) 273111 Fax: (01294) 274063 E-mail: sales@wallacetown.com *Electrical switchgear manufrs*

▶ Aller Engineering, Chantry Farmhouse, Unit 1, Aller, Langport, Somerset, TA10 0RA Tel: (01458) 259550 Fax: (01458) 259512 E-mail: allerengineering@hotmail.co.uk *Specialists in non ferrous welding & fabrication*

Allerayde UK Ltd, Unit 1b Enterprise Park, Brunel Drive, Newark, Nottinghamshire, NG24 2DZ Tel: (01636) 613609 Fax: (01636) 612161 E-mail: sales@allerayde.co.uk *Allergy control products*

Allergan Ltd, Coronation Road, High Wycombe, Buckinghamshire, HP12 3SH Tel: (01494) 444722 Fax: (01494) 473593 *Pharmaceutical product suppliers*

Allertex Ltd, Paradise Street, Bradford, West Yorkshire, BD1 2HP Tel: (01274) 723783 Fax: (01274) 728267 E-mail: info@allertex.co.uk *Machinery agents*

Allerton Construction Ltd, Woodbridge Road, Sleaford, Lincolnshire, NG34 7EW Tel: (01529) 305757 Fax: (01529) 414232 E-mail: sales@allertonuk.com *Sewage system suppliers & installers*

Allerton Engineering Ltd, Allerton House, Thurston Road, Northallerton, North Yorkshire, DL6 2NA Tel: (01609) 774471 Fax: (01609) 780364 E-mail: sales@allertonengineering.co.uk *Steel fabricators*

Allerton Packaging Service, 7 King Close, Leeds, LS17 7AS Tel: 0113-269 1440 Fax: 0113-294 4330 E-mail: packserve@totalise.co.uk *PVC & polythene suppliers*

▶ The Allesley Press Ltd, Leofric House, Waterman Road, Coventry, CV6 5TP Tel: (024) 7663 8844 Fax: (024) 7663 8890 *Printing services*

Allevard Springs Ltd, Cambrian Industrial Park, Clydach Vale, Rhondda, Tonypandy, Mid Glamorgan, CF40 2XX Tel: (01443) 424700 Fax: (01443) 424736 *Coil springs manufrs*

▶ Allfabs Fence Suppliers, Kitson House, Watercock Street, Bradford, West Yorkshire, BD4 7DZ Tel: (01274) 740100 Fax: (01274) 689153 *Steel fabricators*

Allfire Protection Services Ltd, Leigh Court, Leigh St, High Wycombe, Buckinghamshire, HP11 2RH Tel: (01494) 446646 Fax: (0114) 944 6646 *Fire fighting equipment distributors*

Allfix Ltd, 2 Leyland Road, Poole, Dorset, BH12 5HB Tel: (01202) 519066 Fax: (01202) 518353 E-mail: sales@allfix.co.uk *Fastener, fixing systems & bolt & nut distributors*

▶ Allforms Of Print Ltd, 25 Bridges Road, Norton Canes, Cannock, Staffordshire, WS11 9PB Tel: (01543) 276621 Fax: (01543) 450308 E-mail: sales@allforms.co.uk *Printing services*

Allgo Ltd, Unit 9c Bank Hall Park, Wharf Street, Warrington, WA1 2DG Tel: (01925) 570150 Fax: (01925) 570155 E-mail: david.snitch@allgo.biz *Packing contractors*

Allgood Technology, Unit 1 Horton Court, Hortonwood 50, Telford, Shropshire, TF1 7GY Tel: (01952) 677145 Fax: (01952) 677145 E-mail: info@allgoodsmt.com *Contract electronic assembly services*

Allgrind, Unit 8 Century Street, Sheffield, S9 5DX Tel: 0114-244 4491 Fax: 0114-244 4491 E-mail: murbeck@aol.com *Manufacturers of tool steel products & precision grinders*

Allheat & Plumbing Services Ltd, Thames House Charfleets Road, Charfleets Industrial Estate, Canvey Island, Essex, SS8 0PQ Tel: (01268) 684414 E-mail: andy@allheat.com *Heating ventilation & air conditioning contractors*

Alliance Automatic Co., Unit 3 The Pilton Estate, Pitlake, Croydon, CR0 3RY Tel: (020) 8688 1866 Fax: (020) 8686 3381 *Automatic gear box repairers*

Alliance Capital Ltd, Devonshire Ho, 1 Mayfair Pl, London, W1J 8JJ Tel: (020) 7470 0100 *Investment fund management*

▶ Alliance Computing Technologies (ACT) Ltd, Concorde House, Limber Road, Kirmington, Ulceby, North Lincolnshire, DN39 6YP Tel: (01652) 682202 Fax: (01652) 680788 E-mail: sjh@act-it.co.uk *IT services*

Alliance Concrete Ltd, Hargreaves St, Manchester, M4 4EJ Tel: (0800) 7836320 Fax: 0161-819 2624 *Concrete manufacturer (ready mixed)*

Alliance Design & Manufacturing, Westbrook Trading Estate, Westbrook Road, Trafford Park, Manchester, M17 1AY Tel: 0161-872 8881 Fax: 0161-872 8883 E-mail: jimkelly@adm.eu.com *Injection moulders*

▶ Alliance Door Engineering, Unit E3 1 Moss Industrial Estate, St. Helens Road, Leigh, Lancashire, WN7 3PT Tel: (01942) 683601 Fax: (01942) 683607 E-mail: mikelabrey@alliancedoors.co.uk *Industrial door manufrs*

▶ Alliance Electrical Services Ltd, Auld Craichie Inn, Craichie, Forfar, Angus, DD8 2LU Tel: (01307) 819000 Fax: (01307) 819001 E-mail: info@alliance-electrical.co.uk

Alliance Engraving & Lettering Co. Ltd, Unit 18 Barton Hill Trading Estate, Maze Street, Bristol, BS5 9TE Tel: 0117-955 5292 Fax: 0117-955 7518 E-mail: sales@alliance-signs.co.uk *Signs engravers*

Alliance Environmental Pest Control Services, 68 Ellerby Street, London, SW6 6EZ Tel: (020) 7736 1329 Fax: (020) 7610 2071 *Alliance in environmental pest control*

Alliance Fish Whitby Ltd, 1 Pier Road, Whitby, North Yorkshire, YO21 3PT Tel: (01947) 606299 Fax: (01947) 606231 E-mail: alliancefish.1@btconnect.com *Fish Merchants*

Alliance Group, Evans Business Centre, Hartwith Way, Harrogate, North Yorkshire, HG3 2XA Tel: (01423) 504088 E-mail: sales@alliancegroup.co.uk *Records management, documents, imaging & scanning*

Alliance Group (Bristol) Ltd, Unit 303 Central Park, Petherton Road, Hengrove, Bristol, BS14 9BZ Tel: (01275) 892882 Fax: (01275) 892766 E-mail: general@alliancegroupbristol.co.uk *Aluminium & PCVU windows, doors & entrance assemblies*

Alliance Industrial Doors Ltd, Unit 4a Sovereign Works, Deepdale Lane, Dudley, West Midlands, DY3 2AF Tel: (01384) 251951 Fax: (01384) 255888 *Industrial doors manufrs*

▶ Alliance Investigation Services, P.O. Box 1869, Bristol, BS37 9TP Tel: (0845) 6101442 E-mail: jantaylor@allianceinvestigationservices.co.uk *Detective Agency based in Bristol with professional operations nationwide. We provide services to the Private, Legal, and Commercial Sectors. Confidentiality and sensitivity in all matters assured. Surveillance Specialists. Infidelity, Debtor Tracing, Missing Persons, Neighbourhood Reports, Process Serving.*

Alliance Lifting Services Ltd, 95 Stockwell Road, Pembroke Dock, Dyfed, SA72 6TQ Tel: (01646) 621115 Fax: (01646) 622518 *Lifting equipment services & manufrs*

▶ Alliance Log Homes, Lower Newhey Mills, Two Bridges Road, Newhey, Rochdale, Lancashire, OL16 3SR Tel: (01706) 299020 Fax: (0870) 4327879 E-mail: info@allianceloghomes.com *Log cabins manufrs*

Alliance Piling Northwest Ltd, Unit 3-4 Victoria Works, Wallgate, Wigan, Lancashire, WN1 1BA Tel: (01942) 820001 Fax: (01942) 322282 E-mail: enquiries@alliancepiling.co.uk *Piling, foundations, underpinning & structural repairers*

▶ Alliance Publishing Co., 119 Talbot Road, Blackpool, FY1 3QX Tel: (01253) 751614 Fax: (01253) 292915

▶ Alliance Resourcing Ltd, 14 Paul Street, Taunton, Somerset, TA1 3PF Tel: (01823) 48 998 Fax: (08700) 100582 E-mail: contact@allianceresourcing.com *Recruitment services (Perm/Temp). Working within the Legal, IT, Administrative and Finance.*

Alliance Sales (Europe) Ltd, Units 22-24, Brunel Way, Thetford, Norfolk, IP24 1HP Tel: (01842) 822150 Fax: (01842) 820300 E-mail: info@alliance-sales.com *Semiconductor agents services*

Alliance Security Ltd, Alliance House, 180 Kingston Road, Leatherhead, Surrey, KT22 7PZ Tel: (01372) 362213 Fax: (01372) 386249 *Security management & consulting service*

Alliance Snooker Ltd, 45-47 Edge Lane, Edge Hill, Liverpool, L7 2PD Tel: 0151-264 8174 Fax: 0151-281 1490 E-mail: sales@alliancesnooker.co.uk *Snooker table manufrs*

Alliance Spring Co Ltd, 44-46 Queensland Road, London, N7 7AR Tel: (020) 7607 3767 Fax: (020) 7609 2994 E-mail: sales@tascuk.co.uk *Manufacturers of springs, coiled springs & stainless steel springs*

Allianz Cornhill Insurance plc, 57 Ladymead, Guildford, Surrey, GU1 1DB Tel: (01483) 568161 Fax: (01483) 300952 E-mail: cornhill@gho.cornhill.co.uk *Insurance company* Also at: Branches throughout the U.K.

Allianz Cornhill Insurance plc, Allianz Cornhill House, 27 Leadenhall Street, London, EC3A 1AA Tel: (020) 7264 1530 Fax: (020) 7929 3562 *Insurance company*

▶ Alliband Business Services Ltd, 14a-14b Enville Road, Kingswinford, West Midlands, DY6 0JT Tel: (01384) 287483 Fax: (01384) 280186 E-mail: phil@alliband.co.uk *IT solutions & on site support*

Allied Associates Geophysical Ltd, Concept House, Townsend Centre, Blackburn Road, Houghton Regis, Dunstable, Bedfordshire, LU5 5BQ Tel: (01582) 606999 Fax: (01582) 606991 E-mail: info@allied-associates.co.uk *Geophysical equipment sales, repairs & hire*

Allied Bakeries Ltd, 64-66 Orby Road, Belfast, BT5 5HP Tel: (028) 9070 6160 Fax: (028) 9079 3411 E-mail: info@alliedbakeries.co.uk *Wholesale bakery services*

Allied Bakeries Ltd, Dunnings Bridge Road, Bootle, Merseyside, L30 6TG Tel: 0151-523 7566 Fax: 0151-522 6363 *Bakery*

Allied Bakeries, Upper Castle Street, Bradford, West Yorkshire, BD5 7RN Tel: (01274) 738822 Fax: (01274) 745446 *Wholesale distributors*

Allied Bakeries Ltd, 2 Kingsway, Team Valley Trading Estate, Gateshead, Tyne & Wear, NE11 0LT Tel: 0191-491 0077 Fax: 0191-491 0953 *Bakers wholesale manufrs*

Allied Bakeries Ltd, Deacon Road, Lincoln, LN2 4JE Tel: (01522) 528334 Fax: (01522) 537391 E-mail: ab_houghton@alliedbakeries.co.uk *Distribution services*

Allied Bakeries Ltd, 1 Kingsmill Place, Vanwall Business Park, Maidenhead, Berkshire, SL6 4UF Tel: (01628) 764300 Fax: (01628) 764390 E-mail: information@alliedbakeries.co.uk *Bakers wholesale manufrs*

▶ Allied Bakeries Ltd, Cray Avenue, Orpington, Kent, BR5 3RT Tel: (01689) 881111 Fax: (01689) 878155 *Bakery*

Allied Bakeries Ltd, Cartwright Road, Stevenage, Hertfordshire, SG1 4QA Tel: (01438) 359611 Fax: (01438) 316451 *Bakery*

Allied Bakeries Ltd, Birmingham Road, West Bromwich, West Midlands, B71 4JH Tel: 0121-553 2988 Fax: 0121-553 3462 *Bakers wholesale manufrs*

Allied Bakeries Walthamstow, Argall Avenue, Leyton, London, E10 7AB Tel: (020) 8556 1031 Fax: (020) 8558 6636 E-mail: subhirdey@alliedbakeries.com *Bakers wholesale manufrs*

▶ Allied Billiards (Northern) Ltd, Newhouse Road, Huncoat Industrial Estate, Accrington, Lancashire, BB5 6NT Tel: (01254) 390011 Fax: (01254) 385344

Allied Cables Ltd, Liverpool Road, Warrington, WA5 1AP Tel: (01925) 445764 Fax: (01925) 232880 E-mail: alliedcables@absonline.net *Wire & cable distribs*

▶ Allied Catering Equipment, 33 Mayfield Place, Newcastle, Staffordshire, ST5 9LZ Tel: (01782) 711551 Fax: (01782) 711551 *Catering equipment engineers*

Allied Communications Ltd, 7 Hepton Court, Leeds, LS9 6PW Tel: 0113-200 9000 Fax: 0113-200 9001 E-mail: info@alliedcom.co.uk *Telecommunication systems sales & service*

Allied Distillers Ltd, Miltonduff Distillery, Elgin, Morayshire, IV30 8TQ Tel: (01343) 547433 Fax: (01343) 548802 *Whisky distillers* Also at: Brechin, Dumbarton & Tain

▶ Allied Distillers Ltd, Tormore Distillery, Richardson Road, Advie, Grantown-on-Spey, Morayshire, PH26 3LR Tel: (01807) 510244 Fax: (01807) 510352 *Distillers*

▶ Allied Distillers Ltd, Ardmore Distillery, Kennethmont, Huntly, Aberdeenshire, AB54 4NH Tel: (01464) 831213

▶ Allied Drinks System, Mexborough Business Centre, College Road, Mexborough, South Yorkshire, S64 9JP Tel: (0800) 442299 Fax: (01732) 781818 E-mail: sales@allied-drinks.co.uk *Coffee machine suppliers*

▶ Allied Electronic Security Ltd, 10 Town End, Caterham, Surrey, CR3 5UG Tel: (01883) 381382 Fax: (01883) 340267 E-mail: info@allied-security.co.uk *Offer a security service*

Allied Filter Systems Ltd, Huntsman Drive, Northbank Industrial Park, Irlam, Manchester, M44 5EG Tel: 0161-777 9505 Fax: 0161-777 9506 E-mail: sales@alliedfilter.com *Filter bag, pressure vessel manufrs*

Allied Forma, 6 Beacon Road, Poulton Industrial Estate, Poulton-le-Fylde, Lancashire, FY6 8JE Tel: (01253) 884646 Fax: (01253) 899114 E-mail: alangreen1@compuserve.com *PVCu profile bending services & fabricators*

▶ Allied Forming Services, Unit 8 Edwards La Industrial Estate, Liverpool, L24 9HX Tel: 0151-486 3872 Fax: 0151-486 3857 *Soft ceramics*

Allied Glass Containers, Fernley Green Road, Knottingley, West Yorkshire, WF11 8DH Tel: (01977) 672661 Fax: (01977) 607116 E-mail: admin@allied-glass.com *Glass container bottle manufrs*

Allied Glass Containers Ltd, South Accommodation Road, Leeds, LS10 1NQ Tel: 0113-245 1568 Fax: 0113-244 9349 E-mail: sales@allied-glass.com *Glass container manufrs* Also at: Falkirk

Allied Glazing Systems Ltd, 60 Cyclops Street, Sheffield, S4 8EH Tel: 0114-243 3595 Fax: 0114-243 2298 E-mail: info@allied-glazing.co.uk *Aluminium shopfront manufrs*

Allied Grain (South) Ltd, Church Lane, Godmersham, Canterbury, Kent, CT4 7DS Tel: (01227) 731161 Fax: (01227) 731157 *Grain traders*

▶ Allied Industrial Services, 1 Withensfield, Wallasey, Merseyside, CH45 7NP Tel: 0151-734 4242 Fax: 0151-734 4242 *Prevention & control of legionnaire's disease*

▶ Allied International Credit UK Ltd, The Clocktower, Chineham, Basingstoke, Hampshire, RG24 8BQ Tel: (01256) 416400 Fax: (01256) 355155 E-mail: marketing@aiccorp.com *Debt recovery services*

▶ Allied International Trading Ltd, Unit A1, Hubert Road, Brentwood, Essex, CM14 4JE Tel: (01277) 204355 Fax: (01277) 204377 E-mail: sales@supertouch.co.uk *Protective clothing, footwear distributors or agents*

▶ Allied Machine Sales, 23 Saxton Lane, Saxton, Tadcaster, North Yorkshire, LS24 9QD Tel: (01937) 558560 Fax: (01937) 558642 E-mail: info@alliedmachines.co.uk *Vending machines, hot drinks & snacks suppliers*

Allied Machinery Ltd, Star Works, Tong Road, Leeds, LS12 3BH Tel: 0113-279 2792 Fax: 0113-279 9799 *Distribution of safety footwear & protective work wear*

Allied Manufacturing, Sarena House Grove Park Industrial Estate, Grove Park, London, NW9 0EB Tel: (020) 8905 8000 Fax: (020) 8200 9510 E-mail: sandra.mcguire@kingswood-allied.co.uk *Kitchen distributors* Also at: Birmingham, Glasgow, Newcastle & Oldham

Allied Material Handling, Unit 24 Philadelphia Complex, Philadelphia, Houghton le Spring, Tyne & Wear, DH4 4UG Tel: 0191-584 7617 Fax: 0191-584 9797 E-mail: joe@alliedmaterialhandling.fsnet.co.uk *Forklift equipment & forklift driving training*

Allied Maxcut Engineering Co. Ltd, 93 Vantage Point, Pensnett Estate, Kingswinford, West Midlands, DY6 7FR Tel: (01384) 400900 Fax: (01384) 400105 E-mail: rodcrawford@alliedmaxcut.com *Special cutting tools engineers*

Allied Meat Importers, Stuart House, Britannia Road, Queens Gate, Waltham Cross, Hertfordshire, EN8 7TF Tel: (01992) 807950 Fax: (01992) 807951 E-mail: amiuk@alliedmeats.com *Allied Meat Importers based in Waltham Cross, Hertfordshire markets and promotes the following two brands, Botswana Meat Commission products under the ECCO brand and Swaziland Meat Industries products under the SIMUNYE brand.*

Allied Packaging Ltd, Brabant House, Portsmouth Road, Thames Ditton, Surrey, KT7 0EY Tel: (020) 8398 8882 Fax: (020) 8398 4485 E-mail: sales@alliedpackaging.co.uk *Suppliers of packaging* Also at: Claygate

Allied Rubber Products, 15 Cornwall Road Industrial Estate, Smethwick, West Midlands, B66 2JT Tel: 0121-565 0961 Fax: 0121-565 0976 *Rubber products suppliers & manufrs*

Allied Sports & Leisure Ltd, 2 Westminster House, Thorley Street, Failsworth, Manchester, M35 9PA Tel: 0161-688 7049 Fax: 0161-681 9851 E-mail: sales@asll.co.uk *Sports equipment manufacturers*

Allied Stainless Ltd, Newtown Works, Cradley Road, Dudley, West Midlands, DY2 9SW Tel: (01384) 635000 Fax: (01384) 633000 E-mail: info@alliedstainless.co.uk *Stainless steel stockholders*

Allied Tank & Fabrications Ltd, Phoenix Works Industrial Estate, Richards Street, Wednesbury, West Midlands, WS10 8BZ Tel: 0121-568 8166 Fax: 0121-568 8177 E-mail: sales@alliedtanks.co.uk *Carbon & stainless steel tank manufacturers to the industries*

Allied Technical Services Ltd, Aberdeen Studios, 22-24 Highbury Grove, London, N5 2EA Tel: (020) 7226 2220 Fax: (020) 7226 0297 *Employment agency*

Allied (Tooling) Ltd, Unit 2, 19 Willis Way, Poole, Dorset, BH15 3SS Tel: (01202) 675767 Fax: (01202) 684422 E-mail: sales@alliedtooling.com *Regrinding of Engineering Tools. Tooling sales & service inc TCT, HSS, PCD blades. Bandsaw Blades, Abrasives. Shank & profiled tooling.*

Allied Traders, 28 Seaton Place, Jersey, JE4 5XU Tel: (01534) 722213 Fax: (01534) 870613 E-mail: alliedtraders@jerseymail.co.uk *Paper & catering supplies distribs*

▶ Allied Trades Ltd, 14-16 Highholm Street, Port Glasgow, Renfrewshire, PA14 5HJ Tel: (01475) 743666

▶ Allied Transport Scotland Ltd, 120 Springhill Parkway, Glasgow Business Park, Baillieston, Glasgow, G69 6GA Tel: 0141-781 9414

Allied Underwriting Agencies Ltd, 14 Fenchurch Avenue, London, EC3M 5AT Tel: (020) 7265 1166 Fax: (020) 7265 1857 E-mail: info@aua-insurance.com *Insurance underwriters*

Allied Wall Ties, Blade Works, Marriner Road, Keighley, West Yorkshire, BD21 5LW Tel: (01535) 690555 Fax: (01535) 606031 *Manufacturing engineers*

Allied Workshops Ltd, 45 Hatton Garden, London, EC1N 8EU Tel: (020) 7831 7373 Fax: (020) 7242 4644 *Jewellery repairers & manufrs*

▶ Alligator Business Solutions, 17 Whinhill Road, Glasgow, G53 5RQ Tel: 0141-882 5678 Fax: 0141-882 1443 E-mail: enquiries@alligatorsolutions.com

▶ Alligator Pool Products, Unit 27, Station Road Industrial Estate, Southwater, Horsham, West Sussex, RH13 9UD Tel: (01403) 730505 Fax: (01403) 733888 E-mail: info@alligator-pools.co.uk *Swimming pool supplies*

Allins Ltd, Southgate Works, Hartland, Bideford, Devon, EX39 6DG Tel: (01237) 441242 *Steel fabricators*

Allinson's, Allinson House, Lincoln Way, Fairfield Industrial Estate, Louth, Lincolnshire, LN11 0LS Tel: (01507) 600911 Fax: (01507) 600434 E-mail: admin@allinsonwilcox.co.uk *Printers & stationers*

▶ Allis Chalmers Pumps Ltd Ltd, Containerbase Building, Gartsherrie Road, Coatbridge, Lanarkshire, ML5 2DS Tel: (01236) 437000 Fax: (01236) 437037 E-mail: info@allis-chalmerspumps.com *Manufacturers and worldwide supplier of spares, equipment and replacements for Allis Chalmers Pumps*

Allis Welding Services, Unit 6 Bath Street, Newcastle upon Tyne, NE6 3PH Tel: 0191-295 0041 Fax: 0191-263 0614 E-mail: awswelding@ukonline.co.uk *Suppliers & distributors of welding plant & consumables*

Allison Farming Partnership, Thistledown Farm House, Amesbury Road, Newton Toney, Salisbury, SP4 0HN Tel: (01980) 629246 Fax: (01980) 629246 *Farming*

Allison Gray, Longtown Street, Dundee, DD4 8LF Tel: (01382) 505888 Fax: (01382) 507333 E-mail: allison-gray@dpandl.co.uk *Rubber hose & protective clothing & marquees*

▶ Allison Heating Plumbing & Electrical Ltd, Old Station Way, Holt, Norfolk, NR25 6DH Tel: (01263) 713260 Fax: (01263) 713174 *Heating ventilation & plumbing services*

Allison Homes, Wardentree Park, Pinchbeck, Spalding, Lincolnshire, PE11 3ZN Tel: (01775) 724701 Fax: (01775) 762153 *Building contractors*

Allison Hydraulics Ltd, Unit 2, Factory Lane, Rooley Lane, Bradford, West Yorkshire, BD4 9NW Tel: (01274) 687327 Fax: (01274) 688869 E-mail: sales@allisonhydraulics.com *Allison Hydraulics Ltd is a well-established company with 25 years experience within the hydraulics industry, supplying components and providing a component repair and maintenance service. They are able to supply most hydraulic components, in addition to being a major stockholder and distributor for several*

continued

international hydraulic component manufacturers.

Allison International Ltd, 7 Birchin Lane, London, EC3V 9BW Tel: (020) 7626 2266 *Management consultants & recruitment consultants*

Allison Plastics & Paper Ltd, New Pudsey Square, Stanningley, Pudsey, West Yorkshire, LS28 6PX Tel: 0113-256 6435 Fax: 0113-257 5337 *Vacuum forming plastic manufrs*

▶ Allisport Ltd, Little Northend, Newent Lane, Huntley, Gloucester, GL19 3HG Tel: (01452) 751187 Fax: (01452) 830226 *Aluminium fabrications*

Allister Welding Co. Ltd, Unit 30, Horndon Industrial Park, Station Road, West Horndon, Brentwood, Essex, CM13 3XL Tel: (01277) 812534 Fax: (01277) 812616 E-mail: enquiry@allister.co.uk *Steelwork & architectural erectors & fabricators*

Allistone Electrical, 24 Eastbourne Road, Willingdon, Eastbourne, East Sussex, BN20 9LD Tel: (01323) 502998 Fax: (01323) 502998 *Electrical & air conditioning services*

Alljay Plastics Sheet Sales, 321 Sutton Road, Southend-on-Sea, SS2 5PF Tel: (01702) 600320 Fax: (01702) 600325 E-mail: alljayplastics@aol.com *Sign makers & acrylic fabricators services*

Allmakes Ltd, 176 Milton Park, Milton, Abingdon, Oxfordshire, OX14 4SW Tel: (01235) 821122 Fax: (01235) 821133 E-mail: allmakes@allmakes.co.uk *Commercial vehicle component distributors*

Allman Fasteners Ltd, PO Box 5, Wilmslow, Cheshire, SK9 2EF Tel: (01625) 537535 Fax: (01625) 537635 *Fastener & rivet distributors*

Allman Sprayers Ltd, Birdham Business Park, Birdham Road, Chichester, West Sussex, PO20 7BT Tel: (01243) 512511 Fax: (01243) 511171 E-mail: sales@allman-sprayers.co.uk Principal Export Areas: Worldwide *Spray equipment suppliers & manufrs*

Allmat East Surrey Ltd, The Kenley Waterworks, Godstone Road, Kenley, Surrey, CR8 5AE Tel: (020) 8668 6666 Fax: (020) 8763 2110 E-mail: info@allmat.co.uk *Building material distributors*

▶ Allmec Engineering Ltd, 8 Guardian Street Industrial Estate, Guardian Street, Warrington, WA5 1SJ Tel: (01925) 575820 Fax: (01925) 637796 E-mail: allmec@aol.com *Engineering*

Allmi-Care, Biocity Nottingham, Pennyfoot Street, Nottingham, NG1 1GF Tel: 0115-912 4325 Fax: 0115-912 4326 E-mail: admin@allmi-care.co.uk *Medical & cosmetic product development & marketing*

Allnet Ltd, Unit B4, Intergration House, Woton Grange, Reading, RG2 0TG Tel: (01923) 410415 Fax: 0118-921 6006 *Data cable installation services*

Alloageorge Man & Van, 127 Links Way, Croxley Green, Rickmansworth, Hertfordshire, WD3 3RW Tel: 07780 746844 Fax: 0871 2478031 E-mail: sales@alloageorge.com *long base high top transit van*i always help load/unload*full rac breakdown/recovery*see me on e-bay*username(ALLOAGEORGE)*

Allofts Joinery Services, 4 Ladywood Road, Old Hall, Warrington, WA5 9QR Tel: (01925) 638889 Fax: (01925) 638889 E-mail: sales@allofts.co.uk *Loft ladder fittings*

Sam Allon (Contracts) Ltd, Lincoln Street, Hull, HU2 0PE Tel: (01482) 320051 Fax: (01482) 216610 E-mail: user@samallon.co.uk *Demolition contractors*

Allott Bros & Leigh Ltd, Fullerton Road, The Ickles, Rotherham, South Yorkshire, S60 1DJ Tel: (01709) 364115 Fax: (01709) 364696 E-mail: reception@uwilperengineering.com *Structural steelwork engineers*

▶ Allott Steelwork Ltd, Worthing Road, Sheffield, S9 3JB Tel: 0114-276 6882 Fax: 0114-275 4922 E-mail: info@allottsteelwork.co.uk *Engineering construction steelwork*

▶ Alloway Timber Southern Ltd, Forval Close, Wandle Way, Mitcham, Surrey, CR4 4NE Tel: (020) 8640 5544 Fax: (020) 8640 5599 E-mail: sales@allowaytimber.com *Timber merchants*

Alloy Bodies Ltd, Jubilee Works, Clifton Street, Miles Platting, Manchester, M40 8HN Tel: 0161-205 7612 Fax: 0161-202 1917 E-mail: info@alloybodies.co.uk *Commercial vehicle body builders*

Alloy Fabweld Ltd, 5 Zone C Chelmsford Road Industrial Estate, Chelmsford Road, Dunmow, Essex, CM6 1HD Tel: (01371) 859544 Fax: (01371) 878608 *Architectural metalworkers*

Alloy Heat Treatment, Block 6 Grazebrook Industrial Park, Peartree Lane, Dudley, West Midlands, DY2 0XW Tel: (01384) 456777 Fax: (01384) 453900 E-mail: sales@alloyheat.co.uk *Heat treatment services*

Alloy Sales Ltd, B G K House, Travellers Lane, North Mymms, Hatfield, Hertfordshire, AL9 7HF Tel: (01707) 268222 Fax: (01707) 274655 E-mail: info@alloysales.co.uk *Non-ferrous metal stockholders* Also at: London E17

Allpac, Beck View Road, Beverley, North Humberside, HU17 0JT Tel: (01482) 881255 Fax: (01482) 863537 E-mail: sales@allpac.co.uk *Packaging contractors*

▶ All-Pac, Trevilson Business Park, St. Newlyn East, Newquay, Cornwall, TR8 5JF Tel: (01872) 510065 Fax: (01872) 510765 E-mail: sales@all-pac.co.uk *Packaging material manufrs*

Allpac Exports, PO Box 46, Barnsley, South Yorkshire, S75 2BL Tel: (01226) 280033 Fax: (01226) 280044 E-mail: allpacexports@aol.com *Case manufrs*

Allpine, Deardengate, Haslingden, Rossendale, Lancashire, BB4 5QJ Tel: (01706) 220463 Fax: (01706) 220463 *Furniture & bed retailers*

▶ Allpipe & Valve, 103a Pontefract Road, Ackworth, Pontefract, West Yorkshire, WF7 7EL Tel: (01977) 600606 Fax: (01977) 704215 E-mail: allpipe@aol.com *Pipeline & fittings stockholders*

▶ Allpoint Hire Ltd, Emery Court, Heaton Mersey, Stockport, Cheshire, SK4 3GL Tel: 0161-431 8400 Fax: 0161-431 8411 E-mail: ian@allpointhire.com *Repair, testing & hire of equipment used in the removal of asbestos*

Allpoint Packaging Ltd, Witch Lane Industrial Estate, Charter Alley, Basingstoke, Hampshire, RG26 5PY Tel: (01256) 851081 Fax: (01256) 851305 E-mail: allpointp@aol.com *Manufacture corrugated boxes & packaging distributors*

Allpoint Safety Ltd, Unit 49, Hull Micro Firm Centre, 266-290 Wincolmlee, Hull, HU2 0PZ Tel: (01482) 222796 Fax: (01482) 229969 *Insulating material distributors & safety products*

Allport Ltd, 2 The Faraday Centre, Faraday Road, Crawley, West Sussex, RH10 9PX Tel: (01293) 510246 Fax: (01293) 562044 E-mail: info@allport.co.uk *Freight forwarders*

▶ Allport Ltd, 7-8 Nurseries Road, Baillieston, Glasgow, G69 6UL Tel: 0141-773 2266 Fax: 0141-773 3044

Allport Ltd, 26 Chase Road, Park Royale, London, NW10 6QA Tel: (020) 8965 0678 Fax: (020) 8965 1340 E-mail: info@allport.co.uk Principal Export Areas: Worldwide *Freight forwarders*

Allport Overland, Allport House, Thurrock Park Way, Tilbury, Essex, RM18 7HZ Tel: (01375) 487800 Fax: (01375) 487890 E-mail: info@allport.co.uk *Freight forwarders*

Allport Packaging Ltd, Brokenford Lane, Totton, Southampton, SO40 9TF Tel: (023) 8066 3111 Fax: (023) 8066 3049 E-mail: info@allport.co.uk *Case makers & packers*

Allpower 2 Computers, West Bergholt, Colchester, CO6 3WB Tel: (01206) 247094 Fax: (01206) 247094 E-mail: softwaresales@allpower2computers.co.uk *Computer software suppliers*

Allprep Weighing Equipment, 26 Church Lane, Caythorpe, Grantham, Lincolnshire, NG32 3DU Tel: (01400) 273877 Fax: (01400) 273877 *Weighing equipment suppliers*

▶ Allprint Ltd, Llantrisant Business Park, Llantrisant, Pontyclun, Mid Glamorgan, CF72 8LF Tel: (01443) 228555 Fax: (01443) 237477 E-mail: sales@allprint2000.com

Allprint Ltd, Llantrisant Business Park, Llantrisant, Pontyclun, Mid Glamorgan, CF72 8LF Tel: (01443) 228555 Fax: (01443) 237477 E-mail: sales@allprint2000.com *Printers & stationers*

▶ allretailrecruitment, PO Box 551, Chesterfield, Derbyshire, S40 9BX Tel: 01246 551255

Allsafe Protection Ltd, 120 Moorfield Road, Widnes, Cheshire, WA8 3HX Tel: 0151-424 7299 Fax: 0151-424 2040 *Safety work wear distribution*

Allseal Insulation Products Ltd, Phoenix Works Industrial Estate, Richards Street, Wednesbury, West Midlands, WS10 8BZ Tel: 0121-526 4241 Fax: 0121-568 8177 *Gasket & insulating material distributors*

Allsebrook Pump Services Ltd, Unit 10 Van Alloys Industrial Estate, Busgrove Lane, Stoke Row, Henley-on-Thames, Oxfordshire, RG9 5QW Tel: (01491) 680628 Fax: (01491) 682318 E-mail: sales-allsebrookservices@btconnect.co.uk *Pump services*

Allsecure, Unit 4a Arun Buildings, Arundel Road, Uxbridge, Middlesex, UB8 2RP Tel: (01895) 255950 *Shutter rolling manufrs*

Allsigns, 1-1A Havelock Crescent, Bridlington, East Yorkshire, YO16 4JH Tel: (01262) 400700 Fax: (01262) 400701 E-mail: rob@allsigns-bridlington.co.uk *Sign manufacturer*

Allsigns, 122 Connaught Road, Brookwood, Woking, Surrey, GU24 0AS Tel: (01483) 799100 Fax: (01483) 799188 *General sign makers, installers & metal powder coating*

Allslade plc, Dundas Lane, Portsmouth, PO3 5SD Tel: (023) 9266 7531 Fax: (023) 9267 9818 E-mail: accounts@allslade.co.uk *Structural steelwork manufrs*

▶ Allsop & Francis Ltd, Unit 18, Ford Lane Business Park, Ford, Arundel, West Sussex, BN18 0UZ Tel: (01243) 555525 Fax: (01243) 555526 E-mail: sales@allsopandfrancis.co.uk *Sales & service of commercial laundry & catering equipment*

F.F. Allsopp, Union Road, Nottingham, NG3 1FH Tel: 0115-950 7631 Fax: 0115-950 1057 E-mail: info@allsopp.co.uk *Bookbinder manufrs*

Allsoprint Designers, 3 Titan House, Calleva Park, Aldermaston, Reading, RG7 8AA Tel: 0118-982 0000 Fax: 0118-982 0004 *Print designers*

Allsops Ltd, Hope Bank Works, New Mil Road, Honley, Holmfirth, HD9 6QG Tel: (01484) 661447 Fax: (01484) 666808 E-mail: info@allsops.co.uk *Sheet metalworkers*

Allsorts, 33 Kirkby Road, Hemsworth, Pontefract, West Yorkshire, WF9 4BA Tel: (01977) 610955 *Textiles retailer*

Allsorts Inflatables, 8 Kings Road, New Haw, Addlestone, Surrey, KT15 3BG Tel: (01932) 336306 E-mail: sales@inflatafun.co.uk *Inflatable product services*

Allsorts Of Kitchens, Unit 6 Solent Industrial Estate, Shamblehurst Lane, Hedge End, Southampton, SO30 2FX Tel: (01489) 788617 Fax: (01489) 788617 E-mail: info@allsortsofkitchens.co.uk *Fitting of kitchens, from initial design to complete installation*

Allspares Heating Supplies, 60 Frances Street, Newtownards, County Down, BT23 7DY Tel: (028) 9181 7915 Fax: (028) 9181 7915 *Boiler spares & fittings manufrs*

Allspeed Clutches & Brakes, Unit 14c Birches Industrial Estate, East Grinstead, West Sussex, RH19 1XZ Tel: (01342) 322829 Fax: (01342) 300464 *MOT's garage & motor vehicle repairers*

Allspeeds Ltd, Royal Works, Atlas Street, Clayton le Moors, Accrington, Lancashire, BB5 5LP Tel: (01254) 615100 Fax: (01254) 615199 E-mail: sales@allspeeds.co.uk *Manufacturers of Tangye Jacks, Webtool Cutters, John Blake Hydram, Kopp Variators and Millingford subsurface oil pumps*

Allsports Darts & Trophies Ltd, 34 Fairview Drive, Chigwell, Essex, IG7 6HS Tel: (020) 8500 8283 Fax: (020) 8500 8283 *Trophies & medals*

Allstar Services Ltd, 25 Forward Drive, Harrow, Middlesex, HA3 8NT Tel: (020) 8861 6440 Fax: (020) 8861 3134 E-mail: sales@allstar.co.uk *Digital printing, CD & DVD printing, duplication & packaging*

▶ Allstar Sports Equipment, 1 Mid Road Industrial Estate, Mid Road, Prestonpans, East Lothian, EH32 9ER Tel: (01875) 811255 Fax: (01875) 811880 E-mail: sales@allstar-fencing.co.uk *Fencing equipment suppliers*

Allstat Ltd, Bowmans Trading Estate, Bessemer Drive, Stevenage, Hertfordshire, SG1 2DL Tel: (01438) 759084 Fax: (01438) 740958 E-mail: info@allstat.co.uk *Labels & tape manufacturers*

Allsteed Signs & Graphics Ltd, Unit 4 & 5 Palmerston Business Park, New Gate Lane, Fareham, Hampshire, PO14 1DJ Tel: (01329) 234224 Fax: 01329 317659 E-mail: sales@allspeedsigns.co.uk *Signmakers. Manufacturing signs of all types on time to spec & within budget.*

Allstick Decals, 133 Ridge Road, Kingswinford, West Midlands, DY6 9RG Tel: (01384) 271505 Fax: (01384) 271505 E-mail: enquiries@allstickdecals.co.uk *Signs & printing manufrs*

▶ Allstore Solutions Ltd, Regus House, Highbridge Industrial Estate, Oxford Road, Uxbridge, Middlesex, UB8 1HR Tel: (01895) 876192 Fax: (0870) 7348183 E-mail: sales@allstoresolutions.co.uk *Manufacturing materials, handling equipment*

Allstyle Engineering Ltd, Unit 5 60 Arthur Street, Redditch, Worcestershire, B98 8JY Tel: (01527) 527687 Fax: (01527) 500467 E-mail: allstyle@tesco.net *Precision machinists*

Allswell Security Ltd, 3 Saville Road, Peterborough, PE3 7PR Tel: (01733) 333560 Fax: (01733) 332601 E-mail: martintaylor@ukdoor.co.uk *Security door manufrs*

▶ Alltech, 6 The Chimes, Hillsborough, County Down, BT26 6AJ Tel: 028 92681078 Fax: 028 92681079 *Agricultural services*

Alltech Associates Applied Science Ltd, 6 Kellet Road Industrial Estate, Kellet Road, Carnforth, Lancashire, LA5 9XP Tel: (01524) 734451 Fax: (01524) 733599 E-mail: sales@alltechweb.com *Chromatography equipment supplies*

Alltech Moulds, Unit 2, Foxley Court Farm, Ascot Road, Holyport, Maidenhead, Berkshire, SL6 3LA Tel: (01628) 789993 Fax: (01628) 789994 E-mail: andy@alltechmoulds.co.uk *Plastic & injection mould tool makers*

Alltex Ltd, Sladen Mill, Halifax Road, Littleborough, Lancashire, OL15 0LB Tel: (01706) 377374 Fax: (01706) 377256 E-mail: alltex@alltechsdying.co.uk *Dyers, bleachers & finishers*

▶ Alltgoch Construction, Cwrtnewydd, Llanybydder, Dyfed, SA40 9YJ Tel: (01570) 434337 Fax: (01437) 899353

Alltgoch Quarry, Cwrtnewydd, Llanybydder, Dyfed, SA40 9YL Tel: (01570) 434338 Fax: (01570) 434304 *Quarry operators*

Allthread Plastics Ltd, Ridley Road, Burnt Mills Industrial Estate, Basildon, Essex, SS13 1EG Tel: (01268) 726559 Fax: (01268) 725287 E-mail: sales@allthread.co.uk Principal Export Areas: Worldwide *Manufacturers of plastic industrial fasteners*

Allton Contractors Ltd, PO Box 4, Ripon, North Yorkshire, HG4 1JD Tel: (01765) 604351 Fax: (01765) 600669 E-mail: alton@eborconcrete.co.uk *Public works contractors*

Alltube Engineering, 3-9 Siddeley Way, Royal Oak Industrial Estate, Daventry, Northamptonshire, NN11 8PA Tel: (01327) 878250 Fax: (01327) 300478 E-mail: cope@wakefind.co.uk *Rigid & flexible pipe work systems manufrs*

Alltype Fencing Co. Ltd, Howgare Road, Broad Chalke, Salisbury, SP5 5DR Tel: (01722) 780563 Fax: (01722) 780138 E-mail: sales@alltypefencing.fsnet.co.uk *Fencing contractors*

Alltype Hose & Couplings Ltd, Units 14 & 15 Palace Industrial Estate, Bircholt Road, Parkwood, Maidstone, Kent, ME15 9XU Tel: (01622) 757512 Fax: (01622) 757663 E-mail: sales@alltypehose.co.uk *Distributors & agents of Parker UCC filtration products, industrial rubber & PVC hose, hydraulic oils, stainless steel assemblies, fittings & adaptors, high pressure paint spray hose, mild & stainless steel tube & DIN fittings, valves, cylinders & pumps*

Allube Ltd, Thorncliffe Park Estate, Chapeltown, Sheffield, S35 2PH Tel: 0114-245 4979 Fax: 0114-257 0377 E-mail: sales@allube.co.uk *Lubrication equipment & systems*

▶ All-Ways Couriers, Unit 6 Owen O' Cork Mills, Beersbridge Road, Belfast, BT5 5DX Tel: (028) 9073 2468 Fax: (028) 9045 7010 E-mail: info@allwayscouriers.com *Warehouse and forklift facilities in Belfast, Courier service throughout Ireland. Daily deliveries Belfast - Dublin - Belfast.*

Allweld Wrought Ironwork, 3 300 Archer Road, Sheffield, S8 0LA Tel: 0114-236 8239 Fax: 0114-236 8239 E-mail: sales@allweld.com *Wrought iron gates manufrs*

Allwick Patterns, The Shipyard, Upper Brents, Faversham, Kent, ME13 7LB Tel: (01795) 532580 Fax: (01795) 533707 E-mail: allwickpatterns@btconnect.com *Engineers pattern makers*

Allwood Ceiling Services, Shaws Farm, Horsell Common, Woking, Surrey, GU21 4XZ Tel: (01483) 724180 Fax: (01483) 724316 E-mail: acs4you@aol.com *Suspended ceiling manufrs*

Allwood Design, Unit 3 Creek Rd Ind Est, 96-124 Creek Rd, London, SE8 3BZ Tel: (020) 8692 1935 Fax: (020) 8692 1935 *Joinery manufrs*

▶ Allwood Floors, 28 Faraday Road, Rugby, Warwickshire, CV22 5ND Tel: (01788) 569980 Fax: (01788) 569978 E-mail: info@allwood-floors.co.uk *Specialists in the sanding & sealing of wood flooring*

Allworks Ltd, Unit 4 Dene Valley Business Centre, Brookhampton Lane, Kineton, Warwick, CV35 0JD Tel: (01926) 642544 Fax: (01926) 642512E-mail: allworksltd@warwicks.fsnet.co.uk *Civil engineers & builders*

Allyson Fabrications Ltd, Andersen Road, Goole, North Humberside, DN14 6UD Tel: (01405) 762214 Fax: (01405) 768505 *Steel fabricators & manufrs*

Alm Chesterfield, 3 North Wingfield Road, Grassmoor, Chesterfield, Derbyshire, S42 5EB Tel: (01246) 855338 Fax: (01246) 855667 *Lifting gear services*

Alma Engineering Co. Ltd, Montgomery Way, Biggleswade, Bedfordshire, SG18 8UB Tel: (01767) 317814 Fax: (01767) 317002 E-mail: almaen@globalnet.co.uk *Industrial conveyor system developers, mechanical handling equipment suppliers*

Alma Leather Ltd, 12-14 Greatorex Street, London, E1 5NF Tel: (020) 7375 0343 Fax: (020) 7375 2598 E-mail: tisha.richbell@almaleather.co.uk *Leather merchants*

Alma Patterns, Pondfield, Church Lane, Sheering, Bishop's Stortford, Hertfordshire, CM22 7NR Tel: (01279) 734079 Fax: (01279) 734079 *General engineers*

Alma Products Ltd, 51-53 Brindley Road, Astmoor Industrial Estate, Runcorn, Cheshire, WA7 1PF Tel: (01928) 580595 Fax: (01928) 581022 *Plastic extruders manufrs*

Alma Sheet Metal Ltd, Unit 4 Mottram Way, Hurdsfield Industrial Estate, Macclesfield, Cheshire, SK10 2DH Tel: (01625) 427159 Fax: (01625) 669166 E-mail: sales@almasheetmetal.co.uk *Alma Sheet Metal Limited is located in Macclesfield 18 miles south of Manchester and has been established for over 30 years providing high quality sheet metal and allied fabrications to a variety of customers in the Pharmaceuticals, Chemicals, Food, Plastics and Textiles industries. Although we specialise in Stainless Steel, we are experienced in handling a wide range of materials including Aluminium, Galvanised Steel, Mild Steel (H.R. & C.R.), Copper and Brass and we can handle the materials in sheet and section form. Alma Sheet Metal Limited manufactures a wide range of Stainless Steel fabrications from complex pipework to Pharmaceutical products and Textile machinery - each requiring a wide range of welding skills. We have a fully trained workforce including welders coded to either ASME IX or more currently B.S.E.N. 287 Part 1 & B.S.E.N. 288 Part 3. For further information please visit our website vial the link below.*

Alma Steels Ltd, Steetley Industrial Estate, Bean Road, Bilston, West Midlands, WV14 9EE Tel: (01902) 880726 Fax: (01902) 880726 *Import & export merchants*

Almac Sales & Service Ltd, Capelrig Lane, Newton Mearns, Glasgow, G77 6XZ Tel: 0141-639 2578 Fax: 0141-639 2578 *Garage services*

Almaco S.A., PO Box 22, Selby, North Yorkshire, YO8 9YX Tel: (01757) 705979 Fax: (01757) 706383 E-mail: mark.hurst@khass.fsbusiness.co.uk *Aluminium extrusion manufrs*

Almal Engineering Ltd, Derrington Lane, Derrington, Stafford, ST18 9NH Tel: (01785) 255108 Fax: (01785) 248108 E-mail: almalengineering@supanet.com *General engineers*

Alman Engineering Services Ltd, 12 Bradfield Close, Finedon Road Industrial Estate, Wellingborough, Northamptonshire, NN8 4RQ Tel: (01933) 275551 Fax: (01933) 275552 E-mail: sales@alman.co.uk *Precision engineers*

Almar Services Ltd, 33 Marathon Place, Moss Side Industrial Estate, Leyland, PR26 7QN Tel: (01772) 623336 Fax: (01772) 623486 *Electro-mechanical & sheet metal engineers*

▶ Almay Decorative Products & Packaging Ltd, Elam House, Lydd Road, New Romney, Kent, TN28 8HE Tel: (01797) 364559 Fax: (01797) 367049 E-mail: rod@almay-packaging.co.uk *Contract packing & assembly services*

Almaz Food Co Ltd, 2 Raeburn Crescent, Kirkcaldy, Fife, KY2 5QQ Tel: (01592) 646414 Fax: (01592) 646414 *Food products manufrs*

Almec E A S Ltd, Knowl Piece, Wilbury Way, Hitchin, Hertfordshire, SG4 0TY Tel: (01462) 436330 Fax: (01462) 437160 E-mail: enquiries@almec-eas.com *Printed circuit assembly agents*

▶ Almetron Ltd, Unit 24 Abenbury Way, Wrexham Industrial Estate, Wrexham, Clwyd, LL13 9UZ Tel: (01978) 660297 Fax: (01978) 661104 E-mail: info@almetron.co.uk Principal Export Areas: Worldwide *Chemical blending & mixing services. Also chemical manufacturers, distributors & agents*

Almick Sheet Metal, Unit 7h Claymore, Wilnecote, Tamworth, Staffordshire, B77 5DQ Tel: (01827) 251530 Fax: (01827) 260390 *Steel fabricators*

Almik Engineering, Unit 22 Pershore Trading Estate, Pershore, Worcestershire, WR10 2DD Tel: (01386) 553550 Fax: (01386) 556048 E-mail: steve.almik@btconnect.com *Precision & general engineers*

Almit Metal Finishing, Whinfield Drive, Aycliffe Industrial Estate, Aycliffe Industrial Park, Newton Aycliffe, County Durham, DL5 6AU Tel: (01325) 311777 Fax: (01325) 316472 *Electroplaters & metal finishers*

Almit Technology Ltd, 7 Forest Row Business Park, Station Road, Forest Row, East Sussex, RH18 5DW Tel: (01342) 822844 Fax: (01342) 824155 E-mail: info@almit.co.uk *General soldering services*

David Almond Ltd, Union Works, Bacup Road, Rossendale, Lancashire, BB4 7LN Tel: (01706) 214817 Fax: (01706) 214819 E-mail: venor@davidalmond.freeserve.co.uk *Carpet & rug tufting & tufting machine manufrs*

Almond Engineering Ltd, 3A Fleming Road, Kirkton Campus, Livingston, West Lothian, EH54 7BN Tel: (01506) 412647 Fax: (01506) 412647 E-mail: info@almond.co.uk Principal Export Areas: Worldwide *Precision engineering services*

Almond & Mellor Services Ltd, Hampden Mill, Grimshaw Street, Darwen, Lancashire, BB3 2QJ Tel: (01254) 705498 Fax: (01254) 873680 E-mail: sales@almondmellor.freeserve.co.uk *Metal finishing & polishing engineers*

Almonds Engravers, 12 Duke Street, Darlington, County Durham, DL3 7AA Tel: (01325) 464808 Fax: (01325) 464808 *Hand & machine engravers*

Almondsbury Forge Works Ltd, Sundays Hill, Almondsbury, Bristol, BS32 4DS Tel: (01454) 613315 Fax: (01454) 613303 E-mail: sales@almondsburyforge.co.uk *Wrought iron workers*

Almont Plastics Ltd, Lower Road, Ledbury, Herefordshire, HR8 2DH Tel: (01531) 633640 Fax: (01531) 635925 *Plastics injection moulding manufrs*

Almor Ltd, Daleside Road, Nottingham, NG2 3GJ Tel: 0115-986 8773 Fax: 0115-986 6716 E-mail: sales@mpcl.uk.com *Service engineers*

Almura Building Products, Cantay House, 62 St. Georges Place, Cheltenham, Gloucestershire, GL50 3PN Tel: (01242) 262900 Fax: (01242) 221333 E-mail: philipmarsh@almura.co.uk *Importers and Suppliers of Alcoa Vinyl and Aluminium Cladding, CertainTeed Weatherboards, Stoneflex Aggregate Faced Panels, Nichiha Brick and Stone Effect Boards & Werzalit Weatherboard Cladding. Included in the product ranges are architectural trims, balconies & window boards*

Almurad DIY Bradford Ltd, Bell House, Southfield Lane, Bradford, West Yorkshire, BD7 3NN Tel: (01274) 522375 Fax: (01274) 656333 *Tile manufr*

Alno Products Services, 17 Brookside Business Centre Northway Lane, Tewkesbury, Gloucestershire, GL20 8JG Tel: (01684) 291050 Fax: (01684) 290887 E-mail: alno@btconnect.com *Precision engineers*

Alnwick Computerware, Market Place, Alnwick, Northumberland, NE66 1HS Tel: (01665) 604816 Fax: (01665) 604160 E-mail: sales@alnwickcomputerware.co.uk *Computer maintenance & services*

▶ Aloe Forever Living, 12 Kelburn Crescent, Kilmarnock, Ayrshire, KA1 4UE Tel: (01563) 541407 E-mail: madeleine.hannah@virgin.net *Independant Distributor for Forever Living Products.*Aloe Vera based health & nutrition products.*

▶ The Aloe Shop, 17 Ffordd Y Mynydd, Birchgrove, Llansamlet, Swansea, SA7 9QG Tel: (0845) 2570150 E-mail: info@aloeshop.org.uk *Buy aloe vera products directly from a Forever Living Products distributor, we are the world''s largest grower of aloe vera, and offer natural products for diet, health, wellness, beauty and skin needs.*

▶ Aloe Vera, Haydon House, Church Street, Chipping Campden, Gloucestershire, GL55 6JG Tel: (01386) 841521

Aloe Vera Health Products & Information Service, 55 Amity Grove, London, SW20 0LQ Tel: (020) 8947 6528 Fax: (020) 8947 1463 *Health products distribution & information*

▶ Aloe Vera Products, Unit C23, Houghton Enterprise Centre, Lake Road, Houghton Le Spring, Tyne & Wear, DH5 8BJ Tel: 0191-584 8811 Fax: 0191-584 7856 E-mail: sales@aloeveraproducts.co.uk *Natural health products suppliers*

Aloevera Co UK, PO Box 15, Towcester, Northamptonshire, NN12 8DJ Tel: (01327) 830855 Fax: (01327) 831000 *Health & beauty product manufrs*

Alomgate Ltd, Unit 1, Shaw Road, Dudley, West Midlands, DY2 8TS Tel: (01384) 238786 Fax: (01384) 455261 E-mail: john@alomgate.com *Catering equipment manufrs*

▶ Aloof Design, 5 Fisher Street, Lewes, East Sussex, BN7 2DG Tel: (01273) 470887 E-mail: michellekostyrka@aloofdesign.com *Design specialists*

▶ Alp Scaffolding, 58-60 High Street, Sandy, Bedfordshire, SG19 1AJ Tel: (01767) 692811 Fax: (01767) 699233 E-mail: alpscaffolding@supanet.com

Alpa Garden Centre, 142-144 Swallow Street, Iver, Buckinghamshire, SL0 0HR Tel: (01753) 654101 Fax: (01753) 652641 *Garden centre*

▶ Alpa UK Ltd, 497 Saffron Lane, Leicester, LE2 6UG Tel: 0116-244 0880 Fax: 0116-283 4854

Alpac Alloys Holdings Ltd, Dale Street, Burton-on-Trent, Staffordshire, DE14 3TE Tel: (01283) 567737 Fax: (01283) 512359 E-mail: peter@alpacgroup.com *Aluminium gravity die castings & sand castings*

▶ Alpen Signs Ltd, Marlow Road, Leicester, LE3 2BQ Tel: 0116-263 0550 Fax: 0116-263 0579 E-mail: info@alpensigns.co.uk *Sign manufacturers & installers*

Alpen UK Ltd, 1 Laburnum Park, 72 Knutsford Road, Alderley Edge, Cheshire, SK9 7SF Tel: (01625) 586516 Fax: (01625) 586556 *Drill bit importers*

Alpenbury Ltd, 11 Gateway Industrial Estate, Parkgate, Rotherham, South Yorkshire, S62 6JL Tel: (01709) 528186 Fax: (01709) 528287 E-mail: enquiries@alpenbury.co.uk *General engineers & gear manufrs*

Alpha, 2-6 Spottiswoode Road, Edinburgh, EH9 1BQ Tel: 0131-447 9111 Fax: 0131-452 8259 E-mail: alphabm@btconnect.com *Office equipment retailers*

Alpha, Westbury, Sherborne, Dorset, DT9 3RB Tel: (01935) 813722 Fax: (01935) 811822 *Coated fabric & laminated plastic manufrs*

Alpha, Goudhurst Road, Marden, Tonbridge, Kent, TN12 9NW Tel: (01622) 832488 Fax: (01622) 832488 *Air conditioning suppliers*

▶ Alpha 7, 3 Tipping Brow, Mobberley, Knutsford, Cheshire, WA16 7JE Tel: (01565) 880012 E-mail: contactus@alpha7haircare.co.uk *Professional hair products, designed to address the problems associated with thin-looking hair and preventing hair loss through mechanical breakage. Improves the appearance of hair thinning due to male pattern balding.*

▶ Alpha Anglo College, 3 Dean Street, London, W1D 3TH Tel: (020) 7437 6767 E-mail: info@alphaanglocollege.com *Alpha Anglo College situated in a heart of London in Oxford Street. We offer General English, Intensive English, General English and Conversatation, IELTS and Cambridge Preparation, Business English for Specific Purposed Courses.*

Alpha Asbestos Removals Ltd, 158 Hatmore Park, Londonderry, BT48 0QJ Tel: (028) 7126 9167 Fax: (028) 7136 4356 E-mail: alpha_asbestos@btconnect.com *Asbestos removal services*

Alpha Bearings Ltd, Kingsley St, Dudley, West Midlands, DY2 0QA Tel: (01384) 255151 Fax: (01384) 457509 E-mail: info@alpha-bearings.com *Motor cycle bearing manufrs*

▶ Alpha Beta Controls Ltd, 14 Coles Lane, Sutton Coldfield, West Midlands, B72 1NE Tel: 0121-321 3844 Fax: 0121-321 3866 E-mail: sales@alphabetacontrols.co.uk *Control panel manufrs*

Alpha Bio Systems Ltd, Harlaw Way, Hawlaw Road Industrial Estate, Harlaw Road Industrial Estate, Inverurie, Aberdeenshire, AB51 4SG Tel: (01467) 620266 Fax: (01467) 620265 *Water treatment equipment manufrs*

Alpha Blinds, Radnor Chambers, Cheriton Place, Folkestone, Kent, CT20 2BB Tel: (01303) 244010 Fax: (01303) 244010 *Window blinds manufrs*

Alpha Business Centre Ltd, 12 Princes Drive, Colwyn Bay, Clwyd, LL29 8LA Tel: (01492) 531813 Fax: (01492) 531708 E-mail: sales@alpha-business-centre.co.uk *Retail office furniture & supplies*

Alpha Business Computers Ltd, Bentley House Newby Road Industrial Estate, Newby Road, Hazel Grove, Stockport, Cheshire, SK7 5DA Tel: 0161-483 5650 Fax: 0161-483 5576 E-mail: info@alphacom.co.uk *Software consultancy, design & installation*

Alpha Business Machines Ltd, 5 Chorley West Business Park, Ackhurst Road, Chorley, Lancashire, PR7 1NL Tel: (01257) 279000 Fax: (01257) 231010 E-mail: alpha@copfax.freeserve.co.uk *Photocopiers*

Alpha Business Support Ltd, Cavendish House, Cavendish Avenue, New Malden, Surrey, KT3 6QQ Tel: (0845) 1110060 Fax: (020) 8942 1100 E-mail: info@alphabusiness.net *Computer software developers*

▶ Alpha Business Systems Ltd, Chorley Business & Technology Centre, Euxton Lane, Euxton, Chorley, Lancashire, PR7 6TE Tel: (01257) 249017 Fax: (08700) 517171 E-mail: info@alphasys.co.uk *Computer software manufrs*

Alpha Cam, 68 Wilson Street, Alexandria, Dunbartonshire, G83 0EE Tel: (01389) 729333 Fax: (01389) 729444 *CCTV security cameras systems*

Alpha Chemicals Ltd, 29 Winchester Avenue, Denny, Stirlingshire, FK6 6QE Tel: (01324) 824181 Fax: (01324) 822101 E-mail: alphachem@winning.sol.co.uk *Chemical manufrs*

▶ Alpha Computer Maintenance, 22 Lyndon Avenue, Wallington, Surrey, SM6 7JT Tel: (020) 8254 9920 Fax: (020) 8254 9921

Alpha Computer Products, 6 Portershill Drive, Shirley, Solihull, West Midlands, B90 4DS Tel: 0121-744 0377 Fax: 0121-744 2392 E-mail: info@alphacomputers.co.uk *Computer repair & maintenance services*

Alpha Computer Services, Laurel Bank, Chester Road, Kelsall, Tarporley, Cheshire, CW6 0RT Tel: (01829) 759440 Fax: (01829) 741106 E-mail: admin@alphacomputer.uk.com *Hardware & software services*

Alpha Computer Services UK Ltd, 69 Bransgrove Road, Edgware, Middlesex, HA8 6HZ Tel: (020) 8905 7245 Fax: (020) 8905 7245 *Computer systems servicing*

Alpha Co Consulting Engineers Ltd, 30 Stowell Cresent, Wareham, Dorset, BH20 4PZ Tel: (01929) 551207 Fax: (07802) 431378 E-mail: info@alpha-comp.co.uk *Consultant engineers*

Alpha Controls Ltd, Hindley Industrial Estate, Off Swan Lane, Hindley Green, Wigan, Lancashire, WN2 4HR Tel: (01942) 525833 Fax: (01942) 523413 E-mail: technicalsales@alphacontrols.co.uk *Agent & distributor pneumatic controls valve, pumps, switches sensors*

Alpha Design, 1 Didcot Road, Nuffield Industrial Estate, Poole, Dorset, BH17 0GD Tel: (01202) 684248 Fax: (01202) 666190 E-mail: info@alphadesign-poole.co.uk *Electronic services sub-contractors*

▶ Alpha Distribution Sales & Service, Old Doncaster Road, Wath-upon-Dearne, Rotherham, South Yorkshire, S63 7EU Tel: (01709) 515157 Fax: (01709) 515158 *Scuba diving equipment manufrs*

Alpha Dot Ltd, 6 Hollom Down Road, Lopcombe, Salisbury, SP5 1BP Tel: (01264) 781989 Fax: (01264) 782017 E-mail: info@alphadot.co.uk *Printing machine manufrs*

▶ Alpha Electrical, Unit 11 Kingsway, Norwich, NR2 4UE Tel: (01603) 662270 Fax: (01603) 633478 E-mail: info@alpha-electrical.co.uk

Alpha Electrics Ltd, Unit 11, 158 Tithe St, Leicester, LE5 4BN Tel: 0116-276 8686 Fax: 0116-276 6776 E-mail: info@alphaelectrics.com *Electrical machine tools manufrs*

▶ Alpha Engineering Solutions Ltd, 2 Pit Lane, Talke Pits, Stoke-on-Trent, ST7 1UH Tel: (01782) 774444 Fax: (01782) 775525 E-mail: enquires@alphaeng.co.uk *Sub-contract machinists*

Alpha Engraving Co. Ltd, Unit F1 Bounds Green Industrial Estate, South Way, London, N11 2UL Tel: (020) 8368 1674 Fax: (020) 8368 1675 E-mail: alphablocks@btconnect.com *Litho-letterpress & lithographic plate manufrs*

Alpha Fabrications, Unit 53c Notley Enterprise Park, Raydon Road, Great Wenham, Colchester, CO7 6QD Tel: (01473) 827263 Fax: (01473) 829762 *Gates, railings, staircases, balustrades, balconies, fencing.*

Alpha Fasteners, Unit 13 Ffrwdgrech Industrial Estate, Ffrwdgrech Road, Brecon, Powys, LD3 8LA Tel: (01874) 625631 Fax: (01874) 625326 E-mail: sales@alphafasteners.co.uk *Bolt & nut distributors*

Alpha Fire Protection, Unit 30 East Belfast Enterprise Park, Albertbridge Road, Belfast, BT5 4GX Tel: (028) 9046 1681 Fax: (028) 9045 7376 *Fire equipment repair services*

Alpha Fireworks Ltd, Marlie Farm, The Broyle Shortgate, Lewes, East Sussex, BN8 6PH Tel: (01825) 840818 Fax: (01825) 840818 E-mail: sales@sussexfireworks.co.uk *Firework display suppliers*

▶ Alpha Gauging Ltd, 11 Hoo Road, Meppershall, Shefford, Bedfordshire, SG17 5LP Tel: (01462) 819435 Fax: (01462) 812849 E-mail: sales@alphagauging.com *Electronic indicators & transducer systems to the gauging industry*

Alpha Graphics, 40 Carrmere Road, Leechmere Industrial Estate, Sunderland, SR2 9TW Tel: 0191-523 9100 Fax: 0191-523 6045 *Printers*

Alpha Instrumentation Ltd, 6 Stoke Close, Seaford, East Sussex, BN25 3RN Tel: (01323) 897027 Fax: (01323) 897027 *Design control systems*

Alpha Interiors, 1013b Finchley Road, London, NW11 7ES Tel: (020) 8455 6619 Fax: (020) 8951 0093 *Wooden furniture manufrs*

▶ Alpha Leather Goods, Osbourne House, Charles Street, Walsall, WS2 9LZ Tel: (01922) 721804 Fax: (01922) 722733

Alpha Lettering Systems, 10 New Street, Ossett, West Yorkshire, WF5 8BH Tel: (01924) 275747 Fax: (01924) 275740 E-mail: sales@alphalettering.co.uk *Labeling machines*

Alpha Mail Ltd, 18 Victoria Way, Burgess Hill, West Sussex, RH15 9NF Tel: (01444) 871555 Fax: (01444) 871355 E-mail: sales@alphamail.co.uk *Direct mail services*

Alpha Marketing plc, 53 Dargan Road, Belfast, BT3 9JU Tel: (028) 9078 1531 Fax: (028) 9037 0053 E-mail: alphamarketing@msn.com *Office equipment suppliers*

Alpha Media Direct Marketing, 38 Second Drove, Peterborough, PE1 5XA Tel: (01733) 898023 Fax: (01733) 898324 E-mail: sales@alphamedia.co.uk *Direct Mail Company - Alphamedia offers a complete Direct Mail service encompassing Supply of mailing lists, Machine enclosing and Hand Enclosing, Data Processing & Management, Printing & Pre-press, Envelope Supply & Overprinting, Personalisation and Promotional Mailing. Whether producing simple address labels or the more complicated personalised mailings Alphamedia can provide you with a competitively priced solution for all your fulfillment requirements.*

Alpha Metal Finishes Ltd, Bond End Works, Yoxall, Burton-on-Trent, Staffordshire, DE13 8NL Tel: (01543) 472333 Fax: (01543) 473575 E-mail: diane@alphametalfinishesltd.co.uk *Anodisers & polishers services*

Alpha Micro Components Ltd, Springfield House, Cranes Road, Sherborne St. John, Basingstoke, Hampshire, RG24 9LJ Tel: (01256) 851770 Fax: (01256) 851771 E-mail: sales@alphamicro.net *Components design & manufrs*

▶ Alpha One Consultants Ltd, 24 Elm Way, Messingham, Scunthorpe, South Humberside, DN17 3UR Tel: (01724) 764892

▶ Alpha Optics, Manor House, Back Lane, Souldrop, Bedford, MK44 1HQ Tel: (01234) 272746 Fax: (01234) 783093 E-mail: sales@fibre-optic-lighting.co.uk *Manufactures fibre optic lighting kits for unlimited applications. Bathroom lighting or bedroom lighting (star ceiling lighting kits, crystal ceiling lighting kits, colourwash downlight kit & colourwash tube light kit)*

Alpha Packaging, Gooch, Didcot, Oxfordshire, OX11 7PR Tel: (01235) 511500 Fax: (01235) 510543 E-mail: alpha.packaging@btconnect.com *Polythene bag manufrs*

Alpha Pattern Co., Grove Road, Northfleet, Gravesend, Kent, DA11 9AX Tel: (01474) 568669 Fax: (01474) 568669 *Engineers' pattern makers*

▶ Alpha Peerless Fire Systems Ltd, Wiltshire House, Tovil Green, Maidstone, Kent, ME15 6RJ Tel: (01622) 693869 Fax: (01622) 756675

▶ Alpha Pine (Harrogate) Ltd, 55 Knaresborough Road, Harrogate, North Yorkshire, HG2 7LT Tel: (01423) 885196 Fax: (01423) 885196 E-mail: info@alphapine.co.uk *Pine manufrs & furniture retailers*

▶ Alpha Plating Technologies Ltd, Unit 1 2, Block 3, Wednesbury Trading Estate, Wednesbury, West Midlands, WS10 7JN Tel: 0121-506 1720

Alpha Plus, 10 Caputhall Road, Deans Industrial Estate, Livingston, West Lothian, EH54 8AS Tel: (01506) 401401 E-mail: service@alphascot.co.uk *Industrial cleaning contractors & suppliers of machinery*

▶ Alpha Pneumatic Supplies Ltd, Unit 7, The I O Centre, Hearle Way, Hatfield, Hertfordshire, AL10 9EW Tel: (01707) 282700 Fax: (01707) 282701 E-mail: sale@naylors.co.uk *Pneumatic equipment distributors*

Alpha Polymers Ltd, Costain Street, Liverpool, L20 8QJ Tel: (0151-933 3020 Fax: 0151-944 1494 E-mail: neil@alpha-polymers.freeserve.co.uk *Raw plastics converters*

Alpha Pool Table Services, 19 Maple Grove, Tadley, Hampshire, RG26 4ND Tel: 0118-982 0190 Fax: 0118-982 0190 *Pool tables refurbishment services*

Alpha Powder Coatings, 6-10 Benedict Square, Peterborough, PE4 6GD Tel: (01733) 320111 Fax: (01733) 320111 E-mail: alphapowder@aol.com *Powder coating & finishing services*

Alpha Precision Engineering (Poole) Ltd, Units 7-8 Alpha Centre, Upton Road, Poole, Dorset, BH17 7AG Tel: (01202) 683819 Fax: (01202) 665030 E-mail: sales@alphaprecision.net *Machining services*

Alpha Price, Station Road, Harrow, Middlesex, HA1 1NA Tel: (020) 8861 4710 *Cutlery Supplier*

Alpha Print & Design, Unit 12, Sedgemount Industrial Park, Bristol Road, Bridgwater, Somerset, TA6 4AR Tel: (01278) 426958 Fax: (01278) 424001 E-mail: alphaprint@ukonline.co.uk *Label printer suppliers*

Alpha Printing Services, 227b Withington Road, Manchester, M16 8LU Tel: 0161-862 9922 Fax: 0161-862 9944 E-mail: sales@alphaprint.com *Commercial printers*

Alpha Refrigeration, 25 Langdale Road, Blackburn, BB2 5DP Tel: (01254) 209577 Fax: (01254) 209577 *Refrigeration sales & repairers*

Alpha Roofing Ltd, Unit 9 Crompton Mrne Industria, Est Victoria Rd, Oulton Broad, Lowestoft, Suffolk, NR33 9NQ Tel: (01502) 569847 Fax: (01502) 567573 E-mail: info@alpharoof.co.uk *Flat roofing specialists*

Alpha Rowen Treatments Ltd, 3-4 & 7 Brymill Industrial Units, Brown Lion Street, Tipton, West Midlands, DY4 9EG Tel: 0121-557 2376 Fax: 0121-557 2580 E-mail: kevin.p.rowen@btinternet.com *Customer specialists heat treatment services*

Alpha Rowen Treatments Ltd, 3-4 & 7 Brymill Industrial Units, Brown Lion Street, Tipton, West Midlands, DY4 9EG Tel: 0121-557 2376 Fax: 0121-557 2580 *Heat treatment services*

Alpha Safety Supplies Ltd, 18 Jeynes Road, Tewkesbury, Gloucestershire, GL20 5NG Tel: (01684) 298083 Fax: (01684) 850420 E-mail: sales@alphasafetysupplies.co.uk *Suppliers of protective and corporate clothing, transmission products, engineering supplies. Also suppliers and installers of environmental depollution equipment including a range of chem free cleaning products. We can also provide general plant maintenance.*

▶ Alpha Science Editors, Bridge Cottage, Chapelton, Muir of Ord, Ross-Shire, IV6 7XP Tel: (0845) 6448601 E-mail: info@alphascienceeditors.com *Editing services for scientists*

Alpha Sheet Metal Work, Unit 3A, Butlerfield Industrial Estate, Newton Grange, Bonnyrigg, Midlothian, EH19 3JQ Tel: (01875) 822588 *Sheet metal workers*

Alpha Sign Systems, Oakwood Bussiness Park, Oldmixon Crescent, Weston-Super-Mare, Avon, BS24 9AY Tel: (01934) 625444 Fax: (01934) 625358 E-mail: sales@alphasignsystems.com *Signs manufrs*

Alpha Signs, Hamperden End, Debden Green, Saffron Walden, Essex, CB11 3NA Tel: (01279) 850555 *Sign manufrs*

Alpha Signs (Northampton) Ltd, Clarence Avenue, Northampton, NN2 6NY Tel: (01604) 712233 Fax: (01604) 717131 *Sign manufrs*

Alpha Solway Ltd, Queensberry Street, Annan, Dumfriesshire, DG12 5BL Tel: (01461) 202452 Fax: (01461) 205684 E-mail: sales@alphasolway.com *Safety & protective clothing manufrs*

Alpha Stove Enamelling Ltd, Unit 17 Green Lane Industrial Estate, Green Lane, Letchworth Garden City, Hertfordshire, SG6 1HP Tel: (01462) 670761 Fax: (01462) 684466 E-mail: alphastoveltd@aol.com *Stove enamellers*

Alpha Systems, Imperial Works, Coalpit Hill, Talke, Stoke-on-Trent, ST7 1PN Tel: (01782) 783267 Fax: (01782) 776240 E-mail: info@alphasystems-tec.co.uk *Sheet metal engineers*

Alpha Systems, 63-65 High Street, Standish, Wigan, Lancashire, WN6 0HD Tel: (01257) 426617 Fax: (01257) 472148 E-mail: info@alphasolutions.co.uk *Sign & labeling systems suppliers*

▶ Alpha Technologies, Twyford House, Pig Lane, Thorley, Bishop's Stortford, Hertfordshire, CM22 7PA Tel: (01279) 501110 Fax: (01280) 659870 E-mail: sales@alphaeurope.com *Power supplies*

▶ Alpha Technologies, 5 Alpha Technologies, Larkfield Industrial Estate, Greenock, Renfrewshire, PA16 0EQ Tel: (01475) 633333 Fax: (01475) 630055

Alpha Technologies, Unit 2B Crowood House, Gipsy Lane, Swindon, SN2 8YY Tel: (01793) 601100 Fax: (01793) 615214 Principal Export Areas: Worldwide *Testing equipment manufrs*

Alpha Telecommunications Ltd, 359a Hagley Rd, Edgbaston, Birmingham, B17 8DL Tel: 0121-434 4003 Fax: 0121-434 4043 *Facsimile machine distributors/computer manufacturers*

Alpha Therm Ltd, Nepicar House, London Road, Wrotham Heath, Sevenoaks, Kent, TN15 7RS Tel: (01732) 783000 Fax: (01732) 783080 E-mail: info@alphatherm.co.uk *Boiler manufrs*

Alpha Tool Grinding, Unit 6 Stafford Park 4, Telford, Shropshire, TF3 3BA Tel: (01952) 292988 Fax: (01952) 292988 *Tool & cutter grinding services*

Alpha Tools (Northern) Ltd, Grove Road, Wakefield, West Yorkshire, WF1 1UW Tel: (01924) 384227 Fax: (01924) 363525 E-mail: sales@alphatools.co.uk *Power tool sales, hire & repair*

Alpha Tube Co., Tameside Works, Park Road, Dukinfield, Cheshire, SK16 5PT Tel: 0161-339 8901 Fax: 0161-343 1750 E-mail: alpha@alphatube.freeserve.co.uk *Spiral ducting manufrs*

▶ Alpha Tutors, No. 6, Russell Flint House, Royal Docks, London, E16 1UT Tel: 0207 4732360 *Alpha Tutors is the leading online national tuition agency. Due to an*increased demand in many subjects, including elocution, singing and*various instruments, we are seeking exceptional individuals, with a flair*for teaching. Full or part time, online and offline private tutors*required. To apply, please visit www.alphatutors.co.uk**

▶ Alpha Windows Ltd, 30 Town Lane, Denton, Manchester, M34 6LE Tel: 0161-335 0129 Fax: 0161-337 8717 *Windows*

▶ Alphabet Signs (south west) Ltd, Mary Seacole Rd, The Millfields, Plymouth, PL1 3JY Tel: 08447 255456

Alphabet Video Production, 2 The Heywoods, Chester, CH2 2RA Tel: (01244) 380744 Fax: (01244) 380744 E-mail: alan.digby@btconnect.com *Video production, filming, editing, DVD production*

Alphacast Ltd, 139 Park Road, Halesowen, West Midlands, B63 2NR Tel: (01384) 634542 E-mail: alphacast@btconnect.com *Aluminium & copper castings*

Alphachem Ltd, 55 Nutfield Rd, Merstham, Redhill, RH1 3ER Tel: (01737) 644836 Fax: (01737) 644500 *Pharmaceutical export merchants*

▶ Alphaglen Laboratories, Unit 12a Millbrook Business Park, Sybron Way, Crowborough, East Sussex, TN6 3JZ Tel: (01892) 664224 E-mail: kompassenq@alphaglen.co.uk *Manufacturer of air velocity transmitters, condensation detectors, interface modules, thermostatic controllers and water detectors eg for HVAC*

▶ Alphagraphics, 37-39 George Street, Hull, HU1 3BA Tel: (01482) 229111 Fax: (01482) 229090 E-mail: info@alphagraphics-hull.co.uk

▶ Alphagraphics Ltd, 19-21 Collingwood Street, Newcastle upon Tyne, NE1 1JE Tel: 0191-221 2030 Fax: 0191-221 2031

Alphagraphics, 68 Darlington Street, Wolverhampton, WV1 4ND Tel: (01902) 711151 Fax: (01902) 710174 E-mail: wolves016@alphagraphics.co.uk *Printers*

Alphalube Lubricant Distributors, Lincoln Road, Newark, Nottinghamshire, NG24 2DR Tel: (01636) 673705 Fax: (01636) 686660 E-mail: allwoodssales@lineone.net *Cars spares distributors*

Alphamation Ltd, Bassett Road, Halesowen, West Midlands, B63 2RE Tel: (01384) 412255 Fax: (01384) 413191 E-mail: info@alphamation.co.uk *Manufacturers of conveyor systems*

Alphameric Broadcast Solutions Ltd, Pear Mill Industrial Estate, Stockport Road West, Bredbury, Stockport, Cheshire, SK6 2BP Tel: 0161-476 7770 Fax: 0161-476 7771 E-mail: lynsey.rothwell@alphameric.com *Software engineering*

Alphameric Red Onion Ltd, Caxton Close, Andover, Hampshire, SP10 3QN Tel: (01264) 332252 Fax: (01264) 333552 *Book sellers & betting officers*

Alphameric Solutions Ltd, Bishopsgate House, Broadford Park, Guildford, Surrey, GU4 8ED Tel: (01483) 293900 Fax: (01483) 533333 E-mail: enquiries@alphameric.com *IT data communication system*

Alphameric Solutions Ltd, Bishopsgate House, Broadford Park, Guildford, Surrey, GU4 8ED Tel: (01483) 293900 Fax: (01483) 533333 E-mail: enquiries@alphameric.com *Data communication systems*

▶ Alphamet (U K) Ltd, Unit 21 Riverside, Sir Thomas Longley Road, Meadway City Estate, Rochester, Kent, ME2 4DP Tel: (01634) 721122

▶ Alphaone Computing Services, 126 Ladies Mile Road, Brighton, BN1 8TE Tel: (01273) 552955 *Computing services*

Alphaprint Graphic Services Ltd, 18-20 Mark Road, Hemel Hempstead Industrial Estate, Hemel Hempstead, Hertfordshire, HP2 7BN Tel: (01442) 262798 Fax: (01442) 217831 *Lithographic printers*

Alphasense Ltd, 3 Oak Industrial Park, Chelmsford Road, Dunmow, Essex, CM6 1XN Tel: (01371) 878048 Fax: (01371) 878066 E-mail: sensors@alphasense.com *Designers & manufacturers of gas sensors*

▶ Alphasonics Ultrasonic Equipment Mnfrs, Caddick Road, Knowsley Business Park, Prescot, Merseyside, L34 9HP Tel: 0151-547 3777 Fax: 0151-547 1333 E-mail: alphasonics@alphasonics.co.uk *Alphasonics are one of the largest ultrasonic cleaning suppliers to the industry, specialising in a wide range of products and services to the flexographic, sheetfed offset, gravure and specialty printing markets. Alphasound systems are renowned throughout the world for delivering scrupulously clean anilox rolls to a constant level, time after time. At Alphasonics we pride ourselves in delivering the very best and most effective cleaning roll equipment within our industry.*

▶ Alphatalk Ltd, 109 Digbeth, Birmingham, B5 6DT Tel: 0121-633 5200 Fax: (0870) 2005200 E-mail: info@alphatalk.com *Suppliers of peronal name numbers*

▶ Alphatask Salon Solutions, 12B Gaisford Street, London, NW5 2ED Tel: 0870 1417370 E-mail: info@alphatask.net *Salon Software and technology equipment for hair and beauty salons. Xtensions e-Salon Manager, simple to use and learn. Send text messages reminders to customers, Internet booking and report on salon performance.*

▶ Alphatec Software Ltd, Suite 16f, Challenge House, Sherwood Drive, Milton Keynes, MK3 6DP Tel: (01908) 363900 Fax: 01908 363901 E-mail: enquiries@claimcon.net *Alphatec is the creator of the revolutionary online risk analysis and insurance management system - Claim Control. ***Powerful analytical features allow the simple interpretation of complex data, cutting insurance costs and streamlining the administration of all incidents and their associated claims. ***Delivered entirely online, the innovative solution identifies, controls and manages risk, while providing the information necessary to negotiate the best premiums with insurance companies. ** ***

Alphatech Ltd, Green House, Homefield Road, Haverhill, Suffolk, CB9 8QP Tel: (01440) 714709 Fax: (01440) 714706 E-mail: info@alphatech.eu.com *Environmental & information technology products*

Alphawrap Printers, 13 Miners Road, Llay Industrial Estate, Llay, Wrexham, Clwyd, LL12 0PJ Tel: (01978) 856109 Fax: (01978) 852077 E-mail: admin@alphawrap.co.uk *Printed paper/ polythene packaging suppliers*

Alpheus Solutions Ltd, 60 Lombard Street, London, EC3V 9EA Tel: (020) 7464 8444 Fax: (020) 7464 8745 *IT consultancy services*

ALPHR Technology Ltd, Amor Way, Dunhams Lane, Letchworth Garden City, Hertfordshire, SG6 1UG Tel: (01462) 675838 Fax: (01462) 481190 E-mail: alphr@alphrtechnology.co.uk *Automation special purpose equipment manufrs*

▶ Alpine, 8 Millbrook Road, Cramlington, Northumberland, NE23 3GG Tel: (01670) 735402 Fax: (01670) 735402 E-mail: alpinetrans@btinternet.com *A translation and proofreading service specialising in medical and pharmaceutical German.*

Alpine Blinds, 37 Lacy Street, Paisley, Renfrewshire, PA1 1QN Tel: 0141-840 4488 Fax: 0141-840 4499 *Blinds manufrs*

Alpine Computer Systems, 5 Church Road, Bishops Cleeve, Cheltenham, Gloucestershire, GL52 8LR Tel: (01242) 673322 Fax: (01242) 674845 E-mail: sales@alpinesystems.co.uk *Computer services consultants & builders*

▶ Alpine Conservatory Roof Manufacturers, Unit 9 Barnes Road Industrail Estate, Barnes Road, Bradford, West Yorkshire, BD8 9TG Tel: (01274) 494940 Fax: (01274) 484850 E-mail: matt@alpineroofs.co.uk *Manufacturers & suppliers of conservatories roofs & windows*

▶ Alpine Construction Services, Ifield Green, Ifield, Crawley, West Sussex, RH11 0ND Tel: (01293) 412233 Fax: (01293) 514675 E-mail: sales@labour-hire.com *Dry lining & suspended ceiling subcontractors*

▶ Alpine Hygiene Supplies, Unit 6a Bontoft Avenue, Hull, HU5 4HF Tel: (01482) 210021 Fax: (01482) 440060 *Janitorial supply services*

Alpine Precision Engineering, 27 Telford Road, Wimborne, Dorset, BH21 7RX Tel: (01202) 894478 Fax: (01202) 894441 E-mail: alan.codman@virgin.net *Sub-contract precision engineers*

Alpine Preservations, 14 Redpol Avenue, Leigh, Lancashire, WN7 2GA Tel: (01942) 742230 Fax: (01942) 603608 E-mail: p.balickyj@blueyondar.co.uk *Building restoration & refurbishment*

▶ Alpine Sheet Metal Ltd, 21 Porte Marsh Road, PorteMarsh Industrial Estate, Calne, Wiltshire, SN11 9BW Tel: (01249) 813412 Fax: (01249) 815184 E-mail: sales@alpinesheetmetal.co.uk *Metalworking & fabricators*

Alpine Storage Ltd, West Road, Old Hooton Airfield, Hooton, Ellesmere Port, CH65 1BR Tel: 0151-327 5651 Fax: 0151-327 7870 E-mail: alpine@mersinet.co.uk *Warehouse/ distributors & storage - bonded storage. Also enchanced remote transit shed. Warehousing services, bonded warehousing, warehousing and distribution, warehousing, freight, freight import services, dry warehousing, warehousing, hazardous materials*

Alpine Technology Ltd, Unit 12 Tungsten Building, George Street, Portslade, Brighton, BN41 1RA Tel: (01273) 425290 Fax: (0870) 8901087 E-mail: sales@alpinetech.co.uk *Distributors of semiconductor components*

Alpla Plastics Ltd, Wood Street, New Ferry, Wirral, Merseyside, CH62 4ZD Tel: 0151-643 5500 Fax: 0151-643 5512 *Plastic products*

Alpla UK Ltd, Lasborough Road, Kingston, Milton Keynes, MK10 0AB Tel: (01908) 285300 Fax: (01908) 285318 *Plastics*

Alplas Plastics Machinery Services Ltd, 1 Leyside, Bromham, Bedford, MK43 8NF Tel: (01234) 823619 Fax: (01234) 825824 E-mail: sales@alplas.freeserve.co.uk *Machinery services packaging machinery*

Alpress Hydraulic Engineers, 65 Back Sneddon Street, Paisley, Renfrewshire, PA3 2DD Tel: 0141-848 7175 Fax: 0141-889 5280 E-mail: alpresshs@tiscali.co.uk *Cutting manufrs*

▶ ALPS Mobile & Studio photography, Lee Lane, Pinkneys Green, Maidenhead, Berkshire, SL6 Tel: 07779 572360 E-mail: apage@e-work.co.uk *Providing a fast, efficient and high quality photographic service for all occasions*

Alpunch Tooling Ltd, 24 Ganton Way, Techno Trading Estate, Swindon, SN2 8EZ Tel: (01793) 613185 Fax: (01793) 642628 E-mail: johntownsend@alpunch.co.uk *Precision engineers*

Alrad Instruments Ltd, Alder House, Turnpike Road Industrial Estate, Newbury, Berkshire, RG14 2NS Tel: (01635) 30345 Fax: (01635) 32630 E-mail: sales@alrad.co.uk *Through its two trading divisions Alrad Instruments Ltd is a long standing and leading UK leading supplier of machine vision and imaging products, as well as providing Electro Optical detectors and laser products. **Alrad Imaging supplies imaging components and services to both industrial system integrators, OEMs, scientific and research customers. **We provide a comprehensive range of vision products including CCD and CMOS cameras, frame grabbers, lighting solutions, lenses and accessories, and imaging software from the worlds leading manufacturers. Alrad Imaging is a truly "one stop" supplier for all your vision related components. **Alrad Electronics provides a wide range of optical detectors including single channel electron multipliers, micro channel plates and photomultipliers. high voltage components and instruments, infra red detectors, laser lines and 2D laser projectors, densitometers and refractometers. **Visit our web site www.alrad.co.uk for more information.*

Alray Catering Equipment, 30 Prince Andrew Close, Maidenhead, Berkshire, SL6 8QH Tel: (01628) 676099 Fax: (01628) 676099 *Catering equipment repair & installation*

▶ Already Hire Ltd, 469 Malton Avenue, Slough, SL1 4QU Tel: (01753) 512333 Fax: (01753) 533303

Alrian Industries Ltd, Unit 2D Lake Enterprise Park, Sandall Stones Road, Kirk Sandall, Doncaster, South Yorkshire, DN3 1QR Tel: (01302) 885851 Fax: (01302) 885851 E-mail: sales@alrian.idps.co.uk *Electronic recording & industrial equipment manufrs*

Alrog Engineering Ltd, Halifax Road, Cressex Business Park, High Wycombe, Buckinghamshire, HP12 3SD Tel: (01494) 447213 Fax: (01494) 528104 *Sheet metalwork engineers*

▶ alron alarms, Golf View, Main Street, Barry, Carnoustie, Angus, DD7 7RP Tel: 0808-155 3686 E-mail: alron.alarms@virgin.net

Alroy Microwaves & Electronics Ltd, Boulton Road, Stevenage, Hertfordshire, SG1 4QX Tel: (01438) 314753 Fax: (01483) 367430 E-mail: sales@alroymicrowave.co.uk *Waveguide & microwave components manufrs*

Alroy Sheet Metal Ltd, Gunnels Wood Road, Stevenage, Hertfordshire, SG1 2BL Tel: (01438) 355687 Fax: (01438) 367608 E-mail: lorna@alroys.com *Sheetmetal fabrications, welding & machining*

ALS Ultrasonic, Unit 24, Uplands Way, Blandford Forum, Dorset, DT11 7UZ Tel: (01258) 459257 Fax: (01258) 459287 E-mail: als.ultrasonics@virgin.net *Ultrasonic welding equipment manufrs*

Alsager Precision Sheet Metal Ltd, Unit 1C Wistaston Business Centre, Wistaston Road, Crewe, CW2 7RP Tel: (01270) 251271 Fax: (01270) 215614 E-mail: alssheetmetal@talk21.com *Fine limit & prototype sheet metalworkers*

Alsager Printing Co. Ltd, Excalibur Industrial Estate, Fields Road, Alsager, Stoke-on-Trent, ST7 2LX Tel: (01270) 873897 Fax: (01270) 882804 *General printing services*

Alsager & Sandbach Saddlery, Day Green Farm, Hassall Road, Sandbach, Cheshire, CW11 4XU Tel: (01270) 872095 *Saddlery manufrs*

Alsamex Products Ltd, 1 Protea Way, Pixmore Avenue, Letchworth Garden City, Hertfordshire, SG6 1JT Tel: (01462) 672951 Fax: (01462) 480660 E-mail: sales@alsamex.co.uk *Foam converters*

Alsaplas Ltd, Unit 1, Ramsden Road, Rotherwas Industrial Estate, Hereford, HR2 6LR Tel: (01432) 277747 Fax: (01432) 262600 *Polythene film manufrs*

Alserco (UK) Ltd, 111 Fazeley Street, Digbeth, Birmingham, B5 5RR Tel: 0121 643 2421 Fax: 0121 633 3140 E-mail: philip.relph@tkmuk.thyssenkrupp.com *Alserco are a fabrication company specialising in aluminium. We are ablr to make fabrications to your specificatin. Our services include: Cutting, drilling, punching, welding and assembly.*

Alsford Timber Ltd, Montague Road, Brielle Way, Sheerness, Kent, ME12 1YW Tel: (01795) 662363 Fax: (01795) 665806 *Timber merchants*

Alsigns Self Luminous, Hilland Rise, Headley, Bordon, Hampshire, GU35 8LT Tel: (01536) 201525 Fax: (01780) 479032 E-mail: douglas@surelite.co.uk *Manufacturers of lighting tracers*

Alson Controls Ltd, Bolton Enterprise Centre, Washington Street, Bolton, BL3 5EY Tel: (01204) 524262 Fax: (01204) 534888 *Fire & security products*

Alstain Metal Services Ltd, Sapcote Trading Centre, Small Heath Highway, Birmingham, B10 0HR Tel: 0121-773 5655 Fax: 0121-773 5220 E-mail: sales@alstain.co.uk *Stainless steel stockholders*

▶ Alstoe Ltd, The Industrial Estate, York Road, Sheriff Hutton, York, YO60 6RZ Tel: (01347) 878606 Fax: (01347) 878333 E-mail: info@alstoe.co.uk *Veterinary pharmaceutical distributor*

Alstom Combined Cycles International Ltd, Booths Hall, Chelford Road, Knutsford, Cheshire, WA16 8GE Tel: (01565) 758000 Fax: (01565) 758001 *Electrical engineers & power station designers & constructors*

Alstom Power, Kirkton Drive, Pitmedden Industrial Estate, Dyce, Aberdeen, AB21 0BG Tel: (01224) 214500 *Turbine machinery*

Alstom Power Ltd, Newbold Road, Rugby, Warwickshire, CV21 2NH Tel: (01788) 577111 Fax: (01788) 531700 Principal Export Areas: Worldwide *Manufacturers of turbine components*

Alstom Power Generation Ltd, Silverlink Business Park, Silverlink, Wallsend, Tyne & Wear, NE28 9ND Tel: 0191-295 2000 Fax: 0191-295 2011 *Power generation equipment manufrs*

Alstom Traction International Ltd, Channel Way, Preston, PR1 8XL Tel: (01772) 254777 Fax: (01772) 553554 *Railway electrical equipment manufrs*

Alstom Transport Ltd, PO Box 248, Birmingham, B8 2YF Tel: 0121-328 5455 Fax: 0121-695 3500 Principal Export Areas: Worldwide *Rapid transit system assemblers*

Alston Asset Management Services Ltd, Unit 27, 27 Roman Way Industrial Estate, Ribbleton, Preston, PR2 5BD Tel: (01772) 700590 Fax: (01772) 706510 E-mail: info@pre-applied.co.uk *Thread locking & sealing services*

▶ Alston Country Homes, Squirrels Lodge Hards Lane, Frognall, Peterborough, PE6 8RL Tel: (01778) 346773 Fax: (01778) 349131

Alston Lime Stone Co. Ltd, PO Box 8, Chester le Street, County Durham, DH3 2SS Tel: 0191-410 9611 Fax: 0191-492 0729 *Civil engineers & road contractors*

Alston Studio, Unit 4A, Great Northern Works, Hartham Lane, Hertford, SG14 1QN Tel: (01992) 534200 Fax: (01992) 534201 E-mail: gmtech@btconnect.com *Screen process printers*

Alstone Engineering, Unit 1 Towers Business Park, Wheelhouse Road, Rugeley, Staffordshire, WS15 1UZ Tel: (01889) 577775 Fax: (01889) 575111 *Machinists, precision machining & CNC engineering services*

Alstons Upholstery Ltd, Albro Works, Gosbecks Road, Colchester, CO2 9JU Tel: (01206) 765343 Fax: (01206) 763401 E-mail: enquiries@alstons.co.uk *Lounge furniture manufrs*

Alta Systems Ltd, Ashleigh House, 81 Birmingham Road, West Bromwich, West Midlands, B70 6PX Tel: 0121-553 6665 Fax: 0121-553 6661 E-mail: sales@altasystems.co.uk *Cad & cam systems distributors & agents*

Altacontact Call Centres, 21-23 Mill Street, Bedford, MK40 3EU Tel: (01234) 360001 Fax: (0870) 7620812 E-mail: info@altacontact.co.uk *AltaContact provides e-services to clients throughout the UK. AltaContacts mission is to enable not for profit organisations to increase their return from every pound invested in fundraising and administration. *AltaContacts solutions include, e-based cause marketing, online services for events, telephone fundraising, paperless direct debit implementation and interactive supporter websites.*

Altag Tool & Die, 10 3 Wilton Road, Ramsgate, Kent, CT12 5HG Tel: (01843) 588663 Fax: (01843) 853738 E-mail: info@altag.co.uk *Toolmaking service*

Altair Engineering Ltd, Vanguard Centre Sir William Lyons Road, University of Warwick S, Coventry, CV4 7EZ Tel: (01926) 468600 Fax: (024) 7632 3700 E-mail: info@uk.altair.com *Computer aided engineering software & product design*

Altair Filter Technology Ltd, Omega Park, Alton, Hampshire, GU34 2QE Tel: (01420) 541188 Fax: (01420) 541298 E-mail: info@altairfilter.com *Air filtration & acoustic equipment manufrs*

Altaroute Ltd, 10 North Road, Yate, Bristol, BS37 7PA Tel: (01454) 311475 Fax: (01454) 273065 E-mail: sales@altaroute.com *Variable message sign manufrs*

Altec Computer Cleaning, 4 Station Road, Belfast, BT4 1RE Tel: (028) 9047 1937 Fax: (028) 9065 0620 *Computer cleaning services*

Altech Engineering, Brighton Road, Bolney, Haywards Heath, West Sussex, RH17 5NA Tel: (01444) 881964 Fax: (01444) 881816 E-mail: sales@altechengineering.com *General sheet metalwork*

Altech Services, 1 Cemetery Road, Houghton Regis, Dunstable, Bedfordshire, LU5 5BZ Tel: (01582) 472882 Fax: (01582) 471887 *Steel & aluminium fabricators*

Altek, Bath Road, Beckington, Bath, BA11 6SQ Tel: (01373) 831231 Fax: (01373) 831813 E-mail: sales@altek-computers.co.uk *Computer repairers*

Altek Chemical Engineering 2000 Ltd, Cuckoo Hill, Bures, Suffolk, CO8 5JH Tel: (01787) 242007 Fax: (01787) 227000 *Water treatment*

Altek Instruments Ltd, Enterprise House, 44-46 Terrace Road, Walton-on-Thames, Surrey, KT12 2SD Tel: (01932) 244110 Fax: (0870) 0548263 E-mail: info@barcodeman.com *Bar coding systems manufrs*

Alter Air, 6 Holly Grove, Basildon, Essex, SS16 6SB Tel: (01268) 540862 Fax: (01268) 540862 *Ventilation ductwork, ducting & duct contractors*

▶ Alter Vista Landscaping, 1 Manor Cottages, Ladham Road, Goudhurst, Cranbrook, Kent, TN17 1LY Tel: (01580) 211618 Fax: (07789) 763435 E-mail: altervistalandscaping@yahoo.co.uk *All manner of landscaping services, from design & installation to maintenance & remedial work*

Altera Europe Ltd, Holmers Farm Way, High Wycombe, Buckinghamshire, HP12 4XF Tel: (01494) 602000 Fax: (01494) 602001 E-mail: newsroom@altera.com *Computer systems & software sales*

▶ Altered Image, St. Helier, Jersey, JE2 3GH Tel: (01534) 767323 *Graphic designers*

Altered Images, Unit 4 Shepperton Business Park, Govett Avenue, Shepperton, Middlesex, TW17 8BA Tel: (01932) 255666 Fax: (01932) 260646 E-mail: sales@alteredimagesltd.com *Audio visual equipment services & suppliers*

Alterian Holdings Ltd, Century Place, Bond Street, Bristol, BS2 9AG Tel: 0117-970 3200 Fax: 0117-970 3201 E-mail: info@alterian.com *Computer software developers*

Alterlist Ltd, 32 Mason Street, Manchester, M4 5EY Tel: 0161-833 2723 Fax: 0161-833 2723 *Clothing manufrs*

▶ Alternates Clothing Mnfrs, 80 Mary Street, Laurieston, Falkirk, FK2 9PS Tel: (01324) 633606 Fax: (01324) 633606 *Clothing manufrs*

Alternative Autom Fuel Conversions Ltd, Unit 1 Blind Pond Industrial Estate, Woburn Sands Road, Bow Brickhill, Milton Keynes, MK17 9LA Tel: (01908) 641333 Fax: (01908) 641981 E-mail: gas4cars@aol.com *LPG conversions*

▶ Alternative Direct Marketing, 20 Fletcher Gate, Nottingham, NG1 2FZ Tel: (0871) 2202520 Fax: (0871) 2200141 *Alternative Offices is a superb affordable serviced offices in the UK and worldwide.*Just click here and search for your ideal location.*

Alternative Door Style, 9 St. Johns Street, Bridlington, North Humberside, YO16 7NL Tel: (01262) 400626 Fax: (01262) 400626 *Doors distributors*

Alternative Enterprises Ltd, Avocet House Trinity Park, Trinity Way, London, E4 8TD Tel: (020) 8498 4100 Fax: (020) 8498 4200 E-mail: info@alternative.uk.com *Photocopiers & faxes suppliers*

▶ Alternative Focus Media, 68 Castle Gate, Newark, Nottinghamshire, NG24 1BG Tel: (01636) 706106 Fax: (01636) 611149 E-mail: mike@alternativefocusmedia.com *Website development*

▶ Alternative Mobiles, 20 Fletcher Gate, Nottingham, NG1 2FZ Tel: (0870) 1203233 *Alternative Mobiles is the best selling mobile phone offers on the internet!!*

▶ Alternative Packaging Solutions Ltd, The Studio Prospect Place, Mill Lane, Alton, Hampshire, GU34 2SX Tel: (01420) 544800 Fax: (01420) 544850 *Supplying all types of packaging to retail, trade industry*

Alternative Services, Cartref, Laurels Road, Offenham Cross, Evesham, Worcestershire, WR11 8RE Tel: (01386) 443795 Fax: (01386) 423893 *Archery manufrs & exporters*

▶ Alternative Test Equipment, PO Box 3470, Wokingham, Berkshire, RG40 9AH Tel: (0845) 3457791 Fax: (0845) 3457792 E-mail: sales@AlternativeTest.co.uk *Distributors of test & measurement equipment*

▶ Alternatum, 22-24, Homecroft Road, London, N22 5EL Tel: (020) 8888 7956 Fax: (020) 8888 2521

Alternet, 5 Cardiff Road, Luton, LU1 1PP Tel: (0870) 6009968 Fax: (0870) 6009969 E-mail: jimrudd@alternetuk.com *Payroll services*

▶ Altex, 58 Tailors Court, Temple Farm Industrial Estate, Southend-on-Sea, SS2 5SX Tel: (01702) 602220 Fax: (01702) 602215 E-mail: sales@altex-uk.com *Windows & doors manufrs*

Althacam Ltd, Licom House, 8 Davenport Road, Coventry, CV5 6PY Tel: (024) 7671 3434 Fax: (024) 7671 3449 E-mail: sales@uk.althacam.com *CAD & CAM systems software distributors*

▶ Altia Solutions Ltd, 176 St Vincent Street, Glasgow, G2 5SG Tel: 0141-249 6830

Altimed Ltd, 74 Sullington Road, Shepshed, Loughborough, Leicestershire, LE12 9JJ Tel: (01509) 501720 Fax: (01509) 501721 E-mail: enquiries@altimed.co.uk *Medical compression hosiery manufrs*

Altis Consulting Ltd, 11 Thatcham Business Village, Colthrop Way, Thatcham, Berkshire, RG19 4LW Tel: (01635) 867575 Fax: (01635) 867576 E-mail: sales@altisltd.com *Computer consultants*

▶ Altissimo Ltd, Arnish Point, Stornoway, Isle Of Lewis, HS2 9JZ Tel: (01851) 707180 Fax: (01851) 705529 E-mail: mdm@camcal.co.uk *Steel fabrication, renewable energy fabrication*

Altitude Access, Burma Road, Blidworth, Mansfield, Nottinghamshire, NG21 0RT Tel: (01623) 796969 Fax: (01623) 793008 E-mail: info@altitudeaccess.co.uk *Access platform hirers*

▶ Altitude Alloy Towers Ltd, 3 The Aerodrome, Stoke Road, Stoke Orchard, Cheltenham, Gloucestershire, GL52 7RS Tel: (01242) 676662 Fax: (01242) 676662

▶ Altmore General Recruitment, Office 15 Townsend Enterprise Park, 28 Townsend Street, Belfast, BT13 2ES Tel: (028) 9032 8411 Fax: (028) 9032 8400 E-mail: cr@altmore.co.uk *IT recruitment: ad-hoc/temp/contract/perm*

Alto Digital, Sommerville House, Leathley Road, Leeds, LS10 1BG Tel: 0113-244 3016 Fax: 0113-242 4765 *Photocopying machine suppliers*

Alto Digital, Sommerville House, Leathley Road, Leeds, LS10 1BG Tel: 0113-244 3016 Fax: 0113-242 4765 *Sell faxes, photocopiers & computers*

Alto Plant Services Ltd, Railway Road, Brinscall, Chorley, Lancashire, PR6 8RJ Tel: (01254) 832132 Fax: (01254) 832121 *Plant equipment & construction*

Alto Tower Systems, 24 Walkers Road, North Moons, Moons Moat North Industrial Estate, Redditch, Worcestershire, B98 9HE Tel: (01527) 62946 Fax: (01527) 597444 E-mail: sales@alto-towers.co.uk *Aluminium access systems manufrs*

Altodigital Midlands UK Ltd, Pensnett Trading Estate, Kingswinford, West Midlands, DY6 7FZ Tel: (01384) 404660 Fax: (01384) 404665 E-mail: enquiries@altodigital.com *Digital office solutions supply & service*

Alton Bolt & Tool Co. Ltd, Unit E6 West Ham Industrial Estate, Grafton Way, Basingstoke, Hampshire, RG22 6HY Tel: (01256) 461078 Fax: (01256) 323936 *Power tools, hand tools & fastener suppliers*

Alton Chemicals, 4 Bollinbarn Drive, Macclesfield, Cheshire, SK10 3DN Tel: (01625) 425694 Fax: (01625) 610405 *Epoxy consultants*

Alton Design Ltd, Burnham House Park Street, Ripon, North Yorkshire, HG4 2BY Tel: (01765) 643830 Fax: (01765) 643831 E-mail: annabel@altoninteriors.com *Colour design consultants*

Alton Electrical Services, 25-27 Southview Rise, Alton, Hampshire, GU34 2AB Tel: (01420) 86194 Fax: (01420) 86194 *Washing machine distributors & repair services*

▶ Alton It Support Ltd, 51 Greenfields Avenue, Alton, Hampshire, GU34 2EE Tel: (01420) 86315 *IT services for homes & small to medium enterprises*

Alton Precision Engineering Ltd, Unit 27a Chemical Lane, Stoke-on-Trent, ST6 4PB Tel: (01782) 813735 Fax: (01782) 813752 E-mail: altonpre@clara.co.uk *CNC milling engineers*

▶ Alton Pumps, Redwood Lane, Medstead, Alton, Hampshire, GU34 5PE Tel: (01420) 561111 Fax: (01420) 561111 E-mail: altnpumps@supanet.com

Alton Wire Products, Pennypot Industrial Estate, Hythe, Kent, CT21 6PE Tel: (01303) 266061 Fax: (01303) 261080 E-mail: finance@delphinware.co.uk *Wire products manufrs*

Altred & Harrison, Wellington House, 108 Beverley Road, Hull, HU3 1XA Tel: (01482) 611200 Fax: (01482) 225452 E-mail: info@oandh.co.uk *Shipping agents*

Altrincham & Cheshire Security Systems, 16 Trafford Drive, Timperley, Altrincham, Cheshire, WA15 6EJ Tel: 0161-976 3752 Fax: 0161-976 3752 *CCTV & security system installers*

▶ Altrincham Lofts Ltd, 36 Aimson Road East, Timperley, Altrincham, Cheshire, WA15 7DA Tel: 0161-980 6365 E-mail: davebourkelofts@aol.com *Loft Conversion Specialists. Joinery and Building Contractors.**From initial enquiry to completion - we offer a high quality design, planning and build service.*

Altrix Healthcare plc, Garret House, Warrington, WA3 7BP Tel: (01925) 828916 Fax: (01925) 848949 *Software & testing kits suppliers consultants*

Altro Ltd, Works Road, Letchworth Garden City, Hertfordshire, SG6 1NW Tel: (01462) 707604 Fax: (01462) 707504 E-mail: leisure@altro.co.uk *Altro based in Hertfordshire is a world leading manufacturer and supplier of interior surfaces, resin systems, flooring and wall cladding, founded in the UK in 1919.* Also at: Bristol, East Kilbride, Hertford, Leeds & Stafford

▶ Altro Window Frame Mnfrs, Unit 51 Barns Court, Turners Hill Road, Crawley Down, Crawley, West Sussex, RH10 4HQ Tel: (01342) 718702 Fax: (01342) 718942 *Upvc doors & windows installations & manufrs*

Altron Communications Equipment Ltd, Tower House, Parc Hendre, Capel Hendre, Ammanford, Dyfed, SA18 3SJ Tel: (01269) 831431 Fax: (01269) 845348 E-mail: comms@altron.co.uk Principal Export Areas: Worldwide *CCTV manufrs*

Altros Engineering Ltd, Birch House Commercial Square, Leigh Street, High Wycombe, Buckinghamshire, HP11 2QT Tel: (01494) 443082 Fax: (01494) 436186 E-mail: altros_uk@hotmail.com *Printed circuit assembly services*

▶ Altura Extrusions, Horsepool Grange Industrial Estate, Elliotts Lane, Stanton under Bardon, Markfield, Leicestershire, LE67 9TW Tel: (01530) 245500 Fax: (01530) 245599 E-mail: sales@alturaextrusions.com *Plastic Profile Extruders*

Altus Adtek, Unit E The Coppetts Centre, Coneyhatch Lane, London, N12 0AJ Tel: (020) 8920 4800 Fax: (020) 8920 4827 E-mail: info@adtek.co.uk *Copiers & facsimile suppliers*

▶ Altus Computers Ltd, Abbeyfields, Lodge Road, Sandbach, Cheshire, CW11 3HD Tel: (01270) 750800 *Computer maintenance & repair services*

Altus Recruitment Services Ltd, Moseley, Birmingham, B13 9ZQ Tel: 0121-442 4030 Fax: 0121-442 4030 *Selection & search consultants*

Alucare Glaziers, 9 Flitwick Industrial Estate, Maulden Road, Flitwick, Bedford, MK45 1UX Tel: (01525) 713085 Fax: (01525) 715661 E-mail: info@alucare.co.uk *Double glazing manufrs*

Alucast Ltd, Western Way, Wednesbury, West Midlands, WS10 7BW Tel: 0121-556 6111 Fax: 0121-505 1302 E-mail: sales@alucast.co.uk Principal Export Areas: Africa *Diecasting manufrs*

Aluclad Ltd, 140 Woodside Street, Coatbridge, Lanarkshire, ML5 5NS Tel: (01236) 422822 *Double glazed windows*

Aluline (Greasetraps) Ltd, Harbour House, 1 Aldborough Street, Blyth, Northumberland, NE24 2EU Tel: (01670) 544322 Fax: (01670) 544340 E-mail: design@aluline.co.uk *Grease related drainage solutions in commercial, industrial, institutional &and military kitchens*

Aluline T/A Olympic, 59-62 Brindley Road, Astmoor Industrial Estate, Runcorn, Cheshire, WA7 1PF Tel: (01928) 563532 Fax: (01928) 580224 E-mail: accounts@barolympics.co.uk *Catering equipment manufrs*

ALUMAS, Ackhurst Road, Chorley, Lancashire, PR7 1NH Tel: (01257) 266687 Fax: (01257) 267562 E-mail: alumas@nisltd.com Sales Contact: R. Crampton Principal Export Areas: Worldwide *Alumas will build or integrate the profiles with any other equipment, mechanical, pneumatic or electronic. We have a design team with a wide range of knowledge. Alumas offer conveyor systems, either modular aluminium based or of steel construction. The standard types are belt, roller - driven or gravity, pallet carrying, with options of transfer units, turntables, elevators, centring & robotic integration*

Alumasc Exterior Building Products, White House Works, Bold Road, Sutton, St. Helens, Merseyside, WA9 4JG Tel: 01744 648400 Fax: 01744 648401 E-mail: info@alumasc-exteriors.co.uk *Alumasc Exterior Building Products Ltd has been a major force in the UK Construction Industry for over 30 years. During that time Alumasc products and systems have been specified on some of the most prestigious buildings in all sectors, throughout the UK. Highly regarded brands such as Harmer, Apex, Derbigum, ZinCo, Hydrotech, Armaseam and M.R., together with Alumasc''s well known architectural rainwater range are leaders in their respective fields. **Ongoing investment in engineering skills and state of the art technology combined with an ingrained service ethic, provides construction firms, architects, specifiers and building clients with the products, technical support and lifecycle support they require for their projects.*

The Alumasc Group Plc, Station Road, Burton Latimer, Kettering, Northamptonshire, NN15 5JP Tel: (01536) 383848 Fax: (01536) 420147 E-mail: info@alumascprecision.co.uk *Brewery equipment manufrs*

The Alumasc Group Plc, Station Road, Burton Latimer, Kettering, Northamptonshire, NN15 5JP Tel: (01536) 383848 Fax: (01536) 723835 E-mail: info@alumascprecision.co.uk *Fully finished aluminium castings*

Alumasc Interior Building Products Ltd, Unit C1 Halesfield 19, Telford, Shropshire, TF7 4QT Tel: (01952) 580590 Fax: (01952) 587805 E-mail: sales@alumascinteriors.com *Trunking systems manufrs*

▶ Alumet Systems (U K) Ltd, Bourne End, Kineton Road Industrial Estate, Southam, Warwickshire, CV47 0NA Tel: (01926) 811677 Fax: (01926) 811676

Alumeta Glazing Systems Ltd, 123a Gorton Road, Stockport, Cheshire, SK5 6EE Tel: 0161-431 9998 Fax: 0161-431 9195 E-mail: mailbox.alumeta@btopenworld.com *Aluminium shop front & window suppliers*

▶ Aluminium All Parts, 1-5 Meadow Court, Pen Elm, Taunton, Somerset, TA2 6PD Tel: (01823) 323916 Fax: (01823) 323916 E-mail: alluminiumallparts@btinternet.com *Aluminium parts suppliers*

Aluminium Capping Services Ltd, 30-32 Singer Way, Kempston, Bedford, MK42 7AF Tel: (01234) 843301 Fax: (01234) 841820 E-mail: sales@aluminiumcapping.com *Aluminium foil capping presses manufrs*

Aluminium Castings Ltd, 3b Celtic Road, Moss Side Industrial Estate, Callington, Cornwall, PL17 7SD Tel: (01579) 383513 Fax: (01579) 384762 E-mail: info@alcast.co.uk *High pressure die-casting services*

Aluminium Copper & Stainless Co. Ltd, 22-24 Crittall Road, Witham, Essex, CM8 3DR Tel: (01376) 513419 Fax: (01376) 511615 *Craftsmen in all metal fabricators*

The Aluminium Cutting Company Ltd, 2 94 Kitchener Road, High Wycombe, Buckinghamshire, HP11 2SW Tel: (01494) 448790 Fax: (01494) 448794 *Aluminium cutting services*

Aluminium Droitwich, 7 Judge Court, Berry Hill, Berry Hill Industrial Estate, Droitwich, Worcestershire, WR9 9AB Tel: (01905) 794620 Fax: (01905) 797863 *Aluminium stockholders*

Aluminium Extruders Association, Broadway House, Calthorpe Road, Edgbaston, Birmingham, B15 1TN Tel: 0121-456 1103 Fax: 0801389714 E-mail: alfed@alfed.org.uk *Trade association*

Aluminium & Plastics Ltd, 29a Marlborough Road, Newport, Gwent, NP19 0PZ Tel: (01633) 259188 Fax: (01633) 212217 *Plastics fabricators*

Aluminium Powder Co. Ltd, Forge Lane, Minworth Industrial Park, Minworth, Sutton Coldfield, West Midlands, B76 1AH Tel: 0121-351 4686 Fax: 0121-351 7604 E-mail: enquiries@alpoco.co.uk Principal Export Areas: Worldwide *Manufacturers of aluminium, magnesium & metal powder*

Aluminium Products Ltd, Alpro Foundry, Haines Street, West Bromwich, West Midlands, B70 7DA Tel: 0121-553 1911 Fax: 0121-500 5796 E-mail: alpro@compuserve.com *Aluminium castings manufrs*

Aluminium Ramp Company, London, UK, TN15 8EU Tel: 028 90868838 Fax: 028 90861804 E-mail: info@rampcompany.com *Manufacture Aluminium Truck Ramps, Car Ramps, Van Ramps, Container Ramps, Custom Ramps and Disability Access Ramps.*

Aluminium Rolled Products Manufacturers Association, Broadway House, Calthorpe Road, Edgbaston, Birmingham, B15 1TN Tel: 0121-456 1103 Fax: 0121-456 2274 E-mail: alfed@alfed.org.uk *Trade association*

Aluminium Sashes Ltd, Barnett Way, Barnwood, Gloucester, GL4 3RT Tel: (01452) 616581 Fax: (01452) 371923 *Aluminium window frame manufrs*

Aluminium Service Co. (Warwick) Ltd, Millers Road, Warwick, CV34 5AE Tel: (01926) 491824 Fax: (01926) 410072 *Aluminium alloy die casting suppliers*

Aluminium Services Ltd, Aizlewood Road, Sheffield, S8 0YX Tel: 0114-255 3055 Fax: 0114-255 3798 E-mail: ast-info@btconnect.com *Aluminium finishing services*

Aluminium Stockholders Association, Broadway House, Calthorpe Road, Five Ways, Birmingham, B15 1TN Tel: 0121-456 4938 Fax: 0121-456 4937 E-mail: asa@alfed.org.uk *Trade association services*

Aluminium Supply Aerospace, 1 Totteridge Lane, London, N20 0EX Tel: (020) 8700 2000 Fax: (020) 8700 2099 E-mail: *Aluminium stockholders*

Aluminiumwerk Unna AG, 48 Elmsdale Rd, Wootton, Bedford, MK43 9JN Tel: (01234) 768805 Fax: (01234) 767532 E-mail: sales@galupltd.co.uk *Galup Limited represents leading aluminium manufacturers. if you are looking for tubes, wire, rods, extruded profiles, strip or cast billets in aluminium please contact us*

▶ Alumnium Profiles UK, Unit 5, Peckleton Lane Business Park, Peckleton Common, Leicester, LE9 7RN Tel: (01455) 823304 Fax: (01455) 828186 E-mail: sales@kjnltd.co.uk *Aluminium profiles*

▶ Alutech Surface Treatments Ltd, Airedale Mills, Skipton Road, Cross Hills, Keighley, West Yorkshire, BD20 7BX Tel: (01535) 636465 Fax: (01535) 636467 E-mail: overingtoncc@aol.com *Founders & finishers specialists*

Alutrade Ltd, Tat Bank Road, Oldbury, West Midlands, B69 4NH Tel: 0121-552 0330 Fax: 0121-552 0166 E-mail: info@alutrade.co.uk *Scrap metal processors*

▶ Aluvents Ltd, Victory Place, Westow Street, London, SE19 3RW Tel: (020) 8653 9795

Alvan Blanch Development Co. Ltd, Chelworth, Malmesbury, Wiltshire, SN16 9SG Tel: (01666) 577333 Fax: (01666) 577339 E-mail: info@alvanblanch.co.uk *Agricultural machinery manufrs* Also at: Chirnside

Alvechurch Fisheries, Little Stannalls, Bittell Road, Barnt Green, Birmingham, B45 8LT Tel: 0121-445 4274 Fax: 0121-447 7117 *Fishery*

Alvent Heating Contractors, Units 5-6 Alexandra Industrial Estate, Locarno Road, Tipton, West Midlands, DY4 9SJ Tel: 0121-557 6727 Fax: 0121-520 8717 *Installation & maintenance engineers*

▶ Alver Services Ltd, 1 The Anchorage, Gosport, Hampshire, PO12 1LY Tel: (023) 9252 9191 Fax: (023) 9252 9191 *IT consultants*

Alvey & Towers, Unit 9, Enterprise House, Coalville, Leicestershire, LE67 3LA Tel: (01530) 450011 Fax: (01530) 450011 E-mail: office@alveyandtowers.com *Industrial & commercial photographers*

Alvic PVC Ltd, Units 9-10 Brookfield Business Park, Brookfield Road, Cheadle, Cheshire, SK8 2PE Tel: 0161-491 5853 Fax: 0161-491 5852 *PVC powder manufrs*

Alw, Tweedale Industrial Estate, Madeley, Telford, Shropshire, TF7 4JR Tel: (01952) 684100 Fax: (01952) 581611 E-mail: bruce@alws.freeserve.co.uk *Metal finishing & powder coatings suppliers*

▶ Always Under Pressure, 4 Langley Avenue, Ruislip, Middlesex, HA4 9TT Tel: (020) 8868 6694 Fax: (020) 8582 2773 E-mail: office@graffiti-removal.org.uk *Professional anti graffiti coating service*

Alwen Garage, Llanfihangel Glyn Myfyr, Corwen, Clwyd, LL21 9UH Tel: (01490) 420567 Fax: (01490) 420418 *Agricultural & commercial vehicle repairs*

Alzin Engineering Ltd, Century Works, Briggate, Elland, West Yorkshire, HX5 9HG Tel: (01422) 373456 Fax: (01422) 373813 E-mail: info@alzin.co.uk *Die castings in aluminium alloy*

Am Car Care, A4 Bolney Road, Cowfold, Horsham, West Sussex, RH13 8AZ Tel: (01403) 864638 Fax: (01403) 864638 *Vehicle accident repair service*

Am Computing Direct Ltd, International House, Cray Avenue, Orpington, Kent, BR5 3RY Tel: (01689) 896489 Fax: (01689) 896659 E-mail: amaddalo@aol.com *Data management services*

Am Designer Logo Jewellers, Mount Pleasant, Barnet, Hertfordshire, EN4 9HH Tel: (020) 8441 3835 Fax: (020) 8440 7771 E-mail: info@promotionaljewellery.co.uk *Promotional jewellery designers*

▶ AM Electrical & Gas Installations, 41 Irlam Avenue, Eccles, Manchester, M30 0JR Tel: 0161 7079797 *We carryout gas safety inspections for homeowners, landlords and property management agents, providing a landlords gas safety certificate on completion if required. The Gas Safety (Installation and Use) Regulations 1994 (as amended) place duties on gas consumers, installers, suppliers and landlords. All gas appliances/associated pipeworks, flues, portable heaters must be checked annually for safety.**

Am PM Fabrications, Hatfield Cottage, Hardings Elms Road, Billericay, Essex, CM11 2UH Tel: (01268) 285115 Fax: (01268) 285117 E-mail: ampmfabrications@btconnect.com *Steel fabricators*

Am Safe Ltd, Tamian Way, Hounslow, TW4 6BL Tel: (020) 8572 0321 Fax: (020) 8572 2096 E-mail: sales@am-safe.co.uk *Aircraft personnel restraints*

Ama Business Systems Ltd, The Old Tabernacle, Palmyra Road, Bristol, BS3 3JQ Tel: 0117-923 1133 Fax: 0117-923 1144 E-mail: sales@ama-it.com *Accounting software suppliers & resellers*

Amac Services Ltd, 82 Ashenground Road, Haywards Heath, West Sussex, RH16 4QB Tel: (01444) 416305 *Computer consultants*

Amacord Screenprint, Unit 14-16 Arden Business Centre, Arden Road, Alcester, Warwickshire, B49 6HW Tel: (01789) 764926 Fax: (01789) 764797 E-mail: sales@amacord.co.uk *Dry image transfer services*

Amada UK Ltd, 6 Atlas House, St. Georges Square, Bolton, BL1 2HB Tel: (01562) 749555 Fax: (01562) 749510 E-mail: info@amada.co.uk *Metal tools & machinery suppliers*

▶ Amadeus Press Ltd, Ezra House, Littlewood Drive, West 26 Industrial Estate, Cleckheaton, West Yorkshire, BD19 4TQ Tel: (01274) 863210 Fax: (01274) 863211 E-mail: info@hartandclough.co.uk

Amadeus Software Ltd, Orchard Farm, Witney Lane, Leafield, Witney, Oxfordshire, OX29 9PG Tel: (01993) 878287 Fax: (01993) 878042 E-mail: info@amadeus.co.uk *Computer software developers*

Amafiltergroup Ltd, Navigation Road, Stoke-on-Trent, ST6 3RU Tel: (01782) 575611 Fax: (01782) 577001 E-mail: salesuk@amafilter.com *Filters, filtration & separation systems*

Amag U K Ltd, Beckley Lodge Leatherhead Road, Bookham, Leatherhead, Surrey, KT23 3PD Tel: (01372) 450661 Fax: (01372) 450833 E-mail: amag.uk@amag.at *Aluminium/alloy producers & aluminium/alloy plate, sheet & treadplate manufrs*

Amalgam Modelmakers Ltd, The Old Sorting Office, Eastfield Road, Cotham, Bristol, BS6 6AB Tel: 0117-924 9596 Fax: 0117-923 2727 E-mail: admin@amalgam-models.co.uk *Industrial model makers & rapid prototypes suppliers*

Amalgamated Construction Co. Ltd, Whaley Road, Barnsley, South Yorkshire, S75 1HT Tel: (01226) 243413 Fax: (01226) 320202 E-mail: info@amco-construction.co.uk *Civil engineers*

Aman.Smart-Finance, Ammanford, Carmarthenshire, SA18 1JF Tel: (01269) 826643 E-mail: aman@smart-finance.co.uk *Business loans, tenant loans, secured loans. If your looking for any finance- try us first for a professional service*

▶ Amanassas, 2 Briarfield Gardens, Shipley, West Yorkshire, BD18 2BE Tel: (07890) 194132 E-mail: panther1966uk@yahoo.co.uk *Free Quote Given, usual cost for a average semi detached is £30. No call out fee's.**We also are available for Handyman services too. Any job undertaken, free quote. **Our gutter cleaning program is designed to maximize your cleaning investment. We will either clean the gutters by hand, using poles and scoops if the gutters are full of water, or we will blow them out with air if they are dry. We test the downspouts for good drainage. Cosmetic cleaning of the outsides of the gutters is also available. As with our window cleaning program, our gutter cleaning is guaranteed. We will return to check and re-clean any gutters that seem to warrant it.**

▶ Amandas Direct (UK) Washroom Supplies, Amandas Direct Ltd, Po Box 572, Worcester, WR5 3XW Tel: 0800 3898701 E-mail: customercare@amandasdirect.com *Amanda's Direct washroom supplies one of the leading UK suppliers with years experience in the supply and installation of equipment for washrooms and specialist in feminine hygiene. Supplying well know brands from Kimberly-Clarke with branches in Edinburgh, Birmingham, Cardiff and Worcester providing services to customers all over the UK.*

▶ A-Man-With-A-Van, Northcroft, New Park Road, Hockley, Essex, SS5 5JX Tel: (01702) 205320 E-mail: amanwithavan@btinternet.com *Small Removals - Single Items - House Clearances - Household Waste Fully Licenced*

Amar Engineering Consultants, Unit 70 Station Road Workshops, Station Road, Kingswood, Bristol, BS15 4PJ Tel: 0117-956 5522 Fax: 0117-956 5573 E-mail: webe-amar@demon.co.uk *Engineering consultants & CNC support*

Amar Specialised Plastics Ltd, Unit G Alpha Centre, Babbage Road, Totnes, Devon, TQ9 5JA Tel: (01803) 868077 Fax: (01803) 863399 E-mail: amar@specialisedplastics.co.uk *PTFE machined components manufrs*

Amar Textiles, 105 Grange Street, Derby, DE23 8HD Tel: (01332) 365527 Fax: (01332) 731771 *Textiles manufrs*

Amarenda Ltd, Unit 1A Green End Farm Business Unit, 93A Church Lane, Sarratt, Rickmansworth, Hertfordshire, WD3 6HH Tel: (01923) 291550 Fax: (01923) 291660 E-mail: enquiries@amarenda.co.uk *Corporate uniform, leisurewear & workwear*

Amarex Ltd, Newburn Industrial Estate, Shelley Road, Newcastle upon Tyne, NE15 9RT Tel: 0191-264 4781 Fax: 0191-229 0405 E-mail: steel@amerex.demon.co.uk *Steel stockholders*

Amari Copper Alloys, Unit 47, Eagle Rd, Moons Moat North Industrial Estate, Redditch, Worcestershire, B98 9HF Tel: (01527) 405600 Fax: (01527) 405605 E-mail: sales@amaricopperalloys.co.uk *Processors, Stockholders & distributors. Brass, copper, nickel silver, copper nickel, all non-ferrous metal sheets, strips, tubes, plates, coils, slitting, shearing & sawing quality assured & export sales.*

Amari Plastics P.L.C., 11-12 Hillman Close, Hornchurch, Essex, RM11 2SJ Tel: (01708) 452525 Fax: (01708) 437030 E-mail: el@amariplastics.com *Plastic sheet distributors*

Amari Plastics plc, Wednesbury One, Blackcountry New Road, Wednesbury, West Midlands, WS10 7NZ Tel: 0121-567 3400 Fax: 0121-567 3401 E-mail: bm@amariplastics.com *Plastic sheet stockholders*

▶ Amari Plastics PLC, Holmes House, 24-30 Baker Street, Weybridge, Surrey, KT13 8AU Tel: 01932 835000 Fax: 01932 835002 E-mail: ho@amariplastics.com *Nationwide stockholder and distributor of semi finished plastics and associated products to the sign, POP, building, glazing, engineering and industrial markets*

▶ Amark Safety Markings, 78 Shawfield Road, Ash, Aldershot, Hampshire, GU12 6RB Tel: (01252) 320325 Fax: (01252) 320325 E-mail: rjwright2005@yahoo.co.uk *Specialists in paint markings in warehouses, factories, car parks and playgrounds. Markings for Health and Safety purposes.*

▶ Amas Europe, 76 Lancefield Quay, Glasgow, G3 8HP Tel: (0870) 7471350 Fax: (0870) 1277477 *IT support services*

Amasec Airfil Ltd, Unit 1 Colliery Lane, Exhall, Coventry, CV7 9NW Tel: (07739) 974027 Fax: (024) 7664 4325 E-mail: sales@airfil.com *Packaging plastic products manufrs*

Amatar Ltd, Amatar House, Manor Road, Woodley, Stockport, Cheshire, SK6 1RT Tel: 0161-494 6692 Fax: 0161-406 6752 E-mail: djo171135@aol.com *Chemical, pigment & dyestuff manufrs*

▶ Amaya Sales UK Ltd, Trademark House, Ramshill, Petersfield, Hampshire, GU31 4AT Tel: (01730) 711151 Fax: (01730) 711141 E-mail: sales@amayauk.com *Melco amaya embroidery machines & software distributors*

Amazing Bunting Co., Units 1-7, 22 Pleydell Road, Northampton, NN4 8NL Tel: (01604) 675556 Fax: (01604) 675557 E-mail: sales@amazingbunting.co.uk Principal Export Areas: Africa *Manufacturers of bunting, flags & banners in a range of materials for all applications. Finishers to the print trade. Digital printers offering a same day internet service*

▶ Amazing Days, 78 Gallaghers Mead, Andover, Hants, SP10 3BW Tel: 01264 395081 *For all your wedding and party needs. Planning, invitations and finishing touches. Supplier recommendation a speciality.*

▶ Amazing Days Ltd, 90-91 Luddesdown Road, Luddesdown, Gravesend, Kent, DA13 0XE Tel: (01474) 815589 Fax: (01474) 815589 E-mail: dawn.gibson@amazing-days.co.uk *Amazing Days Corporate will offer you the chance to explore your imagination and take your staff or clients for the most enjoyable time they have ever spent at work! Every day is as individual as its client. Imagine... Believe and Achieve with Amazing Days. *By selecting Amazing Days Wedddings you will receive experience backed by a superior reputation. Where dreams come true. Our options are as unlimited as your imagination. With personalized attention to every detail, we promises to guide, assist and stand by you, every step of the way to your happily ever after.**

▶ Amazing Internet Ltd, 82 Heath Road, Twickenham, TW1 4BW Tel: (020) 8607 9535 Fax: (020) 8607 9536 E-mail: contact@amazinginternet.com *Leading web design company*

▶ Amazing Lengths, 7 Gladstone Close, Newport Pagnell, Bucks, MK16 0EU Tel: 01908 612489 E-mail: info@amazinglengths.co.uk *Human hair extensions at a fraction of salon prices! Call now for free consult in friendly, relaxed surroundings. Half & full heads available from £250!!*

▶ Amazing Lengths Hair Extensions, 16 Guernsey Close, Aylesbury, Buckinghamshire, HP19 9GU Tel: (01296) 397046 E-mail: info@amazinglengths.co.uk *Hair extensions at fantastic low prices! Get that salon lookfor a fraction of the price in friendly, relaxed surroundings!*

▶ Amazing Man & Van, Ford Place, Ford Road, Wrotham Heath, Sevenoaks, Kent, TN15 7SE Tel: (0800) 2986802 Fax: (0871) 4338214 E-mail: andrew@questforbest.org *We are a privately owned man and van transport, deliveries and removal company operating in Kent and South East London.* *Our core competencies are B2B and B2C deliveries of small to medium sized consignments. We specialise in fragile and heavy general goods and furnishings transportation. **We also provide home removals, man & van moving, small business removals services. **We have a specialised piano moving service.**In relation to your moving we have an on site warehouse storage facility, and can provide all manner of packaging materials. We will also undertake house clearance.*

▶ Amazing Spanish Villas, 14 Denham Road, Sheffield, S11 8NE Tel: 0114 2756784

▶ Amazon ATV Ltd (Quad Sales & Hire 6-6yrs), Green Street Industrial Estate, 1 Green Street, Eastbourne, East Sussex, BN21 1QN Tel: (01323) 645564 Fax: (01323) 645564 E-mail: elainechild@tiscali.co.uk *QUAD HIRE. Child/Junior Quad Parties, Adult Events. Hen/ Stag/Corporate Events. Birthday/anniversary treat. Groups upto 30 or single hires. Biggest outdoor tracks in East Sussex. Ages 6-6yrs. QUAD SALES. Servicing, parts,Clothing & accessories. Parties, Events, family, friends & Corporate Hire.*

Amazon Business Communications Ltd, Amazon House 2, Pitters Piece, Long Crendon, Aylesbury, Buckinghamshire, HP18 9PP Tel: (01844) 202035 Fax: (01844) 202031 E-mail: info@amazon-business.com *Supply & service canon business machines*

▶ Amazon Consultants, 29 St. Peters Street, Stamford, Lincolnshire, PE9 2PF Tel: (01780) 764430 Fax: (01780) 764430 E-mail: info@amazonconsultants.co.uk *IT consultants*

Amazon Filters Ltd, Albany Park, Frimley Road, Camberley, Surrey, GU15 2RA Tel: (01276) 670600 Fax: (01276) 670101 E-mail: sales@amazonfilters.co.uk Principal Export Areas: Worldwide *Specialists in liquid filtration - Manufacturers of filter cartridges, spunbonded depth and pleated cartridges in both polypropylene or nylon, nominal and absolute. We fabricate a full range of filter housings in 316L and Super Duplex.*

Amazon Herbal Products UK, PO Box 12958, Birmingham, B11 9BG Tel: (0870) 8113611 E-mail: webmaster@amazonherbalproducts.co.uk *AmazonHerbalProducts UK provides herbal shampoo, anti tobacco, natural acne treatment, cellulitis treatment, natural hair care treatment and natural hair loss treatment using natural herbal products like ervamatin, anti smoking, fix amazonia gel and clear gel.*

Amazon Karaoke Disco, Glen Way House, Brightlingsea Road, Thorrington, Colchester, CO7 8JH Tel: (01206) 520756

Amazon Leisure UK Ltd, The Fitness Centre, Hargham Road, Shropham, Attleborough, Norfolk, NR17 1DS Tel: (01953) 498098 Fax: (01953) 498340 E-mail: sales@amazonamazon-leisure.co.uk *Fitness equipment service*

▶ Amazon Personnel, 6 Star Street, London, W2 1QD Tel: (020) 7706 9345 Fax: (020) 7706 9456 E-mail: enquiries@amazonpersonnel.co.uk *Recruitment outsourcing agents*

Amazon Promotions, Unit 126 Oystons Mill, Strand Road, Preston, PR1 8UR Tel: (01772) 722800 Fax: (01772) 722800 E-mail: maria.atherton@rediffmail.com Principal Export Areas: Worldwide *Sportswear, embroidery & print wear suppliers & manufrs*

Amazone Ltd, Blyth Road, Harworth, Doncaster, South Yorkshire, DN11 8NE Tel: (01302) 751 200 Fax: (01302) 751 202 E-mail: info@amazone.co.uk *Agricultural machinery manufrs*

Amb Ltd, Brownell Street, Sheffield, S3 7GR Tel: 0114-272 0489 Fax: 0114-272 0489 E-mail: amb@btinternet.com *Precision engineers*

Amba Dockside Technology Ltd, 1 The Parkwood Centre, Aston Road, Waterlooville, Hampshire, PO7 7HT Tel: (023) 9223 1200 Fax: (023) 9226 7047 E-mail: ambeng@aol.com *Manufacturing & suppliers of straddle carrier parts*

Amba Forwarding Ltd, 6 Trafalgar Business Centre, River Road, Barking, Essex, IG11 0JU Tel: (020) 8591 1600 Fax: (020) 8591 1700 E-mail: info@ambaforwarding.com *Freight forwarders*

Amba Hydraulics Ltd, 25 Schneider Close, Felixstowe, Suffolk, IP11 3SS Tel: (01394) 673830 Fax: (01394) 673380 E-mail: ambahydraulics@hotmail.com *Hydraulic equipment, systems, maintenance & repair service*

Ambass-A-Door Windows & Doors Ltd, 18 Bidwell Road, Rackheath Industrial Estate, Norwich, NR13 6PT Tel: (01603) 720332 Fax: (01603) 721245 E-mail: sales@ambassadoor.fsnet.co.uk *Joinery manufrs*

Ambassador Billiard Co., Priesthorpe Lane, Farsley, Pudsey, West Yorkshire, LS28 5RF Tel: 0113-204 7500 Fax: 0113-204 7501 E-mail: sales@snookermarket.co.uk *Snooker, pool tables & wooden toys manufrs*

▶ Ambassador Caterers, 4 Pollards Moor Road, Copythorne, Southampton, SO40 2NZ Tel: (023) 8081 2434

Ambassador Cleaning Services Company, 18 Ashwin Street, London, E8 3DL Tel: (020) 7241 0937 Fax: (020) 7249 9583 *Office cleaning services*

▶ Ambassador Electrical Services Ltd, 29 The Maples, Broadstairs, Kent, CT10 2PE Tel: (01843) 860258 Fax: (01843) 860258

▶ Ambassador Environmental, 49 Chambers Road, St. Leonards-On-Sea, East Sussex, TN38 9HY Tel: (01424) 201309 *Pest control services*

▶ Ambassador Litho Ltd, 25 Hockeys Lane, Bristol, BS16 3HH Tel: 0117-965 5252 Fax: 0117-965 3275 E-mail: info@ambassador.co.uk *Litho printers services*

Ambassador Marketing, 6 G Belgic Square, Peterborough, PE1 5XF Tel: (01733) 563275 Fax: (01733) 63275 *Specialising in thick wall metals, we supply exactly what you ask for, saving you machining costs*

Ambassador Packaging, Tundry Way, Chainbridge Road, Blaydon-On-Tyne, Tyne & Wear, NE21 5ST Tel: (0870) 6099888 Fax: 0191-414 6627 E-mail: ambassador.blaydon@pactiv.com *Merchants & agents of packaging materials* Also at: Blackwood, Brierley Hill, Crawley, Leeds, Leicester, Livingstone, Newbury, Peter borough, Sheffield & Winsford

Ambassador Packaging, Unit 2 Venture Park, Stirling Way, Bretton, Peterborough, PE3 8YD Tel: (0870) 6099888 Fax: (01733) 330954 E-mail: ambassador.@pactiv.com *Merchants, packaging materials & protective bags, stretch wrap films* Also at: Blackwood, Blaydon-on-Tyne, Brierley Hill, Crawley, Leeds, Leicester, Livingston e, Newbury, Sheffield & Winsford

Ambassador Packaging Ltd, Road One, Winsford Industrial Estate, Winsford, Cheshire, CW7 3QB Tel: (01606) 567000 Fax: (01606) 567001 E-mail: ambassador@pregis.com *Packaging materials & protective bags suppliers* Also at: Blackwood, Blaydon-on-Tyne, Brierley Hil, Crawley, Leeds, Leicester, Livingstone, Newbury, Peterborough & Sheffield

Ambassador Windows Ltd, 8 Heol Gors, Dafen Industrial Estate, Dafen, Llanelli, Dyfed, SA14 8QR Tel: (01554) 752144 Fax: (01554) 753311 E-mail: ambassador@lineone.net *Windows doors & conservatories fabrications*

Amber Christian Workshops, 3a Old Market Avenue, Chichester, West Sussex, PO19 1SP Tel: (01243) 781474 *Jewellers*

Amber Composites Ltd, 94 Station Road, Langley Mill, Nottingham, NG16 4BP Tel: (01773) 530899 Fax: (01773) 768687 E-mail: sales@ambercomposites.co.uk *Composites manufrs*

▶ Amber Computing & It Services Ltd, Coilacriech, Ballater, Aberdeenshire, AB35 5UH Tel: (01339) 742019 Fax: (01339) 742292

▶ Amber Construction Services Ltd, Unit 62 Uplands Business Park, Blackhorse Lane, London, E17 5QJ Tel: (020) 8531 4553 Fax: (020) 8531 7553

▶ Amber Contracts, 29 Lochinvar Road, Cumbernauld, Glasgow, G67 4AR Tel: (01236) 453776

Amber Doors Ltd, Mason Way, Platts Common Industrial Estate Hoyland, Barnsley, South Yorkshire, S74 9TG Tel: (01226) 351135 Fax: (01226) 350176 E-mail: sales@amberdoors.co.uk *Industrial door manufrs*

▶ Amber Green, 135 George Street, Edinburgh, EH2 4JS Tel: 0131-514 4000 Fax: 0131-514 4001 E-mail: info@ambergreen.co.uk

Amber Industries, Amber House, Crompton Street, Chadderton, Oldham, OL9 9AA Tel: 0161-284 2222 Fax: 0161-627 0075 E-mail: sales@amber-industries.ltd.uk *Overhead & automated systems conveyors*

Amber Industries Ltd, Brook House, Brook Street, Tipton, West Midlands, DY4 9DD Tel: 0121-530 8664 Fax: 0121-530 8665 E-mail: info@amber-industries.ltd.uk *Manufacturers of conveyor systems*

Amber Instruments Ltd, Dunston House Sheepbridge Works, Dunston Road, Chesterfield, Derbyshire, S41 9QD Tel: (01246) 260250 Fax: (01246) 260955 E-mail: sales@amberinstruments.com *Control equipment distributors*

Amber Insurance Services, 889 Stockport Road, Manchester, M19 3PG Tel: 0161-224 7268 Fax: 0161-256 4798 *Insurance brokers services*

Amber Langis Ltd, Dene Yard, Green Street Green Road, Dartford, DA2 8DH Tel: (01474) 705897 Fax: (01474) 703941 E-mail: info@amberlangis.co.uk *Traffic control equipment & hire services*

▶ Amber Medical Ltd, Unit 1, Belvedere Trading Estate, Taunton, Somerset, TA1 1BH Tel: (01823) 336362 Fax: (01823) 336364 E-mail: mail@ambermedical.co.uk

Amber Plastics Ltd, Broombank Road, Chesterfield, Derbyshire, S41 9QJ Tel: (01246) 453544 Fax: (01246) 450339 E-mail: sales@amberplastics.co.uk Sales Contact: T. Bunting *Amber Plastics specialise in all types of Rotational Mouldings. From design to manufacture we carry out the whole process. We were founded in 1978 by our current MD's and currently employ over 50 staff.*

▶ Amber Press Ltd, Platt Industrial Estate, Maidstone Road, Platt, Sevenoaks, Kent, TN15 8JL Tel: (01732) 886911

Amber Programmable Design Ltd, Newbie, Annan, Dumfriesshire, DG12 5QJ Tel: (01461) 206000 Fax: (01461) 206200 E-mail: info@apd-ltd.com *Electric control panel suppliers*

▶ Amber Radiator Covers, 14 Freemans Way, Harrogate, North Yorkshire, HG3 1DH Tel: (01423) 883386 Fax: (01423) 883386 E-mail: sales@amberradiatorcovers.co.uk *Amber radiator covers manufrs*

Amber Signs, Pledgdon Hall, Henham, Bishop's Stortford, Hertfordshire, CM22 6BJ Tel: (01279) 850836 Fax: (01279) 850995 E-mail: ambersigns@btconnect.com *Sign manufrs*

▶ Amber Valley Development, 12 Churchill Way, Fleckney, Leicester, LE8 8UD Tel: 0116-240 2968 Fax: 0116-240 2941 *Property services*

Amber Valley Engineering Ltd, Pye Bridge Industrial Estate, Pye Bridge, Alfreton, Derbyshire, DE55 4NX Tel: (01773) 604753 Fax: (01773) 540136 E-mail: ambervalleyeng@hotmail.com *Steel fabricators*

▶ Amber Web Designs, 16 High Street, Baldock, Hertfordshire, SG7 6AS Tel: (01462) 895018

Amberlan Ltd, Building No 2, Brick Kiln Street, Brierley Hill, West Midlands, DY5 1JG Tel: (01384) 74332 Fax: (01384) 74334 E-mail: amberlan@blueyonder.co.uk *Conveyor roller manufrs*

Amberlea Plastics Ltd, 26 Palmerston Business Park, Palmerston Drive, Fareham, Hampshire, PO14 1DJ Tel: (01329) 231031 Fax: (01329) 239995 E-mail: sales@amberlea.co.uk *Plastic fasteners & plastic engineered products suppliers & manufrs*

Amberley Adhesive Labels Ltd, Team House, Higher Shaftesbury Road, Blandford Forum, Dorset, DT11 7FG Tel: (01258) 455772 Fax: (01258) 453215 E-mail: sales@amberley.net *Self adhesive label manufrs*

▶ Amberley Bouncy Castles, 55 The CR, Wallsend, Tyne & Wear, NE28 7RE Tel: 0191-209 2142 E-mail: ian.abc@blueyonder.co.uk *Children's entertainment hirers*

Amberley Security, 185-187 Copnor Road, Portsmouth, PO3 5BT Tel: 0800 0217066 Fax: (023) 9265 0349 E-mail: scottandrews@amberley-security.co.uk *Amberley Security is a family-owned and managed business, trading since 1927. We offer specialist services as locksmiths, keycutting, safe engineering, access control, door entry*

continued

*systems, bars, grilles, anti-climb protection and door controls.*Because we are independent and are not tied to any particular manufacturer's products, we pride ourselves on offering the best value solution to each and every client's individual circumstances.*We have a thriving trade counter and showroom which stocks the largest range of Yale and Chubb locks in the area, and a fully equipped locksmith workshop. As an approved Investors In People company, all staff undergo regular skills reviews to ensure that all staff have the skills necessary to undertake all work asked of us.*We care passionately about doing the right job in the best way.*

Amberley Signs, 144 Frimley Green Road, Frimley Green, Camberley, Surrey, GU16 6NA Tel: (01252) 836436 Fax: (01252) 836436 E-mail: amberleysigns@discali.co.uk *Sign manufrs*

▶ Amberlight Partners, 58 Bloomsbury Street, London, WC1B 3QT Tel: (020) 7307 7770 E-mail: info@amber-light.co.uk *Research & design services*

▶ Ambertex Ltd, 11 Parkhall Road, Walsall, WS5 3HF Tel: (01922) 620908 Fax: (01922) 620403 E-mail: sales@ambertex.com *Shirts & ladies wear manufrs*

▶ Amberwood Construction Contractors, 1088 Tollcross Road, Glasgow, G32 8UN Tel: 0141-778 6163 Fax: 0141-778 6163

▶ Amberwood Direct Ltd, 6 Southwood Close, Walkford, Christchurch, Dorset, BH23 5RW Tel: (01425) 279022

Ambery Metalform Components, Unit F6 Newton Business Park, Talbot Road, Hyde, Cheshire, SK14 4UQ Tel: 0161-367 9616 Fax: 0161-368 0689 E-mail: sales@ambery-metalform.co.uk *General sheet metalwork*

Ambic Ltd, 41-44 Stella Gill Industrial, Estate Pelton Fell, Pelton Fell, Chester le Street, County Durham, DH2 2RH Tel: 0191-389 1888 Fax: 0191-389 1999 E-mail: enquiries@ambic.ltd.uk *Specialists in manufacturing school furniture*

Ambic Equipment Ltd, Avenue 4, Station Lane, Witney, Oxfordshire, OX28 4XT Tel: (01993) 776555 Fax: (01993) 779039 E-mail: sales@ambix.co.uk *Dairy equipment manufrs*

▶ Ambidex Fashions, 82-90 Mile End Road, London, E1 4UN Tel: (020) 7790 7170 Fax: (020) 7790 7178

Ambience Air Conditioning & Refrigeration Services Ltd, 1 Foxlease Terrace, Shrubbs Hill Road, Lyndhurst, Hampshire, SO43 7DJ Tel: (07074) 284837

Ambient Control Ltd, Unit 3b Glevum Works, Upton Street, Gloucester, GL1 4LA Tel: (01452) 303311 Fax: (01452) 330682 E-mail: info@ambientcontrol.co.uk *Refrigerators & air conditioning maintenance*

▶ Ambient Light Productions Ltd, 6 Shipquay Street, Londonderry, BT48 6DN Tel: (028) 7136 3525 E-mail: info@ambient-light.co.uk *Ambient Light Productions are a Derry based company. We produce *digital features/shorts/ documentaries and corporate video in both standard definition and the new high definition **formats. Visit our website for more details.*

▶ Ambient Lounge, Elm Road, Kingston Upon Thames, Surrey, KT2 6HT Tel: (0870) 2851619 Fax: (0870) 2851613 E-mail: info@ambientlounge.com *Online retail*

AmbiRad Ltd, Fens Pool Avenue, Brierley Hill, West Midlands, DY5 1QA Tel: (01384) 489700 Fax: (01384) 489707 E-mail: marketing@ambirad.co.uk Principal Export Areas: Worldwide *Gas fired radiant and warm air energy efficient space heating solutions. Ideal for industrial and commercial buildings such as sports halls, retail premises, factories, hangers, showrooms and storage and distribution centres.*

Ambit Precision Grinding, 38a Kenilworth Drive, Oadby, Leicester, LE2 5LG Tel: 0116-271 1011 Fax: 0161-627 1101 E-mail: adam@ambit.fsnet.co.uk *Grinding services*

Ambit Projects Ltd, North Lynn Industrial Estate, King's Lynn, Norfolk, PE30 2JL Tel: (01553) 692977 Fax: (01553) 692997 E-mail: ambit@btinternet.com Principal Export Areas: Africa *Manufacturers of conveyor systems*

Ambitron Components Ltd, 4 Station Road, Hungerford, Berkshire, RG17 0DY Tel: (01488) 685404 Fax: (01488) 685406 E-mail: sales@ambitron.co.uk *Connector & cable assemblies distributors*

Amble Boat Co. Ltd, The Boatyard, 14 Coquet Street, Amble, Morpeth, Northumberland, NE65 0DJ Tel: (01665) 710267 Fax: (01665) 711354 E-mail: sales@ambleboat.co.uk *Boat builders & repairers*

Amblecote Machine Services, 4 Junction Road, Audnam, Stourbridge, West Midlands, DY8 4YJ Tel: (01384) 374935 Fax: (01384) 373336 *Engineer machinists*

Ambler Patterns, Riverside Works, Todmerton Rd, Littleborough, Lancs, OL15 9EG Tel: (01706) 378197 Fax: (01706) 377826 E-mail: sales@ambler-patterns.co.uk *Pattern makers & model makers*

Amblergem Jewellers, Unit 79 Grainger Market, Newcastle upon Tyne, NE1 5QQ Tel: 0191-232 3555 E-mail: amblergem@fsmail.net *Jewellery retail & manufrs*

▶ Ambleside Joinery Sales, 18, Graystones Close, West Bridgford, Nottingham, NG2 6QU Tel: 01159 819853 Fax: 01159 819853 E-mail: ambleside.sales@ntlworld.com *Purpose made specialist joinery & associated items, staircases*

▶ Ambrisbeg Ltd, 68 Marine Road, Port Bannatyne, Isle Of Bute, PA20 0LT Tel: (01700) 502719

Ambroplastics Ltd, Chamber House, Halesfield 13, Telford, Shropshire, TF7 4PL Tel: (01952) 684922 Fax: (01952) 581414 E-mail: info@ambro.co.uk *Polypropylene materials & packaging products manufrs*

▶ Ambros Travel, 33 LongBanks, Staple Tye, Harlow, Essex, CM18 7NT Tel: (01279) 639412 Fax: (0870) 7051629 E-mail: travel@ambros.plus.com *Travel Agency.*

Ambrose & Cox, Heanor Gate Road, Heanor, Derbyshire, DE7 7RE Tel: (01773) 713094 Fax: (01773) 717709 *Plant hire* Also at: Branches throughout the U.K.

▶ Ambrose Versak Group, Knarr Mill, Oldham Road, Delph, Oldham, OL3 5RQ Tel: (01457) 875901 Fax: (01457) 810687 *Manufacture objects from fibreglass*

Ambrose Wood & Son, Ovenhouse Farm Depot, Henshall Road, Bollington, Macclesfield, Cheshire, SK10 5DN Tel: (01625) 573291 *General engineers*

Ambuco (2000) Ltd, 55 London Rd, Raunds, Northants, NN9 6EH Tel: (01933) 624424 Fax: (01933) 626400 *Air pollution control systems*

Ambush Ltd, 11 Emmott Avenue, Ilford, Essex, IG6 1AL Tel: (020) 8554 0016 Fax: (020) 8554 6375 E-mail: enquiries@ambushed.com *T-shirt production & designers*

Amc, 45 Great Portland Street, London, W1W 7LD Tel: (020) 7468 0130 Fax: (020) 7468 0131 *Overseas purchasing agents*

Amc Diesel Engineering Ltd, Beverley House, Hall Lane, Longton, Preston, PR4 5ZD Tel: (01772) 613003 Fax: (01772) 616364 E-mail: sales@amcdiesel.co.uk *Marine diesel engine manufrs*

AMC Exhibitions, 1 Station Road, Foxton, Cambridge, CB22 6SA Tel: (01223) 871360 E-mail: info@amcexhibitions.co.uk *AMC Exhibitions offers a complete exhibition service. We sell exhibition equipment of all kinds - anything from the simplest of banner stand to a more complex modular system. We also have 25 years experience designing and building custom made stands, so whatever your particular requirement is we're sure to be able to help.*Our exhibition logistics service takes the hassle out of getting to a show - wherever it is in Europe. We'll collect your goods from your premises, and deliver them directly to your stand. We can unpack all the boxes, set up the stand and store all the packaging material for the duration of the event. And when the show is over, we'll bring everything back to the UK for you.*

▶ AMC Refrigeration, Killoch Road, Paisley, Renfrewshire, PA3 1ER Tel: 0141-849 6291 E-mail: amcref@hotmail.co.uk *Domestic & commercial refrigeration repairs.*

Amc Sheet Metal Fabrication, 1 2 3 The Chilterns, Marlborough Road, Lancing, West Sussex, BN15 8SU Tel: (01903) 752127 Fax: (01903) 750426 *Sheet metal fabricators*

▶ Amc Solutions UK Ltd, 16 St. James Avenue, Sutton, Surrey, SM1 2TH Tel: (020) 8642 7214 Fax: 0870 766 9675 E-mail: info@amc-solutions.com *Hotel booking Agency*

Amcast Ltd, Unit 7, Alliance Close, Attleborough Fields Industrial Estate, Nuneaton, Warwickshire, CV11 6SD Tel: (024) 7635 0575 Fax: (024) 7635 0761 E-mail: enquiries@amcast.co.uk *Tyres manufrs*

▶ Amcat, 11 Commerce Way, Westinghouse Road, Manchester, M17 1HW Tel: 0161-772 7100 Fax: 0161-876 4323 E-mail: mjolley@amcat.co.uk *Call centre*

Amcc Electronic Engineers, 15 Enterprise Industrial Estate, Station Road West, Ash Vale, Aldershot, Hampshire, GU12 5QJ Tel: (01252) 377723 Fax: (01252) 377724 E-mail: enquiries@amcc.co.uk *Acoustic & electronic engineering consultants*

Amco, P O Box 61, Camberley, Surrey, GU17 9YU Tel: 01276 31891 Fax: 01276 502239 *Floor maintenance equipment leasers*

▶ Amco Donelon, Unit 4a Birchwood One Business Park, Dewhurst Road, Birchwood, Warrington, WA3 7GB Tel: (01925) 838070 Fax: (01925) 816670

Amco Drilling International, PO Box 1, Barnsley, South Yorkshire, S75 1HT Tel: (01226) 243413 Fax: (01226) 320202 E-mail: info@amco-constrction.co.uk *Ground engineering & drilling contractors*

▶ Amco Engineering Services, Willow Tree House, Inchture, Perth, PH14 9RN Tel: (01828) 686963 Fax: (01828) 685385 E-mail: chatts@callnet.co.uk *Engineering installation services*

Amco FM Ltd, 3 Sun Street, Baldock, Hertfordshire, SG7 6QA Tel: (01462) 896959 Fax: (01462) 896597 E-mail: support@amcofm.co.uk *Computer maintenance engineers*

Amco Marelli Ltd, Meadow Lane, Loughborough, Leicestershire, LE11 1NB Tel: (01509) 615518 Fax: (01509) 615514 E-mail: sales@amco.fki-et.com *High quality electric motor manufrs*

Amco Print Solutions Ltd, 3 Beech Close, Menston, Ilkley, West Yorkshire, LS29 6NU Tel: (01943) 873 455 Fax: (01943) 884 786 E-mail: sales@amcoprint.com *Specialist Print solutions provider offering UNIQUE print solutions, specialists in swing tickets, garment labels, shelf edge labels magazines, colour leaflets, brochures, digital print, NCR pads, continuous stationery, vinyl and polyprop. binders, gift vouchers, loyalty cards and envelopes; with over 30 years experience within the trade supplying corporate and retail operations.*

Amco Products, 5 Orchard Road, Royston, Hertfordshire, SG8 5HD Tel: (01763) 242040 Fax: (01763) 245505 E-mail: sales@Amco-products.co.uk *Manufacturers of injection plastic moulders*

▶ AMCOL Specialty Minerals, Wharton Lodge Mills, Weaver Valley Road, Winsford, Cheshire, CW7 3BU Tel: (01606) 868200 Fax: (01606) 868268 E-mail: asm@amcol.com *Clay sourcing & technology company*

Amcor, Digby Street, Ilkeston, Derbyshire, DE7 5TS Tel: 0115-932 4391 Fax: 0115-932 7506 Principal Export Areas: Worldwide *Flexible packaging film distributors*

Amcor Ltd, Denmark House, Brick Close, Kiln Farm, Milton Keynes, MK11 3DP Tel: (01908) 261333 Fax: (01908) 261334 *Flexible packaging manufrs*

Amcor Flexibles, 1 Gass Close, Highbridge, Somerset, TA9 4JT Tel: (01278) 793232 Fax: (01278) 794996 E-mail: sales@amcor.com *Manufacturers of packaging for flexible products*

Amcor Flexibles Camvac, Burrell Way, Thetford, Norfolk, IP24 3QY Tel: (01842) 755021 Fax: (0845) 0822426 E-mail: steve.jackson@amcor-flexibles.com *Metallising processors services & metallised plastic film manufrs*

Amcor Flexibles Europe, Crompton Road, Ilkeston, Derbyshire, DE7 4BZ Tel: 0115-932 1443 Fax: 0115-944 0644 E-mail: info@amcor-flexibles.com *Polythene bags manufrs*

Amcor Flexibles Ledbury, Lower Road Trading Estate, Ledbury, Herefordshire, HR8 2DJ Tel: (01531) 638638 Fax: (01531) 635716 E-mail: enquiries@rexam.com *Polyethylene bag manufrs*

Amcor Flexibles S & R, Intaglio House, Brucefield Park West, Livingston, West Lothian, EH54 9ES Tel: (01506) 412845 Fax: (01506) 417344 *Flexible packaging products*

▶ Amcor Flexibles (UK) Ltd, Keith House, South Gyle, Edinburgh, EH12 9DQ Tel: 0131-317 2600

▶ Amcor Flexibles Winterbourne, Winterbourne Road, Stoke Gifford, Bristol, BS34 6PT Tel: 0117-987 2000 Fax: 0117-987 2002 E-mail: healthcare_info@amcor-flexibles.com Principal Export Areas: Worldwide *Amcor Flexibles is one of Europe's leading manufacturers of flexible packaging & one of the global leaders in flexible packaging for the healthcare industry. From 47 manufacturing plants throughout the world, Amcor Flexibles supplies a wide range of pharmaceutical, food & beverage markets & offers a comprehensive range of technological capabilities including state-of-the-art gravure & flexographic printing, coating & lamination, co-extrusion, metallising, micro-perforation, film, vented & header bags, pouches, die-cut lids & labels* Also at: Manchester

Amcor Pet Packaging Holdings Ltd, Gresford Industrial Park, Gresford, Wrexham, Clwyd, LL12 8LX Tel: (01978) 856111 Fax: (01978) 854168 *Plastic bottle & perform manufrs*

Amcore Flexibles, Hawkfield Way, Hawkfield Business Park, Bristol, BS14 0BD Tel: 0117-975 3200 Fax: 0117-975 3311 E-mail: sales@amcore.com *Flexible packaging materials*

Amcort Ltd, Field House, McMichaels Way, Hurst Green, Etchingham, East Sussex, TN19 7HJ Tel: (01580) 860500 Fax: (01580) 860171 E-mail: info@amcort.com *Business support services*

Amdale Ltd, 6-7 Culverin Square, Limberline Road, Hilsea, Portsmouth, PO3 5BU Tel: (023) 9266 0726 Fax: (023) 9265 5177 E-mail: sales@amdale.co.uk Principal Export Areas: Worldwide *Precision engineers to markets as diverse as sterile medical implants, through to marine pump manufacturers and formula one industries.*

Amdec Fork Lift Truck, Globe Lane Industrial Estate, Broadway, Dukinfield, Cheshire, SK16 4UU Tel: 0161-330 5151 Fax: 0161-338 8002 *Fork lift truck hire sales & repairs*

Amdocs, Clarify Court, London Road, Earley, Reading, RG6 1BW Tel: 0118-955 5200 Fax: 0118-955 5201 Principal Export Areas: Worldwide *Telecommunications software suppliers*

▶ Amdon Electrical Ltd, 2 The Green, Westerham, Kent, TN16 1AS Tel: (01959) 565635 Fax: (01959) 565783

▶ Amec, Site Office, Longannet Power Station, Alloa, Clackmannanshire, FK10 4AA Tel: (01259) 730474

▶ Amec Construction (Scotland) Ltd, Lundholm Road, Stevenston, Ayrshire, KA20 3LJ Tel: (01294) 605562

Amec Developments Ltd, Tolworth Tower, Ewell Road, Surbiton, Surrey, KT6 7EL Tel: (020) 8390 8300 Fax: (020) 8339 4699 *Property development consultants*

Amec Group Ltd, City Gate, Altens Farm Road, Nigg, Aberdeen, AB12 3LB Tel: (01224) 291000 Fax: (01224) 291001 *Oil & gas contractors*

▶ Amec Internal Asset Management Ltd, Meadowside Street, Renfrew, PA4 8SS Tel: 0141-886 2253 Fax: 0141-886 6510

AMEC Piling, Cold Meeth, Swynnton, Stone, Staffordshire, ST15 0UD Tel: (01785) 760022 Fax: (01785) 760762 *Foundation contractors*

Amec Process & Energy Ltd, 76-78 Old Street, London, EC1V 9RU Tel: (020) 7539 5800 Fax: (020) 7539 5900 E-mail: commercial@amec.com Principal Export Areas: Worldwide *Engineering & construction services*

Amec Process & Energy Ltd, 76-78 Old Street, London, EC1V 9RU Tel: (020) 7539 5800 Fax: (020) 7539 5900 E-mail: m.bell@amec.co.uk Principal Export Areas: Worldwide *Process engineering consultants*

▶ Amec Utilities Design & Build Ltd, 65 Bonnington Road, Edinburgh, EH6 5JQ Tel: 0131-553 7300 Fax: 0131-553 6956

Amech Engineering Ltd, Dudley Road, Yarm Road Industrial Estate, Darlington, County Durham, DL1 4GG Tel: (01325) 488884 Fax: (01325) 382525 E-mail: info@amech.net *Aluminium extrusion fabricators*

Amefa (UK) Ltd, Lion Works, 15 Orgreave Drive, Handsworth, Sheffield, S13 9NR Tel: (0844) 5553234 Fax: (0844) 5553435 E-mail: sales@amefa.co.uk *Amefa (UK) Ltd based in Sheffield offer a wide range in table and kitchen ware to make a feast of all your meals, whatever the occasion. They import and distribute a wide range of cookware and cutlery products.*

Amega Training (Wigan), Hewitt House, Hewitt Business Park, Winstanley Road, Orrell, WIGAN, LANCASHIRE, WN5 7XA Tel: 01695 682057 Fax: 01695 682058

continued

E-mail: info@amegatraining.co.uk *Independent training provider, based in Wigan, covering the North West of England. Delivers professional, accredited, cost effective training to business and the public,on your premises or at our local venues. Deliver training in CIEH Health and Safety, HSE First Aid at Work, Appointed Persons First Aid, Early Years /Children"s First Aid, CIEH Food Hygiene,CIEH HACCP, CIEH Nutrition, CIEH Food Safety Management Procedures, CIEH Manual Handling, CIEH Risk Assessment, CIEH COSHH, Supervising & Managing Safety, Fire Safety, Fire Risk Assessment, Fire Marshal /Warden, CIEH Stress Awareness, Noise, DSE, Working at Heights etc. Courses tailored to meet business /individuals needs, delivered in a fun interactive way. Courses delivered by experienced, qualified staff.*

Amek Conveyors, 17 Bergen Way, Hull, HU7 0YQ Tel: (01482) 838605 Fax: (01482) 838705 E-mail: sales@amek.co.uk *Mechanical engineers*

Amek Precision Engineers, The Hollies, Campton Road, Meppershall, Shefford, Bedfordshire, SG17 5PB Tel: (01462) 851171 Fax: (01462) 851171 *Precision engineers sub contractors*

Amelec Ltd, 101 Moreton Street, Cannock, Staffordshire, WS11 5HN Tel: (01543) 466191 Fax: (01543) 467339 E-mail: info@amelec.co.uk *Electronic component distributors*

Amelec Instruments Ltd, 3-5 Cochran Close, Crownhill, Milton Keynes, MK8 0AJ Tel: (01908) 567003 Fax: (01908) 566735 E-mail: sales@amelec-uk.com *Process control instrument manufrs*

Amenco (Poole) Ltd, Units 14-18, Willis Way, Fleets Industrial Estate, Poole, Dorset, BH15 3ST Tel: 0845 1306660 Fax: (01202) 671436 E-mail: office@amenco.co.uk *Shop fittings & sheet metal workers*

Amer Sports Ltd, Ayr Road, Irvine, Ayrshire, KA12 8HG Tel: (01294) 316200 Fax: (01294) 316300 *Sports goods distributors* Also at: Southall

Amerada Hess Ltd, 33 Grosvenor Place, London, SW1X 7HY Tel: (020) 7823 2626 Fax: (020) 7887 2199 *Oil & gas exploration*

Amerang Ltd, 15b Commerce Way, Lancing, West Sussex, BN15 8TA Tel: (01903) 765496 Fax: (01903) 765178 E-mail: sales@amerang-group.com *Import & export model kits*

Amerex Fire International Ltd, Unit 54 Springvale Industrial Estate, Cwmbran, Gwent, NP44 5BD Tel: (01633) 627000 Fax: (01633) 627005 E-mail: sales@amerexfire.eu *Amerex Fire International Ltd. is a UK based company supplying both UK and overseas markets. Amerex has been providing high quality and innovative fire fighting products for over 35 years and are recognised as leaders in their field. Products include powder, foam, water and wet chemical fire extinguishers.*

American Appraisal UK Ltd, Aldermary House, 10-15 Queen Street, London, EC4N 1TX Tel: (020) 7329 1776 Fax: (020) 7248 1453 E-mail: sales@american-appraisal.co.uk *Property consultants*

American Appraisal (UK) Ltd, Portland Buildings, 127-129 Portland Street, Manchester, M1 4PZ Tel: 0161-237 9907 Fax: 0161-237 9908 *Valuation consultants*

▶ American Drinks Ltd, Maple House, High Street, Potters Bar, Hertfordshire, EN6 5BS Tel: (0870) 3511718 Fax: (0870) 3511719 E-mail: info@arizona.uk.com *Arizona green tea reseller*

American & Efird GB Ltd, Chapelfield, Radcliffe, Manchester, M26 1JF Tel: 0161-766 1333 Fax: 0161-766 9965 E-mail: sales@amefird.co.uk *Industrial sewing thread manufrs*

American Marine Imports, Waterloo Park, Bidford-on-Avon, Alcester, Warwickshire, B50 4JG Tel: (01789) 491673 Fax: (01789) 778377 E-mail: ami1.ltd@btconnect.com *Marine importers*

American Marketing Systems, 13b Palmer Avenue, Blackpool, FY1 5JP Tel: (01253) 401872 *Cleaning materials & equipment*

American Optical UK Ltd, Unit 76-77 Capitol Industrial Park, Capitol Way, London, NW9 0EW Tel: (020) 8205 6575 Fax: (020) 8200 9749 *Lens manufrs* Also at: London E3

American Software (UK) Ltd, St Georges Business Park, Brooklands Road, Weybridge, Surrey, KT13 0TS Tel: (01932) 855554 Fax: (01932) 854563 E-mail: sales@amsoftware.com *Computer software distributors*

▶ American V8 Engines, 266 Orphanage Road, Erdington, Birmingham, B24 0BB Tel: 0121-350 1116 Fax: 0121-350 1116 E-mail: adrian@americanv8engines.co.uk *Suppliers of american v8 engines*

Americhem Ltd, Cawdor Street, Eccles, Manchester, M30 0QF Tel: 0161-789 7832 Fax: 0161-787 7832 *Colour & additive masterbatch manufrs*

Amerind Holdings Ltd, Bilsten House, Blackbushe Business Park, Yateley, Hampshire, GU46 6GE Tel: (01252) 861800 Fax: (01252) 861801 E-mail: admin@amerind.co.uk *Timber agents & veneer merchants*

Amerson Ltd, 9 Albany Road, Granby Industrial Estate, Weymouth, Dorset, DT4 9TH Tel: (01305) 206101 Fax: (01305) 206106 E-mail: amersonsales@amerson.co.uk *Filing cabinet manufrs*

Amery Engineering, Mill Lane, Alton, Hampshire, GU34 2QG Tel: (01420) 80298 Fax: (01420) 549559 E-mail: geoff@ameryeng.swiftserve.net *Precision toolmakers*

Ames Stokes Stevens & Son, Hanley Works, Hanley Street, Birmingham, B19 3SP Tel: 0121-359 5561 Fax: 0121-359 2336 E-mail: sales@amesstokes.com Principal Export Areas: Africa *Metal hinge manufrs*

Amethyst Ltd, Amherst House, Ferring Street, Worthing, West Sussex, BN12 5JR Tel: (01903) 700444 Fax: (01903) 700455 E-mail: production@amethystmailing.co.uk *Direct mail solutions & marketing consultants*

Amethyst Associates Ltd, The Old Barn, Oak House, Main Road, Farthinghoe, Brackley, Northamptonshire, NN13 5PB Tel: (01295) 714056 Fax: (0870) 1219961 E-mail: geoff.wenmouth@amethystassociates.co.uk *Selling & supporting accountancy software services*

Amethyst Designs Ltd, 9 Trafalgar Way, Bar Hill, Cambridge, CB3 8SQ Tel: (01954) 789696 Fax: (01954) 789662 E-mail: sales@amethyst-designs.co.uk *Manufacturers of transformers*

Amethyst Marine Services Ltd, Amethyst House, Royal Stuart Lane, Cardiff, CF10 5EL Tel: (029) 2048 8149 Fax: (029) 2048 6928 *Ship repairers*

▶ Amex Holdings, 5 Cherrywood, Stag Oak Lane, Chineham, Basingstoke, Hampshire, RG24 8WF Tel: (01256) 471000 Fax: (01256) 708989 *Double glazing installers*

Amey plc, Sutton Courtenay, Abingdon, Oxfordshire, OX14 4PP Tel: (01235) 848811 Fax: (01235) 848822 E-mail: amey.fleet@amey.co.uk *Fleet management & specialist plant hire*

Amey Cliff & Son, 12 Clive Road, Canton, Cardiff, CF5 1HJ Tel: (029) 2023 3462 Fax: (029) 2023 3462 E-mail: dennis.amey@talk21.com *Upholsterers & soft furnishing suppliers*

▶ Amey Infer- Structure Services Ltd, Second Floor, 1 Redcliff Street, Bristol, BS1 6QZ Tel: 0117-934 8836

Amfast Fasteners & Fixing Devices, Clifton House Southdown Industrial Estate, Southdown Road, Harpenden, Hertfordshire, AL5 1PW Tel: (01582) 715150 Fax: (01582) 712120 E-mail: ritagill@am-fast.co.uk *Fasteners stockists & distributors*

Amfax Ltd, 3 Clump Farm Industrial Estate, Blandford Heights, Blandford Forum, Dorset, DT11 7TE Tel: (01258) 480777 Fax: (01258) 480728 E-mail: sales@amfax.co.uk *Test & measurement solutions services*

▶ AMG Engineering, Wesleyan House, Lode Lane, Alstonefield, Ashbourne, Derbyshire, DE6 2FY Tel: (01335) 310249 Fax: (01335) 310276 E-mail: sales@amg-engineering.co.uk

▶ AMG People Management, The Springboard Centre, Mantle Lane, Coalville, Leicestershire, LE67 3DW Tel: 01530 510319 E-mail: enquiries@amgpeople.co.uk *AMG People Management offer a pay-as-you-go personnel management service to small and medium sized businesses.**Employment Law, grievance and discipline, absence /attendance management, HR policy and procedure, employee handbooks and employment contracts.**AMG also offer a full learning and development service to business of all sizes, from training design, to delivery and evaluation.**AMG - think of us as your own personnel and training manager, except you only pay for the time you use, not a large annual salary!**AMG work across the UK, with particular strength in the East Midlands, prioritising Nottinghamshire, Derbyshire, and Leicestershire, along with Birmingham, South Yorkshire and Sheffield.*

▶ Amg Stone Products Ltd, Rosedale, Stonehaven Road, Aberdeen, AB12 5UT Tel: (01224) 877283 Fax: (01224 873462 E-mail: info@amgstoneproducts.com *Importer and fabricator of natural stone products such as floor tiles, worktops, sink bowls, wall cladding, laminated worktops, building blocks, blank worktops. Specialist supplier to kitchen and bathroom showrooms, manufacturers, and building & construction industry.*

▶ AmG - Tony Ganchev, 50 Vulcan Close, London, UK, E6 5NY Tel: 07919 446843 Fax: 0207 4769123 E-mail: amgdirector@yahoo.co.uk *Building & Maintenance Service*- Interior & Exterior Painting & Decorating*- Carpenter work*- Locks and hinges*- The inside & outside doors *- General Building*- Tiling*- Changing Baths, Toilets, Flushing systems*

▶ Amgas Fires & Fireplaces Ltd, Unit 12 12 Whingate, Leeds, LS12 3BL Tel: 0113-263 0700 Fax: 0113-263 0700 E-mail: info@amgas.tk *We supply a huge range of gas fires, electric fires,*

▶ Amh Direct Ltd, Units 3-4 Tannock Street, Kilmarnock, Ayrshire, KA1 4DN Tel: (01563) 522000

Amian J Ltd, Lord Nelson Industrial Estate, Commercial Road, Stoke-On-Trent, ST1 3QF Tel: (01782) 267501 Fax: (01782) 267501 *Metal polishing & finishing services*

▶ Amicable Mortgage Services, 32 Twyford Avenue, Southampton, SO15 5NP Tel: (0800) 7810414 Fax: (023) 8032 2832 E-mail: patrick@effectivebusiness.info *Amicable Business Coaching**Effective Business Solutions - How To Increase Profits And Grow Your Company - FREE Phone 0800 781 0414 - http://www.EffectiveBusiness.info/**

▶ Amici Procurement Solutions, Fairwinds House, 31 Main Road, Fairlie, Largs, Ayrshire, KA29 0DL Tel: (01475) 568388 E-mail: info@amiciprocurement.com *Business consultancies*

Amico Packaging Supplies, 4 Robinson Road, Leicester, LE5 4NS Tel: 0116-276 2786 Fax: 0116-276 9786 *Major distributors of packers*

Amicon Engineering, 24-26 Ivatt Way, Peterborough, PE3 7PG Tel: (01733) 331414 Fax: (01733) 261383 E-mail: info@amiconengineering.com *General engineering services*

▶ Amicore Ltd, 8 Ringwood Avenue, Newport, Gwent, NP19 9DW Tel: (01633) 290486 Fax: (01633) 252100 E-mail: care@amicore.co.uk *emarketing and ecommerce service providers; hosting, web marketing, web design and development, shopping carts.*

Amicus, 33-37 Moreland Street, London, EC1V 8HA Tel: (020) 7505 3000 Fax: (020) 7505 3030 *Trade union* Also at: Branches throughout the U.K.

Amicus Aeeu, 396-398 Dunstable Road, Luton, LU4 8JT Tel: (01582) 576271 Fax: (01582) 580031 *Trade union* Also at: Branches throughout the U.K.

▶ Aminibus.co.uk, 92 Grange Lane, Barnsley, South Yorkshire, S71 5QQ Tel: (01226) 246445 Fax: (01226) 246101 E-mail: info@aminibus.co.uk *At A-Team travel we aim to offer Competetive Quality With Comfort & Safety, We provide transportation to most types of destinations from our Main Offices based in Barnsley, we cover the whole of south Yorkshire for collections, and travel nationwide as required.**Who Will You Choose To Travel With ?**BOOK EARLY - THE BEST !**Or Get Left With - THE REST !**

Amipak Ltd, 16-18 Factory Lane, Croydon, CR0 3RL Tel: (020) 8681 8611 Fax: (020) 8688 5314 E-mail: sales@amipak.co.uk *Board material manufrs*

Amir Power Transmission Ltd, Amir House, Maxted Road, Hemel Hempstead Industrial Estate, Hemel Hempstead, Hertfordshire, HP2 7DX Tel: (01442) 212671 Fax: (01442) 246640 E-mail: amirpower@amirpower.co.uk *Speed drive manufrs* Also at: Dewsbury & Lichfield

▶ Amitec UK Ltd, Riverside Farm, Back Lane, Kingston Seymour, Clevedon, Avon, BS21 6UZ Tel: (01275) 342236 Fax: (01275) 342236 E-mail: info@amitec.co.uk *Shot blasting & paint systems suppliers*

▶ Amj Services UK Ltd, 21a Whirlow Grove, Whirlow, Sheffield, S11 9NR Tel: 0114-249 8380 Fax: 0114 2817979 E-mail: tony@amjservices.com *Retail shopfitting specialist in store fit out and refurbishment*

AMJ (UK), Epps Buildings, Bridge Road, Ashford, Kent, TN23 1BB Tel: (01233) 663205 Fax: (01233) 664181 E-mail: info@amj-uk.com *Website & software developers services*

Amko Foods Ltd, Shiffnall Street, Bolton, BL2 1BZ Tel: (01204) 388801 E-mail: sales@amko.fsnet.co.uk *Food manufrs*

Aml Computers, Sir Francis Drake, Gayhurst, Newport Pagnell, Buckinghamshire, MK16 8LG Tel: (01908) 551550 Fax: (01908) 551545 *Recording studio equipment manufrs*

▶ Amlo Electrical Inspections Ltd, 46 Olma Road, Dunstable, Bedfordshire, LU5 5AF Tel: (01582) 535605 Fax: (01582) 535605 E-mail: enquiries@amlo.co.uk *NICEIC approved, electrical safety testing, fixed wiring*

Amman Concrete Products Ltd, Bryncethin Road, Garnant, Ammanford, Dyfed, SA18 1YP Tel: (01269) 823338 Fax: (01269) 823638 *Concrete products manufrs*

▶ Amman Mouldings, Dinefwr House, Pantyffynnon Road, Ammanford, Dyfed, SA18 3HL Tel: (01269) 851603 Fax: (01269) 851603 *Fibreglass moulders*

Amman Valley Fabrication Ltd, Llandeilo Road, Llandybie, Ammanford, Dyfed, SA18 3JG Tel: (01269) 851266 Fax: (01269) 851340 *Sheet metal fabrication & acoustic industry*

▶ Ammar Professionals Ltd, Flat 12, Jellicoe House, Osnaburgh Street, London, NW1 3AY Tel: (020) 7387 7600 Fax: (0870) 1323077 E-mail: ammar@btconnect.com *Management consultants*

Ammeraal Beltech Ltd, John Tate Road, Foxholes Business Park, Hertford, SG13 7QE Tel: (01992) 500550 Fax: (01992) 553010 E-mail: sales@ammeraalbeltech.co.uk Principal Export Areas: Worldwide *Process & conveyor belting distributors*

Ammeraal Beltech Ltd, Parkwood Street, Keighley, West Yorkshire, BD21 4PL Tel: (01535) 667015 Fax: (01535) 610250 E-mail: keighley@ammeraalbeltech.co.uk *Conveyor & transmission belts manufrs*

Ammnet Ltd, Wentworth House, 3 Lichfield Road, Burntwood, Staffordshire, WS7 0HQ Tel: (01543) 305133 Fax: (0870) 0547750 E-mail: sales@ammnet.com *Software warehouse*

Ammonite Flooring, 22 Hayes Street, Bromley, BR2 7LD Tel: (020) 8462 4671 Fax: (020) 8462 1013 *Flooring contractors*

Amnitec Ltd, Abercanaid, Merthyr Tydfil, Mid Glamorgan, CF48 1UX Tel: (01685) 385641 Fax: (01685) 389683 E-mail: sales@amnitec.co.uk *Metal & composite flexible hose manufacturers. Hose assemblies, stainless steel corrugated & stripwound metal hose products formerly known as United Flexible, Compoflex & Willcox*

Amo Blinds & Fabrics, 102 B M K Industrial Estate, Wakefield Road, Liversedge, West Yorkshire, WF15 6BS Tel: (01924) 410100 Fax: (01924) 410170 E-mail: showroom@amoblinds.co.uk *Blinds manufrs*

▶ Amo Security Roller Systems Ltd, Unit 6 Sycamore Industrial Estate, Walkley Lane, Heckmondwike, West Yorkshire, WF16 0NL Tel: (01924) 412666 Fax: (01924) 412233 E-mail: sales@amosecurity.co.uk *Manufacture & installer roller shutters, garage doors & awnings*

Amodil Supplies Ltd, Enterprise Trading Estate, Guinness Road, Trafford Park, Manchester, M17 1SG Tel: 0161-877 4539 Fax: 0161-877 4541 E-mail: mcl@amodilmanchester.demon.co.uk *Stainless steel stockholders*

Amoire Linen, 82 Beech Farm Drive, Macclesfield, Cheshire, SK10 2ER Tel: (01625) 431166 Fax: (01625) 610955 E-mail: sales@armoirelinen.co.uk *Finest linen collection for luxury hotels and resorts, yachts and villas.*

Amonite Ltd, 7b King St, Belper, Derbyshire, DE56 1PW Tel: (01773) 822211 E-mail: sales@amonite.com *Software House*

Amor Flexibles Europe Ltd, Orleans Close, Four Pools Industrial Estate, Evesham, Worcestershire, WR11 1LA Tel: (01386) 45925 Fax: (01386) 41114 *Printed flexible packaging*

Amora Wear, 9 Manningtree Street, London, E1 1LG Tel: (020) 7377 8711 Fax: (020) 7377 8711 *Ladies' fashion wholesalers & manufrs*

Amorim UK Ltd, Suite 1a Bishops Weald House, Albion Way, Horsham, West Sussex, RH12 1AH Tel: (01403) 710001 Fax: (01403) 710003 E-mail: sales@wicanders.co.uk *Manufacturing of cork & rubber products*

Amos Electronics, 4 Little Balmer, Buckingham Industrial Estate, Buckingham, MK18 1TF Tel: (01280) 817877 Fax: (01280) 814140 E-mail: purchasing@paramountelectronics.co.uk *Cable harness manufrs*

▶ AMOS Marketing Ltd, 28 Jermyn Way, Tharston, NORWICH, NR15 2ZA Tel: 01508 531482 E-mail: amosmarketing@btinternet.com *Online suppliers of the very best and latest in digital satellite receivers and accessories.*

Amos Swift Co. Ltd, Boathouse Lane, Stockton-on-Tees, Cleveland, TS18 3AW Tel: (01642) 675241 Fax: (01642) 675241 E-mail: john.hingley@ntlworld.com *Wood turners & brush manufrs*

Amot Controls Ltd, Western Way, Bury St. Edmunds, Suffolk, IP33 3SZ Tel: (01284) 762222 Fax: (01284) 760256 E-mail: info@amot.com Principal Export Areas: Worldwide *Manufacturers of control panel components; control panel; diesel engine safety equipment & thermosta*

Amp Air Conditioning Ltd, Blenheim House Blenhiem Court, Brownfields, Welwyn Garden City, Hertfordshire, AL7 1AD Tel: (01707) 378670 Fax: (01707) 378699 E-mail: info@ampair.co.uk *Air conditioning distributors*

▶ AMP (GB) Ltd, Horton Corner, Small Dole, Henfield, West Sussex, BN5 9XJ Tel: (01903) 817004 Fax: (01903) 817114 E-mail: mphippf@amp.com *Control systems suppliers*

Ampac System Integrators Ltd, Hilton Officers, Shobnall Road, Burton-On-Trent, Staffordshire, DE14 2BW Tel: (01283) 567888 Fax: (01283) 567606 E-mail: info@ampac.co.uk *Systems integration systems*

Ampacet UK Ltd, Unit F1, Halesfield 21, Telford, Shropshire, TF7 4NX Tel: (01952) 581814 Fax: (01952) 581815 *Masterbatch compound manufrs*

Ampack Security Products Ltd, Saxon Way, Melbourn, Royston, Hertfordshire, SG8 6DN Tel: (01763) 261900 Fax: (01763) 261234 *Security bag & durable mailers manufrs*

Ampair, Park Farm, West End Lane, Warfield, Bracknell, Berkshire, RG42 5RH Tel: (01344) 303311 Fax: (01344) 303312 E-mail: sales@ampair.com *Wind & water generator manufrs, solar PV distributors*

Ampco, Unit 4 Prime Buildings, Daux Road, Billingshurst, West Sussex, RH14 9SJ Tel: (01403) 780420 Fax: (01403) 786486 E-mail: sales@ampco.co.uk *Plastic vacuum formed products manufrs*

Ampco Metal Ltd, 17 Binns Close, Coventry, CV4 9TB Tel: (024) 7646 7011 Fax: (024) 7646 1455 E-mail: info@ampcometal.co.uk *Aluminium, bronze & copper alloy stockholders*

▶ Ampere Electrical Ltd, 27 St. Margaret Drive, Epsom, Surrey, KT18 7LB Tel: (0845) 8380825 Fax: (01372) 745580 E-mail: ampere@fsmail.net *Electrical contractors & portable appliance testing services*

Ampetronic Ltd, Northern Road, Newark, Nottinghamshire, NG24 2ET Tel: (01636) 610062 Fax: (01636) 610063 E-mail: sales@ampetronic.com *Audio induction loops & audio visual equipment manufrs*

Amphenol Ltd, Thanet Way, Whitstable, Kent, CT5 3JF Tel: (01227) 773200 Fax: (01227) 276571 E-mail: info@amphenol.co.uk *Electronic component manufrs*

Amphenol Spectrastrip Ltd, Unit 21-23 Romsey Industrial Estate, Greatbridge Road, Romsey, Hampshire, SO51 0HR Tel: (01794) 517575 Fax: (01794) 516246 E-mail: info@spectra-strip.com Principal Export Areas: Worldwide *Cable manufrs*

▶ Ampire Productions, Marino Way, Finchampstead, Wokingham, Berkshire, RG40 4RF Tel: 0118-973 5050 *Repair,Service,Sales and Hire for professional Lighting and Sound equipment.*

▶ Ample Clothing Mnfrs, 15 Yorkshire Road, Leicester, LE4 6PH Tel: 0116-261 3052 Fax: 0116-261 3053 *Fabric manufrs*

Amplicon Liveline Ltd, Unit 11 Centenary Industrial Estate, Hughes Road, Brighton, BN2 4AW Tel: (01273) 570220 Fax: (01273) 570215 E-mail: sales@amplicon.co.uk Principal Export Areas: Africa, Central/East Europe, West Europe, North America & South America *Data communication system distributors*

▶ Amplicore Ltd, 163 Wensley Road, Reading, RG1 6DU Tel: 0118-377 3197 *Electronic equipment manufrs*

▶ Ampliflaire Ltd, Off The Square Trade Centre, Bowmont Street, Kelso, Roxburghshire, TD5 7JH Tel: (01573) 225209 Fax: (01573) 225886

AM-PM Gate Automation, View Gardens Centre, Old Chelmsford Road, Rawreth, Wickford, Essex, SS11 8SJ Tel: 01268 571400 Fax: 05601 150721 E-mail: enquiries@ampmgateautomation.co.uk *Gate automation installation services*

Ampo UK, Holly Tree Cottage, Stocks Lane, Welshampton, Ellesmere, Shropshire, SY12 0NT Tel: (01948) 710764 Fax: (01948) 710914 E-mail: ampouk@aol.com Sales Contact: G. Grant *Ampo is situated in Northern Spain and is dedicated to the casting of stainless steels (austenitic, martensitic, duplex, super duplex), nickel based alloys (monel, inconel, incolloy) heat resistant steels, low alloy, carbon steels etc. We have a static foundry producing castings using silica sand, shell and ceramically moulded processes to 5000kgs unit weight. Our modern centrifugal spinning facility casts thick-walled tube and floating, trunnion and stem balls to 30" diameter. Equipped with the most modern of installations, approved by the world's leading inspection authorities, we offer a wide range of castings to markets such as gas, onshore/ offshore, chemical and petrochemical industries, power generation, hydraulics, naval, heat treatment etc. With our innovative machining facility we can supply customers with fully-machined castings, adding value to the product and shortening final customer delivery times.*

Ampohm Wound Products, Unit 1d Treburley Industrial Estate, Treburley, Launceston, Cornwall, PL15 9PU Tel: (01579) 370025 Fax: (01579) 370051 E-mail: ampcaps15@btconnect.com *Capacitor & suppressor manufrs*

Amps Ltd, Wheatsheaf Buildings, High Street, Rhosymedre, Wrexham, Clwyd, LL14 3YE Tel: (01978) 810808 Fax: (01978) 810700 E-mail: info@amps-ltd.co.uk *Pigment merchants*

▶ Amps International Ltd, 11 Lime Hill Road, Tunbridge Wells, Kent, TN1 1LJ Tel: (01892) 538862 Fax: (01892) 513992 E-mail: sales@ampsl.com *Multimedia packaging manufacturers & importers*

Ampthill Metal Co. Ltd, Station Road Industrial Estate, Ampthill, Bedford, MK45 2QY Tel: (01525) 403388 Fax: (01525) 404908 E-mail: mick@ampthillmetal.co.uk *Metal recycling*

Amracks Ltd, 2 Cockerell Road, Corby, Northamptonshire, NN17 5DU Tel: (01536) 401361 Fax: (01536) 275909 E-mail: info@amracks.co.uk *Storage & mezzanine floorings*

Amrob Engineering Ltd, Unit 14 Garth Works, Taffs Well, Cardiff, CF15 7RN Tel: (029) 2081 3033 Fax: (029) 2081 3272 *Structural engineering & fabricating steelworks*

▶ Ams, 25 Challenge Enterprise Centre, Sharps Close, Portsmouth, PO3 5RJ Tel: (023) 9266 9600 Fax: (023) 9267 9743 E-mail: danny@automotivesecurity.co.uk *Vehicle security & entertainment services*

AMS Group Consultants, PO Box 5586, Milton Keynes, MK4 1ZG Tel: (0870) 0923392 Fax: (0870) 0923393 E-mail: ams@amsgroup.demon.co.uk *Chartered structural & civil engineers*

Ams Steel Fabrications, St Nicholas Industrial Estate, Darlington, County Durham, DL1 2NL Tel: (01325) 254439 Fax: (01325) 254439 *Fabricators*

Amsafe Bridport, The Court, West Street, Bridport, Dorset, DT6 3QU Tel: (01308) 456666 Fax: (01308) 456605 E-mail: david.rumney@amsafe.com *Weavers of fabrics & webbing manufrs*

Amscan International Ltd, Brudenell Drive, Brinklow, Milton Keynes, MK10 0DA Tel: (01908) 288500 Fax: (01908) 288501 E-mail: sales@amscan-uk.co.uk *Party products distributors*

▶ AMS-IT, Merlin House, Langstone Business Village, Priory Drive, Langstone, Newport, Gwent, NP18 2HJ Tel: (01633) 415310 Fax: (01633) 415366 E-mail: peter.oddy@amsolve.co.uk *Computer services*

Amstrad plc, Brentwood House, 169 Kings Road, Brentwood, Essex, CM14 4EF Tel: (01277) 228888 Fax: (01277) 211350 E-mail: admin@amstrad.com *Telecommunications & consumer electronics*

Amsys plc, Byron House, Lower Road, Kenley, Surrey, CR8 5NB Tel: (020) 8660 9999 Fax: (020) 8763 9332 E-mail: info@amsys.co.uk *Computer repair services*

Amtec Ltd, Throop Business Park, Throop Road, Bournemouth, BH8 0DW Tel: (01202) 533557 Fax: (01202) 533567 E-mail: info@amteccorrosion.co.uk *Sheet metal fabricators*

Amtec Automation Ltd, 27 Brooklands Close, Uttoxeter, Staffordshire, ST14 8UH Tel: (07973) 614115 Fax: (01889) 560353 E-mail: info@amt-a.com *AMTec Automation.*Control solutions for your business.*PLC SOFTWARE:*Software written in either ladder Logic or IEC11 format. Full software comments supplied within software and in accompanying documentation* Allen Bradley, Mitsubishi,NAIS ,Omron PLC"s**NETWORK AND COMMUNICATIONS:*Full network systems for PLC - PLC, PLC - HMI, PLC - SCADA supported.**HMI /SCADA SYSTEMS:*Full graphical representations of process, incorporating the use of simple and straight forward menu and sub menu systems. Enabling quick navigation around the screens.***

Amtec Consulting plc, Millennium Centre, 2 Crosby Way, Farnham, Surrey, GU9 7XX Tel: (01252) 737866 Fax: (01252) 737855 E-mail: post@amtec.co.uk *IT computer consultants*

Amtech Industrial Computer Solutions, Ramage House, Samson Close, Newcastle upon Tyne, NE12 6DX Tel: 0191-268 2022 Fax: 0191-268 2092 E-mail: sales@amtechltd.co.uk *Industrial control systems distributors*

Amtech Power Software Ltd, Bank House, 171 Midsummer Boulevard, Milton Keynes, MK9 1EB Tel: (01908) 608833 Fax: (01908) 234355 E-mail: sales@amtech-power.co.uk *Software solution specialists*

Amtek Instrumentation Engineers, 8 Mexico Lane, Phillack, Hayle, Cornwall, TR27 5AG Tel: (01736) 754015 Fax: (01736) 759389 *Electrical instrument distributor*

The Amtico Co. Ltd, Kingfield Road, Coventry, CV6 5AA Tel: (024) 7686 1400 Fax: (024) 7686 1552 E-mail: info@amtico.com *Resilient flooring manufrs*

▶ Amtin Ltd, Manor Barns, The Street, Brundish, Woodbridge, Suffolk, IP13 8BL Tel: (01379) 388385 Fax: (01379) 388386 E-mail: design@amtin.co.uk *Steel Fabricators, Balustrades, Fire Escapes*

▶ Amtrak Express Parcels, Craigshaw Road, West Tullos Industrial Estate, Aberdeen, AB12 3AR Tel: (01224) 894927 Fax: (01224) 879864

▶ Amtrak Express Parcels, 1 Barrs Fold Road, Wingates Industrial Estate, Westhoughton, Bolton, BL5 3XW Tel: (01942) 811542 Fax: (01942) 842036

▶ Amtrak Express Parcels, Unit A3 Mid Craigie Trading Estate, Mid Craigie Road, Dundee, DD4 7RH Tel: (0870) 8110619 Fax: (01382) 458855

▶ Amtrak Express Parcels, Unit 16h Bergen Way, Hull, HU7 0YQ Tel: (01482) 830842 Fax: (01482) 823772

▶ Amtrak Express Parcels, Waleswood House Aldred Close, Norwood Industrial Estate, Killamarsh, Sheffield, S21 2JH Tel: 0114-247 2049 Fax: 0114-247 2831

▶ Amtri Veritas Ltd, Hulley Road, Macclesfield, Cheshire, SK10 2LU Tel: (01625) 425421 Fax: (01625) 427038 E-mail: info@amtri.co.uk *Certification body, marking & training*

Amtv, The Studio, Black Bourton Road, Carterton, Oxfordshire, OX18 3HF Tel: (01993) 841827 Fax: (01993) 842943 E-mail: anthonymorris@amtv.co.uk *Audio visual sales*

Amundsen & Smith Ltd, Cargo Durham Distribution Centre, Seaham, County Durham, SR7 7NZ Tel: 0191-581 2315 Fax: 0191-581 7360 E-mail: enquiries@amundsen-smith.co.uk *Ship brokers & chartering agents of freight forwarders*

▶ Amusement Caterers Sheffield Ltd, 140 Walkley Lane, Sheffield, S6 2NZ Tel: 0114-234 9808 Fax: 0114-285 2342 E-mail: andy@amusementcaterers.com *Suppliers of Juke Boxes, Pin Tables, Pool Tables, Table Football, AWP (Fruit Machines/ Bandits), SWP (Quiz Games), Video Games and Bingo Machines. We offer a sales, rental, or repair service to the licensed trade and the general public within the Sheffield area.*

Amusement Machines Services, Pioneer House, Northgate, Dewsbury, West Yorkshire, WF13 1AP Tel: (0800) 7837313 E-mail: peter@ams-nv.freeserve.co.uk *Amusement machine services*

Amvar Ltd, Unit 2 Mucklow Hill Trading Estate, Mucklow Hill, Halesowen, West Midlands, B62 8DF Tel: (0800) 5424512 Fax: 0121-550 7222 E-mail: amvar@forklift-trucks.uk.com *Forklift truck & storage solution services*

Amx UK Ltd, Auster Road, York, YO30 4GD Tel: (01904) 343100 Fax: (01904) 343101 E-mail: sales@amxuk.co.uk *Systems equipment distributors*

▶ Amy Nicholas Interior Design, Rose Cottage, Main Street, Grindleton, Clitheroe, Lancashire, BB7 4QT Tel: 01200 441854 Fax: 01200 441854 E-mail: info@amynicholas.co.uk *Interior design*

Amy Shutters, 8 Slader Business Park, Witney Roe, Nuffield Industrial Estate, Poole, Dorset, BH17 0GP Tel: (01202) 666702 Fax: (01202) 666705 E-mail: info@amyshutters.co.uk *Industrial doors & shutters*

▶ An Agency Called England, The Old Warehouse, 1 Albert Street, Whitstable, Kent, CT5 1HP Tel: (01227) 770790 Fax: (01227) 770924 E-mail: admin@polcol.co.uk *Advertising agency*

▶ An Other Cleaning Company, 11 Pembrook Road, Holbrook, Coventry, CV6 4FD Tel: (024) 7666 5921 Fax: (024) 7666 5921 E-mail: rob@aocc.co.uk *Professional contract cleaners. Cleaning Offices, Commercial Properties and Light Industry. Driveways /Patios pressure washed and sealed. Builder clean ups. House sale clean ups. Over 15 Year experience.*

▶ An Technology Antech Ltd, 6 Thames Park, Lester Way, Wallingford, Oxfordshire, OX10 9TA Tel: (01491) 824444 Fax: (01491) 832800

Anaconda Belting Co., 2 Ashwood Place, Bean, Dartford, DA2 8BD Tel: (01474) 709784 Fax: (01474) 709896 E-mail: info@anacondabelting.co.uk *Conveyor & elevator belting distributors*

Anaesthesia Technology Ltd, Walshford, Wetherby, West Yorkshire, LS22 5JJ Tel: (01937) 587001 Fax: (01937) 587002 E-mail: sales@anaetech.co.uk *Medical engineers & consultants*

Anage Productions, Quoin House, Adelaide Road, Ashford, Middlesex, TW15 3LJ Tel: (01784) 423993 Fax: (01784) 247203 *Conference organizers*

Analan Supplies Ltd, 62 High Street, Beighton, Sheffield, S20 1ED Tel: 0114-269 7060 Fax: 0114-254 8445 E-mail: analan@talk21.com *Janitorial supply services*

Analog Devices Ltd, Rothwell House, Pembroke Road, Newbury, Berkshire, RG14 1BX Tel: (01635) 555400 Fax: (01635) 555401 E-mail: hilary.abbott@analog.com *Microchip designers*

▶ Analogue Integration Ltd, The Old Village Store, Corston, Malmesbury, Wiltshire, SN16 0HJ Tel: (01666) 823290 Fax: (01666) 825154 E-mail: enquiry@analog.co.uk *Silicon microchip designers*

Analox Instruments Ltd, 8 Goldhawk Industrial Estate, 2a Brackenbury Road, London, W6 0BA Tel: (020) 8749 7644 Fax: (020) 8740 6608 E-mail: info@analox.com *Clinical scientific instrument manufrs*

Analox Sensor Technology Ltd, 15 Ellerbeck Court, Stokesley Business Park, Stokesley, Middlesbrough, Cleveland, TS9 5PT Tel: (01642) 711400 Fax: (01642) 713900 E-mail: admin@analox.net *Air compressor & gas sensor manufrs*

▶ Analytical Columns, 7 Addington Business Centre, Vulcan Way, New Addington, Croydon, CR0 9UG Tel: (01689) 842736 Fax: (01689) 800199 E-mail: analytical@btconnect.com *GC & HPLC column manufacturers & suppliers*

Analytical Measurements Ltd, 14 Selby Road, Ashford, Middlesex, TW15 1JH Tel: (01784) 256236 Fax: (01784) 257938 *PH meters suppliers*

Analytical Technologies Ltd, Lynchford House Lynchford Lane, Farnborough, Hampshire, GU14 6JB Tel: (01252) 514711 Fax: (01252) 511855 E-mail: analyticaltechnologies@aol.com *Chemical, medical analysts & analysing services*

Analytical Technology International Ltd, 5 Heather Close, Lyme Green Business Park, Macclesfield, Cheshire, SK11 0LR Tel: (01625) 616431 Fax: (01625) 612494 E-mail: sales@ati-ltd.co.uk *Scientific instrument parts manufrs*

Ananas & Dansk, The Old Coachworks, Rotterdam Road, Lowestoft, Suffolk, NR32 2EX Tel: (01502) 514848 Fax: (01502) 514828 E-mail: sales@ananasanddansk.com *Furniture wholesalers*

Anaren Microwave Europe Inc, Suites 16-17, Somerset House, Hussar Court, Waterlooville, Hampshire, PO7 7SG Tel: (023) 9223 2392 Fax: (023) 9225 1369 E-mail: anareneurope@anaren.com *Radio frequency & microwave component manufrs*

▶ Anastasia Flowers, 131 Easterly Road, Leeds, LS8 2TP Tel: 0113-235 1010 Fax: 0113-235 1010 E-mail: lana@anastasiaflowers.co.uk *Florist*

Anatric Machine Tools, 3 Sinclair Court, Bletchley, Milton Keynes, MK1 1RB Tel: (01908) 371331 Fax: (01908) 367683 *Machining services*

▶ Anbar Trading Co., 44 Belton Lane, Great Gonerby, Grantham, Lincolnshire, NG31 8NA Tel: (01476) 571966 Fax: (01476) 592093 E-mail: anbar@globalnet.co.uk *Exporters of coles crane parts & industrial automotive parts suppliers*

Anbercraft Furniture, 315 Princes Road, Stoke-on-Trent, ST4 7JS Tel: (01782) 413719 Fax: (01782) 749156 *Occasional furniture manufrs*

▶ Anc Birmingham, 99 Amington Road, Birmingham, B25 8EP Tel: 0121-708 4444 Fax: 0121-708 4433

▶ Anc Launceston, Unit 4b, Pennygillam Indust Estate, Pennygillam Industrial Estate, Launceston, Cornwall, PL15 7ED Tel: (01566) 773330 Fax: (01566) 777486 E-mail: sales0072@anc.co.uk

▶ Anc North Yorkshire Ltd, York Road, Flaxby, Knaresborough, North Yorkshire, HG5 0RP Tel: (01423) 869696 Fax: (01423) 862922

Anca, Leyton Avenue, Mildenhall, Bury St. Edmunds, Suffolk, IP28 7BL Tel: (01638) 717611 Fax: (01638) 717711 *Office equipment & stationery distributors*

Anca Industrial Supplies Ltd, Unit 16 Forge Trading Estate, Mucklow Hill, Halesowen, West Midlands, B62 8TP Tel: 0121-503 0919 Fax: 0121-585 5483 E-mail: admin@anca.co.uk *Distributors of adhesives & packaging products*

▶ Ancar Installations, 208 Amblecote Road, Brierley Hill, West Midlands, DY5 2PP Tel: (01384) 485000 Fax: (01384) 485000 *Mezzanine floors*

▶ Ancholme Discount Furniture, Unit 7 Island Carr Industrial Estate, Island Carr Road, Brigg, South Humberside, DN20 8PD Tel: (01652) 653644 Fax: (01652) 653644 E-mail: chizel@btopenworld.com *Blinds & laminate flooring retailers*

Ancholme Machinery Co. Ltd, Units 3-4, Albert Street, Brigg, North Lincolnshire, DN20 8HQ Tel: (01652) 657521 Fax: (01652) 650073 E-mail: ancholme1@aol.com *Packaging machinery specialists*

Bruce Anchor Ltd, Royston Road, Deans Industrial Estate, Livingston, West Lothian, EH54 8AH Tel: (01506) 415454 Fax: (01506) 461202 E-mail: bruceanchor@lineone.net *Mooring equipment & 'Bruce' anchors manufrs*

Anchor Building Services, 14 Ivy Street, Burnley, Lancashire, BB10 1TD Tel: (01254) 394137 Fax: (01254) 394137 *Wall tie replacements installers*

Anchor Components Ltd, 1 John Street, Biddulph, Stoke-on-Trent, ST8 6BB Tel: (01782) 522844 Fax: (01782) 522828 E-mail: sales@anchorcomponents.co.uk *Electronic component kitting services, distributors, agents*

Anchor Data Systems Ltd, Unit 36 North City Business Centre, 2 Duncairn Gardens, Belfast, BT15 2GG Tel: (028) 9074 0315 Fax: (028) 9035 1531 E-mail: info@anchordata.co.uk *Electronic cash handling machines distributors*

Anchor Employment Agency, 2 The Colonnade, Lind St, Ryde, Isle of Wight, PO33 2NE Tel: (01983) 811244 Fax: (01983) 812866 E-mail: anchoriw@hotmail.com *Employment agency*

Anchor Export Services Ltd, Unit D 1, Gildersome Spur Estate, Wakefield Road, Leeds, LS27 7JZ Tel: 0113-252 6544 Fax: 0113-238 0028 *Export packaging services*

Anchor Fire Protection Ltd, 11 Elkin Road, Morecambe, Lancashire, LA4 5RN Tel: (01524) 832238 Fax: 01524 832238 *Fire protection equipment services*

Anchor Food Service Equipment Ltd, 4 Capital Industrial Estate, Crabtree Manorway South, Belvedere, Kent, DA17 6BJ Tel: (020) 8311 1313 Fax: (020) 8311 4431 E-mail: anchor.food@btclick.com *Catering equipment manufrs*

Anchor Food Service Equipment, Unit F1, Valley Way, Market Harborough, Leicestershire, LE16 7PS Tel: (01858) 468181 Fax: (01858) 467506 E-mail: pennywashtech@1dial.co.uk *Catering equipment suppliers*

▶ Anchor Hydraulics Ltd, Unit 6 Leeds Street, Wigan, Lancashire, WN3 4BW Tel: (01942) 820615 Fax: (01942) 820615 E-mail: anchorhydraulics@btclick.com *Hydraulic spares & repairs*

Anchor Industrial Plastics Ltd, 3 Benjamin Outram Business Centre, Whiteley Road, Ripley, Derbyshire, DE5 3QL Tel: (01773) 513022 Fax: (01773) 570404 E-mail: jkanchorplastics@aol.com *Plastic pipe fitting distributors*

Anchor Inserts, 11 Bayton Road Industrial Estate, Bayton Road, Exhall, Coventry, CV7 9EL Tel: (024) 7636 3979 Fax: (024) 7636 6303 E-mail: info@anchorinserts.co.uk *Threaded insert manufrs*

Anchor Interior Solutions Ltd, 97 Leyland Trading Estate, Wellingborough, Northamptonshire, NN8 1RT Tel: (01933) 275757 Fax: (01933) 270070 *Suspended ceilings, dry lining & partitioning installers*

Anchor Plastics Machinery, The Watermill, Royal Quay, Harefield, Uxbridge, Middlesex, UB9 6SA Tel: (01895) 824301 Fax: (01895) 825344 E-mail: info@anchor-pm.co.uk *Plastics packaging equipment machinery agents*

Anchor Seafoods Ltd, Devonshire House, High Street, Handcross, Haywards Heath, West Sussex, RH17 6BJ Tel: (01444) 400363 Fax: (01444) 400949 E-mail: sales@anchorseafoods.com *Seafood distributors*

Anchor Sound & Security, 474 Hatfield Road, St. Albans, Hertfordshire, AL4 0XS Tel: (01727) 831402 *Intercom & security systems*

continued

Anchor Supplies, Peasehill Road, Ripley, Derbyshire, DE5 3JG Tel: 01773 570139 Fax: 01773 570537 E-mail: ripley@anchorsupplies.com *Government surplus supplier*

Anchor Trust Co. Ltd, PO Box 496, Jersey, JE4 5TD Tel: (01534) 887211 Fax: (01534) 887212 E-mail: anchor@jerseyoffice.com *Trust & company development services*

Anchor Tyres, Unit 6, Oakwood Industrial Park, Gatwick Road, Crawley, West Sussex, RH10 9AZ Tel: (01293) 544577 Fax: (01293) 527477 *Tyre sales & distributors*

Anchor Ventilation Co Britair Ltd, Malt Lane, Stoke-on-Trent, ST3 1RR Tel: (01782) 312809 Fax: (01782) 311138 *Ventilating engineers*

▶ Anchor Woodworking, 3 Mid Row, Croftouterly, Leslie, Glenrothes, Fife, KY6 3DR Tel: (01592) 748900 Fax: (01592) 748900 E-mail: info@anchorwoodworking.co.uk *Manufactures of Timber Sheds, Garages, Summer & Play houses, Dog Kennels & Runs, Tool & Potting Sheds.*

Ancient Barn Ltd, Coxford Abbey Farm, Coxford, King's Lynn, Norfolk, PE31 6TB Tel: (01485) 528860 *Furniture manufrs*

Ancient Recipes, Empire Way, Gretna, Dumfriesshire, DG16 5BN Tel: (01461) 338117 Fax: (01461) 338436 E-mail: mail@solwayveg.co.uk *Food products manufrs*

Ancol Pet Products Ltd, Ancol House, 113 Leamore Lane, Walsall, WS2 7DA Tel: (01922) 402428 Fax: (01922) 404983 E-mail: sales@ancol.co.uk *Pet accessorie suppliers*

Ancorite, Moston Road, Sandbach, Cheshire, CW11 3AB Tel: (01270) 761720 Fax: (01270) 761697 Principal Export Areas: Worldwide *Corrosion prevention coatings*

▶ And Design, 39 Derment Drive, Maidenhead, Berkshire, SL6 6LE Tel: (07747) 782816 E-mail: ant@and-design.co.uk *Print, advertising, web design, point of sale, packaging & printing*

And So To Bed Ltd, Pymore Mills, Pymore, Bridport, Dorset, DT6 5PJ Tel: (01308) 425252 Fax: (01308) 458811 E-mail: sales@andsotobed.co.uk *Bed specialists*

And So To Bed Ltd, 15 Orchard Street, London, W1H 6HG Tel: (020) 7935 0225 Fax: (020) 7487 3434 *Bed suppliers & manufrs*

And Technology Research Ltd, 4 Forest Drive, Theydon Bois, Epping, Essex, CM16 7EY Tel: (01992) 814655 Fax: (01992) 813362 *Software developers & computer systems*

▶ And Then There Was Light, The Digital World Centre, The Quays, Manchester, M50 3UB Tel: 0870 2407507 E-mail: enquiries@andlight.co.uk *And Then There Was Light help to take away the mystery that surrounds the development of a website. We reduce the hassle, confusion and uncertainty that can make the process so costly and time-consuming.**For a new business website or improvement of an existing one.*

Andaire Computer Services, Plainlands, Drake Lane, Dursley, Gloucestershire, GL11 5HF Tel: (01453) 541800 Fax: (01453) 541808 E-mail: mail@andaire.co.uk *Specialists in permanent IT recruitment*

Andante Medical Services Ltd, Brick Kiln Lane, Horsmonden, Tonbridge, Kent, TN12 8ES Tel: (01892) 724881 Fax: (01892) 535853 E-mail: sales@medicalpromotional.co.uk *Surgical instrument manufrs*

Andantex Ltd, Rowley Drive, Bagington, Coventry, CV3 4LS Tel: (024) 7630 7722 Fax: (024) 7630 4499 E-mail: sales@andantex.com Principal Export Areas: Worldwide *Power transmission equipment distributors*

Andark Promotions Ltd, 256 Bridge Road, Swanwick, Southampton, SO31 7FL Tel: (01489) 581755 Fax: (01489) 575223 E-mail: sales@andark.co.uk *Scuba diving teachers*

Andawest Engineering Ltd, Unit 2a Boardman Industrial Estate, Boardman Road, Swadlincote, Derbyshire, DE11 9DL Tel: (01283) 214182 Fax: (01283) 550909 E-mail: andawest@aol.com *Precision machining*

Andel Plastics Ltd, 1 Klaxon Tysley Industrial Estate, 751 Warwick Road, Tyseley, Birmingham, B11 2HA Tel: 0121-765 4042 Fax: 0121-707 3335 E-mail: enquiries@andel-plastics.demon.co.uk Principal Export Areas: North America *Injection mould toolmakers & injection moulders*

Andergauge Ltd, Hareness Road, Altens Industrial Estate, Aberdeen, AB12 3LE Tel: (01224) 336500 Fax: (01224) 336505 E-mail: sales@andergauge.com *Drilling equipment hire*

Anderman & Co. Ltd, 145 London Road, Kingston Upon Thames, Surrey, KT2 6NH Tel: (020) 8541 0035 Fax: (020) 8549 1617 E-mail: enquiries@earthwaterfire.com *Laboratory equipment suppliers*

Anders Elite Ltd, Capital House, Houndwell Place, Southampton, SO14 1HU Tel: (023) 8022 3511 Fax: (023) 8022 7911 E-mail: contactus@anderselite.com *Recruitment consultants*

▶ Anders Glass Ltd, 30 Frederick Road, Salford, M6 6NY Tel: 0161-736 2487 Fax: 0161-745 8183 E-mail: simon.anders@andersglass.co.uk *PVC windows manufrs*

▶ Anders Heating Co Ltd, Unit G Watcombe Manor Industrial Units, Ingham Lane, Watlington, Oxfordshire, OX49 5EB Tel: (01491) 614694 Fax: (01491) 614489 E-mail: info@andersheating.co.uk *Specialists in Underfloor Heating for Commercial and Residential Buildings *Anders Heating Company Ltd provides design concepts through to completion of all types of heating and domestic water services specializing in REHAU under floor heating for both private and commercial applications.*

Anders & Kern UK Ltd, Norderstedt House, James Carter Road, Mildenhall, Bury St. Edmunds, Suffolk, IP28 7RQ Tel: (01638) 510900 Fax: (01638) 510901 E-mail: info@anders-kern.co.uk *Audiovisual demonstration distributors*

Andersen, 4th Floor Forum Ho, Grenville St, St. Helier, Jersey, JE2 4UF Tel: (01534) 707100 Fax: (01534) 707101 E-mail: diane.l.porritt@uk.andersen.com *Assurance/business advisory & business consultants*

▶ Andersen Offshore Company Formations, PO Box 8188, Colchester, CO3 3WW Tel: (020) 8123 1493 E-mail: idpnd@yahoo.co.uk

Andersen Products Ltd, Davy Road, Gorse Lane Industrial Estate, Clacton-On-Sea, Essex, CO15 4XA Tel: (01255) 428328 Fax: (01255) 222987 E-mail: uk@andersenmedical.com *Ventilated medical sterilizers distributors*

Anderside Tools Ltd, 25 Colvilles Place, Kelvin Industrial Estate, East Kilbride, Glasgow, G75 0PZ Tel: (01355) 245455 Fax: (01355) 230703 E-mail: greg@andersidetools.com *Mould makers & precision engineers*

Anderson Apparel Ltd, Unit 4-5 Village Workshops, Pandy Road, Llanbrynmair, Powys, SY19 7AA Tel: (01650) 521880 Fax: (01650) 521880 *Garment design & manufrs*

Anderson Associates, 5 Station Road, Parbold, Wigan, Lancashire, WN8 7NU Tel: (01257) 463149 Fax: (01257) 463149 *Mining consultants*

Anderson & Brooks, 85 New Road, Kidderminster, Worcestershire, DY10 1AE Tel: (01562) 864500 Fax: (01562) 864600 *Air conditioning*

Anderson Cars, Alington Road, Little Barford, St. Neots, Cambridgeshire, PE19 6YH Tel: (01480) 212845 Fax: (01480) 213007 E-mail: jason@peterandersoncars.com *Car dealers*

▶ Anderson Crawler Crane Hire Ltd, Flaxton Grange, Flaxton, York, YO60 7RU Tel: (01904) 468689 Fax: (01904) 468775 E-mail: martyn@andersoncrawler.co.uk *for the hire of 30t 40t + 50t crawler cranes*

D.S. & J. Anderson, Unit 4, Tayview Industrial Estate, Friarton Road, Perth, PH2 8DF Tel: (01738) 444885 Fax: (01738) 444885 *Joiners & building contractors*

▶ David Anderson Associates, Unit 3 Saffron Walden Business Centre, Elizabeth Cl, Saffron Walden, Essex, CB10 2BL Tel: (0797) 3227402 Fax: (0870) 0527516 E-mail: sales@anderson.ath.cx *Internet services, networking & secure systems*

Deven Anderson Ltd, George House, 121 High Street, Henley-in-Arden, West Midlands, B95 5AU Tel: (01564) 795565 Fax: (01564) 795122 E-mail: headhunt@devenanderson.co.uk *Executive search consultants & recruitment*

Anderson Electrical Ltd, PO Box 91, Derby, DE24 8HY Tel: (01332) 343121 Fax: (01332) 294736 *Industrial cleaning equipment distributors*

▶ Anderson Engineering, 1 Lochside Industrial Estate, Irongray Road, Dumfries, DG2 0JE Tel: (01387) 721700 Fax: (01387) 721701 E-mail: sales@andeng.uk *Engineering services*

Anderson Gibb & Wilson, 543 Gorgie Road, Edinburgh, EH11 3AR Tel: 0131-443 4556 Fax: 0131-455 7608 E-mail: tennants.edinburgh@dial.pipex.com *Chemical distributors*

Anderson Greenwood Crosby, Wellheads Terrace, Wellheads Industrial Estate, Aberdeen, AB21 7GF Tel: (01224) 722562 Fax: (01224) 771607 E-mail: cmiln@tyco-valves.com *Valve repair sales & services*

Anderson Haulage Ltd, 85 Channing Street, Belfast, BT5 5GP Tel: (028) 9045 1771 Fax: (028) 9073 9047 E-mail: andersonhaulage@btconnect.com *Road transport, haulage & freight services*

▶ Anderson & Innes Ltd, 15 Nursery Avenue, Kilmarnock, Ayrshire, KA1 3DP Tel: (01563) 523188 Fax: (01563) 523516

▶ Anderson Instruments, East Lodge, Drum, Drumoak, Banchory, Kincardineshire, AB31 5AN Tel: (01224) 733835 Fax: (01224) 733835 E-mail: ian@anderson-instruments.co.uk *Repair of laboratory equipment for the oil industry*

▶ Anderson James Builders Ltd, 35a Kyle Road Irvine Indust Estate, Irvine, Ayrshire, KA12 8LE Tel: (01294) 279245

▶ Anderson Joinery Ltd, 3 Bradford Road, Stanningley, Pudsey, West Yorkshire, LS28 6AT Tel: 0113-255 0788 Fax: 0113-236 1681

▶ Anderson Moves, 45 Maclellan Street, Glasgow, G41 1RR Tel: 0141-419 7070 Fax: 0141-427 9994

▶ Anderson & Partners, 275 Kirkstall Road, Leeds, LS4 2BX Tel: 0113-231 0191

Anderson Refrigeration, 30 Gartclush Gardens, Bannockburn, Stirling, FK7 8QA Tel: (01786) 817677 Fax: (01786) 817677 E-mail: enquiries@andersonrefrigeration.co.uk *Air conditioning & refrigeration engineers*

Anderson Ross Associates, Wellhall Road, Hamilton, Lanarkshire, ML3 9BY Tel: (01698) 493420 Fax: (01698) 493423 E-mail: info@andersonross.com *Software consultants*

Anderson Software, 23 Bernay Gardens, Bolbeck Park, Milton Keynes, MK15 8QD Tel: (01908) 668544 *Computer software*

Anderson Spratt Group Holdings, Anderson House, 409 Holywood Road, Belfast, BT4 2GU Tel: (028) 9080 2000 Fax: (028) 9080 2021 E-mail: info@andersonspratt.com *Advertisers*

Anderson Stewart Castings Ltd, Block 1 Lochshore Industrial Estate, Caledonia Road, Glengarnock, Beith, Ayrshire, KA14 3DB Tel: (01505) 683368 Fax: (01505) 683771 E-mail: mail@ascast.co.uk *Investment casting manufrs*

Andersons Ltd, Powells Farm, Berkham Lane, Bentworth, Alton, Hampshire, GU34 5RP Tel: (01420) 563646 Fax: (01420) 561897 E-mail: sales@andersons-uk.net *Vinyl material suppliers*

Andersons, Denton Holme Sawmills, Denton Street, Carlisle, CA2 5EQ Tel: (01228) 526242 Fax: (01228) 515647 *Timber merchants*

Andersons Ltd, 1 Weston Road, Guildford, Surrey, GU2 8AU Tel: (01483) 578887 Fax: (01483) 578885 E-mail: johnschluter@btconnect.com *Air conditioning, refrigeration & heating engineers*

Andersons Blinds, Penrhewl Works, St. Asaph, Clwyd, LL17 0NH Tel: (01352) 752467 Fax: (01745) 584860 *Blind manufrs*

Anderton Concrete Products Ltd, Anderton Wharf, Soot Hill, Anderton, Northwich, Cheshire, CW9 6AA Tel: (01606) 79436 Fax: (01606) 871590 E-mail: sales@andertonconcrete.co.uk *Concrete products manufrs*

Doric Anderton Ltd, King Edward Street, Grimsby, South Humberside, DN31 3JP Tel: (01472) 362429 Fax: (01472) 343300 E-mail: mandy.pratt@doricandertonltd.com *Solid board fish box suppliers*

Anderton Kitchen Ltd, Braconash Road, Leyland, PR25 3ZE Tel: (01772) 433577 Fax: (01772) 622402 E-mail: anderton-kitchen@btclick.com *Plant hire & civil engineering contractors*

W.R. Anderton Group, Maltings Lane, Castleton, Rochdale, Lancs, OL11 2UY Tel: (01706) 631277 Fax: (01706) 358201 E-mail: info@andertongroup.com *Sub-contract laser cutting service, CNC & conventional machining, Wire & spark erosion, Welding & Fabrication, Engraving, Metal finishing - painting, plating etc*

▶ Andesign Sign Writers, F 11-13 Coleshill Road, Sutton Coldfield, West Midlands, B75 7AA Tel: 0121-354 2272 Fax: 0121-355 8883 E-mail: info@andesignuk.co.uk *Signs, labels, digital print, exhibition boards & vehicle livery services*

Andiamo, Swan Yard, West Market Place, Cirencester, Gloucestershire, GL7 2NH Tel: (01285) 659100 Fax: (01285) 659369 E-mail: sales@andiamo.com *Translation services*

Andiloos Portable Toilets, Crow Trees Farm, Thurvaston Lane, Longford, Ashbourne, Derbyshire, DE6 3DU Tel: (01335) 330053 Fax: (01335) 330053 E-mail: marsh.andrew@btconnect.com *Toilet hire & showers hire services*

Andover Fork Truck Services, Fluens Yard, Picket Piece, Andover, Hampshire, SP11 6LU Tel: (01264) 324055 Fax: (01264) 334735 E-mail: info@andoverforktruckservices.co.uk *Fork truck sales, service, & hire in hampshire*

Andover Natural Products, Unit 7b Apollo House, Calleva Park, Aldermaston, Reading, RG7 8TN Tel: 0118-981 6111 Fax: 0118-981 7778 *Importers of dried food ingredients*

Andover Precision Ltd, Marriott Road, Dudley, West Midlands, DY2 0JZ Tel: (01384) 212655 Fax: (01384) 235863 E-mail: dave.andover@btconnect.com *Precision engineers*

▶ Andover Rubber Stamp Service, Unit 1, Balksbury Estate, Upper Clatford, Andover, Hampshire, SP11 7LW Tel: (01264) 362925 Fax: (01264) 333079 E-mail: service@andover-rubberstamp.com *Rubber stamp manufacturer & glass engraving services*

Andrea Hosiery Manufacturing Co. Ltd, 107-115 Humberstone Road, Leicester, LE5 3AN Tel: 0116-262 5543 Fax: 0116-262 8732 *Hosiery manufrs*

▶ Andream Car Component Mnfrs, 12 Griston Road, Watton, Thetford, Norfolk, IP25 6DL Tel: (01953) 884176 Fax: (01953) 884176 E-mail: admin@addream.co.uk *Glass fibre or fibreglass moulders*

Andrena Direct Furniture, Auction House, Geddings Road, Hoddesdon, Hertfordshire, EN11 0NT Tel: (01992) 451722 Fax: (01992) 466024 E-mail: enquiries@anrenda.co.uk *Furniture reproduction*

Andress Printing Co. Ltd, 17 Abercorn Close, South Croydon, Surrey, CR2 8TG Tel: (020) 8651 3005 Fax: (020) 8651 3025 *Printers & publishers*

Andrew Beattie & Co, 332 Chipstead Valley Road, Coulsdon, Surrey, CR5 3BE Tel: (01737) 557811 *Welding equipment & supplies*

Andrew Beattie & Co., Ilkley House, Brighton Road, Tadworth, Surrey, KT20 6SU Tel: (0845) 3301373 Fax: (0845) 3301373 *Welding equipment suppliers*

Andrew C Alston & Son Ltd, Benston Smithy, Cumnock, Ayrshire, KA18 4QA Tel: (01290) 421234 Fax: (01290) 425889 *Agricultural engineers*

Andrew Charles Associates, 119 Mulberry Road, Northfleet, Gravesend, Kent, DA11 8QA Tel: (01474) 532865 Fax: (01474) 320442 E-mail: enquires@andrewcharles.co.uk *Computer consultants*

Andrew Engineering Ltd, Unit 4, Cobnar Wood Close, Chesterfield, Derbyshire, S41 9RQ Tel: (0845) 1267873 Fax: (0845) 1267874 E-mail: sales@andrew-eng.co.uk *Andrew Engineering Ltd based in Chesterfield, Derbyshire, specialise in the design and installation of energy efficient solutions for mechanical building services including: air conditioning, comfort cooling, ventilation, heating, underfloor heating, ground source heat pumps, air source heat pumps, swimming pool dehumidifiers, rain water harvesting, commercial kitchen canopies and kitchen ventilation systems.*

Andrew Gray & Co Fuels Ltd, Portland Depot, London Road, Kilmarnock, Ayrshire, KA3 7DD Tel: (01563) 525215 Fax: (01563) 541146 E-mail: andrew@graysfuels.freeserve.co.uk *Coal & solid fuel merchants*

▶ Andrew Ingredients Ltd, 141 Dromore Road, Hillsborough, County Down, BT26 6JA Tel: (028) 9268 3030 Fax: (028) 9268 3798 E-mail: info@andrewingredients.co.uk *Specialist suppliers to the food industry.*

James Andrew International Ltd, 72-75 Marylebone High Street, London, W1U 5JW Tel: (020) 7224 4436 Fax: (020) 7486 5277 E-mail: hms@jamesandrew.co.uk *Property surveyors*

Andrew Johnson Knudtzon, Boulevard, Hull, HU3 4DY Tel: (01482) 326873 Fax: (01482) 327934 E-mail: info@ajkltd.co.uk *Cold storage company*

Andrew Lusk & Co., Lower Addicroft, Liskeard, Cornwall, PL14 5AH Tel: (01579) 363104 Fax: (01579) 363162 *Self adhesive labels manufrs*

▶ Andrew Mccall & Son, 11 Simonsburn Road, Loreny Industrial Estate, Kilmarnock, Ayrshire, KA1 5LA Tel: (01563) 571173 Fax: (01563) 571488

▶ Andrew Macphee Ltd, 8b Dochcarty Road, Dingwall, Ross-Shire, IV15 9UG Tel: (01349) 862862 Fax: (01349) 862863

▶ Andrew Mcrobb Ltd, Oldmill Road, Aberdeen, AB11 6EG Tel: (01224) 581327 Fax: (01224) 573828 E-mail: info@andrew-mcrobb.co.uk

Andrew Mark Ltd, Tredgar Wharf, Hancock Road, London, E3 3DA Tel: (020) 8981 2224 Fax: (020) 8980 7037 E-mail: sales@amarka.co.uk *Aluminium fabricators*

Andrew Mitchell & Co. Ltd, Bishops Court Industrial Estate, Sidmouth Road, Exeter, EX2 7JH Tel: (01392) 432228 Fax: (01392) 211589 *Tarpaulin manufrs*

Andrew Mitchell Co. Ltd, Bates Business Centre, Church Road, Harold Wood, Romford, RM3 0JF Tel: (01708) 370800 Fax: (01708) 377190 E-mail: info@mitco.co.uk *Tarpaulin manufrs*

Andrew Paul Bulmer, Mill House, Mill Lane, Topcliffe, Thirsk, North Yorkshire, YO7 3RZ Tel: (01845) 578172 Fax: (01845) 578172 *Furniture designers & manufrs*

Andrew Sidebottom, 8 Overland Road, Cottingham, North Humberside, HU16 4PZ Tel: (01482) 847491 Fax: (01482) 847491 E-mail: info@psydebottom.co.uk *Psychometric testing & assessment for recruitment*

Andrew & Co Spalding Ltd, Welland Sawmills, Little London, Spalding, Lincolnshire, PE11 2UJ Tel: (01775) 723016 Fax: (01775) 722499 E-mail: derek@andrewdiy.co.uk *Timber merchants*

▶ T.M. Andrew (Plant Hire) Ltd, Kirktonfield Road, Neilston, Glasgow, G78 3NY Tel: 0141-880 7119

Andrew Thomas, Crossgates, Llandrindod Wells, Powys, LD1 6RF Tel: (01597) 851810 Fax: (01597) 851810 *Agricultural engineers*

▶ Andrew Thomas (Builders) Ltd, 7 New Street, Musselburgh, Midlothian, EH21 6JH Tel: 0131-665 2792

Andrew Tyler, Berthlwyd, Maesymeillion, Llandysul, Dyfed, SA44 4NG Tel: (01545) 590590 *Agricultural services & consultants*

Andrew Waugh Jewellery Ltd, 34-35 Hatton Garden, London, EC1N 8DY Tel: (020) 7405 8173 Fax: (020) 7405 8174 E-mail: tgwhattongdn@aol.com *Jewellers*

Andrew Webron Ltd, Hareholme Mill, Bacup Road, Rawtenstall, Rossendale, Lancashire, BB4 7JL Tel: (01706) 214001 Fax: (01706) 830003 E-mail: info@andrewwebron.com *Industrial needle, felts & cloths manufrs*

Andrew Wright, 4 Boundary Road, Heathfield Industrial Estate, Ayr, KA8 9DJ Tel: (01292) 611999 Fax: (01292) 610298 *Glazing contractors & glass merchant* Also at: Irvine

Andrew Young Auto Electrical & Air Con Specialists, 4 Prospect Business Park, Langston Road, Loughton, Essex, IG10 3TR Tel: (020) 8508 5880 Fax: (020) 8502 3530 *Air conditioning engineers*

Andrew Young & Son (Engineers) Ltd, 45 Midwharf Street, Glasgow, G4 0LD Tel: (0141) 332 1165 Fax: (0141) 331 2690 *Steel fabricators*

Andrews, Littles Lane, Wolverhampton, WV1 1JY Tel: (01902) 429190 Fax: (01902) 426574 E-mail: info@andrewscoatings.co.uk Principal Export Areas: Worldwide *Paints distributors*

Andrews Auto Panels Ltd, Kimberley Road, Gillingham, Kent, ME7 4NE Tel: (01634) 851292 *Automotive component distributors*

Andrews & Boyd, 24 Old Burlington Street, Mayfair, London, W1S 3AW Tel: (020) 7494 0399 Fax: (020) 7494 0477 E-mail: info@andrewsboyd.co.uk *Quantity surveyors*

Andrews Bros Plastering Ltd, Bridge House, Clyst St. Mary, Exeter, EX5 1BR Tel: (01392) 875755 Fax: (01392) 876617 *Plastering, floor & tiling contractors*

Andrews Computer Services Ltd, Nash House, London Road, Hemel Hempstead, Hertfordshire, HP3 9SR Tel: (01442) 241200 Fax: (01442) 241201 E-mail: admin@andrews-computers.com *Computer systems & software developers*

David Andrews Products Ltd, Kenilworth Lodge, Leamington Road, Kenilworth, Warwickshire, CV8 2AA Tel: (01926) 856653 Fax: (01926) 850067 E-mail: heatleyjames@aol.com *Lightning protection production suppliers*

▶ Andrews Decorating, 79 Mortimer Street, Herne Bay, Kent, CT6 5PR Tel: (07762) 621300 E-mail: laurieandrews@gmail.com *Painting & decorating services*

Andrews & Elmes Engineering Ltd, Unit 58b Arthur Street, Redditch, Worcestershire, B98 8JY Tel: (01527) 522771 Fax: (01527) 522771 *Precision turned parts manufrs*

Andrews Fasteners Ltd, 8 Latchmore Industrial Park, Low Fields Road, Leeds, LS12 6DN Tel: 0113-246 9992 Fax: 0113-243 6463 E-mail: sales@andrewsfasteners.co.uk *Bolt & nut manufacturers & distributors*

Andrews Hydraulics Ltd, Unit 27-28, Craftsmans Way, East Goscote, Leicester, LE7 3SL Tel: 0116-260 1001 Fax: 0116-264 0186 E-mail: design@andrewshydraulics.co.uk *Hydraulic power pack manufrs*

John Andrews Studio, Rear Of Cranham Farm, The Chase, Upminster, Essex, RM14 3YB Tel: 01708 224040 Fax: 01708 641 206 *Plaster suppliers & manufrs*

Andrews Survey, Salmon Road, Great Yarmouth, Norfolk, NR30 3QS Tel: (01493) 332111 Fax: (01493) 332265 *Geophysical surveyors*

Andrews Sykes Hire Ltd, Unit F17 Ashmount Business Park, Upper Fforest Way, Swansea Enterprise Park, Swansea, SA6 8QR Tel: (01792) 701701 Fax: (01792) 701700 *Heating & air conditioning retailers & hirers*

Andrews Sykes Hire Ltd, Premier House, Darlington Street, Wolverhampton, WV1 4JJ Tel: (01902) 328700 Fax: (01902) 422466 E-mail: info@andrews-sykes.com *Heater & pump suppliers*

Andrews Of Wanstead, 10 Woodbine Place, London, E11 2RH Tel: (020) 8989 0377 *Builders merchants*

Company Information

Andritz Ltd, R & B Technology Centre, Speedwell Road, Parkhouse East Industrial Estate, Newcastle, Staffordshire, ST5 7RG Tel: (01782) 565656 Fax: (01782) 566130 E-mail: welcome@andritzltd.com *Filter presses*

Andritz Sprout Ltd, Stockholm Road, Sutton Fields Industrial Estate, Hull, HU7 0XL Tel: (01482) 825119 Fax: (01482) 839806 *Engineers*

▶ Andromeda IT, 124 Selby Road, West Bridgford, Nottingham, NG2 7BA Tel: 0115-974 4891 E-mail: m@andromeda-it.co.uk *PC Supplier. PC Support & Upgrades. Web Design.**

Andromeda Products Ltd, 6 Stanton Close, Finedon Road Industrial Estate, Wellingborough, Northamptonshire, NN8 4HN Tel: (01933) 234448 Fax: (01933) 234449 E-mail: sales@andromeda-ltd.co.uk *Electronic component distributors*

Andromica Video Systems Ltd, Victory House, 54 Wallingford Road, Uxbridge, Middlesex, UB8 2RW Tel: (01895) 257971 Fax: (01895) 273483 E-mail: admin@andromica.co.uk Principal Export Areas: Worldwide *Closed circuit television suppliers*

Andron Contract Services Ltd, 7 Telford Place, Cumbernauld, Glasgow, G67 2NH Tel: (01236) 451143 Fax: (01236) 451134 E-mail: admin@andron.co.uk *Contract cleaning & security services*

Andron Contract Services, 3 Greenwood Court, Risley, Warrington, WA3 6DD Tel: (01925) 767389 Fax: (01925) 766011 E-mail: warrington@andron.co.uk *Industrial cleaning services*

▶ Andros Engineering, Langbridge, Newchurch, Sandown, Isle of Wight, PO36 0NP Tel: (01983) 867722 Fax: (01983) 865333 *Steel fabrication & stock holders*

Andross Electrics Ltd, Unit 12 Twyford Business Centre, London Road, Bishop's Stortford, Hertfordshire, CM23 3YT Tel: (01279) 657661 Fax: (01279) 506164 E-mail: sales@andross.net Principal Export Areas: Worldwide *Control & instrument panel manufrs* Also at: King's Lynn

Andura Coatings Ltd, 20 Murdock Road, Bicester, Oxfordshire, OX26 4PP Tel: (01869) 240374 Fax: (01869) 240375 E-mail: admin@andura.com *Paint manufrs*

▶ Andy Hire Sales & Services Ltd, Wykeham Street, Scarborough, North Yorkshire, YO12 7SB Tel: (01723) 500601 Fax: (01723) 500611

▶ Andy Holehouse, 39 School Lane, Addlestone, Surrey, KT15 1TB Tel: (01932) 849631 E-mail: enquiries@andyholehouse.co.uk *We provide property maintenance, home improvement and handyman services to residential and commercial clients. Including decorating, tiling, kitchen/bathroom refits and hard landscaping.*

Andy Race Ltd, The Harbour, Mallaig, Inverness-Shire, PH41 4PX Tel: (01687) 462626 Fax: (01687) 462060 E-mail: sales@andyrace.co.uk *Fish merchants*

Andy's Concrete Grooving, 29 Redlands, Chippenham, Wiltshire, SN14 0JA Tel: (01249) 654683 E-mail: andytuck3@hotmail.com *Concrete grooving services*

▶ Andy's Machine Start, Block J Ringstones Industrial Estate, Bridgemont, Whaley Bridge, High Peak, Derbyshire, SK23 7PD Tel: (01663) 719710 *Contractors' plant maintenance or repair*

Andy's Sheds, 46 Church Street, Warsop, Mansfield, Nottinghamshire, NG20 0AR Tel: (01623) 844439 E-mail: sales@andys-sheds.co.uk *Sheds manufrs*

▶ Aneataprint Two Ltd, 170a New London Centre, Drury Lane, London, WC2B 5QA Tel: (020) 7841 1280 Fax: (020) 7841 1289 E-mail: sales@aneataprint.co.uk *Digital printing, site printing delivery & litho printing*

Anest Iwata UK Ltd, Little End Road, Eaton Socon, St. Neots, Cambridgeshire, PE19 8JH Tel: (01480) 405419 Fax: (01480) 217610 E-mail: enquiries@anest-iwata.co.uk *Spray equipment manufrs*

Anetus Ltd, 14-30 City Business Centre, Hyde Street, Winchester, Hampshire, SO23 7TA Tel: (020) 7669 4260 E-mail: office@anetus.com *Providing complete services: graphic and web design, site or CMS implementation, training, hosting and administration. Effective, professional solutions based on Open Source.*

▶ Angali Shipping & Trading Co. Ltd, 18 Exeter Street, London, WC2E 7DU Tel: (020) 7379 9002 Fax: (020) 7379 9004 E-mail: ast@angali.co.uk *AC & refrigeration equipment supply, repair & installation*

▶ Angel Archive, Suite 076 - 080, 555 White Hart Lane, London, N17 7RN Tel: (020) 8099 4167 Fax: (020) 8889 1300 E-mail: info@angelarchive.co.uk *Document storage*Archive Management*Relocation Services across the UK*Personal Storage*Digital Scanning*Secure Shredding*

Angel Catering plc, 65 West Ham Lane, London, E15 4PH Tel: (020) 8555 5533 Fax: (020) 8555 2200 E-mail: east@angelhr.org *Employment agencies*

▶ Angel Chemdry, 53 Goodwood Avenue, Hutton, Brentwood, Essex, CM13 1QD Tel: (01277) 217776 Fax: (01277) 217776 E-mail: angelchemdry@talktalk.net *Carpet cleaning, fire & flood restoration*

▶ Angel Designs, 14 West Beech Avenue, Wickford, Essex, SS11 8AL Tel: 01268 570483 Fax: 01268 570483 E-mail: info@angeldesigns.org.uk *t-shirt print~design~merchandise*We specialise in silk screen printing for workwear, leisurewear, sports wear, corporate and promotional products.**

Angel Human Resources plc, 54 Uxbridge Rd, Shepherds Bush, London, W12 8LP Tel: (020) 8740 1999 Fax: (020) 8749 4950 E-mail: west@angelhr.org *Employment agencies*

Angel Human Resources plc, 2-4 Union Street, London, SE1 1SZ Tel: (020) 7940 2000 Fax: (020) 7940 2018 E-mail: admin@angelhr.org Purchasing Contact: D. Merrison Sales Contact: J. Crawford *Employment agencies & recruitment*

▶ Angel Investigations - Privacy Consultants, The 401 Centre, Regent Street, London, W1 Tel: (020) 7692 0000 E-mail: ahunter149@hotmail.com *At Angel Investigations we teach you how anyone with enough determination can and will easily invade your privacy and compile an amazingly damaging list of your personal information that can be used against you through criminal acts such as Identity theft or cloning plus many more serious and complicated acts. We teach you how to hide and shield yourself from all these potential intruders and create a life so private it shows up on no record.*

Angel Multimedia, 32 Blue Street, Carmarthen, Dyfed, SA31 3LE Tel: (01267) 221175 Fax: (01267) 223196 E-mail: sales@angelmm.co.uk *Multimedia authoring*

Angel Net Ltd, 193 Granville Avenue, Long Eaton, Nottingham, NG10 4HE Tel: 0115-973 3013 Fax: 0115-973 3166 E-mail: angelnet@proweb.co.uk *Hairnet manufrs*

▶ Angel Property Services, Silton Road, Bourton, Gillingham, Dorset, SP8 5DD Tel: (08712) 715128 E-mail: rennie@angelpropertyservices.net *On line estate agency with listings for residential & commercial properties. Mortgage facilities available through the site.*

S.P. Angel & Co., East India House, 109-117 Middlesex Street, London, E1 7JF Tel: (020) 7422 4300 Fax: (020) 7422 3401 E-mail: admin@spangel.co.uk *Broker dealers*

▶ The Angel Services Group Ltd, 61 Bridge Street, Walsall, WS1 1JQ Tel: (01922) 424300 E-mail: charles.trivett@ems-gb.com *Recruitment company*

▶ Angel Solutions, 30 Faraday Road, Wavertree Technology Park, Liverpool, L13 1EH Tel: (0845) 8330933 Fax: (0845) 8338561 E-mail: info@angelsolutions.co.uk *Educational software suppliers*

▶ Angel Springs Ltd, Unit 4 Spring Road Indust Estate, Wolverhampton, WV4 6UD Tel: (01902) 353598 Fax: (01902) 385604 E-mail: admin@purecoolers.co.uk *Industrial water cooler suppliers*

Angela Mortimer plc, 37-38 Golden Square, London, W1F 9LA Tel: (020) 7287 7788 Fax: (020) 7470 5578 E-mail: name.surname@angelamortimer.com *Secretarial recruitment consultancy*

Angell Hosiery Ltd, Ashford Road, Leicester, LE2 6AA Tel: 0116-270 0698 Fax: 0116-270 1040 *Hosiery manufrs*

Angell Patterns Ltd, 215a Fosse Road North, Leicester, LE3 5EZ Tel: 0116-253 1964 Fax: 0116-253 1964 *Wooden shoe models & pattern making specialists*

▶ Angels, 9 Town Square, Syston, Leicester, LE7 1GZ Tel: 0116-269 3033

▶ The Angels Communcations Limited, The Round Foundry Media Centre, Foundry Street, Leeds, LS11 5QP Tel: 0870 4202442 Fax: 0870 4202444 E-mail: info@the-angels.com *The Angels Communications - Leeds Continuing to provide unique parties and event with unfaltering flair and technique*

Angels (Cwas) Ltd, 100 Rooley Avenue, Bradford, West Yorkshire, BD6 1DB Tel: (01274) 731532 Fax: (01274) 308290 E-mail: sales@angel-mobile-phones.co.uk *Cellular phones & car satellite systems*

Angelus Machine Corporation International, De Salis Drive, Hampton Lovett, Droitwich, Worcestershire, WR9 0QE Tel: (01905) 779602 Fax: (01905) 771882 E-mail: admin@angelus-machine.co.uk *Can seaming machine manufrs*

Angila Radio Ltd, Branford House, Valley Road, Tasburgh, Norwich, NR15 1NG Tel: (01508) 470720 Fax: (01508) 471393 E-mail: info@angliaradio.com *Two-way radios supplier*

▶ Anglepoise Ltd, 6 Stratfield Park, Elettra Avenue, Waterlooville, Hampshire, PO7 7XN Tel: (023) 9225 0934 Fax: (023) 9225 0696 E-mail: sales@anglepoise.co.uk *Electric light fittings manufrs*

Angler Craft, Greenbogue, Torthorwald, Dumfries, DG1 3QG Tel: (01387) 750247 Fax: (01387) 750247 *Fishing tackle manufrs*

Anglers Corner, 80 Station Road, Llanelli, Dyfed, SA15 1AN Tel: (01554) 773981 Fax: (01554) 773981 *Fishing tackle retailers*

▶ Anglers Den, 26a High Street, Haverfordwest, Dyfed, SA61 2DA Tel: (01437) 760045 *Fishing tackle retailers*

The Anglers Emporium, 64 Cadzow Street, Hamilton, Lanarkshire, ML3 6DS Tel: (01698) 283903 E-mail: info@anglersemporium.co.uk *Fishing tackle suppliers*

▶ Anglers Peg, 4 Ashworth House, Cannock Road, Cannock, Staffordshire, WS11 5DF Tel: (01543) 466946 E-mail: sales@anglerspeg.com *Supply fishing tackle*

Anglers Stop, 161 Rose Avenue, Worcester, WR4 9QN Tel: (01905) 619803 *Angling equipment suppliers*

Anglesey Aluminium Metal Ltd, Penrhos Works, Holyhead, Gwynedd, LL65 2UJ Tel: (01407) 725000 Fax: (01407) 725001 *Chemical manufrs*

Anglesey Geophysical Service Ltd, Unit 1, Mona Industrial Park, Gwalchmai, Holyhead, Gwynedd, LL65 4RJ Tel: (01407) 720333 Fax: (01248) 853874 E-mail: anglesey-geophysical@dial.tipex.com *Renewable energy systems distributors & services*

Anglesey Sand Pits, Ogley Hay Road, Newtown, Brownhills, Walsall, WS8 7PR Tel: (01543) 372344 *Sand merchants*

Anglesey Scaffolding (Ynys Mon) Co. Ltd, Amlwch Industrial Estate, Amlwch, Gwynedd, LL68 9BQ Tel: (01407) 831331 Fax: (01407) 831788 E-mail: sales@angleseyscaffolding.co.uk *Scaffolding erectors*

▶ Anglesey Scanner Security, Cae Cali, Brynteg, Gwynedd, LL78 8JJ Tel: (01248) 853353 Fax: (01248) 853666

Anglesey Wood Products, 101 Gerwin Uchaf, Gaerwen, Gwynedd, LL60 6HN Tel: (01248) 421086 Fax: (01248) 421086 E-mail: heather@angleseywoodproducts.co.uk *Garden furniture manufrs*

Angletheme Partnership, Signal House, Charter Way, Macclesfield, Cheshire, SK10 2NF Tel: (01625) 501204 Fax: (01625) 560911 E-mail: enquiries@angletheme.co.uk *Signing & display manufrs*

Anglia, Oldmedow Road, King's Lynn, Norfolk, PE30 4JJ Tel: (01553) 776790 Fax: (01553) 776790 *Self adhesive labels manufrs*

Anglia, Sandall Road, Wisbech, Cambridgeshire, PE13 2PS Tel: (01945) 474747 Fax: (01945) 474849 E-mail: sales@angliac.com *Electronic component distributors & importers*

Anglia Accommodation, 118 Lexden Road, West Bergholt, Colchester, CO6 3BP Tel: (01206) 240842 Fax: (01206) 240842 *Relocatable building specialists*

Anglia Air Conditioning Ltd, 7 Fletcher Way, Weston Road, Norwich, NR3 3ST Tel: (01603) 787383 Fax: (01603) 403480 E-mail: sales@anglia-aircon.co.uk *Ventilation engineers services*

Anglia Alloys Ltd, Unit 5 Riverside Industrial Estate, Riverside Road, Gorleston, Great Yarmouth, Norfolk, NR31 6PU Tel: (01493) 651028 Fax: (01493) 655391 *Steel, brass & bronze stockholders*

Anglia Autoflow Ltd, The Ling, Wortham, Diss, Norfolk, IP22 1SR Tel: (01379) 651031 Fax: (01379) 652832 E-mail: sales@aaflow.com *Poultry processing equipment*

Anglia Battery & Filter Co., 834 London Road, Leigh-on-Sea, Essex, SS9 3NH Tel: (01702) 470262 Fax: (01702) 470335 E-mail: sales@angliabattery.co.uk *Battery distributors*

Anglia Bearing Co. Ltd, 17 Lealand Way, Boston, Lincolnshire, PE21 7SW Tel: (01205) 357200 Fax: (01205) 351663 *Ball bearing stockists*

Anglia Bearing Co. Ltd, Units 1 & 8, Wulfric Square, Bretton, Peterborough, PE3 8RF Tel: (01733) 268180 Fax: (01733) 268156 E-mail: angliabearings@aol.com *Bearings & transmission products distributors* Also at: Boston

▶ Anglia Building & Decorating Contractors, Anglia House, Newmarket Road, Dyserth, Rhyl, Clwyd, LL18 6BS Tel: (01745) 572100 Fax: (01745) 571658 E-mail: info@angliabuilders.co.uk

Anglia Building Suppliers Ltd, Waltham Road, Boreham, Chelmsford, CM3 3AY Tel: (01245) 467505 Fax: (01245) 467506 E-mail: angliabs@btinternet.com *Re-cycled building material suppliers*

Anglia Business Computers Training Ltd, Harston Mill, Royston Road, Harston, Cambridge, CB22 7GG Tel: (01223) 873400 Fax: (01223) 873401 E-mail: mktg@angliabs.com *IT consultancy & services*

Anglia Circuits Engineering Ltd, Anglia Works, Burrel Road, St. Ives, Cambridgeshire, PE27 3LB Tel: (01480) 464624 Fax: (01480) 494041 E-mail: sales@angliacircuits.com *Printed circuit manufrs*

Anglia Composite, Runway Farm, Parham Airfield, Parham, Woodbridge, Suffolk, IP13 9AF Tel: (01728) 664194 Fax: (01728) 664195 *Manufacturing company - glass fibre or carbon fibre*

▶ Anglia Concrete Products, Skelmersdale Road, Clacton-on-Sea, Essex, CO15 6BZ Tel: (01255) 420018 Fax: (01255) 222880 E-mail: admin@angliagroup.co.uk *Landscaping*

Anglia Electrical, Audley Field House, Audley End, Gestingthorpe, Halstead, Essex, CO9 3AU Tel: (01787) 460597 Fax: (01787) 460792 E-mail: mdutch@anglieeletricaltesting.wanado.co.uk *Portable appliance testing services*

▶ Anglia Electrical Services Ltd, Anglia House, Hamburg Way, North Lynn Industrial Estate, King's Lynn, Norfolk, PE30 2ND Tel: (01553) 773366 Fax: (01553) 771515

Anglia Engineering Ltd, Estate Road, 2 South Humberside Industrial Estate, Grimsby, South Humberside, DN31 2TG Tel: (01472) 359455 Fax: (01472) 242478 E-mail: sales@anglia-eng.co.uk *Sheet metalworkers & fabricators*

Anglia Epos, Hall Lodges, Gateley, Dereham, Norfolk, NR20 5EF Tel: (01328) 829607 Fax: (01328) 829607 *Cash registers & epos systems sales & services*

▶ Anglia Financial Services, 106 Hellesdon Park Road, Drayton High Road, Norwich, NR6 5DR Tel: (01603) 418320 Fax: (01603) 418320 E-mail: sales@anglia.demon.co.uk

Anglia Fixing Supplies, Anglia House, Grange Avenue, Mayland, Chelmsford, CM3 6BG Tel: (01621) 744490 Fax: (01621) 744821 *Power & hand tool fixings distributors & retailers*

Anglia Forwarding Group Ltd, The Anglian Centre, Blackwater Close, Rainham, Essex, RM13 8UA Tel: (01708) 527000 Fax: (01708) 524881 E-mail: london@anglia-forwarding.co.uk *International freight forwarders*

Anglia Glassware & Bar Supplies, 6 Oakfield, Stebbing, Dunmow, Essex, CM6 3SX Tel: (01371) 856857 Fax: (01371) 874040 E-mail: angliaglassware@btclick.com *Glass & bar suppliers*

Anglia Health Care Ltd, Oak Lodge, School Lane, Little Melton, Norwich, NR9 3LB Tel: (01603) 819600 Fax: (01603) 812811 *Healthcare software manufrs*

Anglia Industrial Fire Ltd, 21 Old Court, Long Melford, Sudbury, Suffolk, CO10 9HA Tel: (01787) 883437 *Fire alarm systems*

Anglia Industrial Roofing Co. Ltd, Bunyan Close, Gamlingay, Sandy, Bedfordshire, SG19 3JD Tel: (01767) 651550 Fax: (01767) 651566 E-mail: sales@angliaindustrialroofing.co.uk *Industrial & commercial roofing contractors*

Anglia Jewellers, 270-272 Lincoln Road, Peterborough, PE1 2ND Tel: (01733) 314670 Fax: (01733) 896228 *Jewellery manufr*

▶ Anglia Joinery Ltd, 28-29 Maitland Road, Lion Barn Industrial Estate, Needham Market, Ipswich, IP6 8NZ Tel: (01449) 720070 Fax: (01449) 722817 *Joinery specialists*

Anglia Labels Sales Ltd, Bull Lane Industrial Estate, Bull Lane, Acton, Sudbury, Suffolk, CO10 0BD Tel: (01787) 379118 Fax: (01787) 378840 E-mail: sales@anglialabels.co.uk *Self adhesive label manufrs*

▶ Anglia Landscapes, Brooklands, Straight Road, Boxted, Colchester, CO4 5QY Tel: (01206) 272357 E-mail: sales@anglialandscapes.co.uk

Anglia Laundry & Linen Hire Services, 1a Victoria Place, Peterborough, PE1 2HB Tel: (01733) 314464 Fax: (01733) 314464 *Linen hire services*

Anglia Mechanical Environmental, Unit 38, Mere View Industrial Estate, Yaxley, Peterborough, PE7 3HS Tel: (01733) 244600 Fax: (01733) 244606 E-mail: angliamechanicle@btopenworld.com *Environmental gas engineers*

Anglia Microwave Centre, 51-53 Argyle St, Cambridge, CB1 1AS Tel: 01223 416276 *Microwave servicing*

Anglia Microwaves Ltd, 5 Chandlers Quay, Maldon, Essex, CM9 4LF Tel: (01621) 841420 E-mail: sales@anglia-micro.co.uk *RF & microwave electronic components suppliers*

Anglia Partitions Ltd, Unit 3 Freisian Way, King's Lynn, Norfolk, PE30 4JQ Tel: (01553) 691202 Fax: (01553) 769808 E-mail: info@angliapartitions.demon.co.uk *Partitioning & suspended ceiling suppliers racking shelving*

Anglia Pipework Ltd, 27 Manor Farm Close, Drayton, Norwich, NR8 6EE Tel: (01603) 260199 Fax: (01603) 400722 E-mail: angliaparkwork@aol.com *Pipe work installation & mechanical engineering contractors*

Anglia Precision Engineering, 32 Stapledon Road, Orton Southgate, Peterborough, PE2 6TD Tel: (01733) 703230 Fax: (01733) 703231 E-mail: sales@angliaprecision.com *Engineering subcontract services*

Anglia Recycling Ltd, Crow Hall Farm, Northfield Road, Soham, Ely, Cambridgeshire, CB7 5UF Tel: (01353) 624004 Fax: (01353) 723888 E-mail: sales@angliarecycling.co.uk *Security shredding services*

Anglia Rubber & Plastics Ltd, Unit 27, Saville Road, Westwood, Peterborough, PE3 7PR Tel: (01733) 264100 Fax: (01733) 261823 E-mail: arp.sales@btconnect.com *Polycarbonate, perspex, nylon, acetal, polypropylene, tufnol, foamex, P.T.F.E. Rubber, neoprene, silicone, (sheet & sponge), insulation materials, cork, tico pad & adhesive, P.V.C. (sheet,hose & door strip),jointing, packing & gaskets, industrial rubber hose & ducting, P.V.C. swing door & PVC wall cladding systems.*

Anglia Rustguard Ltd, 26 Crittall Road, Western Industrial Estate, Witham, Essex, CM8 3DR Tel: 01376 514152 Fax: 01376 512802 E-mail: angliarustguard@btconnect.com *Blast cleaning, shot,sand & grit. Industrial painting. Hot metal spray in Zinc & Aluminium. Hot dip galvanizing.*

Anglia Shopfitting Norwich Ltd, Diamond Road, Norwich, NR6 6AB Tel: (01603) 426297 Fax: (01603) 483644 *Shop fitters & joiners*

Anglia Sign Casting Co., 4 Horsbeck Industrial Estate, Horsbeck Way, Horsford, Norwich, NR10 3SS Tel: (01603) 897111 Fax: (01603) 897011 *Memorial plaques*

Anglia Sprayers Ltd, Unit 60, Lancaster Way, Ely, Cambridgeshire, CB6 3NP Tel: (01353) 666615 Fax: (01353) 668763 E-mail: mail@angliasprayers.co.uk *Agricultural spray equipment suppliers*

▶ Anglia Springs Ltd, Unit N Loddon Industrial Estate, Little Money Road, Loddon, Norwich, NR14 6JD Tel: (01508) 528396 Fax: (01508) 528240 E-mail: info@angliasprings.com Sales Contact: M. Basinger *Spring & spring clip manufrs*

Anglia Telecom Centres plc, 166 Handford Road, Ipswich, IP1 2BH Tel: (01473) 382000 Fax: (01473) 225617 E-mail: mandy.stafford@angliatelecom.co.uk *Telecommunications technicians*

Anglia Telecoms, 1 Gateshead Close, Sandy, Bedfordshire, SG19 1RS Tel: (01767) 692792 Fax: (01767) 692992 E-mail: info@angliatelecoms.co.uk *Telecommunications organisation services*

Anglia Textile Manufacturers Ltd, Holly Park Mills, Calverley, Pudsey, West Yorkshire, LS28 5QS Tel: 0113-257 0861 Fax: 0113-257 2391 E-mail: fabrics@angliat.free.online.co.uk *Mens worsted/wool suiting materials*

Anglia Time Recorders Ltd, 3 Cox Close, Kesgrave, Ipswich, IP5 2DW Tel: (01353) 778518 Fax: (01487) 823862 E-mail: sales@angliatime.co.uk *Time control systems services*

Anglia Valves Ltd, Unit 12g West Station Industrial Estate West Station Yard, Spital Road, Maldon, Essex, CM9 6TW Tel: (01621) 858861 Fax: (01621) 855942 *Industrial control valve distributors*

Anglia Window Blinds, 27a Forge Road, Port Talbot, West Glamorgan, SA13 1US Tel: (01639) 891045 Fax: (01639) 884995 *Blind manufrs*

Anglian Awards, The Grove, Hyde Lane, Danbury, Chelmsford, CM3 4LJ Tel: (01245) 223132 Fax: (01245) 222189 E-mail: info@anglianawards.com Principal Export Areas: Worldwide *Trophies specialists suppliers*

Anglian Bridges, 3 Westbrook Close, Steeple Morden, Royston, Hertfordshire, SG8 0NY Tel: (01763) 852839 Fax: (01763) 852839 *Construction advisers*

Anglian Building Products Ltd, 59 Hurricane Way, Norwich, NR6 6JB Tel: (01603) 422000 Fax: (01603) 422066 E-mail: sales@anglian-building.co.uk *Commercial window fabricators*

Anglian Caterers, 4 Hurricane Way, Norwich, NR6 6EN Tel: (01603) 485273 Fax: (01603) 418679 *Airline caterers*

Anglian Chemicals Ltd, Fakenham Industrial Estae, Millers Close, Fakenham, Norfolk, NR21 8NW Tel: (01328) 851407 Fax: (01328) 855701 E-mail: sales@anglianchemicals.com *Janitorial suppliers & distributors*

Anglian Cleaning Services Ltd, 8 Magdalen St, Colchester, CO1 2JT Tel: (01206) 763501 Fax: (01206) 571794 E-mail: info@angliancleaning.com *Office cleaning services*

Anglian Compressors & Equipment Ltd, Storeys Bar Road, Peterborough, PE1 5YS Tel: (01733) 349993 Fax: (01733) 564983 E-mail: business@anglianccomp.co.uk *Air compressor distributors*

Anglian Developments Ltd, School Lane, Neatishead, Norwich, NR12 8BU Tel: (01692) 630808 Fax: (01692) 631591 E-mail: angdev@paston.co.uk *Grp moulded vehicle body builders*

Anglian Energy Services, 23 Windrush Road, Kesgrave, Ipswich, IP5 2NZ Tel: (01473) 614446 Fax: (01473) 620443 E-mail: aessprinklers@aol.com *Residential & domestic fire sprinkler systems suppliers & installers*

Anglian Fasteners Ltd, 16 Millbrook Close, Northampton, NN5 5JF Tel: (01604) 758585 Fax: (01604) 758565 E-mail: anglianf@micromat.net *Industrial fastener distributors* Also at: Bedford

Anglian Home Improvements Ltd, PO Box 65, Norwich, NR6 6EJ Tel: (01603) 787000 Fax: (01603) 422298 E-mail: matt.carey@angliangroup.com *Replacement windows & doors* Also at: Branches throughout the U.K.

▶ Anglian Minimix, Dereham Road, New Costessey, Norwich, NR5 0TL Tel: (01603) 745490 Fax: (01603) 741336 *Ready mix concrete suppliers*

Anglian Nutrition Products Co., Lady Lane Industrial Estate, Crocatt Road, Hadleigh, Ipswich, IP7 6RD Tel: (01473) 822121 Fax: (01473) 822156 E-mail: mail@anupco.com *Animal health & nutrition products manufrs*

Anglian Pest Control, 4 Brick Kiln Barns, Manor Road, North Walsham, Norfolk, NR28 9LH Tel: (01692) 403762 Fax: (01692) 403762 *Pest control*

Anglian Pharma Sales & Marketing Ltd, Titmore Court, Titmore Green, Little Wymondley, Hitchin, Hertfordshire, SG4 7XJ Tel: (01438) 743070 Fax: (01438) 743080 E-mail: admin@anglianpharma.com *Suppliers of pharmaceuticals*

Anglian Playground Services, 6 St.Andrews Court, March, Cambridgeshire, PE15 9GE Tel: (01354) 656174 Fax: (01354) 657182 E-mail: anglian_playgrounds@yahoo.com *Outdoor playground equipment design & installation*

Anglian Pools, 7 Hurricane Way, Airport Industrial Estate, Norwich, NR6 6EZ Tel: (01603) 429441 Fax: (01603) 417274 E-mail: mail@spasandpools.net *Swimming pool contractors*

Anglian Pumping Services Ltd, APS House, The Drift, Nacton Road, Ipswich, IP3 9QR Tel: (01473) 719950 Fax: (01473) 719951 E-mail: info@anglianpumping.com *Pump & motor distributors*

Anglian Siting Services, 3 Mayfield Way, North Walsham, Norfolk, NR28 0DQ Tel: 01692 405885 *Toilet hire*

Anglian Timber Ltd, The Sawmill, Colchester Road, Wix, Manningtree, Essex, CO11 2RS Tel: (01255) 870881 Fax: (01255) 870480 E-mail: sales@angliantimber.co.uk *Softwood distributors & truss manufrs*

Anglian Water, Hendeson House, Lancaster Way, Ermine Business Park, Huntingdon, Cambridgeshire, PE29 6XQ Tel: (01480) 323900 Fax: (01480) 326981 *Water utilities*

▶ Angling Centre, 3 Forrest Street, Airdrie, Lanarkshire, ML6 7BA Tel: (01236) 750288

Angling Centre, 85 St Leonards Road, Northampton, NN4 8DN Tel: (01604) 764847 *Fishing tackle manufrs*

▶ Angling & Out Door Center, 121/122 Ennerdale Road, Cleator Moor, Cumbria, CA25 5LP Tel: (01946) 810377 E-mail: sales@angleingandoutdoor.co.uk *Suppliers of fishing tackle*

▶ Angling Supplies, 49 Retford Road, Worksop, Nottinghamshire, S80 2PU Tel: (01909) 482974 Fax: (01909) 482974 *Angling supplies*

Anglitemp Ltd, Unit A3 Third Avenue, Tyne Tunnel Trading Estate, North Shields, Tyne & Wear, NE29 7SW Tel: 0191-258 6646 Fax: 0191-257 8445 E-mail: anglitemp@anglitemp.freeserve.co.uk *Industrial insulation & subsea systems*

Anglo American Adhesives, Cg10 Warrington Business Park, Long Lane, Warrington, WA2 8TX Tel: (01925) 419111 Fax: (01925) 419222 E-mail: colin.fitz@virgin.net *Industrial adhesive suppliers*

Anglo American Electrical Co., 67 Bradley Lane, Bolton, BL2 6RA Tel: (01204) 527251 Fax: (01204) 527257 E-mail: angloamerican1@btconnect.com *Lighting distributors & manufrs*

▶ Anglo American Security Ltd, 160 Bridport Way, Braintree, Essex, CM7 9FF Tel: 01376 333631 Fax: 01376 333640 E-mail: info@anglo-american-security.com *Anglo American Security Limited specialises in the design, installation and maintenance of a range of electronic security, surveillance, communications and control systems.*

Anglo Aquarium Plant Co. Ltd, Strayfield Road, Enfield, Middlesex, EN2 9JE Tel: (020) 8363 8548 Fax: (020) 8363 8547 E-mail: sales@anglo-aquarium.co.uk *Aquatic plants*

Anglo Assessors Ltd, 23 Canterbury Park, Liverpool, L18 9XP Tel: (07710) 510234 Fax: 0151-475 7867 E-mail: mrb.angloassessors@tiscali.co.uk *Independent insurance claims consultants & loss assessors*

Anglo Beef Processors Ltd, The Abbatoir, Battlefield Road, Harlescott, Shrewsbury, SY1 4AH Tel: (01743) 442322 Fax: (01743) 446326 E-mail: stevenfeehan@abpltd.com *Processed & cooked meat product manufrs*

Anglo Blackwells Ltd, Ditton Road, Widnes, Cheshire, WA8 0NT Tel: 0151-495 1400 Fax: 0151-495 4201 E-mail: sales@angloblackwells.com *Producers of aluminium master alloys*

Anglo Building Products Ltd, Branksome House, Filmer Grove, Godalming, Surrey, GU7 3AB Tel: (01483) 427777 Fax: (01483) 428888 E-mail: sales@anglobuild.co.uk *Protective non slip floor coating*

Anglo Caribbean Shipping Co. Ltd, 14 Skylines Village, Limeharbour, London, E14 9TS Tel: (020) 7537 7420 Fax: (020) 7537 4778 *Ship brokers*

Anglo Eastern Ship Management UK Ltd, The Parks, 107-115 Milton Street, Glasgow, G4 0DN Tel: 0141-353 1020 Fax: 0141-353 2366 E-mail: supplies@tandh.co.uk *Marine spare parts & equipment suppliers* Also at: Aberdeen, Douglas (Isle of Man) & London EC3

Anglo European Pallets, Unit 1 Old Airfield Farm, Moreton Valence, Gloucester, GL2 7NG Tel: (01452) 883305 Fax: (01452) 723082 E-mail: mac@aepallet.demon.co.uk *Suppliers of plastic pallets, wooden collars & wooden pallets*

Anglo European Workforce Ltd, 51 Waterloo Road, Wolverhampton, WV1 4QJ Tel: (01902) 426767 Fax: (01902) 421895 E-mail: contact@angloew.com *Engineering recruitment agency*

Anglo Fabrications Ltd, Saxon Way, Melbourn, Royston, Hertfordshire, SG8 6DN Tel: (01763) 260872 Fax: (01763) 262615 E-mail: sales@anglofabrication.com *Acrylic sheet & plastic fabricators*

Anglo Felt Industries Ltd, Bridge End Mills, Tong Lane, Whitworth, Rochdale, Lancashire, OL12 8BG Tel: (01706) 853513 Fax: (01706) 853625 E-mail: enquiries@anglofelt.com *Friendly, family business manufacturing all industrial felts. We supply felt washers, gaskets, seals and strips. Also display felts, adhesive backed, automotive and carpet underlay, flame retardant non wovens, sound insulation material and capillary matting.*

Anglo Group Ltd, Capital House, Bond Street, Bristol, BS1 3LA Tel: (0870) 5673631 Fax: (0870) 5673649 *Equipment leasing & finance company*

Anglo Irish Asset Finance plc, Town Centre House, Southam Road, Banbury, Oxfordshire, OX16 2EN Tel: (01295) 755500 Fax: (01295) 755100 *Small & medium ticket corporate financiers*

Anglo Irish Bank, 10 Old Jewry, London, EC2R 8DN Tel: (020) 7710 7000 Fax: (020) 7710 7050 E-mail: enquiries@angloirishbank.co.uk *Banking services including commercial lending*

Anglo Leather Craft Ltd, Unit 4 Bellair Estate, Musker Street, Crosby, Liverpool, L23 0UB Tel: 0151-931 3177 Fax: 0151-931 4076 E-mail: angloleather@netscapeonline.co.uk *Leather goods manufrs*

Anglo Norden Forest Products Ltd, Orwell Terminal Eagle Wharf, Helena Road, Ipswich, IP3 0BT Tel: (01473) 233244 Fax: (01473) 230805 E-mail: sales@anglonorden.co.uk *Timber, sheet materials & ships agents*

Anglo Nordic Burner Products Ltd, Units 12-14, Island Farm Avenue, West Molesey, Surrey, KT8 2UZ Tel: (020) 8979 0988 Fax: (020) 8979 6961 E-mail: sales@anglonordic.co.uk *Heating equipment distributors & detector manufrs*

▶ Anglo Overseas Ltd, 1 Ennis Close, Roundthorn Industrial Estate, Manchester, M23 9LE Tel: 0161-945 3333 Fax: 0161-998 2181 E-mail: admin@anglooverseas.com

Anglo Packaging Ltd, 10 Silverdale, Meadow Road, Worthing, West Sussex, BN11 2RZ Tel: (01903) 202333 Fax: (01903) 232333 E-mail: info@anglopackaging.com *Carrier bag suppliers*

Anglo Precision Engineering Co. Ltd, Deans Yard, 15 South Road, Baldock, Hertfordshire, SG7 6BZ Tel: (01462) 491105 Fax: (01462) 491106 E-mail: sales@anglo-precision.co.uk *CNC machining services*

Anglo Pumps Ltd, 4a-B Aston Road, Cambridge Road Industrial Estate, Bedford, MK42 0LJ Tel: (01234) 353525 Fax: (01234) 211655 E-mail: sales@anglo-pumps.co.uk *Industrial & chemical pumps*

▶ Anglo Saxon Coins, PO Box 38444, London, SE16 2WF Tel: (020) 7232 1885 E-mail: info@anglosaxoncoins.com *Anglo saxon coin & artifact specialist suppliers*

Anglo Scottish Packaging, Montrose Avenue, Hillington Industrial Estate, Glasgow, G52 4LA Tel: 0141-882 5151 Fax: 0141-882 5500 E-mail: sales@angloscottish.net *Labelling services*

Anglo Scottish Pest Control, 24 Annandale Street, Edinburgh, EH7 4LS Tel: (0800) 0743606 Fax: (01289) 302257 *Pest control services*

▶ Anglo Security, 33 Morecambe Road, Brighton, BN1 8TL Tel: (01273) 702500 Fax: (01273) 562479 E-mail: kenneth.mees@ntlworld.com *SECURITY GUARDING GUARD DOGS KEY HOLDING ALARM RESPONSE MOBILE PATROLS STATIC GUARDS*

▶ Anglo Sphere Ltd, 97 Commercial Road, London, E1 1RD Tel: (020) 7377 2111 Fax: (020) 7377 2999 *Clothing manufrs*

Anglo Standard Pipework, Arisdale Avenue, South Ockendon, Essex, RM15 5DP Tel: (01708) 858800 Fax: (01708) 858811 E-mail: sales@anglostandard.com *Industrial pipe installers*

Anglo-African Machinery Co. Ltd, Clent House, Bromsgrove Road, Clent, Stourbridge, West Midlands, DY9 9PY Tel: (01562) 883067 Fax: (01562) 885335 E-mail: angloafrican@btconnect.com *Machine tool merchants*

Anglo-Holt Construction Ltd, 150 Birmingham Road, West Bromwich, West Midlands, B70 6QT Tel: 0121-525 6717 Fax: 0121-553 4701 E-mail: sales@angllo-holt.co.uk *Building & civil engineers*

Anglosax Ltd, 3 Pomeroy Drive, Oadby Industrial Estate, Oadby, Leicester, LE2 5NE Tel: 0116-271 1005 *Fabricators & refurbish lifts*

Anglo-Swedish Engineering & Welding (Southern) Ltd, Unit 12, Lansdowne Workshops, Lansdowne Mews, Charlton, London, SE7 8AZ Tel: (020) 8858 2024 Fax: (020) 8858 7301 E-mail: info@metboilerrepairs.co.uk *Boiler maintenance & repair services*

▶ Anglotan Ltd, 47 Cricket Inn Crescent, Sheffield, S2 5AQ Tel: 0114-272 9220 Fax: 0114-272 9220 E-mail: transport@anglotan.com *Nationwide & European removal & delivery services*

Anglowide Marketing Ltd, County Ground Works, Deanstones Lane, Bradford, West Yorkshire, BD13 2AT Tel: (01274) 883668 Fax: (01274) 818980 *Textile household chemicals manufrs*

Angoss Software Ltd, Unit 23 Surrey Technology Centre, Occam Road, Surrey Research Park, Guildford, Surrey, GU2 7YG Tel: (01483) 452303 Fax: (01483) 453303 E-mail: ncb@angoss.com *Delivery data mining software & service solutions*

▶ Angove Associates, 5 Marsh Grove Road, Huddersfield, HD3 3AQ Tel: 01484 539229 Fax: 01484 539229 E-mail: info@angoveassociates.co.uk *Careful creation of bespoke Microsoft Excel Spreadsheets. We write the solution to your problems!*Also the sole source for "Multibuy Management" - the indispensible and most effective "promotion"software available - if you want to know what it will cost you to promote with your customers - you need to use Multibuy Management*

Angram Ltd, Unit 11 Becklands Close, Bar Lane, Roecliffe, York, YO51 9NR Tel: (01423) 324555 Fax: (01423) 324955 E-mail: sales@angramltd.com *Beer dispense equipment manufrs*

Angstrom Video, 16 Chapel Lane, Northorpe, Gainsborough, Lincolnshire, DN21 4AF Tel: (01724) 763594 Fax: (01724) 763594 E-mail: sales@angstromvideo.co.uk *Video producers*

Angus Classic Interiors, 13-17 Bank Street, Brechin, Angus, DD9 6AU Tel: (01356) 623982 E-mail: sales@classicint.fsnet.co.uk *Soft furnishngs manufrs & retailers*

Angus Decorating, Kings Works, Sir William Smith Road, Kirkton Industrial Estate, Arbroath, Angus, DD11 3RD Tel: (01241) 435238 Fax: (01241) 879474 *Painting & Decorating Contractors*

▶ Angus Fertilizers Ltd, River Street, Montrose, Angus, DD10 8DL Tel: (01674) 678400 Fax: (01674) 671318 E-mail: info@cars-feltilizer.co.uk *Fertiliser blenders manufrs*

Angus Fire, Station Road, High Bentham, Lancaster, LA2 7NA Tel: (01524) 261611 Fax: (01524) 264180 *Firefighting equipment manufrs*

Angus Fire, Thame Park Road, Thame, Oxfordshire, OX9 3RT Tel: (01844) 214545 Fax: (01844) 265156 E-mail: general.enquiries@kiddeuk.co.uk *Fire protection equipment suppliers* Also at: Bentham, Dublin & Newton Abbey

▶ Angus Homes Ltd, Markethill Industrial Estate, Markethill Road, Turriff, Aberdeenshire, AB53 4AG Tel: (01888) 562639 Fax: (01888) 568953

Angus Hotel, 46 Wellmeadow, Blairgowrie, Perthshire, PH10 6NH Tel: (01250) 872455 Fax: (01250) 875615 E-mail: reservations@theangushotel.com *Hotel*

Angus Jarvis, 68 Barkby Road, Leicester, LE4 9LF Tel: 0116-246 0258 Fax: 0116-246 0258 *Metal finishing & polishing*

▶ Angus Jordan, Broomknowe House Struthers, Cupar, Fife, KY15 5PG Tel: (01334) 828433 Fax: (01334) 828177

Angus Mcmurtrie Blacksmiths Ltd, 1 Kellas Road, Wellbank, Broughty Ferry, Dundee, DD5 3PE Tel: (01382) 350301 Fax: (01382) 350573

▶ The Angus Plumbing Co. Ltd, 38-40 Glengate, Kirriemuir, Forfar, Angus, DD8 4HD Tel: (01575) 573777

▶ Angus Removals, Peasie Hill, Elliot Industrial Estate, Arbroath, Angus, DD11 2NJ Tel: (01241) 871711

▶ Anhop Metalwork Ltd, 109 Glenpark Street, Glasgow, G31 1NY Tel: 0141-554 7667

Anigold Ltd, 5 Woodhill Industries, Nottingham Lane, Old Dalby, Melton Mowbray, Leicestershire, LE14 3LX Tel: (01664) 823359 Fax: (01664) 823359 E-mail: anigold18@hotmail.com *Polyurethane moulding services*

Anikem Ltd, 18 North Gate, Harborne, Birmingham, B17 9EP Tel: 0121-428 1355 Fax: 0121-428 1366 E-mail: sales@anikem.co.uk *Leaders in chemical surfactants throughout the UK*

▶ Anila's Authentic Sauces, Walton-On-Thames, Surrey, KT12 3WS Tel: (020) 8577 6162 Fax: (020) 8577 6162 E-mail: info@anilassauces.com *Food processors of sauces pickles & chutney*

▶ Animal Bouncers, 122 Forester Road, Crawley, West Sussex, RH10 6EF Tel: (01293) 417346 Fax: E-mail: sales@animalbouncers.co.uk

Animal Systems, Threshing House, Berwick St. Leonard, Salisbury, SP3 5SN Tel: (01747) 827000 Fax: (01747) 820127 E-mail: sales@animalsystems.co.uk *Animal Systems Ltd design and manufacture high quality bespoke computer platforms for industry. Utilising the latest Intel, AMD and industrial SBC architecture we are able to offer an extremely stable but diverse product range*

Animalcare Ltd, Common Road, Dunnington, York, YO19 5RU Tel: (01904) 487687 Fax: (01904) 487611 *Veterinary suppliers*

▶ Animals Cemetery, 16 Skylark Wells, Horsham, West Sussex, RH12 5EA Tel: (01403) 791756

Animm Textiles Ltd, Mangochi House, 107-115 Gwendolen Road, Leicester, LE5 5FL Tel: 0116-212 1234 Fax: 0116-273 3396 E-mail: info@animm.com *Embroidery services*

Anita Business Systems, 29 Bentley Road, London, N1 4BY Tel: (020) 7249 6666 Fax: (020) 7923 1852 E-mail: info@anita.co.uk *Computer repairs support & training*

▶ Anita Grant Ltd, Wycombe Lane, Wooburn Green, Buckinghamshire, HP10 0HL Tel: 0845 4025240 E-mail: atyourservice@anitagrant.com *A tantalizing mix of Fair Trade butters, oils &*

continued

*herbs that go beyond the call of moisture to provide wholesome nourishment from your tresses to your toes. *Freshly made to order JUST for YOU!*

Anite Mobile Working Solutions, 353 Buckingham Avenue, Slough, Slough, SL1 4PF Tel: (01753) 804000 Fax: (01753) 735735 *Software development services*

Anix Computers Ltd, The Alpha Centre, Armstrong Way, Yate, Bristol, BS37 5NG Tel: (01454) 329555 Fax: (01454) 329666 Sales Contact: P. Sheppard *Computer consultants*

▶ Anixper Luton, Unit 10, Sundon Business Park, Dencora Way, Luton, LU3 3HP Tel: (01582) 491748 Fax: (01582) 491280 E-mail: luton.adesco@infast.com *Adhesive distributor*

Anixter, A The Beacons Warrington Road, Birchwood Park, Birchwood, Warrington, WA3 6GP Tel: (01925) 850808 Fax: (01925) 418166 E-mail: jackie.fisher@anixter.com *Wire & cable distributors* Also at: Branches throughout the U.K.

Anixter, A The Beacons Warrington Road, Birchwood Park, Birchwood, Warrington, WA3 6GP Tel: (01925) 850808 Fax: (01925) 418166 *Electrical cable distributors*

Anixter Adhesives, 3 Edmond Road, Sheffield, S2 4EB Tel: 0114-275 1496 Fax: 0114-269 7171 E-mail: sheffield.adesco@infast.com *Adhesives, adhesive tape & sealant distributors*

▶ Anixter Industrial - Barrow, Unit 2D Ashburner Way, Walney Road Industrial Estate, Barrow-In-Furness, Cumbria, LA14 5UZ Tel: (01229) 825871 Fax: (01229) 827442 *Engineers supplies & distributors*

Anixter Industrial - Chesterfield, Brimington Road North, Chesterfield, Derbyshire, S41 9BE Tel: (01246) 452188 Fax: (01246) 455778 E-mail: chesterfield.sales@alistairindustrial.com *Engineers supplies & distributors*

Anixter Industrial - Nottingham, Fastener House, Queens Bridge Road, Sheriffs Way, Nottingham, NG2 1NB Tel: 0115-986 0127 Fax: 0115-986 2574 *Distribution agents*

Anixter UK Ltd, Anixter House, 1 York Road, Uxbridge, Middlesex, UB8 1RN Tel: (0845) 6041301 Fax: (01895) 818136 *Data cabling systems, enterprise cabling, electric & electronic cable manufrs*

Anixter UK Ltd, Anixter House, 1 York Road, Uxbridge, Middlesex, UB8 1RN Tel: (0845) 6041301 Fax: (01895) 818182 *Data communication cables distributors*

Anjec Computer Services, The Mansard Suite The Robbins Building, Albert Street, Rugby, Warwickshire, CV21 2AA Tel: (01788) 540484 Fax: (01788) 540493 E-mail: anjec@via-anjec.co.uk *Computer software consultants*

Anker Of Ellington, Unit 16 Brook Farm, Thrapston Road, Ellington, Huntingdon, Cambridgeshire, PE28 0AE Tel: (01480) 890990 Fax: (01480) 890988 E-mail: enquiries@ankerofcoates.co.uk *Agricultural engineering services & john deer dealers*

Anker Gasquet Ltd, Unit 40 Hollingworth Court, Ashford Road, Maidstone, Kent, ME14 5PP Tel: (01622) 664200 Fax: (01622) 750754 E-mail: anker-gasquet@email.msn.com *Bottling engineers for wines & spirits* Also at: Crail

Anker International plc, Howard House, Howard Way, Interchange Park, Newport Pagnell, Buckinghamshire, MK16 9PX Tel: (01908) 618811 Fax: (01908) 612612 E-mail: info@anker.co.uk *Stationery & janitorial service providers*

Anker & Renton Ltd, 1-2 Caxton Hill, Hertford, SG13 7NE Tel: (01992) 551991 Fax: (01992) 500375 E-mail: info.ankerrenton@btinternet.com *Plastic injection mouldings & tool making*

Ankold Refrigeration Equipment, The Old Shippon, Lily Lane, Byley, Middlewich, Cheshire, CW10 9NH Tel: (01606) 836312 Fax: (01606) 836883

Anly Office Services, 1191 Middleton Road, Chadderton, Oldham, OL9 0NN Tel: 0161-627 5870 Fax: 0161-287 3945 E-mail: enquiry@anly.co.uk *Service & supply of photocopiers & fax machines*

Anlyn Engineering, Taylor Street, Liverpool, L5 5AD Tel: 0151-207 5592 Fax: 0151-207 5594 E-mail: anlynsales@agjengineering.co.uk *Precision engineers & conveyor system manufrs*

Ann Louise Corporatewear Ltd, Unit 3 Shaw Mills, 173 Town Street, Armley, Leeds, LS12 3JF Tel: 0113-279 5397 Fax: 0113-279 3078 *Mens & ladies corporate tailors wear*

▶ Ann Pettengell Gold Helm Ltd, 1 Dover Street, Cambridge, CB1 1DY Tel: (01223) 350234 Fax: (01223) 462929 E-mail: jobs@annpettengell.co.uk *Office support recruitment consultants services*

▶ Ann Summers, 97 Allen Road, Irthlingborough, Wellingborough, Northamptonshire, NN9 5QX Tel: (07840) 587700 E-mail: the2honeys2002@yahoo.com *Recruitment- i need recruits in banbury and surrounding villages *Parties- have a ann summers party in the comfort of your own home *just call for details*

Annalex Bute Ltd, Unit B6 Blaby Industrial Park, Winchester Avenue, Blaby, Leicester, LE8 4GZ Tel: 0116-277 9537 Fax: 0116-277 8623 E-mail: sales@annalexbyute.co.uk *Bolt & nut distributors*

▶ Annandale, 773 Spring Bank West, Hull, HU5 5BA Tel: (01482) 354908 Fax: (01482) 506544

Annasbrook Supply Co. Ltd, Gapton Hall Road, Great Yarmouth, Norfolk, NR31 0HX Tel: (01493) 668721 Fax: (01493) 440250 E-mail: sales@annasbrook.com *Engineers supplies distributors*

▶ Annes Garden Supplies, 68 High Street, Great Broughton, Middlesbrough, Cleveland, TS9 7EG Tel: (01642) 711882 E-mail: sales@annesgardensupplies.co.uk *Garden supplies /Online Shopping*

Company Information

▶ Annesley Woodhouse Working Mens Club, Forest Road, Kirkby-in-Ashfield, Nottingham, NG17 9HW Tel: (01623) 752264 E-mail: gary.cain@ntlworld.com *Pet foods & accessories retail*

Annick Manufacturing Ltd, 13 Kyle Road, Irvine Industrial Estate, Irvine, Ayrshire, KA12 8JN Tel: (01294) 312895 Fax: (01294) 312895 *Joinery manufrs*

Annicom Electronic Equipment Component, Highview, High Street, Bordon, Hampshire, GU35 0AX Tel: (01420) 487788 Fax: (01420) 487799 E-mail: sale@annicom.com *Electrical control panels manufrs*

▶ Annie's Hampers, Bar Farm, Market Weighton Road, Holme-on-Spalding-Moor, York, YO43 4ED Tel: (01430) 860339 E-mail: enquires@annieshampers.com *Luxury Food Hampers,Corporate Gifts*

Annite Public Sector Ltd, Sheridan House, Pitfield, Kiln Farm, Milton Keynes, MK11 3LW Tel: (01908) 264500 Fax: (01908) 264501 E-mail: enquiries@aniteps.com *Software development*

Annodata Business Communications, Shannon House, Station Road, Kings Langley, Hertfordshire, WD4 8SE Tel: (01923) 261733 Fax: (01923) 261678 *Business network systems*

Annolloy Ltd, 135 Garth Road, Morden, Surrey, SM4 4LF Tel: (020) 8330 2211 Fax: (020) 8330 5599 E-mail: sales@annolloy.co.uk *Tungsten carbide products manufrs*

▶ Annoplanna Ltd, 12 Quarry Street, Guildford, Surrey, GU1 3UY Tel: (01483) 302727 Fax: (01483) 506108

Annstar Group Ltd, 57 Sutherland Road, London, E17 6BH Tel: (020) 8503 2323 Fax: (020) 8503 3947 E-mail: info@annstar.co.uk *Architectural ironmongers*

Anoca Ltd, 24 Roman Way, Thetford, Norfolk, IP24 1XB Tel: (01842) 766131 Fax: (01842) 762929 E-mail: sales@anoca.co.uk *Shipping & forwarding agents*

Anochrome Technologies Ltd, Wood Lane, Wolverhampton, WV10 8HN Tel: (01902) 567567 Fax: (01902) 567777 E-mail: enquiries@anochrome-group.co.uk *Electroplaters* Also at: Birmingham, Bloxwich & Wolverhampton

▶ The Anodising Co. Ltd, North Street, Wigston, Leicestershire, LE18 1PS Tel: 0116-288 1333 Fax: 0116-251 1351 E-mail: info@theanodisingco.co.uk *Anodising & dyeing of aluminium, & chromate conversion coatings manufrs*

Anodos Information Systems Strategy Ltd, Rangers, South Rd, Liphook, Hants, GU30 7HS Tel: (01428) 727847 E-mail: info@anodos.com *IT & management consultants*

Anodyne Technology, 140 Castellain Mansions, Castellain Road, London, W9 1HB Tel: (020) 7266 5315 Fax: (020) 7266 5315 *Computer consultants*

▶ Anopol Ltd, PO Box 177, Birmingham, B5 5QA Tel: 0121-693 0280 Fax: 0121-631 2274 E-mail: info@anapol.co.uk *Chemical & electrochemical surface treatment services*

Anotek (Nameplates) Ltd, 22 Simpson Place, Nethermains Industrial Estate, Kilwinning, Ayrshire, KA13 6PT Tel: (01294) 557932 Fax: (01294) 557809 E-mail: anotek@btconnect.com *Screen printers plastics*

Another Dimension Ltd, 167 Ardleigh Green Road, Hornchurch, Essex, RM11 2LF Tel: (01708) 701511 Fax: (01708) 701994 E-mail: info@anotherdimension.co.uk *Software developers*

▶ Another Late Night, 19 Hope Street, Liverpool, L1 9BQ Tel: 0151-708 7103 E-mail: enquiries@anotherlatenight.biz *Another Late Night is a full service marketing and promotions company, and we produce a magazine in Liverpool every six weeks. We offer a range of services, including creative design and print, distribution, publishing, advertising bikes, gimmicks, and consultancy. We pride ourselves on our flexible and hands on approach to business.*

▶ ANOTHER LEVEL CAR PARKS LTD, Tweedale Way, Chadderton, Oldham, OL9 7LD Tel: 0845 345 3835 Fax: 0845 345 3836 E-mail: INFO@ANOTHERLEVELCARPARKS.COM *Hirer of Portable Car Parks*

▶ Another Sampson Scaffold, Samson House, 78 Napier Road, South Croydon, Surrey, CR2 6HG Tel: (020) 8688 2714 Fax: (020) 8667 1327

Anotronic Ltd, Stewkley Road, Soulbury, Leighton Buzzard, Bedfordshire, LU7 0DF Tel: (01525) 270261 Fax: (01525) 270235 E-mail: sales@anotronic.co.uk *Engineering services*

▶ Anova Communications Group, 41 Market Place, Henley-on-Thames, Oxfordshire, RG9 2AA Tel: (01491) 636300 Fax: (0870) 1336271 E-mail: info@futureincoms.com *ICT sector headhunting, executive search & psychometric assessments*

A-Novo UK Ltd, Technology Centre, 5 Finlan Road, Middleton, Manchester, M24 2RW Tel: 0161-654 1400 Fax: 0161-654 1411 *Electronic service providers*

The ANPR Co. Ltd, Link House Unit 5, Bath Road Business Centre, Devizes, Wilts, SN10 1XA Tel: (01380) 739000 Fax: (01380) 739071 E-mail: sales@anpr.com *Automatic number plate recognition cameras & CCTV services & installers*

▶ Anpro Ltd, 1 Northumberland Avenue, London, WC2N 5BW Tel: (020) 7872 5658 Fax: (020) 7872 5611 E-mail: change@anpro.co.uk *Over the last decade, we have carried out a variety of major partnerships projects covering a wide range of business challenges, organising change management and organisational development programmes across diverse industrial and commercial sectors. Visit our web site for case histories and reference letters.*

Anritsu Ltd, 200 Capability Green, Luton, LU1 3LU Tel: (01582) 433200 Fax: (01582) 731303 E-mail: sales@anritsu.co.uk *Test equipment manufrs*

Anross Ltd, Leadgate Industrial Estate, Lope Hill Road, Consett, County Durham, DH8 7RN Tel: (01207) 509448 Fax: (01207) 592158 E-mail: sales@anross.co.uk *Excavator & loader bucket manufrs*

▶ Ans Logistics Ltd, 385 Brentwood Road, Gidea Park, Romford, RM2 5TH Tel: (01708) 500883 E-mail: info@anslogistics.co.uk *Man & van courier & delivery services*

▶ ANS Supplies, 701 Warwick Road, Tyseley, Birmingham, B11 2EZ Tel: 0121- 745 8469 Fax: (0870)7064238 E-mail: sales@anssupplies.co.uk *ANS Supplies is a nickel alloy pipe, pipe fittings and flange specialist supplying the petrochemical industry all over the world.*

▶ Ansaback, Melford Court 2 The Havens, Ransomes Europark, Ipswich, IP3 9SJ Tel: (01473) 322900 Fax: (01473) 321801 E-mail: mtaylor@ansaback.co.uk *Call centre & marketing*

Ansacaller Telecommunication Ltd, Unity House, Main Road, Denholme, Bradford, West Yorkshire, BD13 4BL Tel: (01274) 834366 Fax: (01274) 834593 *Telecommunication equipment suppliers*

Ansacom Telephone Answering Services, Basement Flat, 8 St. Johns Road, Tunbridge Wells, Kent, TN4 9NP Tel: (01892) 612700 Fax: (01892) 616323 E-mail: s.johnson@ansacom.co.uk *Telephone answering*

Ansco Technologies Ltd, 77 Beverley Road, Hull, HU3 1XR Tel: (01482) 222191 Fax: (01482) 225572 *Magnetic lock, child safety lock manufrs*

▶ Anscombe Property Maintenance, 8 Leybourne Parade, Brighton, BN2 4LW Tel: (01273) 693844 Fax: 01273 693844 E-mail: info@anscombepropertymaintenance.co.uk *Property Maintenance, Approved Contractor, Damp Proofing*

Ansell Ltd, Ansell House, 119 Ewell Road, Surbiton, Surrey, KT6 6AL Tel: (020) 8481 1800 Fax: (020) 8481 1828 E-mail: info@ansell.com *Medical products manufrs* Also at: Redditch

▶ Ansell Builders, 7 New Road, Mytholmroyd, Hebden Bridge, West Yorkshire, HX7 5DZ Tel: (01422) 881991 E-mail: Caroline@ansellgroup.com

Ansell Handtools Sheffield Ltd, 72 Catley Road, Sheffield, S9 5JF Tel: 0114-244 8098 Fax: 0114-261 0252 E-mail: enquiries@ansell-handtools.com *Hand tool manufacturers & forging of small items*

Ansell Jones Ltd, Satellite Industrial Park, Neachells Lane, Wolverhampton, WV11 3PQ Tel: (01902) 722117 Fax: (01902) 725533 E-mail: sales@anselljones.com *Lifting & marine equipment manufrs* Also at: Paisley

▶ AnServe, Redbourne Mere, Kirton Lindsey, Gainsborough, Lincolnshire, DN21 4NN Tel: (01652) 641100 Fax: (01652) 640720 E-mail: anserve_uk@yahoo.co.uk *International telephone answering & order taking services*

Anson Ltd, Team Valley Trading Estate, Seventh Avenue, Gateshead, Tyne & Wear, NE11 0JW Tel: 0191-482 0022 Fax: 0191-487 8835 E-mail: anson-gateshead@anson.co.uk *High pressure valve manufrs* Also at: Aberdeen

Anson Packaging Ltd, 62 Station Road, Haddenham, Ely, Cambridgeshire, CB6 3XD Tel: (01353) 740990 Fax: (01353) 741365 E-mail: anson@avroind.com *Thermoplastics products manufrs*

▶ Anson Tactical Equipment, Upper Office, 44 Grove Road, Eastbourne, East Sussex, BN21 2EW Tel: 01323 725333 Fax: 01323 725333 E-mail: info@ansontactical.co.uk *Anson Tactical are suppliers of high quality Tactical and Operational Equipment to the Police, Military, Special Forces and Private Security sectors.*

Ansoroy Ltd, 237 Railton Road, London, SE24 0LX Tel: (020) 7738 6030 Fax: (020) 7738 6030 E-mail: sales@ansoroy.co.uk *Cradle systems design & maintenance*

▶ Anstee Ware Ltd, Unit 59a Thornhill Industrial Estate, South Marston, Swindon, SN3 4TA Tel: (01793) 832828 Fax: (01793) 831955

Anstee & Ware Gloucester Ltd, Bonds Mill, Bristol Road, Stonehouse, Gloucestershire, GL10 3RF Tel: (01453) 826433 Fax: (01453) 827653 E-mail: awglass@aol.com *Electrical & mechanical engineers*

Anstee & Ware Group Ltd, Unit 1 St Georges Industrial Estate, St Andrews Road, Bristol, BS11 9HS Tel: 0117-982 0081 Fax: 0117-982 3501 E-mail: admin@ansteeware.co.uk *Electrical & mechanical engineers*

Anstee & Wear (Wales) Ltd, Foreshore Road, Cardiff, CF10 4DF Tel: (029) 2048 1831 Fax: (029) 2049 6592 E-mail: info@ansteewear.co.uk *Mechanical & electrical engineers*

▶ Anstey Transport Services, London Warehouse, Chittening Industrial Estate, Chittening, Bristol, BS11 0YB Tel: 0117-982 3111 Fax: 0117-982 5111

Ansteygate Dust Extraction, 19 Marlow Road, Leicester, LE3 2BQ Tel: 0116-282 6333 Fax: 0116-282 6336 E-mail: carl@ansteygate.co.uk *Dust extraction*

Ansteys Of Worcester Traditional Cheese Makers, Broomhall Lane, Broomhall, Worcester, WR5 2NT Tel: (01905) 820232 Fax: (01905) 828032 E-mail: gifts@ansteys.com *Cheese makers*

Ansty Computer Systems, 1 North Cottages, Cuckfield Road, Ansty, Haywards Heath, West Sussex, RH17 5AG Tel: (01444) 455760 Fax: (01444) 458067 E-mail: peterhutchinson@lineone.net *Computer consultants*

Ansul Fabrication, Downing Street, Smethwick, West Midlands, B66 2JL Tel: 0121-565 3108 Fax: 0121-558 1339 E-mail: ansulfabricationsuk@tyco-bstd.com *Pipe work fabricating services*

Ansvar Insurance Co. Ltd, 31 St Leonards Road, Eastbourne, East Sussex, BN21 3UR Tel: (01323) 737541 Fax: (01323) 430977 E-mail: ansvar.insurance@ansvar.co.uk *General insurance company* Also at: Larkhall

▶ Answer Transport Express Ltd, Strothers Road, High Spen, Rowlands Gill, Tyne & Wear, NE39 2EX Tel: (01207) 544111

▶ Answerback Ltd, 56a Hatton Garden, London, EC1N 8HP Tel: (020) 7251 9313 E-mail: paul.krisman@answerbackinteractive.com *AnswerBack supplies large-scale high-speed audience response and voting systems. Both wired and wireless systems are available. We are focused at providing professional and design-led audience solutions to service the Broadcast, light entertainment and conferencing industries*

Answering (Scotland) Ltd, Suite 291, 93 Hope Street, Glasgow, G2 6LD Tel: 0141-221 9911 Fax: 0141-204 3998 E-mail: admin@answer4you.co.uk *Telephone answering services*

Answerlink plc, Manton Lane, Manton Industrial Estate, Bedford, MK41 7TL Tel: (0845) 3305577 Fax: (0845) 3305588 E-mail: info@answerlink.com *Telecommunications specialists*

Answerpak Ltd, Unit M, Fircroft Way, Edenbridge, Kent, TN8 6EL Tel: (01732) 869930 Fax: (01732) 869939 E-mail: sales@answerpak.co.uk *Packaging material suppliers*

Answers Training International Ltd, Rose Lodge, Old Potbridge Road, Winchfield, Hook, Hampshire, RG27 8BT Tel: (01252) 845500 Fax: (01252) 845585 E-mail: info@answers-group.com *Business development trainers*

▶ ANSYS Europe Ltd, West Central 127, Milton Park, Abingdon, Oxfordshire, OX14 4SA Tel: (0870) 1420333 Fax: (0870) 1420301 *Software development & sales services*

▶ Ant Creations, 7 Granville Street, Market Harborough, Leicestershire, LE16 9EU Tel: 08444 778910 E-mail: nathan@antcreations.co.uk *Graphic design service*

▶ Ant Marketing, 1 Clarke Drive, Sheffield, S10 2NS Tel: 0114-278 0555 Fax: 0114-278 0666 E-mail: gavin.foster@antmarketing.com *Call centre*

Ant Software Ltd, Cambridge Business Park, Cowley Road, Cambridge, CB4 0WZ Tel: (01223) 716400 Fax: (01223) 716401 E-mail: info@antlimited.com *Embedded communication software agents*

Antalis, Unit 4 Horizon Wade Road, Kingsland Industrial Estate, Basingstoke, Hampshire, RG24 8LJ Tel: (01256) 776200 Fax: (01256) 724734 E-mail: sales@antalis.co.uk *Paper merchants*

Antalis Ltd, Kempson Way, Bury St. Edmunds, Suffolk, IP32 7AR Tel: (0870) 6073103 Fax: (01284) 706116 E-mail: admin@antalis.com *Paper merchants*

Antalis Ltd, Gateway House, Pilsworth Road, Bury, Lancashire, BL9 8RD Tel: (0870) 6073112 Fax: 0161-910 8268 E-mail: info@antalis-print.co.uk *Paper merchants*

▶ Antalis Ltd, Gateway House, Interlink Way West, Bardon Hill, Coalville, Leicestershire, LE67 1LE Tel: (0870) 6079014 Fax: (0870) 6073160 E-mail: contact@antalis.co.uk Principal Export Areas: Worldwide *Corrosion prevention packaging*

Antalis Ltd, Unit C3 Crossways Boulevard, Greenhithe, Kent, DA9 9BT Tel: (0870) 6073117 Fax: (01322) 226297 *Paper merchants*

Antalis Ltd, 2 Blackwater Business Park, Mallusk Way, Newtownabbey, County Antrim, BT36 4AA Tel: (0870) 6073101 Fax: (0870) 6073156 *Distributors of stationary & paper*

Antalis, 3 Imperial Park Imperial Way, Watford, WD24 4PP Tel: (01923) 636600 Fax: (0870) 6073168 E-mail: contact@antalis.co.uk *Paper merchants* Also at: Bristol, Dartford & Exeter

Antalis Ltd, Unit 14, Avenue One, Witney, Oxfordshire, OX29 6XX Tel: (0870) 6073114 Fax: (01993) 779066 *Paper merchants*

Antares Europe Ltd, Chiltern Hill, Chalfont St. Peter, Gerrards Cross, Buckinghamshire, SL9 9UQ Tel: (01753) 890888 Fax: (01753) 891260 E-mail: info@antares.co.uk *Auxiliary electrical systems for specialist vehicles.*

Antartex Village, Lomond Industrial Estate, Alexandria, Dunbartonshire, G83 0TP Tel: (01389) 754263 Fax: (01389) 750656 E-mail: alexav141@ewm.com *Sheepskin clothing manufacturers & tourist shop*

Antec Instrumentation, Unit 1, 59 Queensway North, Team Valley Trading Estate, Gateshead, Tyne & Wear, NE11 0NX Tel: 0191-482 4241 Fax: 0191-487 8835 *Cable fault locator manufrs*

Antech Hydraulics, Cocker Avenue, Poulton Industrial Estate, Poulton-le-Fylde, Lancashire, FY6 8JU Tel: (01253) 890037 Fax: (01253) 890073 E-mail: enquiries@antech-hyd.co.uk *Staffa motors, UFI filters, Kawasaki pumps. Hydraulic equipment including power units, filtration , cylinders and motors. Full design service and installation team.*

▶ Antech Systems, Unit 3, Hackhurst Lane Industrial Estate, Lower Dicker, Hailsham, East Sussex, BN27 4BW Tel: (01323) 442035 E-mail: musicalfix@aol.com *Repairs & servicing of electronic equipment for the music industry*

Antelope Garage Ltd, Swan Close Road, Banbury, Oxfordshire, OX16 5AQ Tel: (01295) 265435 Fax: (01295) 269208 *Nissan franchise dealer*

Antenna Audio, J307-9 Tower Bridge, Business Complex, London, SE16 4DG Tel: (020) 7740 1155 Fax: (020) 7394 6746 *Audio tour production*

Antenna Systems Ltd, Hertford, SG13 8YB Tel: (01707) 878875 Fax: (01707) 876873 E-mail: antenna@euromast.fsbusiness.co.uk *Radio tower suppliers & erectors*

Antex (Electronics) Ltd, 2 Westbridge Industrial Estate, Tavistock, Devon, PL19 8DE Tel: (01822) 613565 Fax: (01822) 617598 E-mail: sales@antex.co.uk *Manufacturers of soldering irons*

Anthan Engineering Ltd, Watford, WD19 4EZ Tel: (01923) 249474 Fax: (01923) 249477 E-mail: anthan@anthan.co.uk Principal Export Areas: Worldwide *Shock absorbers & spring manufrs*

Anthill Debt Collectors, 233a Golders Green Road, London, NW11 9ES Tel: (0800) 0742500 Fax: (020) 8905 5100 *Debt recovery services*

Anthony & Associates, 2 Thorn Road, Poole, Dorset, BH17 9AX Tel: (01202) 380500 Fax: (01202) 380510 *Electronics*

Anthony Bryant & Co Property Services Ltd, 25 Eccleston Square, London, SW1V 1NS Tel: (020) 7630 9696 Fax: (020) 7630 5761 E-mail: info@athonybryant.com *Investment consultants*

Anthony Cundy & Co., 39 South Drive, Sutton Coldfield, West Midlands, B75 7TE Tel: 0121-378 4649 Fax: 0121-378 4670 E-mail: cundys@btconnect.com *Chartered patent agents*

Anthony D Roberts, Westminster Industrial Estate, Station Road, North Hykeham, Lincoln, LN6 3QY Tel: (01522) 689199 Fax: (01522) 689199 *Engineers pattern makers*

Anthony Howard Eaton Ltd, Cursham Street, Sutton-in-Ashfield, Nottinghamshire, NG17 5FD Tel: (01623) 557444 *Swimwear manufrs*

▶ Anthony J Lewis & Co., 63 Leigh Hill Road, Cobham, Surrey, KT11 2HY Tel: (01932) 700063 Fax: (0870) 0940804 E-mail: service@anthonyjlewis.com *Commercial agents & chartered surveyors*

Anthony Jackson, Unit C2 Sheaf Bank Business Park, Prospect Road, Heeley, Sheffield, S2 3EN Tel: 0114-258 9889 Fax: 0114-258 5255 E-mail: info@jacksoncleaning.com *Commercial cleaning contractors*

John Anthony Organistation, Greenwood House, Unity Road, Lowmoor Business Park, Kirkby-in-Ashfield, Nottingham, NG17 7LE Tel: (01623) 755090 Fax: (01623) 755110 E-mail: sales@jao.co.uk *Shop fittings manufrs*

▶ Anthony Leput Ta DTS, 3 Sankey Valley Industrial Estate, Junction Lane, Newton-le-Willows, Merseyside, WA12 8DN Tel: (01925) 225760 Fax: (01925) 291014

Anthony Nixon Furniture, Birch Road, Barnard Castle, County Durham, DL12 8JR Tel: (01833) 690666 Fax: (01833) 690777 *Cabinet makers & furniture manufrs*

▶ Anthony Percival, 22 Swale Drive, Wellingborough, Northamptonshire, NN8 5ZL Tel: (01933) 405449 Fax: (01933) 400310 E-mail: anthony@percival69.freeserve.co.uk *Drawings prepared for Planning Permission & Building Regulation approval to the Commercial & Domestic Market,Bespoke Design Work Undertaken at hourly rates...*Commercial Buildings,Residential Buildings,Parkhomes,Park layouts P.O.A...*

Anthony Pickard, The Depot, Weeton Lane, Harewood, Leeds, LS17 9LP Tel: 0113-288 6524 Fax: 0113-288 6524 *Technical engineers*

Anthony & Pykett, 1 Park Road, Carlton, Nottingham, NG4 3DE Tel: 0115-940 0268 Fax: 0115-956 2494 E-mail: sales@anthonyandpykett.co.uk *Snooker, tables & accessories manufrs*

Anthony Stern Glass Ltd, Unit 205 Avro House, Havelock Terrace, London, SW8 4AL Tel: (020) 7622 9463 Fax: (020) 7738 8100 E-mail: anthony@anthonysternglass.com *Decorative glassware & lighting manufrs*

Anthony Van Tulleken Associates, 88 Brook Green, London, W6 7BD Tel: (020) 7603 7649 Fax: (020) 7603 8762 *Industrial designers*

▶ Anthony Warwick, 73 London Road, Copford, Colchester, CO6 1LG Tel: (01206) 211227 Fax: (01206) 211216 E-mail: sales@anthonywarwick.co.uk *Restorers of fine furniture & bespoke cabinetmakers*

Anthony's, 36 High Street, Stotfold, Hitchin, Hertfordshire, SG5 4LL Tel: (01462) 835452 Fax: (01462) 835452 *Office furniture suppliers*

▶ Anti Aging Laser Lite Ltd, 54 Eton Banks Court, Tangier Lane, Eton, Windsor, Berkshire, SL4 6BB Tel: (01753) 853878 Fax: (01753) 853878 E-mail: Beautylight@bellsouth.net *A Revolutionary Breakthrough in Anti*Ageing Laser Technology for the Home Buyer*

▶ Anti Contamination Equipement Supplies, Carr Mills, Bradford Road, Batley, West Yorkshire, WF17 9JY Tel: (01924) 420750 Fax: (01924) 420530 E-mail: sales@aces.uk.com *Supplier of Personal Protective Equipment, safety wear, work wear, tool, and ancillary products to trade, industry and the general public. Specialist supplier of equipment used for asbestos surveys, removal and management and bird flu protective clothing.*

Anti Noise Ltd, 67 Great Underbank, Stockport, Cheshire, SK1 1PE Tel: 0161-480 8454 Fax: 0161-429 9049 E-mail: sales@freehearingtest.co.uk *Ear plug manufrs*

Anti Vibration Methods Rubber Co. Ltd, 3 Woodcock Industrial Estate, Woodcock Road, Warminster, Wiltshire, BA12 9DX Tel: (01985) 219032 Fax: (01985) 219849 E-mail: sales@antivibrationmethodsrubber.co.uk *Manufacturer of vibration & shock isolation solutions*

Ltd Anti-Corrosion Services, Carrington Business Park, Carrington, Manchester, M31 4QW Tel: 0161-776 4019 Fax: 0161-775 8995 *Anti-corrosion service contractors*

Antics, 16 St Swithins Street, Worcester, WR1 2PS Tel: (01905) 22075 *Model making kit distributor*

Antiference, Eastern Avenue, Lichfield, Staffordshire, WS13 7SB Tel: (01889) 272600 Fax: (01296) 84284 E-mail: sales@antiference.co.uk *Television aerial manufrs*

▶ Antifriction Components Ltd, 8-9 Days Road, St. Philips, Bristol, BS2 0QS Tel: 0117-955 2266 Fax: 0117-955 1287 E-mail: bristolsales@afc-uk.com *Bearing & power transmission stockists & distributors* Also at: Basingstoke, Cwbran, Exeter, Gloucester, Swansea & Worcester

▶ Antifriction Components Ltd, Unit 3 Pearce Way, Gloucester, GL2 5YD Tel: (01452) 529669 Fax: (01452) 423873 E-mail: gloucestersales@afc-uk.com *Retail agricultural machinery*

Antigen Pharmaceuticals UK, NLA Tower, 12-16 Adiscombe Road, Croydon, CR0 0XT Tel: (020) 8649 8500 Fax: (020) 8686 0807 E-mail: info@gshieldplc.com *Pharmaceutical products distributors*

▶ Antimony Communications, 5 Chestnut Way, Godalming, Surrey, GU7 1TN Tel: (0870) 3214807 Fax: (0870) 7656807 E-mail: kelly@antimony.co.uk *Public relations for technology companies*

Antique Furniture Designs Ltd, The Warehouse, Sandy Bank Road, New York, Lincoln, LN4 4YE Tel: (01526) 342821 Fax: (01526) 344186 E-mail: sales@antiquefurnituredesigns.com *Antique Furniture Designs Ltd., is a traditional English furniture maker with a reputation for high quality reproduction furniture manufacturing. Much of their handcrafted production is custom made, bespoke, classic furniture in fine quality mahogany, yew, burr walnut and burr elm. The range of replica furniture at Antique Furniture Designs Ltd., includes dining tables, extending dining tables, dining chairs, sideboards, bookcases, desks, chests of drawers, side tables, coffee tables and other designs of antique furniture from the Georgian, Chippendale, Sheraton and Hepplewhite periods.*

▶ Antique Oak Flooring Co., 94 High Street, London, N8 7NT Tel: (020) 8347 8222 Fax: (020) 8347 8333 E-mail: info@antiqueoakflooring.com *Hardwood flooring specialists*

Antique Renovating Co., 43 Bent Street, Manchester, M8 8NW Tel: 0161-834 8000 *Electroplaters services*

▶ Antique Shop, 100 Bridge Road, Sutton Bridge, Spalding, Lincolnshire, PE12 9SA Tel: (01406) 350535 E-mail: info@theantiqueshop.co.uk *Antique furniture dealer*

▶ Antique Style Reproductions Ltd, Unit 16 Loughbrook Industrial Estate, Bessbrook, Newry, County Down, BT35 7EE Tel: (028) 3083 9232 Fax: (028) 3083 9236 E-mail: info@kanafurniture.com *Furniture*

▶ Anti-Slip, 12 Morningside Terrace, Inverurie, Aberdeenshire, AB51 4FE Tel: (01467) 622721

▶ Antix Pine Furniture, 5 Blatchford Road, Horsham, West Sussex, RH13 5QR Tel: (01403) 265040 E-mail: info@antixfurniture.co.uk *Furniture retailers & manufrs*

Antler Ltd, Pilot Works, Alfred Street, Bury, Lancashire, BL9 9EF Tel: 0161-764 0721 Fax: 0161-764 0723 E-mail: custserv@antler.co.uk *Travel goods manufrs* Also at: Exeter

▶ Antler Office Furniture Ltd, Seedbed Centre, Langston Road, Loughton, Essex, IG10 3TQ Tel: (020) 8787 7097 Fax: (020) 8787 7066 E-mail: enquiries@antleroffice.co.uk *Office furniture suppliers*

Antofagasta, 5 Princes Gate, London, SW7 1QJ Tel: (020) 7808 0988 Fax: (020) 7808 0986 *Holding company & diversified industries*

Anton Graphics Ltd, Unit 3b Duke Close, West Way, Andover, Hampshire, SP10 5AS Tel: (01264) 358544 Fax: (01264) 358242 E-mail: brian@antongraphics.co.uk *Digital reproduction services*

Anton Paar Ltd, 13 Harforde Court, John Tate Road, Hertford, SG13 7NW Tel: (01992) 514730 Fax: (01992) 514739 E-mail: info.gb@anton-paar.com *Density measuring equipment manufrs*

Anton Test & Measurement, Park House, 15-23 Greenhill Crescent, Watford, WD18 8PH Tel: (08704) 280073 Fax: (08704) 280076 E-mail: sales@anton-group.com *Test equipment distributors*

Anton Wylam Personal Computers, 10 Union Place, Tewkesbury, Gloucestershire, GL20 5RE Tel: (01684) 273800 *Computer software maintenance & repairers*

Antone Displays Ltd, Wanstead Road, Leicester, LE3 1TR Tel: 0116-232 4700 Fax: 0116-287 8012 E-mail: lucy.orr@antone.co.uk *Plastic display equipment, fittings & accessories*

Antone Displays Ltd, Wanstead Road, Leicester, LE3 1TR Tel: 0116-232 4700 Fax: 0116-287 8012 *Shop fitters & bespoke joinery contractors*

Antonine Printing Inks Ltd, Block 15, Newhouse Industrial Estate, Motherwell, Lanarkshire, ML1 5RX Tel: (01698) 733768 Fax: (01698) 832861 E-mail: info@antonine-inks.co.uk *Printing inks*

▶ Antony Devine, IFA, 7 Daines Close, Southend-on-Sea, SS1 3PG Tel: (0870) 0427900 Fax: (0870) 8913106 E-mail: akdevine@millfield-ifa.co.uk *Established in March 1998, Millfield Partnership Limited is one of the largest firms of independent financial advisers in the UK and is the principal operating company of Millfield Group plc.**Tony Devine, Independent Financial Adviser with Millfield, and a Chartered Accountant since 1983, has his practise in both London (City) and Thorpe Bay, and covers all of Greater London and Essex. With his extensive experience, plus access to specialists within Millfield where appropriate, you can depend on receiving the best possible independent advice, tailored to your individual needs. ***

▶ Antony Rowe Ltd, 2 Whittle Drive, Eastbourne, East Sussex, BN23 6QH Tel: (01323) 434700 Fax: (01323) 521117 E-mail: info@antonyrowe.co.uk

Antplace Ltd, Ford Airfield Industrial Estate, Ford, Arundel, West Sussex, BN18 0HY Tel: (01903) 714402 Fax: (01903) 732065 *Plastic injection moulding & vacuum forming manufrs*

Antrim Builders Centre, Springfarm Industrial Estate, Antrim, BT41 4NT Tel: (028) 9446 5921 Fax: (028) 9446 1844 E-mail: collin.robinson@mcnoughton-blair.com *Builders merchants*

Antrim Transformers Ltd, 25 Enkalon Industrial Estate, Randalstown Road, Antrim, BT41 4LD Tel: (028) 9442 8734 Fax: (028) 9446 8745 E-mail: technical@antrimtransformers.com *Transformer manufrs*

Antron Engineers Supplies, Unit 11 Broomers Hill Par, Broomers Hill Lane, Pulborough, West Sussex, RH20 2RY Tel: (01798) 872720 E-mail: sales@antroneng.co.uk *Bolt & nut suppliers*

Antruck Ltd, 22-24 Southgate Industrial Estate, Cross Street, Heywood, Lancashire, OL10 1PW Tel: (01706) 366636 Fax: (01706) 669989 E-mail: sales@antruck.co.uk *Trucks importers & distributors*

▶ Ants Recruitment, 11 Bridge Street, Leighton Buzzard, Bedfordshire, LU7 1AH Tel: (01525) 384288 Fax: (01525) 384140 E-mail: pete@antsrecruitment.co.uk *Specialists in the provision of industrial and commercial staff. 24 hour telephone line offering rapid response for immediate requirements for: drivers, warehouse staff, office administrators etc.*

▶ Ants Removals & Storage, 60a Milmead Industrial Centre, Mill Mead Road, London, N17 9QU Tel: (020) 8880 9190 Fax: (020) 8880 3131

▶ Antwerp Africa Metals and Minerals, 79 The Heights, Foxgrove Road, Beckenham, Kent, BR3 5BZ Tel: (020) 8663 0873 E-mail: antwerpafrica@yahoo.co.uk *Scrap lead specialists*

▶ Anubis Protection (UK), 46 Yewlands Avenue, Higher Blackley, Manchester, M9 6QR Tel: 0845 456 8717 Fax: 08712 365 328 E-mail: enquiries@anubis-protection.co.uk *Anubis Protection (UK) provide professionally trained fully uniformed Officers to cover rudimentary security functions through to crisis management & emergency response.*

Anvil Alloys Ltd, 1-2 Benwick Road, Whittlesey, Peterborough, PE7 2HD Tel: (01923) 800721 Fax: (01923) 800722 *Pipeline fittings & fabricators*

▶ Anvil Construction, Anvil House, Whittonstall, Consett, County Durham, DH8 9JN Tel: (01207) 560991 Fax: (01207) 563538

Anvil Engineering, Aiskew Ironworks, Sandhill Lane, Bedale, North Yorkshire, DL8 1DU Tel: (01677) 427362 Fax: (01677) 427364 E-mail: info@anvileng.co.uk *Blacksmiths & metalworkers including art specialists*

Anvil Iron Crafts, The Forge, Gittisham, Honiton, Devon, EX14 3AR Tel: (01404) 42510 Fax: (01404) 42510 *Mobile welders*

Anvil Tubesmiths Southern Ltd, Sedlescombe Sawmills, Hawkhurst Road, Staplecross, Robertsbridge, East Sussex, TN32 5SA Tel: (01580) 830770 Fax: (01580) 830220 E-mail: barry.luckham@btopenworld.com Purchasing Contact: B. Luckman Sales Contact: B.J. Luckham *Tube manipulation/bending services or fabricators, section bending services, Tubular & pipework fabricators. Also light/ non-ferrous & stainless steel fabricators. Metal & non ferrous metal fabricators. Rolls, tube forming, cold rolling and section forming.*

▶ Anville Censors, Westward House, Glebeland Road, Camberley, Surrey, GU15 3DB Tel: (01276) 684613 Fax: (01276) 692606 E-mail: camberleycensorsfuk@online.co.uk *Temperature censors manufrs*

Anville Instruments, Unit 19 Pegasus Court, North Lane, Aldershot, Hampshire, GU12 4QP Tel: (01252) 351030 Fax: (01252) 323492 E-mail: stephen@anvilleinstrumemts.com *Temperature measuring instruments*

▶ Any Garden Ltd, 20 Slonk Hill Road, Shoreham-by-Sea, West Sussex, BN43 6HX Tel: (01273) 440397 E-mail: markoakley@anygarden.com *Garden design, landscaping and maintenance. East and West Sussex, centred around the Brighton, Hove, Shoreham and Worthing area. We cater for private and commercial customers, offering hard and soft landscaping, lawns, patios, decking, planting, pruning, barbecues, water features, arbours, pergolas, clearance work, mulching, jet washing, garden makeovers to name but a few of the services we offer.*

▶ Any Junk, Unit A06 Riverside Business Centre, Haldane Place, London, SW18 4UQ Tel: (020) 8877 1155 Fax: (020) 8875 0055 E-mail: enquiries@anyjunk.co.uk *House, office, garden & site clearance services*

▶ Any Key Training Ltd, 15 Ongar Close, Addlestone, Surrey, KT15 1BX Tel: (01932) 820064 Fax: (0870) 7626550 E-mail: akt@anykeytraining.co.uk *IT training services*

Any Pest Control Services, Apple Trees, Gasden Copse, Witley, Godalming, Surrey, GU8 5QD Tel: (01428) 682359 *Pest control services*

▶ Anypest, Trelawney Lane, Plymouth, PL3 4JU Tel: (0800) 0960016

▶ Anytainment UK, 45 Stevens Lane, Claygate, Esher, Surrey, KT10 0TQ Tel: (01372) 467676 E-mail: info@anytainment.co.uk *Party & event hire of mini marquees, tables chairs, lighting*

Anything in Wood Ltd, 44-46a Hamilton Street, Grimsby, North East Lincolnshire, DN32 7HL Tel: (01472) 344176 Fax: (01472) 344176 *Joinery & building manufrs*

▶ Anything It, 14 Mary Seacole Road, Plymouth, PL1 3JY Tel: (01752) 667771 Fax: (01752) 667771 E-mail: sales@anything-it.biz *Anything IT as the name suggest does anything IT. From website design and programming to database and sofwtare development; from Networking small businesses to sofwtare and PC support all in the Plymouth area and in fact the whole of the UK.*

▶ Anything It, 14 Mary Seacole Road, Plymouth, PL1 3JY Tel: (01752) 667771 Fax: (01752) 667771 E-mail: sales@anything-it.biz *Anything IT means anything! Databases, Websites, Networking, PC troubleshooting, software development*

Anytronics Ltd, 5-6 Hillside Industrial Estate, London Road, Horndean, Waterlooville, Hampshire, PO8 0BL Tel: (023) 9259 9410 Fax: (023) 9259 8723 E-mail: sales@anytronics.com *Lighting control systems manufrs*

▶ Anywhere Same Day Couriers, Manchester Business Park, 3000 Aviator Way, Manchester, M22 5TG Tel: (0845) 4567722 Fax: (0870) 4323377 E-mail: info@anywhere.ltd.uk *Anywhere Couriers is a Manchester courier service operating from the South Manchester, Manchester Airport and Warrington areas and carrying out sameday deliveries throughout the UK and beyond.**They specialise in providing an economical and reliable sameday courier service to clients throughout the North West.**They also offer a specialist late collection service for nextday and international parcels.*

Anzeck Plastics (Packaging Division), Battye St, Bradford, West Yorkshire, BD4 8AG Tel: (01274) 669672 Fax: (01274) 663448 E-mail: sales@anzeck.co.uk *Polythene bag manufrs*

▶ Aodh Hannon, 21 Brankinstown Road, Aghalee, Craigavon, County Armagh, BT67 0DF Tel: (028) 9265 1441 Fax: (028) 9265 1995 E-mail: sales@hannon.transport.co.uk

A-Ok Signs Ltd, Units 21-23 Phoenix Court, Hawkins Road, Colchester, CO2 8JY Tel: (01206) 793683 Fax: (01206) 792895 E-mail: sales@aoksigns.com *Sign manufrs*

Aon Ltd, 21 Golden Square, Aberdeen, AB10 1RE Tel: (01224) 647201 Fax: (01224) 639715 *Commercial insurance brokers*

Aon Ltd, 145 St Vincent Street, Glasgow, G2 5JF Tel: 0141-222 7000 Fax: 0141-222 3345 *Pensions life insurance agents*

Aon Consulting Ltd, Briarcliffe House, Kingsmead, Farnborough, Hampshire, GU14 7TE Tel: (01252) 544484 Fax: (01252) 522206 E-mail: enquiries@aon.com *Pension consultants*

Aon Consulting Ltd, 8 Devonshire Square, London, EC2M 4PL Tel: (020) 7086 8000 Fax: (020) 7767 2001 E-mail: enquiries@aonconsulting.co.uk *Consulting actuaries*

Aon Entertainment Risk Services Ltd, Pinewood Road, Iver, Buckinghamshire, SL0 0NH Tel: (01753) 658200 Fax: (01753) 653152 E-mail: film@aon.co.uk *Insurance brokers*

Aon Risk Services, 3RD Floor, St. Georges Court, Douglas, Isle Of Man, IM1 1EE Tel: (01624) 673325 Fax: (01624) 623664 E-mail: mike.henthorn@ars.aon.co.uk *Financial services*

Aon Trust Corporation Ltd, 8 Devonshire Square, London, EC2M 4PL Tel: (020) 7623 5500 Fax: (020) 7621 1511 E-mail: nicola.fairley@aon.co.uk *Insurance brokers*

A1 Computer Services, 6 Wheatfield Road, Westerhope, Newcastle upon Tyne, NE5 5HQ Tel: (07757) 612978 E-mail: a1computers@mail.com *The North East of Englands leading computer engineers, on call seven days a week. Same day callout. No-Fix No-Fee. Over 8 Years Experience.*

Aonix Europe, Newtown House, Newtown Road, Henley-on-Thames, Oxfordshire, RG9 1HG Tel: (01491) 415000 Fax: (01491) 575033 E-mail: info@aonix.co.uk *Software developers products*

▶ Ap Floors & Doors, 47 Craigs Crescent, Rumford, Falkirk, FK2 0ET Tel: (01324) 710016 E-mail: donna.peat@btinternet.com *Supply & Fit of Hardwood, laminate, solid wood flooring at trade prices. Decking, Sheds, Fencing, internal & external doors, facings & skirtings. Qualified joiner. Regular clients include Behar & Carpet Right.*

▶ AP Office Services, 44 Christchurch Road, Tring, Hertfordshire, HP23 4EH Tel: 01442 890597 Fax: 0871 661 3480 E-mail: alison@aptyping.f9.co.uk *Offering virtual assistant services for your business requirements. Admin, secretarial, photocopying, transcription.*

Apache Electronics, Linc Business Park, Ofbolwick, York, YO10 3JB Tel: (01904) 436456 Fax: (01904) 436567 E-mail: sales@apache-electronics.com *Electronic component distributors*

Apak Group plc, Apak House Badminton Court, Station Road, Yate, Bristol, BS37 5HZ Tel: (01454) 871000 Fax: (01454) 871199 E-mail: enquiries@apakgroup.com *With over 25 years experience of providing specialist financial systems, APAK has become a market leader in the retail banking and asset based finance sectors. Our superior wholesale and retail finance systems are used by major financial institutions worldwide. APAK is also renowned for its expertise in developing and integrating core banking technology.**We believe one of APAK's greatest strengths is its team of dedicated and highly qualified employees. Many key staff have a financial background which helps us to provide the best business focused and technically advanced solutions. Coupled with our commitment to developing new and pioneering software, APAK expects to remain at the forefront of financial systems technology.**

▶ Apartment Liverpool, St Lukes Court, 1 Hardman Street, Liverpool, L1 9AX Tel: 0151 922 7788 E-mail: Sarah@ApartmentLiverpool.com *Luxury self-catering apartment within a restored georgian building. Minutes away from Liverpool"s vibrant restaurants, bars, shops & all tourist attractions. A cheaper luxury alternative to hotels.*

Apaseal Ltd, Battle Road, Hailsham, East Sussex, BN27 1DX Tel: (01323) 842066 Fax: (01323) 440450 E-mail: sales@apaseal.co.uk *Wheel balancing equipment distributors*

Apaseal Ltd, Unit 32 The Willow Estate, Avis Way, Newhaven, East Sussex, BN9 0DD Tel: (01273) 517995 Fax: (01273) 611061 *Industrial skin care products manufrs*

Apax Partners Ltd, 15 Portland Place, London, W1B 1PT Tel: (020) 7872 6300 Fax: (020) 7872 9449 Principal Export Areas: Worldwide *Capital gains venture services*

Apb Precision Engineers, Lakeside Business Park, Swan Lane, Sandhurst, Berkshire, GU47 9DN Tel: (01252) 890061 Fax: (01252) 890062 *Precision engineers*

Apb Products, Unit 30 Tweedale Court Industrial Estate, Madeley, Telford, Shropshire, TF7 4JZ Tel: (01952) 681940 Fax: (01952) 681945 E-mail: malcolm.harris@apbproducts.co.uk *Webbing straps & assemblies*

▶ APC Engineering, Unit 8, Flightway Business Park, Dunkeswell, Honiton, Devon, EX14 4RD Tel: (01404) 891105 Fax: (01404) 891107 E-mail: andy@apcengineering.co.uk *Agricultural machinery manufrs*

Apc Group Ltd, Crown Street, Thornton Road, Bradford, West Yorkshire, BD1 2LA Tel: (01274) 306970 Fax: (01274) 730900 E-mail: info@a-p-c.biz *Engineers pattern makers & shop fitting*

Apcom Computer Services Ltd, 104 Newbury Gardens, Epsom, Surrey, KT19 0PD Tel: (020) 8224 9015 Fax: (020) 8224 9015 E-mail: atul@apcom.co.uk *Computer resellers*

Apd Ltd, 69-71 Lower Bristol Road, Bath, BA2 3BE Tel: (01225) 424221 Fax: (01225) 444357 E-mail: orders@apd.co.uk *Motor Factor selling car and van parts & accessories, Consumables, radios, tools, Satnav and other automotive related products to trade and the general public*

Apd Colour Print & Design, Unit 5-6 Brookfield Farm Gravel Pit Lane, Southam Road, Cheltenham, Gloucestershire, GL52 3NQ Tel: (01242) 529132 Fax: (01242) 262311 E-mail: sales@apdprint.co.uk *Printing services, leaflets, brochures, magazines & flyers*

Ape Image Consultants, 36-40 Bloomfield Avenue, Luton, LU2 0PT Tel: (01582) 483718 Fax: (01582) 454518 E-mail: sales@apeimage.co.uk *Document binding service*

Apec Ltd, Armstrong Way, Bristol, BS37 5NG Tel: (01454) 324644 Fax: (01454) 311414 E-mail: info@apecbraking.co.uk *Brake parts & components distributors*

Apek Design & Developments Ltd, Ferndown Industrial Estate, Wimborne, Dorset, BH21 7RF Tel: (01202) 876149 Fax: (01202) 861210 E-mail: sales@apek.co.uk *Precision engineers*

Apem Components Ltd, Drakes Drive, Long Crendon, Aylesbury, Buckinghamshire, HP18 9BA Tel: (01844) 202400 Fax: (01844) 202500 E-mail: info@apem.co.uk *Miniature & industrial switch manufr*

Apetito, Crackley Way, Peartree Lane Industrial Estate, Dudley, West Midlands, DY2 0UW Tel: (01384) 254389 Fax: (01384) 456334 *Pastry food product manufrs*

Apetito Ltd, Canal Road, Trowbridge, Wiltshire, BA14 8RJ Tel: (01225) 753636 Fax: (01225) 777084 E-mail: sales@apetito.co.uk *Frozen food processors*

Apex Agencies International Ltd, Sportrite House, 155 Tame Road, Witton, Birmingham, B6 7DG Tel: 0121-328 9190 Fax: 0121-328 4175 E-mail: info@apex-world.com Principal Export Areas: Worldwide *Import & export merchants of building materials distribute fruit juice*

Apex Architectural Aluminium, Broadleigh Park, Broadleigh Lane, Stoke Gabriel, Totnes, Devon, TQ9 6PU Tel: (01803) 782929 Fax: (01803) 782929 *Architectural aluminium*

Apex Architecture Ltd, The Old School, Viney Hill, Lydney, Gloucestershire, GL15 4ND Tel: (01594) 516161 Fax: (01594) 516145 E-mail: info@apexarchitecture.co.uk *Architects, residential & commercial properties*

Apex Asphalt & Paving Co. Ltd, 60 Cato Street, Nechells, Birmingham, B7 4TS Tel: 0121-359 8447 Fax: 0121-359 5418 E-mail: apex@apex-asphalt.co.uk *Roofing & surfacing contractors*

▶ Apex Audio Systems Ltd, The Maltings, Roydon Road, Stanstead Abbotts, Ware, Hertfordshire, SG12 8UU Tel: (01920) 870950 Fax: (01920) 870951 E-mail: mikelfod@aol.com *ELECTRONIC SPEECH TRANSFER, CASH SCOOPS,INDUCTION LOOPS,"Q" MANAGEMENT, CCTV,P.A.*

Apex Bacon Co., Milk Street, Leek, Staffordshire, ST13 6BE Tel: (01538) 387363 Fax: (01538) 382204 *Meat merchants*

Apex Belting Co. Ltd, 9 Boldero Road, Bury St. Edmunds, Suffolk, IP32 7BS Tel: (01284) 752486 Fax: (01284) 750542 E-mail: sales@apex-belting.co.uk *Conveyor belting manufrs*

Apex Blinds Ltd, 46-48 Avenue Road, Lurgan, Craigavon, County Armagh, BT66 7BD Tel: (028) 3834 2525 Fax: (028) 3832 7835 E-mail: apexlinesni@hotmail.co.uk *Window blinds & awning manufrs*

Apex Block Cutters Ltd, 21 Murdock Road, Manton Industrial Estate, Bedford, MK41 7PE Tel: (01234) 355255 Fax: (01234) 352575 E-mail: sales@apexbuildingproducts.co.uk *Brick Cutters*

▶ Apex Building Supplies & Joinery Ltd, Lower Street, Baylham, Ipswich, IP6 8JP Tel: (01473) 832484 Fax: (01473) 832494

Apex Cables Ltd, St Johns Road, Meadowfield Industrial Estate, Durham, DH7 8RJ Tel: 0191-378 7900 Fax: 0191-378 7909 E-mail: apex@apexcables.co.uk *Electrical cable distributors*

Apex Closing (Footwear), Radiant Works, Burnley Road, Rossendale, Lancashire, BB4 8EW Tel: (01706) 218981 Fax: (01706) 218981

Apex Coffee Co. Ltd, Unit 4 Langdon Hills Business, Florence Way, Basildon, Essex, SS16 6AJ Tel: (01268) 411940 Fax: (01268) 491688 E-mail: roytaylor@apexcoffee.co.uk *Suppliers of coffee machines*

Apex Computer International Ltd, Apex House, The Mallards, South Cerney, Cirencester, Gloucestershire, GL7 5TQ Tel: (01285) 862100 Fax: (01285) 862111 *Computer distributors*

Apex Computer Services Wales Ltd, Unit 2 St. Michaels Court, Church Street, Newport, Gwent, NP20 2BY Tel: (01633) 215123 Fax: (01633) 215124 E-mail: sales@apexcs.co.uk *Computer maintenance*

▶ Apex Cowls, Lyncombe, Didcot Road, Harwell, Didcot, Oxfordshire, OX11 0DP Tel: (01235) 820876 E-mail: enquiries@apexcowls.co.uk *Chimney cowls*

Apex Diamond Products Ltd, 10 Bartleet Road, Washford Industrial Estate, Redditch, Worcestershire, B98 0DQ Tel: (01527) 529011 Fax: (01527) 510740 E-mail: sales@apexdiamond.co.uk *Diamond tools & turning tools for contact lens trade*

Company Information

continued

▶ Apex Displays, 18-20 Gladstone Street, Leicester, LE1 2BN Tel: 0116-251 1999 Fax: 0116-251 2022 E-mail: team@apax-displays.co.uk *Shop fittings manufrs*

▶ Apex Domestic & Commercial Services Ltd, 43 Eastgate Street, Stafford, ST16 2LY Tel: (01785) 250699 Fax: (01785) 229616 E-mail: enquiries@apexservice.wanado.co.uk *Buildings maintenance*

▶ Apex Drilling Services Ltd, 28 Sturmi Way, Village Farm Industrial Estate, Pyle, Bridgend, Mid Glamorgan, CF33 6BZ Tel: (01656) 749149 Fax: (01656) 749096

Apex Electrical Distribution Ltd, New York Way, New York Industrial Park, Newcastle upon Tyne, NE27 0QF Tel: 0191-293 0900 Fax: 0191-257 7722 *Electrical appliance equipment distributors, lighting design & supply*

▶ Apex Electrical Engineers Ltd, Alpha House Chapel Place, Dentonholme Trading Estate, Carlisle, CA2 5DF Tel: (01228) 520213 Fax: (01228) 514828 E-mail: info@apexelectrical.co.uk *Electrical engineers*

Apex Engineering South Ltd, Apex Business Centre, Queens Farm Road, Shorne, Gravesend, Kent, DA12 3HU Tel: (01474) 825700 Fax: (01474) 825717 E-mail: sales@apex-engineering.co.uk *Steel manufrs*

▶ Apex Enterprises, Kern House, Corporation Road, Birkenhead, Merseyside, CH41 1HB Tel: 0151-647 9323 Fax: 0151-647 9324 *Door & folding door gear manufrs*

▶ Apex Fire Ltd, Broadfieds, Headstone Lane, Harrow, Middlesex, HA2 6NN Tel: (020) 8421 2228 Fax: (020) 8421 5257 *Fire alarm installers*

Apex Fluid Engineering Ltd, 4 Morley Road, Staple Hill, Bristol, BS16 4QT Tel: 0117-907 7555 Fax: 0117-907 7556 E-mail: enquiries@apexpumps.com *Centrifugal pump manufrs*

▶ Apex GB Ltd, Station Approach, Victoria, Roche, St. Austell, Cornwall, PL26 8LG Tel: (0870) 7373771 Fax: (0870) 7373772 E-mail: sales@apexgb.com *Manufacturers of plastic & rubber extrusions*

Apex General Supplies Ltd, Unit 14 Apex House, Radford Crescent, Radford Way, Billericay, Essex, CM12 0DG Tel: (01277) 623269 Fax: (01277) 630739 *Industrial suppliers & manufrs*

▶ Apex Industrial Ltd, 14 Faraday Road, Glenrothes, Fife, KY6 2RU Tel: (01592) 771676 Fax: (01592) 774674

Apex Industrial Ltd, 651 Eccles New Road, Salford, M50 1BA Tel: 0161-789 0909 Fax: 0161-787 7113 *Power tools, engineers & building suppliers*

Apex Industrial Ltd, 26c Orgreave CR, Sheffield, S13 9NQ Tel: 0114-254 0011 Fax: 0114-254 8002 E-mail: sheffield@apexindustrial.co.uk *Distributors of hand machine tools*

Apex Industrial Chemicals Ltd, Peterseat Drive, Altens Industrial Estate, Aberdeen, AB12 3HT Tel: (01224) 878420 Fax: (01224) 871195 E-mail: sales@apex-chemical.co.uk *Chemical hygiene maintenance & manufrs*

▶ Apex Labels UK Ltd, Oyo BSNS Units, Fishers Grove, Portsmouth, PO6 1SH Tel: (023) 9237 2220 Fax: (0845) 1307886 E-mail: andrew@apexlabels.co.uk *Specialist manufacturers of self adhesive labels*

Apex Load Controls Co. Ltd, 8 Galloway Drive, Teignmouth, Devon, TQ14 9UX Tel: (01626) 776490 Fax: (01626) 770877 *Lifting equipment manufrs*

▶ Apex Networks Ltd, Unit 2, Lead Centre, Dane Valley Road, Broadstairs, Kent, CT10 3JJ Tel: (0870) 3303141 Fax: (0870) 3303151 E-mail: info@apex-networks.com *Networks solutions maintenance & supplies*

Apex Office Centre Ltd, 7 Malham Fell, Wildridings, Bracknell, Berkshire, RG12 7DU Tel: (01344) 441061 Fax: (01344) 441061 E-mail: info@apexoffice.com *Stationery suppliers*

Apex Office Solutions Ltd, 147 Bellenden Road, London, SE15 4DH Tel: (020) 7277 5168 *Photocopying machine maintenance, repair & specialist services*

Apex Patterns, Unit 10 Redland Indust Estate, Station Hill St.Georges, Madeley, Telford, Shropshire, TF7 5EF Tel: (01952) 614337 Fax: (01952) 614337 E-mail: apexpatterns1@btclick.com *Engineers patternmakers*

Apex Pest Control, Apex House, 15 Stratton Road, Bournemouth, BH9 3PG Tel: (01202) 523838 Fax: (01202) 293954 E-mail: sales@apexpestcontrol.co.uk *Pest control & fly screening services*

Apex Print & Promotion, Sapphire Way, Rhombus Business Park, Norwich, NR6 6NN Tel: (01603) 410035 Fax: (01603) 410049 E-mail: admin@promotion.co.uk *Promotional gifts*

Apex Radio Systems Ltd, 102 Tantobie Road, Denton Burn, Newcastle Upon Tyne, NE15 7DQ Tel: 0191 228 0466 Fax: 0191 228 0467 E-mail: info@apexradio.com *Radio communication equipment sales*

▶ Apex Roofing and building Maintenance, 28 Binley House, Highcliffe Drive, Roehampton, London, SW15 4PY Tel: 0208 392 9792 E-mail: masterson697@aol.com *New roofs, same day repairs, 24 hr call out, guttering, repointing,exterior/interior painting, free estimates, all work guaranteed*

Apex Roofing Services, Apex Lodge, Great Tey Road, Little Tey, Colchester, CO6 1HZ Tel: (01206) 210762 Fax: (01206) 211622 *Roofing contractors*

▶ Apex Scaffolding Anglia Ltd, Barnards Way, Lowestoft, Suffolk, NR32 2HF Tel: (01502) 537129 Fax: (01502) 537133

▶ Apex Scaffolding Northampton Ltd, 165 St. Andrews Road, Northampton, NN2 6HL Tel: (01604) 719422

Apex Security Engineering Ltd, Flint Road, Letchworth Garden City, Hertfordshire, SG6 1HJ Tel: (01462) 673431 Fax: (01462) 671518 E-mail: sales@apexsecuritiesfurniture.com *Sheet metalwork engineers & fabricators*

Apex Signs, 2a West Telferton, Edinburgh, EH7 6UL Tel: 0131-657 3530 Fax: 0131-669 7305 E-mail: info@apex-signs.co.uk *Sign makers*

Apex Software, 11 Broadway, Knaphill, Woking, Surrey, GU21 2DR Tel: (01483) 797700 Fax: (01483) 797960 *Computer software*

▶ Apex Technology Ltd, PO Box 2364, Stafford, ST16 3DA Tel: (01785) 227989 E-mail: enquiry@apextechnology.co.uk *Data recovery services*

▶ Apex Tubulars, Cairnrobin Pipe Yard, Portlethen, Aberdeen, AB12 4SB Tel: (01224) 786900 Fax: (01224) 784258

Apfel Europe, Unit 2 Station Yard, Station Road, Hungerford, Berkshire, RG17 0DY Tel: (01488) 685183 Fax: (01488) 685430 E-mail: sales@apfel.co.uk *Hard metric press-fit connectors agents*

▶ Apg Precision Engineering & Fabrication, John Street, Warrington, WA2 7UB Tel: (01925) 418790 Fax: (01925) 243403 E-mail: sales@apgprecisionengineeringltd.co.uk

Aph Signs, 1 Pinfold Lane, Llay Industrial Estate, Llay, Wrexham, Clwyd, LL12 0PX Tel: (01978) 856565 Fax: (01978) 856568 *Sign makers*

Aphel Ltd, Wayside Business Park, Wilsons Lane, Coventry, CV6 6NY Tel: (0870) 7541880 Fax: (0870) 7541881 E-mail: sales@aphel.co.uk *Multi-socket outlet manufacturers, supplying power strips, power distribution units, data distribution units.*

Aphrodite, 1a Priory Lane, Penwortham, Preston, PR1 0AR Tel: (01772) 746555 *Health food retailers*

Api Precision Toolmakers, Unit 2 Quell Farm Industrial Estate, Greatham, Pulborough, West Sussex, RH20 2ES Tel: (01798) 875688 Fax: (01798) 872701 E-mail: api@apiprecision.co.uk *Precision toolmakers, mould makers & small batch specialists*

Apiezon Products, Hibernia Way, Trafford Park, Manchester, M32 0ZD Tel: 0161-864 5419 Fax: 0161-864 5444 E-mail: sales@apiezon.com *Producers of high vacuum greases*

Apiffany Interior Design Ltd, Yandell Publishing Ltd, 9 Vermont Place, Tongwell, Milton Keynes, MK15 8JA Tel: (0870) 1212617 Fax: (0870) 1212618 E-mail: info@apiffany.co.uk *Interior design consultancy, design, procurement & full project management services to residential & commercial customers.*

▶ APL Ltd, Eagle Court, 9 Vine Street, Uxbridge, Middlesex, UB8 1QE Tel: (01895) 202600 Fax: (01895) 202698 *Shipping company*

▶ A-Plant Ltd, Ford Airfield Industrial Estate, Ford, Arundel, West Sussex, BN18 0HY Tel: (01903) 717431 Fax: (01903) 732246

▶ A-Plant Ltd, Humber Road, Barton-upon-Humber, South Humberside, DN18 5BN Tel: (01652) 637777 Fax: (01652) 637788

▶ A-Plant Ltd, B Swann Road, Cambridge, CB5 8JZ Tel: (01223) 464367 Fax: (01223) 350050

A-Plant Ltd, Mansfield Road, Derby, DE1 3RF Tel: (01332) 382275 Fax: (01332) 295504 E-mail: derbynorth@aplant.com *Contractors plant hire*

A-Plant Ltd, Unit 8 Bridge End, Egremont, Cumbria, CA22 2RE Tel: (01946) 823073 Fax: (01946) 821792 E-mail: egremont@aplant.com *Tool hire suppliers*

▶ A-Plant Ltd, Speedfields Park, Fareham, Hampshire, PO14 1TS Tel: (01329) 829998 Fax: (01329) 828088

A-Plant, Unit 1 Block E, 19 Nurseries Road, Baillieston, Glasgow, G69 6UL Tel: 0141-771 7388 Fax: 0141-771 4929

▶ A-Plant Ltd, Chaddock Lane Industrial Estate, Kennedy Road, Astley Tyldesley, Manchester, M29 7JY Tel: (01942) 884588

A-Plant Ltd, 5 Wood Street, Openshaw, Manchester, M11 2FB Tel: 0161-231 4035 Fax: 0161-223 3140

A-Plant Ltd, Unit B1 Swinton Bridge Industrial Estate, White Lee Road, Swinton, Mexborough, South Yorkshire, S64 8BH Tel: (01709) 588890 Fax: (01709) 584632 *Plant hire*

A-Plant Ltd, Nuthall Road, Nottingham, NG8 5BU Tel: 0115-942 0567 Fax: 0115-978 8868 E-mail: nottinghamwest@aplant.com *Tool hire services*

▶ A-Plant Ltd, King George Close, Romford, RM7 7PN Tel: (01708) 730206 Fax: (01708) 733839

▶ A-Plant Ltd, Lockheed Close, Preston Farm Industrial Estate, Stockton-on-Tees, Cleveland, TS18 3SE Tel: (01642) 615151 Fax: (01642) 614549

▶ A-Plant Ltd, 102 Dalton Avenue, Birchwood Park Birchwood, Warrington, WA3 6YE Tel: (01925) 281030 Fax: (01925) 281005 E-mail: enquiries@aplant.com *Plant & tool hire specialists*

A-Plant Powered Access, Trent Lane, Nottingham, NG2 4DS Tel: 0115-948 3348 Fax: 0115-950 8275 *Access equipment hire & sales*

▶ Aplomb Ltd, 74 Chancery Lane, London, WC2A 1AD Tel: (020) 7831 9444 Fax: (020) 7831 9445 E-mail: admin@aplombonline.com *Fast accurate translations for business in major world languages*

▶ Aplus Entertainment, Calshot Road, Birmingham, B42 2BY Tel: 0800 9168762 E-mail: sales@aplusentertainment.co.uk *Entertainment agency suppling all types of entertainment across the united kingdom*

▶ APM Group - Interactive Community of Practice (ICP), The APM Group, Sword House, Totteridge Road, High Wycombe, Buckinghamshire, HP13 6DG Tel: (01494) 452450 Fax: (01494) 459559 E-mail: keerin.saeed@apmgroup.co.uk *Examination & accreditation company services*

Apm Metals Ltd, Plantation Works, Eurolink Way, Sittingbourne, Kent, ME10 3HH Tel: (01795) 426021 Fax: (01795) 421858 E-mail: apmmetalsltd@btconnect.com *Non-ferrous scrap metal recycling*

Apmg Ltd, Mount Skip Lane, Little Hulton, Manchester, M38 9AL Tel: 0161-799 2200 Fax: 0161-799 2220 E-mail: enquiries@apmg.co.uk *Laboratory furniture, fume cupboards, fans & extraction system manufacturers*

▶ Apna Marquee.com, 6 Copinger Walk, Edgware, Middlesex, HA8 0AH Tel: (07956) 895677 E-mail: info@ApnaMarquee.com *Marquee Party Tents Hire*Chairs - Table - Heaters - Carpet - Lighting.*The Ideal Solution for all out door occasions.*All sizes and equipment available.*

Apogee Corporation Ltd, Unit 8 Willow Lane Business Park, Nyton Road, Mitcham, Surrey, CR4 4NA Tel: (0845) 3009955 Fax: (0845) 3009944 E-mail: reception@apogeecorp.com *Fax machines, photocopiers & telephone system distributors*

Apollo, 3 Merchant Drive, Mead Lane, Hertford, SG13 7BH Tel: (01992) 558375 Fax: (01992) 501318 E-mail: david@horneandbanks.co.uk *Plastics mould toolmakers & precision engineers*

Apollo, Pond House, Bulmer Lane, Holme-on-Spalding-Moor, York, YO43 4HE Tel: (01430) 860049 Fax: (01430) 861550 E-mail: sales@apolloultrasonics.co.uk *Apollo Ultrasonics is the appointed UK distributor for the Bransonic range of Ultrasonic cleaning equipment & the Branson range of Ultrasonic Sonifier Disintegrators. Our Comprehensive product range includes - Ultrasonic Bench Top equipment, Industrial Cleaning equipment, Immersible transducers & generators, Ultrasonic Cleaning liquids, Ultrasonic Homogenisers, & disintegration equipment*

Apollo Bearings, 8 Priestley Way, Crawley, West Sussex, RH10 9NT Tel: (01293) 539539 Fax: (01293) 538853 E-mail: apollo.bearings@talk21.com *Apollo Bearings are an independent stockist, distributor for a wide range of bearing types, Ball, Roller, Needle, Taper, Plain etc. Also chains, roller, bush, lifting with test certificate. V Belt drives & pulleys, flat belts & conveyor belts Agents for: Nachi Bearings; Sedis Chains; Transmission Development*

Apollo Blinds Ltd, 195 Rosemount Place, Aberdeen, AB25 2XP Tel: (01224) 644600 Fax: (01224) 644292 *Blind manufrs*

Apollo Blinds Ltd, 38 South Bridge Street, Airdrie, Lanarkshire, ML6 6JA Tel: (01236) 768011 Fax: (01236) 768011 *Blinds manufrs*

Apollo Blinds Ltd, 8 Lorne Arcade, Ayr, KA7 1SB Tel: (01292) 261838 Fax: (01292) 261838 *Window blinds*

Apollo Blinds, 3 Bond Street, Bury, Lancashire, BL9 7BE Tel: 0161-761 3211 Fax: 0161-761 3211 *Blind retailers*

Apollo Blinds Ltd, Unit 25 Lordswood Industrial Estate, Revenge Road, Chatham, Kent, ME5 8UD Tel: (01634) 686868 Fax: (01634) 686868 E-mail: midwayblinds@btconnect.com *Window blind manufrs*

Apollo Blinds Ltd, 42 Cow Wynd, Falkirk, FK1 1PU Tel: (01324) 627814 Fax: (01324) 627814 *Blind retailers*

▶ Apollo Blinds Ltd, 64 Main Street, Rutherglen, Glasgow, G73 2HY Tel: 0141-647 0341 Fax: 0141-647 0341 *Supplier & manufacturer of window blinds*

Apollo Blinds Ltd, 212 Argyle Street, Glasgow, G2 8HA Tel: 0141-226 3166 Fax: 0141-226 5444 *Blinds, curtains, shutters, canopies & awnings manufrs*

Apollo Blinds Ltd, 101 Kilmarnock Road, Glasgow, G41 3YR Tel: 0141-649 2768 Fax: 0141-632 6428 *Blind suppliers*

Apollo Blinds Ltd, 160 York Road, Hartlepool, Cleveland, TS26 9DT Tel: (01429) 236666 Fax: (01429) 293004 *Blind distributors & manufrs*

Apollo Blinds Ltd, 19 St. Marnock Street, Kilmarnock, Ayrshire, KA1 1DZ Tel: (01563) 532452 Fax: (01563) 544473 *Blind retailers*

Apollo Blinds Ltd, 254 High Street, Kirkcaldy, Fife, KY1 1LA Tel: (01592) 268841 Fax: (01592) 268841 *Supplier of blinds*

Apollo Blinds Ltd, 102 BMK Industrial Estate, Wakefield Road, Liversedge, West Yorkshire, WF15 6BS Tel: (01924) 413010 Fax: (01924) 410170 E-mail: sales@apollo-blinds.co.uk *Window blind manufrs*

▶ Apollo Blinds Ltd, 4 Mallard Buildings, Station Road, New Milton, Hampshire, BH25 6HY Tel: (01425) 623624 Fax: (01425) 629709 E-mail: apolloblinds1@btconnect.com *Blind retailers*

Apollo Blinds Ltd, 197 Sandyford Road, Newcastle upon Tyne, NE2 1NP Tel: 0191-230 4156 Fax: 0191-232 4498 *Blinds manufacturers & retailers*

▶ Apollo Blinds Ltd, 73 South Methven Street, Perth, PH1 5NX Tel: (01738) 622366 Fax: (01738) 622366

Apollo Blinds Ltd, 43 King Street, Ramsgate, Kent, CT11 8NP Tel: (01843) 589849 Fax: (01843) 589849 *Blind manufrs*

Apollo Blinds Ltd, 6 Senator Industrial Estate, College Close, Sandown, Isle of Wight, PO36 8EH Tel: (01983) 407395 Fax: (01983) 407395 E-mail: apolloexpiowltd@skelly.co.uk *Blind fitting & distributors*

Apollo Blinds Ltd, 35 Westfield Street, St. Helens, Merseyside, WA10 1QD Tel: (01744) 739588 *Blinds distributors*

Apollo Blinds Ltd, 27 Cowane Street, Stirling, FK8 1JW Tel: (01786) 472335 Fax: (01786) 472335 *Blinds manufrs*

Apollo Blinds Ltd, 5 Boldmere Road, Sutton Coldfield, West Midlands, B73 5UY Tel: 0121-321 3337 Fax: 0121-321 3337 *Window blind retailers*

Apollo Blinds Ltd, 3 Horsemarket Street, Warrington, WA1 1TP Tel: (01925) 411404 Fax: (01925) 411404 *Blind suppliers*

Apollo Blinds Ltd, 8 Wigan Gallery, The Galleries, Wigan, Lancashire, WN1 1AR Tel: (01942) 495500 Fax: (01942) 495500 *Blinds manufrs*

Apollo Chemicals Holdings Ltd, Sandy Way, Amington Industrial Estate, Tamworth, Staffordshire, B77 4DS Tel: (01827) 54281 Fax: (01827) 53030 E-mail: sales@apolloadhesives.com Purchasing

continued

Contact: G. Rea Sales Contact: A. Jones *Manufacturers, industrial adhesives & tapes*

Apollo Colours Ltd, 127 Nathan Way, West Thames Mead Business Park, London, SE28 0AB Tel: (020) 8854 0017 Fax: (020) 8316 6956 E-mail: london@apollocolours.co.uk *Printing ink manufrs*

Apollo Computers Ltd, Unit 34, Eurolink Business Centre, 49 Effra Road, London, SW2 1BZ Tel: (020) 7924 0753 Fax: (020) 7274 8376 *Computer repair & sales & data recovery*

Apollo Construction Products, Unit 4 Weights Lane, Redditch, Worcestershire, B97 6RG Tel: (01527) 63999 Fax: (01527) 64999 E-mail: sales@apollofix.co.uk *Structural building fixing systems, resin anchors, innovative fixings & fasteners for scaffolding & access products, safety line & eyebolt installers, mast climbers, hoist erectors & rigging contractors, tne stop shopping for commercial & industrial building contractors*

Apollo Cradles Ltd, 428 Carlton Road, Barnsley, South Yorkshire, S71 3HX Tel: (01226) 700079 Fax: (01226) 707108 E-mail: sales@apollocradles.co.uk *Cradle distributors*

Apollo Dental Ltd, Tempest House, Lyon Road, Walton-on-Thames, Surrey, KT12 3PU Tel: (01932) 240950 Fax: (01932) 246606 *Dental, surgical, healthcare items suppliers & manufrs*

Apollo Distribution Solution, A5 Seedbed Centre, Avenue Road, Nechells, Birmingham, B7 4NT Tel: 0121-359 7707 Fax: 0121-359 7717 *Courier service*

Apollo Electronics Co., Unit 1 Riverside Business Park, Wakefield Road, Scissett, Huddersfield, HD8 9HR Tel: (01484) 864940 Fax: (01484) 865830 E-mail: sales@apollo-electronics.com *Electronic contract manufrs*

Apollo Fabrications Ltd, Unit 20 Canalside Industrial Estate, Brettell Lane, Brierley Hill, West Midlands, DY5 3JU Tel: (01384) 484603 Fax: (01384) 484603 E-mail: ralph-apollo@supanet.com *Steel fabricators*

Apollo Fire Detectors Ltd, 36 Brookside Road, Havant, Hampshire, PO9 1JR Tel: (023) 9249 2412 Fax: (023) 9249 2754 E-mail: sales@apollo-fire.co.uk *Manufacturer of smoke & heat detectors for commercial, marine, offshore & industrial fire detection systems.*

Apollo Fuels Ltd, Templeborough Depot, Sheffield Road, Tinsley, Sheffield, S9 1RT Tel: 0114-243 6814 Fax: 0114-242 3362 *Oil distributors*

Apollo Hifi Furniture Ltd, Castle Works, High Street, Tipton, West Midlands, DY4 8HJ Tel: 0121-520 5070 Fax: 0121-522 2055 E-mail: sales@apollohifi.co.uk *Audio stand manufrs*

Apollo Leisure, Unit 1 Forest Close, Ebblake Industrial Estate, Verwood, Dorset, BH31 6DE Tel: (01202) 812000 Fax: (01202) 827040 E-mail: sales@apolloleisure.co.uk *Sports warehouse & office equipment distributors & agents*

Apollo Leisure Ltd, 90 Hillcroft Crescent, Watford, WD19 4NY Tel: (01923) 221195 Fax: (01923) 334438 E-mail: michaelzapala@ntlworld.com *Supply & maintain amusement machines*

Apollo Light & Sound Ltd, Avonside Enterprise Park, Melksham, Wiltshire, SN12 8BS Tel: (01225) 707429 Fax: (01225) 707429 E-mail: apollo@lightandsound.fsnet.co.uk *Disco & karaoke sales, hire & repair*

Apollo Lighting Ltd, 4 Felnex Trading Estate, Pontefract Lane, Leeds, LS9 0SL Tel: 0113-240 5511 Fax: 0113-240 5151 E-mail: sales@apollolighting.co.uk *Industrial task lighting equipment services*

▶ Apollo London Ltd, Conquest House, Church Street, Waltham Abbey, Essex, EN9 1DX Tel: (01992) 650333 Fax: (01992) 650999

Apollo Multiform Ltd, 14 Gorst Road, London, NW10 6LE Tel: (020) 8965 8571 Fax: (020) 8838 2588 E-mail: info@apolloltd.co.uk *Saw sharpening services*

Apollo Optical Manufacturing Ltd, 12b Carvers Trading Estate, Southampton Road, Ringwood, Hampshire, BH24 1JS Tel: (01425) 479593 Fax: (01425) 479963 *Spectacles, lenses & frames manufrs*

▶ Apollo Plant Hire & Sales, 108 St. Francis Way, Chadwell St. Mary, Grays, Essex, RM16 4RH Tel: (01375) 841050 Fax: (01375) 841050 E-mail: apolloplant@blueyonder.co.uk *Hire service & repair of all pipe threading*

Apollo Plant Holdings Ltd, Redstone Industrial Estate, Boston, Lincolnshire, PE21 8AL Tel: (01205) 351722 Fax: (01205) 360432 E-mail: enquiries@apollo-plant.co.uk *Forklift truck services, sales & hire*

Apollo Plastics, 62 St James Street, Hull, HU3 2DH Tel: (01482) 325394 Fax: (01482) 229826 E-mail: sales@apolloplastics.co.uk *Plastics vacuum formed products manufrs*

Apollo Press, 8 Decoy Road, Worthing, West Sussex, BN14 8ND Tel: (01903) 232444 Fax: (01903) 230354 E-mail: dyerpress72@aol.com *General printers*

▶ Apollo Products Ltd, Rhewl Quarry, Denbigh Road, Rhewl, Ruthin, Clwyd, LL15 2UF Tel: (01824) 702889 E-mail: info@apolloproducts.co.uk *Road construction*

Apollo Scientific Ltd, Bredbury, Stockport, Cheshire, SK6 2QR Tel: (01256) 336097 Fax: (01256) 336097 E-mail: johncaparn@fsmail.net

▶ Apollo Sheet Metal Products, Bayton Road, Bayton Road Industrial Estate, Exhall, Coventry, CV7 9EJ Tel: (024) 7636 0822 Fax: (024) 7664 4415 *Metal working & fabrication specialists*

Apollo Signs & Engraving, Wigwam Lane Unit E1, Imex Enterprise Park, Hucknall, Nottingham, NG15 7SZ Tel: 0115-963 1366 Fax: 0115-961 1355 E-mail: dexterapolo@aol.com *Sign engravers & manufrs*

Apollo Upvc, 19 Aintree Road, Bootle, Merseyside, L20 9DL Tel: 0151-922 1322 Fax: 0151-922 1322 *Windows suppliers*

Apollo Window Blinds, The Courtyard Matthews Green Farm, Matthews Green Road, Wokingham, Berkshire, RG41 1JX Tel: (01344) 669733 Fax: 0118-979 6009

continued

continuation
E-mail: apolloblinds@onetel.com *Blind & patio awning manufrs & suppliers*

▶ Apollo11 Organisation UK, Independent FIlm & Multimedia Studios, Horsham, West Sussex, RH13 5EY Tel: (01403) 739333 Fax: (01403) 254461 E-mail: enquires@apollo11.org.uk *Film making*

Appeal Conservatory Blinds Ltd, Unit 6 Vale Lane, Bristol, BS3 5SD Tel: 0117-963 7734 Fax: 0117-966 6216 E-mail: sales@appealblinds.com *Conservatory blind manufrs*

Robin Appel Ltd, The Town House, The Square, Bishops Waltham, Southampton, SO32 1AF Tel: (01489) 896388 Fax: (01489) 896602 E-mail: enquiries@robin-appel.com *Agricultural merchants*

J.F. Appelbe & Co. Ltd, Littlefair Road, Hedon Road, Hull, HU9 5LN Tel: (01482) 781191 Fax: (01482) 781235 E-mail: enquiries@applebes.com *Steel fabrication engineers*

Apperley Business Supplies Ltd, 1 St Andrews Road, Montpelier, Bristol, BS6 5EH Tel: 0117-942 4972 Fax: 0117-942 4400 E-mail: marklaval@blueyonder.co.uk *Paper, polythene bag & packaging distributors*

▶ Apperley Design, 51 Strathallan Drive, Baildon, Shipley, West Yorkshire, BD17 6QH Tel: (01274) 421410 E-mail: info@apperleydesign.co.uk *Graphic design & web design services*

Apperley Honing Ltd, Alpha Works, Alstone La, Cheltenham, Glos, GL51 8ES Tel: (01242) 525868 Fax: (01242) 224738 E-mail: sales@apperleyhoning.co.uk *Apperley Honing are an experienced specialist contract honing company based in the UK. They are approved to ISO9001:2000, and have capacity to hone all bores between 3.00mm & 750.00mm diameter, up to 15 metres long. Their special purpose machine division designs, manufacturers & sells bespoke honing machines, filters, tooling and consumables.*

Apph Aviation Services Ltd, Unit 1 Rokeby Court, Manor Park, Runcorn, Cheshire, WA7 1RW Tel: (01928) 579791 Fax: (01928) 579811 *Aircraft undercarriage service & repair*

APPH Nottingham Ltd, Urban Road, Kirkby-In-Ashfield, Nottingham, NG17 8AP Tel: (01623) 754355 Fax: (01623) 723904 E-mail: sales@beauforteng.co.uk *Precision machining services*

Applabs Ltd, Preston Technology Centre, Marsh Lane, Preston, PR1 8UQ Tel: (01772) 885850 Fax: (01772) 558881 E-mail: info@isintegration.com Sales Contact: D. Lawlor *IT consultants*

▶ Apple Display Systems Ltd, Units 1-9, Nelson Business Centre, Nelson Street, Manchester, M34 3ET Tel: 0161-335 0660

Apple Engineering Ltd, Unit 23 Gothenburg Way, Hull, HU7 0YG Tel: (01482) 824200 Fax: (01482) 824196 E-mail: sales@appleng.co.uk Principal Export Areas: Worldwide *Custom built machinery*

Apple Freight Ltd, Trafford House, Chester Road, Stretford, Manchester, M32 0RS Tel: 0161-872 0718 Fax: 0161-872 9751 *Road transport, haulage & freight services*

▶ Apple Marquees Ltd, Cranford House, 20 Harborough Rd, Kingsthorpe, Northampton, NN2 7AZ Tel: 01604 627290 E-mail: info@applemarquees.co.uk *Apple Marquees offer event solutions with a dedicated personal service. All of our marquees are brand new for the 2005 season. We also have available for hire linings, flooring, lighting and furniture.*

▶ Apple Transcription, 59 Market Street, Edenfield, Bury, Lancashire, BL0 0JQ Tel: (01706) 828020 Fax: (01706) 870838 E-mail: info@appletranscription.co.uk *typing services to legal, medical and business professionals*

Appledore Developments, Swiss Life House, 24-26 South Park, Sevenoaks, Kent, TN13 1DU Tel: (01732) 469888 Fax: (01732) 469890 E-mail: info@appledoredevelopments.co.uk *A specialist regional house building company providing new homes in Kent and Sussex*

Appledore Packaging, Rose Dene, Green Farm Lane, Shorne, Gravesend, Kent, DA12 3HL Tel: (01474) 770018 Fax: (01474) 770019 E-mail: enquiries@appledore-packaging.co.uk *Suppliers Of Corrugated & Solid Board Packaging. All Made To Measure. Design Service & Sample Making Facilities. Plain or Printed Applications. Bespoke & Die Cut Packaging.*

Appledore Shipbuilders Ltd, Bidna Yard, Hubbastone Road, Appledore, Bideford, Devon, EX39 1LZ Tel: (01237) 473281 Fax: (01237) 426500 E-mail: info@appledore-shipbuilders.co.uk *Shipbuilders*

Appleford Woodworking Machinery, 49 Derham Park, Yatton, Bristol, BS49 4EA Tel: (01934) 838025 E-mail: applewood.machine@virgin.net *Woodwork machinery suppliers*

Applejacks, Unit 28 The Mall, The Stratford Centre, London, E15 1XD Tel: (020) 8519 5809 Fax: (020) 8519 1099 E-mail: robert@applejacks.co.uk *Health food retailers*

▶ Applelec Sign Components, Walker Terrace, Bradford, West Yorkshire, BD4 7HP Tel: (01274) 774477 Fax: (01274) 774478 E-mail: sales@applelecsign.co.uk *Trade suppliers of lighting signage*

▶ AppleSoundShop, 6 Well House Barns, Bretton, Chester, CH4 0DH Tel: (0870) 7410123 Fax: (0870) 7410124 E-mail: info@applesound.com *Buy Sound Systems and Audio Equipment Online. AppleSoundShop has a secure online card payment facility and option to send by post or fax. You''ll find a wide selection of popular audio equipment for school, church or workplace at prices only available online and all with prompt delivery.*

▶ Applestone Music & Sound Ltd, 197 Union Street, Torquay, TQ1 4BY Tel: (01803) 297297 Fax: (01803) 297297 E-mail: admin@theacademy.uk.com *Provider of guitars spare, parts, tuition, studio an rehearsal rooms*

▶ Applestorm Ltd, Unit 3, Homefarm, Luton Hoo Estate, Luton, LU1 3TD Tel: (0800) 5655565 Fax: (0870) 4670447 E-mail: sales@applestorm.com *IT Support services*

Appleton Commercial Engineering, Unit 3c Lyncastle Way, Barleycastle Lane, Appleton, Warrington, WA4 4ST Tel: (01925) 601855 Fax: (01925) 860478 E-mail: email@ace-commercials.com *Commercial vehicle repair services*

Appleton Signs Signwriters, Waterloo Indust Estate, Flanders Road, Hedge End, Southampton, SO30 2QT Tel: (01489) 787203 Fax: (01489) 788281 *Sign manufrs*

Appleton Woods Ltd, Lindon House, Heeley Road, Selly Oak, Birmingham, B29 6EN Tel: 0121-472 7353 Fax: 0121-414 1075 E-mail: info@appletonwoods.co.uk *Laboratory suppliers*

▶ Appleton-Sales.com, 2 Thurlby Way, Maidenhead, Berkshire, SL6 3YZ Tel: (08700) 423600 *Appleton-Estates.com provide residential property sales, rental and management services in Maidenhead and Reading.**Each property is advertised with Slide Shows and 360-degree Virtual Tours.*

Appletree Press Ltd, 14 Howard St South, Belfast, BT7 1AP Tel: (028) 9024 3074 Fax: (028) 9024 6756 E-mail: info@appletree.ie *Book publishers*

Applewade Packaging Ltd, Park House, 15-19 Greenhill CR, Watford, WD18 8PH Tel: (01923) 250202 Fax: (01923) 251101 E-mail: sales@applewade.co.uk *Packaging material manufrs*

▶ Appleworks Recruitment, Mack House, Aviation Court, Crawley, West Sussex, RH10 9RE Tel: (01293) 887709 E-mail: apple.works@virgin.net *Appleworks Recruitment Solutions are a Recruitment Provider specialising in placing Permanent Social Care, Childcare and Commercial, office based positions . We pride ourselves on providing the very best service to all our candidates. Our aim is to provide you with a personal yet professional service and take the hassle of job-hunting out of your hands. **Our dedicated consultants have an in depth knowledge of each sector and will spend time talking with you to establish your needs and actively talk to their clients on your behalf. **Appleworks work with local and national organisations, local governments, blue chip and private organisations and have new vacancies every day, across all sectors.**

The Appley Group, Teesport Works, Middlesbrough, Cleveland, TS6 6UF Tel: (01642) 446100 Fax: (01642) 467176 E-mail: orders@theappleygroup.co.uk *Cement manufrs*

Colin Appleyard Ltd, Worth Way, Keighley, West Yorkshire, BD21 5AJ Tel: (01535) 606311 Fax: (01535) 602585 E-mail: bikes@colinappleyard.co.uk *Motor cycle distributors*

Appleyard Lees, 15 Clare Road, Halifax, West Yorkshire, HX1 2HY Tel: (01422) 330110 Fax: (01422) 330090 E-mail: ip@appleyardlees.com *Chartered patent attorneys, european patent attorneys & european trade mark attorneys* Also at: Bolton, Burnley, Harrogate, Preston, Sheffield & Leeds

Appliance Care Ltd, 1 Swallow Units, Alphinbrook Road, Marsh Barton Trading Estate, Exeter, EX2 8QF Tel: (0871) 2006625 Fax: (01392) 258302 E-mail: steve@appliancecare.tv *Household electrical appliances*

▶ Appliance Testing London, 61 Cambridge Drive, London, SE12 8AG Tel: (0795) 1028089 Fax: E-mail: info@testin.co.uk *PAT TESTING LONDON. All pat testers are expected to be smart professional www.testin.co.uk and on time when pat testing london and kent. www.testin.co.uk When pat testing london, tests are expected to be done quickly and with as little inconvenience to the customer. pat testers in london . www.testin.co.uk portable appliance testing london . All portable appliance testers in london are expected to be smart www.testin.co.uk professional and on time when pat testing in london and kent. PAT TESTING LONDON PAT TESTING www.testin.co.uk LONDON PAT TESTING LONDON PAT TESTING LONDON PAT TESTING LONDON**

Application Solutions Ltd, The Riverside Centre, Railway Lane, Lewes, East Sussex, BN7 2AQ Tel: (01273) 476608 Fax: (01273) 478888 E-mail: sales@aslnet.co.uk *Electronic engineering & consultancy*

Application Specific Computers Ltd, Chapel Lane, Emley, Huddersfield, HD8 9ST Tel: (01924) 844600 Fax: (01924) 844606 *Computer software developers*

Applications Design Ltd, 91 Melciss Road, Wickersley, Rotherham, South Yorkshire, S66 2BU Tel: (01709) 543025 Fax: (01709) 543025 E-mail: appsdesign@btinternet.com *Computer consultancy*

Applications Engineering Ltd, 5 Horsted Square, Bellbrook Industrial Estate, Uckfield, East Sussex, TN22 1QG Tel: (01825) 764737 Fax: (01825) 768330 E-mail: info@appeng.co.uk Sales Contact: S. Banks *Distributors of switches including pressure, vacuum, float, temperature & flow*

▶ Applications Management Ltd, 11g Kingwood Road, Fulham, London, SW6 6SW Tel: (020) 7386 9916 Fax: (020) 7386 9916 E-mail: info@applicationsmanagement.com *Desktop application & information management services*

Applications Unlimited, 20 Glebe Road, Bedlington, Northumberland, NE22 6JT Tel: (01670) 824679 Fax: (01670) 823454 E-mail: sales@aucomputers.com *Computer distributors*

Applied Acoustic Engineering Ltd, 3 Marine House, Marine Park, Great Yarmouth, Norfolk, NR31 0NL Tel: (01493) 440355 Fax: (01493) 440720 E-mail: general@appliedacoustics.com *Electronic sub-sea survey & positioning equipment manufrs*

Applied Biosystems, Lingley House, 120 Birchwood Boulevard, Birchwood, Warrington, WA3 7QH Tel: (01925) 825650 Fax: (01925) 282502 E-mail: abdirect@eur.apliedbiosystems.com *Systems and services for life science research*

Applied Coating Technologies Ltd, Tipton Road, Tividale, Oldbury, West Midlands, B69 3HY Tel: 0121-557 5324 Fax: 0121-557 7064 E-mail: sales@applicoat.com *Conductive paint spraying applicators*

Applied Computer Services, Hunts End, Waterworks Lane, Martin, Dover, Kent, CT15 5JW Tel: (01304) 852772 Fax: (01304) 852772 E-mail: acsjohndyer@aol.com *Computer repairs & suppliers*

Applied Computer Solutions Ltd, 2 Thatched Cottages, Longford, Ashbourne, Derbyshire, DE6 3DR Tel: (01335) 330097 E-mail: enquires@acslimited.org *Computer network systems development & support*

Applied Containment Engineering Ltd, Unit 4, Shaw Cross Business Park, Dewsbury, West Yorkshire, WF12 7RF Tel: (01924) 455339 Fax: (01924) 452295 E-mail: applied.containment@ace-ltd.com Principal Export Areas: Worldwide *Manufacturers of isolation & process containment systems*

▶ Applied Cooling Systems Ltd, M2 Cody Court, Kansas Avenue, Salford, M50 2GE Tel: 0161-877 7262 Fax: 0161-877 7378

Applied Cytometry Systems, Unit 2 Brooklands Way, Brooklands Park Industrial Estate, Dinnington, Sheffield, S25 2JZ Tel: (01909) 566982 Fax: (01909) 561463 E-mail: acs@appliedcytometry.com *Cytometry instruments & software developers*

Applied Data Technologies, 92 Bedminster Parade, Bedminster, Bristol, BS3 4HL Tel: 0117-987 2170 Fax: 0117-941 0935 E-mail: sales@adtsystems.co.uk *Computer maintenance, repairs & distribution & telephone systems*

▶ Applied Design, 215a Worplesdon Road, Guildford, Surrey, GU2 9XJ Tel: (01483) 232678 Fax: (01483) 237991

Applied Design Group, Berberis House, 22 Hollowfields Way, Southcrest, Redditch, Worcestershire, B98 7NR Tel: (01527) 550474 E-mail: applieddesigngrp@btinternet.com *Architects & building design consultants*

Applied Drilling Systems Ltd, 18 Concorde Drive, Five C Business Centre, Clevedon, Avon, BS21 6UH Tel: (01275) 340763 Fax: (01275) 340765 *Woodworking machinery manufrs*

Applied Electronics, Onslow House, Magham Down, Hailsham, East Sussex, BN27 1PL Tel: (01323) 844709 Fax: (01323) 844725 *Computer consultants*

Applied Energy Products Ltd, PO Box 220, Peterborough, PE2 9JJ Tel: (01733) 456789 Fax: (01733) 310606 E-mail: joe.barrasso@applied-energy.com *Centrifugal fan & blower manufrs*

Applied Executive Selection Ltd, Shales House, 17-19 Mealcheapen St, Worcester, WR1 2DQ Tel: (01905) 23444 Fax: (01905) 23393 E-mail: info@aesco.co.uk *Executive recruitment consultants*

▶ Applied Fx, Unit 3, Blatchford Road, Horsham, West Sussex, RH13 5QR Tel: (01403) 280857 Fax: (01403) 280855 E-mail: julie@belsigns.com *Embroidery & printing company*

▶ Applied Generics, Pentlands Science Park, Bush Loan, Penicuik, Midlothian, EH26 0PZ Tel: (0870) 2403694

Applied Hoist Services, Meadows Abbey Meadows, Back Lane, Cotes, Loughborough, Leicestershire, LE12 5TA Tel: (01509) 212711 Fax: (01509) 212722 E-mail: enquire@menz.fsnet.co.uk *Hoist, crane sales & services*

Applied Holographics plc, 40 Phoenix Road, Washington, Tyne & Wear, NE38 0AD Tel: 0191-417 5434 Fax: 0191-417 6591 E-mail: sales@applied-holographics.com *Hologram label producers.*

Applied Imaging International Ltd, International Centre For Life Times Square, Scotswood Road, Newcastle upon Tyne, NE1 4EP Tel: 0191-202 3100 Fax: 0191-202 3101 E-mail: sales@aii.co.uk *Analysis equipment manufrs*

Applied Interactive Ltd, Cranfield Innovation Centre, University Way, Cranfield, Bedford, MK43 0BT Tel: (01234) 756050 Fax: (01234) 756138 E-mail: sales@applied-interactive.co.uk *Computer systems consultants, online training product suppliers*

▶ Applied It Solutions Ltd, Bury Farm, Mill Lane, Stotfold, Hitchin, Hertfordshire, SG5 4NY Tel: (01462) 732020 Fax: 01462 732120 E-mail: info@appliedisolutions.co.uk *Applied IT Solutions is an independent technology solution provider that specialises in meeting the technology needs of small to medium sized businesses. We have proven competency in the design, deployment and customisation of small-business solutions.*

Applied Labels, 4 Cronin Road, Weldon South Industrial Estate, Corby, Northamptonshire, NN18 8AQ Tel: (01536) 406572 Fax: (01536) 406972 E-mail: applied@btinternet.com *Self-adhesive label manufrs*

Applied Lettering, 2 Junction Road, Andover, Hampshire, SP10 3QT Tel: (01264) 357438 Fax: (01264) 357438 *Sign manufrs*

Applied Management Techniques, 33 Harts Leap Road, Sandhurst, Berkshire, GU47 8EW Tel: (01344) 773153 Fax: (01344) 776216 *Consultants & training to improve management, sales & service*

Applied Medical Technical Ltd, 4-5 Orwell Furlong, Cambridge, CB4 0WY Tel: (01223) 420415 Fax: (01223) 420797 E-mail: sales@applied-medical.co.uk *Medical & surgical supplies*

▶ Applied Metal Technology Ltd, 3 Ashfield Close Whitehall Industrial Estate, Whitehall Road, Leeds, LS12 5JB Tel: 0113-279 3708 Fax: 0113-279 3816

▶ Applied Minds Ltd, 48 New Brighton Road, Emsworth, Hampshire, PO10 7QR Tel: (01243) 371813 E-mail: info@appliedminds.co.uk *IT consultancy*

Applied Office Imaging Ltd, Moat Farm, Vicarage Road, Pitstone, Leighton Buzzard, Bedfordshire, LU7 9EY Tel: (01296) 661002 *Microfilm services*

Applied Photophysics, 203 Kingston Road, Leatherhead, Surrey, KT22 7PB Tel: (01372) 386537 Fax: (01372) 386477 E-mail: sales@photophysics.com *Scientific instrument manufrs*

Applied Polymer Technology Ltd, Unit 3 Great Western Court, Ashburton Industrial Estate, Ross-on-Wye, Herefordshire, HR9 7XP Tel: (01989) 764270 Fax: (01989) 764269 E-mail: enquiries@appliedpolytech.com *Polymer engineering services. Specialists in the design and manufacture of polymer systems and products for engineering applications, including **vibration control, *marine engineering, *sub-sea protection, *acoustic signature management.*

Applied Power Techniques Ltd, 7 Maundrell Road, Calne, Wiltshire, SN11 9PU Tel: (01249) 811888 Fax: (01249) 811888 *Rectifiers, transformers; power supplies, custom built; rectifiers (electrical) manufrs*

▶ Applied Precison Coatings Ltd, 1 Lessarna Court, Bowling Back Lane, Bradford, West Yorkshire, BD4 8ST Tel: (01274) 724897 Fax: (01274) 738306 *Metal heat treatment*

Applied Research & Development Ltd, Newfield, Newfield Mains Road, Dundonald, Kilmarnock, Ayrshire, KA2 9AW Tel: (01563) 850180 Fax: 01563 850180 *Electronics manufrs*

Applied Scintillation Technologies, Unit 7-8 Roydenbury Industrial Estate, Horsecroft Road, Harlow, Essex, CM19 5BZ Tel: (01279) 641234 Fax: (01279) 413679 E-mail: ast@appscintech.com *Radiation detector, fluorescent & scintillation manufrs*

Applied Shopfitting Ltd, Hamlyn House, Mardle Way, Buckfastleigh, Devon, TQ11 0NS Tel: (01364) 643855 Fax: (01364) 643888 E-mail: info@appliedshopfitting.co.uk *Joinery, shop fitting.*

Applied Spring Technology Ltd, Unit 8 Chapel Farm, Hartwell, Northampton, NN7 2EU Tel: 01908 511432 Fax: 01908 511432 E-mail: inbox@appliedspring.co.uk *Constant force springs*

Applied Technology Development, Unit K1 Valley Way, Market Harborough, Leicestershire, LE16 7PS Tel: (01858) 461014 Fax: (01858) 461015 E-mail: mail@atduk.com *Industrial ink-jet systems*

Applied Weighing International Ltd, Unit 5 Southview Park, Caversham, Reading, RG4 5AF Tel: 0118-946 1900 Fax: 0118-946 1862 E-mail: info@appliedweighing.co.uk *Weighing equipment manufrs*

Applinet, Unit 14 Thatcham Business Village, Colthrop Way, Thatcham, Berkshire, RG19 4LW Tel: (01635) 848900 Fax: (01635) 848920 E-mail: sales@applinet.co.uk *Voice & data systems integrators*

▶ Appoint Direct Ltd, PO Box 8828, Chelmsford, CM1 7WP Tel: (01245) 442777 Fax: (08456) 443005 E-mail: info@appointdirect.com *Appoint Direct allows job seekers to make applications directly to employers across many sectors throughout the United Kingdom. If you are seeking work why not use our vacancy search section to get started on your job hunt or register and submit your CV to receive free email alerts when suitable jobs and careers are posted to our site. All Job applications are guaranteed to go direct to the employers in box!*

▶ Appointments Direct Ltd, 62 Eden Road, Beckenham, Kent, BR3 4AT Tel: (020) 8402 2776 E-mail: rec@appointmentsdirect.com *Recruitment to Recruitment covering the UK.*

Appor Ltd, Duffield Road Industrial Estate, Little Eaton, Derby, DE21 5EG Tel: (01332) 832455 Fax: (01332) 834427 E-mail: info@appor.com Principal Export Areas: Worldwide *Hygiene product dispensing equipment manufrs*

▶ Approved Construction, Unit 5 Newcastle Enterprise Centre, High Street, Knutton, Newcastle, Staffordshire, ST5 6BX Tel: (01782) 799820 Fax: (01782) 799820 *We are specialists in all types of property maintenance, snag list repairs and are contractors to national house builders.*Members of the guild of builders & contractors.*

Approved Fire Appliances Ltd, Spinney Hill Road, Leicester, LE5 3GG Tel: 0116-276 8991 Fax: 0116-253 8017 E-mail: sales@approvedfire.co.uk *Fire equipment supply & service* Also at: Blackpool & Coventry

Approved Hydraulics Ltd, Brook Business Complex, Bennett Street, Manchester, M12 5AU Tel: 0161-273 1999 Fax: 0161-273 7979 E-mail: approvedhyd@aol.com *Hydraulic components/fittings distributors or agents; hydraulic engineers, installation or service; hydraulic equipment/systems maintenance/repair services & pumps. Also hydraulic power pack manufrs*

▶ Approved Services, 108 Calderglen Avenue, Blantyre, Glasgow, G72 9UN Tel: (0800) 0850295 Fax: (01698) 820444

Approved Services, 180 Long Chaulden, Hemel Hempstead, Hertfordshire, HP1 2JL Tel: (01442) 255081 Fax: (01442) 211185 *Pest control services*

Approved Welding Supplies, Hill Top Farm, 22 Main Street, South Croxton, Leicester, LE7 3RJ Tel: (01664) 840098 Fax: (01664) 840527 *Forklift truck suppliers*

Apreco Ltd, Bruff Works, Suckley, Worcester, WR6 5DR Tel: (01886) 884090 Fax: (01886) 884099 E-mail: info@apreco.co.uk *Pressure relief dampers, clean room & operating theatre manufrs*

▶ Apres Shower Dryers (UK) Ltd, Apres House, Woodhill Street, Bury, Lancashire, BL8 1AT Tel: 0161-761 7014 Fax: 0161-764 7013 E-mail: mike@apresshower.com *Manufacture the worlds only in-shower body-dryer*

Apri Ltd, 8-12 Orpheus Street, London, SE5 8RR Tel: (020) 7701 5494 Fax: (020) 7703 4223 *Garment manufrs*

Apricot Security Ltd, The Rearing Site, Oldbury Lane, Oldbury-on-Severn, Bristol, BS35 1RF Tel: (01454) 419204 Fax: (01454) 417311 E-mail: apricotsecurity@fsmail.net *Manufacture garage doors*

▶ Apricot Studio, 11 Charles CR, Drymen, Glasgow, G63 0BU Tel: (01360) 661028 E-mail: info@apricot-studios.com *Web design*

▶ APS Ltd, PO Box 12333, Birmingham, B43 6LL Tel: 0121-358 0581 Fax: 0121-358 1062 E-mail: pbenning@aradis.co.uk *Free quotations, niceci approved, part p approved, jib registered*

Aps Printers, 4a West Parade, Lincoln, LN1 1JT Tel: (01522) 525066 Fax: (01522) 525066 E-mail: info@apsprinters.co.uk *Commercial printers*

Aps Welding Services, 215 Kirk Road, Wishaw, Lanarkshire, ML2 7DD Tel: (01698) 361601 Fax: (01698) 292555 *Welding services & plastic injection repair*

Apsley Controls Ltd, Unit 14 Kents Avenue, Hemel Hempstead, Hertfordshire, HP3 9XH Tel: (01442) 235464 Fax: (01442) 249479 E-mail: martinturnbull@virgin.net *Electrical control panel manufrs*

Apsley Engineering, High Post, Salisbury, SP4 6AT Tel: (01722) 782488 Fax: (01722) 782632 E-mail: info@apsleyeng.co.uk *Precision engineers*

Apt Art, PO Box 250, Kidlington, Oxfordshire, OX5 2WA Tel: (01865) 372981 E-mail: sales@aptart.co.uk *Designers of brochures*

Apt Electric Ltd, Unit 2 Hopton Indust Estate, Hopton Road, Devizes, Wiltshire, SN10 2DX Tel: (01380) 739837 Fax: (01380) 739839

Aptec Metal Finishing Services, Southbrook Road, Eastern Avenue, Gloucester, GL4 3DN Tel: (01452) 300800 Fax: (01452) 500400 E-mail: admin@poeton.co.uk *Surface coating technology services*

Aptiva Ltd, Shapwick Road, Poole, Dorset, BH15 4AP Tel: (01202) 670597 Fax: (01202) 680789 E-mail: sales@aptiva.co.uk *Asbestos removal & thermal insulators*

Apuro Ltd, Unit 21a Monkspath Business Park, Highlands Road, Shirley, Solihull, West Midlands, B90 4NZ Tel: 0121-744 0968 Fax: 0121-744 0974 E-mail: enquiries@apuro.co.uk *Catering equipment suppliers*

Apv Films, 6 Alexandra Square, Chipping Norton, Oxfordshire, OX7 5HL Tel: (01608) 641798 Fax: (01608) 642177 E-mail: artworks@apvfilms.co.uk *Video producers*

▶ Aqata Ltd, Brookfield, Hinckley, Leicestershire, LE10 3DU Tel: (01455) 896500 Fax: (01455) 896501 E-mail: sales@aqata.co.uk *Manufacturer of luxury shower doors & enclosures*

▶ AQC, 9 Hartfield Road, Eastbourne, East Sussex, BN21 2AP Tel: 01323 720659 E-mail: info@a-q-c.co.uk *Dry Carpet Cleaning Using HOST Dry Extracton System, Wool Sisal Safely Cleaned,*

▶ Aqua Attention, 16 Orchard Way, North Bradley, Trowbridge, Wiltshire, BA14 0SU Tel: (01225) 754599 Fax: (01225) 777878 E-mail: sales@aquaattention.co.uk *Gas & oil boiler specialists covering South & S/West England with offices in Trowbridge (HQ) and Bristol. Genuine 24 hour, 7 days a week service with all work guaranteed.*

Aqua Bell Ltd, Brundall, Norwich, NR13 5PY Tel: (01603) 713013 *Marina moorings & marine engineers*

▶ Aqua Bio UK Ltd, Fenpark Industrial Estate, Park Lane, Stoke-on-Trent, ST4 3JP Tel: (01782) 593263 Fax: (01782) 593263

Aqua Blue Seafoods Ltd, Brookfield, Brook Lane, Westbury, Wiltshire, BA13 4EN Tel: (01373) 824242 Fax: (01373) 825566 E-mail: sales@aquablue.co.uk *Frozen Sea Foods*

Aqua Clenz Ltd, Unit 8-10 Chanters Industrial Estate, Tyldesley Old Road, Atherton, Manchester, M46 9BE Tel: (01942) 882664 Fax: (01942) 883733 *Drain repairs & cleaning*

Aqua Cure P.L.C, Aqua Cure House, Hall Street, Southport, Merseyside, PR9 0SE Tel: (01704) 501616 Fax: (01704) 544916 E-mail: sales@aquacure.plc.uk Principal Export Areas: Africa *Water filter/purification system manufrs*

Aqua Data Services Ltd, Unit 1 Townsend Court, Poulshot, Devizes, Wiltshire, SN10 1SD Tel: (01380) 828971 Fax: (01380) 828971 E-mail: sales@aqua-data.com *Water flow measurement systems manufrs*

Aqua Det Sales Co. Ltd, Bowles House, Blackthorne Road, Colnbrook, Slough, SL3 0AL Tel: (01753) 684282 Fax: (01753) 680305 *Manufacturers of janitorial & hygiene products*

▶ Aqua & Effluence Systems, Witham Friary, Frome, Somerset, BA11 5HA Tel: (01373) 836403 Fax: (01373) 836404

Aqua Engineering Systems, Unit 4 Whitefield Place, Morecambe, Lancashire, LA3 3EA Tel: (01524) 66512 Fax: (01524) 846397 *Water supplies, sewage & swimming pool engineers*

▶ Aqua Flow Drainage Services Ltd, Denton Farm, Lodge Lees, Denton, Canterbury, Kent, CT4 6NS Tel: (01227) 832626

▶ Aqua Force Plumbing Installations, 35 Highfield CR, Barlby, Selby, North Yorkshire, YO8 5HD Tel: (01757) 210136 E-mail: afpi@shoppers-pantry.com *Bathroom design & installation*

Aqua Free Ltd, 1 Avon Industrial Estate, Butlers Leap, Rugby, Warwickshire, CV21 3UY Tel: (01788) 561221 Fax: (01788) 560663 E-mail: info@aquafree.com *Waterless urinal suppliers & maintenance*

▶ Aqua Gas, Unit 300, 405 Kings Road, London, SW10 0BB Tel: (020) 7351 0000

Aqua Heat Ltd, Unit 33 Three Elms Trading Estate, Hereford, HR4 9PU Tel: (01432) 340111 Fax: (01432) 271888 *Plumbing & heating*

▶ Aqua Heat State Sales, 61-67 Commercial Road, Southampton, SO15 1GG Tel: (023) 8057 1107 Fax: (023) 8057 7965 E-mail: enquiries@state-waterheaters.co.uk *Direct fired storage water heater manufrs*

Aqua Home Pools Marketing Ltd, Oteley Road, Shrewsbury, SY2 6QW Tel: (01743) 235081 Fax: (01743) 271043 E-mail: enquiry@aquahome.com *Distribution & installation of home pools & bars*

▶ Aqua Marine Ltd, Units 14 & 15 Penton Hook Marina, Staines Road, Chertsey, Surrey, KT16 8PY Tel: 01932 570202 Fax: 01932 570222 E-mail: info@aquamarineuk.com

Aqua Marine Chemicals Ltd, Unit 6 Strensham Business Park, Strensham, Worcester, WR8 9JZ Tel: (01684) 290077 Fax: (01684) 290608 E-mail: laura@bayer-wood.co.uk *Chemicals for boilers & cooling towers*

Aqua Marine Chemicals Ltd, Unit 6 Strensham Business Park, Strensham, Worcester, WR8 9JZ Tel: (01684) 290077 Fax: (01684) 290608 E-mail: aquamarine@btconnect.com *Suppliers of chemicals*

Aqua Mechanical Services Ltd, Aqua House, Rose & Crown Road, Swavesey, Cambridge, CB4 5RB Tel: (01954) 230948 Fax: (01954) 230593 E-mail: group@aqua.co.uk *Mechanical & electrical building services* Also at: Ruislip

▶ Aqua Pacific Ltd, 87A Warwick Street, Leamington Spa, Warwickshire, CV32 4RJ Tel: (01926) 339100 Fax: (01926) 889134 *Computer software suppliers*

Aqua Process Engineering Ltd, Aqua House, 27 Denison Road, London, SW19 2DJ Tel: (020) 8543 3647 Fax: (020) 8543 2163 E-mail: enquiries@aquaprocess.com *Swimming pool filtration systems & service*

▶ Aqua Rentals, 2 Silkwood Court, Ossett, West Yorkshire, WF5 9TP Tel: (01924) 237440 Fax: (01924) 237441 E-mail: enquiries@aquarentals.co.uk *Rent aquariums*

▶ Aqua Serve, 13 Pinewood, Somerton, Somerset, TA11 6JW Tel: (01458) 272444 Fax: (01458) 272444 E-mail: clive@aqua-serve.co.uk *Water softener, filters treatment services, legionella control*

Aqua Servicing Incorporating Thinktanks, 13 Ponsonby Place, London, SW1P 4PS Tel: (020) 7821 6489 *Aquarium & pond suppliers*

Aqua Signal & Telegraphic Systems Ltd, Belmont House, Garnett Place, Skelmersdale, Lancashire, WN8 9UB Tel: (01695) 51933 Fax: (01695) 51891 *GRP & PVC fabricators*

Aqua Soft Services, Downland, The Vale, Chalfont St. Peter, Gerrards Cross, Buckinghamshire, SL9 9SD Tel: (01753) 885551 Fax: (01753) 885551 *Water softening services*

Aqua Spring Ltd, 177 Kingston Road, Leatherhead, Surrey, KT22 7NX Tel: (01372) 373023 Fax: (01372) 360003 E-mail: sales@aquaspring.co.uk *Water softener manufrs*

Aqua Status Waterbed Centre, 112 Lower Dock Street, Newport, Gwent, NP20 2AF Tel: (01633) 842777 Fax: (01633) 842777 E-mail: waterbeds@aquastatus.co.uk *Bed manufrs*

Aqua Varium, 1 The Green, Ware, Hertfordshire, SG12 0QW Tel: (01920) 464442 Fax: (01920) 464442 *Aquaria suppliers*

▶ Aqua Warehouse, Unit 2, Rignals Lane, Chelmsford, CM2 8RE Tel: (0845) 4024303 Fax: (0845) 4024304 E-mail: richard@aquawarehouse.co.uk *Importers & Distributors to the Pool & Spa Trade. The Voyager Spa, The ECO spas, Sevylor Inflatables, Spazazz, Aquachek Test Strips*

Aqua-Air Ltd, 219 Ashley Road, Hale, Altrincham, Cheshire, WA15 9SZ Tel: 0161-926 9595 Fax: 0161-929 7345 E-mail: sales@aqua-air.co.uk *Vacuum cleaner manufacturers & distributors*

Aquablast Blast Cleaning, Crutched Friars, Little Whelnetham, Bury St. Edmunds, Suffolk, IP30 0UH Tel: (01284) 388700 Fax: (01284) 388701 E-mail: sales@aquablast.uk.com *Blast cleaning contractors*

▶ Aquabrand Bathrooms Ltd, 16 Spinnaker Quay, Plymouth, PL9 9SA Tel: (01752) 223645 Fax: 0870 758 5877 E-mail: markthomas@aquabrand.com *Aquabrand. The Hansgrohe Specialists. Aquabrand are the only company in the bathroom industry to specialise purely in Hansgrohe products.*

Aquabuild Ltd, Woodland Dell, Byers Lane, South Godstone, Godstone, Surrey, RH9 8JH Tel: (01342) 893519 Fax: (01342) 892933 E-mail: aquabuild@yahoo.co.uk *Pool construction, service & maintenance*

Aquacadabra Aquarium & Pond Supplies, 100 Barnehurst Road, Bexleyheath, Kent, DA7 6HG Tel: (01322) 345242 Fax: (01322) 335031 *Aquarium & pond suppliers*

▶ Aquacair Ltd, 40 Parklands Road, Chichester, West Sussex, PO19 3DT Tel: (01243) 790808 Fax: (01243) 790809 E-mail: sales@aquacair.co.uk *Asbestos consultancy*

Aquacare services, 7 Austin cottages, Potters gate, Farnham, Surrey, GU9 7BA Tel: 01252 711126 E-mail: mike@aquacareservices.co.uk *Aquacare services specialise in the maintenance, upgrade & repair of sewage treatment systems.*

Aquachemix Ltd, PO Box 1, Dunstable, Bedfordshire, LU5 6HX Tel: (01525) 872432 Fax: (01525) 872210 *Water treatment equipment distributors*

Aquaculture Holdings Ltd, 24 26 Gold Street, Saffron Walden, Essex, CB10 1EJ Tel: (01799) 28167 Fax: (01799) 25546 E-mail: spaquaculture@spcorp.com *Veterinary sales*

Aquadition Ltd, 220 Copnor Road, Copnor, Portsmouth, PO3 5DA Tel: (023) 9269 1035 Fax: (023) 9261 8200 E-mail: sales@aquadition.co.uk *Water treatment equipment & services*

Aquaduct Systems, Cambridge Street, Ashton-under-Lyne, Lancashire, OL7 0RJ Tel: 0161-339 8828 Fax: 0161-301 5394 E-mail: aquaduct@ukonline.co.uk *Rainwater goods manufrs*

Aquafan Cooling Towers Ltd, 47 Down St, West Molesey, Surrey, KT8 2SY Tel: (020) 8941 4378 *Cooling tower manufrs*

Aquafax Ltd, Unit 14 Dencora Way, Sundon Business Park, Luton, LU3 3HP Tel: (01582) 568700 Fax: (01582) 583913 E-mail: sales@aquafax.co.uk *Marine pumps & engineering equipment distributors*

▶ Aquafern Products, Unit 8, Chapel Lane, Hadleigh, Essex, SS7 2PP Tel: (01702) 551044 Fax: (01702) 551044 *Wholesalers of aquariums*

Aquafibre Mouldings Ltd, Wendover Road, Rackheath Industrial Estate, Rackheath, Norwich, NR13 6LH Tel: (01603) 720651 Fax: (01603) 720654 E-mail: info@aquafibre.co.uk *Glass fibre reinforced plastic moulders*

▶ Aquafirm Heat Transfer Ltd, Racecourse Road, Pershore, Worcestershire, WR10 2EY Tel: (01386) 552251 Fax: (01386) 561948 *Heat exchangers*

Aquaflex Ltd, 1 Edison Road, Salisbury, SP2 7NU Tel: (01722) 328873 Fax: (01722) 413068 E-mail: info@aquaflex.co.uk *PVC bespoke fabrication services*

Aquaflow Ltd, Onneley Works, Newcastle Road, Woore, Crewe, CW3 9RU Tel: (01630) 647111 Fax: (01630) 647734 E-mail: response@aquaflowvalves.com *Waterwork valve manufrs*

Aqua-Gas Avk Ltd, P O Box 143, Northampton, NN4 7ZU Tel: (01604) 601188 Fax: (01604) 604818 E-mail: info@aquagas.co.uk *Valve & pipeline fittings manufrs*

Aqua-Gas Manufacturing Ltd, Arnsley Road, Weldon North Industrial Estate, Corby, Northamptonshire, NN17 5QW Tel: (01536) 275910 Fax: (01536) 204256 E-mail: fran.brody@agmc.co.uk *Valve & fittings manufrs*

Aquaglow Waterbeds, 145 Fox Lane, Leyland, PR25 1HE Tel: (01772) 452462 Fax: (01772) 460669 E-mail: info@aquaglowwaterbeds.co.uk *Waterbed & water accessory distributors*

Aquaid, 22 New Lane, Burscough, Ormskirk, Lancashire, L40 8JA Tel: (01704) 891344 Fax: (01704) 891599 *Water cooler retailers*

▶ Aquaid Liverpool, Bridle Way, Bootle, Merseyside, L30 4UJ Tel: 0151-525 6006 Fax: 0151-525 6116 E-mail: aquaid.liverpool@btconnect.com *Water cooler distributor*

▶ Aquaid (Midlands & South Wales), 36 Bidavon Industrial Estate, Waterloo Road, Bidford-on-Avon, Alcester, Warwickshire, B50 4JW Tel: (01789) 778345 Fax: (01789) 772314 *Water cooler industrial suppliers*

▶ Aquaid North London, Unit 9a Rosebery Industrial Park, Rosebery Avenue, London, N17 9SR Tel: (020) 8801 9789 Fax: (020) 8801 9678 *Water coolers suppliers*

Aquaid South Kent, Eythorne Courtshepherdswell Roadeythorne, Eythorne, Dover, Kent, CT15 4AD Tel: (01304) 831122 Fax: (01304) 832244 *Water cooler distributors*

Aquajoy Aquarium & Pond Supplies, 31 Lower Morden Lane, Morden, Surrey, SM4 4SE Tel: (020) 8337 7373 Fax: (020) 8337 7373 E-mail: enquiries@aquajoy.co.uk *Maintenance & construction services of ponds*

▶ Aquajoy Bathlifts Ltd, Consett Business Park, Villa Real, Consett, County Durham, DH8 6BP Tel: (01207) 501555 Fax: (01207) 599789 E-mail: info@aqua-joy.com *Suppliers of bath lifts of all ages*

▶ Aquakem Technology Ltd, 6 The Elms, Tallarn Green, Malpas, Cheshire, SY14 7HY Tel: (0870) 0887051 Fax: (0870) 0887052 E-mail: aquakem@btinternet.com *Manufacture test kits to analyse water*

▶ Aqualeader Ltd, Sweet Five, 16 Wilbury Gardens, Hove, East Sussex, BN3 6HY Tel: (01273) 299685 Fax: (01273) 377903 *Water coolers suppliers*

▶ Aqualease Ltd, Wigan Road, Leyland, PR25 5XW Tel: (0845) 3905904 E-mail: info@aqualease.co.uk *Large acrylic display systems, acrylic fish tanks suppliers*

▶ Aqua-Leisure International Ltd, The Tannery, Queen Street, Gomshall, Surrey, GU5 9LY Tel: (0870) 4050600 Fax: (0870) 4050601 E-mail: info@aqua-leisure.co.uk *Suppliers of to the aquatic leisure industry*

Aqualift Ltd, Meeting Lane, Brierley Hill, West Midlands, DY5 3LB Tel: (01384) 77255 Fax: (01384) 77254 E-mail: sales@aqualift.co.uk *Ships tackle manufrs*

▶ Aqua-Light, 21 Favourite Road, Whitstable, Kent, CT5 4UB Tel: (01227) 282130 E-mail: info@aqua-light.co.uk *Installation of domestic irrigation & low voltage lighting systems*

▶ Aqualine Services Ltd, 59 Wassand Street, Kingston Upon Hull, Hull, HU3 4AL Tel: (01482) 657709 Fax: (01482) 655777

Aqualisa Products Ltd, Westerham Trade Centre, The Flyers Way, Westerham, Kent, TN16 1DE Tel: (01959) 560000 Fax: (01959) 560030 E-mail: marketing@aqualisa.co.uk *Shower manufrs*

Aqualogic, Brighton Street, Wallasey, Merseyside, CH44 6QJ Tel: 0151-638 6111 Fax: 0151-638 6777 E-mail: info@aqualogic-wc.com *Water conservation equipment manufrs*

Aqualona Products, 50 Moxon Street, Barnet, Hertfordshire, EN5 5TS Tel: (020) 8449 7321 Fax: (020) 8449 7496 E-mail: sales@aqualona.com *Bathroom product manufrs*

▶ Aquamagic, 30 Cambridge Crescent, Rotherham, South Yorkshire, S65 2RB Tel: (01709) 376222 Fax: 07092 877608 E-mail: dene@aquamagicuk.co.uk *Aquamagic are carpet and upholstery cleaners operating in Rotherham, Sheffield and South Yorkshire, we also offer stain removal, anti allergen treatments, and free advise.*

Aquamarine, 216 Fair Oak Road, Eastleigh, Hampshire, SO50 8HU Tel: (023) 8060 0473 Fax: (023) 8060 1381 E-mail: admin@aqua-marine.co.uk *Marine equipment distributors*

Aquamat Ltd, Unit 8g Chalford Industrial Estate, Chalford, Stroud, Gloucestershire, GL6 8NT Tel: (01453) 884411 Fax: (01453) 884499 E-mail: admin@aquamatcovers.co.uk *Swimming pool covers & rollers*

Aquamatic, PO Box 117, Godalming, Surrey, GU8 4FF Tel: (01483) 861598 *Water treatment*

Aquamatic Ltd, Mayfield Industrial Park, Liverpool Road, Irlam, Manchester, M44 6GD Tel: 0161-777 6607 Fax: 0161-777 6617 E-mail: admin@aquamatic.ltd.uk *Waste water samplers manufrs*

Aquamatic Irrigation, Stanroyd Mill, Cotton Tree, Colne, Lancashire, BB8 7BW Tel: (01282) 873322 Fax: (01282) 870904 E-mail: irrigation@lbs-group.co.uk *Irrigation systems distributors*

Aquamix Water Purification, 20 Orville St, St. Helens, Merseyside, WA9 3JJ Tel: (01744) 816990 Fax: (01744) 816990 *Water purification*

Aquapets, 17 Leeland Rd, London, W13 9HH Tel: 020 85672748 *Pet supplies*

Aquaplan, South Cadleigh House, Beech Road, Ivybridge, Devon, PL21 9HN Tel: (01752) 892908 Fax: (01752) 892908 *Swimming pool contractors & suppliers*

▶ Aquapoint Ltd, 9 Rye Close, York Road Business Park, Malton, North Yorkshire, YO17 6YD Tel: (08700) 555333 Fax: (08700) 555600 E-mail: sales@aquapoint.co.uk *Aquapoint Limited provide a range of bottled water coolers and plumbed in water coolers for businesses in the Yorkshire, Humberside and Teesside area.*

Aquapure Water Treatment Equipment, 9 Richmond Mansions, Denton Road, Twickenham, TW1 2HH Tel: (020) 8892 9010 Fax: (020) 8892 9010 E-mail: info@aquapure.co.uk *Water Purifcation & Water Treatment Equipment Supplier*

Aquarest Bedding & Blankets, 86 Holden Road, Brierfield, Nelson, Lancashire, BB9 5PR Tel: (01282) 698671 Fax: (07005) 802409 *Waterbed retail suppliers & manufrs*

Aquaria Aquarium & Pond Supplies, 335 Hollinwood Avenue, Manchester, M40 0JA Tel: 0161-681 6731 *Aquarium suppliers*

▶ Aquarians, 40 Bushby Close, Lancing, West Sussex, BN15 9JW Tel: (01903) 755978 *Bathroom & Kitchen Planning and Installation Services.*Sussex, London & Hampshire.*All works guaranteed - Quality Makes The Difference.*

Aquarium Design Centre, 476 Paisley Road, Glasgow, G5 8RE Tel: 0141-429 0044 Fax: 0141-429 0044 E-mail: aquariumdesigncentre@hotmail.com *Tropical fish suppliers*

▶ AquariumHire.co.uk, PO Box 156, Sevenoaks, Kent, TN15 0WA Tel: (01732) 760991 Fax: (01732) 760992 E-mail: goldfish@aquariumhire.co.uk *Aquarium sales hire maintenance & purchasing*

Aquarius Back Care, The Old Dairy, Broom Hill, Bristol, BS16 1DN Tel: 0117-965 8555 Fax: 0117-965 8444 E-mail: info@backcare.co.uk *Specialist back care equipment*

Aquarius Engineering Ltd, 52 Bergen Way, North Lynn Industrial Estate, King's Lynn, Norfolk, PE30 2JG Tel: (01553) 771716 Fax: (01553) 765164 E-mail: aquarius.eng@easynet.co.uk *Stainless steel fabricators*

▶ Aquarius Paint & Lacquer, Granary Buildings, Eastgate Street, North Elmham, Dereham, Norfolk, NR20 5HF Tel: (07752) 602789 Fax: (01362) 860793 E-mail: aquariuspaintandlacquer@yahoo.co.uk *Furniture finishing & paint spraying services*

Aquarius Press, Aquarius House, Montpelier Business Park, Leacon Road, Ashford, Kent, TN23 4FG Tel: (01233) 662544 Fax: (01233) 662577 E-mail: sales@aquarius.invictornet.co.uk *General printers*

Aquarius Software, The Purlins, Black Robin Lane, Kingston, Canterbury, Kent, CT4 6HR Tel: (01227) 830131 E-mail: aquariussoft@freeuk.com *Computer software for bakeries*

Aquascan International Ltd, Aquascan House, Hill Street, Newport, Gwent, NP20 1LZ Tel: (01633) 841117 Fax: (01633) 254829 E-mail: info@aquascan.co.uk *Sub sea & underwater locating services & manometer manufrs*

Aquascapes, 153 Cardinal Avenue, Morden, Surrey, SM4 4ST Tel: (020) 8337 9880 Fax: (020) 8330 1069 *Water garden specialists*

Aquascutum International Ltd, Ibex House, 42-47 Minories, London, EC3N 1DY Tel: (020) 7675 9050 Fax: (020) 7675 9099 E-mail: john.harper@aquascutum.co.uk *Clothing manufrs*

▶ Aquashoe Ltd, Unit 25 Lamberhurst Farm, Dargate, Faversham, Kent, ME13 9EP Tel: (01227) 752752 Fax: (01227) 752750 *Distributors of sports goods, equipment & accessories*

Aquasource (UK) Ltd, 12 Oaktree Place, Marsh Barton Trading Estate, Matford Business Park, Exeter, EX2 8WA Tel: (01392) 822155 Fax: (01392) 822151 E-mail: info@aquasource.co.uk *Health food products distributors*

Aquaspersions Ltd, Beacon Hill Road, Halifax, West Yorkshire, HX3 6AQ Tel: (01422) 386200 Fax: (01422) 386239 E-mail: info@aquaspersions.co.uk *Emulsion manufrs*

Aquastat West, Hillgate House, Bridgwater Road, Bleadon, Weston-super-Mare, Avon, BS24 0BA Tel: (01934) 811264 Fax: (01934) 811394 *Water hygiene services*

Aquatec, 7 Russell Avenue, Weymouth, Dorset, DT4 9RA Tel: (01305) 776037 Fax: (01305) 769977 E-mail: info@aquatec.co.uk *Sub aqua diving accessory manufrs*

▶ Aquatec Coatings Ltd, Rock Road, Rhosymedre, Wrexham, Clwyd, LL14 3YF Tel: (01978) 822881 Fax: (01978) 821169 E-mail: sales@aquatecpaint.co.uk *Industrial paint manufrs*

Aquatec Consultancy Services Ltd, Pocket Nook Lane, Lowton, Warrington, WA3 1AB Tel: (01942) 603268 Fax: (01942) 261521 E-mail: info@aquatecchemicalservices.com *Effluent treatment systems manufrs*

Aquatec Electronics Ltd, High Street, Hartley Wintney, Hook, Hampshire, RG27 8NY Tel: (01252) 843072 Fax: (01252) 843074 E-mail: sales@aquatec.org.uk *Electronic & software manufacturing engineers*

▶ Aquatic Control Engineering Ltd, Main Street, Rampton, Retford, Nottinghamshire, DN22 0HR Tel: (01777) 249080 Fax: (01777) 249069 E-mail: info@aquaticcontrol.co.uk *Suppliers of kwt flow control range*

Aquatic Design Centre, 107-109 Great Portland Street, London, W1W 6QG Tel: (020) 7580 6764 Fax: (020) 7631 2033 E-mail: nick@aquaticdesign.co.uk *Design, install & manufacture aquariums*

Aquatic Discount Centre, 1a Haydock Street, Newton-le-Willows, Merseyside, WA12 9AB Tel: (01925) 291439 Fax: (01925) 291439 *Aquarium & pond suppliers*

Aquatic Engineering & Construction Ltd, Palmerston Centre, 29-31 Palmerston Road, Aberdeen, AB11 5QP Tel: (01224) 573359 Fax: (01224) 577361 E-mail: admin@aquatic.co.uk *Provision of technical manpower, in house engineering and specialised pipelay equipment for flexibles and umbilicals for the oil and gas industry worldwide.*

Aquatic Style, Wyndham CR, Cardiff, CF11 9EH Tel: (029) 2064 4519

▶ Aquatic Systems Ltd, PO Box 330, Blackburn, BB2 3XX Tel: (01254) 278807 Fax: (01254) 278914 *Pet shops display systems and acrylic tanks. Acrylic aquariums stands and canopys. large bespoke aquariums. Custom design acrylic aquariums*

Aquatide Ltd, 26 Hewell Road, Redditch, Worcestershire, B97 6AN Tel: (01527) 592777 Fax: (01527) 592888 *Water treatment equipment & service*

Aquatools Ltd, 54 Chapel Street, Tipton, West Midlands, DY4 8JB Tel: 0121-520 7978 Fax: 0121-522 2051 E-mail: sales@aquatools.co.uk *Press tool manufrs*

▶ Aquator Water Coolers, Unit 8, Packhorse Place, Watling Street, Kensworth, Dunstable, Bedfordshire, LU6 3QL Tel: (01582) 842828 Fax: (01582) 842727 *Water cooler units.*

Aquatreat Group Ltd, Stanley House, 9 Bunting Close, Mitcham, Surrey, CR4 4ND Tel: (020) 8401 8391 Fax: (020) 8401 8392 E-mail: mailbox@aquatreat.uk.com *Chemical suppliers for water treatment services*

Aquila Computer Services Ltd, 8-11 Waveney Road, Lowestoft, Suffolk, NR32 1BN Tel: (01502) 562555 Fax: (01502) 538149 E-mail: enquiries@aquila.uk.com *Website designs*

Aquila Shelters Ltd, Claremont House, St Georges Road, Bolton, BL1 2BY Tel: (01204) 522424 Fax: (01204) 365110 E-mail: sales@aquila-shelters.co.uk *Tensile structures*

▶ Aquila Switchgear Ltd, The Industrial Estate, Enterprise Way, Edenbridge, Kent, TN8 6HF Tel: (01732) 868138 Fax: (01732) 867101

Aquila Systems, Aquila House, 283 Laygate, South Shields, Tyne & Wear, NE33 4QN Tel: 0191-455 9440 Fax: 0191-456 1259 E-mail: sales@aquilasystems.co.uk *Rebuild computer upgraders*

▶ Aquilar Ltd, Dial Post Court, Horsham Road, Rusper, Horsham, West Sussex, RH12 4QX Tel: (01293) 871874 Fax: (01293) 871717 E-mail: jwaumsley@aquilar.co.uk *Fuel oils, chemical, gas & refrigerant gas leak detection alarm systems*

▶ Aquilegia, 2 Grange Close, Hartlepool, Cleveland, TS26 0DU Tel: (01429) 423165 *Aquilegia Photographic provide a photography service to PR public relations companies, editorial support to newspapers & magazines, and photographs to corporate, lifestyle, wedding, portrait sport, news & event photography throughout Cleveland, Durham, Tyne & Wear, Northumberland Durham & North Yorkshire. 27 years experience photographing royals, national politicians, top models, high society weddings, magazine features & d public relations campaigns and business and event photography.*All inclusive prices our speciality. Quality with no compromise - fully digital from top to bottom.*

Aqute Ltd, 500 Chiswick High Road, London, W4 5RG Tel: (020) 8956 2505 Fax: (020) 8956 2504 E-mail: info@aqute.co.uk *IT recruitment services*

Ar Computing, 8 Friday Street, Minehead, Somerset, TA24 5UA Tel: (01643) 707381 Fax: (01643) 707431 E-mail: enquiries@arcomputing.co.uk *Computer services*

Ar Fabrications Ltd, 21 Rigg Street, Stewarton, Kilmarnock, Ayrshire, KA3 5AG Tel: (01560) 483777 Fax: (01560) 483777 *Structure steel & general fabrication*

Arabesque, 2 Rodney Way, Guildford, Surrey, GU1 2NY Tel: (01483) 825949 E-mail: j_langridge@yahoo.co.uk *Electronic consultants & designers*

Arabesque, 302-304 Westborough Road, Westcliff-on-Sea, Essex, SS0 9PX Tel: (01702) 333244 Fax: (01702) 331066 *Sportswear manufrs*

Aram Picture Framing, 8 Turnham Green Terrace, London, W4 1QP Tel: (020) 8994 8844 Fax: (020) 8994 8844 *Picture framing services*

Aramark Ltd, Caledonia House Lawnswood Business Park, Redvers Close, Leeds, LS16 6QY Tel: 0113-230 5300 Fax: (0870) 1118199 E-mail: client-care@aramark.co.uk *Contract caterers*

▶ Aran Construction, Tarporley Road, Stretton, Warrington, WA4 4NB Tel: (01925) 860002 Fax: (01925) 860101

▶ Aran Proplan, Aran House, Old Tarporley Road, Stretton, Warrington, WA4 4NB Tel: 01925 860002 Fax: 01925 860101 E-mail: a.newton@arangroup.com *Planning consultancy.*Building plans drawn for extensions, alterations and new build to domestic commercial and industrial properties.*Planning and building regulations submittal to the local authority.*Spacial planning.**

Arasco Auto Products Corp, 185 Sunningvale Ave, Biggin Hill, Westerham, Kent, TN16 3TL Tel: (01959) 565535 Fax: (01959) 573131 *Import of car care products*

Araywelds Mobile Services, 6 Flanders Road, London, E6 6DU Tel: (07885) 431727 Fax: (020) 8507 7056 *Mobile welding services*

Arb Sales, 13 School Street, Hazel Grove, Stockport, Cheshire, SK7 4RA Tel: 0161-483 9661 Fax: 0161-483 6160 E-mail: sales.arb@ntlworld.com *Engineers merchants, compressor suppliers & welding supplies*

Arba Engineering, 32g Heming Road, Redditch, Worcestershire, B98 0DH Tel: (01527) 520629 Fax: (01527) 520629 E-mail: arba32g@hotmail.com *Precision engineers & quality pressings*

▶ Arbarr Electronics, Unit 14c Rathenraw Industrial Estate, Antrim, BT41 2SJ Tel: (028) 9442 9333 Fax: (028) 9442 6178 E-mail: johnpaul@arbarr.co.uk *Electronics design & assembly service*

Arbarr Electronics Ltd, 2 Kilgavanagh Road, Antrim, BT41 2LJ Tel: (028) 9442 9334 Fax: (028) 9442 9178 E-mail: enquiries@arbarr.co.uk *Electronic designers & manufrs*

Arbel Electronics, Dyffryn, Rosebush, Clynderwen, Dyfed, SA66 7RH Tel: (01437) 532266 Fax: (01437) 532488 E-mail: arbel@arbelelectronics.co.uk *Electronics manufrs*

▶ Arbell Ltd, Vickers House Vickers Business Centre, Priestley Road, Basingstoke, Hampshire, RG24 9NP Tel: (01256) 810100 Fax: (01256) 486588 E-mail: enquiries@arbell.co.uk *Telephone Answering Services*Message Taking Services*Sales /Order Taking Services*Virtual Reception*FREE 1 WEEK TRIAL OFFER*

Arben Sheet Metal Ltd, 204 Bedford Avenue, Slough Trading Estate, Slough, SL1 4RY Tel: (01753) 531066 Fax: (01753) 694724 E-mail: arben@globalnet.co.uk *Sheet metalwork precision engineers*

▶ Arbico Computers, 120 Franciscan Road, London, SW17 8HL Tel: (020) 8772 4090 Fax: (020) 8772 4090 E-mail: info@arbico.co.uk *Computer hardware retailers*

Arbiter Group Ltd, 2nd Floor, Atlantic House, Stirling Way, Borehamwood, London, Hertfordshire, WD6 2BT Tel: (020) 8207 7860 Fax: (020) 8953 6221 E-mail: sales@arbitergroup.com *Musical instrument suppliers*

Arboga Darenth Ltd, Darenth Works, Ray Lamb Way, Erith, Kent, DA8 2LA Tel: (01322) 342533 Fax: (01322) 331226 E-mail: info@arbogadarenth.co.uk *Filtration & swarf equipment manufrs*

Arboret, 16 Fritchley Close, Huncote, Leicester, LE9 3AR Tel: 0116-286 6897 Fax: 0116-286 6897 E-mail: arboret@btconnect.com *Temperature sensors & control equipment*

▶ Arborplant Ltd, The Log House, Kiln Lane, Henley-on-Thames, Oxfordshire, RG9 4EN Tel: 0118-940 4739 Fax: 0118-940 4739 *Machine hire*

▶ Arbory Group Ltd, Holker Business Centre, Burnley Road, Colne, Lancashire, BB8 8EG Tel: (0870) 0802322 Fax: (0870) 0802325 E-mail: sales@arborygroup.co.uk *Designers & manufacturers of quality GRP (fibreglass) products.*

Arbour Engineering Ltd, Unit 23, West Station Yard Industrial Estate, Spital Road, Maldon, Essex, CM9 6TS Tel: (01621) 857320 Fax: (01621) 874609 *Sheet metalworkers*

Arbour Tech Ltd, Kingsland, Leominster, Herefordshire, HR6 9SF Tel: (01568) 708840 Fax: (01568) 708974 E-mail: enquiries@arbourtech.com *Designers and manufacturers of water treatment plant, systems and units. Utilising ultrafiltration, reverse osmosis, ultraviolet light sterilisation, ionisation for treatment of domestic and industrial water treatment and reclaimation.*

Arbra Instruments, Advance Park, Park Road, Rhosymedre, Wrexham, Clwyd, LL14 3YR Tel: (01978) 823900 Fax: (01978) 822913 E-mail: sales@aslgroup.uk *Exploders, mining accessories & ohmmeters specialists*

The Arbroath Fishermens Association Ltd, 2 Marketgate, Arbroath, Angus, DD11 1AY Tel: (01241) 873132 Fax: (01241) 875442 *Ship chandlers*

Arbscapes, Rawreth Lodge, Church Road, Rawreth, Wickford, Essex, SS11 8SG Tel: (01268) 560006 Fax: (01268) 733251 E-mail: info@arbscapes.co.uk *Plant hire, treework & landscaping services*

Arbuckle Smith & Co., 106 Abercorn Street, Paisley, Renfrewshire, PA3 4AY Tel: (0141) 887 5252 Fax: (0141) 887 4461 E-mail: craig_hodgson@zieglergroup.com *Freight forwarding agents*

Arburg Ltd, Tachbrook Park Drive, Warwick, CV34 6RH Tel: (01926) 457000 Fax: (01926) 457030 E-mail: uk@arburg.com *Injection moulding machinery distributors*

▶ Arbury Tools & Equipment Ltd, Whitacre Road, Industrial Estate, Nuneaton, Warwickshire, CV11 6BY Tel: (024) 7638 4896 Fax: (024) 7638 4896 E-mail: ronsinfo1@yahoo.co.uk *SALES OF SOFT CHUCK JAWS.*NEW AND USED MAHINERY FOR THE*UPVC WINDOW AND DOOR MANUFACTURE,*AND ENGINEERING TRADES.***

Arbutus, Unit 14 The Bridgeway Centre, Bridge Road, Wrexham Industrial Estate, Wrexham, Clwyd, LL13 9QS Tel: (01978) 661572 Fax: (01978) 661572 E-mail: jon@arbutus-watch.co.uk *Watch distributor/sales*

Arc, Western House, 7 Knutsford Road, Wilmslow, Cheshire, SK9 6JA Tel: (01625) 543430 Fax: (01625) 543431 E-mail: sales@arcit.co.uk *Computer transportation storage services*

▶ Arc Colourprint, 16 Timber Bush, Edinburgh, EH6 6QH Tel: 0131-553 1707

▶ Arc Construction Ltd, 14 Lower Green Road, Tunbridge Wells, Kent, TN4 8TE Tel: (01892) 514035 Fax: (01892) 616553

▶ Arc Construction (Grays) Ltd, Unit 3, Translink House, Askew Farm Lane, Grays, Essex, RM17 5XR Tel: (01375) 375937

Arc Electronics, 352 Portswood Road, Southampton, SO17 3SB Tel: (023) 8058 4642 Fax: (023) 8055 9199 E-mail: simon@btclick.com *Hire sales & repair public address equipment*

▶ Arc Electronics Ltd, Lower Ground Floor, 44 Bath Road, Swindon, SN1 4AY Tel: (01793) 549230 Fax: (01793) 549239 E-mail: enquiries@arcsales.co.uk *Electronic component distribution*

Arc Energy Resources Ltd, Unit 12 Eastington Industrial Estate, Meadow Mill, Eastington, Stonehouse, Gloucestershire, GL10 3RZ Tel: (01453) 823523 Fax: (01453) 823623 E-mail: sales@arcenergy.co.uk *Arc Energy Resources specialises in weld overlay cladding & stainless steel fabrication for oil & gas, subsea, water & waste treatment & petrochem industries. * Arc Energy uses dedicated welding workstations & a skilled workforce qualified to international welding standards such as ASME, BS EN 287, NES 706 & BS ISO 9001-2000 quality system. Qualified staff including Chartered & European Welding Engineers and Metallurgists, provide unrivalled knowledge of welding technology & weld cladding, which is produced using corrosion resistant materials & welding processes such as pulsed GTAW, synergic GMAW, SAW & electroslag. * Applications include pressure vessels, pipeline equipment, subsea piping, wellhead components, & storm & wastewater control equipment. * By combining weld cladding & fabrication Arc Energy provides a complete package saving customers' production time and transport costs. * Arc Energy offers heat treatment, rolling, pressbrake, NC plasma profiling, NDT & bead blast facilities.*

Arc Engineering Fabrication Ltd, 311 Bexhill Road, St. Leonards-on-Sea, East Sussex, TN38 8AJ Tel: (01424) 715220 Fax: (01424) 442344 E-mail: steelwork@arcfab.freeserve.co.uk *Steel fabricators*

▶ Arc Euro Trade Ltd, 10 Archdale Street, Syston, Leicester, LE7 1NA Tel: 0116-269 5693 Fax: 0116-260 5805 E-mail: information@arceurotrade.co.uk *Bearing distributions, machine tools suppliers*

Arc Fabrication Ltd, 2 Gourley Place, London, N15 5NF Tel: (020) 8800 2557 Fax: (020) 7706 1248 E-mail: sales@arcfabrications.com *Steel fabrications*

Arc Fabrics Ltd, 47 Morris Road, Leicester, LE2 6BR Tel: 0116-270 0702 E-mail: arcfabrics@aol.com *Knitted fabric manufrs*

ARC Facilities Ltd, 1 Park Circus, Glasgow, G3 6AX Tel: 0141-333 1200 Fax: 0141-332 6002 E-mail: arcfacilities@picardy.co.uk *Production of TV commercials*

Arc Gas Welding Co. Ltd, The Croft, Cheadle Road, Tean, Stoke-on-Trent, ST10 4DR Tel: (01538) 722460 Fax: (01538) 723293 *Mild steel fabricators*

Arc Labels Ltd, The Maltings Industrial Estate, Doncaster Road, Whitley Bridge, Goole, North Humberside, DN14 0HH Tel: (01977) 663063 Fax: (01977) 663064 E-mail: sales@arclabels.com Principal Export Areas: Africa *Self-adhesive label manufrs*

▶ Arc Locksmiths, 181 Mauldeth Road, Manchester, M19 1BA Tel: 0161-256 2551 E-mail: arclocks@yahoo.com *Locksmith*

Arc Pharmacare (2006) Ltd, PO Box 2146, Bolton, BL6 9AY Tel: (01204) 362236 Fax: (01204) 362239 E-mail: sales@arc-ltd.uk.com *Pharmaceutical manufacturers*

Arc Services Ltd, Unit 1-2 Andrews Road Industrial Estate, Andrews Road, Cardiff, CF14 2JP Tel: (029) 2055 1919 Fax: (029) 2055 2777 *Welding fabrication*

Arc Tap & Die Co. Ltd, Delamare Road, Cheshunt, Waltham Cross, Hertfordshire, EN8 9SH Tel: (01992) 629247 Fax: (01992) 636268 *Tap & die manufrs*

Arc Welding Products Ltd, 5 Charlestown Industrial Estate, Robinson Street, Ashton-under-Lyne, Lancashire, OL6 8NS Tel: 0161-330 1671 Fax: 0161-330 1714 *Welding machines, consumables & safety equipment*

Arc Welding Services, 17 Sandy Lane, Aston, Birmingham, B6 5TP Tel: 0121-327 2249 Fax: 0121-327 4797 E-mail: service@arcweld.freeserve.co.uk *Welders*

Arc Welding Supplies & Repairs, 6 Palmbourne Industrial Park, Castle Street, Stafford, ST16 2TB Tel: (01785) 281007 Fax: (01785) 240688 *Welding consumables suppliers & repairers*

Arca Ltd, 237 Branston Road, Burton-on-Trent, Staffordshire, DE14 3BT Tel: (01283) 531126 Fax: (01283) 568228 E-mail: info@arca.org.uk *Trade association*

Arcade Amusements, 10 Shelley Grove, Loughton, Essex, IG10 1BY Tel: (020) 8508 8909 *Amusement arcade suppliers*

▶ Arcade Clearance Ltd, Unit 4 City Mills, Hull Street, Morley, Leeds, LS27 8QL Tel: 0113 2527602 E-mail: sales@arcadeclearance.com *Suppliers of pub pool tables and accessories*

▶ Arcade Warehouse Com, Savile Road, Castleford, West Yorkshire, WF10 1PD Tel: (01977) 790523 *Amusement machines & equipment suppliers*

Arcadia Alive Ltd, Parkfield House, Park Street, Stafford, ST17 4AL Tel: 01785 214921 E-mail: enquiry@conflict-training.co.uk *Uk-wide in-house training courses on conflict prevention, de-escalation and management in the workplace. Our courses include: Conflict Management Skills, Personal Safety, Safe Lone Working, Handling Conflict on the Phone and Train the Trainer. We will travel to any place in the UK and our rates are affordable and all inclusive.*

Arcadia Blinds & Coverings, 47 Main Street, Kilwinning, Ayrshire, KA13 6AN Tel: (01294) 554441 Fax: (01294) 559991 *Blinds & covering suppliers*

Arcadia Coffee Services, 65 Mayflower Road, Park Street, St. Albans, Hertfordshire, AL2 2QN Tel: (01727) 873202 Fax: (01727) 873202 *Coffee machine manufrs*

▶ Arcadia (Engineering) Ltd, 22 & 23 Arcadia Avenue, London, N3 2JU Tel: (020) 8349 4816

Arcadia Group Ltd, Hudson Road, Leeds, LS9 7DN Tel: 0113-249 4949 Fax: 0113-380 6282 *Retailers*

Arcall plc, Westminster Road, Wareham, Dorset, BH20 4SR Tel: (01929) 554884 Fax: (01929) 554466 E-mail: email@arcall.co.uk *Food process equipment manufrs*

Arcam, Pembroke Avenue, Waterbeach, Cambridge, CB25 9QR Tel: (01223) 203200 Fax: (01223) 863384 E-mail: info@arcam.co.uk Principal Export Areas: Worldwide *Hi-fi equipment manufrs*

▶ Arcam Consultancy Ltd, 24 Burghmuir Road, Perth, PH1 1LS Tel: (0845) 0550723 E-mail: rod@arcam-it.com *Information technology services*

Arcana, Cheeks Farm, Farnham, Surrey, GU10 5HD Tel: (01420) 22813 Fax: (01420) 22813 E-mail: sales@cabinetmakers.co.uk *Cabinet makers*

Arcane Lighting Ltd, 1f Avenue One, Chilton Industrial Estate, Chilton, Ferryhill, County Durham, DL17 0SF Tel: (01388) 720103 Fax: (01388) 720126 *Specialist lighting manufrs*

Arcas Computing Ltd, 5 Grange Road, Edinburgh, EH9 1UH Tel: 0131-620 8110 Fax: 0131-620 8112 E-mail: sales@arcas.co.uk *Computer consultants*

Arcelor UK, Arcelor House, 4 Princes Way, Solihull, West Midlands, B91 3AL Tel: 0121-705 5444 Fax: 0121-703 0584 *Steel manufrs*

▶ Arcevia Services, 80 Oakland Avenue, Leicester, LE4 7SF Tel: 0116-220 4655 Fax: (0870) 7625207 E-mail: info@arcevia.com *Web site maintenance, proof reading, typing, data entry, document management, web site management, copy typing, touch typing & online proofreading by Arcevia Services uk.*

Arcflex, Old Bank Mill, Ball Haye Road, Leek, Staffordshire, ST13 6AT Tel: (01538) 386000 Fax: (01538) 398999 E-mail: sales@arcflex.com *Stainless steel flexible hose manufrs*

▶ Arcforce Ltd, 5-9 Berkeley Avenue, Reading, RG1 6EL Tel: 0118-933 3800 Fax: 0118-901 8883 E-mail: enquiries@arcforcelimited.co.uk *Mechanical pipework and plumbing installation contractor.*

Arc-Gen Ltd, Station Road, Four Ashes Industrial Estate, Four Ashes, Wolverhampton, WV10 7DB Tel: (01902) 790824 Fax: (01902) 790355 E-mail: andymunford@arc-gen.co.uk *Arc-Gen Ltd, Wolverhampton, United Kingdom. Welder generators, mobile/engine driven welding equipment. Super silent welder generators. Mobile plasma cutters. Lighting towers, mobile metal halide lighting towers. Portable metal halide lighting units. Automatic lighting towers. Generators. Super silent generators. construction type generators. Multi voltage generators*

Arch 18, Kingsdown Cl, London, W10 6SW Tel: 020 72295391 E-mail: michaelreed@arch18.co.uk *Cabinet makers*

▶ Arch Automation Ltd, Unit 12, North Hylton Enterprise Park, Hepworth Road, Sunderland, SR5 3JT Tel: 0191-549 4969 Fax: 0191-549 6944 E-mail: sales@arch-automation.co.uk *Industrial automation, software & design*

Arch Chemicals UK, Wheldon Road, Castleford, West Yorkshire, WF10 2JT Tel: (01977) 714000 Fax: (01977) 714001 *Timber protection services*

Arch Construction Joinery Ltd, King Edward Court, Gee Cross, Hyde, Cheshire, SK14 5JR Tel: 0161-368 0609 Fax: 0161-367 9052 E-mail: enquiries@archjoinery.co.uk *Joinery manufrs*

Arch Consulting Ltd, The Mews, 1b Elliott Road, London, W4 1PF Tel: (020) 8987 0440 Fax: (020) 8747 8330 E-mail: info@arch.co.uk *Computer consultants*

Arch Engineering Ltd, East Side North Dock, Alexandra Docks, Newport, Gwent, NP20 2NP Tel: (01633) 264154 Fax: (01633) 264154 *General engineers*

Arch Henderson & Partners, 26 Rubislaw Terrace, Aberdeen, AB10 1XE Tel: (01224) 631122 Fax: (01224) 632233 E-mail: headoffice@arch-henderson.co.uk *Civil & structural engineers*

▶ ARCH Marketing Solutions Ltd, Kildare House, 102-104 Sheen Road, Richmond, Surrey, TW9 1UF Tel: (020) 8334 1137 Fax: E-mail: info@archmarketing.co.uk *ARCH Marketing is a full services marketing company providing professional billangual - English and Chinese marketing services to clients including: Market research; PR; advertising; TV commercial production; media planning and buying; branding; marketing strategy; branding strategy; copywriting...**Our services cover the areas in FMCG; financial and IT sectors...***

Arch Motor & Manufacturing Co Co. Ltd, Redwongs Way, Huntingdon Trading Estate, Huntingdon, Cambridgeshire, PE29 7HD Tel: (01480) 459661 Fax: (01480) 450923 E-mail: info@archmotor.co.uk *Sheet metal & welded fabrications for the automotive industry*

Arch Services, Bodymoor Green Farm, Coventry Road, Kingsbury, Tamworth, Staffordshire, B78 2DZ Tel: (01827) 875558 Fax: (01827) 875539 *Plant & haulage refinishing contractors*

Archbold Logistics Ltd, Albert Road, Morley, Leeds, LS27 8TT Tel: 0113-252 2333 Fax: 0113-252 7915 E-mail: enq@archbold.co.uk *Road transport services* Also at: Branches throughout the U.K.

continued

▶ indicates data change since last edition

Company Information

Archbond Ltd, Mill Hill Factory, Desford Road, Enderby, Leicester, LE19 4AD Tel: 0116-284 1222 Fax: 0116-284 9954 E-mail: lizhayes@archbond.co.uk *Laminating fabrics services*

Archco Rigidon, Denso House, 33-35 Chapel Road, London, SE27 0TR Tel: (020) 8761 6244 Fax: (020) 8761 2456 E-mail: mail@denso.net *Corrosion resistant coatings manufrs*

▶ Archer Blinds Ltd, 1 Lodge Street, Middleton, Manchester, M24 6AA Tel: 0161-653 3800 Fax: 0161-653 3800 *Blinds retailers*

Archer Electrical Services, 9 Parkdale Avenue, Wednesbury, West Midlands, WS10 9BG Tel: 0121-556 7024 *Security services & general electrician*

Archer Engineering (Leeds) Ltd, Pepper Road, Hunslet, Leeds, LS10 2RU Tel: 0113-270 5478 Fax: 0113-271 9886 E-mail: richard@archereng.co.uk *Pressed steel section fabricators*

▶ Archer Power, Archer House, Twyford Road, Wokingham, Berkshire, RG40 5QT Tel: (0845) 8330333 Fax: (0845) 8330222 E-mail: admin@archerpower.com *Power suppliers*

Archer Technicoat Ltd, E Progress Road, Sands Industrial Estate, High Wycombe, Buckinghamshire, HP12 4JD Tel: (01494) 462101 Fax: (01494) 463049 E-mail: info@cvd.co.uk *Surface coatings & materials technology*

Archer Woodnutt Ltd, Pit Lane, Talke Pits, Stoke-on-Trent, ST7 1UH Tel: (01782) 785016 Fax: (01782) 776273 E-mail: info@archerwoodnutt.com *Precision sheet metal workers*

Archerdale Ltd, Hirstwood Works, Hirst Wood Road, Shipley, West Yorkshire, BD18 4BU Tel: (01274) 595783 Fax: (01274) 531263 E-mail: sales@archerdale.co.uk *Industrial fastener stockholders*

Archers Stone Restoration Ltd, Winters Farm, North Common Road, Wivelsfield Green, Haywards Heath, West Sussex, RH17 7RJ Tel: (01444) 471090 Fax: (01444) 471095 E-mail: info@archerstone.com *Restoration of historic properties, cleaning & repair services*

Archfact Ltd, 10 Pipers Wood Industrial Park, Waterberry Drive, Waterlooville, Hampshire, PO7 7XU Tel: (023) 9224 0700 Fax: (023) 9223 0157 E-mail: info@archfact.com *CNC precision engineers*

Archfield (Shipping) Ltd, Factory Road, London, E16 2HD Tel: (020) 7476 4386 Fax: (020) 7511 2238 E-mail: sales@archfield.co.uk *International shipping & forwarding agents* Also at: Dover & Heathrow Airport (London)

▶ Archibald Fergusson Ltd, Ardgowan, Strachur, Cairndow, Argyll, PA27 8DG Tel: (01369) 860231

Archibald Mcaulay & Son, Bankend Road, Broadmeadow Industrial Estate, Dumbarton, G82 2RB Tel: (01389) 762778 Fax: (01389) 742350 E-mail: steel@mcaulay.co.uk *Structural steel fabricators*

▶ Archibald Mccorquodale & Son Ltd, 353-355 Langside Road, Glasgow, G42 8XT Tel: 0141-423 1187 Fax: 0141-423 0497

▶ Archibald Russell Of Denny Ltd, Drumbowie Farm, Denny, Stirlingshire, FK6 5LZ Tel: (01324) 822555

Archibald Shaw LLP, One Little London, Chichester, West Sussex, PO19 1PP Tel: (01243) 786 471 E-mail: info@archibaldshaw.co.uk *Consulting engineers & designers*

Archibald Young Ltd, Milton Road, Kirkintilloch, Glasgow, G66 1SY Tel: 0141-776 7701 Fax: 0141-775 1743 E-mail: sales@archibaldyoung.co.uk *Founders & engineers*

Archibald Young Brassfounders Ltd, Motherwell Business Centre, Albert Street, Motherwell, Lanarkshire, ML1 1PR Tel: (01698) 263165 Fax: (01698) 263211 E-mail: enquiries@archibaldyoung.co.uk *General engineers & founders*

▶ Archimage Architectural Photography Ltd, Common Road, Kensworth, Dunstable, Bedfordshire, LU6 2PJ Tel: (01582) 872179 E-mail: anthony.weller@archimage.co.uk *Photographers, architectural*

▶ ArchiTech Surveys Ltd, 86 Easton street, High Wycombe, Bucks, HP11 1LT Tel: (01494) 522455 Fax: (01494) 535667 E-mail: technical@architechsurveys.co.uk *ArchiTech Surveys provide precision land surveys, topographical and measured building surveys, detailed site plans, floor plans as existing plans, elevations and sections to developers and the construction industry; utilising auto cad and leica tools, in the areas of High Wycombe, Buckinghamshire, Birmingham and London.*** *

Architectural Aluminium Systems Ltd, Sandleheath Industrial Estate, 6 Old Brickyard Road, Sandleheath, Fordingbridge, Hampshire, SP6 1PA Tel: (01425) 654080 Fax: (01425) 652038 *Aluminium shop front & curtain walling installers*

Architectural Cladding Association, 60 Charles Street, Leicester, LE1 1FB Tel: 0116-253 6161 Fax: 0116-251 4568 E-mail: info@britishprecast.org *Trade association*

Architectural Contract Services Ltd, Stable Cottage Industries, Wheatsheaf Road, Woodmancote, Henfield, West Sussex, BN5 9AU Tel: (01273) 495188 Fax: (01273) 495199 E-mail: archconserv@onetel.com *GRP manufrs*

Architectural Design, The Courtyard, 28a Great King Street, Macclesfield, Cheshire, SK11 6PL Tel: (01625) 615954 Fax: (01625) 511042 E-mail: post@archdes.co.uk *RIBA chartered architectural practice*

▶ Architectural Glazed Facades Ltd, Wellington House, East Road, Cambridge, CB1 1BH Tel: (01223) 451051 Fax: (01223) 566781 E-mail: office@agfacades.co.uk *Suppliers of glazing glass*

Architectural & Industrial Group, 29 High Street, Hampton Wick, Kingston upon Thames, Surrey, KT1 4DA Tel: (020) 8977 8203 Fax: (01932) 829706 E-mail: sales@boschkitchens.com *Kitchen design consultants*

▶ Architectural Joinery Workshops Ltd, 287-288 Clough Road, Hull, HU6 7PY Tel: (01482) 442300 Fax: (01482) 341880

Architectural Metal Fixing Services, 18 Penshurst Way, Sutton, Surrey, SM2 6HR Tel: (020) 8643 7469 *Wrought ironwork*

Architectural Models Ltd, 275-281 King Street, London, W6 9LZ Tel: (020) 8748 6110 Fax: (020) 8741 3719 E-mail: arcmodels@btinternet.com *Specialist model constructors*

▶ Architectural Plans, Hill House, Hillside, Prestatyn, Clwyd, LL19 9PW Tel: (01745) 854945 E-mail: christopher.parry@virgin.net *Specialising in the preparation and submission of plans and applications for extensions, alterations, loft conversions, new build domestic and industrial buildings**

▶ Architectural Security & Protection Ltd, 22c Orgreave CR, Sheffield, S13 9NQ Tel: 0114-288 0041 Fax: 0114-288 0041 *Security design & installers*

Architectural Steelwork Nottingham, Stapleford, Nottingham, NG9 Tel: 07976 293162 Fax: 0115 9176250 E-mail: auto.marine@ntlworld.com *Tele.0115 9176250 or 07976 293162 All types of architectural steelwork fabricated and installed.including structural steelwork, universal beams and columns, staircases, fire escapes, handrails, balustrades, electric gates, railings, wrought ironwork etc.*

▶ Architectural Stone Ltd, 10 Sheepwalk Road, Lisburn, County Antrim, BT28 3RD Tel: (028) 9264 8048 Fax: (028) 9264 8775

▶ Archival Record Management plc, 53-57 Southampton Way, London, SE5 7SW Tel: (020) 7701 7018 Fax: (020) 7701 7026 E-mail: sales@armplc.com

▶ Archive Attic Ltd, The Farm Office, Grooms Lane, Creaton, Northampton, NN6 8NN Tel: (01604) 505715 E-mail: sales@archiveattic.co.uk *Secure, dry self storage. Suitable for document archiving, car storage, household storage etc. Trade and private. **Flexible terms and excellent rates.**Collection by arrangement.**Please contact for more information.** http:// www.archiveattic.co.uk*

▶ Archive & Data Storage Ltd, 7 Northumberland Court, Chelmsford, CM2 6UW Tel: (01245) 461000 Fax: (01245) 467000

▶ Archive Management Systems Ltd, Unit 2 Sterling Way, Reading, RG30 6HW Tel: 0118-943 1443 Fax: 0118-942 6631 E-mail: postmaster@archivems.co.uk

▶ Archive123.com, Unit 4665, 555 White Hart Lane, London, N17 7RN Tel: (020) 8888 1050 Fax: (020) 8888 0785 E-mail: info-ffg123@wwmail.co.uk *Document archive management services*

Archmate Ltd, 15 Granby House, Granby Row, Manchester, M1 7AR Tel: 0161-236 2762 Fax: 0161-228 7247 *Foam scrap suppliers*

▶ Arch's Plumbing & Heating Services, 37 Teal Crescent, Basingstoke, Hampshire, RG22 5QX Tel: (01256) 472651 E-mail: info@plumberhampshire.co.uk *Plumbing Services, for boiler installations & central heating maintenance*

Archway Brown Ltd, 43 Bury Mead Road, Hitchin, Hertfordshire, SG5 1RT Tel: (01462) 432139 Fax: (01462) 420102 *Manufacturers of aluminum*

Archway Business Centre, The Mill, Boden Street, Chard, Somerset, TA20 2DD Tel: (01460) 64539 Fax: (01460) 61136 E-mail: sales@archway-uk.com *Office furniture & stationer suppliers*

Archway Engineering (UK) Ltd, Ainleys Industrial Estate, Elland, West Yorkshire, HX5 9JP Tel: (01422) 373101 Fax: (01422) 374847 E-mail: sales@archway-engineering.com *Earth boring & drilling equipment manufrs*

▶ Archway Promotions, 7 Kempston Court, Kempston Hardwick, Bedford, MK43 9PQ Tel: (01234) 853500 Fax: (01234) 852826 E-mail: sales@archwaypromotions.co.uk *Promotional products manufrs*

Archway Services plc, Bound Oak, Eversley Road, Arborfield Cross, Reading, RG2 9PN Tel: 0118-976 1610 Fax: 0118-976 1510 E-mail: archway.service@virgin.net *Scaffolding contractors*

Archway Systems Ltd, 31 Parolles Road, London, N19 3RE Tel: (020) 7272 3530 Fax: (020) 7263 1951 E-mail: admin@arsy.co.uk *Computer suppliers & repair services*

Archwright Ltd, Unit 29 Maybrook Road, Brownhills, Walsall, WS8 7DG Tel: (01543) 371971 Fax: (01543) 371009 *UPVC profile bending manufrs*

Arckiv Vintage Eyewear, Unit 87a, The Stables Market, London, NW1 8AH Tel: (07790) 102204 Fax: (020) 7428 0123 E-mail: info@arckiv.net *Museum quality collection of frames and sunglasses, available to hire or purchase. Inexhaustible source of vintage sunglasses, spectacle frames, pince-nez, lorgnettes, goggles for Film, Theatre and television. Working closely with craftsmen in the UK, France and Italy, Arckiv frame made to any design, in acetate, metal or both. We stock Persol, Cazal, Porsche, Ray Ban, Carrera, Dior, and NHS geek chic style frames. Recent projects include the 22nd Bond film, Quantum of Solace. Quick and inexpensive lense service available. Arckiv can fit old lenses to old frames, and it offers an extensive repair servive, also by post. Open to the public Tuesday-Friday 1pm-6pm and Saturday-Sunday am-6pm. Monday closed. All other times please call 07790 2204 for an appointment. Nearest entrance is opposite Morrison''s petrol station. Nearest underground is Chalk Farm. Buses: 24, 27, 31 and 168.*

▶ Arclid.Com Ltd, 506 Building 1, Radway Green Venture Park, Crewe, CW2 5PR Tel: (0844) 8009672 Fax: (01270) 750524 E-mail: info@arclid.com *Web site designers*

Arco, Blackburn Interchange Trade Park, Commercial Road, Darwen, Lancashire, BB3 0DB Tel: (01254) 778680 Fax: (01482) 388029 E-mail: darwen.branch@arco.co.uk *Work & safety wear distributors*

Arco Ltd, Tenax Circle, Trafford Park, Manchester, M17 1EZ Tel: 0161-869 5800 Fax: 0161-869 5858 E-mail: traffordpark.branch@arco.co.uk *Safety & industrial protective clothing suppliers*

Arco, PO Box 78, Watford, WD24 4YT Tel: (01923) 202090 Fax: (01923) 202010 E-mail: arco@watford.co.uk *Safety clothing & equipment manufrs*

Arco East Scotland, Avon Mill Industrial Estate, Mill Road, Linlithgow Bridge, Linlithgow, West Lothian, EH49 7QY Tel: (01506) 844661 Fax: (01506) 847816 E-mail: arco.eastscotland@arco.co.uk *Safety clothing & equipment suppliers* Also at: Branches throughout the U.K.

Arco Ellesmere Port Ltd, Hooton Road, Hooton, Ellesmere Port, CH66 7PA Tel: 0151-327 6666 Fax: 0151-327 7930 *Safety clothing & equipment distributors* Also at: Hull

Arco Engineering & Fabrications Ltd, 68-70 Heath Mill Lane, Deritend, Birmingham, B9 4AR Tel: 0121-771 0936 Fax: 0121-766 7396 *Pipework fabricators*

Arco Glasgow, 210 Edmiston Drive, Glasgow, G51 2YY Tel: 0141-419 3200 Fax: 0141-419 3232 E-mail: arco-glasgow@arco.com *Safety clothing & equipment manufrs* Also at: Hull

▶ Arco Group Ltd, Parkway Avenue, Sheffield, S9 4YX Tel: 0114-272 3333 E-mail: admin@arco.co.uk

▶ Arco Plymouth, Unit A Estover Road, Plymouth, PL6 7PY Tel: (01752) 751650 *Suppliers of safety equipment*

Arco Redman Ltd, The Boardroom Suite, Lingley House, Commissioners Road, Strood, Rochester, Kent, ME2 4EE Tel: (01634) 723372 Fax: (01634) 725572 E-mail: mail@arcoredman.co.uk *Walkway, stairway, sunscreen, balustrade, infill & fence manufrs*

Arco South East, Cray Avenue, Orpington, Kent, BR5 3QB Tel: (01689) 875411 Fax: (01689) 876538 E-mail: orpington.branch@arco.co.uk *Safety clothing & equipment distributors* Also at: Hull

Arco Southwest Ltd, Unit 8a & 8b Point 4, Second Way, Avonmouth, Bristol, BS11 8YA Tel: 0117-982 3751 Fax: 0117-923 5574 E-mail: avonmouth.branch@arco.co.uk *Safety clothing & equipment distributors*

Arco Tyne & Wear Ltd, PO Box 8, Blaydon-on-Tyne, Tyne & Wear, NE21 5TP Tel: 0191-414 7721 Fax: 0191-414 0258 E-mail: arco.tynewear@arco.co.uk *Safety clothing & equipment manuf*

ARCO West Bromwich, PO Box 2210, West Bromwich, West Midlands, B71 1DQ Tel: 0121-500 4444 Fax: 0121-553 7554 E-mail: westbromwich.branch@arco.co.uk *Personal safety clothing & equipment distributors*

Arco West Scotland, PO Box 6, Irvine, Ayrshire, KA12 8LG Tel: (01294) 315900 Fax: (01294) 271335 E-mail: arco.westscotland@arco.co.uk *Protective clothing, equipment & industrial consumables*

Arcode UK Ltd, 41 Ebrington Road, Kenton, Harrow, Middlesex, HA3 0LS Tel: (020) 8907 1309 Fax: (020) 8907 9132 E-mail: sales@arcode.co.uk *Rubber products manufrs*

Arcoe Metal Products, 11 Fairway Drive, Greenford, Middlesex, UB6 8PW Tel: (020) 8575 5541 Fax: (020) 8575 8678 E-mail: metalman@arcoe.freeserve.co.uk *Sheet metalwork engineers or fabricators*

Arcom Control Systems Ltd, 8 Clifton Road, Cambridge, CB1 7EA Tel: (01223) 411200 Fax: (01223) 403400 E-mail: sales@arcom.co.uk *Industrial computer products manufrs*

Arcon Overseas Ltd, 12 Relton Mews, London, SW7 1ET Tel: (020) 7225 1411 Fax: (020) 7225 1811 E-mail: sales@arcon-london.co.uk *Export agents*

Arcontech Ltd, 31-35 Kirby Street, London, EC1N 8TE Tel: (020) 7405 2111 Fax: (020) 7831 6667 E-mail: mail@arcontech.com *Computer systems consultants*

Arcorundum Grinding Wheel Co., Toll End Road, Tipton, West Midlands, DY4 0HF Tel: (0845) 6347171 Fax: (0845) 6347170 *Abrasive segment manufrs*

▶ Arcova Manhole Cover Manufacturers, Willow Tree Farm, Main Street, Laneham, Retford, Nottinghamshire, DN22 0NG Tel: (01777) 228931 Fax: (01777) 228504 E-mail: sales@arcova.co.uk *Specialist access covers, gratings & frames*

Arcraft Products 2005 Ltd, 1 Mousell Street, Cheetham, Manchester, M8 8HY Tel: 0161-833 2269 Fax: 0161-833 2269 E-mail: greetings16@hotmail.com *Greeting card wholesalers*

Arcrite Fabrications, Fleming Road, Corby, Northamptonshire, NN17 4SW Tel: (01536) 204969 Fax: (01536) 402456 E-mail: email@genbridge.fsnet.co.uk *Narrow boat & steel fabricators*

Arcs N Sparks Ltd, The Long House, Villiers Street, Willenhall, West Midlands, WV13 1DF Tel: (01902) 636133 Fax: (01902) 636122 E-mail: sales@arcsnsparks.co.uk *Work wear distribution & retailers*

Arc-Tec, Unit 4 Bound Oak, Eversley Road, Arborfield, Reading, RG2 9PN Tel: 0118-976 1777 Fax: 0118-976 1444 *Steel fabricators & welders*

Arctek Carpentry, 44 The Croft, Marlow, Buckinghamshire, SL7 1UP Tel: (01628) 475624 *Cabinet makers*

Arctic Circle Ltd, Coldnose Court, Coldnose Road, Rotherwas Industrial Estate, Hereford, HR2 6JL Tel: (01432) 273333 Fax: (01432) 264616 E-mail: enquiries@acl-online.com *Refrigeration equipment manufrs*

Arctic Knitwear, 2nd Floor 2 Rochdale Road, Manchester, M4 4JR Tel: 0161-839 8092 Fax: 0161-831 9009 *Knitwear manufrs*

Arctic Paper UK Ltd, Quadrant House, 47 Croydon Road, Caterham, Surrey, CR3 6PB Tel: (01883) 331800 Fax: (01883) 330560 E-mail: info-uk@arcticpaper.com *Paper & board marketing agents* Also at: Manchester

Arctic Refrigeration Ltd, 36 Bath Street, Bolton, BL1 2DJ Tel: (01204) 524655 Fax: (01204) 526557 *Refrigeration & air conditioning ssuppliers*

▶ Arctic Spas Hot Tub Centre, 19b Alston Road, Hellesdon Park Road, Norwich, NR6 5DS Tel: (01603) 416016 Fax: (01603) 416016 E-mail: info@arctichottubcentre.co.uk *Hot tub installation*

Arcusin UK, Walnut Tree House, Oxton, Southwell, Nottinghamshire, NG25 0SZ Tel: (07790) 989024 Fax: 0115-965 5970 E-mail: stephen@arcusin.com *Bail handling equipment suppliers*

▶ Arcwell Mobile Welding, 64 Tansey Green Road, Brierley Hill, West Midlands, DY5 4TE Tel: (07860) 419626 Fax: (01384) 78009 E-mail: patricia@hopton8339fsnet.co.uk *Mobile welders*

Ardan Exhibition, Unit 7 North Medburn Farm, Watling Street, Elstree, Hertfordshire, WD6 3AA Tel: (020) 8207 4957 Fax: (020) 8207 3040 E-mail: info@ardan.co.uk *Exhibition stand design & construction*

Ardath Video, 56 Ardath Road, Birmingham, B38 9PH Tel: 0121-451 3332 Fax: 0121-459 5127 E-mail: sales@ardathvideo.co.uk *Video filming & production*

▶ Ardbeg Distillery Ltd, Ardbeg, Ardbeg, Isle of Islay, PA42 7EA Tel: (01496) 302244 Fax: (01496) 302040

Arden Box Ltd, Unit, Tything Road East, Kinwarton, Alcester, Warwickshire, B49 6ES Tel: (01527) 545635 Fax: (01527) 540299 E-mail: ardenbox@hotmail.com *Manufacturer of silk lined presentation boxes & folding cartons, plain or printed. Also hot foil blocking. All boxes are made to customers own requirements with regard to dimensions and colour,and foil logo if required. Internal fittings made to fit your own product perfectly. Laminated covered cardboard tubes with end caps can be supplied in various lengths and diameters to suit requirements. Reasonably quick turn around from receipt of order.*

▶ Arden Business Consultants, PO Box 9900, Henley-in-Arden, Warwickshire, B95 5QW Tel: (01564) 796600 Fax: (0870) 0516753 E-mail: data@abcon.net *Database management, web on-line databases, remote access databases, e-mail broadcasting, e-newsletters, stakeholder communications, database marketing & database publishing, fulfilment*

Arden Control Systems Ltd, Arden Street, New Mills, High Peak, Derbyshire, SK22 4NS Tel: (01663) 746060 Fax: (01663) 746189 E-mail: sales@ardencontrolsystems.co.uk *Safety & emergency shutdown systems manufrs*

Arden Dies Ltd, Shepley Lane Industrial Estate, Hawk Green, Marple, Stockport, Cheshire, SK6 7JW Tel: 0161-449 6000 Fax: 0161-449 0497 E-mail: orderdies@ardendies.com *Laser form cutters*

Arden Direct Marketing Ltd, Island House, Arthur Street, Barwell, Leicester, LE9 8AH Tel: (0870) 4025220 Fax: (01455) 852249 E-mail: sales@ardendirect.co.uk *Response handling service*

▶ Arden Environmental Ltd, The Arden Centre, Little Alne, Wootton Wawen, Henley-In-Arden, West Midlands, B95 6HW Tel: (01789) 488555 Fax: (01789) 488122 E-mail: enquiries@ardenair.com *Heating ventilation, air conditioning cleaning, dust & fume control*

Arden Fabrications, Packwood Road, Lapworth, Solihull, West Midlands, B94 6EJ Tel: (01564) 770966 Fax: (01564) 771052 E-mail: guy@ardenfabrications.co.uk *Steel fabricators*

Arden Photonics Ltd, Business & Innovation Centre Aston Science Park, Love Lane, Birmingham, B7 4BJ Tel: 0121-250 3588 Fax: (01564) 205043 E-mail: david@ardenphotonics.com *Provides innovative products & services to the photonics industry, including wavefront sensors for optical & surface metrology; laser beam profilers; high magnification interferometer for small objects such as optical fibre ends; a modal profiler for multimode optical fibres*

Arden Power Tools, Albion Works, High Street, Newhall, Swadlincote, Derbyshire, DE11 0EB Tel: (01283) 550347 Fax: (01283) 550720 E-mail: ardenpowertools@btconnect.com *Power tools & pneumatic tools sales, services & repairers*

Arden Precision Ltd, 5 Maidwell Drive, Shirley, Solihull, West Midlands, B90 4QN Tel: 0121-683 5200 Fax: 0121-683 5210 *Aerospace precision engineers*

Arden Winch & Co. Ltd, 116 Station Road, Beeston, Nottingham, NG9 2AY Tel: 0115-925 8222 Fax: 0115-925 8444 E-mail: roger.graves@ardenwinch.co.uk *Workwear, Embroidered/Heat Seal Logos and Paper disposable products to all kinds of business both large and small, throughout the UK.*

Arden Windows Ltd, Arden House, Sparkbrook St, Coventry, CV1 5ST Tel: (024) 7663 2423 Fax: (0870) 7890161 E-mail: enquiries@ardenwindows.net *Quality timber windows & doors manufrs*

▶ Arden Wood Shavings Ltd, Kenilworth Road, Hampton-in-Arden, Solihull, West Midlands, B92 0LP Tel: (01675) 443888 Fax: (01675) 443873

▶ Ardent Ltd, Unit 3 Becklands Close, Barr Lane, Roecliffe, York, YO51 9NR Tel: (0870) 1625400 Fax: (0870) 1625410 E-mail: Info@ardent-uk.com *Ardent are specialists in the supply & maintenance of fire protection systems. specialising in Vehicle and Restaurant and Building Suppression systems. We are also UK distributors for the Ansul Micro-K range of extinguishers.*

Ardep UK Ltd, Unit 34, Spring Vale Industrial Estate, Cwmbran, Gwent, NP44 5BD Tel: (01633) 480496 Fax: (01633) 480497 E-mail: sales@ardep.com *Swimming pool contractors*

▶ indicates data change since last edition

Ardern Healthcare Ltd, Pipers Brook Farm, Eastham, Tenbury Wells, Worcestershire, WR15 8NP Tel: (01584) 781777 Fax: (01584) 781788 E-mail: info@ardernhealthcare.com *Pharmaceutical distributors*

Ardeth Engineering Ltd, Dewsbury Road, Elland, West Yorkshire, HX5 9AZ Tel: (01422) 371014 Fax: (01422) 372218 E-mail: info@ardeth.com Principal Export Areas: Central/East Europe, West Europe, North America, Central America & South America *Pressure vessels manufrs*

Ardfern Yacht Centre, Ardfern, Lochgilphead, Argyll, PA31 8QN Tel: (01852) 500636 Fax: (01852) 500624 E-mail: office@ardfernyacht.co.uk *Boat builders*

Ardington Archives, White Horse Business Park, Ware Road, Stanford in the Vale, Faringdon, Oxfordshire, SN7 8NY Tel: (01367) 718710 Fax: (01367) 718501 E-mail: sales@ardingtonarchives.co.uk *Data storage services*

Ardmac Performance Contracting Ltd, Annesborough Industrial Area, 15 Annesborough Road, Lurgan, Craigavon, County Armagh, BT67 9JD Tel: (028) 3834 7093 Fax: (028) 3834 1604 E-mail: info@ardmac.com *Office & factory fit-outs-clean rooms-sterile rooms*

▶ Ardmair Enterprises Ltd, 82 Brown Edge Road, Buxton, Derbyshire, SK17 7AF Tel: (01298) 78926 Fax: (01298) 25122 E-mail: mail@ardmairenterprises.co.uk *Packaging manufrs*

Ardmaleish Boatbuilding Co Ltd, Ardmaleish, Port Bannatye, Isle of Bute, PA20 0QY Tel: (01700) 502007 Fax: (01700) 502257 E-mail: info@ardmaleishboatbuilding.co.uk *Boat repairers & manufrs*

Ardmore Construction Ltd, Bryne House, 54 Jeffreys Road, Enfield, Middlesex, EN3 7UB Tel: (020) 8805 0101 Fax: (020) 8364 7477 E-mail: millmarsh@mooregroup.co.uk Principal Export Areas: Worldwide *Manufacturers of precision turned parts & fasteners*

▶ Ardmore Construction Ltd, 3 Hollybrook Place, Glasgow, G42 7HB Tel: 0141-433 2588

Ardmore Precast Concrete Ltd, 25 Ballybogie Road, Ardmore, Londonderry, BT47 3RE Tel: (028) 7134 9566 Fax: (028) 7131 1100 E-mail: info@ardmoreprecast.co.uk *Manufacturers of concrete products*

Ardrox Engineering, Godiva Place, Coventry, CV1 5PN Tel: (024) 7655 9986 Fax: (024) 7655 1402 E-mail: sales@ardroxengineering.com *NDT equipment engineers, crack & flaw detection specialists*

Ards Tubular Furniture Ltd, Unit 24E Blocks Industrial Estate, Mark Street, Newtownards, County Down, BT23 4DT Tel: (028) 9181 3499 Fax: (028) 9181 3499 *Tubular furniture*

Arduous Manufacturing, The Old Brewery, Norton Fitzwarren, Taunton, Somerset, TA2 6RN Tel: (01823) 339000 Fax: (01823) 339000 *Bolt & nut manufrs*

Ardvick Trading & Supply Co., 37-39 Peckham Road, Camberwell, London, SE5 8UH Tel: (020) 7703 9135 Fax: (020) 7708 0844 *Buying & purchasing agents*

Area Networks Ltd, Sunningdale Ho, 11 George St, Altrincham, Cheshire, WA14 1RJ Tel: 0161-926 8484 Fax: 0161-926 8921 *Computer networking & installation*

Area Print & Graphic, Unit 8 Marsland Street, Hazel Grove, Stockport, Cheshire, SK7 4ER Tel: 0161-483 5034 Fax: 0161-483 5034 *Commercial printers*

Areco Roofing Supplies, Coppice Lane, Walsall Wood, Walsall, WS9 9AA Tel: (01922) 743553 Fax: (01922) 743554 E-mail: sales@areco.co.uk *Aluminium Roof Edge Trims Upvc Fascias, Soffits & Cladding Polycarbonate Roof Sheets & Access.*

Arefco Special Products Ltd, Jubilee Industrial Estate, Ashington, Northumberland, NE63 8UA Tel: (01670) 819513 Fax: (01670) 816132 E-mail: sales@arefco.co.uk *Hydraulic & pneumatic seal manufrs*

▶ AR-EL Workshop Equipment Ltd, PO Box 200, Aberdeen, AB32 6GW Tel: (01224) 749051 Fax: (01244) 749051 E-mail: raymond@workshop-equipment.co.uk *Supplier of workshop equipment*

Aremco Products, Foxoak Street, Cradley Heath, West Midlands, B64 5DQ Tel: (01384) 568566 Fax: (01384) 634601 E-mail: sales@aremco-products.co.uk *Security barrier posts supply & manufrs*

Arena Books, 6 Southgate Green, Bury St. Edmunds, Suffolk, IP33 2BL Tel: (01284) 754123 Fax: (01284) 754123 E-mail: arenabooks@tiscali.co.uk *Publishers of politics, current affairs & economics business*

Arena Business Machines, Armitage House, Thorpe Lower Lane, Robin Hood, Wakefield, West Yorkshire, WF3 3BQ Tel: 0113-288 0282 Fax: 0113-288 0671 E-mail: admin@arenagroup.net *Office equipment distributors*

Arena Computer Supplies Ltd, 18 Sandeman Way, Horsham, West Sussex, RH13 6EL Tel: (01403) 272156 Fax: (01403) 252620 *Computer consumables*

▶ Arena Display Ltd, 3 Scotch George Lane, Knaresborough, North Yorkshire, HG5 9EH Tel: (01423) 770900 Fax: (01423) 770400 E-mail: steve@arenadisplay.co.uk Principal Export Areas: Worldwide *Exhibition displays sales*

Arena Events, Unit 1 Perimeter Road, The N.E.C., Birmingham, B40 1PJ Tel: (0870) 7203010 Fax: (0870) 7201101 E-mail: info@arenaevents.com *Business entertainment organisers*

Arena Plastics Ltd, 5 Lynmouth Avenue, Stockport, Cheshire, SK5 7AL Tel: 0161-442 4000 Fax: 0161-442 4000 *Plastic fabrication manufrs*

Arena Q S Ltd, Arena House, 23 Plough Way, London, SE16 2LS Tel: (020) 7237 1415 Fax: (020) 7237 1452 *Software development*

Arena Seating Ltd, Membury, Lambourn Woodlands, Hungerford, Berkshire, RG17 7TQ Tel: (01488) 674800 Fax: (01488) 674822 E-mail: info@arenaseating.com *Seating contractors*

Arena Structures, Needingworth Road, St. Ives, Cambridgeshire, PE27 3ND Tel: (01480) 468888 Fax: (01480) 462888 *Marquee & temp structure suppliers*

Arends International Ltd, Sankey Valley Industrial Estate, Anglezarke Road, Newton-le-Willows, Merseyside, WA12 8DJ Tel: (01925) 223323 Fax: (01925) 229800 E-mail: sales@arends.co.uk *Freight forwarding agents*

Arenson Group Ltd, Arenson Centre, Arenson Way, Dunstable, Bedfordshire, LU5 5UL Tel: (01582) 678300 Fax: (01582) 678111 *Office furniture manufrs*

Areton International Plastics Ltd, Unit 47-48, Clywedog Road North, Wrexham Industrial Estate, Wrexham, Clwyd, LL13 9XN Tel: (01978) 664646 Fax: (01978) 664647 E-mail: sales@areton.co.uk *Additives masterbatch manufrs*

▶ Arfary Group, Parliament View APTS, D Block, No. 1 Albert Embankment, London, London, SE1 7XQ Tel: 0870 0053923 E-mail: sales@arfary.com *Arfary is the Pure Silk & Cashmere Company. We offer a wide variety of Cashmere and Silk Garments together with a wide range of accessories in both Men's wear and Ladies wear.*Arfary offers a free tailoring service so you are able to choose your own made to measure garments from our extensive range of cashmere or silk materials. A wide choice of colours and styles is available for your own personal inspiration. visit at:*www.arfary.com for further details.*

▶ Argee Builders Ltd, 1 Rosendale Way, Blantyre, Glasgow, G72 0NJ Tel: (01698) 826824 Fax: (01698) 826828

Argee Instrument Co. Ltd, 14 Albert Road, Romford, RM1 2PL Tel: (01708) 747878 Fax: (01708) 733216 *General engineers*

Argent Engineering Services Ltd, 52 Stockholm Road, Hull, HU7 0XW Tel: (01482) 838698 Fax: (01482) 838668 *Fabrications in stainless steel*

Argent F M Ltd, Unit 8, Penarth Centre, London, SE15 1TW Tel: (0870) 8900399 Fax: (0870) 8900398 E-mail: info@argent.fm.co.uk *Air conditioning contractors*

Argent Fabrications Ltd, Unit 4 Avery Dell, Lifford Lane, Birmingham, B30 3DZ Tel: 0121-459 9617 Fax: 0121-458 6604 E-mail: enquiries@argentfabs.com *Sheet metal fabrications*

Argent Independant Steel (UK) Ltd, Lake Road, Leeway Industrial Estate, Newport, Gwent, NP19 4WN Tel: (01633) 290260 Fax: (01633) 290911 E-mail: info@argentindependantsteel.ltd.uk *Steel stockholders*

Argent Steel Ltd, 1 Matthew Street, Sheffield, S3 7BE Tel: 0114-270 1428 Fax: 0114-272 3717 E-mail: enquiries@argentsteel.co.uk *Steel tool stockholders*

Argo Crane Hire, Greenham Lock Cottage, London Road, Newbury, Berkshire, RG14 5SN Tel: (01635) 30306 *Mobile crane hirer*

Argo Electronic Components Ltd, Leyden Works, Station Road, Great Yarmouth, Norfolk, NR31 0HB Tel: (01493) 652752 Fax: (01493) 655433 E-mail: sales@norfolk-capacitors.com *Relays, electromechanical component distribs*

Argo Plastics Ltd, Unit 6B, Park Street Industrial Estate, Kidderminster, Worcestershire, DY11 6TN Tel: (01562) 823531 Fax: (01562) 825417 Principal Export Areas: Worldwide *Plastics fabricators & marketing display designers*

Argo Products Ltd, Viola Street, Bolton, BL1 8NG Tel: (01204) 595224 Fax: (01204) 307729 *Production engineers*

Argon Arc Ltd, South Nelson Road, South Nelson Industrial Estate, Cramlington, Northumberland, NE23 1WF Tel: (01670) 707888 Fax: (01670) 707889 E-mail: argonarc@btinternet.com *General engineers*

▶ Argon Computing, 125 Southend Road, Rochford, Essex, SS4 1HX Tel: (01702) 547625 E-mail: sales@argoncomputing.com *Computer systems consultants*

Argon Corporation Ltd, Ridgeway, Aycliffe Industrial Park, Newton Aycliffe, County Durham, DL5 6EE Tel: (01325) 304166 Fax: (01325) 304167 *Diamond tooling manufrs*

Argon Electronics, Unit 16, Progress Park, Ribocon Way, Luton, LU4 9UR Tel: (01582) 491616 Fax: (01582) 492780 E-mail: sales@argonelectronics.com *Argon Electronics LLP are world leaders in CBRN / NBC Gas and Hazmat Simulation and training aids. We provide realistic, cost effective radiological, nuclear, chemical and biological training simulators for military and civil use.*

▶ Argonaut Powder Coating Ltd, 13 Nutwood Way, Totton, Southampton, SO40 3SZ Tel: (023) 8087 3455 Fax: (023) 8087 2255 E-mail: info@argonaut-uk.com *Powder coating services*

Argonaut Press, 108 New Cavendish Street, London, W1W 6XP Tel: (020) 7631 1011 Fax: (020) 7631 1011 *Lithographic printers*

Argonaut Press, Kendalls Buildings, Birmingham Road, Stratford-upon-Avon, Warwickshire, CV37 0AQ Tel: (01789) 414478 Fax: (01789) 414478 E-mail: john@argonautpress.co.uk *Printing & labels on rolls*

▶ ARGONAUTIC TRANSPORT, 77 Albany Road, Kensington, Liverpool, L7 8RQ Tel: (0845) 1307133 E-mail: aahbtrans@yahoo.co.uk *Boat Transport and Specialised Marine Transport*

▶ Argoneon Ltd, Unit A6 Continental Approach, Westwood Industrial Estate, Margate, Kent, CT9 4JG Tel: (01843) 226420 Fax: 01843 226420 E-mail: michael@argoneon.co.uk *Lighting & illumination manufrs*

▶ Argo's Bakery, 50-52 Victoria Street, Stromness, Orkney, KW16 3BS Tel: (01856) 850245 Fax: (01856) 851264 E-mail: sales@argosbakery.co.uk *Bakery*

Argos Inspection Co. Ltd, Tower Road, Washington, Tyne & Wear, NE37 2SH Tel: 0191-417 7707 Fax: 0191-415 4979 E-mail: ndt@argosinspection.com *Inspecting & testing engineers*

Argosafe Ltd, Unit 11 Dawsons Lane, Barwell, Leicester, LE9 8BE Tel: (01455) 844801 Fax: (01455) 850280 E-mail: argosafe@btconnect.com *Electronic control system manufrs*

Argosy Ltd, Units 6-7, Ridgeway, Drakes Drive, Long Crendon, Buckinghamshire, HP18 9BF Tel: (01844) 202101 Fax: (01844) 202025 E-mail: sales@argosycable.com *Electrical products for broadcast industry*

Argosy Coffee Services, 44 Rownhams Lane, North Baddesley, Southampton, SO52 9HQ Tel: (023) 8073 2345 Fax: (023) 8073 2234 *Office coffee service*

Argosy Control Engineering Ltd, Murcar Industrial Estate, Denmore Road, Bridge of Don, Aberdeen, AB23 8JW Tel: (01224) 704788 Fax: (01224) 704831 *Corrosion protection services*

Argosy Machinery Ltd, Unit F6, Southwell Road, Horsham St. Faith, Norwich, NR10 3JU Tel: (01603) 893987 Fax: (01603) 893988 E-mail: info@argosymachineryltd.co.uk *Argosy machinery suppliers of New and rebuilt flow wrapping machinery, our flow wrapping machinery are manufactured in the UK. Electronic /Servo and mechanical flow wrappers built at our UK manufacturing site in Norwich. New and re-built 4 side seal packaging machinery for the medical,surgical glove and wound care industries, bespoke feeding systems manufactured to feed our flow wrapping machinery.Electronic upgrades to your existing flow wrapping machinery, print registration systems etc. Flow wrapping machinery for the biscuit, bakery, confectionery, medical, wound care, personal care, printing industries etc.*

Argun Printers, 344 Mare Street, London, E8 1HA Tel: (020) 8985 7879 Fax: (020) 8985 3668 E-mail: info@argun.co.uk *Art materials suppliers, general printers & stationers*

▶ Argus Electrical Services Ltd, 150 Avery Hill Road, London, SE9 2EY Tel: (020) 8850 9947 Fax: (020) 8859 8680 E-mail: arguselecservltd@aol.com *Electrical contractor*

Argus Electronics, Frenches, Chew Valley Road, Greenfield, Oldham, OL3 7AE Tel: (01457) 876951 Fax: (01457) 876951 *Electronic designers & manufrs*

Argus Fire Protection Co, Hendglade House, 46 New Road, Stourbridge, West Midlands, DY8 1PA Tel: (01384) 376256 Fax: (01384) 393955 E-mail: sales@argusfire.co.uk *Fire protection engineers*

Argus Refrigeration Ltd, 21 King Street, Port Glasgow, Renfrewshire, PA14 5JA Tel: (01475) 741053 Fax: (01475) 741038 E-mail: smithargus@yahoo.co.uk *Refrigeration & air conditioning engineers*

▶ Argus Services, H R S House H R S Industrial Estate, Garretts Green Lane, Birmingham, B33 0UE Tel: 0121-683 1168 Fax: 0121-683 1167 E-mail: admin@argus-services.co.uk *Security systems*

Argyle Energy, Stirling University Innovtn Park, Stirling, FK9 4NF Tel: (01786) 451030 Fax: (01786) 473688 E-mail: energy@argyleuk.com *Energy consultancy & management*

▶ Argyle Engineering Ltd, 21-29 Regent Street, Liverpool, L3 7BW Tel: 0151-236 0777 Fax: 0151-236 8073

Argyle Engineering Ltd, 21-29 Regent Street, Liverpool, L3 7BW Tel: 0151-236 0777 Fax: 0151-236 8073 *Toolmakers & precision engineers*

Argyll Cash Register Systems, Unit 25a Anniesland Industrial Estate, Glasgow, G13 1EU Tel: 0141-950 6766 Fax: 0141-950 6750 E-mail: sales@argyllsystems.co.uk *Cash register*

▶ Argyll Computer Services, Unit 3, 46 Argyll Street, Lochgilphead, Argyll, PA31 8NE Tel: (01546) 603674 Fax: (01546) 603674 E-mail: info@argyllcomputers.com *Computer maintenance services*

▶ Argyll & Highland Fire Services, Ben Nevis Drive, Ben Nevis Industrial Estate, Fort William, Inverness-Shire, PH33 6RU Tel: (01397) 700234 Fax: (01397) 705377 *Fire protection suppliers*

▶ Argyll Sawmills Ltd, Strachur, Cairndow, Argyll, PA27 8DW Tel: (01369) 860701 Fax: (01369) 860709

▶ Aria Desktops, Unit 12, Harmill Industrial Estate, Grovebury Road, Leighton Buzzard, Bedfordshire, LU7 4FF Tel: (01525) 853233

Arian Communications Ltd, Unit 14, Gaugemaster Way, Ford, Arundel, West Sussex, BN18 0RX Tel: (0871) 2261481 Fax: (01903) 881510 E-mail: mike@ariancom.com *Telecommunications*

Arian Electronic Systems, 34A High St, Syston, Leicester, LE7 1GP Tel: 0116-260 7663 Fax: 0116-260 7663 *Battery charger manufrs*

▶ Ariazone, Princess of Wales Court Seaway Drive, Seaway Parade Industrial Estate, Port Talbot, West Glamorgan, SA12 7BT Tel: (01639) 822111 Fax: (01639) 822192 E-mail: sales@arizone.co.uk

Ariel Communications Ltd, 2 Harvingwell Place, 129-32 Mark Road, Hemel Hempstead, Hertfordshire, HP2 7BW Tel: (01442) 418460 E-mail: sales@arielcommunications.co.uk *Web site solutions*

Ariel Fastners Ltd, Ariel Works, Temple Road, Leicester, LE5 4JG Tel: 0116-273 6541 Fax: 0116-249 0024 E-mail: enquiries@arielfasteners.com *Rivet & industrial fastener manufrs*

Ariel Machine Products Ltd, Yew Tree Lane, Caerleon, Newport, NP18 1LL Tel: (01633) 420405 Fax: (01633) 430072 *Precision & general engineers*

Ariel Maritime (UK) Ltd, Unit 26, Waters Edge Business Park, Salford, M5 3EZ Tel: 0161-848 9009 Fax: 0161-848 9511 E-mail: manchester@arielmaritime.co.uk *Shipping & freight forwarding agents*

Ariel Plastics Ltd, Speedwell Industrial Estate, Staveley, Chesterfield, Derbyshire, S43 3JP Tel: (01246) 281111 Fax: (01246) 561115 E-mail: info@arielplastics.com *Plastic roofing materials distributors*

Aries Barcoding & Labelling Ltd, Philpot House, Station Road, Rayleigh, Essex, SS6 7HH Tel: (01268) 774494 Fax: (01268) 777959 E-mail: ablltd@btconnect.com *Barcode labels, scanners and verifiers and peripherals. Barcode systems including Inventory control, asset tracking etc. Label overprinting service for barcode labels, sandwich labels etc. Also self adhesive labels on rolls, plain or pre-printed in up to 6 colours.*

Aries Commercial Machinery Ltd, The Hollies School Lane, Auckley, Doncaster, South Yorkshire, DN9 3JR Tel: (01302) 770777 Fax: (01302) 770787 E-mail: info@aries.co.uk *Computer software developers*

Aries Software Service, 23 Surbiton Road, Southend-on-Sea, SS2 4NR Tel: (01702) 463833 Fax: (01702) 466122 E-mail: ariessoftware@btconnect.com *Computer software developers*

Arinsdale Ltd, Block 6 Unit A, Westmains Industrial Estate, Grangemouth, Stirlingshire, FK3 8YE Tel: (01324) 665234 Fax: (01324) 665388 E-mail: info@arinsdale.com *Securing & lifting systems manufrs*

Arise N Shine Cleaning Services & Supplies, 68 Icknield Close, Ickleford, Hitchin, Hertfordshire, SG5 3TE Tel: (01462) 675525 Fax: (01462) 456288 *Office cleaners*

▶ Ariser Computer Services, 188 Blythe Road, London, W14 0HD Tel: (020) 7371 2227

Aristec Ltd, 97 Hildyard Road, Leicester, LE4 5GG Tel: 0116-266 1707 Fax: 0116-266 1995 E-mail: aristec@fsnet.co.uk *Clothing & fabric manufrs*

Aristocast Originals Ltd, 2 Wardsend Road, Sheffield, S6 1RQ Tel: 0114-269 0900 Fax: 0114-234 4885 E-mail: sales@troikaam.co.uk *Moulding & ceramic plaster producers & suppliers*

Aristocrat Home Improvements, Mowsley End, Wigston, Leicestershire, LE18 3LS Tel: 0116-288 9230 Fax: 0116-288 9230 E-mail: sales@aristocrat-mouldings.co.uk *Plaster moulding suppliers & manufrs*

Aristocrat Signs, Unit 6 Mitchell Close, Fareham, Hampshire, PO15 5SE Tel: (01489) 589292 Fax: (01489) 584909 E-mail: aristocrat@zoom.co.uk *Sign contractors & manufrs*

The Aristotle Corporation, Blenheim House, 56 Old Steine, Brighton, BN1 1NH Tel: (01273) 222400 Fax: (01273) 778464 E-mail: candidates@aristotlecorp.com *Computer personnel recruitment services*

Aristotle Corporation Ltd, 6 Hope Street, Edinburgh, EH2 4DB Tel: 0131-220 0420 Fax: 0131-220 1973 *IT recruitment*

Aristrobes, 37-41 Glenbank Pl, Belfast, BT14 8AL Tel: (028) 9039 1900 *Window manufrs*

Arivatex Ltd, 17 Chatley Street, Manchester, M3 1HX Tel: 0161-834 9191 Fax: 0161-834 9161 E-mail: info@arivatex.co.uk *Suppliers of workwear, corporate wear, catering & health care clothing*

Arjay Joinery Co. Ltd, Unit 6, Craufurd Business Park, Silverdale Road, Hayes, Middlesex, UB3 3BN Tel: (020) 8573 3746 Fax: (020) 8569 1807 *Joinery manufrs*

▶ ARJMK PRINT & DESIGN, 25 Sutton Lane, Eastburn, Keighley, West Yorkshire, BD20 7SL Tel: 01535 655390 Fax: 01535 655390 E-mail: roy@rjmk.co.uk *We supply all types and styles of printed products, sage, sage compatible, packaging and stationery*

Arjo Ltd, St. Catherine Street, Gloucester, GL1 2SL Tel: (01452) 428200 Fax: (01452) 428344 E-mail: info@arjo.com *Patient lifting & bathing aid suppliers*

Arjo Wiggins Fine Papers Ltd, Chineham, Basingstoke, Hampshire, RG24 8BA Tel: (01256) 728728 Fax: (01256) 728889 *Speciality paper manufrs* Also at: Branches throughout the U.K.

▶ Arjun International, 36 Cobden Street, Leicester, LE1 2LB Tel: 0116-251 4100 Fax: 0116-251 8789 E-mail: sales@arjuninternational.co.uk *Clothing manufrs*

Ark Forwarding Ltd, Unit 13 Brittania Industrial Estate, Poyle Road, Slough, SL3 0BH Tel: (01753) 685454 Fax: (01753) 684093 E-mail: sales@airfreight.co.uk *Freight forwarders*

Ark H Handling Ltd, 1 Wilstead Industrial Park, Kenneth Way, Wilstead, Bedford, MK45 3PD Tel: (01234) 742777 Fax: (01234) 742999 E-mail: sales@ark-h.co.uk *Marketing services*

Ark Site Fabrications, Unit 7b Greenhill Mills, Grange Road, Batley, West Yorkshire, WF17 6LH Tel: (01924) 420874 Fax: (01924) 359744 E-mail: brian@arksite.co.uk *Steel fabricators, architectural staircases & fire escapes*

Ark Storage Systems, Registered Office:, Riverside House, 31 Cathedral Road, Cardiff, CF11 9HB Tel: 02920 383453 Fax: 02920 383486 E-mail: info@arkstore.co.uk *Ark Storage are specialists in all forms of Archive and Document Storage Management. If you are interested in straight forward archival storage or state of the art paper-to-electronic storage, call us today for a competitive quote.*

▶ Arkadin UK Ltd, 26-28 Hammersmith Grove, London, W6 7JA Tel: (020) 8742 6380 Fax: (020) 8742 6355 E-mail: d.creigh@arkadin.co.uk *Worldwide provider of teleconferencing*

Arkas Ltd, Nubal House, Headcorn Road, Sutton Valence, Maidstone, Kent, ME17 3EH Tel: 0845 5314195 Fax: (01622) 843488 E-mail: danny@arkas.co.uk *Arkas has over thirty years experience in the manufacture, installation, maintenance and repair of Industrial Doors, Roller Shutters, Gates and Barriers for a wide range of industries and applications in the UK and overseas.*

Arkay Clothing Ltd, 5 Easter Langlee Industrial Estate, Melrose Road, Galashiels, Selkirkshire, TD1 2UH Tel: (01896) 754933 Fax: (01896) 754932 *Industrial clothing manufrs*

▶ Arkay Engineering, Unit1 Budds Lane, Romsey, Hampshire, SO51 0HA Tel: (01794) 511644 Fax: (01794) 511678 *Fabricators*

Arkay Windows Ltd, 573-575 Lordship Lane, London, N22 5LE Tel: (020) 8889 6821 Fax: (020) 8888 0398 E-mail: sales@arkaywindows.co.uk Principal Export Areas: Worldwide *Double glazed unit manufacturers/installers*

▶ arken P-O-P Ltd, Studlands Park Avenue, Newmarket, Suffolk, CB8 7EA Tel: (01638) 565656 Fax: (01638) 662770 E-mail: info@arken-pop.com *arken is the market leader in the design and manufacture of award winning POP and graphic display products. Their offering is two fold, firstly providing off the shelf and customised graphic display products such as light boxes, poster frames, free standing pavement and forecourt signs, hanging signs, and literature holders. A number of these products can now be purchased on line on-line at www.arken-direct.com.*Secondly arken provide a full service bespoke design and manufacturing facility creating highly innovative P-O-P display and merchandising solutions, tailor made to customer's individual needs.*arken have won numerous awards for their highly effective display solutions. Having created merchandising displays for various well known brands in sectors such as consumer electronics, cosmetics, tobacco, jewellery and automotive, their experience and knowledge from concept through to installation is vast.*

Arkinstall Ltd, 6 Buntsford Park Road, Bromsgrove, Worcestershire, B60 3DX Tel: (01527) 872962 Fax: (01527) 837127 E-mail: info@arkinstall.co.uk *Cloakroom equipment manufrs*

Arkinstall Galvanizers, Ebro Works, Dudley Road West, Tividale, Oldbury, West Midlands, B69 2PF Tel: 0121-557 1851 Fax: 0121-522 3991 E-mail: arkinstall@galvanizing.co.uk *Galvanizing services*

Arkinstall Galvanizing Ltd, 38 Coventry Street, Birmingham, B5 5NQ Tel: 0121-643 6455 Fax: 0121-643 0192 E-mail: info@galvanizing.co.uk Principal Export Areas: Central/East Europe & West Europe *Galvanizers & galvanising processors or services*

▶ Arkle Bros Ltd, 5 Herbert Road, Ilford, Essex, IG3 8AL Tel: (020) 8590 3321 Fax: (020) 8590 3349 E-mail: arkle@btinternet.com *We are an experienced NICEIC Electrical Installation Company, employing Approved Electricians, covering all of Greater London. We offer a complete electrical service, from Electrical Reports on existing installations though to complete design and installation, on all types of electrical installations, including Portable Appliance (PAT) Testing.*

Arkley Labels, Unit 8, Aslton Works, Alston Road, Barnet, Hertfordshire, EN5 4EL Tel: (020) 8441 2011 Fax: (020) 8441 5909 *Self-adhesive label manufrs*

Arkoss Metals Ltd, 112 Latimer Road, Chesham, Buckinghamshire, HP5 1QQ Tel: (01494) 776163 Fax: (01494) 771511 *Steel stockholders & scrap metal merchants*

Arkrite Fencing Manufacturers Ltd, Progress Drive, Cannock, Staffordshire, WS11 0JE Tel: (01543) 577677 Fax: (01543) 574446 E-mail: arkrite@btconnect.com *Security fencing manufrs*

▶ Arktech UK Ltd, 11 Tower Road, Washington, Tyne & Wear, NE37 2SH Tel: 0191-419 3996 Fax: 0191-419 3096

Arkwell Fasteners Ltd, Unit 1, Chapel Street, Long Eaton, Nottingham, NG10 1EQ Tel: 0115-973 1181 Fax: 0115-946 1123 E-mail: sales@arkwell.co.uk *Industrial fasteners, agents, stockholders & distributors*

▶ Arla Plant Hire Ltd, 64 Foxcroft Drive, Carterton, Oxon, OX18 3HT Tel: 07717 130983 E-mail: arlaplanthire@aol.com *Arla Plant Hire is a newly established company providing the following services and equipment to the construction industry.***Excavators*Our range includes 13.5 tonne and 21 tonne Fiat-Hitachi tracked excavators that are all well serviced and come with a full range of buckets. Rates start from £18.50 an hour depending on distance.***Operators*We can supply all of our machines with operators or can provide them as drivers for companies that require just that. They are all CITB and CPCS certified and are fully insured.***Tipper hire*Arla also have 8 wheel tippers for all aspects of bulk haulage including muck shift and supply of materials for the construction industry.***Ground workers/Skilled labour hire*Arla Plant Hire Ltd will consider all contracts for ground works or can provide skilled labour on a day rate if needed. All ground workers carry either CSCS or CPCS certificates, are competent and are insured.***

Arlen Electrical Ltd, Unit 1, High Point Business Village, Henwood Industrial Estate, Ashford, Kent, TN24 8DH Tel: (01233) 668041 Fax: (01233) 668042 E-mail: efasales@arlen.co.uk *Electronic & fluorescent accessories dis*

▶ Arleys Angels Ltd, 2 Old Farm, Arley Road, Appleton, Warrington, WA4 4RP Tel: (01925) 266834 Fax: (01925) 266895 E-mail: info@arleysangels.co.uk *Commercial & industrial cleaning contractors*

Arlington Ltd, Gloucester Business Park, Hucclecote, Brockworth, Gloucester, GL3 4AA Tel: (01452) 619281 Fax: (01452) 612943 E-mail: kate.parkin@arlington.co.uk *Trading estate administrators*

▶ Arlington Beverge Group, 162-164 Arthur Road, London, SW19 8AQ Tel: (020) 8395 1552 Fax: (020) 8395 1558 E-mail: info@arlingtonbeverage.com *Wine importers*

Arlington Consultants Group Ltd, 32 Brook Street, London, W1K 5DL Tel: (020) 7470 0057 Fax: (020) 7470 0074 E-mail: info@arlington-consultants.co.uk *Recruitment consultants*

Arlington Interiors, 3 Damgate Lane, Acle, Norwich, NR13 3DH Tel: (01493) 751628 *Furniture manufrs*

Arm A-V Services, 57 St. Johns Road, Caversham, Reading, RG4 5AL Tel: 0118-948 2559 E-mail: mekka@lentil.org *Electronic repairs*

ARM Fire Extinguisher Services, 12 Vicarage Way, Arksey, Doncaster, South Yorkshire, DN5 0TG Tel: (01302) 873379 Fax: (01302) 873379 *Fire equipment sales & service*

Arm Services, The Willows, Crays Hill Road, Crays Hill, Billericay, Essex, CM11 2YP Tel: (01268) 530470 Fax: (01268) 530470 *Motor vehicle recovery services*

Arm Sure Security, 97 Occupation Road, Corby, Northamptonshire, NN17 1EE Tel: (01536) 202631 Fax: (01536) 202102 *Security alarms installers*

Armac Brassfounders Group Ltd, 60 Staniforth Street, Birmingham, B4 7DN Tel: 0121-359 4821 Fax: 0121-359 4698E-mail: buyer@armac.co.uk *Reproduction brass cabinet fittings*

Armack Chemicals, 52-53 Brook Street, Lye, Stourbridge, West Midlands, DY9 8SL Tel: (01384) 897531 Fax: (01384) 892448 E-mail: sales@armack.co.uk *Metal finishing chemical suppliers*

Armacoating North West Ltd, Moores Mill, Cathrine Street East, Denton, Manchester, M34 3RQ Tel: 0161-320 9856 Fax: 0161-320 0772 *Powder coating & stove enamelling services*

Armada Engineering, Bransford, Worcester, WR6 5JB Tel: (01886) 833672 Fax: (01886) 833906 *Mould manufrs*

Armada Software, Glendower, Llangynog, Oswestry, Shropshire, SY10 0EX Tel: (01691) 860304 E-mail: armada@onetel.net.uk *Agricultural software developers*

Armada Tube & Steel (SW) Ltd, Tube & Steel Service Centre, Pennygillam Industrial Estate, Launceston, Cornwall, PL15 7ED Tel: (01566) 776699 Fax: (01566) 776500 E-mail: des@armadatube.co.uk *Steel stockholders*

Armadale UK Swimming Pools & Spas, Unit 11 Capenhurst Technology Park, Capenhurst Lane, Chester, CH1 6EH Tel: 0151- 347 1661 Fax: 0151-347 1658 E-mail: post@armadaleuk.com *Design & manufacturer of mosaic tiled spas & swim spas*

Armadale Vending Services Ltd, Armadale House, Bury Road Industrial Estate, Ramsey, Huntingdon, Cambridgeshire, PE26 1NF Tel: (01487) 813892 Fax: (01487) 813021 E-mail: info@armadale-vending-services.co.uk *Vending machine services*

Armadillo Coatings, Unit 3A, Victor Business Centre, Arthur Street, Redditch, Worcestershire, B98 8JY Tel: (01527) 526855 Fax: (01527) 502856 E-mail: msalter@aol.com *Redditch Anodising (accredited with BSI to ISO 9001) offers a full range of finishes on aluminium; clear and coloured sulphuric acid anodised bright or matt, including electrolytic bronzes, for aesthetic or functional applications. Engineering and aerospace requirements can be met with hard anodising and chromic acid anodising and chromate conversion (Alocrom). Through our powder coating company, Armadillo Coatings, we can apply epoxy or polyester powders, with chromate or for severe environments anodised pre-treatment. We also offer passivation of stainless steel and application of dry-film lubricants. Redditch Anodising has extensive in-house testing facilities to ensure compliance with customers specification such as film thickness, sealing quality, microhardness and Taber abrasion resistance. Every specification flightbar processed is checked for seal quality and subjected to a statistical check for appearance and film thickness*

Armadillo Window Protection, 1 The Avenue, Burwell, Cambridge, CB25 0DE Tel: (01638) 610490 Fax: (01638) 742167 *Industrial door & shutter manufrs*

Armagard Ltd, Unit 9 Fortnum Close, Birmingham, B33 0LG Tel: 0121-608 7210 Fax: 0121-608 4477 E-mail: sales@armagard.co.uk *Enclosures mild & stainless steel suppliers*

Armagh Computer World, 43 Scotch Street, Armagh, BT61 7DF Tel: (028) 3751 0002 Fax: (028) 3751 0009 E-mail: sales@computerworlds.co.uk *PC builders & retailers*

Armagh Construction Ltd, 14 Ennislare Road, Armagh, BT60 2AX Tel: (028) 3752 3047 Fax: (028) 3752 3166 E-mail: acl_scc@ireland.com *Building & civil engineers*

Armaghdown Creameries Ltd, Greenbank Industrial Estate, Newry, County Down, BT34 2SJ Tel: (028) 3026 2224 Fax: (028) 3026 9565 E-mail: contact@fanevalley.co.uk *Milk powdered/ processed products manufrs*

Armalines Ltd, Unit 11 Saracen Estate, Mark Road, Hemel Hempstead, Hertfordshire, HP2 7BJ Tel: (01442) 241334 Fax: (01442) 264261 E-mail: armalinesltd@aol.com *Industrial adhesive tape distributor*

Armalon Ltd, 44 Harrowby Street, London, W1H 5HY Tel: (020) 7262 1881 Fax: (020) 7402 0959 E-mail: info@armalon.com *Gunsmiths*

▶ Armana, Talbot House, High Street, Crowthorne, Berkshire, RG45 7AQ Tel: (01344) 780000 Fax: (01344) 769240 E-mail: info@armana.co.uk *Network security consultants*

Armaplate UK Ltd, Central Workshops, Back Longworth Road, Horwich, Bolton, BL6 7DB Tel: (01204) 468295 Fax: (01204) 468356 E-mail: info@armaplate.com *Van security installations specialists*

Armare School Furniture & Equipment, 3 Peartree Industrial Estate, Bath Road, Langford, Bristol, BS40 5DJ Tel: (01934) 853808 Fax: (01934) 853141 *Educational furniture manufrs*

Armari Ltd, 5 Woodshots Meadow, Croxley Business Park, Watford, WD18 8QD Tel: (01923) 225550 Fax: (01923) 221161 E-mail: sales@amari.co.uk *Computer manufrs*

Armeg Ltd, Callywhite Lane, Dronfield, Derbyshire, S18 2XJ Tel: (01246) 411081 Fax: (01246) 411882 E-mail: j.mowthorpe@armeg.co.uk *Hammer drill manufrs*

Armer Quality Components Ltd, Hope Mill, Greenacres Road, Oldham, OL4 2AB Tel: 0161-620 5203 Fax: 0161-627 5139 E-mail: mail@armerqc.co.uk *Sheet metalwork fabricators*

Armex Systems, 130 Park Road, Prestwich, Manchester, M25 0DU Tel: 0161-740 2178 Fax: 0161-740 8414 *Building engineers*

Armfibre Ltd, Unit 7, Wilstead Industrial Park, Kenneth Way, Wilstead, Bedford, MK45 3PD Tel: (01234) 741444 Fax: (01767) 651901 E-mail: sales@armfibre.com *Reinforced plastic moulding manufrs*

Armfield, Heriot House, 88-90 Guildford Street, Chertsey, Surrey, KT16 9AD Tel: (01932) 566633 Fax: (01932) 566639 *Building contractors*

Arminhall Engineering, Shire Hill Industrial Estate, Saffron Walden, Essex, CB11 3AQ Tel: (01799) 524510 Fax: (01799) 526680 *Steel fabricators*

Arminox UK, PO Box 39, Peterborough, PE8 4JT Tel: (01832) 272109 Fax: (01832) 275759 E-mail: info@arminox.com Sales Contact: E. James Principal Export Areas: Worldwide *Leading international Danish supplier of stainless steel rebar: cut and bent stainless reinforcement with subsidiaries in Jebel Ali and UK ; with joint venture in Australia. All Grades of stainless steel relevant to civil engineering supplied: EN1.4301; EN1.4436; EN1.4462; EN1.4571 in Tensile Grades 200; 500; 550 & 650. Also supplying stainless steel dowel bar ; all thread bar ; threading ; studding ; anchor and ties ; bolts ; plate and sheet ; tube and box section. Produced to British BS6744 & BS8666; Danish and German Solasung standards. With UK CARES certification. Major supplier of stainless steel wall ties in Scandinavia: now developing market for stainless steel wall ties with successful unique patented product in UK and Ireland. Produced to exacting Danish standards but conforming to British Standard requirements. Competitively priced*

Armishaws Removals, Wincanton Business Park, Wincanton, Somerset, BA9 9RU Tel: (01963) 34065 E-mail: enquiries@armishaws.com

Armitage Du-Lieu (UK) Ltd, Oakes Mill West, New Hey Road, Lindley, Huddersfield, HD3 4DD Tel: (01484) 648897 Fax: (01484) 648897 *Property business*

Armitage Leisure Services, 121a Acre Street, Huddersfield, HD3 3EJ Tel: (01484) 644404 Fax: (01484) 646315 E-mail: info@armitageleisure.co.uk *Amusement arcade suppliers*

Armitage Monobond, Ilkley Road, Otley, West Yorkshire, LS21 3JP Tel: (01943) 466222 Fax: (01943) 850265 *Bathroom fittings/plastics mouldings manufrs*

Armitage Pet Care Ltd, Private Road Number 3, Colwick Industrial Estate, Colwick, Nottingham, NG4 2BA Tel: 0115-938 1200 Fax: 0115-961 7496 E-mail: sales@armitages.co.uk *Manufacturer of pet products*

Armitage Shanks, Alderflat Drive, Newstead Industrial Estate, Stoke-on-Trent, ST4 8HX Tel: (01782) 277200 Fax: (01782) 657386 *Toilet cubicle manufrs*

Armitage Shanks Group Pension Trustees Ltd, Old Road, Armitage, Rugeley, Staffordshire, WS15 4BT Tel: (01543) 490253 Fax: (01543) 491677 E-mail: merrickj1@aseur.com *Bathroom fittings & accessories manufrs*

Armitage Venesta Washroom Systems Ltd, Imperial Business Estate, West Mill, Gravesend, Kent, DA11 0DL Tel: (01474) 353333 Fax: (01474) 533558 E-mail: info@armitage-venesta.co.uk *Pre-plumbed washroom systems & wc cubicle range*

▶ Armitech Ltd, 149 Mill Lane, Wallasey, Merseyside, CH44 3BJ Tel: 0151-639 0222 Fax: 0151-639 0222 E-mail: chris_wigins@armitec.co.uk *Steel fabricators*

Armley Fashions, Wesley Road, Leeds, LS12 1UH Tel: (07812) 766023 Fax: 0113-263 7053 *Sportswear & head garments manufrs*

▶ Armo UK, Unit A5, Halesfield 9, Telford, Shropshire, TF7 4QW Tel: (07838) 117354 Fax: (01952) 582321 E-mail: david.bruneau@armoweb.com *Supplier of dock levelers lifting tables & loading bay equipment*

Armoloy UK Ltd, Mammoth Drive, Wolverhampton Science Park, Wolverhampton, WV10 9TF Tel: (01902) 310375 Fax: (01902) 310075 E-mail: armoloyuk@aol.com *Hard precision chrome plating manufrs*

▶ Armondi Ltd, Unit 2 Crusader Industrial Estate, 167 Hermitage Road, London, N4 1LZ Tel: (020) 8800 4441

Armor Inox, Fairways Woodlands View, New Rhosrobin, Rhosrobin, Wrexham, Clwyd, LL11 4PT Tel: (01978) 263482 Fax: (01978) 263488 *Food processing equipment manufrs*

Armor Products, Cranfield Road, Lostock Industrial Estate, Lostock, Bolton, BL6 4SB Tel: (01204) 664000 Fax: (01204) 664001 *Protective clothing manufrs*

ArmorGard Security Products, Castle Trading Estate, Portchester, FAREHAM, Hants, PO16 9SF Tel: 02392 380280 Fax: 02392 200715 E-mail: sales@armorgardsecurity.com *Manufacturers of secure and safe storage solutions for tools, equipment, and hazardous substances*

Armour Blinds, Whitehouse Enterprise Centre, Whitehouse Road, Newcastle upon Tyne, NE15 6EP Tel: 0191-228 0912 Fax: 0191-228 0912 E-mail: armoursecurity@cwcom.net *Shop front manufrs and fitters*

Armour Custom Services Ltd, K Holder Road, Aldershot, Hampshire, GU12 4RH Tel: (01252) 350280 Fax: (01252) 350682 E-mail: info@totalinstallations.co.uk *Double glazed product manufacturers & installers*

Armour Guard Films Ltd, 6 Maple Court, Crystal Drive, Smethwick, West Midlands, B66 1RB Tel: 0121-544 4884 Fax: 0121-544 4885 E-mail: sales@armourguardfilms.co.uk *Solar & glare control, one way vision & security window film manufrs*

Armour Print & Design, 92b Audley Street, Reading, RG30 1BS Tel: 0118-958 8957 Fax: 0118-959 4816 E-mail: dave@armourprint.co.uk *Commercial printers*

▶ Armour Sealed Units Bristol Ltd, 62 Barrs Court Road, Barrs Court, Bristol, BS30 8DH Tel: 0117-961 3970 Fax: 0117-961 3533

Armour Supplies Ltd, Units 2-3, Brunel Road, Churchfield Industrial Estate, St. Leonards-on-Sea, East Sussex, TN38 9RT Tel: (01424) 853717 Fax: (01424) 853719 *Packaging material & stationery distributors*

▶ Armour Systems Ltd, Unit D, Lyon Road, Denbigh West, Milton Keynes, MK1 1EX Tel: (01908) 370345 Fax: (01908) 366659 E-mail: info@armoursystems.co.uk *Cases manufrs*

Arms Technical Engineering, Arms House, 29 Glen Road, Oldham, OL4 1LP Tel: 0161-626 5293 Fax: 0161-626 5293 E-mail: sales@armstechnicalengineering.co.uk *Rubber extrusion & mouldings manufrs*

Armson-Boult Ltd, 144b George Street, Coventry, CV1 4HE Tel: (024) 7622 6817 Fax: (024) 7622 6817 *Precision gauge & tool makers*

▶ Armston Group Ltd, The Mill, Middle Street, Elton, Peterborough, PE8 6RA Tel: (01832) 281259 E-mail: enquiries@armstongroup.co.uk *Planning a wedding, special party or corporate event then call Armston Group to ensure the weather does not spoil your special day. When you want your party or event to be remembered by your friends, family and colleagues a marquee will ensure your party and event goes off with style.*

▶ Armstrong, 6 James Carter Road, Mildenhall, Bury St. Edmunds, Suffolk, IP28 7DE Tel: (01638) 715713 Fax: (01638) 713007

▶ Armstrong Blacksmiths & Engineers, Lichfield Road Industrial Estate, Tamworth, Staffordshire, B79 7TA Tel: (01827) 316663 Fax: (01827) 66833 E-mail: armstrong.blacksmiths@btopenworld.com *Metal components manufrs*

Armstrong Bradley Ltd, 35a Middlewich Road, Sandbach, Cheshire, CW11 1DH Tel: (01270) 758960 Fax: (01270) 764797 E-mail: sales@armstrongbradley.com *Armstrong Bradley Limited was established in 1966, specifically to service the highly specialised needs of the plastic packaging industry. The Company has grown to represent some of the most respected plastics manufacturing organisations both in Europe and Worldwide. *Today, Armstrong Bradley supplies flexible and rigid plastics for a wide range of packaging, print and industrial applications. Products are supplied that meet the highest technical specifications and conform to the most demanding health and hygiene regulations. Almost any product which requires protection, promotion or merchandising can be packaged to advantage with Armstrong Bradley supplied materials* Also at: Altrincham

Armstrong Crane Hire, 44 Pemberton Valley, Ayr, KA7 4UB Tel: (01292) 445645 Fax: (01292) 445645 *Crane & lifting equipment hire*

Armstrong Electrical, 109 Hatch Road, Pilgrims Hatch, Brentwood, Essex, CM15 9QA Tel: (01277) 375511 Fax: (01277) 375511 E-mail: Principal Export Areas: Worldwide *Marine electrical equipment suppliers*

Armstrong Fastenings Ltd, PO Box 6, Wednesbury, West Midlands, WS10 8UL Tel: 0121-224 2000 Fax: 0121-224 2007 E-mail: info@armfast.com *Threaded fastener manufrs*

Armstrong Floor Products UK Ltd, Hitching Court, Abingdon Business Park, Abingdon, Oxfordshire, OX14 1RB Tel: (01235) 554848 Fax: (01235) 553583 E-mail: uk-info@armstrong.com *Floor covering manufrs*

Armstrong Glen Metals, 14 Palacecraig Street, Coatbridge, Lanarkshire, ML5 4RY Tel: (01236) 424396 Fax: (01236) 433330 E-mail: glenmetals@asdmetalservices.co.uk *Steel stockholders*

Armstrong Hi-Fi & Video Service Ltd, 32a Blackhorse Lane, London, E17 6HJ Tel: (020) 8523 0051 Fax: (020) 8523 4395 E-mail: ahvsltd@aol.com *Audio visual equipment repair centre*

Armstrong Holden Brooke Pullen, Ormside House, 21 Ormside Way, Redhill, RH1 2JG Tel: (01737) 378100 Fax: (01737) 378140 E-mail: sales@holdenbrookpullen.com *Pump manufrs*

Armstrong Hydraulic Services (Hull) Ltd, Unit 8 Tom Thumb Industrial Estate, English Street, Hull, HU3 2BT Tel: (01482) 210680 Fax: (01482) 211947 E-mail: info@arma-hydraulic.co.uk *ARMSTRONG HYDRAULIC SERVICES (HULL) LIMITED was formed in 1985 to provide a wide ranging but specialist service in hydraulic and pneumatic systems. Today we employ a vastly experienced team of engineers and technicians with the ability to produce and maintain all aspects of marine and industrial hydraulic systems. The Company has vast experience in servicing and repairing all types of marine and industrial hydraulic machinery including steering gear, winches, davits, cranes, engine controls, cargo pump systems, factory conveyor systems, processing machinery and pipe installation. We also have the expertise to design and manufacture HYDRAULIC SYSTEMS and POWER PACKS to customer specification.*

Armstrong Hydraulic Services Hull Ltd, 8 Tom Thumb Industrial Estate, English Street, Hull, HU3 2BT Tel: (01482) 210680 Fax: (01482) 211947 E-mail: info@arma-hydraulic.co.uk *Hydraulic engineers installation service*

Armstrong Laing plc, 25 King Street, Knutsford, Cheshire, WA16 6DW Tel: (01565) 687000 Fax: (01565) 750030 *Computer software consultancy*

Armstrong Laundry Systems, Ampere Road, Newbury, Berkshire, RG14 2AE Tel: (01635) 33881 Fax: (01635) 32434 E-mail: enquiries@armstrong-laundry.co.uk *Armstrong has provided specialist laundry plant since 1878 and their know-how has been gained from the supply, service and manufacture of equipment for virtually every type of laundry installation. They also offer solutions to the rental markets. Products include washers, dryers, ironers, ancillary equipment and spare parts. All products have associated after-sales care, with service centres located country wide throughout the UK.*

Armstrong Lyon Hydraulics Ltd, 13 Faraday Road, Knowsley Industrial Park, Liverpool, L33 7UT Tel: 0151-545 2180 Fax: 0151-547 1309 E-mail: sales@armstronglyon.freeserve.co.uk *Hydraulic systems manufrs*

Armstrong Metal Ceilings Ltd, 9-10 Telford Drive, Tollgate Industrial Estate, Stafford, ST16 3ST Tel: (01785) 222414 Fax: (01785) 226084 *Metal ceilings manufrs*

▶ Armstrong omponents Limited, 57 Groveside, East Rudham, King's Lynn, Norfolk, PE31 8RL Tel: (01485) 529082 Fax: (01485) 529294 E-mail: dave@armstrongsales.f9.co.uk *Precision engineers. CNC & Conventional maching. Toolmaking, Injection Moulding & fabrication. Painting, anodising & plating*1 off to batch quantities 20'000 per week. Prototype design & sub-assembly*

▶ Armstrong Packaging Ltd, Baden-Powell Road, Kirkton Industrial Estate, Arbroath, Angus, DD11 3LS Tel: (01241) 430000 Fax: (01241) 431122 E-mail: admin@apbox.co.uk *Manufacturers of presentation boxes*

Armstrong Priestley, 77 Holbeck Lane, Leeds, LS11 9UL Tel: 0113-244 3138 Fax: 0113-394 4041 E-mail: sales@armstrongpriestley.co.uk *Designers & installations of automatic fire sprinklers*

Armstrong Printing Ltd, Unit 4 Carsebridge Court, Alloa, Clackmannanshire, FK10 3LQ Tel: (01259) 722930 Fax: (01259) 721080 E-mail: sales@armstrongprinting.co.uk *Commercial printers manufrs*

Armstrong Richardson & Co.Limited, Mount Pleasant Way, Stokesley Business Park, Stokesley, Middlesbrough, Cleveland, TS9 5NZ Tel: (01642) 718280 Fax: (01642) 710993 E-mail: sales@armstrongrichardson.co.uk *Animal feed merchants*

Thomas Armstrong Ltd, Park Road, Consett, County Durham, DH8 5SP Tel: (01207) 505655 Fax: (01207) 592345 E-mail: sales@thomasarmstrong.co.uk *Block paving manufacturers in the North of England supplying a full product range of rectangular, hexagonal and cobble pavers. Please log onto our website www.thomasarmstrong.co.uk. Tel: (01207) 505655*

Thomas Armstrong Construction Ltd, Workington Road, Flimby, Maryport, Cumbria, CA15 8RY Tel: (01900) 68211 Fax: (01900) 602672 *Construction contractors*

Armstrong UK Investments, Armstrong House, 38 Market Square, Uxbridge, Middlesex, UB8 1NG Tel: (01895) 251122 Fax: (01895) 231571 *Floor covering & ceiling manufrs*

Armstrongs, Hawthorne Road, Bootle, Merseyside, L20 2DG Tel: 0151-922 1910 Fax: (01704) 896890 *Removal & storage contractors* Also at: Southport

Armthorpe Fabrication, Renny's Lane, Dragonville Industrial Estate, Gilesgate, Durham, DH1 2RS Tel: 0191-386 9502 Fax: 0191-386 2092 *Stainless steel fabricators*

Armtrack Security Services, 127 Moresk Road, Truro, Cornwall, TR1 1BP Tel: (01872) 222022 Fax: (01872) 222022 *Security & wheel clamping services*

Armultra Ltd, Armultra House, Hewett Road, Great Yarmouth, Norfolk, NR31 0RB Tel: (01493) 652150 Fax: (01493) 652842 E-mail: sales@armultra.co.uk *Freezer & pressure vessel manufrs*

Army & Navy, Lockwood Way, London, E17 5RB Tel: (020) 8527 3735 Fax: (020) 8527 6639 *Camping & retailers*

▶ The Army Store, 11 - Wyndham Arcade, St Mary's Street, Cardiff, CF10 1FH Tel: 02920 343141 E-mail: info@thearmystore.co.uk

Arna & Farrington, Langley House, High Street, Thorpe-le-Soken, Clacton-on-Sea, Essex, CO16 0EA Tel: (01255) 862355 Fax: (01255) 862355 E-mail: sales@marisaarna.co.uk *Ceramic products manufrs*

Arndrove Fabrications Ltd, Unit 3 Wyther Lane, Industrial Estate, Kirkstall, Leeds, LS5 3BT Tel: 0113-230 7722 Fax: 0113-230 7207 *Steel fabricators*

Arndt Systems, 23 Falcons Rise, Belper, Derbyshire, DE56 0QN Tel: (01773) 827894 Fax: (01773) 827894 *Textile Machinery Manufacturer*

Arnesys Telecommunications Equipment, Queens Bridge Road, Nottingham, NG2 1NB Tel: 0115-985 2525 Fax: 0115-985 2526 E-mail: admin@arnesys.com *Manufacture & supply of voice communications equipment & systems based on either IP/LAN or Fibre or Analog for arduous & hazardous environments*

▶ Arngrove Construction Services, 3 Easter Park, Teesside Industrial Estate, Stockton-on-Tees, Cleveland, TS17 9NT Tel: (01642) 800666 Fax: (01642) 800688

Arno GB Ltd, Discovery House, 125 Redcliff Street, Bristol, BS1 6HU Tel: 0117-929 2541 Fax: 0117-929 4684 E-mail: display@arno-online.co.uk *Design & manufacture retail display systems*

Arnold B Johnston, Dean Road, Yate, Bristol, BS37 5NR Tel: (01454) 316175 Fax: (01454) 884455 E-mail: mail@erh.co.uk *Civil engineering contractors*

Arnold Building Services Ltd, Rudgeway, Bristol, BS35 3ZQ Tel: (01453) 547730 Fax: (01453) 547766 E-mail: info@abs-radiantheating.co.uk *Heating engineers*

Arnold Designs Ltd, London Rd, Chalford, Stroud, Glos, GL6 8NR Tel: (01453) 882310 Fax: (01453) 886977 *Giftware manufrs*

Arnold Heal Ltd, 86b St. James Street, Newport, Isle of Wight, PO30 1LB Tel: (01983) 523352 *Gunsmiths*

Arnold Hose Ltd, 2 Rothersthorpe Avenue, Rothersthorpe Avenue Industrial Estate, Northampton, NN4 8JH Tel: (01604) 706570 Fax: (01604) 661170 E-mail: ahl@arnoldhose.demon.co.uk Principal Export Areas: Worldwide *Manufacturers of flexible metallic hose/tubing; hose (stainless steel); flexible tubing/hose conduit & hose assembly*

Arnold James St Albans Ltd, 1 Metro Centre, Ronsons Way, Sandridge, St. Albans, Hertfordshire, AL4 9QT Tel: (01727) 851477 Fax: (01727) 842912 *Heating ventilation & air conditioning services*

Arnold Laver, Manningham Sawmills, Canal Road, Bradford, West Yorkshire, BD2 1AR Tel: (01274) 732861 Fax: (01274) 737060 E-mail: sales@bradford.timberworld.co.uk *Timber supplies*

Arnold Laver, 478 Basingstoke Road, Reading, RG2 0QN Tel: 0118-975 1100 Fax: 0118-975 1900 E-mail: sales@reading.timberworld.co.uk *Timber importers & merchants*

Arnold Lift Trucks, 161 Ramsey Drive, Arnold, Nottingham, NG5 6SB Tel: 0115-926 2884 Fax: 0115-926 2884 *Fork lift truck repairers*

Arnold Plant Hire Ltd, Bredbury Park Way, Bredbury Park Industrial Estate, Bredbury, Stockport, Cheshire, SK6 2SN Tel: 0161-406 8734 Fax: 0161-406 8804 E-mail: hire@arnold-plant.co.uk *Arnold Plant Hire Ltd offers a wide range of plant and equipment from ¾ ton mini excavators up to 20 ton Excavators. We specialise in Loading Shovels and Telescopic Handlers. Within the Group we operate JCB 3cx Sitemasters complete with operators if required, JCB 2cx Airmasters, dumpers, rollers, bowsers and small tools. For more information please view our website and click on 'Partners'. We operate our fleet of Loading shovels and telescopic handlers Nationwide servicing and maintaining the fleet from our Stockport, Warrington and Cannock depots. We also offer long term contract hire tailored to meet your specific requirements. Our fleet is never older than four years and most items are fitted with 'Tracker' security devices. Throughout the Group we can offer you a complete package for your plant hire requirements, a 'one stop shop'.*

Arnold Precision Engineering, 3 46 Holton Road, Holton Heath Trading Park, Poole, Dorset, BH16 6LT Tel: (01202) 621128 Fax: (01202) 621128 *Precision engineers*

▶ Arnold Warner Ltd, 247 Goldsmith Avenue, Southsea, Hampshire, PO4 0BS Tel: (023) 9283 2801

Arnold Wragg Ltd, Unit 2, Parkway One, Parkway Drive, Sheffield, S9 4WU Tel: 0114 2519050 Fax: 0114 2446635 E-mail: sales@arnold-wragg.com *Non-standard & special specification bolts & nuts including A series and AGS series locking nuts*

Arnolds Curtains & Blinds, 2-4 Dinsdale Road, Bromborough, Wirral, Merseyside, CH62 3PY Tel: 0151-343 9696 Fax: 0151-343 1838 *Curtains, blinds & flooring suppliers*

Arntz Belting Co. Ltd, Pennyburn Passage, Londonderry, BT48 0AE Tel: (028) 7126 1221 Fax: (028) 7126 3386 E-mail: abcderry@globalnet.co.uk *Belting manufrs*

Arnway Ltd, 24 Burtonwood Industrial Centre, Phipps Lane, Burtonwood, Warrington, WA5 4HX Tel: (01925) 229479 Fax: (01925) 220865 E-mail: steve@arnway.co.uk *Welding fabricators*

Arodix Ltd, Unit 4, 36 Greenford Road, Harrow, Middlesex, HA1 3QH Tel: (020) 8864 2272 Fax: (020) 8423 8870 *Ladies & gents uniform belts manufrs*

▶ Aroma Cleaning Ltd, 4b Coventry Road, Burbage, Hinckley, Leicestershire, LE10 2HL Tel: (0845) 3706106 Fax: (01455) 238480 E-mail: sales@aromacleaning.co.uk *Commercial cleaning services*

▶ Aromapetmats, Roville House, Ford Park Road, Plymouth, PL4 6RB Tel: (01752) 220541 Fax: (01752) 662876 *manufacture of dog and cat beds*

▶ Aromask Motor, 24 Chapel Street, Bradford, West Yorkshire, BD1 5DL Tel: (01274) 777662 Fax: (01274) 777665 E-mail: sales@ukmotorjobs.co.uk *Recruitment specialists for the motor trade*

▶ Aromatic Ingredients Ltd, 33 Melton Road, Tollerton, NG12 4EL Tel: 0115-937 6785 Fax: 0115-937 2206 E-mail: lauramellor@aromaticingredients.com *Suppliers of aroma chemicals*

Aromet Group Ltd, 15 Ballinderry Road, Lisburn, County Antrim, BT28 2SA Tel: (028) 9266 5721 Fax: (028) 9260 1611 *Tyre repairers*

Aronn Interiors Ltd, 17 West Avenue, Aldwick, Bognor Regis, West Sussex, PO21 3QP Tel: (01243) 823904 Fax: (01243) 841132 E-mail: ceilings@aronn.wanadoo.co.uk *Partitions & suspended ceiling installers*

Arp Plastics Ltd, Unit M Westminster Industrial Estate, Measham, Swadlincote, Derbyshire, DE12 7DS Tel: (01530) 514280 Fax: (01530) 514281 E-mail: admin@arpplastics.co.uk *Injection moulders manufrs*

▶ A-R-pcrepairs, Mill Close, Elsenham, Bishop's Stortford, Hertfordshire, CM22 6EG Tel: (01279) 810962 E-mail: richard@a-r-pcrepairs.co.uk *mobile pc repairs stansted harlow*

Arper Quality Products, 1 Ashwood Close, Branton, Doncaster, South Yorkshire, DN3 3UB Tel: (01302) 371133 Fax: (01302) 371777 *Janitorial product suppliers & bar requisites*

Arqadia Ltd, 2 Wolseley Road, Woburn Road Industrial Estate, Bedford, MK42 7AD Tel: (01234) 857488 Fax: (01234) 840190 E-mail: sales@arqadia.co.uk *Picture frame, mount boards & picture frame moulding distributors*

Arqiva Ltd, Unit 13, Garonor Way, Portbury, Bristol, BS20 7XE Tel: (01275) 371371 Fax: (01275) 371269 *Telecommunications contractor*

Arqrva Ltd, Crawley Court, Crawley, Winchester, Hampshire, SO21 2QA Tel: (01962) 823434 Fax: (01962) 822378 *Telecommunication services*

Arr Craibs, Howe Moss Drive, Dyce, Aberdeen, AB21 0GL Tel: (01224) 771122 Fax: (01224) 724461 E-mail: info@arr-craib.co.uk *Road transport & freight contractors*

▶ Arran Construction Ltd, Cleveland Hall, Cleveland Street, Darlington, County Durham, DL1 2PE Tel: (01325) 267221 Fax: (01325) 369521

▶ Arran Deliveries, Dock Road, Ardrossan, Ayrshire, KA22 8DA Tel: (01294) 469492

▶ Arran Haulage Services Ltd, The Home Farm, Brodick, Isle of Arran, KA27 8DD Tel: (01770) 302777 Fax: (01770) 302500

▶ The Arran Lamb Co., The Abattoir, Blackwaterfoot, Isle of Arran, KA27 8EZ Tel: (01770) 850264 Fax: (01770) 850264 E-mail: iain@arranlamb.com *Abattoir*

▶ Arranbrook Miniature Donkeys, Mill Farm, Azerley, Ripon, North Yorkshire, HG4 3JJ Tel: (01765) 658877 E-mail: Anne@minidonks.co.uk *Miniature Donkey stud dedicated to producing the finest stock in the world*

▶ Arrange It Lifestyle Management, 23 Redstart Avenue, Kidderminster, Worcestershire, DY10 4JR Tel: 01562 631682 E-mail: annehope@arrangeitlifestylemanagement.co.uk *We are a professional concierge & lifestyle management business based in worcestershire providing a range of services to those individuals who lead hectic lives & have insufficient time to undertake those regular mundane tasks at home ie walking the dog, arrange household repairs or organise that special event ie birthday parties, wedding anniversaries*

Arranquote Ltd, 4 Heritage Enterprise Acres, Wakefield Road, Fitzwilliam, Pontefract, West Yorkshire, WF9 5BP Tel: (01977) 617319 Fax: (01977) 617390 E-mail: arranquote@globalnet.co.uk *Steel re-rolling mill equipment suppliers*

Arraquip Ltd, Withambrook Industrial Estate, Grantham, Lincolnshire, NG31 9ST Tel: (01476) 573637 Fax: (01476) 590192 E-mail: arraquip@msn.com *Steel stockholders*

▶ Arras People, 47 York Street, Heywood, Lancashire, OL10 4NN Tel: (01706) 366444 Fax: (01706) 366544 E-mail: info@arraspeople.co.uk *The UK's Project Management Recruitment Specialists 100% focused on providing programme managers, project managers, and project support staff. We work across the UK, across many industry sectors & provide both permanent, contract & interim project management professionals. *Roles recruited for include; Programme Managers, Project Managers, Project Directors, Bid Managers, Management Consultants, Junior Project Managers, Stage /Workpackage Managers, Project Office Manager, Project Office Co-ordinators, Project Planners, Project Office Administrators, Project Analysts, Project Accountants, Bid Team Administrator and Business Analysts. *Arras People provides programme & project management recruitment services to a variety of vertical markets, these have included; Central & local government, IT, Professional services, Business /management consultancies, Healthcare, Not-for-profit & charities, Financial & banking, Media, marketing & print, Utilities, Telecoms, Security, Education & Retail.*

▶ Arrest Security Systems, Unit 2 142 Strathcona Drive, Glasgow, G13 1JQ Tel: 0141-958 1555 Fax: 0141-958 1558

Arrestapest Gidding Ltd, Whiteacre 70 Main Street, Great Gidding, Huntingdon, Cambridgeshire, PE28 5NU Tel: (01832) 293463 *Pest control services*

Arri GB Ltd, 2 Highbridge Industrial Estate, Oxford Road, Uxbridge, Middlesex, UB8 1LX Tel: (01895) 457000 Fax: (01895) 457001 E-mail: sales@arri-gb.com *Camera & lighting distributors*

▶ Arris, The Granary, Hunsingore, Wetherby, West Yorkshire, LS22 5HY Tel: (01423) 358881 Fax: (01423) 359490 E-mail: enquires@arris.co.uk *Free-thinking graphic design for corporate/brand identity, brochures, catalogues, leaflets/flyers, posters/ banners, exhibitions, CD/DVD creation, new media, websites and the internet.*

▶ Arriva Vehicle Rental, Cattle Market Road, Nottingham, NG2 3GY Tel: 0115-968 2900

Arrk Product Developement Group Ltd, 79 Sadler Foster Way, Teesside Industrial Estate, Stockton-on-Tees, Cleveland, TS17 9JY Tel: (01642) 769930 Fax: (01642) 762352 E-mail: projects@arrkeurope.com *Engineers*

Arro Signs, Unit 4 Three Springs Industrial Estate, Vincent Road, Worcester, WR5 1BW Tel: (01905) 356333 Fax: (01905) 764406 *Sign makers & suppliers*

▶ Arromax Structures Ltd, Langwith Road, Langwith Junction, Mansfield, Nottinghamshire, NG20 9RN Tel: (01623) 747466

Arromax Structures Ltd, Langwith Road, Langwith Junction, Mansfield, Nottinghamshire, NG20 9RN Tel: (01623) 747466 Fax: (01623) 748197 E-mail: sales@aromax.co.uk *Light to medium engineering services*

Arron Print Ltd, Unit 30 Enfield Industrial Estate, Redditch, Worcestershire, B97 6BY Tel: (01527) 67295 Fax: (01527) 584509 E-mail: info@arron.co.uk *Printers & designers services*

Arrow Auctions, Bartleet Road, Washford, Redditch, Worcestershire, B98 0DQ Tel: (01527) 517707 Fax: (01527) 510924 E-mail: enquiries@arrowauction.co.uk *Auctioneers & valuers to HM customs*

Arrow Aviation Services Ltd, Little Stone, Thorverton, Exeter, EX5 5LL Tel: (01884) 855327 Fax: (01884) 855249 E-mail: arrow@eclipse.co.uk *Aeronautical engineers*

Arrow Butler Castings Ltd, Station Road, Whittington Moor, Chesterfield, Derbyshire, S41 9ES Tel: (01246) 450027 Fax: (01246) 261913 E-mail: sales@arrowbutlercastings.co.uk *Non ferrous foundry*

Arrow Ceilings Ltd, A9 Hucknall Road, Nottingham, NG5 1FD Tel: 0115-985 7016 Fax: 0115-985 6883 E-mail: mail@arrowceilings.co.uk *Suspended ceiling contractors*

▶ Arrow Cleaning Services, 17 The Hudson, Wyke, Bradford, West Yorkshire, BD12 8HZ Tel: (01274) 690805 Fax: (01274) 690805 E-mail: sales@arrow-cleaning.co.uk *cleaning and support services to the UK.*

▶ Arrow Cleaning Services, 17 The Hudson, Wyke, Bradford, West Yorkshire, BD12 8HZ Tel: (01274) 690805 Fax: (01274) 690805 E-mail: sales@arrow-cleaning.co.uk *UK Cleaning and support services*

Arrow Cleaning Services, 17 The Hudson, Wyke, Bradford, West Yorkshire, BD12 8HZ Tel: (01274) 690805 Fax: (01274) 690805 E-mail: sales@cleaningservicesleeds.co.uk *Cleaning janitorial & associated services*

Arrow Components, Unit 5 Mill Court, Spindle Way, Crawley, West Sussex, RH10 1TT Tel: (01293) 558900 Fax: (01293) 558901 *Electronic distributors*

Arrow Display Fittings Ltd, 21 Bartleet Road, Redditch, Worcestershire, B98 0DG Tel: (01527) 527941 Fax: (01527) 510205 E-mail: sales@arrowdisplay.co.uk *Shop display fittings manufrs*

Arrow Electronics, London Road Campus, London Road, Harlow, Essex, CM17 9NA Tel: (01279) 441144 Fax: 01189 683801 E-mail: embedded@arrowuk.com *With over 70 years of industry expertise, Arrow Electronics is one of the world's largest distributors of electronic components and enterprise computing solutions, and a leading provider of service to the electronics industry. In addition to our vast range of Semiconductor products and electronic components Arrow Embedded Solutions, a division of Arrow Electronics, specialises in a range of electronic sub-systems from display products, touch screen, keypads, memory storage, embedded software, wireless modules, power supplies, embedded onboard and single board computers from some of the best manufacturers in the world. The pan-European AES portfolio has been especially selected to serve high growth sectors in the electronics industry. Microsoft Embedded Software* Wireless Modules and Accessories* Displays* Power Supply Units* Industrial Computer Products* Solid State Memory**

Arrow Engineering Scunthorpe, Dawes Lane, Scunthorpe, South Humberside, DN15 6UW Tel: (01724) 869371 Fax: (01724) 270190 *General engineers & fabricators*

Arrow Engineering Supply Co. Ltd, Hunters Lane Industrial Estate, Rugby, Warwickshire, CV21 1EA Tel: (01788) 574107 Fax: (01788) 542179 E-mail: frank@fasteng.co.uk *Engineer suppliers*

Arrow Engineers, 6 Izons Lane Industrial Estate, West Bromwich, West Midlands, B70 9BY Tel: 0121-553 6559 Fax: 0121-553 5872 *General engineers*

Arrow Environmental Services Ltd, Exchange Works, Kelvin Way, West Bromwich, West Midlands, B70 7JW Tel: 0121-525 0757 Fax: 0121-525 1179 E-mail: arrow.environmental@virgin.net *Tank & industrial cleaning services*

Arrow Express Couriers, 387 Railway Arches, Geffrye Street, London, E2 8HZ Tel: (020) 7294 2000 Fax: (020) 7294 2094 E-mail: sales@arrow-express.co.uk *Couriers*

Arrow Fastener (U K) Ltd, Unit 5 ZK Park, 23 Commerce Way, Croydon, CR0 4ZS Tel: 0845 5314109 Fax: (020) 8686 9197 E-mail: arrowfast@aol.com *Manufacturers of stapling machines, industrial staplers, steel measuring tapes, blind riveting systems, adhesives, hot melt & nail guns*

▶ Arrow Film Convertors, Sterling Industrial Park, Carr Wood Road, Castleford, West Yorkshire, WF10 4PS Tel: (01977) 556551 Fax: (01977) 556552

Arrow Flexible Packaging Ltd, Millingford Industrial Estate, Golborne, Warrington, WA3 3QE Tel: (01942) 722383 Fax: (01942) 716502 E-mail: sales@polythene.co.uk *Polythene bag manufrs*

▶ Arrow Geophysics, 14 The Fridays, East Dean, Eastbourne, East Sussex, BN20 0DH Tel: (01323) 423556 Fax: (01323) 423556 E-mail: enquiries@arrowgeophysics.co.uk *Geophysical surveying*

Arrow Group, Smalls Hill Road, Norwood Hill, Horley, Surrey, RH6 0HR Tel: (01293) 863024 Fax: (01293) 864003 E-mail: gatwick@arrow.co.uk *Air conditioning equipment*

Arrow Guard, Byeways, Woodgate Road, Ryarsh, West Malling, Kent, ME19 5LH Tel: (01732) 820444 Fax: (01732) 820333 *Pest & vermin control agents*

Arrow Hydraulics, 76 Heming Road, Redditch, Worcestershire, B98 0EA Tel: (01527) 517120 Fax: (01527) 517123 *Steel tube distributors*

Arrow Imaging Ltd, 34 Pebble Close, Tamworth Business Park, Amington, Tamworth, Staffordshire, B77 4RP Tel: (01827) 310350 Fax: (01827) 313880 E-mail: sales@arrow-imaging.co.uk *Electronic Document Management, Document Scanning, Drawing Scanning, Microfilm Scanning. Specialise in Internet based on-line solutions and in-house document management systems. Archive Off-site to free up space and speed access. Document storage in Arrow's Document Warehouse facility for safe, secure retrievals of paper, CD, microfilm and tapes. Kodak accredited, ISO9001, ISO14001. Invu reseller. Based in the Midlands with a UK wide customer base. Clients include: Aerospace, Automotive, Construction, Financial, Local Government, Healthcare, Housing Associations, Manufacturing, Pharmaceutical, Service Based and Utility companies.*

Arrow Industrial Ltd, 930 Hedon Road, Hull, HU9 5QN Tel: (01482) 228202 Fax: (01482) 218697 E-mail: sales@arrow-industrial.co.uk *Manufacturers of pvc strip curtains & industrial doors*

Arrow Industries Ltd, Unit 13 Tolsons Mill Estate, Lichfield Street, Tamworth, Staffordshire, B78 3QA Tel: (01827) 286959 Fax: (01827) 251952 E-mail: email@arrowindustries.co.uk *Plastic moulders*

Arrow International Technologies Ltd, Arrow House, 4 Malabar Fields, Daventry, Northamptonshire, NN11 4DP Tel: (01327) 301160 Fax: (01327) 301180 E-mail: arrowteks@aol.com *Computer components & semiconductor distributor*

Arrow Lift Trucks Ltd, 9 Kepler, Tamworth, Staffordshire, B79 7XE Tel: (01827) 313335 Fax: (01827) 313336 E-mail: sales@arrowlifttrucks.co.uk *Fork lift truck hire & sales*

▶ Arrow Light Haulage, 18 Fletcher Drive, Wickford, Essex, SS12 9FA Tel: 01375 643897 E-mail: kevinscorpion@aol.com *Professional courier services and transport solutions. Essex based but deliver UK wide. From documents to furniture we deliver everything. For Fast top quality service, fully insured drivers give us a call.*

Arrow Medical Ltd, Unit B1 Hatton Gardens Industrial Estate, Kington, Herefordshire, HR5 3RB Tel: (01544) 231760 Fax: (01544) 231640 E-mail: info@arrowmedical.co.uk *Medical device manufrs*

Arrow Metals Ltd, 200 High Street, Boston Spa, Wetherby, West Yorkshire, LS23 6BT Tel: (01937) 845066 Fax: (01937) 845897 E-mail: arrowmetalsltd@aol.com Principal Export Areas: Worldwide *Aluminium & brass stockholders*

Arrow Plastics Ltd, Arrow Works, Hampden Road, Kingston upon Thames, Surrey, KT1 3HQ Tel: (020) 8546 6258 Fax: (020) 8541 4654 E-mail: mail@arrow-plastics.co.uk *Plastics for the sign & lighting industry suppliers*

Arrow Precision Engineering Ltd, 12 Barley Field, Hinckley Fields Industrial Estate, Hinckley, Leicestershire, LE10 1YE Tel: (01455) 234200 Fax: (01455) 233545 E-mail: sales@arrowprecision.co.uk *Precision engineers*

Arrow Press, 11 Riverside Park Industrial Estate, Dogflud Way, Farnham, Surrey, GU9 7UG Tel: (01252) 722790 Fax: (01252) 721874 E-mail: sales@arrowpress.co.uk *Lithographic printers services*

Arrow Projects Consultants Ltd, 7 Dorset Road, London, SW19 3EY Tel: (020) 8543 9390 Fax: (020) 8543 8748 E-mail: sales@pmpe.co.uk *Paper making consultants*

Arrow Refrigeration & Air Conditioning, 54 Chesterton Close, Redditch, Worcestershire, B97 5XS Tel: (01527) 541420 Fax: (01527) 543843 E-mail: arrowcooling@tiscali.com *Refrigeration & air conditioning engineers*

Arrow Screen Print Ltd, 3 Fletcher Way, Weston Road, Norwich, NR3 3ST Tel: (01603) 485942 Fax: (01603) 485385 E-mail: sales@arrowscreenprint.co.uk *Established 1975 in Norwich the Company has had a steady growth and now occupies 5000 sq ft unit. Specialising in all types of retail & industrial labels, plastic and component printing direct onto customer supplied goods.*

Arrow Security Ltd, 62a Frimley High Street, Frimley, Camberley, Surrey, GU16 7JF Tel: (0800) 0922031 Fax: (01276) 677263 E-mail: info@arrowsecurity.co.uk *ISO and NACOSS accredited. Independent UK supplier and installer of security systems specialising in access control, cctv systems, fire alarms, intruder/burglar alarms. 24 hour call out and maintenance services. 24 hour central monitoring. Offices in Surrey and London.*

Arrow Signs, Nairn Road, Cramlington, Northumberland, NE23 1RQ Tel: (01670) 735922 Fax: (01670) 716269 *Signwriting & lettering services*

Arrow Technical Services Ltd, 58 Nursery Street, Sheffield, S3 8GG Tel: 0114-281 2018 Fax: 0114-281 5404 E-mail: info@arrowtechnical.com *Printed circuit board design services*

Arrow Tool & Cutter Co Ltd, 13 Ireton Avenue, Leicester, LE4 9EU Tel: 0116-276 1633 *Woodworking machinery & tooling merchants*

Arrow Valves Ltd, 68 High Street, Tring, Hertfordshire, HP23 4AG Tel: (01442) 823123 Fax: (01442) 823234 E-mail: info@arrowvalves.co.uk *Water rigs valve specialists*

Arrow Window Systems, Warwick Road, Fairfield Industrial Estate, Louth, Lincolnshire, LN11 0YB Tel: (01507) 601861 Fax: (01507) 607642 *Double glazing services*

Arrow Wire Products Ltd, 15 Boulton Road, Reading, RG2 0NF Tel: 0118-987 4521 Fax: 0118-931 3456 E-mail: sales@arrowwireproducts.co.uk *Shopfitting suppliers & distributors*

Arrowflight, High Croft, Coldharbour Lane, Bletchingley, Redhill, RH1 4NA Tel: (01883) 744644 Fax: (01883) 744530 E-mail: sales@arrowflight.co.uk Principal Export Areas: Central America *Software developers*

Arrowfreight Ltd, Unit D3, Crossgate Drive, Queens Drive Industrial Estate, Nottingham, NG2 1LW Tel: 0115-986 8031 Fax: 0115-986 0607 E-mail: info@arrowfreight.com *Freight & air freight forwarders*

Arrowhead, Barn Owl Cottage, Moretonhmpstead, North Bovey, Newton Abbot, Devon, TQ13 8QT Tel: (01647) 441212 Fax: (01647) 441212 E-mail: info@arrowheaduk.com *Archery equipment manufrs*

Arrowhead Hire, Unit 5 Kennet Weir Bussiness Park, Arrowhead Road, Theale, Reading, RG7 4AD Tel: 0118-930 3703 Fax: 0118-930 4160 *Excavator & tool hire*

▶ Arrowhead Printing Ltd, 1 Alton Business Centre, Omega Park, Alton, Hampshire, GU34 2YU Tel: (01420) 549960 Fax: (01420) 549967

▶ Arrowhead Training and Consultancy Services, 80 Woolmer Road, Nottingham, NG2 2FB Tel: 0115-952 8603 E-mail: admin@arrowheadtraining.co.uk *Training & development consultancy*

▶ Arrowpak International, 11 Crompton Road, Hadleigh Road Industrial Estat, Ipswich, IP2 0UQ Tel: (01473) 210459 Fax: (01473) 210458

▶ Arrowpak Removals & Storage, Westwood Farm, Westwood, Peterborough, PE3 9UW Tel: (01733) 333445 Fax: (01733) 333665

Arrowpak Transport & Warehousing Ltd, Norwood Road, Brandon, Suffolk, IP27 0PB Tel: (01842) 812165 Fax: (01842) 813051 E-mail: sales@arrowpak.co.uk *Removal contractors* Also at: Abingdon, Cambridge & Oxford

Arrowsacks Packaging, PO Box 234, Dover, Kent, CT15 6GD Tel: (01304) 853604 Fax: (01304) 852540 E-mail: arrowsacks@isleoak.freeserve.co.uk *Polythene/polypropylene bags*

Arrowvale Electronics, Shawbank Road, Redditch, Worcestershire, B98 8YN Tel: (01527) 514151 Fax: (01527) 514321 E-mail: info@arrowvale.co.uk *Electronic assembly services*

▶ Art 4 U, The Colonnades, Albert Dock, Liverpool, L3 4AA Tel: 0151-708 7400 Fax: 0151-707 6800 *Artists material suppliers*

Art All, 34 Britannia Way, Britannia Enterprise Park, Lichfield, Staffordshire, WS14 9UY Tel: (01543) 258222 Fax: (01543) 258444 E-mail: signs@artall.co.uk *Sign manufrs*

Art Blinds, 372 London Road, Hadleigh, Benfleet, Essex, SS7 2DA Tel: (01702) 559969 Fax: (01702) 554058 *Blinds manufrs*

Art Bronze Foundry Ltd, 1 Michael Road, London, SW6 2ER Tel: (020) 7736 7292 Fax: (020) 7731 5460 E-mail: service@artbronze.co.uk *Statuary foundry*

Art Equipment, 3 Craven Street, Northampton, NN1 3EZ Tel: (01604) 632447 Fax: (01604) 632447 E-mail: charlesstradling@aol.com Principal Export Areas: Central/East Europe & West Europe *Engineers for the Arts, etchings, lithograph, equipment maintenance and repairs to machinery on and of site.*

▶ Art Exhibition Textile Ltd, 16 Dalesford, Haslingden, Rossendale, Lancashire, BB4 6QH Tel: (01706) 219550 Fax: (01706) 222218 E-mail: sales@artex-online.com *Art Exhibition Textiles Ltd specialise in the production, import and distribution of quality Textiles, Garments, Outdoor goods (camping equipment) and Hi Visibility Clothing.*

Art Forma (Furniture) Ltd, Station Road, Castle Donington, Derby, DE74 2NU Tel: (01332) 810474 Fax: (01332) 810277 E-mail: sales@artforma.co.uk *Furniture manufrs*

Art Founders, 11 Springwood Industrial Estate, Braintree, Essex, CM7 2YP Tel: (01376) 343222 Fax: (01376) 341793 E-mail: info@msaf.co.uk *Bronze casters, sculpture manufrs*

▶ Art Gecko, 59A High Street, East Grinstead, West Sussex, RH19 3DD Tel: (01342) 323007 *Art & craft materials suppliers*

Art Glass Ltd, Ellis Ashton Street, Liverpool, L36 6BN Tel: 0151-489 2214 Fax: 0151-489 2214 E-mail: sales@artglass.co.uk *Glazing repairs including stained glass services*

Art Glass Processing Ltd, Ripley Road, Bradford, West Yorkshire, BD4 7TP Tel: (01274) 393161 Fax: (01274) 393895 *Glass merchants*

▶ Art & Image Ltd, Orchehill Avenue, Gerrards Cross, Buckinghamshire, SL9 8QF Tel: (01753) 884535 Fax: (0870) 4601546 E-mail: valerie@artandimage.co.uk *Printing services*

▶ The Art Library Ltd, 14 West Street, Comberton, Cambridge, CB3 7DS Tel: 01223 264011 E-mail: info@theartlibrary.co.uk *The Art Library leases and sells works of art to corporations, government, hotels and leisure facilities. We create pleasant and stimulating working environments and make offices, boardrooms and corridors more inviting for visitors as well as their personnel.*

▶ Art Logistics Ltd, 1 Victoria Industrial Estate, Victoria Road, London, W3 6UU Tel: (020) 8993 8811 Fax: (020) 8993 8833

▶ Art Marine Ltd, Pythouse Upper Barn, Tisbury, Salisbury, SP3 6PA Tel: (01747) 871272 E-mail: jt@artmarine.co.uk *Publisher & dealer of prints & paintings by marine artists*

Art Media Associates, Beech Croft House, Rugby, Warwickshire, CV22 7TD Tel: (01788) 522779 Fax: (01788) 522779 *Video & multi-media production*

Art Pewter Silver Ltd, 3B Colvilles Road, Kelvin Industrial Estate, East Kilbride, Glasgow, G75 0RS Tel: (01355) 229446 Fax: (01355) 264762 E-mail: service@artpewter.co.uk *Jewellery manufrs*

▶ Art Plus Function Ltd, Macknade, Selling Road, Faversham, Kent, ME13 8XF Tel: (01795) 530400 Fax: (0870) 7627707 E-mail: info@artplusfunction.co.uk *Home decoration*

Art Sales Index Ltd, 194 Thorpe Lea Road, Egham, Surrey, TW20 8HA Tel: (01784) 451145 Fax: (01784) 451144 E-mail: info@art-sales-index.com *Directory publishers*

Art Systems Ltd, Unit 10-12, Glaisdale Point, Glaisdale Parkway, Nottingham, NG8 4GP Tel: (0870) 2243612 Fax: (0870) 2243613 E-mail: sales@artsystems.ltd.uk *Computer wholesaler & distributor*

Art Trade Frames, 2 Dagnan Road, London, SW12 9LQ Tel: (020) 8673 8797 Fax: (020) 8265 2221 *Picture framers & hand finishers*

Art Workshop NW Ltd, Unit 20 Kingston Mill, Chestergate, Stockport, Cheshire, SK3 0AL Tel: 0161-429 9445 Fax: 0161-480 0218 *Graphic design services*

▶ Artastik Ltd, Unit 6 Shorade Industrial Estate, New Street, Bridgtown, Cannock, Staffordshire, WS11 0DH Tel: (01543) 468434 E-mail: info@artastik.co.uk *Art, craft & stationery suppliers*

Artcom Tradebridge Ltd, Unit 2E, South Bridgend, Crieff, Perthshire, PH7 4DJ Tel: (01764) 654666 Fax: (0560) 1163109 E-mail: enquiries@scot-track.co.uk Sales Contact: C. Masson *Vehicle (cross country/rough terrain/off-road) manufacturers & distributors or agents. Also vehicle hire/contract/rental/leasing/ fleet management*

Artd'Sign Sign Manufacturer, Victoria Road, Unit 8, Teknol House, Burgess Hill, West Sussex, RH15 9LH Tel: (01444) 241215 Fax: (01444) 239136 E-mail: info@artdsigns.co.uk *Experts in sign making & sign writing*

Arte Engineering Co., Unit 8 Great Bridge Industrial Estate, Tipton, West Midlands, DY4 0HR Tel: 0121-520 8953 Fax: 0121-520 8953 *General precision engineers*

Arteb Printing Ltd, Unit 13 Lyon Industrial Estate, Brindley Road, Reginald Road Industrial Estate, St. Helens, Merseyside, WA9 4HY Tel: (01744) 820933 Fax: (01744) 815154 E-mail: info@arteb.co.uk *Flexographic printing & slitting services*

Artedi (U K) Ltd, Unit D, Everitt Road, London, NW10 6PL Tel: (020) 8961 6555 Fax: (020) 8961 9996 *Glass & stone furniture importers*

▶ Artefekz, 2 Parbrook Close, Tile Hill, Coventry, CV4 9XY Tel: (024) 7642 2000 Fax: (024) 7646 2694 E-mail: info@artefekz.com *Manufacturer & retail of postal tubes & boxes*

Artek Contracts, 173 Red Lion Road, Surbiton, Surrey, KT6 7RG Tel: (020) 8397 2121 *Office blind manufrs*

Artel Rubber Co., The Studio Unit 3/A, Waterloo Industrial Estate, Waterloo Road, Bidford-on-Avon, Alcester, Warwickshire, B50 4JH Tel: (01789) 774099 Fax: (01789) 774599 E-mail: sales@artelrubber.co.uk *Silicone rubber products manufrs*

Artem Ltd, Perivale Park, Horsenden Lane South, Perivale, Greenford, Middlesex, UB6 7RH Tel: (020) 8997 7771 Fax: (020) 8997 1503 E-mail: info@artem.com *Special effects company*

▶ Artemia Ltd, Keystone House, Grateley, Andover, Hampshire, SP11 8HZ Tel: (01264) 889020 E-mail: pajohnson@doctors.org.uk *Occupational health consultancy, accident or incident investigation & reporting*

Artemide GB Ltd, 106 Great Russell Street, London, WC1B 3NB Tel: (020) 7631 5200 Fax: (020) 7631 5222 E-mail: info@artemide.co.uk *Lighting manufrs*

Artemis Corporation, Kingsclere Park, Kingsclere, Newbury, Berkshire, RG20 4SW Tel: (01635) 291800 Fax: (01635) 291801 E-mail: sales@artemiscorp.com *Network solutions providers*

Arten Co. Ltd, New Bongate Mill, Jedburgh, Roxburghshire, TD8 6DU Tel: (01835) 863380 Fax: (01835) 862148 E-mail: info@halfttern.co.uk *Archery equipment engineers*

Arter Bros Ltd, Barham Services, Folkestone Road, Barham, Canterbury, Kent, CT4 6EX Tel: (01227) 831356 Fax: (01227) 832060 E-mail: sales@arterbros.co.uk *Tractor distributor, forecourt & car repairs*

Arterial Engineering Works Ltd, Morston Road, Blakeney, Holt, Norfolk, NR25 7BE Tel: (01263) 740444 Fax: (01263) 740444 *Electric kilns & potters' wheels & pottery materials*

Artetch Circuits Ltd, Riverside Industrial Estate, Bridge Road, Littlehampton, West Sussex, BN17 5DF Tel: (01903) 725365 Fax: (01903) 730572 E-mail: sales@artetch.co.uk *Printed circuit manufrs*

Artex Rawlplug Ltd, Pasture Lane, Ruddington, Nottingham, NG11 6AE Tel: 0115-984 9124 Fax: 0115-940 5240 *DIY product distribs*

▶ artful construction.co.uk, Old Court Works, Bickleigh, Tiverton, Devon, EX16 8RP Tel: (01884) 855656 Fax: (01884) 855656 E-mail: info@artfulconstruction.co.uk *We are an experienced, multi-disciplinary company that is able to bring together a unique combination of creative skills: Design origination, concept development and project realisation. We have a fully equipped workshop as our Devon base and are able to produce fine quality work in the fields of: Architectural modelmaking, commercial sculpture, 2D & 3D graphics and public art.*

▶ Artful Dodgers, Unit 3-4 Laneside Works, Stockclough Lane, Feniscowles, Blackburn, BB2 5JR Tel: 0161-228 2850 Fax: (01254) 207484 E-mail: sales@artfuldodgers.co.uk *Educational suppliers*

Artful Dodgers, Burrs Hill, Staplehurst Rd, Marden, Tonbridge, Kent, TN12 9BS Tel: 01622 831800 Fax: 01622 831800 *Exhibition & display services*

▶ Artful Image Picture Library, Basildon Business Centre, Bentalls, Basildon, Essex, SS14 3FT Tel: 01268 274456 E-mail: sales@artfulimage.co.uk *Artful Image Picture Library has a large collection of stock photographs available for download direct to your computer.*

Artfull, 12 Victoria Terrace, London, N4 4DA Tel: (020) 7272 9341 Fax: (020) 7281 9252 E-mail: nnewglass@aol.com *Hand blown glass makers*

Arthouse P R, 7a Market Street, Crediton, Devon, EX17 2EE Tel: (01363) 777002 Fax: (01363) 779956 E-mail: sales@arthouse-pr.com *Arthouse PR offers creative Public Relations support. With experience and expertise across the board, our extensive range of activities address all areas of profile raising. Working with both larger corporate clients and smaller businesses, we have particular knowledge of the homes & interiors industry, specialising in the promotion of luxury furnishings.*

Arthritis Research Campaign, Copeman House St. Marys Court, St. Marys Gate, Chesterfield, Derbyshire, S41 7TD Tel: (01246) 558033 Fax: (01246) 558007 E-mail: enquiries@arc.org.uk *Medical research charity*

Arthur A Brown & Co., Fairfield Road, Market Harborough, Leicestershire, LE16 9QH Tel: (01858) 462946 Fax: (01858) 462884 E-mail: partners@aabrown.co.uk *Production engineers*

Anna Arthur & Associates Solicitors, 5 Fieri Facais House, High Street, Ripley, Surrey, GU23 6AF Tel: (01483) 222499 Fax: (01483) 222766 *Solicitors*

Arthur Beesley, 7 Trotters Lane, Harlaxton, Grantham, Lincolnshire, NG32 1JQ Tel: (01476) 565386 *Embroidery agents*

Arthur Black General Smiths Ltd, Clay Lane, Oldbury, West Midlands, B69 4TH Tel: 0121-552 4212 Fax: 0121-552 2208 E-mail: info@arthurblack.com *Blacksmiths & metal bending/forming services. Also manufacturers of forging (hand); bolts, u; bolts, foundation & ladders, steel*

Arthur Bramwell & Co. Ltd, Bronte House, 58-62 High Street, Epping, Essex, CM16 4AE Tel: (01992) 577333 Fax: (01992) 561138 E-mail: arthurbranwell@branwell.com *Gums producers*

▶ Arthur Cooper Construction Ltd, 72 Church St, Greasbrough, Rotherham, South Yorkshire, S61 4DX Tel: (01709) 551086

Arthur Diamond, Atkinson House, 43 Duke Street, Liverpool, L1 5AP Tel: 0151-706 0336 Fax: 0151-706 0336 *Signmaker*

Arthur Elkin Holdings Ltd, Progress Mill, Parsonage Street, Macclesfield, Cheshire, SK11 7LY Tel: (01625) 423502 Fax: (01625) 612994 E-mail: elkin.sales@arthurelkin.co.uk *Pleaters & makers up of school skirts & corporate wear skirts*

Arthur Hayes Opticians Ltd, 1070 Whitgift Centre, Croydon, CR0 1UX Tel: (020) 8686 0707 *Optical goods merchants* Also at: East Grinstead, Thornton Heath & Tunbridge Wells

John Arthur & Son Ltd, Throckley Industrial Estate, Ponteland Road, Throckley, Newcastle upon Tyne, NE15 9EW Tel: 0191-267 1341 Fax: 0191-264 0329 *Steel drum merchants & transporters*

▶ Arthur Mckay & Co. Ltd, 42 Dryden Road, Loanhead, Midlothian, EH20 9LZ Tel: 0131-440 6000 Fax: 0131-440 6001

Arthur Neal & Co. Ltd, 6 Send Road, Caversham, Reading, RG4 8EH Tel: 0118-947 0519 Fax: 0118-946 1418 E-mail: anealco@aol.com *Wholesale cycle component dealers*

Arthur Price, Britannia Way, Lichfield, Staffordshire, WS14 9UY Tel: (01543) 267324 Fax: (01543) 414488 E-mail: catering@arthur-price.com *Cutlery & silverware manufrs* Also at: Glasgow & Sheffield

Arthur Redman Contractors, 9 Moat Farm Lane, Bishampton, Pershore, Worcestershire, WR10 2NJ Tel: (01386) 462426 Fax: (01386) 462426 *Plant hire & ground workers*

▶ Arthur Rostron & Sons Ltd, Forge Lane, Canal Road, Leeds, LS12 2PR Tel: 0113-263 8988 Fax: 0113-279 0234

▶ Arthur Simms New Homes, The Old Barn, Harpenden Road, Wheathampstead, St. Albans, Hertfordshire, AL4 8EE Tel: (01582) 834200 Fax: (01582) 832981

Arthur Stephenson Engineers Ltd, Gibfield Works, Bag Lane, Atherton, Manchester, M46 0RD Tel: (01942) 883046 Fax: (01942) 896025 E-mail: ormerod@enterprise.net *General fabrication engineers*

Arthur Wood Advertising Ltd, 69 Dane Road, Sale, Cheshire, M33 7BP Tel: 0161-968 6900 Fax: 0161-968 6939 E-mail: info@awa.uk *Marketing & advertising consultants*

Artic Air Refrigeration & Air Conditioning, 14 Bell Mead, Studley, Warwickshire, B80 7SH Tel: (01527) 857578 Fax: (01527) 857578 *Maintain & suppliers of refrigeration & air conditioning systems*

▶ Artic Building Services Ltd, Artic House, Business Park, Green Lane, London, SE9 3TL Tel: (020) 8851 0111 Fax: (020) 8517 0011 *Air conditioning*

Artic Trailers, Holton Road, Nettleton, Market Rasen, Lincolnshire, LN7 6AW Tel: (01472) 851314 Fax: (01472) 851314 *Trailer repair & manufrs*

Articole Ltd, 9 Alexander Road, Stotfold, Hitchin, Hertfordshire, SG5 4NA Tel: (01462) 835640 Fax: (01462) 834896 E-mail: steve@articolestudios.co.uk *Plaster & silicone rubber moulds manufrs*

Artifax Signs & Print, 9f New Yard, Clay Flatts Industrial Estate, Workington, Cumbria, CA14 3YE Tel: (01900) 606452 Fax: (01900) 608395 E-mail: m.laidlow@btopenworld.com *Sign manufacturers & screen printers*

Artis Studios Ltd, The Studio 56a High Street, Sunninghill, Ascot, Berkshire, SL5 9NF Tel: (01344) 870033 E-mail: kat@artisstudios.com *Artis Studios is a contemporary photography studio based just off Sunninghill High Street, near Ascot. The studio specialises in social photography, focusing on creating stunning, natural wedding and portrait images.*

▶ Artisan, Phoenix Mills, Phoenix Street, Brighouse, West Yorkshire, HD6 1PD Tel: (01484) 723717 Fax: (01484) 723184

▶ Artisan Ltd, Dean Court, Great Western Business Park, Yate, Bristol, BS37 5NJ Tel: (01454) 321212 Fax: (01454) 313471 *Exhibition display graphics exhibition stand design & build*

▶ Artisan, 4 Riley Road, Telford Way Industrial Estate, Kettering, Northamptonshire, NN16 8NN Tel: (01536) 522777 Fax: (01536) 522666 E-mail: sales@artisansigns.co.uk *Sign makers*

Artisan Control Equipment, 10 Pinfold Workshops, Pinfold La Industrial Estate, Buckley, Clwyd, CH7 3PL Tel: (01244) 550012 Fax: (01244) 549482 *Lifts parts suppliers*

Artisan Precision Engineering Co., Snatchwood Road, Abersychan, Pontypool, Gwent, NP4 7BT Tel: (01495) 772644 Fax: (01495) 773844 E-mail: artisan04@supernet.com *Precision welders & fabricators*

▶ Artisan Press Ltd, 4 Boston Road, Leicester, LE4 1AQ Tel: 0116-235 5221 Fax: 0116-236 6222 E-mail: sales@artisanpress.co.uk

Artisan Refractories Ltd, Hanley Road, Stoke-on-Trent, ST1 6BG Tel: (01782) 266563 Fax: (01782) 266563 E-mail: artisanref@aol.com *Refractory contractors*

▶ Artisan Security Doors, Unit 5 Usher St Business Park, Bradford, West Yorkshire, BD4 7DS Tel: (01274) 723123 Fax: (01274) 727477 E-mail: sales@artisan-doors.co.uk *Roller shutters manufrs*

Artisan Sintered Products Ltd, Unit 15, Shepley Industrial Estate, Audenshaw, Manchester, M34 5DW Tel: 0161-336 5911 Fax: 0161-3350280 E-mail: sales@artisancarbide.co.uk *Tungsten carbide drill tips and saw tips, tungsten carbide blasting nozzles, tungsten carbide wear parts & bespoke tungsten carbide components*

continued

▶ Artisan Software Tools Ltd, 701 Eagle Tower, Montpelier Drive, Cheltenham, Gloucestershire, GL50 1TA Tel: (01242) 229300 Fax: (01242) 229301 E-mail: info@artisansw.com *Software development for business*

▶ Artisan Solutions Ltd, Venture House 2 Arlington Square, Downshire Way, Bracknell, Berkshire, RG12 1WA Tel: (01344) 742808 Fax: (01344) 742908 *Computer consultants*

▶ Artisan Surveyors, 5 Heyes Drive, Southampton, SO19 1SE Tel: (0845) 2579636 Fax: (023) 8039 2209 E-mail: office@artisansurveyors.co.uk *Asbestos surveys & sampling*

Artisan Tools Ltd, Edison Courtyard, Brunel Road, Earlstrees Industrial Estate, Corby, Northamptonshire, NN17 4LS Tel: (01536) 201000 Fax: (01536) 201389 E-mail: sales@artisan-tools.co.uk *Tool & engineers merchants* Also at: Peterborough

▶ Artisan Work Surfaces, Units 3-4, Shelton Court, Shelton Road, Willowbrook Industrial Estate, Corby, Northamptonshire, NN17 5YU Tel: (01536) 409771 Fax: (01536) 201641 E-mail: sales@artisanworksurfaces.co.uk *Artisan work surfaces are fabricators of solid surface*

Artistic Blind Co., 115 Staple Hill Road, Bristol, BS16 5AD Tel: 0117-910 9888 Fax: 0117-910 9890 E-mail: sales@artisticblinds.co.uk *Blinds & awnings*

▶ Artistic Ironwork Supplies, Unit 13 14, Waterfall La Trading Estate, Cradley Heath, West Midlands, B64 6PU Tel: 0121-559 4111 E-mail: info@artisticironsupplies.co.uk

Artistic Solutions Ltd, Coventry Road, Burbage, Hinckley, Leicestershire, LE10 2HL Tel: (01455) 634742 Fax: (01455) 633543 *Glass reinforced plastics designers & manufrs*

Artistic Trims Ltd, Aston House, 77 Upper Trinity Street, Birmingham, B9 4EG Tel: 0121-766 6167 Fax: 0121-766 6360 E-mail: elastic@artistictrims.co.uk *Manufacturers of elastic tape, elastic braid, elastic cord*

Artistic Upholstery Ltd, Bridge Street, Long Eaton, Nottingham, NG10 4QQ Tel: 0115-973 4481 Fax: 0115-946 1018 E-mail: sales@artisticupholstery.co.uk *Manufacturing upholsterers*

Artistic Window Blinds, Shopping Precinct, 28o Lochside Road, Dumfries, DG2 0LW Tel: (01387) 268518 Fax: (01387) 268518 *Window blinds*

▶ Artistry In Iron Ltd, Unit D2 Commercial Avenue, Cheadle Hulme, Cheadle, Cheshire, SK8 6QH Tel: 0161-482 8022 Fax: 0161-482 8023 E-mail: sales@artistryuk.com *Furniture & architectural products manufrs*

Artistuff Framing Ltd, Victoria Road, Swindon, SN1 3BH Tel: (01793) 522152 Fax: (01793) 488379 *Picture framers & fine art gallery*

Artizan Communications, Milton Road, Ware, Hertfordshire, SG12 0QD Tel: (01920) 466678 Fax: (01920) 466821 E-mail: jane@artizan-on-line.com *Strategic communication agents*

▶ Artlines Media Ltd, 54 Cressex Buissness Park, Lincoln Road, High Wycombe, Buckinghamshire, HP12 3RL Tel: (01494) 614600 Fax: (01494) 614601 E-mail: tom@artlines.co.uk *Multi-disciplinary designers*

Arto Chemicals Ltd, Arto House, London Road, Binfield, Bracknell, Berkshire, RG42 4BU Tel: (01344) 860737 Fax: (01344) 860820 E-mail: sales@artochemicals.com *Synthetic rubber & plastic polymers traders*

Artoray Engineering Ltd, 58 Thorney La North, Iver, Buckinghamshire, SL0 9LR Tel: (01753) 655987 Fax: (01753) 651540 *Mechanical engineers*

Artronics Manufacturing Ltd, Old School House, 6 Church Street, Somersham, Huntingdon, Cambridgeshire, PE28 3EG Tel: (01487) 740447 Fax: (01487) 740449 E-mail: sales@itonics.co.uk *Electronics production*

Artrow Metals Co. Ltd, Landywood Lane, Cheslyn Hay, Walsall, WS6 7AL Tel: (01922) 412602 Fax: (01922) 414583 *Steel stockholders*

Arts & Fashion Co. Ltd, Unit 7 Concorde Business Centre, Concorde Road, Acton, London, W3 0TJ Tel: (020) 8896 2929 Fax: (020) 8814 0735 *Furniture & furnishing importers, wholesalers & distributors*

Artseens.com Picture Library, 45 Avondale Court, Avondale Road, London, E16 4PU Tel: (020) 7476 0215 E-mail: info@artseens.com *Online photo library, photographers,designers*

▶ Artside Barnsley, 23 Gerald Place, Kendray, Barnsley, South Yorkshire, S70 3BW Tel: 07947 339658 E-mail: youngbritishartist@hotmail.com *British art, original oils, acrylics & watercolours*

▶ artstop.biz, 29 Red Lion Street, Aylsham, Norwich, NR11 6ER Tel: (01263) 734571 Fax: (01263) 735804 *Art material suppliers*

Artstore (Scotland) Ltd, 94 Queen Street, Glasgow, G1 3AQ Tel: 0141-221 1101 Fax: 0141-204 2902 E-mail: artstore@artstore.co.uk *Art & craft materials suppliers*

▶ Artwork Print Ltd, Unit 29, Wilmer Industrial Estate, Wilmer Place, London, N16 0LW Tel: (020) 7254 3993 E-mail: info@artworkprint.co.uk *graphic design and printing services*

Artworks Solutions Ltd, 22-24 Winterstoke Road, Ashton, Bristol, BS3 2NQ Tel: 0117-966 6331 Fax: 0117-966 6332 E-mail: sales@artworks-solutions.com *Art, graphics & sign manufacturers for the corporate interior sector*

▶ Artworkshops, 43 Broomleaf Road, Farnham, Surrey, GU9 8DQ Tel: 01252 714221 *Artworkshops provides primary art and craft training and resource materials for use by teachers. Specialising in Key Stages 1 and 2.*

Arun Components Ltd, PO Box 281, Bognor Regis, West Sussex, PO21 9AE Tel: (01243) 587215 Fax: (01243) 584382 E-mail: sales@aruncomponents.co.uk *Arun Components Ltd started business in 2003 supplying Marushin connectors within the UK. Our product ranges now include ceramic and tantalum capacitors, trimmer potentiometers, AC and DC fans, a wide range of connectors, fuseholders and heatsinks.*We are fully franchised by our principals.*Popular products include - DC Connectors - we supply the Marushin range, which include parts to EIAJ RC5320A, RC5321 and RC5322 as well as many other sizes and lockable connectors.*Audio Connectors - 2.5mm, 3.5 mm and 6.35 mm miniature plugs and jacks (2 to 6 pole), DIN connectors, Phono /RCA connectors, and audio adaptors.*Fans -a big range of AC fans, DC fans and blowers - datasheets are on our web site.*Heatsinks - our supplier specialises in custom solutions including machining to customers specifications, customer specific extrusions and surface finishing.*Trimmer potentiometers - a wide range of wirewound, precision and trimmer potentiometers - compatible with leading industry types.*

Arun Computer Equipment Ltd, 72-74 Clifton Road, Worthing, West Sussex, BN11 4DP Tel: (01903) 529077 Fax: (01903) 529088 E-mail: sales@aruncomputers.co.uk *Computer consultants*

Arun Environmental, Batten Street, Aylestone Road, Leicester, LE2 7PB Tel: 0116-283 0020 Fax: 0116-244 0430 E-mail: tomwhalley@arunenvironmental.co.uk *Heating & ventilation equipment distributors*

Arun International (Power) Ltd, Unit F1, Dominion Way, Littlehampton, West Sussex, BN16 3HQ Tel: (01903) 850285 Fax: (01903) 850636 E-mail: sales@arunpower.co.uk *Manufacturers of diesel generating sets & associated switchgear*

Arun Sails Ltd, The Sail Centre Southfields Industrial Estate, Delling Lane, Bosham, Chichester, West Sussex, PO18 8NW Tel: (01243) 573185 Fax: (01243) 573032 E-mail: arun@sailmakers.com *Sail makers*

Arun Welding Supplies Ltd, Block B, Rudford Industrial Estate, Ford, Arundel, West Sussex, BN18 0BS Tel: (01903) 717606 Fax: (01903) 730214 E-mail: enquiry@arunwelding.com *Welding equipment & supplies*

Arunday Computer Services, 41 Fairford Cl, Redditch, Worcs, B98 9LU Tel: 01527 63742 *Software development*

Arundel Stone, 62 Aldwick Road, Bognor Regis, West Sussex, PO21 2PE Tel: (01243) 829151 Fax: (01243) 860341 E-mail: info@arundelstone.co.uk *Cast stone manufrs*

Arundel Street Joinery, 151 Arundel Street, Sheffield, S1 2NU Tel: 0114-275 6255 Fax: 0114-275 6255 *Joinery manufrs*

Arundelle Industrial Services Ltd, 250 High Street, Cranleigh, Surrey, GU6 8RL Tel: (01483) 277801 Fax: (01483) 277802 E-mail: sales@arundelle.co.uk *Waste disposal, tank & vessell cleaning, decontamination, environmental cleaning, pollution control & oil spill contractor*

Arup, 13 Fitzroy Steet, London, W1T 4BQ Tel: (020) 7636 1531 Fax: (020) 7755 3716 E-mail: corporate@arup.com *Consulting engineers & designers*

Arup Acoustics, 8 St Thomas Street, Winchester, Hampshire, SO23 9HE Tel: (01962) 829900 Fax: (01962) 867270 E-mail: rob.harris@arup.com *Acoustic consultants*

▶ Aru's 4 Accessories, 4 Courtlands Avenue, Langley, Slough, SL3 7LE Tel: (01753) 549388 Fax: (01753) 549388 E-mail: arus4accessories@yahoo.co.uk *We are designers and manufacturers of fashion accessories. We supply handbags/shawls/scarfs. We also manufacture woven garments for ladies i.e blouses and skirts, childrens and mens clothing.*

▶ ARV Solutions, 27 Southmead Road, Westbury-On-Trym, Bristol, BS10 5DL Tel: 0117 9083173 Fax: 0871 661 3669 E-mail: mail@arvsolutions.co.uk *Recruitment business*

▶ Arvanti UK Ltd, Unit 6, Morley Business Centre, Morley Road, Tonbridge, Kent, TN9 1RA Tel: (01732) 366063 Fax: (01732) 770890 E-mail: info@arvanti.co.uk *Digital printers*

Arvin Motion Control Ltd, 15 New Star Road, Leicester, LE4 9JD Tel: 0116-274 3600 Fax: 0116-274 3620 E-mail: info@camloc.com Principal Export Areas: Worldwide *Gas spring manufacturers & ball & clevis joint distributors*

Arvin Replacement Products, New Haden Road, Cheadle, Stoke-on-Trent, ST10 1UF Tel: (01538) 752561 Fax: (01538) 752202 *Exhaust manufrs*

Arvin Replacment Products, Squires Gate Industrial Estate, Squires Gate Lane, Blackpool, FY4 3RN Tel: (01253) 400400 Fax: (01253) 406475 Principal Export Areas: Central/East Europe & West Europe *Exhaust systems manufrs* Also at: Blackpool, Bristol, Enfield, Falkirk, Redhill, Sheffield, Tamworth & Washington

Arvin Roofing Ltd, Prestage Works, 1 Prestage Way, London, E14 9QE Tel: (020) 7987 4711 Fax: (020) 7538 3177 E-mail: contract@arvin.sons.co.uk *Roofing contractors*

Arvinmeritor, Squires Gate Lane, Blackpool, FY4 3RN Tel: (01253) 345591 Fax: (01253) 402012 E-mail: info@arvin.com *Exhaust manufrs* Also at: Preston & Ramsbottom

ArvinMeritor HVS Ltd, Park Lane, Great Alne, Alcester, Warwickshire, B49 6HT Tel: (01789) 768236 Fax: (01789) 488031 *Assemblers of vehicle axles*

Arvon Die & Tool Co., Oaks Street, Quarry Bank, Brierley Hill, West Midlands, DY5 2JH Tel: (01384) 567970 Fax: (01384) 567970 E-mail: enquires@arvon.co.uk *Diecasting mould manufrs*

▶ Arx Construction Ltd, The Bake House, 43 Bonnyrigg Road, Dalkeith, Midlothian, EH22 3HF Tel: 0131-663 0996

▶ Arx Construction Ltd, Arx House, 22 Cameron Knowe, Philpstoun, Linlithgow, West Lothian, EH49 6RL Tel: (01506) 830114

▶ Arxcis Europe Ltd, Palmerston House, Palmerston Road, Barry, South Glamorgan, CF63 2YZ Tel: (01446) 744381 Fax: (01446) 744381

Aryan Computer Associates Ltd, 5 Pepper Close, Caterham, Surrey, CR3 6BJ Tel: (01883) 344094 Fax: (01883) 341908 *Computer consultancy*

▶ AS Bearings and Drives Services, 5 Oadby Drive, Hasland, Chesterfield, Derbyshire, S41 0YF Tel: 07813 717741 Fax: 01246 224995 E-mail: alastair.stewart@astewart.fsnet.co.uk *Bearings & power transmission equipment suppliers*

As Communications UK Ltd, The Green, Agden Green Farm, Great Staughton, St. Neots, Cambridgeshire, PE19 5DQ Tel: (01480) 861824 Fax: (01480) 869453 E-mail: wmumford@ascomms.co.uk *Radio communications retail & services*

▶ As new, 33 Walnut Avenue, Mansbridge, Southampton, SO18 2HT Tel: (023) 8057 2324 E-mail: as_new@msn.com *Exterior Cleaning.*Gutters fascias and soffits.*Window and window frames*Door and door frames*path and patios*Garden decking*Walls.*

Asa Consulting Engineers Ltd, Surrey Chambers, Surrey Street, Lowestoft, Suffolk, NR32 1LJ Tel: (01502) 518223 Fax: (01502) 567663 E-mail: sue@asaconsultants.co.uk *Consulting engineers*

Asadul Ltd, Hop House, West Bergholt, Colchester, CO6 3TJ Tel: (01206) 241600 *Air conditioning contractors*

▶ Asahi Alumni Associates Limited, 56 Swainstone Road, Reading, RG2 0DX Tel: 0118 9869963 Fax: 0118 9869963 E-mail: julie.bell@can-do.co.uk *Japanese translators - high quality, accurate Japanese translations, either English to Japanese or Japanese to English. Japanese interpreters - confident, appropriate interpreting within UK.*

Asahi Thermofil UK Ltd, 28 New Lane, Havant, Hampshire, PO9 2NQ Tel: (023) 9248 6350 Fax: (023) 9247 2388 *Specialised plastic compound manufrs*

▶ Asap Locksmiths, 123 Silverdale Road, Earley, Reading, RG6 7ND Tel: (07947) 023271 Fax: 0118-926 8641 E-mail: sales@asaplocksmiths.co.uk *Locksmiths services*

Asap Personnel, 5a Sheep Market, Spalding, Lincolnshire, PE11 1BH Tel: (01775) 712212 Fax: (01775) 768090 E-mail: info@asap-personnel.co.uk *Recruitment consultants*

Asap Solutions International Ltd, 233 Uxbridge Road, Mill End, Rickmansworth, Hertfordshire, WD3 8DP Tel: (07985) 378402 Fax: (020) 8566 3653 *IT recruitment*

Asbestos Analysis Services Ltd, 8 Tower Quays, Tower Road, Birkenhead, Merseyside, CH41 1BP Tel: 0151-649 0541 Fax: 0151-649 0547 *Analytical chemists*

▶ Asbestos Consultants Ltd, Vincent Road, Selsey, Chichester, West Sussex, PO20 9DH Tel: (01243) 605229 Fax: (01243) 603685 E-mail: asbestossurveying@btinternet.com *We are an Asbestos Consultants Chartered Building Surveyors Practice principally based in West Sussex, Hampshire and Surrey. We are a professional asbestos consultancy who provide a range of asbestos related services to the commercial, industrial and domestic sectors.*All our surveyors hold the P402 certificate and NIACS qualification and all surveys are conducted in accordance with MDHS 0 and also incorporate the advice and guidance within the ACOP L 127 all in compliance with the Control of Asbestos at Work Regulations 2002.**All Samples analyzed by UKAS accredited Laboratories.**We also supply asbestos consultancy in training courses for managing asbestos in property, which includes health and safety protocols.*

▶ Asbestos Consultants To The Enviroment Ltd, 23 Romney Avenue, Bristol, BS7 9ST Tel: 0117-952 7609 Fax: 0117-952 0947 E-mail: info@asbestos-ace.co.uk

Asbestos & Insulation Co., 765 Maidstone Road, Gillingham, Kent, ME8 0LR Tel: (01634) 232221 Fax: (01634) 233221 E-mail: sales@asbestos-insulation.com *Asbestos surveys, sampling & removal services*

Asbestos Management Co. (Ireland) Ltd, 5 Carthall Manor, Coleraine, County Londonderry, BT51 3GR Tel: (028) 7032 1319 Fax: (028) 7032 1319 E-mail: jimb@asbestos-management-company.com *Asbestos surveys, sampling and management*

▶ Asbestos North Wales, 17 Hamilton Square, Birkenhead, Merseyside, CH41 6AX Tel: 0151-666 2111 Fax: 0151-666 1624

Asbestos Safety Association, Suites 6 - 8 Imperial Centre, Grange Road, Darlington, County Durham, DL1 5NQ Tel: 01325 355009 Fax: 01325 355905 E-mail: info@asbestos-safety.org *The Asbestos Safety Association has been set up to help Dutyholders to comply with the Control of Asbestos at Work Regulations. The Asbestos Safety Association also offers membership benefits to asbestos surveyors, asbestos analysts, asbestos training providers, asbestos laboratories, Health & Safety Consultants and individuals who are likely to come into contact with asbestos through their work. The ASA is also a resource for Union Representatives seeking specialist advice on asbestos. The website is also home to Asbestos World magazine.*

▶ Asbestos Solutions, Carlotta Way, Cardiff, CF10 5FY Tel: (0800) 1973907 *Asbestos Solutions provides total solutions in the areas of Safety Management Services, Asbestos Sampling, Asbestos Decontamination, Asbestos legislation, Asbestos Survey, Asbestos management and many other Asbestos Solutions covering all the major geographical area in the UK - mainly Sunderland, Tyneside, Teeside, North East, Newcastle, County Durham, Durham, Hartlepool, and also providing specialist advice and service in all asbestos related problems to both the public and private sectors throughout the United Kingdom.*

▶ Asbestos Survey & Removal Consultants, 3 Fewston Way, Lakeside, Doncaster, South Yorkshire, DN4 5PR Tel: 01302 556336 Fax: 01302 556336 E-mail: arcu@btinternet.com *Asbestos surveys and asbestos removal service nationwide, free quotations.tel: 07961 521959*

Asbestos Surveys & Advice, Suite 7, Cockenzie Business Centre, Edinburgh Road, Cockenzie, Prestonpans, East Lothian, EH32 0HL Tel: 0845 5314268 Fax: (01875) 819111 E-mail: info@asa-asbestos.uk.com *Based in central Scotland, covering the whole UK, we are an independent, impartial provider of asbestos related services, including; Asbestos surveys, Asbestos removal and disposal, Reports, Registers, Management plans and Risk assessments. Our staff are fully qualified and experienced asbestos surveyors. ASA is quality assured to ISO 9001 2000 standard and Hold a SEPA license. Asbestos reports, Building surveys, Asbestos in buildings, Asbestos, Asbestos cement, Asbestos sampling and testing, Asbestos disposal, H.S.E, ARCA, Artex, Asbestos management, Asbestos insulation, Amosite, Chrysotile, Crocidolite, Asbestos insulating board, Asbestos contamination, Asbestos surveying, Environmental consultants, White asbestos, brown asbestos, Blue asbestos, Asbestos regulations, MDHS 100, Asbestos remedial works, Asbestos floor tiles, Asbestos sheeting, Asbestos roofs, Asbestos abatement, P402 Asbestos surveyors, Asbestos help, Professional asbestos surveyors, Asbestos garages, Asbestos outbuildings.*

▶ Asbestos Technology Solutions Ltd, Astech House, 3 Saxon Crescent, Barton-le-Clay, MK45 4LY Tel: 01582 883938 Fax: 01582 651931 *AS-TECH-S is an asbestos surveying company concerned solely with ensuring businesses are aware of their duties under the Control of Asbestos at Work Regulations 2002. Provides free and confidential information for property owners, tenants and employers on the legal 'Duty to Manage', asbestos facts and health risks and offers free and impartial advice for businesses to ensure they meet their obligations under the Regulations. Specialise in small business solutions.*

▶ Asbestos UK, 13 Station Road, Cam, Dursley, Gloucestershire, GL11 5NS Tel: (01453) 549060 Fax: (08716) 617645 E-mail: info@asbestosmanagementsolutions.co.uk *Qualified asbestos surveyors for type 1, 2 & 3 surveys, asbestos registers and management plans. FREE initial inspection for commercial and industrial premises, fast turnaround for residential and retail. Managing asbestos in buildings and asbestos awareness training. Project management services for independent monitoring of asbestos removal. Call for a sample survey report, information leaflet or free impartial advice.*

Asbestostrip Innovations, Unit 12 Tufthorn Industrial Estate, Stepbridge Road, Coleford, Gloucestershire, GL16 8PJ Tel: (01594) 837755 Fax: (01594) 836633 E-mail: enquiries@asbestostrip.co.uk *Asbestos dust suppression equipment manufrs*

Asbury Associates, 40 Croft Holm, Moreton-in-Marsh, Glos, GL56 0JH Tel: (01608) 652214 Fax: (01608) 652214 *Connectors, cable & PCB assemblies manufrs*

Asbury Brodie & Co. Ltd, 1 Dover Street, Birmingham, B18 5HN Tel: 0121-554 7000 Fax: 0121-554 0242 E-mail: sales@asburybrodie.co.uk *Manufacturers of electroplating chemical products*

▶ ASC Berkshire & Oxfordshire, Suite 7, Stubbings House, Henley Road, Maidenhead, Berkshire, SL6 6QL Tel: 01628 828220 *Commercial Mortgage Brokers*

Asc Metals Lincoln Ltd, Westminster Industrial Estate, Station Road, North Hykeham, Lincoln, LN6 3QY Tel: (01522) 501777 Fax: (01522) 501700 E-mail: sales@ascmetals.com *Aluminium & stainless steel stockholders*

▶ Ascend Recruitment, Trym Lodge, 1 Henbury Road, Westbury-on-Trym, Bristol, BS9 3HQ Tel: 0117-310 1270 Fax: 0117-310 1271 E-mail: mail@ascendrecruitment.net *Ascend Recruitment provides a field sales recruitment service aimed at any vertical market in engineering. It is based in Bristol and covers the South West and South Wales region. It operates on a no placement - no fee basis.*

Ascendis, 15 Queen Square, Leeds, LS2 8AJ Tel: 0845 054 8561 Fax: 0870 766 7985 E-mail: steve.lake@ascendis.co.uk *Increase the amount of time you have available and reduce the stresses associated with managing your accounts with our straightforward and secure outsourcing service that can provide access to financial director level help and support as part of the service.*

Ascent Media, Film House, 142 Wardour Street, London, W1F 8DD Tel: (020) 7878 0000 Fax: (020) 7878 7800 *Full service post-production facilities*

Ascent Media Camden, 13 Hawley Cresent, London, NW1 8NP Tel: (020) 7284 7900 Fax: (020) 7284 1018 *Post production - facilities house*

▶ AsciiTec Computers Ltd, 145-157 St. John Street, London, EC1V 4PY Tel: (020) 8843 0443 Fax: (020) 8843 0453 E-mail: vishal@asciitec.com *AsciiTec Computers is a leading distributor of computer peripherals and components. Specialize in offering our own brand name systems and servers, with complete obligation free consultation for networking. Our unique combination of category experience, personal service, technological expertise and top brand-name product availability assures you the right products and price points every time.*

Asco Components, Unit 19 Green Lane Industrial Estate, Bordesley Green, Birmingham, B9 5QP Tel: 0121-773 3090 Fax: 0121-773 3390 E-mail: info@ascocomponents.co.uk *Transformer components distributors*

Asco Fixings Ltd, Colliery Road, West Bromwich, West Midlands, B71 4JT Tel: 0121-553 1177 Fax: 0121-553 1199 E-mail: info@ascofixings.co.uk *Since 1998 we have been helping our customers to save lots of money by supplying them with very high quality parts, brought in mainly from India, China and Taiwan. Parts such as: Investment Castings using the lost wax method, Gravity Die Castings, Pressure Die Castings, in various materials - aluminium, mild steels, plastics, ceramics, high*

continued

continuation
tensile steel and stainless steel. Working with your engineers, we can supply the tooling designs in both 2d and 3d for any new projects for castings. Once drawings are agreed we can, either supply the tooling for your own production or produce the parts for you. Supply these on a call off basis or to whatever your requirements may be. Special Fasteners are also a speciality of Asco Fixings. We have our own joint venture in India, which can manufacture fasteners in all grades from M2 to M20 in metric sizes or imperial.

Asco Fuel & Lubricants, South Esplanade East, Aberdeen, AB11 3PB Tel: (01224) 890888 Fax: (01224) 890383 *Bulk liquid storage & handling contractors*

Asco UK Ltd, Asco House, Sinclair Road, Aberdeen, AB11 9PL Tel: (01224) 580396 Fax: (01224) 576172 E-mail: info@ascoplc.com *Offshore logistic services & distributors*

Ascobra Ltd, 12 Abbots Rise, Kings Langley, Hertfordshire, WD4 8AP Tel: (01923) 264067 *Audio-visual production & presentation services*

Ascom Tele Nova Ltd, Enterprise Drive, Sutton Coldfield, West Midlands, B74 2DY Tel: 0121-353 6151 Fax: 0121-352 1424 *Telecommunications systems*

Ascon Industrial Roofing Ltd, Hope Street, Dudley, West Midlands, DY2 8RS Tel: (01384) 233171 Fax: (01384) 456162 *Industrial roofing & cladding contractors service*

▶ Ascot Business Solutions, Park View, Stone Road, Fradswell, Stafford, ST18 0HA Tel: (01889) 502014 Fax: (01889) 502350 E-mail: info@ascot-solutions.co.uk *Document management, data collection & business process management*

Ascot Construction Services Ltd, 34 Albert Road, Heaton, Bolton, BL1 5HF Tel: (01204) 847700 Fax: (01204) 393950 *Timber building construction contractors*

▶ Ascot Environmental, Astra House, Christy Way, Southfields Business Park, Basildon, Essex, SS15 6TQ Tel: (01268) 540480 Fax: (01268) 540850

Ascot Heath, Brockhill Farm, Mathon Rd, Colwall, Malvern, Worcs, WR13 6EP Tel: (01684) 541100 Fax: (01684) 541455 E-mail: sales@ascotheath.co.uk *Catering equipment suppliers*

▶ Ascot Industrial Doors Ltd, Unit 1, Viola St, Bolton, BL1 8NG Tel: (01204) 309908 Fax: (01204) 300532 E-mail: sales@ascotdoors.co.uk *Doors & windows suppliers & manufrs*

Ascot Metal Finishers Ltd, 6 David Road, Colnbrook, Slough, SL3 0DG Tel: (01753) 682416 Fax: (01753) 680493 *Electroplating & stove enamelling services*

Ascot Precision Tooling Ltd, Richington Works, Hall Lane, Walsall Wood, Walsall, WS9 9AS Tel: (01543) 452127 Fax: (01543) 452127 *Press tool manufrs*

Ascot Systems (UK) Ltd, Woods Way, Goring-By-Sea, Worthing, West Sussex, BN12 4QY Tel: (01903) 503041 Fax: (01903) 507250 E-mail: sales@ascot-systems.co.uk *Computer training, teaching systems, classroom training services*

Ascotex Ltd, Calder Works, Simonstone, Burnley, Lancashire, BB12 7NL Tel: (01282) 772011 Fax: (01282) 773600 E-mail: sales@ascotex.com Principal Export Areas: Worldwide *Textile & ceramic engineers*

Ascott Clark, 42 Western Lane, Buxworth, High Peak, Derbyshire, SK23 7NS Tel: (01663) 734221 Fax: (01663) 734318 E-mail: info@ascottclark.com *Chimney cowl manufrs*

▶ Ascott Smallholding Supplies Ltd, Unit 9/10, The Old Creamery, Four Crosses, Llanymynech, Powys, SY22 6LP Tel: (0845) 1306285 Fax: (0870) 7740140 E-mail: phil@ascott.biz *Agriculture merchant*

▶ Ascus Concrete Pumping Ltd, Burcott Road, Bristol, BS11 8AB Tel: 0117-982 7272 Fax: (029) 2049 9799 *Plant hire*

Asd, Hamlin Way, King's Lynn, Norfolk, PE30 4LQ Tel: (01553) 761431 Fax: (01553) 692394 E-mail: info@asdplc.co.uk *Steel stockholders*

Asd, Station Road, Stalbridge, Sturminster Newton, Dorset, DT10 2RW Tel: (01963) 362066 Fax: (01963) 363260 E-mail: yeovil@asdplc.co.uk *Steel stockholders* Also at: Leeds

Asd Metal Services, South Humberside Industrial Estate, Grimsby, South Humberside, DN31 2TG Tel: (01472) 353851 Fax: (01472) 240028 E-mail: grimsby@asdmetalservices.co.uk *Steel stockholders, multi metal stockists*

Asd Metal Services, Thames Wharf, Dock Road, London, E16 1AF Tel: (020) 7476 0444 Fax: (020) 7476 0239 E-mail: customer.care@asdmetalservices.co.uk *Steel stockholders*

▶ Asda Distribution Centre, Asda Distribution Centre Portbury Way, Royal Portbury Dock, Portbury, Bristol, BS20 7XN Tel: (01275) 375361 Fax: (01275) 373374

▶ Asda Distribution Centre, Westmains Industrial Estate, Grangemouth, Stirlingshire, FK3 8YE Tel: (01324) 492102 Fax: (01324) 492025

ASDA Securities Ltd, 58 Queen Anne St, London, W1G 8HW Tel: (020) 7224 1030 Fax: (020) 7224 0574 *Property & development*

Asdec Ltd, Unit 7-8 Building 33, Second Avenue, Pensnett Trading Estate, Kingswinford, West Midlands, DY6 7UG Tel: (01384) 402463 Fax: (01384) 402662 E-mail: asdecc@hotmail.com *Paint spraying contractors, on site, plastic finishing services*

Asdon Business Centre, Systems House, Enterprise Crescent, Ballinderry Road, Lisburn, County Antrim, BT28 2BH Tel: (028) 9267 5114 Fax: (028) 9266 0256 E-mail: sales@asdon.co.uk *Computer equipment suppliers*

Ase Ltd, Stanley House, Acorn Business Park Heaton Lane, Stockport, Cheshire, SK4 1AS Tel: 0161-429 1500 Fax: 0161-480 3382 E-mail: info@aselcd.co.uk *Accountants*

▶ Asf, 1 Old Station Road, Station Road, Uppingham, Oakham, Leicestershire, LE15 9TX Tel: (01572) 822486 Fax: (01572) 822475 E-mail: sales@asf-upvc.com *Windows, conservatories install & manufacture*

Asg Midlands, 2 Old Walsall Road, Birmingham, B42 1NN Tel: 0121-358 1524 Fax: 0121-358 1525 *Security systems engineers*

▶ Asgard Crafts, The Smithy Heritage Centre, Strathcarron, Ross-Shire, IV54 8YS Tel: (01520) 722722 E-mail: cat@asgardcrafts.uklinux.net *Reproduction jell*

Ash Of Ancoats Ltd, 166-174 Great Ancoats Street, Manchester, M4 7AB Tel: 0161-273 6986 Fax: 0161-273 6986 E-mail: ashdiy@freenetname.co.uk *Ladder distributors*

▶ Ash Associates, PO Box 5374, Ferndown, Dorset, BH22 0ZX Tel: (0845) 1232701 E-mail: recruit@ash-associates.com *It recruitment*

▶ Ash Build Ltd, 21a Ancaster Road, Beckenham, Kent, BR3 4DZ Tel: (020) 8663 6227 Fax: (020) 8663 6254

▶ Ash Crane Services, 20 Royds Avenue, New Mill, Holmfirth, HD9 1LP Tel: (01484) 691890 Fax: (01484) 691896 E-mail: 1.ashmead@btopenworld.com *Crane hire services*

▶ Ash Employment Services Ltd, Unit 5a Centre Court, Sir Thomas Longley Road, Medway City Estate, Rochester, Kent, ME2 4BQ Tel: (01634) 710999 Fax: (01634) 712283 E-mail: lesley@ashemploymentservices.com *Employment services*

Ash Hill Communications & Electronics Ltd, Keepers Cottage, Combe Raleigh, Honiton, Devon, EX14 4TG Tel: (01404) 44080 Fax: (01404) 44122 *Supplier & installation of telephone systems*

▶ Ash Hill Data, 20 CWRT Pen-Y-Twyn, Dukestown, Tredegar, Gwent, NP22 4DL Tel: (01495) 711422 Fax: (01495) 711439 E-mail: richard@ashhilldata.co.uk *Software systems consultancy*

Ash Information Systems Ltd, Mile End Barn, Hemel Hempstead Road, Dagnall, Berkhamsted, Hertfordshire, HP4 1QR Tel: (01442) 842624 Fax: (01442) 842683 E-mail: ash@ashsys.co.uk *Producers of software*

▶ Ash Internet Services, 3 Punch Croft, New Ash Green, Longfield, Kent, DA3 8HP Tel: 0870 1996484 E-mail: admin@ashinternet.com *High quality, low cost website hosting solutions - with special discounts for local users.*

John Ash Photography Ltd, Church Farm, Ashchurch Road, Ashchurch, Tewkesbury, Gloucestershire, GL20 8JU Tel: (01684) 291200 Fax: (01684) 291201 E-mail: sales@ash-photography.com *Commercial photographers*

Ash & Lacy Building Systems, Bromford Lane, West Bromwich, West Midlands, B70 7JJ Tel: 0121-525 1444 Fax: 0121-524 8435 E-mail: kay.hall@ashandlacy.com Principal Export Areas: Worldwide *Cladding products distributor & manufrs*

▶ Ash Plastering, 8 Benson Road, Kings Heath, Birmingham, B14 4PH Tel: 0121- 430 5058 E-mail: quote@ashplastering.co.uk

Ash Resources Ltd, Lynemouth, Ashington, Northumberland, NE63 9YH Tel: (01670) 811166 Fax: (01670) 856847 *General purpose cement manufrs*

Ash Rubber Stamp Co Ltd, 149 Barford Street, Birmingham, B5 6AS Tel: 0121-622 4040 Fax: 0121-622 6600 E-mail: sales@ashstamp.co.uk *Rubber stamp manufrs*

Ash Tool Co. Ltd, Lord Street, Ashton-under-Lyne, Lancashire, OL6 6HZ Tel: 0161-330 2325 Fax: 0161-343 2229 E-mail: ash.tool@zen.co.uk *Precision engineers*

Ash Tool Hire & Sales, Unit 2 Walker Street, Oldham, OL8 1SX Tel: 0161-678 8088 Fax: 0161-678 8005 *Power tools suppliers*

▶ Ash Transport Solutions, Priory Coach House, Ash Priors, Taunton, Somerset, TA4 3ND Tel: (01823) 431600 *Computer software developers*

Ash UK Ltd, 63 James Watt Place, East Kilbride, Glasgow, G74 5HG Tel: (01355) 224445 Fax: (01355) 223055 E-mail: ashukltd@btopenworld.com *Hydraulic components, power packs, suppliers, spares & repairs*

▶ Asha Womens Centre, 26 London Road, Worcester, WR5 2DL Tel: (01905) 767552 Fax: (01905) 769463 E-mail: ashaprojects@btconnect.com *Support centre*

Ashbee Computer Services, Wood Lea, Priorswood, Guildford, Surrey, GU3 1DR Tel: (01483) 810500 Fax: (01483) 811577 *Quality IT training & consultancy. Access and SQL Server databases developed. Access, Excel, Word, Powerpoint, VBA and All Microsoft Office products trained from Introduction to Advanced and Workshops.*

Ashbee & Wood, 50 Ormside Way, Redhill, RH1 2LW Tel: (01737) 765711 Fax: (01737) 778579 E-mail: asbeewood@hardtoforget.co.uk *Kitchen suppliers*

Ashbourne Engineering UK Ltd, Rear of, 71 Westcote Road, London, SW16 6BN Tel: (020) 8664 7170 Fax: (020) 8664 7459 *Precision engineers*

▶ Ashbourne Property Services, 75 Ashford Avenue, Hayes, Middlesex, UB4 0NB Tel: (020) 8581 2415 Fax: 020 85812415 E-mail: mrdbryn@yahoo.co.uk *Providing routine grounds maintenance, ensuring regular cutting of lawns and hedges and sweeping of pathways & carparks. Also offering window cleaning services.Covering West London and the Home Counties.*

Ashbridge Concrete, Pigeon Cote Industrial Estate, Malton Road, York, YO32 9LD Tel: (01904) 425300 Fax: (01904) 427115 *Concrete production services*

Ashbrittle Ltd, Ashbrittle House, Lower Dagnall Street, St. Albans, Hertfordshire, AL3 4PA Tel: (01727) 854054 Fax: (01727) 865557 E-mail: mail@ashbrittle.com *International recruitment consultants*

Ashbrook Garage Ltd, Ashbrook Garage, Clyro, Hereford, HR3 5SD Tel: (01497) 821046 Fax: (01497) 821182 E-mail: poleposition@lineone.net *Motor vehicle repair*

Ashbrook Simon-Hartley Ltd, Derby Road, Clay Cross, Chesterfield, Derbyshire, S45 9AG Tel: (01246) 252600 Fax: (01246) 252601 E-mail: enquiries@as-h.com *Industrial centrifuge refurbishment services & manufrs*

Ashbrook Simon-Hartley Ltd, 10/11 Brindley Court, Dalewood Road, Lymedale Business Park, Newcastle-under-Lyme, Staffordshire, ST5 9QH Tel: (01782) 578650 Fax: (01782) 260534 E-mail: enquiries@as-h.com Principal Export Areas: Asia Pacific, Central Asia, Middle East, Africa, Central/East Europe, West Europe & South America *Wastewater treatment*

Ashburne, 16-20 Penallta Road, Ystrad Mynach, Hengoed, Mid Glamorgan, CF82 7AP Tel: (01443) 816618 Fax: (01443) 816880 *Curtain & blinds suppliers*

Ashburne, 16-20 Penallta Road, Ystrad Mynach, Hengoed, Mid Glamorgan, CF82 7AP Tel: (01443) 816618 Fax: (01443) 816880 *Dry cleaning services*

Ashburnham Insurance Services Ltd, 80 London Road, Southend-on-Sea, SS1 1PG Tel: (01702) 347400 Fax: (01702) 333890 E-mail: insure@ashburnham-insurance.co.uk *Insurance broker*

Ashburton Instrument Co., Western Road, Ashburton, Newton Abbot, Devon, TQ13 7ED Tel: (01364) 652579 Fax: (01364) 653978 E-mail: phil@ashins.freeserve.co.uk *Instrument engineers & industrial engravers*

Ashby, 33 Ascot Avenue, Kimberley, Nottingham, NG16 2TU Tel: 0115-938 5101 Fax: 0115-938 5102 *Postal equipment distributors*

Ashby Computer Services, Sywell Airport Business Park, Wellingborough Road, Sywell, Northampton, NN6 0BN Tel: (01604) 790979 Fax: (01604) 491859 E-mail: enquiries@ashbycomputers.co.uk *Computer brokers, data cabling, repairs, support & sales*

Ashby Engineering Co., 8 Surbiton Hill Road, Surbiton, Surrey, KT6 4TP Tel: (020) 8399 4034 Fax: (020) 8390 4947 E-mail: ashbyeng@aol.com *Plastics engineers*

Ashby Precision Engineering Drayton Ltd, Marcham Road, Drayton, Abingdon, Oxfordshire, OX14 4JH Tel: (01235) 531279 Fax: (01235) 535801 E-mail: sales@ashbyeng.com *Precision engineers*

Ashby Trade Sign Supplies Ltd, Youngs Industrial Estate, Aldermaston, Reading, RG7 4PW Tel: 0118-981 5343 Fax: 0118-981 5335 E-mail: sales@ashbytrade.co.uk *Sign manufrs*

Ashby Welding, 13 Potters Industrial Park, Church Crookham, Fleet, Hampshire, GU52 6EU Tel: (01252) 815811 *Welding fabricators*

▶ Ashby's Driving School, 29 Acres Gardens, Tadworth, Surrey, KT20 5LP Tel: (01737) 358430 Fax: (01737) 358430 E-mail: info@ashbysdrivingschool.gbr.cc *We are your local driving school covering Tadworth, Reigate, Leatherhead, Epsom, Banstead, Sutton and surrounding areas.**We use Ford Fiesta cars which are renewed regularly ensuring reliability and trouble free driving lessons for our pupils.**They have a manual gearbox and are fitted with dual controls.**Lessons are competitively priced at an hourly rate with discounts for block booking and we operate a complete door to door service.*

Ashcott Equestuirn Ltd, Reme Drive, Heath Park Industrial Estate, Honiton, Devon, EX14 1SE Tel: (01404) 44680 Fax: (01404) 46688 *Shoulder pad & clothing components manufrs* Also at: Honiton

Ashcraft Furniture Ltd, Unit 1, Orchard Industrial Estate, Toddington, Cheltenham, Gloucestershire, GL54 5EB Tel: (01242) 620731 Fax: (01242) 621939 *Furniture manufrs*

Ashcroft Agencies Ltd, 14a Airfield Road, Christchurch, Dorset, BH23 3TG Tel: (01202) 499945 Fax: (01202) 499207 Principal Export Areas: Worldwide *Industrial vacuum motor suppliers*

▶ Ashcroft Transmissions, 5 Stadium Industrial Estate, Cradock Road, Luton, LU4 0JF Tel: (01582) 496040 Fax: (01582) 595040 *Industrial bearings*

Ashcroft Woodworking, Thompsons Yard, Chipping Hill, Witham, Essex, CM8 2DE Tel: (01376) 514771 Fax: (01376) 514771 *Cabinet making & joinery specialists*

▶ Ashdale, 61 Manston CR, Leeds, LS15 8BN Tel: 0113-260 0527 Fax: 0113-260 0527 E-mail: ashdalepat@hotmail.co.uk *electrical installation testing, periodic electrical inspection and test, pat testing specialist services, portable appliance testing*

Ashdale Engineering, Mitchell Close, Andover, Hampshire, SP10 3TJ Tel: (01264) 355642 Fax: (01264) 333641 *Sheet metalwork engineers & fabricators*

Ashdale Lifting Services Ltd, 14 Thornton Industrial Trading Estate, Milford Haven, Dyfed, SA73 2RX Tel: (01646) 695332 Fax: (01646) 693570 *Mechanical plant & lifting equipment maintenance & repair*

Ashdown Blinds, St. Johns Road, Crowborough, East Sussex, TN6 1RT Tel: (01892) 665596 Fax: (01892) 665596 *Blind retailers*

Ashdown Brookworth, 5 Parkway House, Worth Way, Keighley, West Yorkshire, BD21 5LD Tel: (01535) 663336 Fax: (01535) 610338 *Liquid hand soap cleaner distributors*

▶ Ashdown Lyons, Northdown House, 2-4 Station Road, Ashford, Kent, TN23 1PT Tel: (01233) 646491 Fax: (01233) 646498 E-mail: ashford@ashdownlyons.co.uk *Residential & commercial property valuations & surveys throughout London, southern England & Wales. We carry out over 7000 valuations & surveys every month for private & corporate clients.*

Ashdown Lyons, The Estate Office, Common Farm, Biddenden, Ashford, Kent, TN27 8LJ Tel: (01580) 292837 Fax: (0871) 2516479 E-mail: weald@ashdowlyons.co.uk *Residential & commercial valuations and surveys throughout London, southern England and Wales. We carry out over 7000 valuations and surveys every month for private and corporate clients.*

▶ Ashdown Lyons, Marlowe House, Station Road, Sidcup, Kent, DA15 7ET Tel: (020) 8308 1199 Fax: (020) 8308 0261 E-mail: nicholsfrics@aol.com *Residential & commercial valuations and surveys throughout London, southern England and Wales. We carry out over 7000 valuations and surveys every month for private and corporate clients.*

Asher Andell Ltd, Midway House, Main Road, Upper Broughton, Melton Mowbray, Leicestershire, LE14 3BG Tel: (01664) 822131 Fax: (01664) 823332 E-mail: medical@asher-andell.co.uk *Plastics engineers/medical products*

Asher Consulting Ltd, Asher House, Barsbank Lane, Lymm, Cheshire, WA13 0ED Tel: (01925) 751444 Fax: (01925) 751555 E-mail: info@asherconsulting.co.uk *Safety advice service*

Ashfaq Knitwear Ltd, Majid House, 37-49 Devonshire Street North, Manchester, M12 6JR Tel: 0161-272 6368 Fax: 0161-272 6368 *Knitwear manufrs*

Ashfarm Personal Care Ltd, 33 Croft Street, Manchester, M11 4RQ Tel: 0161-223 8265 Fax: 0161-223 7100 E-mail: mark@mpmconsumerproducts.com *Skin care preparations*

Ashfield Extrusion Ltd, B Field Industrial Estate, Clover Street, Kirkby-in-Ashfield, Nottingham, NG17 7LH Tel: (01623) 757333 Fax: (01623) 751771 E-mail: ashfield.sales@btconnect.com *Aluminium extrusion manufrs*

▶ Ashfield Labels, Unit E Draycott Business Park, Cam, Dursley, Gloucestershire, GL11 5DQ Tel: (01453) 890825 Fax: (01453) 890579 E-mail: sales@ashfieldlabels.co.uk *Manufacturers of self adhesive labels, stickers & signs*

▶ Ashfield Personnel, Norwich House, 45 Poplar Road, Solihull, West Midlands, B91 3AW Tel: 0121-711 7811 Fax: 0121-711 7801 E-mail: admin@ashfieldpersonnel.co.uk *Recruitment agency*

▶ Ashfield Precision Engineering Ltd, 59 Eastfield Side, Sutton-in-Ashfield, Nottinghamshire, NG17 4JW Tel: (01623) 551954 Fax: (01623) 514109

Ashfield Springs Ltd, Nunn Brook Rise, Huthwaite, Sutton-in-Ashfield, Nottinghamshire, NG17 2PD Tel: 0845 4941745 Fax: (01623) 455502 E-mail: bryan.smith@ashfield-springs.com *Ashfield Springs are the U.K's leading compression, extension and torsion spring manufacturers and spring suppliers. Whether you require one, one thousand or one million springs, you will benefit from a response time, which is second to none. Good service, quality products and competitive pricing are guaranteed. We are committed to providing a product of consistent quantity that meets all contractual requirements set out by our customers. We continually improve our manufacturing techniques machinery and employee skills to meet future requirements.*

▶ Ashfield Technology, 2 Ashfield Road, Cults, Aberdeen, AB15 9NQ Tel: 07803 015163 Fax: 01224 868545 E-mail: ashfield_tec@hotmail.com *Laboratory equipment rental services*

Ashfield & Wilson, Charlemont Street, Moy, Dungannon, County Tyrone, BT71 7SL Tel: (028) 8778 4671 Fax: (028) 8778 4391 E-mail: ashfieldwilson@btconnect.com *Agricultural machinery distributors*

▶ Ashfield Wood Carvings, Unit 6, Stanmore Industrial Estate, Bridgnorth, Shropshire, WV15 5HR Tel: (01746) 769691

▶ The Ashford Advertiser, PO Box 1, Ashford, Kent, TN23 4ZU Tel: (01233) 624538 Fax: (01233) 641900 E-mail: theadvertiser@aol.com *Printing & publishing*

Ashford Awnings, 4 Hilton Business Centre, Wotton Road, Ashford, Kent, TN23 6LL Tel: (01233) 624471 Fax: (01233) 624471 E-mail: ashford_awnings@hotmail.com *Awning manufrs*

Ashford Borough Council, Civic Centre, Tannery Lane, Ashford, Kent, TN23 1PL Tel: (01233) 330310 Fax: (01233) 330682 *Local government*

Ashford & Campion Ltd, Westfield Terrace, Higham Ferrers, Rushden, Northamptonshire, NN10 8BB Tel: (01933) 359321 Fax: (01933) 410403 *Footwear component manufrs*

Ashford Coachworks Ltd, Ashford Road, Ashford, Middlesex, TW15 1XB Tel: (01784) 888600 Fax: (01784) 888620 *Motor vehicle repair services*

▶ Ashford Domestic Appliances, 1 Tritton Close, Kennington, Ashford, Kent, TN24 9HN Tel: (01233) 613300 Fax: (01233) 613300 *Repair & sales of all domestic appliances & household goods*

Ashford Engineering Services, Unit 3 New Street Farm, Great Chart, Ashford, Kent, TN23 3DL Tel: (01233) 668883 Fax: (01233) 668883 E-mail: clive@asheng.freeserve.co.uk *Manufacturers of metal fabrication, medical testing equipment*

Ashford Flexible Hose & Couplings Supplies Ltd, 110 Ellingham Way, Ashford, Kent, TN23 6LZ Tel: (01233) 629528 Fax: (01233) 625420 *Hose & coupling distribs*

Ashford (Kent) Chamber Of Commerce Industry & Enterprise Ltd, Ashford Business Pointwaterbrook Avenuesevington, Sevington, Ashford, Kent, TN24 0LH Tel: (01233) 503838 Fax: (01233) 503687 E-mail: sales@ashford-chamber.co.uk *Chamber of commerce & industry*

Ashford Metal Spinners Ltd, Unit E, Chilmington Works, Chilmington Green, Great Chart, Ashford, Kent, TN23 3DR Tel: (01233) 610404 E-mail: ams@ashfordmetalspinning.co.uk *Metal spinning manufrs*

Ashford Overload Services, Bottings Industrial Estate, Curdridge, Southampton, SO30 2DY Tel: (01489) 787071 Fax: (01489) 787621 E-mail: ashford.overload@dial.pipex.com *Digital printers*

Ashford Press, Bottings Industrial Estate, Curdridge, Southampton, SO30 2DY Tel: (01489) 785311 Fax: (01489) 780716 E-mail: production@asfordpress.co.uk *Technical printers services*

Ashford Signmakers Ltd, Unit 11q Godinton Way Industrial Estate, Godinton Way, Ashford, Kent, TN23 1JB Tel: (01233) 621447 Fax: (01233) 624327 E-mail: coneysigns@aol.com *Wooden & plastic sign manufrs*

Ashford Signs, 7 Roberts Close, Hempnall, Norwich, NR15 2ND Tel: (01508) 498242 Fax: (01508) 498242 *Signs & sign writing manufrs*

Ashford Woodturners, Old Saw Mill, Hothfield, Ashford, Kent, TN26 1EN Tel: (01233) 623090 Fax: (01233) 643423 E-mail: ashford.woodturners@btinternet.com *Wood turning-carpenters*

Ashgoal Ltd, Cqueens Road, Barnet, Hertfordshire, EN5 4DJ Tel: (020) 8275 5100 Fax: (020) 8441 7240 E-mail: info@ashgoal.co.uk *Computer & accounts system engineers*

Ashington Fabrication Co. Ltd, Ennerdale Road, Kitty Brewster Industrial Estate, Blyth, Northumberland, NE24 4RD Tel: (01670) 365666 Fax: (01670) 364466 E-mail: enquiries@afc-ltd.com *Engineering fabricators*

▶ Ashkent Landscaping, Unit 3 Wissenden Lane, Bethersden, Ashford, Kent, TN26 3EL Tel: (01233) 822040 Fax: (01233) 822540 E-mail: sam@ashkent.co.uk *Ashkent are a BALI (BRITISH ASSOCIATION OF LANDSCAPE INDUSTRIES) Registered company who offer all aspects of hard & soft landscaping to the commercial and domestic customer. Who will recieve a professional service from start to finish.*

Ashland Chemical & Hygiene Supplies Ltd, Unit 17-18 Aghanloo Industrial Estate, Aghanloo Road, Limavady, County Londonderry, BT49 0HE Tel: (028) 7776 7007 Fax: (028) 7776 7008 E-mail: ian.ashfield@ashlandchemicals.co.uk *Hygiene product manufacturers*

Ashland Communications Equipment Ltd, Ashland House, Dobson Park Way, Ince, Wigan, Lancashire, WN2 2DX Tel: (01942) 221122 Fax: (01942) 222127 E-mail: sales@ashlandcomm.com *Supply/install/ maintain telecommunication equipment*

Ashland Foundry Products, Vale Industrial Estate, Kidderminster, Worcestershire, DY11 7QU Tel: (01562) 821300 Fax: (01562) 740785 *Foundry industry chemicals manufrs*

Ashland Resources Ltd, PO Box 3694, Colchester, CO4 5QJ Tel: (01206) 273658 Fax: (01206) 273199 E-mail: sales@ashland.co.uk Purchasing Contact: P. Honeywell Sales Contact: D.W. Eaton Principal Export Areas: Africa *Manufacturers of antislip products, including tiles, treads & flooring.*

Ashland UK, Wimsey Way, Somercotes, Alfreton, Derbyshire, DE55 4LR Tel: (01773) 604321 Fax: (01773) 606901 *Water treatment specialists*

Ashlea Components Ltd, 4 Shrivenham Hundred Business Park, Majors Road, Watchfield, Swindon, SN6 8TZ Tel: (01793) 783784 Fax: (01793) 783646 E-mail: sales@ashlea.co.uk *Electronic component agents & distributors*

Ashleigh Scotland Ltd, Lochar House, Dumfries, DG1 3NU Tel: (01387) 711500 Fax: (01387) 711501

▶ Ashley Ann Ltd, 17 Ormlie Industrial Estate, Thurso, Caithness, KW14 7QU Tel: (01847) 890506 Fax: (01847) 893145 *Furnishings*

Ashley Blind Contracts, 20 Old Mill Road, Hunton Bridge, Kings Langley, Hertfordshire, WD4 8QT Tel: (01923) 270801 Fax: (01923) 270425 E-mail: action@ashleyblinds.co.uk *Blinds & curtain supplier*

Ashley Chase Estate Ltd, Parks Farm, Litton Cheney, Dorchester, Dorset, DT2 9AZ Tel: (01308) 482580 Fax: (01308) 482662 E-mail: cheese@fordfarm.com *Cheese makers*

Ashley Cleaning Supplies, 1 Culcheth Road, Altrincham, Cheshire, WA14 2LU Tel: 0161-928 2436 Fax: 0161-928 2436 *Cleaning product suppliers*

Ashley Competition Exhausts, 1 New Street, Walsall, WS1 3DF Tel: (01922) 720767 Fax: (01922) 721354 E-mail: sales@ashleycompetitionexhausts.com *Ashley competition Exhausts are probably Europe's largest specialist manufacturer of performance mild steel tubular manifolds, systems, sport boxes and fabricated race and rally equipment.*

▶ Ashley Hastings, 20 Manor Heath, Copmanthorpe, York, YO23 3SL Tel: (01904) 700847 E-mail: ashley@ashleyhastings.co.uk *Copywriting for business*

Ashley Industrial, South Wraxall, Bradford-on-Avon, Wiltshire, BA15 2RL Tel: (01225) 868083 Fax: 01225 868089 E-mail: japapps@aol.com *Finished labels nameplate distributors*

Ashley Law Rickmansworth, 11 Shepherds Way, Rickmansworth, Herts, WD3 7NH Tel: (01923) 710392 Fax: (01923) 710392 E-mail: rickmansworth@ashleylaw.co.uk

▶ Ashley Lawrence Upholstery, A Northbrook Trading Estate, Northbrook Road, Worthing, West Sussex, BN14 8PN Tel: (01903) 820899 Fax: (01903) 820959 E-mail: sales@ashleylawrence.co.uk *Furnishing specialists*

▶ Ashley Mulhall Associates, 46 School Lane, Sprowston, Norwich, NR7 8TQ Tel: (01603) 488528 Fax: (01603) 488528 E-mail: info@ashleymulhallassociates.co.uk *Business System Selection, ERP Systems Consultants, Business Process Re-Engineering, Applications Audit, IT Reviews, IT Strategy, IT Project Management*

Ashley Precision (Parkstone) Ltd, 12 Broom Road, Parkstone, Poole, Dorset, BH12 4NL Tel: (01202) 744168 Fax: (01202) 744168 *Precision engineers*

Ashlie Craft, 10 Wheatley Grove, Beeston, Nottingham, NG9 5AG Tel: 0115-922 9735 Fax: 0115-922 9735 E-mail: baglady@ashliecraft.com *Handbag retailers*

Ashling Microsystems Ltd, Studio 9 Intec 2, Wade Road, Basingstoke, Hampshire, RG24 8NE Tel: (01256) 811998 Fax: (01256) 811761 E-mail: ian.harry@ashling.com *Microprocessors*

Ashlyn Computer Services, The Garth, Doddington Road, Stubton, Newark, Nottinghamshire, NG23 5BX Tel: (01636) 627900 Fax: (01636) 627909 E-mail: sales@ashlyn.co.uk *Computer consultants*

Ashman Bros, 43 Swaffham Road, Mundford, Thetford, Norfolk, IP26 5HR Tel: (01842) 879063 *Pest control services*

Ashmead Applications Ltd, 28 Pigeon Farm Road, Stokenchurch, High Wycombe, Buckinghamshire, HP14 3TE Tel: (01494) 483623 E-mail: patrick@ashmeadapplications.co.uk *Data application developers*

Ashmead Building Supplies Ltd, Portview Road, Avonmouth, Bristol, BS11 9LD Tel: 0117-982 8281 Fax: 0117-982 0135 E-mail: avon@ashmead.co.uk *Builders' merchants* Also at: Willand

Ashmond Electronics Ltd, 8 Gadwey House, Leigh Street, High Wycombe, Buckinghamshire, HP11 2QU Tel: (01494) 440925 Fax: (01494) 446795 *Process control services*

Ashmoors Headboard Co., 136 Station Road, Broughton Astley, Leicester, LE9 6PW Tel: (01455) 286633 Fax: (01455) 286633 *Bedroom upholstery manufrs*

▶ Ashmore Press Ltd, Unit 18 Martlets Way, Goring-by-Sea, Worthing, West Sussex, BN12 4HF Tel: (01903) 506735 Fax: (01903) 507225

Ashmores Press Brake Tooling Ltd, Lewis Street, Great Bridge, Tipton, West Midlands, DY4 7EF Tel: 0121-557 1064 Fax: 0121-557 1085 E-mail: ashmores@pressbraketool.co.uk Principal Export Areas: Worldwide *Press brake tool manufrs*

Ashprint London Ltd, 46 South Building 56 Magnet Road, East Lane, Wembley, Middlesex, HA9 7RG Tel: (020) 8904 6479 Fax: (020) 8908 0315 E-mail: sales@ashprint-international.co.uk *Screen & pad printers*

▶ Ashprint Web Offset Ltd, 3 Drumhead Road, Chorley North Industrial Park, Chorley, Lancashire, PR6 7BX Tel: (01257) 230988 Fax: (01257) 230977

▶ Ashridge Construction Ltd, A A Workshop, Enterprise Way, Thatcham, Berkshire, RG19 4AE Tel: (01635) 879400 Fax: (01635) 879401 E-mail: enquiries@ashridge.co.uk *Civil engineering contractors, construction & maintenance*

Ashridge Engineering Ltd, 58 North Road Indust Estate, Okehampton, Devon, EX20 1BQ Tel: (01837) 53381 Fax: (01837) 55022 E-mail: sales@ash-eng.co.uk *Level & pressure transducer sensor manufrs*

▶ Ashridge New Media, 131-151 Great Titchfield Street, London, W1W 5BB Tel: (0845) 2305105

▶ Ashridge Trees, Grove Cross Barn, Castle Cary, Somerset, BA7 7NJ Tel: (01963) 359444 Fax: (01963) 359445 E-mail: julian@ashridgetrees.co.uk *Grower & supplier of native bare-root trees, conifers, hedging, shrubs and planting accessories. Next day delivery.*

Ashstead Group plc, Kings Court, 41-51 Kingston Road, Leatherhead, Surrey, KT22 7AP Tel: (01372) 362300 Fax: 01372 376610 *Plant hire company*

▶ Ashstead Plant Hire, 16 St Machar Road, Aberdeen, AB24 2UU Tel: (01224) 276760

Ashstead Plant Hire Ltd, ST. Johns Road, Dock Approach, Boston, Lincolnshire, PE21 6BE Tel: (01205) 311672 Fax: (01205) 363300 *Contractors plant hire* Also at: Sleaford

Ashtead Engineering Co. Ltd, Unit 2 3 Camphill Industrial Estate, Camphill Road, West Byfleet, Surrey, KT14 6EW Tel: (01932) 353121 Fax: (01932) 342968 E-mail: ashteadeng@byfleet.net *Precision Engineering*

Ashtead Plant Hire Co. Ltd, Greenwell Road, East Tullos Industrial Estate, Aberdeen, AB12 3AX Tel: (01224) 876538 Fax: (01224) 899032 E-mail: whitehaven@aplant.com

Ashtead Plant Hire Co. Ltd, Wylds Road, Bridgwater, Somerset, TA6 4BH Tel: (01278) 423153 Fax: (01278) 444299 E-mail: sales@aplant.com *Plant hire*

Ashtead Plant Hire Co. Ltd, 819 London Road, Alvaston, Derby, DE24 8UU Tel: (01332) 573566 Fax: (01332) 755660 E-mail: derbysouth@aplant.com *Plant and Tool hire*

▶ Ashtead Plant Hire Co. Ltd, Rossfield Road, Ellesmere Port, CH65 3AW Tel: 0151-357 3075 Fax: 0151-356 8588

Ashtead Plant Hire Co. Ltd, Station Works, Westerfield, Ipswich, IP6 9AB Tel: (01473) 254822 Fax: (01473) 212060 *Contractors plant hire*

Ashtead Plant Hire, Mintsfeet Road North, Kendal, Cumbria, LA9 6LZ Tel: (01539) 736444 Fax: (01539) 730870 *Hire company*

Ashtead Plant Hire, 3 Dixon Way, Dixon Street, Lincoln, LN6 7DE Tel: (01522) 520688 Fax: (01522) 513577 *Tool hire*

Ashtead Plant Hire Co Ltd, 119 Bow Road, London, E3 2AN Tel: (020) 8981 2611 Fax: (020) 8980 5627 E-mail: bowtoolhire@aplant.com *Plant hire contractors*

▶ Ashtead Plant Hire Company Ltd, James Corbett Road, Salford, M50 1DE Tel: 0161-736 3779

Ashtead Plant Hire Co. Ltd, St Georges Road, Donnington, Telford, Shropshire, TF2 7RA Tel: (01952) 620320 Fax: (01952) 610708 E-mail: telford@aplant.com *Plant hire*

Ashtead Plant Hire Co. Ltd, Vale Industrial Estate, Tolpits Lane, Watford, WD18 9QP Tel: (01923) 771577 Fax: (01923) 771090 E-mail: watford@aplant.com *Plant hire*

Ashtead Technology Ltd, Unit 3, Kirkton Avenue, Pimedden Road Industrial Estate, Aberdeen, AB21 0BF Tel: (01224) 771888 Fax: (01224) 770129E-mail: rentals@ashtead-technology.com *Electronic marine equipment hire*

Ashtel Systems Ltd, Unit 12, Central Business Centre, Great Central Way, London, NW10 0UR Tel: (0870) 9221140 Fax: (0870) 9221141 *IT & Telco*

A. E. & N. Ashton & Co. Ltd, Sedgeway Farm, Common Road, Wichford, Ely, Cambridgeshire, CB6 2HY Tel: (01353) 662473 Fax: (01353) 667726 Principal Export Areas: West Europe *GRP, Plastic fabricators, chemical tank manufrs*

Ashton Balloon Centre, 34 Gerard Street, Ashton-in-Makerfield, Wigan, Lancashire, WN4 9AE Tel: (01942) 701312 *Balloons & gift suppliers*

▶ Ashton Billige Property Marketing Ltd, 71 Doods Road, Reigate, Surrey, RH2 0NT Tel: 01737 225752 Fax: 01737 225752 E-mail: enquiries@abpropertymarketing.co.uk *We are a dedicated property marketing agency offering advertising, marketing, public relations, design and events services to the UK commercial and residential sectors as well as the overseas property markets.*

▶ Ashton Concrete Floors Ltd, B The Old Brickyard, North End, Ashton Keynes, Swindon, SN6 6QR Tel: (01285) 862344 Fax: (01285) 862655

Ashton Engineering Co. Ltd, Floodgate Street, Birmingham, B5 5SS Tel: 0121-643 5134 Fax: 0121-643 4212 E-mail: sales@ashtonengineering.co.uk *Sell & repair garage equipment*

Ashton Industrial Sales Ltd, 4 Anderson Road, Woodford Green, Essex, IG8 8ET Tel: (020) 8551 4046 Fax: (020) 8551 1433 E-mail: ashton@ashton-industrial.com *Glass processing machinery manufacturers & wholesalers of window components*

▶ Ashton Lake Solicitors, Park House, 25 Park Road, Loughborough, Leicestershire, LE11 2ED Tel: (01509) 262621 Fax: (01509) 233550 E-mail: sales@ashtonlake.com *Solicitors*

Ashton & Moore Ltd, 12 Smith Street, Hockley, Birmingham, B19 3EX Tel: 0845 618 8196 Fax: 0845 618 8197 E-mail: sales@ashton-moore.co.uk *Alocrom, anodising - sulphuric & chromic, bright and dyed alocrom 1200/1000; Electropolishing & passivation of stainless steel; Plating of electroless nickel, cadmium, silver, lead & indium; Phosphating - manganese & zinc; Painting - air dry & stove enamels. Ipcote, spray &: barrel; Lacquer - electrophoretic & spray; Dry film lubricants - PTFE, moly disulphide, hot lube; Non destructive testing - MP1 & dye pen; Approvals - ISO 9002/MOD. Full defence & aerospace*

▶ Ashton Penny, Broadbent House, 64-65 Grosvenor Street, London, W1K 3JH Tel: (020) 7659 0600 Fax: (020) 7659 0601 *Specialising in the provision of interim management solutions, the company supplies chief executives, board directors & functional managers across all industries, functions & public services throughout the UK & Europe***

Ashton Plant Hire Dudley Ltd, Dormston Trading Estate, Burton Road, Dudley, West Midlands, DY1 2UF Tel: (01902) 661151 Fax: (01902) 679070 E-mail: rick@safety-fence.co.uk *Crash barrier distributors*

Ashton Printers, London Street, Fleetwood, Lancashire, FY7 6JE Tel: (01253) 874549 Fax: (01253) 773773 E-mail: ashton@ashtonprinters.fsnet.co.uk *Commercial printers*

Ashton Refrigeration Co., 106 Minto Street, Ashton-under-Lyne, Lancashire, OL7 9DA Tel: 0161-343 1446 Fax: 0161-339 0152 E-mail: ashtonrefrigeration@tiscali.co.uk *Commercial refrigeration suppliers*

Ashton Seals Ltd, PO Box 1030, Barnsley, South Yorkshire, S73 0YP Tel: (01226) 273700 Fax: (01226) 756774 E-mail: sales@ashtonseals.com *Manufacturers of pvc products*

Ashton Steel Stockholders Ltd, Station Yard, Station Road, Hadfield, Glossop, Derbyshire, SK13 1AA Tel: (01457) 862438 Fax: (01457) 861325 *Steel & steel bar suppliers*

▶ Thomas Ashton, Beaufort Court, Admirals Way, London, E14 9XL Tel: (020) 7863 1740 Fax: (020) 7863 7510

Ashton Tyre Specialists Ltd, Adlington Industrial Estate, Adlington, Macclesfield, Cheshire, SK10 4NL Tel: (01625) 859123 Fax: (01625) 850181 *Tyre distributors*

▶ The Ashton Window Company Ltd, Holden Fold Lane, Royton, Oldham, OL2 5BZ Tel: 0161-624 9433 Fax: 0161-652 1326 *Upvc window manufrs*

Ashton-Evans & Associates, PO Box 4, Knaresborough, North Yorkshire, HG5 0AA Tel: (01423) 866125 Fax: (07092) 862117 E-mail: sales@ashtonevans.co.uk *Recruitment & training for the hotel & leisure industry*

Ashtree Glass Ltd, Ashtree Works, Brownroyd Street, Bradford, West Yorkshire, BD8 9AF Tel: (01274) 546732 Fax: (01274) 548525 E-mail: sales@ashtree.yorks.com Principal Export Areas: Worldwide *Ashtree Glass is one of Europe's leading manufacturers of rear view mirrors and safety mirrors. We supply mirrors to many of the worlds leading vehicle and equipment manufacturers. We manufacture truck mirrors, tractor mirrors, bus mirrors, plant mirrors, construction equipment mirrors and forklift truck mirrors. As well as standard rear view mirrors we manufacture an extensive range of blind spot safety mirrors for use on construction equipment and other off highway machinery. These mirrors help operators manoeuvre safely in dangerous environments and so reduce accidents. We also manufacture a range of mirror arms and brackets for mounting mirrors safely. Being a manufacturing company we are able to provide bespoke solutions to individual fleet problems in an efficient and cost effective manner. Using modern communication and transport systems means we are also able to supply our customers all over the world with an efficient service.*

Ashtree Label Systems, 36 Ashtree Hill, Tandragee, Craigavon, County Armagh, BT62 2HP Tel: (028) 3884 9706 Fax: (028) 3884 9706 *Self adhesive labels & labelling equipment suppliers*

Ashtronics Ltd, 119 Meldreth Road, Whaddon, Royston, Hertfordshire, SG8 5RS Tel: (01223) 208308 Fax: (01223) 208308 E-mail: ashtronics@aol.com *Control panel manufrs*

▶ Ashvale Civil Engineering, Dallow Road, Luton, LU1 1TD Tel: (01582) 726650 Fax: (01582) 726652

Ashvale Sawmills Ltd, East Shalford Lane, Shalford, Guildford, Surrey, GU4 8AS Tel: (01483) 537505 Fax: (01483) 451298 *Fencing manufrs*

Ashvale Timber Industries, 62-68 Birling Road, Ashford, Kent, TN24 8BB Tel: (01233) 623592 Fax: (01233) 712611 *Fencing & shed erectors & manufrs*

Ashway Associates, Ashway House, Ickwell Green, Biggleswade, Bedfordshire, SG18 9EQ Tel: (01767) 627449 Fax: (01767) 627799 E-mail: ashcroftashway@aol.com *Customer satisfaction consultants*

Ashwell Construction Co. Ltd, 158 Victoria Rise, Clapham, London, SW4 0NW Tel: (020) 7622 0688 Fax: (020) 7627 1336 E-mail: enquiries@ashwell-interiors.co.uk *Office refurbishment*

Ashwell Engineering Services Ltd, Unit 12, Pinfold Road, Thurmaston, Leicester, LE4 8AT Tel: 0116-260 4050 E-mail: ashwelleng@hotmail.com *Engineering manufrs*

Ashwood, Stanshope Hall, Stanshope, Ashbourne, Derbyshire, DE6 2AD Tel: (01335) 310278 Fax: (01335) 310470 E-mail: jvelas@ashwood.biz *We at Ashwood are acting as UK introduction agents for the Indian company JV Elastomers, a member of the Horiaki group. JV Elastomers are specialists in producing any rubber or rubber-to-metal product required. Everything is custom - made and shipped from India at competitive prices, quickly and efficiently. **The services of JV Elastomers are already widely used throughout Europe, and are beginning to be adopted by many UK companies.**We assure prompt delivery of goods in accord to our customer"s specification by excellent production process and quality control systems. We derive strength from being a part of a Japanese conglomerate, manufacturing and selling rubber extruded and mounted products; packing material; machinery and selling rubber extruded and moulded products; packing materials; machinery and equipment; construction materials etc. *Constant quality checks guarantee that our products meet and exceed the strictest international standards.**

Ashwood, Crown House, Home Gardens, Dartford, DA1 1DZ Tel: (0845) 3700222 Fax: (0845) 3700223 E-mail: sales@ashwood.biz *Visit Ashwood for ice cream products, medical supplies, plastic boxes, plastic food containers, sandwich packs, snack food boxes, biodegradable packaging, and dowel pins and more. They are based in Dartford, Kent.*

Ashwood Designs Ltd, Robertstown House, Aberdare Business Park, Aberdare, Mid Glamorgan, CF44 8ER Tel: (01685) 883388 Fax: (01685) 883399 *Furniture manufrs*

Ashwood Garden Services & Crafts, Blendworth, Waterlooville, Hampshire, PO8 0QG Tel: (07071) 229946 Fax: (023) 9257 1700 *Fencing & garden furniture suppliers*

▶ Ashwood Scotland, 159A West Main Street, Whitburn, Bathgate, West Lothian, EH47 0QQ Tel: (01501) 744988

▶ Ashwood Technical Services Ltd, 1 Middleway Avenue, Stourbridge, West Midlands, DY8 5NJ Tel: (01384) 288763 Fax: (01384) 288763

Ashworth Bros Nelson Ltd, Whitefield Mill, Victoria Street, Nelson, Lancashire, BB9 7HL Tel: (01282) 613997 Fax: (01282) 613997 *Textiles manufrs*

▶ Ashworth Construction (North West) Ltd, 16a Boxer Place, Moss Side, Leyland, PR26 7QL Tel: (01772) 699800

Edwin Ashworth Marine Ltd, 10 Dove Way, Kirkby Mills Industrial Estate, Kirkbymoorside, York, YO62 6QR Tel: (01751) 433039 Fax: (01751) 433039 *Commercial fishing equipment*

▶ Ashworth Electrical Services Ltd, Townfield House, Townfield Street, Oldham, OL4 1HF Tel: 0161-620 2689 Fax: 0161-627 4157 E-mail: sales@ashworthelectrical.co.uk *Electrical installation contractors*

Ashworth Europe Ltd, Building 84, Bay 1 First Avenue, Pensnett Trading Estate, Kingswinford, West Midlands, DY6 7FN Tel: (01384) 355000 Fax: (01384) 355001 E-mail: info@ashworth.com *Conveyor belting manufrs*

John Ashworth & Partners Ltd, PO Box 160, Bacup, Lancashire, OL13 0BW Tel: (01706) 879544 Fax: (01706) 647767 E-mail: johnashworth.paint@virgin.net *Analytical chemists & paint test/research*

▶ Ashworth Norman Ltd, Mellor Street, Rochdale, Lancashire, OL11 5BT Tel: (01706) 648501 Fax: (01706) 345721

▶ Ashworth Preece Logistics, 7 Memorial Road, Walkden, Manchester, M28 3AQ Tel: (0870) 350 1246 Fax: (0870) 350 1248

▶ Ashworth (Screen Printers) Ltd, Westland Square, Leeds, LS11 5SS Tel: 0113-271 7978

Ashworth Springs, 32 Tong Lane, Whitworth, Rochdale, Lancashire, OL12 8BE Tel: (01706) 854161 Fax: (01706) 854171 *Metal spring manufrs*

Ashworth & Tennant, 12 The Moors Shopping Centre, South Hawksworth Street, Ilkley, West Yorkshire, LS29 9LB Tel: (01943) 817614 Fax: (01943) 817614 E-mail: na@working-jewellers.co.uk *Jewellers*

Ashworth & Thompson Ltd, Freestone Drive, Bulwell, Nottingham, NG6 8UZ Tel: 0115-927 8504 Fax: 0115-977 0152 E-mail: sales@ashworthandthompson.co.uk

continued

Company Information

continuation
Picture frame moulding suppliers & framing machinery Also at: Belfast, Dublin, Edinburgh & Nottingham

▶ W.B. Ashworth & Sons Ltd, Tudor Industrial Estate, Ashton Street, Dukinfield, Cheshire, SK16 4RN Tel: 0161-330 3555 Fax: 0161-330 6777 E-mail: wba@btinternet.com *Fashion handbag designers & imports*

Asi, Alliance House, Snape, Saxmundham, Suffolk, IP17 1SW Tel: (01728) 688555 Fax: (01728) 688950 *Shotgun importers*

ASI DataMyte UK Ltd, Estate Office, Luton Hoo Estate, Luton, LU1 3TQ Tel: (0870) 1433020 Fax: (0870) 1433021 E-mail: sales@qgs.co.uk *Quality Gauging Systems provide advanced metrology and data collection systems and equipment to the manufacturing and process industries. We manufacture and market high precision pneumatic and electronic measuring instruments, SPC and data analysis software, laser systems for turbine blade measurment, gap and flush multi gauging systems and other dimensional gauges.*

Asian Chemical News, Quadrant House, The Quadrant, Brighton Road, Sutton, Surrey, SM2 5AS Tel: (020) 8652 3500 *The first dedicated news weekly for Asian Chemicals.*

▶ Asianet UK Ltd, Packaging Company Unit, 10 A Featherby Drive, Glen Parva, Leicester, LE2 9NY Tel: 0116-278 4449 Fax: 0116-224 6431 E-mail: arunk19@aol.com *Manufacturers of bags*

Asig, Pinfold Lane, Manchester Airport, Manchester, M90 5XA Tel: 0161-499 1316 Fax: 0161-499 3700 *Aviation refuelling*

▶ Asj Electrical Services, 6 Woodburn Road, Smethwick, West Midlands, B66 2PU Tel: 0121-555 8801 Fax: 0121-555 8803

▶ Asj Itnet Com Ltd, 10 Morris Close, Croydon, CR0 7RD Tel: (07749) 446211 Fax: (07720) 270771 E-mail: info@asj-itnet.co.uk *Computer consultancy & services*

▶ Ask The Geek, Bruntsfield, Edinburgh, EH3 9LP Tel: (0797) 4224472 E-mail: sales@askthegeek.it *IT Support & services for Edinburgh. ADSL, Wirless, Office IT Moves, desktop support, server support, network support.*

▶ ASK Innovation Limited, Suite 104b, Discovery Court, 551-553 Wallisdown Road, Poole, Dorset, BH12 5AG Tel: 01202 853221 Fax: 01202 853214 E-mail: enquiries@askinnovation.co.uk *We provide product development services for the engineering and scientific community. Our specialism is low power analogue design.*

Ask Web Design, Dam Hill Farm, Malton Road, York, YO32 9TL Tel: (01904) 400047 E-mail: tom@askwebdesign.com *Internet solutions, from domain name registration to web development*

Askern UK Ltd, High Street, Askern, Doncaster, South Yorkshire, DN6 0AA Tel: (01302) 703065 Fax: (01302) 701992 E-mail: info@askern.com *Cable drum & pallet manufrs*

Askew Mailing Services Ltd, 1 Broadmead Business Park, Broadmead Road, Stewartby, Bedford, MK43 9NX Tel: (01234) 766202 Fax: (01234) 766388 E-mail: info@mailinghouse.co.uk *Direct Mail Fulfilment .Laser Printed Personalised Letters. Mono Digital Laser Copying. Direct Ink-Jet Printing to Envelopes. Mailsort Discounted Post Sorting. Overseas Consolidated Discounted Post Service. Mailing Item Pack and Prep*

Askews Library Services Ltd, 218-222 North Road, Preston, PR1 1SY Tel: (01772) 555947 Fax: (01772) 492768 E-mail: info@askews.co.uk *Library & schools book distributors*

Askey Precision Engineering, Neachells Lane, Willenhall, West Midlands, WV13 3SJ Tel: (01902) 306300 Fax: (01902) 306400 *Precision engineers services*

▶ Ask-gutenburg.com Ltd, 2 Frankton Avenue, Haywards Heath, West Sussex, RH16 3QX Tel: (01444) 441444 E-mail: sales@ask-gutenburg.com *Publishers*

Askham Motors Ltd, Gilwilly Road Industrial Estate, Gilwilly Industrial Estate, Penrith, Cumbria, CA11 9BF Tel: (01768) 892233 Fax: (01768) 895522 *Agricultural machinery sales*

Askquith Industrial Marketing Services, PO Box 10, Corbridge, Northumberland, NE45 5BY Tel: (01434) 633068 Fax: (01434) 633068 E-mail: bill@ask-marketing.co.uk *Marketing consultants*

Asl Financial Solutions, Fountain House Suite 9, Great Cornbow, Halesowen, West Midlands, B63 3BL Tel: (0870) 6002131 Fax: 0121-585 7294 E-mail: info@finobj.com *Software house service provider*

Asles (Tool Hire & Sales) Ltd, 82 Broadway, Shifnal, Shropshire, TF11 8AZ Tel: (01952) 461266 Fax: (01952) 462337 *Tool hire & sales*

Aslotel Ltd, Aslotel House, Pebble Close, Pebble Coombe, Tadworth, Surrey, KT20 7PA Tel: (01372) 362533 Fax: (01372) 362284 E-mail: asl@aslotel.co.uk *Aslotel Ltd based in Tadworth, Surrey offer hotel guest products including batchroom accessories and fittings, coathangers, electronic safes and hairdryers as well as a range of cosmetics and toiletries for the hotel industry.*

▶ Asm GmbH, Tanyard House, 37 High Street, Measham, Swadlincote, Derbyshire, DE12 7HR Tel: (01530) 515342 Fax: (0845) 1222124 E-mail: sales@asm-sensor.co.uk *Electrical equipment distributors*

Asm GmbH, Tanyard House, 37 High Street, Measham, Swadlincote, Derbyshire, DE12 7HR Tel: (01530) 515342 Fax: (0845) 1222124 E-mail: sales@asm-sensor.co.uk

Asm Data Ltd, Unit 9-12, Faraday Park, Andover, Hampshire, SP10 3SA Tel: (01264) 336007 Fax: (01264) 336100 E-mail: admin@asmdata.co.uk *Document managers*

Asm Engineering Ltd, 74 Wilbury Way, Hitchin, Hertfordshire, SG4 0TP Tel: 01462 477360 Fax: 01582 454772 E-mail: office@asmeng.co.uk *Air conditioning duct work installers & manufrs*

▶ ASM Group, Unit U1, Rose Business Estate, Marlow Bottom Road, Marlow, Buckinghamshire, SL7 3ND Tel: (01628) 891717 Fax: (01628) 891718 E-mail: sales@asmgroup.info *ASM Group manufacture and supply airfield lighting, signs, airfield ground lighting transformers and docking guidance systems*

ASM Metal Recycling Ltd, Griffin Lane, Aylesbury, Buckinghamshire, HP19 8BB Tel: (01296) 337711 Fax: (01296) 337751 E-mail: asm@asm-recycling.co.uk *Recycling contractors & salvage consultants*

▶ Asm Services, The Wharf Offices, Glynde, Lewes, East Sussex, BN8 6SS Tel: (01273) 858839 Fax: (01273) 858840 E-mail: maintanence@asmprompticle.com

Asmec Electronics Solutions Ltd, 64-68 Wilbury Way, Hitchin, Hertfordshire, SG4 0TP Tel: (01462) 441155 Fax: (01462) 441150 E-mail: nashr@asmec.com *Manufacturers of cable assembly services*

Asmech Systems Ltd, Units 108-111, Old Mill Lane Industrial Estate, Mansfield Woodhouse, Mansfield, Nottinghamshire, NG19 9BG Tel: (01623) 424442 Fax: (01623) 424433 E-mail: sales@asmechsystems.co.uk *Conveyor & holding systems for the food & confectionary markets*

▶ Asmet Engineering & Technical Services Ltd, 27 Highcroft Crescent, Leamington Spa, Warwickshire, CV32 6BN Tel: (01926) 314536 Fax: 0871 2439203 E-mail: asmet@clara.co.uk *Design and procurement of equipment for the support of product development, testing and manufacture. Also engineering services in support of product development: modelling, analysis and drawing.*

Asmex Ltd, Unit 43 Gemini Business Estate, Landmann Way, London, SE14 5RL Tel: (020) 7394 9090 Fax: (020) 7394 9191 *Catering equipment manufrs*

▶ Asociated Agency Co., Factory 1, Pottery Close, Winterstoke Road, Weston-Super-Mare, Avon, BS23 3YH Tel: (01934) 622960 Fax: (01934) 621456 *Suppliers of windows*

▶ Asp Ship Management Ltd, Bergius House, 20 Clifton Street, Glasgow, G3 7XS Tel: 0141-332 8118 Fax: 0141-332 2675

Aspall, The Cider House, Aspall Hall, Debenham, Stowmarket, Suffolk, IP14 6PD Tel: (01728) 860510 Fax: (01728) 861031 E-mail: barry@aspall.co.uk *Apple juice, vinegars & ciders manufacturers or producers*

Aspec Precision Engineers, Unit P1 Dales Manor Business Park, Grove Road, Sawston, Cambridge, CB22 3TJ Tel: (01223) 836710 Fax: (01223) 836294 E-mail: info@aspec.co.uk *Precision engineers*

Aspect 3D - Visualisation and Design, 59 Hawkenbury Way, Lewes, East Sussex, BN7 1LT Tel: (01273) 471606 E-mail: info@aspect3d.co.uk *Architectural services*

Aspect Design, 89 Newtown Road, Malvern, Worcestershire, WR14 1PD Tel: (01684) 561567 Fax: (01684) 560041 E-mail: help@aspect-design.net *Lithographic printers & designers*

Aspect Exhibitions Ltd, 1 Ashton Lodge Farm, Hartwell Road, Ashton, Northampton, NN7 2JT Tel: (01604) 864999 Fax: (01604) 864888 E-mail: sales@aspectexhib.co.uk *Exhibition stand contractors*

Aspect Graphics & Displays, Units 35-36 Bury Business Centre, Kay Street, Bury, Lancashire, BL9 6BU Tel: 0161-763 9955 Fax: 0161-763 9355 E-mail: sales@aspectdisplays.co.uk *Display stands distributors*

Aspect Insurance Services Ltd, Evans Business Centre Sycamore Trading Estate, Squires Gate Lane, Blackpool, FY4 3RL Tel: (0870) 0465540 Fax: (01253) 340551 E-mail: sales@aspectinsurance.co.uk *Commercial & private insurance services*

▶ Aspect It Ltd, County End Business Centre, Jackson Street, Springhead, Oldham, OL4 4TZ Tel: (01457) 872636 Fax: (01457) 872637 *Computer systems consultants*

▶ Aspect Metalcraft, Unit 8, Potts Marsh Industrial Estate, Eastbourne Road, Westham, Pevensey, East Sussex, BN24 5NH Tel: (01323) 735537 Fax: (01323) 765666 E-mail: sales@aspectmetalcraft.com *Metal fabricators*

▶ Aspect Powder Coatings, Coneygre Industrial Estate, Tipton, West Midlands, DY4 8XP Tel: 0121-557 4444

Aspect Print Services Ltd, Main Street, Aslockton, Nottingham, NG13 9AL Tel: (01949) 851611 Fax: (01949) 851609 E-mail: aspect-print@btconnect.com *Label printing services*

▶ Aspect Studio Ltd, 14 Woodland Drive, Watford, WD17 3BX Tel: (01923) 213989 Fax: 01923 213980 E-mail: info@aspectstudio.co.uk *Aspect Studio is a leading market research viewing facility, located in central Watford, United Kingdom.*

▶ Aspecthr Business Consultants, 6 Abbotsford Crescent, Wishaw, Lanarkshire, ML2 7DH Tel: (01698) 385075 E-mail: enquiries@aspectHR.co.uk *Services include: Human Resource Management, Human Resource Consultancy, Management Development, Training, Psychometric Testing, Assessment & Development Centres.*

Aspects Of Beauty, 23 Baldock Street, Ware, Hertfordshire, SG12 9DH Tel: (01920) 466100 Fax: (01920) 822745 *Tyres manufrs*

▶ Aspects Of Stone, Broughton Grounds, Broughton, Newport Pagnell, Buckinghamshire, MK16 0HZ Tel: (01908) 830061 Fax: (01908) 830062 E-mail: sales@aspectsofstone.co.uk *Manufacturers of high quality reconstituted stonework. Our extensive range of standard products include: Balustrading, Columns, Porticos, Strings, Plinths, Window Cills and heads, Pier Caps, Copings and Quoins Etc. We pride ourselves on the personal service given to each customer. Our range of colours include Bath, Cotswold, Portland and Terracotta. A full fitting service is also available.*

Aspectus Global Resource Solutions Ltd, Suite 353, 405 Kings Road, London, SW10 0BB Tel: (07002) 773288 Fax: (020) 8549 8592 E-mail: bmadmin@aspectusltd.co.uk *IT recruitment & resource solutions*

▶ Aspen A C Ltd, Apex Way, Hailsham, East Sussex, BN27 3WA Tel: (0800) 0377220 Fax: (01323) 849966 E-mail: info@aspen-ac.co.uk *Air conditioning installation services*

Aspen Air Conditioning Ltd, Apex Way, Hailsham, East Sussex, BN27 3WA Tel: (0800) 376 0767 Fax: (01323) 849 966 E-mail: info@aspen-ac.co.uk *Air conditioning designers*

Aspen Contracts Ltd, 333 London Road, Hadleigh, Essex, SS7 2BT Tel: (01702) 428899 Fax: (01702) 551899 E-mail: enquiries@aspencontracts.com *Air conditioning engineers*

▶ Aspen Electronics Ltd, 1-3 Kildare Close, Ruislip, Middlesex, HA4 9UR Tel: (020) 8868 1311 Fax: (020) 8866 6596 E-mail: info@aspen-electronics.com *Aspen Electronics are electronic component suppliers.*

Aspen Pumps Ltd, Aspen Building, Apex Way, Hailsham, East Sussex, BN27 3WA Tel: (01323) 848842 Fax: (01323) 848846 *Pump manufrs*

Aspentech Ltd, Birkdale House, Kelvin Close, Warrington, WA3 7RB Tel: (01925) 844400 Fax: (01925) 844455 *Computer software writers*

Aspentech Ltd, Unit 1 Century Court, Tolpits La, Watford, WD18 9RS Tel: (01923) 254499 Fax: (01923) 816456 *Software development*

Aspentech UK Ltd, Sheraton House, Castle Park, Cambridge, CB3 0AX Tel: (01223) 312220 Fax: (01223) 350653 E-mail: info@aspentech.com *Computer software producers*

▶ Aspenwood Holiday Cottage, Inverfarigaig, South Loch Ness Side, Inverness, IV2 6XR Tel: (01456) 486415 E-mail: lyn@lochnesscottage.com *Aspenwood luxury self catering holiday cottage overlooking Loch Ness in the romantic Highlands of Scotland. Sleeps 5 comfortably. Private decking looking onto Loch Ness. Computer access.*

Aspermont UK, Albert House, 1-4 Singer Street, London, EC2A 4BQ Tel: (020) 7216 6060 Fax: (020) 7216 6050 E-mail: info@mining-journal.com *Publishers*

Aspex Technology, Rapid House, 40 Oxford Road, High Wycombe, Buckinghamshire, HP11 2EE Tel: (01494) 558121 Fax: (01494) 558016 E-mail: sales@aspex-semi.com *Semiconductors, ultra high performance software specialists*

Aspfase Ltd, 4 Stepbridge Road, Tufthorn Industrial Estate, Coleford, Gloucestershire, GL16 2PL Tel: (01594) 833939 Fax: (01594) 833939 *Industrial rubber product manufrs*

Asphalt Roofing Ltd, 78b Warwick Road, London, N18 1RT Tel: (020) 8807 9806 Fax: (020) 8807 9806 *Roofing contractors*

Asphaltic Roofing Supplies Ltd, Page Green Road, London, N15 4PG Tel: (020) 8808 0459 Fax: (020) 8801 3259 E-mail: tottenham@asphaltic.co.uk *Roofing suppliers*

Aspin Engineering Ltd, Moss La Industrial Estate, Egremont Close, Whitefield, Manchester, M45 8FH Tel: 0161-766 9622 Fax: 0161-766 1423 E-mail: enquiries@aspin-engineering.com *Aspin Engineering, formed 20 years ago by the present owner primarily manufactures extrusion dieheads and crossheads for plastics, rubber and food processing. Machining services include thread grinding, universal grinding, horizontal boring, CNC turning and CNC milling.*

Frank Aspinall & Co., Unit 7, Offerton Industrial Estate, Hempshaw Lane, Stockport, Cheshire, SK2 5TJ Tel: 0161-480 2707 Fax: 0161-480 2707 E-mail: frankaspinall@hotmail.com *Commercial printers*

Aspinall's Angling Supplies, 36 Cross Street, Barry, South Glamorgan, CF63 4LU Tel: (01446) 742645 Fax: (01446) 742645 E-mail: aspinallangling@aol.com *Fishing tackle wholesalers & manufrs*

▶ Aspiration Jewellery, PO Box 052, Glasgow, G71 7WW Tel: (0870) 757 1512

▶ Aspire Beyond, 2nd Floor 145-157 St John Street, London, EC1V 4PY Tel: 0870-490 4296 Fax: 0870-706 4880 E-mail: info@aspirebeyond.co.uk *We are a professional consultancy and coaching practice, committed to helping our customers to achieve their aspirations for life, career and business. Our services include CV appraisals, CV coaching, CV writing, interview coaching, business writing, business plan support and business startup coaching.*

▶ Aspire Media Design, PO Box 436, Weston-super-Mare, Avon, BS22 8WZ Tel: (0808) 1661515 E-mail: sales@aspiremediadesign.co.uk *Web design*

▶ Aspiredos Ltd, 23 The Chantree, Hillingdon, Uxbridge, Middlesex, UB8 3RA Tel: (01895) 520020 Fax: 01895 520020 E-mail: info@aspiredos.co.uk *Aspiredos provide Cost Effective Management Solutions to the Construction Industry. We offer a complete range of support services to both Building and ME&P Works for both Contractors and Sub-Contractors. These services include Pre and Post Contract , Planning, Management and Commercial.*

Aspland Gauge Co Ltd, Broadway, Hyde, Cheshire, SK14 4QF Tel: 0161-368 3432 Fax: 0161-367 8426 E-mail: sales@aspland.co.uk *Micrometer & gauge servicing*

Aspley Workwear Rental, Robins Wood Road, Nottingham, NG8 3LE Tel: 0115-929 1321 Fax: 0115-929 1239 *Industrial laundry services*

Asplins Oatcakes, 2 Haywood Street, Leek, Staffordshire, ST13 5JX Tel: (01538) 387556 *Bakery & confectionery retailers*

▶ Aspull Electrical Services Ltd, 124-126 Frog Lane, Wigan, Lancashire, WN6 7DS Tel: (01942) 247459 Fax: (01942) 826367 E-mail: info@aspull-electrical.co.uk

Asquith Butler, Huddersfield Road, Brighouse, West Yorkshire, HD6 3RA Tel: (01484) 726620 Fax: (01484) 718708 E-mail: info@asquithbutler.com *Machine tool manufacturer, service, sales & spares specialists*

Asquith & Co Refrigeration Ltd, Searches Lane, Bedmond, Abbots Langley, Hertfordshire, WD5 0SB Tel: (01727) 852488 Fax: (01727) 859226 E-mail: info@asquiths.co.uk *Refrigeration engineers*

▶ Asseal, 139a Hillsborough Old Road, Lisburn, County Antrim, BT27 5QE Tel: (028) 9266 9966 Fax: (028) 9266 9977

Assembleon (UK) Ltd, Philips Ho, Cambridge Business Pk, Cowley Rd, Cambridge, CB4 0HE Tel: (01223) 468268 Fax: (01223) 468269 E-mail: louise.hartley@philips.com *Surface mount equipment*

Assembly Solutions Ltd, Units 4-8 Watermead Works, Slater Lane, Bolton, BL1 2TE Tel: (01204) 537621 Fax: (01204) 381007 E-mail: sales@assembly-solutions.com *Electrical wiring assemblies & components manufrs*

▶ Assent Systems Ltd, Braemar, Nether Compton, Sherborne, Dorset, DT9 4QJ Tel: (01935) 814300 Fax: (01935) 813047

▶ Assert I T Ltd, 10 Knowle Avenue, Blackpool, FY5 3PP Tel: (01253) 865467 Fax: (0871) 2216078 E-mail: info@assert-it.co.uk *Computer Services*

▶ Assertis Ltd, 22 Warwick Park, Tunbridge Wells, Kent, TN2 5TB Tel: (01892) 513688 E-mail: info@assertis.co.uk *Website design & content management specialists*

▶ Asset Brokers (Int) Ltd, 123 Ashgrove Road West, Aberdeen, AB16 5FA Tel: (01224) 666308 Fax: (01224) 698154 E-mail: info@abil.org.uk *International equipment brokerage company*

Asset Business Coaching Ltd, 120 Narbeth Drive, Aylesbury, Buckinghamshire, HP20 1PZ Tel: 01296 394222 E-mail: info@assetbusinesscoaching.com *Asset Business Coaching provide the complete business development and coaching programme for every small to medium enterprise (SME) in the UK that is looking for that elusive "something better"*

Asset Business Systems Ltd, 8a Milburn Road, Bournemouth, BH4 9HJ Tel: (01202) 757599 Fax: (01202) 757588 E-mail: davemac@assetsystems.co.uk *Computer software & hardware designers*

▶ Asset Construction Consultants, 1 Dittons Mews, St. Leonards-on-Sea, East Sussex, TN38 9TQ Tel: (01424) 853754 Fax: (01424) 851210 E-mail: matt@assetconstructionconsultants.co.uk *Chartered building surveyors*

Asset Engineering Ltd, 16 20 Black Lake Industrial Estate, Black Lake, West Bromwich, West Midlands, B70 9QP Tel: 0121-553 0231 Fax: 0121-525 4856 *Flame cut profiles*

▶ Asset Finance Broker, Scotland Farm, Stockwood Road, Bristol, BS4 5LU Tel: (0845) 8380936 E-mail: info@assetfinancebroker.co.uk *Business finance consultants*

Asset Fixings & Tools Ltd, 40 Wilbury Way, Hitchin, Hertfordshire, SG4 0AP Tel: (01462) 440445 Fax: (01462) 440540 E-mail: sales@assetfixings.co.uk *Power tools & accessories*

Asset Co Group Ltd, Ruislip Workshop, 800 Field End Road, Ruislip, Middlesex, HA4 0QH Tel: (020) 8515 3999 Fax: (020) 8515 3999 E-mail: sales@assetco.com *Hire of specialist vehicles*

▶ Asset Manufacturing Ltd, Howletts Way, Thetford, Norfolk, IP24 1HZ Tel: (01842) 763529 Fax: (01842) 752398 E-mail: sales@asset-windows.co.uk *Manufacture instore windows, doors & conservatories*

▶ Asset Protection Administration, The Terminal Building, Union Wharf, Leicester Road, Market Harborough, Leicestershire, LE16 7UW Tel: (01858) 469955 Fax: (01858) 466460 E-mail: apa@apa-admin.co.uk *APA is an insurance intermediary that specialises in extending services warranties for manufacturer and distributors or industrial equipment*

Assicurazioni Generali, 100 Leman Street, London, E1 8AJ Tel: (020) 7265 6200 Fax: (020) 7702 3745 E-mail: sales@generaliglobal.com *Insurance company* Also at: Birmingham, Bristol, Glasgow, Maidstone, Manchester & York

▶ Assign It, 4 Brick Knoll Park, Ashley Road, St. Albans, Hertfordshire, AL1 5UG Tel: (01727) 843888 Fax: (01727) 839999 E-mail: sales@assign-it.co.uk *Computer systems consultants*

Assign Technology, Unit 1 Wadsworth Business Centre, 21 Wadsworth Road, Greenford, Middlesex, UB6 7LQ Tel: (020) 8998 0806 Fax: (020) 8998 1272 E-mail: info@assigntechnology.com *Signs, electronic information, sign contractors/sign makers/suppliers/installation, sign consultant and designers & information display devices manufactures. Products include single line signs, Bi Line Signs, Multi-Line signs, reception boards, time and temperature displays, exchange rate boards, graphic boards, scoreboards, factory and safety boards, queuing systems, carpark and traffic management and bespoke displays. Please quote Kellysearch when calling.*

Assignment Signs & Nameplates, 26 Brindley Road, Dodwells Bridge Industrial Estate, Hinckley, Leicestershire, LE10 3BY Tel: (01455) 891200 Fax: (01455) 619426 *Exhibition display designers*

Assignments Ltd, Unit 6 Broadway Green Farm, Broadway Road, Lightwater, Surrey, GU18 5SU Tel: (01276) 452110 Fax: (01276) 453312 E-mail: sales@assimen.com *Sign maker services*

Assistance Teknica Ltd, York House, Borough Road, Middlesbrough, Cleveland, TS1 2HJ Tel: (01642) 224545 Fax: (01642) 243514 E-mail: enquiries@teknica.co.uk *Steelwork consultants*

▶ Assistpoint Limited, 40 Allendale Road, Barnsley, South Yorkshire, S75 1BJ Tel: 0114 2387569 E-mail: sales@assistpoint.co.uk *Computer software and web site designers and suppliers of 3D glasses and eclipse glasses.*

Associated British Engineering P.L.C., 63 Church Street, Harston, Cambridge, CB2 5NP Tel: (01223) 873600 Fax: (01223) 872652 E-mail: peter.morton@abeplc.co.uk *Holding company*

Associated British Ports, Old Custom House, Key St, Ipswich, IP4 1BY Tel: (01473) 231010 Fax: (01473) 230914 E-mail: ipswich@abports.co.uk *Port authority services*

▶ Associated Building Maintenance, 106 Whitworth Road, Rochdale, Lancashire, OL12 0JJ Tel: (01706) 654730 Fax: (01706) 648169

Associated Cold Stores & Transport Ltd, South Humberside Industrial Estate, Grimsby, South Humberside, DN31 2WR Tel: (01472) 240269 Fax: (01472) 240269 E-mail: acoldnsn@acst.co.uk *Distributors of frozen food*

Associated Compressor Engineers, Sheffield Street, Stockport, Cheshire, SK4 1RU Tel: 0161-476 3800 Fax: 0161-476 6300 E-mail: sales@acecompressors.com *Air compressor distributors or agents*

Associated Consultants Ltd, The Old Mill, Ewenny, Bridgend, Mid Glamorgan, CF35 5BN Tel: (01656) 768916 Fax: (01656) 662007 *Computer software services*

Associated Contract Energy Ltd, 73-75 Church Road, Redfield, Bristol, BS5 9JR Tel: 0117-939 4495 Fax: 0117-939 4496 E-mail: vivre21@hotmail.com *Heating & energy management contractors*

Associated Control Systems Ltd, Unit 15 Spring Road, Industrial Estate, Wolverhampton, WV4 6UA Tel: (01902) 353811 Fax: (01902) 353818 E-mail: rob.acs@btconnect.com *Control panel manufrs*

▶ Associated Cooling Services, Unit 20 Metro Business Centre, Kangley Bridge Road, London, SE26 5BW Tel: (020) 8778 8668 Fax: (020) 8778 1221

Associated Dental Products Ltd, Kemdent Works, Cricklade Road, Purton, Swindon, SN5 4HT Tel: (01793) 770256 Fax: (01793) 772256 E-mail: sales@kemdent.co.uk *Dental & wax products manufrs*

▶ associated drain cleaning services, 80 hawthorn way, shepperton, middlesex, TW17 8QD Tel: 01932 765892 Fax: 01932 765892 E-mail: info@associated-services.co.uk *drain and pipe clearing /cleaning*services sinks toilets urinals*high pressure water jetting colour cctv scans* mechanical and manual rodding*covering surrey middlesex all KT GU and TW post code areas*

Associated Hospital Supply Ltd, Sherwood Road, Aston Fields, Bromsgrove, Worcestershire, B60 3DR Tel: (01527) 876776 Fax: (01527) 872022 E-mail: info@associatedhospitalsupply.com *Medical disposable products*

Associated Independent Stores Ltd, Cranmore Avenue, Shirley, Solihull, West Midlands, B90 4LF Tel: 0121-711 2200 Fax: 0121-711 1334 E-mail: mail@aistores.co.uk *Voluntary buying group*

▶ Associated Industrial Control Solutions, 298 Bath Road, Slough, SL1 4DX Tel: (0845) 6031601 Fax: (01753) 824147 E-mail: mail@aicsolutions.com *Automation & process control services*

▶ Associated Industrial Paints, Park View Works, Park Street, Stalybridge, Cheshire, SK15 2BT Tel: 0161-303 9008 *Powder coating suppliers*

Associated Joinery Techniques Ltd, Marks Hall, Marks Hall Lane, Margaret Roding, Dunmow, Essex, CM6 1QT Tel: (01245) 231881 Fax: (01245) 231818 E-mail: ajt.ltd@btinternet.com *Laboratory furniture manufrs*

Associated Laboratories Services UK Ltd, Unit 55 Lakes Industrial Park, Lower Chapel Hill, Braintree, Essex, CM7 3RU Tel: (01376) 322938 Fax: (01376) 552106 E-mail: info@als-uk-ltd.com *Laboratory equipment manufrs*

▶ Associated Laundry Systems Ltd, Broadfields Court, Broadfields, Aylesbury, Buckinghamshire, HP19 8BU Tel: (01296) 393939 Fax: (01296) 393934 E-mail: alslimited@aol.com *Laundry machine distributors*

Associated Metal Stainless Ltd, 101 Brook Street, Glasgow, G40 3AP Tel: 0141-551 0707 Fax: 0141-551 0690 E-mail: info@assoc-metal.co.uk *Stainless steel products & sanitary ware*

▶ Associated Network Engineers, Mardale Road, Penrith, Cumbria, CA11 9EH Tel: (01768) 868555 Fax: (01768) 868777 E-mail: sales@ane.co.uk *Installers of data cabelling*

Associated Pied Pipers, 37 Bowring Close, Exeter, EX1 3TU Tel: (01392) 461991 Fax: (01392) 205153 *Pest control services*

Associated Pipework, 35 The Swan Centre, Rosemary Road, London, SW17 0AR Tel: (020) 8879 7042 Fax: (020) 8947 9139 E-mail: assocpipework@ukonline.co.uk *Installation & fabrication of pipework*

Associated Print & Training Ltd, PO Box 107, Bury St. Edmunds, Suffolk, IP31 2UF Tel: (01284) 788333 Fax: (01284) 788336 E-mail: sales@apt.gb.com *Computer stationery & training*

Associated Reclaimed Oils, 165 Tunnel Avenue, London, SE10 0PW Tel: (020) 8858 9907 Fax: (020) 8858 9907 *Oil waste processors & contractors*

Associated Roto-Plastics Ltd, Green Grove Mill, Dyehouse Lane, Rochdale, Lancashire, OL16 2QN Tel: (0870) 8303900 Fax: (0870) 8303901 E-mail: sales@haywood-rotomoulding.co.uk *Plastic rotational mouldings & bollard manufrs*

▶ Associated Securities, Unit 14 15, Cam Square, Wilbury Way, Hitchin, Hertfordshire, SG4 0TZ Tel: (01462) 421188 Fax: 01462 421188 E-mail: associatedsecurities@btconnect.com

Associated Security Ltd, 59 London Road, Wallington, Surrey, SM6 7HW Tel: (020) 8669 7811 Fax: (020) 8669 9890 E-mail: sales@associatedsecuritygroup.co.uk

continued

Safe suppliers & repairers Also at: Croydon & London SW6

Associated Security Ltd, 59 London Road, Wallington, Surrey, SM6 7HW Tel: (020) 8669 7811 Fax: (020) 8669 9890 E-mail: sales@associatedsecurity.co.uk *Security services*

Associated Security Group Ltd, 277 Wandsworth Bridge Road, London, SW6 2TX Tel: (020) 7736 7092 Fax: (020) 8669 9890 E-mail: info@associatedsecuritygroup.co.uk *Security services*

Associated Security Group Ltd, 277 Wandsworth Bridge Road, London, SW6 2TX Tel: (020) 7736 7092 Fax: (020) 8669 9890 E-mail: info@associatedsecuritygroup.co.uk *Security services*

Associated Security Group Ltd, 59 London Road, Wallington, Surrey, SM6 7HW Tel: (020) 8669 7722 Fax: (020) 8669 9890 E-mail: sales@associatedsecuritygroup.co.uk *Security equipment engineers* Also at: Croydon & Fulham

Associated Technology Pipeline Ltd, 3b Mansfield Business Park, Lymington Bottom Road, Medstead, Alton, Hampshire, GU34 5PZ Tel: (01420) 565601 Fax: (01420) 565602 E-mail: sales@atpuk.co.uk *Software development services*

Associated Tyre Specialists Ltd, Vantage Point, 20 Upper Portland Street, Aston, Birmingham, B6 5TW Tel: 0121-325 7325 Fax: 0121-325 7333 E-mail: info@ats.euromaster.com *Tyre repairers*

Associated Vehicle Services, 222 Main Rd, Hawkwell, Hockley, Essex, SS5 4EG Tel: 01702 201869 *Vehicle Electrics*

Associated Wire Products, Hendre Mine, The Nant, Rhydymwyn, Mold, Clwyd, CH7 5QD Tel: (01352) 741222 Fax: (01352) 741666 *Abrasive metallic & shot blasting materials suppliers*

I B A Associates, Dorford House, Perks Lane, Prestwood, Great Missenden, Buckinghamshire, HP16 0JD Tel: (01494) 865393 Fax: (01494) 865395 E-mail: miranda@ibaassociates.co.uk *Pharmaceutical consultancy service*

Associates Partnerships, 59 High Street, Maidstone, Kent, ME14 1SR Tel: (01622) 685588 Fax: (01622) 764660 *Computer consultancy*

Association Of The British Pharmaceutical Industry, 12 Whitehall, London, SW1A 2DY Tel: (020) 7930 3477 Fax: (020) 7747 1411 E-mail: abpi@abpi.org.uk *Trade association*

The Association Of Building Engineers, Jubilee House, Billing Brook Road, Northampton, NN3 8NW Tel: (01604) 404121 Fax: (01604) 784220 E-mail: building.engineers@abe.org.uk *Professional association*

Association Of Frozen Food Producers, 6 Catherine Street, London, WC2B 5JJ Tel: (020) 7420 7180 Fax: (020) 7783 6580 *Trade association*

Association of Industrial Laser Users (AILU), Oxford House, 100 Ock Street, Abingdon, Oxfordshire, OX14 5DH Tel: (01235) 539595 Fax: (01235) 550499 E-mail: mike@ailu.org.uk *Association for industrial laser users*

▶ Association Of Industrial Truck Trainers, The Springboard Centre, Mantle Lane, Coalville, Leicestershire, LE67 3DW Tel: (01530) 277857 Fax: (01530) 810231 *Fork lift truck trainers*

Association Of International &Currier Express Services, Global House, Poyle Road, Colnbrook, Slough, SL3 0AY Tel: (01753) 680550 Fax: (01753) 681710 E-mail: sales@aices.org *Trade association*

The Association of Suppliers To The British Clothing Industry, Unit 5, 25 Square Road, Halifax, West Yorkshire, HX1 1QG Tel: (01422) 354666 Fax: (01422) 381184 *Trade association*

Association of Wheelchair Children, 12 Tauntan Road, Brighton, BN2 4JN Tel: (01273) 239162 *Charity*

Assured Fire & Safety, 59 Florist Street, Stockport, Cheshire, SK3 8DW Tel: 0161-666 0204 Fax: 0161-666 0204 E-mail: paul@assuredfireandsafety.fsnet.co.uk *Fire alarm contractors*

▶ Assured I T Services Ltd, Head Office 8 Apsley Mill Cottage, London Road, Hemel Hempstead, Hertfordshire, HP3 9QU Tel: (0870) 4608802 Fax: (0870) 7065656 E-mail: sales@assuredit.com *Computer systems consultants*

Assured Performance Group Ltd, Kenlis Road, Barnacre, Preston, PR3 1GD Tel: (01995) 604600 Fax: (01995) 606651 E-mail: info@apgroup.uk.com *Manufacturers of pneumatic brakes & water pumps*

▶ Assured Sleep Beds, Part Moorbank, Artillery Street, Heckmondwike, West Yorkshire, WF16 0NX Tel: (01924) 406030 Fax: (01924) 400503 E-mail: sales@assuredsleep.com

▶ Assured Systems, 154 London Road, Sevenoaks, Kent, TN13 1DJ Tel: (01732) 455911 Fax: (01732) 465018 *Computer system consultants*

AST Signs, Unit 2, Gilwilly Road, East Lakes Business Park, Penrith, Cumbria, CA11 9BF Tel: (01768) 892292 Fax: (01768) 892294 E-mail: mark@astsigns.com *Sign contractors*

Asta Development plc, 5 Goodson Industrial Mews, Wellington Street, Thame, Oxfordshire, OX9 3BX Tel: (01844) 261700 Fax: (01844) 261314 E-mail: sales@astadev.com *Project management software manufrs*

Astabridge Ltd, Earlstrees Road, Earlstrees Industrial Estate, Corby, Northamptonshire, NN17 4AZ Tel: (01536) 267796 Fax: (01536) 402079 E-mail: info@astabmnge.co.uk *Retail display showcase manufrs*

A-Stat, 15 Hollybush Lane, Wolverhampton, WV4 4JJ Tel: (01902) 342400 Fax: (01902) 342333 E-mail: admin@astat.co.uk *Photocopying machine distributors*

Astec Computing UK Ltd, Astec House, 10-12 Sedlescombe Road South, St. Leonards-on-Sea, East Sussex, TN38 0TA Tel: (01424) 460721 Fax: (01424) 430888 E-mail: enquiries@asteccomputing.com *Computer systems services*

Astec Construction, Northfield, Hull Road, Cliffe, Selby, North Yorkshire, YO8 6NH Tel: (01757) 630374 Fax: (01757) 630609 *Steel fabricators*

Astec Projects Ltd, 187-189 Kings Road, Reading, RG1 4EX Tel: 0118-958 1333 Fax: 0118-958 1337 E-mail: astec@astecprojects.co.uk *Integrated ceiling design & installation services*

Astech Consultants, Albion Street, Chipping Norton, Oxfordshire, OX7 5BL Tel: (01608) 645251 Fax: (01608) 646510 E-mail: info@astech.uk.com *Software developers*

Astech Electronics Ltd, Forge Industrial Estate, The Street, Binsted, Alton, Hampshire, GU34 4PF Tel: (01420) 22689 Fax: (01420) 22636 E-mail: astech@astech.demon.co.uk *Tachometer & thermocouple manufrs*

Astellas Pharma, Lovett House, Lovett Road, Staines, Middlesex, TW18 3AZ Tel: (01784) 419400 Fax: (01784) 419401 *Manufacturing chemists*

Astelle Electrical Contractors Ltd, Mayflower House, 3 Chapel St, Billericay, Essex, CM12 9LT Tel: (01277) 651320 Fax: (01277) 630608 *Electrical engineers & contractors*

Asten Instruments Ltd, 3 Millfields, Caistor, Market Rasen, Lincolnshire, LN7 6PD Tel: (01472) 851831 Fax: (01472) 859927 E-mail: info@asten.co.uk *Instruments distributors*

▶ Aster Maintenance, 3 Kings Road, Fleet, Hampshire, GU51 3DL Tel: (01252) 816111 Fax: (01252) 816070 *Air conditioning suppliers*

Astley Components, 623-625 High Road Leyton, London, E10 6RF Tel: (020) 8556 9711 Fax: (020) 8556 6641 E-mail: sales@astleycomp.co.uk *Distributors of bolts & nuts, fasteners & threaded inserts*

Astley Computer Services, 37 The Farthings, Chorley, Lancashire, PR7 1TP Tel: (01257) 277057 Fax: (01257) 277057 E-mail: ast_com_serve@btinternet.com *Computer systems designers*

Astley Diamond Tools, Unit 10, Chancel Way, Witton Moor Lane Industrial Estate, Witton, Birmingham, B6 7AU Tel: 0121-356 8035 Fax: 0121-356 8035 E-mail: benorpeter@astley-diamontools.co.uk *Electroplated diamond tool manufrs*

Astley Signs, 273 Dukesway, Team Valley Trading Estate, Gateshead, Tyne & Wear, NE11 0PZ Tel: 0191-491 0097 Fax: 0191-491 0158 E-mail: astley@redforrest.co.uk *Established in 1924 and acquired by the existing Directors in 1990, Astley Signs has become one of the largest sign companies in the UK. Services include sign design, manufacture, installation, survey, planning, contract management and maintenance.*

Astleys, Renown Avenue, Coventry Business Park, Coventry, CV5 6UF Tel: (024) 7685 4545 Fax: (024) 7685 4515 E-mail: reception@astleys.co.uk *Janitorial supply services*

Aston Acoustic Ltd, Unit 7, Bay 1 The Woodsbank Trading Estate, Woden Road West, Wednesbury, West Midlands, WS10 7SU Tel: 0121-505 6500 Fax: 0121-505 6515 E-mail: info@astonacoustic.com *Loudspeaker systems distributors, agents, audio visual equipment hire & public address systems*

▶ Aston Carpets, 7 Polmorla Walk, Wadebridge, Cornwall, PL27 7NS Tel: (01208) 812184 Fax: (01208) 816137 E-mail: enquiries@astons-online.co.uk

▶ Aston Chimneys, 6 Bishops Field, Aston Clinton, Aylesbury, Buckinghamshire, HP22 5BB Tel: (0800) 5874098 E-mail: mick@astonchimneys.co.uk *Chimney Sweep Services: Full Brush & Vacuum. Chimney Pots, Vents Cages & Anti-Down Draught Cowls Supplied & Fitted. Advice & Problem Solving, Clean, Reliable & Efficient Service throughout london and the home counties.*

Aston Communications, 2 St. Johns Buildings, Friern Barnet Road, London, N11 3DP Tel: (020) 8361 8711 Fax: (020) 8361 3633 E-mail: john@aston-telex.com *Telephone equipment & telex distributors*

Aston Dane P.L.C., Aston Dane House, Waterloo Road, Widnes, Cheshire, WA8 0QR Tel: 0151-423 4494 Fax: 0151-495 1089 E-mail: postbox@astondane.com *Plant contractors*

Aston Display Ltd, 30 Brewery Street, Aston, Birmingham, B6 4JB Tel: 0121-333 6768 Fax: 0121-333 6769 E-mail: info@astondisplay.com *Exhibition & display equipment & services suppliers & manufrs*

Aston Edwards Electrical Co. Ltd, C Salford Trading Estate, Salford Street, Birmingham, B6 7SH Tel: 0121-327 4064 Fax: 0121-327 7759 *Electric motor repair services*

Aston & Fincher Ltd, Unit 2 Pavillion Drive, Off Holford Drive, Perry Barr, Birmingham, B6 7BB Tel: 0121-331 2000 Fax: 0121-331 2001 *Hairdressers' wholesalers* Also at: Branches throughout the UK.

Aston & Fincher Ltd, 213a Mill Road, Cambridge, CB1 3BE Tel: (01223) 249555 Fax: (01223) 249038 *Hair & beauty*

Aston & Fincher Ltd, 60 Cyprus Road, Leicester, LE2 8QS Tel: 0116-283 3451 *Hairdressing accessories wholesaler*

▶ Aston & Fincher Ltd, 3 Trafalgar Way, Erskine Industrial Estate, Liverpool, L6 1NA Tel: 0151-263 8811 Fax: 0151-263 8855 *Hair & beauty suppliers*

Aston & Fincher Ltd, 9-10 Embankment Lane, Plymouth, PL4 9LQ Tel: (01752) 221213 Fax: (01752) 260275 *Wholesale hair & beauty suppliers*

Aston Fittings, Springcroft Road, Birmingham, B11 3EL Tel: 0121-778 6001 Fax: 0121-778 6002 E-mail: sales@astonfittings.com *Valves & tube fittings manufrs*

Aston Martin Lagonda Ltd, Tickford Street, Newport Pagnell, Buckinghamshire, MK16 9AN Tel: (01908) 610620 Fax: (01908) 613708 E-mail: enquiry@astonmartin.com *Motor car manufrs*

Aston Matthews Ltd, 141-147a Essex Road, London, N1 2SN Tel: (020) 7226 7220 Fax: (020) 7354 5951 E-mail: sales@astonmatthews.co.uk *Bathroom specialists*

Aston Scientific Ltd, 111 Wendover Road, Stoke Mandeville, Aylesbury, Buckinghamshire, HP22 5TD Tel: (01296) 614144 Fax: (01296) 614228 *Scientific software distributors*

Aston Security, Walthamstow Business Centre, Clifford Road, London, E17 4SX Tel: (020) 8527 6888 Fax: (020) 8527 6969 *Security systems & maintenance, gate automation & barriers*

Aston's Bakery, Longpark, Newton Road, Torquay, TQ2 7AL Tel: (01803) 614811 *Wholesale bakery*

Astons Of Dudley Ltd, Shaw Road, Dudley, West Midlands, DY2 8TP Tel: (01384) 456836 Fax: (01384) 211953 *Road transport, haulage & freight services*

Astor Emc, Unit 1-2 Redlake Lane, Wokingham, Berkshire, RG40 3BF Tel: 0118-979 5909 Fax: 0118-979 5791 E-mail: oceangrove@hotmail.com *Electro magnetic compatibility components manufrs*

▶ Astor-Bannerman Medical Ltd, Unit 11f Coln Park, Andoversford Industrial Estate, Andoversford, Cheltenham, Gloucestershire, GL54 4HJ Tel: (01242) 820820 Fax: (01242) 821110 E-mail: sales@astorbannerman.co.uk *Medical & surgical supplies*

Astore Harrison Ltd, PO Box 20, Peterborough, PE1 2DT Tel: (01733) 361361 Fax: (01733) 361360 E-mail: sales@astore-harrison.co.uk *Astore Harrison has a broad spectrum of highly qualified designers, engineers and specialists with many years' experience within the hospitality and leisure industry. They provide bar, restaurant and hotel interior fitting services. Working with architects, interior designers and private clients they have carried out a wide range of high profile projects.*

Astore UK, Walsall Road, Norton Canes, Cannock, Staffordshire, WS11 9PU Tel: (01543) 272400 Fax: (01543) 272413 E-mail: sales@astore.uk.com *PVC, abs pipes & filling manufrs*

Astor-Rack, 579 Gale Street, Dagenham, Essex, RM9 4TS Tel: (020) 8984 8499 Fax: (020) 8984 8412 E-mail: sales@astor-rack.co.uk *Shelving & lockers distributors/agents*

Astra Commerical Doors, 2a Window Lane, Liverpool, L19 8EJ Tel: 0151-494 2880 Fax: 0151-494 9648 *Shutter & door manufrs*

Astra Distribution Ltd, 29 Roseberry Crescent, Great Ayton, Middlesbrough, Cleveland, TS9 6EP Tel: (01642) 724367 E-mail: info@astradistribution.com *Import distribute, computer hardware, software & support services*

Astra Distribution Manchester Ltd, Unit 6, Lowercroft Business Park, Lowercroft Road, Bury, Lancashire, BL8 3PA Tel: 0161-797 3222 Fax: 0161-797 3444 E-mail: support@astra247.com *Ceiling fan specialists*

▶ Astra Electrical Services, Unit D16g Lakeside Park, Neptune Close, Medway City Estate, Rochester, Kent, ME2 4LT Tel: (01634) 291079 Fax: (01634) 291019

▶ Astra Engineering Services, 21 Borough Road, Darlington, County Durham, DL1 1SW Tel: (01325) 389810 Fax: (01325) 355020 *Sub contract precision engineering company*

Astra Leisure Inflatables, 10 Trevithick Close, Crewe, CW1 5GR Tel: 01270 589968 *Bouncy castle & inflatable hirer & seller*

Astra Precision Engineering Ltd, Mnercian Works, Holyhead Road, Ketley, Telford, Shropshire, TF1 5DY Tel: (01952) 616622 Fax: (01952) 616622 *Tool manufrs*

▶ Astra Printing Services Ltd, Old Stoneywood Church, Bankhead Road, Bucksburn, Aberdeen, AB21 9HQ Tel: (01224) 715151

Astra Threads & Trimmings Ltd, Ladderedge, Leek, Staffordshire, ST13 7AG Tel: (01538) 373704 Fax: (01538) 373704 E-mail: astra@ladderedge.fsnet.co.uk *Suppliers of quality sewing threads, zips, trimmings & accessories*

▶ Astra Trading, Glenelg, Ox Lane, St. Michaels, Tenterden, Kent, TN30 6NQ Tel: (01580) 762578 Fax: (01580) 762588 E-mail: astratradingsupplies@hotmail.com *Janitorial supplies*

▶ ASTRAC Ltd, Innovation Centre, Warwick Technology Park, Warwick, CV34 6UW Tel: (01926) 623060 Fax: (01926) 623061 E-mail: info@astrac.com *Computer software & hardware*

Astracast P.L.C., PO Box 20, Birstall, West Yorkshire, WF17 9XD Tel: (01924) 477466 Fax: (01924) 475801 E-mail: marketing@astracast.co.uk *Stainless steel & ceramic kitchen sinks*

Astral Fabrications Ltd, 5 Phoenix House, Castle Street, Tipton, West Midlands, DY4 8HP Tel: 0121-522 4761 Fax: 0121-522 4761 *Steel fabricators*

▶ Astral Installations Ltd, 279 Marlborough Road, Gillingham, Kent, ME7 5HS Tel: (01634) 280763 Fax: (01634) 302110 E-mail: enquiries@astraluklimited.co.uk *Computer net workers*

Astral Max Couriers, 90a High Street, Rickmansworth, Hertfordshire, WD3 1AQ Tel: (01923) 711444 Fax: (01923) 711714 E-mail: sales@maxinternational.co.uk *Courier services*

Astral Pattern Co. Ltd, Roway La, Oldbury, W. Midlands, B69 3EJ Tel: 0121-552 3507 Fax: 0121-544 2471 *Engineers' pattern/gravity die markers*

Astraline Security Door Systems, Unit 6a Waterloo Works, Gorsey Way, Stockport, Cheshire, SK1 3BU Tel: 0161-477 9991 Fax: 0161-477 5742 E-mail: astraline4doors@aol.com *Security equipment manufrs*

▶ Astralite Fabricators Ltd, 4 Marshall Road, Hampden Park Industrial Estate, Eastbourne, East Sussex, BN22 9AT Tel: (01323) 501221 Fax: (01323) 521452 E-mail: sales@astralitefabricators.co.uk *Aluminium cutting, folding and welding fabrication. Also stainless steel, mild and*

continued

Company Information

continuation
galvanised steels. Painting, anodising and delivery services available on appropriate products. Punching, slotting and cutting on both supplied and free issue materials. Patent curtain walling, glazing, rooflight and lantern light fabricators. Order range from single quantity to large contract capabilities.

Astran Cargo Services Ltd, 519, New Hythe Lane, Larkfield, Maidstone, Kent, ME20 6SB Tel: (01622) 716441 Fax: (01622) 791854 E-mail: london@astran-cargo.com *Freight forwarders*

Astranet Systems Ltd, PO Box 734, Cambridge, CB2 5PE Tel: (01223) 872197 Fax: (01223) 872197 E-mail: info@astranetsystems.com *Colour measurement apparatus & instruments manufrs*

Astrapac Midlands Ltd, Mount Road, Burntwood, Staffordshire, WS7 0AJ Tel: (01543) 677262 Fax: (01543) 672718 E-mail: sales@astrapac.co.uk Principal Export Areas: Worldwide *Manufacturers of heat sealing machines*

▶ Astrata Group Ltd, Astrata, 112-113 The Chambers, Chelsea Harbour, London, SW10 0XF Tel: (07841) 213759 E-mail: sales@astratagroup.com *Accurate, quality location base service, military, government & public*

Astratec Electronics Ltd, 2-3 James Watt Close, Drayton Fields Industrial Estate, Daventry, Northamptonshire, NN11 8RJ Tel: (01327) 705936 Fax: (01327) 300665 E-mail: sales@astratec.co.uk *Battery tester manufrs*

▶ Astraware, Unit IC2, Keele Science Park, Newcastle, Staffordshire, ST5 5NH Tel: (01782) 638140 Fax: (01782) 667828 *Computer maintenance & repair services & software suppliers*

▶ Astrazeneca, 600 Capability Green, Luton, LU1 3LU Tel: (01582) 836000 Fax: (01582) 835800 *Pharmaceutical manufrs*

Astrazeneca After 5pm, Alderley Park, Macclesfield, Cheshire, SK10 4TF Tel: (01625) 582828 Fax: (01625) 585022 E-mail: julia.ainsworth@astrazeneca.com *Pharmaceutical production manufrs*

▶ Astric Medical, 36 Blatchington Road, Hove, East Sussex, BN3 3YN Tel: (01273) 716516 Fax: (01273) 716516 E-mail: astricmed@aol.com *Bedwetting alarm manufrs*

Astrin Bros Ltd, 32 Prescot Street, London, E1 8BB Tel: (020) 7481 2110 Fax: (020) 7480 5030 E-mail: trading@johnkellystd.demon.co.uk *Medical drug merchants*

▶ Astro Bounce, 311 Monks Road, Lincoln, LN2 5LB Tel: (01522) 859493

▶ Astro Exhibitions Ltd, Unit 3, Ensor Trading Estate, Ensor Way, New Mills, New Mills, High Peak, Derbyshire, SK22 4NQ Tel: 01663 744868 Fax: 01663 747950 E-mail: info@astroexhibitions.co.uk *Stand exhibition contractors and designers. specialising in high quality bespoke exhibition stands across varied industries.*

▶ Astro Lighting Ltd, Unit 21 Mead Industrial Park, Riverway, Harlow, Essex, CM20 2SE Tel: (01279) 427001 Fax: (01279) 427002 E-mail: sales@astrolighting.co.uk *Design & manufacture domestic lighting products*

Astro Med Inc, Astro Med House 11 Progress Business Centre, Whittle Parkway, Slough, SL1 6DQ Tel: (01628) 668836 Fax: (01628) 664994 E-mail: astromeduk@astromed.com *UK Sales and Service office of US company manufacturing portable data acquisition recorders and telemetry workstations.*

Astro Technologies Ltd, 26 Brunel Way, Segansworth East, Fareham, Hampshire, PO15 5SD Tel: (01489) 555300 Fax: (01489) 555302 E-mail: sales@astrotec.co.uk *Distributors or agents of printed circuit board assembly equipment*

Astrocare Ltd, Bolton Enterprise Centre, Washington Street, Bolton, BL3 5EY Tel: (01204) 370861 Fax: (01204) 548742 E-mail: astrocare@aol.com *Computer & telephone cleaning services*

Astrofade Ltd, Kyle Road, Gateshead, Tyne & Wear, NE8 2YE Tel: 0191-420 0515 Fax: 0191-460 4185 E-mail: sales@astrofade.co.uk *Roof lights & structural glazers*

Astron Marketing Technology, Crawford House, Crawford Way, Liverpool, L7 9NG Tel: 0151-228 8003 Fax: 0151-259 6129 *Direct marketing services & database creation*

Astrosyn International Technology plc, The Old Courthouse, New Road Avenue, Chatham, Kent, ME4 6BE Tel: (01634) 815175 Fax: (01634) 826552 E-mail: astrosyn@btinternet.com *Rotating component manufrs*

▶ Astrum, Bondisle Works, Station Road, Stanhope, Bishop Auckland, County Durham, DL13 2YR Tel: (01388) 528860 Fax: (01388) 528879 E-mail: stevedowson@astrum.uk.com *Steel manufrs*

Astrun Computers, 78 High Street, Lee-on-the-Solent, Hampshire, PO13 9DA Tel: (023) 9255 6007 Fax: (023) 9255 3514 E-mail: sales@smsit.co.uk *Computer maintenance & repairers*

Astute, 44-46 Brechin Road, Forfar, Angus, DD8 3JX Tel: (01307) 464467 Fax: (01307) 464561 E-mail: sales@astute.uk.com *Printers & rubber stamp manufrs*

Astute Electronics Ltd, Church House, Church Street, Ware, Hertfordshire, SG12 9EN Tel: (01920) 483800 Fax: (01920) 486399 E-mail: insales@astute.co.uk *Electronic component distributors*

▶ Astute Electronics, 2 Canyon Road, Netherton Industrial Estate, Wishaw, Lanarkshire, ML2 0EG Tel: (01698) 377450 Fax: (01698) 375860 *Electronic component suppliers*

Astwell Augers Ltd, A14 Huntingdon Road, Thrapston, Kettering, Northamptonshire, NN14 4PT Tel: (01832) 735300 Fax: (01832) 735533 E-mail: sales@astwell.co.uk *Agricultural machinery equipment & implement manufrs*

▶ Asvisual - Architectural Photography, 2 Eddy Street, Berkhamsted, Hertfordshire, HP4 1DQ Tel: (07747) 103334 E-mail: andy@asvisual.co.uk *A complete digital photography service*

Asysco P.L.C., Asisco House, Omega Way, Egham, Surrey, TW20 8RD Tel: (01784) 487000 Fax: (01784) 487060 E-mail: info@rslav.com *Audio visual equipment distributors*

▶ At Chore Service, 10 Oak Court, North Road, South Ockendon, Essex, RM15 6PN Tel: (01708) 850931 *Domestic cleaning & housekeeping services*

▶ At The Source, 192 Clarendon Park Road, Leicester, LE2 3AF Tel: 0116-270 6255 E-mail: beverley@atthesource.co.uk *Holistic Therapy Centre. Room rental and coffee bar selling inspired gifts . Full programme of events - angel workshops, mediatation classes, yoga, therapy taster sessions etc*Subscribe to our free newsletter with a monthly circulation of 400 in Leicester & beyond*

A-T Tool Centre Ltd, 19 Alston Drive, Bradwell Abbey, Milton Keynes, MK13 9HA Tel: 01908 310707 Fax: 01908 220695 E-mail: miltonkeynes@at-toolcentre.co.uk *A.T. Toolcentre is an Industrial Supplies Company covering a radius of 40+ miles from each of our branch locations. We offer a daily delivery service through our own fleet of vehicles. All branches carry an extensive range of quality industrial products supported by the Group Central Warehouse in Northampton. We are able to supply any brand of product and to any specification required.**Our specialist divisions are:*Hand Tools, Power Tools and Accessories, Welding, Fasteners and Fixings, Pipeline, Precision Measurement, Cutting Tools, Carbide Cutting Tools, VMIS, Oils and Lubricants, Adhesives, Abrasives, Paints and Industrial Coatings, Janitorial and Hygiene, First Aid, Safety Flooring, Workwear and PPE, Laundry, Signs and Labels, Storage and Handling, Packaging.**

At Toolcentre Ltd, Studland Road, Kingsthorpe, Northampton, NN2 6RL Tel: (01604) 711711 Fax: (01604) 711111 E-mail: northampton@at-toolcentre.co.uk *A.T. Toolcentre is an Industrial Supplies Company covering a radius of 40+ miles from each of our branch locations. We offer a daily delivery service through our own fleet of vehicles. All branches carry an extensive range of quality industrial products supported by the Group Central Warehouse in Northampton. We are able to supply any brand of product and to any specification required.***Our specialist divisions are:**Hand Tools, Power Tools and Accessories, Welding, Fasteners and Fixings, Pipeline, Precision Measurement, Cutting Tools, Carbide Cutting Tools, VMIS, Oils and Lubricants, Adhesives, Abrasives, Paints and Industrial Coatings, Janitorial and Hygiene, First Aid, Safety Flooring, Workwear and PPE, Laundry, Signs and Labels, Storage and Handling, Packaging.*

▶ At Your Fingertips, 26 Greywell Precinct, Havant, Hampshire, PO9 5AL Tel: (023) 9247 1434 Fax: (023) 9247 1434 *Computer building & repair service*

▶ At Your Service, Clarendon House, 52 Cornmarket Street, Oxford, OX1 3HJ Tel: (0870) 4130424 Fax: (0870) 4130425 E-mail: oxford@ays.co.uk *Event staffing and management.*

Ata, 37 Smiths Way, Water Orton, Birmingham, B46 1TW Tel: 0121-748 5785 Fax: 0121-748 5785 *Partitioning & suspended ceilings manufrs*

ATAC Ltd, 6 Redlands Centre, Redlands, Coulsdon, Surrey, CR5 2HT Tel: (020) 8763 9494 Fax: (020) 8763 9540 E-mail: atac@atacuk.com *Gas detection equipment suppliers*

Atacanter Horsebox Hire, Kimpton House Farm, Oldhurst Road, Woodhurst, Huntingdon, Cambridgeshire, PE28 3BY Tel: (01487) 840448 Fax: (01487) 840448 E-mail: claire@atacanterhorseboxhire.co.uk *Hire horse boxers*

Atack Electrical Co. Ltd, 68 Churchbridge, Oldbury, West Midlands, B69 2AS Tel: 0121-552 3076 Fax: 0121-544 2697 E-mail: atack@atackelec.co.uk *Electrical engineers & contractors*

Atag Heating UK Ltd, Unit 3 Beaver Trade Park, Quarry Lane, Chichester, West Sussex, PO19 8NY Tel: (01243) 815770 Fax: (01243) 839596 E-mail: info@atagheating.co.uk *Manufacturer of gas condensing boilers for domestic & commercial*

Atari Ltd, Landmark House, Hammersmith Bridge Road, London, W6 9EJ Tel: (020) 8222 9700 Fax: (020) 8222 9870 *Computer games manufrs*

Ataroth Plastics Machinery Sales Ltd, 5 Maer Lane, Market Drayton, Shropshire, TF9 1QX Tel: (01630) 655148 Fax: (01630) 654055 *Printing machine distributors*

▶ ATC (Application Tape Co.) Ltd, Calf Hey South, Rochdale, Lancashire, OL11 2JS Tel: (01706) 633043 Fax: (01706) 710086 E-mail: sales@apptape.co.uk *Supplier of sign making material*

Atc Engineering Services Ltd, C1 Oak Park Estate, Northarbour Road, Portsmouth, PO6 3TJ Tel: (023) 9232 6635 Fax: (023) 9221 0907 E-mail: info@atcengineering.co.uk *Service engineering to industry*

Atc Lasham Ltd, Lasham Airfield, Lasham, Alton, Hampshire, GU34 5SP Tel: (01256) 356123 Fax: (01256) 467487 E-mail: sales@atclasham.co.uk *Aircraft maintenance services*

Atco Development, 42 Albemarle Street, London, W1S 4JH Tel: (020) 7491 3664 Fax: (020) 7629 1120 E-mail: liam@atcolondon.com *Middle East export agents*

ATCO Noise Management Ltd, PO Box 3, Newcastle Upon Tyne, NE20 9WY Tel: (01661) 825379 Fax: (01661) 825379 E-mail: jerry.kinver@atconoise.com *Noise control consultants*

Atd Fabrications, Unit D Bromcliffe Park, Barnsley, South Yorkshire, S71 5RN Tel: (01226) 718400 Fax: (01226) 718411 *Structural steel fabrications*

ATE Ltd, Design Office, 56 Nodes Road, Northwood, Cowes, Isle of Wight, PO31 8AD Tel: (01983) 292052 *Electronic equipment deseigner manufrs*

▶ ATE Insurance.com, Riverbank House, Brownhill, Ruyton X1 Towns, Shrewsbury, SY4 1LR Tel: 01939 261730 Fax: 01939 261583 E-mail: bob@ATEinsurance.com *After the Event (ATE) litigation costs insurance for commerial cases and personal injury.*The ATE insurance resource for lawyers and the public.*

Atec Engineering, Albany Park, Cabot Lane, Poole, Dorset, BH17 7BX Tel: (01202) 696260 *Precision engineers*

Atec Hampshire Ltd, Peel Street, Southampton, SO14 5QT Tel: (023) 8063 1391 Fax: (023) 8033 8931 E-mail: sales@atec-hants.co.uk *Marine equipment distributors*

A-Tec Plastics, 6 Queensway, New Milton, Hampshire, BH25 5NN Tel: (01425) 638433 Fax: (01425) 616374 E-mail: sales@atec.co.uk *Plastics injection moulders manufrs*

▶ A-Tec Property Services, 9 Redhill Close, Bassett, Southampton, SO16 7BT Tel: (07957) 830615 Fax: (023) 8032 5178 E-mail: paulewilcox@hotmail.com *Bathroom Fitter, Carpentry & Joinery, Drain Clearance, *Fencing Contractors, General Plumbing, Kitchens, Plasterers, *Screeders & Dry Lining Contractors, Property Maintenance & Repairs, Shop Fitting*all areas within M25*

Atech Computer Systems, 122 Broadway, Didcot, Oxfordshire, OX11 8AB Tel: (01235) 812900 Fax: (01235) 812900 *Hardware & software retailers & manufrs*

▶ Atech Electrical, 269 Church Rd, Sheldon, Birmingham, B26 3YH Tel: 07967 305583 E-mail: atech.electrical@blueyonder.co.uk

A-Tech Fabrications Ltd, Woodham Road, Aycliffe Industrial Park, Newton Aycliffe, County Durham, DL5 6HT Tel: (01325) 304033 Fax: (01325) 304044 *Welded fabrication specialists*

Atelier Screen Print Ltd, 130 Pershore Street, Birmingham, B5 6ND Tel: 0121-622 6301 Fax: 0121-666 6487 E-mail: atelier.screenprint@virgin.net *Traditional screenprinting:*Point of sale material. L/ holders,Car Stickers,Display boards, Banners,PVC wallets,Posters,Header Boards,Price Visors,Window decals,T-Shirts,Sweatshirts, Fence signs,Warning signs,*Magnetic signs,Cut outs, Shelf Talkers,Coasters,Clip boards,Foamex signs,Wobblies,Perspex signs,safety signs.*

Ateq UK Ltd, Unit 71 Heming Road, The Washford Industrial Estate, Redditch, Worcestershire, B98 0EA Tel: (01527) 520011 Fax: (01527) 520022 E-mail: info@ateq.co.uk *Manufacturers of pressure test equipment,*

Atex Ltd, Wilsthorpe Road, Long Eaton, Nottingham, NG10 3LL Tel: 0115-973 5900 Fax: 0115-973 6605 *Software publishing services*

Atex Ltd, 4 Thames Park, Lester Way, Wallingford, Oxfordshire, OX10 9TA Tel: (01491) 839999 Fax: (01491) 839466 E-mail: contactuk@atex-f1.com *Load cell Pressure Transducer Accelerometer Strain gauges and associated electronics manufrs*

Atex Factors Ltd, Canal Street, Brierley Hill, West Midlands, DY5 1JR Tel: (01384) 480500 Fax: (01384) 74820 *Vehicle bodywork consultants*

Atex Media Command Ltd, Woodside House, Latimer, Chesham, Buckinghamshire, HP5 1UQ Tel: (01494) 546500 Fax: (01494) 766761 E-mail: info@atex.com *Suppliers of software solutions*

J. Atha & Son, 9 Norton Church Glebe, Sheffield, S8 8JX Tel: 0114-274 6407 *Plumbers & heating engineers*

Athag Ltd, Well Spring Close, Carlyon Road Industrial Estate, Atherstone, Warwickshire, CV9 1HU Tel: (01827) 713040 Fax: (01827) 717307 E-mail: info@dogcages.uk.com *Security cage manufrs*

▶ Athena Intercultural Services, 12 St. James's Square, London, SW1Y 4RB Tel: (020) 7849 6067 Fax: (020) 7849 6300 E-mail: info@athenaintercultural.com *We are an International Management Training company. Athena Intercultural develops competencies and increases skills to maximise effectiveness in the global market. We listen and we respond with ingenuity, integrity and professionalism adapting to your needs.*Our services include assessment, candidate assessment, developmental assessment, cross cultural training, virtual team building, intercultural professional development, repatriation coaching, executive coaching.*

Athena Solid Surfaces, 14 Sedling Road, Wear Industrial Estate, Washington, Tyne & Wear, NE38 9BZ Tel: 0191-416 7275 Fax: 0191-417 7510 E-mail: admin@athenasolidsurfaces.co.uk *Solid surface manufrs*

Athena Training U K, Suite 3, 13 Sheppey Gardens, Dagenham, Essex, RM9 4LD Tel: (07973) 869163 Fax: (020) 8517 0007 E-mail: enquiries@athenatraininguk.net *High quality training in first aid, health & social care*

▶ Athene Communications, 26 Priestgate, Peterborough, PE1 1WG Tel: (01733) 865040 Fax: (01733) 865013 E-mail: jane@athene-communications.co.uk *Strategic communications consultancy offering innovative advice*

Athenian Tankers UK Ltd, 2 Dartmouth Street, London, SW1H 9BP Tel: (020) 7222 2742 Fax: (020) 7222 4824 E-mail: chartering@athenian.co.uk *Marine tanker operators*

Atherstone Crane Hire & Machinery Installation, 166 High Street, Dosthill, Tamworth, Staffordshire, B77 1LR Tel: (01827) 288271 Fax: (01827) 281800 E-mail: enquiries@atherstone-crane.co.uk *Crane hire*

Atherstone Industrial Coatings Ltd, Spring Hill Industrial Estate, Colliers Way, Arley, Coventry, CV7 8HN Tel: (01676) 541114 Fax: (01676) 541241 *Sheet metal work services*

▶ Atherton & Co., 15 Cheapside, Liverpool, L2 2DY Tel: 0151-236 7977 Fax: 0151-236 7977 *Computer maintenance & office equipment suppliers*

Athertons, 593 Ormskirk Road, Wigan, Lancashire, WN5 8AG Tel: (01942) 214579 *Hairdressers equipment suppliers*

Athrodax Healthcare International Ltd, Hawthorn Business Park, Puddlebrook, Drybrook, Gloucestershire, GL17 9HP Tel: (01594) 544440 Fax: (01594) 545800 E-mail: sales@athrodax.co.uk *Surgical & medical suppliers*

Atis Real, 22 Chancery Lane, London, WC2A 1LS Tel: (020) 7338 4000 Fax: (020) 7430 2628 E-mail: info@atisrealweatheralls.com *Estate, office agents, & charted surveyors*

Atkin John Construction Ltd, Viking Place, Cardiff, CF10 4UU Tel: (029) 2044 2060 Fax: (029) 2044 2065 E-mail: atkintradespec@enterprise.net *Building & civil engineering*

Atkin John Construction Ltd, Viking Place, Cardiff, CF10 4UU Tel: (029) 2044 2060 Fax: (029) 2044 2065 E-mail: atkintrade@atkingroup.co.uk *Steel framers, sto render*

Albert Atkins, 71 Coleraine Road, Garvagh, Coleraine, County Londonderry, BT51 5HR Tel: (028) 2955 7691 Fax: (028) 9255 7692 *Fish tackle manufrs & retailer*

Atkins Consultants Ltd, Bank Chambers, Faulkner Street, Manchester, M1 4EH Tel: 0161-245 3400 Fax: 0161-245 3500 E-mail: jon.baker@atkinsglobal.com *Process, synthetic resin making & pharmaceutical plant contractors. Also chemical engineers*

Atkins Precision, 59 Fairmile Road, Christchurch, Dorset, BH23 2LA Tel: (01202) 478824 *Precision engineers*

▶ Richard Atkins, 132 Kingsley Park Terrace, Northampton, NN2 7HJ Tel: (01604) 710050 Fax: (01604) 710170 E-mail: sales@aps-promotions.com *Embroiders*

Atkins Saws, 53 Richmond Road, Solihull, West Midlands, B92 7RR Tel: 0121-707 1600 *Saw sharpening services*

W.S. Atkins Ltd, Unit 3 Langstone Business Village, Langstone Park, Langstone, Newport, Gwent, NP18 2LG Tel: (01633) 415500 Fax: (01633) 411211 *Computer consultants*

▶ Atkinson Bailey Ceramics, 3a Groveley Road, Christchurch, Dorset, BH23 3HB Tel: (01202) 473330 Fax: (01202) 480686

▶ Atkinson D J Ltd Builders Contractors, 123 North Wingfield Road, Grassmoor, Chesterfield, Derbyshire, S42 5EB Tel: (01246) 855699 Fax: (01246) 854292

Atkinson Dyeing Co. Ltd, Deal Street, Keighley, West Yorkshire, BD21 4LA Tel: (01535) 604288 Fax: (01535) 690710 *Yarn dyers & processors*

Atkinson Engineering, Unit 1 Lancaster Close, Sherburn in Elmet, Leeds, LS25 6NS Tel: (01977) 689665 Fax: (01977) 685624 E-mail: sales@atkinsonprecision.co.uk *Rubber & plastic mould makers & sub contractors*

Atkinson Equipment Ltd, Moat Road, West Wilts Trading Estate, Westbury, Wiltshire, BA13 4JF Tel: (01373) 822220 Fax: (01373) 826996 E-mail: sales@atkinsonequipment.com *Content, gauge & tank accessory manufrs*

John Atkinson Interiors Ltd, Deanfield Mill, Asquith Avenue, Morley, Leeds, LS27 9QT Tel: 0113-253 5661 Fax: 0113-238 0323 E-mail: atkinsoninteriors@btopenworld.com *Suspended ceiling contractors*

Atkinson & Kirby Ltd, 2 Burscough Road, Ormskirk, Lancashire, L39 2XG Tel: (01695) 573234 Fax: (01695) 586902 E-mail: sales@akirby.co.uk *Manufacturers and distributors of all types of hardwood flooring and accessories to the trade sector. From Traditional Unfinished strip flooring, through to solid and multi-layer pre-finished flooring and accessories, we have a range to suit most, if not all specifications.*

Atkinson & Prickett, Crowle House, Hull, HU1 1RJ Tel: (01482) 324191 Fax: (01482) 224914 E-mail: hull@kettlewell.com *Ship brokers & forwarding agents* Also at: Goole, Grimsby & Immingham Dock

Atkinson Print Ltd, 10-11 Lower Church Street, Hartlepool, Cleveland, TS24 7DJ Tel: (01429) 267849 Fax: (01429) 865416 E-mail: enquiries@atkinsonprint.com *Commercial printers*

Richard Atkinson & Co. Ltd, 10 Nicholson Drive, Mallusk, Newtownabbey, County Antrim, BT36 4FD Tel: (028) 9084 3323 Fax: (020) 8908 4850 E-mail: info@atkinsons-irishpoplin-ties.com *Irish poplin weavers*

▶ Atkinson Sanding, 97 Replingham Road, Southfields, London, SW18 5LU Tel: (0770) 4571080 E-mail: tom@atkinsondsanding.co.uk *We provide a full restoration service, Sanding, filling, staining, and sealing wooden floors commercial and domestic*

Atkinson Sons Farmers, Main Street, Warton, Carnforth, Lancashire, LA5 9QF Tel: (01524) 732894 Fax: (01524) 720884 *Dairy farmers*

Atkinson Vari-Tech Ltd, Unit 4, Sett End Road, Shadsworth, Blackburn, BB1 2PT Tel: (01254) 678777 Fax: (01254) 678782 E-mail: sales@vari-tech.co.uk *Tubular steel fabricators & education furniture manufrs*

Atkinson Walker Saws Ltd, Bower Street, Sheffield, S3 8RU Tel: 0114-272 4748 Fax: 0114-272 5065 E-mail: sales@atkinson-walker-saws.co.uk *Saw manufrs*

▶ Atkinsons Fencing Ltd, Green Lane, Cutsyke, Castleford, West Yorkshire, WF10 5JL Tel: (01977) 550441 Fax: (01977) 515321 E-mail: sales@atkinsonfencing.co.uk *Fencing & decking services*

Atl Automation Systems, Cackle Street, Brede, Rye, East Sussex, TN31 6DY Tel: (01424) 882823 Fax: (01424) 882855 *Automation special purpose equipment manufrs*

Atlan Ltd, Six Acre House, 17 Town Square, Sale, Cheshire, M33 7WZ Tel: 0161-282 1770 Fax: 0161-962 0316 E-mail: cbsnorth@atlanrecruitment.com *IT staff recruitment service*

Atlantas Co., 43c-43d Melbourne Place, North Berwick, East Lothian, EH39 4JS Tel: (01620) 893395 Fax: (01620) 894289 *Electrical contractors*

Atlantic Ltd, K Chadwell Heath Industrial Park, Kemp Road, Dagenham, Essex, RM8 1SL Tel: (020) 8599 0600 Fax: (0870) 7774412 E-mail: atlantic@eidosnet.co.uk *Commercial refrigeration sales & services*

Atlantic 2000, PO Box 11, Ashton-under-Lyne, Lancashire, OL6 7TR Tel: 0161-621 5960 Fax: 0161-621 5966 E-mail: info@atlanticboilers.com *Hot water & condensing boilers*

Atlantic Auto Engineering, Unit 7b Fernfield Farm, Little Horwood Road, Little Horwood, Milton Keynes, MK17 0PS Tel: (01908) 501904 Fax: (01908) 501904 *Precision turned parts manufrs*

▶ Atlantic Bathrooms & Kitchens, 21-23 Waterloo Road, Norwich, NR3 1EH Tel: (01603) 402222 Fax: (01603) 402022 E-mail: enquiries@atlanticbathrooms.com *Bathroom & kitchen installations & retail*

Atlantic Bearings Ltd, Unit 1, Milners Road, Yeadon, Leeds, LS19 7JE Tel: 0113-250 6640 Fax: 0113-250 0031 E-mail: user@atlantic-bearings.fsnet.co.uk *Bearing distributors*

Atlantic Bridge Ltd, Zenith House, 11 The Street, Chirton, Devizes, Wiltshire, SN10 3QS Tel: (01380) 848170 Fax: (01380) 840152 E-mail: sales@atlanticbridge.co.uk *Regulatory consultancy CE marking & risk assessment services*

Atlantic Engineering UK Ltd, Depot Road, Middlesbrough, Cleveland, TS2 1LE Tel: (01642) 248525 Fax: (01642) 221950 E-mail: enquire@atlanticeng.co.uk *Steel fabricators*

Atlantic Equine Ltd, Calcutt House, Flecknoe, Rugby, Warwickshire, CV23 8AU Tel: (01788) 891406 Fax: (01788) 890793 E-mail: sales@atlantic-equine.co.uk *Farrier suppliers*

Atlantic Fibre Optics, Lynch Green, Hethersett, Norwich, NR9 3JU Tel: (01603) 811994 Fax: (01603) 810395 E-mail: info@atlanticfo.co.uk *Fibre optic equipment manufrs*

▶ Atlantic Focus, 17 Leachkin Avenue, Inverness, IV3 8LH Tel: 01463 712638 E-mail: info@atlanticfocus.co.uk *PE boats suppliers*

▶ Atlantic Machinery Ltd, Barleyfield, Hinckley, Leicestershire, LE10 1YE Tel: (01455) 251151 Fax: (01455) 890942 E-mail: j.betteridge@atlantic.machinery.co.uk *Machinery, plant & equipment manufrs*

Atlantic Microwave Ltd, 40a Springwood Drive, Braintree, Essex, CM7 2YN Tel: (01376) 550220 Fax: (01376) 552145 E-mail: sales@atlanticmicrowave.co.uk *Microwave component manufrs*

Atlantic Project Co., 828 Manchester Road, Rochdale, Lancashire, OL11 3AW Tel: (01706) 345661 Fax: (01706) 648243 E-mail: aslack@apcpower.com *Turbine & boiler erectors*

Atlantic Refrigeration Ltd, Peel Street, Northam, Southampton, SO14 5QT Tel: (023) 8033 9141 Fax: (023) 8022 9840 E-mail: grantwest@atlantic-refrig.co.uk *Fridge service & installation*

Atlantic Rubber Company Ltd, Castleton Works, Atlantic Street, Altrincham, Cheshire, WA14 5BX Tel: 0161-928 3727 Fax: 0161-926 9755 E-mail: info@atlanticgb.co.uk Principal Export Areas: Worldwide *Manufacturers of gaskets*

Atlantic Rubber & Plastic Ltd, 6 St. Annes Road, Willenhall, West Midlands, WV13 1ED Tel: (01902) 634400 Fax: 01902 634413 E-mail: hintons@blueyonder.co.uk *Rubber sponge products manufrs*

Atlantic Security, Unit 462 Robeson Street, Bow Common Lane, London, E3 4JA Tel: (020) 8981 5559 Fax: (020) 8981 5559 E-mail: atlansecur@yahoo.co.uk *Domestic & commercial decorative & security gates & railings*

Atlantic Service Co. (UK) Ltd, Pen-Y-Fan Industrial Estate, Croespenmaen, Crumlin, Newport, Gwent, NP11 4EG Tel: (01495) 246012 Fax: (01495) 248113 E-mail: sales@atlantic-service.co.uk *Butchers equipment manufrs*

Atlantic Supports Engineering, 3 Llandough Trading Estate, Penarth Road, Cardiff, CF11 8RR Tel: (029) 2070 8461 Fax: (029) 2035 0437 E-mail: sales@atlantic-supports.co.uk *Pipes manufrs*

Atlantic Tyre Co. Ltd, 130 Lowfield Street, Dartford, DA1 1JB Tel: (01322) 273031 Fax: (01322) 289054 E-mail: atlantictyres@aol.com *Tyre distributors*

Atlantic Zeiser Ltd, 53 Central Way, Andover, Hampshire, SP10 5AN Tel: (01264) 324222 Fax: (01264) 324333 E-mail: sales@atlanticzeiseruk.com Principal Export Areas: Central Asia, Africa, Central/East Europe, West Europe, North America & South America *Ink jet printing & numbering machine manufrs*

▶ Atlantis Ceramics, 3 Wilton Way, Exeter, EX1 3UH Tel: (07919) 575300 E-mail: atlantis.ceramics@mail.com *Professional tile fixing. Bathrooms, Kitchens, Swimming Pools, Tanking Systems, Patios, Conservatories and Wet Rooms.*

Atlantis Forwarding Ltd, 1607 Pershore Road, Stirchley, Birmingham, B30 2JF Tel: 0121-451 1588 Fax: 0121-433 4034 E-mail: enquiries@atlantisltd.co.uk *Sea & air freight forwarding* Also at: Edinburgh & Leeds

Atlantis International Ltd T/A Karcher Vehicle Wash, Lion court, Staunton Harold Hall, Melbourne Road, Staunton Road, Ashby-de-la-Zouch, Leicestershire, LE65 1RT Tel: (01332) 695035 Fax: (01332) 695036 E-mail: jodieburgess@atlantisint.co.uk *Water recycling systems manufrs*

▶ Atlantis Promotions UK Ltd, 2 Clements Green Lane, South Woodham Ferrers, Chelmsford, CM3 5JG Tel: (08701) 223247 E-mail: info@atlantispromotions.co.uk *Atlantis is an innovative media design consultancy based in central Essex near Chelmsford. We work pro-actively with our clients to produce inspiring and fresh design ideas for your marketing needs.*

Atlantis Trading Co, Unit 12 Workplace, Highfield Street, Coalville, Leicestershire, LE67 3BZ Tel: (01530) 830840 Fax: (01530) 830850 E-mail: info@atlantisclassics.co.uk *Metal casting hammock chairs manufrs*

Atlas, 4c St. Marys Place, The Lace Market, Nottingham, NG1 1PH Tel: 0115-955 8818 Fax: 0115-941 2238 E-mail: info@atlas-1.org.uk *Steeplejacks & industrial climbers trade association*

Atlas Alarms, 2-8 Blackburn Road, Darwen, Lancashire, BB3 1QJ Tel: (01254) 873232 Fax: (01254) 761277 E-mail: admin@atlasalarms.co.uk *Alarms installation*

Atlas Ball & Bearing Co. Ltd, Leamore Lane, Walsall, WS2 7DE Tel: (01922) 710515 Fax: (01922) 710575 E-mail: sales@atlasball.co.uk *Steel ball & roller distributors*

▶ Atlas Business plc, Globe House, The Gullet, Nantwich, Cheshire, CW5 5RT Tel: (01270) 613016 Fax: (01270) 613012 E-mail: sales@atlasbiz.com *Systems integrators*

▶ Atlas Carpetcare, 93 Heath End Road, Flackwell Heath, High Wycombe, Buckinghamshire, HP10 9ES Tel: (01628) 533329 Fax: E-mail: paul@wiseman250.fsnet.co.uk *Carpet cleaning services*

▶ Atlas Clean Air Ltd, 5 Carrside, Lomeshaye Industrial Estate, Nelson, Lancashire, BB9 6RX Tel: (01282) 447666 Fax: (01282) 447789 E-mail: info@atlascleanair.com *Laboratory, clean room & pharmacy design builders & equipment suppliers*

Atlas Coating Ltd, Unit 15a Hixon Airfield Estate, New Road, Hixon, Stafford, ST18 0PF Tel: (01889) 271002 Fax: (01889) 271178 E-mail: mail@atlascoating.co.uk *Powder coating services*

▶ Atlas Composites Ltd, Chelton House, Merlin Way, Quarry Hill Industrial Estate, Ilkeston, Derbyshire, DE7 4RA Tel: 0115-930 4058 Fax: 0115-930 4558 *Racing car part suppliers*

▶ Atlas Contract Blinds Ltd, 11a Bolton Road, Kearsley, Bolton, BL4 8DB Tel: (01204) 409580 Fax: (01204) 411304 E-mail: sales@atlasblinds.co.uk *Blinds retailers*

Atlas Converting Plc, Wolseley Road, Woburn Road Industrial Estate, Kempston, Bedford, MK42 7XT Tel: (01234) 852584 Fax: (01234) 851151 E-mail: sales.atlas@bobstgroup.com *World leading manufacturer of primary & secondary slitter rewinders for plastic film, foil, paper & labelstock including the widest machines (at metres) and fastest (at 1200m/min).*

Atlas Copco Compressors Ltd, 34 Telford Road, Lenzie Mill Industrial Estate, Cumbernauld, Glasgow, G67 2AX Tel: (01236) 733722 Fax: (01236) 735601 E-mail: admin@atlascopco.com *Compressors manufrs*

Atlas Copco Compressors Ltd, 11 Harvey Close, Crowther, Washington, Tyne & Wear, NE38 0AB Tel: 0191-417 5764 Fax: 0191-415 7452

Atlas Engineering Ltd, Pontefract Street, Derby, DE24 8JD Tel: (01332) 343161 Fax: (01332) 294935 E-mail: tamara@atlaseng.co.uk *Precision engineers*

Atlas Fire & Security Ltd, Unit 8A Lansil Industrial Estate, Caton Road, Lancaster, LA1 3PQ Tel: (01524) 69488 Fax: (01524) 842972 *Burglar & fire alarm installers*

Atlas Food Processing Systems Ltd, Imperial House, 64 Willoughby Lane, London, N17 0SP Tel: (020) 8885 7200 Fax: (020) 8885 7219 E-mail: info@atlasfps.com *Atlas Food Processing Systems Ltd. is a reputable engineering company specialising in the design, engineering and installation of Bulk Materials Handling and Food Processing Equipment and Systems for the food industry.*

▶ Atlas Foods, 11a Grove Street, Salford, M7 2YZ Tel: 0161-792 3000 Fax: 0161-792 3000 *Food distributors*

▶ Atlas Handling Ltd, Unit 15, Bondor Business Centre, London Road, Baldock, Hertfordshire, SG7 6HP Tel: (01462) 491700 Fax: (01462) 491666 E-mail: john.p.johnson@btconnect.com *Shelving, racking & fork lift truck services*

Atlas Industrial Services Ltd, Tofts Farm Industrial Estate East, Brenda Road, Hartlepool, Cleveland, TS25 2BS Tel: (01429) 233018 Fax: (01429) 863316 E-mail: m.gcoop@tiscali.co.uk *Producers of chemical products for cleaning*

Atlas Laser Dies, 3 Northgate Industrial Park, Collier Row Road, Romford, RM5 2BG Tel: (020) 8548 7230 Fax: (020) 8548 7231 E-mail: sales@atlasdies.com *Die cutting forms*

▶ Atlas Machine Knives Ltd, Unit 5 Heath House Mill, Golcar, Huddersfield, HD7 4JW Tel: (01484) 644996 Fax: (01484) 644994 E-mail: sales@atlas-knives.com *Specialist machine knife sales & regrinding services*

Atlas Machinery (UK) Ltd, Unit 1, Flanshaw Way, Wakefield, West Yorkshire, WF2 9LP Tel: (01924) 381999 Fax: (01924) 378999 E-mail: bindmachines@atlasuk.com

Atlas Manufacturers, 61 High Street, West Bromwich, West Midlands, B70 6NZ Tel: 0121-553 7744 Fax: 0121-553 4774 *Clothing manufrs*

Atlas Marine Contractors Ltd, Imperial Dock Road, Lieth Docks, Edinburgh, EH6 7DR Tel: 0131-555 6030 Fax: 0131-555 6040 *Underwater engineers civil engineers, sub sea services*

Atlas Metals Ltd, Cranford Street, Smethwick, West Midlands, B66 2RX Tel: 0121-555 5000 Fax: 0121-558 8600 *Iron & steel metal merchants*

Atlas Office Supplies, 36 Trafalgar Road, Kettering, Northamptonshire, NN16 8DA Tel: (01536) 417414 Fax: (01536) 417528 *Office suppliers*

Atlas Products, Unit F1 Ash Grove Industrial Park, Heath Place, Bognor Regis, West Sussex, PO22 9SL Tel: (01243) 830324 Fax: (01243) 868404 *Point of sale display unit manufrs*

▶ Atlas Quality Fashion Fabrics (Europe), 9 Maidwell Close, Wigston, Leicestershire, LE18 3WU Tel: 0116-292 9685 E-mail: m.kennell@ntlworld.com

Atlas Rubber Moulding Ltd, Unit 4, Marshgate, Widnes, Cheshire, WA8 8UA Tel: 0151-420 2577 Fax: 0151-420 2527 E-mail: sales@atlasrubber.co.uk *Compression moulding of all types of rubber including rubber to metal bonding. Low & high volume enquiries welcome.*

Atlas Security, 226 Psalter Lane, Sheffield, S11 8UT Tel: 0114-266 9850 *General domestic electrical engineers*

Atlas Suspended Ceilings, 27 Beechwood Street, Belfast, BT5 5BQ Tel: (028) 9065 0532 Fax: (028) 9065 3905 *Suspended ceilings fitters*

▶ Atlas Technology, 2 Burwell Meadow, Witney, Oxon, OX28 5JQ Tel: 01993 700824 E-mail: marc@atlastek.co.uk *Atlas Technology (Tel +44 01993 700824) IT consultancy, database systems, web site design, software systems. We also provide home and business computer installations and systems design*

Atlas Telecommunications, Bridge Road, Broughton, Brigg, South Humberside, DN20 0BN Tel: (01652) 654950 Fax: (01652) 658519 *Telecommunications equipment supply & install*

▶ Atlas Trading Group Ltd, Oldham Road, Ashton-under-Lyne, Lancashire, OL7 9AZ Tel: 0161-339 2011 Fax: 0161-343 2453 E-mail: info@atlastrading.co.uk *Builders material suppliers*

▶ Atlas Transfer Printers Ltd, 9 Wanstead Road, Leicester, LE3 1TR Tel: 0116-231 4500 Fax: 0116-231 4600 E-mail: atpl@btconnect.com *Transfer paper manufacturers serving the narrow fabrics trade worldwide.*

Atlas Tube Bending Ltd, Albert Street, Oldham, OL8 3QP Tel: 0161-683 5556 Fax: 0161-683 5557 E-mail: admin@atlastubebending.co.uk *Tube manipulation & bending services or fabricators*

Atlasco Constructional Engineers Ltd, Rowhurst Close, Rowhurst Industrial Estate, Newcastle, Staffordshire, ST5 6BD Tel: (01782) 564711 Fax: (01782) 564591 E-mail: atlasco@steelweb.co.uk *Steel framed building manufrs*

▶ Atmel Smart Card Ics Ltd, Nasmyth Avenue, East Kilbride, Glasgow, G75 0QR Tel: (01355) 803000

Atmel UK Ltd, Coliseum Business Centre, Riverside Way, Camberley, Surrey, GU15 3YL Tel: (01344) 390060 Fax: (01344) 390070 E-mail: jane.sorrell@atmel.com *Semi-conductor component manufrs*

Atmosphere, 3 Manners Corner, Manners Way, Southend-on-Sea, SS2 6QR Tel: (01702) 335186 Fax: (01702) 337218 *Balloon & card suppliers*

Atmosphere Ltd, 14 Suffolk Avenue, Westgate-on-Sea, Kent, CT8 8JG Tel: (01843) 833818 Fax: (01843) 833518 E-mail: info@lexterten.com *Furniture manufacturers & retailers*

▶ Atmosphere Kites, 137 St. Georges Road, Bristol, BS1 5UW Tel: 0117-908 7153 E-mail: sales@atmospherekites.com *Kite & specialist extreme sports shop*

Atmosphere Productions Ltd, 6 Lothair Road, Leicester, LE2 7QB Tel: 0116-244 0041 E-mail: info@atmospheres.co.uk *Video production company*

Atmospheric Products, 7 Bold Industrial Estate, Lunts Heath Road, Widnes, Cheshire, WA8 5RZ Tel: (0870) 2430203 Fax: (0870) 2430204 E-mail: apluk@hotmail.com *Air conditioning installation*

▶ ATMT Group P.L.C., 3 Central Business Centre, Great Central Way, London, NW10 0UR Tel: (0870) 4102868 Fax: (0870) 4102869 E-mail: info@atmtgroup.com *Hardware & software suppliers*

Atol Racking & Building Ltd, Unit A3 Wymeswold Industrial Park, Wymeswold Road, Burton-on-the-Wolds, Loughborough, Leicestershire, LE12 5TY Tel: (01509) 881345 Fax: (01509) 881064 E-mail: office@atol.co.uk *Storage equipment manufrs*

Atom Civil Engineering & Drainage, Carlinlees, Darvel, Ayrshire, KA17 0NG Tel: (0800) 3898986

Atom Hydraulics, 1 Wicks Close, Springwood Industrial Estate, Braintree, Essex, CM7 2GE Tel: (01376) 348889 Fax: (01376) 348311 *Hydraulic coupling pumps manufrs*

▶ Atomiza Ltd, Provident House, 6-20 Burrell Row, Beckenham, Kent, BR3 1AT Tel: (0845) 0066006 Fax: (020) 8402 1221 E-mail: info@atomiza.co.uk *Sprayers & cleaning accessories*

Atos Origin (UK) Ltd, Walsall Road, Cannock, Staffordshire, WS11 0JA Tel: (01543) 465800 Fax: (01543) 464895 *Transaction processing services* Also at: Blackwood, Doncaster, Gateshead, Glasgow, Livingston, St. Helens & Watford

Atos Spa (UK), 17A Longwood Avenue, Cowplain, Waterlooville, Hampshire, PO8 8HX Tel: (023) 9226 5880 Fax: (023) 9226 5881 E-mail: atos-uk@fsmail.net *Hydraulic equipment manufrs*

Atotech UK Ltd, William Street, West Bromwich, West Midlands, B70 0BE Tel: 0121-606 7777 Fax: 0121-606 7200 E-mail: sales.uk@atotech.com *Chemical products* Also at: East Kilbride

▶ Atr, 35 Spring Lane, Wellingborough, Northamptonshire, NN8 1EY Tel: (01933) 229965 Fax: 01933 229965 E-mail: info@atruk.com *We stock Music T-Shirts, Music Hooded Sweatshirts, Hoodies, T Shirts + other Band related Music Merchandise.*Rock t shirts, Old Nu metal t shirts, Death Metal t shirts, Dark Metal t shirts, Punk t shirts, Skinny Fit Baby Doll t shirts,*Gothic, Urban, Rap etc.Plus Movie & Television t shirts, Comedy & Cartoon t shirts, hoodie, beanie, tee shirt, action figures collectables*WE SHIP WORLDWIDE.*

ATR Engineering Ltd, Unit 5, Ashley Group Base, Pitmedden Road, Dyce, Aberdeen, AB21 0DP Tel: (01224) 729855 Fax: (01224) 729913 E-mail: bob@atreng.co.uk *Manufacturers electrical control & distribution equipment*

Atradius, 3 Harbour Drive, Cardiff, CF10 4WZ Tel: (029) 2082 4000 Fax: (029) 2082 4003 E-mail: reception@atradius.com *Credit insurance services*

▶ atretirement.co.uk, Tritton House, 14 Bath Road, Swindon, SN1 4BA Tel: (0870) 1904187 *Pension Review Services.*

Atritor Ltd, PO Box 101, Coventry, CV6 5RD Tel: (024) 7666 2266 Fax: (024) 7666 5751 E-mail: sales@atritor.com *Drying & pulverising equipment manufrs*

Atrium, 6 The Old Foundry, Victoria Road, Kington, Herefordshire, HR5 3DA Tel: (01544) 231769 Fax: (01544) 231008 E-mail: atrium@srump.fsnet.co.uk *Conservatory manufrs*

Atrium Ltd, Yateley Lodge, Reading Road, Yateley, Hampshire, GU46 7AA Tel: (01252) 862423 Fax: (01252) 890596 E-mail: info@atriumcom.com *Computer systems & software developers*

Atrium Facilities Management Ltd, Atrium House, Oakfields, Guildford, Surrey, GU3 3AT Tel: (01483) 889090 Fax: (01483) 889091 E-mail: info@atriumfm.co.uk *Air conditioning installation*

Atronic International, Unit 2b The Courtyard, Alban Park, St. Albans, Hertfordshire, AL4 0LA Tel: (01727) 855966 Fax: (01727) 847957 E-mail: sales@atronic.com *Slot machine manufrs*

ATS Euromaster Ltd, 37 Boucher Road, Belfast, BT12 6HR Tel: (028) 9066 3623 Fax: (028) 9066 3894 *Tyre distributors* Also at: Branches throughout Northern Ireland

ATS Euromaster Ltd, 143 Histon Road, Cambridge, CB4 3HZ Tel: (01223) 454631 Fax: (01223) 454654 E-mail: ats@euromaster.com *Tyre & battery suppliers* Also at: Branches throughout East Anglia & London

Atson Ltd, 3 Marsh Lane, Bootle, Merseyside, L20 4LZ Tel: 0151-922 7486 Fax: 0151-922 1907 E-mail: enquiries@atson.co.uk *Rubber band manufacturers & distributors*

▶ Atspeed Distributors Ltd, Oakendene Industrial Estate, Bolney Road, Cowfold, Horsham, West Sussex, RH13 8AZ Tel: (01403) 864950 Fax: (01403) 864987 E-mail: andy.thompson@atspeed.co.uk *Atspeed is a specialist UK distributor of catnic, ig and birtley lintels, fixings, steelwork and other products for the building industry.***

Attachments Ltd, 6 Peterborough Road, Crowland, Peterborough, PE6 0BA Tel: (01733) 210611 Fax: (01733) 211345 E-mail: sales@attachments.ltd.uk *Attachments manufrs*

▶ Attain Consulting Ltd, 6 Walkers Lane, Lambourn, Hungerford, Berkshire, RG17 8YE Tel: (01488) 72766 Fax: (0870) 4602625 E-mail: info@attain.eu.com *Lean manufacturing and Lean supply chain project management firm, experts in design and introduction of KANBAN systems and Continuous Improvement (KAIZEN)Concepts*

Attenborough Dental Ltd, Viscosa House, George Street, Nottingham, NG1 3BN Tel: 0115-947 3562 Fax: 0115-950 9086 E-mail: info@attenborough.com *Dental technicians & brushes service*

Attenborough Industrial Doors Ltd, Merlin Way, Quarry Hill Industrial Estate, Ilkeston, Derbyshire, DE7 4RA Tel: 0115-930 0815 Fax: 0115-944 8930 E-mail: information@attenboroughdoor.co.uk *Door manufrs*

Atterton & Ellis Ltd, Hamlet Road, Haverhill, Suffolk, CB9 8QH Tel: (01440) 702312 Fax: (01440) 712138 *Lawn mower grinding machine manufrs*

Attewell Ltd, 4 Southbridge Way, Southall, Middlesex, UB2 4BY Tel: (020) 8571 0055 Fax: (020) 8571 7139 E-mail: sales@attewell.co.uk *Aircraft components manufrs*

The Attic, 96 London Road South, Poynton, Stockport, Cheshire, SK12 1LQ Tel: (01625) 876141 *Antique restorers & suppliers*

▶ Attic Life Ltd, Unit 5 Charmborough Farm, Charlton Road, Holcombe, Radstock, BA3 5EX Tel: (01761) 239154 Fax: (01761) 233614 E-mail: contact@atticlife.co.uk *-Loft Conversion Specialists*-From Design To Completion*-19 Years Experience*-Competitive Prices*-5 Year Guarantee**

▶ Atticoustic, 56a Lansdown, Stroud, Gloucestershire, GL5 1BN Tel: (01453) 755592 E-mail: pete@atticoustic.com *Atticoustic is one of the UKs most competitive CD/DVD manufacturers. If you want 10 or 1,000,000 CDs there is a solution for all. For friendly advice on CD duplication, CD tickets, CD Business Cards just call or e-mail & we will be happy to help.*

▶ Atticus Trophies, 244 Manley Road, Manchester, M21 0RD Tel: 0161-746 7115 Fax: (0800) 6528551

▶ Attitude Promotions, Enterprise House, Ocean Way, Southampton, SO14 3XB Tel: (023) 8048 8789 Fax: (0871) 7335764 E-mail: alex@attitudepromotions.co.uk *Quality branded promotional products, carrier bags & design service*

▶ Attitudes PMC, Earls Colne Business Centre, Airfield, Earls Colne, Colchester, CO6 2NS Tel: (0870) 2424814 Fax: (01787) 221149 E-mail: info@attitudesUK.co.uk *Performance Management Consultancy and Accredited Training Supplier of NVQs, CMSs, ILMs and more. We also offer bespoke training sessions.*

Attleborough Camping Hire, 31 Besthorpe Road, Attleborough, Norfolk, NR17 2AN Tel: (01953) 452825 *Camping hire equipment*

Atton Furniture, Church Lane, Church Walk, Little Dalby, Melton Mowbray, Leicestershire, LE14 2UQ Tel: (01664) 454553 Fax: (01664) 454553 *Furniture design & manufrs*

▶ Attract Marketing Ltd, Leonard House, 13 Silver St, Tamworth, Staffordshire, B79 7NH Tel: 01827 65814 Fax: 01827 65867 E-mail: info@attractmarketing.co.uk Attract is a multi-disciplinary consultancy specialising in providing bespoke marketing, business management and implementation consultancy to the leisure and visitor attraction sectors. Our range of business and marketing services include: -**strategic marketing and business planning, quantitative and qualitative market research, branding and corporate identity, general promotional activities; funding, human resources, management and organisational development, access, design and curatorial services. *

▶ Attractive Partners, The Old Coach House, Upper Grove Street, Leamington Spa, Warwickshire, CV32 5AN Tel: 0870 2424212 Fax: 0870 2407227 E-mail: liz@attractivepartners.co.uk A personal introduction agency.

Attributes Associates, 52 Harvey Rd, Guildford, Surrey, GU1 3LU Tel: (01483) 577771 Fax: (01483) 577555 Management consultants

Attunity UK Ltd, 6 Beacontree Plaza, Gillette Way, Reading, RG2 0BS Tel: (01344) 742805 Fax: 0118-975 3005 E-mail: info-uk@attunity.com Internet services & software solution providers

Attwater Group, PO Box 39, Preston, PR1 1TA Tel: (01772) 258245 Fax: (01772) 203361 E-mail: info@attwater.co.uk Principal Export Areas: Worldwide Manufacturers and machinists of industrial composites, high pressure laminates and tubes*Manufacturers of electrical insulating materials and machined components. Manufacturers of high performance thermosets including phenolics, epoxies, polyimides and silicones in various formats. Manufacturers of carbon fibre composite sheets.*

Attwood Aquatics, 187 London Road, Hemel Hempstead, Hertfordshire, HP3 9SQ Tel: (01442) 211077 Fax: (01442) 264849 E-mail: sales@attwoodaquatics.co.uk Aquatic retail

Attwood Evans Consultancy, 10 Olivers Battery Road North, Winchester, Hants, SO22 4JA Tel: (01962) 869672 Mechanical engineering consultancy

Atuglas International, Swadlincote, Derbyshire, DE11 1BD Tel: (0870) 5403050 E-mail: maureen.cairns@atuglasint.com Plastic sheet stockholders suppliers

Atwell Engineering Holdings Ltd, Unit 1, Dinnington Business Park, Outgang Lane, Sheffield, S25 3QU Tel: (01909) 551133 Fax: (01909) 551123 E-mail: admin@ens-precision.com Precision machining & general engineering

Atwell Self-Adhesive Labellers, Unit B2 Haysbridge Business Centre, Brickhouse Lane, South Godstone, Godstone, Surrey, RH9 8JW Tel: (01342) 844146 Fax: (01342) 843666 E-mail: sales@atwell-labellers.co.uk Principal Export Areas: Asia Pacific, Central Asia, Middle East, Africa, Central/East Europe & West Europe Labeling machine systems

▶ Au Consulting, 37 Palmer Rise, Livingston, West Lothian, EH54 6NP Tel: (07986) 494775 Fax: (0871) 6611605 E-mail: enquiries@au-consulting.co.uk Professional business consultancy services and a wide range of document management solutions. From sales and marketing assistance to supplying information management systems, scanning services and low cost, high quality, offshore data capture services. Real business solutions.

▶ Au Pair Professional, Lacewing Close, Plaistow, London, E13 8AD Tel: 079 30540127 E-mail: info@aupairprofessional.com Au Pair Professional is an au pair agency supplying families in the UK with flexible and affordable childcare.*All of our candidates have references and medical clearance confirming they are fit to work as au pairs.

Aubic Bar Supplies, Unit 7, Dominion Way, Rustington, Littlehampton, West Sussex, BN16 3HQ Tel: (01903) 775002 Fax: (01903) 775112 E-mail: info@aubic.co.uk Spirit measure & dispenser manufrs

Aubourn, Rolfes House, 60 Milford Street, Salisbury, SP1 2BP Tel: (01722) 426850 Fax: (01722) 426851 E-mail: salisbury@aubourn-consultancy.co.uk Agricultural consultants

▶ Aubrey Davidson & Co., 137 Barronstown Road, Banbridge, County Down, BT32 3SA Tel: (028) 4066 2379 Fax: (028) 4062 6769

▶ Aubs Villa, 26 Masefield Avenue, Orrel, Wigan, Lancs, WN5 8HR Tel: 01942 744587 E-mail: enquires@aubsvilla.co.uk Orlando, Florida, Holiday, villa, Golf, golfing, private villa, Walt Disney World, Davenport, heated, swimming pool, gated, community, secure, lit, 24 hour, resort, Holiday, homes, attractions, Champions Gate, Sea World, Universal, MGM, Studios, Islands, Adventure, DownTown, Magic Kingdom, Epcot Centre, Kennedy Space, Typhoon Lagoon, Lagoon, Blizzard, Beach, Wet 'n Wild, Bush Gardens, Animal Kingdom, Church Street, International, Drive, Old Town, uk, us, villa, holidays, magic kingdom, MGM studios, Down Town Disney, Water park, animal, disneys, sports, Universal, Universals Islands adventure, mercado centre, pointe, belz, Ripley"s, Ripleys, believe or not, planet hollywood, cirque du soleil, pleasure island, gloria estafan"s bongos, live music, rainforest

▶ Auction Fitness, Unit 10 Bakers Park, Cater Road, Bishopsworth, Bristol, BS13 7TW Tel: (0870) 8519419 Fax: 0117-964 9679 E-mail: info@auctionfitness.com Weight & fitness equipment suppliers

Auctionelec Ltd, 20-22 Bedford Row, London, WC1R 4JS Tel: (0870) 6093195 E-mail: sales@auctionelec.com Online auction of electrical and electronic components

▶ Audace, North Street, Stoke-sub-Hamdon, Somerset, TA14 6QR Tel: (01935) 825910 Fax: (08707) 051692

Audenshaw Steel Ltd, Unit 12 Wharf Parade, Lower Wharf Street, Ashton-under-Lyne, Lancashire, OL6 7PE Tel: 0161-343 8550 Fax: 0161-343 8550 Steel sales & fabricators

▶ Audex Contracts, Block 3, 8 Causewayside Street, Glasgow, G32 8LP Tel: 0141-778 6448 Fax: 0141-764 1731

Audio Ltd, Audio House, Progress Road, Sands Industrial Estate, High Wycombe, Buckinghamshire, HP12 4JD Tel: (01494) 511711 Fax: (01494) 539600 E-mail: info@audioltd.com Radio microphone manufrs

Audio Access Ltd, 9 Romney Road, Rottingdean, Brighton, BN2 7GG Tel: (01273) 300001 Fax: (01273) 390909 E-mail: sound@audioaccess.co.uk Sound & broadcast services

Audio & Acoustics, United House, North Road, London, N7 9DP Tel: (020) 7700 2900 Fax: (020) 7700 6900 E-mail: sales@audioandacoustics.com Acoustic consultants

Audio Agency Europe, PO Box 4601, Kiln Farm, Milton Keynes, MK19 7ZN Tel: (01908) 510123 Fax: (01908) 511123 E-mail: info@audioagencyeurope.com Acoustic products distributor & broadcasting installation service

Audio Communications, 6 Elmcourt Industrial Park, Station Road, Wootton Bassett, Swindon, SN4 7ED Tel: (01793) 851440 Fax: (01793) 851440 Electronic equipment manufrs

Audio Design Services Ltd, St Davids House, Adcroft St, Higher Hillgate, Stockport, Cheshire, SK1 3HW Tel: 0161-476 1010 Fax: 0161-666 6366 E-mail: sales@ads-worldwide.net Principal Export Areas: Asia Pacific, Central Asia, Central/East Europe & West Europe Suppliers of induction loops, assisted listening & manufacture speakers

Audio Developments Ltd, 23 Portland Road, Walsall, WS9 8NS Tel: (01922) 457007 Fax: (01922) 457008 E-mail: sales@audio.co.uk Manufacturer of sound mixers

Audio Education Ltd, 13A Airport Road West, Belfast, BT3 9ED Tel: (028) 9088 3555 Fax: (028) 9088 3539 Departmental store buying services

Audio Engine, 1 Lower Luton Road, Harpenden, Hertfordshire, AL5 5AF Tel: (01582) 768560 Fax: (01582) 469532 E-mail: phaudio@aol.com Electronics design consultancy

Audio Engineering Ltd, New Road, London, N8 8TA Tel: (020) 8341 3500 Fax: (020) 8341 5100 E-mail: sales@micronwireless.co.uk Radio microphone manufrs

Audio Experts, Springboard Business Centre, Ellerbeck Way, Middlesbrough, Cleveland, TS9 5JZ Tel: (01642) 715345 Fax: (01642) 715344 E-mail: office@audio-experts.co.uk Transcribers of PACE interviews, Police station interviews, Legal transcription, Business documentation, Business administration, Conference transcription, Court proceedings, General audio dictation, Customer Service Calls, Disciplinary Hearings, Employment Tribunal proceedings, General correspondence, Group Interviews, Lectures and other academic work, Interviews with clients, Radio and TV, Recorded Video link meetings, Market Research Interviews, Speeches and Presentations, Medical transcription, Study Interviews, Meetings, Teleconference Recordings, Translation work, Religious meetings, University Research Interviews, Telephone Response recordings, Video and CD Rom Webcasts.

Audio Images, 187 Westgate, Bradford, West Yorkshire, BD1 3AD Tel: (01274) 733633 Fax: (01274) 776966 E-mail: sales@audioimages.co.uk Car audio, alarm systems & tracking systems providers

▶ Audio Marketing Ltd, 11 Ravenscourt, Thorntonhall, Glasgow, G74 5AZ Tel: (0870) 3500205

Audio Mouldings Ltd, Unit 4 Langley Terrace, Latimer Road, Luton, LU1 3XA Tel: (01582) 424606 Fax: (01582) 459891 E-mail: audiomouldings@aol.com Headset manufrs

Audio Partnership P.L.C., Units 3-4, Gallery Court, Hankey Place, London, SE1 4BB Tel: (020) 7940 2200 Fax: (020) 7940 2233 Speaker designers & manufrs

Audio Technica Ltd, 2 Royal London Ind Estate, Old Lane, Beeston, Leeds, LS11 8AG Tel: 0113-277 1441 Fax: 0113-270 4836 E-mail: sales@audio-technica.co.uk Microphone manufrs

Audio Visual Consultants Ltd, 107-111 Whitehouse Loan, Edinburgh, EH9 1AT Tel: 0131-447 6211 Fax: 0131-452 8372 E-mail: info@avc-edinburgh.co.uk Audio visual designers & installation services

Audio Visual Machines Ltd, Phoenix House, 2B Upper Teddington Road, Kingston Upon Thames, Surrey, KT1 4DY Tel: (020) 8977 8880 Fax: (020) 8977 8879 E-mail: info@avmachines.com Audio visual installation

▶ Audio Visual & Presentation Systems, 34 Curlew Avenue, Chatteris, Cambridgeshire, PE16 6PL Tel: (01354) 696747 Fax: (01354) 695287 E-mail: sales@av-presentation.co.uk Hire, sales, install audio visual, conference, stage lighting, sound

Audio Visual & Reprographics, 62 Donegall Street, Belfast, BT1 2GT Tel: (028) 9020 7070 Fax: (028) 9020 7071 E-mail: info@avar-online.co.uk Audio visual equipment hire, repair & sales

Audio Visual Unit Ltd, 10 Leslie Road, Ipswich, IP3 9PL Tel: (01473) 705200 Fax: (01473) 705218 E-mail: info@avunit.co.uk Conference staging & production. Video production

Audionics Ltd, 31 Jessops Riverside, Sheffield, S9 2RX Tel: 0114-242 2333 Fax: 0114-243 3913 E-mail: info@audionics.co.uk Principal Export Areas: Worldwide Broadcast equipment manufrs

Audionics Presentation Services, Alpen House, Headley Road, Grayshott, Hindhead, Surrey, GU26 6JG Tel: (01428) 713937 Graphic design

Audioserv Ltd, Beaver Works,, 36 Whitehouse street,, Hunslet,, Leeds, LS10 1AD Tel: 0113 2164255 E-mail: audioserv@gmail.com Installation, sales, hire and servicing of professional audio equipment. We can tailor installations and hires to our customers" exact needs. We can provide sound, staging, lighting and event management services for events up to 180,000 people.

Audiotel International Ltd, Corby Road, Weldon, Corby, Northamptonshire, NN17 3AR Tel: (01536) 266677 Fax: (01586) 277711 E-mail: sales@audiotel-international.com Design & manufacture counter surveillance (de-bugging) equipment

▶ Audioworkshop.Co.Uk, Unit 17 Lynderswood Farm, London Road, Black Notley, Braintree, Essex, CM77 8QN Tel: (01245) 361578 Fax: (01245) 361357 E-mail: sales@audio-workshop.co.uk Suppliers of electrical parts for sound companies

Audit & Computer Security Services Ltd, 46 Queens Road, Hertford, SG13 8AZ Tel: (01992) 582439 Fax: 01992 582439 Computer consultants

▶ Audit Logistics UK, Apex House, 72 Peghouse Rise, Uplands, Stroud, Gloucestershire, GL5 1UR Tel: (01453) 750740 Fax: (01453) 750786 E-mail: contact@auditlogistics.co.uk Freight Auditors in business to reduce freight costs to businesses sending volume overnight deliveries.

Auditel Ltd, 2 Devonport Vernon Trading Estate, Cock Lane, High Wycombe, Buckinghamshire, HP13 7DE Tel: (01494) 465335 Fax: (01494) 446013 E-mail: sales@auditel.ltd.uk Principal Export Areas: Worldwide Conference equipment manufrs

▶ Auditoria Services Ltd, Denby Way, Hellaby, Rotherham, South Yorkshire, S66 8HR Tel: (01709) 543345 Fax: (01709) 700771 E-mail: sales@auditoria-services.com Seating manufrs

Audix Systems Ltd, Station Road, Wendens Ambo, Saffron Walden, Essex, CB11 4LG Tel: (01799) 540888 Fax: (01799) 541618 E-mail: sales@tepg.com Public address system installers Also at: Glasgow

Audnam Metalworkers, 6 Platts Road, Stourbridge, West Midlands, DY8 4YR Tel: (01384) 374468 Fax: (01384) 440947 Kitchen ventilator manufrs

Audus Noble Ltd, Blyth Industrial Estate, Cowpen Road, Blyth, Northumberland, NE24 5TD Tel: (01670) 543100 Fax: (01670) 364800 Plastic bottle & container manufrs

Audyan Blinds, 2 Lynburn Industrial Estate, Halbeath Place, Dunfermline, Fife, KY11 4JT Tel: (01383) 624555 Fax: (01383) 624555 Blind suppliers

Aufait Systems, 54 High Street, Hail Weston, St. Neots, Cambridgeshire, PE19 5JW Tel: (01480) 474779 Fax: (01480) 217288 E-mail: aufaitsystems@btinternet.com Shop equipment suppliers

G. Auger & Son, Old Post Ho, The Street, Hartlip, Sittingbourne, Kent, ME9 7TH Tel: 01795 842490 Fax: 01795 845490 Agricultural contractors

▶ Auger Productions, Suite F16, Scope House, Weston Road, Crewe, CW1 6DD Tel: (01270) 258111 Fax: (01270) 258161 E-mail: info@auger-productions.com Internet service agents

Aughton Automation Ltd, 66 Brindley Road, Astmoor Industrial Estate, Runcorn, Cheshire, WA7 1PF Tel: (01928) 589606 Fax: (01928) 589601 E-mail: brian.duffy@aughtonuk.com Electronic & test equipment hire

▶ Aughton Hire, 66 Brindley Road, Astmoor, Runcorn, Cheshire, WA7 1PF Tel: (01928) 589600 Fax: 01928 589601 E-mail: brian.duffy@aughtonuk.com Control instrumentation & electrical engineers

August P A's & Personnel, 8 Gobbitts Yard, Woodbridge, Suffolk, IP12 1DD Tel: (01394) 388828 E-mail: enquiries@august-pas.com Employment agents

▶ August Personnel, Sheraton House, Castle Park, Cambridge, CB3 0AX Tel: (01223) 370162 E-mail: pauline@augustpersonnel.co.uk Recruitment for technical, architectural & general office staff, offices in Cambridge & Ipswich

Auguste Development Services, Unit 12b Cooksland Industrial Estate, Bodmin, Cornwall, PL31 2QB Tel: (01208) 75593 Fax: (01208) 77499 E-mail: sales@augustedev.fsnet.co.uk Precision engineers & turned part manufrs

Augustus Martin Ltd, 8-20 St. Andrews Way, London, E3 3PB Tel: (020) 7537 4200 Fax: (020) 7537 2184 E-mail: sales@amartin.co.uk Screen printers

Augustus Oils Ltd, 64 Woolmer Way, Bordon, Hampshire, GU35 9QF Tel: (01420) 488555 Fax: (01420) 476777 E-mail: sales@augustus-oils.ltd.uk Essential oils, fragrance and flavour ingredients

Auld Valves Ltd, Finlas Street, Cowlairs Industrial Estate, Glasgow, G22 5DQ Tel: 0141-557 0515 Fax: 0141-558 1059 E-mail: bob@auldvalves.com Valve manufrs

Aulds Delicious Desserts, Inchinnan Industrial Estate, 1 Barnsford Avenue, Renfrew, PA4 9RZ Tel: 0141-812 1126 Fax: 0141-812 1127 E-mail: deliciousdeserts@aulds.co.uk Bakery & confectionery suppliers

Aulton & Butler Ltd, Ashtree Works Bentley Lane Industrial Park, Bentley Lane, Walsall, WS2 8TL Tel: (01922) 623297 Fax: (01922) 613586 E-mail: aulton-butler@tiscali.co.uk Saddle tree makers

Auma Actuators Ltd, Britannia Way, Clevedon, Avon, BS21 6QH Tel: (01275) 871141 Fax: (01275) 875492 E-mail: sales@alma.com Electric valve actuators

Aunt Sandra's Candy Factory, 60 Castlereagh Road, Belfast, BT5 5FP Tel: (028) 9073 2868 Fax: (028) 9073 2868 Confectionery manufrs

▶ Aunty Lesley's, 9 Cornerswell Road, Penarth, South Glamorgan, CF64 2UW Tel: (029) 2070 7923

Aur Telephone, 260 Tottenham Court Road, London, W1T 7RF Tel: (020) 7637 7353 Fax: (020) 7323 9790 Telecommunications

Aura Furniture, Unit 1 The Precinct, Cheadle Hulme, Cheadle, Cheshire, SK8 5BB Tel: 0161-486 6566 Pine & hardwood furniture manufacturers & sales

Aura Q, 33 Grayham Road, Malvern, Worcestershire, WR14 2HU Tel: (01684) 577990 E-mail: sales@ntl-uk.com Computer networks

Auric Metal Finishers Ltd, Herald Way, Binley Industrial Estate, Coventry, CV3 2RP Tel: (024) 7644 7431 Fax: (024) 7663 5719 E-mail: info@auric.co.uk Precious metal finishing services

Auricle Screening, 27 High Street, Petersfield, Hampshire, GU32 3JR Tel: (0800) 1804097 Fax: (01252) 720820 E-mail: iatkinson@noiseatwork.org

▶ Auriga Business Solutions Ltd, Soldon Cross Farm Soldon Cross, Holsworthy, Devon, EX22 7PH Tel: (01409) 241060 E-mail: sales@aurigasolutions.co.uk Auriga offer an extensive range of business training courses supported by a comprehensive consultancy service which takes lessons learnt in the classroom through to practical application and real results in the workplace. If your requirement is Management Systems training or assistance in implementing an approval then Auriga is your first point of call.**Our Quality, Lean and Six Sigma training programmes provide the springboard to drive improvement throughout your organisation.**Public training courses are offered at a range of venues across the UK. Alternatively we can offer in house courses at competitive rates tailored to meet your specific needs.

Auriga Communications Ltd, Auriga House, Thompson Close, Harpenden, Hertfordshire, AL5 4ES Tel: (01582) 466800 Fax: (01582) 466839 E-mail: sales@auriga.co.uk Data communication equipment services

▶ Auriga Europe plc, Davy Avenue, Knowlhill, Milton Keynes, MK5 8ND Tel: (0870) 1219990 Fax: (0870) 1219991 E-mail: sales@aurigaeurope.com Network cabling solutions

Aurion Computer Consultants, Laganside Studios, Ravenhill Business Park, Belfast, BT6 8AW Tel: (028) 9045 5244 Fax: (028) 9045 5244 E-mail: maureen@aurion.co.uk Web design services

Aurora, 6 Little Burrow, Welwyn Garden City, Hertfordshire, AL7 4SW Tel: (01707) 351820 Fax: (01707) 351821 Lighting company

Aurora Business Development Ltd, 9 Ferndown Close, Bristol, BS11 0UP Tel: 0117-962 6500 Fax: 0117-962 6500 E-mail: aurora@btinternet.com Manufacturing & business education, training & consultancy, public & in-house courses run worldwide

▶ Aurora Colors P.L.C., Crossways Park, Caerphilly, Mid Glamorgan, CF83 3NL Tel: (029) 2088 0888 Lithographic & screen printing service

Aurora Conservatories, The Old Station, Naburn, York, YO19 4RW Tel: (01904) 631234 Fax: (01904) 610318 E-mail: info@btconnect.com Timber conservatory manufrs

Aurora Fireworks Ltd, Kiln Industries, Fittleworth Road, Wisborough Green, Billingshurst, West Sussex, RH14 0ES Tel: (0800) 9756573 Fax: (01403) 701085 E-mail: sales@aurorafireworks.co.uk Firework display suppliers

▶ Aurora Imaging, Delfan, Cas-Mael, Haverfordwest, Pembrokeshire, SA62 5RJ Tel: 01348 881444 E-mail: info@photowales.com Professional Commercial Photography, Digital Imaging and Web Design

Aurora Jewellery, St. Ola, Kirkwall, Orkney, KW15 1TR Tel: (01856) 871861 Fax: (01856) 871861 E-mail: info@aurora-jewellery.co.uk Jewellery suppliers & manufrs

Aurora Marble Ltd, Green Lea Mills, Cross Green Road, Huddersfield, HD5 9XX Tel: (01484) 510470 Fax: (01484) 538943 Marble importers for fireplace's

▶ Aurora Services, 58 Kinnaird Close, Slough, SL1 6AS Tel: (0870) 9504617 Fax: (07732) 103565 E-mail: aurora.services@tiscali.co.uk A Professional Carpet & Rug Cleaning service, with very competitive rates. Based in Slough, we service Berks, Bucks, Oxon, & west Surrey.

Aurum Ltd, 1A Crab La, New Invention, Willenhall, W. Midlands, WV12 5BJ Tel: (01922) 404394 Fax: (01922) 338212 Manufacturers' agents

George Ausden Ltd, 253 High Street, Watford, WD17 2HW Tel: (01923) 223530 Fax: (01923) 223530 E-mail: info@geo-ausden.com Scrap metal merchants & steel stockists

Austen Brush Co., Station Street West Business Park, Station Street West, Foleshill, Coventry, CV6 5BP Tel: (024) 7666 1326 Fax: (024) 7668 8603 E-mail: sales@scaleaway-tools.co.uk Rubberised rotary wire brush manufrs

Austick Construction Ltd, West Park View, Dudley, Cramlington, Northumberland, NE23 7AA Tel: 0191-250 2425 Fax: 0191-250 2450 E-mail: austickconstruction@hotmail.co.uk Electrical & civil engineers

Allan Austin Ltd, Crystal Drive, Smethwick, West Midlands, B66 1QG Tel: 0121-552 8513 Fax: 0121-552 1480 E-mail: allan@austinltd.freeserve.co.uk Industrial packaging

▶ Austin Banks Ltd, Hutton Business Centre, Suite 1a High Street, Bentley, Doncaster, South Yorkshire, DN5 9QP Tel: (01302) 822228 Fax: 01302 822237 E-mail: james@austinbanks.co.uk Website offering Jobs in Doncaster in Accountancy, Administration, Customer Service, HR and more. Jobs in South Yorkshire also available. CV Advice, Interview Tips and Salary Survey. Call us for more details or email your enquiry.

Austin Bros Ltd, 413 London Road, Slough, SL3 8PS Tel: (01753) 593007 Fax: (01753) 593329 E-mail: info@austinbrothers.co.uk Commercial vehicle repairs

▶ Austin Design & Manufacture Ltd, Unit 2 Warish Hall, Warish Hall Road, Takeley, Bishop's Stortford, Hertfordshire, CM22 6NZ Tel: (01279) 871527 Fax: (01279) 871544

continued

continuation
E-mail: keith@admfloors.com *Movable swimming pool floor manufrs, car turn tables & lifts*

Austin Engineering Shropshire Ltd, Cargotec Industrial Park, Ellesmere, Shropshire, SY12 9JW Tel: (01691) 622864 Fax: (01691) 622864 E-mail: steve@austinengineering.co.uk *For all your HIAB service & spare part requirements in the West Midlands & North Wales. Austin Engineering is a foremost UK installer of HIAB cranes & a main contractor to HIAB Limited. Austin Engineering holds in continuous stock a range of faster-moving HIAB components & consumables that are available for re-sale. For items outside our shelf stock programme, we are able to provide next day delivery on orders placed by 2.30pm. We can supply; Crane spare parts, Lorry mounted crane spare parts, Lorry loaders, Crane accessories, General purpose crane attachments, Vehicle mounted hydraulic cranes, Lorry loader spare parts, Reconditioned crane spare parts, Used crane spare parts, Crane installation and maintenance, Crane servicing, Crane components. Container hydraulic lifting equipment, Crane installation, Crane test equipment, Hydraulic loaders, Dock or Loading bay lorry loading lifts, Lorry loader Installation, Lorry loader maintenance, Vehicle mounted crane spare parts, Crane modification services, Hydraulic cranes, & much more.*

Austin Leisure, 153-154 Victoria Road, Swindon, SN1 3BU Tel: (01793) 528505 Fax: (01793) 613469 E-mail: office@austingroup.co.uk *Electrical contractors*

Austin Mcgillivray & Co., 124 Scotland Street, Sheffield, S3 7DE Tel: 0114-273 8041 Fax: 0114-275 0290 E-mail: enquiries@sheffieldknives.co.uk *Tool manufrs*

Austin & McLean Ltd, Unit 1, Cookesland Industrial Estate, Bodmin, Cornwall, PL31 2QB Tel: (01208) 264162 Fax: (01208) 73125 *Lifting equipment engineers.*

▶ Austin Marr, 7 The Nelson Centre, Portfield Road, Portsmouth, PO3 5SF Tel: (023) 9269 0900 Fax: (023) 9269 1300 E-mail: enquiries@austinmarr.co.uk *Specialists in made to measure pleated conservatory blinds for the South of England. Free brochure and home consultation.*

Austin Office Furniture Ltd, 19 Millicent Road, London, E10 7LG Tel: (020) 8558 6489 Fax: 0208 558 6499 E-mail: sales@austinoffice.co.uk *We are a bespoke office furniture manufacturer in East London. We supply to the trade and also to the end user, offering tailored individual pieces that are made at our on-site factory. We also offer a hire service, along with free consultations on every aspect of your office needs. Storage wall, executive furniture, reception areas and design are our speciality.*

Austin Reed Ltd, Station Road, Thirsk, North Yorkshire, YO7 1QH Tel: (01845) 573000 Fax: (01845) 525536 E-mail: sales@austinreed.co.uk *Clothing & retailers*

Austin Roberts, Tarran Way South, Tarran Industrial Estate, Wirral, Merseyside, CH46 4UB Tel: 0151-678 6088 Fax: 0151-678 9448 E-mail: austin.roberts@virgin.net *Glass fibre mouldings manufrs*

Austin Semiconductor (Europe) Ltd, Test House, 1 Mill Lane, Alton, Hampshire, GU34 2QG Tel: (01420) 88022 Fax: (01420 87259 E-mail: sales@austinsemi.com *Semi-conductor designers & manufrs*

Stephen Austin & Sons Ltd, Caxton Hill, Hertford, SG13 7LU Tel: (01992) 584955 Fax: (01992) 500021 E-mail: sales@stephenaustin.co.uk *Security printers*

Austin Trumanns Steel Ltd, Moss Lane, Worsley, Manchester, M28 3NH Tel: 0161-799 8882 Fax: 0161-790 1848 E-mail: sales@austin-trumanns.co.uk *Steel stockholders*

Austin (UK) Ltd, Cardinal Point, Park Road, Rickmansworth, Hertfordshire, WD3 1RE Tel: (01923) 432658 Fax: (01923) 432795 E-mail: sales@austin.co.uk *Design construction & management*

Austin West Communications Ltd, New Premier House, 150 Southampton Row, London, WC1B 5AL Tel: (020) 7278 7878 Fax: (020) 7278 0238 *Media independent agency*

▶ Austin Wilkinson Ltd, Coal Pit Lane, Atherton, Manchester, M46 0RY Tel: (01942) 887000 Fax: (01942) 888222

Austin Wolstencroft & Co. Ltd, 56 Broadbent Road, Oldham, OL1 4HY Tel: 0161-624 5236 Fax: 0161-620 8413 E-mail: avrilbrooks20944@aol.com *Hose fittings manufrs*

▶ Austins Cradles Ltd, Unit 7 Sussex Park Indust Estate 270/272 Old Shoreham Road, Hove, East Sussex, BN3 7DX Tel: (01273) 734744 Fax: (01273) 220810

Australian Dried Fruits Europe Ltd, 45a The Mall, London, W5 3TJ Tel: (020) 8566 2944 Fax: (020) 8566 2967 E-mail: john@adfe.co.uk *Bakers ingredient & prepared material producers*

Austria Mikrosysteme International Ltd, Coliseum Business Centre, Watchmoore Park, Riverside Way, Camberley, Surrey, GU15 3YL Tel: 0118-973 1797 Fax: (01276) 29353 E-mail: info@amsint.com *Semi-conductor chip manufrs*

Austrian Airlines, 10 Wardour St, London, W1D 6BQ Tel: (020) 7434 7380 Fax: (020) 7434 7363 *Airline*

Austrian National Tourist Office, 13-14 Cork Street, London, W1S 3NS Tel: (020) 7629 0461 Fax: (020) 7499 6038 E-mail: info@anto.co.uk *Tourist office*

Autac Products Ltd, Bollin Cable Works, London Road, Macclesfield, Cheshire, SK11 7RN Tel: (01625) 619277 Fax: (01625) 619366 E-mail: info@autac.co.uk *Retractable spiral electrical cable manufrs*

Autarky Co. Ltd, Charlwoods Industrial Estate, Charlwoods Place, East Grinstead, West Sussex, RH19 2HY Tel: (01342) 311388 Fax: (01342) 323733E-mail: sales@autarky.com *Food packaging machinery manufrs*

Authentic Asian Snacks, 24-26 Cedar Road, Newcastle upon Tyne, NE4 9XX Tel: 0191-273 4715 Fax: 0191-273 4715 E-mail: rehmansweetcentre@hotmail.com *Food products manufrs*

Authentic Indian Co., 1 Glebe Farm, Dennis Street, Hugglescote, Coalville, Leicestershire, LE67 2FP Tel: (01530) 830308 Fax: (01530) 838978 E-mail: sales@authenticindian.co.uk *Savoury food manufrs*

Authordocs Ltd, 60 Purton Road, Swindon, SN2 2LZ Tel: (0845) 0940387 Fax: (01793) 539640 E-mail: info@authordocs.co.uk *Technical writing*

Auto 2000, 24 College Street, Kempston, Bedford, MK42 8LU Tel: (01234) 210012 *Motor repairers*

Auto Amusements, 21 Stanmore Avenue, Blackpool, FY4 3LX Tel: (01253) 838838 Fax: (01253) 798835 E-mail: info@autoamusements.com *Amusement machine refurbishment & repair*

Auto Amusements Ltd, 31a Coxs Lane, Cradley Heath, West Midlands, B64 5NS Tel: (01384) 564207 Fax: (01384) 566877 E-mail: mike@auto-amusements.co.uk *Hire gaming machines & amusements*

Auto Asylum, 78 Portlock Road, Maidenhead, Berkshire, SL6 6DZ Tel: (01628) 782782 Fax: (01628) 784541 *Car window tinting service*

Auto Audio Leeds Ltd, 35 Wakefield Road, Swillington, Leeds, LS26 8DT Tel: 0113-286 2970 Fax: 0113-287 0222 E-mail: autoaudiosales@aol.com *Car security & alarms services & van livery*

Auto Battery Service, 59 Recreation Road, Guildford, Surrey, GU1 1HE Tel: (01483) 572316 Fax: (01483) 504965 E-mail: guildford@manbat.co.uk *Battery distributors & agents*

▶ Auto Business Solutions Ltd, Ivy Road Industrial Estate, Chippenham, Wiltshire, SN15 1SB Tel: (0870) 7779116 Fax: (0870) 7779115 E-mail: john_mitchell@absol.co.uk *Car & van leasing & finance specialists*

▶ Auto Carriers, Oxford Road, Ryton on Dunsmore, Coventry, CV8 3EF Tel: (024) 7651 1167 Fax: (024) 7663 9661

Auto Components Ltd, 11 Coulman Road, Industrial Estate, Thorne, Doncaster, South Yorkshire, DN8 5JS Tel: (01405) 812424 Fax: (01405) 740072 E-mail: info@auto-components.co.uk *Sub-contract engineers*

▶ Auto Craft Engineering, Unit 1 St. Davids Industrial Estate, Pengam, Blackwood, Gwent, NP12 3SW Tel: (01443) 831748 Fax: (01443) 831758 E-mail: info@autocraftengineering.co.uk *Steel components*

Auto Crash Repairs Ltd, Lorita House, Barkers Lane, Brunel Road, Bedford, MK41 9TG Tel: (01234) 266881 Fax: (01234) 351601 E-mail: acrbedford@btconnect.com *Vehicle repair body shop*

▶ Auto Dark Helmet, 43 Long Hassocks, Rugby, Warwickshire, CV23 0JS Tel: (01788) 573056 Fax: (01788) 573057 E-mail: sales@autodarkhelmet.co.uk *Mail order company*

Auto Design Ltd, 12 Tallon Road, Hutton, Brentwood, Essex, CM13 1TF Tel: (01277) 225000 Fax: (01277) 225002 E-mail: harvey@autodesign.co.uk *Consulting engineers & designers & prototype production engineers*

▶ Auto Design, Workshop, Lincoln Road, Horncastle, Lincolnshire, LN9 5AW Tel: (01507) 525300 Fax: (01507) 525300 E-mail: sales@autodesignkent.com

Auto Electrical Services, Unit 34-36 Harmill Industrial Estate, Grovebury Road, Leighton Buzzard, Bedfordshire, LU7 4FF Tel: (01525) 372330 Fax: (01525) 851685 E-mail: info@aes2.co.uk *Auto-electrical services*

Auto Engineering Supplies Ltd, Forties, Wilnecote, Tamworth, Staffordshire, B77 5DG Tel: (01827) 286161 Fax: (01827) 286042 E-mail: jmurphy@autoengsupplies.co.uk *Precision engineers*

Auto Europe Parts Ltd, Unit 11 Betchworth Works, Ifield Road, Charlwood, Horley, Surrey, RH6 0DX Tel: (01293) 863777 Fax: (01293) 863888 *Reconditioned gear boxes*

Auto Europe Parts Ltd, Unit 11 Betchworth Works, Ifield Road, Charlwood, Horley, Surrey, RH6 0DX Tel: (01293) 863777 Fax: (01293) 863888 E-mail: info@autoeurope.co.uk *Electrical automotive parts importers & exporters*

Auto Exec Account Collections Ltd, Technology House, 492 London Road, Westcliff-on-Sea, Essex, SS0 9LD Tel: (01702) 431731 Fax: (01702) 431804 E-mail: info@accountcollection.com *Debt recovery services*

Auto Extract Systems, Brearley House, Burnley Road, Halifax, West Yorkshire, HX2 6NB Tel: (01422) 888144 Fax: (01422) 888145 *Dust & fume extraction engineers & installers*

▶ Auto Flow Ltd, Sirius House, Alderley Road, Chelford, Macclesfield, Cheshire, SK11 9AP Tel: (01625) 860545 Fax: (0870) 4581616 E-mail: sales@autoflow.ltd.uk *Bespoke software solutions. We also sell and support our leading management system for the vehicle repair industry*

▶ Auto Gas Technology Ltd, Unit 2 Sherriff Street, Worcester, WR4 9AB Tel: (01905) 729662 Fax: (01905) 28410

Auto Gates Scotland Ltd, 4-5 Murray Street, Paisley, Renfrewshire, PA3 1QG Tel: 0141-849 7029 Fax: 0141-849 1224 E-mail: info@auto-gatesscotland.co.uk *Automatic gate manufrs*

Auto Glass York Ltd, Layerthorpe, York, YO31 7YW Tel: (01904) 644723 Fax: (01904) 611624 *Windscreen replacement-vehicle security-vehicle sunroof installers*

Auto Guard Security Centre Ltd, Unit 3 Sandy La Industrial Estate, Stourport-on-Severn, Worcestershire, DY13 9QB Tel: (01299) 878111 Fax: (01299) 871990 *Security vehicle manufrs*

Auto Imaginations, Ranmore Common, Dorking, Surrey, RH5 6SX Tel: (01483) 284114 *Motor cars, tyres, wheels, seats & spare parts specialists*

Auto Interiors, 56 Norfolk Street, Liverpool, L1 0BE Tel: 0151-708 8881 Fax: 0151-708 6002 *Sound proofing interior trim manufrs*

Auto Nest Ltd, Stoke Albany Road, Desborough, Kettering, Northamptonshire, NN14 2SP Tel: (01536) 760332 Fax: (01536) 762712 *Plastics products agents*

Auto Paint, 761 Little Horton Lane, Bradford, West Yorkshire, BD5 9ER Tel: (01274) 522222 Fax: (01274) 522500 *Automotive & industrial paint suppliers*

▶ Auto Plas UK Ltd, 10 Edgware Grove Winstanley, Wigan, Lancashire, WN3 6EF Tel: (01942) 217209 Fax: 01942 218720 E-mail: info@autoplasuk.co.uk *Provide nationwide plastic collection which is granulated and put back into the motor industry*

Auto Plates, Unit 1 Chessington Trade Park, Cox Lane, Chessington, Surrey, KT9 1TW Tel: (020) 8391 9070 Fax: (020) 8391 9075 *Car number plate & sign manufrs*

▶ Auto Point, Bank View, First Drove, Fengate, Peterborough, PE1 5BJ Tel: (01733) 566332 Fax: 01733 352933 E-mail: info@fast-print.net *Self Publishing, Book Printing*

▶ Auto Proud, PO Box 504, Worcester, WR4 0XQ Tel: (01905) 734973 Fax: (01905) 734973 E-mail: info@autoproud.co.uk *Auto Proud Superior Vehicle & Home Care Products - The Ultimate Shine in a Fraction of the Time - If you are one of the many proud automobile owners who love to keep their vehicles in prestige showroom condition but hate the hours of endless rubbing and polishing that takes, we have the solution. Years of research and development have resulted in producing a revolutionary new way to clean, shine and protect your vehicle.*

▶ Auto Refinish Systems, 70 Richardson Street, Belfast, BT6 8DY Tel: (07734) 235952 Fax: (028) 9061 5122 E-mail: robert.warnock@auto-refinish-systems.co.uk *Refinish paints suppliers*

Auto Rentals Ltd, Fleming Road, Skippers Lane Industrial Estate, Middlesbrough, Cleveland, TS6 6TT Tel: (01642) 469000 Fax: (01642) 464475 E-mail: info@autorentalscleveland.co.uk *Commercial vehicle leasing & rental*

▶ Auto Repairs & Recovery, Unit C1 Riverside Industrial Estate, Bridge Road, Littlehampton, West Sussex, BN17 5DF Tel: (01903) 726635 Fax: (01903) 733013 E-mail: autorepair2001@yahoo.com *Vehicle repair & test centre*

Auto Services, 26 Arden Business Centre, Arden Road, Alcester, Warwickshire, B49 6HW Tel: (01789) 763327 Fax: (01789) 763327 E-mail: enquiries@autoservices.co.uk *Motor vehicle repair services*

Auto Shield, 465 Barlow Moor Road, Manchester, M21 8AU Tel: 0161-881 3463 Fax: 0161-881 3463 *Vehicle windscreen repairs*

Auto Sleepers Ltd, Orchard Works Indust Estate, Broadway, Worcestershire, WR12 7QF Tel: (01386) 853338 Fax: (01386) 858343 E-mail: sales@auto-sleepers.co.uk *Motor caravan manufrs*

▶ Auto Smart Repairs Ltd, 8 Riverway, Staines, Middlesex, TW18 2SJ Tel: (01784) 442000 E-mail: michael@autosmartrepairsltd.com *Cosmetic car repair specialist*

Auto Spares & Salvage, Station House, Station Road, Raunds, Wellingborough, Northamptonshire, NN9 6BX Tel: (01933) 626166 Fax: (01933) 625339 E-mail: admin@autospares-salvage.com *New & used car part distributors*

Auto Sport (Engineering) Ltd, Brandon Road, Binley, Coventry, CV3 2AH Tel: (024) 7643 7110 Fax: (024) 7645 9757 *Motor precision engineers*

Auto Style, Unit 16 Little Balmer, Buckingham Industrial Park, Buckingham, MK18 1TF Tel: (01280) 817962 Fax: (01280) 817963 *Car mat manufrs*

▶ Auto Trim, 36 Dorset Close, Bletchley, Milton Keynes, MK3 7HZ Tel: (01908) 368542 E-mail: sales@autotrimmer.co.uk *Car trimming services*

Auto Turned Products Northants Ltd, 1 North Portway Close, Round Spinney Industrial Estate, Northampton, NN3 8RD Tel: (01604) 642214 Fax: (01604) 499319 E-mail: info@autoturned.co.uk *Car parts*

Auto Tyre & Battery Co., Southern Avenue, Leominster, Herefordshire, HR6 0QF Tel: (01568) 615680 *Tyre & battery distributors*

▶ Auto Valeting Services, 7 Ham Close, Collingbourne Kingston, Marlborough, Wiltshire, SN8 3SB Tel: 01264 850621 E-mail: mike@autovaletingservices.co.uk *Mobile Vehicle Valeting Specialist*Covering East Wiltshire, West Berkshire and North Hampshire.*Prompt professional service at your home or work. Free quotations.*

Autobar Packaging & Veriplast International, Dragonville Industrial Estate, Durham, DH1 2RL Tel: 0191-386 5171 Fax: 0191-386 4429 *Plastic cup & container manufrs* Also at: Durham

Autobox Ltd, Unit S1 Cherrycourt Way, Leighton Buzzard, Bedfordshire, LU7 4UH Tel: (01525) 852831 Fax: (01525) 382353 E-mail: enquiries@autobox.co.uk *Corrugated carton machinery manufrs*

▶ Autocal Ltd, Unit 2 Feldspar Close, Enderby, Leicester, LE19 4SD Tel: 0116-286 2444 Fax: 0116-286 3444 E-mail: sales@autocal.co.uk *Garage equipment retailers*

Autocare, 83 Heeley Road, Birmingham, B29 6EJ Tel: 0121-472 5066 Fax: 0121-477 4015 *Garage services*

▶ Autocare Distribution Ltd, Carrington Power Station, Manchester Road, Carrington, Manchester, M31 4AX Tel: 0161-775 7576 Fax: 0161-775 7556

Autochair, Wood St North, Meddow Lane Industrial Estate, Alfreton, Derbyshire, DE55 7JR Tel: (0800) 214045 Fax: (01773) 830444 E-mail: info@autochair.co.uk *Mobility aids for the disabled*

Autoclaved Aerated Concrete Products Association Ltd, 60 Charles Street, Leicester, LE1 1FB Tel: (0116) 253 6161 Fax: (0116) 251 4568 E-mail: briprecast@aol.com *Trade association*

Autoclock Systems Ltd, 93-97 Second Avenue, Newcastle upon Tyne, NE6 5XT Tel: 0191-276 1611 Fax: 0191-265 0586 E-mail: sales@autoclocksystems.co.uk *Fingerprint & biometric time systems, employee & master clock manufrs*

Autoclude, Unit 7, Carnival Park, Carnival Close, Basildon, Essex, SS14 3WN Tel: (01268) 662450 Fax: (01268) 662459 E-mail: info@autocludepumps.com *AUTOCLUDE designer, manufacturer & distribute peristaltic pumps & tubing with flow rates from less than 1ml/min up to 23L/min & tubing in various materials specifically for peristaltic pumps. The extensive range consists of OEM pumps & cased models with variable flow, programming features & IP55 protection*

▶ Autoconnect Contact Centre, Hewell Road, Redditch, Worcestershire, B97 6AY Tel: (01527) 61661 *Automotive consultants*

Autocraft Equipment Ltd, Higher Street, Norton sub Hamdon, Stoke-sub-Hamdon, Somerset, TA14 6SN Tel: (01935) 881848 Fax: (01935) 881793 *Supplier of garage equipment*

Autocraft Equipment Ltd, Higher Street, Norton sub Hamdon, Stoke-sub-Hamdon, Somerset, TA14 6SN Tel: (01935) 881848 Fax: (01935) 881793 E-mail: sales@autocraftequipment.co.uk *Sales of garage equipment*

Autocrafts, Brimscombe Mills, Brimscombe, Stroud, Gloucestershire, GL5 2SB Tel: (01453) 882468 Fax: (01453) 882182 *Body work services & vehicle repairs*

Autocross Plastics, Units 26-27 New Hall Hey Business Park, New Hall Hey Road, Rossendale, Lancashire, BB4 6HL Tel: (01706) 216794 Fax: (01706) 230758 E-mail: bill@euroshel.com *Cycle shelters manufacturer & cycle stands*

Autocruise Group Holdings Ltd, Swinton Meadows Industrial Estate, Meadow Way, Swinton, Mexborough, South Yorkshire, S64 8AB Tel: (01709) 571411 Fax: (01709) 579292 E-mail: sales@autocruise.co.uk *Motor caravan manufrs*

Autodesk Ltd, 1 Meadow Gate Avenue, Farnborough Business Park, Farnborough, Hampshire, GU14 6FG Tel: (01252) 456600 Fax: (01252) 456601 *3D computer graphic software manufrs*

▶ Autoelectronix, PO Box 588, Warrington, WA4 6XT Tel: (07811) 944824 E-mail: enquiries@autoelectronix.co.uk *Car audio, car security, satellite navigation suppliers*

Autoflex Ltd, 15 Steele Road, London, NW10 7AS Tel: (020) 8961 0193 Fax: (020) 8965 0856 *Auto-electrical & mechanical engineers*

Autofour Precision Engineering Ltd, 5 Alstone Trading Estate, Alstone Lane, Cheltenham, Gloucestershire, GL51 8HF Tel: (01242) 582064 Fax: (01242) 224374 E-mail: info@autofour.co.uk *Precision turned parts manufrs*

Autoglass Ltd, 1 Priory Business Park, Cardington, Bedford, MK44 3US Tel: (01234) 273636 Fax: (01234) 831100 E-mail: postmaster@autoglass.co.uk *Motor & agricultural vehicle glaziers* Also at: Branches throughout the U.K.

▶ Autogleam Mobile Valeting, 76 Birkdale, Warmley, Bristol, BS30 8GH Tel: 0117-961 8666 Fax: 0117-914 0777 E-mail: info@autogleam.net *Mobile car & commercial valeting service in Bristol and outskirts*

Autoglide Garage Services, Birkett House, Wellington Road, Bollington, Macclesfield, Cheshire, SK10 5HT Tel: (01625) 574126 Fax: (01625) 574126 *Automatic gear box specialists & code readers & garage services*

Autoglym, Works Road, Letchworth Garden City, Hertfordshire, SG6 1LU Tel: (01462) 677766 Fax: (01462) 677712 E-mail: sales@autoglym.com *Vehicle cleaning product manufrs*

Autograph, Block 2 Beechfield Road, Willowyard Industrial Estate, Beith, Ayrshire, KA15 1LN Tel: (01505) 506366 Fax: (01505) 506344 *Sign manufrs*

Autograph, The Malthouse, 139-141 Eastgate, Worksop, Nottinghamshire, S80 1QS Tel: (01909) 488500 Fax: (01909) 482687 E-mail: autographsigns.uk@btconnect.com *Sign manufrs*

Autographic Sign Co., Offerton Lodge, Offerton, Sunderland, SR4 9JL Tel: 0191-534 6295 Fax: 0191-534 6157 *Signwriting & lettering services sign makers*

Autographics Cheshire Ltd, Unit 2 Henderson Street, Macclesfield, Cheshire, SK11 6RA Tel: (01625) 662092 Fax: (01625) 662093 E-mail: autographics@btinternet.com *Sign manufrs*

Auto-Id.Co.Uk, 13 Telford Way, Severalls Industrial Park, Colchester, CO4 9QP Tel: (01206) 751349 Fax: (01206) 854332 E-mail: sales@auto-id.co.uk *Bar code products distributors*

▶ Autoinstalls UK Ltd, Unit 11B Lincoln Way, Salthill Industrial Estate, Clitheroe, Clitheroe, Lancashire, BB7 1QD Tel: (01200) 420750 Fax: (01200) 420751 E-mail: sales@autoinstallsuk.com *Bespoke car electronics phones hi-fi & competition system design*

Autolec Services, 101 Albert Street, Rugby, Warwickshire, CV21 2SW Tel: (01788) 573475 Fax: (01788) 550530 E-mail: autorug@yahoo.co.uk *Autoelectrical services*

Autolign Inspections Ltd, Unit 3 J B J Business Park, Northampton Road, Blisworth, Northampton, NN7 3DW Tel: (01604) 859424 Fax: (01604) 859428 E-mail: sales@autoligninspections.co.uk *Inspect previously accident damaged vehicles*

Autolok Security Products Ltd, Park Lane, Royton, Oldham, OL2 6PU Tel: 0161-624 8171 Fax: 0161-627 3742 E-mail: enquiries@autolok.uk.com *Anti-theft devices for motor vehicles*

Autolux Control Panel Mnfrs, Sizers Court, Yeadon, Leeds, LS19 7DP Tel: 0113-250 1405 Fax: 0113-250 1449 E-mail: autolux@btconnect.com *Control panel manufrs*

Automaster UK Ltd, Centaur House, Ancells Road, Fleet, Hampshire, GU51 2UJ Tel: (0845) 4666070 Fax: (0845) 4666080 E-mail: info@automaster.ltd.uk *Computer dealers*

Automate UK, 9 Hill La Industrial Estate, Markfield, Leicestershire, LE67 9PN Tel: (01530) 249444 Fax: (01530) 249444 E-mail: sales@automateuk.co.uk *Automatic doors, glass & aluminium shop fronts manufrs*

Automated Access Ltd, Unit F 59 Sibson Road, Birstall, Leicester, LE4 4DX Tel: 0116-267 1122 Fax: 0116-267 1122 E-mail: enquiries@automated-access-solutions.co.uk *At Automated Access Solutions we specialise in the automation of sliding rooflights, awnings, active openings and other moving structures, whether supplied by us or already in situ. We offer a particular specialism in remedial automation work on problem rooflights. Please call us or visit our website for more information.*

▶ Automated Building Controls, Wellesley House, 7 Clarence Parade, Cheltenham, Gloucestershire, GL50 3NY Tel: (01242) 265781 Fax: (01242) 265781 E-mail: mail@abc.uk.net *Automated Building Controls Limited specialises in the Building Management Systems (BMS) industry, and control applications for the Heating Ventilation and Air Conditioning (HVAC) market.*

Automated Entry Systems Ltd, Automation House, 61 East Street, Warminster, Wiltshire, BA12 9BZ Tel: (01985) 215827 Fax: (01985) 219299 E-mail: aeswinchcombe@aol.com *Automatic entry systems*

Automated Garage Doors & Gates Ltd, Burnet Road, Sweet Briar Road Industrial Estate, Norwich, NR3 2BS Tel: (01603) 787069 Fax: (01603) 789209 *Garage doors & automated gate suppliers*

Automated Process & Control Manufacturing Co. Ltd, Unit 11 St. Georges Industrial Estate, Richmond Road, Kingston upon Thames, Surrey, KT2 5BQ Tel: (020) 8549 3331 Fax: (020) 8547 1309 E-mail: info@apcair.co.uk Principal Export Areas: Worldwide *Valves & actuators*

Automated Services (London) Ltd, 42B Oakwood Hill Industrial Estate, Oakwood Hill, Loughton, Essex, IG10 3TZ Tel: (020) 8502 3111 Fax: (020) 8508 0322 *Computer consumables*

Automated Systems, 1-3 Mossley Road, Grasscroft, Oldham, OL4 4HH Tel: (0870) 2402771 Fax: (0870) 2402773 E-mail: stevepage@automatedsystem.org *Air conditioning engineers*

Automatic Alarms Ltd, 5 Kenyon Business Park, Pilkington Street, Bolton, BL3 6HL Tel: (01204) 393883 Fax: (01204) 362059 E-mail: info@automaticgroup.co.uk *Alarm installations*

Automatic Cooling Engineers Ltd, 96 Milnbank Street, Glasgow, G31 3AL Tel: 0141-556 7691 Fax: 0141-554 2928 *Refrigeration consultants*

Automatic Devices Ltd, London Road, Pampisford, Cambridge, CB22 3EE Tel: (01223) 832485 Fax: (01223) 837758 E-mail: info@automaticdevices.co.uk *Precision sheet metalwork engineers*

Automatic Doors & Gates, 64 Standard Road, Hounslow, TW4 7AS Tel: (020) 8568 6781 *Door & gate installers*

Automatic Engineers (Hinckley) Ltd, Burbage Road, Burbage, Hinckley, Leicestershire, LE10 2TP Tel: (01455) 238033 Fax: (01455) 615101 E-mail: roger@automaticengineers.com *CNC engineering, tube manipulation & spark erosion machining & grinding services*

Automatic Forming, 7 Kinwarton Farm Road, Kinwarton, Alcester, Warwickshire, B49 6EH Tel: (01789) 400567 Fax: (01789) 765213 Principal Export Areas: Central/East Europe & West Europe *General engineers services*

▶ Automatic Gates & Garage Doors, De La Rocque, La Route De La Trinite, St. Helier, Jersey, JE2 4JN Tel: (01534) 877927 Fax: (01534) 871333

Automatic Gearboxes Leigh Ltd, Unit 3, Victoria Industrial Estate, Leigh, Lancashire, WN7 5SE Tel: (01942) 677800 Fax: (01942) 677800 *Automatic transmission specialists*

Automatic Industrial Machines Ltd, Units 9 & 10, Hither Green Industrial Estate, Clevedon, Avon, BS21 6XT Tel: (01275) 877695 Fax: (01275) 878463 E-mail: info@aim-ltd.net *Precision engineers*

▶ Automatic Man Ltd, 64 Davis Road, London, W3 7SG Tel: (020) 8740 1020 E-mail: automaticman.ltd@virgin.net *Automatic gearbox specialist*

Automatic Peeler Co., Premier House, 146 Field Lane, Burton-on-Trent, Staffordshire, DE13 0NN Tel: (01283) 565819 Fax: (01283) 565819 E-mail: sales@autopeel.com *Food processing equipment & machinery* Also at: Rugby

Automatic Protection Equipment & Crown Security Se, 73 Lower High Street, Bristol, BS11 0AW Tel: 0117-982 5045 Fax: 0117-982 6046 E-mail: info@apealarms.co.uk *Burglar alarms & security systems*

Automatic Protection Systems, 156 The Bluebells, Bradley Stoke, Bristol, BS32 8DW Tel: 0117-979 8330 Fax: 0117-979 8330 *Security installation*

Automatic Pump Ltd, 36 Lanehead Road, Etruria, Stoke-On-Trent, ST1 5PT Tel: (01782) 279504 Fax: (01782) 279005 E-mail: enquiries@elipse.co.uk *Manufacturers of condensate removal systems*

Automatic Response Telephone Systems Ltd, 153 Marine Drive, Saltdean, Brighton, BN2 8AA Tel: (01273) 304010 E-mail: director@1tripcamera.com *Interactive & automated telephone services*

▶ Automatic Retailing (Scotland LTD), Barrmill Road, Galston, Ayrshire, KA4 8HH Tel: (01563) 821900 Fax: (01563) 820329 E-mail: enquires@automaticretail.co.uk *Vending supplies & machines equipment*

Automatic Systems Equipment UK Ltd, Unit G4, Middlesex Business Centre, Bridge Road, Southall, Middlesex, UB2 4AB Tel: (020) 8744 7669 Fax: (020) 8744 7670 E-mail: sales@automaticsystems.co.uk *Manufacturers of barriers (mechanically/electronically operated), car park entry/exit control systems, turnstiles, security gates/barriers & ticketing gates*

Automatic Transmissions Ltd, 201 Fulwich Road, Dartford, DA1 1UW Tel: (01322) 222608 Fax: (01322) 222608 *Automatic transmission systems supply, fit & repair*

▶ Automatic Transmissions Ltd, Kebs Road, Todmorden, Lancashire, OL14 8SB Tel: (01706) 812291 E-mail: autotrans@uk2.net *Gearbox reconditioning autogas LPG conversions*

Automation Control & Technology Ltd, 149 Tavistock Road, Fleet, Hampshire, GU51 4EE Tel: (01252) 623316 Fax: (01252) 623316 E-mail: sales@automationcontrol.co.uk *Control systems specialists*

Automation Controls Ltd, Musgrave Park Industrial Estate, Stockmans Way, Belfast, BT9 7JU Tel: (028) 9068 1391 Fax: (028) 9066 3533 E-mail: tom@acl.presstel.co.uk *Control panel manufrs*

Automation Conveyors Ltd, Coopies Field, Coopies Lane Industrial Estate, Morpeth, Northumberland, NE61 6JT Tel: (01670) 514354 Fax: (01670) 514328 *Automatic handling equipment manufrs*

Automation Design & Installation Ltd, 1 Melchett Road, Kings Norton Business Centre, Birmingham, B30 3HG Tel: 0121-451 2255 Fax: 0121-459 1415 E-mail: info@adiltd.co.uk *Automation & instrumentation manufrs*

Automation Dynamics Ltd, PO Box 6842, Nottingham, NG9 3SS Tel: 0115-849 9878 E-mail: server@automation-dynamics.com *Adhesive applications/robot systems industrial*

Automation Experts Ltd, Appic Elliot Innovation Centre, Elliot Business Park, 4 Barling Way, Nuneaton, Warwickshire, CV10 7RH Tel: (024) 7679 6666 Fax: (024) 7679 6667 E-mail: info@automationexperts.co.uk *Recruitment*

▶ Automation Integration Limited, C/O 14 Rowfant Close, Worth, Crawley, West Sussex, RH10 7QT Tel: 01293 888586 Fax: 08706 220778 E-mail: info@ai-ltd.co.uk *Systems Integration utilising PLC, SCADA and PC control.*Specialist Siemens, Allen Bradley, Mitsubushi, Ge Fanuc, Wonderware, Intellution and Omron integration providing new and upgraded control solutions for all your automation needs.*

▶ Automation & Lift Co., 9 Marine Parade, Sheerness, Kent, ME12 2AL Tel: (01795) 585050 Fax: (01795) 585051 *Lift installation & manufrs*

Automation Partnership, York Way, Royston, Hertfordshire, SG8 5WY Tel: (01763) 227200 Fax: (01763) 227201 E-mail: sales@automationpartnership.com *Automation components/systems*

Automation Sales, Unit 14 Fowlswick Industrial Estate, Fowlswick Lane, Allington, Chippenham, Wiltshire, SN14 6QE Tel: (01249) 782453 Fax: (01249) 782881 *Ultrasonic transducers manufrs*

Automation & Security, Unit 11C, Victoria Road West Industrial Estate, Hebburn, Tyne & Wear, NE31 1UB Tel: 0191-428 0788 Fax: 0191-428 5127 *Gate security systems manufacture & install*

▶ Automation Security Electrical Ltd, Bridge House, Dock Lane, Shipley, West Yorkshire, BD18 1BU Tel: (01274) 585222 Fax: (01274) 585444

Automatique Hambrid Ltd, 68-70 Elizabeth Street, Blackpool, FY1 3JH Tel: (01253) 620134 *Supply fruit machines*

Automec Equipment & Parts Ltd, 36 Ballmoor, Buckingham, MK18 1RQ Tel: (01280) 822818 Fax: (01280) 823140 E-mail: info@automec.co.uk *Brake pipe & flaring tool manufrs*

Auto-Med Technologies Ltd, 127 North Gate, Nottingham, NG7 7FZ Tel: 0115-919 1234 Fax: 0115-919 1236 E-mail: sales@auto-med.com *Orthopedic sundries & surgical goods*

Automedia Ltd, Prince William Road, Loughborough, Leicestershire, LE11 5GU Tel: (01509) 263411 Fax: (01509) 610062 E-mail: info@automedia.ltd.uk *Printers & designers*

Automobile Association, Fanum House, Basing View, Basingstoke, Hampshire, RG21 4EA Tel: (0870) 5448866 Fax: (01256) 493389 *Recovery services*

▶ Automobile Trimmings Co., Stonebridge Works, Cumberland Road, Stanmore, Middlesex, HA7 1EL Tel: (020) 8204 8242 Fax: (020) 8204 0255 E-mail: sales@automobiletrim.com *Manufacturer of Automotive Door Seals, Edge Trims & Car Carpet. We also supply Leathercloth (upholstery vinyl),foams, Headlinings, rubber mattings and general interior trimmings for the restoration market.*

▶ Automotion (International) Ltd, Alexia House Dunley Hill Court, Ranmore, Dorking, Surrey, RH5 6SX Tel: (01483) 286674 Fax: (01483) 286675 E-mail: info@automotion.co.uk *Source for miniature power transmission & linear motion components*

Automotive Applied Technologies Ltd, PO Box 22, Accrington, Lancashire, BB5 0LA Tel: (01254) 357500 Fax: (01254) 357600 E-mail: info@automotive-tech.co.uk *Plastics injection moulders*

Automotive Cable Products Ltd, Copperworks Road, Llanelli, Dyfed, SA15 2NE Tel: (01554) 752207 Fax: (01554) 749600 E-mail: info@automotivecableproducts.co.uk *Cable controls manufacturers*

Automotive Design Centre, Northern Ireland Technology Centre, Cloreen Park, Malone Road, Belfast, BT9 5HN Tel: (028) 9033 5424 Fax: (028) 9097 4332 E-mail: a.mcbride@qub.ac.uk *Consulting engineers or designers*

▶ Automotive Development Consultants Limited, 3 Chaucer Close, Bridgetown Gardens, Stratford-upon-Avon, Warwickshire, CV37 7PQ Tel: 07974 713316 E-mail: mattbishton@hotmail.com

Automotive Distributors Ltd, Unit 9 Wheelbarrow Park Estate, Pattenden Lane, Marden, Tonbridge, Kent, TN12 9QJ Tel: (01622) 833007 Fax: (01622) 833001 E-mail: info@blueprint-adl.co.uk *Automotive component distributors*

The Automotive Friction Co. Ltd, Park Lane, Handsworth, Birmingham, B21 8LE Tel: 0121-553 1584 Fax: 0121-553 3275 *Assemble brake-pads*

Automotive Industrial Partnerships Ltd, 52 Heming Road, Redditch, Worcestershire, B98 0EA Tel: (01527) 504200 Fax: (01527) 516195 E-mail: sales@aip.demon.co.uk *Automotive component distributors*

▶ Automotive Parts Distribution Ltd, Unit 2, Ash, Kembrey Park, Swindon, SN2 8UN Tel: (01793) 433933 Fax: (01793) 614965 E-mail: swindon@apd.co.uk *Motor factor selling car & van parts & accessories, radios, tools*

Automotive Tanks Ltd, Bilston Lane, Willenhall, West Midlands, WV13 2LH Tel: (01902) 604207 Fax: (01902) 604265 E-mail: sales@automotivetanks.ltd.uk *Pressure vessels & electric harness manufrs*

Automotive Technology Ltd, 3 Morton Street, Leamington Spa, Warwickshire, CV32 5SY Tel: (01926) 882201 Fax: (01926) 420934 E-mail: sidaway@atl-uk.com *Automotive components services*

▶ Automotive Test Equipment, Unit 2 Feldspar Close, Enderby, Leicester, LE19 4SD Tel: 0116-286 5959 Fax: 0116-286 3444 E-mail: sales@automotivetestequipment.co.uk *Garage equipment & suppliers*

Automotive Tools & Supplies Ltd, Old Smithy, Hambledon View, Read, Burnley, Lancashire, BB12 7PD Tel: (01282) 771432 Fax: (01282) 774944 E-mail: sales@auto-tools.co.uk *Garage equipment manufrs*

Autonational Ltd, Troy Industrial Estate, Jill Lane, Sambourne, Redditch, Worcestershire, B96 6ES Tel: (01527) 892003 Fax: (01527) 893310 E-mail: autonational@aol.com *Motor component distributors*

Autonic Engineering Co. Ltd, Salisbury Road, Hoddesdon, Hertfordshire, EN11 0HU Tel: (01992) 471101 Fax: (01992) 471102 E-mail: sales@autonic.co.uk *Manufacturer of Precision Turned Parts and Self Clinching Fasteners for the sheet metal and PCB industries.*

Autonix, 64 Brackley Square, Woodford Green, Essex, IG8 7LL Tel: (020) 8498 9797 Fax: (020) 8491 6331 *Car alarms*

Autonnic Research Ltd, Woodrolfe Road, Tollesbury, Maldon, Essex, CM9 8SE Tel: (01621) 869460 Fax: (01621) 868815 E-mail: info@autonnic.co.uk *Sensor manufrs*

Autonomy Systems Ltd, Cambridge Business Park, Cowley Road, Cambridge, CB4 0WZ Tel: (01223) 448000 Fax: (01223) 448001 *Knowledge management & software development*

Autonumis Ltd, Cirencester Road, Tetbury, Gloucestershire, GL8 8SA Tel: (01666) 502641 Fax: (01666) 505100 E-mail: info@autonumis.co.uk *Autonumis designs, manufactures and markets a discreet range of vending equipment, back bar refrigerated display cabinets and soft drink dispensers. Our products are purchased by multinational brand owners throughout the world and are market leaders in quality, reliability and technical innovation.*

Autool Grinders Ltd, Padiham Road, Sabden, Clitheroe, Lancashire, BB7 9EW Tel: (01282) 775000 Fax: (01282) 773486 E-mail: sales@autool.co.uk Principal Export Areas: Worldwide *Grinding machinery services*

Autopaints (South Wales) Ltd, 233 Penarth Road, Cardiff, CF11 6HF Tel: (029) 2022 4038 Fax: (029) 2034 4448 E-mail: gibsonm@btconnect.com *Car paint suppliers*

Autoparts Ecosse Garage Equipment Services, 175 Castlebank Street, Glasgow, G11 6DP Tel: 0141-271 7400 Fax: 0141-334 0022 E-mail: garage.equipment@arnoldclark.co.uk *Garage equipment manufrs*

▶ Autopoint, Bramshall Industrial Estate, Bramshall, Uttoxeter, Staffordshire, ST14 8TD Tel: (01889) 566605 Fax: (01889) 566684

▶ Autoporters, 20 Arran Drive, Frodsham, WA6 6AL Tel: (01928) 732846 E-mail: chris.wynne@autoporters.co.uk *Car transportation service*

Autopower Car Alarms & Hi Fi Centre, 345 Vicarage Road, Kings Heath, Birmingham, B14 7NN Tel: 0121-441 1856 Fax: 0121-441 5551 E-mail: bobgihair@aol.com *Security company*

Autoquench Ltd, 132 Priory Road, Hall Green, Birmingham, B28 0TB Tel: 0121-693 6888 Fax: 0121-430 6007 E-mail: mail@autoquench.co.uk *Automatic fire suppression systems manufrs*

Autoquip Ltd, 2-4 Church Rd, Lawrence Hill, Bristol, BS5 9JA Tel: 0117-955 6789 Fax: 0117-954 1925 E-mail: autoquip@aol.com *Motor vehicle accessories*

Autoquip Factors Ltd, 2-3 Woodland Close, Torquay, TQ2 7BD Tel: (01803) 612260 Fax: (01803) 618119 *Car spar parts suppliers*

Autoreel Ltd, Palmer Drive, Stapleford, Nottingham, NG9 7BW Tel: 0115-939 0200 Fax: 0115-939 0201 E-mail: autoreel@autoreel.co.uk *Cable handling, rewinding, production measuring & cutting systems*

▶ Autorim Ltd, Unit 6 Botany Business Park, Macclesfield Road, Whaley Bridge, High Peak, Derbyshire, SK23 7DQ Tel: (01663) 735032 Fax: (01663) 733671 E-mail: anne@autorim.net

continued

Polyurethane foam dispensing machinery & equipment providers & manufrs

Autorise Ltd, Maspro House, Chadwick Road, Astmoor Industrial Estate, Runcorn, Cheshire, WA7 1PW Tel: (01928) 561552 Fax: (01928) 591531 *Importers & exporters*

Autorite Ltd, 60-61 Leslie Park Road, Croydon, CR0 6TP Tel: (020) 8654 8977 Fax: (020) 8656 8277 *Car repair specialists & servicing*

▶ Autoroll U K, Wilden Road, Pattinson Industrial Estate, Washington, Tyne & Wear, NE38 8QB Tel: 0191-415 5888 Fax: 0191-419 4800 *Roller garage doors manufacturers & installers*

▶ autosava.com, Dundry Lane, Dundry, Bristol, BS41 8JQ Tel: (020) 7193 0085 Fax: (0845) 280 4950 E-mail: sales@autosava.com *Our objective is simple; to supply automotive service parts directly to the consumer at the best price. We cater for almost all British, European, Japanese and American cars and light commercial vehicles. Even if your part isn"t listed online we will try our best to track it down for you.**Autosava only supplies quality new and reconditioned parts from well known, reputable manufacturers. Our parts are OEM spec, guaranteeing performance, functionality and fit.**Autosava exists on line to keep our prices as low as possible. It doesn"t matter if you are in the motor trade or not, the autosava price is always going to be the best price.**From our Bristol HQ we ship to the UK and overseas, sub 48 hour despatch to our UK customers is our goal, using only quality carriers to ensure delivery direct to your door with the minimum of fuss*

Autoscales & Service Co. Ltd, Truweigh House, Ordnance Street, Blackburn, BB1 3AE Tel: (01254) 676938 Fax: (01254) 682374 E-mail: info@autoscales.co.uk *Weighing machine manufrs*

Autoscan Ltd, 61 High Road, Beeston, Nottingham, NG9 4AJ Tel: 0115-922 4249 Fax: 0115-922 9142 E-mail: info@autoscanuk.co.uk *Storage systems/solutions for both industrial & office environments, vertical carousels & lifts, rotary filing units, service & maintenance*

Autoscript Ltd, Unit 8a Poplar Business Park, Prestons Road, London, E14 9RL Tel: (020) 7538 1427 Fax: (020) 7515 9529 E-mail: sales@autoscript.tv *Prompting equipment manufrs*

Autoscroll Engineering, 5 Morley Street, Daybrook, Nottingham, NG5 6JX Tel: 0115-967 0327 *Metal fabricators*

Autosigns Ltd, North Mills, Frog Island, Leicester, LE3 5DH Tel: 0116-262 9526 Fax: 0116-251 2889 E-mail: enquiries@autosigns.co.uk *Display manufrs* Also at: Huddersfield

Autosmart, Huncote Road, Stoney Stanton, Leicester, LE9 4DJ Tel: (01455) 271166 Fax: (01455) 271166 *Chemical distributors*

Autosmart, 18 Holmfield, Holm Lane, Prenton, Merseyside, CH43 2NZ Tel: 0151-653 4588 Fax: 0151-512 0147 *Cleaning products distributors motor trade*

▶ Autosmart International, 3 Kidwelly Industrial Estate, Pembrey Road, Kidwelly, Dyfed, SA17 4TF Tel: (01554) 890212 Fax: (01554) 890212 *Vehicle cleaners*

Autosmart International Ltd, Lynn Lane, Shenstone, Lichfield, Staffordshire, WS14 0DH Tel: (01543) 481616 Fax: (01543) 481549 E-mail: info@autosmart.co.uk *Vehicle cleaning chemical manufrs*

▶ Autosort, Pier Garage, Fairlie, Ayrshire, KA29 0AU Tel: (01475) 560088 E-mail: webmaster@autosort.co.uk *A garage handling mechanical and body repairs to cars and motorbikes. 24 hour breakdown recovery, MOTs, welding, tuning and motorsport preparation.*

▶ Autosounds, Sungold House, Scotts Wood Road, Newcastle Upon Tyne, NE4 7AP Tel: 0191-273 6100 Fax: 0191-272 3383 E-mail: sales@autosounds.co.uk *Suppliers of audio systems*

Autospark UK Ltd, 284b Water Road, Wembley, Middlesex, HA0 1HX Tel: (020) 8998 9642 Fax: (020) 8810 9349 *Ignition leads & mirrors manufrs*

Autospin, Castle Trading Estate, Fareham, Hampshire, PO16 9SE Tel: (023) 9237 7737 Fax: (023) 9221 9544 E-mail: mariacrawley180@hotmail.com Sales Contact: B. Crawley *Manufacturers of metal spinners/spinnings. In addition lighting fittings/equipment, architectural & sheet metalwork engineers or fabricators & metal smallware manufrs*

Autospin (Oil Seals) Ltd, Birkdale Avenue, Selly Oak, Birmingham, B29 6UB Tel: 0121-472 1243 Fax: 0121-471 3348 E-mail: sales@autospin.co.uk *Rotary shaft fluid seal*

Autosplice Brittanic Ltd, Unit 1/6, Crompton Road, Ilkeston, Derbyshire, DE7 4BG Tel: 0115-944 0258 Fax: 0115-944 0587 E-mail: sales@bpte.com *Plastic mouldings insert moulders*

Autoswitch Electronics Ltd, 46 Lammas Way, Letchworth Garden City, Hertfordshire, SG6 4LW Tel: (01462) 677778 Fax: (01462) 480449 *Electronic, people & hour counters manufrs*

Autotape Systems Ltd, Quakers Coppice, Crewe, CW1 6FA Tel: (01270) 254737 *Packaging machinery manufrs*

▶ Autotech Controls Ltd, Unit K, President Way, Luton, LU2 9NL Tel: (01582) 400690 Fax: (01582) 400392

Autotech UK Ltd, Unit 1, Dyehouse Lane, Glastonbury, Somerset, BA6 9LZ Tel: (01458) 835551 Fax: (01458) 835903 E-mail: colin.autotechukltd@btinternet.com *Tube forming equipment manufrs*

▶ Autotint Ltd, 498 Reading Road, Winnersh, Wokingham, Berkshire, RG41 5EX Tel: (0870) 2402480 Fax: 0118-946 2114 E-mail: autotint@durable.co.uk *Apply window films*

Autotop Signs & Nameplates, Council Street West, Llandudno, Gwynedd, LL30 1ED Tel: (01492) 860667 Fax: (01492) 878050 *Sign writers*

Autotrack (Birmingham) Ltd, Ball Unit House Station Road Industrial Estate, Station Road, Woodchester, Stroud, Gloucestershire, GL5 5EQ Tel: (01453) 873155 Fax: (01453) 878500 E-mail: info@autotrack.co.uk Principal Export Areas: Worldwide *Manufacturers of ball transfer units*

Autotrans Gearbox Centre, Unit 2 Broadhempston, Totnes, Devon, TQ9 6AT Tel: (01803) 762233 Fax: (01803) 762233 *Gearbox reconditioning services*

▶ Autotron Computer Systems, 35 Hazelwood Avenue, New Milton, Hampshire, BH25 5LX Tel: (01425) 612470 Fax: (07092) 308410 *Computer maintenance services*

▶ Autoview UK Ltd, Business & Innovation Centre, Wearfield, Sunderland Enterprise Park (East), Sunderland, SR5 2TA Tel: 0191 5166444 Fax: 0191 5166445 E-mail: info@autoviewsystems.co.uk *Motor trade systems suppliers*

Autoweigh Scales UK Ltd, James Street, Elland, West Yorkshire, HX5 0HB Tel: (01422) 376965 Fax: (01422) 378109 E-mail: autoweigh.sales@virgin.net *Industrial scales sale, service & hire*

Autoy Ltd, 152 Castleton Road, Deepdale, Preston, PR1 6QH Tel: (01772) 556115 Fax: (01772) 204937 E-mail: autoy@btconnect.com *Repetition & precision engineers*

▶ Autrans (Europe) Ltd, Cherry Blossom Way, Sunderland, SR5 3QZ Tel: 0191-416 1133 E-mail: info@autrans.co.uk

Autronica Industrial Ltd, 11 Dudley Bank, Edinburgh, EH6 4HH Tel: 0131-555 1013 Fax: 0131-467 0712 *Fire alarm systems manufrs*

Autumn Engineering Co. Ltd, 58 Bath Street, Gravesend, Kent, DA11 0DF Tel: (01474) 560446 Fax: (01474) 535510 *Mechanical engineering contractors*

▶ Auty Precision Engineering, 5-7 Colndale Road, Colnbrook, Slough, SL3 0HQ Tel: (01753) 770012 Fax: (01753) 770014 *Precision engineering services*

Auwell Electronics Ltd, Units 16-19, Oldends Industrial Estate, Oldends, Stonehouse, Gloucestershire, GL10 3RQ Tel: (01453) 791111 Fax: (01453) 791313 E-mail: enquiries@auwell.co.uk *Circuit boards manufrs*

▶ Auxilior Ltd, 6 Steventon Road, Southampton, SO18 5HA Tel: (023) 8047 3441 E-mail: kevin.haynes@auxilior.co.uk *Web design & information systems consultants*

▶ Auxill UK Ltd, 4 Stockmers End, Capel St. Mary, Ipswich, IP9 2HQ Tel: (01473) 310659 Fax: (01473) 311740 E-mail: drewery@lineone.net *Filters,filtration & seperation techniques*

Av Niche Recording Systems, 5 Heron Court, Cranes Farm Road, Basildon, Essex, SS14 3DF Tel: (01268) 474608 Fax: (01268) 531482 E-mail: avniche@btconnect.com *Video recording equipment suppliers*

▶ Av Shed, 6 West Haddon Road, Guilsborough, Northampton, NN6 8QL Tel: (0870) 2242246 Fax: (0871) 7333866 E-mail: sales@avshed.com *Audio visual equipment & accessory repairers*

Av Surgery Supplies, 29 Cross Road, Croydon, CR0 6TE Tel: (020) 8760 9992 *Doctor & dentist suppliers*

Av2hire.com (Manchester) Ltd, 22 Hardwick Street, Buxton, Derbyshire, SK17 6DH Tel: (0845) 0705168 E-mail: manchester@av2hire.com *Projector hire*

Av4business Ltd, PO Box 123, Batley, West Yorkshire, WF17 6ZZ Tel: (0870) 2412364 Fax: (0870) 2412232 E-mail: sales@av4business.com *Audio visual equipment distributors*

Ava Knit GB Ltd, Dodwells Bridge Industrial Estate, Jacknell Road, Hinckley, Leicestershire, LE10 3BS Tel: (01455) 636419 Fax: (01455) 619989 *Knitted fabric manufrs*

Ava Matic U K Ltd, 24 Padgets Lane, Redditch, Worcestershire, B98 0RB Tel: (01527) 518520 Fax: (01527) 518526 E-mail: info@avamatic.co.uk *Metal tube end forming machine suppliers*

Avac, 38 Comiston Road, Edinburgh, EH10 5QQ Tel: 0131-452 8455 Fax: 0131-664 9085 E-mail: avac@netscapeonline.co.uk *Office cleaning/janitorial supplies*

Avalon and Lynwood, PO Box 608, Altrincham, Cheshire, WA15 7ZP Tel: 0161-904 8642 E-mail: sales@avalonandlynwood.com *Avalon & Lynwood (highvisibilityclothing.net)a work wear company putting health & safety first. All our safety products meet required British & EU standards. Specialists in high visibility clothing, high visibility jackets, high visibility vests high visibility trousers, florescent waistcoats for children supplying schools & organisations nationwide. Products include safety wear, safety boots, safety gloves, corporate work wear, uniforms, protective clothing, sweat shirts, polo shirts, reflective work wear, waterproof work wear, coats, shirts, trousers, drivers jackets, industrial work wear, t shirts, body warmers, combat trousers, hi viz jackets, high viz vests, Denny's chefs whites, chefs trousers, chefs caps. Distributing for "B Seen" Yoko International & Supertouch stocking faridge,fruit of the loom & gildan. WE OFFER A PRINTING & EMBROIDERING SERVICE ADD YOUR COMPANY NAME, LOGO, OR PROMOTIONAL MESSAGE TO YOUR GARMENTS TAKE ADVANTAGE OF OUR SPEEDY ORDER & DELIVERY SERVICE.*

▶ Avalon Blinds, 13 Porlock Grove, Stoke-On-Trent, ST4 8TN Tel: (01782) 657878 Fax: (01782) 657878 *Blinds suppliers & fitters*

Avalon Electronics Ltd, Langhorne Park House, High Street, Shepton Mallet, Somerset, BA4 5AQ Tel: (01749) 345266 Fax: (01749) 345267 E-mail: info@avalon-electronics.com *Designers & manufacturers of advanced tape & disk-based data recorders*

Avalon Plastics Ltd, Imco Works, Beckery New Road, Glastonbury, Somerset, BA6 9NR Tel: (01458) 831563 Fax: (01458) 834384 E-mail: enquiries@avalonplastics.co.uk *Plastic injection mouldings manufrs*

Avalon Sciences, Unit 6-7 Wessex Buildings, Bancombe Road, Somerton, Somerset, TA11 6SB Tel: (01458) 270000 Fax: (01458) 270088 E-mail: sales@avalonsciences.com *Oil exploration electronic equipment manufrs*

A-Valvetech Services Ltd, 4 The Courtyard, D'Arcy Business Park, Llandarcy, Neath, West Glamorgan, SA10 6EJ Tel: (01792) 817708 Fax: (01792) 815298 E-mail: valtec3@hotmail.com *Valve reconditioning & testing services*

Avana Bakeries Ltd, Wern Trading Estate, Rogerstone, Newport, Gwent, NP10 9YB Tel: (01633) 466400 Fax: (01633) 466466 E-mail: avanareception@rhm.com *Bakers wholesale manufrs*

▶ Avanco Engineering Ltd, 1 Manor Court, Grimsby, South Humberside, DN32 0SD Tel: (01472) 344923 E-mail: info@avancoengineering.com

▶ Avandale Maintenance, 6 Roebuck Close, Hertford, SG13 7TE Tel: (01992) 581899 E-mail: alandunnage@ntlworld.com *carpentry services to the commercial and private sector*kitchens bedrooms decking etc*

▶ Avansys UK Ltd, Business & Technology Centre, Radway Green, Crewe, CW2 5PR Tel: (01270) 878555 Fax: (0870) 2010600 *Resellers of computer parts*

▶ Avant Garde, 28 Tadmarton, Downhead Park, Milton Keynes, MK15 9BD Tel: (01908) 675977 Fax: (01908) 675890 E-mail: page@ag-gifts.co.uk *Corporate gifts & promotional items specialists*

Avant Hotel, Windsor Road, Oldham, OL8 4AS Tel: 0161-627 5500 Fax: 0161-627 5896 E-mail: avant@menzies-hotels.co.uk *Hotel & conference facilities*

Avante Digital Ltd, Kirkton Business Centre, 1 Kirk Lane, Livingston Village, Livingston, West Lothian, EH54 7AY Tel: (01506) 419777 Fax: (01506) 415777 E-mail: post@av-digital.com *Computer storage system integrators*

Avantgarde Security Systems, 190 Frant Road, Thornton Heath, Surrey, CR7 7JW Tel: (020) 8239 6989 Fax: (020) 8251 8311 E-mail: avantgardesecurity@blueyonder.co.uk *Door entry, cctv & security alarms systems suppliers*

Avanti Conveyors, Calico Lane, Furness Vale, High Peak, Derbyshire, SK23 7SW Tel: (01663) 740011 Fax: (01663) 745097 E-mail: sales@avanti-conveyors.co.uk *Materials handling for corrugated board industry*

▶ Avanti Elektronik Ltd, 37 Forest Avenue, Aberdeen, AB15 4TU Tel: (01224) 319849

▶ Avanti Fitted Kitchens Ltd, Avanti House, Hayes Lane, Stourbridge, West Midlands, DY9 8RD Tel: (01384) 893929 Fax: (01384) 896734 E-mail: avanti@callnetuk.com *Kitchen & bedroom manufrs*

▶ AVArcher, Arndean, 4 Maggiewoods Loan, Falkirk, FK1 5SJ Tel: (01324) 621216

Avatar, 5 Elizabeth Close, Attleborough, Norfolk, NR17 1QJ Tel: 07747 610805 E-mail: info@avatargraphics.co.uk *Graphic designers*

Avatar Systems, Davis House, 36 Market Place, Brackley, Northamptonshire, NN13 7DP Tel: (01280) 700711 Fax: (01280) 700711 E-mail: avatar.systems@virgin.net *Computer consultants*

Avatea Ltd, Bulldog House, 267-269 Reading Road, Winnersh, Wokingham, Berkshire, RG41 5AB Tel: 0118-977 0270 Fax: 0118-977 0278 E-mail: peter@avatea.co.uk *Computer distributors & manufrs*

Avaya UK Ltd, Avaya House, Cathedral Hill, Guildford, Surrey, GU2 7YL Tel: (01483) 308000 Fax: (01483) 308001 E-mail: sales@avaya.co.uk *Telephone exchange services*

▶ Avc (Classic Woodworkers) Ltd, Newfield Works, High Street, Sandyford, Stoke-on-trent, ST6 5PQ Tel: 01782 832555 Fax: 01782 832666 E-mail: sales@avcwood.com *Staircase Manufacturers*

Avc Europe Ltd, Bessemer Drive, Stevenage, Hertfordshire, SG1 2DT Tel: (01438) 341300 Fax: (01438) 341301 E-mail: info@avcgroup.co.uk *Tele communication equipment distributors*

▶ Avc Productions Ltd, 106 Kings Road, Brighton, BN1 2FU Tel: (01273) 746555 Fax: (01273) 746447 E-mail: sales@avcworld.com *Complete conference production service and audio/visual hire.*

Avdon Bristol Ltd, Ashton Vale Road, Bristol, BS3 2HT Tel: 0117-953 3300 Fax: 0117-966 4948 E-mail: sales@avdon.co.uk *Aluminium window & door specialists*

▶ Avea Organic, Mopla House, Pwllmeyric, Chepstow, Gwent, NP16 6LA Tel: (0870) 1999220 Fax: (0709) 2021615 E-mail: sales@avea.co.uk *Distributor of organic cosmetics & skin care products*

▶ Aveat Heating Ltd, Lambert House, 7 Driberg Way, Braintree, Essex, CM7 1NB Tel: (01376) 325670 Fax: (01376) 551210 E-mail: aveat@btconnect.com *Heating engineers services*

Avebe U K Ltd, Thornton Hall, Thornton Curtis, Ulceby, South Humberside, DN39 6XD Tel: (01469) 532222 Fax: (01469) 531488 *Potato, wheat & waxy starches*

▶ Avecia, Earls Road, Grangemouth, Stirlingshire, FK3 8XG Tel: (01324) 498300 Fax: (01324) 498350 E-mail: admin@avecia.com

Aveco Teesside Ltd, The Slipways, Dockside Road, Middlesbrough, Cleveland, TS3 8AT Tel: (01642) 224994 Fax: (01642) 248138 E-mail: aveco.teeside@ntl.com *Marine engineers & shipbuilders*

Avena Carpets Ltd, Bankfield Mills, Haley Hill, Halifax, West Yorkshire, HX3 6ED Tel: (01422) 330261 Fax: (01422) 348399 E-mail: avena@btconnect.com *Wilton carpet weavers & manufrs*

Avenga Computer Services, 34 Morse Road, Whitnash, Leamington Spa, Warwickshire, CV31 2LH Tel: (01926) 882639 Fax: (01926) 882639 E-mail: nigel@avenga.co.uk *Computer repair & maintenance*

Avent Ltd, Avon Works, Station Street, Walton On The Naze, Essex, CO14 8DA Tel: (01255) 672244 Fax: (01255) 852030 E-mail: Info@aventsltd.co.uk *Furniture manufrs*

▶ Aventis Audio Visual, 7 Rockfort Industrial Estate, Hithercroft Road, Wallingford, Oxfordshire, OX10 9DA Tel: (01491) 836244 Fax: (01491) 838568 E-mail: info@aventisav.com *Audio visual services*

Aventis Behring Ltd, Centeon House, Market Place, Haywards Heath, West Sussex, RH16 1DB Tel: (01444) 447400 Fax: (01444) 447401 *Pharmaceutical products manufrs*

▶ Aventus Design, 7 Leaches Farm Business Centre, Bicester Road, Kingswood, Aylesbury, Buckinghamshire, HP18 0RR Tel: (01296) 770066 Fax: (08707) 066007 E-mail: mail@aventusdesign.co.uk *Consulting Civil and Structural Engineers*

▶ Avenue Audio, Millbrook Road East, Southampton, SO15 1HS Tel: 07789 695567 E-mail: Info@avenueaudio.co.uk *APA hire company, providing sound systems & technicians*

Avenue Coatings, 3 David Road, Colnbrook, Slough, SL3 0TW Tel: (01753) 686888 Fax: (01753) 684684 E-mail: paint@avenue-group.co.uk *Specialist paint manufrs* Also at: London N2 & Wokingham

Avenue Office Supplies, 3 David Road, Colnbrook, Slough, SL3 0TW Tel: (01753) 687687 Fax: (01753) 681681 E-mail: admin@avenue-group.co.uk *Avenue office Supplies supplies in excess of 16,000 items that include stationery , office consumables, office equipment, printers, computers,cartridges, furniture, etc.*

▶ Avenue Pattern Co. Ltd, 10 Scar Bank, Warwick, CV34 5DB Tel: (01926) 498117 Fax: (01926) 497117

▶ Avenue Supplies, 15 The Avenue, London, W13 8JR Tel: (020) 8997 5071 E-mail: sales@avenuesupplies.co.uk *DIY retail & trade services*

Avenue Tools Ltd, 3 David Road, Colnbrook, Slough, SL3 0TW Tel: (01753) 685921 Fax: (01753) 685922 E-mail: avenue@avenue-group.co.uk *Engineers & tool distributors* Also at: Wokingham

Avery Dennison, Unit 7, Astra Centre, Edinburgh Way, Harlow, Essex, CM20 2BN Tel: (01279) 786000 Fax: (01279) 786100 E-mail: Principal Export Areas: Africa *Barcode printing solutions & handheld price market solutions specialists*

Avery Dennison Material (UK) Ltd, Unit 5/6, Gardner Road, Maidenhead, Berkshire, SL6 7PP Tel: (01628) 764095 Fax: (01628) 623713 *Self adhesive papers & vinyls*

Avery Dennison UK Ltd, Business Media Division Thomas Road, Wooburn Industrial Park, Wooburn Green, High Wycombe, Buckinghamshire, HP10 0PE Tel: (01628) 859500 Fax: (01628) 859599 E-mail: sales@averydennison.com Principal Export Areas: Worldwide *Plastic fasteners for textile & apparel*

Avery Dennison UK Ltd, P O Box 16, Oldbury, West Midlands, B69 4LU Tel: 0121-511 2500 Fax: 0121-511 2525 *Office accessory manufrs*

Avery Electronic Services, Unit 4 Wren Industrial Estate, Coldred Road, Parkwood, Maidstone, Kent, ME15 9XN Tel: (01622) 682138 Fax: (01622) 691232 *Audio/visual repair services*

▶ Avery Hardoll, Holland Way, Blandford Forum, Dorset, DT11 7BJ Tel: (01258) 486600 Fax: (01258) 486601 E-mail: sales@meggittfuelling.com Principal Export Areas: Worldwide *Manufacturers of aircraft test equipment, filter*

Avery Knight & Bowlers Engineering Ltd, 33-35 James St West, Bath, BA1 2BT Tel: (01225) 425894 Fax: (01225) 445753 E-mail: sales@averyknight.co.uk *Masonry tool merchants*

Avery Truman DIY & Garden Centre, 13 The Arcade, Eltham High Street, London, SE9 1BE Tel: (020) 8850 9621 Fax: (020) 8850 9621 *DIY & gardening, builders & hardware merchants*

▶ Avery Weigh Tronix Ltd, 13-14 Monckton Road Industrial Estate, Wakefield, West Yorkshire, WF2 7BP Tel: (0870) 9050041 Fax: (0870) 9050042 E-mail: hiredivisionuk@awtxglobal.com *HIRE OF FULL RANGE OF WEIGHING EQUIPMENT FROM BALANCES TO WEIGHBRIDGES*

Avery Weigh-Tronix, Unit D4, Capital Point, Capital Business Park, Wentloog, Cardiff, CF3 2PY Tel: (029) 2083 9510 Fax: (0870) 9018166 *Hire of scales & weighing equipment*

Avery Weigh-Tronix Ltd, Unit 8 Fieldhouse Way, Sheffield, S4 7SF Tel: (0870) 4420000 Fax: 0114-243 2235 E-mail: info@awtxglobal.com *Industrial weighing scale manufrs*

Avery Weigh-Tronix, Foundry Lane, Smethwick, West Midlands, B66 2LP Tel: (01624) 675770 Fax: (0870) 9000366 E-mail: info@awtxglobal.com Sales Contact: T. Fizackerley *Makers of Industrial Scales*

Avery's Garage & Transport Services Ltd, Grovebury Road, Leighton Buzzard, Bedfordshire, LU7 4SQ Tel: (01525) 373385 Fax: (01525) 371900 *Road transport*

Aveva Engineering It Ltd, High Cross, Madingley Road, Cambridge, CB3 0HB Tel: (01223) 556655 Fax: (01223) 556666 E-mail: info@aveva.com *Computer aided design software manufrs*

Avia Signs & Labels, Shore Head, Stonehaven, Kincardineshire, AB39 2JY Tel: (01569) 767290 Fax: (01569) 767290 E-mail: david@aviasigns.freeserve.co.uk *Sign makers, acid etching, metalphoto aluminium labels & nameplates*

Avia Technique Ltd, 1 Fishponds Estate, Fishponds Road, Wokingham, Berkshire, RG41 2QJ Tel: 0118-978 9789 Fax: 0118-979 4511 E-mail: sales@intertechnique.co.uk *Repair & overhaul of aircraft fuel pumps & fuel motoring equipment*

Aviall Product Services Ltd, Unit 10 Polygon Business Centre, Blackthorne Road, Colnbrook, Slough, SL3 0QT Tel: (01753) 689090 Fax: (01753) 680755 *Aircraft batteries sales & service*

▶ Aviation Book Centre Ltd, Unit K, Basin Bridge Farm, Basin Bridge Lane, Stoke Golding, Nuneaton, Warwickshire, CV13 6JJ Tel: (01827) 722115 E-mail: sales@aviationbookcentre.com *Specialist aviation & military book titles from around the world*

Aviation Enterprises Ltd, Membury Airfield, Lambourn, Hungerford, Berkshire, RG17 7TJ Tel: (01488) 72224 Fax: (01488) 72224 E-mail: sales@aviationenterprises.co.uk *Glass fibre moulding manufrs*

Aviation Jersey Ltd, Beaumont, St. Peter, Jersey, JE3 7BR Tel: (01534) 725301 Fax: (01534) 759449 E-mail: sales@aviationjersey.com *Aeronautical engineers*

Aviation Metals Ltd, Michigan Drive, Tongwell, Milton Keynes, MK15 8JE Tel: (01908) 210012 Fax: (01908) 210066 E-mail: sales@aviationmetals.co.uk Principal Export Areas: Worldwide *Aerospace metal stockholders*

Aviation Salvage International Ltd, Unit 2 Valley Court, Basingstoke Road, Beech, Alton, Hampshire, GU34 4BH Tel: (01420) 84183 Fax: (01420) 544266 E-mail: info@airsalvage.co.uk *Aircraft decommission services*

Aviation Spares Ltd, 2 Haviland Road, Ferndown Industrial Estate, Wimborne, Dorset, BH21 7RF Tel: (01202) 875336 Fax: (01202) 894290 E-mail: sales@aviation-spares.co.uk *Aircraft component distributors*

Aviation Tool Corporation P.L.C, Airport Works, Green Lane, Hounslow, TW4 6DE Tel: (020) 8570 9664 Fax: (020) 8570 9660 E-mail: atctools@aol.com *Aircraft precision engineers*

▶ Aviation Warranty Solutions Limited, 3 Fountains Road, Luton, LU3 1LX Tel: 01582 418331 Fax: 01582 458325 E-mail: info@aviationwarranty.com *AWS is engaged in business offering services in relation to the processing and administration of aircraft warranty claims including Boeing and Airbus fleets and has considerable skill, knowledge and experience in that field*

Avid Ltd, Holroyd Suite, Oak Hall, Sheffield Park, Uckfield, East Sussex, TN22 3QY Tel: (01825) 791069 Fax: (01825) 791006 *Animal microchip manufrs*

Avid Tools, 126a Lame Road, Sands, High Wycombe, Buckinghamshire, HP12 4HN Tel: (01494) 465315 Fax: (01494) 465312 *Precision engineers manufrs*

Aviemore Highlands Resort, Aviemore Centre, Aviemore, Inverness-Shire, PH22 1PN Tel: (01479) 815100 Fax: (01479) 811478 E-mail: info@aviemorehighlandsresort.com *Hotel*

Aviform Ltd, Unit 4, G-K Wellesley Road, Tharston Industrial Estate, Long Stratton, Norwich, NR15 2PD Tel: (01508) 530500 Fax: (01508) 530873 E-mail: sales@aviform.co.uk *Animal health product manufrs*

Avilion, Gateway X111 Industrial Estate, Ferry Lane, Rainham, Essex, RM13 9YH Tel: (01708) 526361 Fax: (01708) 550220 E-mail: sales@avilion.co.uk Principal Export Areas: Worldwide *Kitchen & bathroom brassware designers & manufacturers*

Avington Systems Ltd, PO Box 82, Winchester, Hampshire, SO21 1WA Tel: (01962) 779894 E-mail: info@avington.com *Software manufrs*

Avintair Ltd, 150 Regent St, London, W1B 5SJ Tel: (020) 7439 4767 Fax: (020) 7439 4067 *Aviation consultants*

Avionics Mobile Services Ltd, 6 Park Industrial Estate, Frogmore, St. Albans, Hertfordshire, AL2 2DR Tel: (01727) 872605 Fax: (01727) 872605 E-mail: sales@avionics-mobile.co.uk *Sales, installation & repair of aircraft electronic equipment & systems*

▶ Avis Packaging Ltd, Grafton Works, Grafton Road, New Malden, Surrey, KT3 3AD Tel: (020) 8942 0415 E-mail: sales@avispack.co.uk *Cardboard boxes, cases & containers*

Avis Software Consultants, 22 Balmoral Way, Sutton, Surrey, SM2 6PD Tel: (020) 8643 6899 Fax: (020) 8642 6005 E-mail: info@avissoft.co.uk *Software developers*

Avisoft Ltd, 11 Church Street, Kirkby In Ashfield, Nottingham, NG17 8LA Tel: (01623) 755555 E-mail: sales@avisoft.co.uk *Computer software developers*

H.M. Avison & Co. Ltd, 305 Feltham Hill Road, Ashford, Middlesex, TW15 1LT Tel: (01784) 253130 Fax: (01784) 253130 *Hot foil stamping brasses & chemical etching services*

Aviza Technology Ltd, Coed Rhedyn, Ringland Way, Newport, Gwent, NP18 2TA Tel: (01633) 414000 Fax: (01633) 414141 E-mail: sales@trikon.com *Semi-conductor production machinery*

Avm, 6 Hawley Lane Industrial Estate, Hawley Lane, Farnborough, Hampshire, GU14 8EH Tel: (01252) 510363 Fax: (01252) 519874 E-mail: sales@avmltd.co.uk *Audio visual distributors*

Avnet Memec Ltd, 64-65 Rabans Close, Aylesbury, Buckinghamshire, HP19 8TW Tel: (01296) 330061 Fax: (01296) 330065 E-mail: sales@insightuk.memec.com *Semiconductor component distributors or agents*

Avnet Time, Avnet House, Rutherford Close, Stevenage, Hertfordshire, SG1 2EF Tel: (01438) 789789 E-mail: timeuk@avnet.com *Electronic component distributors*

▶ Avo UK Ltd, Caswell Road, Brackmills Industrial Estate, Northampton, NN4 7PW Tel: (01604) 708101 Fax: (01604) 761030 E-mail: sales@avouk.com

Avocet Cleaning Services, 210 Queen Ediths Way, Cambridge, CB1 8NL Tel: (01223) 244038 Fax: (01223) 244038 *Cleaning contractors*

▶ Avocet Electrical Contractors Ltd, Units 2-2a, St. Johns Lane, Bewdley, Worcestershire, DY12 2QY Tel: (01299) 401501 Fax: (01299) 402828 *Established electrical contractors*

Company Information

Avocet Hardware Taiwan Ltd, Brookfoot Mills, Elland Road, Brighouse, West Yorkshire, HD6 2RW Tel: (01484) 711700 Fax: (01484) 720124 E-mail: post@avocet-hardware.co.uk *Manufacture & distribution of window & door security products, ironmongery for large & small retail companies & electronic security systems*

Avoidatrench Ltd, Brooks Lane, Middlewich, Cheshire, CW10 0JQ Tel: (01606) 831600 Fax: (01606) 831620 E-mail: admin@avoidatrench.co.uk *Horizontal drilling services*

Avolites Ltd, Park Avenue, London, NW10 7XL Tel: (020) 8965 8522 Fax: (020) 8965 0290 E-mail: sales@avolites.com *Stage lighting control equipment*

Avon, Unit 22 Wansdyke Workshops, Unity Road, Keynsham, Bristol, BS31 1NH Tel: 0117-986 6001 Fax: 0117-986 6001 E-mail: sales@avonplantrepairs.co.uk *Plant & machinery repairers*

Avon, 28 Charlton Road, Kingswood, Bristol, BS15 1HB Tel: 0117-935 2061 Fax: 0117-947 7533 *Metal fabricators*

Avon, 154 Cannon Hill Road, Coventry, CV4 7BX Tel: 0800 0430154 E-mail: claire630@btopenworld.com *Avon reps and sales leaders required in all areas. Hours to suit and good rates of commission*

Avon Armour Holdings Ltd, Unit 12, 1-2 Portview Road, Bristol, BS11 9LD Tel: 0117-982 6288 Fax: 0117-982 8322 E-mail: sales@avonarmour.co.uk *Manufacturers of security screens & counters*

Avon Automotive, Bumbers Farm Industrial Estate, Bumpers Way, Chippenham, Wiltshire, SN14 6NF Tel: (01249) 667000 Fax: (01249) 667001 E-mail: enquiries@avonauto.com *Motor vehicle component manufrs*

Avon Autopoint, Charles Martin Business Park, Arrow Road North, Redditch, Worcestershire, B98 8NT Tel: (01527) 68109 Fax: (01527) 61264 E-mail: avonautopoint@tiscali.co.uk *Motor vehicle repair & restoration*

Avon Boating, Swans Nest Boathouse, Swans Nest Lane, Stratford-upon-Avon, Warwickshire, CV37 7LS Tel: (01789) 267073 Fax: (01789) 267073 E-mail: boat-hire@avon-boating.co.uk *Boat hire services*

▶ Avon Bridge Conservatories, 8 Bidavon Industrial Estate, Waterloo Road, Bidford-on-Avon, Alcester, Warwickshire, B50 4JN Tel: (01789) 778592 Fax: (01789) 490939 *Conservatory solutions services*

Avon Business Computers, New Road, High Littleton, Bristol, BS39 6JH Tel: (01761) 470543 *Software publishers*

Avon Construction, 850 Wimborne Road, Bournemouth, BH9 2DS Tel: (01202) 523006 *Technical staff recruitment*

Avon Control Engineering & Software, The Old Vicarage, Somerset Square, Nailsea, Bristol, BS48 1RN Tel: (01275) 853721 Fax: (01275) 857746 E-mail: sales@graynailsea.freeserve.co.uk *Computer software developers*

Avon Cosmetics Ltd, Nunn Mills Road, Northampton, NN1 5PA Tel: (01604) 232425 Fax: (01604) 232444 E-mail: info@avon.com *Cosmetic & jewellery manufrs* Also at: Corby

Avon Dies Bristol Ltd, Unit 5-6 Carrick Business Centre, 4-5 Bonville Road, Bristol, BS4 5NZ Tel: 0117-977 1872 Fax: 0117-972 3703 E-mail: cad@avon-dies.co.uk *Shaped cutter manufrs*

Avon Displays, Unit 4, Redhill Business Park, Elberton, Bristol, BS35 4AL Tel: (01454) 411144 E-mail: info@avondisplays.com *Sign & display manufrs*

Avon Engraving Services, 15 Barratt Street, Bristol, BS5 6DE Tel: 0117-951 0234 Fax: 0117-952 0234 *Engravers*

Avon Equipment Ltd, Unit 7-8 Dixon Business Centre, Dixon Road, Bristol, BS4 5QW Tel: 0117-972 3210 Fax: 0117-972 1120 E-mail: sales@avonequipment.co.uk *Power tool distributors*

Avon Extinguishers, Hanham Business Park, Memorial Road, Hanham, Bristol, BS15 3JE Tel: 0117-960 2266 Fax: 0117-960 2233 E-mail: avon-extinguish@btconnect.com *Extinguishers & fire alarms services*

Avon Fastenings & Industrial Supplies Ltd, Unit 10, Western Road Industrial Estate, Stratford-Upon-Avon, Warwickshire, CV37 0AH Tel: (01789) 269661 Fax: (01789) 267051 E-mail: avonfastenings@aol.com *Distributors & stockholders of fasteners*

Avon Group Manufacturing Ltd, 30 Vale Lane, Bristol, BS3 5RU Tel: 0117-904 3355 Fax: 0117-904 3366 E-mail: admin@avon-group.co.uk *Converters of non-metallic materials*

Avon Hydraulics Ltd, Waterloo Road, Bidford-on-Avon, Alcester, Warwickshire, B50 4JN Tel: (01789) 772613 Fax: (01789) 490051 *Hydraulic systems & cylinder distributors*

Avon Joinery Manufacturers, 8 Minto Road Industrial Centre, Ashley Parade, Bristol, BS2 9YW Tel: 0117-955 8142 *Joinery manufrs*

Avon Lighting, 4 Fenbrook Close, Hambrook, Bristol, BS16 1QJ Tel: 0117-956 5511 Fax: 0117-935 3678 E-mail: avonlite@bbcopenworld.com *Electrical lighting suppliers & manufrs*

Avon Lighting, Unit 23, Avondale Business Centre, Woodland Way, Bristol, BS15 1AW Tel: 0117-935 3678 Fax: 0117-935 3678 E-mail: sales@avonlighting.co.uk *Lighting fittings manufrs*

Avon Manufacturing Ltd, Viande House, Kineton Road, Southam, Warwickshire, CV47 0DR Tel: (01926) 817292 Fax: (01926) 814156 E-mail: sale@avonova.co.uk *Builders ironmongers of garage doors, special fabrication & alucobond*

Avon P D C, 40 Holford Way, Witton, Birmingham, B6 7AX Tel: 0121-681 1160 Fax: 0121-344 3902 E-mail: enquiries@avonpdc.co.uk Principal Export Areas: Asia Pacific, Africa, Central/East Europe, West Europe & North America *Precision pressure die castings manufrs*

Avon Partitioning Services, Unit 10 Evercreech Way, Highbridge, Somerset, TA9 4AR Tel: (01278) 788575 Fax: (01278) 782252 E-mail: enquiries@avonpartitioning.co.uk *Office partitioning services*

Avon Pine Ltd, 34 Old Broughton Road, Melksham, Wiltshire, SN12 8BX Tel: (01225) 700878 Fax: (01225) 793540 E-mail: sales@avonpine.co.uk *Furniture retailers & timber building manufrs*

▶ Avon Polishing Ltd, Unit 4 & 5 Rollingmill Business Park, Rollingmill Street, Walsall, WS2 9EQ Tel: (01922) 633937 Fax: (01922) 633937 *Metal polishing*

Avon Rubber P.L.C., European Headquarters, Hampton Park West, Melksham, Wiltshire, SN12 6NB Tel: (01225) 896800 Fax: (01225) 896302 E-mail: enquiries@avon-rubber.com *Motor industry rubber products manufrs*

▶ Avon Rubber, Cory Way, West Wilts Trading Estate, Westbury, Wiltshire, BA13 4QT Tel: (01373) 863106 Fax: (01373) 863107

Avon Ruber P.L.C., Hampton Park West, Melksham, Wiltshire, SN12 6NB Tel: (01225) 896300 Fax: (01225) 896302 E-mail: enquiries@avon-rubber.com *Rubber manufrs*

Avon Scale Co. Ltd, 1 Claremont Street, London, N18 2RP Tel: (020) 8807 2254 Fax: (020) 8803 6653 E-mail: accounts@avonscale.freeserve.co.uk Principal Export Areas: Central/East Europe *Scale & weighing machine*

▶ Avon Security, 21 Salisbury Street, Amesbury, Salisbury, SP4 7AW Tel: (01980) 626000 Fax: (01980) 626464 E-mail: info@avonsecurity.net *LOCKSMITHSKEY CUTTINGLOCKS SUPPLIED & FITTEDEMERGENCY CALL OUTSSAFES ACCESS CONTROLPVCu LOCKSMASTER KEY SYSTEMSCODE KEY CUTTINGCAR TRANSPONDER KEYS CUTLOCK REFURBISHMENTSBARS & GRILLES*

▶ Avon Solar Control Ltd, Avon House, Kineton Road Industrial Estate, Southam, Warwickshire, CV47 0DR Tel: (01926) 818992 Fax: (01926) 811676 E-mail: enquiries@avonsolarcontrol.co.uk *Design, manufacture & install solar shading, brise soleil & louvres*

Avon Stainless Fasteners, Unit 10 Riverside Business Park, St. Annes Road, St. Annes Park, Bristol, BS4 4ED Tel: 0117-972 8560 Fax: 0117-972 8570 E-mail: sales@avonstainlessfasteners.co.uk *The company is a specialist supplier of a wide range of Stainless Steel fasteners in both metric and imperial. As well as standard items, we are also known for our expertise of sourcing non-standard, and those difficult to find items. Specials can also be quoted to your sketch or drawing. Other corrosion resistant materials available on request (Brass, Bronze, Aluminium, Titanium and Nylon etc) Detailed product guide available please ask.*

Avon Steel Co. Ltd, Unit 18 Midsomer Enterprise Park, Radstock Road, Midsomer Norton, Radstock, BA3 2BB Tel: (01761) 416721 Fax: (01761) 412870 E-mail: charles@avonsteel.co.uk *Steel & stainless steel stockholders*

Avon Trophies, Wharfside, Couch Lane, Devizes, Wiltshire, SN10 1EB Tel: (01380) 724630 Fax: (01380) 720122 E-mail: sales@avontrophies.co.uk *Trophy & gift presentation suppliers*

▶ Avon Valley Landscapes, 10 Ashman Avenue, Long Lawford, Rugby, Warwickshire, CV23 9AG Tel: (01788) 550195 E-mail: mark@avonvalleylandscapes.co.uk *BLOCK PAVING,BESPOKE NATURAL STONE PATIOS*

Avon Welding & Marine, 50 Grace Drive, Kingswood, Bristol, BS15 4JU Tel: 0117-975 4443 *Welding fabricators*

Avon Welding Supplies, Unit D6 Avondale Works, Woodland Way, Bristol, BS15 1PA Tel: 0117-947 7532 Fax: 0117-947 7532 E-mail: info@aws-ltd.co.uk *Suppliers of Safety Equipment,Protective clothing, Work Wear, First Aid Supplies & Safety signs, In house clothing logo service*

Avonbank Joinery, Unit 3 Stratford Agri Park, Clifford Chambers, Upper Quinton, Stratford-upon-Avon, Warwickshire, CV37 8LP Tel: (01789) 720444 Fax: (01789) 720444 *Joinery manufrs*

Avonbridge Alarms, 87 Bradley Crescent, Bristol, BS11 9SR Tel: 0117-982 2088 Fax: 0117-982 1292 E-mail: info@avonbridgealarms.co.uk *Install, fault find & maintain wired or wire-free security systems*

Avonchem Ltd, 10 Waterloo Street West, Macclesfield, Cheshire, SK11 6PJ Tel: (01625) 434300 Fax: (01625) 869777 E-mail: sales@avonchem.co.uk *Laboratory chemical product wholesalers*

Avonchem Chemicals, Waterloo House, 10 Waterloo St West, Macclesfield, Cheshire, SK11 6PJ Tel: (01625) 869769 Fax: (01625) 869777 E-mail: info@avonchem.co.uk *Distributors of laboratory consumables & chemicals*

Avoncolour Professional Imaging, 131-133 Duckmoor Road, Bristol, BS3 2BJ Tel: 0117-963 3456 Fax: 0117-966 3456 E-mail: sales@avoncolour.co.uk *Professional imaging centre services* Also at: Luton

Avoncraft Ltd, 12 West Burrowfield, Welwyn Garden City, Hertfordshire, AL7 4TW Tel: (01707) 330000 Fax: (01707) 333026 E-mail: sales@avoncraft.co.uk *Kayak & canoe distributors*

Avoncroft Joinery, 1c Shaw Lane, Stoke Prior, Bromsgrove, Worcestershire, B60 4DY Tel: (01527) 579229 Fax: (01527) 579229 *Joinery manufrs*

▶ Avoncroft Plastics Ltd, 23 Charlestone Road, Burnham-on-Sea, Somerset, TA8 2AP Tel: (01278) 794732 Fax: (01278) 794344 E-mail: duncan@avoncroftplastics.co.uk *Suppliers of thermoplastic polyurethane materials*

Avondale Engineering Ltd, Phoenix Works, Pontnewynydd Industrial Estate, Pontypool, Gwent, NP4 6PD Tel: (01495) 750133 Fax: (01495) 763488 E-mail: sales@avondale-engineering.com *Precision engineers*

Avonmouth Pallets Ltd, King Road Avenue, Avonmouth, Bristol, BS11 9HG Tel: 0117-982 9012 Fax: 0117-982 5108 E-mail: sales@avonmouthpallets.co.uk *Reconditioned pallet suppliers*

Avonmouth Shipping & Salvage, Chittening Industrial Estate, Chittening, Bristol, BS11 0YB Tel: 0117-982 9608 Fax: 0117-982 9559 E-mail: avonmouthsigns@btconnect.com *Vehicle graphics & safety signs engraving & manufrs*

Avonquest (UK) Ltd, 151 Freston Road, London, W10 6TH Tel: (020) 7221 4600 Fax: (020) 7792 1611 E-mail: jobs@mediagold.com *Computer consultants*

Avonride Ltd, Spelter Site, Caerau, Maesteg, Mid Glamorgan, CF34 0AQ Tel: (01656) 739111 Fax: (01656) 737677 E-mail: salesmaesteg@knottuk.com *Avonride Ltd manufacturers of trailer axles & suspension systems to a capacity of four tonnes per axle. Manufacturer of trailer couplings, coupling devices, T bar chassis including "Ackerman" steering systems*

Avonside Insulation Supplies Ltd, Unit 6a Pucklechurch Trading Estate, Pucklechurch, Bristol, BS16 9QH Tel: 0117-937 2232 Fax: 0117-937 2387 *Insulating material distributors*

▶ Avonside Plumbing & Heating Ltd, Unit 19, Colvilles Park, Glasgow, G75 0GZ Tel: (01355) 237021

Avonside Plumbing & Heating Yorkshire Ltd, Dunswell Road, Cottingham, North Humberside, HU16 4JU Tel: (01482) 841146 Fax: (01482) 875137 *Heating & plumbing contractors* Also at: Stockton

Avonstar Trading Co. Ltd, 44 Barn Street, Digbeth, Birmingham, B5 5QB Tel: 0121-643 0408 Fax: 0121-643 1104 E-mail: kevin.taylor@avonstar.co.uk *Manufacture of catering equipment.*

Avontech Computer Systems, Dark Lane, Backwell, Bristol, BS48 3NP Tel: (01275) 462260 Fax: (01275) 462203 E-mail: sales@avontech.co.uk *Computer systems manufrs*

Avontech Machines, Park Yard, Old Down, Tockington, Bristol, BS32 4PB Tel: (0845) 070 4343 Fax: (0845) 070 4346 E-mail: avontech@blueyonder.co.uk *Woodwork machinery retailers & service*

▶ Avonwood Developments Ltd, Knoll Technology Centre, Stapehill Road, Wimborne, Dorset, BH21 7ND Tel: (01202) 868000 Fax: (01202) 868001 E-mail: sales@avonwood.co.uk *Avonwood is an established developer and manufacturer of the Eureka® RFID range of products and services.*Providing complete end-to-end solutions to identify and manage assets and personnel in areas of safety, security and control as well as more specialised asset management applications within industry, commerce and the service sector.*Avonwood offers a complete service from bespoke system design and integration to turnkey RFID technology solutions.**

Avp, School Hill Centre, Chepstow, Gwent, NP16 5PH Tel: (01291) 625439 Fax: (01291) 629671 E-mail: sales@info.avp.co.uk *Educational software mail order company*

Avpower, C11 Acre Business Park, Acre Road, Reading, RG2 0SA Tel: 0118-975 2555 Fax: 0118-975 3074 E-mail: sales@avpower.com *Power analysists*

Avprod Lighting Mnfrs, Ravenscroft House, 39 St Annes Road, Aigburth, Liverpool, L17 6BN Tel: 0151-427 0444 Fax: 0151-427 0666 *Lighting manufrs*

▶ AVRS Systems Ltd, Choices House, Maybrook Road, Stratford-upon-Avon, Warwickshire, CV37 0BT Tel: (01789) 268252 Fax: (01789) 297078 E-mail: technical@avrssystems.co.uk *Motor control centres, control panels instrumentation suppliers*

▶ AVS UK Ltd, Business Centre, High Street, Guilsborough, Northampton, NN6 8PU Tel: (0870) 2242246 Fax: (0871) 7333866 *Suppliers of audiovisual products, sales, hire, repairs & install*

Avtech Ltd, Building 170 Churchill Way, Biggin Hill Airport, Biggin Hill, Westerham, Kent, TN16 3BN Tel: (01959) 575679 Fax: (01959) 576968 E-mail: avtech@btconnect.com *Aircraft engineers & sales*

▶ Av-Tech Manufacturing Co. Ltd, Unit 33 London Road Industrial Estate, Baldock, Hertfordshire, SG7 6NG Tel: (01462) 893336 Fax: (01462) 893336 *We are a well-established precision engineering company with a highly skilled work force currently supplying components for the Automotive Industry, Optical Instruments, Medical & Test Equipment, Jigs, Fixtures, Tool Design, Rail & Transport, Aerospace etc*

Avw Controls Ltd, Finningham Road, Rickinghall, Diss, Norfolk, IP22 1LT Tel: (01379) 898340 Fax: (01379) 898386 E-mail: info@avw.co.uk *Control panel manufrs*

Aw Computer Systems Ltd, 16 Dundry Lane, Winford, Bristol, BS40 8AN Tel: (01275) 474591 Fax: (0870) 9004911 E-mail: awcs@dial.pipex.com *Computer software*

▶ Aw Crane Solutions Ltd, 78 Ellison Road, Sidcup, Kent, DA15 8BL Tel: (020) 8300 3109 Fax: 020 83024867 E-mail: cranesolutions@aol.com

▶ Aw Developments, 436 Queens Drive, West Derby, Liverpool, L13 0AR Tel: 0151-228 0001 Fax: 0151-252 1472

▶ Awan Electronics, 32-34 Abbey Barn Road, High Wycombe, Buckinghamshire, HP11 1RW Tel: (0870) 8798455 Fax: 01494 471700 E-mail: info@awanelectronics.com *To provide contract manufacturing and test facilities which meets customer"s needs in relation to printed circuit boards, electromechanical equipment and cable assemblies.**

▶ Awanstars Leather Fashion, 42 Foxton Road, Birmingham, B8 3HP Tel: (0781) 2817248 E-mail: awanstars@yahoo.co.uk *We take the pleasure in introducing ourselves as one of the Leading Manufacturer and Exporter dealing in Leather Garments and Goods .Our Factory is in pakistan We are manufacturing Ladies, Men?s Fashion Overcoat, Fetish Fashion, Top,Short,Harness,Mask,Underwear,Whips, Bandages,belts, Blazer ,Motorbike Leather Jackets, Pant and Police & Army Gloves etc.. We are making garments in different type of leather skins like Sheep /Lamb Napa, Goat, Cow & Buff in various colours and quality as per our customers requirement. We can supply our customers with above-mentioned items of different materials and of many styles. Also, we can produce the production according to buyer"s brand, buyer"s model as well.*For all your queries, please feel free to write us in our following URL: www.awanstars.com**Looking forward to hear from you for mutual business development and interest. *Assuring you of our best services at all times* *With best regards**MR.Awan*Awanstars Leather Fashion*

▶ Award Electrical Contractors, 40 Pennycroft, Pixton Way, Croydon, CR0 9LL Tel: (020) 8150 6357 E-mail: awardelectricalcontractors@g2gm.com *Award Electrical Contractors.*Re-wires,Alarms,cctv and Door entry systems.*Showers,Baths,sinks,toilet,Emergency callout and much more.Free Estimates and best rates.*

Awardco Group, Mile Road, 9 Bedford Business Centre, Bedford, MK42 9TW Tel: (01234) 300555 Fax: (01234) 348871 E-mail: sales@awardco.co.uk *Promotional product manufrs*

Aware Marketing Consultants, 16 Craigweil Close, Stanmore, Middlesex, HA7 4TR Tel: (020) 8954 9121 Fax: (020) 8954 2102 E-mail: aweiss@marketing-intelligence.co.uk

▶ Awareness Centre Of Natural Health, 41 Abbeville Road, London, SW4 9JX Tel: (020) 8673 8844 Fax: (020) 8673 8844 E-mail: sales@awarness.com *Services designed to address various physical & emotional needs*

Away & Away, The Stables, Goulds Green, Hillingdon, Uxbridge, Middlesex, UB8 3DG Tel: (01895) 442260 Fax: (01895) 447561 *Hire & put up camping tents & marquees*

Awe, 147 Victoria Road, Southend-on-Sea, SS1 2TD Tel: (01702) 469898 Fax: (01702) 610042 E-mail: awescales@aol.com *Food processing & weighing machinery distributors*

AWE Newtech Ltd, Brunel Drive, Northern Road Industrial Estate, Newark, Nottinghamshire, NG24 2EG Tel: (01636) 703793 Fax: (01636) 701210 E-mail: sales@awe-newtech.com *Automation & control systems manufrs*

▶ Awelfor Ltd, 2 Marine Drive, Rhyl, Clwyd, LL18 3AT Tel: (01745) 361801

▶ Awesome Bouncy Castles, 45 Woodlands Road, Stafford, ST16 1QP Tel: (01785) 600950 Fax: (07817) 128319 *Bouncy castle hire services*

▶ Awesome Catering, Crome Cottage, Coxford, King's Lynn, Norfolk, PE31 6TB Tel: (01485) 528816 E-mail: peter@theawesomechef.com *private in house catering for weddings garden parties and company functions, offering a different cusine type in cajun and creole food as well as traditional fayre*

Awlwood Joinery, Unit 4 Bruce Grove, Wickford, Essex, SS11 8BP Tel: (01268) 735994 Fax: (01268) 730451 E-mail: joconnor@abalone-awlwood.co.uk *Joiners*

Awnings & Blinds By Morco, Riverside, Lombard Wall, London, SE7 7SG Tel: (020) 8858 2083 Fax: (020) 8305 2431 E-mail: sales@morcoblinds.co.uk *Blinds & shop fascia manufrs*

Awon Engineering, 26 Dunlop Road, Redditch, Worcestershire, B97 5XP Tel: (01527) 404699 Fax: (01527) 524868 *General engineers*

Awr Engineering Services, Unit A11 Abbey Close, Redwither Business Park, Wrexham, Clwyd, LL13 9XG Tel: (01978) 661928 Fax: (01978) 661928 *Precision engineers*

Axa Couriers Ltd, Axa House, Blandford Road, Southall, Middlesex, UB2 4JY Tel: (020) 8571 4747 Fax: (020) 8574 5697 *Courier services*

Axa Insurance, Windsor House, 9-15 Bedford Street, Belfast, BT2 7FT Tel: (028) 9033 3222 Fax: (028) 9053 5010 *Insurance company*

Axa Insurance, 1 Aldgate, London, EC3N 1RE Tel: (020) 7702 3109 Fax: (020) 7369 3909 *Insurance company*

Axa Insurance, 1 Aldgate, London, EC3N 1RE Tel: (020) 7702 3109 Fax: (020) 7369 3909 *Insurance*

Axa Investment Managers Ltd, 7 Newgate Street, London, EC1A 7NX Tel: (020) 7645 1000 Fax: (020) 7575 8585 *Investment management company* Also at: High Wycombe

Axa PPP Healthcare Group plc, P P P House, Vale Road, Tunbridge Wells, Kent, TN1 1BJ Tel: (01892) 512345 Fax: (01892) 515143 E-mail: enquiries@axappphealthcare.com *Private health insurance*

Axe & Status Ltd, 2 Holdom Avenue, Bletchley, Milton Keynes, MK1 1QU Tel: (01908) 647707 Fax: (01908) 648087 E-mail: sales@axestatus.com *Machine tool merchants*

▶ Axem Computers, 30-31 Caroline Street, Hull, HU2 8DY Tel: (01482) 226899 E-mail: sales@axemcomputers.co.uk *Computer suppliers*

Axeon Ltd, Unit 1-2, Nobel Court, Nobel Road, West Gourdie Industrial Estate, Dundee, DD2 4UH Tel: (01382) 400040 Fax: (01382) 400044 E-mail: info@axeon.com *Electronics developers, batteries*

▶ Axess, 1 Orchard Close, Pinchbeck, Spalding, Lincolnshire, PE11 3RL Tel: (01775) 724066 Fax: (01775) 712812 E-mail: lowe.john@btconnect.com *Website design specialists*

Axestone Engineering, North Cresent, London, E16 4TQ Tel: (020) 7473 3737 Fax: (020) 7473 3738 *Fabrication & welding engineers*

Axflow Ltd, 3 Harlaw Centre Howe Moss Crescent, Kirkhill Industrial Estate, Dyce, Aberdeen, AB21 0GN Tel: (01224) 729367 Fax: (01224) 729368 E-mail: infoscot@axflow.co.uk *AxFlow are the leading UK supplier of air operated double diaphragm pumps, specialist centrifugal pumps, rotary positive displacement pumps, reciprocating positive displacement pumps, metering pumps, canned motor centrifugal pumps, plastic lined centrifugal pumps, magnetic drive centrifugal pumps, self cleaning filters and gas compressors. Manufacturers represented by AxFlow include, Wilden air operated double diaphragm pumps, Waukesha rotary circumferential piston pumps, Blackmer rotary sliding vane pumps, Pulsafeeder diaphragm metering pumps, Hermetic canned motor centrifugal pumps, Wernert plastic lined centrifugal pumps, Borger rotary lobe pumps, External gear pumps from Zenith, Eco, Isochem and Cucchi, Mono progressing cavity - helical rotor pumps, FMC reciprocating piston and plunger pumps, Blackmer - Mouvex principle eccentric disc pumps, Almatec aodd pumps, Ronningen & Petter and Burton Corblin.*

A. Axford Ltd, The Workshop, Bark Street, Bolton, BL1 1AZ Tel: (01204) 520931 Fax: (01204) 520931 *Timber merchants & builders' hardware suppliers*

Anthony Axford Ltd, Atlas Saw Mills, King Street, Farnworth, Bolton, BL4 7AD Tel: (01204) 571697 Fax: (01204) 795627 E-mail: sales@anthonyaxford.co.uk *Timber merchants & importers* Also at: Walkden

▶ Axford Decorating Services Ltd, 49 Hollingbourne Road, Rainham Gillingham, Gillingham, Kent, ME8 6SN Tel: (01634) 232031 Fax: 01634 377882 E-mail: axfords@hotmail.co.uk *We cover most aspects of house renovations. Interior and exterior decorating, plastering, artexing, coving, ceramic tiling, guttering, upvc fashias/soffits, fencing/shed erection, screeding/shed bases, laminate flooring, kitchen and bathroom fitting*

Axfords Clothing Mnfrs, 82 Centurion Road, Brighton, BN1 3LN Tel: (01273) 327944 Fax: (01273) 220680 *Foundation garment & corset manufrs*

Axgro Foods Ltd, 39 West Street, West Butterwick, Scunthorpe, South Humberside, DN17 3JZ Tel: (01724) 783214 Fax: (01724) 782198 E-mail: admin@axgrofoods.fsnet.co.uk *Food manufrs*

Axia Distribution Ltd, Axia House, 111 St Albans Road, Watford, WD17 1UH Tel: (01923) 227007 E-mail: sales@axia.co.uk *Computer software & peripherals distributors*

▶ Axicon Auto Id Ltd, Church Road, Weston-on-the-Green, Bicester, Oxfordshire, OX25 3QP Tel: (01869) 351166 Fax: (01869) 351205 E-mail: info@axicon.com *Bar codes suppliers*

Axiom Connection Ltd, 2A Station Yard, Hungerford, Berkshire, RG17 0DY Tel: (01488) 683033 Fax: (01488) 683133 E-mail: axiom@axiomconnection.com *Computer software developers*

▶ Axiom Contractors Ltd, The Cavendish Centre, Winnall Close, Winchester, Hampshire, SO23 0LB Tel: (01962) 890888 Fax: (01962) 890888 E-mail: gtabner@axiomcontractors.co.uk *Working as Pricipal Contractor within the building and refurbishment sectors of the construction industry.*

Axiom Displays Ltd, Mersey Road North, Failsworth, Manchester, M35 9LT Tel: 0161-681 1371 Fax: 0161-683 4641 E-mail: info@axiom-displays.co.uk *Specialist in point of purchase design & manufrs*

Axiom NDT Services Ltd, 72-74 Clifford Lane, Glasgow, G51 1NR Tel: 0141-427 3302 Fax: 0141-427 7240 E-mail: enquiries@axiomndt.co.uk *Non destructive testing services*

Axiom Quality Control Equipment, Chapel House, The Hill, Kirkby-In-Ashfield, Nottingham, NG17 8JS Tel: (01623) 759836 Fax: (01623) 755103 E-mail: info@handh-services.co.uk *Sampling equipment & industrial weighing equipment manufrs*

Axiom Software Solutions Ltd, 1 Olympic Way, Wembley, Middlesex, HA9 0NP Tel: (0845) 2305665 E-mail: info@biztechsolutions.co.uk *Systems integration service*

Axiom Transmissions Ltd, 18 Manor Road, Folksworth, Peterborough, PE7 3SU Tel: (01733) 241234 Fax: (01733) 242435 *Variable speed drive distributors*

Axiomatic Design Services, 43 St. Marys Lane, Ecclesfield, Sheffield, S35 9YE Tel: 0114-246 0160 E-mail: james@axiomatic.biz *Electronic consultants*

Axis Alloys FP Ltd, 4 Popes Lane, Oldbury, West Midlands, B69 4PN Tel: 0121-552 7733 Fax: 0121-552 3682 E-mail: axisalloys@aol.com *Foundry supply agents*

▶ Axis Display LLP, Unit B, Centurion Way, Erith, Kent, DA18 4AF Tel: (020) 8319 7743 Fax: (020) 8319 7776 E-mail: sales@axisdisplay.co.uk *UK's largest range of display and presentation products. pop-ups, banner stands, portable display, notice boards, glass cases.Full catalogue or on-line shop. Next day delivery*

Axis Electronics, Manton Lane, Bedford, MK41 7NY Tel: (01234) 342932 Fax: (01234) 364941 E-mail: sales@axis-electronics.com *Provider of contract electronic manufacturing services, specialising in complex PCB assembly on a variety of substrates including FR4, Polyimide, Rogers, PTFE, Flexi-Rigid and metal backed laminate.*

Axis Group, Unit 5 The Lion Centre, Hanworth Trading Estate, Hampton Road West, Feltham, Middlesex, TW13 6DS Tel: (020) 8893 8339 Fax: (020) 8893 8439 E-mail: sales@axis-gb.com *Distribution of precision instruments*

Axis Intabuild Ltd, PO Box 50, Cranbrook, Kent, TN18 4EL Tel: (01580) 753798 Fax: (01580) 754079 E-mail: richardaxis@btopenworld.com *Partitioning/suspended ceilings/interior finishes general builders*

▶ Axis International plc, 40 Park Street, London, W1K 2JG Tel: (020) 7290 9570 Fax: (020) 7629 1917 E-mail: admin@axisinternational.com *Corporate finance - specialising in corporate recovery and turnaround.*

Axis International Ltd, Antry Avenue, White Horse Business Park, Trowbridge, Wiltshire, BA14 0XB Tel: (01225) 768491 Fax: (01225) 716100 *Toiletries manufrs*

Axis Scotland Ltd, 12 Auchingramont Road, Hamilton, Lanarkshire, ML3 6JT Tel: (01698) 785000 Fax: (01698) 785111 E-mail: enquiries@axis.gb.com *Partitioning & furniture contractors*

Axis Shield plc, Dundee Technology Park, Dundee, DD2 1XA Tel: (01382) 422000 Fax: (01382) 422088 E-mail: shield@uk.axis-shield.com *Medical & diagnostic equipment manufrs*

▶ Axis Well Technology, Kettock Lodge Campus Aberdeen Science Park, Balgownie Drive, Bridge of Don, Aberdeen, AB22 8GU Tel: (01224) 829200 Fax: (01224) 829201

Axisclaim Ltd, 11 Leap Cross Small Business Centre, London Road, Hailsham, East Sussex, BN27 3PD Tel: (01323) 442717 Fax: (01323) 442717 E-mail: enquiries@axisclaimelectronics.co.uk *Electronic contract manufrs*

Axminster Carpets Ltd, Woodmead Road, Axminster, Devon, EX13 5PQ Tel: (01297) 33533 Fax: (01297) 35241 E-mail: sales@axminster-carpets.co.uk *Carpet manufrs*

Axminster Electronics Ltd, Unit 1, Millwey Indust Estate, Axminster, Devon, EX13 5HU Tel: (01297) 32360 Fax: (01297) 35454 E-mail: mail@axminster-electronics.co.uk *Electronic design & manufrs*

Axminster Power Tool Centre, Chard Street, Axminster, Devon, EX13 5DZ Tel: (01297) 33656 Fax: (01297) 35242 *Sell power tools & machinery*

Axon Buildbase, Unit 1 McKenzie Industrial Park, Bird Hall Lane, Cheadle Heath, Stockport, Cheshire, SK3 0SB Tel: 0161-428 0314 Fax: 0161-491 0844 E-mail: stockport@buildbase.co.uk *Buildbase is one of the UK's fastest growing builders merchants. All of our branches are long established companies which have been serving local trades people for many years, with knowledge and experience to match. We believe strongly in understanding the needs of trades professional and our business has been developed specifically to meet those demands. Massive stocks, top quality products, competitive pricing, reliable delivery, specialist staff and exceptional customer service.*

Axon Cable Ltd, 22 Ridge Way, Donibristle Industrial Park, Hillend, Dunfermline, Fife, KY11 9JN Tel: (01383) 821081 Fax: (01383) 821080 E-mail: sales@axon-cable.co.uk *AXON CABLE is a provider of custom designed interconnect solutions including wires, round or flat cables, composite cables, coaxial cables, assemblies and connectors for any application: *'Aeromil and space *'Automotive *'Consumer electronics *'Industry *'Medical *'Research centres *'Telecommunications, *Our strengths are that 10 % of our turnover is invested in Research & Development. *We have engineers with expertise in physics, mechanics, electronics, chemistry, plastics technologies, robotics, microwave. We offer a world-wide sales support via our subsidiaries and sales representatives. Our manufacturing facilities in France, China, Hungary, Latvia and Mexico offer a global presence.*

▶ Axon Enterprises Ltd, 8a & 8b St. Martins Street, Hereford, HR2 7RE Tel: (01432) 359906 Fax: (01432) 352436 E-mail: sales@axon-enterprises.co.uk *We are Catering equipment wholesalers, operating nationally, offering equipment resellers and engineers a wide range of quality equipment and spares at competitive resale discounts. *In addition, within Herefordshire only, we are able to offer competitive prices and friendly advice to local restaureaurs,publicans etc whether the enquiry is for one item or a complete kitchen layout.*

Axon Power & Control, 347 Pomeroy Road, Pomeroy, Dungannon, County Tyrone, BT70 3DT Tel: (028) 8775 8923 Fax: (028) 8775 8937 *Electrical services*

Axon Systems, 108 Bartholomew Street, Newbury, Berkshire, RG14 5DT Tel: (01635) 33033 Fax: (07050) 300603 E-mail: sales@axon-systems.co.uk *Mobile communications dealer*

Axon Welding & Fabrication, Green Lane, Challock, Ashford, Kent, TN25 4BL Tel: (01233) 740691 Fax: (01233) 740691 *Welding fabricators*

Axsia Mozley, 370 Bristol Road, Gloucester, GL2 5DH Tel: (01452) 833800 Fax: (01209) 211068 E-mail: asbl@axsia.com *Process design manufacture & project management of oil & gas power refinery*

Axtell Perry Simm Masonry Ltd, Osney Mead, Oxford, OX2 0EQ Tel: (01865) 254600 Fax: (01865) 254617 E-mail: sales@apsmasonry.com *Stone masonry sub-contractors*

▶ Axxess 28 Ltd, 18 Rosemary Lane, Blackwater, Camberley, Surrey, GU17 0LS Tel: (01276) 36915 Fax: (01276) 36917 E-mail: sales@axxess28.com *Design, install & maintain electronic security systems*

Axxicon Moulds Cleveleys Ltd, Dorset Avenue, Thornton-Cleveleys, Lancashire, FY5 2DB Tel: (01253) 823241 Fax: (01253) 869717 E-mail: cleveleys@axxicon.co.uk *Plastic mould toolmakers precision engineers*

Axyswebs Ltd, Host Media Centre, Saville Mount, Leeds, LS7 3HZ Tel: 0113-200 7070 Fax: 0113-200 7071 E-mail: info@axyswebs.com

▶ AXYZ Engineering Ltd, 34 Rotherford Road, Southfield Industrial Estate, Glenrothes, Fife, KY6 2RT Tel: (01592) 772500 Fax: (01592) 771170 *CNC engineering*

▶ Axzona Ltd, 36 Dean Park Mews, Edinburgh, EH4 1ED Tel: 0131-315 0181 Fax: 0131-315 0185

▶ Ayce Systems Ltd, C Snaygill Industrial Estate, Keighley Road, Skipton, North Yorkshire, BD23 2QR Tel: (01756) 709709 Fax: (01756) 709409 E-mail: info@aycesystems.co.uk *Smart repair suppliers*

▶ Aycliffe Engineering Ltd, Beaumont Way, Aycliffe Industrial Park, Newton Aycliffe, County Durham, DL5 6SN Tel: (01325) 300223 Fax: (01325) 300233 E-mail: altringham@aycliffe-engineering.onyxnet.co.uk *Tyre mould manufrs/injection mould manufrs*

Aycliffe Plastics (Fabrications) Ltd, Ketton Way, Aycliffe Industrial Estate, Newton Aycliffe, County Durham, DL5 6AU Tel: (01325) 310000 Fax: (01325) 301987 E-mail: info@aycliffefabrications.co.uk *Fly screens for kitchens & steel fabricators*

Aydon Silver & Co. Ltd, Units 1-2 Stoney Lane Industrial Estate, Red Suns Road, Kidderminster, Worcestershire, DY10 2LG Tel: (01562) 820107 Fax: (01562) 822253 E-mail: enquiries@aydonsilver.co.uk *Label printers*

Ayfab Industrial Plastics, Leaside, Aycliffe Industrial Estate, Aycliffe Industrial Park, Newton Aycliffe, County Durham, DL5 6HX Tel: (01325) 310510 E-mail: ayfab@aycliffe16fsnet.co.uk *Plastic fabricators*

Ayh plc, 1 East Harding Street, London, EC4A 3AH Tel: (020) 7216 1000 Fax: (020) 7216 1001 E-mail: info@ayh.co.uk *Quantity surveyors & project managers* Also at: Stockport

Aylesbury Automation Ltd, Unit 2 Farmbrough Cl, Stocklake Industrial Pk, Aylesbury, Buckinghamshire, HP20 1DQ Tel: (01296) 314300 Fax: (01296) 482424 E-mail: enquiry@aylesbury-automation.co.uk *The company has now been divided into three divisions, AA Robotics, Automation and The Bifurcated & Tubular Rivet Company operating from a 10,000 square ft site in Aylesbury. The company aims to be solution providers to its customers and has achieved and maintained ISO 9001:2000 and investors in people accreditation. Machine designs are produced on the 3D SolidWorks 2007 CAD system and 3D robot simulations are offered at the quotation stage.*

Aylesbury Box, 19 Faraday Road, Rabans La Industrial Area, Rabans Lane Industrial Area, Aylesbury, Buckinghamshire, HP19 8RY Tel: (01296) 436888 Fax: (01296) 481955 E-mail: sales@abcbox.co.uk *Corrugated box manufrs*

Aylesbury Fire Systems Ltd, Queens Park, Aylesbury, Buckinghamshire, HP21 7SG Tel: (01296) 399994 Fax: (01296) 394692 E-mail: jane@aylesburyfire.co.uk *Installation of fire alarm systems*

Aylesbury Flooring, 3 Jansel Square, Aylesbury, Buckinghamshire, HP21 7ES Tel: (01296) 415038 Fax: (01296) 393891 E-mail: carpets@aylesburyflooring.co.uk *Carpet & wood flooring contractors*

▶ Aylesbury Limousines, 279 Tring Road, Aylesbury, Buckinghamshire, HP20 1PH Tel: (01296) 484051 Fax: (01296) 420791 E-mail: lisa@aylesburylimousines.co.uk *American stretch limousine hire. Chauffeur driven latest style limos available in black & white.*

▶ Aylesbury Mains Ltd, Colts Holm Road, Old Wolverton, Milton Keynes, MK12 5QD Tel: (01908) 222041 Fax: (01908) 222037

Aylesbury Training Group, Gatehouse Close, Gatehouse Industrial Area, Aylesbury, Buckinghamshire, HP19 8DN Tel: (01296) 481818 Fax: (01296) 437391 E-mail: training@atg-training.co.uk *Training providers*

Aylesbury Trophies, 102 Tring Road, Aylesbury, Buckinghamshire, HP20 1LS Tel: (01296) 421475 Fax: (01296) 421475 *Sport trophy suppliers*

Aylesford Paper Sales, Consolidated Paper House, Forstal Road, Aylesford, Kent, ME20 7AE Tel: (01622) 716353 Fax: (01622) 716663 E-mail: sales@aylesfordpaper.co.uk *Paper merchants*

▶ Ayne Engineers Ltd, Cocker Avenue, Poulton Industrial Estate, Poulton-le-Fylde, Lancashire, FY6 8JU Tel: (01253) 896007 Fax: (01253) 896006 E-mail: sales@ayneengineers.co.uk *Steel fabrication & erection*

Ayneson Engineering Co. Ltd, Commercial Road, Wolverhampton, WV1 3RD Tel: (01902) 452862 Fax: (01902) 455383 *General engineers*

Mike Ayres Design Ltd, Unit 8, Shepherds Grove, Stanton, Bury St. Edmunds, Suffolk, IP31 2AR Tel: (01359) 251551 Fax: (01359) 251707 E-mail: enquiries@mikeayresdesign.co.uk *Mike Ayres Design designs, manufactures, installs, maintains and provides training for Multi Sensory rooms, Sensory Studios and Soft Play rooms. These environments are installed in schools, hospitals, early years centre, children's centre and adult care homes. *Individual products include: Bubble tubes, switch control systems, fibre optic lights, soft cushions, Sensory Trolley, Soundbeam, switches, LED lighting system, Tactile panels and murals, Ultra violet Blacklights, Moving light scanner and activity panels. All of this can be used individually or as part of a fully integrated system giving opportunity for people with learning difficulties physical disability, visual impairment, behavioural difficulties, autism, communication needs and many other special needs. *Mike Ayres Design has a policy of designing the best possible equipment and environments for inclusive education and life long learning.*

Ayrshire Chamber Of Commerce & Industry, Suite 1005 Terminal Building, Prestwick Airport, Glasgow Prestwick Intnl Airport, Prestwick, Ayrshire, KA9 2PL Tel: (01292) 678666 Fax: (01292) 678667

continued

E-mail: enquires@ayrshire-chamber.org *Chambers of commerce*

Ayrshire Metal Products, Royal Oak Way North, Royal Oak Industrial Estate, Daventry, Northamptonshire, NN11 8NR Tel: (01327) 300990 Fax: (01327) 300885 E-mail: sales@ayrshire.co.uk *Cold rolled steel sections manufrs*

Ayrshire Metal Products plc, Pocket Nook Street, St. Helens, Merseyside, WA9 1LT Tel: (01744) 29145 Fax: (01744) 451257 E-mail: ampsth@compuserve.com Principal Export Areas: Worldwide *Metal forming manufrs*

Ayrshire Paint & Paper Co, 15 Church Street, Troon, Ayrshire, KA10 6HU Tel: (01292) 312111 *Decorators merchants*

Ayrshire Precision Engineering Ltd, Low Coylton, Coylton, Ayr, KA6 6LF Tel: (01292) 570450 Fax: (01292) 570891 E-mail: enquiries@ayrshire-precision.co.uk *Sub-contract engineering*

Ayrshire Service, 7 Campsie Avenue, Bourtreehill South, Irvine, Ayrshire, KA11 1JF Tel: (01294) 212410 Fax: (01294) 312223 *Weighing system suppliers*

Ayrshire Shop Fronts Ltd, Unit 3 & 4, Moorfield Industrial Estate, Kilmarnock, Ayrshire, KA2 0DP Tel: (01563) 542991 Fax: (01563) 538195 *Shop front & screen manufacturers & suppliers*

▶ Ayshire Curtain Makers, 3 Montgomery Place, Irvine, Ayrshire, KA12 8PN Tel: (01294) 275603 Fax: (01294) 275603 *Soft furnishing manufrs*

Aytans Manufacturing Co., 107-115 Whitechapel Road, London, E1 1DT Tel: (020) 7247 0089 Fax: (020) 7375 1837 E-mail: sales@aytans.com *Clothing wholesalers*

Aythen Fashions Co., 19 Hamstead Road, Hockley, Birmingham, B19 1BX Tel: 0121-523 2815 Fax: 0121-523 2815 *Anorak, promotional & leisure wear manufrs*

Ayton Asphalte, Browick Works, Ayton Road, Wymondham, Norfolk, NR18 0RJ Tel: (01953) 602002 Fax: (01953) 604965 E-mail: sales@ayton.co.uk *Asphalt bituminous compound manufrs*

Ayton Equipment Ltd, Station Yard, Station Road, Stokesley, Middlesbrough, Cleveland, TS9 7AB Tel: (01642) 711455 Fax: (01642) 710100 E-mail: marketing@ayton.com *Chemical plants & equipment distributors*

▶ Ayudar, Sheraton House, Castle Park, Cambridge, CB3 0AX Tel: (08709) 9 01090

A-Z Analytical Services, 82 Allens Rd, Poole, Dorset, BH16 5BX Tel: (01202) 624985 Fax: (01202) 624985 *Materials testing services*

A-Z Group Ltd, Darby House, Bletchingley Road, Merstham, Redhill, RH1 3TT Tel: (01737) 645777 Fax: (01737) 645888 E-mail: sales@a-zgroup.com *Specialist publishers & directory advertisement agents*

A-Z Windscreens, 17 Boar Green Close, Manchester, M40 3AW Tel: 0161-682 2399 Fax: 0161-682 2399 *Windscreen & car alarm suppliers*

Azcon Components Solutions Ltd, Waterside Business Park, Eastways, Witham, Essex, CM8 3YQ Tel: (01376) 517642 Fax: (01376) 519333 E-mail: info@qualitycomponents.co.uk *Suppliers of electronic components*

Azgard Engineering Products, 10 Compton Road, Kinver, Stourbridge, West Midlands, DY7 6DN Tel: (01384) 872286 Fax: (01384) 878203 *Suppliers of fasteners, tubes, fittings*

Azigo Technology Services, Systems House, Wade Road, Basingstoke, Hampshire, RG24 8FL Tel: (01256) 811811 Fax: (01256) 811855 E-mail: niel-raggett@rtgh.com *Electronic components*

Azimex Fabrications Ltd, Cartwright Road, Northampton, NN2 6HF Tel: (01604) 717712 Fax: (01604) 791087 *Sheet metalwork fabricators*

Aziz Textiles Ltd, 19-21 Portland St, Aston, Birmingham, B6 5RX Tel: 0121-328 4456 Fax: 0121-328 6941 *Textile fabric importers*

Azizoff Co. Ltd, 2 Beechfield Road, London, N4 1PE Tel: (020) 8809 6902 Fax: (020) 8800 5795 E-mail: azizoffltd@tiscali.co.uk *Pen & pencil distributors & manufrs*

Azizollahoff & Co., Building A Oriental Carpet Centre, 105 Eade Road, London, N4 1TJ Tel: (020) 8802 3107 Fax: (020) 8442 8949 E-mail: azizcocarpets@mserve.com *Carpet merchants*

Nathan Azizollahoff, Top Floor Building A, 105 Eade Road, London, N4 1TJ Tel: (020) 8802 0077 Fax: (020) 8802 1144 E-mail: joseph@jazico.com *Oriental carpets & rugs distributors*

▶ Aztec Assemblies Ltd, Bryn Brithdir, Oakdale Business Park, Blackwood, Gwent, NP12 4AA Tel: (01495) 247788 Fax: (01495) 247080 *Metal pressings engineering*

Aztec Cleaning Services Ltd, 10 Birkbeck Road, Sidcup, Kent, DA14 4DE Tel: (020) 8300 6571 Fax: (020) 8308 0502 E-mail: ray@aztec-cleaning.prestel.co.uk *Window cleaning specialists*

Aztec Composites, Unit 9 Queens Park Industrial Estate, Studland Road, Northampton, NN2 6NA Tel: (01604) 721727 Fax: (01604) 720420 E-mail: rgoodman@azteccomposites.co.uk *Manufacturer motor racing carbon fibre*

Aztec Computing, Monument House, Marsh Road, Pinner, Middlesex, HA5 5NE Tel: (020) 8866 5577 E-mail: info@azteccomputing.com *Software consultants*

▶ Aztec Conservatory Roof Systems Ltd, Haydock Lane, Haydock, St. Helens, Merseyside, WA11 0SN Tel: (01942) 720044 E-mail: sales@aztecsystems.co.uk *Conservatory roofs specialists*

▶ Aztec Electrical Ltd, Cheney Manor Industrial Estate, Swindon, SN2 2PJ Tel: (01793) 484401 Fax: (01793) 484407

Aztec Garage, 6-8 Emery Road, Bristol, BS4 5PF Tel: 0117-977 0314 Fax: 0117-977 4431 E-mail: myrtletree@holding4337.freeserve.co.uk *Coach services & repairs*

Aztec Group, Unit 18 Chiltern Business Village, Arundel Road, Uxbridge, Middlesex, UB8 2SN Tel: (01895) 520600 Fax: (01895) 520650 E-mail: sales@aztecgroup.net *Sign consultants or designers*

▶ Aztec Innovations, Burnhouse Industrial Estate, Whitburn, Bathgate, West Lothian, EH47 0LQ Tel: (01506) 204188 *Hirers of Giant Inflatables, Bouncy Castles, Sky Dancers, Junior Quad Bikes, Bronco Bull, Surf Simulator, Gladiator Duel, Bungee Run and many more. Discos, Karaoke, Quiz Nights, Themed Events.*

Aztec Interiors, Hillcrest, Long Lane, Bursledon, Southampton, SO31 8BZ Tel: 023 80457036 Fax: 023 80457036 *Interior fitters & contractors*

▶ Aztec Interiors Leicester, 62 Constance Road, Leicester, LE5 5DD Tel: 01162 218674 Fax: 01162 490480 E-mail: sales@azteceinteriorsleic.co.uk *Kitchen & bedroom furniture retailer*

Aztec Labels, Kidderminster Industrial Estate, Spennells Valley Road, Kidderminster, Worcestershire, DY10 1XS Tel: (01562) 66518 Fax: (01562) 69802 E-mail: sales@azteclabel.co.uk *Label manufrs*

Aztec Oils Ltd, 31 Intake Road, Bolsover Business Park, Bolsover, Chesterfield, Derbyshire, S44 6BB Tel: (01246) 823007 Fax: (01246) 823014 E-mail: sales@aztecoils.co.uk *Industrial oil products & lubricants*

Aztec Plant Displays, 18 Eden Way, Pages Industrial Estate, Leighton Buzzard, Bedfordshire, LU7 4TZ Tel: (01525) 372322 Fax: (01525) 379426 E-mail: info@aztec.co.uk *Office cleaning contractors*

Aztec Precision Engineering, Pixmore Avenue, Letchworth Garden City, Hertfordshire, SG6 1JG Tel: (01462) 677888 Fax: (01462) 677888 *Precision engineers*

Aztec Presentations Ltd, Unit 7B, Browns Place, Leeds, LS11 0EF Tel: 0113-277 7799 E-mail: sales@aztecpresentations.co.uk *Computer graphic presentations services & sign manufrs*

Aztec Signs, 10 Lound Road, Kendal, Cumbria, LA9 7DT Tel: (01539) 724897 Fax: (01539) 724897 *Sign manufrs*

▶ Aztec Software & Technology Services Ltd., 1, Berkeey Street, London, W1J 8DJ Tel: (020) 7016 9852 E-mail: rphanee@aztecsoft.com

Aztec Tooling & Moulding Co. Ltd, Buckholt Drive, Worcester, WR4 9ND Tel: (01905) 754466 Fax: (01905) 754475 E-mail: aztectmltd@aol.com *Toolmakers & moulders*

Aztec Upvc Specialists, Unit 29-30, Colliery Close, Dinnington, Sheffield, S25 3QX Tel: (01909) 564946 Fax: (01909) 550418 E-mail: northfibre@aol.co.uk *Asbestos, environmental consultants, testing, recovery, analysts services*

Aztech Components Ltd, 78 Atcham Close, Winyates East, Redditch, Worcestershire, B98 0NZ Tel: (01527) 500151 Fax: (01527) 500151 E-mail: sales@aztech.uk.net *Manufacturer of bespoke robot covers. Distributor of pneumatics and fittings. Distributor of galvanised channel, conduit tray, fixings and fittings. Distributor of environmental storage and clean-up products include drum and IBC storage units, plus portable berms and containment pools. Consumables include absorbent booms, socks, pads plus both static and mobile spill kits.*

Aztech Microcentres Ltd, 322 Hemdean Road, Caversham, Reading, RG4 7QS Tel: 0118-946 6600 Fax: 0118-946 1076 E-mail: sales@aztechmicros.com *IT solution centre*

Aztech Precision Ltd, Church Lane, Barnham, Bognor Regis, West Sussex, PO22 0BP Tel: (01243) 555140 Fax: (01243) 555870 E-mail: mail@aztech-precision.co.uk *Plastic mould toolmakers*

Aztecs Pheonix Environmental Ltd, Ashmore, Maygersbury Park, Stow On The Wold, Cheltenham, Gloucestershire, GL54 1DU Tel: (01451) 830456 Fax: (01451) 830678 E-mail: info.apel@virgin.net *Flat roofing suppliers*

Aztek Services Ltd, Unit 8 Hall Barn Industrial Estate, Isleham, Ely, Cambridgeshire, CB7 5RB Tel: (01638) 781799 Fax: (01638) 781768 E-mail: sales@aztekservices.co.uk *Alarm systems installation*

▶ Azura Soft Furnishings, Chapter Street, Manchester, M40 2AY Tel: 0161-202 4148

Azure Ltd, Unit 10 Herrington Barn, Herrington, Dorchester, Dorset, DT2 9PU Tel: (01305) 251771 Fax: (01305) 251779 E-mail: info@azure.com *Computer vision system manufrs*

Azure Blue Design, 61 Viceroy Court, Wilmslow Road, Didsbury, Manchester, M20 2RH Tel: (07886) 443129 E-mail: sales@azure-blue.co.uk *Azure-Blue is a small multi-disciplinary 3-D design agency based in Manchester specialising in the design and supply of Point-of-Purchase display stands and retail equipment. We can design, visualise, prototype and supply point of purchase displays to compliment your product or services.*

▶ Azure Hygiene, 14 Chalgrove Way, Emmer Green, Reading, RG4 8SJ Tel: 0845 2572727 E-mail: info@azurehygiene.co.uk *Established washroom hygiene and waste management services. Registered Waste Carriers with the Environment Agency we collect sanitary, clinical, sharps and nappy waste. We also supply quality air care systems, water sanitizers, vending machines and general washroom products and consumables. Flexible and reliable servicing to suit. Azure offers outstanding value for money..*

Azure Leisure Pools, 150 London Road, Bagshot, Surrey, GU19 5DG Tel: (01276) 475566 Fax: (01276) 475201 *Swimming pools manufrs*

▶ Azure Mobile Communications, 36a Church Hill, Loughton, Essex, IG10 1LA Tel: 0871 2714075 Fax: 0871 2714074 E-mail: mail@azuremobile.com *Mobile Phone Dealer - Specialising in Business mobile phones, Satellite Navigation, Car Kits, Tracking. Trade Enquiries also Welcome for Mobile Phones, Software, VOIP Products, Memory Cards Etc.. (Buy & Sell)*

▶ Azurra Mosaics, PO Box 2801, Purley, Surrey, CR8 1WX Tel: (0845) 0908110 Fax: (0870) 1313319 E-mail: info@mosaics.co.uk *Online mosaic tile store, selling Azurra brand original vitreous glass mosaics, crystal clear glass*

continued

mosaics, gold streak /gold fleck mosaics and craft mosaics. Tile sizes are 2cm x 2cm and 1cm x 1cm. Ideal for kitchens, bathrooms, pools, spas and mosaic art. Hardwearing, colourfast and frostproof tiles make them ideal for use indoors and outdoors.

Azzuri Connection Ltd, Haleworth House, Tite Hill, Egham, Surrey, TW20 0LT Tel: (01784) 486550 Fax: (01784) 486587 *Communication system installers*

Azzurri Communications Ltd, Elmhirst Lane, Dodworth, Barnsley, South Yorkshire, S75 4LS Tel: (01226) 777111 Fax: (01226) 777100 *Office equipment distributors*

Azzurri Communications Ltd, 6 Manor Court, Barnes Wallis Road, Fareham, Hampshire, PO15 5TH Tel: (01489) 889300 Fax: (01489) 553554 E-mail: sales@azzu.co.uk *One stop telephone shop*

B A A Lynton, Medici Court, 67-69 New Bond Street, London, W1S 1DF Tel: (020) 7907 9200 Fax: (020) 7907 9299 *Property developers*

B A Amusements Ltd, Hayfield Road, Kirkcaldy, Fife, KY1 2HP Tel: (01592) 641133 Fax: (01592) 642345 *Amusements machines hire*

B A Beds & Pine, 4 Joyce Dawson Way, London, SE28 8RA Tel: (020) 8310 0200 Fax: (020) 8312 1208 *Sell beds & bedroom furniture*

B A C Ltd, Faringdon Avenue, Romford, RM3 8SP Tel: (01708) 382200 Fax: (01708) 382308 E-mail: sales@bac.ltd.uk *Window & door installers & manufrs*

B A C Corrosion Control Ltd, Stafford Park 11, Telford, Shropshire, TF3 3AY Tel: (01952) 290321 Fax: (01952) 290325 E-mail: sales@bacgroup.com *Cathodic protection systems & services*

B A C Fire & Security, 591 Fishponds Road, Fishponds, Bristol, BS16 3AA Tel: 0117-958 3838 Fax: 0117-958 3848 E-mail: admin@bacsecurity.com *CCTV installation services also intruder & fire alarm systems*

B & A Chamberlain Ltd, Trowell Lane, Sutton Bonington, Loughborough, Leicestershire, LE12 5RW Tel: (01509) 856357 Fax: 0115-985 3221 E-mail: cabins@bachamberlain.fsnet.co.uk *Portable buildings, modular building & jack leg building suppliers*

▶ B A Corry Ltd, 24 Whitelaw Road, Southampton, SO15 8LJ Tel: (023) 8077 2854 Fax: (023) 8078 7013 E-mail: office@bacorryltd.co.uk

B A E, 8 Eagle Estate, Brookers Road, Billingshurst, West Sussex, RH14 9RZ Tel: (01403) 782696 *Motor vehicle repairs & recovery*

▶ B A E Systems Ltd, Hillend Industrial Park, Dunfermline, Fife, KY11 9HQ Tel: (01383) 822131

B A E Systems plc, Stirling Square, 6 Carlton Gardens, London, SW1Y 5AD Tel: (01252) 373232 Fax: (01252) 383000 *Aeronautical designing & engineering services*

B A E Systems, Elettra Avenue, Waterlooville, Hampshire, PO7 7XS Tel: (023) 9226 4466 Fax: (023) 9226 0246 *Geophysical equipment manufrs*

B A E Systems, Spares Logistic Centre Vickers Drive South, Brooklands Busin, Weybridge, Surrey, KT13 0UJ Tel: (01932) 352611 Fax: (01932) 353355 *Logistics centre*

B A E Systems Avionics Ltd, Christopher Martin Road, Basildon, Essex, SS14 3EL Tel: (01268) 522822 Fax: (01268) 883140 *Navigation equipment manufrs* Also at: Southampton

B A E Systems Land Systems (Weapons & Vehicles) Ltd, Scotswood Road, Newcastle Upon Tyne, NE99 1BX Tel: 0191-273 8888 Fax: 0191-273 2324 *Manufacturers of armoured military vehicles* Also at: Leeds

B A E Systems Land Systems (Bridging) Ltd, P O Box 37, Wolverhampton, WV4 6YN Tel: (01902) 405050 Fax: (01902) 355354 E-mail: kathryn.fisher@baesystems.com Principal Export Areas: Worldwide *Aluminium fabricators; consulting engineers, designers*

B A E Systems Marine Ltd, 1048 Govan Road, Glasgow, G51 4XP Tel: 0141-445 8000 Fax: 0141-445 2325 E-mail: sales.marketing@baesystems.com *Shipbuilders*

B A Engineering, 4a Tulnacross Road, Cookstown, County Tyrone, BT80 9NH Tel: (028) 8675 1117 Fax: (028) 8675 1017 *Plant, machinery engineering & manufrs*

B A F Printers Ltd, Portland House, Cross Chancellor Street, Leeds, LS6 2TG Tel: 0113-243 9788 Fax: 0113-243 8741 E-mail: office@bafprinters.co.uk *Label printers & medication technologies suppliers*

B A Halston Heating, Stoney Croft, The Lynch, Kensworth, Dunstable, Bedfordshire, LU6 3QZ Tel: (01582) 872445 Fax: (01582) 872445 *Heating engineers & plumbers*

▶ B A Henderson, Princess Court, 4 Princess Way, Prudhoe, Northumberland, NE42 6PL Tel: (01661) 831613 Fax: (01661) 831731 E-mail: bahendersontcs@aol.com

B A Jones & Co., 27 Padgets Lane, Redditch, Worcestershire, B98 0RB Tel: (01527) 523377 Fax: (01527) 523377 E-mail: stevethewoodturner@blueyonder.co.uk *Hand wood turners, batch work or one off's*

B A Kirk, Tadwell Farm, Elm Lane, Minster on Sea, Sheerness, Kent, ME12 3SQ Tel: (01795) 876723 Fax: (01795) 876723 *Motor vehicle & agricultural engineers*

B A L Broadcast, Unit 23 Croft Road Industrial Estate, Newcastle, Staffordshire, ST5 0TW Tel: (024) 7631 6500 Fax: (024) 7649 1117 E-mail: sales@bal.co.uk *Broadcast electronics manufrs*

▶ B & A Metal Finishers Ltd, Unit 4, Ellingham Way Industrial Estate, Ashford, Kent, TN23 6NF Tel: (01233) 661652 Fax: (01333) 624500 E-mail: julie@kmd.co.uk *Powder coating*

B A P Air Co Ltd, 10a West St, Southend-on-Sea, SS2 6HJ Tel: (01702) 347222 Fax: (01702) 331508 *Air conditioning*

B A Pest Control, 9 Palmerston Road, Stockport, Cheshire, SK2 7EA Tel: 0161-483 0123 Fax: 0161-483 0123 *Pest control services*

B & A Quilting Co. Ltd, Oxford Mill, Oxford Street East, Ashton-under-Lyne, Lancashire, OL7 0LT Tel: 0161-330 5030 Fax: 0161-339 0418 E-mail: info@ba-quilting.co.uk *Quilters to the trade, sofa bed & mattress manufrs*

▶ B A S Castings Ltd, Wharf Road Industrial Estate, Pinxton, Nottingham, NG16 6LE Tel: (01773) 812028 Fax: (01773) 861948 E-mail: sales@bascastings.com *Iron foundy*

B A S Components Ltd, 2 Cramptons Road, Sevenoaks, Kent, TN14 5EF Tel: (01732) 450011 Fax: (01732) 455884 E-mail: info@bas-airospace.co.uk *Aircraft, aerospace & automotive industry fasteners manufrs*

B A S Knitwear, 8 Woolley Street, Manchester, M8 8WE Tel: 0161-833 9870 Fax: 0161-833 9870 *Knitwear wholesaler*

B A S S Hydro Coatings Ltd, Unit 101 Tenth Avenue, Deeside Industrial Park, Deeside, Clwyd, CH5 2UA Tel: (01244) 281315 Fax: (01244) 281316 E-mail: coil-coatings-uk@coatings.basf.org *Metal coating manufrs*

B A S Systems Land Systems Weapons & Vehicles, PO Box 106, Telford, Shropshire, TF1 6QW Tel: (01952) 224500 Fax: (01952) 243910 *Customer support services for armoured vehicles*

▶ B & A Scaffolding Ltd, Unit D, Therm Road, Hull, HU8 7BF Tel: (01482) 325952

B A Shaw Contractors Ltd, 90 Mount Pleasant Road, Newtownabbey, County Antrim, BT37 0NQ Tel: (028) 9036 5706 Fax: (028) 9036 5570 *Building contractors*

B A T A Lloyds Ltd, 7 Norwood, Beverley, North Humberside, HU17 9ET Tel: (01482) 868135 Fax: (01482) 861173 *Agricultural merchants*

B A Thorne Ltd, Eagle Road, Moons Moat North Industrial Es, Redditch, Worcestershire, B98 9HF Tel: (01527) 584714 Fax: (01527) 584784 E-mail: bat@bathorne.co.uk Principal Export Areas: Worldwide *Import cable production machinery*

B A W Precision Engineering Ltd, Cwmtawe Business Park, Alloy Industrial Estate, Pontardawe, Swansea, SA8 4EZ Tel: (01792) 862141 Fax: (01792) 865545 E-mail: peter@bawengineering.co.uk *Electronic engineers & machine builders*

▶ B & A Whelan, 52-54 High Street, Blue Town, Sheerness, Kent, ME12 1RW Tel: (01795) 663879 Fax: (01795) 661934

▶ B A Williams, Unit 21, Top Barn Business Centre, Worcester Road, Holt Heath, Worcester, WR6 6NH Tel: (01905) 620791 Fax: (01905) 621751 E-mail: info@dawbulidingcontractors.co.uk

B A X Global Ltd, Unitair Centre, Great South West Road, Feltham, Middlesex, TW14 8NT Tel: (020) 8899 3000 Fax: (020) 8899 3111 Principal Export Areas: Worldwide *Air freight forwarders*

▶ B Amberg, 31 Elkstone Road, London, W10 5NT Tel: (020) 8960 2000 Fax: (020) 8960 2321

B & B Attachments Ltd, Unit 39 Colbourne Cresent, Nelson Park, Cramlington, Northumberland, NE23 1WB Tel: (01670) 737373 Fax: (01670) 736286 *Distributor of fork lift truck attachments*

B & B Attachments Ltd, Guildgate House, Pelican Lane, Newbury, Berkshire, RG14 1NX Tel: (01635) 232000 Fax: (01635) 237444 E-mail: info@bandbattachments.com *Fork lift truck attachment distributors*

B B Beresford, Goods Road, Belper, Derbyshire, DE56 1UU Tel: (01773) 825959 Fax: (01773) 821213 E-mail: beresford@btconnect.com Sales Contact: J. Beresford *Glass fibre fabricators & mouldings manufacturers. In addition, manufacturers of motor vehicle bodies (glass fibre) & plastic vacuum formed products*

▶ B & B Builders Ltd, Tolver Farm Cottage, Tolver, Long Rock, Penzance, Cornwall, TR20 8YL Tel: (01736) 330996 Fax: (01736) 330996

B & B Business Equipment, 137 Lovibonds Avenue, Orpington, Kent, BR6 8EN Tel: (01689) 853821 Fax: (01689) 851114 E-mail: info@ukofficeshop.com *Office equipment maintenance & supplies*

B B C Fire Protection Ltd, St Florian House, Ayton Road, Wymondham, Norfolk, NR18 0RD Tel: (01953) 857700 Fax: (01953) 857750 E-mail: sales@bbcfire.co.uk *Fire alarms & security systems*

B & B Catering, 5 Cross Lane West, Gravesend, Kent, DA11 7PZ Tel: (01474) 535427 Fax: (01474) 322500 E-mail: sally@bandbcatering.co.uk *Catering equipment hire*

B B Christorfersen, Crimond Airfield, Crimond, Fraserburgh, Aberdeenshire, AB43 8QQ Tel: (01346) 532686 Fax: (01346) 532294

B & B Construction Ltd, Baulker Farm, Baulker Lane, Farnsfield, Newark, Nottinghamshire, NG22 8HP Tel: (01623) 883771 Fax: (01623) 883771 E-mail: bernard@bbconstruction.freeserve.co.uk *Building work*

B & B Contractors Ltd, Tamar Ridge, Cox Park, Coxpark, Gunnislake, Cornwall, PL18 9BD Tel: (01822) 834397 Fax: (01822) 834397 *Waste & agricultural contractors & farming services*

B B Conveyors Ltd, 5 Hallcroft Industrial Estate, Aurilac Way, Retford, Nottinghamshire, DN22 7PX Tel: (01777) 711111 Fax: (01777) 711501 *Conveyor belting/systems & materials handling*

B & B Event Hire, Lyon Road, Walton-on-Thames, Surrey, KT12 3PU Tel: (01932) 253253 Fax: (01932) 254976 *Event hire*

B B F Co. Ltd, Unit 5 Bishopsgate Industrial Estate, Cashs Lane, Coventry, CV1 4NN Tel: (024) 7622 7925 Fax: (024) 7655 3097 E-mail: nikki@bbfco.ltd.uk *Steel fabricators*

B B F CNC Machining, 31 Knowl Piece, Hitchin, Hertfordshire, SG4 0TY Tel: (01462) 432700 Fax: (01462) 431414 E-mail: bbf.cnc@btinternet.com *CNC engineers*

B B F Fencing, Victoria Street Sawmills, Stoke-on-Trent, ST4 6HD Tel: (01782) 717757 Fax: (01782) 712565 E-mail: trentwoodtimber@talktalkbusiness.net *Timber merchants*

B B F Services Ltd, 49 Saxon Road, Whitby, North Yorkshire, YO21 3NU Tel: (01947) 601173 Fax: (0870) 7598439 E-mail: bbfservicesltd@aol.com *Service engineers, cutting & creasing machine*

▶ B & B Fabrications Ltd, Units B & D, Bedewell Industrial Park, Adair, Hebburn, Tyne & Wear, NE31 2XQ Tel: 0191-430 1908 Fax: 0191-428 0615 *Fabrication supplier*

B B Fencing Ltd, Foxley Farm, Draycote Water, Kytes Hardwick, Rugby, Warwickshire, CV23 8AB Tel: (01788) 812800 Fax: (01788) 812500 *Fencing contractors*

B B Glass Ltd, 7a Buddle Road, Clay Flatts Industrial Estate, Workington, Cumbria, CA14 3YD Tel: (01900) 65445 Fax: (01900) 64789 *Glass suppliers/PVC window manufrs*

▶ B B H Ltd, Unit 9-10, 251 Holt Road, Horsford, Norwich, NR10 3EB Tel: (01603) 897350 Fax: (01603) 890080 E-mail: bbh@bbhltd.fx.co.net *Plastic products*

B B J Engineering Ltd, Apex Way, Diplocks Industrial Estate, Hailsham, East Sussex, BN27 3WA Tel: (01323) 848842 Fax: (01323) 848846 E-mail: sandy@aspenpumps.com *Manufacturers of accessories & equipment of pumps*

B & B Knitwear Ltd, Westgate, Long Eaton, Nottingham, NG10 1EF Tel: 0115-972 2471 Fax: 0115-946 3815 *Clothing manufrs*

B B M Audio Visual Specialists Ltd, Studio 2, Northbrook, Mitcheldever, Winchester, Hampshire, SO21 3AJ Tel: (01962) 774857 Fax: (01962) 774144 E-mail: audiovisual.bbm@btinternet.com *Audio visual equipment hire*

B B M Electronics Group Ltd, Kestral House, Garth Road, Morden, Surrey, SM4 4LP Tel: (020) 8330 3111 Fax: (020) 8330 3222 E-mail: enquiries@trantec.co.uk *Radio microphones manufrs*

B B Mathias Ltd, 102 St Davids Road, Letterston, Haverfordwest, Dyfed, SA62 5SJ Tel: (01348) 840318 Fax: (01348) 840900 *Refrigeration contractors*

▶ B B Moulding Ltd, Unit 2 New Street, Bridgtown, Cannock, Staffordshire, WS11 0DD Tel: (01543) 468698

▶ B B N Communicatios, 18 Strand Street, Poole, Dorset, BH15 1SB Tel: (01202) 669922 Fax: (01202) 669922 E-mail: sales@bbncomms.co.uk *Computer systems for emergency services*

B B P Marketing Ltd, Lowland Works, Lowland Road, Mirfield, West Yorkshire, WF14 8LY Tel: (01924) 480393 Fax: (01924) 480632 E-mail: sales@bb-plastics.co.uk Principal Export Areas: Worldwide *One of the UK's largest manufacturers of reusable & virtually unbreakable plastic glassware into the catering distribution network*

B & B Precision Engineering, 9 Station Court, Park Mill Way, Clayton West, Huddersfield, HD8 9XJ Tel: (01484) 866386 Fax: (01484) 866300 *Precision engineers*

B B R Engineering (Shropshire) Ltd, King Street, Broseley, Shropshire, TF12 5LT Tel: (01952) 882597 Fax: (01952) 883955 E-mail: sales@bbrengineering.co.uk *General machining services*

B B R Graphic Engineers, Kings Yard, Low Mill Road, Ossett, West Yorkshire, WF5 8ND Tel: (01924) 263339 Fax: (01924) 280164 E-mail: service@bbrgraphics.com *Printing engineers*

B B S Building Components, Spon Lane, West Bromwich, West Midlands, B70 6AP Tel: 0121-553 5509 Fax: 0121-500 5425 E-mail: mail@bbsrooflights.co.uk *Roof light & glazed structure manufrs* Also at: Manchester & Newcastle upon Tyne

B B S Cutter, 282 Upper Balsall Heath Road, Birmingham, B12 9DR Tel: 0121-440 4034 Fax: 0121-446 4090 E-mail: info@bbscutters.co.uk Principal Export Areas: Worldwide *Rotary knife manufrs*

B B S Gloucester Ltd, Unit 1 Ross Site, Alton Road Industrial Estate, Ross-on-Wye, Herefordshire, HR9 5NB Tel: (01989) 564404 Fax: (01989) 566635 *Pressings manufrs*

B B S Packaging, Wakeford Farm, Aldermaston Road, Pamber End, Tadley, Hampshire, RG26 5QN Tel: (01256) 851281 Fax: (01256) 850429 *Distributors or agents of packaging material*

▶ B B S Roof Light Co., Bedes Way, Bede Industrial Estate, Jarrow, Tyne & Wear, NE32 3HG Tel: 0191-489 0960 Fax: 0191-489 2303 E-mail: bbs.factory@keme.co.uk *Roof lights manufrs*

▶ B B S Security Systems Ltd, Vision House, 25 Dick O' The Banks Road, Crossways, Dorchester, Dorset, DT2 8BJ Tel: (01305) 851516 Fax: (01305) 851517 E-mail: mail@bbssecurity.co.uk *CCTV systems & networked cctv systems*

▶ B B S Transport Ltd, 26 Bayton Road, Exhall, Coventry, CV7 9EJ Tel: (024) 7664 5666

B B Services, 75 Ballyutoag Road, Belfast, BT14 8SS Tel: (028) 9082 5393 Fax: (028) 9082 5393 *Machinery importers*

B & B Supplies, 641 Garratt Lane, London, SW18 4SX Tel: (020) 8946 2957 Fax: (020) 8946 2435 *Plumbing, heating equipment suppliers & distributors*

B B T Thermo Technology UK Ltd, Danesmoor Works, Pilsley Road, Danesmoor, Chesterfield, Derbyshire, S45 9BY Tel: (01246) 250251 Fax: (01246) 250313 *Domestic central heating boiler manufrs*

B & B Tractors, Windmill House Farm, Forest Road, Warsop, Mansfield, Nottinghamshire, NG20 0EP Tel: (01623) 847171 Fax: (01623) 847485 E-mail: enquiries@bbtractors.co.uk *Agricultural machinery distributors*

B B W Engineering Co Aston Ltd, 55 Stanhope Street, Birmingham, B12 0UX Tel: 0121-446 5223 Fax: 0121-446 5305 E-mail: m.eaton@btconnect.com *Engineers machinists & turned parts*

B B & W W Erectors Ltd, 51 Uckfield Road, Enfield, Middlesex, EN3 6AS Tel: (01992) 717417 Fax: (01992) 767894 *Steel erectors*

B & B Zinc Alloys Ltd, 233 Station Road, Knowle, Solihull, West Midlands, B93 0PU Tel: (01564) 773062 Fax: (01564) 778907 *Metal brokers*

B Batch Electrical Ltd, 2025 Spring Bank West, Hull, HU5 5ER Tel: (01482) 506903 Fax: (01482) 571900 E-mail: tristan@bbatch.karou.co.uk *Shop fitters manufrs*

▶ B Brackenborough, 44 Westfield Road, Birchington, Kent, CT7 9RN Tel: (07751) 546520 E-mail: benplaster1@msn.com *all plastering undertaken no job too big or small please call im sure ill be able to assist you thanks for looking*

B. Braun Medical Ltd, Brookdale Road, Thorncliffe Park Estate, Chapeltown, Sheffield, S35 2PW Tel: 0114-225 9000 Fax: 0114-225 9111 E-mail: info@bbraun.com *Medical supply & surgical instrument manufrs* Also at: London W1

B Brooks Norwich Ltd, Beckhithe, Little Melton, Norwich, NR9 3NP Tel: (01603) 810137 Fax: (01603) 812272 E-mail: sales@ppcsfoodservice.co.uk *Meat processors*

▶ B B's Copy & Stationery Shop, Hawthorne House, 1 Exeter Road, Ivybridge, Devon, PL21 0BN Tel: (01752) 893959 Fax: (01752) 893959

B C A S Ltd, Unit 8 Thames Park, Lester Way, Wallingford, Oxfordshire, OX10 9TA Tel: (01491) 821737 Fax: (01491) 821730 E-mail: sales@bcaslimited.co.uk *Air compressor distributors & agents*

B C Abrasives Ltd, Cleeton Cottage, Cleeton St. Mary, Kidderminster, Worcestershire, DY14 0QU Tel: (01584) 891202 Fax: (01584) 891002 E-mail: bcabrasives2@btconnect.com *Glass bead, alu oxides, metallic & abrasive media*

B C Agricultural Services, 26 Corsend Road, Hartpury, Gloucester, GL19 3BP Tel: (01452) 700521 Fax: (01452) 700521 E-mail: bcagricultural@btconnect.com *Agricultural contractors*

▶ B C Aviation, Old Lamb House, Walton Elms, Marnhull, Sturminster Newton, Dorset, DT10 1QG Tel: (01258) 820491 Fax: (01258) 821464 E-mail: sales@bcaviation.co.uk *Ground support equipment*

B C B International Ltd, Units 7-8, Clydesmuir Road Industrial Estate, Cardiff, CF24 2QS Tel: (029) 2043 3700 Fax: (029) 2043 3701 E-mail: info@bcbin.com *Survival equipment manufrs*

B C Barton & Son Ltd, Granville Iron Works, Oldbury, West Midlands, B69 2NJ Tel: 0121-557 2272 Fax: 0121-557 2276 E-mail: pressworkers@b-c-b.co.uk Principal Export Areas: Middle East & North America *Heavy steel pressings*

B C C Ltd, PO Box 5875, Halesowen, West Midlands, B63 4RF Tel: 0121-501 2288 Fax: 0121-585 5757 E-mail: seb@bcclimited.co.uk *Project collaboration tools suppliers*

B C C Marketing Services Ltd, Belgrade Centre, Denington Road, Denington Industrial Estate, Wellingborough, Northamptonshire, NN8 2QH Tel: (01933) 443322 Fax: (01933) 441844 E-mail: info@bccmarketing.co.uk *Telephone marketing service*

B C Computing Ltd, 57 Ferrybridge Road, Castleford, West Yorkshire, WF10 4JW Tel: (01977) 667777 Fax: (01977) 667701 *Computer systems consultancy*

▶ B C Connections Ltd, 27a Erewash Square, Ilkeston, Derbyshire, DE7 5SP Tel: 0115-977 0586 Fax: (0870) 1319548 E-mail: bcconnection@emailaccount.com *We supply logistic enforcement & marketing support to clients, personal & house security, bluetooth products, golf trolley, metal products & storage equipment*

B C D Marine Ltd, Vanguard House, Vanguard Road, Gapton Hall Industrial Estate, Great Yarmouth, Norfolk, NR31 0NT Tel: (01493) 444002 Fax: (01493) 652576 *Diving services or contractors*

B C Dyson & Co., Prescott Lodge, Prescott Street, Halifax, West Yorkshire, HX1 2QW Tel: (01422) 360934 Fax: (01422) 320379 E-mail: b.c.dyson@bt.openworld.com *Industrial plant, structural & civil engineers*

B C E Scotland Ltd, 4 119 Cambuslang Road, Rutherglen, Glasgow, G73 1BW Tel: 0141-613 1850 Fax: 0141-613 1850 *Catering equipment & catering trailers manufrs*

B C Electrical, 8 Hurstleigh Heights, Thornton-Cleveleys, Lancashire, FY5 5NY Tel: (01253) 824781 E-mail: sales@bcelectrical.co.uk *electrical services*

B C Electrical Techniques Ltd, Stocklake, Aylesbury, Buckinghamshire, HP20 1DA Tel: (01296) 481995 Fax: (01296) 394158 E-mail: info@bcet.co.uk *Transformer manufrs*

B & C Express Ltd, Station Road, Potterhanworth, Lincoln, LN4 2DX Tel: (01522) 791369 Fax: (01522) 794262 E-mail: sales@bandcexpress.co.uk *Motor cycle part wholesalers*

B C F Technology Ltd, 3 Rutherford Square, Brucefield Industrial Estate, Livingston, West Lothian, EH54 9BU Tel: (01506) 460023 Fax: (01506) 460045 E-mail: office@bcftech.demon.co.uk *Electronic product manufrs*

▶ B & C Fabrications, Unit I Stonebridge Court, Nottingham, NG3 2GY Tel: 0115-947 2444 Fax: 0115-947 2777 *Steel fabricators*

B & C Fixings Ltd, Archimedes House, 20 Cleveland Trading Estate, Darlington, County Durham, DL1 2PB Tel: (01325) 286842 Fax: (01325) 352563 *Fixing specialists*

B C H Relays Ltd, Unit 15, Phoenix Business Park, Brindley Road, Dodwells Bridge Industrial Estate, Hinckley, Leicestershire, LE10 3BY Tel: (01455) 239675 Fax: (01455) 238795 E-mail: billpower@btconnect.com *Relay manufacturers including electromechanical & flag*

B C Harper Ltd, 7-9 Vincent Street, Derby, DE23 8BT Tel: (01332) 773333 Fax: (01332) 773777

▶ B C I Electronics Ltd, 20 Mercers Row, Cambridge, CB5 8HY Tel: (01223) 472360 Fax: (01223) 352386 *Contract Manufacturer of Electronic products*

B C I Stretchers Ltd, 386-388 South Eldon Street, South Shields, Tyne & Wear, NE33 5SY Tel: 0191-455 3984 Fax: 0191-456 9653 E-mail: info@bci-stretchers.co.uk Principal Export Areas: Worldwide *Rescue stretcher suppliers & manufrs*

B C L, 12 The Square, Caterham, Surrey, CR3 6QA Tel: (01883) 340311 Fax: (01883) 342144 E-mail: solutions@bclsystems.com *Office equipment*

B C L Construction Ltd, 263 Haydons Road, London, SW19 8TY Tel: (020) 8543 6221 Fax: (020) 8543 9725 E-mail: sales@bclltdconstruction.co.uk *Office designers & refurbishers*

B C L Distribution, Hornbeam Park, Hookstone Road, Harrogate, North Yorkshire, HG2 8QT Tel: (01423) 879787 Fax: (01423) 879030 E-mail: information@bcldistribution.com Principal Export Areas: Worldwide *Electronic component distributors or agents*

B C M Group P.L.C., Unit 1, Wildmere Close, Banbury, Oxfordshire, OX16 3TL Tel: (01295) 267671 Fax: (01295) 269142 *Photocopy & fax sales & service*

B C Marketing Ltd, 7 Eastway Business Village, Olivers Place, Fulwood, Preston, PR2 9WT Tel: (01772) 654654 Fax: (01772) 652233 E-mail: mail@bcmarketing.co.uk *Marketing consultants & advertising agents*

B & C Non-Ferrous Foundry Ltd, Unit 3, Bedwas House Industrial Estate, Caerphilly, Mid Glamorgan, CF83 8DW Tel: (029) 2088 6871 Fax: (029) 2086 9916 E-mail: ceri@bcfoundry.co.uk *Non ferrous casting manufrs*

B & C Office Cleaning Services, 25 Castlereagh St, London, W1H 5YR Tel: (020) 7636 0519 *Cleaning service agents*

B C P Industrial Coatings, Unit 14 Hitchin Business Centre, Wilbury Way, Hitchin, Hertfordshire, SG4 0AP Tel: (01462) 440804 Fax: (01462) 440804 *Powder coating services*

B C P Paterson Ltd, Boyle Street, Blackburn, BB1 6EG Tel: (01254) 687900 Fax: (01254) 681736 *Packaging manufrs*

B C P Search & Selection Ltd, Unit 9b Intec 2, Wade Road, Basingstoke, Hampshire, RG24 8NE Tel: (01256) 470704 Fax: (01256) 844054 E-mail: mail@bcprecruitment.co.uk *Personnel consultants*

B C R Publishing Ltd, 3 Cobden Court, Wimpole Close, Bromley, BR2 9JF Tel: (020) 8466 6987 Fax: (020) 8466 0654 E-mail: bcr@bcrpub.co.uk *Publishers of books on factoring*

B C S A Ltd, 4 Whitehall Court, Westminster, London, SW1A 2ES Tel: (020) 7839 8566 Fax: (020) 7976 1634 E-mail: gillian.mitchell@steelconstruction.org *Trade association*

B C S Steel Fabrication, Carron Works, Stenhouse Road, Carron, Falkirk, FK2 8DR Tel: (01324) 631528 Fax: (01324) 630729 *Steel fabricators*

B C Security Ltd, 8 Sandbach Rd South, Alsager, Stoke-on-Trent, ST7 2LU Tel: 01270 884646 *Security & CCTV*

▶ B & C Services, Premier House, 46 Victoria Road, Burgess Hill, West Sussex, RH15 9LR Tel: 01444 248474 Fax: 01444 870146 E-mail: info@redwellassociates.co.uk *Full Bookkeeping and Payroll Services catering for any size of business. Mentoring service also available.*

B & C Supplies Ltd, Unit 1 Burnham Way, London, SE26 5AG Tel: (020) 8776 5757 Fax: (020) 8776 5750 E-mail: sales@bandcsupplies.co.uk *Janitorial cleaning & hygiene products services*

B.C. & T. Consultants Ltd, Arundel House, Byland Road, Whitby, North Yorkshire, YO21 1JH Tel: (01947) 604871 Fax: (01947) 600010 E-mail: general@bct-consultants.co.uk *Consulting engineers*

B C T Engineering Ltd, 4 Manor Way, Woking, Surrey, GU22 9JX Tel: (01483) 767756 Fax: (01483) 740548 E-mail: mr.dental@virgin.net *Precision & development engineers*

B C Technology Ltd, 3 Wallis Close, Park Farm Industrial Estate, Wellingborough, Northamptonshire, NN8 6AG Tel: (01933) 405050 Fax: (01933) 405454 E-mail: info@bctechnologyltd.co.uk *Audio video door entry equipment agents services*

B C Thornell, Churchleaze, Codrington Road, Westerleigh, Bristol, BS37 8RQ Tel: (01454) 316935 Fax: (01454) 329642 E-mail: manc@bcthornell.fsnet.co.uk *Second hand farm machinery retailers*

B C Whitmore Ltd, 146 Bridgeman Street, Walsall, WS2 9PG Tel: (01922) 646212 Fax: (01922) 627591 *Saddlery manufrs*

B Carnegie, 154 Stonhouse Street, London, SW4 6BE Tel: (020) 7627 3119 *Leather garment repairs, alterations & manufrs*

B Clatworthy & Sons, Greyhouse Farm, St Brides Wentlodge, Newport, Gwent, NP10 8SQ Tel: (01633) 680235 Fax: (01633) 680235 *Agricultural contractors*

▶ B Clean Cleaning Services Ltd, 110 Methil Brae, Methil, Leven, Fife, KY8 3LR Tel: (01333) 426871 E-mail: bcleanservices@aol.com *Cleaning services*

B Conway Mechanical Handling Ltd, Hamilton Street, Oldham, OL4 1DA Tel: 0161-624 6621 Fax: 0161-627 2419 E-mail: admin@bconway.co.uk *Fork lift truck distributors*

B Cooke & Son Ltd, 58-59 Market Place, Hull, HU1 1RH Tel: (01482) 224412 Fax: (01482) 219793 E-mail: bcs@cooke.karoo.co.uk *Admiral chart shipping agents & nautical instrument manufrs*

B D B Marketing Ltd, D161-162 Fruit & Vegetable Market, New Covent Garden, Vauxall, London, SW8 5LL Tel: (020) 7720 4444 Fax: (020) 7720 4808 E-mail: bryan1brown@hotmail.com *Fruit & vegetable wholesalers*

B & D Blinds, 153 Castle Road West, Oldbury, West Midlands, B68 0EL Tel: 0121-421 1000 Fax: 0121-602 6008 *Blind suppliers & manufrs*

B & D Bolts Ltd, Central Warehouse, Bradford Road, Batley, West Yorkshire, WF17 5LW Tel: (01924) 470331 Fax: (01924) 473749 *Bolt & nut distributors/agents*

B D C, Unit 4 Redfields Industrial Estate, Redfields Lane, Church Crookham, Fleet, Hampshire, GU52 0RD Tel: (01252) 851688 Fax: (01252) 850577 *Data networking & installation services*

▶ B D C Ltd, Marshall Stevens Way, Trafford Park, Manchester, M17 1PP Tel: 0161-848 9988

B & D Clays & Chemicals Ltd, 10 Wandle Way, Willow Lane Trading Estate, Mitcham, Surrey, CR4 4NB Tel: (020) 8640 9221 Fax: (020) 8648 5033 E-mail: sales@bdclays.co.uk *Industrial cleaning materials distributors*

▶ B D Cravens, Rossfield Road, Ellesmere Port, CH65 3AW Tel: 0151-356 5654 Fax: 0151-356 7822 E-mail: bdcraveneng@tiscali.co.uk *CNC machining services & jigs, fixtures, special tools, gauges manufrs*

B & D Electrical Security & Surveillance Ltd, Unit 12 Grinnall Business Centre, Sandy Lane, Stourport-on-Severn, Worcestershire, DY13 9QB Tel: (01299) 822758 Fax: (01299) 827995 *Security & electrical installations*

▶ B D G Ceramics, Ure Street, Dundee, DD1 5JD Tel: (01382) 225985 Fax: (01382) 229866 *Dental laboratory*

B D G Group Ltd, 5 Wenlock Road, Lurgan, Craigavon, County Armagh, BT66 8QR Tel: (028) 3832 7741 Fax: (028) 3832 4358 E-mail: bdg@bdg.co.uk *Windows & conservatory manufrs*

▶ B D & H Ltd, 37 Europa Way, Martineau Lane, Norwich, NR1 2EN Tel: (01603) 620780 Fax: (01603) 630186

B D H Engineering, Unit 3, Granta Terrace, Great Shelford, Cambridge, CB2 5DJ Tel: (01223) 845088 Fax: (01223) 841973 E-mail: bdheng@aol.com *Precision engineers & turned parts manufrs*

B D & J M Heslop, Newton Grange, Shipton by Beningbrough, York, YO30 1BA Tel: (01347) 848206 Fax: (01347) 848443 *Engineering, haulage & storage*

▶ B D L Litho Ltd, 3 Bat & Ball Enterprise Centre, Bat & Ball Road, Sevenoaks, Kent, TN14 5LJ Tel: (01732) 464111 Fax: (01732) 462020

B D L Systems Ltd, 14 Denmark Lane, Poole, Dorset, BH15 2DG Tel: (01202) 669000 Fax: (01202) 682660 *Electronic engineers*

B D M, Unit 2 Hudcar Mill, Hudcar Lane, Bury, Lancashire, BL9 6HD Tel: 0161-764 1200 Fax: 0161-764 1235 E-mail: bdmmetal@absonline.net *Powder coating services*

B D M Fastenings, 10 Royce Road, Crawley, West Sussex, RH10 9NX Tel: (01293) 548186 Fax: (01293) 553274 E-mail: sales@bdm-fastenings.demon.co.uk *Stockists of nuts & bolts*

B & D Manufacturing Ltd, 15 Albert Road, Aldershot, Hampshire, GU11 1SZ Tel: (01252) 341553 Fax: (01252) 328824 Principal Export Areas: Worldwide *Cake decorating equipment sales*

B D P Computers & Data Processing Centre, 88-90 Tredworth Road, Gloucester, GL1 4QS Tel: (01452) 381425 Fax: (01452) 414718 *Computer reseller*

▶ B & D Patterns Ltd, Alan Bray Close, Hinckley, Leicestershire, LE10 3BP Tel: (01455) 445500 Fax: (01455) 445501 E-mail: sales@bdpatterns.co.uk *Aerospace machining fabricators*

B & D Print Services Ltd, Moss Side Industrail Estatemarathon Place, Leyland, PR26 7QN Tel: (01772) 435050 Fax: (01772) 426601 E-mail: sales@bdprints.co.uk *Commercial printers*

B D Profiles Ltd, PO Box 65, Cradley Heath, West Midlands, B64 5PP Tel: 0121-559 5136 Fax: 0121-561 4265 E-mail: syoung@bdprofiles.co.uk Principal Export Areas: Asia Pacific, Central Asia, Middle East, Africa, Central/East Europe, West Europe & South America *Flange manufacturers includiing stainless steel, pipeline & higher alloy*

B D R Micro Instruments Ltd, The Bringey, Church Street, Great Baddow, Chelmsford, CM2 7JW Tel: (01245) 476777 Fax: (01245) 475761 E-mail: info@bdr-micro.co.uk *Precision engineers*

B D S Ltd, Grangestone Industrial Estate, Ladywell Avenue, Girvan, Ayrshire, KA26 9PL Tel: (01465) 714848 Fax: (01465) 713857 E-mail: contact@bdf.ltd.uk *Hospital disposal products manufrs*

▶ B D S Dental Equipment Ltd, 2b Stanley Road, Barnsley, South Yorkshire, S70 3PG Tel: (01226) 208810 Fax: (01226) 208815 E-mail: info@bds-dental.co.uk *Independent wholesaler & retailer of dental surgery equipment*

B D S Electrical, 10 Calverley Drive, Leeds, LS13 3LN Tel: 0113-255 2389 *Alarm systems distributors & fitters*

▶ B D S Marketing & Research Ltd, Lonsdale, Single Hill, Shoscombe, Bath, BA2 8LZ Tel: (01761) 433035 Fax: (01761) 434579 E-mail: julian.clapp@bdsmarketing.co.uk *Marketing and research consultancy in building materials.*

B D S Solutions, Heywood House, 12 High Street, Cullompton, Devon, EX15 1AA Tel: (01884) 33221 Fax: (01884) 34555 E-mail: info@bds-solutions.co.uk *Computer consultancy*

B D S Sponsorship Ltd, 19 Waterside, 44-48 Wharf Road, London, N1 7UX Tel: (020) 7689 3333 Fax: (020) 7689 3344 E-mail: bds@sponsorship.co.uk *Sponsorship & marketing consultants*

B & D Shelving, Hadley Park Road Industrial Estate, Leegomery, Telford, Shropshire, TF1 6PY Tel: (01952) 247987 Fax: (01952) 247987 *Shelving & racking distribs*

▶ B D Structures Ltd, James Street, Westhoughton, Bolton, BL5 3QR Tel: (01942) 817770 Fax: (01942) 810438 E-mail: office@bdstructures.co.uk *Steel work suppliers*

▶ B D T (uk) Ltd, Beaconsfield Lodge, Fore Street, Ashton Keynes, Swindon, SN6 6NP Tel: (01285) 862399 Fax: (01285) 862399 E-mail: richard.long@bduk.ltd.com *Consulting sturctural engineers & architects*

B D Technical Polymers Ltd, 202b Cooks Road, Weldon North Industrial Estate, Corby, Northamptonshire, NN17 5JT Tel: (01536) 200913 Fax: (01536) 400836 E-mail: sales@bdtechnicalpolymer.co.uk *Rubber compound & products manufrs*

B D UK Ltd, 21 Between Towns Road, Cowley, Oxford, OX4 3LY Tel: (01865) 748844 Fax: (01865) 717313 *Medical supply & surgical supply distributors*

B D Welding Supplies, 203 Halesowen Road, Netherton, Dudley, West Midlands, DY2 9PU Tel: (01384) 214577 Fax: (01384) 214577 *Welding supplies*

B & D Willett Fabrications Ltd, 131 Mereside, Soham, Ely, Cambridgeshire, CB7 5EG Tel: (01353) 721374 Fax: (01353) 722567 E-mail: rujwillett@bdwillett.co.uk *Steel fabricators*

B D X Insect Screen Sales, The Onsite Building, Stephenson Way, Crawley, West Sussex, RH10 1TN Tel: (01293) 744426 *Insect screen distributors & manufrs*

B Danby & Company Ltd, English Street, Hull, HU3 2DZ Tel: (01482) 599599 Fax: (01482) 599211 E-mail: enquiries@danbys.co.uk *Plumbers merchants & electrical wholesalers* Also at: Grimsby, Hessle & Leeds

B Danby & Co., Milners Road, Yeadon, Leeds, LS19 7JE Tel: 0113-250 6511 Fax: 0113-250 0328 E-mail: enquires@danbys.co.uk *Builders, plumbers & electrical merchants*

B Danby & Co, Albermarle Back Road, Scarborough, North Yorkshire, YO11 1YA Tel: (01723) 360580 Fax: (01723) 352010 *Plumbing merchants*

B E C Distribution Ltd, Unit 5, Coronation Grove, Harrogate, North Yorkshire, HG2 8BU Tel: (0845) 4900405 Fax: (0845) 4900406 E-mail: sales@bec.co.uk *Distributors of coils filters & inductors*

▶ B E C Engineering, Richmond Road, Atherstone, Warwickshire, CV9 2AH Tel: (01827) 718198 Fax: (01827) 715498 *Engineering company*

B E C Global Ltd, Gore Road Industrial Estate, New Milton, Hampshire, BH25 6SA Tel: (01425) 613131 Fax: (01425) 616551 E-mail: info@becgroup.com *Manufacturers of plastic filters, plastic injection mouldings and tooling design for production.*

B E C Systems Ltd, 11 Glen Grove, East Kilbride, Glasgow, G75 0BG Tel: (01355) 242302 E-mail: sales@becsystems.co.uk *Software & hardware control engineers services*

B E Ebdon, Leafdale, London Road, Addington, West Malling, Kent, ME19 5PL Tel: (01732) 843351 Fax: (01732) 843351 *Plastic moulding & tool makers*

B & E Engineering Services, First Avenue, Crewe, CW1 6BG Tel: (01270) 586958 Fax: (01270) 585042 E-mail: sales@deengineering.co.uk *Precision machining services*

B E I Distribution, Wyndham Way, Brackla, Bridgend, Mid Glamorgan, CF31 2NB Tel: (01656) 645414 Fax: (01656) 669231 E-mail: info@beilighting.com *Exterior lighting equipment distribs*

B E K Engineering Ltd, Unit C1, New St, Charfield, Wotton-under-Edge, Gloucestershire, GL12 8ES Tel: (01453) 844372 Fax: (01453) 842050 E-mail: bek@harris-pye.com *Marine catering equipment manufrs*

B E L Precision Engineers Ltd, Wyre Street, Padiham, Burnley, Lancashire, BB12 8DF Tel: (01282) 770315 Fax: (01282) 770152 *Toolmakers*

B E Moors Ltd, Kemp House, 152-160 City Road, London, EC1V 2NP Tel: (020) 7855 5300 Fax: (020) 7454 9090 E-mail: admin@bemoors.co.uk *Ship brokers*

B E P Signs Ltd, 8a South Street, Greenock, Renfrewshire, PA16 8TX Tel: (01475) 784423 Fax: (01475) 729213 E-mail: enquiries@bepsigns.co.uk *Sign manufrs*

B E S Controls Ltd, Unit 7c Silver End Industrial Estate, Brettell Lane, Brierley Hill, West Midlands, DY5 3LA Tel: (01384) 75000 Fax: (01384) 74000 E-mail: bescontrol@aol.com *Control panel manufrs*

B.E.S (Europe) Ltd, 3 Oriel Court, The Green, Twickenham, TW2 5AG Tel: (020) 8898 8396 Fax: (020) 8898 8419 E-mail: info@beseurope.com *Export services*

B E S T, Morton Street, Brooke House, Middleton, Manchester, M24 6AN Tel: 0161-655 3000 Fax: 0161-655 3001 E-mail: info@bestservices.co.uk *Church restoration steeple jacks lightning system protection*

B & E Security Systems, 10 Oakland Avenue, Portrush, County Antrim, BT56 8JP Tel: (028) 7082 5119 Fax: (028) 7082 3757 E-mail: team@eonde.prestel.co.uk *CCTV & security alarms distribs*

B & E Services, Greenhill Mills, Grange Road, Batley, West Yorkshire, WF17 6LH Tel: (01924) 420800 Fax: (01924) 420800 *Access platform repairers*

▶ B E W O (UK) Ltd, Unit 3 Bay 2, Eastacre, The Willenhall Estate, Willenhall, West Midlands, WV13 2JZ Tel: (01902) 635027 Fax: (01902) 635843 E-mail: info@bewo.co.uk *Tube machinery distributors laser cutting machines*

B E W T Environmental Services Ltd, Warwick, CV35 8PY Tel: (01926) 843233 Fax: (01926) 843233 *Effluent treatment specialists*

B E Wedge Holdings Ltd, Stafford Street, Willenhall, West Midlands, WV13 1RZ Tel: (01902) 630311 Fax: (01902) 366353 E-mail: wedge.holdings@wedge-galv.co.uk *Galvanizing services*

B E White, Brantwood Road, London, N17 0ED Tel: (020) 8887 1690 Fax: (020) 8884 1865 E-mail: info@bewhite.co.uk *Electric motor, control gear & transformer supplier manufrs*

B E Williams Ltd, Sennybridge, Brecon, Powys, LD3 8RR Tel: (01874) 636711 Fax: (01874) 638902 *Agricultural wholesale distributors*

B F C Brava Ltd, 26 Store Street, London, WC1E 7BT Tel: (020) 7631 1501

B F Components Ltd, Unit 6, Cobham Centre, Westmead Industrial Estate, Westlea, Swindon, SN5 7UJ Tel: (01793) 498020 Fax: (01793) 542019 E-mail: sales@bfgroup.co.uk *Electronic component distributors*

B F Elton, The Bungalow, Bristol Road, Rooksbridge, Axbridge, Somerset, BS26 2TF Tel: (01934) 750433 *Metal gates*

B F F Technical Fabric Ltd, Bath Road, Bridgwater, Somerset, TA6 4NZ Tel: (01278) 428500 Fax: (01278) 429499 E-mail: information@bff-technicalfabric.com *Non-woven textile manufrs*

B & F Group Ltd, Sovereign Way, Chester West Employment Park, Chester, CH1 4QJ Tel: (01244) 390215 Fax: (01244) 382747 *Electrical power equipment fabrication services*

B F Group Ltd, Unit 6 Cobhan Centre, Westmead Industrial Estate, Westlea, Swindon, SN5 7UJ Tel: (01793) 498020 Fax: (01793) 542019 E-mail: sales@bfgroup.co.uk *Manufacturers of display systems*

B F I Optilas Ltd, Mill Square, Featherstone Road, Wolverton Mill, Milton Keynes, MK12 5ZY Tel: (01908) 326326 Fax: (01908) 221110 E-mail: info.uk@bfioptilas.com *Distributors, agents of fibre optic equipment*

B F M Plastics Ltd, Unit 17c Orgreave Close, Sheffield, S13 9NP Tel: 0114-269 1688 Fax: 0114-269 3995 E-mail: sales@bfmplastics.com *Injection & compression moulders & finishers*

B F P Instruments Ltd, Unit 9b Alstone Trading Estate, Alstone Lane, Cheltenham, Gloucestershire, GL51 8HF Tel: (01242) 251281 Fax: (01242) 251468 *Industrial instrumentation service providers*

B F P Wholesale Ltd, 1 Manson Square, Deans Industrial Estate, Deans, Livingston, West Lothian, EH54 8SD Tel: (01506) 462444 Fax: (01506) 419888 E-mail: sales@bfpwholesale.com *Bakery ingredients & confectionary wholesalers*

B F S Enterprise Fabrications Ltd, 6 Ellough Industrial Estate, Ellough, Beccles, Suffolk, NR34 7TD Tel: (01502) 716383 Fax: (01502) 717416 E-mail: m.spence@bfs-fabs.co.uk Purchasing Contact: D. Doddington Sales Contact: M. Spence Principal Export Areas: Worldwide *Steel fabricators, skid package unit & pressure vessel manufrs.*

B F S International, Willowbrook, 20 Bray Road, Bray, Maidenhead, Berkshire, SL6 1UE Tel: (01628) 671458 Fax: (01628) 784337 E-mail: sales@bfs-international.co.uk *Petrochemical plant & equipment manufrs*

B F T Automation, Unit 8e Newby Road Industrial Estate, Newby Road, Hazel Grove, Stockport, Cheshire, SK7 5DA Tel: 0161-456 0456 Fax: 0161-456 9090 E-mail: info@bftautomation.co.uk *Security product distributors*

B F T Engineering Ltd, Hill Street, Kidderminster, Worcestershire, DY11 6TD Tel: (01562) 824225 Fax: (01562) 741692 E-mail: info@bft-eng.com *Plastics mould toolmakers*

B F T Northern, Units 14-16, Bassington Industrial Estate, Cramlington, Northumberland, NE23 8AD Tel: (01670) 737645 Fax: (01670) 736558 *Gate automation services*

▶ B & G, Market Street, Farnworth, Bolton, BL4 8EX Tel: (01204) 796844 Fax: (01204) 796844

B & G Ltd, Premier Way, Abbey Park, Romsey, Hampshire, SO51 9DH Tel: (01794) 518448 Fax: (01794) 518077 E-mail: sales@bandg.co.uk *Navigation aids manufrs*

B G B Services & Supply Ltd, Unit 52, Sovereign Road, Kings Norton Business Centre, Birmingham, B30 3HN Tel: 0121-458 5424 Fax: 0121-459 4756 E-mail: ian@bgbservices.co.uk *Fastener (furniture) & turned parts distributors, agents & stockholders*

B & G Cleaning Systems Ltd, Abeles Way, Holly Lane Industrial Estate, Atherstone, Warwickshire, CV9 2QZ Tel: (01827) 717028 Fax: (01827) 714041 E-mail: sales@bgclean.co.uk *Cleaning, industrial, food processing plants. Cleaning systems, industrial. Washing systems, pressure. Chemical mixing/dilution equipment. Cleaning (industrial) equipment manufacturers. Cleaning (industrial) equipment/materials distribution. Floor cleaning machine or equipment distributors or agents. Steam cleaning equipment distributors/agents/suppliers. Steam cleaning equipment manufacturers. Vacuum cleaners. Vacuum cleaners, industrial. Washers, pressure. Water jet (high pressure) cleaning/washing equipment.*

▶ B G Contracts, Unit 1 Brown Street, Coatbridge, Lanarkshire, ML5 4AS Tel: (01236) 435335 Fax: (01236) 449894 *Fire sprinkler engineers*

B & G Controls Ltd, Broadoak Enterprise Village, Broadoak Road, Sittingbourne, Kent, ME9 8AQ Tel: (01795) 423554 Fax: (01795) 428873 E-mail: sales@bt-controls.co.uk *Control panel manufrs/design consultants*

B G Developments Ltd, Unit 9 West Court, Buntsford Park Road, Bromsgrove, Worcestershire, B60 3DX Tel: (01527) 832453 Fax: (01527) 575403 E-mail: info@bgdevelopments.co.uk *Motor sport components distributors & manufrs*

B G E UK Ltd, Brighouse Bay Compressor Station, Borgue, Kirkcudbright, DG6 4TR Tel: (01557) 870349 Fax: (01557) 870292 *Gas station*

B G Electrical Accessories, Unit 1 Highpoint Business Village, Henwood, Ashford, Kent, TN24 8DH Tel: (01233) 668000 Fax: (01233) 668100 E-mail: efasales@arlen.co.uk *Fluorescent lighting control gear manufrs*

B G Europa (U K) Ltd, Pipers Drove, Giffords Road, Newmarket, Suffolk, CB8 8PQ Tel: (01440) 821155 Fax: (01440) 821156 E-mail: sales@bgeuropa.co.uk *Asphalt plant manufrs*

B G H Joinery Co. Ltd, Unicorn Business Centre, Ridgeway, Chiseldon, Swindon, SN4 0HT Tel: (01793) 741330 Fax: (01793) 741310 E-mail: sales@bghjoinery.wanadoo.co.uk *Joinery*

B G I Direct Furniture Fittings, 8 Harpur Road, Omagh, County Tyrone, BT78 5BY Tel: (028) 8289 8089 Fax: (028) 8289 8033 *Fitted kitchen services*

B & G Lock & Tool Co. Ltd, Chapel Green, Willenhall, West Midlands, WV13 1RD Tel: (01902) 630290 Fax: (01902) 633794 E-mail: sales@bgpadlocks.co.uk *Manufacturers of 'sta-lok,' 'sta-secure' & 'B & G' padlocks*

B G N Boards Co. Ltd, Bromford Road, West Bromwich, West Midlands, B70 7JB Tel: 0121-552 7777 Fax: 0121-552 7722 E-mail: sales@bgn.co.uk *Laminated board distributors*

▶ B G P Bicester, Chaucer Business Park, Launton Road, Bicester, Oxfordshire, OX26 4QZ Tel: (01869) 363333 Fax: (01869) 363306 E-mail: marketing@bgprint.co.uk *Web offset printers of catalogues, magazines & directories*

B G Penny & Co. Ltd, Unit 3, Three Spires Industrial Estate, Ibstock Road, Coventry, CV6 6JR Tel: (024) 7636 7636 Fax: (024) 7636 7636 *Shot blasting, powdering & surface treatments service providers*

B G Perimeter Systems Ltd, Tomo Industrial Estate, Packet Boat Lane, Uxbridge, Middlesex, UB8 2JP Tel: (01895) 441794 Fax: (01895) 448597 E-mail: sales@bgperimeter.co.uk *Perimeter heating equipment manufrs*

B G Petchell Ltd, Church Farm, Langar, Nottingham, NG13 9HH Tel: (01949) 860509 Fax: (01949) 861156 *Building contractors & gate manufrs*

▶ B & G Products Ltd, Norbury House Farm Buildings, Norbury, Stafford, ST20 0PB Tel: (01785) 284222 Fax: (01785) 284613

B & G Repairs, Ditchling Common, Ditchling, Hassocks, West Sussex, BN6 8SG Tel: (01444) 245691 Fax: (01444) 236041 *Car body repairs*

B G Romeril Ltd, Dumaresq Street, St. Helier, Jersey, JE2 3WP Tel: (01534) 738806 Fax: (01534) 767016 E-mail: enquiry@romerils.co.je *Building & plumbing material merchants*

B G Saunders & Son, Orchard View, Long Lane, Maidenhead, Berkshire, SL6 3TA Tel: (01628) 621491 *Agricultural services*

B G Slattery & Son, Unit 3 Martlets Way, Goring-by-Sea, Worthing, West Sussex, BN12 4HF Tel: (01903) 506128 *Refrigeration engineers*

B & G Software Consultancy Ltd, The Barn, Watery Lane, Monmouth, Gwent, NP25 5AT Tel: (01600) 715105 Fax: (01600) 772802 E-mail: info@bandgsoftware.com *Computer software developers*

B & G Softwater Services, Barnside, Wrotham Road, Meopham, Gravesend, Kent, DA13 0AU Tel: (01474) 812005 E-mail: contact@softwaterservices.co.uk *Water softener distributors*

B & G Spreaders, Back Meadow Cottage, 23, Denham, Bury St. Edmunds, Suffolk, IP29 5EW Tel: (01284) 811082 Fax: (01284) 810234 E-mail: phorner@jhbunn.co.uk *Agricultural contractors services*

B G T Automatics Ltd, 2 Paragon Court, Tongham Road, Aldershot, Hampshire, GU12 4AA Tel: (01252) 318111 Fax: (01252) 311831 E-mail: carol@bgtcnc.freeserve.co.uk *Repetition turned parts manufrs*

B G Transmission, Unit 1a Brickworks Trading Estate, Buckle Street, Honeybourne, Evesham, Worcestershire, WR11 8QE Tel: (01386) 830870 Fax: (01386) 831611 *Reconditoned gear box retailers*

B G U Manufacturing Co., Meadow Lane, Nottingham, NG2 3JQ Tel: 0115-986 2460 Fax: 0115-986 2522 E-mail: info@bgu-man.co.uk *Library stationary book protection & book covering manufrs*

B & G Ventilation Ltd, Coppice Trading Estate, Kidderminster, Worcestershire, DY11 7QY Tel: (01562) 740815 Fax: (01562) 751123 E-mail: office@bgvent.co.uk *Distribution of heating & ventilation*

B G Ventilation, Lynton Industrial Estate, Stanley, Perth, PH1 4QQ Tel: (01738) 828800 Fax: (01383) 420216 E-mail: bgvent@aol.com *Ventilation specialists*

B G W Woodcraft Ltd, 1 Retreat Pl, London, E9 6RH Tel: (020) 8533 9885 *Instrument case manufrs*

B & G Williams Ltd, Garratts Lane, Cradley Heath, West Midlands, B64 5RH Tel: 0121-559 2811 Fax: 0121-559 9412 *Chain makers & crane aids*

B Garrad Ltd, Water Lane, Kings Langley, Hertfordshire, WD4 8HW Tel: (01923) 264088 Fax: (01923) 264089 E-mail: artcraft@bgarrad.co.uk *Art & educational supplies distributors*

B H Associates 2000 Ltd, Cromwell House, Elland Road, Brighouse, West Yorkshire, HD6 2RG Tel: (01756) 700138 Fax: (01422) 371337 E-mail: sales@bhassociates.sagehost.co.uk *Accountancy software & training providers*

▶ B H C Ltd, 1 Edinburgh Road, Carnwath, Lanark, ML11 8HS Tel: (01555) 840006 Fax: (01555) 840036

B H C Coach Builders, The Stables, Stanwell New Road, Staines, Middlesex, TW18 4HZ Tel: (01784) 453148 *Coach Builders*

B & H Canvas Products Ltd, 33a Chester Street, Cardiff, CF11 6PY Tel: (029) 2034 3610 Fax: (029) 2056 3753 *Canvas goods manufrs*

B H Carpets, Unit 24 Oakwood Place, Oakwood Road, Croydon, CR0 3QS Tel: (020) 8665 9110 Fax: (020) 8665 6611 *Carpets & tailoring suppliers*

▶ B H Custom Made Furniture, Stowmarket, Suffolk, IP14 2AG Tel: (01449) 676004

B H D Building Products, Unit 5 And 6, Judson Road, Northwest Industrial Estate, Peterlee, County Durham, SR8 2QJ Tel: 0191-415 5220 Fax: (0870) 2421846 Principal Export Areas: Worldwide *Pvc window frame, conservatory & door manufrs*

B H E Sports Ltd, Units 4-5 Sharbrook Trading Estate, Mullineux Street, Manchester, M28 3DZ Tel: 0161-790 5071 Fax: 0161-703 7324 *Sportswear manufrs*

B H F Engineering Ltd, 4a Churchward, Southmead Industrial Park, Didcot, Oxfordshire, OX11 7HB Tel: (01235) 811111 Fax: (01235) 817676 E-mail: peter_vilk@bh-fing.com *Glass making machinery manufrs*

▶ B H F Printers, G 1 Unit Riverside Industrial Estate, Riverside Way, Dartford, DA1 5BS Tel: (01322) 285286 Fax: (01322) 287070

▶ B & H Group, 3 Caxton Way, Watford, WD18 8UA Tel: (01923) 247466 Fax: (01923) 246476 E-mail: sales@bh-group.com

B H James, Great Penlan, Brilley, Whitney-on-Wye, Hereford, HR3 6JW Tel: (01497) 831224 *Farming contractors*

▶ B H L Builders Oxford Ltd, Unit 5 Station Field Industrial Estate, Kidlington, Oxfordshire, OX5 1JD Tel: (01865) 378049 Fax: (01865) 378050

B H L Manufacturing Ltd, Llewellyns Quay, Port Talbot, West Glamorgan, SA13 1RG Tel: (01639) 884878 Fax: (01639) 890317 *Stainless steel fabricators*

B H M Plastics Ltd, The Station, High Street, Meldreth, Royston, Hertfordshire, SG8 6JR Tel: (01763) 260452 Fax: (01763) 261152 E-mail: bhm.plastics@virgin.net *Plastic injection moulders*

B & H (Nottingham) Ltd, Middlemore Lane West, Aldridge, WS9 8EB Tel: (01922) 744144 Fax: (01922) 744150 *Cable jointing accessory manufrs*

B H P Alarms, Unit B3, Balliniska Business Park, Springtime Industrial Estate, Londonderry, BT48 0LY Tel: (028) 7126 2757 Fax: (028) 7137 2225 E-mail: info@bhpalarms.com *Alarms & security system manufrs*

B H & P Direct Mail Ltd, Darby House, Bletchingley Road, Redhill, RH1 3DN Tel: (01737) 645233 Fax: (01737) 644283 E-mail: bhpdirectmailltd@onyxnet.co.uk *Direct mail marketing consultants*

B H Panels Ltd, 4 Waterloo Avenue, Fordbridge, Birmingham, B37 6RE Tel: 0121-779 6971 Fax: 0121-779 6217 *Accident repair centre*

▶ B & H Plastics Ltd, Anchorage Works, New Road, Radford, Nottingham, NG7 3FR Tel: 0115-970 1655

B & H Precision Tooling Ltd, Unit 14 Glover Estate, Egmont Street, Mossley, Ashton-Under-Lyne, Lancashire, OL5 9PY Tel: (01457) 833434 Fax: (01457) 835685 E-mail: sales@bh-precision.co.uk *Engineers' pattern makers & aero tooling services*

B & H Pumps & Engineering Services, Unit 19 Whitemoor Court Industrial Estate, Nottingham, NG8 5BY Tel: 0115-929 9746 Fax: 0115-942 5091 *Pump repair & maintenance services*

B H R Ltd, Unit 16, Peerglow Industrial Estate, Watford, WD18 9SR Tel: (01923) 776683 Fax: (01923) 776683 *Stainless steel fabricators*

B.H.R. Precision Engraving, Units 215 Victory Business Centre, Somers Road North, Portsmouth, PO1 1PJ Tel: (023) 9281 6613 Fax: (023) 9281 6613 *Industrial engravers*

▶ B H Salvage, Kensworth Industrial Estate, Isle of Wight Lane, Kensworth, Dunstable, Bedfordshire, LU6 2PP Tel: (01582) 873677 Fax: (01582) 872177 E-mail: sales@bhsalvage.com *Car parts & accessories some new, some used*

▶ B & H Sound Services Ltd, The Old School Studio, Crowland Road, Eye, Peterborough, PE6 7TN Tel: (01733) 223535 Fax: (01733) 223545 E-mail: sound@bhsound.co.uk *Sound services video equipment hire*

B & H Surgical Instrument Makers, Unit C2 Up Bounds Green Industrial Estate, South Way, London, N11 2UL Tel: (020) 8368 1616 Fax: (020) 8368 0243 E-mail: office@bhsi.co.uk *Surgical instrument manufrs*

B H T Engineering Ltd, Unit 8, Hayes Lane Factory Estate, Lye, Stourbridge, West Midlands, DY9 8RH Tel: (01384) 422294 Fax: (01384) 422562 E-mail: bhteng@compuserve.com *General & precision engineering services*

B.H.W Ceramics Ltd, Adelaide Street, Stoke-on-Trent, ST6 2BD Tel: (01782) 813855 Fax: (01782) 575647 E-mail: info@bhwceramics.sagehost.co.uk *Electrical ceramics distributors & manufrs*

B H W Components Ltd, 1a-2b Unit, Worthington Way, Wigan, Lancashire, WN3 6XE Tel: (01942) 821205 Fax: (01942) 821377 E-mail: info@hampson-industries.plc.uk Principal Export Areas: North America, Central America & South America *Aircraft component*

B H W Glass, The Gables, Church Road, Partridge Green, Horsham, West Sussex, RH13 8JS Tel: (01403) 713757 Fax: (01403) 864932 E-mail: enquiries@bhwglass.co.uk *UPVC window frame & conservatory distributors*

▶ B Harper, North Road, Insch, Aberdeenshire, AB52 6XP Tel: (01464) 820011 Fax: (01464) 821145

B Healthy Solutions Ltd, Brookside, Pinmill Road, Chelmondiston, Ipswich, IP9 1JF Tel: (01473) 780155 Fax: (01473) 780155 *Health product distributors*

B Horrocks Fabrications, Mill Street Works, Mill Street, Adlington, Chorley, Lancashire, PR6 9QY Tel: (01257) 482560 Fax: (01257) 474259 *Steel fabricators*

B I Ltd, 2 Robinson Road, Leicester, LE5 4NS Tel: 0116-276 6344 Fax: 0116-276 6187 E-mail: info@biltd.com *Sauce manufrs*

B I B Cutters & Formes, Hertford, SG14 3BT Tel: (07710) 255485 Fax: (01992) 419275 *Forme cutter manufrs.*

B I Communications, 7 Buckwins Square, Burnt Mills Industrial Estate, Basildon, Essex, SS13 1BJ Tel: (01268) 729393 Fax: (01268) 727987 E-mail: bicomms@dircon.co.uk *Design & manufacture of test equipment*

B I Composites Ltd, Green Lane, Cannock, Staffordshire, WS11 0JW Tel: (01543) 466021 Fax: (01543) 574157 E-mail: firstname.lastname@bi-composites.co.uk *Plastics foam manufrs*

B I Composites Halesowen Ltd, 270 Coombs Road, Halesowen, West Midlands, B62 8AA Tel: 0121-550 7577 Fax: 0121-585 5315 E-mail: bi-composites@bi-composites.co.uk *Manufacturers of automotive interior polyurethane products* Also at: Dudley

B I Engineering Ltd, Crane Close, Denington Industrial Estate, Wellingborough, Northamptonshire, NN8 2QG Tel: (01933) 228012 Fax: (01933) 441935 E-mail: biengineering@btconnect.com Principal Export Areas: Worldwide *Manufacturers of heat exchangers*

B & I Fabrications, Farrington Place, Rossendale Road Industrial Estate, Burnley, Lancashire, BB11 5TY Tel: (01282) 411434 Fax: (01282) 838963 *General engineers*

B I L Steels Ltd, Eyre Street, Birmingham, B18 7AA Tel: 0121-456 5886 Fax: 0121-454 6213 *Steel shearers & stockholders*

B I P (Oldbury) Ltd, PO Box 3180, Oldbury, West Midlands, B69 4PG Tel: 0121-544 2333 Fax: 0121-552 4267E-mail: enquiries@bip.co.uk *Plastic material resins & manufrs*

B I P Organics Ltd, Brooks Lane Industrial Estate, Middlewich, Cheshire, CW10 0JG Tel: (01606) 835271 Fax: (01606) 835274 *Chemical manufrs*

B I S Trent Rosettes, 7 Railway Enterprise Centre, Shelton New Road, Stoke-on-Trent, ST4 7SH Tel: (01782) 279797 Fax: (01782) 279797 *Rosette & personalised badge manufrs*

B I S Valves Ltd, Unit 17 Kingfisher Park, Three Cross Road, West Moors, Wimborne, Dorset, BH21 6US Tel: (01202) 896322 Fax: (01202) 896718 E-mail: info@bisvalves.co.uk *Specialist valve manufacturers*

B I T S Heritage Ltd, 2 Assarts Lane, Malvern, Worcestershire, WR14 4JR Tel: (01684) 565709 Fax: (01684) 560977 E-mail: tony@bits.co.uk *Computer services*

▶ B I Worldwide Ltd, 1 Vantage Court, Tickford Street, Newport Pagnell, Buckinghamshire, MK16 9EZ Tel: (01908) 214700 Fax: (01908) 214777 E-mail: enquires@eu.biworldwide.com *BI is a communication and motivation company that provides employees, customers, channels with live events, reward and recognition programmes, and marketing initiatives that deliver measurable results. With over 25 years of market expertise, BI's solution neutral approach starts from the issues customers face rather than a product BI can sell. Whether motivating a salesforce to increase revenues or raising the profile of a business or product, BI provides advice on the best combination of approaches that deliver cost-effective, creative and compelling solutions. This is supported with strong analytics that demonstrate return on investment and achievement of objectives. enquiries@eu.biworldwide.com*

▶ B I Z Engineering Ltd, Millmarsh Lane, Brunsdown, Enfield, Middlesex, EN3 7QA Tel: (020) 8443 3300 Fax: (020) 8804 6672 E-mail: sales@bizengineering.com

B & J Alloys Ltd, The Leys, Brierley Hill, West Midlands, DY5 3UJ Tel: (01384) 485533 *Metal merchants*

B J Ashpole Ltd, Southmill Road, Bishop's Stortford, Hertfordshire, CM23 3DJ Tel: (01279) 653211 Fax: (01279) 651694 *Motor spare parts factors & precision engineers*

B J B (UK) Ltd, 9 Ivory House, Plantation Wharf, York Road, London, SW11 3TN Tel: (020) 7924 1177 Fax: (020) 7924 5357 E-mail: bjbuk@bjb.com *Lighting component manufrs*

B & J Builders, 98 Lightwood Road, Buxton, Derbyshire, SK17 7AN Tel: (01298) 79832 *Joinery manufrs*

B J C Communication Contracts Ltd, 198 Hydean Way, Stevenage, Hertfordshire, SG2 9YD Tel: (07879) 605543 Fax: (0844) 5875728 E-mail: mail@bjccommunications.co.uk *Access control security specialists*

B J C Mudguards Ltd, 14 Floodgate Street, Birmingham, B5 5ST Tel: 0121-643 3295 *Mudguard & trailer equipment manufrs*

B J Cheese, 345 Heath Street, Smethwick, West Midlands, B66 2QY Tel: 0121-565 1188 Fax: 0121-565 1188 *Cheese & dairy products manufrs*

▶ B J Communications Ltd, 12 Riverside Industrial Estate, Gorleston, Great Yarmouth, Norfolk, NR31 6TU Tel: (01493) 441187 Fax: (01493) 444200 E-mail: mail@bjcommunications.co.uk *Telecommunication systems & equipment manufrs*

B J Completion Services, Blackness Avenue, Altens Industrial Estate, Aberdeen, AB12 3PG Tel: (01224) 897929 Fax: (01224) 896118 E-mail: sales@bjservices.com *Coiled tubing & oilfield services*

B J Computers Ltd, 259 Eversholt Street, London, NW1 1BA Tel: (020) 7383 3444 E-mail: jass@bjcomputers.co.uk *Networking*

B J Construction, Units 29-30, Manor Industrial Estate, Flint, CH6 5UY Tel: (01352) 730111 Fax: (01352) 730444 *Refractories engineers*

B & J Controls, Spa Fields Industrial Estate, New Street, Slaithwaite, Huddersfield, HD7 5BB Tel: (01484) 843449 Fax: (01484) 842058 *Electrical control panel manufrs*

B J Cope (Electrical) Ltd, D6 Ivinghoe Bus Centre, Blackburn Road, Houghton Regis, Dunstable, Bedfordshire, LU5 5BQ Tel: (01582) 662434 Fax: (01582) 472753 *Electrical contractors*

B J Corridan Plant Hire Ltd, 42 Midland Road, Scunthorpe, South Humberside, DN16 1DQ Tel: (01724) 859228 Fax: (01724) 859228 *Plant hire*

B J Crowther & Sons, Windsor House, Windsor Street, Oldham, OL1 4AE Tel: 0161-652 0505 Fax: 0161-628 5187 *Excavation & groundwork contractors*

B J D Crushers Ltd, B B I Centre, Innovation Way, Wilthorpe, Barnsley, South Yorkshire, S75 1JL Tel: (01226) 241425 Fax: (01226) 296713 E-mail: sales@bjdcrushers.co.uk Principal Export Areas: Worldwide *Industrial crushing & quarry plant services*

B J Dawson Coins, 52 St Helens Road, Bolton, BL3 3NH Tel: (01204) 63732 Fax: (01204) 63732 *Medal dealer*

B J Doughty Engineering Ltd, Hereford Way, King's Lynn, Norfolk, PE30 4JD Tel: (01553) 773537 Fax: (01553) 767859 E-mail: admin@bjdoughty.co.uk *Steel & sheet metal fabricators*

▶ B J Electricians, 79 Charles Street, Glasgow, G21 2PS Tel: 0141-553 1133 Fax: 0141-552 5333

B & J Engineering Co., 7 Brampton Sidings Industrial Estate, Hempstalls Lane, Newcastle, Staffordshire, ST5 0SR Tel: (01782) 632132 Fax: (01782) 628591 E-mail: bjenglttd@aol.com *Engineers*

▶ B J Express Ltd, 106 Abercorn Street, Paisley, Renfrewshire, PA3 4AY Tel: 0141-887 1429 Fax: 0141-887 3467

B J Forster Electrical Contractors, 16 Powys Close, Dinas Powys, South Glamorgan, CF64 4LQ Tel: (029) 2051 4326 Fax: (029) 2051 4326 *Electrical contractors*

B J Industrial Supplies Ltd, 6 Harwood Street, Blackburn, BB1 3BD Tel: (01254) 675244 Fax: (01254) 663061 E-mail: info@thetradeshop.co.uk *Distributors of janitorial supplies, work wear packaging & tools*

B J Industries Ltd, Dukeries Industrial Estate, Claylands Avenue, Worksop, Nottinghamshire, S81 7DJ Tel: (01909) 501771 Fax: (01909) 501022 E-mail: info@bj-industries.co.uk *Providers of gas safety & gas control equipment*

B J Kenny, Z Cartwright Business Park, Brue Avenue, Bridgwater, Somerset, TA6 5LT Tel: (01278) 421168 Fax: (01278) 444421 *Ready mix concrete suppliers*

B J Lashbrook & Son, Red Lion Street, Redcar, Cleveland, TS10 3HF Tel: (01642) 482629 Fax: (01642) 489720 E-mail: bj@bjlashbrook.freeserve.co.uk *Cash registers & scales*

B J Leisure Installations Ltd, The Courtyard, Reddicap Trading Estate, Sutton Coldfield, West Midlands, B75 7BU Tel: 0121-311 1166 Fax: 0121-311 1885 *Landscaping services*

▶ B J M Joinery Manufacturers, Battye Street, Bradford, West Yorkshire, BD4 8AG Tel: (01274) 665000 Fax: (01274) 667000 *Window & door manufrs*

B J Mailing Services, 25-27 Whittle Road, Ferndown Industrial Estate, Wimborne, Dorset, BH21 7RP Tel: (01202) 897717 Fax: (01202) 870277 E-mail: admin@bjmailing.co.uk *Direct mail & fulfillment services*

B & J Material Handling Ltd, 3 Hardy Drive, Hardingstone, Northampton, NN4 6UX Tel: (01604) 769977 Fax: (01604) 708151 *Fork lift truck services*

B J P Window Controls Ltd, Unit 11 Springvale Industrial Park, Off Millfields Road, Bilston, West Midlands, WV14 0QL Tel: (01902) 409461 Fax: (01902) 494672 E-mail: sales@bjp-windowcontrols.co.uk *Leading suppliers and installers of Teleflex window systems and smoke ventilatoin systems. Systems suitable for most windows, sliding sashes, roof lights, louvres and dampers*

▶ B J Process & Pipeline Service, Suffolk Road, Great Yarmouth, Norfolk, NR31 0ER Tel: (01493) 442398 Fax: (01493) 656258

B J Promotions & Trophies, 68 Church Street, Gainsborough, Lincolnshire, DN21 2JR Tel: (01427) 614976 *Trophey supplier & dance promotion s*

B J S Co. Ltd, 65 Bideford Avenue, Greenford, Middlesex, UB6 7PP Tel: (020) 8810 5779 Fax: (020) 8810 5883 E-mail: enquiries@bjsco.com Principal Export Areas: Worldwide *Electroplating, electroforming & gold plating services*

B J Services Co (U K) Ltd, Marine Base, Southtown Road, Great Yarmouth, Norfolk, NR31 0JJ Tel: (01493) 680680 Fax: (01493) 680780 *Coiled tubing & pipeline commissioning*

B J Services Co UK Ltd, Badentoy Avenue, Badentoy Industrial Estate, Portlethen, Aberdeen, AB12 4YB Tel: (01224) 401401 Fax: (01224) 401501 *Oil service company* Also at: Great Yarmouth

B & J Signs, 14 Farrington Court, Burnley, Lancashire, BB11 5SS Tel: (01282) 454807 Fax: (01282) 831781 E-mail: sales@bjsigns.co.uk *Sign makers*

B J Special Steels, 14 Burrell Buildings, Chartwell Road, Lancing, West Sussex, BN15 8TZ Tel: (01903) 851059 Fax: (01903) 851037 *Tool steel stockholders*

B & J Stevenson, 19 Peverel Road, Cambridge, CB5 8RN Tel: (01223) 241901 Fax: (01223) 241901 E-mail: bansjstevenson@freenet.co.uk *Induction loops manufrs*

B J Supplies, Merlin Way, Quarry Hill Industrial Park, Quarry Hill Industrial Estate, Ilkeston, Derbyshire, DE7 4RA Tel: 0115-944 1949 Fax: 0115-944 1945 E-mail: bjsupplies@hotmail.com *Buying & purchasing agents*

▶ B & J Swindells Masonry Ltd, 9-11 Mill Lane, Macclesfield, Cheshire, SK11 7NN Tel: (01625) 420221

B J T Print Services Ltd, Common La, Kenilworth, Warwickshire, CV8 2EL Tel: (01926) 852085 Fax: (01926) 859591 *Litho printers/colour printing*

▶ B.J.Travel, 9, Woodview, Paulton, Bristol, BS39 7XQ Tel: 01761 412822 Fax: 01761 412822 E-mail: quotes@bj-travel.co.uk *Family run coach & car hire business for schools, groups, societies, the film industry etc.*For local, national & international travel and trips.*

B J Tubular Services, Hareness Circle, Altens Industrial Estate, Aberdeen, AB12 3LY Tel: (01224) 249678 Fax: (01224) 249106 E-mail: jbaglee@bjservices.co.uk *Casing & tubing contractors*

B James, Green Park, West Moore, Diptford, Totnes, Devon, TQ9 7PE Tel: (01364) 73501 Fax: (01364) 73501 *Engineers & metal fabricators*

▶ B Jeffrey Construction Ltd, Control Tower, Rufforth Airfield, Wetherby Road, Rufforth, York, YO23 3QA Tel: (01904) 738326

B Jenkinson & Sons, 5 Wellington Road East, Dewsbury, West Yorkshire, WF13 1HF Tel: (01924) 454681 Fax: (01924) 458696 E-mail: sales@elico.co.uk *Equestrian wholesalers*

B J's Blinds, Hillend Bridge, Pudford Lane, Worcester, WR6 6QL Tel: (01886) 888966 Fax: (01886) 888481 *Vertical & pleated blind manufrs*

B K A Solutions, Unit 13 Headley Park Area Ten, Woodley, Reading, RG5 4SW Tel: (0870) 2403586 Fax: (0870) 2403587 E-mail: sales@bka.co.uk *Distributor of voice & data networking products* Also at: Salford

B K Automations, 4 Talisman Business Centre, Duncan Road, Park Gate, Southampton, SO31 7GA Tel: (01489) 582712 Fax: (01489) 583294 E-mail: bkautomamation@tinyworld.co.uk *Automation & material handling specialists*

B K Bluebird Ltd, Mannings Heath Road, Parkstone, Poole, Dorset, BH12 4NF Tel: (01202) 740182 Fax: (01202) 715545 E-mail: uksales@bkbluebird.co.uk *Manfrs static holiday caravan*

▶ B & K Boiler Services Ltd, 2-4 Vicarage Road, Blackwater, Camberley, Surrey, GU17 9AX Tel: (01276) 705000 Fax: (01276) 705009

B & K Building Services Ltd, Peveril House, Alfreton Road, Derby, DE21 4AG Tel: (01332) 331444 Fax: (01332) 291067 E-mail: bkbs@rwkhouse.co.uk *Builders Construction agents*

B & K Ceilings Ltd, Unit B8 Manor Development Centre, 40 Alison Crescent, Sheffield, S2 1AS Tel: 0114-253 1620 Fax: 0114-239 4976 *Suspended ceilings & partitions contractors*

B K Consultants Ltd, Paxton Lodge, London Road, Coventry, CV1 2JT Tel: (024) 7625 6423 Fax: (024) 7652 0783 E-mail: engineers@bkconsultants.co.uk *Consulting structural engineers*

▶ B K E Business Services Ltd, 77 Oxford Street, Pontycymmer, Bridgend, Bridgend, Mid Glamorgan, CF32 8DD Tel: 01656 871605 E-mail: louise@bkebusiness.co.uk *Book keeping & payroll services, marketing, pr and sales management.*

B K Electronics, Unit 1 3 & 5 Comet Way, Southend-on-Sea, SS2 6TR Tel: (01702) 527572 Fax: (01702) 420243 E-mail: sales@bkelec.com *Test & measurement equipment*

B K Engineering Ltd, Kingswood Works, Heath and Reach, Leighton Buzzard, Bedfordshire, LU7 0AZ Tel: (01525) 237411 Fax: (01525) 237827 E-mail: sales@bkengineering.com *Precision sheet metal subcontract engineers*

B K Engineering Services, 4 Eye Green Industries, Crowland Road, Eye, Peterborough, PE6 7SZ Tel: (01733) 222711 Fax: (01733) 222711 *Engineering industry regrinding services*

B & K Fabrications Ltd, 60-64 Heath Mill Lane, Deritend, Birmingham, B9 4AR Tel: 0121-772 2667 Fax: 0121-772 2667 *Sheet metalwork & fabrications*

B.K. Gas Supplies, 35 Kings Road, West Drayton, Middlesex, UB7 9EF Tel: (01895) 446115 Fax: (01895) 446115 *Gas appliances & spares stockists*

B K Grain Handling Engineers, Littlecoate Road, Froxfield, Marlborough, Wiltshire, SN8 3JY Tel: (01488) 684154 Fax: (01488) 684455 E-mail: info@bkgrain.co.uk *Design Build Agricultural building, Grain Handling machinery.*

▶ B K H Paper Converters Ltd, Unit 1, Eurolink Industrial Estate, Sittingbourne, Kent, ME10 3RN Tel: (01795) 479534

B K International Freight Ltd, Unit 13 Maguire Industrial Estate, 219 Torrington Avenue, Coventry, CV4 9HN Tel: (024) 7646 4983 Fax: (024) 7669 4184 E-mail: admin@bkfreight.co.uk Principal Export Areas: Worldwide *Freight forwarders*

B K S Survey Group Ltd, Ballycairn Road, Coleraine, County Londonderry, BT51 3HZ Tel: (028) 7035 2311 Fax: (028) 7035 7637 E-mail: sales@bks.co.uk *Aerial surveying, mapping, data conversion*

B K Screen Print, Queen Street, Carlisle, CA2 5TP Tel: (01228) 542957 Fax: (01228) 514736 *Screen process printers*

B & K Steelwork Fabrications Ltd, High Edge Court, Church Street, Heage, Belper, Derbyshire, DE56 2BW Tel: (01773) 853400 Fax: (01773) 857389 E-mail: bksf@bksf.prestel.co.uk *Structural steel manufrs*

B K W Instruments Ltd, Weymouth Road, Winton, Eccles, Manchester, M30 8NN Tel: 0161-707 4838 Fax: 0161-787 7580 E-mail: sales@bkwinstruments.co.uk *Pressure instrumentation & temperature manufrs*

B K Webster, Main Street, West Tanfield, Ripon, North Yorkshire, HG4 5JH Tel: (01677) 470505 E-mail: info@gunfitting.co.uk *Gun repair & maintenance*

B K Whalley Ltd, 41 Chiswick Staithe, Hartington Road, London, W4 3TP Tel: (020) 8742 7371 Fax: (020) 8742 8371 *Food import agents*

B L Acoustics Ltd, 152 Enterprise Court, Eastways, Witham, Essex, CM8 3YS Tel: (01376) 521525 Fax: (01376) 521526 E-mail: male@blacoustics.net *Fire & voice alarm systems maintenance & manufrs*

B L C Scotland Ltd, 20 Garrell Road, Kilsyth, Glasgow, G65 9JX Tel: (01236) 822365 Fax: (01236) 826446 *Metal fabrication services*

B L Computer Services, McPhail Ho, 1 Alexandra Rd, Clevedon, Avon, BS21 7QE Tel: (01275) 340500 Fax: (01275) 340470 E-mail: admin@blcomp.co.uk *Computer consultants*

B L Cranes Ltd, 60 Granary Street, Burghead, Elgin, Morayshire, IV30 5UA Tel: (01343) 835360 Fax: (01343) 830771 *Crane hire & services*

B L D Refrigeration, 104 Castle Lea, Caldicot, Gwent, NP26 4PL Tel: (01291) 420854 Fax: (01291) 420894 E-mail: bldref@btconnect.com *Refrigeration & air conditioning repairers*

B & L Engineering & Castings, Darenth Mill, Darenth Road South, Dartford, DA2 7QT Tel: (01322) 289665 Fax: (01322) 289664 E-mail: blengineering@aol.com *Precision engineers*

▶ B L P (Hamble) Ltd, Mercury Yacht Harbour, Satchell Lane, Hamble, Southampton, SO31 4HQ Tel: (023) 8045 5537

▶ B L Penwarden Haulage, Chalk Pit, College Road, Epsom, Surrey, KT17 4JA Tel: (01372) 749977 Fax: (01372) 739284

B L Precision Ltd, Unit 6-7 Focal Point, Lacerta Court, Letchworth Garden City, Hertfordshire, SG6 1FJ Tel: (01462) 670800 Fax: (01462) 816865 E-mail: info@blprecision.co.uk *Precision engineers*

B L Refrigeration & Air Conditioning Ltd, Unit 3, Channel Commercial Park, Queens Island, Belfast, BT3 9DT Tel: (028) 9045 3325 Fax: (028) 9045 0073 E-mail: info@blgroup.co.uk *Install & service refrigeration units*

B & L Sheetmetal (2003) Ltd, Ramsden Road, Rotherwas Industrial Estate, Hereford, HR2 6LR Tel: (01432) 355040 Fax: (01432) 343844 E-mail: bandl2003@btconnect.com *Steel fabricators*

B L T Circuit Services Ltd, Airfield Industrial Estate, Eye, Suffolk, IP23 7HN Tel: (01379) 870870 Fax: (01379) 870970 E-mail: sales@blt.keme.co.uk *Printed circuit industry suppliers*

▶ B L T V Security Systems, 20 Broad Acres, Haxby, York, YO32 3WL Tel: (01904) 758555

B L Tooling & Moulding, 7 Hall Road Industrial Estate, Hall Road, Southminster, Essex, CM0 7DA Tel: (01621) 772608 Fax: (01621) 772608 *Injection moulding & tool manufrs*

B L W Associates Ltd, 1 Alexandra Drive, Lockerbie, Dumfriesshire, DG11 2PD Tel: (01576) 203595 Fax: (01576) 202276 *PVC window manufrs*

B Line L, Channel View, Cilonen, Three Crosses, Swansea, SA4 3UR Tel: (01792) 874449 Fax: (01792) 874449 *Groundwork contractors*

▶ B Loony Ltd, 1 Cape House, 105 Bellingdon Road, Chesham, Buckinghamshire, HP5 2HQ Tel: (01494) 774664 Fax: (01494) 792787

B M A C Ltd, Units 13 14, Shepley Industrial Estate South, Shepley Road, Audenshaw, M34 5DW Tel: 0161-367 3070 Fax: 0161-336 5691 E-mail: enquiries@bmac.ltd.uk *Lighting manufrs**

B M A Partitioning Group, 3 Ashburn Grove, Wetherby, West Yorkshire, LS22 6WB Tel: (01937) 581421 Fax: (01937) 581421 *Office partitioning , suspended ceilings & storage walls manufrs*

B & M Automatics Ltd, The Dingle, 56a New Penkridge Road, Cannock, Staffordshire, WS11 1HW Tel: (01543) 468138 *Fruit machine distributors*

B M B Ltd, 194 Newbold Road, Chesterfield, Derbyshire, S41 7AF Tel: (01246) 273500 Fax: (01246) 235252 E-mail: chesterfield@buildbase.co.uk *Builders merchants*

B M B Engineers (Newcastle) Ltd, 96 Millrise Road, Milton, Stoke-on-Trent, ST2 7DN Tel: (01782) 543004 Fax: (01782) 543288 E-mail: steve@bmbengineersltd.co.uk *General engineers & fabricators*

B M B Menswear Ltd, Granary Buildings, Canal Wharf, Holbeck, Leeds, LS11 5BB Tel: 0113-259 5500 Fax: 0113-259 5512 *Gentleman's clothing manufrs*

B M B Weatherproof Canopies, Arrowe Brook Road, Wirral, Merseyside, CH49 1SX Tel: 0151-678 7888 Fax: 0151-678 7999 E-mail: sales@bmb-weatherproofcanopies.co.uk *Fork lift truck hood manufrs*

B M Brown, Pincents Kiln Industrial Park, Pincents Kiln, Calcot, Reading, RG31 7SB Tel: 0118-930 5333 Fax: 0118-930 5111 E-mail: enquiries@bmbrowne.co.uk *Surgical instrument & scope manufrs*

B & M Business Machines Ltd, 30 Military Road, Colchester, CO1 2AJ Tel: (01206) 576872 Fax: (01206) 576873 *Shop fittings distributors*

B M C Security Systems N I Ltd, 2 Orchard Road, Strabane, County Tyrone, BT82 9QR Tel: (028) 7138 2936 Fax: (028) 7138 2937 E-mail: bmcsecsys@hotmail.com *Shutter doors suppliers & manufrs*

B M Commercials, Firbank Industrial Estate, Dallow Road, Luton, LU1 1TW Tel: (01582) 400262 Fax: (01525) 406089 *Commercial vehicle repairers*

B & M Concrete Products, Grange Works, 22 Falkenham Road, Kirton, Ipswich, IP10 0NW Tel: (01394) 448556 Fax: (01394) 448586 *Concrete products manufrs*

▶ B & M Consultancy, 118 Colinton Mains Drive, Edinburgh, EH13 9BL Tel: 0131-441 9576 *Computer services consultants*

▶ B & M Contract Services Ltd, B & M House, Gordon Road, Southbourne, Emsworth, Hampshire, PO10 8AZ Tel: (01243) 377444 Fax: (01243) 377666

▶ B & M Davies Plant Hire Ltd, Lakeside, Lees Lane, Dalton, Wigan, Lancashire, WN8 7RE Tel: (01257) 254343

B M Door Services, 34 Brookside, Totton, Southampton, SO40 9FL Tel: (023) 8086 1601 Fax: (023) 8086 9466 *Industrial door installation*

B & M Europe Ltd, Heath End House, West Street, Tadley, Hampshire, RG26 3ST Tel: 0118-981 1880 Fax: 0118-981 1881 E-mail: info@bmeurope.com *European technical consultants*

B & M Fencing Centre Ltd, Reading Road, Rotherwick, Hook, Hampshire, RG27 9DB Tel: (01256) 762739 Fax: (01256) 766891 *Fencing contractors & suppliers*

B M G Industries Ltd, Amwell Lane, Stanstead Abbotts, Ware, Hertfordshire, SG12 8EB Tel: (01920) 870240 Fax: (01920) 870652 E-mail: bmgprint@aol.com *Digital printing labels banners, decals embossed domed, leisurewear*

B & M Glazing Ltd, 330 Eastcote Lane, Harrow, Middlesex, HA2 9AJ Tel: (020) 8423 6031 Fax: (020) 8423 6171 *Glazing contractors services*

B M H Construction Co Clifton Ltd, 52 Clifton Road, Henlow, Bedfordshire, SG16 6BL Tel: (01462) 816555 E-mail: info@bmhconstruction.co.uk *Design & Build/Building & construction company*

B M Hire & Sales, 203 Askern Road, Bentley, Doncaster, South Yorkshire, DN5 0JR Tel: (01302) 876225 Fax: (01302) 876225 *Fire extinguishers hire & sales*

B M I Engineering Ltd, Vernon Road, Halesowen, West Midlands, B62 8HN Tel: 0121-559 3406 Fax: 0121-561 2603 E-mail: sales@bmi-engineering.co.uk *Metal merchants*

B M I Engineering Ltd, Vernon Road, Halesowen, West Midlands, B62 8HN Tel: 0121-559 3406 Fax: 0121-561 2603 E-mail: sales@bmi-engineering.co.uk *Turned parts manufrs*

▶ B & M Industrial Floor Cleaning Machinery, 6 Town Lane, Denton, Manchester, M34 6LE Tel: 0161-320 4291 Fax: 0161-320 4291 *Industrial floor cleanign specialists*

▶ B M J Parr Packaging Ltd, Unit 22, Boston Industrial Estate, Power Station Road, Rugeley, Staffordshire, WS15 2HS Tel: (01889) 578915

B M J Power Ltd, 25-27 Stokes Croft, Bristol, BS1 3QA Tel: 0117-924 5018 Fax: 0117-942 8902 *Power tools*

B M K Industrial I D Systems, 1 Claremont Street, Aberdeen, AB10 6QP Tel: (01224) 213325 Fax: (01224) 213377E-mail: bmk.id@talk21.com *Label manufrs*

B & M Labelling Supplies, 41 High Street, Linton, Cambridge, CB21 4HS Tel: (01223) 890569 Fax: (01223) 892366 E-mail: sales@bandmlabelling.co.uk *Labelling, bar codes & sticky labels suppliers*

B M Packaging Ltd, Unit 4 Crosland Road Industrial Estate, Netherton, Huddersfield, HD4 7DQ Tel: (01484) 667855 Fax: (01484) 663280 E-mail: sales@bmpackaging.co.uk *Specialised packaging & corrugated box*

B M Prickett, Unit 1 Dodwell Trading Estate, Dodwell, Stratford-upon-Avon, Warwickshire, CV37 9ST Tel: (01789) 204930 Fax: (01789) 204930 *Joinery manufrs*

B M Printers Ltd, Units 8-9, Queens Mill Road, Huddersfield, HD1 3PG Tel: (01484) 422593 Fax: (01484) 519399 E-mail: john@bmprinters.fsnet.co.uk *Lithographic printers*

B M S Ltd, 1 Dalzells Lane, Burwell, Cambridge, CB5 0GA Tel: (01638) 741275 Fax: (01638) 742236 E-mail: reception@burmech.co.uk *Mechanical service contractors*

B M S Ltd, Sproughton House, Sproughton, Ipswich, IP8 3AW Tel: (01473) 240024 Fax: (01473) 240043 E-mail: info@b-m-s.co.uk *Computer software/hardware*

B M S Janitorial, 351 Nuthall Road, Nottingham, NG8 5BX Tel: 0115-913 2200 Fax: 0115-913 2222 *Cleaning materials suppliers*

▶ B & M Scientific, 13 Goodwood Cresent, Timperley, Altrincham, Cheshire, WA15 7BD Tel: 0161-904 9149 Fax: 0161-904 9149 E-mail: info@b-mscientific.co.uk *Suppliers of balances, scales, microscopes & laboratory instruments.*

B & M Services, 7 Pioneer Way, Lincoln, LN6 3DH Tel: (01522) 695272 Fax: (01522) 500092 *Agricultural machinery sales & service*

▶ B & M Sheet Metal Ltd, Building 32 Bay 4 Second Avenue, The Pensnett Estate, Pensnett Trading Estate, Kingswinford, West Midlands, DY6 7PP Tel: (01384) 402558 Fax: (01384) 402557 *Sheet metal work*

B & M Supplies, 99 Church Road, Formby, Liverpool, L37 3ND Tel: (01704) 876665 Fax: (01704) 380046 E-mail: bandmsupplies@hotmail.com *Nursing home suppliers*

B M T Cordah Ltd, Scotstown Road, Bridge of Don, Aberdeen, AB23 8HG Tel: (01224) 414200 Fax: (01224) 414250 E-mail: main@cordah.co.uk *Environmental consultants*

B M T Cordah Ltd, Pentlands Science Park, Bush Loan, Penicuik, Midlothian, EH26 0PZ Tel: 0131-445 6120 Fax: 0131-445 6110 E-mail: enquiries@bmtcordah.com *Environmental consultants*

B M T Defence Services Ltd, 210 Lower Bristol Road, Bath, BA2 3DQ Tel: (01225) 448712 Fax: (01225) 448714 E-mail: info@bmtdsl.co.uk *Naval architects*

B.M.W. Building Products Ltd, Unit 52, Stella Gill Industrial Estate, Pelton Fell, Chester le Street, County Durham, DH2 2RG Tel: 0191-388 9145 Fax: 0191-387 1756 E-mail: johnj@bmwbuilding.co.uk *PVCu Window & Door manufrs*

B & M Wireworks, Prescot Trade Centre, Oliver Lyme Road, Prescot, Merseyside, L34 2SH Tel: 0151-431 0101 Fax: 0151-431 0101 E-mail: rickymartin@supanet.co.uk *Manufacturers of security gauges & grilles*

▶ B McDougal Ltd, 7 Erskine Square, Hillington Industrial Estate, Glasgow, G52 4BJ Tel: 0141-882 4600

B Mason & Sons Ltd, Wharf Street, Aston, Birmingham, B6 5SA Tel: 0121-327 0181 Fax: 0121-322 8341 E-mail: sales@bmason.co.uk *Rolled metal manufrs*

▶ B Mullen & Sons Ltd, Crookston, Musselburgh, Midlothian, EH21 8QF Tel: 0131-665 2335

B Murphy, 2 Avenue Mews, London, N10 3NP Tel: (020) 8883 4555 Fax: (020) 8883 3363 E-mail: hathersichroger@hotmail.com *Joinery manufrs*

B.N.B Vehicle Lifting Equipment, 17 Grasmere Park, Carrickfergus, County Antrim, BT38 7TP Tel: (028) 9336 5677 *Garage equipment engineers*

B N D Abrasives & Tapes Ltd, Unit 3a Stephenson Close, Andover, Hampshire, SP10 3RU Tel: (01264) 354133 Fax: (01264) 323873 E-mail: info@bnd-abrasives.co.uk *Abrasive products distributors*

B N E Electronics Ltd, 44 Main Street, Toomebridge, Antrim, BT41 3TF Tel: (028) 7965 0502 Fax: (028) 7965 4830 E-mail: edward.duffin@bne.onyxnet.co.uk *Computer systems manufacturers & computer programmers*

B N Group Ltd, Bembridge Airport, Bembridge, Isle of Wight, PO35 5PR Tel: (020) 3371 4000 Fax: (01983) 873246 E-mail: customer.services@britten-norman.com Principal Export Areas: Worldwide *Aircraft components importers & distributors*

B N International, Metro Centre, Dwight Road, Watford, WD18 9YD Tel: (01923) 219132 Fax: (01923) 219134 *Book covering manufrs*

B N P Leasing Ltd, 10 Hareward Avenue, London, NW1 6AA Tel: (020) 7595 2000 Fax: (020) 7595 2555 *Worldwide banking services*

Company Information

▶ B & N Plastics, Unit 5-6 Haslam Business Centre, Haslam Street, Bolton, BL3 6LB Tel: (01204) 529112 Fax: (01204) 529112 E-mail: sales@bnplastics.co.uk *We at B & N Plastics have a highly skilled work force with on-site pattern making and mould making facilities. We can manufacture all your GRP needs from your own drawings. All our products will enhance or compliment any type of house or apartment block. GRP products are widely used in the construction industry because they are easy to fit, thus saving labour and precious time, because after all "time is money". GRP canopies, dormers, columns and filials are virtually maintenance free.*

B N Precision Assemblies, Unit 10, Portsmouth Enterprise Centre, Quartremaine Road, Portsmouth, PO3 5QT Tel: (023) 9266 6444 Fax: (023) 9266 6444 *PCB assembly services*

▶ B Neale & Son Builders Ltd, 61 Weltmore Road, Luton, LU3 2TN Tel: (01582) 595541

B.O.B Stevenson Ltd, Coleman Street, Derby, DE24 8NL Tel: (01332) 574112 Fax: (01332) 757286 E-mail: sales@bobstevenson.co.uk Principal Export Areas: Worldwide *Fans manufrs*

B O C Edwards, Manor Royal, Crawley, West Sussex, RH10 9LW Tel: (01293) 528844 Fax: (01293) 533453 E-mail: admin@edwards.boc.com Sales Contact: I. Smith *Manufacturers of vacuum pumps, exhaust gas management systems, thin film coating equipment, vacuum measuring instruments, pharmaceutical freeze dying & filling systems, speciality gases & gas/chemical dispense systems. All products are available globally*

B O C Group P.L.C., Chertsey Road, Windlesham, Surrey, GU20 6HJ Tel: (01276) 477222 Fax: (01276) 471333 *Industrial Gases agents*

B O M Light Engineering Ltd, B O M Engineering Tools, Station Road, Morley, Leeds, LS27 8JT Tel: 0113-253 7544 Fax: 0113-252 7851 E-mail: sales@bomeng.co.uk *Turned parts & CNC machining agents*

B O P P Precision Engineers Ltd, A Emms Court, Meeting Lane, Brierley Hill, West Midlands, DY5 3LB Tel: (01384) 78646 Fax: (01384) 78646 E-mail: mail@bopppe.fsnet.co.uk *Precision engineers, press tools & toolmakers*

B O'Leary & Sons Engineering Ltd, Blacklands, East Malling, West Malling, Kent, ME19 6DR Tel: (01732) 845313 Fax: (01732) 874397 *Steel fabricators & sheetmetal work*

B P, Burnside Road, Farburn Industrial Estate, Dyce, Aberdeen, AB21 7PB Tel: (01224) 832000 Fax: (01224) 725273 *Oil exploration*

▶ B P, Saltend, Hull, HU12 8DS Tel: (01482) 896251 *Chemical plant*

B P Plc, Witan Gate House, 500-600 Witan Gate, Milton Keynes, MK9 1ES Tel: (01908) 853000 Fax: (01908) 852020 E-mail: clarkez@bp.com *Automotive lubricants & speciality products*

B P Air Ventilation, 284 Coulsdon Road, Coulsdon, Surrey, CR5 1EB Tel: (01737) 556499 Fax: (01737) 552955 E-mail: brian.knightingale@britishlibrary.net *Air conditioning repairs*

B P B Paperboard Ltd, B P B UK Service Centre, East Leake, Loughborough, Leicestershire, LE12 6JU Tel: 0115-945 1000 Fax: 0115-945 1199 *Paperboard & packaging materials manufrs*

B P C Building Products Ltd, Flanshaw Way, Wakefield, West Yorkshire, WF2 9LP Tel: (01924) 364794 Fax: (01924) 373846 E-mail: sales@bpcfixings.com *BPC Building Products Ltd. (established 1977) is a UK manufacturer of a huge range of builders' metalwork including joist hangers, restraint straps, angle brackets, timber frame wall ties, nail plates and timber connectors. Distributors of plasterers angle beads, fibreglass joint tape, wall ties and brickwork reinforcement. In addition, BPC incorporates a special fabrications department and in house tool-making & testing facilities.*

B P C Courseware, 4 Apple Barn Court, Old Church Lane, Bury St. Edmunds, Suffolk, IP33 3TJ Tel: (01284) 703300 *Educational publishers*

B P C EMEA Ltd, B P C House, Romsey Industrial Estate, Greatbridge Road, Romsey, Hampshire, SO51 0HR Tel: (01794) 521200 Fax: (01794) 521400 E-mail: sales@bpc-ups.com *Power supply systems*

▶ B P Cabling & Communications Ltd, Unit 7-8 The Old Brewery, Shore Street, Barrow-in-Furness, Cumbria, LA14 2UB Tel: (01229) 825525 Fax: (01229) 870208 *Fibre optics manufrs*

▶ B P Cabling & Communications Ltd, Unit 7-8 The Old Brewery, Shore Street, Barrow-in-Furness, Cumbria, LA14 2UB Tel: (01229) 825525 Fax: (01229) 870208 E-mail: info@bpcomms.co.uk *Data communications service*

B P Chemicals Marketing Ltd, 1 St James Square, London, SW1Y 4PD Tel: (020) 7496 4000 Fax: (020) 7496 4630 *Petrochemical suppliers*

▶ B P Consultancy, Unit 3, Plot 14, Eagle Road, Quarry Hill Industrial Estate, Ilkeston, Derbyshire, DE7 4RB Tel: 0115-930 9275 Fax: 0115-930 4083

B P D Building Services, 7 Sunnyside Grove, Ashton-under-Lyne, Lancashire, OL6 6TN Tel: 0161-612 7514 E-mail: paul@bpd-ltd.com *Electrical contractors*

B P Engineering Ltd, John Harper Street, Willenhall, West Midlands, WV13 1RE Tel: (01902) 609167 Fax: (01902) 605766 *Turned parts manufrs*

B P Engineering Co. Ltd, 5 Railway Buildings, Carr Lane, Hoylake, Wirral, Merseyside, CH47 4AY Tel: 0151-632 1364 Fax: 0151-632 3364 E-mail: bpeng@btconnect.com *Steel fabricators*

B & P Engineering (Poole) Ltd, Unit 14, Chelwyn Industrial Estate, Parkstone, Poole, Dorset, BH12 4PE Tel: (01202) 743401 Fax: (01202) 730088 *Precision engineering services*

B P Exploration, Britannic House, 1 Finsbury Circus, London, EC2M 7BA Tel: (020) 7496 4000 Fax: (020) 7496 4630 *Oil & gas exploration services*

B P Exploration Operating Co. Ltd, Wytch Farm, Wytch, Corfe Castle, Wareham, Dorset, BH20 5JR Tel: (01929) 476000 Fax: (01929) 476072 *Oil exploration company*

B P F Plastics, 33 The Vintners, Temple Farm Industrial Estate, Southend-on-Sea, SS2 5RZ Tel: (01702) 616224 Fax: (01702) 616224 E-mail: brian@bpf6r.freeserve.co.uk *Plastic injection mouldings manufacturers/sales & toolmaking*

B & P Fabrications Ltd, 6 Euston Street, Leicester, LE2 7ST Tel: 0116-249 4440 Fax: 0116-249 4444 E-mail: bandp@webleicester.co.uk *Sheetmetal contractors*

B P Fire Protection Services, 37 Emerson Road, Poole, Dorset, BH15 1QS Tel: (01202) 665506 Fax: (01202) 669990 *Fire extinguisher sales & service*

B P H Equipment Ltd, PO Box 12, Barton-upon-Humber, South Humberside, DN18 5XD Tel: (01652) 633340 Fax: (01652) 635920 E-mail: info@bphequipment.co.uk *Contractors plant & crane hire* Also at: Aberdeen, Lowestoft & Great Yarmouth

B P H Plastics, Woods Farm, Woodham Road, Battlesbridge, Wickford, Essex, SS11 7QU Tel: (01245) 328801 Fax: (01245) 328717 E-mail: bph@btinternet.com *Design consultants & plastic fabricators*

B P Hydraulics Ltd, Douglas Drive, Godalming, Surrey, GU7 1JX Tel: (01483) 423321 Fax: (01483) 426581 E-mail: enquiry@bp-hydraulics.fsnet.co.uk *Hydraulic manifold manufrs*

B P I Consumer V M B, Block C, Blackpole East, Blackpole Road, Worcester, WR3 8ZL Tel: (01905) 755000 Fax: (01905) 456378 E-mail: enquiries@vmb.co.uk *Polythene converters & printers*

B P I Films, 40 Thursby Road, Croft Business Park, Wirral, Merseyside, CH62 3PZ Tel: 0151-334 8091 Fax: 0151-334 0066 E-mail: enquiries@bpipoly.com Principal Export Areas: Worldwide *Plastic products manufrs*

▶ B P I Industrial Ardeer, Lundholm Road, Stevenston, Ayrshire, KA20 3NQ Tel: (01294) 605111 Fax: (01294) 842032

▶ B P I Packaging Services, 3-4 Manor Industrial Estate, Flint, Clwyd, CH6 5UY Tel: (01352) 735122 Fax: (01352) 734032 E-mail: packagingsales@bpipoly.com *Polythene manufrs*

▶ B P I Packaging Services, 96 Port Glasgow Road, Greenock, Renfrewshire, PA15 2UL Tel: (01475) 501100 Fax: (01475) 744868 *Printed & plain carrier bags, manufrs*

B P I Recycled Products, Heanor Gate Industrial Estate, Heanor, Derbyshire, DE75 7RG Tel: (01773) 530530 Fax: (01773) 533347 Principal Export Areas: Central/East Europe *Waste polythene recycling services*

B P I Recycled Products, Unit N Bath Road Trading Estate, Lightpill, Stroud, Gloucestershire, GL5 3QF Tel: (01453) 751471 Fax: (01453) 752843 *Refuse sack manufrs*

B P I Stretchville, Bath Road, Bridgwater, Somerset, TA6 4BF Tel: (01278) 446262 Fax: (01278) 452252 E-mail: pswexports@brithene.com *Plastic, flexible & polyethylene packaging manufrs*

B P Instruments, Unit 1 Oak Street Trading Estate, Oak Street, Quarry Bank, Brierley Hill, West Midlands, DY5 2JQ Tel: (01384) 569531 Fax: (01384) 569531 *Automatic test equipment*

B & P Joiners Ltd, Thomas Street, Crewe, CW1 2BD Tel: (01270) 250969 Fax: (01270) 250969 *Joinery company*

B P Marine, 11 Durham Road, Basildon, Essex, SS15 6PH Tel: (01268) 541737 Fax: (01268) 541737 E-mail: bpmarine@blueyonder.co.uk *Glass fibre mouldings manufrs*

B P Newbould Ltd, 15 Hilltop Road, Hamilton, Leicester, LE5 1TT Tel: 0116-274 3303 Fax: 0116-274 3301 E-mail: sales@bpnewbould.co.uk *Engineering & machining services*

▶ B P Rolls Ltd, West Portway, Andover, Hampshire, SP10 3LF Tel: (01264) 361516 Fax: (01264) 333473 E-mail: sales@bprolls.co.uk *Vehicle repair service*

B P S, Pinnacle House, 17-25 Hartfield Road, London, SW19 3SE Tel: (020) 8296 1000 Fax: (020) 8296 1010 *Telephone marketing & sales service*

B P S Dorline, Hermes Court, Hermes Close, Warwick, CV34 6NJ Tel: (01926) 332620 Fax: (01926) 332629 E-mail: bpsdorline@bandps.co.uk *Architectural ironmongers*

▶ B P S Printers, 1 Holtspur Top Lane, Beaconsfield, Buckinghamshire, HP9 1DN Tel: (01494) 678823 Fax: (01494) 674457

B P T Automation Ltd, Unit 16 Sovereign Park, Cleveland Way, Hemel Hempstead, Hertfordshire, HP2 7DA Tel: (01442) 235355 Fax: (01442) 244729 *Industrial gates*

B P V Servicing, The Workshop, Ely Avenue, Slough, SL1 3AE Tel: (01753) 692386 Fax: (01753) 692383 *Air conditioning for cars*

B P Y Plastics, J Lincoln Park, Borough Road, Buckingham Road Industrial Estate, Brackley, Northamptonshire, NN13 7BE Tel: (01280) 706335 Fax: (01280) 705675 E-mail: tony@bpy-plastics.com *Manufacturers of injection mouldings (plastic) & plastic mouldings*

B Plan Information Sytems, The Square, Basing View, Basingstoke, Hampshire, RG21 4EB Tel: (01256) 691111 Fax: (01256) 692450 E-mail: enquiries@fiinfo.com *Engineering subcontractors*

B Plan Shop Equipment, Unit 4e Bellair, Musker Street, Liverpool, L23 0UB Tel: 0151-932 1002 Fax: 0151-932 1002 *Shop fittings suppliers*

B Preece & Son, Plowden Mill, Plowden, Lydbury North, Shropshire, SY7 8BG Tel: (01588) 680279 *Agricultural building*

▶ B Proudfoot, 151 Balmoral Street, Glasgow, G14 0HB Tel: 0141-959 4555

B R C Special Products, Carver Road, Astonfields Industrial Estate, Stafford, ST16 3BP Tel: (01785) 222288 Fax: (01785) 240029 *Construction products manufrs*

B R E Ltd, Fowler Road, West Pitkerro Industrial Estate, Broughty Ferry, Dundee, DD5 3RU Tel: (01382) 739848 Fax: (01382) 739849 E-mail: info@breuk.com *Engineering*

B R E Europe Ltd, London Road, Feering, Colchester, CO5 9ED Tel: (01376) 572500 Fax: (01376) 572600 E-mail: sales@breltd.com *CNC drilling machine merchants*

B & R Fabrication, 3g Lyncastle Way, Barley Castle Lane, Appleton, Warrington, WA4 4ST Tel: (01925) 601728 Fax: (01925) 602261 E-mail: brfabrications@lineone.net *Steelwork fabricators*

B & R Fabrication & Welding, 115 Spalding Road, Deeping St. James, Peterborough, PE6 8SD Tel: (01778) 341355 Fax: (01778) 341355 *Fabrication & welding sub-contractors & gate manufrs*

B R G International Ltd, Carrington Field Street, Stockport, Cheshire, SK1 3JN Tel: 0161-477 4487 Fax: 0161-480 3573 E-mail: sales@brginternational.co.uk *Manufacturers of rubber extrusions & rubber sports surfaces*

B R L Consulting Ltd, 1 Amersham Road, Penn Street, Amersham, Buckinghamshire, HP7 0QW Tel: (01494) 716541 Fax: (01494) 716541 *Computer consultants*

B R M Computers, 101 Winchester Road, Chandler's Ford, Eastleigh, Hampshire, SO53 2GG Tel: (023) 8034 1094 Fax: (023) 8064 7207 E-mail: info@brmcomputers.demon.co.uk *PC repairs, upgrades & replacements*

B R M Precision Engineers & Toolmakers Ltd, Unit 3, Brooks Street Business Centre, Brook Street, Colchester, CO1 2UZ Tel: (01206) 794617 Fax: (01206) 793839 *CNC engineering services or machinists*

▶ B & R Maintenance, 140 Harport Road, Redditch, Worcestershire, B98 7PD Tel: (01527) 460344 E-mail: brmaintenance@hotmail.co.uk *general property maintenance*

B R Saunders Ltd, Molesey Road, Walton-on-Thames, Surrey, KT12 3PW Tel: (01932) 245161 Fax: (01932) 254764 E-mail: info@brsaunders.co.uk *Road haulage*

B R Sippy & Co., 118 Pepys Road, London, SW20 8NY Tel: (020) 8946 5964 Fax: (020) 8944 6083 *Generating set distribs*

▶ B R V Technologies Ltd., Unit 18a, Challenge House,, Sherwood Drive, Bletchley, Milton Keynes, MK3 6DP Tel: (01908) 484753 Fax: (01908) 484901 E-mail: vasu@brvtech.com

B & R Welding Fabrications, Unit 1a Ribble Business Park, Challenge Way, Blackburn, BB1 5QB Tel: (01254) 670503 Fax: (01254) 670503 *Welding & fabrication contractors services*

▶ B Rogers, Unit 23 Mold Business Park, Wrexham Road, Mold, Clwyd, CH7 1XP Tel: (01352) 700096 Fax: (01352) 753100

B Rourke & Co. Ltd, Accrington Road, Burnley, Lancashire, BB11 5QD Tel: (01282) 422841 Fax: (01282) 458901 E-mail: info@rourkes.co.uk *Wrought ironwork manufrs*

B S & A, Unit 8 Imex Business Centre, Station Lane, Birtley, Co. Durham, DH3 1QT Tel: 0191-411 1411 Fax: 0191-411 1410 *Power press repair*

B S A Advanced Sintering Ltd, Hadleigh Road, Ipswich, IP2 0HX Tel: (01473) 233300 Fax: (01473) 230424 E-mail: Sales@bsasintering.com *Sintered metal component manufrs*

B S A Bath, 91 Mount Road, Southdown, Bath, BA2 1LL Tel: (01225) 313088 Fax: (01225) 303341 E-mail: bsa.lg@btinternet.com *Fire & security systems service*

B S A Machine Tools, Mackadown Lane, Kitts Green, Birmingham, B33 0LE Tel: 0121-783 4071 Fax: 0121-789 9509 E-mail: sales@bsamachinetools.co.uk *B S A Machine Tools Ltd - The ONE stop source for Quality Machine Tools, from major manufactures around the world. Whether your requirement is for a conventional machine or a CNC model in either Milling or Turning, we have the highest level of quality and technology available. Explore the possibilities !!! The Products we can offer... Conventional Centre Lathes with D.R.O. Milling Machines - 2 and 3 Axis with D.R.O. Heavy Duty Engine Lathes. CNC Lathes and Turning Centre's CNC Multi Axes Automatic Lathes. CNC Multi Spindle Automatic Lathes. CNC Machining Centre's. Spares & Service Support. Applications & Customer Training. Machine tools, cnc mahcine tools*

▶ B S A Metal Powders, Montgomery Street, Birmingham, B11 1DT Tel: 0121-773 7386 Fax: 0121-772 3587 E-mail: sales@mbc-meta1-powders.co.uk

B S A Mouldings Ltd, Larch Road, Saddlebow, King's Lynn, Norfolk, PE34 3HW Tel: (01553) 772555 Fax: (01553) 776294 E-mail: bsamouldings@compuserve.com *Injection moulders*

▶ B S & A Power Press, Unit 7-8 Tanfield Lea Industrial Estate South, Tanfield Lea, Stanley, County Durham, DH9 9QX Tel: (01207) 283377 Fax: (01207) 283366 E-mail: bsassociates@aol.com *Power pressing services*

B S A Prophet Systems Ltd, 3 Church Street, Leamington Spa, Warwickshire, CV31 1EG Tel: (01926) 430023 Fax: (01926) 431010 E-mail: sales@hccm.co.uk *Computer system developers*

B & S Adams, Fairy Cross, Bideford, Devon, EX39 5DA Tel: (01237) 451254 Fax: (01237) 451254 *Agricultural contractors*

B S B, 28 Heathfield Road, Bexleyheath, Kent, DA6 8NP Tel: (020) 8303 0196 Fax: (020) 8303 6466 *Car paints manufrs*

B S B Engineering Co. Ltd, Phoenix Street, Bolton, BL1 2SY Tel: (01204) 535343 Fax: (01204) 389287 E-mail: enquiries@bsbengineering.com *Sheet metal fabricators*

▶ B S B Engineering Services Ltd, Unit E, Trinity Trading Estate, Mill Way, Sittingbourne, Kent, ME10 2PD Tel: (01795) 422609 *Engineers for air conditioning*

B & S Builders Ltd, Churchill Farm, Dale Road, Haverfordwest, Dyfed, SA62 3AD Tel: (01437) 779303 *WE WILL UNDER TAKE ANY BUILDING WORKS FROM MAINTENANCE TONEW BUILDS AND WILL OFFER A 24 HOUR SERVICE.*

B S C (Contracts) Ltd, Unit 4 Inoic Park, Birmingham New Road, Dudley, West Midlands, DY1 4SJ Tel: 0121-557 4651 Fax: 0121-557 7375 E-mail: sales@bsc-contracts.co.uk *Racor filter separator stockists*

B S C (Diecasting) Ltd, Fryers Close, Walsall, WS3 2XQ Tel: (01922) 710070 Fax: (01922) 408008 E-mail: tech@bscdiecasting.co.uk *Die casting*

B S C L Ltd, Horndon Industrial Park, West Horndon, Brentwood, Essex, CM13 3XD Tel: 01268 578940 Fax: 01277 810157 E-mail: info@bscl.com *Telecommunications*

B S C Management Ltd, 150 Minories, London, EC3N 1LS Tel: (0870) 2406117 Fax: (0870) 2406118 E-mail: bsc@bscconsulting.com *Risk management consultants*

B S C Packaging, 127 Mereside, Soham, Ely, Cambridgeshire, CB7 5EG Tel: (01353) 723024 Fax: (01353) 723333 E-mail: mark@brimur.co.uk *Corrugated cardboard box, case & container manufrs*

B S C Print, B S C House, 48 Weir Road, Wimbledon, London, SW19 8UG Tel: (020) 8947 8571 Fax: (020) 8947 3319 E-mail: sales@bscprint..co.uk *Commercial colour printers & typesetters*

B S C Snooker Equipment, 24 Newbiggin Road, Grangemouth, Stirlingshire, FK3 0LF Tel: (01324) 473069 Fax: (01324) 473069 *Snooker equipment alarms & surveillance*

B & S Chains (Midlands) Ltd, 29 Toys Lane, Halesowen, West Midlands, B63 2JX Tel: (01384) 413088 Fax: (01384) 413066 E-mail: enquiries@bandschains.co.uk *Chain assembling services*

B S Commercial Repairs Ltd, 3 Clothier Road, Bristol, BS4 5PS Tel: 0117-977 2608 Fax: 0117-972 1967 E-mail: sales@bs-commercial.co.uk *Commercial vehicle body repairs*

B & S Dental Laboratory, 18 Chilham Way, Bromley, BR2 7PR Tel: (020) 8462 7007 Fax: (020) 8462 7007 *Dental technicians*

B S Eaton Ltd, Coppice Lane, Cheslyn Hay, Walsall, WS6 7EY Tel: (01922) 413678 Fax: (01922) 416515 E-mail: enquiries@bseaton.co.uk *Concrete products manufrs*

B S Ellis, Unit 5 Chillington Fields, Wolverhampton, WV1 2BY Tel: (01902) 459111 Fax: (01902) 459111 *Jig & fixture manufrs*

▶ B S Engineering Ltd, 5 Kings Mill Way, Mansfield, Nottinghamshire, NG18 5ER Tel: (01623) 636899

B S Fashions, 187 Plashet Rd, London, E13 0QZ Tel: 020 84720439 *Manufacture of leather garments*

B S Fibre Glass Moulding, 1 Carloggas, St. Columb Major Industrial Estate, St. Columb, Cornwall, TR9 6SF Tel: (01637) 880700 Fax: (01637) 880056 E-mail: enquiries@bspanelvanconversions.gbr.fm *Glass fibre moulding manufrs*

B & S Glass Industries Ltd, 47 Sutherland Road, London, E17 6BH Tel: (020) 8527 7575 Fax: (020) 8531 4875 E-mail: colin.tucker4@btopenworld.com *Glass decorating & bending services*

B S Group Consultancies, 36 Woodpond Avenue, Hockley, Essex, SS5 4PX Tel: (01702) 204073 Fax: (01702) 200759 E-mail: bob41@onetel.com *Software engineers*

B S H Ltd, 15 Powdrake Road, Grangemouth, Stirlingshire, FK3 9UT Tel: (01324) 474242 Fax: (01324) 665456 E-mail: sales@bshltd.co.uk *Hydraulics pneumatics transmission distributors*

B S I Technology Ltd, 11 Whittle Road, Phoenix Parkway, Corby, Northants, NN17 5DX Tel: (01536) 201555 Fax: (01536) 401660 E-mail: bsilubron@netscapeonline.com *Lubricant distributors*

B & S Injection Moulders Ltd, Units 14-15 Joseph Wilson Industrial Estate, Millstrood Road, Whitstable, Kent, CT5 3PS Tel: (01227) 262599 Fax: (01227) 770767 E-mail: sales@bandsinjection.co.uk *Plastics mouldings manufrs*

▶ B S J Mechanical & Plumbing Services Ltd, 87 Princess Street, Sheffield, S4 7UU Tel: 0114-276 6004

▶ B S Joinery Services, 2 Harlaw Business Centre, Inverurie, Aberdeenshire, AB51 4FR Tel: (01467) 625300 Fax: (01467) 625643 E-mail: bsjoinery@bsjoinery.com *manufacturers of high quality garden sheds,garden workshops,timber garages,dog kennels,dog runs,childrens playhouses,summer houses, solar cabins,potting sheds,pine welsh dressers and just about any sectional timber garden building you could think of*

B S K Ltd, Murdock Rd, Bedford, MK41 7PD Tel: (01234) 217096 Fax: (01234) 271537 E-mail: info@bsk.co.uk *Sewing & knitting machines distributors & retail*

▶ B S L Hire Ltd, 11 Churchill Road, Wimborne, Dorset, BH21 2AT Tel: (01202) 882126 Fax: (01202) 882126 E-mail: billy@bslhire.wanadoo.co.uk *Industrial roofing & cladding & safety netting installation*

B S Labels Ltd, Wood Street, Earl Shilton, Leicester, LE9 7NE Tel: (01455) 844451 Fax: (01455) 842607 E-mail: sales@bslabels.co.uk *Labels*

B & S Leicester Ltd, 33 Parker Drive, Leicester, LE4 0JP Tel: 0116-232 3222 *Plumbers merchants*

▶ B S M Knitware, Majid House, 39 Devonshire St North, Manchester, M12 6JR Tel: 0161-273 6033 Fax: 0161-273 6033 *Knitted garment manufrs*

B S Motors, 42 Tyne Road, Sandy, Bedfordshire, SG19 1SA Tel: (01767) 682206 Fax: (01767) 682208 E-mail: sales@bsmotors.com *Motor engineers*

B S P Ltd, 26 Balmer Cut, Buckingham Industrial Estate, Buckingham, MK18 1UL Tel: (01280) 813881 Fax: (01280) 822429 E-mail: sales@buckscreenprint.co.uk *Screen printers & printing services*

B S P Electrics, 10 Horwood Court, Bletchley, Milton Keynes, MK1 1RD Tel: (01908) 645500 Fax: (01908) 647700

B S P Engineering Ltd, Maitland Road, Lion Barn Industrial Estate, Needham Market, Ipswich, IP6 8NZ Tel: (01449) 722222 Fax: (01449) 721989 E-mail: sales@bspengineering.co.uk *CNC machiners*

▶ B S P Method Ltd, 3 Millbrook Business Centre, Floats Road, Roundthorn Industrial Estate, Manchester, M23 9YJ Tel: 0161-998 1999 Fax: 0161-946 1697 E-mail: info@bspmethod.com *Manufacturers & suppliers of laboratory fittings, safety showers & eyewashes*

B S Panel Van Conversions, 1 Carloggas Industrial Units, St. Columb Major Industrial Estate, St. Columb, Cornwall, TR9 6SF Tel: (01637) 880700 Fax: (01637) 880056 E-mail: enquiries@bspanelvanconversions.gbr.fm *Vehicle refrigeration equipment manufrs*

B & S Quality Joinery, 3 Aylesham Industrial Estate, Covert Road, Aylesham, Canterbury, Kent, CT3 3EQ Tel: (01304) 842336 Fax: (01304) 841104 *Joinery manufrs*

B S R Technical Mouldings Services Ltd, Unit 13/14/18 Lagrange, Lichfield Road Industrial Estate, Tamworth, Staffordshire, B79 7XD Tel: (01827) 63626 Fax: (01827) 63242 *Injection mouldings manufrs*

B S R Wickens, Hambridge Farm, Martley, Worcester, WR6 6QT Tel: (01886) 812228 Fax: (01886) 812228 *Farming & agricultural contractors*

B S S Group plc, Fleet House, Lee Circle, Leicester, LE1 3QQ Tel: 0116-262 3232 Fax: 0116-253 1343 E-mail: sales@bssuk.co.uk *Pipeline fittings & flanges stockholders*

B S S Trading Co. Ltd, Worton Hall Worton Hall Industrial Estate, Worton Road, Isleworth, Middlesex, TW7 6ER Tel: (020) 8569 7007 Fax: (020) 8569 8008 E-mail: bss@freenetname.co.uk *Masking products distributors*

B S Sales, 149 Hale Lane, Edgware, Middlesex, HA8 9QW Tel: (020) 8201 0101 Fax: (020) 8201 0022 *Office furniture & banqueting hire*

B S Sectional Buildings, Stapleford Road, Trowell, Nottingham, NG9 3PS Tel: 0115-932 3280 Fax: 0115-932 3290 E-mail: sales@bssectional.co.uk *Garden sheds manufrs*

B S Security, 25 Barnes Wallis Road, Fareham, Hampshire, PO15 5TT Tel: (01489) 885870 Fax: (01489) 889801 E-mail: enquiries@bssecurity.co.uk *Security systems distributors*

B S Security, PO Box 115, Fareham, Hampshire, PO15 5TT Tel: (01489) 885870 Fax: (01489) 889801 E-mail: enquiries@bssecurity.co.uk *Alarm equipment suppliers*

B S Steels, 1 Shawcross Industrial Park, Ackworth Road, Portsmouth, PO3 5HU Tel: (023) 9267 3778 Fax: (023) 9269 1528 E-mail: bssteels@btconnect.com *Steel fabricators & stockholders*

B & S Threaded Products Ltd, 28 Newtown Street, Cradley Heath, West Midlands, B64 5LD Tel: (01384) 569899 Fax: (01384) 410392 *Industrial fasteners*

B S Tickle, Unit 5, Waterside Trading Estate, Leigh, Lancashire, WN7 2BG Tel: (01942) 676914 Fax: (01942) 676914 *Joiners*

B S W Engineering UK Ltd, 115a West End Road, Southall, Middlesex, UB1 1JF Tel: (020) 8574 6685 Fax: (020) 8571 5751 E-mail: bswenguk@aol.com *Precision engineers*

B S W Timber plc, East End, Earlston, Berwickshire, TD4 6JA Tel: (01896) 849255 Fax: (01896) 848080 E-mail: sales@bsw.co.uk *Sawmiller & timber merchants*

B Safe Security Systems, Security Buildings, Storforth Lane, Chesterfield, Derbyshire, S40 2TU Tel: (01246) 556400 Fax: (01246) 232050 E-mail: sales@bsafesecurity.co.uk *Security systems installation*

B Saxton & Co. Ltd, Unit 6a Arrow Trading Estate, Corporation Road, Audenshaw, Manchester, M34 5LR Tel: 0161-320 1444 Fax: 0161-320 1555 E-mail: sales@banshaws.com *Engineering*

B Sheldon, Burrs Hill Barn House, Horsmonden Road, Brenchley, Tonbridge, Kent, TN12 7AT Tel: (01892) 723857 *Architects*

B Shelsher & Son, Bridge Cottage, The Druce, Clavering, Saffron Walden, Essex, CB11 4QP Tel: (01799) 550350 Fax: (01799) 550135 *Excavation & groundwork contractors*

B Sinclair, Kirkton Cottage, Auchterless, Turriff, Aberdeenshire, AB53 8BA Tel: (01888) 511406 Fax: (01888) 511406 *Marine engineering & diesel generating sets*

B Sipling Covermakers, Broughton, Brigg, South Humberside, DN20 0BZ Tel: (01652) 652343 Fax: (01652) 652343 E-mail: becky@sipling.freeserve.co.uk *Tarpaulin manufrs*

B Snelling, 1 The Laurels, Netherfield, Battle, East Sussex, TN33 9QJ Tel: (01424) 838886 Fax: (01424) 838273 *Joinery manufrs*

B & T Angling, 11 Briar Road, Romford, RM3 8AH Tel: (01708) 370033 Fax: (01708) 370004 *Retail & wholesale angling suppliers*

B T B, Supreme House, 1 Pitt Lane, Bideford, Devon, EX39 3JA Tel: (01237) 424046 Fax: (01237) 423376 *Closed circit television designers/consultants*

B T Blinds, 26 Winsover Road, Spalding, Lincolnshire, PE11 1EJ Tel: (01775) 760620 Fax: (01775) 760620 E-mail: info@btblinds.co.uk *Blinds suppliers*

▶ B T C Euro Ltd, Bond Street, Nuneaton, Warwickshire, CV11 4BX Tel: (024) 7632 8104 Fax: (024) 7664 1948 E-mail: sales@btceuro.co.uk *Footwear*

▶ B & T Family Caterers, 54 Duffryn Street, Ferndale, Mid Glamorgan, CF43 4EP Tel: (01443) 755499

B T & G Midson, 39 Mere View Industrial Estate, Yaxley, Peterborough, PE7 3HS Tel: (01733) 243833 Fax: (01733) 243833 *Stainless steel finishing & polishing service providers*

B T G Plant Hire & Repairs Ltd, Hallsford Bridge Industrial Estate, Ongar, Essex, CM5 9RB Tel: (01277) 364444 Fax: (01277) 365239 *Contractors plant hire, leasing & rental hire*

B T G Plastics Ltd, Corporation Road, Sparth Bottoms, Rochdale, Lancashire, OL11 4HJ Tel: (01706) 640400 Fax: (01706) 653434 E-mail: btg.plastics@tiscali.co.uk *Plastic injection mouldings extruders & manufrs*

B T I Computer Systems UK Ltd, Burnt Meadow Road, Moons Moat North Industrial Estate, Redditch, Worcestershire, B98 9PA Tel: (01527) 598500 Fax: (01527) 598555 E-mail: sales@bticomputer.com *Early warning systems manufacturer*

B T J Drives & Controls Ltd, Heath Holdings, Stone Heath, Leigh, Stoke-on-Trent, ST10 4PG Tel: (01889) 505315 Fax: (01889) 505604 E-mail: enquiries@btjdrives.co.uk Principal Export Areas: Worldwide *Supply computer systems & repair*

B T L Powertec Ltd, 4 Station Yard, Old Furnace Road, Coniston, Cumbria, LA21 8HU Tel: (01539) 441904 Fax: (01539) 441907 *Transformers & power supply systems manufrs*

B T M Automation Products (UK) Ltd, Unit 6, Stephenson Road, St. Ives, Cambridgeshire, PE27 3WJ Tel: 0845 5314209 Fax: (01480) 497479 E-mail: btmautomation@btconnect.com Principal Export Areas: Worldwide *Are you looking for a solution to your metal joining needs? If so, then BTM bring you Tog-L-Loc®, a sheet metal joining process that is both simple and economical. We specialise in joining sheet metal components with this patented clinching system offering a full turn-key package from initial enquiry to equipment commissioning. Our specialist engineers have served the Automotive, White Goods, Office furniture, Heating & Ventilation industries and others for over 15 years and will provide the customer the best solution whether it is a hand-held unit for low production or a robot cell or dedicated special purpose machine for high output.*

B T M Services, Unit 16 The Lays Farm Trading Estate, Charlton Road, Keynsham, Bristol, BS31 2SE Tel: 0117-986 8390 Fax: 0117-986 1031 E-mail: btmservs@yahoo.co.uk *Engineering, design, manufacture & installers*

B T M Sports Services, Columbia House, Columbia Avenue, Worcester Park, Surrey, KT4 7SP Tel: (020) 8337 3327 Fax: (020) 8337 3328 *Grounds maintenance services*

▶ B T N L Ltd, 291 High Street, Epping, Essex, CM16 4DA Tel: (01992) 574070 Fax: (01992) 578848 E-mail: bramsden@btnl.co.uk *Telecommunication systems*

B & T Printed Circuits Services Ltd, B&T House, 27 Eastways, Witham, Essex, CM8 3YG Tel: (01376) 519500 Fax: (01376) 500388 E-mail: btcircuits@clara.co.uk *Manufacturers of bare printed circuit boards*

B & T Quality Engineering, Unit B Pooley Lane, Polesworth, Tamworth, Staffordshire, B78 1JA Tel: (01827) 895377 Fax: (01827) 895377 *Toolmakers supplier & manufrs*

B T Refrigeration, 20 Nelson Street, Bradford, West Yorkshire, BD5 0HD Tel: (01274) 727777 Fax: (01274) 739797 E-mail: btrefrigeration@btconnect.com *Transport refrigeration specialist*

B & T Rewinds Ltd, 134 Brearley Street, Hockley, Birmingham, B19 3XJ Tel: 0121-359 8398 Fax: 0121-359 7072 E-mail: bandt.rewind@btconnect.com *Electric motor repair agents*

▶ B T S Haulage Ltd, Manchester Road, Carrington, Manchester, M31 4BD Tel: 0161-775 5277 Fax: 0161-777 9267 E-mail: admin@btshaulage.co.uk

B T S Industrial Supplies, Unit 6, 692 Stratford Road, Sparkhill, Birmingham, B11 4AT Tel: 0121-702 2404 Fax: 0121-778 6092 E-mail: sales@btssupplies.co.uk *Industrial supplies*

B T S Scotland Ltd, 15 Croft Road, Balmore, Torrance, Glasgow, G64 4AL Tel: (01360) 620761 Fax: (01360) 622236 *Air conditioning & refrigeration contractors*

B T U (Europe) Ltd, Unit 14 Armstrong Mall, Southwood Business Park, Farnborough, Hampshire, GU14 0NR Tel: (01252) 660010 Fax: (01252) 660011 E-mail: sales@btu.co.uk *Electric furnace sales & service*

B T U (Heating) Ltd, 38 Weyside Road, Guildford, Surrey, GU1 1JB Tel: (01483) 590600 Fax: (01483) 590601 E-mail: enquiries@btu-heating.com *Heating & ventilating engineers*

B T U Pool Services Ltd, 38 Weyside Road, Guildford, Surrey, GU1 1JB Tel: (01483) 727444 Fax: (01483) 766254 E-mail: sales@btu-group.com *Central heating engineers, installation or service* Also at: Ashford, Basingstoke, Erith, Middleton-on-Sea, Southampton & Watford

B T U (Pool Services) Ltd, Wyevale Garden Centre, Egley Road, Woking, Surrey, GU22 0NH Tel: (01483) 727444 Fax: (01483) 766254 E-mail: sales@btu-poolservices.com *Swimming pool maintenance*

▶ B Tattersall, Unit 4a1 Strathspey Industrial Estate, Woodlands Terrace, Grantown-on-Spey, Morayshire, PH26 3NB Tel: (01479) 872184 Fax: (01479) 872184

B Tech International Ltd, Vulcan House, Vulcan Way, New Addington, Croydon, CR0 9UG Tel: (01689) 848535 Fax: (01689) 841073 E-mail: info@b-tech-int.com *Audio & visual equipment accessories manufrs*

▶ B Thompson & Sons Ltd, Station Road, Moretonhampstead, Newton Abbot, Devon, TQ13 8NQ Tel: (01647) 440505 Fax: (01647) 440507

▶ B Tyler & Sons, 30 Mallory Road, Bishops Tachbrook, Leamington Spa, Warwickshire, CV33 9QX Tel: (01926) 335476 E-mail: btyler@tylerandsonsroofing.co.uk *a family run business for over 30 years,operating in warwickshire and Leamington spa,supplying quality roof repairs,roof surveys,EPDM rubber roofs,fibreglass roof coverings and roof renewals,including plastic facias,soffits and guttering.All roofing works guaranteed*

B U Industrial Components Ltd, Units B2-B5, Tweedale Industrial Estate, Madeley, Telford, Shropshire, TF7 4JR Tel: (01952) 586016 Fax: (01952) 586062 *Decorative trim & control knob manufrs*

▶ B U Interiors Ltd, Unit 15 Nonsuch Industrial Estate, Kiln Lane, Epsom, Surrey, KT17 1DH Tel: (01372) 747677 Fax: (01372) 747706 E-mail: sales@buinteriors.co.uk *Welcome to BU Interiors, suppliers and installers of carpets,vinyl, linoleum, rubber, resin and hardwood flooring*

B U P A, BUPA House, 15-19 Bloomsbury Way, London, WC1A 2BA Tel: (020) 7656 2000 Fax: (020) 7656 2701 *Health insurance* Also at: Branches throughout the U.K.

B & V Fowler, Lowmans Farm, Beacon, Honiton, Devon, EX14 4TX Tel: (01404) 42683 Fax: (01404) 47411 *Agricultural contractors*

B V Senior Engineering Co. Ltd, Hall Road, Maltby, Rotherham, South Yorkshire, S66 8ET Tel: (01709) 818511 Fax: (01709) 812557 *Steel fabricators*

B V Z Marketing Ltd, Unit 34, Meadow Lane, Ellesmere Port, CH65 4EH Tel: 0151-355 3055 Fax: 0151-355 5055 *Laboratory plastic ware distributors*

B Vaughan & Partners, 14 Northbourne Avenue, Shanklin, Isle of Wight, PO37 7LT Tel: (01983) 864175 E-mail: mark.harrison@tiscali.co.uk *Removal contractors*

B.W.B Engineering Company Ltd, Baltimore Trading Estate, Baltimore Road, Birmingham, B42 1DD Tel: 0121-356 2879 Fax: 0121-356 2880 *Press tool manufrs*

B & W Billiards & Snooker Services Ltd, Unit 3 Sapcote Trading Centre, Powke Lane, Old Hill, Cradley Heath, West Midlands, B64 5QR Tel: (01384) 638191 Fax: (01384) 638195 E-mail: sales@bandwbilliards.co.uk *B & W Billiards manufacture and supply the finest quality handcrafted cues. We are a small, specialised firm of experienced craftsmen who take real pride in their work. Dean Jones is our in house Cue maker & Julian Westwood is our in house Table fitter. We offer; the NEW - Flexi-rest head, pool accessories, pool tables, pool table restoration, snooker accessories, snooker cues, snooker tables, snooker table restoration, billiard table restoration, billiard tables, bar billiards, French polishing services, hand spliced cue, custom made cues, we also have our standard range of cues, air hockey tables, football tables, dart boards, Unicorn darts, Gunn & Moore Cricket bats & accessories, Hockey accessories, Cue Cases, Poker products. Although we restore and sell antique Burroughes & Watts tables and accessories, please note that there is no link between B & W Billiards Limited and Burroughes & Watts® or Burroughes & Watts Cues Limited.*

B W Blinds, 127a Frankwell, Shrewsbury, SY3 8JU Tel: (01743) 341290 Fax: (01743) 341290 *Blinds manufrs*

B W C L, B W C L House, Brook Farm Estate, Kimbolton, Leominster, Herefordshire, HR6 0ES Tel: (01568) 750365 Fax: (01568) 750369 E-mail: admin@bwcl.co.uk *Computers & software*

▶ B W Cook Construction, Rutland Farm, Wimblington Road, Manea, March, Cambridgeshire, PE15 0JR Tel: (01354) 688062 Fax: (01354) 680934

B W Dove & Son, The Old Dairy, Darrow Green Road, Denton, Harleston, Norfolk, IP20 0BA Tel: (01986) 788377 *Joinery manufrs*

B W F Kunststoffe GmbH, Unit 4, Orchard Court, Nunn Brook Road, Huthwaite, Sutton-in-Ashfield, Nottinghamshire, NG17 2HZ Tel: (01908) 516177 Fax: (01908) 290468 E-mail: sales@bwfprofiles.co.uk Principal Export Areas: Central/East Europe *Extrusion rod & polycarbonate tubes manufrs*

B W Fabrications Ltd, 3 Market Side, Albert Road, St. Philips, Bristol, BS2 0XS Tel: 0117-972 4002 Fax: 0117-972 3094 E-mail: bwfabrications@hotmail.com *Ventilation & air conditioning manufrs*

▶ B W Fire Engineering, Moorgreen Industrial Park, Engine Lane, Newthorpe, Nottingham, NG16 3QU Tel: (01773) 715978 *Fire fighting equipment manufrs*

B W Grinding Services, 15 Bourne End Lane, Hemel Hempstead, Hertfordshire, HP1 2RL Tel: (01442) 872819 Fax: (01442) 872819 *Precision grinders*

B & W Group, Elm Grove Lane, Steyning, West Sussex, BN44 3SA Tel: (01903) 817200 Fax: (01903) 815801 *Hi-fi manufrs*

B & W Group Ltd, Dale Road, Worthing, West Sussex, BN11 2BH Tel: (01903) 221800 Fax: (01903) 221801 E-mail: info@bwgroup.com *High fidelity sound equipment manufrs*

B & W Joinery Ltd, 2 50 Bradfield Road, Finedon Road Industrial Estate, Wellingborough, Northamptonshire, NN8 4HB Tel: (01933) 279800 Fax: (01933) 279881 E-mail: r.webb@bwjoinery.fsnet.co.uk *Shopfitting manufrs*

B & W Lifting, Unit 2e Grangetown Centre, Stapylton Street, Middlesbrough, Cleveland, TS6 7BJ Tel: (01642) 467900 Fax: (01642) 467900 E-mail: bwlifting@hotmail.com *Lifting equipment manufrs*

▶ B W M Ribs, Satchell Lane, Hamble, Southampton, SO31 4HQ Tel: (023) 8045 4719 Fax: (023) 8045 4719

B W Machine Tools, 4 Lyon Close, Wigston, Leicestershire, LE18 2BJ Tel: 0116-288 6070 Fax: 0116-288 0014 E-mail: toolsbw@aol.com Principal Export Areas: Worldwide *Machine tool merchants*

B & W Machinery Installations Ltd, Eagle Iron Works, Tame Street, Stalybridge, Cheshire, SK15 1ST Tel: 0161-338 6588 Fax: 0161-338 6385 *Machinery removal contractors*

B W Manufacturing Plastics Ltd, Rear of, 74 Castle Street, Grimsby, South Humberside, DN32 7TE Tel: (01472) 344444 Fax: (01472) 359523 *Plastic moulders*

▶ B W May & Son Ltd, West La Trading Estate, West Lane, Sittingbourne, Kent, ME10 3TT Tel: (01795) 423021 Fax: (01795) 426974 E-mail: sales@bwmay.co.uk

B. & W. Mechanical Handling Ltd, Gemini House Cambridgeshire, Business Park, Ely, Cambridgeshire, CB7 4EA Tel: (01353) 665001 Fax: (01353) 666734 E-mail: sales@bwmech.co.uk Principal Export Areas: Worldwide *Conveying & handling systems*

B W P Ltd, 24 Bloomsbury Way, London, WC1A 2SL Tel: (020) 7404 2525 Fax: (020) 7404 2084 E-mail: host@bwp.co.uk *Conference organisers & advertising agents*

B W P Advertising, 5 Long Meadow Mills Industrial Estate, Dixon Street, Kidderminster, Worcestershire, DY10 1HH Tel: (01562) 744513 Fax: (01562) 820045 *Letterpress & litho printers*

B W P Technical Services Ltd, 543 Wallisdown Road, Poole, Dorset, BH12 5AD Tel: (01202) 546733 Fax: (01202) 546733 E-mail: info@hats.org.uk *Biotechnology*

B W Services Ltd, St. James Road, Goffs Oak, Waltham Cross, Hertfordshire, EN7 6TR Tel: (01707) 872099 Fax: (01707) 876440 E-mail: pwservices@btinternet.com *Agricultural equipment services & suppliers*

▶ B W W Printers Ltd, Axe Road, Bridgwater, Somerset, TA6 5LW Tel: (01278) 423637 Fax: (01278) 444032 *Printing services*

B Webster & Sons Eastrington Ltd, Lilac Villa, Eastrington, Goole, North Humberside, DN14 7XL Tel: (01430) 440336 Fax: (01430) 441826 *Fell mongers & maggot farm*

B Wilson & Sons, 4 Martins Lane, Newry, County Down, BT35 8PJ Tel: (028) 3026 3342 Fax: (028) 3026 7919 *Steel fabricators*

B X Tech Ltd, 19 Wainright Street, Aston, Birmingham, B6 5TH Tel: 0121-327 6411 Fax: 0121-327 6681 *Courier services & logistics* Also at: Cambridge & Warrington

▶ B & Y Engineering, 5 The Cross, Baltonsborough, Glastonbury, Somerset, BA6 8QW Tel: (01458) 850136 Fax: (01458) 851291 E-mail: info@byengineering.co.uk *Food processor manufrs*

B Y G Systems Ltd, 1-2 William Lee Building, Nottingham Science & Technical Park, University Boulevard, Nottingham, NG7 2RQ Tel: 0115-925 2221 Fax: 0115-922 3496 E-mail: info@bygsystems.com *Bespoke multimedia solutions, simulation software & services*

B Young, The Riverside Workshop, John Martin Street, Haydon Bridge, Hexham, Northumberland, NE47 6AB Tel: (01434) 688007 Fax: (01434) 601938 *Joinery*

B & Z, O2, Cherrycourt Way, Leighton Buzzard, Bedfordshire, LU7 4UH Tel: (01525) 373018 Fax: (01525) 851439 E-mail: enquiries@bandz.co.uk *Manufacturers of electrical & electronic enclosure equipment*

▶ B Z C International Ltd, Waterbury Hill, Horsted Keynes, Haywards Heath, West Sussex, RH17 7BA Tel: (01342) 813748 Fax: (01342) 813748 E-mail: info@bzc.co.uk *Building design & construction services*

B&D, Church Lane, Tydd St. Giles, Wisbech, Cambridgeshire, PE13 5LG Tel: (01945) 870204 Fax: (01945) 870820 *Supply refrifgeration & instalation*

B&M Longworth (Edgworth) Ltd, Sett End Road North, Shadsworth Business Park, Blackburn, BB1 2QG Tel: (01254) 680501 Fax: (01254) 54041 E-mail: enquiries@bmlongworth.com *B&M Longworth Process Technology provides a unique contract cleaning service that offers an economic alternative to component replacement. Our facility is equipped with the latest cleaning technologies which is complemented with an advanced validation programme. The technology in operation at the Blackburn, UK facility includes a variety of ultrasonic & aqueous processes, enclosed high temperature solvent systems, controlled pyrolysis ovens, auto spray wash, slurry flushing and super heated steam.*

B&T, Ironmould Lane, Bristol, BS4 5SA Tel: 0117-971 5295 Fax: 0117-971 5295 *General engineers & toolmakers manufrs*

▶ B2basics Translations, The Old Smithy, Main Street, Gisburn, Clitheroe, Lancashire, BB7 4HD Tel: (01200) 445749 Fax: (01200) 445576 E-mail: sales@translations-translation.com *We specialize in the translation of documents in the following languages: Polish, German, French*

▶ Baas Construction Ltd, The Old Chapel, Brooklandsroad, Burnley, Lancashire, BB11 3PR Tel: (01282) 437304 Fax: (01282) 452200

BAB Industrial & Commercial, 7 Stainburn Avenue, Leeds, LS17 6PQ Tel: 0113-269 5936 Fax: 0113-269 5936 E-mail: brian@boardman-online.co.uk *Industrial ceramic product suppliers*

Babbage Software Ltd, Victoria House, Victoria Street, Totnes, Devon, TQ9 5EF Tel: (01803) 864328 *Computer software processors*

Babbis Ltd, Deopham Road, Great Ellingham, Attleborough, Norfolk, NR17 1LJ Tel: (01953) 455422 Fax: (01953) 456491 *Forklift trucks servicing & sales*

Babcock Defence Services, Hangar 4, RAF Leeming, Leeming, Northallerton, North Yorkshire, DL7 9NJ Tel: (01677) 425952 Fax: (01677) 425952 *Aircraft engineers*

▶ Babcock International Group PLC, Rosyth Business Park, Rosyth, Dunfermline, Fife, KY11 2YD Tel: (01383) 412131 Fax: (01383) 417774

Babcock PTI, Lorne Road, Larbert, Stirlingshire, FK5 4AT Tel: (01324) 552599 Fax: (01324) 552006 *Compressed air, refrigeration & hvac engineers*

Babcock Scientific Services, Rosyth Dockyard, Rosyth, Dunfermline, Fife, KY11 2YD Tel: (01383) 412131 Fax: (01383) 422699 E-mail: bs-info@babcock.co.uk *Engineering support services*

Babcock Wanson UK Ltd, 7 Elstree Way, Borehamwood, Hertfordshire, WD6 1SA Tel: (020) 8953 7111 Fax: (020) 8207 5177 E-mail: *Manufacturers of industrial boilers*

continued

▶ indicates data change since last edition

Company Information

Baber Rollaprint Ltd, Coombs Road, Halesowen, West Midlands, B62 8AJ Tel: 0121-559 5111 Fax: 0121-559 6594 E-mail: creativity@baber-rollaprint.co.uk *Printers & printing services*

► Babla's Jewellers, 517 High Road, Wembley, Middlesex, HA0 2DH Tel: (020) 8900 9229 Fax: (020) 8900 9229E-mail: info@bablas.co.uk *Professional watch repair service*

Babs UK Ltd, Plot 1 Oakwood Hill Industrial Estate, Oakwood Hill, Loughton, Essex, IG10 3TZ Tel: (020) 8965 9821 Fax: (020) 8502 4187 E-mail: info@babs.co.uk *Shredding & print finishing equipment manufrs*

Babtie Group Ltd, Sheldon Court, Wagon Lane, Birmingham, B26 3DU Tel: 0121-700 1250 Fax: 0121-700 1251 E-mail: birmingham@babtie.com *Consulting engineers*

► Babtie Group Ltd, 95 Bothwell Street, Glasgow, G2 7HX Tel: 0141-204 2511 Fax: 0141-226 3109 *Babtie Asia; Babtie spol s r.o, Babtie India, Babtie Murdoch Green, Babtie Fichtner, Babtie Pettit, Babtie Ringway - Le Crossing, BEAR Scotland Ltd, Babtie Ross Silcock, Babtie Consulting, Babtie International, technical and management consultants, consultancy, consulting engineers, civil engineering, design, management consulting, strategic planning, programme management, project management, design consulting, supervision, operations, support services*

Babtie Group Ltd, 224-226 Tower Bridge Road, London, SE1 2UP Tel: (020) 7403 3330 Fax: (020) 7939 1418 *Consulting engineers* Also at: Birmingham, Manchester, Norwich, Nottingham, Reading & Winchester

Babtie Group Murdoch Green, 1 Grand Parade, Brighton, BN2 9QB Tel: (01273) 676766 Fax: (01273) 696977 E-mail: mgk.brighton@babtie.com *Cost consultancy* Also at: London EC4 & Stockport

► Baby Agency, 479 Hartshill Road, Stoke-on-Trent, ST4 6AA Tel: (01782) 626613 *Baby care equipment suppliers*

► Baby B, 155-157 Portland Road, Hove, East Sussex, BN3 5QJ Tel: (01273) 220789 Fax: (01273) 220789 *Baby care equipment manufrs*

► Baby B Gifts, 33A Wilberforce Road, London, N4 2SN Tel: 020 76908992 *Online baby & new mum gift shop*

► Baby Boom 2000, Long Lane, Ickenham, Uxbridge, Middlesex, UB10 8QS Tel: (01895) 675596 Fax: (01895) 675596 E-mail: sales@babyboom2000.co.uk *BabyBoom 2000 specialize in Baby Travel Systems, Sleeping Bags, Rockers and Bouncers, Pushchairs, Highchairs, Bedding, Car seats, Nursery Furniture and Moses Baskets and Cribs for babies.**

Baby Daze, 132 Main Street, Lochgelly, Fife, KY5 0YF Tel: 01592 784218 Fax: 01592 784218

Baby Point Ltd, PO Box 28, Stowmarket, Suffolk, IP14 3AZ Tel: (01449) 770607 Fax: (01449) 678444 E-mail: sales@babypoint.co.uk *Baby changing equipment manufrs*

► Baby Prints, 41 Tivoli Road, Cheltenham, Gloucestershire, GL50 2TD Tel: (01242) 238029

► Baby Rug, 61 Pepys Road, London, SW20 8NL Tel: (020) 8944 8674 E-mail: info@babyrug.co.uk *Importers of baby accessories*

► Baby Travel, St. Annes Road, Willenhall, West Midlands, WV13 1DY Tel: (01902) 366333 Fax: (01902) 366333 *Baby care retailers*

► Baby Unique, 35 King Street East, Stockport, Cheshire, SK1 1XJ Tel: 0161-477 1666 Fax: 0161-477 0666 *Nursery retailers*

► Baby World, 23 High Street, Hucknall, Nottingham, NG15 7HJ Tel: 0115-964 0008 Fax: 0115-964 0008

Babyfayre Nursery Equipment, 10-12 Orchard Street, Weston-super-Mare, Avon, BS23 1RQ Tel: (01934) 418746 E-mail: angelasbabyfayre@hotmail.com *Independant nursery equipment specialist*

► Babyjacks Nursery Equipment, 40 Comberton Hill, Kidderminster, Worcestershire, DY10 1QN Tel: (01562) 741717 *Nursery & baby store*

Babyland & Pramcots, 76 Yorkshire Street, Oldham, OL1 1SR Tel: 0161-628 9754 Fax: 0161-628 9754 *Baby & nursery equipment*

► Babylon Garden Design, 5 Linksway, Leigh-on-Sea, Essex, SS9 4QY Tel: (01702) 527242 E-mail: discover@babylon-gardens.co.uk *Garden designers & landscapes*

Babylon Hanging Gardens, 11 Stirling Crescent, Horsforth, Leeds, LS18 5SJ Tel: 0113-239 0909 Fax: 0113-239 0909 *Floral display contractors*

Babylon Health Ltd, 57 Uxbridge Road, Shepherds Bush, London, W12 8NR Tel: (020) 8749 0037 Fax: (020) 8749 5628 E-mail: merrell@globalnet.co.uk *Export merchants*

Babytec International Ltd, 5B Sunrise Business, Blandford Forum, Dorset, DT11 8ST Tel: (01258) 459554 Fax: (01258) 480225 E-mail: stephenbenson@babytec.co.uk *Bottle warmers & goods for baby market*

Babyworld, New Portreath Road, Redruth, Cornwall, TR16 4QQ Tel: (01209) 843311 Fax: (01209) 842206 *Baby shop*

Bac Air Conditioning Ltd, Lea Vale, South Normanton, Alfreton, Derbyshire, DE55 3NA Tel: (01773) 814670 Fax: (01773) 814680 *Distributor of air conditioning equipment*

► Bacchus Interiors Exhibition & Display, Stadium Works, Dogford Road, Royton, Oldham, OL2 6UA Tel: 0161-652 6520 Fax: 0161-652 6529 E-mail: sales@bacchusgroup.co.uk *Joiners, manufacturers of shop fitting, interior design*

► Baccus Model Makers, Bardwell Road, Sheffield, S3 8AS Tel: 0114-272 4491 Fax: 0114-272 4491 *Toy soldier manufrs*

► Bace Ltd, Willoughby House, 439 Richmond Road, Twickenham, TW1 2AG Tel: (020) 7060 1620 Fax: (070) 0580 6646 E-mail: h.quinn@baceltd.com *BACE is a specialist building design and engineering company established to provide complete and coordinated building solutions for petrochemical,*

continued

power and heavy industrial industry. Capabilities include engineering from Front-End to Detail Design stages. We deliver the following quality services: Architectural, Civil/Structural, HVAC, Electrical

Bache Pallets Ltd, Bromley Street, Stourbridge, West Midlands, DY9 8HU Tel: (01384) 897799 Fax: (01384) 891351 E-mail: sales@bache-pallets.co.uk Principal Export Areas: Worldwide *Steel pallets*

► Bache Treharne, Cornwall House, 31 Lionel Street, Birmingham, B3 1AP Tel: 0121-212 0005 Fax: 0121-212 0009 E-mail: sales@bachellp.com

Bachy Soletanche, Units 2 & 5 Prospect Place, Mill Lane, Alton, Hampshire, GU34 2SX Tel: (01420) 594700 Fax: (01420) 86971 E-mail: geotech@bacsol.co.uk *Structural foundation contractors & pile driving contractors* Also at: Burscough & York

► Back Scatter Ltd, 7 Grantley Gardens, Glasgow, G41 3PY Tel: 0141-636 1222 *Computer software developers*

Back To Black Ltd, 55 Barkby Road, Leicester, LE4 9HN Tel: 0116-261 1817 Fax: 0116-261 1841 E-mail: sales@back2black.co.uk *Printer, laser photocopier consumables cartridge recycling services*

Back To Fashion, 78 Kimberley Rd, London, E6 1EN Tel: (020) 8470 0054 Fax: (020) 8470 0054 *Clothing manufrs*

► Back To Natural, 115, Montagu Street, Kettering, Northants, NN16 8XJ Tel: (01536) 481881

► Back Up & Running, Tong Hall, Tong Lane, Bradford, W. Yorkshire, BD4 0RR Tel: 0113-285 2004

► Backer Electric Co. Ltd, Fitzwilliam Road, Eastwood Trading Estate, Rotherham, South Yorkshire, S65 1TF Tel: (01709) 828292 Fax: (01709) 828388 E-mail: sales@backer.co.uk *Heating Element*Immersion Heaters*Sheathed Heating Elements Immersion heaters*Industrial Heaters*Industrial Immersion Heaters*

Backlane Farm, Back Lane Farm, Back Lane, Goosnargh, Preston, PR3 2WE Tel: (01772) 782247 Fax: (01772) 782247 *Agricultural contractors*

Backmuir Trading Ltd, Backmuir Farm, Keith, Banffshire, AB55 5PE Tel: (01542) 882543 Fax: (01542) 886065 E-mail: philipsimmers@moraybroadband.com *Farming*

► Backstop Support Ltd, 9 Disraeli Road, London, SW15 2DR Tel: 0870 2247800 Fax: 020 8785 9904

► Backtracks Record Mart, 17 Brougham Street, Edinburgh, EH3 9JS Tel: 0131-228 4898 E-mail: kelly@backtracksmusic.co.uk *BACKTRACKS sell records, tapes and videos , deletions and rarities. it has become the Aladdin's Cave of 'hard to find oldies' on 7 inch, 12 inch, LP, 78's, 8 Track, Reel to Reel Tapes- right up to and, including, CD & DVD.Computer Games and electronic equipment. Check out the glowing article in Edinburgh Evening News 10 Nov 2004. Successfully running alongside the retail operation is MAD HATMAN DISCOS - possibly the most experienced music host serving Edinburgh and surrounding regions. Always providing top quality entertainment but at reasonable prices for your special party or event. We can adapt to a large or small occasion - if reliability and versatility is what you are looking for then you have found your man.*

BACO Metal Centres, Unit 1 Lombard Centre, Kirkhill Pl, Dyce, Aberdeen, AB21 0GU Tel: (01224) 802600 Fax: (01224) 802699 E-mail: bmc.marketing@british-aluminium.ltd.uk *Aluminium & stainless steel stockholders*

Baco Metal Centres, Edison Road, Elm Farm Industrial Estate, Bedford, MK41 0HU Tel: (01234) 684100 Fax: (01234) 684199 E-mail: bmc.sales@alcoa.com *Aluminium & stainless steel stockholders*

Baco Metal Centres, Coegnant Close, Brackla Industrial Estate, Bridgend, Mid Glamorgan, CF31 2AH Tel: (01656) 683900 Fax: (01656) 683999 E-mail: bridgend@bacometalcentres.co.uk *Aluminium & stainless steel stockholders*

Baco Metal Centres, Unit 14 St Andrews Trading Estate, Third Way, Avonmouth, Bristol, BS11 9YE Tel: 0117-948 2600 Fax: 0117-948 2699 E-mail: bmc.sales@alcoa.com *Aluminium & stainless steel stockholders*

Baco Metal Centres, 13 Concorde Road, Norwich, NR6 6BJ Tel: (01603) 243900 Fax: (01603) 243999 E-mail: norwich@blackburnsm.com *Aluminium & stainless steel stockholders*

Baco Metal Centres, 1 Eagle Road, Plympton, Plymouth, PL7 5JY Tel: (01752) 612400 Fax: (01752) 612499 E-mail: plymouth@bacometalcentres.co.uk *Aluminium & stainless steel stockholders*

Baco Metal Centres, Unit 4 Stadium Way, Tilehurst, Reading, RG30 6BX Tel: 0118-980 3300 Fax: 0118-980 3399 E-mail: bmc.sales@alcoa.com *Aluminium & stainless steel stockholders*

Bacogold (1965) Ltd, 18a Malyons Rd, London, SE13 7XG Tel: (020) 8690 4665 *Woodworm eradication*

Bacol Fine Blanking Ltd, Tramway, Oldbury Road, Smethwick, West Midlands, B66 1NY Tel: (01527) 874205 Fax: (01527) 833761 E-mail: info@bacolfineblanking.co.uk *Fine blanking pressworkers*

Bacol Industries Ltd, Middlemore Road, Middlemore Industrial Estate, Smethwick, West Midlands, B66 2EQ Tel: 0121-558 3911 Fax: 0121-555 5720 E-mail: eng@bacol.co.uk Principal Export Areas: South America & Worldwide *Presswork*

Bacou Dalloz Ltd, Osborn Way Industrial Estate, Osborn Way, Hook, Hampshire, RG27 9HX Tel: (01256) 693200 Fax: (01256) 693300 E-mail: info@dalloz.co.uk *Protective equipment sales & manufrs*

► Bacton Transport Services Ltd, Tomo Industrial Estate, Creeting Road, Stowmarket, Suffolk, IP14 5AY Tel: (01449) 618210 Fax: (01449) 676406 E-mail: haulage@bacton.co.uk

Bacup Shoe Co. Ltd, Atherton Holme Mill, Railway Street, Bacup, Lancashire, OL13 0UF Tel: (01706) 873304 Fax: (01706) 873216 E-mail: admin@bacupshoe.co.uk *Shoe & slipper importers, wide-fit footwear & footwear wholesalers*

H. & F. Badcock (Fibrous & Solid Plastering) Ltd, Unit 9, 57 Sandgate Street, Old Kent Road, London, SE15 1LE Tel: (020) 7639 0304 Fax: (020) 7358 1239 E-mail: info@hf-badcock.co.uk *Fibrous plaster products & plaster contractors*

Baddeley Brothers London Ltd, Bayford St Indust Units, Bayford Street, London, E8 3SE Tel: (020) 8986 2228 Fax: (020) 8986 4383 E-mail: enquiries@baddeleybrothers.com *Stationers & specialist envelope manufrs*

Baddeley Reynolds & Dix Ltd, 23-31 Dennett Road, Croydon, CR0 3JD Tel: (020) 8684 1277 Fax: (020) 8689 8791 *Lithographic printers*

Badenoch & Clark, 16-18 New Bridge Street, London, EC4V 6HU Tel: (020) 7583 0073 Fax: (020) 7353 3908 E-mail: corp.comms@badenochandclark.com *Recruitment specialists*

Badge Design Ltd, Unit 4e Crofts End Industrial Estate, Crofts End Road, Bristol, BS5 7UW Tel: 0117-952 5856 Fax: 0117-952 5857 E-mail: badge.design@btconnect.com *Embroidery services*

► Badge UK, 58 Crossgate, Cupar, Fife, KY15 5HS Tel: (01334) 656677 Fax: (01334) 656678 E-mail: mail@badgeuk.co.uk *Badge suppliers & manufrs*

Badgemans Recognition Express, 8 Hillside Industrial Estate, London Road, Horndean, Waterlooville, Hampshire, PO8 0BL Tel: (023) 9259 5509 Fax: (023) 9259 5528 E-mail: sales@re-southern.co.uk *Identity badge manufrs*

Badgemaster Ltd, Unit 2-8, Hazelford Way, Newstead Industrial Park, Newstead, Nottingham, NG15 0DQ Tel: (01623) 723112 Fax: (01623) 723113 E-mail: customerservices@badgemaster.co.uk *Leading International manufacturers and suppliers of personalised name badges, promotional badges, conference and event badges, corporate jewellery and custom made signage. Very fast turnaround, no minimum order. Best price guarantee. Free no-obligation award-winning design service. For full product information and to receive free samples and obtain an instant quotation on-line, visit www.badgemaster.co.uk or simply click on the link above and let us know where to send your comprehensive enquiry pack.*

Badger Anodising Ltd, 52-54 Bissell Street, Birmingham, B5 7HP Tel: 0121-622 1850 Fax: 0121-622 1218 E-mail: sales@badgeranodising.co.uk *Anodising services*

► Badger Associates Ltd, Pottergate Street, Aslacton, Norwich, NR15 2JU Tel: 01508 536013 Fax: 0871 7501925 E-mail: info@badgerassociates.co.uk Sales Contact: M. Bolger *Badger Associates has grown and developed to become a full service HR and Senior and Specialist recruitment company operating mainly in Norfolk, Suffolk and Cambridgeshire. Badger Associates works with many of the region's most discerning organisations offering recruitment in the fields of executive, professional, sales, marketing, IT, accountancy, financial, manufacturing, engineering, administration and customer service. In addition to its recruitment services Badger Associates also offers full psychometric testing using both traditional methods and more focused testing for specific needs. Badger Associates offers individual ability and aptitude testing, management audits, HR audits, management of assessment centres, appraisal scheme management, organisation development, personal development training and team development training. A comprehensive package designed for appointing senior and specialist staff so critical to the future of the organisation.*

► Badger Bars, The Post Office, Firsby Road, Great Steeping, Spilsby, Lincolnshire, PE23 5PT Tel: 07731 576864 *Outside bars for weddings, parties, exhibitions, product promotions, concerts sporting events and much more. Quality service with highly trained staff to make your event a success.*

► Badger Computer Services Ltd, The Business Innovation Centre 1 Innova Business Park, Electric, Enfield, Middlesex, EN3 7XU Tel: (020) 8344 8344 Fax: (020) 8344 8345 E-mail: sales@badgercomputerservices.co.uk *Computer maintenance services*

► Paul Badger Commercials, Badger House, 15 Rothwell Road, Desborough, Kettering, Northamptonshire, NN14 2NS Tel: (01536) 763246 Fax: (0871) 2425181 E-mail: badgercommercials@tiscali.co.uk *Buyer and seller of quality light commercials,Vans and Tractors*

► Paul Badger Pipelines Ltd, Pinley Farm, Hatton, Warwick, CV35 8XQ Tel: (01926) 840247 Fax: (01926) 840249 E-mail: pbpipelines@btinternet.com *Installation of water & gas pipelines*

Badger Print, 1 Blatchford Close, Horsham, West Sussex, RH13 5RG Tel: (01403) 257722 Fax: (01403) 263276 E-mail: info@mrprinters.com *General print agents*

Badgers, 4 Beach Road, Emsworth, Hampshire, PO10 7JS Tel: (01243) 378147 Fax: (01243) 379408 E-mail: sales@badges4all.co.uk *Badge & sign manufrs*

Badgers Removals, Unit 11 Nathan Way, London, SE28 0BQ Tel: (020) 8317 4500 Fax: (020) 8317 3539 *Business removal contractors*

Allan Badman Transport Ltd, Bamfield House, Bristol, BS14 0XD Tel: (01275) 839417 Fax: (01275) 839375 E-mail: enquiries@badmantransport.co.uk *Machinery removal contractors*

Badman & Badman Ltd, The Drill Hall, Langford Road, Weston-super-Mare, Avon, BS23 3PQ Tel: (01934) 644122 Fax: (01934) 628189 E-mail: sales@badman.co.uk *Joinery distributors, installers & furniture manufrs*

► BAE Systems, Crewe Toll, World Markets House, Edinburgh, EH4 2PY Tel: 0131-343 4409

Bae Systems Defence Systems Ltd, Warwick House, P O Box 87, Farnborough, Hampshire, GU14 6YU Tel: (01252) 373232 Fax: (01252) 383000 *Aeronautical designers*

► Baer Cargolift, Birch Lane Business Park, Unit 9, Aldridge, Walsall, WS9 0NF Tel: (01922) 456700 Fax: (01922) 455551 *Commercial vehicle tail lift suppliers*

► Bag a Card, 2 Falmouth Way, London, E17 7NZ Tel: (0845) 6445787 E-mail: sales@bag-a-card.com *Beautiful handmade greeting cards for all occasions.**Specialising in Jewish and religious cards.*We can also Personalise all of our designs with wording and Photographs.*Take a look at our site*

► Bag Building Society Ltd, 10 Viscount"s Pend, Dundee, DD4 9RJ Tel: (01382) 509000

BAG Supplies Ltd, Unit J, East Lakes Business Park, Cowper Road, Gilwilly Industrial Estate, Penrith, Cumbria, CA11 9BN Tel: (07798) 723040 Fax: (01786) 892779 E-mail: info@bagsupplies.com *BAG Supplies is a family run business supplying a range of packaging materials throughout the United Kingdom, specialising in Polypropylene Sacks, Flexible Intermediate Bulk Containers (Bulk Bags), and all types of Net and Plastic Bags. We purchase and collect "Used Bulk Bags" for recycling in high volumes. We offer "Vented Bulk Bags" which are idle for the storage and drying of Fire wood logs which can be reused over and over. If customers require a smaller bulk bag, then we offer our "Barrow Bag" this is idle for moving a product through small doorways to get a product to another area where a folk lift with a bulk bag is not able to get to. "Cubic Log Nets" which is a low cost way of storing and handling products. We also offer many different types and sizes of Small "Net bags" which have a pull tie included. All our products can have a customers own label/Logo printed onto the bags at manufacturing stage. If we do not offer a product that a customer is looking for, then we can offer a bespoke service. We cover the UK and over seas.*

Bagfast Ltd, Unit 2, Morris Court, Colwick Industrial Estate, Nottingham, NG4 2JN Tel: 0115-940 1658 Fax: 0115-961 1714 E-mail: sales@bagfast.com *Silos & bakery equipment manufrs*

Baggeridge Brick plc, Fir Street, Sedgley, Dudley, West Midlands, DY3 4AA Tel: (01902) 880555 Fax: (01902) 880432 *Brick manufrs* Also at: Hartlebury & Tamworth

Baggeridge Brick plc, Lynwick Street, Rudgwick, Horsham, West Sussex, RH12 3DH Tel: (01403) 822212 Fax: (01403) 823357 E-mail: info@baggeridge.co.uk *Stock facing bricks*

Baggeridge Brick plc, Gresham House, 24 Holborn Viaduct, London, EC1A 2BN Tel: (020) 7236 6222 Fax: (020) 7248 6363 *Brick manufrs*

Bagnall Group Ltd, 940 Lakeside Drive, Centre Park, Warrington, WA1 1RY Tel: (01925) 651191 Fax: (01925) 651192 E-mail: admin@bagnallgroup.co.uk *Asbestos removal specialists/demolition contractors*

Bagnall & Kirkwood Ltd, 28 Grey Street, Newcastle upon Tyne, NE1 6AE Tel: 0191-232 5873 Fax: 0191-230 5656 *Gunsmith repairs*

► Bagpress, Unit 6, Flint Road, Letchworth Garden City, Hertfordshire, SG6 1HJ Tel: (01462) 483366 Fax: (01462) 483377 E-mail: tim.kucuk@bagpress.com *We supply vacuum press equipment used for veneering, laminating and making curved panels. We also have our own manufacturing service from one-offs to production runs.*If you need veneering or a curved panels made for whatever reason please call for a quote.*

► Bags Of Fun, 9 Crofton Avenue, Corringham, Stanford-le-Hope, Essex, SS17 7TD Tel: (01375) 404716 E-mail: sales@rodeobullrides.co.uk *Leisure equipment hire services*

► Bags Of History, 8 Lovett Drive, Prescot, Merseyside, L35 5HJ Tel: 0151-431 1444 Fax: 0151-431 1444

► Bagwell Ltd, Station Yard, Station Road, Sidmouth, Devon, EX10 9DN Tel: (01395) 577194 Fax: (01395) 577132

Bahadur Garments, 29 Wood Hill, Leicester, LE5 3SP Tel: 0116-251 3538 Fax: 0116-262 3423 E-mail: bahadurgarments@yahoo.com *Clothing & garment manufrs*

Bahco Metal Saws Ltd, Moorhead Way, Bramley, Rotherham, South Yorkshire, S66 1YY Tel: (01709) 731600 Fax: (01709) 731700 *Bandsaw blade manufrs*

► Bahi Group, 68 Pullman Road, Wigston, Leicestershire, LE18 2DB Tel: 0116-281 3111

Bahlsen Ltd, Hannover House, Packhorse Road, Gerrards Cross, Buckinghamshire, SL9 7QE Tel: (01753) 889822 Fax: (01753) 889786 *Continental biscuit importers*

Bahr Forwarding, Suite 16b Unit 4 Orwell House, Ferry Lane, Felixstowe, Suffolk, IP11 3QR Tel: (01394) 675686 Fax: (01394) 674232 E-mail: admin@bahrforwarding.co.uk *Shipping forwarding & transport agents*

► Bahson Colour Print, Unit 4b Adwalton Moor Bus Park, Inmoor Road, Birkenshaw, Bradford, West Yorkshire, BD11 2PS Tel: (01274) 474500 Fax: (01274) 474577

► Bailey, 5 South Gyle CR Lae, Edinburgh, EH12 9EG Tel: 0131-316 4443 Fax: 0131-316 4244

Bailey, Blatchford Close, Horsham, West Sussex, RH13 5RF Tel: (01403) 261844 *Manufacture aluminium products*

Albert E. Bailey & Sons Ltd, 25 Holywell Row, London, EC2A 4XE Tel: (020) 7729 1442 E-mail: baileyprintgroup@talk21.com *Printers & office services*

Bailey Bros (Engineers) Ltd, 105 Hospital St, Newtown, Birmingham, B19 3XB Tel: 0121-359 8361 Fax: 0121-359 0909 E-mail: sales@cerro-ems.co.uk *Sink & bath wastes & drain rods*

D. & J. Bailey (Flooring) Ltd, Churchill House, Farncote Drive, Four Oaks, Sutton Coldfield, West Midlands, B74 4QS Tel: 0121-308 0402 Fax: 0121-308 7327 E-mail: lisab@bailey-flooring.co.uk *Flooring contractors*

Bailey & Davidson Ltd, The Street, Bishop's Cannings, Devizes, Wiltshire, SN10 2LD Tel: (01380) 860386 Fax: (01380) 860897 E-mail: nbailey@kwikbuild.com *Export merchants kwikbuild low cost housing systems*

Bailey Employment Services Ltd, Crown House, Market Place, Melksham, Wiltshire, SN12 6ES Tel: (01225) 709494 Fax: (01225) 709044 E-mail: melksham@baileyemploy.co.uk *Employment agency*

James Bailey Ltd, Empire Works, Howgate Road, Huddersfield, HD7 5AX Tel: (01484) 842316 Fax: (01484) 846537 E-mail: sales@jamesbailey.co.uk *Textile finishing machinery manufrs*

Bailey Johnson, Wyther Lane, Leeds, LS5 3BT Tel: 0113-275 9048 Fax: 0113-230 4328 E-mail: info@baileyjohnson.co.uk *Fibrous plasterers & suspended ceiling contractors*

Bailey Johnson Hayes, Dane House, 55 London Road, St. Albans, Hertfordshire, AL1 1LJ Tel: (01727) 841172 Fax: (01727) 841085 E-mail: wb@bjh.co.uk *Consulting engineers*

Bailey & Mackey Ltd, Baltimore Road, Birmingham, B42 1DE Tel: 0121-357 5351 Fax: 0121-357 8319 E-mail: enquiries@baileymackey.com *Pressure gauge, switch/transducer manufrs*

▶ Bailey Maintenance Services, Caxton House, Caxton Place, Cardiff, CF23 8HA Tel: (029) 2054 9097 Fax: (029) 2073 5972

Bailey Marine, 53 Rempstone Road, Wimborne, Dorset, BH21 1TR Tel: (01202) 885052 Fax: (01202) 842817 E-mail: john@bailey-marine.co.uk Principal Export Areas: Worldwide *Designers & suppliers of marine equipment*

Oswald Bailey Ltd, 72-74 Palmerston Road, Bournemouth, BH1 4JT Tel: (01202) 397273 Fax: (01202) 397274 *Camping equipment suppliers*

Oswald Bailey Ltd, 317 Ashley Road, Poole, Dorset, BH14 0AP Tel: (01202) 740724 *Outdoor equipment manufrs*

Bailey Packaging Ltd, PO Box 64, Solihull, West Midlands, B93 9NZ Tel: (01564) 774259 Fax: (01564) 777859 *Flexible packaging material manufrs*

Bailey Packaging Ltd, Unit 26 Garden Estate, Lowtherville Road, Ventnor, Isle of Wight, PO38 1YD Tel: (01983) 855535 Fax: (01983) 853358 *Polyethylene & polythene bag manufrs* Also at: Solihull

Bailey Paints Ltd, London Road, Thrupp, Stroud, Gloucestershire, GL5 2AZ Tel: (01453) 882237 Fax: (01453) 731413 E-mail: info@baileypaints.demon.co.uk *Paint makers & distributors*

Bailey & Partners Ltd, 30 South Park Road, Gatley, Cheadle, Cheshire, SK8 4AN Tel: 0161-428 8212 Fax: 0161-428 8212 *Water treatment equipment & service*

Bailey Polythene Co. Ltd, Unit 26, Garden Estate, Ventnor, Isle Of Wight, PO38 1YJ Tel: (01983) 855535 Fax: (01983) 853358 E-mail: sales@baileypolythene.co.uk *Convert polythene to product*

Bailey & Smith Ltd, Hammerstone Road, Gorton, Manchester, M18 8EF Tel: 0161-223 5000 Fax: 0161-223 2989 E-mail: info@baileysmith.co.uk *Manufacturers of Custom Built Hot & Cold Counters.*

Bailey Streetscene Ltd, Bailey Business Park, Grimshaw Lane, Bollington, Macclesfield, Cheshire, SK10 5NY Tel: (0870) 0928928 Fax: (0870) 0929929 E-mail: info@baileystreetscene.co.uk *Suppliers of street furniture*

▶ Bailey Taylor Haulage Ltd, Winter Closes, Underwood, Nottingham, NG16 5GR Tel: (01773) 530339 Fax: (01773) 530528

Bailey Telecom Ltd, 7 Brown Lane West, Leeds, LS12 6EH Tel: 0113-243 9921 Fax: (0845) 128128 E-mail: enquiries@baileyteswaine.co.uk *Communications solutions* Also at: Denton

▶ Bailey Teswaine, Etna House, 78 New Coventry Road, Birmingham, B26 3AY Tel: 0121-771 7288 Fax: 0121-771 7268 E-mail: enquiries@baileyteswaine.co.uk *Communications solutions, implementation, management of voice, video, data solutions over both wired, wireless network infrastructures for customers in both the private & public sector*

Bailey Textiles, 9-10 The Warren, East Goscote, Leicester, LE7 3XA Tel: 0116-269 4694 Fax: 0116-269 3956 E-mail: sales@baileysdirect.plus.com *Textile & equestrian goods wholesalers*

Bailey Trailers Ltd, Main Street, Aunsby, Sleaford, Lincolnshire, NG34 8TA Tel: (01529) 455232 Fax: (01529) 455248 E-mail: sales@baileytrailers.co.uk *Trailer manufrs*

N. & J. Bailey Transport, Canal Lane, Tunstall, Stoke-on-Trent, ST6 4PA Tel: (01782) 575740 Fax: (01782) 837096 *Freight services*

Bailey Walsh & Co., 5 York Place, Leeds, LS1 2SD Tel: (0800) 7837623 Fax: 0113-244 5699 E-mail: mail@bailey-walsh.com *Patent agents*

William Bailey Ltd, Merlin Court, Ripley Road, Ambergate, Belper, Derbyshire, DE56 2EP Tel: (01773) 853703 Fax: (01773) 856930 E-mail: enquiries@williambailey.co.uk *Air conditioning engineers*

Baileys Blinds Ltd, 211 High Street, Gosforth, Newcastle upon Tyne, NE3 1HQ Tel: 0191-284 6284 Fax: 0191-284 1464 E-mail: baileys@btconnect.com *Manufacturer of blinds & awnings, fitting services*

Baileys Blinds Ltd, Unit 15 Bellway Industrial Estate, Whitley Road, Newcastle Upon Tyne, NE12 9SW Tel: 0191-270 0501 Fax: 0191-266 8993 E-mail: info@baileys-blinds.co.uk *Blind retailers & manufrs*

Baileys Of Bromsgrove Ltd, 12a St. John Street, Bromsgrove, Worcestershire, B61 8QY Tel: (01527) 873128 Fax: (01527) 873128 E-mail: sales@baileyphotographic.com *Social commercial & industrial photographers*

Baileys Carpets Of Bristol Ltd, Broadmead Lane, Keynsham, Bristol, BS31 1ST Tel: 0117-986 8431 Fax: (0800) 212701 E-mail: baileybristol@mcd.co.uk *Carpet & flooring wholesalers* Also at: Newton Abbott & Swansea

Bailie Connor Partnership Ltd, Landmark House, 5 Cromac Quay, Belfast, BT7 2JD Tel: (028) 9023 1062 Fax: (028) 9023 1273 E-mail: info@bailieconnor.co.uk *Quantity surveyors*

▶ Baillando Dancewear, 12a Market Buildings, Maidstone, Kent, ME14 1HP Tel: (01622) 691190 E-mail: manager@baillando.co.uk *Dance shoes, childrens & adults dancewear suppliers*

Baillie Associates Ltd, 50 Main Street, Lowdham, Nottingham, NG14 7BE Tel: 0115-966 3929 Fax: 0115-966 4745 E-mail: binfo@baillies.com *Supply of business management systems*

Baillie Sign Services, 184-186 Queensferry Road, Edinburgh, EH4 2BW Tel: 0131-315 2800 Fax: 0131-315 2797 E-mail: sales@bailliesigns.co.uk *Sign design, installation & manufrs*

▶ Bailstar Ltd, Unit 7-8 Zennor Road Industrial Estate, Zennor Road, London, SW12 0PS Tel: (020) 8675 3419 Fax: (020) 8673 5951 *Engineering, fabrication & sheet metal work*

Bain & Co., 40 Strand, London, WC2N 5RW Tel: (020) 7969 6000 Fax: (020) 7969 6666 *Strategic management consultants*

Bainbridge Farms, Donkin Rigg, Cambo, Morpeth, Northumberland, NE61 4LA Tel: (01670) 774246 Fax: (01670) 774246 *Farming*

Bainbridge GRP Ltd, Unit 3D, Peel Mill, Chamberhall Street, Bury, Lancashire, BL9 0JU Tel: 0161-764 5034 Fax: 0161-764 5020 *House building component manufrs*

Bainbridge International Ltd, 8 Flanders Park, Flanders Road, Hedge End, Southampton, SO30 2FZ Tel: (01489) 776000 Fax: (01489) 776005 E-mail: mail@bainbridgeint.co.uk *Marine product manufrs*

Bainbridge Joinery, Faraday Road, Kirkby Stephen, Cumbria, CA17 4QL Tel: (01768) 372100 Fax: (01768) 372303 *Joinery manufrs*

Bainbridge Liversidge Group, Pepper Road, Hunslett, Leeds, LS10 2NL Tel: 0113-270 5431 Fax: 0113-276 0379 *Scrap metal processors*

▶ Baineport Engineering Services, 4 The Dock, Ely, Cambridgeshire, CB7 4GS Tel: (0870) 2414806 Fax: (0870) 2417172

Baines Herbert Ltd, No 2 Passage Chester Street, Stockport, Cheshire, SK3 0BR Tel: 0161-480 9796 *Building contractors*

Baines Simmons Ltd, Fairoaks Airport, Chobham, Woking, Surrey, GU24 8HX Tel: (01276) 855412 Fax: (01276) 856285 E-mail: bob@bainessimmons.com *Aviation safety training & consultants*

Bains Fashions, 104 Bridge Road, Leicester, LE5 3LD Tel: 0116-276 1525 Fax: 0116-210 0562 E-mail: admin@ambni.co.uk *Manufacturers of school wear & promotional wear*

Baird & Co, 2 Park Place, Kirkcaldy, Fife, KY1 1XL Tel: (01592) 268608 Fax: (01592) 203369

Baird Lends A Hand Ltd, 75 Beardmore Way, Clydebank, Dunbartonshire, G81 4HT Tel: 0141-952 0962 Fax: 0141-941 2205 E-mail: jb@baird-uk.com *Storage contractors & freight services*

W.F.B. Baird & Co, Ltd, 72 Shankbridge Road, Kells, Ballymena, County Antrim, BT42 3DL Tel: (028) 2589 8144 Fax: (028) 2589 8153 *Linen manufrs*

▶ Baiss & Co Advances, 2 St. Peters Street, Ipswich, IP1 1XB Tel: (01473) 400033 E-mail: info@baiss.co.uk *Baiss & Co Advanced brings to East Anglia a level of contemporary luxury rarely seen outside of the West End of London.**Established 15 years ago, Baiss & Co has grown to become the one of the most respected names in hair in East Anglia with its stylish and buzzing town centre salon. **Baiss & Co also offers an extensive range of beauty and self-improvement services for men and women in its custom built private treatment rooms.**

▶ Bait & Tackle Supplies, 692 Bolton Road, Pendlebury, Swinton, Manchester, M27 6EL Tel: 0161-728 4400 *Retailers of fishing tackle*

Baizecraft Snooker & Pool Tables, 120a Saintfield Road, Lisburn, County Antrim, BT27 5PG Tel: (028) 9263 8649 Fax: (028) 9263 8994 E-mail: sales@baizecraft.com *Snooker tables manufrs*

Bakehouse Ltd, 3 Tanners Yard, London Road, Bagshot, Surrey, GU19 5HD Tel: (01276) 850500 E-mail: info@bakehouse.co.uk *Bakehouse Ltd, based in Bagshot Surrey, supply delicious bakery products to the UK market through their partnerships with European bakery specialists. Their wide range includes Danish pastries, viennoiserie, Continental savouries, speciality breads and more.*

Bakels Foodservice, Granville Way, Launton Road, Bicester, Oxfordshire, OX26 4JT Tel: (01869) 247098 Fax: (01869) 242979 E-mail: bakels@bakels.com *Bakers ingredient & prepared material producers*

A.J. Baker (Grinding) Ltd, Middlemore Lane West, Redhouse Industrial Estate, Aldridge, Walsall, WS9 8BG Tel: (01922) 745075 Fax: 0121-378 3291 E-mail: enquiries@ajbaker.com *Dealers & rebuilders of centreless grinding machines*

Baker Auto Care, 18 Bankside, Station Approach, Kidlington, Oxfordshire, OX5 1JE Tel: (01865) 376008 Fax: (01865) 841511 *Vehicle repairers*

▶ Baker Automation, 3 Butternab Road, Huddersfield, HD4 7AH Tel: (07802) 495848 Fax: 0161-881 9376 E-mail: john@ukelo.co.uk *We design, develop and manufacture many different kinds of electronic devices for use in industry and commerce worldwide.*

Baker Blower Engineering Co. Ltd, 39 Stanley Street, Sheffield, S3 8HH Tel: 0114-272 5527 Fax: 0114-272 7533 E-mail: bakerblower@aol.com Principal Export Areas: Worldwide *CNC engineering services or machinists & grinding services*

C.T. Baker Ltd, 133 High Street, Stalham, Norwich, NR12 9BB Tel: (01692) 580210 Fax: (01692) 581412 *Builders' merchants*

▶ Baker Dougan, Unit 4 Oyster Estate, Jackson Close, Portsmouth, PO6 1QN Tel: (023) 9237 0777 Fax: (023) 9237 1777

Douglas Baker Plastics Ltd, Doubak Works Barton Industrial Estate, Mount Pleasant, Bilston, West Midlands, WV14 7LH Tel: (01902) 353800 Fax: (01902) 353855 E-mail: sales@dbplastics.co.uk *Manufacturer of composite pigments for the thermoplastics industry*

Baker Engineering, Devon Road, Bordon, Hampshire, GU35 0BB Tel: (01420) 473953 Fax: (01420) 473953 *Precision engineering services*

Baker Engineering, 15 Bishops Orchard, East Hagbourne, Didcot, Oxfordshire, OX11 9JS Tel: (01235) 512447 Fax: (01235) 512447 E-mail: georgebakerengineering@freeserve.co.uk *Industrial cleaning equipment sales & service*

Baker Engineering Co., Unit 11 Paramount Industrial Estate, Sandown Road, Watford, WD24 7XA Tel: (01923) 229309 Fax: (01923) 801182 E-mail: sales@bakereng.co.uk *Electroplaters & shot blasting contractors*

▶ Baker Environmental Lining Services Ltd, Darlei House Friars, Capel St. Mary, Ipswich, IP9 2XS Tel: (01473) 312161 Fax: 01473 312161 E-mail: sales@baker-els.com *Tank Linings & Modifications, Bund Linings, Protective Coatings, Floor & Wall Linings, Flat Roof Linings, Grit Blasting, Advice on Oil Storage Regulations Deadline : September 2005 - DOES YOUR BUND COMPLY?*

Baker & Finnemore Ltd, 199 Newhall Street, Birmingham, B3 1SN Tel: 0121-236 2347 Fax: 0121-236 7224 E-mail: sales@bakfin.com *Fixing washer manufrs*

Baker Flooring Ltd, Unit D2-D4 Guy Motors Industrial Park, Park Lane, Wolverhampton, WV10 9QG Tel: (01902) 730990 Fax: (01902) 722012 E-mail: mail@bakerflooringltd.co.uk *Floor covering contractors*

Fred Baker Ltd, 30 Park Street, Birmingham, B5 5JH Tel: 0121-643 5409 Fax: 0121-643 0914 *General press workers*

G.E. Baker (UK) Ltd, Heath Road, Woolpit, Bury St. Edmunds, Suffolk, IP30 9RN Tel: (01359) 240529 Fax: (01359) 242086 E-mail: baker@quality-equipment.co.uk *Manufacturers & suppliers of equipment to the livestock industry*

G.P.& J. Baker, Po Box 30, London, SW10 0XE Tel: (020) 7351 7760 Fax: (020) 7351 7752 E-mail: sales@gpjbaker.co.uk *Fabric covering distributors*

George Baker (Insurance Brokers) Ltd, Richmond House, 1 Richmond Parade, Brighton, BN2 9GB Tel: (01273) 603066 Fax: (01273) 670324 *General insurance brokers*

H. Baker (Haulage) Ltd, Florence Street, Leeds Road, Bradford, West Yorkshire, BD3 8EX Tel: (01274) 664249 Fax: (01274) 668224 E-mail: julie.todd@btconnect.com *Warehouse & distribution*

Baker Hughes Ltd, Campus 1, Aberdeen Science And Technology Centre, Bridge Of Don, Aberdeen, AB22 8GT Tel: (01224) 226000 Fax: (01224) 226006 *Subsea survey services* Also at: Great Yarmouth

Baker Hughes Production Quest, Rowan Court, North Leigh Business Park, Woodstock Road, North Leigh, Witney, Oxfordshire, OX29 6SW Tel: (01993) 883366 Fax: (01993) 881123 E-mail: baker@hughes.com *Oil flow measurement instrumentation manufrs*

Baker Metals Ltd, Great Northern Road, Derby, DE1 1LT Tel: (01332) 340186 Fax: (01332) 344130 Principal Export Areas: Central/East Europe *Aluminium refiners*

Mike Baker Timber Merchants, Boston Industrial Estate, Power Station Road, Rugeley, Staffordshire, WS15 2HS Tel: (01889) 583306 Fax: (01889) 575263 *Timber merchants*

Baker Oil Tools UK Ltd, Kirkhill Road, Kirkhill Industrial Estate, Dyce, Aberdeen, AB21 0GQ Tel: (01224) 223500 Fax: (01224) 771400 E-mail: jim.moir@bakeroiltools.com *Oil tool manufrs*

Baker Petrolite, Howe Moss Avenue, Kirkhill Industrial Estate, Dyce, Aberdeen, AB21 0GP Tel: (01224) 405700 Fax: (01224) 405705 *Chemical suppliers*

Baker Print System, Forms House, 20 Lyons Cresent, Tonbridge, Kent, TN9 1EY Tel: (01732) 771188 Fax: (01732) 771999 *Printing & design services*

R. Baker (Electrical) Ltd, Evans Road, Speke, Liverpool, L24 9PB Tel: 0151-486 6760 Fax: 0151-448 1225 E-mail: mail@rbaker.co.uk *Servicing & manufacturing engineers*

The Baker Self-Adhesive Label Company Ltd, 37 Sutherland Road, London, E17 6BH Tel: (020) 8523 2174 Fax: (020) 8527 6556 *Printing labels services*

Baker & Sons Danbury Ltd, Eves Corner, Danbury, Chelmsford, CM3 4QB Tel: (01245) 225876 Fax: (01245) 226821 E-mail: enq@bakersofdanbury.co.uk *Building contractors*

▶ Baker & Sons Margate Ltd, 29 St. Augustines Avenue, Margate, Kent, CT9 4DN Tel: (01843) 220958 Fax: (01843) 292467

Baker Thompson Ltd, 371 Selsdon Road, South Croydon, Surrey, CR2 6PT Tel: (020) 8681 1952 Fax: (020) 8760 9935 E-mail: sales@thompsonplastics.com *Plastic fabricators services*

Baker Ward Ltd, 1137 Yardley Wood Road, Birmingham, B14 4LS Tel: 0121-474 3185 Fax: 0121-474 6291 E-mail: sales@bakerward.co.uk *Sign contractors & manufrs*

Baker Wilkins & Smith, 57-63 Church Road, London, SW19 5DQ Tel: (020) 8406 4422 Fax: (020) 8944 6767 E-mail: dedwards@bakerwilkins.com *Chartered quantity surveyors*

Bakers, 2 Hainge Road, Tividale, Oldbury, West Midlands, B69 2NH Tel: 0121-557 1935 Fax: 0121-557 4245 E-mail: sales@bfsltd.co.uk *Design, manufacture, repair & testing of forklift forks & attachments*

Bakers Farm Feeds, Bakers Farm, Coat, Martock, Somerset, TA12 6AR Tel: (01935) 823417 *Animal feed supplier*

▶ Bakers & Larners Of Holt, 10 Market Place, Holt, Norfolk, NR25 6BW Tel: (01263) 712323 Fax: (01263) 712720 E-mail: sales@bakersandlarners.com *Large department store in Holt, Norfolk*

Bakers Of North Walsham, Midland Road, North Walsham, Norfolk, NR28 9JR Tel: (01692) 403718 Fax: (01692) 500545 *Builders merchants*

▶ Bakers Of Oakley, Bakers Yard, Pardown, Oakley, Basingstoke, Hampshire, RG23 7DY Tel: (01256) 780266 *Coal merchants*

The Bakery, Manor Gardens, Farmborough, Bath, BA2 0AS Tel: (01761) 470598 Fax: (01761) 479072 E-mail: info@thebakeryrestaurant.com *Bakery suppliers*

The Bakery, Dwyran, Llanfairpwllgwyngyll, Gwynedd, LL61 6YU Tel: (01248) 430717 Fax: (01248) 430717 *Bakers*

▶ The Bakery, The Shop, Edward Street, Stone, Staffordshire, ST15 8HN Tel: (01785) 812118 *Bakery wholesalers*

▶ Bakery Maintenance Solutions, Channing House, Mart Road, Minehead, Somerset, TA24 5BJ Tel: (0845) 2239007 E-mail: info@bakerymaintenance.co.uk *Bakery plant & equipment maintenance*

▶ Bakes & Lord Ltd, 529 Beacon Road, Bradford, West Yorkshire, BD6 3NB Tel: (01274) 521717

Bakewell Engineering Ltd, 99 North Western Street, Ardwick, Manchester, M12 6JL Tel: 0161-273 2822 Fax: 0161-273 3829 *Mild steel sheet metal fabricators*

Bakewell Fly Fishing, 3a Hebden Court, Matlock Street, Bakewell, Derbyshire, DE45 1EE Tel: (01629) 813531 Fax: (01629) 813531 *Fishing equipment suppliers*

▶ Baking Solutions Ltd, Avenue Two, Witney, Oxfordshire, OX28 4YQ Tel: (01993) 864777 Fax: (01993) 777440 E-mail: info@bakingsolutions.co.uk *Manufacture & wrapping of muffins, flapjacks, cupcakes, cereal bars*

Bakkavor, 86 Carver Street, Birmingham, B1 3AL Tel: 0121-236 6464 Fax: 0121-233 2711 E-mail: info@bakkavor-bham.co.uk *Fresh dressings manufrs*

Balaban Ltd, Sneath Farm, High Green, Great Moulton, Norwich, NR15 2HU Tel: (01379) 677296 Fax: (01379) 677296 *Pest control services*

Balance, 59 High St, Fochabers, Morayshire, IV32 7DU Tel: 01343 820780 *Natural health food retailers & manufrs*

Balance Books Ltd, 306 Aberdeen House, 22 Highbury Grove, London, N5 2DQ Tel: (020) 7704 1515 Fax: (020) 7226 0491 E-mail: admin@balance_uk.com *Payroll & accounting services*

Balanced Solutions Ltd, 20 Juniper Road, Southampton, SO18 4EJ Tel: (023) 8063 8393 Fax: (023) 8063 8393 E-mail: info@balancedsolutions.co.uk *IT solutions & consultants*

▶ Balancing, Unit 12, Logan Road, Birkenhead, Merseyside, CH41 1JJ Tel: 0151-639 9898 Fax: 0151-639 9898 E-mail: enquiries@dp-engineering.co.uk *Dynamic balancing services*

▶ Balblair, Balblair Residential Home, Edderton, Tain, Ross-Shire, IV19 1LB Tel: (01862) 821272 Fax: (01862) 821360

▶ Balby Electric Co. Ltd, Heavens Walk, Doncaster, South Yorkshire, DN4 5HZ Tel: (01302) 367986 Fax: (01302) 340727

Balcan Engineering, Banovallum Court, Boston Road Industrial Estate, Horncastle, Lincolnshire, LN9 6JR Tel: (01507) 528500 Fax: (01507) 528528 E-mail: info@balcan.co.uk *Manufacturers of lamp crushers, needle destructors & lamp recycling*

Balco Engineering Ltd, 35 Nursery Road, Hockley, Birmingham, B19 2XN Tel: 0121-523 0853 Fax: 0121-554 0597 E-mail: balcoeng@aol.com *Metal finishing equipment manufrs*

▶ Balco Jewellery Finishing, 35 Nursery Road, Hockley, Birmingham, B19 2XN Tel: 0121-554 1026

Balco Prescision Engineering, 24 Benfield Way, Braintree, Essex, CM7 3YS Tel: (01376) 347767 Fax: (01376) 347767 *Precision engineers*

▶ Balcombe Glass Ltd, Unit 5, Avocet Industrial Estate, Burgess Hill, West Sussex, RH15 9NH Tel: (01444) 230986 Fax: (01444) 230987 E-mail: glazing@balcombeglass.co.uk *Double glazed sealed unit manufrs*

Balcon Plastics, Unit 6a Challenger Way, Peterborough, PE1 5EX Tel: (01733) 347012 Fax: (01733) 558232 E-mail: wayne.hutton@balconplastics.co.uk *Heat benders of rigid plastics*

Baldane Ltd, Auchterhouse, Dundee, DD3 0QS Tel: (01382) 320404 Fax: (01382) 320461 E-mail: info@baldane.co.uk *Computer repairs*

▶ Baldock Advanced Motorcycle Training, 31 Bush Spring, Baldock, Hertfordshire, SG7 6QT Tel: (01462) 641775 Fax: (0871) 4335485 E-mail: tclarke@evprecruit.com *Executive recruitment & outplacement services*

Baldock Blinds, 3-4 Charles Street, Wrexham, Clwyd, LL13 8BT Tel: (01978) 264441 Fax: (01978) 353638 E-mail: baldockblinds@aol.com *Blinds manufrs*

E.J. Baldock, 1A Cambridge Road, Ellesmere Port, CH65 4AE Tel: 0151-355 5689 Fax: 0151-355 5689 *Jewellery manufacturers & repairers*

Baldock Reproduction Furniture, Mansfield Road, Baldock, Hertfordshire, SG7 6EB Tel: (01462) 892134 Fax: (01462) 892134 *Reproduction furniture*

Baldock Tyres, 22 London Road Industrial Estate, Baldock, Hertfordshire, SG7 6LE Tel: (01462) 894772 Fax: (01462) 491412 *Battery distributors*

Baldwin Boxall Communications Ltd, Wealden Industrial Estate, Farningham Road, Crowborough, East Sussex, TN6 2JR Tel: (01892) 664422 Fax: (01892) 663146 E-mail: mail@baldwinboxall.co.uk *Manufacturers of public address systems & voice evacuation systems*

Baldwin Construction Ltd, The Old School, Arrow, Alcester, Warwickshire, B49 5PJ Tel: (01789) 762125 Fax: (01789) 400367 E-mail: bill.@baldwin-constr.fsnet.co.uk *Building contractors*

Baldwin & Francis, President Park, Sheffield, S4 7UQ Tel: 0114-286 6000 Fax: 0114-286 6059 E-mail: enquiries@baldwinandfrancis.com *Mining & industrial switchgear manufrs*

Baldwin Glass Ltd, Spyvee St/Durban Street, Hull, HU8 7JU Tel: (01482) 223128 Fax: (01482) 586583 *Glass merchants*

Baldwin & Moore Ltd, Unit 7 Elton Road Business Park, Derby, DE24 8EG Tel: (01332) 385356 Fax: (01332) 385377 E-mail: baldwinandmoore@derby22.fsnet.co.uk *Shop fitters & furniture manufrs*

Baldwin Plastic Laminates Ltd, 57 Tallon Road, Hutton, Brentwood, Essex, CM13 1TG Tel: (01277) 225235 Fax: (01277) 222586 *Laminated plastic fabricators*

Baldwin & Wiser Ltd, Urban Road, Kirkby-in-Ashfield, Nottingham, NG17 8AP Tel: (01623) 754982 Fax: (01623) 754983 *Mining fabricators & engineers*

▶ Baldwins Crane Hire Ltd, 52-54 River Road, Barking, Essex, IG11 0DW Tel: (020) 8591 9901 Fax: (020) 8591 9981 E-mail: info@baldwinscranehire.co.uk *Crane hire*

Baldwins Crane Hire Ltd, Crane House, Rover Way, Cardiff, CF24 2RX Tel: (01753) 648682 Fax: (01753) 648685 *Crane hire, sales & service, 7ton to 1000 ton, M&E division*

▶ M. & E. Baldwins, Finmere Road, Eastbourne, East Sussex, BN22 8QG Tel: (01323) 417101 Fax: (01323) 417102

K.K. Balers Ltd, Victory House, Victory Park Road, Addlestone, Surrey, KT15 2AX Tel: (01932) 852423 Fax: (01932) 847170 E-mail: sales@kkbalers.com Principal Export Areas: Worldwide *Baler, baling machine manufrs*

Balform Patterns Ltd, Unit 28 Soho Mills Industrial Estate, Wooburn Green, High Wycombe, Buckinghamshire, HP10 0PF Tel: (01628) 528021 Fax: (01628) 810213 E-mail: enquiries@balform.co.uk *Plastic vacuum forming toolmakers*

Balfour Beatty plc, Fourth Floor, 130 Wilton Road, London, SW1V 1LQ Tel: (020) 7216 6800 Fax: (020) 7216 6950 *Civil engineering & construction*

Balfour Beatty, Chaddock Lane, Worsley, Manchester, M28 1XW Tel: 0161-790 3000 Fax: 0161-703 5307 *Civil engineers & public works* Also at: Exeter & Chesterfield

▶ Balfour Beatty Ltd, 361-365 Coleford Road, Sheffield, S9 5NF Tel: 0114-256 1656 Fax: 0114-256 2656 *Railway material contractors*

Balfour Beatty Construction Ltd, Neville House, 42-46 Hagley Road, Birmingham, B16 8PE Tel: 0121-224 6600 Fax: 0121-224 6601 E-mail: reception.edgbaston@bbcl.co.uk *Building contractors*

Balfour Beatty Construction Ltd, 23 Ravelston Terrace, Edinburgh, EH4 3TW Tel: 0131-332 9411 Fax: 0131-332 5937 E-mail: info@bbcl.co.uk *Civil engineering contractors*

▶ Balfour Beatty Construction Ltd, Churchill House, 29 Mill Hill Road, Pontefract, West Yorkshire, WF8 4HY Tel: (01977) 602120 Fax: (01977) 602181

Balfour Beatty Construction Ltd, Balfour House, Churchfield Road, Walton-on-Thames, Surrey, KT12 2TD Tel: (020) 7922 0000 Fax: (01932) 229032 *Building contractors*

Balfour Beatty Construction International Ltd, 7 Mayday Road, Thornton Heath, Surrey, CR7 7XA Tel: (020) 8684 6922 Fax: (020) 8710 5222 *Civil engineers* Also at: Ramsbottom & Rugby

Balfour Beatty Power Networks Ltd, PO Box 5064 West Service Road, Derby, DE21 7ZP Tel: (01332) 661494 Fax: (01332) 288312 *Modular building & portable rail plant hire services*

Balfour Beatty Rail Projects Ltd, Acornfield Road, P O Box 12, Kirby Industrial Estate, Liverpool, L33 7TY Tel: 0151-548 5000 Fax: 0151-548 5320 *Railway electrification*

Balfour Beatty Rail Track Systems Ltd, Osmaston Street, Sandiacre, Nottingham, NG10 5AN Tel: 0115-921 8218 Fax: 0115-541 8219 E-mail: phil.bean@bbrail.com *Rail tracks repairs & manufrs*

▶ Balfour Kilpatrick Ltd, Unit 2B, Bankhead Crossway South, Edinburgh, EH11 4TA Tel: 0131-453 4842

Balfour Kilpatrick Ltd, Glasgow Road, Deanside, Renfrew, PA4 8XZ Tel: 0141-885 4321 Fax: 0141-885 4480 E-mail: enquiry@balfourkilpatrick.com *Electrical & mechanical contractors*

Balgownie Machine Centre Ltd, 78a Powis Terrace, Aberdeen, AB25 3PQ Tel: (01224) 485291 Fax: (01224) 482344 E-mail: sales@balgownie.co.uk *Garden equipment distributors & services*

Balham Glass & Joinery, 260-262 Cavendish Road, London, SW12 0BT Tel: (020) 8675 1640 Fax: (020) 8657 6784 E-mail: balhamglass@btclick.com *Glazing & joinery manufacturers, supplier & distributor*

Balham Joinery Works, Rear 102 Upper Tooting Road, London, SW17 7EN Tel: (020) 8767 9902 Fax: (020) 8767 9718 *Joinery*

Balham Wholefoods & Health Store, 8 Bedford Hill, London, SW12 9RG Tel: (020) 8673 4842 *Whole food & supplements retailers*

Balkan & Black Sea Shipping Co. Ltd, Black Sea House, 72 Wilson Street, London, EC2A 2DH Tel: (020) 7684 2800 Fax: (020) 7684 2790 E-mail: enquiries@bbss.uk *Marine chartering & ship management*

▶ Balkany Enterprise Ltd, 144 Page Road, Feltham, Feltham, Middlesex, TW14 8DN Tel: (07951) 767106 Fax: (020) 8707 6636 E-mail: bobbi_mk@yahoo.com *Internal & external painter & decorator*

Ball & Co., 5 Harpton Parade, Villiage Way, Yateley, Hampshire, GU46 7SB Tel: (01252) 879884 Fax: (01252) 878067 *Computer supplier maintenance & distributors*

Ball Bearing Centre Ltd, Unit 1-55, 57 Park Royal Road, London, NW10 7JJ Tel: (020) 8965 8833 Fax: (020) 8965 7080 E-mail: ballbrgctr@btconnect.com Principal Export Areas: Worldwide *Ball bearing & electric motor distributors*

Ball Bros, 42 Church Road, Dromara, Dromore, County Down, BT25 2NS Tel: (028) 9753 2379 Fax: (028) 9753 2379 *Agricultural merchants*

G.L. Ball Components Ltd, 41 Lancaster Road, Bowerhill Industrial Estate, Melksham, Wiltshire, SN12 6SS Tel: (01225) 702657 Fax: (01225) 790066 E-mail: gb.sherwood@btconnect.com *Manufacturer of archery accessories*

▶ Graham Ball Joiners & Builders Ltd, 11 Sedgwick Street, Preston, PR1 1TP Tel: (01772) 250481 Fax: (01772) 823383 E-mail: gbjb11s@awell.com *Timber manufrs*

Ball Hill Blinds, 221 Walsgrave Road, Coventry, CV2 4HH Tel: (024) 7645 1615 Fax: (024) 7645 1615 *Blinds manufrs*

Ball J & L Curtains Blinds, 16 North Street, Stamford, Lincolnshire, PE9 1EH Tel: (01780) 481416 Fax: (01780) 481416 E-mail: info@jlball.co.uk *Made to measure curtains, blinds & awnings at realistic prices*

Ball Packaging Europe UK Ltd, Lakeside, Chester Business Park, Chester, CH4 9QT Tel: (01244) 681155 Fax: (01244) 680320 E-mail: chester_reception@ball-europe.com *Can manufrs*

Ball Spinning Co. Ltd, Unit 34 Park Farm Industrial Estate, Ermine Street, Buntingford, Hertfordshire, SG9 9AZ Tel: (01763) 273506 Fax: (01763) 273509 E-mail: enquiries@ballspinning.co.uk *Metal spinning manufrs*

Ball & Young Division Of Vitafoan Ltd, 53 Causeway Road, Earlstrees Industrial Estate, Corby, Northamptonshire, NN17 4DU Tel: (01536) 200502 Fax: (01536) 269554 E-mail: sales@underlay.com *Manufacturers of carpet underlay*

Ballachree Ltd, Canal Road, Frizinghall, Bradford, West Yorkshire, BD2 1AU Tel: (01274) 593131 Fax: (01274) 596752 E-mail: sales@ballachree.co.uk Principal Export Areas: Africa *Steel & steel plate stockholders & steel plate flattening services*

Michael Ballance Plastics Ltd, Suite 8 Worthington House, 146 High Street, Burton-On-Trent, Staffordshire, DE14 1JE Tel: (01283) 511632 Fax: (01283) 517400 E-mail: mb@ballance-plastics.co.uk *Suppliers of pvc tpe compounds*

Ballantine Engineering Ltd, Links Road, Bo'Ness, West Lothian, EH51 9PW Tel: (01506) 822721 Fax: (01506) 827326 E-mail: sales@ballantineboness.co.uk *Iron casting manufrs*

▶ Ballantyne Cashmere, 303 Westbourne Grove, London, W11 2QA Tel: (020) 7792 2563 Fax: (020) 7243 5816 *Knitwear retailers*

Ballantyne Cashmere UK Ltd, Caerlee Mills, Innerleithen, Peeblesshire, EH44 6HP Tel: (01896) 830222 Fax: (01896) 831128 E-mail: enquiries@ballantyne-cashmere.co.uk *Knitwear manufrs*

Ballard Chalmers Ltd, 1 Christopher Road, East Grinstead, West Sussex, RH19 3BT Tel: (01342) 410223 Fax: (01342) 410225 E-mail: info@ballardchalmers.com *Software developments*

▶ Ballard Communications Management, The Malthouse, Milton Street, Westcott, Dorking, Surrey, RH4 3PX Tel: (01306) 882288 Fax: (01306) 881803 E-mail: info@ballard.co.uk *Press relations for the engineering and life science industries.**Generating favourable press comment within the Europe, Middle East and Africa (EMEA) region.**Press relations is an important and cost effective communication channel to businesses within the engineering and life sciences sector. In a market where the decision making process is extended beyond the purchasing department to senior management, press relations plays an important role in creating and maintaining customer awareness through a wide variety of specialist publications. *Ballard Communications Management is focused on the production, co-ordination and placement of technical and application articles, scientific papers, in addition to standard product releases. Technical authors are all qualified engineers or scientists and write in the native language of each individual European market.*

Ballast Tools (UK) Ltd, Unit 4 County Park Business Centre, Shrivenham Road, Swindon, SN1 2NR Tel: (01793) 697800 Fax: (01793) 527020 E-mail: btukltd@aol.com Principal Export Areas: Worldwide *Railway track maintenance equipment*

Ballcock & Bits Ltd, Broad Lane, Bracknell, Berkshire, RG12 9BJ Tel: (01344) 481212 Fax: (01344) 302512 *Plumbing & heating suppliers*

Ballinliss Forge Works, 17 Tamnaghbane Road, Newry, County Down, BT35 8RF Tel: (028) 3084 8694 Fax: (028) 3084 8694 E-mail: info@ballinliss.co.uk *Staircases manufacturers & glass manufrs*

▶ Ballistic Research Ltd, PO Box 263, Romsey, Hampshire, SO51 7WY Tel: (01794) 521113 Fax: (01794) 521623 E-mail: info@ballisticresearch.co.uk *Electrical & electronic test engineers. Specialists in the calibration & repair of electrical & electronic test equipment.*

Balloo Hire Centre Ltd, 21 Balloo Drive, Bangor, County Down, BT19 7QY Tel: (028) 9145 4457 Fax: (028) 9127 1239 E-mail: dan@balloohire.com *Industrial power tool specialists*

▶ Balloo Hire Centre Ltd, 31 Sydenham Road, Belfast, BT3 9DH Tel: (028) 9045 8080 Fax: (028) 9127 1239 E-mail: laura.corrigan@balloohire.com *Scaffold Supply and Erect*Plant and Machinery Hire*

▶ Balloon Addict, 15 Broom Close, Wath-upon-Dearne, Rotherham, South Yorkshire, S63 7JU Tel: (07800) 906846 *Party balloon suppliers*

▶ Balloon Arcade, 32 Shillito Road, Poole, Dorset, BH12 2BW Tel: (01202) 743465 Fax: (01202) 718488 E-mail: sales@balloon-arcade.co.uk *Balloon decor*

Balloon Art Design Studio, 2 Whitehall Ave, Rumney, Cardiff, CF3 8DQ Tel: (029) 2079 0207 *Novelty balloons*

Balloon Box, 9 Elizabeth Court, Collingham, Wetherby, West Yorkshire, LS22 5JL Tel: (01937) 579549 Fax: (01937) 574585 E-mail: enquiries@balloonbox.co.uk *Giftware & balloons retailers*

Balloon Buddies, 26 Oxford Street, St. Philips, Bristol, BS2 0QU Tel: 0117-945 1822 E-mail: sales@balloonbuddies.co.uk *Balloon decorators commercial & private*

▶ Balloon Celebration (A), 1 Mill Lane, Broxbourne, Hertfordshire, EN10 7AZ Tel: (01992) 467555 Fax: (01920) 872719 E-mail: sales@aballooncelebration.co.uk *Celebration & balloon retail*

Balloon Elegance, 53 Love Street, Paisley, Renfrewshire, PA3 2DZ Tel: 0141-848 6119 Fax: 0141-848 9161 E-mail: jb-promotions@btclick.com *Novelty balloon design wholesalers*

Balloon Express UK Ltd, Dart Mills, Buckfastleigh, Devon, TQ11 0NF Tel: (01364) 643497 Fax: (01364) 642172 E-mail: ballonexpress@btconnect.com *Balloon printers & wholesalers*

Balloon Flights Co, Dovecote House, Gaulby Lane, Kings Norton, Leicester, LE7 9BA Tel: 0116-259 6990 E-mail: bookings@balloonflightscompany.co.uk *Novelty balloons supply & manufrs*

Balloon Options, 66 Scotchman Lane, Morley, Leeds, LS27 0BJ Tel: 0113-252 3800 Fax: 0113-252 7400 *Novelty balloon suppliers*

▶ Balloon Print, 22 Hammond Road, Woking, Surrey, GU21 4TQ Tel: (01483) 722229 Fax: (01483) 722229 E-mail: balloons.partyworld@ntlworld.com *Party service balloons, streamers, bunting, to business & individuals*

The Balloon Store Ltd, 106 Cheriton Road, Folkestone, Kent, CT20 2QN Tel: (01303) 256337 E-mail: info@balloonstore.com *Balloon suppliers & designers*

Balloon Studio Ltd, 44 Sandhill Oval, Leeds, LS17 8EA Tel: 0113-225 5666 Fax: 0113-226 2845 E-mail: janice@balloonstudio.co.uk *Novelty balloon suppliers*

Balloon World, 18 Norfolk Street, King's Lynn, Norfolk, PE30 1AN Tel: (01553) 760909 Fax: (01553) 760909 *Balloon suppliers*

Balloon Wrap & Decoration, 12 Downlands Parade, Upper Brighton Road, Worthing, West Sussex, BN14 9JH Tel: (01903) 203549 Fax: (01903) 203549 *Balloon suppliers*

Balloonatics, 21 Mytham Road, Little Lever, Bolton, BL3 1TH Tel: (01204) 792340 E-mail: enquiries@balloonaticsofstockton.co.uk

Balloonatics, 76 Penkville Street, Stoke-On-Trent, ST4 5AJ Tel: (01782) 844616 *Balloon decoration suppliers*

Ballooning Network Ltd, Vauxhall House, Coronation Road, Southville, Bristol, BS3 1RN Tel: 0117-963 7858 Fax: 0117-963 9555 *Balloons - hot air flights*

▶ Balloonprint Balloons, Trevordale House, Pius Drove, Upwell, Wisbech, Cambridgeshire, PE14 9AL Tel: (01945) 773559 Fax: (0845) 0090903 E-mail: peter@balloonprint.co.uk *Quality screen printed latex & foil balloons*

▶ Balloons Afloat, 90 Freeman Road, Didcot, Oxfordshire, OX11 7DB Tel: (01235) 819904 E-mail: sales@balloonsafloat.co.uk

▶ Balloons For All Occasions, 52 King Street, Ramsgate, Kent, CT11 8NT Tel: (01843) 851087 Fax: (01843) 851087 *Party balloon manufrs*

Balloons Are Taking Off, 390 Gorgie Road, Edinburgh, EH11 2RQ Tel: 0131-346 4446 Fax: 0131-346 2608 E-mail: sales@balloonsaretakingoff.co.uk *Balloon suppliers*

▶ Balloons By Emma, 62 High Street, Cefn Coed, Merthyr Tydfil, Mid Glamorgan, CF48 2PL Tel: (01685) 721210 Fax: (01685) 721210 *Balloon suppliers*

Balloons By Post, 1 Audley End, Saffron Walden, Essex, CB11 4JB Tel: (01799) 513335 E-mail: contact@ballonsbypost.com *Balloon suppliers*

Balloons Direct, Lyn Court, The Common, Holt, Trowbridge, Wiltshire, BA14 6QL Tel: (01225) 784040 *Publicity balloon services*

Balloons & Flora, 53 The Broadway, Loughton, Essex, IG10 3SP Tel: (020) 8508 8977 Fax: (020) 8508 8977 *Party suppliers*

Balloons Galore, 61 Leedham Avenue, Tamworth, Staffordshire, B77 3LZ Tel: (01827) 62995 *Balloons for all occasions distributors*

Balloons 'N' Things, 27 Essex Street, Birmingham, B5 4TR Tel: 0121-622 2331 Fax: 0121-622 1779 E-mail: david@balloons-n-things.co.uk *Balloon & party supply agents*

Balloons On Tour, Dart Mills, Old Topnes Road, Buckfastleigh, Devon, TQ11 0NF Tel: (0800) 7834546 Fax: (01364) 642172 *Novelty balloon suppliers*

Balloons R Us, 25 Military Road, Colchester, CO1 2AD Tel: (01206) 545556 Fax: (01206) 545556 *Balloons*

▶ Balloons & Tunes, Bottom Lock Cottages, Glascote Road, Tamworth, Staffordshire, B77 2AE Tel: (01827) 316600 Fax: (01827) 311066 E-mail: us@balloonsandtunes.co.uk *Balloon decorations & entertainer hire*

Balloons UK Hot Air Flights, School Farm, School Lane, Stretton, Stafford, ST19 9LJ Tel: (01785) 280450 Fax: (01952) 541856 E-mail: tony@balloonsuk.co.uk *Hot air balloon flying services*

Balloons Worldwide Ltd, London Road, Brown Street, Alderley Edge, Cheshire, SK9 7EQ Tel: (01625) 583168 Fax: (01625) 586098 *Balloons wholesalers & distributors*

▶ Balloonz 'N' Cakes, 94 Delamere Street, Winsford, Cheshire, CW7 2LU Tel: (01606) 860668 E-mail: balloonz@cakes.co.uk *Wedding catering & decoration services*

Ballpoint Office Supplies, Unit 21 The Bell Centre, Newton Road, Crawley, West Sussex, RH10 9FZ Tel: (01293) 433330 Fax: (01293) 434484 E-mail: sales@ballpoint.co.uk *Suppliers of office & computer products very low prices to businesses*

Balls Grinding Ltd, Unit K, Chosenview Road, Cheltenham, Gloucestershire, GL51 9LT Tel: (01242) 576621 Fax: (01242) 584298 E-mail: ballsgrinding@btconnect.com *Engineering services*

Ballymena Guardian, 83-85 Wellington Street, Ballymena, County Antrim, BT43 6AD Tel: (028) 2564 1229 Fax: (028) 2565 3920 E-mail: advertising@ballymenaguardian.co.uk *Newspaper publishers*

Ballymena Meats, Pennybridge Industrial Estate, Ballymena, County Antrim, BT42 3HB Tel: (028) 2565 3710 Fax: (028) 2564 7593 E-mail: ballymena.meats@nireland.com *Cold storage services*

▶ Balmedie Quarry, Balmedie Quarry, Belhelvie, Aberdeen, AB23 8WT Tel: (01358) 742203 Fax: (01358) 742203 *Aberdeenshire council quarry*

Balmer Lawn Hotel, Lyndhurst Road, Brockenhurst, Hampshire, SO42 7ZB Tel: (01590) 623116 Fax: (01590) 623864 E-mail: blh@btinternet.com *Hotel with conference facilities*

Balmer Lindley Group, Dragonby Vale Enterprise Park, Mannaberg Way, Scunthorpe, South Humberside, DN15 8XF Tel: (01724) 289119 Fax: (01724) 281478 E-mail: mail@balmer-group.co.uk *Steel & aluminium handrail & parapet fencing manufrs*

Balmoral Group Ltd, Balmoral Park, Aberdeen, AB12 3GY Tel: (01224) 859000 Fax: (01224) 859059 E-mail: group@balmoral.co.uk *Anchor, chain and load testing services.*

Balmoral Knitwear (Scotland) Ltd, 16 Church Lane, Galston, Ayrshire, KA4 8HF Tel: (01563) 820213 Fax: (01563) 821740 E-mail: info@balmoralknitwear.co.uk *Knitwear & embroidery manufacturers & stockists*

Balmoral Tanks Ltd, Wellington Road, Aberdeen, AB12 3GY Tel: (01224) 859100 Fax: (01224) 859123 E-mail: tanks@balmoral.co.uk *Single source designer & manufacturer of liquid storage tanks, covering the water, wastewater, chemical, environmental & fuel sectors, provides rotationally moulded seamless tanks up to capacities of 67,000 litres & hot press GRP& steel sectional water tanks*

Baloris Ltd, Oakfield House, 35 Perrymount Road, Haywards Heath, West Sussex, RH16 3BW Tel: (01444) 441252 Fax: (01444) 452107 E-mail: seanhickey@valoris.com *Strategic marketing consultancy*

Baltairco West Ltd, Ivy House Farm, Wolvershill, Banwell, Avon, BS29 6LB Tel: (01934) 824411 Fax: (01934) 824477 *Air conditioning distributors*

Baltec UK Ltd, Danehill, Lower Earley, Reading, RG6 4UT Tel: 0118-931 1191 Fax: 0118-931 1103 E-mail: sales@baltec.co.uk Principal Export Areas: Central/East Europe *Precision tooling for assembled machinery*

Baltex Clothing, 63 Hume Street, Smethwick, West Midlands, B66 3PN Tel: (07956) 365202 *Wholesale clothing*

Baltic Exchange Ltd, 24 St.Mary Axe, London, EC3A 8EX Tel: (020) 7623 5501 Fax: (020) 7369 1622 E-mail: admin@balticexchange.com *International shipping exchange*

Baltic Wharf Boatyard Ltd, Baltic Wharf Business Centre, St. Peters Quay, Totnes, Devon, TQ9 5EW Tel: (01803) 867922 Fax: (01803) 866795 E-mail: sales@balticwharf.co.uk *Site management & property development*

Balticare Ltd, Princewood Road, Earlstrees Industrial Estate, Corby, Northamptonshire, NN17 4AP Tel: (01536) 200312 Fax: (01536) 408623 E-mail: info@baltaircoil.be *Cooling towers & industrial fluid cooler services*

Balvac Whitley Moran Ltd, 24 Woodside Business Park, Birkenhead, Merseyside, CH41 1EL Tel: 0151-650 0184 Fax: 0151-650 0358 E-mail: info@balvac.co.uk *Concrete repairers*

BAM Ritchies, Nailsea Wall, Kenn Pier, Clevedon, North West Somerset, BS21 6UE Tel: 01275 875338 Fax: 01275 870076 E-mail: ritchies@bamritchies.co.uk *Ground Engineering Contractors*Ground Investigation Contractors*Concrete Techniques Contractors*Drilling and Blasting Contractors*

▶ Bambach Saddle Seat Europe, Unit A2 Seedbed Centre, Langston Road, Loughton, Essex, IG10 3TQ Tel: (0800) 581108 Fax: (020) 8532 5109 E-mail: info@bambach.co.uk *Furnishings*

▶ Bam-Bams, 106 Castle Street, Forfar, Angus, DD8 3HR Tel: (01307) 462244

▶ Bambe Ltd, 3 Granville Industrial Estate, Granville Road, London, NW2 2LD Tel: (020) 8381 4567 Fax: (020) 8381 4589 E-mail: sales@bambeltd.co.uk *Packaging material manufrs*

Bamber Roof Trusses, Church Farm Works, Oulton, Norwich, NR11 6NT Tel: (01263) 584255 Fax: (01263) 584166 E-mail: ronny.bamber@btinternet.com *Timber fabricators*

▶ Bamber's Special Projects, 5 Challenge Court, Love La Industrial Estate, Bishops Castle, Shropshire, SY9 5DW Tel: (01588) 638111 Fax: (01588) 638111 E-mail: info@specialprojects.co.uk *Designers & manufacturers of bespoke furniture & interiors*

Bambi Air Compressors Ltd, 152 Thimble Mill Lane, Birmingham, B7 5HT Tel: 0121-322 2299 Fax: 0121-322 2297 E-mail: sales@bambi-air.co.uk *Dentistry & industrial air compressor spray equipment manufrs*

Bamboozled Gifts, 44 Alexandra Road, Swadlincote, Derbyshire, DE11 9AZ Tel: 01283 552888 E-mail: sales@bamboozledgifts.co.uk *Professional service offering stunning balloon decor, unique gifts/gift baskets, favours & party goods all under one roof. We are based in Swadlincote & cover venues throughout Derbyshire, Staffordshire & Leicestershire.*

Bambury Metal Fabrications, Short Street, Bristol, BS2 0SW Tel: 0117-971 9216 Fax: 0117-971 1898 *Sheet metalworkers & fabricators*

The Bamford Group, Millgate, Market Street, Shawforth, Rochdale, Lancashire, OL12 8NX Tel: (01706) 897100 Fax: (01706) 897101 E-mail: bamford.group@virgin.net *Energy conservation consultants*

► Bamond Civil Engineering Ltd, The Maltings, East Tyndall Street, Cardiff, CF24 5EA Tel: (029) 2047 1189 Fax: (029) 2048 5053

Bampton Packaging Holdings Ltd, Lenton Lane, Nottingham, NG7 2NR Tel: 0115-986 8601 Fax: 0115-986 2984 E-mail: sales@bamtonpacking.co.uk *Export packing manufrs*

Bana Bags, Market Hall, Earle Street, Crewe, CW1 2BL Tel: (01270) 255703 *Bags suppliers*

► Banbury Alarms, Unit 5 Thorpe Close, Banbury, Oxfordshire, OX16 4SW Tel: (01295) 263552 *Burglar alarm systems installers*

Banbury Badges Ltd, Brooklands, Brook Street, Moreton Pinkney, Daventry, Northamptonshire, NN11 3SL Tel: (01295) 768758 Fax: (01295) 768759 E-mail: info@banburybadges.co.uk *Advertising gifts & badges manufrs*

Banbury Blinds, Bell Hill, Hook Norton, Banbury, Oxfordshire, OX15 5NG Tel: (01608) 737205 Fax: (01608) 730679 *Blind manufrs*

Banbury Computers, 55 Middleton Road, Banbury, Oxon, OX16 3QR Tel: (01295) 272627 E-mail: sales@banburycomputers.com *Computer systems house*

Banbury Environmental Products Ltd, Yorke Street, Mansfield Woodhouse, Mansfield, Nottinghamshire, NG19 9NX Tel: (01623) 662002 Fax: (01623) 640864 *Plastic fence post & gravel board*

Banbury Farm General Supplies Ltd, Grove Farm Building, Burton Dassett, Southam, Warwickshire, CV47 2AB Tel: (01295) 770707 Fax: (01295) 770787 *Agricultural suppliers*

Banbury Gunsmiths, 47a Broad Street, Banbury, Oxfordshire, OX16 5BT Tel: (01295) 265819 Fax: (01295) 265810 E-mail: sales@banburygunsmiths.com *Guns & fishing tackle distributors*

Banbury Nameplates Ltd, Dashwood Road, Banbury, Oxfordshire, OX16 5HD Tel: (01295) 267638 Fax: (01295) 271745 E-mail: sales@banburynameplates.co.uk *Screen printers*

► Banbury Pat Testing Services, 157 Delapre Drive, Banbury, Oxfordshire, OX16 3WS Tel: (01295) 271049 E-mail: enquiries@pat-testing-uk.org *A1 pat testing portable appliance testing electrical safety*

Banbury Plastic Fittings Ltd, Unit 13, Overfield, Thorpe Way Industrial Estate, Banbury, Oxfordshire, OX16 4XR Tel: (01295) 264800 Fax: (01295) 264901 E-mail: sales@bpfittings.co.uk *BPF manufacture & supply plastic injection moulded components to a whole host of industries particularly the office sector with furniture components, widgets & gadgets. Products include Pop Up Electrical Power & Data Units, Cable Ports, Wire Management, Desk Tidies, Organisers, Keyboard & Pen Trays & Monitor Arms.** We have a 40-page standard plastic parts catalogue which caters for a variety of industry sectors such as the Medical, Fabrication,Shopfitting & Fastener solutions industries. Key components include Tube Inserts, Grommets, Glides, Adjustable & Tilt Feet, Ironmongery, Hardware, Castors, Handles, Threaded Inserts, Bath Height Adjusters, Handwheels, Chair Mouldings, Caps & Plugs, Steel Inserts, Ferrules,Self Adhesive Feet, Bumpers, Washers, Concrete Spacers & countless more!** The company also offers a bespoke custom moulding service & produce Steel & Aluminium Tools to rapid lead times & can run them in low-cost commodity materials through to sophisticated engineering polymers.*

Banbury Traffic Signals, 1 Overfield, Thorpe Way, Banbury, Oxfordshire, OX16 4XR Tel: (01295) 259922 Fax: (01295) 251478 *Traffic signalling*

Banbury Windows Ltd, Alton Works, Long Bank, Bewdley, Worcestershire, DY12 2UL Tel: (01299) 266332 Fax: (01299) 266676 *Double glazing*

► Banburys Ltd, Castle Park Road, Whiddon Valley Industrial Estate, Barnstaple, Devon, EX32 8PA Tel: (01271) 326200 Fax: (01271) 327880 E-mail: removals@banburys.com

R. Bance & Co. Ltd, Coc Crow Hill House, St. Marys Road, Surbiton, Surrey, KT6 5HE Tel: (020) 8398 7141 Fax: (020) 8398 4765 E-mail: admin@bance.com *Railway track fastners & fittings manufrs*

Banchory Contractors Ltd, The Minklets, Crathes, Banchory, Kincardineshire, AB31 5QQ Tel: (01330) 844767 Fax: (01330) 844788 E-mail: info.bcl@bancon.co.uk *Building contractors*

► Banchory Dental Practice, 9 Station Road, Banchory, Kincardineshire, AB31 5XX Tel: (01330) 823400 E-mail: smile@banchorydentalpractice.com *Dental practices*

Bancom Communications Ltd, P O Box 280, Cambridge, CB2 2DY Tel: (01223) 566577 Fax: (01223) 566588 E-mail: tony@bancom.co.uk *Radio communications retailer*

Bancroft & Co., 5 Stairbridge Court, Stairbridge Lane, Bolney, Haywards Heath, West Sussex, RH17 5PA Tel: (01444) 248884 Fax: (01444) 242767 E-mail: sales@bancroft.co.uk *Electric motors pressure test systems*

Band International, Woodlands, Middleton, Freshwater, Isle of Wight, PO40 9RW Tel: (01983) 755858 Fax: (01983) 756273 E-mail: will@band.co.uk *Band International, based on the Isle of Wight, manufactures and*

continued

supplies wedding and banquet chairs and event seating for functions and events worldwide.

► Band Systems, Unit 3, Twyford Business Park, Station Road, Twyford, Reading, RG10 9TU Tel: 0118-377 9000 Fax: 0118-970 6804 *Security installers for burglar alarms access control cctv*

Bandai UK Ltd, Jellicoe House, Grange Drive, Hedge End, Southampton, SO30 2AF Tel: (01489) 790944 Fax: (01489) 790643 *Toys distributor*

Bandapac Packaging Materials, 9 Fieldings Road, Cheshunt, Waltham Cross, Hertfordshire, EN8 9TL Tel: (01992) 622799 Fax: (01992) 628873 *Distributors or agents of strapping systems*

Bandor Loudspeakers, 11 Penfold Cottages, Penfold Lane, Holmer Green, High Wycombe, Buckinghamshire, HP15 6XR Tel: (01494) 714058 Fax: (01494) 715903 *Loudspeakers & drivers designers*

Bandsaw Service Ltd, Fairacres Industrial Estate, Dedworth Road, Windsor, Berkshire, SL4 4LE Tel: (01753) 862029 Fax: (01753) 830051 E-mail: saws@eclipse.co.uk *Saw distributors, services & sharpening*

Band-Tite Co. Ltd, 9 Aizlewood Road, Sheffield, S8 0YX Tel: 0114-250 0393 Fax: 0114-250 0394 E-mail: sales@band-tite.co.uk *Stainless steel sign, fixings manufrs*

Banfield Engineering Wisbech Ltd, Unit 8b Tinkers Drove, Wisbech, Cambridgeshire, PE13 3PQ Tel: (01945) 585554 Fax: (01945) 463874 E-mail: sales@banfield-uk.com *Steel & pipework fabricators*

Banfield Fencing, 2 Alexander Way, Yatton, Bristol, BS49 4HE Tel: (01934) 838885 Fax: (01934) 838885 *Fencing contractors*

Banfield Suspended Ceilings, Culzean, Wexham Park La, Wexham, Slough, SL3 6LX Tel: 01753 532421 Fax: 01753 532421 *Suspended ceilings*

Bang Communications Ltd, The Black Barn, Farleigh Road, Cliddesden, Basingstoke, Hampshire, RG25 2JL Tel: (01256) 370900 Fax: (01256) 370901 E-mail: info@bang-on.net *Graphic designers*

Bang & Olufsen, 147 Kings Road, London, SW3 5TX Tel: (020) 7376 5222 Fax: (020) 7376 5333 E-mail: chelsea@bang-olufsen.uk.com *Luxury audio visual retailers*

► Bang & Olufsen, 3 Market Place, Reading, RG1 2EG Tel: 0118-959 0770 Fax: 0118-959 0980 *Audio visual equipment & accessory retailers*

Bang & Olufsen, Unit 630 Wharfdale Road, Winnersh Triangle, Wokingham, Berkshire, RG41 5TP Tel: 0118-969 2288 Fax: 0118-969 3388 *Audio systems manufrs*

► Bang on Baits, 273 Senwick Drive, Wellingborough, Northamptonshire, NN8 1SD Tel: (01933) 274968 E-mail: bangonbaits@yahoo.co.uk

Bangor Blinds, 2 Dew Street, Menai Bridge, Gwynedd, LL59 5AU Tel: (01248) 714666 Fax: (01248) 715161 E-mail: bangorblinds@aol.com *Blind, roller shutter garage doors sales & manufrs*

Bangor Yacht Services, 98 Warren Road, Donaghadee, County Down, BT21 0PQ Tel: (028) 9188 8600 Fax: (028) 9188 8481 *Yacht repairers*

Banham Security Ltd, 10 Pascal Street, London, SW8 4SH Tel: (020) 7622 5151 Fax: (020) 7498 2461 E-mail: security@banham.com *Security specialist manufrs & distributors*

► Banico Ltd, Tilson Road, Roundthorn Industrial Estate, Manchester, M23 9GF Tel: (0845) 1700740 Fax: (0845) 1700750 E-mail: sales@banico.co.uk *Air conditioning, humidity, heat control suppliers & manufrs*

Baniftec Ltd, Farley Edge, Farley Common, Westerham, Kent, TN16 1UB Tel: (01959) 564526 E-mail: enquiries@baniftec.com *Computer consultants*

Banjo Inc Ltd, Unit 4d Green End Business Centre, 93a Church Lane, Sarratt, Rickmansworth, Hertfordshire, WD3 6HH Tel: (01923) 266887 Fax: (01923) 266887 E-mail: sales@banjocreative.com *Prototype models & model making services*

Bank Farm Trailers, The Garage, Llangunnor, Carmarthen, Dyfed, SA31 2PG Tel: (01267) 231565 Fax: (01267) 222154 E-mail: sales@bankfarm-trailers.co.uk *Industrial trailer suppliers & manufrs*

Bank Farm Trailers Ltd, Robeston Wathen, Narberth, Dyfed, SA67 8EN Tel: (01834) 860605 Fax: (01834) 861498 E-mail: sales@bankfarm-trailers.co.uk *Industrial & leisure road trailer suppliers & manufrs*

Bank Farm Trailers, Bank Farm, Spytty Road, Newport, Gwent, NP19 4QW Tel: (01633) 290291 Fax: (01633) 270400 *Road & exhibition trailer manufrs*

Bank Farm Trailers Ltd, Unit 1 Mill Brook Yard, Landore, Swansea, SA1 2JG Tel: (01792) 795834 Fax: (01792) 799251 E-mail: sales@bankfarm-trailers.co.uk *Industrial trailer suppliers & manufrs*

Rose Bank Stores & Saddlery, Middle Lane, Kings Norton, Birmingham, B38 0DX Tel: (01564) 822112 Fax: (01564) 822112 *Equestrian equipment retailers*

Bankhead Bakery, 8 Wallace Street, Rutherglen, Glasgow, G73 2SA Tel: 0141-613 0405 Fax: 0141-613 0405 E-mail: akelly@bankheadbakery.fsnet.co.uk *Suppliers of quality Scottish bakery products to upmarket retail & wholesale outlets*

Banking Automation Ltd, Unit 2 Woodley Park Estate, Reading Road, Reading, RG5 3AW Tel: 0118-969 2224 Fax: 0118-944 1191 E-mail: robinguest@bankingautomation.co.uk *Deposit machines*

Banks & Burr, 25 Claremont Road, Rugby, Warwickshire, CV21 3NA Tel: (01788) 576782 Fax: (01788) 560774 E-mail: sales@tackleup.com *Fishing tackle suppliers*

Banks Cargill Agriculture Ltd, Unit 7 Spalding Road Business Park, Bourne, Lincolnshire, PE10 9LF Tel: (01778) 422454 Fax: (01778) 426200 *Agricultural services*

Banks Cargill Agriculture Ltd, Unit 6 Bury Road Industrial Estate, Ramsey, Huntingdon, Cambridgeshire, PE26 1NF Tel: (01487) 813361 Fax: (01487) 814600 *Agricultural merchants*

Banks Cargill Agriculture Ltd, Lineside, Weston, Newark, Nottinghamshire, NG23 6TL Tel: (01636) 821074 Fax: (01522) 822235 E-mail: enquiries@cargill.com *Agricultural merchants*

Banks Dave Electric, 9 Harewood Road, Holymoorside, Chesterfield, Derbyshire, S42 7HT Tel: (01246) 567333 Fax: (01246) 567444 *Electrical installation contractors*

G. Banks (Nu-Co), Unit 9, Atlantic Trading Estate, Barry, South Glamorgan, CF63 3RF Tel: (01446) 742861 Fax: (01446) 742861 *Shot blasting contractors*

J. Banks & Co. Ltd, Excelsior Works, Wood Street, Willenhall, West Midlands, WV13 1JY Tel: (01902) 605084 Fax: (01902) 603248 E-mail: contact@jbanks.co.uk *Locks, hardware & housewares manufr*

Banks Sails Ltd, 372 Brook Lane, Sarisbury Green, Southampton, SO31 7ZA Tel: (01489) 582444 Fax: (01489) 589789 E-mail: enquiries@banks.co.uk *Yacht & dinghy sail manufrs*

Banks Software Ltd, 74 Forest Road, Oldbury, West Midlands, B68 0EF Tel: (0121) 421 8295 E-mail: sales@banks-software.co.uk *Software consultants*

Bankside Engineering Ltd, Woodhouse St, Hedon Road, Hull, HU9 1RJ Tel: (01482) 337700 Fax: (01482) 337742 E-mail: users@bie.co.uk Principal Export Areas: Worldwide *Machinists & precision machining services*

Bankside Patterson Ltd, Catwick Lane, Brandesburton, Driffield, East Yorkshire, YO25 8RW Tel: (01964) 545454 Fax: (01964) 545459 E-mail: sales@bankside-patterson.co.uk *Chassis & sheet metal products*

► Bankton Developments, 76 New Row, Tranent, East Lothian, EH33 2AA Tel: (01875) 616888 Fax: (01875) 616836

► Banlaw Europe Ltd, Unit 1-3 Rosendale Way, Blantyre, Glasgow, G72 0NJ Tel: (01698) 824431 Fax: (01698) 826725 E-mail: andymcateer@banlawsystems.com

Banner Ltd, Banner House, Greg Street, Stockport, Cheshire, SK5 7BT Tel: 0161-474 8000 Fax: 0161-474 7655 E-mail: admin@bannergroup.co.uk *Children's & school wear distributors*

► Banner Batons Majorette Cheerleading Supplies, 9 Cornfield Lane, Eastbourne, East Sussex, BN21 4NE Tel: (01323) 439914 Fax: (01323) 439485 E-mail: sales@bannerbatons.co.uk *Mail order for majorette & cheer leader supplies*

Banner Chemicals Ltd, Unit B, Hampton Court, Manor Park, Runcorn, Cheshire, WA7 1TU Tel: (01928) 597000 Fax: (01928) 597001 E-mail: reception@bannerchemicals.co.uk *Speciality chemical distributors* Also at: Glasgow & London

► Banner & Flag Co., 9 Lubnaig Gardens, Bearsden, Glasgow, G61 4QX Tel: 0141-577 9141 Fax: 0141-563 7147 E-mail: graphics@bf-c.co.uk *Design & manufacture of flag or banner & signs*

Banner Homes Group plc, Riverside House, Holtspur Lane, Wooburn Green, High Wycombe, Buckinghamshire, HP10 0TJ Tel: (01628) 536200 Fax: (01628) 536201 E-mail: info@banner-homes.co.uk *Building contractors*

Banner Plant Services, 36 London Road, Datchet, Slough, SL3 9JN Tel: (01753) 543029 Fax: (01753) 580511 *Management consultants*

► Banner & Shields Ltd, Mabgate Mills, Mabgate, Leeds, LS9 7DZ Tel: 0113-243 2860

► Banner Solutions, Banner House, Central Buildings, Parkfield Road, Rugby, Warwickshire, CV21 1QJ Tel: (01788) 559300 Fax: (01788) 559333 E-mail: joanne.lewis@bannerholdings.co.uk *Rail maintenance & refurbishment*

► Banner Sports Surfaces, Banner House, Parkfield Road, Rugby, Warwickshire, CV21 1QJ Tel: 01788 559332 Fax: 01788 559333 E-mail: joanne.lewis@bannerholdings.co.uk *Sports Surface construction Company - installers of artificial and natural grass football, Rugby, hockey pitches, tennis courts and MUGAS, clubhouses and pavilions*

Banner Total Maintenance Ltd, Callywhite Lane, Dronfield, Derbyshire, S18 2XS Tel: (01246) 299400 Fax: (01246) 290253 E-mail: dronfield@bannerplant.co.uk *Non operator plant hire.*

Banner Warehouse, Unit 4 & 5 Knowle Business Centre, Wadhurst Road, Frant, Tunbridge Wells, Kent, TN3 9EJ Tel: (0800) 0523659 Fax: (0800) 0523658 E-mail: regencysigns@btclick.com *Banner manufacturers & print finishing services*

► Bannermakers.co.uk, 79 Pickford Lane, Bexleyheath, Kent, DA7 4RW Tel: (0845) 4660172 E-mail: info@bannermakers.co.uk *Designers & suppliers of PVC, mesh & full colour outdoor banners, building wraps, flags, signs & graphics*

B.J. Banning Ltd, 501-527 Lichfield Road, Birmingham, B6 7SR Tel: (0121) 327 2741 Fax: (0121) 327 0704 *Motor tyre & battery distributors*

Bannocks Of Solihull, 117 Streetsbrook Road, Shirley, Solihull, West Midlands, B90 3PF Tel: 0121-744 1727 Fax: 0121-733 1651 *Marble granite slate & stone manufrs*

Bannons Ltd, 75 North Street, Belfast, BT1 1NL Tel: (028) 9032 9335 Fax: (028) 9023 5152 *Furniture retailers*

Bannvalley Guns & Tackle, 20 Finlayston, Portglenone, Ballymena, County Antrim, BT44 8EA Tel: (028) 2582 1383 Fax: (028) 2582 1383 *Gunsmiths*

Banson Tool Hire Ltd, 125 Pellon Lane, Halifax, West Yorkshire, HX1 5QN Tel: (01422) 254999 Fax: (01422) 254778 *Tool hire, sale & services* Also at: Batley, Bradford, Huddersfield, Keighley, Leeds, Oldham, Manchester, Rochdale, Rotherham & Wakefield

Bantel Investments Ltd, 45-47 North Bridge Street, Hawick, Roxburghshire, TD9 9PX Tel: (01450) 373352 Fax: (01450) 377531 *Commercial property agents*

► Banwall Cars, Westwood Farm, Westwood, Peterborough, PE3 9UW Tel: (01733) 332913 Fax: (01733) 268295 E-mail: sales@vanwallcars.com *Carbon fibre fabricators & automotive components manufrs*

Bap Factory, 2 Fitzroy Street, Cardiff, CF24 4BL Tel: (029) 2022 5255 *Bakery wholesalers*

► Bapco Closures, Unit 267, Jurby Industrial Estate, Jurby, Isle of Man, IM7 3BD Tel: (01624) 896166 Fax: (0870) 1383885 E-mail: info@bapcoclosures.com *Bapco Closures is a manufacturer of next generation packaging solutions. At our core is an innovative new closure technology which we have pioneered and developed. **BAP® closures constitute a fundamental innovation in packaging technology, and mean that our closures have inherent features and benefits ahead of other capping techniques.**The integral design features of BAP® closures enable them to be used under many demanding filling and liquid processing conditions, including Hot fill, Aseptic, Pasteurized and Sterilized processes.*

Bapp Industrial Supplies Castleford Ltd, Methley Road, Castleford, West Yorkshire, WF10 1PA Tel: (01977) 510640 Fax: (01977) 516514 E-mail: sales@bappcastleford.co.uk *Bolt & nut distributors*

Bapp Industrial Supplies Doncaster Ltd, Chappell Drive, Doncaster, South Yorkshire, DN1 2RW Tel: (01302) 364444 Fax: (01302) 321409 Principal Export Areas: Worldwide *Industrial fasteners distributors*

Bapp Industrial Supplies Lancs Ltd, Trafalgar Centre, Belfield Road, Rochdale, Lancashire, OL16 2UX Tel: (01706) 359500 Fax: (01706) 640270 *Industrial fastener distributors*

Bapp Industrial Supplies Preston Ltd, 57 Roman Way Industrial Estate, Ribbleton, Preston, PR2 5BE Tel: (01772) 704700 Fax: (01772) 704701 *Industrial fasteners & engineering supplies services*

► Bar Code Data Systems Ltd, Ashton House, Margaret Street, Ashton-under-Lyne, Lancashire, OL7 0SH Tel: 0161-330 0077 Fax: 0161 330 0088 E-mail: keith.hardy@bcdata.co.uk *Systems Integrator for bar code scanning solutions using 'Best of Breed' radio frequency terminals and complete RFid solutions encompassing RFid encoding and reading across the full range of RFid frequencies.*

► Bar Code Systems (London) Ltd, Lakeside House, 1 Furzeground Way, Stockley Park, Uxbridge, Middlesex, UB11 1BD Tel: (0870) 3516496 Fax: (020) 8622 3249 E-mail: robertmoorman@barcode-systems.com *Accreditation from GS1 UK,*Alliance Member GS1 UK Solution Provider.Retail Supply Chain Compliance.REA ScanCheck II.Quick Check Barcode Scanners.*Symbol & Zebra partner, REA bar code verifier master distributor, Axicon bar code verifier reseller*ISO Compliant Verification.*Retail Supply Chain Reports, ANSI & CEN.Training Academy, Barcode Audits.Verification Specialists.Pharmaceutical,Automotive & Food Packaging Bar Coding. Thermal Transfer Printers, Labeling Software, Labels & Ribbons.Axicon HHP Hand Held Products. Scanners Verifiers. Mobile Printing Solutions.Barcode Training & Consultancy. Supermarket Compliant. Retail Supply Chain.Transwin, Arcticle Look Up. 2D BarCodes, Datamatrix, PDF 417 Bar Codes & Verification Service.*

Bar Codes For Business Ltd, 56 Packhorse Road, Gerrards Cross, Buckinghamshire, SL9 8EF Tel: (01753) 888833 Fax: (01753) 888834 E-mail: sales@barcodesforbusiness.co.uk *Barcodes & label printers*

Bar Engineering, 20 West Dock Avenue, Hull, HU3 4JR Tel: (01482) 224966 Fax: (01482) 211443 *Precision engineers*

Bar Knight Precision Engineers Ltd, 588-588a Glasgow Road, Clydebank, Dunbartonshire, G81 1NH Tel: 0141-952 4000 Fax: 0141-952 1157 E-mail: sales@barknight.co.uk *Veterinary instrument manufacturers & sub contract precision engineers*

Bar Mutual Indemnity Fund Ltd, International Ho, 26 Creechurch La, London, EC3A 5BA Tel: (020) 7283 4646 Fax: (020) 7283 5988 *Insurance company*

► Bar Products & Services Ltd, Hanworth Road, Low Moor, Bradford, West Yorkshire, BD12 0SG Tel: (01274) 693249

Bar Refractories Ltd, Moorfield Rd, Alcester, Warwickshire, B49 5DA Tel: (01789) 764448 Fax: (01527) 821238 *Suppliers of labour and materials to repair all types of furnaces*

Bar & Restaurant Foods Ltd, Nine Mile Point Industrial Estate, Newport, Gwent, NP11 7HZ Tel: (01495) 202100 Fax: (01495) 200869 E-mail: sales@barfoods.com *Bar & Restaurant Foods Ltd based in Newport, Gwent are food processors. They are suppliers of soups, sauces and recipe dishes to the UK's foodservice and manufacturing industries.*

Baracuda UK, Unit 2, Swinford Farm, Swinford, Witney, Oxon, OX29 4BY Tel: (01865) 881988 Fax: (01865) 883717 *Swimming pool servicing*

Baram Ltd, Unit 1 Station Hill, Curdridge, Southampton, SO30 2DN Tel: (01489) 785086 Fax: (01489) 785929 E-mail: baramltd@aol.com *Civil engineers*

Barana P.L.C., 2-3 Charter Street, Leicester, LE1 3UD Tel: 0116-253 9380 Fax: 0116-262 7023 E-mail: enquiries@barana.co.uk *Leisurewear & knitwear manufrs*

Baratix, 15b Regency Mews High Road, London, NW10 2TE Tel: (020) 8459 0832 Fax: (020) 8459 0832 *Ladies' fancy belt manufrs*

Baravon Systems, Sanctus Street, Stratford-upon-Avon, Warwickshire, CV37 6DH Tel: (01789) 299668 Fax: (01789) 414230 *Emergency lighting & fire alarm systems manufrs*

Barb Security Systems, Reeds, Colliers End, Ware, Hertfordshire, SG11 1EH Tel: (0845) 2304248 *Security alarms installers*

Barbara Caterers Hire, 20 Almond Crescent, Swanpool, Swanpool, Lincoln, LN6 0HN Tel: (01522) 859457 *Catering equipment hire*

Barber Bros, Unit 1-6 Clifton Road Industrial Estate, Clifton Road, Balsall Heath, Birmingham, B12 8SX Tel: 0121-440 4737 Fax: 0121-440 2480 *Fire extinguisher refillers*

Barber Pumps Ltd, Jacksons Yard, Douglas Road North, Fulwood, Preston, PR2 3QH Tel: (01772) 715502 Fax: (01772) 712716 E-mail: barberpumps@aol.com *Specialist pump distributors, agents & stockholders for the building services industry*

Barber Refrigeration, Hazelwood Row, Cwmavon, Port Talbot, West Glamorgan, SA12 9DP Tel: (01639) 871675 Fax: (01639) 871675 E-mail: barber.refridge@btconnect.com *Repairers & restorers of refrigeration equipment*

Barber Wilson & Co. Ltd, Crawley Road, London, N22 6AH Tel: (020) 8888 3461 Fax: (020) 8888 2041 E-mail: sales@barwil.co.uk *Water fittings manufrs*

Barbican Centre, Silk Street, Barbican, London, EC2Y 8DS Tel: (020) 7382 7043 Fax: (020) 7382 7237 E-mail: admin@barbican.org.uk *Conferences & arts specialists*

Barbour ABI, Hinderton Piont, Lloyd Drive, Cheshire Oaks, Ellesmere Port, CH65 9HQ Tel: 0151 353 3512 Fax: 0151 353 3637 E-mail: info@barbour-abi.com *Barbour ABI delivers construction sales leads about construction contracts to industry professionals. Our extensive database of construction projects covers 0% of all planning applications throughout the UK.*

Barbour Engineering Ltd, 3 Balloo Avenue, Bangor, County Down, BT19 7QT Tel: (028) 9146 6622 Fax: (028) 9146 6535 *Fabrication engineers services*

▶ Barbour European Ltd, Craig Leith Road, Springkerse Industrial Estate, Stirling, FK7 7BA Tel: (07764) 162640

Barbour Index, Kingswood, Kings Ride, Ascot, Berkshire, SL5 8AD Tel: (01344) 884999 Fax: (01344) 899377 E-mail: reception@barbourindex.co.uk *Specialist information services*

Barbra Coats Ltd, Hilden Mill, Lisburn, County Antrim, BT27 4RR Tel: (028) 9267 2231 Fax: (028) 9267 8048 E-mail: mail@coats.com *Sewing thread*

Barbrak Ltd, 5 Eden Court, Eden Way, Leighton Buzzard, Bedfordshire, LU7 4FY Tel: (01525) 376605 Fax: (01525) 370505 E-mail: chris@barbrak.co.uk *Construction equipment specialists*

Barbuys Bar Equipment, 19 Index Drive, Dunstable, Bedfordshire, LU6 3TU Tel: (01582) 605477 Fax: (01582) 605477 *Bar equipment supplier*

Barcare Supreme Ltd, 39 Railway Street, Stafford, ST16 2DS Tel: (01785) 247267 Fax: (01785) 247311 *Bar suppliers*

Barcham Sewing Machinery, 59 Harbour Street, Whitstable, Kent, CT5 1AG Tel: (01227) 264271 Fax: (01227) 264271 E-mail: sales@barchams.co.uk *Sewing machine suppliers & repair service*

Barchem Construction Ltd, 3 Barton Court, 11-12 High Street, Highworth, Swindon, SN6 7AG Tel: (01793) 762380 Fax: (01793) 766005 E-mail: barchonpr@aol.com *Building contractors*

▶ Barclay Bros Ltd, Station Road, Methil, Leven, Fife, KY8 3HA Tel: (01333) 422955 Fax: (01333) 422966

▶ Barclay Communications, Grove House, 145-149 Donegall Passage, Belfast, BT7 1DT Tel: (028) 9096 0366 Fax: (028) 9023 2679 E-mail: info@barclaycomms.com *Business to Business mobile phone specialists.*

Barclay Engineering, Southend Arterial Road, Gallows Corner, Romford, RM3 0BZ Tel: (01708) 345390 Fax: (01708) 370047 E-mail: terry.barclay@lineone.net Purchasing Contact: T. Barclay Sales Contact: T. Barclay Principal Export Areas: Worldwide *Press tool, spark erosion machining & wire erosion machining services*

J.H. Barclay & Co., 53 Burnfield Road, Giffnock, Glasgow, G46 7PY Tel: 0141-638 9382 Fax: 0141-638 9848 E-mail: solutions@jhbarclay.co.uk *Dimensional measuring equipment manufrs*

Jack Barclay Ltd, 18 Berkeley Square, London, W1J 6AE Tel: (020) 7629 7444 Fax: (020) 7629 8258 E-mail: administration@jackbarclay.co.uk *Motor vehicle body builders*

Barclay & Mathieson Ltd, Cloverhill Road, Bridge of Don, Aberdeen, AB23 8FE Tel: (01224) 702771 Fax: (01224) 826227 E-mail: aberdeen@bmsteel.co.uk *Steel stockholders*

Barclay & Mathieson Ltd, 180 Hardgate Road, Glasgow, G51 4TB Tel: 0141-445 6161 Fax: 0141-445 6964 E-mail: admin@bmsteel.co.uk *Steel stockholders*

Barclay & Mathieson Ltd, Arnold Road, Nottingham, NG6 0EF Tel: 0115-970 1171 Fax: 0115-942 2181 E-mail: nottingham@bmsteel.co.uk *Steel stockholders*

Barclay & Mathieson Ltd, Coleford Road, Sheffield, S9 5NF Tel: 0114-244 2094 Fax: 0114-243 5965 E-mail: sheffield@bmsteel.co.uk *Steel stockholders*

Barclay & Purvis Ltd, 8 Baker St, Weybridge, Surrey, KT13 8AU Tel: (01932) 845247 Fax: (01932) 850448

Barclay Tarpaulins, New Beke Hall, Beke Hall Chase South, Rayleigh, Essex, SS6 9EX Tel: (01268) 780353 Fax: (01268) 780353 E-mail: enquiries@barcleytarpaulin.co.uk *PVC coated fabric manufrs*

Barclays Capital, 7th Floor, 5 North Colonnade, London, E14 4BB Tel: (020) 7623 2323 Fax: (020) 7621 5290 *Investment bankers*

Barclays Mercantile Business Finance Ltd, Churchill Plaza, Churchill Way, Basingstoke, Hampshire, RG21 7GP Tel: (01256) 314108 Fax: (01256) 791850 E-mail: bassf@barclays.co.uk *Finance company* Also at: Branches throughout the U.K.

▶ Barclays Print, 6 Dorma Trading Park, Staffa Road, London, E10 7QX Tel: (020) 8556 5955 Fax: (020) 8556 2134 E-mail: admin@barclaysprint.co.uk

Barcode Concepts, 4 Beckfield Drive, Glasgow, G33 1SF Tel: 0141-558 3311 Fax: 0141-558 3322 E-mail: 2johnl@barcodeconcept.com *Bar-coding field service.*

Barcode Connections Ltd, 18 King Harry Lane, St. Albans, Hertfordshire, AL3 4AR Tel: (01727) 833391 Fax: (01727) 838819 E-mail: info@tele-ticket.co.uk Principal Export Areas: Africa *Bar code equipment distributors & bar code system manufrs*

▶ Barcodesolutions, Faraday House, Wolfreton Drive, Anlaby, Hull, HU10 7BY Tel: 08454 300798 Fax: 08454 300799 E-mail: david.newton@barcodesolutions.co.uk *Supplier of Thermal Printheads, Auto-id products, Thermal Printers, Scanners and Maintenace Contracts. For all the major manufacturers including Intermec, Datamax, Sato, Tec, Markem, Zebra and Avery.*

Barcol Ltd, Oak Lodge, Studland Avenue, Wickford, Essex, SS12 0JF Tel: (01268) 764642 Fax: (01268) 764644 *Diamond drilling & cutting services*

▶ Barcon Systems Ltd, Unit 12a Horwich Loco Industrial Estate, Chorley New Road, Horwich, Bolton, BL6 5UE Tel: (01204) 690088 Fax: (01204) 690779

▶ Barconn Ltd, Roostinghill Gravel Pit, Beetley, Dereham, Norfolk, NR20 4DH Tel: (01362) 869089 Fax: (01362) 860555

Bard Holdings Ltd, Forest House, Brighton Road, Crawley, West Sussex, RH11 9BP Tel: (01293) 527888 Fax: (01293) 552428 *Bio-feedback equipment suppliers*

Bardek Precision Tools, Britten Street, Redditch, Worcestershire, B97 6HD Tel: (01527) 67358 Fax: (01527) 65145 *Machine tool manufrs*

Barden Engineering, Unit 20-21 Joseph Wilson Industrial Estate, Millstrood Road, Whitstable, Kent, CT5 1PP Tel: (01227) 272665 Fax: (01227) 770268 *Toolmaking specialists*

Barden Print Ltd, Bay Hall Print Works, Common Road, Huddersfield, HD1 5EU Tel: (01484) 422522 Fax: (01484) 435158 E-mail: design@bardenprint.com *Offset printers & website design services*

Barden Roofing Services, 199 Alverthorpe Road, Wakefield, West Yorkshire, WF2 9PT Tel: (01924) 378094 Fax: (01924) 378094 *Suspended ceiling installation services*

Bardini Bros, 1a St Johns Avenue, London, NW10 4ED Tel: (07811) 105727 Fax: (020) 8961 2526 *Joinery*

Bardini Plastics, Unit 4 Ellesmere, Manners Industrial Estate, Ilkeston, Derbyshire, DE7 8EF Tel: 0115-944 2733 Fax: 0115-944 2723 E-mail: bardini@bigfoot.com *Plastic extrusion manufrs*

▶ Bardo Environmental, Brunel Gate, Harworth, Doncaster, South Yorkshire, DN11 8QB Tel: (01302) 755821 Fax: (01302) 755824 E-mail: davidd@bardoenvironmental.co.uk *Retailers of washroom & hygiene products*

▶ Bardo Midlands, 115 Spalding Road, Deeping St. James, Peterborough, PE6 8SD Tel: (01778) 345609 Fax: (01778) 349258 E-mail: bardo.midlands@btconnect.com

▶ Bardon Aggregate, Fledmyre Quarry, Forfar, Angus, DD8 2HX Tel: (01307) 464728

Bardon Aggregates Ltd, Thorney Mill Road, West Drayton, Middlesex, UB7 7EZ Tel: (01895) 442852 Fax: (01895) 421464 *Aggregate producers*

Bardon Concrete Ltd, Lichfield Road, Barton under Needwood, Burton-on-Trent, Staffordshire, DE13 8EF Tel: (01283) 712677 Fax: (01283) 716598 E-mail: general@aggregate.com *Sand & ready mixed concrete*

Bardon Concrete Ltd, Stephenson Industrial Estate, Willowholme, Carlisle, CA2 5RN Tel: (01228) 599980 Fax: (01228) 599980 *Quarry & concrete (ready mixed) manufrs*

Bardon Concrete Ltd, Eskett Quarry, Eskett, Frizington, Cumbria, CA26 3UN Tel: (01946) 862414 Fax: (01946) 862757 E-mail: general@aggregate.com *Concrete (ready-mixed) manufrs*

Bardon Concrete Ltd, Balmore Road, Torrance, Glasgow, G64 4AF Tel: (01360) 622135 Fax: (01360) 620575 *Ready mixed concrete suppliers*

Bardon Concrete Ltd, Unit 7, Robert Way, Wickford, Essex, SS11 8DD Tel: (01268) 769696 Fax: (01268) 769097 *Ready-mixed concrete suppliers*

▶ Bardon Contracts Ltd, 45-47 River View, Chadwell St Mary, Grays, Essex, RM16 4BJ Tel: (01375) 841555

Bardon Engineering, 9 Douglas Court, Eleventh Avenue, Team Valley Trading Estate, Gateshead, Tyne & Wear, NE11 0JY Tel: 0191-482 4407 Fax: 0191-482 4407 *Engineering fabricators*

▶ Bardon Musker Ltd, Unit 9, Guild Hall Industrial Estate, Sandal Stones Road, Doncaster, South Yorkshire, DN3 1QR Tel: (01302) 886102 Fax: (01302) 887632 E-mail: bardonmusker@aol.com

Bardon Vectis Ltd, St Georges Down, Blackwater, Newport, Isle of Wight, PO30 3BX Tel: (01983) 524822 Fax: (01983) 825676 *Quarrying & building services*

▶ Bardra Building Services Ltd, 43 London Road, Brentwood, Essex, CM14 4NN Tel: (01277) 211609 Fax: (01277) 262726

▶ Sarah Bardsley Contemporary Artist, Church Fields, Nutley, Uckfield, East Sussex, TN22 3NA Tel: (07884) 495007 E-mail: info@artbyslb.co.uk *I take commisions for individuals or businesses. Contemporary artwork in acrylics on canvases or framed. I always have a selection of work for sale. I will take commisions for short deadlines. Please call to discuss your requirements.*

S.P. Bardwell Ltd, Mapledean Indi Estate, Maldon Rado, Latchingdon, Chelmsford, CM3 6LG Tel: (01621) 742742 Fax: (01621) 741723 E-mail: steve@spbardwell.co.uk *Civil engineers*

Bardyke Chemicals Ltd, Hamilton Road, Cambuslang, Glasgow, G72 7XJ Tel: (01698) 823361 Fax: (01698) 820535 E-mail: sales@bardyke.com *Copper compounds*

Fred Bare Ltd, 74 Alexandra National Ho, Seven Sister Rd, London, N4 2PE Tel: (07958) 955707 *Hotel & corporate uniform suppliers*

Barenson Engineering Co., Deseronto Estate, St Marys Road, Slough, SL3 7EW Tel: (01753) 543140 Fax: (01753) 540615 E-mail: info@barenson.co.uk *Precision engineers*

David Barfield Associates, Tylston Cottage, Tunbridge Lane, Liphook, Hampshire, GU30 7QA Tel: (01428) 723325 Fax: (01428) 723325 E-mail: dab295@aol.com *Engineering consultancy covering structural engineering*

Barfield UK Ltd, 3A Parker Road, Bournemouth, BH9 1AX Tel: (01202) 515132 Fax: (01202) 515133 E-mail: sales@barfielduk.com *E M I shielding products*

▶ Barfil Management Centre, Barfil Farm, Crocketford, Dumfries, DG2 8RW Tel: (01387) 266079 Fax: (01387) 266118

▶ Barfoot & Powell Ltd, Coal Park Lane, Swanwick, Southampton, SO31 7GW Tel: (01489) 576281 Fax: (01489) 576298

Barford Bros Ltd, 111 North Street, Luton, LU2 7QG Tel: (01582) 720371 Fax: (01582) 611098 *Dyers to the millinery trade*

▶ Barford Sails, 11 Nothe Parade, Weymouth, Dorset, DT4 8TX Tel: (01305) 768282 *Sail manufrs*

Bargain Bedstores Ltd, 155 Hornsey Road, London, N7 6DU Tel: (020) 7609 6320 Fax: (020) 7278 6025 *Furniture & bedding retail*

Bargain Buys, 35 Shafto Way, Newton Aycliffe, County Durham, DL5 5QN Tel: (01325) 321678 *Washing machines*

▶ Bargain Outlet Ltd, Unit 18 Mildmay House, Foundry Lane, Burnham-on-Crouch, Essex, CM0 8BL Tel: (0871) 2211422 Fax: (01621) 781199 E-mail: sales@bargainoutlet.co.uk *Computer software developers*

Bargate Computer Services, Suite 3, 84 High Street, Burton-on-Trent, Staffordshire, DE14 1LJ Tel: (01283) 510249 Fax: (01283) 512330 E-mail: bargate@internet-uk.net *Computer manufrs*

Bargate International Ltd, 6 Premier Court, Boarden Close, Moulton Park Industrial Estate, Northampton, NN3 6LF Tel: (01604) 679500 Fax: (01604) 495919 E-mail: sales@bargateinternational.com *Import & export agents freight forwarders*

▶ Barhale Construction plc, Redburn Industrial Estate, Woodall Road, Enfield, Middlesex, EN3 4LE Tel: (020) 8443 0333 Fax: (020) 8804 9597 E-mail: info@barhale.co.uk

▶ Barhale Construction plc, Bushey & Oxhey Railway Yard, Pinner Road, Watford, WD19 4EA Tel: (01923) 800864 Fax: 01923 655656 E-mail: info@barhale.co.uk

Barham & Moore Ltd, 8 Grafton Place, Chelmsford, CM2 6TG Tel: (01245) 450554 Fax: (01245) 450845 E-mail: sales@barham-print.co.uk *Renting agents services*

Baric Systems, 11 Telford Court, Morpeth, Northumberland, NE61 2DB Tel: (01670) 505944 Fax: (01670) 505923 E-mail: sales@baricsale.co.uk *Lube seal oil & control systems*

Baring Asset Management, 155 Bishopsgate, London, EC2M 3XY Tel: (020) 7628 6000 Fax: (020) 7638 7928 E-mail: enquiries@baring-asset.com *Pension fund & charity investment finance*

Baring Insulation Ltd, Unit A, 223A Hatfield Road, St. Albans, Hertfordshire, AL1 4TB Tel: (01727) 860004 Fax: (01727) 847253 E-mail: admin@baringinsulation.co.uk *Insulation contractors*

Barkat Knitwear Manufacturing Co. Ltd, 64-66 Dale Street, Manchester, M1 2HR Tel: 0161-832 3388 Fax: 0161-228 7465 *Knitwear manufrs*

Barkby Knives Ltd, 41 Cannock Street, Leicester, LE4 9HR Tel: 0116-276 1101 Fax: 0116-233 2433 E-mail: sales@barkbyknives.co.uk *Knife manufrs*

Barke Machinery Ltd, 274 Manchester Road, Audenshaw, Manchester, M34 5GL Tel: 0161-370 1313 Fax: 0161-301 5993 E-mail: info@barke.demon.co.uk *Textile machinery agents*

Barker, 44 Main Street, Irton, Scarborough, North Yorkshire, YO12 4RH Tel: (01723) 865044

Barker Billiards, 32 Greenhead Gardens, Chapeltown, Sheffield, S35 1AR Tel: 0114-245 6738 Fax: 0114-245 6738 *Snooker, billiards & pool table distributors*

Barker Brettell Ltd, 138 Hagley Road, Birmingham, B16 9PW Tel: 0121-456 1364 Fax: 0121-456 1368 E-mail: admin@barkerbrettell.co.uk *Chartered patent attorneys* Also at: Cambridge, Gloucester, Southampton, Telford & Worcester

Barker Bros Aggregates Ltd, The Green, Railway Road, Downham Market, Norfolk, PE38 9DY Tel: (01366) 382525 Fax: (01366) 383002 *Aggregates distributors & manufrs*

▶ Barker Building Ltd, Dormston Trading Estate, Burton Road, Dudley, West Midlands, DY1 2UF Tel: (01902) 885098

John Barker & Dixon Ltd, Lincoln Works, Smithfield, Sheffield, S3 7AR Tel: 0114-272 4962 Fax: 0114-276 0299 *Cutlery manufrs*

J. Barker Electrical Services Ltd, The Old School Buildings, Churchill Street, Hull, HU9 1RR Tel: (01482) 588500 Fax: (01482) 594699 E-mail: enquiries@jbe1.com *Electrical contractors*

Barker Ross Contracts, 7 Faraday Court, 36 Conduit Street, Leicester, LE2 0JN Tel: 0116-255 1055 Fax: 0116-255 0811 E-mail: recruitment@barkerross.co.uk *Recruitment agency*

Barker Shoes Sales Ltd, 3 Station Road, Earls Barton, Northampton, NN6 0NT Tel: (01604) 810387 Fax: (01604) 812350 E-mail: barker@barkershoes.co.uk *Shoe manufrs*

Barker & Simpkins Ltd, 205 Wincolmlee, Hull, HU2 0PZ Tel: (01482) 320151 Fax: (01482) 320199 *Precision machinists*

C.F. Barker & Sons (Marquees) Ltd, 47 Osborne Road, Thornton Heath, Surrey, CR7 8PD Tel: (01883) 337099 Fax: (020) 8653 2932 *Tent & marquee manufrs & Hire*

George Barker (Transport) Ltd, Gallions Close, Thames Road, Barking, Essex, IG11 0JD Tel: (020) 8594 7911 Fax: (020) 8591 8828 *Refrigerated transport contractors*

Barkers Engineering, Etna Works, Duke Street, Stoke-on-Trent, ST4 3NS Tel: (01782) 319264 Fax: (01782) 599724 E-mail: sales.enquiries@churchill.com *General engineering services*

Barkers International Communication Ltd, Barkers Lane, Bedford, MK41 9TR Tel: (01234) 327772 Fax: (01234) 325526 E-mail: richard@barkers-int.co.uk *Computer network installers*

▶ Barkers Plumbing Services, 83 Sketchley Road, Burbage, Hinckley, Leicestershire, LE10 2DU Tel: (01455) 446784 E-mail: barkersplumbingservices@ntlworld.com

Barking & Dagenham Chamber Of Commerce, Suite A Roycraft House, 15 Linton Road, Barking, Essex, IG11 8HE Tel: (020) 8591 6966 Fax: (020) 8594 1576 E-mail: info@bdchamber.co.uk *Chamber of commerce, business support & networking services*

Barking Electronics, 432 Barking Rd, London, E6 2SA Tel: 020 84707722 Fax: 020 84707788 *Install, supply & repair technical equipment*

Barking Engineering, Barking Forge, Barking, Ipswich, IP6 8HJ Tel: (01449) 720087 Fax: (01449) 723131 *Wrought iron suppliers*

▶ Barking Mad, Wishing Well Cottage, 285 Headley Road East, Woodley, Reading, RG5 4SE Tel: 0118 9693115 E-mail: val.walls@barkingmad.uk.com *Barking Mad provides an alternative to kennelling where pets stay with a select host family whose environment is similar to their own and where daily home life routine can be maintained.*

Barking Shopfronts Ltd, Unit 1 Barking Industrial Park, Alfreds Way, Barking, Essex, IG11 0TJ Tel: (020) 8591 0504 Fax: (020) 8594 3060 *Shop front fitters*

Barkley Plastics Ltd, 120 Highgate Street, Birmingham, B12 0XR Tel: 0121-440 1303 Fax: 0121-440 4902 E-mail: mharwood@barkley.co.uk *Plastic injection moulding manufrs*

Barkshire Group, 40 Ivanhoe Road, Hogwood Industrial Estate, Finchampstead, Wokingham, Berkshire, RG40 4QQ Tel: 0118-973 2919 Fax: 0118-973 0899 E-mail: sales@barkshiregroup.co.uk *Stationery & furnishing supplies*

▶ Barkston Plastics Ltd, D5-D7 Unit, Drypool Way, Hull, HU9 1LG Tel: (01482) 323886 Fax: (01482) 214193 E-mail: mailbox@barkstonltd.co.uk *Plastic materials products distributors*

Barkwood Ltd, 5 Erb Buildings, Claybank Road, Portsmouth, PO3 5NQ Tel: (023) 9265 2078 Fax: (023) 9265 2063 E-mail: barkwoodmetalspinners@hotmail.com Sales Contact: B. Trend *Metal spinners & sheetmetal fabrication engineers. Also welding services, & can supply your product painted or plated*

Anthony Barkworth, Dorchester Road, Lytchett Minster, Poole, Dorset, BH16 6HS Tel: (01202) 632838 Fax: (01202) 632838 *Furniture manufrs*

Barlass Shutters Ltd, 59 Shaw Street, Liverpool, L6 1HL Tel: 0151-427 1340 Fax: 0151-207 2801 *Steel roller shutter manufrs*

Barley Chalu Ltd, Ayton Road, Wymondham, Norfolk, NR18 0QH Tel: (01953) 602771 Fax: (01953) 606631 E-mail: sales@barleychalu.co.uk *Powder coating services*

Barley Mow Reprographics Ltd, 10 Barley Mow Passage, London, W4 4PH Tel: (020) 8995 7042 Fax: (020) 8747 8530 E-mail: enjayrepro@btinternet.com *Reprographic printing services, photocopying*

Barley Reproduction, Arch 3 Pedley Street, London, E1 5EW Tel: (020) 7377 2081 Fax: (020) 7247 9241 *Furniture reproduction*

Barlis Pine Ltd, 5-6 Tentercroft Street Industrial Estate, Lincoln, LN5 7ED Tel: (01522) 567745 Fax: (01522) 544336 E-mail: barlispine@hotmail.com *Pine furniture, fixture, fixing suppliers & manufrs*

Barllaeth Bakery & Confectionery Supplies, London House, St Peters Square, Ruthin, Clwyd, LL15 1AA Tel: (01824) 707000 *Sandwich suppliers*

Barlow Blinds Ltd, 54 Uppingham Road, Leicester, LE5 0QE Tel: 0116-276 9771 Fax: 0116-246 0490 E-mail: brian@barlow-bellows.co.uk *Manufacturers of industrial & protective bellows & blinds*

Barlow Farm Services Ltd, New Farm, Wilkin Hill, Barlow, Dronfield, Derbyshire, S18 7TE Tel: 0114-289 0209 Fax: 0114-289 1496 *Animal health remedies & health foods*

Barlow Tyrie Ltd, Springwood Industrial Estate, Braintree, Essex, CM7 2RN Tel: (01376) 557600 Fax: (01376) 557610 E-mail: sales.uk@teak.com *Outdoor leisure furniture manufrs*

Barloworld, 2 Brook Office Park, Emersons Green, Bristol, BS16 7FL Tel: 0117-970 9450 Fax: 0117-982 1465 E-mail: marketing@handling.barloworld.co.uk *Fork lift truck distributors*

Barloworld Handling Ltd, Unit 1 Minto Drive, Altens Industrial Estate, Aberdeen, AB12 3LW Tel: (01224) 878959 Fax: (01224) 896226 E-mail: aberdeen@handling.barloworld.co.uk *Fork lift truck distributors.*

Barloworld Handling Ltd, Portobello Road, Birtley, Chester Le Street, County Durham, DH3 2RZ Tel: 0191-410 6221 Fax: 0191-410 5795 E-mail: birtley@handling.barloworld.co.uk *Fork lift truck distributors & materials handling*

Barloworld Handling Ltd, 6 Rutherford Road, Dryburgh Industrial Estate, Dundee, DD2 3XH Tel: (01382) 811523 Fax: (01382) 858640 E-mail: sales@barlow.co.uk *Fork lift truck distributors.*

Barloworld Handling Ltd, Unit G Cumbernauld Business Park, Wardlaw Road, Cumbernauld, Glasgow, G67 3JZ Tel: (01236) 725061 Fax: (01236) 736212 E-mail: cumbernauld@handling.barloworld.co.uk *Fork lift truck distributors.*

Barloworld Handling Ltd, Farthing Road Indust Estate, Ipswich, IP1 5BL Tel: (01473) 740241 Fax: (01473) 740903 *Fork lift truck distributors*

Barloworld Handling Ltd, Barlow House, Howley Park Road East, Morley, Leeds, LS27 0SW Tel: 0113-252 1711 Fax: 0113-253 4339 *The distribution of fork lift trucks & materials handling equipment*

Barloworld Handling Ltd, Unit 4, Vitruvius Way, Meridian Business Park, Leicester, LE19 1WA Tel: 0116-282 7500 Fax: 0116-282 3888 *Fork lift truck distribs*

Barloworld Handling Ltd, Unit 5 Burrington Way, Plymouth, PL5 3LR Tel: (01752) 782540 Fax: (01752) 768467 E-mail: plymouth@handling.barloworld.co.uk *Fork lift truck distributors.*

Barloworld Handling Ltd, Barlow House, Dolphin Way, Purfleet, Essex, RM19 1NZ Tel: (01708) 257300 Fax: (01708) 257310 E-mail: haydock@handling.barloworld.co.uk Principal Export Areas: Worldwide *Fork lift trucks & handling equipment supply & hire*

Barloworld Handling Ltd, Unit 1 30 Stevenston Industrial Estate, Stevenston, Ayrshire, KA20 3LR Tel: (01294) 463350 Fax: (01294) 462410 E-mail: knelson@handling.barloworld.co.uk *Fork lift truck retailers*

Barloworld Handling Ltd, Barlow House, Yew Tree Way, Golborne, Warrington, WA3 3JD Tel: (01942) 721111 Fax: (01942) 408100 E-mail: warrington@handling.barloworld.co.uk *Fork lift truck distributors*

Barloworld Handling Ltd, 2 Cygnus Way, West Bromwich, West Midlands, B70 0XB Tel: 0121-521 2500 Fax: 0121-521 2550 E-mail: birmingham@barlow.co.uk *Fork lift trucks*

Barloworld Handling Ltd, 104 Coed Aben, Wrexham, Clwyd, LL13 9NY Tel: (01978) 661333 Fax: (01978) 664234 E-mail: wrexham@handling.barloworld.co.uk *Material handling specialists services*

Barloworld Vacuum Technology P.L.C, Harbour Road, Gosport, Hampshire, PO12 1BG Tel: (0870) 0107666 Fax: (0870) 0106916 E-mail: marketing@barloworldvt.com *Conveying system manufrs*

Barlows Boards Ltd, 8 Rushey Lane, Birmingham, B11 2BL Tel: 0121-706 2067 Fax: 0121-707 9550 E-mail: bugbashbar@yahoo.co.uk *Sheet materials & worktops*

Barlows Electrical, St.Josephs Bus Park, 3 St. Josephs Close, Hove, East Sussex, BN3 7EZ Tel: (01273) 710077 Fax: (01273) 710066 E-mail: office@barlowselectrical.co.uk

Barlows Securities plc, Chepstow House, Dee Hills Park, Chester, CH3 5AR Tel: (01244) 350202 Fax: (01244) 311522 *Commercial property development & investment*

Barlows & Sons Hermitage Ltd, Red Shute Hill Industrial Estate, Red Shute Hill, Hermitage, Thatcham, Berkshire, RG18 9QL Tel: (01635) 200253 Fax: (01635) 201092 *Timber & fencing merchants*

▶ Barmaid Joinery Manufacturers, 3 Wesley Street, Swinton, Manchester, M27 6AD Tel: 0161-728 1122 Fax: 0161-728 2233 *Bespoke joiners & bar manufrs*

The Barn, 48 Walcott Road, Billinghay, Lincoln, LN4 4EH Tel: (01526) 861881 Fax: (01526) 861881 *Furniture manufrs*

Barn Glassworks Ltd, 7 Sandiford Road, Sutton, Surrey, SM3 9RN Tel: (020) 8644 7444 Fax: (020) 8641 5853 *Patent glazing contractors*

Barn Studios, The Old Barn Manor Farm, Woodstock Lane South, Claygate, Esher, Surrey, KT10 0TA Tel: (01372) 467755 *Cabinet makers*

Barnaby Climax Ltd, White Ladies Close, Little London, Worcester, WR1 1PZ Tel: (01905) 22014 Fax: (01905) 723828 E-mail: wildon@sweepaxpumps.co.uk *Water pump manufrs*

Barnard Mircosystems Ltd, 134 Crouch Hill, London, N8 9DX Tel: (020) 8341 0566 E-mail: enquiries@barnardmicrosystems.com *Software development consultants*

Barnards Ceilings & Partitions Ltd, Mulberry House, Holders Green, Lindsell, Dunmow, Essex, CM6 3QQ Tel: (01371) 870104 Fax: (01371) 870105 *Ceiling (suspended) systems, partition installers & suppliers*

Barnbrook Systems Ltd, 25 Fareham Park Road, Fareham, Hampshire, PO15 6LD Tel: (01329) 847722 Fax: (01329) 844132 E-mail: barnbrook@aol.co.uk *Electro mechanical component manufrs*

Barnby Engineering, 2 Lakeside Park, Neptune Close, Medway City Estate, Rochester, Kent, ME2 4LT Tel: (01634) 711801 Fax: (01634) 711766 *Engineers*

Barnes Branch & Co Ltd, Brook Street, High Wycombe, Buckinghamshire, HP11 2EQ Tel: (01494) 525761 Fax: (01494) 464582 E-mail: sales@barnesbranch.demon.co.uk *Timber merchants*

Barnes E A & Sons Ltd, Unit 5, Vulcan Road, Lichfield, Staffordshire, WS13 6RW Tel: (01543) 250480 Fax: (01543) 250480 E-mail: sales@eabarnes.co.uk *Waste disposal & steel merchants*

Barnes & Gannon Ltd, Charles House, Royle Barn Road, Rochdale, Lancashire, OL11 3DT Tel: (01706) 344997 Fax: (01706) 641653 E-mail: sales@aqua-check.co.uk *Non-return water valves, check valves & automatic repetition work*

Grant Barnes & Son, Horsefair, Malmesbury, Wiltshire, SN16 0AP Tel: (01666) 822316 Fax: (01666) 822316 *Saddlers & riding wear*

Barnes Group Ltd, 6 Bermuda Road, Ransoms Euro Park, Ipswich, IP3 9RU Tel: (01473) 272222 Fax: (01473) 272955 E-mail: cbruce@barnesconstruction.co.uk *Building contractors & construction*

Barnes Interiors Ltd, Unit 1 Urban Hive 410, Avenue West Syline 120, Great Notley, Braintree, Essex, CM77 7AA Tel: (01376) 528627 Fax: (01376) 325935 E-mail: info@barnesinteriors.co.uk *Partitions & suspended ceilings installators*

Barnes Lifting Services Ltd, Station Works, Main Road, Unstone, Dronfield, Derbyshire, S18 4AQ Tel: (01246) 417941 Fax: (01246) 410244 *Chain sling & tackle manufrs*

Barnes Of Lincoln Ltd, Fort Barnes, Freeman Road, North Hykeham, Lincoln, LN6 9AP Tel: (01522) 686404 Fax: (01522) 681000 *Removals & storage service*

Barnes Morris Steels, Bay 3 5 Grazebrook Industrial Park, Peartree Lane, Dudley, West Midlands, DY2 0XW Tel: (01384) 233393 Fax: (01384) 253111 E-mail: info@barnesmorris.co.uk *Steel stockholders*

Neville Barnes Ltd, Padmoor Lane, Upton, Gainsborough, Lincolnshire, DN21 5NH Tel: (01427) 838245 Fax: (01427) 838417 *Agricultural engineers*

Barnes Plastic Welding Equipment Ltd, Unit 4 New Plough Yard, Queen Street, Great Harwood, Blackburn, BB6 7AX Tel: (01254) 882525 *Welding equipment distributors*

Barnes Steel Fabrications, 3 Brooklyn Farm, North Hill, Horndon-on-the-Hill, Stanford-le-Hope, Essex, SS17 8QA Tel: (01375) 644048 Fax: (01375) 644049 *Steel fabricators*

Barnes & Thomas Ltd, Cheetham Mill, Park Street, Stalybridge, Cheshire, SK15 2BT Tel: 0161-338 3630 Fax: 0161-304 8055 E-mail: brian_richard@barnesandthomas.com *Engineers*

▶ Barnes Webster & Sons Ltd, 29 Crown Street, Brentwood, Essex, CM14 4BA Tel: (01277) 233344 Fax: (01277) 200379 E-mail: post@barneswebster.co.uk

Barnes & Woodhouse Cases, Commercial Street, Middlesbrough, Cleveland, TS2 1JT Tel: (01642) 224092 Fax: (01642) 251272 *Packing case suppliers*

▶ Barnet Bath & Kitchen Ltd, 2 Castle Road, St Albans, St. Albans, Hertfordshire, AL1 5DL Tel: (01727) 899155 Fax: (01727) 899153 E-mail: barnetbandk@aol.com *Bathroom fitters*

Barnet Leisure 2000, 28a Westerham Avenue, London, N9 9BU Tel: (020) 8807 3598 *Game machines manufrs*

Barnet Lock & Security, 123-125 Baker Street, Enfield, Middlesex, EN1 3HA Tel: (020) 8342 0040 Fax: (020) 8342 0230 E-mail: barnetlock@btconnect.com *Locksmiths*

Barnet Metal Engineering Co. Ltd, Stirling Works, Tewin Road, Welwyn Garden City, Hertfordshire, AL7 1AG Tel: (01707) 324327 Fax: (01707) 371375 *Steel sheet stockholders*

Barnett Confectioners Ltd, Stansfield Street, Nottingham, NG7 2AE Tel: 0115-978 4642 Fax: 0115-944 9236 *Sweet manufrs*

▶ Barnett Construction Ltd, Gannow Lane, Rose Grove, Burnley, Lancashire, BB12 6JJ Tel: (01706) 833900 Fax: (0845) 2268822

▶ Barnett Consulting Services Ltd, Providence House, River Street, Windsor, Berkshire, SL4 1QT Tel: (01753) 856723 Fax: (01753) 866297 E-mail: barnettgp@aol.com

Grant Barnett & Co. Ltd, Waterfront House, 55-61 South Street, Bishop's Stortford, Hertfordshire, CM23 3AL Tel: (01279) 758075 Fax: (01279) 758095 E-mail: enquiries@grantbarnett.com *Umbrella manufacturers & distributors*

Barnett Lawson Trimmings Ltd, 16-17 Little Portland Street, London, W1W 8NE Tel: (020) 7636 8591 Fax: (020) 7580 0669 E-mail: info@bltrimmings.com *Wholesale trimmings*

Barnett Window Blinds, 66 Dunmore Road, Ballynahinch, County Down, BT24 8PR Tel: (028) 9756 2635 Fax: (028) 9756 1174 *Blind manufrs*

Barnetts Buglawton, 24 Brook Street, Congleton, Cheshire, CW12 1RH Tel: (01260) 273170 Fax: (01260) 298150 E-mail: barnetsbuglawltd@thomasarmstrong.co.uk *Concrete blocks manufrs*

Barnetts Of Canterbury, 1 Wealden Forest Park, Herne Common, Herne Bay, Kent, CT6 7LQ Tel: (01227) 710174 Fax: (01227) 713113 *Steel stockholders & fabricators*

▶ Barnetts Catering Co., Burnmill Depot, Philiphaugh, Selkirk, TD7 5AU Tel: (01750) 23333 *Catering & hospitality services*

Barneys Advertising Ltd, Royal London Buildings, 42-46 Baldwin Street, Bristol, BS1 1PN Tel: 0117-921 4551 Fax: 0117-926 2529 E-mail: info@barneys.co.uk *Advertising agents & public relations services*

▶ Barney's Bouncers, 54 Foster Road, Kempston, Bedford, MK42 8BU Tel: (01234) 303823 *Bouncy castle hire*

▶ Barneys Sarnies, Byron House, Westbury Road, Nottingham, NG5 1EJ Tel: 0115-970 6661 Fax: 0115-970 6669 E-mail: barneysarnies@tiscali.co.uk *Catering manufrs*

Barnfather Wire Ltd, Willenhall Road, Wednesbury, West Midlands, WS10 8JG Tel: 0121-526 2880 Fax: 0121-526 3130 E-mail: sales@barnfatherwire.co.uk *Galvanised wire, cold headed wire, bright drawn wire to various specifications supplied on formers and cut to length. Size range 1.6 mm to 16 mm diameter*

▶ Dennis Barnfield Ltd, Main Bye Pass Road, Bolton le Sands, Carnforth, Lancashire, LA5 8JA Tel: (01524) 823156 Fax: (01524) 823156 *Contract plant*

Dennis Barnfield Ltd, Lodge Quarry, Carnforth, Lancashire, LA5 9DW Tel: (01524) 733422 Fax: (01524) 736450 E-mail: malcolm@dennisbarnfield.co.uk *Contractors plant sales & hire*

▶ Barnfield Engineering Services Ltd, Lane End Farm, Hatt Common, East Woodhay, Newbury, Berkshire, RG20 0NG Tel: (01635) 255330 Fax: (01635) 255338 E-mail: barnfield@btclick.com *Steel work fabrication & installation*

Barnfield Hughes Ltd, Barnfield, Leek, Staffordshire, ST13 5QG Tel: (01538) 385626 Fax: (01538) 386302 *Concrete drainage manufrs*

Barnham Telecottage, 49 Barnham Rd, Barnham, Bognor Regis, W. Sussex, PO22 0ER Tel: (01243) 553725 Fax: (01243) 554898 E-mail: barnham.telecottage@saqnet.co.uk *Computer systems*

Barnket Ltd, 128 Milton Road, Gravesend, Kent, DA12 2PG Tel: (01474) 327576 Fax: (01474) 567318 *Industrial fastener distributors*

George Barnsdale & Sons Ltd, 24 High Street, Donington, Spalding, Lincolnshire, PE11 4TA Tel: (01775) 823000 Fax: (01775) 823010 E-mail: lnewell@gbstp.com *Manufacturers of Timber Windows Doors and Stairs*

Barnshaw Plate Rollers Ltd, Anchor Lane, Coseley, Bilston, West Midlands, WV14 9NE Tel: (01902) 880250 Fax: (01902) 880505 *Plate rollers*

Barnshaw Steel Benders, 89 Bothwell Road, Hamilton, Lanarkshire, ML3 0DW Tel: (01698) 421010 Fax: (01698) 421177 E-mail: hamilton@barnshaws.com *Steel bending services*

Barnshaw's Bending Centre Ltd, 2 Arrow Trading Estate, Corporation Road, Audenshaw, Manchester, M34 5LR Tel: 0161-320 9696 Fax: 0161-335 0918 *Steel plate bendng services*

Barnshaws Plate Bending, Anchor Lane, Bilston, West Midlands, WV14 9NE Tel: (01902) 880250 Fax: (01902) 880505 *Pressing & shearing services*

Barnshaws Profiles, Anchor Lane, Bilston, West Midlands, WV14 9NE Tel: (01902) 663553 Fax: (01902) 887379 E-mail: enquiries@barnshaws.com *CAD, CAM plasma cutting services*

Barnsley Cash Registers, 2the Parade, Clough Fields Road, Hoyland, Barnsley, South Yorkshire, S74 0HR Tel: (01226) 744003 Fax: (01226) 744003 E-mail: barnsleytills@aol.com *Cash registers & scales, sales, rental & maintenance services*

▶ Barnsley Optical, Unit 16 Zenith Park, Whaley Road, Barnsley, South Yorkshire, S75 1HT Tel: (01226) 284646 Fax: (01226) 205306 E-mail: info@barnsleyoptical.co.uk *Manufacturing opticians & suppliers of prescription optical lenses*

▶ Barnsley Refrigeration Services Ltd, D Beevor Industrial Estate, Beevor Street, Barnsley, South Yorkshire, S71 1HN Tel: (01226) 732068 Fax: (01226) 732068 *Complete installation, service and repair of all types of commercial, retail and industrial refrigeration and air-conditioning systems.*

Barnsley Yesco, 17 Fishdam La, Monk Bretton, Barnsley, S. Yorkshire, S71 2PX Tel: (01226) 200338 Fax: (01226) 200338 E-mail: yesco@computers97.freeserve.co.uk *Computer maintenance & repair*

▶ Barnstaple Removals, 14-15 Tree Beech Rural Estate, Goodleigh, Barnstaple, Devon, EX32 7NZ Tel: (01271) 831164 Fax: (01271) 831165

▶ Barnstaple Sewing Machines, Hallsannery, Bideford, Devon, EX39 5HE Tel: (01237) 470032 Fax: (01237) 470032 E-mail: sewingmachines@hallsannery.go-plus.net *Needles, sewing machine manufrs*

M. Barnwell Services Ltd, 5 Bessemer Crescent, Rabans Lane Industrial Estate, Aylesbury, Buckinghamshire, HP19 8TF Tel: (01296) 431429 Fax: (01296) 435716 E-mail: aylesbury@barnwell.co.uk *Plastic seal suppliers*

Barnwood Shopfitting Ltd, 203 Barnwood Road, Gloucester, GL4 3HS Tel: (01452) 614124 Fax: (01452) 371061 E-mail: email@barnwoodshopfitting.com *Building contractors*

Baron Contracts Ltd, 72 Cross Road, Maldon, Essex, CM9 5ED Tel: (01621) 856991 Fax: (01621) 850326 *Office furnishers*

Baron Fire, Lubbards Lodge, Hullbridge Road, Rayleigh, Essex, SS6 9QG Tel: (01702) 230082 Fax: (01702) 230082 E-mail: info@baronfire.co.uk *Fire fighting equipment services*

Baron Pipework Services, Unit 2 Baron Business Centre, 75 Cemetery Road, Lye, Stourbridge, West Midlands, DY9 8AD Tel: (01384) 422082 Fax: (01384) 422082 *Pipework erection & installation contractors*

Baron Springs, Unit 3 70 Strathclyde Street, Glasgow, G40 4JR Tel: 0141-550 3477 Fax: 0141-554 7240 *Spring manufrs*

Baroney Universal Products plc, Barony Industrial Estate, Auchinleck, Cumnock, Ayrshire, KA18 2BL Tel: (01290) 426400 Fax: (01290) 426399 *Aerosol manufrs*

Barong Windows Ltd, Doves Barn, Copthorne, Felbridge, East Grinstead, West Sussex, RH19 2QQ Tel: (01342) 300903 *Replacement windows & conservatories manufacturers & installers*

▶ Baronmead International Ltd, 1 Flansham Business Centre, Hoe Lane, Flansham, Bognor Regis, West Sussex, PO22 8NJ Tel: (01243) 586692 Fax: (01243) 586312 E-mail: info@baronmead.com *Mobile stair climbers manufrs*

▶ Barons, Unit 7 Tyndall St Industrial Estate, Cardiff, CF10 4BG Tel: (029) 2046 4090 Fax: (029) 2046 3130 E-mail: admin@baronsestateagents.co.uk *Food & drink services*

Barpest Pest & Vermin Control, 42 Bittams Lane, Chertsey, Surrey, KT16 9QX Tel: (01932) 872289 Fax: (01932) 872289 *Pest control services*

Barplas Ltd, Barplas Industrial Park, Raymond Street, Bradford, West Yorkshire, BD5 8DG Tel: (01274) 727111 Fax: (01274) 726111 E-mail: ken@barplas.com *Manufacturers of plastic containers for the paint industry*

Barpoint Ltd, Willenhall Trading Estate, Midacre, Willenhall, West Midlands, WV13 2JW Tel: (01902) 608021 Fax: (01902) 601652 *Stainless steel bars*

▶ Barr Ltd, Killoch Depot, Ochiltree, Cumnock, Ayrshire, KA18 2RL Tel: (01290) 700681

▶ Barr Ltd, Maybury House, Turnhouse Road, Edinburgh, EH12 8LX Tel: 0131-339 1000

▶ Barr Ltd, Brayhead, Barrhill, Girvan, Ayrshire, KA26 0QR Tel: (01465) 821300

▶ Barr Ltd, Barr Quarry, Glenluce, Newton Stewart, Wigtownshire, DG8 0JQ Tel: (01581) 300329 Fax: (01581) 300523 *Construction*

Barr + Wray Ltd, 324 Drumoyne Road, Glasgow, G51 4DY Tel: 0141-882 5757 Fax: 0141-882 3690 E-mail: sales@barrandwray.com Principal Export Areas: Worldwide *Filtration/water treatment engineers* Also at: London

▶ Barr Construction, Dunollie Road, Oban, Argyll, PA34 5PL Tel: (01631) 567362

Barr Electrical Ltd, 1 Ladywell Road, Motherwell, Lanarkshire, ML1 3JA Tel: (01698) 263231 Fax: (01698) 263231 *Electrical contractors*

Barr & Grosvenor Ltd, Jenner Street, Wolverhampton, WV2 2AE Tel: (01902) 352390 Fax: (01902) 871342 E-mail: sales@bargrosvenorwannado.co.uk *Architectural casting restorators*

Barr Holdings Ltd, 100 Inchinnan Road, Paisley, Renfrewshire, PA3 2RE Tel: 0141-848 8000 Fax: 0141-848 8001 E-mail: info@barr.co.uk *Civil engineers, building contractors, concrete manufrs*

Barr Mason Ltd, 10 Greycaine Road, Watford, WD24 7GG Tel: (01923) 222248 Fax: (01923) 817024 E-mail: sales@barrmason.co.uk Principal Export Areas: Worldwide *Manufacturers of injection mouldings, custom, plastic (technical, industrial)*

▶ Perry Barr Fencing, 72 Walsall Road, Perry Barr, Birmingham, B42 1TX Tel: 0121-356 9405 *Fencing manufrs*

Barr Printers Glenrothes Ltd, 4 Faraday Road, Glenrothes, Fife, KY6 2RU Tel: (01592) 776870 Fax: (01592) 770779 E-mail: sales@barrprinters.co.uk *Commercial printers*

Barr R & T Electrical Ltd, 142-158 Pittencrieff Street, Dunfermline, Fife, KY12 8AN Tel: (01383) 722096 Fax: (01383) 739226 E-mail: rtbarr@hotmail.co.uk *Electrical engineers, armature winders*

Barr Radcliffe Ltd, 97 Grace Road, Leicester, LE2 8AE Tel: 0116-244 0414 Fax: 0116-244 0268 E-mail: info@barr-radcliffe.co.uk *Fashion trimmings & zip fasteners*

Barracks Fabrics Printing Co. Ltd, Caton Road, Lancaster, LA1 3PA Tel: (01524) 389308 Fax: (01524) 381057 *Textile printers.*

Joseph Barraclough Ltd, Bankfield Mills, Mirfield, West Yorkshire, WF14 9DD Tel: (01924) 493147 Fax: (01924) 490702 E-mail: info@barrayarn.co.uk *Carpet yarn spinners*

P. Barraclough & Associates Ltd, 48 Top Lane, Copmanthorpe, York, YO23 3UJ Tel: (01904) 704065 Fax: (01904) 700496 *Consulting engineers*

▶ Barracuda Safety & Training Services, 19 Kingsmead, Nailsea, North Somerset, BS48 2XH Tel: (01275) 859285 Fax: (01275) 859285 E-mail: info@barracudatraining.co.uk *Health and safety training*Manual handling training *Risk assessments*Forklift truck training*ADR training*general awareness training*dangerous goods safety advisor*health and safety advisor, MIIRSM, MIOSH,*Fire Safety Training*

▶ Barrass Hull Ltd, 16 Alfred Street, Hull, HU3 2DD Tel: (01482) 324954 Fax: (01482) 213598 E-mail: user@barrasshull.co.uk *Industrial roofing & insulation*

Barratt Homes Ltd, Barratt House Almondsbury Business Centre, Woodlands, Bradley Stoke, Bristol, BS32 4QH Tel: (01454) 202202 Fax: (01454) 612277

Barratt, Vico House, Ring Road, Lower Wortley, Leeds, LS12 6AN Tel: 0113-279 0099 Fax: 0113-279 0038 *Builders*

Barratt Computing Ltd, Larbreck House, Quernmore, Lancaster, LA2 9EF Tel: (01524) 388000 Fax: (01524) 388333 E-mail: enquiries@barcom.co.uk *Computer software data base manufrs*

Barratt Developments plc, Rotterdam House, 116 Quayside, Newcastle upon Tyne, NE1 3DA Tel: 0191-227 2000 Fax: 0191-227 2001 *Property investment services*

▶ Barratt East Midlands Ltd, 16 Regan Way, Chilwell, Beeston, Nottingham, NG9 6RZ Tel: 0115-907 8300 Fax: 0115-973 2329

Barratt East Midlands Ltd, 16 Regan Way, Chilwell, Beeston, Nottingham, NG9 6RZ Tel: 0115-907 8300 Fax: 0115-907 8301 E-mail: ianrose@barratt-eastmidlands.co.uk *Builders* Also at: Branches throughout the U.K.

▶ Barratt (East Scotland) Ltd, Craigcrook Castle, Craigcrook Road, Edinburgh, EH4 3PE Tel: 0131-336 3655

▶ Barratt Eastern Counties plc, Lorne Stewart House, 7 Springfield Lyons Approach, Springfield, Chelmsford, CM2 5EY Tel: (01245) 232200

Barratt Homes, 60 Whitehall Road, Halesowen, West Midlands, B63 3JS Tel: 0121-585 5303 Fax: 0121-585 5304 *Building contractors*

Michael Barratt, Field House, Ascot Road, Holyport, Maidenhead, Berkshire, SL6 3LD Tel: (01628) 770800 Fax: (01628) 627737 E-mail: michael@mbarrett.co.uk *Conference organising services*

Barratt Newcastle Ltd, Barratt House, City West Business Park, Newcastle upon Tyne, NE4 7DF Tel: 0191-298 6100 *Builder contractors*

Barratt & Swann, Hardigate Road, Cropwell Butler, Nottingham, NG12 3AH Tel: 0115-933 2642 Fax: 0115-933 3957 E-mail: info@barrattandswan.co.uk *Kitchen furniture manufrs*

Barratt (West Scotland) P.L.C., Mayfield House, 7 Maggie Woods Loan, Falkirk, FK1 5SJ Tel: (01324) 620011 Fax: (01324) 625916 *Home builders* Also at: Aberdeen

Barratt's International Resorts Ltd, Dalfaber Village, Aviemore, Inverness-Shire, PH22 1ST Tel: (01479) 810810 Fax: (01479) 811510 E-mail: ownerservices@mcdonald-hotel.co.uk *Management & holding company*

Barrel Lighting Ltd, Southend Airport, Southend-on-Sea, SS2 6YF Tel: (01702) 530995 Fax: (01702) 531030 E-mail: sales@barrel-lighting.com *Light fittings/ airport equipment manufrs*

Barrell Bearing, Unit G Sawtry Business Park, Sawtry, Huntingdon, Cambridgeshire, PE28 5GQ Tel: (01487) 834053 Fax: (01487) 832887 *Roller & ball bearing*

Barrett Bros Electrical Ltd, 198 Hither Green Lane, London, SE13 6QB Tel: (020) 8852 4271 Fax: (020) 8852 0892 E-mail: barrettbros@btconnect.com *Electrical contractors/building contractors*

Barrett Electrical Contracts Ltd, Unit 29 Gortrush Industrial Estate, Omagh, County Tyrone, BT78 5EJ Tel: (028) 8224 9111 Fax: (028) 8224 6815 E-mail: barrett.electric@btconnect.com *Electrical contractors*

Barrett Europe Ltd, 19 Lenten Street, Alton, Hampshire, GU34 1HG Tel: (01420) 542254 Fax: (01420) 543373 E-mail: sales@barretteurope.co.uk *Radio communication equipment services*

▶ Barrett Homes Ltd, 1 Silver Street, Kettering, Northamptonshire, NN16 0BN Tel: (01536) 511711 Fax: (01536) 511042 E-mail: liz@johnbarratt.co.uk

▶ Barrett Homes, 900 Pavilion Drive, Northampton, NN4 7RG Tel: (01604) 664500 Fax: (01604) 664501

Barrett Inter Signs Co Ltd, 18 Farlow Road, Northfield, Birmingham, B31 3AE Tel: 0121-477 7396 Fax: 0121-477 7414 *Sign contractors & suppliers*

V.O. Barrett Joinery, 4 Goodson Road, London, NW10 9LR Tel: (020) 8963 1198 Fax: (020) 8963 1231 E-mail: barretjoinery@hotmail.com *Joinery manufrs*

Joseph Barrett & Sons Ltd, 128 Eglish Road, Dungannon, County Tyrone, BT70 1LB Tel: (028) 3754 8646 Fax: (028) 3754 8863 E-mail: info@barrettconcrete.com *Concrete (ready mix) suppliers*

Barrettine (Industrial) Ltd, St. Ivel Way, Bristol, BS30 8TY Tel: 0117-960 0060 Fax: 0117-935 2437 E-mail: sales@barrettine.co.uk *Insecticide & pest control manufrs*

Barrett's, Tivoli Road, Margate, Kent, CT9 5TA Tel: (01843) 228581 Fax: (01843) 228878 *Soft drink manufrs*

Barretts Of Aspley Ltd, North Common Farm, Woburn Road, Marston Moretaine, Bedford, MK43 0NN Tel: (01525) 280136 Fax: (01525) 280137 *Steel manufrs*

▶ Barretts Bathrooms & Tiles, Derrylin, Enniskillen, County Fermanagh, BT92 9LA Tel: (028) 6774 2009 Fax: (028) 6774 8229 *Bathroom design & installation services*

Barretts Of Feckenham, Astwood Lane, Feckenham, Redditch, Worcestershire, B96 6HQ Tel: (01527) 892935 Fax: (01527) 892455 *Camping equipment suppliers*

Barretts Garden Buildings Ltd, Portsmouth Road, Ripley, Woking, Surrey, GU23 6EW Tel: (01483) 224186 E-mail: info@barrettsgardenbuildings.co.uk *Manufacture timber buildings*

Barretts Glass & Window Centre Ltd, 24a Edward Road, Dorchester, Dorset, DT1 2HL Tel: (01305) 264299 Fax: (01305) 260083 E-mail: sales@barrettsglass.com *Glazing contractors & uPVC windows*

Barretts Leisure Buildings Ltd, 347 Leverington Common, Leverington, Wisbech, Cambridgeshire, PE13 5JR Tel: (01945) 410361 Fax: (01945) 419038 E-mail: enquiries@barretts-leisure.co.uk *Agents for greenhouses*

Barric Ltd, Vinces Road, Diss, Norfolk, IP22 4WY Tel: (01379) 644202 Fax: (01379) 652361 E-mail: sales@barric.co.uk *Electronic contract manufacturing services*

Barricade Roller Shutters, 7 St. Thomas's Place, Manchester, M8 8TP Tel: 0161-833 0007 Fax: 0161-835 1546 E-mail: shutters@barricade.fsnet.co.uk *Security gates, shutters & doors*

Barrie Knitwear, Burnfoot Industrial Estate, Hawick, Roxburghshire, TD9 8RJ Tel: (01450) 365500 Fax: (01450) 365501 E-mail: saleas@barrie.co.uk *Knitwear manufrs*

▶ Barrie Lewis & Co. Ltd, Units 1 & 2, Bedwas Business Centre, Bedwas, Caerphilly, Mid Glamorgan, CF83 8DU Tel: (029) 2088 6846

▶ Barrie Scott & Co., 16-18 Weir Street, Falkirk, FK1 1RA Tel: (01324) 637654 Fax: (01324) 635678

Barrier Foil Products, Unit 9, Sutton Fold Sullivans Way, St. Helens, Merseyside, WA9 5GL Tel: 0161-480 4007 Fax: (01744) 451000 E-mail: barrierfoil@aol.com *Flexible packaging manufrs*

Barrier Offshore Engineering Ltd, Joyce Buildings, Haverton Hill Industrial Estate, Billingham, Cleveland, TS23 1PZ Tel: (01642) 565202 Fax: (01642) 563061 *Steel fabrication for onshore & offshore industry*

Barrier Surveillance Services, 77 Main Street, Shildon, County Durham, DL4 1AN Tel: (01388) 776833 Fax: (01388) 775886 *Security product installers*

Barriers International Ltd, PO Box 999, Malmesbury, Wiltshire, SN16 0JJ Tel: (01666) 829100 Fax: (01666) 823800 E-mail: admin@barriersint.com *Specialist impact absorbing sports fencing suppliers*

▶ Barrimon Solutions, Jersey Crescent, Stoke-on-Trent, ST3 4TJ Tel: (01384) 823828 *Welcome to Barrimon Solutions* *Drama is at our core. Actors, directors, writers and producers fusing their skills, disciplines, and experience to create a dynamic tool for training and development. **Harnessing the art of stagecraft, which at its very heart pulses with ensemble reliance and co-operation, we deliver a positive product through a positive approach. **Over our collective years in the arts we have observed, experienced and learned a multitude of techniques. Techniques for releasing people's inhibitions, creating fresh insight and creating true group dynamics. From these we have cultivated those ideas which we believe to be most effective and formed them into our packages. Packages that can help you and your company succeed. **

▶ Barrington Engineering Ltd, New Parkhall Industrial Estate, Parkhall Road, Stoke-on-Trent, ST3 5AT Tel: (01782) 370200 *Supplier of new and refurbished machinery for the Ceramic/Food/Pharmaceutical Industry *Plus Fabrication and Sheetmetal work*

Jean Barrington, 32 Dove Way, Kirkby Mills Industrial Estate, Kirkbymoorside, York, YO62 6QR Tel: (01751) 430081 Fax: (01751) 430081 E-mail: nigelboyes@onetel.com *Stationery manufrs*

▶ Barrington Sports, 3 Wolfe Close, Parkgate Industrial Estate, Parkgate Industrial Estate, Knutsford, Cheshire, WA16 8XJ Tel: (01565) 650269 Fax: (01565) 634104 E-mail: neil@barringtonsports.com *Wholesaler, retailer & distributor of hockey & cricket equipment*

Barritt Associates Ltd, 6 Firwood Close, Longridge, Preston, PR3 3HB Tel: (01772) 780555 Fax: (01772) 780777 E-mail: sales@barrittglassprint.co.uk *Printed & engraved glassware*

Barron Glass, Unit 11 Lansdown Industrial Estate, Gloucester Road, Cheltenham, Gloucestershire, GL51 8PL Tel: (01242) 228000 Fax: (01242) 226555 E-mail: admin@barronglass.co.uk *Decorative glass manufrs*

Barron Mccann Ltd, Meteor Centre, Mansfield Road, Derby, DE21 4SY Tel: (01332) 866500 Fax: (01332) 866501 *IT communications services*

Barron Mccann Technology Ltd, Fifth Avenue, Letchworth Garden City, Hertfordshire, SG6 2HF Tel: (01462) 482333 Fax: (01462) 482112 E-mail: info@bemac.com *IT software services*

Barron-Clark Castings Ltd, Royce Road, Peterborough, PE1 5YB Tel: (01733) 551141 Fax: (01733) 896004 E-mail: info@barronclark-castings.co.uk *Engineers pattern makers*

▶ Derek Barrott Packaging Ltd, Unit 1 B, Oak Business Park, Oaks Drive, Newmarket, Suffolk, CB8 7SX Tel: (01638) 660909 Fax: (01638) 666649 E-mail: admin@barrottpackaging.co.uk *Corrugated cardboard cartons*

Barrow (Don), Sandy Lane, Whirley, Macclesfield, Cheshire, SK10 4RJ Tel: (01625) 429092 Fax: (01625) 429092 E-mail: info@donbarrow.co.uk *Supplier of rally navigation equipment & electronic road survey equipment*

Barrow Lane Products, Cherry Tree Farm, Charlton Musgrove, Wincanton, Somerset, BA9 8HW Tel: (01963) 34279 E-mail: info@roosterbooster.co.uk *12-volt poultry lighting for free range chickens distributors*

▶ Barrow Models, St. Vincents Primary School, Greenside Street, Manchester, M11 2EX Tel: 0161-231 2272 *Promotional models manufrs*

▶ A & D Barrowclough Ltd, Elm Street Works, Elm Street, Burnley, Lancashire, BB10 1NY Tel: (01282) 427048

Barrowfield Leather Co. Ltd, 47 Solway Street, Glasgow, G40 4JG Tel: 0141-554 7863 Fax: 0141-554 8053 E-mail: office@barrowfield.com Principal Export Areas: Central/East Europe & West Europe *Leather goods & leather thonging & laces*

Barrowmore Industries, Barrowmore Enterprise Estate, Barnhouse Lane, Great Barrow, Chester, CH3 7JA Tel: (01829) 742590 Fax: (01829) 742571 E-mail: kat@barrowmore.org.uk *Manufacturers of timber summer houses, fencing, garden furniture and hand made oak furniture for over 80 years. All buildings are pressure treated and come with a superb 20 year guarantee against rot. We offer flat-pack delivery or delivery and erection. Feel free to click on the map and visit our display centre.*

Barrows Cartons Ltd, Unit 1a Squires Mill, Micklehurst Road, Mossley, Ashton-under-Lyne, Lancashire, OL5 9JL Tel: (01457) 835253 Fax: (01457) 835898 E-mail: kel.b@btinternet.com *Box suppliers*

Barrs Court Engineering Ltd, Netherwood Road, Rotherwas Industrial Estate, Hereford, HR2 6JU Tel: (01432) 353450 Fax: (01432) 353452 E-mail: paul@barrscourt.com *Architectural metalwork manufrs*

Barrs Security Locksmiths Ltd, 329 Fulham Palace Road, London, SW6 6TE Tel: (020) 7731 4502 Fax: (020) 7731 4502 *Locksmith & security specialists*

Barry Air Service, Hafod Lon, Port Road West, Barry, South Glamorgan, CF62 3BA Tel: (01446) 734153 Fax: (01446) 734153 *Garage equipment distributors*

Barry Bennett Ltd, Unit 15a Bankfield Business Park, Quebec Street, Bolton, BL3 5JN Tel: (01204) 534311 Fax: (01204) 362783 E-mail: info@baarybennett.co.uk *Office equipment furniture distributors*

Barry Bros Security, 121-123 Praed Street, London, W2 1RL Tel: (0800) 3168547 Fax: (020) 7262 5005 E-mail: info@barrybros.com *Locksmiths & burglar alarms & security engineers*

Barry Cousins, High House Wharf, Heyford Lane, Weedon, Northampton, NN7 4SF Tel: (01327) 342300 Fax: (01327) 342300 *Boat fitting & repairers*

▶ David Barry (London) Ltd, 7-9 Solebay St, London, E1 4PW Tel: (020) 7790 1952 *Manufacture ladies wear outerwear*

▶ Barry Ives Haulage Ltd, Rippers Court, Sible Hedingham, Halstead, Essex, CO9 3PY Tel: (01787) 462111 Fax: (01787) 462178

Barry M Cosmetics, Unit 1 Bittacy Business Centre, Bittacy Hill, London, NW7 1BA Tel: (020) 8349 2992 Fax: (020) 8346 7773 E-mail: info@barrym.co.uk *Cosmetics manufrs*

Barry P Millard, 3 Underhill Lane, Lower Bourne, Farnham, Surrey, GU10 3NF Tel: (01252) 711002 Fax: (01252) 711002 *Electrical contractors*

Barry Sharman Caravans Ltd, The Caravan Centre, Colchester Road, Ipswich, IP4 4RU Tel: (01473) 713284 Fax: (01473) 273166 E-mail: sharmancaravans@supanet.com *Secondhand caravan sales, repairs & servicing*

Barry & Son Ltd, 37 Bute Street, Salford, M50 1DU Tel: 0161-737 6888 Fax: 0161-745 8159 E-mail: sales@barryandson.co.uk *Engineers' suppliers*

▶ Barry Ward, 10 Vowell Close, Bristol, BS13 9HS Tel: (07831) 447764 Fax: 0117-904 4859 E-mail: barry@barrywardcourierservices.co.uk *Van + Driver operating from the Bristol area.*

Barry Wehmiller Europe Ltd, 16 Roman Way, Thetford, Norfolk, IP24 1XB Tel: (01842) 754171 Fax: (01842) 755318 E-mail: info@hayssen.co.uk *Refurbish machinery & spares service centre*

Barry Wheatley & Sons, King Street, Hodthorpe, Worksop, Nottinghamshire, S80 4XA Tel: (01909) 720692 *Wrought iron gate manufrs*

Barry's Signs, 2 High Street, Wavertree, Liverpool, L15 8HG Tel: 0151-733 9741 Fax: 0151-734 0800 *Sign contractors*

▶ Barsby Lightning Protection, 31 Trinity Road, Whetstone, Leicester, LE8 6JW Tel: 0116-278 7996 Fax: 0116-278 7996 E-mail: info@barsbylightning.co.uk *Lightning Protection Installers of Faraday Cage Systems to BS 6651:1999 and Single Mast Systems.Earthing Specialists to BS 7430. Steeplejacks.*

Barson Lift Co. Ltd, Unit 1, Bellgrave Industrial Estate, Honeywell Lane, Oldham, OL8 2JP Tel: 0161-678 9209 Fax: 0161-627 5009 *Lift manufrs*

▶ BarTax Services Ltd, 3 Rose Bank, Bollington, Cheshire, SK10 5JA Tel: 01625 268482 Fax: 01625 268483 E-mail: info@bartaxbusiness.co.uk *Expert UK-wide business accountant - covers London, Cheshire & Manchester. Accountancy support: Outsourced, Year End Accounts, Tax Returns & Payroll.*

▶ Bartec Paper & Packaging, Wincham Avenue, Wincham, Northwich, Cheshire, CW9 6GB Tel: (01606) 354664 Fax: (01606) 354665 E-mail: ute.cooper@good.co.uk *Flexible packaging converters, specialising in waxed papers, glassines, greaseproof & parchments for fish, confectionery, cosmetics, arts/crafts industries & others. Our new gift bags are designed to decrease packaging. Also new; non stick liners, PTFE coated*

Bartec (UK) Ltd, Arundel House, Hollins Brook Park, Pilsworth Road, Bury, Lancashire, BL9 8RN Tel: (0844) 4992710 Fax: (0844) 4992715 E-mail: info@bartec.co.uk *Display terminals & junction box manufrs*

Bartech Marine Engineers, 11-12 Rushmere Close, West Mersea, Colchester, CO5 8QQ Tel: (01206) 384677 Fax: (01206) 385329 E-mail: sales@bartechmarine.com *Marine engineers & consultants*

Bartek Engineering Ltd, 24 Industrial Estate, Cornwall Road, Smethwick, West Midlands, B66 2JS Tel: 0121-555 8885 Fax: 0121-555 8885 *Engineers & welding fabricators*

Bartell Contract Furnishings Ltd, Bartell House, 733 Oldham Road, Manchester, M40 5AP Tel: 0161-205 0222 Fax: 0161-205 0444 E-mail: info@bar-tell.co.uk *Window furnishings installers & manufrs*

Bartham Press (Watford) Ltd, Unit A, Park Avenue Estate, Sundon Park, Luton, LU3 3BP Tel: (01582) 573471 Fax: (01582) 582024 *Printers*

Bartholomew C & Son Ltd, 15 Hatton Place, London, EC1N 8RU Tel: (020) 7405 9557 Fax: (020) 7404 4706 *Haberdashery manufacturers' agents*

Bartholomew Joinery Ltd, The Workshop Great Hidden Farm, Wantage Road, Eddington, Hungerford, Berkshire, RG17 0PW Tel: (01488) 685407 Fax: (01488) 681624 E-mail: bart.joinery@amserve.net *Contract joiners*

Bartholomews Chartered Surveyors, 15 Greycoat Place, London, SW1P 1SB Tel: (020) 8546 9441 Fax: (020) 8546 9442 E-mail: enquires@batholomew.com *Property consultants*

Bartholomews (Chichester) Ltd, Mullaney Business Park, Deanland Road, Golden Cross, Hailsham, East Sussex, BN27 3RP Tel: (01825) 872697 Fax: (01825) 872850 E-mail: goldencross@bartholomews.fsnet.co.uk *Agricultural products distributors*

Bartholomews Specialist Distribution Ltd, Bognor Road, Chichester, West Sussex, PO19 7TT Tel: (01243) 539224 Fax: (01243) 536341 E-mail: agri@bartholomews.co.uk *Agricultural merchants*

Bartington Instruments Ltd, 10 Thorney Leys Park, Witney, Oxfordshire, OX28 4GG Tel: (01993) 706565 Fax: (01993) 774813 E-mail: sales@bartington.com *Manufacturers of magnetic field sensors, magnetometers*

Bartlett Catering Equipment Ltd, 171 Camford Way, Luton, LU3 3AN Tel: (01582) 847462 Fax: (01582) 566172 E-mail: sales@bartlettcatering.com *Manufacturers of catering equipment*

Bartlett Printing, Swan Yard, Okehampton Street, Exeter, EX4 1HU Tel: (01392) 254086 Fax: (01392) 256224 E-mail: sales@bartlett-printing.co.uk *Commercial printers*

Bartlett Refrigeration Ltd, Marsh Green Road West, Marsh Barton Trading Estate, Exeter, EX2 8PT Tel: (01392) 203000 Fax: (01392) 203001 E-mail: sales@bartlett.uk.com *Air conditioning & refrigeration engineers* Also at: Camborne, Paignton & Plymouth

William Bartlett & Son Ltd, Grafton Street, High Wycombe, Buckinghamshire, HP12 3AJ Tel: (01494) 526491 Fax: (01494) 451021 E-mail: sales@williambartlett.co.uk *Furniture manufrs*

▶ Bartletts Battlefields Journeys, Broomhill, Edlington, Horncastle, Lincolnshire, LN9 5RJ Tel: (01507) 523128 Fax: (01507) 523130 E-mail: info@battlefields.co.uk *Battlefield tour specialists*

Bartling Designs Ltd, Staplehurst Road, Sittingbourne, Kent, ME10 1TA Tel: (01795) 476424 Fax: (01795) 475751 E-mail: bartlingdesigns@bartlingdesigns.com *Holding fixtures manufrs*

Bartoline, Barmston Close, Woodmansey, Beverley, North Humberside, HU17 0LW Tel: (01482) 678710 Fax: (01482) 872606 E-mail: info@bartoline.co.uk *DIY products & adhesives suppliers*

Barton Aluminium Foundries, Rayboulds Bridge Rd, Walsall, WS2 8PG Tel: (01922) 637551 Fax: (01922) 644481 E-mail: sales@barton-aluminium.co.uk *A unique service in cast components*

Barton Blinds Ltd, Unit B3, Imex Enterprise Park, Rands Lane, Armthorpe, Doncaster, South Yorkshire, DN3 3DY Tel: (01302) 830810 Fax: (01302) 830810 *Blind retailer & manufrs*

Barton Carbide Tooling Ltd, PO Box 5243, Milton Keynes, MK17 0YL Tel: (0870) 7466390 Fax: (08707) 466391 E-mail: info@barton.uk.com *Cigarette machinery spare part manufrs*

Barton Chemicals Ltd, Greendykes Industrial Estate, Broxburn, West Lothian, EH52 6PG Tel: (01506) 862299 Fax: (01506) 862288 E-mail: barton.chemicals@virgin.net *Chemical suppliers to transport*

Barton Civil Engineering, 537 Durham Road, Gateshead, Tyne & Wear, NE9 5EY Tel: 0191-487 9609 Fax: 0191-487 4814

Barton Cruisers, Welford Road, Barton, Bidford-on-Avon, Alcester, Warwickshire, B50 4NP Tel: (01789) 772003 Fax: (01789) 772112 *Marina services*

Barton Drilling Ltd, 1 Station Road Industrial Estate, Latchford, Warrington, WA4 1LB Tel: (01925) 653354 Fax: (01925) 230151 E-mail: sales@bartondrilling.co.uk *Concrete drilling contractors*

Barton Electrical Ltd, Leondore House, 142 Molesdey Avenue, West Molesey, Surrey, KT8 2RY Tel: (020) 8979 4444 Fax: (020) 8979 6555 *Cleaning equipment manufrs*

Barton Engineering, Birchills, Walsall, WS2 8QE Tel: (01922) 433100 Fax: (01922) 646675 *Cable management systems manufrs*

▶ Barton Engineering & Export Ltd, Diamond Road, Whitstable, Kent, CT5 1LN Tel: (01227) 272141 Fax: (01227) 771653 E-mail: susan@bartoneng.co.uk *Screen enclosures computer server racks*

Barton Fabrication Ltd, Harbour Road Trading Estate, Portishead, Bristol, BS20 7BL Tel: (01275) 845901 Fax: (01275) 849462 E-mail: barton.fabrication@virgin.net *Steel & aluminium fabricators*

Barton Firtop Engineering, Stoke Heath Works, Hanbury Road, Stoke Heath, Bromsgrove, Worcestershire, B60 4LT Tel: (01527) 831664 Fax: (01527) 832638 E-mail: sales@bartonfirtop.co.uk Principal Export Areas: Worldwide *Filter & strainers manufrs*

Barton Forge & Ironwork Ltd, 48 Alexandra Road, Enfield, Middlesex, EN3 7EH Tel: (020) 8804 1752 *Heat treatment & chemical blacking*

Barton Industrial Services Ltd, 6 Longlands Avenue, Newtownabbey, County Antrim, BT36 7NE Tel: (028) 9085 4535 Fax: (028) 9036 5133 E-mail: mail@barton-industrial.com *Arch frame manufrs*

Barton Instrument Systems Ltd, 3 Steyning Way, Southern Cross Trading Estate, Bognor Regis, West Sussex, PO22 9TT Tel: (01243) 826741 Fax: (01243) 860263 E-mail: bartonuk@nuflotech.com *Manufacturers of flow measurement systems & process controllers*

Barton Kendal, 122 Yorkshire Street, Rochdale, Lancashire, OL16 1LA Tel: (01706) 653214 Fax: (01706) 341476 E-mail: sales@barton-kendal.co.uk *Estate agents & chartered surveyors*

Barton Marine Equipment Ltd, Marine House, Tyler Way, Whitstable, Kent, CT5 2RS Tel: (01227) 792979 Fax: (01227) 793555 E-mail: sales@bartonmarine.com *Marine suppliers*

Barton Petroleum Ltd, 6-7 Vaux Road, Finedon Road Industrial Estate, Wellingborough, Northamptonshire, NN8 4TG Tel: (01933) 224317 Fax: (01933) 441039 E-mail: enquiries@bartonpetroleum.co.uk *Fuel distributors*

Barton Plant Ltd, Cranford Road, Burton Latimer, Kettering, Northamptonshire, NN15 5TB Tel: (01536) 722100 Fax: (01536) 722714 E-mail: enquiries@barton-plant.co.uk *Earth moving contractors plant hire*

Barton Precision Engineers Ltd, Dabell Avenue, Blenheim Industrial Estate, Nottingham, NG6 8WA Tel: 0115-927 2368 Fax: 0115-977 0101 E-mail: info@bartonprecision.co.uk *Precision engineers*

Barton Products Ltd, Barton Road, Long Eaton, Nottingham, NG10 2FN Tel: 0115-972 5134 Fax: 0115-946 1370 E-mail: sales@barton-products.co.uk *Furniture parts manufrs*

Barton & Sons (Coach Trimmers), 2 New Town Trading Estate, Chase Street, Luton, LU1 3QZ Tel: (01582) 412932 Fax: (01582) 726867 E-mail: sales@carinteriors.net *Car upholstery manufrs*

Barton Steel Services Ltd, Unit 6 Severnside Trading Estate, Textilose Rd, Trafford Park, Manchester, M17 1WA Tel: 0161-872 3084 Fax: 0161-872 0759 *Steel stockholders*

Barton Timber Co. Ltd, 50 North Street, Hornchurch, Essex, RM11 1SR Tel: (01708) 448805 Fax: (01708) 453561 *Timber merchants*

Barton Willmore Partnership, Netherton House, 23-29 Marsh Street, Bristol, BS1 4AQ Tel: 0117-929 9677 Fax: 0117-929 4569 E-mail: planning@bartonwillmore.co.uk *Town planning consultants*

Barton Willmore Partnership, 35 Kings Hill Avenue, Kings Hill, West Malling, Kent, ME19 4BW Tel: (01732) 845845 Fax: (01732) 223808 E-mail: architects@eastern.bartonwillmore.co.uk *Environmental consultants*

Bartons Of Bawtry Ltd, Market Place, Bawtry, Doncaster, South Yorkshire, DN10 6JL Tel: (01302) 710212 Fax: (01302) 710212 *Motor engineers services*

David Bartram, The Raveningham Centre, Beccles Rd, Raveningham, Norwich, NR14 6NU Tel: (01508) 548721 Fax: (01508) 548721 *Cabinet makers*

Bartram Mowers, Bluebell Road, Norwich, NR4 7LG Tel: (01603) 458916 Fax: (01603) 250643 E-mail: sales@bartrammowers.co.uk *Horticultural distributors* Also at: Ipswich

S.G. Bartram, Edward Street, Burton-On-Trent, Staffordshire, DE14 2JF Tel: (01283) 517300 Fax: (01283) 517401 E-mail: sgbartram@tiscali.co.uk *Joinery manufrs*

▶ Bartram Walker, Bowburn North Industrial Estate, Bowburn, Durham, DH6 5PF Tel: 0191-377 4620 Fax: 0191-377 4621 E-mail: sales@bartramwalker.co.uk

Bartram Walker, Bowburn North Industrial Estate, Bowburn, Durham, DH6 5PF Tel: 0191-377 4620 Fax: 0191-377 4621 E-mail: sales@bartramwalker.co.uk *Electrical plumbing & mechanic agents*

▶ Bartram Walker, Esh Burn, Burn Lane, Hexham, Northumberland, NE46 3HN Tel: (01434) 602441 Fax: (01434) 601975 E-mail: info@robsonwalker.co.uk

Bartrums Haulage & Storage Ltd, Langton Green, Eye, Suffolk, IP23 7HN Tel: (01379) 870693 Fax: (01379) 870942E-mail: info@bartrums.com *Haulage contractors & storage services*

▶ Bartrum's Road Services Ltd, 57 Victoria Road, Diss, Norfolk, IP22 4JD Tel: (01379) 642384

Baruch Enterprises Ltd, Watkins House, Pegamoid Road, London, N18 2NG Tel: (020) 8803 8899 Fax: (020) 8965 5448 E-mail: info@baruch.co.uk *Battery suppliers*

▶ Barum & Dewer Ltd, Unit 11 Two Rivers Industrial Estate, Braunton Road, Barnstaple, Devon, EX31 1JY Tel: (01271) 375197 Fax: (01271) 344870 *Industrial cases distributors*

▶ Barwell Litho Ltd, Unit 34 First Avenue, Westfield Industrial Estate, Midsomer Norton, Radstock, BA3 4BS Tel: (01761) 419161 Fax: (01761) 418098

Barwick Commercials, Rennesley Works, Anchor Lane, Wadesmill, Ware, Hertfordshire, SG12 0TE Tel: (01920) 462370 *Lorry repairers*

Barwick Systems Ltd, Merchants Wharf, Teesdale Park, Thornaby, Stockton-on-Tees, Cleveland, TS17 6BA Tel: (01642) 632900 Fax: (01642) 632915 E-mail: admin@barwicksystems.co.uk *Software developers*

Barwood Developments Ltd, The Grange, Warren Office Village, Wolverton Mill, Milton Keynes, MK12 5NE Tel: (01908) 577600 Fax: (01908) 312017 E-mail: info@barwood.co.uk *Commerical property developers*

▶ Barwoods Bedrooms Ltd, 34 Market Street, Mottram, Hyde, Cheshire, SK14 6JG Tel: (01457) 763355 Fax: (01457) 763355 E-mail: mbardsley@barwoods.com *Fitted bedroom furniture manufrs*

Barzillai Hingley & Sons Ltd, Lion Chain Works, Providence Street, Cradley Heath, West Midlands, B64 5DT Tel: (01384) 569141 Fax: (01384) 639177 E-mail: sales@barzillai.com *Lifting gear, shackles & deep sea fishing equipment manufrs*

Base 1 Ltd, 41-43 Roebuck Road, Hainault Industrial Estate, Ilford, Essex, IG6 3TU Tel: (020) 8500 5649 Fax: (020) 8559 9456 E-mail: phil@base1.co.uk *Promotional products designers & suppliers*

Base 2 Professional Ltd, 1 Bracklinn Road, Callander, Perthshire, FK17 8EH Tel: (01877) 331331 Fax: (01877) 331711 *Computer software for accountants*

Base Camp, 1a Clifton Road, Littlehampton, West Sussex, BN17 5AS Tel: (01903) 723853 Fax: (01903) 723853 E-mail: sales@base-camp.co.uk *Outdoor equipment suppliers*

Base Computer Services Ltd, 154 Eltham Hill, London, SE9 5EA Tel: (020) 8488 4448 Fax: (020) 8488 4449 E-mail: sales@base.uk.com *Computer repairers*

▶ Base Creative Ltd, 46 Parkway, Dorking, Surrey, RH4 1EU Tel: (01306) 875447 E-mail: info@base-creative.co.uk *We offer creative design solutions for all corporate needs and a high quality Artwork service.*

Base Enamellers Ltd, 1 Power Works, Slade Green Road, Erith, Kent, DA8 2HU Tel: (01322) 338052 Fax: (01322) 334360 E-mail: info@base-enamellers.co.uk *Stove enamelling services*

Base Handling Products Ltd, Unit 20 Barleyfield Industrial Estate, Barleyfield Way, Nantyglo, Ebbw Vale, Gwent, NP23 4LU Tel: (01495) 312172 Fax: (01495) 312089 E-mail: info@baseproducts.co.uk *Materials handling equipment manufrs*

▶ Base Line, 4 The Square, Notley Green, Great Notley, Braintree, Essex, CM77 7WT Tel: (01376) 551030 Fax: (01376) 551251 E-mail: sales@base-line.co.uk *Static & mobile racking & shelving for hand loaded environments. Bespoke systems for specialist requirements. Picture storage racking for museums & art galleries. Data storage racking & Archive shelving. Fire protection rooms for specialist environments, stand alone & internal. Raised storage areas, mezzanine floors plus associated equipment. Trucks, trolleys & handling equipment, see our 300 page catalogue. Bespoke trucks & trolleys also available to your detailed drawing. special hospital trolleys*

Base Minimix Concrete, A29 Red Scar Industrial Estate, Longridge Road, Ribbleton, Preston, PR2 5NA Tel: (01524) 720344 Fax: (01772) 655515 *Supply ready mix concrete*

▶ Basegold Rail Ltd, 51 William Hunter Way, Brentwood, Essex, CM14 4WQ Tel: (01277) 228788 Fax: (01277) 228122 E-mail: info@basegoldrail.co.uk *Suppliers to the Rail Industry of safety critical labour, and RTAS licensed Track Safety training provider.*

Baselica Ltd, 3 Somers Place, London, SW2 2AL Tel: (020) 8671 6622 Fax: (020) 8678 6151 E-mail: enquires@fineitalianfood.co.uk *Italian food importers & distributors*

Basell (UK) Ltd, Mount Farm, Bramley Road, Milton Keynes, MK1 1LZ Tel: (01908) 360000 Fax: (01908) 360036 *Polymeric, resin & alloy manufrs*

▶ Basement 4 Creating Space, 288 Oxford Road, Gomersal, Cleckheaton, West Yorkshire, BD19 4PY Tel: (0800) 1381998 Fax: (01274) 852937 E-mail: enquiries@basement4.com *Basement 4 specialise in newbuild, retro-fit & basement conversions including tanking & converting damp cellars into dry useable living spaces, we undertake a comprehensive service from initial survey through to design, dealing with planning permission, structural engineering services & building regulations, we have our own* continued *team of dedicated specialist tradesmen to carry out the groundworks, underpinning, new basement formations, tanking, plastering, joinery, electrics & plumbing*

▶ Baseresult Holdings Ltd, Dudnance Lane, Pool, Redruth, Cornwall, TR15 3QT Tel: (01209) 715777 Fax: (01209) 716777 E-mail: baseresult@btconnect.com *Mining tin ores & mining services*

Basf Public Ltd Company, Earl Road, Cheadle Hulme, Cheadle, Cheshire, SK8 6QG Tel: 0161-485 6222 Fax: 0161-486 0891 E-mail: info.service@basf-plc.co.uk *Chemical manufrs*

Basford Plant Ltd, 12 Pinxton Lane, Kirkby-in-Ashfield, Nottingham, NG17 8LT Tel: (01623) 451010 Fax: (01623) 451011 *Plant manufrs*

Bashir & Sons London Ltd, 178-180 Brick Lane, London, E1 6SA Tel: (020) 7739 0834 Fax: (020) 7739 8115 *Leather garment manufrs*

Basic Business Systems Ltd, Brookside Road, Ruddington, Nottingham, NG11 6AT Tel: 0115-940 5000 Fax: 0115-940 5450 *Computer reseller & solutions provider*

Basic Electronics Ltd, 5 Leapale Road, Guildford, Surrey, GU1 4JX Tel: (01483) 539984 Fax: (01483) 539984 E-mail: sales@basicelectronics.co.uk *Electronic component distributors*

Basic Strategies Ltd, Network Ho, 222 Ewell Rd, Surbiton, Surrey, KT6 7AF Tel: 020 83954240 Fax: 020 83399550 *Computer consultancy*

Basil Paterson College, 66 Queen Street, Edinburgh, EH2 4NA Tel: 0131-225 3802 Fax: 0131-226 6701 E-mail: info@basilpaterson.co.uk *English language computer training*

Basildon Glassworks Ltd, 12 Winstanley Way, Basildon, Essex, SS14 3BP Tel: (01268) 282424 Fax: (01268) 532348 E-mail: basildonglass@aol.com *Glass processors & mirrors*

Basingstoke Control Systems, 12 Mallard Close, Basingstoke, Hampshire, RG22 5JP Tel: (01256) 466639 Fax: (01256) 842876 E-mail: basingstokecobtrolsystems@ukonline.co.uk *Heating & air conditioning panels manufrs*

Basingstoke Packaging, 24 London Road, Thatcham, Berkshire, RG18 4LQ Tel: (01635) 863783 Fax: (01635) 861675 *Export packing services & wooden packing case manufrs*

Basingstoke Pressure Vessels & Pipework Ltd, 11 Brunel Gate, Andover, Hampshire, SP10 3SL Tel: (01264) 351559 Fax: (01264) 332173 E-mail: acole@bpbp.co.uk *Fabricators & welding engineers*

▶ Baskerville, 30 Long Wood Road, Trafford Park, Manchester, M17 1PZ Tel: 0161-888 2345 Fax: 0161-888 2345 E-mail: admin@baskervilleautoclaves.co.uk *Autoclave manufacturers. Pressure Vessels, (5ml-1000L) reactors and test rigs for industry and research. All materials. Standard and custom built equipment with electronic controls/ data output. Multi-cells for chemical screening and parallel synthesis. Maintenance/servicing.*

G. Baskerville Demolition Contractors Ltd, Leek New Road Trading Estate, Cobridge, Stoke-On-Trent, ST6 2PL Tel: (01782) 219455 Fax: (01782) 263666 *Demolition contractors*

▶ Baskets & Bows Fingers & Toes, 22 Queen Street, Dalton-in-Furness, Cumbria, LA15 8EG Tel: (01229) 467868 Fax: (01229) 467868 E-mail: sue@basketsandbows-fingersandtoes.co.uk *Reproduction 3d hand & foot casting"s. Don"t let time fade your memories, capture them forever with our unique cast"s. Every crease, wrinkle & line of your baby or childs hands & feet, they grow so fast.*Visit our website for details on our range of ideas for Castings, Gift baskets and unique Nappy Cake"s*

Basmati Rice UK Ltd, Pari House, Stambourne Road, Great Yeldham, Halstead, Essex, CO9 4RB Tel: (01787) 237173 Fax: (01787) 237318 E-mail: admin@basmatiriceukltd.co.uk Principal Export Areas: Central/East Europe, West Europe & Worldwide *Food product manufrs*

Basover Construction Ltd, Gweedore, Newnham Lane, Old Basing, Basingstoke, Hampshire, RG24 7AT Tel: (01256) 461949 *Groundwork & excavation contractors*

Bass Stobart Ltd, 20 Obelisk Road, Southampton, SO19 9BN Tel: (023) 8068 5485 Fax: (023) 8068 5469 E-mail: sales@bass-stobart.co.uk *Engineering tooling distributors*

Terry Bass Garden Machinery Services, Mortimer Trading Estate, Hereford, HR4 9SP Tel: (01432) 357933 Fax: (01432) 357933 E-mail: tcbass@freenetname.co.uk *Garden machinery sales & services*

Bassaire Ltd, Duncan Road, Park Gate, Southampton, SO31 1ZS Tel: (01489) 885111 Fax: (01489) 885211 E-mail: sales@bassaire.co.uk *Clean air equipment & clean room (environmental) manufrs*

Bassett Down Balancing, Unit 19 Lower Bassett Down Workshops, Basset Down, Wroughton, Swindon, SN4 9QP Tel: (01793) 812331 Principal Export Areas: Asia Pacific, Central/East Europe & West Europe *Specialist engine balancing services*

Bassett Electronic Systems Ltd, Unit 15 Whitehill Industrial Estate, Whitehill Lane, Wootton Bassett, Swindon, SN4 7DB Tel: (01793) 851013 Fax: (01793) 848765 E-mail: sales@bassettelectronics.com *Printed circuit board building & services*

Bassett & Findley Ltd, Talbot Road North, Wellingborough, Northamptonshire, NN8 1QS Tel: (01933) 224898 Fax: (01933) 227731 E-mail: info@bassettandfindley.ltd.uk *Specialist architectural metalwork*

Bassett Transport Training Ltd, Transport House, Stoke-on-Trent, ST12 9HD Tel: (01782) 371018 Fax: (01782) 371028 E-mail: training@bassett-group.co.uk *Bassett Transport Training provides quality-assured LGV, PCV and FLT Driver Training services, delivered by DSA qualified instructors.*

Basta Parsons Ltd, Alma Street, Wolverhampton, WV10 0EY Tel: (01902) 877770 Fax: (01902) 877771 E-mail: sjohnson@bastaparsonsqb.com *Brass/stainless steel hinge manufrs*

Bastion Glassfibre Rod & Sections Ltd, 12 Harvey Close, Crowther Industrial Estate, District 3, Washington, Tyne & Wear, NE38 0AB Tel: 0191-416 6394 Fax: 0191-415 4961 E-mail: gf-admin@bastion-ltd.co.uk *Glass fibre rod manufrs*

Bastion Security Ltd, Claremont House, Holly Road, Slough, SL2 3QT Tel: (01753) 646488 Fax: (01753) 646488 E-mail: bastion@tinyworld.co.uk *Security door installers & manufrs*

Bastow & Ryder Ltd, 157 Sunbridge Road, Bradford, West Yorkshire, BD1 2NU Tel: (01274) 724358 *Poster writers*

▶ Bat & Bottle, 24 Pillings Road, Oakham, Leicestershire, LE15 6QF Tel: (0845) 1084407 Fax: (0870) 4582505 E-mail: post@batwine.co.uk *Wine importers*

▶ Bat I T Solutions Ltd, 20 Briskman Way, Oakwood Park, Aylesbury, Buckinghamshire, HP21 8FP Tel: (01296) 483631 Fax: (01296) 331510 E-mail: tris@bat-it.com *We are an independant computer services company, established in 2001 providing a comprehensive range or realistically-priced i.t.services.**Our client base ranges from businesses with 5 employees to multi-national and international corporations.*

Batalas Ltd, PO Box 8770, Pershore, Worcestershire, WR10 2NU Tel: (0870) 7504400 E-mail: enquiries@batalas.co.uk *Quality management & training agents*

Batch Control Systems Ltd, Govanhill Workspace, 69 Dixon Road, Glasgow, G42 8AT Tel: 0141-423 0413 Fax: 0141-424 3149 E-mail: sales@bcs2000.co.uk *Industrial software suppliers*

Batchelor Air Conditioning, 3 Stilebrook Road, Olney, Buckinghamshire, MK46 5EA Tel: (01234) 241781 Fax: (01234) 241781 *Refrigeration & air conditioning*

Batchelor Concrete Products, Wood End Gardens, Northolt, Middlesex, UB5 4QH Tel: (020) 8422 6892 Fax: (020) 8863 1268 *Concrete products manufrs*

Batchglow Ltd, Unit 1-2 Bookers Way, Dinnington, Sheffield, S25 3SH Tel: (01909) 563051 Fax: (01909) 564164 E-mail: info@batchglow.co.uk *Powder coating specialists*

Batching & Blending Systems Ltd, 48 Marlow Road, Stokenchurch, High Wycombe, Buckinghamshire, HP14 3QJ Tel: (01494) 484952 Fax: (01494) 485696 E-mail: sales@bbsys.uk.com *Industrial processes computer control systems services*

Batchit Ltd, 204 Halesowen Road, Dudley, West Midlands, DY2 9FD Tel: (01384) 633900 Fax: (01384) 566941 E-mail: info@batchit.co.uk *Second hand laboratory furniture manufrs*

L.M. Bateman & Co. Ltd, Five Bridges, Cullompton, Devon, EX15 1QP Tel: (01884) 33453 Fax: (01884) 34410 E-mail: info@lmbateman.co.uk *Agricultural suppliers*

L.M. Bateman & Co. Ltd, Island Works, Cheadle Road, Chedleton, Leek, Staffordshire, ST13 7EE Tel: (01538) 361326 Fax: (01538) 360803 E-mail: info@lmbateman.co.uk *Livestock equipment manufrs*

Bateman Sewing Machines, 14 Helena Close, Hockley, Essex, SS5 4DJ Tel: (01702) 203306 *Sewing machines repairs*

W. Bateman & Co., Garstang Rd, Barton, Preston, PR3 5AA Tel: (01772) 862948 Fax: (01772) 861639 E-mail: sales@bateman-sellarc.co.uk Sales Contact: S.J. Cox Principal Export Areas: Worldwide *Based in the North West we specialise in the manufacture of various types of air compressors & pressure washers. Our product range includes heavy duty air compressors, industrial air compressors, diesel air compressors, mobile air compressors, belt driven and direct drive air compressors plus many more. Our pressure washers include cold water, hot water, heavy duty, diesel driven, mobile, portable, electric etc. We handle inquiries from all over the UK, please feel free to call for a quotation.*

Adrian Bates Ltd, 10 Curlew Close, Porthcawl, Mid Glamorgan, CF36 3QB Tel: (01656) 785658 Fax: (01656) 785658 *IT consultancy*

Bates & Davis 1998, 82 Pikehelve Street, West Bromwich, West Midlands, B70 0TU Tel: 0121-557 3346 Fax: 0121-557 4162 E-mail: sales@wpmgroupltd.co.uk *Non-ferrous scrap metal merchants*

Bates Furniture, 21 Newton Road, Rushden, Northamptonshire, NN10 0PS Tel: (01933) 358295 Fax: (01933) 358295 *Kitchen & bedroom furniture suppliers*

▶ Bates Millfield, Sherbourne House, 119 Cannon Street, London, EC4N 5AT Tel: (08452) 309092 Fax: 0870 891 3106 E-mail: akdevine@millfield-partnership.co.uk *Established in March 1998, Millfield Partnership Limited is one of the largest firms of independent financial advisers in the UK and is the principal operating company of Millfield Group plc.**Offering a professional financial planning service, we combine the vitality of a young dynamic company with traditional ethics, total customer focus and substantial experience in the financial services industry. Millfield-s City office, fielding over 60 qualified advisers, services clients throughout the Central London, Greater London and the South East. With specialists in all financial areas, you can depend on receiving the best possible independent advice, tailored to your individual needs. **

Bates Office Service Ltd, Unit 26-29 Ropery Business Park, Anchor & Hope Lane, London, SE7 7RX Tel: (020) 8858 0988 Fax: (020) 8858 1136 E-mail: sales@thestationers.co.uk *Stationers*

▶ Bates & Sons Ltd, 18 Vyse Street, Hockley, Birmingham, B18 6LE Tel: 0121-515 2550 Fax: 0121-515 3383 *Jewellery manufrs*

Bates Textile Machine Co. (Leicester) Ltd, Harding Street, Leicester, LE1 4DH Tel: 0116-262 9661 Fax: 0116-251 3041 E-mail: sales@bates-textile.demon.co.uk *Textile machinery*

Bateson Trailers Ltd, Doodfield Works, Windlehurst Road, Marple, Stockport, Cheshire, SK6 7EN Tel: 0161-426 0500 Fax: 0161-426 0245 E-mail: sales@bateson-trailers.co.uk *Trailer manufrs*

Batey Metallic Packing Co. Ltd, Back Ellison Road, Gateshead, Tyne & Wear, NE11 9TR Tel: 0191-460 4167 Fax: 0191-493 2148 *General presswork services*

▶ Bath Accessory Store, Jolen House, Solartron Road, Farnborough, Hampshire, GU14 7QL Tel: (01252) 794454 E-mail: sales@bath-accessory-store.com *Bathroom Accessories from the One stop bathroom shop for stylish, reliable and*affordable bathroom accessories and bathroom suite products.*

Bath Blind Co., Lower Bristol Road, Bath, BA2 7DL Tel: (01225) 837517 Fax: (01225) 837517 E-mail: stewart.davies@ukonline.co.uk *Window blind retailers*

Bath Chamber Of Commerce, Trimbridge House, Trim Street, Bath, BA1 2DP Tel: (01225) 460655 Fax: (01225) 462612 E-mail: info@bathchamber.co.uk *Chamber of commerce*

▶ Bath House, 3a Saunterne Road, Prestwick, Ayrshire, KA9 2JQ Tel: (01292) 470222

▶ Bath Knight, Paladin, Atlas Street, Stoke-on-Trent, ST4 3AL Tel: (01782) 840840 Fax: (01782) 209243 *Mobility company*

Bath Marina & Caravan Park, Brassmill Lane, Bath, BA1 3JT Tel: (01225) 424301 Fax: (01225) 424301 E-mail: sales@bwml.co.uk *Marina & caravan park*

Bath Panel Beating Co. Ltd, Roseberry Road, Bath, BA2 3DX Tel: (01225) 320060 Fax: (01225) 320062 E-mail: bodyshop@bathpanel.sagehost.co.uk *Motor body repairers*

Bath Patio Slab Centre, Whiteway Road, Bath, BA2 2RG Tel: (01225) 319334 Fax: (01225) 319334 E-mail: info@bathslabs.com *Concrete slabs*

▶ Bath Press, 14-18 Block 2-First Road, Blantyre Industrial Estate, Blantyre, Glasgow, G72 0ND Tel: (01698) 822727 Fax: (01698) 710105

▶ The Bath Stone Co. Ltd, Stoke Hill Mine, Midford Lane, Limpley Stoke, Bath, BA2 7GP Tel: (01225) 723792

▶ Bath Time Creations, 23 Cherry Tree Grove, Wokingham, Berkshire, RG41 4UZ Tel: 0118-989 4194 E-mail: info@bathtimecreations.com *Bathroom design & installation*

Bath & West Fire & Safety, 61 Winsley Road, Bradford-on-Avon, Wiltshire, BA15 1NX Tel: (01225) 868199 Fax: (01225) 868118 *Distributors of safety equipment*

Frank Bather & Son Ltd, 248-258 New Chester Road, Birkenhead, Merseyside, CH41 9BQ Tel: 0151-645 1494 Fax: 0151-644 7171 *Motor tyre distributors*

Bathgate & Co Cork Ltd, 75 Trafalgar Lane, Edinburgh, EH6 4DQ Tel: 0131-625 5485 Fax: 0131-625 5485 E-mail: bathgateco@aol.com *Cork products manufrs*

Bathgate Flooring Ltd, 1 Fir Tree Lane, Rotherwas, Hereford, HR2 6LA Tel: (01432) 353003 Fax: (01432) 353004 *Manufacturers & installers of raised access flooring*

▶ Bathgate Silica Sand Ltd, Arclid Quarry, Congleton Road, Arclid, Sandbach, Cheshire, CW11 4SN Tel: (01270) 762492 Fax: (01270) 759449 E-mail: sales@bathgatesilica.co.uk *Top dressings & root zone mixes for sports turf applications*

Bathgate Silica Sand Ltd, Arclid Quarry, Congleton Road, Arclid, Sandbach, Cheshire, CW11 4SN Tel: (01270) 762492 Fax: (01270) 759449 E-mail: info@bathgatesilica.co.uk *Quarrying & processing of silica sand*

▶ Bathroom Beauty Of Bolton, 509 Tonge Moor Road, Bolton, BL2 3BG Tel: (01204) 592306 Fax: (01204) 595970 E-mail: enquires@bathroombeautyofbolton.co.uk *Fit bathroom suits*

Bathroom City, Seeleys Road, Birmingham, B11 2LQ Tel: 0121-753 0700 Fax: 0121-753 1110 E-mail: 101460.273@compuserve.com *Bathroom retailers*

▶ Bathroom Deals, 102 Finlay Road, Gloucester, GL4 6TP Tel: (01452) 336250 Fax: (01452) 332338 E-mail: sales@bathroomdeals.com *Bathroom suit manufrs*

Bathroom Emporium, Galgate Mill, Chapel Lane, Galgate, Lancaster, LA2 0PR Tel: (01524) 752929 Fax: (01524) 751031 E-mail: sales@bathroomemporiumltd.co.uk *Bathroom retailers*

▶ Bathroom Outlet, 77 Bicester Road, Kidlington, Oxfordshire, OX5 2LD Tel: (01865) 847546 Fax: (01865) 370740 *Bathroom distributors*

▶ Bathroom Refurbishments Specialists, 71 Beltony Drive, Crewe, CW1 4TX Tel: (01270) 255116 *Bathroom installers*

▶ Bathroom Studio Birtley, The Whitehouse, Durham Road, Birtley, County Durham, DH3 2QQ Tel: 0191 4922022 E-mail: enquiries@bathroomstudiobirtley.co.uk *Bathroom design or installation*

▶ Bathroombits4u Ltd, 26 Fraiary Gardens, Newport Pagnell, Buckinghamshire, MK16 0JZ Tel: (01908) 614012 E-mail: leonmaclean@bathroombits4u.co.uk *Online shop for bathrooms, showers, taps, toilets & sinks*

▶ Bathrooms Etc, 102-104 Hammersmith Road, London, W6 7JP Tel: (020) 8563 2255 Fax: (020) 8563 0333

▶ Bathrooms To Go, Unit 9 First Avenue, Marlow, Buckinghamshire, SL7 1YA Tel: (01628) 484443 Fax: (01628) 483688 *Suppliers of bathrooms*

▶ Bathstore, 23 Gloucester Road, Brighton, BN1 4AD Tel: (01273) 608088 Fax: (01273) 609099 *Bathrooms retailer*

▶ Bathstore.com Ltd, York Buildings, Edinburgh, EH2 1HY Tel: 0131-556 0333 Fax: 0131-557 4884 E-mail: edinburgh.central@bathstore.com *Bathroom product retailers*

▶ Bathstore.com Ltd, 87-89 Leeds Road, Harrogate, North Yorkshire, HG2 8BE Tel: (01423) 874400 Fax: (01423) 874400 E-mail: harrogate@bathstore.com *Bathrooms retail services*

▶ Bathstore.com Ltd, 62-82 Commercial Road, London, E1 1NU Tel: (020) 7702 9898 Fax: (020) 7702 3399 *Bathroom fittings or accessory retailers*

▶ Bathstore.com Ltd, 455 Yarmouth Road, Slough, SL1 4HB Tel: (01753) 516400 Fax: (01753) 539800 E-mail: slough@bathstore.com *Bathroom fitting manufrs*

▶ Bathstore.com Ltd, 4 The Pompey Centre, Fratton Way, Southsea, Hampshire, PO4 8SL Tel: (023) 9287 7000 Fax: (023) 9287 5900 *Bathroom retailers*

▶ Bathstore.com Ltd, Unit T4 Io Trade Centre, Hobley Drive, Swindon, SN3 4NS Tel: (01793) 834111 Fax: (01793) 834222 E-mail: swindon@bathstore.com *Minimalist & designer bathrooms sales*

Bathstore.com Ltd, Unit 2a Felnex Trading Estate, Wallington, Surrey, SM6 7EL Tel: (01923) 694740 Fax: (020) 8773 5004 E-mail: enquiries@bathstore.com *Bathroom retail chain*

▶ Bathtimes Bathroom Equipment, 3 New Road, Newhaven, East Sussex, BN9 0HE Tel: (01273) 513022 Fax: (01273) 513848 E-mail: info@bathtimesltd.co.uk *Bathroom showroom services*

Batley Body Builders Ltd, Thomas St, Bradford Road, Batley, West Yorkshire, WF17 8PR Tel: (01924) 473602 Fax: (01924) 471161 *Commercial vehicle body builders*

Batley & Robinson (Worsteds) Ltd, 7-9 Valley Road Business Park, Keighley, West Yorkshire, BD21 4LZ Tel: (0845) 1235516 Fax: (01535) 610047 E-mail: sales@batleyandrobinson.com *Worsted cloth manufrs*

Batley Wire Products, 268 Bradford Road, Batley, West Yorkshire, WF17 6HT Tel: (01924) 470739 Fax: (01924) 520946 *Bedspring manufrs*

▶ Baton Consulting Ltd, 41 Maple Crescent, Penketh, Warrington, WA5 2LE Tel: (01925) 790111 Fax: (01925) 790101 *Computer systems consultants*

Baton Lock Ltd, Baton House, 4TH Avenue The Village, Trafford Park, Manchester, M17 1DB Tel: 0161-877 4444 Fax: 0161-877 4545 E-mail: kevin.bratt@batonlockuk.com Principal Export Areas: Central/East Europe & West Europe *Locks manufrs*

Batoyle Freedom Group, 1 Charles Wood Road, Dereham, Norfolk, NR19 1SX Tel: (01362) 698728 Fax: (01362) 690254 *Lubricants & greases distributor*

Batoyle Freedom Group, Colne Vale Road, Milnsbridge, Huddersfield, HD3 4NT Tel: (01484) 653015 Fax: (01484) 460078 E-mail: bfgsales@aol.com Principal Export Areas: Worldwide *Lubricant manufrs* Also at: Nuneaton

▶ Batt Networks, The Belfry, Fraser Road, Erith, Kent, DA8 1QH Tel: (01322) 441165 Fax: (01322) 440492 E-mail: battnetworks.sales@batt.co.uk *Specialists in the supply of data & voice networking equipment*

▶ Batt Sails, 10 Broadbridge Business Centre, Delling Lane, Bosham, Chichester, West Sussex, PO18 8NF Tel: (01243) 575505 Fax: (01243) 574404 E-mail: info@battsails.com *Sail manufrs*

▶ Battech International Ltd, 83 Shropshire Street, Market Drayton, Shropshire, TF9 3DQ Tel: (0871) 5500051 E-mail: sales@bat-tech.co.uk *Batteries & power solutions suppliers*

Batten & Allen Ltd, Bridge End, Cirencester, Gloucestershire, GL7 1NQ Tel: (01285) 655220 Fax: (01285) 652650 E-mail: admin@batten-allen.co.uk *Precision pressings*

Battenfeld UK Ltd, 6 Valley Business Centre, Gordon Road, High Wycombe, Buckinghamshire, HP13 6EQ Tel: (01494) 450911 Fax: (01494) 444546 E-mail: abek.r@vuk.battenfeld.com *Plastics machinery manufrs*

Battersea Fire Protection Services, 35 Culmstock Road, London, SW11 6LY Tel: (020) 7228 6838 Fax: (020) 7738 2830 E-mail: battersea@btopenworld.com *Retailing fire protection equipment*

Battery Centre Ltd, 224 Neath Road, Landore, Swansea, SA1 2JG Tel: (01792) 774528 Fax: (01792) 772464 *Auto electrical diesel repair services & spares manufrs*

Battery Services (Standby) Ltd, 71 Thomson Drive, Bearsden, Glasgow, G61 3PB Tel: (0141) 956 5575 Fax: (0141) 943 1134 *Battery distributors & emergency lighting specialists*

Battery Specialists South East, 35 High Dewar Road, Rainham, Gillingham, Kent, ME8 8DN Tel: (01634) 262343 Fax: (01634) 262343 *Battery suppliers*

Battle Hayward & Bower Ltd, Crofton Drive, Lincoln, LN3 4NP Tel: (01522) 529206 Fax: (01522) 538960 E-mail: bhb@battles.co.uk *Animal health, veterinary medicines, pharmaceutical manufrs*

J. Battle, Pipers Drier Studio, Clarendon Park, Salisbury, SP5 3ES Tel: (01722) 711770 Fax: (01722) 506707 E-mail: jay.battle@ntlworld.com *Architectural stone carving, stone & monumental masonry specialists*

Batty & Dixon, Raymond Road, Doncaster, South Yorkshire, DN5 9PP Tel: (01302) 783130 Fax: (01302) 390440 *Contractors & joinery manufrs*

Batty Joinery Manufacturers, Bridge Works, 101 West Dock Street, Hull, HU3 4HH Tel: (01482) 326377 Fax: (01482) 585566 E-mail: colinsmith@battyjoinery.co.uk *Joinery manufrs*

Baty International, Victoria Road, Burgess Hill, West Sussex, RH15 9LB Tel: (01444) 235621 Fax: (01444) 246985 E-mail: sales@baty.co.uk *Manufacture, service & calibration*

Malcolm Baucher Ltd, Cavendish House, Brighton Road, Waterloo, Liverpool, L22 5NG Tel: 0151-920 8030 Fax: 0151-949 0527 E-mail: baucherbuild@aol.com *Building work & extensions*

▶ Baudains Trade Supplies Ltd, Les Amballes, St. Peter Port, Guernsey, GY1 1WT Tel: (01481) 724642 Fax: (01481) 714399 E-mail: peter@btsgsy.com *Engineering supplies & storage equipment supplies & handling*

▶ Baudelaire Ltd, 7 Prospect Business Centre, Prospect Road, Alresford, Hampshire, SO24 9UH Tel: (0870) 7776380 Fax: (0870) 7776382

Bauder Ltd, Broughton House, 26 Broughton Road, Ipswich, IP1 3QR Tel: (01473) 257671 Fax: (01473) 230761 E-mail: marketing@bauder.co.uk *Bauder leads the market in single source flat roof waterproofing systems. Our established pre-eminent reputation is founded on our long and successful track record across Europe for the manufacture, supply and installation of failure-free flat roof systems.*

▶ Bauer Inner City, The Dallam Court, Dallam Lane, Warrington, WA2 7LT Tel: (01925) 428940 Fax: (01925) 244133 E-mail: info@bauerinnercity.co.uk *Suppliers of barriers*

Baugh & Weedon Ltd, Beech Business Park, Tillington Road, Hereford, HR4 9QJ Tel: (01432) 267671 Fax: (01432) 359017 E-mail: sales@bandwndt.co.uk Principal Export Areas: Worldwide *Crack detection & magnetic particle inspection machinery manufrs*

▶ Baule UK Ltd, Baule House Earl Road, Stanley Green Trading Estate, Cheadle, Cheshire, SK8 6PT Tel: 0161-485 7000 Fax: 0161-485 7700 E-mail: d.walker@bauleuk.com *Manufacture of polyurethane & epoxy resin systems*

Herbert Baumann Ltd, Bago Ho, 11-15 Chase Rd, Park Royal, London, NW10 6PT Tel: (020) 8955 6400 Fax: (020) 8883 3833 *Cosmetic bags & grooming sets manufrs*

Baumann Springs & Pressings UK Ltd, East Mill Lane, Sherborne, Dorset, DT9 3DR Tel: (01935) 818100 Fax: (01935) 814141 E-mail: info@baumann-springs.com *Stainless steel spring & coil spring manufrs*

Bauromat UK, Beauchamp Business Centre, Sparrowhawk Close, Malvern, Worcestershire, WR14 1GL Tel: (01684) 575757 Fax: (01684) 569887 E-mail: info@bauromat.co.uk *Robot systems & industrial machinery design & manufrs*

Bauschlinnemann UK, Widow Hill Road, Heasandford Industrial Estate, Burnley, Lancashire, BB10 2TB Tel: (01282) 686850 Fax: (01282) 412361 E-mail: armabord@armabord.co.uk *Melamine edge banding manufrs*

▶ Bav Presentation Services, Rookhurst, Forest Road, Effingham Junction, Leatherhead, Surrey, KT24 5HD Tel: (01483) 280041 E-mail: info@bavltd.co.uk *Audio video maintenance services*

Bawa Engineering Ltd, Units 4 & 5 Fenlake Industrial Estate, Fenlake Road, Bedford, MK42 0ET Tel: (01234) 215906 Fax: (01234) 327858 *General engineers*

▶ Bawden Quinn Associates, Sanderum House, 38 Oakley Road, Chinnor, Oxfordshire, OX39 4TW Tel: (01844) 355622 Fax: (01844) 353553 E-mail: contact@bawden-quinn.co.uk *Your strategic partner: over 15 years running IT; IT Strategy, CRM, Security & Data Protection. 8 years within the Recruitment and Financial Services Sectors; British Computer Society Members.*

▶ Bawden Quinn Associates Ltd, Manchester Business Park, 3000 Aviator Way, Manchester, M22 5TG Tel: 0161-266 1017 Fax: 0161-266 1001 E-mail: sales@bawden-quinn.co.uk *Your strategic partner: over 15 years running IT; IT Strategy, CRM, Security & Data Protection. 8 years within the Recruitment and Financial Services Sectors; British Computer Society Members.*

Bawtry Pine Furniture, Woodhouse, Cooke Street, Bentley, Doncaster, South Yorkshire, DN5 0BH Tel: (01302) 875578 *Pine furniture manufrs*

Baxa Ltd, Radius Court, Eastern Road, Bracknell, Berkshire, RG12 2UP Tel: (01344) 890916 Fax: (01344) 890917 *Medical device distributors*

Baxenden Chemicals Ltd, Paragon Works, Rising Bridge, Accrington, Lancashire, BB5 2SL Tel: (01254) 872278 Fax: (01254) 871247 *Speciality chemical manufrs*

Baxi Heating Ltd, Brook House, Coventry Road, Warwick, CV34 4LL Tel: (01772) 693700 Fax: (01926) 410006 E-mail: service@heatteam.co.uk *Manufacturers boilers & fires*

▶ Baxter Ltd, 8 Smith Street, Dundee, DD3 8AZ Tel: (01382) 832900

Baxter, 103 Arundel Street, Sheffield, S1 2NT Tel: 0114-272 1575 Fax: 0114-272 5354 E-mail: anne@wjabaxter.co.uk *Silverware manufacturing blacksmiths*

Baxter Associates, 24 Ben Madigan Heights, Newtownabbey, County Antrim, BT36 7PY Tel: (028) 9037 0567 Fax: (028) 9028 3324 E-mail: sales@baxterworld.com *Chartered accountants*

Baxter Avey & Co. Ltd, The Hill House, Castor, Peterborough, PE5 7BS Tel: (01733) 380597 Fax: (01733) 380365 E-mail: william.baxter@virgin.net *Agricultural merchants*

▶ Baxter (Consultants) Ltd, Floor 6, 456-458 The Strand, London, WC2R 0DZ Tel: 07092 090755 E-mail: enquiries@baxterconsultants.com *Operating from the UK and Argentina, Baxter Consultants are able to offer a wide range of consultancy solutions focussing on Business Development. Our expertise is primarily in the operational activities where technical or functional know-how is required. We are a small company; accepting each assignment on merit*

continued

*not value. We work with the client to provide a specific service in pursuit of the wider strategic aims, be that market growth, product development, process improvement, cost reduction etc. *Alternatively we can carry out an assessment of the business with recommendations of our own, taking direction from the clients' own vision for success.*Whatever stage of growth your are experiencing, we offer a helping hand. *BC is a consultancy unique in its strengths and expertise, competitively priced, professionally trained and experienced in several industries.*

David Baxter, Unit J, Minvera Business Park, Miller Street, Johnstone, Renfrewshire, PA5 8HP Tel: (01505) 344998 Fax: (01505) 344942 E-mail: dbaxtermb@aol.com *Medical suppliers*

Baxter Hart & Abraham Ltd, 141 New Bedford Road, Luton, LU3 1LF Tel: (01582) 721381 Fax: (01582) 451033 E-mail: hornbha@aol.com *Hat trade suppliers & ribbon merchants*

Baxter Healthcare Ltd, Wallingford Road, Compton, Newbury, Berkshire, RG20 7QW Tel: (01635) 206000 Fax: (01635) 206115 E-mail: admin@baxterhealthcare.co.uk *Suppliers of medical products* Also at: Cumbernauld, Northampton & Thetford

Baxter Healthcare Ltd, Mount Vernon Hospital, Rickmansworth Road, Northwood, Middlesex, HA6 2RN Tel: (01923) 828230 Fax: (01923) 844764 *Chemotherapy medicines*

Leigh Baxter Associates Ltd, 15-17 Robert Leonard Industrial Site, Stock Road, Southend-on-Sea, SS2 5QD Tel: (01702) 460970 Fax: (01702) 600544 E-mail: sales@leighbaxter.co.uk *General purpose hoses*

Baxter Murray, Unit 2 69a Aigburth Park, Belfast, BT4 1PQ Tel: (028) 9065 0209 Fax: (028) 9065 0209 *Chocolates manufrs*

Baxters Food Group, Baxters Of Speyside, Fochabers, Morayshire, IV32 7LD Tel: (01343) 820393 Fax: (01343) 820286 E-mail: info@baxters.co.uk *Food soup, beetroot & preserves manufrs*

▶ Bay Area Sign Solutions, Unit 1, Farfield Business Park, Main Road, Wykeham, Scarborough, North Yorkshire, YO13 9QB Tel: (01723) 866680 Fax: (01723) 865509 E-mail: info@bay-area.co.uk *Sign & display manufacturers commercial & industrial engravers*

Bay Class Yachts Ltd, Conyer Wharf, Teynham, Sittingbourne, Kent, ME9 9HN Tel: (01795) 520787 Fax: (01795) 520788 *Boating company*

▶ Bay Computer Maintenance, 231 Torquay Road, Paignton, Devon, TQ3 2HW Tel: (01803) 555367 E-mail: sales@baycomputers.co.uk *www.baycomputers.co.uk*

▶ Bay Design, 1 Stanways Cottage, Hatfield Broad Oak, Bishop's Stortford, Hertfordshire, CM22 7JS Tel: (01279) 718139 Fax: (01279) 718139 E-mail: michele@bay-design.co.uk *Collection of bespoke lampshades and offering commissions to suit any interior*

▶ Bay House, Unit 1 New Rookery Farm, Little London, Silverstone, Towcester, Northamptonshire, NN12 8UP Tel: (01327) 856988 Fax: (01327) 856967 E-mail: sales@bay-house.co.uk *Aromatherapy products suppliers*

Bay Management Services Ltd, Applegarth House, Heversham, Milnthorpe, Cumbria, LA7 7FD Tel: (01539) 564642 *Laundry consultancy & facility management services*

Bay Plastics Ltd, Unit H1, High Flatworth, Tyne Tunnel Trading Estate, North Shields, Tyne & Wear, NE29 7UZ Tel: 0191-258 0777 Fax: 0191-258 1010 E-mail: sales@bayplastics.co.uk *Bay Plastics Limited are plastic stockist and plastic fabricators, supplying customers all over the world with quality plastic materials and products at competitive prices. The company offers an extensive range of stock to accommodate the diverse market for semi-finished plastic materials from global brands such as Perspex Acrylic, Palram Polycarbonate Sheets to Quadrant Engineering Plastics. Our main focus is providing exceptional level of service through our professional cutting department allowing customers to purchase custom sizes in plastic sheets and rods, with rapid delivery time. Bay Plastics Fabrication can produce finished plastic parts for all your industrial and commercial plastic applications. We can fulfil all your professional bespoke plastic manufacturing requirements from prototypes to batch production runs. Our commitment to service and unrivalled product knowledge enables us to guide you in all aspects of plastics material selection and component design.*

▶ Bay Precision, 20 Westgate, Morecambe, Lancashire, LA3 3LN Tel: (01524) 409955

▶ Bay Recruitment, The Enterprise Centre, Town Hall Approach road, London, London, N15 4RX Tel: 0800 014 4249 Fax: 020 8509 8752 E-mail: info@bayconstruction.co.uk *supply of construction wokers,project managers,general building maitenance.*

▶ Bay Ridge, Design House, 20-22 Beulah Road, London, SW19 3SB Tel: (020) 8543 8598 Fax: (020) 8542 6831 E-mail: office@bayridge-uk.com

▶ Bay Tile Company, 90 Canterbury Road, Herne Bay, Kent, CT6 5SB Tel: (01227) 283838 Fax: (01227) 283838 *Ceramic tile retail*

Bay Tree, 15 Pennys Walk, Ferndown, Dorset, BH22 9TH Tel: (01202) 896096 Fax: (01202) 895296 *Health product suppliers*

Bay Tree Candies, Unit 1f Barbican Rise Industrial Estate, Looe, Cornwall, PL13 1QQ Tel: (01503) 262413 Fax: (01503) 262413 E-mail: baytreecandies@btconnect.com *Confectionary manufrs*

Bayard Packaging Ltd, Unit 16 Deptford Trading Estate, Blackhorse Road, London, SE8 5HY Tel: (020) 8692 4444 Fax: (020) 8692 3851 E-mail: sales@bayardpackaging.co.uk *Polythene bag & envelope manufrs*

Baybridge Press Tools Ltd, 151 Charles Henry Street, Birmingham, B12 0SD Tel: 0121-622 3878 Fax: 0121-622 3743 E-mail: baybridgetools@aol.com *Press tool manufrs*

Baydel Ltd, Brook Way, Leatherhead, Surrey, KT22 7NA Tel: (01372) 378811 Fax: (01372) 386960 E-mail: enquiry@baydel.com *Computer system manufrs*

Bayer, 230 Science Park, Milton Road, Cambridge, CB4 0WB Tel: (01223) 226500 Fax: (01223) 426240 Principal Export Areas: Worldwide *Crop science* Also at: Kings Lynn, Saffron Walden & Widnes

Bayer P.L.C., 47 Deerdykes View, Westfield, Glasgow, G68 9HN Tel: (01236) 458909 Fax: (01236) 458828 *Chemist suppliers & distributors*

Bayer UK plc, Bayer House, Strawberry Hill, Newbury, Berkshire, RG14 1JA Tel: (01635) 563000 Fax: (01635) 563393 E-mail: corporate.communications@bayer.co.uk *Chemical manufacturers; pharmaceutical manufacturers/contract manufacturing; pharmaceutical chemical manufacturers & plastic raw/basic materials suppliers/factors*

Bayer UK plc, Bayer House, Strawberry Hill, Newbury, Berkshire, RG14 1JA Tel: (01635) 563000 E-mail: corporate.communications@bayer.co.uk *Chemicals, pharmaceutical industry & diagnostic products distributors*

Bayford & Co. Ltd, Bowcliffe Hall, Bramham, Wetherby, West Yorkshire, LS23 6LP Tel: (01937) 541111 Fax: (01937) 841465 E-mail: sales@bayford.co.uk *Fuel oil distributors*

Bayford Cambria, Tir Llwyd Enterprise Park, Kinmel Bay, Rhyl, Clwyd, LL18 5JH Tel: (01745) 332121 Fax: (01745) 332122 E-mail: sales@BAYFORDCAMBRIA.co.uk *Fuel oil & lubricating oil distributors*

▶ Bayford Foods Ltd, Unit 24, Wynford Farm Industrial Estate, Belbins, Romsey, Hampshire, SO51 0PW Tel: (01794) 367567

Bayham Ltd, Rutherford Road, Daneshill West, Basingstoke, Hampshire, RG24 8PG Tel: (01256) 464911 Fax: (01256) 464366 E-mail: sales@bayham.demon.co.uk *Liquid level control equipment manufrs*

Bayham Foods Ltd, PO Box 2081, Hope Valley, Derbyshire, S32 5BW Tel: (01433) 639717 Fax: (01433) 639718 *Cheese importer & distributors*

Bayles & Wylie Ltd, Forge Mill, Bestwood, Nottingham, NG6 8SX Tel: 0115-927 8227 Fax: 0115-977 0281 *Vermin destroyer manufrs*

Bayline Systems Ltd, 76 Abergele Road, Colwyn Bay, Clwyd, LL29 7PP Tel: (01492) 535445 Fax: (01492) 535443 E-mail: sales@bayline.co.uk *Communications & security distributors*

Baylis Automotive, Unit 49g, Pipers Road, Park Farm Industrial Estate, Redditch, Worcestershire, B98 0HU Tel: (01527) 517220 Fax: (01527) 517114 E-mail: tclews@baylisautomotive.com Principal Export Areas: Central/East Europe & South America *Wired formed components*

▶ Baylis Distribution Ltd, Dealain House 72 Napier Road, Wardpark North, Cumbernauld, Glasgow, G68 0DF Tel: (01236) 736510 Fax: (01236) 736525 E-mail: admin@bayliss.co.uk

Baylis Distribution Ltd, New Potter Grange Road, Goole, North Humberside, DN14 6BZ Tel: (01405) 766174 Fax: (01405) 766270 *Haulage & storage contractors*

Baylis Distribution Ltd, Billington Road, Leighton Buzzard, Bedfordshire, LU7 9HH Tel: (01525) 375550 Fax: (01525) 850149 E-mail: email@baylislogistics.com *Road transport contracting services*

Baylis Distribution Ltd, Hamilton House, Birchwood Lane, Moore, Warrington, WA4 6XJ Tel: (01925) 656770 Fax: (01925) 571049 *Haulage and storage contractors*

▶ Baylis & Harding, Unit 10 The I O Centre, Nash Road, Redditch, Worcestershire, B98 7AS Tel: (01527) 505000 Fax: (01527) 505001 E-mail: post@bayhar.com *Toiletries manufrs*

Baylis Hargreaves Ltd, Unit 2b2 Seacroft Industrial Estate, Coal Road, Leeds, LS14 2AQ Tel: 0113-273 6689 Fax: 0113-265 0236 E-mail: sales@baylishargreaves.com *Lining fabric distributors*

Baylis Logistics Ltd, Unit 11, Pucklechurch Trading Estate, Pucklechurch, Bristol, BS16 9QH Tel: 0117-937 2580 Fax: 0117-937 4161 *Road transport& haulage agents*

A.J. Bayliss Petroleum Engineers Ltd, Unit 1, Hodfar Road, Stourport-On-Severn, Worcestershire, DY13 9QB Tel: (01299) 824541 Fax: (01299) 827638 E-mail: simon@ajbayliss.demon.co.uk *Petrol pump maintenance & petroleum engineers*

C.J. Bayliss (Hereford) Ltd, Albert House, Holmer, Hereford, HR1 1JN Tel: (01432) 265130 Fax: (01432) 274435 E-mail: cjbayliss@btconnect.com *Building contractors*

Bayliss & Miles Construction, 20 Park Way, Newbury, Berkshire, RG14 1EE Tel: (01635) 32280 Fax: (01635) 32260 E-mail: baylissandmiles@lineone.net *Ground workers services*

Bayliss Patterns Walsall Ltd, Rollingmill Street, Walsall, WS2 9EG Tel: (01922) 626972 Fax: (01922) 633748 *Non-ferrous founders*

Bayliss Precision Components Ltd, Blenheim Road, Airfield Industrial Estate, Ashbourne, Derbyshire, DE6 1HA Tel: (01335) 342981 Fax: (01335) 343860 E-mail: info@bayliss.uk.com *Greenhouse autovents; Precision engineering services*

Bayliss Wright Gados Ltd, 50 Park Street, Luton, LU1 3ET Tel: (01582) 722186 Fax: (01582) 727780 E-mail: baylisswright@eurotelbroadband.com *Art supply distributors*

Baymarine Industrial Services Ltd, Aqua-Plan House, Burt Street, Cardiff, CF10 5FZ Tel: (029) 2045 3700 Fax: (029) 2045 0077 *Ship repairers & tank clean repair*

Baymont Alarms York, 137 Brecksfield, Skelton, York, YO30 1YE Tel: (01904) 471120 Fax: (01904) 471121 E-mail: sales@baymontalarms.uk *Burglar alarms installers*

Baynell, 85-86 Darlington Street, Wolverhampton, WV1 4NG Tel: (01902) 425616 Fax: (01902) 311242 *Bedding manufrs*

▶ Baynes & Son Ltd, Unit 16 Llandygai Industrial Estate, Llandygai, Bangor, Gwynedd, LL57 4YH Tel: (01248) 353533 Fax: (01248) 361144

▶ Baynham Meikle Partnership, 8 Meadow Road, Harborne, Birmingham, B17 8BU Tel: 0121-434 4100 Fax: 0121-434 4073

Baynham & Stanfield Badge Co. Ltd, 32b Coppice Industrial Trading Estate, Kidderminster, Worcestershire, DY11 7QY Tel: (01562) 60738 Fax: (01562) 829747 E-mail: sales@baynhambadges.co.uk *Badge manufrs*

▶ Bayphase Ltd, Clearglen House, 151 Frimley Road, Camberley, Surrey, GU15 2PS Tel: (01276) 682828 Fax: (01276) 63334 E-mail: sales@bayphase.com *Engineering consultancy*

▶ Baystream, Unit 4 Metro Trading Centre, Second Way, Wembley, Middlesex, HA9 0YJ Tel: (020) 8903 5552 Fax: (020) 8903 9595

Bayswater Tubes & Sections Ltd, The Tube Mills, Pencoed, Bridgend, Mid Glamorgan, CF35 6UG Tel: (01656) 860581 Fax: (01656) 860906 E-mail: sales@aluminiumtubes.com *Aluminium welded tube manufrs*

▶ Baytree Industries Ltd, Resource House, Brunel Road, St. Leonards-on-Sea, East Sussex, TN38 9RT Tel: (01424) 854460 Fax: (01424) 854461 E-mail: sales@bt-ind.com *Sheet metal work & precision engineers & electronics*

▶ Bayview Angling, 12 Greenfield Road, Colwyn Bay, Clwyd, LL29 8EL Tel: (01492) 535888 *Fishing tackle manufrs*

Baz Light Design & Installation, 6 Golden Court, Bridge Road, Lowestoft, Suffolk, NR32 3LU Tel: (01502) 501628 Fax: (01502) 501628 *Designers*

Baz Roll Products Ltd, Portemarsh Road, Calne, Wiltshire, SN11 9BW Tel: (01249) 822222 Fax: (01249) 822300 E-mail: sales@bazroll.co.uk *Castor distributors & manufrs*

Bazen & Page, 127 Whyke Lane, Chichester, West Sussex, PO19 8AU Tel: (01243) 782067 Fax: (01243) 869862 E-mail: bazen.page@tiscali.co.uk *Electrical contractors*

▶ Bazeray, PO Box 3936, Bracknell, Berkshire, RG42 7PX Tel: (01344) 884916 Fax: (01344) 884916 E-mail: info@bazeray.co.uk *Personalisation & printing service*

▶ BB Online UK Ltd, PO Box 2162, Luton, LU3 2JL Tel: (01582) 572148 Fax: (01582) 585057 E-mail: info@bb-online.co.uk *Iccan accredited registrar*

BBC Childrens Learning, P O Box 234, Wetherby, West Yorkshire, LS23 7EU Tel: (0870) 8308000 Fax: (0870) 8308002 *School books & equipment distributor & manufrs*

▶ BBC Security Systems, 11 Franklyn Avenue, Southampton, SO19 8AN Tel: (0845) 2306611 Fax: (0845) 2306622 *Security installation*

BBN Industrial Fasteners Ltd, Locksley, London End, Beaconsfield, Buckinghamshire, HP9 2JB Tel: (01494) 680078 Fax: (01494) 680093 *Bolt nut & fastener distributors*

BBS, Unit 2-3 Cauldwell Walk, Bedford, MK42 9DT Tel: (01234) 268838 Fax: (01234) 359071 *Crash repairers*

BBS Graphix Group, Market St, Bingley, W. Yorkshire, BD16 2HP Tel: (01274) 510562 Fax: (01274) 510562 E-mail: info@bbsgraphixs.com *Signs & graphics manufrs*

▶ BC Corporate Interiors Ltd, Front Office - David Bletsoe Brown Site, Telford Way, Telford Way Industrial Estate, Kettering, Northamptonshire, NN16 8UN Tel: (01536) 521793 Fax: (01536) 521778 E-mail: mail@bcci-ltd.co.uk *Commercial interior fitting specialists*

BC Plastic Mouldings Ltd, Commercial Road, Walsall, WS2 7NQ Tel: (01922) 497888 Fax: (01922) 478600 E-mail: cjms@btconnect.com *Plastic injection moulders*

▶ BCB Environmental Management Ltd, Liverpool Road, Eccles, Manchester, M30 7HZ Tel: (0870) 2432341 Fax: 08702 432389 E-mail: sales@bcbenvironmental.co.uk *BCB specialises in providing a national hazardous waste collection and disposal service for all types of wastes in packages and drums.*

BCC, B Station Road, Newcastle Emlyn, Dyfed, SA38 9BY Tel: (01239) 710823 Fax: (01239) 711449 E-mail: sales@bccit.co.uk *Computer software & hardware suppliers*

BCC Stockholders Ltd, Pontardulais Road, Gorseinon, Swansea, SA4 4FQ Tel: (01792) 893985 Fax: (01792) 893124 E-mail: sales@rollaclad.com *Steel roofing & cladding sheets manufrs*

BCCB Trade Organisations, 1 Westminster Palace Gardens, Artillery Row, London, SW1P 1RJ Tel: (020) 7222 3651 Fax: (020) 7222 3664 E-mail: mail@bccb.co.uk *Trade association*

BCD Cables Ltd, The E-Tech Centre, Boundary Road, Great Yarmouth, Norfolk, NR31 0LY Tel: (01493) 604604 Fax: (01493) 604606 E-mail: john.milne@etechcentre.com *Electrical cable distributors*

Bce Ltd, 9 Whitehall Trading Estate, Gerrish Avenue, Whitehall, Bristol, BS5 9DF Tel: 0117-955 1770 Fax: 0117-955 2271 E-mail: admin@bce-uk.com *Pool & snooker equipment distributors*

▶ BCF Designs Ltd, Phoenix House, Phoenix Way, Cirencester, Gloucestershire, GL7 1QG Tel: (01285) 642434 Fax: (01285) 640606 *Design & supply of operational level ground support equipment*

▶ BCHR Ltd, 14 Marlborough Crescent, Sevenoaks, Kent, TN13 2HP Tel: (01732) 459743 Fax: 01732 779271 E-mail: barry@bchr.com *Job evaluation, reward systems, performance management, personnel policies*

▶ BCM Technologies Ltd, Battle Court, Mill Lane Boroughbridge, York, YO51 9LH Tel: (01423) 324842 Fax: (08701) 38757 E-mail: martin.henry@battlecourt.fsnet.co.uk *Design and manufacture of industrial control and*

continued

*instrumentation systems. Supply of PLC, HMI and drive systems and software.**Design and manufacture of special purpose machines and manufacturing cells.**

BCP Fabrication Ltd, Dormston Trading Estate, Burton Road, Dudley, West Midlands, DY1 2UF Tel: (01902) 885777 Fax: (01902) 883344 *Structural steelwork & security grille manufrs*

BCP Fluted Packaging Ltd, Crompton House, Nuttall Way Shadsworth, Shadsworth Business Park, Blackburn, BB1 2JT Tel: (01254) 677790 Fax: (01254) 681736 E-mail: info@bcpflute.com Principal Export Areas: Worldwide *Corrugated converters*

▶ BCR, 8-9 171 Church Hill Road, Thurmaston, Leicester, LE4 8DH Tel: 0116-269 7774 Fax: 0116-210 9209 E-mail: enquireies@bouncycastlerepairs.com *Bouncy castle repairers*

▶ bcrodda, bcrodda, Tavistock, Devon, PL19 8BN Tel: 07989 893658 *I am a Freelance IT consultant based in the South West of England.*I help both business (SME"s) and home computer users maintain, repair and upgrade their systems, and by so doing, make the most out of their IT systems and infrastructure.*If it"s a small network upgrade or a full system overhaul I"m the man to speak to.*

▶ BCS, 364 Two Mile Hill Road, Bristol, BS15 1AH Tel: 0117-967 5707 Fax: 0117-940 7555 E-mail: b.c.s@virgin.net *Computer maintenance & repair*

BCS Uk Ltd, Marle Place, Brenchley, Tonbridge, Kent, TN12 7HS Tel: (01892) 724534 Fax: (01892) 724099 *Chemical distributors*

Bda, The Studio, Pipits Croft, Bicester, Oxfordshire, OX26 6XW Tel: (01869) 322158 Fax: (01869) 322158 E-mail: info@bda-uk.com *New product development, design, packaging & technical illustration*

▶ B-Dacs Ltd, 1 Cameron Gate, 145 New Edinburgh Road, Uddingston, Glasgow, G71 6NF Tel: (01698) 801181 Fax: (01698) 801111

BDC Materials Handling, Airedale Works, Fountain Street, Morley, Leeds, LS27 0AA Tel: 0113-219 7200 Fax: 0113-219 7201 E-mail: info@bdcgroup.co.uk *Lifting equipment, fork lifts & repairs*

▶ BDE Group, 5 Tun Yard, Peardon Street, London, SW8 3HT Tel: 0870 128 7800 Fax: 020 7801 8866 E-mail: sales@bdegroup.co.uk *IT support consultancy*

▶ Bde Group, Blackpole Trading Estate West, Worcester, WR3 8ZP Tel: (0870) 1287800 Fax: (01905) 756574 E-mail: sales@bdegroup.co.uk *BDE provide the complete range of sage business software for all your financial, manufacturing, retail and distribution needs. We provide solutions for small, medium and large businesses, providing over 25 years of experience in professional I.T services. Services include the supply and support of Sage Line 50, Sage Line 100/MMS, Sage Line 200, Sage Line 500 and CRM software - ACT & SalesLOGIX. BDE Group operates from four UK locations in Worcester, London, Leeds and Bristol.*

BDJ Engineering Worcester Ltd, A Carden Close, Worcester, WR1 2AR Tel: (01905) 23616 Fax: (01905) 22242 E-mail: brian@bdjengineering.wanadoo.co.uk *Precision & production engineers*

BDJR Computers Ltd, 6 St Albans Square, Bootle, Merseyside, L20 7BA Tel: 0151-922 0430 Fax: 0151-474 0703 E-mail: kevin@bdjr.com *Computer sales & network installers*

BDK Industrial Products, Levington Park, Bridge Road, Levington, Ipswich, IP10 0JE Tel: (01473) 659059 Fax: (01473) 659104 E-mail: sales@bdk.uk.com *BDK, the adhesive technology specialists, are a leading distributor, converter and developer of adhesive products for over 48 years. Providing a range of industrial adhesives, converted technical adhesive tapes and bespoke medical adhesive products, BDK apply their expertise to find solutions to meet your requirements in industries as diverse as Medical to Automotive, Photographic to Security. Operating in accordance with ISO 9001:2000 and ISO 485 with a class 7 (,000) clean room facility. BDK has a trained and experienced Technical Sales team available to advise customers on the suitability, cost effectiveness presentation of adhesive technology from some of the worlds leading adhesive manufactures. BDK's Quality Assurance employ appropriate testing procedures to ensure product consistency. Statistical process Control (SPC) data, FMEA, Cpk studies etc can also be provided as required.*

BDP Surfacing Ltd, Raynesway, Derby, DE24 0DW Tel: (01332) 571806 Fax: (01332) 574278 *Asphalt & macadam contractors*

▶ BDR Civil, 4c Belmont Buildings, High Street, Crowborough, East Sussex, TN6 2QB Tel: (01892) 660057 Fax: (01892) 660063

BDS Computer, 1 Rookery Court, Weller Drive, Finchampstead, Wokingham, Berkshire, RG40 4QZ Tel: 0118-973 7000 Fax: 0118-973 7070 E-mail: gen@bds.co.uk *Computer peripheral equipment*

BDS Consultants, 4 Cumberland Road, Urmston, Manchester, M41 9HS Tel: 0161-748 2712 Fax: 0161-748 2378 E-mail: info@bds-consultants.co.uk *Health & safety, food safety, fire safety,& first aid consultancy services*

BDS Industrial Fabrics, 44-46 Percy Road, Leicester, LE2 8FP Tel: 0116-283 9933 Fax: 0116-283 9966 *Industrial fabrics manufrs*

▶ Be Modern Ltd, 19 Bedesway, Jarrow, Tyne & Wear, NE32 3HQ Tel: 0191-428 0444 Fax: 0191-489 0620 E-mail: info@bemodern.co.uk

Be Modern Ltd, Head Office, Western Approach, South Shields, Tyne & Wear, NE33 5QZ Tel: 0191-455 3571 Fax: 0191-456 5556 E-mail: justina.hathaway@bemodern.co.uk *Fire surrounds & bathroom manufrs*

Be Spares Marine, 9 Town Quay Wharf, Abbey Road, Barking, Essex, IG11 7BZ Tel: (020) 8594 9409 Fax: (020) 8594 9429 E-mail: sales@besparesmarine.co.uk *Marine equipment suppliers*

Be Textiles Ltd, 5 London Street, Leicester, LE5 3RL Tel: 0116-221 3300

Be That Body, Christs Hospital Sports Centre, Christs Hospital, Horsham, West Sussex, RH13 0YP Tel: (023) 8025 1125 E-mail: enquiries@bethatbody.com *Exclusive gym, leisure & sports clothing*

Bea Fastening Systems Ltd, Waterside Road, Beverley, North Humberside, HU17 0ST Tel: (01482) 889911 Fax: (01482) 871804 E-mail: sales@uk.bea-group.com Principal Export Areas: Worldwide *Manufacturers of nail collated coils, strips & industrial stapling machines & staplers*

▶ Beach Display, 7 Ormont Avenue, Thornton-Cleveleys, Lancashire, FY5 2BT Tel: (01253) 869202 Fax: (01253) 869202 E-mail: phill@beachdisplay.com *Christmas supplies for retailers*

▶ Beach Entertainments, 89 The Ridgway, Brighton, BN2 6PB Tel: (01273) 388424 *Professional mobile disco entertainment. Superb light show and top quality sound system. Karaoke, bands and PA hire also available.*

▶ Beach Huts.com, 23 Richmond Park Avenue, Bournemouth, BH8 9DL Tel: (01202) 315437 E-mail: beach-huts@jxwd.co.uk *Find a beach hut or chalet to rent this summer /Advertise your beach hut or chalet to rent...*

Beach Signs Ltd, Leigh Street, Sheffield, S9 2PR Tel: 0114-243 7382 Fax: 0114-262 6550 E-mail: sales@beachsign.net *Sign manufrs*

Beacon Associates, The Pines, Templewood Lane, Farnham Common, Slough, SL2 3HQ Tel: (01753) 648234 Fax: (01753) 648234 *Industrial door manufrs*

▶ Beacon Associates, 18 Wrekin Drive, Wergs, Wolverhampton, WV6 8UJ Tel: (01902) 755347 Fax: (01902) 754446 E-mail: mpb@beacon-associates.co.uk *IT system improvements & project management services*

Beacon Blinds Ltd, 15 Fore Street, Totnes, Devon, TQ9 5DA Tel: (01803) 867200 Fax: (01803) 867952 *Blinds retailers*

Beacon Computer Technology Ltd, 43 Clifton Road, Cambridge, CB1 7ED Tel: (01223) 506616 Fax: (01223) 506620 E-mail: sales@beacon-ct.co.uk *Software house*

Beacon Dodsworth Ltd, Garth Mews, Sim Balk Lane, Bishopthorpe, York, YO23 2UE Tel: (01904) 701020 Fax: (01904) 701030 E-mail: info@beacon-dodsworth.co.uk *Software development specialists*

Beacon Horseboxes, The Haulage Yard, Wyck Beacon, Upper Rissington, Cheltenham, Gloucestershire, GL54 2NE Tel: (01451) 821289 Fax: (01451) 810423 *Horsebox refurbishment & suppliers*

Beacon Insulation Supplies Ltd, Bleak Hall Farm, Bleak Lane, Lathom, Ormskirk, Lancashire, L40 4BP Tel: (01704) 897878 Fax: (01704) 897879 *Insulation conversion contractors*

▶ Beacon Lights, Capel Grange, Bedford Road, Holwell, Hitchin, Hertfordshire, SG5 3RT Tel: (01462) 711919

Beacon Metal Finishers Ltd, Unit 10 Sirhowy Industrial Estate, Thomas Ellis Way, Sirhowy, Tredegar, Gwent, NP22 4QZ Tel: (01495) 711383 Fax: (01495) 711383 *Electroplaters*

Beacon Printers Penarth Ltd, Leyshons Buildings, Cornerswell Road, Penarth, South Glamorgan, CF64 2XS Tel: (029) 2070 8415 Fax: (029) 2070 3754 E-mail: sales@beaconprinters.co.uk *Digital & litho printing, full finishing department & studio service*

Beacon Training Co., 21 Thetford Road, Birmingham, B42 2JA Tel: 0121-357 2992 Fax: 0121-357 2992 *Fork lift operations training*

Beacon Water Treatments Ltd, 4 Parsons Hall, High Street, Irchester, Wellingborough, Northamptonshire, NN29 7AB Tel: (01933) 410066 Fax: (01933) 410077 E-mail: beaconwt@ukf.net *Water treatment*

Beacon Woodcraft Ltd, Queen Street, Premier Business Park, Walsall, WS2 9NT Tel: (01922) 613255 Fax: (01922) 634720 E-mail: info@beaconwoodcraft.co.uk *Publicans bar fitters*

Beaconsfield Footwear Ltd, 2 Peel Road, Skelmersdale, Lancashire, WN8 9PT Tel: (01695) 712720 Fax: (01695) 712715 E-mail: info@hotter.co.uk *Footwear manufrs*

Beaconsfield Products Halesowen Ltd, Foxoak Street, Cradley Heath, West Midlands, B64 5DE Tel: (01384) 569571 Fax: (01384) 566328 E-mail: sales@beacoproducts.co.uk *Manufacturers of forgings & fabrications*

▶ Bead Envy, 4 Killerby Lane, Cayton, Scarborough, North Yorkshire, YO11 3TP Tel: 01262 470229 E-mail: emma@beadenvy.co.uk *Manufacture glass lamp worked beads, bead sets, focal beads*

Bead Exclusive, 119-121 Teignmouth Road, Torquay, TQ1 4HA Tel: (01803) 322000 Fax: (01803) 322250 E-mail: sales@beadexclusive.com *Mail order beads*

Bead Shop Retail Wholesale, 21a Tower Street, London, WC2H 9NS Tel: (020) 7240 0931 E-mail: sales@beadworks.com *Beads wholesalers & retailers*

▶ Bead Solutions, 13 Seaway Road, Paignton, Devon, TQ3 2NX Tel: (01803) 552072 Fax: 01803 552072 E-mail: beads@beadsolutions.co.uk *Suppliers of glass, crystal beads metal findings to the jewellery*

▶ Bead Training, Development House, 24 Heaton Close, Poulton-Le-Fylde, Lancashire, FY6 7TY Tel: 01253 890790 Fax: 01253 890790 E-mail: enquiries@beadtraining.com *We provide training for nurses, doctors and healthcare assistants in primary care on aspects of patient assessment, emergency assessment, cardiovascular disease, chronic heart failure and diabetes. All of our courses are very practical based, teaching skills that are needed for every*

continued

day practice, by doctors and nurses that are working in the field they teach. Courses are run either over weekends or commissioned by primary care trusts for local services.

Beadles Group Ltd, 370 Princes Road, Dartford, DA1 1LN Tel: (01322) 222201 Fax: (01322) 289896 E-mail: info@beadles-dartford.volkswagen.co.uk *Volkswagen & manufacture franchise*

▶ Beads By Design, 4, Nunnery Walk, South Cave, Brough, East Yorkshire, HU15 2JA Tel: (01430) 471007 E-mail: info@beadsbydesign.co.uk *Beads & findings supplies*

▶ Beads & Sparkly Things, 24 Larchwood Avenue, Romford, RM5 2QJ Tel: (07976) 035539 E-mail: carol.norman@ntlworld.com *Handmade jewellery that has been made using mainly sterling silver and swarovski crystals or semi precious beads. Free P+P on all orders.*

▶ BeadVoodoo!, 134 Sicily Park, Belfast, BT10 0AP Tel: (020) 8123 0703 E-mail: admin@beadvoodoo.com *Beads & pendants wholesaler*

Beagle Aircraft Ltd, Stony Lane, Christchurch, Dorset, BH23 1EX Tel: (01202) 482296 Fax: (01202) 499449 *Aircraft engineers & repairers*

Beagle Cookware, 72-78 Stour Street, Birmingham, B18 7AJ Tel: 0121-454 3323 Fax: 0121-454 3342 *Cookware distributors*

Beak Bros, Clover Cottage, 3 Butts Road, Ryde, Isle of Wight, PO33 3JH Tel: (01983) 611509 Fax: (01983) 611509 *Agricultural contractors*

Beakbane Ltd, Stourport Road, Kidderminster, Worcestershire, DY11 7QT Tel: (01562) 820561 Fax: (01562) 820560 E-mail: sales@beakbane.co.uk Principal Export Areas: Africa *Designers & manufacturers of specialist machinery protection components including steel/fabric slideway covers & flexible bellows*

▶ Beaky.net, 35 Vaughan Drive, Kemsley, Sittingbourne, Kent, ME10 2UB Tel: (07729) 163996 Fax: (01795) 438113 *Logistics consultancy*

▶ Beal Developments Ltd, Tower House Lane, Hedon Road, Hull, HU12 8EE Tel: (01482) 899114

Tony Beal Ltd, 18 Station Road, Baillieston, Glasgow, G69 7UF Tel: 0141-773 2166 Fax: 0141-773 2904 E-mail: tbl@bealgroup.com *Tarpaulin manufrs*

Arthur Beale Ltd, 194 Shaftesbury Avenue, London, WC2H 8JP Tel: (020) 7836 9034 Fax: (020) 7836 5807 *Yacht chandlers*

▶ Beale & Cole Ltd, 3 Limber Road, Lufton, Yeovil, Somerset, BA22 8RR Tel: (01935) 444660 Fax: (01935) 433523

Beam Structural Services Ltd, Creek Road, March, Cambridgeshire, PE15 8RE Tel: (01354) 660895 Fax: (01354) 661361 E-mail: sales@bssmarchltd.co.uk *Steel fabrication manufrs*

Beam Vacuum Systems, 65 Deerpark Road, Castledawson, Magherafelt, County Londonderry, BT45 8BS Tel: (028) 7963 2424 Fax: (028) 7938 6869 E-mail: enquiries@beamvacuums.ie *Central vacuum system installers & distributors throughout Ireland*

Len Beaman Ltd, Eccleston Street, St. Helens, Merseyside, WA10 2PG Tel: (01744) 20717 Fax: (01744) 453012 E-mail: sales@beaman.co.uk *Plumbers & bathroom showrooms manufrs*

G.W. Beamand & Son Ltd, 7-9 Gibraltar Walk, Bethnel Green, London, E2 7LH Tel: (020) 7729 1442 Fax: (020) 7729 0178 E-mail: baileyprintgroup@talk21.com *Printers & stationers*

Beamglow Ltd, Somersham Road, St. Ives, Cambridgeshire, PE27 3LP Tel: (01480) 465012 Fax: (01480) 494826 E-mail: cartons@beamglow.co.uk *Carton manufrs*

▶ Beamshape Rhinosports, Rotherside Road, Eckington, Sheffield, S21 4HL Tel: 0114-276 2233 E-mail: info@rhinosports.co.uk

▶ Bean Bag Chair UK, 11 Belgrave Court, Blackwater, Camberley, Surrey, GU17 9JE Tel: (07866) 630026 E-mail: Info@Bean-Bag.org *Bean Bag UK - Provider of Bean Bag Chair, Giant Bean Bag, Child Bean Bag, Foot Rest Bean Bag, Bean Bag Filling, Bean Bag Refill, Bean Bag Fillings, Cheap Bean Bag, beanbag. bean bag london, bean bag uk, leather bean bag, faux leather bean bag, leatherette bean bag.**We pride ourselves on delivering a friendly service together with competitively priced quality bean bags.*

▶ Bean Bag Refill, Beanbag Filling, 11 Belgrave Court, Blackwater, Camberley, Surrey, GU17 9JE Tel: 0 870 285 1593 E-mail: info@bean-bag.co.uk *bean bag filling, bean bag refill, beanbag filler, competitively priced flame retardant polystyrene beans available in 5, and 20 cubic foot bags. top up or completely refill an old or new bean bag.*

▶ Bean Processed, 177 Adnitt Road, Northampton, NN1 4NJ Tel: (01604) 634452 Fax: (01604) 601610 E-mail: info@photorestorations.co.uk *Photo Restorations, Northampton, U.K. established 1997 - Old, Faded or Damaged Photographs Restored to as new, printed on Fuji Crystal Archive photographic paper for longevity, from your original prints or films.*

▶ Beanacre Enterprises Ltd, Juliet Way, Aveley, South Ockendon, Essex, RM15 4YD Tel: (01708) 864231 Fax: (01708) 862327

Beanfeast Wholefoods, 2 The Arcade, Fore Street, Okehampton, Devon, EX20 1EX Tel: (01837) 52387 *Health food retailers*

Beanfreaks, 5 Chartist Tower, Upper Dock Street, Newport, Gwent, NP20 1DX Tel: (01633) 251823 Fax: (01633) 666150 *Health foods*

Beans Ltd, 4 Sumner Place, Addlestone, Surrey, KT15 1QD Tel: 01932 841171 E-mail: sales@beansltd.co.uk *Beans is your Virtual Marketing Department bringing you a team of marketing professionals providing a fully integrated marketing & communications service spanning the full marketing mix*

▶ Beanwebs and Beandesigns, Georgian House, Orchard lane, East Hendred, Wantage, Oxfordshire, OX12 8JW Tel: 01235 832192 E-mail: enquiries@beanwebs.co.uk *Website Design and Search Engine Optimisation Specialists*

▶ Bear Assembly, 203 Longford Road, Longford, Coventry, CV6 6BG Tel: (024) 7636 7771 Fax: (024) 7664 5020

Bear Ramada Jarvis, 41 Charnham Street, Hungerford, Berkshire, RG17 0EL Tel: (01488) 682512 Fax: (01488) 684357 E-mail: enquiries@jarvishotels.co.uk *Conference facilities*

▶ Bearcomm.Com, 10 Thornberry Terrace, Penzance, Cornwall, TR18 3AH Tel: (01736) 333355 Fax: (01736) 350488 E-mail: sales@bearcomm.com *IT consultancy, web & print design*

Beard Engineering Co. Ltd, Pye Hill Road, Jacksdale, Nottingham, NG16 5LR Tel: (01773) 602535 Fax: (01773) 540185 E-mail: admin@beardengineering.co.uk *Sub-contract planning & milling*

Beard Evans Joinery, Shepherd Road, Gloucester, GL2 5EL Tel: (01452) 423123 Fax: (01452) 501055 E-mail: sales@beardevansjoinery.co.uk *Joiners*

▶ Beard & Tandy, Stenders Business Park, The Stenders, Mitcheldean, Gloucestershire, GL17 0JE Tel: (01594) 542997

Ken Beardall Ltd, 67 Howards Wood Drive, Gerrards Cross, Buckinghamshire, SL9 7HS Tel: (01753) 884974 Fax: (01753) 880553 *Industrial cleaning equipment exporters*

Beardshaw Bolts & Fixings, Stalham Road, Hoveton, Norwich, NR12 8DU Tel: (01603) 783811 Fax: (01603) 783859 E-mail: sales@beardshaw.co.uk *Fastener & bolt distributors*

Frederick Beardsley & Co. Ltd, 1 Cotmanhay Road, Ilkeston, Derbyshire, DE7 8HR Tel: 0115-932 4502 Fax: 0115-944 1298 E-mail: sales@frederickbeardsley.com *Warp knitted fabric manufrs*

Bearing Brokers Ltd, Unit 13a Limestone Cottage Lane, Sheffield, S6 1NJ Tel: 0114-231 0310 Fax: 0114-232 2320 E-mail: sales@bearingbrokers.co.uk *Bearing distributors*

Bearing Centre Ltd, 19 Nevanthon Road, Leicester, LE3 6DR Tel: 0116-275 7799 Fax: 0116-275 7799 *Ball & roller bearing suppliers*

Bearing & Engineering Products, 2 Downley Road, Havant, Hampshire, PO9 2NJ Tel: (023) 9247 7760 Fax: (023) 9247 7800 E-mail: adrian@1bep.co.uk *Bearing distributors & agents*

Bearing Factors, Progress Road, Whitewalls Industrial Estate, Nelson, Lancashire, BB9 8TE Tel: (01282) 693540 Fax: (01282) 691881 E-mail: sales@bearingfactors.co.uk *Ball bearing stockists & lubricants*

Bearing Power Ltd, 60 Church Road, Aston, Birmingham, B6 5TY Tel: 0121-327 5133 Fax: 0121-557 6644 E-mail: aperks@aol.com *Bearing distributors*

Bearing Shop, Grace Road Central, Marsh Barton Trading Estate, Exeter, EX2 8QA Tel: (01392) 680880 Fax: (01392) 437131 E-mail: info@thebearingshop.co.uk *All major brands of bearings suppliers*

Bearing Supplies Thetford, Unit 1 Brunel Way, Thetford, Norfolk, IP24 1HP Tel: (01842) 765074 Fax: (01842) 754709 *Bearing/power transmission distributors*

Bearing Traders Ltd, 18-20 Desborough Street, High Wycombe, Buckinghamshire, HP11 2LY Tel: (01494) 441301 Fax: (01494) 438085 E-mail: hwsales@bearingtraders.com *Bearing distributors*

Bearing Transmission & Pneumatics Ltd, 6 Chieftain Way, Tritton Road Trading Estate, Lincoln, LN6 7RY Tel: (01522) 560060 Fax: (01522) 560040 E-mail: btplimited@aol.com *Bearing/power transmission distributors* Also at: Derby

Bearing & Transmission Supplies Ltd, Watling House, Sutherland Street, Stoke-on-Trent, ST4 4HS Tel: (01782) 846216 Fax: (01782) 749080 E-mail: sales@btslimited.freeserve.co.uk *Bearing distributors*

Bearings & Drives Ltd, 4 Greenfield Farm Industrial Estate, Congleton, Cheshire, CW12 4TR Tel: (01260) 299744 Fax: (01260) 298285 E-mail: sales@bearingsanddrives.co.uk *Bearing distributors, agents & stockholders*

Bearings & Drives, Angel Road Works, Advent Way, London, N18 3AH Tel: (020) 8884 2111 Fax: (020) 8884 2112 E-mail: bearings2004@hotmail.co.uk *Pump repairs & sales*

Bearings Supplies, Southwell Road, Horsham St. Faith, Norwich, NR10 3JU Tel: (01603) 898918 Fax: (01603) 891801 E-mail: sales@bearing-supplies.co.uk *Bearing distributors*

Bearward Ltd, Main Road, Far Cotton, Northampton, NN4 8HJ Tel: (01604) 762851 Fax: (01604) 766168 E-mail: bernard.harrison@bearward.com Principal Export Areas: Worldwide *Motor diesel radiator manufrs*

Bearwood Builders Supply Co Smethwick Ltd, Three Shires Oak Road, Smethwick, West Midlands, B67 5BS Tel: 0121-429 2011 Fax: 0121-429 2226 *Builders & plumbers merchants*

Bearwood Finance Services, 39 Friar Street, Reading, RG1 1DX Tel: 0118-958 5880 Fax: 0118-958 5599 E-mail: mail@bearwood.co.uk *Merger & acquisition consultants, brokers & intermediaries*

Beasley (Joiners) Ltd, Bangor Terrace, Leeds, LS12 5PS Tel: 0113-263 0524 Fax: 0113-279 2389 E-mail: sales@beasleyjoiners.co.uk *Shop fitters*

▶ Beat Creative Design & Print Management, Cedar House, Vine Lane, Hillingdon, Uxbridge, Middlesex, UB10 0BX Tel: (01895) 252152 Fax: (01895) 230233 E-mail: enquiries@beat-creative.co.uk *Graphic design*

▶ Beat Route Music, 27 Branscombe Drive, Wootton Bassett, Swindon, SN4 8HS Tel: (01793) 850086 E-mail: Disco@Swindon-Disco.co.uk *Beat Route Music is the best quality mobile disco and light show around the Wiltshire and Gloucestershire area on a price for price basis. We play the music YOU want the way YOU want it! We can even send you our complete track list for you to choose the music for your special event. Give DJ Mo a call on 01793 850086 or email me at Disco@Swindon-Disco.co.uk.*

▶ Beat Suite, Studio 1, 5-7 Pink Lane, Newcastle upon Tyne, NE1 5DW Tel: 0191-261 2400 Fax: 0191-261 5746E-mail: info@beatsuite.com *Royalty free music library*

Beatson Clark P.L.C., The Glass Works, Greasbrough Road, Rotherham, South Yorkshire, S60 1TZ Tel: (01709) 828141 Fax: (01709) 828476 E-mail: sales@beatsonclark.co.uk *Glass container manufrs* Also at: Barnsley

Beatson Drake Ltd, Quarry Road, Handsworth, Sheffield, S13 9AZ Tel: 0114-244 6873 Fax: 0114-243 5915 E-mail: beatsondrakeltd@aol.com *Cutlery handle manufrs*

▶ Beatsons Building Supplies Ltd, 2 Glencryan Road, Cumbernauld, Glasgow, G67 2UQ Tel: (01236) 722580 Fax: (01236) 722589 *Building construction*

▶ Beattie Architectural Aluminium, 2-4 Abercorn Street, Paisley, Renfrewshire, PA3 4AB Tel: 0141-561 7567

Beattie Flanigan & Partners, 174 Castlereagh Road, Belfast, BT5 5GX Tel: (028) 9073 2121 Fax: (028) 9073 2630 E-mail: info@beattieflanigan.com *Engineering consultants*

Beattie Watkinson, Network House, 1 Ariel Way, London, W12 7SL Tel: (020) 8743 2021 Fax: (020) 8740 5921 E-mail: london@beawat.co.uk *Consulting civil/ structural engineer agents*

Beaubelle Interiors Urmston, 410 Flixton Road, Flat 1, Urmston, Manchester, M41 6QY Tel: 0161-749 8525 Fax: 0161-749 8525 *Blinds & retailers*

Curtis Beauclair Automatics Ltd, 99 Wills Crescent, Hounslow, TW3 2JE Tel: (020) 8894 4463 Fax: (020) 8894 4463 E-mail: cutejuke@aol.com *Juke boxes*

Beaucrest Ltd, Holdford Road, Birmingham, B6 7EP Tel: 0121-356 5668 Fax: 0121-356 6049 E-mail: sales@beaucrest.ltd.uk *Corrugated packaging manufrs*

Beaufort Air Sea Equipment Ltd, Beaufort Road, Birkenhead, Merseyside, CH41 1HQ Tel: 0151-652 9151 Fax: 0151-653 6639 E-mail: cgreen@rfdbeaufort.com *Air sea rescue equipment manufrs* Also at: London

▶ Beaufort Maintenance Ltd, Ashcombe House, Upper Swainswick, Bath, BA1 8AL Tel: (01225) 859286 Fax: (01225) 859286 E-mail: beaufortmaintenance@fsbdial.co.uk *Specialists in conveyor hire,conveyor servicing and installation,new and used spares available for all types of conveyors,metal fabrications from our workshop/mobile workshop*

▶ Beaulieu Chocolates, High Street, Beaulieu, Brockenhurst, Hampshire, SO42 7YA Tel: (01590) 612279 Fax: (01590) 611192 E-mail: sales@beaulieuchocolates.co.uk *Food & tobacco*

Beaumanor Engineering Ltd, 47 Highmeres Road, Leicester, LE4 9LZ Tel: 0116-276 4728 Fax: 0116-246 0133 E-mail: info@beaumanor.com *Fluid fit accessories fittings manufrs*

Beaumanor Press Ltd, 23 Bath Lane, Leicester, LE3 5BF Tel: 0116-233 1337 Fax: 0116-233 5337 E-mail: sales@beaumanor.co.uk *Printers*

Beau-Monde, Unit 7 Old Pottery Court, Fore Street, Chudleigh, Newton Abbot, Devon, TQ13 0HX Tel: (01626) 852500 Fax: (01626) 852500 *Soft furnishing manufrs*

Beaumont Beds Ltd, 5-31 Eastmoor St, London, SE7 8LX Tel: (020) 8853 1155 Fax: (020) 853 2337 *Bedroom furniture sales & distributors*

Bill Beaumont Textiles Ltd, Park Mills, Deighton Road, Chorley, Lancashire, PR7 2HP Tel: (01257) 263065 Fax: (01257) 241348 E-mail: sales@billbeaumont.co.uk *Home furnishing manufrs*

Beaumont & Blackburn Ltd, 21 Wellington Road, Dewsbury, West Yorkshire, WF13 1HL Tel: (01924) 461067 Fax: (01924) 430971 *Electrical, heating & plumbing contractors*

Beaumont Blending Co. Ltd, Ings Dyeworks, Wakefield Road, Scissett, Huddersfield, HD8 9JL Tel: (01484) 863526 Fax: (01484) 865479 *Commission textile blenders*

Beaumont Colson Ltd, 133 New Bridge Street, Newcastle upon Tyne, NE1 2SW Tel: 0191-261 7117 Fax: 0191-230 4090 *IT solutions*

Beaumont D Gearbox Reconditioners, Lumb Cottage, Wainstalls, Halifax, West Yorkshire, HX2 7UJ Tel: (01422) 244587 Fax: (01422) 243758 *Gearbox reconditioners*

Beaumont Engineering, Unit G11 Rudford Industrial Estate, Ford Road, Ford, Arundel, West Sussex, BN18 0BD Tel: (01903) 730822 Fax: (01903) 730315 *Steel fabricators*

Beaumont Forest Products Ltd, Swinley Sawmills, Swinley Road, Ascot, Berkshire, SL5 8AZ Tel: (01344) 874137 Fax: (01344) 874139 E-mail: sales@beaumontforest.co.uk *Timber merchants*

Beaumont H Landrover Specialist, Square Mill, Wainstalls, Halifax, West Yorkshire, HX2 7UG Tel: (01422) 244823 Fax: (01422) 247397 E-mail: info@beaumontlandrovers.co.uk *Engine reconditioners*

John Beaumont Ltd, Riverside Mills, Firth Street, Huddersfield, HD1 3BD Tel: 0845 8510215 Fax: (01484) 435302 E-mail: peter@beaumont-ltd.co.uk *A long established manufacturer of Control & Instrument Panel Facias, Backpanels, Enclosures, Chassis, Membrane Overlays, Mimic Diagrams, Nameplates, Dials & Scales for the Electronic and Mechanical Industries. Our in house, design, artwork production, manufacture & surface finishing capability means that we*

continued

have total control of all aspects of production so that customers can rely on receiving a quality product at short lead times that offer value for money

Michael Beaumont, PO Box 8, Nottingham, NG4 4QZ Tel: 0115-987 8361 Fax: 0115-987 8361 E-mail: michael.beaumont1@ntlworld.com *Coin & jewellery sales*

Beaumont PPS Ltd, 537 Sauchiehall Street, Glasgow, G3 7PQ Tel: 0141-226 3411 Fax: 0141-221 9249 E-mail: sales@beaumontpps.com *Gifts & incentives*

Beaumont Products Ltd, Cleves Farm, Barby, Rugby, Warwickshire, CV23 8TF Tel: (01788) 899100 Fax: (01788) 891671 E-mail: sales@beaumontcastiron.com *Cast iron radiator manufrs*

▶ Beaumont Service, 21 Donaldson Crescent, Kirkintilloch, Glasgow, G66 1XF Tel: 0141-777 6363

Beaumont Structural Consultants, Goose Green Marsh, La Rue Du Craslin, St. Peter, Jersey, JE3 7BU Tel: (01534) 822888 Fax: (01534) 822889 *Home improvement suppliers*

Beaumont Structural Consultants, Goose Green Marsh, La Rue Du Craslin, St. Peter, Jersey, JE3 7BU Tel: (01534) 822888 Fax: (01534) 822889 E-mail: mail@bsc.co.je *Consulting civil & structural engineers*

T.W. Beaumont Ltd, Spafield Mill, Upper Road, Batley, West Yorkshire, WF17 7LS Tel: (01924) 461401 Fax: (01924) 461378 E-mail: helen.miles@yorkshirewiter.co.uk *Textile recycling & clothing sort agents*

Beaumont TM Ltd, 1-4 Lyall Court, Commerce Way, Flitwick, Bedford, MK45 1UQ Tel: (01525) 722500 Fax: (01525) 718902 E-mail: info@beaumonttm.co.uk *Bar equipment*

Beaumonts Robinson Risk Services, 1 Clifton Villas, Bradford, West Yorkshire, BD8 7BY Tel: (01274) 404050 Fax: (01274) 404060 *Insurance brokers & financial agents*

▶ Beautelle Supplies, 1a Railway Terrace, Nechells, Birmingham, B7 5NG Tel: 0121-322 0920 Fax: 0121-322 0921 E-mail: enquiry@beautelle.co.uk *Leading therapy & healthcare equipment manufrs*

Beautiful Food Ltd, Unit 10 Block C, Juno Way, London, SE14 5RW Tel: (020) 8469 4117 E-mail: info@beautifulfoods.co.uk *Catering food suppliers*

Beautimatic International Ltd, Abbey House, Eastways, Witham, Essex, CM8 3YL Tel: (01376) 535535 Fax: (01376) 503503 *Perfume manufrs*

Beauty, 103-105 Cheetham Hill Road, Manchester, M8 8PY Tel: 0161-833 9163 Fax: 0161-833 1687 E-mail: beautyuk@btconnect.com *Cosmetic wholesalers*

▶ The Beauty Preference, 33 Lyon Close, Maidenbower, Crawley, West Sussex, RH10 7ND Tel: (01293) 883716 E-mail: rose@beautypref.com *In today's busy lifestyle it is so easy to find excuses not to book a nail treatment for yourself and not to mention how difficult it is to actually find the time to go to the salon. **My name is Rose Timms, I am a fully qualified and insured Mobile Nail Technician and I offer a competitive range of treatments using top quality products from Creative Nail design to achieve the ultimate in beauty and relaxation in the comfort of your own home. I work within a 15 mile radius of Crawley, West Sussex and all my prices include travel expenses in this area.**I provide a friendly yet professional service at all times and offer a full client consultation before every treatment to ensure all my clients are left feeling totally rejuvenated and more beautiful after every visit.**Escape from your daily routine, treat yourself to one of my luxurious treatments and experience beauty expertise at first hand!*

▶ Beauty Spot, 84 Gunville Down Road, Blandford Camp, Blandford Forum, Dorset, DT11 8BD Tel: (01258) 458229 *Holistic beauty therapist and nail technician providing a wide range of fantastic treatments including facials, swedish and aromatherapy massage, reflexology, hopi ear candles, a selection of body wraps and conditioning treatments, waxing, make up and eye treatments as well as spray tanning, luxury spa manicures and pedicures and uv gel nail enhancements.**Soon to come....indian head massage and TH Stone massage therapy.**Stockist of JESSICA and Susan Molyneux.**Products and gift vouchers available to buy.*

▶ The Beauty Studio, 33 Greystone Avenue, Worthing, West Sussex, BN13 1LR Tel: (01903) 262447 E-mail: wendy.greaves2@ntlworld.com *facials,manicure-pedicure, wedding makeup, in relaxing beauty room or mobile. One to one in complete privacy.*

▶ Beauty Styles Ltd, The Agora Centre, Church Street, Wolverton, Milton Keynes, MK12 5LG Tel: (07946) 599661 *Hairdressing services*

▶ Beauty Tech International Ltd, Golf House, Horsham Road, Pease Pottage, Crawley, West Sussex, RH11 9SG Tel: (01293) 530300 *Chemical manufrs*

▶ BeautyFromWithin, Spencer Road, Priestwood, Bracknell, Berkshire, RG42 1UP Tel: 07941 494669 E-mail: caroline_beautyfromwithin@yahoo.com *Mobile beauty treatments in Berkshire, available 7 Days a Week - specialising in evening & weekend appointments*

Beavan & Hodges Ltd, 29-35 Portland Street, Hereford, HR4 9JF Tel: (01432) 272188 Fax: (01432) 351173 *Building contractors*

Beaven & Sons Ltd, 183 Westgate Street, Gloucester, GL1 2RN Tel: (01452) 314384 Fax: (01452) 300195 *Maintenance engineers & refrigeration* Also at: Cheltenham

Beaver Co. Ltd, 968 North Circular Road, London, NW2 7JR Tel: (020) 8208 1839 Fax: (020) 8452 4610 E-mail: bopco@aol.com *Heating & ventilation engineers*

▶ Beaver 84 Ltd, Thingoe Hill, Bury St. Edmunds, Suffolk, IP32 6BE Tel: (01284) 724824 Fax: (01284) 765824 E-mail: sales@beaver84.co.uk

▶ Beaver 84 Ltd, Watson Close, Grays, Essex, RM20 3EF Tel: (01708) 861821 Fax: (01708) 869537

▶ Beaver 84 Ltd, Bunny Lane, Sherfield English, Romsey, Hampshire, SO51 6FT Tel: (01794) 884876 Fax: (01794) 884277

▶ Beaver Architectural Ironmongery, Unit D 18 Imperial Way, Croydon, CR0 4RR Tel: (020) 8681 3939 Fax: (020) 8649 8213 E-mail: gary@beaverai.co.uk *Architectural hardware & ironmongers*

Beaver Business Gifts, 5 Telford Road, Middlesbrough, Cleveland, TS3 8BL Tel: (01642) 252890 Fax: (01642) 773277 *Corporate gifts &promotional items manufrs*

Beaver Graphic Services, Graphic House, Wiggenhall Road, Watford, WD18 0FG Tel: (01923) 229387 Fax: (01923) 223957 E-mail: sales@beaver.co.uk *Digital print, lithographic printing & graphic design specialist*

Beaver Healthcare Equipment, Beaver House, 1 Vale Rise, Tonbridge, Kent, TN9 1TB Tel: (01732) 367777 *Medical suppliers*

Beaver Industrial Coatings, Singer Court, Singer Way, Kempston, Bedford, MK42 7AW Tel: (01234) 843614 Fax: (01234) 843309 E-mail: derekjbeaver@aol.com *High quality powder coating services*

Beaver International, Station Road, Plumtree, Plumtree, Nottingham, NG12 5NA Tel: 0115-937 5900 Fax: 0115-937 4074 *Engineers.*

Beaver Leeds Ltd, Elder Mills, Elder Road, Leeds, LS13 4DL Tel: 0113-239 3363 Fax: 0113-236 1264 E-mail: info@beaverleeds.ltd.uk *Shop-fitting manufrs*

Beaver Mats, PO Box 305, Eastleigh, Hampshire, SO53 3XR Tel: (023) 8062 0304 *Service entrance floor matting*

Beaver Power Ltd, Goat Mill Road, Dowlais, Merthyr Tydfil, CF48 3TF Tel: (01685) 353270 Fax: (01685) 353271 E-mail: sales@beaverpower.co.uk *Generating set manufrs*

Beaver Timber Co., Barcaldine Sawmills, Barcaldine, Oban, Argyll, PA37 1SG Tel: (01631) 720353 Fax: (01631) 720430 E-mail: info@beavertimber.co.uk *Sectional wooden buildings & log cabin importers & distributors*

Beaver Tool Hire Ltd, 15-17 Kingston Road, Portsmouth, PO1 5RX Tel: (023) 9282 6632 Fax: (023) 9282 6639 *Tool hire & sales*

Beavers Ltd, Holden House, 57 Rathbone Place, London, W1T 1JU Tel: (020) 7636 0825 Fax: (020) 7255 1237 E-mail: dam@beaver.co.uk *Recruitment consultants*

Beaves & Son, Haroden, Woodrolfe Road, Tollesbury, Maldon, Essex, CM9 8SD Tel: (01621) 868870 *Boat builders & repairers*

Beavin Engineering Ltd, 33 Haviland Road, Ferndown Industrial Estate, Wimborne, Dorset, BH21 7SA Tel: (01202) 894404 Fax: (01202) 894404 E-mail: beavineng@btconnect.com *Beavin Engineering in Ferndown, Dorset offers a working partnership you can rely on. Call today on 01202 894404. Since 1987, we have been providing plastic insert moulding, injection moulding, tool-making, mould design, mould trials and assembling and finishing services for customers in, amongst others, the electronics, leisure and building industries. Our extensive in-house technical injection moulding, tool-making and precision engineering capabilities allow for fast turnaround and we have a machine capacity of 25 - 100 tonnes with a maximum shot weight of 200 grams. We mould most types of material and are happy to accommodate both short and long runs.*

Beazer Road Springs, 2 The Pheasantry, Scarborough, North Yorkshire, YO12 4UH Tel: (01723) 864234 *Vehicle suspension manufrs*

Beazley's (Savile Row) Ltd, 9-10 Savile Row, London, W1S 3PF Tel: (020) 7437 1831 Fax: (020) 7439 2166 *Woollen fabric merchants*

Bebbington Steps Ltd, Unit 1-2 Finnimore Industrial Estate, Ottery St. Mary, Devon, EX11 1NR Tel: (01404) 813817 Fax: (01404) 813817 E-mail: martin@bebbingtonsteps.co.uk Principal Export Areas: Central/East Europe & West Europe *Steel fabricators*

Bec Plastics, 18-20 Lenziemill Road, Cumbernauld, Glasgow, G67 2RL Tel: (01236) 781255 Fax: (01236) 781299 E-mail: enquires@becplastics.co.uk *Plastic materials, fabricators & machinists*

Becatech Ltd, The Olde Farm, Stone Allerton, Axbridge, Somerset, BS26 2NP Tel: (01934) 713608 Fax: (01934) 713737 E-mail: sales@becatech.com *Electronic engineers*

Becc Signs, 9a Orchard Rise, Croydon, CR0 7QZ Tel: (020) 8777 9377 Fax: (020) 8776 2224 E-mail: mail@beccs.co.uk *Sign makers & general building work*

Beccis International Ltd, Saxon Way, Melbourn, Royston, Hertfordshire, SG8 6DN Tel: (01763) 262160 Fax: (01763) 261980 E-mail: beccisinternational@tascali.co.uk *Exports of packing goods*

Beccles Heat Treatments, Gosford Road, Beccles, Suffolk, NR34 9QP Tel: (01502) 717738 Fax: (01502) 711001 E-mail: admin@b-h-t.co.uk *Machine shop manufrs*

▶ Becher Joinery Ltd, 7 Worton Hall Industrial Estate, Worton Road, Isleworth, Middlesex, TW7 6ER Tel: (020) 8568 9488 Fax: (020) 8568 9311

Bechtel Holdings Ltd, 245 Hammersmith Road, London, W6 8DP Tel: (020) 8846 5111 Fax: (020) 8846 6940 *Construction engineers*

Beck Engineering Co (Bridlington) Ltd, Camlock Works, 13 & 15 Bridlington Road, Hunmanby, Filey, North Yorkshire, YO14 0LR Tel: (01723) 890631 Fax: (01723) 891554 E-mail: shane@becktransglobal.co.uk *Blast, security & steel doors, electrical insulation & strapping tapes manufrs*

Beck Farm Cottages, Beck Farm, Trunch Hill, Denton, Harleston, Norfolk, IP20 0AE Tel: (01986) 788454 Fax: (01986) 788454 E-mail: pearlcharnick@tesco.net *Rosettes & self catering holiday cottages*

Beck Greener, Fulwood House, 12 Fulwood Place, London, WC1V 6HR Tel: (020) 7693 5600 Fax: (020) 7693 5601 E-mail: mail@beckgreener.com Principal Export Areas: Worldwide *Beck Greener was established in 1867, making it one of the oldest intellectual property firms in the world. They provide a comprehensive service in relation to patents, trade marks, designs, copyright and related rights. Their offices are in the heart of London's historic legal district, within walking distance of the London Patent Office and The High Court.* Also at: London WC1

▶ Beck Interiors Ltd, Victory House, Cox Lane, Chessington, Surrey, KT9 1SG Tel: (020) 8974 0500 Fax: (020) 8974 0555 E-mail: mail@beckinteriors.com *Office furniture manufrs*

O.N. Beck & Co. Ltd, 104 Fox Lane, Palmers Green, London, N13 4AX Tel: (020) 8886 3444 Fax: (020) 8886 9218 E-mail: sales@onbeck.co.uk *Manufacturers of compressed air/gas blow guns & nozzles, air driven & industrial vacuum cleaners. Also portable & air driven fans & portable ventilators*

Beck & Pollitzer, Rochester Way, Dartford, DA1 3QT Tel: (01322) 528291 Fax: (01322) 525461 E-mail: info@beck-pollitzer.com *Crane & forklift hire services*

Beck & Pollitzer Engineering Ltd, 6 Locksbrook Court, Locksbrook Road, Bath, BA1 3EN Tel: (01225) 425383 Fax: (01225) 448385 E-mail: info@beck-pollitzer.com *Engineering service specialists*

Beck & Pollitzer Engineering Ltd, Wetmore Road, Burton-on-Trent, Staffordshire, DE14 1SN Tel: (01283) 508976 Fax: (01283) 508978 E-mail: glenda.watson@beck-pollitzer.com *Beck & Pollitzer Engineering is Europe's leading outsourced engineering services contractor with experience in all industry sectors. From a single internal machine move to multisite relocations around the world, we possess the experience, skills and resources.Established in 1863 Beck & Pollitzer Engineering has gained many years experience in the provision of industrial engineering services, and with a constantly growing number of operating locations in the UK and Europe Beck & Pollitzer can undertake any kind of factory or machinery removal throughout the world. Our expertise in heavy lifting and our specialized equipment ensure high quality services and customer satisfaction. The services we offer include: Project Management-Machinery Installations and Relocations-Mechanical, Electrical and Maintenance Services-Printing Engineering-Heavy Haulage-Crane & Forklift Truck Hire-Contract Lifting. Beck & Pollitzer Engineering - Innovative, flexible and cost conscious engineering services with a proven record of excellence and reliability.*

▶ Beck Powersports, Suite 2, 27 Colmore Row, Birmingham, B3 2EW Tel: 0121 557 8837 Fax: 08701 257572 E-mail: info@beckpowersports.co.uk *Motorcycle Clothing, Accessories and Spares we stock a full range of Clothing including helmets, leathers, race suits, gloves, boots, textile jackets and trousers from manufacturers such as OGK, Nitro, Akito, Swift and many more please visit our online shop to view the full product range.*

Beck Sack Co., 3 Hermitage Lane, London, SE25 5HH Tel: (0845) 0720750 *Polyethylene sack distributors*

Will Beck Ltd, Kitchener Road, High Wycombe, Buckinghamshire, HP11 2SW Tel: (0845) 4500444 Fax: (0845) 4500445 E-mail: sales@wil.co.uk *Furniture suppliers*

Beckart Environmental International Ltd, 62 Upper Way, Upper Longdon, Rugeley, Staffordshire, WS15 1QA Tel: (01543) 493189 Fax: (0870) 3835292 E-mail: beckart.uk@virgin.net *Wastewater treatment system manufrs*

Becker Acroma Ltd, Rookwood Way, Haverhill, Suffolk, CB9 8PF Tel: (01440) 703611 Fax: (01440) 761091 E-mail: frar@beckeracroma.com *Wood finish manufacturers. Producing stains, lacquers, enamels, varnishes and paints.* Also at: Liverpool

E. Becker Ltd, 2 Hazlemere View, Hazlemere, High Wycombe, Buckinghamshire, HP15 7BY Tel: (01494) 713777 Fax: (01494) 713888 E-mail: e.becker@breathemail.net *Manufacturers of fancy paper, educational & packaging equipment*

Becker Industrial Coatings Ltd, Goodlass Road, Liverpool, L24 9HJ Tel: 0151-448 1010 Fax: 0151-448 2589 E-mail: info-uk@beckers-bic.com *Industrial paint manufrs*

Becker Powder Coatings Ltd, Goodlass Road, Liverpool, L24 9HJ Tel: 0151-486 0486 Fax: 0151-486 0484 *Thermosetting powder coating manufrs*

Becker Sliding Partitions Ltd, Wemco House, 477 Whippendell Road, Watford, WD18 7QY Tel: (01923) 236906 Fax: (01923) 230149 E-mail: sales@becker.uk.com *Sliding & folding partitioning services*

Becker U K Ltd, Unit C, Brighton Street Trading Park, Hull, HU3 4XS Tel: (01482) 835280 Fax: (01482) 831275 E-mail: sales@becker.co.uk *Vacuum pumps & low pressure air compressors*

Beckett Construction Solutions Ltd, 99 Kingsway, Dunmurry, Belfast, BT17 9NU Tel: (028) 9066 3631 Fax: (028) 9055 1309 E-mail: mail@whbeckett.com *Flooring, ceiling & roofing contractors*

Beckett Instruments Ltd, 533 Rayleigh Road, Benfleet, Essex, SS7 3TN Tel: (01268) 773653 Fax: (01268) 745697 E-mail: beckettinstruments@btinternet.com *Surgical instrument manufrs*

Becketts Bakery Engineers Ltd, Fir Street, Heywood, Lancashire, OL10 1NP Tel: (01706) 364103 Fax: (01706) 625057 E-mail: sales@becketts.co.uk *The company was established in 1867 and initially the business was that of manufacturing chemist. In the mid 1930's the direction of the firm changed to that of Rebuilding Bakery Equipment and rapid expansion of the company followed this change.*

continued

*Since the 1970's the company has also taken on agencies for New Equipment from manufacturers all around the world enabling Becketts to offer the most comprehensive range of Equipment possible. A number of New Machines are manufactured 'in house'.**The equipment offered today has uses in many areas of the baking industry including Bread, Rolls, Pies, Sausage Rolls, Pizzas, Biscuits, Cakes, Puddings and Ethnic Products. The equipment offered ranges from small bench top machines for the small producer to complete bread plants capable of outputs of many thousand of loaves per hour. We are also able to offer a complete installation and commissioning service for the equipment.*

Beckford Silk Ltd, Ashton Road, Beckford, Tewkesbury, Gloucestershire, GL20 7AU Tel: (01386) 881507 Fax: (01386) 882019 E-mail: sales@beckfordsilk.co.uk *Printed silk scarf manufrs*

▶ BECKFORD'S ART WORKS, 7 JURY ROAD, DULVERTON, SOMERSET, TA22 9DX Tel: 01398 323746 Fax: 01398 323746 E-mail: l.beckford@tiscali.co.uk *WOOD CARVERS. STONE CARVERS MEMORIALS, HEADSTONES, LETTERING. DECORATIVE INTERIORS, JOINERY, PLASTERWORK. HISTORIC BUILDING RESTORATION. WINDOWS, DOORS, STAIRCASES.*

▶ Beckingham Solutions, Walsall Road, Sutton Coldfield, West Midlands, B74 4NP Tel: 0121-580 8669 *Computer system consultants*

Beckman Coulter (UK) Ltd, Oakley Court, Kingsmead Business Park, London Road, High Wycombe, Buckinghamshire, HP11 1JU Tel: (01494) 441181 Fax: (01494) 447558 *Medical supply services*

Beckmass Scientific Apparatus, 25 The Brambles, Haslington, Crewe, CW1 5RA Tel: (01270) 586707 Fax: (01270) 586707 *Infrared Instrument suppliers*

Beckox Plastic Fabrications Ltd, 4-6 Wool Road, Poole, Dorset, BH12 4NG Tel: (01202) 736725 Fax: (01202) 738352 E-mail: reg@beckox.co.uk *Plastic fabrications*

Beckwith & Son, St. Nicholas Hall, 43 St. Andrew Street, Hertford, SG14 1HZ Tel: (01992) 582079 Fax: (01992) 581009 E-mail: sales@beckwithandsonantiques.co.uk *Antique dealers, restorers & valuers*

Beckworth Technical Plating Ltd, 16 Caker Stream Road, Alton, Hampshire, GU34 2QF Tel: (01420) 80880 Fax: (01420) 80881 E-mail: admin@beckworth.net *Precious metal platers*

Beco Products Ltd, Becco House, Wrawby Road, Brigg, North Lincolnshire, DN20 8DT Tel: (01652) 651641 Fax: (01652) 652796 E-mail: info@becowallform.co.uk *Building suppliers*

Becool Radiators Ltd, Paterson Road, Wellingborough, Northamptonshire, NN8 4BZ Tel: (01933) 230420 Fax: (01933) 279902 E-mail: sales@gallay.co.uk *Cooling system manufrs*

Becosolar, 8-10 Speedwell Units, Nelson Road Industrial Estate, Dartmouth, Devon, TQ6 9SZ Tel: (01803) 833636 Fax: (01803) 835379 E-mail: info@becosolar.com *Manufacturers of solar powered electricity supply systems*

Becro Engineering Services Ltd, 117 Brooker Road, Waltham Abbey, Essex, EN9 1JH Tel: (01992) 713045 Fax: (01992) 700157 E-mail: admin@becro.co.uk *Metalwork engineers & steel fabricators structural steelwork*

Bed & Bath UK Ltd, Orston Lane, Bottesford, Nottingham, NG13 0AU Tel: (01949) 844441 Fax: (01949) 844001 E-mail: sales@bedandbath.co.uk *Towels & bathrobes suppliers*

Bed Bedroom, 124-126 Walsgrave Road, Coventry, CV2 4AX Tel: (024) 7645 3924 Fax: (024) 7645 3924 *Bedroom furniture retailer*

▶ Bed & Breakfast Edinburgh @14 Hart Street - Scotland, 14 Hart Street Guest House, New Town, Edinburgh, EH1 3RN Tel: 0131-557 6826 E-mail: info@14hartstreet.com *Hart Street enjoys an ideal, central location; it is close to a number of visitor attractions - the Playhouse Theatre, the Scottish National Portrait Gallery, the monuments on the Calton Hill and the Royal Botanic Gardens. Princes Street - the main thoroughfare of the city - is a mere five minutes" stroll away, and a large number of museums, galleries and other visitor sites are within comfortable walking distance. ***

Bed Factory, 139 Regent Street, Leamington Spa, Warwickshire, CV32 4NX Tel: (01926) 426405 Fax: (01926) 314802 E-mail: admin@thebedfactory.co.uk *Retail beds & furniture distributors*

Bed Linen Shop Southport, 65a London Street, Southport, Merseyside, PR9 0TH Tel: (01704) 501183 *Linen & pram supplies*

Bed & Pine Centre, 20 Wallsgreen Road, Cardenden, Lochgelly, Fife, KY5 0JF Tel: (01592) 720373 Fax: (01592) 721665 *Beds & furniture retailers*

Bed Post, 193-195 Eltham High Street, London, SE9 1TS Tel: (020) 8294 1319 Fax: (020) 8294 1755 *Bed & bedding suppliers*

Bed Post, 4-5 Elm Parade, Main Road, Sidcup, Kent, DA14 6NF Tel: (020) 8309 6016 Fax: (020) 8309 6017 *Bed sales*

Bed Shed, 135 King Street, Kilmarnock, Ayrshire, KA1 1QJ Tel: (01563) 522151 Fax: (01563) 522151 *Bed retailers*

▶ Bed Shop, 21 Brunel Road, Manor Trading Estate, Benfleet, Essex, SS7 4PS Tel: (01268) 569155 Fax: (01268) 569156 E-mail: sales@thebedshopltd.com *Bed suppliers*

▶ Bed Shops, 2a Buckland Road, Pen Mill Trading Estate, Yeovil, Somerset, BA21 5EA Tel: (01935) 431331 *Bed & lounge suites retailers*

Bed Warehouse, Wrea Lane, Scarborough, North Yorkshire, YO12 7PN Tel: (01723) 351313 Fax: (01723) 353971 *Bed retailers*

Bed Workshop, Braunton Road, Bristol, BS3 3AA Tel: 0117-963 6659 E-mail: info@thebedworkshop.co.uk *Import antiques & bed manufrs*

▶ Bedbugz Bedding & Blankets, 243-245 Dewsbury Road, Leeds, LS11 5HZ Tel: 0113-277 7753 Fax: 0113-277 7753 *Bedroom furniture retailers*

Bedcrest Ltd, Old Hall Street, Middleton, Manchester, M24 1AG Tel: (0870) 7662324 *Continental quilt & pillow manufrs*

Bedding Superstore Studley, 1 Marble Alley, Studley, Warwickshire, B80 7LD Tel: (01527) 854488 Fax: (01527) 854488 *Beds & bedding suppliers*

▶ Beddis Kenley Engineering Ltd, Unit 6, Astra Park, Parkside Lane, Leeds, LS11 5TD Tel: 0113-270 9674

T.G. Beddoe & Sons Ltd, Pontygwindy Industrial Estate, Caerphilly, Mid Glamorgan, CF83 2WF Tel: (029) 2088 3040 Fax: (029) 2088 3040 *Pressing services*

Beddoes Bros, Pentre Hyling, Church Stoke, Montgomery, Powys, SY15 6HU Tel: (01588) 620199 Fax: (01588) 620499 E-mail: paul@beddoesplant.co.uk *Machinery dealers*

Bedeck Ltd, 189 Lurgan Road, Craigavon, County Armagh, BT67 0QS Tel: (028) 3832 5836 Fax: (028) 3831 3001 E-mail: cust.services@bedeck.co.uk Principal Export Areas: Worldwide *Bed linen manufrs*

Bedestone Ltd, Boulton Ho, 41 Icknield St, Hockley, Birmingham, B18 5AY Tel: 0121-554 3283 Fax: 0121-507 0140 E-mail: bedestone@aol.com *Since 1978 Bedestone Ltd have continued to provide the UK industry with a high class sub-contract service, not only in CNC Jig Grinding; CNC Milling; Wire EDM; Spark Erosion, but complete Toolmaking and Mould Making facilities.*The directors, Eric Handford and Roger Tromans are qualified and experienced engineers with a highly trained workforce, all with one objective - to produce accurate high quality work at an economic price with reliable delivery.*This is mirrored in our BS EN ISO 9001:2000 and AS9100 quality approvals along with our many other accreditations.*

Bedestone Ltd, 41 Icknield Street, Hockley, Birmingham, B18 5AY Tel: 0121-554 3283 Fax: 0121-507 0140 E-mail: bedestone@aol.com *Precision engineers & jig & fixture construction, boring & grinding engineers & custom builders*

Bedewear Manufacturing Co. Ltd, Bede Street, Leicester, LE3 5LD Tel: 0116-254 9031 *Hosiery & children's wear manufrs*

Bedfont Scientific Ltd, 105 Rochester Airport Industrial Estate, Laker Road, Rochester, Kent, ME1 3QX Tel: (01634) 673720 Fax: (01634) 673721 E-mail: info@bedfont.com *Gas analyser equipment manufrs*

Bedford Balloons, 165 Castle Road, Bedford, MK40 3RT Tel: (01234) 212232 Fax: (01234) 346289 E-mail: bedfordflorist@amserve.net *Balloon display services*

Bedford Battery Co. Ltd, 1-3 & 2-12 Wellington Street, Bedford, MK40 2HZ Tel: (01234) 340661 Fax: (01234) 217205 *Motor accessories distributors service* Also at: Wellingborough

▶ Bedford Bears Ltd, 21 Broom Hall, High Street, Broom, Biggleswade, Bedfordshire, SG18 9ND Tel: 01767 318626 Fax: 01767 631131 E-mail: ann@bedfordbears.wanadoo.co.uk *Manufacture and retail of traditional English mohair collectors teddy bears and a unique range of hand puppets. Commissions welcomed for teddy bears to meet special occassions: anniversaries, christenings, etc.*Est. 20 years.*

▶ Bedford Building Plastics, 11 Grisedale Court, Woburn Road Industrial Estate, Kempston, Bedford, MK42 7EE Tel: (01234) 855388 Fax: (01234) 855399 *Building plastic wholesalers*

Bedford Dials Ltd, Corn Exchange, Teme Street, Tenbury Wells, Worcestershire, WR15 8BB Tel: (01584) 810345 Fax: (01584) 810683 E-mail: info@bedforddials.co.uk *Design, development, printing and manufacture of dials for instruments for the clock, watch, gauge and automotive industries. Design, development, printing and manufacture of graphic overlays, fascia panels and membrane switches. Component printing services. Lithographic printing, screen printing and pad printing. Prototyping and design to specification.*

Bedford Engineering Co Manchester Ltd, Hollingworth Road, Bredbury, Stockport, Cheshire, SK6 2AU Tel: 0161-430 2650 Fax: 0161-494 6589 E-mail: bedeng@btconnect.com *Precision engineers*

▶ Bedford Engineering Services, Blanche House, Cross Blanche Street, Dowlais, Merthyr Tydfil, CF48 3PD Tel: (01685) 350798 Fax: (01685) 350798

Bedford Estates, 29a Montague Street, London, WC1B 5BL Tel: (020) 7636 2885 Fax: (020) 7255 1729 E-mail: enquiries@woburnabbey.co.uk *Property Management*

Bedford Fencing Co. Ltd, 8 Sargeant Turner Trading Estate, Bromley Street, Stourbridge, West Midlands, DY9 8HZ Tel: (01384) 422688 Fax: (01384) 422688 *Fencing gate manufrs*

Bedford Fixings, 1a Dean Street, Bedford, MK40 3EQ Tel: (01234) 360747 Fax: (01234) 217414 *Power tools & fixing systems wholesaler*

▶ Bedford Home Computers, Poplar Avenue, Bedford, MK41 8BL Tel: (07754) 093885 *Internet, & wireless broadband, computer upgrades & repairs etc*

Bedford Pump Ltd, Brooklands, Woburn Road Industrial Estate, Kempston, Bedford, MK42 7UH Tel: (01234) 852071 Fax: (01234) 856620 E-mail: sales@bedfordpumps.co.uk *Pump manufrs*

Bedford Saw & Tool Co., Ampthill Road, Bedford, MK42 9JP Tel: (01234) 217417 Fax: (01234) 270663 E-mail: info@bedfordsaw.co.uk *Saw & woodworking machinery distributors, sharpening services*

Bedford Stainless Ltd, 11c Dock Road, Connah's Quay, Deeside, Clwyd, CH5 4DS Tel: (01244) 830271 E-mail: bedfordstainless@hotmail.co.uk *Stainless & mild steel fabricators*

Bedford Stainless Engineering, Blyth Road, Harworth, Doncaster, South Yorkshire, DN11 8NE Tel: (01302) 752003 Fax: (01302) 752006 *Welders*

Bedford Timber Supplies Ltd, Cauldwell Walk, Bedford, MK42 9DT Tel: (01234) 272171 Fax: (01234) 269235 E-mail: matt@batfordtimbersupplies.co.uk *Timber merchants*

Bedford Transmissions Ltd, Unit 26-27, Raynham Road, Bishop's Stortford, Hertfordshire, CM23 5PE Tel: (01279) 461397 Fax: (01279) 659017 E-mail: enquires@btlgears.co.uk *CNC turning & milling in 2,3,4,5 axis for small to medium batch services*

Bedford Typesetters, 36 Woburn Road Industrial Estate Singer Way, Woburn Road Industrial Estate, Kempston, Bedford, MK42 7AF Tel: (01234) 840125 Fax: (01234) 840909 *Typesetters*

W.R. Bedford Stonemasonry Ltd, 57-65 Whitehouse Lane, Bedminster, Bristol, BS3 4DN Tel: 0117-963 7756 Fax: 0117-963 4223 E-mail: wr.bedford@1way.co.uk *Stone masonry contractor services*

▶ Bedhampton Piano Shop Ltd, 90 Bedhampton Road, Havant, Hampshire, PO9 3EZ Tel: (023) 9248 4802 Fax: (0800) 2985087 E-mail: graham@bpspianos.com *Piano restoration services*

Bedingfield Hirebase Ltd, Faraday Road, Harfreys Industrial Estate, Great Yarmouth, Norfolk, NR31 0NH Tel: (01493) 440522 Fax: (01493) 442555 *Tool plant hire services*

▶ Bedlum Beds Ltd, 2 Mansfield Road, Baldock, Hertfordshire, SG7 6ED Tel: (01462) 642921 Fax: (01462) 635370 E-mail: bedlum.beds@ntlworld.com *Bed & mattress retail & wholesale*

▶ Bedmakers Co., Unit 5-7, Clayhill, Fish Bound Industrial Trading Estate, Fishbound, Bristol, BS5 7ES Tel: 0117-965 6400 Fax: 0117-965 7300 E-mail: bedmakerbristol@aol.com *Furniture retailer*

Bedrock Business Finance Ltd, 29/30 Fleet Street, Torquay, TQ1 1BB Tel: 01803 217917 Fax: 01803 217916 E-mail: finance@bedrock.uk.com **Commercial Finance Specialists.**We provide specialist advice and guidance for all business finance and loan requirements.**Loans avaialable for purchase, remortgage or capital raising. **We can fund pubs, hotels, guest houses, care homes, shops,industrial units property development, property investment, boats.**Non status, adverse and self certification loans available**Asset and leasing finance*

▶ Bedrock Crushing & Recycled Materials Ltd, Bow Depot, Marshgate Sidings, London, E15 2PB Tel: (020) 8503 0006

Bedrock Engineering, Unit 7, Palmers Road Industrial Estate, Emsworth, Hampshire, PO10 7DH Tel: (01243) 377435 Fax: (01243) 377443 E-mail: info@bedrockengineering.co.uk *Welders & tooling suppliers*

The Bedroom, 61 Market Place, Shaw, Oldham, OL2 8NN Tel: (01706) 299522 Fax: (01706) 299522 *Bed distributors*

Bedroom Options, 13 Wychwood Avenue, Edgware, Middlesex, HA8 6TL Tel: (020) 8952 3200 Fax: (020) 8952 3200 *Bespoke bedroom furniture manufrs*

Beds Beds Bed Centre, 313-321 North End Rd, London, SW6 1NN Tel: 020 76103000 Fax: 020 73857711 *Bed retailer*

Beds Beds Beds London Ltd, 313-321 North End Road, London, SW6 1NN Tel: (020) 7385 2000 Fax: (020) 7385 7711 *Bed suppliers*

Beds Compressor Service Ltd, Unit 4h, Cambridge Road Industrial Estate, Bedford, MK42 0LJ Tel: (01234) 364446 Fax: (01234) 217344 *Air compressor distributors*

Beds Direct From Sleepers, 4 Boxer Trading Estate, Ponthir Road, Caerleon, Newport, NP18 3NY Tel: (01633) 430022 Fax: (01633) 430011 *Beds & furniture distributors*

Beds Flooring Distributors, Cambridge Road, Bedford, MK42 0LH Tel: (01234) 342444 Fax: (01234) 364925 E-mail: sales@bedsflooring.co.uk *Wholesale floor covering distributors* Also at: Branches throughout the U.K.

Beds & Furniture Superstore, 280 Oxlow Lane, Dagenham, Essex, RM10 8LP Tel: (020) 8593 7776 Fax: (020) 8593 7776 *Bed suppliers*

Beds To Go London Ltd, 43 Windmill Hill, Enfield, Middlesex, EN2 7AE Tel: (020) 8363 3323 Fax: (020) 8363 5545 *Bed retail*

▶ Bedside Manor, 108 Burley Road, Leeds, LS3 1JP Tel: 0113-242 5600 Fax: 0113-242 6100 *Beds & bedroom furniture showroom*

Bedsons Ltd, A1 Bodmin Road, Coventry, CV2 5DB Tel: (024) 7661 4542 Fax: (024) 7661 4523 E-mail: info@bedsons.com *Hand lamp manufrs*

Bedstead Collection, 1 & 2 Montpellier Walk, The Ginnel, Harrogate, North Yorkshire, HG1 2RB Tel: (01423) 528111 Fax: (01423) 538321 *Bedstead suppliers*

Bedtime, 691 London Road, Isleworth, Middlesex, TW7 4ES Tel: (020) 8568 2574 Fax: (020) 8568 4761 E-mail: sales@bedtimesuperstores.co.uk *Sale of beds & bedding*

Bedtime Bed Centre, 8 Falcon Road, Wisbech, Cambridgeshire, PE13 1AU Tel: (01945) 466788 Fax: (01945) 466788 *Bed & bedding suppliers*

Bedtime Bedding Centre, 21-23 Windmill Street, Gravesend, Kent, DA12 1AS Tel: (01474) 321249 Fax: (01474) 320009 E-mail: info@wellsbedding.co.uk *Bedroom furniture*

Bedworld Ltd, 36 Bridge Street, Castleford, West Yorkshire, WF10 1JS Tel: (01977) 511577 Fax: (01977) 511577 *Bed distributors*

Bedworld, Unit 3 Bulmer Way, Middlesbrough, Cleveland, TS1 5JT Tel: (01642) 860086 Fax: (01642) 862488 E-mail: admin@bedworld.org *Bed retailers*

▶ Bedworld.net, Calder House, Saville Road, Castleford, West Yorkshire, WF10 1BJ Tel: (01977) 669690 Fax: (01977) 669693 E-mail: sales@bedworld.net *Bed retailer*

BEE, Yardes Cott, Dewlish, Dorchester, Dorset, DT2 7LT Tel: 01258 837234 *Caravan & camping accessories*

Company Information

Bee Gee Brushes Ltd, Unit 3c Saxon Business Park, Hanbury Road, Stoke Prior, Bromsgrove, Worcestershire, B60 4AD Tel: (01527) 837001 Fax: (01527) 837001 E-mail: mar_r_goddard@hotmail.com *Brushes, general & industrial. Also paint brush manufrs*

▶ Bee Inspired, 236 Windmill Avenue, Kettering, Northamptonshire, NN15 7DQ Tel: (01536) 514646 *Craft supplies retailers*

Bee Instruments Ltd, 46 Spindus Road, Speke Hall Industrial Estate, Liverpool, L24 1YA Tel: 0151-486 5775 Fax: 0151-448 1677 *Industrial instrument manufrs*

Bee Line Fitted Bedrooms, 71 Station Road, Flitwick, Bedford, MK45 1JU Tel: (01525) 712090 Fax: (01525) 712090 *Furniture to specification manufrs*

▶ Bee Online Ltd, 24 Taphouse Avenue Witney, Witney, Oxfordshire, OX28 1JJ Tel: (01993) 200852 Fax: (01993) 200852 E-mail: info@buzzonline.biz *Bee Online provide total web design solutions for small to medium-sized businesses. Our team combines both the technical and the creative talents to design and build effective and practical websites at prices that won''t break the bank.** Based in Witney, near Oxford, Bee Online is a full-service web consultancy, built in partnership with Spear Solutions - a fast growing Internet services company. We have access to resources including graphic designers, user-interface planners and software engineers who work together at every stage of a project to meet your specific requirements. **We offer template or bespoke website design, flash media, e-commerce systems, cd-rom business cards, secure data back-up and much more.**

Bee Tee Products, Cemetery Lane, Carlton, Wakefield, West Yorkshire, WF3 3QT Tel: 0113-282 4494 Fax: 0113-282 4706 *Inflatable products manufrs*

Beebee & Beebee Ltd, 48 Lower Forster Street, Walsall, WS1 1XB Tel: (01922) 623407 Fax: (01922) 722575 *Saddle tree manufrs*

Beebys, The Depot, High Street, Stilton, Peterborough, PE7 3RA Tel: (01733) 244584 Fax: (01733) 244946 E-mail: info@beebys.co.uk *Industrial cleaning services*

C. Beech & Sons (Netherton) Ltd, Waterside Estate, Primrose Hill, Cradley Road, Netherton, Dudley, West Midlands, DY2 9RG Tel: (01384) 456654 Fax: (01384) 238656 E-mail: sales@cbeech-steel.co.uk *Steel Stockholders. Suppliers of mild steel flats, angles, rounds, squares, plates, sheets, universal beams (RSJ's), universal columns, welded mesh. We also offer cutting, shearing, drilling, painting. Daily delivery throughout the Midlands.*

Beech Dene Craft Centre, Beechdene, Carr Lane, Hambleton, Poulton-le-Fylde, Lancashire, FY6 9DW Tel: (01253) 701371 Fax: (01253) 701848 *Furniture restoration & furniture cabinet manufrs*

Beech Hill Electronics, Beechcroft, Beech Hill Road, Beech Hill, Reading, RG7 2AU Tel: 0118-988 4622 E-mail: sales@beech-hill.co.uk *Computer software & electronic design & manufrs*

Beech & James, 8 Vyse Street, Hockley, Birmingham, B18 6LT Tel: 0121-236 6589 Fax: 0121-236 6589 *Jewellery manufrs*

▶ Beech Systems, Riversmead 1 Longridge Road, Hurst Green, Clitheroe, Lancashire, BB7 9QW Tel: (01254) 826570 Fax: (01254) 826763

▶ Beechams, 167 Fleet Street, London, EC4A 2EA Tel: (020) 7427 5700 Fax: (020) 7427 5701 E-mail: ian.wright@beechams.com *Provinding expert tax and accounting services and advice in central London. Specialising in property capital gains tax issues and outsourcing solutions. Services include audits, management accounts, tax returns, payroll, capital gains, inhertance tax planing, corporate tax issues and VAT assistance.*

Beechbrook Consulting Ltd, 24 Clermont Terrace, Brighton, BN1 6SH Tel: (01273) 561714 Fax: (01273) 561772 E-mail: info@fastrak-consulting.co.uk *Computer consultants*

Beechcraft Ltd, First Avenue, Westfield Industrial Estate, Midsomer Norton, Radstock, BA3 4BS Tel: (01761) 416642 Fax: (01761) 419267 E-mail: info@beechcraft-ltd.com *Enclosures for electronic equipment manufrs*

▶ The Beeches, Boston Road, Heckington, Sleaford, Lincolnshire, NG34 9JQ Tel: (01529) 462059 E-mail: thebeeches@lycos.co.uk *Bed and Breakfast Accommodation. Superior Ensuite double room, in former stable annex. Lovely grounds to relax in. Situated between Boston and Sleaford. Please contact for dates and prices.*

▶ Beechgrove Woodworking Ltd, 7-8 Lancaster Park Industrial Estate, Bowerhill, Melksham, Wiltshire, SN12 6TT Tel: (01225) 792920 Fax: (01225) 792131 E-mail: sales@beechgrovefurniture.co.uk

Beechwood, 5 Havelock Terrace, Plymouth, PL2 1AT Tel: (0870) 7395000 Fax: (01752) 318332 E-mail: enquiries@bwcom.co.uk *Beechwood Communications offer range web design services to improve your business communications. Based in Plymouth, Devon, South West England UK we specialise in developing e-commerce strategies and solutions for businesses in the UK.*

▶ Beechwood Developments, 70 Albion Road, Edinburgh, EH7 5QZ Tel: 0131-661 5999

▶ Beechwood Hire & Sales Ltd, 264-272 Corporation Rd, Newport, Gwent, NP19 0DZ Tel: (01633) 244444 Fax: (01633) 251111 E-mail: sales@beechwoodhire.co.uk *Plant & tool hire centre*

Beechwood House Publishing Ltd, Beechwood House 2-3 Commercial Way, Christy Close, Southfields Business Park, Basildon, Essex, SS15 6EF Tel: (01268) 495600 Fax: (01268) 495601 E-mail: info@binleys.co.uk *Publishing agents*

▶ Beechwood Press, 1 Park Gate Close, Bredbury Park Way, Bredbury, Stockport, Cheshire, SK6 2SZ Tel: 0161-612 0102 Fax: 0161-612 9889

Beechwood Recruitment Ltd, 221 High Street, London, W3 9BY Tel: (020) 8992 8647 Fax: (020) 8992 5658 E-mail: mail@beechwoodrecruit.com *Technical recruitment register engineering & technical recruitment*

Beechwood Saab, 8 Siddals Roaf, Derby, DE1 2QD Tel: (01332) 381900 Fax: (01332) 381999 *Car dealership*

Beecroft & Co. Ltd, Huddersfield, HD1 9WB Tel: (01422) 374801 Fax: (01422) 370681 E-mail: sales@warmalux.co.uk *Electrical under floor heating manufrs*

Beecroft Engineering Co., South Parade, Pudsey, West Yorkshire, LS28 8NZ Tel: 0113-256 5131 Fax: 0113-239 3126 *General engineers*

Beecroft & Partners Ltd, Northfield Road, Rotherham, South Yorkshire, S60 1RR Tel: (01709) 377881 Fax: (01709) 369264 E-mail: sales@beecroft-science.co.uk *General laboratory assay suppliers*

Beecroft & Wightman Bradford Ltd, 94 Garnett Street, Bradford, West Yorkshire, BD3 9HB Tel: (01274) 725276 Fax: (01274) 725276 *Timber merchants*

Beedle & Cooper Photograpy, Orchard Studio, 8 Beech Lane, Kislingbury, Northampton, NN7 4AL Tel: (01604) 832555 E-mail: beedle.cooper@btinternet.com *Photographers*

Eddie Beedle Ltd, Unit 1 Jenning Street, Hull, HU8 7AN Tel: (01482) 323648 Fax: (01482) 211461 *Architectural metalwork fabricator*

▶ Beefast Contractors Ltd, 85 Highlands Close, Kidderminster, Worcestershire, DY11 6JU Tel: (01562) 630861 Fax: (01562) 630861 E-mail: beefast85@aol.com *beefast contractors supplys a expert carpentry and building service all over the uk*

Bee-Fast Fasteners Ltd, Montrose House, Lancaster Road, Cressex Business Park, High Wycombe, Buckinghamshire, HP12 3PY Tel: 0845 4940703 Fax: (01494) 436270 E-mail: sales@themontosegroup.com *Montrose Fasteners is a Leading Supplier of Industrial Fasteners and Stainless Steel Bars to the whole UK market place. Inventory Management / Vendor Management Systems specialists. Bespoke manufacturing or off the shelf screws, bolts, nuts, rivets, washers, turned parts, studs, and fasteners for every conceivable application! Please visit our website or call us today to discuss your requirements. Our friendly advisors will be delighted to take your call. Please mention Kellysearch when calling.*

Beehive Coils Ltd, Studlands Park Industrial Estate, Newmarket, Suffolk, CB8 7AU Tel: (01638) 664134 Fax: (01638) 661623 E-mail: info@beehivecoils.co.uk *Coil, heat transfer & air conditioning equipment manufacturer. Full design service. Established in 1968!*

Beehive Joinery, 3 Beehive Trading Estate, Crews Hole Road, Bristol, BS5 8AY Tel: 0117-955 8974 Fax: 0117-955 8974 *Joinery contractors*

Beejay Welding Engineers, 5 Newlyn Road, Cradley Heath, West Midlands, B64 6BE Tel: (01384) 566205 Fax: (01384) 565245 *Welding fabricators*

Beekay Products, 152-154 Ilderton Road, London, SE15 1NT Tel: (020) 7732 8608 Fax: (020) 7277 6996 *Promotional aids to sport*

Beeland Controls Ltd, Unit 14 Marcon House, Wyther Lane, Leeds, LS5 3BT Tel: 0113-278 2351 Fax: 0113-278 9663 E-mail: beelandc@aol.com Principal Export Areas: Central/East Europe & West Europe *Pneumatic manifold manufrs*

▶ Beeley Fabrications Ltd, 11 Beeley Wood Road, Sheffield, S6 1NH Tel: 0114-234 3244 Fax: 0114-234 3063

Beeline, 9 London Road, Pakefield, Lowestoft, Suffolk, NR33 7AA Tel: (01502) 514756 Fax: (01502) 516043 E-mail: sales@beeline-refrigeration.co.uk *Refrigeration & air conditioning services*

Beeline Engineering Products Ltd, 82 Alston Drive, Bradwell Abbey, Milton Keynes, MK13 9HF Tel: (01908) 222999 Fax: (01908) 222998 E-mail: sales@beeline.co.uk *Industrial transmissions & drive belts engineers*

Beeney & Co. Ltd, Oakville Farm, Easons Green, Blackboys, Uckfield, East Sussex, TN22 5JH Tel: (01825) 840276 Fax: (01825) 840276 *Water engineering services*

Beer on Tap Ltd, Units 1-3 Townsend Farm Business Park, Melbury Osmond, Dorchester, Dorset, DT2 0LP Tel: (01935) 83683 Fax: (01935) 83683 E-mail: beerontapsales@aol.com *Beer, wine & spirits wholesalers*

Steve Beer, 44 Archery Steps, St. Georges Fields, London, W2 2YF Tel: (020) 7723 2049 E-mail: stevebeer@talk21.com *Film & video production*

▶ Bees Marquees, Satchell Lane, Hamble, Southampton, SO31 4HQ Tel: (023) 8045 8400 Fax: E-mail: john@beesmarquees.co.uk *Marquee hire*

Beesley Fuel Services Ltd, Whitehall Road, Greatbridge, Tipton, West Midlands, DY4 7JT Tel: 0121-557 4239 Fax: 0121-520 4536 *Fuel oil distributors*

Beesley's S S H Ltd, 15 Ashbourne Parade, London, W5 3QS Tel: (020) 8998 1291 Fax: (020) 8998 2112 *Power & hand tools distributors & maintenance*

Beeston Joinery & Upvc, Littleworth Road, Cannock, Staffordshire, WS12 1QQ Tel: (01543) 877342 *Joinery manufrs*

▶ Beeswitched, PO Box 413, Horsham, West Sussex, RH12 2YD Tel: (01403) 242003 E-mail: info@beeswitched.com *Decorative Light Switch Covers for childrens rooms*

▶ Beetecs Investigations, 1 Cranwell Rise, Mile Oak, Tamworth, Staffordshire, B78 3PU Tel: (01827) 285401 E-mail: petespencer1@ntlworld.com *Friendly and discreet Detective Agency specialising in confidential enquiries, surveillance and process serving.*

Beetee, 139 Taplow, Thurlow Street, London, SE17 2UJ Tel: (07956) 868418 E-mail: lewis@btcomputers.com *Computer maintenance*

Beetham Engineering Systems Ltd, 5 Hutchwns Close, Porthcawl, Mid Glamorgan, CF36 3LD Tel: (01656) 784882 Fax: (01656) 773332 E-mail: h.howard@btconnect.com *Engineering consultants*

Beetlenut, Abbey Barn Farm, Abbey Barn Lane, High Wycombe, Buckinghamshire, HP10 9QQ Tel: (0870) 460 5626 Fax: (0870) 460 5627 E-mail: Debbie@beetlenut.com *The design and production of live events, video & film, exhibitions, print, design and communications consultancy*

H.V. Beever Ltd, Unit 2, Marshgate Trading Estate, Marshgate Lane, London, E15 2NG Tel: (020) 8519 1777 Fax: (020) 8534 5420 E-mail: sales@hvbeeverltd.com *Paper merchants*

Beeversales Components Ltd, Aurillac Way, Retford, Nottinghamshire, DN22 7PX Tel: (01777) 700611 Fax: (01777) 701799 E-mail: sales@beeversales.com *Agricultural machinery component distributors*Agricultural wearing parts*Agricultural fasteners*

Beeweb Lifting Equipment, Ambrose Street, Rochdale, Lancashire, OL11 1QX Tel: (01706) 648717 Fax: (01706) 653012 E-mail: beeweb@btconnect.com *Webbing & cargo & lifting slings*

Begg & Co Thermoplastics Ltd, 71 Hailey Road, Erith, Kent, DA18 4AW Tel: (020) 8310 1236 Fax: (020) 8310 4371 E-mail: darrenw@fsmail.net *Master batch & raw material suppliers to the plastics industry*

Behind Closed Doors Ltd, 20 Sands Road, South Moreton, Didcot, Oxfordshire, OX11 9AB Tel: (01235) 818278 Fax: (01235) 818278 *Rollers & industrial door manufrs*

▶ Bei Giardini, 69 Braycourt Avenue, Walton-on-Thames, Surrey, KT12 2BA Tel: (01932) 244403 Fax: (01932) 244403 E-mail: beigiardini@aol.com *Bei Giardini designs, installs and maintains residential & Commercial irrigation systems in South England*

Beighton Construction Ltd, 58 Dunston Road, Whittington Moor, Chesterfield, Derbyshire, S41 8XA Tel: (01246) 451098 Fax: (01246) 455421 E-mail: beightonconstruction@hotmail.com *Civil engineers & public works contractors*

Beith Printing Co. Ltd, 1-7 Earl Haig Road, Hillington Industrial Estate, Glasgow, G52 4JU Tel: 0141-882 9088 Fax: 0141-882 3204 E-mail: mail@beith-printing.co.uk *Commercial & colour printers*

BEKA Associates Ltd, Old Charlton Road, Hitchin, Hertfordshire, SG5 2DA Tel: (01462) 438301 Fax: (01462) 453971 E-mail: sales@beka.co.uk *BEKA manufacture ATEX approved display instruments including 4-20mA loop-powered indicators, batch controllers, rate totalisers, temperature transmitters, counters, timers and clocks, alongside associated equipment such as lamps, beacons and sounders. Serial indicators and FIELDBUS displays are also available.*

Bekenal, PO Box 8494, Solihull, W. Midlands, B91 2BS Tel: 0121-705 2478 Fax: 0121-705 2478 *Cake decorating equipment*

Beko Technologies Ltd, Unit 2-3 Buntsford Park Road, Bromsgrove, Worcestershire, B60 3DX Tel: (01527) 575778 Fax: (01527) 575779 *Compressed air equipment suppliers*

Bel Air Sub Aqua Supplies, 82 Fairfax Drive, Westcliff-on-Sea, Essex, SS0 9AF Tel: (01702) 353205 Fax: (01702) 353205 *Diving equipment suppliers & wet & dry suit manufrs*

Bel Fuse Europe Ltd, G 7 Unit Preston Technology Centre, Marsh Lane, Preston, PR1 8UQ Tel: (01772) 556601 Fax: (01772) 883666 E-mail: bel_europe@belfuse.com *Electronic components manufrs*

Bela Electronic Design Ltd, 12-14 Brooklands, Kempston, Bedford, MK42 7UH Tel: (01234) 840242 Fax: (01234) 843066 E-mail: sales@bela.co.uk *PCB assemblers & design engineers*

Belair Research Ltd, Broadway, Bourne, Cambridge, CB23 2TA Tel: (01954) 718366 Fax: (01954) 718355 E-mail: brl@acoustical.co.uk *Noise vibration control consultants*

Belair Software, Unit 16 Orchard Road Industrial Estate, Strabane, County Tyrone, BT82 9FR Tel: (07710) 344940 Fax: (028) 7138 3792 *Computer software suppliers*

C.P. Belcher (Welding) Ltd, 115B Blythswood Road, Tyseley, Birmingham, B11 2BX Tel: 0121-706 9689 Fax: 0121-706 8477 E-mail: steve@cpbsteel.fsnet.co.uk *Steel fabrications of all types*

Belcher Cammack Transport Ltd, Norton Way, Moss Lane Industrial Estate, Sandbach, Cheshire, CW11 3YT Tel: (01270) 750992 Fax: (01270) 762882 *Road transport, haulage & freight services*

Belcom Cable & Wire Suppliers, Warish Hall, Warish Hall Road, Takeley, Bishop's Stortford, Hertfordshire, CM22 6NZ Tel: (01279) 871150 Fax: (01279) 871129 E-mail: dave@belcom.co.uk *Cable design & distribution*

Beldam Burgmann Ltd, Neachells Lane, Wednesfield, Wolverhampton, WV11 3QG Tel: (01902) 307711 Fax: (01902) 305201 E-mail: sales@beldamburgmann.com *Manufacturers and distributors of sealing products for industrial applications. Suppliers of Rubber Sheeting and Jointing materials.*

▶ Beldam Crossley Ltd, PO Box 7, Bolton, BL1 6PB Tel: (01204) 494711 Fax: (01204) 493203 E-mail: sales@beldam-crossley.co.uk *PTFE slide bearings,encapsulated 'O' seals, plane bearings & rotary shaft seals, PTFE & crossflow & sealing technology*

Beldam Lascar Seals Ltd, Lascar Works, Staines Road, Hounslow, TW3 3JL Tel: (020) 8570 7722 Fax: (020) 8570 4438 E-mail: enquiries@beldamlascargroup.com *Packaging seal services* Also at: Branches throughout the U.K.

Belden C D T Ltd, Littleborough, Lancashire, OL15 8YJ Tel: (01706) 374015 Fax: (01706) 370576 *Electric cable & wire manufrs*

Beldorm Ltd, Kearsley Mill, Crompton Road, Radcliffe, Manchester, M26 1RH Tel: (01204) 702300 Fax: (01204) 854854 E-mail: sales@ruia.co.uk *Textile suppliers manufrs*

Belfast Boiler Services, 574-576 Ballysillan Rd, Belfast, BT14 6RN Tel: (028) 9071 0000 Fax: (028) 9039 1062 *Heating & plumbing engineers*

Belfast International Airport Ltd, Belfast International Airport, Belfast, BT29 4AB Tel: (028) 9442 2888 Fax: (028) 9445 2096 E-mail: info@bial.co.uk *Airport service suppliers*

▶ Belfast Skills Development, 98 Carryduff Road, Lisburn, County Antrim, BT27 6YL Tel: (028) 9263 9459 Fax: (028) 9263 9510

Belfor Relectronic UK Ltd, Imbach House, Gerard, Tamworth, Staffordshire, B79 7UW Tel: (01827) 310100 Fax: (01827) 310200 E-mail: tamworth@uk.belfor.com *Specialist disaster management & contingency agents*

▶ Belfuse Eu, Riverside Estate, Sir Thomas Longley Road, Medway City Estate, Rochester, Kent, ME2 4DP Tel: (01634) 722890 Fax: (01634) 716677 *Electrical component manufrs*

Belgrade Insulations Ltd, Belgrade Centre, Denington Road, Denington Industrial Estate, Wellingborough, Northamptonshire, NN8 2QH Tel: (01933) 222205 Fax: (01933) 441433 E-mail: sales@belgrade-polymer.com *Plastics injection mouldings manufrs*

Belgrave Graphics Ltd, Belgrave House, Hatfield Business Park, Frobisher Way, Hatfield, Hertfordshire, AL10 9TQ Tel: (01707) 274549 Fax: (01707) 630660 E-mail: mail@intg.co.uk *Gift cards & tag manufrs*

Belgrave Press Ltd, 320 Melton Road, Leicester, LE4 7SL Tel: 0116-266 2516 Fax: 0116-261 0053 E-mail: sales@belgravepress.co.uk *Printing & Packaging products manufrs*

Belgrave Shipping Co. Ltd, Fishers Way, Belvedere, Kent, DA17 6BS Tel: (020) 8310 1890 Fax: (020) 8312 3505 E-mail: belgrave@ukfraite.co.uk *Shipping & forwarding agents*

▶ Belgravia Colour Printers, 12a Uplands Business Park, Blackhorse Lane, London, E17 5QJ Tel: (020) 8527 0101 Fax: (020) 8527 0105

Belgravium, 6 Campus Road, Listerhills Science Park, Bradford, West Yorkshire, BD7 1HR Tel: (01274) 741860 Fax: (01274) 741862 E-mail: sales@belgravium.com *Radio data*

Believe, The Business Centre, Padbury Hill Farm, Padbury, Buckingham, MK18 2BN Tel: 01296 730230 Fax: 01296 730121 E-mail: natacha@believeuk.co.uk *Marketing and fundraising services to local businesses and charities - strategic plans, marketing plans, website design, design, brochures and leaflets, copy writing, customer care, mailings, research and events*

Belimo Automation UK Ltd, Unit 10 Shepperton Business Park, Govett Avenue, Shepperton, Middlesex, TW17 8BA Tel: (01932) 260460 Fax: (01932) 269222 E-mail: welcome@belimo.co.uk *Air conditioning component manufrs*

Belix Services Ltd, 2 Hazel Business Park Sandwash Close, Rainford Industrial Estate, Rainford, St. Helens, Merseyside, WA11 8LY Tel: (01744) 885110 Fax: (01744) 885110 E-mail: belixservices@barclays.net *Electrical*

Alan Bell & Partners Ltd, Manor House, Front St South, Trimdon, Trimdon Station, County Durham, TS29 6LY Tel: (01429) 883664 Fax: (01429) 883664 E-mail: abell@criticalstrategy.com *Management consultants & accountants*

Bell Amusements Ltd, Unit 11 Queens Park Industrial Estate, Studland Road, Northampton, NN2 6NA Tel: (01604) 708398 Fax: (01604) 714347 *Amusement machine suppliers*

▶ Bell Architects, Main Street, Ballymoney, County Antrim, BT53 6AN Tel: (028) 2766 6406 Fax: (028) 2766 9982 E-mail: murray@bell-architects.com *Architects, planning advice, urban design, interior design*

▶ Bell Asphalt Company, 2e Penhill Road, Bexley, Kent, DA5 3EN Tel: (020) 8304 1901 Fax: (020) 8304 1901 E-mail: l-collins@ntlworld.com *Asphalt and felt roofing services*

▶ Bell Bros Pudsey Ltd, Green Lane, Pudsey, West Yorkshire, LS28 8JN Tel: 0113-256 5715 Fax: 0113-256 9255 E-mail: info@bellbros.com *Aluminium, sheet metalwork & steel fabricators*

Bell Brush Co., 286 Alma Road, Enfield, Middlesex, EN3 7BB Tel: (020) 8804 4144 Fax: (020) 8804 4235 E-mail: sales@bellbrush.com *Brush & janitorial suppliers service*

Bell Brush Co., 286 Alma Road, Enfield, Middlesex, EN3 7BB Tel: (020) 8804 4144 Fax: (020) 8804 4235 E-mail: sales@bellbrush.com *Janitorial supplier*

▶ Bell College Of Technology, Almada Street, Hamilton, Lanarkshire, ML3 0JB Tel: (01698) 283100 Fax: (01698) 282131

Bell Communications, 196-198 Cheltenham Road, Bristol, BS6 5QZ Tel: 0117-923 2323 Fax: 0117-923 2031 E-mail: info@bellcomm.co.uk *Telephone system services*

David K. Bell, 12 Church Street, Coatbridge, Lanarkshire, ML5 3ER Tel: (01236) 424617 Fax: (01236) 433866 E-mail: general@dkbell.co.uk *Messenger service providers*

Bell Display Ltd, Fernie Road, Market Harborough, Leicestershire, LE16 7PH Tel: (01858) 432652 Fax: (01858) 431621 *Plastic moulders & fabricators*

Bell Donaldson Steele, 17 Westfield Street, Edinburgh, EH11 2QQ Tel: 0131-337 6303 Fax: 0131-313 5328 E-mail: sales@belldonaldsonsteele.fsnet.co.uk *Wholesale ironmongers*

Bell Dunn & Keenlyside Ltd, Dale House, 21 Sussex St, Blyth, Northumberland, NE24 2AY Tel: (01670) 352213 Fax: (01670) 352767 *Ship chandler services*

Edmund Bell & Co. Ltd, Belfry House, Roydsdale Way, Euroway Industrial Estate, Bradford, West Yorkshire, BD4 6SU Tel: (01274) 680000 Fax: (01274) 680699 E-mail: sales@edmundbell.co.uk *Edmund Bell Contract supplies Flame Retardant Linings, Blackout and Interlinings for the Hospitality, Healthcare, Leisure and Education sectors as well as technical upholstery and curtain fabrics for Education and Healthcare.*

Bell Equipment UK, Unit 6c Graycar Business Park, Barton Turns Barton Under, Barton Under Needwood, Burton-on-Trent, Staffordshire, DE13 8EN Tel: (01283) 712862 Fax: (01283) 712687 E-mail: web@bell.co.za *Construction plant vehicle distributors*

G. Bell & Sons Ltd, 11 Kilmore Road, Crossgar, Downpatrick, County Down, BT30 9HJ Tel: (028) 4483 0301 Fax: (028) 4483 2301 E-mail: enquiries@crossgarpoultry.com *Poultry food manufrs*

Bell Gears Ltd, Frestan Works, Carwood Road, Sheffield, S4 7SE Tel: 0114-243 1938 Fax: 0114-243 2428 E-mail: sales@bell-gears.co.uk *Gear cutter manufrs*

Bell Glass, 2 Bloors Lane, Rainham, Gillingham, Kent, ME8 7EG Tel: (01634) 377776 Fax: (01634) 265813 *PVC & aluminium window manufrs*

Bell Hydraulic Services Ltd, Chapel Lane, Cwmbran, Gwent, NP44 2PP Tel: (01633) 861423 Fax: (01633) 864472 E-mail: dave.bell@bellhydraulics.co.uk *Hydraulic equipment manufrs*

John Bell Surveyor & Valuer, The Corner House, Tuttington Road, Aylsham, Norwich, NR11 6TA Tel: (01263) 734403 *Independent Chartered Surveyors covering the Norwich, Broadland and North Norfolk Areas*

Bell Lawrie & Co., 7 Drumsheugh Gardens, Edinburgh, EH3 7QH Tel: 0131-225 2566 Fax: 0131-225 3134 E-mail: abj@blw.co.uk *Stockbrokers*

Bell Lawrie White, 25 Albyn Place, Aberdeen, AB10 1YL Tel: (01224) 589345 Fax: (01224) 573199 E-mail: enquiries@blw.co.uk *Stockbrokers*

Bell Lawrie White Ltd, 43 Buccleuch Street, Dumfries, DG1 2AB Tel: (01387) 252361 Fax: (01387) 257288 E-mail: gmckerrow@b/w.co.uk *Stockbrokers*

M.M. Bell & Sons Ltd, 102 Arundel Street, Sheffield, S1 3BA Tel: 0114-272 4740 Fax: 0114-273 7523 E-mail: packaging@mmbell.co.uk *Presentation packaging agents*

Bell Machinery Ltd, PO Box 56, Tadcaster, North Yorkshire, LS24 9WS Tel: (01937) 830777 Fax: (01937) 830888 E-mail: hbellmt@aol.com *Machine tool merchants & fabrication machinery*

Bell Packaging Ltd, Barratt Industrial Park, Airport Way, Luton, LU2 9NH Tel: (01582) 459292 Fax: (01582) 450181 E-mail: info@bellpackaging.com *Transparent display manufrs*

Bell Perkins Ltd, Channing Houidses, Mart Road, Minehead, Somerset, TA24 5BJ Tel: (01643) 704541 Fax: (07643) 705646 E-mail: info@brookfood.co.uk *Food processing equipment manufrs*

Bell Polishing & Engineering Ltd, Pool Street, Wolverhampton, WV2 4HN Tel: (01902) 421714 Fax: (01902) 424517 E-mail: bell.polishing@virgin.net *Metal finishing services*

Bell Pottinger, 14 Curzon Street, London, W1J 5HN Tel: (020) 7495 4044 Fax: (020) 7861 8506 *Public relations* Also at: Cardiff & Glasgow

Bell Pottinger Public Affairs, 330 High Holborn, London, WC1V 7LU Tel: (020) 7861 2400 Fax: (020) 7861 2401 E-mail: enquiries@bpcf.co.uk *Public relations consultants*

▶ Bell Press Ltd, Jeans Lane Bells Hill, Bishop's Stortford, Hertfordshire, CM23 2NN Tel: (01279) 652976 Fax: (01279) 652770

▶ R.W. Bell Electrical Ltd, Atholl Road, Pitlochry, Perthshire, PH16 5BX Tel: (01796) 472263

S.A. Bell Ltd, The Old Spital Beck, Barton Hill, York, YO60 7JX Tel: (01653) 618578 Fax: (01653) 618824 *Haulage contractors*

Bell Security, Roding House, 970 Romford Road, London, E12 5LP Tel: (020) 8477 7500 Fax: (020) 8478 8052 E-mail: info@bellsec.com *Security specialists services*

▶ Bell Sheet Metal Ltd, Unit 1 Coin Street, Off Edge Lane Street Royton, Oldham, OL2 6EE Tel: 0161-627 0748 Fax: 0161-628 2511 E-mail: info@bellsheet.com *Specialised stainless steel manufrs*

Bell & Sime, Balunie Drive, Balunie Field Trading Estate, Dundee, DD4 8XE Tel: (01382) 730630 Fax: (01382) 739639 E-mail: dundee@buildbase.co.uk *Buildbase is one of the UK's fastest growing builders merchants. All of our branches are long established companies which have been serving local trades people for many years, with knowledge and experience to match. We believe strongly in understanding the needs of trades professional and our business has been developed specifically to meet those demands. Massive stocks, top quality products, competitive pricing, reliable delivery, specialist staff and exceptional customer service*

Bell Sons & Co Druggists Ltd, Slaidburn CR, Southport, Merseyside, PR9 9YF Tel: 0151-422 1200 Fax: 0151-422 1211 E-mail: sales@bells-healthcare.com *Pharmaceuticals*

Bell Sons & Co. (Druggists) Ltd, Tanhouse Lane, Widnes, Cheshire, WA8 0RD Tel: 0151-422 1200 Fax: 0151-422 1211 E-mail: sales@bells-healthcare.com *Pharmaceutical manufrs*

▶ Bell Stretchers, Unit 1B, Boundary Bank, Underbarrow Road, Kendal, Cumbria, LA9 5RR Tel: (01539) 732281 E-mail: info@bellstretchers.co.uk *Stainless steel rescue stretchers*

Bell System Telephones Ltd, Presley Way, Crownhill, Milton Keynes, MK8 0ET Tel: (01908) 261106 Fax: (01908) 261116 E-mail: sales@bellsystem.co.uk *Door entry systems manufrs*

Thomas Bell & Sons (Corn Merchants) Ltd, PO Box 5, Brigg, South Humberside, DN20 8RA Tel: (01652) 652933 Fax: (01652) 651313 *Agricultural merchants*

Bell Trailers Ltd, Finedon Sidings, Finedon, Wellingborough, Northamptonshire, NN9 5NY Tel: (01536) 723695 Fax: (01536) 724054 E-mail: belltrailers@lineone.net *Caravan chassis manufrs*

▶ Bell Truck Sales, Macklin Avenue, Cowpen Lane Industrial Estate, Billingham, Cleveland, TS23 4BY Tel: (01642) 561333 Fax: (01642) 561999 *Truck suppliers*

Bell Woven Brake, New Market Street, Colne, Lancashire, BB8 9DA Tel: (01282) 864000 Fax: (01282) 864325 E-mail: info@bellwoven.co.uk *Packaging manufrs*

Bella Moda, 48-66 Queensland Road, London, N7 7AS Tel: (020) 7609 2123 Fax: (020) 7609 1144 *Women's blouse, skirt, clothes manufrs*

Bellamy & Co Plymouth Ltd, Millbay Docks, Plymouth, PL1 3SA Tel: (01752) 665154 Fax: (01752) 263572 E-mail: ballamyagency@plymouth-chamber.co.uk *Shipping agents*

H & T Bellas Ltd, 14 Mountsandel Road, Coleraine, County Londonderry, BT52 1JD Tel: (028) 7034 2205 Fax: (028) 7035 2413 E-mail: info@bellas.co.uk *Established in 1825, the company is involved in timber & plywood importing, sawmilling operations, & builders merchants, selling both to trade & the public*

▶ Bellcraig Medical Ltd, 8 Muriel Street, Barrhead, Glasgow, G78 1QB Tel: 0141-880 4141 Fax: 0141-876 0301

▶ Belle Balloons & Florist, 184 The Chesils, Coventry, CV3 5BH Tel: (024) 7650 6177 Fax: (024) 7650 6177 E-mail: sales@belleballoons.co.uk *Retail, balloons & flowers*

Belle Coach Works, 26-28 Pinbush Road, Lowestoft, Suffolk, NR33 7NL Tel: (01502) 514001 Fax: (01502) 562217 E-mail: marton@shreevem.freeserve.co.uk *Commercial vehicle rebuilding services*

Bellerby Engineering Ltd, 6 Queens Gardens, Hornsea, North Humberside, HU18 1AU Tel: (01964) 532176 Fax: (01964) 532176 *Horticultural & agricultural engineering services*

Bellet Ltd, White House Nurseries, Colchester Main Road, Alresford, Colchester, CO7 8DH Tel: (01206) 827360 Fax: (01206) 823360 *Garden machines suppliers*

Bell-Fruit Games Ltd, Leen Gate, Lenton, Nottingham, NG7 2LX Tel: 0115-970 6707 Fax: 0115-978 0963 E-mail: sales@bellfruitgames.co.uk *Amusement machine manufrs*

Bellingdon End Farm Supplies, Bellingdon End Farm, Bellingdon, Chesham, Buckinghamshire, HP5 2UR Tel: (01494) 758239 Fax: (01494) 758051 E-mail: enquires@bel.co.uk *Equestrian sales*

Bellingham & Stanley Ltd, Longfield Road, Tunbridge Wells, Kent, TN2 3EY Tel: (01892) 500400 Fax: (01892) 543115 E-mail: sales@bellinghamandstanley.co.uk Principal Export Areas: Worldwide *Quality manufacturers of most types of Refractometers and Polarimeters based in UK and USA.*

Belliss & Morcom Ltd, Chequers Bridge, Gloucester, GL1 4LL Tel: (01452) 338338 Fax: (01452) 338307 E-mail: indsales@gardnerdenver.co.uk Principal Export Areas: Worldwide *Manufacturers of gas, industrial & oil free compressors*

Bellman Carter 2000 Ltd, Rear of, 358-374 Grand Drive, London, SW20 9NG Tel: (020) 8540 1372 Fax: (020) 8544 9424 *Builders merchants*

Bellmaster UK Ltd, 5 Victoria Street, Cinderford, Gloucestershire, GL14 2ET Tel: (01594) 822490 Fax: (01594) 822480 *Railway contractors, training & installation services*

▶ Bellmatic Leisure Ltd, 10-12 Boswell Square, Hillington Industrial Estate, Glasgow, G52 4BQ Tel: 0141-882 8320 Fax: 0141-810 4098 E-mail: carrigan@bellmatic.com *Pool tables, games supplier*

Bellpumps & Pollution Control, La Petite Fosse, St. Ouen, Jersey, JE3 2GN Tel: (01534) 485555 Fax: (01534) 482245 E-mail: enquiries@bellpumps.com *Pollution consultants*

Bells Control Equipment Ltd, 49 Scrutton Street, London, EC2A 4XJ Tel: (020) 7729 1979 Fax: (020) 7729 3731 E-mail: bells@mcmh.clara.net *Generating sets & power supply systems manufrs*

Bells Engineering Products Ltd, 874 Plymouth Road, Slough, SL1 4LP Tel: (01753) 567788 Fax: (01753) 567799 E-mail: bells.engineering@virgin.net *Valve distributors, agents & stockholders*

▶ Bell's Fencing Specialists, Robinia Close, London, SE20 8BF Tel: (020) 8778 6080

Bells Heat Transfer Ltd, Factory Road, Blaydon-on-Tyne, Tyne & Wear, NE21 5SA Tel: 0191-414 6789 Fax: 0191-414 5890 E-mail: bells.heat.transfer@talk21.com *Heat exchanger cleaning, coil air conditioning services*

Bells Instrument Engineers, 153 Sunbridge Road, Bradford, West Yorkshire, BD1 2NU Tel: (01274) 720677 Fax: (01274) 720677 E-mail: bells@legend.co.uk *Counters service & repairers*

Bells Tool Hire, Unit 337 Rushock Trading Estate, Rushock, Droitwich, Worcestershire, WR9 0NR Tel: (01299) 250578 Fax: (01299) 250578 *Tool hire & computer services*

Bellshill Metal Works Glasgow Ltd, 60-82 Hamilton Road, Bellshill, Lanarkshire, ML4 1AG Tel: (01698) 747132 Fax: (01698) 746908 *Sheet metalworkers*

▶ Bellstan Ltd, Old Post House, Wood Lane, Beech Hill, Reading, RG7 2BE Tel: 0118-988 3413 Fax: 0118-988 2820

▶ Bellville Computers Ltd, 53 Second Drove, Peterborough, PE1 5XA Tel: (01733) 891414 Fax: (01733) 891415 E-mail: sales@bellville-computers.co.uk *Suppliers of computer systems to trade & public*

▶ Bellway Homes Ltd, Bothwell House Hamilton Business Park, Caird Park, Hamilton, Lanarkshire, ML3 0QA Tel: (01698) 477440 Fax: (01698) 477441

▶ Bellwether Inventory Software, Bickerton House, Bickerton Road, Archway, London, N19 5JT Tel: 0871 309 8353 E-mail: enq@bellwethersoftware.com *Supplier of inventory software used on a lightweight handheld PDA. Produces highly detailed reports with photographs at the touch of a button. All typing eliminated, reports can range from 20-0 + pages. The software has been designed by inventory clerks for inventory clerks. Suitable for independent clerks and in-house clerks, long list of established clients.*

Belmar Engineering Services Ltd, Abbotswell Road, Aberdeen, AB12 3AJ Tel: (01224) 875038 Fax: (01224) 879125 E-mail: postmaster@belmar.co.uk *Machine engineers*

Belmay Ltd, Turnells Mill Lane, Denington Industrial Estate, Wellingborough, Northamptonshire, NN8 2RN Tel: (01933) 440343 Fax: (01933) 274414 E-mail: postmaster@belmay.co.uk Principal Export Areas: Asia Pacific, Africa, Central/East Europe & West Europe *Food flavour manufrs*

Belmey Industrial Supplies, Unit 12 & 17 Oldbury Business Centre, Oldbury Road, Cwmbran, Gwent, NP44 3JU Tel: (01633) 872474 Fax: (01633) 875557 E-mail: sales@belmey.co.uk *Distributor of fasteners & fixings*

Belmont Bakery Machinery, Slater Lane, Watermead Works, Bolton, BL1 2TE Tel: (01204) 370743 Fax: (01204) 399355 E-mail: sales@bakerymachinery.co.uk *Bakery machinery sales & service*

Belmont Bleaching & Dyeing Co. Ltd, Belmont Works, Egerton Road, Belmont, Bolton, BL7 8BN Tel: (01204) 811247 Fax: (01204) 811408 E-mail: info@belmont-bleaching.co.uk *Textile dyers & finishers*

▶ Belmont Blinds, 1 Brookside, Red Marsh Industrial Estate, Thornton-Cleveleys, Lancashire, FY5 4HD Tel: (01253) 820084 Fax: (01253) 820084 E-mail: pculley3@aol.com *Blind manufrs*

Belmont Fabrications Ltd, Unit 7, 15 Headley Road, Woodley, Reading, RG5 4JB Tel: 0118-944 8782 Fax: 0118-944 8757 E-mail: belmontfabltd@aol.com *Steel fabricators*

Belmont Hair & Beauty, 2 Plot 46 Colville Road, London, W3 8BL Tel: (020) 8992 7708 Fax: (020) 8992 7709 *Hairdressers sundries & equipment* Also at: London W3

Belmont Tool Hire Ltd, 310 Brighton Road, Belmont, Sutton, Surrey, SM2 5SU Tel: (020) 8770 9480 Fax: (020) 8770 9480 *Plant & tool hire*

Belmonte Business Equipment Ltd, Carlton House, 230 Manchester Road, Stockport, Cheshire, SK4 1NN Tel: 0161-480 5556 Fax: 0161-480 6546 E-mail: sales@belmonte.co.uk *Hewlett packard & canon printer sales & maintenance supplier*

Belmos Electrical Services Ltd, 19 Hagmill Road, East Shawhead Industrial Estate, Coatbridge, Lanarkshire, ML5 4XD Tel: (01236) 443382 Fax: (01236) 443384 E-mail: belmos@btconnect.com *Control panels & systems manufacture including the following services: Manufacture, Design & Installation of the following: Control Panels, MCC"s, PLC systems, Drive Systems, for all type of industrial applications.*

Belpac Ltd, Heath Mill Road, Wombourne, Wolverhampton, WV5 8AP Tel: (01902) 897343 Fax: (01902) 893708 E-mail: sales@belpac.co.uk *Vacuum formed packaging & contract packing services*

Belper Tools Ltd, 7 Chapel Street, Levenshulme, Manchester, M19 3QB Tel: 0161-224 7240 Fax: 0161-257 2875 *Plough grinding & welding fabrication services*

Belso's Cereals Research & Development, 45-46 Stapledon Road, Orton Southgate, Peterborough, PE2 6TD Tel: (01733) 234076 Fax: (01733) 235799 E-mail: info@belso.co.uk *Cereal food products manufrs*

Belstan Metals Non-Ferrous Ltd, 21-27 Hunters Road, Hockley, Birmingham, B19 1DP Tel: 0121-554 5531 Fax: 0121-515 2824 *Non-ferrous scrap metal merchants*

The Belt Company Ltd, Springvale House, Doncaster Road, Askern, Doncaster, South Yorkshire, DN6 0AD Tel: (01302) 708383 Fax: (01302) 708527 *Conveyor belts manufrs*

Belt Technologies Europe, Pennine House, Washington, Tyne & Wear, NE37 1LY Tel: 0191-415 3010 Fax: 0191-415 0333 E-mail: sales@bte.co.uk *Metal belting technology & manufrs*

Beltech Belting Mnfrs, 7 Acacia Close Business Estate, Off Cherrycourt Way, Leighton Buzzard, Bedfordshire, LU7 4QE Tel: (01525) 851155 Fax: (01525) 851156 E-mail: beltech@globalnet.co.uk *Conveyor belting distributors*

Belting & Mechanical Leather Co. Ltd, 20 Cloberfield Road, Milngavie, Glasgow, G62 7LN Tel: 0141-956 6577 Fax: 0141-956 2126 E-mail: sales@beltingmechanical.co.uk *Conveyor belting manufrs*

Belton & Slade, 84 Wandsworth High Street, London, SW18 4LB Tel: (020) 8871 1000 Fax: (020) 8874 3117 E-mail: sales@beltonandslade.co.uk *Tools & general engineers suppliers*

Belton Technological Services Ltd, 2 Church Street, Henfield, West Sussex, BN5 9NR Tel: (01273) 492320 Fax: (01273) 494849 E-mail: bts.ltd@btopenworld.com *Electronics design development*

Belts Conveyors & Accessories Ltd, Unit 8 Terry Dicken Industrial Estate, Station Road, Stokesley, Middlesbrough, Cleveland, TS9 7AE Tel: (01642) 711270 Fax: (01642) 711919 E-mail: geoflett@btinternet.com *Belts & conveyor supplies pvc curtains & doors*

Belvedere, Kite Hill Studios, Kite Hill, Selborne, Alton, Hampshire, GU34 3LA Tel: (01420) 511524 Fax: (01420) 511491 E-mail: m.hackman@btclick.com *Mirrors*

Belvedere Manufacturing Co. Ltd, The Old Printing Works, Waterloo Road, Radstock, BA3 3EP Tel: (01761) 437621 Fax: (01761) 436616 E-mail: belvederemfg@aol.com *Joinery specialists*

Bemas Boiler Erectors Ltd, PO Box 28, Nottingham, NG10 2GA Tel: 0115-972 8954 Fax: 0115-946 1857 E-mail: paul@bemasboilers.co.uk *Boiler erectors, repairers & services*

Bemasan Ltd, Owen Road, Wolverhampton, WV3 0BB Tel: (01902) 772975 Fax: (01902) 424374 E-mail: nevasales@bemasan.com *NEVA is the UK's leading brand of brass servicing valves and check valves for water and gas applications in the HVAC market. The NEVA brand is well known for leading the marketplace and providing innovative solutions for everyday applications.*

Bembridge & Jenkins Ltd, Moland Forge, Central Trading Estate, Shaw Road, Dudley, West Midlands, DY2 8QX Tel: (01384) 243833 Fax: (01384) 455628 *Marine & ships' chandlery equipment manufrs* Also at: Dudley

▶ Bemis Associates, 5 Turnpike Close, Grantham, Lincolnshire, NG31 7XU Tel: (01476) 594000 Fax: (01476) 576922

Bemis Packaging Ltd, The Flarepath, Elsham Wolds Industrial Estate, Brigg, South Humberside, DN20 0SP Tel: (01652) 680680 Fax: (01652) 680630 *Flexible packaging manufrs*

Bemrose Booth, PO Box 18, Derby, DE21 6XG Tel: (01332) 294242 Fax: (01332) 290366 E-mail: promote@bemrose.co.uk *Advertising calendar designers, producers & publishers*

F. Bemrose Ltd, Manby Road, Immingham, South Humberside, DN40 2LL Tel: (01469) 572961 Fax: (01469) 571498 E-mail: frankbemrose@aol.com *Blast cleaning & specialist coating*

Bemrosebooth Ltd, Stockholm Road, Hull, HU7 0XY Tel: (01482) 826343 Fax: (01482) 826667 E-mail: contact@bemrosebooth.co.uk *Security printers*

Ben Burgess Beeston, Dereham Road, Beeston, King's Lynn, Norfolk, PE32 2LE Tel: (01328) 701347 Fax: (01328) 700111 E-mail: beestonsales@benburgess.co.uk *Agricultural engineers* Also at: Aylsham & Norwich

▶ Ben Burgess Newmarket Ltd, Windmill Hill, Exning, Newmarket, Suffolk, CB8 7NP Tel: (01638) 577877 Fax: (01638) 577977 E-mail: newmarket@benburgess.co.uk *Agricultural machinery suppliers & repairers*

Ben Bydawell, Noth Barn, Wayners, Ashton, Leominster, Herefordshire, HR6 0DN Tel: (01584) 711580 Fax: (01584) 711580 *Joinery specialists*

Ben Ford Paul Ltd, 41 West Princes Street, Glasgow, G4 9BU Tel: 0141-332 0585 Fax: 0141-333 1607 E-mail: benfordpaul@aol.com *Engineers merchant supplying fasteners, hand tools, abrasives & sundries to the industry as well as tamper resistant security screws for over 75 years.*

▶ Ben & Jerry's Homemade Ltd, 10 Charter Place, High Street, Egham, Surrey, TW20 9EA Tel: (01784) 439900 Fax: (01784) 439999

Ben Kent Precision Engineers, Riverside Industrial Estate, Marsh Lane, Boston, Lincolnshire, PE21 7PJ Tel: (01205) 362681 Fax: (01205) 362681 *Fuel injection pump reconditioners*

▶ Ben Mundell, Bardaravine, Tarbert, Argyll, PA29 6YF Tel: (01880) 820223 Fax: (01880) 820491

▶ Ben 'N' Jack's Bouncy Castles, 65 Bollington Road, Stockport, Cheshire, SK4 5ER Tel: 0161-432 1932 E-mail: michael.thompson93@ntlworld.com

Ben Nevis Clothing, 237 Royal College Street, London, NW1 9LT Tel: (020) 7485 9989 Fax: (020) 7916 2324 E-mail: info@bennevisclothing.com *Suppliers of all aspects of safety and protective wear, outdoor, camping and hiking equipment, corporate, industrial and embroidered clothing and uniforms. We are the manufacturers of the original Combat labelled Harrington Jackets.*

Ben Nevis Distillery Fort William Ltd, Lochy Bridge, Fort William, Inverness-Shire, PH33 6TJ Tel: (01397) 700200 Fax: (01397) 702768 E-mail: colin.ross@bennevis.co.uk *Ben Nevis Distillery (Fort William) Ltd offers the finest whisky products, produced in a distillery in Fort William, Scotland. They offer various whisky blends, crystal products, pewterware and embroidered clothing.*

Ben Shaws Western, 5 Avon Gorge Industrial Estate, Portview Road, Bristol, BS11 9LQ Tel: 0117-982 4742 Fax: 0117-938 1169 *Draught soft drink & wine dispense specialist*

Ben Singer Machinery, Woolley Grange Farm, Woolley Green, Bradford-On-Avon, Wiltshire, BA15 1TY Tel: (01225) 866487 Fax: (01225) 865742 E-mail: ben@woolley59.fsnet.co.uk *Agricultural machinery suppliers*

▶ Ben Transport Services, Centurion House, Leyland Business Park, Farington, Leyland, PR25 3GR Tel: (01772) 459909 Fax: (01772) 459899

▶ Ben Walton Contractors, Mill Pit, Houghton le Spring, Tyne & Wear, DH4 4RA Tel: 0191-385 2517 Fax: 0191-385 2517

Benaim (UK) Ltd, Dilke House, 1 Malet Street, London, WC1E 7JN Tel: (020) 7580 6000 Fax: (020) 7580 6090 E-mail: london@benaimgroup.com *Consulting civil & structural engineers*

Benardout John & Robert Reproduction Furnisher Dealers, 168 Upper Richmond Road West, London, SW14 8AW Tel: (020) 8878 7775 Fax: (020) 8876 4620 E-mail: sales@benardoutfurniture.com *Furniture reproduction*

continued

Company Information

▶ Benben, 5 Trafalgar Road, Cambridge, CB4 1EU Tel: (07771) 902020 E-mail: benben@benben.co.uk *award winning short videos for events, corporate, promos, titles and ads. our aim is to make engaging, entertaining, & crafted films.*

Benbow Interiors, Bradley Mill, Newton Abbot, Devon, TQ12 1NF Tel: (01626) 367861 Fax: (01626) 355591 E-mail: mail@benbow-interiors.co.uk *Joiners & architectural metalworkers*

Benbow Metal Works Ltd, Townley Street, London, SE17 1DZ Tel: (020) 7701 0208 Fax: (020) 7703 3254 *Blacksmith railings & gates*

Benbrook Foods Ltd, The Manor Crown Business Centre, 5 Market Place, Whittlesey, Peterborough, PE7 1AB Tel: (01733) 350003 Fax: (01733) 350565 E-mail: jeanette.benner@benbrookfoods.co.uk *Benbrook Foods Ltd based in Peterborough are distributors of soft drinks, mineral water and syrups.*

Bencere Elliott Ltd, Broadstone Hill, Old Chalford, Chipping Norton, Oxfordshire, OX7 5QL Tel: (01608) 672800 Fax: (01789) 450785 E-mail: sales@bencere.co.uk *Cutting tools, design, manufacture & distribution*

▶ Bench Sheet Metal, 20c Beauchamp Industrial Park, Watling Street, Wilnecote, Tamworth, Staffordshire, B77 5BZ Tel: (01827) 265533 Fax: (01827) 265533 E-mail: craig.belford@btinternet.com *Sheet metal & sectional fabrication*

Benchmark, 5 Oxwich Court, Fendrod Business Park Valley Way, Morriston, Swansea, SA6 8RA Tel: (01792) 772292 Fax: (01792) 771458 *Kitchen furniture manufrs*

▶ Benchmark Cleaning Services Ltd, 59 Grantock Road, Walthamstow, London, E17 4DF Tel: (020) 8297 9136 Fax: (020) 8418 5866 E-mail: info@benchmarkcleaning.co.uk *Cleaning & staffing to the construction industry*

▶ Benchmark Dental Laboratories Ltd, Renwick House, Brixham Road, Paignton, Devon, TQ4 7RE Tel: (01803) 555741 Fax: (01803) 664273 E-mail: mail@1stdental.co.uk *Dental laboratory*

Benchmark Fabrication Ltd, Jubilee House, Jubilee Road, Letchworth Garden City, Hertfordshire, SG6 1WU Tel: (01462) 633000 Fax: (01462) 481450 E-mail: sales@bench-mark.co.uk *Manufacturers of shop display equipment*

Benchmark Interiors Ltd, Unit 2, Trading Estate, Kelvin Way, West Bromwich, West Midlands, B70 7TN Tel: 0121-553 0023 Fax: 0121-553 0024 *Shop fitters*

▶ Benchmark Scaffolding Ltd, Unit 32 The Waterside Trading Centre, Trumpers Way, London, W7 2QD Tel: (020) 8867 9977 Fax: (020) 8867 9900 E-mail: info@benchmarkscaffolding.com

Benchmaster Ltd, Glover Centre, Egmont Street, Mossley, Ashton-under-Lyne, Lancashire, OL5 9PY Tel: (01457) 837146 Fax: (01457) 837981 E-mail: sales@benchmaster.co.uk *Benchmaster have been a major manufacturer and supplier of workbenches for nearly 30 years. Benchmaster benches are all steel framed fully welded with a choice of tops. In addition to our extensive range of static work benches we have a range of mobile and semi-mobile benches which allow the fitter or service engineer to take the workbench to the job. We also supply a range of accessories including vices, cupboards and drawer units. In addition to our range of work benches and accessories we have a range of industrial cupboards and drawer units.*

Benchmaster Machine Tool Co., Holmfield Industrial Estate, Holmfield, Halifax, West Yorkshire, HX2 9TN Tel: (01422) 247185 Fax: (01422) 247234 *Machine tool manufrs*

The Bend It Shape It Co Ltd, Elswick Way Industrial Estate, Newcastle Road, South Shields, Tyne & Wear, NE34 0LW Tel: 0191-455 1209 Fax: 0191-456 4671 E-mail: sales@tecform.com *Plastic sheet shapers & suppliers*

Bendall, Brunthill Road, Kingstown Industrial Estate, Carlisle, CA3 0EH Tel: (01228) 526246 Fax: (01228) 525634 E-mail: info@bendalls.co.uk *Pressure vessels & specialist steel fabrication designers & manufrs*

Bendcrete Climbing Walls, Aquaduct Mill, Tame Street, Stalybridge, Cheshire, SK15 1ST Tel: 0161-338 3046 Fax: 0161-338 7956 E-mail: mail@bendcrete.com *Climbing wall manufrs*

▶ F. Bender Ltd, Gresford Industrial Park, Chester Road, Wrexham, LL12 8LX Tel: (01978) 855661 Fax: (01978) 855101 E-mail: info@benders.co.uk *Benders are the UK's leading manufacturer of Paper Disposable Tableware. We provide a complete service in the tabletop disposable products to meet all the needs of the Catering Industry. Our customers are caterers of every size, from multinational groups to individual cafes, who benefit from all the advantages that our deep market knowledge and continuity of service brings. Our unrivalled range of products consists of paper napkins, cups, plates, table coverings, doyleys and cutlery. Nevertheless we are always looking for ways to improve and expand the product line we offer to professional caterers. Our design experts spot trends, our production team keeps us at the fore front of manufacturing capability, our Custom Print service creates the unique identity needed for our customers business; and our sales and distribution network listens carefully to what our customers think. We are experts in our field, so let the experts do the hard work for you!*

Bender Machine Services Ltd, Manchester Road, Haslingden, Rossendale, Lancashire, BB4 5SL Tel: (01706) 225521 Fax: (01706) 218844 E-mail: info@bendermachine.com *Roll grinding engineers, metal finishing*

Bender UK, Low Mill Business Park, Ulverston, Cumbria, LA12 9EE Tel: (01229) 480123 Fax: (01229) 480345 E-mail: info@bender-uk.com *Electrical monitoring & earth fault detection equipment*

Bendigo Mitchell Ltd, 104 Windy Arbour, Kenilworth, Warwickshire, CV8 2BH Tel: (01926) 857626 Fax: (01926) 850609 E-mail: sales@bendigomitchell.com *Fork lift truck distributors*

Bendles Print Ltd, Unit 2, Higher Furzeham, Brixham, Devon, TQ5 8QP Tel: (01803) 616161 Fax: (01803) 859446 E-mail: sales@bendles.co.uk *Printers*

Bendrey Bros, Bath Road, Bridgeyate, Bristol, BS30 5JW Tel: 0117-967 4382 Fax: 0117-967 4383 *Timber merchants*

▶ Benefit 2 Business, 2A Red Lions Business Centre, Burnham Road, Latchingdon, Chelmsford, CM3 6JH Tel: 01621 743699 E-mail: info@benefit2business.com *Network support*

Benegraph & Academie Signs, 12 Market Place, Adlington, Chorley, Lancashire, PR7 4EZ Tel: (01257) 480366 Fax: (01257) 483499 *Sign manufrs*

Benetec Ltd, PO Box 472, Edgware, Middlesex, HA8 7ZR Tel: (0845) 4563082 Fax: (0845) 4563085 E-mail: sales@benetecmetleb.com *Metal cutting machine manufrs*

Benetec Cutting Tools, Unit 5b Midland Trading Estate, Consul Road, Rugby, Warwickshire, CV21 1PB Tel: (01788) 561133 Fax: (01788) 560223 E-mail: sales@benetecmetlab.com Principal Export Areas: Worldwide *Manufacturers of cutting-off machines including abrasive*

Benfells Ltd, Durham Road, Blackpool, FY1 3QB Tel: (01253) 295500 Fax: (01253) 295100 *Car alarm installation services*

▶ Benfield & Loxley Ltd, Old Bank House, 166 Oxford Road, Cowley, Oxford, OX4 2LA Tel: (01865) 717855 Fax: (01865) 715368 E-mail: mail@benfieldandloxley.co.uk

Benfleet Scrap Co. Ltd, 16 Brunel Road, Manor Trading Estate, Benfleet, Essex, SS7 4PS Tel: (01268) 756525 Fax: (01268) 566121 *Scrap metal merchants*

Benflow UK, 395 Crewe Road, Wistaston, Nantwich, Cheshire, CW5 6NW Tel: (07813) 158317 Fax: (01270) 664551 E-mail: enquiries@belflow.co.uk *Paint stripper*

Benham Goodhead Print Ltd, Newcomen Way, Severalls Industrial Park, Colchester, CO4 9PF Tel: (01206) 752525 Fax: (01206) 752255 E-mail: psimons@bgprint.co.uk *Directory printers*

Phil Benham Heavy Haulage Ltd, Heddons Cottage, Back Lane, Baydon, Marlborough, Wiltshire, SN8 2JL Tel: (01672) 541611 Fax: (01672) 541610 E-mail: info@benham-haulage.co.uk *Heavy, abnormal road haulage up to 100T, low loaders, stepframes, hiab, flat beds, extenables and abnormal load escort services. Nationwide coverage 24/7*

Benhar Blinds, Rimmon Cottage, Benhar Road, Shotts, Lanarkshire, ML7 5BJ Tel: (01501) 821835 Fax: (01501) 821835 *Blind manufrs*

Benhar Systems Ltd, Fleming House, 18a Garrell Road,, Burnside Industrial Estate, Kilsyth, Glasgow, G65 9JX Tel: (01236) 827070 Fax: (01236) 827071 Purchasing Contact: W. Curle Sales Contact: W. Curle Principal Export Areas: Worldwide *Conveyor systems, pneumatic; dust extraction engineers, installation or service. Also silo manufrs.*

Benier (UK) Ltd, 56 Alston Drive, Bradwell Abbey, Milton Keynes, MK13 9HB Tel: (01908) 312333 Fax: (01908) 311481 E-mail: sales@benier.co.uk *Benier (UK) Ltd based in Milton Keynes are bakery machinery importers. Products include ingredient storage, handling and metering, dough mixing, fermentation and delivery, dough dividing, resting and moulding, baking ovens, conveyors, bakeware, proofers and many more.*

Benita's Bread Shop, Market Place, Louth, Lincolnshire, LN11 9NR Tel: (01507) 600180 Fax: (01507) 450781 *Bakers*

▶ Benjamin Armitage (Hyde) Ltd, 238 Stockport Road, Gee Cross, Hyde, Cheshire, SK14 5RG Tel: 0161-368 2319

Benjamin R Vickers & Sons Ltd, Clarence Road, Leeds, LS10 1ND Tel: 0113-386 7654 Fax: 0113-386 7676 E-mail: inbox@vickers-oil.com *Manufacturers of technical oils*

Benmar Textiles Ltd, Cheetwood Road, Off Broughton Street, Manchester, M8 8AQ Tel: 0161-839 7000 Fax: 0161-839 2500 E-mail: info@benmartextiles.co.uk *Textile merchants*

Benn & Sons (Halifax) Ltd, Essex Street Industrial Park, Essex Street, Bradford, West Yorkshire, BD4 7PG Tel: (01422) 365308 Fax: (01274) 393537 *Removal & storage specialists*

Bennett, 1 Iremonger Road, Off London Road, Nottingham, NG2 3BL Tel: 0115-955 8000 Fax: 0115-955 8008 E-mail: sales@bennittsykes.co.uk *Sales & service of office products, office furniture, office stationery, office machines & consumables*

Bennett Architectural Aluminium Solutions Ltd, Parsonage Street, Stoke-on-Trent, ST6 5HL Tel: (01782) 834633 Fax: (01782) 835395 E-mail: helpdesk@baasl.co.uk *Manufacture aluminium frames*

Bennett & Dean Ltd, 9a Edison Road, Salisbury, SP2 7NU Tel: (01722) 413303 Fax: (01722) 414281

Bennett Electrical Co, 6-8 Reginald St, Burslem, Stoke-on-Trent, ST6 1DU Tel: (01782) 825281 Fax: (01782) 575120 E-mail: motors@bennettelectrical.com *Electric & geared motor distributors*

Bennett Engineering, Mintsfeet Industrial Estate, Mintsfeet Road, Kendal, Cumbria, LA9 6LU Tel: (01539) 722275 Fax: (01539) 730516 E-mail: s.bennett@bennett-engineering.co.uk *Sheet metal work engineers*

Bennett & Fountain Ltd, 2-4 Argyle Road, London, W13 8AD Tel: (020) 8998 0061 Fax: (020) 8998 0085 E-mail: bandf@ealing514.fsbusiness.co.uk *Electrical goods distributors*

James Bennett Ltd, Benco Works, Rugby Road, Hinckley, Leicestershire, LE10 0QG Tel: (01455) 637841 Fax: (01455) 636314 E-mail: sales@james-bennett.co.uk Principal Export Areas: Africa *Knitwear manufrs*

Bennett & Sayer, Wetherby Road, Derby, DE24 8HN Tel: (01332) 345546 Fax: 01332 293215 E-mail: info@holdenengineering.co.uk *Brick machine manufacturers & cnc engineers*

▶ Bennett Secretarial Services Ltd, 51a-52 Market Street, Hyde, Cheshire, SK14 2AB Tel: 0161-368 5511 Fax: 0161-627 1793 E-mail: hyde@bennettstaff.co.uk *Suppliers of temporary and permanent staffing solutions across commercial, catering and industrial sectors.*

Bennett Silks Ltd, Crown Royal Park, Higher Hill Gate, Stockport, Cheshire, SK1 3HB Tel: 0161-476 8600 Fax: 0161-480 5385 E-mail: sales@bennett-silks.co.uk *Silk fabric manufrs*

Bennett & Skelland Ltd, 306 Liverpool Road, Warrington, WA5 1DP Tel: (01925) 634066 Fax: (01925) 445505 E-mail: bennettandskelland@tiscali.co.uk *Pipe work & metal fabrication*

Bennett & Sons, Mowlem Trading Estate, Leeside Road, London, N17 0QJ Tel: (020) 8365 0033 Fax: (020) 8836 5161 E-mail: tottenham@bennetts.com *Motor spare part suppliers*

▶ Bennett Staff Bureau, 22 St Petersgate, Stockport, Cheshire, SK1 1HD Tel: 0161-480 0411 Fax: 0161-474 7610 E-mail: stockport@bennettstaff.co.uk *Supplier of temporary and permanent staffing solutions for the commercial, catering and industrial sectors.*

Bennett Sykes Group, 84 Vaughan Way, Leicester, LE1 4SH Tel: 0116-253 0454 Fax: 0116-253 6127 E-mail: enquiries@bennettsykes.co.uk *Office equipment suppliers*

Bennett Verby, 7 St. Petersgate, Stockport, Cheshire, SK1 1EB Tel: 0161-476 9000 Fax: 0161-476 9001 E-mail: enquiries@bennettverby.co.uk *Business consultants & accountants business advisors*

Bennett-Mahler Ltd, Merse Road, North Moons Moat, Redditch, Worcestershire, B98 9HL Tel: (01527) 62304 Fax: (01527) 591668 E-mail: bennettmahler@msn.com *Spring end grinding machines*

Bennett's, Chapel Pond Hill, Bury St. Edmunds, Suffolk, IP32 7HT Tel: (01284) 766166 Fax: (01284) 769634 E-mail: burystedmunds@bennetts.com *Warehouse distribution of motor components* Also at: Airdrie, Bury St. Edmunds, Leeds, Stoke-on-Trent & West Bromwich

▶ Bennetts Angling Stores Ltd, 9 Market Place, Mountsorrel, Loughborough, Leicestershire, LE12 7BA Tel: 0116-230 2818 Fax: 0116-237 4333 E-mail: fishing@bennettsangling.com *Fishing tackle on-line store*

Bennetts Of Bromsgrove Ltd, 53 Sherwood Road, Aston Fields Industrial Estate, Bromsgrove, Worcestershire, B60 3DR Tel: (01527) 870440 Fax: (01527) 575595 E-mail: sales@bennettsbathrooms.co.uk *Disabled person handrail manufrs*

Bennetts & Co (Grimsby) Ltd, 101 Charlton St, Grimsby, South Humberside, DN31 1SW Tel: (01472) 350151 Fax: (01472) 250053 E-mail: bennettstimber@aol.com *Timber merchants*

Bennetts & Son Ltd, 2 Centre Point, Knights Way, Battlefield Enterprise Park, Shrewsbury, SY1 3AB Tel: (01743) 467226 Fax: (01743) 467238 E-mail: shewsbury@bennetts.com *Tools & motor factor distributors*

W.D. Bennett's Plant & Services Ltd, Burma Road, Sharpness, Gloucestershire, GL13 9UQ Tel: (01453) 811754 Fax: (01453) 811657 E-mail: sales@newsilencers.freeserve.co.uk *Tower crane sales & hire* Also at: Sharpness

▶ Bennex (Aquaculture), Bennex House, The Enterprise Park, Forres, Morayshire, IV36 2AB Tel: (01309) 678270 Fax: (01309) 673215 E-mail: aquaculture@bennex.co.uk *Welding equipment*

Bennie Contracts, Leafy Lodge, Bridgecastle, Bathgate, West Lothian, EH48 3DR Tel: (01501) 730369 Fax: (01501) 730369 *Agricultural & public works contractors*

Peter Bennie Ltd, Oxwich Close, Brackmills Industrial Estate, Northampton, NN4 7BH Tel: (01604) 766101 Fax: (01604) 760671 E-mail: admin@peter.bennie.co.uk *Quarrying contract crushing haulage building stone*

Benning UK Ltd, Oakley House, Hogwood Lane, Finchampstead, Wokingham, Berkshire, RG40 4QW Tel: 0118-973 1506 Fax: 0118-973 1508 E-mail: info@benninguk.com *Power conversion technology electronic equipment distributors*

Benninghoven UK Ltd, Incendium House Centurion Way, Meridian Business Park, Leicester, LE19 1WH Tel: 0116-263 0345 Fax: 0116-282 8741 E-mail: enquiries@benninghoven.co.uk *Mining, quarrying & road making equipment*

Bennington Bait, The Bait Factory, Valley Lane, Long Bennington, Newark, Nottinghamshire, NG23 5EE Tel: (01400) 281525 *Fishing bait manufr*

▶ Bennys Bouncers, 802 Burnley Road, Rossendale, Lancashire, BB4 8BH Tel: (07867) 877813 *Inflatable bouncy castle hire services*

Benoil Services Ltd, Norcombe House, Tile Barn, Woolton Hill, Newbury, Berkshire, RG20 9UZ Tel: (01635) 253412 Fax: (01635) 253899 E-mail: sales@benoil.com *Polyurethane products/oil exploration consultants*

▶ Benriach Distillery Co, Longmorn, Elgin, Morayshire, IV30 8SE Tel: (01343) 862888 Fax: (01343) 862999

Benring Ltd, Glebe Tail, Quarnford, Buxton, Derbyshire, SK17 0TG Tel: (01298) 74026 Fax: (01298) 72391 *Epoxy resin formulation services & manufrs*

Benross Marketing Ltd, Benross House, Speke Hall Road, Liverpool, L24 9WD Tel: 0151-448 1200 Fax: 0151-448 1221 E-mail: sales@benross.com *Import merchants*

Benruss Fabrications Ltd, 10 Derby Road, Bootle, Merseyside, L20 8LN Tel: 0151-922 5478 Fax: 0151-922 7835 *Fabrication engineers*

Benson Beltings Ltd, Spenvale Works, Balme Road, Cleckheaton, West Yorkshire, BD19 4EW Tel: (01274) 851600 Fax: (01274) 851620 E-mail: sales@benson-beltings.co.uk *Industrial conveyor belt manufrs*

Benson Bros Bristol Ltd, Carlton Lodge, 90 Gloucester Road, Patchway, Bristol, BS34 6PZ Tel: 0117-969 4241 Fax: 0117-931 2028 *Civil engineers services*

▶ Benson Cairns Communications, 30B/9 Chambers Street, Edinburgh, EH1 1HR Tel: 0131 220 3785 Fax: 0131 220 3786 E-mail: rachelle@bensoncairns.co.uk *Benson Cairns Communications develops communication strategies, content and digital media for companies that wish to use information and communication technologies to drive their businesses forward. We focus on strategy, content development and project management.*

▶ Chris Benson Signs Ltd, 96-98 Great Howard Street, Liverpool, L3 7AX Tel: 0151-298 1567 Fax: 0151-298 1568 E-mail: info@benson-signs.co.uk *Sign manufrs*

Benson Components Ltd, Saxon Works, South St, Openshaw, Manchester, M11 2FY Tel: (0845) 1300000 Fax: 0161-231 6866 E-mail: sales@bensonexhausts.com *Manufacturers of exhaust systems & components*

Benson Engineering Ltd, Units 14-16, Houghton Road, Sheffield, S25 4JJ Tel: (01909) 563551 Fax: (01909) 569953 E-mail: bensons@heh.co.uk *Food processing plant manufrs*

Benson Heating, Ludlow Road, Knighton, Powys, LD7 1LP Tel: (01547) 529245 Fax: (01547) 520399 E-mail: information@bensonheating.co.uk Principal Export Areas: Worldwide *Heating & ventilation equipment manufrs*

Benson Industries Ltd, 5 Norcroft Industrial Estate, Norcroft Street, Bradford, West Yorkshire, BD7 1JA Tel: (01274) 722204 Fax: (01274) 306319 E-mail: enquiries@bensonindustries.co.uk *Builders trowel manufrs*

Benson Lund Ltd, Aviation Way, Southend Airport, Southend-on-Sea, SS2 6UN Tel: (01702) 547683 Fax: (01702) 530884 E-mail: bensonsales@ipeco.co.uk *Aircraft seating to customer's requirements worldwide*

Benson Refrigeration Ltd, Kings Cottage, Starlings Green, Clavering, Saffron Walden, Essex, CB11 4PP Tel: (01279) 777963 Fax: (01279) 777869 *Refrigeration engineers*

Benson Viscometers Ltd, Croft Quarry, West Williamston, Kilgetty, Dyfed, SA68 0TN Tel: (01646) 650065 *Measuring, analysing & controlling instruments*

Bensons Bed Centres Ltd, 1-5 St James Barton, Bristol, BS1 3LT Tel: 0117-927 2695 *Bed specialists*

▶ Bensons Bed Centres Ltd, Gallagher Retail Park, Stoney Stanton Road, Coventry, CV6 5QQ Tel: (024) 7666 1055 *Furniture manufrs*

Bensons Bed Centres Ltd, Debenhams, 36 Prospect Street, Hull, HU2 8PQ Tel: (01482) 589068 Fax: (01482) 211926 *Distributor*

Bensons Bed Centres Ltd, 8 Newbury Retail Park, Pinchington Lane, Newbury, Berkshire, RG14 7HU Tel: (01635) 569893 Fax: (01635) 569893 *Selling of beds*

▶ Bensons Bed Centres Ltd, 7 Sprowston Retail Park, Salhouse Road, Norwich, NR7 9AZ Tel: (01603) 301959 *Bed suppliers*

▶ Bensons Bed Centres Ltd, 786 Mansfield Road, Nottingham, NG5 3GG Tel: 0115-920 3852 *Bed manufrs*

Bensons Bed Centres Ltd, Unit 4 Alexandra Centre, Park Road, Oldham, OL8 1DB Tel: 0161-624 8893 *Bed suppliers*

▶ Bensons Bed Centres Ltd, Botley Road, Oxford, OX2 0HA Tel: (01865) 202795 *Beds retailers*

Bensons Bed Centres Ltd, Glamorgan Vale Retail Park, Talbot Green, Pontyclun, Mid Glamorgan, CF72 8RP Tel: (01443) 222889 Fax: (01925) 237601 *Bed retailers*

Bensons Bed Centres Ltd, Carpet World, Mariners Way, Ashton-on-Ribble, Preston, PR2 2YN Tel: (01772) 768565 Fax: (01772) 723027 *Bed distributors*

Bensons Bed Centres Ltd, Stadium Way, Retail World, Parkgate, Rotherham, South Yorkshire, S60 1TG Tel: (01709) 780030 *Bed retailers*

Bensons Bed Centres Ltd, 18 Goodwood Square, Teesside Retail Park, Thornaby, Stockton-on-Tees, Cleveland, TS17 7BW Tel: (01642) 670800 *Bed & bedding retailers*

Bensons Bed Centres Ltd, Unit 4 Taurus Park, Europa Boulevard, Westbrook, Warrington, WA5 7ZT Tel: (01925) 237600 *Bed manufacturers & retailers*

Bensons Bed Centres Ltd, 6 Winterstoke Road, Weston-super-Mare, Avon, BS23 3YT Tel: (01934) 635946 Fax: (01934) 413228 *Bed retailer*

Bensons International Systems Ltd, Bensons House, 104 Bath Road, Stroud, Gloucestershire, GL5 3TJ Tel: (01453) 755888 Fax: (01453) 753300 *Loose leaf ring mechanisms*

Bentalls, Wood Street, Kingston Upon Thames, Surrey, KT1 1TX Tel: (020) 8546 1001 Fax: (020) 8549 6163 E-mail: bentallsonline@bentalls.co.uk *Departmental store head office*

Benteler UK Ltd, 31 Waterloo Road, Wolverhampton, WV1 4DP Tel: (01902) 712212 Fax: (01902) 712899 E-mail: sales@benteleruk.com *Manufacturer of Steel Tubes*

Bentham Instruments Ltd, 2 Boulton Road, Reading, RG2 0NH Tel: 0118-975 1355 Fax: 0118-931 2971 E-mail: sales@bentham.co.uk *Light measuring equipment manufrs*

▶ Bentheim Interior Design, 3 Rosetti Studios, 72 Flood Street, London, SW3 5TF Tel: (020) 7376 3427 Fax: (020) 7376 3428 E-mail: david@bentheim.co.uk *Cutting edge interior design for retail, restaurant, hotel, exhbition, office and all commercial and residential interiors. Maximum design impact within budget constraints.*

Bentley Chemicals Ltd, Unit 17 Hoo Farm Industrial Estate, Worcester Road, Kidderminster, Worcestershire, DY11 7RA Tel: (01562) 515121 Fax: (01562) 515847 E-mail: info@bentleychemicals.co.uk *Silicone Specialists - sealants, lubricants & adhesives*

Bentley Computer Consultants, Lower Bush, Stoke St. Milborough, Ludlow, Shropshire, SY8 2ES Tel: (01584) 823667 Fax: (01584) 823667 E-mail: tonybentley@hotmail.com *Computer consultants*

Bentley Contracts, Brook Farm, Thorrington Road, Great Bentley, Colchester, CO7 8QP Tel: (01206) 250213 *Agricultural Contractors*

Bentley Copying Services, 1 Harewood Close, Sandiacre, Nottingham, NG10 5PL Tel: 0115-939 5577 Fax: 0115-939 5512 *Copying machines suppliers*

David Bentley Ltd, Greengate, Salford, M3 7NS Tel: 0161-834 8851 Fax: 0161-835 3303 E-mail: sales@davidbentley.co.uk Principal Export Areas: Worldwide *Calendar bowl manufrs*

F. Bentley & Co. (Heating & Plumbing) Ltd, 312 Ware Road, Hertford, SG13 7ER Tel: (01992) 500009 Fax: (01992) 505005 *Heating & plumbing engineers*

Bentley Instrument Co Ltd, 1 Block 2, Pennyburn Industrial Estate, Londonderry, BT48 0LU Tel: (028) 7126 1023 Fax: (028) 7126 6629 E-mail: sales@bentley-instruments.com *Instrumentation engineers*

Bentley Insurance Services Ltd, Pyms Lane, Crewe, CW1 3PL Tel: (01270) 255155 Fax: (01270) 586548 E-mail: recruitment@bentley.co.uk *Car manufrs*

▶ Bentley Mechanical Services Ltd, 140 Barton Road, Comberton, Cambridge, CB23 7BT Tel: (01223) 264240 Fax: (01223) 264240 E-mail: office@bentleymechanicalservices.co.uk *AC, heating, plumbing & ventilation contractors, domestic & commercial*

Bentley Wessex, 64 Third Avenue, Teignmouth, Devon, TQ14 9DP Tel: (01626) 770830 Fax: (01626) 770830 *Commercial laundry supplier & service*

Bentleys Fabrications, Gatesland, Stafford Road, Huntington, Cannock, Staffordshire, WS12 4NQ Tel: (01543) 570911 Fax: (01543) 570911 *Wrought iron manufr*

Benton & Johnson Ltd, Regalia House, Newtown Road, Bedworth, Warwickshire, CV12 8QR Tel: (024) 7684 8800 Fax: (024) 7664 3018 E-mail: bentonandjohnson@toye.com *Embroidery wires manufrs*

Benton Security Locks Ltd, 16 Victoria Street, Willenhall, West Midlands, WV13 1DR Tel: (01902) 602102 Fax: (01902) 366512 E-mail: info@bentonsecuritylocks.co.uk *Lock manufrs*

Bentsfield Engineering Ltd, Holme Mills, West Slaithwaite Road, Huddersfield, HD7 6LS Tel: (01484) 841100 Fax: (01484) 841919 E-mail: enquries@bentsfield.com *Catering equipment manufrs*

Bentwood Ltd (Sterling Group), Atlantic Street, Broadheath, Altrincham, Cheshire, WA14 5FY Tel: 0161-926 7000 Fax: 0161-926 7029 E-mail: info@stirlinggroup.com *Clothing manufrs*

Russell Benussi Associates, 3 Pebble Close, Tamworth, Staffordshire, B77 4RD Tel: (01827) 68008 Fax: (01827) 69265 E-mail: sales@benussi.com *Manufacturers representatives*

BenweldSecure, Unit 14a Hartlebury Trading Estate, Hartlebury, Kidderminster, Worcestershire, DY10 4JB Tel: (01299) 251750 Fax: (01299) 253576 E-mail: info@benweld.co.uk *Security door manufrs*

Benwell Cebard Ltd, 24 Crimscott Street, London, SE1 5TE Tel: (020) 7237 5111 Fax: (020) 7252 0683 E-mail: info@benwellsebard.co.uk *Printers foil blockers & embossers*

Benz Industrial Heating Ltd, 15 Dover Road, Northfleet, Gravesend, Kent, DA11 9PH Tel: (01474) 332522 Fax: (01474) 564267 *Warm air heating installers & servicing*

Beoley Building Services, 19 Druids Lane, Birmingham, B14 5SL Tel: 0121-436 5717 Fax: (01527) 597103 *Building refurbishment contractors*

Beolia Enviromental Services plc, 154a Pentonville Road, London, N1 9PE Tel: (020) 7812 5000 Fax: (020) 7812 5026 E-mail: edward.demaslatrie@veolia.co.uk Principal Export Areas: Worldwide *Veolia Environmental Services is the UK leading waste management company. Globally, the company serves over 45 million customers across 35 countries with 80,700 partners. Veolia Environmental Services provides a full range of services for handling solid and liquid waste. It provides waste management and logistic services, as well as material recovery and recycling.*

▶ Bep Industrial Supplies, Unit 11, Appleby Business Centre, Blackburn, BB1 3BL Tel: (01254) 279841 Fax: (01254) 290129 *Plastic Stockholders*Plastic Welding Equipment*

BEP Surface Tecnologies, Eton Hill Road, Radcliffe, Manchester, M26 2XT Tel: 0161-724 9090 Fax: 0161-725 9539 E-mail: info@bepsurfacetecnologies.co.uk *Grinding & electroplating services*

Bepco UK Ltd, Unit 2, Hatton Gardens Industrial Estate, Kington, Herefordshire, HR5 3RB Tel: (01544) 231144 Fax: (01544) 231484 E-mail: jbrett@bepco.co.uk *Tractor spare parts distributors*

Be-Plas Marketing Ltd, Unit 2 & 3 Old Hall Industrial Estate, Grisedale Road, Old Hall Industrial Estate, Wirral, Merseyside, CH62 3QA Tel: 0151-334 5133 Fax: 0151-334 9399 E-mail: sales@beplas.com *Plastics distributors*

Ber Polishing Co. Ltd, 8 A1 Trading Estate, Lewisham Road, Smethwick, West Midlands, B66 2BN Tel: 0121-565 2735 Fax: 0121-565 2735 *Metal polishing services*

▶ Berber Ltd, 18 Rosebank, Lymm Warrington, Lymm, Cheshire, WA13 0JH Tel: (07961) 905903 E-mail: nicksteed@supanet.com *Berber provide a besoke Recruitment Service to UK and European companies for both permanent and contract opportunities.*

▶ Beresford Blake Thomas Ltd, Fifth Floor, 52 Grosvenor Gardens, London, SW1W 0AU Tel: (020) 7881 2700 Fax: (020) 7881 2702 E-mail: administrator@bbt.co.uk *Recruitment agency services*

James Beresford & Sons, Bridge Street, Belper, Derbyshire, DE56 1BA Tel: (01773) 822117 Fax: (01773) 822117 *Monumental masons*

Beresford Pumps Ltd, Unit 7, Network Park, Duddeston Mill Road, Saltley, Birmingham, B8 1AU Tel: 0121-503 3001 Fax: 0121-503 3002 E-mail: info@beresfordpumps.co.uk *Manufacturers of industrial & chemical pumps*

Bereton Electronics Ltd, Unit 49 Kettley Business Park, Ketley, Telford, Shropshire, TF1 5JD Tel: (01952) 253222 Fax: (01952) 244445 E-mail: mail@bereton.co.uk *Electronic engineers subcontract design build service repair*

Bergas, 35 Keithleigh Gardens, Pitmedden, Ellon, Aberdeenshire, AB41 7GF Tel: (0771) 1205998 Fax: (01651) 842793 E-mail: bergas.scotland@talk21.com *Sales & service of cylinder gas control equipment*

▶ Bergen Transport Ltd, Mellors Road, New Bridge, Trafford Park, Manchester, M17 1PB Tel: 0161-873 0300 Fax: 0161-872 4379 E-mail: sales@bergen.co.uk

Berger Tools Ltd, Units B 1-2 Chaucer Business Park, Watery Lane, Kemsing, Sevenoaks, Kent, TN15 6QY Tel: (01732) 763377 Fax: (01732) 763335 E-mail: sales@berger-tools.co.uk ***Press & Mould Tooling****Berger Tools Ltd supplies all your Press and Mould tool requirements. Our client service is backed with over 25 years experience in this niche market, allowing us to offer extensive technical support.****Standard Parts****Berger Tools Ltd offer a comprehensive range of Standard Machine Elements for Clamping and Operating requirements including Tube Clamp Connectors & Linear Actuators.**We hold an extensive range of products in stock. If you product is not listed or needs to be modified we can offer the part as a special, manufactured to your exact requirement. **

Berges UK Ltd, 3 Nelson Business Centre, Nelson Street, Denton, Manchester, M34 3ET Tel: (0161) 335 0995 Fax: 0161-335 0935 *Drive manufrs*

▶ Bergman Direct, Lindum Business Park, Station Road, North Hykeham, Lincoln, LN6 3QX Tel: (01522) 852610 Fax: (01522) 852615

Bergmans, Grainger Suite, Dobson House, Regent Centre, Gosforth, Newcastle Upon Tyne, NE3 3PF Tel: 0191-233 6311 Fax: 0191-233 6341 E-mail: bergmans@north-house.com *Public relations agents*

Bergstrom Inc., Hengoed, Mid Glamorgan, CF82 7YH Tel: (01443) 865100 Fax: (01443) 865157 *Vehicle heating/ventilation systems*

Bericap (U K) Ltd, Oslo Road, Hull, HU7 0YN Tel: (01482) 826666 Fax: (01482) 832839 E-mail: info.uk@bericap.com *Metal & plastic closures manufrs*

Berigood Cooked Meats, 23 Preston Old Road, Freckleton, Preston, PR4 1PB Tel: (01772) 632215 *Food manufrs*

Bering Heating Supplies Ltd, Unit 9 Station Industrial Estate, Oxford Road, Wokingham, Berkshire, RG41 2YQ Tel: 0118-978 9886 Fax: 0118-978 7460 *Heating engineers*

Berisfords Ltd, Thomas Street, Congleton, Cheshire, CW12 1EF Tel: (01260) 274011 Fax: (01260) 274014 E-mail: office@berisfords-ribbons.co.uk Principal Export Areas: Worldwide *Ribbon & trimmings suppliers*

Berk, 46-49 Burlington Arcade, London, W1J 0ET Tel: (020) 7493 0028 Fax: (020) 7499 4312 *Cashmere retailers*

Berkeley Car Company Scotland Ltd, Berryfauld, Forfar Road, Arbroath, Angus, DD11 3RA Tel: (01241) 875013 Fax: (01241) 875013 E-mail: berkeleycarco@btconnect.com *Machinists & general engineers, subcontracting engineering*

Berkeley Guard Ltd, The Pottery, Ham Lane, Baughurst, Tadley, Hampshire, RG26 5SD Tel: 0118-981 1428 Fax: 0118-981 0487 E-mail: info@berkeleyguard.com *NSI approved alarm installers & alarm system engineers*

▶ Berkeley Homes, 3 Arsenal Way, London, SE18 6TF Tel: (020) 8319 5900

▶ Berkeley Homes (Southern) Ltd, Broadlands Business Campus, Langhurstwood Road, Horsham, West Sussex, RH12 4QP Tel: (01403) 211240

Berkeley Partnership, 55 Blandford Street, London, W1U 7HW Tel: (020) 7224 2671 Fax: (020) 7935 1892 E-mail: sales@berkeleypartnership.com *Management consultants*

Berkeley Stainless Fittings Ltd, 5 Novers Hill Trading Estate, Novers Hill, Bedminster, Bristol, BS3 5QY Tel: 0117-966 5544 Fax: 0117-966 5548 E-mail: bristol@berkeleystainless.co.uk *Hygienic stainless steel tube, valves & fittings. Specialist hygienic fabricated fittings.*Stainless Steel flanges,BSP threaded fittings.*

▶ Berkeley Trade Management Limited, PO Box 25, Darlington, County Durham, DL2 3WX Tel: 01325 710111 Fax: 01325 710108 E-mail: info@trademanagement.co.uk *Strategic offshore sourcing & supply chain management consultancy.*Supply Chain risk management*

Berks & Bucks Air Conditioning, Unit G2 Rose Business Estate, Marlow Bottom Road, Marlow, Buckinghamshire, SL7 3ND Tel: (01628) 472267 Fax: (01628) 472262 E-mail: info@berksbucksaircon.co.uk *Planning & installation of air conditioning systems*

Berks Extinguisher Services, 48 Ardingly, Bracknell, Berkshire, RG12 8XR Tel: (01344) 425015 Fax: (01344) 304924 E-mail: enquiries@berksext.co.uk *Fre extinguisher distributors*

Berkshire Bearings & Transmsns Ltd, 27-31 Meadow Road, Newbury, Berkshire, RG14 7AH Tel: (01635) 43449 Fax: (01635) 35447 E-mail: sales@bbt1.sagehost.co.uk *Engineering products distributors*

Berkshire Building Services, Blounts Court Road, Sonning Common, Reading, RG4 9PA Tel: 0118-972 1199 Fax: 0118-972 1155

▶ Berkshire Clearance, 9 Church Road, Earley, Reading, RG6 1EY Tel: 0118-961 0112 Fax: (0870) 4321014 E-mail: help@berkshireclearance.com *IT recycling, house & office clearance service*

▶ Berkshire Cutouts Ltd, Unit 7-8 Redfields Industrial Park, Church Crookham, Fleet, Hampshire, GU52 0RD Tel: (01252) 850491 Fax: (01252) 851370 E-mail: sales@chromatec.co.uk

▶ Berkshire Finance, 6 The Litten, Kingsclere, Newbury, Berkshire, RG20 5NH Tel: 01635 299474 Fax: 01635 291352 E-mail: info@berkshirefinance.co.uk *Arranging corporate finance*

Berkshire Foods, 210 166 Fareham Road, Gosport, Hampshire, PO13 0FW Tel: (01329) 230000 Fax: (01329) 236611 *Snack food retailers*

▶ Berkshire Heating & Plumbing, 299 Basingstoke Road, Reading, RG2 0JA Tel: 0118-942 8300

Berkshire Labels Ltd, Swangate, Hungerford, Berkshire, RG17 0YX Tel: (01488) 683628 Fax: (01488) 684186 E-mail: sales@berkshirelabels.co.uk *Label printers & manufrs*

Berkshire Metals Ltd, 10-12 Armour Road, Tilehurst, Reading, RG31 6HS Tel: 0118-942 9476 Fax: 0118-942 4800 *Aluminium, brass, stainless steel & steel stockholders*

Berkshire Microwave Services, 3 Cavendish Meads, Sunninghill, Ascot, Berkshire, SL5 9TB Tel: (01344) 623867 Fax: (01344) 623867 *Installation of microwaves*

▶ Berkshire Opthalmic Laboratories Ltd, Unit 6 Pipers Court, Berkshire Drive, Thatcham, Berkshire, RG19 4ER Tel: (01635) 865050 E-mail: sales@berkshirelabs.co.uk *Spectacles manufrs*

Berkshire Pallets Ltd, Unit 2 Membury Business Park, Lambourn Woodlands, Hungerford, Berkshire, RG17 7TJ Tel: (01488) 73700 Fax: (01488) 73701 *Pallet & packing case manufrs*

Berkshire Telephone Systems Ltd, PO Box 4229, Reading, RG8 9XT Tel: (01491) 682552 Fax: (01491) 682551 *Telecommunications installation & equipment services*

Berleburger, Lumbrook Mills, Westercroft Lynn, Northowram, Halifax, West Yorkshire, HX3 7TY Tel: (01422) 200143 Fax: (01422) 200144 E-mail: maguirejbswuk@aol.com *Rubber matting suppliers*

Berma Ltd, 31 Brooke Avenue, Harrow, Middlesex, HA2 0NB Tel: (020) 8423 6568 Fax: (020) 8864 6615 *Building contractors & distributors*

▶ Bermar Building Co. Ltd, 2 Bull Royd Industrial Estate, Bull Royd Lane, Bradford, West Yorkshire, BD8 0LH Tel: (01274) 493427 Fax: (01274) 483502

▶ Bernafon UK Ltd, Cadzow Industrial Estate, Hamilton, Lanarkshire, ML3 7QE Tel: (01883) 331730 Fax: (01883) 331739 *Instrumentation, to specification*

Bernard Group Ltd, Bernard House 52-54 Peregrine Road, Hainault, Ilford, Essex, IG6 3SZ Tel: (020) 8501 2599 Fax: (020) 8559 9922 E-mail: corporate@bernardgroup.plc.uk *Global logistics management*

▶ Bernard Hunt (Electrical Contractors) Ltd, Northfield, Kilburn, Belper, Derbyshire, DE56 0LW Tel: (01332) 880665

Bernard J Arnull & Co. Ltd, 17-21 Sunbeam Road, London, NW10 6JP Tel: (020) 8965 6094 Fax: (020) 8961 1585 E-mail: bernard.arnull@easynet.co.uk *Ceramic tile distributors* Also at: London W1

Bernard L Haywood Sales Ltd, 89-91 New Town Row, Birmingham, B6 4HG Tel: 0121-333 6656 Fax: 0121-359 1530 E-mail: sales@hbl.co.uk *Exhaust silencer manufrs*

Bernard Mccartney Ltd, Unit 2 National Trading Estate, Bramhall Moor Lane, Hazel Grove, Stockport, Cheshire, SK7 5AA Tel: 0161-456 0102 Fax: 0161-483 5399 E-mail: mccartney@macpactor.co.uk *Steel landfill compactor wheels & ancillary equipment supplier & manufrs*

Bernard Matthews plc, Upper Holton, Halesworth, Suffolk, IP19 8NJ Tel: (01986) 872162 Fax: (01986) 872188 *Food manufrs*

Robert Bernard & Son Ltd, 26 Oxton Road, Birkenhead, Merseyside, CH41 2QJ Tel: 0151-652 3136 Fax: 0151-652 7552 E-mail: sales@bernards.co.uk *Ironmongery, tools, plumbing & security*

Bernard Uniforms Ltd, Harbour Crescent, Main Road, Harwich, Essex, CO12 3NT Tel: (01255) 502281 Fax: (01255) 241457 *Uniform clothing manufrs*

▶ Bernard Ward Ltd, Dean House Accent Park, Bakewell Road, Peterborough, PE2 6XS Tel: (01733) 390190

Bernie Richardson, Unit 2 Abbey Manor Industrial Estate, Yeovil, Somerset, BA21 3AR Tel: (01935) 413317 *Blasting contractors*

▶ Bernie's Bait & Tackle, Snuff Court, Snuff Street, Devizes, Wiltshire, SN10 1HU Tel: (01380) 730712 *Fishing tackle retailers*

Bernley Packaging, Unit 13 Wilton Industrial Court, 851 Bradford Road, Batley, West Yorkshire, WF17 8NN Tel: (01924) 471188 Fax: (01924) 471199 E-mail: burnpack@aol.com Principal Export Areas: Worldwide *Packaging machinery manufrs*

Bernlite Ltd, 3 Brookside, Colne Way, Watford, WD24 7QJ Tel: (01923) 200160 Fax: (01923) 246057 *Sign component suppliers & manufrs*

Bernstein Ltd, Westgate Trading Estate, Westgate, Aldridge, Walsall, WS9 8EX Tel: (01922) 744999 Fax: (01922) 457555 E-mail: sales@bernstein-ltd.co.uk *Switch, safety, sensor & enclosure manufacturer*

Berrico Ltd, 57 Churchfield Road, London, W3 6AU Tel: (020) 8992 6454 Fax: (020) 8752 0670 E-mail: berrico@berrico.co.uk *Printing services*

Austin Berridge Ltd, 2 Buckminster Road, Blackbird Road, Leicester, LE3 9AR Tel: 0116-251 9922 Fax: 0116-251 9922 *Blinds & curtain manufrs*

▶ Berridge Electrical Services Ltd, Unit 2 38a Rosemary Lane, Blackwater, Camberley, Surrey, GU17 0LT Tel: (01276) 32707 Fax: (01276) 36538

Berriman & Chapman, 41-43 Victoria Road, Scarborough, North Yorkshire, YO11 1SQ Tel: (01723) 360604 Fax: (01723) 378819 *Builders' ironmongers*

Berrington Press, Barton Yard, Hereford, HR4 0AZ Tel: (01981) 241360 Fax: (01432) 353877 E-mail: david@berrington-press.co.uk *Self-adhesive labels, swing tickets & lithograqphic printers*

Berrington Spring Water Co., Little Berrington Farm, Marden, Hereford, HR1 3EY Tel: (01568) 797552 Fax: (01568) 797224 E-mail: sales@berringtonwater.com *Bottling of spring water*

▶ Angela Berry, Hag Hill Rise, Taplow, Maidenhead, Berkshire, SL6 0LS Tel: (01628) 661073 Fax: (01628) 661073 E-mail: design@angelaberry.co.uk *Graphic designers or artists*

▶ Berry Bank Bank Farm, Windmill Lane, Hundall, Apperknowle, Dronfield, Derbyshire, S18 4BQ Tel: (01246) 415986 E-mail: mark@berrybankfarm.co.uk *Darainage & foundation contractors & mini digger hire*

▶ Berry Computers, Grove House, Lutyens Close, Lychpit, Basingstoke, Hampshire, RG24 8AG Tel: (01256) 316525 E-mail: info@berrycomputers.com *Build & sell computers & offer a wide range of IT consultancy services*

E. Berry & Sons, Unit 19, 308A Melton Road, Leicester, LE4 7SL Tel: (0845) 1306862 Fax: (0845) 3892144 E-mail: eberryson@aol.com *Dental lathe brush manufrs*

Berry Engineering, 3 Severnside, Brue Avenue, Bridgwater, Somerset, TA6 5LT Tel: (01278) 444861 Fax: (01278) 444865 E-mail: leeberryeng@aol.com *General engineering & machining manufrs*

John Berry, 187 Meriden Drive, Birmingham, B37 6BT Tel: 0121-770 6226 Fax: 0121-770 6226 E-mail: enquiries@jhberry.co.uk *Playground equipment installation*

▶ Berry & Marshall Bolton Woods Ltd, Order Number Bolton Wood Quarries, Bolton Hall Road, Bradford, West Yorkshire, BD2 1BQ Tel: (01274) 595534 Fax: (01274) 626146 E-mail: sales@pickardgroup.co.uk *Stone quarrying*

Peter Berry Associates, Unit 1B, Station Road, Tewkesbury, Gloucestershire, GL20 5DR Tel: (01684) 290629 Fax: (01684) 275231 E-mail: info@pbaservice.co.uk *EPOS, cash registers, weighing scales service & consumables*

Berry Place Models Ltd, 1 Berry Place, Sebastian Street, London, EC1V 0HE Tel: (020) 7490 8222 Fax: (020) 7336 8482 E-mail: enquiries@berryplace.co.uk *Model (CAD) industrial process manufrs*

Berry Plastics UK. Ltd, Stanford Tuck Road, North Walsham, Norfolk, NR28 0TY Tel: (01692) 404488 Fax: (01692) 404373 *Injection mouldings manufrs*

▶ Berry Street Studio, 1 Berry Street, London, EC1V 0AA Tel: (020) 7253 5885 E-mail: info@berrystreetstudio.com *Recording studio servicing the music & broadcast industries*

Berry & Vincent Ltd, 18 Union Road, Crediton, Devon, EX17 3AS Tel: (01363) 772078 Fax: (01363) 772814 E-mail: berryandvincent@btinternet.com *General construction services*

Berrymans Lace Mawer, Salisbury House, London Wall, London, EC2M 5QN Tel: (020) 7638 2811 Fax: (020) 7920 0361 E-mail: damian.greiff@blm-law.com *Solicitors*

▶ Berry's Plumbing & Heating Ltd, 141 Manchester Road East, Little Hulton, Manchester, M38 9AN Tel: 0161-790 9933 Fax: 0161-790 9944

F.H. Bertling Ltd, York House, Empire Way, Wembley, Middlesex, HA9 0PA Tel: (020) 8900 2060 Fax: (020) 8900 1248 E-mail: sales@bertling.com *Freight forwarders & project management services*

▶ The Bertrand Russell Peace Foundation Ltd, Russell House, Bulwell Lane, Nottingham, NG6 0BT Tel: 0115-978 4504 Fax: 0115-942 0433

Berwick Salmon Co. Ltd, 1 Main Street, Spittal, Berwick-upon-Tweed, TD15 1QY Tel: (01289) 307474 Fax: (01289) 305913 *Salmon products*

Berwickshire Electronic Manufacturing Ltd, G Industrial Estate, Station Road, Duns, Berwickshire, TD11 3EJ Tel: (01361) 883888 Fax: (01361) 883888 *Electronic manufrs*

▶ Berwin Group Ltd, 39 A & B Broadway, Globe Lane Industrial Estate, Dukinfield, Cheshire, SK16 4UJ Tel: 0161-330 2504

Berwyn Engineering Ltd, Euridge Works, Thickwood, Colerne, Chippenham, Wiltshire, SN14 8BG Tel: (01225) 742301 Fax: (01225) 743457 E-mail: info@jetway.co.uk Principal Export Areas: Worldwide *Grain treatment plant marine safety equipment*

Berystede Hotel, Bagshot Road, Ascot, Berks, SL5 9JH Tel: (01344) 623311 Fax: (01344) 872301 *Hotel & conference centre*

Bes Ltd, 3 Junction 6 Industrial Park, 66 Electric Avenue, Birmingham, B6 7JA Tel: 0121-322 6400 Fax: 0121-322 6440 E-mail: sales@bes.ltd.uk *Gas & plumbing fittings distributors*

Besafe Protective Clothing Ltd, Somerton Works, Prince Avenue, Westcliff-on-Sea, Essex, SS0 0ER Tel: (01702) 333344 Fax: (01702) 433590 E-mail: sales@besafe.co.uk *Head-to-toe personal protective clothing & equipment suppliers*

Besblock Ltd, Halesfield 21, Telford, Shropshire, TF7 4NF Tel: (01952) 586778 Fax: (01952) 585224 E-mail: sales@besblock.com *Building block manufrs*

Besco Industrial Supplies Ltd, Unit 3, The Glenmore Centre, Eurolink Industrial Centre, Castle Road, Sittingbourne, Kent, ME10 3GL Tel: (0845) 2960050 Fax: (0845) 2960056 E-mail: sales@besco.co.uk *Abrasive products*

Bescol Ltd, Unit 8a Number One Industrial Estate, Consett, County Durham, DH8 6SS Tel: (01207) 582555 Fax: (01207) 583951 E-mail: name@btconnect.com *Industrial engineer & tools distributors*

Bescot Constuction, Besot Crescent, Walsall, WS1 4NX Tel: (01922) 621286 Fax: (01922) 621321
E-mail: enquiries@chillingtonbarrows.co.uk *Wheelbarrows, sack trucks, builders trestles & crowd barriers*

▶ Beserved Virtual Offices Ltd, Newlands, 13 The Green, Tuddenham, Bury St. Edmunds, Suffolk, IP28 6SD Tel: (0845) 2268064
E-mail: bev@beserved.co.uk *Beserved is a Virtual Office. Our core services include Call handling, order taking, appointment setting and a web diary - all packaged as part of our Virtual PA service. Service is available for any period of time from 1 hour, 1 week, 1 month or 1 year & 24 x 7. Also, make use of our 50 years sales experience for your telesales and telemarketing campaigns. Call us on 08000 430023.*

Besglos Polish Co Ltd, George Street, Burnley, Lancashire, BB11 1ND Tel: (01282) 432351 Fax: (01282) 421558
E-mail: sales@besglos.co.uk *Cleaning chemical manufrs*

▶ Bespoke Bedrooms, 68 Huntingdon Road, Chatteris, Cambridgeshire, PE16 6ED Tel: (01354) 693392 Fax: (01354) 696807
E-mail: sales@bespokebedroomfurniture.co.uk *Manufacture & installation of fitted bedroom furniture*

▶ Bespoke Cards, 9B Higham Road, Woodford Green, Essex, IG8 9JN Tel: (0845) 270 1410 Fax: (0845) 270 1411
E-mail: theteam@bespokecards.net *Creators of the world's finest wedding & personal stationery. We use the highest quality materials and techiniques to produce stunning products. We usually work on individual commissions and offer face-to-face consultations to ensure a perfect result.*

Bespoke Concrete Products Ltd, Tynedale Works, Princess Way, Prudhoe, Northumberland, NE42 6PL Tel: (01661) 839340 Fax: (01661) 833923 E-mail: info@bespokeconcrete.co.uk *Pre-cast concrete products*

Bespoke Furniture, 63A Road A, Boughton Industrial Estate, Boughton, Newark, Nottinghamshire, NG22 9LE Tel: (07768) 847737
E-mail: enquiries@bespokefurn.co.uk *Bespoke cabinet maker & architectural joinery manufrs*

▶ Bespoke Granite Worktops, Goosey Lodge Farm, Wymington Lane (off A6), Rushden, Northamptonshire, NN10 9LU Tel: (07905) 401697 Fax: (01933) 387059
E-mail: neil@stoneinstallations.co.uk *Granite Worktops and Granite Kitchen Worktops are our speciality. Granite worktop samples can be brought to your home for you to view. We personally inspect each granite slab for your worktops to ensure the highest quality of material and your peace of mind. We are traditional stonemasons who offer a bespoke service to the trade and public. Granite worktop restoration service,expert advice on how to care for your granite worktops.*

▶ Bespoke Integrated Systems, 131 Foley Road West, Sutton Coldfield, West Midlands, B74 3NZ Tel: 0121-352 1204 Fax: 0121-352 1204
E-mail: support@bespokeis.co.uk *electronic security systems-CCT,network video,access control, integrated systems*

▶ Bespoke Interiors Of Cheshire Ltd, Tameside Works, Dukinfield, Cheshire, SK16 5PT Tel: 0161-343 7972 Fax: 0161-343 7973 *Cabinet manufrs*

▶ Bespoke Kitchens, 1 Hillcrest, Stoodleigh, Tiverton, Devon, EX16 9PJ Tel: (01398) 351467 *Stephen Smith of Stoodleigh in devon has been supplying high quality, bespoke handmade kitchens for more than ten years*

▶ Bespoke Lighting, 116 Chester Street, Birkenhead, Merseyside, CH41 5DL Tel: 0151-649 8649 Fax: 0151-649 8648 *Lighting manufrs*

Bespoke Precast Ltd, 2 Concrete Works Wellthorne Lane, Ingbirchworth, Penistone, Sheffield, S36 7GJ Tel: (01226) 761000 Fax: (01226) 761216
E-mail: bespokeprecast@btconnect.com *Pre-cast concrete staircase manufrs*

Bespoke Services (Manchester) Ltd, Whitehill Industrial Estate, Whitehill Street, Reddish, Stockport, Cheshire, SK5 7LW Tel: 0161-476 3522 Fax: 0161-476 0522
E-mail: info@bespoke-services.co.uk *Wood veneered fire door & furniture manufrs*

▶ Bespoke Tables - Stainless steel, Wood & Glass., The Old School House, Traboe, St Martin, Helston, Cornwall, TR12 6EA Tel: 01326 231020 E-mail: Jules@bespoke-tables.co.uk *Beautiful minimalist KITCHEN TABLES, DINING TABLES and COFFEE TABLES. Made from STAINLESS STEEL table bases and WOOD or GLASS table tops. Each is unique, tough and affordable. Amaze your friends and clients with your urban-chic style! SEE SITE FOR EXAMPLES. Bespoke tables and ready-to-buy tables for sale. We also sell minimalist stainless steel office desks and Boardroom tables. We also deliver free to the UK mainland.*

▶ Bespoke Timber Design, Harrier House, Unit 2C Rossbank Road, Ellesmere Port, CH65 3AN Tel: 0151-355 8183

▶ Bespoke Timberworks, Unit 25, Brockley Cross Business Centre, Endwell Road, London, SE4 2PD Tel: (020) 7639 8060 Fax: (020) 7639 8060

Besseges Ltd, Riverside, Dukinfield, Cheshire, SK16 4HE Tel: 0161-308 3252 Fax: 0161-339 5003 E-mail: sales@besseges.co.uk *Sprinkler & fire protection system services*

Besseges Valves Tubes & Fittings Ltd, Jackson House, Turner Lane, Ashton-under-Lyne, Lancashire, OL6 8LP Tel: 0161-343 2225 Fax: 0161-339 0307
E-mail: sales@besseges-vts.co.uk *Valve, tube & fitting stockists manufrs*

Best Boots, Nettleton, Chippenham, Wiltshire, SN14 7NS Tel: (01249) 783530 Fax: (01249) 782058 E-mail: info@bestboots.co.uk *Outdoor footwear manufrs*

Best Building Supplies, 12-16 Platt Fold Street, Leigh, Lancashire, WN7 1JH Tel: (01942) 673876 Fax: (01942) 608038 *Builders merchants*

Best Buy Carpet & Divan Centre, 2 Arksey Lane, Bentley, Doncaster, South Yorkshire, DN5 0RR Tel: (01302) 873586 Fax: (01302) 873586 *Beds & Carpets Retail*

▶ Best Computer Training Ltd, 189 London Road, Staines, Middlesex, TW18 4HR Tel: (01784) 451288 Fax: (01784) 451287
E-mail: staines@best-training.co.uk *Computer training services*

▶ Best Connection Group Ltd, 10-12 Pall Mall, Liverpool, L3 6AL Tel: 0151-236 0111 Fax: 0151-236 0999
E-mail: liverpool@thebestconnection.co.uk *Employment agency*

Best Connection Group Ltd, Hanger Lane Station, Hanger Lane, London, W5 1DL Tel: (020) 8998 9910 Fax: (020) 8997 4928
E-mail: sales@sharestaff.co.uk *Recruitment agency for industrial staff*

Best Deals, 58 London Road, Dover, Kent, CT17 0SP Tel: (01304) 208255 *Electrical goods retailers*

Best Electroplating, 1 Columbia Works, Fleming Way, Crawley, West Sussex, RH10 9JU Tel: (01293) 532843 Fax: (01293) 523688
E-mail: mark@bestelectroplating.co.uk *Electroplaters in gold, silver, rhodium & nickel*

Best Frames, 14 Clyde Drive, Livingston, West Lothian, EH54 5LS Tel: (01506) 444598 *Ironing & laundry services*

Best International Equipment Ltd, Unit 5 Centre One, Old Sarum Park Lysander Way, Old Sarum, Salisbury, SP4 6BU Tel: 01722 410203 Fax: 01722 320831 *Car parts manufrs*

Best Knitwear Ltd, 24-28 George Leigh Street, Manchester, M4 5DQ Tel: 0161-228 2526 Fax: 0161-228 2522
E-mail: info@bestknitwear.com *Knitwear manufrs*

Best Office Services Sussex, Five Ash Down, Uckfield, East Sussex, TN22 3AP Tel: (01825) 732020 Fax: (01825) 733506
E-mail: bos.s@virgin.net *Office equipment repair services, & sales*

Best Pest, 4 Waterloo Place, Duncombe Street, Kingsbridge, Devon, TQ7 1LX Tel: (01548) 854353 Fax: (01548) 857256 *Fumigation services*

Best Pneumatics Ltd, Units 6-7, Short Way, Thornbury Industrial Estate, Thornbury, Bristol, BS35 3UT Tel: (01454) 415761 Fax: (01454) 414607 *Air compressor*

Best Rest Beds, 18-20 Grosvenor Street, Manchester, M1 7JJ Tel: 0161-273 7700 Fax: 0161-273 7711 *Bed manufrs*

Best Security, 39b Moss Bank Road, St. Helens, Merseyside, WA11 7DD Tel: (01744) 757065 Fax: (01744) 600548 *Intruder alarm system installations services*

Best Services, M C F Complex, New Road, Kidderminster, Worcestershire, DY10 1AQ Tel: (01562) 829565 Fax: (01562) 829286 *Lightning conductors*

Best Training, 18 Fisher Street, Carlisle, CA3 8RH Tel: (01228) 590750 Fax: (01228) 596740
E-mail: carlisle@best-training.co.uk *Computer training*

▶ Best Web Site Design, 13 Larkspur Close, Bishop's Stortford, Hertfordshire, CM23 4LL Tel: (01279) 303878 Fax: (0870) 7058397 *Web site design including web site builder to allow you to produce your own site with e-commerce using your web browser.**Web site promotion and search engine optimisation*

Best Western Mount Sorrel, Porthkerry Road, Barry, South Glamorgan, CF62 7XY Tel: (01446) 740069 Fax: (01446) 746600
E-mail: reservations@mountsorrel.co.uk *Hotel with conference facilities*

Best Windings Ltd, Viking Works, Bucklesham Road, Kirton, Ipswich, IP10 0NX Tel: (01394) 448424 Fax: (01394) 448430
E-mail: kevin@bestwindings.co.uk *Best Windings is an established design and manufacturing company for transformers, inductors and other wound magnetics. ISO9001 approved, we supply quality magnetics into telecoms, aerospace, military, audio, video, automotive, security, medical, and other markets. Our capabilities range from miniature signal components to substantial power devices found in critical and specialist applications as well as cost-sensitive commercial and industrial areas.**We work closely with customers to ensure complete satisfaction. From our site in eastern England we can supply low to medium volumes produced in the UK, and medium to high volume using our offshore partners, thus meeting your price, performance, quality and delivery expectations. **We support with full custom design, build-to-print and standard products. Whether a new design, a cost reduction exercise, a second source, or an obsolescence problem, we offer first class support based on knowledge, skills and experience acquired over many years.*

▶ Bestaire Conditioning, Unit 2 Wessex Business Centre, Cheddar, Somerset, BS27 3EJ Tel: (01934) 741174 Fax: (01934) 741141

Bestalinks Engineers Ltd, 2 Wood Street, Dukinfield, Cheshire, SK16 4UT Tel: 0161-330 8515 Fax: 0161-343 2228
E-mail: bestlink@aol.com *Toolmaking engineers*

Best-Chem Ltd, Barracks Road, Sandy Lane, Stourport-On-Severn, Worcestershire, DY13 9QB Tel: (01299) 827232 Fax: (01299) 827608 *Janitorial supplies manufrs*

Bestco Surfacing Ltd, Hope Yard, Monroe Industrial Estate, Waltham Cross, Hertfordshire, EN8 7LX Tel: (01992) 652477 Fax: (01992) 652479 *Asphalt contractors*

▶ Beste Fashions, 10 Millers Avenue, London, E8 2DS Tel: (020) 7241 1009 Fax: (020) 7241 1011 *Outerwear for ladies*

Bestobell Valves, President Way, Sheffield, S4 7UR Tel: 0114-224 0200 Fax: 0114-278 4974
E-mail: sales@bestobellvalves.com Principal Export Areas: Worldwide *Valve manufrs*

▶ Bestway Nottingham Ltd, 5 Chestnut Drive, Broadmeadows, South Normanton, Alfreton, Derbyshire, DE55 3AH Tel: (01773) 860844 *Haulage services*

Bestway Tyres Ltd, Leopold Street, Pemberton, Wigan, Lancashire, WN5 8DH Tel: (01942) 214827 Fax: (01942) 226311
E-mail: jdc@lancasterhouse.fsnet.co.uk *Commercial vehicle tyre retreaders*

Bestwood Joinery, 141 Mansfield Street, Nottingham, NG5 4BD Tel: 0115-960 7955 Fax: 0115-969 2843 *Joinery manufrs*

Bestworld Packing Ltd, Spur Road, Feltham, Middlesex, TW14 0SL Tel: (020) 8893 2930 Fax: (020) 8893 2476
E-mail: gcecil@bestworldpacking.com *Export packers*

Besure Security Systems, Belcrest House, 114 Battle Road, St. Leonards-on-Sea, East Sussex, TN37 7EP Tel: (01424) 852343 Fax: (01424) 200999 E-mail: enquiries@besuresecurity.co.uk *Intruder alarms installers*

Beswick Engineering Co. Ltd, 21 Cowley Road, Blackpool, FY4 4NE Tel: (01253) 761661 Fax: (01253) 761661 *Injection mouldings (plastic) manufacturers & precision engineers*

Beta, 1 Letts Builder Yard, Dock Road, Worksop, Nottinghamshire, S80 1RX Tel: (01909) 489988 *Concrete manufrs*

Beta Air, Unit 6, Cheltenham Trade Park, Arle Road, Cheltenham, Gloucestershire, GL51 8LZ Tel: (01242) 570995 Fax: (01242) 226131
E-mail: betaair.storacall@btinternet.com *Air conditioning suppliers*

Beta Electronics Ltd, 11 Indescon Court, Docklands, London, E14 9TN Tel: (020) 7531 2828 Fax: (020) 7531 2929 *Office equipment distributors*

Beta Electronics, Dukesway, Teesside Industrial Estate, Stockton-on-Tees, Cleveland, TS17 9LT Tel: (01642) 765321 Fax: (01642) 760155
E-mail: jks@betaelectronics.co.uk *Printed circuit assemblers*

Beta Engineering Services Ltd, Unit 3a Goldthorpe Industrial Estate, Commercial Road, Goldthorpe, Rotherham, South Yorkshire, S63 9BL Tel: (01709) 898848 Fax: (01709) 880856
E-mail: enquiries@betaengineeringservices.co.uk *CNC precision services*

Beta Engineering Stotfold Ltd, Taylors Road, Stotfold, Hitchin, Hertfordshire, SG5 4AX Tel: (01462) 730910 Fax: (01462) 835325 *Sheet metalwork manufrs*

Beta Engravers (Northampton) Ltd, Clarence Avenue, Northampton, NN2 6NY Tel: (01604) 715152 Fax: (01604) 717131 *General engravers*

Beta Heat Treatment Ltd, Summerton Road, Oldbury, West Midlands, B69 2EL Tel: 0121-511 1190 Fax: 0121-511 1192
E-mail: beta@claytonholdings.com *Contract heat treatment suppliers*

Beta Lasermike Ltd, Stirling Road, Cressex Business Park, High Wycombe, Buckinghamshire, HP12 3RT Tel: (01494) 894400 Fax: (01494) 894401
E-mail: sales@uk.betalasermike.com *Gauging electronic inspection systems manufrs*

Beta Plant Ltd, Alpha Works, Ashton Road, Bredbury, Stockport, Cheshire, SK6 2QF Tel: 0161-430 7549 Fax: 0161-494 2758 Principal Export Areas: Worldwide *Generator suppliers*

Beta Power Engineering Ltd, Beta House Discovery Park, Crossley Road, Stockport, Cheshire, SK4 5BN Tel: 0161-432 9995 Fax: 0161-431 7800 E-mail: beta_power@btconnect.com *Power transmission engineers & manufrs*

▶ Beta Print Ltd, Unit 1c, Larkin Industrial Estate, Springfield Road, Chesham, Buckinghamshire, HP5 1PW Tel: (01494) 791463

Beta Research & Development Ltd, 50 Goodsmoor Road, Sinfin, Derby, DE24 9GN Tel: (01332) 770500 Fax: (01332) 771591
E-mail: project@betard.co.uk *Researchers & developers*

Beta Security Systems, Llandegai Industrial Estate, Llandygai, Bangor, Gwynedd, LL57 4YH Tel: (01248) 364967 Fax: (01248) 364967 *Security & fire systems installers*

Beta Signs, Unit 1 Block 6 Shenstone Trading Estate, Bromsgrove Road, Halesowen, West Midlands, B63 3XB Tel: 0121-501 3535 Fax: 0121-501 3545
E-mail: sales@betasigns.co.uk *Sign makers*

Beta Telecom, 1 Southborough Terrace, Brunswick Street, Leamington Spa, Warwickshire, CV31 2DT Tel: (01926) 311479 Fax: (01926) 337704 E-mail: tara@betatelecom.co.uk *Telecommunications equipment supply & installation*

▶ Beta Tools (UK) Ltd, Unit D, Horton Enterprise Park, Hortonwood 50, Telford, Shropshire, TF1 7GZ Tel: (01952) 677977 Fax: (01952) 677545

Beta Training Ltd, Thompsons Lane, Hough-on-the-Hill, Grantham, Lincolnshire, NG32 2BB Tel: (01400) 251848 Fax: (01400) 251849 E-mail: info@betatraining.com *Industrial training services*

Beta Valve Systems Ltd, Parkhouse Business Centre, Desborough Park Road, High Wycombe, Buckinghamshire, HP12 3DJ Tel: (01494) 459511 Fax: (01494) 461136
E-mail: info@betavalve.com Principal Export Areas: Worldwide *Valve distributors*

Betablinds Blinds & Awnings, Spooner Drive, Killamarsh, Sheffield, S21 1SH Tel: 0114-248 7262 E-mail: info@beta-blinds.co.uk *Supply & installation window blinds domestic and commercial*

▶ Betalec Ltd, Unit 29, Neath Abbey Business Park, Neath Abbey, Neath, West Glamorgan, SA10 7DR Tel: (01792) 324555

Betapest Pest & Vermin Control, 9 Canfield Road, Brighton, BN2 4DN Tel: (0800) 2949332 Fax: (01273) 672270 *Pest & vermin control service providers*

▶ Betaquip, 4 Farm Road, Buckingham Road Industrial Estate, Brackley, Northamptonshire, NN13 7EA Tel: (01280) 840297

Betarange Ltd, Leverington Road, Wisbech, Cambridgeshire, PE13 1PJ Tel: (01945) 583200 Fax: (01945) 463099 *Bar drinks wholesalers and suppliers*

Betchworth International Heavy Transport, Old Reigate Road, Betchworth, Surrey, RH3 7LW Tel: (0870) 1671671 Fax: (0870) 1671672 *Road transport & haulage & freight services*

Betco Packaging Supplies, 12 Gregston Industrial Estate, Birmingham Road, Oldbury, West Midlands, B69 4EX Tel: 0121-552 8400 Fax: 0121-511 1324
E-mail: sales@betcofasteners.co.uk *Collated staples & nails & associated machinery*

Betech 100pt Ltd, Four Square Building, Thomas Street, Heckmondwike, West Yorkshire, WF16 0LS Tel: (0870) 7573344 Fax: (0870) 7573388 E-mail: sales@betech100pt.co.uk *Industrial drive & control systems service*

George Bethell Ltd, Unit 9 Rugby Park, Bletchley Road, Heaton Mersey, Stockport, Cheshire, SK4 3EJ Tel: 0161-442 8805 Fax: 0161-442 8818 E-mail: sales@bethell.com *General mechanical engineering services*

Bethell Group plc, Dane House Europa Trading Estate, Stoneclough Road, Radcliffe, Manchester, M26 1GE Tel: (01204) 439100 Fax: (01204) 439101 E-mail: mail@bethell.co.uk *Sewer inspection & construction services*

Bethell Group plc, Dane House Europa Trading Estate, Stoneclough Road, Radcliffe, Manchester, M26 1GE Tel: (01204) 439100 Fax: (01204) 439101 E-mail: mail@bethell.co.uk *Multi-disciplined construction services*

Betrex Flooring Supplies, 3 Dollman Street, Birmingham, B7 4RP Tel: 0121-333 3432 Fax: 0121-333 3436
E-mail: sales@floorwise.co.uk *Floor covering distributors*

Betrix Industrial Models Ltd, 18-20 Waterloo Road, Stockport, Cheshire, SK1 3BD Tel: 0161-477 1766 Fax: 0161-474 7052
E-mail: betrixmodels@aol.com *Manufacturers of models & plastic fabricators*

Bett Homes Ltd, Argyll Court, The Castle Business Park, Stirling, FK9 4TT Tel: (01786) 477777 Fax: (01786) 477666
E-mail: betthomes@bett.co.uk *Building contractors*

Betta Blinds, Unit Ps5, Market Precinct, Carmarthen, Dyfed, SA31 1QY Tel: (01267) 232263 Fax: (01267) 232263 *Window blinds installers*

▶ Betta Solutions Limited, 86, Enfield Road, Redditch, Worcs, B97 5NH Tel: (01527) 541171

Betta Tech Controls Ltd, 104 Tanners Drive, Blakelands, Milton Keynes, MK14 5BP Tel: (01908) 616784 Fax: (01908) 216264 *Temperature control manufrs*

▶ Bettapack, 37 Portland Drive, Biddulph, Stoke-on-Trent, ST8 6RY Tel: (01782) 510833 Fax: (01782) 510833

▶ BettaPat, Hillcrest, Cooks Cross, Alveley, Bridgnorth, Shropshire, WV15 6LS Tel: 0870 8508667 Fax: 01746 780961
E-mail: adam@bettapat.co.uk *Portable appliance testing specialists*

Bettaprice Systems Ltd, 23k Bridge St Industrial Estate, Lower Mantle Close, Clay Cross, Chesterfield, Derbyshire, S45 9NU Tel: (01246) 865508 Fax: (01246) 865441 *PVC-u door & window manufrs& installation*

▶ Better 4 Business, 11 Brook Hey Avenue, Bolton, BL3 2EQ Tel: (0870) 8749500
E-mail: enquiries@better4business.co.uk *Better4Business provide real time Internet solutions for small to medium companies in Greater Manchester. Whether you want to get a website, increase your traffic or research your competition, we are the people to talk to.*

Better Badges, C 9 Garman Road, London, N17 0UR Tel: (020) 8365 1035 Fax: (020) 8365 1905 E-mail: john@abetterbadge.com *Promotional badge manufrs*

Better Blind Co., Wych Fold, Hyde, Cheshire, SK14 5ED Tel: (0800) 1693765 Fax: 0161-367 9318 E-mail: info@newblinds.co.uk *Blind manufrs*

Better Engineers, Abatec House, Oldmixon Crescent, Weston-Super-Mare, Avon, BS24 9AX Tel: (01934) 621262 Fax: (01934) 620619
E-mail: mail@betterengineers.co.uk *Engineering recruitment consultants*

▶ Better Environment & Security Technologies B E S T Ltd, Glen Rose, The Hollow, West Hoathly, East Grinstead, West Sussex, RH19 4QE Tel: (01842) 811990 Fax: 01342 811990
E-mail: britsectec@aol.com *NACOSS NSI Gold approved intruder alarm /CCTV /access control installation and maintenance. We cover Sussex London Kent Surrey Essex*

▶ Better Life Healthcare, 3 Sherdley Road, Lostock Hall, Preston, PR5 5LP Tel: (01772) 626777 Fax: (01772) 626770
E-mail: gabrahams@betterlifehealthcare.com *NHS, public & trade, medical, mobility & healthcare aids suppliers*

▶ Better Plumbing Services, 4 Exchange Road, Lincoln, LN6 3JZ Tel: (01522) 688866 Fax: (01522) 688855 *Plumbing & heating*

Better Sound Ltd, 31 Cathcart Street, London, NW5 3BJ Tel: (020) 7482 0177 Fax: (020) 7482 2677 E-mail: admin@bettersound.co.uk *Audio equipment suppliers*

▶ Better Start Here, Ashford Road, Faversham, Kent, ME13 8XL Tel: (07890) 617747
E-mail: info@betterstarthere.co.uk *Better Start Here is dedicated to helping businesses establish themselves as visible and viable brands.*We work closely with firms to ensure that they become and remain competitive.*Our services include brand design, copywriting for print and web, proofreading, research and marketing advice.*We are fully committed to good customer service and offer affordable pricing to new businesses, non-profit organisations and charities.*

▶ Better Strategy Ltd, 22 The Grove, Farnborough, Hampshire, GU14 6QR Tel: (01252) 682167 *We develop the strategy skills of senior executives and aspiring senior executives. We cover strategy development and implementation, managing change, project management, consulting skills, consultative b2b sales and marketing. We use traditional workshops, computer simulations, project-based learning, coaching and consulting depending on our client"s need. We deliver performance improvement by being relevant, practical and engaging.*

▶ Betterlight Ltd, Carey Street, Kettering, Northamptonshire, NN16 0JL Tel: (01536) 415138 Fax: (01536) 415843 *Lighting import, export & manufrs*

▶ Betterplace Property Maintenance, T M S House, Cray Avenue, Orpington, Kent, BR5 3QB Tel: (01689) 875957 Fax: (01689) 885035 E-mail: betterplace1@aol.com *Property maintenance services*

▶ Bettershred, Thornborough Road, Thornton, Milton Keynes, MK17 0HE Tel: (01280) 821444 Fax: (01280) 821190 *Shredding services*

Betterware UK Ltd, Stanley House, Park Lane, Castle Vale, Birmingham, B35 6LJ Tel: (0845) 1294500 Fax: (0845) 1294654 E-mail: info@betterware.co.uk *Household products*

Betterweigh Leicester, 48 The Half Croft, Syston, Leicester, LE7 1LD Tel: (0845) 2602602 Fax: 0116-269 7767 E-mail: enquiries@betterweighleicester.com *Specialists in industrial and laboratory weighing systems.*

Bettix Ltd, Lever Street, Bolton, BL3 6NZ Tel: (01204) 526241 Fax: (01204) 521958 E-mail: sales@bettix.co.uk *Special containers, technical mouldings & post fluorination services*

Betts UK Ltd, 505 Ipswich Road, Colchester, CO4 9HE Tel: (01206) 753400 Fax: (01206) 844002 E-mail: simon.jones@betts-uk.com *Laminate tube manufrs*

Betttavend Ltd, 5 Speedwell Close, Chandlers Ford Industrial Estate, Eastleigh, Hampshire, SO53 4BT Tel: (023) 8025 5222 Fax: (023) 8027 6644 E-mail: enquiries@bettavend.co.uk *Vending machine distributors & ingredients*

Beulah Packaging Cards Ltd, 25 Scotts Road, Bromley, BR1 3QD Tel: (020) 8466 8610 Fax: (020) 8466 8612 E-mail: info@beulahpackaging.co.uk *Printed folding cartons*

Beva Investments Ltd, Chichester Business Centre, Chichester Street, Rochdale, Lancashire, OL16 2AU Tel: (01706) 710740 Fax: (01706) 710536 E-mail: investments@beva.co.uk *Property developers*

Bevan, 53a Frederick Street, Birmingham, B1 3HS Tel: 0121-236 9263 Fax: 0121-236 9263 *Press toolmakers & wire erosion*

Bevan Carp Tackle, 3 Havengore, Chelmsford, CM1 6JP Tel: (01245) 266833 Fax: (01245) 344249 E-mail: sales@bevancarptackle.co.uk *Fishing tackle retailers*

Bevan Funnell Ltd, Reprodux House, Norton Road, Newhaven, East Sussex, BN9 0BZ Tel: (01273) 513762 Fax: (01273) 516735 E-mail: enquiries@bevan-funnell.co.uk *Reproduction furniture manufrs*

Bevan Motor Bodies Ltd, Blakeley Hall Road, Oldbury, West Midlands, B69 4ET Tel: 0121-533 2000 Fax: 0121-544 7783 *Commercial body builders*

Bevan Simpson Foundry Ltd, Hainge Road, Tividale, Oldbury, West Midlands, B69 2PB Tel: 0121-557 3621 Fax: 0121-520 6622 *Iron castings manufrs*

Bevans Holdings Leicester Ltd, Gloucester Cresent, Wigston, Leicestershire, LE18 4YR Tel: 0116-278 2331 Fax: 0116-277 8307 E-mail: sales@bevanscomponents.co.uk Principal Export Areas: Worldwide *Springs & wire formed & shaped component products*

▶ Bevanwood Joinery Ltd, 6 Albany Trading Estate, Albany Street, Newport, Gwent, NP20 5NQ Tel: (01633) 858811 Fax: (01633) 858811 E-mail: bevanwood@btconnect.com *Joiners*

Bevenden Moulds & Tools Ltd, Unit 5c Triumph Trading Estate, Tariff Road, London, N17 0EB Tel: (020) 8801 2488 Fax: (020) 8808 0982 E-mail: bevendenmandt@btconnect.com *Plastics mould toolmakers*

Beverage Plastics Ltd, 70 Silverwood Road, Craigavon, County Armagh, BT66 6LN Tel: (028) 3832 2221 Fax: (028) 3832 1888 E-mail: enquires@lurgan.plastic.boxmore.com *Plastic bottle & container manufrs*

▶ David Beveridge Ltd, 43-51 Jeanfield Road, Perth, PH1 1NZ Tel: (01738) 636736 Fax: (01738) 630100

Beverley Analytical Laboratories, Hull Bridge Mills, Tickton, Beverley, North Humberside, HU17 9SB Tel: (01964) 542144 Fax: (01964) 543060 E-mail: admin@beverlyanalytical.co.uk *Analysis in agriculture & food*

Beverley Electric Ltd, Annie Reed Road, Beverley, North Humberside, HU17 0LF Tel: (01482) 862379 Fax: (01482) 865811 E-mail: robkitchen@beverleyelectric.co.uk *Electrical contractors*

▶ Beverley Foster Wedding Photographer, 14 Moorfields, Leek, Staffordshire, ST13 5LU Tel: (01538) 386403 E-mail: admin@weddingstorybook.co.uk *Wedding photographers*

▶ Beverley Hewitt Designs, Studio 11, The Hot House, Webberley Lane, Longton, Stoke-On-Trent, ST3 3SL Tel: (01782) 597004 E-mail: beverley@beverleyhewittdesigns.co.uk *Ceramic designers*

Beverley Veneers Ltd, Grovehill Road, Beverley, North Humberside, HU17 0JJ Tel: (01482) 882537 Fax: (01482) 869520 *Veneered panel manufrs*

Beverleyblinds, 93 Nunts Park Avenue, Holbrooks, Coventry, CV6 4GX Tel: (024) 7664 4727 Fax: (024) 7666 6232 *Blinds manufrs*

▶ Beverleyhills Beauty Clinic, 88-90 Liverpool Road, Eccles, Manchester, M30 0WZ Tel: (07979) 794223 E-mail: shaabanahhmad@yahoo.co.uk *Experience the latest technology of laser treatment*In skincare and hair care **

BEVI Group UK, 62 Alleyn Park, London, SE21 8SF Tel: (020) 8670 0806 Fax: (0870) 4601131 E-mail: sales@bevi.co.uk *Motor generator frequency converters*

▶ Bevington Evans & Associates, 53 Harrowby Street, Cardiff, CF10 5GA Tel: (029) 2048 5221 Fax: (029) 2048 5231 E-mail: cbevev@ntlbusiness.com *Independent Financial Advisers*Mortgages /Life critical illness cover /pensions /investments*

Bevpak Ltd, 27-28 Arkwright Road, Astmore Industrial Estate, Runcorn, Cheshire, WA7 1NU Tel: (01928) 574815 Fax: (01928) 589487 E-mail: bevpak@hotmail.co.uk *Conveyor systems manufacturers, belt conveyors, overhead conveyors, screw conveyors, mechanical handling & pipework fabrication & sheet metal, stainless steel fabricators, steel stairs, safety barriers, access ladders, handrails, balustrades and much more.*

Bewa (UK) Ltd, Noble Square Industrial Estate, Brynmawr, Ebbw Vale, Gwent, NP23 4BS Tel: (01495) 310170 Fax: (01495) 311816 E-mail: bewauk@yahoo.co.uk *Manufacturers of cable handling systems*

Bewator Ltd, Albany Street, Newport, Gwent, NP20 5XW Tel: (08713) 860800 Fax: (01633) 850893 E-mail: sales@bewator.co.uk *CCTV electronic access control systems & distributors*

▶ Bewebsmart Web Design Solutions, 24 Canolblas Avenue, Bodelwyddan, Rhyl, Denbighshire, LL18 5TW Tel: (01745) 583418 E-mail: mail@bewebsmart.co.uk *Smart & artistic custom built website solutions services*

Bewick Engineering Ltd, 4 Walker Riverside, Wincomblee Road, Newcastle upon Tyne, NE6 3PF Tel: 0191-295 1975 Fax: 0191-295 1973 E-mail: robq@bewick.clara.co.uk *Hydraulic systems & components manufrs*

▶ Bewick Homes Ltd, 40 Mill Street, Bedford, MK40 3HD Tel: (01234) 267459 Fax: (01234) 212864

▶ Bewley & Scott Ltd, Ellison Road, Gateshead, Tyne & Wear, NE11 9TS Tel: 0191-460 4219 Fax: 0191-460 1901

Bewley's Coffee Man, 5 Mill Paddock, Letcombe Regis, Wantage, Oxfordshire, OX12 9JE Tel: (01235) 764145 Fax: (01235) 764145 *Coffee distributor*

Bex Contracts plc, Bex House, Crabtree Manorway South, Belvedere, Kent, DA17 6BJ Tel: (020) 8311 2992 Fax: (020) 8311 2303 *Cable trunking manufrs*

Bex Design Services Ltd, Stainer Road, Porte Marsh Industrial Estate, Calne, Wiltshire, SN11 9PX Tel: (01249) 821127 Fax: (01249) 817072 E-mail: sales@bexdesign.co.uk *Industrial screen printers*

Bexley Council For Racial Equality, 1 Maran Way, Erith, Kent, DA18 4BP Tel: (020) 8310 0138 Fax: (020) 8312 0238 E-mail: EDUBBC@bexley.gov.uk *Local authority economic development*

Bexley Steel, 8 Power Industrial Estate, Slade Green Road, Erith, Kent, DA8 2HU Tel: (01322) 335420 Fax: (01322) 335984 E-mail: bexleysteel@supernet.com *Steel fabricators & steel section stockholders*

Bexley Vehicle Bodies, Unit 14, Belvedere Industrial Estate, Fishers Way, Belvedere, Kent, DA17 6BS Tel: (020) 8311 6100 Fax: (020) 8311 6101 *Commercial vehicle body builders*

▶ Bexwell Construction Ltd, 27 Stamford Hill, London, N16 5TU Tel: (020) 8802 4109 Fax: (020) 8802 0523

Bexwell Tractors Ltd, Bexwell, Downham Market, Norfolk, PE38 9LU Tel: (01366) 383301 Fax: (01366) 384930 E-mail: admin@bexwell-tractors.co.uk Principal Export Areas: Worldwide *Agricultural repairs*

E.T. & A. Beynon, Bryncelyn, Blaenpennal, Aberystwyth, Dyfed, SY23 4TL Tel: (01974) 251294 Fax: (01974) 251294 E-mail: bryncelyn@supanet.com *Commercial car & four by four sales*

Beyond 2000 PC Systems Software, 97-103 Upper Parliament Street, Nottingham, NG1 6LA Tel: 0115-924 3000 Fax: (0870) 3304300 *Computer maintainers & manufrs*

Beyond Engineering Ltd, Bidewell Close, Drayton High Road, Norwich, NR8 6AP Tel: (01603) 868423 Fax: (01603) 261712 E-mail: sales@claydale.co.uk *Enclosure manufrs*

▶ Beyond Retreats, PO Box 46523, London, N1 2WN Tel: (020) 7226 4044

▶ Beyond Solutions, 90-91 Luddesdown Road, Luddesdown, Gravesend, Kent, DA13 0XE Tel: (01474) 815589 E-mail: neill.gibson@beyond.eu.com *beyond provides IT services, support, security solutions and project management to clients of small to corportate size.*

Bezalel Gems Ltd, St Georges House, 44 Hatton Garden, London, EC1N 8ER Tel: (020) 7405 5923 Fax: (020) 7405 2021 *Precious stone merchants*

Bezier Corporate Print, 145 Sterte Road, Poole, Dorset, BH15 2AF Tel: (01202) 681466 Fax: (01202) 670010 E-mail: sales@bezier.co.uk *Brochure design & printing services*

Bezier Creative Printers, Balne Lane, Wakefield, West Yorkshire, WF2 0DF Tel: (01924) 362921 Fax: (01924) 372615 E-mail: bdw@bezier.co.uk *Point of sale display manufrs*

Bezier P O P, Church Road, Wick, Bristol, BS30 5RF Tel: 0117-937 3989 Fax: 0117-937 2662 E-mail: bdb@bezier.co.uk *Point of sale display producers*

▶ BF Interactive, 128 Frankwell, Shrewsbury, SY3 8JX Tel: (01743) 270444 Fax: (01743) 368381 E-mail: mitch@bfgroup.co.uk *Major vendor of all finished flat screens in plasma and LCD technologies. Also audio systems from BOSE and others*

▶ BFCC Garage Doors, The Garage Door Showroom, Tendring Road, Thorpe-le-Soken, Clacton-on-Sea, Essex, CO16 0AA Tel: (01255) 863815 Fax: (01255) 813527 E-mail: rogersmith888@aol.com *GARAGE DOORS SUPPLIED, INSTALLED, AUTOMATED & REPAIRED.*GATES AND RAILINGS SUPPLIED & AUTOMATED*

BFL Trading Ltd, 314 Regents Park Road, London, N3 2LT Tel: (020) 8371 6000 Fax: (020) 8371 6010 E-mail: info@bfl.com *Exporters*

BFS Sheet Metal & Engineering Ltd, 42 Woodham Lane, New Haw, Addlestone, Surrey, KT15 3NA Tel: (01932) 848142 Fax: (01932) 841937 E-mail: stephen@bfssheetmetal.co.uk *Subcontract engineering, machining, sheet metalwork engineers*

▶ BFS Transport Ltd, Dove Court, West Lane, Sykehouse, Goole, North Humberside, DN14 9BD Tel: (01405) 785373 Fax: (01405) 785249

BFSS Ltd, 2 Strawberry Lane, Tiptree, Colchester, CO5 0RX Tel: (01621) 810500 Fax: (01621) 810500 E-mail: sales@blackwaterfss.co.uk *Fire equipment maintenance & training*

BG Group, 100 Thames Valley Park Drive, Reading, RG6 1PT Tel: 0118-935 3222 Fax: 0118-929 3710 E-mail: admin@bg-group.com *Gas & oil exploration & production services*

▶ BG IT Services, 3, Glen Court, Grasmere Road, Bromley, BR1 4BD Tel: 070 9223 1080 Fax: 070 9223 1080 E-mail: us@bg-it.com

B-G Kleen, 94 Radegund Road, Cambridge, CB1 3RS Tel: (01223) 242677 Fax: (01223) 242677 *Office cleaning contractors*

▶ BG Properties, 15 Palgrave Road, London, W12 9NB Tel: 07968 034592 Fax: 07092 038898 *Plumbing, Heating contractors. Bathroom and Kitchen installers, Property refurbishment and maintenance.*

BH & Sons Ltd, 6 Hazel End, Swanley, Kent, BR8 8NU Tel: (01322) 667610 Fax: (01322) 614569 *Ductwork installers*

Bhallatex Fabric Importers, 93 Parker Drive, Leicester, LE4 0JP Tel: 0116-236 3660 Fax: 0116-236 3680 *Wholesale fabrics & distributors*

Bharat Alarms, 32-34 Constitution Hill, Birmingham, B19 3JT Tel: 0121-236 7449 Fax: 0121-236 8996 E-mail: bharatuk@aol.com *Burglar alarm installation agents*

▶ BHCS, 64a Market Place, Chippenham, Wiltshire, SN15 3HG Tel: (01249) 652682 Fax: (0871) 2771259 E-mail: nstuart@businessandhome.co.uk *Computer services*

BHG Grinding Ltd, Unit A Drury Lane, Chadderton, Oldham, OL9 8EU Tel: 0161-682 6519 Fax: 0161-683 4682 *Grinding tools manufrs*

▶ Bhi Solutions, Coombe Lodge, Bourne Lane, Bristol, BS40 7RG Tel: (01761) 462244 Fax: (01761) 462775

BHM Knitwear Ltd, 31 Churchill Way, Fleckney, Leicester, LE8 8UD Tel: 0116-240 2909 Fax: 0116-240 2708 E-mail: info@bhmknitwear.co.uk *Knitwear manufrs*

Bhor (Hallbridge Ltd), 28 Brookdene Drive, Northwood, Middlesex, HA6 3NS Tel: (020) 8961 1614 Fax: (020) 8961 1614 E-mail: hallbridge@aol.com *Wholesale distributors*

Bhs Ltd, Marylebone House, 129-137 Marylebone Road, London, NW1 5QD Tel: (020) 7262 3288 Fax: (020) 7723 1115 *Retail outlets home & clothing* Also at: Branches throughout the U.K.

BHSF, 2 Darnley Road, Birmingham, B16 8TE Tel: 0121-454 3601 Fax: 0121-454 7725 E-mail: sales@bhsff.co.uk *Healthcare plans specialists*

▶ BI Electronics, Greenmoss, Kinellar, Aberdeen, AB21 0SE Tel: (01224) 790615 *Electronics manufrs*

Biachem Ltd, Boundary House, 91-93 Charterhouse Street, London, EC1M 6HR Tel: (020) 7250 1905 Fax: (020) 7250 1913 E-mail: info@biachem.com *Chemical distributors*

Biacore International, 2 Meadway Court, Rutherford Close, Stevenage, Hertfordshire, SG1 2EF Tel: (01438) 846200 Fax: (01438) 846201 E-mail: enquiries@biacore.com *Scientific instrument sales*

Bianca UK, 56 Eastcastle Street, London, W1W 8EQ Tel: (020) 7580 0085 Fax: (020) 7436 3938 *Ladies fashion distributors*

Biasys Health Care, Manor Way, Woking, Surrey, GU22 9JU Tel: (01483) 770331 Fax: (01483) 727193 *Medical monitoring systems*

Bib Cochran Ltd, Newbie Works, Annan, Dumfriesshire, DG12 5QU Tel: (01522) 510510 Fax: (01461) 205511 E-mail: enquiries@bibcochran.com *Industrial boilers*

▶ Bibase Rental POS Point of Sale Software, 33 Burnt Stones Drive, Sheffield, S10 5TT Tel: 0114 2302050 E-mail: info@bibase.co.uk *POS Point of sale inventory & rental software*

Bibby Distribution Ltd, 3 West Bank Road, Belfast, BT3 9JL Tel: (028) 9077 3997 Fax: (028) 9077 3117

▶ Bibby Distribution Services Ltd, 7 Yeadon Airport Industrial Estate, Harrogate Road, Yeadon, Leeds, LS19 7WP Tel: 0113-250 6787 Fax: 0113-239 1293 E-mail: info@bibbydist.co.uk

Bibby Distributions Ltd, 105 Duke St, Liverpool, L1 5JQ Tel: 0151-708 8000 Fax: 0151-794 1001 E-mail: iain.speak@bibbydist.co.uk *Road transport haulage, freight services, logistics services*

▶ Bibby Logistics Ltd, P9 Parklands, Heywood Distribution Park, Heywood, Lancashire, OL10 2TT Tel: (01706) 620222 Fax: (01706) 367107

Bibby Sterlin Ltd, Pengam Road, Aberbargoed, Bargoed, Mid Glamorgan, CF81 9FW Tel: (01443) 830830 Fax: (01443) 821545 *Disposable medical products manufrs*

Bibby Tranmissions Ltd, Cannon Way, Dewsbury, West Yorkshire, WF13 1EH Tel: (01924) 460801 Fax: (01924) 457668 E-mail: sales@bibbytransmissions.co.uk *Couplings including disc pack, torsion ally rigid, flexible, fluid suppliers*

Bibbys Of Halifax Ltd, Jasper Street Works, Queens Road, Halifax, West Yorkshire, HX1 4NT Tel: (01422) 366331 Fax: (01422) 330086 E-mail: bibbysofhalifax@aol.com *Stainless steel fabricators*

Biblio Products Ltd, The Broadway, High Street, Chesham, Buckinghamshire, HP5 1EG Tel: (01494) 776655 Fax: (01494) 776677 E-mail: sales@biblioproducts.com *Promotional products & incentive gifts*

▶ Bibliographic Data Services Ltd, Annandale House, The Crichton, Bankend Road, Dumfries, DG1 4TA Tel: (01387) 702251 Fax: (01387) 702259 E-mail: info@bibdsl.co.uk *Information services*

Bibra International Ltd, Woodmansterne Road, Carshalton, Surrey, SM5 4DS Tel: (020) 8652 1000 Fax: (020) 8661 7029 E-mail: help@bibra.co.uk *Biological researchers*

Bicel Industries Ltd, 64 Sandown Avenue, Swindon, SN3 1QQ Tel: (01793) 491988 Fax: (01793) 692462 *Computer consultants*

▶ Bicester Credit Services, The Buntings, Bicester, Oxon, OX26 6WE Tel: 07791 482964 E-mail: bicestercs@aol.com *Debt Collection . No Win No Fee .Company Reports and Consultancy*Let us manage your collections or collect those non payers.*WE GET RESULTS**We also stop rogue companies from burning your bottom line by tracking who they are dealing with . We can forewarn you of a potential bad debt .**Great strides in the forklift Industry.**

▶ Bicester Furniture Studio, 24 Church Street, Bicester, Oxfordshire, OX26 6AZ Tel: (01869) 325669 Fax: (01869) 323164 E-mail: sezzybfs@tesco.net *Corndell furniture retailers*

Bicester Products Squash Court Manufacturers Ltd, 55 West End, Witney, Oxfordshire, OX28 1NJ Tel: (01993) 774426 Fax: (01993) 779569 E-mail: sales@squashcourts.co.uk *Squash & racquetball court designers, manufacturers & erectors*

▶ Bicester Sweepers Ltd, Glebe Court, Fringford, Bicester, Oxfordshire, OX27 8RJ Tel: (01869) 277410 Fax: (01869) 277704

Bickers, 6 Maple Close, St. Columb, Cornwall, TR9 6SL Tel: (07977) 147294 E-mail: info@bickerslocksmiths.co.uk *Locksmiths*

▶ Bickerstaffe Containers Ltd, Grave Yard Lane, Bickerstaffe, Ormskirk, Lancashire, L39 9EG Tel: (01695) 424244 Fax: (01695) 424387 *Packaging manufrs*

Bickerton Bros, 8 Arden Road, Alcester, Warwickshire, B49 6HN Tel: (01789) 763834 Fax: (01789) 400512 E-mail: bickbros@aol.com *Fabricators & metal workers*

Bickerton Jewellery, 23 Vyse Street, Hockley, Birmingham, B18 6LE Tel: 0121-551 0509 Fax: 0121-523 0366 *Jewellery manufrs*

Bico Ltd, Rosemary Lane, Beaumaris, Gwynedd, LL58 8EB Tel: (01248) 810463 Fax: (01248) 810998 E-mail: bicoltd@aol.com *Precision turned parts & tools manufrs*

Bicycle Association Of GB Ltd, 3 The Quadrant, Coventry, CV1 2DY Tel: (024) 7655 3838 Fax: (024) 7622 8366 E-mail: info@ba-gb.co.uk *Trade association*

BID Group Ltd, Elland Close, Wingates Industrial Estate, Westhoughton, Bolton, BL5 3XE Tel: 0870 607 5050 Fax: 0870 6081271 E-mail: sales@bidgroup.co.uk *Industrial door manufrs*

▶ Bid Management UK Limited, PO Box 629, Haywards Heath, West Sussex, RH16 4WU Tel: 01444 415548 Fax: 01444 415548 E-mail: info@bidmanuk.com *Bid Management UK offer a specialist range of Bid Management services to companies large or small for competitive tendering and the production of unsolicitied proposals to customers.*

Bidcorp P.L.C., 6 Stratton Street, London, W1J 8LD Tel: (020) 7408 0123 Fax: (020) 7495 8284 *Transportation property & shipping*

Biddle Air Curtains Ltd, St Mary's Road, Nuneaton, Warwickshire, CV11 5AU Tel: (024) 7638 4233 Fax: (024) 7637 3621 E-mail: info@biddle-air.co.uk *Heating manufrs*

Biddle & Mumford Gears Ltd, 8-18 Kings Place, Buckhurst Hill, Essex, IG9 5EA Tel: (020) 8505 4615 Fax: (020) 8505 3718 E-mail: sales@biddleandmumford.co.uk Principal Export Areas: Worldwide *small gears, Gear Manufaturers, Precision Gears,fine pitch, Helicals, Spur, Bevel, worm,ratchet, pulleys, toothed pulleys, sprockets, CNC Turning, CNC Milling, assembly*

Biddle Sawyer Silks, 22 Rook Street, St Mary''s Courtyard, Manchester, M15 5PS Tel: 0161-227 9428 Fax: 0161-227 8023 E-mail: info@biddlesawyersilks.com *Silk merchants*

Biddlecombe Engineering Ltd, Unit 18 Landford Common Farm, New Road, Landford, Salisbury, SP5 2AZ Tel: (01794) 322992 Fax: (01794) 323001 *Precision engineers*

Biddles, 24 Rollesby Road, King's Lynn, Norfolk, PE30 4LS Tel: (01553) 764728 Fax: (01553) 764633 E-mail: enquiries@biddles.co.uk *Lithographic printers & lithographers*

Bidlift Ltd, 1-3 Dudley Street, Grimsby, South Humberside, DN31 2AW Tel: (01472) 341932 Fax: (01472) 341919 E-mail: jacking@bidlift.co.uk *Heavy lifting specialists*

Bidmuthin Technologies, Dudley House, 31 Lower Road, Harrow, Middlesex, HA2 0DE Tel: (020) 8866 9988 Fax: (020) 8422 9555 E-mail: info@bidmuthin.co.uk *Apple & PC computer resellers*

Bidwell Metals Ltd, Tiger Works, Clandown, Radstock, BA3 3BR Tel: (01761) 432391 Fax: (01761) 432522 *Metal merchants*

▶ Biele UK Ltd, 24 Wilton Court, Newton Aycliffe, County Durham, DL5 7PU Tel: (01325) 321478 Fax: (01325) 312537 E-mail: sales@biele.co.uk

Bierrum Structural Services Ltd, 105 High Street, Houghton Regis, Dunstable, Bedfordshire, LU5 5BJ Tel: (01582) 845745 Fax: (01582) 845746 E-mail: admin@bierrum.co.uk *Reinforced concrete engineers*

Bierton & Staniforth Ltd, Crescent Works, 71-73 St. Mary's Road, Sheffield, S2 4AN Tel: (0114) 272 0514 *Cutlery manufrs*

Biffa Holdings Ltd, Coronation Road, Cressex, High Wycombe, Buckinghamshire, HP12 3TZ Tel: (0800) 307307 E-mail: marketing@biffa.co.uk *Industrial waste disposal & refuse disposal contractors* Also at: Branches throughout the U.K.

Biffa Waste Services Ltd, Gavell Road, Twechar, Kilsyth, Glasgow, G65 9LP Tel: (01236) 821607 Fax: (01236) 822007 *Waste disposal contractors*

Biffa Waste Services Ltd, Boiling Plant, Stoneferry Road, Hull, HU8 8BZ Tel: (01482) 322311 Fax: (01482) 322321 *Waste disposal & industrial waste recycling*

Company Information

Biffa Waste Services Ltd, Private Road 2, Colwick Industrial Estate, Nottingham, NG4 2JR Tel: 0115-961 6424 Fax: 0115-940 0102 *Waste recovery services*

Biffa Waste Services Ltd, Rixton Old Hall, Manchester Road, Rixton, Warrington, WA3 6EW Tel: 0161-775 1011 Fax: 0161-775 7291 *Waste disposal services*

Biffa Waste Services Ltd, Potters Lane, Wednesbury, West Midlands, WS10 7NR Tel: 0121-502 5500 Fax: 0121-505 2120 E-mail: wednesbury@biffa.co.uk *Waste disposal services*

Bifold Fluidpower Ltd, Greenside Way, Middleton, Manchester, M24 1SW Tel: 0161-345 4777 Fax: 0161-345 4780 E-mail: sales@bifold-fluidpower.co.uk Principal Export Areas: Worldwide *Directional control valves*

Bifrangi (UK) Ltd, PO Box 22, Lincoln, LN2 5DT Tel: (01522) 585800 Fax: (01522) 529116 *Press forging manufrs*

Bifrangi UK Ltd, PO Box 129, Sheffield, S9 1HR Tel: (01709) 562766 Fax: (01709) 857888 *Crankshaft manufrs*

▶ Big Al's, The Old Vicarage, 24 Zetland Street, Wakefield, West Yorkshire, WF1 1QT Tel: 07971 635051 E-mail: big_als_comics@hotmail.co.uk *Selling retail - Comics, Vintage Toys and Collectibles, Manga and Anime figures and much much more. E mail for mail order or give us a ring, we might just have what you are looking for!**We guarantee we have something which will make you say: " I remember that!"*

Big Apple, Unit 1 Queen Street, Morley, Leeds, LS27 8EG Tel: 0113-253 4525 *Herbalist*

Big Badge Co., Old School House, Victoria Avenue, London, N3 1GG Tel: (020) 8371 8752 Fax: (020) 8371 8751 E-mail: sales@theknightgroup.com *Enamel badge manufrs*

The Big Bale Company North Ltd, Heck Lane, Great Heck, Goole, North Humberside, DN14 0BL Tel: (01405) 862240 Fax: (01405) 862328 E-mail: northern.straw@virgin.net *Machinery bailers sales*

▶ Big Bang Balloon, 38 Parkfield Road, Ruskington, Sleaford, Lincolnshire, NG34 9HS Tel: (07906) 951961 *Professional balloon decor for weddings, parties and special events. Printed/personalised balloons.*

Big Bang Productions Ltd, 45 Oakleys Road, Long Eaton, Nottingham, NG10 1FQ Tel: 0115-973 0435 Fax: 0115-946 3937 E-mail: bb.fireworks@virgin.net *Firework displays & retail sales*

Big Bear Ltd, Fox'S Confectionery, Sunningdale Road, Braunstone, Leicester, LE3 1UE Tel: 0116-287 3561 Fax: 0116-232 0117 E-mail: info@foxs.co.uk *Confectionery production*

Big Bear Plastic Products Ltd, Fantastic Works, Wassage Way, Hampton Lovett, Droitwich, Worcestershire, WR9 0NX Tel: (01905) 792500 Fax: (01905) 792501 E-mail: louises@big-bear.co.uk *Design & manufacture high quality vacuum formed products*

Big Bite, Rowles House, Weston-on-the-Green, Bicester, Oxfordshire, OX25 3QQ Tel: (01869) 351383 Fax: (01869) 351383 *Buffet catering & sandwich manufrs*

▶ Big Blue Marketing Ltd, 24 Grove Lane, Wolverhampton, WV6 8NJ Tel: (01902) 756836 Fax: (01902) 756836 E-mail: support@bigbluemarketing.co.uk *Sage act software support*

Big Boss (London) Ltd, 201 Whitechapel Road, London, E1 1DE Tel: (020) 7377 6068 Fax: (020) 7377 6068 *Clothing retail*

▶ Big Bounce, 11a Venachar Avenue, Callander, Perthshire, FK17 8JQ Tel: (01877) 339952 E-mail: info@big-bounce-entertainment.co.uk *bouncy castle, sumo suits, bungee run, gladiator jousting and inflatble hire for Children and Adults. All events catered for including birthday parties and corporate entertainment.*

▶ Big Brother Security (UK) Ltd, Harmer Street, Gravesend, Kent, DA12 2AX Tel: (01474) 354086 Fax: (01474) 354086 E-mail: info@bigbrothersecurity.org.uk *Big Brother Security, installs & maintains CCTV, intruder alarms, fire and access control systems to domestic and comercial premises all over the UK and Europe Contact us for a free quotation*

Big Brother UK, 23 Castalia Square, London, E14 3NG Tel: (0800) 0186315 Fax: (0871) 8713816 E-mail: bigbrotheruk@hotmail.com *Detective agency & all aspects of security, tracing & surveillance systems*

▶ Big Cooker Repair Co., 41 Balcarres Road, Leyland, PR25 2EL Tel: (01772) 465676 Fax: (01772) 464757 E-mail: enquiry@bigcookerrepair.co.uk *Repair & install cookers*

The Big Do Co. Ltd, PO Box 104, Manchester, M26 4WU Tel: (0870) 8907585 Fax: 0161-724 8790 E-mail: mail@bigdo.co.uk *The business supplies chair covers and table linen both to hire and purchase. We also offer towelling products and a sourcing service*

Big Egg Designs, 1 Parade Mews, Norwood Road, London, SE27 9AX Tel: (020) 8674 3600 Fax: (020) 8674 3600 *Furniture manufrs*

Big Fish, Unit 10 Glenpark Industrial Estate, Glenpark Street, Glasgow, G31 1NU Tel: 0141-550 2001 Fax: 0141-556 1131 *Office consumables (printing) suppliers*

Big Fish Ltd, Ribbon Light House, Newtown Street, Prestwich, Manchester, M25 1HU Tel: 0161-798 0040 Fax: 0161-798 8884 E-mail: manvent@bigfishhook.com *Consumables, computer printers, accessories & repairs*

▶ Big Fish Training, Huntingdon House, 35 Field Road, Reading, RG1 6AP Tel: 0845 833 0072 Fax: 0870 705 8562 *Specialists in media training, public relations training, publicity advice & communications skills*

Big Fun Casino Co., Crackley Lane, Kenilworth, Warwickshire, CV8 2JT Tel: (01926) 863090 Fax: (01926) 511533 E-mail: sales@bigindoorgames.co.uk *Event organisers*

▶ Big Green Carpet, 31 Grange Road, Hove, East Sussex, BN3 5HU Tel: (07900) 890977 E-mail: oli@biggreencarpet.co.uk *Big Green Carpet offer landscaping, garden design and construction services, lawn maintenance and specialist fencing; based in Sussex.*

▶ Big Green Carpet, Flat 4 Clearview House, London Road, Ashington, Pulborough, West Sussex, RH20 3DD Tel: (07810) 611236 E-mail: luke@biggreencarpet.co.uk *Garden landscapers*

The Big Internet, 32 Lipson Road, Plymouth, PL4 8PW Tel: (01752) 256162 Fax: (01752) 250733 *Computer systems & software development service*

Big John Rubbish Removals, 25 Lister Road, Dudley, West Midlands, DY2 8JR Tel: (01384) 232359 *Waste disposal services*

Big K Charcoal Merchants, Whittington Hill, Whittington, King's Lynn, Norfolk, PE33 9TE Tel: (01366) 500252 Fax: (01366) 500395 E-mail: sales@bigk.co.uk *Charcoal merchants*

▶ Big Limo Co. Ltd, 13 Waterloo Road, Wolverhampton, WV1 4DJ Tel: (0845) 6442290 Fax: (0845) 6442290 E-mail: ask@thebiglimo.co.uk *Chauffeur driven limo services for weddings, business, stag & hen nights*

▶ Big Marketing, 82-84 Newport Road, New Bradwell, Milton Keynes, MK13 0AA Tel: (01908) 326666 Fax: (01908) 326601 E-mail: sales@bigmarketing.co.uk *Advertising & marketing agency*

Big On Bouncing, 17 Wendover Road, Burnham, Slough, SL1 7ND Tel: (01628) 410736 E-mail: bigonbouncing@aol.com *Inflatable Hire*

Big Red Computers P.L.C., 84 Aldermans Hill, London, N13 4PP Tel: (0870) 0711117 Fax: (0870) 0733337 *Computer software manufrs*

▶ Big Rigs LGV Driver Training, Hereford, Hereford, HR4 7SG Tel: 01432 761004 Fax: 01432 769305 E-mail: info@bigrigstraining.com *DSA registered LGV/HGV Driving Instructors based in Herefordshire, providing quality training Nationwide. Car & Trailer, CPC, Rigid and Artic, Company assessments. Tailor made courses to suit the individual.*

Big Screen, Church Lane, Gorleston, Great Yarmouth, Norfolk, NR31 7BG Tel: (01493) 662913 Fax: (01493) 440677 E-mail: sales@bigscreenonline.co.uk *LCD giant plasma projection screens supplier*

Big Screen, 5 Dace Road, London, E3 2NG Tel: (020) 8986 3300 Fax: (020) 8986 3742 E-mail: sales@thebigscreen.co.uk *Promotional clothing manufrs*

Big Stuff, 4 Hall Road Industrial Estate, Southminster, Essex, CM0 7DA Tel: (01621) 774981 Fax: (01621) 774672 *Promotional product producers*

Big Table Furniture Co Op Ltd, 56 Great Western Road, London, W9 3BT Tel: (020) 7221 5058 Fax: (020) 7229 6032 E-mail: sales@bigtable.co.uk *Pine beds & mattress manufacturers & retailers*

▶ Big Window Co., Smallwood Street, Redditch, Worcestershire, B98 7AZ Tel: (01527) 585258 Fax: (01527) 585258

Bigbury Mint Ltd, Ermington Mill, Ermington, Ivybridge, Devon, PL21 9NT Tel: (01548) 830717 Fax: (01548) 830046 E-mail: sales@bigburymint.com *Medal dealers*

Bigdug.Co.Uk, Unit 41 Staunton Court Business Park, Ledbury Road, Staunton, Gloucester, GL19 3QS Tel: (0845) 0654000 E-mail: racking9@gmail.com *Suppliers of shelving, racking, boxes, storage equipment*

Bigfish, Unit 8 Adam Smith Street, Grimsby, South Humberside, DN31 1SJ Tel: (01472) 268180 Fax: (01472) 268170 E-mail: humberside@bigfishhooked.com *Print consumables & repairs*

▶ Bigfoot Play Systems Ltd, Hamilton House, 111 Marlowes, Hemel Hempstead, Hertfordshire, HP1 1BB Tel: (01442) 243355 Fax: (01442) 244330 E-mail: info@bigfootplay.com *Design, manufacture & installation of playground equipment, includes play equipment, sports systems, skateboard parks, youth shelters, site furniture & safer surfacing*

▶ Biggabyte Computer Maintenance, 47 Medway Drive, Wellingborough, Northamptonshire, NN8 5XT Tel: (01933) 392375 E-mail: john@biggabyte.com *Computer services & training*

▶ Bigger Scene Ltd, 172 Monks Wood, North Shields, Tyne & Wear, NE30 2UB Tel: 0191-272 8998 *Exhibition stands & display manufrs*

Biggins Bros Ltd, 154 Arundel St, Sheffield, S1 4RE Tel: 0114-272 2612 Fax: 0114-275 6296 *Electroplaters*

Biggleswade Auto Supplies Ltd, 132 Shortmead Street, Biggleswade, Bedfordshire, SG18 0BH Tel: (01767) 316666 Fax: (01767) 318362 E-mail: biggsautosupplies@ntlworld.com *Motor accessories & factors service*

Biggleswade Linen Services Ltd, Potton Road, Biggleswade, Bedfordshire, SG18 0EJ Tel: (01767) 313159 Fax: (01767) 601958 *Linen hire services*

Biggleswade Saddlery, South View, Biggleswade, Bedfordshire, SG18 8BZ Tel: (01767) 316089 E-mail: sales@biggleswadesaddlery.co.uk *Saddlery & riding gear suppliers*

Biggleswade Sheet Metal Co, The Old Forge, Rose Lane, Biggleswade, Bedfordshire, SG18 0JT Tel: (01767) 318509 Fax: (01767) 318509 *Sheet metalwork engineers*

▶ Biggs Building & Landscaping, 12 Westray Place, Bishopbriggs, Glasgow, G64 1UQ Tel: 0141-762 0004 Fax: 0141-762 0007

M.C. Bignell Ltd, Horton Road, West Drayton, Middlesex, UB7 8EJ Tel: (01895) 448181 Fax: (01895) 431157 *Electrical control panels manufrs*

▶ Bigstudio Glass Design Ltd, Hunter House Farm, Tees Road, Hartlepool, Cleveland, TS25 2DX Tel: (01429) 270777 Fax: (01429) 270888 E-mail: sales@big-studio.co.uk *Glass design & manufrs*

▶ Bigtoolbox, Unit 12, Hampstead Avenue, Mildenhall, Bury St. Edmunds, Suffolk, IP28 7AS Tel: (01638) 716170 Fax: (01638) 510728 E-mail: john@bigtoolbox.co.uk *Tradesman wholesaler*

▶ Biject Ltd, 4 Kingston Close, Knott End-on-Sea, Poulton-le-Fylde, Lancashire, FY6 0DJ Tel: (01253) 812363 *Network security products & services*

Bijou, Unit 60a Castle Court, Royal Avenue, Belfast, BT1 1DD Tel: (028) 9023 5595 Fax: (028) 9023 5595 E-mail: sales@bijou.ltd.com *Fashion accessories suppliers*

Bilanco Ltd, Units 3-4, Powdrake Road, Grangemouth, Stirlingshire, FK3 9OT Tel: (01324) 473707 Fax: (01324) 471926 *Window blinds distributors*

▶ Bilbate Ltd, 24 High March, High March Industrial Estate, Daventry, Northamptonshire, NN11 4HB Tel: (01327) 871467 Fax: (01327) 300619 *Laboratory glassware manufacturers, pipettes & capillary tubes*

Bilbeck Ltd, Yorke Street, Mansfield Woodhouse, Mansfield, Nottinghamshire, NG19 9NU Tel: (01623) 651101 Fax: (01623) 653387 E-mail: sales@bilbeck.com *Plumbing & heating merchants*

▶ Bilbo Tools Ltd, Steamhouse Group, 555 White Hart Lane, London, N17 7RN Tel: 020 88196076 E-mail: sales@bilbotools.com

Bilco UK Ltd, 3 Park Farm Business Centre, Fornham Park, Fornham St. Genevieve, Bury St. Edmunds, Suffolk, IP28 6TS Tel: (01284) 701696 Fax: (01284) 702531 E-mail: admin@bilco.com Principal Export Areas: Asia Pacific, Middle East, Central/East Europe, West Europe, North America & South America *Lift access cover manufrs*

Bildabin Agricultural Machinery, Harrison House, Benson Lane, Catforth, Preston, PR4 0HY Tel: (01772) 690575 Fax: (01772) 691681 E-mail: enquiries@bildabin.co.uk *Animal feeding systems*

▶ Bi-Link Europe, 2 Little Drum,, Cumbernauld,, Glasgow, G68 9LH Tel: (01236) 780107

Bill Blind Spot, 904 Shettleston Road, Glasgow, G32 7XN Tel: 0141-778 1866 Fax: 0141-778 2759 *Blinds manufrs*

▶ Bill Carver Ltd, Unit 2 Turner Industrial Estate, Turner Street, Denton, Manchester, M34 3EG Tel: 0161-320 3400 Fax: 0161-320 3433

Bill Dawson Sign Consultants, Nailford House, Brewery Lane, Bridge, Canterbury, Kent, CT4 5LF Tel: (01227) 831044 Fax: (01227) 831044 *Sign designers & contractors*

Bill Dibden G R P, 8 Littletowns Estate, Blandford Heights, Blandford Forum, Dorset, DT11 7UR Tel: (01258) 459703 Fax: (01258) 459714 *Fibre glass moulding*

Bill Heaney Ltd, Hume Street, Newcastle upon Tyne, NE6 1LN Tel: 0191-265 8511 Fax: 0191-209 0203 E-mail: heaneyacc@aol.com *Motor body repairers services*

▶ Bill Mackie, 3 Baltic Place, Peterhead, Aberdeenshire, AB42 1TF Tel: (01779) 480290 Fax: (01779) 480559 E-mail: sales@billmackieengltd.co.uk *Marine engineering commercial & vehicle repairs &ships carpenter*

Bill Quay Engineering Co., Unit 10 Wagonway Road, Hebburn, Tyne & Wear, NE31 1SP Tel: 0191-483 7355 Fax: 0191-428 0603 *Precision engineers*

▶ Billaboing Bouncy Castle, 9 Wilfrid Grove, West Bridgford, Nottingham, NG2 7AT Tel: (07875) 703971 E-mail: info@billaboing.co.uk *Telephone: 0787 5703971*Absolutely, definitely the cheapest bouncers in town. Bouncy castle prices start from just £38 per day. Based in Nottingham. We also hire outdoor toys and games.*

Billcar Engineering Ltd, Unit 1a March Way, Battlefield Enterprise Park, Shrewsbury, SY1 3JE Tel: (01743) 469398 Fax: (01743) 450084 E-mail: billcarengine@hotmail.com *Precision engineers*

Billenness Keith Ltd, 22 Birch Road, Eastbourne, East Sussex, BN23 6PD Tel: (01323) 411028 Fax: (01323) 411704 E-mail: keith@kbglass.fsnet.co.uk *Glazing contractors*

Billericay Farm Services Ltd, School Road, Downham, Billericay, Essex, CM11 1QU Tel: (01268) 710237 Fax: (01268) 711040 E-mail: sales@bfs.uk.com *Fuel oil distributors & liquid fertilisers*

Billet Auto Sales Ltd, Archers Fields, Basildon, Essex, SS13 1DN Tel: (01268) 286764 Fax: (01268) 532349 *Used commercial vehicle dealers*

Billiard Supply Co., 21 Beacon Street, Huddersfield, HD2 2RS Tel: (01484) 424333 Fax: (01484) 424333 *Billiard table maintenance services*

Billing Aquadrome Ltd, Crow Lane, Little Billing, Northampton, NN3 9DA Tel: (01604) 408181 Fax: (01604) 784412 E-mail: brochures@aquadrome.co.uk *Tackle shop*

Billingham Aquatic Centre, 12 Mill Lane, Billingham, Cleveland, TS23 1HF Tel: (01642) 360058 Fax: (01642) 359444 E-mail: sales@billinghamaquaticcentre.co.uk *Tropical marine fish & cold water specialist*

Billingham Machine Co. Ltd, Alvis Close, Billingham, Cleveland, TS23 4JB Tel: (01642) 560981 Fax: (01642) 565523 E-mail: bmc@billinghammachinecompany.fsnet.co.uk *General engineers*

Billings & Edmonds Ltd, Shop, 132 High Street, Eton, Windsor, Berkshire, SL4 6AR Tel: (01753) 818290 Fax: (01753) 831145 E-mail: sales@billingsandedmonds.co.uk

▶ Billings & Hathaway Ltd, Unit 3, Centenary Industrial Estate, Hughes Road, Brighton, BN2 4AW Tel: (01273) 570680

Billington Export Ltd, Units 1e-2e, Gilmans Industrial Estate, Billingshurst, West Sussex, RH14 9EZ Tel: (01403) 784961 Fax: (01403) 783519 E-mail: sales@bel-tubes.co.uk *Electronic valve distributors*

Billington Group, 280 Bawtry Road, Wickersley, Rotherham, South Yorkshire, S66 1JY Tel: (01709) 543837 Fax: (01709) 531215 E-mail: info@billington-group.co.uk *Supplier of pallet collars & accessories*

Billington Modern Structures Ltd, 456 Badminton Road, Yate, Bristol, BS37 5HY Tel: (01454) 318181 Fax: (01454) 318231 E-mail: postroom@billington-modern.co.uk *Structural engineers*

Billington Press Ltd, 20 Hepscott Road, London, E9 5HB Tel: (020) 8985 7561 Fax: (020) 8533 3692 *Lithographic printers*

Billington Structures Ltd, Barnsley Road, Wombwell, Barnsley, South Yorkshire, S73 8DS Tel: (01226) 340666 Fax: (01226) 755947 E-mail: sales@billington-structures.co.uk *Steel, structural steelwork & welded fabricators*

Billion UK Ltd, 2 Fitzhamon Court, Wolverton Mill, Milton Keynes, MK12 6LB Tel: (01908) 223344 Fax: (01908) 223006 E-mail: sales@billion-uk.co.uk *Plastic injection moulding machine sales & services*

Billown Lime Quarries Ltd, Billown Quarry, Ballasalla, Isle Of Man, IM9 3DW Tel: (01624) 828765 Fax: (01624) 824477 *Agricultural limestone producers*

Henry T. Billson (Kettering) Ltd, Glendon Ironworks, Sackville St, Kettering, Northants, NN16 9EQ Tel: (01536) 512194 Fax: (01536) 484152 E-mail: sales@billsonssteel.co.uk *Steel stockholders, structural steelwork engineers, steel fabricators, steel tube stockholders & reinforcing steel stockholders*

▶ Billy Boy Frozen Foods Ltd, Park Industrial Estate, Liverpool Road, Ashton In Makerfield, Wigan, Lancashire, WN4 0YU Tel: (01942) 764000

▶ Billy Walker, Shandonan, The Belts, Turriff, Aberdeenshire, AB53 5PN Tel: (01888) 562738

▶ Billy's Bouncers, Keepers Lodge, Benington Lordship, Benington, Stevenage, Hertfordshire, SG2 7BS Tel: (01438) 356777

▶ Billys Leisure, Unit 4 A Country House Estate, Whimple, Exeter, EX5 2NL Tel: (01395) 268595 E-mail: sales@billysleisure.com *Boing are the creative forcr behind some of the best inflatable and custom designed adventure play on earth. Whether making an impact on land or water, the football pitch or film and television, our huge range of products are packed with more thrills more spills and mre playability than ever before.*Inflatable fun including Bouncy Castles in all shapes and sizes, Inflatable games, football games, pool inflatables, sof play and accessories.*

▶ Bilston Angling Centre, 48 Church Street, Bilston, West Midlands, WV14 0AH Tel: (01902) 495366 *Fishing tackle suppliers*

Bilston & Battersea Enamels, 14-16 Barton Park, Mount Pleasant, Bilston, West Midlands, WV14 7LH Tel: (01902) 408440 Fax: (01902) 492162 E-mail: sales@bilstonandbattersea.com *Decorative enamelled ware manufrs*

Bilston Engineering Ltd, Spring Road, Wolverhampton, WV4 6LF Tel: (01902) 492004 Fax: (01902) 354510 E-mail: sales@bilston-engineering.co.uk *Steel fabricators & general engineers*

▶ Bilston Precision Engineering Ltd, Lady Victoria Business Centre, Newtongrange, Dalkeith, Midlothian, EH22 4QN Tel: 0131-454 0044 Fax: 0131-454 0045 *Engineering manufrs*

▶ Bilt Hamber Ltd, Tye Barn, Tye Common Road, Little Burstead, Billericay, Essex, CM12 9SB Tel: (01277) 658899 Fax: (01277) 657533 E-mail: enquiries@bilthamber.com *Formulators & manufacturers of surface care & protection products*

Biltmore Printers, 14 Manners View, Newport, Isle of Wight, PO30 5FA Tel: (01983) 529788 Fax: (01983) 825528 E-mail: info@biltmoreprinters.co.uk *General printer services*

David Bilton Engineering Ltd, 77 Hudson Street, North Shields, Tyne & Wear, NE30 1DL Tel: 0191-296 1429 Fax: 0191-257 8611 E-mail: info@dbeltd.com *Pipework fabricators & installers*

Bilton Flooring Contractors, 11 Firside Grove, Sidcup, Kent, DA15 8WB Tel: (020) 8300 3250 *Floor coverings specialists*

Bilton & Johnson Co. Ltd, Chadwell Heath Industrial Park, Kemp Road, Dagenham, Essex, RM8 1SL Tel: (020) 8598 8088 Fax: (020) 8599 4311

Bin UK Ltd, Prince Street, Bolton, BL1 2NP Tel: (01204) 366997 Fax: (01204) 366998 E-mail: uk_sales@binkemi.com *Water based adhesives & speciality chemicals*

▶ binbagloader.co.uk, 1 Stone Cottages, Green End, Goathland, Whitby, North Yorkshire, YO22 5LQ Tel: (01947) 896398 Fax: (01947) 896398 E-mail: info@binbagloader.co.uk *Bin bag loader manufrs*

Binder Ltd, Progress Works, Ipswich Road, Claydon, Ipswich, IP6 0AG Tel: (01473) 830582 Fax: (01473) 832175 E-mail: info@binder.co.uk *Waste disposal of effluence*

Bindmont Print Services Ltd, Heywood Distribution Park, Heywood, Lancashire, OL10 2TT Tel: (01706) 360011 E-mail: bps@btinternet.com *Manufrs of printers*

Bindoff, 23 Linton Crescent, Leeds, LS17 8PZ Tel: 0113-268 1526 *Web designers*

Bindon Auto Body Centre Ltd, Cook Way, Bindon Road, Taunton, Somerset, TA2 6BJ Tel: (01823) 338582 Fax: (01823) 321854 *Car body repairs*

Bindon Engineering Co. Ltd, Johns Road, Wareham, Dorset, BH20 4BG Tel: (01929) 553477 Fax: (01929) 554858 *Precision engineers*

Bindra Bros Ltd, 6-8 Hazel Street, Leicester, LE2 7JN Tel: 0116-247 0116 Fax: 0116-247 0126 E-mail: hazelfashion@hotmail.com *Leisure wear manufrs*

Bingham Appliances, Unit 83 Hillgrove Business Park, Nazeing Road, Nazeing, Waltham Abbey, Essex, EN9 2HB Tel: (01992) 899033 Fax: (01992) 899158 E-mail: binghamappliance@aol.com *Food processing equipment manufrs*

Bingham Engineering Ltd, Wentdale, Doncaster Road, East Hardwick, Pontefract, West Yorkshire, WF8 3EQ Tel: (01977) 620517 Fax: (01977) 620863 E-mail: sales@universalbingham.co.uk Principal Export Areas: Central/East Europe, West Europe, North America, Central America & South America *Sub contract machining & fabrication*

▶ Bingham Pine Furniture, Grantham Road, Radcliffe-on-Trent, Nottingham, NG12 2JP Tel: 0115-933 2555 Fax: 0115-933 2555 E-mail: binghampine@aol.com *Pine furniture manufrs*

▶ Bingham Transport Ltd, Woodkirk International Freight, Terminal, Quarry Lane, Dewsbury, West Yorkshire, WF12 7JJ Tel: (01924) 423655

Bingo Office Supplies Ltd, PO Box 845, Halifax, West Yorkshire, HX3 6YR Tel: (0800) 0424646 Fax: (0800) 0424329 E-mail: sales@bingo-office.co.uk *Computer consumables & stationery*

Binney & Smith Europe Ltd, Ampthill Road, Bedford, MK42 9RS Tel: (01234) 266702 Fax: (01234) 342110 *Children's colouring products*

Binney & Son Ltd, Unit H Spring Hill Industrial Park, Steward Street, Birmingham, B18 7AF Tel: 0121-454 4545 Fax: 0121-454 1145 E-mail: binney.eng@btconnect.com *Valves, toilet rolls, oils, hand cleaners engineering supplies* Also at: Coventry

Binneys Coventry, Unit 1 Challenge Business Park, Challenge Close, Coventry, CV1 5JG Tel: (024) 7622 0228 Fax: (024) 7652 5342 E-mail: info@binneys.co.uk *Engineering & industrial supplies*

Binns Security Fencing Ltd, Pressmetal House St. Augustines Business Park, Estuary Close, Whitstable, Kent, CT5 2QJ Tel: (01227) 794490 Fax: (01227) 794488 *Pressings, general presswork; sheet metal & sheet metalwork engineers & fabricators. Also punching (CNC) & (sheet metal) services. In addition sign contractors*

John Binns Springs Co. Ltd, Ghyll Way, Airedale Business Centre, Keighley Road, Skipton, North Yorkshire, BD23 2TZ Tel: (01434) 681111 Fax: (01434) 681100 E-mail: sales@jbsprings.co.uk Principal Export Areas: Africa *Springs manufrs*

Binoray Ltd, Elm Grove, London, SW19 4HL Tel: (020) 8946 5157 Fax: (020) 8944 1476 E-mail: sales@binoray.co.uk Principal Export Areas: Worldwide *Freight forwarders/forwarding agents & removal contractors operating overseas. Cargo delivered world wide together with through bills of lading.Personal service.Help given to first time importers and exporters. Well versed in the requirements for Letters of Credit. Commercial cargo, household effects, cars, etc. shipped worldwide. Crosstrade services offerred*

▶ Bins and Things Ltd, 30 High Warren Close, Appleton, Warrington, WA4 5SB Tel: 07771 638413 *Bins and Things Ltd - Cigarette Bin manufacturer. BEST PRICES IN UK. Range includes Wall Mounted Cigarette Bin, Stainless Steel Cigarette Bin, Stainless Steel Outdoor Ash Tray, Wall Mounted Outdoor Ashtray, Cigarette Litter Bins, Floor Standing Ash Bin, Floor Standing Ashtrays, Wallmounted Ash Bins, Cigarette Butt Bins, Cigarette Disposal Bins, Cigarette Disposal Units, External Ashtray. Cigarette Bin Scotland ? Cigarette Bin Wales ? Cigarette Bin Ireland ? Cigarette Bin UK ? Call 07771 6384*

▶ Bins & Recycling, Aireview Court, Leeds, LS17 8YX Tel: 0113-237 0039 Fax: 0113-237 0041 E-mail: sales@binsrecycling.co.uk *Specialist suppliers of all types of bins, waste & recycling containers*

Binson Bearing Co., 335 A Round Hay Road, Leeds, LS8 4HT Tel: 0113-249 0251 Fax: 0113-235 0375 E-mail: sales@binsonbearings.ssnet.co.uk *Chain & bearing distributors*

▶ Binsted Group plc, Attwood House Mansfield Business Park, Lymington Bottom Road, Medstead, Alton, Hampshire, GU34 5PZ Tel: (01420) 568900 Fax: (01420) 565994 E-mail: info@binstedgroup.com *Book & magazine publishers*

Bio Crop Science Ltd, Sweet Briar Road, Norwich, NR6 5AP Tel: (01603) 242424 Fax: (01603) 242331 *Agricultural chemicals manufrs*

Bio Diagnostics Ltd, Upton Industrial Estate, Rectory Road, Upton Upon Severn, Worcester, WR8 0LX Tel: (01684) 592262 Fax: (01684) 592501 E-mail: info@bio-diagnostics.co.uk *Medical diagnostics products manufrs*

Bio Green Dairy Products, Home Farm, Hayes End Road, Hayes, Middlesex, UB4 8EN Tel: (020) 8848 1051 Fax: (020) 8813 5833 *Dairy products manufrs*

Bio Natura Ltd, PO Box 2, Ilkley, West Yorkshire, LS29 8AS Tel: (01943) 816816 Fax: (01943) 816818 E-mail: sales@bionutura.co.uk *Design & develop a range of chemicals*

Bio Seekers Ltd, 7 Notley Farm, Chearsley Road, Long Crendon, Aylesbury, Buckinghamshire, HP18 9ER Tel: (01844) 201745 Fax: (01844) 201963 E-mail: bioseekers@aol.com *Water testing products manufrs*

▶ Bio Vite, Unit 9A Albany Park, Cabot Lane, Poole, Dorset, BH17 7BX Tel: (01202) 606660 Fax: (01202) 694321

Biocare Ltd, Lakeside Centre, 180 Lifford Lane, Birmingham, B30 3NU Tel: 0121-433 3727 Fax: 0121-433 3879 E-mail: info@biocare.co.uk *Vitamin manufrs*

Biocatalysts Ltd, Cefn Coed, Nantgarw, Cardiff, CF15 7QQ Tel: (01443) 843712 Fax: (01443) 846500 E-mail: sales@biocats.com *Enzymes producers & suppliers*

Biochek UK Ltd, Unit 11 Mill Farm Business Park, Millfield Road, Hounslow, TW4 5PY Tel: (020) 8893 3000 Fax: (020) 8893 3101 E-mail: admin@biochek.com *Produce veterinary diagnostics*

Bio-chem Fluidics Ltd, Unit 2, College Park, Coldhams Lane, Cambridge, CB1 3HD Tel: (01223) 416642 Fax: (01223) 416787 E-mail: sales@omnifit.com *Chromatographic equipment manufrs*

Bio-Claire International Ltd, 48 Bathurst Walk, Iver, Buckinghamshire, SL0 9BH Tel: (01753) 774778 Fax: (01753) 774788 *Water conditioning suppliers & manufrs*

Bio-Clean Equipment Sales Ltd, Waterhouse, Greenfields Road, Horley, Surrey, RH6 8HW Tel: (01293) 424200 Fax: (01293) 424444 E-mail: sales@bioclean.co.uk *Industrial parts cleaning technologies services*

Bioclear Environmental Ltd, Unit 10, Carver Road, Astonfields Industrial Estate, Stafford, ST16 3HR Tel: (01785) 254410 Fax: (01785) 254553 E-mail: sales@bioclear.fsnet.co.uk *Effluent treatment plant manufrs*

Biocote Ltd, Technology Centre Glaisher Drive, Wolverhampton Science Park, Wolverhampton, WV10 9RU Tel: (01902) 824450 Fax: (01902) 824453 E-mail: info@biocote.com *Biotechnology services*

▶ Biocraft Ltd, 25b Chapel Hill, Tilehurst, Reading, RG31 5BT Tel: 0118-945 1144 E-mail: sales@biocraft.co.uk *Biocraft offers a comprehensive range of basement conversion, damp proofing and ventilation services throughout Berkshire, Oxfordshire, Surrey, Hampshire and London*

▶ The Bio-Energy Clinic, Maritime House, 14 - 16 Balls Road, Oxton, Birkenhead, Merseyside, CH43 5RE Tel: (07930) 933960 Fax: (0845) 8380793 E-mail: info@oxtonltd.com *We supply a variety of detox foot spa units starting from £ 349. We stock Platinum Detox, The Detox Box, PediTox, Bio-Detox and Detox Box Lite, Baby D units. Replacement arrays and adaptors also available suitable for a wide variety of units including Bio-Energiser, Total Style, O2, Scanda Sol and more. We supply units worlwide for clinic, business and home use - contact us to discuss your requirements.**Also stockists of Zetacap Stomach Blocker Tablets, Chi-Swing Machines, Ion Toothbrushes, Innerlight Supergreens, Bio-Patch Detox Foot Pads and portable steam saunas.**All stock available Worldwide.****We are a clinic ourselves operating in the Merseyside area, specialising in Bio-Energetic Medicine - Allergy Testing for foods, environmental and E-numbers (Bach Flowers also available), MORA Therapy, Allergy Desensitisation and Detox foot spa treatments.***

▶ BioExport Ltd, Parkside Court, Weybridge, Surrey, KT13 8AG Tel: (0796) 0555313 Fax: (0870) 7061864 E-mail: info@bioexport.co.uk *BioExport Ltd. specializes in the manufacture and acquisition of bacterial products to serve the environment. The company was established to develop and supply environmentally sound, microbiological products to resellers around the world at cost effective rates.*

Biogas Technology Ltd, Brookside Industrial Estate, Sawtry, Huntingdon, Cambridgeshire, PE28 5SB Tel: (01487) 831701 Fax: (01487) 830962 E-mail: info@biogas.co.uk *Biogas Technology Ltd brings together the resources and expertise of over 17 years experience as a leading Landfill Gas specialist to be able to deliver a one stop shop for all your landfill gas needs*

Biogen Idec, Thames House, Foundation Park, Maidenhead, Berkshire, SL6 3UD Tel: (01628) 823200 Fax: (01628) 501010 E-mail: ukrecpt@biogenidec.com *Pharmaceutical suppliers*

Biohit, Unit 1 Barton Hill Way, Torquay, TQ2 8JG Tel: (01803) 315900 Fax: (01803) 315530 *Biomedical product suppliers*

Biomerieux UK Ltd, Grafton Way, Basingstoke, Hampshire, RG22 6HY Tel: (01256) 461881 Fax: (01256) 816863 *Micro biological diagnostic equipment*

Biomet Merck Ltd, Waterton Industrial Estate, Waterton Industrial Estate, Bridgend, Mid Glamorgan, CF31 3XA Tel: (01656) 655221 Fax: (01656) 645454 *Orthopaedic implants instruments* Also at: Swindon

▶ Bio-Plus, PO Box 6726, Northampton, NN5 6WQ Tel: (01604) 751222 Fax: (01604) 592777 E-mail: sales@bio-plus.co.uk *Sewage treatment plant manufrs*

Bio-Productions, 72 Victoria Road, Burgess Hill, West Sussex, RH15 9LH Tel: (01444) 244000 Fax: (01444) 244999 E-mail: info@bio-productions.co.uk *Chemical blenders*

Bioquell UK Ltd, 52 Royce Close, West Portway, Andover, Hampshire, SP10 3TS Tel: (01264) 835835 Fax: (01264) 835836 E-mail: enquiries@bioquell.com Principal Export Areas: Worldwide *Clean air equipment*

Bio-Rad Laboratories Ltd, Bio-Rad House, Maylands Avenue, Hemel Hempstead, Hertfordshire, HP2 7TD Tel: (020) 8328 2000 Fax: (020) 8328 2500 E-mail: uk.lsg.marketing@bio-rad.com *Sales & service of diagnostic kits & systems*

▶ Bioresonance Therapy Centre, St. Justins Close, Orpington, Kent, BR5 3LU Tel: (01689) 834405 E-mail: bioresonancetherapycentre@yahoo.co.uk *Bioresonance Therapies - Specialising in Nicotine Addiction. OUr success rate for 1 45 minute Therapy session is 80%. Stop Smoking now, Based in Kent. Can visit clients at their own homes.*

Biorex Laboratories Ltd, 2 Crossfield Chambers, Gladbeck Way, Enfield, Middlesex, EN2 7HT Tel: (020) 8366 9301 Fax: (020) 8357 4627 E-mail: sales@biorex.co.uk *Pharmaceutical manufrs*

▶ Bioroute Ltd, Flint House, 25 Charing Cross, Norwich, NR2 4AX Tel: (01603) 724714 Fax: (01603) 724700 E-mail: biodiesel@bioroute.co.uk *Biodiesel suppliers in the UK and Europe*

Biosil Ltd, Tournament Way, Ashby-de-la-Zouch, Leicestershire, LE65 2UU Tel: (01530) 560204 Fax: (01530) 412715 E-mail: biosil@griffin.co.uk *Medical devices & plastics materials manufrs*

▶ Biosilico, 34, Maple Street, London, W1T 6HD Tel: (020) 7436 8554 Fax: (020) 7436 8476

▶ Bio-Synergy Licensing Ltd, 10a Nutford Place, London, W1H 5YL Tel: (020) 7569 2528 E-mail: lisa@bio-synergy.co.uk *Suppliers of health & sports nutrition*

Bio-Synergy Licensing Ltd, 10a Nutford Place, London, W1H 5YL Tel: (020) 7569 2528 Fax: (020) 7487 2581 E-mail: natalie@bio-synergy.co.uk *Health food product suppliers*

▶ Bioteknik Ltd, Unit 1, City Business Park Marshwood Close, Canterbury, Kent, CT1 1DX Tel: (01227) 470007 Fax: (01227) 470070 E-mail: enquiries@bioteknik.net *Computer recycling, sales & networking, web design*

Biotest (U.K.) Ltd, Unit 28 Monkspath Business Park, Highlands Road Shirley, Shirley, Solihull, West Midlands, B90 4NZ Tel: 0121-733 3393 Fax: 0121-733 3066 E-mail: sales@biotestuk.com *Diagnostic kits manufrs*

Biotige Ltd, Duffryn Business Park, Ystrad Mynach, Hengoed, Mid Glamorgan, CF82 7RJ Tel: (01443) 811811 Fax: (01443) 816552 E-mail: sales@jones-chrom.co.uk *Chromatography services*

Biozyme Holdings Ltd, Tnit 6 Gilchrist Thomas Estate, Bleanavon, Pontypool, Gwent, NP4 9RL Tel: (01495) 790678 Fax: (01495) 791780 E-mail: sales@biozyme.co.uk *Biochemical preparations manufrs*

▶ Bip Banners, Wesley Close, Crawley, West Sussex, RH11 6AE Tel: (01293) 562619 E-mail: bipbanners@btinternet.com *Low Cost Banner Design Service. Fast 48-72 Hours. Cheap from £9.50. No Advance Payment. Animated & Static Web Banners.*

Birch Bros Kidderminster Ltd, Barracks Road, Sandy Lane Industrial Estate, Stourport-On-Severn, Worcestershire, DY13 9QB Tel: (01299) 826227 Fax: (01299) 826229 E-mail: civils@birch-brothers.co.uk *Birch Brothers (Kidderminster) Ltd celebrates its 25th anniversary in 2007. We have always prided ourselves on providing high quality civil engineering services at a competitive rate. We specialise in services to the water and sewage industries including: Flood prevention, protection, alleviation and repairs, Pumping stations, Reservoir and dam refurbishment ? repair, Reed beds, River Works, High rise refuse chute, Sewerage and drainage, Sewage treatment works, Waterway and lake work. We also offer expertise and experience in general civil engineering, groundworks and retaining wall construction. A long-standing speciality is the replacement of refuse chutes in high rise developments. Our recent clients include: Environment Agency Midlands (Framework Contractors), Severn Trent Water Ltd, Defra, Borough and County Councils throughout the Midlands. Our accreditations include ISO 9001, ISO 14001, OHSAS 18001.*

Charles Birch Ltd, Holly House, 43 Cavendish Street, Leeds, LS3 1LY Tel: 0113-243 1155 Fax: 0113-242 3593 *Leather factors suppliers* Also at: Birmingham, Glasgow, Manchester & Southend

Charles Birch (Essex) Ltd, Units 7-8, Fleet Hall Road, Purdeys Industraal, Rochford, Essex, SS4 1NF Tel: (01702) 530656 Fax: (01702) 531417 E-mail: info@charlesbirch.com *Shoe repair service suppliers*

Birch Hotel, Lewes Road, Haywards Heath, West Sussex, RH17 7SF Tel: (01444) 451565 Fax: (01444) 440109 E-mail: sales@birchhotel.co.uk *Hotel with conference facilities*

▶ Birch House Construction Ltd, 31 Icen Road, Weymouth, Dorset, DT3 5JL Tel: (01305) 785787 Fax: (01305) 781117

Birch Sales & Marketing Ltd, 41 Green Lane, Burnham, Slough, SL1 8DZ Tel: (01628) 661475 Fax: (01628) 667999 E-mail: bob@birch-sales.co.uk *Air conditioning & equipment*

Birch Valley Plastics Ltd, Darklake View, Estover, Plymouth, PL6 7TL Tel: (01752) 696515 Fax: (01752) 696724 E-mail: admin@birchvalley.co.uk *BVP is a manufacturing company producing Heat Shrinkable Sleeving and PVC insulating tubing. Specializing in extruding flexible insulation sleeving and flexible and rigid profiles we also manufacture small bore EVA, Nylon, Polythene and Polypropylene. Other than tubing Birch Valley Plastics supplies spiral binding, neoprene sleeves, silicone sleeving, polyester expandable braided monofilament sleeving, PTFE, Motor Insulation products, Heat Resisting sleeving such as Vidaflex, specialty tapes, Paxolin sheets and Switchgear matting. Our Heat shrink sleeving range includes PVC heat shrink and Polyolefin heat shrink of all grades including adhesive lined products.*

W. Birch & Son (Polishers) Ltd, 42-50 Bissell Street, Birmingham, B5 7HP Tel: 0121-666 6164 Fax: 0121-622 1218 E-mail: sales@badgeranodising.co.uk *Anodises & metal polishers services*

William Birch & Sons Ltd, 1 Link Road Court, Osbaldwick, York, YO10 3JQ Tel: (01904) 411411 Fax: (01904) 428428 E-mail: info@williambirch.co.uk *Building contractors*

Birchall Engineering Ltd, Birchwood Park Old School, Cottingham Street, Goole, North Humberside, DN14 5RR Tel: (01405) 767930 Fax: (01405) 767876 *Engineering & steel fabricators*

Birchdale Associates, Unit A, Chiltern Trading Estate, Leighton Buzzard, Bedfordshire, LU7 4TU Tel: (01525) 852513 Fax: (01525) 850462 E-mail: sales@signtec.co.uk *Sign making component manufrs*

Michael Birchell Structural Engineers, 61 Cotton Road, Potters Bar, Hertfordshire, EN6 5JJ Tel: (01707) 657996 Fax: (01707) 657996 *Structural engineers*

▶ Birches Printers Ltd, 39-43 Temple Bar, Willenhall, West Midlands, WV13 1SH Tel: (01902) 605410 Fax: (01902) 637746

Birchfield Sheet Metal Sheet Metal, 15 Hadfield Industrial Estate, Waterside, Hadfield, Glossop, Derbyshire, SK13 1BS Tel: (01457) 865536 Fax: (01457) 865536 *Sheet metal fabricators*

Birchley Products, 7 Bush Hay, Church Down, Gloucester, GL3 2QR Tel: (01452) 855312 Fax: (01452) 859245 E-mail: ab@birchleyproducts.co.uk *Diving equipment manufrs*

Birchmoor Associates, 16 Norris Way Industrial Estate, Norris Way, Rushden, Northamptonshire, NN10 6BP Tel: (01933) 314499 Fax: (01933) 410495 E-mail: lionel@birchmoorassociates.co.uk *Shelving distributors*

Birchwood Marine Ltd, Fulwood Road North, Sutton-in-Ashfield, Nottinghamshire, NG17 2NB Tel: (01623) 515133 Fax: (01623) 440328 E-mail: info@birchwood.co.uk *Boat builders*

Bird Associates, 7 Larksfield, Englefield Green, Egham, Surrey, TW20 0RB Tel: (01784) 438963 Fax: (01784) 432319 *Structural engineers*

Bird & Davis Ltd, 45 Holmes Road, London, NW5 3AN Tel: (020) 7485 3797 Fax: (020) 7284 0509 E-mail: birdltd@aol.com *Artists material manufrs*

M.E.C. Bird Associates Ltd, Horsleys Green, High Wycombe, Buckinghamshire, HP14 3UX Tel: (01494) 482348 Fax: (01494) 483348 E-mail: mecbird@aol.com *Building services consulting engineers*

Bird & Moore Ltd, The Vicarage, Church Street, Uttoxeter, Staffordshire, ST14 8AA Tel: (01889) 565111 Fax: (01889) 565700 E-mail: birdandmoore@btinternet.com *Provides integrated communications to advertising, design & marketing services*

▶ Bird Solutions, 26 Sturt Close, Charlbury, Chipping Norton, Oxfordshire, OX7 3SS Tel: (01608) 819000 Fax: (01608) 819000 E-mail: birdsolutions@btconnect.com *Pest controllers*

Bird Stainless Ltd, Box Mill, Sheffield Road, Penistone, Sheffield, S36 6HQ Tel: (01226) 766766 Fax: (01226) 766841 E-mail: sales@birdstst.com *Stainless steel stockholders*

Bird Stevens & Co. Ltd, Sun Street, Brierley Hill, West Midlands, DY5 2JE Tel: (01384) 567381 Fax: (01384) 637357 E-mail: sales@birdstevens.co.uk *General presswork, galvanized hollow-ware manufrs*

▶ Bird-e Video, The Old Granary, Scotterthorpe, Gainsborough, Lincolnshire, DN21 3JL Tel: (01724) 761101 Fax: (01724) 761101 E-mail: steve.bird-e@virgin.net *Video and DVD production. Corporate, Marketing, Promotion, Training, Performance, Travel, Wedding.*

Birds Baskets, The Old School House, Butt Lane, Burgh Castle, Great Yarmouth, Norfolk, NR31 9QE Tel: (01493) 843392 Fax: (01493) 843392 E-mail: basketsbirds@aol.com Principal Export Areas: Central/East Europe & West Europe *Baskets & furniture manufrs*

Birds Groupage Services Ltd, Tat Bank Road, Oldbury, West Midlands, B69 4NQ Tel: 0121-543 6400 Fax: 0121-544 4928 E-mail: ken@birds.co.uk *Transport contractors*

Birdsall Services Ltd, 6 Frogmore Road, Apsley, Hemel Hempstead, Hertfordshire, HP3 9RW Tel: (01442) 212501 Fax: (01442) 248989 E-mail: lynne.culliton@birdsall.co.uk *Air conditioning engineers*

Birichen Beverage Equipment & Supplies, Tudor Stud Farm, Chinnor road, Bledlow Ridge, High Wycombe, Buckinghamshire, HP14 4AA Tel: 01494 481056 Fax: 01494 481056 E-mail: quintinjuckes@birichenbeverages.wanadoo.co.uk *suppliers of beverage and vending equipment.*suppliers of the finest ingredients.*on-site engineering and loan equipment facility*

Birkbys Plastics Ltd, Headlands Road, Liversedge, West Yorkshire, WF15 6QA Tel: (01924) 414200 Fax: (01924) 400051 E-mail: admin@birkbys.co.uk Principal Export Areas: Worldwide *Plastics moulding manufrs*

Birkdale Engineering Co., 56-62b Cemetery Road, Southport, Merseyside, PR8 5EF Tel: (01704) 538763 Fax: (01704) 544256 E-mail: birkdalejohn@aol.com *Precision engineers*

Birkdale Plastics Ltd, Unit 2-4 Fowler Industrial Estate, Chorley New Road, Horwich, Bolton, BL6 5LU Tel: (01204) 698715 Fax: (01204) 698716 E-mail: sales@birkdaleplastics.com *Specialists in rigid & plastic extruding*

Birkdale Sales, Granville House Lees Parade, Uxbridge Road, Uxbridge, Middlesex, UB10 0PQ Tel: (01895) 272112 *Fencing accessories manufrs*

Birkdale Trophies, 97 Old Watford Road, Bricket Wood, St. Albans, Hertfordshire, AL2 3UN Tel: (01923) 671225 Fax: (01923) 662522 E-mail: sales@birkdale-trophies.co.uk *Trophies, medals & rosettes manufrs*

Birkett Cutmaster Ltd, PO Box 30, Cleckheaton, West Yorkshire, BD19 5LY Tel: (01274) 870311 Fax: (01274) 862754 E-mail: bryn.pritchard@birkett-cutmaster.co.uk *Machine suppliers*

▶ Birkett Electric Ltd, Bridge House, Longwick Road, Princes Risborough, Buckinghamshire, HP27 9RS Tel: (01844) 274480 Fax: (01844) 274470 E-mail: info@birkett-electric.com *Cable jointing kits manufrs*

▶ Birkhull Engineering Ltd, Mangham Road, Parkgate, Rotherham, South Yorkshire, S62 6EF Tel: (01709) 524115 Fax: (01709) 710110

Birkin Cleaning Services Ltd, Unit 8 Little Mundells, Welwyn Garden City, Hertfordshire, AL7 1EW Tel: (01707) 322228 Fax: (01707) 387666 E-mail: sales@birkinclean.co.uk *Contract cleaners*

Guy Birkin & Co. Ltd, Bains Drive, Borrowash, Derby, DE72 3FS Tel: (01332) 680680 Fax: (01332) 680681 *Lace manufrs*

Birla Technologies Ltd, 5th Floor Congress House, 14 Lyon Road, Harrow, Middlesex, HA1 2FD Tel: (020) 8424 7320 Fax: (020) 8861 5062 E-mail: ketanm@birlatechnologies.com *IT services, out sourcing*

Birlasoft UK Ltd, Cromwell House, 142 High Street, Stevenage, Hertfordshire, SG1 3HN Tel: (01438) 350270 Fax: (01438) 749309 E-mail: corp@birlasoft.co.uk *Software developers*

▶ Birley Park Financial Advisers Ltd, 40 Chadderton Drive, Bury, Lancashire, BL9 8NL Tel: 0161 796 3383 E-mail: phillm36@aol.com *Independent financial advice including,life assurance, pensions, home insurance, investments,and mortgage consultants.* * * *

Birley Ventures Ltd, Mountfield Road, New Romney, Kent, TN28 8LH Tel: (01797) 361100 Fax: (01797) 367700 E-mail: birleyventures@aol.com *General engineers*

Birmingham Air Conditioning Ltd, Firswood Road, Birmingham, B33 0TG Tel: 0121-786 1842 Fax: 0121-786 2689 E-mail: bhamair@aol.com *Air handling units distributors*

Birmingham Alarm Technicians Ltd, 28-30 Hall Street, Birmingham, B18 6BS Tel: 0121-236 7828 Fax: 0121-236 6114 *Supply & instal security equipment*

The Birmingham Assay Office, P O Box 151, Birmingham, B3 1SB Tel: 0121-236 6951 Fax: (0121) 236 9032 *Assay/hallmarking metal testing services*

Birmingham Cash Registers Ltd, 135 Quinton Road West, Birmingham, B32 2RE Tel: 0121-565 3131 Fax: 0121-565 3213 E-mail: lesley@birminghamcash.co.uk *Distributors of cash registers*

Birmingham Catering Equipment Ltd, Unit 139a, Middlemore Road, Middlemore Industrial Estate, Birmingham, B21 0AY Tel: 0121-558 2451 Fax: 0121-558 2452 E-mail: enquiries@bceltd.com *Stainless steel fabricators*

Birmingham Chamber Training Ltd, 75 Harbourne Road, Edgbaston, Birmingham, B15 3DH Tel: 0121-454 1999 Fax: 0121-455 8700 E-mail: enquiries@birminghamchamber.org.uk Principal Export Areas: Worldwide *Chambers of commerce*

Birmingham City Laboratories, Phoenix House, Valepits Road, Garretts Green, Birmingham, B33 0TD Tel: 0121-303 9300 Fax: 0121-303 9301 E-mail: trevor_box@birmingham.gov.uk *Regulatory services*

Birmingham Export Billiards, 2 Red Rooster Industrial Estate, Tintagel Way, Aldridge, Walsall, WS9 8ER Tel: (01922) 455554 Fax: (01922) 455558 E-mail: sales@birminghambilliards.com *Billiard & pool table manufrs*

Birmingham Fan UK Ltd, Old Walsall Road, Hampstead Industrial Estate, Birmingham, B42 1EA Tel: 0121-357 2941 Fax: 0121-357 5805 E-mail: birmfansales@aol.com *Fan manufrs*

Birmingham Garage & Industrial Doors Ltd, Griffin Industrial Estate, Rowley Regis, West Midlands, B65 0SN Tel: 0121-559 8666 Fax: 0121-561 5373 E-mail: sales@bgid.net *Roller shutter manufrs*

Birmingham Glass Fibre Mouldings, 5 Weston Works, Weston Lane, Birmingham, B11 3RP Tel: 0121-708 1400 Fax: 0121-707 5312 E-mail: info@birminghamglassfibre.co.uk *Glass fibre mouldings manufrs*

Birmingham Glass Studios Ltd, Units 5 & 6 The Stained Glass Centre, 100-102 Edward Road, Balsall Heath, Birmingham, B12 9LS Tel: 0121-706 3131 Fax: 0121706 3130 E-mail: bhamglass@aol.com *Specialist leaded light makers with over 0 years experience in the trade between them & their skill & quality of work ensure that every contract is carried out to the highest standard.New projects can be designed, manufactured & installed by our own professional staff. We can provide toughened & laminated safety glass, armour plate assemblies, shop front glazing,new aluminium shop front frames,specialising in sand blasted glass, etched glass, glass balustrade & mirrors,can fit reflective/solar safety films to suit almost every requirement.emergency glazing & boarding service is utilised by many other country wide glass companies.We offer our own glass laminating service, & give free advice on the current safety glass regulations.*

Birmingham Gun Barrel Proof House, Banbury Street, Birmingham, B5 5RH Tel: 0121-643 3860 Fax: 0121-643 7872 E-mail: sales@gunproof.com *Testing & proving house*

Birmingham Machine Tool Services Ltd, 312-314 Bradford Street, Birmingham, B5 6ET Tel: 0121-622 6339 Fax: 0121-666 6406 E-mail: bhammctool@aol.com *Machine tool rebuilders*

Birmingham Mailing Cases Ltd, Machin Road, Birmingham, B23 6DR Tel: 0121-373 0401 Fax: 0121-377 7671 E-mail: birmingham.mailingcases@virgin.net *Manufacturers of cardboard tubes, cardboard cores & display tubes. We can produce a full range of tubes and cores that can be finished with a printed, coloured or textured paper. Any length of tube can be made up to 8 metres and we keep a number of tubes in stock. All tubes can be supplied with plastic end caps in a variety of colours and styles. Composite tubes can also be produced which include tubes with metal crimped ends, suitable for whisky bottles and diploma tubes.*

Birmingham Metal Co. Ltd, Garrison Street, Bordesley, Birmingham, B9 4BN Tel: 0121-766 6022 Fax: 0121-766 7485 *Precious metal alloy manufrs*

Birmingham Motor Tyre, 11 Washington Street, Birmingham, B1 1JS Tel: (0121) 643 7656 Fax: 0121-643 7606 E-mail: pat@bmtrgroup.com *Motor tyre factors exporters* Also at: Coleshill

Birmingham Packaging Co., 40 Rushey Lane, Tyseley, Birmingham, B11 2BL Tel: 0121-706 9171 Fax: 0121-708 2565 E-mail: sales@birminghampackaging.co.uk *Packaging material wholesalers*

Birmingham Partitioning Supplies Ltd, Unit 54 Rovex Business Park, Hay Hall Road, Birmingham, B11 2AQ Tel: 0121-706 0666 Fax: 0121-708 1355 E-mail: sales@bhampartitions.co.uk *Partition component distributor*

Birmingham Powder Coatings, Clonmel Road, Birmingham, B30 2BU Tel: 0121-459 4341 Fax: 0121-451 1735 E-mail: sales@b-p-c.co.uk *Powder coating services*

Birmingham Pump Supplies, 7 Network Park Industrial Estate, Duddeston Mill Road, Saltley, Birmingham, B8 1AU Tel: 0121-503 3000 Fax: 0121-503 3002 E-mail: sales@bhampumps.co.uk *Pump distributors*

Birmingham Rubber Stamp Co Ltd, 209 Streetly Road, Erdington, Birmingham, B23 7AH Tel: 0121-377 7757 Fax: 0121-377 7718 E-mail: sales@britishstamp.com *Rubber stamp manufrs*

▶ Birmingham Safety Deposit Ltd, Westbourne Manor, 17 Westbourne Road, Edgbaston, Birmingham, B15 3TR Tel: 0121-456 2627 Fax: 0121-454 4299 E-mail: info@swordsecurity.co.uk

Birmingham Safety Wear, Unit 14 Mount Street Business Centre, Mount Street, Nechells, Birmingham, B7 5RD Tel: 0121-327 0873 Fax: 0121-327 0873 E-mail: sales@birminghamsafetywear.co.uk *Workwear & safety wear manufrs*

Birmingham Saw Blades Ltd, 117 Station Road, Cradley Heath, West Midlands, B64 6PL Tel: 0121-559 5931 Fax: 0121-561 5121 E-mail: sales@dynashape.co.uk *Saw blades*

Birmingham Stone Cutting Co. Ltd, 59 Caroline Street, Birmingham, B3 1UF Tel: 0121-236 1418 Fax: 0121-248 1418 *Stone cutting & jewellery repairers*

Birmingham Stopper, 235 Icknield Street, Hockley, Birmingham, B18 6QU Tel: 0121-551 7781 Fax: 0121-554 4567 E-mail: robertp@birminghamstopper.co.uk *Presswork to 500 tonnes. Bed areas 3 meters by 1.2 meters. Coil feed equipment. CNC Turret Pressing & Fabrication. Profiling bending to 3 meters. CNC Machining. Surface Grinding/ Duplex to 1500mm diameter. Welding MIG, TIG, Projection. Quality currently registered to QS-9000.*

Birmingham Tile & Mosaic Co. Ltd, Ceramic House, 198 Kings Road, Tyseley, Birmingham, B11 2AP Tel: 0121-707 4505 Fax: 0121-707 5585 E-mail: mail@btandm.co.uk *Ceramic floor & wall tiling fixers*

Birmingham Time Recorder Services Ltd, Rumbow House, Rumbow, Halesowen, West Midlands, B63 3HU Tel: 0121-585 6660 Fax: 0121-585 6661 E-mail: info@ctrn.co.uk *Time recorder sales service rental*

Birmingham Tin Box Co., 82 Cliveland Street, Birmingham, B19 3SN Tel: 0121-359 7974 Fax: 0121-359 7975 E-mail: btb@regton.com *Tin Box Suppliers*

Birmingham Transformers Ltd, 6 Weston Works, Weston Lane, Birmingham, B11 3RP Tel: 0121-764 5600 Fax: 0121-764 5551 E-mail: sales@birminghamtransformers.co.uk *Electric transformers manufrs*

Birmingham Trophies & Awards, Unit 10 Summerhill Industrial Estate, 4 Goodman Street, Birmingham, B1 2SS Tel: 0121-236 1327 Fax: 0121-233 9021 *Sports trophy distributors*

Birmingham Woodcrafts, Units 9-10 All Saints Industrial Estate, Hockley, Birmingham, B18 7RJ Tel: 0121-523 8007 Fax: 0121-507 0685 *Wood turners & machinists*

Birmtool Engineering Ltd, 74 Warwick Street, Birmingham, B12 0NH Tel: 0121-772 3534 Fax: 0121-766 7548 *Toolmakers*

▶ Birns (Scotland) Ltd, Denmore Road, Bridge of Don, Aberdeen, AB23 8JW Tel: (01224) 706816 Fax: (01224) 707280

Birotech Food Machinery, 34 Beveridge Road, Kirkcaldy, Fife, KY1 1UY Tel: (01592) 260288 Fax: (01592) 644150 E-mail: biro.tech@virgin.net *Food machinery distributors*

Birse Construction Ltd, Humber Road, Barton-upon-Humber, South Humberside, DN18 5BW Tel: (01652) 633222 Fax: (01652) 633360 E-mail: birseho@birse.co.uk *Constructors manufrs*

▶ Birstall Secretarial, 94 Gelderd Road, Birstall, Batley, West Yorkshire, WF17 9LP Tel: (01924) 440291 Fax: (0870) 1334078 E-mail: sales@birstallsecretarial.co.uk *Secretarial services*

Simon Birtall, West Kirby, Wirral, Merseyside, CH48 2HL Tel: (0779) 0471098 E-mail: simon@birtall.co.uk *Art work & web design*

Birthstone Jewellery, 20 Ashley Gardens, Harpenden, Herts, AL5 3EY Tel: (01582) 766254 Fax: (02582) 712270 *Jewellery repairers & manufrs*

Birtley Building Products Ltd, Mary Avenue, Birtley, Chester le Street, County Durham, DH3 1JF Tel: 0191-492 1059 Fax: 0191-410 0650 E-mail: info@birtley-building.co.uk *Residential door galvanizes & steel lintel*

Birtley C B Services, 33 Penshaw View, Birtley, Chester le Street, County Durham, DH3 2JL Tel: 0191-492 0681 Fax: 0191-411 1341 E-mail: bev@phoenixcomms.freeserve.co.uk *Radio communications*

Birtley Construction North East, West Line Industrial Estate Station Lane, Birtley, Ouston, Chester le Street, County Durham, DH2 1ZZ Tel: 0191-410 2707 Fax: 0191-492 0583 *Structural steelwork engineers*

J.H. Birtwistle Ltd, Grane Road Mill, Grane Road, Haslingden, Rossendale, Lancashire, BB4 5ES Tel: (01706) 215351 Fax: (01706) 831054 E-mail: birtwhistle@johnlewis.co.uk *Acrylic yarn & cotton fabric manufrs*

BISC, 10 Park Lane, Reigate, Surrey, RH2 8JX Tel: (01737) 222119 Fax: (01737) 222119 E-mail: bs@bisconsultants.co.uk *Advice & support*

Bischof & Klein UK Ltd, Unit C Hortonwood 2, Telford, Shropshire, TF1 7XX Tel: (01952) 606848 Fax: (01952) 606698 E-mail: info@bk-packaging.co.uk Principal Export Areas: Worldwide *Flexible packaging manufrs*

Biscor Ltd, Kingsmark Freeway, Bradford, West Yorkshire, BD12 7HW Tel: (01274) 694684 Fax: (01274) 694685 E-mail: info@biscor.com *PTFE coated glass fabric & adhesive tapes*Silicone rubber coated fabric*Fabrication of conveyor belts*

Bruce Bishop & Sons Ltd, Lake Avenue, Slough, SL1 3BZ Tel: (01753) 525206 Fax: (01753) 532801 *Ferrous & non-ferrous scrap metal merchants*

Bishop Consultancy, 639 Galleywood Road, Chelmsford, CM2 8BT Tel: (01245) 346985 Fax: (01245) 490736 E-mail: enquiries@bishop-consultancy.com *Computer consultants*

▶ Bishop Developments, 176 York Way, London, N1 0AZ Tel: (020) 7713 0455 Fax: (020) 7278 1594

Bishop Pipefreezing Ltd, Pipefreezing House, 58A Shirley Road, Croydon, CR0 7EP Tel: (0800) 132750 Fax: (020) 8654 5459 E-mail: bishop@pipefreezingsales.co.uk *We offer the most comprehensive pipefreezing, hot tapping & line stopping services, from our regional offices in the UK. Also at:- ABERDEEN :- 01224 524060 GLASGOW:- 01412 486789 STOCKTON (Northern Head Office):- 01642 679200 MANCHESTER:- 01612 286464 BIRMINGHAM:- 01212 362288 SWANSEA:- 01792 468801 LONDON (UK Head Office):- 020 8656 8234 FRANCE - 00 33 442 65 96 41 IRELAND - WATERFORD 00 353 51 845490 FRANCE:- N0 114 - Z.I. Avon - 13120 Gardanne, France 33 (0)4 42 65 96 41*

Bishop & Smith Stainless Fabrication, Unit 2 Thorn Business Park, Rotherwas, Hereford, HR2 6JT Tel: (01432) 342355 Fax: (01432) 352399 E-mail: alan@bishop-smith.fsnet.co.uk *Stainless steel fabricators & sheet metalwork*

Bishop Sports & Leisure Ltd, Bishops House, Crown Lane, Farnham Royal, Slough, SL2 3SF Tel: (01753) 648666 Fax: (01753) 648989 E-mail: sales@bishopsport.co.uk *Sports & leisure equipment distributors.*

Syd Bishop & Sons (Demolitition) Ltd, Waldens Depot, Waldens Road, St. Mary Cray, Orpington, Kent, BR5 4EU Tel: (01689) 820315 Fax: (01689) 873784 E-mail: info@sydbishop.co.uk *Demolition contractors*

▶ Bishopcraft Ltd, 7 Otley Road, Shipley, West Yorkshire, BD17 7DY Tel: (01274) 599466

Bishops plc, Halden House, High Halden, Ashford, Kent, TN26 3BT Tel: (01233) 649000 Fax: (01233) 850052 E-mail: enquiry@bishopsltd.com *Insurance brokers* Also at: Coventry

Bishop's Blatchpack, Kestrel Way, Sowton Industrial Estate, Exeter, EX2 7PA Tel: (01392) 202040 Fax: (01392) 201251 E-mail: blatchpack@bishops-move.co.uk *Removal contractors*

Bishops Castle Meat Ltd, Love Lane Industrial Estate, Bishops Castle, Shropshire, SY9 5DW Tel: (01588) 638770 Fax: (01588) 638008 E-mail: bcmeats@btopenworld.com *Abattoir*

Bishop's Express, 8-9 Flexi Units, Budlake Road, Marsh Barton Trading Estate, Exeter, EX2 8PY Tel: (01392) 271237 Fax: (01392) 272171 *Catering equipment suppliers*

Bishop's Express, 8-9 Flexi Units, Budlake Road, Marsh Barton Trading Estate, Exeter, EX2 8PY Tel: (01392) 271237 Fax: (01392) 272171 *Catering equipment distributors*

Bishops Glass, 164-166 Main Road, Romford, RM2 5HT Tel: (01708) 744870 Fax: (01708) 733643 *Glazing contractors & glass merchants*

Bishops Move, 1-5 Kelvin Way, Crawley, West Sussex, RH10 9SP Tel: (01293) 512646 Fax: (01293) 550105 E-mail: crawley@bishopsmove.com *Removal contractors* Also at: Branches throughout the U.K.

▶ Bishops Move Ltd, Unit 12 Moor La Trading Estate, Sherburn in Elmet, Leeds, LS25 6ES Tel: (01977) 680061 Fax: (01977) 680063

▶ Bishops Move, Unit 11, South Hampshire Industrial Park, Totton, Southampton, SO40 3SA Tel: (023) 8023 7100 Fax: (023) 8086 7888 E-mail: southampton@bishopsmove.com

Bishop's Move, Bishops House, Lodge Road, Long Hanborough, Witney, Oxfordshire, OX29 8LQ Tel: (01993) 883377 Fax: (01993) 883646 E-mail: oxford@bishops-move.co.uk *Removal contractors* Also at: Branches throughout the U.K.

▶ Bishops Move Aberdeen, Howe Moss Terrace, Kirkhill Industrial Estate, Dyce, Aberdeen, AB21 0GR Tel: (0800) 1696126 Fax: (01224) 729722

▶ Bishops Move Birmingham, Unit 10 The I O Centre, Nash Road, Redditch, Worcestershire, B98 7AS Tel: (01527) 522925 Fax: (01527) 528252 E-mail: liverpool@bishopsmove.com

Bishops Move Chichester Ltd, 3 The Nelson Centre, Portfield Road, Portsmouth, PO3 5SF Tel: (023) 9266 9350 Fax: (023) 9266 9399 E-mail: portsmouth@bishopsmove.co.uk *Removal contractors services*

Bishops Move (Guildford) Ltd, Unit 3 Riverway Industrial Estate, Portsmouth Road, Peasmarsh, Guildford, Surrey, GU3 1LZ Tel: (01483) 722207 Fax: (01483) 302454 E-mail: gillford@bishopsmove.com *Removal contractors & warehousing* Also at: Branches throughout UK

Bishop's Move Industrial & Household, South Road, Brighton, BN1 6SB Tel: (01273) 557423 Fax: (01273) 501295 E-mail: brighton@bishops-move.co.uk *Removal contractors*

Bishops Move Maidstone, 14 Spa Industrial Park, Longfield Road, Tunbridge Wells, Kent, TN2 3EN Tel: (01892) 530191 Fax: (01892) 540201 E-mail: tunbridgewells@bishopsmove.com *Removal contractors* Also at: Branches throughout the U.K.

Bishop'S Move Overseas, Bishops House, 102-104 Stewarts Road, London, SW8 4UG Tel: (020) 8391 8222 Fax: (020) 7498 0749 E-mail: commercial@bishops-move.co.uk *Removal & storage contractors & shippers* Also at: Branches throughout the U.K.

Bishops Move Wokingham Ltd, Oaklands Business Centre, Oaklands Park, Wokingham, Berkshire, RG41 2FD Tel: (01276) 685515 Fax: 0118-977 3183 E-mail: wokingham@bishopsmove.co.uk *Removal contractors* Also at: Branches throughout the U.K.

Bishops Stortford Scaffolding Ltd, 64 Garnetts, Takeley, Bishop's Stortford, Hertfordshire, CM22 6RN Tel: (01279) 870680 Fax: (01279) 870680 E-mail: arthouseint@btconnect.com *Scaffolding contractors*

▶ Bishops Waltham Removals, 33 Claylands Road, Bishops Waltham, Bishops Waltham, Southampton, SO32 1BH Tel: (07802) 824547 Fax: (01489) 895387

Bishopsworth Group Ltd, Unit 14A Fiveways Industrial Estate, Westwells Road, Hawthorn, Corsham, Wiltshire, SN13 9RG Tel: (01225) 812177 Fax: (01225) 812188 E-mail: sales@keiron.demon.co.uk *Bishopsworth Group based in Corsham, Providing solutions for Industry, **Product design*Prototype and Production*Tool making*Moulding*Machining*Fabrication*Pcb, cba's *And turn key Electro-Mechanical assembly.*

Bishopton Joinery, Burton Farm, Bishopton, Stratford-upon-Avon, Warwickshire, CV37 0RW Tel: (01789) 298448 Fax: (01789) 298448 *Joinery*

Bi-Silque UK Ltd, 72c Noramn Way Industrial Estate, Longbridge Road, Preston, PR2 5BB Tel: (01772) 655353 Fax: (01772) 655525 *Office suppliers*

▶ The Bisky Batz, Wix's Lane, London, SW4 0AH Tel: (0870) 7659867 E-mail: sales@biskybatz.com *Imaginative music, arrangements and recordings for children - with their grown-ups in mind too.*Traditional and favourite songs rub shoulders with Edward Lear, Noel Coward and music hall to introduce the little ones to a wonderful fusion of styles that may be new to them.**The Bisky Batz support PACE - helping children with Autistic Spectrum Disorders.*

Bisley Computency, 1 The Cottages, Stroud Road, Bisley, Stroud, Gloucestershire, GL6 7BQ Tel: (01452) 770832 Fax: 08717 333315 E-mail: enquiries@bisleydesign.co.uk *No Fix - No Fee PC repairs & maintenance for the Stroud area of Gloucestershire. Website design & hosting country wide.*

Bisley Shooting Ground Ltd, Bisley Camp, Brookwood, Woking, Surrey, GU24 0NY Tel: (01483) 797017 Fax: (01483) 476953 E-mail: office@bisleyshooting.co.uk *Corporate entertainment agents*

Bison Bede Ltd, Unit 9 Number One Industrial Estate, Consett, County Durham, DH8 6ST Tel: (01207) 585000 Fax: (01207) 585085 E-mail: sales@bisonbede.co.uk *Stair lifts manufrs*

Bison Concrete Products Ltd, Millennium Court, First Avenue, Centrum One Hundred, Burton-On-Trent, Staffordshire, DE14 2WR Tel: (01283) 495000 Fax: (01283) 544900 E-mail: concrete@bison.co.uk *Pre-cast concrete products manufrs* Also at: Falkirk, Iver, Leeds & Lichfield

Bison Metalworking Machinery, Common Road, Stafford, ST16 3EQ Tel: (01785) 214242 Fax: (01785) 254232 *Buying & selling metalworking machinery*

▶ Bison Paper Ltd, Bison House, 6 Museum Street, Maidstone, Kent, ME14 1QD Tel: (01622) 677541 Fax: (01622) 687685 E-mail: mark@bisonprint.co.uk *Printing services*

Bison Supplies, 31 Garland Avenue, Belfast, BT8 6YH Tel: (028) 9040 2292 Fax: (028) 9040 2292 *Office equipment suppliers*

G.E. Bissell & Co. Ltd, Malt Mill Lane, Halesowen, West Midlands, B62 8JL Tel: 0121-559 2241 Fax: 0121-559 1168 E-mail: sales@bissell.co.uk Principal Export Areas: Worldwide *Manufacturers of spring pins & disc springs*

Bissell Homecare, The Boatyard, 105 Straight Road, Old Windsor, Windsor, Berkshire, SL4 2SE Tel: (0870) 2250109 Fax: (01753) 867684 *Carpet sweeper manufrs*

Bisset & Ross, Riverside Drive, Aberdeen, AB11 7SL Tel: (01224) 580659 Fax: (01224) 583295 *Tarpaulins maintenance & manufrs*

▶ Bissett & Taylor Ltd, Unit 29-31, Tyock Industrial Estate, Elgin, Morayshire, IV30 1XY Tel: (01343) 544055 Fax: (01343) 548422 *Retail office furniture, fax machines, office supplies*

Bistech plc, 137 Victoria Road, Ferndown, Dorset, BH22 9HX Tel: (01202) 863200 Fax: (01202) 896465 *Telecommunication system installation services*

▶ BitBolt Software Limited, 22b Petticoat Tower, Petticoat Square, London, E1 7EF Tel: 08704 860 498 Fax: 08704 860 497 E-mail: info@bitbolt.com *London based software development company, offering bespoke software development and consulting solutions.*

▶ Bitch Skateboards, 11 Flag Square, Shoreham-by-Sea, West Sussex, BN43 5RZ Tel: (07766) 001121 E-mail: bitchskates@yahoo.co.uk *Handcrafted, custom skateboard manufacturers*

Bitco Systems Ltd, 46 Bankfield Avenue, Stockport, Cheshire, SK4 2JH Tel: 0161-442 8178 Fax: 0161-442 8178 E-mail: mark@bitco.co.uk *Databases & websites*

▶ Bites to Banquets, 6 Park Avenue, Sleaford, Lincolnshire, NG34 7JQ Tel: 01529 410522 E-mail: bites@mprl.co.uk *Bites to Banquets provide a complete catering service tailored to the individual needs of the customers. Offering a full range of hot & cold buffets, for corporate or private needs. Licenced outside bars available. Boasting an impressive list of corporate clients, Bites to Banquets combines excellent service with reliability.*

▶ Bites UK Ltd, PO Box 2294, Woodford Green, Essex, IG8 0YF Tel: (0845) 2211000 Fax: (0870) 1350684 E-mail: sales@bites-uk.com *IT outsourcing, business systems support*

▶ Bitrex, 10 Wheatfield Road, Edinburgh, EH11 2QA Tel: 0131-337 2434 Fax: 0131-337 9813 *Chemicals manufrs*

BITS Ltd, 45 Manor Fields, Bratton, Westbury, Wiltshire, BA13 4ST Tel: (0845) 0940458 E-mail: info@bits-solutions.co.uk *Business information technology support services*

Bits N Bytes Computer Solutions Ltd, 22-24 Ravendale St North, Scunthorpe, South Humberside, DN15 6NJ Tel: (01724) 282627 Fax: (01724) 280605 E-mail: sales@bitsnbytes.co.uk *Computer services*

▶ Bits & P C's Bognor Regis, 92 Highfield Road, Bognor Regis, West Sussex, PO22 8PH Tel: (01243) 849001 Fax: (01243) 849001 E-mail: sales@computerandy.co.uk

▶ Bits & PC's, Unit 10 Cwmtillery Industrial Estate, Cwmtillery, Abertillery, Gwent, NP13 1LZ Tel: (01495) 321300 E-mail: bitznpcz@aol.com *Computer maintenance services*

▶ Bits & PC's, High Cross Street, St. Austell, Cornwall, PL25 4AB Tel: (01726) 76999 *Computer suppliers & maintenance services*

E.A. Bitterling Ltd, Poulton Drive, Daleside Road Industrial Estate, Nottingham, NG2 4BN Tel: 0115-986 2934 Fax: 0115-986 3027 E-mail: info@bitterling.co.uk *Machinery manufrs*

Bitton Precision Engineering Ltd, Unit 9f Aldermoor Way, Longwell Green, Bristol, BS30 7DA Tel: 0117-961 2128 Fax: 0117-947 6908 E-mail: john.coggins@bittonprecision.co.uk *Precision engineers*

Bituchem Group, Laymore Road, Forest Vale Industrial Estate, Cinderford, Gloucestershire, GL14 2YH Tel: (01594) 826768 Fax: (01594) 826948 E-mail: sales@bituchem.com *Bituminous materials manufrs*

Bitwise Ltd, Crescent House, Carnegie Campus, Dunfermline, Fife, KY11 8GR Tel: (01383) 625151 Fax: (01383) 625152 E-mail: admin@bitwise.co.uk *Software writing services*

Biwater International Ltd, Biwater House, Station App, Dorking, Surrey, RH4 1TZ Tel: (01306) 740740 Fax: (01306) 885233 E-mail: corporate.communications@biwater.com *Water filter manufrs*

▶ Biwater Leslie, PO Box 2, Glasgow, G78 1DU Tel: (01301) 703497

Biwater Treatment Ltd, The Compound White Horse Business Park, Ware Road, Stanford in the Vale, Faringdon, Oxfordshire, SN7 8NY Tel: (01367) 710088 Fax: (01367) 710266 *Water engineers*

Bizarre Balloons, Unit B 43 Foregate Street, Stafford, ST16 2PJ Tel: (01785) 256668 Fax: (01785) 605680 E-mail: sales@bizarreballoons.co.uk *Balloon suppliers*

▶ BizEquip Ltd, 6 Kingscroft Road, Hucclecote, Gloucester, GL3 3RF Tel: (01452) 618888 Fax: (01452) 542621 E-mail: sales@bize-mail.info *Cash register & EPOS system supply*

Bizerba UK Ltd, Eastman Way, Hemel Hempstead Industrial Estate, Hemel Hempstead, Hertfordshire, HP2 7DU Tel: (01442) 240751 Fax: (01442) 231328 E-mail: info@bizerba.co.uk *Labelling machine & weighing manufrs*

Bizley Cleaning Services Ltd, Unit 1, Kings Cliffe Industrial Estate, Kings Cliffe Road, Wansford, Peterborough, PE8 6PB Tel: (0870) 9033323 Fax: (0870) 9033324 E-mail: info@bizley.com *Industrial cleaning contractors*

Biznet Services, 63 Abingdon Villas, London, W8 6XA Tel: (020) 7565 0909 Fax: (020) 7565 0111 E-mail: translate@biznetserv.com *Translation services*

▶ Biztech Business Consultants, Field Farm, Ashton Road, Minety, Malmesbury, Wiltshire, SN16 9QP Tel: (01666) 862000 Fax: (01666) 860594

▶ Bizvizion Limited, Brighton Media Centre, 15-17 Middle Street, Brighton, BN1 1AL Tel: (01273) 275832 E-mail: info@bizvizion.co.uk *Bizvizion is a consultancy specialising in working within the creative industries, providing advice to public organisations, business support to small & medium sized creative companies; and desk space and incubation facilities.*

Bizzy Balloons, 4 Old Hall Drive, Dersingham, King's Lynn, Norfolk, PE31 6JT Tel: (01485) 541744 *Novelty balloon services*

▶ BJB Lift Trucks Ltd, Armstrong Street, Grimsby, South Humberside, DN31 1XD Tel: (01472) 230244 Fax: (01472) 230245

BJL Business Consultants, The Old Rectory, St Marys Lane, Claxby, Market Rasen, Lincolnshire, LN8 3YX Tel: (01673) 828345 Fax: (01673) 828345 *Computer consultants*

BJN Roofing Contractors Ltd, Gladstone House, Gladstone Road, Horsham, West Sussex, RH12 2NN Tel: (01403) 255155 Fax: (01403) 211794 *Roofing contractors*

▶ bjsedgwick.com, 23 Meadowbrook Close, Norwich, NR1 2HJ Tel: (01603) 618514 E-mail: barry@supasedg.freeserve.co.uk *Renewable energy consultant*

BK Safety, 20 Pembroke Rise, Cusworth, Doncaster, South Yorkshire, DN5 8PP Tel: (01302) 785063 Fax: (01302) 785063 E-mail: info@bksafety.co.uk *Safety and Environmental Consultants.*Suppliers of the "Sumo" fluorescent lighting tube disposal device.*

▶ BKB-Consultancy, Firtree Cottage, Oakenshaw, Crook, County Durham, DL15 0TH Tel: (01388) 745182 E-mail: bryan.burke@bkb-consultancy.co.uk *The key focus is on working with businesses to develop robust management systems,ISO9001:2000 implementation and auditing, to drive out costs, improve the customer experience, grow the customer base and profits. develop a culture of continual improvement.*

BKS Plastics Ltd, Unit 2 Station Road Industrial Estate, Great Harwood, Blackburn, BB6 7BB Tel: (01254) 889139 Fax: (01254) 889187 E-mail: bksplastics@btclick.com *Plastic components moulders*

▶ BKS Webdesign, 29 Allensbank Road, Cardiff, CF14 3PN Tel: (029) 2064 5761 Fax: (029) 2064 5729 E-mail: accounts@bkswebdesign.co.uk *BKS Webdesign is a Cardiff website design*

continued

company that specialises in building, rebuilding and advertising companies" web presence.

▶ BL1 : I.T. Specialists, 7 Trevarrick Court, Horwich, Bolton, BL6 6TF Tel: (07005) 968828 E-mail: bl1@hotmail.co.uk *We are an international UK based I.T. services company who offer computer sales, system repair and a whole consortium of related services including website design and hosting, internet access and more for businesses across the world! **See how we can help you today!*

▶ Blaby Alarms Ltd, 12 Waterloo Crescent, Wigston, Leicestershire, LE18 3QH Tel: 0116-288 3493 Fax: 0116-288 4138 E-mail: beba@btconnect.com *Electrical products suppliers & installers*

Blaby Electrical Ltd, 12 Waterloo Crescent, Wigston, Leicestershire, LE18 3QH Tel: 0116-288 3493 Fax: 0116-288 4138 E-mail: beba@btconnect.com *Alarms installation & electrical contracting services*

▶ black and white marketing, 5 Laundon Way, Whetstone, Leicester, LE8 6ZL Tel: 07092 003119 E-mail: andrew@blackwhite.uk.com *Professional marketing advice and consultancy from a B2B and Service Excellence.*

▶ Black Arrow Group P.L.C., 748 London Road, Hounslow, TW3 1PD Tel: (020) 8572 7474 *Office furniture manufrs*

Black Box A V Ltd, Unit 25, Aberafon Road, Baglan Industrial Park, Port Talbot, West Glamorgan, SA12 7DJ Tel: (01639) 767007 Fax: (01639) 767008 E-mail: sales@blackboxav.co.uk Principal Export Areas: Central/East Europe & West Europe *Audio visual equipment manufrs*

Black Box Computers, 2 Norfolk Street, Lancaster, LA1 2BW Tel: (01524) 389400 Fax: (01524) 62925 *Computer services*

Black Box Network Services Ltd, 464 Basingstoke Road, Reading, RG2 0BG Tel: 0118-965 5000 Fax: 0118-965 5001 E-mail: info@blackbox.co.uk *Data communication & transmission systems distributors*

Black Box Network Services (Nottingham) Ltd, 464 Basingstoke Road, Reading, RG2 0BG Tel: 0115-900 3333 Fax: 0115-900 3390 Principal Export Areas: Worldwide *Computer network engineers*

▶ Black Boy Inn, Northgate Street, Caernarfon, Gwynedd, LL55 1RW Tel: (01286) 673604 Fax: (01286) 674130 E-mail: black@welsh-historic-inns.com *Hotel & accommodation provider*

▶ Black Cat Cars Ltd, 312 Channelsea Business Centre, Canning Road, London, E15 3ND Tel: (020) 8555 4545 Fax: (020) 8519 2333 E-mail: office@BlackCatCouriers.co.uk *Motorbike & small van couriers*

Black Cat Fabrications Ltd, Unit 12, Marsland Street Industrial Centre, Hazel Grove, Stockport, Cheshire, SK7 4ER Tel: 0161-482 2272 Fax: 0161-482 2272 E-mail: blackcatfabs@hotmail.com *Light steel fabricators*

Black Country Chamber & Business Link, Dudley Court South The Waterfront, Level Street, Brierley Hill, West Midlands, DY5 1XN Tel: (0845) 1131234 Fax: (01384) 360560 E-mail: sales@blackcountrybusinesslink.com *Business information advisory services*

Black Country Chamber & Business Link, Dudley Court South The Waterfront, Level Street, Brierley Hill, West Midlands, DY5 1XN Tel: (0845) 1131234 Fax: (01384) 360560 E-mail: sales@blackcountrybusinesslink.com *Business information advisory services*

Black Country Narrow Boats, Waterside Cottage, Prestwood Drive, Stourbridge, West Midlands, DY7 5QT Tel: (01384) 872135 Fax: (01384) 878968 *Boat builders & repairers*

▶ Black Country Pressings Ltd, 2 Alma Works, Darlaston Road, Wednesbury, West Midlands, WS10 7TG Tel: 0121-568 8787 Fax: 0121-568 8788

Black Country Rag & Wiper Co. Ltd, Greets Green Road Industrial Estate, Greets Green Road, West Bromwich, West Midlands, B70 9EW Tel: 0121-520 7586 Fax: 0121-522 3340 E-mail: mail@bcrglobaltextiles.co.uk *Secondhand clothing wholesale dealers*

▶ Black Country Saddles, 59-61 Wednesbury Road, Walsall, WS1 4JL Tel: (01922) 626936 Fax: (01922) 636022 E-mail: sales@blackcountrysaddles.com *Saddle manufrs*

Black & Decker Ltd, 210 Bath Road, Slough, SL1 3YD Tel: (01753) 511234 Fax: (01753) 551155 E-mail: info@blackdecker.co.uk *Tool manufrs*

Black & Decker, Unit 25 Clarks Village, Farm Road, Street, Somerset, BA16 0BB Tel: (01458) 840205 Fax: (01458) 840206 *Power tools suppliers & manufrs*

▶ Black Diamond Ltd, Units 2-7 Guardian St Industrial Estate, Guardian Street, Warrington, WA5 1SJ Tel: (01925) 416619 Fax: (01925) 230472 *Service centre & remanufacture of differentials gear boxes & axels*

Black Gold Oil Tools Ltd, Souter Head Road, Altens Industrial Estate, Aberdeen, AB12 3LF Tel: (01224) 894019 Fax: (01224) 879731 E-mail: info@blackgoldoiltools.co.uk *Oilfield equipment manufrs*

Black Gold Oil Tools Ltd, Steven Road, Huntly, Aberdeenshire, AB54 8SX Tel: (01466) 793457 Fax: (01466) 793095 *Oil field equipment*

▶ Black Lion, Unit 14 Mayfield Avenue Industrial Park, Fyfield Road, Weyhill, Andover, Hampshire, SP11 8HU Tel: (01264) 771199 Fax: (01264) 773993

▶ Black Market Tools, Unit 19 Faraday Mill Business Park, Faraday Road, Plymouth, PL4 0ST Tel: (01752) 205905 Fax: (01752) 302232 E-mail: sales@blackmarket-tools.co.uk *Power tool & fastener distributors*

Black Millwork Co Incorporated, Anderson House, Dallow St, Burton-on-Trent, Staffordshire, DE14 2PQ Tel: (01283) 511122 Fax: (01283) 510863 E-mail: enquiries@andersenwindows.com *Windows & patio door distributors*

Penni Black Ltd, 14 Lyminge Gardens, Wandsworth, London, SW18 3JS Tel: (0800) 3896107 Fax: (020) 8870 9422 E-mail: charlotte@penniblack.co.uk *Penni Black is a catering company based in Wandsworth, London. we use our 15 years of experience in the catering industry to create delicious food specifically tailored to meet our customers? individual requirements.*

▶ Black Seal UK, Smallfield Road, Horne, Horley, Surrey, RH6 9JP Tel: (07932) 782435 E-mail: bermuda@blackseal.co.uk *Resellers and distributors of Black Seal Rum*

▶ Black Sun plc, Fulham Palace, Fulham, London, SW6 6EA Tel: (020) 7736 0011 Fax: (020) 7736 1294 E-mail: jobs@blacksunplc.com *We are the customer management arm of Black Sun Plc, the strategic, marketing and communications agency. **Our mission is to help our clients build more rewarding relationships with their customers by securing their loyalty and maximising their value. **We achieve this by harnessing client data to generate powerful customer insights. We use this insight to create the right customer management strategy, and to build compelling loyalty propositions that retain and grow your customer base. We communicate these propositions through data-driven mixed media solutions that engage the target audience and deliver powerful business results. ***Our work is underpinned by a commitment to thought leadership, creative excellence and superior client service. As testament to our success, we have worked extensively with some of the UK"s largest organisations such as Barclay's Capital, British Airways, Eurostar, Friends Provident, Legal & General, Pfizer Nicorette, Sainsbury"s and WWF.**

Black Swan Printers, Unit 7 Shutterton Industrial Estate, Dawlish, Devon, EX7 0NH Tel: (01626) 865463 Fax: (01626) 888224 E-mail: sales@blackswanprinting.co.uk *Printing company & design works*

Black Swan Restoration Ltd, 27 Gloucester Street, Coventry, CV1 3BZ Tel: (024) 7625 6061 Fax: (024) 7625 6061 *Boat builders & restorers*

▶ Black Van Removals, Unit 5a-5b Ribbleton La Trading Estate, Crook Street, Preston, PR1 5LS Tel: (01772) 794160 Fax: (01772) 702540

Black & Veatch, Grove House, 100 High Street, Hampton, Middlesex, TW12 2ST Tel: (020) 8783 1055 Fax: (020) 8979 5397 *Consulting engineers*

Black & Veatch Ltd, Stirling House, Danebury Court Old Sarum Park, Old Sarum, Salisbury, SP4 6EB Tel: (01722) 413339 Fax: (01722) 413306 *Effluent treatment plant designers & contractors*

Black & Veatch Group Ltd, Grosvenor House 69 London Road, Redhill, RH1 1LQ Tel: (01737) 789918 Fax: (01737) 772767 E-mail: bvcs@bv.com *A multi-disciplinary engineering consultancy, specialising in water supply; wastewater collection & disposal; environmental management; infrastructure technology; and information solutions. We also have specialist applications in geotechnical engineering, structural engineering and safety & risk management.*

Black & White Consumables Ltd, 22 St.Johns North, Wakefield, West Yorkshire, WF1 3QA Tel: (01924) 210236 Fax: (01924) 782037 E-mail: info@bwconsumables.co.uk *Computer consumables, stationery, hardware & software*

Black & White Systems, 11 Castle Mews, London, N12 9EH Tel: (020) 8446 9999 Fax: (020) 8446 8426 E-mail: blackandwhite@london.com *Photocopiers services & suppliers*

Black & White Telephone Co., John Street, Royston, Hertfordshire, SG8 9BE Tel: (01763) 248216 Fax: (01763) 249475 *Telecommunication installers & retailer*

▶ Blacka Acoustics, Storage World, Reddish Road, Stockport, Cheshire, SK5 7BW Tel: 0161-477 9700 Fax: 0161-477 9300 E-mail: sales@blackaacoustics.co.uk *Blacka Acoustics is a Manchester based PA hire and sound system services company, providing hire, manufacturing, installation and system support services throughout the UK.*

Blackberry Forge, Bar Forge, Barcelona, Looe, Cornwall, PL13 2JU Tel: (01503) 272886 *Blacksmiths*

▶ Blackboard Associates, 5 Barton Villas, Dawlish, Devon, EX7 9QJ Tel: (01626) 863888 Fax: (0709) 219048 E-mail: info@blackboard-associates.com *Computer consumables specialists*

Blackbourn Geological Services, Carriden House, Bo'Ness, West Lothian, EH51 9SN Tel: (01506) 826777 Fax: (01506) 826888 E-mail: carriden_house@compuserve.com *Rock analysis & geological consulting services*

Blackbourne Electrical Co. Ltd, Springfarm Industrial Estate, Antrim, BT41 4NZ Tel: (028) 9446 4231 Fax: (028) 9446 7109 E-mail: bec@karl.co.uk *Power line manufrs*

Blackburn Bailey Ltd, Wantz Road, Dagenham, Essex, RM10 8PS Tel: (020) 8593 7346 Fax: (020) 8984 0813 E-mail: info@blackburngroup.co.uk *Steel fabricators & balustrade manufrs*

Blackburn Chemicals Ltd, Cunliffe Road, Whitebirk Industrial Estate, Blackburn, BB1 5SX Tel: (01254) 52222 Fax: (01254) 664224 E-mail: info@bbchem.co.uk *Anti-foam specialists*

Blackburn Circuit Design Ltd, Cunliffe Road, Whitebirk Industrial Estate, Blackburn, BB1 5UA Tel: (01254) 680819 Fax: (01254) 682395 E-mail: peter@bc-design.co.uk *PCB assembly design & assembly*

Blackburn Clothing Co., Unit 1, Willow Street, Blackburn, BB1 5NQ Tel: (01254) 264762 Fax: (01254) 279464 *Jeans manufrs*

▶ Blackburn Conveyor, Delph Road, Great Harwood, Blackburn, BB6 7HT Tel: (01254) 888866 Fax: (01254) 829826 *Conveyor systems manufrs*

Blackburn Conveyor, Delph Road, Great Harwood, Blackburn, BB6 7HT Tel: (01254) 888866 Fax: (01254) 829826 *Conveyors & conveyor belting*

▶ Blackburn Heavy Engineering Ltd, Spring Bank Works, Albert Street, Blackburn, BB2 4BL Tel: (01254) 677817 Fax: (01254) 673260 E-mail: info@millhillpaper.com *Metal work services*

▶ Blackburn Marshall Construction Ltd, Wooler Street, Darlington, County Durham, DL1 1RQ Tel: (01325) 352109 Fax: (01325) 488146

Blackburn Products Co. Ltd, Whalley Banks, King Street, Blackburn, BB2 1NU Tel: (01254) 51655 Fax: (01254) 51740 *Animal waste recycling*

Blackburn Starling & Co. Ltd, Queens Drive, Nottingham, NG2 3AY Tel: 0115-986 6331 Fax: 0115-986 0301 E-mail: sales@blackburn-starling.co.uk *Electrical control engineers*

▶ Blackburn Trailers Ltd, Whitestone Farm, Main Road, Birdham, Chichester, West Sussex, PO20 7HU Tel: (01243) 513550 Fax: (01243) 513865 E-mail: info@kompak.co.uk *Exhibition & catering trailer manufacturer*

Blackburn With Darwen Borough Council, Town Hall, King William St, Blackburn, BB1 7DY Tel: (01254) 585585 E-mail: regeneration@blackburn.gov.uk *Business advice & financial assistance service*

Blackburn Yarn Dyers Ltd, Grimshaw Park Dye Works, Haslingden Road, Blackburn, BB2 3HN Tel: (01254) 53051 Fax: (01254) 672233 E-mail: info@bydltd.co.uk *Dyers to textile trade (yarn dyers)*

Blackburns, Fircroft Way, Edenbridge, Kent, TN8 6ES Tel: (01732) 582700 Fax: (01732) 582799 E-mail: edenbridge@blackburnsmetals.com *Aluminium & stainless steel stockholders*

Blackburns Of Bolton, Unit H, Lecturers Close, Bolton, BL3 6DG Tel: (01204) 532121 Fax: (01204) 396670 E-mail: sales@blackburns.co.uk *Commercial form management & digital printers*

▶ Blackburns Harleston Ltd, 37 Station Road, Harleston, Norfolk, IP20 9EW Tel: (01379) 852131 Fax: (01379) 853363 E-mail: mail@blackburns-harleston.co.uk

▶ Blackburns Metal Centres, Units 3-4, Haydock Lane, Haydock Industrial Estate, Haydock, St. Helens, Merseyside, WA11 9UY Tel: 0161-254 8800 Fax: (01942) 758899 E-mail: haydock@blackburnsmetalcentre.com *Aluminium & stainless steel stockholders*

Blackburns Metals Ltd, 4 Wellington Road, Leeds, LS3 1LE Tel: 0113-296 1500 Fax: 0113-296 1599 E-mail: leeds@blackburnsmetals.com *Aluminium & stainless steel stockholders*

▶ Blackdog Services Ltd, 22 Harefield Avenue, Bedford, MK42 9RL Tel: (01234) 294230 Fax: (01234) 295876 E-mail: enquiries@blackdogservices.co.uk *Web designers & hosting services*

Blackdown Plant Ltd, The Cross, 2 Midhurst Road, Haslemere, Surrey, GU27 3EE Tel: (01428) 643309 Fax: (01428) 661630 E-mail: sales@blackdownpress.co.uk *Self-adhesive label printers*

▶ Blackfin Translation, Lynnwood Business Ce, 116 Kayside, Rotterdam House, Newcastle Upon Tyne, NE1 3DI Tel: 0191-206 4071 Fax: 0191-206 4001 E-mail: info@blackfin-translation.com *Translation & interpreting services*

Blackfive Engineering Ltd, 16 Beeston Court, Stuart Road, Manor Park, Runcorn, Cheshire, WA7 1SS Tel: (01928) 579140 Fax: (01928) 579514 E-mail: blackfive@btconnect.com *Sample valves & precision engineers*

Blackford Fencing Contractors, 92 Blackford Road, Shirley, Solihull, West Midlands, B90 4BX Tel: 0121-745 6691 Fax: 0121-745 6691 *Fencing contractors*

Blackfriars Ltd, Roman Way, Market Harborough, Leicestershire, LE16 7PQ Tel: (01858) 462249 Fax: (01858) 464755 E-mail: sales@blackfriars.com *Reclamation machinery manufrs*

Blackfriars Bakery, 185 Gloucester Crescent, Wigston, Leicestershire, LE18 4YH Tel: 0116-278 6029 Fax: 0116-278 5348 E-mail: bfriars@blackfriarsbakery.co.uk *Food manufrs*

Blackfriars Scenery Ltd, Blackfriars Studio, 33 Bear Lane, London, SE1 0UH Tel: (020) 7928 6413 Fax: (020) 7261 1994 E-mail: staging@compuserve.com *Scenery builders & stage lighting*

▶ Blackhammer Ltd, 30 Theydon Road, London, E5 9NA Tel: (020) 8442 4040 Fax: (020) 8806 7040 E-mail: mark@blackhammer.net *Commercial print*

Blackheath Car Service, 2a Blackheath Village, London, SE3 9LA Tel: (020) 8318 5432 Fax: (020) 8297 0734 E-mail: sales@blackheath-car-services.co.uk *Courier services & mini cabs*

▶ Blackheath Mini-Cabs, 75-77 Lee High Road, London, SE13 5NS Tel: (020) 8297 1234 Fax: (020) 8297 4044 E-mail: info@blackheathcabs.com *CABS, TAXIS, TAKING YOU FROM AND TO LONDON AIRPORTS, TO SOUTH EAST LONDON, SE3, SE6, SE7, SE, SE12, SE*

Blackheath Products Ltd, Fairfield Park, Halesowen, West Midlands, B62 9JL Tel: 0121-561 4245 Fax: 0121-561 5904 E-mail: sales@blackheathproducts.co.uk *Formica laminate/kitchen furniture distribs*

Blackheath Tube Co Ltd, Castle Mill Works, Birmingham New Road, Dudley, West Midlands, DY1 4DA Tel: (01384) 255300 Fax: (01384) 255400 E-mail: sales@blackheathtube.co.uk *Non ferrous tube manufacturer. Ideally located in the West Midlands, We are a major UK supplier of copper based alloy tubes to the heat exchanger, engineering, electrical, lighting and water industry market. We are a supplier of quality tube to a variety of specifications and specialise in medium to large quantities at extremely competitive prices. Call us today to discuss your requirements. Please tell us you found our information on Kellysearch.*

▶ Blackhill Engineering Services Ltd, Blackhill Quarry, Woodbury, Exeter, EX5 1JL Tel: (01395) 232701 Fax: (01395) 232571 *Engineering*

Company Information

Blacklake Systems Ltd, Unit 6a Whitebridge Estate, Stone, Staffordshire, ST15 8LQ Tel: (01785) 817170 Fax: (01785) 812406 E-mail: charles@whitebridge.co.uk Principal Export Areas: Worldwide *Milling*

Blacklands Fire, Britannia Enterprise Centre, Waterworks Road, Hastings, East Sussex, TN34 1RT Tel: (01424) 722200 Fax: (01424) 722200 *Fire protection services*

Chris Blackler Farm Buildings, Oaklands, Loddiswell, Kingsbridge, Devon, TQ7 4EA Tel: (01548) 821489 Fax: (01548) 821489 *Farm building erection & manufrs*

Blackmore Ltd, Longmead, Shaftesbury, Dorset, SP7 8PX Tel: (01747) 853034 Fax: (01747) 854500 E-mail: sales@.blackmore.co.uk *Quality print agents*

Blackmore Commercials, Little Tennis Street, Nottingham, NG2 4EL Tel: 0115-958 6696 Fax: 0115-979 9698 *Commercial vehicle repairers*

▶ Blackmore Heath Ltd, Luffield House Eurolink Industrial Centre, Stadium Way, Sittingbourne, Kent, ME10 3SD Tel: (01795) 470471 Fax: (01795) 470475 E-mail: steve@bhl-insurance.co.uk *Insurance Brokers*

▶ Blackmore Hurrell, Rear of, 103 Wolseley Road, Plymouth, PL2 3BL Tel: (01752) 567056 *Servicing vehicles*

Blacknor Technology Ltd, 1d South Way, Southwell Business Park, Portland, Dorset, DT5 2NJ Tel: (01305) 860922 Fax: (01305) 860912 E-mail: enquiries@blacknor.com Principal Export Areas: Worldwide *Marine electronic equipment distributors, ship security systems*

Blackpool DIY & Door Centre Ltd, 43b Caunce Street, Blackpool, FY1 3ND Tel: (01253) 622176 *Timber & door manufrs*

Blackpool & The Fylde College Fleetwood Office Shore Survival Cen, Fleetwood Road, Nautical Campus, Fleetwood, Lancashire, FY7 8JZ Tel: (01253) 779123 Fax: (01253) 773014 E-mail: jbo@blackpool.ac.uk *Offshore oil, gas emergency training short course services*

Blackpool Laundry Co. Ltd, Unit 6e Moor Park Industrial Estate, Kincraig Road, Blackpool, FY2 0JY Tel: (01253) 500014 Fax: (01253) 500014 E-mail: sales@blackpoollaundry.com *Linen hire & hospital laundry services*

Blackpool Snooker Co., 245 Dickson Road, Blackpool, FY1 2JH Tel: (01253) 299710 Fax: (01253) 299710 *Snooker table repairs & sales*

▶ Blackpool Trim Shops Ltd, 9-15 Brun Grove, Blackpool, FY1 6PG Tel: (01253) 766762 Fax: (01253) 798443

▶ Blackpool Utilities Independent Energy, 94 Newcastle Avenue, Blackpool, FY3 9DH Tel: (01253) 390441 Fax: (01253) 393548 E-mail: sales@blackpool-utilities.co.uk *Utilities procurement*

Blackroc Systems Ltd, Drummond Road, Astonfields Industrial Estate, Stafford, ST16 3HJ Tel: (01785) 213777 Fax: (01785) 251546 E-mail: sales@blackroc.com *System distributors of automatic Identification products*

▶ Blackrock Computers, 85 Church Road, Caldicot, Gwent, NP26 4HT Tel: (07906) 329794 *Computer maintenance & repair services*

▶ Blackrow Engineering Co. Ltd, 7 Estate Road, South Humberside Industrial Estate, Grimsby, South Humberside, DN31 2TP Tel: (01472) 889200 Fax: (01472) 889201 E-mail: sales@blackrow.co.uk

Blacks Ltd, 38-39 Long Causeway, Peterborough, PE1 1YJ Tel: (01733) 340674 Fax: (01733) 347683 *Outdoor & camping accessories suppliers*

Blacks Equipment Ltd, Barton La, Armthorpe, Doncaster, S. Yorkshire, DN3 3AA Tel: (01302) 834444 Fax: (01302) 831834 E-mail: sales@blacksequipment.com Principal Export Areas: Worldwide *Friction welding equipment & services. In addition, charpy preparation equipment & materials & engineering industry test equipment*

Blacks Leisure Group plc, 74 Bull Street, Birmingham, B4 6AD Tel: 0121-233 1678 Fax: 0121-236 8209 *Camping equipment distributor*

Blacks Leisure Group plc, Unit 11 254-284 Sauchiehall Street, Glasgow, G2 3EQ Tel: 0141-353 2344 Fax: 0141-331 0614 *Outdoor equipment retailers*

Blacks Leisure Group plc, 10 Phoenix Court, Guildford, Surrey, GU1 3EG Tel: (01483) 506432 *Outdoor camping suppliers service*

Blacks Leisure Group plc, Shopping Centre, Brent Cross, London, NW4 3FP Tel: (020) 8203 9895 *Outdoor equipment*

Blacks Leisure Group plc, 8 The Arcadia Centre, The Broadway, London, W5 2ND Tel: (020) 8840 1514 *Camping equipment supply & manufrs*

Blacks Leisure Group plc, 8-10 Old Hall Street, Stoke-on-Trent, ST1 1QT Tel: (01782) 212870 *Outdoor leisure equipment suppliers*

Blacks Outdoor Group, 61b Friargate Walk, St. Georges Shopping Centre, Preston, PR1 2NQ Tel: (01772) 252669 *Outdoor equipment retailer*

▶ Blacks Shrewsbury, 27-28 Shoplatch, Shrewsbury, SY1 1HS Tel: (01743) 368272 *Outdoor clothing retailers*

Blackshaw Sykes & Morris Ltd, PO Box 18, Bolton, BL3 6NH Tel: (01204) 521438 Fax: (01204) 364819 *Printers*

▶ Blacksmith Collection Ltd, West Park, Kings Nympton, Umberleigh, Devon, EX37 9TN Tel: (01769) 580004 Fax: (01769) 581125 E-mail: info@blacksmithcollection.com *Hand forged curtain poles in black & stainless steel manufrs*

▶ Blackstaff It, 1 Mill Court, 500-502 Falls Road, Belfast, BT12 6EP Tel: (028) 9062 9991

Blackstone Developments South West Ltd, 8 Kingswood Trading Estate, Southey Avenue, Bristol, BS15 1QX Tel: 0117-961 1122 Fax: 0117-961 1122 *Joinery manufrs*

▶ Black-Thong Limited, 23 Danestone Close, Middleleaze, Swindon, SN5 5GP Tel: 07977 717893 E-mail: enquiries@black-thong.com *Mail Order Lingerie*

▶ Blackthorn Enviromental Ltd, Forum House, Stirling Road, Chichester, West Sussex, PO19 7DN Tel: (0870) 0101800 Fax: (0870) 0101811 E-mail: contact@blackthorn.eu.com *Emission control specialists*

▶ Blacktoe Ltd, 53 The Slough, Redditch, Worcestershire, B97 5JR Tel: (01527) 458954 *Blacktoe offer a comprehensive range of outdoor camping and hiking equipment.* Our range offers some of the best equipment available at an affordable price without loosing quality or technical specification; we want a product that will do the job.*

Blackwater Manufacturing Ltd, 2 Faraday Road, Glenrothes, Fife, KY6 2RU Tel: (01592) 774637 Fax: (01592) 775160 E-mail: sales@blackwatermfg.co.uk *Tube & pipe fittings manufrs*

Blackwater Photographic Co., 69 Fleet Road, Fleet, Hampshire, GU51 3PJ Tel: (01252) 613243 Fax: (01252) 811223 E-mail: keithe@patrol.i-way.co.uk *Photographers printed circuit photomechanical services*

C.A. Blackwell (Contracts) Ltd, Coggeshall Road, Earls Colne, Colchester, CO6 2JX Tel: (01787) 223131 Fax: (01787) 224391 E-mail: enquires@cablackwell.co.uk *Civil engineers & earth moving services* Also at: Swansea

Blackwell Hydraulics Ltd, Unit 13 Industrial Estate, Llandudno Junction, Gwynedd, LL31 9SX Tel: (01492) 583821 Fax: (01492) 593591 E-mail: sales@blackwellhydrolics.co.uk *Hydraulic hose distributors*

Blackwell Stanistreet, 64 Talbot Road, Old Trafford, Manchester, M16 0PP Tel: 0161-872 2821 Fax: 0161-848 7427 *Industrial roofers & cladders*

Blackwell UK Ltd, Beaver House, Hythe Bridge Street, Oxford, OX1 2ET Tel: (01865) 792792 Fax: (01865) 791438 E-mail: enquries@blackwell.co.uk *Books sellers*

▶ Blackwells Stone Craft, Overleigh Road, Chester, CH4 7HW Tel: (01244) 680704 Fax: (01244) 671772

Blackwood Communications, 2a New Road, Mytholmroyd, Hebden Bridge, West Yorkshire, HX7 5DZ Tel: (01422) 883688 Fax: (01422) 881376 E-mail: info@blackwood-pr.co.uk *PR & marketing services consultancy*

Blackwood Discount Jewellers, 168 High Street, Blackwood, Gwent, NP12 1AH Tel: (01495) 222709 *Jewellery repairers*

Blackwood Engineering Ltd, Glandwr Industrial Estate, Aberbeeg, Abertillery, Gwent, NP13 2LN Tel: (01495) 214331 Fax: (01495) 217309 *Grey iron castings*

Blackwood S Consultants Ltd, 15 Glengarry Crescent, Falkirk, FK1 5UD Tel: (01324) 630043 *Computer consultants*

Blade & Cutter Ltd, Unit 5 Hattersley Industrial Estate, Stockport Road, Hyde, Cheshire, SK14 3QT Tel: 0161-367 8240 Fax: 0161-367 8785 *Blade & cutter grinding services*

Blade Interactive Studios, Suite A, Great Northern Warehouse, Deansgete Mews, Manchester, M3 4EN Tel: 0161-839 6622 Fax: 0161-839 6688 E-mail: info@bladeinteractive.com *Computer games developers*

Blade Rubber Stamps Ltd, 12 Bury Place, London, WC1A 2JL Tel: (020) 7831 4123 Fax: (020) 7831 4242 E-mail: sales@bladerubber.co.uk *Rubber stamps made to order from customer designs*

▶ Bladonmore Ltd, 10-11 Percy Street, London, W1T 1DA Tel: (020) 7631 1155 Fax: (020) 7631 1444 E-mail: info@bladonmore.com *Contract publishing*

Blaenau Plastics Ltd, Tanygrisiau Trading Estate, Tanygrisiau, Blaenau Ffestiniog, Gwynedd, LL41 3RY Tel: (01766) 833700 Fax: (01766) 833701 *Extrusion manufrs*

Blagden Hydraulic Ltd, 110 Tuddenham Road, Ipswich, IP4 2SZ Tel: (01473) 252623 Fax: (01473) 233732 E-mail: brianblagden@lineone.net *Hydraulic cylinders & ram suppliers*

Blagdon Pump Ltd, 2 Lambert Road, Armstrong Estate, Washington, Tyne & Wear, NE37 1QP Tel: 0191-417 7475 Fax: 0191-417 5435 E-mail: sales@blagdonpump.com *Pumps*

Blair Engineering Ltd, Balmoral Road, Rattray, Blairgowrie, Perthshire, PH10 7AH Tel: (01250) 872244 Fax: (01250) 872244 E-mail: sales@blairengineering.co.uk *Agricultural machinery manufrs*

▶ Blair Neill Ltd, 13 Comber Road, Newtownards, County Down, BT23 4QR Tel: (028) 9182 6868 E-mail: peter.blair@blairneill.com *Pvc manufrs company windows doors conservatories*

Robert Blair, 50 Waterfall Road, Larne, County Antrim, BT40 3NQ Tel: (028) 2827 6898 *Agricultural farmers*

Blairgowrie Bedding Centre, 67 Perth Street, Blairgowrie, Perthshire, PH10 6DL Tel: (01250) 873148 Fax: (01250) 873148 *Beds & pines furniture suppliers*

Blairgowrie Printers, 7 Reform Street, Blairgowrie, Perthshire, PH10 6BD Tel: (01250) 872102 *Printers*

A.W. Blake Ltd, Commerce Road, Black Park Industrial Park, Stranraer, Wigtownshire, DG9 7DF Tel: (01776) 706665 Fax: (01776) 889669 *Agricultural engineers*

▶ Blake Contractors Ltd, 10 Bircham Road, Southend-on-Sea, SS2 5DN Tel: (01702) 613641 Fax: (01702) 467002 E-mail: info@blakecontractors.co.uk *Electrical contractors & install alarms*

Blake & Horlock, 286 Church Street, London, N9 9HJ Tel: (020) 8807 3992 Fax: (020) 8807 3992 *Monumental memorial manufrs*

▶ James Blake & Co. (Engineers) Ltd, 30-32 South Fort Street, Leith, Edinburgh, EH6 5NU Tel: 0131-554 1646 Fax: 0131-553 4128 E-mail: info@blakegroup.co.uk *Bunded storage tank manufacturers. Also steel & stainless steel tanks*

Blake Joinery Co. Ltd, 17 St John Street, Bridgwater, Somerset, TA6 5HR Tel: (01278) 444333 Fax: (01278) 439298 *Joinery manufrs*

Blake UK Ltd, 177-187 Rutland Road, Sheffield, S3 9PT Tel: 0114-275 9729 Fax: 0114-275 6061 E-mail: sales@blake.uk.com *TV aerials manufrs*

Blakeacre Ltd, Austin Way, Hampstead Industrial Estate, Birmingham, B42 1DU Tel: 0121-358 5066 Fax: 0121-358 1721 E-mail: sales@blakeacre.co.uk Principal Export Areas: Africa *Manufacturer & stockist of industrial fasteners*

Blakelan Communications Ltd, Railway Cottage, Mill Road, Brighton, BN1 8ZF Tel: (01273) 564092 Fax: (01273) 564111 E-mail: mike.blakeman@blakelan.com *Relocations consultancy & computers*

Blakeley Tonge & Partner Ltd, 3 Lever Bridge Mills, Radcliffe Road, Bolton, BL3 1RU Tel: (01204) 535580 Fax: (01204) 535581

Blakell Europlacer Ltd, 30 Factory Road, Poole, Dorset, BH16 5SL Tel: (01202) 266500 Fax: (01202) 266599 E-mail: gas@europlacer.co.uk *Gas detection equipment/systems manufrs*

Blakemar Briars, 10 Northampton Road, Litchborough, Towcester, Northamptonshire, NN12 8JB Tel: (01327) 830213 E-mail: mike@blakemar.co.uk *Tobacco pipe manufrs*

Blakemore & Chell Ltd, New Street, Leek, Staffordshire, ST13 6EB Tel: (01538) 382387 Fax: (01538) 399726 *Agricultural machinery distributors*

Blakemore & Kent Ltd, Cliftonville, Grove Lane, Brenzett, Romney Marsh, Kent, TN29 9RR Tel: (01797) 344577 *Plastering contractors*

Blaker Specialised Welding Repairs Ltd, Worthing Road, Dial Post, Horsham, West Sussex, RH13 8NJ Tel: (01403) 710333 Fax: (01403) 711234 E-mail: simon@blaker.co.uk *Welding repairs & fabricating engineers*

▶ Blake-Robson Northumbria Tuning Machines, Low Lambton Farm, Penshaw, Houghton le Spring, Tyne & Wear, DH4 7NQ Tel: 0191-246 2007 Fax: 0191-385 8013 E-mail: tuningmachines@aol.com *Blake Robson Northumbria Tuning Machines are producers of hand crafted, precision engineered tuning machine heads for classical and acoustic guitar. Offering a custom facility for eight string and ten string guitars.*Eighteen toothed gear wheel with chamfered teeth designed and crafted using the latest technology.*

Blakes Building Profiles Ltd, Unit 7 Jupiter House, Calleva Park, Reading, RG7 8NN Tel: 0118-981 2872 Fax: 0118-981 2872 *Sell building profiles to the building industry*

▶ Blakes Of Farnham, 20 Caker Stream Road, Alton, Hampshire, GU34 2QA Tel: (01420) 86196 Fax: (01420) 86736 E-mail: sales@blakesoffarnham.com *Providers of fixings & support products*

▶ Blakes Interior Design, Unit 14, Lakes Farm, Rayne, Braintree, Essex, CM77 6TE Tel: (01371) 850826 Fax: (01371) 850826 E-mail: wayne@blakesinteriordesign.co.uk *Design & supply of bespoke kitchens*

Blakes Sheds & Fencing, Salop Street, Dudley, West Midlands, DY1 3AT Tel: (01384) 456800 Fax: (01384) 459585 *Wood fencing manufrs*

Blakes Woodcrafts, Holme Pierrepont Hall, Holme Lane, Holme Pierrepont, Nottingham, NG12 2LD Tel: 0115-933 6106 *Cabinet manufrs*

Blakey Engineering Ltd, Caleb Close, Dunstable Road, Luton, LU4 8DR Tel: (01582) 571640 Fax: (01582) 492055 E-mail: blakey@engineeringco.fsnet.co.uk *Steel fabricators*

Blakiston Ltd, 38 St. Helens Road, Hayling Island, Hampshire, PO11 0BT Tel: (023) 9246 9698 Fax: (023) 9246 9716 E-mail: sales@partitions.net *Office partitioning & suspended ceilings*

▶ Blåkläder Workwear Ltd., P.O Box 3965, Warwick, CV34 9AJ Tel: 0800 028 8234 Fax: 0800 028 8235 E-mail: Jeff.Adams@blaklader.com *Manufacturers of workwear and safety clothing.*

Blakley Electrics Ltd, 1 Thomas Road, Crayford, Dartford, DA1 4GA Tel: (0845) 0740084 Fax: (0845) 0740085 E-mail: sales@blakley.co.uk *Electrical engineering manufacturers & distributors* Also at: London SE13

Blanc De Bierges, Eastrea Road, Whittlesey, Peterborough, PE7 2AG Tel: (01733) 202566 Fax: (01733) 205405 E-mail: sales@blancdebierges.com *Manufrs for construction industry* Also at: London N1

Blanchard Security, 51 Mill Street, Bideford, Devon, EX39 2JS Tel: (01237) 472084 Fax: (01237) 423703 E-mail: Kellysearch@blanchards.f9.co.uk *Security system installers*

▶ Blanchards Construction, 3 Newland Drive, Wallasey, Merseyside, CH44 2AX Tel: 0151-637 1222

Blanchards Home Hardware, 51 Mill Street, Bideford, Devon, EX39 2JS Tel: (01237) 472084 E-mail: kellysearch@blanchardsecurity.co.uk *Installation of fire alarms & security equipment*

Blanchet & Co., G7-G9 Blackpole Trading Estate East, Blackpole Road, Worcester, WR3 8SG Tel: (01905) 757144 Fax: (01905) 755705 *Paper disposable product distributors*

Blandford Engineering, Unit 7 Littletowns Estate, Blandford Heights, Blandford Forum, Dorset, DT11 7UR Tel: (01258) 454222 Fax: (01258) 480433 E-mail: blandfordpumps@btinternet.com *Pump installation*

Blandford Forum Timber Ltd, Holland Way, Blandford Forum, Dorset, DT11 7SX Tel: (01258) 452692 Fax: (01258) 459589 E-mail: talkwood@talk21.com *Timber & builders merchants*

▶ Blandford Office Furniture, 20a Sunrise Business Park, Higher Shaftesbury Road, Blandford Forum, Dorset, DT11 8ST Tel: (01258) 450006 Fax: (01258) 459933 E-mail: ian@officefurniture.demon.co.uk *Office furniture retail*

Blandford Sub Aqua, Unit C Holly Industrial Park, Ryan Way, Watford, WD24 4YP Tel: (01923) 801572 Fax: (01923) 801573 *Diving equipment wholesalers*

Blandon Group, Unit 12, Spring Mill Industrial Estate, Old Bristol Road, Avening Road, Nailsworth, Stroud, Gloucestershire, GL6 0BS Tel: (01453) 832358 Fax: (01453) 834878 E-mail: admin@blandon.com *Sheet metal manufrs*

Blanford Engineering, Forum Buildings, Main Road, Minsterworth, Gloucester, GL2 8JS Tel: (01452) 750510 Fax: (01452) 750553 *Engineers & fabricators*

John Blanks, 17 Presburg Road, New Malden, Surrey, KT3 5AH Tel: (020) 8942 2100 Fax: (020) 8336 2337 *Graphic designers*

Blantyre Castings Ltd, Block 9a West Avenue, Blantyre, Glasgow, G72 0UZ Tel: (01698) 829572 Fax: (01698) 824093 E-mail: blantyrecastings@btconnect.com *Castings manufrs*

Blastech Ltd, The Innovation Centre, 217 Portobello, Sheffield, S1 4DP Tel: (01298) 25951 Fax: 0114-222 4430 E-mail: jwarren@blastechltd.co.uk *Blastech offers explosive and ballistic testing services. Including experiment design and execution, trial oversight and numerical model validation.*

Blastline Ltd, Grove Street, Mansfield Woodhouse, Mansfield, Nottinghamshire, NG19 8BU Tel: (01623) 623333 Fax: (01623) 655208 E-mail: sales@blastline.co.uk *Blast cleaning equipment manufrs*

Blastman Robotics Ltd, 68 Cunliffe Cl, Oxford, OX2 7BL Tel: (01865) 512654 Fax: (01865) 311874 *Manufacturers of blast cleaning equipment*

Blastpride Holdings Ltd, Units 7-8 Curran Buildings, Curran Road, Cardiff, CF10 5NE Tel: (029) 2037 1959 Fax: (029) 2022 2351 *Shop blasting*

Blastreat Arundel Ltd, 14 Fitzalan Road, Arundel, West Sussex, BN18 9JS Tel: (01903) 883262 Fax: (01903) 884185 E-mail: blastreat@btconnect.com *Shot blasting contractors*

Blaxill Bros Ltd, 122 Stanstead Road, London, SE23 1BX Tel: (020) 8699 3431 Fax: (020) 8699 3431 *Property management & building services*

Blaze Bright Trading As Exterior, 8B Langthwaite Road, Langthwaite Grange Industrial Estate, South Kirkby, Pontefract, West Yorkshire, WF9 3AP Tel: (0845) 6440977 Fax: (0845) 6440988 E-mail: gareth.jones@exterior.innovations.co.uk *Designers, manufacturers & suppliers of sensory rooms & (mile)*

▶ Blaze Heating, 75 Milborough Crescent, London, SE12 0RP Tel: (020) 3149 3488 E-mail: info@blazeheating.co.uk *Boiler installation, repairs, and servicing.*

Blaze Maintenance Ltd, 15 Tonbridge Road, Hildenborough, Tonbridge, Kent, TN11 9BH Tel: (01732) 832555 Fax: (01732) 833002 E-mail: info@blazemaintenance.co.uk *Electronic sign maintenance services*

Blaze Neon Ltd, Patricia Way, Pysons Road Industrial Estate, Broadstairs, Kent, CT10 2XZ Tel: (01843) 601075 Fax: (01843) 867924 E-mail: chrisa@blazeneon.com *Sign manufrs*

Blazeneon Ltd, Units 3-4 Arden Road, Rednal, Birmingham, B45 0JA Tel: 0121-457 7715 Fax: 0121-453 9356 E-mail: victorl@blazeneon.com *Sign manufrs*

Blazepoint Ltd, Unit 2 Tower Estate, Warpsgrove Lane, Oxford, OX44 7XZ Tel: (01865) 891666 Fax: (01865) 891118 E-mail: sales@blazepoint.co.uk *Blazepoint, a specialist design and engineering company based in the UK, designs, manufactures and develops IT systems and peripheral products using innovative technology combined with technical excellence.*Blazepoint also are an Elite Distributor for Zebra Plastic Card Printers, ribbons, cards and card design and printing sofware.*

▶ Blazes Fireplaces & Heating Centres, 5 Riverpark Industrial Estate, Ampere Road, Newbury, Berkshire, RG14 2DQ Tel: (01635) 36624 Fax: (01635) 47273 E-mail: marc@blazes-newbury.co.uk *2300 sq feet showroom with around 50 displays half of which are live, free parking outside for over cars, custom designs & full installation service, coupled with professional, friendly design & technical guidance*

Blazon Fabrication, Unit 31 125-127 London Road, Stone, Dartford, DA2 6BH Tel: (01322) 280561 Fax: (01322) 228825 E-mail: blazon@btconnect.com *Ventilating ductwork distributors*

Ble Ltd, Church Street, Eckington, Sheffield, S21 4BH Tel: (01246) 436361 Fax: (01246) 436726 E-mail: sales@blegroup.co.uk *Access control & alarm system engineers also emergency lighting*

Bleep Computing Ltd, 7 St. Saviours Wharf, 23 Mill Street, London, SE1 2BE Tel: (020) 7717 0200 Fax: (020) 7717 0201 E-mail: jay@bleep2000-demon.co.uk *Computer development*

Bleep (UK) P.L.C., Rown House, 9-31 Victoria Road, Park Royal, London, NW10 6DP Tel: (020) 7724 2000 Fax: (020) 7706 1935 E-mail: info@bleepplc.com Principal Export Areas: Worldwide *Cash register agents*

Bleepers, PO Box 71, Barnet, Hertfordshire, EN4 0QD Tel: (07000) 253373 Fax: (020) 8440 8024 E-mail: sales@bleepers.co.uk *Paging systems contractors*

Blem Information Management Ltd, Fox House, 135 High Street, Bromley, BR1 1JF Tel: (020) 8313 1616 Fax: (020) 8313 1919 E-mail: info@blem.com *Insurance software developers*

Blemkleen NW Ltd, PO Box 688, Lancaster, LA2 6WY Tel: (01524) 812832 Fax: (01524) 811747 E-mail: tony@blemkleen.freeserve.co.uk *Scaffolding refurbishment*

▶ Blends Ltd, Units 14-18 Manor Complex, Kirkby Bank Road, Knowsley Industrial Park, Liverpool, L33 7SY Tel: 0151-548 3000 Fax: 0151-548 3111 E-mail: sales@blendsltd.co.uk *Suppliers of food additives, colours & flavourings*

▶ Blenham Window Systems Ltd, 212 Windmill Lane, Cheshunt, Waltham Cross, Hertfordshire, EN8 9AF Tel: (01992) 642300 *PVC framed window manufrs*

▶ Blenheim & Moorcroft, Unit 123 Lee Valley Technopark, Ashley Road, London, N17 9LN Tel: (020) 8880 4091 Fax: (020) 8880 4113 E-mail: info@blenheimandmoorcroft.com

continued

Blenheim Systems, 31 Blenheim Gardens, Wembley, Middlesex, HA9 7NP Tel: (020) 8904 9317 Fax: (07092) 215433 E-mail: enq@blenheim-systems.com *Computer consultants*

▶ Blenkins Computer Services Ltd, 34 Rochester Road, Bournemouth, BH11 8AQ Tel: (01202) 568794 E-mail: info@blenkins.co.uk

▶ Blevins Ltd, 189 Old Shettleston Road, Glasgow, G32 7HN Tel: 0141-764 3733 Fax: 0141-764 3734 *Manufacturers of joinery products*

▶ Blevins Road Haulage Services, 23 Derryhubbert Road, Dungannon, County Tyrone, BT71 6NW Tel: (028) 3885 2880 Fax: (028) 3885 2700 E-mail: sales@pablevinshaulage.co.uk

Blezard Ltd, 44 Garstang Road, Preston, PR1 1NA Tel: (01772) 258511 Fax: (01772) 258265 E-mail: mail@blezard.co.uk *Energy conservation consultants & building services specialists*

Blickglen Lifts Ltd, 27 Wentworth Avenue, Southbourne, Bournemouth, BH5 2EQ Tel: (01202) 429155 Fax: (01202) 429550 E-mail: info@blickglenlifts.co.uk *Lift services*

Blickle Castors & Wheels Ltd, 30 Vincent Avenue, Crownhill, Milton Keynes, MK8 0AB Tel: (01908) 560904 Fax: (01908) 260510 E-mail: sales@blickle.co.uk *Manufacturers, stock holders & distributors of castors*

Bligh Appointments Ltd, 70 North End Road, London, W14 9EP Tel: (020) 7603 6123 Fax: (020) 7371 6898 E-mail: info@bligh.com.uk *Employment agency*

▶ Blight & Scoble Ltd, Mardle Way, Buckfastleigh, Devon, TQ11 0JS Tel: (01364) 642253 Fax: (01364) 642074 E-mail: enquiries@blightandscoble.co.uk

▶ Blind Co., Foundry House, Polmorla Road, Wadebridge, Cornwall, PL27 7NB Tel: (01208) 815000 *Blind retailers*

Blind Ambition, 2 Brighton Way, Chippenham, Wiltshire, SN14 0YR Tel: (01249) 446868 Fax: (01249) 446868 *Window & blinds manufrs*

▶ Blind Bolt Co., Tollgate Drive, Tollgate Industrial Estate, Stafford, ST16 3HS Tel: (01785) 270629 Fax: (01785) 270601 E-mail: sales@blindbolt.co.uk *Blind Fixings*

Blind Business, Arturi's Garden Centre, Allington Lane, Fair Oak, Eastleigh, Hampshire, SO50 7DE Tel: (023) 8060 2211 Fax: (023) 8060 2211 E-mail: info@theblindbusiness.co.uk *Suppliers of All types of interior & exterior window blinds*

Blind Cleaning Services, Unit 5a, High St Indust Estate, Kirkintilloch, Glasgow, G66 1PU Tel: 0141-775 0133 Fax: 0141-775 0301 *Cleaning of blinds*

Blind Date, 58 East Main Street, Whitburn, Bathgate, West Lothian, EH47 0RD Tel: (01501) 740166 Fax: (01501) 740166 *Blinds & cloths retailers*

Blind Design, 28-29 Springbank Industrial Estate, Pembroke Loop Road, Dunmurry, Belfast, BT17 0QL Tel: (028) 9030 0999 Fax: (028) 9030 0999 E-mail: blindesign@hotmail.com *Blinds manufrs*

Blind Design, 2a North End Grove, Portsmouth, PO2 8NG Tel: (023) 9266 4476 Fax: (023) 9267 0077 *Blinds manufrs*

Blind Design, Northminster Business Park, Northfield Lane, Upper Poppleton, York, YO26 6QU Tel: (01904) 799647 Fax: (01904) 799793 *Blind manufrs*

Blind Design (Scotland) Ltd, 17 George Street, Bathgate, West Lothian, EH48 1PH Tel: (01506) 632813 Fax: (01506) 69366 *Window blind manufrs*

Blind Design (Stirling) Ltd, Unit 5, Heren Square, Deans Industrial Estate, Livingston, West Lothian, EH54 8QY Tel: (0800) 3281791 Fax: (01506) 418229 *Blind manufrs*

Blind Galleries, Unit 6g Skillion Business Park, Thames Road, Barking, Essex, IG11 0JP Tel: (020) 8594 4772 Fax: (020) 8594 7436 E-mail: blindgallery@aol.com *Blind contractors & manufrs*

Blind Image, 9 Auster Road, York, YO30 4XA Tel: (01904) 693069 Fax: (01904) 693569 *Commercial & domestic blind manufrs*

Blind Man, 40 Stockdale Avenue, Redcar, Cleveland, TS10 5EE Tel: (01642) 488979 Fax: (01642) 488979 *Blinds suppliers*

The Blind Man Ltd, The Stables, Great Farm, Wilstone Green, Tring, Hertfordshire, HP23 4PA Tel: (01296) 661545 Fax: (01296) 668631 *Blind supplier & installer*

▶ Blind Rack Ltd, 32 Navigation Drive, Glen Parva, Leicester, LE2 9TB Tel: 0116-242 5934 *Blind retailers*

Blind Spot, 44 Hardhillock Avenue, New Elgin, Elgin, Morayshire, IV30 6UG Tel: (01343) 549939 Fax: (01343) 55522 *Interior blinds manufacturers & retailers*

▶ Blind Technique, 4 Kildare Close, Ruislip, Middlesex, HA4 9LG Tel: (020) 8866 6088

Blindate Blinds & Awnings, 91 North Drive, Troon, Ayrshire, KA10 7DN Tel: (01292) 315905 Fax: (01292) 313377 *Blinds manufrs*

Blindcraft, 2 Peffer Place, Edinburgh, EH16 4BB Tel: 0131-661 1205 Fax: 0131-652 2095 E-mail: sales@blindcraft.co.uk *Manufacturers of beds*

Blindfix, Wickens Place, Godstone Hill, Godstone, Surrey, RH9 8AP Tel: (01883) 743600 Fax: (01883) 731199 *Suppliers & fitters of blinds & curtains*

Blinding Ideas, Landsdown Lane, Torquay, TQ2 5AJ Tel: (01803) 299880 Fax: (01803) 299880 E-mail: fran_kim@feaves.freeserve.co.uk *Blinds manufrs*

▶ Blinding Web Site Design, 8 Dalkeith Street, Barrow-in-Furness, Cumbria, LA14 1SP Tel: (01229) 828028 E-mail: info@blindingwebdesign.co.uk *Online animation & web design*

▶ Blindmans Brewery Ltd, Talbot Farm, Leighton, Frome, Somerset, BA11 4PN Tel: (01749) 880038 Fax: (01749) 880379 E-mail: info@blindmansbrewery.co.uk *Brewers of hand crafted real ales*

Blinds, Bremilham House, Bremilham Road, Malmesbury, Wiltshire, SN16 0DQ Tel: (01666) 822680 *Blinds suppliers*

Blinds 2000, 8 Spinney Avenue, Goostrey, Crewe, CW4 8JE Tel: (01477) 533472 Fax: (01477) 533472 E-mail: sales@blinds2000.co.uk *Blind manufrs*

Blinds 2000, 98a Fountain Street, Morley, Leeds, LS27 0PH Tel: 0113-259 7741 Fax: 0113-259 7802 *Blind service & manufrs*

Blinds 2000, The Blinds Factory, Croft Road, Neath, West Glamorgan, SA11 1RW Tel: (0800) 0688876 Fax: (0800) 0688876 E-mail: rob@blinds2000.co.uk *Blind manufrs*

Blinds Of Allkinds, Sussex House, Park Lane, Crowborough, East Sussex, TN6 2QN Tel: (01892) 610780 *Awnings & blinds manufrs*

Blinds By Athena, 47 Longstone Avenue, East Linton, East Lothian, EH40 3BS Tel: (01620) 861729 Fax: (01620) 861729 *Blind retailers*

Blinds By Design Ltd, 34 Wagg Street, Congleton, Cheshire, CW12 4BA Tel: (01260) 299866 Fax: (01260) 290099 E-mail: blindsbydesign@compuserve.com *Furniture suppliers*

Blinds By Design, 48 Park Lane, Poynton, Stockport, Cheshire, SK12 1RE Tel: (01625) 858558 Fax: (01625) 858558 *Blinds & curtains manufrs*

Blinds By Elizabeth, 352 Southchurch Road, Southend-on-Sea, SS1 2QB Tel: (01702) 603659 Fax: (01702) 522657 *Sellers of blinds*

Blinds By Sovereign, Sovereign House, Newsome Street, Leyland, PR25 2SY Tel: (01772) 421789 Fax: (01772) 421789 E-mail: sales@sovblinds.com *Blind manufrs*

Blinds Direct, 61 Annacloy Road, Downpatrick, County Down, BT30 9AQ Tel: (028) 4483 1713 Fax: (028) 4483 1710 E-mail: sales@blinds-direct.co.uk *Blind manufrs*

Blinds Direct Solar Control Systems, 20 Blue Chalet Industrial Park, West Kingsdown, Sevenoaks, Kent, TN15 6BQ Tel: (01474) 854156 Fax: (01474) 855361 E-mail: woodblinds@btconnect.com *Blinds & curtain manufrs*

Hillary's Blinds (Northern) Ltd, Glover Industrial Estate, Spire Road, Washington, Tyne & Wear, NE37 3ES Tel: 0191-416 2354 Fax: 0191-416 2369 *Blind manufrs*

Blinds & Co. Leeds Ltd, 64 Hall Lane, Armley, Leeds, LS12 2LH Tel: 0113-263 4186 Fax: 0113-231 1083 *Blinds, awnings & canopy suppliers*

Blinds Solutions, 30 Vale Street, Denbigh, Clwyd, LL16 3BE Tel: (01745) 815549 Fax: (01745) 812226 *Window blind manufrs*

Blinds Unlimited, 4 Carpenters Close, Barnet, Hertfordshire, EN5 1EX Tel: (020) 8441 3663 Fax: (020) 8449 0012 E-mail: blindsunlimited1@aol.com *Blind suppliers*

Blinds Wholesale, 7 Pound Close, Great Oakley, Corby, Northamptonshire, NN18 8JA Tel: (01536) 745575 Fax: (01536) 460369 *Blinds wholesale*

▶ Blinds4uk, Devon House, Church Hill, London, N21 1LE Tel: (0870) 4460550 E-mail: grant.deacon@blinds4uk.co.uk *Blinds4UK - Quality made-to-measure blinds, venetian blinds, wood blinds, roller blinds, vertical blinds and roman blinds. Order online, order by phone. Stunning range of blinds.*

▶ Blingy Things, 45 Briston Road, Melton Constable, Norfolk, NR24 2AP Tel: 01263 861124 *LED scrolling message pendants*

▶ Blinkin Ink Cartridge Service, 15 Bucknall New Road, Stoke-on-Trent, ST1 2BA Tel: (01782) 859933 Fax: (01782) 861130

Blisters Ltd, Second Avenue, Midsomer Norton, Radstock, BA3 4AR Tel: (01761) 418277 Fax: (01761) 418900 E-mail: enquiries@blisters.ltd.uk *Packing services*

Blithfield Events Ltd, Cawarden Springs Farm, Blithbury Road, Rugeley, Staffordshire, WS15 3HL Tel: (01889) 582228 Fax: (01889) 575695 E-mail: marquees@blthfieldevents.co.uk *Marquee events organisers*

Blitz Communications Ltd, Unit 100 Centennial Park, Centennial Avenue, Elstree, Borehamwood, Hertfordshire, WD6 3SA Tel: (0870) 1621000 Fax: (0870) 1621111 E-mail: enquiries@blitzvision.com *Audio visual equipment*

Blitz Vision Ltd, Unit 10, Centennial Avenue, Elstree, Borehamwood, Hertfordshire, WD6 3SA Tel: (020) 8327 1000 Fax: (020) 8327 1111 E-mail: info@blitzcomm.com *Audio visual equipment hire*

Blizard Electronic Assembly Ltd, 8 Greenlea Park, Prince Georges Road, London, SW19 2JD Tel: (020) 8685 9460 Fax: (020) 8840 8688 *Printed circuit assembly services*

Blizzard Signs, 13 Schoolhall Lane, Bury St. Edmunds, Suffolk, IP33 1HA Tel: (01284) 754651 Fax: (01284) 754651 E-mail: sales@blizzardsigns.com *Sign writing & graphics*

▶ Bloc Interiors, 25 Lodge Road, Little Houghton, Northampton, NN7 1AE Tel: (01604) 891110 Fax: (01604) 899478 E-mail: alisonparker@blocinteriors.co.uk *Interior designers & space planning*

▶ Block Engineers, 87 Church Road, Kessingland, Lowestoft, Suffolk, NR33 7SJ Tel: (01502) 740293 Fax: (01502) 742003 E-mail: agblockkessingland@hotmail.com *Training products*

▶ Blocker Products Ltd, Pals Haven, Hook Lane, Aldingbourne, Chichester, West Sussex, PO20 3TE Tel: (01243) 545465 Fax: (01243) 545475 E-mail: millerbrian@btconnect.com *Ventilation equipment suppliers*

Blockleys Brick Ltd, Sommerfeld Road, Trench Lock, Telford, Shropshire, TF1 5RY Tel: (01952) 251933 Fax: (01952) 265377 E-mail: info@blockleys.com *Brick Manufacturers*

▶ Blockstopper Greasetraps, Unit 6, Priestfield Industria Estate, Blantyre, Glasgow, G72 OJA Tel: (01698) 828131 E-mail: cyoker@hotmail.com *We supply greasetraps for Commercial Kitchens and restaurants.*

Bloctube Marine Services Ltd, 5 Felnex Close, Leeds, LS9 0SR Tel: 0113-248 4827 Fax: 0113-240 3351 E-mail: enquiries@bloctube.co.uk *Deep sea hose manoeuvring systems*

Bloodaxe Boats, 9 Somerton Industrial Park, Newport Road, Cowes, Isle of Wight, PO31 8PB Tel: (01983) 298716 Fax: (01983) 299397 E-mail: sales@bloodaxeboats.co.uk *Boat builders*

▶ Bloomers, 820 Bury Road, Bolton, BL2 6PA Tel: (01204) 531487 E-mail: sales@bloomersballoons.co.uk *Gifts & party ware retailers & manufrs*

Bloomfield Ltd, 7b Waterloo Industrial Estate, Waterloo Road, Bidford-on-Avon, Alcester, Warwickshire, B50 4JH Tel: (01789) 490528 Fax: (01789) 490461 E-mail: info@bloomfieldprinters.co.uk *Lithographic printers*

Bloomfield Blinds & Curtains, 84 Bloomfield Road, Belfast, BT5 5LU Tel: (028) 9065 2524 Fax: (028) 9065 2524 E-mail: davidsonr@btconnect.com *Blind distributors*

Bloomfield Books, 26 Meadow Lane, Sudbury, Suffolk, CO10 2TD Tel: (01787) 376374 Fax: (01787) 376967 *Publishers & wholesale booksellers*

Bloomfield Guns & Tackle, 157 Bloomfield Avenue, Belfast, BT5 5AB Tel: (028) 9020 9730 Fax: (028) 9058 0222 *Guns & fishing tackle distributors*

Bloomfield Packaging Ltd, Unit 33 Bloomfield Park, Bloomfield Road, Tipton, West Midlands, DY4 9AH Tel: 0121-520 5480 Fax: 0121-520 3580 E-mail: info@bloomfieldpackaging.co.uk *Polythene product manufrs*

Bloomfield Supplies, Naas Lane, Gloucester, GL2 5RG Tel: (01452) 883354 Fax: (01452) 725115 E-mail: info@bloomfieldsupplies.co.uk *Industrial packaging services*

▶ Bloomfield Trophies, 72 St. Osyth Road, Clacton-on-Sea, Essex, CO15 3BU Tel: (01255) 435888 Fax: (01255) 221450 *Trophies & engraving service*

▶ Blooming Good Jobs, BGJ House, Ashford, Kent, TN21 0LT Tel: (0871) 24225232 E-mail: info@blooming goodjobs.com *Blooming Good jobs is a specialist recruitment website for Horticultural Jobs, Agricultural Jobs and Floristry Jobs. New Vacancies are added daily*

▶ Blooms Blinds, 3 Aspen Close, Timperley, Altrincham, Cheshire, WA15 7YF Tel: 0161-980 0449 Fax: 0161-980 0437 *Supply & installation of interior sunblinds*

▶ Blooms Blinds, 95 Swinton Hall Road, Swinton, Manchester, M27 4AU Tel: 0161-727 8810 Fax: 0161-980 0437 E-mail: sales@bloomsblinds.co.uk

Bloomsbury Cheeses, 61b Judd Street, London, WC1H 9QT Tel: (020) 7387 7645 Fax: (020) 7387 7645 *Specialist cheese producers & distributors*

Bloomsbury International Ltd, Hoghton Street, Southport, Merseyside, PR9 0PA Tel: (01704) 514646 Fax: (01704) 514848 *Seafood suppliers*

B-Looney, Buck House, Sunnyside Road, Chesham, Buckinghamshire, HP5 2AR Tel: (01494) 793904 Fax: (01494) 791268 E-mail: balloons@b-loony.co.uk *Plain & printed advertising balloons manufrs*

▶ Bloor Homes, Rivermead Industrial Estate, Rivermead Drive, Westlea, Swindon, SN5 7EX Tel: (01793) 513938 Fax: (01793) 486953

▶ Blootoon Design Network, Windyridge, Blackhills, Peterhead, Aberdeenshire, AB42 3JW Tel: (0709) 2394531 Fax: (0870) 1302125

Blount UK, Unit 3 Arianda Warwhouses, Steinhoff Business Park, Tewkesbury, Gloucestershire, GL20 8GY Tel: (01684) 297600 Fax: (01684) 855497 E-mail: sales@blount.co.uk *Forestry & horticultural equipment suppliers*

Blow & Scrimshaw Ltd, 10 Dixon Way, Lincoln, LN6 7XN Tel: (01522) 521319 Fax: (01522) 545718 E-mail: contact@blowandscrimshaw.com *Shop fitters & joinery services*

Bloxwich Co., Park Road, Bloxwich, Walsall, WS3 3SS Tel: (01922) 710588 Fax: (01922) 710588 *Woodwork machinists & general woodworking*

Bloxwich Engineering Ltd, Fryers Road, Walsall, WS2 7LZ Tel: (01922) 710510 Fax: (01922) 713510 E-mail: bloxwich@bloxwich.u-net.com *Commercial vehicle component & spare parts manufrs*

W. Bloy & Son, King Edward Street, Grimsby, North East Lincolnshire, DN31 3JP Tel: (01472) 354069 Fax: (01472) 354069 *Non-ferrous metal merchants*

BLP UK Ltd, B L P House, Sandall Stones Road, Kirk Sandall Industrial Estate, Doncaster, South Yorkshire, DN3 1QR Tel: (01302) 890555 Fax: (01302) 886724 E-mail: mail@blpuk.com *Furniture component manufrs*

BLP UK Ltd, B L P House, Sandall Stones Road, Kirk Sandall Industrial Estate, Doncaster, South Yorkshire, DN3 1QR Tel: (01302) 890555 Fax: (01302) 886724 E-mail: mail@blpuk.com Principal Export Areas: Worldwide *Manufacturers of components*

▶ BLP Window Cleaning Services, 15 Laburnum Terrace, Portskewett, Caldicot, Gwent, NP26 5UJ Tel: (01291) 421382 E-mail: blpwindowcleaningservices@hotmail.co.uk

▶ Blue Aardvark Design, The Grange Business Centre, Belasis Avenue, Billingham, Cleveland, TS23 1LG Tel: (01642) 658783 Fax: (01642) 552820 E-mail: blueaardvarkdesign@tiscali.co.uk *Drafting services*

▶ Blue Apple, 6 The Wroe, Higham Ferrers, Rushden, Northamptonshire, NN10 8NB Tel: (01933) 316149 Fax: (01933) 316149 E-mail: steve@theblueapple.co.uk *We specialise in mystery shopping,customer/employee satisfaction surveys & market research*

Blue Arrow, 5 Colston Centre, Colston Avenue, Bristol, BS1 4UB Tel: 0117-929 8435 Fax: 0117-925 0231 E-mail: info@bluearrow.co.uk *Employment agency*

Blue Arrow, Portland House, Longbrook Street, Exeter, EX4 6AB Tel: (01392) 424733 Fax: (01392) 490486 E-mail: enquiries@bluearrow.co.uk *Recruitment agency for south west*

Blue Arrow Ltd, Capability Greenthe Boulevard, Luton, LU1 3BA Tel: (01582) 692692 Fax: (01582) 698698 E-mail: enquiries@bluearrow.co.uk *Employment agency* Also at: Branches throughout the U.K.

Blue Arrow, 32 Friar Lane, Nottingham, NG1 6DQ Tel: 0115-947 2252 Fax: 0115-950 3766 E-mail: nottingham@bluearrow.co.uk *Recruitment agency*

Blue Baron, 1089 Pollokshaws Road, Glasgow, G41 3YG Tel: 0141-649 3101 Fax: 0141-649 3101 E-mail: bluebar@btconnect.com *Computer retail & repair services*

▶ Blue Bell Computers, 14 Chalfont Walk, Norwich, NR4 7NH Tel: (01603) 507777 Fax: (01603) 507701 E-mail: sales@bluebellcomputers.co.uk *Maintain computers & website design*

Blue Boar, Unit D3 New Yatt Business Centre, Kite Lane, New Yatt, Witney, Oxfordshire, OX29 6TJ Tel: (01993) 868878 Fax: (01993) 868878 E-mail: helen.cook@virgin.net *Packing services*

Blue Boats Boat Yard, Bryher, Isles of Scilly, TR23 0PR Tel: (01720) 423095 Fax: (01720) 423011 *Boat builders & boat yard*

Blue Box Design Ltd, 2a Craig Leith Road, Broadleys Industrial Park, Stirling, FK7 7LQ Tel: (01786) 446098 Fax: (01786) 446097 *Presentation packing design & manufrs*

▶ Blue Box One Ltd, 8 Sturt Road, Frimley Green, Camberley, Surrey, GU16 6HX Tel: (01276) 500253 Fax: (0845) 4334450 E-mail: info@blueboxone.co.uk *Supplier & service provider of photocopiers & network printing systems*

▶ Blue Box Technology Ltd, Unit 54, Works Road, Hollingwood, Chesterfield, Derbyshire, S43 2PE Tel: (01246) 472233 Fax: (01246) 477788 E-mail: sales@bb24.co.uk *IT consultants*

Blue C Marine Ltd, Firs Industrial Estate, Kidderminster, Worcestershire, DY11 7QN Tel: (01562) 746336 Fax: (01562) 742255 E-mail: info@bluecmarine.com *Boat builders services*

Blue Chip Customer Engineering Ltd, Franklin Court, Prioy Business Park, Bedford, MK44 3JZ Tel: (01234) 327700 Fax: (01234) 831580 E-mail: sales@bluechip.co.uk Principal Export Areas: Worldwide *Computer maintenance repair services*

Blue Chip Technology Ltd, Chowley Oak, Chowley Oak Lane, Tattenhall, Chester, CH3 9EX Tel: (01829) 772000 Fax: (01829) 772001 E-mail: sales@bluechiptechnology.co.uk *Blue Chip Technology is a leading UK designer and manufacturer of embedded boards, industrial computers and data acquisition modules: 2U; 4; Rack Mount; Bench Top; Passive; ATX; Slot Cards; PC104; Biscuits; ETX; X86; MIPS; Custom Design Service.*

Blue Circle Cement, 84 Eccleston Sq, London, SW1V 1PX Tel: (020) 7828 3456 Fax: (020) 7245 8400 *Cement manufrs*

Blue Circle Industries UK P.L.C., West Medina Wharf, Stag Lane, Newport, Isle Of Wight, PO30 5TS Tel: (01983) 522271 Fax: (01983) 524972 *Cement manufrs*

Blue Code Labelling Technology, Great Central Way Industrial Estate, Great Central Way, Rugby, Warwickshire, CV21 3XH Tel: (01788) 576100 Fax: (01788) 578900 E-mail: sales@bluecode.co.uk *Labels manufacturers including bar coded & self adhesive*

▶ Blue.com, 76 Landedmans, Westhoughton, Bolton, BL5 2QJ Tel: (07841 708495 E-mail: pfreek@10Blue.com *Blue is a importer of the latest Electronic items, i,e Sony PSP Console and games, Sony playstation 3, Xbox, Digital Cameras at cheap prices*

Blue Cube, Bordesley Hall, The Holloway, Alvechurch, Birmingham, B48 7QA Tel: (01527) 595595 E-mail: theteam@thebluecube.com *Creative web design agency specialising in online communication solutions, web design, E-marketing solutions such as email newsletters and e-postcards.*

▶ Blue Cube Design, 6 Keble Park North, Bishopthorpe, York, YO23 2SX Tel: (01904) 778222 Fax: (01904) 708828 E-mail: admin@bluecubedesign.com *Exhibition & interior designers*

Blue Curve, 17-29 Sun Street, London, EC2M 2PT Tel: (020) 7392 1390 *Computer applications services*

▶ Blue Design & Print, 1 Rumsey Row, The Green, Writtle, Chelmsford, CM1 3DU Tel: (01245) 423822 Fax: (01245) 423833

Blue Diamond Bearings Ltd, Rolwey House, School Close, Chandler's Ford, Eastleigh, Hampshire, SO53 4BY Tel: (023) 8025 8966 Fax: (023) 8025 8925 E-mail: bdsales@rolwey.com *Rubber seal manufrs*

Blue Diamond Hygiene Supplies, 104 Havest Lane, Sheffield, S3 8EG Tel: 0114-278 7777 *Janitorial supply services*

Blue Diamond Industrial Supplies, Hatton, Peterhead, Aberdeenshire, AB42 0RX Tel: (01779) 841899 *Mat & matting manufrs*

Blue Diamond Services, 106 Pembroke Road, Ruislip, Middlesex, HA4 8NW Tel: (01895) 671500 Fax: (01895) 671509 E-mail: info@blued.co.uk *Office cleaners, industrial & commercial sevice*

Blue Dolphin Supplies Ltd, 4 Portland Place, Hamilton, Lanarkshire, ML3 7JU Tel: (0870) 7479101 Fax: (01698) 297048 E-mail: info@bluedolphinsupplies.co.uk *Computer consumables suppliers*

▶ Blue Earth Web Solutions, Globe House, 17 Vale Walk, Worthing, West Sussex, BN14 0BS Tel: (0845) 3311396 E-mail: info@blueearthsolutions.co.uk *Web solutions*

▶ Blue Enterprises, 130 Shaftesbury Avenue, London, W1D 5EU Tel: (0845) 3702583 Fax: (0845) 3702584 E-mail: info@blue-enterprises.co.uk *Recruitment agency*

▶ Blue Eye Design, 38 Westway, Caterham, Surrey, CR3 5TP Tel: (0870) 7701090 Fax: (0870) 7701091 E-mail: info@blueeyedesign.co.uk *Manufacturers of software*

▶ Blue Fire Consulting Ltd, Il Palazzo 7 Water Street, Liverpool, L2 0RD Tel: (0870) 7521080 Fax: (0870) 7521090 E-mail: sales@bluefireconsulting.co.uk *IT engineering, finance, clerical, recruitment consultancy, agency*

Blue Fish Co., The Barm, Holt Lane, Ashby Magna, Lutterworth, Leicestershire, LE17 5NJ Tel: (01455) 201010 Fax: (01455) 201001 E-mail: bluefish@thebluefishcompany.com *Web designers & IT support*

▶ Blue Flame Gas & Heating, Waterside House, Falmouth Road, Penryn, Cornwall, TR10 8BE Tel: (01326) 378122 Fax: (01326) 374891 E-mail: sales@blueflamegas.co.uk *Gas engineers*

▶ Blue Goose Gallery, 87 High Street, West End, Southampton, SO30 3DS Tel: (023) 8047 1818 E-mail: kellysearch@bluegoosegallery.co.uk *Art gallery*

Blue Goose Systems, 44 Whitebridge Road, Onchan, Isle of Man, IM3 4HR Tel: (01624) 671719 Fax: (01624) 620179 E-mail: enquiries@bluegoosesystems.co.uk *IT hardware supply & sourcing*

Blue Ice Refrigeration, 8 Harpham Road, Marshchapel, Grimsby, South Humberside, DN36 5TR Tel: (01472) 388491 Fax: (01472) 388491 *Refrigeration Components Services & Supplies*

Blue Jay Of London, 2 Shillingford Street, London, N1 2DP Tel: (020) 7359 4800 Fax: (020) 7704 9654 *Uniform & workware manufrs*

Blue Keld Springs Ltd, Fossil Nest Cranswick, Cranswick, Driffield, North Humberside, YO25 9RE Tel: (01377) 275302 Fax: (01377) 271360 E-mail: sales@bluekeld.co.uk *Fruit flavoured mineral water & mineral water suppliers*

Blue Lagoon Aquatics, 157-159 Broad Street, Dagenham, Essex, RM10 9HX Tel: (020) 8595 9635 Fax: (020) 8592 3173 *Aquatics retailers*

▶ Blue Light Office Supplies Ltd, 1 Cedar Wood Drive, Watford, WD25 0RR Tel: (01923) 677005 Fax: (01923) 673584 E-mail: sales@bluelightoffice.com *Suppliers of office stationery, furniture & printing*

Blue Line Office Furniture, Endeavour House, London Stansted Airport, Stansted, Essex, CM24 1SJ Tel: (01279) 669470 Fax: (01279) 669471 E-mail: sales@blueline.uk.com *Manufacturer of wood and veneered furniture for office and home, (contract and bespoke)suppliers of standard office furniture, storage and seating, interior designers and space planners*

▶ Blue Line Trading Ltd, Grapes House, 79A High Street, Esher, Surrey, KT10 9QA Tel: (01372) 468141 Fax: (01372) 467891

Blue Line Trailers, New Office, Main Road, Algarkirk, Boston, Lincolnshire, PE20 2BE Tel: (01205) 460777 Fax: (01205) 460014 *Manufacturers of trailers*

Blue Machenary (Scotland) Ltd, 9 Broadways Road, Spring Kerse Industrial Estate, Stirling, FK7 7ST Tel: (01786) 469444 *Quarry machinery*

▶ Blue Mobiles, 6 Hampson Gardens, Edenthorpe, Doncaster, South Yorkshire, DN3 2TN Tel: 07921 996869 E-mail: bluemobiles@tiscali.co.uk

Blue Moon Insurance, Church Street, Wellingborough, Northamptonshire, NN8 4PD Tel: (01933) 303020 Fax: (01933) 303021 E-mail: sales@bluemooninsurance.co.uk *Unbiased mortgage and insurance advice and recommendation from the whole of the mortgage market. Mortgages, remortgages, bad credit mortgages, self employed and council right to buy welcomed. Call Blue Moon Mortgages 0800 011 20 21*

Blue Moon Leisure, Unit 9 The Old Retort House Hele Business Park, Witheridge Place, Ilfracombe, Devon, EX34 9RA Tel: (01271) 864922 Fax: (01271) 864922 E-mail: sales@bluemoonleisure.com *Telescopic snooker & pool cues extensions distributors & manufrs*

▶ Blue Osprey Ltd, 9 Gala Avenue, Deanpark, Renfrew, PA4 0UH Tel: 0141-885 0715 E-mail: alastairm@blueosprey.com *A range of accounting based business services within a context of continous improvement*

▶ Blue Print, 7 Barton House, Barton Industrial Estate, Upper Wield, Alresford, Hampshire, SO24 9RN Tel: (01420) 560600 Fax: (01420) 560600 *Screen printers*

▶ Blue Ribbons, 29 Walton Road, East Molesey, Surrey, KT8 0DH Tel: (020) 8941 1591 E-mail: sales@blueribbons.co.uk *Cake decorations & equipment suppliers*

Blue Rocket Group Ltd, 115 Church Road, Hove, East Sussex, BN3 2AF Tel: (01273) 779196 E-mail: daniel@bluerocketgroup.com *Blue Rocket is a full service independent agency. We develop and manage high impact business to business and consumer PR campaigns across a wide range of sectors. **We know how to fulfil journalists' expectations and that means results for our clients. Many of our consultants are established journalists in their fields. We act as newshounds, seeking out and generating positive media opportunities. Our excellent working relationships with the media and our proactive approach make our clients first choice when it comes to media comment. **We work closely with clients to understand their business and ensure the right messages are delivered to the right audiences. We plan and implement full retainer or shorter project based campaigns, according to the client need. **We offer a flexible approach based on honest advice, good value and great results. **Our intelligent thinking coupled with guided enthusiasm makes us stand out from the crowd* *

▶ Blue Sails, Garage Street, Llandudno, Conwy, LL30 1DW Tel: (01492) 879914 *Manufacture and repair of Sails and covers*

Blue Sheep Ltd, West Wing Arle Court, Hatherley Lane, Cheltenham, Gloucestershire, GL51 6PN Tel: (01242) 545300 E-mail: richard@blueskyuk.com *Corporate dvd production*

▶ Blue Silicon, 214 Kings Ash Road, Paignton, Devon, TQ3 3XL Tel: (0870) 7070005 E-mail: kellysearch@bluesilicon.co.uk *Engineering recruitment*

▶ Blue Skin, Blue Skin, Hoxton Works, 128 Hoxton Street, London N1 6SH, London, United Kingdom, N1 6SH Tel: 020 7012 1720 E-mail: info@blueskin.com *Established since 1996, Blue Skin is the creative love child of Niki Kerr. Operated and designed by Niki, Blue Skin aims to bring quirky humour, combined with clean graphics and bold colour to your inner wardrobe. Inspired by brands such as X-girl and Supreme in the mid nineties,*Blue Skin began its road trip into the world!*

Blue Sparkle Cleaning Contractors, 2 Clarenden Place, Dartford, DA2 7HL Tel: (01322) 669494 *Industrial cleaning contractors*

Blue Spring, Hanney Road, Steventon, Abingdon, Oxfordshire, OX13 6DJ Tel: (01235) 861000 Fax: (01235) 861999 *Water coolers manufrs*

▶ Blue Star Jeans Ltd, Chesterfield Road, Leicester, LE5 5LF Tel: 0116-273 3533

Blue Systems, 34 Clifton Road, Cambridge, CB1 7EB Tel: (01223) 404100 Fax: (01223) 414900 *Audio services & distribution providers*

▶ Blue Team, 6 Eton Garages, Lambolle Place, London, NW3 4PE Tel: (020) 7794 3777 Fax: (020) 7794 4651

Blue Tree Recruitment, Suite 3 The Sanctuary, 23 Oak Hill Grove, Surbiton, Surrey, KT6 6DU Tel: (020) 8399 4908 Fax: (020) 8399 4909 E-mail: claire@bluetreerecruitment.co.uk *Blue Tree Recruitment is about people. We provide a personal, reliable and efficient recruitment service driven by personal communication to our clients and candidates alike to ensure quality and effectiveness at all times.***We recruit for permanent, temporary and contract positions at all levels of authority throughout London and the South East in the following sectors:* *Sales, Marketing and PR*Design and Creative Services*Accounting*Office Support*Retail Services*

▶ Blue U V, 121 Loverock Road, Reading, RG30 1DZ Tel: 0118-959 7444 *UV lighting manufrs*

▶ Blue Water International, Blue Water House, Howe Moss Drive, Dyce, Aberdeen, AB21 0GL Tel: (01224) 771191 Fax: (01224) 724591 E-mail: sales@bluewater-offshore.com

▶ Blue White Brown Ltd, 22 Fellows Avenue, Kingswinford, West Midlands, DY6 9ET Tel: (01384) 296666 Fax: (01384) 296666 E-mail: asbestos@bluewhitebrown.ltd.uk *Independent asbestos surveying & management, cost effective solutions, highly professional impartial advice by qualified surveyors*

Bluearc, Queensgate House, Cookham Road, Bracknell, Berkshire, RG12 1RB Tel: (01344) 408200 Fax: (01344) 408202 *Network attached storage*

Bluebell Associates Ltd, Cresta House, 42 Water Lane, Wilmslow, Cheshire, SK9 5AL Tel: (01625) 539288 Fax: (01625) 539211 *Computing & communication services*

Blueberry Consultants Ltd, 22 Clarendon Street, Leamington Spa, Warwickshire, CV32 4PG Tel: (01926) 430168 Fax: (01926) 430133 E-mail: penny.oddy@bbconsult.co.uk *Bespoke computer software developers & consultants*

Bluebird Fixings Ltd, Westminster Industrial Estate, Station Road, North Hykeham, Lincoln, LN6 3QY Tel: (01522) 697776 Fax: (01522) 697771 E-mail: info@bluebird-fixings.ltd.uk *Fixing systems distributors & manufrs*

Bluebird Packaging Machines Ltd, 43 Boulton Road, Reading, RG2 0NU Tel: 0118-987 4611 Fax: 0118-987 4575 E-mail: sales@bluebird-machines.co.uk *Shrink wrapping machinery manufrs*

▶ Blueblossom Ltd, 61 St. Albans Hill, Hemel Hempstead, Hertfordshire, HP3 9NQ Tel: (01442) 219795 Fax: (01442) 219795 E-mail: info@blueblossom.co.uk *IT and Business Services*Drop Shipping*e-returns management*Order fulfilment*Web designing*Business-in-a-Box*

Blueboar Farm Contracts Ltd, London Road, Dunchurch, Rugby, Warwickshire, CV23 9LH Tel: (01788) 810854 Fax: (01788) 817100 E-mail: enquiries@blueboarcontracts.co.uk *Dredging & civil engineering contractors*

▶ BlueChip Admin Services, 30, Pennyacre Road, Teignmouth, Devon, TQ14 8LB Tel: 01626 774143 Fax: 01626 779059 E-mail: bluechipcasework@yahoo.co.uk *Virtual secretarial and administration services. Professional, confidential and reliable. Word processing, book-keeping,tele-marketing and many more office services.*

▶ Blueclaw, 21 Denton Avenue, Leeds, LS8 1LE Tel: 0113-226 2760 E-mail: info@blueclaw.co.uk *Blueclaw specialises in bespoke Web Design, Organic Search Engine Optimisation (SEO), RSS/XML Feed Generation, Viral Marketing, Flash Games, Visitor Tracking and Pay Per Click Campaign Management. We will make your web site more effective.*

▶ Bluedelta, Unit 2 Saxon Way, Melbourn, Royston, Hertfordshire, SG8 6DN Tel: (01763) 263120 Fax: (01763) 261958 E-mail: trade@bluedelta.co.uk *Cat5 video design, distribution & manufrs*

▶ Bluefin Solutions Ltd, Utell House, 2 Kew Bridge Road, Brentford, Middlesex, TW8 0JF Tel: (0870) 2330404 Fax: (0870) 2330405 E-mail: enquiries@bluefinsolutions.com *Business intelligence consultancy*

▶ Bluefinger Computer Systems, Underwood Business Park, Wells, Somerset, BA5 1AF Tel: (01749) 834900 Fax: (01749) 834901 E-mail: info@bluefinger.com *Asset tracking solutions*

Bluefrog Design, 21 St Margarets Street, Leicester, LE1 3EB Tel: 0116-253 0612 Fax: 0116-226 5737 E-mail: mail@bluefrogdesign.co.uk *Design consultants*

▶ Bluejam Ltd, 26-30 Stoney Street, Nottingham, NG1 1LL Tel: 0115-959 8000 Fax: 0115-959 8001 E-mail: sales@bluejam.com *Design & marketing*

▶ Bluejays PC Services, 76 Davidson Road, Croydon, CR0 6DB Tel: 0208 6561056 E-mail: info@bluejayspc.co.uk *PC repairs*

Blueleaf Ltd, 73 Steventon Road, Drayton, Abingdon, Oxfordshire, OX14 4LA Tel: (01235) 554677 Fax: (01235) 554977 *Handheld computers suppliers & software solutions designers*

▶ Blueleafcreative .Co.Uk, 22 Greenacre Road, Worksop, Nottinghamshire, S81 0SL Tel: (07828) 218092 E-mail: info@blueleafcreative.co.uk *Web site design services for small businesses & organizations*

Bluelimit Surveys Ltd, 6 Riverside Road, Gorleston, Great Yarmouth, Norfolk, NR31 6PU Tel: (01493) 653900 Fax: (01493) 442774 E-mail: bluelimit@paston.co.uk Principal Export Areas: Asia Pacific, Central Asia, Middle East, Africa, Central/East Europe, West Europe & North America *Non-destructive testing*

Blueline Buildings, Rowms Lane, Swinton, Mexborough, South Yorkshire, S64 8AA Tel: (01709) 578333 Fax: (01709) 578444 E-mail: sales@bluelinebuildings.com *Importers of steel frameworks*

▶ Blueline Business Solutions Ltd, The iD Centre, rtc Business Park, London Road, Derby, DE24 8UP Tel: 01332 258837 Fax: 01332 258833 E-mail: enquiry@bluelinesolutions.co.uk *Discover the Personal Touch!**Every client is different, so you won"t find our consultants trying to force a standard solution on you and your business.**Our services range from Process Design and CHange Management to Staff Development and cover all aspects of IT and Operational Management.**Contact us today to see how we can help you.*

▶ Blueline Hire, Sellwood Court Enterprise Park, Sleaford, Lincolnshire, NG34 8GJ Tel: (01529) 300233

Bluemay Weston, Cooks Cross, South Molton, Devon, EX36 4AW Tel: (01769) 574574 Fax: (01769) 512944 E-mail: sales@bluemayweston.co.uk Sales Contact: M. Appleyard Principal Export Areas: Worldwide *Punched & pressed parts in non-metallic materials. Gaskets & washers*

▶ Bluemonday Recruitment, 18 Soho Square, London, W1D 3QL Tel: (020) 7025 8747 Fax: (020) 7025 8100 E-mail: sales@bluemondayrecruitment.com

▶ Bluemoon Bottle Neck Co., 2 Lintonville Terrace, Ashington, Northumberland, NE63 9UN Tel: (01670) 858888 E-mail: sales@bluemoonbottleneck.co.uk *Guitar slide manufrs*

Blueprint Dental Equipment Ltd, 12 Lessness Road, Morden, Surrey, SM4 6HP Tel: (0870) 4329786 Fax: (0870) 4324665 E-mail: info@blueprintdental.co.uk *Dental equipment manufrs*

▶ Blueprint Engineering Services Ltd, Units 1-5, 28A Wellington Road, Prenton, Merseyside, CH43 2JE Tel: 0151-652 3516 Fax: (0870) 8362181 E-mail: sales@blueprint-eng.com *Professional liquid and vacuum pump repair company.**Delivering guaranteed MTBF improvements at lowest prices.**Factory trained engineers and mechanical seal experts.*

Blueprint Management Systems, 1 Pemberton Row, London, EC4A 3BG Tel: (020) 7832 1800 Fax: (020) 7832 1801 *Computer consultants*

▶ Blueprint for Training, Pembroke Cotttage, Vicarage Road, Waresley, Sandy, Bedfordshire, SG19 3DA Tel: 01767 651200 Fax: 01767 654147 E-mail: info@blueprint4all.com *Training Consultants. Bespoke learning and development programmes including: Management Development, supervisory skills, team building, time management, motivation, delgation, influencing and negotiation, coaching and mentoring, customer service skills, effective telephone handling skills.Provision of training needs analysis and learning and development strategies.*

Blueridge, 10 Chillingham Way, Camberley, Surrey, GU15 2NS Tel: (07773) 334000 Fax: (07092) 862302 E-mail: info@blueridge.org.uk *Scaffolding hire & sale & erections*

▶ Bluerock Security Ltd, St. James Road, Brackley, Northamptonshire, NN13 7XY Tel: (01280) 706969 Fax: (01280) 706969 E-mail: sales@bluerocksecurity.com *Security products & services*

Blues Clothing Ltd, Brigade House, Parsons Green, London, SW6 4TN Tel: (020) 7371 9900 Fax: (020) 7371 9782 E-mail: marketing@blues-clothing.co.uk *Corporate identity clothing manufrs*

▶ Bluesky Designers, College Road, Bromley, BR1 3PU Tel: (020) 8313 9881 Fax: (020) 8290 5932 E-mail: bluesky@easynet.co.uk *Graphic design services*

▶ Bluespier International Ltd, Priory Barn, The Priory, Alcester Road, Feckenham, Redditch, Worcestershire, B96 6JD Tel: (01527) 894216 Fax: (01527) 893089

Bluespier International Ltd, Wood End House, Grafton Flyford, Worcester, WR7 4PH Tel: (01905) 391120 Fax: (01905) 391121 E-mail: susan.williams@bluespier.com *Clinical information systems for medical sector*

▶ Bluestone plc, Waterside Centre, 4215 Solihull Parkway, Birmingham Business Park, Birmingham, B37 7YN Tel: 0121-329 1500 Fax: 0121-329 1501

Bluestone Ltd, Unit F3 Fareham Heights, Standard Way, Fareham, Hampshire, PO16 8XT Tel: (01329) 822888 Fax: (01329) 827272 *Building contractors*

▶ Bluestone Plc, Nations House, 103 Wigmore Street, London, W1U 1AQ Tel: (020) 7659 3333 Fax: (020) 7659 3300 *Bluestone is one of Britain's leading construction services providers delivering projects to local communities across the country. From the schools, hospitals & commercial buildings we construct & refurbish, to the major projects we design & deliver, we want every customer to be an advocate of our business.**

Bluestone plc, 4 Phoenix Place, Nottingham, NG8 6BA Tel: 0115-964 7000 Fax: 0115-964 7001 E-mail: admin@bluestonesolutions.net .

▶ Bluestone plc, The Meads Business Centre, Ashworth Road, Bridgemead, Swindon, SN5 7YJ Tel: (01793) 648000 Fax: (01793) 648001

▶ Bluestone plc, 3 Heron Gate Office Park, Hankridge Way, Taunton, Somerset, TA1 2LR Tel: (01823) 624100 Fax: (01823) 624101

▶ Bluestone Technology Ltd, 1 Paiges Farm, Bovisand Lane, Down Thomas, Plymouth, PL9 0AE Tel: (01752) 862436 Fax: (01752) 862436E-mail: sales@bluestonetechnology.com *Specialists in the manufacture of rugged lcd displays*

▶ Blueton Ltd, 19c Winchester Avenue, Winchester Industrial Estate, Denny, Stirlingshire, FK6 6QE Tel: (01324) 829661 Fax: (01324) 829551 E-mail: blueton@btinternet.com *manufacturer of Street Furniture, bollards, tree grills, cycle stands, seating, litter bins, planters and signage*

▶ Bluetree Specific Skills, 18 Croftfield Road, Godmanchester, Huntingdon, Cambridgeshire, PE29 2ED Tel: (0845) 4534500 Fax: (0870) 8681610 E-mail: graham@bluetreeuk.com *Change Management*Team Builing & Training*Executive Coaching*NLP & Marketing*Business Strategy Planning*

Blundell Files & Tools Ltd, Pottery Fields, Prescot, Merseyside, L34 5RL Tel: 0151-426 6745 Fax: 0151-493 1576 E-mail: enquiries@blundell-files.com *Engineering & hand tool distributors*

Blundell Harling Ltd, 9 Albany Road, Granby Industrial Estate, Weymouth, Dorset, DT4 9TH Tel: (01305) 206000 Fax: (01305) 760598 E-mail: sales@blundellharling.co.uk *Office furniture & drawing board manufrs*

Blundell Woodworking Machinery Ltd, Park Drive, Braintree, Essex, CM7 1AP Tel: (01376) 346565 Fax: (01376) 551230 E-mail: blundell@btconnect.com *Sellers of woodwork machinery*

▶ Blundeston Property Maintenance, 61 Lakeside Rise, Blundeston, Lowestoft, Suffolk, NR32 5BD Tel: (07887) 604133 E-mail: philip.hannant@btinternet.com *Blundeston Property Maintenance can offer you the property owner the complete package. From a simple job to a large project such as a loft conversion. From conception to completion we will work with you and offer the benefit of our experience to guide you through what can be a stressful time, to enable you to have peace of mind regardless of the job in hand. ELECTRICAL, PLUMBING, SMALL BUILDING WORKS, DECORATING.* *

Bluntray Ltd, 55 Lonsdale Road, London, NW6 6RA Tel: (020) 7624 8151 Fax: (020) 7624 2533 *Sheet metal fabricators*

▶ Bluprint Design & Copy, 79 Wellgate, Rotherham, South Yorkshire, S60 2LZ Tel: (01709) 838965 Fax: (01709) 365449 E-mail: info@bluprintdesign.co.uk *Design print & marketing services*

▶ Bluroc Leasing4u, 4 Mallard Way, Crewe, CW1 6ZQ Tel: (01270) 617540 Fax: (0870) 0941442 E-mail: info@leasing4u.co.uk *Contract hire of cars & vans*

▶ Bluu Group, Princess House, 50 Eastcastle Street, London, W1W 8EA Tel: (020) 7079 3400 Fax: (020) 7323 1723

Blyford Dairy Services, Oakley, Primes Lane, Blyford, Halesworth, Suffolk, IP19 9JS Tel: (01986) 872578 Fax: (01986) 875569 *Dairy services*

▶ Blygold Air Conditioning Consultants, 4 Beacon Road, Poulton Industrial Estate, Poulton-le-Fylde, Lancashire, FY6 8JE Tel: (01253) 890666 Fax: (01253) 890222

Charles Blyth & Co. Ltd, Carnival Way, Castle Donington, Derby, DE74 2NJ Tel: (01332) 810283 Fax: (01332) 855810 E-mail: info@charlesblyth-co.co.uk *Upholstery & bedding spring manufrs*

Blyth Marble Ltd, Lawn Road, Carlton-in-Lindrick, Worksop, Nottinghamshire, S81 9LB Tel: (01909) 730807 Fax: (01909) 730114 E-mail: admin@blyth-marble.co.uk *Marble & granite importers*

Blyth Pest Control Ltd, Worksop Road, Blyth, Worksop, Nottinghamshire, S81 8DX Tel: (01909) 591150 Fax: (01909) 591860 *Pest control services*

William Blyth, Pasture Road North, Barton-upon-Humber, South Humberside, DN18 5RB Tel: (01652) 632175 Fax: (01652) 660966 E-mail: sales@williamblyth.co.uk *Natural clay roofing tile manufrs*

Blyth Woodmachinery Ltd, 15 Ashville Way, Cambridge Road Industrial Estate, Whetstone, Leicester, LE8 6NU Tel: 0116-286 1617 Fax: 0116-286 1618 E-mail: jonathan@blythmachinery.co.uk *Dealers and Agents specialising in the supply of New & Used Equipment for use in the Woodworking Industry. Family run business formed in 1986. Based in Leicestershire with a modern purpose built 10,000 sq. ft. factory showroom offering the widest choice of machines to suit all budgets. Delivery, Installation and Servicing.*

A.P. Blythe & Sons Ltd, Will-o-the-wisp, Main Rd, Wrangle, Boston, Lincs, PE22 9AE Tel: (01205) 870738 *Plant hire contractor (agricultural)*

Blythe Business Equipment Ltd, 161-165 Newcastle Street, Stoke-on-Trent, ST6 3QJ Tel: (01782) 817121 Fax: (01782) 575087 E-mail: sales@blythebusiness.co.uk *Retailers of copiers & facsimile machines*

William Blythe Ltd, Bridge Street, Church, Accrington, Lancashire, BB5 4PD Tel: (01254) 320000 Fax: (01254) 320001 E-mail: ian.pearce@wm-blythe.co.uk *Inorganic chemical manufrs* Also at: Hapton

William Blythe Ltd, Hapton Works, Manchester Road, Hapton, Burnley, Lancashire, BB12 7LF Tel: (01254) 320000 Fax: (01254) 320001 *Chemical manufrs*

▶ Blythewood Plant Hire Ltd, Fenland District Industrial Estate, Station Road, Whittlesey, Peterborough, PE7 2EY Tel: (01733) 203201 Fax: (01733) 350308 E-mail: enquiries@blythewood-plant.co.uk *Plant hire contractors* Also at: Welwyn Garden City

▶ BM Bijoux, 174 New Bond Street, London, W1S 4RG Tel: (020) 7409 3539 Fax: (020) 7409 2425 E-mail: sales@bmbijoux.com *Jewellery designers & manufrs*

BMB Builderbase, Wakefield Road, Barnsley, South Yorkshire, S71 1NH Tel: (01226) 730400 Fax: (01226) 730600 E-mail: barnsley@buildbase.co.uk *Buildbase is one of the UK's fastest growing builders merchants. All of our branches are long established companies which have been serving local trades people for many years, with knowledge and experience to match. We believe strongly in understanding the needs of trades professional and our business has been developed specifically to meet those demands. Massive stocks, top quality products, competitive pricing, reliable delivery, specialist staff and exceptional customer service.*

BMF Business Services, 211 Piccadilly, London, W1J 9HF Tel: (020) 7353 8688 Fax: (020) 7895 1353 E-mail: info@211piccadilly.co.uk *Business centre*

Bmg Labtech Ltd, PO Box 73, Aylesbury, Buckinghamshire, HP20 2QJ Tel: (01296) 336650 Fax: (01296) 336651 *Laboratory instruments supplier*

▶ BMH, 37 Crow Lane, Little Billing, Northampton, NN3 9BZ Tel: (01604) 403322 Fax: (01604) 403329

▶ Bmib Scotland Ltd, 18 Melford Road, Righead Industrial Estate, Bellshill, Lanarkshire, ML4 3LR Tel: (01698) 844021 Fax: (01698) 845888 *Industrial batteries distributors*

BMM Heaters Ltd, 1 Copeland Court, Forest Grove, Middlesbrough, Cleveland, TS2 1RN Tel: (01642) 240700 Fax: (01642) 240708 E-mail: sales@bmmheaters.co.uk *Manufacturers of gas & oil fired heater, oil boilers & air heaters*

Bmo Group, 95 Queen Victoria Street, London, EC4V 4HG Tel: (020) 7489 8844 Fax: (020) 7236 7041 *Commercial banking agents*

BMP, 6 The Half Croft, Syston, Leicester, LE7 1LD Tel: 0116-260 2916 Fax: 0116-260 7296 E-mail: bnpengineers@btconnect.com *Precision & general engineers*

BMP Europe Ltd, Shorten Brook Drive, Altham Business Park, Altham, Accrington, Lancashire, BB5 5YH Tel: (01282) 772000 Fax: (01282) 777700 E-mail: bmp@bmp-europe.co.uk *Photocopier parts*

BMR Presswork, Market Street, Draycott, Derby, DE72 3NB Tel: (01332) 875384 Fax: (01332) 874022 *Presswork manufrs*

BMRB Ltd, Ealing Gate Way, 26-30 Uxbridge Road, Ealing, London, W5 2VP Tel: (020) 8566 5000 Fax: (020) 8579 9208 E-mail: mailbox@bmrb.co.uk *Market research services*

BMS, Mead House, 49 High Street, Egham, Surrey, TW20 9EW Tel: (01784) 434334 Fax: (01784) 435584 E-mail: jobs@bms-uk.com *Sales professionals recruitment*

▶ BMS Electrical, Windmill Farm, Benenden Road, Rolvenden, Cranbrook, Kent, TN17 4PF Tel: (01580) 241841 Fax: (01580) 241873

BMS Group, 3 Faversham Road, Challock, Ashford, Kent, TN25 4BQ Tel: (01233) 740134 Fax: (01233) 740943 E-mail: sales@bms-ltd.com *The BMS Group incorporates Bigwood Mechanical Services and Bulk Meter Services Limited. Bigwood Mechanical Services are the master European Distributor for the Veeder-Root Petroleum range of products, as well as being distributors for Danaher Controls & Hengstler counters. Bulk Meter Services Ltd., is a young vibrant field service company, carrying out meter calibrations, meter/system repairs and planned maintenance programs.*

BMT, Chapel Street, Wincham, Northwich, Cheshire, CW9 6DA Tel: (01606) 43886 Fax: (01606) 49059 E-mail: crosswarehouse@btconnect.com *Packing service agents*

▶ BMT Combustion Systems Ltd, Foxbourne Business Center, Heathmill Close, Wombourne, Wolverhampton, WV5 8EX Tel: (01902) 896183 Fax: (01902) 897372 E-mail: trevor@bmtcombustion.co.uk *Combustion systems & heating equipment suppliers*

BMT Cordah Ltd, Grove House, 7 Ocean Way, Southampton, SO14 3TJ Tel: (023) 8023 2222 Fax: (023) 8023 2891 E-mail: jenny.bell@bmtcordah.com *Environmental consultants & information systems*

BMT Murray Fenton Ltd, 70 Newcomen Street, London, SE1 1YT Tel: (020) 7234 9160 Fax: (020) 7234 9161 E-mail: enquiries@bmtmarcon.com *Marine consultants*

BMT The Salvage Association, 37-39 Lime Street, London, EC3M 7AY Tel: (020) 7648 9650 Fax: (020) 7234 9187 E-mail: sales@wreckage.org *Marine surveyors*

BMTGroup Ltd, Goodrich House, 1 Waldegrave Road, Teddington, Middlesex, TW11 8LZ Tel: (020) 8943 5544 Fax: (020) 8943 5347 E-mail: enquiries@bmtmail.com *Research organisation & developers*

BMW (GB) Ltd, Ellesfield Avenue, Bracknell, Berkshire, RG12 8TA Tel: (01344) 426565 Fax: (01344) 480203 E-mail: customer.service@bmw.co.uk *Motor car & cycle importers*

▶ BN Pork Products Ltd, Unit 23-24-25 Riverside, Power Station Road, Rugeley, Staffordshire, WS15 2YR Tel: (01889) 570088 Fax: (01889) 583550 E-mail: raygrey@btconnect.com *Food processors*

BN Thermic Ltd, 34 Woodside Road, London, SE25 5DY Tel: (01293) 547361 Fax: (01293) 531432 E-mail: sales@bnthermic.co.uk *Electric heater manufrs*

Bna International, Millbank Tower, 21-24 Millbank, London, SW1P 4QP Tel: (020) 7559 4800 Fax: (020) 7559 4848 E-mail: sales@bnai.com *Publications & information services*

▶ BNB Tax Consultants, Union Chambers, 63 Temple Row, Birmingham, B2 5LS Tel: 0121 483 6850 Fax: 0121 483 6851 E-mail: info@bnbtax.com *Tax consultancy services*

▶ BNC, 7 Old Gasworks, Station Road, Moretonhampstead, Newton Abbot, Devon, TQ13 8SA Tel: (01647) 440231 E-mail: info@bncelectrical.co.uk *Electrical contractors, domestic installation, agricultural,commercial and industrial installations.*

▶ BND UK Limited, Suite 501,, International House,, 223 Regent Street,, London, W1R 8QD Tel: 0870 2863725 Fax: 0870 7064636 E-mail: ht-sales@bndhardware.co.uk *Bnd UK limited are the sole importer and distributors of excellent quality "forge" branded hand tools and hardware in the UK. Providing our UK wholesale customers with great value and excellent products, we can supply almost every type of hand tool, INC. Allen keys, hammers, blades, bolsters, knifes, clamps, chisels, cutters, drywall knives, files, hatchets, ladders, tape measures, spirit levels, screwdrivers, spanners, tool sets, riveters, sockets, wheelbarrows, wrenches and much much more. Please visit our website for more details. We look forward to hearing from you.*

BNFL, Birchwood Park Avenue, Birchwood, Warrington, WA3 6GR Tel: (01925) 832000 Fax: (01925) 822711 E-mail: sales@britishnucleargroup.com *Reprocesses*

Bo Mac Sheffield Ltd, 63 Jenkin Road, Sheffield, S9 1AT Tel: 0114-244 8170 Fax: 0114-243 7104 E-mail: sales@bo-mac.co.uk *Precision engineers*

Bo Mic Engineering, 1 Brickyard Lane, New Road, Gillingham, Dorset, SP8 4JL Tel: (01747) 824216 Fax: (01747) 821726 E-mail: sale@bomic.co.uk *Precision engineers*

Boalloy Ltd, Radnor Park Trading Estate, West Heath, Congleton, Cheshire, CW12 4QA Tel: (01260) 275155 Fax: (01260) 279696 E-mail: buying@boalloy.org *Commercial vehicle body builders*

Boar Engineering Ltd, 39a Barking Industrial Park, Alfreds Way, Barking, Essex, IG11 0TJ Tel: (020) 8594 0526 Fax: (020) 8507 8050 E-mail: boareng@aol.com *Precision engineers & toolmakers*

Board Bros, 103 St John's Hill, London, SW11 1SY Tel: (020) 7228 6846 Fax: (020) 7228 8136 *Piston & piston ring wholesalers*

▶ Board Envelopes, Unit 15 Newark Storage Industrial Estate, Bowbridge Road, Newark, Nottinghamshire, NG24 4EQ Tel: (01636) 700611 Fax: (01636) 700084 E-mail: sales@boardenvelopes.com *Manufacturers of heavy duty mailing products*

Boarder Contract Services, Castlemains, Duns, Berwickshire, TD11 3TP Tel: (01361) 882809 Fax: (01361) 882871 *Agricultural contracting & technical services*

Boardley & Roberts Ltd, Plummers Dell, Gipping Road, Great Blakenham, Ipswich, IP6 0JG Tel: (01473) 830272 Fax: (01473) 830274 E-mail: carl@boardley-roberts.co.uk *Motor rewind contractors*

Boardman & Co., 8 Clydesdale Street, Oldham, OL8 1BT Tel: 0161-624 2058 Fax: 0161-652 0427 E-mail: boardmanscopiers@btconnect.com *Photocopying machines*

Boardman Bros Ltd, 50 Red Bank, Manchester, M4 4HF Tel: 0161-832 2381 Fax: 0161-833 2456 E-mail: reception@boardmanbros.co.uk *Glove & scarf merchants*

James Boardman Ltd, Weir Street, Blackburn, BB2 2BB Tel: (01254) 59755 Fax: (01254) 682482 E-mail: eng@jboardman.co.uk *Industrial heating engineers*

Boart UK Ltd, Littlemoor, Eckington, Sheffield, S21 4EF Tel: (01246) 435601 Fax: (01246) 435903 E-mail: sales@boartlongyear.com *Rock & quarry drilling equipment distributors*

Boat Care UK, 1Turpins Ride, Welwyn, Herts, AL6 0QS Tel: 0845 6521415. E-mail: enquires@boatcareuk.com *Boat Cleaning, Boat Valeting.*

Boat Electrics & Electronics Ltd, Harbour Road, Troon, Ayrshire, KA10 6DJ Tel: (01292) 315355 Fax: (01292) 315825 E-mail: sales@boatelectronics.com *Marine equipment*

Boat Harbour London Ltd, 40 High Street Colliers Wood, London, SW19 2AB Tel: (020) 8542 5857 Fax: (020) 8542 0284 *Boat builders & chandlers*

Boat & Jet Ski World, 94 Newhall Street, Willenhall, West Midlands, WV13 1LQ Tel: 0121-323 5335 Fax: (01902) 366136 E-mail: post@boatandjetskiworld.co.uk *Marines sales, service & repair*

Boat Store, Falmouth Yacht Marina, North Parade, Falmouth, Cornwall, TR11 2TD Tel: (01326) 318314 Fax: (01326) 318314 *Yatch chandling agents*

▶ Boatcoat, Fox House, Whimple Street, Plymouth, PL1 2DH Tel: (01752) 227333 Fax: (01752) 227333 E-mail: sales@boatcoat.co.uk *Shrink wrapping service*

▶ Boatcraft Boatbuilders, Clyde Marina, The Harbour, Ardrossan, Ayrshire, KA22 8DB Tel: (01294) 603047 Fax: (01294) 607076 E-mail: info@boatcraft.info *Boat repairs*

Boathunters Boatbuilders, The Docks, Burry Port, Dyfed, SA16 0LT Tel: (01554) 834030 *Boat builders, repairers & marina operators*

▶ Boatman Air Conditioning Ltd, Unit 1a Abbey Trading Estate, Bell Green Lane, London, SE26 5TW Tel: (0500) 300971 Fax: (020) 8778 9500

Boatman Plastics, Newport Road, Market Drayton, Shropshire, TF9 2AA Tel: (01630) 657286 Fax: (01630) 655545 *Plastic tank manufrs*

▶ Boats4fun, Averys Oak, Laughton, Lewes, East Sussex, BN8 6BY Tel: (07710) 000410 E-mail: sales@boats4fun.co.uk *Fishing, pleasure boats, dinghies, boat trailers & chandlery for sale*

The Boatworks, Benson, Wallingford, Oxfordshire, OX10 8SJ Tel: (01491) 833526 *Boat repairs & restoration service*

▶ Bob Francis, 31 Deeside Industrial Estate, Welsh Road, Deeside, Clwyd, CH5 2LR Tel: (01745) 591753 Fax: (01745) 591929

▶ Bob Heath Visors Ltd, 6 Birmingham Road, Walsall, WS1 2NA Tel: (01922) 614747 Fax: (01922) 644956 E-mail: b.heath@virgin.net *Plastic manufrs*

Bob Jackson Cycles 1993 Ltd, 320-322 Stanningley Road, Leeds, LS13 3EG Tel: 0113-255 9844 Fax: 0113-255 4444 E-mail: factory@bobjacksoncycles.demon.co.uk *Cycle retailers & manufrs*

Bob Langrish, The Old Court House, High Street, Bisley, Stroud, Gloucestershire, GL6 7AA Tel: (01452) 770140 Fax: (01452) 770146 *Equestrian photographers*

Bob Martin UK Ltd, 8 Wemberham Lane, Yatton, Bristol, BS48 4BS Tel: (01934) 831000 Fax: (01934) 831050 E-mail: sales@bobmartin.co.uk *Animal health care products manufrs*

Bobak Precision Engineers, 11 Berkeley Place, London, SW19 4NN Tel: (020) 8947 6323 Fax: (020) 8947 6323 E-mail: bobak_eng@lineone.net *General engineers*

▶ Bobcat Midlands Limited, Ridgeway, Well Lane, Little Witley, Worcester, WR6 6LN Tel: 01886 888413 Fax: 01886 888561 E-mail: adam.bobcat@virgin.net *Sales, Repairs, Hire and Spare Parts for all Bobcat machines - Herefordshire, Worcestershire and the West Midlands*

▶ Bobdonutandbird Ltd, 15 Beechwood Avenue, Ruislip, Middlesex, HA4 6EG Tel: (0870) 1995461 Fax: 020 8863 4148 E-mail: info@bobdonutandbird.co.uk *Cool t-shirts and slogan,designer t-shirts. Suppliers to Hollyoaks and other TV shows. Very silly funny t-shirts. Safe and secure website. Available for retail. Also clothing available for events, parties, shows, teams and groups, call or email for a quotation.*

Boc Ltd, The Priestley Centre, 10 Priestley Road, Surrey Research Park, Guildford, Surrey, GU2 7XY Tel: (01483) 579857 Fax: (01483) 244658 *Oxygen & nitrogen plant manufrs*

Boc Edwards Pharmaceutical Systems, P O Box 7, Huntly, Aberdeenshire, AB54 4SY Tel: (01542) 870633 Fax: (01542) 870222 E-mail: paul.vadler1@btinternet.com *Pharmaceutical equipment manufrs*

▶ Boc Gases Ltd, Chapelknowe Road, Motherwell, Lanarkshire, ML1 5LF Tel: (01698) 860721 Fax: (01698) 861870 *Suppliers of gases, equipment, consumables & services*

▶ BOCA REPAIRS MP Repairs Boca printer repairs, 78 Collingwood Road, South Woodham Ferrers, Chelmsford, CM3 5YD Tel: 07833 528725 E-mail: mprepairs@fsmail.net *BOCA REPAIRS. - Boca printer repair specialists and sales - Eltron /Zebra plastic card printer specialists. Most types of printer covered - Please contact for more details.07833 528725 (Mobile)*

Bocco Ltd, Fitzroy House, Lynwood Park, Worcester Park, Surrey, KT4 7AT Tel: (020) 8330 7007 Fax: (020) 8330 3351 E-mail: bocco@lineone.net *Bathroom fittings or accessories manufrs*

▶ The Boddington Collection, Castle Farm, Cholmondeley, Malpas, Cheshire, SY14 8AQ Tel: (0870) 2406135 Fax: (01948) 822151 E-mail: info@theboddington collection.co.uk *Cabinet manufrs*

Boddingtons Ltd, Blackwater Trading Estate, The Causeway, Maldon, Essex, CM9 4GG Tel: (01621) 874200 Fax: (01621) 874299 E-mail: sales@boddingtons-ltd.com *Extruded plastic mesh & netting manufacturers. Ground reinforcement products - plastic grass and paving.*

Boddingtons Shipping Ltd, Blackbirds, Little Bardfield, Braintree, Essex, CM7 4TU Tel: (01371) 810983 Fax: (01371) 811854 E-mail: robinbodd@aol.com *Shipping lines & ship owners*

Bodel Distributors Ltd, 9 Hulls Lane, Lisburn, County Antrim, BT28 2SR Tel: (028) 9267 2412 Fax: (028) 9267 1873 E-mail: sales@badel.com *Hardware manufrs*

Bodel Manufacturing Ltd, 9 Hulls Lane, Lisburn, County Antrim, BT28 2SR Tel: (028) 9266 5266 Fax: (028) 9267 1873 E-mail: sales@bodel.com *Kitchen furniture*

▶ Bodelwyddan Cold Stores Ltd, Royal Welsh Avenue, Kinmel Park, Bodelwyddan, Rhyl, Clwyd, LL18 5TY Tel: (01745) 582966

Boden Clark Ltd, George Henry Rd, Greatbridge, Tipton, W. Midlands, DY4 7BZ Tel: 0121-557 1700 Fax: 0121-557 3788 *Combustion consultants or consulting engineers*

Boden Engineers, Unit 9 Moorfields Industrial Estate, Cotes Heath, Stafford, ST21 6QY Tel: (01782) 791777 Fax: (01782) 791777 *Punches for ceramic products*

Boden Sheet Metal Ltd, Drake House, Drake Avenue, Staines, Middlesex, TW18 2AW Tel: (01784) 452683 Fax: (01784) 465889 E-mail: info@bodensheetmetal.co.uk *Sheet metal engineers & fabricators*

Bodenham & Shorthouse, 50 Albion Street, Birmingham, B1 3EA Tel: 0121-236 5464 Fax: 0121-236 5465 E-mail: jb@bodshort.fsnet.co.uk *Jewellery manufrs*

Bodet UK Ltd, 4 Sovereign Park, Cleveland Way, Hemel Hempstead Industrial Estate, Hemel Hempstead, Hertfordshire, HP2 7DA Tel: (01442) 418800 Fax: (01442) 234345 E-mail: enquiries@bodet.co.uk *Manufacturer and Distributor of clocks, clocks systems, time and attendance systems, access control*

Bodigian & Co. Ltd, Wenman Road, Industrial Estate, Thame, Oxfordshire, OX9 3SD Tel: (01844) 213555 Fax: (01844) 214120 E-mail: sales@bodigianofthame.co.uk *Carpet merchants*

Bodill Parker Group Ltd, Barnfield Industrial Estate, Speed Road, Tipton, West Midlands, DY4 9DY Tel: 0121-557 4164 Fax: 0121-557 4177 E-mail: sales@bodill-parker.co.uk Principal Export Areas: Worldwide *We are a small proactive presswork company which has been trading for over 150 years. We were the first to manufacture sail eyelets and still make a full range to BS3102. We also make brass grommets, cable thimbles, wire hooks.*

continued

Bodmin Blocks Ltd, Penwithick, St. Austell, Cornwall, PL26 8YL Tel: (01726) 850461 Fax: (01726) 850866 E-mail: bodblocks@callnet.com *Concrete blocks & slabs*

▶ Bodmin Flooring Centre & Carpetworld Ltd, Dunmere Road, Bodmin, Cornwall, PL31 2QN Tel: (01208) 76859 Fax: (01208) 78644 E-mail: mail@bodminflooring.com *Suppliers of carpets, beds, furniture & flooring*

▶ Body Buddies Lingerie, 41 Ely Close, Southminster, Essex, CM0 7AQ Tel: (07762) 059557 E-mail: sales@bodybuddies.co.uk *We sell top of the range Lingerie and Adult Toys at rock bottom prices*

Body Casual UK Ltd, 76 Dorothy Road, Leicester, LE5 5DQ Tel: 0116-273 6776 Fax: 0116-273 6776 *Clothing manufrs*

Body Coat Heat Treatment, Stillington, Stockton-on-Tees, Cleveland, TS21 1LD Tel: (01740) 630353 Fax: (01740) 630075 *Heat treatment services*

Body Coating Treatments Ltd, Cranbourne Road, Gosport, Hampshire, PO12 1RW Tel: (023) 9258 0946 Fax: (023) 9251 0292 E-mail: markdavies@bodycoat.com *Heat treatment specialist services*

Body Fitnesse, Unit 15B National Trading Estate, Hazel Grove, Stockport, Cheshire, SK7 5AA Tel: 0161-456 8556 *Gymnasium*

▶ Body Perfect, 524 Blackburn Road, Bolton, BL1 8NW Tel: (01204) 308100 E-mail: enquires@bodyperfectsalon.co.uk *Beauty treatment Decleor facials and body massage waxing eye care Decleor St Tropez self-tanning Pedicure manicure extensions electrolysis Bolton Astley Bridge Horwich Bury Darwen, Blackburn, Farnworth Chorley Leyland Manchester*Aromatherapy massage essential oils body envelope Isogei non-surgical face lift body treatment fine lines wrinkles skin rejuvenation bridal packages mother to be safe self-tan Gold Salon organic wax Hopi ear candling excessive ear wax, vertigo, colds, migraines, glue ear, sinusitis, rhinitis, tinitus, Menieres disease snoring Nailtiques, Warm Mitts Sixtus*

Body Sculpture (International Europe) Ltd, Morley Carr Road, Low Moor, Bradford, West Yorkshire, BD12 0RW Tel: (01274) 693888 Fax: (01274) 693700 E-mail: hi-markgroup@btinternet.co.uk *Weight training equipment distributors*

The Body Shop International P.L.C., Watersmead, Littlehampton, West Sussex, BN17 6LS Tel: (01903) 731500 Fax: (01903) 726250 E-mail: info@bodyshop.co.uk *Cosmetic manufrs*

▶ Body Talk, 48-57, Market Hall, Derby, DE1 2DB Tel: (01332) 298989 Fax: (01332) 296661

Bodycare Health & Beauty Ltd, 100 Albany Way, Salford, M6 5HR Tel: 0161-736 6522 *Cosmetic suppliers*

Bodycare Toiletries Ltd, A4-A5 Red Scar Industrial Estate, Longridge Road, Ribbleton, Preston, PR2 5NA Tel: (01772) 662400 Fax: (01772) 662401 *Toiletries manufrs*

Bodycoat Materials Testing, Shotton Works, Deeside Industrial Park, Deeside, Clwyd, CH5 2NH Tel: (01244) 818927 Fax: (01244) 836535 E-mail: shotton@bodycote.com *Analytical chemists*

Bodycoat Materials Testing Ltd, Lochend Industrial Estate, Queen Anne Drive, Newbridge, Midlothian, EH28 8PL Tel: 0131-333 4360 Fax: 0131-333 5135 E-mail: sales@bodycote.com *Pharmaceutical testing laboratory*

Bodycote, Carlisle Close, Sheffield Road, Sheepbridge, Chesterfield, Derbyshire, S41 9ED Tel: (01246) 260888 Fax: (01246) 260889 *Hot isostatic processing*

Bodycote, Unit 6-7 Furlong Business Centre, The Furlong, Berry Hill Industrial Estate, Droitwich, Worcestershire, WR9 9AH Tel: (01905) 774861 Fax: (01905) 776598 E-mail: droitwich@bodycote-mt.com *Non-destructive test services*

Bodycote Birmingham, Britannia House, Austin Way, Hampstead Industrial Estate, Birmingham, B42 1DU Tel: 0121-358 7266 Fax: 0121-358 0478 E-mail: info@bodycote.co.uk *Metal heat treatment services*

Bodycote Birmingham, Britannia House, Austin Way, Hampstead Industrial Estate, Birmingham, B42 1DU Tel: 0121-358 7266 Fax: 0121-358 0478 E-mail: sales@bodycote.com *Metal heat treatment services*

Bodycote Health Sciences, 121 Shady Lane, Great Barr, Birmingham, B44 9ET Tel: 0121-206 4100 Fax: 0121-251 4040 E-mail: healthsciences@bodycote.com *Food analysts & legal consultants*

Bodycote Heat Treatment Ltd, 11 Bamfurlong Industrial Park, Staverton, Cheltenham, Gloucestershire, GL51 6SX Tel: (01452) 714440 Fax: (01452) 856097 E-mail: sales@bodycote.co.uk *Vacuum heat treatment specialists*

Bodycote Heat Treatment Ltd, Field Way, Rotherham, South Yorkshire, S60 1QG Tel: (01709) 361047 Fax: (01709) 828529 E-mail: sales@bodycote.co.uk *Metal heat treatment services*

Bodycote Heat Treatment Ltd, 437 Chester Road, Woodford, Stockport, Cheshire, SK7 1QP Tel: 0161-440 0288 Fax: 0161-440 8017 E-mail: sales@bodycote.co.uk *Heat treatment services*

Bodycote Heat Treatment Ltd, Macclesfield Road, Hazel Grove, Stockport, Cheshire, SK7 5EN Tel: 0161-483 0511 Fax: 0161-483 5450 E-mail: sales@bodycote.co.uk *Heat treatment services*

Bodycote Heat Treatments Ltd, Springwood Court, Springwood Close, Tytherington Business Park, Macclesfield, Cheshire, SK10 2XF Tel: (01625) 505300 Fax: (01625) 505320 E-mail: info@bodycote.co.uk *Heat treatment services*

Bodycote Heating Treatment Ltd, 18 Westgate, Skelmersdale, Lancashire, WN8 8AZ Tel: (01695) 716500 Fax: (01695) 50105 E-mail: sales@bodycote.co.uk *Vacuum heat treatment services*

Bodycote Materials Engineering, White Cross Industrial Estate, South Road, Lancaster, LA1 4XQ Tel: (01524) 841070 Fax: (01524) 62983 E-mail: sales-uk@bodycote-mt.com *Materials testing services & specialists*

Bodycote Materials Testing Ltd, 4 Bleasdale Court, 2 South Avenue, Clydebank Business Park, Clydebank, Dunbartonshire, G81 2LE Tel: 0141-941 2022 Fax: 0141-952 7099 E-mail: analytical@bodycote.com *Environmental testing services laboratory*

Bodycote Materials Testing, 12 High March, High March Industrial Estate, Daventry, Northamptonshire, NN11 4HB Tel: (01327) 702964 Fax: (01327) 871119 E-mail: daventry@bodycote.com *Subcontract testing & proving house* Also at: Branches throughout the U.K.

Bodycote Materials Testing Ltd, Denison House, Hexthorpe Road, Doncaster, South Yorkshire, DN4 0BF Tel: (01302) 384340 Fax: (01302) 384341 E-mail: sales-uk@bodycote.com *Materials testing laboratory*

Bodycote Materials Testing Ltd, Shields Road, Newcastle upon Tyne, NE6 2YD Tel: 0191-275 2800 Fax: 0191-276 0177 E-mail: sales-mt@bodycote-mt.com *Providers of creep & stress rupture tests*

Bodycote Metallurgical Coatings Ltd, Harrison Way, Brunswick Business Park, Liverpool, L3 4BG Tel: 0151-709 8411 Fax: 0151-709 2622 E-mail: info@aerogistics.com *Electroplating services*

Bodycote Metallurgical Coatings Ltd, Shakespeare Street, Wolverhampton, WV1 3LR Tel: (01902) 452915 Fax: (01902) 352917 E-mail: sales.bmc@bodycote.co.uk *Rust proofers & sherardisers* Also at: Caerphilly & Rochdale

Bodycote Metallurgical Coatings Uxbridge Ltd, 5 Carleton House, 549 Eskdale Road, Uxbridge, Middlesex, UB8 2RT Tel: (01895) 252185 Fax: (01895) 810755 *Electroplaters*

Bodycote Radiography, 1 Blackbrook Valley Industrial Estate, Narrowboat Way, Dudley, West Midlands, DY2 0XQ Tel: (01384) 455880 Fax: (01384) 457250 E-mail: dudley@bodycote-mt.com *Testing services materials*

Bodycote (Somerset) Ltd, Leach Road, Chard Business Park, Chard, Somerset, TA20 1FA Tel: (01460) 67957 Fax: (01460) 67962 E-mail: sales@bodycote.co.uk *Metal heat treatment services*

Bodycraft 2004, Unit A4, Worcester Trading Estate, Worcester, WR3 8HR Tel: (01905) 753631 Fax: (01905) 756790 E-mail: bobbycraft@tiscali.co.uk *Commercial motor body builders*

BodyLaser Clinic, 58 Broadway, Peterborough, PE1 1SU Tel: 01733 555200 *The BodyLaser Clinic now offers the Titan skin tightening laser treatment for sagging skin. It also specialises in laser treatment for hair removal, facial veins and leg veins. Other services include Microdermabrasion, Genesis skin rejuvenation, Botox, Sculptra, and Restylane. Free consultation; call (01733) 555200.*www.BodyLaser.co.uk*

▶ Bodyline, 18 Park Farm Industrial Estate, Evesham Road, Greet, Cheltenham, Gloucestershire, GL54 5BX Tel: (01242) 621257 Fax: (01242) 603781 *Manufacturer van vehicle lining kits*

Bodylines, Autograph House, Frank Street, Preston, PR1 1PB Tel: (01772) 561177 Fax: (01772) 556993 *Sign writers*

Bodys Surgical Care Centre, 631 London Road, Westcliff-on-Sea, Essex, SS0 9PE Tel: (01702) 346204 Fax: (01702) 338631 *Surgical appliance suppliers*

▶ The Bodyshop Associates, 22 The Crescent, Littleport, Ely, Cambridgeshire, CB6 1HS Tel: (01353) 863800 Fax: (01353) 863800 E-mail: clive@cbservices.fsnet.co.uk *Auto paint supplies*

▶ Bodyshop Consumables Ltd, Wilne Road, Long Eaton, Nottingham, NG10 3AN Tel: 0115-946 1571 E-mail: orders@bodyshopconsumables.co.uk *On line store serving body shops*

Bodytreats International Ltd, 21, Manor Rd, Upper Beeding, Steyning, W. Sussex, BN44 3TJ Tel: (07768) 908486 E-mail: ksinfo@bodytreats.com *Aromatherapy products & essential oils*

Boehringer Ingelheim Ltd, Ellesfield Avenue, Bracknell, Berkshire, RG12 8YS Tel: (01344) 746959 Fax: (01344) 741349 E-mail: vetmedica.uk@boehringer-ingelheim.com *Pharmaceutical manufrs*

Boen UK Ltd, Elgar House, Green Street, Kidderminster, Worcestershire, DY10 1JF Tel: (0800) 6525280 Fax: (0870) 7704340 E-mail: sales@boen.co.uk *Hardwood flooring manufrs*

Boettcher U K Ltd, Cwmdraw Industrial Estate, Newtown, Ebbw Vale, Gwent, NP23 5AE Tel: (01495) 350300 Fax: (01495) 350064 E-mail: admin@boettcher.co.uk *Rubber & polyurethane roller manufrs*

Boewood Prevention Ltd, PO Box 44, Newtown, Powys, SY16 1WD Tel: (01686) 622228 Fax: (01686) 622451 E-mail: sales@doorsafety.co.uk *Door safety products suppliers*

▶ Bofa Electrical Ltd, 22 Broadleys Road, Stirling, FK7 7ST Tel: (01786) 450260 Fax: (01786) 451763

Bofa UK Ltd, Unit 13 Fleetsbridge Business Park, Upton Road, Poole, Dorset, BH17 7AF Tel: (01202) 699444 Fax: (01202) 699446 E-mail: sales@bofa.co.uk *Laser Fume Extraction Systems for Soldering, Electronics, Printing and Mechanical Engineering. *Market leaders in fume extraction, dust extraction and filtration systems for laser, solder, welder, engineering and printing environments. Laser Fume*

continued

Extraction and Fume Control for Laser Marking, Laser Coding and Laser Engraving industries.

Boge Compressors, Units 1-4, Bowen Industrial Estate, Aberbargoed, Bargoed, Mid Glamorgan, CF81 9EP Tel: (01443) 875163 Fax: (01443) 820909 *Compressed air engineers*

Bogod Group P.L.C., Fortran Road, St. Melons, Cardiff, CF3 0WJ Tel: (029) 2079 2079 Fax: (029) 2077 4999 *Suppliers of spare parts to sewing machines*

Bogod Machine Co., Bogod House, 50-52 Great Sutton Street, London, EC1V 0DJ Tel: (020) 7253 1198 Fax: (020) 7250 0016 E-mail: info@bernina.co.uk *Sewing machine distributors*

▶ Bogyoch Transport Co. Ltd, Fortrie Cottage, Fortrie, Turriff, Aberdeenshire, AB53 4HG Tel: (01466) 730310 Fax: (01466) 730347

Bohan Engineering, Unit 14a Fiveways Trading Estate, Westwells Road, Hawthorn, Corsham, Wiltshire, SN13 9RG Tel: (01225) 812730 Fax: (01225) 812188E-mail: sales@bohan.co.uk *Printed circuit equipment manufrs*

Bohemia Crystal (UK) Ltd, Hammond Road, Elms Industrial Estate, Bedford, MK41 0UD Tel: (01234) 347069 Fax: (01234) 271553 *Czech crystal & chinaware importers & distributors*

Bohle, Unit 7 Fifth Avenue, Dukinfield, Cheshire, SK16 4PP Tel: 0161-342 1100 Fax: 0161-344 0111 E-mail: bohleuk@bohle.de *Flat glass industry suppliers*

Bohler Special Steels, European Business Park, Taylors Lane, Oldbury, West Midlands, B69 2BN Tel: 0121-552 2575 Fax: 0121-552 0023 E-mail: sales@bohlersteels.co.uk *Manufacturers of special steels, tool steels & HSS*

Bohler Thyssen Welding (UK) Ltd, European Business Park, Taylors Lane, Oldbury, West Midlands, B69 2BN Tel: 0121-569 7700 Fax: 0121-544 2876 E-mail: info@btwuk.co.uk *Welding consumables*

Bohler-Uddeholm, Taylors Lane, Oldbury, West Midlands, B69 2BN Tel: 0121-511 1121 Fax: 0121-544 2911 E-mail: info@bohler-uddeholm.co.uk *Holding company*

Marcus Bohn Associates Ltd, Studio House, Delamare Road, Cheshunt, Waltham Cross, Hertfordshire, EN8 9SH Tel: (01992) 633882 Fax: (01992) 627831 E-mail: sales@marcusbohn.co.uk *Management & sales training specialists*

▶ Boho Chic, 35 Bridge Street, Dollar, Clackmannanshire, FK14 7DG Tel: (01259) 743311 *Fashion retailers*

Boil Irrigation Ltd, 46 Montford Road, Sunbury-on-Thames, Middlesex, TW16 6EJ Tel: (01932) 788301 Fax: (01932) 780437 E-mail: davidjones@boilirrigation.co.uk *Irrigation equipment & systems manufrs & installers*

▶ Boiler & Burner Maintenance, Unit 317 Woodside Way, Springvale Industrial Estate, Cwmbran, Gwent, NP44 5BR Tel: (01633) 871377 Fax: (01633) 838670

▶ Boiler Diagnostics Ltd, 127 Simpson Road, Snodland, Kent, ME6 5QH Tel: (01634) 244120 Fax: (01634) 245305 E-mail: matt@boilerdiagnostics.co.uk *Domestic & commercial heating service & repair*

▶ Boiler Healthcare, 16 Kent Road, Folkestone, Kent, CT19 4NT Tel: (01303) 275729 Fax: (01303) 279081 E-mail: sales@boilerhealthcare.co.uk

Boiler Management Systems (International) Ltd, 189-191 Rutland Road, Sheffield, S3 9PT Tel: 0114-275 5500 Fax: 0114-275 5533 E-mail: isd@bmsint.com *Heat transfer & process control systems manufrs*

▶ Boiler Scot Ltd, Victoria Buildings Business Ce, Violet Street, Paisley, Renfrewshire, PA1 1PA Tel: 0141-889 5447

Boiler Tech Services, Unit 22 Demmings Road, Cheadle, Cheshire, SK8 2PE Tel: 0161-428 2967 Fax: 0161-428 6487 E-mail: peter@mead4656.fsnet.co.uk *Boiler maintenance & repair services*

▶ Boing Boing, 36 Oakleigh Avenue, Chaddesden, Derby, DE21 6GZ Tel: (01332) 603010 Fax: (01332) 603010

Boiswood Ltd, Unit A1 Spinnaker Park, Hempsted, Gloucester, GL2 5JA Tel: (01452) 330011 Fax: (01452) 330088 E-mail: ian.taylor@boiswood.co.uk *Pressure regulator distributors or agents*

▶ Bojangle Communications Ltd, 2 Virginia Close, Ashtead, Surrey, KT21 2NW Tel: (01372) 274975 E-mail: lindsey@bojangle.co.uk *A fresh approach to public relations. The company has expertise in trade show promotion and the aerospace, automotive, construction, defence, and financial services industries.*

Boka Bolt Supplies, 10 Cormorant Drive, Picow Farm Road, Runcorn, Cheshire, WA7 4UD Tel: (01928) 590440 Fax: (01928) 590400 *Stockist of industrial fasteners*

Bolam & Shaw Ltd, Red Doles Works, Red Doles Lane, Huddersfield, HD2 1YF Tel: (01484) 425705 Fax: (01484) 430480 E-mail: sales@bolamandshaw.co.uk *Wooden pallet & packing cases manufrs*

▶ Boland Jarrett (Edinburgh) Ltd, 49 Northumberland St, Edinburgh, EH3 6JJ Tel: 0131-557 8155 E-mail: mail@johnstonfinancial.co.uk

Bold Transmission Parts Ltd, Webber Road, Knowsley Industrial Park North, Knowsley Industrial Park, Liverpool, L33 7SW Tel: 0151-548 2303 Fax: 0151-549 1117 E-mail: sales@engineerskeys.co.uk *Engineers key manufrs*

▶ Boldmere Plumbing, 377 Chester Road, Sutton Coldfield, West Midlands, B73 5BL Tel: 0121-382 7020 E-mail: simonawhite@hotmail.com *Plumbing service, maintenance & contractor*

Boldon Drilling Ltd, Private Road 3, Colwick Industrial Estate, Nottingham, NG4 2BB Tel: 0115-961 1250 Fax: 0115-961 7338 E-mail: drill@bds.co.uk *On-land drilling contractors*

Boldvale Engineering Ltd, Unit 15 Cambridge Industrial Estate Montague Road, Hanwell, London, W7 3PG Tel: (020) 8840 2398 Fax: (020) 8566 3125

continued

E-mail: john.dwight@boldvaleeng.co.uk *Aircraft component manufrs*

Bolenda Engineering Ltd, Birds Hill, Clopton, Woodbridge, Suffolk, IP13 6SE Tel: (01473) 601982 Fax: (01473) 690954 E-mail: lee@bolenda.ndo.co.uk *Engineering & fabrication manufrs*

Boler S E Ltd, 16-20 Princess Street, Sheffield, S4 7UW Tel: 0114-272 0833 Fax: 0114-272 0838 E-mail: sales@boler-se.com *Electrical contractors*

Bolhoff Fastenings Ltd, Midacre, Willenhall, West Midlands, WV13 2JW Tel: (01902) 637161 Fax: (01902) 609495 E-mail: enquiries@bollhoff.co.uk *Rivets & fasteners distributor*

The Bolholt Hotel, Walshaw Road, Bury, Lancashire, BL8 1PU Tel: 0161-762 4000 Fax: 0161-762 4100E-mail: sales@bolholt.co.uk *Hotel, conference & leisure centre services*

Bolivar Ltd, Unit 9B Devonshire Works, Riparian Way, Cross Hills, Keighley, West Yorkshire, BD20 7BW Tel: (01535) 631222 Fax: (01535) 637555 E-mail: sales@bolivar-limited.com *Pipe clip distributors & manufrs*

Bollegraaf UK Ltd, 93-96 William Street, West Bromwich, West Midlands, B70 0BG Tel: 0121-557 9700 Fax: 0121-557 9800 E-mail: info@bollegraaf.co.uk *Design & manufacture of recycling machinery & MRF systems*

Bollin Dale Engineering Ltd, Pownall Square, Macclesfield, Cheshire, SK11 8DT Tel: (01625) 422620 Fax: (01625) 614322 E-mail: sales@bollineng.co.uk *CNC engineering services or machinists*

Bollman Headwear Europe Ltd, Cleator Mills, Cleator, Cumbria, CA23 3DJ Tel: (01946) 810312 Fax: (01946) 811087 E-mail: enquireies@kangolheadweareurope.com *Headwear distributors* Also at: Luton

Bolne Materials Handling, Unit 2 Stoken Place, Steventon, Basingstoke, Hampshire, RG25 3BD Tel: (01256) 398585 Fax: (01256) 398484 E-mail: sales@bolne.co.uk *Hire Of Handling Equipment*

Bolsons Ltd, The Gatehouse, Cooks Road, London, E15 2PW Tel: (020) 8555 7137 Fax: (020) 8519 6641 E-mail: info@bolsons.co.uk *Founded in the East End of London in 1894 as M. Bolson & Co. Limited, was acquired on a management buyout by Bolsons Limited in 1983. Historically Bolsons concentrated on the production of Company Seals and embossing presses. Bolsons also produce perforators for validating voting papers and a vast range of rubber stamps. Since the Companies Act 1985 made the need for a Company Seal no longer mandatory, the demand for Company Seals has reduced, but the computerisation of artwork and production has enabled Bolsons to improve its service and speed of delivery of the Heraldic and specialised logo work. A Company Seal can be manufactured and delivered from the factory near the Bow flyover, to the City of London, within three hours of the order. Seals and presses are exported to Switzerland, Nigeria, Uganda, Australia, United States of America and The Republic of Ireland. In addition, Bolsons supplies the Seals for Government Departments, Archbishops & Bishops, College of Arms, British Embassies, Universities (for Sealing degrees) and the Central Chancery of Knighthoods at St. James's Palace. Bolsons Ltd are specialists in company seals, wax seals, perforators, heraldic seals, Rubber stamps, steel stamps, medals and company registers and we are also manufacturers of the largest range of paper embossing tools.*

Bolt Ltd, Bluebridge Industrial Estate, Colchester Road, Halstead, Essex, CO9 2EX Tel: (01787) 477261 Fax: (01787) 475680 E-mail: enquiries@boltbuildingsupplies.co.uk *Timber & builders merchants*

Bolt & Bearing London, 21s Queensway, Enfield, Middlesex, EN3 4UL Tel: (020) 8805 7250 Fax: (020) 8804 0126 E-mail: sales@boltandbearing.co.uk *Fixing distributors*

▶ Bolt Burdon Kemp, 338 City Road, London, EC1V 2PY Tel: 0870 0201650 *No win, no fee lawyers we specialise in personal injury claims, medical negligence, lawyers negligence, case of child abuse and less serious personal injuries*

▶ Bolt Fabrications & Site Services, Unit 5, Albany Trading Estate, Albany Street, Newport, Gwent, NP20 5NQ Tel: (07799) 835958 Fax: (01633) 872143 E-mail: mike@boltfabs.co.uk *Steel fabrications & site installations*

Bolt & Nut Manufacturing, White Lee Road, Swinton, Mexborough, South Yorkshire, S64 8BH Tel: (01709) 570212 Fax: (01709) 584125 E-mail: sales@tachart.com *CNC turned parts, bolts, nuts, fastener manufrs*

Bolt & Nut Supplies Ltd, 35-37 Chapeltown, Pudsey, West Yorkshire, LS28 7RZ Tel: 0113-255 6336 Fax: 0113-256 9242 *Engineers merchants*

Boltdown Power Press Repairs Ltd, Unit 10 Cato Street, Birmingham, B7 4TS Tel: 0121-359 7862 Fax: 0121-359 4645 E-mail: bolstownppr@aol.com *Power press maintenance & repair*

▶ Boltight, Unit 2 Junction 10 Business Park, Bentley Mill Way, Walsall, WS2 0LE Tel: (01922) 631289 Fax: (01922) 633728 E-mail: sales@boltight.com *Bolt tensioners, hydraulic nuts, pumps hydraulic, bolt tightening systems, HydraNuts, hydraulic bolt tightening tools, Hand pumps, bolt tensioning equipment, Hydraulic bolt tensioners.*

▶ Bolton Bros Shoe & Appliance Makers Ltd, Penn Street, Newcastle upon Tyne, NE4 7BG Tel: 0191-273 2012 Fax: 0191-226 0143

Bolton Business Ventures Ltd, 46 Lower Bridgeman Street, Bolton, BL2 1DG Tel: (01204) 391400 Fax: (01204) 380076 E-mail: sales@bbvonline.net *Business advisors*

Bolton Enamellers, Unit 19 Portland Industrial Estate, Portland Street, Bury, Lancashire, BL9 6EY Tel: 0161-763 1333 Fax: 0161-763 1341 E-mail: dave@boltonenamellers.co.uk *Industrial paint spray specialists*

Bolton Gate Co. Ltd, 6 Dutton Court, Chainbridge Road, Blaydon-on-Tyne, Tyne & Wear, NE21 5ST Tel: 0191-414 0112 Fax: 0191-414 3011 E-mail: sales@boltongate.co.uk *Manufacture roller shutter doors*

Bolton Gate Co. Ltd, Waterloo Street, Bolton, BL1 2SP Tel: (01204) 871000 Fax: (01204) 871049 E-mail: general@boltongate.co.uk *Industrial folding door manufrs* Also at: Branches throughout the U.K.

Bolton Hemming Ltd, Halliwell Industrial Estate, Wapping Street, Bolton, BL1 8DP Tel: (01204) 492614 Fax: (01204) 492088 E-mail: enquiries@bolton-hemming.co.uk *Household textile products*

Bolton Labelling Systems, 53-55 Bridgeman Place, Bolton, BL2 1DE Tel: (01204) 526079 Fax: (01204) 384348 E-mail: sales@boltonlabelling.co.uk *Self adhesive & fabric labels manufrs*

Bolton Linen Services, Minerva Road, Farnworth, Bolton, BL4 0JR Tel: (01204) 390613 Fax: (01204) 390693 *Laundry & linen hire*

Bolton Metropolitan Borough Council Commercial Services Bolmoor I, St Helens Road, Bolton, BL3 3NS Tel: (01204) 336855 Fax: (01204) 658072 E-mail: sales@bolmoor.co.uk *Manufacturers of newspaper courier bags & work wear*

▶ Bolton P C, 57 Bramhall Avenue, Harwood, Bolton, BL2 4ES Tel: (0870) 0174010 Fax: (0870) 0174011 E-mail: sales.kellysearch@boltonpc.co.uk *Computer Hardware delivered UK wide, but free in any BL (Bolton) post code. At Bolton PC, we will always endeavor to provide the best brands on Earth with prices that are down to Earth. Our product portfolio contains such names as AMD, Intel, Adaptec, Twinmoss, Sandisk, Intenso, ADATA, Relisys, Chaintech, Epson, HP Lexmark, Alps, Artec, Acer, Benq, Fujitsu, Hitachi, Inex, Jetway, Toshiba, Genius, LG, Maxtor, Mercury, Microsoft, NEC, Pioneer, Ronin, Samsung, Seagate, Sony, Thermal Take, and Western Digital, the list goes on.*

Bolton Profiles Ltd, Brittania Way Industrial Park, Union Road, Bolton, BL2 2HG Tel: (01204) 386441 Fax: (01204) 385705 E-mail: paul@boltonprofiles.co.uk *High - definition plasma, underwater plasma and gas steel profile cutting and grinding. Full on site CNC machine shop. CAD/CNC controlled. ISO9001:200 UKAS approved.*

Bolton Scaffolding, Unit 4b-C Horwich Loco Estate, Chorley New Road, Horwich, Bolton, BL6 5UE Tel: (01204) 478910 Fax: (01204) 478919 E-mail: hardmana@biltonscaffolding.co.uk *Scaffolding contract services*

Bolton Sign Contractors, Unit 4 Printers Lane, Bolton, BL2 3DW Tel: (01204) 594700 Fax: (01204) 595424 E-mail: info@boltonsign.co.uk *Sign contractors & signwriting services*

▶ Bolton Stone Restoration Ltd, Winter House, Winter Street, Bolton, BL1 8AZ Tel: (01204) 843853 Fax: (01204) 849841 E-mail: enquiries@boltonstone.co.uk *Stone Restoration. Stone Cleaning. Wet Abrasive. Dry Abrasive. Chemical Cleaning. Specialist Coatings. Terra Cotta. Retaining Walls. Dry Stone Walls.*

Bolton Tarpaulins, Unit 16 Brownlow Business Centre, Darley Street, Bolton, BL1 3DX Tel: (01204) 380837 Fax: (01204) 380837 E-mail: boltontarps@btconnect.com *Tarpaulin manufrs*

Bolton's Superheaters Ltd, Wellington Works, Wellington Road, Ashton-U-Lyne, Ashton-under-Lyne, Lancashire, OL6 7EF Tel: 0161-344 0208 Fax: 0161-343 3305 E-mail: sales@superheater.co.uk *Boiler & pipework fabricators*

Bolts Of Hereford, 5-7 Perseverance Road, Hereford, HR4 9SN Tel: (01432) 269508 Fax: (01432) 263835 E-mail: nick.bolt@btclick.com *Suspended ceiling & partition installers*

Boltworthy Ltd, Unit I1 Cowlairs, Nottingham, NG5 9RA Tel: 0115-977 0432 Fax: 0115-977 0424 *Fastener distributors*

Bolwell Rowcliffe Ltd, 54-56 Brigstocke Road, Bristol, BS2 8TY Tel: 0117-924 6844 Fax: 0117-942 5589 E-mail: info@bolwell-rowcliffe.co.uk *Plastic mould toolmakers, plastic injection moulders specialists*

Bolyer Engineering Co. Ltd, Bayton Road, Bayton Road Industrial Estate, Exhall, Coventry, CV7 9EL Tel: (024) 7636 1600 Fax: (024) 7636 5151 E-mail: info@bolyer.co.uk *Pressing works manufrs*

Bolzoni Auramo Ltd, Unit 10 Taurus Park, Europa Boulevard, Westbrook, Warrington, WA5 7ZT Tel: (01925) 624570 Fax: (01925) 624578 E-mail: admin@bolzoni-auramo.com *Fork lift truck attachment manufrs*

Bom Group Ltd, Clue House, Petherton Road, Bristol, BS14 9BZ Tel: (01275) 890100 Fax: (01275) 890111 E-mail: info@bom.co.uk *Software developers*

▶ Bomac Electric Ltd, Randles Road, Knowsley Business Park, Prescot, Merseyside, L34 9HX Tel: 0151-546 4401 Fax: 0151-549 1661 E-mail: sales@bomac-elec.co.uk *General appliance heating element manufrs*

Bomag Great Britain Ltd, Sheldon Way, Larkfield, Aylesford, Kent, ME20 6SE Tel: (01622) 715252 Fax: (01622) 710233 E-mail: sales@bomag.com *Site refuse compactors & compaction equipment*

Bombardier, Litchurch Lane, Derby, DE24 8AD Tel: (01332) 344666 Fax: (01332) 266271 E-mail: bombardi@transportation.bombardier.com Principal Export Areas: Worldwide *Railway equipment manufrs*

Bombardier Transportation, West Street, Crewe, CW1 3JB Tel: (01270) 538700 Fax: (01270) 538669 E-mail: info@transportation.bombardier.com *Engineering & railway repairers*

Bombardier Transportation (Signal Management) U K Ltd, Letcombe Street, Reading, RG1 2HN Tel: 0118-953 8000 Fax: 0118-9538009 *Railway signalling equipment manufrs*

▶ BOMBER COUNTY CUSTOMS, Drakes holdings, Ferry Road, Fiskerton, Lincoln, LN3 4HU Tel: (07958) 018368 E-mail: petescustom24@yahoo.co.uk *MOTORCYCLE AND TRIKE BUILDER MANUFACTURER OF ONE OFF PARTS IN ALLOY,STEEL AND STAINLESS STEEL,ALSO SUPPLIER OF CUSTOM PARTS FROM HIGHWAY HAWK,ALLOY WELDING REPAIRS AND POLISHING TO A HIGH STANDARD IF YOU WANT THE BEST AT AN AFFORDABLE PRICE call for quote.,*

▶ Bombers Bouncys, 4 Buttercup Close, Stamford, Lincolnshire, PE9 4BS Tel: (01780) 753152 *Bouncy castle hirers*

Bomet UK (Threaded Bar) Ltd, Unit H3, Eastacre, Off Longacre, Willenhall, West Midlands, WV13 2JZ Tel: (01902) 368400 Fax: (01902) 606877 E-mail: j.shuffe@bomet.com *Threaded rod manufrs*

Bomford Turner Ltd, Station Road, Salford Priors, Evesham, Worcestershire, WR11 8SW Tel: (01789) 773383 Fax: (01789) 773238 E-mail: sales@bomford-turner.com *Cultivator & flail mower manufrs*

Bominflot Ltd, Ravensbourne Road, Bromley, BR1 1HN Tel: (020) 8315 5400 Fax: (020) 8315 5429 E-mail: mail@bominflot.co.uk *Marine fuel bunkering services*

▶ Bomphray Signs, 38 Central Avenue, Troon, Ayrshire, KA10 7AZ Tel: (01292) 319555 Fax: (01292) 319444 E-mail: karen.bomphray@ukonline.co.uk *Sign manufacturers*

Bomphray Signs, 38 Central Avenue, Troon, Ayrshire, KA10 7AZ Tel: (01292) 319555 Fax: (01292) 319444 *Sign manufrs*

Bon Accord Glass, Bon Accord House, Riverside Drive, Aberdeen, AB11 7SL Tel: (01224) 588944 Fax: (01224) 582731

Bon Accord Metal Supplies Ltd, 86 Sinclair Road, Aberdeen, AB11 9PP Tel: (01224) 878898 Fax: (01224) 879730 E-mail: info@bonaccordmetals.co.uk Principal Export Areas: Worldwide *Industrial fastener manufrs*

Bon Accord Sparkling Drinks Ltd, 12 Station Rd, Larkhall, Lanarkshire, ML9 2DB Tel: 01698 883295 Fax: 01698 883295 *Soft drinks distribution.*

Bon Accord Trophies, 121 Crown Street, Aberdeen, AB11 6HN Tel: (01224) 576226 Fax: (01224) 585089 E-mail: info@soccerworldscotland.co.uk *Engravers*

▶ Bon Bons Office, 17 Sandbeck Park, Sandbeck Lane, Wetherby, West Yorkshire, LS22 7TW Tel: (01937) 584600 Fax: (01937) 584600 E-mail: info@bonbon.co.uk *Confectionery wholesale & retail*

Bon Groundwork Ltd, 47 Windsor Drive, Orpington, Kent, BR6 6EY Tel: (01689) 862285 Fax: (01689) 850917 *Ground workers*

Bonair Air Conditioning, 8 Westfield Close Rawreth Industrial Estate, Rawreth Lane, Rayleigh, Essex, SS6 9RL Tel: (01268) 782828 Fax: (01268) 783287 E-mail: mike@bonair.co.uk *Vehicle air conditioning specialists*

Bonair Plastics Ltd, Old Forge Yard, Swanley Village Road, Swanley, Kent, BR8 7NF Tel: (01322) 664347 Fax: (01322) 664347 E-mail: dave@bonair.freeserve.co.uk *Plastics moulding manufrs*

Bonaprene Products, Clywedog Road South, Wrexham Industrial Estate, Wrexham Industrial Estate, Wrexham, Clwyd, LL13 9XS Tel: (01978) 661478 Fax: (01978) 661190 E-mail: sales@polybush.co.uk *Manufacturers of Polyurethane elastomer products; roller manufacture, refurbishment and recovery; specialists in Polyurethane to metal bonding; vehicle bushes; bespoke Polyurethane mouldings; sheets; cyclones. Complete design service and tooling service is also available.*

Bonar Floors, 92 Seedlee Road, Walton Summit Centre, Bamber Bridge, Preston, PR5 8AE Tel: (01772) 646900 Fax: (01772) 646912 *Carpet tiles distributors*

Bonar Floors Ltd, High Holborne Road, Ripley, Derbyshire, DE5 3XD Tel: (01773) 744121 Fax: (01773) 744142 E-mail: enquires@bonarfloors.com *Safety & anti-slip matting manufrs*

Bonar Yards & Fabrics Ltd, St Salvador Street, Dundee, DD3 7EU Tel: (01382) 227346 Fax: (01382) 202378 E-mail: ascott@bonaryarns.com *Artificial grass & polypropylene yarn manufrs*

Bonart Ltd, 19 Stilebrook Road, Olney, Buckinghamshire, MK46 5EG Tel: (01234) 711171 Fax: (01234) 711979 E-mail: hq@bonart.co.uk *Menswear wholesalers*

Bonas Machine Co. Ltd., Dukesway, Team Valley Trading Estate, Gateshead, Tyne & Wear, NE11 0LF Tel: 0191-491 0444 Fax: 0191-491 0999 E-mail: sales@bonas.co.uk *Textile machinery sales (UK)*

Bond Air Services Ltd, Boreham Airfield, Boreham, Chelmsford, CM3 3BG Tel: (01245) 362627 Fax: (01245) 362624 *Helicopter operators*

Bond Catering Manufacturers, Bond Street, Denton, Manchester, M34 3AJ Tel: 0161-320 4065 *Catering equipment manufrs*

Bond Engineering Ltd, Harrowbrook Road, Hinckley, Leicestershire, LE10 3DJ Tel: (01455) 632775 Fax: (01455) 632738 E-mail: bondeng31@aol.com *Precision turned parts manufrs*

Bond Engineering Maintenance Ltd, Unit P-Q Little Moor Lane, North Road, Loughborough, Leicestershire, LE11 1RL Tel: (01509) 266662 Fax: (01509) 231638 E-mail: sales@cranesandhoist.co.uk *Lifting gear distributors*

Bond Estates Ltd, Bond Avenue, Bletchley, Milton Keynes, MK1 1JJ Tel: (01908) 270900 Fax: (01908) 270052 E-mail: info@terrapin-ltd.co.uk *Property developers*

Bond Instrumentation & Process Control Ltd, Woodrope Building, Woodrolfe Road, Tollesbury, Essex, CM9 8SE Tel: (01621) 862140 Fax: (01621) 862141 E-mail: bond@bond.ipc.com *Control for land & marine industries*

Bond International, Unit 10 Coped Hall Business Park, Wootton Bassett, Swindon, SN4 8DP Tel: (01793) 856300 Fax: (01793) 856301 E-mail: helpdesk@infosupport.co.uk *Personnel system software*

Bond International Software Ltd, Courtlands, Parklands Avenue, Goring-by-Sea, Worthing, West Sussex, BN12 4NG Tel: (01903) 707070 Fax: (01903) 707080 E-mail: sales@bond.co.uk *Computer & data processing services.*

Bond Lovis Insurance Brokers Ltd, 522 Barking Road, London, E13 8QE Tel: (020) 8552 6900 Fax: (020) 8470 3051 E-mail: sales@bondlovis.co.uk *Insurance brokers*

Bond Pearce, Ballard House, West Hoe Road, Plymouth, PL1 3AE Tel: (0870) 1200000 Fax: (023) 8020 8050 E-mail: elcroft@bondpearce.com *Solicitors*

Bond Precision Grinding Ltd, Trafalgar Works, Effingham Road, Sheffield, S9 3QA Tel: 0114-273 1212 Fax: 0114-276 5387 E-mail: bondpreci@aol.com *Spring steel stockholders*

Bond R S C Associates Ltd, Unit 3 Mercy Terrace, Ladywell, London, SE13 7UX Tel: (020) 8314 1188 Fax: (020) 8314 1221 E-mail: info@bondmailrooms.com *Mailroom equipment*

Bond Scaffolding Ltd, 31 Lamb Lane, London, E8 3PL Tel: (020) 7254 4444 Fax: (020) 7254 9046 *Scaffolding contractors*

Bond Street Business Base, 3 Bond Street, St. Helier, Jersey, JE2 3NP Tel: (01534) 724100 Fax: (01534) 759662 E-mail: info@bondbase.info *Business centre including desk*

Bond Street Personnel Ltd, 22 South Molton Street, London, W1K 5RB Tel: (020) 7629 3692 Fax: (020) 7409 1524 E-mail: enquires@bondstreetpersonnel.co.uk *Recruitment specialists*

Bond Trading GB Ltd, 2 Gillingham Green, Gillingham, Kent, ME7 1SS Tel: (01634) 580670 Fax: (01634) 855455 E-mail: bondtradingltd@aol.com *Import & export buying house*

▶ Bond Trucking Co, The Old Brickyard, Ashton Keynes, Swindon, SN6 6QR Tel: (01285) 861875 Fax: (01285) 861875

Bond & White Buildbase, 40 Muswell Hill Road, Highgate, London, N6 5UN Tel: (020) 8883 9722 Fax: (020) 8444 5146 E-mail: highgate@buildbase.co.uk *Buildbase is one of the UK's fastest growing builders merchants. All of our branches are long established companies which have been serving local trades people for many years, with knowledge and experience to match. We believe strongly in understanding the needs of trades professional and our business has been developed specifically to meet those demands. Massive stocks, top quality products, competitive pricing, reliable delivery, specialist staff and exceptional customer service*

▶ Bond Williams Professional Recruitment, 23 Hinton Road, Bournemouth, BH1 2EF Tel: (01202) 201700 Fax: (01202) 201645 E-mail: enquiry@bondwilliams.co.uk *As an independent recruitment agency, Bond Williams specialise in the placing of professional, high calibre, permanent office staff within quality companies on the South Coast. **With our extensive local knowledge and experience in the business we have built an enviable reputation founded on integrity, honesty and quality of service.*"

Bond-a-Band Transmissions Ltd, Vale Mills, Oakworth, Keighley, West Yorkshire, BD22 0EB Tel: 01535 643123 Fax: 01535 646795 E-mail: sales@bondaband.com Principal Export Areas: Worldwide *Manufacturers extensible, polyurethane, round & conveyor belting. In addition, polyurethane extrusion & sheet/film manufrs*

Bondaglass Voss Ltd, 158 Ravenscroft Road, Beckenham, Kent, BR3 4TW Tel: (020) 8778 0071 Fax: (020) 8659 5297 E-mail: bondaglass@btconnect.com *Suppliers of cold curing plastics*

Bondaglass Voss Ltd, Sunderland Road, Sandy, Bedfordshire, SG19 1QY Tel: (01767) 681432 Fax: (01767) 691720 *Chemical manufrs*

Bondation Fabrications, 4-6 Abingdon Road, Nuffield Industrial Estate, Poole, Dorset, BH17 0UG Tel: (01202) 677828 Fax: (01202) 677861 *Sheet metal engineers*

Bondcote Ltd, Unit 15, Lister Road Industrial Estate, Sherrington Way, Basingstoke, Hampshire, RG22 4DQ Tel: (01256) 465983 Fax: (01256) 328818 E-mail: mail@bondcote.co.uk *Laminated metal materials manufrs*

Bonded Abrasives Ltd, Green Street, Macclesfield, Cheshire, SK10 1JQ Tel: (01625) 429009 Fax: (01625) 610076 E-mail: p.d.bailey@btinternet.com *Abrasive products manufrs*

Bonded Components Ltd, Brookside, Glatton Road, Sawtry, Huntingdon, Cambridgeshire, PE28 5SB Tel: (01487) 831278 Fax: (01487) 832274 *Sandwich panel manufrs*

Bonded Motor Spares Ltd, 95 Cooperative Street, Stafford, ST16 3DA Tel: (01785) 250850 Fax: (01785) 250852 *Rubber to metal bonders*

Bonded Services, Unit 1, Aerodrome Way, Cranford Lane, Hounslow, TW5 9QB Tel: (020) 8990 9192 Fax: (020) 8990 9028 E-mail: sales@ftsbonded.com *Freight forwarders of agents*

▶ Bondelivery, Dundrod Road, Nutts Corner, Crumlin, County Antrim, BT29 4SR Tel: (028) 9082 5151 Fax: (028) 9082 5296

Bondelivery, TT Complex, Dundrod Road, Crumlin, County Antrim, BT29 4SS Tel: (028) 9082 5151 Fax: (028) 9068 3300 E-mail: bondelivery@demon.co.uk *Storage distributors*

Bondex Adhesives & Coatings Ltd, C.P Farms, Woburn Road, Wootton, Bedford, MK43 9EL Tel: (01234) 757763 Fax: (01234) 765550 *Adhesive supply & manufrs*

Bonding & Reline Services Co. Ltd, Unit 4, Carls Way, Thurmaston, Leicester, LE4 8DL Tel: 0116-260 1717 Fax: 0116-260 1958 *Brake & clutch reline & hydraulic components specialists*

Bonding Techniques (Stotfold) Ltd, Taylors Road, Stotfold, Hitchin, Hertfordshire, SG5 4AX Tel: (01462) 733120 Fax: (01462) 732822 E-mail: info@bondingtechniques.com *Panel laminators*

Bondlabels Ltd, Wollaston Way, Burnt Mills Industrial Area, Basildon, Essex, SS13 1DJ Tel: (01268) 590555 Fax: (01268) 590999 E-mail: sales@bondlabels.co.uk *Self-adhesive products manufrs*

Bondloc UK Ltd, Alton Works, Long Bank, Bewdley, Worcestershire, DY12 2UJ Tel: (01299) 269269 Fax: (01299) 269210 E-mail: sales@bondloc.co.uk *Adhesive formulators & manufrs*

▶ Bondrite Adhesives Ltd, Unit 12, Meadow Lane Industrial Estate, Gordon Road, Loughborough, Leicestershire, LE11 1JP Tel: (01509) 262121 Fax: (01509) 262122 E-mail: sales@bondrite.co.uk *We pride ourselves on a fast response, competitive pricing, deliveries to customer requirements and an overall high level of service. If you need reliability and the willingness to "pull out all the stops" from a supplier then you will not be disappointed. Our Range is very extensive covering virtually every adhesive manufactured in many different pack sizes. Consequently, you can take advantage of a single source for all your adhesive requirements. If you have a gluing problem we can advise the best adhesive to resolve it and, if necessary, undertake bond testing in our lab using your sample substrates to ensure you get a product to match your requirements exactly.*

Bonds Foundry Co., Wards End, Tow Law, Bishop Auckland, County Durham, DL13 4JS Tel: (01388) 730328 Fax: (01388) 731034 E-mail: bfc@bondsfoundry.com *Steel casting manufrs*

Bondworth Ltd, Townshend Works, Puxton Lane, Kidderminster, Worcestershire, DY11 5DF Tel: (01562) 745000 Fax: (01562) 732827 E-mail: sales@bondworth.co.uk *Carpets manufrs*

John K. Bone, 404 Cremer Business Centre, Cremer Street, London, E2 8HD Tel: (020) 7739 2470 Fax: (020) 7739 2470 E-mail: terryberry321@hotmail.com *Furniture restorers & manufrs*

▶ Bone Steel Ltd, Pickering Park Works, Netherton Road, Wishaw, Lanarkshire, ML2 0EQ Tel: (01698) 375000 Fax: (01698) 372727 E-mail: sales@bonesteel.co.uk *Industrial steel manufrs*

Bonefish Adventure Ltd, 75 Bargates, Christchurch, Dorset, BH23 1QE Tel: 01202 474343 E-mail: info@bonefishadventure.com *Fly fishing in Bahamas & fishing*

Bonfiglioli UK Ltd, 3-5 Grosvenor Grange, Woolston, Warrington, WA1 4SF Tel: (01925) 852667 Fax: (01925) 852668 E-mail: sales@bonfiglioliuk.co.uk *Gear boxes & allied products suppliers*

Bong UK Ltd, Envelope Buildings, Michigan Drive, Tongwell, Milton Keynes, MK15 8HQ Tel: (01908) 216216 Fax: (01908) 216217 *Envelope manufrs*

Bonhoeffer, Manor Drive, Sileby, Loughborough, Leicestershire, LE12 7RZ Tel: (01509) 817570 Fax: (01509) 817586 E-mail: enquiries@bonhoeffer.eu.com *Specialist manufacturer of sandwich vans, hot and cold catering vehicles, refrigerated trucks, and bespoke conversions.*

Bonlea Ltd, Q Net House, Malleable Way, Stockton-on-Tees, Cleveland, TS18 2SZ Tel: (01642) 617611 Fax: (01642) 674490 E-mail: enquiries@bonlea.co.uk *Joinery manufrs*

Bonlea Engineering, 4 Ajax Works, Hertford Road, Barking, Essex, IG11 8DY Tel: (020) 8591 2183 Fax: (020) 8594 3605 *General engineers*

▶ Bonnar Sand & Gravel Co. Ltd, Clachan Gravel Pit, Cairndow, Argyll, PA26 8BL Tel: (01499) 600269 *Quarry company*

Bonnay Ltd, 4 Wood Lane, Isleworth, Middlesex, TW7 5ER Tel: (020) 8568 1567 Fax: (020) 8568 3660 *Plastic injection mouldings*

Bonnell Engineering Ltd, 28-33 Stewart Street, Wolverhampton, WV2 4JW Tel: (01902) 712855 Fax: (01902) 712855 *Toolmakers & precision engineers*

▶ Bonnells Electrical Contractors Ltd, 9 Long Drive, Ruislip, Middlesex, HA4 0HH Tel: (020) 8845 8455 Fax: (020) 8845 8745

Bonner & Cook Ltd, 14 South Road, Luton, LU1 3UD Tel: (01582) 732151 Fax: (01582) 480424

Bonner International, 19 Kennet Road, Dartford, DA1 4QN Tel: (020) 8303 6261 Fax: (01322) 556882 E-mail: moving@dbonner.co.uk *International removal & domestic storage specialists* Also at: Dublin

Bonner-Regis Manufacturing Ltd, High Street, Princes End, Tipton, West Midlands, DY4 9HR Tel: 0121-522 2616 Fax: 0121-557 6864 E-mail: sales@regis-bolt.co.uk *Manufacturers of special cold forged components, fasteners & studs*

▶ Bonners Music Superstore, 56 Langney Road, Eastbourne, East Sussex, BN21 3JN Tel: (01323) 639335 Fax: (01323) 649100 E-mail: info@bonnersmusic.co.uk *Music instrument retailers*

Bonnett Maintenance Chemicals, Unit 44 Corringham Industrial Estate, Corringham Road, Gainsborough, Lincolnshire, DN21 1QB Tel: (01427) 613240 Fax: (01427) 617308 E-mail: enquiries@bonnetts.f9.co.uk *Cleaning chemicals supplier*

Bonnett's (Bakers) Ltd, 103 High Street, Somersham, Huntingdon, Cambridgeshire, PE28 3EH Tel: (01487) 840243 Fax: (01487) 740397 *Bakery suppliers*

▶ Bonnington Contract Ltd, 58 Southcroft Road, Rutherglen, Glasgow, G73 1UG Tel: 0141-613 6132

▶ Bonny Bouncy, 21 Morrison Avenue, Bonnybridge, Stirlingshire, FK4 1ET Tel: (07969) 995976 Fax: (01324) 878509 E-mail: bonnybrig@blueyonder.co.uk *Bouncy castle hire*

Bonomi UK Ltd, The Fluid Power Centre, Watling Street, Nuneaton, Warwickshire, CV11 6BQ Tel: (024) 7635 4535 Fax: (024) 7635 4143 E-mail: sales@bonomi.co.uk *Valve & actuator distributors*

▶ Bonser Building Contractors Ltd, Scotlands Industrial Estate, The Scotlands, Coalville, Leicestershire, LE67 3JJ Tel: (01530) 810336 Fax: (01530) 813409

Bonsers Cleaning Nottingham, 19a Forester Street, Netherfield, Nottingham, NG4 2LJ Tel: 0115-988 7520 Fax: (01636) 815926 E-mail: contact@bonsersrestoration.co.uk *Building Restoration & Conservation*

Bonus Accessories, Citadel Trading Park, Citadel Way, Hull, HU9 1TQ Tel: (01482) 580077 Fax: (01482) 588753E-mail: bonusacc@aol.com *Lighting equipment manufrs*

Bonus Plug In Systems, Citadel Trading Park, Citadel Way, Hull, HU9 1TQ Tel: (01482) 313700 Fax: (01482) 588753 *Electrical product distributors & electronic systems manufrs*

▶ Bonus Wind Turbine UK Ltd, 4 Dyffryn Industrial Estate, Pool Road, Newtown, Powys, SY16 3BD Tel: (01686) 621801 Fax: (01686) 621802

Bonut Engineering Ltd, Universal Works, Hibbert Street, Stockport, Cheshire, SK4 1NS Tel: 0161-480 1068 Fax: 0161-480 6173 E-mail: info@bonutengineering.co.uk *Manufacture keys, collars, turned parts, stainless steel keys*

Bonwitco Boatbuilders, Torr Quarry Industrial Estate, East Allington, Totnes, Devon, TQ9 7QQ Tel: (01548) 521561 Fax: (01548) 521560 E-mail: franciswills@aol.com *Boat builders*

Booja Booja Company Ltd, Howe Pits, Norwich Road, Brooke, Norwich, NR15 1HJ Tel: (01508) 558888 Fax: (01508) 557844 E-mail: info@boojaboojj.com *Chocolate manufrs*

▶ The Book Wiz, White Hart Drive, Newsome, Huddersfield, HD4 6JD Tel: (01484) 325444 E-mail: katie.myers1@ntlworld.com *fed up of clutter?*come to my site for cheap e-books*that you can download in a minute*we have a great variety at really*supurb prices*

Bookcraft Supplies, Kennedy Way, Green Lane, Stockport, Cheshire, SK4 2JX Tel: 0161-480 2118 Fax: 0161-480 3679 E-mail: info@fjratchford.co.uk *Supplier of covering materials*

Booker & Best, Windmill House, Windmill Road, St. Leonards-on-Sea, East Sussex, TN38 9BY Tel: (01424) 434391 Fax: (01424) 446833 E-mail: adrianstallworthy@bookerbest.co.uk *Building Contractor, Electrical & Mechanical Engineers*

▶ Booker Cash & Carry Ltd, Lacy Street, Paisley, Renfrewshire, PA1 1QP Tel: 0141-889 7997 Fax: 0141-848 5279

Booker Tate Ltd, Masters Court, Church Road, Thame, Oxfordshire, OX9 3FA Tel: (01844) 251000 Fax: (01844) 251020 E-mail: info@booker-tate.co.uk *Agricultural management consultants*

Bookham, Caswell, Towcester, Northamptonshire, NN12 8EQ Tel: (01327) 350581 Fax: (01327) 356775 Principal Export Areas: Worldwide *Telecommunications*

Bookham Print & Design, Homestead, Eastwick Road, Bookham, Leatherhead, Surrey, KT23 4BA Tel: (01372) 454506 Fax: (01372) 452087 *Printers & lithographers*

▶ Bookham Saddlery Ltd, 10 Grove Corner, Lower Shot, Bookham, Leatherhead, Surrey, KT23 4LP Tel: (01372) 450555 Fax: (01372) 450555 *Saddlery*

Bookham Technology Ltd, Brixham Road, Paignton, Devon, TQ4 7BE Tel: (01803) 662000 Fax: (01803) 559218 *Fibre optic electronics manufrs & supplier*

▶ The Booking Agency, 152 Malpas Road, Newport, NP20 5PN Tel: (01633) 671498 Fax: (0871) 6612184 E-mail: info@thebookingagency.co.uk *Thank you for visiting The Booking Agency our core service includes:*celebrity acquisition, entertainment and a full casting service.**Whatever the service you chose us for you'll find that we will bring professionalism, creativity, objectivity and loyalty.**Whatever YOUR needs The Booking Agency is here to assist you!**Please take a moment to browse around our site to see how we can help you.*

▶ Bookkeeper Blandford Dorset accountant, 9 The Pebbles, Chettle Village, Blandford Forum, Dorset, DT11 8DB Tel: (01258) 830624 E-mail: info@bookkeeper.org.uk *Blandford dorset business accountancy bookkeeping bookkeeper accountant service 01258 830624 www.bookkeeper.org.uk*

▶ Bookmarque Printers, 110 Beddington Lane, Croydon, CR0 4TD Tel: (020) 8612 3400 Fax: (020) 8612 3401

▶ BookShelving, 40 Marlborough Road, Romford, RM7 8AJ Tel: 01708 736305 *Book shelving, book cases, joinery carpentry shelving*

▶ Bookspeed, 16 Salamander Yards, Edinburgh, EH6 7DD Tel: 0131-467 8100 Fax: 0131-467 8008

▶ Bookworm Services Ltd, Kingsnorth, Ashford, Kent, TN23 Tel: 07593 741917 Fax: 07593 741917 E-mail: sc9771@aol.com *Small business offering Bookkeeping and Accounting services, ranging from general bookkeeping, PAYE, VAT, P11D"s, P60"s, Sage, Management Accounts, Temporary accounts staff cover. Competitive hourly rates.*

Boole's Tools & Pipe Fittings Ltd, Haigh Avenue, Whitehill Trading Estate, Stockport, Cheshire, SK4 1NU Tel: 0161-480 7900 Fax: 0161-474 7142 E-mail: enquiries@booles.co.uk *Pipeline fitters & flange stockholders, distributors or agents*

Boomer Industries Ltd, Vale Works, Stockfield Road, Chadderton, Oldham, OL9 9HD Tel: (028) 9266 2881 Fax: 0161-643 7299 E-mail: enquiries@boomer.co.uk *PVC extruders & plastic building product manufrs*

continued

Boon Edam Ltd, Holldan House, Crowbridge Road, Orbital Park, Ashford, Kent, TN24 0GR Tel: 0113-287 6300 Fax: (01233) 505909 E-mail: sales@boonedam.co.uk *Supply, install & maintain revolving doors, security revolving doors*

Boon Edam, Moss Dean Lodge, Nelson Road, Bristol, BS16 5HX Tel: 0117-956 6910 Fax: 0117-956 6911 E-mail: sales@boonedam.co.uk *Supply, install & maintain revolving doors, security revolving doors & turnstiles*

Boone & Lane Ltd, 7-11 Taylor Street, Luton, LU2 0EY Tel: (01582) 723224 Fax: (01582) 402298 *Hat block makers*

Boost Machine Co., Diamond Road, Whitstable, Kent, CT5 1LN Tel: (01227) 272947 Fax: (01227) 272947 *Machine tool service engineers*

Boot Computers Ltd, Stapeley House, London Road, Stapeley, Nantwich, Cheshire, CW5 7JW Tel: (01270) 611299 Fax: (01270) 611302 *Computer software for finance institutes*

Boot Robin Design Associates, 295a Lichfield Road, Sutton Coldfield, West Midlands, B74 4BZ Tel: 0121-308 5913 Fax: 0121-308 5913 *Industrial designers & model makers*

▶ BootBay.co.uk Ltd, New Barn, Hawk Hill, Battlesbridge, Wickford, Essex, SS11 7RJ Tel: (0870) 4447338 E-mail: info@bootbay.co.uk *Online virtual CarBoot Sale 24/7 365 days a year*

Booth Industries, PO Box 50, Bolton, BL3 2RW Tel: (01204) 366333 Fax: (01204) 380888 E-mail: sales@booth-industries.co.uk *Blast resistant steel doors, acoustic steel doors, hangar doors, security doors, flood barriers and watertight doors, blast resistant windows & wall systems. Commercial steel doors and doors for specialist applications.*

Booth Industries Group P.L.C, 1-4 The Courtyard, Gaulby Lane, Stoughton, Leicester, LE2 2FL Tel: 0116-271 2713 Fax: 0116-271 6786 *General engineers*

Booth & Openshaw Blackburn Ltd, 17-19 St. Peter Street, Blackburn, BB2 2HH Tel: (01254) 52828 *Industrial chemists*

Booth Signs, 45 Stafford Road, Wallington, Surrey, SM6 9AP Tel: (020) 8669 1625 Fax: (020) 8773 3429 E-mail: boothsigns@lineone.net *Signwriting services*

Booth Welsh Automation Ltd, The A P L Centre, Stevenston Industrial Estate, Stevenston, Ayrshire, KA20 3LR Tel: (01294) 605123 Fax: (01294) 605555 E-mail: sales@boothwelsh.com *Instrumentation & control panels manufrs*

William Booth & Sons, Spring Street, Ramsbottom, Bury, Lancashire, BL0 9JQ Tel: (01706) 823104 Fax: (01706) 821874 *Joinery manufrs*

▶ Booth Wire Products, Springvale Works, Elland Road, Brookfoot, Brighouse, West Yorkshire, HD6 2RN Tel: (01484) 714837 Fax: (01484) 710515 E-mail: sales@boothwire.co.uk *Wire goods*

Bootham Engineers Mechanical Services, Amy Johnson Way, Clifton Moor, York, YO30 4WT Tel: (01904) 477670 Fax: (01904) 691826 E-mail: engineering.location@dowdingandmills.com Principal Export Areas: Worldwide *Mechanical & general engineers* Also at: Bacup, London, Scarborough & Weedon

▶ Bootham Removals & Storage, Compass House, Common Road, Dunnington, York, YO19 5PD Tel: (0500) 011355 Fax: (01904) 488519

Boothmans (Agriculture) Ltd, 6 Hereward, Cherry Holt Road, Bourne, Lincolnshire, PE10 9LA Tel: (01778) 394040 Fax: (01778) 394499 E-mail: info@boothman.co.uk *Agro-chemical specialists*

▶ Boothright, Glaisdale Dr East, Nottingham, NG8 4GU Tel: 0115-942 8585 Fax: 0115-942 8586 E-mail: sales@boothright-electrical.co.uk

▶ Boothroyden Boarding Cattery, Boothroyden Cottage, Boothroyden Terrace, Manchester, M9 0SB Tel: 0161-653 6483 Fax: 0161-653 7191 E-mail: peter.graham7@btinternet.com *Horse transport*

Booths Blinds, 282 Derby Road, Chesterfield, Derbyshire, S40 2ER Tel: (01246) 207568 Fax: (01246) 278212 E-mail: enquiries@boothsblinds.co.uk *Blinds, awnings install & manufrs*

Boothville Computer Services, 4 Boothville Green, Northampton, NN3 6JR Tel: (01604) 452967 E-mail: info@boothville.co.uk *Computer services*

▶ Bootle Bros Ltd, 42B Banstead Road, Carshalton, Surrey, SM5 3NW Tel: (020) 8770 1347

Bootle Containers Ltd, 72 St Johns Road, Bootle, Merseyside, L20 8BH Tel: 0151-922 0610 Fax: 0151-944 1280 E-mail: sales@bootlecontainers.co.uk Sales Contact: H. Daly Principal Export Areas: Worldwide *Bootle Containers was founded in the mid 1970s to provide refurbishment, repair and manufacturing services to the container industry. Located in Merseyside, England, we quickly established a reputation for quality and service second to none. We have become a respected innovator of designs and uses to which the container can be adapted ranging from general cargo to machinery plant rooms, offshore work cabins and specialised intermodal transportation equipment*

Boots, 32 The Broadway, Joel Street, Northwood, Middlesex, HA6 1PF Tel: (01923) 820841 Fax: (01923) 825555 *Pharmacy*

Boots Chemists P.L.C., Unit 23-24, Buttercrane Shopping Centre, Buttercrane Quay, Newry, County Down, BT35 8HJ Tel: (028) 3026 8234 Fax: (028) 3026 7902 *Wholesale chemists* Also at: Branches throughout Northern Ireland

Boots Contract Manufacturing, P O Box 429, Nottingham, NG90 2PR Tel: 0115-968 6390 *Contract manufrs*

▶ Bop TV (E-Video Productions), Alexander House, Foxlands Drive, Wolverhampton, WV4 5NB Tel: (01902) 344844 Fax: (01902) 340544 E-mail: sara_longman@fish.co.uk *Quick & professional video production services for presentations*

Borahurst Ltd, Devonshire House, 31 Holmesdale Road, Reigate, Surrey, RH2 0BJ Tel: (01737) 221733 Fax: (01737) 223512 E-mail: info@borahurst.com *Mechanical services*

Borchard Lines Ltd, 24 Chiswell Street, London, EC1Y 4XY Tel: (020) 7628 6961 Fax: (020) 7588 1884 E-mail: headoffice@borlines.com *Shipping line*

Borden Chemical, Station Road, Cowie, Stirling, FK7 7BQ Tel: (01786) 814045 Fax: (01786) 816476 *Synthetic resin manufrs*

▶ Borden Electrical Services Ltd, Riddles Road Off Borden Lane, Bredgar, Sittingbourne, Kent, ME9 8HP Tel: (01795) 410186 Fax: (01795) 410142

▶ Border Barrier Systems Ltd, Head Office, Alstonby Grange, Westlinton, Carlisle, CA6 6AF Tel: (01228) 675764 Fax: (01228) 675215 E-mail: info@borderbarriers.com *Suppliers of road & pedestrian safety barriers for hire or sale*

▶ Border Biscuits Ltd, Block 4, Caldwellside Industrial Estate, Lanark, ML11 7SR Tel: (01555) 662886 Fax: (01555) 665106 E-mail: sales@borderbiscuits.co.uk *Biscuit supplier*

▶ Border Blinds Ltd, 103 Whalley Road, Clitheroe, Lancashire, BB7 1EE Tel: (01200) 428555 E-mail: borderblinds@tiscali.co.uk *Blind retailers*

Border Concrete Products Ltd, Jedburgh Road, Kelso, Roxburghshire, TD5 8JG Tel: (01573) 224393 Fax: (01573) 226360 E-mail: sales@borderconcrete.co.uk *Pre-cast & cast stone manufrs*

Border Construction Ltd, Marconi Road, Brough Road Industrial Estate, Carlisle, CA2 7NA Tel: (01228) 522296 Fax: (01228) 514928 E-mail: admin@border-construction.co.uk *Building & civil engineers services* Also at: Earlston

▶ Border Construction Ltd, Rhymers Mill, Mill Road, Earlston, Berwickshire, TD4 6DG Tel: (01896) 849660 Fax: (01896) 848917

Border Converters, Second Avenue, Deeside Industrial Park, Deeside, Clwyd, CH5 2NX Tel: (01244) 289988 Fax: (01244) 289300 E-mail: admin@borderconverters.co.uk *Manufacture flexible packaging products*

▶ Border County Foods, The Old Vicarage, Crosby-On-Eden, Carlisle, CA6 4QZ Tel: (01228) 573500 Fax: (01228) 672021 E-mail: info@cumberland-sausage.net *Specialist meats suppliers*

Border Farm Supplies Ltd, Turfford Park, Earlston, Berwickshire, TD4 6GZ Tel: (01896) 848911 Fax: (01896) 848006 *Agricultural suppliers*

▶ Border Fine Arts, Townfoot, Langholm, Dumfriesshire, DG15 0ET Tel: (01387) 383027 Fax: (01387) 383020 E-mail: norman.maxwell@enesco.co.uk *Gift wear importers designers & manufrs*

Border Food Machinery, 39 Kingstown Broadway, Kingstown Industrial Estate, Carlisle, CA3 0HA Tel: (01228) 534996 Fax: (01228) 514260 *Catering equipment suppliers*

Border Frames Lochmaben Co., Dumfries Road, Lochmaben, Lockerbie, Dumfriesshire, DG11 1RF Tel: (01387) 810455 Fax: (01387) 810693 E-mail: info@borderframes.com *Photo (wood-aluminium) frame manufrs*

Border Holdings Coldstore (UK) Ltd, Avonmouth Way, Avonmouth, Bristol, BS11 9LX Tel: 0117-982 8589 Fax: 0117-982 4565 *Freezers suppliers*

Border Holdings UK Ltd, The Grove, Craven Arms, Shropshire, SY7 8DA Tel: (01588) 672711 Fax: (01588) 672660 E-mail: info@britparc.co.uk *Landrover parts & accessories*

Border Hydraulics & Pneumatics Ltd, 9 Currock Road Trade Centre, Currock Road, Carlisle, CA2 5AD Tel: (01228) 530010 Fax: (01228) 818087 *Hydraulic hose distributors & manufrs*

Border Label Company Ltd, Glenview Catrail Road, Galashiels, Selkirkshire, TD1 1NW Tel: (01896) 759074 Fax: (01896) 759074 *Self adhesive label printers*

Border Line Arts Ltd, 17 Macklin Street, Covent Garden, London, WC2B 5NQ Tel: (020) 7691 8938 Fax: (020) 7691 8969 E-mail: info@borderlinearts.co.uk *Picture frames*

Border Oak Ltd, Kingsland Sawmills, Kingsland, Leominster, Herefordshire, HR6 9SF Tel: (01568) 708752 Fax: (01568) 708295 E-mail: sales@borderoak.com *Oak framed building manufrs*

Border Office Equipment, 4 Block 14 Amber Business Centre, Greenhill Lane, Riddings, Alfreton, Derbyshire, DE55 4BR Tel: (01773) 608039 Fax: (01773) 609145 E-mail: borderofficeriddings@btopenworld.com *Office equipment suppliers*

Border Offset Printers, Church Street, Caldewgate, Carlisle, CA2 5TJ Tel: (01228) 526675 Fax: (01228) 515245 *Fire extinguisher service*

Border Offset Printers Ltd, Rigg Street, Caldewgate, Carlisle, CA2 5TN Tel: (01228) 526675 Fax: (01228) 515245 *Printers*

Border Oils, 34 Turnberry Way, Carlisle, CA3 0QL Tel: 01228 536960 *Lubricating oil distributors*

▶ Border Paving Ltd, Maltkiln Farm, Chapel Lane, Bronington, Whitchurch, Shropshire, SY13 3HR Tel: (01948) 780902 Fax: (01948) 780630

▶ Border Plastering Services, 33 Elizabeth Road,, Kington, Herefordshire, HR5 3DB Tel: 01544 230099 E-mail: terry@townsend33.fsworld.co.uk *All Types of Internal and external plastering. Slaked lime hair mortar render,Hydraulic lime mortar render, Hydrated lime and cement mortar render. Incl: Ashlar lining, block rendering, pebbledash and roughcast finish.*All types of internal render finished with lime finishing plaster or gypsum finishing plaster. Plasterboard ceilings and partitions finished with gypsum finishing plaster. *Fibrous cornice work run in situ and repairs to old cornice work.*Fixing of all cast's and archway's*Our forty-five years experience in thr trade is your guarantee of quality workmanship and service.*

Border Precision Ltd, Pinnaclehill Industrial Estate, Kelso, Roxburghshire, TD5 8DW Tel: (01573) 224941 Fax: (01573) 225220 E-mail: sales@borderprecision.com *Precision engineers & pressworkers*

Border Pumps & Transmissions, Station Road, Sandycroft, Deeside, Clwyd, CH5 2PT Tel: (01244) 533065 Fax: (01244) 535635 *Bearing distributors, pump repairers & distributors*

Border Reprographics, Tuppenny Lane, Emsworth, Hampshire, PO10 8HG Tel: (01243) 377721 Fax: (01243) 379200 E-mail: info@border-repro.co.uk *Exhibition graphics*

▶ Border Scaffold Services LLP, Unit 2-3 Holmer Trading Estate, Hereford, HR1 1JS Tel: (01432) 352530 Fax: (01432) 352533

Border Shearing Supplies, The Hagg, Cornhill-on-Tweed, Northumberland, TD12 4RT Tel: (01890) 850219 Fax: (01890) 850219 *Shearing equipment manufrs*

Border Signs & Graphix Ltd, St. Marys Industrial Estate, Dumfries, DG1 1NA Tel: (01387) 269582 Fax: (01387) 259396 *Sign manufrs*

Border Telecom, Heather Drive, Ascot, Berkshire, SL5 0HT Tel: (01344) 873873 Fax: (01344) 873872 *Phone installation service providers*

Border Television Ltd, The Television Centre, Carlisle, CA1 3NT Tel: (01228) 525101 Fax: (01228) 541384 E-mail: ian@border-tv.com *Television broadcaster*

Border Textiles UK Ltd, Whitechapel Road, Cleckheaton, West Yorkshire, BD19 6HY Tel: (01274) 866200 Fax: (01274) 866220 E-mail: sales@bordertextiles.co.uk *Textile machinery agents* Also at: Galashiels

▶ Border Traffic Service Ltd, Border View, Norham, Berwick-upon-Tweed, TD15 2JZ Tel: (01289) 382400 Fax: (01289) 382312 *Road haulage services*

▶ Border Vending Group, Unit 4 Willow Court, West Quay Road, Winwick, Warrington, WA2 8UF Tel: 01925 423900 Fax: 01925 423902 *Suppliers of high quality vending machines and services locally and nationally.*

Borderfoam Ltd, Lingen Road, Ludlow Business Park, Ludlow, Shropshire, SY8 1XD Tel: (01584) 877107 Fax: (01584) 874073 Principal Export Areas: Africa *Foam polyurethane mouldings manufrs*

Borderloos, Alstonby Grange, West Linton, Westlinton, Carlisle, CA6 6AF Tel: (01228) 792792 Fax: (01228) 792791 E-mail: philip.a@borderloos.co.uk *Vast range of toilet hire*

Borders Coffee Co. Ltd, Unit 5, Station Yard, Newtown St. Boswells, Melrose, Roxburghshire, TD6 0PP Tel: (01835) 823005 Fax: 01835 822999 *Suppliers of quality coffee and teas to business users within Scottish Borders, Dumfries & Galloway, Cumbria and Northumberland.Suppliers of Rancilio Italian coffee machines offering full maintainance and back up.We supply coffee beans, ground coffees, satchet coffees and herbal, and speciality teas.*

▶ Bore Electrical Services, 3 Venture Works, Charleywood Road, Knowsley Industrial Park, Liverpool, L33 7SG Tel: 0151-547 4447 Fax: 0151-547 4437

Bored Bar Engineering Ltd, New Street, Halfway, Sheffield, S20 3GH Tel: 0114-248 3631 Fax: 0114-247 7133 E-mail: sales@bored-bar.co.uk *Bored bar manufrs*

Boreflex Ltd, Unit 9 Gateway Court, Parkgate, Rotherham, South Yorkshire, S62 6LH Tel: (01709) 522333 Fax: (01709) 522663 E-mail: sales@boreflex.co.uk *Protective bellows & machine guards*

Boremasters, High Street, Cleobury Mortimer, Kidderminster, Worcestershire, DY14 8DS Tel: (01299) 270942 Fax: (01299) 270212 E-mail: sales@boremasters.co.uk *Boring tools, grinding machines, spade drills & holders manufrs*

Borer Data Systems Ltd, Gotelee House, Market Place, Wokingham, Berkshire, RG40 1AN Tel: 0118-979 1137 Fax: 0118-977 3526 E-mail: borer@borer.co.uk Principal Export Areas: Middle East, Central/East Europe & West Europe *Access control & security product distributors*

Bores Signal Processing, Pond Road, Woking, Surrey, GU22 0JZ Tel: (01483) 740138 Fax: (01483) 740136 *DSP hardware & software*

Borg & Ranalli Ltd, 364a Clapham Road, London, SW9 9AR Tel: (020) 7627 3962 Fax: (020) 8947 1501 *Restoration services in marble*

▶ Borglass Laminated Ltd, Quay Road, Rutherglen, Glasgow, G73 1LD Tel: 0141-613 1400 Fax: 0141-647 5750

Borgwarner Holdings Ltd, Roydsdale Way, Euroway Industrial Estate, Bradford, West Yorkshire, BD4 6SE Tel: (01274) 684915 Fax: (01274) 689671 *Turbocharger fan drive specialists*

Borgwarner Trustees Ltd, Borg Warner Ltd, Kenfig Industrial Estate, Margam, Port Talbot, West Glamorgan, SA13 2PG Tel: (01656) 741001 Fax: (01656) 745811 *Motor vehicle accessory manufrs*

Borough Ltd, 65 Progress Road, Leigh-on-Sea, Essex, SS9 5JT Tel: (01702) 425425 Fax: (01702) 425400 E-mail: sales@borough.co.uk *Plastics finishing & electroplating services*

Borough Green Sand Pits Ltd, Commercial Road, Strood, Rochester, Kent, ME2 2AD Tel: (01634) 717515 Fax: (01634) 717153 *Sand producers*

Borough Motor Services Ltd, 226 Cleveland Street, Birkenhead, Merseyside, CH41 3QJ Tel: 0151-647 8019 Fax: 0151-650 0666 E-mail: bmsltd@btinternet.com *Motor vehicle spares & dismantlers*

Borregaard (UK) Ltd, Clayton Road, Risley Employment Area, Warrington, WA3 6QQ Tel: (01925) 285400 Fax: (01925) 285434 E-mail: marketing_europe@borregaard.com *Chemical blenders & distributors*

Borries, 28 Coalbrookdale Road, Clayhill Light Industrial Park, Neston, CH64 3UG Tel: 0151-336 3101 Fax: 0151-336 3217 E-mail: rob@borriesuk.fsnet.co.uk *Marking device manufrs*

▶ Borsdane Wood Ltd, 76a Market Street, Farnworth, Bolton, BL4 7NY Tel: (01204) 577776 Fax: (01204) 575600 E-mail: info@borsdane.com *Computer software developers*

▶ Bosa Contracts Ltd, Unit 5A, Ahed Business Centre, Dewsbury Road, Ossett, West Yorkshire, WF5 9ND Tel: (01924) 274930 Fax: (01924) 271728 E-mail: stevebosa@btconnect.com

▶ Bosal UK Ltd, Unit 330 Four Oaks Road, Walton Summit Centre, Bamber Bridge, Preston, PR5 8AP Tel: (01772) 771000 Fax: (01772) 312750 E-mail: marketing@eur.bosal.com Also at: Glasgow & West Thurrock

Bosch Lawn & Garden Limited, Suffolk Works, Stowmarket, Suffolk, IP14 1EY Tel: (01449) 742000 Fax: (01449) 675444 *Lawn & garden machinery manufrs*

▶ Bosch Rexroth Ltd, 23 Queensbrook, Bolton, BL1 4AY Tel: (01204) 534083 Fax: (01204) 534084 E-mail: steve.smith@boschrexroth.co.uk *Supplier of industrial hydralic equipment & systems*

Bosch Rexroth Ltd, Viewfield Industrial Estate, Glenrothes, Fife, KY6 2RD Tel: (01592) 631515 Fax: (01592) 631888

Bosch Rexroth Ltd, Viewfield Industrial Estate, Glenrothes, Fife, KY6 2RD Tel: (01592) 631515 Fax: (01592) 631888 *Hydraulic cylinder/ram manufrs*

Bosch Rexroth Ltd, Cromwell Road, St. Neots, Cambridgeshire, PE19 2ES Tel: (01480) 223200 Fax: (01480) 219052 E-mail: info@boschrexroth.co.uk *Hydraulic equipment systems manufrs*

Robert Bosch Ltd, Cardiff Plant, Miskin Industrial Park, Miskin, Pontyclun, Mid Glamorgan, CF72 8XQ Tel: (01443) 221000 Fax: (01443) 221201 *Alternator plants*

Robert Bosch Ltd, PO Box 98, Uxbridge, Middlesex, UB9 5HJ Tel: (01895) 834466 Fax: (01895) 838388 *Warehouse centre & distributors*

Boscombe Beds & Suites, 40 Ashley Road, Bournemouth, BH1 4LJ Tel: (01202) 300909 Fax: (01202) 720888 E-mail: sales@boscombebeds.com *Furniture distributors*

Bose Ltd, 138-139 Cheshire Oaks Outlet Village, Kinsey Road, Ellesmere Port, CH65 9JJ Tel: 0151-357 8300 Fax: (08707) 415546 E-mail: cheshire_oaks@bose.com *Speaker system distributors*

Bose, Unit 1 Ambley Green, Gillingham Business Park, Gillingham, Kent, ME8 0NJ Tel: (0870) 7414500 Fax: (0870) 7414545 E-mail: shane_wheatcroft@bose.com *Hi-fi equipment importers*

Bosprint, Units 38 & 40, Hastings Road Industrial Estate, Hastings Road, Leicester, LE5 0LJ Tel: 0116-274 3308 Fax: 0116-276 1254 E-mail: info@bosprint.co.uk *Lithographic printers*

The Boss Corporation, 31 Wren Gardens, Alderholt, Fordingbridge, Hampshire, SP6 3PJ Tel: (0845) 2574685 Fax: (0871) 4332393 E-mail: sales@thebosscorporation.co.uk *Specialist financier of IT Solutions including Software only funding. Also offering competitive, flexible terms on other business equipment.*

Boss Design Ltd, Boss Drive, Dudley, West Midlands, DY2 8SZ Tel: (01384) 455570 Fax: (01384) 241628 E-mail: sales@boss-design.co.uk *Contract furniture manufrs*

Boss Plant Hire Ltd, Shelford Farm Cottages, Shalloak Road, Broad Oak, Canterbury, Kent, CT2 0PR Tel: (01227) 454445 Fax: (01227) 769822 *Contractors' plant hire*

▶ Boss Scaffolding Ltd, Repton Street, London, E14 7RW Tel: (020) 7702 7805

▶ Bosstech UK, Borodin Close, Basingstoke, Hampshire, RG22 4EW Tel: (01256) 470444 Fax: (0871) 6613031 E-mail: phil@bosstechuk.co.uk *Computer consumables suppliers*

Bosta Agricultural Services, Chapel Pond Hill, Bury St. Edmunds, Suffolk, IP32 7HT Tel: (01284) 716580 Fax: (01284) 716588 E-mail: sales@uk.bosta.com *Irrigation pipes & fittings manufrs*

Bostel Brothers Ltd, 1-3 The Compound, Northease Close, Hove, East Sussex, BN3 8LJ Tel: (01273) 430264 Fax: (01273) 422605 *Heating engineers*

▶ Bostik Findley Ltd, Common Road, Stafford, ST16 3EH Tel: (01785) 272727 Fax: (01785) 257236 E-mail: jackie.scarfe@bostikfindley.com Principal Export Areas: Worldwide *Manufacturers of industrial & pressure sensitive adhesives, sealant (structural), sealant (industrial) & hot melt adhesives*

Bostitch, Europa Views, Sheffield Business Park, Sheffield, S9 1XH Tel: (0870) 1630630 Fax: (0870) 1670670 E-mail: bostitchuksales@stanleyworks.com *Power tool manufrs*

Boston Acoustics Distribution UK Ltd, 16 Bridge Road, Cirencester, Gloucestershire, GL7 1NJ Tel: (01285) 654432 Fax: (01285) 654430 E-mail: info@acoustic-energy.co.uk *Loudspeaker manufrs*

▶ Boston Acoustics Distribution UK Ltd, 16 Bridge Road, Cirencester, Gloucestershire, GL7 1NJ Tel: (01285) 650814 Fax: (01285) 654430 E-mail: uksales@acoustics-energy.co.uk *Speakers manufrs*

Boston Anorak Co., Church Road, Freiston, Boston, Lincolnshire, PE22 0NX Tel: (01205) 769130 Fax: (01205) 769131 *Protective clothing manufrs*

Boston Chamber Of Commerce & Industry, Boston Business Centre, Norfolk Street, Boston, Lincolnshire, PE21 9HH Tel: (01205) 358800 Fax: (01205) 359388 E-mail: bcci@btclick.com *Chambers of commerce & industry*

Boston Chemical Co. Ltd, 48 Millbeck Green, Collingham, Wetherby, West Yorkshire, LS22 5AJ Tel: (01937) 579522 Fax: (01937) 907473 E-mail: bccinfo@bostonchemicals.co.uk *Floor levelling compound manufrs*

Boston Engineering Supplies & Services, Riverside Industrial Estate, Marsh Lane, Boston, Lincolnshire, PE21 7PJ Tel: (01205) 361218 Fax: (01205) 361218 *Bearing stockists & engineering services*

▶ Boston Freight Services Ltd, St. Johns Road, Boston, Lincolnshire, PE21 6HG Tel: (01205) 311666 Fax: (01205) 310471 E-mail: judybarnes@rsboston.com

Boston Matthews Machinery Ltd, Navigation Road, Diglis, Worcester, WR5 3DE Tel: (01905) 763100 Fax: (01905) 763101 E-mail: info@bostonmatthews.co.uk *Manufacturers of plastics machinery*

Boston Office Solutions, Moor La Trading Estate, Sherburn in Elmet, Leeds, LS25 6ES Tel: (01977) 681068 Fax: (01977) 681619 E-mail: sales@bostonoffice.co.uk *Office equipment suppliers*

Boston Radiator Services Ltd, Maud Street, Boston, Lincolnshire, PE21 6TP Tel: (01205) 369555 Fax: (01205) 364829 *Radiator manufacturers & repairers*

Boston Retail Products, 10a Lower Guildford Road, Knaphill, Woking, Surrey, GU21 2EW Tel: (0870) 7706680 Fax: (0870) 7706681 E-mail: sales@bostonretail.com *Damage protection & custom extrusions suppliers & manufrs*

Boston Sausage, 13 High Street, Boston, Lincolnshire, PE21 8SH Tel: (01205) 362167 *Butchers*

Boston Signs & Displays, Unit 1, Spalding Road, Boston, Lincolnshire, PE21 8XL Tel: (01205) 363849 Fax: (01205) 367725 E-mail: boston_signs@yahoo.co.uk *Sign manufrs*

Boston Tapes UK Ltd, Unit 12 Block 2, Wednesbury Trading Estate, Wednesbury, West Midlands, WS10 7JN Tel: 0121-556 9900 Fax: 0121-556 9034 E-mail: avantitapes@yahoo.co.uk *Self-adhesive protective tape distributors*

Boston Tractors Ltd, Eagle Iron Works, Creake Road, Scultthorpe, Fakenham, Norfolk, NR21 9NH Tel: (01328) 862333 Fax: (01328) 856249 *Tractors agricultural machinery*

Bosuns Locker, 10 Military Road, Ramsgate, Kent, CT11 9LG Tel: (01843) 597158 Fax: (01843) 597158 *Yacht chandler*

▶ Bosus, 8 Dickson Street, Liverpool, L3 7EB Tel: 0151-298 9393 Fax: 0151-298 9500 E-mail: sales@bosus.com

Boswell Bros (Salisbury) Ltd, Ford, Salisbury, SP4 6DJ Tel: (01722) 333781 Fax: (01722) 327858 E-mail: boswell.broth@virgin.net *Ballast, sand & concrete products*

Boswell & Davis, 1 Sunbury Workshops, Swanfield Street, London, E2 7LF Tel: (020) 7739 5738 *Restoration of antique furniture*

▶ Boswell Printers & Office Supplies, Graphic House, 9 Dunlop Road, Hadleigh Road Industrial Estate, Ipswich, IP2 0UG Tel: (01473) 212000 Fax: (01473) 214000

Boswell Rod & Wire Ltd, 4 The Wallows Industrial Estate, Wallows Road, Brierley Hill, West Midlands, DY5 1QB Tel: (01384) 263238 Fax: (01384) 480223 E-mail: sales@boswellrod.co.uk *Manufacturers of wire straightening & steel products*

Boswell & Co. (Steels) Ltd, Bassett Road, Park Lane Industrial Estate, Cradley, Halesowen, West Midlands, B63 2RE Tel: (01384) 637375 Fax: (01384) 410103 E-mail: boswellsteel@aol.com *Steel & steel bar stockholders*

▶ Bosworth Business Management Limited, 37 Northumberland Avenue, Market Bosworth, Nuneaton, Warwickshire, CV13 0RJ Tel: 07050 369499 E-mail: contact@bbml.org *Part time Finance Directors to the SME market place. General business advice, change and transformation projects undertaken. CEO Hans Skeat*

Bosworth Tools (Cutters) Ltd, Unit 19 20, Sketchley Meadows Industrial Estate, Hinckley, Leicestershire, LE10 3ES Tel: (01455) 250066 Fax: (01455) 250077 *Precision grinders*

Bosworth Wright, Express Works, Hollow Road, Anstey, Leicester, LE7 7FP Tel: 0116-236 2231 Fax: 0116-235 2230 E-mail: bosworthwright@hotmail.com *Carton & rigid box manufrs*

Botanica Nurseries, Crown Lane, Farnham Royal, Slough, SL2 3SG Tel: (01753) 647476 Fax: (01753) 647476 *Interior office plant display exhibitioners & contractors services*

▶ Botanical Interiors Ltd, 98 Glenfield Park One, Philips Road, Blackburn, BB1 5PF Tel: (01254) 267999 Fax: (01254) 267992 E-mail: info@botanicalgroupservices.co.uk *Horticultural services*

▶ Botes Maintenance, Harvey Road, Basildon, Essex, SS13 1EP Tel: (0800) 0730317

Elizabeth Botham & Sons, 35-39 Skinner Street, Whitby, North Yorkshire, YO21 3AH Tel: (01947) 602823 Fax: (01947) 820269 *Bakery & confectionery retailers*

Bott, Unit 9 Ivanhoe Industrial Estate, Tournament Way, Ashby-de-la-Zouch, Leicestershire, LE65 2UU Tel: (01530) 410600 Fax: (01530) 410629 E-mail: v-sales@bottltd.co.uk *Vehicle storage equipment manufrs*

Bott Ltd, Bude-Stratton Business Park, Bude, Cornwall, EX23 8LY Tel: (01288) 357788 Fax: (01288) 352692 E-mail: info@bottltd.co.uk *Workshop & Storage Equipment, Drawer Cabinets, Workbenches, Mobile Equipment, Cupboards & Shelving, CNC Tool Storage, Perfo Panel Systems, Tool & Transport Cases, Chairs & flooring & Secure Storage Systems.*

Bott Builders Ltd, Birmingham Road, Whitacre Heath Coleshill, Birmingham, B46 2ET Tel: (01675) 462214 *Building & plumbing contractors*

▶ Bott Shaun Upholstery, 18 Leicester Road, Blaby, Leicester, LE8 4GQ Tel: 0116-277 9705 E-mail: info@handmadesofas.co.uk *Custom - made sofa & chair makers, sofa beds*

Bottcher UK, Jubilee Way, Shipley, West Yorkshire, BD18 1QG Tel: (01274) 530531 Fax: (01274) 530532 *Rubber & polyurethane rollers for industry*

Botterills, Block, 9 South Avenue, Blantyre, Glasgow, G72 0XB Tel: (01698) 824311 Fax: (01698) 824231 E-mail: info@botterillconveniencestores.co.uk *Convenience store*

Bottlestore Ltd, Icknield Way Industrial Estate, Icknield Way, Tring, Hertfordshire, HP23 4JX Tel: (01442) 820920 Fax: (01442) 820939 E-mail: sales@bottlestore.co.uk *UK manufacturer of custom printed sports bottles and promotional drinkware products. We also manufacture packaging containers for the medical, health, beauty and retail industries.*

Bottling & Packaging Enterprises, 2 Becklands Park Industrial Estate, York Road, Market Weighton, York, YO43 3GA Tel: (01430) 871990 Fax: (01430) 871999 *Packing machinery specialist suppliers*

Bottom Line Technologies Ltd, Ground Floor, Cromwell House, Bartley Wood Business Park, Bartley Way, Hook, Hampshire, RG27 9XA Tel: (01252) 618600 Fax: 0118-956 9988 E-mail: info@bottomline.com *IT software multi service providers*

▶ Bottomline Technologies Europe Ltd, 115 Chatham Street, Reading, RG1 7JX Tel: 0118-925 8250 Fax: 0118-956 9988 E-mail: sales@bottomline.co.uk *Finance & leasing services*

Bouchier Fencing Ltd, Goring Road, Woodcote, Reading, RG8 0QD Tel: (01491) 681265 Fax: (01491) 681737 *Fencing suppliers*

Boucon Network Solutions Ltd, 2 Minster Court, Valley Way, Swansea Enterprise Park, Swansea, SA6 8RN Tel: (01792) 762200 Fax: (01792) 762201 *Telecommunication services*

▶ Boughey Distribution Ltd, Wardle Industrial Estate, Wardle, Nantwich, Cheshire, CW5 6RS Tel: (01829) 260704

The Boughton Group, Graycar Business Park, Barton Turn, Barton under Needwood, Burton-on-Trent, Staffordshire, DE13 8EN Tel: (01283) 711771 Fax: (01283) 711669 E-mail: enquiries@reynoldsboughton.com *Waste disposal container manufrs*

The Boughton Group, Graycar Business Park, Barton Turn, Barton under Needwood, Burton-on-Trent, Staffordshire, DE13 8EN Tel: (01283) 711771 Fax: (01283) 711669 E-mail: enquiries@reynoldsboughton.com *Transportation & earth moving equipment manufrs*

Boughtons Bedroom Design, 319 Grafton Street, Liverpool, L8 4YB Tel: 0151-709 5195 Fax: 0151-709 7390 *Bedroom sales & installers*

Boulevard Business Partnership Ltd, Island Farm, Black Lane, Nateby, Preston, PR3 0LH Tel: (0845) 4560050 Fax: (01995) 606045 *Computer software suppliers*

▶ John Boult & Sons, 2a Farnell Street, Glasgow, G4 9SE Tel: 0141-333 1966 Fax: 0141-333 1456

Boult Wade Tennant, Verulam Gardens, 70 Gray's Inn Road, London, WC1X 8BT Tel: (020) 7430 7500 Fax: (020) 7831 1768 E-mail: boult@boult.com *European patent & trade mark agents services*

Boult Wade Tennant, 34 Bridge Street, Reading, RG1 2LU Tel: 0118-956 5900 Fax: 0118-950 0442 E-mail: boult@boult.com *European patent attorneys*

Boulter Boilers Ltd, Magnet House, Whitehouse Road, Ipswich, IP1 5JA Tel: (01473) 241555 Fax: (01473) 241321 E-mail: sales@boulter-buderus.com *Domestic & industrial boiler manufrs*

Boulting Group plc, Chapel Road, Penketh, Warrington, WA5 2PL Tel: (01925) 726661 Fax: (01925) 723508 E-mail: info@boulting.co.uk *Project management, design, installation, electrical contractor*

Boulting Mechanical Services, Unit 11, Warrington Central Trading Estate Bewsey Road, Warrington, WA2 7LP Tel: (01925) 831151 Fax: (01925) 581120

Boulting Mechanical Services, Unit 11, Warrington Central Trading Estate Bewsey Road, Warrington, WA2 7LP Tel: (01925) 831151 Fax: (01925) 581120 E-mail: mechanical@boulting.co.uk *Project management services*

Boulton Ltd, Cannon Business Park, Darkhouse Lane, Bilston, West Midlands, WV14 8XQ Tel: (01902) 385300 Fax: (01902) 385330 E-mail: info@boultonlimited.com *Scaffolding services*

Bounce Higher, 20 Harland Street, Glasgow, G14 0AT Tel: 0141-950 6009 *Bouncing castles & inflatable hire*

▶ Bounce Higher, 32 Ryefield Road, Eastfield, Scarborough, North Yorkshire, YO11 3DW Tel: (01723) 585542 E-mail: info@no1bouncehigher.com *Bounce Higher.*Bouncy castle hire in Scarborough and surrounding areas. Free local delivery. Tel:01723 585542 Moblie: 07949646812 www.no1bouncehigher.com*

▶ Bounce Krazee, 14 Green Leys, High Wycombe, Buckinghamshire, HP13 5UH Tel: (01494) 464902 E-mail: info@bouncekrazee.co.uk *Bouncy castle & slide hire for children & adults in Buckinghamshire, Berkshire and Oxfordshire. Free delivery, set-up & collection. Free of charge cancellation option in the event of bad weather. Member of the BIHA and NAIH. Pictures, prices and sizes are available on our web site www.bouncekrazee.co.uk*

▶ Bounce Now, 8 Morfa Clwyd Business Centre, Marsh Road, Rhyl, Clwyd, LL18 2AF Tel: (01745) 354194 Fax: (01745) 354194 E-mail: scottousey@tiscali.co.uk *Manufacturers of quality bouncy castles*

Bounceabout, 5 Warner Road, Selsey, Chichester, West Sussex, PO20 9AL Tel: (01243) 607772 *Bouncy castle hire*

Bounceabouts Leisure Ltd, Asfare Business Park, Hinckley Road, Wolvey, Hinckley, Leicestershire, LE10 3HQ Tel: (01455) 220886 Fax: (01455) 220988 E-mail: sales@bounceabouts.co.uk *Children's inflatables manufrs*

▶ Bouncers, 14 Villiers Street, Sunderland, SR1 1HA Tel: 0191-567 1668 Fax: 0191-567 1668

▶ Bounceuk Biz, 77 Stranding Street, Eastleigh, Hampshire, SO50 5GR Tel: (023) 8064 1669 *Bouncy castle's, mini-marquees & hot tub hire*

▶ Bouncing Castles, 10 Grafton Close, St. Albans, Hertfordshire, AL4 0EX Tel: (01727) 837031 E-mail: sales@bouncingcastles.co.uk

▶ Bouncing Off The Walls, 2 Proud Close, Purton, Swindon, SN5 4EH Tel: (01793) 771320 *Distributors of bouncy castles*

Bouncy Castle Company.com, 366 Brook Street, Birkenhead, CH41 7LB Tel: (08702) 406050 E-mail: sarahbyron@btinternet.com *We offer a huge range of Bouncy Castles, Slides, inflatables for manufacture or hire purposes. Our customers include major PLC companies all over the UK. Our range of products include castle slides, adventure play centres, soft play facilities, obstacles, jungle dens etc. We handle inquiries from all over the Wirral, Merseyside, North West and Wales and the UK. For all hire products we cover an approximate 50 miles radius. To view our products please go to our E-commerce website, Online catalogue or feel free to give us a call.*

▶ Bouncy Castle Hire Ltd, 6 Des Roches Square, Witney, Oxfordshire, OX28 4BE Tel: (01993) 709851 E-mail: enquiries@bouncycastlehire.ltd.uk *Bouncy castle hire*

Bouncy Castle Kingdom, 43 Higher Road, Liverpool, L25 0QG Tel: 0151-486 2050 *Bouncy castle hire*

▶ Bouncy Castle Warehouse, 2 Osborne Court, Thelwall New Road, Grappenhall, Warrington, WA4 2LS Tel: (01925) 606060 Fax: (01925) 606061

▶ Bouncy Time Bouncy Castles, 31 Castercliff Bank, Colne, Lancashire, BB8 8DJ Tel: (01282) 871091 *Bouncy castle equipment suppliers*

▶ Bouncycastlesforhire.com, 7A High Street, Marlow, Buckinghamshire, SL7 8DW Tel: (01494) 464902 E-mail: info@bouncycastlesforhire.com *Bouncy castles & slides for hire*

▶ Bound Around Ltd, 51 Livesey Street, Wateringbury, Maidstone, Kent, ME18 5BQ Tel: (01622) 817717 Fax: (01622) 817717 *Stationery manufacturers & distributors*

Boundary Fencing Supplies, Unit 1, Vale View Business Park, Crown Lane South, Ardleigh, Colchester, CO7 7PL Tel: (01206) 230231 *Fencing contractors*

Boundary Precision Engineering Ltd, Limber Road, Lufton, Yeovil, Somerset, BA22 8RR Tel: (01935) 472094 Fax: (01935) 382488 *Precision engineers*

Bounty Pest Control, Unit 108, Ellingham Industrial Estate, Willesborough, Ashford, Kent, TN23 6LZ Tel: (01233) 640191 *Pest control services*

Bourbon Fabi UK Ltd, North Portway Close, Round Spinney Industrial Estate, Northampton, NN3 8RE Tel: (01604) 493126 Fax: (01604) 644547 E-mail: simon.t@bourbonfabi.co.uk *Motor vehicle trimmings & assembly manufrs*

Bourdon Haenni Ltd, Unit A Central Estate, Albert Road, Aldershot, Hampshire, GU11 1SZ Tel: (01252) 354000 Fax: (01252) 354009 E-mail: info@bourdon-haenni.co.uk Sales Contact: J. Good *Transmitters, gauges, switches, temperature controller manufrs*

Bourjois Ltd, Bourjois House, Queensway, Croydon, CR9 4DL Tel: (020) 8688 7131 Fax: (020) 8688 0012 *Distributors of cosmetics*

Bourne Building Services, Builders Yard, Wool Road, Poole, Dorset, BH12 4NG Tel: (01202) 749105 Fax: (0870) 7707306

▶ Bourne Fibre Manufacturing Ltd, The Chapel, The Street, Brockdish, Diss, Norfolk, IP21 4JY Tel: (01379) 668743 Fax: (01379) 669032 E-mail: hopeatthechapel@aol.com *Case manufrs*

▶ Bourne Gas Bournemouth Ltd, Unit 3 Broom Road Business Park, Broom Road, Poole, Dorset, BH12 4PA Tel: (01202) 716665 E-mail: gas@bournebg.ltd.uk *Mechanical & electrical engineers*

Bourne Joinery, 196 London Road, Bexhill-On-Sea, East Sussex, TN39 4AE Tel: (01424) 212066 *Joinery manufrs*

▶ Bourne & Kemp Jewellers, 35 Station Road, Longfield, Kent, DA3 7QD Tel: (01474) 702121 Fax: (01474) 702121 E-mail: bourne.kemp1@ticali.co.uk *Jewellery manufrs*

Bourne Salads, Spalding Road, Bourne, Lincolnshire, PE10 0AT Tel: (01778) 393222 Fax: (01778) 393001 *Prepared salads*

▶ Bourne & Son Ltd, Unit 23a Firsland Park Estate, Henfield Road, Albourne, Hassocks, West Sussex, BN6 9JJ Tel: (01273) 491554 Fax: (01273) 491554 E-mail: furniture@bourneandson.com *Wooden furniture manufrs*

Bourne Steel Ltd, St. Clements House, St. Clements Road, Poole, Dorset, BH12 4GP Tel: (01202) 746666 Fax: (01202) 732002 E-mail: sales@bourne-steel.demon.co.uk *Structural engineers*

▶ Bourne Training, Bourne House, Sandy Lane, Romsey, Hampshire, SO51 0PD Tel: 01794 523301 Fax: 01794 516720 E-mail: info@bournetraining.co.uk *Computer based e-learning solutions training*

Bournemouth Balloon Co., 1440 Wimbpourne Road, Bournemouth, BH10 7AF Tel: (01202) 590890 Fax: (01202) 590890 *Balloon decorators*

Bournemouth Chamber Of Trade & Commerce, 15 Alum Chine Road, Bournemouth, BH4 8DT Tel: (01202) 540870 Fax: (01202) 751997 E-mail: sales@bournemouthchamber.org.uk *Chamber of trade & commerce*

▶ Bournemouth Fishing Lodge, 904 Wimborne Road, Bournemouth, BH9 2DW Tel: (01202) 514345 Fax: (01202) 514345

Bournlea Instruments Ltd, The Old Rectory, 34 Pauls Lane, Overstrand, Cromer, Norfolk, NR27 0PF Tel: (01263) 578186 Fax: (01263) 579186 E-mail: enquiries@bournlea.com Principal Export Areas: Worldwide *High voltage electronic component*

Bournville Engineering, Lifford Trading Estate, Lifford Lane, Birmingham, B30 3DY Tel: 0121-459 9339 Fax: 0121-459 9242 *Plastic mould toolmakers & pressure diecasting toolmakers*

▶ Bournville Heating Service, 50 Camp Hill Industrial Estate, John Kempe Way, Birmingham, B12 0HU Tel: 0121-753 3456 Fax: 0121-753 3698

Bournville Mot Centre Ltd, Bournville Road, Blaina, Abertillery, Gwent, NP13 3ER Tel: (01495) 290013 Fax: (01495) 290269 *Amusement machine distributors*

Bourton Group Ltd, Bourton Hall, Bourton, Rugby, Warwickshire, CV23 9SD Tel: (01926) 633333 Fax: (01926) 633450E-mail: info@bourton.co.uk *Management consultants to industry*

Bousfield Ltd, Southway Drive, North Common, Bristol, BS30 5JE Tel: 0117-988 8899 Fax: 0117-988 8866E-mail: sales@bousfield.net *Printing products & pre-press system printers* Also at: Hull & Leicester

Boustead International Heaters Ltd, Southwick Square, Southwick, Brighton, BN42 4UA Tel: (01273) 596868 Fax: (01273) 596860 E-mail: sales@bihl.com *Designers & suppliers of direct fired process heaters*

Boverton Precision, Unit 2 Oxbutts Industrial Etate, Woodmancote, Cheltenham, Gloucestershire, GL52 9HW Tel: (01242) 675405 Fax: (01242) 677411 E-mail: bovertonprecision@wwmail.co.uk *Mouldmaker, injection moulds & press tools*

Bovey Handloom Weavers, 1 Station Road, Bovey Tracey, Newton Abbot, Devon, TQ13 9AL Tel: (01626) 833424 Fax: (01626) 833424 *Woolen material retailers & manufrs*

James Boville, 35 Culnafay Road, Toomebridge, Antrim, BT41 3QG Tel: (028) 2587 8213 Fax: (028) 2587 8213 *Agricultural contractors*

Bovingdon Brickworks Ltd, Pudds Cross, Bovingdon, Hemel Hempstead, Hertfordshire, HP3 0NW Tel: (01442) 833176 Fax: (01442) 834539 E-mail: info@bovingdonbrickworks.co.uk *Facing & general purpose brick manufrs*

Bovingdon M.A, Stanwell Road, Ashgood Farm, Horton, Slough, SL3 9PA Tel: (01753) 682063 *Livestock*

▶ Bovis Construction Contractors, 33 Bothwell Street, Glasgow, G2 6NL Tel: 0141-226 8500 Fax: 0141-226 8513

Bovis Land Lease Ltd, Third Floor The Vinus, 1 Old Park Lane, Trafford, Manchester, M41 7HG Tel: 0161-254 1700 Fax: 0161-254 1701 *Building contractors*

Bovis Lend Lease, 32 Cumberland Street, Bristol, BS2 8NL Tel: 0117-924 8094 Fax: 0117-924 7314

Bow Aquatic Centre, Willowbrook Garden Centre, West Buckland, Wellington, Somerset, TA21 9HX Tel: (01823) 461822 Fax: (01823) 461822 *Aquatic retail centre*

Bow Brand International Ltd, Highgate, King's Lynn, Norfolk, PE30 1PT Tel: 0800 282355 Fax: (01553) 762887 E-mail: sales@bowbrand.co.uk *Sports & music string manufrs*

Bow Finishing, Stansted House, Tilburstow Hill Road, South Godstone, Godstone, Surrey, RH9 8NA Tel: (01342) 892220 Fax: (01342) 892220 E-mail: sales@bowfinishing.co.uk *Polyester lacquer manufrs*

▶ The Bow Group, 2274 Dunbeath Road, Elgin, Swindon, SN2 6EA Tel: (01793) 651000

Bow Metals, 49 Moody Street, London, E1 4BZ Tel: (020) 8981 0903 *Scrap metal merchants*

Bow Tyre Service, Unit 263A, Carpenters Road, Stratford, London, E15 2DU Tel: (020) 8519 7072 Fax: (020) 8519 7072 E-mail: bowservice@talk21.com *Tyre & battery distributors*

Bowater Cordell Ltd, Dukesway, Teesside Industrial Estate, Thornaby, Stockton-On-Tees, Cleveland, TS17 9LT Tel: (01642) 750303 Fax: (01642) 750164 E-mail: bowater@cordellgroup.com *General engineers*

▶ Bowater Engineering (EU), PO Box 63, Stamford, Lincs, PE9 4SW Tel: 01780 480877 Fax: 01780 480878 E-mail: info@bowater.eu.com *Bowater provide engineering, sales and marketing consulting to the paper,plastics, printing and packaging sectors*

Bowater S J, Sidney Street, Wolverhampton, WV2 4HH Tel: (01902) 425677 Fax: (01902) 771540 *Scrap iron & steel merchants*

Bowbrook Studios Ltd, Unit 7, Highgrove Farm, Seaford, Pinvin, Pershore, Worcestershire, WR10 2LF Tel: (01905) 840694 Fax: (01905) 840695 E-mail: sales@bowbrookstudios.co.uk *Giftware manufrs*

▶ Bowbros Ltd, Newby Road Industrial Estate, Newby Road, Hazel Grove, Stockport, Cheshire, SK7 5DD Tel: (01656) 661224 Fax: (01656) 660009 *Flexible tubing manufrs*

Bowburn Hall Hotel, Ramside Estates, Bowburn, Durham, DH6 5NH Tel: 0191-377 0311 Fax: 0191-377 3459 E-mail: info@bowburnhallhotel.co.uk *Conference facilities*

Bowcom Ltd, Florence Works, Brindley Road, Cardiff, CF11 8TX Tel: (029) 2038 8349 Fax: (029) 2034 3235 E-mail: info@bowcom.co.uk *Road & sports ground marking equipment*

Bowcourt Ltd, 7 Gardner Industrial Estate, Kent House Lane, Beckenham, Kent, BR3 1JR Tel: (020) 8659 1931 Fax: (020) 8676 8939 E-mail: sales@bowcourt.co.uk *Printers*

Bowdell Steel Services Ltd, 57 Bradford Street, Walsall, WS1 3QD Tel: (01922) 720989 Fax: (01922) 635960 E-mail: bowdellsteel@tinyworld.co.uk *Steel stockholders, fabricators & sub-contractors*

Bowden Bros Ltd, Brickworks House, Spook Hill, North Holmwood, Dorking, Surrey, RH5 4HR Tel: (01306) 743355 Fax: (01306) 876768 E-mail: info@bowdon-bros.com *High voltage power system manufrs*

Bowden Bros & Co. (Manchester) Ltd, Newby Road Industrial Estate, Hazel Grove, Stockport, Cheshire, SK7 5DD Tel: 0161-483 9311 Fax: 0161-483 1080 E-mail: sales@bowbros.co.uk *Gas fittings manufrs*

▶ Bowden Close Hotel, Teignmouth Road, Maidencombe, Torquay, TQ1 4TJ Tel: (01803) 328029 E-mail: enquiries@bowdenclose.co.uk *Bowden Close House is a large Victorian house with 6 self-catering holiday apartments set in an acre of gardens overlooking Lyme Bay in South Devon.*

Company Information

Bowden & Dolphin Ltd, 16 Cherrywood Road, Birmingham, B9 4UD Tel: 0121-773 6000 Fax: 0121-773 4070 E-mail: info@bowdenanddolphinsigns.com *Sign & kiosk manufrs*

Bowden Precision Engineering Co. Ltd, Riverside, Market Harborough, Leicestershire, LE16 7PU Tel: (01858) 467508 Fax: (01858) 431656 E-mail: enquiries@bowdenprecision.co.uk *Precision engineers*

Bowden-Jackson (Construction) Ltd, PO Box Hk7, Leeds, LS11 7DY Tel: 0113-277 9539 Fax: 0113-277 9539 *Refractory contractors & building contractors*

Bowdery & Wilkinson, 7 Powke Lane Industrial Estate, Powke Lane, Rowley Regis, West Midlands, B65 0AH Tel: 0121-561 3448 Fax: 0121-561 3448 *Commercial vehicle repairs*

▶ Bowe Digitl:Access, 27 Lansdowne Terrace, Newcastle Upon Tyne, NE3 1HP Tel: 0191-284 2002 E-mail: david.rosher@bowe.co.uk *IT consultants & bespoke software programmers*

Boweld Engineering, Pentre Halkyn, Rhes-y-Cae, Holywell, Clwyd, CH8 8JP Tel: (01352) 781566 Fax: (01352) 781141 *Commercial vehicle body builders*

Bowen Barrack & Co., 9 SMM Business Park, Dock Road, Birkenhead, Merseyside, CH41 1DT Tel: 0151-653 7948 Fax: 0151-653 7990 *Marine consultants or consulting engineers*

Bowen Hopkins Ltd, 854 Carmarthen Road, Fforestfach, Swansea, SA5 8HS Tel: (01792) 581022 Fax: (01792) 583321 *Electrical contractors*

Bowen Tools Div I R I International, Kirkton Avenue, Pitmedden Road Industrial Estate, Dyce, Aberdeen, AB21 0BF Tel: (01224) 771339 Fax: (01224) 723034 *Fishing tool, drilling rigs & equipment manufrs*

Bowen Water Systems, Pasture House, Main Street, Kirkby Malzeard, Ripon, North Yorkshire, HG4 3SD Tel: (01765) 658293 Fax: (01765) 658830 *Water engineers*

Bowens International Ltd, 355 Old Road, Clacton-on-Sea, Essex, CO15 3RH Tel: (01255) 422807 Fax: (01255) 475503 E-mail: sales@bowensinternational.co.uk *Electronic flash equipment manufrs*

Bower & Child Ltd, 91 Wakefield Road, Huddersfield, HD5 9AB Tel: (01484) 425416 Fax: (01484) 517353 *Domestic heating engineers*

Bower Fuller Ltd, 6 Bermuda Road, Ransomes Industrial Estate, Ipswich, IP3 9RU Tel: (01473) 272277 Fax: (01473) 270100 E-mail: services@bowerfuller.co.uk *Complete mechanical & electrical services*

Bower Green Ltd, Dryden Street, Bradford, West Yorkshire, BD1 5ND Tel: (01274) 733537 Fax: (01274) 393511 E-mail: info@bowergreen.co.uk *Freight forwarding agents*

Bower Green Ltd, Station Road, Norwood Green, Halifax, West Yorkshire, HX3 8QD Tel: (01274) 672450 Fax: (01274) 693136 E-mail: norwood@bowergreen.co.uk *Freight forwarders*

Bower Roebuck & Co. Ltd, Glendale Mills, New Mill, Holmfirth, HD9 7EN Tel: (01484) 682181 Fax: (01484) 683469 E-mail: info@bowerroebucks.com *Worsted manufrs*

▶ Bowers & Co, York House, 4 Sheepscar Way, Leeds, LS7 3JB Tel: 0113 2379500 Fax: 0113 2379550 E-mail: ajb@companydoctor.co.uk *Intensive care for your business. Commercial finance & business turnaround solutions*

Bowers Electricals Ltd, Slack Lane, Heanor, Derbyshire, DE75 7GX Tel: (01773) 531531 Fax: (01773) 716171 E-mail: enquiries@bowerselec.co.uk *Electric motor repairers & rewind specialist*

Bowers & Jones Ltd, Patrick Gregory Road, Wolverhampton, WV11 3DU Tel: (01902) 732110 Fax: (01902) 864654 E-mail: jim.willmott@bowers.jones.freeserve.co.uk *Engineers & general engineering*

Bowers Systems Ltd, 293 Wallisdown Road, Poole, Dorset, BH12 5BT Tel: (01202) 512790 Fax: (01202) 524663 *Bakery equipment manufrs*

V.J. Bowers & Sons, 11 Rydal Road, Little Lever, Bolton, BL3 1DT Tel: (01204) 578358 Fax: (01204) 578358 *Shop fitters*

Bowey Construction Ltd, Albany Court, Newcastle Business Park, Newcastle upon Tyne, NE4 7YB Tel: 0191-273 3311 Fax: 0191-273 6620 E-mail: info@boweyconstruction.co.uk *Building contractors*

Bowhill & Elliott East Anglia Ltd, 65 London Street, Norwich, NR2 1HL Tel: (01603) 620116 Fax: (01603) 620066 *Footwear retailers services*

T.A. Bowkett, 3 Cox Industustrial Estate, Three Cocks, Brecon, Powys, LD3 0SD Tel: (01497) 851650 Fax: (01497) 847766 *Agricultural merchants*

Bowland Cumbria Ltd, Under Railway Bridge, Dockray Hall Mill, Kendal, Cumbria, LA9 4RU Tel: (01539) 723600 Fax: (01539) 740776 E-mail: sales@boland-stone.com *Cast concrete manufrs*

Bowland Paving Centre, Mogul Lane, Halesowen, West Midlands, B63 2QQ Tel: (01384) 636564 Fax: (01384) 411744 *Landscape material retailers, suppliers & manufrs*

▶ Bowland Trading Ltd, Units 2-4, Springhill Works, Edleston Street, Accrington, Lancashire, BB5 0HG Tel: 01254 395553 Fax: 01254 384728 E-mail: sales@bowlandtrading.com *Bowland Trading Ltd specialises in quality used machine tools and provides manufacturing companies with a range of services to enable them to sell surplus or redundant manufacturing equipment.**We have the product to maximise return on surplus equipment from single items of equipment, to complete manufacturing plants, from commission based sales, to outright purchase.**Bowland Trading Ltd was formed to offer a cost efficient service to engineering companies who have redundant assets. The principal partners involved in the business have over a decade of experience in the market.**Our offices are alongside our 20,000sq ft warehouse of where we hold our stock and invite customers to call and visit us.**

Bowlea Trailers & Caravan Sales, Bowlea Smithy, Penicuik, Midlothian, EH26 8PX Tel: (01968) 673571 Fax: (01968) 673571 *Trailer hire*

▶ Bowlen Packaging Ltd, Castle Clough Mill, Hapton, Burnley, Lancashire, BB12 7LN Tel: (01282) 770770

Colin Bowler, Church Farm, Main Street, Great Casterton, Stamford, Lincolnshire, PE9 4AP Tel: (01780) 752895 *Specialist joiners*

▶ Bowler Group Ltd, Bowler House Harvey Road, Burnt Mills Industrial Estate, Basildon, Essex, SS13 1DD Tel: (01268) 470700 Fax: (01268) 477717 E-mail: info@hjbowlerandsons.com *Specialists in the procurement & supply of secondary tinplate & tfs*

Bowler Group Ltd, Bowler House Harvey Road, Burnt Mills Industrial Estate, Basildon, Essex, SS13 1DD Tel: (01268) 470700 Fax: (01268) 470900 *Metal stampers manufrs*

Bowling Finishing Services Ltd, Bowling Mill, Lonsdale Street, Nelson, Lancashire, BB9 9HQ Tel: (01282) 612336 *Commissioners bleachers dyeing finishers services*

Bowling International UK Ltd, Bushacre Court, 14 Garrard Way, Kettering, Northamptonshire, NN16 8TD Tel: (01536) 412244 Fax: (01536) 410350 *Ten pin bowling equipment suppliers & installers*

Bowller Roofing Supplies, Station Road, Harston, Cambridge, CB22 7QP Tel: (01223) 872260 Fax: (01223) 871143 E-mail: admin@bowller.co.uk *Roofing, suspended ceilings & environmental systems suppliers*

Bowman E Sons Building Contractors, Cherryholt Road, Stamford, Lincolnshire, PE9 2EP Tel: (01780) 751015 Fax: (01780) 759051 E-mail: mail@ebowman.co.uk *Building contractors & stone masons*

Bowman Group Ltd, 1200 Century Way, Thorpe Park Business Park, Leeds, LS15 8ZB Tel: (01422) 322211 Fax: (01325) 151100 E-mail: info@bowman-group.co.uk *Management consultancy*

Bowman & Porter Security Ltd, 678 High Road, North Finchley, London, N12 9PT Tel: (020) 8446 2541 Fax: (020) 8445 6016 *Gate security services*

Bowman Power Group Ltd, Ocean Quay, Belvidere Road, Southampton, SO14 5QY Tel: (023) 8023 6700 Fax: (023) 8035 2565 E-mail: sales@bowmanpower.co.uk *Research & development services*

Bowman & Sanderson Ltd, Icknield Way, Baldock, Hertfordshire, SG7 5BD Tel: (01462) 892292 Fax: (01462) 490457 E-mail: bowsand@tiscali.co.uk *Precision engineers*

Bowmans, Westland Square, Leeds, LS11 5SS Tel: 0113-272 0088 Fax: 0113-272 0261 E-mail: mail@bowmans77.co.uk

Bowmans Blinds & Canopies, 8 Whinfield Close, Stockton-on-Tees, Cleveland, TS19 8UA Tel: (07762) 581158 Fax: (01642) 583625 *Blinds & canopy suppliers*

Bowmer Bond Narrow Fabrics Ltd, Hanging Bridge Mills, Ashbourne, Derbyshire, DE6 2EA Tel: (01335) 342244 Fax: (01335) 300651 E-mail: sales@bowmerbond.co.uk Principal Export Areas: Worldwide *Narrow fabric, fabric tape & webbing manufrs*

Bowmer & Kirkland Ltd, High Edge Court, Church Street, Heage, Belper, Derbyshire, DE56 2BW Tel: (01773) 853131 Fax: (01773) 856710 E-mail: sales@bandk.co.uk *Building & civil engineers* Also at: Cambridge, Harrow & Warrington

Bowmer & Kirkland Ltd, Aspect Gate, 166 College Road, Harrow, Middlesex, HA1 1BH Tel: (020) 8427 4322 Fax: (020) 8863 5627 E-mail: enquiries@bandk-harrow.co.uk

Bowmonk Ltd, Diamond Road, St. Faiths Industrial Estate, Norwich, NR6 6AW Tel: (01603) 485153 Fax: (01603) 418150 E-mail: info@bowmonk.co.uk *Dynamometers & brake test equipment manufrs*

Bowne Global Solutions Ltd, Eaton House, Wigmore Place, Luton, LU2 9EZ Tel: (01582) 702000 Fax: (01582) 702222 E-mail: info.luton@bowneglobal.co.uk *Desk top publishing services & translation*

John Bownes Ltd, Courthouse Farm, Swanlow Lane, Darnhall, Winsford, Cheshire, CW7 4BS Tel: (01606) 592639 Fax: (01606) 861410 E-mail: sales@jbownes.co.uk *Tractors & agricultural machinery*

▶ Bowpak Ltd, 191 Station Road, Shotts, Lanarkshire, ML7 4BA Tel: (01501) 825185 E-mail: bowpak@aol.com *Hand labellers, Price Guns,Labels till rolls plain paper carrier bags*

▶ Bowron Motor Care, Hatton House, Flaunden Lane, Flaunden, Hemel Hempstead, Hertfordshire, HP3 0PQ Tel: (01442) 834634 Fax: (01442) 834488 E-mail: sales@bowron-motorcare.co.uk *Car Body Repairs, Light Commercial Body Repairs, Insurance repairs, Mechanical Servicing and Repairs, Courtesy Cars available*

▶ Bowser Bros, Stainton by Langworth, Lincoln, LN3 5BL Tel: (01673) 862423 Fax: (01673) 862423

Harry Bowser & Son, Providence Place, Driffield, North Humberside, YO25 6QQ Tel: (01377) 252134 *Scrap metal merchants*

Bowsey Hill Sawmill, Bear Lane, Wargrave, Reading, RG10 8QJ Tel: 0118-940 2240 *Wood sawmill*

Bowshers Ltd, 19 Buckland Road, Pen Mill Trading Estate, Yeovil, Somerset, BA21 5HA Tel: (01935) 423926 Fax: (01935) 432865 E-mail: bowshers@bowshers-electrical.co.uk *Electrical contractors*

Bowson Engineering Ltd, Oak House, Dewsbury Road, Fenton Industrial Estate, Stoke-on-Trent, ST4 2TE Tel: (01782) 749000 Fax: (01782) 749299 E-mail: sales@bowson.co.uk *Precision sheet metal workers & light steel fabricators*

Bowsprit Contracting Ltd, J The Henfield Business Park, Shoreham Road, Henfield, West Sussex, BN5 9SL Tel: (01273) 491499 Fax: (01273) 491982 E-mail: enquiries@bowspritltd.co.uk *Civil engineers*

Bowtech Products Ltd, Howe Moss Cresent, Kirkhill Industrial Estate, Dyce, Aberdeen, AB21 0GN Tel: (01224) 772345 Fax: (01224) 772900 E-mail: bowtech@bowtech.co.uk *Sub-sea equipment suppliers*

Bowyer Engineering Ltd, South Way, Walworth Industrial Estate, Andover, Hampshire, SP10 5AF Tel: (01264) 365921 Fax: (01264) 356547 E-mail: sales@bowyerengineering.co.uk *Precision engineers & instrumentation manufrs*

Bowyers Office Equipment, Church Road, Penn, High Wycombe, Buckinghamshire, HP10 8LP Tel: (01494) 816585 Fax: (01494) 813684 E-mail: charles.bowyer@bowyersoffice.co.uk *Office equipment suppliers*

Box 42 Ltd, PO Box 42, St. Helens, Merseyside, WA10 3BF Tel: (0845) 3700442 Fax: (0845) 3700542 E-mail: welcome@box42.com *Computer services for special needs*

▶ Box Clever Solutions Ltd, PO Box 427, Southport, Merseyside, PR8 2WG Tel: (0845) 1235730 Fax: (0845) 1235736 E-mail: info@business-made-simple.co.uk *Business Development Consultants for small to medium sized businesses in the UK - in a language you can understand at an affordable price. Website development and promotion specialists.*

▶ Box Clever Wholesale, 1e Britannia Estate, Leagrave Road, Luton, LU3 1RJ Tel: (01582) 722990 Fax: (01582) 450030

Box Factory Ltd, 2 Caswell Road, Leamington Spa, Warwickshire, CV31 1QD Tel: (01926) 430510 Fax: (01926) 430505 *Cardboard box manufrs*

Box Products Ltd, The Lodge 3 Russell House, Cambridge Street, London, SW1V 4EQ Tel: (020) 7976 6791 Fax: (020) 7828 7133 E-mail: boxproducts@btinternet.com *Custom lighting design & production*

Box & Seal, Unit 30 Whitehill Industrial Estate, Whitehill Lane, Wootton Bassett, Swindon, SN4 7DB Tel: (01793) 855855 Fax: (01793) 855853 *Box manufrs*

Box Wise Ltd, Rayne House, 3 The Street, Rayne, Braintree, Essex, CM77 6RH Tel: (01376) 551166 Fax: (01376) 551429 E-mail: sales@boxwise.ltd.uk *Carton boxing manufrs*

Box42 Ltd, PO Box 42, Prescot, Merseyside, L35 4PH Tel: 0151-426 9988 Fax: 0151-426 994 E-mail: jeffhughes@box42.com *Computers special needs*

Boxall Engineering, Unit 50 Grace Business Centre, Willow Lane, Mitcham, Surrey, CR4 4TU Tel: (020) 8648 8468 Fax: (020) 8648 4162 E-mail: info@boxall-industrial.co.uk *Precision & general engineers industrial cleaning vessel*

T.A. Boxall & Co. Ltd, 20 Balcombe Road, Horley, Surrey, RH6 9HR Tel: (01293) 820133 Fax: (01293) 776139 E-mail: ronransley@taboxall.co.uk *Electrical contractors & motor repair services*

Boxclever, The Mount, Selby Road, Garforth, Leeds, LS25 2AQ Tel: 0113-286 0795 Fax: 0113-286 4525 E-mail: sales@boxcleverbrokers.com *Computer consultants & brokers*

▶ Boxdvdsets, 33 Rye Road, Hoddesdon, Hertfordshire, EN11 0JE Tel: (0871) 2002082 Fax: E-mail: sales@boxdvdsets.com *DVD players & dvd products suppliers*

Boxer Designs & Manufacturing, Unit 2 Boundary Court, Heaton Chapel, Stockport, Cheshire, SK4 5GA Tel: 0161-975 1830 Fax: 0161-431 3364 E-mail: sales@boxer-design.co.uk Principal Export Areas: Worldwide *Design & manufacture of lock forming & sheet metalworking machinery*

▶ Boxes And Packaging (Cambridge)Ltd, Edison Road, St. Ives Industrial Estate, St. Ives, Cambridgeshire, PE27 3LF Tel: (01480) 467633 Fax: (01480) 309100 E-mail: cambridge@boxesandpackaging.com *Designers, Manufacturers and Stockists of corrugated packaging. From Big Brown Boxes (even beyond conventional sizes) through to FULL COLOUR retail display units. FREE 'Pack Rationalisation' or 'Cost Down Exercises' survey - please contact our sales office*

Boxes G H Ltd, Palatine Mill, Meadow Street, Great Harwood, Blackburn, BB6 7EJ Tel: (01254) 888151 Fax: (01254) 889569 E-mail: carton@boxesgh.co.uk *Printed folding cartons & folding box manufrs*

Boxes Kelvin Fenton Ltd, George Street, Burnley, Lancashire, BB11 1LX Tel: (01282) 477047 Fax: (01282) 477048 E-mail: boxeskf@discali.co.uk *Box manufrs*

Boxes & Packaging Ltd, Unit 2/A, Drakes Farm, Drakes Drive, Long Crendon, Aylesbury, Buckinghamshire, HP18 9BA Tel: (01844) 202188 Fax: (01844) 202198 E-mail: sales@mondipackaging.com *Corrugated cases manufrs*

Boxes & Packaging, Unit 10 Southside, Bredbury Park Industrial Estate, Bredbury, Stockport, Cheshire, SK6 2SP Tel: 0161-406 4200 Fax: 0161-406 7217 E-mail: manchester@boxesandpackaging.co.uk *Corrugated boxes, cases & containers manufrs*

Boxes & Packaging Ltd, Dunbeath Road, Elgin Industrial Estate, Swindon, SN2 8EA Tel: (01793) 513233 Fax: (01793) 513225 E-mail: swindon@boxesandpackagingltd.co.uk *Cardboard boxes or cases or containers*

Boxes & Packaging (Manchester) Ltd, Gorse Lane, Tarleton, Preston, PR4 6LH Tel: (01772) 815689 Fax: (01772) 812234 E-mail: info@boxesandpackaging.co.uk *Corrugated box & fitment manufrs*

Boxford Ltd, Boy Lane, Wheatley, Halifax, West Yorkshire, HX3 5AF Tel: (01422) 358311 Fax: (01422) 355924 E-mail: info@boxford.co.uk *Machine tool manufrs*

Boxline Ltd, Bradgate Street, Leicester, LE4 0AW Tel: 0116-262 7571 Fax: 0116-251 5090 E-mail: sales@boxline.co.uk *Cardboard packaging suppliers*

BoxMart Ltd, Unit 1C, Ringway Industrial Estate, Eastern Avenue, Lichfield, Staffordshire, WS13 7SF Tel: (01543) 411574 Fax: (01543) 258952 E-mail: enquiries@boxmart.co.uk *BoxMart are trade suppliers of gift boxes and speciality packaging, primarily serving UK, Ireland and continental Europe customers. They hold a wide range of gift boxes, bottle boxes and florist sundries in stock for swift despatch. This allows you to meet urgent deadlines and saves you the expense of holding stocks. Minimum order quantity is just one pack of any product. You can browse and order via their user friendly website. Their boxes are 95% recycled material and are fully recyclable. All can be customised with an overprint. Available off-the-shelf: small and large presentation boxes, pillow packs, CD boxes, bottle boxes for 1, 2, 3, 4, 6 or 12 bottles, magnum presentation packs, wine box K, promotional ice buckets, hamper boxes, balloon boxes, Posy Boxes for hand-tied bouquets, Supa Posy Boxes, buttonhole boxes, delivery boxes, POS Bottle Display, NotWood, Tag Box, Christmas designs, Valentine's and other seasonal designs.*

continued

Boxmoor Precision Engineering, 439A London Road, Hemel Hempstead, Hertfordshire, HP3 9BD Tel: (01442) 250147 Fax: (01442) 250147 *Precision engineers*

Boxmore Packaging Ltd, Gateway, Crewe, CW1 6YA Tel: (01270) 582137 Fax: (01270) 581615 E-mail: enquiries@boxmoreplastics.com *Plastic blow moulders*

Boxpads Ltd, 59-61 Camden Street, Birmingham, B1 3BT Tel: 0121-236 2337 Fax: 0121-212 0977 *Jewellery case manufrs*

Boxpak Ltd, 65 Church Road, Newtownabbey, County Antrim, BT36 7LR Tel: (028) 9036 5421 Fax: (028) 9086 6731 E-mail: sales@boxpak.co.uk *Printed folded cartons & hot-foil blocking manufrs*

Boxrite Hydraulics, 1A May Avenue, Northfleet, Gravesend, Kent, DA11 8RH Tel: (01474) 327722 Fax: (01322) 327722 *Hydraulic engineers, repairers & manufrs*

Boxshop Ltd, 1-3 Manson Place, Kelvin Industrial Estate, East Kilbride, Glasgow, G75 0QW Tel: (01355) 222960 Fax: (01355) 223147 E-mail: boxes@boxshop.com *Corrugated packaging manufrs*

▶ Boxstar Ltd, Hill Street, Clayton-le-moors, Accrington, Lancashire, BB5 5EA Tel: 01254 395631 Fax: 01254 391573 E-mail: info@boxstarltd.com *Boxstar Limited is the UK's newest print & packaging Group, formed in September 2004. Comprising 4 sites within the UK, Boxstar focuses on the manufacture of folding cartons, self-adhesive labels, foil laminate sachets, wet glue labels, the unique T-tube® and Concept Boxes as well as digital imaging for many leading blue-chip groups.*

Boyce & Co., Exeter Airport Industrial Estate, Exeter Airport, Clyst Honiton, Exeter, EX5 2LJ Tel: (01392) 368891 Fax: (01392) 365598 *Packaging material distributors*

Boyco Co., Europa Way, Stockport, Cheshire, SK3 0XE Tel: 0161-428 7077 *Manufacturers cloak room furniture*

Alexander Boyd Displays Ltd, Lambeg Mills, Ballyskeagh Road, Lisburn, County Antrim, BT27 5SX Tel: (028) 9030 1115 Fax: (028) 9030 1305 E-mail: sboyd@alexanderboyd.com *Screen process printers*

▶ Boyd Cooper Ltd, Bruton House, Stadium Way, Harlow, Essex, CM19 5FT Tel: (01279) 621900 Fax: (01279) 641779 E-mail: enquiries@boydcooper.com *Uniform clothing manufrs*

Boyd Food Machinery, Ramas, Buckie, Banffshire, AB56 4BA Tel: (01542) 835885 Fax: (01542) 835080 E-mail: boyd@boydfood.com *Used food machinery, processing equipment, reconditioned & refurbished food processing machinery, packaging equipment & used refrigeration plant, export worldwide*

John Boyd Textiles Ltd, Higher Flax Mills, Castle Cary, Somerset, BA7 7DY Tel: (01963) 350451 Fax: (01963) 351078 E-mail: enquiries@johnboydtextiles.co.uk *Weavers, horsehair fabrics & upholstery*

Boyd Line, The Orangery Hesslewood Country Office Park, Ferriby Road, Hessle, North Humberside, HU13 0LH Tel: (01482) 324024 Fax: (01482) 323737 E-mail: info@boydline.co.uk *Trawler owners & vessel management*

Boyd & Co (Metalworkers) Ltd, Chainbridge Road, Blaydon-on-Tyne, Tyne & Wear, NE21 5SW Tel: 0191-414 3331 Fax: 0191-414 0340 E-mail: info@boydduct.co.uk *Ductwork contractors & sheet metal fabricators*

Boyd & Sons Bendooragh Ltd, 80 Bann Road, Bendoragh, Ballymoney, County Antrim, BT53 7LP Tel: (028) 2766 3116 Fax: (028) 2766 3116 *Agricultural machinery distributors*

Boydell & Jacks Ltd, Marlborough Street, Burnley, Lancashire, BB11 2HW Tel: (01282) 456411 Fax: (01282) 437496 E-mail: sales@featherwing.com *Commercial vehicle component manufrs*

Boydell Pipeworks & Fabrications, Poplar Street, Leigh, Lancashire, WN7 4HL Tel: (01942) 672951 Fax: (01942) 262042 E-mail: info@boydellfab.com *Sheet metalwork manufrs*

George Boyden & Son Ltd, York House, 17 Rother Street, Stratford-Upon-Avon, Warwickshire, CV37 6NB Tel: (01789) 266261 Fax: (01789) 269519 E-mail: news@stratford-herald.co.uk *Printers*

Boyer Bransden Electronics Ltd, Frinsbury House, Cox Street, Detling, Maidstone, Kent, ME14 3HE Tel: (01622) 730939 Fax: (01622) 730930 E-mail: sales@boyerbransden.com *Electronic ignition for classic motorbikes*

Boyer Leisure Ltd, Ford Lane, Iver, Buckinghamshire, SL0 9LL Tel: (01753) 630302 Fax: (01753) 630302 E-mail: tackleshop@boyer.co.uk *Fishing lakes leisure & equipment*

Boyerman Ltd, Unit C Chesham Close, Romford, RM7 7PJ Tel: (01708) 742854 Fax: (01708) 737737 E-mail: sales@boyerman.co.uk *Machinery maintenance & repair services*

John Boyes Consulting, May House, Tanners Lane, Hathern, Loughborough, Leicestershire, LE12 5JG Tel: (01509) 646530 Fax: (01509) 646530 E-mail: john@johnboyes.com *Management consultants*

Boygle & Co. Ltd, Chichester Road, Romiley, Stockport, Cheshire, SK6 4BL Tel: 0161-406 8280 Fax: 0161-406 8244 *Shop fitters*

Boyland Joinery Ltd, Stony Lane, Christchurch, Dorset, BH23 1EZ Tel: (01202) 499499 Fax: (01202) 499037 E-mail: enquires@boylandjoinery.co.uk *Wood windows, doors & staircases manufrs*

Daniel Boyle & Son, 1 Carruthers Street, Liverpool, L3 6BY Tel: 0151-255 0055 Fax: 0151-255 0011 E-mail: sales@titherleys.co.uk *Paper merchants*

R. Boyle Motor Engineering Ltd, Blackwall Way, London, E14 9QG Tel: (020) 7987 2683 Fax: (020) 7987 2683 *Accident repairs, servicing & mot's*

▶ Boyle Transport Ltd, Block F, Porterfield Road, Renfrew, PA4 8DJ Tel: 0141-886 6000

Boys & Boden Ltd, Mill Lane, Welshpool, Powys, SY21 7BL Tel: (01938) 556677 Fax: (01938) 555773 *Builders & timber merchants* Also at: Newtown

BP Exploration Operating Co. Ltd, Sullom Voe Oil Terminal, Mossbank, Shetland, ZE2 9TU Tel: (01806) 243000 Fax: (01806) 243200

BP International Ltd, Research & Engineering Centre, Chertsey Rd, Sunbury-on-Thames, Middx, TW16 7LN Tel: (01932) 762000 Fax: (01932) 762999 *Research & engineering centre*

BP Self Adhesive Labels Ltd, Cypress Drive, St Mellons Business Park, St. Mellons, Cardiff, CF3 0EG Tel: (029) 2077 8500 Fax: (029) 2077 8388 E-mail: hello@bplabels.co.uk *Manufacturers self-adhesive labels cosmetic toiletries electronics*

BPC (Anglia) Ltd, Unit 1, 22-24 Brunel Way, Thetford, Norfolk, IP24 1HP Tel: (01603) 721197 Fax: (01603) 721197 *Fly screens installers, manufacturers & pest control*

BPC Circuits Ltd, Sheene Road, Leicester, LE4 1BF Tel: 0116-233 4444 Fax: 0116-233 4466 E-mail: info@circuitcontroltechnology.com Principal Export Areas: Worldwide *Dust control industry specialists*

Bpe Signs, B135 Stourvale Road, Bournemouth, BH6 5HF Tel: (01202) 430066 Fax: (01202) 430066 E-mail: info@bpesigns.co.uk *Sign manufrs*

bpi.agri, Worcester Road, Leominster, Herefordshire, HR6 0QA Tel: (01568) 617220 Fax: (01568) 611435 E-mail: sales@bpiagri.com *Polythene film manufrs*

BPI Films, Warrington Road, Widnes, Cheshire, WA8 0SX Tel: 0151-422 3600 Fax: 0151-422 3620 *Polythene sheeting manufrs*

▶ BPI.Industrial Swansea, Swansea Enterprise Park, Clarion Close, Morriston, Swansea, SA6 8QZ Tel: (01792) 772441 Fax: (01792) 701134 E-mail: salesswansea@bpipoly.com *Polyethylene manufrs*

▶ Bpi Packaging, Brook Road, Buckhurst Hill, Essex, IG9 5TU Tel: (020) 8504 9151 Fax: (020) 8506 1892 E-mail: salesessex@bpipoly.com *Printed & plain carrier bags, polythene & polyethylene/polythene converters. Also environmental spillage containment products, layflat tubing polyethylene/polythene), packaging material/goods/products & polyethylene/ polythene bag/carrier/sack, film/sheet & packaging products manufrs*

BPM Engineering Services Ltd, Unit 18 Failsworth Indust Estate, Morton Street, Failsworth, Manchester, M35 0BN Tel: 0161-682 3377 Fax: 0161-682 7711 E-mail: brian.bpm@btconnect.com *Manufacturers of hot & cold needle perforators*

▶ BPMG Ltd, Peratone House, Gatehouse Way, Aylesbury, Buckinghamshire, HP19 8DB Tel: (01296) 436791 Fax: (01296) 380100 E-mail: sales@bpmg.co.uk

BPS Knowsley Ltd, Haven House, Kirkby Bank Road, Knowsley Industrial Park, Liverpool, L33 7RG Tel: 0151-548 1882 Fax: 0151-548 3884 *Industrial chemical power & pipe work installation building services*

BPX Electro Mechanical Co, Unit 8 Decade Close, High Carr Business Park, Newcastle, Staffordshire, ST5 7UH Tel: (01782) 565500 Fax: (01782) 565500 E-mail: bpxstaffs@bpx.co.uk *Electrical goods distributors*

Brabbin & Rudd Ltd, Walker Street, Bolton, BL1 4TB Tel: (01204) 521171 Fax: (01204) 364972 E-mail: sales@brabbin-and-rudd.co.uk *Engineers suppliers*

Brabiner Maintenance, 3 Brabiner Lane, Whittingham, Preston, PR3 2AP Tel: 01772 865182 Fax: 01772 865182 E-mail: thegavaghanhouse@msn.com *Weed control NPTC registered. Sensitive weed control for land & water. Chemical - heat - organic. Japanese knotweed Himalayan balsam specialist treatments. Contracts and one off treatments.Chimney sweeping - sales of stoves - flexi liners & fire parts & accessories.*

▶ Brabourne Communications Ltd, PO Box 6417, Derby, DE1 2BU Tel: (0845) 6039770 Fax: (01332) 294347 E-mail: simon@brabournecommunications.com *Two way radios & accessories suppliers*

Brace, Main Road, Milfield, Wooler, Northumberland, NE71 6JD Tel: (01668) 216306 Fax: (01668) 216348 E-mail: david@braceltd.co.uk *Refrigerator & catering equipment*

Brace Bakery Ltd, Cambrian House, Croespenmaen Industrial Estate, Kendon, Crumlin, Newport, Gwent, NP11 3AG Tel: (01495) 241400 Fax: (01495) 241441 *Bakers*

Bracebridge Motor Body Works Ltd, 246 Newark Road, Lincoln, LN6 8RP Tel: (01522) 520383 Fax: (01522) 537137 *Car bodywork, repairs & spraying*

Bracehand Ltd, Stanford Bury, Stanford Road, Shefford, Bedfordshire, SG17 5NS Tel: (01462) 817039 Fax: (01462) 816325 Principal Export Areas: North America, Central America & South America *CNC engineering or machining*

Braces, South Cornelly, Bridgend, Mid Glamorgan, CF33 4RE Tel: (01656) 742830 Fax: (01656) 744463 *Builders merchant*

Dr Barry Bracewell-Milnes, 26 Lancaster Court, Banstead, Surrey, SM7 1RR Tel: (01737) 350736 Fax: (01737) 371415 *Economic consultants*

A.G. Bracey Ltd, Unit 13, Pucklechurch Trading Estate, Pucklechurch, Bristol, BS16 9QH Tel: 0117-937 2705 Fax: 0117-937 4243 *Commercial body builders*

▶ Brachot Hermant UK Ltd, Wood Lane, Erdington, Birmingham, B24 9QJ Tel: 0121-382 8778 Fax: 0121-382 8700 *Marble & stone product manufrs*

Brack Meekins Partnership, Aberdeen House, 22 Highbury Grove, London, N5 2DQ Tel: (020) 7359 9245 Fax: (020) 7226 9522 E-mail: info@qs_1.com *Construction cost consultants & quantity surveyors* Also at: Bournemouth

▶ Bracken Hill Preserves, 7 Cranbrook Close, Wheldrake, York, YO19 6BY Tel: (01904) 448286 Fax: (01904) 607799 E-mail: info@brackenhillfinefoods.co.uk *Manufacturers of hand made preserves*

▶ Bracken Lea Homes Ltd, Unit 9 Main Street, Dunfermline, Fife, KY12 8QY Tel: (01383) 882882 Fax: (01383) 882244

▶ Bracken Lea Homes Planning Department Ltd, Culross, Dunfermline, Fife, KY12 8ET Tel: (01383) 880800

▶ Bracken Press, Print House, Swallowfields, Welwyn Garden City, Hertfordshire, AL7 1JD Tel: (01707) 896999

Bracken Wood Craft, The Stanway Centre, Peartree Road, Colchester, CO3 0JX Tel: (01206) 561316 Fax: (01206) 575619 *Pine furniture manufacturer & supplier*

▶ Bracken Wood Furniture, Unit 8 Headway Business Park, Denby Dale Road, Wakefield, West Yorkshire, WF2 7AZ Tel: (01924) 381580 Fax: (01924) 290811 E-mail: sales@brackenwoodfurniture.co.uk *Cane furniture specialists wide range available*

Bracken Woodcraft, Chelmsford Road, Rawreth, Wickford, Essex, SS11 8SJ Tel: (01268) 571800 Fax: (01268) 571870 *Pine furniture retailers & manufrs*

▶ Brackley Glass & Windows Ltd, PO Box 6911, Brackley, Northamptonshire, NN13 7ZX Tel: (01280) 703277 Fax: (0871) 7143685 E-mail: info@brackleyglass.co.uk *Glass & glazing services*

▶ Brackley Labels Ltd, A Nigel Court, Ward Road, Buckingham Road Industrial Estate, Brackley, Northamptonshire, NN13 7LF Tel: (01280) 704979 Fax: (01280) 705256 E-mail: sales@brackleylabels.net *Self-adhesive label manufrs*

Bracknell Fireworks Ltd, 2 Bullbrook Row, Bracknell, Berkshire, RG12 2NL Tel: (01344) 425321 Fax: (01344) 861006 E-mail: sales@bracknell-fireworks.co.uk *Firework retailers & suppliers*

Bracknell Pest Control Ltd, 2 Talbot Cotts, Forest Road, Wokingham, Berkshire, RG40 5SG Tel: (01344) 482202 Fax: (01344) 482202 *Pest control services*

Brad Ken Uk Ltd, Heath Road, Wednesbury, West Midlands, WS10 8JL Tel: 0121-526 4111 Fax: 0121-526 4174 *Iron alloy casting manufrs*

Brad Scott Estates Ltd, 137 Stonnall Road, Walsall, WS9 8JY Tel: (01543) 454098 Fax: (01543) 453352 *Surples services*

▶ Bradbury Flooring Ltd, 39-41 Carlisle Street, Leicester, LE3 6AH Tel: 0116-254 2655 Fax: 0116-254 2656 E-mail: sales@bradburyflooring.co.uk *Commercial carpet & flooring contractors*

Bradbury Graphics Ltd, 6-14 Donegall Pass, Belfast, BT7 1BS Tel: (028) 9023 3535 Fax: (028) 9057 2057 E-mail: info@bradbury-graphics.co.uk *Imaging bureau & digital printers*

▶ Bradbury Security Grilles, Dunlop Way, Queensway Enterprise Estate, Scunthorpe, South Humberside, DN16 3RN Tel: (01724) 271999 Fax: (01724) 271888 E-mail: sales@bradburyuk.com *Security product manufrs*

Bradbury's Engineering, The Crossways, Loggerheads, Market Drayton, Shropshire, TF9 4BX Tel: (01630) 672900 Fax: (01630) 673858 E-mail: bradburyeng@aol.com *Engine reconditioners*

Braddicks Amusements Ltd, 37 Mill Street, Bideford, Devon, EX39 2JJ Tel: (01237) 471897 Fax: (01237) 424434 *Amusement machines*

Brade Engineering Ltd, Atlas Works, Gibbet Street, Halifax, West Yorkshire, HX1 4DB Tel: (01484) 711003 Fax: (01422) 350066 E-mail: sales@ormandyltd.com *Manufacturers of industrial process water heaters*

Brade-Leigh Bodies Ltd, Albion Industrial Estate, Oldbury Road, West Bromwich, West Midlands, B70 9EH Tel: 0121-553 4361 Fax: 0121-500 6139 E-mail: sales@brade-leigh.co.uk *Commercial vehicle body builders*

Bradfabs Ltd, 61A Plane Trees Road, Laisterdyke, Bradford, West Yorkshire, BD4 8AE Tel: (01274) 400401 Fax: (01274) 773335 E-mail: sales@bradfabs.co.uk *Bradfabs Ltd (Bradford Fabrications) are a steel fabricator in Bradford West Yorkshire *fabricating specific specialist engineering products.***We design, engineer, manufacture and finish a wide range of products to a high quality and cost *effective fabrication methods from all grades of carbon steel, stainless steel and aluminium. ***Our products include: staircases, fire escapes, balconies, balconettes, railings, fencing, balustrade, *I beams, construction frames, trolleys through to casings, gearboxes, storage and pressure vessels*and any other bespoke product you might require*

Bradfield Storage Handling Ltd, Forty Horse Close, Codnor Gate Business Park, Ripley, Derbyshire, DE5 3ND Tel: (01773) 748748 Fax: (01773) 749998 E-mail: sales@bradfield-storage.co.uk *Buy direct from UK's leading manufacturer of Mezzanine floors. Our Company provides a fast professional service from enquiry /quotation /site survey /design through to final installation. All our Installation Teams are SIERS registered and work to the SEMA Code of Practice. We are*

continued

specialists in full project work, including two and three tier floors

Bradfor Aircraft Services, Forestbrook Mill, Forestbrook Avenue, Rostrevor, Newry, County Down, BT34 3BX Tel: (028) 4173 8835 Fax: (028) 4173 8694 E-mail: patricia@bradfor.co.uk *Aircraft seat cover manufrs*

Bradford Armature Winding Co. Ltd, 429 Bowling Old Lane, Bradford, West Yorkshire, BD5 8HN Tel: (01274) 728379 Fax: (01274) 731518 E-mail: info@bawco.com *Founded in 1919, BAWCO Ltd has 88 years experience in the Electric Motors /Transformers sector, with the focus on providing Motor /Transformer Repairs and Manufacture to clients throughout the world. BAWCO also provides other electrical equipment such as Inverters, Control Gears, Starters as well as other associated equipment. The company is based in Bradford as well as having a new branch in the North East (BAWCO NE).*

Bradford Bar Supplies, Unit 2 Napoleon Business Park, Wakefield Road, Bradford, West Yorkshire, BD4 7NL Tel: (01274) 741739 Fax: (01274) 741739 *Glass wear & janitorial suppliers*

Bradford & Bingley plc, PO Box 88, Bingley, West Yorkshire, BD16 2UA Tel: (01274) 555555 Fax: (01274) 554422 E-mail: enquiries@bbg.co.uk *Banking services*

Bradford Business Machines, 155 Bradford Road, Cleckheaton, West Yorkshire, BD19 3SX Tel: (01274) 879608 Fax: (01274) 879608 E-mail: bradfordbusiness@aol.com *Office equipment sales & repairers*

Bradford Chamber Of Commerce & Industry, Devere House Vicar Lane, Little Germany, Bradford, West Yorkshire, BD1 5AH Tel: (01274) 772777 Fax: (01274) 771081 E-mail: sales@bradfordchamber.co.uk *Chamber of commerce*

▶ Bradford Community Enviroment Project, Unit 14 Carlisle Business Centre, Carlisle Road, Bradford, West Yorkshire, BD8 8BD Tel: (01274) 223236 Fax: (01274) 223353 E-mail: info@bcep.org.uk *BCEP is Bradford largest environmental charity offering a range of community based programmes from reclaiming derelict land to sustainablity issues awareness work with schools and youth groups to supporting local food co-ops and others (please see our web site).*

Bradford Cylinders Ltd, Soho Works, Allerton Road, Bradford, West Yorkshire, BD8 0BA Tel: (01274) 495611 Fax: (01274) 547119 E-mail: sales@bradfordcylinders.co.uk *Hydraulic Cylinder Manufacturers.*

Bradford Grinders UK Ltd, Mount Street, Bradford, West Yorkshire, BD3 9SN Tel: (01274) 733141 Fax: (01274) 734610 E-mail: sales@bradfordgrinders.co.uk *Engine reconditioners engine part suppliers*

Bradford Moor Iron & Steel Co. Ltd, Cow Lane, Newark, Nottinghamshire, NG24 1HQ Tel: (01636) 703645 Fax: (01636) 672167 *Scrap iron & steel merchants*

Bradford Piston & Piston Ring Co. Ltd, Unit 22, Missouri Avenue, Salford, M50 2NP Tel: 0161-736 5211 Fax: 0161-736 4785 E-mail: bppr@btconnect.com *Piston ring manufrs*

Bradford Rubber Services Ltd, 25 Annison Street, Garnet Street, Bradford, West Yorkshire, BD3 9HJ Tel: (01274) 307030 Fax: (01274) 305699 E-mail: sales@bradfordrubber.co.uk *Gasket & rubber matting manufrs*

▶ Bradford Skip Hire, Cottingley Moor Road, Bingley, West Yorkshire, BD16 1UU Tel: (01274) 733999 Fax: (01274) 546343 *Contract skip hire & waste management services*

Bradford & Sons Ltd, 98 Hendford Hill, Yeovil, Somerset, BA20 2QR Tel: (01935) 845245 Fax: (01935) 845242 E-mail: bradfords@bradfords.co.uk *Builders merchants* Also at: Branches throughout the S.W.

Bradford Tool Group, Beta Works, 1 Tong Street, Bradford, West Yorkshire, BD4 9PW Tel: (01274) 683902 Fax: (01274) 651168 E-mail: sales@bradtool.co.uk *Special cutting tool manufrs*

Bradford Welding & Sheet Metal Co. Ltd, 340b Thornton Road, Bradford, West Yorkshire, BD8 8LD Tel: (01274) 480288 Fax: (01274) 480284 *General fabricators*

Bradfords Building Supplies Ltd, 139 Bristol Road, Bridgwater, Somerset, TA6 4AQ Tel: (01278) 422654 Fax: (01278) 450574 E-mail: bbs.bridgwater@bradford.co.uk *Builders merchant*

Bradfords Underwood, Tolladine Road, Worcester, WR4 9EG Tel: (01935) 845245 Fax: (01905) 723743 *Builders merchants* Also at: Worcester

Bradgate Containers Ltd, Leicester Road, Shepshed, Loughborough, Leicestershire, LE12 9EG Tel: (01509) 508678 Fax: (01509) 503224 E-mail: sales@bradgate.co.uk *Industrial noise control equipment manufrs*

▶ Bradgate Lace, Leciester Outdoor Market, Stall Nos D7/8 (Opposite Bewise), Market Place, Leicester, LE1 5HQ Tel: (07917) 466959 E-mail: enquiries@bradgatelace.com *WE ARE A SPEACILIST RETAILER OF NET CURTAINS , VOILES, LACE CURTAINS, TIEBACK SETS, CAFE LACES, JARDINIERES, TIE UP BLINDS*WHITE /CREAM AND COLOURS*OPEN 9-4 4 DAYS ONLY ON LEICESTERS OUTDOOR MARKET RIGHT IN THE CENTER OF LEICESTER*

Bradite Ltd, Ogwen Valley Works, Bethesda, Bangor, Gwynedd, LL57 4YP Tel: (01248) 600315 Fax: (01248) 602782 E-mail: sales@bradite.co.uk *Paint manufrs*

Bradlee Boilers Ltd, 3 Stambermill Industrial Estate, Timmis Road, Stourbridge, West Midlands, DY9 7BJ Tel: (01384) 423859 Fax: (01384) 895435 E-mail: sales@bradleeboilers.com Principal Export Areas: Worldwide *Boiler manufrs*

Bradley Builders, Talbot Buildings, Newnham Bridge, Tenbury Wells, Worcestershire, WR15 8JF Tel: (01584) 781489 Fax: (01584) 781489 *Portable building manufrs*

Bradley D.B.& D.K Farmers, Thelbridge Hall, Witheridge, Tiverton, Devon, EX16 8NZ Tel: (01884) 860226 *Agricultural engineering & contracting services*

Bradley Doublelock Ltd, Victoria Works, Victoria Street, Bingley, West Yorkshire, BD16 2NH Tel: (01274) 560414 Fax: (01274) 551114 E-mail: larry.lambert@bradleydoublelock.co.uk *Trailer equipment manufrs*

▶ Bradley Electrical Services & Technicians Ltd, Hilton Trading Estate, Hilton Road, Lanesfield, Wolverhampton, WV4 6DW Tel: (01902) 493555 Fax: (01902) 493888 E-mail: sales@bradleyelectrical.co.uk

Bradley Furniture Kent Ltd, Bradley House, Park Farm Close, Park Farm Industrial Estate, Folkestone, Kent, CT19 5ED Tel: (01303) 850011 Fax: (01303) 244028 E-mail: info@bradleyfurniture.co.uk *Furniture manufrs*

▶ G.L. Bradley (Lace Draughtsmen) Ltd, 126 Derby Road, Long Eaton, Nottingham, NG10 4LS Tel: 0115-972 0095 Fax: 0115-972 2379 E-mail: ian@bradleylace.co.uk *Lace designers & lace draughtsman for raschel, tectonic*

Bradley Glass Ltd, 19 Ham Bridge Trading Estate, Willowbrook Road, Worthing, West Sussex, BN14 8NA Tel: (01903) 205411 Fax: (01903) 214395 E-mail: enquiries@bradleyglass.co.uk *Automotive mirror manufrs*

H.E.L.& H.M. Bradley & Son, Waddings Farm, Knighton-on-teme, Tenbury Wells, Worcs, WR15 8LY Tel: 01584 781243 *Agricultural merchants*

Bradley Hire Southern Ltd, Biltam Farm, Stan Hill, Charlwood, Horley, Surrey, RH6 0EP Tel: 01293 863205 Fax: 01293 862775 *Tower hire*

Humphrey Bradley Ltd, Tingley Bar Industrial Estate, Tingley Mills, Morley, Leeds, LS27 0HE Tel: 0113-253 2581 Fax: 0113-238 0069 *Holding & property company*

Bradley Industrial Services, Thornleigh, Summerhill, Kingswinford, West Midlands, DY6 9JF Tel: (01384) 271911 Fax: (01384) 273104 *Gas central heating installation & service*

John Bradley Ltd, 1 Levens Road, Newby Road, Industrial Estate, Stockport, Cheshire, SK7 5DL Tel: 0161-483 5200 Fax: 0161-483 5101 E-mail: office@samuelbradley.com *Textile machinery agents providing sales service & support*

John Bradley & Son Ltd, Spring Works, Russell Street, Heywood, Lancashire, OL10 1NU Tel: (01706) 360353 Fax: (01706) 366154 E-mail: jbs@johnbradleygroup.co.uk *Presswork, spring & railway track fasteners*

Bradley Pulverizer Co., 15 Kennet Road, Crayford, Crayford, Dartford, DA1 4QN Tel: (01322) 559106 Fax: (01322) 528690 E-mail: bradley.pulverizer@btinternet.com *Grinding mills & air classifiers*

Bradley Refrigeration Ltd, 929 Abbeydale Road, Sheffield, S7 2QD Tel: 0114-236 9971 Fax: 0114-236 8681 E-mail: ecroft@bradley-refrigeration.com *Commercial refrigeration equipment & air conditioning services*

Bradley Steels Ltd, Dawley Brook, Kingswinford, West Midlands, DY6 7AS Tel: (01384) 293855 Fax: (01384) 297440 *Steel stockholders*

Bradley Textiles Ltd, 6 Huss Row, Belfast, BT13 1EE Tel: (028) 9032 5434 Fax: (028) 9031 5350 E-mail: bradleytextiles@btopenworld.com *Leisure wear & embroidery distributors*

Bradley Thallon Industries Ltd, Kiltonga Industrial Estate, Belfast Road, Newtownards, County Down, BT23 4TJ Tel: (028) 9181 5403 Fax: (028) 9181 5409 E-mail: terence@bradleythallon.co.uk *Manufrs of cargo slings*

Bradleys Electronic & Computer Services, Andross, Forest Road, Ruardean Woodside, Ruardean, Gloucestershire, GL17 9XW Tel: (01594) 544093 Fax: (01594) 544093 E-mail: becs@aic.co.uk *Computer systems supplier & maintenance agents*

Bradleys Rivets Ltd, Unit 8b Reddicap Trading Estate, Sutton Coldfield, West Midlands, B75 7BU Tel: 0121-326 7468 Fax: 0121-327 1092 E-mail: enquiries@bradleysrivets.com Principal Export Areas: Worldwide *Screw & rivet manufrs*

Bradleys (Stowmarket) Ltd, 49 Knightsdale Road, Ipswich, IP1 4JJ Tel: (01473) 461400 Fax: (01473) 461490 *Contractor or services of metal spraying, shot blasting, zinc spraying, nylon coating & powder coating*

▶ Bradma Furniture, Unit 12 Suprema Business Park, Suprema Avenue, Edington, Bridgwater, Somerset, TA7 9LF Tel: (01278) 723467 Fax: (01278) 723129

Bradmeres Engineering Ltd, Unit 42 Wilford Industrial Estate, Ruddington Lane, Wilford, Nottingham, NG11 7EP Tel: 0115-981 7814 Fax: 0115-981 9782 E-mail: bradmeres@btconnect.com *Mechanical & electrical engineers*

Bradmore Garden Centres, Pendock Lane, Bradmore, Nottingham, NG11 6PQ Tel: 0115-984 7990 Fax: 0115-940 6175 *Garden centre*

Bradney Chain & Engineering Co. Ltd, Quarry Road, Dudley, West Midlands, DY2 0EB Tel: (01384) 636233 Fax: (01384) 634289 E-mail: sales@bradneychain.co.uk *Chain makers & engineers*

Bradrail Blinds & Awnings, 7-15 Main Street, Bulwell, Nottingham, NG6 8QH Tel: 0115-927 5251 Fax: 0115-977 0274 E-mail: enquiries@bradrail.co.uk *Venetian, Vertical, Roller Blinds, Curtains & Poles Largest Patio and Shop Awning Showroom in the UK Patio and Shop Awnings. *Manufacture, Supplier & Installation Service. *Measuring & Fittings service or DIY Supply *Large Retail Showroom and Agent /Trade Account*

Brads Fencing Co. Ltd, 22 Hare Lane, Godalming, Surrey, GU7 3EE Tel: (01483) 414745 Fax: (01483) 419394 *Fencing & security fencing contractors*

Company Information

Bradshaw Associates, P O Box 415, Maidstone, Kent, ME16 0LR Tel: (01622) 751747 Fax: (01622) 675050 E-mail: ivorbradshaw@cwcom.net *Industrial remote controls*

Bradshaw Boiler & Heating Services Ltd, 624 Tonge Moor Road, Bolton, BL2 3BJ Tel: (01204) 307484 Fax: (01204) 593835 E-mail: bradshawboilers@fsbdial.co.uk *Industrial & domestic heating contractors services*

Bradshaw & Bradshaw, 18 Hanson Street, London, W1W 6UE Tel: (020) 7255 2333 Fax: (020) 7255 3131 *Textile agents*

John Bradshaw Ltd, New Lane, Stibbington, Peterborough, PE8 6LW Tel: (01780) 782621 Fax: (01780) 783694 E-mail: sales@john-bradshaw.co.uk *Electric vehicle distributors*

The Bradshaw Pattern Company Ltd, Rowland House Lion Mill, Fitton Street, Royton, Oldham, OL2 5JX Tel: 0161-624 5043 Fax: 0161-628 3245 *Specialised woodworking*

Bradshaw Sheet Metal Works Ltd, Bradshaw Works, Printers Lane, Bolton, BL2 3DW Tel: (01204) 303300 Fax: (01204) 595797 *Sheet metalwork engineers*

Bradshaws Body Repairs Ltd, 329 London Road, Hemel Hempstead, Hertfordshire, HP3 9AN Tel: (01442) 211711 Fax: (01442) 251788 *Motor car body builders repairs commercial*

Bradshaws Direct Ltd, James Nicolson Link, Clifton Moore, York, YO30 4XX Tel: (01904) 691169 Fax: (01904) 691133 E-mail: ferrey@aol.com *Water gardening products & tarpaulins mail order services*

▶ Bradworthy Glass, Units 3d, Langdon Road, Bradworthy, Holsworthy, Devon, EX22 7SF Tel: (01409) 241010 Fax: (01409) 241160 *Manufacture decorative glass, install glazing pvc windows & doors*

Brady Fabrications, Units 20& 22, Wedgewood Road, Bicester, Oxfordshire, OX26 4UL Tel: (01869) 252750 Fax: (01869) 247394 E-mail: bradyfabs@btopenworld.com *Sheet metal fabricators*

▶ Brady & Gallagher, 13 Cattle Street, St. Helier, Jersey, JE2 4WP Tel: (01534) 758267 *Electrical contractors*

Braefield Precision Engineers Ltd, High Lane, Stanstead, Stansted, Essex, CM24 8LQ Tel: (01279) 815686 Fax: (01279) 815647 E-mail: braefield@tiscali.co.uk *Quality machining & sheet metalwork*

Braehead (S F O Enterprises) Ltd, West Shore Road Industrial Estate, Fraserburgh, Aberdeenshire, AB43 9LG Tel: (01346) 513777 Fax: (01346) 514123 E-mail: gwatt@scottishfisherman.co.uk *Cold storage for prawns*

▶ Braeside Joinery, Unit 1-5 Moore Acre, Manor Furlong, Marston Trading Estate, Frome, Somerset, BA11 4RL Tel: (01373) 451213 Fax: (01373) 451860

Brafe Engineering Ltd, Grundisburgh Road, Woodbridge, Suffolk, IP13 6HX Tel: (01394) 380000 Fax: (01394) 380300 E-mail: sclarke@brafe.com *Corrosion resistant casting manufrs*

Bragman Flett Ltd, 34 Holmethorpe Avenue, Redhill, RH1 2NL Tel: (01737) 779200 Fax: (01737) 779600 E-mail: bragman.flett@btopenworld.com *Sheet metalworkers*

Braham & Dixon Ltd, 88 Hodgson Street, Hull, HU8 7JB Tel: (01482) 211853 Fax: (01482) 211865 E-mail: eric@bd-eng.co.uk *Mechanical handling & processing equipment*

Brahler Ics UK Ltd, Unit 2 The Business Centre, Church End, Cambridge, CB1 3LB Tel: (01223) 411601 Fax: (01223) 411602 E-mail: info@brahler-ics.co.uk *Hire & sell conference equipment*

Braidbar Boats Ltd, Lyme Road, Poynton, Stockport, Cheshire, SK12 1TH Tel: (01625) 873471 *Boat builders & repairers*

Braidway Ltd, Unit 14 198 Swanston Street, Glasgow, G40 4HH Tel: 0141-550 0333 Fax: 0141-554 3863 *Emergency service uniforms, country wear & corporate wear*

▶ Alexander Braidwood Ltd, Rosendale Way, Blantyre, Glasgow, G72 0NJ Tel: (01698) 822633

▶ Braille Translations, 9 Wadham Gardens, Greenford, Middlesex, UB6 0BP Tel: (07005) 860169 Fax: (020) 8422 2237 E-mail: ghow@brailletranslations.co.uk

Brailsford Bros Barnsley Ltd, Langdale Road, Barnsley, South Yorkshire, S71 1AF Tel: (01226) 282703 Fax: (01226) 204897 E-mail: brailsfordbros@smartone.co.uk *Sheet metal workers & welders*

Brain Power International Ltd, 3 Prospect Way, Butlers Leap, Rugby, Warwickshire, CV21 3UU Tel: (01788) 568686 Fax: (01788) 568686 E-mail: paul@callbpi.com *Optical dyes & machinery suppliers*

Brainsmead Ltd, Tangley Brainsmead Close, Cuckfield, Haywards Heath, West Sussex, RH17 5EZ Tel: (01444) 441951 E-mail: richard@brainsmead.co.uk *Computer programmers*

Brainstorm Computing Ltd, 3 White Hart Close, Sevenoaks, Kent, TN13 1RH Tel: (01732) 465786 E-mail: mark@brainstorm-uk.co.uk *Software developers*

Braintree Build Base, Manor Street, Braintree, Essex, CM7 3HS Tel: (01376) 322944 Fax: (01376) 550046 E-mail: briantree@buildbase.co.uk *Buildbase is one of the UK's fastest growing builders merchants. All of our branches are long established companies which have been serving local trades people for many years, with knowledge and experience to match. We believe strongly in understanding the needs of trades professional and our business has been developed specifically to meet those demands. Massive stocks, top quality products, competitive pricing, reliable delivery, specialist staff and exceptional customer service*

Braintree Electro Platers Ltd, 12-13 Springwood Drive, Braintree, Essex, CM7 2YN Tel: (01376) 344265 Fax: (01376) 328927 *Electroplating services*

Braintree Pine Centre, Spring Wood Industrial Estate, Warner Drive, Braintree, Essex, CM7 2YW Tel: (01376) 349493 Fax: (01376) 349553 *Pine furniture manufrs*

Braintree Precision Components Ltd, 2-8 Blackwell Drive, Springwood Industrial Estate, Braintree, Essex, CM7 2QJ Tel: (01376) 552989 Fax: (01376) 552995E-mail: sales@hepco.co.uk *Ball bearing specialists*

Braithwaite Engineers Ltd, Neptune Works Cork Wharf, Mill Parade, Newport, Gwent, NP20 2UY Tel: (01633) 262141 Fax: (01633) 250631 E-mail: tanks@braithwaite.co.uk *Sectional & one-piece water storage tank manufrs*

▶ Braithwaite Excavations Ltd, Claycliffe Road, Barnsley, South Yorkshire, S75 1HS Tel: (01226) 779527 Fax: (01226) 203080

Braithwaite Paul Outdoor Sports, Rhodes Bank, Oldham, OL1 1TA Tel: 0161-620 3900 Fax: 0161-620 2863 E-mail: sales@paulbraithwaites.co.uk *Outdoor equipment retail*

Braithwaite Rebuild, Pinfold La Industrial Estate, Bridlington, North Humberside, YO16 6XS Tel: (01262) 606691 Fax: (01262) 606691 *Bridgeport machine tool rebuilbers*

Braithwaite Telescopes, Old School, Manse Brae, Dalserf, Larkhall, Lanarkshire, ML9 3BN Tel: (01698) 881004 E-mail: john@dalserf.demon.co.uk *Telescope manufacturers & retailers*

Braitrim Group Ltd, Braitrim House, 98 Victoria Road, London, NW10 6NB Tel: (020) 8723 3000 Fax: (020) 8723 3001 E-mail: service@braitrim.com *Suppliers of packaging for clothing garments*

Brake Direct Ltd, PO Box 11, Bordon, Hampshire, GU35 9YR Tel: (01420) 474834 Fax: (01420) 474834 *Brake shoe manufacturers & distribs*

Brake Engineering, Redwither Road, Wrexham Industrial Estate, Wrexham, Clwyd, LL13 9RD Tel: (01978) 667803 Fax: (01978) 667801 E-mail: sales@brake-eng.com *Brake drum manufrs*

▶ The Brake Fit Centre, Unit 3, 171 New Road, Rainham, Essex, RM13 8SH Tel: (01708) 555552 Fax: (01708) 555552 E-mail: info@brakesessex.com *Quality vehicle repairs, carried out only by trained technicians*

Brake Grocery, Alpha Way, Egham, Surrey, TW20 8SG Tel: (0845) 6076777 Fax: (01784) 485040 E-mail: marketing@brake.co.uk Purchasing Contact: N. Adrien Sales Contact: J. Vokes *Wholesale food distributors & caterers supply services* Also at: Branches throughout the U.K.

Brake Logistics, Queensway, Rochdale, Lancashire, OL11 2RG Tel: (01706) 525211 Fax: (01706) 525213 *Food distributors*

Brakes Ltd, Enterprise House Nicholas Road, Eureka Science Park, Ashford, Kent, TN25 4AG Tel: (01233) 206206 Fax: (01223) 206035 E-mail: customer.service@brake.co.uk *Brakes based in Asford, Kent are frozen food processors and product manufacturers. Products include chilled and frozen foods and meats.*

Brakes Catering Equipment, Unit 3 Gloucester Court, Gloucester Terrace, Armley Road, Leeds, LS12 2ER Tel: (0845) 9319494 Fax: 0113-231 9495 *As part of the Brakes Group, UK''s leading supplier to the foodservice industry, Catering Equipment Warehouse understands the needs of the caterer. Catering Equipment Warehouse specialise in the supply of commercial catering equipment at extremely competitive prices and extended warranties, backed with the assurances of dealing with a industry leader. Products include crockery, cutlery, glassware, workwear, knives, bakewear, janitorial supplies and many other solutions.*

▶ Brakewater Blinds, 14 Bromhead Court, Plymouth, PL6 5NJ Tel: (01752) 776636

▶ Braking Systems Co. Ltd, Doctors Piece, Willenhall, West Midlands, WV13 1PZ Tel: (01902) 609543 Fax: (01902) 609359 E-mail: sales@brakingsystemsltd.co.uk *Quality brakes & braking products suppliers*

Bralo UK Ltd, Leabrook Road, Wednesbury, West Midlands, WS10 9NB Tel: 0121-567 3230 Fax: 0121-505 1378 E-mail: bralouk@bralo.net *Rivet distribution & manufrs*

Bramah Security Centres Ltd, 31 Oldbury Place, London, W1U 5PT Tel: (020) 7486 1757 Fax: (020) 7935 2779 E-mail: locksmiths@bramah.co.uk *Locksmiths & alarm installers*

Bramall Construction, 3 Callflex Business Park, Golden Smithies Lane, Wath-upon-Dearne, Rotherham, South Yorkshire, S63 7ER Tel: (01709) 766000 Fax: (01709) 766001 E-mail: info@bramall.com *Building contractors*

Bramall Construction, The Quays, Salford, M50 3BF Tel: 0161-876 6000 Fax: 0161 876 6001 E-mail: info@bramallnw.com *Part of the Keepmoat Group, Bramall are building contractors specialising in public sector regeneration*

Bramall Quicks Ltd, Lower Bridge Street, Chester, CH1 1DX Tel: (01244) 320444 Fax: (01244) 349536 *Main ford dealers*

▶ Bramber Construction Ltd, 370 Brighton Road, Shoreham-by-Sea, West Sussex, BN43 6RE Tel: (01273) 465111 Fax: (01273) 440799 E-mail: info@bramber-construction.co.uk

▶ Bramble.cc Ltd, 9e Albert Embankment, London, SE1 7SP Tel: (020) 7735 0030 Fax: (07092) 189532 E-mail: contact@bramble.cc *Bramble.cc is an independent, UK-based consultancy company specialising in the management of change (MoC) aspects of information management (IM) projects and programmes. We provide expert business and IT services in information management and records management (EDRM) and enterprise content management (ECM) to both the public and private sectors.*

Bramblee Design, 4 Tilgate Park Craft Units, Tilgate Drive, Crawley, West Sussex, RH10 5PQ Tel: (01227) 792716 Fax: (01293) 528486 *Celtic jewellery gifts & manufrs*

Brambletye Hotel, Lewes Road, Forest Row, East Sussex, RH18 5EZ Tel: (01342) 824144 Fax: (01342) 824833 E-mail: brambletye.hotel@fullers.co.uk *Hotel & conference services, restaurant & bar*

Brambley Furniture, 108 Westmoor Street, Charlton, London, SE7 8NQ Tel: (020) 8293 6662 Fax: (020) 8305 0907 *Aluminium garden furniture manufrs*

Bramco Steel Services Ltd, Thorncliffe Park Estate, Chapeltown, Sheffield, S35 2PH Tel: 0114-246 3033 Fax: 0114-245 5901 *Sawing & grinding services*

Bramigk & Co. Ltd, Chelmsford, CM2 7WG Tel: (01245) 477616 Fax: (01245) 477498 E-mail: info@bramigk.co.uk *Food machinery sales & service*

Bramlands Aviation Ltd, Bramlands Stables, Bramlands Lane, Woodmancote, Henfield, West Sussex, BN5 9TQ Tel: (01273) 494774 Fax: (01273) 494799 E-mail: sales@bramlands.com *Aircraft component distributors*

Brammer Ltd, Unit A Berkeley Court Earl Russell Way, Lawrence Hill, Bristol, BS5 0BX Tel: 0117-935 0422 Fax: 0117-935 0435 *Bearing & lubricant distributors* Also at: Branches throughout the U K

Brammer Ltd, 8a Blackbrook Valley Industrial Estate, Narrowboat Way, Dudley, West Midlands, DY2 0XQ Tel: (01384) 456783 Fax: (01384) 456795 E-mail: dudley@branner.biz *Bearing steel distributors*

Brammer Ltd, Claverton Court, Claverton Road, Roundthorn Industrial Estate, Manchester, M23 9NE Tel: 0161-953 8600 Fax: 0161-953 8680 E-mail: enquiries@bslbrammer.co.uk *Bearing & power transmission distributors* Also at: Branches throughout the U.K.

Brammer plc, Claverton Court, Claverton Road, Roundthorn Industrial Estate, Manchester, M23 9NE Tel: 0161-902 5599 Fax: 0161-902 5595 E-mail: sales@brammer.plc.uk *Holding company*

Brammer Ltd, 11 Canons Road, Old Wolverton Industrial Estate, Old Wolverton, Milton Keynes, MK12 5TL Tel: (01908) 317464 Fax: (01908) 311113 E-mail: miltonkeynes@brammer.biz *Bearing distributors*

Brammer Ltd, 16 Javelin Road, Airport Industrial Estate, Norwich, NR6 6HP Tel: (01603) 423756 Fax: (01603) 424693 E-mail: norwich@brammer.biz *Bearing & power transmission equipment distributors*

Brammer Ltd, Unit 1, Manor Grove Business Centre, Vicarage Farm Road, Peterborough, PE1 5TP Tel: (01733) 565222 Fax: (01733) 896014 E-mail: peterb@bsl.co.uk *Engineering distributors*

Brammer Ltd, 25 Buckingham Avenue, Slough, SL1 4QA Tel: (01753) 537695 Fax: (01753) 572311 E-mail: slough@brammer.biz *Bearing & power transmission distributors & maintenance*

Brammer UK Ltd, Headway Road, Wolverhampton, WV10 6PZ Tel: (01902) 395949 Fax: (01902) 395945 E-mail: export@brammer.biz *Bearing & power transmission distributors*

Brampton Gun Room, 47-49 Old Hall Road, Chesterfield, Derbyshire, S40 1HD Tel: (01246) 211294 *Gunsmiths*

Bramtool Precision Engineering, 13 109 Sydenham Road, Birmingham, B11 1DG Tel: 0121-773 1345 Fax: 0121-773 1345 *Precision & general machinists*

▶ Alan Bramwell General Property Maintenance, 7 Holt Drive, Matlock, Derbyshire, DE4 3BB Tel: (07708) 557289 E-mail: handyman@brammy.co.uk *General property maintenance*

Bramwell Furniture Ltd, Unit 50 Crayford Industrial Estate, Swaisland Drive, Crayford, Dartford, DA1 4HS Tel: (01322) 556223 Fax: (01322) 550900 E-mail: sales@bramwellfurniture.co.uk *Office & residential furniture manufrs*

▶ The Bramwell Label Company Ltd, 33 Long Wood Road, Trafford Park, Manchester, M17 1PZ Tel: 0161-876 7444 Fax: 0161-876 7555

▶ Bramwells, 14 Nelson Avenue, St. Albans, Hertfordshire, AL1 5RY Tel: (01727) 860703 Fax: (01727) 860703 E-mail: bramwells@hotmail.com

Bran Tub Ltd, 20 Lavant Street, Petersfield, Hampshire, GU32 3EW Tel: (01730) 267043 Fax: (01730) 267043 *Health food wholesalers*

▶ Jo Branagan Business Support Services, 188 Danube Road, Hull, HU5 5UX Tel: (07973) 511026 E-mail: info@jo-branagan.co.uk

Branberg Machine Tools, Unit 15 Marino Way, Finchampstead, Wokingham, Berkshire, RG40 4RF Tel: 0118-973 4044 Fax: 0118-973 2707 *Turned part manufrs*

Branch Hydraulic Systems Ltd, Unit H, Innsworth Technology Park, Innsworth Lane, Gloucester, GL3 1DL Tel: (01452) 730562 Fax: (01452) 731579 E-mail: branch@dowco.co.uk *Hydraulic equipment manufrs*

Branch Signs, 7 Dalmeny Road, Worcester Park, Surrey, KT4 8UU Tel: (020) 3277 1060 Fax: (020) 8949 3690 E-mail: michaelbranch@freenet.co.uk *Signwriters & manufrs*

Branchand Ltd, Ashwellthorpe Industrial Estate, Ashwellthorpe, Norwich, NR16 1ER Tel: (01508) 488450 Fax: (01508) 488451 E-mail: info@branchand.co.uk *Maintenance & cleaning services*

▶ Branches Design Ltd, Unit 4, Shawbridge Sawmill, Taylor Street, Clitheroe, Lancashire, BB7 1LY Tel: (01200) 444443 E-mail: info@branchesdesign.co.uk *Web site design & e-commerce web site design*

Branchsound Ltd, Unit 9, Springfield Road Industrial Estate, Burnham-on-Crouch, Essex, CM0 8TE Tel: (01621) 782964 Fax: (01621) 783314 E-mail: tecnauticwindow@btclick.com *Windows & clean room equipment manufrs*

▶ Brand 5, 19 Portico Road, Derby, DE23 3NJ Tel: 0845 2261883

▶ Brand Attention Ltd, 30A Bridge Street, Hitchin, Hertfordshire, SG5 2DF Tel: (01462) 435330 E-mail: info@brandattention.com *Optimisation plus website submission & marketing services*

▶ Brand Creative, Slackcote Lane, Delph, Oldham, OL3 5TP Tel: (01457) 874016 Fax: (01457) 874016 E-mail: design@brand-creative.co.uk *Graphic designers*

Brand Development Co., 50 Long Acre, London, WC2E 9JR Tel: (020) 7497 9727 Fax: (020) 7497 3581 E-mail: info@brandevo.com *Development consultants*

▶ The Brand in a Box Co. Ltd, Damery Works, Damery Lane, Woodford, Berkeley, Gloucestershire, GL13 9JR Tel: (0845) 2011266 Fax: (0845) 2011265 E-mail: info@brandinabox.biz *Food packaging suppliers*

Brand Managers Ltd, Ambasidor House, 3rd Floor, Cavendish Avenue, Sudbury Hill, Harrow, Middlesex, HA1 3RW Tel: (020) 8869 4444 Fax: (020) 8869 4455 *Toiletries distributor & manufrs*

▶ Nigel Brand, Unit H, Tollgate Business Centre, Tollgate Industrial Estate, Stafford, ST16 3HS Tel: (01785) 259988 E-mail: penshop@premierprint.uk.com *Promotional printers*

Brand Packaging Ltd, Bridge Mills, Holland Street, Pendleton, Salford, M6 6EL Tel: 0161-736 8941 Fax: 0161-745 7141 *Flexible packaging manufrs*

Brand Partnership Ltd, Southfork Industrial Estate, Dartmouth Way, Leeds, LS11 5JL Tel: 0113-270 6061 Fax: 0113-277 5319 E-mail: patrick.barrow@brandpartnership.co.uk *Dry Food manufrs*

▶ Brand Phoenix, Caledonian House, Tatton Street, Knutsford, Cheshire, WA16 6AG Tel: (01565) 621345 Fax: (01565) 621456 *Wine brokers*

Brand Precast, 2 Lockwood Court, Market Pl, Pocklington, York, YO42 2QW Tel: (01759) 304130 Fax: (01759) 306727 *Concrete flooring*

Brand & Rae Ltd, Russell Mill, Springfield, Cupar, Fife, KY15 5QX Tel: (01334) 652828 Fax: (01334) 655967 *Concrete block manufacturers & bagged aggregate suppliers*

Brand Rex Ltd, Viewfield Industrial Estate, Glenrothes, Fife, KY6 2RS Tel: (01592) 772124 Fax: (01592) 775314 E-mail: loswald@brand-rex.com Principal Export Areas: Worldwide *Fibre optic cable manufrs*

▶ Brand & Ross Ltd, 29 Admiral Street, Glasgow, G41 1HP Tel: (0500) 454549 E-mail: sales@nu-rest.co.uk

▶ Brandart Giftware, Studio House, Heckworth Close, Severalls Industrial Park, Colchester, CO4 9TB Tel: (01206) 224466 Fax: (01206) 224460 *Suppliers of souvenirs*

Brandbright Ltd, The Old School, Cromer Road, Bodham, Holt, Norfolk, NR25 6QG Tel: (01263) 588755 E-mail: sales@brandbright.co.uk *Model makersaw*

Branded Bargains, Ilford House, 6-12 Audley Street, Liverpool, L3 8LB Tel: 0151-207 2797 Fax: 0151-207 1433 E-mail: info@taylorsuperstore.co.uk *Toy & fancy goods retailers*

Branded Champagne, 15 Belmont Business Centre, Belmont Farm, East Hoathly, Lewes, East Sussex, BN8 6QL Tel: (0845) 3303769 Fax: (01825) 841315 E-mail: info@ambassadorleisure.com *Branded champagne, wine, beer & spirits suppliers*

Brandenburg, 24 Navigation Drive, Hurst Business Park, Brierley Hill, West Midlands, DY5 1UT Tel: (01384) 472900 Fax: (01384) 472911 E-mail: sales@b-one.com *Manufacturer & designer of flying insect control systems*

▶ Brandford, Majestic Mill, Greenacres Road, Lees, Oldham, OL4 3NT Tel: 0161-345 4858 E-mail: info@storagecompany.co.uk

Brandl Engineering Ltd, 1st Floor, 5 Nimrod Pass, London, N1 4BU Tel: 020 72492375 Fax: 020 72545525 *Industrial engineering*

Brandlab, The Royal British Legion, 14 Arwenack Street, Falmouth, Cornwall, TR11 3JA Tel: (01326) 311488 Fax: (01326) 313678 E-mail: studio@brandlab.co.uk *Consultancy based we have a range of design & branding experience*

Brandon Bolt Co., 4 Faraday Place, Thetford, Norfolk, IP24 3RG Tel: (01842) 766612 Fax: (01842) 755526 E-mail: sales@brandonbolt.fsnet.co.uk *Bolt, nut & industrial fastener distributors service*

Brandon Hire plc, St Helen Way, St. Helen Auckland, Bishop Auckland, County Durham, DL14 9AX Tel: (01388) 663085 Fax: (01388) 607264 *Plant hirers*

Brandon Hire plc, 151 Bute Street, Cardiff, CF10 5HQ Tel: (029) 2048 9898 Fax: (029) 2048 0772 E-mail: cardiff23@brandonhire.plc.uk *Contractor's plant hire*

Brandon Hire plc, Llangunnor Road, Carmarthen, Dyfed, SA31 2PB Tel: (01267) 237405 Fax: (01267) 238299 E-mail: carmarthen@brandonhire.plc.uk *Tool equipment hire* Also at: Camarthen

Brandon Hire plc, Unit 7-9, Holmstone Road, Dover, Kent, CT17 0UF Tel: (01304) 241622 Fax: (01304) 241981 *Contractors small plant & tool hire* Also at: Ashford & River

Brandon Hire plc, 63 Lyde Green, Halesowen, West Midlands, B63 2PQ Tel: (01384) 566936 Fax: (01384) 410134 E-mail: info@brandonhire.plc.uk *Lifting gear & tool hire*

Brandon Hire plc, 1 Stadium Way, Leeds, LS11 0EW Tel: 0113-270 7373 Fax: 0113-270 7322 *Tool specialists*

▶ Brandon Hire plc, Long Wood Road, Trafford Park, Manchester, M17 1PZ Tel: 0161-877 7720 Fax: 0161-877 7741 *Hire tools*

Brandon Hire plc, 48 Ratcliffe Gate, Mansfield, Nottinghamshire, NG18 2JL Tel: (01623) 635136 Fax: (01623) 624006 *Power tool hire services* Also at: Branches throughout the UK

Brandon Hire P.L.C., 184 New Road, Rainham, Essex, RM13 8RS Tel: (01708) 553541 Fax: (01708) 521010 Principal Export Areas: Worldwide *Tool hire services* Also at: Bristol, Norwich & London

Brandon Medical Co. Ltd, Holme Well Road, Leeds, LS10 4TQ Tel: 0113 2777393 Fax: 0113 2728844 E-mail: enquiries@brandon-medical.com *Brandon Medical is an award winning, UK*

continued

continuation
medical technology company with over 40 years healthcare experience. Our products include medical lighting products, operating theatre lights, medical video, medical AV systems, operating theatre control panels, surgical lights, examination lights, medical power systems and many more. We carry out installation and commissioning work in hospitals in the UK and abroad as well as offering servicing on all types of operating theatre lights and medical video systems.

Brandon Pipe Hire, Unit 1 Claremont Centre, Cornwall Street South, Kinning Park, Glasgow, G41 1AA Tel: 0141-427 9000 Fax: 0141-427 9009 E-mail: glagow.k65@wilsley.co.uk *Tools & plant hire*

Brandon Precision, Holmewall Road, Leeds, LS10 4TQ Tel: 0113-277 5671 Fax: 0113-271 2161 E-mail: enquiries@brandon-medical.com *Sub-contract high precision engineering services*

Brandone Machine Tool Ltd, Unit 1, 57 Bushey Grove Road, Bushey, WD23 2JW Tel: (01923) 637893 Fax: (01923) 248055 E-mail: brandone@btconnect.com *Machinery importers*

Brandoni Music Ltd, Unit 3-6 Wembley Commercial Centre, East Lane, Wembley, Middlesex, HA9 7XJ Tel: (020) 8908 2323 Fax: (020) 8908 2323 *Wholesale of musical instruments & guitar parts*

▶ Brands Electronics, Faulds Park, Faulds Park Road, Gourock, Renfrewshire, PA19 1BN Tel: (01475) 657700

Brandsby Agricultural Trading Association Ltd, Station Yard, Green Lane, Lebberston, Scarborough, North Yorkshire, YO11 3PF Tel: (01723) 584455 Fax: (01723) 586247 *Agricultural feed merchants*

Brandsby Agricultural Trading Association Ltd, Ruswarp, Whitby, North Yorkshire, YO21 1NJ Tel: (01947) 602522 Fax: (01947) 602522 *Agricultural suppliers*

Brandsby Agricultural Trading Association Ltd, Sawmill Lane, Helmsley, York, YO62 5DQ Tel: (01439) 770372 Fax: (01439) 770372 *Farmers co-operative*

Brandt, Badentoy Way, Badentoy Park, Portlethen, Aberdeen, AB12 4YS Tel: (01224) 787700 Fax: (01224) 784555 E-mail: sales@brandt-uk.com *Solids control systems*

Brandt Computer Systems Ltd, 20 Barclay Road, Croydon, CR0 1JN Tel: (020) 8760 9173 Fax: (020) 8760 9180 E-mail: croydon@brandt.co.uk *Computer solutions suppliers*

▶ Brandtjen & Kluge, Inc. International, 5, Spring Mill Business Center, Avening Road, Nailsworth, Stroud, Gloucestershire, GL6 0BS Tel: (01453) 836522 Fax: (01453) 836009 E-mail: tandersen@kluge.biz *Print finishing equipment, foil stamping & embossing manufrs*

Brank Brook, Bescot Crescent, Walsall, WS1 4ND Tel: (01922) 728600 Fax: (01922) 728644 *Staircase manufrs*

▶ Branlow Ltd, 8-9 St Peters Way, Warrington, WA2 7BT Tel: (01925) 639979 Fax: (01925) 411627 E-mail: info@branlow.co.uk *Piling foundation specialists*

▶ Branlow Piling Solutions, Denzil, Main Road, Yapton, Arundel, West Sussex, BN18 0DX Tel: (01243) 555890 Fax: (01243) 555943 E-mail: info@branlow.co.uk *Piling solutions*

▶ Branlow Piling Solutions, 66 Waverley Crescent, Kirkintilloch, Glasgow, G66 2DA Tel: 0141-776 6659 Fax: 0141-776 6660 E-mail: admin@branlow.co.uk *Range of piling solutions ideally suited to restricted access*

▶ Branova Cleaning Services, Meadow Mills, Carlton Road, Dewsbury, West Yorkshire, WF13 2BA Tel: (01924) 486000 Fax: (01924) 486010 E-mail: sales@branova.com *Branova Ltd was set up to market a range of world-class innovative products for the cleaning industry. We offer effective, value-for-money products. Branova markets exclusively through distributors and has 3 main brands: The very popular range of Handies impregnated wipes provide superb performance plus 'on-shelf appeal' for distributors. The range includes Heavy-Duty wipes , All-Purpose wipes , Sanitiser wipes, Graffiti wipes, Disinfectant wipes and Probe wipes. Meleco is a lightweight sponge, made from melamine resin, which is extremely effective in removing all types of dirt without chemicals. It works rather like microfibre and can be used, wet or dry, on office equipment, work-surfaces, paintwork - almost anything. Zybax gets nature to work for you by using thoroughly safe, non-pathogenic, non-toxic micro-organisms to digest bacteria causing problems such as unpleasant smells or clogged drains. There are 4 Zybax products: OdourMaster, ClogMaster, PottiMaster and ChannelMaster.*

Bransby Components, Unit 7, Minafon Yard, Betws Yn Rhos, Abergele, Clwyd, LL22 8AW Tel: 01492 680682 Fax: 01492 680286 *Motor vehicle filter suppliers*

Bransom Retail Systems Ltd, The Old Church, 48 Verulam Road, St. Albans, Hertfordshire, AL3 4DH Tel: (01727) 810509 Fax: (01727) 854607 E-mail: rob@bransom.co.uk *Computer system & software developers*

Branson Boats Design, Crease Drove, Crowland, Peterborough, PE6 0BN Tel: (01733) 211966 Fax: (01733) 211966 E-mail: bransonboats@btinternet.com

Branson Leisure Ltd, Fosters Croft, Foster Street, Harlow, Essex, CM17 9HS Tel: (01279) 432151 Fax: (01279) 450542 E-mail: sales@bransonleisure.co.uk *Contract hardwood seating, outdoor furniture, steel furniture manufrs*

Branston Engineering Ltd, Grange Farm Cottages, Grange Lane, Nocton Hth, Lincoln, LN4 2AQ Tel: (01522) 791101 Fax: (01522) 793242 E-mail: branston@globalnet.co.uk *Engineers & general engineers*

Branston Plastics Ltd, 60 Spencer Street, Birmingham, B18 6DS Tel: 0121-236 8253 Fax: 0121-236 8253 *Jewellery & souvenir box manufrs*

Brantham Electronics, The Gattinetts, Unit 2b Hadleigh Road, East Bergholt, Colchester, CO7 6QT Tel: (01206) 298951 E-mail: paul.oliver@branthamelectronics.co.uk *Electronic & computer design services*

Brantham Engineering Ltd, 3l Moss Road, Witham, Essex, CM8 3UQ Tel: (01376) 518384 Fax: (01376) 518900 E-mail: mail@brantham.com *Sub-contract electronic assembly*

Branwell Graphite Ltd, 58-62 High St, Epping, Essex, CM16 4AE Tel: (01992) 577334 Fax: (01992) 561138 E-mail: sales@branwell.com *Graphite powder & granule products*

Brapack Ltd, Brapack Moreton Avenue, Hithercroft Industrial Estate, Wallingford, Oxfordshire, OX10 9DE Tel: (01491) 833131 Fax: (01491) 825409 E-mail: sales@brapack.com *Cleaning chemicals manufrs*

Brasec, Anchorage House, Stoke Street, Rodney Stoke, Cheddar, Somerset, BS27 3UP Tel: (01749) 870888 Fax: (01749) 870999 E-mail: bristec_radar_uk@compuserve.com *Radar consultants*

Brash Industrial Scales, 3 I Anchor Bridge Way, Dewsbury, West Yorkshire, WF12 9QS Tel: (01924) 465169 *Weighing machinery manufrs*

The Brass Decorative Grille & Repolishing Co. Ltd, Unit B7 Phoenix Industrial Estate, Rosslyn Cresent, Harrow, Middlesex, HA1 2SP Tel: (020) 8863 8558 Fax: (020) 8863 5330 E-mail: sales@brassgrille.co.uk *Grilles manufrs*

Brass Fittings & Supplies Ltd, Hawkshead Mill, Hope Street, Glossop, Derbyshire, SK13 7SS Tel: (01457) 854415 Fax: (01457) 855403 E-mail: b.f.s@btconnect.com Principal Export Areas: Central/East Europe & West Europe *Gas & gas meter fittings*

▶ Brass Maintenance Ltd, Unit 8a G W S Trading Estate, Leabrook Road, Wednesbury, West Midlands, WS10 7NB Tel: 0121-556 2010 Fax: 0121-556 2040

▶ Brass Master Antiques, 36 Oakhill Road, Maple Cross, Rickmansworth, Hertfordshire, WD3 9RF Tel: 0771 3526495 Fax: 01923 896565 E-mail: sales@brassmasterantiques.com *Antique services*

Brass Reproductions, 226 Barr Street, Birmingham, B19 3AG Tel: 0121-554 8556 Fax: 0121-554 8556 *Brassware manufrs*

Brass Tacks Fittings Ltd, 8 Kildare Close, Ruislip, Middlesex, HA4 9LG Tel: (020) 8866 8664 Fax: (020) 8866 8446 E-mail: sales@brasstacksfittings.co.uk *Architectural ironmongery manufrs*

Brass Turned Parts Ltd, 160 Dollman Street, Birmingham, B7 4RS Tel: 0121-359 1234 Fax: 0121-359 4698 E-mail: enquiries@brassturnedparts.co.uk *Capstan & automatic work manufrs*

Brassart Ltd, 76 Attwood Street, Lye, Stourbridge, West Midlands, DY9 8RY Tel: (01922) 740512 Fax: (01384) 898705 E-mail: davidgregory@brassards.co.uk *Brass door furniture manufrs*

▶ Brasscraft E K Ltd, 3a Hawbank Road, East Kilbride, Glasgow, G74 5EG Tel: (01355) 221089

Brassey Export Co., Starbell House, Carr Lane, Hoylake, Wirral, Merseyside, CH47 4FB Tel: 0151-632 6464 Fax: 0151-632 6392 E-mail: bec@starbell.com *Drum taps manufrs*

Brassington & Co., Easing Moor Farm, Thorncliffe Road, Thorncliffe, Leek, Staffordshire, ST13 7LW Tel: (01538) 300243 Fax: (01538) 300333 *Abattoir*

Brassware Sales Ltd, Unit 5 Junction 6 Industrial Park, 66 Electric Avenue, Witton, Birmingham, B6 7JJ Tel: 0121-327 1234 Fax: 0121-327 4066 *Plumbing suppliers*

Brassworld Bar Equipment, Unit 22 Royal Industrial Estate, Jarrow, Tyne & Wear, NE32 3HR Tel: 0191-428 2233 Fax: 0191-483 8893 E-mail: lisa@ahlpipework.co.uk *Manufactures of brass fittings & fixtures*

Bratherton Manufacturers' Agents, 4 Old Park Road, Sheffield, S8 7DT Tel: 0114-274 9922 Fax: 0114-274 9933 E-mail: richard.bratherton@btinternet.com *Brick making machinery agents & manufrs*

David Bratt & Sons (Haulage) Ltd, 102 Grove Lane, Cheadle Hulme, Cheadle, Cheshire, SK8 7ND Tel: 0161-439 8124 Fax: 0161-439 9002 *Road transport, haulage & freight services*

Brattonsound Engineering Ltd, Unit 4 Kimpton Trade & Business Centre, Minden Road, Sutton, Surrey, SM3 9PF Tel: (020) 8254 6800 Fax: (020) 8641 9991 *Gun safe manufrs*

E. Braude (London) Ltd, Liberta House, Scotland Hill, Sandhurst, Berkshire, GU47 8JR Tel: (01252) 876123 Fax: (01252) 875281 E-mail: sales@braude.co.uk *Non-corrosive tank heaters, coolers & chemical pumps manufrs*

Brauer Limited, Dawson Road, Mount Farm, Milton Keynes, MK1 1JP Tel: (01908) 374022 Fax: (01908) 641628 E-mail: sales@brauer.co.uk *Wheel & toggle clamp manufrs*

Brauncewell Quarries Ltd, Brauncewell Quarry, Brauncewell, Sleaford, Lincolnshire, NG34 8RL Tel: (01526) 832767 Fax: (01526) 833075 *Limestone quarry specialists*

▶ Brave Little Soldiers, The Waterside Centre, Unit 6 Abbey Meadows, Leicester, LE4 5AE Tel: 0116-251 9333 Fax: 0116-251 9335

Bray Display Ltd, 23 Woodside Industrial Park, Works Road, Letchworth Garden City, Hertfordshire, SG6 1LA Tel: (01462) 482323 Fax: (01462) 482324 E-mail: jim@braydisplay.co.uk *Point of sale purchasers*

E.P. Bray & Co. Ltd, Coombes Lane Works, Charlesworth, Glossop, Derbyshire, SK13 5DQ Tel: (01457) 853277 Fax: (01457) 856114 E-mail: epbray@charlesworth81.fsnet.co.uk *Colour manufrs*

Bray Group Ltd, Olive House, Regal Way, Faringdon, Oxfordshire, SN7 7BX Tel: (01367) 240736 Fax: (01367) 242625 E-mail: info@bray.co.uk *Chemists, sports & leisure sundries suppliers & manufrs*

Bray Management Ltd, Bray Studios, Down Place, Water Oakley, Windsor, Berkshire, SL4 5UG Tel: (01628) 622111 Fax: (01628) 770381 E-mail: bray.studios@btinternet.com *Film studios & facilities*

Nigel Bray Ltd, 3 Grandstand Business Centre, Westfields Trading Estate, Hereford, HR4 9NS Tel: (01432) 351400 Fax: (01432) 351888 E-mail: sales@nigelbrayltd.fsbusiness.co.uk *Clutch, brakes (agricultural) & plant equipment distributors*

▶ Braycot Construction Ltd, 56 Malt Mill Lane, Halesowen, West Midlands, B62 8JF Tel: 0121-559 2955 Fax: 0121-561 2324

Brayford Plastics, Horncastle Lane, Dunholme, Lincoln, LN2 3QF Tel: (01522) 530557 Fax: (01522) 730372 E-mail: info@brayfordplastics.com *Polythene & polypropylene bag manufrs*

Brayman Springs & Production Engineering, 7 28 Heming Road, Redditch, Worcestershire, B98 0DH Tel: (01527) 510004 Fax: (01527) 510004 *Spring clip & pressing manufrs*

Braythorn Ltd, Phillips Street, Birmingham, B6 4PT Tel: 0121-359 8800 Fax: 0121-359 8412 E-mail: sales@braythorn.co.uk Sales Contact: Hammond *Manufacturers of quality packaging products. Cardboard tubes or PVC/PET clear tubes, plain to process printed with curled ends, metal ends, ring pulls or plastic plugs. Polythene envelopes from stock or bespoke. ISO9001 and BRC/IOP approved.*

Braywhite & Co. Ltd, Halligan Buildings, Johnstone Street, Birmingham, B19 1SZ Tel: 0121-551 6001 Fax: 0121-511 7120 E-mail: info@braywhite.co.uk *Air conditioning industrial refrigeration engineers*

Braywood Joinery, Home Farm, Middle Green, Langley, Slough, SL3 6BS Tel: (01753) 534542 Fax: (01753) 546460 E-mail: braywood@homechoice.co.uk *Joinery manufrs*

▶ Brayzel Narrow Boats, Nateby Crossing Lane, Nateby, Preston, PR3 0JJ Tel: (01995) 601515 Fax: (01995) 601515 *Boats distributors & manufrs*

W.W. Brazell Ltd, Raeburn Street, Hartlepool, Cleveland, TS26 8PT Tel: (01429) 272937 Fax: (01429) 274950 *Building contractors*

Brazier Interior Systems Ltd, Medino House Rushington Business Park, Rushington Lane, Totton, Southampton, SO40 9LU Tel: (023) 8058 0000 Fax: (023) 8066 1900 *Office interior contractors*

▶ Braziers Dairies, Bellingdon Road, Chesham, Buckinghamshire, HP5 2NN Tel: (01494) 784232 Fax: (01494) 792500

BRC Ltd, 79-81 Station Road, Sutton-in-Ashfield, Nottinghamshire, NG17 5FR Tel: (01623) 440932 Fax: (01623) 440932 E-mail: sales@eastmidlands.brc.ltd.uk *Reinforcing steel & allied products* Also at: Branches Throughout the UK

BRC, 11 Mulberry Business Park, Fishponds Road, Wokingham, Berkshire, RG41 2FH Tel: 0118-977 3822 Fax: 0118-977 3913 E-mail: sales@brc-uk.co.uk *Reinforcing steel* Also at: Daventry, Darlington, Chelmsford, Glasgow, Sittingbourne & Wakefield

BRC Industrial Roofing (Midlands) Ltd, Unit 1, Merchants Way, Aldridge, Walsall, WS9 8SW Tel: (01922) 454044 Fax: (01922) 454254 E-mail: sales@brcroofing.co.uk *Roofing specialists*

BRC Welded Mesh, Whaley Road, Barugh, Barnsley, South Yorkshire, S75 1HT Tel: 01226 283438 Fax: 01226 248738 E-mail: industrialmesh@brc.ltd.uk *BRC Welded Mesh are medium to high volume manufacturers to customer requirements of:**- Bespoke Welded Mesh sheets*- Standard Welded Mesh sheets**Finish Types Offered:**- Self Colour Wire Mesh*- Pre-galvanised Wire Mesh*- Hot Dipped Galvanised Wire Mesh*- Powder Coated Wire Mesh**Product Type Offered:**- Wire diameters from 2.5mm to 8mm.*- Ability to vary mesh pitch to supply a flush panel.*- Panels with flying ends on any side.*- Infinitely variable centres on line & cross wires.*- Mesh panels supplied with mixed wire diameters.*- Panel corners notched & areas removed.*- Wire supplied cut to length from 2mm to 12mm.*- Panels upto 30 mm x 1650 mm in size.**BRC manufacture welded mesh from bright drawn mild steel wire to BS 4482.**The company has achieved ISO 9001 and CARES accreditation.*

▶ Bread Co., Unit 8+9 Premier Trading Estate, Dartmouth Middleway, Birmingham, B7 4AT Tel: 0121-359 6163 Fax: 0121-359 5153 E-mail: sales@breadbin.co.uk *Bakers*

Bread Bin, 3 Hay Street, Sunderland, SR5 1BG Tel: 0191-514 3933 *Bakery & confectionery suppliers*

The Bread Roll Company, Lyon Way, St Albans, St. Albans, Hertfordshire, AL4 0LQ Tel: (0845) 6070324 Fax: (01727) 818009 E-mail: info@breadroll.co.uk *Wholesalers of baking products*

Breakaway Tackle Development Co. Ltd, 376 Bramford Road, Ipswich, IP1 5AY Tel: (01473) 741393 Fax: (01473) 462482 *Fishing tackle manufrs*

Breakthrough Ltd, 145 Willington Street, Maidstone, Kent, ME15 8QX Tel: (01622) 670609 Fax: (01622) 670212 *Computer value added resellers*

▶ Breakwells Glass Ltd, 5 Villiers Trading Estate, Marston Road, Wolverhampton, WV2 4LA Tel: (01902) 420457 E-mail: sales@breakwellsglass.com

Breakwells Paints Ltd, 1 Harden Road, Walsall, WS3 1EL Tel: (01922) 400444 Fax: (01922) 400555 E-mail: sales@breakwellspaints.co.uk *Paint specialists*

Breamfold Packaging Ltd, 129 Richmond Road, London, E8 3NJ Tel: (020) 7249 6735 Fax: (020) 7249 6737 E-mail: sales@breamfoldpackaging.co.uk *Packaging material agents*

Breamhurst Ltd, Gorsey Lane, Clock Face, St. Helens, Merseyside, WA9 4SE Tel: (01744) 811208 Fax: (01744) 820004 E-mail: info@breamhurstdytran.co.uk *Pigment dispersion manufrs*

Breaston Chair Frames Co. Ltd, Unit 21b Merlin Way, Quarry Hill Industrial Estate, Ilkeston, Derbyshire, DE7 4RA Tel: 0115-944 0626 *Wood turners, polishers & chair frame manufrs*

Breathing Space, Two Stepps Cottage Studios , Old Road, Harbertonford, Totnes, Devon, TQ9 7TE Tel: 01803 732171 E-mail: interested@breathingspacedevon.com *A new exciting independent publication sympathetic with holistic green & organic concerns in your local area.*Over 8,000 readers per month.*Delivered Free promptly to over 60 pick up points across Devon,30 of which have bespoke display stands.Ecologically printing and production with the environment in mind.**Radio Station . Online Video*Tel our team now on:01803 732 171*

▶ Breathing Space Advertising Directory & Search Shop, Breathing Space Head OfficeHarbertonford, Two Stepps Cottage Studios, Old Road, Harbertonford, Totnes, Devon, TQ9 7TE Tel: (01803) 732171 E-mail: directory@breathingspacedevon.com *Showcasing the very best in health, beauty, healthy eating, fitness, and wellbeing, the Breathing Space Advertising Directory is the perfect place to focus on YOU. **Pick up your copy today in *Devon . Birmingham . Worcester**www.breathingspacedevon.com*

▶ Breathing Space Printing and Graphic Design, Breathing Space Head Office, Two Stepps Cottage Studios, Old Road, Harbertonford, Totnes, Devon, TQ9 7TE Tel: 01803 732171 E-mail: design@breathingspacedevon.com *Design with a spiritual connection in mind.*

▶ Breathing Space Worcester, Breathing Space Publishing Head Office, Two Stepps Cottage, Old Road, Harbertonford, Totnes, Devon, TQ9 7TE Tel: (01803) 732 171 *Local Listing Guide for Worcester and surrounding areas. Will Provide event listing, local holistic shops, and features from local practitioners.* interested@breathingspaceworcester.com Breathing Space will be distributed free to Tourist Information Centres, B&B's, Hotels & Shops. *If you would like copies of Breathing Space available in your premises, telephone us on 01803 732 171 for free delivery. For free listings of your event or activity in Worcester and surrounding areas, please send details to: Breathing Space, 2 Stepps Cottage, Harbertonford, Devon TQ9 7TE.*

Brec Ltd, Moor Park Court, St. Georges Road, Preston, PR1 6AQ Tel: (01772) 555000 Fax: (01772) 555422 E-mail: info@brec-ltd.com *Conveyor belt & vulcanising specialists*

▶ Breckenridge Conservatories Ltd, Unit 16, Sawston Trade Park, London Road, Sawston, Cambridge, CB2 4TR Tel: (01223) 839976 Fax: (01223) 839339 E-mail: sales@breckenridgeconservatories.co.uk *Suppliers of conservatories*

Brecker Grossmith & Co., 63 Wigmore Street, London, W1U 1BQ Tel: (020) 7486 3531 Fax: (020) 7935 3074 E-mail: enquiries@breckergrossmith.co.uk *Estate agents, surveyors & property consultants*

Breckhouse Engineering, Middle Farm, Sproxton, York, YO62 5EF Tel: (01439) 770579 Fax: (01439) 770772 *Agricultural engineers*

▶ Breckland Precision Engineering, Church Road, Watton, Thetford, Norfolk, IP25 6QA Tel: (01953) 885363 Fax: (01953) 885933 E-mail: bpe03@aol.com *Prototype & precision engineers*

The Brecks Co. Ltd, Breighton Airfield, Breighton, Selby, North Yorkshire, YO8 7DH Tel: (01757) 288943 Fax: (01757) 289119 *Food ingredient manufrs*

Brecon Beacon Natural Waters, Llwyn Dewi, Trapp, Llandeilo, Dyfed, SA19 6TT Tel: (01269) 850175 Fax: (01269) 851181 E-mail: info@breconwater.co.uk *Water bottling plant*

Brecon Pharmaceuticals Ltd, Pharos House Wye Valley Business Park, Brecon Road, Hay-on-Wye, Hereford, HR3 5PG Tel: (01497) 820829 Fax: (01497) 820050 E-mail: admin@brecon-pharm.co.uk *Packaging services*

▶ Brecon Scaffolding Ltd, Box Bush Farm, Three Cocks, Brecon, Powys, LD3 0SH Tel: (01874) 754262 Fax: (01874) 754862

Breconcherry Ltd, Lower Road Trading Estate, Ledbury, Herefordshire, HR8 2DH Tel: (01531) 632476 Fax: (01531) 633839 E-mail: cip@breconcherry.com *Design & manufacture tank cleaning equipment specialists*

Nina Breddal Ltd, Mermaid House, Chertsey Road, Byfleet, West Byfleet, Surrey, KT14 7AP Tel: (01932) 340433 Fax: (01932) 336578 *Jewellery importers & manufrs*

▶ Bredero Shaw Ltd, Bredero House, Imperial Dock, Leith, Edinburgh, EH6 7DT Tel: 0131-553 9700 Fax: 0131-553 9604 *Pipe coating suppliers*

▶ Bredero Shaw Ltd, Castle Street, Castlepark Industrial Estate, Ellon, Aberdeenshire, AB41 9RF Tel: (01358) 723435 Fax: (01358) 723371 E-mail: ellon.reception@brederoshaw.shawcor.com *Metal distributors*

▶ Bredon Forge, Newton Farm, Natton, Ashchurch, Tewkesbury, Gloucestershire, GL20 7BE Tel: (01684) 299494 Fax: (01684) 299494 E-mail: allan_marden@tiscali.co.uk *Small independant forge manufacturing garden gates, railings, weather vanes, boot scrapers, candlesticks, ornamental ironwork and much more.*

▶ Breedmax.co.uk, PO Box 7774, Harlow, Essex, CM18 6WJ Tel: (01279) 324509 E-mail: sales@breedmax.co.uk *Bird feed supplements & specialist chick identification marker pen.*

Breeze Ltd, Breeze House, Albert Close Trading Estate, Whitefield, Manchester, M45 8EH Tel: 0161-796 3600 Fax: 0161-796 3700 E-mail: info@breez.co.uk *Mailing house*

Breeze Cool Air Conditioning & Refrigeration Ltd, 37 Amberley Road, Macclesfield, Cheshire, SK11 8LX Tel: (01625) 511336 Fax: (01625) 511288 E-mail: enquiries@breezecool.co.uk *"Air conditioning refrigeration & ventilation Design,*

continued

Company Information

continuation
sales, installations, repairs & planned maintenance. We operate a fleet of engineers across the UK providing solutions for over a decade. We welcome all new business large & small'

▶ Breeze Design Ltd, Studio 4, Weston Farm, The Street, Albury, Guildford, Surrey, GU5 9BZ Tel: (0845) 0943701 E-mail: info@breezedesign.co.uk *Graphic Design Agency, design, branding, identity, advertising & websites*

Breeze It Ltd, 5 Colwick Quays Business Park, Colwick, Nottingham, NG4 2JY Tel: (0845) 0092788 Fax: (0845) 0092789 E-mail: steve.watkins@breezeassist.com *Bespoke software & intranet design specialists*

▶ Breeze Media Ltd, Gleann Cottage, 1 The Terrace, Glenlomond, Kinross, KY13 9HF Tel: (01592) 840640 E-mail: info@breezemedia.co.uk *Software programmers*

▶ Breeze Mount Transport, Topcliffe Lane, Tingley, Wakefield, West Yorkshire, WF3 1SP Tel: 0113-218 9541 Fax: 0113-218 9541

Breeze UK Ltd, 18 St. Pancras Way, London, NW1 0QG Tel: (020) 7383 2288 Fax: (020) 7383 2288 E-mail: reception@breezeuk.com *Fashion manufrs*

Breg Products Ltd, Tower Works, Birkhouse Lane, Huddersfield, HD1 4SF Tel: (01484) 469944 Fax: (01484) 469955 E-mail: sales@bregproducts.co.uk *Truck & trolley manufrs*

Brega Blinds, Poplar Farm House, Charles Tye, Ringshall, Stowmarket, Suffolk, IP14 2HU Tel: (01449) 740013 Fax: (01449) 744392 *Blind fitters & manufrs*

Brellant Engineering Co. Ltd, Hole Bottom Mills, Huddersfield, HD5 8HF Tel: (01484) 428892 Fax: (01484) 431712 *Precision engineers*

Brenal Optical Services, Great Western Street, Wednesbury, West Midlands, WS10 7LL Tel: 0121-556 1506 Fax: 0121-556 9792 *Optical manufrs*

Brencliffe Ltd, Rossendale Road, Burnley, Lancashire, BB11 5HD Tel: (01282) 435226 Fax: (01282) 436147 E-mail: sales@brencliffe.com *Stockinette, dishcloth manufacturers & distributors of car care products*

▶ Brendata UK Ltd, Nevendon Hall, Nevendon Road, Basildon, Essex, SS13 1BX Tel: (01268) 471777 Fax: (01268) 466101 E-mail: response@brendata.co.uk *IT consultants & network security for medium to large businesses*

▶ Brenden Fern Heating & Plumbing, 27 Paradise Street, Stoke-on-Trent, ST6 5AG Tel: (01782) 818577 Fax: (01782) 818578 E-mail: info@bfplum.co.uk *Plumbing heating, gas work services*

Brenig Outdoor Clothing, Greenfield Road, Greenfield, Holywell, Clwyd, CH8 7GR Tel: (01352) 718025 Fax: (01352) 718025 E-mail: sales@brenig.co.uk *Quality outdoor clothing manufrs*

▶ Brenmar Electrical, Glen Eyre, Brickyard Road, Swanmore, Southampton, SO32 2PJ Tel: (01489) 891196 Fax: (01489) 891197

Brenmark Holdings Ltd, 1 Newbridge Road, St Annes, Bristol, BS4 4GH Tel: 0117-971 3121 Fax: 0117-971 3428 E-mail: info@brenmark.co.uk *Fastener & tool stockists* Also at: Plymouth

▶ Brennan Lettings & Property Management, Weddington Road, Nuneaton, Warwickshire, CV10 0EG Tel: (024) 7635 2537 *We are a local independant firm specialising in Residential sales and Property Management.*

S.N. & C. Brennan, The Old Workshop, The Common, Cranleigh, Surrey, GU6 8RZ Fax: (01483) 274228 *Carpenters & joiners*

Brennan Site Services Ltd, Mill Way, Old Mill Lane Industrial Estate, Mansfield Woodhouse, Mansfield, Nottinghamshire, NG19 9BG Tel: (01623) 654221 Fax: (01623) 420390 *Crane hire services*

Brennan Tool & Engineering Co. Ltd, Unit 9-11 Brooke Trading Estate, Lyon Road, Romford, RM1 2AT Tel: (01708) 736600 Fax: (01708) 735500 E-mail: david.brennan@brennan-tools.co.uk *Precision engineers & toolmakers*

▶ Brennand Clothing Ltd, Halliwell Industrial Estate, Rossini Street, Bolton, BL1 8DL Tel: (01204) 493160 Fax: (01204) 493190

Brennans Of Wiltshire Ltd, Harepath Farm, Burbage, Marlborough, Wiltshire, SN8 3BT Tel: (01672) 810380 Fax: (01672) 811157 E-mail: bofwilts@aol.com *Groundwork & haulage contractors*

Brenson Fashions Ltd, 32 Fortesque Avenue, London, E8 3QB Tel: (020) 8533 1525 Fax: (020) 8533 4427 *Ladies fashion manufrs*

▶ Brent Cross, Sayer House, Oxgate Lane, London, NW2 7JN Tel: (020) 8208 2626 Fax: (020) 8208 2012 E-mail: sales@brentxofficefurniture.co.uk Sales Contact: Green *New office furniture to suit your premises. We will prepare floor plans of your premises and suggest the most suitable furniture. This will be full office quality and at competitive prices. Please see the furniture gallery on our web site for pictures of many of the styles and ranges available. Reliable delivery and installation nationwide. We also deliver to shippers for export worldwide.*

Brent Engineering Co. Ltd, The Barn, 13 Wycombe Gdns, Golders Green, London, NW11 8AN Tel: (020) 8455 4701 *Line transformers manufacturers*

Brent Group Ltd, Brent House, Travellers Lane, North Mymms, Hatfield, Hertfordshire, AL9 7HF Tel: (01707) 282300 Fax: (01707) 282333 E-mail: hq@brentgroup.com *Holding company*

▶ Brent Precision, Upcott Avenue, Pottington Business Park, Barnstaple, Devon, EX31 1HN Tel: (01271) 324172 Fax: (01271) 324173 E-mail: karl@brentprecision.co.uk *Sheet metal fabrication*

Brent Products Develompent Ltd, Old House Lane, Bisley, Woking, Surrey, GU24 9DB Tel: (01483) 797655 Fax: (01483) 797475 E-mail: sales@brentltd.co.uk *New product developers*

▶ Brent Scaffold Boards Ltd, The Airfield, Breighton, Selby, North Yorkshire, YO8 6DJ Tel: (01757) 289199 Fax: (01757) 289105 *Scaffolding*

Brent Taunton Joinery, 3 Coopers Industrial Estate, Littlehampton Road, Ferring, Worthing, West Sussex, BN12 6PW Tel: (01903) 248169 Fax: (01903) 248169 *Joinery manufrs*

Brentmere Leisure, 18 Mallard Close, Earls Barton, Northampton, NN6 0JF Tel: (01604) 810700 Fax: (01604) 812497 *Static holiday caravan manufrs*

Brenton Handbags Ltd, Darren Mill, Wash Lane, Bury, Lancashire, BL9 7DU Tel: 0161-764 8528 Fax: 0161-763 1503 E-mail: info@brentonbags.com *Suppliers of fashion for the retail trade*

Brentwood, 2 Whitehouse Road, Dordon, Tamworth, Staffordshire, B78 1QF Tel: (01827) 705450 Fax: (01827) 705450 E-mail: bob.kind@ntlworld.com *Rubber moulding & rubber extrusion distributors & agents*

Brentwood Angling, 118 Warley Hill, Warley, Brentwood, Essex, CM14 5HB Tel: (01277) 225585 Fax: (01277) 219500 E-mail: enquiries@brentwoodangling.co.uk *Angling equipment sales*

Brentwood Communications Ltd, 178 Warley Hill, Warley, Brentwood, Essex, CM14 5HF Tel: (01277) 225254 Fax: (01277) 223089 E-mail: info@bc-ltd.co.uk *Two way radios*

▶ Brentwood Electrical Contractors Ltd, 5 St. James Road, Brentwood, Essex, CM14 4LF Tel: (01277) 216121

Brentwood Marketing, Lockhill Mills, Holmes Road, Sowerby Bridge, West Yorkshire, HX6 3LD Tel: (01422) 831185 Fax: (01422) 831186 E-mail: info@brentwoodmarketing.co.uk *Personalised clothing & printing*

▶ BresnanWalsh, 1 Water Street, Liverpool, L2 0RD Tel: 0151 236 1494 Fax: 0151 258 1516 E-mail: mail@bresnanwalsh.co.uk *Chartered Accountants*

Bressingham Engineers Ltd, High Road, Bressingham, Diss, Norfolk, IP22 2AT Tel: (01379) 688163 Fax: (01379) 687437 E-mail: bresseng@enterprise.net *Fabrication engineers*

Bretby Nurseries Ltd, Bretby Lane, Bretby, Burton-on-Trent, Staffordshire, DE15 0QS Tel: (01283) 703355 Fax: (01283) 704035 E-mail: bretby.nurseries@virgin.net *Garden nursery*

▶ Bretby Services, Ashby Road East, Bretby, Burton-on-Trent, Staffordshire, DE15 0PS Tel: (01283) 550491

Breton International Ltd, Havelock Buildings, Jubilee Street, Llandudno, Gwynedd, LL30 2NZ Tel: (01492) 875268 Fax: (01492) 860731 E-mail: info@breton-international.com *Diamond tool manufrs*

Brett Aggregates Ltd, Brett House, Bysing Wood Road, Faversham, Kent, ME13 7UD Tel: (01795) 594051 Fax: (01795) 594027 *Aggregate producers & suppliers*

Brett Aggregates, Waldringfield Road, Brightwell, Ipswich, IP10 0BL Tel: (01473) 621007 Fax: (01473) 736721 *Ready mixed concrete producers* Also at: Brightlingsea & Wivenhoe

Brett Aggregates, Waldringfield Road, Brightwell, Ipswich, IP10 0BL Tel: (01473) 621007 Fax: (01473) 736721 *Plant hire, aggregates & earthmoving contractors*

Brett Aggregates, North Sea Terminal, Cliffe, Rochester, Kent, ME3 7SX Tel: (01634) 220631 Fax: (01634) 220067 *Concreting aggregate producers*

Brett Concrete Ltd, Oare Road, Faversham, Kent, ME13 7TW Tel: (01795) 533436 Fax: (01795) 536047 *Ready mix concrete suppliers*

Brett Concrete Ltd, Foxhall Four Quarry, Foxhall Road, Brightwell, Ipswich, IP10 0HT Tel: (01473) 736441 Fax: (01473) 736721 *Ready mixed concrete manufacturers & suppliers*

Brett Concrete Ltd, 7-9 Chapman Road, London, E9 5DW Tel: (020) 8986 6616 Fax: (020) 8985 8182 *Ready mixed concrete*

Brett Concrete Ltd, Jurys Gap Road, Lydd, Romney Marsh, Kent, TN29 9JW Tel: (01797) 320462 Fax: (01797) 320074 E-mail: sales@fullsupply.co.uk *Ready mix concrete manufrs*

Brett Martin, Brierley Close, Speedwell Industrial Estate Staveley, Staveley, Chesterfield, Derbyshire, S43 3JP Tel: (01246) 280001 Fax: (01246) 280001 E-mail: building@brettmartin.com *Plastics tube & pipe distributors*

▶ Brett Martin Ltd, 9 Blairlinn Road, Cumbernauld, Glasgow, G67 2TF Tel: (01236) 725536 Fax: (01236) 725871 *PBC materials & plastics supplies*

Brett Martin Daylight Systems Ltd, Sandford Close, Aldermans Green Industrial Estate, Coventry, CV2 2QU Tel: (024) 7660 2022 Fax: (024) 7660 2745 *Roof light & skylight manufrs*

Brett Martin Roofing Products Ltd, Langley Road, Burscough Industrial Estate, Ormskirk, Lancashire, L40 8JR Tel: (01704) 895345 Fax: (01704) 894229 E-mail: contact@daylightsystems.co.uk *Plastics drainage systems*

Brett Specialised Aggregates, Sturry Quarry, Fordwich Road, Sturry, Canterbury, Kent, CT2 0BW Tel: (0845) 6080572 Fax: (0845) 6080573 E-mail: sales@brett-specialised-aggregates.co.uk *Specialised aggregate producers*

Brettell Bros, Hungary Hill, Stourbridge, West Midlands, DY9 7NH Tel: (01384) 395711 Fax: (01384) 372948 E-mail: sales@brettellbrothersgates.co.uk *Specialists in steel fabrication & wrought iron work*

H. Brettell & Sons Ltd, 20 Chestnut Ave, Forest Gate, London, E7 0JH Tel: (020) 8555 4037 Fax: (020) 8555 2106 E-mail: sales@brettells.co.uk Purchasing Contact: R. Brettell Sales Contact: R. Brettell

continued

Wood turnery manufacturers/wood turners; fitting, handrails, wood. Also stair parts

Brettell & Shaw, Allfor House, Hayes Lane, Stourbridge, West Midlands, DY9 8QT Tel: (01384) 898911 Fax: (01384) 899100 E-mail: jpc@bretshaweltex.com *Galvanized hollow-ware manufrs*

▶ brettonmobiles.2u.co.uk, 172 Kirkmeadow, Bretton, Peterborough, PE3 8JN Tel: (01733) 332390 E-mail: brettoncomputers@ukonline.co.uk *free nokia mobile phones*ringtones*logos*the best contract deals*

Bretts Oils, Pipewellgate, Gateshead, Tyne & Wear, NE8 2BN Tel: 0191-477 0856 Fax: 0191-490 0360 E-mail: uksales@ovoline.co.uk *Oil & grease manufrs*

Bretts Transport Ltd, Thorney Road, Guyhirn, Wisbech, Cambridgeshire, PE13 4AG Tel: (01733) 849245 Fax: (01733) 849363 *Haulage & storage contractors*

Bretvents Ltd, Bradfords Farm, Little Horsted, Uckfield, East Sussex, TN22 5QP Tel: (01825) 841227 Fax: (01825) 841294 *General sheet metal working engineers*

Brevitt Rieker Ltd, 37 Tenter Road, Moulton Park Industrial Estate, Northampton, NN3 6AX Tel: (01604) 491222 Fax: (01604) 499512 E-mail: sales@rieker.net *Footwear merchants*

Brew Bros Fabrications Ltd, 30 Hailey Road, Erith, Kent, DA18 4AP Tel: (020) 8311 1150 Fax: (020) 8312 4224 *Specialists in all areas of structural steel, architectural metalwork, fire escapes, gates, railings, balustrades, fencing, security grilles and screens.*

C. Brewer & Sons Ltd, 81 Alston Drive, Bradwell Abbey, Milton Keynes, MK13 9HF Tel: (01908) 316719 Fax: (01908) 311423 *Decorators merchants*

Brewer Sign Services, 24 Meredith Road, Portsmouth, PO2 9NN Tel: (023) 9266 8602 Fax: (023) 9266 8602 *Signwriters & lettering services*

T. Brewer & Co. Ltd, 110 Dunmow Road, Bishop's Stortford, Hertfordshire, CM23 5HN Tel: (01279) 658338 Fax: (01279) 757023 E-mail: stortford@tbrewer.co.uk *Timber & builders merchants*

▶ Brewer & Turnbull Ltd, The Royal Hall, 40 Arthurstone Terrace, Dundee, DD4 6QT Tel: (01382) 226437

Brewers Ltd, Priory Bridge Road, Taunton, Somerset, TA1 1QD Tel: (01823) 284532 Fax: (01823) 353712 *Decorators merchants* Also at: Bournemouth & Taunton

Brewers Business Solutions Ltd, Water-Ma-Trout, Helston, Cornwall, TR13 0LW Tel: (01326) 563424 Fax: (01326) 563606 *Office stationery, furniture & printers distributor & supplier*

▶ Brewery Equipment Refurbishers, 3a Moorfield Road, Wolverhampton, WV2 4QT Tel: (01902) 421170 Fax: (01902) 421168 *Brewery plant equipment*

▶ Brewfitt Refrigeration & Air Conditioning, International House, Penistone Road, Fenay Bridge, Huddersfield, HD8 0LE Tel: (01484) 340800 Fax: (01484) 340900 E-mail: sales@brewfitt.com *Refrigeration & air conditioning equipment suppliers*

Brewin Dolphin, Old Bank of England Court, Queen Street, Norwich, NR2 4SX Tel: (01603) 767776 Fax: (01603) 767476 E-mail: richardl@hillosborne.co.uk *Stockbrokers*

Brewin Dolphin Securities Ltd, Edmund House, 12-22 Newhall Street, Birmingham, B3 3DB Tel: 0121-236 7000 Fax: 0121-212 0011 E-mail: martin.lord@brewin.co.uk *Stock brokers*

Brewin Dolphin Securities, Auburn House, Upper Piccadilly, Bradford, West Yorkshire, BD1 3NU Tel: (01274) 728866 Fax: (01274) 370483 E-mail: rupertf@hillosborne.co.uk *Stock brokers*

Brewin Dolphin Securities Ltd, Sutherland House, Cowbridge Road East, Cardiff, CF11 9BB Tel: (029) 2034 0100 Fax: (029) 2034 4999 E-mail: catherin.thomas@brewin.co.uk *Stockbrokers*

Brewin Dolphin Securities, 50 South Street, Dorchester, Dorset, DT1 1DQ Tel: (01305) 259333 Fax: (01305) 269111 E-mail: david.evans@brewin.co.uk *Stock brokers*

Brewin Dolphin Securities, 1 Courthouse Square, Dundee, DD1 1NH Tel: (01382) 317200 Fax: (01382) 317201 E-mail: david.chalmers@blw.co.uk *Stock brokers & financial advisors*

Brewin Dolphin Securities Ltd, 2 Hyde Gardens, Eastbourne, East Sussex, BN21 4PN Tel: (08452) 131190 Fax: (01323) 644109 *Stockbrokers*

Brewin Dolphin Securities, 12-14 Fountain Street, Halifax, West Yorkshire, HX1 1LW Tel: (01422) 367707 Fax: (01422) 348362 E-mail: scott.cresswell@brewin.co.uk *Stock brokers*

Brewin Dolphin Securities, Kintail House, Beechwood Park, Inverness, IV2 3BW Tel: (01463) 225888 Fax: (01463) 226777 E-mail: john.clarkson@blw.co.uk *Stock brokers*

Brewin Dolphin Securities, 27 Charing Cross, St. Helier, Jersey, JE2 3RP Tel: (01534) 703000 Fax: (01534) 731910 E-mail: stuart.sangan@brewin.co.uk *Stockbrokers*

Brewin Dolphin Securities Ltd, 34 Lisbon Street, Leeds, LS1 4LX Tel: 0113-245 9341 Fax: 0113-243 5666 E-mail: sales@brewin.co.uk *Stockbrokers*

Brewin Dolphin Securities, Permanent House, Horsefair Street, Leicester, LE1 5BU Tel: 0116-242 0700 Fax: 0116-253 6585 E-mail: cjh@hillosborne.co.uk *Stockbrokers*

Brewin Dolphin Securities, Wigford House, Brayford Wharf East, Lincoln, LN5 7AY Tel: (01522) 585100 Fax: (01522) 513965 E-mail: peters@hillosborne.co.uk *Stockbrokers*

Brewin Dolphin Securities Ltd, 59 Madoc Street, Llandudno, Gwynedd, LL30 2TW Tel: (01492) 874391 Fax: (01492) 871990 E-mail: colin.wickens@brewin.co.uk *Stock brokers*

Brewin Dolphin Securities Ltd, 5 Giltspur Street, London, EC1A 9BD Tel: (020) 7248 4400 Fax: (020) 7236 2034E-mail: info@brewin.co.uk *Stockbrokers, financial planners & investment services*

Brewin Dolphin Securities Ltd, 98 High St, Lymington, Hampshire, SO41 9AP Tel: (01590) 674288 Fax: (01590) 679039 *Stockbrokers*

Brewin Dolphin Securities Ltd, PO Box 512, Manchester, M2 7LE Tel: 0161-833 0961 Fax: 0161-839 1651 E-mail: neil.harding@brewin.co.uk *Stockbrokers*

Brewin Dolphin Securities Ltd, Cross Keys House The Parade, Marlborough, Wiltshire, SN8 1NE Tel: (01672) 519600 Fax: (01672) 515550 E-mail: beverley.mcilvar@brewin.co.uk *Investments, Pensions and Financial Planning*

Brewin Dolphin Securities, Pilgrim Street, Newcastle Upon Tyne, NE1 6RQ Tel: 0191-279 7300 Fax: 0191-279 7301 *Stockbrokers*

Brewin Dolphin Securities Ltd, Park House, 77-81 Bell Street, Reigate, Surrey, RH2 7AN Tel: (01737) 223722 Fax: (01737) 224848 E-mail: paul.cannons@brewin.co.uk *Stockbrokers*

Brewin Dolphin Securities, 5 Alma Square, Scarborough, North Yorkshire, YO11 1JR Tel: (01723) 372478 Fax: (01723) 500116 *Stockbrokers*

Brewin Dolphin Securities, Progress House, Fudan Way, Thornaby, Stockton-On-Tees, Cleveland, TS17 6EN Tel: (01642) 608855 Fax: (01642) 604488 E-mail: william.bakerbaker@wise-speke.co.uk *Stockbrokers*

Brewin Dolphin Securities Ltd, 2 Mendip House, High Street, Taunton, Somerset, TA1 3SX Tel: (01823) 332042 Fax: (01823) 335166 E-mail: terry.leach@brewin.co.uk *Stockbrokers*

Brewin Dolphin Security Ltd, The Lypiatts, Lansdown Road, Cheltenham, Gloucestershire, GL50 2JA Tel: (01242) 577677 Fax: (01242) 520030 E-mail: edward.mawle@brewin.co.uk *Stockbrokers*

Brewing Research International Ltd, Lyttel Hall, Coopers Hill Road, Redhill, RH1 4HY Tel: (01737) 822272 Fax: (01737) 822747 E-mail: bri@brewingresearch.co.uk *Research laboratory*

Brewing-Solutions Co UK Ltd, Unit 31, Osborne Mill Osborne Street, Oldham, OL9 6QQ Tel: 0161-622 1603 Fax: 0161-622 1662 E-mail: info@brewing-solutions.co.uk *Designers & builders of breweries & brewing equipment*

Brewis Engineering, Handlemaker Road, Frome, Somerset, BA11 4RW Tel: (01373) 451387 Fax: (01373) 452714 E-mail: sales@brewisdirect.com *Trenchless technology*

Brewpack Ltd, 2 Sky Business Park, Eversley Way, Thorpe Industrial Estate, Egham, Surrey, TW20 8RG Tel: (01784) 431331 Fax: (01784) 472313 E-mail: sales@brewpack.ltd.uk *Conveyor systems, bottling, canning & packaging*

Breydon Enterprises Ltd, Fenner Road, Unit 1, Great Yarmouth, Norfolk, NR30 3PS Tel: (01493) 331411 Fax: (01493) 331411 E-mail: breydonenterprises@fsmail.net *Export packers*

Brian A Powles, Staunton-on-Wye, Hereford, HR4 7LY Tel: (01981) 500327 Fax: (01981) 500683 *Joinery manufrs*

Brian Bass, 285 Fleet Road, Fleet, Hampshire, GU51 3BT Tel: (01252) 625202 Fax: (01252) 625978 E-mail: info@brianbass.com *Computer & office equipment & networking manufrs*

▶ Brian Brass, Kardale, Sandwick, Stromness, Orkney, KW16 3HY Tel: (01856) 841733

▶ Brian Burgess, 18 Fairway Drive, Greenford, Middlesex, UB6 8PW Tel: (020) 8578 7233 Fax: (020) 8578 7180

Brian Cook Engineering Ltd, Calder Road Works, Ravensthorpe, Dewsbury, West Yorkshire, WF13 3JT Tel: (01924) 469469 Fax: (01924) 849099 *Shotblast engineers*

Brian Cooper, 1 Market Street, Hollingworth, Hyde, Cheshire, SK14 8NE Tel: (01457) 763861 Fax: (01457) 855712 *Industrial heating services*

Brian Currie, 3 Brunel Road, Bedford, MK41 9TG Tel: (01234) 325737 Fax: (01234) 360804 *DAF franchise & vehicle repair services*

Brian Fawcett Joinery, Ellifoot Lane, Burstwick, Hull, HU12 9EF Tel: (01964) 670818 Fax: (01964) 671138 E-mail: enquiries@brianfawcett-joinery.com *Joinery products, windows, conservatories, staircases, doors etc*

▶ Brian Fenton Wide Load Escorts, 17 Weatherdon Drive, Ivybridge, Plymouth, PL21 0DD Tel: 01752 690373 Fax: 01752 690373 E-mail: mail@wide-load-escorts.co.uk *We are Plymouth based and run by Brian Fenton, serving the whole of the UK and also Europe.**We are approved by the Highways Agency Dept. for transport and also the Police, plus we are listed by the police as a recommended company and can supply many references from satisfied customers.**Specialist''s in delivery through the lanes of Devon and Cornwall with over 37 years experience delivering abnormal /wide loads such as boats, mobile homes, machinery etc throughout the UK and Europe.**Our Vehicle''s are also marked up in the correct marking''s that are required by the UK Highways Agency and are also required by Insurance companies to be correctly insured.**We carry full equipment as required by the code of practice for private escort vehicles plus many extras**Vehicle''s insured specifically to cover the escorting of abnormal /wide loads on public highways and also covered by public liability insurance*

Brian Green, D B H House, Boundary Street, Liverpool, L5 9YJ Tel: 0151-207 5225 Fax: 0151-207 3300 E-mail: sales@brian-green.co.uk *Office machinery system suppliers*

Brian Harris Ltd, Pottery Road, Bovey Tracey, Newton Abbot, Devon, TQ13 9DS Tel: (01626) 833371 Fax: (01626) 834680 *Freight services*

Brian J Hetherington Joiner & Contractor, 2 Barras La Industrial Estate, Station Road, Dalston, Carlisle, CA5 7LX Tel: (01228) 710314 Fax: (01697) 476568 *Joinery contractors*

▶ Brian Knight Electrical Ltd, 2 Summers Road, Godalming, Surrey, GU7 3BB Tel: (01483) 414477 Fax: (01483) 424300

Brian Lowndes Print Ltd, Graphichouse, Portland Street, Walsall, WS2 8BE Tel: (01922) 725282 Fax: (01922) 720981 E-mail: mail@blprint.co.uk *Commercial printers*

Brian Mccance Steel Ltd, 1 Dargan Road, Belfast, BT3 9JU Tel: (028) 9077 2326 Fax: (028) 9077 9698 E-mail: admin@mccancesteel.com *Steel stockholders & processors*

Brian Matthews Licensed Trade Suppliers, 17 Malmesbury Road, Chippenham, Wiltshire, SN15 1PS Tel: (01249) 444803 Fax: (01249) 462650 *License trade suppliers*

▶ Brian Pierpoint & Co., Amberley Ridge, Church Road, Woolton, Liverpool, L25 6DD Tel: 0151-428 4019 Fax: 0151 428 4019 E-mail: brian.pierpoint@tiscali.co.uk *Chartered Quantity Surveyors and Construction Contracts Consultants*

Brian Plant, Wickham Road, Grimsby, South Humberside, DN31 3SL Tel: (01472) 241342 Fax: (01472) 354329 *Skip hire*

Brian S Pope Ltd, 200 Manchester Road, Stockport, Cheshire, SK4 1NN Tel: 0161-480 8322 Fax: 0161-474 1406 E-mail: sales@brianpope.com *Engineer suppliers*

Brian Walker & Son, 87 Garraways, Coffee Hall, Milton Keynes, MK6 5DU Tel: (01908) 666690 Fax: (01908) 233211 *Bolt & nut distributors/ agents/stockholders*

▶ Brians Locksmiths, 125 Rotterdam Road, Lowestoft, Suffolk, NR32 2EY Tel: (01502) 572176 Fax: (01502) 572176 E-mail: brianslocksmiths@aol.com *Locksmith, master systems & access control*

Briant Curtaining Ltd, 147-149 Albany Road, Coventry, CV5 6ND Tel: (024) 7671 3334 Fax: (024) 7671 2055 E-mail: bc@briantcurtaining.co.uk *Soft furnishings suppliers, Makers of Curtains and Blinds, Suppliers of all types of curtains, blinds, curtains rails, electric curtain rails and Awnings*

Brican Fabrications Ltd, 12 Alder Road, Broadmeadow Industrial Estate, Dumbarton, G82 2EL Tel: (01389) 731410 Fax: (01389) 730711 *Steel fabrications*

▶ Brice-Baker Group, Rookery Road, The Lane, Wyboston, Bedford, MK44 3AX Tel: (01480) 216618 Fax: (01480) 406226 E-mail: info@bricebaker.co.uk *Agricultural dealers*

Brick Bond Northern, 7 Healey New Mills, Healey Road, Ossett, West Yorkshire, WF5 8NF Tel: (01924) 266194 Fax: (01924) 266195 E-mail: admin@brickmanufacturers.com *Specialised brick manufrs*

The Brick Business Ltd, Todhills Factory, Newfield, Bishop Auckland, County Durham, DL14 8BA Tel: (01388) 603008 Fax: (01388) 450356 *Brick manufrs*

Brick Business, Steer Point Factory, Brixton, Plymouth, PL8 2DG Tel: (01752) 880659 Fax: (01752) 881734 E-mail: info@thebrickbusiness.com *Brick manufrs*

Brick House Ceramic Supplies Ltd, The Barn, Sheepcotes Lane, Silver End, Witham, Essex, CM8 3PJ Tel: (01376) 585655 Fax: (01376) 585656 E-mail: sales@brickhouseceramics.co.uk *Kilns pottery manufrs*

Brick Lock Ltd, 8 Brexdale Avenue, Kippax, Leeds, LS25 7EJ Tel: 0113-232 0800 *Wall tie replacements*

▶ Brick Peers, Milton Priory House, Gate Lane, Wells, Somerset, BA5 1UA Tel: (01749) 683110 Fax: (01749) 683117

Brick Specialists (Midlands) Ltd, 2 Cottage Terrace, The Rope Walk, Nottingham, NG1 5DX Tel: 0115-985 9100 Fax: 0115-947 8960 E-mail: rgb@bricks99.freserve.co.uk *Brick distributors*

▶ Brick & Steel Construction Co., 4-6 Boswell Square, Hillington Industrial Estate, Glasgow, G52 4BQ Tel: 0141-810 1919 Fax: 0141-810 1929

▶ Brick & Stone Cosmetics Western Ltd, 56 Pinewood Road, Belper, Derbyshire, DE56 2TS Tel: (01773) 826160

Brick & Stone Doctors, 139 Newgate Lane, Mansfield, Nottinghamshire, NG18 2LG Tel: (01623) 402427 Fax: (01623) 402208 E-mail: brick.stonedoctors@ntlworld.com *Brick tinting & stone repairs cleaning*

Brickell Swimming Pools Ltd, 84a Oakley Lane, Basingstoke, Hampshire, RG23 7JU Tel: (01256) 780567 Fax: (01256) 782385 E-mail: info@brickellpools.co.uk *Swimming pool construction & servicing*

Bricknells, 35 Fore Street, Bodmin, Cornwall, PL31 2JD Tel: (01208) 77088 Fax: (01208) 78497 *Independent newsagents, stationery, toy & nursery suppliers*

▶ Brid Fish Ltd, Old Laundry Trading Estate, Sea Road North, Bridport, Dorset, DT6 3BD Tel: (01308) 456306 Fax: (01308) 456367 E-mail: info@thegourmetworld.com *Fish processors*

Briddon Baker Labels, Monkham Wood, Purley Ford, Luxborough, Watchet, Somerset, TA23 0SA Tel: (01984) 640084 Fax: (01984) 640521 E-mail: briddon.baker@virgin.net *Label printers*

Bride Hall, 49 Hays Mews, London, W1J 5QQ Tel: (020) 7493 3996 Fax: (020) 7499 4388 E-mail: developments@bride-hall.co.uk *Property developers*

▶ Bridenprint Ltd, Briden House, Condor Road, Quarry Hill Industrial Park, Ilkeston, Derbyshire, DE7 4RE Tel: 0115-944 7111 Fax: 0115-944 7222 E-mail: sales@bridenprint.co.uk *Lithographic printers*

Bridge Abrasives Ltd, Unit E, Ford Road, Totnes Industrial Estate, Totnes, Devon, TQ9 5LQ Tel: (01803) 866667 Fax: (01803) 866001 E-mail: info@bridge-abrasives.co.uk *Diamond grinding tools manufrs*

Bridge Associates, 22 Greville Drive, Birmingham, B15 2UU Tel: 0121-440 4503 Fax: 0121-440 4503 *Recruitment consultants*

▶ Bridge Bathrooms, Bridge Works, Stockport Road, Romiley, Stockport, Cheshire, SK6 3AN Tel: 0161-406 6454 Fax: 0161-494 2222

Bridge Bearings Ltd, Heath Field Road, Sandy Lane Industrial Estate, Stourport-On-Severn, Worcestershire, DY13 9AQ Tel: (01299) 878443 Fax: (01299) 878318 E-mail: bearingsales@bridge-bearings.co.uk *Bridge Bearings are the largest privately owned Bearing and Conveyor Component manufacturer in the U.K.Our range includes both steel and plastic housed semi-precision and precision bearings and bearings for all types of Conveyor Rollers. With full CNC machining and moulding facilities we are more than happy to quote for a wide range of bespoke components.The Conveyor Roller range consists of steel and plastic rollers for both gravity and powered applications, including motorised and sprocketed rollers covering the majority of material handling requirements. A new range of fabricated steel drums to suit most belt conveyor and general heavy-duty applications has also been introduced to compliment them.Standard rollers range from 20mm, to a robust 219mm diameter. Also available is a range of segmented true taper rollers for lineshaft applications, with finishes ranging from self-colour to zinc plated, stainless steel, rubber and polyurethane coatings.*

Bridge Boats Ltd, Fry's Island, De Montfort Road, Reading, RG1 8DG Tel: 0118-959 0346 Fax: 0118-959 1114 E-mail: sales@bridgeboats.com *Boat repairers & hire service*

Bridge Ceilings Ltd, Interiors House, Samson Road, Coalville, Leicestershire, LE67 3FP Tel: (01530) 834777 Fax: (01530) 813388 E-mail: info@bridgeinteriors.co.uk *Bridge Interiors is an interiors contracting company involved in the fitting out and refurbishment of industrial and commercial interiors, specializing in the installation of suspended ceilings, demountable partitioning and design led turnkey projects.*

▶ Bridge Consultants, 19 Beck Ford, Teal Farm, Washington, Tyne & Wear, NE38 8TP Tel: (07967) 383105 Fax: (0870) 1692863 E-mail: enquiries@bridgeconsultants.co.uk *Bridge Consultants are the experts in the implementation and maintenance of quality - ISO9000, environmental - ISO14001, and health and safety management systems.*

▶ Bridge County, 25 Francis Street, Hull, HU2 8DT Tel: (01482) 588288 Fax: (01482) 588388 *Manufacture of educational furniture*

Bridge Engineering Ltd, Station Road, Thorney, Peterborough, PE6 0QE Tel: (01733) 270308 Fax: (01733) 270985 E-mail: bridgeeng@btopenworld.com *Fork lift truck attachment manufrs*

Bridge Greenhouses Ltd, Keynor Farm, Keynor Lane, Sidlesham, Chichester, West Sussex, PO20 7NQ Tel: (01243) 641789 Fax: (01243) 641788 E-mail: south@bridgegreenhouses.co.uk *Commercial greenhouse manufrs*

▶ Bridge Hall Stockbrokers Ltd, Fairbank House, 27 Ashley Road, Altrincham, Cheshire, WA14 2DP Tel: 0161-927 9568 Fax: (0845) 9289287 E-mail: info@bridgehall.co.uk *Share Dealing from £17.50 for telephone dealing. Certificated trading available and self-select ISA, PEP and SIPP accounts provided.*

Bridge House Services Ltd, Rectory House, Maltings Lane, Ingham, Bury St. Edmunds, Suffolk, IP31 1NS Tel: (01284) 728100 Fax: (0870) 1671963 *Computer services*

James Bridge Steel Services Ltd, B S A Business Park, Armoury Road, Birmingham, B11 2RQ Tel: 0121-753 4444 Fax: 0121-753 4446 E-mail: sales@steelplates.co.uk *Steel plate stockholders & processors*

Bridge Joinery, Unit 1, Limberline Spur, Hilsea, Portsmouth, PO3 5HJ Tel: (023) 9266 6479 Fax: (023) 9266 6479 *Joinery manufrs*

Bridge Metals Birmingham Ltd, 4 Landor Street, Birmingham, B8 1AE Tel: 0121-359 6991 *Non-ferrous scrap metal merchants*

Bridge Musical Instruments Ltd, 28 Boston Road, Sleaford, Lincolnshire, NG34 7ET Tel: (01529) 415372 Fax: (01529) 415372 E-mail: sales@electricviolins.com *Stringed instruments manufrs*

Bridge Steel Sections, PO Box 92, Smethwick, West Midlands, B66 2PA Tel: 0121-555 1460 Fax: 0121-555 1461 E-mail: sales.ssl@hadleygroup.co.uk *Cold rolled steel sections & metal purlin manufrs*

Bridge Steel Sections Ltd, Ridgeacre Road, West Bromwich, West Midlands, B71 1BB Tel: 0121-553 6771 Fax: 0121-556 6325 E-mail: sales.bss@hadleygroup.co.uk *Steel section manufrs*

Bridge Of Weir Leather Co. Ltd, 98 Kilbarchan Road, Bridge of Weir, Renfrewshire, PA11 3RH Tel: (01505) 612132 Fax: (01505) 614964 E-mail: mail@bowleather.co.uk *Leather upholstery manufrs*

▶ Bridgeford and Associates, 54 Richmond Road, Cambridge, CB4 3PT Tel: (07977) 613207 E-mail: michaeljgfjennings@yahoo.de *Books & spare parts for kitchen appliances*

Bridgeforth Engineering, Unit 13-14, Belleknowes Industrial Estate, Inverkeithing, Fife, KY11 1HZ Tel: (01383) 413441 Fax: (01383) 418391 E-mail: sales@bridgefothl.co.uk *Sub-contract precision machinists*

▶ Bridgehead Software Ltd, 215 Barnett Wood Lane, Ashtead, Surrey, KT21 2DD Tel: (01372) 221950 Fax: (01372) 221977 E-mail: bridgehead@bridgeheadsoftware.com *Data backup services*

Bridgelock Engineering & Marketing Ltd, 137 Slough Road, Datchet, Slough, SL3 9AE Tel: (01753) 549373 Fax: (01753) 580269 E-mail: sales@bridgelock.com Principal Export Areas: Worldwide *Identification systems suppliers*

▶ Bridgemary Library, 74 Brewers Lane, Gosport, Hampshire, PO13 0LA Tel: (0845) 6035631 Fax: (01329) 511390 E-mail: bridgemaryaquatics@ntlworld.com *Aquarium & pond specialists,massive selection fish foods, treatments, equipment,air pumps' aquarium filters, pond pumps & fish care products for goldfish, pond fish & tropical aquariums 17 ponds 64 tropical aquariums 6 coldwater aquariums tropica aquarium plants & reptile food & accessories.*

Bridgend Boat Co., Western Hangar, Lawrence Road, Plymouth, PL9 9SJ Tel: (01752) 404082 Fax: (01752) 403405 *Boat building*

▶ Bridgend Joinery, Lake District Business Park, Mint Bridge Road, Kendal, Cumbria, LA9 6NH Tel: (01539) 738387 Fax: (01539) 738388 *Joinery manufrs*

Bridgend Printers Edinburgh Ltd, 40 Constitution Street, Edinburgh, EH6 6RS Tel: 0131-554 3883 Fax: 0131-555 0516 *Commercial printing services*

John Bridger Marine, Haven Road, Exeter, EX2 8DP Tel: (01392) 250970 Fax: (01392) 410955 E-mail: bridgermarine@btconnect.com *Yacht chandlers & marine engineers*

Bridger & Co Office Interiors, South Ease Cottage, Send Marsh Road, Ripley, Woking, Surrey, GU23 6JQ Tel: (01483) 224920 Fax: (01483) 211599 *Office designers & partition contractors*

Bridger Packaging, Avenue One, Letchworth Garden City, Hertfordshire, SG6 2WP Tel: (01462) 636465 Fax: (01462) 636433 E-mail: postmaster@bridger.co.uk *Carton manufrs*

Bridges of Minworth, Kingsbury Road, Minworth, Sutton Coldfield, West Midlands, B76 9DD Tel: 0121-351 1965 Fax: 0121-351 7793 E-mail: sales@bridges-bridmin.co.uk *Contractors plant & HGV sales*

Bridgeshire Packaging Ltd, 1 Wimsey Way, Alfreton Trading Estate, Somercotes, Alfreton, Derbyshire, DE55 4LS Tel: (01773) 601000 Fax: (01773) 606075 E-mail: sales@bridgeshire.co.uk *Packaging designers & manufrs*

Bridgestone Industrial Ltd, 2nd Floor West, CP House, 97 -107 Uxbridge Road, Ealing, London, W5 5TL Tel: (020) 8567 8080 Fax: (020) 8567 2066 E-mail: info@bsil.co.uk Principal Export Areas: Worldwide *Rubber foam product industrial manufrs*

Bridgestone UK Ltd, Athena Drive, Tachbrook Park, Warwick, CV34 6UX Tel: (01926) 488500 Fax: (01926) 488600 E-mail: bfuk.reception@bridgestone-eu.com *Tyre manufrs*

Bridgewater Computers, 42 Green End, Whitchurch, Shropshire, SY13 1AA Tel: (01948) 666630 Fax: (01948) 666630 E-mail: bridgewatermcg@aol.com *Computer suppliers & manufrs*

▶ Emma Bridgewater Ltd, Eastwood Pottery, Lichfield Street, Stoke-on-Trent, ST1 3EJ Tel: (01782) 201200 Fax: (01782) 271508 *Pottery manufrs*

Bridgewater Europe Ltd, 132 Windmill Rd, Gillingham, Kent, ME7 5PD Tel: (01634) 311717 Fax: (01634) 310632 E-mail: riaz@zoom.co.uk *Inport and export merchants*

Bridgewater Glass, 44-52 Vicarage Road, Watford, WD18 0EN Tel: (01923) 237533 Fax: (01923) 817118 E-mail: bridgewaterglass@aol.com *Glazing contractors & glass merchants*

Bridgewater International Recruitment Direct, 109 Bodmin Road, Astley, Tyldesley, Manchester, M29 7PE Tel: (01942) 873158 Fax: (01942) 896946 E-mail: birdrecruit@blueyonder.co.uk *Bridgewater International recruits western trained nurses, midwives and doctors to tax free positions in the Emirates, Oman, Bahrain and Saudi. There is also some recruitment to Australia and New Zealand. Middle East positions have free accommodation, free flights and end of contract bonuses. Contact us by Email or phone for a fast, friendly service. We do NOT charge recruits for our services.*

Bridgewater Software Development, Audley House, Northbridge Road, Berkhamsted, Hertfordshire, HP4 1EH Tel: (01442) 870244 Fax: (01442) 879993 E-mail: info@bridgewater.it *It consultancy, bespoke software development*

Bridgewell Ltd, Old Change House, 128 Queen Victoria Street, London, EC4V 4BJ Tel: (020) 7003 3000 Fax: (020) 7369 0301 *Institution stock brokers*

Bridgeworks Ltd, 135 Summerford Road, Christchurch, Dorset, BH23 3PY Tel: (01425) 478811 Fax: (0870) 1210709 E-mail: sales@4bridgeworks.com *Storage area networks*

Bridgford Pressings Ltd, Building No. 3 Gotham Business Complex, Leake Road, Gotham, Nottingham, NG11 0LB Tel: 0115-983 0884 Fax: 0115-983 0155 E-mail: enquiries@bridgfordpressings.co.uk *Metal pressing services*

Bridgland Moulders Ltd, Rectory Road, Ashmanhaugh, Norwich, NR12 8YP Tel: (01603) 783130 Fax: (01603) 783701 *GRP mouldings manufrs*

Bridgman, Market Fields, Kilkhampton, Bude, Cornwall, EX23 9QZ Tel: (01288) 321777 Fax: (01288) 321211 E-mail: info@bridgmans.co.uk *Agricultural merchants*

Bridgnorth Castings Ltd, Alveley Industrial Estate, Alveley, Bridgnorth, Shropshire, WV15 6HG Tel: (01746) 781177 Fax: (01746) 781188 E-mail: vp32@dial.pipex.com *Aluminium casting & machining services*

▶ Bridgnorth Transport Co. Ltd, Stourbridge Road, Bridgnorth, Shropshire, WV15 6AN Tel: (01746) 762681 Fax: (01746) 765152

Bridgwater Electronics Ltd, Unit 15 Westmans Industrial Estate, Love Lane, Burnham-on-Sea, Somerset, TA8 1EY Tel: (01278) 789552 Fax: (01278) 789782 E-mail: sales@bridgwater-electronics.co.uk *Offering an automotive electronics design & manufacturing service and a large range of automotive electronic products. Electronic vehicle security devices such as alarms, immobilisers and Thatcham Approved systems,*

continued

Universal central locking modules, solar powered battery trickle chargers, CAN Bus interfaces, power supplies, reversing/parking sensors, vehicle tracking systems and speed conversion/ sensing/alarm products. In-house design capability, offering custom-designed solutions, supported by our UK manufacturing facilities.

Bridgwater Glass, Unit 2-3 Park View, Gallamore Lane, Market Rasen, Lincolnshire, LN8 3HZ Tel: (01673) 842388 Fax: (01673) 842388 *Double glazing, UPVC windows & doors*

Bridgwater Joinery Ltd, Crofton Drive, Allenby Industrial Estate, Lincoln, LN3 4NR Tel: (01522) 546699 Fax: (01522) 546644 E-mail: joinery@bridgwater.fsbusiness.co.uk *Joinery manufrs*

Bridgwater Metalcraft Ltd, Brue Avenue, Bridgwater, Somerset, TA6 5LT Tel: (01278) 452867 Fax: (01278) 423167 *Sheet metalwork & fabricators*

Bridgwater Pallets Ltd, 13 Parrett Way, Colley Lane Industrial Estate, Bridgwater, Somerset, TA6 5LB Tel: (01278) 444039 Fax: (01278) 446888 *Pallet recovery services*

Bridgwater Warehousing Co. Ltd, Colley Lane Industrial Estate, Bridgwater, Somerset, TA6 5LN Tel: (01278) 424921 Fax: (01278) 431168 *Warehousing contractors*

Bridgwaters Ltd, Unit 19 Excelsior Works, Rollins Street, London, SE15 1EP Tel: (020) 7639 2003 Fax: (020) 7252 9627 *Roofing contractors*

Bridisco Ltd, Devonshire House, 550 White Hart Lane, London, N17 7RQ Tel: (020) 8881 2001 Fax: (020) 8829 9210 *Electrical distributors*

Bridle Way At Gauntleys, Mill House, Laneham Road, Dunham-on-Trent, Newark, Nottinghamshire, NG22 0UW Tel: (01777) 228040 Fax: (01777) 228977 *Saddlery retailers*

▶ Bridledene Steel Fabricators, Little Marsh Quarter, Sandhurst, Cranbrook, Kent, TN18 5NY Tel: (01580) 850860 Fax: (01580) 850870 E-mail: info@bridledene.com *Storage facilities manufrs*

Bridley Equestrian Centre, Berry Lane, Worplesdon, Guildford, Surrey, GU3 3QG Tel: (01483) 232272 Fax: (01483) 232070 E-mail: pan.edwards@bridleyec.demon.co.uk *Agricultural contractors*

▶ Bridon, Denmore Road, Bridge of Don, Aberdeen, AB23 8JW Tel: (01224) 822288 Fax: (01224) 708573 E-mail: sales@bridon.com *Lifting gear hirers & inspection service providers*

Bridon Wire Special Steels Division, Sheephouse Wood, Stocksbridge, Sheffield, S36 4GS Tel: 0114-288 4207 Fax: 0114-288 4874 *Stainless & alloy steel wire & bar*

▶ Bridoon, Heywood Equestrian Centre, Westbury, Wiltshire, BA13 4LP Tel: (01985) 848485 *Equestrian equipment suppliers*

▶ Brier Construction Ltd, Upper Whittimere Cottage, Upper Whittimere, Bobbington, Stourbridge, West Midlands, DY7 5EP Tel: (01384) 221298 Fax: (01384) 221268

Brierley Bros Ltd, Albert Mills, Albert Street, Huddersfield, HD1 3PZ Tel: (01484) 426511 Fax: (01484) 430244 E-mail: office@brierleybrothers.com *Woollen yarn spinners*

Brierley Hill Glass Co. Ltd, Mount Pleasant, Quarry Bank, Brierley Hill, West Midlands, DY5 2YS Tel: (01384) 77486 Fax: (01384) 77486 E-mail: sales@brierleycrystal.com Principal Export Areas: Worldwide *Lead crystal glassware manufrs*

Brierley Lifting Tackle Co. Ltd, Timmis Road, Lye, Stourbridge, West Midlands, DY9 7BQ Tel: (01384) 893000 Fax: (01384) 898000 E-mail: brilift@aol.com *Lifting gear distributors*

Brierley Machine Tools Ltd, Ferry Farm Road, Llandudno Junction, Gwynedd, LL31 9SF Tel: (01492) 581777 Fax: (01492) 592558 *Machine toolmakers*

▶ Briers Horticultural Equipment, 1 St. Martins Courtyard, Chapel Lane, Zeals, Warminster, Wiltshire, BA12 6NZ Tel: (0870) 8015650 Fax: (0870) 8015651 E-mail: sales@briersuk.com *Gardening equipment*

W.M. Briers & Son (Tamworth) Ltd, Anchor Siding, Glascote Road, Tamworth, Staffordshire, B77 2AN Tel: (01827) 62668 Fax: (01827) 53721 E-mail: equiries@wmbriers.co.uk *Scrap iron merchants*

Brifrost Engineering, 9 The Drive, Wheathampstead, St. Albans, Hertfordshire, AL4 8LE Tel: (01438) 832402 Fax: (01438) 833526 *Air conditioning engineers*

Brigg Motor Springs Ltd, 79 Bridge Street, Brigg, South Humberside, DN20 8NF Tel: (01652) 653280 Fax: (01652) 659029 *Spring manufrs*

▶ Briggs Accountancy Services, Congleton, Cheshire, CW12 3WT Tel: (01260) 270620 E-mail: allisons3s@aol.com *Bookkeeping final accounts, profit & loss, payroll services*

Alfred Briggs (Alwood) Ltd, PO Box 6, Lurgan, County Armagh, BT66 8DD Tel: (028) 3832 3296 Fax: (028) 3832 4256 E-mail: mail@alwood.co.uk *Kitchen & bedroom manufrs*

Brian Briggs, 58-60 Chadwick Road, Sheffield, S13 8DF Tel: 0114-247 5288 Fax: 0114-247 5288 E-mail: sales@briggs-snooker.co.uk *Snooker table repairers*

Briggs Bros Engineers Ltd, 39 Walkers Road, Moons Moat North Industrial Estate, Redditch, Worcestershire, B98 9HD Tel: (01527) 66779 Fax: (01527) 596130 E-mail: sales@briggsairmotors.com *Pneumatic motor manufrs*

Briggs Environmental Services Ltd, Leading Light Building, 142 Sinclair Road, Aberdeen, AB11 9PR Tel: (01224) 898666 Fax: (01224) 896950 E-mail: marketing@briggsmarine.com Principal Export Areas: Worldwide *Environmental consultants & testing services*

George Briggs & Son, Wirswall, Whitchurch, Shropshire, SY13 4LF Tel: (01948) 663733 *Livestock farmers*

Briggs Holdings Ltd, Briggs House, Derby Street, Burton-on-Trent, Staffordshire, DE14 2LH Tel: (01283) 566661 Fax: (01283) 545978 *Food process plant manufrs*

▶ Briggs Kidz Ltd, 38 Kirkintilloch Road, Bishopbriggs, Glasgow, G64 2AL Tel: 0141-772 3322 Fax: 0141-772 3322

Briggs Land Drainage & Excavations Ltd, Liley Lane, Mirfield, West Yorkshire, WF14 8EB Tel: (01924) 492588 Fax: (01924) 491545 *Land drainage contractors*

Briggs Marine Contractors Ltd, West Dock, Seaforth Place, Burntisland, Fife, KY3 9AU Tel: (01592) 872939 Fax: (01592) 873975 *Marine contractors*

Briggs & Partner Ltd, The Storth, Huddersfield Road, Elland, West Yorkshire, HX5 9JR Tel: (01422) 372515 Fax: (01422) 311093 E-mail: briggs@zen.co.uk *Contractors plant hirers*

Briggs Priestley Ltd, 1-3 Lord Street, Halifax, West Yorkshire, HX1 5AE Tel: (01422) 354565 Fax: (01422) 356687 E-mail: dan@briggspriestley.ndo.co.uk *Engravers, signmakers & silk screen printers*

Briggs & Stratton Power Products Group, Road Four, Winsford Industrial Estate, Winsford, Cheshire, CW7 3QN Tel: (01606) 862182 Fax: (01606) 862201 *Portable generating sets*

Briggs Trading Co Southern Ltd, Ebblake Industrial Estate, 21 Blackmoor Road, Verwood, Dorset, BH31 6AX Tel: (01202) 825555 Fax: (01202) 823980 E-mail: enquiries@briggsproducts.com *Production wood turners*

Briggs William & Co., Unit 52 Halliwell Industrial Estate, Rossini Street, Bolton, BL1 8DL Tel: (01204) 599100 Fax: (01204) 599149 *Needlecrafts manufrs*

▶ Briggsbits.co.uk, Hutton Garden Centre, Banwell Road, Hutton, Weston-super-Mare, North Somerset, BS24 9UB Tel: (01934) 813261 Fax: (01934) 815356 E-mail: graham@westongm.eclipse.co.uk *The online store for Briggs and Stratton spares and Briggs and Stratton service spare parts including parts lookup diagrams.*

Brighouse Engineering Ltd, Martin House, 2 Martin Street, Brighouse, West Yorkshire, HD6 1DA Tel: (01484) 719999 Fax: (01484) 720422 E-mail: brigeng@compuserve.com *Materials handling engineers & consultants*

Bright A Blind Ltd, Unit 5, 1-3 North Road, London, N7 9HA Tel: (020) 7700 6000 Fax: (020) 7700 6303 E-mail: info@brightablind.com *Window blind cleaning services*

Bright Cook & Co Shipbrokers Ltd, 139 Upper Richmond Road, London, SW15 2TX Tel: (020) 8785 4288 Fax: (020) 8785 2571 E-mail: ships@brightcook.com *Ship sales & purchase*

Bright Designs, Station Road, Mexborough, South Yorkshire, S64 9AQ Tel: (01709) 570838 Fax: (01709) 570838 *Lighting manufrs*

Bright Enterprises Ltd, Enterprise House, London Road, West Kingsdown, Sevenoaks, Kent, TN15 6AP Tel: (01474) 852222 Fax: (01474) 853944 E-mail: sales@rfbright.co.uk *Polyurethane production machinery*

▶ Bright Eyes Nanny Agency, 11 Gatley Drive, Guildford, Surrey, GU4 7JJ Tel: (01483) 506150 Fax: 01483 506150 E-mail: Brighteyesnannys@aol.com *Established 1987 to provide a much needed quality Nanny / Childcare service. We pride ourselves 90% of our business is generated by recommendation.*

▶ Bright Green Energy, 26 Woodmere Way, Beckenham, Kent, BR3 6SL Tel: (020) 8663 3273 Fax: (020) 8650 9037 E-mail: sales@brightgreenenergy.co.uk *Renewable energy products suppliers, designers & installers*

Bright Instrument Co. Ltd, St. Margarets Way, Stukeley Meadows Industrial Estate, Huntingdon, Cambridgeshire, PE29 6EU Tel: (01480) 454528 Fax: (01480) 456031 E-mail: sales@brightinstruments.com *Scientific instrument manufrs*

▶ Bright Lemon Ltd, Unit 12, Zeus House, London, N1 7NG Tel: (020) 7608 2838 E-mail: info@brightlemon.com *Development solutions & products*

▶ Bright Look Fashions, 33-35 Mere Lane, Rochdale, Lancashire, OL11 3TD Tel: (01706) 345322 Fax: (01706) 711611 *Manufacturers of children's & ladies clothing*

Malcolm Bright Haulage, 18 Castlefields Industrial Estate, Bingley, West Yorkshire, BD16 2AG Tel: (01274) 561994 Fax: (01274) 566665 *Road transport, haulage & freight services*

▶ Bright New World, 3 Woodbrook Crescent, Billericay, Essex, CM12 0EQ Tel: (01277) 656200 Fax: (01277) 653342 *Computer systems consultants*

Bright Screw Co. Ltd, Bagley Lane, Rodley, Leeds, LS13 1JB Tel: 0113-256 4166 Fax: 0113-239 3480 E-mail: sales@brightscrew.co.uk *Bolt & nut manufrs*

Bright Shade Blinds, 2 Bosden Fold Road, Hazel Grove, Stockport, Cheshire, SK7 4LQ Tel: 0161-487 3901 Fax: 0161-487 3901 *Blind manufrs*

Bright Shades Manufacturer Ltd, High Road, London, NW10 2EA Tel: (020) 8830 0736 Fax: (020) 8830 0736 *Lampshade manufrs*

Bright Spark Ltd, 178-180 Hotwell Road, Bristol, BS8 4RP Tel: 0117-925 9300 Fax: 0117-925 9301 E-mail: sales@bsmg.co.uk *Graphic designers & artists*

▶ Bright Star, 4 Barra Close, Hull, HU8 9JB Tel: (0845) 2578501 Fax: (0845) 2578501 E-mail: info@brightstarwebdesign.co.uk *Custom web design*

Bright Steels Ltd, Norton Works, Malton, North Yorkshire, YO17 9BD Tel: (01653) 694961 Fax: (01653) 695856 E-mail: info@bright-steels.com *Bright steel bars & sections manufrs*

▶ Bright Window Cleaning, 53 Hurdford Drive, Thatcham, Berkshire, RG19 4WA Tel: 07818 403736 E-mail: Info@brightwindowcleaning.co.uk *A quality Thatcham-based domestic window cleaning service offering a friendly, uniformed, reliable service.*

Brightarc Welding, Newlands Farm, Canterbury Road, Selsted, Dover, Kent, CT15 7HL Tel: (01303) 844319 Fax: (01303) 844666 *Steel fabricators*

▶ Brightcast Plant Hire Ltd, 18-22 Hertford Road, London, N1 5SH Tel: (020) 7249 1492 Fax: (020) 7254 6567 E-mail: brightcast@aol.com

Brightcross Insulation Ltd, Shaftesbury Street, Derby, DE23 8XA Tel: (01332) 331808 Fax: (01332) 292697 E-mail: sales@brightcross.co.uk *Insulating material processors*

Brightel Datanet Ltd, Unit 3 Moulsecoomb Way, Brighton, BN2 4PB Tel: (01273) 244400 Fax: (01273) 244410 *Telephone distributors*

Brighter Blinds Ltd, 59 Church Street, Walshaw, Bury, Lancashire, BL8 3BN Tel: (01204) 883301 Fax: (01204) 887073 E-mail: bighterblinds@aol.com *Blind retail & manufrs*

Brighter Blinds & Services, 3 Croft Estate, Glasgow Road, Dennyloanhead, Bonnybridge, Stirlingshire, FK4 1QP Tel: (01324) 840654 Fax: (01324) 840860 E-mail: brighterblinds@blueyonder.co.uk *Blinds manufrs*

▶ Brighter Recruiting, Elmsland House, Kirk Hammerton, York, YO26 8BX Tel: (01423) 331535 Fax: (01423) 331536 E-mail: recruiting@brighter-recruiting.co.uk *Placement of permanent, contract & temporary sales, hr & management*

▶ Brighters, 20 Spring Lane, Cambridge, CB5 9BL Tel: 01223 812549 E-mail: info@brighters.co.uk *A seamless solution for busy people who want a regular housekeeper to help with domestic cleaning and ironing in Cambridgeshire and Bury St Edmunds areas*

Brightmedia Computer Consumables, 3 Chiltern Street, London, W1U 7PB Tel: (020) 7224 3363 Fax: (020) 7224 3373 *Computer consumables*

Brighton Carpet Centre, 102 Preston Drove, Brighton, BN1 6EW Tel: (01273) 564037 Fax: (01273) 561622 E-mail: sales@brightoncarpetcentre.co.uk *Carpet retailers*

Brighton Centre, Kings Road, Brighton, BN1 2GR Tel: (01273) 290131 Fax: (01273) 779980 E-mail: info@brightoncentre.co.uk *Exhibition & entertainments venue*

▶ Brighton Communications Systems, Scallow Wish, Moat Lane, Waldron, Heathfield, East Sussex, TN21 0RT Tel: (01273) 888788 Fax: (0845) 1232934 E-mail: mail@commsdirect.com *Business telephone systems & computer net workers*

Brighton Electrical Assemblies Ltd, Cradle Hill Industrial Estate, Seaford, East Sussex, BN25 3JE Tel: (01323) 893295 Fax: (01323) 897429 E-mail: info@bealtd.co.uk *Electronic equipment manufrs*

Brighton Festival Society Ltd, 29 New Road, Brighton, BN1 1UG Tel: (01273) 700747 Fax: (01273) 707505 E-mail: info@brighton-festival.org.com *Entertainment & conference venue specialists*

Brighton Foam Shop, 99 North Road, Brighton, BN1 1YE Tel: (01273) 606291 Fax: (01273) 606291 *Foam products retail & wholesale*

▶ Brighton & Hove Removals, 190 Portland Road, Hove, East Sussex, BN3 5QN Tel: (01273) 735111 E-mail: sales@brightonandhovekitchens.com *We supply and fit affordable kitchens for everyone. High quality, high standards but not high prices. Free quotes given with complete pre-install computer design so you can see your dream kitchen before the install*

▶ Brighton & Hove Removals, 190 Portland Road, Hove, East Sussex, BN3 5QN Tel: (01273) 735111

▶ Brighton Scaffolding, 98a Pelham Rise, Peacehaven, East Sussex, BN10 8BD Tel: (01273) 691454 E-mail: brightonscaffolding@fsmail.net *Scaffolding Erectors & Hirers*

Brighton Sheet Metal Ltd, The Hyde, Brighton, BN2 4JE Tel: (01273) 602216 Fax: (01273) 674153 E-mail: sales@brightonsheetmetal.co.uk *Sheet metal fabricators*

Brighton Sign Co., Foredown House, 2-4 Foredown Drive, Portslade, Brighton, BN41 2BB Tel: (01273) 424900 Fax: (01273) 412006 E-mail: sales@brightonsigns.co.uk *Sign manufrs*

Brighton Systems Ltd, Unit 24 Euro Business Park, New Road, Newhaven, East Sussex, BN9 0DQ Tel: (01273) 515563 Fax: (01273) 611533 E-mail: sales@brightonsystems.co.uk *Biotechnological plant & equipment manufrs*

Brighton Tools & Fixings Ltd, 7 Centenary Industrial Estate, Hughes Road, Brighton, BN2 4AW Tel: (01273) 620456 Fax: (01273) 620611 E-mail: info@brightontools.co.uk *Distribution Of Tools*

Brights Of Nettlebed, The Old Gaol, The Strand, Topsham, Exeter, EX3 0JB Tel: (01392) 877443 Fax: (01392) 877633 *Furniture manufrs*

Brights Of Nettlebed, 61-63 Leigh Road, Wimborne, Dorset, BH21 1AE Tel: (01202) 884613 Fax: (01202) 885679 E-mail: enquiries@brightsofnettlebed.com *Furniture reproduction*

Brightside Industries Ltd, Empire Works, Brewery Lane, Thornhill Lees, Dewsbury, West Yorkshire, WF12 9HQ Tel: (01924) 455717 Fax: (01924) 450220 E-mail: bsind@globalnet.co.uk *Machinery dealers*

▶ Brightspark, 1 Blackthorn Court, Soham, Ely, Cambridgeshire, CB7 5DT Tel: (01353) 723902 Fax: (01353) 723902 E-mail: info@brightspark-recruitment.co.uk *Recruitment in Cambridgeshire and Suffolk **Dedicated to finding the right people for work and the right work for people **Based in Cambridgeshire, BrightSpark is ideally situated to provide a full recruitment service to the entire Cambridgeshire and Suffolk region.**Specialising in providing staff for full and part time office support roles, from Junior to Management positions - Not forgetting all other vital roles included in the running of an office*

▶ Brightspark Precision Engineering Ltd, 3 Carrside, Lomeshaye Industrial Estate, Nelson, Lancashire, BB9 6RX Tel: (01282) 613444 E-mail: brightsp@globalnet.co.uk *Precision engineering*

The Brightstart Company Services Ltd, Kersal, Woodlands Lane, Windlesham, Surrey, GU20 6AH Tel: (01276) 850644 Fax: (0870) 1384969 E-mail: promotions@brightstart.plus.com *Sales promotion recruitment*

Brightview Blinds, 91 Charlock Way, Watford, WD18 6JT Tel: (01923) 243392 Fax: (01923) 231092 *Blind*

Brightwake Ltd, Sidings Road, Lowmoor Industrial Estate, Kirkby-in-Ashfield, Nottingham, NG17 7JZ Tel: (01623) 751151 Fax: (01623) 757636 E-mail: sales@brightwake.co.uk *Hospital & medical supplies manufrs*

Brightwater Engineering, Unit 2 The Business Centre, Avenue One, Letchworth, Letchworth Garden City, Hertfordshire, SG6 2HB Tel: (01462) 485005 Fax: (01462) 485003 E-mail: enquiries@brightwater.uk.com *Sewage treatment plant equipment manufrs*

Brightwell Warehouse, 11 Barr Street, Birmingham, B19 3EH Tel: 0121-236 2112 Fax: 0121-236 2112 E-mail: manj97@hotmail.com *Clothing wholesalers*

▶ Briliant Products, PO Box 7956, Chelmsford, CM2 9WG Tel: (0870) 2403853 E-mail: info@briliant.biz *Briliant metal polish for polishing and cleaning aluminium, silver, gold, brass, bronze, chrome, stainless steel, copper and bronze.*

J.H. Brill & Son Ltd, 1A Merivale Rd, Putney, London, United Kingdom, SW15 2NW Tel: (020) 8788 2217 Fax: (020) 8788 5800 E-mail: info@brillandson.co.uk *Zinc & copper roofing contractors we also undertake slating & tiling*

▶ Brilliant Hi Fi, 35 Cumberland Road, Urmston, Manchester, M41 9HR Tel: (07963) 117341 E-mail: sales@brilliancehifi.co.uk *Brilliance Hi-Fi manufacture well reviewed hi-fi interconnects, speaker cables and video leads for both audio and home theatre enthusiasts alike through carefully selected dealerships or direct. The comprehensive and co-ordinated range of Teflon-insulated cables includes digital and audio interconnects, (RCA and XLR), video leads and speaker cables, with offerings to suit the requirements of both the entry level and advanced audiophile.*

Brilliant Signs & Fabrications, Unit 2 Forty Green, Bledlow, Princes Risborough, Buckinghamshire, HP27 9PN Tel: (01844) 273602 Fax: (0871) 4330112 E-mail: peter.snellgrove@brilliant-signs.com *Sign manufrs*

Brilliant Stages Ltd, 2 Hillgate, Hitchin, Hertfordshire, SG4 0RY Tel: (01462) 455366 Fax: (01462) 436219 E-mail: sales@brilliantstages.com *Stage & concert fabricators*

Brilliant (UK) Ltd, Hanworth Trading Estate, Hampton Road West, Feltham, Middlesex, TW13 6DR Tel: (020) 8898 3131 Fax: (020) 8898 3232 E-mail: sales@brilliant-ag.com *Domestic lighting manufrs*

Brillopak, 29 Victory Park, Trident Close, Rochester, Kent, ME2 4ER Tel: (01634) 295050 Fax: 01825 840882 E-mail: info@brillopak.co.uk *Engineering designers and manufacturers, specialists in factory automation - pick and place systems, pallet dispensers, pallet pushers, pallet/load presses, specialist conveyors, turntables, specialist manipulators, robot palletising/ automation systems, bag-lifting heads and pick-up/station conveyors.*

▶ Bri-Mac Engineering Ltd, Unit 2 Stambermill Works, Bagley Street, Lye, Stourbridge, West Midlands, DY9 7AR Tel: (01384) 423030 Fax: (01384) 422774 E-mail: sales@bri-mac.co.uk *Designer & manufacturer of bearing housings*

▶ Brimak Joinery Manufacturers, Unit 5 Wood Lane, Rothwell, Leeds, LS26 0RS Tel: 0113-393 4392

Brimalk Ltd, Unit 8, Apollo, Lichfield Road Industrial Estate, Tamworth, Staffordshire, B79 7TA Tel: (01827) 51550 Fax: (01827) 51188 E-mail: sales@brimalk.co.uk *Air conditioning engineers*

Briman Contracts Ltd, Unit 2b Building B Wembley Commercial Centre, East Lane, Wembley, Middlesex, HA9 7UR Tel: (020) 8908 0102 Fax: (020) 8904 0664 E-mail: info@briman.co.uk *Manufacture stage curtains & blinds*

Brimar Ltd, Greenside Way, Middleton, Manchester, M24 1SN Tel: 0161-681 7072 Fax: 0161-683 5978 E-mail: dave.eldridge@brimar.ltd.uk *Electronics designers & manufrs*

Brimar Plastic Ltd, North Road, Yate, Bristol, BS37 7PR Tel: (01454) 322111 Fax: (01454) 316955 E-mail: brimar@brimarplastics.co.uk *Water storage tank manufrs*

Brimglades Ltd, 1 Deans Factory Estate, Lambs Lane, Rainham, Essex, RM13 9XL Tel: (01708) 552085 Fax: (01708) 520237 *Shop fitting manufrs*

Brimor Engineering Ltd, Blandford Heights, Blandford Forum, Dorset, DT11 7TE Tel: (01258) 452222 Fax: (01258) 480320 *Precision engineers*

Brimotor Ltd, 10-12 Culverden Down, Tunbridge Wells, Kent, TN4 9SA Tel: (01892) 537588 Fax: (01892) 527724 E-mail: info@brimotor.co.uk *Generator, pump, floodlight & engine manufrs*

Brimset Ltd, 2 Stocks Lane, Rawmarsh, Rotherham, South Yorkshire, S62 6NL Tel: (01709) 522270 Fax: (01709) 527240 E-mail: contracts@brimset.f9.co.uk *Structural fire protection*

Brimur Packaging Ltd, 1-3 Hostmoor Avenue, March Industrial Estate, March, Cambridgeshire, PE15 0AX Tel: (01354) 658585 Fax: (01354) 653780 *Corrugated packaging manufrs*

Brinard Joinery Ltd, 257 Somercotes Hill, Somercotes, Alfreton, Derbyshire, DE55 4HX Tel: (01773) 608693 Fax: (01773) 540743 *Joinery manufrs*

Brindley Lift Truck Services Ltd, Unit 4, Aston Lane, Sharnford, Hinckley, Leicestershire, LE10 3PA Tel: (01455) 272800 Fax: (01455) 274712 E-mail: rhayes@lift-truck.co.uk *Fork lift truck hire & leasing*

Brindley Twist Tafft & James, Lowick Gate Coventry Trading Estate, Siskin Drive, Middlemarch Business Park, Coventry, CV3 4FJ Tel: (024) 7653 1532 Fax: (024) 7630 1300 E-mail: admin@bttj.com *Solicitors & debt recovery services*

Brineton Engineering Co., Alma Street, Walsall, WS2 8JQ Tel: (01922) 620070 Fax: (01922) 722875 E-mail: sales@brineton-eng.co.uk *General engineers*

Bringate Sheet Metals, Cross Green Industrial Estate, Cross Green, Leeds, LS9 0SG Tel: 0113-240 7711 Fax: 0113-240 7722 E-mail: sales@bringate.co.uk *Fencing panels manufrs*

Bringover Ltd, Unit 6, Boathouse Lane, Stockton-On-Tees, Cleveland, TS18 3AW Tel: (01642) 605111 Fax: (01642) 615880 E-mail: bringover@bringovr.demon.co.uk *Machinery repair service*

▶ Brink (UK) Ltd, Unit 7 Centrovell Industrial E, Caldwell Road, Nuneaton, Warwickshire, CV11 4NG Tel: (024) 7635 2353

Brinksway Electro Plating Ltd, Unit 17 Latham Close, Bredbury Park Industrial Estate, Bredbury, Stockport, Cheshire, SK6 2SD Tel: 0161-494 6161 Fax: 0161-406 6447 *Plating services*

Brinsmoor Solutions, Unit 2 Aerial Way, Hucknall, Nottingham, NG15 6DW Tel: 0115-964 0961 Fax: 0115-964 1819 *Sign manufrs*

Brintex Ltd, 32 Vauxhall Bridge Road, London, SW1V 2SS Tel: (020) 7973 6404 Fax: (020) 7233 5054 E-mail: sales@brintex.com *Exhibition organisers*

Brintons Carpets (U S A) Ltd, PO Box 16, Kidderminster, Worcestershire, DY10 1AG Tel: (01562) 820000 Fax: (01562) 634540 E-mail: solutions@brintons.co.uk *Carpet manufrs* Also at: Bristol, Glasgow, London, Manchester & Newcastle

Brio Ltd, Sutton House, Bishop Meadow Road, Loughborough, Leicestershire, LE11 5RE Tel: (01509) 231874 Fax: (01509) 234547 E-mail: info@brio.co.uk *Wooden toy distributors*

Brioni UK Ltd, 32 Britton Street, London, EC1M 5UH Tel: (020) 7491 7701 Fax: (020) 7491 7701 *Italian clothing manufrs*

Bripak UK Ltd, Delta Works, Devonshire Road, Eccles, Manchester, M30 0WX Tel: 0161-787 8770 Fax: 0161-707 0009 *Pallets & heavy duty packaging plywood boxes manufrs*

Bripat Engineering, Unit 7 Steel Close, Eaton Socon, St. Neots, Cambridgeshire, PE19 8TT Tel: (01480) 211322 Fax: (01480) 210761 E-mail: brian.raffaelli@btconnect.com *Steel fabrication*

Brisbane Moss Corduroys Corduroy Manufacturers, Halifax Road, Bridgeroyd Works, Todmorden, Lancashire, OL14 6DF Tel: (01706) 815121 Fax: (01706) 818598 E-mail: brimoss@brisbanemoss.co.uk *Corduroy cloth & cotton fabric manufrs*

Brisbay Plastics Ltd, Adamsez Industrial Estate, Scotswood Road, Newcastle upon Tyne, NE15 6XA Tel: 0191-274 4774 Fax: 0191-228 0146 E-mail: steve@brisbay.co.uk *Plastics fabricators*

▶ Brisco Trading Ltd, Old Bankend Farm House, Touch, Stirling, FK8 3AD Tel: (01786) 474114 Fax: (01786) 474114

Brisco Waste Disposal Ltd, 87 Ystrad Road, Fforestfach, Swansea, SA5 4BU Tel: (01792) 584585 Fax: (01792) 586811 *Waste disposal merchants*

Brissco Signs & Graphics, 25 Cater Road, Bristol, BS13 7TX Tel: 0117-311 3777 Fax: 0117-311 6777 E-mail: sales@brissco.co.uk *Screen printers* Also at: Cardiff & Great Yarmouth

Bristan Group Ltd, 30 Lagrange, Lichfield Road Industrial Estate, Tamworth, Staffordshire, B79 7XD Tel: (01827) 68525 Fax: (01827) 68553 E-mail: enquire@bristan.com *Bathroom taps, showers & mixers suppliers*

Bristlecone UK Ltd, Fulton House, Fulton Road, Wembley, Middlesex, HA9 0TF Tel: (0870) 7368880 Fax: (0870) 7368889 E-mail: sunilk@bcone.co.uk *Software company*

Bristlewand Ltd, 48 Ashton Vale Road, Bristol, BS3 2HQ Tel: 0117-963 6141 Fax: 0117-963 1954 E-mail: bristlewand@kennygroup.co.uk *Building & civil engineers*

Bristol Acoustic Ceilings Ltd, 40 Shellards Road, Longwell Green, Bristol, BS30 9DU Tel: 0117-932 2073 Fax: 0117-932 9950 *Suspended ceilings installation*

▶ Bristol Angling Centre, 12-16 Doncaster Road, Bristol, BS10 5PL Tel: 0117-950 0201 Fax: 0117-959 2799 E-mail: admin@bristolangling.co.uk *On-line and retail fishing tackle, all the top brands at discount prices*

Bristol Batteries Ltd, 3 Dove Lane, St. Pauls, Bristol, BS2 9HP Tel: 0117-955 0536 Fax: 0117-935 1791 E-mail: admin@bristolbatteries.com *Battery & charger distributors*

Bristol Batteries, Axis Business Centre, Westmead Trading Estate, Westmead, Swindon, SN5 7YS Tel: (01793) 616646 Fax: (01793) 490011 E-mail: sales@bristolbatteries.com *Specialist battery distributors*

Bristol Bending Sanoh Ltd, Fourth Way, Bristol, BS11 8DL Tel: 0117-982 8260 Fax: 0117-982 2040 *Bend tubular components suppliers for the car industry*

▶ Bristol Bending Sanoh Ltd, Quedgeley Court, Shepherd Road, Gloucester, GL2 5EL Tel: (01452) 303062 Fax: (01452) 300575 *Brake pipe manufrs*

▶ Bristol Blue Glass Ltd, 7 Whitby Road, Bristol, BS4 3QF Tel: 0117-972 0888 Fax: 0117-972 1050 E-mail: bristolblueglass@bristol-glass.co.uk *Glass manufacturers free blown*

Bristol Boats Ltd, Mead Lane, Saltford, Bristol, BS31 3ER Tel: (01225) 872032 Fax: (01225) 872032 *Boat retailers*

Bristol Bouncy Castles Ltd, 22 Green Dragon Road, Winterbourn, Bristol, BS36 5EH Tel: (07796) 775522 Fax: (01454) 778888 *Bouncy castles & inflatable hire*

Bristol Business Cards, Cater Road, Bridge House, Bristol, BS13 7TW Tel: 0117-978 4777 *Printed & embossed plastic card manufrs*

▶ Bristol Business Interiors, CastleMead, Lower Castle Street, Bristol, BS1 3AG Tel: 08450 090514 E-mail: info@bristol-business-interiors.com *Bristol Business Interiors for office interior design and consultancy services that will transform your office interiors*

Bristol Cars Ltd, 368-370 Kensington High Street, London, W14 8NL Tel: (020) 7603 5554 *Motor manufrs*

▶ Bristol Computer Training, 92 Egerton Road, Bishopston, Bristol, BS7 8HP Tel: 0117 9247567 E-mail: mail@bristolcomputertraining.co.uk *Computer training in excel & word*

Bristol Crown Company, Albert Road Unit 7, Ferry Steps Trading Estate, St. Philips, Bristol, BS2 0XW Tel: 0117-977 3593 Fax: 0117-977 3593 E-mail: bcrown@dircon.co.uk *Dental technicians*

Bristol Design (Tools) Ltd, 14 Perry Road, Bristol, BS1 5BG Tel: 0117-929 1740 *Specialists in older hand tools of high quality*

▶ Bristol Ferry Boat Co., Welsh Back, Bristol, BS1 4SP Tel: 0117-927 3416 Fax: 0117-929 4077

Bristol Fire, Covert End, Westleigh Close, Yate, Bristol, BS37 4PR Tel: (01793) 480040 Fax: (01454) 273312 E-mail: sales@bristolfire.com *Fire protection sales & services*

▶ Bristol Forklifts, The Grove Industrial Estate, Gloucester Road, Patchway, Bristol, BS34 5BB Tel: 0117-969 4141 Fax: 0117-969 1211 E-mail: info@bristolforklifts.co.uk *Bristol Forklifts based in Bristol supply and hire forklift trucks throughout the South West.Their range includes electric or diesel forklift trucks, reach forklift trucks, used forklift trucks, pedestrian forklift trucks, articulating forklift trucks, wire guided forklift trucks, rail guided forklift trucks and man up machines. Bristol Forklifts also provide forklift truck repairs and maintenance. Bristol Forklifts based from our head office in Filton we are ideally located to serve Somerset, Wiltshire, Bath, Avon and Gloucestershire. Cities include Weston Super Mare, Taunton, Bridgewater, Yeovil, Radstock, Frome, Chippenham, Gloucester, Cheltenham, Tewkesbury and Stroud.*

Bristol Industrial Protection Ltd, Avonmouth Docks Estate, Chittening, Bristol, BS11 0YB Tel: 0117-982 7418 Fax: 0117-923 5961 E-mail: eip@netgates.co.uk *Protective & safety clothing distributors*

▶ Bristol Mac Centre, 233 Gloucester Road, Bishopston, Bristol, BS7 8NR Tel: (0800) 0714417

Bristol Office Products, Woodview House, 47 Woodleaze, Bristol, BS9 2HX Tel: 0117-968 5016 Fax: 0117-968 5993 E-mail: sales@bop.uk.com *Office furniture & equipment suppliers*

▶ Bristol Oil Storage Ltd, Royal Edward Dock, Bristol, BS11 9BT Tel: 0117-923 5868 Fax: 0117-923 5854

Bristol Packaging Co., 29 Stoneberry Road, Bristol, BS14 0UA Tel: (01275) 540800 Fax: (01275) 541266 *Packaging merchants*

Bristol Panel Formers, Unit 606 Central Park, Petherton Road, Bristol, BS14 9BZ Tel: (01275) 830544 Fax: (01275) 830563 E-mail: sales@bristolpanelformers.co.uk *Post form laminators*

Bristol Plastic Containers, Unit 10, Ashley Trading Estate, Ashley Parade, Bristol, BS2 9XS Tel: 0117-955 8500 Fax: 0117-955 8600 E-mail: frwarrencoltd@btconnect.com *Plastic container manufacturers & stockists*

Bristol Product Coating Ltd, The Mill Bath Road, Swineford, Bitton, Bristol, BS30 6LW Tel: 0117-932 3647 Fax: 0117-932 6183 *Stove enamellers & powder coaters*

Bristol Scientific Services, 7 Redcross Street, Bristol, BS2 0BA Tel: 0117-903 8666 Fax: 0117-903 8667 E-mail: labmail@sciserv.demon.co.uk *Chemical analysis*

Bristol Steel Stockholders Ltd, Unit 13-14 Avonbridge Trading Estate, Atlantic Road, Bristol, BS11 9QD Tel: 0117-982 8131 Fax: 0117-982 8137 E-mail: steel@bristolsteel.co.uk *General steel stockists*

Bristol Street Motors, Southam Road, Banbury, Oxfordshire, OX16 2RS Tel: (01295) 253511 Fax: (01295) 261325 E-mail: mja49@bristolstreet.co.uk *Car dealers, servicing & MOT's*

▶ Bristol Sweet Mart, 71 St Marks Road, Bristol, BS5 6HX Tel: 0117-951 2257 Fax: 0117-952 5456 E-mail: sales@sweetmart.co.uk *Spices & sweets retail*

Bristol Tank Ltd, Princess House, Princess Street, St Philips, Bristol, BS2 0RR Tel: 0117-954 0838 Fax: 0117-954 0839 E-mail: bristoltank@aol.com *Tank cleaning & waste disposal services*

Bristol Transmissions, Unit 4, Strachan & Henshaw Building, Foundry Lane, Fishponds, Bristol, BS5 7UF Tel: 0117-952 4920 Fax: 0117-951 4982 E-mail: service@bristoltransmissions.co.uk *Gear box repairs agents*

▶ Bristol (UK) Ltd, 3 Sutherland Court, Tolpits Lane, Watford, WD18 9SP Tel: (01923) 779333 Fax: (01923) 779666 E-mail: tech.sales@bristolpaint.com *Paint wholesalers special effect & fabric*

Bristol Uniforms Ltd, Victoria Street, Staple Hill, Bristol, BS16 5LL Tel: 0117-956 3101 Fax: 0117-956 5927 E-mail: enquiries@bristoluniforms.co.uk *Fireman uniform manufrs*

Bristol Water Holdings plc, Bridgwater Road, Bridgwater Road, Bristol, BS99 7AU Tel: 0117-966 5881 Fax: 0117-963 3755 E-mail: corporate.affaires@bristolwater.co.uk *Water authority*

Bristol Waterworld, Wyevale Garden Centre, Hicks Gate, Keynsham, Bristol, BS31 2AD Tel: 0117-977 2955 Fax: 0117-977 2956 E-mail: sales@fishkeeper.com *Aquarium & pond suppliers*

Bristol & West Copiers Ltd, 196-198 Cheltenham Road, Bristol, BS6 5QZ Tel: 0117-923 2333 Fax: 0117-923 2031 *Photocopying machines*

Bristol & West Joinery & Turnings, 56-58 Park Rd, Stapleton, Bristol, BS16 1AU Tel: 0117-965 8662 Fax: 0117-965 8662 *Joinery manufrs*

Bristol & West Windscreens, 5 Chardstock Avenue, Bristol, BS9 2RY Tel: 0117-908 2256 Fax: 0117-908 2256 E-mail: sales@bristolwindscreens.com *Bristol & West Windscreens, provide a fast and efficient windscreen replacement service, 24hrs, 7 days a week. Covering; Bristol, Bath, Gloucester, Cheltenham & Swindon. Also specialists in windscreen stone chip repair & executive windscreen tinting.*

Bristol Woodtech Ltd, 208 South Liberty Lane, Bristol, BS3 2TY Tel: 0117-953 2592 Fax: 0117-953 2595 *Wooden windows, doors & staircase manufrs*

Bristol Workshop Services, St. Francis Road, Bristol, BS3 2AN Tel: 0117-953 0381 Fax: 0117-953 7353 E-mail: bwsequip@aol.com *Garage equipment*

▶ Bristol Yacht Brokerage Ltd, Junction Lock, Cumberland Basin, Bristol, BS1 6XL Tel: 0117-930 4891 Fax: 0117-930 4882 E-mail: tim@bristolyachtbrokerage.com *Suppliers & dealers of boats & yachts, crown line, harbor yachts*

Bristolfridge Air Conditioning, 343 Southmead Road, Westbury-on-Trym, Bristol, BS10 5LW Tel: 0117-950 6800 Fax: 0117-950 0483 E-mail: bristolfridge@tiscall.co.uk *Commercial refrigeration installation & maintenance*

R. Bristoll Ltd, Timothy Bridge Road, Stratford-upon-Avon, Warwickshire, CV37 9NQ Tel: (01789) 204881 Fax: (01789) 204883 *Welding fabricators*

Bristol-Myers Squibb Pharmaceuticals, Reeds Lane, Wirral, Merseyside, CH46 1QW Tel: 0151-552 1500 Fax: 0151-552 1615 E-mail: office@bms.com *Pharmaceutical researchers & developers* Also at: Hounslow

Bristol-Myers Squibb Trustees Ltd, Uxbridge Business Park, Sanderson Road, Uxbridge, Middlesex, UB8 1DH Tel: (01895) 523000 Fax: (01895) 523010 *Pharmaceutical administration* Also at: Cramlington, Uxbridge & Wirral

Bristols & Round Ltd, Longford Road, Cannock, Staffordshire, WS11 0LF Tel: (01543) 503027 Fax: (01543) 505693 E-mail: sales@bristolround.co.uk *Hose fittings & turned parts manufrs*

Bri-Stor Systems Ltd, Church Lane, Hixon, Stafford, ST18 0PS Tel: (01889) 271202 Fax: (01889) 271178 E-mail: systems@bristor.co.uk *Vehicle storage & security system manufrs*

Bristow Buildbase, Kensington Way, Oakengates, Telford, Shropshire, TF2 6ER Tel: (01952) 613561 Fax: (01952) 616555 E-mail: telford@buildbase.co.uk *Buildbase is one of the UK's fastest growing builders merchants. All of our branches are long established companies which have been serving local trades people for many years, with knowledge and experience to match. We believe strongly in understanding the needs of trades professional and our business has been developed specifically to meet those demands. Massive stocks, top quality products, competitive pricing, reliable delivery, specialist staff and exceptional customer service*

Bristow Johnson & Partners, 146 Oxford St, London, W1D 1LZ Tel: (020) 7636 1036 Fax: (020) 7436 5347 E-mail: bristowjohnson@compuserve.com *Quantity surveyors*

Bristow's Of Devon Holdings Ltd, Marsh Lane, Crediton, Devon, EX17 1ET Tel: (01363) 774631 Fax: (01363) 772792 E-mail: sweets@bristows-of-devon.co.uk *Confectionery manufrs*

▶ Brit Bit Ltd, Technology & Manufacturing Centre, Souter Head Road, Altens Industrial Estate, Aberdeen, AB12 3LF Tel: (01224) 380050 Fax: (01224) 380291

▶ Brit Software Ltd, Unit 6, Quayside Business Centre, Lowestoft Enterprise Park, School Road, Lowestoft, Suffolk, NR33 9NW Tel: (0870) 7664965 Fax: (0870) 0117596 E-mail: info@britsoftware.com *Software distributors*

▶ Britain China Trading Co. Ltd, Cinnabar Wharf, East Block, 26 Wapping High Street, London, E1W 1NG Tel: (020) 7680 8032 Fax: (020) 7680 8001 E-mail: mars@buj.co.uk *Construction materials suppliers*

Britain Fabricators Ltd, Watnall Road, Hucknall, Nottingham, NG15 6EP Tel: 0115-963 2901 Fax: 0115-968 0335 E-mail: sales@britonsltd.co.uk *Fabrication of footbridges sign gantries*

Britain & Overseas Trading (Bristles) Ltd, 12 Willow St, London, EC2A 4BH Tel: (020) 7729 2487 Fax: (020) 7739 2795 *Bristle merchants*

Britainia Hotels Wigan, Almond Brook Road, Standish, Wigan, Lancashire, WN6 0SR Tel: (01257) 499988 Fax: (01257) 427327 *Conference facility services*

Britains Aquatic Superstore Ltd, 225 Folds Road, Bolton, BL1 2TW Tel: (01204) 534343 Fax: (01204) 364642 *Aquarium & pond suppliers*

Britalco Engineering Ltd, 3 Villiers Trading Estate, Marston Road, Wolverhampton, WV2 4LA Tel: (01902) 771836 Fax: (01902) 717766 *Crankshaft manufrs*

Britania Leatherbarrows, Building, 105 Aviation Park West, Hurn, Christchurch, Dorset, BH23 6NW Tel: (01202) 495600 Fax: (01202) 581639 E-mail: admin@1eatherbarrows.co.uk *National & international removal contractors*

Britania Towing, Unit 2 Kensington Road, Canterbury, Kent, CT1 1QZ Tel: (01227) 457010 Fax: (01227) 784080 *Car alarm installers*

Britannia Adhesives Ltd, 4b Horndon Industrial Park, Station Road, West Horndon, Brentwood, Essex, CM13 3XL Tel: (01277) 810480 Fax: (01277) 812028 E-mail: john.lown@britannia-adhesives.co.uk *Industrial adhesive manufacturers*

Britannia Construction Ltd, Britannia House, Staverton Technology Park, Staverton, Cheltenham, Gloucestershire, GL51 6TQ Tel: (01452) 859880 Fax: (01452) 859881 E-mail: info@britanniaconstruction.co.uk *Building & civil engineering contractors*

Britannia Cooling Ltd, Britannia Road, Morley, Leeds, LS27 0DD Tel: 0113-253 6159 Fax: 0113-253 0111 *Automotive radiators exchanger manufrs*

Britannia Dynamics, 1 Southside Industrial Park, North Road, Atherton, Manchester, M46 0RE Tel: (01942) 887811 Fax: (01942) 887818 E-mail: sales@britannia-dynamics.com *Toolmakers distributors*

Britannia Enterprises Ltd, Unit 14 Canal Industrial Park, Canal Road, Gravesend, Kent, DA12 2PA Tel: (01474) 328051 Fax: (01474) 320564 *Electrical equipment suppliers*

Britannia Fasteners, 4/6 Auckland Street, Hot Lane Industrial Estate, Stoke-on-Trent, ST6 2AT Tel: (01782) 833233 Fax: (01782) 833255 E-mail: sales@britanniafasteners.co.uk *Fastener distributors*

Britannia Greer's of Elgin Ltd, The Depository, Edgar Road, Elgin, Morayshire, IV30 6YQ Tel: (01343) 542229

Britannia Labels Ltd, 22b Centurion Way, Meridian Business Park, Leicester, LE19 1WH Tel: 0116-281 5300 Fax: 0116-281 5301 E-mail: sales@britannialabels.com *Clothing label manufacturers*

▶ Britannia Lanes Of Somerset, Crossways Road, Bridgwater, Somerset, TA6 6DD Tel: (01278) 447099 Fax: (01278) 421500

Britannia Lightning Prevectron Ltd, Longue Drive, Calverton, Nottingham, NG14 6QF Tel: 0115-847 7113 Fax: 0115-847 5185 E-mail: sales@lightninguk.fsnet.co.uk *Lightning conductors*

Britannia Machinery Pontefract Ltd, Stuart Street, Pontefract, West Yorkshire, WF8 4PW Tel: (01977) 790818 Fax: (01977) 600333 E-mail: britannia.machinery@btinternet.com *Used printing machinery distributors & engineers*

Britannia Marine Services, Unit 11 50 Windsor Avenue, London, SW19 2TJ Tel: (020) 8408 6020 Fax: (020) 8408 6040 E-mail: sales@britannia.com *Marine spare parts*

▶ Britannia Mounts Co. Ltd, Unit E3-E4, Meltham Mills Industrial Estate, Meltham, Holmfirth, HD9 4DS Tel: (01484) 854444 Fax: (01484) 854433 E-mail: sales@britannia-mounts.co.uk *Picture mounts & art boards suppliers*

▶ Britannia Mounts Co. Ltd, Unit E3-E4, Meltham Mills Industrial Estate, Meltham, Holmfirth, HD9 4DS Tel: (01484) 854444 Fax: (01484) 854433 E-mail: sales@britannia-mounts.co.uk

▶ Britannia Movers Of Edinburgh, 26 Bath Road, Edinburgh, EH6 7JU Tel: 0131-553 4374 Fax: 0131-554 9357

Britannia Nurseries, 103 Eleanor Cross Road, Waltham Cross, Hertfordshire, EN8 7NS Tel: (01992) 713696 *Florist wholesale & distribution*

Britannia Paints Ltd, Units 7-8, King Street Trading Estate, Middlewich, Cheshire, CW10 9LF Tel: (01606) 834015 Fax: (01606) 837006 E-mail: sales@britanniapaints.co.uk *Paints & sports surface & weatherproofing materials manufrs*

▶ Britannia Pine, Unit 9b Watling St Business Park, Watling Street, Cannock, Staffordshire, WS11 9XG Tel: (01543) 379888 Fax: (01543) 276901 *Manufacturers & wholesalers of pine furniture*

Britannia Powder & Plastic Coating Ltd, Unit 8 Thistlebrook Industrial Estate, Eynsham Drive, London, SE2 9RB Tel: (020) 8311 0991 Fax: (020) 8311 0773 *Specialists in powder & plastic coatings to the metal trade*

▶ Britannia Precision Engineering Ltd, Unit 6 M1 Commerce Park, Markham Lane, Duckmanton, Chesterfield, Derbyshire, S44 5HS Tel: (01246) 241555 Fax: (01246) 241599

Britannia Refined Metals Ltd, Britannia Works, Botany Road, Northfleet, Gravesend, Kent, DA11 9BG Tel: (01474) 538200 Fax: (01474) 538203 *Metal refiners*

Britannia Security Group UK Ltd, Britannia House, Lake Street, Stockport, Cheshire, SK2 7NU Tel: 0161-456 2103 Fax: 0161-487 4174 *Industrial door & grille manufrs*

Britannia Security Services Ltd, Eden Business Centre, South Stour Avenue, Ashford, Kent, TN23 7RS Tel: (01233) 628684 Fax: (01233) 628684 *Security systems equipment installation services*

Britannia Services UK Ltd, Lysways House, 45 Britannia Way, Lichfield, Staffordshire, WS14 9UY Tel: (01543) 418855 Fax: (01543) 418699 E-mail: sales@britanniagroup.co.uk *Industrial cleaning contractors* Also at: Branches throughout the U.K.

Britannia Soft Drinks Ltd, Britvic House, Broomfield Road, Chelmsford, CM1 1TU Tel: (01245) 261871 Fax: (01245) 267147 E-mail: forename.surname@britvic.co.uk *Soft drink & fruit juice manufrs*

Britannia Steam Ship Insurance Association Ltd, New City Court, 20 St Thomas Street, London, SE1 9RR Tel: (020) 7407 3588 Fax: (020) 7403 3942 *Marine insurance company*

Britannia Storage Systems, Airfield, Earls Colne, Colchester, CO6 2NS Tel: (01787) 223884 Fax: (01787) 223038 E-mail: enquires@britannia-storage.co.uk *Shelving & storage systems manufrs*

▶ Britannia Support Services Ltd, 17 Ensign House, Admirals Way, London, E14 9XQ Tel: 020 7474 6108 Fax: 020 7474 1668 E-mail: info@britannia-supportservices.co.uk *Process Serving, Surveillance, Test Purchasing, Mystery Shopping, Tracing, Company Reports, Property Reports, Credit Card & Cheque Recovery.*

Britannia Transprint, 38 Burgess Road, Saffron Works, Leicester, LE2 8QL Tel: 0116-283 8485 E-mail: info@tranfereprint.co.uk *Textile heat transfer printers*

▶ Britannia Tusons (Waltham Cross) Ltd, Marsh Lane, Ware, Hertfordshire, SG12 9QN Tel: (01920) 461616

▶ Britannia Wardrobes Ltd, Ebberns Road, Hemel Hempstead, Hertfordshire, HP3 9QS Tel: (01442) 239900 Fax: (01442) 244121

Britannia Welding Supplies Ltd, 7 Rotunda Estate, Aldershot, Hampshire, GU11 1TG Tel: (01252) 350866 Fax: (01252) 330938 E-mail: debbie@britweld.co.uk *Welding supplies distributors*

Britannia Windows (UK) Ltd, Britannia Houd, Stroud Road, Clevedon, Avon, BS21 6QH Tel: (01275) 878153 Fax: (01275) 343134 E-mail: info@britanniawindows.co.uk *Double glazed unit manufrs*

Britannia Wiper Co., Tidal Basin Road, London, E16 1AD Tel: (020) 7476 6888 Fax: (020) 7476 9888 E-mail: sales@britannia-wiper.co.uk *Industrial wiper manufrs*

Britannic Assurance P.L.C., 1 Wythall Green Way, Wythall, Birmingham, B47 6WG Tel: (01564) 828888 Fax: (0870) 8870002 E-mail: info@britannic.co.uk *Assurance company* Also at: Branches throughout the U.K.

Britannic Engineering Co Ltd, The Old Bakery, Market St, Charlbury, Chipping Norton, Oxfordshire, OX7 3PH Tel: (01608) 810332 Fax: (01608) 811566 E-mail: office@britannickengineering.co.uk *Electro-mechanical engineering services*

Britannic Garden Furniture Ltd, Costers Close, Alveston, Bristol, BS35 3HZ Tel: (01454) 411601 Fax: (01454) 417941 *Garden furniture manufrs*

The Britannic Lift Company plc, Riverview Buildings, Bradford Road, Riddlesden, Keighley, West Yorkshire, BD20 5JH Tel: (01535) 600066 Fax: (01535) 600077 E-mail: sales@lifts.co.uk *Lift maintenance, repair & installation services*

Britannic Security Systems Ltd, The Exchange, Haslucks Green Road, Shirley, Solihull, West Midlands, B90 2EL Tel: 0121-744 0770 Fax: (0870) 2000772 E-mail: information@britannic-security.com *Security installation services*

Britannic Technologies Ltd, Britannic House, Merrow Business Park, Guildford, Surrey, GU4 7WA Tel: (01483) 242526 Fax: 0845-050 1001 E-mail: enquiries@btlnet.co.uk *Telecommunication equipment installation, maintenance & repairs*

Britannic Warehouse, 142 Sand Pits, Birmingham, B1 3RJ Tel: 0121-236 7271 Fax: 0121-236 8266 E-mail: sales@britannicwarehouse.co.uk *Wholesale cash & carry*

Britax Excelsior Ltd, 1 Churchill Way West, Andover, Hampshire, SP10 3UW Tel: (01264) 333343 Fax: (01264) 334146 *Child car seats & nursery products*

Britax International Holdings Ltd, Seton House, Warwick Technology Park, Warwick, CV34 6DE Tel: (01926) 400040 Fax: (01926) 406350 E-mail: info@britax.com *Holding company*

Britax P S V Wypers Ltd, Navigation Road, Diglis, Worcester, WR5 3DE Tel: (01905) 350500 Fax: (01905) 763928 E-mail: sales@psvwypers.com *Windscreen wiper systems roof ventilators*

Britcast Plant & Machinery Dealer, Green Acres, Shere Road, West Clandon, Guildford, Surrey, GU4 8SG Tel: (01483) 223696 Fax: (01483) 223696 E-mail: britcast@lineone.net *Design & supply of cast wearparts*

Britcon Ltd, Midland Road, Scunthorpe, South Humberside, DN16 1DQ Tel: (01724) 280022 Fax: (01724) 270616 E-mail: robinallen@britcon.co.uk *Civil engineers & building contractors*

Brite Band 1990 Ltd, Manywells Brow Industrial Estate, Cullingworth, Bradford, West Yorkshire, BD13 5DX Tel: (01535) 271427 Fax: (01535) 275676 E-mail: j.hanson@briteband.co.uk *Stainless steel processing & stockholders*

Brite Technology, Unit C Radford Business Centre, Radford Way, Billericay, Essex, CM12 0DP Tel: (01277) 655922 Fax: (01277) 655949 E-mail: j.creek@britetec.com *Sign engravers & manufrs*

Britech Industries Ltd, Cinderhill Trading Estate, Weston Coyney Road, Longton, ST3 5JU Tel: (01782) 388280 Fax: (01782) 392441 E-mail: sales@britech.co.uk *Ceramic engineering services*

Britelec Network Services Ltd, 39 London Road, Braintree, Essex, CM7 2LD Tel: (01376) 552323 Fax: (01376) 340006 *Computer consultants*

▶ Britelite Signage, 1 Wallis Court, James Carter Road, Mildenhall, Bury St. Edmunds, Suffolk, IP28 7DD Tel: (01638) 583879 Fax: (01638) 515237 *Illuminated sign maker*

Briter Components & Manufacturing Ltd, 8 Sandwich Industrial Estate, Ramsgate Road, Sandwich, Kent, CT13 9LN Tel: (01304) 617155 Fax: (01304) 617741 E-mail: brian@britercomponents.com *Precision machining services & turned parts manufrs*

Britestar Plastics Ltd, Unit 7, Broomfield Works, London Road, Swanley, Kent, BR8 8DF Tel: (01322) 669964 Fax: (01322) 660083 E-mail: info@britestar.gb *Plastic, injection moulders & toolmakers*

Britim Computer Products Ltd, Broadway Unit 1, Horseshoe Yard, Crowland, Peterborough, PE6 0BJ Tel: (01733) 212121 Fax: (01733) 212122 E-mail: sales@britim.biz *Office suppliers*

British Adhesives & Sealants Association, 5 Alderson Road, Worksop, Nottinghamshire, S80 1UZ Tel: (01909) 480888 Fax: (01909) 473834 E-mail: sales@basa.uk.com *Adhesive trade association*

British Airways plc, PO Box 365, West Drayton, Middlesex, UB7 0GB Tel: (020) 8759 5511 Fax: (020) 8738 9800 *Airline*

British Airways Cargo, Cargo Centre, Belfast Int Airport, Belfast, BT29 4AA Tel: (028) 9442 2731 Fax: (028) 9445 2570 E-mail: belfast@baregionalcargo.com *Road transport & haulage contractors*

Company Information

British American Offshore Ltd, 39 Upper Brook Street, London, W1K 7QW Tel: (020) 7499 2957 Fax: (020) 7409 2738 *Oil well drilling contractors*

British & American Retail Systems Ltd, 151b Dentons Green Lane, Dentons Green, St. Helens, Merseyside, WA10 6RG Tel: (01744) 750221 Fax: (01744) 750222 E-mail: britishamerican@btopenworld.com *Cash register retailers*

▶ British American Tax, 8 Forest View, London, E11 3AP Tel: (020) 8989 0088 Fax: (020) 8530 3528 E-mail: referredbyKelleysearch@BritishAmericanTax.com *BritishAmericanTax provides international and expatriate tax advice and compliance on matters of individual, corporate, partnership, and trust US taxation. We also help foreign nationals with US tax issues such as purchasing US property or moving to the US. With over 19 years of experience, let us help you reduce your combined US and foreign tax.*

British American Tobacco plc, Globe House, 4 Temple Place, London, WC2R 2PG Tel: (020) 7845 1000 Fax: (020) 7240 0555 *Tobacco manufrs*

British American Tobacco (UK) Ltd, Oxford Road, Aylesbury, Buckinghamshire, HP21 8SZ Tel: (01296) 335000 Fax: (01296) 335999 *Tobacco products manufrs*

British Antarctic Survey, High Cross, Madingley Road, Cambridge, CB3 0ET Tel: (01223) 221400 Fax: (01223) 362616 E-mail: information@bas.ac.uk *Government research organisation*

British Approvals Board Telecommunications Ltd, Claremont House, 34 Molesey Road, Hersham, Walton-on-Thames, Surrey, KT12 4RQ Tel: (01932) 251200 Fax: (01932) 251201 E-mail: m.brain@babt.com *Certification of radio & telecom equipment, manufacturing systems*

British Arab Commercial Bank Ltd, 8-10 Manson House Place, London, EC4N 8BJ Tel: (020) 7648 7777 Fax: (020) 7600 3318 *Commercial bankers*

British Association for Chemical Specialities, The Gatehouse, White Cross, Lancaster, LA1 4XQ Tel: (01524) 849606 Fax: (01524) 849194 E-mail: enquiries@bacsnet.org *Trade associations*

The British Association For Shooting & Conservation, Marford Mill, Rossett, Wrexham, Clwyd, LL12 0HL Tel: (01244) 573000 Fax: (01244) 573001 E-mail: enquiries@basc.org.uk *Membership association*

British Autogard Ltd, Siddington, Cirencester, Gloucestershire, GL7 6EU Tel: (01285) 640333 Fax: (01285) 659476 E-mail: sales@autogard.co.uk Principal Export Areas: Worldwide *Torque control equipment manufrs*

British Bakeries Ltd, Gain Lane, Bradford, West Yorkshire, BD3 7DX Tel: (01274) 665211 Fax: (01274) 663895 E-mail: info@britishbakeries.co.uk *Fabrication & distribution of baked goods*

British Bakeries Ltd, Toynbee Road, Eastleigh, Hampshire, SO50 9YU Tel: (0870) 7288888 Fax: (023) 8064 1612 *Bakery suppliers*

British Bakeries Ltd, Belmont Road, Erith, Kent, DA8 1JZ Tel: (01322) 341144 Fax: (01322) 350249 *Bread manufrs*

British Bakeries Ltd, 783 Duke Street, Glasgow, G31 1LL Tel: 0141-556 5211 Fax: 0141-554 3508 *Bakery & confectionery suppliers*

British Bakeries Ltd, Chaucer Road, London, E7 9NA Tel: (020) 8472 9881 Fax: (020) 8548 0842 *Bakers*

▶ British Bakeries Ltd, Wheatfield Road, Newcastle upon Tyne, NE5 5LB Tel: 0191-286 9831 Fax: 0191-214 5246

British Bakeries Ltd, Main Road, Watnall, Nottingham, NG16 1HB Tel: 0115-938 3391 Fax: 0115-945 8274 *Bakery products manufrs*

British Bakeries Ltd, PO Box 527, Windsor, Berkshire, SL4 3HD Tel: (0870) 7288888 Fax: (01753) 791739 *Bakers wholesale manufrs*

British Bakers, Avonmouth Way, Bristol, BS11 8DQ Tel: 0117-988 3900 Fax: 0117-988 3962 E-mail: admin@britishbakeries.co.uk *Bakery*

British Benzol, Roentgen Road, Staineshill East, Basingstoke, Hampshire, RG24 8NT Tel: (01256) 811020 Fax: (01256) 355151 *Petroleum products distributors* Also at: Barking, Basingstoke, Pitsea, Port Talbot & Stoke

British & Brazilian Produce Co. Ltd, Silvertown House, Orion Avenue, Great Blakenham, Ipswich, IP6 0LW Tel: (01473) 835640 Fax: (01473) 835657 E-mail: mail@produceworld.co.uk *Fresh produce*

British Bung Manufacturing Co. Ltd, Lowlands Works, Mirfield, West Yorkshire, WF14 8LY Tel: (01924) 493071 Fax: (01924) 480632 E-mail: brit.bung@telinco.co.uk *Faucet plug makers*

▶ British Business Club Ltd, 12 Gatwick Road, Birmingham, B35 6NE Tel: 0121-749 7940 Fax: 08444 844748 E-mail: info@britishbusinessclub.com *The UK"s largest independent business club offering members advice,information and global business contacts*

British Cables Association, 37a Walton Road, East Molesey, Surrey, KT8 0DH Tel: (020) 8941 4079 Fax: (020) 8783 0104 E-mail: admin@bcauk.org *Trade association*

British Carton Association, 29-35 Farringdon Point, Farrindon Road, London, EC1M 3JF Tel: (020) 7915 8300 Fax: (020) 7405 7784 E-mail: sigs@bpis.org.uk *Trade association agents*

British Ceramic Confederation, Federation House, Station Road, Stoke-on-Trent, ST4 2SA Tel: (01782) 744631 Fax: (01782) 744102 E-mail: bcc@ceramfed.co.uk *Trade association*

British Chemical Engineering Contractors Association, 1 Regent Street, London, SW1Y 4NR Tel: (020) 7839 6514 Fax: (020) 7930 3466 E-mail: ian.corbidge@bceca.org.uk *Chemical engineers*

British Coffee Manufacturers Association, 12 Market Street, Chipping Norton, Oxfordshire, OX7 5UD Tel: (01608) 644995 *Trade Association*

British & Continental Traders Ltd, Oxford House, North Bridge Road, Berkhamsted, Hertfordshire, HP4 1EH Tel: (01442) 877415 Fax: (01442) 872782 E-mail: sales@b-ct.co.uk *Metal working equipment agents*

British Contractors Plant Ltd, Feathers Lane, Wraysbury, Staines, Middlesex, TW19 5AN Tel: (01784) 482122 Fax: (01784) 483781 *Contractors plant hire*

British Cushion Co., Unit 28 Narborough Wood Park, Desford Road, Enderby, Leicester, LE19 4XT Tel: 0116-239 2390 Fax: 0116-239 2397 E-mail: sales@britishcushions.com *Hire cushions for sports events*

British Dental Trade Association, Mineral Lane, Chesham, Buckinghamshire, HP5 1NL Tel: (01494) 782873 Fax: (01494) 786659 E-mail: admin@bdta.org.uk *Trade association*

British Diamalt, Maltkiln Lane, Newark, Nottinghamshire, NG24 1HN Tel: (01636) 614730 Fax: (01636) 614740 E-mail: sales@diamalt.co.uk Principal Export Areas: Worldwide *Cereal syrup producers or suppliers & malt/malt extract/malt flour processors/roasters/manufrs*

British Diamond Wire Die Co. Ltd, 66 Old Wareham Road, Poole, Dorset, BH12 4QS Tel: (01202) 745104 Fax: (01202) 746125 E-mail: sales@bdwd.freeserve.co.uk *Light precision engineers*

British Drilling and Freezing Co. Ltd, Private Road No 3, Colwick Industrial Estate, Colwick, Nottingham, NG4 2BB Tel: 0115-961 1300 Fax: 0115-961 7338 E-mail: drill@bdf.co.uk *We are the UK's largest & longest established drilling company for coal, oil, gas, salt water & other important minerals. BDF own rigs that can cover all on-shore operational requirements to a depth capacity of over 4,000 metres. It has more back-up facilities than other UK drilling company & is not dependant upon other contractors. BDF offer rotary borehole drilling for salt caverns for gas storage, water wells, site investigation, oil & gas borehole drilling & workovers, mineral exploration, coal bed methane drainage among others. Our rotary drilling rigs range in their drilling capacity from 1m to in excess of 4000m.Our waterwell drilling rigs can drill boreholes up to a diameter of 60" to a depth of over 300m.We can also provide water well boreholes for household use as well as for ground source heat pumps. We have been drilling boreholes for oil gas & coal for over 80 years & have highly experienced staff capable of helping deliver a full drilling package to your specifications.*

British Electrometals Co, Netherward Works, Dens Road, Arbroath, Angus, DD11 1RU Tel: (01241) 875757 Fax: (01241) 874599 E-mail: bem@btconnect.com *Electroplaters & Metal finishers*

British Encoder Products Co., Unit 33, Whitegate Industrial Estate, Wrexham, Clwyd, LL13 8UG Tel: (01978) 262100 Fax: (01978) 262101 E-mail: sales@brit-encoder.com *Optical shaft encoders manufrs*

British Energy Ltd, 3 Redwood Crescent, East Kilbride, Glasgow, G74 5PR Tel: (01355) 262000 Fax: (01355) 262626 *Suppliers of energy to businesses*

▶ British Energy Generation UK Ltd, Torness Power Station, Torness, Dunbar, East Lothian, EH42 1QU Tel: (01368) 873000 Fax: (01368) 873846

British Engineering Productions Ltd, 19 Arnside Road, Waterlooville, Hampshire, PO7 7UP Tel: (023) 9226 8733 Fax: (023) 9225 1104 E-mail: sales@bep-manifolds.com *Hydraulic equipment & manifold manufrs*

British Engines Ltd, St Peters, Newcastle upon Tyne, NE6 1BS Tel: 0191-265 9091 Fax: 0191-276 3244 E-mail: sales@bel.co.uk Principal Export Areas: Central/East Europe & West Europe *Iron castings*

British Essential Oil Association Ltd, Flat 15 Exeter Mansions, Exeter Road, London, NW2 3UG Tel: (020) 8450 3713 Fax: (020) 8450 3197 E-mail: beoa@btinternet.com *Trade association agents*

British Estate Services Ltd, 132 Bath Road, Reading, RG30 2EU Tel: 0118-957 2263 Fax: 0118-951 2267 *Tennis court refurbishment*

British & European Sales Ltd, Plummer, Tenterden, Kent, TN30 6TU Tel: (01580) 762415 Fax: (01580) 764466 *Iron ore merchants*

British Exhibition Contractors Association, Beca House Uplands Business Park, Blackhorse Lane, London, E17 5QJ Tel: (020) 8543 3888 Fax: (020) 8523 5204 E-mail: info@beca.org.uk *Exhibition trade association*

British Exporters Association, Broadway House, Tothill Street, London, SW1H 9NQ Tel: (020) 7222 5419 Fax: (020) 7799 2468 E-mail: bexamail@aol.com *Trade association for exporters*

British Falcon Plastics, Kemmings Close, Paignton, Devon, TQ4 7TW Tel: (01803) 551313 Fax: (01803) 664548

British Filters Ltd, 11-12 Porsham Close, Roborough, Plymouth, PL6 7DB Tel: (01752) 703900 Fax: (01752) 703901 E-mail: pdenyer@britishfilters.co.uk *Specialist filtration aviation brewery*

British & Foreign (Exporters) Ltd, 53 Park Royal Rd, London, NW10 7LQ Tel: (020) 8965 4833 Fax: (020) 8961 3377 E-mail: leea@brit-foreign.demon.co.uk *Leather garment wholesalers*

British Gas Business, Spinneyside, Penman Way, Grove Park, Leicester, LE19 1SZ Tel: 0845 850 0056 E-mail: customerservice@britishgasbusiness.co.uk *British Gas Business is the UK's largest business energy supplier with over 950 thousand customers, from small businesses to large commercial organisations.*We were voted most trusted utility company in the 2008 Readers Digest Most Trusted Brands Survey, and you can trust us to deliver more than just business gas and electricity:*Extensive portfolio of products tailored to your business needs.*Average customer online energy savings of £300.*Fixed price energy tariffs for 1, 2 or 3 years*Dedicated Account Managers in UK based call centres.*Save money with expert energy efficiency advice.*Visit our business website today for instant online energy quotes, product information, business advice and more.*

▶ British Gas Services Ltd, 30 The Causeway, Staines, Middlesex, TW18 3BY Tel: (01784) 874000

British Gas Trading, Bridge St, Leeds, LS2 7PE Tel: (0845) 609 1122 *Natural gas producer (accounts)*

British Gaskets Ltd, Bulmer Road Industrial Estate, Bulmer Road, Sudbury, Suffolk, CO10 7HJ Tel: (01787) 881188 Fax: (01787) 880595 E-mail: sales@british-gaskets.co.uk Principal Export Areas: Asia Pacific, Middle East, Africa, Central/East Europe, West Europe, North America & South America *Manufacturers of gaskets*

British Gaskets Ltd, Bulmer Road Industrial Estate, Bulmer Road, Sudbury, Suffolk, CO10 7HJ Tel: (01787) 881188 Fax: (01787) 880595 Principal Export Areas: Worldwide *Rubber mouldings, rubber extrusions & grommets & gaskets manufrs*

British Gates & Timber Ltd, Biddenden, Ashford, Kent, TN27 8DN Tel: (01580) 291555 Fax: (01580) 292011 E-mail: sales@britishgates.co.uk *Timber merchants, woodworkers & retailers*

British Gypsum Ltd, Gotham Road, East Leake, Loughborough, Leicestershire, LE12 6JQ Tel: 0115-945 1050 Fax: 0115-945 1154 E-mail: bgtechnical.enquiries@bpb.com *Plaster & plasterboard manufrs* Also at: Belfast, Leeds, Penrith & Robertsbridge

British Heat Treatments, 40 Milton Road, East Kilbride, Glasgow, G74 5BU Tel: (01355) 225288 Fax: (01355) 265845 E-mail: jbridges@ajt-engineering.co.uk *Heat treatment contractors*

▶ British Hide Collection, Chorley Road, Fourgates Mill, Westhoughton, Bolton, BL5 3NB Tel: (01942) 819740 Fax: (01942) 816587

British Hospitality Association, Queens House, 55-56 Lincolns Inn Fields, London, WC2A 3BH Tel: (020) 7404 7744 Fax: (020) 7404 7799 E-mail: bha@bha.org.uk *Trade association*

British Inspecting Engineers Ltd, Chatsworth Technology Park, Dunston Road, Chesterfield, Derbyshire, S41 8XA Tel: (01246) 260260 Fax: (01246) 260919 E-mail: info@bieltd.co.uk *Inspection engineers & worldwide expediting services*

British Institute of Agricultural Consultants, Estate Office, Torry Hill, Milstead, Sittingbourne, Kent, ME9 0SP Tel: (01795) 830100 Fax: (01795) 830243 E-mail: info@biac.co.uk *Research organisation*

British Institute Of Cleaning Science Ltd, Anglia Way, Moulton Park Industrial Estate, Northampton, NN3 6JA Tel: (01604) 678710 Fax: (01604) 645988 E-mail: info@bics.org.uk *Professional institute*

British Institute Of Non Destructive Testing, 1 Spencer Parade, Northampton, NN1 5AA Tel: (01604) 630124 Fax: (01604) 231489 E-mail: enquiries@bindt.org *Professional association*

British Jewellery & Giftware Federation Ltd, Federation House, 10 Vyse Street, Hockley, Birmingham, B18 6LT Tel: 0121-236 2657 Fax: 0121-236 3921 E-mail: info@bjgf.org.uk *Trade federation*

The British Land Corporation Ltd, York House, 45 Seymour Street, London, W1H 7LX Tel: (020) 7486 4466 Fax: (020) 7935 5552 E-mail: info@britishland.com *Property investers*

British Lead Mills, Unit C & D Abbotsfield Rd, St. Helens, Merseyside, WA9 4HU Tel: (01744) 819126 Fax: (01744) 819335 E-mail: info@guhring.co.uk *Lead sheet manufrs* Also at: Branches throughout U.K.

British Lead Mills, Peartree Lane, Welwyn Garden City, Hertfordshire, AL7 3UB Tel: (01707) 324595 Fax: (01707) 328941 E-mail: sales@britishlead.co.uk *Lead sheet manufrs*

The British Library, The British Library STB, London, NW1 2DB Tel: (020) 7412 7000 Fax: (020) 7412 7609 *Library*

The British Library, The British Library STB, London, NW1 2DB Tel: (020) 7412 7000 Fax: (020) 7412 7609 E-mail: business-information@bl.uk *Business information services*

The British Linen Bank Ltd, PO Box 49, Edinburgh, EH3 7NZ Tel: (0131) 243 8386 Fax: (0131) 243 8393 E-mail: blb@blb.co.uk *Merchant bankers*

British Luggage Association, 10 Vyse Street, Hockley, Birmingham, B18 6LT Tel: 0121-237 1107 Fax: 0121-237 1124 E-mail: info@sea.org.uk *Trade association*

British Lymphology Society, 1 Webbs Court, Buckhurst Avenue, Sevenoaks, Kent, TN13 1LZ Tel: (01732) 740850 Fax: (01732) 459225 E-mail: bhta@bhta.com *Trade association*

Britihsh Marine Federation, Marine House, Thorpe Lea Road, Egham, Surrey, TW20 8BF Tel: (01784) 473377 Fax: (01784) 439678 E-mail: enquiries@bmif.co.uk *Trade association*

British Market Research Association, Devonshire House, 60 Goswell Road, London, EC1M 7AD Tel: (020) 7566 3636 Fax: (020) 7689 6220 E-mail: admin@bmra.org.uk *Trade association*

British Markitex Ltd, PO Box 52, Waltham Cross, Hertfordshire, EN8 7AF Tel: (01992) 650455 Fax: (01992) 700319 E-mail: markitex@compuserve.com *Trade finance services*

British Metal Treatments Ltd, 40 Battery Road, Great Yarmouth, Norfolk, NR30 3NN Tel: (01493) 844153 Fax: (01493) 330303 E-mail: sales@bmtgalv.co.uk *Hot tip galvanising services*

British Metallic Packings Co 1933 Ltd, 15 Invicta Road, Dartford, DA2 6AY Tel: (01322) 224514 *Steel packing makers*

British Metallurgical Plant Constructors Association, c/o EEF, Broadway House, Tothill Street, London, SW1H 9NQ Tel: (0778) 5255218 Fax: (020) 7222 3531 E-mail: enquiries@bmpca.co.uk *Trade association*

British Mica Co. Ltd, 123 Barkers Lane, Bedford, MK41 9RR Tel: (01234) 327977 Fax: (01234) 352016 E-mail: info@britishmica.co.uk *Plastic compression mouldings manufrs*

The British Millerain Company Ltd, Melloroid Works, Belfield Road, Rochdale, Lancashire, OL16 2XA Tel: (01706) 649242 Fax: (01706) 527611 E-mail: sales@britishmillerain.com *Suppliers & finishers of dyed, proofed & polyurethane laminated fabric*

British Movietone Ltd, North Orbital Road, Denham, Uxbridge, Middlesex, UB9 5HQ Tel: (01895) 833071 Fax: (01895) 834893 E-mail: library@mtone.co.uk Principal Export Areas: Worldwide *Archive film library*

British Office Supplies & Services Federation, Farringdon Point, 29-35 Farringdon Road, London, EC1M 3JF Tel: (0845) 4501565 Fax: (0870) 7706789 E-mail: sales@bossfed.co.uk *Trade association services*

British Petroleum Co. P.L.C., 1 St. James's Square, London, SW1Y 4PD Tel: (020) 7496 4000 Fax: (020) 7496 4630 *Oil company*

The British Piano Manufacturing Co., Woodchester Mill, Selsley Road, North Woodchester, Stroud, Gloucestershire, GL5 5NN Tel: (01453) 872871 Fax: (01453) 872822 *Piano makers & piano maintenance*

British Plastics Federation, 6 Bath Place, Rivington Street, London, EC2A 3JE Tel: (020) 7457 5000 Fax: (020) 7457 5038 E-mail: bpf@bpf.co.uk *Technical design or supply consultants on plastics*

British Polar Engines Ltd, 133 Helen Street, Glasgow, G51 3HD Tel: 0141-445 2455 Fax: 0141-445 2185 E-mail: sales@polareng.sagehost.co.uk *Diesel engine manufrs*

British Polythene Industries, 96 Port Glasgow Road, Greenock, Renfrewshire, PA15 2UL Tel: (01475) 501000 Fax: (01475) 743143 E-mail: carolanderson@bpipoly.com *Packaging material product manufrs*

British Precast Concrete Federation Ltd, 60 Charles Street, Leicester, LE1 1FB Tel: 0116-253 6161 Fax: 0116-251 4568 E-mail: info@britishprecast.org.uk *Trade association*

British Property Federation, 1 Warwick Row, London, SW1E 5ER Tel: (020) 7828 0111 Fax: (020) 7834 3442 E-mail: info@bpf.org.uk *Trade association*

British Publishing Co., Messenger House, 33 St Michaels Square, Gloucester, GL1 1HX Tel: (01452) 418191 Fax: (01452) 300069 E-mail: info@british-publishing.com *Guidebooks for local authorities*

British Quality Foundation, 32-34 Great Peter Street, London, SW1P 2QX Tel: (020) 7654 5000 Fax: (020) 7654 5001 E-mail: mail@quality-foundation.co.uk *Quality assurance consultants & trade association*

British Refractory Metals, 27 Nobel Square, Burnt Mills Industrial Estate, Basildon, Essex, SS13 1LP Tel: (01268) 591386 Fax: (01268) 591389 E-mail: pcurtisbrm@aol.com Principal Export Areas: Worldwide *Powders & exotic metal & refractory metal producers & suppliers*

British Rema Manufacturing Co. Ltd, Image Works, Foxwood Close, Chesterfield, Derbyshire, S41 9RN Tel: (01246) 269955 Fax: (01246) 269944 E-mail: sales@britishrema.co.uk *Manufacturers of powder classifiers*

British Rototherm Co. Ltd, Kenfig Industrial Estate, Margam, Port Talbot, West Glamorgan, SA13 2PW Tel: (01656) 740551 Fax: (01656) 745915 E-mail: rototherm@rototherm.co.uk *Temperature & pressure instruments*

British Rubber Co., Station Road, Baildon, Shipley, West Yorkshire, BD17 6SE Tel: (01274) 585427 Fax: (01274) 532816 E-mail: britishrub@aol.com *Tyre wholesalers & distributors*

British Safety Council Services, 70 Chancellors Road, London, W6 9RS Tel: (020) 8741 1231 Fax: (020) 8741 4555 E-mail: mail@britsafe.org *Independent health & safety body*

British Salt Ltd, Cledford Lane, Middlewich, Cheshire, CW10 0JP Tel: (01606) 832881 Fax: (01606) 835999 E-mail: sales@british-salt.co.uk Principal Export Areas: Worldwide *Manufacturers of salt*

British Seals & Rubber Mouldings Ltd, Unit 7 Childerditch Indust Park, Childerditch Hall Drive, Brentwood, Essex, CM13 3HD Tel: (01277) 815300 Fax: (01277) 815350 E-mail: seals@british-gaskets.co.uk *Rubber & plastic factors suppliers & manufrs*

British Security Industry Association Ltd, Kirkham House, John Comin Drive, Worcester, WR3 7NS Tel: (0845) 3893889 E-mail: info@bsia.co.uk *Trade association*

British Security Technologies, 19 Hackford Walk, 119-123 Hackford Road, London, SW9 0QT Tel: (01424) 883275 E-mail: britsectec@aol.com *Security systems company*

British Shielding Windows, Unit 16 Ffordd Richard Davies, St. Asaph Business Park, St. Asaph, Clwyd, LL17 0LJ Tel: (01745) 536730 Fax: (01745) 536735 E-mail: sales@bswin.com *Shielding window manufrs*

British Silverware Ltd, Windsor Street, Sheffield, S4 7WB Tel: 0114-286 0500 Fax: 0114-286 0501 E-mail: office@britishsilverware.co.uk *Sterling silver & silver plated gifts, cutlery & silverware manufrs*

British Soft Drinks Association Ltd, 20-22 Stukeley Street, London, WC2B 5LR Tel: (020) 7430 0356 Fax: (020) 7831 6014 E-mail: bsda@britishsoftdrinks.com *Trade protection association*

British Standard Gratings, 2 Springhill Trading Eastate, Aston Street, Shifnal, Shropshire, TF11 8DR Tel: (01952) 277777 Fax: (01952) 277778 *Steel fabricators*

British Standards Institution, 389 Chiswick High Road, London, W4 4AL Tel: (020) 8996 9000 Fax: (020) 8996 7400 E-mail: info@bsi-global.com *British standard publishing & sales*

British Sugar plc, Cantley Sugar Factory, Cantley, Norwich, NR13 3ST Tel: (01493) 700351 Fax: (01493) 724203 *Sugar manufrs*

British Timbermasters, Thame Road, Brill, Aylesbury, Buckinghamshire, HP18 9SA Tel: (01844) 237633 E-mail: sales@swedish-log-cabins.com *Timber framed buildings*

British Trimmings Ltd, Coronation Street, Stockport, Cheshire, SK5 7PJ Tel: 0161-480 6122 Fax: 0161-477 1789 E-mail: uk.sales@btrim.co.uk *Furnishing trimmings manufrs*

The British Turned Parts Manufacturers Association, Heathcote House, 136 Hagley Road, Edgbaston, Birmingham, B16 9PN Tel: 0121-454 4141 Fax: 0121-454 4949 E-mail: heathcotes@btinternet.com *Trade association*

British Velvets Ltd, Wyre Street, Padiham, Burnley, Lancashire, BB12 8DQ Tel: (01282) 778134 Fax: (01282) 772168 E-mail: sales@britishvelvets.co.uk *Velvet manufrs*

British Water Ltd, 1 Queen Annes Gate, London, SW1H 9BT Tel: (020) 7957 4554 Fax: (020) 7957 4565 E-mail: info@britishwater.co.uk *Trade association for water industry*

British Wood Preserving & Damp Proofing Association, 1 Gleneagles House, Vernon Gate, Derby, DE1 1UP Tel: (01332) 225100 Fax: (01332) 225101 *Trade association*

▶ Britmilk, Ballantrae House, Collin, Dumfries, DG1 4PT Tel: (01387) 750459 Fax: (01387) 750243 E-mail: info@britmilk.co.uk

Britom Contractors Ltd, Valley Ind Est, Valley Rd, Earlswood, Solihull, W. Midlands, B94 6AA Tel: 01564 703366 *Excavation & groundwork contractors*

Briton EMS Ltd, 4 Shuttleworth Road, Elms Industrial Estate, Bedford, MK41 0EP Tel: (01234) 266300 Fax: (01234) 266488 E-mail: sales@britonems.co.uk *Electronics manufrs*

Briton Ferry Stevedoring Ltd, Giants Wharf, Briton Ferry, Neath, West Glamorgan, SA11 2LP Tel: (01639) 825700 Fax: (01639) 822912 E-mail: bfss@dial.pipex.com *Stevedoring services & ship agents*

Briton Plant Installation, 8 Woodfield Road, Welwyn Garden City, Hertfordshire, AL7 1JQ Tel: (01707) 885732 Fax: (01707) 882566 E-mail: britton.plant@ntlbusiness.com *Engineering to plastics industry*

Britool Ltd, Churchbridge Works, Walsall Road, Cannock, Staffordshire, WS11 3JR Tel: (01922) 702100 Fax: (01922) 702101 E-mail: uk_sales@britool.co.uk Principal Export Areas: Worldwide *Tool box & wrench manufrs*

Britorion Ltd, PO Box 98, Alton, Hampshire, GU34 4YL Tel: (01420) 22134 Fax: (01420) 520345 E-mail: britorion@aol.com *Military equipment, protective clothing & footwear*

Britsoft Barcode Systems Ltd, 1 Kings Road, Hertford, SG13 7EY Tel: (01992) 554552 Fax: (01992) 552426 E-mail: sales@britsoft.com *Barcode systems integrators*

Britspace Modular Buildings, Unicorn House, Broad Lane, Gilberdyke, Brough, East Yorkshire, HU15 2TS Tel: (01430) 444400 Fax: (01430) 444401 E-mail: info@britspace.com *Bespoke modular building manufacturers*

Brittain Adams (Holdings) Ltd, 40 The Boulevard, Stoke-on-Trent, ST6 6DP Tel: (01782) 834175 Fax: (01782) 834176 *Plumbers merchant & heating contractors*

M. Brittain (York) Ltd, Unit 12 Barclay Curle Works, 739 South Street, Glasgow, G14 0AH Tel: 0141-950 1400 Fax: 0141-950 1393 *Steel stockholders*

▶ Brittains Removals, Alington Road, Eynesbury St Neots, St. Neots, Cambridgeshire, PE19 6YH Tel: (01480) 405161 E-mail: admin@brittainsremovals.co.uk

Brittan Design Partnership, 7 The Old Fire Station Annexe, Fairfield Road, Market Harborough, Leicestershire, LE16 9QJ Tel: (01858) 466950 Fax: (01858) 434632 E-mail: enquiry@goto-bdp.co.uk *Advertising design & web development consultants*

▶ Brittania Heatex Ltd, Unit 36-38 Coleshill Industrial Estate, Station Road, Coleshill, Birmingham, B46 1JP Tel: (01675) 466060 Fax: (01675) 467675 E-mail: info@britheat.co.uk *New design, or the replacement of existing equipment (often superior to the original), expertise in the design & manufacture of heat exchanger for a wide variety of market sectors. With an emphasis on producing innovative solutions on short lead times, from failure investigation, through repair or remanufacture, to new design & build**

Brittania Leeds Bradford Airport, Leeds Road, Bramhope, Leeds, LS16 9JJ Tel: 0113-284 3966 Fax: (0845) 8385552 *Conference facilities & hotel services*

Brittanic Software Services Ltd, 2 Mount Pleasant Rd, Aldershot, Hants, GU12 4NL Tel: 01252 334469 Fax: 01252 334434 *Software consulting*

▶ Brittany Ferries Freight, New Harbour Road, Poole, Dorset, BH15 4AJ Tel: (0870) 9013300 Fax: (0870) 9011200

Britten Engineering Ltd, 12 Morris Road, Leicester, LE2 6BR Tel: 0116-270 0448 Fax: 0116-270 4998 *Engineering sub-contractors*

Britter & Co., Enterprise House, 14B White Horse Street, Baldock, Hertfordshire, SG7 6QN Tel: (01462) 894200 Fax: (01462) 893636 E-mail: britterco@aol.com *Chartered patent agents & trade mark agents*

Britton Decoflex Ltd, Skerne Road, Oakesway Industrial Estate, Hartlepool, Cleveland, TS24 0RH Tel: (01429) 272102 Fax: (01429) 860388 E-mail: smrsales@britton-group.com *Flexible packaging manufrs*

Britton Engineering, Carlyon Road, Atherstone, Warwickshire, CV9 1LQ Tel: (01827) 712578 Fax: (01827) 713561 E-mail: malcolm.crane@btconnect.com *General engineers*

Britton Gelplas Ltd, Venture House, 5th Avenue, Letchworth Garden City, Herts, SG6 1JT Tel: (01462) 480808 Fax: (01462) 481398 E-mail: roger.young@britton-group.com *Britton Gelplas is part of the Britton Group. Manufacturers of a diverse & flexible range of*

continued

polythene products. Servicing many markets, but highly geared to supplying the food industry certified manufacturer

▶ Britton Mailing, Unit 10 B, Temple Farm Industrial Estate, Sutton Road, Southend-on-Sea, SS2 5RD Tel: (01702) 468976 Fax: (01702) 469221 E-mail: enquiries@britton-group.co.uk *Polyethylene & polythene envelopes manufrs*

▶ Britton Packbourne Ltd, Unit 11, Ponders End Industrial Estate, Duck Lees Lane, Enfield, Middlesex, EN3 7UP Tel: (020) 8805 8000 Fax: (020) 8805 7727

Britton Packbourne Ltd, Unit 11 Ponders End Industrial Estate, 35 East Ducklees Lane, Ponders End, Enfield, Middlesex, EN3 7UP Tel: (020) 8805 8000 Fax: (020) 8805 7727 E-mail: sales@brittongrp-enfield.ffnet.co.uk *Polythene product manufrs*

Britton Price Ltd, Unit 14 Hove Business Centre, Fonthill Road, Hove, East Sussex, BN3 6HA Tel: (01273) 235035 Fax: (01273) 235036 E-mail: sales@brittonprice.co.uk *Passenger lift designers installers & maintenance services*

Ronald Britton & Co., Lower Eccleshill Road, Darwen, Lancashire, BB3 0RP Tel: (01254) 874750 Fax: (01254) 873009 E-mail: lara.thornhill@r-britton.com *Metal powder, glitter & bronze suppliers*

▶ Britton Taco Ltd, Road One Industrial Estate, Winsford Industrial Estate, Winsford, Cheshire, CW7 3RD Tel: (01606) 593434 Fax: (01606) 866423 E-mail: team@taco.co.uk *Polyethylene film extruders*

Brittons Ltd, Waterlip Works, Cranmore, Shepton Mallet, Somerset, BA4 4RW Tel: (01749) 880371 Fax: (01749) 880347 E-mail: sales@brittons-uk.com *Reconditioned gear boxes & electric motors repairers*

Britvic Northern Ireland, 468-472 Castlereagh Road, Belfast, BT5 6RG Tel: (028) 9079 9335 Fax: (028) 9070 7206 E-mail: james.simpson@candcgroup.ie *Soft drinks distributors*

Britvic Soft Drinks Ltd, Wellington Parkway, Magna Park, Lutterworth, Leicestershire, LE17 4XW Tel: (01455) 559772 Fax: (01455) 551449 *Soft drinks manufrs*

Britvic Soft Drinks Ltd, Aventine Way, Glebe Farm Industrial Estate, Rugby, Warwickshire, CV21 1HA Tel: (01788) 538800 Fax: (01788) 538817 *Soft drinks manufacturer*

Brixham Joinery, 8 Brixham Enterprise Estate, Rea Barn Road, Brixham, Devon, TQ5 9DF Tel: (01803) 853138 Fax: (01803) 853138 *Joinery manufrs*

Brixham Marine Services Ltd, Unit 21 Northfields Industrial Estate, Brixham, Devon, TQ5 8UA Tel: (01803) 854224 Fax: (01803) 857363 E-mail: salesandservice@bmslimited.co.uk *Marine engineers*

Brixton Plc, 50 Berkeley St, London, W1J 8BX Tel: (020) 7399 4500 Fax: (020) 7399 4550 *Property development company*

BRM, 1 Block 4, Cocker Avenue, Poulton Industrial Estate, Poulton-le-Fylde, Lancashire, FY6 8JU Tel: (01253) 885270 Fax: (01253) 884485 E-mail: enquiries@brmeng.co.uk Sales Contact: G Worrall *Suppliers of Nut, Bolts, Abrasives, Cutting Wheels, Set Screws, Cap Screws, Wood Screws, Taps, Dies, Rivets, Hand & Electrical tools, Fixings. Welding Suppliers. Full range of "V" Belts. Welding and Fabrication in mild steel and stainless steel.*

Broad Lane Caravans Ltd, 1 Somers Road, Rugby, Warwickshire, CV22 7DB Tel: (01788) 542672 Fax: (01788) 546109 E-mail: rugby@broadlane.co.uk *Caravan sales & service*

▶ Broad Oak Colour Printers, A-D 254 Broad Oak Road, Canterbury, Kent, CT2 7QH Tel: (01227) 767856 Fax: (01227) 762593

Broad Oak Gears Ltd, Old Warburton Bakery, Jacob Street, Accrington, Lancashire, BB5 1HU Tel: (01254) 397489 Fax: (01254) 390550 E-mail: bogears@aol.com *Gear wheel manufrs*

Broad Oak Toiletries Ltd, Tiverton Way, Tiverton Business Park, Tiverton, Devon, EX16 6TG Tel: (01884) 242626 Fax: (01884) 242602 *Manufacturers of toiletries & soaps*

Broad Oak Woodcraft Ltd, Grange Farm Regis, Hatfield Broad Oak, Bishop's Stortford, Hertfordshire, CM22 7JZ Tel: (01279) 718549 Fax: (01279) 718549 *Pine furniture manufrs*

▶ Broad System, Building 1, Chalfont Park, Gerrards Cross, Buckinghamshire, SL9 0GA Tel: (01753) 433000 Fax: (01753) 433333 E-mail: enquiries@broadsystem.com *Broadsystem is the UK"s leading provider of outsourced marketing communications. Broadsystem creates, manages and delivers multi-channel customer communication strategies. We develop, host, and manage marketing databases for our clients and, through the intelligent analysis of marketing data, deliver and handle their messages through integrated multi-channel communications.**Our services include: Data Management, Data Processing, Data Analytics, Customer Campaign Management, Email MArketing, In and Outbound Call Handling, IVR, Voice Recognition, Logistics and Fulfilment, Mobile Marketing Services and Information Lines.**Our extensive experience spans a wide range of industry sectors including; Retail, Travel & Lesiure, Utilities, Publishing, Charity, Public Sector, Loyalty & Subscriptions, Healthcare & Pharmaceuticals, Financial Services and IT & Telecoms.*

▶ Broadband Ltd, 46 Station Road, North Harrow, Harrow, Middlesex, HA2 7SE Tel: (0845) 658 1110 Fax: (08715) 227 075 E-mail: gsmgateways@broadbandltd.co.uk *Broadband ltd is a leading independent value added reseller of a complete range of broadband, GSM Gateways and all telecommunication solutions. GSM Gateways, Broadband, High speed Internet access, CPS (carrier pre-selection), LCR (least cost routing), Premicells, Business Mobile, Telecommunications, Telecom's, FCT Fixed Cellular Terminals, GSM Gateway, Mobile, Cheap mobile calls, Low Cost Calls, ADSL, SDSL, IP Leased line, Voip, Vpn, HDSL, Business broadband, Broadband provider,*

continued

Bandwidth, Voice over IP, Pbx, modems/Routers, Voip switch, voip gateway, Isdn pbx, Dial-up internet access, SMS Messages.

Broadband Connections Ltd, 6-8 Oakway, London, SW20 9JE Tel: (020) 8543 5228 Fax: (020) 8241 2061 *Computer consultants*

Broadbent & Co. Ltd, Unit 14a Colwick Business Park, Private Road No 2, Colwick Industrial Estate, Nottingham, NG4 2JR Tel: 0115-940 0777 Fax: 0115-987 3744 E-mail: info@industrialcleaningequipment.co.uk *Industrial cleaning equipment, scrubber driers & sweepers*

Broadbent Drives, Britannia Mills, Portland Street, Bradford, West Yorkshire, BD5 0DW Tel: (01274) 783434 Fax: (01274) 390527 E-mail: sales@broadbent-drives.co.uk *Based in Bradford, covering the whole of the UK and exporting throughout Europe we manufacture the Broadbent range of clutches and brakes and distribute the Noram and Marzorati ranges of clutches and gearboxes. We supply centrifugal clutches, centrifugal brakes, clutch brakes, electromagnetic brakes, and torque limiting clutches. We specialize in the Noram range of karting clutches and also Marzorati gearboxes, bevel gearboxes, angle gearboxes, phasing systems, coaxial phasing systems, angle phase shiffting units, change speed gear units and screw jacks. We also supply compactor clutches, wacker plate clutches, rammer clutches, lawn tractor clutches and lawn tractor clutch-brakes. Our large workshop is able to produce a large variety of bespoke components using CNC horizontal machining centres, CNC vertical machining centres, CNC lathes, and CNC Drills as well as conventional machining and fabrication.*

Broadbent Engineering, The Forge, Pavement Lane, Mobberley, Knutsford, Cheshire, WA16 7ED Tel: (01565) 889000 Fax: (01565) 872067 E-mail: sales@broadbentsforge.com *Iron workers*

Broadbridge Precision Engineering Ltd, 1-5 Marters Avenue, Langley Green, Crawley, West Sussex, RH11 7RX Tel: (01293) 525260 Fax: (01293) 561668 E-mail: broadbridge.eng@pncl.co.uk *Prototype & instrument engineers*

▶ Broadcast Services, The Coach House, Ruxbury Road, Chertsey, Surrey, KT16 9EP Tel: (01932) 570001 Fax: (01932) 570443 E-mail: hire@broadcast-services.co.uk *Broadcast equipment production & facilities hire*

▶ Broadcast Traffic Systems, Chapel Barns, Merthyr Mawr, Bridgend, CF32 0LS Tel: (01656) 648181 *Supply of computer software applications to the broadcast industry*

Broadcliffe Fabrications, Cragg Vale, Hebden Bridge, West Yorkshire, HX7 5RU Tel: (01422) 884030 Fax: (01422) 884030 *Steel fabrications*

Broadfield Plastics Ltd, Foxcroft Street, Littleborough, Lancashire, OL15 8LB Tel: (01706) 378636 Fax: (01706) 377131 E-mail: sales@broadfieldplastics.co.uk *Glass fibre moulding manufrs*

▶ Broadhay Consulting Services, PO Box 6448, Poole, Dorset, BH12 9BZ Tel: 01202 650069 Fax: 0870 762 6135 E-mail: csh@broadhay.co.uk *We are a services company specialising in electrical engineering services to create safe environments within buildings and to meet electrical legislation. Staff members include MIEE Engineer, NICEIC Inspector*Services include Design services for all types of Buildings Design Components include electrical installations, Fire Alarms & Emergency lighting, Power, Air Conditioning & Ventilation, Lighting, Data and Audio Visual Installations. *Production of detailed specifications & drawings of Electrical Service requirements to satisfy IEE requirements and to enable NICEIC Certification.*Electrical Site Surveys Anytime anywhere. Full reports with photographic evidence within 24 hours with survey benchmarks to Industry regulations NICEIC - BSI - IEE standards*Information on equipment and fittings to advise on: Safety, cost effectiveness, mintainability, Site Audits, Feasibility studies, Options Appraisals**

▶ Broadhempston Plant Hire Ltd, Fairfax Road, Heathfield Industrial Estate, Newton Abbot, Devon, TQ12 6UD Tel: (01626) 832290 Fax: (01626) 201131

Broadhurst Bros Burslem Ltd, Waterloo Road, Burslem, Stoke-on-Trent, ST6 2EL Tel: (01782) 834561 Fax: (01782) 832102 *China manufrs*

Broadhurst Clarkson & Fuller Ltd, 63 Farringdon Road, London, EC1M 3JB Tel: (020) 7405 2156 Fax: (020) 7430 2471 E-mail: info@telescopehouse.co.uk *Telescope suppliers*

Broadland Ceramics, 8 Moores Industrial Estate, High Street, Stalham, Norwich, NR12 9AN Tel: (01692) 582528 Fax: (01692) 583403 E-mail: sales@broadlandceramics.co.uk *Ceramic manufrs*

Broadland Foods Ltd, Great Barr Street, Birmingham, B9 4BB Tel: 0121-773 5955 Fax: 0121-771 1207 E-mail: broadland@chobby.fsnet.co.uk *Edible oil & fat producers, refiners & merchants*

▶ Broadland Hosting, 11 Mill Crescent, Acle, Norwich, NR13 3BL Tel: (01493) 750428 *Quality Shared cPanel Hosting.*

▶ Broadland Interior Systems, The Bearings, Bowbridge Road, Newark, Nottinghamshire, NG24 4BZ Tel: (01636) 700744 *Ceiling manufrs*

Broadland Passenger Craft, George Smith & Sons, The Rhond, Hoveton, Norwich, NR12 8UE Tel: (01603) 782527 Fax: (01603) 784124 *Boat repairers & hirers*

▶ Broadland Plastics Ltd, Sutton Road, Catfield, Great Yarmouth, Norfolk, NR29 5BG Tel: 01692 580080 Fax: 01692 580801 E-mail: simon@broadlandplastics.co.uk *We are a manufacturing company that"s based in Norfolk in the Broadland area we have been in business since 1994 specializing in flexible plastics such as PVC, PEVA and PU coated fabrics. We use the method of high frequency welding, sewing and impulse heat sealing.*

▶ Broadland Products, Unit 22 Littlewood Lane, Hoveton, Norwich, NR12 8DZ Tel: (01603) 783083 Fax: (01603) 783084 E-mail: sales@broadlandproducts.co.uk *Steel fabrication*

Broadland Radiators & Heat Exchangers Ltd, Burton Road, Norwich, NR6 6AU Tel: (01603) 413050 Fax: (01603) 413066 E-mail: sales@broadlandradiators.co.uk *Diesel engine, radiator & heat exchanger manufacturer & designers & repair*

Broadland Sevices Ltd, 2D Wellesley Road, Tharston, Norwich, NR15 2PD Tel: (01508) 532100 Fax: (01508) 532292 E-mail: info@bstrip.com *Suspended ceilings & partitions services*

Broadland Stainless Ltd, New Road, Acle, Norwich, NR13 3BD Tel: (01493) 753933 Fax: (01493) 753944 E-mail: sales@broadlandstainless.co.uk *Manufacture stainless steel products*

▶ Broadland Windows Ltd, 148 Hellesdon Park Road, Drayton High Road, Norwich, NR6 5DR Tel: (01603) 483002 Fax: (01603) 485946 E-mail: sales@broadlandwindows.co.uk

Broadleaf Engineering, 1 Craven Street, Leicester, LE1 4BX Tel: 0116-253 9200 Fax: 0116-253 0598 *Precision engineers & fabricators*

▶ Broadleaze Transport, Noahs Cottage, Cricklade, Swindon, SN6 6HU Tel: (01793) 751129 Fax: (01793) 750022

Broadmoor Brickworks Ltd, Whimsey Industrial Estate, Steam Mills, Whimsey, Cinderford, Gloucestershire, GL14 3JA Tel: (01594) 822255 Fax: (01594) 826782 E-mail: sales@broadmoor-brickworks.co.uk *Brick manufrs*

▶ Broadnet Systems & Solutions, 1st Floor, 148 High Street, Berkhamsted, Hertfordshire, HP4 3AT Tel: (01442) 879090 Fax: (01442) 873210 E-mail: sales@broadnetsystems.com *Net workers*

▶ Broadoak Construction Southeast Ltd, Triumph House, Guildford Road, Bookham, Leatherhead, Surrey, KT23 4HB Tel: (01372) 453111 Fax: (01372) 452193 E-mail: sales@broadoak-construction.co.uk

Broadoak Controls Ltd, Broadoak Enterprise Centre, Broadoak Road, Sittingbourne, Kent, ME9 8AQ Tel: (01795) 421900 Fax: (01795) 421900 *Control panels designers & manufrs*

Broadoak Manufacturing Ltd, The Forge, Cricket Hill Lane, Yateley, Hampshire, GU46 6BB Tel: (01252) 890707 Fax: (01252) 890808 *Rubber mouldings manufrs*

Broads Tours Ltd, Faircroft Loynes, The Bridge, Wroxham, Norwich, NR12 8RX Tel: (01603) 782207 Fax: (01603) 784272 E-mail: info@broads.co.uk *Boat Hire /Leasing*

Broadskill Ltd, Hinderton Grange, Quarry Road, Neston, CH64 7UD Tel: 0151-336 8899 Fax: 0151-336 7799 E-mail: admin@broadskill.com *Business training & development services*

Broadstock Office Furniture Ltd, Brunel Road, Lyme Green Business Park, London Road, Macclesfield, Cheshire, SK11 0TA Tel: (01625) 431979 Fax: (01625) 511136 E-mail: enquire@broadstock.co.uk *Office furniture manufrs*

Broadsword Projects Ltd, Unit 13 Westwood Court, Brunel Road, Totton, Southampton, SO40 3WX Tel: (023) 8067 5888 Fax: (023) 8067 5999 *Suspended ceilings & partitioning installation services*

Broadview Blinds Ltd, 57 Hatch Pond Road, Nuffield Industrial Estate, Poole, Dorset, BH17 0JZ Tel: (01202) 679012 Fax: (01202) 671885 E-mail: sales@broadview-blinds.co.uk *The UK's leading manufacturer, supplier & installer to the trade, contract & retail, of all types of interior & exterior window blinds, awnings, garage doors & shutters for domestic & commercial premises. We also produce Venetian and pinoleum blinds as well as canopy shades and roller garage doors. Please contact us for a helpful, personal service.*

▶ Broadview Builders, Marshlands Lane, Heathfield, East Sussex, TN21 8EX Tel: (01435) 864924 Fax: (01435) 867544

Broadwater Mouldings Ltd, Denham Site, Horham Road, Denham, Eye, Suffolk, IP21 5DQ Tel: (01379) 384145 Fax: (01379) 384150 E-mail: info@broadwater.co.uk *Glass fibre mouldings manufrs*

Broadway & Co. Ltd, Shady Lane, Birmingham, B44 9ER Tel: 0121-360 0606 Fax: 0121-360 7880 E-mail: information@broadwaysilver.uk.com *Manufacturing silversmiths*

▶ Broadway Ceramics, 23 Broadway Market, London, E8 4PH Tel: (020) 7923 7632 *Ceramic suppliers*

Broadway Computer Cleaning Service, 45 Broadway, Gillingham, Kent, ME8 6BA Tel: (01634) 232974 *Computer & telephone cleaning services*

Broadway Electrical Services, 36 The Broadway, Grays, Essex, RM17 6EW Tel: (01375) 372782 Fax: (01375) 381457 E-mail: broadwayelectrical@lycos.co.uk *Auto electrical services*

Broadway Group, 136 Stanwell Road, Ashford, Middlesex, TW15 3QP Tel: (0845) 6019006 Fax: (0845) 6019007 E-mail: ppstechnical@yahoo.co.uk *Water industry component designers & contractors manufrs*

Broadway Malyan, 3 Weybridge Business Park, Addlestone Road, Addlestone, Surrey, KT15 2BW Tel: (01932) 845599 Fax: (01932) 856206 E-mail: man@broadwaymalyan.com *Town planning consultants*

Broadway Signs, Unit 18 Elmbourne Industrial Estate, Crabtree Manorway, Belvedere, Kent, DA17 6AW Tel: (020) 8310 8100 Fax: (020) 8310 1950 E-mail: curwood1954@hotmail.com *General sign makers*

Broadway Stamping Ltd, Denbigh Road, Bletchley, Milton Keynes, MK1 1DT Tel: (01908) 647703 Fax: (01908) 649279 E-mail: broadways@broadwaysstampings.co.uk *Pressed parts manufrs*

Company Information

Broadweave, Hayhill Industrial Estate, Barrow Upon Soar, Loughborough, Leicestershire, LE12 8LD Tel: (01509) 816123 Fax: (01509) 814867 E-mail: sales@broadweaveltd.co.uk *Workwear suppliers*

Broadwood International, Trading Estate, Oakhanger Road, Bordon, Hampshire, GU35 9HH Tel: (01420) 478111 Fax: (01420) 483000 E-mail: info@wessexmachinery.co.uk *Agricultural implement manufrs*

D.J. Broady Ltd, Foster Street, Kingston Upon Hull, East Yorkshire, Hull, HU8 8BT Tel: (01482) 585985 Fax: (01482) 585995 *Demolition contractors, plant & transport hire*

▶ Broch Computer Services, 21 Commerce Street, Fraserburgh, Aberdeenshire, AB43 9AQ Tel: (01346) 512754 *Computer software consultants*

▶ Broch Information Services, Glendale, Bridge Street, Halkirk, Caithness, KW12 6YG Tel: (01847) 831828

Brochure Holders International Ltd, Victor Unit, Earls Colne Business Park, Earls Colne, Colchester, CO6 2NS Tel: (01787) 220700 Fax: (01787) 220701 E-mail: sales@brochureholders.co.uk *Injection moulded plastic & brochure holders*

Brock plc, New Hey, Chester Road, Great Sutton, Ellesmere Port, CH66 2LS Tel: 0151-339 8113 Fax: 0151-347 1254 *Land reclamation, plant & transport hire*

Brock plc, New Hey, Chester Road, Great Sutton, Ellesmere Port, CH66 2LS Tel: 0151-339 8113 Fax: 0151-347 1254 *Civil engineers & building developments*

Brock Brothers Builders Ltd, 20 Field Lane, Kessingland, Lowestoft, Suffolk, NR33 7QB Tel: (01502) 740617

Brock Carmichael Architects, 19 Old Hall Street, Liverpool, L3 9JQ Tel: 0151-242 6222 Fax: 0151-236 4467 E-mail: office@brockcarmichael.co.uk *Architects & planning consultants*

Brock Farm Supplies, Foxhouses Farm Cottage, Long Lane, Scorton, Preston, PR3 1DB Tel: (01524) 791170 *Farm supplies*

▶ L. & T.I. Brock & Co. Ltd, Unit 1 Falkland House, 19 Falkland Close, Charter Avenue Industrial Estate, Coventry, CV4 8AG Tel: (024) 7642 1200 Fax: (024) 7642 1459 E-mail: enquiries@tangi-flow.com *Precision Engineering*

Brock Metal Co., Walsall Road, Norton Canes, Cannock, Staffordshire, WS11 9NR Tel: (01543) 276666 Fax: (01543) 276418 E-mail: brock@brock-metal.co.uk *Metal alloy manufrs*

Brock Signs & Graphics Ltd, 32 Kansas Avenue, Salford, M50 2GL Tel: 0161-877 8484 Fax: 0161-877 8444 E-mail: sales@brocksigns.co.uk *Sign making*

Brocket Hall Ltd, Brocket Hall, Brocket Park, Lemsford, Welwyn Garden City, Hertfordshire, AL8 7XG Tel: (01707) 335241 Fax: (01707) 375166 E-mail: mail@brocket-hall.co.uk *Conference & incentive venue incorporating golf*

Brockham Computers, 7 Bishops Cottages Chalkpit Lane, Betchworth, Dorking, Surrey, RH3 7HA Tel: (01737) 842075 E-mail: keith@brockhamcomputers.co.uk *We offer a range of personal computer, laptop & software services*

Brockhill Enterprises Ltd, Hobson Lane, Kirkby Stephen, Cumbria, CA17 4RN Tel: (01768) 372027 Fax: (01768) 372049 E-mail: sales@brockhill.sagehost.co.uk Principal Export Areas: Worldwide *Cable assembly harness suppliers*

Brockinwood French Polishing, Unit 16 Admington Lane, Admington, Shipston-on-Stour, Warwickshire, CV36 4JJ Tel: (01789) 450914 *French polisher & furniture restorer*

John Brocklesby & Sons Ltd, Courtney Street, Hull, HU8 7QF Tel: (01482) 320120 Fax: (01482) 587005 *Ferrous & non-ferrous scrap merchants*

Brockmoor Foundry, The Leys, Brierley Hill, West Midlands, DY5 3UJ Tel: (01384) 480026 Fax: (01384) 480032 E-mail: sales@brockmoor.co.uk *Spherical graphite iron specialists & castings services*

Brock's Explosives Ltd, Gateside Factory, Sanquhar, Dumfriesshire, DG4 6JP Tel: (01659) 50531 Fax: (01659) 50526 *Pyrotechnics & explosive manufrs*

▶ Brocks Haulage Ltd, Beacon Hill Industrial Estate, Botany Way, Purfleet, Essex, RM19 1SR Tel: (01708) 861021 Fax: (01708) 864224

Brockstock, Overend Road, Corngreaves Trading Estate, Cradley Heath, West Midlands, B64 7DD Tel: 0121-568 6161 Fax: (01384) 567191 E-mail: sales@brockstock.co.uk *Steel stockholders & processors*

Brockway Carpets Ltd, Hoobrook, Kidderminster, Worcestershire, DY10 1XW Tel: (01562) 824737 Fax: (01562) 863598 E-mail: sales@brockway.co.uk *Carpets manufrs*

Brockwood Collection, Brockwood Hill Farm, Park Lane, Audley, Stoke-On-Trent, ST7 8HR Tel: (01782) 722569 Fax: (01782) 722569 E-mail: louise@brockwood.freeserve.co.uk *Furniture & gifts manufrs*

Brocol Engineers Supplies Ltd, 58 Hotchkiss Way, Binley Industrial Estate, Binley Industrial Estate, Coventry, CV3 2RL Tel: (024) 7644 1303 Fax: (024) 7644 1353 E-mail: sales@gtssltd.co.uk *Industrial fastener suppliers*

▶ Brocol Pipe Work Ltd, 62a Thornes Lane, Wakefield, West Yorkshire, WF1 5RR Tel: (01924) 380048 Fax: (01924) 380588

Brodersen Control Systems, Unit 11 Canbury Business Park, Elm Cresent, Kingston upon Thames, Surrey, KT2 6HJ Tel: (020) 8546 4283 Fax: (020) 8547 3628 E-mail: bcs@brodersen.co.uk *Control system distributors*

Brodex Ltd, Unit 4, 76 Stevenson Way, Formby, L37 8EG Tel: (01704) 834477 Fax: (01704) 833104 E-mail: brodex@ukonline.co.uk *Water treatment*

▶ Brodie Group Of Companies, Bathville Business Park, Armadale, Bathgate, West Lothian, EH48 2JS Tel: (01501) 733667

Brodie Label Services Ltd, 4 Dunnwoods Road, Cumbernauld, Glasgow, G67 3EN Tel: (01236) 736984 Fax: (01236) 731953 E-mail: info@brodielabels.co.uk *Label printers*

Brody International Ltd, Units 1-2, 18 Gillender Street, London, E3 3JW Tel: (020) 7538 5666 Fax: (020) 7510 1099E-mail: sales@brody.co.uk *Sequin manufrs*

Broen Valves Ltd, 7 Cleton Street Business Park, Cleton Street, Tipton, West Midlands, DY4 7TR Tel: 0121-522 4505 Fax: 0121-522 4535 E-mail: broenvalves@broen.com *Based in the West Midlands in the heart of the United Kingdom, BROEN Valves Ltd are ideally placed for the distribution of its product range throughout the United Kingdom and Ireland. BROEN Valves Ltd stock, market and distribute the products manufactured by the BROEN Lab Group, these products include Laboratory service fittings for water and gas, emergency shower and eye wash systems and ultra clean pressure regulators and quick release couplings for laboratory applications. The BROEN lab group are the world market leaders in the production and design of laboratory service fittings. Please see our website for more information, or contact us to discuss your requirements.*

Brogan Fuels, Nethan Street, Motherwell, Lanarkshire, ML1 3TF Tel: (01698) 265132 Fax: (01698) 262547 *Road transport, haulage & freight services*

▶ Broker Partners Ltd, Studio A Dean Mill, Plumbe Street, Burnley, Lancashire, BB11 3AG Tel: (01282) 453629 Fax: (01282) 453629 E-mail: sales@brokerpartners.co.uk *Computer software*

Brolyn Butchers Supplies, New Street, Bridgend Industrial Estate, Bridgend, Mid Glamorgan, CF31 3UD Tel: (01656) 668614 Fax: (01656) 668614 *Butchers sundries suppliers*

Bromac Machining Services Ltd, Cradley Heath Factory Centre, Woods Lane, Cradley Heath, West Midlands, B64 7AQ Tel: (01384) 637838 Fax: (01384) 637838 *Precision machinists*

Bromag Structures Ltd, Burford Road, Witney, Oxfordshire, OX29 0RE Tel: (01993) 703584 Fax: (01993) 772149 E-mail: jo@bromag.demon.co.uk *Mezzanine floor manufrs*

Bromak Ltd, Capitol House, 51 Churchgate, Bolton, BL1 1LY Tel: (01204) 532500 Fax: (01204) 363163 E-mail: enquiries@bromak.com *Recruitment consultancy, employment agency, recruitment agency; construction, social housing refurbishment, Civil Engineering, residential development,*

Bromakin Wheelchairs, 12 Prince William Road, Loughborough, Leicestershire, LE11 5GU Tel: (01509) 217569 Fax: (01509) 233954 E-mail: sales@bromakin.co.uk *Wheelchair manufrs*

Bromborough Plastics Ltd, Unit 1b Spencer Industrial Estate, Liverpool Road, Buckley, Clwyd, CH7 3LY Tel: (01244) 545202 Fax: (01244) 545202 *Plastic scrap recycling recovery contractors*

Paul Bromfield Aquatics, Maydencroft Lane, Gosmore, Hitchin, Hertfordshire, SG4 7QD Tel: (01462) 457399 Fax: (01462) 422652 *Aquatic nurseries*

Bromfield Precision Engineering Ltd, 905 Uxbridge Road, Uxbridge, Middlesex, UB10 0NH Tel: (020) 8573 8422 Fax: (020) 8569 2589 *CNC milling & engraving services*

Bromford Iron & Steel Co. Ltd, Bromford Lane, West Bromwich, West Midlands, B70 7JJ Tel: 0121-553 6121 Fax: 0121-525 0913 E-mail: enquiries@bromfordsteels.co.uk *Hot rolled flats, bars & sections*

Bromhead & Co., 37 Great James Street, London, WC1N 3HB Tel: (020) 7405 7010 Fax: (020) 7831 5118 E-mail: mail@bromhead-johnson.com *Chartered patent & trade mark agents*

Bromhead Johnson, Kingsbourne House, 19 Buckingham Street, London, WC2N 6EF Tel: (020) 7839 4935 Fax: (020) 7839 6898 E-mail: mail@bromhead-johnson.com *Trademark agents*

Bromley Brush Co Kent Ltd, 1 Pembroke Road, Bromley, BR1 2TJ Tel: (020) 8464 1707 Fax: (020) 8313 3494 *Brush makers & janitorial suppliers*

Bromley Car Audio, 50 Homesdale Road, Bromley, BR2 9LD Tel: (020) 8460 8704 Fax: (020) 8460 8704 E-mail: sales@caraudioonline.co.uk *Car audio equipment manufrs*

Bromley Demolition Co. Ltd, 75 Siward Road, Bromley, BR2 9JY Tel: (020) 8464 3610 Fax: (020) 8313 3623 E-mail: info@bromleydem.co.uk *Demolition contractors*

Bromley Enterprises UK Ltd, Unit 7 Bruntingthorpe Industrial Estate, Upper Bruntingthorpe, Lutterworth, Leicestershire, LE17 5QZ Tel: 0116-247 8912 Fax: 0116-247 8969 E-mail: bromleyenterprises@googlemail.com *Metal treatment for rubber industry*

Norman Bromley Partnership, Bridge House, 99-101 High Street, Tonbridge, Kent, TN9 1DR Tel: (01732) 773737 Fax: (01732) 773353 E-mail: mail@normanbromley.co.uk *Engineering consultants*

Bromley Pest Control, 4-20 Oaklands Road, Bromley, BR1 3SL Tel: (020) 8466 5079 Fax: (020) 8466 5079 *Pest & vermin controllers property hygiene service*

Bromley Sameday Couriers, 16 Amesbury Road, Bromley, BR1 2QJ Tel: (07783) 238436 E-mail: jamesmaycock@bromleysamedaycouriers.co.uk *Sameday courier services. Specialists in Direct Dispatch. Nationwide coverage. Professional and reliable service.*

Bromley Sewing Machines, 30 Homesdale Road, Bromley, BR2 9LD Tel: (020) 8460 7865 Fax: (020) 8313 9993 *Sewing machines*

Bromsgrove Advertiser & Messenger, 5 High Street, Bromsgrove, Worcestershire, B61 8AJ Tel: (01527) 837000 Fax: (01527) 877456 E-mail: carol.hinett@newsquestmidlands.co.uk *Media*

Bromsgrove Glass & Windows Ltd, Sherwood Road, Aston Fields Industrial Estate, Bromsgrove, Worcestershire, B60 3DR Tel: (01527) 836777 Fax: (01527) 579148 E-mail: enquiries@bromsgroveglass.co.uk *Glass processors & aluminium, upvc windows manufrs*

Bromsgrove Guild Ltd, 233 Worcester Road, Stoke Heath, Bromsgrove, Worcestershire, B61 7JA Tel: (01527) 833198 *Concrete products manufrs*

Bromsgrove & Redditch Trophies Ltd, 485 Evesham Road, Redditch, Worcestershire, B97 5JJ Tel: (01527) 550556 Fax: (01527) 550866 E-mail: admin@brchc.u-net.com *Engravers & sports trophy retailers*

Bromyard Engineering Company Ltd, 23 Rowberry Street, Bromyard, Herefordshire, HR7 4DT Tel: (01885) 483257 Fax: (01885) 488028 E-mail: linda@bromyard.com *Sub-contract engineering services*

Bromyard Timber & Fencing Ltd, Station Road, Bromyard, Herefordshire, HR7 4NT Tel: (01885) 482443 Fax: (01885) 489053 *Fencing manufrs*

▶ Bronte Precision Engineering, Unit 1, Hanworth Road, Low Moor, Bradford, West Yorkshire, BD12 0SG Tel: (01274) 698900 Fax: (01274) 698909 E-mail: mail@bpel.co.uk *Bronte Precision offer a full CNC Manufacturing Service combined with a comprehensive Gear Manufacturing Capability. We specialise in the manufacture of Medium to Large Sized Components in Low to Medium Volumes. CNC Turning up to 800mm Dia and CNC Milling up to 2000mm x 00mm x 00mm. Based in Bradford, West Yorkshire. Click the links below to visit our website or contact us via our profile page.*

Bronze Mechanical Ltd, Trading Estate, Motherwell Way, Grays, Essex, RM20 3XD Tel: (01708) 862444 Fax: (01708) 867890 E-mail: bronze@machanicalhandling.freeserve.com *Fork lift trucks, sales, hire & repair*

Bronzefern Ltd, 9 Orchard Close, Gravenhurst, Bedford, MK45 4JF Tel: (01462) 711400 Fax: (01462) 713162 E-mail: john@bronzefern.demon.co.uk *Computer consultants*

Bronzeshield Lifting Ltd, Vitbe Bungalow, Thames Road, Crayford, Dartford, DA1 4QH Tel: (01322) 555050 Fax: (01322) 550099 *Crane hire & services*

Bronzeshield Lifting Ltd, Vitbe Bungalow, Thames Road, Crayford, Dartford, DA1 4QH Tel: (01322) 555050 Fax: (01322) 550099 *Crane hire, sales & service*

Arthur Brook Ltd, Low Mill Lane, Ravensthorpe Industrial Estate, Dewsbury, West Yorkshire, WF13 3LN Tel: (01924) 492457 Fax: (01924) 480466 *Scrap iron & metal merchants*

Brook Bank Joinery, 15 Lenton Street, Sheffield, S2 4BH Tel: 0114-273 9086 *Joinery manufrs*

Brook Crompton, St. Thomas Road, Huddersfield, HD1 3LJ Tel: (01484) 557200 Fax: (01484) 557201 E-mail: csc@brookcrompton.com *Electric motor manufrs* Also at: Leicester

Brook Design Hardware Ltd, Brook House, Dunmurry Industrial Estate, Dunmurry, Belfast, BT17 9HU Tel: (028) 9061 6505 Fax: (028) 9061 6518 E-mail: sales@brookvent.co.uk *Ventilation systems manufrs & distributors*

Brook Dyeing Co. Ltd, Slaithwaite Dyeworks, Britannia Mills, Slaithwaite, Huddersfield, HD7 5HE Tel: (01484) 842345 Fax: (01484) 843640 *Commission dyers*

Brook International, Flagship House, Riparian Way, Cross Hills, Keighley, West Yorkshire, BD20 7BW Tel: (01535) 639020 Fax: (01535) 639029 E-mail: info@brookinternational.com *Suppliers of flag & banner fabrics & fabrics for digital printing*

Brook & Mayo Electrical, Acorn House, Lindum Business Park, Station Road, North Hykeham, Lincoln, LN6 3YL Tel: (01522) 686851 Fax: (01522) 686843 E-mail: nick@brookandmayo.co.uk *Electrical contractors & alarm installers*

▶ Brook Metal Design Ltd, Brook Farm Industrial Estate, Stapleford Road, Romford, RM4 1EJ Tel: (01708) 687420 *Metal workers*

Brook Miller Mobility Ltd, Ability House, Owler Ings Road, Brighouse, West Yorkshire, HD6 1EH Tel: (01484) 721772 Fax: (01484) 401242 E-mail: sales@brookmobility.co.uk *Specialist mobility services*

Brook Signs, 6 Cedar House, Caen Street, Braunton, Devon, EX33 1AH Tel: (01271) 812300 *Sign making*

Brook Street Bureau, Hatfield Road, St. Albans, Hertfordshire, AL1 4JB Tel: (01727) 848292 Fax: (01727) 846654 *Recruitment consultants*

Brook Street Metal Co. Ltd, Bridge Street, Bury, Lancashire, BL9 6HH Tel: 0161-764 4950 Fax: 0161-764 4619 *Scrap metal merchants & waste contractors skip hire*

Brooke Ltd, 324a Holderness Road, Hull, HU9 3DE Tel: (01482) 320592 Fax: (01482) 213193 *Tools, hardware & ceramics manufrs*

Brooke Air, J C House, Hurricane Way, Wickford, Essex, SS11 8YB Tel: (01268) 572266 Fax: (01268) 560606 E-mail: jcv@jchouse.freeserve.co.uk *Air diffusion equipment, heating & ventilating grilles suppliers*

Brooke Concrete Products Ltd, Monksbridge Road, Dinnington, Sheffield, S25 3QS Tel: (01909) 550455 Fax: (01909) 568780 E-mail: claz.smyth@brooke.concrete.co.uk *Concrete block paving services*

Brooke Cutting Tools (UK) Ltd, Denby Way, Hellaby, Rotherham, South Yorkshire, S66 8HU Tel: (01709) 314500 Fax: (01709) 314501 E-mail: info@brooke.co.uk *Cutting tools manufacturers & distributors*

▶ K Brooke & Son, 7 Broomfield Road, Marsh, Huddersfield, HD1 4QD Tel: (01484) 425286 Fax: (01484) 364727 E-mail: michael@brookeprinters.com *Specialists in printing letter headings & business cards*

Brooker Mouldings Ltd, 4 Vickers Business Centre, Priestley Road, Basingstoke, Hampshire, RG24 9NP Tel: (01256) 356523 Fax: (01256) 328281 *Plastic mould manufrs*

Brookers Builders Merchants Ltd, 43-53 Norman Road, St. Leonards-on-Sea, East Sussex, TN38 0EQ Tel: (01424) 423107 Fax: (01424) 718341 *Plumber's & builders merchants*

Brookes Batchellor, 102-108 Clerkenwell Road, London, EC1M 5SA Tel: (020) 7253 1563 Fax: (020) 7253 1214 *Chartered patent & trademark agents*

Brookes Bell Jarrett Kirman LLP, Martins Building, Exchange Flags, Liverpool, L2 3PG Tel: 0151-236 0083 Fax: 0151-236 2945 E-mail: liv@brookesbell.com *Marine consultants, consulting engineers & marine surveyors* Also at: London E14

D. Brookes & Son (Timber) Ltd, Oldfields, Corngreaves Road, Cradley Heath, West Midlands, B64 6BS Tel: (01384) 568821 *Fencing suppliers*

Brookes Data Products Ltd, Brookes House, Cradock Street, Loughborough, Leicestershire, LE11 1AJ Tel: (01509) 237410 Fax: (01509) 610506 E-mail: sales@brookesdata.co.uk *Hardware component dealers*

Brookes Engineers Ltd, Hope Street, Rotherham, South Yorkshire, S60 1LH Tel: (01709) 365418 Fax: (01709) 828453 E-mail: sales@brookeseng.co.uk *Precision CNC Machinists - turning and milling.*

Brookes Machine Tools Ltd, Derby Road, Kegworth, Derby, DE74 2EN Tel: (01509) 672256 Fax: (01509) 674502 E-mail: bmtlimited@aol.com *Machine tool merchants* Also at: Melbourne

Brookes & Simms Joiners, Corfe, Waltham Road, Thorpe Arnold, Melton Mowbray, Leicestershire, LE14 4SD Tel: (01664) 566565 Fax: (01664) 566565 *Joinery manufrs*

Brookes & Sons Ltd, Bangor Road, Penmaenmawr, Gwynedd, LL34 6LF Tel: (01492) 622685 Fax: (01492) 622943 E-mail: gavin@brookestarpaulins.co.uk *Merchants & road safety equipment*

Brookes Specialist Engineers Ltd, Gospel End Street, Sedgley, Dudley, West Midlands, DY3 3LS Tel: (01902) 882233 Fax: (01902) 885284 E-mail: mike@brookes-engineering.co.uk *Tools, jigs & fixtures manufrs*

▶ Brookes (UK) Ltd, Unit 5, Gaw End Lane, Lyme Green, Macclesfield, Cheshire, SK11 0LB Tel: (0800) 0729812 Fax: (0870) 2422995 E-mail: sales@ebrookes.co.uk *Safety equipment & clothing suppliers*

W.J. Brookes Sraigh Devine, 44 King Street, Earls Barton, Northampton, NN6 0LQ Tel: (01604) 810217 Fax: (01604) 812511 E-mail: providerwb@aol.com *Boot & shoe retailers & wholesalers*

▶ Brookfield, Kent Street, Wigan, Lancashire, WN1 3BB Tel: (07971) 484695 *management consultant training free websites manchester mentoring business growth development start up grants, equity funding advice, limited company*

Brookfield Business Centre Ltd, 333 Crumlin Road, Belfast, BT14 7EA Tel: (028) 9074 5241 Fax: (028) 9074 8025 *Business advisors*

Brookfield Engineering Co., James Street, Littleborough, Lancashire, OL15 8LT Tel: (01706) 378042 Fax: (01706) 378042 *Engineers toolmakers*

Brookfield Viscometers Ltd, 1 Whitehall Estate Flex Meadow, Pinnacles West, Harlow, Essex, CM19 5TP Tel: (01279) 451774 Fax: (01279) 451775 E-mail: sales@brookfield.co.uk *Viscometer sales, designers & manufrs*

Brookfields Garden Centre, 431 Mapperley Plains, Nottingham, NG3 5RW Tel: 0115-926 8200 Fax: 0115-967 3261 *Pond aquatic supplies & fish breeding*

Brookhaven Instruments Ltd, Chapel House, Stockwood, Redditch, Worcestershire, B96 6ST Tel: (01386) 792727 Fax: (01386) 792720 E-mail: info@brookhaven.co.uk *Particle & polymer characterisation equipment distributor*

Brookite Ltd, Brightly Mill, Okehampton, Devon, EX20 1RR Tel: (01837) 53315 Fax: (01837) 53223 E-mail: enquiries@brookite.com *Kite & toy manufrs*

▶ Brooklands Automation, 27a Brindley Road, Bayton Road Industrial Estate, Coventry, CV7 9EP Tel: (024) 7667 1030 Fax: (024) 7636 2244 *Control systems manufrs*

Brooklands International Freight Services Ltd, Airport House Redhill Aerodrome, Kings Mill Lane, Redhill, RH1 5JY Tel: (01737) 823575 Fax: (01737) 823634 E-mail: sales@bifs.net *Freight forwarding agents*

Brookley Case Co. Ltd, Shaw Road, Dudley, West Midlands, DY2 8TP Tel: (01384) 259908 Fax: (01384) 241624 E-mail: brookley.case@btinternet.com *Export packing cases & pallet manufrs*

Brooklin Models Ltd, Unit A3, Pinesway Industrial Estate, Ivo Peters Road, Bath, BA2 3QS Tel: (01225) 332400 Fax: (01225) 447438 *Miniature model cars distributor*

Brooklyn Bow & Ribbon Co. Ltd, Herald Business Park, Golden Acres Lane, Coventry, CV3 2RT Tel: (024) 7663 5599 Fax: (024) 7663 5525 E-mail: sales@brooklynbow.co.uk *Ribbon trim manufrs*

Brooks Ltd, Causeway Park Manchester Road, Audenshaw, Manchester, M34 5UU Tel: 0161-666 5000 Fax: 0161-666 5050 E-mail: sales@brooks.ltd.uk *Water system manufrs*

Brooks Ltd, Beckhithe, Little Melton, Norwich, NR9 3NP Tel: (01603) 810137 Fax: (01603) 812272 *Meat (processed/cooked) products manufrs*

Brooks Associates, Honeyhill, Bismore, Eastcombe, Stroud, Gloucestershire, GL6 7DG Tel: (01452) 770060 Fax: (01452) 770078 E-mail: admin@brooksassociates.com *Computer consultants*

Brooks Bourne Venture, Manning Road, Bourne, Lincolnshire, PE10 9EU Tel: (01778) 394900 Fax: (01778) 394218 *Laundry suppliers*

Brooks Bros (London) Ltd, Kingsbridge Wharf, Kingsbridge Road, Barking, Essex, IG11 0BT Tel: (020) 8591 5300 Fax: (020) 8594 7133 E-mail: enquires@brooksbroslondon.com *Timber merchants*

Brooks Composites Ltd, Percival Lane, Runcorn, Cheshire, WA7 4DS Tel: (01928) 574776 Fax: (01928) 577067 E-mail: sales@brooks-composites.co.uk *Chemical plants manufrs*

Brooks Crownhill Patternmakers Ltd, North Way, Andover, Hampshire, SP10 5AZ Tel: (01264) 355136 Fax: (01264) 332145 E-mail: info@bcplimited.co.uk Principal Export Areas: Central Asia, Central/East Europe & West Europe *Metal casting*

Brooks Crownhill Patternmakers Ltd, North Way, Andover, Hampshire, SP10 5AZ Tel: (01264) 355136 Fax: (01264) 332145 E-mail: info@bcplimited.co.uk *Casting manufrs*

▶ Brooks Decorating & Maintenance Services, 2 Old Brompton Road, London, SW7 3DQ Tel: (020) 7823 4382 Fax: (020) 7823 4382 E-mail: brooks@metronet.co.uk *We are a well established building & maintenance services, covering all aspects of the bulding trade. We cover Kensington & Chelsea. City of Westminster, Knightsbridge & Belgravia. All our work is guaranteed.*

Brooks Engineering Services, Unit 3 Park La Industrial Estate, Stourport Road, Kidderminster, Worcestershire, DY11 6TJ Tel: (01562) 740661 Fax: (01562) 740661 *General engineering services*

Brooks Forgings Ltd, Doulton Road, Cradley Heath, West Midlands, B64 5QJ Tel: (01384) 566772 Fax: (01384) 637380 E-mail: sales@brooksforgings.co.uk *Established in 1960 we have a reputation built on quality, service & rapid reaction to customers' needs & requirements. The following is a list of our products & services: Forgings, cold & hot pressed, drop, hot, upset & cold forged, hot & cold bent, eyebolts, eye-nuts, lifting eyes, special & agricultural forgings, railheads, wrought iron & heritage components, in house tool room, machining, milling, drilling, turned parts, threading, welded & fabricated steel products. Galvanised fasteners, bolts, nuts, security & construction fixings & fasteners, all threads, tie bars, & foundation bolts. Stock, warehousing & distribution services available as well as a global sourcing & procurement service. Fencing & gate components, gate automation systems, handrail components, bollards, security & parking posts, skip & trailer components & much more. Go to our website www.brooksforgings.co.uk please quote ref. Kellys01. All new customers will be entitled to an introductory discount on request.*

G.B. Brooks & Co. Ltd, Mackenzie Industrial Park, Bird Hall Lane, Cheadle Heath, Stockport, Cheshire, SK3 0SB Tel: 0161-428 7330 Fax: 0161-428 7294 E-mail: enquiries@gbbrooks.co.uk *Cutters & converters of materials*

Brooks Group (U K) Ltd, 27 Duncrue Street, Belfast, BT3 9AR Tel: (028) 9074 4201 Fax: (028) 9074 8952 E-mail: brooks.belfast@brooksgroup.ie *Timber importers & building suppliers* Also at: Downpatrick

▶ Brooks Haulage Ltd, Apy Hills Lane, Tickhill, Doncaster, South Yorkshire, DN11 9PD Tel: (01302) 742999

Brooks Haulage, Redcliffe Street, Sutton-in-Ashfield, Nottinghamshire, NG17 4ES Tel: (01623) 441255 *Plant & haulage*

Brooks Inspection Equipment Ltd, 1 Parsons Lane, Colchester, CO1 2NN Tel: (01206) 799170 Fax: (01206) 798238 E-mail: sales@brooksinspection.com *Mechanical testing equipment manufrs*

J.L. Brooks (Provisions) Ltd, Unit 16, Waterloo Mills, Waterloo Road, Pudsey, West Yorkshire, LS28 8DQ Tel: 0113-257 0975 *Snack foods*

Brooks & Jackson Engineering Ltd, P O Box 186, Macclesfield, Cheshire, SK10 4RE Tel: 01625 611550 Fax: 01625 611550 *Steel fabricators & erectors*

Brooks McRobbie Ltd, 43 St. John Street, London, EC1M 4LX Tel: (020) 7490 0304 Fax: (020) 7490 0307 E-mail: john.brooks2@ukonline.co.uk *Dairy traders*

Brooks Manson, Colne Rd, Earby, Barnoldswick, Lancs, BB18 6XT Tel: (01282) 842777 Fax: (01282) 843361 E-mail: brooks.earby@upm-kymmene.com *Timber merchants*

▶ Brooks Marquee Hire, Chart Hill Road, Staplehurst, Tonbridge, Kent, TN12 0DE Tel: (0800) 7837089 Fax: (01622) 844662 *Marque hire with a difference in the south east. 0800 783 7089*www.brooksmarquees.com*email: info@brooksmarquees.com*

Brooks Packaging Ltd, 37-39 North Acton Road, London, NW10 6PF Tel: (020) 8961 2733 Fax: (020) 8965 9841 E-mail: sales@brookpackaging.co.uk *Packaging material distributors*

Brooks Partners Ltd, The Paddocks, Honey Hill, Wokingham, Berkshire, RG40 3BD Tel: (01344) 772456 Fax: (01344) 776733 E-mail: sales@brookspartners.co.uk *Electric under floor heaters*

Brooks Precision Engineering Ltd, 6 Chamberlain Road, Aylesbury, Buckinghamshire, HP19 8DY Tel: (01296) 393862 Fax: (01296) 421014 *Precision engineers*

Brooks Service Group Plc, Bowling Hall Road, Bradford, West Yorkshire, BD4 7ST Tel: (01274) 390225 Fax: (01274) 725464 *Laundry retailers*

Brooks Service Group, 6 Lansdowne Hill, London, SE27 0AR Tel: (020) 8761 3001 Fax: (020) 8761 8275 *Linen, garment hire & rental*

Brooks Stairlifts Ltd, Telecom House Millenium Business Park, Station Road, Steeton, Keighley, West Yorkshire, BD20 6RB Tel: (0800) 834730 Fax: (01535) 290014 E-mail: brooks@stairlifts.co.uk *Lift manufrs*

T.A. Brooks, 1 Staffa Drive, Tibshelf, Alfreton, Derbyshire, DE55 5PJ Tel: (01773) 872361 Fax: (01773) 872361 *Joiners*

T.M. Brooks Ltd, Unit 4, Dawley Estate, Stallings Lane, Kingswinford, West Midlands, DY6 7AP Tel: (01384) 400777 Fax: (01384) 400167 E-mail: office@tmbrooks.co.uk *Constructional steelwork & steel fabricators*

Brooks Textile Rentals P.L.C., 400 Centenary Way, Batley, West Yorkshire, WF17 8JY Tel: (01924) 444964 Fax: (01924) 477487 *Workwear rental*

▶ Brooks & Wood Ltd, 365 Foxhall Road, Ipswich, IP3 8LH Tel: (01473) 719191

▶ Brookside Construction, 19a Church Street, Oadby, Leicester, LE2 5DB Tel: 0116-271 0680 Fax: 0116-271 0991 E-mail: caroline@brooksideconstruction.co.uk

Brookside Engineering, Unit 32j The Washford Industrial Estate, Heming Road, Redditch, Worcestershire, B98 0DH Tel: (01527) 502092 Fax: (01527) 502092 *Precision tool room & engineers*

Brookside Engineering, Brookside Business Park, Cold Meece, Stone, Staffordshire, ST15 0RZ Tel: (01785) 761000 Fax: (01785) 761361 E-mail: brooksideb@aol.com *Precision engineers*

Brookside Metal Co. Ltd, 28 Bilston Lane, Willenhall, West Midlands, WV13 2QE Tel: (01902) 365500 Fax: (01902) 636671 E-mail: richard.payne@brooksidemetal.com *Brass & bronze ingot manufrs*

Brookside Products Ltd, Harbour View, Glasson Industrial Estate, Maryport, Cumbria, CA15 8NT Tel: (01900) 815757 Fax: (01900) 814606 E-mail: brooksideproducts.co.uk@onetel.net.uk Principal Export Areas: West Europe *Smoked foods producers*

Brookside Refurbishers, Unit 1/2, Brookside Garage, Wellingborough Road, Wellingborough, Northamptonshire, NN8 4BW Tel: (01933) 279288 *Paint sprayers*

Brookside Services Ltd, Station Road, Harrietsham, Maidstone, Kent, ME17 1JA Tel: (01622) 858995 Fax: (01622) 859793 *Steel fabricators*

▶ Brookside Southern Ltd, 2 The Shops, Wonersh Common, Wonersh, Guildford, Surrey, GU5 0PJ Tel: (01483) 893182 Fax: (01483) 894331

▶ Brooktherm Refrigeration Ltd, 3 Kelvin Park, Dock Road, Birkenhead, Merseyside, CH41 1LT Tel: 0151-650 1070 Fax: 0151-649 9001 E-mail: sales@brooktherm.co.uk

Brookthorpe Engineering, Tiltups End, Horsley, Stroud, Gloucestershire, GL6 0QE Tel: (01453) 832420 Fax: (01453) 832420 *Agricultural engineers*

Brookthorpe Joinery, Stroud Road, Brookthorpe, Gloucester, GL4 0UQ Tel: (01452) 813007 Fax: (01452) 813007 *Joinery manufrs*

Brookvale Manufacturing Co. Ltd, 15 Reddicap Trading Estate, Sutton Coldfield, West Midlands, B75 7DQ Tel: 0121-378 0833 Fax: 0121-311 1794 E-mail: enquiries@brookvale-manufacturing.co.uk *Pressings, Wireforms and Assemblies, Ford Q1 and TS16949 accredited. The Brookvale Manufacturing Company (est1949) Also manufacturers , Oil Dipsticks for both Automotive and Off Highway markets. We have the capacity to resistance and projection weld, Brazing, riveting, drill and tap, thread roll 3.5mm to 8mm and assemble/assembly production to your requirements from prototype and low quantity manufacture to high volume requirements. We manufacture pressings, Stampings, wireforms for UK and export automotive and non automotive sectors. We have our own toolroom facilities. and can open and translate most CAD data files. We also have our own logisticsdept for delivery of components. Areas of Export: France, Hungary, Czech Republic, Germany, Mexico and Spain.*

Brookvine, Flitch Industrial Estate, Chelmsford Road, Dunmow, Essex, CM6 1XJ Tel: (01371) 875663 Fax: (01371) 875665 E-mail: brookvine@essex-x-ray.com *Encapsulation services to electronics industry*

▶ Brook-Water-Design, The Downs, Woodhouse Hill, Uplyme, Lyme Regis, Dorset, DT7 3SL Tel: (01297) 446060 Fax: (0871) 7505306 E-mail: sales@brookwater.co.uk *BrookWater, Contemporary Designed Bathrooms & Kitchens, Ceramic Sinks, Ceramic Basins, Glass Sinks, Glass Basins, Chromed Bottle Traps, Chromed Sink & Basin Plugs, Chromed Sink & Basin Wastes, Modern Designer Showers, Venturi Showers, Chromed, Brushed Steel, Chromed Satin Kitchen & Bathroom Taps & Mixers, Water Softeners, Water Conditioners, Stainless Steel Bathroom Cabinets, Frameless Shower & Bath Screens*

Brookwick Ward, Fearby Road, Masham, Ripon, North Yorkshire, HG4 4ES Tel: (0870) 1118610 Fax: (0870) 1118609 E-mail: sales@brookwickward.com *Animal health & grooming product distributors*

Broom Boats Ltd, Brundall, Norwich, NR13 5PX Tel: (01603) 712334 Fax: (01603) 714803 E-mail: enquiries@broomboats.com *Boat builders*

John Broom Boats Ltd, Covey Lane, Surlingham, Norwich, NR14 7AL Tel: (01508) 538929 Fax: (01508) 538909 E-mail: info@johnbroom.co.uk *Boat & engine repair services & marina operators*

Broom Joinery Ltd, 14 Arden Business Centre, Arden Road, Alcester, Warwickshire, B49 6HW Tel: (01789) 764156 Fax: (01789) 764156 *Joinery & woodworking services*

Broome Signs, Old Bridge Way, Shefford, Bedfordshire, SG17 5HQ Tel: (01462) 851919 Fax: (01462) 851595 E-mail: sales@broomesigns.com *Sign manufrs*

Broome & Wellington Aviation Ltd, 86 Princess Street, Manchester, M1 6NG Tel: 0161-236 2317 Fax: 0161-228 1326 E-mail: broom@broomwell.com *Grey cloth & loom state fabric merchants*

Broomecupboard.com, Knole Ho, Otham La, Bearsted, Maidstone, Kent, ME15 8SJ Tel: (01622) 738006 E-mail: info@broomecupboard.com *Interior design tips*

Broomfield Carbide Gauges Ltd, Unit 7 Crossley Mills, New Mill Road Honley, Honley, Holmfirth, HD9 6PL Tel: (01484) 664982 Fax: (01484) 664982 E-mail: info@broomfieldgauges.com *Tungsten carbide gauge manufrs*

Broomhall Joinery Co. Ltd, Sunley House, Olds Approach, Tolpits Lane, Watford, WD18 9TB Tel: (01923) 777714 Fax: (01923) 771077 *Joinery manufrs*

Broomhill Agricultural Spares, BA Country Store, Lyne Of Skene, Duthethe, Westhill, Aberdeenshire, AB32 7DA Tel: (01330) 860840 Fax: (01330) 860841 *Agricultural spares suppliers*

Broomhill Holdings Ltd, 189 Lurgan Road, Maralin, Craigavon, County Armagh, BT67 0QS Tel: (028) 3831 3000 Fax: (028) 3831 3001 *Bed linen manufrs*

Broomstair Metal Co., 328 Hyde Road, Denton, Manchester, M34 3EH Tel: 0161-336 3240 Fax: 0161-336 8888 *Sheet metalworkers*

Broomstick Car & Commercials Ltd, Willow Farm, Ivinghoe Aston, Leighton Buzzard, Bedfordshire, LU7 9DF Tel: (01525) 220123 Fax: (01525) 221351 *Commercial vehicles painters & repairers*

Stevie Broons Ltd, Murraysgate Industrial Estate, Whitburn, Bathgate, West Lothian, EH47 0LE Tel: (01501) 745607 Fax: (01501) 745819 *Meat wholesalers*

▶ Brophy Castings, Building 15 Soho Mills, Wooburn Green, High Wycombe, Buckinghamshire, HP10 0PF Tel: (01628) 525068 Fax: (01628) 525129 E-mail: info@brophycastings.co.uk *Aluminium castings manufrs*

▶ Broplant Fabrications Ltd, Moorfield Industrial Estate, Cotes Heath, Stafford, ST21 6QY Tel: (01782) 791232 Fax: (01782) 791611 E-mail: broplantfabs@ukonline.co.uk *Steel fabrications*

▶ Brora Transport Ltd, West End Garage, Brora, Sutherland, KW9 6NY Tel: (01408) 621223

▶ Broseley Computers, 6 Instones Building, The Square, Broseley, Shropshire, TF12 5EW Tel: (01952) 884682

Broson Ltd, Church Hill Road, Thurmaston, Leicester, LE4 8DJ Tel: 0116-269 8899 Fax: 0116-269 8898 E-mail: sales@broson.co.uk *Steel tubes stockholders & processors*

Brost Forge Motorspring Service, Unit 7 149 Roman Way, London, N7 8XH Tel: (020) 7607 2311 Fax: (020) 7619 0370 *Road spring manufrs*

Broste Ltd, Unit 8 North Lynn Business Village, Bergen Way, North Lynn Industrial Estate, King's Lynn, Norfolk, PE30 2JG Tel: (01553) 776066 Fax: (01553) 767319 E-mail: broste.uk@broste.com *Salt merchants, road gritting materials, water softening chemical products distributors & salt import & export merchants/agents*

Brother (U K) Ltd, Shepley St, Guide Bridge, Manchester, M34 5JD Tel: 0161-330 6531 Fax: 0161-308 3281 E-mail: sales@brother-uk.com *Office & domestic product manufrs*

Brotherton Speciality Products Ltd, Calder Vale Road, Wakefield, West Yorkshire, WF1 5PH Tel: (01924) 371919 Fax: (01924) 290408 E-mail: info@brotherton.co.uk Principal Export Areas: Worldwide *Producers & suppliers of chemicals to food industry*

Brough & Horner Ltd, Station Road, Loftus, Saltburn-by-the-Sea, Cleveland, TS13 4QB Tel: (01287) 640374 *Railing manufrs*

Broughton & Co Bristol Ltd, 4 Axis, Hawkfield Way, Hawkfield Business Park, Bristol, BS14 0BY Tel: 0117-964 1300 Fax: 0117-964 1003 E-mail: broughtons1bristol@btinternet.com *Office machines distributors*

Broughton Civil Engineers, 7-9 Station Road, Newport Pagnell, Buckinghamshire, MK16 0AG Tel: (01908) 500888 Fax: (01908) 500889 E-mail: consult@bbltd.co.uk *Engineering consultants* Also at: Wokingham

Broughton Controls Ltd, Shaw Road, Oldham, OL1 4AW Tel: 0161-627 0060 Fax: 0161-627 1362 E-mail: info@broughton-controls.co.uk *Installers of barriers & turnstiles*

Broughton Electroair Products, Clive Works, Edward Street, Redditch, Worcestershire, B97 6HA Tel: (01527) 597567 Fax: (01527) 67603 E-mail: sales@broughtoneap.com *Air conditioning, heater & dehumidifier equipment & fans suppliers*

Broughton Mechanical & Civil Engineering Ltd, Ditton Road, Widnes, Cheshire, WA8 0TH Tel: 0151-423 5273 Fax: 0151-495 1390 E-mail: enquiries@jep-engineering.co.uk *Mechanical & civil engineer contractors*

▶ Broughton Minerals, 2 Station Yard, Kirkby Stephen, Cumbria, CA17 4LA Tel: (01768) 371155 Fax: (01768) 371166 *Importers & wholesalers of gifts*

▶ Broughtons Distribution Ltd, Brailwood Road, Bilsthorpe, Newark, Nottinghamshire, NG22 8UA Tel: (01623) 411114 Fax: (01623) 411010 E-mail: sales@broughtonsdistribution.co.uk *We specialise in vehicle collection/delivery, both driven and transported, all transporter drivers wear uniformes with collor and tie, and are versed in hand over procedures*

Alister Brown, Unit 3 Huddersfield Street, Galashiels, Selkirkshire, TD1 3BF Tel: (01896) 758668 Fax: (01896) 758668 *Paint retailers*

▶ Brown & Armstrong Ltd, The Workshop, Glasson Industrial Estate, Maryport, Cumbria, CA15 8NT Tel: (01900) 812410

▶ Brown & Biggs, Continental House, Avis Way, Newhaven, East Sussex, BN9 0DH Tel: (01273) 515919 Fax: (01273) 515939

Brown Brothers, Unit 2, Wild Street, Lowestoft, Suffolk, NR32 1XH Tel: (01502) 573196 Fax: (01502) 508076 *Motor body paint merchants*

Brown Brothers Group Ltd, 168/170 South Street, Dorking, Surrey, RH4 2ES Tel: (01306) 742611 Fax: (01306) 742601 E-mail: duncan@brownbros.co.uk *Suppliers of high quality packaging, printed & plain*

Brown Bros Harriman Ltd, Veritas House, 125 Finsbury Pavement, London, EC2A 1PN Tel: (020) 7588 6166 Fax: (020) 7614 2440 *Broker dealers*

Brown Bros Wines Europe Ltd, Ray Mead Road, Maidenhead, Berkshire, SL6 8NJ Tel: (01628) 776446 Fax: (01628) 776136 *Wine distributors*

▶ Brown Bryan & Son, South Gable, Southsea Road, Flamborough, Bridlington, North Humberside, YO15 1AD Tel: (01262) 850477 Fax: (01262) 850477

Brown Butlin, Northons Lane, Holbeach, Spalding, Lincolnshire, PE12 7QA Tel: (01406) 422666 Fax: (01406) 422757 *Agricultural chemicals distributors*

Brown Butlin Group Ltd, Brook House, Ruskington, Sleaford, Lincolnshire, NG34 9EP Tel: (01526) 831000 Fax: (01526) 832967 E-mail: ken.matthews@bbgdirect.co.uk *Holding company*

Brown & Cayton Coachworks Ltd, Unit 8 The Airfield, Little Staughton, Bedford, MK44 2BN Tel: (01234) 376591 Fax: (01234) 376202 E-mail: brown.cayton@btopenworld.com *Commercial vehicle body repairs & repainters*

Brown & Cook Ltd, 77 Allcock Street, Birmingham, B9 4DY Tel: 0121-766 7117 Fax: 0121-753 2155 E-mail: sales@brownandcook.co.uk *Suppliers to the upholstery trade since 1912. Suppliers of foam, fillings, springs, upholstery cloths, tools & sundries, comprehensive range of vinyls, tweeds & furniture fabrics.*

David Brown Engineering Ltd, Park Works, Park Road, Huddersfield, HD4 5DD Tel: (01484) 465500 Fax: (01484) 465586 E-mail: sales@davidbrown.textron.com *David Brown is an engineering group focused on manufacturing and supplying customers with the best solution in power transmission products. David Brown has been in business since 1860 and operates on a global scale manufacturing and supplying - Industrial gearboxesGeared motorsWorm gearsServo motorsScrew jacksGear CouplingsFlexible CouplingsPin & Bush CouplingsCone Ring CouplingsIndustrial ReducersHigh Speed GearboxesMill Drive GearboxesGeared Pumps All of the above are offered with a world class service and repair experience to ensure we offer our customers 0% satisfaction.*

Denis Brown & Son (Nailsworth) Ltd, Broadmead, Bath Road, Woodchester, Stroud, Gloucestershire, GL5 5EG Tel: (01453) 873516 Fax: (01453) 873333 *Timber merchants*

Edward & John Brown (Contractors) Ltd, 288 Bordesley Grange, Birmingham, B9 5NA Tel: 0121-772 1191 Fax: 0121-766 5130 *Demolition contractors*

▶ Brown Engineering (Fochabers) Ltd, Garmouth Road, Mosstodloch Industrial Estate, Garmouth Road, Fochabers, Morayshire, IV32 7LH Tel: (01343) 820753 Fax: (01343) 821400 E-mail: enquiries@brownengineering.fochabers.co.uk *Metalworking & fabrication services*

Ray Brown (Engineers) Ltd, Caroline Place, Plymouth, PL1 3QY Tel: 01752 662084 *Precision engineers*

F. Brown P.L.C., 75 Moor Lane, Preston, PR1 1JQ Tel: (01772) 824141 Fax: (01772) 203383 E-mail: fbrownplc@btconnect.com *Refurbishment & internal fit out contractors* Also at: Clydebank & Dumbarton

Francis Brown Ltd, Church Road, Stockton-on-Tees, Cleveland, TS18 2HL Tel: (01642) 806000 Fax: (01642) 806001 E-mail: sales@francisbrown.co.uk *Steel fabricators & wire workers*

Frank Brown & Son (Luton) Ltd, 87-105 Wingate Road, Luton, LU4 8QA Tel: (01582) 597246 Fax: (01582) 505959 E-mail: enquiries@frankbrown.co.uk *Aircraft ground support equipment manufrs*

Gary Brown Steels Ltd, Unit 21 Izons Industrial Estate, Oldbury Road, West Bromwich, West Midlands, B70 9BS Tel: 0121-525 2700 Fax: 0121-525 6200 *Steel coil stockholders*

George Brown, 12 Crosby Street, Bangor, County Down, BT20 5EE Tel: (028) 9146 6136 Fax: (028) 9146 6136 *Sign manufrs*

Brown & Glegg Edinburgh Ltd, Bankhead Crossway South, Sighthill Industrial Estate, Edinburgh, EH11 4EZ Tel: 0131-453 6611 Fax: 0131-453 1848 E-mail: info@brownglegg.co.uk *Steel stockholders* Also at: Glasgow

Gordon Brown, White Hill, Springfield, Enniskillen, County Fermanagh, BT74 8AL Tel: (028) 6634 1717 Fax: (028) 6634 1717 *Agricultural equipment maintenance services*

Brown Hills Tackle, 5 Silvercourt, Walsall, WS8 6HA Tel: (01543) 372395 *Fishing tackle suppliers*

▶ Brown & Illingworth, Ford 5 5 Hoults Estate, Walker Road, Newcastle upon Tyne, NE6 1AB Tel: 0191-265 3860 Fax: 0191-265 3860

▶ Brown Ink, 6 Home Ground, Shirehampton, Bristol, BS11 0HN Tel: 0117-938 1413 E-mail: rachel@brown-ink.co.uk *brown ink web design offers professional bespoke website design and graphical services for small businesses and organisations throughout the south west and the UK.**Whether you are working to update your existing site or developing from scratch, we maintain a flexible approach to ensure we provide the right solution for you.**Our aim is to develop highly useable, affordable websites that attract and keep customers. Our websites are custom built from the ground up, not from pre-made templates so you can be sure that your website will be a unique design. We can help you create the professional image you need to take your business to the next level.*

▶ Brown Ink, 309 St. Michaels Avenue, Yeovil, Somerset, BA21 4ND Tel: (01935) 424607 E-mail: info@brown-ink.co.uk *brown ink web design offers professional bespoke website design and graphical services for small businesses and organisations throughout the south west and the UK.**Whether you are working to update your existing site or developing from scratch, we maintain a flexible approach to ensure we provide the right solution for you.**Our aim is to develop highly useable, affordable websites that attract and keep customers. Our websites are custom built from the ground up, not from pre-made templates so you can be sure that your website will be a unique design. We can help you create the professional image you need to take your business to the next level.*

James Brown & Sons Ltd, 92 The Grove, Marton-in-Cleveland, Middlesbrough, Cleveland, TS7 8AP Tel: (01642) 318370 Fax: (01642) 318370 *Metal fabricators & machinists*

Joe Brown, Capel Curig, Betws-y-Coed, Gwynedd, LL24 0EN Tel: (01690) 720205 Fax: (01690) 720224 *Camping & climbing equipment suppliers*

Company Information

Joseph Brown & Sons, 72 Balvenie Street, Dufftown, Keith, Banffshire, AB55 4FS Tel: (01340) 820265 Fax: (01340) 820265 E-mail: jbvat@fsmail.net *Wooden vat manufrs*

Brown & Kirby Ltd, Sidwell Street, Leicester, LE5 4GQ Tel: 0116-273 4613 Fax: 0116-273 3844 E-mail: brown.kirby@talk21.com *Joinery & building contractors*

Brown Knight & Truscott Holdings Ltd, North Farm Road, High Brooms, Tunbridge Wells, Kent, TN2 3BW Tel: (01892) 511678 Fax: (01892) 511343 *Colour & commercial printers & direct mailers*

L. Brown & Sons Ltd, St. Anns House, St. Anns Parade, Alderley Road, Wilmslow, Cheshire, SK9 1HG Tel: (01625) 522251 Fax: (01625) 533653 E-mail: mikemason@lbrowns.co.uk *Building contractors*

M. & A. Brown (Engravers) Ltd, Stable Fold, Barton Road, Worsley, Manchester, M28 2PE Tel: 0161-794 2397 Fax: 0161-794 4982 E-mail: masigns@ukonline.co.uk *Sign makers & engravers*

M. & C. Brown Ltd, Maryland, Highfield Road, Sunbury-on-Thames, Middlesex, TW16 6DL Tel: (01932) 787332 *Floral Services*

Brown McFarlane Ltd, 239 Myreside Street, Glasgow, G32 6DR Tel: 0141-551 9191 Fax: 0141-554 6825 E-mail: info@brownmac.co.uk *Steel stockholders manufrs/distributors* Also at: Stoke on Trent

▶ Brown & Mcrae, 10 High Street, Turriff, Aberdeenshire, AB53 4DS Tel: (01888) 568950 Fax: (01888) 563031

▶ Brown & Martin Engineering Limited, Unit AA37, Hastingwood Industrial Park, Wood Lane, Erdington, Birmingham, B24 9QR Tel: 0121 3868412 Fax: 0121 3866742 E-mail: adam.wle@hastmail.com *Presswork, Tube Manipulation, Welding & Brazing*

Martin Brown Paints Ltd, 265 Dickson Road, Blackpool, FY1 2JJ Tel: (01253) 626907 Fax: (01253) 753494 E-mail: enquiries@martinbrownpaints.com *Car panel beaters & paint suppliers*

▶ Brown & Mason Ltd, New Loom House, 101 Back Church Lane, London, E1 1LU Tel: (020) 7264 1120 Fax: (020) 7481 8244 E-mail: b&m@brownandmason.ltd.uk *One of the largest UK demolition companies with over 45 years experience working nationwide. We undertake asbestos removal, decommissioning, land remediation, decontamination, industrial/ environmental services, asset recovery, reclamation, recycling & demolition by controlled explosives. Twice winners of the British Safety Council's "Sword of Honour" Award, recognised as the pinnacle of safety achievement. We are long standing members of the NFDC & ARCA & are accredited to OHSAS 18001, BS EN ISO 14001 & BS EN ISO 9001:2000. Winners of Contract Journal's "Demolition Contractor of the Year" Award & finalists on five other occasions. Winners of Building Magazine/HSE Awards 2006 in the category of "Best Occupational Health Initiative". Numerous successful demolition/ dismantling projects carried out eg. traditional/ domestic/residential/commercial, city centre redevelopments, façade retention, internal soft stripping, temporary works, industrial, power station, chimney, bridge & much more*

Matthew Brown Blacksmiths Ltd, East Grange Farm, A179 Hartlepool, Hartlepool, Cleveland, TS27 4RA Tel: (01429) 865777 Fax: (01429) 865777 *Blacksmiths & steel forgings manufrs*

▶ Brown & May, Progress Way, Mid Suffolk Business Park, Eye, Suffolk, IP23 7HU Tel: (01379) 870181 Fax: (01379) 870673 *Specialists suppliers in fresh & frozen fish*

N.C. Brown (Storage Equipment) Ltd, Firwood Industrial Estate, Thicketford Road, Bolton, BL2 3TR Tel: (01204) 590200 Fax: (01204) 590210 *Steel storage equipment manufrs*

Neil Brown Engineering Ltd, Wardentree Lane Industrial Estate, Benner Road, Pinchbeck, Spalding, Lincolnshire, PE11 3TZ Tel: (01775) 723052 Fax: (01775) 710570 E-mail: admin@nbe.co.uk *Competition engines manufrs*

Oliver Brown, 75 Lower Sloane Street, London, SW1W 8DA Tel: (020) 7259 9494 Fax: (020) 7259 9444 E-mail: info@oliverbrown.org.uk *Clothes retailer*

Owen Brown, Station Road, Castle Donington, Derby, DE74 2NL Tel: (01332) 850000 Fax: (01332) 850005 E-mail: info@owen-brown.co.uk *Marquee hire*

Brown & Potter Ltd, The Quarry, Boroughbridge Road, Ripon, North Yorkshire, HG4 1UG Tel: (01765) 603710 Fax: (01765) 698801 *Aggregate materials manufrs*

R.W. Brown Precision Engineering, 9 Buchanan Building, Stephenson Road, Clacton-On-Sea, Essex, CO15 4XA Tel: (01255) 220230 Fax: (01255) 220202 E-mail: bob@the-machining-centre.co.uk *Precision CNC engineers*

Robert Brown Engineering Ltd, Douglas Close, Preston Farm Industrial Estate, Stockton-on-Tees, Cleveland, TS18 3SB Tel: (01642) 675201 Fax: (01642) 615902 *General engineers & fabricators*

Roger Brown Trophies, 372 Carden Avenue, Brighton, BN1 8LJ Tel: (01273) 559110 Fax: (01273) 500298 *Sports trophy manufrs*

Brown Rutter Ltd, Salisbury Street, Barton Hill, Bristol, BS5 9UD Tel: 0117-955 0781 Fax: 0117-941 3685 E-mail: sales@brownrutter.com *Bearing mounting components manufrs*

▶ Sam Brown Furniture, Unit 12 Berlin Bank, North London Freight Depot, York Way, London, N1 0UZ Tel: (07778) 615980 E-mail: sam@sambrownfurniture.co.uk *Designer & maker of bespoke furniture in solid & veneered wood*

Brown Shipley Asset Management Ltd, Founders Court, Lothbury, London, EC2R 7HE Tel: (020) 7606 9833 Fax: (020) 7606 6657 *Financial consultants*

Brown & Son, Crow Arch Lane, Ringwood, Hampshire, BH24 1PD Tel: (01425) 476133 Fax: (01425) 477063 E-mail: sales@vanboorn.co.uk *Printers service*

Steve Brown Engineering Ltd, 40 Tyne Road, Middlefield Industrial Estate, Sandy, Bedfordshire, SG19 1SA Tel: (01767) 681224 Fax: (01767) 681224 *Precision engineers*

T.H. Brown Ltd, Estate Road No. 1, South Humberside Industal Estate, Grimsby, North East Lincolnshire, DN31 2TA Tel: (01472) 362603 Fax: (01472) 360112 E-mail: admin@thbrown.co.uk *Road transport contractors*

Brown & Wakelin Sales Ltd, The Croft, Marsh Gibbon, Bicester, Oxfordshire, OX27 0EU Tel: (01869) 277337 Fax: (01869) 278844 E-mail: sales@brownandwakling.co.uk *Based in Oxfordshire with trade customers throughout the UK, we supply turned and cnc machined timber components including: turned legs, wooden knobs, wooden toys and games, wooden puzzles, and components to your own specification. We are also the sole UK distributor for T-Lock, the innovative new range of Point of Sale Display Solutions designed for major permanent or seasonal sales campaigns. Options include floor standing displays, counter top displays, dump bins, poster display units, and wine display shelving. The displays are supplied flat-packed, and assemble in minutes without tools, clips, or screws. They are customised with colour and printed logos to suit your requirements. Visit our web site for full details.*

Alan Browne Gauges Ltd, Blackdown Mill, Blackdown, Leamington Spa, Warwickshire, CV32 6QT Tel: (01926) 424278 Fax: (01926) 451865 E-mail: sales@alanbrowne.co.uk *Gauge blocks calibration & manufrs*

Browned Off, 10 Farr Avenue, Barking, Essex, IG11 0NZ Tel: (020) 8507 0707 E-mail: browned.off@btinternet.com *Tanning & beauty services*

Brownell Ltd, Commercial Way, Abbey Road, London, NW10 7XF Tel: (020) 8965 9281 Fax: (020) 8965 3239 E-mail: sales@brownell.co.uk *Manufacturers of desiccant moisture drying agents*

Browne's Chocolates, Throwleigh, Okehampton, Devon, EX20 2HX Tel: (0845) 4560568 Fax: (01647) 231289 E-mail: sales@brownes.co.uk *Chocolate manufrs*

Brownhills Engineering Co, Progress Drive, Cannock, Staffordshire, WS11 0JE Tel: (01543) 502700 Fax: (01543) 520700 *Engineers machinists & general machinists*

Brownieside Coopereage, Airdrie Road, Caldercruix, Caldercruix, Airdrie, Lanarkshire, ML6 8PA Tel: (01236) 767774 *Barrel repair*

Don Browning Trophies, 4 St. Georges Street, Cheltenham, Gloucestershire, GL50 4AF Tel: (01242) 690314 Fax: (01242) 690313 E-mail: richard@dbtrophies.co.uk *Computerised engravers*

Brownings Electric Co. Ltd, 11 Thames Road, Barking, Essex, IG11 0HG Tel: (020) 8591 3030 Fax: (020) 8594 7708 E-mail: enquiries@browningselectric.co.uk *Motor rewinders & repairers* Also at: Watford

Brownlow Way Garage, Topping Street, Off Brownlow Way, Bolton, BL1 3UB Tel: (01204) 533300 Fax: (01204) 533300 *Motor vehicle repair services & MOT services*

Browns, 2 Hallam Mill, Hallam Street, Stockport, Cheshire, SK2 6PT Tel: (01925) 759740 Fax: 0161-476 4533 *Furniture restorers & suppliers*

▶ Browns Associated Cleaners, Tamarind House, 41 Marshall Avenue, Bridlington, North Humberside, YO15 2DT Tel: (01262) 606779 E-mail: brownscleaners@btinternet.com *Established 1985 now based in Bridlington fully insured professional cleaning services incorporating window cleaning car valeting pressure cleaning industrial cleaning*

▶ Browns Bedrooms & Kitchens, Colbourne Avenue, Nelson Park, Cramlington, Northumberland, NE23 1WD Tel: (01670) 590556 Fax: (01670) 738206 E-mail: brown.2000@virgin.net *Manufacture doors*

Browns Of Burwell Ltd, 7 North Street, Burwell, Whittlesford, Cambridge, CB4 3QW Tel: (01638) 741306 Fax: (01638) 743497 E-mail: sales@brownsofburwell.co.uk *Fuel distribution & motor engineers*

Browns Coachworks Ltd, 282 Moira Road, Lisburn, County Antrim, BT28 2TU Tel: (028) 9262 1711 Fax: (028) 9262 1962 E-mail: info@brownscoachworks.com *Specialised coachbuilders & manufrs*

Browns Fasteners Ltd, PO Box 13, Leeds, LS27 9QS Tel: 0113-252 2185 Fax: 0113-252 0826 E-mail: browns_fasteners@yahoo.com *Fastener distributors*

▶ Brown's French Polishers, Unit A2 Pixmore Estate, Pixmore Avenue, Letchworth Garden City, Hertfordshire, SG6 1JJ Tel: (01462) 680241 Fax: (01462) 482999 E-mail: info@brownsfrenchpolishing.co.uk *French polishers and furniture restoration. Industrial wood finishers & spray finishing.*

Browns Glass & Glazing, 6 Silver Street, Bridgwater, Somerset, TA6 3EG Tel: (01278) 423157 Fax: (01278) 423157 *Sheet glass & diy merchants*

▶ Browns Homes Ltd, St. Anns House, St. Anns Parade, Wilmslow, Cheshire, SK9 1HG Tel: (01625) 445606 Fax: (01625) 528527

Browns Ladders & Ceilings, Glen Way, Brierfield, Nelson, Lancashire, BB9 5NH Tel: (01282) 615517 Fax: (01282) 615515 E-mail: sales@brownsladders.co.uk *Suspended ceilings & ladder retailers & on site ladder inspection*

▶ Brown's Lock Stock & Barrel, 224 Holme Lane, Sheffield, S6 4JZ Tel: 0114-234 6222 Fax: 0114-234 6222 *Gunsmiths*

Brown's Operating System Services Ltd, Brigade Street, London, SE3 0TW Tel: (020) 8297 9797 Fax: (020) 8318 3939 E-mail: mail@browns.co.uk *Remote access dialling solutions distributors*

Brown's Photocopier Repairs, 57 Leybourne Road, London, E11 3BS Tel: (020) 8530 3569 *Photocopier, printer & fax repair*

Browns of Wem Ltd, Four Lane Ends, Wem, SY4 5UQ Tel: (01939) 232382 Fax: (01939) 234032 E-mail: mail@brownsofwem.com *Building manufacturers, designers & construction*

▶ BROWNWARRIORSOURCING, 112 Findhorn Street, Fintry, Dundee, DD4 9PN Tel: 01382 506814 E-mail: duncanscott@brownwarriorsourcing.co.uk *BROWNWARRIORSOURCING provides professional Product,Parts,Component and Services Sourcing ,along with Ordering and Supply Chain Management , run by experienced purchasing personnel,for the manufacting and service market.We will source your product,part,component or services for you,getting the best possible deal for you, then place an order on your behalf,progessing it to delivery,and allowing you to reap the benefits of more time spent on other areas of you business,and more importantly,increasing you competetiveness by reducing your input costs and lowering your lead times.*

Browse Engineering Services, 34b Cowleigh Road, Malvern, Worcestershire, WR14 1QD Tel: (01684) 567125 Fax: (01684) 568240 E-mail: sales@ibrowse2.com *General fabricators*

Broxap Dorothea, Rowhurst Industrial Estate, Chesterton, Newcastle, Staffordshire, ST5 6BD Tel: (01782) 564411 Fax: (01782) 565357 E-mail: sales@broxap.co.uk *Architectural contractors*

Broxap Mawrob, 121A-125A Sefton Street, Southport, Merseyside, PR8 5DR Tel: (01704) 513330 Fax: (01704) 500380 E-mail: sales@broxap.co.uk *Street furniture manufrs*

Broxbarn Joineries, Millbrook House, Chertsey Road, Shepperton, Middlesex, TW17 9LA Tel: (01932) 877600 Fax: (01932) 269261 *Joinery manufrs*

▶ Broxburn Bottlers Ltd, 3 Dunnet Way, East Mains Industrial Estate, Broxburn, West Lothian, EH52 5NN Tel: (01506) 854373 Fax: (01506) 854611

▶ Broxburn & Dundee Pallet Recovery Ltd, Baldovie Industrial Estate, Piper Street, Dundee, DD4 0NT Tel: (01382) 736888

▶ Broxden Ltd, 8 Algo Business Centre, Glenearn Road, Perth, PH2 0NJ Tel: (01738) 450422 Fax: (01738) 783685 E-mail: sales@broxden.co.uk *Web designers*

Broxted Furniture, Chickney Hall Farm, Chickney, Broxted, Dunmow, Essex, CM6 2BY Tel: (01279) 850733 *Furniture manufrs*

Broyce Control Ltd, Pool St, Wolverhampton, WV2 4HN Tel: (01902) 773746 Fax: (01902) 420639 E-mail: sales@broycecontrol.com Principal Export Areas: Worldwide *Earth leakage equipment manufrs*

BRS, 8 Expodite Works, Stuart Road, Bredbury, Stockport, Cheshire, SK6 2SR Tel: 0161-430 8380 Fax: 0161-406 6634 Principal Export Areas: Worldwide *Refrigeration, bakery & air conditioning engineers*

BRT Bearings Ltd, 9 Common Bank Industrial Estate, Ackhurst Road, Chorley, Lancashire, PR7 1NH Tel: (01257) 264266 Fax: (01257) 274698 *Automotive transmission specialists*

BRT Bearings Ltd, 43 Deerdykes View, Cumbernauld, Glasgow, G68 9HN Tel: (01236) 452976 Fax: (01236) 736604 E-mail: info@brt-group.com Principal Export Areas: Worldwide *Bearings, belts, pulleys , gear boxes & pneumatics distributors*

Brtitish Bed Exports, Lower Clough Mill, Pendle Street, Barrowford, Nelson, Lancashire, BB9 8PH Tel: (01282) 694777 Fax: (01282) 447777 E-mail: sales@silentnightexport.co.uk *Bed & furniture distributors*

Bruce Boxes Ltd, Timothys Bridge Road, Stratford-Upon-Avon, Warwickshire, CV37 9NQ Tel: (01789) 269811 Fax: (01789) 414489 E-mail: sales@brucebox.co.uk *Carton manufrs*

▶ Bruce Collie Building Co Ltd, 46 Silverknowes Road, Edinburgh, EH4 5LF Tel: 0131-336 5050

▶ Bruce Contracts, 72 Brand Street, Glasgow, G51 1DG Tel: 0141-427 5331 Fax: 0141-427 5639

Bruce Data Networks, 22 Duthie Road, Tarves, Ellon, Aberdeenshire, AB41 7JX Tel: (01651) 851568 Fax: (01651) 851416 E-mail: jim.bruce@btinternet.com *Computer services, networking & fibre optics*

Bruce Douglas Ultratape Ltd, Kilspindie Road, Dunsinane Industrial Estate, Dundee, DD2 3JP Tel: (01382) 832999 Fax: (01382) 833422 E-mail: sales@ultratape.com *Adhesive tape distributors or agents. Also manufacturers of adhesive tapes (double sided)/industrial & packaging materials*

Bruce & Hyslop (Brucast) Ltd, 1 Well Lane, Bootle, Merseyside, L20 3BS Tel: 0151-922 2404 Fax: 0151-922 5994 E-mail: colin.appleton@bruceandhyslop.com *Cast iron decorative metalwork manufrs*

Bruce R.I.D. Recycling Ltd, March Street, Sheffield, S9 5DQ Tel: 0114-243 3637 Fax: 0114-244 8521 E-mail: info@weee-recycler.co.uk *Bruce RID Recycling is a specialist electrical recycling company offering a complete solution to the WEEE directive.*

Robert Bruce Construction Ltd, Unit 40 Thornleigh Trading Estate, Blowers Green Road, Dudley, West Midlands, DY2 8UB Tel: (01384) 457780 Fax: (01384) 259921 *Building & painting contractors*

▶ Bruce Stevenson Risk Management, 38-40 New City Road, Glasgow, G4 9JT Tel: 0141 353 3539 Fax: 0141 353 3888 E-mail: mark.costello@brucestevenson.co.uk *Bruce Stevenson Risk Management are an owner managed Insurance Broker, we specialize in property,manufacturing and leisure industry.*

Bruce's Shellfish, 9 Balconie Street, Evanton, Dingwall, Ross-Shire, IV16 9UN Tel: (01349) 830187 Fax: (01349) 830187 *Shellfish merchants*

Bruck Lighting Ltd, 1 Cherrytrees, Stanbridge Road Terrace, Leighton Buzzard, Bedfordshire, LU7 4QU Tel: 01525 372645 Fax: 01525 378777 *Lighting manufrs*

Brucklay Garage, Maud, Peterhead, Aberdeenshire, AB42 4RA Tel: (01771) 613500 Fax: (01771) 613789 *Agricultural engineers*

▶ Brucom Distribution Ltd, Unit 7 & 13 Jupiter Business Park, Airfield Industrial Estate, Hixon, Stafford, ST18 0PF Tel: (01889) 272645 Fax: (01889) 271737 E-mail: sales@brucom.co.uk *Wiring harnesses manufrs*

Bruderer Ltd, Cradock Industrial Estate, Cradock Road, Luton, LU4 0JF Tel: (01582) 560300 Fax: (01582) 570611 E-mail: mail@bruderer.co.uk *Machinery manufrs*

Bruel & Kjaer Ltd, Bedford House, Rutherford Close, Stevenage, Hertfordshire, SG1 2ND Tel: (01438) 739000 Fax: (01438) 739099 E-mail: ukinfo@bksv.com *Noise & vibration Equipment Engineers*

Bruhn Newtech Ltd, The Portway Centre, 1 Old Sarum Park, Old Sarum, Salisbury, SP4 6EB Tel: (01722) 417000 Fax: (01722) 417014 E-mail: info@bruhn-newtech.co.uk *Hazard prediction & sensor integration software suppliers*

Bruker BioSpin Ltd, Banner Lane, Coventry, CV4 9GH Tel: (024) 7685 5200 Fax: (024) 7646 5317 E-mail: admin@bruker.co.uk *Spectrometers manufrs*

Brumfitt Factory Equipment Ltd, Foundry Works, Gibson Street, Laisterdyke, Bradford, West Yorkshire, BD3 9TF Tel: (01274) 666760 Fax: (01274) 666760 *Truck & trailer manufrs*

Brummells Foods Ltd, Old Ryes, Stebbing Green, Stebbing, Dunmow, Essex, CM6 3TE Tel: (01371) 856880 Principal Export Areas: Worldwide *Shortbread*

▶ Brune & Blond, PO Box 4143, Lichfield, Staffordshire, WS14 9WT Tel: (01543) 411458 E-mail: info@bruneandblond.co.uk *Gift packs of European Brune and Blond beers. Presentation bottled beer for corporate, business and Christmas hampers delivered to your door*

Brunel Computer Services Ltd, 87 - 89 Prince Avenue, Southend-on-Sea, SS2 6RL Tel: (01702) 302000 Fax: (01702) 305000 E-mail: brunel@email.com *Commercial computer services offering to build PC's to individual customer requirements. Also carrying out diagnostics & repairs & are also able to offer a range of upgrade options. Delivery & commissioning of new systems. We install & maintain networks, Internet routers, backup systems, wireless networking & network printers. Also commercial PC repairs*

Brunel Plastics, Unit A1 Hennock Road North, Marsh Barton Trading Estate, Exeter, EX2 8NJ Tel: (01392) 277466 Fax: (01392) 410526 *PVCU distributors service*

▶ Brunel Scaffolding Ltd, 5 James Watt Close, Hawkesworth Trading Estate, Swindon, SN2 1EL Tel: (01793) 531539 Fax: (01793) 542510

Brunel Signs, Unit 8b, St. Marks Road, St. James Industrial Estate, Corby, Northamptonshire, NN18 8AN Tel: (01536) 205335 Fax: (01536) 408509 E-mail: brunelsign@aol.com *Sign manufrs*

▶ Brunels Removal Services Ltd, 4 Crown Industrial Estate, Crown Road, Warmley, Bristol, BS30 8JB Tel: 0117-907 7855 Fax: 0117-907 7856 E-mail: info@brunel.co.uk

Brunner Machine Tools Ltd, 6 Colville Road, London, W3 8BL Tel: (020) 8992 6011 Fax: (020) 8992 7559 E-mail: sales@brunnermachine.co.uk *Sales & service of tool & wheel grinding machines*

Brunner Mond Group Ltd, PO Box 4, Northwich, Cheshire, CW8 4DT Tel: (01606) 724000 Fax: (01606) 781353 E-mail: sales.enquiries@brunnermond.com *Chemical manufrs*

Brunner Scientific, Unit 4c Hunmanby Industrial Estate, Hunmanby, Filey, North Yorkshire, YO14 0PH Tel: (01723) 891611 Fax: (01723) 890872 E-mail: sales@brunnerscientific.com *Laboratory & scientific supply services & calibration repairers*

Bruno Timber Products, Weston Court, Holton Road, Barry, South Glamorgan, CF63 4JD Tel: (01446) 732693 Fax: (01446) 732693 *Wood pallet & fencing manufrs*

▶ Bruno's Access, 20 Regent Street, Treorchy, Mid Glamorgan, CF42 6PP Tel: (01443) 777997 Fax: (01443) 777997 E-mail: brunopink@aol.co.uk *Access hire*

Brunshaw Light Engineering Co., 19 Athletic Street, Burnley, Lancashire, BB10 4LP Tel: (01282) 420080 Fax: (01282) 420080 E-mail: brunshaw@btconnect.com *Precision engineers & toolmakers*

Brunstock Engineering, Brunstock Works, Brunstock, Carlisle, CA6 4QG Tel: (01228) 525334 Fax: (01228) 525334 *Sheet metalworkers & steel fabricators*

Brunswick Engineering, 27 Sterling Road, Enfield, Middlesex, EN2 0LN Tel: (020) 8882 1877 Fax: (020) 8886 7933 E-mail: brunswick@wwmail.co.uk *Heating & ventilation engineers*

▶ Brunswick Instrumentation Ltd, Maritime House, Basin Road North, Portslade, Brighton, BN41 1WR Tel: (01273) 704949 Fax: (01273) 248900 E-mail: info@brun-inst.co.uk *Sample system components for gas analysis/UK distributor for Perma Pure Nafion dryers and humidifiers. Genie membrane separators for protecting analysers from liquid water. Unisearch Associates high performance optical gas analysers for process and CEMS*

Brunswick Tooling Ltd, Unit 3, The Tiding Industrial Park, Birds Royd Lane, Brighouse, West Yorkshire, HD6 1LQ Tel: (01484) 719900 Fax: (01484) 404727 E-mail: sales@brunswicktooling.co.uk *Tungsten carbide tipped tools, engineering services*

Bruntech Equipment, Easthills, Laurencekirk, Kincardineshire, AB30 1EJ Tel: (01561) 378866 Fax: (01561) 378877 E-mail: robin@bruntech.com *Garage equipment factors automotive & body shop suppliers*

Brunton Business Publications Ltd, Thruxton Down House, Thruxton Down, Andover, Hampshire, SP11 8PR Tel: (01264) 889533 Fax: (01264) 889524 E-mail: publications@brunton.co.uk *Book & magazine publishers*

Bruntons Propellers Ltd, Oakwood Business Park, Stephenson Road West, Clacton-on-Sea, Essex, CO15 4TL Tel: (01255) 420005 Fax: (01255) 427775 E-mail: info@bruntons-propellers.com *Ships propeller & stern gear manufrs*

Brupac Drinks & Machine Co. Ltd, 147a Richmond Road, Crewe, CW1 4AX Tel: (01270) 587700 Fax: (01270) 501129 E-mail: sales@brupac.co.uk *Vending machines manufrs*

The Brush Co., 36 North Lane, Aldershot, Hampshire, GU12 4QG Tel: (01252) 341300 Fax: (01252) 332993 E-mail: sales@lincolnfloor.co.uk *Industrial floor cleaner brushes manufrs*

Brush Electrical Machines Ltd, PO Box 18, Loughborough, Leicestershire, LE11 1HJ Tel: (01509) 611511 Fax: (01509) 610440 E-mail: sales@bem.fki-et.com *Heavy electrical engineers*

▶ Brush Strokes, 801 London Road, Stoke-on-Trent, ST4 5NZ Tel: (01782) 874178 E-mail: foxy1@ntlworld.com *Domestic and commercial work undertaken to. Allwork carried out to a high standard.*Free quotations*

Brush Technology Ltd, 3 Throckley Industrial Estate, Ponteland Road, Throckley, Newcastle upon Tyne, NE15 9EW Tel: 0191-229 1666 Fax: 0191-229 1777 E-mail: info@brushtec.com *Industrial brushes & injection mouldings manufrs*

Brush Traction, PO Box 17, Loughborough, Leicestershire, LE11 1HS Tel: (01509) 617000 Fax: (01509) 617001 E-mail: sales@brushtraction.com *Locomotives overhaul & manufrs*

▶ Brushers Ltd, Marston Gate, Frome, Somerset, BA11 4DJ Tel: (01373) 467418

Brushes North West Ltd, 16 Offerton Industrial Estate, Hempshaw Lane, Offerton, Stockport, Cheshire, SK2 5TJ Tel: 0161-477 4805 Fax: 0161-477 4805 *Industrial brushes*

Brushstrokes Signs, Station Road, Buckhaven, Leven, Fife, KY8 1JH Tel: (01592) 714804 Fax: (01592) 714103 *Sign makers*

Brushwork Magazine, 59-61 The Broadway, Haywards Heath, West Sussex, RH16 3AS Tel: (01444) 440188 Fax: (01444) 414813 E-mail: info@airstream.co.uk *Based in Haywards Heath, England Airstream Communications Ltd publishes two magazines: Brushwork which is aimed at the worldwide brushmaking industry and gives global coverage of the supply situation for materials machinery and semi finished brush and applicator goods such as tooth brushes, paintbrushes, household brushes, Industrial brushes, Paint Rollers, Power Brushes as well as all kinds of Brush making machinery and materials. It has a website www.brushworkonline.com. The second magazine is called Tool Business+Hire, which is a UK (England, Wales Scotland and Northern Ireland) based trade magazine which together with associated website www.toolweb.co.uk gives details of new products and company developments affecting the UK hand and power tool trade as well as covering Plant Hire and construction related issues.*

Bruton Classic Furniture Ltd, Riverside, Station Road, Bruton, Somerset, BA10 0EH Tel: (01749) 813266 Fax: (01749) 813266 E-mail: sales@brutonclassic.co.uk *Import & export furniture*

Bruva Renaissance, The Old Mill, Miry Lane, Yeadon, Leeds, LS19 7ER Tel: 0113-250 4499 *Curtain access distributors*

Bruynzeel Multipanel, 8 High Street, Southminster, Essex, CM0 7DE Tel: (01621) 774728 Fax: (01621) 773825 E-mail: lbundy@bruynzeelmultipanel.com *Plywood manufacturers & import merchants*

▶ Bryan C Cooper Ltd, 96 Newland, Sherborne, Dorset, DT9 3DT Tel: (01935) 814946 Fax: (01935) 816306

Bryan & Clark Ltd, Ground Floor, West Cumberland House, 80 Scrubs Lane, London, NW10 6RF Tel: (020) 8969 9933 Fax: (020) 8960 7430 E-mail: sales@bryanandclark.co.uk *Exhibition display fabric suppliers*

Bryan Contract Seating Services, Bass Industrial Estate, Sleaford, Lincolnshire, NG34 7JT Tel: (01529) 306281 Fax: (01529) 414303 E-mail: sales@bryan-seating.co.uk *Manufacture & supply contract seating*

Bryan Donkin Ltd, Enterprise Drive, Holmewood, Chesterfield, Derbyshire, S42 5UZ Tel: (01246) 501501 Fax: (01246) 501500 E-mail: sales@bdrmg.co.uk *Gas & pressure regulator manufrs*

Bryan Gelder Joinery, 7 Jack Straws Lane, Headington, Oxford, OX3 0DL Tel: (01865) 247197 Fax: (01865) 247197 *Joinery manufrs*

▶ Bryan Madge Associates LLP, Vale Forge, North Road, Cowbridge, South Glamorgan, CF71 7DF Tel: (01446) 775959 Fax: (01446) 775758 E-mail: symmons@bryanmadge.co.uk *Training & business development consultancy*

Bryan Packman Marcel, 26 Moreton Street, London, SW1V 2PE Tel: (020) 7834 7899 Fax: (020) 7931 0568 E-mail: consulting@bpm.uk.com *Civil & structural engineers*

Bryan Powercom, 19 University Street, Belfast, BT7 1FY Tel: (028) 9032 6315 Fax: (028) 9032 3144 E-mail: bryanprcom@aol.com *Computer suppliers, integrated power & communication systems*

▶ Bryan & Son, 165a Camden Road, Tunbridge Wells, Kent, TN1 2RF Tel: (01892) 544635 Fax: (01892) 544635 *Specialists in both modern & vintage car radiator repair & rebuilding*

▶ Bryan's Ltd, Gorhuish, Northlew, Okehampton, Devon, EX20 3BU Tel: (01837) 810501 Fax: (01837) 810705

Bryant Broadcast, 70b Stafford Road, Croydon, CR0 4NE Tel: (020) 8404 4050 Fax: (020) 8404 4080 E-mail: sales@bryant-broadcast.co.uk *Broadcasting industry cables & metalwork manufrs*

▶ Bryant & Cairns, Borthwick View, Pentland Industrial Estate, Loanhead, Midlothian, EH20 9QH Tel: 0131-440 2855 Fax: 0131-448 2096 E-mail: sales@bryantandcairns.co.uk *Installation & joinery services*

Bryant Electrical Ltd, 3 Shamel Business Centre, Commissioners Road, Rochester, Kent, ME2 4HQ Tel: (01634) 297211 Fax: (01634) 226863 E-mail: bryant.electrical@bryantelectrical.com *Industrial control, switch gear & distribution systems*

Bryant Fixings Ltd, 21 Blatchford Road, Horsham, West Sussex, RH13 5QR Tel: (01403) 265652 Fax: (01403) 218070 *Fixing system stockists & distributors*

▶ Bryant Homes Southern Counties, Templars House, Lulworth Close, Chandler''s Ford, Eastleigh, Hampshire, SO53 3TJ Tel: (023) 8025 5288 Fax: (023) 8025 1344

Bryant Plastic Products Ltd, Walk Mills, The Walk, Coney Lane, Keighley, West Yorkshire, BD21 5AR Tel: (01535) 606676 Fax: (01535) 602966 E-mail: sales@bryantplastics.co.uk *Plastics & metal manufrs*

▶ Bryant & Towbridge Ltd, 47 Elizabeth Avenue, Christchurch, Dorset, BH23 2DN Tel: (01202) 484174

Bryant Welding Supplies, PO Box 100, Southampton, SO40 9LA Tel: (023) 8086 7789 Fax: (023) 8066 3688 E-mail: sales@bryantwelding.co.uk *Welding supplies & abrasive product distributors or agents*

Bryar Group Ltd, 41 Catley Road, Darnall, Sheffield, S9 5JF Tel: 0114-291 7020 Fax: 0114-261 8186 E-mail: info@bryar.co.uk *Metal fabrication & railway maintenance equipment supply & manufrs*

Bryce Curdy Productions, PO Box 400, Ayr, KA7 4NB Tel: (01292) 443398 Fax: (01292) 443398 E-mail: mail@bryce-curdy.com *Events organisers & video production*

▶ Bryce Metalwork Ltd, 111 Deerdykes View, Cumbernauld, Glasgow, G68 9HN Tel: (01236) 453503 Fax: (01236) 453503

Bryco Ltd, Greystones, Langwith Road, Scarcliffe, Chesterfield, Derbyshire, S44 6TH Tel: (01246) 823407 Fax: (01246) 827899 E-mail: brycoltd@btinternet.com *Mine consulting engineers*

Bryen & Langley Ltd, 48-60 Footscray Road, London, SE9 2SU Tel: (020) 8850 7775 Fax: (020) 8850 6772 E-mail: info@bryen-langley.com *Building contractors*

▶ Bryers & Heaton Ltd, Richmond Hill, Wigan, Lancashire, WN5 8AA Tel: (01942) 211726 Fax: (01942) 214171

Bry-Kol Group of Companies, 10 Newcastle Street, Burslem, Stoke-On-Trent, ST6 3QF Tel: (01782) 577991 Fax: (01782) 577511 E-mail: info@bry-Kol.co.uk *Air conditioning specialists*

Brymore Group, 8 Tavistock Court, Tavistock Road, Croydon, CR9 2ED Tel: (020) 8688 3926 Fax: (020) 8688 6979 *Private property services*

Bryn Thomas Training Services Ltd, 421 Chester Road, Oakenholt, Flint, CH6 5SE Tel: (01352) 733984 Fax: (01352) 761052 E-mail: nik@brynthomastrainingservices.co.uk *CPCS Training provider*

Bryning & Wright Printers, Buckley House, Buckley Road Indust Estate, Rochdale, Lancashire, OL12 9EF Tel: (01706) 345897 Fax: (01706) 632767 E-mail: info@atecgroupe.co.uk *Printers*

Brynkir Woollen Mill Ltd, Brynkir Woollen Factory, Golan, Garndolbenmaen, Gwynedd, LL51 9YU Tel: (01766) 530236 *Bedspread manufrs*

Brynleigh Technology, Unit 11 Heybridge House, Industrial Estate, Maldon, Essex, CM9 4XL Tel: (01621) 877920 Fax: (01621) 877921 E-mail: sales@brynleigh.co.uk *Electronic assembly*

Brynmawr Tools & Engineering Co. Ltd, Heritage Court Road, Gilchrist Thomas Industrial Estate, Blaenavon, Pontypool, Gwent, NP4 9RL Tel: (01495) 790230 Fax: (01495) 792757 E-mail: wnquiries@gosengomeering.co.uk *Steel fabricators*

▶ Brynymor Digital, 14 Brynymor Road, Swansea, SA1 4JQ Tel: (01792) 456661 Fax: (01792) 456777 E-mail: info@digipress.co.uk *Quality photocopying, colour copying & digital print services*

Brysdales Interiors Ltd, Brysdale House Drumhead Road, Chorley North Business Park, Chorley, Lancashire, PR6 7DE Tel: (01257) 240000 Fax: (01257) 240024 E-mail: enquiries@brysdales.co.uk *Shelving, racking & partition systems*

Brystewood Veneering Co., The Hatcheries, Brackner Lane, Bilsthorpe, Newark, Nottinghamshire, NG22 8TU Tel: (01623) 411415 Fax: (01623) 411416 E-mail: brystewood@aol.com *Joinery & door manufrs*

Brystewood Veneering Co., The Hatcheries, Brackner Lane, Bilsthorpe, Newark, Nottinghamshire, NG22 8TU Tel: (01623) 411415 Fax: (01623) 411416 E-mail: brystewood@aol.com *Joinery & door manufrs*

▶ Bryteworks Ltd, 24 Hampden Road, Caversham, Reading, RG4 5ED Tel: (0870) 7770477 Fax: (0870) 7620794 E-mail: info@bryteworks.com *Website design services*

BS&B Safety Systems (UK) Ltd, Adamson House, Tower Business Pk, Wilmslow Rd, Didsbury, Manchester, M20 2YY Tel: 0161-955 4202 Fax: 0161-955 4282 E-mail: sales@bsb-systems.co.uk *Manufacturers offering a wide selection of rupture disks, bursting safety disks & venting explosion protection equipment. Disk sizes ranging from 1/8 inches (3mm) to 44 inches (1120mm). Pressures from in. WC (mbar g) to 100,000 psig (6900). Custom engineered & designed rupture disks* Also at: London SW14

▶ B-SafeUK, 77 Power Street, Newport, NP20 5FS Tel: (01633) 673372 E-mail: clive.blake@ntlworld.com

BSB Electronics Ltd, Cambridge Street, Great Harwood, Blackburn, BB6 7BU Tel: (01254) 883348 Fax: (01254) 889113 E-mail: sales@progeny.co.uk *Security electronic manufrs*

BSB Signs.Co.Uk, Orchard Works, Grove Road, London, E4 9SU Tel: (020) 8529 3330 Fax: (020) 8529 3331 E-mail: info@bsbsigns.co.uk *Sign manufrs*

BSC Filters Ltd, Jorvik House, Outgang Lane, Osbaldwick, York, YO19 5UP Tel: (01904) 438438 Fax: (01904) 438123 E-mail: sales@bscfilters.com Principal Export Areas: Worldwide *Design microwave filters*

BSC Sales Specialists, BSC House, 16 Blackfriars Street, Salford, M3 5BQ Tel: 0161-834 6234 Fax: 0161-835 3114 *Sales recruitment specialists*

▶ BSCL Ltd, Unit 1 Stoke View Business Park, Stoke View Road, Bristol, BS16 3AE Tel: 0117-958 3540 Fax: 0117-958 3539 E-mail: info@bscl.com

BSI Quality Assurance, 389 Chiswick High Road, London, W4 4AL Tel: (020) 8996 9000 Fax: (020) 8996 7400 E-mail: info@bsi-global.com *Testing services*

BSS, Unit 6-7 Industrial Estate, Thomas Road, London, E14 7BN Tel: (020) 7531 3900 Fax: (020) 7537 4849 E-mail: 1920.sales@bssgroup.com *Copper tube fittings specialist services & distribution* Also at: Castle Bromwich & Gateshead

BSS Steelstrip Co. Ltd, 42 Gatcombe Way, Priorslee, Telford, Shropshire, TF2 9GZ Tel: (01952) 290313 E-mail: bss@steelstrip.co.uk *Hot and Cold Rolled mild, carbon and alloy steel strip*

▶ BSS UK Ltd Export Services, Fleet House, Lee Circle, Leicester, LE1 3QQ Tel: 0116-256 7084 Fax: 0116-256 7096

▶ BST Precision Ltd, Unit D 10, Hortonwood 7, Hortonwood, Telford, Shropshire, TF1 7XU Tel: (01952) 603952 Fax: (01952) 604947 E-mail: tony.edgley@bstprecision.co.uk *Precision engineers*

▶ BSTMS, River Court, 27 Brewhouse Lane, Putney Wharf, London, SW15 2JX Tel: (020) 8780 0805 *BSTMS design and deliver Management Training and Personal Effectiveness programmes and workshops to a range of organisations in the UK, US and Europe. We supply tailored programmes and workshops, short Learning Bites and a variety of Open Courses.*

▶ BSW Building Services TD, Rock Lodge Vineyard, Lewes Road, Scaynes Hill, Haywards Heath, West Sussex, RH17 7NG Tel: (01444) 831138 Fax: (01444) 831183

BSW Heating Ltd, 3 Old Barn Lane, Kenley, Surrey, CR8 5AT Tel: (020) 8763 5300 Fax: (020) 8763 5353 E-mail: enquiries@bsw-heating.com

BT, Annandale House, 1 Hanworth Road, Sunbury-On-Thames, Middlesex, TW16 5DJ Tel: (01932) 765766 Fax: (01932) 772277 *IT E-commerce*

BT International Ltd, Regatta House, 67-71 High Street, Marlow, Buckinghamshire, SL7 1AB Tel: (01628) 470040 Fax: (01628) 470041 E-mail: info@bt-international.com *Fork lift truck manufrs*

BT Products Engineering, Unit U Penfold Works, Imperial Way, Watford, WD24 4YY Tel: (01923) 240950 Fax: (01923) 255932 *Stove enamelling services*

▶ BT Showroom, 155 Tailyour Road, Crownhill, Plymouth, PL6 5DJ Tel: (01752) 791222 E-mail: sales@btshowroom.com *bt Showroom supplies the widest range of audio visual equipment for the home user or the av professionals. Including multimedia projectors & screens, CD & DVD duplicators , PA systems plasma & LCD screens, a complete range of hi fi and audio products and the best customer service in the business.*

Bta Ltd, 100 The High Street, Wandsworth, London, SW18 4LA Tel: (020) 8871 4240 Fax: (020) 8871 4584 E-mail: info@bta.com *IT consultancy*

▶ Btatraining Ltd, 32 Cornwall Crescent, Brighouse, West Yorkshire, HD6 4DS Tel: (01484) 718218 E-mail: stuart@btatraining.co.uk *BTA provides training in management, health & Safety, Fire safety and Certificate of professional competence*

BTB Exhausts Ltd, 3-5 The Beaver Centre, Great Central Way, Woodford Halse, Daventry, Northamptonshire, NN11 3DP Tel: (01327) 261797 Fax: (01327) 263577 *Exhaust system manufrs*

BTC Group Ltd, Unit 9 Millington Road, Hayes, Middlesex, UB3 4AZ Tel: (020) 8569 2250 Fax: (020) 8587 3350 E-mail: sales@btcgroup.co.uk *T-shirt & sweatshirt printers*

BTC Speciality Chemical Distribution Ltd, PO Box 4, Cheadle, Cheshire, SK8 6QG Tel: 0161-488 5223 Fax: 0161-486 6184 E-mail: sales@btc-uk.com *Colour, chemical & plastic distributors*

BTG UK, Unit 1 Churchill Court, 58 Station Road, North Harrow, Harrow, Middlesex, HA2 7SA Tel: (020) 8515 6050 Fax: (020) 8515 6099 E-mail: sales@btg-group.com *Pulp paper distributors*

BTM Ltd, 1 Nagi Business Centre, Marsh Road, Wembley, Middlesex, HA0 1ES Tel: (020) 8566 8866 Fax: (020) 8566 8188 E-mail: sales@btmltd.co.uk *We are specialist suppliers, fixers and restorers of marble, granite, slate and limestone for kitchen worktops, bathrooms, vanity tops, shelves, fire surrounds, hearths, shop fronts, walls and floor tiles, entrances, etc. Existing marble and granite can be cut down, altered, re-shaped, re-moulded etc to fit that new location.*Our large stock, reliable and prompt delivery, and customer service are what set us apart from others in the stone industry.**

BTS Holdings plc, B T S House, 69-73 Manor Road, Wallington, Surrey, SM6 0DD Tel: (020) 8401 9000 Fax: (020) 8401 9101 E-mail: sales@bts.co.uk *Electronic directory & phone call logging equipment manufrs*

Bubball Systems Ltd, 60-62 Jenkin Road, Horbury, Wakefield, West Yorkshire, WF4 6DT Tel: (01924) 261158 Fax: (01924) 261158 *Computer game developers*

▶ Bubble Distribution Ltd, Edison Court, Pinchbeck, Spalding, Lincolnshire, PE11 3FX Tel: (0845) 4084671 Fax: (0845) 4084672 *Inkjet cartridges supplier*

The Bubble Factory Ltd, Grove Road, Preston, Canterbury, Kent, CT3 1EF Tel: (01227) 722228 Fax: (01227) 722399 E-mail: thebubble.factory@yahoo.co.uk *The Bubble Factory & Converters Ltd are specialist suppliers of bubble wrap to the fruit packaging industry, trade and retail. The Bubble Factory are pioneers in degradable bubble wrap and biodegradable bubble wrap. For further information on this great new product contact us direct on 01227 722228. We supply a range of bubble wrap packaging and associated products including fruit box packaging and card board box packaging The Bubble Factory provide: Bubble wrap sheets Bubble wrap rolls card board boxes fruit box packaging For further information on bubble wrap and fruit box packaging or to place an order with The Bubble Factory & Converters Ltd please call 01227 722228.*

▶ Bubbles Bathrooms, 13 High Street, Linlithgow, West Lothian, EH49 7AB Tel: (01506) 840060 *Bathroom suppliers*

Bucbricks Ardleigh Sands, Martells Industrial Estate, Slough Lane, Ardleigh, Colchester, CO7 7RU Tel: (01206) 230310 Fax: (01206) 231057 E-mail: sands@bucbricks.co.uk *Filtration media & sand producers*

Buccaneer Boats & Mouldings, Unit 20 The Forge Industrial Park, North Roskear, Camborne, Cornwall, TR14 0AW Tel: (01209) 710398 Fax: (01209) 710398 *Boat builders & repairers*

▶ Buccaneer Trading, Spire Hill Farm, Thornhill, Stalbridge, Dorset, DT10 2SG Tel: 01258 821389 *Based in Dorset, we are suppliers of 0% Arabica coffees, flavoured coffees, teas.*

Buccleuch Printers Ltd, Carnarvon Street, Hawick, Roxburghshire, TD9 7EB Tel: (01450) 372566 Fax: (01450) 375146 E-mail: info@buccleuchprinters.co.uk *General printers*

Buchan Agricultural Consultants, Fridayhill, Maud, Peterhead, Aberdeenshire, AB42 4QQ Tel: (01771) 637721 Fax: (01771) 637888 E-mail: bac.ltd@farmline.com *Agricultural consultants*

▶ Buchan Bros Ltd, Glenugie, Longside, Peterhead, Aberdeenshire, AB42 4XE Tel: (01779) 821419 Fax: (01779) 472737

Buchan Ceilings Ltd, 7 Curtis Road, Coventry, CV2 3AG Tel: (024) 7644 5589 Fax: (024) 7644 5589 E-mail: robbie@robbiebuchan.co.uk *Suspended ceilings*

Buchan Chemicals & Janitorial Supplies, Unit 2 Maxwell Place Industrial Estate, Fraserburgh, Aberdeenshire, AB43 9SX Tel: (01346) 517758 Fax: (01346) 510473 *Chemicals & janitorial suppliers*

Buchan Hall & Mitchell, Reclaimed Ground, Fraserburgh, Aberdeenshire, AB43 9TD Tel: (01346) 513336 Fax: (01346) 513345 *Boat repairers*

▶ Buchan Observer, 28-30 Seagape, Peterhead, Aberdeenshire, AB42 1JP Tel: (01779) 472017 Fax: (01779) 871331 E-mail: sales@buchanobserver.com

Buchan Refrigeration, Ivy Place, Worthing, West Sussex, BN11 3LN Tel: (01903) 204655 Fax: (01903) 204657 *Refrigeration & air conditioning services*

Buchanan Business Systems Ltd, 14 Barrow Close, Sweet Briar Road Industrial Estate, Norwich, NR3 2AT Tel: (01603) 400550 Fax: (01603) 400770 E-mail: sales@buchananforce9.co.uk *Cash register supplies & services*

▶ Buchanan Clark & Wells, 24 George Square, Glasgow, G2 1EG Tel: 0141-221 3535

Buchanan Communications Ltd, 107 Cheapside, London, EC2V 6DN Tel: (020) 7466 5000 Fax: (020) 7466 5001 E-mail: contact@buchanan.uk.com *Public relations consultants*

Buchanan Computing, Newcombe House, 45 Notting Hill Gate, London, W11 3PB Tel: (020) 7674 3150 E-mail: sales@buchanancomputing.co.uk *Software design for transportation*

Buchanan & Curwen (Leatherhead) Ltd, Fairfield Works, Upper Fairfield Road, Leatherhead, Surrey, KT22 7HJ Tel: (01372) 373481 Fax: (01372) 377458 E-mail: buchanans@b-and-c.co.uk *Electrical contractors*

▶ Buchanan Mcpherson Ltd, 2 Portland Place, Hamilton, Lanarkshire, ML3 7JU Tel: (01698) 282903

Buchanan Orthotics Ltd, Suite 4-2 Sky Park SK5, 45 Finnieston Street, Glasgow, G3 8JU Tel: 0141-221 9997 Fax: 0141-221 1345 E-mail: sales@buchananorthotics.freeserve.co.uk *Manufacturers of surgical appliances*

Buchanan Wire Mesh Ltd, 21b Drapersfield Road, Cookstown, County Tyrone, BT80 8RS Tel: (028) 8675 8644 Fax: (028) 8676 5764 E-mail: info@buchananwire.com *Wire goods to specification*

Bucher Hydraulics Ltd, 9 Hemdale Business Park, Hemdale, Nuneaton, Warwickshire, CV11 6GY Tel: (024) 7635 3561 Fax: (024) 7635 3572 E-mail: info.uk@bucherhydraulics.com *Hydraulic control systems*

Buck & Hickman Ltd, 4 Block A Hareness Park, Hareness Circle, Altens Industrial Estate, Aberdeen, AB12 3QY Tel: (01224) 895272 Fax: (01224) 895248 E-mail: aberdeen@buckhickmaninone.com *Industrial supplies distributors*

Buck & Hickman Ltd, 5 Mod Department, Spitfire Road, Birmingham, B24 9PR Tel: 0121-386 8000 Fax: 0121-386 8011 E-mail: manchester@buckhickman.co.uk *Industrial supplies distributors*

Buck & Hickman Ltd, 203 Longmead Road, Emersons Green, Bristol, BS16 7FG Tel: 0117-957 9797 Fax: 0117-957 9799 E-mail: bristol@buckhickmaninone.com *Industrial supplies distributors*

Buck & Hickman Ltd, R Kingsville Road, Kingsditch Trading Estate, Cheltenham, Gloucestershire, GL51 9NZ Tel: (01242) 519665 Fax: (01242) 224097

continued

continuation
E-mail: cheltenham@buckhickmaninone.co.uk *Industrial supplies distributors**

Buck & Hickman Ltd, Unit 16 Gatwick Int Distribution Centre, Cobham Way, Crawley, West Sussex, RH10 9RX Tel: (01293) 561651 Fax: (01293) 561637 E-mail: crawley@buckhickmaninone.com *Industrial tool distributors*

Buck & Hickman Ltd, Sterling Industrial Estate, Rainham Road South, Dagenham, Essex, RM10 8TA Tel: (020) 8593 8177 Fax: (020) 8984 1163 E-mail: exports@buckhickmaninone.com *Industrial supplies distributors*

Buck & Hickman Ltd, Rosswood Road, Rossmore Industrial Estate, Ellesmere Port, CH65 3BU Tel: 0151-356 2160 Fax: 0151-357 2019 E-mail: ellesmere@buckhickmaninone.com *Industrial supplies distributors*

Buck & Hickman Ltd, Unit 19 Ringway Industrial Estate, Beck Road, Huddersfield, HD1 5DG Tel: (01484) 426611 Fax: (01484) 435368 E-mail: huddersfield@buckhickman.co.uk *Industrial supplies distributors*

▶ Buck & Hickman Ltd, C2 Waterside Road, Hamilton, Leicester, LE5 1TL Tel: 0116-299 2990 Fax: 0116-299 3301 E-mail: leicester@buckhickmaninone.com *Industrial supplies distributors*

Buck & Hickman Ltd, Unit 9a, Finway, Dallow Road, Luton, LU1 1TR Tel: (01582) 419887 Fax: (01582) 425824 E-mail: luton@buckhickmaninone.co.uk *Industrial supplies distributors*

Buck & Hickman Ltd, Unit 5 Waterside, Trafford Park, Manchester, M17 1WD Tel: 0161-877 7888 Fax: 0161-877 7111 E-mail: manchester@buckhickmaninone.com *Industrial supplies distributors*

Buck & Hickman Ltd, 7 Cannon Park Way, Cannon Park Industrial Estate, Middlesbrough, Cleveland, TS1 5JU Tel: (01642) 240116 Fax: (01642) 245299 E-mail: middlesbrough@buckhickmaninone.com *Industrial supplies distributors*

Buck & Hickman Ltd, A Hambridge Road, Newbury, Berkshire, RG14 5SS Tel: (01635) 521747 Fax: (01635) 32605 E-mail: newbury@buckhickmaninone.com *Industrial supplies distributors*

Buck & Hickman Ltd, Hamar Close, Tyne Tunnel Trading Estate, North Shields, Tyne & Wear, NE29 7UY Tel: 0191-296 0333 Fax: 0191-296 0335 E-mail: newcastle@buckhickman.co.uk *Industrial tool distributors*

Buck & Hickman Ltd, Unit 2 Longwall Avenue, Queens Drive Industrial Estate, Nottingham, NG2 1NA Tel: 0115-986 8282 Fax: 0115-986 8486 E-mail: nottingham@buckhickmaninone.com *Industrial tool distributors*

Buck & Hickman Ltd, Unit 2a Treelyn Park, Welbeck Way Woodston, Peterborough, PE2 7WH Tel: (01733) 371737 Fax: (01733) 232245 E-mail: peterborough@buckhickmaninone.co.uk *Industrial supplies distributors*

Buck & Hickman Ltd, 4 Phoenix Business Park, Estover Road, Plymouth, PL6 7PY Tel: (01752) 692700 Fax: (01752) 692701 E-mail: plymouth@buckhickmaninone.com *Industrial supplies distributors*

Buck & Hickman Ltd, Unit 12, Riverside Court, Don Road, Sheffield, S9 2TJ Tel: 0114-244 1012 Fax: 0114-244 5372 E-mail: sheffield@buckhickman.co.uk *Industrial supplies distributors*

Buck & Hickman Ltd, Building 110 Nursling Industrial Estate, Mauretania Road, Nursling, Southampton, SO16 0YS Tel: (023) 8074 2300 Fax: (023) 8074 2301 E-mail: southampton@buckhickmaninone.com *Industrial supplies distributors*

Buck & Hickman Ltd, Lyme Vale Court, Parklands Business Park, Parklands, Stoke-on-Trent, ST4 6NW Tel: (01782) 279927 Fax: (01782) 286355 E-mail: stoke@buckhickman.co.uk *Industrial supplies distributors*

Buck & Hickman Ltd, Unit 12 Ferryboat Close, Enterprise Park, Swansea Enterprise Park, Swansea, SA6 8QN Tel: (01792) 799998 Fax: (01792) 700678 E-mail: swansea@buckhickman.co.uk *Industrial supplies distributors**

Buck & Hickman Ltd, 103-109 Waldegrave Road, Teddington, Middlesex, TW11 8LL Tel: (020) 8977 8844 Fax: (020) 8943 2826 E-mail: teddington@buckhickman.co.uk *Industrial supplies distributors*

Buck Hickman In One Ltd, 70 Lancefield Street, Glasgow, G3 8JD Tel: 0141-221 7174 Fax: 0141-221 8877 E-mail: glasgow@buckhickman.co.uk *Industrial supplies distributors*

Buck In Hickman, Neptune Point, Vanguard Way, Ocean Park, Cardiff, CF24 5PG Tel: (029) 2030 6000 Fax: (029) 2030 6030 E-mail: cardiff@buckhickmaninone.co.uk *Industrial supplies distributors*

Buck Systems, 257 Wharfdale Road, Birmingham, B11 2DP Tel: 0121-765 5800 Fax: 0121-765 5802 E-mail: sales@buck-systems.com *Intermediate bulk container systems*

J.K. Buckenham Ltd, 1 America Square, 17 Crosswall, London, EC3N 2LB Tel: (020) 7377 0110 Fax: (020) 7680 4080 E-mail: jkb@jkb.co.uk *Insurance brokers*

Bucket & Grab Handling Ltd, Bevington Farm, Belchamp Otten, Sudbury, Suffolk, CO10 7BE Tel: (01787) 278781 Fax: (01787) 278783 *Agricultural machinery hire*

Buckfield Plastic Mould Tool, Moor Lane, Witton, Birmingham, B6 7AE Tel: 0121-356 9044 Fax: 0121-344 3108 E-mail: plastic@aol.com *Plastic mould & moulded parts manufrs*

Buckhickman Ltd, Castleton Road, Armley, Leeds, LS12 2EN Tel: 0113-246 0911 Fax: 0113-244 6888 E-mail: sales@buckhickmaninone.com *Industrial supplies distributors*

BuckHickman InOne, Unit 2, Chartergate, Moulton Park, Northampton, NN3 6QF Tel: (01604) 797400 Fax: (01604) 797401 E-mail: northampton@buckhickmaninone.co.uk *Industrial supplies distributors*

Buckie Shipyard Ltd, Commercial Road, Buckie, Banffshire, AB56 1UR Tel: (01542) 832727 Fax: (01542) 831825 E-mail: office@buckieshipyard.com *Boat & yacht builders & repairers*

Buckingham Aggregates Ltd, Unit 6 Ballmoor, Buckingham Industrial Estate, Buckingham, MK18 1RT Tel: (01280) 817611 Fax: (01280) 817749 *Aggregate & hard core merchants*

▶ Buckingham Balloons Ltd, 113 St Thomas Road, Trowbridge, Wiltshire, BA14 7LT Tel: (01225) 752410 E-mail: sales@buckinghamballoons.co.uk *Balloons, party balloons, fancy dress, face paints, wigs, hats*

Buckingham Foods Ltd, Wimblington Drive, Redmoor, Milton Keynes, MK6 4AH Tel: (01908) 838900 Fax: (01908) 838920 *Sandwich production & distribution*

▶ Buckingham Plant Hire Ltd, Blackpit Farm, Silverstone Road, Stowe, Buckingham, MK18 5LJ Tel: (01280) 823355 Fax: (01280) 812830 E-mail: mail@buckinghamplant.co.uk

Buckingham Swimming Pools Ltd, Dalehouse Lane, Kenilworth, Warwickshire, CV8 2EB Tel: (01926) 852351 Fax: (01926) 512387 E-mail: info@buckinghampools.com *Reinforced concrete swimming pools*

Buckinghamshire Fastener Co. Ltd, 14 Wilverley Road, Christchurch, Dorset, BH23 3RU Tel: (01202) 488202 Fax: (01202) 474442 E-mail: sales@buckfastener.co.uk *Industrial fastener distributors & stockists*

Buckland Press Ltd, Barwick Road, Dover, Kent, CT17 0LG Tel: (01304) 205900 Fax: (01304) 205619 E-mail: info@buckland.co.uk *Printers*

Bucklands Independent Land Rover, Court Farm Workshops, Huntley Road, Tibberton, Gloucester, GL19 3AF Tel: (01452) 790788 *Sell used four wheel drive*

Buckle & Davies Construction Ltd, 4 Little Langlands, East Hagbourne, Didcot, Oxfordshire, OX11 9TA Tel: (01235) 819586 Fax: (01235) 819586 *Groundwork contractors*

Buckler Ltd, 3 Angus Works, North Isla Street, Dundee, DD3 7JQ Tel: (01382) 828200 Fax: (01382) 828882 E-mail: info@bucklerboots.com *Work wear manufrs*

▶ Buckler Engineering Services Ltd, King Road Avenue, Bristol, BS11 9HG Tel: 0117-982 9135 Fax: 0117-982 6197

▶ Buckler Haulage Ltd, Marsh Road, Middlesbrough, Cleveland, TS1 5LB Tel: (01642) 222489 Fax: (01642) 249144 E-mail: mrk@bucker.fsbusiness.co.uk *Demolition contractors*

Bucklers Hard Boat Builders Ltd, The Agamemnon Yard, Bucklers Hard, Beaulieu, Brockenhurst, Hampshire, SO42 7XB Tel: (01590) 616214 Fax: (01590) 616267 *Boat builders*

Buckley Elements Ltd, Galveston Grove, Fenton, Stoke-on-Trent, ST3 2JT Tel: (01782) 333071 Fax: (01782) 593485 E-mail: sales@buckleyelements.co.uk *Elements, electric heating elements, industrial ovens, temperature sensors, pressure switches, industrial heating elements, ceramic, thermocouples, molybdenum, iron chrome, nickel chrome, tubular cartridge, wire wound, immersion, commercial, heating elements, mineral insulated, thermometers, digital thermometers, resistance thermometers, thermostats, temperature control/measurement, conditioning ovens*

▶ Buckleys, Welkin Mill, Welkin Road, Bredbury, Stockport, Cheshire, SK6 2BL Tel: 0161-430 4211 Fax: 0161-494 2837 E-mail: tony.stevens@buckleys-print.co.uk *Specialists in all types of wet glue label production & management. Also producers of direct mail & general promotional print.*

Buckleys Brushes, Lowland Works, Hurst Lane, Mirfield, West Yorkshire, WF14 8LY Tel: (01924) 498214 Fax: (01924) 480632 E-mail: brit.bung@telincon.co.uk *Brush manufrs*

▶ Buckley's Crane Hire, Bryn Garth, Garth Road, Glan Conwy, Colwyn Bay, Clwyd, LL28 5TD Tel: (01492) 580227 Fax: (01492) 580725 E-mail: enquiries@buckleyscranehire.co.uk *Mobile crane & lorry hire*

Buckman Hardy Associates, The Old Bakehouse, Albert Road, Deal, Kent, CT14 9RD Tel: (01304) 365918 Fax: (01304) 369737 E-mail: sales@buckman-hardy.co.uk *Electronic equipment & electronic engineering services*

Buckman Laboratories Ltd, Millbank House, Bollin Walk, Wilmslow, Cheshire, SK9 1BJ Tel: (01625) 524875 Fax: (01625) 525988 *Special chemical product manufrs*

A.C. Buckoke & Sons Ltd, Factory 11-25 Chatfield Road, London, SW11 3SE Tel: (020) 7223 3746 Fax: (020) 7223 3746 E-mail: acbuckoke@yahoo.co.uk *Cabinet makers, wooden*

Bucks Metal Finishers Ltd, 19 March Place, Gatehouse Industrial Area, Aylesbury, Buckinghamshire, HP19 8UG Tel: (01296) 420301 Fax: (01296) 420302 E-mail: jacqui.carlisle@btconnect.com *Metal finishing services*

▶ BucksBouncers.Co.Uk, 258 Main Road, Naphill, High Wycombe, Buckinghamshire, HP14 4RX Tel: (01494) 566132 E-mail: info@bucksbouncers.co.uk *Bouncy castle hire*

▶ Buckstop Print Services, Unit 2, Wisloe Road, Cambridge, Gloucester, GL2 7AF Tel: (01453) 890767 Fax: (01453) 890392 *Graphic design & digital print*

▶ Buddies, 60 George Street, Hastings, East Sussex, TN34 3EE Tel: (01424) 427290 Fax: (01424) 427290 *Florists shop*

Bude Angling Supplies, 6 Queen Street, Bude, Cornwall, EX23 8BB Tel: (01288) 353396 Fax: (01288) 353396 E-mail: petsgalorebude@aol.com *Fishing tackle & pets & reptiles suppliers*

Bude Precision Engineering Ltd, Unit 14a Bude Business Centre, Kings Hill Industrial Estate, Bude, Cornwall, EX23 8QN Tel: (01288) 356656 Fax: (01288) 356657 E-mail: bpneng@tiscali.co.uk *Precision engineers*

Bude Time Enterprises Ltd, Higher Wharf, Bude, Cornwall, EX23 8LW Tel: (01288) 353832 Fax: (01288) 355562 E-mail: sales@budetime.co.uk *Clock wholesalers*

Budelpack March Ltd, Martin Avenue, March, Cambridgeshire, PE15 0BJ Tel: (01354) 660400 Fax: (01354) 661270 E-mail: info@budelpack.com *Contract packers manufrs*

▶ Budget, 13 865 Ringwood Road, Bournemouth, BH11 8LW Tel: (01202) 582700 Fax: (01202) 573200 E-mail: info@budgetbatteries.co.uk *Internet battery sales*

Budget Blinds Ltd, Enterprise House, Chorley New Road, Horwich, Bolton, BL6 5NY Tel: (01204) 669898 Fax: (01204) 469696 *Blind manufrs*

Budget Blinds, 10 Heol Cwm Ifor, Caerphilly, Mid Glamorgan, CF83 2EU Tel: (029) 2088 8763 Fax: (029) 2085 3167 *Blinds manufrs*

Budget Blinds, 50 William Street, Cookstown, County Tyrone, BT80 8NB Tel: (028) 8676 7875 Fax: (028) 8676 7875 *Vertical roller & plated blinds manufacturers & installers*

Budget Blinds, 119 Higher Lomax Lane, Heywood, Lancashire, OL10 4RU Tel: (01706) 369402 Fax: (01706) 625525 *Window blinds manufrs*

Budget Blinds, 4 Tangier Street, Whitehaven, Cumbria, CA28 7UZ Tel: (01946) 64287 Fax: (01946) 64287 *Blind manufrs*

▶ Budget Estimate Ltd, 124 Cliff Road, Crigglestone, Wakefield, West Yorkshire, WF4 3EJ Tel: (01924) 250211 E-mail: info@budgetestimate.co.uk *Estimating service to contractors and subcontractors.Bill of quantities. Plan & spec.*

Budget Furniture, Unit 1 Manor St, Manchester, M12 6HE Tel: 0161-272 6876 *Furniture wholesalers & bed manufrs*

Budget Gas Ltd, Halesfield 21, Telford, Shropshire, TF7 4NX Tel: (01952) 583908 Fax: (01952) 586692 *Propane & butane bulk suppliers*

▶ Budget Marquees, 18 Cliff Hill, Gorleston, Great Yarmouth, Norfolk, NR31 6DQ Tel: (01493) 300721 E-mail: info@BudgetMarquees.co.uk *Marquees & gazebos suppliers*

Budget Paper Supplies Ltd, Arborfield Mill, Helpston, Peterborough, PE6 7DH Tel: (01733) 252868 Fax: (01733) 253555 E-mail: enquiries@budget-paper.co.uk *Specialist educational suppliers*

Budget Steel Fabrications, 48 English Street, Hull, HU3 2DT Tel: (01482) 320346 Fax: (01482) 215799 E-mail: business@budgetsteel.co.uk *Steel fabricators*

Budget Tyre & Auto Service, 95 Orbiston Street, Motherwell, Lanarkshire, ML1 1PY Tel: (01698) 275070 Fax: (01698) 276667 *Exhaust & tyre distribs*

Budget Windows, 2 Chain Lane, Newport, Isle of Wight, PO30 5QA Tel: (01983) 520327 Fax: (01983) 521600 E-mail: sales@bwconline.net *Double glazing manufrs*

Budjit Textile Services, 53 Love Street, Paisley, Renfrewshire, PA3 2DZ Tel: 0141-887 8480 Fax: 0141-887 8480 *Linen distributors*

▶ Budweiser Budvar UK Ltd, Hamilton House, Mabledon Place, London, WC1H 9BB Tel: (020) 7554 8810 Fax: (020) 7554 8811 E-mail: john.harley@budvar.co.uk *Beer, larger & wine distributors*

▶ Buffers & Stackers Ltd, Creative Industries Centre, Wolverhampton Science Park, Wolverhampton, WV10 9TG Tel: (01902) 420877 Fax: (01902) 716312 E-mail: info@buffstack.co.uk *Design automation handling equipment for stacking and buffering*

▶ Buffet Car, The, 25 Maplewood Park, Deans, Livingston, West Lothian, EH54 8BB Tel: 01506 415055 Fax: 07931 796940 E-mail: Eileen@TheBuffetCar.com *We make and deliver buffets, cakes and drinks to the general public, business and for social events. We supply outside catering with a quality low cost product.Email Eileen@TheBuffetCar.com*

Bugbusters, Mcb Business Centre, Argoed Rd, Buckley, Clwyd, CH7 3HZ Tel: (01244) 546299 Fax: (01244) 543926 *Computer services*

Bugbusters Pest Control Ltd, 40 Goodrich Avenue, Bedford, MK41 0DE Tel: (0800) 854757 Fax: (01234) 312426 E-mail: bugbusters.2002@virgin.net *Pest control services*

Francis Bugler Ltd, Barrowfield, Broadwindsor Road, Beaminster, Dorset, DT8 3PP Tel: (01308) 862239 Fax: (01308) 863511 E-mail: info@buglers.co.uk *Agricultural tractor & machinery distributors*

Build Center, Cambrian Works, Station Approach, Wrexham, Clwyd, LL11 2NY Tel: (01978) 354444 Fax: (01978) 351688 *Builders' merchants*

Build Centre Ltd, Unit 8 Etna Court, Falkirk, FK2 9ED Tel: (01324) 611787 Fax: (01324) 621375 E-mail: sales@buildcentre.co.uk *Abrasive & power tool distribrs* Also at: Edinburgh, Glasgow & Inverness

Build Centre, 555 South Street, Glasgow, G14 0QT Tel: 0141-954 5051 Fax: 0141-954 7322 *Ironmongers*

Build-A-Van, Riverside Mill, Brunswick Street, Nelson, Lancashire, BB9 0HZ Tel: (01282) 693025 Fax: (01282) 603921 E-mail: graham.hardman@btconnect.com *Passenger welfare safety manufrs*

Buildbase, Simpson Road, Bletchley, Milton Keynes, MK1 1BB Tel: (01908) 644222 Fax: (01908) 270243 *Timber & builders merchants* Also at: Braintree, Horsham, Luton & Oxford

Buildbase, Crinoline Commercial Area, Rawmarsh Road, Rotherham, South Yorkshire, S60 1SA Tel: (01709) 365686 Fax: (01709) 362365 *Builders & plumbers merchants*

Builder Center Ltd, Windsor Road, Bedford, MK42 9SU Tel: (01234) 272292 Fax: (01234) 365395 E-mail: peter.abbott@wolseley.co.uk *Builders merchants*

Builder Center Ltd, Dunmere Road, Bodmin, Cornwall, PL31 2QN Tel: (01208) 78211 Fax: (01208) 72934 *Builders merchants*

Builder Center Ltd, Martin Street, Burnley, Lancashire, BB10 1SH Tel: (01282) 421811 Fax: (01282) 831723 E-mail: admin@buildercenter.co.uk *Builders & plumbers merchants*

Builder Center Ltd, New Station Road, Dalbeattie, Kirkcudbrightshire, DG5 4AP Tel: (01556) 610208 Fax: (01556) 611514 *Builders merchants* Also at: Dumfries

Builder Center Ltd, Finmere Road, Eastbourne, East Sussex, BN22 8QJ Tel: (01323) 725121 Fax: (01323) 738879 *Builders merchants*

Builder Center Ltd, 29 Wellside Place, Falkirk, FK1 5RL Tel: (01324) 632634 Fax: (01324) 670900 *Builders merchants*

Builder Center Ltd, Conway Street, Hove, East Sussex, BN3 3LA Tel: (01273) 778778 Fax: (01273) 722413 *Builders merchants*

Builder Center Ltd, 80 Low Hill, Liverpool, L6 1BT Tel: 0151-263 5544 Fax: 0151-263 1432 *Building material merchants* Also at: Birkenhead, Isle of Man, Kirkdale & Maghull

Builder Center, 1 Knowsley Street, Cheetham Hill Road, Manchester, M8 8QL Tel: 0161-834 9437 Fax: 0161-833 2706 E-mail: wolseley@center.co.uk *Builders merchants* Also at: Cadishead

Builder Center Ltd, Cradle Hill Industrial Estate, Alfriston Road, Seaford, East Sussex, BN25 2AT Tel: (01323) 893243 Fax: (01323) 891072 *Builders merchants*

Builder Center Ltd, 591 Sedlescombe Road North, St. Leonards-on-Sea, East Sussex, TN37 7PY Tel: (01424) 756946 Fax: (01424) 751481 *Building materials merchants*

Builder Centre, Clay Flatts Industrial Estate, Workington, Cumbria, CA14 2DB Tel: (01900) 62231 Fax: (01900) 67631 *Builders merchant*

▶ Builder Express co uk Ltd, 16 Rheidol Mews, Islington, London, N1 8NU Tel: (0800) 6191248 *We are a London based construction company . We offer a wide range of building services , from small paint jobs , flooring fitting , adding (or removing) an extension , electric work , and all the refurbishment jobs around the house to a complete make over . "We proud ourselves in the reliable and quick service we provide , on top of a job well performed .*

▶ Builders Beams Ltd, Unit 15 Cosgrove Way, Luton, LU1 1XL Tel: (01582) 429151 Fax: (01582) 429155 *Steel fabricators*

Builders Centre Sheffield Ltd, Nunnery Drive, Sheffield, S2 1TA Tel: 0114-272 4001 Fax: 0114-241 2840 E-mail: info@builderscentre.co.uk *Builders & plumbers merchants*

▶ Builders Equipment Ltd, City Road, Norwich, NR1 3AN Tel: (01473) 236316 Fax: (01473) 281788 E-mail: mail@builders.equipment.co.uk *Lifting gear & plant hire, leasing & rental services* Also at: Ipswich

Builders Equipment (Norwich) Ltd, 24 City Road, Norwich, NR1 3AN Tel: (01603) 616211 Fax: (01603) 630408 E-mail: mail@builders-equipment.co.uk *Building equipment suppliers*

Builders Merchants Confederation Ltd, 15 Soho Square, London, W1D 3HL Tel: (020) 7439 1753 Fax: (020) 7734 2766 E-mail: info@bmf.org.uk *Federation trade association*

Builders Supplies (West Coast) Ltd, Kilbane Street, Fleetwood, Lancashire, FY7 7PF Tel: (01253) 776600 Fax: (01253) 776800 E-mail: sales@bswc.biz *Builders Supplies (West Coast) Ltd has been established on the Fylde coast since 1938. As one of the areas leading independent builders' merchants, we have a wealth of experience and a vast product range including bricks, concrete block, landscaping materials, paving, walling, timber, insulation, fence panels, underground drainage, plumbing, plaster, cement, aggregates, power tools and we are also a HSS Hire agency. We can, therefore, offer almost every product that you would need for a building project, and we can source most others. Our impressive 16-strong delivery fleet includes 8 vehicles with crane off-load facilities, all of which make prompt and efficient daily deliveries. Also at:- Kilbane Street, Fleetwood, Lancashire Dorset Avenue, Cleveleys, FY5 2DB Chain Caul Way, Riversway, Preston PR2 2TD (01772 766500) Middlegate, White Lund Industrial Estate, Morecambe LA3 3BN (01524 842299)*

Builders' Supply Co. Ltd, 8 Inglis Green Road, Edinburgh, EH14 2HX Tel: 0131-443 4474 Fax: 0131-455 7297 *Builders' merchants*

Builders Supply Co. (Kendal) Ltd, Ann Street, Kendal, Cumbria, LA9 6AA Tel: (01539) 721911 Fax: (01539) 740481 E-mail: info.kendal@builders-supply.co.uk *Building materials merchants*

Builders Supply Co Leabrooks, 33 Greenhill Lane, Leabrooks, Alfreton, Derbyshire, DE55 4AS Tel: (01773) 602727 Fax: (01773) 540324 *Builders merchants*

Builders Supply Stores Coventry Ltd, 45 Spon End, Coventry, CV1 3HG Tel: (024) 7671 2000 Fax: (024) 7671 4072 E-mail: info@bsscov.co.uk *Builders merchants*

Builders Supply (Wakefield) Ltd, 2 Thornes Lane, Wakefield, West Yorkshire, WF1 5QH Tel: (01924) 376821 Fax: (01924) 362018 *Builders merchants*

Building Adhesives Ltd, Longton Road, Stoke-on-Trent, ST4 8JB Tel: (01782) 591100 Fax: (01782) 591101 E-mail: info@building-adhesives.com *Industrial, structural & structural sealant adhesives*

The Building Centre Bookshop, 26 Store Street, London, WC1E 7BT Tel: (020) 7692 4040 Fax: (020) 7636 3628 E-mail: bookshop@buildingcentre.co.uk *Books for the construction industry retailers*

The Building Centre Bookshop, 26 Store Street, London, WC1E 7BT Tel: (020) 7692 4040 Fax: (020) 7636 3628 E-mail: agagliano@buildingcentre.co.uk *Building information centres*

▶ Building Craftsmen Dumfries Ltd, The Hollies, Lockerbie, Dumfriesshire, DG11 1BJ Tel: (01387) 263131 Fax: (01387) 263131

Building Design Patnership, 7 Hill Street, Bristol, BS1 5RW Tel: 0117-929 9861 Fax: 0117-922 5280 E-mail: bristol@bdp.co.uk *Architects & engineers*

▶ Building Diagnostic & Assessment Services Ltd, Liberator House, Glasgow Prestwick International, Glasgow Prestwick Intnl Airpor, Prestwick, Ayrshire, KA9 2PL Tel: (0800) 7314364 Fax: (01292) 471146

▶ Building Environmental Services P.L.C., The Church House, Kneesworth Street, Royston, Hertfordshire, SG8 5AB Tel: (01763) 248752

Building & Industrial Tool Supplies, 78 Chester Avenue, Lancing, West Sussex, BN15 8PG Tel: (01903) 766983 Fax: (01903) 764190 *Tool repairers*

▶ Building Movement Services, Unit 5 Little Orange Farm, Hedingham Road, Gosfield, Halstead, Essex, CO9 1SA Tel: (01787) 478890 Fax: (01787) 472623

Building Product Design Ltd, 2 Brooklands Road, Sale, Cheshire, M33 3SS Tel: 0161-905 5700 Fax: 0161-905 2085 E-mail: postmaster@buildingproductdesign.com *Ventilation manufrs*

Building Product Design Ltd, 6 Tonbridge Chambers, Pembury Road, Tonbridge, Kent, TN9 2HZ Tel: (01732) 355519 Fax: (01732) 355536 E-mail: info@bpd.com *Building products distributors*

Building Products Design Ltd, Brook Hill Industrial Estate, Pinxton, Nottingham, NG16 6NS Tel: (01773) 814123 Fax: (01773) 814101 E-mail: info@buildingproductsdesign.com *Building industry plastic products manufrs*

Building Products Index, 30 Gorst Road, London, NW10 6LE Tel: (020) 8838 1904 Fax: (020) 8838 1905 E-mail: bpindex@netscapeonline.co.uk *Building information service*

Building Profiles Ltd, Timothys Bridge Road, Stratford-upon-Avon, Warwickshire, CV37 9NQ Tel: (01789) 414044 Fax: (01789) 415273 E-mail: info@building-profiles.co.uk *Window & door hardware distribs*

▶ Building & Property Defence Ltd, R A F Beaconside, Stafford, ST18 0AQ Tel: (01785) 250749

Building Research Establishment Ltd, Bucknalls Lane, Garston, Watford, WD25 9XX Tel: (01923) 664237 Fax: (01923) 664994 E-mail: enquiries@brecertification.com *Fire testing /evaluation services.*

Building Research Establishment Ltd, Bucknalls Lane, Garston, Watford, WD25 9XX Tel: (01923) 664000 Fax: (01923) 664010 E-mail: enquiries@bre.co.uk *Research laboratories, environmental research consultants & publishers of technical building information. Also risk management consultants*

▶ Building Restoration Co., Kinbreac, Duror, Appin, Argyll, PA38 4DA Tel: (01631) 740300 Fax: (01631) 740216

Building Restoration & Cleaning (Leeds) Ltd, Abbey Mills, Kirkstall, Leeds, LS5 3HP Tel: 0113-278 6472 Fax: 0113-275 4644 E-mail: brcleeds@btconnect.com *Building restoration contractors*

▶ Building Sciences Ltd, The Carriage House, School Road, Ardington, Wantage, Oxfordshire, OX12 8PQ Tel: (01235) 835323 Fax: (01235) 863220 E-mail: sborland@buildingsciences.co.uk *Building air pressurisation testing, Air leakage consultancy, Acoustic testing and consultancy*

▶ Building Services Ltd, Unit 2 Avon Court, Avon Close, Granby Industrial Estate, Weymouth, Dorset, DT4 9UX Tel: (01305) 770773

▶ Building Services Design, 5 Melbourne House Corby Gate Business Park, Priors Haw Road, Corby, Northamptonshire, NN17 5JG Tel: (01536) 403304 Fax: (01536) 403838

▶ Building Services Easton Ltd, Dereham Road, Easton, Norwich, NR9 5EH Tel: (01603) 742274 Fax: (01603) 741377

Building Services Research & Information Associati Ltd, Old Bracknell Lane West, Bracknell, Berkshire, RG12 7AH Tel: (0845) 1309030 Fax: (01344) 465626 E-mail: bsria@bsria.co.uk *Test research association & consultancy services*

▶ Building Services Scotland, Midlothian Inovation Centre, Roslin, Midlothian, EH25 9RE Tel: 0131-440 2020 Fax: 0131-448 0542

Building Supplies (Holme Lane) Ltd, 115 Holme Lane, Sheffield, S6 4JR Tel: 0114-234 2501 Fax: 0114-285 2836 *Building material suppliers*

▶ Building Surveying Solutions, 376 City Road, London, EC1V 2QA Tel: (020) 7278 4060 Fax: (020) 7287 4717

Building Tecnics, Regents Trade Park, Barwell Lane, Gosport, Hampshire, PO13 0EQ Tel: (01329) 282900 Fax: (0870) 200517 E-mail: info@buildingtecnics.com *Partitioning, ceiling contractors & commercial fit out services*

Buildings Unlimited, Unit 20 Hollins Business Centre 6, Rowley Street, Stafford, ST16 2RH Tel: (01785) 211503 Fax: (01785) 259042 E-mail: enquires@buildingsunlimited.co.uk *Design & supply of steel framed industrial buildings*

Buildswift Ltd, 2 Fleet La Industrial Estate, Fleet Lane, St. Helens, Merseyside, WA9 1TA Tel: (01744) 731494 Fax: (01744) 731506 E-mail: glee@buildswift.co.uk *Conveyors & steel fabrication services*

▶ Builth Building Services, Castle Road, Builth Wells, Powys, LD2 3EL Tel: (01982) 552746 Fax: (01982) 552746

▶ Bulk Food Transport Ltd, Crossway Farm, Thurlton, Norwich, NR14 6NZ Tel: (01508) 548338

▶ Bulk GSM, Unit 25 Cygnus Business Centre, Dalmeyer Road, London, NW10 2XA Tel: (020) 8459 7373 Fax: (020) 8459 0202 E-mail: sales@bulkgsm.com *Telecommunications*

▶ Bulk Lift Europe Ltd, Monkswell House, Manse Lane, Knaresborough, North Yorkshire, HG5 8NQ Tel: (01423) 860100 Fax: (0845) 4301296 E-mail: agh@eds.gb *Structural engineers*

Bulk Meter Services, 3 Faversham Road, Challock, Ashford, Kent, TN25 4BQ Tel: (0845) 2307887 Fax: (01233) 740943E-mail: sales@bms-ltd.com *Flow meter calibration services*

Bulk Storage & Process Systems Ltd, 1 Colekitchen Lane, Gomshall, Guildford, Surrey, GU5 9LH Tel: (01483) 202211 Fax: (01483) 205110 E-mail: sales@bulk-systems.co.uk *Bulk product handling*

Bulkbag Ltd, Block 20, Kilspindie Road, Dunsinane Industrial Estate, Dundee, DD2 3QH Tel: (01382) 833111 Fax: (01382) 832272 E-mail: sales@bulkbuy.co.uk *Bulkbag Limited, established in 1984, service a broad customer base, producing FIBCs to carry foodstuff, aggregate, chemicals, pharmaceuticals through to hazardous goods within the U.N. Dangerous Goods category.*

Bulkrite Commercial Vehicle Bodybuilders, Dorrington, Shrewsbury, SY5 7EB Tel: (01743) 718232 Fax: (01743) 718293 E-mail: bulkrite_1@lineone.net *Motor body builders* Also at: Acton Burnell

Bull & Co., 61 La Colomberie, St. Helier, Jersey, JE2 4QA Tel: (01534) 866688 Fax: (01534) 866699 E-mail: enquiries@bullandcompany.com *Business transfer agents & property management*

▶ Bull Electrical Services Westminster Ltd, 13-15 Johns Mews, London, WC1N 2PA Tel: (020) 7242 1282 Fax: (020) 7242 1909

Bull Group Ltd, Unit D Henfield Business Park, Sussex, Henfield, West Sussex, BN5 9SL Tel: (01273) 491490 Fax: (01273) 490813 E-mail: sales@bullnet.co.uk *Internet mail orders*

▶ Bull Hotel, Bulkley Square, Llangefni, Gwynedd, LL77 7LR Tel: (01248) 722119 Fax: (01248) 750488 E-mail: bull@welsh-historic-inns.com *stay at the bull hotel to experiance one of the best hotels on the island of anglesey. centarl for north wales and the ferry to ireland*

Bull Information Systems Ltd, Maxted Road, Hemel Hempstead, Hertfordshire, HP2 7DZ Tel: (01442) 232222 Fax: (01442) 884361 E-mail: information@bull.co.uk *Computerised simulators*

Bull Signs, Bayhorne Lane, Horley, Surrey, RH6 9ES Tel: (01293) 821313 Fax: (01293) 821414 E-mail: sales@bullsigns.com *Sign makers*

Bull Tubes Ltd, Unit 4, Park Road, Willenhall, West Midlands, WV13 1AH Tel: (01902) 608881 Fax: (01902) 602221 E-mail: enquiries@bulltube.com *Steel tube stockholders*

Bulldog Door Services Ltd, Unit D1 Adamson Industrial Estate, Hyde, Cheshire, SK14 1EF Tel: 0161-368 6011 Fax: 0161-368 5566 *Door manufrs*

Bulldog Engineering Recruitment & Management, 223a-225 South Coast Road, Peacehaven, East Sussex, BN10 8LB Tel: (01273) 580580 E-mail: recruitment@bulldog.co.uk *Engineering recruitment*

Bulldog Industrial Holdings Ltd, Carrington Road, Stockport, Cheshire, SK1 2JT Tel: 0161-477 0775 Fax: 0161-480 0133 E-mail: sales@bulldogprocess.com *Supply of coil process, roll forming & folding machinery, new & used*

Bulldog Intruder Detection Systems, 29 Arthur Street, Derby, DE1 3EF Tel: (01332) 360220 Fax: (01332) 384854 E-mail: sales@bulldog-security.co.uk *Security services*

Bullen Consultants Ltd, Copthall House, Station Square, Coventry, CV1 2GT Tel: (024) 7663 2299 Fax: (024) 7663 2221 E-mail: coventry@bullen.co.uk *Consulting engineers*

Geoff Bullen Electronics, Unit 1-2 Woods Way, Goring-by-Sea, Worthing, West Sussex, BN12 4QY Tel: (01903) 244500 Fax: (01903) 700715 E-mail: sales@gbelectronics.com *Electronic product, firmware and software design. Sub-contract board assembly, obsolete component sourcing specialists.*

Bullen Health Care Group, 85-87 Kempston Street, Liverpool, L3 8HE Tel: 0151-207 1239 Fax: 0151-207 3804 E-mail: info@bullens.com *Surgical suppliers*

Bullen Healthcare Group, 479a Alfreton Road, Nottingham, NG7 5NH Tel: 0115-970 4072 Fax: 0115-970 8993 E-mail: info@bullens.com *Stoma care products suppliers*

▶ Buller Ltd, Unit 1G,, Passfield Mill Business Park, Mill Lane, Liphook, Hampshire, GU30 7QU Tel: (0845) 0043748 E-mail: sales@bullerltd.co.uk *Furniture accessories & fittings distributor. *We specialise in supply of kitchen accessories such as magic corners, pullout larders or cabinet handles. Please visit our site for full range of products.*

Bullet Engineering Ltd, Vale Road, Spilsby, Lincolnshire, PE23 5HE Tel: (01790) 753320 Fax: (01790) 754530 *Sheet metalwork engineers or fabricators*

▶ Bullet Express, 5 Ashley Drive, Bothwell, Glasgow, G71 8BS Tel: (01698) 811777 Fax: (01698) 811222 E-mail: info@bulletexpress.co.uk

Bullfinch (Gas Equipment) Ltd, Diadem Works, Kings Road, Tyseley, Birmingham, B11 2AJ Tel: 0121-706 6301 Fax: 0121-707 0995 E-mail: sales@bullfinch-gas.co.uk *Supply of good quality equipment and service at a fair Price. That is our speciality. Leading manufacturer and Supplier of LP Gas equipment. Over 40 years' experience in the production of LPG equipment and appliances. Gas supplies companies (LPG) Diesel engine manufacturers Motorhome manufacturers Central heating boiler manufacturers Telecom companies Defence equipment manufacturers.*

Bulli Computer Maintenance, Gatehouse Lane, Goddards Green, Hassocks, West Sussex, BN6 9LD Tel: (01444) 871609 Fax: (01444) 871216 E-mail: bullicomputers@btconnect.com *Computer maintenance suppliers*

▶ Bullimore Plant Hire, 3 Spalding Road Industrial Esta, Bourne, Lincolnshire, PE10 9LE Tel: (01778) 423309 Fax: (01778) 393139

▶ The Bullit Courier Company Ltd, 12 Charlotte Street, Brighton, BN2 1AG Tel: (0845) 2268556 E-mail: info@bullitcouriers.com *Specialists in same day urgent deliveries nationwide*

Roger Bullivant Ltd, Walton Road, Drakelow, Burton-on-Trent, Staffordshire, DE15 9UA Tel: (01283) 511115 Fax: (01283) 540826 E-mail: marketing@roger-bullivant.co.uk *Piling, house foundations & under pinning contractors, dock pits* Also at: East Bolden, Norwich, Pontefract, Port Talbot, Preston & Westbury

Bullock & Bosson, Unit 6, Victoria Road, Stoke-on-Trent, ST4 2HS Tel: (01782) 747222 Fax: (01782) 746200 E-mail: phillips@bullockandbosson.co.uk *Office equipment suppliers*

Bullock Bros Edge Tools Ltd, Landywood Lane, Cheslyn Hay, Walsall, WS6 7AL Tel: (01922) 414360 Fax: (01922) 410359 E-mail: sales@bullocktools.co.uk *Hand & edge tool manufrs*

Bullock Bros Electronics, 132 Cheltenham Road, Gloucester, GL2 0LY Tel: (01452) 529806 Fax: (01452) 529806 E-mail: sales@bullock-bros.com *Electronic repair services*

Bullock Construction Ltd, Northgate, Aldridge, Walsall, WS9 8TU Tel: (01922) 458311 Fax: (01922) 459589 E-mail: admin@bullock.co.uk *General building contractor*

Bullock & Driffill Ltd, Staunton Works, Newark Road, Staunton in the Vale, Nottingham, NG13 9PF Tel: (01400) 280000 Fax: (01400) 280010 E-mail: bullock.driffill@btopenworld.com *Timber framed system buildings*

Bullock & Driffill Ltd, Staunton Works, Newark Road, Staunton in the Vale, Nottingham, NG13 9PF Tel: (01400) 280000 Fax: (01400) 280010 E-mail: bullock.driffill@btopenworld.com *Roof trusses & timber frames manufrs*

Colin Bullot & Sons Ltd, 7 Glendale Walk, Cheshunt, Waltham Cross, Hertfordshire, EN8 9RJ Tel: (01992) 627407 Fax: (01992) 633198 E-mail: colin@bullot.co.uk *Central heating engineers*

Bullseye Awards & Garments Ltd, 1-2 Norbbeck Parade, Hanger Lane, London, NW10 7HR Tel: (0844) 8009047 Fax: (020) 8997 3840 E-mail: sales@bullseyeuk.com *Trophies, garments, awards, selling & engraving manufrs*

Bullseye Awards & Garments Ltd, 127 Bath Road, Slough, SL1 3UW Tel: (01753) 578830 Fax: (01753) 825679 E-mail: admin@bullseyeuk.com *Trophies & garments services*

Bullus & Co., Rumbolds House, Hammonds Road, Sandon, Chelmsford, CM2 7RS Tel: (01245) 474035 Fax: (01245) 477175 E-mail: search@bullus.co.uk *Recruitment of top executives*

▶ Bullus & Co., Rumbolds House, Hammonds Road, Sandon, Chelmsford, CM2 7RS Tel: (01245) 474035 Fax: (01245) 477175 E-mail: search@bullus.co.uk *Executive recruitment services*

Bulmer Brick Cutting Services, The Brickfields, Hedingham Road, Bulmer, Sudbury, Suffolk, CO10 7EF Tel: (01787) 269132 Fax: (01787) 269044 E-mail: info@brickcutter.com *Brick cutter & arch manufrs*

▶ Bulmer Interior Contracts Ltd, Lauren House, 164 Brinkburn Street, Newcastle upon Tyne, NE6 2AR Tel: 0191-276 4781 Fax: 0191-276 2663

Bulmer & Lumb, Royds Hall Lane, Buttershaw, Bradford, West Yorkshire, BD6 2NE Tel: (01274) 676321 Fax: (01274) 691239 E-mail: sales@bulmerandlumb.com Principal Export Areas: Worldwide *Worsted yarn spinner manufrs*

Bulmer & Lumb Group Ltd, Albert Street, Lockwood, Huddersfield, HD1 3PE Tel: (01484) 423231 Fax: (01484) 435313 E-mail: headoffice@taylor-and-lodge.co.uk *Worsted manufrs*

Bulmers Business Machines Ltd, Royston House, 267 Cranmore Boulevard, Shirley, Solihull, West Midlands, B90 4QT Tel: 0121-745 5529 Fax: 0121-733 6180 *Labelling machine distributors*

Bulmers Logistics (Malton) Ltd, Eston Road, Lazenby, Middlesbrough, Cleveland, TS6 8DR Tel: (01642) 462608 Fax: (01642) 462932 *Haulage company*

▶ Bulpitts Ltd, 30 Plume Street, Birmingham, B6 7RT Tel: 0121-328 5530

Bulpitts Lampshades Ltd, Jarvis House, Yarlet Bank, Stafford, ST18 9SD Tel: (01889) 508977 Fax: (01543) 508966 *Lampshades*

Bulroc (UK) Ltd, Station Lane, Old Whittington, Chesterfield, Derbyshire, S41 9QX Tel: (01246) 450608 Fax: (01246) 454621 E-mail: info@bulroc.com *Rock drilling manufrs*

Bulwell Precision Engineers Ltd, Wharf Road Industrial Estate, Pinxton, Nottingham, NG16 6LE Tel: (01773) 863969 Fax: (01773) 861644 E-mail: bpe@bulwell.com *Precision components manufrs*

Bumble End Barn Old Pine, Grove Lane, Wishaw, Sutton Coldfield, West Midlands, B76 9PH Tel: 0121-351 3993 Fax: 0121-351 3993 E-mail: bumblepine@aol.com *Manufacture & retail of pine & hardwood furniture*

▶ Bumford Heating Ltd, Millhouses Street, Hoyland, Barnsley, South Yorkshire, S74 9LU Tel: (01226) 749300 Fax: (01226) 747952 E-mail: sales@bhl.co.uk

▶ Bumper Centre Ltd, Unit 4 Birds Hill, Letchworth Garden City, Hertfordshire, SG6 1HX Tel: (01462) 487070 Fax: (01462) 620456 E-mail: bumpercentre@btconnect.com *Car bumper retail & repair*

▶ Bumps Maternity Wear, 19 Frederick Street, Sunderland, SR1 1LT Tel: 0191-565 3232 Fax: 0191 5520988 E-mail: info@bumpsmaternity.com *Online collection of affordable and fashionable maternity clothes. Sizes 8 to 26. Also some irresistable 0-12 month baby clothes and nursery products.*

▶ Bumptastic Maternity Wear, Worthing Road, Lowestoft, Suffolk, NR32 4HD Tel: 01502 583568 E-mail: sarah@bumptastic.co.uk

▶ Bumpy Jumpy, 2 Treetops, Southwater, Horsham, West Sussex, RH13 9GE Tel: (01403) 731836 *Bouncy castle hire services*

Bunce Sheet Metal Work, Unit B5 Crabtree Road, Thorpe Industrial Estate, Egham, Surrey, TW20 8RN Tel: (01784) 433556 Fax: (01784) 433556 E-mail: sales@buncesheetmetal.co.uk *Sheet metalworks*

Bunce's Home Hardware, 112-114 Chapel Road, Worthing, West Sussex, BN11 1BX Tel: (01903) 235321 Fax: (01903) 823279 E-mail: enquiries@bunce-co.co.uk *Builders, ironmongers & merchants*

Bunchmakers Ltd, Bagley Lane, Farsley, Leeds, LS28 5UH Tel: 0113-255 6933 Fax: 0113-239 3459 *Pattern card & book manufrs*

Bundz Vending Services Ltd, Southern Messsenger Close, Loughborough, Leicestershire, LE11 5SR Tel: (01509) 230481 Fax: (01509) 233572 *Vending machine operators & service providers*

Bunk A Bin Ltd, Tweedale Way, Oldham, OL9 7LD Tel: (0845) 4567899 Fax: (0845) 4566899 E-mail: hires@bunkabin.co.uk *Manufacturers & hirer of bunk a bin accommodation*cabins**

A.G. Bunker & Sons, Old House Stud Farm, Station Road, Stanbridge, Leighton Buzzard, Bedfordshire, LU7 9JF Tel: (01525) 210984 Fax: (01525) 210984 *Farmers*

J.J. Bunker & Son Ltd, 73 Common Road, Chandlers Ford, Eastleigh, Southampton, SO53 1HE Tel: (023) 8026 8176 Fax: (023) 8027 0668 *Joinery manufrs*

Bunkerfuels UK Ltd, 21-24 Mill Bank Tower, London, SW1P 4QP Tel: (020) 7828 3299 Fax: (020) 7834 4951 E-mail: bunkers@bunkerfuels.co.uk *Oil & bunker brokers*

J. & H. Bunn Ltd, South Beach Parade, Great Yarmouth, Norfolk, NR30 3QA Tel: (01493) 744700 Fax: (01493) 744701 E-mail: info@jhbunn.co.uk *Fertilizer supplier & manufrs*

Bunney & Young Engineering Ltd, Unit V4 Willments Industrial Estate, Hazel Road, Southampton, SO19 7HS Tel: (023) 8042 0993 Fax: (023) 8042 2358 *Precision engineers*

Bunns Lane Welding, Bunns Lane Works, Bunns Lane, London, NW7 2AJ Tel: (020) 8959 8046 *Welding services*

▶ Bunny Connect Ltd, 11 Parade House, 135 The Parade High Street, Watford, WD17 1ND Tel: (0800) 0970238 *Mobile phones, Mobile phone extra, Broadband, Home Phone, Calling cards, PC 2 Phone, Digital TV, Free SMS, Dial up Services and other telecom related services from Xpert4u.co.uk.*

Bunny's Bolts, The Depot The Mayford Centre, Mayford Green, Woking, Surrey, GU22 0PP Tel: (01483) 727227 Fax: (01483) 727995 E-mail: sales@bunnysbolt.com *Bolt & nut distributors*

Bunting Engineering Ltd, Unit 14/20, Manor Industrial Estate, Pleck Road, Walsall, WS2 9XX Tel: (01922) 623888 Fax: (01922) 623888 *CNC turning on latest machines*

P.H. Bunting & Son Ltd, 2A Grange Avenue, Burntwood, Staffordshire, WS7 0BD Tel: (01543) 686481. *Jewellery repairs*

Bunzl Ltd, 5 Bonnington Road Lane, Edinburgh, EH6 5BJ Tel: 0131-553 5555 Fax: 0131-554 6068 E-mail: service@bunzlcleaningsupplies.co.uk *Cleaning & hygiene & packaging suppliers* Also at: Glasgow & Newcastle upon Tyne

Bunzl plc, 110 Park Street, London, W1K 6NX Tel: (020) 7495 4950 Fax: (020) 7495 4953 E-mail: enquiries@bunzl.com *Holding company*

Bunzl Cleaning & Hygiene Supplies, Stansted Distribution Centre, Start Hill, Great Hallingbury, Bishop's Stortford, Hertfordshire, CM22 7DG Tel: (01279) 655544 Fax: (01279) 757899 *Janitorial equipment suppliers*

Bunzl Cleaning & Hygiene Supplies, Henson Road, Darlington, County Durham, DL1 4QD Tel: (01325) 353551 Fax: (01325) 465952 E-mail: darlington@bunzlchs.co.uk *Hygiene & catering consumable distributors*

Bunzl Cleaning & Hygiene Supplies, Unit 4c Swallowfield Way, Hayes, Middlesex, UB3 1DQ Tel: (020) 8581 2345 Fax: (020) 8581 3344 E-mail: admin@bunzlcleaningsupplies.co.uk *Janitorial suppliers*

Bunzl Cleaning & Hygiene Supplies, Bone Lane, Newbury, Berkshire, RG14 5SH Tel: (01635) 528550 Fax: (01635) 528822 E-mail: newbury@bunzlchs.co.uk *Hygiene & janitorial specialised wipers products*

Bunzl Lockhart Catering Equipment, Lockhart House, Brunel Road, Theale, Reading, RG7 4XE Tel: (0870) 1678678 Fax: (0870) 1678679 E-mail: marketing@bunzl.co.uk *Bunzl Lockhart Catering Equipment supply the largest range of light and heavy catering equipment available to the UK caterer. They offer exclusive warranties on many heavy equipment products, dedicated light and heavy equipment field sales teams, next day delivery on orders received before 2pm, nationwide coverage, and a full catering design service. *Their 2008 catalogue features an updated and greatly expanded selection of products to keep your catering facility running like clockwork - if you haven't received your new catalogue please request one by calling on 08701 678678.*

Bunzl Retail Supplies Ltd, Lamplight Way, Swinton, Manchester, M27 8UJ Tel: 0161-743 2222 Fax: 0161-743 2233 E-mail: info@bunzlretail.com *Packaging distributors*

Bunzl Safety & Work Wear, Unit 2b, Adergellay Road, Swansea, SA5 4DY Tel: (01792) 355600 Fax: (01792) 355700 E-mail: sales@bunzlsws.com *Industrial workwear suppliers & safety footwear*

Bunzl Vending Services Ltd, 7 Sandpiper Way, Strathclyde Business Park, Bellshill, Lanarkshire, ML4 3NG Tel: (01698) 574580 Fax: (01698) 841517 E-mail: sales.glasgow@bunzlvend.com *Repair vending machines*

Bunzl Vending Services Ltd, 19 Aintree Road, Greenford, Middlesex, UB6 7LG Tel: (020) 8998 2828 Fax: (020) 8998 0704 E-mail: enquiries@bunzlvend.com *Food, snack & beverage vending machines* Also at:

continued

continuation
Bankside, Bristol, Colchester, Glasgow, Leeds, London & Tamworth

Bunzl Workware Ltd, Unit 2B, Abergelly Road, Forest Fach, Swansea, SA5 4DY Tel: (01792) 355600 Fax: (01792) 355700 E-mail: sales@unzlsws.com *Protective clothing distributors*

Buoyant Upholstery Ltd, Hallam Road, Nelson, Lancashire, BB9 8AJ Tel: (01282) 691631 Fax: (01282) 697298 *Upholstery manufrs*

▶ Bur Boing, 8 Beacon Court, Northampton, NN4 8JU Tel: (01604) 674733 E-mail: bur-boing@tesco.net *Large range of brand new bouncy castles for hire some with unique combination bouncy slides.We can also deliver Helium balloon bouquets & also supply matching themed party accessories to complement your childs birthday.All at amazing low prices.So contact us right now to book your special ones party.*

Burall, PO Box 7, Wisbech, Cambs, PE13 2SZ Tel: (0870) 728 7272 Fax: (0870) 728 7273 *Printed label manufrs*

▶ Burall Infocard Ltd, Cromwell Road, Wisbech, Cambridgeshire, PE14 0SN Tel: (01945) 468100 Fax: (01945) 467095

Burau Verater Ltd, 91 Winchester Road, Chandlers Ford, Eastleigh, Hampshire, SO53 2GG Tel: (023) 8024 2300 Fax: (023) 8024 2399 *Noise & vibration control consultants*

Burbage Gates Ltd, Sapcote Road, Burbage, Hinckley, Leicestershire, LE10 2AU Tel: (01455) 613844 Fax: (01455) 611333 E-mail: sales@burbagegates.co.uk *Architectural metalwork engineers*

Burbage Iron Craft Ltd, Unit 16, Sketchley Industrial Estate, Hinckley, Leicestershire, LE10 3ER Tel: (01455) 251656 Fax: (01455) 614136 E-mail: sales@burbageironcraft.co.uk *Iron gates, arches & garden features manufrs*

Burberry, 18-22 Haymarket, London, SW1Y 4DQ Tel: (020) 7930 3343 Fax: (020) 7839 6691 E-mail: sales@burberry.com *Weatherproof clothing manufrs*

Burberry Ltd, Abergorki Industrial Estate, Ynyswen Road, Treorchy, Mid Glamorgan, CF42 6EF Tel: (01443) 772020 Fax: (01443) 775956 E-mail: info@burberry.com *Clothing manufrs*

▶ Burberrys Of London, Coniston Road, Kitty Brewster Industrial Estate, Blyth, Northumberland, NE24 4RF Tel: (01670) 352524 Fax: (01670) 369350

Richard Burbidge Ltd, Whittington Road, Oswestry, Shropshire, SY11 1HZ Tel: (01691) 655131 Fax: (01691) 657694 E-mail: info@richardburbidge.co.uk *Timber home improvement products*

Burbidge & Son Ltd, Burnsall Road, Coventry, CV5 6BS Tel: (024) 7667 1600 Fax: (024) 7669 1010 E-mail: sales@burbidge.co.uk *Wooden door manufrs*

Burbridge 2000 Ltd, Studio's 1 & 2, Channocks Farm, Gilston, Harlow, Essex, CM20 2RL Tel: (01279) 445630 Fax: (01279) 418779 E-mail: enquiries@burbridge2k.co.uk *Precision engineers*

Burcart Clacton Ltd, 259-265 Old Road, Clacton-on-Sea, Essex, CO15 3LU Tel: (01255) 422213 Fax: (01255) 476751 E-mail: burcart@supanet.com *Timber merchants & diy shop*

Burcas Ltd, Park Lane, Handsworth, Birmingham, B21 8LT Tel: 0121-553 2777 Fax: 0121-553 1284 E-mail: info@burcas.co.uk *Engineers toolmakers manufrs*

▶ Burchell Design & Print, Rope Walk, Littlehampton, West Sussex, BN17 5DE Tel: 01903 717633 Fax: 01903 724823 E-mail: mark@burchell.co.uk *Free advice and guidance for all your printing needs. Full colour printing offered at exceptional rates - ask for details.**Ask about our exclusive online ordering system. It makes ordering your stationery a breeze*

Burco Commercial Catering Equipment Ltd, Glen Dimplex Professional Appliances, Stoney Lane, Prescot, Merseyside, L35 2XW Tel: (0871) 2225118 Fax: (0871) 2229636 E-mail: info@gdpa.co.uk *'Burco Appliances Ltd, the established market leader in manual fill electric and gas water boilers. Burco continues to manufacture urns in the UK as it has done for over a century, under the Burco and Cygnet brand. Today the Burco brand has moved into new areas of commercial catering equipment from manual and autofill filter coffee makers, catering slot toasters, conveyor belt toasters, a coffee maker and a mobile handwash unit plus many more.*

Burcombe Crane Hire, 23 Ridgeway, Coalpit Heath, Bristol, BS36 2PN Tel: (01454) 775471 Fax: (01454) 852845 E-mail: sales@burcombes.co.uk *Crane hire to trade & domestic*

George Burdekin Ltd, 9-11 Holbrook Lane, Coventry, CV6 4AD Tel: (024) 7666 7272 Fax: (024) 7666 8050 E-mail: sales@gburdekin.co.uk *Specialists in Centreless Grinding*

Burden Groundcare, 7 Main Street, North Kyme, Lincoln, LN4 4DF Tel: (01526) 860060 Fax: (01526) 861347 E-mail: sales@burdens.com *Agricultural & ground care machinery*

Burdens, Blackdog Centre, Bridge of Don, Aberdeen, AB23 8BT Tel: (01224) 823664 Fax: (01224) 823667 E-mail: acm@burdens.co.uk *Drainage pipe & fittings suppliers*

▶ Burdens, Whitehall Industrial Estate, Whitehall Road, Leeds, LS12 5JB Tel: 0113-231 1339 Fax: 0113-231 1889

Burdens Distribution Ltd, Spalding Road, Sutterton, Boston, Lincolnshire, PE20 2EX Tel: (01205) 460466 Fax: (01205) 460122 E-mail: sales@burdens.com *Agricultural machinery & grass machinery distributors*

Burdens Group, Main Road, Old Leake, Boston, Lincolnshire, PE22 9AT Tel: (01205) 870011 Fax: (01205) 871252 *Agricultural machinery distributors*

Burdett Metals, Railway Arch 214-216, Witan Street, London, E2 6JX Tel: (020) 7739 3951 Fax: (020) 7739 3951 *Scrap metal merchants*

Bureau Of Analysed Samples Ltd, Newham Hall, Stokesley Road, Newby, Middlesbrough, Cleveland, TS8 9EA Tel: (01642) 300500 Fax: (01642) 315209 E-mail: enquiries@basrid.co.uk *Certified reference material producers & suppliers*

Bureau Veritas, Pavilion 1 Craig Shaw Business Park, Craig Shaw Road, Tullos, Aberdeen, AB12 3AR Tel: (01224) 892100 Fax: (01224) 898437 *Oil & gas condition monitoring services & consultants*

Bureau Veritas, The Oast, Newnham Court, Bearsted Road, Maidstone, Kent, ME14 5LH Tel: (01622) 632100 Fax: (01622) 739620 E-mail: oasts@uk.bureauveritas.com *Project managers & consulting engineers*

Burfield & Co Gloves Ltd, Manor Road, Martock, Somerset, TA12 6JH Tel: (01935) 823278 Fax: (01935) 826075 E-mail: burfield.gloves@btconnect.com *Glove manufrs*

Burford Bridge Hotel, London Road, Mickleham, Dorking, Surrey, RH5 6BX Tel: (01306) 884561 Fax: (01306) 880386 *Conference facilities, restaurant & licensed bar*

Burford Controls Ltd, Unit 18 Applins Park, Farrington, Blandford Forum, Dorset, DT11 8RA Tel: (01747) 811173 Fax: (01747) 811171 E-mail: information@burfordcontrols.co.uk *Burford Controls & Instrumentation are leading fluid control engineers based in Dorset, South West England. Burford Controls are UK suppliers of Rochester Gauges International liquid level switches, sensors and gauges. Key markets include tank manufacturers. Quote Kellysearch when calling.*

Burford Engineering, 11 Denesway, Meopham, Gravesend, Kent, DA13 0EA Tel: (01474) 815228 Fax: 07970 086211 E-mail: pete@burfordair.co.uk *Compressed air engineers & distributors*

Burgess & Co. Ltd, New North Road, Heckmondwike, West Yorkshire, WF16 9DP Tel: (01924) 402406 Fax: (01924) 410175 E-mail: info@cburgess.co.uk *Sheet metalworkers*

Burgess, Europa Way, Martineau Lane, Norwich, NR1 2EN Tel: (01603) 628251 Fax: (01603) 762194 E-mail: enquiries@benburgess.co.uk *Horticultural engineers, agriculture services*

Burgess Agricultural Engineers Ltd, 1 Dyffryn Trading Estate, Rhyl Road, Denbigh, Clwyd, LL16 5SJ Tel: (01745) 816776 Fax: (01745) 812772 E-mail: denbigh@burgessae.co.uk *Agricultural & horticultural parts suppliers*

Burgess Architectural Products Ltd, Brookfield Road, Burbage, Hinckley, Leicestershire, LE10 2LL Tel: (01455) 618787 Fax: (01455) 251061 E-mail: info@burgessceilings.co.uk *Metal, acoustic & suspended metal ceiling systems, & acoustic telephone hood manufacturers*

Burgess Architectural Products Ltd, Brookfield Road, Burbage, Hinckley, Leicestershire, LE10 2LL Tel: (01455) 618787 Fax: (01455) 251061 E-mail: sales@fleetguard.com *Vehicle silencer & filtration systems*

Burgess Bedding Ltd, 123 Pollard Street, Manchester, M4 7JB Tel: 0161-273 5528 Fax: 0161-273 5563 *Mattress manufrs*

Burgess & Bowes, 14 Durham Avenue, Romford, RM2 6JS Tel: (01708) 458990 Fax: (01708) 459885 *Bookbinders & business gifts*

Burgess Group P.L.C., Woodlands, Priestmans Lane, Thornton Dale, Pickering, North Yorkshire, YO18 7RT Tel: (01751) 476430 Fax: (01751) 477633 E-mail: burgess@dial.pipex.com *Pet food manufrs*

Burgess Hats Ltd, 21 Parkside Centre, Potters Way, Temple Farm Industrial Estate, Southend-on-Sea, SS2 5SJ Tel: (01702) 617231 Fax: (01702) 460613 E-mail: admin@burgesshats.co.uk *Manufacturers of hats*

Burgess Marine Services, Channel View Road, Dover, Kent, CT17 9TJ Tel: (01304) 207707 Fax: (01304) 207727 E-mail: info@burgessengineering.co.uk *Welding specialists*

▶ Burgess Optical, 22 Northfield Avenue, Knottingley, West Yorkshire, WF11 0JE Tel: (01977) 670395 Fax: (01977) 670394 E-mail: burgessoptical@btinternet.com *Ophthalmic Glazing Laboratory.*All types of frames including Rimless.*

Burgess Printing Ltd, Unit M3 Cody Court, Salford, M50 2GE Tel: 0161-872 7881 Fax: 0161-876 0636 *Lithographic colour printers services*

Burgess Systems, 3 Friars Close, Whitstable, Kent, CT5 1NU Tel: (01227) 263035 Fax: (01227) 263035 *Blind suppliers*

Burghead Boat Centre, Findhorn Boat Yard, Findhorn, Forres, Morayshire, IV36 3YE Tel: (01309) 690099 Fax: (01309) 690165 *Boat builders & repairers*

Angela Burgin Furnishing & Design Ltd, 2a Hazelbury Crescent, Luton, LU1 1DF Tel: (01582) 722563 Fax: (01582) 616131 E-mail: sales@abfd.co.uk *Curtains & drapery manufrs*

Burgins News, 167 Wolverhampton Street, Dudley, West Midlands, DY1 3AH Tel: (01384) 255807 *Electrical consultants*

▶ Burgopak Ltd, 64 Great Suffolk Street, London, SE1 0BL Tel: (020) 7593 1444 Fax: (020) 7593 1414 E-mail: info@burgopak.com *Innovative packaging materials manufrs*

Burgoynes Lyonshall Ltd, Lyonshall, Kington, Herefordshire, HR5 3JR Tel: (01544) 340283 Fax: (01544) 340228 E-mail: enquiries@burgoynes-lyonshall.co.uk *Road haulage & marquee hirers*

Burkard Scientific (Sales) Ltd, PO Box 55, Uxbridge, Middlesex, UB8 2RT Tel: (01895) 230056 Fax: (01895) 230058 E-mail: sales@burkardscientific.co.uk *Scientific instrument manufrs*

▶ Burke Bros, Foxs Lane, Wolverhampton, WV1 1PA Tel: (01902) 714555 Fax: (01902) 427837

Burke Bros, Foxs Lane, Wolverhampton, WV1 1PA Tel: (01902) 714555 Fax: (01902) 427837 E-mail: sales@burkebros.co.uk *Furniture removers & storage*

Burke Bros Cheltenham Ltd, Hayricks Wharf, Tewkesbury Road, Cheltenham, Gloucestershire, GL51 9AH Tel: (01242) 519227 Fax: (01242) 231293 *Scrap metal merchants*

John Burke & Co. Ltd, 141 York Street, Belfast, BT15 1AB Tel: (028) 9032 2841 Fax: (028) 9032 3395 E-mail: smcready@burkebelfast.com *Shipping & customs clearance agents* Also at: Cork, Dublin, Foynes & Londonderry

Burke Office Furniture & Equipment, Unit 28 Ormeau Business Park, 8 Cromac Avenue, Belfast, BT7 2JA Tel: (028) 9087 6020 Fax: (028) 9087 6677 E-mail: enquiries@burke-office.co.uk *Stationery wholesalers & office equipment retailers*

Burkett Quicksign, Unit 19 Carbrook Hall Industrial Estate, Dunlop Street, Sheffield, S9 2HR Tel: 0114-256 0720 Fax: 0114-256 0192 E-mail: sales@burkettquicksign.co.uk *Sign manufrs*

S. Burland & Son Ltd, 19-29 Redchurch Street, London, E2 7DJ Tel: (020) 7739 6366 Fax: (020) 7729 5041 *Furriers*

Burlen Fuel Systems Ltd, Spitfire Hous, Castle Road, Salisbury, SP1 3SA Tel: (01722) 412500 Fax: (01722) 334221 E-mail: info@burlen.co.uk *Carburettor & fuel pump manufrs*

Burley Hydraulics Cambridgeshire Ltd, 27 Stephenson Road, St. Ives, Cambridgeshire, PE27 3WJ Tel: (01480) 497725 Fax: (01480) 497778 E-mail: burley-hydraulics@tiscali.co.uk *Hydraulic hose manufrs*

Burley UPVC Windows, Unit 6-9, Bridle Way, Netherton, Liverpool, L30 4UW Tel: 0151-922 4888 Fax: 0151-944 2300 *Window frame manufrs*

Burlington Bertie's, 329 Haydons Road, London, SW19 8LA Tel: (020) 8543 9700 E-mail: bertie@burlingtonberties.co.uk *Fancy dress hire shop*

Burlington Engineers Ltd, Unit 11 Perival Industrial Park, Horsenden Lane South, Perivale, Greenford, Middlesex, UB6 7RL Tel: (020) 8810 7266 Fax: (020) 8998 3517 E-mail: info@burlington-engineers.co.uk *Contractors plant sales & distributors*

Burlington Slate Production Ltd, Cavendish House, Kirkby-in-Furness, Cumbria, LA17 7UN Tel: (01229) 889661 Fax: (01229) 889466 E-mail: sales@burlingtonstone.co.uk *Roofs & architectural products manufrs*

Burls Gordon & Rolland Ltd, 7 Loxford Way, Caterham, Surrey, CR3 6BX Tel: (01883) 331288 Fax: (01883) 342181 E-mail: surveyor@burlsgordon.demon.co.uk *Marine surveyors*

Burman Laminates, 30 Broomfield Green, Canvey Island, Essex, SS8 9TY Tel: (01268) 690820 Fax: (01268) 690820 E-mail: andre@burmanlaminates.co.uk *Glass fibre fabricators & manufrs*

Burman Tool Co Ltd, Rye Road, Hoddesdon, Hertfordshire, EN11 0DZ Tel: (01992) 466311 Fax: 01992 468900 E-mail: info@burman.co.uk *Precision engineers*

Burmatex Ltd, Victoria Mills, The Green, Ossett, West Yorkshire, WF5 0AN Tel: (01924) 262525 Fax: (01924) 280033 E-mail: info@burmatex.co.uk *Carpet & carpet tile manufrs*

▶ Burmor Construction Ltd, 23 Horsegate, Deeping St. James, Peterborough, PE6 8EN Tel: (01778) 342606 Fax: (01778) 344090

▶ Burn Stewart Distillers Ltd, 101 Carlisle Road, Airdrie, Lanarkshire, ML6 8AG Tel: (01236) 764838 Fax: (01236) 768141

▶ Burn Stewart Distillers Ltd, Deanston Distillery, Doune, Perthshire, FK16 6AG Tel: (01786) 841422 Fax: (01786) 841439 E-mail: sales@burnstewartdistillers.com *Whisky distillery*

▶ Burn Stewart Distillers plc, Ledaig, Tobermory, Isle of Mull, PA75 6NR Tel: (01688) 302645 Fax: (01688) 302643 E-mail: enquiries@burnstewartdistillers.com

▶ Burn Technology Ltd, Building C51, Winfrith Newburgh, Dorchester, Dorset, DT2 8DH Tel: (01305) 852090 Fax: (01929) 463214 E-mail: rob@burntec.com *Distributor of device programmers*

Burnac Ltd, Ohio Grove, Hot Lane Industrial Estate, Stoke-on-Trent, ST6 2BL Tel: (01782) 837599 Fax: (01782) 837149 E-mail: burnac@burnac.co.uk *CNC machinists services*

Burnbank Garage, Burnbank Street, Campbeltown, Argyll, PA28 6JD Tel: (01586) 552772 Fax: (01586) 551414 E-mail: accounts@burnbankgarage.com *Vauxhall repairs, services & motor cycle sales*

▶ Burne & Walsh Ltd, Regus House, 268 Bath Road, Slough, SL1 4DX Tel: (01753) 708419 Fax: (01753) 708810 E-mail: info@burnewalsh.co.uk *Employment agency*

▶ Burnertech Heating Contractors, Unit 2a Osman House, Prince Street, Bolton, BL1 2NP Tel: (01204) 393222 Fax: (01204) 394222

Burness Corlett & Partners, 12-20 Camomile Street, London, EC3A 7PT Tel: (020) 7621 2943 Fax: (020) 7929 4167 E-mail: enquiries@bctq.com *The integrated maritime specialists. Marine design, naval architecture,marine engineering, marine expert services, marine surveying, marine safety services, marine procurement. Offices in London, Southampton, Newcastle, Bristol, Isle of Man, Dubai and Sydney.*

Burnett & Hillman Engineers, Havyatt Road, Coxs Green, Wrington, Bristol, BS40 5NL Tel: (01934) 862980 Fax: (01934) 862616 E-mail: sales@burnettandhillman.co.uk *Hydraulic adaptor manufrs*

▶ Burnham Group, Charwell House, Wilsom Road, Alton, Hampshire, GU34 2PP Tel: (0870) 0607372 Fax: (01420) 540216 E-mail: jo@burnhamgroup.co.uk *IT Recruitment Agency*

Burnham Pottery, 2-4 Maryland, Wells-Next-The-Sea, Norfolk, NR23 1LY Tel: (01328) 710847 Fax: (01328) 711566 E-mail: oldstation.books@btinternet.com *Pottery manufrs*

Burnham Signs Ltd, Burnham Way, London, SE26 5AG Tel: (020) 8659 1525 Fax: (020) 8659 4707 E-mail: sales@burnhamsigns.com *Garnier & Co. is a specialist vitreous enamel sign maker. Established in 1891.*

Burnham Yacht Harbour, Foundry Lane, Burnham-on-Crouch, Essex, CM0 8BL Tel: (01621) 782150 Fax: (01621) 785848 E-mail: admin@burnhamyachtharbour.co.uk *Boat yard & mooring facilities*

Burnholme Fisheries, 1 Gerard Avenue, York, YO31 0QT Tel: (01904) 421360 Fax: (01904) 421365 E-mail: fluid2002uk@yahoo.com *Fish wholesalers*

▶ Burnhouse Engineering Ltd, Lochlibo Road, Burnhouse, Beith, Ayrshire, KA15 1LE Tel: (01560) 484433 Fax: (01560) 484632 E-mail: enquiry@burnhouse-eng.co.uk *Engineering & fabrication services*

Burnison Engineering plc, PO Box 24, Newbury, Berkshire, RG14 5GX Tel: (01635) 552255 Fax: (01635) 552944 *Marine consultants*

C.P. Burns & Associates Ltd, Peter's Farm, Helmdon, Brackley, Northants, NN13 5QH Tel: (01295) 768271 Fax: (01295) 768298 E-mail: enquiries@burnsassociates.demon.co.uk Sales Contact: P. Burns *Supplier of Sorbarix, A20 Water Absorbent Cushions & Sorbarix 08 Oil Absorbent Cushions*

Burns & Churchill, Unit 10 Tudor Yard, Lawnside Road, Ledbury, Herefordshire, HR8 2BZ Tel: (01531) 636177 Fax: (01531) 636177 *Joinery manufrs*

▶ Burns Construction Ltd, Midland Road, Barnsley, South Yorkshire, S71 4DR Tel: (01226) 726786

▶ Burns Construction (Aberdeen) Ltd, 34-36 St Peter Street, Aberdeen, AB24 3HU Tel: (01224) 562000

Burns E-commerce Solutions, Mansion House, Manchester Road, Altrincham, Cheshire, WA14 4RW Tel: 0161-929 8673 Fax: 0161-929 8674 E-mail: info@burnsecs.com *Software services*

▶ Burns Express Freight Ltd, 4 Fulbar Road, Paisley, Renfrewshire, PA2 9AP Tel: 0141-848 0555

Burns & Harris (Retail) Ltd, 97-99 Commercial St, Dundee, DD1 2AF Tel: (01382) 322591 Fax: (01382) 226979 E-mail: shop@burns-harris.co.uk *Commercial Stationary retailers*

W. Burns Tractors Ltd, Blaircochrane, West Linton, Peeblesshire, EH46 7BD Tel: (01968) 673003 Fax: (01968) 678663 E-mail: wburnstractors@btinternet.com *Agricultural machine exporter*

William Burns & Sons, 1 School Road, Millisle, Newtownards, County Down, BT22 2DZ Tel: (028) 9048 4140 Fax: (028) 9048 4140 *Gates & fencing manufrs*

Burnsall Engineering Co. Ltd, Brandon Road, Binley, Coventry, CV3 2AN Tel: (024) 7644 0444 Fax: (024) 7665 2696 E-mail: info@burnsallengineering.com *Mould makers*

Burnside Pine Co, Unit 1 Back Grange Avenue, Harrogate, North Yorkshire, HG1 2AN Tel: (01423) 528116 *Pine furniture manufrs*

▶ Burnsides Marketing Aids Ltd, 62 Station Road, Langley Mill, Nottingham, NG16 4BH Tel: (01773) 713687 Fax: (01773) 715801 E-mail: sales@burnsides.co.uk *Promotional suppliers*

Burnt Oak Builders Merchant Ltd, 41 Barnfield Road, Edgware, Middlesex, HA8 0AY Tel: (020) 8952 1257 Fax: (020) 8952 2538 *Timber merchants & general builders*

Burntisland Fabrications, Seaforth Place, West Shore, Burntisland, Fife, KY3 9AU Tel: (01592) 222000 Fax: (01592) 874688 E-mail: enquiries@bifab.co.uk Principal Export Areas: Worldwide *Fabrication engineers, sub sea & underwater constructors & fabricators*

Burntwood Fasteners Ltd, Hawks Green Business Park, Cannock, Staffordshire, WS11 7XN Tel: (01543) 572731 Fax: (01543) 572735 E-mail: sales@burntwoodfasteners.co.uk *Cold forged parts, screws, sems & rivets manufrs*

Burntwood Spray Booth & Systems, Prospect Road, Burntwood, Staffordshire, WS7 0BU Tel: (01543) 685565 Fax: (01543) 684931 E-mail: spraybooths@unitech.uk.com *Spray booths, ventilation equipment & fume extraction hoods*

Buro Four Project Services Ltd, 296-300 St. John Street, London, EC1V 4PP Tel: (020) 7833 8663 Fax: (020) 7833 8560 E-mail: rbirchmore@burofour.co.uk *Project management-construction*

Burrafirm Ltd, Croxstalls Road, Walsall, WS3 2XY Tel: (01922) 476836 Fax: (01922) 479442 E-mail: user@albert-jagger.co.uk *A quick responsive 3D design, toolroom and production facility containing medium presses, autoturn and general engineering capability. Specialists in small to medium batch quantities.*

James Burrell Ltd, Deptford Road, Gateshead, Tyne & Wear, NE8 2BR Tel: 0191-477 2249 Fax: 0191-490 0359 E-mail: jamesburrell@compuserve.com *Builders merchants*

James Burrell Ltd, Lockheed Close, Preston Farm Industrial Estate, Stockton-on-Tees, Cleveland, TS18 3SE Tel: (01642) 660820 Fax: (01642) 678616 E-mail: jamesburrell@compuserve.com *Builders merchants*

Burrell & Sons Ltd, Fair View, Belton Road, Epworth, Doncaster, South Yorkshire, DN9 1JL Tel: (01427) 874747 Fax: (01427) 875392 E-mail: burrell.construction@virgin.net *Construction & car franchise*

T.W. Burrell & Sons Ltd, Abbey Park Road, Leicester, LE4 5AJ Tel: (0116) 253 8485 Fax: (0116) 251 4554 *Knitted outerwear manufrs*

William Burrell & Sons, Joinery Works, Main Street, Great Ouseburn, York, YO26 9RQ Tel: (01423) 330291 Fax: (01423) 331386 *Joinery Manufacturer*

Burrhart Machinery Ltd, Cradock Road, Luton, LU4 0JF Tel: (01582) 563400 Fax: (01582) 493993 E-mail: sales@burrhart.co.uk *Machinery & standard tooling part distributors*

▶ Burridge Coursewear, Unit 23 The Steadings, Maisemore Court, Maisemore, Gloucester, GL2 8EY Tel: (01452) 872080 Fax: (01452) 872081E-mail: sales@burridge-courseware.com *E-learning & multimedia services*

▶ Burridge Drilling Contractors, 84 Clun Street, Sheffield, S4 7JS Tel: 0114-278 7688 Fax: (0800) 3898508

P.F. Burridge & Sons Ltd, Units 8 & 9, Wesley Way, Benton Square Industrial Estate, Newcastle Upon Tyne, NE12 9TA Tel: 0191-266 5332 Fax: 0191-266 9250 E-mail: info@pfburridge.co.uk *General building contractors*

Burrows Communications Ltd, 106 Stafford Road, Wallington, Surrey, SM6 9AY Tel: (020) 8773 3000 Fax: (020) 8773 8888 E-mail: generalservices@burrows.co.uk *Publishers*

Burrows GM Ltd, Wigan Road, Leyland, PR25 5UE Tel: (01772) 421778 Fax: (01772) 622530 *Horticultural engineers* Also at: Stafford

Jack Burrows & Sons, Unit 10 Field Gate Works, New Street, Walsall, WS1 3DN Tel: (01922) 644150 Fax: (01922) 724375 *Conveyor systems, overhead; conveyor engineers/installation/ service/maintenance & conveyor (industrial) systems manufrs*

Ken Burrows Ltd, 40 Ogle Street, Hucknall, Nottingham, NG15 7FR Tel: 0115-963 2088 Fax: 0115-968 1737 *Electrical contractors*

Burrows & Smith Ltd, Saffron Works, Saffron Lane, Leicester, LE2 6UH Tel: 0116-244 0400 Fax: 0116-244 1100 E-mail: enquiries@burrowsmith.demon.co.uk *Precision engineers*

▶ Burrpark Ltd, Imperial Dock, Edinburgh, EH6 7DT Tel: 0131-553 1188 Fax: 0131-554 5111

Burrups Ltd, St. Ives House, Lavington Street, London, SE1 0NX Tel: (020) 7928 8844 Fax: (020) 7902 6572 E-mail: london@burrups.com Principal Export Areas: Worldwide *Printers*

Burrwill Moulds, Hillside, London Road, Washington, Pulborough, West Sussex, RH20 3BN Tel: (01903) 892023 Fax: (01903) 892136 *Mouldings manufrs*

▶ Burscough Packaging Ltd, Unit 1a Abbey Lane Industrial Estate, Burscough, Ormskirk, Lancashire, L40 7RS Tel: (01704) 896216 Fax: (01704) 896659

Burscough Rewinds, Units 1-10, Red Cat Lane, Burscough, Ormskirk, Lancashire, L40 0RA Tel: (01704) 894501 Fax: (01704) 897787 E-mail: sales@burscough-rewinds.co.uk *Electric motor repair & rewind specialists*

Burson Marsteller, 24-28 Bloomsbury Way, London, WC1A 2PX Tel: (020) 7831 2969 Fax: (020) 7340 1033 E-mail: enquiries@bein.com *Public relations consultants*

A.P. Burt & Sons Ltd, Severn Paper Mill, Harbour Road, Portishead, Bristol, BS20 7DJ Tel: (01275) 842454 Fax: (01275) 849613 E-mail: tdavies@apburt.co.uk *Paper & polythene bag manufrs*

Burt Bros Hosiery Ltd, A-C Willow Road, Nottingham, NG7 2TA Tel: 0115-970 6133 Fax: 0115-942 0576 E-mail: burtbros@premier.co.uk *Hosiery manufrs*

Burtech Precision Ltd, First Avenue, Flixborough Industrial Estate, Flixborough, Scunthorpe, South Humberside, DN15 8SE Tel: (01724) 866406 Fax: (01724) 280614 *Precision engineers*

▶ Burtenshaw Garden Buildings, Maidstone Road, Paddock Wood, Tonbridge, Kent, TN12 6QJ Tel: (01892) 838027 Fax: (01892) 838027 E-mail: enquiries@burtenshawgardenbuildings.co.uk

▶ Burtenshaw Garden Buildings Ltd, c/o Notcutts Garden Centre, Tonbridge Road,, Pembury, Tunbridge Wells, Kent, TN2 4QN Tel: (01892) 825338 E-mail: enquiries@burtenshawgardenbuildings.co.uk

Burton Beer Mats Ltd, Moor St Works, Burton-on-Trent, Staffordshire, DE14 3TA Tel: (01283) 564769 Fax: (01283) 535492 E-mail: sales@burtonbeermatsltd.co.uk *Drip mat manufrs*

Burton Bell & Co. Ltd, 3 Kildonan Road, Liverpool, L17 0BU Tel: 0151-727 2231 Fax: 0151-727 2231 *Builders & plumbing merchants*

Burton Box Co. Ltd, Burton Road Works, Burton-On-Trent, Staffordshire, DE14 3DH Tel: (01283) 540023 Fax: (01283) 565985 *Box manufrs*

Burton Distribution Ltd, 1 Brewster Place, Riverside Business Park, Irvine, Ayrshire, KA11 5DD Tel: (01294) 277766 Fax: (01294) 315381 *Distribution agents*

Burton & District/Tamworth Chamber of Commerce & Industry, Greton House, Waterside Court, Third Avenue, Centrum 100, Burton-On-Trent, Staffordshire, DE14 2WQ Tel: (01283) 563761 Fax: (01283) 510753 E-mail: services@burtonchamber.co.uk *Business support services*

Burton Engineering, Burton, Chippenham, Wiltshire, SN14 7LT Tel: (01454) 218431 Fax: (01454) 218431 *Agricultural engineers*

Burton Environmental Ltd, Unit 1, Wetmore Lane, Burton-On-Trent, Staffordshire, DE14 1RH Tel: (01283) 517374 Fax: (01283) 500360 E-mail: info@bef-online.com *Asbestos removals & encapsulation services*

▶ Burton Environmental Associates, The Old Schoolhouse, 141 Main Road, Clenchwarton, King's Lynn, Norfolk, PE34 4DT Tel: (07761) 256231 E-mail: enquiries@burtonenvironmental.co.uk *Environmental Management consultancy. Services: - ISO14001:2004 EMS implementation, training, internal audit. Waste management & minimisation. Legal compliance.*

Burton Fabrications, 1a Pearson Street, Netherfield, Nottingham, NG4 2JA Tel: 0115-961 8261 Fax: 0115-961 8261 *Stainless steel fabricators*

Burton Hydraulics & Pneumatics, Paget Street, Burton-on-Trent, Staffordshire, DE14 3TQ Tel: (01283) 532745 Fax: (01283) 530637 E-mail: sales@burtonhydraulics.co.uk *Hydraulic & pneumatic component distributors*

Burton Industrial Braking Co. Ltd, 1 Eton Park, Derby Road, Burton-On-Trent, Staffordshire, DE14 1RR Tel: (01283) 565118 Fax: (01283) 565118 *Manufacturers of clutches & brakes*

Burton Insulations Ltd, Crown Industrial Estate, Anglesey Road, Burton-On-Trent, Staffordshire, DE14 3NX Tel: (01283) 536190 Fax: (01283) 540693 *Insulation contractors*

Burton Photography, 19 Britton Street, Clerkenwell, London, EC1M 5NQ Tel: (020) 7253 6111 Fax: (020) 7253 6444 E-mail: info@burtonphoto.co.uk *Photographers*

Burton Saw International Ltd, Trading Estate, Valmar Road, London, SE5 9NW Tel: (020) 7737 3577 Fax: (020) 7733 2368 E-mail: blades@burtonsaw.co.uk Principal Export Areas: Worldwide *Blade manufrs*

Burton Sheet Metal Ltd, Wetmore Road, Burton-on-Trent, Staffordshire, DE14 1SN Tel: (01283) 564019 Fax: (01283) 562626 *General fabricators & welders*

Burton & Smith Ltd, Unit 32p The Washford Industrial Estate, Heming Road, Redditch, Worcestershire, B98 0DH Tel: (01527) 516925 Fax: (01527) 514900 E-mail: burtonandsmith@lycos.co.uk *Jig boring, CNC & precision engineers*

Burton & Smith Moving Ltd, Movement House Soho Mills, London Road, Wallington, Surrey, SM6 7HN Tel: (020) 8773 1122 Fax: (020) 8773 0590 E-mail: sales@burton-smith.co.uk *Commercial removal specialists*

Colin Burton Supplies Ltd, 9 George Avenue, Mile Oak, Tamworth, Staffordshire, B78 3PN Tel: (01827) 289091 *Sell cleaning materials manufrs*

Burtons Foods Ltd, P O Box 39, Blackpool, FY3 7AN Tel: (01253) 394133 Fax: (01253) 300238 *Biscuit manufrs*

Burtonwood Generator & Switchgear Services Ltd, St Michaels Road, St. Helens, Merseyside, WA9 4WZ Tel: (01744) 814444 Fax: (01744) 814455 E-mail: sales@burtonwoodgroup.com *Generators & switchgear services*

Burway Computer Services, 24 Central Avenue, Church Stretton, Shropshire, SY6 6EF Tel: (01694) 722520 Fax: (01694) 724070 E-mail: kevan@burwaycomputers.co.uk *Computer repairers*

▶ Burwood Aviation Supplies, Fairoaks Airport, Chobham, Woking, Surrey, GU24 8HU Tel: (01276) 855966 Fax: (01276) 855977 E-mail: sales@burwoodaviation.co.uk *Aviation supplies, components, fasteners, bolts & nuts suppliers*

Burwood Joinery Ltd, 46 Ridgeway Road, Sheffield, S12 2SX Tel: 0114-281 4113 Fax: 0114-281 4115 *Joinery manufrs*

Bury Bank Pine, Bury Bank, Meaford, Stone, Staffordshire, ST15 0QA Tel: (01785) 813928 Fax: (01785) 813928 E-mail: secured@burybankpine.fsnet.co.uk *Pine furniture manufrs*

Bury Soft Furnishings Ltd, 9 Brantwood Road, Salford, M7 4EN Tel: 0161-792 1492 Fax: 0161-792 1492 *Curtain & bedding manufrs*

▶ The Bus Business, The Coach House, Spofforth Hall, Nickols Lane, Spofforth, Harrogate, North Yorkshire, HG3 1WE Tel: (0845) 2250320 Fax: (0845) 2802461 E-mail: info@thebusbusiness.com

Bus Shelters (Wales) Ltd, Unit 60, Llantwit Major Road, Dyffryn Business Park, Cowbridge, South Glamorgan, CF71 7PY Tel: (01446) 795444 Fax: (01446) 793344 E-mail: bus@shelters.co.uk *Rail, street & bus furniture manufrs*

▶ Bus Tees, 36 Stiby Road, Yeovil, Somerset, BA21 3EG Tel: (01935) 478026 E-mail: bustees@btinternet.com *T-shirt printers, work wear printers & embroiderers*

Bush Baby Ltd, PO Box 61, Stockport, Cheshire, SK3 0AP Tel: 0161-474 7097 Fax: 0161-476 2647 E-mail: sales@bushbaby.com *Clothing manufrs*

Bush Radio P.L.C., Bush House, The Waterfront, Elstree Road, Elstree, Borehamwood, Hertfordshire, WD6 3BS Tel: (020) 8238 7650 Fax: (020) 8953 7117 E-mail: durochers@albaplc.co.uk *Radio receiver manufrs*

Bush Tyres Ltd, Station Yard, Horncastle, Lincolnshire, LN9 5AQ Tel: (0800) 801054 Fax: (01507) 525439 E-mail: ericcorragan@bushtyres.co.uk *Tyre retail*

Bush Tyres, 3-5 Bridge Road Industrial Estate, London Road, Long Sutton, Spalding, Lincolnshire, PE12 9EH Tel: (01406) 365930 Fax: (01406) 365933 *Tyre & exhaust retailers*

Bush Welding & Engineering, 6 Grainger Road Industrial Estate, Southend-on-Sea, SS2 5DD Tel: (01702) 610871 Fax: (01702) 610871 *Welded fabricators*

Bush & Wilton Ltd, 6 Millennium Place, Tiverton Business Park, Tiverton, Devon, EX16 6SB Tel: (01884) 242233 Fax: (01884) 252555 E-mail: sales@bushandwilton.com *Rotary & slider valves suppliers*

▶ Bushboard Ltd, Rixon Road, Wellingborough, Northamptonshire, NN8 4BA Tel: (01933) 232200 Fax: (01933) 232280 E-mail: washrooms@bushboard.co.uk Principal Export Areas: Worldwide *Industrial & private cubicle manufacturers, distributors or agents. Also laminated plastic fabricators/f abricated products manufacvturers & vanitory units*

▶ Dave Bushby Plant Hire Ltd, Clovelly Road Industrial Estate, Bideford, Devon, EX39 3HN Tel: (01237) 472878

Bushell & Meadows Ltd, Northway Lane, Tewkesbury, Gloucestershire, GL20 8HG Tel: (01684) 292000 Fax: (01684) 855763 E-mail: info@bushell-meadows.co.uk *Precision engineers*

Bushell Nicol Wawn & Son, Howden Terminal, Willington Quay, Wallsend, Tyne & Wear, NE28 6UL Tel: 0191-263 1213 Fax: 0191-263 0987 *Marine surveyors* Also at: Middlesbrough

Bushey Hall Garage, Bushey Hall Drive, Bushey, WD23 2QE Tel: (01923) 237135 Fax: (01923) 235372 E-mail: bushey.hall@virgin.net *Garage services /recovery /accident repair /MOT Test Station. Garage Customers Only Please - individual and fleet.*

▶ Bushwear, Unit 5 Crest Business Centre, 2 Glen Tye Road, Stirling, FK7 7LH Tel: (0845) 2260469 Fax: (0845) 2269329 E-mail: sales@bushwear.co.uk *Outdoor wear retail*

▶ Bushy Tail Ltd, Staveley Mill Yard, Back Lane, Staveley, Kendal, Cumbria, LA8 9LR Tel: (01539) 822244 Fax: 0870 8362158 *We manufacture an extensive range of the finest herbal medicines, natural skin care, and aromatherapy products.**All our products are made by hand using 0% pure and natural ingredients. We source our herbs from certified organic growers in the UK and Europe.*

Busi & Stephenson Ltd, 101 Bold Street, Liverpool, L1 4HL Tel: 0151-709 8998 Fax: 0151-709 8919 E-mail: busico@boldst.demon.co.uk *Export procurement agents*

▶ The Business, PO Box 3696, Sheffield, S6 4FF Tel: 0114-233 5233 E-mail: mail@businessstudysolutions.com *Providing quality online study resources tailored for MBA, business and management studies. Free Sample of material is available for immediate download.*

▶ Business 2 Home Carpet Care, 37 Thompson Road, uolands, Stroud, Gloucestershire, GL5 1TE Tel: 01453 751409 E-mail: cleancarpetcarpetclean@yahoo.co.uk *Carpet,rug and upholstery cleaning, odour control and allergy control to the highest standard. Members off the National Carpet Cleaners Association (NCCA).*

▶ Business Advisor Partnership, Hamlet House, 63 High Street, Eccleshall, Stafford, ST21 6BW Tel: (01785) 851536 Fax: (01785) 859437 E-mail: pat@thebusinessadvisor.org *The Business Advisor Partnership - supporting creativity and innovation in business.**Through our team of experienced business professionals, The Business Advisor Partnership provides high calibre, relevant expertise, at the precise point at which you and your management team recognise that you need some professional external assistance.**The Business Advisor Partnership will help you visualise and implement a plan to achieve your full potential - your company may be ready to re-energise the business, plan a new direction, improve operational efficiency or re-engage with your customer base. **Whether it's mentoring support, guidance or startegic advise you are looking for, the development of a business plan to help you raise funds, or the involvement of an interim manager to help you implement a plan - we are able to support you. ****

Business Air Centre Ltd, The Terminal Building, Gloucestershire Airport, Cheltenham, Gloucestershire, GL51 6SR Tel: (01452) 859500 Fax: (01452) 715010 E-mail: charter@businessaircentre.co.uk *Air charter brokers*

▶ Business Angel Finance, 21 Dapps Hill, Keynsham, Bristol, BS31 1ES Tel: (0845) 8380936 E-mail: info@businessangelfinance.co.uk

Business Assessment Service Ltd, 462 Holdenhurst Road, Bournemouth, BH8 9AF Tel: (01202) 392772 Fax: (01202) 392760 E-mail: info@basltd.co.uk *Assessment & certification services*

▶ Business Baubles, North Oast, Reed Court Farm, Hunton Road, Tonbridge, Kent, TN12 9SX Tel: (01622) 820005 Fax: (01622) 820006 E-mail: sales@businessbaubles.com *Promotional merchandise manufrs*

Business By Technology Midlands Ltd, 5 Portway Close, Torrington Avenue, Coventry, CV4 9UY Tel: (024) 7647 1507 Fax: (024) 7646 3838 E-mail: sales@bbt-direct.com *Photocopier repairs, maintenance & sales*

▶ Business Calls Direct, Pentland House, Pentland Park, Glenrothes, Fife, KY6 2AH Tel: (01592) 777800 Fax: (01592) 772860 *Outsource call centre facilities*

Business Cartoons, 4 Reyntiens View, Odiham, Hook, Hampshire, RG29 1AF Tel: (01256) 703004 Fax: (01256) 703004 E-mail: flantoons@btinternet.com *Tailor made cartoons for advertising & catalogues*

▶ Business Cartoons, 4 Auckland Way, Stockton-On-Tees, Cleveland, TS18 5LF Tel: (01642) 581847 E-mail: vh2@businesscartoons.co.uk *Business cartoons for newsletters or presentations etc*

Business Centre, 132 Samlet Road, Swansea Enterprise Park, Swansea, SA7 9AF Tel: (01792) 310110 Fax: (0870) 4280925 E-mail: enquiries@thebusinesscentre.info *CIS Vouchers, self Assessments and accounts done for the building Industry. £800 start up grant for tools etc. Tradesmans Insurance*

▶ Business Collaborator, North Reading Bridge House, George Street, Reading, RG1 8LS Tel: (0870) 1632555 Fax: (0870) 1632550 E-mail: sales@groupbc.com *Produces project collaboration & document management software*

Business Communications, Units 2 Bramshot Barns, Bramshot Lane, Fleet, Hampshire, GU51 2RU Tel: (01252) 617116 Fax: (01252) 626216 E-mail: info@businesscomms.co.uk *Communications services*

Business Computer Resources Ltd, 1b Dyke Road Drive, Brighton, BN1 6AJ Tel: (01273) 542759 Fax: (01273) 889898 E-mail: sales@bcrltd.co.uk *Computer sales & service*

Business Computers Hillsborough Ltd, Unit 225, City Business Park, Belfast, BT17 9HY Tel: (028) 9030 1526 Fax: (028) 9061 7766 E-mail: info@bch.eu.com *Computer networks & specialist software*

Business Computing Services, Linden, East Side, North Littleton, Evesham, Worcestershire, WR11 8QW Tel: (01386) 830444 Fax: (01386) 830444 *Business computing services*

The Business Connection, 4 Heritage Court, Lower Bridge Street, Chester, CH1 1RD Tel: (01244) 350303 Fax: (01244) 313004 E-mail: info@tbc-recruit.com *Recruitment consultants*

Business Database Production Ltd, 19 Hatherley Road, Sidcup, Kent, DA14 4BH Tel: (020) 8300 3661 Fax: (020) 8300 7367 E-mail: marilynbdp@aol.com *Database design & production*

Business Design Centre Ltd, 52 Upper Street, London, N1 0QH Tel: (020) 7359 3535 Fax: (020) 7226 0590 *Conference/exhibition & trade centre*

▶ Business Development Associates Ltd, 18 Rodney Street, Liverpool, L1 2TQ Tel: 0151-707 2308 Fax: 0151-709 9457 E-mail: bda_uk@hotmail.com

▶ Business Development International, Business House, Higher Wych, Malpas, Cheshire, SY14 7JT Tel: (01948) 780515 E-mail: info@bdinternational.co.uk *Management & international business development consultancy services*

▶ Business Direct Ltd, 2NF Floor, Somerset House, Somerset Road, Teddington, Middlesex, TW11 8RT Tel: (020) 8943 1871 Fax: (020) 8977 3048

▶ Business Dispatch, Unit 3-4 Kingspark Business Centre, Kingston Road, New Malden, Surrey, KT3 3ST Tel: (020) 8605 1771 Fax: (020) 8605 1886 E-mail: sales@businessdispatch.com *Computer software developers*

Business Electronic & Computer Services, 74-75 Victoria Road, Great Yarmouth, Norfolk, NR30 3BA Tel: (01493) 330498 Fax: (01493) 332436 *Software engineers*

Business & Employment Skills Training Ltd, 20 Eglinton Street, Irvine, Ayrshire, KA12 8AS Tel: (01294) 313144 Fax: (01294) 313177 *Sales training specialists*

▶ Business Engineering Ltd, 15 The Maples, Banstead, Surrey, SM7 3QZ Tel: (01737) 373121 Fax: (01737) 211837 E-mail: peter@business-engineering.co.uk *Selling engineering or construction for businesses*

▶ Business Envelopes, 11 Juniper Grove, Livingston, West Lothian, EH54 5JF Tel: (07790) 439975 *We supply envelopes to businesses and offer free next day delivery within the West Lothian and Midlothian area.*

Business Equipment Distributors, 16 Swanlow Avenue, Winsford, Cheshire, CW7 1PB Tel: (01606) 551755 Fax: (01606) 551755 E-mail: info@business-labels.co.uk *Labelling system suppliers*

▶ Business Equipment Service, 6 Titan Court, Laporte Way, Luton, LU4 8EF Tel: (01582) 417332 Fax: (01582) 417334 E-mail: mike@besluton.co.uk *Dictating equipment maintenance*

▶ Business Express, Unit 2, Hareness Park, Hareness Circle, Altens Industrial Estate, Aberdeen, AB12 3QY Tel: (01224) 879038

▶ Business Friend Ltd, 5 Mayland Quay, Maylandsea, Chelmsford, CM3 6GJ Tel: (07931) 759611 Fax: (01621) 744292 E-mail: telmemore@businessfriend.net *Professional & friendly business support service*

▶ The Business Garden Limited, 1 Market Hill, Calne, Wiltshire, SN11 0BT Tel: (07867) 900708 E-mail: enquiries@thebusinessgarden.co.uk *The Business Garden Limited offer management training courses, team development courses and personal growth training.*

▶ Business Hospitality Bureau Ltd, 12 Aubrietia Close, Romford, RM3 0XG Tel: (01708) 384140 Fax: (01708) 340204 E-mail: info@bhb.uk.com *The Business Hospitality Bureau is a dynamic, highly creative company, with a refreshingly simple vision - to provide quality events that exceed expectations, within budget and on time. **Whether you are planning an exclusive corporate hospitality event, *a spectacular themed party, a major conference, a vibrant product launch, or a global incentive - every proposal is tailor-made to meet your marketing and motivational objectives.**With over fifteen years' experience, The Business Hospitality Bureau has served many UK and International Companies, from their bases in the UK, USA and Europe.*

Business Improvement Techniques Ltd, 11 Capricorn Centre, Cranes Farm Road, Basildon, Essex, SS14 3JJ Tel: (01268) 663320 Fax: (0845) 1232931 *Office furniture manufrs*

Business In Focus Ltd, Enterprise Centre, Bryn Road, Aberkenfig, Bridgend, Mid Glamorgan, CF32 9BS Tel: (01656) 724414 Fax: (01656) 721163 E-mail: opt@businessinfocus.co.uk *Enterprise agencies*

▶ Business Information Systems, 11 Upper Church Park, Mumbles, Swansea, SA3 4DD Tel: (01792) 361121 Fax: (01792) 361421 E-mail: peter@bizis.co.uk *Chartered accountancy, accountancy, taxation & business advice service*

Business Information Technology Services Ltd, 75 Longford Road, Coventry, CV6 6DY Tel: (024) 7683 5600 Fax: (024) 7683 5601 E-mail: bits@b-i-t-s.co.uk *Epos systems suppliers*

▶ Business Initiatives BDS Ltd, Hardhams Cottage Clay Lane, Fishbourne, Chichester, West Sussex, PO18 8BT Tel: (01243) 775785 Fax: (01243) 528923 E-mail: adrian@business-initiatives.com *WE specialise in providing Business development , sales and account management services to software and allied businesses from overseas*

Business Insights Group Ltd, Brandiston House, 98 High Street, Ingatestone, Essex, CM4 0BA Tel: (01277) 355755 Fax: (01277) 355753 E-mail: info@digroup.co.uk *Software computer, business & accounting consultants service*

▶ The Business Insurance Centre Ltd, 2nd Floor, 17 Pedder Street, Morecambe, Lancashire, LA4 5DY Tel: 01524 418566 Fax: 01524 424537 E-mail: tbicl@hotmail.co.uk *We are part of the F P Hepworth group of companies EST.1976 and are able to offer a wide range of competative premiums for all aspects of business insurance including: Fish and Chip shops, Takeaways,*

continued

Company Information

continuation
Newsagents, sports and social clubs, motor and travel insurance plus many more. If you would like a quotation, then please give our friendly team of advisors a call, who will be happy to assist with your insurance needs or email over your details and we call you within 24 hours with our best quotation.We are fully Authorised and Regulated by the Financial Services Authority Reg: No. 306550.

Business Intelligence International Ltd, 37 Kirkton St, Carluke, Lanarkshire, ML8 4AD Tel: 01555 750783 Fax: 01555 770168 E-mail: sales@businessit.net *Computer software development accountancy*

▶ Business Intelligence Solutions Ltd, 9 Southlands Close, Badsworth, West Bridgford, Pontefract, West Yorkshire, WF9 1AU Tel: (01977) 650944 E-mail: info@bi-solutions.co.uk *Business Intelligence Solutions are a small independent company who specialise in the area of management reporting and analysis. **We have been established since 1997 and are based in Yorkshire. We have a full range of IT and business skills to provide you with the competitive advantage that business intelligence can give. we have successfully provided solutions for major companies like Fox's Biscuits, Express Dairies, Fletchers Bakeries, Capespan, learndirect, Travelsphere and Hoseasons. Our skills encompass key areas such as Data Warehousing and Business Reporting and analysis. We also cover a wide range of industry sectors including FMCG, Travel and Food and work in a number of business areas like HR, production, finance, CRM and sales. **

Business Interface Ltd, 7 Garden Court, Wheathampstead, St. Albans, Hertfordshire, AL4 8RE Tel: (01582) 834477 Fax: (01582) 833200 E-mail: info@business-interface.co.uk *Computer consultants*

▶ Business Interiors Direct Ltd, Unit C19, Alison Centre, 39 Alison Crescent, Sheffield, S2 1AS Tel: (0845) 4300880 Fax: (0845) 4300990 E-mail: sales@businessinteriorsdirect.co.uk *Interior furniture suppliers, designers & installers*

▶ Business It Central, Sussex College, College Road, Crawley, West Sussex, RH10 1NR Tel: (01293) 442326 Fax: (01293) 453421 E-mail: business1@centralsussex.ac.uk *One day software training courses in Microsoft Office & other software products.*

▶ Business Jungle Ltd, Hammerain House, Hookstone Avenue, Harrogate, North Yorkshire, HG2 8ER Tel: 0845-838 2240 Fax: 0845-838 2260 E-mail: david@businessjungle.co.uk *Commercial Finance*Interim Management*Business Development*Business Solutions*

Business Link, Pity Me Business Centre, Abbey Road Business Park, Pity Me, Durham, DH1 5JZ Tel: 0191-374 4000 Fax: 0191-374 4010 E-mail: customerservices@blcd.co.uk *Business information advisory services*

Business Link, Kingsgate House, 66-74 Victoria Street, London, SW1E 6SW Tel: (020) 7215 5000 Fax: (020) 7215 5001 E-mail: enquiries@businesslink.org

Business Link, Tees Valley Business Centre, 2 Queens Square, Middlesbrough, Cleveland, TS2 1AA Tel: (01642) 806666 Fax: (01642) 341425 E-mail: enquiries@businesslinknortheast.co.uk *Business information advisory services*

Business Link, 5 Phoenix Place, Nottingham, NG8 6BA Tel: (0845) 7586644 Fax: 0115-977 7399 E-mail: info@blnotts.com *Business information advisory services*

Business Link, Merck House, Seldown Lane, Poole, Dorset, BH15 1TD Tel: (01202) 785400 Fax: (01202) 448838 *Business information advisory services*

Business Link, 45a Newdown Road, Scunthorpe, South Humberside, DN17 2TX Tel: (01724) 291510 Fax: (01724) 291511 E-mail: info@blhumber.co.uk *Business information advisory services*

Business Link, Bus & Innovation Centre, Sunderland Enterprise Park, Wearfield, Sunderland, SR5 2TA Tel: 0191-516 6700 Fax: 0191-516 6777 E-mail: enquiries@businesslinktw.co.uk *Business information advisory services*

Business Link, Emlyn Square, Swindon, SN1 5BP Tel: (0845) 6004141 Fax: (01722) 415447 E-mail: info@blbw.co.uk *Business information advisory services*

Business Link, Creech Castle, Bathpool, Taunton, Somerset, TA1 2DX Tel: (0845) 7211112 Fax: (01823) 274862 E-mail: sales@somerset.businesslink.co.uk *Business information advisory services*

Business Link, 34 Tower View Kings Hill, Kings Hill, West Malling, Kent, ME19 4ED Tel: (01732) 878000 Fax: (01732) 841109 E-mail: info@businesslinkkent.co.uk *Business information advisory services*

Business Link, Arabesque House, Monks Cross Drive, Huntington, York, YO32 9WU Tel: (01904) 686000 Fax: (01904) 686020 E-mail: info.centre@blyny.co.uk *Business information advisory services*

Business Link Berkshire & Wiltshire, Thames Tower, 37-41 Station Road, Reading, RG1 1LX Tel: (0845) 6004141 *Business information advisory services*

Business Link For Cambridgeshire, Centenary House, St. Marys Street, Huntingdon, Cambridgeshire, PE29 3PE Tel: (0845) 6097979 *Business information advisory services*

Business Link Cheshire & Warrington Ltd, International Business Centre, Delta Crescent, Westbrook, Warrington, WA5 7WQ Tel: (01925) 715200 Fax: (01925) 715005 E-mail: info@blinkcw.co.uk *Business information advisory services*

Business Link For Cumbria, Capital Buildings Hilltop Heights, London Road, Carlisle, CA1 2NS Tel: (0870) 7571177 Fax: (01228) 613233 *Business information advisory services*

Business Link Derbyshire, Canal Wharf, Chesterfield, Derbyshire, S41 7NA Tel: (0845) 6011038 Fax: (01246) 233228 *Business information advisory services*

Business Link Derbyshire, Innovation Ho, Riverside Pk, Raynesway, Derby, DE21 7BF Tel: (0845) 6011038 Fax: (01332) 548088 *Business information advisory services*

Business Link Devon & Cornwall Ltd, Prosper House, Buddshead Road, Plymouth, PL6 5XR Tel: (01752) 785785 Fax: (01752) 770925 *Business information advisory services*

Business Link East, 4 Bishops Square Business Park, Hatfield, Hertfordshire, AL10 9NE Tel: (0845) 7171615 Fax: (0845) 6076117 E-mail: info@businesslinkeast.org.uk *Information, advice & business support for small to medium enterprises*

Business Link East Midlands, Innovation House, East Service Road, Raynesway, Spondon, Derby, DE21 7BF Tel: (0845) 0586644 Fax: (01332) 280792 E-mail: info@businesslinkem.co.uk *Business information advisory services*

Business Link For Greater Merseyside, Halton Business Forum, Victoria Sq, Widnes, Cheshire, WA8 7QZ Tel: (0845) 3300151 Fax: 0151-420 9424 E-mail: questions@halton-businesslink.co.uk *Business information advisory services*

Business Link Hertfordshire, 45 Grosvenor Road, St. Albans, Hertfordshire, AL1 3AW Tel: (01727) 813813 Fax: (01727) 813776 E-mail: stevem@exemplas.com *Business information advisory services*

Business Link Humber, 1B Osborne Street, Grimsby, North East Lincolnshire, DN31 1EY Tel: (01472) 362868 Fax: (01472) 356052 *Business information advisory services*

Business Link Humber, Owen Avenue, Priory Park, Hessle, North Humberside, HU13 9PD Tel: (0845) 1243333 Fax: (01482) 641044 *Business information advisory services*

Business Link London Ltd, Link, 298-308 Southbury Road, Enfield, Middlesex, EN1 1TS Tel: (0845) 6000787 Fax: (020) 7111 0301 E-mail: info@bllondon.com *Business information advisory services*

Business Link For Norfolk, PO Box 36, Swaffham, Norfolk, PE37 7WZ Tel: (0845) 7218218 Fax: (01760) 726727 E-mail: success@businesslinknorfolk.co.uk *Business information advisory services*

Business Link North West, St. Nicholas House, Old Church Yard, Liverpool, L2 8TY Tel: (0845) 0066888 Fax: (01772) 790140 E-mail: info@businesslinknw.co.uk *Business information advisory services*

Business Link North & Western Lancashire, Lancashire Enterprises Business Park, Centurion Way, Leyland, PR26 6TY Tel: (01772) 790200 Fax: (01772) 443002 E-mail: info@nwl.businesslink.co.uk *Business information advisory services*

Business Link Shropshire Ltd, Trevithick House, Unit B1 Stafford Park 4, Telford, Shropshire, TF3 3BA Tel: (0845) 7543210 Fax: (01952) 208208 E-mail: enquiries@bl-shropshire.co.uk *Business support services*

Business Link Shropshire Ltd, Trevithick House, Unit B1 Stafford Park 4, Telford, Shropshire, TF3 3BA Tel: (0845) 7543210 E-mail: enquiries@blwm.com *Business information advisory services*

Business Link Solutions Ltd, Eastern By Pass, Thame, Oxfordshire, OX9 3FF Tel: (01844) 210400 Fax: (01235) 468200 *Business information advisory services*

Business Link South Yorkshire, Reresby House, Bow Bridge Close, Rotherham, South Yorkshire, S60 1BY Tel: (01709) 386300 Fax: (01709) 386330 E-mail: enquiries@blsy.com *Business information advisory services*

Business Link South Yorkshire, Albion House, Savile Street, Sheffield, S4 7UQ Tel: (0800) 0737474 Fax: 0114-201 2525 E-mail: enquiries@blsy.com *Business information advisory services*

Business Link Suffolk Ltd, Felaw Maltings, 42 Felaw Street, Ipswich, IP2 8PN Tel: (01473) 417000 Fax: (01473) 417070 E-mail: admin@bls.org.uk *Business information advisory services*

Business Link Surrey, 5th Floor Hollywood House, Church St East, Woking, Surrey, GU21 6HJ Tel: (0845) 7494949 Fax: (01483) 771507 E-mail: sales@businesslinksurrey.co.uk *Business information advisory services*

Business Link Sussex, Sussex Enterprise Greenacre Court, Station Rd, Burgess Hill, W. Sussex, RH15 9DS Tel: (0845) 0360144 Fax: (01444) 259255 E-mail: marketing@sussexenterprise.co.uk *Business information advisory services*

Business Link Wessex, Wates House, Wallington Hill, Fareham, Hampshire, PO16 7BJ Tel: (0845) 4588558 Fax: (01329) 223223 E-mail: info@businesslink.co.uk *Business information advisory service*

Business Link Wessex, Suite 1 Slade Bldgs, The Square, Gillingham, Dorset, SP8 4AY Tel: (0845) 4588558 Fax: (01747) 821613 *Business information advisory services*

Business Link Wessex, Mill Court, Furrlongs, Newport, Isle of Wight, PO30 2AA Tel: (08454) 588558 Fax: (01983) 533508 E-mail: tbutler@iwpartnership.com *Business information advisory services*

Business Link West Yorkshire, Unit 4 Meadow Court, Millshaw Business Pk, Millshaw, Leeds, LS11 8LZ Tel: 0871 220 5000 Fax: 0113-383 7700 E-mail: info@blinkleeds.co.uk *Business information advisory services*

Business Links For Northumberland, Wansbeck Business Centre, Rotary Parkway, Ashington, Northumberland, NE63 8QZ Tel: (01670) 528000 Fax: (01670) 813355 *Business information advisory services*

Business Lists (U K), Cheadle Court, Turves Road, Cheadle Hulme, Cheadle, Cheshire, SK8 6AW Tel: 0161-482 0500 Fax: 0161-488 4160 E-mail: info@businesslistsuk.com *Direct mail services*

▶ Business Management, 107 Market Street, Manchester, M1 1NN Tel: 0161-832 5647 Fax: 0161-832 5651 E-mail: manchester@btmonline.co.uk *Business travel agent for further information please view our website on www.btmonline.co.uk*

Business Management Promotions Ltd, Lower Weaven, Little Dewchurch, Hereford, HR2 6QB Tel: (01432) 840456 Fax: (01432) 840450 E-mail: bmpltd@ticali.co.uk *Internet & computer services organization*

▶ Business Management Services, 58 South Road, Sully, Penarth, South Glamorgan, CF64 5SJ Tel: (029) 2053 1691 Fax: (029) 2053 1691 E-mail: beads@btinternet.com *Import & export agents, computerised export documentation, training courses*

Business Management Software Ltd, Old Music School, West Street, Oundle, Peterborough, PE8 4EJ Tel: (01832) 275004 Fax: (01832) 275006 E-mail: enquiries@bms.uk.com *Computer software*

Business Micros, Main Street, Penpont, Thornhill, Dumfriesshire, DG3 4BP Tel: (01848) 330588 Fax: (01848) 331531 E-mail: info@businessmicros.co.uk *Software house*

▶ Business Moves Ltd, Offco House, Town Street, Stanningley, Pudsey, West Yorkshire, LS28 6HQ Tel: 0113-236 0136 Fax: 0113-236 0185

Business Moves Ltd, 4 Acre Road, Reading, RG2 0SX Tel: 0118-933 6600 Fax: 0118-975 3586 E-mail: info@businessmove.com *Business removal contractors*

▶ Business Moves, Unit 5 The Three Sisters Enterprise Park, Antler Court, Ashton-In-Makerfield, Wigan, Lancashire, WN4 8DU Tel: (01942) 724167 Fax: (01942) 724440

Business Needs.Co.UK, Elwin House, 13 Alford Road, Cromer, Norfolk, NR27 9AN Tel: (01263) 512170 *Office supplies distributors*

▶ Business Network Ltd, 5 Alcester Street, Redditch, Worcestershire, B98 8AE Tel: (01527) 405500 Fax: (01527) 65375 *Training services*

Business Numbers Ltd, 2 Magnolia Wharf, Strand On The Green, London, W4 3NY Tel: (020) 8995 8316 Fax: (020) 8995 8316 *Specialist software developers services*

Business Plants, 34D St. Phillips Avenue, Worcester Park, Surrey, KT4 8JT Tel: (01424) 777452 *Interior plants suppliers*

▶ Business Post Ltd, 6 Block 1, Hareness Road, Altens Industrial Estate, Aberdeen, AB12 3LE Tel: (01224) 248336 Fax: (01224) 248311

▶ Business Post Ltd, Unit B-C Ronald Close, Woburn Road Industrial Estate, Kempston, Bedford, MK42 7SH Tel: (01234) 840088 Fax: (01234) 853918

▶ Business Post Ltd, Unit 23 Nelson Way, Camberley, Surrey, GU15 3DH Tel: (01276) 686757 Fax: (01276) 686558

▶ Business Post Ltd, 11 Crystal Way, Harrow, Middlesex, HA1 2BJ Tel: (020) 8861 1599 Fax: (020) 8424 0708

▶ Business Post Ltd, Arden Grange, London Road, Albourne, Hassocks, West Sussex, BN6 9BJ Tel: (01273) 831832 Fax: (01273) 835301

▶ Business Post Ltd, Gillsleigh Villas, Gills Green, Cranbrook Road, Hawkhurst, Kent, TN18 5ES Tel: (01580) 754499 Fax: (01580) 754400

▶ Business Post Ltd, Access Point, Eastman Way, Hemel Hempstead Industrial Estate, Hemel Hempstead, Hertfordshire, HP2 7DU Tel: (01442) 439700 Fax: (01442) 261167

▶ Business Post Ltd, 73 St James Mill Road, St James Business Park, Northampton, NN5 5JP Tel: (01604) 592929 Fax: (01604) 592930

Business Post Ltd, 14 The Midway, Nottingham, NG7 2TS Tel: 0115-986 1086 Fax: 0115-986 1102

Business Premises Cleaning Services Ltd, Long Acre, Pewitt Hill, Bursledon, Southampton, SO31 8BL Tel: (023) 8040 5060 Fax: (023) 8040 7549 E-mail: enquiries@businesspremisescleaning.com *Industrial cleaning contractors covering the southern region of the u.k.*

Business Presentations Ltd, Hillfoot Farm, Hitchin Road, Shefford, Bedfordshire, SG17 5JD Tel: (01462) 817406 Fax: (01462) 850130 E-mail: sally@business-presentations.co.uk *Audio visual presentation services*

▶ Business Printing Co., 6 Nene Road, Bicton Industrial Park, Kimbolton, Huntingdon, Cambridgeshire, PE28 0LF Tel: (01480) 861911 Fax: (01480) 861922 E-mail: sales@theprinters.nu

▶ Business & Professional Partners, 1 Gurney Lane, Norwich, NR4 7SB Tel: (0870) 0505144 E-mail: welcome@bppartners.co.uk *Executive search & selectrion, online recruitment,training,development,change management & HR consultancy, IT Services*

Business Resource, 30 High Street, Winterbourne, Bristol, BS36 1JN Tel: (01454) 250758 Fax: (01454) 858125 *Computer consultants*

Business Seating Manufacturing Supplies Ltd, 8 Bridgewater Close, Reading, RG30 1JT Tel: (0800) 9179848 Fax: 0118-951 4505 E-mail: sales@businessandseating.co.uk *Suppliers of office furniture &repair specialist* Also at: Tamworth

▶ Business Sense, Suite 296, 17 Holywell Hill, St. Albans, Hertfordshire, AL1 1DT Tel: (0870) 0201694 *Computer security system suppliers*

Business Services Bureau, 11 Greenland Road, Barnet, Hertfordshire, EN5 2AL Tel: (020) 8440 3474 Fax: (020) 8440 3676 E-mail: bsb@busybee.demon.co.uk *Bereau services*

Business Strategies Ltd, Nightingale House, 65 Curzon Street, London, W1J 8PE Tel: (0870) 1968201 Fax: (0870) 1968200 E-mail: business-strategies@uk.experian.com *Economics consultants*

▶ Business Supplies, 71 Inglis Green Road, Edinburgh, EH14 2EZ Tel: 0131-455 7474 Fax: 0131-455 7940 E-mail: admin@bartill.com *Cash registers manufrs*

Business Systems Design Ltd, 185 Upper Selsdon Rd, South Croydon, Surrey, CR2 0DY Tel: 020 86514421 *Computer consultants*

▶ Business Systems UK Ltd, 462 London Road, Isleworth, Middlesex, TW7 4ED Tel: (020) 8326 8200 Fax: (020) 8326 8400 E-mail: sales@businesssystemsuk.com *Telephone call recording systems suppliers*

Business Tax Centre Ltd, Dte House, Hollins Mount, Bury, Lancashire, BL9 8AT Tel: 0161-796 6090 Fax: 0161 767 1212 E-mail: payroll@dtegroup.com *Payroll Services, Weekly and Monthly Calculations. SSP,SMP, Tax Credits and Attachment of Earnings. Completion of P45, P46s and Year End Returns. Customised reporting facilities. On-line filing offered.*

▶ Business to Web, 14 Quantock Road, Worthing, West Sussex, BN13 2HG Tel: (0845) 8382158 E-mail: support@businesstoweb.co.uk *Fully managed internet services*

Business Training Partnership, 96 High Street, Burnham, Slough, SL1 7JT Tel: (01628) 664040 Fax: (01628) 660042 E-mail: dawn.oxley@btp.uk.com *Training managers*

▶ Business Voice & Data, 324 Birmingham Road, Lickey End, Bromsgrove, Worcestershire, B61 0HJ Tel: (01527) 832552 Fax: (01527) 832542 *Telecommunication systems & equipment manufrs*

▶ Business West, Trimbridge House, Trim Street, Bath, BA1 2DP Tel: (01225) 338383 Fax: (01225) 321971 E-mail: katherine_jenner@bathnes.gov.uk *Business Matters is a one-stop shop for all businesses in Bath and North East Somerset. The site provides information for new, existing and relocating companies on B&NES as a location for business, business start ups and support services, commercial property and land availability, business to business initiatives, local business organisations, economic intelligence and training providers.*

Business West, Leigh Court Business Centre, Pill Road, Abbots Leigh, Bristol, BS8 3RA Tel: (01275) 373373 Fax: (01275) 370706 E-mail: info@businesswest.co.uk *Business information consultants*

Business West, Leigh Court Business Centre, Pill Road, Abbots Leigh, Bristol, BS8 3RA Tel: (01275) 373373 Fax: (01275) 370706 E-mail: info@businesslinksw.co.uk *Business information advisory services*

Business Wise, Bank House, Bank Cresent, Ledbury, Herefordshire, HR8 1AA Tel: (01531) 634636 Fax: (01531) 634637 *Computer stationery retailers*

▶ Business24, Welton House, Lime Kiln Way, Lincoln, LN2 4WH Tel: (01522) 574204 Fax: 01522 574035 E-mail: enquiries@business24.co.uk *Business24 provides a wide range of business support services covering information, networks, business learning and trading opportunities.*

▶ Business-at.com Ltd, Croft Ford, Watercrook Farm, Natland, Kendal, Cumbria, LA9 7QB Tel: 0845 1200665 E-mail: info@jobs4.com *JOBS4 recruitment directory*

BusinessGift.UK.Com, 92 Langdale Road, Leyland, PR25 3AS Tel: (01772) 435010 Fax: (01772) 457280 E-mail: steve@ad-options.co.uk *Promotional business gift manufrs*

▶ BusinessGrowth UK, Bristol & West House, Post Office Road, Bournemouth, BH1 1BL Tel: (01202) 313611 Fax: (01202) 313601 E-mail: info@businessgrowthuk.com *A business directory to address all back office business needs*

Business-ip Ltd, 60 High Street, Measham, Swadlincote, Derbyshire, DE12 7HZ Tel: (01530) 272229 Fax: (01530) 272229 E-mail: info@business-ip.co.uk *At business-ip, our aim is to provide you with a high quality web site solution that complements your business strategy and reflects your style. We blend business, technical and creative skills to offer a range of services from convenient web site packages through to database integration and web applications. Please click on the www. weblink or telephone us to find out more.*

▶ Businesslegal Ltd, Holgrave House, 9 Holgrave Close, High Legh, Knutsford, Cheshire, WA16 6TX Tel: (01925) 757887 Fax: (01925) 758611 E-mail: mike@businesslegal.ltd.uk *UK Company formation and registration agents. Same day on-line incorporation. Registered office and Company secretarial services, Vat and trademark registration. Commercial and company legal advice and consultancy.*

▶ Businessline, Wrexham Library, Rhosddu Road, Wrexham, Clwyd, LL11 1AU Tel: (01978) 292092 Fax: (01978) 292611 E-mail: businessline@wrexham.gov.uk *Business information*

▶ Businets Web Design Ltd, 19 Spencers Way, Harrogate, North Yorkshire, HG1 3DN Tel: (0845) 3457849 Fax: (0870) 0119435 E-mail: help@businets.co.uk *Web developers*

▶ Busiprint Ltd, 64 Well Street, Buckingham, MK18 1EN Tel: (01280) 823000 Fax: (01280) 816464

Bussens & Vigrass, Bexwell Road, Downham Market, Norfolk, PE38 9LH Tel: (01366) 382294 Fax: (01366) 382878 *Agricultural building services*

Buswell Machine Electronics, Peel House, Peel Road, Skelmersdale, Lancashire, WN8 9PT Tel: (01695) 726518 Fax: (01695) 726518 E-mail: rbuswell@buswell.co.uk *Electronic circuit designers & manufrs*

Busy Bee Aero Engineering, Sibson Airfield, Sibson, Peterborough, PE8 6NE Tel: (01832) 280579 Fax: (01832) 280579 *Aircraft engineering maintenance*

Busy Bees, 311 Broad Lane, Leeds, LS13 3BU Tel: 0113-257 7757 *Bouncy castle hire*

Busy Bees, Wath Road, Wath-upon-Dearne, Rotherham, South Yorkshire, S63 7EN Tel: (01709) 760195 Fax: (01709) 877829 *Concrete suppliers & manufrs*

Busy Embroidery, 3 Village Farm Industrial Estate, Pyle, Bridgend, Mid Glamorgan, CF33 6ZR Tel: (01656) 741274 Fax: (01656) 741274 E-mail: sales@fusionembroidery.co.uk *Printing for work ware & sports ware*

▶ Busy Fingers, 2 Elliott Road, Love Lane Industrial Estate, Cirencester, Gloucestershire, GL7 1YS Tel: (01285) 656757 Fax: (01285) 657665 E-mail: bfcopying@aol.com *Copying & duplicating services*

Busy Life, 5 Abingdon Road, Leicester, LE2 1HA Tel: (07729) 288515 E-mail: busy.life@ntlworld.com *Lifestyle management and concierge services for busy people. If your to do list is getting out if hand give Busy Life a call and we will help you out!*

▶ Butbro, Yew Tree Way, Golborne, Warrington, WA3 3JD Tel: (01942) 272872 Fax: 0 1689 845689 E-mail: sales@butbro.co.uk

Butcher Plasterworks Ltd, 8 Fitzroy Road, Primrose Hill, London, NW1 8TX Tel: (020) 7722 9771 Fax: (020) 7586 2953 *Fibrous plastering contractors*

Butchers Arms Gallery & Coffee Shop, Heol-Y-Sarn, Llantrisant, Pontyclun, Mid Glamorgan, CF72 8DA Tel: (01443) 229285 Fax: (01443) 238436 *Pine furniture distributors*

Butchers Printed Products Ltd, 498-506 Moseley Road, Birmingham, B12 9AL Tel: 0121-440 2612 Fax: 0121-440 3239 E-mail: md@bppscreengraphics.co.uk *Specialist screen printers of industrial & promotional graphics* Also at: Stoke-on-Trent

▶ Butchers Removals & Storage Co., 6b Quarry Wood Industrial Estate, Mills Road, Aylesford, Kent, ME20 7NA Tel: (01622) 725888 Fax: (01622) 725219 E-mail: info@butchersremovals.co.uk *Domestic and Commercial Removals and Storage. Member of British Association of Removers sice 1982.*

▶ Bute Blacksmiths, 88 High Street, Rothesay, Isle of Bute, PA20 9BB Tel: (01700) 504235 Fax: (01700) 504235 E-mail: enquiries@buteblacksmiths.fsnet.co.uk *Metal-workers, fabricators, welders*

Butedean Ltd, Springfield Mill, Sherborne Street West, Salford, M3 7LT Tel: 0161-832 4724 Fax: 0161-832 2746 *Yarn merchants & importers*

▶ Butherway Electrical, Rhiw, Rosebush, Clynderwen, Dyfed, SA66 7RH Tel: (01437) 532511 Fax: (01437) 532964 E-mail: sales@butherwayelectrical.com

Butler Engineering, Fen Road Garage, Fen Road, Heighington, Lincoln, LN4 1JH Tel: (01522) 790375 Fax: (01522) 790375 *Motor vehicle repair services*

Butler & England Ltd, 20 The Ferns, Larkfield, Aylesford, Kent, ME20 6NE Tel: (01732) 849247 Fax: (020) 8244 9463 E-mail: info@butlerandengland.com *Used & Reconditioned Soap Machinery, Confectionery Machinery, Chocolate Machinery & Ink Machinery. Servicing, Reconditioning & Maintenance*

Butler Equipment Sales, Glovers Meadow, Maesbury Road Industrial Estate, Oswestry, Shropshire, SY10 8NH Tel: (01691) 676199 Fax: (01691) 679376 *Machine sales case dealers*

John Butler (Hatfield) Ltd, 1 Bury Road, Hatfield, Hertfordshire, AL10 8BQ Tel: (01707) 262257 Fax: (01707) 251929 *Food products manufrs*

Nelson Butler & Son Ltd, Elmhirst Road, Horncastle, Lincolnshire, LN9 5AU Tel: (01507) 523451 Fax: (01507) 522182 *Timber merchants*

Butler Reynolds Ltd, Loughborough Road, Costock, Loughborough, Leicestershire, LE12 6XB Tel: (01509) 854144 Fax: (01509) 854199 E-mail: sales@butlerreynolds.co.uk *Construction equipment sales*

Butler Saddlery Ltd, 4 Fieldgate Works, New Street, Walsall, WS1 3DJ Tel: (01922) 627192 Fax: (01922) 627192 *Saddlery manufrs*

Butler School Of Languages, 170 Victoria Street, London, SW1E 5LB Tel: (020) 7834 0606 Fax: (020) 7828 1184 *Language school for executives*

Simon Butler, Unit 10E, Wincombe Park Business Centre, Shaftesbury, Dorset, SP7 9QJ Tel: (01747) 850150 Fax: (01747) 850250 E-mail: info@comptonsmith.co.uk *Cabinet manufrs*

Stephen Butler Blinds, The Street, Walberton, Arundel, West Sussex, BN18 0PF Tel: (01243) 555222 Fax: (01243) 555222 E-mail: sales@stephenbutlerblinds.co.uk *Blind manufrs*

▶ T.J Butler (Electronics) Ltd, Unit 2 Catherine Court, Airfield View, Hawarden Industrial Park, Hawarden, Deeside, Flintshire, CH5 3NU Tel: (0871) 2224230 Fax: (01244) 538438 E-mail: service@tjbutlers.co.uk *Service centre for plasma, lcd & lcd projectors*

Butler & Tanner Ltd, Caxton Road, Frome, Somerset, BA11 1NF Tel: (01373) 451333 Fax: (01373) 451333 *Printers & bookbinders*

Butler Wentwood Ltd, Units 2-4, New Road, New Inn, Pontypool, Gwent, NP4 0TL Tel: (01495) 763040 Fax: (01495) 763505 E-mail: inquiries@butlerwentwood.sagehost.co.uk *Chemicals & janitorial suppliers*

Butler & Willow Ltd, 7 Harrington Mills, Leopold Street, Long Eaton, Nottingham, NG10 4QE Tel: 0115-946 8687 Fax: 0115-946 9446 E-mail: sales@butler-willow.co.uk *Shelving & racking*

Butler & Young Associates, 54-62 Station Road East, Oxted, Surrey, RH8 0PG Tel: (01883) 717172 Fax: (01883) 717174 E-mail: enquiries@bya.co.uk *Building construction consultants*

John Butlin Ltd, Arthur Road, Yardley, Birmingham, B25 8HA Tel: 0121-772 0313 Fax: 0121-773 4383 E-mail: john.butlin@virgin.net *Road transport haulage freight services*

Butlins Fork Trucks Ltd, Unit 5 Bourne End, Kineton Road Industrial Estate, Southam, Warwickshire, CV47 0NA Tel: (01926) 812334 Fax: (01926) 811734 *Butlin Fork Trucks Ltd are a family business who have been established since 1981, and are ideally situated in Southam, Warwickshire, close to the motorway network. With time served engineers, we can offer you the best advice for your Fork Lift Truck requirements, from Hire, Sales and Service to Parts.*

Butonia, 260-264 Kingsland Road, London, E8 4DG Tel: (020) 7249 5141 Fax: (020) 7249 8859 E-mail: bltd@butonia-group.com *Buckle & button merchants*

Butser Rubber Ltd, Mint Road, Liss, Hampshire, GU33 7BQ Tel: (01730) 894034 Fax: (01730) 894344 E-mail: butserrubber@btinternet.com Purchasing Contact: N. Easton Sales Contact: N. Easton Principal Export Areas: Asia Pacific, Central/East Europe, West Europe & North America *UK based Manufacturer & supplier of high quality rubber mouldings, extrusion, sheeting & precision rubber components to both national & international markets. Located on the Hampshire, Surrey & West Sussex boarder, Butser Rubber is a key producer & distributor to the Aerospace, Defence, Maritime, Medical, Autosport & Motor industries. Butser Rubber's product range includes: precision rubber mouldings, gaskets (From rubber, foam & paper), rubber to metal bondings, Rubber C.V. boots, Extrusions in silicone, solid rubber & sponge, Rubber & sponge 'O' rings, moulded hoses, bellows, anti-vibration mounts, seals & grommets, Sponge mouldings, moulded rubber housings and polyurethane elastomers products. We are very happy to quote for all your rubber needs & can manufacture from both drawing & pattern part. We are an ISO9002 producer & can manufacture using B.S. & Defence DTD standard Materials. Recent investment in a computerised MRP system gives rapid responses & full lot traceability.*

A.B. Butt Ltd, Frog Island, Leicester, LE3 5AZ Tel: 0116-251 3344 Fax: 0116-253 6377 E-mail: sales@abbutt.co.uk *Auto-motive engineers*

Butt Bros, Charlton Musgrove, Wincanton, Somerset, BA9 8HP Tel: (01963) 31771 *Agricultural contractors*

▶ Butt Foods Ltd, The Midway, Nottingham, NG7 2TS Tel: 0115-985 0009 Fax: 0115-985 1460 E-mail: robert@buttfoods.co.uk *Producers of specialty & value added bread products*

Butterfield Morris Bushell Ltd, Bute Mills Mill Yard, Guildford Street, Luton, LU1 2NH Tel: (01582) 725454 Fax: (01582) 480024 E-mail: enquiries@bmb.uk.com *BMB is a full service creative agency that delivers effective marketing programmes for our clients. Public Relations, Exhibition and Event solutions, Interactive and Web, Strategic Marketing and Advertising.*

Butterfield Private Bank, 99 Gresham Street, London, EC2V 7NG Tel: (020) 7776 6700 Fax: (020) 7776 6701 E-mail: info@butterfieldprivatebank.co.uk *Merchant & private bankers*

Butterfield Signs Ltd, 174 Sunbridge Road, Bradford, West Yorkshire, BD1 2RZ Tel: (01274) 722244 Fax: (01274) 848998 E-mail: general@butterfield-signs.co.uk *Sign contractors & suppliers*

Butterflies Catering Equipment Hire, 4 Elm Tree Farm, Sheepway, Portbury, Bristol, BS20 7TF Tel: (01275) 375545 Fax: (01275) 374425 *Catering equipment hire*

Butterfly Blinds, Cambridge Road, Milton, Cambridge, CB24 6AT Tel: (0500) 011363 Fax: (01223) 425355 E-mail: butterflyblinds@tiscali.co.uk *Pleated & vertical blind manufrs*

▶ Butterfly Bronze, 2 Bons Farm Cottages, Stapleford Road, Stapleford Tawney, Romford, RM4 1RP Tel: (020) 8500 3037 Fax: (01708) 687 488 E-mail: links@butterflybronze.com *Using the 'Lost Wax' process and a uniquely developed 'Live Casting' technique, artist William Hayes produces made to measure bronze and aluminium sculptures that are breathtakingly beautiful.*

Butterfly Collection Ltd, Rutland Street, Ilkeston, Derbyshire, DE7 8DG Tel: 0115-944 7469 Fax: 0115-944 7158 E-mail: lester.price@btinternet.com *Soft furnishing distributors*

▶ Butterfly Occasions Ltd, 56 Foxholes Road, Chelmsford, CM2 7HS Tel: (01245) 472529 E-mail: info@butterflyoccasions.co.uk *Wedding favours, reception design products, hen nights and jewellery.*

▶ The Butterfly Within - Life Coaching, 55 Sundridge Road, Addiscombe, Croydon, CR0 6RL Tel: (020) 8090 5007 E-mail: regine.grove@thebutterflywithin.co.uk *Together we can turn your "I can"t" into "I can"!*

Butterley Ltd, Langthwaite Grange Industrial Estate, South Kirkby, Pontefract, West Yorkshire, WF9 3AP Tel: (01977) 643461 Fax: (01977) 655353 *Civil engineers*

Butterley Nuclear Engineering Ltd, Engineering Works, Ripley, Derbyshire, DE5 3BQ Tel: (01773) 573573 Fax: (01773) 749898 E-mail: admin@butterley.com *Cranes, machines & bridges designers & manufrs*

H.E. Butters & Co., Baldwins Gate, Newcastle, Staffordshire, ST5 5DA Tel: (01782) 680253 *Precision engineers*

Butterworth Heinemann, Linacre House Jordan Hill Business Park, Banbury Road, Oxford, OX2 8DP Tel: (01865) 888190 Fax: (01865) 314455 E-mail: bhmarketing@repp.co.uk Principal Export Areas: Worldwide *Book publishers*

Butterworth Steel Processing, Bilport Lane, Wednesbury, West Midlands, WS10 0NT Tel: 0121-556 8541 Fax: 0121-502 4644 *Shearing steel sheet & steel coil cutting*

Butties, 657 Ashton New Road, Manchester, M11 4QJ Tel: 0161-220 8000 *Sandwiches bar*

Buttle plc, 38-41 Castle Mews, London, NW1 8SY Tel: (020) 7485 8511 Fax: (020) 7482 3480 E-mail: bee@buttle.co.uk *Timber & builders merchants* Also at: St. Albans

Jason Buttons Ltd, Unit 40 Mgi Estate, Milkwood Road, London, SE24 0JF Tel: (020) 7274 0724 Fax: (020) 7737 0022 *Button carders & merchants* Also at: Eglinton

Buttons Saddlery, 44 Guildford Road, West End, Woking, Surrey, GU24 9PW Tel: (01276) 857771 Fax: (01276) 857771 E-mail: sales@buttonssaddlery.com *Equestrian saddlery & clothing suppliers*

▶ Buttonwood Marketing Ltd, Buttonwood House, Main Road, Shutlanger, Nr Towcester, Northampton, NN12 7RU Tel: (01604) 862404 Fax: (01604) 862404 E-mail: info@buttonwoodmarketing.com *Marketing services from pr to advertising & direct mail*

Buxactic Ltd, Sedgwick Lane, Horsham, West Sussex, RH13 6QE Tel: (01403) 218880 Fax: (01403) 274111E-mail: chris@buxatic.co.uk *Wholesale for equestrian products*

Buxo Plas, Quarters Farm, Hazle Badge, Bradwell, Hope Valley, Derbyshire, S33 9HX Tel: (01433) 620175 Fax: (01433) 620047 E-mail: sales@buxoplas.co.uk *Plastics extrusion manufrs*

Buxted Construction Ltd, Lower Lowlands Farm, Shepherds Hill, Buxted, Uckfield, East Sussex, TN22 4PX Tel: (01825) 890091 Fax: (01825) 890181 *Excavation & groundwork contractors*

Buxton Associates Consulting Engineers Ltd, Dawson House, 131-135 High Street, New Malden, Surrey, KT3 4BH Tel: (020) 8949 8779 Fax: (020) 8942 9941 E-mail: mail@buxtonassociates.co.uk *Structural engineers*

Buxton Building Supplies Ltd, Charles Street, Buxton, Derbyshire, SK17 7BD Tel: (01298) 28800 Fax: (01298) 28808 E-mail: info@bbs.fsnet.co.uk *Joinery manufrs*

Buxton & Cawthorne, 48 Cheney Hill, Heacham, King's Lynn, Norfolk, PE31 7BS Tel: (01485) 570139 Fax: (01485) 570545 *Groundwork contractors & skip hire*

Buxton Lime Ltd, Tunstead Quarry, Buxton, Derbyshire, SK17 8TG Tel: (01298) 768444 Fax: (01298) 72195 E-mail: buxton.sales@buxtonlime.co.uk *Quick & hydrated lime manufrs*

Buxton Mineral Water, Station Road, Buxton, Derbyshire, SK17 6AQ Tel: (01298) 766000 Fax: (01298) 72088 *Mineral water manufrs*

Buxton Press Ltd, Palace Road, Buxton, Derbyshire, SK17 6AE Tel: (01298) 212000 Fax: (01298) 212001 E-mail: sales@buxtonpress.co.uk *General printers & typesetters*

Buyers Mate, 218F Sackville Place, 44-48 Magdalen Street, Norwich, NR3 1JU Tel: (01603) 611642 Fax: (01603) 115792 E-mail: sales@buyersmate.net *Catering equipment suppliers furniture suppliers *hotel supplies **

Buzi Cleaning & Hygiene Centre, Units 64-65 Livestock Market, Hall Road, Norwich, NR4 6EQ Tel: (01603) 416226 Fax: (01603) 454872 *Janitorial supplier*

▶ Buzitech Computer Systems & It Support, 23 Furzy Park, Haverfordwest, Dyfed, SA61 1HG Tel: (01437) 779201 Fax: (01437) 767892 E-mail: info@buzinetsolutions.com *Internet & web designers*

▶ Buzz Connections, Unit 19 Govan Workspace, Harmony Row, Glasgow, G51 3BA Tel: 0141-440 2600 Fax: 0141-445 3217 E-mail: info@buzzconnections.co.uk *Creative & Graphic Design, Artwork, Print, Marketing, Media Analysis, Media Planning & Buying,*Media Recruitment, Media Sales Training and Development, Interim Management Services.*

▶ Buzz Electrical Ltd, Cornmill Road, Evesham, Worcestershire, WR11 2LL Tel: (01386) 423600 Fax: (01386) 423900

▶ Buzz House Keeping, Trocoll House, Wakering Road, Barking, Essex, IG11 8PD Tel: (020) 8507 9906 Fax: (020) 8507 9066 E-mail: peter@buzzservices.co.uk *Recruitment services*

Buzzard Environmental Services, 28 Hillyfields, Dunstable, Bedfordshire, LU6 3NS Tel: (01582) 477597 Fax: (01582) 477597 *Pest control services*

Buzzard Screen Print Ltd, 17 Wing Road, Leighton Buzzard, Bedfordshire, LU7 2NG Tel: (01525) 373527 Fax: (01525) 851260 E-mail: sales@buzzardscreenprint.co.uk *Buzzard Screen Print Ltd (based in Leighton Buzzard) have been offering high quality screen printing services to many customers for over two decades. *Key services include: POS, large format digital printing, panel printing plus more. We welcome both UK nationwide & worldwide screen printing enquiries.*

Bva Tools & Plastics Ltd, Oaks Road, Batley, West Yorkshire, WF17 6LT Tel: (01924) 474455 Fax: (01924) 477566 *Tool makers & injection moulders*

bValued Ltd, Unit 2, Dyfrig Road Industrial Estate, Cardiff, CF5 5AD Tel: (0845) 1309438 Fax: (0845) 1309439 E-mail: enquiries@bvalued.co.uk *Chartered Surveyor and Estate Agent*

BW Plastics Ltd, Acton Holdings, Long Lane, Essington, Wolverhampton, WV11 2AA Tel: (01922) 405114 Fax: (01922) 405114 *Plastic fabrications*

BWB Engineering, 145-149 Stanwell Road, Ashford, Middlesex, TW15 3QN Tel: (01784) 254321 Fax: (01784) 243451 *Precision sheet metalwork manufrs*

BWC Engineering, Unit 11, Westwood Business Park, Dulverton Road, Birmingham, B6 7DS Tel: 0121-326 6920 Fax: 0121-327 7517 E-mail: dalkeydalton@hotmail.com *Precision turning/grinding/milling. Small batchwork, local service, quick turnaround*

▶ BWH Special Cases, Applebys Business Centre, 1 - 3 Mossley Road, Grasscroft, Oldham, OL4 4HH Tel: (01457) 810800 Fax: (01457) 877244 E-mail: tim.bristow@bwh-cases.co.uk *Bespoke case solutions & standard cases for presentation manufrs*

BWS Security Systems Ltd, BWS Security Systems, Unit18 Church Farm Business Park, Corston, Bath, BA2 9AP Tel: (01225) 872385 Fax: (01225) 874565 *Security systems installers*

BX Plant Ltd, 20 Eastmead Industrial Estate, Lavant, Chichester, West Sussex, PO18 0DE Tel: (01243) 781970 Fax: (01243) 533547 E-mail: rhodge@bxplant.com *Concrete cure spraying equipment & bitumen emulsion spraying equipment manufacturers*

By Design plc, Unit 6 Mountheath Industrial Park, Prestwich, Manchester, M25 9WB Tel: 0161-281 4400 Fax: 0161-281 4481 E-mail: worldwide@by-design.co.uk *Importation of ladies clothing*

By Design Sealants, D The Business Centre, Faringdon Avenue, Romford, RM3 8EN Tel: (01708) 377010 Fax: (01708) 377080 E-mail: info@byds.co.uk *Sales By Design Sealants Ltd are the sole Distributor for Otto Chemie Sealants & Adhesives within the UK, we specialize in all types of Sealants, Adhesives & K-Grip Anti Slip Products. We have the largest colour range for silicone in the UK with 72 plus standard colours. Ottoseal S70 is a silicone sealant that GUARANTEES not to stain any natural stone and can also be used in bathrooms and Kitchens. please check our catalogue for all our products. All products can be bought by the tube or by the box. DISCOUNTS available for large orders. Application By Design Sealants Ltd are Specialist Sealant & K-Grip Applicators, we are approved applicators by all the main sealant manufacturers such as Dow Corning, Fosroc, Sika, Adshead Ratcliff, Mapei to name but a few. We also have applicators carrying out K-Grip application all over the UK, this product is the perfect solution for all your anti-slip /visual aid requirements, perfect for the Disability Discrimination Act*

By Products Keighley Ltd, Deal Street, Keighley, West Yorkshire, BD21 4LA Tel: (01535) 607008 Fax: (01535) 691480 *Sausage casings manufrs*

By Request Ltd, 6 Demmings Road, Demmings Industrial Estate, Cheadle, Cheshire, SK8 2PE Tel: 0161-428 0833 Fax: 0161-491 0411 E-mail: sales@byrequest.co.uk *Outside catering*

Byas, Mosley & Co. UK Ltd, William Byas Ho, 14-18 St. Clare St, London, EC3N 1JX Tel: (020) 7481 0101 Fax: (020) 7481 3442 E-mail: uk-div@bya-mosley.co.uk *Insurance brokers*

▶ Bybell Industrial Services, PO Box 406, Sunderland, SR6 7YB Tel: 0191- 536 5014 Fax: 0191- 536 5014 E-mail: mail@bybell.co.uk *Suppliers of odour control systems & air purification products*

Byford Interiors Ltd, Canterbury Court, Camberwell New Road, London, SE5 0TG Tel: (020) 7793 0777 Fax: (020) 7793 0377 E-mail: reception@cealings-uk.com *Suspended ceiling & partition specialists services*

▶ Bygones Reclaimation Canterbury, Merton Lane, Canterbury, Kent, CT4 7BA Tel: (01227) 767453 Fax: (01227) 762153 E-mail: bob@bygones.net *Reclamation services*

▶ Bylaw Ltd, Norwich Road, Lenwade, Norwich, NR9 5SH Tel: (01603) 872890 Fax: (01603) 872122 E-mail: info@bylaw.co.uk *Manufacturers of furniture reproduction antiques*

Bymax Ltd, Glengarnock Workshops, Glengarnock, Beith, Ayrshire, KA14 3DA Tel: (01505) 683242 Fax: (01505) 683242 *Engineering fabrication & welders*

A.W. Byrde & Associates, Stonefield, Kimmeridge, Wareham, Dorset, BH20 5PE Tel: (01929) 480064 Fax: (01929) 481304 E-mail: yachtsurvey@btopenworld.com *Marine surveyors consultants*

Byrne Bros Formwork Ltd, 13-15 White Hart Lane, London, SW13 0PX Tel: (020) 8878 9161 Fax: (020) 8878 3848 E-mail: info@byrne-bros.co.uk *Building contractors*

▶ Byrne Consultancy Ltd, 34 Ashburnham Loan, South Queensferry, West Lothian, EH30 9LE Tel: 0131-331 3694 Fax: 0131-331 3694

James Byrne Printing Ltd, Unit 10 Sandleheath Industrial Estate, Old Brickyard Road, Sandleheath, Fordingbridge, Hampshire, SP6 1PA Tel: (01425) 655090 Fax: (01425) 656844 E-mail: studio@jamesbyrne.co.uk *Design & print solutions, lithographic printers*

Byrom Clark Roberts Ltd, Maclaren House, Talbot Road, Stretford, Manchester, M32 0FP Tel: 0161-875 0600 Fax: 0161-875 0601 E-mail: bcrmcr@bcr.uk.com *Architects, surveyors & engineers* Also at: Bury & Sheffield

▶ Byron Advertising Ltd, Byron House, Wallingford Road, Uxbridge, Middlesex, UB8 2RW Tel: (01895) 252131 Fax: (01895) 252137 E-mail: enquiries@thebyrongroup.com *Advertising agency*

▶ Byron Finance, 41 London Road, Reigate, Surrey, RH2 9QE Tel: (01737) 228777 Fax: (01737) 735200 E-mail: recruitment@byronfinance.com *Finance & Accountancy Recruitment within Surrey, Sussex and Kent*

Byron George, 2 Gellideg, Pencoed Isaf Road, Bynea, Llanelli, Dyfed, SA14 9TL Tel: (01554) 773010 *Dental laboratory*

Bysel Ltd, Selby House, 27a Batley Road, Heckmondwike, West Yorkshire, WF16 9ND Tel: (01924) 403857 Fax: (01924) 405368 E-mail: export@byselcandy.com *Confectionery distributors & manufrs*

Michael Bysouth & Son, The Barn Trueloves, Trueloves Lane, Ingatestone, Essex, CM4 0NQ Tel: (01277) 355315 Fax: (01277) 355315 *Cabinet manufrs*

Bystone Engineers Ltd, Price Street, Bilston, West Midlands, WV14 7EE Tel: (01902) 494604 Fax: (01902) 353147 *Steel fabricators*

Bystronic UK Ltd, Chard Junction, Chard, Somerset, TA20 4QR Tel: (01460) 222100 Fax: (01460) 222108 E-mail: sales@bystronic.com *Sheet metalworking machinery*

Bystronic UK Ltd, Maple Park, Lowfields Avenue, Leeds, LS12 6HH Tel: 0113-277 8112 Fax: 0113-271 9862 *Sheet metalworkers*

Byte Back, 4 Rex Corner, Broxholme Lane, Doncaster, South Yorkshire, DN1 2LP Tel: (01302) 812809 *Computer consumables & stationery*

Byte Systems, 50 Hoskyn Close, Rugby, Warwickshire, CV21 4LA Tel: (01788) 331495 Fax: (0870) 941027 E-mail: sales@byte-solutions.co.uk *Computer services*

Byte Technology, 12-13 The Street, Yatesbury, Calne, Wiltshire, SN11 8YG Tel: (01672) 539559 *Computer consultants*

▶ Byteback Computers Ltd, 69 Princess Avenue, Stainforth, Doncaster, South Yorkshire, DN7 5RA Tel: (01302) 846555 E-mail: enquiries@bytebackcomputers.net *Computer suppliers*

Bytecraft Ltd, 5 The Quad, Mercury Court, Chester, CH1 4QP Tel: (01244) 390109 Fax: (01244) 390051 E-mail: sales@bytecraft.co.uk *Computer service & peripherals*

Bytes & PC's, 4 Stockwell Head, Hinckley, Leicestershire, LE10 1RE Tel: (01455) 613232 Fax: (01455) 615164 E-mail: derrick@themousepad.co.uk *Computer repairers*

Bytes & PC's UK Ltd, Gosford House, 26/27 Far Gosford Street, Coventry, CV1 5DW Tel: (024) 7655 5265 Fax: (024) 7655 1100 E-mail: sales@bytespcs.co.uk *Computer systems building, maintenance & repair*

Bytes Technology, Matrix House, North Fourth Street, Milton Keynes, MK9 1NJ Tel: (08707) 774646 Fax: (08707) 771021 *Computer consultants*

Bytomic Distribution, Unit 15-17 Top Angel, Angel Vale Business Park, Buckingham Industrial Estate, Buckingham, MK18 1TH Tel: (01280) 818640 Fax: (01280) 823083 E-mail: sales@bytomic.com *Sport equipment distributor*

Byways Ltd, Bramingham Business Park, Enterprise Way, Luton, LU3 4BU Tel: (01582) 524444 Fax: (01582) 491301 E-mail: info@byways.co.uk *Garment label manufrs*

Bywell Shooting Ground, Bywell Farm, Felton, Morpeth, Northumberland, NE65 9QQ Tel: (01670) 787827 Fax: (01670) 787093 *Shooting grounds*

Bywell Springs & Pressings Ltd, Unit 4, Millsborough House, Ipsley St, Redditch, Worcestershire, B98 7AL Tel: (01527) 66551 Fax: (01527) 66024 E-mail: sales@bywell.co.uk Principal Export Areas: Africa *Hydraulic hose spring armoring & spring manufrs*

Byworth Engineering Ltd, Albion Works, Royd Ings Ave, Keighley, W. Yorkshire, BD21 4BZ Tel: (01535) 602780 Fax: (01535) 611319 *Steel fabricators, machinists & flange manufrs*

Byworth Material Services, 12 Stonehouse Commercial Centre, Bristol Road, Stonehouse, Gloucestershire, GL10 3RD Tel: (01453) 821609 Fax: (01453) 821471 E-mail: byworth@aol.com *Stainless alloy-heat treatment & machining engineer machining service*

C 2 P Automotive Ltd, Bradbourne Drive, Tilbrook, Milton Keynes, MK7 8AT Tel: (01908) 362400 Fax: (01908) 362401 *Car manufrs*

C 3 Imaging (Glasgow), 126 Hydepark Street, Glasgow, G3 8BW Tel: 0141-226 3344

▶ C 3 Midlands Ltd, Faraday Wharf, Holt Street, Birmingham, B7 4BB Tel: 0121-260 6144 Fax: 0121-260 6145 E-mail: enquiries@c3midlands.co.uk *C3 Midlands Ltd. have extensive resources for most types of small, medium, large and grand format printing. Printed products can range from business stationery, 2D. and 3D. POS. materials to the production and installation of building wraps, retail display matter and much more!**We provide a single point solution and a single point of contact (if preferred) in our supply of printed matter whether digital, litho or screen printed. These products and services are delivered inclusive of any necessary on site fitting services, collation and packing, packaging, despatch, monitoring, auditing and /or marketing service required.*

▶ C 3 S Projects Ltd, Canal Mills, Elland, West Yorkshire, HX5 0SQ Tel: (01422) 313800 Fax: (01422) 313808

C 4 Carbides (International) Ltd, 9 Nuffield Road, Cambridge, CB4 1TF Tel: (01223) 506406 Fax: (01223) 225405 E-mail: janice@c4carbides.com *Specialist tungsten grit product manufrs*

C A B Joinery Services Ltd, C A B Joinery Services Ltd, Unit 3, Block A, Bescot Industrial Estate, Woden Road West, Wednesbury, West Midlands, WS10 7SG Tel: 0121-556 5445 Fax: 0121-505 4352 E-mail: enquiries@cab-joinery.co.uk *CAB Joinery has been established for over 35 years and is one of the midlands finest companies specialising in bespoke joinery. We have developed an enviable reputation with clients both locally and nationally. From the initial design concept right through to product installation, our team of designers and craftsman ensure a result which is guaranteed to please.*

C A Baldwin & Co. Ltd, 146-154 Wells Way, London, SE5 7SY Tel: (020) 7703 2138 Fax: (020) 7701 8436 E-mail: info@baldwin.co.uk *Heating engineers' merchants*

C A Bengry Ltd, Spring Road, Stoke-on-Trent, ST3 4PX Tel: (01782) 313405 Fax: (01782) 596633 *Bakery*

C A Brown, 5 Young Street Industrial Estate, Young Street, Bradford, West Yorkshire, BD8 9RE Tel: (01274) 488099 Fax: (01274) 498868 E-mail: sales@castortruckladder.co.uk *Material handling*

C A C I Anadata Ltd, Thomas Yeoman House, Coventry Canal Basin, St. Nicholas Street, Coventry, CV1 4LY Tel: (024) 7684 6846 Fax: (024) 7683 7099 E-mail: marketing@caci.co.uk *Information solutions*

C A C Industrial Products Ltd, Thornton Industrial Trading Estate, Milford Haven, Dyfed, SA73 2RU Tel: (01646) 692626 Fax: (01646) 690144 E-mail: sales@cac-industrial.co.uk *Industrial gloves & clothing manufrs*

C A Clase (UK) Ltd, 20 Woolmer Way, Bordon, Hampshire, GU35 9QF Tel: (01420) 488422 Fax: (01420) 488522 E-mail: sales@caclase.co.uk *Marine monitoring equipment*

C A Clemson & Sons Ltd, Shenstone Trading Estate, Bromsgrove Road, Halesowen, West Midlands, B63 3XB Tel: 0121-550 8833 Fax: 0121-550 7617 E-mail: halesowen.sales@toolbank.com *Hand tool distributors* Also at: Gwent

▶ C A Cornish, 21 High Street, Street, Somerset, BA16 0EF Tel: (01458) 442746 Fax: (01458) 443850 *Leather component manufrs*

▶ C A D E Electrical Contractors Ltd, 16 Evelyn Grove South, Grimsby, South Humberside, DN32 8LB Tel: (01472) 591713 Fax: (01472) 230576 E-mail: sales@cadeelectrical.co.uk *Electrical contractors, domestic, commercial & industrial installations worldwide*

C A D (Sales) Ltd, Unit 6, Waldegraves Business Park, West Mersea, Colchester, CO5 8SE Tel: (01206) 386611 Fax: (01206) 385959 *Industrial acoustic, noise control consultants & engineers*

C A Davies & Sons Ltd, Dovefields, Uttoxeter, Staffordshire, ST14 8AE Tel: (01889) 564844 Fax: (01889) 568578 *Country store equestrian sales centre*

C A Design Services Ltd, The Design Centre, Hewett Road, Gapton Hall, Great Yarmouth, Norfolk, NR31 0NN Tel: 01493 440444 Fax: 01493 442480 E-mail: sales@cadesignservices.co.uk *National company providing CAD services, measured building surveying, topographical surveying, scanning, space planning, GIS & mapping, CAD software, CAD training, CAD development, retail design & store planning (www.cadsretail.co.uk), healthcare planning.*

C A Designs Ltd, The Coach House, 54 The Ridgeway, Rothley, Leicester, LE7 7LE Tel: 0116-237 5248 Fax: (08700) 521513 E-mail: sales@cadesigns.co.uk *Computer peripherals design & manufrs*

C A E Diesel Ltd, 49a Chingford Mount Road, London, E4 8LU Tel: (020) 8527 8077 *Diesel fuel injection specialists*

C A E Solutions Ltd, Unit D4 Hilton Trading Estate, Hilton Road, Lanesfield, Wolverhampton, WV4 6DW Tel: (01902) 403555 Fax: (01902) 401952 E-mail: sales@cae-solutions.co.uk *Computer aided design & analysis*

C A E UK plc, Innovation Drive, York Road, Burgess Hill, West Sussex, RH15 9TW Tel: (01444) 247535 Fax: (01444) 244895 E-mail: cae_plc@cae.co.uk *Simulators & process industry training services*

C A F (Charities Aid Foundation), 25 Kings Hill Avenue, West Malling, Kent, ME19 4TA Tel: (01732) 520000 Fax: (01732) 520001 E-mail: enquiries@cafonline.org *Charity finance advisers*

C A Grant, Orgreave Crescent, Sheffield, S13 9NQ Tel: 0114-269 5498 Fax: 0114-269 5412 E-mail: sales@cagrant.co.uk Principal Export Areas: Worldwide *Founded in 1957, we have a broad customer base supplying marking dies & tooling of many types to a wide variety of manufacturing industries including motor vehicles, engineers cutting tools, turned parts & motor vehicle components such as exhaust systems, springs, bearings & shock absorbers. We manufacture all types of engraved products - both standard & special, using the latest technology & offer quick deliveries & competitive prices*

C A Honemaster Ltd, Unit 14 Malmesbury Road, Kingsditch Trading Estate, Cheltenham, Gloucestershire, GL51 9PL Tel: (01242) 584326 Fax: (01242) 226158 E-mail: kieran.reel@btconnect.com *Honing specialists*

▶ C A J Services Ltd, Unit K,, Higham Business Park, Bury Close, Higham Ferrers, Northamptonshire, NN10 8HQ Tel: (01933) 355001 Fax: (01933) 355009 E-mail: mail@cajservices.co.uk *Demolition Contractors covering the South East,Home Counties,Midlands & East Anglia. Asbestos removal,general demolition,materials recycling, contamination land remediation work, Industrial demolition, site clearance, minor civil engineering works, landscape works.*

C A L Software Ltd, Rivington House, Drumhead Road, Chorley North Industrial Estate, Chorley, Lancashire, PR6 7BX Tel: (01257) 231011 Fax: (01257) 230927 E-mail: sales@calsoftware.co.uk *Programming services*

C A M Tyre & Welding Co. Ltd, Frome Road, Radstock, BA3 3PY Tel: (01761) 434226 Fax: (01761) 435541 E-mail: enquiries@camequipment.co.uk *Lifting equipment services*

C A M X L Ltd, Avon Court, Cowbridge Road, Bridgend, Mid Glamorgan, CF31 3SR Tel: (01656) 303100 Fax: (01656) 658054 E-mail: andy@camxl.co.uk *Computer aided software manufrs*

▶ C A Maddox, 150 Widemarsh Street, Hereford, HR4 9HN Tel: (01432) 267156 Fax: (01432) 267556 E-mail: ca.maddox@btconnect.com *Electrical contractors*

C A N (Offshore) Ltd, Hareness Road, Altens, Aberdeen, AB12 3LE Tel: (01224) 870100 Fax: (01224) 876015 E-mail: mailserve@cangroup.net *On & offshore maintenance services*

C A P Aluminium Systems Ltd, Systems House, Spon Lane, West Bromwich, West Midlands, B70 6AA Tel: 0121-525 1000 Fax: 0121-525 5010 *Aluminium glazing system manufrs*

C A P Furnaces, 2 Upper Interfields, Leigh Sinton Road, Malvern, Worcestershire, WR14 1UT Tel: (01886) 833663 Fax: (01886) 833663 E-mail: cap@furnaces.fsn.co.uk *Furnace manufrs*

C A P S Ltd, 80 Pike Helve St, Golds Hill, West Bromwich, West Midlands, B70 0TU Tel: 0121-557 9553 Fax: 0121-522 2795 E-mail: caps.ltd@lineone.net *Ceiling & partition distributors*

C A Palmer & Sons, Clayford Cottages, Clayford, Wimborne, Dorset, BH21 7BJ Tel: (01202) 893467 Fax: (01202) 893467 *Gate & fencing manufrs*

C A R E S GB Ltd, Suite, 8 Stoke Road, Stoke-on-Trent, ST4 2DP Tel: (01782) 212613 Fax: (01782) 212046 *Debt collectors*

C A Sothers Ltd, 156 Hockley Hill, Birmingham, B18 5AN Tel: 0121-554 2054 Fax: 0121-554 4090 E-mail: cas@sothers.com *Electrical & mechanical installation & maintenance contractors*

C A Sperati The Special Agency plc, 54 Westcombe Hill, London, SE10 0LR Tel: (020) 8858 7069 Fax: (020) 8853 5349 E-mail: enquires@casperatiplc.com *Buttons, buckles & trimmings distributors*

C & A Supplies Ltd, Bidder Street, London, E16 4ST Tel: (020) 7474 0474 Fax: (020) 7474 5055 E-mail: info@cabp.co.uk *Plastic sheeting distributors*

C A T Engineering Ltd, Glendale Works, 25 Sandhurst Road, Crowthorne, Berkshire, RG45 7HR Tel: (01344) 772934 Fax: (01344) 779283 E-mail: len@cateng.fsnet.co.uk *Security fixings & consultants*

C A T Industrial Flooring Ltd, 34 Laburnum Avenue, Garden Village, Hull, HU8 8PH Tel: (01482) 783259 Fax: (01482) 783259 E-mail: sales@catindustrialflooring.co.uk *CAT Industrial Flooring Ltd serving the UK from its base in Hull supplying and installing epoxy and polyurethane coatings and screeds to suit all types of working environments including manufacturing , engineering and food and drink processing. *Like the thousands of other flooring companies we offer free advice on all aspects of industrial floor and wall systems. From epoxy and polyurethane coatings to simple floor and cove repairs or trowel applied floor screeds, anti slip coatings, pumpable cementitious screeds, bridge and car park deck systems to polished terazzo floors we have the skill and knowledge to complete. *We have thousands of satisfied customers who have benefited from asking us to undertake works for them. *CAT Industrial Flooring Ltd only use manufacturers with proven track records, with the knowledge and technical resources to supply materials of the highest standard used over many years with success in various industrial and production environments.*

▶ C A Treble, 88-90 Hatton Garden, London, EC1N 8PN Tel: (020) 7405 5556 Fax: (020) 7405 5556 *Food processors products manufrs*

C A Trott Plant Hire Ltd, 21 Hurricane Way, Airport Industrial Estate, Norwich, NR6 6EZ Tel: (01603) 426487 Fax: (01603) 417837 E-mail: enquiries@trott-rentals.com *Commercial vehicle hire*

C A V Aerospace Ltd, Unit 11, Ashville Way, Whetstone, Leicester, LE8 6NU Tel: 0116-284 1520 Fax: 0116-286 7493 E-mail: sales@cav-aerospace.net *Precision engineers*

C A V (Sheffield) Ltd, Meadowbank Works, Meadow Bank Road, Rotherham, South Yorkshire, S61 2NF Tel: (01709) 740744 Fax: (01709) 740755 *Profile cutting services*

C Adams, Unit 18 Barton Hill Trading Estate, Maze Street, Bristol, BS5 9TE Tel: 0117-954 2331 Fax: 0117-954 2331 *Sign acrylic & manufrs*

▶ C Adams & Sons Midlands Ltd, Potters Lane, Wednesbury, West Midlands, WS10 7LH Tel: 0121-556 1774 Fax: 0121-556 5045 E-mail: sales@c-adams.co.uk *Bolt & nut distributors & agents*

C Aiano & Sons Ltd, 64-70 Chrisp Street, London, E14 6LR Tel: (020) 7987 1184 Fax: (020) 7538 2786 E-mail: caianoandson@aol.com *Industrial machine guard manufrs*

C Alexander, Dumbleton Lane, Eardiston, Tenbury Wells, Worcestershire, WR15 8JR Tel: (01584) 881501 Fax: (01584) 881168 *Fitted kitchen planners & manufrs*

C & B Co., Wholesale Warehouse, Chappell Drive, Doncaster, South Yorkshire, DN1 2RF Tel: (01302) 361357 Fax: (01302) 361357 *Packaging materials distributors & agents*

▶ C B A Cleaning Solutions, 6-7 Bunting Road, Bury St. Edmunds, Suffolk, IP32 7BX Tel: (01284) 702233 Fax: (01284) 749300 *Cleaning equipment distributors*

C B Adhesives, Adlington Industrial Estate, Adlington, Macclesfield, Cheshire, SK10 4NL Tel: (01625) 850180 Fax: (01625) 875932 *Tape suppliers & industrial adhesives manufrs*

C B Baggs Ltd, 1 Claremont Industrial Estate, London, NW2 1AL Tel: (020) 8905 5111 Fax: (020) 8905 5222 E-mail: info@cbbaggs.co.uk Principal Export Areas: Africa *Adhesive packing contractors*

C B C International Ltd, Coneygre Industrial Estate, Tipton, West Midlands, DY4 8XP Tel: 0121-557 3154 Fax: 0121-557 9570 E-mail: cklowe@cbcint.com *Bearing distributors*

C B Collections Ltd, 11 Grosvenor Road, Batley, West Yorkshire, WF17 0LX Tel: (01924) 476977 Fax: (01924) 478315 E-mail: silks@dial.pipex.com *Promotional tie, scarf & accessory manufrs*

C B Construction, 96 North Ormesby Road, Middlesbrough, Cleveland, TS4 2AG Tel: (01642) 231928 Fax: (01642) 211949 E-mail: keith@cbcon-cleveland.co.uk *Steel fabricators*

C & B Consultants Ltd, 194 Stanley Green Road, Poole, Dorset, BH15 3AH Tel: (01202) 673666 Fax: (01202) 671776 E-mail: candbaero@candbconsultants.com *Aerodynamics, carbon composites testing specialists*

C B D Research Ltd, 15 Wickham Road, Beckenham, Kent, BR3 5JS Tel: (0871) 2223440 Fax: (020) 8650 0768 E-mail: cbd@cbdresearch.co.uk *Directory publishers*

C & B Engineering Ltd, I Edison Courtyard, Brunel Road, Earlstrees Industrial Estate, Corby, Northamptonshire, NN17 4LS Tel: (01536) 202583 Fax: (01536) 269402 E-mail: ian.candbeng@btopenworld.com *Steel fabricators*

C B F Aluminium Treatments Ltd, Claybank Road, Portsmouth, PO3 5NH Tel: (023) 9266 5253 Fax: (023) 9266 7710 *Anodising services*

C B Fabrications, Units 4-4a The Old Co-Op Bakery, Kellet Road, Carnforth, Lancashire, LA5 9LR Tel: (01524) 736577 Fax: (01524) 736577 E-mail: sales@cbfabrications.co.uk *GRP smoking shelters, gatehouses & security kiosks manufrs*

C B H (Joinery) Ltd, Meadow Street, Walsall, WS1 3QP Tel: (01922) 646690 Fax: (01922) 615244 *Joinery manufrs*

C B Horne, 1a Coteroyd Avenue, Churwell/Morley, Leeds, LS27 7TU Tel: (07748) 086633 E-mail: info@tilersuk.com *INDUSTRIAL, COMMERCIAL & RESIDENTIAL WORK UNDERTAKEN.*COMPANY IN BUSINESS OVER 50 YEARS.*ALL WORK CARRIED OUT TO HIGHEST SPECIFICATION, FROM THE SMALLEST SPLASH-BACK TO LARGE TILING PROJECTS.**CONTACT CHRIS ON:*OFFICE: 01 216 8234*MOBILE: 07748 086633*EMAIL: info@tilersuk.com*WEB: http:// www.tilersuk.com***ALL TYPES OF TILING WORK CARRIED OUT.* BATHROOMS* KITCHENS* PATIOS* CONSERVATORIES* WET ROOMS * SWIMMING POOLS**SPECIALISTS IN CERAMIC TILING & NATURAL STONE.* CERAMIC TILES* SLATE* TRAVERTINE* LIMESTONE* MARBLE* PORCELAIN* GRANITE**

C & B Joinery, 8 Dowding Mews, Lincoln, LN3 4PN Tel: (01522) 568868 Fax: (01522) 568868 *Windows, doors & conservatories manufrs*

▶ C B K Ltd, 90 Bristol Road, Gloucester, GL1 5SQ Tel: (01452) 422333 Fax: (01452) 312822 *Conservatory roofs*

C B Kaymich & Co Ltd, Leigh Street, Sheffield, S9 2PR Tel: 0114-244 6071 Fax: 0114-244 2476 E-mail: info@kaymich.com *Manufacturers of spare parts for cigarette making machines*

▶ C B L Ltd, Banyard Road, Portbury, Bristol, BS20 7XH Tel: (01275) 372229

C B L Ltd, Holmbush Potteries, Crawley Road, Faygate, Horsham, West Sussex, RH12 4SE Tel: (01293) 851352 Fax: (01293) 851205 *Contractors plant rentals sales & services* Also at: Brdigend, Bristol, Crawley, Newton Abbot, Saltash & Southampton

C B Lighting Co., 56 Staplehill Road, Fishponds, Bristol, BS16 5BS Tel: 0117-907 4906 Fax: 0117-966 0311 *Light fittings wholesalers & manufrs*

C & B Marine Ltd, Chichester Marina, Chichester, West Sussex, PO20 7EJ Tel: (01243) 511273 Fax: (01243) 511273 *Precision engineers & boat fitting manufrs*

C B Metal Casements Ltd, Beardmore Place, Clydebank, Dunbartonshire, G81 4HS Tel: 0141-952 6431 Fax: 0141-941 1952 E-mail: cdmetal@supanet.co.uk *Aluminium & steel window manufrs*

▶ C B Morgan Farmers King's Somborne Ltd, Shaftesbury, Shaftesbury, Dorset, SP7 9HD Tel: (01747) 851003

C B North Ltd, 65 Hedon Road, Hull, HU9 1LW Tel: (01482) 329847 Fax: (01482) 215048 *Timber importers*

C B Packaging Ltd, Ballo Drive, Bangor, County Down, BT19 7QY Tel: (028) 9146 3015 Fax: (028) 9127 0048 *Paper sack manufrs*

C B Powell Ltd, 10 St Josephs Close, Hove, East Sussex, BN3 7ES Tel: (01273) 771144 Fax: (01273) 726966 E-mail: cbpowel@btconnect.com *Precision engineers*

C B R P Ltd, 20 Fernwood Drive, Radcliffe-on-Trent, Nottingham, NG12 1AA Tel: 0115-933 6123 Fax: 0115-841 3328 E-mail: enquiries@cbrp.co.uk *IT consultants*

▶ C B S Construction Ltd, Bunny Lane, Sherfield English, Romsey, Hampshire, SO51 6FT Tel: (01794) 884481 Fax: (01794) 884042

C B S Genios Ltd, Garman Road, Tottenham, London, N17 0QN Tel: (020) 8801 6444 Fax: (020) 8808 3650 E-mail: sales@cbsgenios.co.uk *Wholesale distribution of chemists sundries*

C B S L Softech, 10 Bridge Street, Hatherleigh, Okehampton, Devon, EX20 3HU Tel: (01837) 811133 Fax: (01837) 810782 E-mail: info@cbslsoftech.net *Computer networking services*

C B S (Midlands) Ltd, Kenilworth House, 118 Stourbridge Road, Dudley, West Midlands, DY1 2DP Tel: (01384) 254015 Fax: (01384) 456856 *Architectural ironmongery specialists*

C B S Office Supplies Ltd, 1 Winship Road, Milton, Cambridge, CB4 6BQ Tel: (01223) 225555 Fax: (01223) 225550 E-mail: mail@cbsofficesupplies.co.uk *Office equipment suppliers*

C B S Power Tools Ltd, 2 Bramhall Place, Storeys Bar Road, Peterborough, PE1 5YS Tel: (01733) 343031 Fax: (01733) 897151 E-mail: sales@cbspowertools.co.uk *Power tool distributors*

C B S Rotary Power Motion Ltd, Unit 14 Grandstand Business Centre, Westfields Trading Estate, Hereford, HR4 9NS Tel: (01432) 276630 Fax: (01432) 357140 E-mail: hereford@cbs-rpm.co.uk *Bearings, pneumatics & transmission equipment distributors* Also at: Birmingham, Dudley, Kidderminster & Kingswinford

C B S Rotary Power Motion Ltd, Lupin Works, Worcester Road, Kidderminster, Worcestershire, DY10 1JR Tel: (01562) 741808 Fax: (01562) 744312 E-mail: kidderminster@cbs-rpm.co.uk *Bearing & pneumatic equipment systems distributors* Also at: Birmingham & Hereford

C B Screenprinting & Display, 87 Foxholes Road, Hyde, Cheshire, SK14 5AP Tel: 0161-367 8072 Fax: 0161-367 8764 *Point of sale designers & printers*

C B Shack, Unit 1 Cliffe Lane, Lymm, Cheshire, WA13 0TE Tel: (01925) 757200 Fax: (01925) 757300 E-mail: sales@cbshack.com *CB Radio & Truck accessory specialists. Over 1000 products available in our secure on-line store.*

▶ C B Skip Hire Ltd, Southbourne, St. Thomas Farm, London Road, Salisbury, SP1 3YU Tel: (01722) 320544 Fax: (01722) 410329 E-mail: info@cbskiphire.co.uk *Skip hire, waste disposal services*

C & B Timbers/Custom Sheds, 12 Old Mill La Industrial Estate, Mansfield Woodhouse, Mansfield, Nottinghamshire, NG19 9BG Tel: (01623) 632872 Fax: (01623) 632872 *Shed manufrs*

C B Tool Engineers (Cambridge) Ltd, 5 Viking Way, Bar Hill, Cambridge, CB3 8EE Tel: (01954) 780411 Fax: (01954) 781075 E-mail: chapman.c@cbtoolengineers.com *General presswork manufrs*

C B Veneers Ltd, Progress Rd, Sands Industrial Estate, High Wycombe, Bucks, HP12 4JD Tel: (01494) 471959 Fax: (01494) 471961 E-mail: cbveneers@msn.com *Wood veneer merchants*

C B W Associates Ltd, 15 Station Rise, Marlow, Buckinghamshire, SL7 1EJ Tel: (01628) 482282 E-mail: bm.watson@btclick.com *Computer consultants*

C Bain Of Upminster, 164 Upminster Road, Upminster, Essex, RM14 2RB Tel: (01708) 440113 Fax: (01708) 454321 *Removal contractors*

C Biggs, Lankelly, Lankelly Lane, Fowey, Cornwall, PL23 1HN Tel: (01726) 833350 Fax: (01726) 833860 E-mail: chrisbiggs.engineering@virgin.net *Steel fabricators service*

C Blumsom Ltd, Maple Wharf, 36-38 River Road, Barking, Essex, IG11 0DN Tel: (020) 8594 5175 Fax: (020) 8594 1089 E-mail: sales@blumson.co.uk *Hardwood importers, milling & kiln drying*

C Blumsom Ltd, Maple Wharf, 36-38 River Road, Barking, Essex, IG11 0DN Tel: (020) 8594 5175 Fax: (020) 8507 1334 E-mail: sales@blumson.co.uk *Softwood & hardwood importers*

C Bolter Ltd, Carlton Works, St Johns Hill, Sevenoaks, Kent, TN13 3NS Tel: (01732) 457010 Fax: (01732) 740904 *Surgical & dental instruments wholesalers*

▶ C Bradley Engineering, 4-5 Sedgemount Industrial Park, Bristol Road, Bridgwater, Somerset, TA6 4AR Tel: (01278) 426550 Fax: (01278) 446913

C Brandauer & Co. Ltd, 235 Bridge Street West, Birmingham, B19 2YU Tel: 0121-359 2822 Fax: 0121-359 2836 E-mail: aedwards@brandauer.co.uk *Electromagnet intereference shielding materials; pressings, precision; pressings & pressings, beryllim copper*

C Brewer & Sons Ltd, 49 New England Street, Brighton, BN1 4GQ Tel: (01273) 570243 Fax: (01273) 693592 E-mail: brighton@brewers.co.uk *Decorators merchants*

C Brewer & Sons Ltd, Albany House, Ashford Road, Eastbourne, East Sussex, BN21 3TR Tel: (01323) 437801 Fax: (01323) 721435 E-mail: decorating@brewers.co.uk *Decorators merchant* Also at: Branches throughout Southern England

C Brewer & Sons Ltd, 5 Sphere Industrial Estate, Campfield Road, St. Albans, Hertfordshire, AL1 5HT Tel: (01727) 844737 Fax: (01727) 846672 *Decorators supply distributors*

C Bright, Elms Farm, Mount Bures, Bures, Suffolk, CO8 5BA Tel: (01787) 227730 Fax: (01787) 229027 *Farm machinery*

C Brown & Sons Steel Ltd, Pedmore Road, Dudley, West Midlands, DY2 0RL Tel: (01384) 480048 Fax: (01384) 263838 E-mail: sales@cbrownsteels.co.uk *Steel stockholders*

▶ C Burr, Vanguard Court Rear of, 36-38 Peckham Road, London, SE5 8QT Tel: (020) 7358 5225 Fax: (020) 7358 5225 E-mail: info@coryburr.com *Custom fabrication of furnishings*

C & C Auto Services Ltd, 13 Kingston Road, London, SW19 1JX Tel: (020) 8540 8871 Fax: (020) 8542 8903 *Motor spare parts factors*

C C C Express Couriers Ltd, Office 1, The Roundhouse, Dormans Park Road, East Grinstead, West Sussex, RH19 2EN Tel: (01342) 322550 Fax: (01342) 316200 E-mail: courtesycarraige@btconnect.com *Express couriers delivery services. 24hr availability. Same day service. Est. 15yrs. Based in Sussex, offering same day nationwide coverage.*

C C C & School Care Ltd, Unit 1, Armtech Row, Yeovil, Somerset, BA22 8RT Tel: (01935) 470300 Fax: (01935) 470302 E-mail: all@schoolcare.co.uk *Computer sales & distributors*

▶ C & C Cabinet Makers, Unit F5 The Brickyards, Steep Marsh, Petersfield, Hampshire, GU32 2BN Tel: (01730) 891400 Fax: (01730) 891403 E-mail: glyn@candccabinetmakers.co.uk *Kitchens, bedrooms, studies & commercial projects & cabinet manufrs*

▶ C C Contracting Ltd, Forge House, Dudley Road, Stourbridge, West Midlands, DY9 8EL Tel: (01384) 891891 Fax: (01384) 891831 E-mail: sales@cccontracting.co.uk *Construction of roads, yards, car parks, machine foundations, drainage & steel framed buildings*

▶ C & C Contractors London Ltd, 123 Wennington Road, Rainham, Essex, RM13 9TH Tel: (01708) 550008 Fax: (01708) 551009

CCE Group Ltd, Bentley Farm, Unit 1, Old Church Hill, Langdon Hills, Basildon, Essex, SS16 6HZ Tel: (01268) 412121 Fax: (01268) 412600 E-mail: sales@contractcateringequipment.co.uk *For 20 years CCE have come up with solutions to operational issues in commercial catering through design, re-design, refurbishment and procurement of equipment. Efficiency, speed of service, safety, workflow, EHO issues - we deal with them all week in, week out. CCE always aspire to achieve a long-term relationship with our clients in the belief that continuity and better understanding of the issues bring better solutions.*

C & C Engineering, Unit 3C, Cliffe St, Nelson, Lancashire, BB9 7QR Tel: (01282) 695912 Fax: (01282) 615764 E-mail: sales@candcengineering.co.uk *Precision polishers*

C & C Fire Extinguisher Service Ltd, 39 Pencricket Lane, Oldbury, West Midlands, B68 8LX Tel: 0121-559 6611 Fax: 0121-559 3399 *Fire fighting equipment distributors*

C & C Frames Ltd, 3 Hugomont Avenue, Ballymena, County Antrim, BT43 6HW Tel: (028) 2563 0146 Fax: (028) 2563 0146 E-mail: admin@ashgrovecentre.com *Conservatory design & manufrs*

C C G Corporate Consulting Group Ltd, 24 Buckingham Gate, London, SW1E 6LB Tel: (020) 7828 1123 Fax: (020) 8828 2604 E-mail: info@ccg.co.uk *Management consultants*

▶ C C H Engineering Ltd, 33 Peterfield Road, Kingstown Industrial Estate, Carlisle, CA3 0EY Tel: (01228) 818125 Fax: (01228) 514720

C C I International, 5 Priors Haw Road, Corby, Northamptonshire, NN17 5JG Tel: (01536) 260933 Fax: (01536) 401138 E-mail: info@cci-international.com *Clay pigeon manufrs*

▶ C & C James, Stowford Barton, Halwill, Beaworthy, Devon, EX21 5UN Tel: (01409) 221632 Fax: (01409) 221993

▶ C C Jessop Haulage Co. Ltd, North Side, King George Dock, Hull, HU9 5PR Tel: (01482) 796135

C C K Stainless Products Ltd, Units 17-18, SDH Industrial Estate, West Street, Sowerby Bridge, Halifax, West Yorkshire, HX6 3BS Tel: (01422) 834293 Fax: (01422) 839306 *Stainless steel catering equipment*

C C L A Investment Management, 80 Cheapside, London, EC2V 6DZ Tel: (020) 7489 6000 Fax: (020) 7489 6126 E-mail: info@ccla.co.uk *Church/charity investment management services*

C C L Software Ltd, Battenhall Lodge, 60 Battenhall Road, Worcester, WR5 2BX Tel: (0800) 0199853 Fax: (0845) 4900201 E-mail: nick@ccl-uk.com *Financial software consultants*

C C L Stressing Systems Ltd, Unit 4, Park 2000, Millennium Way, Leeds, LS11 5AL Tel: 0113-270 1221 E-mail: sales@cclstressing.com *Construction industry & components manufrs*

C C L Supplies, 153 High Street, Chesterton, Cambridge, CB4 1NL Tel: (01223) 520575 Fax: (01223) 520175 E-mail: sales@cclsupplies.co.uk *Cleaning & hygiene products suppliers*

C C L Veloduct Ltd, 10 Redburn Industrial Estate, Woodall Road, Enfield, Middlesex, EN3 4LE Tel: (020) 8805 3656 Fax: (020) 8805 0558 E-mail: sales@cclveloduct.co.uk Principal Export Areas: Worldwide *Flexible ducting suppliers* Also at: Bathgate, Belverdere, Birmingham, Enfield, Manchester & Southampton

C C L Veloduct Ltd, Unit 3 Eleventh Avenue, Team Valley Trading Estate, Gateshead, Tyne & Wear, NE11 0JY Tel: 0191-414 0888 Fax: 0191-487 4260 *Ventilation systems & components*

C C M Ltd, Pittman Way, Fulwood, Preston, PR2 9ZD Tel: (01772) 662500 Fax: (01772) 662510 E-mail: sales.dir@ccmltd.co.uk *Protective workwear manufrs*

▶ C C M A Services, Chappell, High Peak, Derbyshire, SK23 9HF Tel: (0870) 7559700 Fax: (0870) 7559707 *Computer software manufrs*

C C M Flintex Ltd, Linden Lea House, High Pitfold, Hindhead, Surrey, GU26 6BN Tel: (01483) 426980 Fax: (01428) 608608 E-mail: tony@flintex.freeserve.co.uk *Cash register & computer distributors*

▶ C C M South West Ltd, 6 Crown Close, Crown Industrial Estate, Taunton, Somerset, TA2 8RX Tel: (01823) 331166 Fax: (01823) 270393 *Office machines & equipment suppliers*

C C M Sussex Ltd, PO Box 2004, Peacehaven, East Sussex, BN10 7HZ Tel: (01273) 586963 Fax: (01273) 584000 E-mail: sales@ccm.gb.com *General office machinery distributors*

C C Moore & Co. Ltd, Church Hill, Sturminster Newton, Dorset, DT10 2RL Tel: (01963) 362234 Fax: (01963) 363837 *Animal feeds & fishing baits wholesalers & retailers* Also at: Weymouth

C C N Ltd, Spence Mills, Mill Lane, Leeds, LS13 3HE Tel: 0113-236 0033 Fax: 0113-236 0069 E-mail: info@ccn-ac.co.uk *Air conditioning & heating specialists*

▶ C C Outdoor Ltd, Exhibition Centre, Hostingley Lane, Middlestown, Wakefield, West Yorkshire, WF4 4PZ Tel: (01924) 272877 Fax: (01924) 261927 *Outdoor equipment manufrs*

C C P Gransden Bi-Chem, 17 Moss Road, Ballygowan, Newtownards, County Down, BT23 6JQ Tel: (028) 9752 8501 Fax: (028) 9752 1024 E-mail: info@ccp-gransden.com *Chemical distributor & GRP manufrs*

C C Power Electronics Ltd, Unit 19, Haigh Park, Whitehill Industrial Estate, Stockport, Cheshire, SK4 1QR Tel: 0161-429 7923 Fax: 0161-474 1174 E-mail: info@ccpowerltd.co.uk *DC control systems specialists & suppliers*

C C Process Engineering Ltd, Unit 44 Carlisle Enterprise Centre, James Street, Carlisle, CA2 5BB Tel: (01228) 819550 Fax: (01228) 819551 E-mail: sales@ccprocessengineering.com *Design & manufacture of process equipment*

C & C Property Consultants, 145-157 St. John Street, London, EC1V 4PY Tel: (0845) 0538867 Fax: (0707) 5209515 E-mail: pmsgwentltd@yahoo.com *We specialise in all aspects of Domestic and Commercial Property Maintenance and Disaster Recovery.*Fully insured and proffesional service at all times.*From a new build to a new tap washer we are the complete solution*

C C S Computers Ltd, 13 Clarkes La, Pocklington, York, YO42 2AW Tel: 01759 302251 Fax: 01759 302251 *Computer repairs & manufrs*

C C S Division Of Consumerdata Ltd, Meridian House, Artist St, Armley, Leeds, LS12 2EW Tel: 0113-242 0520 Fax: 0113-242 0050 E-mail: info@consumerdata.com *Computer bureau*

C C S Fuel Injection, Industrial Estate, Hallcroft Road, Retford, Nottinghamshire, DN22 7SS Tel: (01777) 711715 Fax: (01777) 711719 *Diesel injection engineers*

C C S IT Ltd, The Octagon, Middleborough, Colchester, CO1 1RA Tel: (01206) 216200 Fax: (01206) 767770 E-mail: info@ccsit.co.uk *Computer consultants*

▶ C C S (Leeds) Ltd, 31 Birchfields Avenue, Leeds, LS14 2HT Tel: 0113-294 6699 Fax: 0113-273 0058 *Computer consultancy*

C C S Technology Ltd, School Street, Wolston, Coventry, CV8 3HG Tel: (024) 7654 5711 Fax: (024) 7654 5722 E-mail: markf@ccstech.co.uk *Industrial Control System Design & Manufacture. Utilising PLC, CNC, Motion controllers with AC Servo Drive systems for machine control*

C & C Sales, 18 Nelson Place, Stirling, FK7 7PA Tel: (01786) 474439 Fax: (01786) 474439 *Badge manufrs*

▶ C C Scaffolding Surrey, 1 Croft End Close, Chessington, Surrey, KT9 1RD Tel: (020) 8391 5618 Fax: (020) 8397 7927 E-mail: sales@ccscaffolding.co.uk *Supply and Erection specialists since 1981.*Covering South London and Surrey areas*

▶ C C Systems Ltd, Aldsworth Avenue, Goring-by-Sea, Worthing, West Sussex, BN12 4XG Tel: (01903) 246299 E-mail: info@ccsystems.co.uk *We design, manufacture commission Process Control systems for all types of industry using customer prefered equipment. We also design and manufacture electronic equipment to your requirements.* ****

C C T Ltd, Park Road, Holmewood, Chesterfield, Derbyshire, S42 5UY Tel: (01246) 855995 Fax: (01246) 854028 E-mail: cctltd@breathemail.net *Hydraulic engineers*

C C T Infotech Ltd, Unit 7C Priory Tech Park, Saxon Way, Hull, HU13 9PB Tel: (01482) 647044 Fax: (01482) 647046 E-mail: sales@cct-infotech.co.uk *Networking consultants & computer hardware resellers*

C C T V Installations, 47 Sussex Road, Southport, Merseyside, PR9 0SP Tel: (01704) 884244 Fax: (01704) 884243 E-mail: sales@cctvinstallations.gbr.cc *CCTV installation*

C C T V People Ltd, PO Box 89, Cleckheaton, West Yorkshire, BD19 6YL Tel: (0800) 318748 Fax: (01274) 852188 *CCTV for security & management information*

C C T V Systems, 18 Avondale Road, Waterlooville, Hampshire, PO7 7ST Tel: (023) 9226 7999 Fax: (023) 9223 3664 E-mail: cctvsystems@btinternet.com *CCTV installation & services*

C Canavan, 5 Annaghmore Road, Coalisland, Dungannon, County Tyrone, BT71 4QZ Tel: (028) 8774 7015 Fax: (028) 8774 7427 *Joinery manufrs*

C Churchfield, Unit 7 Howsell Road Industrial Estate, Malvern, Worcestershire, WR14 1UJ Tel: (01684) 892150 Fax: (01684) 892150 *Augers, milling engineers & turned part manufrs*

C Clayton, The Brindles, Frolesworth, Lutterworth, Leicestershire, LE17 5EL Tel: (01455) 209350 *Agricultural contractor*

C Cooper & Sons Amusements, 49 Festival Walk, Spennymoor, County Durham, DL16 6AB Tel: (01388) 810272 *Sun beds & amusement services*

C Cromie, 31 Reservoir Road, Banbridge, County Down, BT32 4LD Tel: (028) 4066 2448 Fax: (028) 4062 9291 E-mail: thomas@futuregenetics.co.uk *Livestock breeders & dealers*

C D A R T Engineering, 1-2 Willow Road, Castle Donington, Derby, DE74 2NP Tel: (01332) 811150 Fax: (01332) 811306 *Commercial vehicle repair services*

C & D Aerials, 25 Howard Avenue, Rochester, Kent, ME1 2AW Tel: (01634) 844448 *Aerial contractors*

C D Atkinson Engineering Co. Ltd, Whitacre Road Industrial Estate, Whitacre Road, Nuneaton, Warwickshire, CV11 6BX Tel: (024) 7637 0119 Fax: (024) 7637 0811 *Precision engineers*

C D Bissell Engineering Services Ltd, Unit 28, Moorfields Industrial Estate, Cotes Heath, Stafford, ST21 6QY Tel: (01782) 791711 Fax: (01782) 791511 E-mail: mick@cdbissell.com *Sewage treatment systems engineers*

C D Bramall Plc, Etherstone Avenue, Newcastle upon Tyne, NE7 7LQ Tel: 0191-266 3311 Fax: 0191-215 0762 E-mail: newcastlehyundaisales@evanshalshaw.com *Rover subaru & daihatsu & hyundai dealership*

C D C 2020, 1 Forest Gate Tilgate Forest Business Centre, Brighton Road, Crawley, West Sussex, RH11 9PT Tel: (0845) 8502020 Fax: (01403) 756341

C & D Cartons Ltd, Third Cross Road, Twickenham, TW2 5DU Tel: (020) 8894 1181 Fax: (020) 8898 1608 *Carton merchants*

C D Contracts Ltd, 50 Garendon Road, Shepshed, Loughborough, Leicestershire, LE12 9NX Tel: (01509) 505511 Fax: (01509) 505522 E-mail: cdcontractsltd@aol.com *Designers & shop fitters*

▶ C D Duplicator, 51 New Chester Road, New Ferry, Wirral, Merseyside, CH62 1AA Tel: (0845) 0940947 E-mail: info@cdduplicator.co.uk *At CDduplicator we provide media duplication, replication, and mastering facilities to businesses and individuals. Apart from CD duplication & DVD duplication, we also provide a range of other services including:**Video to dvd, for copying your video tapes to DVD, video tape copying, design for artwork and print, video and audio mastering. Infact anything to do with: CD, DVD, Video, Audio, Design and copying.*

C D E Ireland Ltd, Ballyreagh Industrial Estate, Sandholes Road, Cookstown, County Tyrone, BT80 9DG Tel: (028) 8676 7900 Fax: (028) 8676 1414 E-mail: info@cdeireland.com *Turn-key sand & aggregate plant, water treatment & filtration*

C D Engineering, 1 Bartleet Road, Redditch, Worcestershire, B98 0DQ Tel: (01527) 524661 Fax: (01527) 510889 E-mail: cdeng100@yahoo.co.uk *Hydraulic manifold manufrs*

C D F Supplies Ltd, Unit 16 Highfield Industrial Estate, North Street, Chorley, Lancashire, PR7 1QD Tel: (01257) 274775 Fax: (01257) 233262 E-mail: sales@cdfsupplies.co.uk *Repairs, fixings & fastenings*

▶ C & D Facilities & Ground Maintenance, 38 Wendover Way, Tilehurst, Reading, RG30 4RU Tel: 0118-942 3999 Fax: 0118-942 6682

C & D Fork Truck Services, Drapers Yard, Warrenwood Industrial Estate, Stapleford, Hertford, SG14 3NU Tel: (01992) 503463 Fax: (01992) 501584 *Forklift trucks repair, service & sales*

▶ C & D Group Of Companies, Kingsnorth & Grain Power Stations, Hoo, Rochester, Kent, ME3 9NQ Tel: (01634) 255726 Fax: (01634) 255726 *Thermal insulation contractors*

▶ C & D Heating Services Ltd, 3 Balgray Road, Glengarnock, Beith, Ayrshire, KA14 3AG Tel: (01505) 683131

C D I Polytek Ltd, 130 Oldfield Road, Hampton, Middlesex, TW12 2HT Tel: (020) 8481 8300 Fax: (020) 8941 3107 E-mail: sales@cdipolytek.co.uk *Rubber mouldings manufrs*

▶ C D I Services, 8 Oak Road, Epping, Essex, CM16 5DJ Tel: (0845) 8382390 Fax: (0845) 8382391 E-mail: sales@cdiservices.co.uk *Cdi security & electrical engineers*

C & D Industrial Services Ltd, 9 Rolling Mill Road, Jarrow, Tyne & Wear, NE32 3DP Tel: 0191-428 7200 Fax: (0870) 9019199 E-mail: cdjarrow@canddgroup.co.uk *Provide insulation, painting & specialist coating & asbestos treatment*

▶ C & D Industrial Services Ltd, 63 Portland Street, Mansfield Woodhouse, Mansfield, Nottinghamshire, NG19 8BE Tel: (01623) 781200 Fax: (01623) 420496 *Industrial insulation, scaffolding & asbestos removal contractors*

C D K Machine Tool Services, Buckingway Business Park, 2 Rowles Way, Swavesey, Cambridge, CB4 5QX Tel: (01954) 230383 Fax: (01954) 230821 E-mail: info@barwell.com *Hydraulic press rebuilders & suppliers*

C D L Co. Ltd, 29 Grafton Road, Croydon, CR0 3RP Tel: (020) 8680 3077 Fax: (020) 8686 9225 E-mail: annaaustin@cdlco.fsnet.co.uk *Exhibition stand fitters*

C D L Construction Co Egham Ltd, Lynchford Lane, Farnborough, Hampshire, GU14 6JD Tel: (01252) 513388 Fax: (01252) 518791 *Civil engineering contractors*

▶ C D L Products, Kennoway House, 34 Kennoway Place, Broughty Ferry, Dundee, DD5 3HT Tel: (01382) 732580 E-mail: sales@cdl-products.com *Computer software*

C D M, Central Boulavard, Blythe Valley Park, Solihull, West Midlands, B90 8AG Tel: (0870) 0116682 Fax: (01264) 711396 E-mail: cdmcontrol@aol.com *Digital instrumentation/electronic control suppliers*

C D M Ductwork, 19 Prince William Road, Loughborough, Leicestershire, LE11 5GU Tel: (01509) 611118 Fax: (01509) 232345 E-mail: cdmductwork@aol.com *Ductwork & ducting manufrs*

C D Measurements Ltd, Chomlea, Hadfield Road, Hadfield, Glossop, Derbyshire, SK13 2ER Tel: (01457) 852929 Fax: (01457) 860619 *Specialists in engineering metrology*

C D N Windings Ltd, Units 9 & 10 Brockwell Court, Low Willington Industrial Estate, Crook, Co. Durham, DL15 0UT Tel: (01388) 745570 Fax: (01388) 745150 E-mail: cdn.windings@ukf.net *Transformer designers/distributors & manufrs*

C D O Electronics Ltd, 17 Bowater Road, Westminster Industrial Estate, London, SE18 5TF Tel: (020) 8855 9508 Fax: (020) 8316 1892 E-mail: jim@cdo-electronics.com *Printed circuit designers/manufrs/assemblers*

C & D Precision, Bluebird House, Povey Cross Road, Horley, Surrey, RH6 0AG Tel: (01293) 820092 Fax: (01293) 820093 E-mail: dedman@cdprecision.freeserve.co.uk *Press tools & fixture makers*

C D R Computing Ltd, 12-14 Thames Street, Sunbury-on-Thames, Middlesex, TW16 5QP Tel: (01252) 838400 Fax: (0845) 3452396 E-mail: support@crdcomputing.com *Computer consultants*

C D R Pumps UK Ltd, 28 Trojan Centre, Finedon Road Industrial Estate, Wellingborough, Northamptonshire, NN8 4ST Tel: (0870) 7561428 Fax: (01933) 226225 E-mail: sales@cdrpumps.com *CDR Pumps have been designing and manufacturing centrifugal pumps for the Chemical, Pharmaceutical, biodiesel and allied Industries for in excess of 40 years, and boast magnetic drive pumps, lined chemical process pumps, Stainless Steel magnetic drive and Stainless steel chemical process pumps to their current portfolio. CDR Pumps are manufactured at their central European headquarters based in Milan, Italy, and themselves are the countries largest and most prestigious manufacturer of such products. CDR Pumps (UK) Ltd serve the UK and Irish markets, based in Northants, England exclusively promoting the CDR product into these markets. Our customer base benefit from dealing with skilled Engineers to ensure the correct pump is selected for the specification, and to ensure an excellent after sales service and support, to ensure all CDR Pumps are operational 24/7 365 days a year as your chemical plant is expected to.*

C & D Recruitment, College Court, Regent Circus, Swindon, SN1 1PZ Tel: (01793) 488057 Fax: (01793) 488056 E-mail: enquiries@cdrecruitment.co.uk *Recruitment agency*

C D S & Co., 245 New Road, Croxley Green, Rickmansworth, Hertfordshire, WD3 3HE Tel: (01923) 441122 Fax: (01923) 440799 E-mail: david@cds-co.co.uk *Market innovation & development consultants*

C D S Cleaning Supplies, 177A Ash Road, Aldershot, Hampshire, GU12 4DB Tel: (01252) 342922 Fax: (01252) 342924 E-mail: sales@cleaningrepairs.co.uk *Cleaning supplies & machine repair specialists*

C D S Interiors, 26 Westover Road, Fleet, Hampshire, GU51 3DG Tel: (01252) 623047 *Furniture manufrs*

▶ C D S Security Ltd, 8-9 Dragonville Industrial Park, Dragon Lane, Durham, DH1 2XH Tel: 0191-384 0079 Fax: 0191-384 0071

▶ C D S Transport Ltd, Craigshaw Drive, West Tullos Industrial Estate, Aberdeen, AB12 3BE Tel: (01224) 872828

C.D.S Yorks Ltd, Ledgard Way, Reprographic House, Armley, Leeds, LS12 2ND Tel: 0113-263 0601 Fax: 0113-231 0305 E-mail: sales@cds-yorks.com *Drawing office material distributors*

C & D Sheet Metal Engineering Ltd, Station Road North, Belvedere, Kent, DA17 6JL Tel: (020) 8311 2056 Fax: (020) 8310 7727 E-mail: sales@cdsheetmetal.com *Sheet metal engineers*

C D Smith, Strine Acres, Crudgington Green, Crudgington, Telford, Shropshire, TF6 6JY Tel: (01952) 541419 Fax: (01952) 541128 *Joining services*

C D Stone Dunstable Ltd, Fairway Works, Southfields Road, Dunstable, Bedfordshire, LU6 3EP Tel: (01582) 605353 Fax: (01582) 660103 *Building services engineers*

C D T Signs, 9 Woodlands Road, Cirencester, Gloucestershire, GL7 1SP Tel: (01285) 640680 Fax: (01285) 652346 *Sign makers*

C.D Tarpaulins, Unit W Rudford Industrial Estate, Ford Road, Ford, Arundel, West Sussex, BN18 0BD Tel: (01903) 732305 Fax: (01903) 732305 *Tarpaulin manufrs*

▶ C D Topp, Lyndhurst, Carlton Husthwaite, Thirsk, North Yorkshire, YO7 2BJ Tel: (01845) 501415 Fax: (01845) 501072 E-mail: enquiries@christopp.co.uk *Heritage metalwork, wrought iron, bronze, copper*

▶ C & D Transport Ltd, 9 New Line Industrial Estate, The Sidings, Bacup, Lancashire, OL13 9RW Tel: (01706) 870333

▶ C D Welding & Inspection Services, Crofton Road, Stockton-on-Tees, Cleveland, TS18 2QZ Tel: (01642) 616987 Fax: (01642) 607799 *Welding fabrication manufrs*

C Davidson Agricultural Contractors, Lincote, Southwaite, Carlisle, CA4 0EP Tel: (01697) 473506 *Agricultural contractors*

C E A Towne Ship Riggers Ltd, 19 Wiltshire Road, Dairycoates Industrial Estate, Hull, HU3 6PA Tel: (01482) 572121 Fax: (01482) 504730 *Retailers, testers & repairers of lifting gear*

C E B Computer Services, 12 Elm Lane, Capel St. Mary, Ipswich, IP9 2HS Tel: (01473) 312072 E-mail: info@cebcom.fsnet.co.uk *Computer services*

C E Bunch, 87 Chapel Street, Dudley, West Midlands, DY2 9PN Tel: (01384) 459241 Fax: (01384) 255166 E-mail: sales@cebunch.co.uk *Building contractors & plumbers*

C E C Engineering Services Ltd, 2 Cantelupe Mews, Cantelupe Road, East Grinstead, West Sussex, RH19 3BG Tel: (01342) 315935 Fax: (01342) 311526

C E C P Ltd, 819a Chorley Old Road, Bolton, BL1 5SL Tel: (01204) 849484 Fax: (01204) 849192 *Structural & civil engineers*

C E D Ltd, 728 London Road, Grays, Essex, RM20 3LU Tel: (01708) 867237 Fax: (01708) 867230 E-mail: sales@ced.ltd.uk *Natural stone & aggregate suppliers*

C E D O Ltd, Halesfield 11, Telford, Shropshire, TF7 4LZ Tel: (01952) 272727 Fax: (01952) 274102 Principal Export Areas: Worldwide *Manufacturers of household disposable products*

C E Davidson Ltd, South View New Street, Fressingfield, Eye, Suffolk, IP21 5PJ Tel: (01379) 586606 Fax: (01379) 586511 *Poultry house manufrs*

C E Davis Marshfield Ltd, 94 High Street, Marshfield, Chippenham, Wiltshire, SN14 8LS Tel: (01225) 891444 Fax: (01225) 891910 *Agricultural engineers*

▶ C E E, Millars Three, Southmill Road, Bishop's Stortford, Hertfordshire, CM23 3DH Tel: (01279) 508204 Fax: (01279) 508206

C E E Norm UK Ltd, Unit A1, Stafford Park 11, Telford, Shropshire, TF3 3AY Tel: (01952) 212700 Fax: (01952) 212711 E-mail: sales@ceenorm.co.uk *Industrial plug & socket manufrs*

C E Edwards Engineers Ltd, Eagle Works, Leek New Road, Stoke-on-Trent, ST6 2LD Tel: (01782) 202400 Fax: (01782) 262781 E-mail: sales@ceedwards.co.uk *Sub contracting precision engineers*

C E F Precision Ltd, Beachs Drive, Chelmsford, CM1 2NU Tel: (01245) 353019 Fax: (01245) 491675 E-mail: sales@cef-precision.co.uk *Precision engineers*

C E Fagg Engineering, 539 Ipswich Road, Slough, SL1 4EP Tel: (01753) 538432 *Precision engineers*

▶ C E I Electrical Ltd, Unit 19 Mitchell Point, Ensign Way, Hamble, Southampton, SO31 4RF Tel: (023) 8045 4822 Fax: (023) 8045 6832 E-mail: email@dmelectrical.co.uk

C & E Joinery, 10 Rear Carr Street, Hindley, Wigan, Lancashire, WN2 3LG Tel: (01942) 254285 *Joinery manufrs*

C E Marshall Wolverhampton Ltd, Church Street, Willenhall, West Midlands, WV13 1QW Tel: (01902) 364500 Fax: (01902) 634908 *Automotive component manufrs*

▶ C E Moore Ltd, 37 Disraeli Road, London, NW10 7AX Tel: (020) 8961 2225 Fax: (020) 8963 0122 *Supply & fit of soft tops for convertible cars*

C E P Ceilings Ltd, Welshmill Lane, Frome, Somerset, BA11 2LL Tel: (01373) 463185 Fax: (01373) 461437 *Ceiling tile manufrs*

C E P Ceilings Ltd, Common Road Industrial Estate, Verulam Road, Stafford, ST16 3EA Tel: (01785) 223435 Fax: (01785) 251309 E-mail: cep@cepgroup.co.uk *Ceiling tile manufrs* Also at: Uxbridge

C E P Cladding Ltd, Wainwright Close, St. Leonards-On-Sea, East Sussex, TN38 9PP Tel: (01424) 852641 Fax: (01424) 852797 E-mail: claddings@cepgroup.co.uk *Cladding distributors & manufrs*

C E Recruitment, First Floor, 65 Seamoor Road, Bournemouth, BH4 9AE Tel: (01202) 752275 Fax: (01202) 768203 E-mail: info@cer.uk.com *Construction & engineering recruitment*

C E S Holdings Ltd, Unit 11 Shepley Industrial Estate South, Audenshaw, Manchester, M34 5EX Tel: 0161-337 9337 Fax: 0161-337 9099 E-mail: sales@cesholdings.co.uk *Educational equipment & suppliers*

C E S Telecom Ltd, 15-17 Newgate Street Village, Hertford, SG13 8RA Tel: (01707) 874775 Fax: (01707) 873165 E-mail: emily.dean@cestelecom.com *Telecommunications manufrs*

▶ C E S TF Software, Suite 12, Venture House, Fifth Avenue, Letchworth Garden City, Hertfordshire, SG6 2HW Tel: (01462) 484333 Fax: (01462) 484422 *Computer software services*

C E S UK Ltd, Knutsford Way, Sealand Industrial Estate, Chester, CH1 4NS Tel: (01244) 372555 Fax: (01244) 371248 E-mail: sales@cesuk.com *Wholesale distribution of exhausts*

C & E Scaffolding, M Waterside, 25-27 Willis Way, Poole, Dorset, BH15 3TD Tel: (01202) 661714 Fax: (01202) 661760 E-mail: lynn@cescaffolding.sagehost.co.uk *Erection & dismantling of scaffolding materials*

▶ C E T Group, Tavistock Road, West Drayton, Middlesex, UB7 7QT Tel: (01895) 439439 Fax: (01895) 439438

C E-Air UK Ltd, Newton Moor Industrial Estate, Newton, Hyde, Cheshire, SK14 4LG Tel: 0161-368 1476 Fax: 0161-367 8145 E-mail: sales@ceair.co.uk *Industrial fan & air cleaning equipment/systems distributors or agents*

C F Airflow, Tameside Works, Dukinfield, Cheshire, SK16 5PT Tel: 0161-339 0707 Fax: 0161-339 0808 *Ventilation equipment suppliers*

C F Anderson & Son Ltd, 228 Old London Road, Marks Tey, Colchester, CO6 1HD Tel: (020) 7226 1212 Fax: (020) 7359 1112 E-mail: cfanderson@cfanderson.co.uk *Timber importers & distributors*

C F Booth Engineering Ltd, Northfield Road, Rotherham, South Yorkshire, S60 1RR Tel: (01709) 829523 Fax: (01709) 829710 E-mail: p.a.hardey@btconnect.com *Engineers*

C F Booth Engineering Ltd, Clarence Metal Works, Armer Street, Rotherham, South Yorkshire, S60 1AF Tel: (01709) 559198 Fax: (01709) 561859 E-mail: enquiries@cfboothltd.com *Scrap metal processors*

C F C Group Ltd, Kilnbrook House, Rosekiln Lane, Reading, RG2 0BY Tel: (0845) 0540040 Fax: (0845) 0540041 E-mail: cfc@cfcgroup.co.uk *Suspended ceiling systems/partition contractors*

C F C Sollutions, 1310 Solihull Parkway, Birmingham Business Park, Birmingham, B37 7YB Tel: 0121-717 7040 Fax: 0121-717 7011 E-mail: enquiries@cfcsolutions.co.uk *Fleet workshop & contract hire software*

C F Cases Ltd, 13 Consul Road, Rugby, Warwickshire, CV21 1PB Tel: (01788) 535484 Fax: (01788) 570933 E-mail: sales@cfcases.co.uk *Flight packing case manufrs*

C F Ceilings, Howgill Garage, Low Road, Whitehaven, Cumbria, CA28 9HS Tel: (01946) 691188 Fax: (01946) 591770 *Ceilings & partitions manufrs*

C F Dodson Ltd, Birch Close, Charlton Marshall, Blandford Forum, Dorset, DT11 9AJ Tel: (01258) 488955 *Agricultural engineers*

C F E Fasteners Ltd, Unit 18, Central Trading Estate, Cable Street, Wolverhampton, WV2 2HX Tel: (01902) 871777 Fax: (01902) 351410 E-mail: sales@cfe.co.uk *Precision parts & special fasteners*

C F E Hydraulics Ltd, Unit 3, Milton Industrial Estate, Milton, Cambridge, CB24 6AZ Tel: (01223) 420466 Fax: (01223) 423233 E-mail: cfehydraulics@tiscali.co.uk *Hydraulic hose distributors*

C & F Electrics, Brookside Offices, Rassau Road, Rassau, Ebbw Vale, Gwent, NP23 5BL Tel: (01495) 350333 Fax: (01495) 305333 *Electrical contractors*

C F Environmental Services Ltd, Unit 3, Bentley Park, Blacknest, Alton, Hampshire, GU34 4PX Tel: (01420) 22622 Fax: (01420) 22612 E-mail: sales@cfes.co.uk *Air conditioning equipment service & installation*

C & F Fabrications Ltd, Cross Street, Darwen, Lancashire, BB3 2PN Tel: (01254) 772418 Fax: (01254) 760830 *Sheet metalwork*

C F Gill & Son Ltd, The Yard, Bedford Street, Peterborough, PE1 4DN Tel: (01733) 566403 *Scrap metal merchants*

C F I, Unit 9B, Thorpe Close, Banbury, Oxfordshire, OX16 4SW Tel: (01295) 257014 Fax: (01295) 272405 E-mail: sales@cfiswin.co.uk *Office ceiling & partitioning components suppliers & powder coaters*

C F James Ltd, 68 Stoke Newington High Street, London, N16 7PA Tel: (020) 7254 5224 Fax: (020) 7254 3431 E-mail: cfjames@btconnect.com *Architectural & general ironmongers*

C F M Blindmaker Supplies Ltd, 18 20 James Road, Tyseley, Birmingham, B11 2BA Tel: (0870) 7702965 Fax: (0871) 4332309 E-mail: sales@cfmblinds.co.uk *Fabric & component suppliers & blinds manufrs*

C F & M Tatlow, 47 Sutherland Road, Derby, DE23 8RX Tel: (01332) 761405 Fax: (01332) 761405 *General purpose joiners*

C & F Office Supplies Ltd, Units 16 Lye Business Centre, Enterprise Drive, Stourbridge, West Midlands, DY9 8QH Tel: (01384) 898370 Fax: (01384) 898370 *Stationery suppliers, distributors & wholesalers*

C F P Software, Propser House, Cardrew Industrial Estate, Redruth, Cornwall, TR15 1SS Tel: (01209) 314371 Fax: (01209) 314368 E-mail: general@cfp-software.co.uk *Software for estate agents*

C F P Supplies, Unit 6-7 Building, 53b Third Avenue, Pensnett Trading Estate, Kingswinford, West Midlands, DY6 7XG Tel: (01384) 400220 Fax: (01384) 400160 *Supply builders merchants*

C F Parkinson Ltd, Marsh Lane, Riverside Industrial Estate, Boston, Lincolnshire, PE21 7FP Tel: (01205) 313900 Fax: (01205) 310124 E-mail: nicholson-r@parkinsontech.co.uk *Auto electrical & harness specialists*

C F R Giesler Ltd, Empson Street, London, E3 3LT Tel: (020) 7987 2161 Fax: (020) 7515 0483 E-mail: sales@giesler.co.uk Purchasing Contact: M. Levey Sales Contact: P.R. Fenton Principal Export Areas: Worldwide *Vibration test equipment & balancing (dynamic) machine manufacturers. Also balancing (dynamic) services & noise control (industrial) consultants or designers*

▶ C F S Aeroproducts, Alvis Works, Bubbenhall Road, Baginton, Coventry, CV8 3BB Tel: (024) 7630 5873 Fax: (024) 7630 2088 E-mail: mslater@cfsaeroproducts.co.uk *Aircraft component maintenance agents*

C F Smith Precision Grinding, The Station, Station Hill, Overton, Basingstoke, Hampshire, RG25 3JH Tel: (01256) 770457 Fax: (01256) 771701 E-mail: cfsmith@btconnect.com *Precision grinding & honing services*

▶ C F Systems Ltd, 17 Trewirgie Hill, Redruth, Cornwall, TR15 2TB Tel: (01209) 210195 Fax: (01209) 313841 E-mail: info@cfsystems.biz *Network specialists*

▶ C F Systems UK Ltd, 7 Metro Centre, Ronsons Way, Sandridge, St. Albans, Hertfordshire, AL4 9QT Tel: (01727) 841048 Fax: (01727) 840944 E-mail: sales@cfsystems.co.uk *Sales & leases, new & refurbished canon copiers & fax machines*

C F Telecom, 36 Regent Street, Great Yarmouth, Norfolk, NR30 1RR Tel: (0845) 4582363 Fax: (0845) 4582364 E-mail: sales@cftele.com *Business phone system suppliers*

C F Whaler Ltd, Bridge Works, Horncastle Road, Wragby, Market Rasen, Lincolnshire, LN8 5RB Tel: (01673) 857575 Fax: (01673) 857788 E-mail: mail@cfwhaler.co.uk *Environmental control systems engineers for livestock*

▶ C Fare Products, 7e Glengallan Road, Oban, Argyll, PA34 4HG Tel: (01631) 565569 Fax: (01631) 566558

C Fewster & Son Ltd, 2 Church Lane, Patrington, Hull, HU12 0RJ Tel: (01964) 630228 Fax: (01964) 631309 E-mail: enquiries@cfewster.co.uk *Building contractors & joinery manufrs*

C Fish, 11 Main Road, Portavogie, Newtownards, County Down, BT22 1EL Tel: (028) 4277 1560 Fax: (028) 4277 2345 *Fish processing*

C & G, 284 North Road, Yate, Bristol, BS37 7LQ Tel: (01454) 228387 Fax: (01454) 228145 E-mail: cgtoolcutter@aol.com *Precision toolmakers*

C & G Alarms, 1 Spencer Street, Barnsley, South Yorkshire, S70 1QX Tel: (01226) 203139 Fax: (01226) 203139 *Electrical contractors*

C G B Humbertherm Ltd, Middleplatt Road, Immingham, South Humberside, DN40 1AH Tel: (01469) 572726 Fax: (01469) 571728 E-mail: sales@cgbhumbertherm.com *Thermal insulation contractors*

▶ C & G Brewster, Lanark House, Kirriemuir, Angus, DD8 5QF Tel: (01307) 466166 Fax: (01307) 468800

C G C Agricultural & Motor Engineers, Five Down, Puddock Road, Warboys, Huntingdon, Cambridgeshire, PE28 2UB Tel: (01487) 823248 Fax: (01487) 823248 E-mail: sales@cgcagricultural.co.uk *Agricultural & motor engineers*

▶ C G C Technology Ltd, E Grovebell Industrial Estate, Wrecclesham Road, Wrecclesham, Farnham, Surrey, GU10 4PL Tel: (01252) 724274 Fax: (01252) 722624 E-mail: enquiries@cgctech.com *Mechanical design & materials consultancy*

C & G Concrete Ltd, Mansgate Hill, Caistor, Market Rasen, Lincolnshire, LN7 6NT Tel: (01472) 851281 Fax: (01472) 851117 *Quarried products suppliers*

C & G Concrete Ltd, Uffington Road, Stamford, Lincolnshire, PE9 2HA Tel: (01780) 482000 Fax: (01780) 480066 E-mail: fhgilman@ibm.net *Ready mixed concrete*

C & G Cutters & Grinding Ltd, Clarendon Road, Blackburn, BB1 9SS Tel: (01254) 663193 Fax: (01254) 665139 E-mail: sales@cg-grind-eng-serv.co.uk *Machining & grinding services CNC*

C G Duffy & Sons, 6 Ratcliffe Road, Fakenham, Norfolk, NR21 8AY Tel: (01328) 862990 Fax: (01328) 853438 *Abattoirs*

C G F Automation Ltd, York House, Fernie Road, Market Harborough, Leics, LE16 7PH Tel: (01858) 414616 Fax: (01858) 410196 E-mail: cgfnormondsales@veeder.co.uk *Dip sticks, gauges & liquid levels*

▶ C & G Hydraulic Services, 4 Newark Storage Industrial Estate, Bowbridge Road, Newark, Nottinghamshire, NG24 4EQ Tel: (01636) 613113 Fax: (01636) 613113 E-mail: cghydraulic@btconnect.com *Engineering services*

C G I International Ltd, International House, Millfield Lane, Haydock, St. Helens, Merseyside, WA11 9GA Tel: (01942) 710720 Fax: (01942) 710730 E-mail: info@cgii.co.uk *Specialist glass manufrs*

C & G Industrial Chemicals Ltd, Sovereign Works, Deep Dale Lane, Lower Gornal, Dudley, West Midlands, DY3 2AF Tel: (01384) 455225 E-mail: angiegroves@tiscali.co.uk *Chemical suppliers & consultants to industry*

▶ C G J Building Services Ltd, 51 Station Road, Knowle, Solihull, West Midlands, B93 0HN Tel: (01564) 732000 Fax: (01564) 732001

▶ C & G Joinery Services Ltd, Unit 13 W & G Industrial Estate, Faringdon Road, East Challow, Wantage, Oxfordshire, OX12 9TF Tel: (01235) 763233 Fax: (01235) 760259 E-mail: info@cgjoinery.co.uk *Designers & manufacturers of all types of internal & external joinery*

C G L Systems, 2 Young Place, East Kilbride, Glasgow, G75 0TD Tel: (01355) 235561 Fax: (01355) 247189 E-mail: sales@cglsystems.co.uk *Rainwater goods & rainscreen cladding manufrs*

C G M Partners Ltd, Carradine House, 237 Regents Park Road, London, N3 3LF Tel: (020) 8349 2011 Fax: (020) 8349 2014 E-mail: cgmpartners@c.co.uk *Electrical power engineers*

▶ C G Metal Spinners, Unit 34 Fairways Business Park, Lammas Road, London, E10 7QB Tel: (020) 8558 6233 Fax: (020) 8558 4568 E-mail: spincraft1@yahoo.co.uk *Metal spinners*

C G P Associates Ltd, 2 Maple Road, Enigma Business Park, Malvern, Worcestershire, WR14 1GQ Tel: (01684) 584700 Fax: (0870) 0522410 E-mail: derekc@cgp.co.uk *Independent software & systems*

C G P Engineering Ltd, Cross Street, Oadby, Leicester, LE2 4DD Tel: 0116-271 7715 Fax: 0116-272 0701 E-mail: info@cgp-engineering.com Principal Export Areas: Worldwide *Toolmakers to the plastics industry*

C G Plastic Fabrications, Unit 41 New Enterprise Workshops, Mount Street, Nechells, Birmingham, B7 5RD Tel: 0121-327 3895 Fax: 0121-327 3895 *Microchip industry to large fume extract for sewerage treatment plants*

C & G Platforms Ltd, PO Box 14, Mirfield, West Yorkshire, WF14 8XH Tel: (01924) 498660 Fax: (01924) 491778 E-mail: sales@candgplatforms.co.uk *Sales of new & used mobile platforms*

C.G.R. Polythene Company Ltd, Unit 72 Powder Mill Lane, Questor Trade Park, Dartford, DA1 1JA Tel: (01322) 292681 Fax: (0845) 6800084 E-mail: gary@cgrpolythene.co.uk *Packaging material, goods & products merchants or agents*

C G Rees Stainless Ltd, 325 North Road, Cardiff, CF14 3BP Tel: (029) 2061 5911 Fax: (029) 2061 8612 E-mail: cgrees@netcomuk.co.uk *Metal merchants services*

C G Removal, 184-186 Oakleigh Road North, London, N20 0UA Tel: (020) 8361 7273 Fax: (020) 8368 9590

C G Resources Ltd, 62 Wellington Street West, Broughton, Manchester, M7 2FD Tel: 0161-792 8234 Fax: 0161-792 7080 E-mail: enq@cgresources.com *IT training*

C G S Brighton Ltd, Unit B4 Modern Moulds Business Centre, Commerce Way, Lancing, West Sussex, BN15 8TA Tel: (01903) 533349 Fax: (01903) 750996 E-mail: admin@cgs-brighton.com *Mould bases importers & suppliers*

C G S Photographers, 102 Ewell By-Pass, Epsom, Surrey, KT17 2PP Tel: (020) 8394 0010 Fax: (020) 8393 0372 E-mail: info@cgs-photographers.co.uk *Commercial, industrial photographer & colour printing*

C G T Ltd, 314 Midsummer Boulevard, Milton Keynes, MK9 2UB Tel: (01908) 690361 Fax: (01908) 669922 E-mail: sales@cgt.co.uk *Computer consultants*

C G & W Young Ltd, 15a Colne Road, Twickenham, TW2 6QQ Tel: (020) 8894 5168 Fax: (020) 8898 1316 E-mail: ryoung@youngswelding.co.uk *Electric welding equipment manufrs*

C Gearing & Son, 28-30 Seabeach Lane, Eastbourne, East Sussex, BN22 7NZ Tel: (01323) 726029 Fax: (01323) 726029 *Scrap metal merchants & recyclers*

C Goodman & Son Ltd, Pensbury Place, London, SW8 4TR Tel: (020) 7622 6444 Fax: (020) 7498 3842 E-mail: goodmangarage@aol.com *MOT testing & vehicle repairers*

C Griffiths & Son, The Foundry, Brimfield, Ludlow, Shropshire, SY8 4NG Tel: (01584) 711264 Fax: (01584) 711805 E-mail: sales@autogasdevelopmentsltd.co.uk *Agricultural engineers & garage with mot centre*

C & H Alarm Systems, 12 Park Hill Gardens, Swallownest, Sheffield, S26 4WL Tel: 0114-293 9000 Fax: 0114-293 9000 *Burglar alarms*

C H B Engineering, Mantra House, South Street, Keighley, West Yorkshire, BD21 1SX Tel: (01535) 607741 Fax: (01535) 690539 *Classic car parts suppliers*

▶ C H B & W Ltd, Brickfield Cottages, 54 Kings Highway, London, SE18 2BG Tel: (020) 8855 8303 Fax: (020) 8855 5480

C H Barnett Ltd, 18 Tyseley Industrial Estate, Seeleys Road, Birmingham, B11 2LQ Tel: 0121-773 5222 Fax: 0121-773 7800 E-mail: sales@chbarnett.co.uk *Machine guards manufacturer & sheet metalwork*

C H Bennett & Son, Plasheulwen, Llanfair Road, Newtown, Powys, SY16 3JY Tel: (01686) 626872 Fax: (01686) 621479 E-mail: chbennett@virgin.net *Haulage contractors*

▶ C H C Solutions, Thorley Health Centre, Villiers-Sur-Marne, Bishop's Stortford, Hertfordshire, CM23 4EG Tel: (01279) 210088 Fax: (0870) 1417242 E-mail: contactus@chcsolutions.co.uk *CHC Solutions is an IT and network support business based in Bishops Stortford. Friendly and professional consultants provide computer support and computer repair services at competitive rates. We provide for and support both home and business users with multimedia PCs, workstations and servers. **CHC Solutions offer the complete IT solution, from your bespoke software package to web site and email hosting.*

C H C Waste Facilities Management, Blackwell, Bromsgrove, Worcestershire, B60 1BE Tel: 0121-445 3344 Fax: 0121-445 3245 E-mail: infodesk@chcwastemgt.co.uk *Recycling services*

C H E Coach House Engineering Ltd, 23 Squares Road, Chilton Trinity, Bridgwater, Somerset, TA5 2BW Tel: (01278) 456557 Fax: (01278) 456557 *Steel fabricators*

C H E Coach House Engineering Ltd, 23 Squares Road, Chilton Trinity, Bridgwater, Somerset, TA5 2BW Tel: (01278) 456557 Fax: (01278) 456557 *Steel fabricators*

C H E Engineering, Unit 59, Bergen Way, North Lynn Industrial Estate, King's Lynn, Norfolk, PE30 2JL Tel: (01553) 691999 Fax: (01553) 691999 *Precision engineering & toolmakers*

▶ C H F Supplies, Crane Hall, Wyreside, Out Rawcliffe, Preston, PR3 6TP Tel: (01995) 670888 Fax: (01995) 670305 E-mail: alex@chfsupplies.co.uk Sales Contact: I. Mackie *CHF SUPPLIES are tank specialists based in the North West. We supply, manufacture and install all types of storage tanks including fuel tanks, bunded steel tanks, oil storage tanks, Harlequin plastic tanks, water tanks, septic tanks, sewage treatment plants and reconditioned tanks. We have an established reputation and several decades of experience within the tank industry. All bunded steel tanks, oil storage tanks and bunded tanks are designed and manufactured to exceed the toughest regulations, technical and environmental requirements. We supply and install the complete range of Harlequin plastic tanks. CHF Supplies are OFTEC registered and undertake tank inspections, site surveys and risk assessments according to fuel storage regulations.*

C H Fowler & Co., 32 Bellgrove Road, Welling, Kent, DA16 3PY Tel: (020) 8304 4805 Fax: (020) 8304 7068 E-mail: c.h.fowler@btconnect.com *Hand tool distributors of king dick,britool,gedore,ceka,knipex,draper tools, norbar torque wrenches,starrett,record,footprint,faithfull tools, clarkson,presto,dormer cuting tools, stubs silver steel,ground flat stock*

C & H Hauliers, Broker House, Tilbury, Essex, RM18 7EH Tel: (01375) 842683 Fax: (01375) 847095 E-mail: cnh.hauliers@btinternet.com *Road transport, haulage & freight services*

▶ C & H Howe Ltd, Progress Drive, Cannock, Staffordshire, WS11 0JE Tel: (01543) 577575 Fax: (01543) 504289

C H I C Fireplaces, 116 Red Lane, Coventry, CV6 5EQ Tel: (024) 7663 8063 E-mail: chicmarbleandgranite@hotmail.co.uk *Stonemasons*

C H Jones & Son, 1 The Square, North Tawton, Devon, EX20 2EW Tel: (01837) 82237 Fax: (01837) 82526 E-mail: chjengineers@aol.com *General engineers steel stockists & fabricators blacksmiths*

C H K Engineering Ltd, Pyms Lane, Crewe, CW1 3PJ Tel: (01270) 255520 Fax: (01270) 211263 E-mail: sales@chk-engineering.co.uk *Steel fabricators & laser cutting services*

C H Lindsey & Son Ltd, Brunel Way, Severalls Industrial Park, Colchester, CO4 9QW Tel: (01206) 844567 Fax: (01206) 844483 E-mail: info@lindsey-aircon.com *Air conditioning & heating engineers*

C H Media, 20 Marigold Walk, Bristol, BS3 2PD Tel: 0117-939 4061 Fax: (08701) 328330 E-mail: enquiries@chmedia.co.uk *Website design for small to medium sized businesses & IT support & consultancy*

C H Medical Ltd, 8 Oaktree Place, Matford Business Park, Marsh Barton, Exeter, EX2 8WA Tel: (01392) 824668 Fax: (01392) 823747 E-mail: sales@chmedical.com *Medical devices*

C H Middleton Ltd, 65-71 Sprotbrough Road, Doncaster, South Yorkshire, DN5 8BW Tel: (01302) 783731 Fax: (01302) 390024 E-mail: c.h.middleton@btconnect.com *Skip Hire Waste Disposal & Recycling Services*

C H Morgan & Co. Ltd, 1 Clifton Business Park, Chamberlain Road, Aylesbury, Buckinghamshire, HP19 8DY Tel: (01296) 434878 Fax: (01296) 338520 *Bolts & nuts distributors*

C & H Plastics Ltd, Burrel Road, St. Ives, Cambridgeshire, PE27 3LE Tel: (01480) 496959 Fax: (01480) 492105 E-mail: sales@chplastics.co.uk *Plastic injection mould manufrs*

▶ C H Power Tools, Bentley Road, Doncaster, South Yorkshire, DN5 9QP Tel: (01302) 821821

C & H Precision Finishers Ltd, Derby Road Trade Centre, Derby Road, Sandiacre, Nottingham, NG10 5HU Tel: 0115-939 4707 Fax: 0115-949 0146 E-mail: admin@chprecision.co.uk *Metal finishing services for aerospace industry*

C & H Quickmix Ltd, Woodlands, Dereham Road, New Costessey, Norwich, NR5 0TL Tel: (01603) 740333 Fax: (01603) 741336 E-mail: enquiries@tarmac-southern.co.uk *Ready mixed concrete suppliers*

C H Rewinds Ltd, Smithfold Lane, Worsley, Manchester, M28 0GP Tel: 0161-702 8737 Fax: 0161-702 8730 E-mail: sales@chrewinds.com *Electric motor repairs & stockists*

C H Reynolds & Sons Ltd, 1358 Stratford Road, Hall Green, Birmingham, B28 9EH Tel: 0121-777 3675 Fax: 0121-777 4883 E-mail: reysigns@aol.com *Sign manufrs*

C H S M, Victoria Mill, Manchester Road, Droylsden, Manchester, M43 6EQ Tel: 0161-370 3600 Fax: 0161-370 8454 *Sheet metal workers*

C H S Switchgear Ltd, 3 Batford Mill Industrial Estate, Lower Luton Road, Harpenden, Hertfordshire, AL5 5BZ Tel: (01582) 766008 Fax: (01582) 461386 E-mail: mailbox@chsswitchgear.co.uk *Electrical control equipment & switchgear manufrs*

C H Sandall & Son Precision Engineers, Whiteleather Square, Billingborough, Sleaford, Lincolnshire, NG34 0QP Tel: (01529) 240277 Fax: (01529) 241543 *Precision engineers*

C & H Storage & Handling Systems Ltd, PO Box 42, Uttoxeter, Staffordshire, ST14 7ED Tel: (01889) 567662 Fax: (01889) 562493 E-mail: jhunt@chstorage.co.uk *Storage & handling systems*

C H Sundries, Willows, Langford Lane, Pen Elm, Taunton, Somerset, TA2 6NZ Tel: (01823) 253441 Fax: (01823) 321410 *Butchers equipment suppliers*

C & H Textile Menders, Market Street, Milnsbridge, Huddersfield, HD3 4HT Tel: (01484) 640850 Fax: (01484) 640850 *Textile merchants*

C H Thompson Ltd, Hargreaves Street, Oldham, OL9 9ND Tel: 0161-620 0211 Fax: 0161-627 4480 E-mail: chthompson@boiler-repairs.co.uk *Boiler repair specialists*

C H W (Metal Components) Ltd, Unit 1A, Abercromby Industrial Estate, Abercromby Avenue, High Wycombe, Buckinghamshire, HP12 3AX Tel: (01494) 530883 Fax: (01494) 463581 *CNC & sheet metal work engineers*

C & H Weston Ltd, 12 East Street, Brighton, BN1 1HP Tel: (01273) 326338 Fax: (01273) 720107 E-mail: info@chweston.co.uk *Gun retailers*

C H Whitehouse Ltd, Buckhurst Works, Bells Yew Green, Tunbridge Wells, Kent, TN3 9BN Tel: (01892) 750247 Fax: (01892) 750247 *Cedarwood greenhouse manufrs*

C H Wood Security Bradford Ltd, 221 Wakefield Road, Bradford, West Yorkshire, BD4 7PE Tel: (01274) 725072 Fax: (01274) 731626 E-mail: info@woodsecurity.co.uk *Locksmith safe distributors* Also at: Sheffield

C H Young Tools (Cov) Ltd, Oban Road, Coventry, CV6 6HH Tel: (024) 7636 1209 Fax: (024) 7664 4270 E-mail: info@chyoung.ndo.co.uk *Precision engineers*

C Hanson & Son, Aynhams Hill, Bracewell, Skipton, North Yorkshire, BD23 3JS Tel: (01200) 445905 *Hay & straw suppliers*

C Hargreaves, Stockfield Mill, Melbourne Street, Chadderton, Oldham, OL9 9ES Tel: 0161-633 5330 Fax: 0161-633 5330 *Welding & fabricators*

C Hemstock, The Old Malt Kiln, Main Street, Carlton-on-Trent, Newark, Nottinghamshire, NG23 6NW Tel: (01636) 822326 Fax: (01636) 821556 *Ceramics restoration*

C Herring & Son Ltd, Windermere Road, Hartlepool, Cleveland, TS25 1NX Tel: (01429) 221104 Fax: (01429) 861989 E-mail: gareth@cherring.co.uk *Scrap metal merchants & skip hire*

C Hoare & Co., 37 Fleet Street, London, EC4P 4DQ Tel: (020) 7353 4522 Fax: (020) 7353 4521 E-mail: e-mail@hoaresbank.co.uk *Bankers*

C Holland & Sons Ltd, 71 Whitecroft Road, Meldreth, Royston, Hertfordshire, SG8 6LS Tel: (01763) 261873 Fax: (01763) 262764 E-mail: robert@holland&son.u-net.com *Bakery & catering wholesalers*

▶ C Howe, 100 High Street, Deal, Kent, CT14 6EE Tel: (01304) 368897 E-mail: cjuk@xln.co.uk *Retail jeweller, swiss watch agent, clock & watch repairs*

C I A Ltd, Froghall Road, Aberdeen, AB24 3JL Tel: (01224) 626364 Fax: (01224) 624005 E-mail: sales@c-i-a.co.uk *Ship chandlers lifting gear services* Also at: Peterhead

C I A 2000 Ltd, 72 High Street, Lees, Oldham, OL4 5AA Tel: 0161-624 8500 Fax: 0161-633 0479 E-mail: info@cialtd.com *Electronic security specialists*

C I Automation Ltd, Shaftesbury Centre, Percy Street, Swindon, SN2 2AZ Tel: (01793) 530063 Fax: (01793) 530064 *Fuel monitoring system manufrs*

C I B C World Markets P.L.C., Cotton Centre, Cotton Lane, London, SE1 2QL Tel: (020) 7234 7100 Fax: (020) 7407 4127 E-mail: firstname.surname@cibc.co.uk *Stock & share brokers*

C I C Co Ltd, 95-97 Palmerston Road, Bournemouth, BH1 4HP Tel: (01202) 301033 Fax: (01202) 300006 *Work wear distributors & manufrs*

C I E Group, Blenheim Industrial Estate, Widdowson Close, Bulwell, Nottingham, NG6 8WB Tel: 0115-977 0075 Fax: 0115-977 0081 E-mail: marketing@cie-ltd.co.uk *Amplifiers (audio) & electric measuring instrumentation agents*

▶ C I E International Ltd, Isle of Grain, Rochester, Kent, ME3 0EP Tel: (01634) 271601 Fax: (01634) 270723

C I Holdings Ltd, 2 Priory Road, Strood, Rochester, Kent, ME2 2EG Tel: (01634) 717747 Fax: (01634) 731115 *Automatic clutch transmission rebuilders & manufrs*

C I Logistics, 43 Wenlock Way, Troon Industrial Area, Leicester, LE4 9HU Tel: 0116-276 1691 Fax: 0116-276 9836 E-mail: sales@conveyors.co.uk *Conveyor systems round/spiral & belt manufrs*

C I M Systems Ltd, 1st Floor, Ross House, Kempson Way, Suffolk Business Park, Bury St. Edmunds, Suffolk, IP32 7AR Tel: (01284) 727200 Fax: (01284) 706602 E-mail: info@cimsystems.co.uk *Computer integration*

▶ C I Products, Lexden Lodge, 7 Crowborough Hill, Crowborough, East Sussex, TN6 2EG Tel: (01892) 654477 Fax: (01892) 653399

C I S Communications Ltd, 85 Victoria Road, Netherfield, Nottingham, NG4 2NN Tel: 0115-961 3220 Fax: 0115-911 9449 E-mail: paul.tys@ntlworld.com *Telecommunication services*

▶ C I S Industrial Storage Ltd, Owler Lane, Birstall, Batley, West Yorkshire, WF17 9BW Tel: (01924) 443290

▶ C I S Office Furniture Ltd, Furniture House, Potters Lane, Wednesbury, West Midlands, WS10 7LP Tel: 0121-556 8741 Fax: 0121-556 9588 E-mail: sales@cisoffice.co.uk *Office furniture, seating repair & reupholsters service*

▶ C & I Solutions Ltd, Unit 4 Fortuna, Watermill Lane, Pett, Hastings, East Sussex, TN35 4HY Tel: (01424) 814757 Fax: (01424) 814754 E-mail: info@candisolutions.co.uk *Manufactures of recording & reporting systems, process & environment*

C I Systems Ltd, Brunel Road, Churchfields, Salisbury, SP2 7PX Tel: (01722) 336938 Fax: (01722) 323222 E-mail: sales@cielec.com *Precision weighing instruments & systems*

C J A Group Ltd, 2 London Wall Buildings, London, EC2M 5UX Tel: (020) 7588 3588 Fax: (020) 7256 8501 E-mail: cja@cjagroup.com *Recruitment & advertising*

C J Armstrong Manufacturing Co. Ltd, Unit 7-8 River Brent Business Park, Trumpers Way, London, W7 2QA Tel: (020) 8574 4602 Fax: (020) 8574 1078 E-mail: cjarmstrong@lycos.co.uk *Electronic engineers, sheet metal manufrs*

C J & B Parr & Sons, Mill Farm, Pilham Lane, Corringham, Gainsborough, Lincolnshire, DN21 5RB Tel: (01427) 838253 Fax: (01427) 838253 *Agricultural contractors*

C & J Blackburn, West End Mills, Watergate Road, Dewsbury, West Yorkshire, WF12 9QB Tel: (01924) 465958 Fax: (01924) 454155 E-mail: carol@cjblackburn.co.uk *Waste paper merchants/processors/recyclers*

▶ C J Burgess & Son Ltd, The Old Mutton House, Bodiam, Robertsbridge, East Sussex, TN32 5UP Tel: (01580) 830888 Fax: (01580) 830284

▶ C J Carpentry & Design, Unit 12 Hybris Business Park, Warmwell Road, Crossways, Dorchester, Dorset, DT2 8BF Tel: (01305) 854555 Fax: (01305) 854555 *Manufacturers of furniture*

C & J Castings, 42 Bayton Road, Exhall, Coventry, CV7 9EJ Tel: (024) 7636 3031 Fax: (024) 7636 3556 E-mail: clive@42baytonroad.freeserve.co.uk *Suppliers of aluminum heavy zinc castings*

C J Coleman Holdings Ltd, Portsoken House, 155 Minories, London, EC3N 1BT Tel: (020) 7488 2211 Fax: (020) 7488 4436 E-mail: sales@cj-coleman.co.uk *Insurance brokers*

C & J Commercials, Falcon Garage, Sparth Bottoms Road, Rochdale, Lancashire, OL11 4HT Tel: (01706) 632680 Fax: (01706) 632680 *Commercial vehicle repairers*

C J Consulting Ltd, 1 Hyde Drive, Worsley, Manchester, M28 3SG Tel: 0161-703 9972 E-mail: sales@cjconsulting.co.uk *Computer consultant*

C J Controls Ltd, Crofty Industrial Estate, Penclawdd, Swansea, SA4 3RS Tel: (01792) 851083 Fax: (01792) 850442 E-mail: sales@cjcontrols.co.uk *Electronic control systems manufrs*

C J Cooke, Unit 31 Park Farm Industrial Estate, Ermine Street, Buntingford, Hertfordshire, SG9 9AZ Tel: (01763) 272523 Fax: (01763) 272955 *Precision engineers*

C J Covers Ltd, 30 Williamson Street, Hull, HU9 1EP Tel: (01482) 226970 Fax: (01482) 327218 *Cover makers*

▶ C J Deighton & Co., 1 Main Street, West Wilts Trading Estate, Westbury, Wiltshire, BA13 4JU Tel: (01373) 824801 Fax: (01373) 824802

▶ C J Design, 47 St. Dunstans Road, Bristol, BS3 5NZ Tel: (07798) 808594 Fax: (0870) 8555366 *Workplace design consultancy & office furniture advice service*

C J Diesel Injection, 6 Wood Lane, Isleworth, Middlesex, TW7 5ER Tel: (020) 8560 2297 Fax: (020) 8560 1282 E-mail: sales@cjdiesel.com *Diesel fuel injection engineers*

C J Dolton, Browning Road, Heathfield, East Sussex, TN21 8DB Tel: (01435) 866350 Fax: (01435) 866416 E-mail: info@cjdoltonjoinery.co.uk *Purpose made joinery*

C J E Micros Ltd, 78 Brighton Road, Worthing, West Sussex, BN11 2EN Tel: (01903) 523222 Fax: (01903) 523679 E-mail: sales@cjemicros.co.uk *Computer systems*

C J Ellmore & Co. Ltd, Henshaw Lane, Yeadon, Leeds, LS19 7RZ Tel: 0113-250 2881 Fax: 0113-239 1227 E-mail: mail@ellmore.co.uk *Building contractor*

C J Engineering Ltd, 2 Faraday Place, Thetford, Norfolk, IP24 3RG Tel: (01842) 761726 Fax: (01842) 761119 E-mail: kevin@cjeng.co.uk *Turning, conventional & cnc milling machinists*

▶ C & J Engineering Services, 47a Park Lane, Poynton, Stockport, Cheshire, SK12 1RD Tel: (01625) 850710 Fax: (01625) 850711 E-mail: info@candjeng.co.uk *Business consultancy, health & safety management services*

▶ C J Express, Unit 6, Spedition House, Holme Industrial Estate, York, YO43 4BB Tel: (01430) 861450

▶ C & J Fabrications Ltd, Unit 5 & 6 Scout Bottom Business, Park Waterfoot, Rossendale, Lancashire, BB4 9JR Tel: (01706) 250084 Fax: (01706) 211113

C & J Fabrics, 11 Norford Way, Rochdale, Lancashire, OL11 5QS Tel: (01706) 633973 Fax: (01706) 638445 E-mail: cjfabrics@compuserve.com *Textile supplies & merchants*

▶ C J G, Box Bush Farm, Oxenhall Lane, Gorsley, Ross-on-Wye, Herefordshire, HR9 7BJ Tel: (01989) 720788 Fax: (01989) 720788 E-mail: cathy@cjgcatering.co.uk *Award Winning mobile quality event catering covering horse/dog shows, fetes/balls, sales/auctions,etc Gloucestershire, Herefordshire, Monmouthshire, Worcestershire, Forest of Dean etc Est.15yrs*

C J G Consultants Ltd, 21e Heathmans Road, Parsons Green, London, SW6 4TJ Tel: (020) 7371 8889 Fax: (020) 7371 9998 *Computer consultants*

C J Harris Electronic Components, Rosebank, Chafford Lane, Fordcombe, Tunbridge Wells, Kent, TN3 0SH Tel: (01892) 740000 Fax: (01892) 740100 E-mail: chrisharris2@btconnect.com *Electronic components distributors*

C & J Industries, Northern House, Station Approach, Hitchin, Hertfordshire, SG4 9UW Tel: (01462) 452414 Fax: (01462) 421105 *Precision turning services*

C.J.Jordan & Son Ltd, Zero, Alfred Road, London, W3 6LH Tel: (020) 8992 0638 Fax: (020) 8992 0073 *Monumental masons distributors*

C J Keitch Engineering, Dunkeswell Airfield, Dunkeswell Industrial Estate, Honiton, Devon, EX14 4LH Tel: (01404) 891796 Fax: (01404) 891796 E-mail: sales@cjkeitchengineering.co.uk *Agricultural engineers*

C J L Construction Ltd, The Stables, Honeyhall Lane, Congresbury, Bristol, BS49 5JX Tel: (01934) 853227 Fax: (01934) 853042

C J & L Fenwick, 2 Station Industrial Estate, Low Prudhoe, Prudhoe, Northumberland, NE42 6NP Tel: (01661) 833474 Fax: (01661) 833474 *Sheet metalworkers & fabricators*

C J Leonard, Clevestone Works, Whitby Road, Guisborough, Cleveland, TS14 7DA Tel: (01287) 633842 Fax: (01287) 633871 E-mail: sales@cjleonard.co.uk *Commercial vehicle & plant hire*

C J Machine Services Ltd, A Commercial Road, Walsall, WS2 7NQ Tel: (01922) 409777 Fax: (01922) 478600 E-mail: cjms@btconnect.com *Plastic machinery & accessories merchants*

▶ C & J Marine Services Ltd, Stephenson Street, Wallsend, Tyne & Wear, NE28 6UE Tel: 0191-295 0072 *Boat builders & repairers*

C & J Marine Textiles, Clay Lane, Chichester, West Sussex, PO19 3JG Tel: (01243) 785485 Fax: (01243) 785487 E-mail: sales@cjmarine.co.uk *Marine manufrs*

C & J Medals, 14 Fairford Road, Tilehurst, Reading, RG31 6QB Tel: 0118-942 5356 Fax: 0118-942 5356 *Mount medals*

C J Microsystems, Walnut Tree Cottage, Sutton Road, Cookham, Maidenhead, Berkshire, SL6 9SY Tel: (01628) 520113 E-mail: colin@cjmicro.co.uk *Computer software developers*

▶ C J Murfitt Ltd, 12a The Shade, Soham, Ely, Cambridgeshire, CB7 5DE Tel: (01353) 720002 Fax: (01353) 722931

C J P Sales Ltd, The Pavilion, Eastgate, Cowbridge, South Glamorgan, CF71 7AB Tel: (01446) 772015 Fax: (01446) 773755 E-mail: sales@cjpsales.co.uk *Plastic raw & basic materials distributors*

C J Penn Sales Ltd, 49 Hardwick Road, Sutton Coldfield, West Midlands, B74 3DN Tel: 0121-580 9099 Fax: 0121-580 9088 *Export merchants*

C J Powder Coatings, Unit 8 Jackson Place, Humberston, Grimsby, South Humberside, DN36 4AS Tel: (01472) 211222 Fax: (01472) 211333 *Powder coating services*

C J Security Systems Ltd, Unit 3 Fence Avenue, Macclesfield, Cheshire, SK10 1LT Tel: (01625) 613707 Fax: (01625) 617898 E-mail: sales@cheshirelock.co.uk *Security installation engineers*

C J Smith, 1 New Mill Street, Dudley, West Midlands, DY2 8PB Tel: (01384) 255172 Fax: (01384) 255172 *Domestic door retailers*

C J Smith, 21 Stoneleigh Court, Westcroft, Milton Keynes, MK4 4BS Tel: (01908) 502386 Fax: (01908) 502386 *Agricultural contractors*

C J Thorne & Co. Ltd, Union Point, Ridgewood, Uckfield, East Sussex, TN22 5SS Tel: (01825) 764123 Fax: (01825) 764126 E-mail: info@thornegroupuk.com *Civil engineering contractors including design*

C J Tools Southern CNC Ltd, Precision House, Northarbour Road, Portsmouth, PO6 3TJ Tel: (023) 9238 9489 Fax: (023) 9237 7119 E-mail: sales@cjtools.com *Sub-contract manufacturing engineers*

C J Trethewy, Waverley Farm, Waverley Lane, Farnham, Surrey, GU9 8EP Tel: (01252) 783008 *Cabinet manufrs*

C J Uniques Ltd, Unit 12 Magnus, Tame Valley Industrial Estate, Wilnecote, Tamworth, Staffordshire, B77 5BY Tel: (01827) 261682 Fax: (01827) 261682 *Design & manufacturing engineers*

C J Upton & Sons Ltd, 7 Stamford Square, Ashton-under-Lyne, Lancashire, OL6 6QU Tel: 0161-339 3330 Fax: 0161-339 3304 E-mail: sales@cjupton.com *Galvanized & cold reduced steel sheet & galvanized steel stockholders*

C J W Printers Ltd, South Lane, Elland, West Yorkshire, HX5 0HQ Tel: (01422) 374082 Fax: (01422) 379335 *Lithographic printers*

C J Wade & Co., 4 Warden Street, Ballymena, County Antrim, BT43 7DT Tel: (028) 2564 0370 Fax: (028) 2564 2823 *Home fitness equipment*

C J Welding, Hall Court Farm Cottage, Ripe, Lewes, East Sussex, BN8 6AY Tel: (01323) 811448 Fax: (01323) 811350 E-mail: cj.welding@virgin.net *Site welding & fabrication service*

▶ C J Worship & Co. (Hull) Ltd, King Edward Road, Thorne, Doncaster, South Yorkshire, DN8 4HU Tel: (01405) 814939

C Jackson & Sons, Keysoe Road, Thurleigh, Bedford, MK44 2EA Tel: (01234) 771311 Fax: (01234) 771128 E-mail: info@cjacksonandsons.co.uk

C Jenkins Ltd, Scotia Place, Falkirk, FK2 7AJ Tel: (01324) 631326 Fax: (01324) 629339 *Double glazing installers*

▶ C JS Coffee Bar, 55 High Street, East Grinstead, West Sussex, RH19 3DD Tel: (01342) 301910 *Cafe bar & wine club*

▶ C K Badges, 7 Oaklands Close, Bexleyheath, Kent, DA6 7AP Tel: (020) 8304 3758 Fax: (020) 8304 3758 *Badge manufrs*

C K Chemicals, Unit 16 Lady La Industrial Estate, Hadleigh, Ipswich, IP7 6BQ Tel: (01473) 822836 Fax: (01473) 824044 E-mail: sales@ckchemicals.co.uk *Manufacturers of industrial chemical products which include solvents, degreasers and cleaning products including, swimming pool chemicals*

C K Communications, 128 St. Andrews Road, Bridport, Dorset, DT6 3BN Tel: (01308) 422133 Fax: (01308) 422133 *Radio communications*

C & K Extrusions Ltd, 12 Drayton Road, Tonbridge, Kent, TN9 2BE Tel: (01732) 361434 Fax: (01732) 771009 E-mail: admin@ckextrusions.co.uk *Thermoplastic extrusion manufrs*

C K Gas Products Ltd, Unit 3, Murrell Green Business Park, London Road, Hook, Hampshire, RG27 9GR Tel: (01256) 766633 Fax: (01256) 766630 E-mail: sales@ckgas.com Principal Export Areas: Worldwide *Flow meter, gas & pressure regulator specialists*

C K International, 38 Eglish Road, Dungannon, County Tyrone, BT70 1LA Tel: (028) 8775 3966 Fax: (028) 8772 5528 E-mail: sales@ckinternational.co.uk *Engineering*

▶ C K Media (UK) Ltd, 300 Westfield Lane, Mansfield, Nottinghamshire, NG19 6NQ Tel: (01623) 652200

Company Information

▶ C K R, 74-76 West Street, Erith, Kent, DA8 1AF Tel: (01322) 445200 Fax: (01322) 439242 E-mail: ckr@accountant.com Certified Accountants, specialists in Construction industry, IT and Medical.**Deal with all tax, accountancy and VAT needs from Self assessments to Tax investigations

▶ C K Recruitment Specialists, 38 Preston Street, Faversham, Kent, ME13 8PE Tel: (0870) 0555821 Fax: (01795) 591116 E-mail: info@ckrecruitment.com Specialists in office & industrial recruitment throughout Kent.

▶ C K S Consulting Ltd, Regent House, Beam Heath Way, Nantwich, Cheshire, CW5 6PQ Tel: (01270) 619571 Fax: (0871) 2360387 E-mail: sales@cksconsulting.com

C K S Entertainment Systems, Logistics Centre, Willoughby Road, Bracknell, Berkshire, RG12 8FD Tel: (01344) 307788 Fax: (01344) 456710 E-mail: sales@cksgroup.co.uk Computer systems & software developers

C K S Entertainment Systems, Logistics Centre, Willoughby Road, Bracknell, Berkshire, RG12 8FD Tel: (01344) 307788 Fax: (01344) 456710 E-mail: sales@cksgroup.co.uk IT equipment recyclers services

C K S Holdings Ltd, Swallow End, Swallowfields, Welwyn Garden City, Hertfordshire, AL7 1JA Tel: (01707) 322528 Fax: (01707) 372851 E-mail: info@cksholdings.com Industrial computer product manufrs

C K S Precision Ltd, Unit 12, Ptarmigan Place, Attleborough Fields Industrial Estate, Nuneaton, Warwickshire, CV11 6RX Tel: (024) 7664 1693 Fax: (024) 7638 3971 E-mail: sales@cks-precision.co.uk Precision engineers

C K Supplies (UK) Ltd, 128 Grange Road, Wigston, Leicestershire, LE18 1JJ Tel: 0116-288 4252 Fax: 0116-288 8072 E-mail: sales@airtrac.co.uk Roof ventilators

C & K Systems Ltd, Cunliffe Drive, Northfield Ave., Kettering, Northamptonshire, NN16 8LF Tel: (01536) 410595 Fax: (01536) 416602 Toggle switch manufrs

▶ C K T Express, Sandybank Garage, Bacup Road, Rossendale, Lancashire, BB4 7JE Tel: (01706) 230666

C L A Manufacturing Ltd, 10 Binns Close, Coventry, CV4 9TB Tel: (024) 7646 5535 Fax: (024) 7669 4543 E-mail: info@clatools.co.uk Engineering sub-contractors, burnishing tool & reamer manufrs

▶ C L B Engineering, 19 Phoebe La Industrial Estate, Halifax, West Yorkshire, HX3 9EX Tel: (01422) 383803 Fax: (01422) 383802 E-mail: Lisa@clbengineers.co.uk Sub contract precision engineers

▶ C L C Construction, Littlebrook Business Centre, Littlebrook Manorway, Dartford, DA1 5PS Tel: (01322) 292636

C L C Contractors Ltd, 21 Oswin Road, Leicester, LE3 1HR Tel: 0116-254 4105 Fax: 0116-254 2784 E-mail: leicester@clcgroup.com Painting contractors Also at: Bolton, Cambridge, Derby, Nottingham, Southampton & Walsall

C L C Contractors Ltd, Northbrook Industrial Estate, Vincent Avenue, Southampton, SO16 6PQ Tel: (023) 8070 1111 Fax: (023) 8070 1171 E-mail: mail@clcgroup.com Painting contractors & building maintenance services

C L C Contractors Anglia, 7 Station Way, Brandon, Suffolk, IP27 0BH Tel: (01842) 813972 Fax: 01842 813113 E-mail: brandon@clcgroup.com Painting & decorating contractors & maintenance works

C L C Presentation Systems, Mill Road Industrial Estate, Linlithgow Bridge, Linlithgow, West Lothian, EH49 7SF Tel: (01506) 848779 Fax: (01506) 202779 E-mail: sales@clc-online.co.uk Binding presentation suppliers

C L D Fencing Systems Suppliers, Unit 11, Springvale Business Centre, Millbuck Way, Sandbach, Cheshire, CW11 3HY Tel: (01270) 764751 Fencing distributors

C & L Developments, 25 Lyon Road, Walton-on-Thames, Surrey, KT12 3PU Tel: (01932) 244699 Fax: (01932) 241660 E-mail: info@cl-devs.co.uk Principal Export Areas: Africa Automation special purpose equipment/systems manufacturers/constructors, laser marking systems distributors & special purpose custom built machinery constructors/ manufrs

C L E Design Ltd, 69-71 Haydons Road, London, SW19 1HQ Tel: (020) 8540 5772 E-mail: admin@cle-design.com Lighting designers & manufrs

C L Edwards & Sons Ltd, Amy Johnson Way, Blackpool, FY4 2RP Tel: (01253) 345311 Fax: (01253) 343610 E-mail: signet@cledwards.co.uk Jewellery wholesalers

C L Electrical Controls Ltd, Unit 1 Kendleshire Farm Down, Road Winterbourne, Bristol, BS36 1AU Tel: (01454) 250555 Fax: (01454) 250540 E-mail: enquiries@clelectricalcontrols.co.uk Electric control panel manufrs

C L F Packaging, Orchard House, Heath Road, Warboys, Huntingdon, Cambridgeshire, PE28 2UW Tel: (01487) 823222 Fax: (01487) 824011 E-mail: sales@clfpack.co.uk Packaging suppliers

C L Hichins & Sons, Carn Farm, Morvah, Pendeen, Penzance, Cornwall, TR19 7TT Tel: (01736) 788309 Agricultural contractors & farmers

▶ C L I Heating Ltd, Unit 56, Bowen Industrial Estate, Aberbargoed, Bargoed, Mid Glamorgan, CF81 9EP Tel: (01443) 828100

C & L Joinery, 30 The Retreat, Frome, Somerset, BA11 5JU Tel: (01373) 466722 Fax: (01373) 466722 Joinery manufrs

C L M Fleet Management plc, Corporate House, Jenna Way, Interchange Park, Newport Pagnell, Buckinghamshire, MK16 9QB Tel: (01908) 210100 Fax: (01908) 210102 E-mail: clm@clm.co.uk Fleet management

C L P Holding Co. Ltd, Tudor Works, Windmill Lane, Smethwick, West Midlands, B66 3EU Tel: 0121-558 2618 Fax: 0121-558 8825 E-mail: sales@clpzips.co.uk Haberdashery manufacturers, wholesalers & trimming merchants

C L P Structured Finance Ltd, 131 Baker Street, London, W1U 6SE Tel: (020) 7486 0655 Fax: (020) 7935 5489 E-mail: mail@cpl.uk.com Property finance brokers

C & L Patterns, Unit 5 Field Gate, Walsall, WS1 3DJ Tel: (01922) 628377 Fax: (01922) 628377 Brass gravity die specialists

C & L Pine Bros Ltd, A B Draycott Cross Road, Cheadle, Stoke-on-Trent, ST10 1PN Tel: (01538) 750110 Fax: (01538) 750110 Pine furniture manufrs

C L Plastics Ltd, Furnace Road, Oakenshaw, Bradford, West Yorkshire, BD12 7BH Tel: (01274) 603344 Fax: (01274) 691541 E-mail: sales@clplastics.com Polythene packaging manufrs

▶ C & L Plumbing Services, Bridge Works, Wood Lane, Rothwell, Leeds, LS26 0RS Tel: 0113-282 3728 Fax: 0113-282 2105

C & L Products, Tall Trees, Lazenbys Estate, Walliswood, Dorking, Surrey, RH5 5RE Tel: (01306) 627721 Fax: (01306) 627721 E-mail: sales@c-lproducts.co.uk Water sport clothing manufrs

C L S, 71 Bankhouse Road, Bury, Lancashire, BL8 1DY Tel: 0161-764 9898 Fax: 0161-764 9898 Hirers & distributors of work wear

C L S Europe, Heritage House, 11 Heritage Court, Chester, CH1 1RD Tel: (01244) 313022 Fax: (01244) 318455 E-mail: sales@clseurope.com Management consultants

C L S Fabrication Ltd, 1 Caswell Road, Leamington Spa, Warwickshire, CV31 1QD Tel: (01926) 336126 Fax: (01926) 312022 E-mail: sales@clsfab.co.uk Laminate fabrication services

C L S Laundry Equipment, Unit A17-19, Holmer Trading Estate, Hereford, HR1 1JS Tel: (01432) 275712 Fax: (01432) 275712 E-mail: intercountyservices@orange.net Purchasing Contact: S. Robinson Sales Contact: S. Robinson Principal Export Areas: Worldwide Catering & laundry equipment suppliers

C L S Offshore Ltd, Bessemer Way, Harfreys Industrial Estate, Great Yarmouth, Norfolk, NR31 0LX Tel: (01493) 668730 Fax: (01493) 667548 E-mail: info@clsoffshore.co.uk Fabrication & engineering & offshore

C L Shredders, Unit 1, Angeldown Farm, Manor Rd, Wantage, Oxon, OX12 8NQ Tel: (0800) 9757235 Fax: (01235) 765474 E-mail: cluton@clshredders.co.uk Purchasing Contact: C. Luton Sales Contact: C. Luton Baler, baler machine/press/industrial & paper manufacturers, reconditioned rebuilders or suppliers. In addition, aerosol disposal equipment shredding, industrial machine, security machine, paper machine & horticultural machine manufacturers. Also industrial shredding machine & security shredding machine distributors or agents. Refuse sorting/ shredding/bailing equipment manufrs

C L T (Essington) Ltd, Unit 2C Bloxwich Business Pk, Fryers Rd, Walsall, WS2 7LY Tel: (01922) 713367 Fax: (01922) 713368 Steel stockholder

C L T Timber & Transport Ltd, Olds Approach, Coalpits Lane, Watford, WD18 9TD Tel: (01923) 711888 Fax: (01923) 711675 E-mail: wood@wattim.co.uk Timber, plywood importers, merchants

▶ C L Transport, Unit 22 Wireworks Estate, Bristol Road, Bridgwater, Somerset, TA6 4AP Tel: (01278) 439062 Fax: (01278) 447194

C Lear & Sons Ltd, Unit 7-8 Rassbottom Industrial Estate, Stalybridge, Cheshire, SK15 1RH Tel: 0161-303 7410 Fax: 0161-338 4214 E-mail: learandsons@aol.com Foundry engineers services

C M A Holdings Ltd, Torr Hill, Plymouth, PL8 2HQ Tel: (01752) 881333 Fax: (01752) 882101 Advertising & internet design consultants

C M A Solutions Ltd, Fleet Mill, Minley Road, Fleet, Hampshire, GU51 2RD Tel: (01252) 861500 Fax: (01252) 861550 E-mail: cma@cma-sol.co.uk Bespoke software development

C M Alloys, Peartree Business Centre, Cobham Road, Ferndown Industrial Estate, Wimborne, Dorset, BH21 7PT Tel: (01202) 850370 Fax: (01202) 850379 Aircraft aluminium extrusions suppliers

C & M Apostolides Ltd, 257 Wood Street, Walthamstow, London, E17 3NG Tel: (020) 8923 5050 Fax: (020) 8923 6060 E-mail: mail@cama.co.uk Office & removals specialists

▶ C M C Aluminium Systems, Unit 4-5 Calow Brook Drive, Hasland, Chesterfield, Derbyshire, S41 0DR Tel: (01246) 555255 Fax: (01246) 555266 E-mail: sales@cmcaluminium.co.uk

C M C Asbestos Surveys Ltd, Elker House, Elker Lane, Billington, Clitheroe, Lancashire, BB7 9HZ Tel: (01254) 822029 Fax: (01254) 825771 E-mail: info@cmcasestsossurveys.com CMC asbestos survey services

C M C Controls Ltd, Chaucer Business Park, Watery Lane, Kemsing, Sevenoaks, Kent, TN15 6PL Tel: (01732) 763278 Fax: (01732) 763279 E-mail: sales@cmccontrols.co.uk Manufacturers of web tension control equipment

▶ C M C Mobile Computing Ltd, The Heath Business & Technical Park, Runcorn, Cheshire, WA7 4QX Tel: (0870) 1651465 Fax: (0870) 7623701 E-mail: sales@cmc.org.uk UK distributor of rugged, full screen mobile computers

C M C Products, Cuxham, Watlington, Oxfordshire, OX49 5NH Tel: (01491) 612676 Fax: (01491) 613771 E-mail: johncarr.cmc@myopal.net Manufacturers & agents for coated-laminated paper-film products-woven labels

C M C (U K) Ltd, Bradwall Court, Bradwall Road, Sandbach, Cheshire, CW11 1GE Tel: (01270) 759444 Fax: (01270) 759888 E-mail: uksteeltrading@cmcukltd.com Steel trading

C & M Communications Consultants Ltd, Tanners Court, Tanners Lane, East Wellow, Romsey, Hampshire, SO51 6DP Tel: (01794) 518508 Fax: (01794) 518182 E-mail: stephen.michaelides@candmcommunications.co.uk Principal Export

continued

Areas: Middle East Telecommunication system integrators

C & M Components, 47 East End, Long Clawson, Melton Mowbray, Leics, LE14 4NG Tel: (01664) 822476 Fax: (01664) 822645 E-mail: chris@cmcomponents.com Pointer/ indicator/hand (dial/gauge/instrument/meter) manufrs

C & M Corporation, Dunfermline, Fife, KY12 9YX Tel: (01383) 621225 Fax: (01383) 623455 E-mail: sales@cmcorporation.co.uk Cable manufrs

C M D Ltd, Flixborough Industrial Estate, Ninth Avenue, Flixborough, Scunthorpe, South Humberside, DN15 8SL Tel: (01724) 851873 Fax: (01724) 874411 E-mail: cm.developments@virgin.net Structural steelwork & architectural metalwork

▶ C M Downton Haulage Ltd, Brook Farm, Bristol Road, Moreton Valence, Gloucester, GL2 7ND Tel: (01452) 720242 Fax: (01452) 722446 General distribution

C M E, 6 Ascot Park Estate, Lenton Street, Sandiacre, Nottingham, NG10 5DL Tel: 0115-949 9066 Fax: 0115-939 3102 E-mail: gcb@cme.globalnet.co.uk Medical equipment distributors

C & M Electrical Contracts & Maintenance Ltd, 2f Vaughan Court, Stapylton Street, Middlesbrough, Cleveland, TS6 7BJ Tel: (01642) 440640 Fax: (01642) 460595 E-mail: jd@cmelec.co.uk Electrical engineers & industrial contractors

C M Engineering, 45 College Street, Kempston, Bedford, MK42 8LU Tel: (01234) 214906 Fax: (01234) 217755 Precision engineers

▶ C M Engineering, Unit 8 Fleet La Industrial Estate, Fleet Lane, St. Helens, Merseyside, WA9 1TA Tel: (01744) 28571 Fax: (01744) 28571 E-mail: denis@marshst.wanadoo.co.uk Precision Engineering and Light Fabrication components manufactured. Design and build sevice. Planned plant maintenance services devised and implemented.

C & M Environmental Ltd, 52 Strathmore Road, Glasgow, G22 7DW Tel: 0141-336 7774 Fax: 0141-336 5559 E-mail: enfor@cmenvironmental.co.uk Refrigeration engineers service

C M F Ltd, Falcon Way, Feltham, Middlesex, TW14 0XJ Tel: (020) 8844 0940 Fax: (020) 8751 5793 E-mail: info@cmf.co.uk Steel fabricators

C M Fair Joinery, Rigby Court, Bolton, BL3 6QY Tel: (01204) 528540 Fax: (01204) 396100 Joinery manufrs

▶ C & M Flooring & Maintenance, 9 Hammonds Lane, Great Warley, Brentwood, Essex, CM13 3AH Tel: (07950) 933025 Fax: (01277) 228414 E-mail: nigel.magee@virgin.net Supply & fit of wooden flooring, sanding, sealing & restoration

▶ C & M Group Ltd, 5-19 Holland Street, Aberdeen, AB25 3UJ Tel: (01224) 625928 Fax: (01224) 625914

C M I Plastics Ltd, Wood Street Works, Wood Street, Burnley, Lancashire, BB10 1QH Tel: (01282) 420021 Fax: (01282) 831387 E-mail: sales@cmi-ltd.com Manufacturers of coated fabric processors

C & M Installations, 11 Craven Close, Longwell Green, Bristol, BS30 7BX Tel: 0117-983 0310 Car accessory installators

▶ C M J Consultants, Glenville, Gwern y Gaer, Rhosesmor, Mold, Flintshire, CH7 6PP Tel: (01352) 781933 Fax: (01352) 781933 E-mail: chrisj@cmjconsultants.org We offer an Asbestos Surveying service as well as Management of Asbestos - your legal duty*We are also conversant with all aspects of Health and Safety at Work legislation

C M Joinery, Coggeshall Road, Bradwell, Braintree, Essex, CM77 8EU Tel: (01376) 331666 Fax: (01376) 331444 E-mail: info@wood-work.demon.co.uk Joinery manufrs

▶ C M Joinery, 9, Drovers Road, East Mains Industrial Estate, Broxburn, West Lothian, EH52 5ND Tel: (01506) 859949 Fax: (01506) 859949

C & M Joinery, Unit 1, Plot 7 Claymore, Tame Valley Industrial Estate, Wilnecote, Tamworth, Staffs, B77 5DQ Tel: (01827) 250849 Fax: (01827) 287913 Staircase manufrs

C M L Alloys Ltd, Units 44-45 Stretford Motorway Estate, Barton Dock Road, Trafford Park, Manchester, M32 0ZH Tel: 0161-864 5001 Fax: 0161-865 5751 E-mail: sales@cmlimited.com Flanges consumables manufrs

C M L Group Ltd, Price Street, Birkenhead, Merseyside, CH41 3PT Tel: 0151-647 5531 Fax: 0151-650 0668 E-mail: enquiries@cml-group.com Precision & composite engineers

C M L Group Ltd, Unit 5 Wheatland Business Park, Wheatland Lane, Wallasey, Merseyside, CH44 7ER Tel: 0151-631 5600 Fax: 0151-631 5601 E-mail: enquiries@cml-group.com Electroplating, anodising, non-destructive test & paint spraying

C M L Innovative Technologies Ltd, Beetons Way, Bury St. Edmunds, Suffolk, IP32 6RA Tel: (01284) 762411 Fax: (01284) 754406 E-mail: sales@cml-it.com Electric suppliers

▶ C M Lane Distribution Services Ltd, Unit A, Monarch Courtyard 11 Salthouse Road, Brackmills Industrial Estate, Northampton, NN4 7BD Tel: (01604) 587781 Fax: (01604) 826030 E-mail: sales@cmlane.co.uk

C M Los (London) Ltd, Coppergate House, 16 Brune Street, London, E1 7NJ Tel: (020) 7721 7977 Fax: (020) 7721 7967 E-mail: mail@cmlos.com Ship brokers

C M M Services Ltd, Butlers Leap, Rugby, Warwickshire, CV21 3RQ Tel: (01788) 570357 Fax: (01788) 567991 E-mail: cmm@itpgroup.co.uk Calibration manifesto manufrs

C & M Machine Tools Ltd, Station Road, Coleshill, Birmingham, B46 1JN Tel: (01675) 433100 Fax: (01675) 433101 E-mail: info@candmtools.com Machine tool reconditioning

C M Machinery, 50 Seagoe Industrial Area, Portadown, Craigavon, County Armagh, BT63 5QE Tel: (028) 3833 3341 Fax: (028) 3833 0915 E-mail: info@cmmachinery.co.uk Purpose built & standard converting equipment suppliers

C & M Mould Tools Ltd, Unit 1-3 Brunel Close, Ebblake Industrial Estate, Verwood, Dorset, BH31 6BA Tel: (01202) 813019 Fax: (01202) 814219 E-mail: cmmoulds@aol.com Injection mould toolmakers

C M Nicholls Timber Products, The Sawmill, Ketsby, Louth, Lincolnshire, LN11 8QW Tel: (01507) 480672 Timber saw millers

C M P Batteries Ltd, PO Box 1, Bolton, BL5 1DD Tel: (01204) 64111 Fax: (01204) 62981 E-mail: sales@cmpbatteries.co.uk Industrial & general purpose batteries & charger manufrs

C M P Data & Information Services, Riverbank House, Angel Lane, Tonbridge, Kent, TN9 1SE Tel: (01732) 377591 Fax: (01732) 377479 E-mail: orders@ubminternational.com Directory publishers

C M P Products, 36 Nelson Way, Nelson Park East, Cramlington, Northumberland, NE23 1WH Tel: 0191 2657411 Fax: 0191 2650581 E-mail: cmp@cmp-products.com CMP Products is the leading specialist manufacturer of industrial & hazardous area cable glands for use in conjunction with power, control, instrumentation & lighting cables.

C & M Partitioning Ltd, 10-12 Stirling Road, London, E17 6BT Tel: (020) 8531 3834 Fax: (020) 8531 3837 Office partitioning installators

C M Precision, 3 Brannish Road, Downpatrick, County Down, BT30 6LL Tel: (028) 4461 9920 Fax: (028) 4461 4733 E-mail: dpk@cmprecision.co.uk Precision engineers

C M Precision Components, Killyhelvin Industrial Estate, Killyhevlin, Enniskillen, County Fermanagh, BT74 4EJ Tel: (028) 6632 3361 Fax: (028) 6632 6958 E-mail: martin@cmprecisioncomponents.co.uk Precision machinists

C M R Chemical Services Ltd, Moorhey Street, Oldham, OL4 1JE Tel: 0161-626 4143 Fax: 0161-628 5081 Detergent powder manufrs

▶ C M R Intech, 124 Churchill Road, Bicester, Oxfordshire, OX26 4XD Tel: (01869) 248400 Computer systems consultants

C M R International (UK) Military Firearms & Antiquities, 53 High Street, Ashford, Kent, TN24 8SG Tel: (0871) 2301318 Fax: (0871) 2301318 E-mail: cmrinternational@aol.com Firearms procurement & equipment

C M Railton & Son Ltd, Poplar, Sunk Island Road, Ottringham, Hull, HU12 0DX Tel: (01964) 626105 Fax: (01964) 626105 Joiners

C & M Refrigeration, Unit C, The Loddon Centre, Wade Road, Basingstoke, Hampshire, RG24 8FL Tel: (01256) 811400 Fax: (01256) 801200 E-mail: coldkit@btconnect.com Refrigerator distributors

▶ C M Rent, 2 Freeport Office Village, Century Drive, Braintree, Essex, CM77 8YL Tel: (01376) 329090 Fax: (01376) 329393 E-mail: enquiries@cmrent.com Letting Agent covering the CM postcode area of Essex, pre-dominantly Chelmsford, Braintree & Witham. Low Fees and Quality Homes for Quality Tenants, Rent Guarantee Insurance included

C M S, Telford Mill, Telford Street, Horwich, Bolton, BL6 6DY Tel: (01204) 694832 Fax: (01204) 690286 Janitorial supply services

C M S Alarms, 603 Newport Road, Cardiff, CF3 4FA Tel: (029) 2079 5697 Fax: (029) 2079 5796 Alarm installation agents

▶ C M S Building Services, 30 St Dunstans Hill, Sutton, Surrey, SM1 2UD Tel: (020) 8641 5520 Fax: (020) 8641 1905

C M S Software Ltd, 9 Saxon House, Warley Street, Upminster, Essex, RM14 3PJ Tel: (01708) 640382 Fax: (01708) 640385 E-mail: sales@cms.co.uk Our solutions scan, store and retrieve mission critical text, graphics and documents to help automate your business processes. We have over 15 years experience in document management, providing document automation to healthcare professionals in many varying departments, multi franchised automotive dealerships, distribution & transport companies and the legal sector. We have the pre and post sales expertise to correctly identify the document control software for you. If you need to catch up with a large backlog of documentation we can provide a Bureau Service for you.

C M S Sports & Leisure, 57 Pen Street, Boston, Lincolnshire, PE21 6TF Tel: (01205) 366730 Fax: (01205) 359119 Sports coaching

C M S Tools Ltd, Don Pedro Close, Normanton Industrial Estate, Normanton, West Yorkshire, WF6 1TD Tel: (01924) 895999 Fax: (01924) 896999 Roof tool manufacturers & wholesalers

C M S Tools Ltd, Don Pedro Close, Normanton Industrial Estate, Normanton, West Yorkshire, WF6 1TD Tel: (01924) 895999 Fax: (01924) 896999 E-mail: info@cmstools.co.uk Roofing accessories suppliers

C M Services, 22 Lowbell Lane, London Colney, St. Albans, Hertfordshire, AL2 1AZ Tel: (01727) 825535 Fax: (01727) 825568 E-mail: info@cmbservices.co.uk Accommodation

C M Shaw Ltd, Clarence Row, Stockton-on-Tees, Cleveland, TS18 2HD Tel: (01642) 606668 Fax: (01642) 617845 E-mail: cmshaw@stkn.freeserve.co.uk Ships agents & road transport services

▶ C M Shop Equipment Ltd, 567 Eastern Avenue, Ilford, Essex, IG2 6PJ Tel: (020) 8518 1986 Fax: (020) 8518 3610 E-mail: info@cmshopequipment.co.uk Shop fitters with showroom, offering full design & installation service

C & M Smith Partnership, 4 Potters Lane, Kiln Farm, Milton Keynes, MK11 3HE Tel: (01908) 265577 Fax: (01908) 265567 E-mail: salescandm@aol.com Protective clothing distributors

C M Supplies, 8 Brothock Bridge, Arbroath, Angus, DD11 1NG Tel: (01241) 434800 Fax: (01241) 434800 E-mail: cmsupplies1@aol.com Suppliers of work wear,footwear,janitorial and*household supplies.

C M T Dynamics, PO Box 36, Cradley Heath, West Midlands, B64 7DQ Tel: (01384) 563220 Fax: (01384) 563225 E-mail: sales@cmt-dynamics.co.uk *Vibration shock & noise control mountings manufrs*

C M T Flexibles, Unit 14D Two Locks, Hurst Business Park, Brierley Hill, West Midlands, DY5 1UU Tel: (01384) 480197 Fax: (01384) 74840 E-mail: sales@cmtflexibles.com *Rubber PVC flexible hoses assemblers*

C M T S, 7 Churchfield Road, Sudbury, Suffolk, CO10 2YA Tel: (01787) 468685 Fax: (01787) 468687 E-mail: sales@cmts.co.uk *Distribution of control products*

C M T Steel Services Ltd, Overend Road, Corngreaves Trading Estate, Cradley Heath, West Midlands, B64 7DD Tel: (01384) 565166 Fax: (01384) 633586 E-mail: sales@cmt-steel.co.uk *Steel stockholder*

C & M Trophies & Engraving, 5 Arundel Road, Littlehampton, West Sussex, BN17 7BY Tel: (01903) 717766 Fax: (01903) 731377 E-mail: enquires@candmtrophies.co.uk *Engraving services*

C M W Controls Ltd, Bryn Lane, Wrexham Industrial Estate, Wrexham, Clwyd, LL13 9UT Tel: (01978) 661516 Fax: (01978) 661626 E-mail: geoff.roberts@cmwcontrols.com *Electrical contractors*

C & M Welding Services, Crabtree Road, Thorpe Industrial Estate, Egham, Surrey, TW20 8RN Tel: (01784) 438127 Fax: (01784) 470223 *Steel fabricators & mobile welding services*

C M Whitby Ltd, King John Bank, Walpole St. Andrew, Wisbech, Cambridgeshire, PE14 7JT Tel: (01945) 780304 Fax: (01945) 780827 *Joinery services*

C M Z Machinery Ltd, Fullers End, Elsenham, Bishop's Stortford, Hertfordshire, CM22 6DU Tel: (01279) 814491 Fax: (01279) 814541 E-mail: info@cmzweb.co.uk *Suppliers of sheet metal machinery*

C Mac Microcircuits Ltd, South Denes, Great Yarmouth, Norfolk, NR30 3PX Tel: (01493) 856122 Fax: 01493 858536 E-mail: mssinfo@cmac.com *The C-MAC Test & Calibration centre is a one-stop shop for manufacturers who need access to a full range of testing and calibration services. These include performing climatic and dynamic tests, making precision electrical, mechanical, optical, and temperature calibrations, a specification consultancy service, and a test jig manufacturing capability.*

▶ C Mac Microcircuits Ltd, South Denes, Great Yarmouth, Norfolk, NR30 3PX Tel: (01493) 856122 Fax: (01493) 858536 E-mail: KenTurrell@cmac.com *Hybrid microcircuits manufacturers*

▶ C Mccullam & Son Transport Ltd, Chapel Street, Stalybridge, Cheshire, SK15 2AW Tel: 0161-338 4616 Fax: 0161-338 4616

C Moore, Drift End Stables, The Drift, Bourn, Cambridge, CB23 2TB Tel: (01954) 719565 *Blacksmiths*

▶ C Morgan, 172 Crown Lane, Horwich, Bolton, BL6 7QX Tel: (01204) 697982

C N A Europe Holdings Ltd, 77 Gracechurch Street, London, EC3V 0DL Tel: (020) 7548 1171 *Insurance*

C N Air Mach Ltd, 255 Monton Road, Eccles, Manchester, M30 9PS Tel: 0161-788 7465 Fax: 0161-787 7002 E-mail: airmachltd@aol.com *Industrial fan manufrs*

C N Associates, 18 Albemarle Street, London, W1S 4HR Tel: (020) 7491 2521 Fax: (020) 7355 3169 *Quantity surveyors*

▶ C N C Check Machine Tools Ltd, Kitchener Road, Leicester, LE5 4AT Tel: 0116-274 1044 Fax: 0116-274 1046 E-mail: mail@cnccheckmachinetools.co.uk *CNC machining centre specialists*

C N C Consulting, Kemnay, Inverurie, Aberdeenshire, AB51 5GB Tel: (01467) 643210

C N C Engineering, 69 Haviland Road, Ferndown Industrial Estate, Wimborne, Dorset, BH21 7PY Tel: (01202) 892892 Fax: (01202) 893114 E-mail: euromation@btconnect.com *Automation systems manufacturers & subcontract manchinists*

C N C Fluids Ltd, Whitehall Trading Estate, Gerrish Avenue, Whitehall, Bristol, BS5 9DF Tel: 0117-935 0033 Fax: 0117-935 0440 E-mail: sales@cncfluids.co.uk *Cutting lubricants suppliers & distributors*

▶ C N C Heating Ltd, Fawkham Road, Longfield, Kent, DA3 7BE Tel: (01474) 700111 Fax: (01474) 700123

▶ C N C Joinery Ltd, Unit 5, Venture Court, Bradley Lane, Newton Abbot, Devon, TQ12 1NB Tel: (01626) 332203 Fax: (01626) 332204 E-mail: customer.service@cncjoinery.co.uk *Joiners*

C N C Loughborough Ltd, 35 Bakewell Road, Loughborough, Leicestershire, LE11 5QY Tel: (01509) 215302 Fax: (01509) 215302 E-mail: cncloughborough@btconnect.com *Electrical enclosures, engineering services & signs*

C N C Moss, Sunnyview, Chatteris Road, Somersham, Huntingdon, Cambridgeshire, PE28 3DN Tel: (01487) 840285 *Machine tools service*

C N C Punching Ltd, 47 Percy Road, Leicester, LE2 8FQ Tel: 0116-283 2350 Fax: 0116-244 0374 *Sheet metal fabricators*

▶ C & N Control Systems Ltd, Units 7-8 Sterling Industrial Park, Carr Wood Road, Castleford, West Yorkshire, WF10 4PS Tel: (01977) 603803 Fax: (01977) 603161 E-mail: info@cn-controls.co.uk

C N Controls Ltd, Thorpe Way Indust Estate, Thorpe Way, Banbury, Oxfordshire, OX16 4SP Tel: (01295) 266704 Fax: (01295) 266704 E-mail: sales@cncontrols.co.uk *Electrical control systems & panel manufrs*

C N F Precision Engineering Ltd, C N F Factory, Southern Road, Aylesbury, Buckinghamshire, HP19 9AY Tel: (01296) 481727 Fax: (01296) 434940 E-mail: sales@cnfengineering.com *Precision engineers, cnc turning & milling*

C N G Foodservice Equipment Ltd, Unit 2, Parker Court, Dunston, Gateshead, Tyne & Wear, NE11 9EW Tel: 0191-460 9408 Fax: 0191-460 7070 E-mail: info@cngfoodserv.co.uk *Commercial kitchen agents*

C N Greene & Sons Ltd, 22 Ashtree Bank, Rugeley, Staffordshire, WS15 1HN Tel: (01889) 582509 Fax: (01889) 582509 E-mail: cng.plants@aol.com *Plant hire & earth moving* Also at: Stafford

▶ C N Hickson General Builder, 62 Thorn Tree Drive, Leighton, Crewe, CW1 4UA Tel: 01270 505593 *Extensions, Renovations, New Build, Property Repairs*

C N P Ltd, Basilica, 2 King Charles Street, Leeds, LS1 6LS Tel: 0113-220 7330 Fax: 0113-266 0022 *Building surveyors*

C N Ross-Feld MJ Ltd, Premier House, 12-13 Hatton Garden, London, EC1N 8AN Tel: (020) 7242 5037 Fax: (020) 7404 5413 *Jewellery manufrs*

C N S, Earley, Reading, RG10 8NF Tel: 0118-940 1313 Fax: 0118-940 3754 E-mail: enquire@cnscommunications.co.uk *Computer hardware suppliers*

▶ C N S Farnell, Elstree Business Centre, Elstree Way, Borehamwood, Hertfordshire, WD6 1RX Tel: (020) 8238 6900 Fax: (020) 8238 6901 E-mail: sales@cnsfarnell.com *Manufacturer of test equipment for concrete, ceramics, roads & soils*

C N S Powertools Sales & Repairs, 111 Neath Road, Briton Ferry, Neath, West Glamorgan, SA11 2BZ Tel: (01639) 824217 Fax: (01639) 824218 *Power tools sales & repairers*

▶ CNS Systems, 29 Fen Road, Watlington, King's Lynn, Norfolk, PE33 0JA Tel: (01553) 811838 Fax: (01553) 810363 E-mail: sales@cns-systems.co.uk

C N Smart (UK) Ltd, Unit 3, Baltimore Trading Estate, Baltimore Road, Great Barr, Birmingham, B42 1DD Tel: 0121-356 2920 Fax: 0121-356 6129 E-mail: cnsmart@hotmail.com *Precision turned parts manufrs*

C N Systems U K Ltd, Unit 1 Wellington St Workshops, Wellington Street, Warrington, WA1 2DB Tel: (01925) 445190 Fax: (01925) 445190 E-mail: info@c-nsystems.com *Industrial instrumentation suppliers*

C & N Transport Services Ltd, Coundon Industrial Estate, Coundon, Bishop Auckland, County Durham, DL14 8NR Tel: (01388) 664500 Fax: (01388) 664550 E-mail: cntransport@btconnect.com *UK & international haulage services*

C O B Engineering, Midland Road, Luton, LU2 0BL Tel: (01582) 736721 Fax: (01582) 402497 E-mail: info@cobengineering.co.uk *General engineers*

C O P Autogas Ltd, Somersall Mill, Grove Lane, Doveridge, Ashbourne, Derbyshire, DE6 5PB Tel: (01283) 585240 Fax: (01283) 585738 *Gas conversion, agricultural engineers & manufrs*

C O S, Unit 9, Hastingwood Business Centre, Hastingwood, Harlow, Essex, CM17 9GD Tel: (0845) 3893030 Fax: (0845) 3893031 E-mail: sales@colouroffset.co.uk *Office stationary*

C O S Marketing Ltd, Bradford Road, Idle, Bradford, West Yorkshire, BD10 8SQ Tel: (01274) 617373 Fax: (01274) 615129 *Pattern book manufrs*

C O S Print, Blakehill Works, Bradford Road, Idle, Bradford, West Yorkshire, BD10 8SQ Tel: (01274) 615142 Fax: (01274) 615129 E-mail: cospresentation@ndirect.co.uk *General printers*

C & O Tractors Ltd, West Street, Wilton, Salisbury, SP2 0DG Tel: (01722) 742141 Fax: (01722) 744497 E-mail: admin@candotractors.co.uk *Agricultural & horticultural engineers* Also at: Blandford

C O'Connor Engineers Ltd, Halberton Street, Smethwick, West Midlands, B66 2QP Tel: 0121-555 5992 Fax: 0121-555 6007 *General engineers*

C Olley & Sons Ltd, Iberia House, 14 Finchley Avenue, Mildenhall, Bury St. Edmunds, Suffolk, IP28 7BJ Tel: (01638) 712076 Fax: (01638) 717304 E-mail: sales@olley-cork.com Principal Export Areas: Worldwide *Ant vibration mounting, bottle cap, liner disc & gasket manufrs*

C P A Ltd, Calderhead Road, Shotts, Lanarkshire, ML7 4EQ Tel: (01501) 825024 Fax: (01501) 825029 E-mail: cpa@cpa-group.com *Compressed air sales & service*

C P A Engineering Ltd, Fircroft Way, Edenbridge, Kent, TN8 6EJ Tel: (01732) 866565 Fax: 01732 866541 *Repetition work*

C P A Laboratories Ltd, 318 Worple Road, London, SW20 8QU Tel: (020) 8946 8621 Fax: (020) 8947 1206 E-mail: admincpa@eurofins.com *Pollution control consultants*

▶ C P A Products, 9 Warrior Business Centre, Fitzherbert Road, Portsmouth, PO6 1TX Tel: (023) 9221 0330 Fax: (023) 9220 1594 *Tool making & injection moulding*

C P Arts Ltd, Alphin Brook Road, Marsh Barton Trading Estate, Exeter, EX2 8QF Tel: (01392) 210574 Fax: (01392) 412107 E-mail: cparts@cparts.co.uk *Screen & digital printers & point of sale manufrs*

▶ C P C, Component House, Faraday Drive, Fulwood, Preston, PR2 9PP Tel: (01772) 654455 Fax: (01772) 654466 E-mail: webadmin@cpc.co.uk *Top quality products online, ranging from audio, video, computing, office equipment, cables, connectors, electrical, security components, tools, in the work place, spares & test equipment all available in just two clicks*

C P C Communications, 56 Clive Road, Cardiff, CF5 1HG Tel: (029) 2066 5213 Fax: (01639) 646003 *Radio communications services*

C P C Computers Ltd, Hay House, 21 Stroud Road, Gloucester, GL1 5AA Tel: (01452) 553344 Fax: (01452) 553345 E-mail: sales@cpccomputers.co.uk *Computer engineers, document and data management, computer maintenance, computer hardware and software. Computer training. Computer security. Covering Gloucestershire, Wiltshire, Avon, Herefordshire, Worcestershire, Cotswolds, Monmouthshire, Somerset. Intel premier provider, Microsoft certified partner. INVU certified partner. ALTO Hiway. Sophos. Anti virus software.*

C P C Engineers Ltd, Adderley Road, Market Drayton, Shropshire, TF9 3SW Tel: (01630) 652904 Fax: (01630) 652904 *Engineering sub-contractors*

C P C Kings Lynn, Oldmedow Road, Hardwick Industrial Estate, King's Lynn, Norfolk, PE30 4LL Tel: (01553) 761481 Fax: (01553) 766203 Principal Export Areas: Worldwide *Printed cartons*

C P Cases Scotland Ltd, 4 Howe Moss Avenue, Kirkhill Industrial Estate, Dyce, Aberdeen, AB21 0GP Tel: (01224) 774384 Fax: (01224) 774123 E-mail: admin@cpcases.com

C P Ceramics, 150 Columbia Road, London, E2 7RG Tel: (020) 7366 9570 Fax: (020) 7366 9715 E-mail: sales@cpceramics.com *Ceramic model & mould making*

▶ C P Construction Gwent Ltd, Newtown Industrial Estate, Cross Keys, Newport, Gwent, NP11 7PZ Tel: (01495) 270804 Fax: (01495) 270728 E-mail: info@cpconstruction.co.uk

▶ C P Covers Ltd, 18 Hanson Close, Middleton, Manchester, M24 2HD Tel: 0161-654 9396 Fax: 0161-654 6017 E-mail: cpcovers@btopenworld.com *Fire & heat protective covers retail & manufrs*

C P D Ltd, Copenhagen Road, Suttonfields Industrial Estate, Hull, HU7 0XQ Tel: (01482) 625625 Fax: (01482) 625626 E-mail: info@cpd-clean.co.uk *Disposable paper & cleaning product suppliers*

C P D Distribution P.L.C., Unit 94 Roding Road, The London Industrial Park, Beckton, London, E6 6LS Tel: (020) 7474 5485 Fax: (020) 7474 6374 *Suspended ceilings*

C P D Distribution P.L.C., Units 11-12, Stadium Industrial Estate, Craddock Road, Luton, LU4 0JF Tel: (01582) 594222 Fax: (01582) 595222 *Supply interior finishing & office equipment*

C P E Precision Engineering Co. Ltd, Sutherland House, Arlington Way, Sundorne Retail Park, Shrewsbury, SY1 4YA Tel: (01743) 444250 Fax: (01743) 462563 *Precision engineers & special purpose machinery*

C P E (Pressure Vessels) Ltd, Apollo, Lichfield Road Industrial Estate, Tamworth, Staffordshire, B79 7TA Tel: 01827 68710 Fax: (01827) 54396 E-mail: sales@cpe-ltd.com *Pressure vessels & pipe work in stainless steel, carbon steel manufrs*

C P Electronic Ltd, Unit 2 Abbey Manufacturing Estate, Wembley, Middlesex, HA0 1RR Tel: (020) 8900 0671 Fax: (020) 8900 0674 E-mail: enquiry@cpelectronics.co.uk *Electronic process controls manufrs*

C P Engineering, Sandys Road, Malvern, Worcestershire, WR14 1JJ Tel: (01684) 584850 Fax: (01684) 573088 E-mail: sales@cpengineering.com *Engine & vehicle test equipment manufrs*

▶ C P F Engineers Stores Ltd, 65 Marmion Road, Southsea, Hampshire, PO5 2AX Tel: (023) 9281 8334 Fax: (023) 9283 3040 E-mail: sales@cpfastenings.co.uk *Retailers of hardware ironmongery*

C P Films, 13 Acorn Business Centre, Northarbour Road, Cosham, Portsmouth, PO6 3TH Tel: (023) 9221 9112 Fax: (023) 9221 9102 E-mail: marketing.cosham@cpfilms.co.uk *Transparent film manufrs*

C P Flooring Services Ltd, The Heysoms, 163 Chester Road, Northwich, Cheshire, CW8 4AQ Tel: 0161-432 9688 Fax: 0161-437 4042 E-mail: sales@cpflooringservices.co.uk

▶ C P Formstyle, 3 Weirside Court, Dockfield Road, Shipley, West Yorkshire, BD17 7AD Tel: (01274) 591400 Fax: (01274) 591811 E-mail: sales@formstyle.co.uk *Print management direct mail & tranactional mailing*

C P H Thurmaston Ltd, 2 Upperton Road, Leicester, LE3 0BG Tel: 0116-254 1322 E-mail: martyngoode@cphthurmaston.co.uk *General engineers*

C P I, Concorde House, 56 Station Road, Finchley Central, London, N3 2SA Tel: (020) 8235 3535 Fax: (020) 8235 3555 E-mail: info@cpilondon.com *Design, print & internet services*

C P I Euromix Ltd, Unit 27 Fountain Business Centre, Ellis Street, Coatbridge, Lanarkshire, ML5 3AA Tel: (01236) 431700 Fax: (01236) 432090 *Dry mortar suppliers*

▶ C P I Pneumatics, Redcliffe Road, Mansfield, Nottinghamshire, NG18 2QH Tel: (01623) 626684 Fax: (01623) 422255 E-mail: sales@cpi-pneumatics.co.uk *Pneumatic equipment distributors & manufrs*

C P I UK Ltd, 107 Boston Road, Gorse Hill, Leicester, LE4 1AW Tel: 0116-234 0600 Fax: 0116-235 2592 E-mail: uk.info@cpiglobal.com *Point of sale display designers*

C P International Chemical Ltd, New Town Road, Bishop's Stortford, Hertfordshire, CM23 3SA Tel: (01279) 506330 Fax: (01279) 755873 E-mail: chemicals@cpgroup.co.uk *Chemical importers & exporters*

C P K Industrial Finishers Ltd, C P K House, Colndale Road, Colnbrook, Slough, SL3 0HQ Tel: (01753) 684666 Fax: (01753) 685272 E-mail: cpk@technicalwebservices.com *Powder coating services*

C P Kelco UK Ltd, Cleeve Court, Cleeve Road, Leatherhead, Surrey, KT22 7UD Tel: (01372) 369400 Fax: (01372) 369401 *Xanthan & food gum manufrs*

C P Knitwear, Victoria Centre, Waterloo Road, Blackpool, FY4 1AD Tel: (01253) 406011 *Knitwear manufrs*

C P L, 2 St. James Road, Brackley, Northamptonshire, NN13 7XY Tel: (01280) 706661 Fax: (01280) 706671 E-mail: canonbury@canonbury.com *Chiropody products*

C P L Ltd, Liverpool House, Penlan Street, Pwllheli, Gwynedd, LL53 5DE Tel: (01758) 613035 Fax: (01758) 612485 E-mail: cplltd@compuserve.com *I.T. specialists*

continued

C P L, Anglo House, Worcester Road, Stourport-On-Severn, Worcestershire, DY13 9AW Tel: (01299) 877004 Fax: (01299) 877226 E-mail: enquiries@computerproof.co.uk *Computer manufacturers & suppliers*

C P L Aromas, Barrington Hall, Dunmow Road, Hatfield Broad Oak, Bishop's Stortford, Hertfordshire, CM22 7LE Tel: (01279) 718573 Fax: (01279) 718527 E-mail: uk.enquiries@cplaromas.com *Fragrances manufrs*

C P L Carbon Link, Sterling House, 2 Park Street, Wigan, Lancashire, WN3 5HE Tel: (01942) 824240 Fax: (01942) 824133 E-mail: support@activated-carbon.com Principal Export Areas: Worldwide *Activated carbon importers*

C P L Electronics Ltd, Unit 8-14 Highcroft Industrial Estate, Enterprise Road, Waterlooville, Hampshire, PO8 0BT Tel: (023) 9259 9333 Fax: (023) 9259 3127E-mail: cpl@dsl.pipex.com *Printed circuit board manufrs*

▶ C P L Engineering, 78 Main Street, Crumlin, County Antrim, BT29 4UU Tel: (028) 9445 3225

C P L Filters, Unit 1-2 Alma Industrial Estate, Regent Street, Rochdale, Lancashire, OL12 0HQ Tel: (01706) 642823 Fax: (01706) 642537 E-mail: dorothy.clarke@pure-filters.com *Filtration and pure air solutions. Odour control, grease control, factories, clean air solutions, bags, carbon, chemical control. Dust control, smoke control, gas control. Typical installations include hospitals, restaurants, air-conditioning and micro-electronics. Products include: grease filters, washable filters, uniglass, disposable panels, bag filters, longlife bag filters, rigid bag filters, rigid box filters, unimat pads, absolute filters. Get in touch for all your filtration needs.*

C P L Industries Ltd, Mill Lane, Chesterfield, Derbyshire, S42 6NG Tel: (01246) 277001 Fax: (01246) 212212 E-mail: corporate@cplindustries.co.uk *Energy products*

C P L Petroleum Ltd, Prince Regent Way, Diss, Norfolk, IP22 4GW Tel: (01379) 652235 Fax: (01379) 643529 E-mail: diss@cplpetroleum.co.uk *Fuel oil distributors*

C P L Petroleum, 22 Hawbank Road, East Kilbride, Glasgow, G74 5HA Tel: (01355) 249077 Fax: (01355) 264043 E-mail: eastkilbride@cplpetroleum.co.uk *Oil distributors*

C P L Scientific Information Services Ltd, Nosworthy Way, Mongewell, Wallingford, Oxfordshire, OX10 8DE Tel: (01491) 829346 Fax: (01491) 836232 E-mail: sis@cplsis.com *Technical & marketing consultants*

C P Lubricants, Drivers Wharf, Northam Road, Southampton, SO14 0YD Tel: (023) 8033 7800 Fax: (023) 8033 7801 E-mail: cp@cplubricants.co.uk *Lubricants oil gear hydraulic axle transmission suppliers*

C P Mechanical Designs Ltd, 48 Wellington Road, Portslade, Brighton, BN41 1DT Tel: (01273) 430001 Fax: (01273) 424654 E-mail: enquiries@cpmechanical.co.uk *Precision engineers*

C P Offset Ltd, Kellaw Road, Darlington, County Durham, DL1 4YA Tel: (01325) 462315 Fax: (01325) 462767 E-mail: administrator@banff-buchan.ac.uk *Lithographic printers*

C P S, Drury Lane, St. Leonards-on-Sea, East Sussex, TN38 9BA Tel: (01424) 442663 Fax: (01424) 433835 *Computer systems & software developers*

C P S Engineering, Wentworth Road, Mapplewell, Barnsley, South Yorkshire, S75 6DU Tel: (01226) 386515 Fax: (01226) 380165 E-mail: cpsengineering@aol.com *Fabrications engineers*

C P S Oxford Ltd, Partridge Yard, Eynsham Road, Cassington, Witney, Oxfordshire, OX29 4EU Tel: (01865) 881204 Fax: (01865) 880617 *Commercial vehicle painters*

C P S Seating & Staging, Station Yard, Station Road, Bawtry, Doncaster, South Yorkshire, DN10 6QD Tel: (01302) 711183 Fax: (01302) 711171 *Seating & staging system manufrs*

C & P Services Northern Ltd, 11 Burtonwood Industrial Centre, Phipps Lane, Burtonwood, Warrington, WA5 4HX Tel: (01925) 229118 Fax: (01925) 228022 E-mail: info@candpservices.co.uk *Compressor & pump maintenance*

C P S-Lanmear Ltd, 158 Little Hardwick Rd, Aldridge, Walsall, WS9 0SF Tel: 0121-353 5705 Fax: 0121-353 5705 E-mail: csiddell@compuserve.com *Communication system consultants*

C P Steel, Salamanca Road, Tharston, Norwich, NR15 2PF Tel: (01508) 531316 Fax: (01508) 531364 *Steel fabricators*

C & P Structural Engineers, 169 Cromford Road, Langley Mill, Nottingham, NG16 4EU Tel: (01773) 530189 Fax: (01773) 530446 E-mail: candp@btconnect.com *Structural engineers services*

C P Supplies Ltd, 95 Chester Street, Aston, Birmingham, B6 4AE Tel: 0121-380 1600 Fax: 0121-380 1616 E-mail: admin@cpsupplies.co.uk *Partition (demountable & dry construction) constructors*

▶ C P Supplies Ltd, Unit A389, Western Avenue, Team Valley Trading Estate, Gateshead, Tyne & Wear, NE11 0SZ Tel: 0191-296 2233 Fax: 0191-482 3500 *Suspended ceilings distribution & dry lining distribution*

C P Supplies Ltd, 1-3 Brixton Road, London, SW9 6DE Tel: (020) 7582 2911 Fax: (020) 7582 0271 E-mail: bmkennington@cpsupplies.co.uk *Partition component distributor or agents*

C P Supplies Ltd, Sheridale Business Centre, Knight Road, Rochester, Kent, ME2 2EL Tel: (01634) 290029 Fax: (01634) 290888 *Suspended ceilings & furniture*

C P Supplies Ltd, Twickenham Trading Estate, Rugby Road, Twickenham, TW1 1DQ Tel: (020) 8891 5971 Fax: (020) 8892 5218 E-mail: michellephelan@cpsupplies.co.uk *Partition & suspended ceiling material suppliers*

▶ indicates data change since last edition

C P T Enterprises, 143 White Hart Lane, Portchester, Fareham, Hampshire, PO16 9BB Tel: (023) 9238 9521 Fax: (023) 9237 5181 E-mail: info@cptenterprises.co.uk *Conveyor belt manufrs*

C P U Direct, 20 Westerham Avenue, London, N9 9BU Tel: (020) 8887 0044 Fax: (020) 8887 0099 *Computer insurance*

C P V Watercoolers, 90 Cannon Lane, Pinner, Middlesex, HA5 1HR Tel: (020) 8866 1585 Fax: (020) 8558 6780 E-mail: sales@c-p-v.co.uk *Cigarette vending machine services*

C Pac, 33a Morland Way, Nelson Park, Cramlington, Northumberland, NE23 1WE Tel: 0191-491 0405 Fax: 0191-491 0465 E-mail: sales@c-pac.co.uk *Computer system manufrs*

▶ C Parducci, 1 Miller Street, Johnstone, Renfrewshire, PA5 8HP Tel: (01505) 324541 Fax: (01505) 324966

C Pawson & Son, Caister House, 19 Market Place, Caistor, Market Rasen, Lincolnshire, LN7 6TR Tel: (01472) 851434 E-mail: paul@houndogtp-net.co.uk *Joiners*

C Perkin Ltd, 6 Shaw Cross Court, Horace Waller V C Parade, Shaw Cross Business Park, Dewsbury, West Yorkshire, WF12 7RF Tel: (01924) 439449 Fax: (01924) 438908 E-mail: info@cperkin.com Principal Export Areas: Worldwide *Spiral paper tube converting machines, cardboard tube making machinery manufrs*

C Potter, 2-6 Grover Street, Tunbridge Wells, Kent, TN1 2QB Tel: (01892) 522208 Fax: (01892) 543515 *Guns & sport clothing suppliers*

C Q Alarms 1982 Ltd, 1a Dora Road, Birmingham, B10 9RF Tel: 0121-772 1566 Fax: 0121-766 8231 *Burglar & fire alarm engineers*

C Q C Ltd, Riverside Road, Pottington Business Park, Barnstaple, Devon, EX31 1NB Tel: (01271) 345678 Fax: (01271) 345090 E-mail: pjg@cqc.co.uk *Made-up textile manufrs*

▶ C Q M, 3 Westbrook Court, Sharrow Vale Road, Sheffield, S11 8YZ Tel: 0114-281 5781 Fax: 0114-281 5785 E-mail: enquireies@cqmltd.co.uk *Telemarketing, marketing & recruitment*

C Q R Security, 125 Pasture Road, Wirral, Merseyside, CH46 4TH Tel: 0151-606 9595 Fax: 0151-606 1122 E-mail: info@cqr.co.uk *Security companies*

C & R, Bruce House, Warren Park Way, Enderby, LE19 4ZW Tel: 0116-284 7464 Fax: 0116-284 7440 E-mail: info@candr.co.uk *General lithographic printers*

C R A Manufacturing Ltd, 15a Oglander Road, London, SE15 4EQ Tel: (020) 7635 8201 Fax: (020) 7277 5667 *Transformer manufrs*

C R Allen, Lower Hoddern Farm, Glynn Road, Peacehaven, East Sussex, BN10 8AP Tel: (01273) 584987 Fax: (01273) 580904 *Agricultural machine repairs & land rovers service parts & sales*

▶ C R Blinds, 55 Warmington Road, Sheldon, Birmingham, B26 3SX Tel: 0121-244 0803 Fax: 0121-244 0803 *Blind retailers*

C R Building Plastics, 40 Main Road, Christian Malford, Chippenham, Wiltshire, SN15 4AZ Tel: (01249) 721700 E-mail: sales@crbuildingplastics.co.uk *Double glazing installation*

C R Business Equipment Ltd, Unit 11 Stephenson Way, Formby Business Park, Formby, Liverpool, L37 8EG Tel: (01704) 834083 Fax: (01704) 834083 *Stationery & office furniture distributors*

▶ C R Carpets, 25-26 Stable Hobba, Newlyn, Penzance, Cornwall, TR20 8TL Tel: (01736) 874500 E-mail: crcarpets@goldsites.co.uk *Carpets & flooring, we also have a carpet fitting & re-fitting service*

C R Cradock Tractors, Woodside, Heywood, Westbury, Wiltshire, BA13 4LW Tel: (01373) 826403 Fax: (01373) 824414 *Agricultural engineers*

▶ C R Crane & Son Ltd, Manor Farm, Main Road, Nether Broughton, Melton Mowbray, Leicestershire, LE14 3HB Tel: (01664) 823366 Fax: (01664) 823534 E-mail: sales@crcrane.co.uk

C R D Devices Ltd, 3 All Saints Industrial Estate, Darlington Road, Shildon, County Durham, DL4 2RD Tel: (01388) 778400 Fax: (01388) 778800 E-mail: sales@crd-devices.co.uk Principal Export Areas: Worldwide *Manufacturers of solenoids. In addition, linear actuators*

▶ C R D Interiors Ltd, 245 High Street, Aldershot, Hampshire, GU12 4NG Tel: (01252) 319588 Fax: (01252) 310698 E-mail: crd-interiors@lycos.co.uk *CRD manufactures & installs high quality bespoke kitchens, bedrooms & home offices, CRD also offers a full interior design service & an installation service for all types of kitchens & bathrooms.*

C R D Refrigeration, Field House, Pudleston, Leominster, Herefordshire, HR6 0RG Tel: (01568) 750620 Fax: (01568) 750386 *Refrigeration & conditioning suppliers*

▶ C R F Coatings Ltd, Unit 1 Bullock Street, West Bromwich, West Midlands, B70 7HE Tel: 0121-525 1888 Fax: 0121-525 0888

C R F Sections Ltd, Hale Trading Estate, Lower Church Lane, Tipton, West Midlands, DY4 7PQ Tel: 0121-557 1234 Fax: 0121-522 3003 *Door components manufrs*

C R F (UK) Ltd, Unit B8 Wem Industrial Estate, Soulton Road, Wem, Shrewsbury, SY4 5SD Tel: (01939) 235000 Fax: (01939) 235111 E-mail: crf-sales@spunwebs.net *Steel fabricators*

C & R Fabrications, Abbey Hill Trading Estate, Stourton Way, Yeovil, Somerset, BA21 3AR Tel: (01935) 427940 Fax: (01935) 414728 *Steel fabricators*

C R Gibbs & Sons (Sheffield) Ltd, Nunnery Drive, Sheffield, S2 1TA Tel: 0114-273 7003 Fax: 0114-275 3500 E-mail: crgibbs@btconnect.com *Shop fitters & building contractors*

▶ C & R Graphics Ltd, 30 Deerdykes View, Cumbernauld, Glasgow, G68 9HN Tel: (01236) 726552 Fax: (01236) 730219

C & R Grieveson, Station Road, Walker, Newcastle upon Tyne, NE6 3PN Tel: 0191-262 8470 Fax: 0191-295 4469 *Scrap iron & steel merchants*

C R I Ltd, 8 Langley Court, Langley Road, Burscough Industrial Estate, Ormskirk, Lancashire, L40 8JR Tel: (01704) 895950 Fax: (01704) 896260 E-mail: cri@cybase.co.uk *Electronic & mechanical calibration services of instruments*

C R I Grinding Ltd, 2a Goodridge Avenue, Gloucester, GL2 5EA Tel: (01452) 529475 Fax: (01452) 306362 E-mail: cri.grinding@virgin.net *Precision centre less & internal grinding services*

C R M Associates, 72 Mytchett Rd, Mytchett, Camberley, Surrey, GU16 6EZ Tel: (01252) 513232 Fax: (01252) 517298 *Computer cleaning services*

▶ C R M Print Finishers Ltd, 3 80-81 Walsworth Road, Hitchin, Hertfordshire, SG4 9SX Tel: (01462) 441644 Fax: (01462) 442744 E-mail: crm@mcng.co.uk *Trade print finishing house, full & complete finishing services*

C & R Munro Ltd, Unit 7e, Bandeath Industrial Estate, Throsk, Stirling, FK7 7NP Tel: (01786) 813618 Fax: (01786) 815113 *Motor rewinds industrial installations & repairers*

C & R Plastics, E4 Unit, Formal Industrial Estate, Treswithian, Camborne, Cornwall, TR14 0PY Tel: (01209) 711878 Fax: (01209) 711895 *PVC building suppliers*

C R Reynolds Construction Ltd, Gibson Lane, Melton, North Ferriby, North Humberside, HU14 3HH Tel: (01482) 637373 Fax: (01482) 637370 E-mail: crreynold@dial.hightec.com *Civil engineers*

C R Robinson & Son, 247 Broad Street, Crewe, CW1 4JJ Tel: (01270) 584531 Fax: (01270) 588054 *Joinery manufrs*

C R S Cash Registers, Low Sell, Gateshead, Tyne & Wear, NE9 5WY Tel: 0191-491 3530 Fax: 0191-491 3530 E-mail: terence.cullen@talk21.com *Sales & service of electronic cash registers*

C R S (London) Ltd, 98A Blackstock Road, London, N4 2DR Tel: (020) 7226 0404 Fax: (020) 7226 1806 E-mail: crslondonltd@hotmail.com *Printing machinery suppliers*

C R S Solutions Ltd, Provincial House, 6 High Street, Southampton, SO14 2DH Tel: (023) 8063 2440 Fax: (023) 8063 2550 *PC parts*

C R S Specialised Building Services Ltd, 45a Stoke Road, Gosport, Hampshire, PO12 1LS Tel: (023) 9258 3084 Fax: (023) 9258 3084 E-mail: enq@crsbuilders.co.uk *Wall ties & electrics services*

C R S Stamps, Cheltenham, Gloucestershire, GL52 2YS Tel: (01242) 241141 Fax: (01242) 690032 E-mail: sales@crsstamps.com *Rubber stamp manufrs*

C R Supplies, 143 Ballysnod Road, Larne, County Antrim, BT40 3NP Tel: (028) 2827 8800 Fax: (028) 2827 8800 *Agricultural merchants*

C R Telecom, 27 Langcliffe Avenue, Warwick, CV34 5XT Tel: (01926) 408399 Fax: (01926) 408401 E-mail: clive@crtelecom.demon.co.uk *Data cables distributors*

▶ C & R Transport Ltd, 24-26 High Street, Snodland, Kent, ME6 5DF Tel: 08703 121247 *available from C & R Transport Ltd based in Snodland, Kent. Click the links below to visit our website or contact us via our profile page.*

C & R Walne, 74 Burnley Road, Accrington, Lancashire, BB5 1AF Tel: (01254) 231384 Fax: (01254) 390737 E-mail: info@walne-engravers.co.uk *Engravers & sign manufrs*

▶ C Raymond Heating Co. Ltd, 93-97 Pall Mall, Leigh-on-Sea, Essex, SS9 1RF Tel: (01702) 714959

C Robathon & Sons Ltd, 63 Hunters Vale, Birmingham, B19 2XH Tel: 0121-554 6990 Fax: 0121-554 4389 E-mail: sales@c-robathan.com *Silversmith manufrs*

C Roberts Steel Services Manchester Ltd, Clement Works, Long Wood Road, Trafford Park, Manchester, M17 1PZ Tel: 0161-874 5200 Fax: 0161-848 7820 E-mail: sales@roberts-steel-mcr.co.uk *Steel stockholders*

C S A, Broad Lane, Cottenham, Cambridge, CB24 8SW Tel: (01954) 251573 Fax: (01954) 206506 E-mail: csaeagle@fsbdial.co.uk *Industrial cleaning equipment*

C S A Electronics, 59 High Street, Findon, Worthing, West Sussex, BN14 0ST Tel: (01903) 877781 Fax: (01903) 877781 *PCB assembly*

C S Alloys, Unit 32 Jubilee Trade Centre, Jubilee Road, Letchworth Garden City, Hertfordshire, SG6 1SP Tel: (01462) 481273 Fax: (01462) 481092 E-mail: csalloys@hotmail.com *Metal slitters & shearers manufrs*

C S B Design Consultants Ltd, 10 Marathon Paddock, Gillingham, Kent, ME7 4HE Tel: (01634) 571749 Fax: (01634) 322206 E-mail: chrisb@cka1.fsnet.co.uk *Industrial controllers*

C S B Supplies, Unit 10 Dale Mill, Burnley Road East, Rossendale, Lancashire, BB4 9HU Tel: (01706) 213333 Fax: (01706) 217733 E-mail: sales@csbsupplies.co.uk *Cleaning material manufrs*

▶ C & S Banners, 244 North Lane, Aldershot, Hampshire, GU12 4TJ Tel: (01252) 317701 Fax: (01252) 324375 *Fishing tackle suppliers*

C & S Bouncy Castles, 8 Duke Close, Nottingham, NG6 7BG Tel: 0115-976 3935 *Bouncy castle hire*

C & S Builders Merchants Stamford Hill Ltd, 278-286 Stamford Hill, London, N16 6TY Tel: (020) 8809 5373 Fax: (020) 8800 3243 *Building materials merchants* Also at: London E11

C S C Ltd, Westlakes Science & Technology, Moor Row, Cumbria, CA24 3JZ Tel: (01946) 502234 Fax: (01946) 502221 E-mail: ijohnson@csc.com *Information technology services*

C S C Construction Ltd, Stanley House, 15-17 Ladybridge Road, Cheadle Hulme, Cheadle, Cheshire, SK8 5BL Tel: 0161-486 9321 Fax: 0161-488 4399 *Building Contractors, Residential Building Contractors available from C S C Construction Ltd based in Cheadle, Cheshire. Click the links below to visit our website or contact us via our profile page.*

continued

▶ C S C Engineers Ltd, Shirley Road, Southampton, SO15 3EY Tel: (023) 8063 0626 Fax: (023) 8033 4065 E-mail: cscengineers@btclick.com

C S C Screeding Ltd, Chancery Court, Lincolns Inn, Lincoln Road, High Wycombe, Buckinghamshire, HP12 3RE Tel: (0845) 500 4055 Fax: (0845) 500 4056 E-mail: info@cscscreeding.co.uk *Total Floor Screeding Solutions, Nationwide.*

▶ C & S Castles, 117 Walsingham Close, Rainham, Kent, ME8 9SN Tel: (01634) 377427 *Bouncy castle equipment hire*

C & S Catering Supplies Ltd, Whitehouse Farm, Littlefield Green, White Waltham, Maidenhead, Berkshire, SL6 3JL Tel: 0118-934 1300 Fax: 0118-932 0304 E-mail: candscatering@candscatering.freeserve.co.uk *China & glass wholesalers & catering disposables*

C S Communication Services Ltd, 19 Sutton Oak Corner, Sutton Coldfield, West Midlands, B74 2DH Tel: (0845) 6771000 E-mail: sales@comms.co.uk *Telecommunications equipment distributors & service providers*

C & S Crane Hire, 54 Pondhills Lane, Arnold, Nottingham, NG5 8DS Tel: 0115-926 3273 Fax: 0115-967 6491 *Crane hire*

▶ C S D, 10 New Road, Rayne, Braintree, Essex, CM77 6TG Tel: (01376) 340240 Fax: (01376) 550853 E-mail: info@csd-it.co.uk *Computer systems consultants*

C S D Controls (U K), Britannia Way, Malvern, Worcestershire, WR14 1GZ Tel: (01684) 567044 Fax: (01604) 567017 E-mail: retrofit@csdcontrols.co.uk *CNC engineering services*

C S D Sealing Systems Ltd, Offshore House, Albert Street, Blyth, Northumberland, NE24 1LZ Tel: (01670) 353300 Fax: (01670) 369503 E-mail: info@csdsealingsystems.co.uk *Passive fire protection manufrs*

C S D Technology, 1 Mclachlan Street, Stenhousemuir, Larbert, Stirlingshire, FK5 3HJ Tel: (01324) 882515 Fax: (01324) 882516 E-mail: sales@csdtechnology.co.uk *Hardware builders, designers & retailers*

▶ C S D Training Partnership, 33 Grange Drive, Castle Donington, Derby, DE74 2QU Tel: (01332) 810117 E-mail: admin@csd-training.co.uk *It training delivered professionally*

C S Digital Systems, 63 Seaview Road, Wallasey, Merseyside, CH45 4QW Tel: 0151-691 1783 Fax: 0151-691 1079 *Copier sales*

C S E Alarms, 13 Haigh Close, Chorley, Lancashire, PR7 2QR Tel: (01257) 275549 *Security equipment installers*

C S E Seprol Ltd, Rotherside Road, Eckington, Sheffield, S21 4HL Tel: (01246) 436331 Fax: (01246) 432461 E-mail: products@cse-seprol.com *Data acquisition systems manufrs*

▶ C & S Electrical Engineering Services Ltd, Unit 30 Salford University BP, Winders Way, Salford, M6 6AR Tel: 0161-736 6486

C S Ellis Group Ltd, Wireless Hill Ind Estate, South Luffenham, Oakham, Leicestershire, LE15 8NF Tel: (01780) 720133 Fax: (01780) 721801 E-mail: mail@csellis.co.uk *Haulage & storage contractors*

C S Environmental Services, 270 Manchester Road, Audenshaw, Manchester, M34 5GJ Tel: 0161-371 1638 Fax: 0161-371 7081 *Heating & ventilating engineers*

C & S Equipment Ltd, Unit 9D, Wingbury Courtyard Business Village, Wingrave, Aylesbury, Buckinghamshire, HP22 4LW Tel: (01296) 688500 *Pneumatic lift platforms manufrs*

▶ C & S Erections Ltd, 31 Cuddington Avenue, Worcester Park, Surrey, KT4 7DB Tel: (020) 8330 3307

C S F Print, 6 Hockliffe Brae, Walnut Tree, Milton Keynes, MK7 7BQ Tel: (01908) 550643 Fax: (01908) 550611 E-mail: sales@csfprint.com *Printing & design agency*

C S F Solutions Ltd, 920 Birchwood Boulevard, Birchwood, Warrington, WA3 7QS Tel: (01925) 852020 Fax: (01925) 811522 *Computer reseller*

C & S Fabrications Ltd, Club Mill Road, Sheffield, S6 2FH Tel: 0114-234 7567 Fax: 0114-231 4513 E-mail: postmaster@scfabs.co.uk *Fabricating engineers & sheet metalwork*

▶ C S Gallagher Ltd, Deans Farm, 2 Phillips Lane, Stratford sub Castle, Salisbury, SP1 3YR Tel: (01722) 421988 Fax: (01722) 421421

C S Howard, 73 Grasscroft, Northampton, NN2 8QL Tel: (01604) 845888 Fax: (01604) 820213 E-mail: colin@the-boardman.co.uk *Sign erecting, boardman, estate agents signs, signs*

▶ C S I, 36 Luzley Brook Road, Royton, Oldham, OL2 6SQ Tel: (01706) 843249 E-mail: spencer.marsden1@btinternet.com *Burglar alarms, CCTV, emergency lighting & access control repairs, upgrades & services*

C S I P Ltd, Unit 11 Granby Court, Surrey Close, Granby Industrial Estate, Weymouth, Dorset, DT4 9XB Tel: (01305) 779020 Fax: (01305) 778095 E-mail: sales@csip.co.uk Principal Export Areas: Africa *Defence contractors*

C S J Enterprises, Unit 96 Spring Hill Farm, Salters Lane, Lower Moor, Pershore, Worcestershire, WR10 2PE Tel: (01386) 861777 Fax: (01386) 861666 E-mail: csjent@aol.com *Bar loading machine services*

▶ C S J Plant Ltd, Harboro House Fairhills Industrial Estate, Woodrow Way, Irlam, Manchester, M44 6ZQ Tel: 0161-775 0805 Fax: 0161-775 0711

C S L Copy Shop, 84 St. Marys Road, Market Harborough, Leicestershire, LE16 7DX Tel: (01858) 465208 Fax: (01858) 465208 *Photocopying services*

C S L Recruitment & Consulting Ltd, Hurst House, 157-169 Walton Road, East Molesey, Surrey, KT8 0DX Tel: (020) 8224 9840 Fax: (020) 8941 4095 E-mail: sales@imesconsulting.com Principal Export Areas: Middle East *Management consultants*

C S L Technical Engineering Services, Office 2 Rainbow Business Centre, Phoenix Way, Swansea Enterprise Park, Swansea, SA7 9EH Tel: 01792 702200 E-mail: sales@csl-ltd.co.uk *Automation Industrial Machines Rework*

C S M Archives Storage & Distribution, Chequers Lane, Dagenham, Essex, RM9 6PR Tel: (020) 8596 0088 Fax: (020) 8596 0099

▶ C S M Electronics, 2 Century Road, High Carr Business Park, Newcastle, Staffordshire, ST5 7UG Tel: (01782) 563334 Fax: (01782) 563345 E-mail: sale@csmelectronics.co.uk *Pcb manufrs*

C S M Plating Ltd, Progress Works, Heath Mill La, Birmingham, B9 4AP Tel: 0121-772 2084 Fax: 0121-772 5190 *Gold, zinc & chrome electroplaters*

C S M Services Ltd, Bradley Hall Trading Estate, Bradley Lane, Standish, Wigan, Lancashire, WN6 0XQ Tel: (01257) 424548 Fax: (01257) 424548 *Fork lift truck hire*

C S Manufacturing Ltd, 13-14 Feeder Road, St. Phillips, Bristol, BS2 0SB Tel: 0117-977 3388 Fax: 0117-977 3397 E-mail: csmanufacturing@btconnect.com *Polystyrene packaging manufrs*

C S Marine, Newmet House, Rue De St. Lawrence, Waltham Abbey, Essex, EN9 1PF Tel: (01992) 703403 Fax: (01992) 768393 E-mail: materials@newmet.co.uk *Paint distributors*

C S Milne Engineering, Unit 2 Peckleton Lane Business Park, Peckleton Common, Elmesthorpe, Leicester, LE9 7SH Tel: (01455) 822569 Fax: (01455) 824012 E-mail: sales@cs-milne.co.uk Principal Export Areas: Worldwide *Gas control ,cylinder manifold systems*

C & S Nameplate Co. Ltd, 37 Vale Road, Portslade, Brighton, BN41 1GD Tel: (01273) 419646 Fax: (01273) 411316 E-mail: sales@candsnameplate.com *Nameplates & labels manufrs*

C S P, Astra House, Christy Close, Southfields Business Park, Basildon, Essex, SS15 6TQ Tel: (01268) 493377 Fax: (01268) 493399 E-mail: sales@cspuk.co.uk *Pharmaceutical test equipment importers*

C S P Audio Visual Ltd, Unit 55 Third Avenue, Deeside Industrial Park, Deeside, Clwyd, CH5 2LA Tel: (01244) 288322 Fax: (01244) 288344 E-mail: sales@cspaudiovisual.co.uk *Audio visual equipment hire*

C & S Packaging, Vestry Industrial Estate, Vestry Road, Sevenoaks, Kent, TN14 5EL Tel: (01732) 456663 Fax: (01732) 459296 *Packaging material distributors*

▶ C S & S Ltd, 5 Tavistock Road, West Bridgford, Nottingham, NG2 6FH Tel: 0115-974 5146 Fax: 0870 762 0539 E-mail: info@chinasourceandsupply.com *Importing business*

C S S P, 29 London Road, Bromley, BR1 1DG Tel: (020) 8460 0022 Fax: (020) 8460 1196 *Computer software construction industry*

C & S Steels Wolverhampton Ltd, Highfields Road, Bilston, West Midlands, WV14 0LQ Tel: (01902) 404771 Fax: (01902) 353348 E-mail: sales@prosol-electronics.co.uk *Bright steel bar stockholders*

C S Struthers, Valletta Street, Hull, HU9 5NU Tel: (01482) 707766 Fax: (01482) 787479 E-mail: sales@csstruthers.co.uk *Pressure vessel manufrs*

C S Surface Coating Ltd, 2 Mackay Transport, Colonial Way, Watford, WD24 4JU Tel: (01923) 246982 Fax: (01923) 237841 E-mail: mail@cs-surface-coating.co.uk *Wood finishing, lacquer & surface coating services*

C S T Group Ltd, 94 Lewes Road, Brighton, BN2 3QA Tel: (01273) 621393 Fax: (01273) 621390 E-mail: info@cst-group.com *Computer web design services*

C & S Tooling Ltd, 103 Nathan Way, London, SE28 0AQ Tel: (020) 8854 0888 Fax: (020) 8854 0888 *Engineers' pattern makers*

C S W Erlang Ltd, Unit 10, Green Farm, Fritwell, Bicester, Oxfordshire, OX27 7QU Tel: (01869) 345050 Fax: (01869) 345954 E-mail: mandy.jenkins@erlangcsw.co.uk *Antenna system installation for mobile communications networks*

C S W Tiling Ltd, 22-24 Nuffield Road, Nuffield Industrial Estate, Poole, Dorset, BH17 0RB Tel: (01202) 675836 Fax: (01202) 668219 E-mail: csw.tiling@cswtiles.com *Ceramic tile distributors*

▶ C Sam, Bridge House, 1-2 Riverside Drive, Aberdeen, AB11 7LH Tel: (01224) 586855 Fax: (01244) 586866 E-mail: sales@c-sam.co.uk *Specialists in asset management solutions for oil & gas*

▶ C Sharp Ltd, 76-80 Old Road, Morley, Leeds, LS27 7TH Tel: 0113-270 9944 Fax: 0113-270 9955 E-mail: enquiries@bsharpconstructions.com *Steel metal fabricators*

▶ C Shearer, Kilmaurs Road, Fenwick, Kilmarnock, Ayrshire, KA3 6AX Tel: (01560) 600552 Fax: (01560) 600670

C Silverman Office Furniture Centre, Fen Road, Cambridge, CB4 1UN Tel: (01223) 425168 Fax: (01223) 424826 E-mail: info@silvermanfurniture.co.uk *Office furniture suppliers*

C Soar & Sons, Tank Row, Grange Lane, Barnsley, South Yorkshire, S71 5AD Tel: (01226) 287951 Fax: (01226) 293146 E-mail: info@csoarandsons.co.uk *Electrical transformer contractors*

▶ C Software, Tayside Software Centre, Dundee Technology Park, Dundee, DD2 1TY Tel: (01382) 598450 Fax: (01382) 598449 *Web software development*

C Sparks & Sons Ltd, Wells Road, Glastonbury, Somerset, BA6 9AG Tel: (01458) 831742 Fax: (01458) 835078 E-mail: info@sparkstransport.co.uk *Road transport, haulage, freight & warehousing services*

▶ C Spencer, The Pentagon Centre, 310 Washington Street, Glasgow, G3 8AZ Tel: 0141-221 4859 Fax: 0141-221 8872

▶ C Spencer Ltd, Grainger House, Clayton St West, Newcastle upon Tyne, NE1 5EE Tel: 0191-261 1116 Fax: 0191-261 7829

C Stanley Jones Paints, Plot 8a Plough Lane Industrial Estate, Hereford, HR4 0EH Tel: (01432) 278613 Fax: (01432) 341089 E-mail: signs.stan@ukonline.co.uk *Signwriters & signmakers*

C Steinweg London Ltd, 106 Leadenhall Street, London, EC3A 4AA Tel: (020) 7626 4769 Fax: (020) 7929 1451 *Commodity warehousing*

C Syms & Sons Ltd, Systems Building, Bristol Road, Bumpers Farm, Chippenham, Wiltshire, SN14 6LH Tel: (01249) 654461 Fax: (01249) 443527 *Building contractors*

C T A Services, 1 Drake Road, Newport, Isle of Wight, PO30 1EQ Tel: (01983) 524129 Fax: (01983) 528001 E-mail: sales@ctaservices.co.uk *Computer consultants*

C T C, 12 Whiteladies Road, Bristol, BS8 1PD Tel: 0117-311 9009 Fax: 0117-311 9010 E-mail: info@ctcuk.com *Advertising & marketing agency*

C T C Container Trading (U.K.) Ltd, Hillview Base, Hillview Rd, East Tullos, Aberdeen, AB12 3HB Tel: (01224) 879111 Fax: (01224) 879015 E-mail: information@ctccontainers.com *Freight container rental services*

C T C & Co. (Essex) Ltd, Benbridge Indust Estate, The Square, Heybridge, Maldon, Essex, CM9 4LT Tel: (01621) 841100 Fax: (01621) 842233 E-mail: sales@ctcandcompany-essex.co.uk *Fibre optic cable management solutions & suppliers*

C T Composites, 2 Industrial Estate, Kempshott Park, Beggarwood, Basingstoke, Hampshire, RG23 7LP Tel: (01256) 396400 Fax: (01256) 397664 E-mail: sales@ctcomposites.co.uk *Distributors of spray machines*

C T D Carlisle, Viaduct Estate Road, Carlisle, CA2 5BN Tel: (01228) 536601 Fax: (01228) 520242 E-mail: sales@ctdtiles.co.uk *Tile distributors*

C T & E F Thomas, 12 Greenbank Terrace, Callington, Cornwall, PL17 7BU Tel: (01579) 384643 *Agricultural contractors*

▶ C T Electrical Rewinds Ltd, 58 Spindus Road, Speke Hall Industrial Estate, Liverpool, L24 1YA Tel: 0151-486 9654 Fax: 0151-486 3802

C T F Ltd, 11 Langley Park Road, Sutton, Surrey, SM1 4TB Tel: (020) 8642 5871 Fax: (020) 8770 1590 E-mail: info@ctfpestcontrol.co.uk *Pest control services*

C T Farr, Timothys Bridge Road, Stratford-upon-Avon, Warwickshire, CV37 9NQ Tel: (01789) 267161 Fax: (01789) 415719 *Fabricating engineers*

C T Finishings (Services) (Manufacturing), Unit 29 Enterprise House, Balloo Industrial Estate, Bangor, County Down, BT19 7QT Tel: (028) 9127 1525 Fax: (028) 9127 0080 *Furniture restorers*

C & T Fire, Stammerham Business Centre, Capel Road, Rusper, Horsham, West Sussex, RH12 4PZ Tel: (01306) 712421 Fax: (01306) 713225 E-mail: info@ctfire.co.uk *Fire & safety product distributors & servicing*

C T Flow Solutions, 24 Second Drove, Peterborough, PE1 5XA Tel: (01733) 319009 Fax: (01733) 319906 E-mail: ctflowsolutions@yahoo.co.uk *Pipeline suppliers*

C & T Harnesses Ltd, Unit 2 Lanwades Business Park, Kennett, Newmarket, Suffolk, CB8 7PN Tel: (01638) 751511 Fax: (01638) 751965 E-mail: info@ctharnesses.com *Assemblies for electronic & telecommunications industry*

C T Hayton Ltd, Sandylands Road, Kendal, Cumbria, LA9 6EX Tel: (01539) 721518 Fax: (01539) 722977 E-mail: sales@cthayton.co.uk *Agricultural & horticultural engineers*

C T I Ltd, 329 Goodyers End Lane, Bedworth, Warwickshire, CV12 0JA Tel: (024) 7664 4475 Fax: (024) 7636 2259 *Ultra sonic cleaner manufrs*

▶ C T I Ltd, 11 Murrills Estate, Fareham, Hampshire, PO16 9RD Tel: (023) 9232 7020 Fax: (023) 9221 5925 E-mail: lisa@cti-int.net *Bespoke antenna manufrs*

▶ C T Joinery, 29 Hillcot Close, Gloucester, GL2 4FU Tel: (01452) 387300 Fax: (01452) 387300 E-mail: ctjoineryglos@msn.com *Joiners*

C T L Components Ltd, Newman Lane, Alton, Hampshire, GU34 2QR Tel: (01420) 86009 Fax: (01420) 87711 *Powder spraying services*

C T L Engineering Co. Ltd, Cromwell Road, Bredbury, Stockport, Cheshire, SK6 2RH Tel: 0161-430 3173 Fax: 0161-430 8643 E-mail: sales@ctl-eng.com *Precision engineers*

C T M Root Crop Systems - Harpley Engineering Ltd, Cross Street, Harpley, King's Lynn, Norfolk, PE31 6TJ Tel: (01485) 520355 Fax: (01485) 520062 E-mail: sales@ctmharpley.co.uk *Agricultural machinery manufrs*

C T M Systems Ltd, Unit 8, Arkwright Road Industrial Estate, Cambridge Road, Bedford, MK42 0LE Tel: (01234) 355700 Fax: (01234) 351155 E-mail: sales@ctm-systems.demon.co.uk *Conveyor systems manufrs*

C & T Metals Ltd, 10 Carlyle Avenue, Hillington Industrial Estate, Glasgow, G52 4JJ Tel: 0141-810 4411 Fax: 0141-810 4414 E-mail: information@ctmetals.com *Plaster bead manufrs*

C T P Wipac Ltd, London Road, Buckingham, MK18 1BH Tel: (01280) 822800 Fax: (01280) 822802 E-mail: sales@wipac.com *Automotive component manufrs*

C T Precision, Hicks Road, Markyate, St. Albans, Hertfordshire, AL3 8LJ Tel: (01582) 840042 Fax: (01582) 840042 *Precision engineers*

C T Refrigeration Services, 16 Linton Dann Close, Hoo, Rochester, Kent, ME3 9DQ Tel: (01634) 250915 Fax: (01634) 255181 *Air conditioning & refrigeration contractors*

C T S, 17 Pages Walk, London, SE1 4SB Tel: (020) 7252 1849 Fax: (020) 7252 3241 E-mail: sales@ctslimited.co.uk *Sales leasing & rental of radio communications equipment & communication systems, mobile.*

C T S Security Ltd, Southgates Corner, Wisbech Road, King's Lynn, Norfolk, PE30 5JH Tel: (01553) 765429 Fax: (01553) 769078 *Security alarms installation*

C T Supplies Ltd, Unit 94 Northwick Business Centre, Blockley, Moreton-in-Marsh, Gloucestershire, GL56 9RF Tel: (01386) 700884 Fax: (01386) 700126 E-mail: sales@ct-supplies.co.uk *Chemical & tack cloth manufrs*

▶ C T Transport Castleford Ltd, Carr Wood Industrial Estate, Carr Wood Road, Castleford, West Yorkshire, WF10 4SB Tel: (01977) 557817 Fax: (01977) 557817

C Tech Electronics, Easting Close, Worthing, West Sussex, BN14 8HQ Tel: (01903) 524600 Fax: (01903) 524603 E-mail: sales@c-techelectronics.co.uk *Electronics sub-contract assembly*

C Tech Handling, 6 The Cloisters, Peterborough, PE6 7SX Tel: 01733 221143 Fax: 01733 221145

▶ C Todd & Co, Riverdale House, 89 Graham Road, Ranmoor, Sheffield, S10 3GP Tel: 0114 2306565 Fax: 0114 2309932 E-mail: chris@c-todd.co.uk *Chartered Certified Accountants in the Ranmoor district of Sheffield.**We offer a friendly and efficient service to meet our clients indivdual needs.**The business and accountancy services we offer includes accounts preparation, audit, management accounts, bookkeeping and payroll services.*

C Toms & Son Ltd, East Hill, East Street, Polruan, Fowey, Cornwall, PL23 1PB Tel: (01726) 870232 Fax: (01726) 870318 *Boat builders & repairs*

C Tyres Ltd, Littleburn Industrial Estate, Langley Moor, Durham, DH7 8HJ Tel: 0191-378 0621 Fax: 0191-378 1758 E-mail: info@c-tyres.co.uk Principal Export Areas: Worldwide *Tyre repairers*

C U Lighting Ltd, 35 Westgate, Cleckheaton, West Yorkshire, BD19 5LE Tel: (01274) 876887 Fax: (01274) 876888 E-mail: sales@cuphosco.co.uk *Steel mast & floodlighting manufrs*

C U Lighting Ltd, 35 Westgate, Cleckheaton, West Yorkshire, BD19 5LE Tel: (01274) 876887 Fax: (01274) 876888 *Steel fabrication*

▶ C U Lighting Ltd, Speech House Road, Broadwell, Coleford, Gloucestershire, GL16 7EG Tel: (01594) 833369 Fax: (01594) 836186 E-mail: s.bray@cuphosco.co.uk *Street lighting*

C U Thosco Lighting Ltd, Charles House, Furlong, Ware, Hertfordshire, SG12 9TA Tel: (01920) 462272 Fax: (01920) 485915 E-mail: export@cuphosco.co.uk *Road & floodlighting equipment manufrs*

C V Instruments, 32 Leeds Old Road, Bradford, West Yorkshire, BD3 8HU Tel: (01274) 223456 Fax: (01274) 223444 E-mail: sales@bowersmetrology.com *Hardness testing equipment manufrs*

▶ C V M S L, Millside, The Moor, Melbourn, Royston, Hertfordshire, SG8 6ED Tel: (01763) 262112 Fax: (01763) 263335 E-mail: service@cvmsl.co.uk *Environmental tester maintenance repair services*

C V P, Neales Yard, Queen Victoria Street, Blackburn, BB2 2QG Tel: 01254 679028 *Commercial vehicle painter & repairs*

▶ C & V Plumbing & Heating Ltd, Hanrhys House, Main Road, New Brighton, Mold, Clwyd, CH7 6QW Tel: (01352) 751800 Fax: (01352) 751802 E-mail: info@cvplumbing.co.uk

C V S Pentapower, St. Andrews Road, Northampton, NN1 2LF Tel: (01604) 638537 Fax: (01604) 634927 E-mail: sales@pentapower.com *Marine engineers*

C V Screen, 12 Octagon Court, High Wycombe, Buckinghamshire, HP11 2HS Tel: (01494) 769191 Fax: (01494) 447621 E-mail: matt@cvscreen.co.uk *IT recruitment agency service*

C & W Berry Ltd, Golden Hill Lane, Leyland, Leyland, PR25 2YH Tel: (01772) 431216 Fax: (01772) 622314 E-mail: enquiries@cwberry.com *Timber, building & plumbing merchants*

▶ C W Bolton, Uplands Farm, Highstreet Road, Hernhill, Faversham, Kent, ME13 9EJ Tel: (01227) 752207 Fax: (01227) 751281

C W Burrows Ltd, 4 Roydenbury Industrial Estate, Horsecroft Road, Harlow, Essex, CM19 5BZ Tel: (01279) 426558 *Furniture distributors*

C W Cole & Co. Ltd, 15 Copthorne, Luton, LU2 8RL Tel: (01582) 726622 Fax: (01582) 731622 *Proximity switches & sensor manufrs*

C W Computer Services Ltd, 62 St Anns Road, Southend-on-Sea, SS2 5AU Tel: (01702) 466161 Fax: (01702) 466162 E-mail: charles.whitmore@cwcomputerservices.com *Computer consultants*

C W D Scotland Ltd, 24 Dundonald Road, Kilmarnock, Ayrshire, KA1 1EG Tel: (01563) 540413 Fax: (01563) 574155 *Process cooling systems engineers & services*

▶ C W Davis Ltd, Baxter Place, Seaton Delaval, Whitley Bay, Tyne & Wear, NE25 0AP Tel: 0191-237 2232 Fax: 0191-298 0036

C W E Stavely Ltd, Unit 1A Hartington Industrial Estate, Deepdale Close, Staveley, Chesterfield, Derbyshire, S43 3YF Tel: (01246) 280046 Fax: (01246) 474975 *Precision engineers*

C & W Electronics Ltd, Pool Street, Wolverhampton, WV2 4HN Tel: (01902) 426714 Fax: (01902) 422544 *Control panels manufrs*

C W F Country Wide, Station Approach, Wrexham, Clwyd, LL11 2AA Tel: (01978) 361561 Fax: (01978) 364328 E-mail: enquiries@nwf.co.uk *Equine & gardening suppliers*

▶ C W F Group, 54 Brighton Road, Purley, Surrey, CR8 2LJ Tel: (0774) 2023084 Fax: (0906) 4062563 E-mail: Kate@cwfgroup.co.uk *CWF. CWF GROUP is a number one Commercial Facilities Services Company. Our highly trained & certified engineers provide our clients with the Professional service they require, From light bulb changing to decorating to boiler repairs. We truly believe in our proactive approach to your office and retail environments., we offer clients a complete package keeping their environments bright, clean, warm, and dry. Our technical board ensures that you are getting the best service, By*

continued

understanding and listening to our clients we have been able to adapt to varying circumstances. We enjoy what we do email us we are here to help

C W Fasteners, Unit 60 Sandy Way, Amington Industrial Estate, Tamworth, Staffordshire, B77 4DS Tel: (01827) 67091 Fax: (01827) 61552 E-mail: cwdfasteners@btopenworld.com *Tool distributors*

C W Fletcher & Sons Ltd, Sterling Works, Mansfield Road, Wales Bar, Sheffield, S26 5PQ Tel: 0114-294 2200 Fax: 0114-294 2211 *Precision engineers*

C W G Ltd, Priory Depot, Uffington Road, Stamford, Lincolnshire, PE9 2HD Tel: (01780) 762543 Fax: (01780) 755152 E-mail: sales@cwg.co.uk *Farming and country supplies. Limited domestic and pet supplies. Large selection of equestrian equiptment and feeds. Also at: Dereham, Fauld, Kentford, Market Rasen, Melton Mowbray, Newark, Towcester & Worksop*

C W Headdress Ltd, Unit 7, Witan Park, Avenue Two, Station Lane, Witney, Oxfordshire, OX28 4FH Tel: (01993) 703535 Fax: (01993) 775904 E-mail: sales@christy.techex.co.uk *Manufacturers of hats & clothing*

C.W. (Industrial) Fans Ltd, Unit 25, Thornleigh Trading Estate, Dudley, West Midlands, DY2 8UB Tel: (01384) 211010 Fax: (01384) 238086 *Profile cutting services & fabricators*

C W Jones Flooring Ltd, 10 Vale Lane, Bristol, BS3 5RU Tel: 0117-966 1454 Fax: 0117-963 9733 E-mail: info@cwjfloorings.co.uk *Carpet, laminate, wood & vinyl flooring & beds*

▶ C W & M A Evans Ltd, Everite Road, Widnes, Cheshire, WA8 8PT Tel: 0151-423 2771

C W Micro-Systems, 11 Mitchell Point, Ensign Way, Southampton, SO31 4RF Tel: (023) 8045 6888 Fax: (023) 8045 6542 E-mail: info@signblazer.com *Electronic display design & manufrs**

C W Polymers Ltd, 10 Felspar Road, Tamworth, Staffordshire, B77 4DP Tel: (01827) 60943 Fax: (01827) 54008 E-mail: sales@cwpollowmas.co.uk *Plastic raw materials suppliers compounders*

C & W Production Engineering Ltd, Unit 9 Vaughan St Industrial Estate, Manchester, M12 5BT Tel: 0161-223 9993 Fax: 0161-231 3113 E-mail: info@candwengineering.com *General & heavy metal engineers*

C W Property Services Ltd, 126 Ashleigh Road, London, SW14 8PX Tel: (020) 8876 9941 Fax: (020) 8878 3942 E-mail: cwps126@hotmail.com *Roofing contractors & decorating services*

C W R General Fabrications Ltd, 93-94, Leechmere East Industrial Estate, Sunderland, SR2 9TE Tel: 0191-521 2106 Fax: 0191-523 6216 E-mail: cwrfabrications@btconnect.com *Sheet metal fabricators*

C & W Scott, 23 West Street, St. Ives, Cambridgeshire, PE27 5PL Tel: (01480) 469999 *Scrap metal merchants*

C & W Summers, 131 Sydney Street, Glasgow, G31 1JF Tel: 0141-554 7997 Fax: 0141-556 2882 *Glazing contractors*

C W T Ltd, Hempstalls Lane, Newcastle, Staffordshire, ST5 0SW Tel: (01782) 625222 Fax: (01782) 625333 E-mail: cwtlimited@aol.com *Pipework fabricators, erection & installation contractors*

C W T Advertising, 121 Becontree Avenue, Dagenham, Essex, RM8 2UJ Tel: (020) 8590 0083 *Circular distribution services*

C W Tents, Unit 9a Backworth Workshops, Station Road, Backworth, Newcastle upon Tyne, NE27 0RT Tel: 0191-268 0110 Fax: 0191-268 9943 *Suppliers & services of tents*

C W Trading, Units 1-4 Danes Grave, Cottam, Driffield, North Humberside, YO25 3BG Tel: (01377) 267400 Fax: (01377) 267444 *Skip contractors*

C W W Engineers Supply Co. Ltd, 7 Stanlake Mews, London, W12 7HA Tel: (020) 8743 0651 Fax: (020) 8740 7731 E-mail: sales@cww.uk *Engineering merchants*

C Wall, 11c St Peters Street, Ipswich, IP1 1XF Tel: (01473) 214366 Fax: (01473) 214366 *Antique & marble furniture merchants*

C Watts, Rear of, 27-29 Buller Street, Grimsby, South Humberside, DN32 8BL Tel: (01472) 359547 Fax: (01472) 359547 E-mail: sales@companyhospitality.com *Cabinet makers*

C Ways, Lora House, Wykeham, Scarborough, North Yorkshire, YO13 9QP Tel: (0870) 3502920 Fax: (0870) 3502919 E-mail: info@c-ways.co.uk *Computer consultants*

▶ C Winfield, Smestow Bridge Industrial Estate, Bridgnorth Road, Wombourne, Wolverhampton, WV5 8AY Tel: (01902) 896666 Fax: (01902) 326611

▶ C Wren, 29 Woodchurch Road, Birkenhead, Merseyside, CH42 9LG Tel: 0151-653 4848 Fax: 0151-653 4425

C Wynne Jones, Ty Brith, Pentre Celyn, Ruthin, Clwyd, LL15 2SR Tel: (01978) 790279 Fax: (01978) 790265 E-mail: jones@tybrith.fsnet.co.uk *Bee keeping bottles & jars supplies*

C X Access Systems Ltd, Unit 5, Cricketts Lane Industrial Park, Chippenham, Wiltshire, SN15 3EQ Tel: (01249) 443898 Fax: (01249) 443336 E-mail: cxaccess@aol.com *Security & access control systems*

C Y Education, 33 Foy Lane, Portadown, Craigavon, County Armagh, BT62 1PY Tel: (028) 3833 4916 Fax: (028) 3833 4916 *Educational products*

C Y Electrical & Cranes Co. Ltd, Hayes Lane, Stourbridge, West Midlands, DY9 8QT Tel: (01384) 895570 Fax: (01384) 892877 E-mail: sales@cyequip.co.uk *Crane suppliers & services*

C Y Finishes Ltd, 4 Arnhem Road, Newbury, Berkshire, RG14 5RU Tel: (01635) 43860 Fax: (01635) 38547 E-mail: sales@cyfinishes.com *Powder coating services*

C Y Inflatables Ltd, Units 3-3a Queniborough Industrial Estate, Melton Road, Queniborough, Leicester, LE7 3FP Tel: 0116-260 2506 E-mail: steve@inflatables.uk.com *Portable inflatable building manufrs*

▶ C Y Logistics Ltd, Deanland Road, Golden Cross, Hailsham, East Sussex, BN27 5 GT Tel: 01825 873333 Fax: 01825 873311 E-mail: yvonne@cylogistics.co.uk *CY Logistics Ltd. A pick, pack, fulfilment, storage house uniquely placed to receive 40ft trailer to a packet throughout the South, UK and then on to Europe. 60,000 sq ft of modern and secured storage available for Web fulfilment and general picking.*

▶ C & Y Transport, Lockerbie Road, Dumfries, DG1 3PG Tel: (01387) 259800 Fax: (01387) 259800

▶ C&C Property solutions ltd, 72 / 74 Birkendale Road, Sheffield, S6 3NL Tel: 0114 2444008 *At C&C we aim to have all the property solutions to suit your needs. Whether your looking to rent a property or require a fully qualified joiner from our joinery divison please contact us.*

C&D, 2a Hoghatch Lane, Farnham, Surrey, GU9 0BY Tel: (01252) 714956 *Consultancy services*

▶ C&D Industrial Services Ltd, Drovers Road, East Mains Industrial Estate, Broxburn, West Lothian, EH52 5ND Tel: (01506) 856000 Fax: (01506) 858000

▶ C&K CLEANING SERVICES, 18 SEVERN WALK, CORBY, NORTHANTS, NN17 2HZ Tel: 01536 391460 *window cleaning,carpet cleaning,gutter cleaning,floor cleaning*

C2 Composites, 7 Venture Court, Bradley Lane, Newton Abbot, Devon, TQ12 1NB Tel: (01626) 356611 Fax: (01626) 356659 E-mail: silvan@c2-composites.co.uk *Composite engineers*

C2c Network Solutions Ltd, The Stripe, Riverside, Sinnington, York, YO62 6RY Tel: (01751) 430063 Fax: (01751) 431999 *Data installation & telecommunication services*

▶ C2m(Uk) Ltd, Suite 48 Gear House, Saltmeadows Road, Gateshead, Tyne & Wear, NE8 3AH Tel: 0191-490 1154 E-mail: c2muk@aol.com *We provide the SME, Individual and entrepreneur with impartial advice in the development of products from Concept to Manufacture. We specialise in concept design, design for manufacture, rapid prototyping, manufacturing and specialise in tool design and development.*

C3 Ltd, St. Johns Innovation Centre, Cowley Road, Cambridge, CB4 0WS Tel: (01223) 427700 Fax: (01223) 427711 E-mail: admin@c3ltd.co.uk *Computer telephony systems manufrs*

C3 Consulting, 2 The Hawthorns, Woodbridge Road, Birmingham, B13 9DY Tel: 0121-449 8717 Fax: 0121-442 4082 E-mail: contact@c3consulting.co.uk *Management consultants*

▶ C3 Emulet Ltd, Caledonian House, High Street, Dingwall, Ross-Shire, IV15 9RY Tel: (01349) 865554 Fax: (01349) 865558 E-mail: enquires@c3emulet.com *Software services*

C3 Imaging Ltd, Severalls Business Park, Telford Way, Colchester, CO4 9QP Tel: (01206) 845544 Fax: (01206) 845856 E-mail: jacqueline@hilocolour.co.uk *Colour printing services*

▶ C3 Imaging, Back New Bridge Street, Newcastle upon Tyne, NE1 2TY Tel: 0191-232 1517 Fax: 0191-232 0572 E-mail: info@c3newcastle.co.uk *Printing*

Cab Glazing Services, Unit D3, Button End Industrial Estate, Harston, Cambridge, CB2 5NX Tel: (01223) 872400 Fax: (01223) 872866 E-mail: sales@cabglazing.co.uk *Glazing contractors*

▶ CabAds - Taxi Advertising, Unit 1A, West Craigs Industrial Estate, Turnhouse Road, Edinburgh, EH12 0BD Tel: (0845) 2268595 Fax: (0845) 2268595 E-mail: info@cabads.co.uk *Taxi advertising*

The Cabair Group Ltd, Elstree Aerodrome, Elstree, Borehamwood, Hertfordshire, WD6 3AW Tel: (020) 8236 2400 Fax: (020) 8207 0995 E-mail: group@cabair.com *Flight training schools & aircraft maintenance*

Cabarfeidh Hotel, Perceval Road South, Stornoway, Isle of Lewis, HS1 2EU Tel: (01851) 702604 Fax: (01851) 705572 E-mail: cabarfeidh@calahotels.com *Hotel & conference facilities*

Cabbola Food Service Equipment, 47 New Street, Hinckley, Leicestershire, LE10 1QY Tel: (01455) 612020 Fax: (01455) 636364 E-mail: sales@cabbola.com *Catering equipment distributors*

Cabcare Products, Unit 6 Raleigh Hall Industrial Estate, Eccleshall, Stafford, ST21 6JL Tel: (01785) 851944 Fax: (01785) 851961 E-mail: sales@cabcare.com *CabCare security vandal guards. Cab care "Snap Lock" vandal guard for cab and cage contruction machinery plant protection*

▶ Caber Developments, 10-12 Pall Mall, Liverpool, L3 6AL Tel: 0151-255 0595 Fax: 0151-255 0601

Cabin Centre Ltd, Sandtoft Industrial Estate, Belton Road Road, Sandtoft, Doncaster, South Yorkshire, DN9 1PN Tel: (01427) 873285 Fax: (01427) 874248 E-mail: sales@cabincentreltd.co.uk *Portable building hire, leasing, rental & boiler services*

▶ The Cabinet Makers, Unit 12 Brighton Road Industrial Estate, Heaton Mersey, Stockport, Cheshire, SK4 2BQ Tel: 0161-432 4455 E-mail: duncan@thecabinetmakers.net *Craftsman built furniture manufrs*

Cable Access Solutions Ltd, 11 Stanley Street, Luton, LU1 5AL Tel: (01582) 411022 Fax: (01582) 727117 E-mail: sales@zyteltd.demon.co.uk *Plastic injection moulding manufrs*

Cable and Wireless P.L.C., Redlion Square, London, WC1R 4HQ Tel: (020) 7315 4000 Fax: (020) 7315 5182 *Telecommunication services*

Cable Check Systems, Unit 18 Quay Lane, Hardway, Gosport, Hampshire, PO12 4LJ Tel: (023) 9252 8396 Fax: (023) 9258 9748 E-mail: info@greenpersonnel.co.uk *Cable test equipment manufrs*

Cable Detection Ltd, 16 Alderflat Drive, Newstead Indsustrial Trading Estate, Trentam, Stoke-On-Trent, ST4 8HX Tel: (01782) 654450 Fax: (01782) 642584 *Cable locators service & manufrs*

Cable First Ltd, 32-40 Harwell Road, Poole, Dorset, BH17 0GE Tel: (01202) 687337 Fax: (01202) 672501 E-mail: sales@cablefirst.co.uk *Cable connection & power cord manufrs*

Cable Grips (Minehead) Ltd, Ponsford Road, Minehead, Somerset, TA24 5DX Tel: (01643) 702177 Fax: (01643) 704012 E-mail: rodgerwood@cablegripsltd.co.uk Principal Export Areas: Worldwide *Cable grips & cable laying equipment manufrs*

Cable Harnesses, Unit 16, Trostre Industrial Park, Llanelli, Dyfed, SA14 9UU Tel: (01554) 777200 Fax: (01554) 777224 E-mail: reception@cableharnessesuk.com Purchasing Contact: M. Davies Sales Contact: N. Gregory Principal Export Areas: Worldwide *Cable assembly harness manufrs*

▶ Cable Jointing Scotland, Tandle Hill Road, Kilbarchan, Johnstone, Renfrewshire, PA10 2AL Tel: (01505) 703445 E-mail: chaddow1111@fsmail.net *ALL ASPECTS OF HV AND LV CABLE JOINTING AND TERMINATING FROM 415v TO 33kv*

Cable Jointing Services Ltd, Cedric Works, Cedric CR, Sunderland, SR2 7QP Tel: 0191-514 1165 Fax: 0191-564 0005 E-mail: sales@cablejointingservices.com *Electrical contractors*

Cable Management Centre Ltd, 3 C M T Industrial Estate, Broadwell Road, Oldbury, West Midlands, B69 4BQ Tel: 0121-544 0077 Fax: 0121-544 0088 *Cable management distributors*

Cable Management Centre Ltd, 3 C M T Industrial Estate, Broadwell Road, Oldbury, West Midlands, B69 4BQ Tel: 0121-544 0077 Fax: 0121-544 0088 *Cable trunking, floor systems manufrs & specialist distributor of PVC & metal*

▶ Cable Management Products Ltd, Station Road, Coleshill, Birmingham, B46 1HT Tel: (01675) 468200 E-mail: info@cm-products.com *Cable and electrical management products from a market leading manufacturing group. Cable management has a worldwide distributor program*

Cable Pressure Systems Ltd, Borrowmeadow Road, Springkerse Industrial Estate, Stirling, FK7 7UW Tel: (01786) 449292 Fax: (01786) 449393 E-mail: cps@fernan.com *Dry air systems maintenance & repairers*

Cable Print, Unit 1, Black Ven Farm, Hartgrove, Shaftesbury, Dorset, SP7 0AS Tel: (0845) 2267012 Fax: (0845) 2267012 E-mail: cableprint@tiscali.com *Motor trade system forms*

Cable Services Liverpool, 43 St.Johns Road, Bootle, Merseyside, L20 8BH Tel: 0151-933 9022 Fax: 0151-933 9765 E-mail: lpool@cableservices.co.uk *Cable distributors or agents*

Cable Services UK Ltd, Rhosddu Industrial Estate, Main Road, Rhosrobin, Wrexham, Clwyd, LL11 4YZ Tel: (01978) 340450 Fax: (01978) 311315 E-mail: uk@cableservices.co.uk *Cable distributors*

▶ Cable Solutions Worldwide Ltd, Unit A1, Wellheads Crescent, Wellheads Industrial Estate, Aberdeen, AB21 7GA Tel: (01224) 727910 Fax: (01224) 725360 E-mail: ricky.gill@1st4cables.com *Electrical wire & cable distributors*

Cable Systems, 61 Corbett Road, Waterlooville, Hampshire, PO7 5TA Tel: (023) 9226 9187 Fax: (023) 9226 9187 *Intercom systems installation*

Cable Team UK Limited, Unit 3, Daaker House, Two Rivers, Station Lane, Witney, Oxfordshire, OX28 4BH Tel: 01993 702300 Fax: 08709 509369 E-mail: enquiries@ct-uk.net *Providing organisations with a range of certified IT, Telecom or Infrastructure related solutions with on-going support services.*

Cable & Wire Technical Services Ltd, 12 Tudor Grove, Gillingham, Kent, ME8 9AF Tel: (01634) 234786 Fax: (01634) 370980 *Cable & wire machinery manufrs*

▶ Cable & Wireless Ltd, Carnbroe House, 1 Finch Way, Strathclyde Business Park, Bellshill, Lanarkshire, ML4 3PE Tel: (01908) 845000 Fax: (01908) 502001

▶ Cablebility Ltd, 26 Beech Road, Shipham, Winscombe, Avon, BS25 1SB Tel: (01934) 843019 Fax: (01934) 844310 E-mail: cablebility@aol.com *Manufacturers & suppliers of custom made cables for data communications & other industries*

▶ Cablecom, 8 Abbeyhill, Edinburgh, EH8 8EE Tel: 0131-656 9151 Fax: 0131-659 5709

▶ Cablecomm Voice & Data Solutions Ltd, Aztec House, 187-189 Kings Road, Reading, RG1 4EX Tel: (0800) 0582662 Fax: 0118-988 3716 E-mail: sales@cablecomm.co.uk *Data cabling manufrs*

Cableflow International Ltd, Windsor House, Abbey Barn Road, High Wycombe, Buckinghamshire, HP11 1NN Tel: (01494) 528811 Fax: (01494) 531188 E-mail: sales@cableflow.com *Aluminium trunking & cable-management systems manufrs*

Cablelines (Nottingham) Ltd, Unit 4 Orchard Park Industrial Estate, Sandiacre, Nottingham, NG10 5BP Tel: 0115-949 1010 Fax: 0115-949 1019 E-mail: sales@cablelines.com *Computer cable manufrs*

Cablelink UK Ltd, Lisle Road, High Wycombe, Buckinghamshire, HP13 5SH Tel: (01494) 525224 Fax: (01494) 525224 E-mail: sales@cablelink.co.uk *Telecommunication cable manufacturers & cable assembly/harness, SCSI & coaxial*

Cablenet Cable & Wire Suppliers, Cablenet House, Lightwater Road, Lightwater, Surrey, GU18 5XQ Tel: (01276) 851900 Fax: (01276) 851909 E-mail: sales@cablenet.uk.com *Networking distributors*

▶ CableNet Tension Wire Grids, Regent Street, Rochdale, Lancashire, OL12 0HH Tel: 01706 632225 Fax: 01706 649025 E-mail: sales@slingco.com *CableNet manufacture tension wire grids and virtual floors for performance venues. Custom steel wire rope cable assemblies for lifting and controlling tensile structures.*

Cablepoint Ltd, Phoenix House, Amsterdam Road, Sutton Fields Industrial Estate, Hull, HU7 0XP Tel: (01482) 837400 Fax: (01482) 839651 E-mail: sales@cablepoint.co.uk *Sub contract electro manufrs*

Cables Direct Ltd, C Industrial Estate, Heage Road, Ripley, Derbyshire, DE5 3GH Tel: (01773) 514514 Fax: (01773) 514515 E-mail: sales@cablesdirect.co.uk *Manufacture cables*

Cablespeed, 447 Oakshott Place, Bamber Bridge, Preston, PR5 8AT Tel: (0870) 6098025 Fax: (0870) 6098026 E-mail: sales@cablespeed.co.uk *Cable stripping & welding equipment manufrs*

Cablink UK Ltd, 74 Tenter Road, Moulton Park Industrial Estate, Northampton, NN3 6AX Tel: (01604) 670005 Fax: (01604) 670011 *On-board computer systems manufrs*

Cabot Carbon Ltd, Lees Lane, Stanlow, Ellesmere Port, CH65 4HT Tel: 0151-355 3677 Fax: 0151-356 0712 *Carbon black processors manufrs*

Cabot G B Ltd, Gate Street, Dukinfield, Cheshire, SK16 4RU Tel: 0161-934 4500 Fax: 0161-934 4502 E-mail: webmaster@cabot-corp.com *Plastics masterbatch manufrs*

Cabot Industrial Doors, 105 Garnet Street, Bristol, BS3 3JN Tel: 0117-940 1242 Fax: 0117-902 0567 E-mail: carbotdoors@msn.com *Industrial door manufrs*

Cabrio Management Services, 6 Ash Meadow, Willesborough, Ashford, Kent, TN24 0LW Tel: (01233) 623230 E-mail: enquiries@cabrio.co.uk *Project management consultants*

Cabsoft Ltd, Orwell House, Cowley Road, Cambridge, CB4 0PP Tel: (01223) 470022 Fax: (01223) 470023 *Software development*

Caburn Hope, Unit D Rusbridge Lane, Lewes, East Sussex, BN7 2XX Tel: (01273) 480404 Fax: (01273) 480505 E-mail: info@caburnhope.co.uk *Design consultants*

▶ Caburn UHV, 45 Southover High Street, Lewes, East Sussex, BN7 1HX Tel: (01273) 488414 Fax: (01273) 488415 E-mail: mario@allectra.com *Manufacturers of vacuum components*

Cabus Garage, Lancaster New Road, Cabus, Preston, PR3 1AD Tel: (01524) 791417 Fax: (01524) 791417 *Petrol station*

Caci Consulting, Manor Court Yard, Grateley, Andover, Hampshire, SP11 8LE Tel: (01264) 889845 Fax: (01264) 889846 E-mail: sales@imaj.co.uk *Financial data analysis*

Cactus Ceramics & Crafts, 4 Merville Garden Village, Newtownabbey, County Antrim, BT37 9TF Tel: (028) 9085 9869 Fax: (028) 9084 0113 *Ceramic studio*

▶ Cactus Marketing, 109a Hamilton Road, Felixstowe, Suffolk, IP11 7BL Tel: (01394) 275275 Fax: (01394) 275275 *International licensing agents for toy & game inventors*

CAD Academy Ltd, Sherwood House, Gregory Boulevard, Nottingham, NG7 6LB Tel: 0115-969 1114 Fax: 0115-969 1115 E-mail: info@cadacademy.co.uk *Autocad facilities management*

Cad Capture Ltd, Greenbank Technology Park, Challenge Way, Blackburn, BB1 5RR Tel: (01254) 504400 Fax: (01254) 504401 E-mail: info@cadcap.co.uk *Internet service providers*

Cad Fab Ltd, 7 The Courtyards, Victoria Road, Leeds, LS14 2LB Tel: 0113-265 5010 Fax: 0113-265 5012 E-mail: cadfab@aol.com *Precision sheetmetal workers*

Cadalec Control Systems, Three Boundaries Business Park, Coventry Road, Croft, Leicester, LE9 3GP Tel: (01455) 286900 Fax: (01455) 286999 E-mail: sales@cadalec.com *Automation control systems manufrs*

▶ Cadamp Ltd, Wharfedale House, Great Pasture Lane, Burley in Wharfedale, Ilkley, West Yorkshire, LS29 7DB Tel: (01943) 863884 Fax: (01943) 862630 E-mail: info@cadamp.co.uk Sales Contact: A. Monaghan *Fan Speed Control, Fan Control - Cadamp manufactures and supplies electrical and electronic controllers for the heating and ventilation industry.*

Cadar Ltd, Unit 3 The Point, Market Harborough, Leicestershire, LE16 7QU Tel: (01858) 410101 Fax: (01858) 433934 E-mail: sales@cadar.ltd.uk Principal Export Areas: Africa *Refractometer & spray nozzle distributors & manufrs. Also ;nozzles, filter, water indu;stry & strainers filtering*

Cadar Measurement Solutions Ltd, 100 Fitzwalter Road, Sheffield, S2 2SP Tel: 0114-275 0722 Fax: 0114-275 2912 E-mail: info@cadar.co.uk *Gauging electronic inspection equipment manufrs*

Cadbury Ltd, Somerdale, Keynsham, Bristol, BS31 2AU Tel: 0117-986 1789 Fax: 0117-937 6590 *Cadburys chocolate manufrs*

Cadbury Garden & Leisure, Smallway, Congresbury, Bristol, BS49 5AA Tel: (01934) 876464 Fax: (01934) 875701 E-mail: info@cadbury.g-l.co.uk *Garden centre*

Cadbury Schweppes P.L.C., Franklin House, Bournville Lane, Bournville, Birmingham, B30 2NB Tel: 0121-625 7000 Fax: 0121-458 2826 *Confectionery manufrs*

Cadbury Schweppes P.L.C., 25 Berkeley Square, London, W1J 6HB Tel: (020) 7409 1313 Fax: (020) 7830 5200 E-mail: info@cadburyschweppes.com *Soft drink manufrs*

Cadbury Trebor Bassett Ltd, PO Box 12, Birmingham, B30 2LU Tel: 0121-458 2000 Fax: 0121-451 4139 *Confectionary manufrs*

Cadbury Trebor Bassett Ltd, PO Box 12, Birmingham, B30 2LU Tel: 0121-458 2000 Fax: 0121-451 4139 *Confectionery manufrs*

▶ Cadbury Trebor Bassett Ltd, Station Avenue, Chirk, Wrexham, Clwyd, LL14 5LT Tel: (01691) 774168 Fax: (01691) 776211 *Chocolate manufrs*

▶ Cadburys, 14-18 Perivale Industrial Park, Horsenden La South, Greenford, Middlesex, UB6 7RW Tel: (020) 8997 3011

Cadcam Technology, 5 Crocus Street, Nottingham, NG2 3DE Tel: 0115-844 8050 Fax: 0115-844 8059 E-mail: info@cct-uk.com *Laser cutting machines, laser systems & equipment manufrs*

Caddum Design Furniture Products Ltd, Dominion Way, Easting Close, Worthing, West Sussex, BN14 8NW Tel: (01903) 232355 Fax: (01903) 232356 E-mail: sales@caddumdesign.com *Upholstery frame manufrs*

Caddy Castings Ltd, Springfield Road, Grantham, Lincolnshire, NG31 7BQ Tel: (01476) 566667 Fax: (01476) 570220 E-mail: caddycastings@btinternet.com Principal Export Areas: Africa & North America *Manufacturers of castings*

Cade Brothers Ramsey Ltd, 94 Great Whyte, Ramsey, Huntingdon, Cambridgeshire, PE26 1HR Tel: (01487) 813318 Fax: (01487) 710449 *Storage & freight services*

Cadence Design Systems Ltd, Bagshot Road, Bracknell, Berkshire, RG12 0PH Tel: (01344) 360333 Fax: (01344) 869647 *Software consultants*

Cadence Design Systems Ltd, Bagshot Road, Bracknell, Berkshire, RG12 0PH Tel: (01344) 360333 Fax: (01344) 360324 *Electronic design automation products & services*

Cades Ltd, Commerce Close, Challenge Way, Bradford, West Yorkshire, BD4 8NW Tel: (01274) 661156 Fax: (01274) 661756 *Dust extraction*

Cadgrange Ltd, 38-40 Sandy Road, Liverpool, L21 3TW Tel: 0151-949 0216 Fax: 0151-949 0419 E-mail: mail@cadgrange.co.uk *Joiners.*

Cadlay Designs Ltd, Sleight House, Sleight Lane, Corfe Mullem, Wimborne, Dorset, BH21 3HL Tel: (01202) 693233 Fax: (01202) 658747 E-mail: sales@cadlay.co.uk *Printed circuit board designers*

Cadlow Enclosures, Bridge House, The Green, Redgrave, Diss, Norfolk, IP22 1RR Tel: (01379) 898810 Fax: (01379) 898812 E-mail: info@cadlow.co.uk *Electrical & electronic enclosures distributors & manufrs*

Cadman Cranes Ltd, Moss Road, Stanway, Colchester, CO3 0LF Tel: (01206) 543232 Fax: (01206) 763231 E-mail: info@cadmancontracts.com *Contractors plant & crane hirers*

Cadman Group, The Twitchell, Sutton-In-Ashfield, Nottinghamshire, NG17 5BT Tel: (01623) 553005 Fax: (01623) 440370 E-mail: bcadman@ypm.net *Injection mouldings (plastic) manufrs*

Cadnam Metalcraft, Southampton Road, Cadnam, Southampton, SO40 2NB Tel: (023) 8081 2489 Fax: (023) 8081 2976 E-mail: cadnammetalcraft@btconnect.com *Steel fabricators*

▶ Cadogan Consultants Ltd, 39 Cadogan Street, Glasgow, G2 7AB Tel: 0141-270 7060 Fax: 0141-270 7061 E-mail: enquiries@cadoganconsultants.co.uk *Consulting engineers*

Cadogan Consultants, 4th Floor The Market Building, 72-82 Rosebury Avenue, Clerkenwell, London, EC1R 4RW Tel: (020) 7837 5918 Fax: (020) 7490 2160 *Mechanical & electronically engineers*

▶ Cadogon Ltd, Unit 55, Park Royal Business Centre 9-17, Acton, London, NW10 7LQ Tel: (020) 7193 1425 Fax: (020) 8965 7679 *Closed circuit television (CCTV) equipment suppliers*

Cadonmain Ltd, 3 Aspen Court, Lancing, West Sussex, BN15 8UN Tel: (01903) 750522 Fax: (01903) 851111 *Carpet accessories wholesalers*

Cadserve Ltd, Beede House, St. Cuthberts Way, Newton Aycliffe, County Durham, DL5 6DX Tel: (01325) 318111 Fax: (01325) 318444 E-mail: info@cadserve.co.uk *Computer aided design (CAD) systems*

Cadtek Systems Ltd, Cadek House, Station Road, Furness Vale, High Peak, Derbyshire, SK23 7QA Tel: (01663) 741405 Fax: (01663) 741605 E-mail: info@cadtek.co.uk *3D CAD software solutions*

▶ Caduceus Medical Training Ltd, Studio 2, Silverdale Enterprise Centre, Kents Lane, Newcastle, Staffordshire, ST5 6SR Tel: 0845 0763507 E-mail: info@cmtltd.com *First Aid Training, Health and safety training and consultancy services, Medical training, Emergency medical technician courses, clinical skills, food hygiene*

▶ CADVanced Ltd, 5 Thorne Rd, Doncaster, S. Yorkshire, DN1 2HJ Tel: (01909) 506655 Fax: (01909) 506655 E-mail: info@cadvancedltd.co.uk *CATIA, auto cad design & conversions*

▶ Cadwell IT Services Ltd, 14 Magisters Lodge, Croxley Green, Rickmansworth, Hertfordshire, WD3 3SZ Tel: (0845) 8900819 Fax: (0845) 8900813 E-mail: info@cadwellit.com *IT support & consultancy services*

▶ Cadzow Plant Hire Ltd, 15 Forrest St, Blantyre, Glasgow, G72 0JP Tel: (01698) 713344 Fax: (01698) 713355

Cae Gwyn Farm Supplies, Caegwyn, Harford, Llanwrda, Dyfed, SA19 8EA Tel: (01558) 650318 *Agricultural supplies*

Caerbont Automotive Instruments Ltd, Caerbont, Abercrave, Swansea, SA9 1SH Tel: (01639) 732200 Fax: (01639) 732201 *Switches, transducers & tachometer manufrs*

Caerleon Ready Mixed Concrete Ltd, Western Industrial Estate, Caerleon, Newport, NP18 3NN Tel: (01633) 423549 Fax: (01633) 430413 *Ready mixed concrete distributors*

▶ Caernarfon Sun Studio, 25 Bangor Street, Caernarfon, Gwynedd, LL55 1AT Tel: (01286) 672754 *Sunbed shop*

▶ Caerneagle Furniture Ltd, Cibyn Industrial Estate, Caernarfon, Gwynedd, LL55 2BD Tel: (01286) 662950 *Furniture manufacturers & designers*

Caerphilly Metal Polishers, 1 The Rhos, Bedwas Road, Caerphilly, Mid Glamorgan, CF83 3AU Tel: (029) 2086 7837 Fax: (029) 2086 7837 *Metal finishing & polishing*

Cafco International, Bluebell Close, Clover Nook Industrial Park, Somercotes, Alfreton, Derbyshire, DE55 4RA Tel: (01773) 837900 Fax: (01773) 836710E-mail: info@cafcoimtl.com *Fire protection services*

▶ Cafe Espress First Service, Regent Park, Booth Drive, Park Farm Industrial Estate, Wellingborough, Northamptonshire, NN8 6GR Tel: (01933) 670999 Fax: (01933) 670998 *Coffee machines suppliers*

▶ Cafe Society, 18C Moor Street, Chepstow, Gwent, NP16 5DB Tel: (01291) 636338 Fax: (01291) 630402 E-mail: jim@jamdmgroup.co.uk *Trade association*

Cafédirect plc, City Cloisters Suite B2, 196 Old Street, London, EC1V 9FR Tel: (020) 7490 9520 Fax: (020) 7490 9521 E-mail: info@cafedirect.co.uk *Cafédirect is the UK's leading Fairtrade hot drinks company. Out-of-home sales have grown 41% in the last year (Source: Cafédirect). Our brands which have driven our growth in the out-of-home market, include: Classic Blend Freeze Dried Coffee, Roast & Ground Coffee and Cafédirect Espresso coffee beans (decaffeinated and organic variants are available); Teadirect, Cafédirect's quality tea, in standard black tea and Earl Grey tea bags; Cocodirect Drinking Chocolate and Instant Hot Chocolate are available respectively as add milk and add water variants.*

▶ Cafenet UK, 63 Watergate Street, Chester, CH1 2LB Tel: (01244) 401116 E-mail: info@cafenetuk.com *Chester''s number one internet cafe. Offering high speed Broadband Internet access at an affordable rate. Many other services available including photo printing, digital camera downloads and refreshments.*

▶ Cage Clothing, 43-68 Lower Villiers Street, Wolverhampton, WV2 4NA Tel: (01902) 717396

▶ CageFabricator, Heath Road, Leighton Buzzard, Bedfordshire, LU7 3AT Tel: (01525) 378185 Fax: (01525) 378185 E-mail: info@cagefabricator.com *Supply of Cut,Bent, reinforcing bars, prefabricated pile cage, ground beam, pile cags, etc...*

▶ Caine Douglas, Unit 2b Little Tennis St South, Nottingham, NG2 4EU Tel: 0115-958 2020 Fax: 0115-958 2030

Caine Precision Ltd, Unit 13 Stocklake Park Industrial Estate, Farmborough Cl, Aylesbury, Bucks, HP20 1DQ Tel: (01296) 435586 Fax: (01296) 432683 E-mail: rcaine@nildron.co.uk *Toolmakers & precision engineers*

J. Cainer & Sons (Bolton) Ltd, Knavebrook House, Morris Street, Radcliffe, Manchester, M26 2HF Tel: 0161-796 8444 Fax: 0161-796 1444 *Ladies jacket manufrs*

Cairn Energy plc, 50 Lothian Road, Edinburgh, EH3 9BY Tel: 0131-475 3000 Fax: 0131-475 3030 E-mail: pr@cairn-energy.plc.uk *Oil & gas exploration*

Cairn Research Ltd, Graveny Road, Faversham, Kent, ME13 8UP Tel: (01795) 590140 Fax: (01795) 594510 E-mail: sales@cairnweb.com *Scientific instrument manufrs*

▶ Cairney Hardware Ltd, 1 Distillery Lane, Edinburgh, EH11 2BD Tel: 0131-313 1303 Fax: 0131-313 1305 E-mail: enquiries@cairney.com *Architectural ironmongery*

▶ Cairney & Smith Construction Ltd, Unit 5, Murray Court, Hillhouse Industrial Estate, Hamilton, Lanarkshire, ML3 9SL Tel: (01698) 286888 Fax: (01698) 286888

Cairnhill Structures Ltd, Watson Towers, Waverley St, Coatbridge, Lanarkshire, ML5 2BE Tel: (01236) 449393 Fax: (01236) 449334 E-mail: enquiries@cairnhillstructures.co.uk *Structural steelwork engineers*

▶ Cairnport Ltd, Lloyd Street, Rutherglen, Glasgow, G73 1NP Tel: 0141-613 1333 Fax: 0141-647 8444 *Shed services*

Cairns Machine Tool Repair Ltd, 18 Haddow Street, Hamilton, Lanarkshire, ML3 7HX Tel: (01698) 457741 Fax: (01698) 283358 *Machine tool repair*

Caithness & Co. Ltd, 47 Old London Road, Kingston upon Thames, Surrey, KT2 6NG Tel: (020) 8549 8011 Fax: (020) 8547 2238 E-mail: mail@caithnessandco.com *Insurance brokers & independent financial advisers*

Caithness Creels Ltd, 17c Airport Industrial Estate, Wick Airport, Wick, Caithness, KW1 4QS Tel: (01955) 602979 Fax: (01955) 602993 *Metal fabricators*

Caithness Crystal, 9-12 Hardwick Industrial Estate, Paxman Road, King's Lynn, Norfolk, PE30 4NE Tel: (01553) 765111 Fax: (01553) 767628 E-mail: sales@caithnessglass.co.uk *Hand-made glass & visitor centre*

▶ Caithness Stone Industries Ltd, The Shore, Wick, Caithness, KW1 4JX Tel: (01955) 605472 Fax: (01955) 605907 *Stone products*

Cake Corner, 33 Orchard Street, Weston-super-Mare, Avon, BS23 1RH Tel: (01934) 626587 *Cake decorations*

Cake Dec Centre, 59 Victoria Terrace, Whitley Bay, Tyne & Wear, NE26 2QN Tel: 0191-251 0663 Fax: 0191-251 0663 *Cake decorators*

Cakeboards Ltd, George Street, Burnley, Lancashire, BB11 1LX Tel: (01282) 423142 Fax: (01282) 477048 E-mail: sales@cakeboards.co.uk Principal Export Areas: Worldwide *Cake boards & decoration manufrs*

Caketops Cake Decorating Equipment, 7 The Pantiles, Bexleyheath, Kent, DA7 5HH Tel: (01322) 448602 *Cake decorating tool suppliers*

Cal Chem Ltd, Unit A3 Hortonwood 10, Telford, Shropshire, TF1 7ES Tel: (01952) 606220 Fax: (01952) 676278 *Electroplating chemical products suppliers*

Cal Controls Ltd, Bury Mead Road, Hitchin, Hertfordshire, SG5 1RT Tel: (01462) 436161 Fax: (01462) 451801 E-mail: sales@cal-controls.com Principal Export Areas: Worldwide *Manufacturers of process controller & control systems*

Cal Gavin Ltd, 1 Station Road, Alcester, Warwickshire, B49 5ET Tel: (01789) 400401 Fax: (01789) 400411 E-mail: info@calgavin.co.uk *Manufacturers of heat exchanger tube enhancement*

▶ Cal Vent Ltd, Somervell Street, Cambuslang, Glasgow, G72 7EB Tel: 0141-641 6633 Fax: 0141-641 6333 *Ventilation manufacturers & installation*

Cala Management Ltd, Adobe House, 5 Mid New Cultins, Edinburgh, EH11 4DU Tel: 0131-453 6192 Fax: 0131-535 5201 E-mail: info@cala.co.uk *Construction services*

▶ Caladonian Plant, Unit 9 Harlaw Way, Harlaw Road Industrial Estate, Inverurie, Aberdeenshire, AB51 4SG Tel: (01467) 623616 Fax: (01467) 624411 *Powered access service, certification, repair & sales services*

Calando Finance Ltd, 115a St. Johns Hill, Sevenoaks, Kent, TN13 3PE Tel: (01732) 743400 Fax: (01732) 743335 E-mail: broughfame@yahoo.com *Leasing company*

Calanpoint Ltd, 52 Linford Street, London, SW8 4UN Tel: (020) 7627 4740 Fax: (020) 7627 5091 E-mail: enq@calanpoint.co.uk *Joinery manufrs*

Calbourne Classics, Three Gates Farm, Yarmouth Road, Shalfleet, Newport, Isle of Wight, PO30 4NA Tel: (01983) 531204 Fax: (01983) 555065 E-mail: sales@calbourneclassics.co.uk *Frozen food & ice creams manufrs*

Calcarb Ltd, 12 North Road, Bellshill, Lanarkshire, ML4 1EN Tel: (01698) 740818 Fax: (01698) 841979 E-mail: sales@calcarb.com *Carbon bonded fibre thermal insulation manufrs*

▶ Calco Instruments, 2 Leonard Street, Beverley Road, Hull, HU3 1SA Tel: (01482) 339300 Fax: (01482) 339301 E-mail: enquiries@calco-instruments.com *Calibration services*

Cal-Com Systems Ltd, Calibration House, Moorefield Grove, Bolton, BL2 2LQ Tel: (01204) 383311 Fax: (01204) 382556 *Test equipment & services suppliers*

Calculated Solutions UK Ltd, 69 Ivy Road, Macclesfield, Macclesfield, Cheshire, SK11 8QN Tel: (01625) 269198 Fax: (01625) 265512 E-mail: calsol@ntlworld.com *Chemical engineering consultants*

▶ Calculus Business Solutions, 15 St Marys Street, Newport, Shropshire, TF10 7AF Tel: 0870 1996823 Fax: 0870 7669347 E-mail: mail@calculus-bs.com *Book keeping services from as little as £1 A DAY INCULSIVE OF VAT*

▶ Calcutt Matthews Ltd, 30 North Street, Ashford, Kent, TN24 8JR Tel: (01233) 623300 Fax: (01233) 623400 E-mail: reception@calcutt-m.co.uk *Accountants*

Calcutt & Sons Ltd, Bullington Lane, Sutton Scotney, Winchester, Hampshire, SO21 3RA Tel: (01962) 760210 Fax: (01962) 760702 E-mail: calcutts@msn.com *Riding wear retailers*

▶ Calder Ltd, Gregory's Bank, Worcester, WR3 8AB Tel: (01905) 723255 Fax: (01905) 723904 E-mail: pumps@calder.co.uk *Calder Pressure Systems has the products, the technology and the expertise to provide complete high pressure solutions. Whatever application you are in, whatever the size and scale of the problem, we can design, manufacture, supply, commission and service high pressure reciprocating positive displacement systems that get the job done, Fast.*Our range includes; Water jet nozzles, High pressure pumps, High pressure cleaning equipment, Ultra high pressure, High pressure plunger pumps, Water jet equipment maintenance, High pressure hoses, Water jetting units, Heat exchanger tube cleaning equipment, and many more. We are representatives for Hammelmann, Stoneage products.* From providing an environmentally sound way to remove disintegrating concrete from a bridge, to high-pressure pumping of liquid butane propellant in household aerosols in a three shift manufacturing facility, we can handle it.*

Calder Building & Civil Engineering, 22 Tomich Industrial Estate, Muir Of Ord, Ross-Shire, IV6 7UA Tel: (01463) 870521

▶ Calder Building Services, 4 Keighley Road, Halifax, West Yorkshire, HX3 6QP Tel: (01422) 383113 Fax: (01422) 383117 E-mail: info@calderbuild.com

Calder Clutch Co. Ltd, Mill Lane, Brighouse, West Yorkshire, HD6 1PN Tel: (01484) 721045 Fax: (01484) 721009 E-mail: sales@calderclutch.co.uk *Car clutch remanufactures and supliers of clutches, clutch kits, clutch Covers,Clutch Plates, Release Bearings, Shot Blasting, Serface Grinding and Phosphating*

Calder Colours Ashby Ltd, Dents Road, Nottingham Road Indust Estate, Ashby DeLa Zouch, Ashby-de-la-Zouch, Leicestershire, LE65 1JS Tel: (01530) 412885 Fax: (01530) 417315 E-mail: office@caldercolours.co.uk *Colour & art & crafts materials manufrs*

Calder Engineering Ltd, Unit 15 Ormlie Industrial Estate, Thurso, Caithness, KW14 7QU Tel: (01847) 892122 Fax: (01847) 892345 E-mail: admin@calderengineering.co.uk *Engineers*

Calder Foods, Unit 20, Harrison Way, Carlisle, CA1 2SS Tel: (01228) 514518 Fax: (01228) 514518 *Sandwich filling manufrs*

Calder Industrial Materials Ltd, Jupiter Drive, Chester West Employment Park, Chester, CH1 4EX Tel: (01244) 390093 Fax: (01244) 389191 E-mail: enquiries@caldergroup.co.uk Principal Export Areas: Worldwide *Manufacturers of lead products, including casting. Also manufacturers of diecastings, radiation shielding & battery terminals. In addition, fabricators of lead, leadwork & nuclear plant lead-work*

continued

Calder Lifting Services Ltd, Warehouse 1, Cromwell House, Elland Road, Brighouse, West Yorkshire, HD6 2RG Tel: (01422) 376589 Fax: (01422) 374686 E-mail: sales@calderlifting.com *Lifting equipment manufrs*

Calder Metal Spinning Co. Ltd, Victoria Mills, Wharfe St, Mill Lane, Brighouse, West Yorkshire, HD6 1PP Tel: (01484) 713061 Fax: (01484) 400096 E-mail: david@caldermetspin.co.uk *Manufacturers of metal spinners & spinning's*

Calder Oils Ltd, Netherfield Road, Dewsbury, West Yorkshire, WF13 3JX Tel: (01924) 461058 Fax: (01924) 459773 E-mail: sales@calder-oils.co.uk *Lubricant manufrs*

Calder Security Services Ltd, 219 King Cross Road, King Cross, Halifax, West Yorkshire, HX1 3JL Tel: (01422) 347313 Fax: (01422) 321106 E-mail: mickyb@promapropertys.co.uk *Electrical installation specialists*

Calder Textiles Ltd, Anchor House Dewsbury Mills, Thornhill Road, Dewsbury, West Yorkshire, WF12 9QE Tel: (01924) 456411 Fax: (01924) 457387 E-mail: info@caldertextilex.co.uk *Woollen carpet yarn spinners*

Calder Trade Supplies Ltd, Unit 11-12 Halifax Industrial Centre, Marshway, Halifax, West Yorkshire, HX1 5RW Tel: (01422) 330008 Fax: (01422) 349437 E-mail: sales@caldertrade.co.uk *Wholesale ironmongers*

Calder Weaving Co. Ltd, Scout Road, Hebden Bridge, West Yorkshire, HX7 5HZ Tel: (01422) 882382 Fax: (01422) 883381 E-mail: sales@calderweaving.co.uk *Interlining & textiles manufrs*

Calderbrook Jute Co., Stansfield Mill, Calderbrook Road, Littleborough, Lancashire, OL15 9NP Tel: (01706) 378711 Fax: (01706) 371345 *Black sheathing felt manufrs*

▶ Calderbrook Woodworking Machinery, Unit 7 New Line Industrial Estate, The Sidings, Bacup, Lancashire, OL13 9RW Tel: (01706) 873344 Fax: (01706) 873388 *Woodworking machine supplier & manufrs*

▶ Calderdale Distribution Ltd, Unit 3A Royds Mill, Royd Business Park, Dye House Lane, Brighouse, West Yorkshire, HD6 1LL Tel: (01484) 722011

Calderdale Economic Development Services, North Gate House, North Gate, Halifax, West Yorkshire, HX1 1UN Tel: (01422) 392222 Fax: (01422) 392260 E-mail: john.hodgson@calderdale.gov.uk *Industrial development authority*

Calderglen Computers Ltd, Calder House, Spring Lane, Colne, Lancashire, BB8 9BD Tel: (01282) 866481 Fax: (01282) 861726 E-mail: steve.alcock@calderglen.net *Voice IT & telephone system manufrs*

Calderprint, 80 Manchester Road, Burnley, Lancashire, BB11 1QZ Tel: (01282) 831530 Fax: (01282) 831524 E-mail: enquiries@calderprint.co.uk *General printers*

Calders & Grandidge, 194 London Road, Boston, Lincolnshire, PE21 7HJ Tel: (01205) 358866 Fax: (01205) 312400 E-mail: enquiries@caldersandgrandidge.com *Electric, telegraph & fencing poles suppliers*

Caldervale Forge Co. Ltd, Dunrobin Road, Airdrie, Lanarkshire, ML6 8LS Tel: (01236) 763388 Fax: (01236) 765259 E-mail: rockeater@btinternet.com *Hydraulic breaker steel manufrs*

Calderys UK Ltd, 5-8 Ashfieldway, Leeds, LS12 5JB Tel: 0113-263 6268 Fax: 0113-279 0539 E-mail: uksales@calderys.com *Refractories manufrs* Also at: Port Talbot, Redcar & Scunthorpe

▶ Caldic Services Ltd, 20 Lightwoods Hill, Smethwick, West Midlands, B67 5EA Tel: 0121-420 4267 Fax: 0121-420 4267 E-mail: caldic@talktalk.net *Office supplies & dictation machine repairs & sales services*

Caldic UK Ltd, Stainsby Close, Holmewood Industrial Estate, Holmewood, Chesterfield, Derbyshire, S42 5UG Tel: (01246) 854111 Fax: (01246) 856222 E-mail: info@caldic.com *Chemical merchants*

Caldicot Engineering Ltd, Sudbrook Shipyard, Sudbrook, Caldicot, Gwent, NP26 5SY Tel: (01291) 421452 Fax: (01291) 422965 *Steel fabricators*

Caldicot Joinery, Unit 5g Castle Way, Severn Bridge Industrial Estate, Portskewett, Caldicot, Gwent, NP26 5PR Tel: (01291) 430532 Fax: (01291) 430532 *Joiners*

▶ Caldicot Printing, 2 Newport Road, Caldicot, Gwent, NP26 4HX Tel: (01291) 423294 Fax: (01291) 423294 E-mail: cal.print1@tiscali.co.uk *Printing services*

Caldo Oils Ltd, Unit 4 Rapier Court Sabre Close, Heathfield Industrial Estate, Newton Abbot, Devon, TQ12 6TW Tel: (01626) 835046 Fax: (01626) 836833 *Lubricating distributors*

Caldo Oils Ltd, Worsley Brow, St. Helens, Merseyside, WA9 3EZ Tel: (01744) 813535 Fax: (01744) 816031 E-mail: info@caldo.co.uk *General purpose lubricant manufrs*

Caldwell Consulting Engineers, 8 Lorne Street, Belfast, BT9 7DU Tel: (028) 9066 9456 Fax: (028) 9066 2219 E-mail: admin@caldwellconsulting.net *Mechanical & electrical engineers*

Caldwell Filtration Ltd, Unit 3d, Lyncastle Way, Barley Castle Trading Estate, Warrington, WA4 4ST Tel: (01925) 267111 Fax: (01925) 267744 E-mail: info@caldwellfiltration.co.uk *Caldwell Filtration Limited based in Warrington United Kingdom has become synonymous within the wire mesh industry for efficient friendly fair price structure. Specialists in Rotex screens wire cloth stockists, filter manufacturer, screen manufacturer, & sieve manufacturer serving industries WORLDWIDE intruder screens, discs & packs, insect screens, flymesh, cut wrap, wire mesh, wire cloth, taped & eyeletted screencloths for both original equipment manufacturers & end users. Caldwell Filtration serves the plastic recycling industry distributing filter discs & working across Europe & Worldwide. Please do contact one of our friendly sales team to discuss your enquiry quoting Kellysearch.*

Caldwell Hardware Ltd, Herald Way, Binley Industrial Estate, Binley Industrial Estate, Coventry, CV3 2RQ Tel: (024) 7643 7900 Fax: (024) 7643 7969 E-mail: sales@caldwell.co.uk *Window manufrs*

Caldwell Metalwork Fabrication, Units 10-11 Shaftsbury Industrial Estate, Icknield Way, Letchworth Garden City, Hertfordshire, SG6 1HE Tel: (01462) 670505 Fax: (01462) 670500 *Steel fabricators*

▶ Caldwells Dairy, 72 Inglefield Street, Glasgow, G42 7AW Tel: 0141-422 1828

Caledon Controls Ltd, Unit 2, Block 4, Castlehill Industrial Estate, Carluke, Lanarkshire, ML8 5UF Tel: (01555) 773355 Fax: (01555) 772212 E-mail: info@caledoncontrols.co.uk *Thyristor control panels manufrs*

▶ Caledonia Homes, 81 Shore, Edinburgh, EH6 6RG Tel: 0131-454 3580

▶ Caledonia Homes, Unit 10 Castle Street, Castlepark Industrial Estate, Ellon, Aberdeenshire, AB41 9RF Tel: (01358) 721661 Fax: (01358) 722955 *Construction*

Caledonia Instrumentation, Unit 26 Dalsetter Avenue, Glasgow, G15 8TE Tel: 0141-949 0000 Fax: 0141-949 1154 E-mail: sales@cal-inst.com *Process instrumentation distributors*

Caledonia Sterne & Wyld Ltd, 5 Queens Cres, Glasgow, G4 9BW Tel: 0141-353 3153 Fax: 0141 353 2435 *Television production company*

▶ Caledonia Textiles, Bridgeton Business Centre, 285 Abercromby Street, Glasgow, G40 2DD Tel: 0141-556 2705 Fax: 0141-564 5123

▶ Caledonia Training & Consultancy Ltd, Silverburn Crescent, Bridge of Don Industrial Estate, Aberdeen, AB23 8EW Tel: (01224) 708141 Fax: (01224) 705718

Caledonian Air Service, St. Andrews Works, Bonnyhill Road, Bonnybridge, Stirlingshire, FK4 2EJ Tel: (01324) 812122 Fax: (01324) 812128 E-mail: caledonian@airservice.fsnet.co.uk *Compressed air specialists*

Caledonian Airborne Engineering Ltd, Dove Hanger Ninian Road, Aberdeen Airport, Aberdeen, AB21 0PD Tel: (01224) 772071 Fax: (01224) 773800 E-mail: cae.line@bt.internet.com *Aircraft maintenance & repair specialist services*

Caledonian Airbourne Systems Ltd, 6 Ninian Road, Dyce, Aberdeen, AB21 0PD Tel: (01224) 722274 Fax: (01224) 722896 *Aircraft maintenance services*

Caledonian Building Services South East Ltd, 31 Slewins Lane, Hornchurch, Essex, RM11 2BZ Tel: (01708) 454305 Fax: (01708) 437375 *Electrical & air conditioning installations*

Caledonian Building Systems Ltd, Carlton Works, Ossington Road, Carlton-on-Trent, Newark, Nottinghamshire, NG23 6NT Tel: (01636) 821645 Fax: (01636) 821261 *Secure accommodation manufrs*

Caledonian Contracts (Aberdeen) Ltd, 8 Holland Place, Aberdeen, AB25 3UW Tel: (01224) 630355 Fax: (01224) 639504 *Partition & ceiling contractors*

Caledonian Control Technology Ltd, 2 Kelsey Close, Attleborough Fields Industrial Estate, Nuneaton, Warwickshire, CV11 6RS Tel: (024) 7634 2071 Fax: (024) 7635 1443 E-mail: info@caledonian-control.co.uk *Industrial gas control manufrs*

Caledonian Ferguson Timpson Ltd, 5 Atholl Avenue, Hillington Park, Glasgow, G52 4UA Tel: 0141-882 4691 Fax: 0141-810 3402 E-mail: ask@caledonian-group.co.uk *Performance packaging services*

▶ Caledonian Freight, Unit 1A, West Mains Industrial Estate, Grangemouth, Stirlingshire, FK3 8YE Tel: (01324) 472611 Fax: (01324) 472334

Caledonian Furniture Co. Ltd, 17 Glencryan Road, Cumbernauld, Glasgow, G67 2UH Tel: (01236) 735180 Fax: (01236) 734670 E-mail: sales@calfurn.co.uk *Office furniture manufrs*

▶ Caledonian Industrial Ltd, Unit 23 Eldin Industrial Estate, Edgefield Road, Loanhead, Midlothian, EH20 9QX Tel: 0131-448 0889 Fax: 0131-448 0891

▶ Caledonian Logistics Ltd, Weatherford House, Lawson Drive, Dyce, Aberdeen, AB21 0DR Tel: (01224) 723905 Fax: (01224) 725253

▶ Caledonian Macbrayne Ltd, Colintraive Office, Colintraive, Argyll, PA22 3AH Tel: (01700) 841235

Caledonian Macbrayne Ltd, The Pier, Station Road, Gourock, Renfrewshire, PA19 1QP Tel: (01475) 650100 Fax: (01475) 637607 E-mail: marketing@calmac.co.uk *Car ferry operators* Also at: Ardrossan & Largs

▶ Caledonian Macbrayne Ltd, The Pier, The Promenade, Largs, Ayrshire, KA30 8BG Tel: (01475) 674134 Fax: (01475) 672784

▶ Caledonian Macbrayne Ltd, Railway Pier, Oban, Argyll, PA34 4DB Tel: (01631) 566688 Fax: (01631) 566588

Caledonian Paper plc, Meadowhead Road, Irvine, Ayrshire, KA11 5AT Tel: (01294) 312020 Fax: (01294) 314400 E-mail: sales@upn-kymmene.com *Coated paper manufrs*

Caledonian Quilting, Rigby Lane, Bolton, BL2 3EQ Tel: (01204) 304462 Fax: (01204) 309770 *Textile manufrs*

▶ Caledonian Roofing Co. Ltd, Holyrood Business Park, 146 Duddingston Road West, Edinburgh, EH16 4AP Tel: 0131-538 6422 Fax: 0131-661 6253 E-mail: info@caledonianblacksmiths.com *Traditiona & contemporary blacksmith company*

Caledonian Stone Co., Marchlands, Lonmay, Fraserburgh, Aberdeenshire, AB43 8RN Tel: (01346) 532747 Fax: (01346) 532547 E-mail: sales@caledonianstone.com *Natural stone distributors*Aggregates*Scottish Highland Pebbles*Beach Cobbles*

Caledonian Storage Ltd, Broadhouse Lea, Cleghorn, Lanark, ML11 8PA Tel: (0870) 2406115 Fax: (0870) 2401146 *Material handling*

The Caledonian Tree Company Ltd, Cowbraehill, Tynehead, Pathhead, Midlothian, EH37 5XT Tel: (01875) 835360 Fax: (01875) 835636 E-mail: single@superoots.co.uk *Tree growing systems*

▶ Caledonian Waste Compactors, Caledonian House, 415 Oakwood Lane, Leeds, LS8 3LF Tel: 0113-205 1750 Fax: 0113-248 1175 E-mail: lukecaledonian@yahoo.co.uk

▶ Caledus G P E Ltd, Linton Industrial Estate, The Haughs, Inverbervie, Montrose, Angus, DD10 0QB Tel: (01561) 361660 Fax: (01561) 362823

Calendar Club, Vulcan Works, Water Lane, Exeter, EX2 8BY Tel: (01392) 207001

▶ Calendar Lady Promotions Ltd, 2 Barnfield Cottages, Upton Bishop, Ross-on-Wye, Herefordshire, HR9 7TZ Tel: (01989) 780727 Fax: (01989) 780276 E-mail: info@calendarlady.co.uk *Suppliers of promotional calendars, gifts & diaries*

Calendar Sales, 192 Oritor Road, Cookstown, County Tyrone, BT80 9RF Tel: (028) 8676 3377 Fax: (028) 8676 3706 E-mail: info@calendarsales.co.uk *Calendar manufrs*

Caletrim Fabrications Ltd, 7a Bowes Road, Middlesbrough, Cleveland, TS2 1LU Tel: (01642) 224121 Fax: (01642) 224121 *Steel & pipework fabricators*

Caleva Process Solutions Ltd, Butts Pond Industrial Estate, Sturminster Newton, Dorset, DT10 1AZ Tel: (01258) 471122 Fax: (01258) 471133 E-mail: info@caleva.co.uk *Pharmaceutical manufrs*

Caley Fisheries Ltd, Castle Street, Peterhead, Aberdeenshire, AB42 1EN Tel: (01779) 479121 Fax: (01779) 474813 *Fish processors*

▶ Caley Print & Stationery Ltd, 26 New Albion Industrial Estate, Halley Drive, Glasgow, G13 4DJ Tel: 0141-951 1500 Fax: 0141-951 1600 E-mail: sales@caleyprint.com *Printing & suppliers of stationary & furniture*

▶ Calf Hey Design Ltd, Unit 23, Colne Valley Business Park, Linthwaite, Huddersfield, HD7 5QG Tel: (01484) 846419 Fax: (01484) 847163

▶ Cali Catering, 54 Corston Park, Livingston, West Lothian, EH54 5NT Tel: (01506) 435304 E-mail: mcalisterkimmy@aol.com *Finger buffets from £3 per head. Fresh quality catering. All events catered for.*

Caliach Ltd, 7 The Green, West Drayton, Middlesex, UB7 7PL Tel: (01895) 430313 Fax: (01895) 448226 E-mail: sales@caliach.com *Software developers*

Caliba Spraying, Wallet Street, Nottingham, NG2 3EL Tel: 0115-986 9200 Fax: 0115-986 9204 E-mail: sales@surface-coating.co.uk *Specialists in powder coating, stove enamelling, spray finishing, incorporating, pre-treating & blast cleaning. Please call for a free copy of our brochure or visit our website*

Calibra Weighing Systems Ltd, Calibra House, Sandy La Industrial Estate, Stourport-on-Severn, Worcestershire, DY13 9QB Tel: (01299) 879944 Fax: (01299) 871188 E-mail: enquiries@calibraweighingsystems.co.uk *Sales & services of weighing equipment*

Calibration & Repair Services Ltd, Cars House, 137a Inkerman Street, Ashton-on-Ribble, Preston, PR2 2HN Tel: (01772) 728233 Fax: (01772) 768031 E-mail: sales@carslimited.co.uk *MOT equipment distributors*

Calibration Services Ltd, 29 Tennant Avenue, East Kilbride, Glasgow, G74 5NA Tel: (01355) 248102 Fax: (01355) 248102 E-mail: calibriation@dial.pipex.com *Calibrating services*

Calibre Computing, 19 Daish Way, Newport, Isle of Wight, PO30 5XJ Tel: (01983) 530548 Fax: (01983) 530548 E-mail: sales@calibrecomputing.co.uk *Computer consumables*

Calibre Recruitment, 71 Patrick Way, Aylesbury, Buckinghamshire, HP21 9XJ Tel: (01296) 420456 Fax: (01296) 393723 E-mail: calibre_uk@compuserve.com *Specialist computer recruitment*

▶ Calibre Recruitment, Unit 10 River Court Brighouse Business Village, Brighouse Road, Middlesbrough, Cleveland, TS2 1RT Tel: (01642) 244020 Fax: (01642) 243480 E-mail: careers@calibre-recruitment.co.uk *Calibre Resource & Recruitment specialise in permanent recruitment and search and selection of graduate calibre personnel from entry level to executive Director. Positions include engineering in all disciplines, construction,manufacturing, sales & marketing, human resources, information technology, junior to senior management,directors, finance,purchasing, logistics etc.**Calibre Resource & Recruitment also provide Human Resource Services and can assist clients with psychometric assesment, personality profiling, personnel development and general business process improvements that are personnel related.**We predominantly operate in the north east of England, but also have the facility to recruit for overseas assignments and UK wide*

Calibre UK Ltd, Cornwall House, Cornwall Terrace, Bradford, West Yorkshire, BD8 7JS Tel: (01274) 394125 Fax: (01274) 730960 E-mail: lisas@calibreuk.com *VDU systems designers & manufrs*

▶ Calico Plant & Transport Ltd, Dawber Industrial Area, Skull House Lane, Appley Bridge, Wigan, Lancashire, WN6 9DN Tel: (01257) 252962 Fax: (01257) 254199

Calido Trading Ltd, Unit 4A, Market Hill, Maldon, Essex, CM9 4PZ Tel: (01621) 842828 Fax: (01621) 840064 E-mail: enquiries@calido.co.uk *Mica products manufrs*

Calig Industrial Wipers, Saw Mill Lane, Great Yarmouth, Norfolk, NR31 0AE Tel: (01493) 603762 Fax: (01493) 442846 E-mail: denisecalig@lineone.net *Industrial cloth manufrs*

Caligen Foam Ltd, Broad Oak, Accrington, Lancashire, BB5 2BS Tel: (01254) 355000 Fax: (01254) 355111 E-mail: info@caligen.co.uk Principal Export Areas: Worldwide *Manufacturers & converters of Polyurethane foams for use in noise insulation within heavy machinery, air compressors & automotive interior trim manufrs*

Caligraving Ltd, Brunel Way, Thetford, Norfolk, IP24 1HP Tel: (01842) 752116 Fax: (01842) 755512 *Music book printers & binders*

Caljan Rite Hite Ltd, Moorbridge Road, Bingham, Nottingham, NG13 8GG Tel: (01949) 838850 Fax: (01949) 836953 E-mail: caljanritehite@caljanritehite.co.uk *Automated storage systems*

Calkin Pattinson & Co. Ltd, 40 Piccadilly, London, W1J 0HR Tel: (020) 7734 2176 Fax: (020) 7437 0604 E-mail: info@calkin.org *Independent financial advisors*

Calkit Maintenance Supplies, 1 Nutfield Road, Merstham, Redhill, RH1 3EB Tel: (01737) 647900 Fax: (01737) 647949 E-mail: sales@calkit.co.uk *Janitorial & nursing product distributors*

▶ Call Aid UK Ltd, 3 Buxton Avenue, Carlton, Nottingham, NG4 3RR Tel: 0115-940 1985 Fax: 0115-940 3369 E-mail: info@callaiduk.com *Healthcare patient & nurse call, panic & disabled alarm system manufrs*

▶ Call Centre Recruitment Experts Ltd, Greyfriars Chambers, Greyfriars, Bedford, MK40 1HJ Tel: (01234) 400233 Fax: (01234) 272155 E-mail: sian@callrecruit.co.uk *Recruitment company*

▶ Call One Ltd, 5 The Foxwood, Charnock Richard, Chorley, Lancashire, PR7 5JQ Tel: (01257) 791599 Fax: (01257) 791599 E-mail: info@callone.uk.com *CallOne Ltd are an independent call centre consultants specialising in providing high quality solutions for the call and contact centre marketplace. We offer truly independent and tangible results based on over 15 years award-winning experience in both sales and customer service environments. Our call centre consultants do this by adopting a friendly and close working relationship with our customers, ensuring that both business and personal requirements are taken into account.*

▶ Call Preformance Ltd, 85-87llington Street, Gravesend, Kent, DA12 1JQ Tel: (01474) 574300 Fax: (01474) 574359 E-mail: sales@callperformance.co.uk *Supply franking machines on a 30 day trial!*

Call Print 16 Ltd, 201 Shenley Road, Borehamwood, Hertfordshire, WD6 1AT Tel: (020) 8207 1188 Fax: (020) 8207 0193 E-mail: bwood@callprint.co.uk *Print & reprographic printers*

Callaghan Engineering, Pembroke Avenue, Waterbeach, Cambridge, CB25 9QP Tel: (01223) 863330 Fax: (01223) 863223 *Precision engineers & sheet metal work fabricators*

▶ Callaghan Fine Paintings, 22 St. Marys Street, Shrewsbury, SY1 1ED Tel: (01743) 343452 E-mail: art@callaghan-finepaintings.com *Fine art gallery specialising in contemporary fine art & sculptures also restore fine works of art*

P W Callaghan, Emerys, 2 Bucks Lane, Little Eversden, Cambridge, CB3 7HL Tel: (01223) 262444 Fax: (01223) 263241 E-mail: callaghanpw@aol.com *An international Chief Executive who has worked for over 20 years in demanding company change roles. Assignments have included business development, caring for orphan companies and activities, disposal, restructuring and turnaround. Known for gaining lasting results quickly in complicated situations. Worked in large and mid-sized companies around the world including UK, Germany, Hungary, North America, Australia, India and South Africa. Detailed knowledge across a number of sectors including logistics, Retail, Engineering, Contracting, Automotive, Steel and Manufacturing.*

▶ Callaghan & Walker, 129 Washington Road, Sheffield, S11 8DP Tel: 0114-278 0876 *Building contractors*

Callan School Of English, 139 Oxford Street, London, W1D 2JB Tel: (020) 7734 5600 Fax: (020) 7494 3204 E-mail: csl@callan.co.uk *Language school*

Callancote plc, Unit 11 Deptford Trading Estate, Blackhorse Road, London, SE8 5HY Tel: (020) 8469 3969 Fax: (020) 8691 6403 E-mail: callancote@aol.com Sales Contact: T. Moore *Manufacturers of polythene bags & carriers, polyethylene refuse sacks & polythene film/sheet*

▶ Callidus Computer Centre, 91 Pall Mall, Leigh-on-Sea, Essex, SS9 1RF Tel: (01702) 478600 Fax: (01702) 479122 E-mail: enquirer@caladercomputercentre.com *Instillation & sales of software*

Callinan Hair & Beauty Products, Glebe Farm, Dennis Street, Hugglescote, Coalville, Leicestershire, LE67 2FP Tel: (01530) 814074 *Hair & beauty products wholesale*

▶ Callisto Trading Ltd, 2 Duckett Mews, London, N4 1BP Tel: (07092) 008537 Fax: (07092) 020256 E-mail: info@callistotrading.co.uk *Bulgarian natural stone importers*

▶ Callmonitor, 207 Regent Street, London, W1B 4ND Tel: (020) 7292 9200 Fax: (0800) 0747458 E-mail: sales@satphone.co.uk

Callow Shopfitters Ltd, 2 Middlemore La West, Walsall, WS9 8DR Tel: (01922) 744888 Fax: (01922) 744555 E-mail: davidrcallow@netscapeonline.co.uk *Shopfitters, joinery specialists & metal fabricators*

Callscan Ltd, Callscan House Priestley Wharf, 20 Holt Street, Birmingham, B7 4BZ Tel: 0121-359 8941 Fax: 0121-359 1417 E-mail: info@epcuk.com *Telephone call management systems*

Callsure Business Telephone Numbers, 36 Duncroft, Windsor, Berkshire, SL4 4HH Tel: (0844) 4780121 E-mail: sales@callsure07050.co.uk *Callsure Business Telephone Numbers provides SMEs with intelligent Phone Numbers. Our range includes: 0800 Freephone, 0870 National Rate, 0845 Local Rate, 0871 Euro/USA Free Divert, International Freephone/Toll Free, UK City Numbers, Fax to Email/Email to Fax Services and Live Answering Services. Our numbers are ideal for businesses who have a single location with multiple departments, multiple location businesses or for growing businesses on the move. A typical example of how are numbers are used is where a customer is starting a new business, and does not want to go through the expense of having to change his phone number if he relocates or changes his business.*

Callworth Ltd, 294 High Street, Rochester, Kent, ME1 1HS Tel: (01634) 402381 Fax: (01634) 201770 E-mail: pj.crook@btinternet.com *Chartered surveyors*

▶ Cally Sawmill Ltd, Cally Sawmill, Dunkeld, Perthshire, PH8 0HU Tel: (01350) 727305

▶ Calm Control Systems Ltd, 7 Mead Walk, Didcot, Oxfordshire, OX11 7PA Tel: (01235) 811117 Fax: (01235) 511551 E-mail: sale@calm-controls.co.uk *Control systems manufrs*

Calmac Metal Finishers Ltd, Unit 10 Quay Lane Industrial Estate, Hard Way, Gosport, Hampshire, PO12 4LJ Tel: (023) 9251 1440 Fax: (023) 9252 8814 *Specialists in blast treatment & powder coating & electroplating services*

▶ Calmag Ltd, Unit 3-6, Crown Works, Bradford Road, Sandbeds, Keighley, West Yorkshire, BD20 5LN Tel: (01535) 210320 Fax: (01535) 210321 E-mail: sales@calmagltd.com *Water conditioning products manufrs*

Calmels Design Ltd, 3-7 Southville, London, SW8 2PR Tel: (020) 7622 6181 Fax: (020) 7498 2889 E-mail: lois@calmels.co.uk *Art metal workers*

Calmore Machinery Co. Ltd, 4 28 Black Moor Road, Ebblake Industrial Estate, Verwood, Dorset, BH31 6BB Tel: (01202) 827701 Fax: (01202) 813053 E-mail: info@calmorehinges.co.uk *Supplier of weld-on hinges & drum mixers*

Calmtoken Ltd, 32C Ellesmere Court, Leechmere Industrial Estate, Sunderland, SR2 9UA Tel: 0191-521 4316 Fax: 0191-521 4317 E-mail: robert@safetechsystems.com Principal Export Areas: Africa & North America *Conveyor safety, personnel detection systems manufrs*

Calne Engineering Ltd, Stanier Road, Porte Marsh Industrial Estate, Calne, Wiltshire, SN11 9PX Tel: (01249) 813288 Fax: (01249) 821266 E-mail: sales@calne-engineering.co.uk *Sheet metalworkers*

Calomax Ltd, Lupton Avenue, Leeds, LS9 7DD Tel: 0113-249 6681 Fax: 0113-235 0358 E-mail: sales@calomax.co.uk *Catering boiler manufrs*

Calor Gas Ltd, Dockyard Road, Ellesmere Port, CH65 4EG Tel: 0151-355 3700 Fax: 0151-357 1944 E-mail: querynw@calor.co.uk *Gas distribution*

Calor Gas Ltd, Cambridge Works, Mornington Road, Smethwick, West Midlands, B66 2JE Tel: 0121-565 0703 Fax: 0121-558 5992 *Calor gas distributors* Also at: Walsall

Calor Gas Ltd, Athena House, Athena Drive, Warwick, CV34 6RL Tel: (0800) 0224199 Fax: (0870) 4006904 E-mail: commercial@calor.co.uk *Calor Gas is the UK's largest supplier of LPG and has for long been taking care of power, heating and lighting needs of UK businesses. On the road, in the field, in the factory or wherever you conduct your business, Calor is there to help.*

Calor Gas (Northern Ireland) Ltd, Airport Road West, Belfast, BT3 9EE Tel: (028) 9045 5588 Fax: (028) 9045 8072 *Calor gas L.P.G. suppliers*

Calorex Heat Pumps Ltd, Unit 2, The Causeway, Heybridge, Maldon, Essex, CM9 4XL Tel: (01621) 856611 Fax: (01621) 850871 E-mail: sales@calorex.com *Manufacturers of dehumidifiers & swimming pool heater pumps*

▶ Calp UK Ltd, Tuscanny House, Crackley Bank Indust Estate, Newcastle Stfs, Newcastle, Staffordshire, ST5 8ET Tel: (01782) 566111 Fax: (01782) 561222

Calpar Electronics, Calpar House, 1 Windermere Road, Beeston, Nottingham, NG9 3AS Tel: 0115-925 8335 Fax: 0115-925 8335 E-mail: keith@calpar-electronics *Electronics engineers*

Calpeda Ltd, Wedgwood Road Industrial Estate, Bicester, Oxfordshire, OX26 4UL Tel: (01869) 241441 Fax: (01869) 240681 E-mail: pumps@calpeda.co.uk *Pump manufrs*

Calserv Surveying Instruments, 5 Prospect Way, Rugby, Warwickshire, CV21 3UU Tel: (01788) 553666 Fax: (01788) 551666 E-mail: calserv@calserv.freeserve.co.uk *Surveying equipment hire, repair & sales*

Calsonic Automotive Products Ltd, 5 Bentall Business Park, Washington, Tyne & Wear, NE37 3JD Tel: 0191-417 0084 Fax: 0191-417 0184 *Exhaust systems & catalytic converters manufrs*

▶ Caltak Aluminium Systems, 9 Napier Square, Houstoun Industrial Estate, Livingston, West Lothian, EH54 5DG Tel: (01506) 444644 Fax: (01506) 444700 *Aluminium fabricators*

Caltec Electronic Equipment, L Quarry Road, Newhaven, East Sussex, BN9 9DG Tel: (01273) 517516 Fax: (01273) 517278 *Manufacturers of temperature controlls*

Caltec Publications Ltd, Petticoat Court, Strait Bargate, Boston, Lincolnshire, PE21 6EE Tel: (01205) 358877 Fax: (01205) 359977 E-mail: sales@caltec.co.uk *Computer consultancy*

Caltech Lifts Servicing, Stannergate Road, Dundee, DD1 3NA Tel: (01382) 462810 Fax: (01382) 454134 E-mail: caltechlifts@btinternet.com *Passenger & goods lift engineers*

Caltest Instruments Ltd, PO Box 7717, Lockerbie, Dumfriesshire, DG11 1YF Tel: (01387) 811910 Fax: (01387) 810195 E-mail: sales@caltest.co.uk *Instrumentation for electrical power systems.*

Caltherm UK Ltd, Rowhurst Industrial Estate, Newcastle, Staffordshire, ST5 6BD Tel: (01782) 563865 Fax: (01782) 561607 E-mail: info@caltherm.co.uk *Industrial ovens manufrs*

Calumet Ltd, 93-103 Drummond Street, London, NW1 2HJ Tel: (0870) 6030303 E-mail: website@calumetphoto.co.uk *Photographic retailer* Also at: Birmingham, Bristol & Manchester

Calumet Photographic Ltd, 4 Downing St Industrial Estate, Charlton Place, Ardwick, Manchester, M12 6HH Tel: 0161-274 4455 Fax: 0161-274 3406 E-mail: michael.collins@calumetphoto.co.uk *Photographic equipment retailers*

Calumite Ltd, Brigg Road, Scunthorpe, North Lincolnshire, DN16 1AW Tel: (01724) 282211 Fax: (01724) 270435 E-mail: info@applebygroup.co.uk Principal Export Areas: Worldwide *Glass making raw material producers*

Calver Ltd, 22 The Drive, Orpington, Kent, BR6 9AP Tel: (01689) 898828 Fax: (01689) 898848 E-mail: sales@calver.com *Promotional designers, clothing & leather goods*

Calverley Control Installations, Blacup House, Royds Close, Leeds, LS12 6LL Tel: 0113-279 6611 Fax: 0113-231 0391 E-mail: info@calverley-control-systems.co.uk *Control systems design & manufrs*

Calvert Brain & Fraulo, 3 Portland Street, King's Lynn, Norfolk, PE30 1PB Tel: (01553) 761771 Fax: (01553) 766033 E-mail: info@c-b-f.co.uk *Chartered civil & structural engineers*

Calyon, Broadwalk House, 5 Appold Street, London, EC2A 2DA Tel: (020) 7214 5000 Fax: (020) 7588 0290 *Broker dealers*

Calypso Blinds, Unit 14 Royal Elizabeth Yard, Kirkliston, West Lothian, EH29 9EN Tel: 0131-319 1190 Fax: 0131-319 1191 *Blind manufrs*

Calypso Soft Drinks Ltd, Spectrum Business Park, Wrexham Industrial Estate, Wrexham, Clwyd, LL13 9QA Tel: (01978) 668400 Fax: (01978) 668440 E-mail: contactus@calypso.co.uk *Soft drinks manufrs*

Calzeat & Co. Ltd, 16 Maddox Street, London, W1S 1PH Tel: (020) 7493 1866 *Fabric manufrs*

Cam, East Carlton Hall, East Carlton Park, East Carlton, Market Harborough, Leicestershire, LE16 8YF Tel: (01536) 771775 Fax: (01536) 771832 *Manufacturers of pharmaceutical products*

▶ Cam Com Radio, Gusto Mills, Huntingdon Road, Cambridge, CB3 0DL Tel: (01223) 277274 Fax: (01223) 277207 E-mail: camcom@metronet.co.uk *Specialists in two-way radio communications*

Cam Hydraulics, Unit 8 Hillfoot Industrial Estate, 17 Hoyland Road, Sheffield, S3 8AB Tel: 0114-231 4833 Fax: 0114-285 5810 E-mail: info@camhydraulics.co.uk *Hydraulic engineers*

Cam Technologies Manufacturing Ltd, 2 Starley Court, Hotchkiss Way, Binley Industrial Estate, Coventry, CV3 2RL Tel: (024) 7644 5829 Fax: (024) 7645 8269

▶ Cam Water Ltd, Cam House, 5 York Street, Aberdeen, AB11 5DL Tel: (01224) 596777 Fax: (01224) 594477

Camale Engineering Ltd, Halas Industrial Estate, Forge Lane, Halesowen, West Midlands, B62 8EB Tel: 0121-550 8089 Fax: 0121-550 8089 *Precision engineers*

Camanchi Leathers Ltd, 184 Brick Lane, London, E1 6SA Tel: (020) 7739 5181 Fax: (020) 7256 0491 *Leather garments manufrs*

Camasonics Ultrasonic Equipment Mnfrs, Unit C2 Fiveways Trading Estate, Westwells Road, Hawthorn, Corsham, Wiltshire, SN13 9RG Tel: (01225) 812223 Fax: (01225) 812223 E-mail: camasonics@hotmail.com *Ultrasonic testing equipment service providers*

Cambashi Ltd, 52 Mawson Road, Cambridge, CB1 2HY Tel: (01223) 460439 Fax: (01223) 461055 E-mail: info@cambashi.com *IT services in industry marketing consultants*

▶ Camber Castles, 6 Academy Close, Camberley, Surrey, GU15 4BU Tel: (01276) 500324

Camberley Auto Factors Ltd, Units 6-7, 196 Old Shoreham Road, Hove, East Sussex, BN3 3TW Tel: (01273) 775488 Fax: (01273) 822821 E-mail: sales@camberleyautofactors.co.uk *Motor factors distributors*

Camberley Glass Ltd, 453 London Road, Camberley, Surrey, GU15 3JA Tel: (01276) 684444 Fax: (01276) 28277 E-mail: sales@camberleyglass.co.uk *PVC-u fabricators & installers*

Camberley Printers Ltd, 357 London Road, Camberley, Surrey, GU15 3HQ Tel: (01276) 63048 Fax: (01276) 23477 E-mail: sales@camberleyprinters.co.uk *Printing & typesetting services*

Camberley Rubber Mouldings Ltd, Unit 10, Springlake Industrial Estate, Aldershot, Hampshire, GU12 4UH Tel: (01252) 330200 Fax: (01252) 330218 E-mail: sales@camberleyrubber.com *Rubber mouldings manufrs*

▶ Camberley Travel Centre Ltd, 2a Princess Way, Camberley, Surrey, GU15 3SR Tel: (01276) 28761 Fax: (01276) 692194 E-mail: jo@camberleytravel.co.uk *Advantage Business Travel Centre**

▶ Cambit Support, 16 Chesterton Hall CR, Cambridge, CB4 1AP Tel: (01223) 576705 E-mail: sales@cambit.net *Online computer support forum*

Cambmac Ltd, 4 Commercial Road, March, Cambridgeshire, PE15 8QP Tel: (01354) 655270 Fax: (01354) 657447 E-mail: info@cambmac.fsnet.co.uk *Machining titanium & stainless ophthalmic blanks*

▶ Camborne Joinery Ltd, Trevu Industrial Estate, Unit 2 Trevu Road, Camborne, Cornwall, TR14 8DX Tel: (01209) 716000

Camborne Mattress & Bed Centre, 85 Pendarves Street, Tuckingmill, Camborne, Cornwall, TR14 8NP Tel: (01209) 718029 *Furniture retailers*

▶ Cambot Technologies Ltd, 135 Edgar Street, Hereford, HR4 9JR Tel: (01432) 370950 E-mail: adrian@camcot.co.uk *Computer software house*

Cambrake Ltd, Crescent Mill, Foundry Street, Todmorden, Lancashire, OL14 7NA Tel: (01706) 815711 Fax: (01706) 817967 E-mail: info@cambrake.co.uk *Photoelectric safety guard manufrs*

Cambray Bindery, 17 Warden Hill Road, Cheltenham, Gloucestershire, GL51 3AU Tel: (01242) 241216 *Book binders manufrs*

Cambrian Caledonian Ltd, Llandygai Industrial Estate, Bangor, Gwynedd, LL57 4YH Tel: (01248) 370248 Fax: (01248) 370406 *Structural & mechanical engineers*

Cambrian Concrete Products, Old Sand Gravel Quarry, Rhosesmor Road, Rhosesmor, Mold, Clwyd, CH7 6PE Tel: (01352) 741412 Fax: (01352) 741531 *Building blocks manufrs*

Cambrian Containers, Unit 32 Mochdre Industrial Estate, Mochdre, Newtown, Powys, SY16 4LE Tel: (01686) 611360 Fax: (01686) 611361 *Plastic container distributors or agents*

Cambrian Fencing, Rhydlydan Yard, Llywernog, Ponterwyd, Aberystwyth, Dyfed, SY23 3AB Tel: (01970) 890502 Fax: (01970) 890502 *Agricultural fencing material manufrs*

Cambrian Foundry Ltd, Unit 34 Vastre Indust Estate, Kerry Road, Newtown, Powys, SY16 1DZ Tel: (01686) 626209 Fax: (01686) 629500 E-mail: camfound@hotmail.com *General engineers*

Cambrian Marine Services Ltd, Ferry Road, Cardiff, CF11 0JL Tel: (029) 2034 3459 Fax: (029) 2034 5116 E-mail: cambrianmarine@aol.com *Boat repairers*

Cambrian News Ltd, Unit 7, Cefn Llan Science Park, Waunfawr, Aberystwyth, Dyfed, SY23 3AH Tel: (01970) 615000 Fax: (01970) 624699 E-mail: edit@cambrian-news.co.uk *Newspaper & magazine publishers*

Cambrian Powder Paints, Site B Unit 200 Rednal Indust Estate, Llanyblodwel, Oswestry, Shropshire, SY10 8NH Tel: (01691) 610596 Fax: (01691) 610596 *Powder coaters*

Cambrian Power Tools, Glendale, Tregaron, Dyfed, SY25 6QT Tel: (01974) 298244 Fax: (01974) 298288 *Power tools, equipment supply, hire, service & sales*

▶ Cambrian Printers (Aberystwyth) Ltd, Llanbadarn Road, Llanbadarn Fawr, Aberystwyth, Dyfed, SY23 3TN Tel: (01970) 627111 Fax: (01970) 615497 E-mail: info@cambrian-printers.co.uk

▶ Cambrian Securities, 3 John Street, Llanelli, Carmarthenshire, SA15 1 UH Tel: (01554) 780502 Fax: (01554) 777708 E-mail: cambrian@clara.net *Private investigation and tracing service,process servers to the legal community and private individuals, authoriesd debt consultancy service.*

Cambrian Signs, 10 Burnell Road, Sheffield, S6 2AX Tel: 0114-233 0233 Fax: 0114-233 0233 *Sign manufrs*

Cambrian Software UK Ltd, 26 Lombard Street, Porthmadog, Gwynedd, LL49 9AP Tel: (01766) 514969 *Software house*

Cambrian Windows Ltd, Units 11-13 Thomas Court, London Road Industrial Estate, Pembroke Dock, Dyfed, SA72 4RZ Tel: (01646) 687455 *Window manufrs*

Cambrian Woollen Mill, Top Floor Weaving Unit, Llanwrtyd Wells, Powys, LD5 4SD Tel: (01591) 610473 Fax: (01591) 610314 E-mail: cambrianwool@tiscali.co.uk *Woollen manufrs*

Cambridge Algorithmica Ltd, 9 Oakdene, Beaconsfield, Buckinghamshire, HP9 2BZ Tel: (01494) 678989 Fax: (01494) 678990 E-mail: info@camalg.co.uk *Telecommunication consultancy services & software developers*

Cambridge (Auto Bulbs) Ltd, Unit 30 Over Industrial Park, Norman Way, Over, Cambridge, CB24 5QE Tel: (01954) 231611 Fax: (01954) 230552 E-mail: cabulbs@tesco.net *Lighting fitting manufrs*

Cambridge Blind Spot, 394 Mill Road, Cambridge, CB1 3NN Tel: (01223) 213984 Fax: (01223) 576657 *Blind suppliers*

Cambridge Capacitors Ltd, Budds Lane, Romsey, Hampshire, SO51 0ZQ Tel: (01794) 513481 Fax: (01794) 523940 E-mail: sales@camcap.co.uk *AC/DC electrical capacitor manufrs*

Cambridge Clinical Research, Tunbridge Court, Tunbridge Lane, Bottisham, Cambridge, CB5 9DU Tel: (01223) 811882 Fax: (01223) 813539 E-mail: marrowsmith@cambridge-clinical-research.co.uk *Clinical trials*

Cambridge Computer Systems, Rosemary House, Lanwades Business Park, Kennett, Newmarket, Suffolk, CB8 7PW Tel: (01638) 751485 Fax: (01638) 751058 E-mail: linda@ccsys.co.uk *Computer consultants*

▶ Cambridge Computers, The Boiler House, Botley Mills Botley, Southampton, SO30 2GB Tel: (01489) 799955 E-mail: info@cambridgeci.com *Computer consultants*

Cambridge Consultants Ltd, Science Park, Milton Road, Cambridge, CB4 0DW Tel: (01223) 420024 Fax: (01223) 423373 E-mail: info@cambridgeconsultants.com *Production & design*

Cambridge Country Furniture, Main Hall Farm, Conington, Cambridge, CB3 8LR Tel: 01954 267156 Fax: 01954 267156 *Pine furniture supplier*

Cambridge Database Technologies Ltd, 102 Long Road, Cambridge, CB2 8HF Tel: (01223) 843840 *Computer consultants*

Cambridge Dive Centre, 252 Cherry Hinton Road, Cambridge, CB1 7AU Tel: (01223) 240818 Fax: (01223) 240818 E-mail: sales@cambridge-dive-centre.co.uk *Diving training centre*

Cambridge Door Services, 127 Mereside, Soham, Ely, Cambridgeshire, CB7 5EG Tel: (01353) 725000 Fax: (01353) 725001 E-mail: alan@camdoor.fsnet.co.uk *Roller shutter & industrial door manufrs*

Cambridge Electro Plating Ltd, 21 25 Union Lane, Cambridge, CB4 1PR Tel: (01223) 352464 Fax: (01223) 361085 E-mail: cep@btinternet.com *Electroplaters & stove enamellers*

Cambridge Electron Beam, 3 High Street, Toft, Cambridge, CB23 2RL Tel: (01223) 263588 Fax: (01223) 263391 E-mail: t.e.burns@talk21.com *Electron beam welding engineers*

Cambridge Electronic Design Ltd, Science Park, Milton Road, Cambridge, CB4 0FE Tel: (01223) 420186 Fax: (01223) 420488 E-mail: info@ced.co.uk *Laboratory computer systems manufrs*

Cambridge Electronic Industries Ltd, Denny Industrial Centre, Denny End Road, Waterbeach, Cambridge, CB25 9PB Tel: (01223) 860041 Fax: (01223) 863625 E-mail: sales@cambridgeconnectors.com *Manufacturer of Interconnection Products, including Connectors, Baluns for Telecom & Data Networks, Cable Assemblies, Harnesses, Enclosures, Patch Leads & Panels.*

▶ Cambridge Engineering Technology Ltd, 17 Fennec Close, Cambridge, CB1 9GG Tel: (01223) 413797 E-mail: enquiries@cambridge-engineering.com *Cambridge Engineering Technology offer a wide range of consultancy services. We utilise the wealth of engineering and technology experience in the Cambridge area. Consultants have previously been employed in the region's consulting and high technology companies and can now offer quality services at competitive rates.**Plesae contact us to discuss your business, technology, development, design, engineering or sourcing needs.**

▶ Cambridge Flow Solutions, Compass House, Vision Park, Histon, Cambridge, CB4 9AD Tel: 01223 257978 Fax: 01223 257800 E-mail: ed.lewis@cambridgeflowsolutions.com *Formed as a spin-out from the University of Cambridge Engineering Department, we develop software products and service offerings to solve complex problems for Engineering blue chips. We are specialists in Computational Fluid Dynamics (CFD), a rapidly growing sector of fluid mechanics and aeronautics that leverages high performance computing to simulate fluid flows and combustion. Our expertise is forged from years of working to the demanding standards of Aerospace and we are now diversifying into additional challenging arenas. **We provide bespoke and heavily customised products that remove costly bottlenecks from our Clients" mission-critical design, certification and R&D processes. **Our vision is to use our expertise to develop disruptive products that extend the limits of the science and the capacity of dependant industries.*

Cambridge Fluid Systems, 12 Trafalgar Way, Bar Hill, Cambridge, CB3 8SQ Tel: (01954) 786800 Fax: (01954) 786818 E-mail: uhp@cam.cambridge-fluid.com *High purity gas systems & suppliers*

▶ Cambridge Food Co., 156 Cowley Road, Cambridge, CB4 0DL Tel: (01223) 433433 Fax: (01223) 433434

▶ Cambridge Glass House Co. Ltd, 236 Main Road, Newport, Brough, North Humberside, HU15 2RH Tel: (01430) 449440 Fax: (01430) 449331 E-mail: info@cambridgeglasshouse.co.uk *Design & build of high specification glasshouses*

Cambridge Glass House Co. Ltd, 236 Main Road, Newport, Brough, North Humberside, HU15 2RH Tel: (01430) 449440 Fax: (01430) 449331 E-mail: info@cambridgeglasshouse.co.uk *Greenhouse distributors & manufrs*

Cambridge Insitu Ltd, Rectory Farm, 39 High Street, Little Eversden, Cambridge, CB3 7HE Tel: (01223) 262361 Fax: (01223) 263947 E-mail: caminsitu@aol.com *Geotechnical instruments*

▶ Cambridge Interiors Ltd, 71 Nelson Street, Kettering, Northamptonshire, NN16 9QL Tel: (01536) 481586 Fax: (01536) 481586 *Footwear manufrs*

Cambridge IT Solutions Ltd, May Ho, 4 Sheepcoat Clo, Shenley Church End, Milton Keynes, MK5 6JL Tel: (01908) 506888 Fax: (01908) 507088 *Computer software manufr*

Cambridge Joinery Ltd, 23 Fen End, Over, Cambridge, CB4 5NE Tel: (01954) 231008 Fax: (01954) 232263 E-mail: jim@cambridgejoinery.co.uk *Joinery manufrs*

▶ Cambridge Magnetic Refrigeration, Britannia House, 19-21 Godesdone Road, Cambridge, CB5 8HR Tel: (01223) 473631 Fax: (01223) 474164 *Scientific instruments manufrs*

Cambridge Manufacturing Services, 3 Hale Close, Melbourn, Royston, Hertfordshire, SG8 6ET Tel: (01763) 260070 Fax: (01763) 260070 E-mail: cammas_uk@yahoo.co.uk *Abrasive products distributors or agents*

Cambridge Micro Engineering Ltd, 83 High Street, Linton, Cambridge, CB21 4JT Tel: (01223) 893872 Fax: (01223) 891760 E-mail: enquiries@cme.co.uk *Electronic design consultancy*

Cambridge Microprocessor Systems Ltd, 17-18 Zone D, Chelmsford Road Industrial Estate, Great Dunmow, Dunmow, Essex, CM6 1XG Tel: (01371) 875644 Fax: (01371) 876077 E-mail: info@cms.uk.com *Control systems manufrs*

▶ Cambridge Multimedia Computing, Gough Way, Cambridge, CB3 9LN Tel: (01223) 579100 *Telecommunications*

▶ Cambridge Nutrtional Sciences Ltd, Eden Research Park, Henry Crabb Road, Littleport, Ely, Cambridgeshire, CB6 1SE Tel: (01353) 862220 Fax: (01353) 863330 E-mail: mike@elisa.co.uk *Cambridge Nutritional offers blood tests for food intolerance by post.*

▶ Cambridge Online Learning Ltd, Barnsley Business & Innovation Centre, Innovation Way, Barnsley, South Yorkshire, S75 1JL Tel: (01226) 321717 Fax: (01226) 290888 E-mail: info@cambridge-online-learning.co.uk *Management training specialists/schools. Training, computer based, distance learning*

▶ Cambridge Online Systems Ltd, 163 Milton Road, Cambridge, CB4 0GP Tel: (01223) 422600 Fax: (01223) 422601 E-mail: enquiries@cosl.co.uk *Incorporated in 1978, Cambridge Online Systems Limited is a highly experienced and trusted provider of value-added information technology solutions and supporting services. Specialists in applications software for financials, logistics, enterprise resource planning (ERP) and customer relationship management (CRM) for industrial and commercial organisations across a number of vertical markets. It is a leading UK Microsoft certified business solutions partner.****

continued

Cambridge Optical Group Ltd, PO Box 76, Cambridge, CB3 8SH Tel: (01954) 781259 Fax: (01954) 789807 E-mail: admin@cambridge-optical.com *Optical supply manufrs*

Cambridge Overseas Trading Ltd, 13 Richmond Walk, St. Albans, Hertfordshire, AL4 9BA Tel: (01727) 833211 Fax: (01727) 810320 E-mail: cambost@aol.com *Machinery & component exporters*

Cambridge Plant Interiors Ltd, Manor Farm, Royston Road, Harston, Cambridge, CB2 5NJ Tel: (01223) 872828 Fax: (01223) 872886 E-mail: hortus@cambplant.co.uk *Interior landscaping*

Cambridge Rapid Components Ltd, Unit 4-5 Shire Hill, Saffron Walden, Essex, CB11 3AQ Tel: (01799) 522151 Fax: (01799) 521686 E-mail: sales@cambridgerapid.co.uk *Sheet metalwork engineers*

Cambridge Rewinds Ltd, Cambridge Road Ind Estate, Milton, Cambridge, CB4 6AZ Tel: (01223) 420555 Fax: (01223) 424113 *Electric motor repairers*

Cambridge Rubber Stamps Direct, 58 Victoria Road, Cambridge, CB4 3DU Tel: (01223) 361600 Fax: (01223) 461391 E-mail: admin@stampsdirect.co.uk *Rubber stamp manufrs* Also at: Lincoln, Norwich & Nottingham

Cambridge Scaffolding Ltd, 56 Cowley Road, Cambridge, CB4 0DN Tel: (01223) 504422 Fax: (01223) 570888 *Scaffolding contractors*

Cambridge Scientific Instruments Ltd, 12-15 Sedgway Business Park, Common Road, Witchford, Ely, Cambridgeshire, CB6 2HY Tel: (01353) 669916 Fax: (01353) 669917 E-mail: camsci@btconnect.com *Scientific equipment manufrs*

Cambridge Sensotec Ltd, Unit 8, Royce Court, Burrel Road, St. Ives, Cambridgeshire, PE27 3NE Tel: 0845 5314235 Fax: (01480) 466032 E-mail: sales@cambridge-sensotec.co.uk *Cambridge Sensotec are manufacturers and distributors of a wide range of portable and on-line gas analysers, gas detectors and gas detection equipment. Specialists in performance zirconia oxygen analysers, sensors and probes. Specialist analysers for SF6, dewpoint, CO2, CO, H2 & He available Distributors of ISC-Oldham personal toxic, oxygen and explosive gas monitors both for personal and fixed installations (fully ATEX approved). Distributors of Witt Gas modified atmosphere packaging (MAP) analysers for the food packaging industry. Distributors of Viamed and Vandagraph oxygen monitors for the Health Service and the diving industry. Distributors of Hitech gas analysers (dual gas) and Orbitec welding gas monitors. Offering calibration gas bottles and a full gas detector calibration service. The company is fully ISO9001 certified and sells products Worldwide through an established distributor network. Founded in 1996 and based in St. Ives, Cambridgeshire, England.*

Cambridge Silicon Radio, Churchill House, Cambridge Business Park, Cowley Road, Cambridge, CB4 0WZ Tel: (01223) 692000 Fax: (01223) 692001 E-mail: sales@csr.com *Single-chip bluetooth devices*

Cambridge Structures Ltd, 2 Huntingdon Street, St. Neots, Cambridgeshire, PE19 1BG Tel: (01480) 477700 Fax: (01480) 477766 E-mail: contact@cambridgestructures.com *Staircases including helical manufrs*

Cambridge Systems Engineering Ltd, Fordham Technology Centre, 5 Station Road, Fordham, Ely, Cambridgeshire, CB7 5LW Tel: (01638) 720727 Fax: (01638) 720724 E-mail: mailbox@cseltd.co.uk *Special purpose custom built machinery designers & manufrs*

Cambridge Tool Supplies Ltd, Unit 1 Brookfield Business Centre, Twentypence Road, Cottenham, Cambridge, CB4 8PS Tel: (01954) 251862 Fax: (01954) 251073 E-mail: camtool@btconnect.com *Engineers tool merchants distributors & agents*

Cambridge Traditional Products, Millfield, Cottenham, Cambridge, CB4 8RE Tel: (01954) 251380 Fax: (01954) 251387 E-mail: info@bees-wax.co.uk *Bees wax furniture polishes natural ingredients sub-aqua dry suit zips manufrs*

Cambridge Transformers Ltd, Quiet Waters, High Street, Earith, Huntingdon, Cambridgeshire, PE28 3PN Tel: (01487) 842154 Fax: (01487) 843445 E-mail: sales@transformers.demon.co.uk Sales Contact: S. Taylor *Cambridge Transformers Limited was incorporated in 1980 and has established a reputation for producing top quality transformers and wound components for incorporation into products sold around the world. They are made in various formats including toroidal. laminated and ferrite. You can be assured of our intent to provide the highest levels of customer service and satisfaction. We are an owner managed company and know that customers are our future. We want to work together with you for our combined benefit. to us, it does matter!*

Cambridge Venture Management Ltd, Unit 54, St. Johns Innovation Centre, Cowley Road, Cambridge, CB4 0WS Tel: (01223) 423828 Fax: (01223) 420418 E-mail: cvm@dial.pipex.com *Provision of management & finance*

Cambridge Water plc, 90 Fulbourn Road, Cherry Hinton, Cambridge, CB1 9JN Tel: (01223) 706050 Fax: (01223) 214052 E-mail: info@cambridge-water.co.uk *Water suppliers*

Cambridgeshire Chamber Of Commerce, 5 The Forum, Minerva Business Park, Lynch Wood, Peterborough, PE2 6FT Tel: (01733) 393330 Fax: (01733) 393335 E-mail: emquiries@cambscci.co.uk *Economic development*

Cambrook Elliott, Clutton, Bristol, BS39 5WB Tel: (0871) 2205230 Fax: (0871) 2205230 *PC sales & network installation*

▶ Cambs Compressor Engineering, Grovemere House, Lancaster Way Business Park, Ely, Cambridgeshire, CB6 3NW Tel: (01353) 668925 Fax: (01353) 669595 E-mail: sales@cambscompressors.co.uk *Air compressor sales & service, pipe work installations, vacuum pump*

▶ Cambs Quality Ltd, St. Johns Innovation Park, Cowley Road, Cambridge, CB4 0WS Tel: (0800) 0130623 Fax: (0870) 1372532 E-mail: info@cambsquality.com *Quality environmental consultants auditors*

▶ Cambs Trading High Road Elm, Holly Cottage, Low Road, Wisbech, Cambridgeshire, PE14 0DD Tel: (01945) 474540 Fax: (01945) 474540 E-mail: admin@cambstrading.co.uk *Garden machinery retailers*

Cambtec Pattern & Model Making, Unit 3, Nene Road, Bicton Industrial Park, Kimbolton, Huntingdon, Cambridgeshire, PE28 0LF Tel: (01480) 860240 Fax: (01480) 860240 *Engineers pattern makers*

Camco Engineering Ltd, Malvito House, Dale Street, Bilston, West Midlands, WV14 7JX Tel: (01902) 404090 Fax: (01902) 402070 E-mail: sales@camcoengineering.co.uk *Bearings, power transmission & electric motors*

Camco Metalcraft Ltd, Eastern Avenue Industrial Estate, Eastern Avenue, Dunstable, Bedfordshire, LU5 4JY Tel: (01582) 476204 Fax: (01582) 475602 E-mail: sales@camcometalcraft.co.uk *Sheet metal fabrications & welding*

Camco UK Ltd, 432 Perth Avenue, Slough, SL1 4TS Tel: (01753) 786100 Fax: (01753) 786101 E-mail: sales@camcoindex.com *Camco Ferguson is a world class manufacturer of motion control components for the global automation market. IMC's products include index drives, custom cams, parts handlers, precision link conveyors and servo-mechanical drives.*

Camden Hire Ltd, Unit C, 125 Brantwood Road, Tottenham, London, N17 0DX Tel: (020) 8961 6161 Fax: (020) 8961 6162 E-mail: contact@thorns.co.uk *TV, exhibitions & event furniture hire*

James Camden Engineering Ltd, Scar Bank, Warwick, CV34 5DB Tel: (01926) 491347 Fax: (01926) 411362 E-mail: jamescamden@btinternet.com *General & subcontract engineering services*

Camden Plant Display Ltd, 116 Eversholt Street, London, NW1 1BP Tel: (020) 7387 7019 Fax: (020) 7387 7824 *Floral & plant displays retailers*

Came Automation Ltd, Design House, 27 Salt Hill Way, Slough, SL1 3TR Tel: (01753) 550660 Fax: (01753) 552424 E-mail: info@atlasgroup.co.uk *Access control systems installers*

Camel Tableware, Camel House, Six Ashes, Bridgnorth, Shropshire, WV15 6ER Tel: (01746) 781610 Fax: (01746) 781607 E-mail: info@cameltableware.com *Tableware distributors*

Cameleon Systems, Cuckoo Lane, Pinchbeck, Spalding, Lincolnshire, PE11 3XT Tel: (01775) 680481 E-mail: martin@chameleon-systems.net *Computer retailers & consultants*

Camelia P.L.C., Linton Park, Maidstone, Kent, ME17 4AB Tel: (01622) 746655 Fax: (01622) 747422 E-mail: camelia@lintonpark.plc.uk *Holding company*

Camellia Contracts, Unit 3 & 10, Walronds Park, Isle Brewers, Taunton, Somerset, TA3 6QP Tel: (01460) 281848 Fax: (01460) 281868 *Grp moulders*

▶ Camellia Universal Ltd, 102 Brewers Hill Road, Dunstable, Bedfordshire, LU6 1AF Tel: (01582) 690442 Fax: 08716 618740 E-mail: camelliauniversal@yahoo.co.uk *China business specialist - Consulting on doing business & investing in China, product sourcing & manufacturing, Chinese business culture coaching. For more information please visit on www.camelliauniversal.com*

▶ Camellia Universal Ltd, 3 Cornwall Road, Harpenden, Hertfordshire, AL5 4TQ Tel: (01582) 690442 Fax: 01582 690442 E-mail: camellia@camelliauniversal.com *Camellia Universal Limited offers an International Business platform between the UK and China. It provides China business investment consultancy, lower cost of high quality product sourcing and development with its various product manufacturer networks in China, cross-cultural coaching, translation and interpretation. We can build relationships between British and Chinese companies and facilitate a vital component to any successful joint business venture, interaction with the Chinese government.**We offer a tailor-made service to your specification, bridging the knowledge gap and providing our expertise to match your needs. Camellia Universal Limited has been approved as a member of UK Trade & Investment. Currently, Camellia Universal Limited is working together with Thomas McMillan & Associates on certain land deals for several potential foreign investors and developers, including major international hotel groups , in China.*

▶ Camelot Kids, 117 Aysgarth, Bracknell, Berkshire, RG12 8SF Tel: (01344) 301726 *Camelot kids offer a range of childrens clothes at affordable prices. online shopping with quick delivery.*

Camelot Silverware Ltd, 173 Gibraltar Street, Sheffield, S3 8UA Tel: 0114-272 4935 Fax: 0114-273 7149 E-mail: enquiries@camelotsilverware.co.uk *Silversmiths manufrs*

Cameo Abrasives, Unit 4 Langley Drive, Chester Road Industrial Estate, Castle Bromwich, B35 7AD Tel: 0121-747 7100 Fax: 0121-748 5000 *Abrasive products suppliers*

▶ Cameo Chauffeur Services, 43 Claremont Crescent, Croxley Green, Rickmansworth, Hertfordshire, WD3 3Qp Tel: 01923 238397 E-mail: enquiry@cameoservices.co.uk

Cameo Computer Services Ltd, Unit 6, Maizefield, Hinckley, Leicestershire, LE10 1YF Tel: (01455) 618893 Fax: (01455) 254878 E-mail: info@cameouk.com *Computer sales, maintenance, installation & repair services*

Cameo Engineering Ltd, Unit 20 Brookside Business Park, Cold Meece, Stone, Staffordshire, ST15 0RZ Tel: (01785) 761134 Fax: (01785) 761837 *Steel fabricators & welding services*

Cameo Glass, Old Saw Mills Road, Faringdon, Oxfordshire, SN7 7DS Tel: (01367) 242421 Fax: (01367) 242978 E-mail: sales@camio-glass.com *Glass processors & merchants*

▶ Cameo It, 5 Elizabeth Drive, Wantage, Oxfordshire, OX12 9YA Tel: (01235) 768660 Fax: (01235) 768660

Cameo Mirror & Glass, Anglian Road, Walsall, WS9 8EP Tel: (0845) 1709881 Fax: (0845) 1709882 E-mail: enquiries@cameoglass.co.uk *Glass & mirror manufrs*

Cameo Network Services Ltd, 91 Gainsborough Road, Felixstowe, Suffolk, IP11 7HR Tel: (01394) 672004 E-mail: info@cameo.co.uk *Training & consultants services*

Cameo Shop Fitting Ltd, 47 Broughton Street, Manchester, M8 8AN Tel: 0161-839 6799 Fax: 0161-839 6798 E-mail: joanne@cameoshopfitting.co.uk *Shop fittings installer & manufrs*

Cameo Systems Ltd, 29 Haviland Road, Ferndown Industrial Estate, Wimborne, Dorset, BH21 7SA Tel: (01202) 892088 Fax: (01202) 861449 E-mail: rob@cameosystems.co.uk *Manufacturers of voice alarm system & safety alarms*

Dave Camepa Lighting, Dragon Works, Leigh Upon Mendip, Radstock, BA3 5QZ Tel: (01373) 813600 Fax: (01373) 813731 E-mail: david@canepalighting.co.uk *Lighting manufrs*

Camera Bellows, Units 3-5, St. Pauls Road, Birmingham, B12 8NG Tel: 0121-440 1695 Fax: 0121-440 0972 E-mail: sales@camerabellows.com *Photographic bellows & machine guard manufrs*

Camera Crewing Co., 2 Kingslea Road, Manchester, M20 4UA Tel: 0161-446 2666 Fax: 0161-448 2666 E-mail: ccc@cameracrewing.co.uk *TV production*

Camera One Ltd, 1275 Stratford Road, Hall Green, Birmingham, B28 9AJ Tel: 0121-733 1999 *Closed circuit television*

Camera Technical Services, 1b St Lawrences Rd, Coventry, CV6 7AE Tel: 024 76661133 *CCTV systems*

Cameras Stop Crime, Hillcrest, Roucan Road, Collin, Dumfries, DG1 4JF Tel: (01387) 750689 Fax: (01387) 750689 *CCTV installers*

Cameron & Andrew, The A P L Centre, Stevenston Industrial Estate, Stevenston, Ayrshire, KA20 3LR Tel: (01294) 603778 Fax: (01294) 603778 E-mail: rcamaron@btconect.com *Design engineers*

Cameron Balloons Ltd, St Johns Street, Bedminster, Bristol, BS3 4NH Tel: 0117-963 7216 Fax: 0117-966 1168 E-mail: sales@cameronballoons.co.uk *Publicity airship & balloon manufrs*

Cameron Brook & Associates, 1 Royal Oak Passage, High Street, Huntingdon, Cambridgeshire, PE29 3EA Tel: (01480) 436236 Fax: (01480) 436336 E-mail: sales@cameronbrook.co.uk *Construction recruitment*

Cameron Coatings Ltd, 18 Forest Vale Road, Forest Vale Industrial Estate, Cinderford, Gloucestershire, GL14 2PH Tel: (01594) 826088 Fax: (01594) 826092 E-mail: cameron@holscot.com *PTFE & fluorocarbon coating processors or services*

Cameron Communications (Aberdeen) Ltd, Suite B Colts Business Centre, Station Road, Colts, Aberdeen, AB15 9NP Tel: (01224) 865005 Fax: (01224) 865205 E-mail: camcomabdn@aol.com *Video conferencing systems distributors, audio visual*

▶ Cameron Controls, I C S House Badentoy Road, Badentoy Industrial Estate, Portlethen, Aberdeen, AB12 4YA Tel: (01224) 785500 Fax: (01224) 783355 E-mail: sales@camerondiv.com

Cameron Durley Consulting, 110 Main Road, Sidcup, Kent, DA14 6NG Tel: (020) 8309 2400 Fax: (020) 8309 2401 E-mail: sidcup@camerondurley.co.uk *Building services consultants*

Cameron Forecourt, Chambers Road, Platts Common Industrial Estate, Hoyland, Barnsley, South Yorkshire, S74 9SE Tel: (01226) 742441 Fax: (01226) 747441 E-mail: info@cameron-forecourt.co.uk *Petrol pump installers* Also at: Barnsley

Cameron Fuller Ltd, Duchy Road, Heathpark Industrial Estate, Honiton, Devon, EX14 1YD Tel: (01404) 47568 Fax: (01404) 44425 E-mail: sales@cameronfuller.co.uk *Curtain & blind fittings*

Cameron Furnace Co. Ltd, 7a Alleysbank Road,, Fameloan Industrial Estate, Rutherglen, Glasgow, G73 1LX Tel: (0141) 643 2244 Fax: (0141) 643 0088 E-mail: cameron.furnace@dial.pipex.com *Refractory installation & repairs*

Cameron Graham, Crosland Road Industrial Estate, Netherton, Huddersfield, HD4 7DQ Tel: (01484) 667822 Fax: (01484) 667817 E-mail: info@cameron-graham.co.uk *Health care consultants*

▶ Cameron Homes Ltd, 53 High Street, Chasetown, Burntwood, Staffordshire, WS7 3XE Tel: (01543) 671818 Fax: (01543) 672367

Cameron Industrial Services Ltd, 351 Hale Road, Widnes, Cheshire, WA8 8TS Tel: 0151-423 3892 Fax: 0151-423 3892 E-mail: enquiries@cameronltd.co.uk *Industrial cleaning contractors*

Cameron Interiors Ltd, 458-462 Crow Road, Glasgow, G11 7DR Tel: 0141-334 9532 Fax: 0141-357 3869 E-mail: sales@cameroninteriors.co.uk *Kitchens & bedroom interiors suppliers*

Cameron Linn Ltd, Belgrave Street, Bellshill Industrial Estate, Bellshill, Lanarkshire, ML4 3NP Tel: (01698) 300400 Fax: (01698) 300900 E-mail: info@cameronlinn.co.uk *Carton manufrs*

▶ Cameron Peters Ltd, The Old Dairy Home Farm, Ardington, Wantage, Oxfordshire, OX12 8PD Tel: (01235) 835000 Fax: (01235) 835005 E-mail: info@cameronpeters.co.uk *Decorative lighting service*

▶ Cameron Plant Hire Holdings Ltd, Brownside Farm, Loganswell, Newton Mearns, Glasgow, G77 6RZ Tel: (01355) 500286

▶ Cameron Wallace - International Accountancy Recruiters, Caledonia Business Centre, Caledonia House, Evanton Drive, Glasgow, G46 8JT Tel: 0141 270 9713 E-mail: info@cameronwallace.com *Cameron Wallace is a UK based financial recruitment consultancy offering clients and candidates a professional, innovative and fresh approach to recruitment in the International Accountancy sector. **Our consultancy will assist worldwide accountancy firms identify and attract newly qualified accountants, both from the UK and overseas marketplace. With an extensive network throughout the globe we ensure only the best opportunities are offered by us. We work with newly qualified positions through to middle management positions.*

Cameron Water Ltd, 6 Belgrave Street, Bellshill Industrial Estate, Bellshill, Lanarkshire, ML4 3NP Tel: (01698) 845050 Fax: (01698) 748368 *Water cooler company suppliers*

▶ Cameronaire Environmental Ltd, Willow House, Kestrel View, Strathclyde Business Park, Bellshill, Lanarkshire, ML4 3PB Tel: (01698) 464321

Cameron-Price Medical Division Ltd, Charlotte Road, Stirchley, Birmingham, B30 2BT Tel: 0121-459 2121 Fax: 0121-451 2303 E-mail: info@cameron-price.co.uk *Industrial plastics mouldings*

Camerson Productions, Deane, Basingstoke, Hampshire, RG25 3AR Tel: (01256) 780600 E-mail: richardcutler@camerson.co.uk *Multimedia internet & video producers*

Camfil Ltd, Knowsley Road, Haslingden, Rossendale, Lancashire, BB4 4EG Tel: (01706) 238000 Fax: (01706) 226736 E-mail: info@camfil.com Principal Export Areas: Worldwide *Air filter filtration equipment specialists*

Camfire Protection, 10 Hythe Close, Burwell, Cambridge, CB25 0EZ Tel: (01638) 741894 Fax: (01638) 741895 E-mail: sales@camfire.co.uk *Fire equipment*

▶ Caminus, Unit 17 North East Suffolk Business Centre, Pinbush Road, Lowestoft, Suffolk, NR33 7NQ Tel: (01502) 513100

Camis Electronics Ltd, Platts Road, Amblecote, Stourbridge, West Midlands, DY8 4YR Tel: (01384) 441402 Fax: (01384) 370354 E-mail: sales@camis.demon.co.uk *Electronic control systems & switches manufrs*

Camis Motors & Drives, Wallows Industrial Estate, Brierley Hill, West Midlands, DY5 1QA Tel: (01384) 480645 Fax: (01384) 480745 E-mail: sales@camis.com Principal Export Areas: Worldwide *Electric motor distributors*

Camlab Computer Systems, 27 Faringdon Road, Swindon, SN1 5AR Tel: (01793) 534917 Fax: (01793) 513120 E-mail: sales@camlab.net *Computer & electronic component suppliers*

▶ Camlachie Cooperage Ltd, R Clyde Workshops, Fullarton Road, Glasgow East Investment Park, Glasgow, G32 8YL Tel: 0141-641 9284 Fax: 0141-641 9294

▶ Camlinks Ltd, Dallas, Newtown, Little Neston, Neston, CH64 4BP Tel: 0151-353 1441 Fax: 0151-353 1441 E-mail: kjs@camlinks.com *Camlinks sells software that lets you model machines, typically packaging machines, that may have many moving independent cam or servo mechanisms. The motion editor/designer is very powerful. We also provide a service to help machine designers improve their machine designs*

Camlit Precision Engineering Ltd, Sand Road Industrial Estate, Sand Road, Great Gransden, Sandy, Bedfordshire, SG19 3AH Tel: (01767) 677263 Fax: (01767) 677720 *Precision engineers*

Camlock Engineering Ltd, Unit 12F, Thorn Business Park, Rotherwas, Hereford, HR2 6JT Tel: (01432) 279553 Fax: (01432) 266010 E-mail: camlock@tactronics.com *Fabrication engineers*

Camlok Lifting Clamps Ltd, 1 Knutsford Way, Chester, CH1 4NZ Tel: (01244) 375375 Fax: (01244) 377403 E-mail: sales@camlok.co.uk *Lifting gear specialists*

Camlon, Camlon House, Unit 10 D, The Grip Industrial Estate, Linton, Cambridge, CB21 4NR Tel: (01223) 897989 Fax: (01223) 897904 E-mail: sales@camlon.com *Medical equipment distributors & construction equipment*

Camlough Joinery Works, 12 Carrivekeeney Road, Newry, County Down, BT35 7LU Tel: (028) 3026 4218 Fax: (028) 3026 0848 *Joinery manufrs*

▶ Camm Management Consultants, 63 Ganton Road, Bloxwich, Walsall, WS3 3XQ Tel: 07917 026719 E-mail: marcus@cammconsulting.co.uk *Consultancy services*

Camm Precision Engineers Ltd, 45 Winpenny Road, Parkhouse Industrial Estate East, Parkhouse Industrial Estate East, Newcastle, Staffordshire, ST5 7RH Tel: (01782) 565611 Fax: (01782) 562747 *Milling engineering services & precision engineers*

▶ Cammach Group Oilfield Services, Greenbank Business Centre, Greenbank Road, East Tullos, Aberdeen, AB12 3BN Tel: (01224) 249977 Fax: (01224) 248977 *Oil & gas services company*

Cammax Precima Ltd, 4 Brunel Way, Severalls Industrial Park, Colchester, CO4 9QX Tel: (01206) 855542 Fax: (01206) 855543 E-mail: sales@cammax.co.uk *Microelectronics assembly technology & equipment*

▶ Camnet, 11 Mill View, London Road, Great Chesterford, Saffron Walden, Essex, CB10 1PD Tel: (01799) 530831 E-mail: james@camnet-communications.co.uk *Computer networking & pc support*

Camouflage Protective Equipment, 82 High Street, Boston, Lincolnshire, PE21 8SX Tel: (01205) 353514 Fax: (01205) 353514 *Work wear retailers*

Camp Steel, 29 Grafton Road, Sparkbrook, Birmingham, B11 1JP Tel: 0121-772 7821 Fax: 0121-771 0435 E-mail: dave-campsteel@btconnect.com *Steel stockholders*

▶ The Campaign For Leadership Ltd, Peter Runge House, 3 Carlton House Terrace, London, SW1Y 5DG Tel: (020) 7004 7200 Fax: (020) 7004 7111 E-mail: info@thecampaignforleadership.com *The Campaign for Leadership improves the performance of individuals and organisations by focusing on practical solutions that bring out the best in people. We work with a wide variety of individuals, teams and companies throughout the UK and Europe - transforming their leadership, influencing and communication skills by designing and delivering leadership programmes around specific organisational issues, objectives, culture and desired outcomes.*

▶ Campaign Marketing, Communications House, 63 Woodfield Lane, Ashtead, Surrey, KT21 2BT Tel: (01372) 277020 Fax: (01932) 860312 E-mail: info@campaignmarketing.net *Sales promotion company*

▶ Campaign Paintball Park, Old Lane, Cobham, Surrey, KT11 1NH Tel: (01932) 865999 Fax: (01932) 865744 E-mail: sales@campaignpaintball.com *Leisure activity venue*

Campak Ltd, Burkitt Road, Earlstrees Industrial Estate, Corby, Northamptonshire, NN17 4DT Tel: (01536) 261501 Fax: (01536) 443656 E-mail: sales@campak.freeserve.co.uk *Packaging machinery specialists*

A. Campbell, 7 Blane Avenue, Blanefield, Glasgow, G63 9HU Tel: (01360) 770437 Fax: (01360) 770495 E-mail: info@campbellcontrols.com *Electrical control panels manufrs*

A.R. Campbell (Construction) Ltd, Unit 86, Bandeuth Industrial Estate, Stirling, FK7 7ND Tel: (01786) 812900 Fax: (01786) 813388 E-mail: info@arcampbell.co.uk *Building contractors*

Alistair Campbell, Wembly, Bridge of Marnoch, Huntly, Aberdeenshire, AB54 7UN Tel: (01466) 780826 Fax: (01466) 780230 *Agricultural machinery manufrs*

Campbell Birch Executive Recruitment, Broadway, Bracknell, Berkshire, RG12 1AG Tel: (01344) 424117 Fax: (01344) 360534 E-mail: info@campbellbirch.com *Recruitment & human resources consultants*

▶ Campbell Bros Ltd, Sherwood Industrial Estate, Bonnyrigg, Midlothian, EH19 3LW Tel: 0131-654 0050 Fax: 0131-654 0080 E-mail: sales@campbellbrothers.co.uk *Wholesale butchers*

Campbell & Campbell, 100 University Street, Belfast, BT7 1HE Tel: (028) 9023 4541 Fax: (028) 9023 2860 E-mail: info@candc.co.uk *Accountants:management consultants*

Campbell Collins Ltd, 162 High St, Stevenage, Hertfordshire, SG1 3LL Tel: (01438) 369466 Fax: (01438) 316465 E-mail: sales@camcol.co.uk *Capacitor, electronic component & power supply distributors*

▶ Campbell Construction (Liverpool) Ltd, Westport Business Complex, Bankhall Lane, Liverpool, L20 8EW Tel: 0151-922 2244

▶ Campbell Control Services, Dalhousie Business Park, Carrington Road, Bonnyrigg, Midlothian, EH19 3HY Tel: 0131-660 4791 Fax: 0131-660 6793 E-mail: admin@campbellcontrols.com *HVAC controls manufrs*

Campbell Control Services, Dalhousie Business Park, Carrington Road, Bonnyrigg, Midlothian, EH19 3HY Tel: 0131-660 4791 Fax: 0131-660 6793 *Electrical controls for the HVAC industry*

Campbell Crane Hire, 112 Lisaclare Road, Stewartstown, Dungannon, County Tyrone, BT71 5QJ Tel: (028) 8773 8105 Fax: (028) 8774 0020 E-mail: kevincranehire@aol.com *Crane hire services*

Campbell Engineering, Gosforth Road, Derby, DE24 8HU Tel: (01332) 347344 Fax: (01332) 364385 *Metal fabricators*

Campbell Engineering & Design, 67 Valley Business Centre, Church Road, Newtownabbey, County Antrim, BT36 7LS Tel: (028) 9055 1611 Fax: (028) 9055 1666 E-mail: mail@cednet.co.uk *Engineering design consultants*

Campbell Fisk & Partners Ltd, Campbell Fisk House, Eridge Road, Crowborough, East Sussex, TN6 2SW Tel: (01892) 664141 Fax: (01892) 665556 E-mail: info@greeninsurance.co.uk *Insurance brokers & financial advisers*

▶ Campbell Fitzpatrick, 51 Adelaide Street, Belfast, BT2 8FE Tel: (028) 9032 7388 Fax: (028) 9032 7732 E-mail: sales@campbell-fitzpatrick.co.uk *A Leading Legal Firm Providing Legal Services To Northern Ireland From Offices In Belfast And Derry /Londonderry. Specialists In Conveyancing, Property Purchase, Property Sale, Employment Law, Commercial, Litigation, Industrial Tribunals, Mediation, Debt Recovery.*

Campbell & Gordon, 29 Evan Drive, Giffnock, Glasgow, G46 6NQ Tel: 0141-638 6666 Fax: 0141-638 9999 E-mail: melody@camass.freeserve.co.uk *Identification systems (software)*

▶ Campbell Gus, 23 Avondale Road, Rayleigh, Essex, SS6 8NJ Tel: (01268) 778519 E-mail: sales@justix.com *Photography of people, places and events. Weddings and portraits are a speciality.*

Campbell Lee Computer Services Ltd, Unit G1 Exploration House, Exploration Drive, Bridge Of Don, Aberdeen, AB23 8GX Tel: (01224) 355435 Fax: (01224) 677201 E-mail: info@campbell-lee.co.uk *Internet & e-business & electronic commerce services*

Campbell Lee Computer Services Ltd, 24 Finlas Street, Cowlairs Industrial Estate, Glasgow, G22 5DT Tel: 0141-557 6400 Fax: 0141-557 6451 E-mail: hugh.gillan@cl-is.co.uk *Internet, e-business & e-commerce services*

Campbell & Mabbs Liverpool Ltd, 1 Regent Street, Liverpool, L3 7BN Tel: 0151-236 1555 Fax: 0151-236 1698 E-mail: camabbs@aol.com *Architectural ironmongers*

▶ Campbell & Mchardy Ltd, Unit 12 Linkwood Industrial Estate, Elgin, Morayshire, IV30 1XS Tel: (01343) 543516 Fax: (01343) 543516

Campbell Miller (Tools) Ltd, 16-22 Jordanvale Avenue, Clydeside Industrial Estate, Glasgow, G14 0QU Tel: 0141-954 9557 Fax: 0141-954 9979 E-mail: sales@cmtl.co.uk *Air, electric, hydraulic & hand tool distributors*

Campbell Murray Guitar Tutor - Scotland, 3 Cedar Gardens, Newarthill, Motherwell, Lanarkshire, ML1 5TP Tel: 01698 290525 E-mail: guitartutor@fsmail.net *Guitar Tuition Central Scotland UK*

Campbell Plastics Ltd, 6 Robinson Close, Telford Way Industrial Estate, Kettering, Northamptonshire, NN16 8PU Tel: (01536) 516563 Fax: (01536) 310086 *Liquid coating manufrs*

▶ Campbell Pryde, 10 Hampton Gardens, Sawbridgeworth, Hertfordshire, CM21 0AN Tel: (01279) 425283 E-mail: sales@campbellpryde.com *Marketing consultancy services*

▶ R.E. Campbell (Joinery) Ltd, Station Road, Spean Bridge, Inverness-Shire, PH34 4EP Tel: (01397) 712561

Campbell Reith Hill LLP, Artillery House, 11-19 Artillery Row, London, SW1P 1RT Tel: (020) 7340 1700 Fax: (020) 7340 1777 E-mail: engineers@campbellreith.com *Consulting engineers*

Campbell Rigg Associates, 12 Apollo Studios, Charlton Kings Road, London, NW5 2SB Tel: (020) 7284 1515 Fax: (020) 7267 4112 E-mail: design@campbellrigg.com *Design consultants*

Campbell Scientific Ltd, Campbell Park, 80 Hathern Road, Shepshed, Loughborough, Leicestershire, LE12 9GX Tel: (01509) 601141 Fax: (01509) 601091 E-mail: sales@campbellsci.co.uk *Data logging & meteorological equipment manufrs*

▶ Campbell & Smith Construction Group Ltd, Old Sawmill, Ormiston, Tranent, East Lothian, EH35 5NQ Tel: (01875) 610343

▶ Campbell Telecom Services, 57 Western Way, Sandy, Bedfordshire, SG19 1DU Tel: (01767) 682838 E-mail: a.campbell19@ntlworld.com *We provide a complete service to the Domestic and Business work place, providing and shifting extensions on Exchange lines and telephone systems.*We also Provide and Install small to medium telephone Systems, these are Programmed and configured to our Customers requirements.*All our work is carried out by fully qualified Telephone Engineers and all the work is guaranteed.*We also provide a Maintenance Service on Internal Wiring on Extensions (Systems or Exchange Lines)*

Campbell-lee Contracts, 84 Greasby Road, Greasby, Wirral, Merseyside, CH49 3NG Tel: 0151-606 8779 Fax: 0151-678 1640 E-mail: sales@campbelllee.co.uk *Hygienic wall cladding*

Campbells Grocery Products Ltd, Batchelors Factory, Kennington Road, Willesborough, Ashford, Kent, TN24 0LU Tel: (01233) 644111 Fax: (01233) 644203 *Food processing*

▶ Campbells Grocery Products, 2020 Cambourne Business Park, Cambourne, Cambridge, CB3 6EZ Tel: (01954) 714100 Fax: (01954) 714101

Campbells Grocery Products Ltd, Hardwick Road, King's Lynn, Norfolk, PE30 4HS Tel: (01553) 615000 Fax: (01553) 615501 E-mail: enquiries@homepride.co.uk *Food manufrs*

Campbell's Shortbread, Ancaster Square, Callander, Perthshire, FK17 8BL Tel: (01877) 330013 Fax: (01877) 331290 E-mail: sales@campbellsshortbread.co.uk *Shortbread & biscuit manufrs*

Camper & Nicholsons (Yachting) Ltd, 229 West Street, Fareham, Hampshire, PO16 0HZ Tel: (023) 9258 0221 *Power boat & yachts suppliers*

Camping & General, 126 Arterial Road, Leigh-on-Sea, Essex, SS9 4DG Tel: (01702) 525536 Fax: (01702) 420230 *Camping equipment suppliers*

▶ Camping & Surplus, 53-59 Woodhouse Road, London, N12 9ET Tel: (020) 8445 4747

▶ Campion Homes, Pitreavie Drive, Pitreavie Business Park, Dunfermline, Fife, KY11 8UH Tel: (01383) 432600 Fax: (01383) 620467

▶ Camplex Ltd, 6 Albemarle Link, Springfield, Chelmsford, CM2 5AG Tel: (0870) 2422462 Fax: (0870) 2422463

Camplins Ltd, Portland Lane, Great Yarmouth, Norfolk, NR31 0JN Tel: (01493) 660000 Fax: (01493) 660006 E-mail: sales@camplings-linen.co.uk *Linen hire manufrs*

Campmuir Ltd, Leanaig Road, Conon Bridge, Dingwall, Ross-shire, IV7 8BE Tel: (01349) 866021 Fax: (01349) 866020 E-mail: campuir@dinwald.net *Agricultural merchants*

Campmuir Ltd, Bourtie Works, Inverurie, Aberdeenshire, AB51 0HL Tel: (01467) 621591 Fax: (01467) 624414 E-mail: richard@campmuir.com *Agricultural engineers*

Campsie Paper Co. Ltd, Courtauld Way, Eglinton, Londonderry, BT47 3DN Tel: (028) 7181 1243 Fax: (028) 7181 1626 *Packaging merchants*

Campsie Spring Scotland Ltd, Veich Place, Lennoxtown, Glasgow, G66 7JQ Tel: (01360) 312121 Fax: (01360) 312672 *Mineral water suppliers*

Camrascan Ltd, Clarence House, Minerva Business Park, Lynch Wood, Peterborough, PE2 6FT Tel: (01733) 239633 Fax: (01733) 362706 E-mail: sales@camrascan.co.uk *Closed circuit TV specialists*

Camrex Chugoku Ltd, Norris House, 4 Norris Street, London, SW1Y 4RJ Tel: (020) 7925 2535 Fax: (020) 7925 2443 E-mail: mailbox@chugoku.co.uk *Marine paint manufrs*

Camrose Air Conditioning Ltd, Unit D4 Brunswick Place, Cranbourne Lane, Basingstoke, Hampshire, RG21 3NN Tel: 0845 4941703 Fax: (01256) 322801 E-mail: peter@camroseair.co.uk *Formed in 1983, Camrose Air Conditioning are specialists in heating, ventilation, air conditioning and heat pump installation and servicing. We employ staff that include electrical, mechanical, heating and refrigeration engineers to provide a dedicated service to our customers. From our own workshop we operate a ductwork manufacture and erection service, allowing direct control over all aspects of the HVAC installation. Camrose Air Conditioning is well equipped to provide you the best system to suit your needs, with a professional personal service.*

▶ CAMS Fire & Security P.L.C., 6 Wedgwood Court, Wedgwood Way, Stevenage, Hertfordshire, SG1 4QR Tel: (01438) 740840 Fax: (01438) 737969 E-mail: info@camssecurity.co.uk *Install, sell, maintain & service fire & security alarms*

▶ Cams Software, Whitehall, 75 School Lane, Hartford, Northwich, Cheshire, CW8 1PF Tel: (01606) 781261 Fax: (01606) 784566 E-mail: info@camssoftware.com *Software developers*

Camsoft, 10 Wheatfield Close, Maidenhead, Berkshire, SL6 3PS Tel: (01628) 825206 Fax: (01628) 820431 *Retailers of language learning software*

Camson Envelopes, Woodlands Mills, Woodlands Road, Tonbridge, Kent, TN9 2NE Tel: (01732) 368949 Fax: (01732) 362429 E-mail: sales@camson.co.uk *Paper envelope manufrs*

▶ Camstruction Ltd, Cam House, 5 York Street, Aberdeen, AB11 5DL Tel: (01224) 593777 Fax: (01224) 594477 E-mail: sales@camstruction.com

Cam-Tec Surveillance Systems, 190 Uttoxeter Road, Blythe Bridge, Stoke-on-Trent, ST11 9JR Tel: (01782) 396619 Fax: (01782) 388549 E-mail: sales@cam-tec.com *CCTV installers*

▶ Camtech Solutions, Oakeys Close, Stow on the Wold, Cheltenham, Gloucestershire, GL54 1FB Tel: (0845) 0505837 E-mail: info@camtechsolutions.co.uk *Camtech Solutions is a leading Information Technology (IT) services Company based in Gloucestershire within easy reach of Birmingham, Warwickshire, Worcestershire, Herefordshire and Oxfordshire.***Camtech Solutions is a 'value added solutions provider' (VASP) and has been responsible for providing IT services, consultancy, solutions, support and products to all types of small to medium businesses.***Using the latest technology we aim to deliver a cost effective, reliable, powerful and robust IT infrastructure, ensuring we are always a 'safe pair of hands', constantly delivering working and appropriate services and solutions to our clients. Our regular customers particularly value our vast technical experience, knowledge and ability to deliver.***

Camtek Ltd, Camtek House, 117 Church Street, Malvern, Worcestershire, WR14 2AJ Tel: (01684) 892290 Fax: (01684) 892269 E-mail: sales@camtek.co.uk *Camtek develop and supply the PEPS SolidCut suite of CADCAM Software for Milling, Turning, Wire EDM and multi-axis laser applications. Systems are supplied around the globe via a network of sales partners, each providing professional sales, training and applications support services.*

▶ Camtek Surveillance Systems Ltd, Bagshot, Surrey, GU19 5XX Tel: (01276) 470999 Fax: (01276) 850679 E-mail: ks@camteksurveillance.co.uk *Design & sale of cctv equipment*

Camtex Fabrics Ltd, Blackwood Road, Lillyhall Industrial Estate, Lillyhall, Workington, Cumbria, CA14 4JJ Tel: (01900) 602646 Fax: (01900) 66827 E-mail: info@cambrelle.com *Fabric shoe lining manufrs*

Camtool Engineering, 6b Purdy Road, Bilston, West Midlands, WV14 8UB Tel: (01902) 403562 Fax: (01902) 403562 E-mail: camtool.eng@btconnect.com *Special purpose machines, press tools, jigs & fixtures suppliers*

Camtrex Ltd, Amington Road, Birmingham, B25 8ET Tel: 0121-706 1167 Fax: 0121-706 5565 E-mail: j.thomas@camtrex.co.uk *Steel stockholders & processors*

Camtronics Ltd, The Walnut Tree, 38 High Street, Bluntisham, Huntingdon, Cambridgeshire, PE28 3LA Tel: (01487) 843278 Fax: (01487) 843280 E-mail: sales@camtronics.ltd.uk *Sub contract manufrs*

Camtronics Vale Ltd, Unit 1 Gwent Court, Victoria Park, Ebbw Vale, Gwent, NP23 8AN Tel: (01495) 352323 Fax: (01495) 352324 E-mail: info@camtronicsvale.com *PCB assembly*

Camwatch Ltd, 128 Maltravers Road, Sheffield, S2 5AZ Tel: 0114-281 9999 Fax: 0114-241 2864 E-mail: enquiries@camwatch.co.uk *CCTV installers & monitoring services*

▶ Camwheat Pie Machine Co. Ltd, Adelaide Street, Halifax, West Yorkshire, HX1 4LY Tel: (01422) 323202 Fax: (01422) 321113

▶ Camwood, 5-25, Scrutton Street, London, EC2A 4HJ Tel: (020) 7426 9700 Fax: (020) 7749 1201 *IT consultants*

Can Geotechnical Ltd, Smeckley Wood Close, Chesterfield Trading Estate, Chesterfield, Derbyshire, S41 9PZ Tel: (01246) 261111 Fax: (01246) 261626 E-mail: info@can.ltd.uk *Civil & structural engineering contractors*

▶ Can It Ltd, 53 Awsworth Lane Cossall, Cossall, Nottingham, NG16 2SA Tel: (0870) 4329919 E-mail: Sale@Can-IT.co.uk *Computer and Network Information Technologies. We employ a tri-view Service Orientated strategy that not only supports but also adds value to the business.*We provide a cost effective, quality, fully managed infrastructure service, which meets the individual requirements of your business. Underpinned by clearly defined, interconnecting processes deployed on a robust, standard infrastructure platform all in accordance with an appropriate customer Service Level Agreement.*We want you to view us as your IT department.*

▶ Can London Ltd, Unit A Springhead Enterprise Park, Springhead Road, Northfleet, Gravesend, Kent, DA11 8HB Tel: (01474) 538100 Fax: (01474) 538101 E-mail: info@canlondon.co.uk *Access workers*

Canaan Carbides Ltd, Unit 13, 13 Briar Close, Evesham, Worcestershire, WR11 4JQ Tel: (01386) 442818 Fax: (01386) 40564 E-mail: canaancarbides@btconnect.com *Cutter manufacturers, paper cutting & guillotining services*

Canada-Uk Chamber Of Commerce, 38 Grosvenor Street, London, W1K 4DP Tel: (020) 7258 6572 Fax: (020) 7258 6594 E-mail: info@canada-uk.org *Exportation advice, commercial & trade relations*

Canadean Ltd, Unit 9-12 Faraday Court, Rankine Road, Basingstoke, Hampshire, RG24 8PF Tel: (01256) 394200 Fax: (01256) 394201 E-mail: sales@canadean.com *Market research services for beverage industries*

Canadian Log Homes UK Ltd, Maple Lodge, Rose Hill, Little Pertherick, Wadebridge, Cornwall, PL27 7QT Tel: (01841) 540680 Fax: (01841) 540580 E-mail: admin@canadianloghomes.co.uk *Import & build canadian log structures*

Canadian Pine Co., 159 Victoria Street, Stoke-on-Trent, ST4 6HA Tel: (01782) 710909 Fax: (01782) 710909 *Pine furniture manufrs*

Canal Cruising Co. Ltd, Crown Street, Stone, Staffordshire, ST15 8QN Tel: (01785) 813982 Fax: (01785) 819041 E-mail: kwyatt5745@aol.com *Boat hiring, leasing & rental services*

Canal Engineering Ltd, Lenton Lane, Nottingham, NG7 2PQ Tel: 0115-986 6321 Fax: 0115-986 0211 E-mail: enquiries@canalengineering.co.uk *Sheet metal work engineers*

Canalside Autos, Unit 6, Finnington Lane, Feniscowles, Blackburn, BB2 5JD Tel: (01254) 200170

Canard Design Ltd, Sidney House, 262 Aylestone Lane, Wigston, Leicestershire, LE18 1BD Tel: 0116-279 6532 Fax: 0116-291 0081 E-mail: info@canard-design.co.uk *Design (CAD) consultants*

▶ Canary Divers, 188 Burnley Road, Blackburn, BB1 3HW Tel: (01254) 696690 Fax: (01254) 696690 E-mail: info@canarydivers.com *Canary Divers is Blackburn's newest PADI dive center. With excellent customer service and a wide range of products and courses, you can't go wrong.*

Canarycliff Co. Ltd, Maple Works, Old Shoreham Road, Hove, East Sussex, BN3 7ED Tel: (01273) 726325 Fax: (01273) 203070 E-mail: sales@ticketmedia.com *Paper converters & roll manufrs*

Canatronics Delta Ltd, Unit 5, Dewhurst Row, Bamber Bridge, Preston, PR5 6SW Tel: (01772) 629429 Fax: (01772) 698611 E-mail: info@canatronics-uk.com *Lighting manufrs*

Canavan Clockmakers, Unit 24, 24 Ulster Street, Lurgan, Craigavon, County Armagh, BT67 9AN Tel: (028) 3832 1100 E-mail: sales@canavanclockmakers.com *Exterior clock manufrs*

Cancarp Ltd, Unit 28 Willan Industrial Estate, Vere Street, Salford, M50 2GR Tel: 0161-736 9026 Fax: 0161-745 8657 E-mail: disc@cancarp.com *Bimetallic disc manufrs*

▶ Cancom, 5 Clifton Court, Cambridge, CB1 7BN Tel: (01223) 247111 Fax: (01223) 213522 E-mail: michael.swales@cancomuk.com *Europe's largest Apple dealer*

▶ CanCreative, 16 The Mallards, Silsden, West Yorkshire, BD20 0NT Tel: 01535 652600 E-mail: candie@cancreative.co.uk *Website designers*

▶ Candagrove Ltd, Regent Road, Great Yarmouth, Norfolk, NR30 2AS Tel: (01493) 844676 Fax: (01493) 858381 E-mail: candagrove@btconnect.com *Confectioners*

Candair Engineering Co. Ltd, Newton Moor Industrial Estate, Mill Street, Hyde, Cheshire, SK14 4LF Tel: 0161-368 7111 *Fabrication engineers*

Candela Traditional Lighting Ltd, 319 Long Acre, Birmingham, B7 5JT Tel: 0121-678 6700 Fax: 0121-678 6701 E-mail: sales@candela.co.uk *Lighting manufrs*

▶ Cando It, 42 Wolfe Road, Norwich, NR1 4HT Tel: (01603) 498999 E-mail: sales@cando-it.co.uk *IT outsource support services*

▶ Can-Do Services, 39 Ellison Street, Lincoln, LN5 8QH Tel: 01522 827894 Fax: 01522 827894 E-mail: can-do.services@ntlworld.com *Patios & Blockpaving*Concrete & Tarmac Finishes*Decking & Fencing*All aspects of building & maintenance*

Candover Investments Public Ltd Company, 20 Old Bailey, London, EC4M 7LN Tel: (020) 7489 9848 Fax: (020) 7248 5483 E-mail: info@candover.com *Investment company*

▶ Candy Designer, The Candy & Chocolate Factory, Hawthorn Road, Skegness, Lincolnshire, PE25 3TD Tel: 01754 896667 E-mail: info@candydesigner.co.uk *Manufacturers and suppliers of bespoke confectionery products. Specialists in personalised confectionery and chocolate.*

Candy Floss Machine Manufacturers Ltd, Gables West, Barrow Hill, Sellindge, Ashford, Kent, TN25 6JG Tel: (01303) 813171 Fax: (01303) 813171 E-mail: malcolm.frazer@virgin.net *Candy floss machine manufrs*

Cane Collection Ltd, 70 Fred Dannatt Road, Mildenhall, Bury St. Edmunds, Suffolk, IP28 7RD Tel: (01638) 714832 Fax: (01638) 510840 E-mail: sales@canecollection.co.uk *Cane furniture importers & manufrs*

Cane Communications Ltd, River Side House, Turnac Avenue, Woking, Surrey, GU22 0AJ Tel: (01483) 727150 Fax: (01483) 223311 *Public relations consultants, advertising & marketing services*

▶ Cane Contractors, 14 Wadhurst Close, Bognor Regis, West Sussex, PO21 5LD Tel: (01243) 825139 Fax: (01243) 825139 E-mail: elieencane@btconnect.com *Civil engineers*

Cane Direct, Goyt Mill, Upper Hibbert Lane, Marple, Stockport, Cheshire, SK6 7HX Tel: 0161-427 7774 Fax: 0161-427 7225 E-mail: admin@cane-direct.co.uk *Cane furniture suppliers*

Cane Workshop, The Gospel Hall, Westport, Langport, Somerset, TA10 0BH Tel: (01460) 281636 *Cane furniture services & material suppliers*

Canecrown Ltd, 34 London Road, Croydon, CR0 2TA Tel: (020) 8649 8349 Fax: (020) 8649 8349 E-mail: tilcluk@aol.com *Telecommunication export merchants*

Can-Eng Furnaces UK Ltd, Unit 8, Ninian Park, Ninian Way, Wilnecote, Tamworth, Staffordshire, B77 5ES Tel: (01827) 262601 Fax: (01827) 262602 E-mail: can-enguk@mcmail.com *Furnace manufrs*

Canford Audio, Crowther Road, Washington, Tyne & Wear, NE38 0BW Tel: 0191-418 1133 Fax: 0191-418 1001 E-mail: admin@canford.co.uk *Pro-audio equipment manufrs*

Canford Hill Engineering Ltd, 30 Benson Road, Nuffield Industrial Estate, Poole, Dorset, BH17 0GB Tel: (01202) 671119 Fax: (01202) 671119 E-mail: canfordhill@btconnect.com *Precision engineers*

▶ Canford Magna Storage, Unit 11, Canford Business Park, Magna Road, Wimborne, Dorset, BH21 3BT Tel: (01202) 570970 Fax: (01202) 577971 E-mail: storage@1stchoiceremovals.net *Self storage facilities*

Canham Controls Ltd, 14 Dodson Way, Peterborough, PE1 5XJ Tel: (01733) 894489 Fax: (01733) 894488 E-mail: canhamcontrols@compuserve.com *Control panel manufrs*

▶ Canine Spirit Ltd, 7 Westfield Road, Lymington, Hampshire, SO41 3PZ Tel: (01590) 610358 Fax: (01590) 676375 E-mail: info@canine-spirit.com *Canine Spirit is the leading outfitter for dogs and their owners who just love to be hiking, camping, sailing, travelling or simply interacting together! **We supply and distribute the largest selection of practical, quality outdoor and active gear and accessories to ensure carefree and safe adventuring with your canine companion.**

Canlin Castings Ltd, Star Foundry, North Street, Langley Mill, Nottingham, NG16 4BS Tel: (01773) 715412 Fax: (01773) 530434 E-mail: sales@canlincastings.co.uk *Non ferrous founders*

Canmec Global Ltd, 7 Dawley Brook Road, Kingswinford, West Midlands, DY6 7BD Tel: (01384) 271203 Fax: (01384) 400179 E-mail: sales@canmecglobal.com *Fastener & pipeline fittings manufrs*

Nick Cann Pest Control, Sturridge Farm, Sandford, Crediton, Devon, EX17 4ED Tel: (01363) 772017 Fax: (01363) 775997 *Pest control*

Canning Conveyor Co. Ltd, Sandy Lane Industrial Estate, Sandy Lane, Worksop, Nottinghamshire, S80 1TN Tel: (01909) 486166 Fax: (01909) 500638 E-mail: andrew.canning@canningconveyor.co.uk *Conveyor belt & quarry manufrs*

▶ Cannington Coldstores, Swang Farm, Cannington, Bridgwater, Somerset, TA5 2NJ Tel: (01278) 671347 Fax: (01278) 671841 E-mail: tim.roe@canningtoncoldstores.co.uk

Cannizaro House, West Side Common, London, SW19 4UE Tel: (0870) 3339124 Fax: (0870) 3339224 E-mail: sales@cannizarohouse.co.uk *Conference centre & hotel restaurant*

▶ Cannoc Electrical, Unit 5 Martindale Industrial Estate, Hawks Green, Cannock, Staffordshire, WS11 7XN Tel: (01543) 505104 Fax: (01543) 466034 E-mail: sales@cannockelectrical.com *Electrical wholesaler*

Cannon Computers Ltd, 2 Kingsmead Road, London, SW2 3JB Tel: (020) 8671 4140 E-mail: leonard@cannon-computers.co.uk *Computer sales & maintenance*

Cannon Electrical Contractors (Manchester) Ltd, Unit 2 Derwent Street Industrial Estate, Odsall Lane, Salford, M5 4RE Tel: 0161-832 7320 Fax: 0161-839 4298 E-mail: cannonelectrical@btopenworld.com *Electrical engineers & contractors*

Cannon Electronics & Automation Ltd, White Gates Factory, Dunmow Road, Hatfield Heath, Bishop's Stortford, Hertfordshire, CM22 7ED Tel: (01279) 730709 *Industrial control systems*

▶ Cannon Fire Protection, 1 Industrial Estate, Hallcroft Road, Retford, Nottinghamshire, DN22 7SS Tel: (01777) 710975 Fax: (01777) 719628

Cannon Groundwork, 9 Cannon Street, Lydd, Romney Marsh, Kent, TN29 9AS Tel: (01797) 320988 Fax: (01797) 320988 *Groundwork civil engineers*

Cannon Horticulture, Unit 21 22 Pelham Court, Pelham Place, Crawley, West Sussex, RH11 9SH Tel: (01293) 562068 Fax: (01293) 562788 *Grounds maintenance & interior plant display suppliers*

Cannon Plastics, Units 2-3 Barrs Fold Road, Wingates Industrial Estate, Westhoughton, Bolton, BL5 3XP Tel: (01942) 810081 Fax: (01942) 814311 E-mail: sales@cannon-plastics.co.uk *Plastics screen printing services*

Cannon & Reading Ltd, A 9 Oakendene Industrial Estate, Bolney Road, Cowfold, Horsham, West Sussex, RH13 8AZ Tel: (01403) 865947 Fax: (01403) 865950

Cannon Steels Ltd, 22 Walcot Road, Enfield, Middlesex, EN3 7NF Tel: (020) 8805 4070 Fax: (020) 8805 4525 E-mail: enquiries@cannonsteelsltd.co.uk *Steel stockholders & fabricators*

Cannon Street Jersey Fabrics Ltd, Ashley Works, Ashley Road, London, N17 9LJ Tel: (020) 8885 9400 Fax: (020) 8885 9410 E-mail: enquiries@csjf.co.uk *Knitted fabrics manufacturers & finishers-printers*

Cannon Technologies Europe Ltd, 13 Queensway, Stem Lane Industrial Estate, New Milton, Hampshire, BH25 5NU Tel: (01425) 638148 Fax: (01425) 619276 E-mail: sales@cannontech.co.uk *Data networking enclosure manufrs*

Cannon.Co.Uk, 214-224 Barr Street, Birmingham, B19 3AG Tel: 0121-551 4131 Fax: 0121-554 9292 E-mail: peter.cannon@cannon.co.uk *Manufacturing silversmiths*

Cannop Foundry 1981 Ltd, Forest Vale Indust Estate, Crabtree Road, Forest Vale Industrial Estate, Cinderford, Gloucestershire, GL14 2YQ Tel: (01594) 822143 Fax: (01594) 824200 E-mail: sales@cannop.co.uk *Ferrous & non-ferrous casting manufrs*

Canon Ltd, The Braccens, London Road, Bracknell, Berkshire, RG12 2AT Tel: (01344) 354700 Fax: (01344) 354850 *Product development & research*

Canon Business Solutions, 1 Cromac Quay, Belfast, BT7 2JD Tel: (028) 9072 7500 Fax: (028) 9072 7555 *Photocopier machine manufrs*

Canon Davis Hangers, Cranford House, Coombe Way, Byfleet, West Byfleet, Surrey, KT14 7DP Tel: (01932) 411288 Fax: (01932) 411289 *Hangers display & shop fitting*

Canon Fire Protection, The Wharf, Midhurst, West Sussex, GU29 9PX Tel: (01730) 815209 Fax: (01730) 816377 E-mail: cfp@canonfire.co.uk *Fire protection equipment suppliers*

▶ Canon Hill Potteries, Canon Street, Barry, South Glamorgan, CF62 7RH Tel: (01446) 740612 Fax: (01446) 738000

Canon (UK) Ltd, 7TH Floor, 6-16 St. Andrew Street, London, EC4A 3LX Tel: (0870) 6081144 Fax: (0870) 6081145 *Business showroom*

Canon UK Ltd, Cockshot Hill, Reigate, Surrey, RH2 8BF Tel: (01737) 220000 Fax: (01737) 220022 *Business systems engineers & suppliers*

Canonbury Asphalte Co. Ltd, The Street, Sheering, Bishop's Stortford, Hertfordshire, CM22 7LY Tel: (01279) 734077 Fax: (01279) 734568 E-mail: canonburyasphalt@aol.com *Asphalt & felt roofing contractors*

Canongate Technology Ltd, 17 Edgefield Road Industrial Estate, Loanhead, Midlothian, EH20 9TB Tel: 0131-448 0786 Fax: 0131-440 1739 E-mail: sales@canongatetechnology.co.uk *Process measurement & control equipment manufrs*

▶ Canopies Ireland, 105 Cavan Road, Dungannon, County Tyrone, BT71 6QN Tel: (028) 8775 1770 Fax: (028) 8772 9922 E-mail: john@canopies-ireland.com *Manufacturers of GRP door canopies, carports & architectural building products*

Canopius Management Services Ltd, 36 Gracechurch Street, London, EC3V 0BT Tel: (020) 7369 3000 Fax: (020) 7337 3999 *Management service company*

Cansco Equipment & Rentals Ltd, Units 2-3 Teesland Development, Hareness Circle, Altens, Aberdeen, AB12 3LY Tel: (01224) 872228 Fax: (01224) 897541 E-mail: enquiries@cansco.com *Drilling equipment distributors*

Cansco Greig Engineering Ltd, Souter Head Road, Altens Industrial Estate, Aberdeen, AB12 3LF Tel: (01224) 898810 Fax: (01224) 878542 E-mail: mail@cansco.co.uk *Stainless steel fabricators*

Cansco Pressure Control Ltd, Badentoy Road, Portlethen, Aberdeen, AB12 4YA Tel: (01224) 782211 Fax: (01224) 782266 E-mail: sales@3plus.co.uk *Engineering contractors*

Mark Cansick & Co., 44a Highgate High Street, London, N6 5JE Tel: (020) 8340 0094 Fax: (020) 8340 0096 E-mail: markcansick@btconnect.com *Export merchants & export managers*

Cantab Millennium Ltd, 95 Mill Road, Cambridge, CB1 2AW Tel: (01223) 322306 Fax: (01223) 322816 E-mail: cantab.millennium@virgin.net *Computer repairs & components manufrs*

Canteen Smithy, Crow Carings Mill North, Stansfield Road, Todmorden, Lancashire, OL14 5DL Tel: (01706) 818375 Fax: (01706) 818375 E-mail: cse@ntlbusiness.com *Injection mould toolmakers*

Cantell & Son Ltd, Robinson Road, Newhaven, East Sussex, BN9 9BL Tel: (01273) 514118 Fax: (01273) 513375 *Ship, yacht, boat repairers & chandlers*

Canterbury Cane, 358 Abergele Road, Old Colwyn, Colwyn Bay, Clwyd, LL29 9LS Tel: (01492) 514448 Fax: (01492) 514448 *Cane furniture suppliers*

Canterbury Joinery Ltd, Faussett Hill, Street End, Canterbury, Kent, CT4 7AL Tel: (01227) 700011 Fax: (01227) 700022 *Joinery manufrs*

Canterbury Tools & Fasteners, 16 Herne Bay Road, Whitstable, Kent, CT5 2LJ Tel: (0845) 4264015 Fax: (01227) 266841 E-mail: normanctf@hotmail.com *Tools & fasteners manufrs*

Canterbury Wholefoods, Jewry Lane, Canterbury, Kent, CT1 2JB Tel: (01227) 464623 Fax: (01227) 764838 E-mail: enquiries@canterbury-wholefoods.co.uk *Food retailers*

Cantrill Cork Products, 3 Alma Works, Darlaston Road, Wednesbury, West Midlands, WS10 7TG Tel: 0121-567 3140 Fax: 0121-567 3149 E-mail: cancork@cantrill.fsbusiness.co.uk *Rubber, cork, neoprene product manufacturers cork producers merchants*

▶ Canty Designs Ltd, 17 Westbourne Avenue, Hull, HU5 3HN Tel: (01480) 491654 Fax: (0870) 7627278 E-mail: info@cantydesigns.com

Canusa Systems Ltd, 3 Sterling Park, Gatwick Road, Crawley, West Sussex, RH10 9QT Tel: (01293) 541254 Fax: (01293) 541777 E-mail: sales@canusa-cps.co.uk Principal Export Areas: Middle East, Africa, Central/East Europe & West Europe *Manufacturers of heat shrinkable products, pipeline coating*

Canute Haulage Company Ltd, Gamston Airfield, Retford, Nottinghamshire, DN22 0QL Tel: (01777) 833300 Fax: (01777) 838880 E-mail: traffic@canutegroup.com *Road transport, haulage & freight services*

▶ Canute LLP, 77, Holbeck Lane, Leeds, LS11 9UL Tel: 0845 056 0390 Fax: 0845 056 0391 E-mail: sales@canutesoft.com *Canute is the leading supply of hydraulic analysis software for the fire protection industry. The FHC program has been used in the design of thousands of fire protection systems worldwide and is accepted by all leading fire insurers and design authorities. **FHC is suitable for performing calculations for the following type of systems:*All types of fire sprinkler systems *Fire hydrant systems*Water deluge systems*Foam monitor systems*Watermist systems (Low and high pressure - NFPA 750) **

▶ Canvas Art, 81 East High Street, Forfar, Angus, DD8 2EQ Tel: (01307) 465715 Fax: (0870) 0569440 *Picture framing*

Canvey Supply Co. Ltd, 101 Point Road, Canvey Island, Essex, SS8 7TJ Tel: (01268) 696666 Fax: (01268) 696724 E-mail: canveysupply@btconnect.com *Builders merchants* Also at: South Benfleet

▶ Canwell Engineering, Redhouse Industrial Estate, Anglian Road, Walsall, WS9 8EP Tel: (01922) 745100

Canwire Services Ltd, 14 Gospel End Street, Dudley, West Midlands, DY3 3LS Tel: (01902) 881460 Fax: (01902) 881393 E-mail: canwireservices1@aol.com *Wire erosion machining & precision manufacturing services*

▶ CanYouDIY Ltd, 1 Queen Alexandra Road, North Shields, Tyne & Wear, NE29 9AS Tel: 0191 2580070 Fax: 0191 2580075 E-mail: questions@canyoudiy.com *UK model shop that specialises in mail order.*

▶ Caol Ila Distillery, Caolila Distillery, Port Askaig, Isle of Islay, PA46 7RL Tel: (01496) 302760 Fax: (01496) 302763 E-mail: sales@malts.com *Whisky distillery*

Cap Gemini, 1 Forge End, Woking, Surrey, GU21 6DB Tel: (01483) 764764 Fax: (01483) 786161 E-mail: sales@uk.ggey.com Principal Export Areas: Worldwide *Computer consultants*

Cap Gemini Ernst & Young, 36 South Gyle Cresent, Edinburgh, EH12 9EB Tel: 0131-339 9339 Fax: 0131-200 3700 E-mail: sales@uk.cgey.com *IT consultants*

▶ Cap Gemini Ernst & Young, Regent Court, 70 West Regent Street, Glasgow, G2 2QZ Tel: 0141-331 0414 Fax: 0141-353 5858

Cap It All Closures Ltd, 149d Pack Lane, Basingstoke, Hampshire, RG22 5HN Tel: (01256) 466178 Fax: (01256) 816333 *Bottle & cap suppliers*

▶ Capability Garden Services, 21 Lavington Road, Croydon, CR0 4PQ Tel: (020) 8680 2880 E-mail: dodge291972@hotmail.com *Garden Design, Construction and Maintenance*

Capacitec, PO Box 4022, Reading, RG8 8HG Tel: 0118-984 5351 Fax: 0118-984 3979 E-mail: sales@sensortronic.co.uk *Electronic gauge manufrs*

Capalex, Cleator Moor, Cumbria, CA25 5QB Tel: (01946) 811771 Fax: (01946) 813681 E-mail: sales@capalex.com *Capalex, Capital Aluminium Extrusions, is a versatile and highly reactive independent extruded aluminium component manufacturer, producing small or large order quantities with very fast lead times. Flexible and responsive service, capalex provides a full range of services including extrusion, design advice, CNC machining, fabrication, assembly, finishing, painting, and special packing. High tolerance aluminium extrusions in a wide range of alloys; 1050, 1200, 2014, 2024, 3003, 5083, 6005, 6061, 6063, 6082, 7020, 7050, 7075. ISO9001:2000 certified.*

Caparo Fabrications Ltd, Macrome Road, Tettenhall, Wolverhampton, WV6 9HF Tel: (01902) 753041 Fax: (01902) 742375 *Steel fabricators*

Caparo Group Ltd, 101-103 Baker Street, London, W1U 6LN Tel: (020) 7486 1417 Fax: (020) 7224 4109 E-mail: sales@caparo.co.uk *Holding company for manufacturers of steel products for industry*

Caparo Industries P.L.C., Caparo House, Popes Lane, Oldbury, West Midlands, B69 4PJ Tel: 0121-202 4400 Fax: 0121-202 4401 *General engineers*

Caparo Merchant Bar plc, Brigg Road, Scunthorpe, South Humberside, DN16 1XJ Tel: (01724) 853333 Fax: (01724) 403044 E-mail: sales@cmbplc.co.uk *Hot rolled steel bar manufrs*

▶ Capatex Ltd, 127 North Gate, Nottingham, NG7 7FZ Tel: 0115-978 6111 Fax: 0115-978 6222 E-mail: info@capatex.com *Hook and Loop fastener, narrow webbings, reflective tapes and plastic fittings, converting services and strap assembly, agro & horticultural textiles, nettings, geo-textiles, woven & non-woven textiles.*

Capco Interior Supplies Ltd, Unit 5, Moreton Industrial Estate, Swanley, Kent, BR8 8DE Tel: (01322) 661199 Fax: (01322) 662299 E-mail: bmswanley@cpdplc.co.uk *Interior distributors*

Capco Presswork, Bel House, Shady Lane, Birmingham, B44 9ER Tel: 0121-325 1344 Fax: 0121-366 6619 *Distributors of bearings, also bearings, solid turned, unground & bearings special or non-standard*

Capco Test Ltd, Riverside View, Wickham Market, Suffolk, IP13 0TA Tel: (01728) 747407 Fax: (01728) 747599 E-mail: sales@capco.co.uk Principal Export

continued

continuation
Areas: Worldwide *Civil engineering test equipment manufrs*

Cape Diamond Products Ltd, Castle Vale Industrial Estate, Maybrook Road, Minworth, Sutton Coldfield, West Midlands, B76 1DJ Tel: 0121-351 4371 Fax: 0121-351 3094 E-mail: sales@cape-diamond.co.uk *Diamond tool manufrs*

Cape Hire Ltd, Unit 4 Eastmoors, Cardiff, CF24 2EE Tel: (029) 2049 3184 Fax: (029) 2049 3186 *Scaffolding supplier*

Cape Industrial Services Ltd, Kirkton Drive, Dyce, Aberdeen, AB21 0BG Tel: (01224) 215800 Fax: (01224) 722879 E-mail: sales@capeindustrialservices.co.uk *Offshore maintenance contractors*

▶ Cape Industrial Services Ltd, Q Fort Wallington Industrial Estate, Military Road, Fareham, Hampshire, PO16 8TT Tel: (01329) 828813 Fax: (01329) 822867

Cape Industrial Services Ltd, Cape House, No 3 Redhall Avenue, Paragon Business Village, Wakefield, West Yorkshire, WF1 2UL Tel: (01924) 871000 Fax: (01924) 876291 *Scaffolding contractors* Also at: Aberdeen, Humberside, Linlithgow, Port Talbot, Sutton Coldfield & Warrington

Cape Warwick Ltd, 47 Britannia Way, Britannia Enterprise Park, Lichfield, Staffordshire, WS14 9UY Tel: (01543) 414544 Fax: (01543) 414599 E-mail: enquiries@cape-warwick.co.uk *Suppliers of Hospitalwares to the Healthcare environment. Manufacturer of standard issue Right Angle Torch to the MOD. Range of mixing bowls etc to the Beauty Sector. Producer of Buffet Maid Clip for the Catering Industry.*

▶ Capel Faces 2 Paint, 17 Long Perry, Capel St Mary, Ipswich, IP9 2XD Tel: (01473) 311609 E-mail: jd@ogalligan.freeserve.co.uk *Face painting, private parties, police checked, liability insurance*

Capel Mills Friction UK Ltd, Unit 6, Maple Works, Maple Road, Redhill, RH1 5HE Tel: (01737) 779090 Fax: (01737) 778040 *Brake lining retailers*

Capel Plant Holdings Ltd, Stephenson Road, Severalls Industrial Park, Colchester, CO4 9QR Tel: (01206) 844004 Fax: (01206) 841409 *Plant hire*

Capel Security Solutions Ltd, 22 Sychem Lane, Five Oak Green, Tonbridge, Kent, TN12 6TR Tel: (01892) 836036 Fax: (01892) 834844 E-mail: info@capelfencing.co.uk *Fencing contractors*

Capell Construction Ltd, Tollemache Road North, Spittlegate Level, Grantham, Lincolnshire, NG31 7UH Tel: (01476) 592000 Fax: (01476) 592100 E-mail: janem@capellconstruction.co.uk *Civil engineering contractors & ground workers*

▶ Capell's Building Stores, Les Petites Capelles Road, St. Sampson, Guernsey, GY2 4GR Tel: (01481) 245897 Fax: (01481) 247399

Capelrig Ltd, Tern Place, Denmore Road, Bridge of Don, Aberdeen, AB23 8JX Tel: (01224) 702211 Fax: (01224) 702219 E-mail: sales@capelrig.co.uk *Instrument & electrical engineers*

Capemist Gloves Ltd, 158 Fenaghy Road, Cullybackey, Ballymena, County Antrim, BT42 1DZ Tel: (028) 2588 1190 Fax: (028) 2588 1682 E-mail: capemist.gloves@virgin.net *Glove, hat & scarf manufrs*

Capers UK Ltd, 8 Raymond Road, Leicester, LE3 2AS Tel: 0116-282 5557 *Knitwear manufrs*

Capeside Steamship Co. Ltd, Charter House, 13-15 Carteret Street, London, SW1H 9DJ Tel: (020) 7222 4923 Fax: (020) 7222 0493 *Shipping company*

▶ Capita, The Capita Building, Kingmoor Business Park, Carlisle, CA6 4SJ Tel: (01228) 673000 Fax: (01228) 673111

Capita Building Services Ltd, Salter House, 263-265 High Street, Berkhamsted, Hertfordshire, HP4 1AB Tel: (01442) 872121 Fax: (01442) 866565 *Consulting engineers*

Capita Business Services Ltd, Kemp House, Cumnor Hill, Cumnor, Oxford, OX2 9PH Tel: (01865) 861300 Fax: (01865) 861301 *Computer consultants*

Capita Business Services Ltd, Manvers House, Manvers Street, Trowbridge, Wiltshire, BA14 8YX Tel: (01225) 773000 Fax: (01225) 777625 *Computer systems & software developers*

▶ Capita Construction Ltd, Beech Court, 27 Summers Road, Burnham, Slough, SL1 7EP Tel: (01628) 665009 Fax: (01628) 559358

Capita Education Services, 5 Mercian Close, Cirencester, Gloucestershire, GL7 1LT Tel: (01285) 647500 Fax: (01285) 647599 E-mail: sales@dolphin-cs.co.uk *Computer software & systems house*

Capita Financial Ltd, Beaufort House, 15 St. Botolph Street, London, EC3A 7HH Tel: (020) 7556 8800 Fax: (020) 7556 8850 *Collective investment schemes administrators*

Capita Hartshead, Castle House, Park Road, Banstead, Surrey, SM7 3BX Tel: (01737) 357272 Fax: (01737) 363106 E-mail: enquires@captia.co.uk *Pensions consultants*

▶ Capita Learning & Development, 17-19 Rochester Row, London, SW1P 1LA Tel: (0870) 1648900 Fax: (0870) 1658974 E-mail: cpdwebinfo@capita.co.uk *Capita People Development provide a comprehensive range of outplacement, transition services and career management solutions nationwide, including one-to-one counselling, workshops, onsite resource centres and online career management.*

Capita Printing Services, Unit C Croydon Road Industrial Estate, Tannery Close, Beckenham, Kent, BR3 4BY Tel: (020) 8662 7010 Fax: (020) 8662 7003 E-mail: sales@capita.co.uk *Security printers*

▶ Capita Social Housing Resourcing, Dean Bradley House, 52 Horseferry Road, London, SW1P 2AF Tel: (020) 7481 8383 Fax: (020) 7202 0045 *Recruitment agents*

▶ Capita Symonds Ltd, Edwinstowe House, High Street, Edwinstowe, Nottinghamshire, NG21 9PR Tel: (01623) 821506 Fax: (01623) 821507 *Building Services Engineers.*

Capita Symonds Services, Sunlight House, Quay Street, Manchester, M3 3JZ Tel: 0161-833 0711 Fax: 0161-835 2624 E-mail: man@mpmcapita.co.uk *Quantity surveyors & cost consultants* Also at: Edinburgh, Glasgow, London SW1 & Oxford

▶ Capital Binder Services, 287 Green Lanes, The Triangle, London, N13 4XS Tel: (020) 8882 4612 Fax: (020) 8882 8949

Capital Blinds, Factory Place, Docklands, London, E14 3AN Tel: (0800) 0433442 *Suppliers & installations of interior blinds*

Capital Building Services, 123 High Street, Rainham, Gillingham, Kent, ME8 8AN Tel: (01634) 360210 Fax: (01634) 310724 E-mail: ray.capital@blueyonder.co.uk *Building contractors & developers*

Capital Cables, D 20 Frogmore Industrial Estate, Motherwell Way, Grays, Essex, RM20 3XD Tel: (01708) 864464 Fax: (01708) 865385 *Industrial flexible cable distributors*

Capital Case Co, 55 Lonsdale Road, London, NW6 6RA Tel: (020) 7624 3333 Fax: (020) 7624 2533 *Case manufrs*

Capital Catering Co. Ltd, 4 Bear Court, Daneshill East Industrial Estate, Basingstoke, Hampshire, RG24 8QT Tel: (01256) 470044 Fax: (01256) 818485 E-mail: admin@capitalsandwiches.co.uk *Established in 1979 as a Caterer and now as a Producer and Distributor of quality sandwiches in the south of England, Capital is an accredited supplier to the NHS and a large university group as well as a small number of high profile venues. Our daily delivery service operates 364 days of the year through a fleet of vehicles with upgraded refrigeration capabilities*

▶ Capital City Cars Ltd, 92 Roan Street, Greenwich, London, SE10 9JT Tel: (08702) 404041 E-mail: colin@capitalcity.info *Private hire taxi company providing an alternatively fuelled green fleet of vehicles for the business community.*

Capital Cleaning Service, 25 Camps Rigg, Livingston, West Lothian, EH54 8PD Tel: (01506) 440333 Fax: (01506) 431318 *Office cleaning contractors*

Capital Cleaning Supplies, 105 Sedlescombe Road North, St. Leonards-on-Sea, East Sussex, TN37 7EJ Tel: (01424) 718666 Fax: (01424) 782798 *Cleaning equipment suppliers*

Capital Coated Steel, East Tyndall Street, Cardiff, CF24 5DA Tel: (029) 2046 0606 Fax: (029) 2048 8687 E-mail: email@capitalcs.com Principal Export Areas: Worldwide *Steel coil cutting services*

Capital Coffee Roasters, 5 Saxon Business Centre, Windsor Avenue, London, SW19 2RR Tel: (020) 8540 5000 Fax: (020) 8543 4444 E-mail: sales@capitalcoffeeroasters.co.uk *Suppliers of espresso, filter and bean-to-cup coffee machines to rent, lease, purchase or free-loan from a range of manufacturers including Vibiemme, Wega and Rex Royal. Roasters of the finest espresso and filter coffees including organic and Fair-trade.*

Capital Communications, 41 Bankhead Crossway South, Edinburgh, EH11 4EP Tel: 0131-442 4314 Fax: 0131-442 2636 *Mailing house*

Capital Communications Group Ltd, Farm Castle Estate, Duchess Place, Rutherglen, Glasgow, G73 1DR Tel: 0141-613 1314 Fax: 0141-643 1032 E-mail: info@scotsmail-online.com *Direct mail services*

Capital & Countys, 40 Broadway, London, SW1H 0BU Tel: (020) 7887 7000 Fax: (020) 7887 0004 *Property developers*

Capital Design Services Ltd, Bridge Buildings, 11A Ladybridge Road, Cheadle Hulme, Cheadle, Cheshire, SK8 5LL Tel: 0161-486 9524 Fax: 0161-485 8605 *Powder coating design engineers*

Capital Engineering Personnel Ltd, Broadway House, 112-134 The Broadway, London, SW19 1RL Tel: (020) 8605 2800 Fax: (028) 8946 3899 E-mail: admin@cap-recruit.co.uk *Employment agency*

Capital Equipment & Machinery Ltd, Mill Mead, Staines, Middlesex, TW18 4UQ Tel: (01784) 456151 Fax: (01784) 466481 E-mail: sales@capital-equipment.com *Used machine tool merchants*

Capital Fire & Security Alarm Systems, Ferry Road, Beauly, Inverness-Shire, IV4 7EA Tel: (01463) 782475 Fax: (01463) 782475 *Security systems & equipment manufrs*

▶ Capital Fireplaces Ltd, Units 12-17, Henlow Trading Estate, Henlow, Bedfordshire, SG16 6DS Tel: (01462) 813138 Fax: (0800) 9804847

▶ Capital Fit, 8 Tynewydd Terrace, Newbridge, Newport, Gwent, NP11 4LU Tel: (01495) 248082 Fax: (01495) 248082 E-mail: sales@capitalfit.com

Capital Group, 1a Bridge Street, Bishop's Stortford, Hertfordshire, CM23 2JU Tel: (01279) 508632 Fax: (01279) 758903 E-mail: admin@cap-recuirt.co.uk *Recruitment manpower & labour agencies, consultants & services*

Capital Group of Companies Ltd, Broadway House, 112-134 The Broadway, London, SW19 1RL Tel: (020) 8542 8131 Fax: (020) 8540 7385 E-mail: admin@cap-recruit.co.uk *Recruitment agency*

Capital Hair & Beauty Ltd, 6 Sackville Trading Estate, Sackville Road, Hove, East Sussex, BN3 7AN Tel: (01273) 215735 Fax: (01273) 735305 E-mail: hove@capitalhairandbeauty.co.uk *Hairdressing & beauty wholesalers*

▶ Capital Hair & Beauty Ltd, Unit 18, Chiltonian Industrial Estate, Manor Lane, Lee, London, SE12 0TX Tel: (020) 8852 9959 E-mail: lee@capitalhairandbeauty.co.uk *Hairdressing & beauty wholesalers*

▶ Capital Hair & Beauty Ltd, 3 Burton Road, Norwich, NR6 6AX Tel: (01603) 788778 Fax: (01603) 788856 E-mail: norwich@capitalhairandbeauty.co.uk *Hairdressing & beauty wholesalers*

Capital Hygiene, 2 Colne Road, Sible Hedingham, Halstead, Essex, CO9 3JP Tel: (01787) 460088 *Distributors of janitorial suppliers*

Capital IFX, 235, Regents Park Road, london, London, N3 3LF Tel: 020 83431188 Fax: 020 83431186 E-mail: K35@btinternet.com *Capital IFX is a foreign exchange specialist providing foreign exchange for importers and exporters. We provide the best rates in the Market.*

Capital Inspection Services, 3 Poyle Technical Centre, Willow Road, Colnbrook, Slough, SL3 0DP Tel: (01753) 684896 Fax: (01753) 681739 E-mail: cap.inspection@btconnect.com *Radiographic test services*

Capital Lift Trucks, Worting House, Basingstoke, Hampshire, RG23 8PY Tel: (01256) 882047 Fax: (01256) 811876 *Fork lift truck retailers*

Capital Lift Trucks Ltd, Reading Road, Sherdon House, Sherfield-On-Loddon, Hook, Hampshire, RG27 0EX Tel: (01256) 882047 Fax: (01256) 811876 *Fork lift trucks sales & hire*

Capital Lock & Safe Company Ltd, 91 Lancaster Road, Enfield, Middlesex, EN2 0DN Tel: (020) 8367 2775 Fax: (020) 8366 5091 *Locksmiths*

Capital Patterns & Plastics, 18 The Grove, West Wickham, Kent, BR4 9JS Tel: (020) 8777 9276 Fax: (020) 8777 9276 E-mail: graham@cap-patt.fsnet.co.uk *Plastic vacuum forming services*

Capital Plant Services Ltd, Elys Estate, Angel Road, London, N18 3BH Tel: (020) 8807 1672 Fax: (020) 8807 1639 *Excavator machinery parts suppliers*

▶ Capital Plumbing, 138 Comiston Road, Edinburgh, EH10 5QN Tel: 0131-447 7555 Fax: 0131-447 7556

▶ Capital Plumbing & Heating, 20 Mylo Griffiths Close, Cardiff, CF5 2RQ Tel: (029) 2057 8268 E-mail: rmr.roberts@virgin.net *Plumbing & heating engineers*

Capital Refractories Ltd, 2 Station Road, Clowne, Chesterfield, Derbyshire, S43 4AB Tel: (01246) 811163 Fax: (01246) 819573 E-mail: info@capital-refractories.com *Refractory suppliers & manufrs*

Capital Repro, Tech West House, Warple Way, London, W3 0UE Tel: (020) 8743 0111 Fax: (020) 8743 0112 E-mail: info@caprep.co.uk *Design & pre press*

Capital Rubber & Plastics Ltd, Units 9-11 Deans Factory Estate, Lambs Lane, Rainham, Essex, RM13 9XL Tel: (01708) 552214 Fax: (01708) 524004 E-mail: sales@capitalrubber.co.uk *Rubber product manufacturers. Also silicone & rubber extruders*

Capital Safety Group Ltd, 7 Christleton Court, Manor Park, Runcorn, Cheshire, WA7 1ST Tel: (01928) 571324 Fax: (01928) 571325 E-mail: csgne@csgne.co.uk *Fall arrest & rescue systems providers*

Capital Sheds, 12 Western Terrace, Edinburgh, EH12 5QF Tel: 0131-313 3515 Fax: 0131-313 3515 E-mail: info@capitalsheds.com *Portable & sectional building suppliers*

Capital Springs & Pressings Ltd, Commerce Way, Edenbridge, Kent, TN8 6ED Tel: (01732) 867130 Fax: (01732) 867140 E-mail: sales@capitalsprings.com Principal Export Areas: Central/East Europe *Spring manufacturers including compression & coil. Also general pressings & wire formed/shaped components/products manufrs*

Capital Steel Fabrications, 21-23 Parkhouse Street, London, SE5 7TQ Tel: (020) 7252 5445 Fax: (020) 7703 5212 *Steel fabrication manufrs*

▶ Capital Steelworks, Unit 1 Kingsnorth Works, Hoo, Rochester, Kent, ME3 9NZ Tel: (01634) 256420 Fax: (01634) 255938 E-mail: capsteelltd@aol.com *Steel fabricators*

Capital Structures plc, 6 Blackstone Road, Stukeley Meadows Industrial Es, Huntingdon, Cambridgeshire, PE29 6EF Tel: (01480) 431188 Fax: (01480) 434210 E-mail: info@capital-structures.com *Fabrication & erection of steel structures, architectural metalworkers*

Capital Supplies Ltd, 87 Boston Road, Croydon, CR0 3EJ Tel: (020) 8665 5520 Fax: (020) 8665 5838 E-mail: info@capitalsupplies.co.uk *Fixings, fasteners & engineering supplies*

Capital Systems Ltd, 17 Princess Victoria Street, Bristol, BS8 4BX Tel: 0117-973 0506 Fax: 0117-973 0811 *Computer software distribution*

Capital Technical Services Ltd, Broadway Ho, 112-134 The Broadway, London, SW19 1RL Tel: (020) 8542 8131 Fax: (020) 8540 7385 E-mail: admin@cap-recruit.co.uk *Recruitment agency*

Capital Tiles Supplies Ltd, P O Box 80, Coventry, CV1 2RJ Tel: (024) 7663 3336 Fax: (024) 7663 1447 *Tile distributors*

▶ Capital Trophies, Unit B1-B2 Peills Yard, Bourne Road, Bromley, BR2 9NS Tel: (020) 8466 9577 Fax: (020) 8466 9579 *Trophy retailers*

Capital Valves Ltd, Wembley Point, Harrow Road, Wembley, Middlesex, HA9 6DE Tel: (020) 8900 0471 Fax: (020) 8900 0808 E-mail: sales@capitalvalves.co.uk *Valve distributors* Also at: Cambridge

Capital Vehicle Maintenance Ltd, 207-209 Worton Road, Isleworth, Middlesex, TW7 6DS Tel: (020) 8758 0888 Fax: (020) 8758 0777 *Commercial workshop for machinery*

Capital Waste Paper Ltd, Dayton Drive, Darent Industrial Park, Erith, Kent, DA8 2LE Tel: (01322) 350555 Fax: (01322) 351758 E-mail: capitalwastepaper@tiscali.co.uk *Waste paper merchants*

Capital Water Treatment Ltd, 79a Lansdowne Road, Croydon, CR0 2BF Tel: (020) 8649 9503 Fax: (020) 8649 9504 E-mail: sales@capitalwater.co.uk *Water services installation & maintenance*

▶ Capital Windows Manfacturing, Unit 9, Sarum Complex, Salisbury Road, Uxbridge, Middlesex, UB8 2RZ Tel: (01895) 271061

Capitan (Europe) Ltd, Capitan House, 1C Church Road, Croydon, CR0 1SG Tel: (020) 8688 2617 Fax: (020) 8688 2821 E-mail: sales@capitan.co.uk *Export & procurement services*

Capitb Trust Ltd, 80 Richardshaw Lane, Stanningley, Pudsey, West Yorkshire, LS28 6BN Tel: 0113-227 3345 Fax: 0113-227 3322 E-mail: sales@capitb.co.uk *Holding company*

Capitol Window Systems Ltd, Unit 58, Third Avenue, Deeside Industrial Park, Deeside, Clwyd, CH5 2LA Tel: (01244) 281777

Capix Ltd, Capix House, Forge Close, Eaton Socon, St. Neots, Cambridgeshire, PE19 8TP Tel: (01480) 470022 Fax: (01480) 215236 E-mail: info@capix.com *Photographic equipment & importers*

▶ Caplin Building Services, Valley Farm Cottages, London Road, Frostenden, Beccles, Suffolk, NR34 7HW Tel: (01502) 675291 Fax: (01502) 676027

Caplin Glass, Unit 9a Queens Yard, White Post Lane, London, E9 5EN Tel: (020) 8986 0047 Fax: (020) 8986 0455 *Plate glass processors.*

Caplugs Ltd, Unit 7, Overfield Industrial Estate, Off Thorpe Way, Banbury, Oxfordshire, OX16 4XR Tel: (01295) 263753 Fax: (01295) 263788 E-mail: support@caplugs.co.uk Principal Export Areas: Central/East Europe & West Europe *Plastic protective caps & plugs*

Capon Computer Environmental Services Ltd, 149 Putnoe Street, Bedford, MK41 8JR Tel: (01234) 359791 Fax: (01234) 269995 *Building services, data network & contractors*

R.S. Capp Ltd, Masters House, Guildford Road, Westcott, Dorking, Surrey, RH4 3NG Tel: (01306) 887785 Fax: (01306) 887800 E-mail: info@rscapp.ltd.uk *Consultants*

Cappa Pinking Machinery Ltd, 25 Westgate, Otley, West Yorkshire, LS21 3AT Tel: (01943) 467655 Fax: (01943) 850362 E-mail: sales@emberfern.co.uk *Textile cutting machine manufrs*

▶ Cappagh Contractors Construction London Ltd, 8 Waterside Way, London, SW17 0HB Tel: (020) 8947 4000 Fax: (020) 8944 9447

Capper Fuels, 124 Tamnamore Road, Dungannon, County Tyrone, BT71 6HW Tel: (028) 8772 6888 Fax: (028) 8772 7276 E-mail: info@cappertrading.com *Haulage agents*

Capper Print, Lanelay Road Industrial Estate, Talbot Green, Pontyclun, Mid Glamorgan, CF72 8XX Tel: (01443) 225500 Fax: (01443) 235290 E-mail: sales@capperprint.co.uk *Printing & designing services*

▶ Cappers Plant Hire, Station Road, Armadale, Bathgate, West Lothian, EH48 3LJ Tel: (01501) 733999 Fax: (01501) 735310 E-mail: sales@cphltd.com

Cappo International Ltd, Global House, 38-40 High Street, West Wickham, Kent, BR4 0NJ Tel: (020) 8776 1850 Fax: (020) 8777 9952 E-mail: info@cappo.co.uk *Provision chemical plant engineers & technicians*

▶ Cappuccino & Gateau Ltd, 173 Crickelwood Broadway, London, NW2 3HT Tel: (020) 8208 4668 E-mail: cappucinogateau@ukcom.com *Café*

Caprari Pumps (UK) Ltd, Caprari House, Bakewell Road, Orton Southgate, Peterborough, PE2 6XU Tel: (01733) 371605 Fax: (01733) 371607 E-mail: info@caprari.co.uk *Pump manufacturers borehole & submersible*

Capri Catering Equipment Services, 55 Great Tindal Street, Birmingham, B16 8DR Tel: 0121-236 5015 Fax: 0121-454 4011 E-mail: capricatering@blueyonder.co.uk *Catering equipment installers*

Capri Electrical Developments Ltd, 45-47 Whalley Road, Clitheroe, Lancashire, BB7 1EE Tel: (01200) 425070 Fax: (01200) 423070 E-mail: roger@storageheater.co.uk *Storage heater spares & thermostats, thermal relays & thermal fuses suppliers*

▶ Capri Fast Foods, 105 High Street, Brockmoor, Brierley Hill, West Midlands, DY5 3JB Tel: (01384) 74100

▶ Capri Mechanical Services Ltd, 53-55 Cutlers Road, South Woodham Ferrers, Chelmsford, CM3 5WA Tel: (01245) 321144 E-mail: info@caprimechanical.co.uk

Capri Mouldings Ltd, 45 Padgets Lane, Redditch, Worcestershire, B98 0RD Tel: (01527) 510008 Fax: (01527) 518288 *Plastics mould makers*

Capri TV Video Productions, 6 Bell Hill, Histon, Cambridge, CB4 9JQ Tel: (01223) 233588 E-mail: capri@capri-video.com *Video production*

Caprice Clothing Co Ltd, Boreham Road, London, N22 6SL Tel: (020) 8888 3513 Fax: (020) 8888 5095 *Ladies clothing manufacturer*

Capricorn Blinds Ltd, 1072 Coventry Road, Yardley, Birmingham, B26 2DT Tel: 0121-772 5366 Fax: 0121-766 7504 E-mail: info@capricornblinds.com *Capricorn Blinds have been serving the West Midlands retail market for 25 years. Over this time we have built up a reputation for manufacturing and installing quality products and a friendly, professional customer service.**As a family run business we have created an excellent customer focused atmosphere and pride ourselves on the level of service and customer care we provide. We have expanded over the years and become one of the most successful Blind companies in the West Midlands**To get more information please call us on the number below or visit out showroom where we will be able to offer you 1-to-1 advice. **

Capricorn Controls, Thorpe Close, Banbury, Oxfordshire, OX16 4SW Tel: (01295) 272360 Fax: (01295) 264766 E-mail: sales@capricorn-controls.com *Electronic controls for the power*

▶ Capricorn Diesinking Services, Unit 13, Pivington Mill, Pluckley, Ashford, Kent, TN27 0PG Tel: (01233) 840968 *Tool manufrs*

Capricorn Mouldings Ltd, Unit 23, Trench Lock 3, Telford, Shropshire, TF1 5ST Tel: (01952) 201090 Fax: (01952) 222744 *Plastics injection mouldings manufrs*

Capricorn Roofing Ltd, 96a Dundonald Road, London, SW19 3PN Tel: (020) 8542 5393 Fax: (020) 8542 3593 *Industrial roofing contractors*

Caprin, Unit 2 Park Industrial Estate, Frogmore, St. Albans, Hertfordshire, AL2 2DR Tel: (01727) 872021 Fax: (01727) 875012 E-mail: office@caprin.co.uk *General printers & stationers*

Caprina Ltd, Woodacre Outbarn, Hazelhead Lane, Barnacre, Preston, PR3 1BN Tel: (01995) 606519 Fax: (01995) 600242 E-mail: prefcable@aol.com *Recyclers of electrical cable*

Capro Europe, Building 54, Second Avenue, Pensnett Trading Estate, Kingswinford, West Midlands, DY6 7XJ Tel: (01384) 276300 Fax: (01384) 402010 *Manufacturers of control cables*

Caprock UK Ltd, Caprock Building, Denmore Road, Bridge Of Don, Aberdeen, AB23 8JW Tel: (01224) 707377 Fax: (01224) 707254 E-mail: info@caprock.co.uk *Assemble satellite communication*

Caproco plc, 31 Davey House, St Neots Road, Eaton Ford, St. Neots, Cambridgeshire, PE19 7BA Tel: (01480) 407600 Fax: (01480) 407619 E-mail: caproco@btconnect.com Principal Export Areas: Worldwide *Corrosion control/monitoring systems & chemical injection equipment manufrs*

▶ Caps Cases Ltd, Nurseries Road, Baillieston, Glasgow, G69 6UL Tel: 0141-773 3337 Fax: 0141-773 4443 *Makers of cardboard boxes*

Caps Cases Ltd, Studlands Park Industrial Estate, Newmarket, Suffolk, CB8 7AU Tel: (01638) 667326 Fax: (01638) 667407 E-mail: info@capscases.co.uk *Cardboard box manufrs*

▶ Capsolutions Ltd, 41 Airmyn Road, Goole, East Yorkshire, DN14 6XB Tel: (01405) 763040 Fax: (01405) 763041 E-mail: sales@capsolutions.co.uk *Suppliers of plastic cap manufacturing equipment*

▶ Capss Electronic Component Distributors, Unit 8 Hotchkiss Way, Binley Industrial Estate, Coventry, CV3 2RL Tel: (024) 7644 4664 Fax: (024) 7644 4585 *Distribution systems, electrical suppliers*

Capstan Food Equipment, 1 Wyndham House, High Street, Kentisbeare, Cullompton, Devon, EX15 2AA Tel: (01884) 266750 Fax: (01884) 266750 *Sales & services of food processing machinery*

Capstan Lift Services, 3 Marlowe Business Centre, Batavia Road, London, SE14 6BQ Tel: (020) 8694 7557 Fax: (020) 8694 6088 E-mail: capstanlifts@aol.com *Lift engineers*

Capstan Screws & Fastenings Ltd, Unit 4 Evingar Trading Estate, Ardglen Road, Whitchurch, Hampshire, RG28 7BB Tel: (01256) 895245 Fax: (01256) 892440 *Industrial fastener distributors*

▶ Capstan Security Ltd, 127 East Barnet Road, Barnet, Hertfordshire, EN4 8RF Tel: (020) 8441 9700 Fax: (020) 8449 5319 E-mail: admin@capstansecurity.com

Gary Capstick Ltd, Green La West, Garstang, Preston, PR3 1NJ Tel: (01995) 600844 Fax: (01995) 600841 E-mail: enquiries@capstick.co.uk *Building & joinery manufrs*

L. Capstick, Middlegate, White Lund Industrial Estate, Morecambe, Lancashire, LA3 3BN Tel: (01524) 63141 Fax: (01524) 846173 *Waste disposal contractors*

Capstone Systems, Oak Mead, Honington, Bury St. Edmunds, Suffolk, IP31 1RE Tel: (01359) 268711 Fax: (01359) 268870 E-mail: dcg@capstonesystems.co.uk *Software development consultancy for charities, Hospices and businesses*

Captain Packaging Ltd, 5 Clarence Wharf, Mumby Road, Gosport, Hampshire, PO12 1AJ Tel: (023) 9251 1125 Fax: (023) 9252 5844 E-mail: sales@captain.co.uk *Packaging material distributors*

▶ Captain Seo, 3 The Croft, Park Hill, London, W5 2NB Tel: (020) 8816 8877 Fax: (0870) 1258147 E-mail: info@captainseo.com *captain seo, a division of Milestones adds value to people''s websites:**1. by increasing the number of visitors applying ethical search engine optimisation (SEO) tactics and web analytics, and**2. by improving the visitors-to-sales/ registration conversion rate analysing the user behaviour and the web traffic.*

Captec Ltd, Fareham, Hampshire, PO15 5TX Tel: (01489) 866066 Fax: (01489) 866088 E-mail: info@captec.co.uk *Industrial computer manufrs*

Captivair Pneumatics Ltd, Unit B2 Imperial Business Estate, Gravesend, Kent, DA11 0DL Tel: (01474) 334537 Fax: (01474) 333657 E-mail: sales@captivair.co.uk *Distributors of flexible tubing & pneumatic equipment*

▶ Captive Calendars, 12 Fairway*, Sawbridgeworth, Hertfordshire, CM21 9NJ Tel: 01279 319769 *Personalized calendars and fridge magnets*

Captive Closures, Burma Road, Blidworth, Mansfield, Nottinghamshire, NG21 0RT Tel: (01623) 491112 Fax: (01623) 491113 E-mail: captive.mick@btconnect.com *Injection moulders*

Captive Clothing Ltd, Great Titchfield House, 14-18 Great Titchfield Street, London, W1W 8BD Tel: (020) 7436 7744 Fax: (020) 7436 8500 *Manufacture clothing*

Captive Minds, Studio 23, The London Fruit & Wool Exchange, 56 Brushfield Street, London, E1 6HB Tel: (020) 7392 2662 Fax: E-mail: info@captiveminds.co.uk *Creating fresh and evocative campaigns for a wide range of brand and entertainment clients, Captive Minds provides a complete and integrated marketing solution - from design and PR, through to SMS, field marketing and film production.*

▶ Captive Systems UK Ltd, 82 Caunce Street, Blackpool, FY1 3ND Tel: (01253) 627600 Fax: (01253) 627560 E-mail: info@captivesystems.co.uk *CCTV installers*

▶ Captured Image Photography, 7 Dunstans Croft, Mayfield, East Sussex, TN20 6UH Tel: 01435 874894 E-mail: andy@capturedimagephotography.co.uk *Freelance photography covering a wide range of commissions, from weddings to web images and company literature. Stock images are available for print, magazine or literature.*

Capvond Plastics Ltd, 32 Welbeck Road, Glasgow, G53 7SD Tel: 0141-876 9000 Fax: 0141-876 4123 E-mail: office@capvond.co.uk *Glass fibre mouldings manufrs*

The Capworth Panel & Timber Company Ltd, 27 Capworth Street, London, E10 5AN Tel: (020) 8539 3374 Fax: (020) 8539 5872 *Timber merchants*

▶ Car Air Conditioning Services, 104 Bennett Way, Dartford, DA2 7JU Tel: (01474) 705370 E-mail: bobr@caraircon.co.uk *Car air-conditioning parts service recharging & fault diagnosis*

▶ Car Air Freshener.Co.UK, 47 Holmewood Gardens, London, SW2 3NB Tel: (0845) 6066204 E-mail: info@carairfreshener.co.uk *Promotional merchandise supplier*

Car Alarm Centre, Unit 5 Hatton Garden Industrial Estate, Johnson Street, Liverpool, L3 2BR Tel: 0151-227 1241 Fax: 0151-236 4673 *Car alarms centre*

▶ Car Alarm Service Ltd, Drakes Lane Industrial Estate, Drakes Lane, Boreham, Chelmsford, CM3 3BE Tel: (01245) 362754

Car & Business Cosmetics, 1 Maxwell Street, South Shields, Tyne & Wear, NE33 4PU Tel: 0191-456 3795 Fax: 0191-454 4078 *Vehicle graphics designers*

Car Care, 153 St. Johns Road, Kettering, Northamptonshire, NN15 5AZ Tel: (01536) 524512 E-mail: sales@carcare-mvs.co.uk *Mobile Car & Commercial Vehicle Valeting Service. Based in Kettering Northamptonshire.*

Car Care Plan, Mid Point, Thornbury, Bradford, West Yorkshire, BD3 7AG Tel: (0870) 7527000 Fax: (0870) 7527100 *Vehicle warranty administrator*

Car Clinic Co. Ltd, Cannal Road, Bradford, West Yorkshire, BD1 4AJ Tel: (01274) 386400 Fax: (01274) 735185 *Motor accident repairers*

Car Colour Services Ltd, 92-94 Mawney Road, Romford, RM7 7JB Tel: (01708) 705005 Fax: (01708) 732618 E-mail: ccsromford@aol.com *Wholesale & trade paint distributors*

Car Comm Aid Ltd, 47-49 Henshall Road, Parkhouse Industrial Estate, Parkhouse Industrial Estate West, Newcastle, Staffordshire, ST5 7RY Tel: (01782) 563474 Fax: (01782) 563550 E-mail: mail@carcommaid.co.uk *Specialist commercial vehicle repairs & paintwork services*

▶ Car & Commercial Components, Freckleton St, Blackburn, BB2 2AL Tel: (01254) 670121 *Motorcycle suppliers*

▶ Car Communications, 33 London Road, Blackburn, BB1 7HA Tel: (0845) 2266454 E-mail: info@carcommunications.co.uk *Handsfree Phone Kits, SimplyTrak Vehicle Tracking Systems, Satellite Navigation (SmartNav). *Nationwide Installations, Established 15 yrs, Liability & Damage Insurance, Fleet Installation Specialists - Cars/ Vans/Trucks. Accredited by the Federation of Communication Services. All our installations are carried out to the industry standard MPT 1362 by fully qualified and insured engineers.*

Car Connection, Unit 7b, Sovereign Way Dock Road, Birkenhead, Merseyside, CH41 1DL Tel: 0151-652 4317 Fax: 0151-652 4317 E-mail: carconnection@talktalkbusiness.net *Hoods & interiors manufacturer & supply and fit. Electrical car equipment, alarms, reversing sensors*

▶ Car Design Jobs, PO Box 8208, Colchester, CO3 3WU Tel: 0845 838 1598

Car Glass Replacement, Norwich Road, Cardiff, CF23 9AB Tel: (029) 2049 0151 Fax: (029) 2049 9431 *Glass & windscreen fitters*

▶ Car Nation Yaxley, Station Road Garage, Broadway, Yaxley, Peterborough, PE7 3EG Tel: (01733) 243424 E-mail: ishy@carnationcars.com *looking for a new car, let us make it easier for you, we have a wide range of cars and vans for sale, warranty and finance available.*

▶ Car Paint Warehouse, Shaunak House, Netham Road, Bristol, BS5 9PJ Tel: 0117-955 4797 Fax: 0117-955 4809 E-mail: carpaintwarehouse@yahoo.com *Motor trade consumables suppliers*

Car Parking Solutions, St. Peters, Ellachie Mews, Gosport, Hampshire, PO12 2DR Tel: (023) 9252 2017 Fax: (023) 9252 2017 E-mail: infosales@parkingsolutions.co.uk *Domestic & commercial vehicle turntables*

Car Radio Alarms, Clarence Road, Sutton, Surrey, SM1 1RJ Tel: (020) 8661 1122 Fax: (020) 8770 7114 E-mail: admin@carradioalarms.co.uk *Car security services*

Car Radio & Security Centre Halifax, 6 Trinity Road, Halifax, West Yorkshire, HX1 2QF Tel: (01422) 363207 Fax: (01422) 321450 *Car radio & security systems distributors*

Car Spares Cheshunt Ltd, Delamare Road, Cheshunt, Waltham Cross, Hertfordshire, EN8 9AP Tel: (01992) 639844 Fax: (01992) 623871 E-mail: sales@carspares.co.uk *Motor vehicle spare parts factors*

Car Spares (Stony Stratford), 98 High Street, Stony Stratford, Milton Keynes, MK11 1AH Tel: (01908) 564333 Fax: (01908) 568386 *Car accessories & component supplier*

▶ Car Trans Vehicle Delivery Services, Spencer Park, Greasbrough Street, Rotherham, South Yorkshire, S60 1RF Tel: (01709) 368577 Fax: (01709) 362228 E-mail: sales@car-trans.co.uk

Car Transmissions, 122 Elmton Road, Creswell, Worksop, Nottinghamshire, S80 4DE Tel: (01909) 721437 Fax: (01909) 721437 *Gearboxes service & repair*

▶ Car Treat (Mobile Car Valeting), 135 Rylands Road, Kennington, Kennington, Ashford, Kent, TN24 9LU Tel: (01233) 629247 E-mail: jonathan4reeves@uk2.net *Give your car a treat.I come to you with fully equiped van which carrys own power and water supply.Have your car washed,polished,vacuumed and shampooed.Covering Ashford,Faversham,Folkstone,Canterbury, Dymchurch and Tenterden.*

▶ Car & Van Hire, Unit 6-7 Harlaw Way, Harlaw Road Industrial Estate, Inverurie, Aberdeenshire, AB51 4SG Tel: (01467) 629999 Fax: (01467) 622211 E-mail: info@carandvanhire.net *Car & van rental*

Car Wash Consultants Ltd, The Platt, Amersham, Buckinghamshire, HP7 0HX Tel: (01494) 723819 Fax: (01494) 723796E-mail: carwashc@aol.com *Car washing equipment & suppliers*

Car Wash UK Ltd, 9-11 Hikers Way, Drakes Drive, Long Crendon, Aylesbury, Buckinghamshire, HP18 9RW Tel: (01844) 202123 Fax: (01844) 202831 E-mail: carwashuk@btconnect.com *Car washing machine distributors*

▶ Car Wrights, Ocean Street, Atlantic Street, Altrincham, Cheshire, WA14 5DH Tel: 0161-925 2250 *Bouncy castle inflatable hire services*

▶ Carabou Gifts & Ballons, 105 Market Street, Cannock, Staffordshire, WS12 1AD Tel: (01543) 878201 E-mail: carabou@hotmail.co.uk *Balloon & party suppliers*

▶ CaraClean.Com, 70 Warwick Road, London, W5 5PT Tel: (0800) 0112272 E-mail: info@caraclean.com *Laundry & dry cleaning collection & delivery services*

Caractor Graphics, 330 Moorhey Road, Liverpool, L31 5LR Tel: 0151-520 0500 Fax: 0151-520 0900 E-mail: caractorgraphics@yahoo.co.uk *Sign manufrs*

Caradale Traditional Bricks Ltd, Goremire Road, Carluke, Lanarkshire, ML8 4PQ Tel: (01555) 771397 Fax: (01555) 771397 *Brick manufrs*

▶ Caradan Designs, 13 Burrows Road, Kingswinford, West Midlands, DY6 8LS Tel: (01384) 273491 *Exquisite handcrafted bridal tiaras & other fine accessories manufrs*

▶ Caraleisure Direct, 205 Elliott Street, Tyldesley, Manchester, M29 8DR Tel: (01942) 894949 Fax: (01942) 894400 E-mail: sales@caraleisuredirect.co.uk *Online retailer of caravan & camping accessories manufrs*

▶ Carallon Ltd, Studio G9 Shepherds Studios, Rockley Road, London, W14 0DA Tel: (020) 7371 2032 *Computer software developers*

Caramex Ltd, PO Box 2599, Bishop's Stortford, Hertfordshire, CM23 2AQ Tel: (01279) 506895 Fax: (01279) 501454 *Agency for ceramic tiles manufrs*

Caranco Ltd, Caranco House, Wilford Road, Nottingham, NG2 1EB Tel: 0115-986 2272 Fax: 0115-986 3705 E-mail: sales@caranco.co.uk *Shop fitting suppliers & sign manufrs*

▶ Carander Construction Ltd, 97 Portman Street, Glasgow, G41 1EJ Tel: 0141-429 1021 Fax: 0141-429 2623

Caraustar Industrial & Consumer Products Group Ltd, 86 Bison Place, Moss Side, Leyland, PR26 7QR Tel: (01772) 621562 Fax: (01772) 622263 E-mail: david.dredge@caraustar.com *Cardboard tube manufrs*

Caravan Accessories Kenilworth Ltd, Unit 10 Princes Drive Industrial Estate, Coventry Road, Kenilworth, Warwickshire, CV8 2FD Tel: (01926) 854271 Fax: (01926) 853954 E-mail: sales@caktanks.co.uk *Caravan accessories retailers*

▶ Caravan Hire Butlins, Minehead, Somerset, TA24 5SH Tel: (01793) 339832 E-mail: gina.traynor1@ntlworld.com *caravan for hire butlins minehead.sleeps up to 8 people.full use of facilities,inside the caravan.cooker, microwave,tv,dvd,etc.for more information you can contact us on 01793 339832 or 07704885565.*

▶ Caravan & Leisure Technology, The Courtyard, Sevenacres, Smallfield Road, Horne, Horley, Surrey, RH6 9JP Tel: (0845) 2262675 Fax: (01342) 844552 E-mail: sales@caravantechnology.com *Caravan fixtures & fittings service*

Carbern Pipes & Fittings, Unit 3 Bevan Industrial Estate, Brierley Hill, West Midlands, DY5 3TF Tel: (01384) 76111 Fax: (01384) 262309 E-mail: sales@carbern.co.uk *Manufacturers of pipeline components & industrial fasteners*

▶ Carberry Haulage, Colesleigh House, Bury Road, Stanton, Bury St. Edmunds, Suffolk, IP31 2BZ Tel: (01359) 252212 Fax: (01359) 252220

Carbide Dies (Birmingham) Ltd, 7 Port Hope Road, Birmingham, B11 1JS Tel: 0121-772 0817 Fax: 0121-773 9342 E-mail: jim@ctr-uk.com *Tooling for the fastener industry*

▶ Carbide Finger, Unit 2 Christy Court, Christy Way, Southfields Business Park, Basildon, Essex, SS15 6TL Tel: 01268 419555 E-mail: sales@carbidefinger.com *Website design, three dimensional 3d animation*

Carbide (UK) Ltd, 8 Park Street, Anlaby Road, Hull, HU3 2JF Tel: (01482) 227234 Fax: (01482) 212902 E-mail: carbideuk@carbideuk.com *Tooling specialists & manufrs*

Carbody Banbury Ltd, Thorpe Lane, Banbury, Oxfordshire, OX16 4UT Tel: (01295) 273945 Fax: (01295) 270226 E-mail: philatcbl@aol.com *Crash repairers*

▶ Carbon Enterprises Ltd, 77A High St, Esher, Surrey, KT10 9QA Tel: (01372) 462892 Fax: (01372) 467043 E-mail: ce@carbonenterprises.co.uk *Carbon Enterprises, formed in 1983, is a supplier of primary and secondary industrial raw materials to a wide range of industries in Europe and Worldwide. We are Suppliers of Microsilica, Calcined Polishing Alumina and Aluminium Silicate. Along with technical expertise on all our products, Carbon Enterprises offers a complete logistics package comprising transport on land and sea, container freight, packaging and repackaging to quoted or individual requirements, including biodegradeable bags.*

▶ Carbon Lodge, Church Road, Catsfield, Battle, East Sussex, TN33 9QP Tel: (01424) 893333 *Music publishers*

Carbonlite Converting Equipment Ltd, Britannia Foundry, Lomax Street, Rochdale, Lancashire, OL12 0DN Tel: (01706) 359000 Fax: (01706) 654378 E-mail: sales@ccequipment.co.uk Principal Export Areas: Worldwide *Precision engineers machine building*

▶ Carbonomics Machine Tools, 14 Waleswood Road, Wales Bar, Sheffield, S26 5PY Tel: (01909) 774777 Fax: (01909) 774779

▶ Carbro Sheet Metal Co. Ltd, Unit 7, 106 Richardson Street, Stockport, Cheshire, SK1 3JL Tel: 0161-477 0900 Fax: 0161-477 0370 E-mail: info@carbro.co.uk *Sheet Metalwork Engineers.*

Carclo Engineering Group, PO Box 14, Ossett, West Yorkshire, WF5 9LR Tel: (01924) 268040 Fax: (01924) 283226 E-mail: investor.relations@carclo-plc.com *Manufacturers of technically demanding plastic injection*

Carclo Technical Plastics, 111 Buckingham Avenue, Slough, SL1 4PF Tel: (01753) 575011 Fax: (01753) 811359 E-mail: optics@carclo-optics.com *Plastics lenses & optical systems*

Carcroft Joinery & Glassglass, 29-31 Owston Road, Carcroft, Doncaster, South Yorkshire, DN6 8DA Tel: (01302) 728260 Fax: (01302) 728260 E-mail: enquiries@carcroftjoinery.co.uk *Joinery manufrs*

▶ Card Professionals Ltd, Sandhurst House, 297 Yorktown Road, College Town, Sandhurst, Berkshire, GU47 0QA Tel: (01276) 609777 Fax: (01276) 609888 *Electric component manufrs*

▶ Card Scanning Solutions Ltd, 14 Coleridge Road, Finchley, London, N12 8DE Tel: (020) 7748 0818 E-mail: sales@cardscanning.com *Unique OCR based solutions for document scanning and data collection. Our portable scanner collect data from any ID card, driving licence, passport etc. Range of portable scanners and magnetic readers.*

Cardair, 7 Fieldon Court, Lower Gravenhurst, Gravenhurst, Bedford, MK45 4NL Tel: (07836) 378640 Fax: (01525) 861890 E-mail: d.skinner545@btinternet.com *Motor car air conditioning accessory suppliers, service & repairs*

Cardale Assurance Facilities Ltd, Old Bank Chambers, Station Road, Horley, Surrey, RH6 9HW Tel: (01293) 786295 Fax: (01293) 820353 *Insurance brokers consultants*

Cardboard Box Co. Ltd, Clayton Park Enterpsise Centre, Petre Road, Clayton Le Moors, Accrington, Lancashire, BB5 5JB Tel: (01254) 232223 Fax: (01254) 232636 E-mail: info@thecardboardbox.co.uk *Cartons manufrs*

▶ Cardboard Boxes, 1 Ivanhoe Street, Leicester, LE3 9GX Tel: 0116-275 2039 *Cardboard boxes suppliers & distributors*

Cardboard Tubes Ltd, Unit D2 Zenith, Paycocke Road, Basildon, Essex, SS14 3DW Tel: (01268) 247380 Fax: (01268) 271979 E-mail: sales@cardboardtubes.co.uk *Manufacturers of composite containers & cardboard tubes.*

▶ Cardehar Rubber Stamps, PO Box 159, Consett, County Durham, DH8 7WT Tel: (01207) 508003 Fax: (01207) 508826 E-mail: seals@crown-stamps.co.uk *Rubber stamps manufrs*

▶ Alexander Cardew Ltd, Unit 27 Chelsea Wharf, 15 Lots Road, London, SW10 0QJ Tel: (020) 7235 3785 Fax: (020) 7352 4635 E-mail: sales@cardew.com Sales Contact: J. Perre Principal Export Areas: Worldwide *Manufacturers of corrosion prevention/protection coatings/linings, flow switches & pig (oilfield/ pipelines). Distributors or agents of pipeline equipment & pipeline supplies*

Cardex Facilities, Essex Technology & Innovation Centre, The Gables, Ongar, Essex, CM5 0GA Tel: (01277) 364455 Fax: (01277) 366330 E-mail: lillian.hill@cardex.co.uk *Plastic card printers & ID card bureau*

Cardiem Ltd, Station Road, Strines, Stockport, Cheshire, SK6 7GP Tel: (01663) 764861 Fax: (01663) 762377 E-mail: sales@cardiem.co.uk *Manufacturers of point of sales displays*

▶ Cardiff Archives, Unit 7-8 Curran Buildings, Curran Road, Cardiff, CF10 5NE Tel: (029) 2066 8915 Fax: (029) 2034 3158

Cardiff Castor Co. Ltd, The Handling Centre, Penarth Road, Cardiff, CF11 8TW Tel: (029) 2071 1171 Fax: (029) 2070 6464 E-mail: sandadirect@ukonline.co.uk *Material handling equipment distributors*

Cardiff Chamber of Commerce, Suite 1, 2nd Floor, St. Davids House, Wood Street, Cardiff, CF10 5AS Tel: (029) 2034 8280 Fax: (029) 2048 9785 E-mail: enquiries@cardiffchamber.co.uk *Business development & support*

▶ Cardiff Craftsmen Ltd, Unit S1 Cardiff Bay Business Centre, Titan Road, Cardiff, CF24 5EL Tel: (029) 2049 5312 Fax: (029) 2048 8182 E-mail: info@cardiffcraftsmen.co.uk *Marine engineering*

Cardiff Door Centre Ltd, 185 Broadway, Cardiff, CF24 1QH Tel: (029) 2025 5674 Fax: (029) 2045 5534 *Doors manufacturers & suppliers*

Cardiff International Arena, Mary Ann Street, Cardiff, CF10 2EQ Tel: (029) 2022 4488 Fax: (029) 2023 4501 E-mail: cia.sales@clearchannel.co.uk *Service industry*

Cardiff M Light & Sound, Unit 2 The Highway Man Pub, Castle View, Bridgend, Mid Glamorgan, CF31 1NJ Tel: (01656) 648170 Fax: (01656) 648412 E-mail: sales@cardiffm.co.uk *Disco equipment sales, service, hire & installation services*

Cardiff Trade Print & Design Ltd, 6 Coed Glas Road, Llanishen, Cardiff, CF14 5EN Tel: (029) 2075 0561 Fax: (029) 2076 1448 *Print brokers*

▶ Cardigan Windows Ltd, The Workshops, Castle Street, Cardigan, Dyfed, SA43 3AB Tel: (01239) 621824 Fax: (01239) 621844

Cardinal Consultants, 46 Church Lane West, Aldershot, Hampshire, GU11 3LW Tel: (01252) 333977 Fax: (01252) 310810 E-mail: info@cardinal.inuk.com *Consultancy*

Cardinal Health Ltd, Sedge Close, Headway, Great Oakley, Corby, Northamptonshire, NN18 8HS Tel: (01536) 461146 Fax: (01536) 461011 *Pharmaceutical packaging services*

Cardinal Healthcare Ltd, Frankland Road, Blagrove, Swindon, SN5 8RU Tel: (0870) 6011011 Fax: (01793) 613394 *Pharmaceutical manufrs*

Cardinal Packaging Ltd, Unit 29, Rassau Industrial Estate, Ebbw Vale, Gwent, NP23 5SD Tel: (01495) 308800 Fax: (01495) 301776 E-mail: sales@cardinal-pkg.co.uk *Cardinal Packaging Limited, are manufacturers of high quality printed paper and plastic carrier bags. We manufacture printed plastic and paper bags in many different styles and designs. We can accommodate lower quantities down to 1,000 on all bag sizes. State of the art Ink Blending and Colour Matching equipment. Special requirements including all over ink coverages or line, tight registration, tone and process work. Product range includes cosmopolitan, boutique and studio, flexi loop handle, patch and turnover handle, duffel drawstring, clip close handle, barrier tapes.*

▶ Cardinal Sports Ltd, Newbridge Industrial Estate, Newbridge, Midlothian, EH28 8PJ Tel: 0131-335 3145 Fax: 0131-333 2133 *Sales & servicing of sports equipment*

▶ Cardinale, Regus House, 400 Thames Valley Park Drive, Reading, RG6 1PT Tel: 0118-965 3444 Fax: 0118-965 3544 *Computer software developers*

▶ Cardine Windows & Doors, 10b Barleyfield, Hinckley, Leicestershire, LE10 1YE Tel: (01455) 890555 Fax: (01455) 891888 *Window frame manufrs*

Cardionetics Ltd, Centaur House, Ancells Road, Fleet, Hampshire, GU51 2UJ Tel: (01252) 761040 Fax: (01252) 761117 E-mail: sales@cardionetics.com *Cardionetics is a highly innovative software solutions company committed to the provision of intelligent systems for unmet diagnostic, monitoring and screening needs to help patients and healthcare professionals fight against cardiovascular disease more effectively.*

Cardium Solutions, Unit 4 Dominion Court, Billington Road, Burnley, Lancashire, BB11 5UB Tel: (01282) 425111 Fax: (01282) 425444 E-mail: info@cardium.co.uk *IT consultants services*

Cardmaster UK, 2 Christopher Road, Leeds, LS6 2JX Tel: 0113-244 2265 Fax: 0113-244 2265 E-mail: bouncers@inname.com *Plastic business & membership cards*

Cardno Ltd, 128a New Town Street, Luton, LU1 3ED Tel: (01582) 405080 Fax: (01582) 412054 E-mail: sales@cardno.co.uk *Protective clothing distributors*

Cardowan Creameries Ltd, 49 Holywell Street, Glasgow, G31 4BT Tel: 0141-554 1137 Fax: 0141-551 0619 *Edible oil & fat producers, refiners & merchants*

▶ Cardrona Cashmere, 50 High Street, Peebles, EH45 8SW Tel: (01721) 724323 *Retailers of knitwear*

▶ Cardtoon Creations, 7 Kiln Crescent, Bishop Middleham, Ferryhill, County Durham, DL17 9AP Tel: (07747) 746123 E-mail: sales@cardsgifts.co.uk *The Web's leading source of wholesale greeting cards -supplier to UK retail greeting card outlets- -Active market place of greeting cards for UK retail greeting card outlets at trade prices and with free samples.*

▶ Cardworks Ltd, 23-25 Great Hollands Square, Bracknell, Berkshire, RG12 8UX Tel: (01344) 450333 Fax: (01344) 483295 E-mail: info@cardworks.co.uk *Packaging design consultants*

Care Centres Ltd, 75 Rowlands Road, Worthing, West Sussex, BN11 3JN Tel: (01903) 821515 Fax: (01903) 235132 E-mail: carecentresltd@supanet.com *Disabled equipment supply & service* Also at: Hove

Care Com Ltd, Unit 24 Kenfig Industrial Estate, Margam, Port Talbot, West Glamorgan, SA13 2PE Tel: (01656) 749500 Fax: (01656) 749200 E-mail: sales@carecom.co.uk *Nurse call equipment manufrs*

Care Data Systems Ltd, Patrick House Lakeside, Lifford Lane, Birmingham, B30 3NU Tel: 0121-458 7887 Fax: 0121-451 2166 *Computer software suppliers & manufrs*

Care Group Ltd, Unit 7 Hartham Lane, Hertford, SG14 1QN Tel: (01992) 505100 Fax: (01992) 509599 E-mail: caregroup@btconnect.com *Commercial cleaning contractors*

Care Labels, 181 Green La Road, Leicester, LE5 4PD Tel: 0116-276 1511 Fax: 0116-276 1511 *Label manufrs*

▶ Care Micro Systems, Columbus House, 77-79 Columbus Ravine, Scarborough, North Yorkshire, YO12 7QU Tel: (01723) 351111 Fax: (01723) 351199 E-mail: sales@caremicro.co.uk *Computer & printer maintenance services*

Care Signs, 1 Sutton Industrial Park, Sea Road, Winchelsea Beach, Winchelsea, East Sussex, TN36 4LZ Tel: (01797) 223999 Fax: (01797) 222264 E-mail: sales@caresigns.co.uk *Signwriters & sign manufrs*

Care UK, Unit 15C, Ground Floor, Imex Business Park, Shobnall Road, Burton-On-Trent, Staffordshire, DE14 2AU Tel: (01283) 568254 Fax: (01283) 512010 *Care agency*

Care Vending Services Ltd, Unit 16 Gunnels Wood Park, Gunnels Wood Road, Stevenage, Hertfordshire, SG1 2BH Tel: (01438) 760600 Fax: (01438) 760602 E-mail: sales@carevending.co.uk *Vending machine supplies & ingredients wholesalers* Also at: Bristol, Droitwich & Risca

▶ Care4yourskin.com, 7-9 Railway Avenue, Newry, County Down, BT35 6BA Tel: (028) 3025 0707 E-mail: customer.services@care4yourskin.com *Northern Ireland based supplier of dermalogica skincare, tanning,nailcare & slimming products worldwide, we operate from 2 Salons in Newry & Lisburn where we offer skin consultations, nailcare clinic & indoor tanning*

Careclean Dry Cleaners, 117 Snakes Lane, Woodford Green, Essex, IG8 0DY Tel: (020) 8504 6955 *Curtain cleaning services*

Carecross Wood Craftsmen, Higher Lake Farm, Woodland, Ashburton, Newton Abbot, Devon, TQ13 7JR Tel: (01364) 652638 Fax: (01364) 652638 E-mail: sales@quizecall.com *Commercial vehicle manufrs*

The Career Centre Ltd, 3 The Courtyard, New North Road, Exeter, EX4 4EP Tel: 01392 277882 E-mail: thecareercentre1@star.co.uk *Parent company of a group providing registration services to UK based individuals seeking employment, consultancy, interim manager or non executive director roles and appointments.*

▶ Career Energy, 4 Staple Inn, London, WC1V 7QH Tel: (020) 7831 2015 E-mail: info@careerenergy.co.uk *Career Consultancy helping you make the career choices that will affect your life. Identify your ideal career path, excel in the job market and win jobs!*

▶ Career Finder, Church Drive, Hucknall, Nottingham, NG15 7BX Tel: 0115-840 1105 E-mail: support@look4jobs.net *recruitmeny website.*

Career Soft Ltd, Mulcture House, 3 Mulcture Hall Road, Halifax, West Yorkshire, HX1 1SP Tel: (01422) 330450 Fax: (01422) 348024 E-mail: info@careersoft.co.uk *Computer software & guidance*

Career Vision Ltd, Unit 3-4 Brickfield Business Centre, 60 Manchester Road, Northwich, Cheshire, CW9 7LS Tel: (0870) 0116713 Fax: (01606) 836977 E-mail: hq@careervision.co.uk *Computer systems & software developers*

Careers In Design Recruitment Ltd, 28 New Road, Ware, Hertfordshire, SG12 7BU Tel: (01920) 486125 Fax: (01920) 412599 E-mail: recruit@careersindesign.com *Our expertise & market knowledge of interior product design*

Carefields Ltd, 5 Atherton Way, Brigg, South Humberside, DN20 8AR Tel: (01652) 653584 Fax: (01652) 650417 E-mail: carefields@carefields.ltd.uk *Contract packers*

▶ Careflex Ltd, 1-2 Anchor Buildings 5 Battle Road, Heathfield Industrial Estate, Newton Abbot, Devon, TQ12 6RY Tel: (01626) 836440 Fax: (01626) 836441 E-mail: sales@careflex.co.uk

▶ Carefree Bathing Ltd, 30 Church Street, Wellington, Telford, Shropshire, TF1 1DS Tel: (01952) 402468 Fax: (01952) 406355 E-mail: sales@carefreebathing.co.uk *Latest design in walk in baths, showers built to match your needs*

▶ Careful Co., Burnfield House, 4 Burnfield Avenue, Thornliebank, Glasgow, G46 7TL Tel: 0141-637 1010 Fax: 0141-637 1010

Carel Components, 24 Endeavour Way, London, SW19 8UH Tel: (020) 8946 9882 Fax: (020) 8946 6259 E-mail: ccs@carel.co.uk *Industrial & scientific components*

Caresafe Electrics, 15 Shorton Road, Paignton, Devon, TQ3 2NB Tel: (01803) 521003 Fax: (01803) 521003 *Electrical contractors*

Caress Precision Products Ltd, Alington Road, Little Barford, St. Neots, Cambridgeshire, PE19 6YH Tel: (01480) 472262 Fax: (01480) 217235 E-mail: caressprescision@btconnect.com *Precision alloy castings manufrs*

Caressa Kahn, Wellfield Road, Hatfield, Hertfordshire, AL10 0BS Tel: (01707) 262287 Fax: (01707) 263297 E-mail: mail@i-kahn.co.uk *Cosmetic application accessories*

▶ Caretaker Cleaning & Electrical Supplies, 12 Whingate, Leeds, LS12 3BL Tel: 0113-263 0055 Fax: 0113-263 3770 E-mail: caretaker@htmirage.co.uk *Janitorial cleaning & electrical supplies*

Caretech Systems Ltd, 114 Cateran Way, Cramlington, Northumberland, NE23 6HG Tel: (01670) 739987 Fax: (0845) 2827347 E-mail: sales@caretechsystems.co.uk *Burglar alarms suppliers & installers*

Carew, Shutterton Bridge, Exeter Road, Dawlish, Devon, EX7 0LX Tel: (01626) 864856 Fax: (01626) 867168 *Granite product supplier & manufrs*

Carew Patio Products, Unit 1 Carew Airfield, Sageston, Tenby, Dyfed, SA70 8SQ Tel: (01646) 651116 Fax: (01646) 650100 *Concrete products manufrs*

▶ Carewright Ltd, Vivary Buildings, Spring Lane, Colne, Lancashire, BB8 9BD Tel: (01282) 869802 Fax: (01282) 865449 E-mail: info@carewright.co.uk *Manufacture of Specialised Pressure Care Chairs, Recliners and Beds. The Airelite Seating System.*

▶ Carey B Restoration, Units 2-3, 63A Westcote Road, London, SW16 6BN Tel: (020) 8696 7555 E-mail: info@antiquerestoration.co.uk *French & lacquer polishing & furniture restoration*

Carey Camelot Chauffeur Drive Ltd, Headfort Place Garage, 11-15 Headfort Place, London, SW1X 7DE Tel: (020) 7201 1706 Fax: (020) 7823 1278 E-mail: res@careyuk.com *Chauffeur driven car hire*

▶ Carey Construction Ltd, 20B Royal Chase, Tunbridge Wells, Kent, TN4 8AY Tel: (01892) 522069 E-mail: careybuild@aol.com *Brickwork & groundwork, drainage, landscaping*

Careybrook Ltd, PO Box 205, Southam, Warwickshire, CV47 0ZL Tel: (01926) 813619 Fax: (01926) 814898 E-mail: cb.ltd@btinternet.com *Management consultants*

▶ Carfabrics, 40a Algernon Road, London, NW4 3TA Tel: (020) 8202 3748 Fax: (020) 8202 3748 E-mail: enquiries@carfabrics.com *Wholesale of seconds and end of lines automotive upholstery fabrics. Original automotive upholstery fabrics for car interior reconditioning.*

Carfax Bearings Ltd, 30-34 Birmingham New Road, Wolverhampton, WV4 6RY Tel: (01902) 338111 Fax: (01902) 341334 E-mail: sale@mainlinebearings.com *Ball bearing stockists*

Carfax Cards Ltd, 76 Glentham Road, London, SW13 9JJ Tel: (020) 8748 1122 Fax: (020) 8748 7110 E-mail: carfax@business-cards.co.uk *Card printing specialists*

Carfax Gowns Ltd, 1st Floor, 15 Poland Street, London, W1F 8QE Tel: (020) 7287 3300 Fax: (020) 7287 6542 *Childrens' wear manufrs* Also at: Liverpool

Carford Group Ltd, Units 1-4, Mitchell Road, Ferndown Industrial Estate, Wimborne, Dorset, BH21 7SG Tel: (01202) 851900 Fax: (01202) 851921 E-mail: sales@carford.co.uk *Sheet metal fabricators*

Carford Transmissions Ltd, 68 Rea Street South, Birmingham, B5 6LB Tel: 0121-622 7060 Fax: 0121-622 4060E-mail: admin@carford.com *Gear manufrs*

Cargill P.L.C., Cargill, Guiness Road, Trafford Park, Manchester, M17 1PA Tel: 0161-872 5959 Fax: 0161-848 9034 E-mail: graham_fletcher@cargill.com Principal Export Areas: Worldwide *Glucose refiners & starch suppliers*

Cargill Cotton, 12 Princes Parade, Liverpool, L3 1BG Tel: 0151-242 7500 Fax: (01932) 576256 E-mail: cotton_uk@cargill.com *Cotton merchants, agents & brokers services*

Cargill Finance Ltd, Knowle Hill Park, Fairmile Lane, Cobham, Surrey, KT11 2PD Tel: (01932) 861000 Fax: (01932) 861200 *Commodity traders*

Cargill Flavor Systems UK Ltd, Old Trafford Essence Distillery, 416 Chester Road, Manchester, M16 9HJ Tel: 0161-872 0225 Fax: 0161-848 7331 E-mail: sales_enquiries@cargi.com *Food flavour manufrs*

Cargo Forwarding, Transit 1, West Bank Way, Belfast, BT3 9LB Tel: (028) 9037 3700 Fax: (028) 9037 3736 E-mail: sales@cargo-forwarding.co.uk *Shipping & forwarding agents*

▶ Cargo Insurance Services, Room 111, Building 308, World Freight Terminal, Manchester Airport, Manchester, M90 5PZ Tel: 0161-498 4908 Fax: 0161-498 6222 E-mail: groche@cargoInsuranceservices.co.uk *Cargo Insurance Specialists whether Air, Sea or Land. Shipper or freight forwarder enquiries welcome*

▶ Cargo Labels Ltd, 12 Culford Walk, Felixstowe, Suffolk, IP11 2YF Tel: (01394) 273357 Fax: (01394) 276828 E-mail: sales@cargolabels.com *Safety signs & equipment*

▶ Cargo Overseas Ltd, Room 110 Building 308, World Freight Terminal, Manchester Airport, Manchester, M90 5PZ Tel: 0161-498 6111 Fax: 0161-498 6222 E-mail: groche@cargo-overseas.co.uk *Freight forwarders, Import and Export specialists*

Cargo Packing Services Ltd, Portland Works, Hill Street, Ashton-under-Lyne, Lancashire, OL7 0PZ Tel: 0161-343 4737 Fax: 0161-343 4738 *Export packing case manufrs*

Cargo Packing Services Ltd, Portland Works, Hill Street, Ashton-under-Lyne, Lancashire, OL7 0PZ Tel: 0161-343 4737 Fax: 0161-343 4738 E-mail: contact@cargopack.co.uk *Export packing services*

Cargo Pallets Ltd, West Lane, Grangetown, Middlesbrough, Cleveland, TS6 7AA Tel: (01642) 468878 Fax: (01642) 461868 E-mail: cargopallets@btconnect.com *Pallet manufrs*

▶ Cargostrap, South Mills, Jubilee Road, Newtownards, County Down, BT23 4YH Tel: (028) 9181 8853 Fax: (028) 9182 0009 E-mail: cargostrap@utvinternet.com *Manufacturers of polyester strap*

Cariad, 105 Bancroft, Hitchin, Hertfordshire, SG5 1NB Tel: (01462) 421200 Fax: (01462) 421210 E-mail: shop@cariad.co.uk *Aromatherapy manufrs*

▶ Caribee Garden Furniture, Chartwell Court, Fort Fareham, Fareham, Hampshire, PO14 1AH Tel: (01329) 825205 Fax: (01329) 825207

▶ Caricature/Cartoon Portrait Wedding Invitations, 5 Hillview Cottages (Off Plough Hill), Basted, Borough Green, Sevenoaks, Kent, TN15 8PS Tel: (01732) 883555 E-mail: weddings@christmanncreative.co.uk *Caricature/cartoon portrait handmade Wedding invitations service.*The artwork is created from your photos which gives you an invitation totally unique to you.*Highly finished digitally rendered quality. Our caricature/cartoon portrait invitations are printed on matte heavyweight double sided card to the*specifications of A5 folded to make A6 cards. *Contemporary and Cute designs also available. All designs come with envelopes included and optional reply cards.*** ***

Carill Aviation Ltd, Southampton International Airport, Southampton, SO18 2NL Tel: (023) 8062 7225 E-mail: enquiries@carillavation.co.uk *Aircraft operation services*

Carillion plc, Green Park Road, Bath, BA1 1XH Tel: (01225) 428441 Fax: (01225) 422577 *Building contractors* Also at: Bournemouth, Bristol, Cardiff, Cheltenham, Llanelli, Swindon & Trowbridge

Carillion, 37 Stirling Road, Kilsyth, Glasgow, G65 0HW Tel: (01236) 823333 Fax: (01236) 825926 E-mail: solutions.scotland@mowlems.com *Building contractors*

Carillion, Webb Road, Skippers Lane Industrial Estate, Middlesbrough, Cleveland, TS6 6HD Tel: (01642) 459000 Fax: (01642) 454111 *Pipework erection & installation contractors*

Carillion P.L.C., 24 Birch Street, Wolverhampton, WV1 4HY Tel: (01902) 422431 Fax: (01902) 316165 E-mail: n.simms@carillionplc.com *Civil engineers & building contractors* Also at: Branches throughout the U.K.

Carillion Building, 3 Abbots Key, Monks Ferry, Wirral, Merseyside, CH41 5LH Tel: 0151-666 5700 Fax: 0151-666 5777 *Building contractors*

▶ Carillion Construction, Hamilton House, Phoenix CR, Strathclyde Business Park, Bellshill, Lanarkshire, ML4 3NJ Tel: (01698) 738930 Fax: (01698) 738931

Carillion Mowlems, Foundation House, Eastern Road, Bracknell, Berkshire, RG12 2UZ Tel: (01344) 720001 *Sewage treatment plant & equipment & water treatment plant contractors or designers. Also tunnelling contractors*

Carillion Regional Civil Engineering, Port Causeway, Bromborough, Wirral, Merseyside, CH62 3PS Tel: 0151-482 3502 Fax: 0151-482 3584 E-mail: martin.c.smith@carillionplc.com *Multi disciplinary projects for the treatment of water*

Carillion Industrial Services, 7 Marlborough Road, Colmworth Business Park, Eaton Socon, St. Neots, Cambridgeshire, PE19 8YP Tel: (01480) 225850 Fax: (01480) 225860 E-mail: sales@cis-tools.co.uk *Precision tooling manufrs*

▶ Caring Industries Ltd, Unit 7, Kenfig Industrial Estate, Margam, Port Talbot, West Glamorgan, SA13 2PE Tel: (01656) 749085

▶ Caring Touch Ltd, Unit 16 Grays Farm Production Village, Grays Farm Road, Orpington, Kent, BR5 3BD Tel: (020) 8300 0770 Fax: (020) 8300 0770 E-mail: sales@caringtouch.co.uk *Suppliers of childrens educational and safe play products including safety flooring.*

Carino Communications, 143 Boundary Road, Wooburn Green, High Wycombe, Buckinghamshire, HP10 0DL Tel: (01628) 526005 Fax: (01628) 851205 E-mail: andy@carino.co.uk *For business-to-business Web design, development and maintenance, Carino Communications delivers exceptional service and professional standards. Our team of graphic designers, programmers, content creators and editors has worked with technology leaders like Fujitsu, Murata, Quin Systems and Parthenon Computing since 1996. Click the links to find out more...*

Caritas Music Publishing, Achmore, Moss Road, Ullapool, Ross-Shire, IV26 2TF Tel: (01854) 612 236 Fax: (01854) 612 236 E-mail: caritas@caritas-music.co.uk *Music publishers*

Carkeek Engineers, 15 Valley Road, Plympton, Plymouth, PL7 1RS Tel: (01752) 517460 Fax: (01752) 347470 *Mechanical engineers*

Carl Bro Group, Grove House, Mansion Gate Drive, Leeds, LS7 4DN Tel: 0113-262 0000 Fax: 0113-262 0737 E-mail: enquiries@carlbro.com *Consulting engineers*

Carl Communications Ltd, 84 Beal Lane, Shaw, Oldham, OL2 8PH Tel: (01706) 292700 Fax: (01706) 880800 E-mail: sales@carlcomms.co.uk *Computer software services*

▶ Carl J Brogan, Martindale, Cannock, Staffordshire, WS11 7XN Tel: (01543) 505001 Fax: (01543) 579406

Carl Stuart, 20 Station Street, Leek, Staffordshire, ST13 8BP Tel: (0845) 2304030 Fax: (0845) 2305030 E-mail: sales@carlstuart.com *Distributor, sales & services*

▶ Carlac Ltd, Green La Industrial Estate, Pelaw, Gateshead, Tyne & Wear, NE10 0UW Tel: 0191-438 0333 Fax: 0191-438 3320 *Supplies dry goods & car body shops*

Carleton Optical Equipment Ltd, Pattisson House, Addison Road, Chesham, Buckinghamshire, HP5 2BD Tel: (01494) 775811 Fax: (01494) 774371 E-mail: carleton@carletonltd.com *Ophthalmic instruments distributors*

Carlex Ltd, Unit 19 Rivington Court, Hardwick Grange, Woolston, Warrington, WA1 4RT Tel: (01925) 811073 Fax: (01925) 817235 E-mail: sales@carlex.co.uk *Electrical & engineering distributor*

Carley & Webb, 52 The Thoroughfare, Woodbridge, Suffolk, IP12 1AL Tel: (01394) 385650 Fax: (01394) 388984 *Deli & natural food merchants*

▶ Carlier Asphalt, Factory Lane, Croydon, CR0 3RL Tel: (020) 8688 4351

Carlight Caravans Ltd, Unit 5-7 Tamson Way, Church Lane, Sleaford, Lincolnshire, NG34 7DE Tel: (01529) 302120 Fax: (01529) 302240 E-mail: mail@carlight.co.uk *Caravan & special vehicle builders*

▶ Carlinden Marquees, 12 Wordsworth Close, Bishops Waltham, Southampton, SO32 1RT Tel: (01489) 893151 Fax: (01489) 893151 E-mail: info@hampshire-marquees.co.uk *Marquee hire*

Carling Hydraulics (Mfg) Ltd, Hawkins Drive, Cannock, Staffordshire, WS11 0XT Tel: (01922) 701600 Fax: (01922) 701606 E-mail: sales@carlinghydraulics.com *Hydraulic equipment manufrs*

Carlingwood Ltd, 1 Bridge Green, Prestbury, Macclesfield, Cheshire, SK10 4HR Tel: (01625) 828342 Fax: (01625) 827471 *Heating element distributors*

Carlisle Engineering Ltd, Edgeworth House, 20 High Street, Northchurch, Berkhamsted, Hertfordshire, HP4 3LS Tel: (01442) 874534 Fax: (01442) 878525 E-mail: info@accessequipment.net Principal Export Areas: Middle East & West Europe *Access equipment manufrs*

Carlisle Facility Ltd, Block C, Albany Place, Hyde Way, Welwyn Garden City, Hertfordshire, AL7 3BG Tel: (01707) 824200 E-mail: mail@carlislefacility.com *Security services*

Carlisle Refrigeration Thermoking Ltd, Brunthill Road, Kingstown Industrial Estate, Carlisle, CA3 0EH Tel: (01228) 531449 Fax: (01228) 511514 E-mail: info@carlislerefrigeration.co.uk *Commercial & transport refrigeration service & repairers.*

Carlisle Staffing plc, 3 Albany Place, Hyde Way, Welwyn Garden City, Hertfordshire, AL7 3BG Tel: (01707) 323000 Fax: (01707) 393398 *Employment agency*

Carlisle Staffing plc, 3 Albany Place, Hyde Way, Welwyn Garden City, Hertfordshire, AL7 3BG Tel: (01707) 323000 Fax: (020) 8498 8851 *Security guard services*

Carlo Services, 71 Childwall Park Avenue, Liverpool, L16 0JE Tel: 0151-737 1030 Fax: 0151-737 2040 .

Carlon Plastics Leicester Ltd, 128 Fairfax Road, Leicester, LE4 9EL Tel: 0116-276 9562 Fax: 0116-276 1267 E-mail: chris@carlonplastics.co.uk *Plastics fabricators*

Carl's Castles, 51 Clydesmuir Road, Tremorfa, Cardiff, CF24 2PX Tel: (029) 2033 1309 Fax: (029) 2033 1309 E-mail: carl@dvsmail.co.uk *Bouncy castle hire*

Carlsbro Electronics Ltd, Cross Drive, Kirkby-in-Ashfield, Nottingham, NG17 7LD Tel: 08452 582910 Fax: 01623 755436 E-mail: sales@carlsbro.co.uk *PA & amplification systems manufacturers & distributors*

Carlson Companies (U K) Ltd, Performance Improvement Belgrave House, 1 Greyfriars, Northampton, NN1 2LQ Tel: (01604) 234300 Fax: (01604) 230219 E-mail: sales@carlson-europe.com *Marketing services*

Carlson Filtration Ltd, The Buttmill, Barnoldswick, Lancashire, BB18 5HP Tel: (01282) 811000 Fax: (01282) 811001 E-mail: sales@carlson.co.uk *Filter manufrs*

▶ Carlson Vehicle Transfer, Bradfield Road, Wix, Manningtree, Essex, CO11 2SP Tel: (01255) 871600 Fax: (01255) 871606

Carlton Automotive Refinishing Supplies, Mirravale Trading Estate, Selinas Lane, Dagenham, Essex, RM8 1YY Tel: (020) 8592 6300 Fax: (020) 8595 9550 E-mail: c-a-r-s@supanet.com *Car paint suppliers*

Carlton Books Ltd, 20 Mortimer Street, London, W1T 3JW Tel: (020) 7612 0400 Fax: (020) 7612 0401 E-mail: enquiries@carltonbooks.co.uk *Book publishers*

Carlton Building Plastics Ltd, 6 Beddington Trading Estate, Bath House Road, Croydon, CR0 4TT Tel: (020) 8665 1221 Fax: (020) 8665 1444 *UPVC building product suppliers*

Carlton Cards Ltd, Mill St East, Dewsbury, West Yorkshire, WF12 9AW Tel: (01924) 465200 Fax: (01924) 453908 *Greeting card manufrs*

▶ Carlton Construction Ltd, 12 Oak Hill, Epsom, Surrey, KT18 7BT Tel: (01372) 749760 Fax: (01372) 745339

Carlton Controls Ltd, 3c Lea Road, Waltham Abbey, Essex, EN9 1AE Tel: (01992) 767609 Fax: (01992) 788446 E-mail: mail@carlton-controls.co.uk *Electrical control panel builders*

Carlton Corporate Finance Ltd, 38 Berkeley Square, London, W1J 5AE Tel: (020) 7355 2211 Fax: (020) 7355 1633 E-mail: ccf@carltoncf.com *Finance short advisory*

Carlton Downs Holdings Ltd, Hulley Road, Hurdsfield, Macclesfield, Cheshire, SK10 2LZ Tel: (01625) 616570 Fax: (01625) 427427 E-mail: enquiries@carltondowns.co.uk *Manufacturers and suppliers of garage servicing equipment, gas bottle & security cages and material handling and storage equipment.*

Carlton Engineering Products Ltd, Unit 1 Airborne Industrial, Estate Arterial Road, Leigh-on-Sea, Essex, SS9 4EX Tel: (01702) 420300 Fax: (01702) 529542 E-mail: sales@cep.uk.com *Fine limit sheet metal & fabrication in all materials*

Carlton House International Ltd, 19 Ayleswater, Aylesbury, Buckinghamshire, HP19 0FD Tel: (01296) 399507 Fax: (01296) 399507 *Furniture suppliers*

Carlton Hydraulics Ltd, Chesterton Road, Eastwood Trading Estate, Rotherham, South Yorkshire, S65 1SU Tel: (01709) 378999 Fax: (01709) 820292 E-mail: sales@carlton-hydraulics.co.uk *Hydraulic hose assembly manufrs*

Carlton Industries Ltd, Units 1-4, Progress Business Park, Progress Way, Croydon, CR0 4XD Tel: (020) 8686 9898 Fax: (020) 8686 9848 *Door & window furniture*

Carlton Lifts Ltd, 8 Bessemer Close, Ebblake Industrial Estate, Verwood, Dorset, BH31 6AZ Tel: (01202) 894025 Fax: (01202) 870982 E-mail: chris.stott@carltonlifts.co.uk *Sales & installation of lifts*

Carlton Main Brickworks Ltd, Grimethorpe, Barnsley, South Yorkshire, S72 7BG Tel: (01226) 711521 Fax: (01226) 780417 E-mail: office.admin@carltonbrick.co.uk *Brick manufrs*

Carlton Press Group N W Ltd, 3-7 Britannia Road, Sale, Cheshire, M33 2AA Tel: 0161-962 8686 Fax: 0161-969 6300 E-mail: sales@carltonpressgroup.com *Colour printers*

▶ Carlton Screens Ltd, 1 Real Workshops, Westfield Road, Parkgate, Rotherham, South Yorkshire, S62 6EY Tel: (01709) 525414 Fax: (01709) 710158

Carlton Sheet Metal Works Ltd, 16-18 Ashley Street, Nottingham, NG3 1JG Tel: 0115-950 5304 Fax: 0115-950 4976 E-mail: info@bagfast.com *Sheet metalwork engineers*

▶ Carlton Shopfitting Ltd, Carlton House, Carlton Road, Dewsbury, West Yorkshire, WF13 2AT Tel: (01924) 454612 Fax: (01924) 460042 *Joinery services*

Carlton Smith Projects Ltd, Station Approach, Station Road, Pershore, Worcestershire, WR10 2DB Tel: (01386) 555770 Fax: (01386) 556432 E-mail: info@carlton-smith.co.uk *Joinery manufrs*

Carlyle Metal Goods Ltd, Carlyle Business Park, Great Bridge Street, Swan Village, West Bromwich, West Midlands, B70 0XA Tel: 0121-525 6614 Fax: 0121-525 6770 E-mail: markcashmore@carlyleplc.co.uk *Aluminium stockholders & fabricators*

Carmac, Burton Road, Finedon, Wellingborough, Northamptonshire, NN9 5HX Tel: (01933) 682345 Fax: (01933) 682555 E-mail: admin@carmac.co.uk *Civil engineers*

Carman (Air Conditioning) Ltd, Winters Cottage, Magdalen Laver, Ongar, Essex, CM5 0EW Tel: (01279) 412314 *Air conditioning contractors*

Carmarthen & Pumpsaint Farmers Ltd, Myrtle Hill, Pensarn, Carmarthen, Dyfed, SA31 2NG Tel: (01267) 236794 Fax: (01267) 230721 *Agricultural merchants* Also at: Branches throughout Wales

Carmarthen & Pumpsaint Farmers Ltd, Station Yard, Station Road, Llangadog, Dyfed, SA19 9LS Tel: (01550) 777281 Fax: (01550) 777955 *Agricultural merchants*

Carmarthenshire C C S C H, Pwllmarl Farm, Velindre, Llandysul, Dyfed, SA44 5YN Tel: (01559) 371629 Fax: (01559) 371188 *Interior blind manufrs*

Carmel, 287 Haggerston Road, London, E8 4EN Tel: (020) 7275 7037 Fax: (020) 7275 7038 *Women's clothing manufrs*

Carmen Plumbing & Heating, 20 The Borough, Aldreth, ELY, Cambs, CB6 3PJ Tel: 01223 655367 Fax: 01223 280298 E-mail: carmenltd@msn.com *Gas, Oil, LPG and Solar powered domestic & commercial heating & plumbing installers*

Carmichael Engineering Ltd, 62 Burkitt Road, Earlstrees Industrial Estate, Corby, Northamptonshire, NN17 4DT Tel: (01536) 261431 Fax: (01536) 201477 E-mail: mail@carmichael-eng.co.uk *Packaging machinery engineers*

Carmo Ltd, 11-19 Bancrofts Road, Eastern Industrial Area, South Woodham Ferrers, Chelmsford, CM3 5UG Tel: (01245) 322130 Fax: (01245) 328695E-mail: brian@carmo.co.uk *Plastic products suppliers*

Carn Fasteners Ltd, 29 Garvagh Road, Swatragh, Maghera, County Londonderry, BT46 5QE Tel: (028) 7940 1248 Fax: (028) 7940 1533 E-mail: info@carnfasteners.com *Wood screw manufrs*

Carn Plastics, Victoria Street, Lurgan, Craigavon, County Armagh, BT67 9DH Tel: (028) 3832 4721 Fax: (028) 3832 4523 E-mail: info@carnplastics.co.uk *Fibreglass moulders*

Carnaby Holdings Ltd, Carnaby Industrial Estate, Lancaster Road, Carnaby, Bridlington, North Humberside, YO15 3QY Tel: (01262) 679971 Fax: (01262) 670315 E-mail: info@carnabycaravans.com *Caravan manufrs*

Carnation Engineering Co, 19 Highmeres Road, Leicester, LE4 9LZ Tel: 0116-276 0124 Fax: 0116-276 0124 *Precision automatic repetition work*

Carnaud Metal Box Engineering, Dockfield Road, Shipley, West Yorkshire, BD17 7AY Tel: (01274) 846200 Fax: (01274) 846201 E-mail: william.jowitt@eur.crowncorrk.com *Can production machinery manufrs* Also at: Alperton, Shipley & Worcester

Carnaud Metalbox P.L.C., Perry Wood Walk, Worcester, WR5 1EG Tel: (01905) 762000 Fax: (01905) 762357 *Food can manufrs*

Carnaud Metalbox Closures Europe UK, Lake Road, Hamworthy, Poole, Dorset, BH15 4LJ Tel: (01202) 774200 Fax: (01202) 774390 *Jar caps & metal closures manufrs*

Carnaudmetalbox, Golf Course Lane, Leicester, LE3 1TX Tel: 0116-291 3300 Fax: 0116-291 3312 *Can manufrs*

D.M. Carnegie Precast, Steelstrath, Laurencekirk, Kincardineshire, AB30 1RN Tel: (01674) 840288 Fax: (01674) 840395 *Agricultural contractors*

▶ Carnell Contruction, Carlbury Crossing Cottage, Durham Lane, Piercebridge, Darlington, County Durham, DL2 3TW Tel: (01325) 374575 Fax: (01325) 374578

▶ Carnell L & J, Delamare Road, Cheshunt, Waltham Cross, Hertfordshire, EN8 9SH Tel: (01992) 642261 E-mail: enquiries@ljcarnell.co.uk *Polypropylene binders screen printing services*

▶ Carney Print Ltd, 141 New Bedford Road, Luton, LU3 1LF Tel: (01582) 737082 Fax: (01582) 402608

Carnhill Transformers Ltd, 68 Sandford Lane, Kennington, Oxford, OX1 5RW Tel: (01865) 327843 Fax: (01865) 736538 E-mail: sales@carnhill.co.uk *Transformer designers & manufrs*

Carnhill Transformers Ltd, 4 Edison Road, St. Ives, Cambridgeshire, PE27 3LT Tel: (01480) 462978 Fax: (01480) 496196 E-mail: sales@carnhill.co.uk *Transformers manufrs*

▶ Carnmeal Cottage Flowers, Carnmeal Cottage, Carnmeal, Breage, Helston, Cornwall, TR13 9NL Tel: (01326) 572901 Fax: (01326) 565698 E-mail: sales@carnmeal.com *Suppliers of a large range of bridal & wedding accessories*

▶ Carnochan Brown, 19 Taylor Close, London, N17 0UB Tel: 07770 254470 Fax: 01992 850749 E-mail: will@carnochanbrown.co.uk *Property Management & Consultancy Services. Surveying & Project Management.*

▶ Carntyne Transport Co. Ltd, 440 Petershill Road, Glasgow, G21 4AA Tel: 0141-557 1199 Fax: 0141-557 2272

Carnwood Engineering Ltd, Penn Industrial Estate, Providence Street, Cradley Heath, West Midlands, B64 5DJ Tel: (01384) 569787 Fax: (01384) 633508 E-mail: sales@carnwoodeng.co.uk *Fabricators & general machinists*

Carol Cable Ltd, 61 Stewarts Road, Finedon Road Industrial Estate, Wellingborough, Northamptonshire, NN8 4RJ Tel: (01933) 277700 Fax: (01933) 273696 *Ignition lead manufrs*

▶ Carola.Co.Uk :Web Development & Consultancy, 45 Queens Drive, London, N4 2SZ Tel: (020) 8802 5570 E-mail: caterina@carola.co.uk *Web design, development & consultancy*

The Carole Group Ltd, Oaklands Business Centre, Oaklands Park, Wokingham, Berkshire, RG41 2FD Tel: 0118-977 1424 Fax: 0118-977 2479 E-mail: sales@carolegroup.com *Sourcing & distribution of promotional gifts*

Carolina Blind Co., 24 Leigh Drive, Elsenham, Bishop's Stortford, Hertfordshire, CM22 6BY Tel: (01279) 816580 Fax: (01279) 817132 E-mail: carolina@elsex.demon.co.uk *Awning & blind manufrs*

▶ Carolina Lighting, 1 Wandle Trading Estate, Goat Road, Mitcham, Surrey, CR4 4HW Tel: (020) 8648 6800 Fax: (020) 8648 6822 E-mail: info@carolina-lighting.co.uk *Lamp shades manufacturers in dupion, silk, suede & damask fabrics*

The Caroline Blind Co., 151 Cocklaw Street, Kelty, Fife, KY4 0DH Tel: (01383) 831609 Fax: (01383) 831609 *Window blind retailers*

Caroline Construction Ltd, PO Box 267, Sittingbourne, Kent, ME10 4HX Tel: (01795) 470722 Fax: (01795) 470121 *Suspended ceilings*

▶ Caroline Hughes, 19, Carlyle Grove, Springbank, Cheltenham, Glos, GL51 0PW Tel: 01242 575670 E-mail: caroline@aromatherapy-makes-scents.co.uk *A small family business run by a qualified Aromatherapist. With information on all aspaects of Aromatherapy together with an online shop.*

Caromal Lesiure, The Willows, Foundry Lane, Copford, Colchester, CO6 1BH Tel: (01206) 210741 Fax: (01206) 212173 *Swimming pool designers*

Carona Reuter Industrial Ltd, Coppen Road, Selinas Lane, Dagenham, Essex, RM8 1HN Tel: (020) 8592 2576 Fax: (020) 8595 8024 E-mail: carona_reuter@hotmail.com *General fastener distributors*

▶ Carousel, Unit 17-18 The Metropolitan Centre, Derby Road, Greenford, Middlesex, UB6 8UJ Tel: (020) 8575 9090 Fax: (020) 8575 3900

▶ Carousel, Gateway Centre Eurolink Industrial Centre, Castle Road, Sittingbourne, Kent, ME10 3RN Tel: (01795) 413600 Fax: (01795) 413610 E-mail: sales@carousellogistics.co.uk *Air Courier, Airfreight, Seafreight,Road Transport/ haulage/freight services, logistics management services & storage/distribution (product) combined services.*

Carousel Bridal Veils Ltd, 174-176 Carlton Road, Nottingham, NG3 2BB Tel: 0115-947 6205 E-mail: info@carouselveils.com *Embroidery & bridal accessory manufrs*

▶ Carousel Coin Machines, Beansheaf Farm, Malton Road, Kirby Misperton, Malton, North Yorkshire, YO17 6UE Tel: (01653) 668547 Fax: (01653) 668434 E-mail: sales@carousel-snooker.co.uk *Suppliers of pool & snooker tables, pool & snooker dining tables*

Carousel Copiers, 148 Westborough Road, Westcliff-on-Sea, Essex, SS0 9JF Tel: (01702) 300886 Fax: (01702) 321083 *Photocopiers*

▶ Carousel Entertainments, 18 Westbury Lodge Close, Pinner, Middlesex, HA5 3FG Tel: (0870) 7518688 Fax: (0870) 7518668 E-mail: sales@carouselentertainments.co.uk *Suppliers of quality entertainment for corporate and private events. Roadshows, DJ's, magicians, function bands, entertainers, jazz, themed parties and so much more.*

Carousel & Intersun, Nant Hall Road, Prestatyn, Clwyd, LL19 9LR Tel: (01745) 886677 Fax: (01745) 857399 *Blind manufrs*

Caroway Fabrications Ltd, 40 Aston Road, Waterlooville, Hampshire, PO7 7XF Tel: (023) 9226 7614 Fax: (023) 9226 2290 *Steel fabricators & welders*

Carparts, Hyberry, Ashlands Meadow, Crewkerne, Somerset, TA18 7NN Tel: (01460) 74600 *Vehicle repairers*

▶ Carparts, 3 Sentry Lane, Newtownabbey, County Antrim, BT36 4XU Tel: (028) 9084 8218 Fax: (028) 9083 5490 E-mail: admin@carpartsuk-ire.com *Motor vehicle equipment wholesaler*

▶ Carpe Diem Inc, Xpidia Cinnamon House Cinnamon Park, Crab Lane, Fearnhead, Warrington, WA2 0XP Tel: (0871) 4341610 Fax: (0871) 4345370 E-mail: info@cd-inc.co.uk *New media services, web site design, e-commerce, hosting, branding*

Carpenter Certech, 92b Brunel Road, Earlstrees Industrial Estate, Corby, Northamptonshire, NN17 4JW Tel: (01536) 202282 Fax: (01536) 202261 *Investment casting ceramic cores manufrs*

Carpenter Communications Group Ltd, Old Greenfield House, Greenfield, Christmas Common, Watlington, Oxfordshire, OX49 5HF Tel: (01491) 614144 Fax: (01491) 613416 E-mail: sales@carpentercomms.co.uk *Audio visual hire & conference equipment suppliers*

Carpenter Goodwin Ltd, 31 Bridge Street, Leominster, Herefordshire, HR6 8DU Tel: (01568) 612666 Fax: (01568) 616276 E-mail: sales@carpentergoodwin.co.uk *Agricultural machinery spare parts sales*

N. Carpenter Custom Made Joinery & Furniture, Unit 7, Parklands Farm, Parklands, Shere, Guildford, Surrey, GU5 9JQ Tel: (01483) 203759 Fax: (01483) 203759 *Joiners*

Carpenter Oak Ltd, The Framing Yard, Cornworthy, Totnes, Devon, TQ9 7HF Tel: (01803) 732900 Fax: (01803) 732901 *Structural timber framers*

Carpenter Oak & Woodland Co. Ltd, Lintrathen, Kirriemuir, Angus, DD8 5JA Tel: (01575) 560393 Fax: (01575) 560295 *Carpenters*

Carpenter & Paterson Holdings Ltd, Crown Works, Henfaes Lane, Welshpool, Powys, SY21 7BE Tel: (01938) 552061 Fax: (01938) 555306 E-mail: info@cp-ltd.co.uk *Pipe clips, pipe support systems, spring hangers manufrs*

Carpenter Technology UK Ltd, 6 The I O Centre, Nash Road, Redditch, Worcestershire, B98 7AS Tel: (01527) 512200 Fax: (01527) 512201 E-mail: afoulkes@cartech.com Purchasing Contact: S. Reinert Sales Contact: P. Bugler Principal Export Areas: Africa *Stainless steel bar stockholders & manufrs*

Carpenters Ltd, Bee Mill, Shaw Road, Royton, Oldham, OL2 6EH Tel: 0161-627 0044 Fax: 0161-627 0951 E-mail: sales.uk@carpenter.com Principal Export Areas: Worldwide *Foam & fibre suppliers*

▶ Carpentry & Structures, 19 Parkside, Northampton, NN3 5EW Tel: (01604) 415198 E-mail: cassinjohn@tiscali.co.uk *Specialist in bespoke design and manufacturing, engineering *solution, natural stone fabrications, bespoke carpentry, from concept *to completion, supplying to the domestic and commercial sector.*

Carpet Accessory Trims Ltd, Unit 24c Park Avenue Estate, Sundon Park Road, Luton, LU3 3BP Tel: (01582) 561500 Fax: (01582) 561900 E-mail: sales@tat-accs.com *Carpet fitting supplies*

Carpet Cleaners London UK, 37 Muswell Avenue, London, N10 2EB Tel: (0800) 0436001 E-mail: info@carpet-cleaner.co.uk *Carpet cleaning equipment*

▶ Carpet Cleaning, 30 Kipling Close, Llanrumney, Cardiff, CF3 5JZ Tel: (029) 2021 2599 E-mail: enquiries@carpetcleaningwales.com *carpet and upholstery cleaning commercial and domestic full insured free estimates criminal records bureau checked 16 yrs experience*

Carpet Cleaning Co., 40 Scotstoun Street, Glasgow, G14 0UN Tel: 0141-958 0759 *Carpet cleaning equipment & supplier*

▶ Carpet Cleaning In Hampshire, 7 Buttermere Drive, Camberley, Surrey, GU15 1QU Tel: (01276) 66217 Fax: (01276) 66217 E-mail: muz15@hotmail.com *Carpet cleaning in Hampshire*

▶ Carpet Cleaning London UK, Colton House, Princes Avenue, London, N3 2EB Tel: (0870) 0052895 E-mail: clients@professional-carpet-cleaning-london.co.uk

▶ Carpet Clearance Corner, 41 Whitby Road, Ellesmere Port, CH65 8AB Tel: 0151-355 7733

Carpet Guard, 9-11 Hoborn Square, Birkenhead, Merseyside, CH41 9HQ Tel: 0151-649 8800 Fax: 0151-649 8800 E-mail: mail@carpetgard.co.uk *Carpet cleaning products & machine suppliers*

Carpet Industry Training Council, C/O 6 Llangorse Close, Stourport-On-Severn, Worcestershire, DY13 8LJ Tel: (01299) 824245 Fax: (01299) 824245 E-mail: jleach.citc@btconnect.com *Industrial training organisation*

▶ Carpet It, 517 Leeds Road, Huddersfield, HD2 1YJ Tel: (01484) 519840 Fax: (01484) 519835 *Carpet retailers*

Carpet Services London Ltd, 79a Russell Road, London, SW19 1QN Tel: (020) 8543 9131 Fax: (020) 8540 2911 E-mail: csll@btconnect.com *Carpet contractors*

▶ Carpet Shop, New Road, Sheerness, Kent, ME12 1BW Tel: (01795) 661060 Fax: (01795) 661060 *Carpet retailers*

▶ Carpet Style, Unit 1 Great Northern Way, Netherfield, Nottingham, NG4 2HD Tel: 0115-940 4110 Fax: 0115-940 4611 *Carpet retailers*

▶ Carpet Time, 47-49 Gaol Road, Stafford, ST16 3AR Tel: (01785) 252707 Fax: (01785) 252707 *Carpets & retail*

▶ Carpet Whipping & Fringing Services, Unit H Union Drive, Sutton Coldfield, West Midlands, B73 5TE Tel: 0121-321 3830 Fax: 0121-321 3569 *Carpet binders & fringers*

▶ Carpetright plc, Unit 2c Northwich Retail Park, Manchester Road, Northwich, Cheshire, CW9 5LY Tel: (01606) 47585 Fax: (01606) 47285 *Carpet retailers*

Carpetright plc, Amberley House, New Road, Rainham, Essex, RM13 8QN Tel: (01708) 525522 Fax: (01708) 559361 E-mail: enquiries@carpetright.co.uk *Carpet retailers*

Carpetronic Flooring Services, 15 Scotts Road, Paisley, Renfrewshire, PA2 7AN Tel: 0141-887 7733 Fax: 0141-887 1771 E-mail: carpetronic@horncroft.co.uk *Fitting of carpet & vinyl flooring*

▶ Carpets 4 Less, Carleton New Road, Skipton, North Yorkshire, BD23 2DE Tel: (01756) 795432 E-mail: sales@carpets4less.com *Carpet retailers*

▶ Carpets Direct, 1 Dominion Works, Denholme Gate Road, Hipperholme, Halifax, West Yorkshire, HX3 8JG Tel: (01422) 202220 Fax: (01422) 202220 *Carpet manufrs*

Carpigiani U.K. Ltd, Faculty House, 214 Holme Lacy Road, Hereford, HR2 6BQ Tel: (01432) 346010 Fax: (01432) 346019 *Ice cream equipment manufrs*

Carr Arthur & Henry Ltd, Lakeside, Drake Road, Tavistock, Devon, PL19 0EJ Tel: (01822) 612868 Fax: (01822) 614508 *Joinery*

Harry Carr Ltd, Armstrong Street, Grimsby, North East Lincolnshire, DN31 1LG Tel: (01472) 246600 Fax: (01472) 240466 E-mail: engineers@harrycarr.co.uk *Electrical & mechanical refrigeration engineers* Also at: Hull

Carr Of Nottingham Ltd, Ronald Street, Radford, Nottingham, NG7 3GY Tel: 0115-942 2252 Fax: 0115-942 2276 E-mail: carrofnottm@btconnect.com *Gymnastic & sporting equipment manufacturers & repairers*

Carr Reinforcements, Carr House, Brighton Road, Stockport, Cheshire, SK4 2BE Tel: 0161-443 3377 Fax: 0161-443 3388 E-mail: erictaylor@btconnect.com *Carbon fibre fabric manufrs*

Carr Sheppards Crosthwaite, 25 Imperial Square, Cheltenham, Gloucestershire, GL50 1QZ Tel: (01242) 514756 Fax: (01242) 533000 *Stockbrokers*

Carr Sheppards Crosthwaite Ltd, 2 Gresham Street, London, EC2V 7QN Tel: (020) 7597 1234 Fax: (020) 7597 1000 E-mail: clientservices@carr-sheppards.co.uk *Stockbrokers*

Carr & Westley Ltd, Bourne Mill, Carpenters Lane, Hadlow, Tonbridge, Kent, TN11 0EU Tel: (01732) 850280 Fax: (01732) 850280 *Mail order ladies' clothing manufrs*

Carrack Ltd, Badentoy Crescent, Badentoy Industrial Estate, Portlethen, Aberdeen, AB12 4YD Tel: (01224) 783100 Fax: (01224) 783400 E-mail: sandym@carrackltd.com *Carrack buy & sell new & surplus certified casing*

▶ Carrara-Tiling, 17 Lytham Close, Doncaster, South Yorkshire, DN4 6UT Tel: (01302) 370352 Fax: (01302) 370352 E-mail: carrara-tiling@tiscali.co.uk

Carratt Suspended Ceilings Ltd, 8 Whitehart Mews, Southgate, Sleaford, Lincolnshire, NG34 7RY Tel: (01529) 305704 Fax: (01529) 307263 *Suspended ceiling installers*

▶ Carrera Dancewear Ltd, 17 Sanders Lodge Industrial Estate, Wellingborough Road, Rushden, Northamptonshire, NN10 6BQ Tel: (01933) 315622 Fax: (01933) 311137 E-mail: sales@carrera.co.uk *Dance shoe manufrs*

Carrick Marketing, 13 Mossgiel Avenue, Kilmarnock, Ayrshire, KA3 7DN Tel: (01563) 524320 Fax: (01563) 524320 E-mail: jcarrick@btconnect.com Principal Export Areas: Worldwide *Audio systems manufrs*

Carrick Read Ltd, Norwich House, Savile Street, Hull, HU1 3ES Tel: (01482) 585795 Fax: (01482) 585798 E-mail: thepartners@cri-hull.co.uk *Solicitors & insolvency practitioners* Also at: Leeds

▶ Carrier Air Conditioning, 133 Barfillan Drive, Glasgow, G52 1BE Tel: 0141-810 2300 Fax: 0141-810 2313

Carrier Refrigeration, United Technologies House, Guildford Road, Fetcham, Leatherhead, Surrey, KT22 9UT Tel: (01865) 337700 Fax: (01372) 230190 *Refrigerator unit suppliers*

Carrier Service, Kettles Wood Drive, Birmingham, B32 3DB Tel: 0121-421 9610 Fax: 0121-421 8147 E-mail: tosibha.carrier@utc.com *Air conditioning equipment suppliers*

▶ Carrier Services, Europa Boulevard, Westbrook, Warrington, WA5 7TN Tel: (01925) 656464 Fax: (01925) 656404

Carrier Sutrak, Unit 6, The IO Centre, Lodge Farm Industrial Estate, Northampton, NN5 7UW Tel: (01604) 581468 Fax: (01604) 758132 *Transport air conditioning manufacturers & installers*

Carrier Transicold UK Ltd, 260 Cygnet Court, Centre Park, Warrington, WA1 1RR Tel: (01925) 401200 Fax: (01925) 401222 *Refrigerator manufrs*

Carrifreight International Ltd, 35 Knighton Rd, Romford, RM7 9BU Tel: (01708) 508603 Fax: (01708) 505981 *International freight forwarders*

Carrimor Outdoor Clothing, Red Lion Square, Grasmere, Ambleside, Cumbria, LA22 9SP Tel: (01539) 435614 Fax: (01539) 435122 *Outdoor equipment retailer*

Carrington Co. Ltd, Vulcan Way, New Addington, Croydon, CR9 0BN Tel: (01689) 842211 *Property management services*

Carrington Architectural Joiners Ltd, Unit 10 Stock Industrial Park, Stock Road, Southend-on-Sea, SS2 5QN Tel: (01702) 616894 Fax: (01702) 602894 E-mail: cajltd@supanet.com *Joiners*

Carrington Bearings & Engineering Ltd, 8 Torridge Close, Telford Way Industrial Estate, Kettering, Northamptonshire, NN16 8PY Tel: (01536) 518666 Fax: (01536) 412131 E-mail: sales@carringtonbearings.co.uk *Industrial distributor for bearing & power transmission equipment*

Carrington Binns Ltd, Lowfields Way, Lowfields Business Park, Elland, West Yorkshire, HX5 9DA Tel: (01422) 372372 Fax: (01422) 315100 E-mail: sales@carringtonwire.com Principal Export Areas: Worldwide *Wire manufrs*

Carrington Career & Workwear Ltd, Market Street, Adlington, Chorley, Lancashire, PR7 4HE Tel: (01257) 476850 Fax: (01257) 476852 E-mail: info@carrington.uk.com Principal Export Areas: Worldwide *Fabric manufrs*

Carrington House, Ancaster Square, Llanrwst, Gwynedd, LL26 0LD Tel: (01492) 642500 Fax: (01492) 642500 E-mail: richard@carringtonhouse.co.uk *Antique furniture retailers*

Carrington Novare, Calder Works, Thornhill Road, Dewsbury, West Yorkshire, WF12 9QQ Tel: (01924) 465161 Fax: (01924) 457596 E-mail: enquiries@cpf.co.uk *Textile finishing services*

▶ Carrington Wire, P O Box 56, Cardiff, CF24 2WR Tel: (029) 2025 6100 Fax: (029) 2025 6101 E-mail: sales@carringtonwiregroup.co.uk *Producer of cold leading wire for the fastener industry & pre-stressing wire & s trand for the construction industry*

Carringtons, The Streams, Eight Acre Lane, Three Oaks, Hastings, East Sussex, TN35 4NL Tel: (01424) 756111 *Fax & printing specialists*

▶ Carroll Bros, Units 51 & 52 Mackley Industrial Estate, Henfield Road, Small Dole, Henfield, West Sussex, BN5 9XR Tel: (01273) 494911 Fax: (01273) 494912 E-mail: brothers@carolmanufacturing.co.uk *Furniture manufrs*

Carroll Bros Engineers Keighley Ltd, Grafton Works, Waddington Street, Keighley, West Yorkshire, BD21 5LP Tel: (01535) 603358 Fax: (01535) 602522 E-mail: sales@acetarc.co.uk *Sub-contract engineering services*

▶ Carroll Ian Professional Building Services Ltd, East Street, Grantham, Lincolnshire, NG31 6QW Tel: (01476) 594300 Fax: (01476) 594300

J. Carroll & Sons, Unit 14, Lyon Gate Enterprise Park, Mouldon Road, Mitcham, Surrey, CR4 4NY Tel: (020) 8640 5424 Fax: (020) 8646 0990 E-mail: lee@jcarrolandsons.fsnet.co.uk *Architectural metalworkers*

M.A. Carroll Engineers Ltd, Birkby, Huddersfield, HD1 5EY Tel: (01484) 510846 Fax: (01484) 425953 E-mail: macengs@cs.com *Building design & construction services*

▶ Carroll Plant, Brookfield Drive, Liverpool, L9 7HJ Tel: 0151-525 1947 Fax: 0151-523 8322

Carroll & Son Fleet Ltd, Willow Cottage, The Hurst, Winchfield, Hook, Hampshire, RG27 8DF Tel: (01252) 843214 Fax: (01252) 845159 *Ground work contractors*

Carroll Tools Ltd, 16-18 Factory Lane, Croydon, CR0 3RL Tel: (020) 8781 1268 Fax: (020) 8781 1278 E-mail: info@carrolltools.com *Abrasive products distributors*

Carron Bathrooms Ltd, PO Box 32, Falkirk, FK2 8UW Tel: (01324) 638407 Fax: (01324) 611490 E-mail: mailroom@carronbathrooms.com *Bathroom manufrs*

Carron Phoenix, Carron Works, Carron, Falkirk, FK2 8DW Tel: (01324) 638321 Fax: (01324) 620978 E-mail: fgp-sales@carron.com *Stainless steel & plastic sink manufrs*

Carron Practicals, 8 Harley Drive, Condover, Shrewsbury, SY5 7AY Tel: (01743) 872120 Fax: (01743) 872792 *Educational software developers*

Carron Tooling, 80 Shelley Road, Bournemouth, BH7 6HB Tel: (01202) 303811 Fax: (01202) 303811 *Precision engineers*

Carronbridge Sawmill Ltd, Carronbridge, Thornhill, Dumfriesshire, DG3 5AY Tel: (01848) 331661 Fax: (01848) 331121 *Timber saw manufrs*

Carrs Billington Agriculture Ltd, 78-80 Stirling Road, Milnathort, Kinross, KY13 9UZ Tel: (01577) 862381 Fax: (01577) 863057 *Agricultural merchants*

Carrs Billington Agriculture Ltd, Highland House, St Catherines Road, Perth, PH1 5YA Tel: (01738) 643022 Fax: (01738) 643022 *Agricultural merchants*

Carrs Fertilisers, Inverbreakie Industrial Estate, Invergordon, Ross-Shire, IV18 0QR Tel: (01349) 853745 Fax: (01349) 854066 E-mail: enquiries@carrs-fertiliser.co.uk *Fertilizer*

Carrs Fertilisers Ltd, Wath, Silloth, Wigton, Cumbria, CA7 4PH Tel: (01697) 332333 Fax: (01697) 332279 *Fertilizer production*

▶ Carrs Of Sheffield Manufacturing Ltd, Troy House 2 Holbrook Avenue, Holbrook Industrial Estate, Holbrook, Sheffield, S20 3FH Tel: 0114-251 0610 Fax: 0114-251 0685

Carrs Special Steels, Wadsley Bridge, Penistone Road North, Sheffield, S6 1LL Tel: 0114-285 5866 Fax: 0114-285 5734 E-mail: info@elgcarrs.co.uk Principal Export Areas: Asia Pacific, Central Asia, Middle East, Central/East Europe, West Europe, North America & South America *Manufacturers of stainless steel ingots, billets & bars*

Carrtech Ltd, Crossfield Road, Birmingham, B33 9HP Tel: 0121-683 2600 Fax: 0121-683 2601 E-mail: sales@carrtech.com *Automotive consumable suppliers & paint & plating jig manufrs*

▶ Carruthers Ltd, Staunton Court Business Park Ledbury Road, Unit 17c, Staunton, Gloucester, GL19 3QS Tel: (01452) 849099 E-mail: info@carruthers-equipment.com *Technical sales consultancy*

▶ Carrwood Homes P.L.C., Carrwood House, 109 Shaw Heath, Stockport, Cheshire, SK2 6QH Tel: 0161-476 2255

▶ Carry Gently Ltd, 7 The Brook Trading Estate, Deadbrook Lane, Aldershot, Hampshire, GU12 4XB Tel: (01252) 318841 Fax: (01252) 311066 E-mail: ops@carry-gently.co.uk

Carryduff Forklift, 5 Cadger Road, Carryduff, Belfast, BT8 8AU Tel: (028) 9081 2864 Fax: (028) 9081 4532 E-mail: sales@carryduff.co.uk.*Fork lift service hire & sales*

▶ Carrylift Materials Handling Ltd, Unit 7 Bamburgh Court, Team Valley Trading Estate, Gateshead, Tyne & Wear, NE11 0TX Tel: 0191-491 4700 Fax: 0191-491 4702 *Forklift truck repairs & sales*

Carrylift Materials Handling Ltd, Peel Road, Skelmersdale, Lancashire, WN8 9PT Tel: (01695) 455000 Fax: (01695) 455099 E-mail: info@carryliftgroup.com *Fork lift truck hire, sale & repair*

Carryon Clothing Mnfrs, Ravenscroft, Stoney Lane, Urpeth, Stanley, County Durham, DH9 0SJ Tel: 0191-370 0250 Fax: 0191-370 1226 E-mail: sales@carryonclothing.co.uk *Clothing manufrs*

▶ Cars For Stars, Great Northern Warehouse, 275 Deansgate, Manchester, M3 4EL Tel: (0845) 2264195 Fax: (01942) 701521 E-mail: nigel@carsforstars-manchester.co.uk *Chauffeur driven cars and American stretched limousines.*

▶ Cars For Stars Ltd, 105 London Street, Reading, RG1 4QD Tel: (0845) 2264205 Fax: 0118-951 7989 E-mail: info@carsforstars-reading.co.uk *Reading based company providing American stretched limousines and executive chauffeur driven cars for hire. Part of the Cars for Stars network.*

▶ Cars for Stars (Cambridge), The Old Brickworks, Little Fen Drove, Burwell, Cambridge, CB5 0BN Tel: 0845 2264202 Fax: 01638 743244 E-mail: info@carsforstars-cambridge.co.uk *Cambridge based company providing American stretched limousines and executive chauffeur driven cars for hire. Part of the Cars for Stars network.*

▶ Cars for Stars (Lincoln), Yew Tree House, Summergates Lane, Batoft, Skegness, Lincolnshire, PE24 5BZ Tel: 0845 2264216 Fax: 0845 1235238 E-mail: info@carsforstars-lincoln.co.uk *Local company providing the latest model American stretched limousines for hire within the LN postcode area with onward travel to any UK destination. Part of the Cars for Stars network of limousine hire companies.*

▶ Cars for Stars (Preston), Unit 22, Sycamore Trading Estate, Squires Gate Lane, Blackpool, FY4 3RL Tel: 0845 2264207 Fax: 01253 349111 *Blackpool based company providing American stretched limousines for hire within the PR, BL and FY postcode areas. Part of the Cars for Stars network.*

Carsem Europe, 1 Potters Walk, 134 High Street, Wootton Bassett, Swindon, SN4 7AY Tel: (01793) 853888 Fax: (01793) 855388 *Semiconductor manufrs*

H D L Carson, Trafford Park Road, Trafford Park, Manchester, M17 1WH Tel: 0161-872 2694 Fax: 0161-877 9755 E-mail: fredrickcarson@aol.com *Warehousing, container handling & group age services*

Carson Stationery & Print Ltd, 107-109 West Street, Sheffield, S1 4EQ Tel: 0114-272 0342 Fax: 0114-281 2996 E-mail: carson-sp@zoom.co.uk *Printers & commercial stationers* Also at: Dronfield

Warren Carson Ltd, Dean Court, Upper Dean, Huntingdon, Cambridgeshire, PE28 0NL Tel: (01234) 708881 Fax: (01234) 708677 *Digital readout systems*

Carstone Windows Ltd, Unit 7 Mount Industrial Estate, Stone, Staffordshire, ST15 8LL Tel: (01785) 814487 Fax: (01785) 816194 *UPVC window frame installers & manufrs*

Cartek Vehicle Solutions, Craven House Lansbury Estate, 102 Lower Guildford Road, Knaphill, Woking, Surrey, GU21 2EP Tel: (01483) 799499 Fax: (01483) 487400 E-mail: sales@cartek.co.uk *Vehicle or trailer hire*

Cartel Communications, Radio House, 15 Sutton Street, Birmingham, B1 1PG Tel: 0121-622 3301 Fax: 0121-622 3328 E-mail: sales@cartel.co.uk *Established since 1983, Midlands based CarTel Communications specialises in the Sale, Service*

continued

& Hire of two way radio nationwide. Manufacturer products include:- Kenwood, Tait Mobile Radio, Entel, Maxon, Motorola, Icom, Key plus Automatic Vehicle Location (AVL) systems. PMR446, Atex Intrinsically Safe and Submersible Radios. PDA Mobile Data Solutions. CarTel specialises in MPT1327 Protocol Trunking systems for both "on-site" and "multi-site" systems from design to implementation. They cover market sectors like Local Authorities, Retail Sector, Shopping Centres, Shopwatch Schemes, Distribution Warehouse Sites, Airports, Hospitals, Large Factory Complexes with access to the Public Switched Telephone Network (PSTN) or Private Access Branch Exchange (PABX). CarTel also supplies Mobile Eye fleet management and vehicle tracking addresses the simplest of vehicle tracking needs whilst catering for the more advanced user requirements with its multi-modular design which easily integrates with in-cab mobile data despatch terminals with signature capture.

Cartel Security, Chesham Close, Romford, RM7 7PJ Tel: (01708) 756100 Fax: (01708) 756200 E-mail: sales@openviewgroup.com *Security systems installation*

▶ Cartel Uk Ltd, 20 Colwell Road, Leicester, LE3 9AX Tel: (07977) 777742 Fax: 0116-223 9702 E-mail: cartel_uk@hotmail.co.uk *Hands free kits car phones car kits tracker monitor retrieve car security*

Cartem Ltd, Wharf Way, Glen Parva, Leicester, LE2 9TF Tel: (0870) 0665122 Fax: (0870) 0665133 E-mail: info@cartem.co.uk *Bitumen tank & sprayer manufrs*

Carter Advertising, 11 Kirkhouse Road, Blanefield, Glasgow, G63 9BX Tel: (01360) 770235 Fax: (01360) 770235 E-mail: sales@carteradvertising.co.uk *Gifts & promotional products advertisers*

▶ Carter Cabin Hire, Garage Lane, Setch, King's Lynn, Norfolk, PE33 0BE Tel: (01553) 810778 Fax: (01553) 810793

Carter Ceilings Ltd, 2 Cunningham Road, Stirling, FK7 7SW Tel: (01786) 464914 Fax: (01786) 450012 E-mail: info@carter.co.uk *Suspended ceilings & partitions contractors*

Carter Concrete Ltd, Stone Hill Way, Holt Way Industrial Estate, Cromer, Norfolk, NR27 9JW Tel: (01263) 511009 Fax: (01263) 519053 *Concrete products*

Carter Concrete Ltd, Britons Lane, Beeston Regis, Sheringham, Norfolk, NR26 8TP Tel: (01263) 823434 Fax: (01263) 825678 E-mail: mail@carter-concrete.co.uk *Contractors & suppliers*

Carter Construction Ltd, Richardson Street, Derby, DE22 3GR Tel: (01332) 381601 Fax: (01332) 290722 E-mail: sales@carterconstruction.co.uk *Building design & construction services.*

Carter Environmental Engineers Ltd, 2 Lawley Middleway, Birmingham, B4 7XL Tel: 0121-250 1000 Fax: 0121-250 1400 E-mail: sales@cee.co.uk *Filtration systems contractors*

Carter Fielding Associates Ltd, 19 Dryden Court, Parkleys, Richmond, Surrey, TW10 5LJ Tel: (020) 8546 7211 Fax: (020) 8546 7008 E-mail: surveyors@carterfielding.co.uk *Surveyors & structural engineers* Also at: Teddington & Weybridge

G. Carter & Son (Thornton) Ltd, Brookside, Thornton-Cleveleys, Lancashire, FY5 4EZ Tel: (01253) 821068 Fax: (01253) 862072 E-mail: steve@gcarter.co.uk *Engineers*

▶ Carter Haulage & Storage Ltd Nfk, Woodside, Mill Road, Shouldham Thorpe, King's Lynn, Norfolk, PE33 0EA Tel: (01366) 347626 Fax: (01366) 347520 E-mail: carterhaulage@supanet.com *Haulage & storage contractors*

Carter Horsley (Tyres) Ltd, 10-11 Thurrock Park Way, Thurrock Park Industrial Estate, Tilbury, Essex, RM18 7HZ Tel: (01375) 489509 Fax: (01375) 489501 E-mail: info@mswuk.com *Tyre import, export merchants & agents*

▶ Kennedy Carter Ltd, Hatchlands, East Clandon, Guildford, Surrey, GU4 7SJ Tel: (01483) 226180 Fax: (01483) 226199 E-mail: sales@kc.com *Computer systems consultant services*

M.J. Carter Associates, Baddesley Colliery Offices, Main Road, Baxterley, Atherstone, Warwickshire, CV9 2LE Tel: (01827) 717891 Fax: (01827) 718507 E-mail: mailbox@mjca.co.uk *Environmental consultants*

Carter Machine Tool Co. Ltd, Aldon Road, Poulton Industrial Estate, Poulton-le-Fylde, Lancashire, FY6 8JL Tel: (01253) 890289 Fax: (01253) 891615 E-mail: sales@cartermachinery.co.uk *Sheet metalworking machinery agents*

▶ Mark Carter Ltd, Slough, SL3 6RR Tel: (01753) 534777 E-mail: markgcarter@bulldoghome.com *Medal dealer militaries & medal fair organiser*

Carter Origin Ltd, Holmes Street, Rochdale, Lancashire, OL12 6AQ Tel: (01706) 656600 Fax: (01706) 524909 E-mail: sales@carterorigin.co.uk *Plastics material distributors & steel fabrication services*

Philip Carter, Unit 21, Enterprise Centre, Bryn Road, Aberkenfig, Bridgend, Mid Glamorgan, CF32 9BS Tel: (01656) 729406 Fax: (01656) 724888 E-mail: baileyorion@aol.com *Signs*

Carter Refrigeration, 111-115 Marsh Lane, Bootle, Merseyside, L20 4JD Tel: 0151-922 2342 Fax: 0151-922 4004 E-mail: liverpool.contracts@crrs.co.uk *Refrigeration engineers*

▶ Carter Retail Equipment, 90 Lea Ford Road, Birmingham, B33 9TX Tel: 0121-250 1111 Fax: 0121-250 1122 E-mail: info@cre-ltd.co.uk *Manufacturers of display cases & cold rooms*

Carter Services, 12A The Butts, Belper, Derbyshire, DE56 1HX Tel: (01773) 821235 Fax: (01773) 821235 E-mail: carterservices@ndcarter.freeserve.co.uk *Electromagnetic manufrs*

Carter Steel Ltd, Yarm Road, Stockton-on-Tees, Cleveland, TS18 3SA Tel: (01642) 679831 Fax: (01642) 670346 *Steel stockholders*

Carter Voce Access Control Ltd, 111 Chiltern Drive, Surbiton, Surrey, KT5 8LS Tel: (020) 8339 9111 Fax: (020) 8390 1727 *Access control systems.*

▶ Carter & Ward, Construction House, 82 Runwell Road, Wickford, Essex, SS11 7HJ Tel: (01268) 733421 Fax: (01268) 767686

Carterian Joinery, 38 Brearley Street, Hockley, Birmingham, B19 3NR Tel: 0121-359 4340 Fax: 0121-333 4115 E-mail: ian.carter@carterian.co.uk *Shop fitters & joiners*

Carter-Parratt Ltd, Crossens Way, Marine Drive, Southport, Merseyside, PR9 9YL Tel: (01704) 228990 Fax: (01704) 228981 E-mail: storage@carter-parratt.co.uk *Steel filing cabinet manufrs*

Carters, 19a Belper Road, Luton, LU4 8RG Tel: (01582) 571477 Fax: (01582) 480980 *Shop window replacement glass*

Carter's, 99-113 Caversham Road, Reading, RG1 8AR Tel: 0118-959 9022 Fax: 0118-950 0618 E-mail: info@carterse.com *Manufacturers & stockists of tents marquees & equipment*

▶ Carters Consumables Ltd, 70 Princess Street, Castle Gresley, Swadlincote, Derbyshire, DE11 9LA Tel: (01283) 550500 *Abrasive product suppliers*

Carters Gate & Fencing Specialists, 12 Sea Road, East Preston, Littlehampton, West Sussex, BN16 1JP Tel: (01903) 785324 Fax: (01903) 783580 *Specialist gate & fencing suppliers & fitters*

Carters Glass Company Ltd, 14-16 Crouch End Hill, London, N8 8AA Tel: (020) 8340 2297 *Glass merchants*

▶ Carters Heating & Plumbing Ltd, Unit 45a Enterprise House, 44-46 Terrace Road, Walton-on-Thames, Surrey, KT12 2SD Tel: (01932) 262521 Fax: (01932) 262521

Carters Packaging Ltd, Station Road, Pool, Redruth, Cornwall, TR15 3QJ Tel: (01209) 612333 Fax: (01209) 612444 E-mail: info@carterpackaging.com *Packaging supplies*

▶ Carters Removals Ltd, Penlan Works, Llandegai, Llandygai, Bangor, Gwynedd, LL57 4AA Tel: (01248) 370109 Fax: (0870) 7059127 E-mail: mail@cartersremovals.plus.com *Removal & storage*

▶ Carter's Safety Training Service, Haven Court Flat 8, 27 Stocks Lane, East Wittering, Chichester, West Sussex, PO20 8NH Tel: (0700) 5982243 Fax: (0700) 5982432 *Low cost, high quality First Aid, Fire & Safety training, delivered on site. Prices from just £23 per delegate for One Day Emergency First Aid (Appointed Person) course. HSE Four Day First Aid at Work Training from just £80 per delegate (subject to suitable numbers and facilities). Where possible training is delivered within the workplace. See our website or contact us to discuss costings.*

Carters Tools Ltd, 74-76 Elmers End Road, Anerley, London, SE20 7UX Tel: (020) 8659 7222 Fax: (020) 8659 2727 E-mail: sales@carterstools.co.uk *Power tool & hand tool distributors*

▶ Carthouse Furniture, Glebe Farm, Carlton Miniott, Thirsk, North Yorkshire, YO7 4NJ Tel: (01845) 525110 Fax: (01845) 574326 E-mail: enquire@carthousefurniture.com *Hand made furniture suppliers*

Cartier Communications International, 7 Hazelbury Rd, High Wycombe, Bucks, HP13 7RZ Tel: 01494 538354 Fax: 01494 443468 *Medical equipment suppliers & manufrs*

▶ Cartledge, Brookenby Business Park, Brookenby, Binbrook, Market Rasen, Lincolnshire, LN8 6HF Tel: (01472) 399935 Fax: (01472) 399920 *Timber frame builders*

Cartmell Transmissions, 4 Lytham Road, Warton, Preston, PR4 1XD Tel: (01772) 631679 *Gearbox repairs*

J.& M. Cartney, Currarie Farm, Lendalfoot, Girvan, Ayrshire, KA26 0JB Tel: (01465) 891213 E-mail: moraghornse@aol.com *Agricultural services*

Cartology Wheel Mnfrs, Unit 3 Llanhilleth Industrial Estate, Llanhilleth, Abertillery, Gwent, NP13 2RX Tel: (01495) 216612 Fax: (01495) 211108 E-mail: mfc@cartology.co.uk *General joinery, cart & kiosk manufrs*

Carton Creations Ltd, Unit 17, Waterside Industrial Park, Waterside Road, Leeds, LS10 1RW Tel: 0113-270 1333 *Carton finishing services*

Carton Packaging Supplies Ltd, Unit 5F, Nobel Road, Eley Estate, London, N18 3BH Tel: (020) 8807 7244 Fax: (020) 8807 7327 E-mail: cartonpack93@msn.com *Cardboard boxes manufrs*

▶ Cartoons By Landers, PO Box 7539, Bishop's Stortford, Hertfordshire, CM23 4JP Tel: (07767) 435571 E-mail: sales@landers.co.uk *Cartoons for all kinds of applications*

▶ Cartotecnica Ltd, Regent Park, 10 Booth Drive, Park Farm Industrial Estate, Wellingborough, Northamptonshire, NN8 6GR Tel: (01933) 675300 Fax: (01933) 675270 E-mail: info@c-pecnica.co.uk *Packaging suppliers*

▶ Cartrefi Dyfed Homes, Unit 8a Glan Yr Afon Industrial Estate, Llanbadarn Fawr, Aberystwyth, Dyfed, SY23 3JQ Tel: (01970) 626686 Fax: (01970) 626026 *Timber frame builders*

▶ Cartridge Cellar, 10 Blenheim Parade, Allestree, Derby, DE22 2GP Tel: (01332) 551514 Fax: (01332) 606790 E-mail: sales@cartridgecellar.co.uk *PC & laptop repairs & printing & fax consumable suppliers*

▶ Cartridge City, 187 Queensway, Bletchley, Milton Keynes, MK2 2ED Tel: (01908) 366616 *Computer accessory & consumable suppliers*

▶ Cartridge City, 49 Midland Road, Wellingborough, Northamptonshire, NN8 1HF Tel: (01933) 226555 Fax: (01933) 275372 *IT consumables*

Cartridge Concept, 5 Grampian Road, Elgin, Morayshire, IV30 1XN Tel: (01343) 544828 Fax: (01343) 544313 E-mail: alan@cartcon.co.uk *Ink jet & laser printing cartridge retailers*

Cartridge Express, 1 Phoenix Business Centre, Low Mill Road, Ripon, North Yorkshire, HG4 1NS Tel: (0870) 2435610 Fax: (0870) 2435611 E-mail: sales@cartex.co.uk *Computer consumables manufrs*

▶ Cartridge Swop Shop, 201 Hoylake Road, Wirral, Merseyside, CH46 0SJ Tel: 0151-606 1435 Fax: 0151-606 0763 E-mail: Mark@cartridgeswopshop.com *Office supplies*

▶ Cartridge World Ltd, 203 Whalley Road, Accrington, Lancashire, BB5 5AD Tel: (01254) 399991 Fax: (01254) 399199 E-mail: cwaccrington@cartridgeworld.org *Manufacture, original & compatible ink & toner cartridges*

▶ Cartridge World Ltd, Unit K-20 Westminster House, Town Centre, Basingstoke, Hampshire, RG21 7LS Tel: (01256) 323000 Fax: (01256) 323011 E-mail: cwbassingstoke@cartridgeworld.org *Computer accessory suppliers*

▶ Cartridge World Ltd, 3 Bassett Avenue, Bicester, Oxfordshire, OX26 4TZ Tel: (01869) 252627 Fax: (01869) 252625 E-mail: cwbicester@cartridgeworld.org *Computer printer accessories suppliers*

▶ Cartridge World Ltd, 24 Hockerill Street, Bishop's Stortford, Hertfordshire, CM23 2DW Tel: (01279) 466664 Fax: (01279) 467466 *Recycle printer cartridges*

▶ Cartridge World Ltd, 22 Temple Street, Keynsham, Bristol, BS31 1EH Tel: 0117-986 8686 Fax: 0117-986 6222 E-mail: cwkeynsham@cartridgeworld.org *Re-manufacturers of laser cartridges & re-fillers of ink cartridges*

▶ Cartridge World Ltd, 40 Duke Street, Doncaster, South Yorkshire, DN1 3EA Tel: (01302) 325511 Fax: (01302) 360607 *Computer accessories suppliers*

▶ Cartridge World Ltd, 7 Shellons Street, Folkestone, Kent, CT20 1BW Tel: (01303) 247474 Fax: (01303) 247427 E-mail: cwfolkstone@cartridgeworld.org *Computer consumables & accessory manufrs*

Cartridge World Ltd, 15 Woodford Avenue, Ilford, Essex, IG2 6UF Tel: (020) 8551 2277 Fax: (020) 8551 2442 *Manufacturers of printer consumables*

▶ Cartridge World Ltd, 8 Clarendon Avenue, Leamington Spa, Warwickshire, CV32 5PZ Tel: (01926) 888131 Fax: (01926) 888787 E-mail: cartridgeworld@leamingtonspa.org *Refill ink cartridges suppliers*

▶ Cartridge World Ltd, 1 Stainburn Parade, Leeds, LS17 6NA Tel: 0113-268 6868 Fax: 0113-268 1614 *Computer accessory suppliers*

Cartridge World Ltd, 1575 London Road, Leigh-on-Sea, Essex, SS9 2SG Tel: (01702) 477449 Fax: (01702) 474449 E-mail: Franchise@cartridgeworld.org *Computer accessories sales*

▶ Cartridge World Ltd, 20 Surrey Street, Littlehampton, West Sussex, BN17 5BG Tel: (01903) 714444 Fax: (01903) 717102 E-mail: cwlittlehampton@cartridgeworld.org *Computer accessory suppliers*

▶ Cartridge World Ltd, 458 Romford Road, London, E7 8DF Tel: (020) 8470 2189 Fax: (020) 8475 0486

▶ Cartridge World, 192 King Street, London, W6 0RA Tel: (020) 8834 7070 Fax: (020) 8834 7171 E-mail: cwhammersmith@cartridgeworld.org *Computer accessories suppliers*

▶ Cartridge World Ltd, 2-2a Greenford Avenue, London, W7 3QP Tel: (020) 8566 3666 Fax: (020) 8566 0111 E-mail: cwgreenford@cartridgeworld.org *Computer accessories suppliers*

▶ Cartridge World Ltd, 370 Hornsey Road, London, N19 4HT Tel: (020) 7281 7600 Fax: (020) 7281 8789 *Manufacturers of cartridges*

▶ Cartridge World Ltd, 464 Hoe Street, London, E17 9AH Tel: (020) 8556 6030 Fax: (020) 8556 6050 E-mail: cwwalthamstow@cartridgeworld.org *Computer accessory suppliers printer consumables*

▶ Cartridge World Ltd, 367 Green Lanes, Palmers Green, London, N13 4JG Tel: (020) 8886 8877 *Printer cartridge suppliers & reselling*

▶ Cartridge World Ltd, 49 St. Georges Terrace, Jesmond, Newcastle upon Tyne, NE2 2SX Tel: 0191-212 1610 Fax: 0191-212 1611 E-mail: cwjesmond@cartridgeworld.org *Printer cartridge manufrs*

▶ Cartridge World Ltd, 96 High Street, Newport, Isle of Wight, PO30 1BQ Tel: (01983) 532323 Fax: (01983) 825477 *Computer consumables distributors*

▶ Cartridge World, 165 Queen Street, Newton Abbot, Devon, TQ12 2BS Tel: (01626) 337444 Fax: (01626) 334819 *Computer accessory distributors*

▶ Cartridge World Ltd, 46 High Street, Northallerton, North Yorkshire, DL7 8EG Tel: (01609) 771123 Fax: (01609) 771203 *Computer accessories suppliers*

▶ Cartridge World Ltd, 78 Witton Street, Northwich, Cheshire, CW9 5AE Tel: (01606) 354554 Fax: (01606) 354553 *Computer accessory suppliers*

▶ Cartridge World Ltd, 126 Front Street, Arnold, Nottingham, NG5 7EG Tel: 0115-967 1133 Fax: 0115-967 6644 E-mail: cwarnold@cartridgeworld.org *Computer accessories suppliers*

▶ Cartridge World Ltd, 19 Shoe Market, Pontefract, West Yorkshire, WF8 1AP Tel: (01977) 600111 Fax: (01977) 600222 *Printer accessory suppliers*

▶ Cartridge World Ltd, High Street, Street, Somerset, BA16 0EX Tel: (01458) 841269 Fax: (01458) 841269 E-mail: cwstreet@cartridgeworld.co.uk *Cartridge retailers*

▶ Cartridge World Ltd, Faringdon Road, Swindon, SN1 5AR Tel: (01793) 714100 Fax: (01793) 714100

▶ Cartridge World Ltd, 25 Broad Street, Truro, Cornwall, TR1 1JD Tel: (01872) 222121 Fax: (01872) 222262 *Printers manufrs*

▶ Cartridge World Ltd, 8 Monson Road, Tunbridge Wells, Kent, TN1 1ND Tel: (01892) 614142 Fax: (01892) 614142 E-mail: cwturnbridgewells@cartridgeworld.co.uk *Printing cartridge manufrs*

▶ Cartridge World Ltd, 152 Widnes Road, Widnes, Cheshire, WA8 6BA Tel: 0151-422 9876 *Cartridge refillers*

▶ Cartridge World Ltd, 902 New Chester Road, Wirral, Merseyside, CH62 6AU Tel: 0151-343 0999 Fax: 0151-343 0008 *Computer accessory suppliers*

Cartridge World Ltd, 506 Stafford Road, Wolverhampton, WV10 6AN Tel: (01902) 788240 Fax: (01902) 789283 E-mail: cwoxley@cartridgeworld.org *Ink & toner cartridges*

▶ Cartridge World Ltd, 74 Clifton Green, York, YO30 6AW Tel: (01904) 733999 Fax: (01904) 700770 *Computer consumables retailers*

▶ Cartridge World Ltd, 16 Hull Road, York, YO10 3JG Tel: (01904) 870870 *Computer accessories suppliers*

Cartridges UK, Corunna House, 42-44 Ousegate, Selby, North Yorkshire, YO8 4NH Tel: (01757) 212747 Fax: (01757) 212321 E-mail: nikki@cartridgesuk.com *Printer consumables agents*

▶ Cartwright Computers, 35 The Arches, Maryport, Cumbria, CA15 8JE Tel: (0845) 2578630 Fax: (0870) 7060333 E-mail: lee@cartwrightcomputers.co.uk *Covering all of Cumbria.*We come to your Home or Business*NO CALL OUT FEE*NO FIX NO FEE**Tel Carlisle: 01228 808085*Whitehaven: 01946 7588*Maryport: 01900 818947*(*Subject to terms)*

Cartwright Hardware, Cartwright House, Springwell Road, Leeds, LS12 1AX Tel: 0113-243 6931 Fax: 0113-242 1716 E-mail: sales@cartwrighthardware.co.uk *Architectural & builders ironmongers*

Cartwright Marsdon, 121-123 New Union Street, Coventry, CV1 2NT Tel: (024) 7625 6616 Fax: (024) 7655 1318 E-mail: sales@cartwright-marston.co.uk *Chartered surveyors & estate agents*

Cartwright Plastics, 1a Birdcroft Lane, Ilkeston, Derbyshire, DE7 4BE Tel: 0115-932 2744 Fax: 0115-932 9762 *Injection mouldings & small insert mouldings manufrs*

S. Cartwright & Sons, Atlantic Street, Broadheath, Altrincham, Cheshire, WA14 5DH Tel: 0161-928 0966 Fax: 0161-926 8410 E-mail: sales@cartwright-group.co.uk *Trailer manufrs*

Carval Computing Ltd, Innovation & Technology Transfer Centre, Tamar Science Park, Plymouth, PL6 8BX Tel: (01752) 764290 Fax: (01752) 764291 E-mail: mail@carval.co.uk *Computer consultants*

▶ carvalet.co.uk Limited, Iron Walls, Tutbury, Burton-on-Trent, Staffordshire, DE13 9NH Tel: 08006 985589 Fax: 08702 646647 E-mail: info@carvalet.co.uk *Mobile car valeting service covering the Southeast & Midlands regions. Qualified staff. Money-back guarantee. Only Autoglym and Swissol products used. We pride ourselves on our quality of service.*

Carvansons LLP, Hollins Vale Works, Hollins Village, Bury, Lancashire, BL9 8QG Tel: 0161-766 3768 Fax: 0161-767 9437 E-mail: enquiries@carvansons.demon.co.uk *Perfume & fragrance compounders*

Carver Gases Ltd, Littles Lane, Wolverhampton, WV1 1JY Tel: (01902) 577000 Fax: (01902) 712145 E-mail: mail@carvers.co.uk *Builders, plumbers, timber merchants & ironmongers*

Carville Engineering, Unit 11 Seymour Hill Industrial Estate, Dunmurry, Belfast, BT17 9PH Tel: (028) 9062 6999 Fax: (028) 9062 7300 E-mail: carvilleng@btconnect.com *Fork truck sales & service*

Carwood Motor Units Ltd, Herald Way, Binley Industrial Estate, Coventry, CV3 2RQ Tel: (024) 7644 9533 Fax: (024) 7645 2074 E-mail: carwood@carwood.co.uk *Auto electrical, fuel injection equipment re-manufrs*

▶ Carworks, 9 Enkalon Industrial Estate, Randalstown Road, Antrim, BT41 4LD Tel: (028) 9446 0111 E-mail: info@carworksni.com *CarWorks is a Car Servicing Garage specialising in the servicing, repair and advanced diagnostics of BMW, Audi, VW, Skoda and SEAT vehicles.**Situtated centrally in the Enkalon Industrial Estate in Antrim, Northern Ireland, CarWorks offers a combination of technical expertise, high quality service and competitive pricing.**We offer the following services:* - Full Dealer Level Diagnostics and Coding (including Engine Management, ABS and Airbags)*- Servicing to Manufacturers" Specification *- Air Conditioning Servicing and Repairs*- Headlight Alignment*- Other Additional Services (including the repair of clutches, brakes, suspensions, exhausts and batteries)**

Cary Concrete Ltd, Tor View Farm, Galhampton, Yeovil, Somerset, BA22 7AE Tel: (01963) 350409 Fax: (01963) 351712 *Concrete products manufrs*

Cas Coatings, Old Mill, Victoria Road, Bradford, West Yorkshire, BD2 2BH Tel: (01274) 634493 Fax: (01274) 634493 *Powder coating & shot blasting services*

Cas Corporation UK Ltd, 29A Junction Street South, Oldbury, West Midlands, B69 4TA Tel: 0121-552 0009 Fax: 0121-511 1317 E-mail: sales@casuk.co.uk *Scales distributors*

▶ Casa Designer Interiors Ltd, 47 Vaughan Way, Leicester, LE1 4SG Tel: 0116-262 8001 Fax: 0116-262 8001 E-mail: info@casadi.co.uk *Design kitchens*

Casa Tiana Ltd, 6 Honey Hill, Emberton, Olney, Bucks, MK46 5LT Tel: 01234 717079 Fax: 01234 717079 *Baby blankets*

Casachi Hydrotheraphy Ltd, Unit A, 1 Wanborough Business Centre, Wanborough, Guildford, Surrey, GU3 2JS Tel: (01483) 813181 Fax: (01483) 813182 *Bath, spa & whirlpool type services*

▶ Casada Cushions, 20 Museum Street, London, WC1A 1JN Tel: (020) 7580 8878 Fax: (020) 7580 8870 E-mail: casadacushions@aol.com *Bespoke feather cushion makers*

Casargon Ltd, Genei House, Bentinck Street, Bolton, BL1 4QG Tel: (01204) 840500 Fax: (01204) 840600 E-mail: sales@casargon.sagenet.co.uk *Safety shower & handrail manufrs*

Cascade Blinds, Trevol Business Park, Torpoint, Cornwall, PL11 2TB Tel: (01752) 815512 Fax: (01752) 823554 E-mail: info@cascadeblinds.co.uk *Blinds manufrs*

Cascade Electrolite Ltd, Gorse Mill, Gorse Street, Chadderton, Oldham, OL9 9RJ Tel: 0161-628 6622 Fax: 0161-628 2831 *Lighting fitting distributors*

Cascade Kenhar Ltd, 3 Kelbrook Road, Manchester, M11 2DD Tel: 0161-230 7472 Fax: 0161-230 7879 *Manufacturer of forks for the materials handling industry*

Cascade Springs Water Co, High Furze Farm, St. Breock, Wadebridge, Cornwall, PL27 7LF Tel: (01208) 814544 Fax: (01208) 813064 *Water cooler company*

Cascade Systems (UK) Ltd, Unit 10, West Place, West Road, Harlow, Essex, CM20 2GY Tel: (01279) 626695 Fax: (01279) 626799 E-mail: infocascade@aol.com *Heating & air-conditioning installers*

Cascade (UK) Ltd, Unit 5, Eden Close, Hellaby Industrial Estate, Hellaby, Rotherham, South Yorkshire, S66 8RW Tel: (01709) 704500 Fax: (01709) 704501 E-mail: uk-sales@cascorp.com *Fork lift truck attachment & distributors*

Cascade Water Gardens, Bury Road, Radcliffe, Manchester, M26 2WW Tel: 0161-725 8142 Fax: 0161-723 0004 E-mail: info@cascadekoi.com *Specialist aquatic suppliers*

Cascade Water Systems Ltd, Cascade House, 35a King Street, Hoyland, Barnsley, South Yorkshire, S74 9JU Tel: (01226) 361665 Fax: (01226) 361671 E-mail: mail@cascade-water-filters.co.uk *Water treatment services*

Cascaid Ltd, Holywell Buildings, Holywell Way, Loughborough, Leicestershire, LE11 3UZ Tel: (01509) 283390 Fax: (01509) 283401 E-mail: enquire@cascaid.co.uk *Computer software*

▶ Casco Ltd, Unit 21, Lawson Hunt Industrial Park, Guildford Road, Broadbridge Heath, Horsham, West Sussex, RH12 3JR Tel: (01403) 248244 Fax: (01403) 218347 E-mail: contactus@casco-group.com *Livestock sales systems design & installation services*

Cascos UK Ltd, Unit 2 Conyer Farm Estate, Conyer, Sittingbourne, Kent, ME9 9HH Tel: (01795) 522201 Fax: (01795) 522281 E-mail: sales@cascos.uk.com *Garage service equipment sales*

Case Co., Leighton Court, Lower Eggleton, Ledbury, Herefordshire, HR8 2UN Tel: (01531) 640543 Fax: (01531) 640759 E-mail: julie@thecasecompany.co.uk Principal Export Areas: Central/East Europe & West Europe *We sell tailor-made cases to suit you, so the insides & outsides look exactly how you want them to. A complete bespoke case presentation service. We have also launched our new online shop which provides a Next Day delivery service for all our standard products which include, Laptop Cases, Plastic Cases, Presentation cases, Aluminium Cases, Flight Cases, CD Presentation Cases, Brief cases, A4 and A3 Cases and much more. All available with accessories such as foam inserts for you to cut and shape to suit your products. We sell cases into many sectors and have vast experience with quick solutions and small, medium or large quantities.*

Case Alarms Ltd, Unit 5 Taff Workshops, Tresillian Terrace, Cardiff, CF10 5DE Tel: (029) 2038 7006 Fax: (029) 2038 7006 E-mail: cardiff@casesecurity.co.uk *Security distributors*

▶ Case Computer Services Ltd, 5 Valleyview Close, Highwoods, Colchester, CO4 9UN Tel: (01206) 845508 E-mail: kelly@casecomputers.co.uk *Supplier of computer services to North Essex businesses and private customers. Supply of hardware and software. Repair and maintenance services.*

Case & Container Supply Co Ltd, 11 Wilson Road, Wigston, Leicestershire, LE18 4TP Tel: 0116-277 0000 Fax: 0116-277 0072 E-mail: sales@casecontainer.co.uk *Carton manufrs*

Casebourne Leach & Co., Room 506, Coppergate House 16 Brune Street, London, E1 7NJ Tel: (020) 7375 2575 Fax: (020) 7953 8411 E-mail: office@casebourne-leach.co.uk *Marine surveyors*

Casella Hazmat, 10-17 Seven Ways Parade, Woodford Avenue, Ilford, Essex, IG2 6JX Tel: (020) 8551 6195 Fax: (020) 8551 3554 E-mail: admin@casellagroup.com *Environmental consultants*

Casemir Chocolates UK Ltd, 5a Tetherdown, London, N10 1ND Tel: (020) 8365 2132 E-mail: info@casemirchocolates.co.uk *Manufacturers of luxury hand made chocolates*

▶ Caseonline, Unit 13, Roman Way Business Park, Godmanchester, Huntingdon, Cambridgeshire, PE29 2LN Tel: (01480) 453288 Fax: (01480) 451088 E-mail: sales@caseonline.co.uk *Media storage solutions services*

▶ Casewest, Moorton Avenue, Burnage, Manchester, M19 2NQ Tel: 07870 409130 E-mail: enquiry@casewest.co.uk *CASEWEST.co.uk Automotive Technical Documentation Consultancy including :*IMDS / International Material Data System / MDSystem*Training*QS9000*Automotive specifications*DVP&R*PPAP*Design FMEA*

Casey Bros, St Georges Drive, Brinsworth, Rotherham, South Yorkshire, S60 5NG Tel: (01709) 378386 Fax: (01709) 373308 *Sub-contract precision engineers*

▶ Casey Group Of Companies, Rydings Road, Rochdale, Lancashire, OL12 9PS Tel: (01706) 860032 Fax: (01706) 861156 E-mail: admin@casey.co.uk *Main contractor for social housing refurbishment, environmental improvements and land remediation, as well as health and education building projects. Also, we undertake commercial and residential development, waste management and hire of plant and equipment.*

Caseys Camping, Pool Road, Otley, West Yorkshire, LS21 1DY Tel: (01943) 465462 Fax: (01943) 850825 E-mail: sales@caseyscamping.com *Camping retailer*

Cash Bases Ltd, The Drove, Newhaven, East Sussex, BN9 0LA Tel: (01273) 616300 Fax: (01273) 512010 E-mail: info@cashbases.co.uk *Cash bases develop point of sale solutions*

Cash Control Equipment, 390 Cathcart Road, Glasgow, G42 7DF Tel: 0141-423 9999 Fax: 0141-423 0690 E-mail: epos@cashcontrol.co.uk *Cash registers, epos equipment sales & services*

Cash Register Services, Eastwood Court, Manor Lane, Hawarden, Deeside, Clwyd, CH5 3QB Tel: (01244) 528998 Fax: (01244) 528998

Cash Register Services London Ltd, Hertford Rdedmonton, London, N9 7ES Tel: (0800) 3580593 Fax: (020) 8443 0446 E-mail: crs5143@aol.com *Cash register distributors*

Cash Register Supply Co., 94-96 Rushmere Road, Ipswich, IP4 4JY Tel: (01473) 723515 Fax: (01473) 405631 E-mail: sales@crs-ipswich.co.uk *Cash registers*

Cashmores, Upper Brook Street, Walsall, WS2 9PD Tel: (01922) 720930 Fax: (01922) 648304 E-mail: sales@cashmores.co.uk *Aluminium & stainless steel stockholders & processors*

Cashmores Joinery Ltd, 86-88 Essex Road, Leicester, LE4 9EG Tel: 0116-276 9948 Fax: 0116-276 9948 *Timber product manufrs*

Cash's, Torrington Avenue, Coventry, CV4 9UZ Tel: (024) 7646 6466 Fax: (024) 7646 2525 E-mail: sales@jjcash.co.uk *Woven label & badge manufrs*

▶ Casino Slots Leisure Centre, 144 The Centre, Feltham, Middlesex, TW13 4BS Tel: (020) 8844 1046 E-mail: richardbg@hotmail.com *Amusement machines*

▶ Casino-To-Go, Unit 3 Foulswick Business Park, Fowlswick Lane, Allington, Chippenham, Wiltshire, SN14 6QE Tel: (01793) 686402 E-mail: info@casino-to-go.co.uk *Fun casino hire for parties, functions & events*

Casio Electronics Co. Ltd, 6 1000 North Circular Road, London, NW2 7JD Tel: (020) 8450 9131 Fax: (020) 8452 6323 *Manufacturers of conveyors & systems*

▶ Casp Products Ltd, W.H.S. Building, Harcourt Road, Harrogate, North Yorkshire, HG1 5NL Tel: (01423) 525206 Fax: (01423) 536500 E-mail: sales@casp-products.com *Manufacturers & distributors of environmental monitoring equipment*

Casper Shipping Ltd, 1 Cleveland Business Centre, Watson Street, Middlesbrough, Cleveland, TS1 2RQ Tel: (01642) 243662 Fax: (01642) 243936 *Shipping & forwarding agents*

Cass Bros, 153 Hastings Road, Bromley, BR2 8NQ Tel: (020) 8462 2387 Fax: (020) 8462 2387 *Motor trimming & upholstery manufrs*

D. Cass, 1 Park Road, Hull, HU3 1TH Tel: (01482) 225866 *Cabinet manufrs*

▶ Cass Electric Co. Ltd, Unit 10-11, The Gateway Industrial Estate, Parkgate, Rotherham, South Yorkshire, S62 6JL Tel: (01709) 528822 Fax: (01709) 528882

Cass Productions Ltd, The Point, Leigh Road, Eastleigh, Hampshire, SO50 9DE Tel: (023) 8065 2220 Fax: (023) 8065 2220 E-mail: sales@cassproductions.co.uk *Audio-visual production*

Cassells Industrial Products, 60 Littleworth, Mansfield, Nottinghamshire, NG18 2SH Tel: (01623) 622439 Fax: (01623) 420134 E-mail: enquiries@cip-ltd.co.uk *Engineers merchants suppliers*

▶ Cassels Transport Ltd, Rollestone Crossroads, Shrewton, Salisbury, SP3 4DS Tel: (01980) 621701

Casserly's Removals & Storage Ltd, Unit 10, Gledrid Industrial Park, Gledrid, Chirk, Wrexham, LL14 5DG Tel: (0800) 3581822 Fax: (01691) 778580 *Removal & storage specialists*

▶ Casshurst Coatings Ltd, 6 Power Works, Slade Green Road, Erith, Kent, DA8 2HY Tel: (01322) 351812 Fax: (01322) 351816

Cassidy Brothers plc, Mitcham Road, Marton, Blackpool, FY4 4QW Tel: (01253) 766411 Fax: (01253) 691486 E-mail: toys@casdon.co.uk *Toy & nursery goods manufrs*

Cassidy Insurance Services, First Floor Anchor House, 24 Anchor Road, Walsall, WS9 8PW Tel: (0870) 0422200 Fax: (0870) 0422201 *Insurance consultants*

Cassidy Sunblinds Ltd, Henry Boot Way, Hull, HU4 7DY Tel: (01482) 473173 Fax: (01482) 473191 E-mail: sales@cassidy-sunblinds.co.uk *Sunblind manufrs*

▶ Cassini, 141 Shirley Road, Southampton, SO15 3FH Tel: (023) 8022 1740 Fax: (023) 8033 9220 E-mail: enquiry@cassinigroup.co.uk *Building Services*

Casson & Co. Ltd, 117 Huddersfield Road, Oldham, OL1 3NY Tel: 0161-624 2227 Fax: 0161-627 5231 *Footwear & leather goods wholesalers*

▶ Casson & Co Handbags Ltd, Market Hall, The Mall, Bury, Lancashire, BL9 0BD Tel: 0161-761 6479 E-mail: info@handbag.uk.net

Casswells Ltd, 6 High Street, Midsomer Norton, Radstock, BA3 2HR Tel: (01761) 413331 Fax: (01761) 410327 *Builders merchants* Also at: Chipping Sodbury, Woodrow (Salisbury)

The Cast Iron Company Ltd, 8 Old Lodge Place, Twickenham, TW1 1RQ Tel: (020) 8744 9992 Fax: (020) 8744 1121 E-mail: info@castiron.co.uk *Architectural metalworkers & fabricators*

▶ Cast Iron Fires.Com, Grove Mill, Commerce Street, Carrs Industrial Estate, Haslingden, Lancashire, BB4 5JT Tel: 0845 230 1991 E-mail: enquiries@castironfires.com *Online shop of reproduction cast iron fireplaces in Victorian, Edwardian, Art Nouveau styles, stoves, mantels, spares and fire accessories.*

▶ Cast Iron Range Cookers Ltd, 50 High Street, Princes Risborough, Buckinghamshire, HP27 0AX Tel: (01844) 344475 Fax: (01844) 342080 *Cookers retailers*

Company Information

Cast Iron Welding Service Ltd, 2 Samson Road, Hermitage Industrial Estate, Coalville, Leicestershire, LE67 3FP Tel: (01530) 811308 Fax: (01530) 835724 E-mail: sales@castironwelding.co.uk *Cast iron welding services*

Cast Metal Repairs Ltd, High Street Mills, High St, Heckmondwike, W. Yorkshire, WF16 0DL Tel: (01924) 403444 Fax: (01924) 410164 E-mail: tranter@rhodesengineering.co.uk *Cold metal stitching specialists*

▶ Cast Tec, Unit 3b East Side, Tynedock, South Shields, Tyne & Wear, NE33 5SP Tel: 0191-497 5438 Fax: 0191-497 4288 E-mail: sales@casttec.co.uk *Importing fire places*

Castacrete Ltd, Plantation Works, Clevedon Road, Failand, Bristol, BS8 3UA Tel: (01275) 851131 Fax: (01275) 851133 *Concrete products*

▶ Castacrete Ltd, Commissioners Road, Rochester, Kent, ME2 4EQ Tel: (01634) 724667 Fax: (01634) 290284 *Construction materials*

Castaline Angling Equipment, 18-20 Upgate, Louth, Lincolnshire, LN11 9ET Tel: (01507) 602149 Fax: (01507) 603163 *Fishing tackle suppliers*

Castech (UK) Ltd, Unit 10 Manor Farm, Main Road, Newport Pagnell, Buckinghamshire, MK16 9JS Tel: 01234 391973 Fax: 01234 391185 E-mail: info@castech.co.uk *Castech Ltd manufacturer of precision aluminium castings and precision sand castings, specialise in embracing every stage of the process, from initial design consultation to delivery of finished components. Production tooling can be modified at any stage to accommodate design changes. Precision Castings are hand finished by our highly skilled workforce enabling anodising alochroming or painting to be applied without further surface treatment. Machining facilities include CNC milling and turning and the painting facilities include powder coating & wet spray painting. All of Castech's Precision Castings are individually inspected during production, all to ISO 9001:2000 standards. Castech manufacture precision aluminium castings, precision sand castings and precision aluminium sand castings with Tolerances of + - 0.4mm on dimensions up to 250mm (pro rata) Thickness down to 3mm or as low as 2mm in local areas."*

Castell Ceilings Co, Willow View, 62 Marshfield Road, Castleton, Cardiff, CF3 2UW Tel: (01633) 681411 Fax: (01633) 681700 *Suspended ceilings & partitions installation*

▶ Castell Howell Foods, Unit 2 Merthyr Tydfil Industrial Park, Pentrebach, Merthyr Tydfil, Mid Glamorgan, CF48 4DR Tel: (01443) 693491 Fax: (01443) 620938 *Wholesale*

Castell Iso Lok, The Castell Building, 217 Kingsbury Road, London, NW9 9PQ Tel: (020) 8511 1858 Fax: (020) 8205 0055 E-mail: sales@castell.com Principal Export Areas: Worldwide *Products for all of your Lockout Tagout needs!**Padlocks - keyed alike, differ and master and differ options availiable.**Clasps, Signs, Tags, Valve lockoff, key cabinets and document control.*

Castell Safety International Ltd, The Castell Building, 217 Kingsbury Road, London, NW9 9PQ Tel: (020) 8200 1200 Fax: (020) 8205 0055 E-mail: sales@castell.com *Castell Safety International, design, manufacture and supply safety systems and solutions. **We are manufacturers of Trapped Key Interlocks for the safety of switchgear and machine guarding applications. **Our Iso-Lok brand offer Lockout Tagout Equipment. **Salvo provides Loading Bay safety systems through drive away prevention.*

Castellum Fine English Reproduction Furniture, 30 Upgate, Louth, Lincolnshire, LN11 9ET Tel: (01507) 602207 Fax: (01507) 602207 *Furniture reproduction*

▶ Casterbridge Fires, Unit 15 Casterbridge Industrial Estate, London Road, Dorchester, Dorset, DT1 1PL Tel: (01305) 262829 Fax: (01305) 257483 *Fires & fire places retailers*

Casting Repairs Ltd, Hipper St South, Chesterfield, Derbyshire, S40 1SS Tel: (01246) 246700 Fax: (01246) 206519 E-mail: andrea.peck@casting-repairs.co.uk *Cold repairers*

▶ Casting Services, 64 Highway Road, Thurmaston, Leicester, LE4 8FQ Tel: (07717) 734483 Fax: 0116-210 2647 E-mail: casting.services@ntlworld.com *Engineering services*

Casting Supplies Ltd, Unit 19 Trent Trading Park, Botteslow Street, Joiners Square, Stoke-on-Trent, ST1 3LY Tel: (01782) 289574 Fax: (01782) 279272 *Ceramics manufrs*

Castings plc, Lichfield Road, Brownhills, Walsall, WS8 6JZ Tel: (01543) 374341 Fax: (01543) 377483 E-mail: mail@castings.plc.uk *Iron castings, malleable & spheriodical graphite*

Castings Technology International, Waverley Advance Manufacturing Park, Brunel Way, Rotherham, South Yorkshire, S60 5WG Tel: 0114-272 8647 Fax: 0114-273 0852 E-mail: info@castingstechnology.com *Castings research & development consultants*

▶ Castle, Chelsham Place, Limpsfield Road, Warlingham, Surrey, CR6 9DZ Tel: (01883) 627300 Fax: (01883) 624571 E-mail: info@castlecon.com

Castle Alarms, Millennium House, Boundary Bank, Kendal, Cumbria, LA9 5RR Tel: (01539) 731394 Fax: (01539) 735367 E-mail: sales@fp.castlealarms.f9.co.uk *Fire,Security alarm service & installation. CCTV systems, Emergency lights, Door Access,*

▶ Castle Architectural Ltd, Duke Street, New Basford, Nottingham, NG7 7JN Tel: 0115-970 1000 Fax: 0115-970 0099 E-mail: info@castle-arc.co.uk *Suppliers of commercial aluminium windows & doors*

Castle Ashby House, Castle Ashby, Northampton, NN7 1LQ Tel: (01604) 696696 Fax: (01604) 696516 E-mail: admin@castleashby.co.uk *Exclusive residential venue*

Castle Blinds, 2 Ayton House, North Road, Berwick-upon-Tweed, TD15 1PR Tel: (01289) 306090 Fax: (01289) 332020 E-mail: micheal@mullan4245.fsnet.co.uk *Awning & canopy manufrs*

▶ Castle Business Services Ltd, 28 Grange Road, South Croydon, Surrey, CR2 0NA Tel: (020) 8407 0632 Fax: (020) 8407 0587 E-mail: service@faxandprinterrepairs.co.uk *Fax & printer repairs, home & on-site, maintenance contracts*

Castle Care Cosmetics Ltd, Invincible Road, Farnborough, Hampshire, GU14 7QP Tel: (01252) 548887 Fax: (01252) 548880 E-mail: sales@castlecare.co.uk *Cosmetic manufrs*

Castle Care Tech Ltd, North Street, Winkfield, Windsor, Berkshire, SL4 4SY Tel: (01344) 890582 Fax: (01344) 890024 E-mail: sales@castle-caretech.com *Manufacturers of intruder alarms and bespoke security products.*

Castle Cartons Ltd, Kings Road, Kings Heath, Birmingham, B14 6TN Tel: 0121-444 6060 Fax: 0121-441 1446 E-mail: jgreen@castlecartons.co.uk *Cardboard container manufrs*

Castle Clay Sales, Podmore Street, Stoke-on-Trent, ST6 2EZ Tel: (01782) 575992 Fax: (01782) 575995 E-mail: claysales@ukonline.co.uk *Clay suppliers*

Castle Colour Press Ltd, 3 Morgan Way, Bowthorpe Employment Area, Norwich, NR5 9JJ Tel: (01603) 741278 Fax: (01603) 749227 E-mail: reception@castlecolour.co.uk *Reprographics & printing agents*

Castle Computers, 347 Barnsley Road, Wakefield, West Yorkshire, WF2 6AS Tel: (01924) 257291 Fax: (01924) 257291 *Alarm installers*

Castle Concrete Ltd, Castle Meadow Road, Nottingham, NG2 1AG Tel: 0115-941 1162 Fax: 0115-948 3362 E-mail: sales@castleconcrete.co.uk *Precast concrete*

Castle Contracts, 1 Koln Close, Charfleets Industrial Estate, Canvey Island, Essex, SS8 0SB Tel: (01268) 696225 Fax: (01268) 512250 *Marble renovation work*

Castle Corrugated Cases Ltd, Hadnock Road, Monmouth, Gwent, NP25 3NQ Tel: (01600) 715727 Fax: (01600) 714942 *Cardboard box manufrs*

Castle Dairies Ltd, Pontygwindy Industrial Estate, Caerphilly, Mid Glamorgan, CF83 3HU Tel: (029) 2088 3981 Fax: (029) 2088 6506 E-mail: sales@castledairies.fsnet.co.uk *Cheese, butter & dairy product manufrs*

Castle Data Imaging Ltd, 2a Mandalay Street, Nottingham, NG6 0BH Tel: 0115-927 4122 Fax: 0115-927 4122 E-mail: imaging@castledata.freeserve.co.uk *Microfilm & scanning bureau & document storage*

Castle Diamond Technology Ltd, Unit 27 Tir Llwyd Industrial Estate, Kinmel Bay, Rhyl, Clwyd, LL18 5JA Tel: (01745) 360877 Fax: (01745) 360862 E-mail: sales@castle-tech.co.uk *Industrial tooling suppliers*

Castle Document Management, The Foundry, London Road, Kings Worthy, Winchester, Hampshire, SO23 7QN Tel: (01962) 882281 Fax: (01962) 882204 E-mail: scanning@castledoc.freeserve.co.uk *Image processing systems & scanning distributors*

Castle Embroidering, Unit J Stonebridge Court, Nottingham, NG3 2GY Tel: 0115-947 2888 Fax: 0115-947 2888 E-mail: sales@castle-embroidery.co.uk *Embroidered leisure wear*

▶ Castle Engineering Ltd, Unit 1, Palmbourne Industrial Park, Castle Street, Stafford, ST16 2TB Tel: (01785) 228808 Fax: (01785) 257883

Castle Engineering Lancaster Ltd, River Street, St Georges Quay, Lancaster, LA1 1TA Tel: (01524) 67604 Fax: (01524) 67604 *Precision & general engineers*

Castle Engineering Resources Ltd, 4 Central Works, Peartree Lane, Dudley, West Midlands, DY2 0QU Tel: (01384) 230233 Fax: (01384) 230757 E-mail: castle.eng@btclick.com *Storage & process tank manufrs*

Castle Fabrication & Installation Ltd, 3a Cold Hesledon Industrial Estate, Cold Hesledon, Seaham, County Durham, SR7 8ST Tel: 0191-581 5177 Fax: 0191-581 4792 E-mail: sales@castlefab.com *Steel fabricators*

Castle Fire Ltd, Ghyll Mill, Beehive Lane, New Hutton, Kendal, Cumbria, LA8 0AJ Tel: (01539) 722500 Fax: (01539) 741044 *Fire protection services*

Castle Gates, Castlelaurie Works, Falkirk, FK2 7XF Tel: (01324) 633510 *Wrought iron work*

Castle Hardware Company Ltd The, Park Road, Hockley, Birmingham, B18 5JA Tel: 0121-551 6021 Fax: 0121-554 7507 *Wholesale hardware merchants*

Castle Hill Quarry Co. Ltd, Cannington, Bridgwater, Somerset, TA5 2QF Tel: (01278) 652280 Fax: (01278) 653724 E-mail: sales@castlehillquarry.co.uk *Manufactures of feed products & agricultural lime spreading*

▶ Castle Home Products, 1 Mount Place, Boughton, Chester, CH3 5BF Tel: (0800) 3897959

Castle Hydraulics & Pneumatics Ltd, 3 Amherst Business Centre, Budbrooke Road Industrial Estate, Budbrooke Industrial Estate, Warwick, CV34 5WE Tel: (01926) 419926 Fax: (01926) 497196 *Hydraulic & pneumatic equipment*

▶ Castle I T Consulting Ltd, 128/7 Brunton Gardens, Edinburgh, EH7 5ET Tel: 0131-477 9536 E-mail: gillian@castleitconsulting.co.uk *Software Development, Database Design, IT Training, Website Design, Project Management, Service Delivery Management, Software Applications, Bespoke Software*

Castle International, 9 Woodcocks Cresent, Bournemouth, BH7 7JW Tel: (01202) 422447 *Computer programmers*

Castle Labelling, Unit 15A Redwell Court, Harmire Enterprise Park, Harmire Road, Barnard Castle, County Durham, DL12 8BN Tel: (01833) 637647 Fax: (01833) 690942 E-mail: sales@castleautoid.co.uk *Bar code products & services suppliers*

▶ Castle Languages, 27 Oakland Drive, Netherton, Wakefield, West Yorkshire, WF4 4LZ Tel: (01924) 262891 Fax: (01924) 262891 E-mail: lisacastillo@castlelanguages.co.uk *Translation & language services*

Castle Lifting Gear Ltd, Porters FLD Road, Corngreaves Trading Estate, Cradley Heath, West Midlands, B64 7BL Tel: (01384) 560924 Fax: (01384) 566452 E-mail: lynn@castleliftinggear.co.uk *Lifting gear engineers*

Castle Marquees & Portable Toilets, 22 Georgian Drive, Coxheath, Maidstone, Kent, ME17 4QT Tel: (01622) 745818 Fax: (01622) 745818 *Portable toilets suppliers*

Castle Meats Burnham Ltd, 11 Harrison Way, Slough, SL1 5LG Tel: (01628) 666034 Fax: (01628) 660768 *Catering butchers supplier & distributor*

Castle Microwave Ltd, 5 Park Street, Newbury, Berkshire, RG14 1EA Tel: (01635) 271300 Fax: (01635) 271301 E-mail: sales@castlemicrowave.com *Microwave component distributors*

Castle Milk & Corrie Estates, Norwood, Tundergarth, Lockerbie, Dumfriesshire, DG11 2QX Tel: (01576) 510203 Fax: (01576) 510362 *Country estate, farms & timber suppliers*

Castle Monolithics Europe Ltd, Sheaf Bank Works, Prospect Road, Heeley, Sheffield, S2 3EN Tel: 0114-273 0588 Fax: 0114-276 2045 *Refractory installers glass tank demolition*

Castle Mouldings, 1 Dew Farm, Church Lane, Peasmarsh, Rye, East Sussex, TN31 6XD Tel: (01797) 230734 E-mail: castlemouldings@hotmail.com *Glass fibre molding manufrs*

Castle Neroche Ltd, Neroche House, Bason Bridge, Highbridge, Somerset, TA9 4RN Tel: (01278) 787840 Fax: (01278) 781825 E-mail: sales@castleneroche.com *Specialist healthcare furniture manufrs*

Castle Oils Ltd, Valley Works, Chemical Lane, Stoke-on-Trent, ST6 4PB Tel: (01782) 577422 Fax: (01782) 839432 E-mail: darren.tistion@castle-stoke.co.uk *Liquid waste disposal manufrs*

Castle Packaging Ltd, Bott Lane, Walsall, WS1 2JG Tel: (01922) 625451 Fax: (01922) 722202 E-mail: sales@castlepackaging.co.uk *Industrial adhesive tape distributors & packaging*

Castle Pine Trading Co., Burcroft Hill, Conisbrough, Doncaster, South Yorkshire, DN12 3EF Tel: (01709) 865999 Fax: (01709) 865999 *Pine furniture suppliers*

▶ Castle Plant Deeside Ltd, Abergairn, Bridge of Gairn, Ballater, Aberdeenshire, AB35 5TY Tel: (01339) 756070

Castle Plastic, Unit 16b Raleigh Hall Industrial Estate, Eccleshall, Stafford, ST21 6JL Tel: (01785) 851842 Fax: (01785) 851370 E-mail: sales@castleplastics.co.uk *Acrylic Fabricators & CNC machining, & vacuum forming*

Castle Pneumatics, Dormston Trading Estate, Burton Road, Dudley, West Midlands, DY1 2UF Tel: (01902) 883727 Fax: (01902) 881208 *Pneumatic tool repair services, distributors & agents*

Castle Point Hand Looms, Unit 32 Brittania Court, Basildon, Essex, SS13 1EU Tel: (01268) 729707 Fax: (01268) 728330 *Solid wood kitchen & bedroom door manufrs*

Castle Portable Buildings Ltd, Wharf Street, Dukinfield, Cheshire, SK16 4PG Tel: 0161-339 3911 Fax: 0161-339 3911 E-mail: info@castleportable.co.uk *Garden shed & concrete garage builders*

Castle Precision Engineering Glasgow Ltd, 241 Drakemire Drive, Glasgow, G45 9SZ Tel: 0141-634 1377 Fax: 0141-634 3678 E-mail: sales@castleprecision.com *Precision engineers*

▶ Castle Properties, 7-9 Portland Street, Cheltenham, Gloucestershire, GL52 2NZ Tel: 0870 240 7113 E-mail: info@castleprop.co.uk *Castle Properties have let and managed our own private portfolio since 1994. In April 2004 we began trading as a limited company. We specialise in shared accommodation, whilst still retaining a selection of individual one, two and three bedroom properties for letting in Cheltenham, Gloucestershire.**

Castle Reproduction Furniture, 461 Hackney Road, London, E2 9DY Tel: (020) 7739 2074 Fax: (020) 7256 1218 E-mail: enquiries@castlefurniture.demon.co.uk *Furniture restoring manufrs*

Castle Reproductions Skipton Ltd, 26-27 North Street, Ripon, North Yorkshire, HG4 1HJ Tel: (01765) 690307 Fax: (01423) 712116 *Furniture manufrs*

▶ Castle Rock Geotech, 22 Morley Road, Colwick, Nottingham, NG3 6LL Tel: 0115-979 9228 Fax: 0115-982 7060 E-mail: enquiry@crgeo.co.uk *Geotechnical & Environmental Services*Geotechnical Investigations*Contaminated Land Assessments*

Castle Saddlery, Hendra Farm, Liskeard, Cornwall, PL14 3LJ Tel: (01579) 344998 Fax: (01579) 344998 *Saddler manufrs*

Castle Steel Services Ltd, Pensnett House, Pensnett Trading Estate, Kingswinford, West Midlands, DY6 7PP Tel: (01384) 401600 Fax: (01384) 292785 E-mail: mikeb@tidentsections.co.uk *Steel stockholders*

Castle Tools Ltd, 33 Trent Street, Sheffield, S9 3XU Tel: 0114-261 7200 Fax: 0114-261 7370 E-mail: sales@castletools.co.uk *Engineering tools distribs*

Castle View Services Ltd, Steuart Road, Bridge of Allan, Stirling, FK9 4JX Tel: (01786) 834060 Fax: (01786) 832658 E-mail: enquiries@castleview.co.uk *Services management company* Also at: Branches throughout the U.K.

▶ Castlebridge Plant, Ketley Business Park, Ketley, Telford, Shropshire, TF1 5JD Tel: (01952) 254422 Fax: (01952) 254433

▶ Castledene Motor Co. Ltd, Mill Hall, Aylesford, Kent, ME20 7JN Tel: (01622) 710717 Fax: (01622) 792828 E-mail: sales@castledenetransport.co.uk

▶ Castlegate Electrics, Dundas Mall, Middlesbrough, Cleveland, TS1 1HR Tel: 01642 244934 E-mail: info@castlegateelecrics.co.uk *Electrical lighting retail*

Castlemoor Demolition Ltd, Transfer House, 53 Marshgate Lane, Stratford, London, E15 2NQ Tel: (020) 8503 1505 Fax: (020) 8519 5035 *Industrial demolition contractors*

Castlepar, 37 Lodlow Avenue, Luton, LU1 3RW Tel: (01582) 726976 Fax: (01582) 459200 *Flooring contractors services*

Castlepoint Associates Ltd, Castle Point House 180 Kiln Road, Benfleet, Essex, SS7 1SU Tel: (01702) 558165 Fax: (01702) 552550 E-mail: sales@castle-point-computers.co.uk *Computer consultants*

Castlerigg Engineering Co. Ltd, Browfoot Works, Penrith Road, Keswick, Cumbria, CA12 4LH Tel: (01768) 772876 Fax: (01768) 772885 E-mail: info@castlerigg-eng.co.uk *Steel fabricators*

Castles In The Air, Spring Bank West, Hull, HU3 1LD Tel: (01482) 470366 Fax: (01482) 470366 *Bouncy castle hire*

Castles Shopfitters Limited, Bowland Street Works, Bowland Street, Bradford, West Yorkshire, BD1 3BW Tel: (01274) 724271 E-mail: mail@castle_shopfitters.co.uk *Shop & bank fitters*

Castleton Signs Ltd, 25 Mitcham Lane, London, SW16 6LQ Tel: (020) 8769 8741 Fax: (020) 8769 9699 E-mail: sales@castletonsigns.co.uk *Sign production & installation services*

Castleton Transformers, Unit C14 Fieldhouse Industrial Estate, Fieldhouse Road, Rochdale, Lancashire, OL12 0AA Tel: (01706) 342086 Fax: (01706) 861286 *Transformer manufrs*

Castlewest Ltd, 6 Greenwood Court, Ramridge Road, Luton, LU2 0TN Tel: (01582) 455757 Fax: (01582) 413114 E-mail: info@castlewest.co.uk *Industrial & hygiene disposable wiping systems*

Castlework Contractors Ltd, 98 College Street, Kempston, Bedford, MK42 8LU Tel: (01234) 217941 Fax: (01234) 357232 E-mail: sales@castlework-contractors.co.uk *Concrete structural repair contractors*

▶ Castmaster Roll Co., Eagle Foundry, Stevenson Road, Sheffield, S9 3XG Tel: 0114-244 0381 Fax: 0114-243 1317 E-mail: sales@castmasterrolls.com *Cast steel roll maker manufrs*

▶ Castor Services Ltd, The Wheel House, Egmont Street, Mossley, Ashton-Under-Lyne, Lancashire, OL5 9NB Tel: (01457) 838001 Fax: (01457) 838998 E-mail: sales@castorserviceslimited.co.uk *Castor distributors*

Castrol (U K) Ltd, 65 Stanlow Works South, Wirrel, Ellesmere Port, CH65 4ES Tel: 0151-355 3737 Fax: 0151-357 1130 E-mail: *Lubricant (general purpose) manufrs*

Caststitch Engineering Ltd, Unit 18, Daneside Business Park, Riverdane Road, Congleton, Cheshire, CW12 1UN Tel: (01260) 298188 Fax: (01260) 298188 E-mail: sales@caststitch/laser/cutting.fsnet.co.uk *Laser cutting press break & welding facilities*

▶ Castyle Ltd, Sandbach Road, Stoke-on-Trent, ST6 2DR Tel: (01782) 838333 Fax: (01782) 838306 *Designers & decorators of ceramic tiles*

▶ Casual Productions, Unit 52, Stafford Business Village, Staffordshire Technology Park, Stafford, ST18 0TW Tel: 01785 887979 Fax: 01785 887825 E-mail: info@casualproductions.com *Casual Productions LTD is a video media company producing corporate video and interactive DVD products as well as independent film. ***We specialise in the production of creative corporate video for promotional, marketing, informative and training applications. Our services cover the whole production process from scriptwriting and casting right through to DVD authoring, packaging design, print and duplication.***Our aim is to provide a unique service and build a strong relationship with our clients to create a difference. We can help your company communicate the right message and discover new ways to effectively inform, influence and inspire your audience. ****

Caswell & Co Ltd, 6 Princewood Road, Earlstrees Industrial Estate, Corby, Northamptonshire, NN17 4AP Tel: (01536) 464800 Fax: (01536) 464801 E-mail: sales@caswell-adhesives.co.uk *Industrial adhesive manufrs*

C. Caswell Engineering Services Ltd, Knowsley Road Industrial Estate, Knowsley Road, Haslingden, Rossendale, Lancashire, BB4 4RR Tel: (01706) 227935 Fax: (01706) 210282 E-mail: enquiries@caswell.com *Vent ductwork installers & manufrs*

Caswells, Lagonda Road, Cowpen Lane Industrial Estate, Billingham, Cleveland, TS23 4JA Tel: (01642) 379600 Fax: (01642) 562978 E-mail: sales@caswellsgroup.com *Engineer suppliers*

Caswick, Sandtoft Road, Belton, Doncaster, South Yorkshire, DN9 1PN Tel: (01427) 872017 Fax: (01427) 873541 *Plastic & rubber drainage products*

▶ Catalan IS Services Ltd, Glenbervie Business Centre, Larbert, Stirlingshire, FK5 4RB Tel: (01324) 682150 Fax: 01324 682149 *Software sellers*

Catalent Pharma Solutions, Lancaster Way, Wingates Industrial Estate, Westhoughton, Bolton, BL5 3XX Tel: (01942) 790000 Fax: (01942) 799799 *Pharmaceutical developers*

Catalent Pharma Solutions, Lancaster Way, Wingates Industrial Estate, Westhoughton, Bolton, BL5 3XX Tel: (01942) 790000 Fax: (01942) 799799 Principal Export Areas: Worldwide *Pharmaceutical packaging services*

Catalyst, 175 Tottenham Court Road, London, W1T 7NU Tel: (020) 7436 3636 Fax: (020) 7580 7449 E-mail: newbuisness@cgsuk.com *Management training specialists*

Catalyst International Ltd, Capital Court, 30 Windsor Street, Uxbridge, Middlesex, UB8 1AB Tel: (01895) 450400 Fax: (01895) 450401 E-mail: europe@catalystinternational.com *Supply chain software & consultancy solutions*

Catalytic Support Systems Ltd, Thelwall New Road Industrial Estate, Thelwall, Warrington, WA4 2LY Tel: (01928) 566344 Fax: (01925) 264995 E-mail: adrian_wood@knitwire.com *Wire mesh for automotive industry, seals and gaskets*

▶ Catch Monitored Security, 38 Portrack Grange Road, Stockton-On-Tees, Cleveland, TS18 2PH Tel: (01642) 677747 Fax: (01642) 602517 E-mail: monitering@cgsl.org.uk *Burglar alarm systems fitters*

Catchwater Meadow, Orby Road, Burgh le Marsh, Skegness, Lincolnshire, PE24 5JD Tel: (01754) 811097 Fax: (01754) 811151 *Aquatic nursery & fish farmers*

Catena Inspection Services, D3 Unit, Amberley Drive, Sinfin, Derby, DE24 9RE Tel: (01332) 722011 Fax: (01332) 764099 E-mail: enquiries@catenais.co.uk *Lifting gear maintenance services & manufrs*

Catena Software Ltd, Terence House, 24 London Road, Thatcham, Berkshire, RG18 4LQ Tel: (01635) 866395 E-mail: sales@catenauk.com *Electronic computer software design*

Catenate Consulting Ltd, Beech Leigh, Rectory Hill, Berrynarbor, Ilfracombe, Devon, EX34 9SE Tel: (01271) 882460 Fax: (01271) 882460 E-mail: sales@catenate-consulting.co.uk *Electronic subcontract assembly specialist services*

Cater Direct Ltd, Unit 6 Pasadena Close, Hayes, Middlesex, UB3 3NQ Tel: (020) 8561 7706 Fax: (020) 8561 7748 E-mail: info@caterdirect.co.uk *Sole Distributors for : Masafi Pure Natural Mineral Water Masafi Fragrant Tissues Prima Halal - Value Added Chicken Products Baguz: Halal Cold Cuts & Hot Dogs Halal Meal Components for Airlines & Contract Catering*

Cater Hire Ltd, Bray House, Pottersheath Road, Welwyn, Hertfordshire, AL6 9TA Tel: (01438) 815428 Fax: (01438) 815428 E-mail: caterhireagd@aol.com *Catering equipment hire service*

Cater Hire Ltd, Unit J Gregorys Bank, Worcester, WR3 8AB Tel: (01905) 23260 Fax: (01905) 23152 E-mail: info@cater-hire.co.uk *Catering equipment & online catalogue & ordering services*

▶ Cater For You Ltd, Unit 4, Wessex Road, Bourne End, Buckinghamshire, SL8 5DT Tel: (01494) 583743 Fax: (01628) 810093 E-mail: info@cater4you.co.uk *On-line retailer of reusable and disposable plastic glasses, plastic champagne flutes and more and the Goodsphere Air Purifier.*

Catercall Ltd, 1 Facet Road, Birmingham, B38 9PT Tel: 0121-433 5444 Fax: 0121-433 4876 E-mail: admin@catercalltechservices.co.uk *Catering Equipment Installation or Maintenance or Repair.*

Caterclean Supplies, Meadow Street, Townhill, Swansea, SA1 6RZ Tel: (01792) 582000 *Catering, cleaning & janitorial supply services*

Caterelle Ltd, Downs Road Boat Yard, Downs Road, Maldon, Essex, CM9 5HG Tel: (01621) 853330 Fax: (01621) 853330 *Boat builders & repairers*

Caterers Equipment World, 121 Avenue Street, Parkhead, Glasgow, G40 3SA Tel: 0141 5565740 Fax: 0141 5565740 E-mail: enquiries@cew-soltan.co.uk *Design equipment manufrs*

The Caterers Linen Supply, 6-8 Jackson Way, Great Western Industrial Park, Southall, Middlesex, UB2 4SF Tel: (020) 8843 5810 Fax: (020) 8843 5865 E-mail: customerservice@caterersIinen.co.uk *The Caterers Linen Supply provide a national linen hire and laundry service for caterers. They offer cost effective, high quality products including chefs wear, uniform, workwear, garments, kitchen wear and table linen. They operate a 'no contract' policy and offer their customers complete flexibility. High quality and excellent customer service are priorities for them. Part of the London Linen Supply Group, they are specialists in linen rental and laundry services for the catering industry. They offer permanent and temporary hire and one-off hire is possible. Additional services, including embroidery, are provided. Gold members of the Association of Catering Excellence, the company is run by experienced, dedicated staff and once a customer you will receive regular visits and communication from your designated Account Manager. They take corporate social responsibility very seriously and do their very best to ensure that their laundry process is as modern and environmentally friendly as possible.*

Caterfab UK, Haleys Yard, Leeds, LS13 3LA Tel: 0113-228 9101 Fax: 0113-228 9201 *Ventilation engineers*

Caterform Works, Victoria Road, Eccleshill, Bradford, West Yorkshire, BD2 2BN Tel: (01274) 626751 Fax: (01274) 626752 E-mail: aireseal@airedale-group.co.uk *Refrigeration & stainless steel manufrs*

Caterfreeze Products Ltd, 59 Main Street, Castlederg, County Tyrone, BT81 7AN Tel: (028) 8167 1247 Fax: (028) 8167 9863 E-mail: caterfreeze@btopenworld.com *Catering equipment suppliers*

Caterham Cars Ltd, 32 Station Avenue, Caterham, Surrey, CR3 6LB Tel: (01883) 333700 Fax: (01883) 333707 E-mail: sales@caterham.co.uk *Sports car retailers*

Caterham Surgical Supplies Ltd, 89A Gloucester Road, Croydon, CR0 2DN Tel: (020) 8683 1103 Fax: (020) 8683 1105 E-mail: info@caterhamsurgical.co.uk *Surgical instrument manufacturers & distributors*

Catering Concepts Ltd, Duck Pool Farm, Duck Pool Lane, Beckington, Frome, Somerset, BA11 6TX Tel: (01373) 831180 Fax: (01373) 831170 E-mail: info@cateringconceptsltd.com *Catering designers & installers*

Catering Engineers NW Ltd, 3 Ketlan Court, River Lane, Saltney, Chester, CH4 8SB Tel: (01244) 676999 Fax: (01244) 676886 E-mail: info@cenw.fsnet.co.uk *Commercial catering equipment repairs*

Catering Equipment Ltd, Unit 7, Speedwell Trading Estate, 106 Kings Road, Tyseley, Birmingham, B11 2AT Tel: 0121-773 2228 Fax: 0121-772 4731 E-mail: sales@celonline.co.uk *Gastronorm, containers, sinks, basins, hygiene sinks, anti-spill lids, lids, chafing dishes, ice cream containers, cutlery cylinders, insulated boxes, food transport, weld in sinks, insert sinks, waste kits, pre rinse spray units, janitorial sinks, taps, sound deadening, knee operated sinks, electronic valves, buffet trays, flat flange containers, dough trays, bulk storage, air pots, insulated flasks, insulated jugs, ice packs, perforated containers, adapter bars, insulated food transport boxes, stainless steel, polycarbonate, polypropylene, waste fittings, strainer wastes, overflow pipes, stand pipes*

Catering Equipment Engineers Ltd, Kildrum Indust Estate, Kildrum Road, Shankbridge, Ballymena, County Antrim, BT42 3EY Tel: (028) 2589 2122 Fax: (028) 2589 8208 E-mail: info@cee-group.com *Catering equipment distributors, catering equipment service engineers*

Catering Equipment (Newcastle Under Lyne) Ltd, Metfab House, Montrose Street, Stoke-On-Trent, ST4 3PB Tel: (01782) 313226 Fax: (01782) 327260 *Catering equipment distributors*

Catering Installation & Service Ltd, 536-537 Ipswich Road, Slough, SL1 4EQ Tel: (01753) 820166 Fax: (01753) 824885 E-mail: sales@orangeflame.co.uk *Service catering equipment*

Catering Kitchen Sheffield, 100 Lyons Street, Sheffield, S4 7QS Tel: 0114-276 3550 Fax: 0114-270 6128 *Catering equipment suppliers*

Catering Linen Hire, Unit E7 Aladdin Centre, Long Drive, Greenford, Middlesex, UB6 8UH Tel: (020) 8575 1844 Fax: (020) 8575 9025 E-mail: maureen.cooper@ukonline.co.uk *'Catering Linen Hire based in Greenford, Middlesex offering catering linen hire including wedding tableware, wedding accessories and paper tableware.*

Catering Supplies & Repair Co. Ltd, 122 Muirhall Road, Larbert, Stirlingshire, FK5 4AP Tel: (01324) 552601 Fax: (01324) 563329 E-mail: info@csr-ltd.co.uk *Complete catering equipment designers & suppliers*

▶ Catering Systems Ltd, 9 Compton Road, Brighton, BN1 5AL Tel: (01273) 508626 Fax: (01273) 505852 E-mail: info@cateringsystems.co.uk *Catering equipment agents*

Catering World, Millcroft Road, Rutherglen, Glasgow, G73 1EN Tel: 0141-613 2075 Fax: 0141-613 2085 E-mail: enquiries@catering-world.co.uk *Suppliers of new & guaranteed reconditioned catering equipment*

Catering-Suppliers.com, PO Box 12976, Witton, B6 7AP Tel: 0121-331 4200 E-mail: cateringsuppliers@gmail.com *We offer a range of Catering Products at reduced prices. We are able to offer these products at the prices stated due to the volume buying discounts we obtain from manufacturers*

Caterlec Services Ltd, 1 Charles Watling Way, Norwich, NR5 9JH Tel: (01603) 742888 Fax: (01603) 742711 *Catering equipment suppliers*

Caterline, 20 John Newington Close, Kennington, Ashford, Kent, TN24 9SG Tel: (01622) 661696 Fax: (01233) 663144 *Catering equipment services*

▶ Caterline Commercial Kitchens Ltd, Unit 16 Primrose Trading Estate, Cradley Road, Dudley, West Midlands, DY2 9SA Tel: (01384) 459111 Fax: (01384) 456986 *Industrial kitchens repair & installations*

Caterlink, 20 Newton Rd, Great Barr, Birmingham, B43 6BN Tel: 0121-358 5844 Fax: 0121 358 6914 *Electric & gas repairs*

Catermech Ltd, Unit 3 Racecourse Court, Racecourse Road, Gallowfields Trading Estate, Richmond, North Yorkshire, DL10 4SP Tel: (01748) 850396 Fax: (01748) 850396 *Catering equipment suppliers*

Caterpillar Peterlee Ltd, North West Industrial Estate, Peterlee, County Durham, SR8 2HX Tel: 0191-569 2200 Fax: 0191-569 2298 *Articulated dump truck manufrs*

Caterpillar Remanufacturing Ltd, Sanders Lodge Industrial Estate, Rushden, Northamptonshire, NN10 6AZ Tel: (01933) 316622 Fax: (01933) 354601 E-mail: sales@wealdstone.co.uk *Engine & transmission manufrs*

Caterpillar Remanufacturing Services, Lancaster Road, Shrewsbury, SY1 3NX Tel: (01743) 212000 Fax: (01743) 212700 *Remanufacturing services*

Caterpillar UK Ltd, Peckleton Lane, Desford, Leicester, LE9 9JU Tel: (01455) 826826 Fax: (01455) 826900 *Materials handling equipment manufrs*

Cater-Quip Ltd, 81 Dargan Road, Belfast, BT3 9JU Tel: (028) 9077 0195 Fax: (028) 9037 0238 *Catering equipment suppliers*

Caterquip (GB) Ltd, Unit 3 Euro-Seas Centre, Blyth, Northumberland, NE24 1LZ Tel: (01670) 546363 Fax: (01670) 546260 E-mail: enquiries@caterquip-gb.co.uk *We are a leading supplier of commercial catering and refrigeration equipment to a wide range of clients in Newcastle, Sunderland, Gateshead, North, South Tyneside, Northumberland and across the North East. We supply commercial catering equipment to a wide range of establishments including: hotels, nursing homes, restaurants, pubs, shops supermarkets, offices, factories, schools, colleges and prisons. With over twenty five year's experience of meeting the commercial catering equipment requirements of organisations in the North East, we are able to offer advice on specification and a complete design and supply package.*

Caterquip Midlands, 4 Albion Parade, Kingswinford, West Midlands, DY6 0NP Tel: (01384) 402345 Fax: (01384) 402345 *Catering equipment suppliers*

Caters Advertising, The Old Mill, Sunfield Place, Stanningley, Pudsey, West Yorkshire, LS28 6DR Tel: 0113-257 5757 Fax: 0113-255 5100 E-mail: info@caters.net *Advertising agency & full marketing services*

Catershop Catering Equipment, 3 Robberds Way, Bowthorpe Employment Area, Norwich, NR5 9JF Tel: (01603) 741133 Fax: (01603) 744255 E-mail: sales@catershop.co.uk *Commercial catering equipment suppliers & distributors* Also at: Boston

Catertech, 4e Haverscroft Industrial Estate, New Road, Attleborough, Norfolk, NR17 1YE Tel: (01953) 454200 Fax: (01953) 454207 *Catering equipment engineers*

Catertech, 18 Brynards Hill, Wootton Bassett, Swindon, SN4 7ER Tel: (01793) 848002 Fax: (01793) 848002 E-mail: enquires@catertech.net *Commercial catering engineering & equipment supplier*

Catesby Packing Case Co Ltd, 647 Melton Road, Thurmaston, Leicester, LE4 8EB Tel: 0116-269 3503 Fax: 0116-269 3503 *Packing case manufrs*

▶ Catex Catering Equipment (2002) Ltd, Unit 2 La Rue Le Gros, La Rue Des Pres Trading Estate, St. Saviour, Jersey, JE2 7QP Tel: (01534) 725582 Fax: (01534) 734314 E-mail: catex@jerseymail.co.uk *Commercial catering*

Catford Agencies, 23a Harberson Road, London, SW12 9QX Tel: (020) 8675 7492 Fax: (020) 8675 7469 *Hair products supplier*

Catford Timber Co., 161 Rushey Green, London, SE6 4BD Tel: (020) 8698 7277 Fax: (020) 8697 0790 E-mail: sales@catfordtimber.co.uk *Timber merchants*

▶ Cathartic Designs, 20 Albert Mews, Lockside, London, E14 8EH Tel: (07976) 718081 E-mail: info@cathartic.co.uk *Production of Storyboards, Concept Art, Illustration and Fine Art Commissions*

Cathay Pacific Airlines, 3 Shortlands, London, W6 8AQ Tel: (020) 8834 8888 Fax: (020) 8741 6118 E-mail: sales@cathaypacific.com *Airline company* Also at: Manchester

▶ Cathay Pigments, Norman House, Friar Gate, Derby, DE1 1NU Tel: (01332) 371759

▶ Cathedral Appointments, 33 Southernhay East, Exeter, EX1 1NX Tel: (01392) 413577 Fax: (01392) 425690 E-mail: sales@cathedralappointments.co.uk *Executive recruitment agents*

▶ Cathedral City Furniture Ltd, Millennia Park, Thornes Road, Wakefield, West Yorkshire, WF2 8PW Tel: (01924) 379100 Fax: (01924) 376136 *Wholesale furniture retailers*

Cathedral Garden Furniture, Unit 9 Hetton Lane Industrial Estate, Colliery Lane, Hetton-Le-Holey, Houghton Le Spring, Tyne & Wear, DH5 0BD Tel: 0191-517 1700 Fax: 0191-517 1700 E-mail: sales@cathedralgardenfurniture.co.uk *Garden furniture manufrs*

Cathedral Stationery, 2 Park Avenue, Lincoln, LN6 0BY Tel: (01522) 692366 Fax: (01522) 684015 *Stationary suppliers*

Cathedral Works Organisation, Terminus Road, Chichester, West Sussex, PO19 8TX Tel: (01243) 784225 Fax: (01243) 813700 E-mail: info@cwo.uk.com *Stonemasons*

Cathelco Ltd, 18 Hipper St South, Chesterfield, Derbyshire, S40 1SS Tel: (01246) 277656 Fax: (01246) 206519 E-mail: sales@cathelco.co.uk *Electrolytic anti-fouling systems manufrs*

Catherines Castles, 11 Villa Way, Wootton, Northampton, NN4 6JH Tel: (01604) 877792 E-mail: info@catherinescastles.co.uk *Catherine's Castles, bouncy castle hire for childrens parties, birthdays, weddings and special occasions, serving Northampton, Milton Keynes, Wellingborough, Kettering, Daventry and surrounding areas.*

Catherwell Engineering Co. Ltd, Unit 7 & 9 Stanley Lane Industrial Estate, Stanley Lane, Bridgnorth, Shropshire, WV16 4SF Tel: (01746) 766154 Fax: (01746) 766154 *Precision & production engineers*

Cathian Leather Goods, Compstall Mills Estate, Andrew Street, Compstall, Stockport, Cheshire, SK6 5HN Tel: 0161-427 4871 Fax: 0161-427 4871 E-mail: cathian@ukonline.co.uk *Leather goods manufrs*

Cathodic Protection Co. Ltd, Venture Way, Grantham, Lincolnshire, NG31 7XS Tel: (01476) 590666 Fax: (01476) 570605 E-mail: cpc@cathodic.co.uk Principal Export Areas: Worldwide *Cathodic protection systems & protection services*

Cathro Air Compressor Services, 48 Winpenny Road, Parkhouse Industrial Estate, Parkhouse Industrial Estate East, Newcastle, Staffordshire, ST5 7RH Tel: (01782) 561191 Fax: (01782) 563348 E-mail: tom@cathrocompressors.wanadoo.co.uk *Specialize in industrial air compressors supply's*

Cathryn Grosvenor Ltd, 3 Elystan Street, London, SW3 3NT Tel: (020) 7584 2112 Fax: (020) 7591 0905 E-mail: sales@cathryngrosvenor.co.uk *Knitwear designers & manufrs*

Tim Catley Ltd, 15, Oakwood Gardens, Knaphill,, Woking, Surrey, GU21 2RX Tel: (01483) 799595 Fax: (01483) 799595 E-mail: tim@tim-catley.co.uk *IT computer services*

▶ Catnic, Pontygwindy Industrial Estate, Caerphilly, Mid Glamorgan, CF83 2WJ Tel: (029) 2033 7900 Fax: (029) 2086 3178 E-mail: sali.morris@corusgroup.com Principal Export Areas: Worldwide *Standard duplex coated Cougar,classic combined box steel manufacture lintels. Arch,feature steel lintels.Bead & mesh plasterer's profiles - galvanised,stainless steel and PVC-U. Lath, mesh, arch formers in galvanised /stainless steel. Wall connectors & wall ties (stainless steel). Litetile,steel profiles available in sheet profiles Tufftile, Elitetile, Academytile or Tuffslate profiles*

Cato Associates Ltd, 13 Chelsea Crescent Chelsea Harbour, Chelsea Harbour, London, SW10 0XB Tel: (020) 7352 1406 Fax: (020) 7326689 E-mail: mac@cato.co.uk *Strategic image consultants*

▶ Catplant Ltd, The Bungalow, Holmsley Lane, Brierley, Barnsley, South Yorkshire, S72 9EX Tel: (01226) 716058 Fax: (01226) 781114

▶ Cats Direct, 70-72 Acton Road, Long Eaton, Nottingham, NG10 1FR Tel: 0115-983 5280 Fax: 0115-972 1112 E-mail: mail@cats-direct.com *Exhausts & catalytic converter specialists*

▶ Cats-Whiskers.com Ltd, 14 Camelot Court, Somerton, Somerset, TA11 6SB Tel: (01458) 274383 Fax: (01458) 274388 *Computer maintenance services*

Catterall & Wood Ltd, Unit 2 Primrose Bank Mill, Friday Street, Chorley, Lancashire, PR6 0AA Tel: (01257) 272192 Fax: (01257) 261432 *Sheet metalwork engineers*

Cattles plc, Kingston House Centre 27 Business Park, Woodhead Road, Birstall, Batley, West Yorkshire, WF17 9TD Tel: (01924) 444466 Fax: (01924) 442255 *Holding company*

▶ Cattles Invoice Finance Ltd, St. James House, Charlotte Street, Manchester, M1 4DZ Tel: 0161-237 1483 Fax: (0870) 0438333 E-mail: hotline@cattlesif.co.uk *Factoring & invoice discounting services*

Cattletech, Leeds Road, Hambleton, Selby, North Yorkshire, YO8 9HJ Tel: (01757) 708870 Fax: (01757) 213604 *Agricultural services*

Catton Control Cables Ltd, 33-35 Kings Road, Yardley, Birmingham, B25 8JB Tel: 0121-772 4297 Fax: 0121-766 6075 E-mail: nick@catton.co.uk Principal Export Areas: Worldwide *Control cable manufrs*

Cattron Theimeg UK Ltd, Riverdene Industrial Estate, Molesey Road, Hersham, Walton-On-Thames, Surrey, KT12 4RY Tel: (01932) 247511 Fax: (01932) 220937 E-mail: sales@cattronuk.com *Remote control system manufrs*

Catwalk Ltd, 69 St Barnabas Rd, Leicester, LE5 4BE Tel: 0116-246 1909 Fax: 0116-276 6403 E-mail: Office@catwalk.ltd.uk *Garment manufrs*

▶ Caudle Contracts & Design Ltd, Everglades, Maiden St, Weston, Hitchin, Hertfordshire, SG4 7AA Tel: (01462) 790580 Fax: (01462) 790398 E-mail: sales@caudle.co.uk *Industrial door specialists*

Caudles, 23 West One House, St. Georges Road, Cheltenham, Gloucestershire, GL50 3DT Tel: (01242) 222307 Fax: (01242) 222665 *Consulting engineers & designers*

Cauldron Business Systems, 2 Walley Grove, High Road Well, Halifax, West Yorkshire, HX2 0AE Tel: (01422) 329500 Fax: (01422) 329500 E-mail: cauldronuk@aol.com *Computer software designers*

John Caunt Scientific Ltd, Oxford, OX2 6YE Tel: (01865) 511848 Fax: (01865) 310986 E-mail: johncaunt@johncaunt.com *Analysis equipment distributors*

Caunton Engineering Ltd, Moorgreen Industrial Park, Engine Lane, Newthorpe, Nottingham, NG16 3QU Tel: (01773) 531111 Fax: (01773) 532020 E-mail: sales@caunton.co.uk *Structural steelwork fabricators & services*

Caurnie Soap Co., The Soaperie, Canal Street, Kirkintilloch, Glasgow, G66 1QZ Tel: 0141-776 1218 Fax: 0141-776 1218 E-mail: office@caurnie.com *Handmade herbal soaps*

Causeway Associates, Clophill House, High Street, Clophill, Bedford, MK45 4AA Tel: (01462) 810033 *Project management for warehousing systems*

Causeway Carpets, Roe Lee Mill, Whalley New Road, Blackburn, BB1 9SU Tel: (01254) 676996 Fax: (01254) 680510 E-mail: info@causewaycarpets.com *Carpet manufrs*

Causeway Electricial Services, Catherine Street, Warrington, WA5 0LH Tel: (01925) 633390 Fax: (01925) 243214 *Electrical contractors*

▶ Causeway Property Services, 17b Church Road, Bebington, Wirral, Merseyside, CH63 7PG Tel: 0151-645 8000 E-mail: jn@cpsbuilders.co.uk *Builders & property renovations for commercial & domestic*

Causeway Steel Products Ltd, Five Ash Road, Gravesend, Kent, DA11 0RF Tel: (01474) 567871 Fax: (01474) 328993 E-mail: causewaysteel@causeway-steel.co.uk *Refractory anchor manufrs*

Causeway Technologies Ltd, Comino House Furlong Road, Bourne End, Buckinghamshire, SL8 5AQ Tel: (01628) 552000 Fax: (01628) 552001 E-mail: sales@causeway.com *With over 2,500 customers and more than 40,000 users, the benefits of Causeway's solutions are proven, helping you to win more work, increase your margins, support corporate governance and compliance, embrace industry initiatives, reduce costs, increase efficiency and integrate your supply chain.*

Causeway Technologies Ltd, Bucknalls Lane, Watford, WD25 9XX Tel: (01923) 892600 Fax: (01923) 679288 E-mail: partners@ecl.uk.com *Computer software developers*

Cautaulds UK, West Mill, Bridge Foot, Belper, Derbyshire, DE56 1BH Tel: (01773) 525525 Fax: (01773) 525545 E-mail: *Hosiery manufrs* Also at: Belper

Cauthery Reid, Kingfisher House, 2 Barry Close, Braunstone, Leicester, LE3 3TP Tel: 0116-239 4022 Fax: 0116-238 8330 E-mail: sales@cautheryreid.co.uk *Polyester manufrs*

Cavaghan & Gray Group Ltd, Brunel House, Brunel Way, Durranhill Industrial Estate, Carlisle, CA1 3NQ Tel: (01228) 518200 Fax: (01228) 518215 E-mail: enquiries@northern-foods.co.uk *Fresh food manufrs*

Cavalcade Blinds, 34 Hope Street, Stoke-on-Trent, ST1 5BS Tel: (01782) 287674 Fax: (01782) 287674 *Blind retailers & manufrs*

Cavalier Of Brighton, 9-11 Nevill Road, Rottingdean, Rottingdean, Brighton, BN2 7HH Tel: (01273) 309224 Fax: (01273) 306321 E-mail: cavalierofbrighton@tiscali.co.uk *Bakery foods wholesale & distributors*

Cavalier Carpets Ltd, Thompson St Industrial Estate, Blackburn, BB2 1TX Tel: (01254) 268000 Fax: (01254) 268001 E-mail: info@cavalier-carpets.co.uk *Wilton carpets manufrs*

▶ Cavalier Mailing Services Ltd, Mackintosh Road, Rackheath Industrial Estate, Norwich, NR13 6LJ Tel: (01603) 720303 Fax: (01603) 721247 E-mail: a.kerridge@cavaliermailing.com *International direct mailing*

▶ Cavalier Marketing, North Dean Road, Keighley, West Yorkshire, BD22 6QY Tel: (01535) 613830 Fax: (01535) 613831 *Furniture manufrs*

Cavalier Software, 1 Bryn Tirion, Nebo Road, Llanrwst, Gwynedd, LL26 0HL Tel: (01492) 641548 *Computer software manufrs*

Cavalry Creative Services, 11 Bury Road, Hatfield, Hertfordshire, AL10 8BJ Tel: (01707) 274584 Fax: (01707) 321043 E-mail: cavalry@ntlworld.com *Printing services*

Cavanagh Roofing Ltd, 36 Dalkeith Avenue, Glasgow, G41 5BN Tel: 0141-427 5555 Fax: 0141-427 5555 *Bitumen & felt roofing contractors*

Cavat, 7 New Road, Burton Lazars, Melton Mowbray, Leicestershire, LE14 2UU Tel: (01664) 561761 Fax: (01664) 410280 E-mail: cavattools@cavattools.co.uk *Cutting tool specialists*

The Cavendish, 81 Jermyn Street, London, SW1Y 6JF Tel: (020) 7930 2111 Fax: (020) 7839 2125 *Hotel & conference facilities*

Cavendish Fabrics Ltd, 140 New Cavendish Street, London, W1W 6YE Tel: (020) 7631 0768 Fax: (020) 7580 8481 *Textile merchants*

Cavendish Hardware, 8 242 Tithe Street, Leicester, LE5 4BN Tel: 0116-274 1746 Fax: 0116-246 1545 E-mail: sales@cavendish-hardware.co.uk Principal Export Areas: Worldwide *Window & door hardware*

Cavendish Hosiery Ltd, 77 Cannock Street, Leicester, LE4 9HR Tel: 0116-276 6477 E-mail: cavendishhos@aol.com *Ladies' & children's sock manufrs*

Cavendish Joinery, Cavendish House, Plumpton Road, Hoddesdon, Hertfordshire, EN11 0LB Tel: (01992) 464506 Fax: (01992) 469506 E-mail: sales@liftcars.net *Joinery manufrs*

▶ Cavendish Management Training, Kings Court, 17 School Road, Hall Green, Birmingham, B28 8JG Tel: (0870) 3219451 Fax: 0121-733 2902 E-mail: sales@mgt-services.com *Personnel services*

Cavendish Packaging Ltd, Manor Royal, Faraday Road, Crawley, West Sussex, RH10 9UR Tel: (01293) 525556 Fax: (01293) 528886 *Carton manufrs*

Cavendish Resources, 57 Chaldon Road, London, SW6 7NH Tel: (020) 7381 0276 Fax: (020) 7386 8183 *Aircraft accessories suppliers*

Cavendish Upholstery Ltd, Mayfield Mill, Briercliffe Road, Chorley, Lancashire, PR6 0DA Tel: (01257) 277664 Fax: (01257) 261665 E-mail: suites@cavendish-upholstery.co.uk *Upholstery manufrs*

▶ Cavern Crystals, 376 Wakefield Road, Denby Dale, Huddersfield, HD8 8RT Tel: 01484 865427 Fax: 01484 865427 E-mail: info@crystalcavern.com *New age online store - Specialising in amethyst, rose quartz, quartz crystals, rune stones and crystal healing stones for alternative health use. Also offers The A-Z of crystals for crystal healers.*

Cavity Trays Ltd, Boundary Avenue, Lufton Trading Estate, Lufton, Yeovil, Somerset, BA22 8HU Tel: (01935) 474769 Fax: (01935) 428223 E-mail: sales@cavitytrays.co.uk *Cavity trays, cavity wall & closures manufrs*

▶ Cawdell Contracts, Malting Lane, Dagnall, Berkhamsted, Hertfordshire, HP4 1QY Tel: (01442) 843100 Fax: (01442) 842170 *Suspended ceilings & dry wall lining manufrs*

▶ Cawl Bunker Services, Albion Mills, 18 East Tenter St, London, E1 8DM Tel: (020) 7216 2000 Fax: (020) 7216 2001 E-mail: bunkers@cawl-group.com *Oil brokers*

Caws Cenarth, Glyneithinog, Lancych, Boncath, Dyfed, SA37 0LH Tel: (01239) 710432 *Cheese manufrs*

Caws Cymru, Wervil Grange, Pentregat, Llandysul, Dyfed, SA44 6HW Tel: (01239) 654800 Fax: (01239) 654800 *Dairy products wholesalers*

Cawthra Bros Ltd, Milton Shed, Gibbet Street, Halifax, West Yorkshire, HX1 5BA Tel: (01422) 352464 Fax: (01422) 354215 *Weaving manufrs*

▶ Caxton Supplies, Eastbridge Road, Burmarsh, Romney Marsh, Kent, TN29 0HY Tel: (01303) 872692 Fax: (01303) 873799 E-mail: caxtonsupplies@tiscalli.co.uk *Cleaning materials*

Cayley Chemical Corporation Ltd, 10 Manor Park Business Centre, Mackenzie Way, Swindon Village, Cheltenham, Gloucestershire, GL51 9TX Tel: (01242) 222971 Fax: (01242) 227634 E-mail: cayley@btinternet.com *International chemical traders*

▶ Cayline Cabinets, Cliff Road, Hornsea, North Humberside, HU18 1JB Tel: (01964) 532221 Fax: (01964) 533872 E-mail: admin@caylinecabinets.co.uk *Kitchen, bedroom & bathroom manufrs*

Cazaly Hillstead Holdings Ltd, 9-10 Industrial Estate, Thomas Road, London, E14 7BN Tel: (020) 7515 4444 Fax: (020) 7537 2650 E-mail: nmp@cazaly.fsbusiness.co.uk *Contract furnishers*

▶ CB CNC UK Ltd, Apartment 113, Whitfield Mill, Meadow Road, Apperley Bridge, Bradford, West Yorkshire, BD10 0LP Tel: (07881) 922680 Fax: (01274) 612808 E-mail: cc.silv-birch@fsmail.net *CNC machine tool repair & service*

▶ CB Neon Signmakers, Humberstone Lane, Leicester, LE4 9HA Tel: 0116-246 1838 Fax: 0116-246 1838 E-mail: justin@aol.com *Sign makers, suppliers, contractors & installers*

CB Richard Ellis, 7 Castle Street, Edinburgh, EH3 3AH Tel: 0131-469 7666 Fax: 0131-469 0131 E-mail: info@cbre.com *Surveyors*

CB Services, 5 Building 14 Mallusk Park, Mallusk Road, Newtownabbey, County Antrim, BT36 4FS Tel: (028) 9083 7738 Fax: (028) 9083 2093 E-mail: iaininfo@cb-services.com *Car wash distributors & chemical manufrs*

▶ CB Solutions, Wise Field, Beverley Road, Beeford, Driffield, East Yorkshire, YO25 8AD Tel: (01262) 488919 Fax: (01262) 488986 E-mail: info@cbsol.co.uk *UPVC windows & doors manufrs*

CBC Ltd, 91C-91D Mora Road, London, NW2 6TB Tel: (020) 8450 9185 Fax: (020) 8450 6090 *Computer builders*

CBC Computer Systems Ltd, 64 Balby Road, Doncaster, South Yorkshire, DN4 0JL Tel: (01302) 768500 Fax: (01302) 761783 E-mail: sales-donc@cbccomputers.com *Computer resellers*

▶ CBF, Holly Farm Business Park, Honiley, Kenilworth, Warwickshire, CV8 1NP Tel: (01926) 484060 Fax: (01926) 486340

CBISS Ltd, 11 Ark Royal Way, Lairdside Technology Park, Tranmere, Birkenhead, Merseyside, CH41 9HT Tel: 0151-666 8300 Fax: 0151-666 8329 E-mail: sales@cbiss.com *Monitoring & environmental control services*

CBL Ceramics, Marble Hall Road, Milford Haven, Dyfed, SA73 2PP Tel: (01646) 697681 Fax: (01646) 690053 *Specialist ceramics manufrs*

CBM Construction Group Ltd, 44 Goodman Street, Leeds, LS10 1NY Tel: 0113-271 0200 Fax: 0113-271 2446 E-mail: info@cbm-construction.co.uk *Building construction contractors*

▶ c-breeze communications Ltd, The Picturehouse, 309-315 Holdenhurst Road, Bournemouth, BH8 8BX Tel: (01202) 303335 Fax: (01202) 303336 E-mail: info@c-breezecommunications.co.uk *Marketing, brand & corporate communications agency*

CB's Aerials, Glendale, Heath Road, Holmewood, Chesterfield, Derbyshire, S42 5RB Tel: (01246) 852667 E-mail: carlboulter@aol.com *Analogue, digital aerials & satellite television installers & services*

CBS Butler, Kings Mill, Kings Mill Lane, South Nutfield, Redhill, RH1 5NB Tel: (01737) 822000 Fax: (01737) 823031 E-mail: admin@uk.butler.com *Recruitment consultants*

CBS Products Ltd, Pillings Road, Oakham, Leicestershire, LE15 6QF Tel: (01572) 723665 Fax: (01572) 756009 E-mail: sales@cbsproducts.com *Cable laying equipment providers & manufrs*

▶ CC Groundworks, 49 Bridge Street, Usk, Gwent, NP15 1BQ Tel: (01291) 671116

CCD Pumps Ltd, 212 Ilderton Road, London, SE15 1NT Tel: (020) 7639 4864 Fax: (020) 7635 0102 E-mail: sales@ccdpumps.co.uk *Pump sales, installation & repairs*

CCF, Newark Road, Peterborough, PE1 5YX Tel: (01733) 551333 Fax: (01733) 311921 *Insulation & dry lining manufrs*

CCF Couriers, 5a Wild Ridings Square, Bracknell, Berkshire, RG12 7SJ Tel: (01344) 452113 Fax: (01344) 489509 E-mail: ccfcouriers@btconnect.com *Courier delivery services*

▶ CCI Legal Services Ltd, Unit 5, Snowdonia Business Park, Minffordd, Penrhyndeudraeth, Gwynedd, LL48 6LD Tel: (01766) 771166 Fax: (01766) 771840 E-mail: sales@ccilegal.co.uk

▶ CCL Components, Unit 22 Evans Business Centre, 70 Queen Elizabeth Avenue, Hillington Industrial Estate, Glasgow, G52 4NQ Tel: (0870) 8705522 Fax: (0870) 8705525 E-mail: kd@cclcomponents.com

CCL Label, Pioneer Way, Castleford, West Yorkshire, WF10 5QU Tel: (01977) 711111 Fax: (01977) 711102 *Label manufrs*

CCL Veloduct, 1-3 Dean Road, Lincoln, LN2 4DR Tel: (01522) 567087 Fax: (01522) 563525 *Heating & ventilation distributors* Also at: Nottingham

CCM, 452 Holdenhurst Road, Bournemouth, BH8 9AF Tel: (01202) 302666 Fax: (01202) 302999 E-mail: sales@rakretail.co.uk *Cash registers*

CCM Ace Ltd, 223 Bury New Road, Whitefield, Manchester, M45 8GW Tel: 0161-766 4686 Fax: 0161-767 9217 E-mail: sales@ccmace.co.uk *Software developers*

Cconline Computer Systems, 33 Main Street, Turriff, Aberdeenshire, AB53 4AB Tel: (01888) 562180 E-mail: sales@cconlineuk.com *Computer hardware suppliers*

▶ CCR, 4 Woodend Street, Stoke-on-Trent, ST4 3JS Tel: (01782) 323601 Fax: (01782) 323626 E-mail: mail@ccrsales.co.uk *Cash register manufrs*

CCR Services Ltd, 128 Vale Road, Rhyl, Clwyd, LL18 2PD Tel: (01745) 360788 Fax: (01745) 360788 E-mail: info@ccrservices.co.uk *Cash registers sales & repairs*

CCS, Peashill Farm, Peashill Lane, Cotgrave, Nottingham, NG12 3HD Tel: 0115-989 2423 Fax: 0115-989 4951 *Selling & repairing fax machines & photocopiers & printers*

CCS Media Holdings Ltd, Old Birdholme House, Derby Road, Chesterfield, Derbyshire, S40 2EX Tel: (01246) 200200 Fax: (01246) 207048 E-mail: enquiries@ccsmedia.com *Computer consumables suppliers*

CCS Neon Ltd, Mabgate Mills, Mabgate, Leeds, LS9 7DZ Tel: 0113-242 1390 *Neon signs & lighting manufrs*

CCSS Europe Ltd, 6 The Courtyard, Campus Way, Gillingham Business Park, Gillingham, Kent, ME8 0NZ Tel: (01634) 370444 Fax: (01634) 370555 E-mail: info@ccssltd.com *Computer software developers*

▶ The CCTV Co., Crows Nest, Ashton Road, Billinge, Wigan, Lancashire, WN5 7XY Tel: (01744) 891702 Fax: (01744) 891710 E-mail: john@thecctvcompany.com

CCTV 4U Ltd, Unit A5, Maritime Park, Pembroke Dock, Pembrokeshire, SA72 6UL Tel: 0 845 226 31 91 Fax: 0 845 226 31 94 E-mail: info@cctv4u.co.uk *Digital Security components in Pembrokeshire, specialising in CCTV, Alarms and Physical security*

▶ CCTV Consultation & Sales, 381 London Rd., Deal, Kent, CT14 9PS Tel: 07050 228885 Fax: 0870 169 6707 E-mail: enquiries@cctv-information.co.uk *The World's leading CCTV information web site. Includes information on design, sales, consultation, equipment and the pitfalls to avoid*

▶ CCTV Services Ltd, Unit 11, Plot 27, Llandegai Industrial Estate, Bangor, Gwynedd, LL57 4YH Tel: (08703) 770100 Fax: (08703) 770108 E-mail: mike@cctvserviceslimited.com *CCTV system consultancy, installation, integration & maintenance*

CCTV Systems Manchester Ltd, 31a Astley Street, Tyldesley, Manchester, M29 8HG Tel: (01942) 894008 Fax: (01942) 893339 E-mail: info@cctv.tv *CCTV equipment remote monitoring services*

CD Team Group Ltd, Unit 1 Fairview Trading Estate, Reading Road, Henley-on-Thames, Oxfordshire, RG9 1HE Tel: (01491) 636373 Fax: (01491) 636374 E-mail: info@cdteam.co.uk *CD & DVD duplication service*

▶ CD Web Design, Forester's Cottage, Kilmaron Estate, Cupar, Fife, KY15 4NE Tel: (07715) 707953 Fax: (01334) 650908 *Website design*

▶ CD Writer Com Ltd, Greenwich High Road, London, SE10 8JL Tel: (020) 8694 7820 Fax: (020) 8694 3754

CDC Instant Space Ltd, Bissoe, Truro, Cornwall, TR4 8QZ Tel: (08706) 082808 Fax: (01872) 862502 *Portable modular building suppliers*

CDC Software, 7 Rushmills, Northampton, NN4 7YB Tel: (01604) 630050 Fax: (01604) 630495 *Computer systems consultants*

▶ CDI DEBT RECOVERY, 9A The Esplanade, Sunderland, SR2 7BQ Tel: 0191 6666666

Cdi Group plc, 5-7 Melchett Road, Kings Norton Business Centre, Birmingham, B30 3HG Tel: 0121-458 4888 Fax: 0121-433 2800 *Electrical contractors*

CDK Engineering Services Ltd, 30 The Avenue, Stoke-Sub-Hamdon, Somerset, TA14 6QB Tel: 01935 825592 Fax: 01823 261066 E-mail: sales@cdkengineering.com *Supply & service solutions to the food & beverage, cosmetic & allied industries*

▶ CDL Couriers, 32 Raymond Drive, Bradford, West Yorkshire, BD5 8HS Tel: (01274) 206329 E-mail: cdlcouriers@yahoo.co.uk *C.D.L. Couriers are a small family run company with over 28 years experiance in UK Road Haulage, Parcel Delivery,and Transport Managment,We provide a one to one friendly service to everyone. Fully Insured, G.I.T., & Public Liability*

CDM Software Services Ltd, The Business Centre, Edward Street, Redditch, Worcestershire, B97 6HA Tel: (01527) 68688 Fax: (01527) 68816 E-mail: support@cdmsoftware.co.uk *Computer & software consultants*

CDM Solutions Ltd, 60 Carter Street, Uttoxeter, Staffordshire, ST14 8EU Tel: (01889) 563434 Fax: (01889) 562797 E-mail: info@cdmsolutions.co.uk *Software development services*

▶ CDMS, Fallows Way, Whiston, Prescot, Merseyside, L35 1RZ Tel: 0151-290 5500 Fax: 0151-290 5599 E-mail: sales@edns.co.uk *Commercial printers & direct mail*

CDP Ltd, Old Popplewell Lane, Scholes, Cleckheaton, West Yorkshire, BD19 6DW Tel: (01274) 697697 Fax: (01274) 697797 E-mail: webtech@cdpltd.co.uk *Shaped wire manufrs*

CDS, Belvoir Way, Fairfield Industrial Estate, Louth, Lincolnshire, LN11 0LQ Tel: (01507) 610555 Fax: (01507) 610500 *Packaging service*

CDS, 3 Avon Path, South Croydon, Surrey, CR2 6AX Tel: (020) 8651 4240 Fax: (020) 8651 0812 *Confidential document shredding*

CDS Consultants, Bwlch Tocyn Farm, Bwlchtocyn, Pwllheli, Gwynedd, LL53 7BN Tel: (01758) 712245 Fax: (01758) 712014 E-mail: cdsconsultants@btinternet.com *suppliers of abrasive blast cleaning plant and equipment worldwide**Procurement specialists of any item of equipment to overseas government governmental agencies **Suppliers to USA ARMY AND MARINE CORPS OF ENGINEERS*

CDS Meter Operatorrs, Little Wood Ho, Wheatley Rd, Sturton-le-steeple, Retford, Notts, DN22 9HU Tel: 01427 881551 Fax: 01427 881511 *Meter operation systems*

CDT Response, Bourne Road Industrial Park, Bourne Road, Dartford, DA1 4BZ Tel: (01322) 555888 Fax: (01322) 555004 E-mail: helpdesk@responseuk.org *Building maintenance service suppliers*

▶ CDV UK Ltd, Unit B1 Knaves Beech Industrial Estate, Knaves Beech Way, Loudwater, High Wycombe, Buckinghamshire, HP10 9QY Tel: (01628) 531300 Fax: (01628) 531003 E-mail: sales@cdvuk.com *Electrical contractors*

Ceag Ltd, Zenith Park, Whaley Road, Barnsley, South Yorkshire, S75 1HT Tel: (01226) 206842 Fax: (01226) 731645 E-mail: sales@ceag.co.uk *Vehicle industrial lighting rail & marine lighting manufrs*

Ceandess Ltd, Ashford Industrial Estate, Dixon Street, Wolverhampton, WV2 2BX Tel: (01902) 872000 Fax: (01902) 872019 E-mail: sales@ceandess.co.uk *Tank filler cap & metallic washer manufrs*

Ceasefire, 4 Reedmace, Tamworth, Staffordshire, B77 1BH Tel: (01827) 56556 Fax: (01827) 54364 *Fire protection*

Ceaton Security Services, The Lodge, 128 Newport Road, Cardiff, CF24 1DH Tel: (029) 2047 2288 Fax: (029) 2047 3377 *Security installation, maintenance & sales*

Cebo UK Ltd, Badentoy Road, Portlethen, Aberdeen, AB12 4YA Tel: (01224) 782020 Fax: (01224) 782340 E-mail: info@cebo-uk.com *Cebo UK provide bulk materials (Cement, Baryte & Bentonite), Bulk Delivery Hose and Rotary Drilling Hose to the Oil & Gas drilling industry. Products used in Industrial Drilling are also provided. As a service Cebo inspect, repair, re-certify and manage the changeout of large bore Tanker Load hose offshore*

continued

Cebo UK Ltd, Boundary Road, Great Yarmouth, Norfolk, NR31 0LY Tel: (01493) 656100 Fax: (01493) 650020 E-mail: nick@cebo-yarmouth.fsnet.co.uk *Oil distributors*

Cebotec Ltd, 26 Castle Road, Bankside Industrial Estate, Falkirk, FK2 7UY Tel: (01324) 877778 Fax: (01324) 882525 E-mail: sales@cebotec.co.uk *Commercial vehicle bodybuilders, repairs & hire*

▶ cebuc, The Pewfist Spinney, Westhoughton, Bolton, BL5 2UN Tel: 07981 172552 Fax: 0870 1341267 E-mail: chris.kelly@cebuc.com

Cecil Instruments Ltd, Cambridge Road Industrial Estate, Milton, Cambridge, CB24 6AZ Tel: (01223) 420821 Fax: (01223) 420475 E-mail: info@cecilinstruments.com *Scientific instrument manufrs*

Cecil W Tyzack, 79-81 Kingsland Road, London, E2 8AH Tel: (020) 7739 2630 Fax: (020) 7729 3373 *Woodworking machinists*

Ceco Packaging Services, The Forge, Kirk Eaton, Huddersfield, HD5 0JS Tel: (01484) 424673 Fax: (01484) 519727 E-mail: james@kirkeng.co.uk *Shrink wrapping equipment manufrs*

▶ Cecube Ltd, 5 Mayfair, Radcliffe On Trent, Radcliffe-on-Trent, Nottingham, NG12 2NP Tel: 0115-933 2673 Fax: 0115-933 2679 E-mail: info@cecube.co.uk *Industrial supplier of railway technical solutions*

Ced Fabrications Ltd, Clayton House, Clayton Business Park, Clayton le Moors, Accrington, Lancashire, BB5 5JD Tel: (01254) 238282 Fax: (01254) 238228 E-mail: sales@cedfabsltd.demon.co.uk *food service display equipment, hotcupboards, steel fabrication*

Cedabond Catering Equipment Ltd, 42 Brook Lane, Warash, Southampton, SO31 9FG Tel: (01489) 576 779 E-mail: pnewman@cedabond.co.uk *Catering equipment suppliers*

Cedalion Ltd, Great Michael House, 14 Links Place, Edinburgh, EH6 7EZ Tel: 0131-477 7741 Fax: 0131-477 7742 E-mail: info@cedalion.co.uk *Software developers*

▶ Cedar Building Services, 27 Sackville Road, Heaton, Newcastle upon Tyne, NE6 5SY Tel: 0191-265 3406 Fax: 0191-265 3406 E-mail: jon@cedarbs.wanadoo.co.uk *Established joiners and building contractors in the North East offering a high quality service encompassing all aspects of joinery and building construction including loft conversions, building extensions and building operations. Prompt quotations, free estimates and excellent workmanship.*

Cedar Glade Foods Ltd, George House, 3 St Davids Court, Kenn, Clevedon, Avon, BS21 6UP Tel: (01934) 834095 Fax: (01934) 835778 E-mail: cfoodsltd@aol.com *Food & drink wholesalers*

Cedar Supplies Ltd, PO Box 59, Crowborough, East Sussex, TN6 3NQ Tel: (01892) 853389 Fax: (01892) 853411 E-mail: sales@cedarsupplies.com *Export merchants*

Cedar Systems Ltd, 2440 The Quadrant, Aztec West, Almondsbury, Bristol, BS32 4AQ Tel: (01454) 878708 Fax: (01454) 878608 E-mail: cedar@cedar.co.uk *Software company*

▶ Cedardell Ltd, 3 Collingwood Street, Newcastle upon Tyne, NE1 1JW Tel: 0191-260 2600 Fax: 0191-260 2606 E-mail: sales@cedardell.com

▶ Cede Tech, 78 London Road, Worcester, WR5 2DY Tel: (01905) 831599 *Software developers*

Cedesa Ltd, Chater Lea Building, Icknield Way, Letchworth Garden City, Hertfordshire, SG6 1WT Tel: (01462) 480764 Fax: (01462) 480765 E-mail: neil.wildon@cedesa.co.uk *Adhesive packing & filling contract services, including collapsible tube filling, bottle filling, blister packing, two component filling, thermoforming & cartridge filling.*

Cee Gee Agencies, Cee Gee House, College Road, Harrow Weald, Harrow, Middlesex, HA3 6EF Tel: (020) 8863 8596 Fax: (020) 8427 1827 *Label printers*

▶ Cee Jay Markings, Summerfield House, 127a Burnham Lane, Slough, SL1 6LA Tel: (01628) 663758 Fax: (01628) 660329 E-mail: contact@ceejaymarkings.co.uk *Line marking specialists services, car parks, playgrounds & sports halls*

Cee Tel, Unit 8 Manners View, Northumberland Rd, Newport, Isle of Wight, PO30 5SA Tel: (01983) 537171 Fax: (01983) 882444 *Environmental chamber manufrs*

Cee Vee Engineering Ltd, Shepherds Close, Cooden Sea Road, Bexhill-on-Sea, East Sussex, TN39 4SL Tel: (01424) 845566 Fax: (01424) 842144 E-mail: sales@ceevee.co.uk *Disabled, handicapped person aid designers*

Cee-Jay, 4-6 Beeching Close, Bexhill-on-Sea, East Sussex, TN39 3YF Tel: (01424) 734126 Fax: (01424) 734126 *Sign manufrs*

Ceejay Maintenance Ltd, Unit 49 Fairways Business Park, Lammas Road, London, E10 7QB Tel: (020) 8518 7644 Fax: (020) 8518 7678 *Steel fabricators & architectural metalworkers*

Ceejay Photographic, 290 Ashby High Street, Scunthorpe, South Humberside, DN16 2RX Tel: (01724) 280510 Fax: (01724) 289966 E-mail: sales@ceejaysystems.com *Commercial & industrial photography*

▶ Cee-Lite & Sound Ltd, Unit 52, Imex Business Park, Ormonde Street, Stoke-on-Trent, ST4 3NP Tel: (01782) 596666 Fax: (01782) 596666 E-mail: sales@cee-lite.com *Sales of Lighting And Sound,P.A. Effects Lighting, Controllers,Dmx Lighting,Lamps, Cables,Theatre Lighting,Dimmers,EFX Lighting,Stands,Package Deals,Headphones,Par Cans,Clamps,Cheap Deals.*

Ceema Technology, 4 The Omega Centre, Stratton Business Park, Biggleswade, Bedfordshire, SG18 8QB Tel: (01767) 319800 Fax: (01767) 317621 E-mail: reception@ceema.co.uk *Engineering design & recruitment*

Ceep Ltd, Unit 7 Weydown Industrial Estate, Haslemere, Surrey, GU27 1DW Tel: (01428) 661515 Fax: (01428) 644147 E-mail: sales@ceep.co.uk Principal Export Areas: Asia Pacific, Middle East, Africa, Central/ East Europe, West Europe, North America & South America *Connector manufrs*

▶ CeeT UK, 20 Lewis Street, Eccles, Manchester, M30 0PX Tel: (07793) 537512 Fax: 0161-707 9145 E-mail: sales@ceetuk.co.uk *Agents for suppliers of packaging film, lamination, flexible packaging*

Ceetak Ltd, Fraser Road, Priory Business Park, Bedford, MK44 3WH Tel: (01234) 832200 Fax: (01234) 832299 E-mail: ceetakltd@ceetak.com *Electrometric sealing solutions*

Ceetak Engineering Ltd, 1 Napier Road, Elm Farm Industrial Estate, Bedford, MK41 0QR Tel: (01234) 343232 Fax: (01234) 341133 E-mail: ceetakengineering@bedford.com *Pump distributors & spare parts suppliers*

Ceetak Engineering Ltd, Unit 10 Easter Court, Europa Boulevard, Westbrook, Warrington, WA5 7ZB Tel: (01925) 710500 Fax: (01925) 710605 *Pump repair & maintenance services & supplies*

Ceetek Chemicals Ltd, Firs Industrial Estate, Kidderminster, Worcestershire, DY11 7QN Tel: (01562) 755337 Fax: (01562) 865660 E-mail: ceetek@aol.com *Cleaning chemicals manufacture & automated vehicle wash system manufrs*

Ceeway Bike Building Supplies, 80-82 West Street, Erith, Kent, DA8 1AQ Tel: (01322) 442990 Fax: (01322) 442886 E-mail: sales@framebuilding.com *Bicycle frame components importers & sales*

Cefn Strain Gauges, Unit E26 Hirwaun Industrial Estate, Hirwaun, Aberdare, Mid Glamorgan, CF44 9UP Tel: (01685) 814451 Fax: (01685) 814342 E-mail: rob@cefn-sg.sfnet.co.uk *Metal pressings manufrs*

Cegedim Ltd, Fourth Floor, Nicholsons House, Nicholsons Walk, Maidenhead, Berkshire, SL6 1LD Tel: (01628) 773533 Fax: (01628) 771488 *Maintenance of pharmaceutical databases*

Cegelec Repair & Maintenance Services, Pyewipe, Gilbey Road, Grimsby, South Humberside, DN31 2SJ Tel: (01472) 355869 Fax: (01472) 250363 E-mail: info.uk@cegelec.com *Cegelec is a global company employing over 500 people in the UK. Providing innovative technological solutions and services, Cegelec designs, installs and maintains electrical and mechanical systems for Industry, Infrastructure and the Service Sector. Our expertise covers HV, MV, LV electrical systems and instrumentation, repair and maintenance services for rotating electrical plant as well as building services.*

▶ CeilCote, 26 Fenlake Business Centre, Fengate, Peterborough, PE1 5BQ Tel: (01733) 558251 Fax: (01733) 558251 E-mail: lloyd@ceilcote.com *Spraying specialists for ceiling & shopfronts.*

▶ Ceiling 2 Ltd, Hazel Grove, Linthwaite, Huddersfield, HD7 5TQ Tel: (01484) 300106 Fax: (01484) 300114 *Suspend ceilings manufrs*

Ceiling Craft, 44 Vernon Drive, Stanmore, Middlesex, HA7 2BT Tel: (020) 8427 4560 Fax: (020) 8426 0599 *Suspended ceiling specialists*

Ceiling Grids Ltd, Branson Street, Manchester, M40 7FJ Tel: 0161-273 4511 Fax: 0161-274 3914 *Suspended ceilings & dry wall partitions suppliers*

Ceiling Installation Ltd, Sanserra House, Mayfield Road, Bournemouth, BH9 1TW Tel: (01202) 539700 Fax: (01202) 535652 E-mail: cil2srs@aol.com *Ceiling services*

Ceiling Services, 4 North Grove, Dalry, Ayrshire, KA24 5DW Tel: (01294) 835336 *Ceiling services*

Ceiling Services Ltd, 3 West Hill, Dunstable, Beds, LU6 3PN Tel: 01582 668822 Fax: 01582 665586 *Suspended ceilings installation*

Ceilings Distribution Ltd, 2a-Elland Way, Leeds, LS11 0EY Tel: 0113-270 0333 Fax: 0113-270 2839 *Suspended ceiling specialists & supplier*

▶ Ceilings Distribution Ltd, Cameron Court, Winwick Quay, Warrington, WA2 8RE Tel: (01925) 635405 Fax: (01925) 417291 *Manufactures of ceiling components*

▶ Ceilings & Partitions Ltd, Alexander House, Robinson Terrace, Washington, Tyne & Wear, NE38 7BD Tel: 0191-417 8089 Fax: 0191-417 1486 *Ceilings installers*

▶ Ceilite Air Conditioning Ltd, 1 The Alcorns, Cambridge Road, Stansted, Essex, CM24 8DF Tel: (01279) 815503 Fax: (01279) 813971 E-mail: sales@ceilte.com *Design, installation, servicing & maintenance of airconditioning units*

Ceipart Ltd, 1 Bowker Street, Worsley, Manchester, M28 0SG Tel: 0161-790 5905 Fax: 0161-703 8673 E-mail: ceipt@aol.com *Ceiling & partition contractors*

Cel International, Cel House Westwood Way, Westwood Business Park, Coventry, CV4 8HS Tel: (024) 7686 2000 Fax: (024) 7686 2200 E-mail: info@cel-international.com *Engineering project management services*

Celab Ltd, 25 Woolmer Way, Bordon, Hampshire, GU35 9QE Tel: (01420) 477011 Fax: (01420) 472034 *Power supply manufrs*

Celcius Refrigeration, Sunnyside, Tilthams Green, Godalming, Surrey, GU7 3BT Tel: (01483) 418703 Fax: (01483) 421096 E-mail: celsius_refrigeration@hotmail.com *Commercial refrigeration services*

Celco Ltd, 14 Forest Hill Business Centre, Clyde Vale, London, SE23 3JF Fax: (020) 8699 5056 E-mail: sales@celco.co.uk *Stage lighting equipment suppliers*

Celcoat Ltd, 3 Crown Works, Rotherham Road, Beighton, Sheffield, S20 1AH Tel: 0114-269 0771 Fax: 0114-254 0495 E-mail: celcoatltd@tiscali.co.uk *Ceramic, metal & plasma spraying contractors & services*

▶ Celebrati Newspaper, Somerset House, 40-49 Price Street, Birmingham, B4 6LZ Tel: (0870) 4324175 Fax: (0870) 4324196 E-mail: editor@celebrati.co.uk *There is no other tabloid like Celebráti in the United Kingdom. Unique to it''s core with its insider coverage on*

continued

*fashion, music, film, accessories, wellbeing, fitness, beauty, culture and travel written by key fashion figures and luminaries. It is an intelligent, witty, contemporary tabloid which has an attractive and enchanting enticement.**The emergence of celebrity style during the past century has witnessed the acceptance of charismatic ladies and gentlemen as cultural and aesthetic ideals. Image has become a marketing device to extend sales and popularity. **With the ever growing public obsession of fashion, music, film, health, beauty, wellbeing, fitness, travel and prominent life styling, Celebráti is born. The weekly Bible of aspiration, appropriating western ideals of perfection not only for work but also for leisure.**Celebráti explores the marriage of luminary culture with vogue through intimate interviews, lifestyle and sub cultures.*

Celebration Balloon Co. Ltd, 90 The Broadway, High Street, Chesham, Buckinghamshire, HP5 1EG Tel: (01494) 791969 Fax: (08700) 526501 *Venue decorators*

Celebration File Ltd, Oakwood House, Spa Road, Melksham, Wiltshire, SN12 7TA Tel: (01225) 705582 Fax: (01225) 700277 E-mail: direct@cflmarketing.co.uk *Direct marketing services*

▶ Celebration Stationery, Unit 1, The Caxton Centre, Porters Wood, St. Albans, Hertfordshire, AL3 6XT Tel: (01727) 868237 Fax: (01727) 847883 E-mail: chris@celebrationstationery.co.uk *Provide wedding stationary & accessories*

▶ Celebration-Balloons, 859 Whittingham Lane, Goosnargh, Preston, PR3 2AU Tel: (01772) 861190 Fax: (01772) 861190 E-mail: info@celebration-balloons.co.uk *Card & gift shop picture frame etc*

Celebrity Motion Furniture Ltd, Unit 1 Wimsey Way, Somercotes, Alfreton, Derbyshire, DE55 4LS Tel: (01773) 604607 Fax: (01773) 541408 E-mail: reception@celebrity-furniture.co.uk *Upholster reclining furniture manufrs*

▶ Celebrity Voices Ltd, 23 Springfeilds, Waltham Abbey, Essex, EN9 1UD Tel: (01992) 611097 E-mail: stuart@celebrityvoices.co.uk *Mobile phone content, audio, web services and greeting card publisher.*

Celect Tools, Ainsworth Street, Rochdale, Lancashire, OL16 5QX Tel: (07814) 349636 Fax: (01706) 648106 E-mail: sales@celect-tools.co.uk *Plastics mould toolmakers & injection moulders*

Celectron Printing, 18-18a Unit, Vale Business Park, Llandow, Cowbridge, South Glamorgan, CF71 7PF Tel: (01446) 774801 Fax: (01446) 775285 E-mail: info@soprint.co.uk *General & lithographic printers*

▶ Celerity Payroll Services Ltd, 21 Longhill Road, Brighton, BN2 7BF Tel: (01273) 306836 Fax: (01273) 304604 E-mail: info@payline.co.uk *Payroll & BACS bureau services*

Cell Ltd, Hallsteads, Dove Holes, Buxton, Derbyshire, SK17 8BJ Tel: (01298) 816692 Fax: (01298) 816277 E-mail: sales@cell-limited.co.uk *Carton merchants & agents*

Cellande Cleaning Materials, Cellande House, 118 Gristhorpe Road, Birmingham, B29 7SL Tel: 0121-472 2903 Fax: 0121-246 7446 E-mail: e-mail@cellande.co.uk *Natural cleansing & cleaning products suppliers*

Cellar Services, 39 Middle Park Way, Leigh Park, Havant, Hampshire, PO9 4AB Tel: (0845) 021 2337 Fax: (023) 9213 2047 E-mail: beerclear@hotmail.com *Who are we? **We are a privately owned cellar services and maintainance company **providing cellar services to the trade and to small and large companies.**Beer Clear Cellar services**has been the U.K''s number one beer line cleaning company since 1993. **During this period we have been working hard** on behalf of pubs, clubs, hotels and restaurants **saving them both time and money. **Our company remains number one due to our commitment** to providing a "first class" and reliable service, and we will **continue to save landlords, time and money. Guaranteed!***

Cellar Systems Ltd, 7 Grange Mills, Weir Road, London, SW12 0NE Tel: (020) 8673 5104 Fax: (020) 8673 2649 *Computer anti virus resellers*

Cellbeam Ltd, Unit 516, Thorp Arch Trading Estate, Thorp Arch, Wetherby, West Yorkshire, LS23 7DB Tel: (01937) 840600 Fax: (01937) 840601 E-mail: sales@cellbeam.co.uk *Structural steelworkers*

Cellbond Composites Ltd, 4-5 Blackstone Road, Stukeley Meadows Industrial Es, Huntingdon, Cambridgeshire, PE29 6EF Tel: (01480) 435302 Fax: (01480) 450181 E-mail: sales.precision@cellbond.com *Precision engineers & toolmakers*

Cellhire plc, Park House, Clifton Park Avenue, York, YO30 5PB Tel: (01904) 610610 Fax: (01904) 611028 E-mail: rentals@cellhire.com *Mobile phone hire* Also at: Glasgow, London & Manchester

Celloglas Speciality Products, Unit 12C, Exeter Way, Theale Commercial Park, Theale, Reading, RG7 4AW Tel: 0118-930 3656 Fax: 0118-932 3256 E-mail: andy.kirbycelloglas@alcan.co.uk *Reflective material manufrs*

Celloglass Ltd, Headley Road East, Woodley, Reading, RG5 4UA Tel: 0118-944 1441 Fax: 0118-944 1913 E-mail: yvonne.parks@celloglas.co.uk *Print finishers* Also at: Branches throughout the U.K.

Cellpath plc, Unit 66 Mochdre Industrial Estate, Mochdre, Newtown, Powys, SY16 4LE Tel: (01686) 611333 Fax: (01686) 622946 E-mail: sales@cellpath.co.uk Principal Export Areas: Worldwide *Medical supplies*

▶ Cellspot Technologies Ltd, 81 Barkham Road, Wokingham, Berkshire, RG41 2RJ Tel: 0118-978 5311 E-mail: john@cellspottechnologies.com *RF product development*Microwave power amplifiers*Radar Depth measurement products*Telemetry systems*

Celltech, Unit 3, Bldg 6 Tameside Bus Development Centre, Windmill Lane, Denton, Manchester, M34 3QS Tel: 0161-320 8096 Fax: 0161-320 3526 E-mail: sales@celltech-battery.co.uk *Battery distributors, wet, seals & chargers*

Celltech R & D Ltd, 4-10 The Quadrant, Abingdon Science Park, Abingdon, Oxon, OX14 3YS Tel: (01235) 543200 Fax: (01235) 543270 E-mail: info@celltechgroup.com *Pharmaceutical & researchers*

Celltex Fabrications Ltd, Unit 9a Barnfield Trading Estate, Ramsey Road, Tipton, West Midlands, DY4 9DU Tel: 0121-520 3443 Fax: 0121-520 1772 E-mail: sales@celltex.co.uk *One of the market leaders in the supply of foam protection packaging, edge protection & cushioning. Also the largest suppliers of all types of expansion joint filler materials, incl. foam rubber, cork, fire rated & expanding foam seals*

Celltherm Coldrooms Ltd, Unit 4, Acan Way, Narborough, Leicester, LE19 2GW Tel: 0116-275 1331 Fax: 0116-275 1304 E-mail: sales@celltherm.co.uk *Established as one of the foremost specialist manufacturers of cold and freezer rooms in Europe, Celltherm's reputation for quality and strength has been hard earned. With a choice of models every 175mm, Celltherm boasts the largest range of standard size rooms available in Europe today and with a choice of three height options there will always be a Celltherm room to suit your purpose and your premises.*

Cellular Mouldings Ltd, 2 Pytchley Lodge Industrial Estate, Pytchley Lodge Road, Kettering, Northamptonshire, NN15 6JQ Tel: (01536) 513452 Fax: (01536) 411206 E-mail: sales@cellularmouldings.co.uk *Polyurethane mouldings components manufrs*

▶ Cellular Solution Engineers Ltd, 691-693 Warrington Road, Risley, WA3 6AY Tel: 0870 1993403 Fax: 0870 1991641 E-mail: installs@csemail.co.uk *installation of Mobile Phone Handsfree car kits parking sensors telematics premicell paknet nationwide service*

▶ Cellular Surplus, Norwich Road, Colton, Norwich, NR9 5BZ Tel: (01603) 882800 Fax: (01603) 882015 *Telecommunication systems or equipment*

▶ Cellustar Ltd, Unit 8C, Beta Close, Tewkesbury Business Centre, Tewkesbury, Gloucestershire, GL20 8SR Tel: (01684) 273080 Fax: (01684) 273081 E-mail: info@cellustar.co.uk *Plastic manufrs*

Celoxica Ltd, 66 Milton Park, Abingdon, Oxfordshire, OX14 4RX Tel: (01235) 863656 Fax: (01235) 863648 E-mail: sales.emea@celoxica.com *Design software to hardware*

Celsius Air Conditioning, 1 Well Street, Heywood, Lancashire, OL10 1NT Tel: (01706) 367500 Fax: (01706) 367355 E-mail: sales@celsiusair.co.uk *Air conditioning suppliers*

Celsius Cooling, The Hollies, Swanley Lane, Ravensmoor, Nantwich, Cheshire, CW5 8PZ Tel: (01270) 626453 Fax: 01270 624759 *Refrigeration & air conditioning*

Celsius Energy Control Ltd, Systems House, 15 Station Road, High Wycombe, Buckinghamshire, HP13 6AD Tel: (01494) 688000 Fax: (01494) 688019 E-mail: general@celsiusenergy.co.uk *Heating systems manufrs*

Celsius First Ltd, Scania House, Annwell St, Hoddesdon, Hertfordshire, EN11 8TT Tel: 01992 449600 Fax: (01992) 467148 E-mail: information@celsiusfirst.com *Frozen food transport service.* Also at: Bristol, Doncaster, Glasgow, Grimsby, King's Lynn, Liverpool, London, & Pontefract

▶ Celsius First Ltd, High Meads, Temple Mill Lane, London, E15 2EW Tel: (020) 8534 5577 Fax: (020) 8519 0263 *Cold storage*

▶ Celsius Mechanical Services Ltd, Viking House, 29 High Street, Woodville, Swadlincote, Derbyshire, DE11 7EH Tel: (01283) 550330 Fax: (01283) 229300 E-mail: midway@btinternet.com *Heating & air conditioning services*

▶ Celsum Technologies Ltd, Willow House, 17 Braemar Close, Mountsorrel, Loughborough, Leicestershire, LE12 7ES Tel: 0116-210 6319 Fax: (0870) 1206319 E-mail: sales@celsum.com *Distribution of process control and serial connectivity products, design and manufacture of materials testing instruments, consultancy.*

Celsur Plastics Ltd, 3 Lovett Road, The Causeway, Staines, Middlesex, TW18 3AZ Tel: (01784) 457175 Fax: (01784) 454605 E-mail: info@celsurplastics.co.uk *PVC welded goods manufrs*

Celtech UK Electronics Ltd, Unit 12 Barton Business Park, Cawdor Street, Eccles, Manchester, M30 0QR Tel: 0161-788 0267 Fax: 0161-787 8212 E-mail: celtech@celtech-uk.co.uk *Automotive diagnostic equipment services*

Celtic Art Ltd, 3 Hawbank Road, East Kilbride, Glasgow, G74 5EG Tel: (01355) 244493 Fax: (01355) 232541 E-mail: info@celtic-art.ltd.uk *Manufacturing jewellers*

Celtic Displays, Unit 17 Newport Business Centre, Corporation Road, Newport, Gwent, NP19 4RF Tel: (01633) 271133 Fax: (01633) 271135 E-mail: jackie@celticdisplays.co.uk *Sign manufrs*

Celtic Kilncare Ltd, Celtic House, Langland Way, Newport, Gwent, NP19 4PT Tel: (01633) 271455 Fax: (01633) 290663 E-mail: celtic.kilns@btinternet.com *Pottery equipment maintenance & distributors*

Celtic Knitwear Ltd, 37 Victoria St, Kirkwall, Orkney, KW15 1DN Tel: 01856 873171 *Clothing manufrs*

Celtic Leathers, 287 Marshfield Road, Castleton, Cardiff, CF3 2UW Tel: (01633) 680093 Fax: (01633) 680949 E-mail: sales@celtic-leathers.com *Leather goods manufrs*

Celtic S M R Ltd, Unit 9-10, Dolphin Court, Brunel Quay, Neyland, Milford Haven, Dyfed, SA73 1PY Tel: (01646) 603150 Fax: (01646) 603159 E-mail: gmacphail@celticsmr.co.uk *X-ray suppliers & services*

Celtic Tyre Services Ltd, Brindley Road, Cardiff, CF11 8TX Tel: (029) 2022 1201 Fax: (029) 2066 4985 E-mail: enquiries@celtictyres.co.uk *Tyre wholesaler & retailer*

Celtic Tyre Services (Bridgend) Ltd, Princes Way, Bridgend Industrial Estate, Bridgend, Mid Glamorgan, CF31 3TT Tel: (01656) 657424 Fax: (01656) 647743 E-mail: enquiries@celtictyres.co.uk *Tyre retailers & wholesalers*

Celtic Tyre Services Maesteg Ltd, Talbot Street, Maesteg, Mid Glamorgan, CF34 9BT Tel: (01656) 733514 Fax: (01656) 733514 E-mail: enquiries@celtictyres.co.uk *Tyre distribution & fitting*

▶ Celtic Water Management Ltd, Dolfedwen, Tresaith, Cardigan, Ceredigion, SA43 2JG Tel: (01239) 811465 Fax: (01239) 811918 E-mail: info@celticwater.co.uk *rainwater harvesting components, waterbutts, rainwater filters,*

Cem Microwave Technology Ltd, 2 Middle Slade, Buckingham Industrial Estate, Buckingham, MK18 1WA Tel: (01280) 822873 Fax: (01280) 822342 E-mail: info.uk@cem.com *Laboratory microwave suppliers*

▶ Cema Universal Engineering, Bordesley Hall, The Holloway, Alvechurch, Birmingham, B48 7QA Tel: (01527) 596106 Fax: (01527) 69362 E-mail: cema.engineering@tiscali.co.uk *Engineering*

▶ Cemac Building Services, 514, Filton Avenue, Horfield, Bristol, BS7 0QE Tel: 0117-979 3053

Cemak Catering Equipment Ltd, The Atrium, Curtis Road, Dorking, Surrey, RH4 1XA Tel: (01306) 646860 Fax: (01306) 646363 E-mail: sales@cemak.co.uk *Cemak Catering Equipment Ltd based in Dorking, Surrey are catering equipment distributors.*

Cembre Ltd, Fair View Industrial Estate, Kingsbury Road, Curdworth, Sutton Coldfield, West Midlands, B76 9EE Tel: (01675) 470440 Fax: (01675) 470220 E-mail: sales@cembre.co.uk *Cembre is a leading European manufacturer of cable terminations and installation tooling for the industrial, transportation, power utility & public sector markets. Recent product developments include Zeta terminal & distribution blocks, Maxiblock cable glands & General Marking cable and component marking systems. Cembre's UK manufacturing facilities also offer design & production of customised termination products & cable assemblies*

Cement Glaze Decorators Ltd, 5 Barry Parade, Barry Road, London, SE22 0JA Tel: (020) 8299 2553 Fax: (020) 8299 2346 *Specialist wall finishings*

Cement UK, Lappel Bank, Sheerness Docks, Sheerness, Kent, ME12 1RS Tel: (01795) 669023 Fax: (01795) 669510 *Cement distribution*

Cementation Skanska, Bentley House, Jossey Lane, Doncaster, South Yorkshire, DN5 9ED Tel: (01302) 821100 Fax: (01302) 821111 *Mining consulting engineers*

Cementcraft Concrete Products Ltd, Beckhythe, Little Melton, Norwich, NR9 3NP Tel: (01603) 810394 Fax: (01603) 812821 *Concrete products*

Cemex, Station Yard, Bletchley, Milton Keynes, MK2 2JU Tel: (01908) 370259 *Concrete suppliers*

Cemex Ltd, Caird Avenue, New Milton, Hampshire, BH25 5QA Tel: (01425) 620332 *Ready mix concrete*

Cemex, Long Lane, Attenborough, Beeston, Nottingham, NG9 6BL Tel: 0115-943 2260 Fax: 0115-943 1966 E-mail: webmanager.hbm@cemex.co.uk *Ready mixed concrete suppliers*

Cemex Ltd, Haughmond Quarry, Uffington, Shrewsbury, SY4 4RW Tel: (01743) 709256 Fax: (01743) 709462 *Ready mixed concrete*

Cemex Ltd, Leeman Road, York, YO26 4HX Tel: (01904) 621280 Fax: (01904) 619399 *Ready mixed concrete suppliers*

Cemex Floors, London Road, Wick, Bristol, BS30 5SJ Tel: (01788) 542111 Fax: 0117-937 4695 E-mail: rmc@concreteproducts.co.uk *Concrete floors*

▶ Cemex Materials, Forcegarth Quarry, Middleton, Barnard Castle, County Durham, DL12 0EP Tel: (01833) 622255

Cemex Materials Ltd, Cemex House, Elland Road, Leeds, LS11 8BA Tel: 0113-271 3881 Fax: 0113-271 9793 *Concrete manufrs*

Cemex (NI) Ltd, 30 Creagh Road, Toomebridge, Antrim, BT41 3SE Tel: (028) 7965 0626 Fax: (028) 7965 0204 *Sand & gravel merchants*

Cemex (NI) Ltd, 41 Manse Road, Carrowdore, Newtownards, County Down, BT22 2EZ Tel: (028) 9186 1450 Fax: (028) 9186 1555 *Stone & gravel suppliers*

Cemex RMC Ltd, Lucknow Road South, Bodmin, Cornwall, PL31 1DR Tel: (01208) 74321 Fax: (01208) 74327 *Ready mixed concrete & mortar* Also at: Bodmin & Honiton

▶ Cemex UK Ltd, Aston Church Road, Saltley, Birmingham, B8 1QF Tel: 0121-327 6581 Fax: 0121-328 9359

Cemex UK Ltd, St Helens Industrial Estate, Bishop Auckland, County Durham, DL14 9AJ Tel: (01388) 603961 Fax: (01388) 450056 E-mail: john.metcalfe@cemex.co.uk *Pre-cast concrete products*

Cemex UK Ltd, Coldharbour Lane, Thorpe/, Egham, Surrey, TW20 8TE Tel: (0845) 1559210 Fax: (01932) 568933 E-mail: enquiries@cemex-group.com *Concrete supplier* Also at: Branches throughout the U.K.

▶ Cemex UK Ltd, Core Utilities, Kilmartin Place, Glasgow, G71 5PH Tel: (01355) 243011 Fax: (01698) 816068 *Concrete manufacturers & aggregates*

Cemex (UK) Ltd, Whitby Street, Hartlepool, Cleveland, TS24 7LP Tel: (01429) 275269 Fax: (01429) 860898 *Ready mixed concrete suppliers*

Cemex UK Ltd, Town Mead Road, London, SW6 2QL Tel: (020) 7790 3232 Fax: (020) 7371 0339 *Concrete & mortar ready mixed*

Cemex UK, Aerodrome, Scorton, Catterick, Richmond, North Yorkshire, DL10 7NP Tel: (01748) 811362 Fax: (01748) 810808 *Concrete manufrs*

Cemex UK Ltd, Crown House, Evreux Way, Rugby, Warwickshire, CV21 2DT Tel: 0114-242 6050 Fax: (01788) 517221 *Concrete distributors & manufrs*

Cemex UK Ltd, Crown House, Evreux Way, Rugby, Warwickshire, CV21 2DT Tel: 0114-242 6050 Fax: (01788) 540166 *Roadstone aggregates*

Cemex UK Ltd, Crown House, Evreux Way, Rugby, Warwickshire, CV21 2DT Tel: 0114-242 6050 Fax: (01788) 517220 *Ready mixed concrete suppliers* Also at: Kingsmead

▶ Cemex UK Construction Services Ltd, Smithfold Lane, Little Hulton, Worsley, Manchester, M28 0GP Tel: 0161-702 6366 Fax: 0161-702 6422

▶ Cemex Uk Materials Ltd, Airdrie Road, Caldercruix, Airdrie, Lanarkshire, ML6 8PA Tel: (01236) 843040 Fax: (01236) 842529 *Quarrying*

Cemex UK Materials, Equinox North, Great Park Road, Bradley Stoke, Bristol, BS32 4QL Tel: (01454) 451851 Fax: (01454) 451860 *Ready mixed concrete, mortar & stone suppliers*

Cemoc Ltd, Cemoc House, Rectory Drive, Wootton Bridge, Ryde, Isle of Wight, PO33 4QQ Tel: (01983) 884321 E-mail: sales@cemoc.co.uk *IT consultants*

Cemplas Ltd, Holbrook House, 72 Lower Addiscombe Road, Croydon, CR9 6AD Tel: (020) 8654 3149 Fax: (020) 8656 6984 E-mail: info@cemplas.co.uk *Waterproofing, building & concrete contractors*

Cem-Spec Ltd, Harby Mill, Colston Lane, Harby, Melton Mowbray, Leicestershire, LE14 4BE Tel: (01949) 860193 Fax: (01949) 860324 E-mail: office@cemspec.co.uk *Fast setting cement producers*

Cemx, R M C House, Littleburn Industrial Estate, Langley Moor, Durham, DH7 8HH Tel: 0191-378 7700 Fax: 0191-378 7752 *Ready mixed concrete & mortar suppliers* Also at: Branches throughout the U.K.

▶ Cendant Mobility Ltd, Frankland Road, Swindon, SN5 8RS Tel: (01793) 756000 Fax: (01793) 756400 E-mail: salesemea@cartus.com *Relocation consultants*

Cengar Ltd, 70 Lister Lane, Halifax, West Yorkshire, HX1 5DN Tel: (01422) 354626 Fax: (01422) 349024 E-mail: enquiries@cengar.com *Portable pneumatic saw manufrs*

Cennin Ltd, Pen-Y-Maes Lodge, Clocaenog, Llanfwrog, Ruthin, Clwyd, LL15 2AP Tel: (01824) 750369 Fax: (01824) 750544 *Computer company*

▶ Censor Security, Unit 342 Camberwell Business Centre, 99-103 Lomond Grove, London, SE5 7HN Tel: (0845) 2309816 Fax: (020) 7703 7243 E-mail: admin@censorgroup.co.uk *Providing security solutions tailored to the individual Business or Companies requirements, through the provision of the highest quality, reliable and dedicated service-dispensed by an equally experienced and dedicated office staff that other Companies can only try to emulate.'*

Centa Transmissions Ltd, Thackley Court, Thackley Old Road, Shipley, West Yorkshire, BD18 1BW Tel: (01274) 531034 Fax: (01274) 531159 E-mail: post@centa-uk.co.uk *Flexible & power transmission couplings. In addition, precision & differential epicycle gears & gear box unit manufacturers. Industrial/mechanical power transmission equipment manufrs*

Centagraphics Labels & Tags, Pitcairn Works, Pitcairn Road, Ipswich, IP1 5BX Tel: (01473) 463883 Fax: (01473) 462333 E-mail: sales@elabel.co.uk *Label design print & production services*

Centaur Communications Ltd, St. Giles House, 50 Poland Street, London, W1F 7AX Tel: (020) 7970 4000 Fax: (020) 7970 4398 *Publishers*

▶ Centaur Foods Ltd, Pucklechurch Trading Estate, Pucklechurch, Bristol, BS16 9QH Tel: 0117-303 9337 Fax: 0117-303 9338 E-mail: mark@centaurfoods.com *Importers & exporters of specialist food ingredients*

Centaur Fuel Management, 251 Manchester Road, Walkden, Manchester, M28 3HE Tel: (0870) 7576323 Fax: 0161-794 8031 E-mail: mc@centauronline.co.uk *Manufacturers & suppliers of fuel monitoring equipment*

Centaur Grain Ltd, Barrow Hill Barns, Barrow Hill, Goodworth Clatford, Andover, Hampshire, SP11 7RG Tel: (01264) 356666 Fax: (01264) 350200 E-mail: sales@centaurgrain.com *Farmers grain co-operative marketing*

Centaur Manufacturing Ltd, Pipers Road, Park Farm Industrial Estate, Redditch, Worcestershire, B98 0HU Tel: (01527) 528049 Fax: (01527) 500882 E-mail: sales@centaurmfg.co.uk *Cable management & trunking systems*

▶ Centaur Van & Truck, 20-22 Kenyon Lane, Manchester, M40 9JQ Tel: 0161-205 3885 E-mail: parts@cvtmercaid.co.uk *parts for the mercedes sprinter and vito, repairs, servicing, recovery and diagonostics*

Centec, Brooks Lane, Middlewich, Cheshire, CW10 0JG Tel: (01606) 737720 Fax: (01606) 737511 E-mail: enquiry@centec.uk.com *Chemical engineers, consultants & manufrs*

Centech Hydraulics, 62 Arnold Road, Nottingham, NG6 0DZ Tel: 0115-924 4822 Fax: 0115-924 4818 *Hydraulic cylinder manufrs*

Centek International, Unit 30 Lawson Hunt Industrial Park, Guildford Road, Broadbridge Heath, Horsham, West Sussex, RH12 3JR Tel: (01403) 263323 Fax: (01403) 270651 E-mail: info@nuplas.co.uk *Spirit measure dispenser manufrs*

▶ Centeng Ltd, Unit 6C Hessay Industrial Estate, Hessay, York, YO26 8LE Tel: (01904) 737247 Fax: (01904) 737248 E-mail: centeng@hessay58fsnet.co.uk *Gas cutting & welding equipment suppliers*

Centiflex Systems Ltd, PO Box 54, Saffron Walden, Essex, CB10 2AN Tel: (01799) 527602 Fax: (01799) 501961 E-mail: sales@centiflex.com *Control system engineers*

Centigrade Ltd, 9 Beverley Road, Tilehurst, Reading, RG31 5PT Tel: 0118-942 4939 Fax: 0118-942 4939 *Refrigeration engineers*

Centigrade Refrigeration Ltd, Unit 17 South Quay Industrial Estate, Douglas, Isle of Man, IM1 5AT Tel: (01624) 622114 Fax: (01624) 624450 *Refrigeration engineers*

Centinel Security Services, 2 Corn Kiln Close, Cogenhoe, Northampton, NN7 1NX Tel: (01604) 890686 Fax: (01604) 890686 E-mail: sales@centinel.fsnet.co.uk *Security post manufrs*

Cento Engineering Co. Ltd, Baddow Park, West Hanningfield Road, Great Baddow, Chelmsford, CM2 7SY Tel: (01245) 477708 Fax: (01245) 477748 *Cradle systems design & manufrs*

Centra Controls Ltd, 14 Landywood Lane, Cheslyn Hay, Walsall, WS6 7AH Tel: (01922) 415510 Fax: (01922) 415510 E-mail: centra@tiscala.co.uk *Electrical contractors*

Central Access Ltd, Unit 21, Hazelford Way, Newstead, Nottingham, NG15 0DQ Tel: (01623) 750500 Fax: (01623) 750400 E-mail: info@central-access.co.uk *Access hire, sales, training & services*

Central Air International Ltd, 47-59 Green Lane, Small Heath, Birmingham, B9 5BU Tel: 0121-773 5630 Fax: 0121-773 1378 E-mail: info@centralaircompressors.com *Air & gas compressors sales parts*

Central Aircoil Service Ltd, 5 Icknield Street, Bidford On Avon, Alcester, Warwickshire, B50 4BX Tel: (01789) 774558 Fax: (01789) 774559 E-mail: sales@central-aircoil.co.uk *Design/supply/install fin coils for replacement, upgrades and retrofits. Water, steam or refrigeration. Associated pipe-work, valves, flow commissioning/re-balancing. Aircoils, coils, batteries: heating, cooling, condensers, evaporators, AHU refurbishment, LPHW, LTHW, glycol, moisture elimination, filtration.*

▶ Central Axle Services Midlands Ltd, 220 Montgomery Street, Birmingham, B11 1DS Tel: 0121-772 0121 Fax: 0121-772 0711

▶ Central Bar Supplies, Unit 4 1 Alice Street, Derby, DE1 2BY Tel: (01332) 296683 Fax: (01332) 296683

Central Bearings & Transmissions Ltd, 43 Padgets Lane, Redditch, Worcestershire, B98 0RD Tel: (01527) 500803 Fax: (01527) 510462 E-mail: sales@centralbearings.com *Ball & roller bearing distributors*

Central Bottling International Ltd, Plumtree Farm Industrial Estate, Plumtree Road, Bircotes, Doncaster, South Yorkshire, DN11 8EW Tel: (01302) 711056 Fax: (01302) 710802 E-mail: sales@centralbottling.com *Bottling equipment suppliers*

Central Box Co. Ltd, 14-16 Lithgow Place, College Milton, East Kilbride, Glasgow, G74 1PW Tel: (01355) 233725 Fax: (01355) 265166

Central Business Machines Ltd, 112-118 Kingsland Road, London, E2 8DJ Tel: (020) 7729 5588 Fax: (020) 7729 9137 *Office equipment & stationery supplier*

Central Business Services, C B S House, 153 Enderby Road, Whetstone, Leicester, LE8 6JJ Tel: 0116-277 8111 Fax: 0116-278 8332 E-mail: info@cbs-osn.co.uk *Computer network support & installation*

Central c.n.c. Machinery Ltd, Unit 12B, Scar La, Milnsbridge, Huddersfield, HD3 4PE Tel: 0845 4941645 Fax: (01484) 460101 E-mail: enquiries@centralcnc.co.uk Principal Export Areas: Worldwide *Central c.n.c. Machinery Ltd, formerly Central Woodworking Machinery Co Ltd, specialise in supplying affordable c.n.c. Routers for applications in woodworking, plastics and non-ferrous metals. We also supply traditional woodworking machinery such as saws, planers, thicknessers, mortisers, tenoners, spindle moulders, etc., and are stockists of a wide range of woodworking machinery tooling and accessories. We are suppliers to both industry and education. In our showroom in Huddersfield, we have c.n.c. Routers from Trend and Victor available for demonstration, along with Delcam software, for which we are authorised resellers. We offer on-site training, maintenance and servicing of c.n.c. routers and woodworking machinery, as well as a programming and in-house machining service.*

Central Cables, Unit 15 Brindley Business Park, Chaseside Drive, Hednesford, Cannock, Staffordshire, WS11 7GD Tel: (01543) 422477 Fax: (01543) 422420 E-mail: sales@centralcables.co.uk *Specialist electrical cable & wire distributors*

Central Canopies & Car Ports, PO Box 32, Nuneaton, Warwickshire, CV11 9XU Tel: (024) 7634 4680 Fax: (024) 7634 4667 *Sectional buildings suppliers & contractors*

▶ Central Capital Mortgages, 2nd Floor, Edward Hyde Building, 38 Clarendon Road, Watford, WD17 1JJ Tel: 0800 032 23 20 E-mail: contact.us@centralcapital.com *Mortgage quotes with no obligation and no upfront fees, all situations considered. Specialists in finding the right deal, no matter what the situation or credit history.*

Central Car Paints, 93 Crafton St East, Leicester, LE1 2DG Tel: 0116-262 9727 E-mail: info@centralcarparts.co.uk *Automotive component suppliers*

Central Catering Supplies, 140 Wood Street, Rugby, Warwickshire, CV21 2SP Tel: (01788) 546547 Fax: (01788) 565180 E-mail: sales@centralcatering.co.uk *Catering supplies distributors*

▶ Central Ceramics, 44 Higher Bridge Street, Bolton, BL1 2HA Tel: (01204) 361887 Fax: (01204) 362577

Central Cladding Systems Ltd, Unit C4 Staverton Technology Park, Gloucester Road, Staverton Technology Park, Cheltenham, Gloucestershire, GL51 6TQ Tel: (01452) 856252 Fax: (01452) 856136 E-mail: ccs@centralcladding.co.uk *Roofing & cladding contractors*

Central Cold Storage Co., Leamore Lane, Walsall, WS2 7DQ Tel: (01922) 401307 Fax: (01922) 710033 E-mail: johncoxcoldstoresltd@btinternet.com *Cold storage distributors & temperature control*

Central Communications Group, 54 Glen Road, Castle Bytham, Grantham, Lincolnshire, NG33 4RJ Tel: (01780) 411194 E-mail: cswright@walkietalkie.co.uk *Portable radio supply & hire company*

Central Computer Corporation (UK) Ltd, 32 St. Peters Street, London, N1 8JT Tel: (020) 7454 1222 Fax: (0870) 2408871 E-mail: info@ccc-uk.net *On site & off site maintenance*

Central Computer Technology, 11 Greskine Clo, Bedford, MK41 0NW Tel: (01234) 357932 *Computer upgrades, repairs & manufrs*

Central Computers Supplies, Washwood Heath Road, Birmingham, B8 2HQ Tel: (0870) 0434049 Fax: 0121-684 8885 *Computer supplier & manufrs*

▶ Central Computers UK Ltd, Shop 284, Brentwood Road, Romford, RM2 5TA Tel: (01708) 453311 Fax: (01708) 458930 E-mail: sales@centralcomputersuk.co.uk *Computer repair services*

▶ Central Construction Norwich, 115 City Road, Norwich, NR1 2HL Tel: (01603) 762804 E-mail: info@centralconstruction.co.uk

Central Convertors, Unit 3 Bandeath Industrial Estate, Throsk, Stirling, FK7 7NP Tel: (01786) 814033 Fax: (01786) 817477 E-mail: convertors@superglass.co.uk *Insulating material converters*

Central Cooling Services Ltd, Garrison House, Garrison Street, Bordesley, Birmingham, B9 4BN Tel: 0121-766 7227 Fax: 0121-766 6156 E-mail: centralcoolingservices@btinternet.com Principal Export Areas: Worldwide *Cooler, cooling (industrial) systems distributors or agents*

▶ Central Crane Hire Hull, Albert Dock, Hull, HU1 2DY Tel: (01482) 223859 Fax: (01482) 581098

Central Diesel, Unit 18 Erdington Industrial Park, Chester Road, Birmingham, B24 0RD Tel: 0121-386 1700 Fax: 0121-386 1744 *Diesel engine services*

Central Diesel, Unit 15 Hawksley Industrial Estate, Hawksley Street, Oldham, OL8 4PQ Tel: 0161-620 7070 Fax: 0161-620 6007 E-mail: steve.kay@central-diesel.co.uk *Diesel engine distributors* Also at: Nottingham

Central Display Production, B Gresham Way Industrial Estate, Gresham Way, London, SW19 8ED Tel: (020) 8944 5156 Fax: (020) 8944 5950 E-mail: dudley@centraldisplay.com *International exhibition & shop fitting contractors*

Central Doors, 3 Arleston Drive, Nottingham, NG8 2FR Tel: 0115-913 0071 Fax: 0115-928 2814 *Industrial door manufrs*

Central Drivers Ltd, Carlyle Business Centre, Queen Victoria Street, Bristol, BS2 0QR Tel: (0870) 7770544 Fax: 0117-955 9040 *Employment agents*

Central Electrical Co., West Midland House, Gipsy Lane, Willenhall, West Midlands, WV13 2HA Tel: (01902) 482477 Fax: (01902) 482478 E-mail: sales@centralelec.co.uk Principal Export Areas: Worldwide *Inverters & starters specialists*

Central Electrical Engineering Services Properties Ltd, 6-8 Edison Road, Rabans Lane Industrial Area, Aylesbury, Buckinghamshire, HP19 8TE Tel: (01296) 424561 Fax: (01296) 394907 *Electrical contractors*

▶ Central Electrical Installations Ltd, Bradley Mill, Bradley Lane, Newton Abbot, Devon, TQ12 1NF Tel: (01626) 330054 Fax: (01626) 331915 E-mail: devon@central-electrical.com *Domestic, commercial, industrial electrical & mechanical engineers*

▶ Central Electrical Services Hinckley Ltd, 10a Ashby Road, Hinckley, Leicestershire, LE10 1SL Tel: (01455) 890860

Central Engineering & Hydraulic Services Ltd, Brook Works, 174 Bromyard Road, St. Johns, Worcester, WR2 5EE Tel: (01905) 748569 Fax: (01905) 420700 E-mail: chs0999@aol.com *Hydraulic cylinder repairers*

Central Engineering Services Ltd, Star Works, Burton St, Leek, Staffordshire, ST13 8BX Tel: (01538) 398127 Fax: (01538) 373774 E-mail: inquire@cepltd.co.uk *Engineering subcontract services & production engineers*

▶ Central European Staffing, Thanet Way, Whitstable, Kent, CT5 3JF Tel: (01227) 771888 Fax: (01227) 771666 E-mail: sales@centraleuropeanstaffing.co.uk *Central European Staffing (CES) recruits workers from Poland and other Eastern European countries. We supply skilled and semi-skilled construction and industrial workers (builders, welders, bricklayers, steel fabricators, carpenters, excavator and crane operators etc.),comanies who would work as subcontractors, seasonal summer staff (for hotels, amusement parks, food processors etc.), farm workers, care assistants doctors andnurses, general labour for heavy and unpopular jobs.*

Central Fabrications, 72 Burnmoor Street, Leicester, LE2 7JJ Tel: 0116-247 1515 Fax: 0116-247 1117 *General sheet metalworker*

Central Fans Colasit Ltd, Unit 19 Lakeside Industrial Estate, New Meadow Road, Redditch, Worcestershire, B98 8YW Tel: (01527) 517200 Fax: (01527) 517195 E-mail: nt@central-fans.co.uk *Manufacturers of plastic corrosion resistant fans*

Central Fasteners (Staffs) Ltd, Airfield Trading Estate, Hixon, Stafford, ST18 0PY Tel: (01889) 270163 Fax: (01889) 271270 E-mail: centralfasteners@aol.com *Bolts, nuts & power tools distribution*

Central Fire Curtains, 80 Blackmore Drive, Leicester, LE3 1LP Tel: 0116-247 0247 E-mail: firecurtains@lycos.com *Smoke & Fire Curtains for the protection of people and buildings. Smoke & fire containment. BS 476: Part 22 fire regulations. Smoke & fire barriers.*

Central Fire Protection, 5 Bewsey Road, Warrington, WA2 7LN Tel: (01925) 414464 Fax: (01925) 244298 E-mail: cfp.warrington@central-fire.co.uk *Fire protection engineers*

Central Fire Security, 9 Gateworth Industrial Estate, Barnard Street, Warrington, WA5 1DD Tel: (01925) 230071 Fax: (01925) 652201 *Fire fighting equipment suppliers*

Central Flooring & Tile Co., 51 Mullaghboy Heights, Magherafelt, County Londonderry, BT45 5NU Tel: (028) 7963 3076 *Tile manufacturers*

Central Grinding Services, 3a Pomeroy Drive, Oadby, Leicester, LE2 5NE Tel: 0116-271 8188 Fax: 0116-271 8199 E-mail: central@grinding.fsnet.co.uk *Precision & production grinders*

▶ Central Health Care Midlands, Unit 46 Rumer Hill Business Estate, Rumer Hill Road, Cannock, Staffordshire, WS11 0ET Tel: (01543) 467407 Fax: (01543) 469741 E-mail: sales@centralhealthcare.net *Providers of specialist medical equipment*

Central Heat Pumps Ltd, 1 Mill Street, Islip, Kidlington, Oxfordshire, OX5 2SZ Tel: (01865) 370998 Fax: (01865) 370902 *Heat pump service & repairers*

▶ Central Heating Advisory Service, 120 A-B, Eastwoodmains Road, Clarkston, Glasgow, G76 7HH Tel: 0141-571 7711

▶ Central Heating Services, 46 Camp Road, Farnborough, Hampshire, GU14 6EP Tel: (01252) 524649 Fax: (01252) 376765 E-mail: service@chsltd.co.uk

Central High Rise Ltd, Central House, Thoresby Avenue, Nottingham, NG2 3GA Tel: 0115-958 7637 Fax: 0115-941 1279 E-mail: info@abseiling.uk.com *Steeplejack services, lightning protection, chimney inspection, fallarrest systems, abseiling services, rope access & difficult access*

Central Home Alarms, 66 Strowan Road, Comrie, Crieff, Perthshire, PH6 2EH Tel: (01764) 670540 Fax: (01764) 679652 *Home alarms installation*

Central Hydraulic Systems Ltd, Walker Street, Rochdale, Lancashire, OL16 2AB Tel: (01706) 343007 Fax: (01706) 645354 *Hydraulic equipment distributors*

Central Hygiene Ltd, Unit 4e Brymau Three Trading Estate, River Lane, Saltney, Chester, CH4 8RQ Tel: (01244) 675066 Fax: (01244) 680129 E-mail: sales@central-hygiene.co.uk *Washdown food systems design & manufrs*

Central Independent Newspapers Ltd, Ventura Park Road, Tamworth, Staffordshire, B78 3LZ Tel: (01827) 848586 Fax: (01827) 848640 *Newspaper publishers & printers*

Central Iron Craft, Bissell Street, Birmingham, B5 7HP Tel: 0121-622 3123 Fax: 0121-622 3123 *Wrought ironworks*

▶ Central Janitorial Supplies, Unit 3, 64 Pritchett Street, Birmingham, B6 4EX Tel: 0121-333 6699 Fax: 0121-333 3848 *Cleaning material suppliers*

Central Joinery Co., 2 Cross Street, Honley, Holmfirth, HD9 6AN Tel: (01484) 667459 *Joinery manufrs*

▶ Central Joinery Services Ltd, 33 Bower Way, Slough, SL1 5HW Tel: (01628) 550900 Fax: (01628) 666991

Central Lifting Services, 17 Eastburn Road, Kintore, Inverurie, Aberdeenshire, AB51 0FG Tel: (01467) 634944 Fax: (01467) 632115 *Lifting & handling equipment*

Central London Office Supplies, 182 Parkview Road, Welling, Kent, DA16 1ST Tel: (020) 8303 2679 Fax: (020) 3223 0068 *Office equipment suppliers*

Central Mechanical Handling Services Ltd, 7 Hanley Terrace, Malvern, Worcestershire, WR14 4PF Tel: (01684) 891042 Fax: (01684) 891042 *Large mechanical handling services*

Central Metal Manufacturing Ltd, Leeside, Merrylees Industrial Estate, Desford, Leicester, LE9 9FS Tel: (01530) 230833 Fax: (01530) 230302 *Sheet metalwork engineers*

Central Metallurgical Laboratory, 53 Sussex Street, Sheffield, S4 7YY Tel: 0114-272 1735 Fax: 0114-275 6797 E-mail: neilellis@centralmet.co.uk *Metallurgists & assayers*

Central Moulding Services Ltd, Unit 6, Barrington Industrial Estate, Bedlington, Northumberland, NE22 7DQ Tel: (01670) 821166 Fax: (01670) 821500 *Designers & suppliers of plastic components*

Central Mouldings Ltd, Reform Street Industrial Estate, Reform Street, Sutton-In-Ashfield, Nottinghamshire, NG17 5DB Tel: (01623) 553005 Fax: (01623) 440370 E-mail: bcadman@ypm.net *Plastics injection moulders*

Central Paints Automotive Ltd, Burncross Road, Chapeltown, Sheffield, S35 1RX Tel: 0114-257 8857 Fax: 0114-257 8857 *Car paint supplier*

Central Pallet Company Ltd, 36-51 Lower Dartmouth Street, Bordesley, Birmingham, B9 4LG Tel: 0121-772 5620 Fax: 0121-766 5778 *New & reconditioned pallet suppliers*

Central Parts Ltd, 222 New John Street West, Birmingham, B19 3UA Tel: 0121-523 4067 Fax: 0121-507 0960 E-mail: centralparts@supanet.com *Textile machinery*

▶ Central Pine, 28-29 Lower Tower Street, Birmingham, B19 3NH Tel: 0121-333 6162 Fax: 0121-333 6162 *Pine furniture manufrs*

Central Plate Services Ltd, Phoenix Works Industrial Estate, Richards Street, Wednesbury, West Midlands, WS10 8BZ Tel: 0121-526 3770 Fax: 0121-526 4770 *Steel plate stockholders*

Central Polishing Supplies, Unit 33 Innage Park, Abeles Way, Holly Lane Industrial Estate, Atherstone, Warwickshire, CV9 2QX Tel: (01827) 714839 Fax: (01827) 714879 E-mail: c.polishing@talk21.com *Abrasive belts & polishing mops manufrs*

Central Polythene Packaging, Unit 60, Abbey Park Street, Leicester, LE4 5AF Tel: 0116-253 0275 Fax: 0116-253 1832 *Polythene suppliers & manufrs*

▶ Central Presentations Ltd, Innsworth Technology Park, Innsworth, Gloucester, GL3 1DL Tel: (01452) 731123 Fax: (01452) 731333 E-mail: dave@centralhospitality.co.uk

continued

continuation
Conferences & events audio equipment hire services, stage events

Central Print, 2 Swan Village Industrial Estate, Swan Lane, West Bromwich, West Midlands, B70 0NY Tel: 0121-500 6230 Fax: 0121-500 6230 *Lithographic printers*

Central Refractories (Scotland) Ltd, PO Box 14871, Falkirk, FK1 1RP Tel: (01324) 624412 Fax: (01324) 626923 *Refractory merchants*

Central Saddlery, Drumbroider Farm, Avonbridge, Falkirk, FK1 2HN Tel: (01324) 861229 Fax: (01324) 861462 *Saddlery & riding wear*

Central Safety Ltd, 30 North Street Industrial Estate, Droitwich, Worcestershire, WR9 8JB Tel: (01905) 774737 Fax: (01905) 796356 *Protective clothing & equipment*

Central Safety (Telford) Ltd, Unit 42 Business Development Centre, Stafford Park 4, Telford, Shropshire, TF3 3BA Tel: (01952) 290216 Fax: (01952) 275050 E-mail: info@centralsafetylimited.co.uk *Protective clothing & equipment manufrs*

Central School Of English, 1 Tottenham Court Road, London, W1T 1BB Tel: (020) 7580 2863 Fax: (020) 7255 1806 E-mail: sales@centralschool.co.uk *English language school*

Central Scientific Laboratories, 445 New Cross Road, London, SE14 6TA Tel: (020) 8694 9330 Fax: (020) 8694 9163 *Analytical & consulting chemists*

▶ Central Seafoods, 7 Festival Drive, Loughborough, Leicestershire, LE11 5XJ Tel: (01509) 239249 Fax: (01509) 233616 *Fish wholesalers*

Central Service Fire Protection, Central House, Vivars Way, Canal Road, Selby, North Yorkshire, YO8 8BE Tel: (01757) 213360 Fax: (01757) 210022 E-mail: csfp@btconnect.com *Sales & services of fire extinguishers & fire safety equipment*

▶ Central Shopfitters Ltd, Palm Street, New Basford, Nottingham, NG7 7HS Tel: 0115-942 2671 Fax: 0115-919 1993

Central Shutters & Doors, Unit 39 Phoenix International Industrial Estate, Charles Street, West Bromwich, West Midlands, B70 0AY Tel: 0121-557 3434 Fax: 0121-557 3403 *Industrial door manufrs*

Central Signs, 4 Glentye Gardens, Falkirk, FK1 5NT Tel: (01324) 610070 Fax: (01324) 610070 *Sign manufacturers & vehicle graphic designers*

Central Signs & Graphics, 6 Saltley Industrial Centre, Adderley Road, Birmingham, B8 1AW Tel: 0121-326 7744 Fax: 0121-326 8123 E-mail: reginold1@aol.com *Sign printers, engravers & manufrs*

Central Sounds, 66 Laurel Road, Loughborough, Leicestershire, LE11 2NL Tel: (01509) 215560 Fax: (01509) 215560 *Discos hire & services*

Central Southern Security Ltd, Station Street, Lymington, Hampshire, SO41 3BA Tel: (01590) 677366 Fax: (01590) 678024 E-mail: enquiries@central southern security.co.uk *Supply security systems*

Central Spares Ltd, Units 3-7, Brook Road, Wimborne, Dorset, BH21 2BH Tel: (01202) 882000 Fax: (01202) 881783 E-mail: sales@the-trolley-shop.co.uk *Distributors of spare parts for garden machinery*

▶ Central Steel Fabrications, 75-77 Chequers Lane, Dagenham, Essex, RM9 6QJ Tel: (020) 8592 7292 Fax: (020) 8517 4848 E-mail: centralsteelltd@aol.com *Steel fabricators & stock holders*

Central Steel Fabrications North West, Unit 5 Brickfields, Wilson Road Huyton, Liverpool, L36 6HY Tel: 0151-480 7504 Fax: 0151-480 7504 E-mail: enquiries@centralsteel.co.uk *Fabricators including sheet, metal & steel*

Central Steel Pickling Ltd, Nomex House, Powke Lane, Cradley Heath, West Midlands, B64 5PX Tel: (01384) 566373 Fax: (01384) 566376 *Pickling & oiling sheet & bar steels*

Central Steel Pickling Ltd, Nomex House, Powke Lane, Cradley Heath, West Midlands, B64 5PX Tel: (01384) 566373 Fax: (01384) 566376 *Crane & hoist repairs*

▶ Central Supplies Brierley Hill Ltd, Unit 55 Enterprise Trading Estate, Pedmore Road, Brierley Hill, West Midlands, DY5 1TX Tel: (01384) 484629 Fax: (01384) 484829 *Wholesalers*

Central Surgical Co. Ltd, 82a-84a Hornsey Road, London, N7 7NN Tel: (020) 7609 7259 Fax: (020) 7700 1328 E-mail: info@centralsurgical.co.uk *Surgical instrument makers*

Central Systems Installations Ltd, 100 Central Street, London, EC1V 8AJ Tel: (020) 7608 0070 Fax: (020) 7253 0891 E-mail: shop@csigroup.co.uk *Data cabling contractors*

Central Theatre Supplies, Midshire House, 1186 Stratford Road, Hall Green, Birmingham, B28 8AB Tel: 0121-778 6400 Fax: 0121-702 2046 E-mail: sales@centraltheatresupplies.co.uk *Theatre & performance equipment hire*

Central Tiles, 19 Highfield Road, Hall Green, Birmingham, B28 0EL Tel: 0121-777 7422 Fax: 0121-778 2414 E-mail: sales@centraltilestudio.co.uk *Ceramic tile suppliers*

▶ Central Timber Frame Ltd, Unit 6, 31 Jubilee Drive, Loughborough, Leicestershire, LE11 5XS Tel: (01509) 269990

Central Tin Canister Co. Ltd, Orrell Mount, Bootle, Merseyside, L20 6NS Tel: 0151-933 6704 Fax: 0151-933 5315 E-mail: centralplastic@freenetname.co.uk *Plastic packaging manufrs*

Central Tin Containers Ltd, Wilbraham Place, Scotland Road, Liverpool, L5 5BJ Tel: 0151-207 2775 Fax: 0151-298 1487 E-mail: dhunt@centraltincontainers.ltd.co.uk *Metal packaging manufrs*

Central Tools & Consumables, 18-19 Haverscroft Industrial Estate, New Road, Attleborough, Norfolk, NR17 1YE Tel: (01953) 453919 Fax: (01953) 456410

continued

E-mail: carlwcentral@aol.com *Tool consumables distributors*

Central Tools & Pressings, Unit D1, Bill House, Birmingham, B19 1AP Tel: 0121-523 7522 Fax: 0121-523 9922 *Press tools & pressings manufrs*

Central Tyre Ltd, 4 Rashs Green, Dereham, Norfolk, NR19 1JG Tel: (01362) 693901 Fax: (01362) 691502 E-mail: info@centraltyre.net *Tyre & exhaust retail outlets*

Central Video Studios, 70 Main Street, Shieldhill, Falkirk, FK1 2DT Tel: (01324) 631317 *Video production company*

Central Waste Oil Collections Ltd, 143 Queen Street, Walsall, WS2 9NT Tel: (01922) 725966 Fax: (01922) 721966 *Oil water waste recycling & disposal services*

Central Welding, 50 Creagh Road, Toomebridge, Antrim, BT41 3SE Tel: (028) 7965 0841 Fax: (028) 7965 9772 E-mail: info@centralwelding.co.uk *Oil tanker manufrs*

Central & West Lancashire Chamber Of Commerce & Industry, Unit 9-10 Eastway Business Village, Olivers Place, Fulwood, Preston, PR2 9WT Tel: (01772) 653000 Fax: (01772) 655544 E-mail: info@lancschamber.co.uk *Business support services*

Central Wheel Components Ltd, Station Road Industrial Estate, Station Road, Coleshill, Birmingham, B46 1HT Tel: (01675) 462264 Fax: (01675) 466412 E-mail: info@central-wheel.co.uk *Headed & threaded wires manufrs*

Central Window Cleaners Ltd, 21 Sussex Close, Nuneaton, Warwickshire, CV10 8JZ Tel: (024) 7675 7615 Fax: E-mail: enquires@centralwindowcleaners.co.uk *With 15 Years of experience, we can provide you with a professional and affordable service to make your windows sparkle - we can guarantee that you won"t be disappointed. *Fed up with an unreliable and poor quality window cleaning service? We offer a reliable regular window cleaning service to both domestic and commercial customers to the Nuneaton, Bedworth, Arley, Witherley, Berkswell and surrounding areas. *We also offer a number of other service such as conservatory cleaning,gutter clearing, house painting and general maintenance. We are fully insured up to 2 million pounds and are friendly and considerate at all times.*

Centralis Ltd, Centralis House Upper Wawensmoor, Wawensmere Road Wootton Wawen, Wootton Wawen, Henley-in-Arden, West Midlands, B95 6BS Tel: (01564) 795911 Fax: (01564) 795912 E-mail: recruitment@centralis.co.uk *Computer consultants services*

Centralised Services, Piccadilly, Nottingham, NG6 9FN Tel: 0115-913 5000 Fax: 0115-977 0744 E-mail: centser@btconnect.com *Security grill manufrs*

Centralised Services, Piccadilly, Nottingham, NG6 9FN Tel: 0115-913 5000 Fax: 0115-977 0744 E-mail: centser@btconnect.com *Engineers*

Centravent Ltd, Churchbridge, Oldbury, West Midlands, B69 2AX Tel: 0121-543 6878 *Ventilation & ductwork services*

Centre Bar Concepts, Willow House, New Road, Droitwich, Worcestershire, WR9 0PQ Tel: (01299) 851649 Fax: (01299) 851550 E-mail: centrebarconcept@aol.com *Refrigeration bar concepts catering, fabrication & air conditioning*

Centre Cane Co., 16 Shakletons, Ongar, Essex, CM5 9AT Tel: (01277) 363285 Fax: (01277) 366682 E-mail: centrcane@aol.com *Horticultural material importers*

Centre for Economics & Business Research Ltd, Unit 1, 4 Bath Street, London, EC1V 9DX Tel: (020) 7324 2850 Fax: (020) 7324 2855 E-mail: enquiries@cebr.com *Business advisors*

Centre Glass & Hygiene, Worrall Street, Salford, M5 4TH Tel: 0161-873 3000 Fax: 0161-877 2717 E-mail: zentreglassmail@aol.com *Glassware distributors*

▶ Centre Index Ltd, Units 5-7, Village Court, Village Farm Industrial Estate, Pyle, Bridgend, Mid Glamorgan, CF33 6BX Tel: (01656) 742100 Fax: (01656) 742251 E-mail: suzannah.bourne@ggtg.net *Assembly systems design & manufrs*

▶ Centre For Integrative Medical Training Ltd, 11 North Claremont Street, Glasgow, G3 7NR Tel: 0141-331 0393 Fax: (01383) 417850

▶ Centre Plant Ltd, 28 Muriel Street, Barrhead, Glasgow, G78 1QB Tel: 0141-880 4433 Fax: 0141-881 0828

Centre Point Associates, 16 St. Helen's Place, London, EC3A 6AU Tel: (020) 7562 1600 Fax: (020) 7562 1651 E-mail: hrservices@centrepointgroup.co.uk *Employment agency*

Centre Point Display Ltd, 91 Parker Drive, Leicester, LE4 0JP Tel: 0116-234 0077 E-mail: center.point.display@orbworld.net *Point of sale manufrs*

Centre Signs Ltd, 14 Iliffe Avenue, Oadby, Leicester, LE2 5LH Tel: 0116-271 4247 Fax: 0116-272 0260 E-mail: graphics@centresigns.co.uk *Sign manufrs*

Centreless Precision Grinding Ltd, Unit 19b Tyseley Industrial Estate, Seeleys Road, Birmingham, B11 2LQ Tel: 0121-772 1616 Fax: 0121-772 7099 *Centreless grinder suppliers*

Centreline Air Charter Ltd, Bristol Flying Centre, Bristol International Airport, Bristol, BS48 3DP Tel: (01275) 474357 Fax: (01275) 476539 E-mail: operations@centrelineair.co.uk *Chartering aircraft, freight, air taxi charter services*

Centreline Machine Guards Ltd, 2 Old Forge Trading Estate, Dudley Road, Stourbridge, West Midlands, DY9 8EL Tel: (01384) 422751 Fax: (01384) 422824 E-mail: neil.centreline@btconnect.co.uk *Industrial machine guards*

Centremark Design Ltd, 143 New London Road, Chelmsford, CM2 0QT Tel: (01245) 345143 Fax: (01245) 345144 E-mail: info@centremark-design.co.uk *Graphic designers & photographers*

Centreprint Graphics Ltd, Units 1-2, Lanesfield Drive, Ettingshall, Wolverhampton, WV4 6UA Tel: (01902) 402693 Fax: (01902) 491794 E-mail: sales@centreprint.co.uk *Commercial printers*

Centrereed Ltd, Thames House, Thames Street, Rotherham, South Yorkshire, S60 1LU Tel: (01709) 827700 Fax: (01709) 827715 E-mail: sales@centrereed.co.uk *Business forms stationery manufrs*

Centrescan Ltd, Centrescan Ho, 59 Great Eastern St, London, EC2A 3HS Tel: (020) 7739 5493 Fax: (020) 7739 6509 *Scanning/litho plate makers/printers*

Centresoft Ltd, 6 Pavilion Drive, Holford, Birmingham, B6 7BB Tel: 0121-625 3399 Fax: 0121-625 3236 E-mail: sales@centresoft.co.uk *Retail computer software distributors*

▶ Centric, 2nd Floor, Europe House, Bancroft Road, Reigate, Surrey, RH2 7RP Tel: (0870) 7703769 Fax: (0870) 7703769 E-mail: sales@centriccc.co.uk *Contract service centre who hosts websites*

Centrical Solutions, 20a West Park, Harrogate, North Yorkshire, HG1 1BJ Tel: (01423) 817555 Fax: (01423) 817999 E-mail: karen@centricalsolutions.com *Graphic design & web site design & consultancy*

Centri-Force Engineering Co. Ltd, 1-7 Montrose Avenue, Hillington Industrial Estate, Glasgow, G52 4DX Tel: 0141-882 3351 Fax: 0141-882 9965 E-mail: enquiries@centri-force.co.uk *High speed centrifuge manufrs*

Centriforce Products Ltd, 14/16 Derby Road, Liverpool, L20 8EE Tel: 0151-207 8109 Fax: 0151-298 1319 E-mail: sales@centriforce.co.uk *Centriforce is the UK market leader in converting low value plastic waste into a range of high value extruded products. From its modern factory in Liverpool, equipped with the latest sorting, cleaning and extrusion equipment, it processes more than 15,000 tonnes of waste plastics each year into quality sheet and boards and sells to markets throughout the world. They are fabricated into useful products such as Stokbord® cable covers and Centritile® warning tape for underground cable protection in the construction industry. Holloplas solid and hollow profiles for fencing, walkways, land management, outdoor furniture, sports and playground equipment. Stokbord® and economy grade sheet for animal house lining, transit packaging and protection and other industrial applications. All Centriforce products are independently verified, perform to the highest standards, and are supported by an innovative product development team. Centriforce ? inbuilt sustainability that benefits everyone*

Centrifugal Pump Services Ltd, Pump House, Bird Hall Lane, Cheadle Heath, Stockport, Cheshire, SK3 0XX Tel: 0161 4280133 Fax: 0161 4280188 E-mail: sales@centrifugalpumps.co.uk *Centrifugal Pump services Ltd supply the following types of pumps CENTRIFUGAL PUMPS, SUBMERSIBLE, GEAR, SELF PRIMING, MULTISTAGE, AIR OPERATED, DRUM, PRESSURISATION, HEATING, VACUUM, GENERATORS, 12/24 VOLTS, POND, FUEL OIL, MACHINE TOOL, HAND, DRAINAGE, SEWAGE, BIO DIESEL, CHEMICAL POOL & SPA, to name a few. They also supply equipment that is used along side the pumps like HOSE, VALVES, CONTROL PANELS & SPARES. *The products they provide are backed up by qualified time served engineers. *Many manufactures are represented through distribution and they pride themselves on being impartial, selecting the right pump for the application. Advice is free so please call with your requirements. *If you require any further information please telephone or visit the website via the link below.*

Centrilift, Howe Moss Place, Kirkhill Industrial Estate, Dyce, Aberdeen, AB21 0ES Tel: (01224) 772233 Fax: (01224) 771021 E-mail: sales@centrilift.com *Electrical & submersible pump manufrs*

Centristic Ltd, 1 Cavalier Road, Heathfield Industrial Estate, Newton Abbot, Devon, TQ12 6TQ Tel: (01626) 834310 Fax: (01626) 834681 E-mail: centristic@btconnect.com *Quarry plant manufrs*

Centrix Networking Ltd, Centrix House, Oxford Road, Newbury, Berkshire, RG14 1PD Tel: (01635) 239800 Fax: (01635) 239801 E-mail: sales@centrix.co.uk *Computer consultants*

Centromed International Ltd, Anglo House, Wotton Road, Ashford, Kent, TN23 6LN Tel: (01233) 635353 Fax: (01233) 635351 E-mail: info@centromed.com *Medical equipment distributors*

Centronic Ltd, Centronic House, King Henrys Drive, New Addington, Croydon, CR9 0BG Tel: (01689) 808000 Fax: (01689) 841822 E-mail: info@centronic.co.uk *Radiation monitor equipment & electronic components manufrs*

▶ Centura Foods Ltd, Altrincham Road, Manchester, M22 9AH Tel: 0161-998 2272

Centurian Products Ltd, 3-7 Bombay Street, London, SE16 3UX Tel: (020) 7237 2273 Fax: (020) 7231 8285 E-mail: sales@cent.demon.co.uk *General fabrication engineers*

Centurion Blinds Ltd, Oakdale Trading Estate, Ham Lane, Kingswinford, West Midlands, DY6 7JH Tel: (01384) 279797 Fax: (01384) 292354 E-mail: paulmorris@centruionblinds.com *Venetian & vertical louver blind manufrs*

Centurion Communications Ltd, Centurion House, Leyland Business Park, Centurion Way, Farington, Leyland, PR25 3GR Tel: (01772) 628362 Fax: (0870) 2113008 E-mail: post@telecomcentral.co.uk *Telecommunications installers*

Centurion Components Ltd, 38 Carron Place, East Kilbride, Glasgow, G75 0TS Tel: (01355) 265222 Fax: (01355) 230331 E-mail: sales@centurionsigns.co.uk *Safety sign manufrs*

Centurion Concrete Products, Centurion Industrial Estate, Centurion Way, Farington, Leyland, PR25 4GU Tel: (01772) 622926 Fax: (01772) 622926 *Concrete manufrs*

Centurion Europe Ltd, Hunt Lane, Doncaster, South Yorkshire, DN5 9SH Tel: (01302) 788700 Fax: (01302) 390004 E-mail: sales@centurioneurope.co.uk *Signs & nameplates distributors & manufrs*

Centurion Furniture plc, Centurion Building, Farington Road, Farington Moss, Leyland, PR26 6JW Tel: (01772) 450111 Fax: (01772) 453511 E-mail: sales@centurion.telme.com *Furniture manufrs*

▶ Centurion Plumbing, 3 Cecil Court, Wall Road, Ashford, Kent, TN24 8NW Tel: 01233 336378 E-mail: mail@centurionplumbing.co.uk

Centurion Safety Products Ltd, 21 Howlett Way, Thetford, Norfolk, IP24 1HZ Tel: (01842) 754266 Fax: (01842) 765590 E-mail: sales@centurionsafety.co.uk *Safety helmet, breathing apparatus & accessories manufrs*

Centurion Security System, Centurion House, Park Road West, Huddersfield, HD4 5RX Tel: (01484) 321321 Fax: (01484) 351888 E-mail: sales@centurion.net *Intruder CCTV & access control installers*

▶ Century Blinds, Lurgan Road, Portadown, Craigavon, County Armagh, BT63 5QR Tel: (028) 3833 6776 Fax: (028) 3833 6776 *Window blind wholesalers*

Century Box & Packaging Ltd, The Tunnels Elms Farm, Gretton Fields, Cheltenham, Gloucestershire, GL54 5HQ Tel: (01242) 620895 Fax: (01242) 620999 E-mail: sales@centurybox.co.uk *Cardboard box manufrs*

▶ Century Builders Ltd, 217 Danes Drive, Glasgow, G14 9AQ Tel: 0141-954 3845

Century Business Systems, 19-21 Mid Stocket Road, Aberdeen, AB15 5JL Tel: (01224) 644064 Fax: (01224) 643407 E-mail: info@century.uk.net *Computer network services*

Century Cables & Controls Ltd, Century House, 8 South Street, Crowland, Peterborough, PE6 0AJ Tel: (01733) 211600 Fax: (01733) 211082 E-mail: kwhincup@yahoo.com *Century Cables Ltd is active in the following markets, and manufactures /supplies the products below: Either a list or description would be great. Market Areas: Marine Cables, Industrial Cables, Aerospace Cables, Motorsports Cables, Agricultural Cables, Offroad Vehicle Cables, Plant Cables. We manufacture and Supply: Brake Cables, Brake Balance Bar Cables, Gearshift Cables,Throttle Cables,Push-Pull Cables,Wire Ropes,Valve Control Cables,Trim Tabs Cables,Speedo Cables,Tacho Cables,Architectural Stainless Steel Wire,Rope and Turnbuckles,Valve Control, Levers,Hydrostatic Drive Levers,Multi Purpose Levers, Self Locking Levers,Forward Neutral and Reverse,Levers,Detent Levers,Hand Throttle Levers, Footpedals*

Century Clothing, Swinburne Street, Nottingham, NG3 2GD Tel: 0115-950 4744 Fax: 0115-924 1896 E-mail: paul@centuryclothing.co.uk *Clothing, workwear, corporate, safety, protective, promotional.*

Century Composites Ltd, 58-59 Hutton Close, Crowther, Washington, Tyne & Wear, NE38 0AH Tel: 0191-416 8200 Fax: 0191-415 5962 *Carbon composite tube manufrs*

Century Computers UK Ltd, 48 Barry Road, Barry, South Glamorgan, CF63 1BA Tel: (01446) 410070 Fax: 01446 410070 *Computer repairs & development*

Century Dyeing Co., Century Road, Elland, West Yorkshire, HX5 9HQ Tel: (01422) 379411 Fax: (01422) 376592 E-mail: info@centurydyeing.co.uk *Polyester & nylon piece dyers*

▶ Century Fabrications, Dunston Trading Estate, Foxwood Road, Chesterfield, Derbyshire, S41 9RF Tel: (01246) 450619 Fax: (01246) 260233 E-mail: cenfab@aol.com *Metalworking & fabrication services*

Century IT Group, 88 Watling Street, Radlett, Hertfordshire, WD7 7AB Tel: (01923) 856590 Fax: (01923) 853025 E-mail: info@century-networks.co.uk *Systems & network sales*

Century Life P.L.C., Century House, 5 Old Bailey, London, EC4M 7BA Tel: (01708) 758196 *Life insurance company*

Century Litho (Truro) Ltd, Kernick Industrial Estate, Penryn, Cornwall, TR10 9EP Tel: (01326) 376666 Fax: (0870) 0010305 E-mail: sales@centryprint.com *Lithographic printer services*

Centurywise Chemicals, Oaker Mount, 175 Stockport Road West, Bredbury, Stockport, Cheshire, SK6 2AP Tel: 0161-430 8773 Fax: 0161-430 8773 E-mail: centurywise@aol.com *Chemical cleaning & pressure washing suppliers*

▶ Ceotronics Ltd, The Clocktower, Park Road, Bestwood Village, Nottingham, NG6 8TQ Tel: 0115-977 0100 Fax: 0115-977 0300 *Radio communications equipment manufrs*

▶ Cer, 7 Monaco Works, Station Road, Kings Langley, Hertfordshire, WD4 8LQ Tel: (01923) 266866 Fax: (01923) 261784

Ceramaspeed Ltd, Zortech Avenue, Kidderminster, Worcestershire, DY11 7DY Tel: (01562) 756000 Fax: (01562) 756030 *Ceramic cooker element manufrs*

Ceramet Plasma Coatings Ltd, Ryeford Industrial Estate, Ryeford, Stonehouse, Gloucestershire, GL10 2LA Tel: (01453) 828416 Fax: (01453) 823068 E-mail: sales@ceramet.co.uk *We offer a complete Thermal Spray coating service including coating choice, development, coating application & finishing (surface/cylindrical grinding, lapping, superfinishing) We service whole spectrum of industries including*

continued

continuation
Petrochemical, Printing, Aerospace, Pumps, Textile, Paper, Electronics.

▶ Ceramic Art, 41 Whitehouse Meadows, Leigh-on-Sea, Essex, SS9 5TY Tel: (01702) 526348 E-mail: ceramicart_uk@msn.com *Established Wall and floor tiling contractors. Natural stone, mosaics, marble, porcelain and ceramics.*

Ceramic Choice, Unit 12 Mossedge Industrial Estate, Moss Road, Linwood, Paisley, Renfrewshire, PA3 3HR Tel: (01505) 336644 Fax: (01505) 335138 *Ceramics suppliers*

Ceramic Core Systems Ltd, Unit F Sawtry Business Park, Sawtry, Huntingdon, Cambridgeshire, PE28 5GQ Tel: (01487) 832283 Fax: (01487) 832887 *Cast ceramic parts suppliers*

Ceramic Decals Ltd, Anderton Works, Port Street, Stoke-on-Trent, ST6 3PF Tel: (01782) 838000 Fax: (01782) 822993 E-mail: maxine@ceramicdetails.co.uk *Ceramic decals manufrs*

Ceramic Design & Installations, 3 St Pauls Close, Farington Moss, Leyland, PR26 6RT Tel: (01772) 311902 Fax: (01772) 311992 *Ceramic tiling installation*

Ceramic Drying Systems Ltd, Weston Coyney Road, Stoke-on-Trent, ST3 5JU Tel: (01782) 336666

Ceramic Gas Products Ltd, Albion Works, Uttoxeter Road, Stoke-on-Trent, ST3 1PH Tel: (01782) 599922 Fax: (01782) 598037 E-mail: joan@ceramicgasproducts.co.uk *Industrial ceramic manufrs*Ultralite high temperature insulation*Ultralite refractory castable.*Kiln insulation*

▶ Ceramic Hair Straighteners, 3 Pye Road, Heswall, Wirral, Merseyside, CH60 0DB Tel: 0151-342 4591 Fax: 0151-342 1130 E-mail: sales@ceramicstraighteners.com *Sells hairdressing products*

Ceramic Research Ltd, Queens Road, Stoke-on-Trent, ST4 7LQ Tel: (01782) 764444 Fax: (01782) 412331 E-mail: sales@ceram.co.uk *Research laboratory*

Ceramic Seals Ltd, Westwood Industrial Estate, Arkwright Street, Oldham, OL9 9LZ Tel: 0161-627 2353 Fax: 0161-627 2356 E-mail: admin@ceramicseals.co.uk *Ceramic seal manufrs*

Ceramic Substrates & Components Ltd, Lukely Works, 180 Carisbrooke Road, Newport, Isle of Wight, PO30 1DH Tel: (01983) 528697 Fax: (01983) 822252 E-mail: sales@ceramic-subtrates.co.uk Purchasing Contact: J. Blain Sales Contact: J. Blain Principal Export Areas: Worldwide *Manufacturers of advanced technical ceramic components for industry, research, motor and aerospace applications.*

Ceramic Tile Distributors, Quarry Lane, Chichester, West Sussex, PO19 8PE Tel: (01243) 787664 Fax: (01243) 776695 *Glazed tile merchants* Also at: Branches throughout the U.K.

Ceramic Tiles Ltd, Unit 46, Bosshall Business Park, Bosshall Road, Ipswich, IP1 5BN Tel: (01473) 745478 Fax: (01473) 240133 E-mail: customer.support@ceramic-tiles.co.uk *Adhesives, accessories & ceramic tiles suppliers* Also at: Bury St. Edmunds

▶ Ceramica Blue, 10 Blenheim Cresent, London, W11 1NN Tel: (020) 7727 0288 Fax: (020) 7221 6694 E-mail: shop@ceramicablue.co.uk *Ceramics, tableware & cookware retailer*

Ceramicast Precision Investment Castings Ltd, Castings House, Boundary Road, Woking, Surrey, GU21 5BX Tel: (01483) 751666 Fax: (01483) 751888 E-mail: sales@ceramicast.com Principal Export Areas: Worldwide *Casting manufrs*

Ceramicos, The Warehouse, Whitehill Cottage, Oxhill, Warwick, CV35 0RH Tel: 01295 680176 Fax: 01295 680174 E-mail: sales@ceramicos.co.uk *Ceramic pot distribs*

Ceramics Cafe, 6 Argyle Road, London, W13 8AB Tel: (020) 8810 4422 Fax: (020) 8810 5593 *Ceramic painters*

Ceramics Cafe, High Street, Ripley, Woking, Surrey, GU23 6BB Tel: (01483) 224477 *Ceramics painting shop*

▶ Ceramics Channel Island Ceramics, Forest Road, Forest, Guernsey, GY8 0AB Tel: (01481) 234000 Fax: (01481) 234007

Ceramics & Crystal Ltd, 7 Montpelier Gardens, London, E6 3JB Tel: (020) 8552 3122 Fax: (020) 8552 3122 *Importers of ceramics*

Ceramics Studios Ltd, 59a Chesson Road, London, W14 9QT Tel: (020) 7385 2061 Fax: (020) 7385 2235 *Dental laboratory*

Ceramiks, Hadfield Road, Cardiff, CF11 8AQ Tel: (0808) 1555629 Fax: (029) 2022 0559 E-mail: ceramiks@comptongroup.com *Ceramic tile suppliers & distributors*

Ceramique (International) Ltd, Unit 1, Royds Lane, Lower Wortley Ring Road, Leeds, LS12 6DU Tel: 0113-231 0218 Fax: 0113-231 0353 E-mail: info@ceramiqueinternationale.co.uk *Ceramic tile importers, distributors & retailers*

Ceramodo Tiles, 236 Easterly Road, Leeds, LS8 3ES Tel: 0113-249 0041 Fax: 0113-248 5665 E-mail: sales@ceramodotiles.co.uk *Tile designers & importers*

Ceramtec UK Ltd, Sidmouth Road, Colyton, Devon, EX24 6JP Tel: (01297) 552707 Fax: (01297) 553325 E-mail: sales@ceramtec.co.uk *Ceramic products manufrs*

▶ Ceram-Tech, 52 Crossgreen Drive, Uphall, Broxburn, West Lothian, EH52 6DR Tel: (01506) 857805 *Supply of standard or custom designed products in 95% or >99% alumina.*

Ceratech Holdings plc, Ceratech House, Omega Park, Alton, Hampshire, GU34 2QE Tel: (01420) 85470 Fax: (01420) 83545 E-mail: sales@ceratech.co.uk *Personal computer peripheral equipment distributors*

Ceratex Engineering Ltd, Church La Works, Church Lane, Kelbrook, Barnoldswick, Lancashire, BB18 6UF Tel: (01282) 842900 Fax: (01282) 844093 E-mail: sales@ceratex.co.uk Principal Export Areas: Worldwide *Vibratory finishing services*

Ceratizit UK Ltd, Cliff Lane, Grappenhall, Warrington, WA4 3JX Tel: (01925) 261161 Fax: (01925) 267933 *Tungsten carbide tool sales and distribution company*

Ceravision Lighting Mnfrs, Innovation Centre, Bletchley Park, Bletchley, Milton Keynes, MK3 6EB Tel: (01908) 371463 Fax: (01908) 370792

Cerberus Engineering Services Ltd, Coker Road, Weston-super-Mare, Avon, BS22 6BX Tel: (01934) 517747 Fax: (01934) 512633 E-mail: info@ceberus-eng.co.uk *General sheet metalwork engineers*

Cerdan Ltd, Silver Street Workshops, 37 Silver Street, Ashwell, Baldock, Hertfordshire, SG7 5QH Tel: (01462) 742837 Fax: (01462) 743130 E-mail: info@cerdan.co.uk *Furniture designers & manufacturers & consultancy*

Cerdic Foundries Ltd, Beeching Close, Chard, Somerset, TA20 1BB Tel: (01460) 64301 Fax: (01460) 63961 E-mail: sales@cerdicfoundries.co.uk *Engineers*

Cereal Partners UK, Port Causeway, Bromborough, Wirral, Merseyside, CH62 4TH Tel: 0151-512 4700 Fax: 0151-512 4702 *Manufacturers of cereal food products*

Cerec, 95 Ashby High Street, Scunthorpe, South Humberside, DN16 2JX Tel: (01724) 846866 Fax: (01724) 280358 E-mail: colin-wilson@ntlworld.com *Tank & boiler manufrs*

Ceres Health Food, 29 Goring Road, Goring-by-Sea, Worthing, West Sussex, BN12 4AR Tel: (01903) 242023 *Health food retailers*

Ceres System Ltd, Unit 15 The Old Malthouse, Springfield Road, Grantham, Lincolnshire, NG31 7BG Tel: (01476) 563188 E-mail: sales@vertexplus.co.uk *Control system software manufrs*

Cerium Group Ltd, Cerium Industrial Park, Appledore Road, Tenterden, Kent, TN30 7DE Tel: (01580) 765211 Fax: (01580) 765573 E-mail: ceriumgrp@aol.com *Optical component manufacturers custom coaters*

Cermag Ltd, 94 Holywell Road, Sheffield, S4 8AS Tel: 0114-244 6136 Fax: 0114-256 1769 E-mail: sales@cermag.co.uk Principal Export Areas: Central Asia, Africa, Central/East Europe, West Europe & North America *Manufacturers of magnets including ceramic, industrial, neodymium, permanent & injection moulded. Also gaussmeter manufrs*

Cermatco Ltd, Aylesham Industrial Estate, Aylesham, Canterbury, Kent, CT3 3EP Tel: (01304) 842222 Fax: (01304) 842434 E-mail: info@cermatco.co.uk *Crush & grade ceramic raw material*

Cermeteq, Treswell, Retford, Notts, DN22 0EQ Tel: 01777 248822 Fax: 01777 248666 *Refractory suppliers*

Cermex UK Ltd, PO Box 12, Huntingdon, Cambridgeshire, PE29 6EF Tel: (01480) 455919 Fax: (01480) 451520 E-mail: sales@cermexuk.com *Packing machinery distributors*

▶ Cerrig Ltd, Glanydon Industrial Estate, Pwllheli, Gwynedd, LL53 5YT Tel: (01758) 612645 Fax: (01758) 612410 E-mail: sales@cerrig-granite.co.uk *Specialists in granite & slate worktops*

Cerrig Furniture, Cae Bryn, Cerrigydrudion, Corwen, Clwyd, LL21 9SW Tel: (01490) 420372 *Furniture manufrs*

Cerro Ems Ltd, Liverpool Street, Birmingham, B9 4DS Tel: 0121-772 6515 Fax: 0121-772 6126 *Hot brass pressings & stampings*

Cerro (Manganese Bronze) Ltd, PO Box 22, Ipswich, IP2 0EG Tel: (01473) 252127 Fax: (01473) 218229 E-mail: sales@scerromb.com *Aluminium bronze forging & rod manufrs*

▶ Cert plc, Hellaby Lane, Hellaby, Rotherham, South Yorkshire, S66 8HN Tel: (01709) 544822 Fax: (01709) 531365

Cert Consultancy & Training, Dairy Farm, Little Gringley, Retford, Nottinghamshire, DN22 0DU Tel: (01777) 860835 Fax: (01777) 702353 E-mail: cert@certuk.com *Human resources consultancy*

▶ Cert Tax Accounting, 47 Clarence Road, Chesterfield, Derbyshire, S40 1LQ Tel: (01246) 200255

Certa Ceto Sandbach, 45 Hightown, Crewe, CW1 3BZ Tel: (01270) 251333 Fax: (01270) 251444 E-mail: mellorremstar@aol.com *Sign making, t-shirt printers, exhibitionists & embroidery*

▶ Certex UK Ltd, 17 Gravelly Industrial Park, Birmingham, B24 8HZ Tel: 0121-327 1255 Fax: 0121-327 6966 E-mail: sales@certex.co.uk *Lifting gear hire & leasing*

▶ Certex UK Ltd, Unit 7a-7b, Pennine Close, Llanishen, Cardiff, CF14 5DN Tel: (029) 2068 3650 Fax: (029) 2068 3659 E-mail: sales@certex.co.uk *Lifting gear hire & inspection services*

Certex UK Ltd, 8 Trafford Court, Doncaster, South Yorkshire, DN1 1PN Tel: (01302) 731000 Fax: (01302) 731000 E-mail: sales@certex.co.uk Principal Export Areas: Worldwide *Listing equipment*

▶ Certex UK Ltd, Units 1-3, Viking Way, Erith, Kent, DA8 1EW Tel: (01322) 442323 Fax: (01322) 441044 E-mail: sales@certex.co.uk *Lifting gear hire & inspection*

▶ Certex UK Ltd, Dukesway Court, Team Valley Trading Estate, Gateshead, Tyne & Wear, NE11 0BH Tel: 0191-491 0696 Fax: 0191-491 0787 E-mail: sales@certex.co.uk *Lifting gear hire & inspection*

▶ Certex UK Ltd, 125 Business Park, Llanthony Road, Gloucester, GL2 5JQ Tel: (01452) 526119 Fax: (01452) 307632 E-mail: gloucester@certex.co.uk *Lifting gear hire & inspection service*

▶ Certex UK Ltd, Ordsall Wire Mills, Ollerton Road, Retford, Nottinghamshire, DN22 7XN Tel: (01777) 708264 Fax: (01777) 705878 E-mail: glasgow@certex.co.uk *Lifting gear hire & inspection services*

▶ Certex UK Ltd, Unit 4 Third Avenue, Southampton, SO15 0LD Tel: (023) 8070 3894 Fax: (023) 8070 3901 E-mail: admin@certex.co.uk *Lifting gear hire & inspection*

▶ Certex UK Ltd, Delphwood Drive, Sherdley Road Industrial Estat, St. Helens, Merseyside, WA9 5JE Tel: (01744) 20590 Fax: (01744) 24059 E-mail: sthelens@certex.co.uk *Lifting gear sales & inspection services*

▶ Certex UK Ltd, Flanshaw Way Industrial Estate, Flanshaw Way, Wakefield, West Yorkshire, WF2 9LP Tel: (01924) 375431 Fax: (01924) 290538 E-mail: sales@certex.co.uk *Lifting gear hire & inspection services*

Certiforms Ltd, Lower Heys Mill, Black Lane, Macclesfield, Cheshire, SK10 2AY Tel: (01625) 433390 Fax: (01625) 511333 E-mail: sales@certiforms.co.uk *wicketed bags.*

Certikin International Ltd, 2 Station Lane Industrial Park Estate, Witney, Oxfordshire, OX28 4FH Tel: (01993) 778855 Fax: (01993) 778620 E-mail: export@certikin.co.uk *Swimming pool equipment manufrs*

Certis, The Crown Business Park, Old Dalby, Melton Mowbray, Leicestershire, LE14 3NQ Tel: (01664) 820052 Fax: (01664) 820216 E-mail: enquiry@luxan.co.uk *Manufacturers of crop protection & pest control products*

▶ Certus Sales Recruitment Ltd, 3RD Floor Sussex House, 143 Long Acre, London, WC2E 9AD Tel: (0845) 2304230 Fax: (020) 7257 6299 E-mail: london@certussales.com *Certus Sales Recruitment are a specialist sales recruitment consultancy providing sales recruitment services to the business to business marketplace. We are experts in the recruitment of sales professionals from Graduate & Sales Trainee through to Sales Manager and Sales Director level.*

Certwood Ltd, Laporte Way, Luton, LU4 8EF Tel: (01582) 456955 Fax: (01582) 485855 E-mail: sales@certwood.com *Injection moulders*

▶ Cerub Limited, 17a Peterborough Avenue, High Wycombe, Buckinghamshire, HP13 6DX Tel: 01494 461784 Fax: 08707 062603 E-mail: ceri@cerubpr.co.uk *Cerub PR is an agency which specialises in providing PR for small to medium sized businesses. We pride ourselves on providing a tailored PR service to suit the individual needs of our clients. **Cerub PR provides an unrivalled service for an unbeatable price.**Services include:**Public relations, event organisation, copywriting and promotions.*

Ces Microcare Ltd, 1 Muirhall Road, Larbert, Stirlingshire, FK5 4RR Tel: (01324) 552121 Fax: (01324) 562299 E-mail: service@ces-microcare.co.uk *Microwave repairers*

Cesab Ltd, Unit 10 Regent Park, Booth Drive Park Farm South, Park Farm Industrial Estate, Wellingborough, Northamptonshire, NN8 6GR Tel: (01933) 670460 Fax: (01933) 679854 E-mail: sales@cesab.net *Fork lift truck distributors & manufrs*

Cesalpinia UK Ltd, Mare House, 1 Bilton Way, Luton, LU1 1UU Tel: (01582) 811900 Fax: (01582) 811901 E-mail: sales@cesalpinia.co.uk *Food stabilizers & suppliers*

▶ Cesano Signs & Graphics, 20 St. Georges Road, Badshot Lea, Farnham, Surrey, GU9 9LX Tel: (01252) 341491 E-mail: dragonheartz@btinternet.com *We offer a full spectrum sign service from traditional sign writting to vehicle wraps and loads more*

Cesar Janitorial Supplies, 35-39 Old Street, London, EC1V 9HX Tel: (020) 7253 4655 Fax: (020) 7250 1516 E-mail: brad@cesar.demon.co.uk *Cleaning equipment suppliers*

Cestradent Mckesson Ltd, Trident House, 110 Park Road, Chesterfield, Derbyshire, S40 2JX Tel: (01246) 276111 Fax: (01246) 230825 E-mail: mail@mckesson.plus.com *Dental anaesthetic equipment wholesalers & manufrs*

Cestrian, Stanley Green TRDG Estate, Earl Road, Cheadle Hulme, Cheadle, Cheshire, SK8 6QD Tel: 0161-488 3300 Fax: 0161-488 3301 E-mail: reception@cestrian.co.uk *Billboard poster printers*

Ceta Precision Engineering Ltd, Tweedbank Industrial Estate, Tweedbank, Galashiels, Selkirkshire, TD1 3RS Tel: (01896) 757200 Fax: (01896) 758307 *CNC machinsts*

Ceto Engineering Ltd, Howard Road, Eaton Socon, St. Neots, Cambridgeshire, PE19 8ET Tel: (01480) 406646 Fax: (01480) 406605 *Staircases (metal) manufrs*

Cetuem Cosmetics Ltd, 115 Brunswick Park Road, London, N11 1EA Tel: (020) 8368 0008 Fax: (020) 8368 9579 E-mail: info@centuem.co.uk *Hair, nail & skincare manufrs*

Ceuta Healthcare Ltd, Hill House, 41 Richmond Hill, Bournemouth, BH2 6HS Tel: (01202) 780558 Fax: (01202) 780559 *Healthcare distributors*

Ceva Animal Health Ltd, 7 Awberry Court, Hatters Lane, Watford, WD18 8PE Tel: (01494) 781510 Fax: (01923) 243001 *Animal health care product suppliers*

▶ Ceva Automotive Logistics UK Ltd, Hawleys Lane, Warrington, WA2 8JR Tel: (01925) 652277 Fax: (01925) 231215

Ceva Logistics, Tunnel Estate, Easton Avenue, Grays, Essex, RM20 3LW Tel: (01708) 258200 Fax: (01708) 258299 *Export buying agents & shippers*

▶ Ceva News Fast, Earn Avenue, Righead Industrial Estate, Bellshill, Lanarkshire, ML4 3LW Tel: (01698) 844737 Fax: (01698) 740862 E-mail: sales@newsfast.co.uk

Cevac & Co., 4 Marechal Niel Parade, Main Road, Sidcup, Kent, DA14 6QF Tel: (020) 8308 0808 Fax: (020) 8308 0181 *Air conditioning engineers*

Cewal UK Ltd, Unit 4C, Woodhall Business Park, Sudbury, Suffolk, CO10 1WH Tel: (01787) 882038 Fax: (01787) 882039 E-mail: info@cewal.co.uk *Pressure & temperature instrumentation manufrs*

CEX Ltd, 143 Whitfield Street, London, W1T 5EP Tel: (020) 7916 8422 Fax: (020) 7916 8434 *Second hand computer games & hardware retailers*

CFBS, 1 Progress Works, Parkwood Street, Keighley, West Yorkshire, BD21 4NX Tel: (01535) 681839 Fax: (01535) 681887 E-mail: mail@cfbs.co.uk *Refurbisher & manufacturer of beer dispensing equipment for real ale.*

CFG Site Services Ltd, Forest Vale Road, Forest Vale Industrial Estate, Cinderford, Gloucestershire, GL14 2PH Tel: (01594) 826364 Fax: (01594) 822807

▶ CFM Building Services Ltd, Units 1-2 Crathie Court, Castlehill Industrial Estate, Carluke, Lanarkshire, ML8 5UF Tel: (01555) 771178 Fax: (01555) 771226

▶ CFM Electrical Contractors, Elizabeth Terrace, Tower Road, St. Helier, Jersey, JE2 3HS Tel: (01534) 870722 Fax: (01534) 780757

▶ CFR Consulting Group Limited, Sixth Floor, Caxton House, 2 Farringdon Street, London, EC1M 3HN Tel: 0207 729 0929 Fax: 01962 849255 E-mail: cfr@freurope.com *European and International Management & Executive Search & Selection Recrtuitment Services Offices in UK (London, Newark, Winchester), Austria (Linz, Innsbruck, Graz), Belgium (Gent, Zaventem, Antwerp, Hasselt), China (shanghai), Czech Republic Prague, Budweis), France (Paris 3 offices), Germany (Munich, Bochum, Dusselfdorf, Stuttgart), Hungary (Budapest), Italy (Milan), The Netherlands (Gorinchem), Poland (Warsaw), Slovenia (Ljubljana), Spain (Barcelona, Madrid), Switzerland (Bern, Zurich)*

▶ CG Computing, 21 Greenlands Avenue, Whitehaven, Cumbria, CA28 6TY Tel: 01946 692871 E-mail: sales@cgcomputing.net *SAVINGS OF UPTO 80% !!!!!!**For all your computer and camera consumables try Cumbria"s No 1 company*

CGB Engineering Services Ltd, 2 Britannia House, Gorton Road, Manchester, M11 2DA Tel: 0161-231 7347 Fax: 0161-231 7077 E-mail: cgbservices@aol.com *Design & manufacture of cutting machines & cutting wires for the rigid foam insulation market. Materials include rigid Phenolic, PU, Styrofoam, Mineral wool & all Polystrene products. Machines for specialised cutting applications also catered for*

Cgi, Wigwam Lane, Hucknall, Nottingham, NG15 7TA Tel: 0115-963 5991 Fax: 0115-968 0334 *Steel fabricators*

Cgi Europe, Unit C3 Enterprise Business Park, Millharbour, London, E14 9TE Tel: (020) 7531 0500 Fax: (020) 7531 0531 *Commercial & financial printers*

CGS Signs Ltd, 23 Railway Road, Adlington, Chorley, Lancashire, PR6 9RG Tel: (01257) 482790 Fax: (01257) 482791 E-mail: sales@cgssigns.co.uk *Sign manufrs*

CH Design Installation Co. Ltd, 31 Southwold Mansions, Widley Road, London, W9 2LE Tel: (020) 7289 1792 Fax: (020) 7266 4607 *Audio-visual equipment supplies & services*

CH Field Services Ltd, 3A Albert Court, Prince Consort Road, London, SW7 2BJ Tel: (020) 7589 1256 Fax: (020) 7591 4994 E-mail: tlovekin@charleskendall.com *Purchasing agents*

Ch2m Hill, Avon House, Avonmore Road, London, W14 8TS Tel: (020) 7471 6100 Fax: (020) 7471 6101 *Project delivery company*

Cha Cha Dum Dum, 16 Osram Road, East Lane Business Park, East Lane, Wembley, Middlesex, HA9 7NG Tel: (020) 8908 0743 Fax: (020) 8904 9117 E-mail: info@chachadumdum.co.uk *Wholesale jewellers & Gifts*

Chad Containers Ltd, Burrell Way, Thetford, Norfolk, IP24 3QS Tel: (01842) 763583 Fax: (01842) 750055 *Container & recycling bank manufrs*

Chad Engineering (UK) Ltd, Unit 2, Business Village, Wexham Road, Slough, SL2 5HF Tel: (01753) 537980 Fax: (01753) 553472 E-mail: enquiries@chad-engineering.co.uk *General engineers*

Chadburns Fence Suppliers, 22 Wortley View, Blacker Hill, Barnsley, South Yorkshire, S74 0RD Tel: (01226) 744028 *Wood bending*

Chadderton Metal Products Ltd, Unit F2 Westwood Industrial Estate, Arkwright Street, Oldham, OL9 9LZ Tel: 0161-620 7907 Fax: 0161-627 4486 E-mail: sales@cmplimited.wanadoo.co.uk *Laser cutting & sheet metalworkers*

Chadfield Signs, 6 Highfield Road, Stockton-on-Tees, Cleveland, TS18 5HG Tel: (01642) 582082 *Sign writers*

Chadfort Engineering Ltd, Unit 6c, Blakewater Road, Blackburn, BB1 5QH Tel: (01254) 582075 Fax: (01254) 661062 E-mail: andrew.chadwick@chadfort.co.uk

Chadha & Son, 112-116 Whitechapel Rd, London, E1 1JE Tel: 020 72470348 *Importers & wholesalers of childrens clothing*

▶ Chadwell Construction Ltd, Tralin House, Chesham Close, Romford, RM7 7PJ Tel: (01708) 767100 Fax: (01708) 759920 E-mail: info@chadwell.co.uk

Chadwell Safety Glass Ltd, Maldon Road, Latchingdon, Chelmsford, CM3 6LF Tel: (01621) 743084 Fax: (01621) 742977 *Motor vehicle window manufrs*

Chadwick Engineering Co. Ltd, 173-179 Tyburn Road, Erdington, Birmingham, B24 8NQ Tel: 0121-327 7997 Fax: 0121-327 7987 *Precision engineers*

Thomas Chadwick & Sons, Eastfield Mills, Goods Lane, Dewsbury, West Yorkshire, WF12 8EH Tel: (01924) 465023 Fax: (01924) 465279 E-mail: tchadwick@standard-wool.co.uk *Wool scouring services*

Chadwick Web Processing Ltd, Aspinall Street, Heywood, Lancashire, OL10 4HR Tel: (01706) 369182 Fax: (01706) 623719 E-mail: info@chadwick.com *Printing press equipment manufrs*

Chadwicks Liverpool Ltd, 62-64 Kitchen Street, Liverpool, L1 0AN Tel: 0151-709 3081 Fax: 0151-709 9115 *Builders merchants & drain cleaning equipment suppliers*

Chaffey & Son, 10 Hollow Lane, Shinfield, Reading, RG2 9BT Tel: 0118-969 2424 *Builders' merchants*

▶ Chafford Landscapes, 14 St. James Avenue East, Stanford-le-Hope, Essex, SS17 7BQ Tel: (01375) 676003 E-mail: ianholloway@btconnect.com *Landscape & horticultural contractors undertaking domestic & commercial contracts*

Chaggar Engineering, Murdock Road, Manton Industrial Estate, Bedford, MK41 7PE Tel: (01234) 360557 Fax: (0871) 2422493 E-mail: premchaggar@hotmail.com *Sheet metal fabricators*

Chain Products Ltd, 49 Ward Street, Birmingham, B19 3TD Tel: 0121-359 0697 Fax: 0121-359 3672 E-mail: chainproducts@aol.com Principal Export Areas: Asia Pacific, Africa & North America *Chain manufrs*

Chain Saw Services, 16 Pinfold Lane, North Luffenham, Oakham, Leicestershire, LE15 8LE Tel: (01780) 721070 Fax: (01780) 729455 *Chain saw & safety clothing distributors*

Chainbond Ltd, Rose Mill, Union Street, Middleton, Manchester, M24 6DD Tel: 0161-653 2931 Fax: 0161-653 2931 *Rubber manufrs*

Chainings Ltd, Pomona Works, Newent Business Park, Newent, Gloucestershire, GL18 1DZ Tel: (01531) 822244 Fax: (01531) 821555 E-mail: sales@chainings.com *Fine filtration products*

Chains Ltd, Winterbottom Lane, Mere, Knutsford, Cheshire, WA16 0QQ Tel: (01565) 830747 Fax: (01565) 830331 E-mail: sales@chainandconveyor.com *Conveyor chains manufrs*

Chains & Lifting Tackle Midlands Ltd, Dewsbury Road, Fenton Industrial Estate, Stoke-on-Trent, ST4 2TD Tel: (01782) 747400 Fax: (01782) 744508 E-mail: info@chainsandlifting.co.uk *Lifting gear sales, hire, repair, service & site installation*

Chains North West Ltd, 180 Rimrose Road, Bootle, Merseyside, L20 4QS Tel: 0151-933 2633 Fax: 0151-922 6739 *Marine consultants*

Chaintabs Ltd, 6 Grafton Rd, Sparkbrook, Birmingham, B11 1JP Tel: 0121-430 7957 Fax: 0121-430 7964 *Lifting gear safety marker manufrs*

Chaintec Ltd, Unit 43, Westbrook Trading Estate, Westbrook Road, Trafford Park, Manchester, M17 1AY Tel: 0161-877 7373 Fax: 0161-876 0365 E-mail: info@chaintec.co.uk *Chaintec are leading suppliers of off-the-shelf and specialist leaf chains for the FLT (fork lift truck) replacement market, plus chain for hoist and conveyor applications. We supply Leaf chain, Zi-Co Chain for hostile environments, Leaf Chain with plastic inserts, Roller Chain, Leaf Chain Accessories, Chain Inspection & Wear Gauges. We carry the widest range of chains in the UK, stocking ½" through to 3" pitch. As a result, our customers receive platinum quality service with stock items delivered next day in the UK, and two-day delivery across mainland Europe. Our chains are tried and tested for all the leading FLT brands such as Rexnord & Flexon, and Chaintec products are used in Scandinavia, Germany, France, Italy and The Middle East and new markets are opening up each year. Due to significant demand within the Italian marketplace for replacement chain, including Chaintec's Zi-Co chain for hostile environments, Leben srl joined our export network in 2007 as our distributor in Italy*

▶ Chaintech Northern Ltd, 22 Ganners Lane, Leeds, LS13 2NX Tel: (07767) 307497 Fax: 0113-256 2379 E-mail: keith@chaintech.fsbusiness.co.uk *Chain suppliers*

▶ Chairs for Work, 28 Loreny Drive, Kilmarnock, Ayrshire, KA1 4SU Tel: (0870) 4280155 Fax: (0870) 4280166 E-mail: sales@chairsforwork.com *Quality Chairs for Work. ESD, Clean Room, Lab, Factory and Office Chairs. All with Comprehensive 5 Year Guarantee.*

▶ Chakir Hairdressing, 62 High Street, Linlithgow, West Lothian, EH49 7AQ Tel: (01506) 671800 E-mail: info@chakirhair.co.uk *Hairdressing*

Chalcross Ltd, Unit 7, Cromford Road Industrial Estate, Langley Mill, Nottingham, NG16 4FL Tel: (01773) 530178 Fax: (01773) 530178 *Structural engineering & fabrication*

Chalford Chairs Ltd, Victoria Works, London Road, Chalford, Stroud, Gloucestershire, GL6 8HN Tel: (01453) 882279 Fax: (01453) 731955 *Upholstered furniture manufrs*

ChaliT Richards & Co. Ltd, The Sovereign Distillery, Wilson Road, Liverpool, L36 6AD Tel: (01403) 250500 Fax: (0870) 6000866 E-mail: admin@chailt-richards.co.uk *Wine importers*

Challenge Alarm Services, Unit 1a, Grange Hill Industrial Estate, Bratton Fleming, Barnstaple, Devon, EX31 4UH Tel: (01598) 710853 Fax: (01598) 710500 *Install fire alarms*

Challenge Europe Ltd, Shuttleworth Road, Elm Farm Industrial Estate, Bedford, MK41 0EP Tel: (01234) 346242 Fax: (01234) 327349 E-mail: sales@challenge-indfast.co.uk *Stockists & distributor of industrial fastenings*

Challenge Fencing Contractors Ltd, The Sawyard, Downside Road, Downside, Cobham, Surrey, KT11 3LY Tel: (01932) 860101 Fax: (01932) 866445 E-mail: sales@challengefencing.com *Fencing & concrete post, gates, wood & railway & sheds suppliers*

Challenge Innovations, 41-43 Mill Street, Bedford, MK40 3EU Tel: (01234) 354025 Fax: (01234) 354025 *Semi-conductor test equipment manufrs*

Challenge Maintenance, 3 Daniels Way, Hucknall, Nottingham, NG15 7LL Tel: (0870) 9502221 Fax: (0870) 9503222 E-mail: sales@challengemaintenance.com *Refrigeration installation & maintenance service providers*

Challenge Packaging Ltd, Ridgewood Indust Park, New Road, Ridgewood, Uckfield, East Sussex, TN22 5SX Tel: (01825) 761836 Fax: (01825) 768408 E-mail: sales@chalpak.co.uk *Packaging materials & corrugated cases manufrs*

Challenge Power Transmission plc, Unit 1 2 Merryhills Enterprise Park, Park Lane, Wolverhampton, WV10 9TJ Tel: (01902) 866116 Fax: (01902) 866117 E-mail: uksales@challengept.com *Power Transmission manufacturers /distributors*

▶ Challenge & Response, 16 Whiteladies Road, Bristol, BS8 2LG Tel: (0870) 2403893 Fax: 0117-973 6403 E-mail: sales@aquapacer.com

▶ Challenge Technical Services Ltd, Alloa Business Centre, The Whins, Alloa, Clackmannanshire, FK10 3SA Tel: (01324) 556772

Challenger Handling Ltd, 1 Warwick Street, Hull, HU9 1ET Tel: (01482) 224404 Fax: (01482) 210808 E-mail: S. Sweryda@challenger-group.co.uk Sales Contact: S. Sweryda *Manufacturers of a wide range of equipment such as woodshaving balers, drum crushers, engine crushers, non-ferrous balers, waste compactors, belt conveyors, roller conveyors, scraper chain conveyors, slat chain conveyors, screw conveyors, goods lifts, bin lifting tippers, ram assist hoppers, disabled platform lifts, etc*

Challenger Hydraulics Ltd, Shaw Cross Business Pk, Owl La, Dewsbury, West Yorkshire, WF12 7RF Tel: (01924) 464433 Fax: (01924) 456292 E-mail: sales@challenger-group.co.uk Purchasing Contact: P. Prideaux Sales Contact: S. Pepper *Manufacturers of hydraulic cylinders, hydraulic power units and hydraulic systems. A good in-house machining capability means that hydraulic cylinder bore diameters of 300 mm can be readily manufactured in addition to being able to offer a low-cost range of standard rams from stock. Electric motor, engine driven and pneumatic power units are manufactured to order for a wide range of applications.*

Challenger Marine Ltd, Freemans Wharf, Falmouth Road, Penryn, Cornwall, TR10 8AD Tel: (01326) 377222 Fax: (01326) 377800 E-mail: sales@challengermarine.co.uk *Marine engineers*

▶ Challenger Site Services, 50 Winton Street, Ashton-under-Lyne, Lancashire, OL6 8NL Tel: 0161-344 2581 Fax: 0161-330 8406 E-mail: sales@challenger-site-services.co.uk *Manufacture portable toilets*

Challenger Solutions Ltd, Unit 85 Haltwhistle Road, South Woodham Ferrers, Chelmsford, CM3 5ZA Tel: (01245) 325252 Fax: (01245) 325301 E-mail: jon@challengersolutions.com *Electronic manufacturing services*

Challenger Trophies & Awards Ltd, 195 Salisbury Road, Totton, Southampton, SO40 3LL Tel: (023) 8086 8119 Fax: (023) 8086 3244 E-mail: challengertrophiesandawards@btinternet.com *Engraving & trophy manufrs*

Challinor & Sons, Malverne, Church Bank, Goostrey, Crewe, CW4 8PG Tel: (01477) 533282 Fax: (01260) 276924 *Agricultural & industrial buildings*

▶ Challis Rubber & Plastic Product, 8 Thorne Farm House, Thorne Hill, Ramsgate, Kent, CT12 5DS Tel: (01843) 826006 Fax: (01843) 826005 E-mail: jwchallis@aol.com *Rubber product manufrs*

▶ Challis Rubber & Plastic Product, 8 Thorne Farm House, Thorne Hill, Ramsgate, Kent, CT12 5DS Tel: (01843) 826006 Fax: (01843) 826005 E-mail: jwchallisco@aol.com *Rubber fabrication services*

Challoner Marketing Ltd, Quill Hall Lane, Amersham, Buckinghamshire, HP6 6LL Tel: (01494) 431163 Fax: (01494) 725732 E-mail: challonermarketing@compuserve.com *Manufacturers of envelope insert & animal heaters*

Chalmers Bakery Ltd, 13-15 Auchmill Road, Bucksburn, Aberdeen, AB21 9LB Tel: (01224) 712631 Fax: (01224) 712464 *Cheesecake suppliers & manufrs*

Raymond Chalmers Electrical Contractor, 25A Kinloch Street, Ladybank, Cupar, Fife, KY15 7LF Tel: (01337) 831272 Fax: (01337) 831272 E-mail: rayspark1@aol.com *Electrical contractor*

Chalmit Lighting, 388 Hillington Road, Hillington Industrial Estate, Glasgow, G52 4BL Tel: 0141-882 5555 Fax: 0141-883 3704 E-mail: sales@chalmit.com *Lighting for oil & gas industry manufrs*

Chalmor Ltd, 1 Telmere Industrial Estate, Albert Road, Luton, LU1 3QF Tel: (01582) 748700 Fax: (01582) 748748 E-mail: sales@chalmor.co.uk *Energy management systems manufrs*

Chalon UK Ltd, Hambridge Mill, Hambridge, Langport, Somerset, TA10 0BP Tel: (01458) 254600 Fax: (01458) 251192 *Kitchen, bedroom & bathroom furniture manufrs*

▶ Chalvington Communications, Unit 3 Northfield Business Park, Lower Dicker, Hailsham, East Sussex, BN27 4BZ Tel: (01323) 440555 Fax: (0870) 7516902 E-mail: info@chalvingtoncomms.co.uk *Communication agents*

Chalwyn Estates Ltd, Chalwyn Industrial Estate, St Clement Road, Poole, Dorset, BH12 4PF Tel: (01202) 715400 Fax: (01202) 715600 E-mail: sales@chalwyn.co.uk *Manufacturers of diesel engine protection systems & safety equipment*

Cham Ltd, 40 High St Wimbledon, London, SW19 5AU Tel: (020) 8947 7651 Fax: (020) 8879 3497 E-mail: phoenics@cham.co.uk *Computational fluid dynamics*

The Chamber Business, Kimpton Road, Luton, LU2 0SX Tel: (01582) 522448 Fax: (01582) 522450 E-mail: info@chamber-business.com *Business information advisory services*

Chamber Business Connections, Commerce House, Bridgeman Place, Bolton, BL2 1DW Tel: (01204) 363212 Fax: (01204) 363212 E-mail: enquiries@chamberhelp.co.uk *Chamber of commerce*

Chamber Business Enterprise, Churchgate House, 56 Oxford Street, Manchester, M60 7HJ Tel: 0161-237 4070 Fax: 0161-236 9945 E-mail: mgore@blnm.co.uk *Business information advisory services*

Chamber Business Enterprise, Churchgate House, 56 Oxford Street, Manchester, M60 7HJ Tel: 0161-237 4070 Fax: 0161-236 9945 E-mail: info@chamber-link.co.uk *Provision of chamber of commerce services*

Chamber Of Commerce, 2 Berkley Crescent, Gravesend, Kent, DA12 2AD Tel: (01474) 320805 Fax: (01474) 537152 E-mail: sales@gravesham.co.uk *Chamber of commerce*

Chamber Of Commerce, Charles House, 5-11 Regent Street, London, SW1Y 4LR Tel: (020) 7930 0219 Fax: (020) 7930 7946 E-mail: info@norwegian-chamber.co.uk *Chamber of commerce*

Chamber Of Commerce (Barnsley & Rotherham) Ltd, Barnsley Business Innovation Centre, Innovation Way, Barnsley, South Yorkshire, S75 1JL Tel: (01226) 217770 Fax: (01226) 784464 *Chamber of Commerce*

Chamber Of Commerce & Business Link West Mercia, Severn House, Prescott Drive, Worcester, WR4 9NE Tel: (0845) 6414641 Fax: (0845) 6414641 E-mail: enquiries@hwchamber.co.uk *Membership organization of products*

Chamber of Commerce (Medway), Medway Business Point, Stirling House, Sunderland Quay, Culpeper Close, Medway City Estate, Rochester, Kent, ME2 4HN Tel: (01634) 311411 Fax: (01634) 311440 E-mail: chamber@medway.co.uk *Chambers of commerce & industry*

Chamber Of Commerce Trade & Industry, Commerce House, Fenton Street, Lancaster, LA1 1AB Tel: (01524) 381331 Fax: (01524) 389505 E-mail: sales@lancaster-chamber.org.uk *Chamber of commerce*

▶ Chamberlain Construction Ltd, Laurel House, Station Approach, Alresford, Hampshire, SO24 9JH Tel: (01962) 733056 Fax: (01962) 734841 E-mail: projects@chamberlainconstruction.co.uk

▶ Chamberlain Corporate Advisors, Gatsby Court, 1 Holliday Street, Birmingham, B1 1TJ Tel: 0121-248 5400 Fax: 0121-551 9606 E-mail: james@thechamberlaingroup.com *Financial Advisors specialising in Inhetitance Tax Planning, Retirement Planning, Corporation and Income Tax Mitigation, On-Shore and Off-Shore Investment Solutions, Specialists in delivering Seminars and Workshops on all subjects listed for both corporate and private clients.*

Chamberlain Plastics Ltd, Bury Close, Higham Ferrers, Rushden, Northamptonshire, NN10 8HQ Tel: (01933) 353875 Fax: (01933) 410206 E-mail: sales@chamberlain-plastics.co.uk *Pvc laminate distributors*

Chamberlain Transport Ltd, Duchy Road, Crewe, CW1 6NB Tel: (01270) 502800 Fax: (01270) 502809 E-mail: sales@palletforce.com *A member of the PalletFORCE distribution network- palletised distribution, timed, next day, economy, tail loft, Ireland and services to mainland Europe. Through its expanding shareholder member depot network, full and part loads, warehouse and logistics services are available.*

Chamberlaine Plant Hire Ltd, Station Road, Odsey, Baldock, Hertfordshire, SG7 5RT Tel: (01462) 742501 Fax: (01462) 742866 *Crane hire*

Chamberlains Falkirk Bed Centre, 54 Cow Wynd, Falkirk, FK1 1PU Tel: (01324) 670060 Fax: (01324) 670060 E-mail: sales@bedsscotland.co.uk *Beds & furniture retailers*

Chamberlin & Hill plc, Chuckery Foundary, Chuckery Road, Walsall, WS1 2DU Tel: (01922) 492000 Fax: (01922) 638370 E-mail: plc@chamberlin.co.uk *Grey & malleable iron casting manufrs*

B.R. Chambers Ltd, 15 Southcroft Road, Rutherglen, Glasgow, G73 1SP Tel: 0141-647 9777 Fax: 0141-613 2068 E-mail: artwork@brchambers.co.uk *Photopolymer printing plate manufrs*

Chambers Communications Ltd, 29-30 High Holborn, London, WC1V 7JZ Tel: (020) 7440 9450 Fax: (020) 7405 5457 E-mail: sales@chamberscomms.com *Employment agency services*

Chambers & Cook Ltd, European House, Perrywell Road, Witton, Birmingham, B6 7AT Tel: 0121-356 1441 Fax: 0121-356 7880 E-mail: admin@chambers-and-cook.co.uk *A member of the PalletFORCE distribution network- palletised distribution, timed, next day, economy, tail loft, Ireland and services to mainland Europe. Through its expanding shareholder member depot network, full and part loads, warehouse and logistics services are available.*

Chambers Engineering Ltd, Warmstone Lane, Waddesdon, Aylesbury, Buckinghamshire, HP18 0NQ Tel: (01296) 651380 Fax: (01296) 651063 E-mail: chameng@btconnect.com *Commercial vehicle repairers & coachbuilders*

Chambers Gunmakers, Ideal Gunworks, River Close South, Alness, Ross-Shire, IV17 0XS Tel: (01349) 883310 Fax: (01349) 883310 *Gun makers*

Chambers Medical Care Ltd, Unit 5, Beresford Gate, South Way, Andover, Hampshire, SP10 5BN Tel: (01264) 332172 Fax: (01264) 332247 E-mail: derek@chambers-medical.co.uk *Approved suppliers to the Ministry of Defence, NHS, the trade and export. Our product range include: pressure care mattresses and cushions, comprehensive range of high quality surgical instruments, nursing bags and cases, polypropylene /stainless steel holloware, general medical equipment such as infusion drip stands, mayo tables etc. Emergency care equipment include: stretchers, evacuation chairs, splints, silicone resuscitators - all sizes, complete range of silicone oxygen therapy products etc.*

▶ Chameeya Software Services Ltd, 4 Aintree Drive, Blackburn, BB3 0QW Tel: (07792) 071655 E-mail: chameeyass@hotmail.com *IT consulting, databases, business analysis, bespoke applications*

Chameleon, PO Box 34, Kilgetty, Pembrokeshire, SA68 0WZ Tel: (07792) 706440 E-mail: info@chameleoncreations.co.uk *Manufacturers of tie dye t-shirts, childrens clothing & tie dye bags*

Chameleon AV, Swallowfields, Welwyn Garden City, Hertfordshire, AL7 1JD Tel: (01707) 339444 Fax: (01707) 377400 E-mail: sales@chameleonav.com *Specialist manufacturers of electrical goods*

▶ Chameleon - Global ITIL Experts, Bracken Lodge, Bay Horse Lane, Scarcroft, Leeds, LS14 3JQ Tel: 0113-289 3661 Fax: 0113-289 2335 E-mail: info@chameleon-itil.com *IT infrastructure training services*

▶ Chameleon Interior Design, 253 Greystones Road, Greystones, Sheffield, S11 7BT Tel: 0114-266 6252 E-mail: louise@chameleoninteriors.wanadoo.co.uk *Interior Design, Property Presentation and Project Coordination. Art suppliers.*

▶ Chameleon Personnel Services Ltd, 1 West Street, Leighton Buzzard, Bedfordshire, LU7 1DA Tel: (01525) 218068 Fax: (01525) 218067 E-mail: info@chameleonpersonnel.co.uk *A specialist Accountancy Recruitment Agency specialising in the supply of Finance Staff to the Commercial and Public Sector and Private Practice.*

Chameleon Print Ltd, Unit 3, Palmerston Drive, Fareham, Hampshire, PO14 1DJ Tel: (01329) 280197 Fax: (01329) 822379 *Digital printing services*

▶ Chameleon Products Ltd, 8 Grange Close, Bradley Stoke, Bristol, BS32 0AH Tel: (01425) 655952 Fax: (01425) 655607 E-mail: tsw@chameleonproducts.net *Suppliers of Decorative coatings to products in aviation,transportation and commercial markets*

▶ Chameleon Services, Senior House, 59-61 High Street, Rickmansworth, Hertfordshire, WD3 1RH Tel: (01923) 896939 Fax: (01923) 896526 E-mail: cims@infoflex-cims.co.uk *Computer software developers*

Chameleon Services, Senior House, 59-61 High Street, Rickmansworth, Hertfordshire, WD3 1RH Tel: (01923) 896939 Fax: (01923) 896526 E-mail: sims@infoflex-sims.co.uk *Software design*

Chameleon Systems Ltd, Great Central House, Great Central Avenue, Ruislip, Middlesex, HA4 6TS Tel: (020) 8839 8526 Fax: (020) 8839 8527 E-mail: sales@chameleonsystems.co.uk *Fire alarm & detection systems suppliers & service*

Chamjtes Ltd, Mason Fold, Lea Lane, Lea Town, Preston, PR4 0RN Tel: (01772) 726975 Fax: (01772) 721277 E-mail: john@chamjets.com *Repair of industrial pressure washers*

Chamois Furnishings Ltd, Units 1-4, Showell Road, Wolverhampton, WV10 9LN Tel: (01902) 864685 Fax: (01902) 865828 E-mail: sales@chamois.co.uk *Kitchen manufrs*

Champ Consultants Ltd, 13 Deacon Place, Caterham, Surrey, CR3 5FN Tel: (01883) 330580 Fax: (0870) 4215242 E-mail: chantal@champconsultants.co.uk *Business & taxation advisors*

Champ Knitwear, 82 Gipsy Road, Leicester, LE4 6QH Tel: 0116-266 9332 Fax: 0116-266 9332 *Knitwear manufrs*

Champ Telephones Holdings Ltd, 11-15 Station Street, Coventry, CV6 5FL Tel: (024) 7666 7757 Fax: (024) 7668 2290 E-mail: gary@champtel.co.uk *Telephones & telephone equipment suppliers*

Champagne Flights, 1 Uppings Farm Cottage, Buckingham Road, Weedon, Aylesbury, Buckinghamshire, HP22 4DR Tel: (01296) 641153 Fax: (01296) 640084 *Balloon flights*

Champion Global Ltd, 33 Branbridges Industrial Estate, Branbridges Road, East Peckham, Tonbridge, Kent, TN12 5HF Tel: (01622) 873366 Fax: (01622) 873388 E-mail: a.chouchane@champion-global.co.uk *Heavy machinery parts exporters*

▶ Champion Hire Ltd, Craven House, Craven Street South, Hull, HU9 1AP Tel: (0845) 3456905 Fax: (01482) 214840 E-mail: marknorrie@championshire.com *Specialists in plant & tool hire services*

Champion Hire Ltd, 2 Roman Ridge Road, Sheffield, S9 1XG Tel: (0845) 3456900 Fax: 0114-249 4100 E-mail: sales@champion-hire.com *Small plant hire specialists* Also at: Bradford, Chesterfield, Hull & Leeds

Champion Photochemistry S.L., 23 Robjohns Road, Chelmsford, CM1 3AG Tel: (01245) 214940 Fax: (01245) 214957 E-mail: sales@championphotochemistry.co.uk *Photographic chemical manufrs*

Champion Plastics Ltd, Bristol Road, Portishead, Bristol, BS20 6QG Tel: (01275) 845105 Fax: (01275) 843081 E-mail: info@albionplastics.co.uk *Albion plastics manufrs*

Champion Print & Web Services, 8 Marritt Close, Chatteris, Cambridgeshire, PE16 6PJ Tel: (01354) 692132 Fax: (07092) 144187 E-mail: tony@championprintandwebservices.co.uk *We provide East Anglian businesses with helpful and flexible printing and website services at a competitive price.**Printed products include business stationery, catalogues, flyers and so on. For example* 250 full-colour business cards for £56* 500 full-colour A4 letterheads for £155**Websites designed to be simple and quick to use . A 3-page site will typically cost around £165, Domain Registration costs £ - £15 for two years, and Hosting is £129. Existing websites can be maintained, updated or completely revamped, as required. If you just want web-based email address (you@your company.co.uk), this costs £35 plus Domain Registration if required.**Other products include PVC ringbinders - either plain or printed, metal pin badges - 50 badges @ 70p each, 0 badges @ 43p each.**Our maintained database of Cambridgeshire business customers - mostly with named addressees - means we can provide*

continued

Company Information

continuation
mailing services. NB, We do NOT disclose customers details to third parties.

Champion Saddlery, 3 Singers Yard, Torquay Road, Paignton, Devon, TQ3 2AH Tel: (01803) 521704 *Leather goods*

Champion Technolgies Ltd, W Sam White Building, Peter Seat Drive, Altens, Aberdeen, AB12 3HT Tel: (01224) 879022 Fax: (01224) 876022 E-mail: champion@champion-servo.com *Chemicals for oil & gas production*

Chana Garments Ltd, 169 Booth Street, Birmingham, B21 0NU Tel: 0121-551 1601 Fax: 0121-507 0471 *Jogging suit manufrs*

Chance Glass Ltd, Pickersleigh Avenue, Malvern, Worcestershire, WR14 2LP Tel: (01684) 892353 Fax: (01684) 892647 E-mail: sales@chanceglass.co.uk *Glass tubing & rod manufactures - Chance Glass is in a unique position to offer a range of highly specialised and skilled services, to provide industry with precision glass components. Specialists if the machining of precision bore or standard tubing to meet your requirements. We also offer a wide range of site glasses manufactured to your design.*

Chance & Hunt Ltd, Alexander House, Crown Gate, Runcorn, Cheshire, WA7 2UP Tel: (01928) 793000 Fax: (01928) 714351 E-mail: passport@chance-hunt.com *Chemical sales & marketing imports export*

▶ Chancery Footwear Ltd, 86 Bunting Road, Northampton, NN2 6EE Tel: (01604) 712159 Fax: (01604) 722397 *Manufacturing of specialist footwear*

F. Chand & Co. Ltd, 81 Rabone Lane, Smethwick, West Midlands, B66 3JH Tel: 0121-565 3959 Fax: 0121-565 3959 *Barbour CMT Manufacturer*BHS supplier wax jackets*John Partridge Supplier wax jackets*Toggi supplier wax jackets*Royal Spencer supplier wax jakets*

Chandis Ltd, 5 Great Union Road, St. Helier, Jersey, JE2 3YA Tel: (01534) 736401 Fax: (01534) 768442 E-mail: admin@chandis.com *Pharmaceutical wholesalers*

▶ Chandler & Co., Red Hill, Wateringbury, Maidstone, Kent, ME18 5NN Tel: (01622) 817484 Fax: (01622) 817152 E-mail: info@chandlerandco.co.uk

R.A.C. Chandler Contractors Ltd, Villiers Farm, Frisby Road, Hoby, Melton Mowbray, Leicestershire, LE14 3DS Tel: (01664) 434813 Fax: (01664) 434134 *Farmers & contractors*

Chandlers Building Supplies Ltd, The Broyle, Ringmer, Lewes, East Sussex, BN8 5NP Tel: (01273) 812721 Fax: (01273) 813958 E-mail: sales@chandlersbs.co.uk *Building materials merchants*

Chandlers Engraver & Sign Co., 42 Market Row, Great Yarmouth, Norfolk, NR30 1PB Tel: (01493) 844126 Fax: (01493) 844126 *Engravers & sign makers*

Chandlers Farm Equipment Ltd, Boston Road, Horncastle, Lincolnshire, LN9 6JN Tel: (01507) 527211 Fax: (01507) 524498 E-mail: enquries@chandlersfe.co.uk *Chandlers are Massey Ferguson, Fendt and Challenger dealers covering Lincolnshire from Grantham (NG32 2LX), Horncastle (LN9 6JN), Spilsby (PE23 5HQ), Holbeach (PE12 7NJ) and Stamford (PE9 3DW), specialising in the hire and sale of used MF, Fendt and Challenger tractors and farm machinery from leading manufacturers. Chandlers also sell vehicles from Subaru, Isuzu, Daihatsu and Ssangyong, www.chandlerscars.co.uk, and country store/ equine visit www.4dobbin.com.*

Chandlers Garage Holdings Ltd, B M W House, Water Lane, Littlehampton, West Sussex, BN16 4EH Tel: (01903) 784147 Fax: (01903) 785289 E-mail: enquiries@chandlers-bmw.co.uk *Mechanical body work repairs & sales*

Tom Chandley Ltd, Windmill La Industrial Estate, Denton, Manchester, M34 3RB Tel: 0161-337 3700 Fax: 0161-335 0972 E-mail: info@chandleyovens.co.uk *Bakery oven manufrs*

Chandos Intercontinental, 6 St Anns Close, Chapel-en-le-Frith, High Peak, Derbyshire, SK23 9SG Tel: (01298) 814949 Fax: (01298) 814949 E-mail: chandos6@highpeak14.freeserve.co.uk *Scientific apparatus distributors*

▶ Chandoz Ltd, Krattigen, Toynton St. Peter, Spilsby, Lincolnshire, PE23 5AT Tel: (01754) 830279 Fax: (01754) 830279 E-mail: ray@pidgley7229.fslife.co.uk *Transport Management & Legal Consultants & Trainers,Operators Licensing, Maintenance, Tachographs & Driver training*Expert Witness services*Courts & Public Inquiries*

Chandra Enterprises, 3 Lower Place Business Centre, Steele Road, London, NW10 7AT Tel: (020) 8453 1990 Fax: (020) 8838 4649 *Food products manufacturer*

Chandris England Ltd, 17 Old Park Lane, London, W1K 1QT Tel: (020) 7412 3900 Fax: (020) 7412 0901 *Ships' agents*

Chandu Mouldings, Unit 10 Corton Trading Estate, Benfleet, Essex, SS7 4QN Tel: (01268) 566048 Fax: (01268) 757740 E-mail: chandu@easynet.co.uk *Plastic injection moulders*

Chandu Toolmakers, Church Road, Benfleet, Essex, SS7 4QN Tel: (01268) 565960 Fax: (01268) 757740 E-mail: chandutools@btconnect.com *Tool making & plastic injection moulding manufrs*

▶ Chaner Engineering Ltd, Norwest Quarry Yard, Quarry Lane, Sandside, Milnthorpe, Cumbria, LA7 7HG Tel: (01539) 564376 Fax: (01539) 564753 E-mail: jacky@chaner-ltd.co.uk *Sheet metal manufrs*

The Change Organisation, Units 70-71, John Wilson Business Park, Harvey Drive, Chestfield, Whitstable, Kent, CT5 3QT Tel: (01227) 779000 Fax: (01227) 779222 *Computer services*

▶ Changing Constants Ltd, 58 Rivers Road, Yeovil, Somerset, BA21 5RJ Tel: (07779) 156217 E-mail: sales@changingconstants.co.uk *E-commerce web design services*

▶ Changing Faces.Biz, 1 Courtney Road, Rushden, Northamptonshire, NN10 9FL Tel: (01933) 419910 E-mail: info@changingfaces.biz *Professional face painters specialising in corporate events,promotion and marketing. for all childrens entertainment.Adorable Costume Characters now available for walkabout,mix and mingle,meet and greet promotional bookings*

▶ Changing Light, 14 Lancaster Drive, Broadstone, Dorset, BH18 9EJ Tel: (07790) 633558 E-mail: andy@changinglight.co.uk *The Landscape photography of Andy J Lock. Scenic landscape images along the South Coast and North Wales Countryside.*

▶ Changing Wood Ltd, Unit 2, Manor Farm, Risborough Road, Aylesbury, Buckinghamshire, HP17 8LU Tel: (01844) 290899 Fax: (01844) 291448 E-mail: andy@changingwood.co.uk *Furniture manufrs*

Channel Ltd, Fairway, Orpington, Kent, BR5 1EG Tel: (01689) 871522 Fax: (01689) 833428 *We design and manufacture high-quality thermoplastic and metal fabricated products, copper termination products, heat shrink products, connectors and much more* Also at: Branches throughout the U.K.

▶ Channel, The Praze, Penryn, Cornwall, TR10 8AA Tel: (01326) 375657 Fax: (01326) 375676 E-mail: enquiries@channelgroup.co.uk *We have seen progressive growth throughout the last few years allowing us to provide a larger range of quality products at competitive prices.*

▶ Channel Commercials plc, Cobbswood Industrial Estate, Brunswick Road, Ashford, Kent, TN23 1EH Tel: (01233) 629272 Fax: (01233) 636322 E-mail: louisedodds@channelcommercials.co.uk *Dealer for daf trucks & ldv vans*

Channel Cutters, Unit 18 Lawrence Hill Industrial Park, Croydon Street, Bristol, BS5 0EB Tel: 0117-955 2443 Fax: 0117-955 2443 E-mail: channelcutters@btconnect.com *Form cutting tool manufrs*

Channel Fisheries, Unit 4 Metherell Avenue Industrial Estate, Brixham, Devon, TQ5 9QL Tel: (01803) 858126 Fax: (01803) 857941 E-mail: martin@channelfisheries.com *Fish merchants*

▶ Channel Line Sewer Systems Ltd, Invicta House, Sandpit Road, Dartford, DA1 5BU Tel: (01322) 281112 Fax: (01322) 281113 *Manufacturing grp mouldings*

Channel Matrix plc, 44 Sanders Road, Finedon Road Industrial Estate, Wellingborough, Northamptonshire, NN8 4NL Tel: (01933) 273444 Fax: (01933) 229277 E-mail: info@channel-creasing.com *Printing trade material suppliers*

Channel Partners Ltd, Albury Park, Albury, Guildford, Surrey, GU5 9BH Tel: (01483) 205011 Fax: (01483) 205022 E-mail: astbury@channelp.co.uk *Computer network consultants*

Channel Safety Systems Ltd, 9 Petersfield Business Park, Bedford Road, Petersfield, Hampshire, GU32 3QA Tel: (01730) 268231 Fax: (01730) 265552 E-mail: sales@channelsafety.co.uk *Fire alarm equipment & maintenance*

▶ Channel Sports Boats, PO Box 872, Canterbury, Kent, CT4 6WA Tel: (01227) 831611 Fax: (01227) 831671 E-mail: sales@channel-sportsboats.com *Boat transportation service*

Channel Steel Fabrications Ltd, Brocklebank Industrial Estate, Brocklebank Road, London, SE7 7SX Tel: (020) 8858 6666 *Steel fabricators*

▶ Channel Strategy Research, European Communication Centre, Flag Business Exchange, Vicarage Farm Road, Fengate, Peterborough, PE1 5TX Tel: 01733 704070 Fax: 01733 704080 E-mail: marketing@channelstrategy.co.uk *Specialist Market Research services, from Product Benchmarking to Customer Satisfaction.*

Channel Weighing, Unit 16 Chislet Close, Lakesview International Business Park, Hersden, Canterbury, Kent, CT3 4LB Tel: (01227) 711020 Fax: (01227) 711040 E-mail: sales@channel-weighing.co.uk *We are an ISO9001:2000 accredited company based in Canterbury, covering Kent, Surrey, Sussex and SE London, we are an independent supplier of all types of mechanical scales, battery operated scales, electronic scales, digital scales, price computing scales, balances and weighing equipment including medical weighing, height measuring, laboratory balances, educational balances, catering scales, kitchen scales, jewellery scales, retail scales, industrial scales, butchery scales, fruit and vegetable scales, pack house scales, veterinary scales, animal weighing, weighbridges, platform scales, floor scales, bench scales, mobile scales, counting scales, liquid measures. We also provide scale service, scale repairs, scale calibration, weight calibration*

Channel Woodcraft Ltd, Bowles Well Gardens, Dover Road, Folkestone, Kent, CT19 6NP Tel: (01303) 850231 Fax: (01303) 850734 E-mail: enquiry@channelwoodcraft.co.uk *Joinery manufacturers & timber merchants*

▶ Channels4profit Ltd, 56 Rosamond Avenue, Bradway, Sheffield, S17 4LT Tel: 0114-235 3773 E-mail: channels4profit@btinternet.com *Management Consultancy specialising in Business Start-ups. Areas of specialism include:*1) Raising seed capital*2) Creating Robust Business Plans*3) Creating web/sales material*4) Establishing profitable routes to market for products/services gaining competitive advantage*

Donal Channer & Co., 50-52 Tower Hill, Dilton Marsh, Westbury, Wiltshire, BA13 4DA Tel: (01373) 824895 Fax: (01373) 824895 *Bespoke furniture & woodwork*

Chantec, Toddbrook House, 120 Padfield Main Road, Padfield, Glossop, Derbyshire, SK13 1ET Tel: (01457) 852376 Fax: (01457) 852376 E-mail: sales@chantec.freeserve.co.uk *Electrical industrial control equipment suppliers*

Chantelle Originals Ltd, 70 Elm Grove, Southsea, Hampshire, PO5 1LN Tel: (023) 9283 0273 Fax: (023) 9283 0273 *Children's clothing manufrs*

Chanter Bio Med Ltd, 1 Hanworth Road, Low Moor, Bradford, West Yorkshire, BD12 0SG Tel: (01274) 414666 Fax: (01274) 414470 E-mail: info@chanterbiomed.co.uk *Boiler fittings & spares. Also medical & dental laboratory equipment manufrs*

Chanterlands Pine Centre, 157 Chanterlands Avenue, Hull, HU5 3TJ Tel: (01482) 492682 Fax: (01482) 492682 *Pine furniture & giftware suppliers*

▶ Chantesse, 25 Orchard Estate, Twyford, Reading, RG10 9JY Tel: 0118-970 6846 Fax: (0870) 1383878 E-mail: sally@chantesse.com *Importers of beaded evening handbags, scarves & jewellery*

▶ Chantilly, Reading Road, Cholsey, Wallingford, Oxon, OX10 9HL Tel: 01491 652848 Fax: 07889 644848 E-mail: susiegsmith@btinternet.com *For a complete interior design and decoration service for offices, units and the home*

Chantilly Blinds, 476 Hartshill Road, Stoke-on-Trent, ST4 6AD Tel: (0800) 0564282 Fax: (01782) 714515 E-mail: enquiries@chantillyblinds.freeserve.co.uk *Blind manufrs*

Chantry Builders Ltd, Bower Close, St. Johns Green, Rotherham, South Yorkshire, S61 3JL Tel: (01709) 550058 Fax: (01709) 555011

Chantry Simonard (Bradford) Ltd, The Granary, Bleach Mill Lane, Menston, Ilkley, West Yorkshire, LS29 6AW Tel: (01943) 878882 Fax: (01943) 872999 *Wool brokers & export merchants*

▶ Chaos Lighting, 36 Hollicondane Road, Ramsgate, Kent, CT11 7PH Tel: 01843 596997 Fax: 01843 596997 E-mail: russell@chaoslighting.co.uk *We provide consultancy, design and electrical installation services to the entertainment industry. incl. theatre television studio etc*

▶ ChaosArtworks.com, 10 Ambleside Way, Donnington, Telford, Shropshire, TF2 7QE Tel: (01952) 604190 E-mail: info@chaosartworks.com *ChaosArtworks.com is dedicated to bringing you some of the freshest new British based urban art, modern art, abstract art & contemporary art.*

▶ CHAP (Holdings) Ltd, Enterprise Drive, Westhill Industrial Estate, Westhill, Aberdeen, AB32 6TQ Tel: (01224) 748500 Fax: (01224) 748501

▶ Chap Quarries Ltd, Park Quarry, Durris, Banchory, Kincardineshire, AB31 6BA Tel: (01330) 811771 Fax: (01330) 811497 *Sand & gravel quarry*

Chap Quarries (Aberdeen) Ltd, Westhill Industrial Estate, Westhill, Aberdeenshire, AB32 6TQ Tel: (01224) 748500 Fax: (01224) 748501 E-mail: mail@chap.co.uk *Quarry operators*

Alexander Chapel Associates, Fountain Court, 2 Victoria Square, Victoria Street, St. Albans, Hertfordshire, AL1 3TF Tel: (01727) 859977 Fax: (01727) 859594 E-mail: stalbans@alexanderchapel.co.uk *Sales & marketing recruitment consultancy*

Chapel Bakers, 384a Katherine Street, Ashton-under-Lyne, Lancashire, OL7 0AL Tel: 0161-330 6745 Fax: 0161-330 6745 *Bakery*

Chapel Forge Farriers Ltd, Upper Lambourn, Hungerford, Berkshire, RG17 8QP Tel: (01488) 72613 Fax: (01488) 73835 E-mail: gary@chappelforge.co.uk *Horse shoe service*

Chapel Press Ltd, Parkgate Close, Bredbury, Stockport, Cheshire, SK6 2SZ Tel: 0161-406 9495 Fax: 0161-292 0200 E-mail: info@chapelpress.com *Lithographic colour printers*

Chapel Sheet Metal Ltd, Bowden Lane, Chapel-en-le-Frith, High Peak, Derbyshire, SK23 0QG Tel: (01298) 813041 Fax: (01298) 816256 E-mail: paul_csm@btinternet.com *Stainless steel fabricators*

Chapel Windows Ltd, Bevan Industrial Estate, Brierley Hill, West Midlands, DY5 3TF Tel: (01384) 571315 Fax: (01384) 480403 *Manufacturers & installers upvc windows & conservatories*

Chapelhouse Farm, Roaring Gate Lane, Hale, Altrincham, Cheshire, WA15 8TZ Tel: 0161-903 9016 Fax: 0161-980 4303 E-mail: info@chapelhouseairportparking.co.uk *Car storage*

▶ Chaplais Ltd, 9 High Street, Fairford, Gloucestershire, GL7 4AD Tel: (01285) 713610 E-mail: mauricechaplais@aol.com *Bakery and Delicatessen Consultant*

Chaplin Bros Birmingham Ltd, Unit 11a Reddicap Trading Estate, Sutton Coldfield, West Midlands, B75 7BU Tel: 0121-378 0565 Fax: 0121-378 0157 *Fine wire manufrs*

Chaplin Computer Consultants, 331 Walsall Road, Great Wyrley, Walsall, WS6 6DR Tel: (01922) 411117 Fax: (01922) 411001 E-mail: chris@ccc1.demon.co.uk *Computer consultants*

Chapman Ltd, Chapmans Corner, Reddal Hill Road, Cradley Heath, West Midlands, B64 5JG Tel: (01384) 569958 Fax: (01384) 413190 *Electrical contractors*

Chapman, Bridgeroyd Works, Halifax Road, Todmorden, Lancashire, OL14 6DF Tel: (01706) 818587 Fax: (01706) 818598 E-mail: chapmans@chapmangroup.co.uk *Textile manufrs*

▶ Chapman Bathurst, 5 Prescot Street, London, E1 8PA Tel: (020) 7553 8850 Fax: (020) 7553 8851

Clifford Chapman Metalworks Ltd, Armstrong Estate, District 2, Washington, Tyne & Wear, NE37 1PB Tel: 0191-417 3135 Fax: 0191-417 8519 E-mail: email@cliffordchapman.com *Architectural metalworkers*

Chapman Drivers Seating, 68 Burners Lane, Kiln Farm, Milton Keynes, MK11 3HD Tel: (01908) 265030 Fax: (01908) 265499 *Drivers seat manufrs*

Chapman Envelopes Ltd, Grimshaw Bridge, Johnson Road, Eccleshill, Darwen, Lancashire, BB3 3PF Tel: (01254) 682387 Fax: (01254) 775920 *Commercial envelope manufrs*

Chapman Foods, 57 Battlehill Road, Portadown, Craigavon, County Armagh, BT62 4ES Tel: (028) 3887 1225 Fax: (028) 3887 0088 *Apple processors*

Chapman Fork Lift Services Ltd, Wood Lane Industrial Estate, Wood End, Marston Moretaine, Bedford, MK43 0NZ Tel: (01234) 766855 Fax: (01234) 766855 *Fork lift hire*

Chapman Freeborn Airchartering Ltd, 5 Hobart Place, London, SW1W 0HU Tel: (020) 7393 1234 Fax: (020) 7393 1275 E-mail: info@chapman-freeborn.com *Air charter brokers & agents* Also at: Gatwick, Heathrow & Stanstead

Chapman G, 36 Dycote Lane, Welbourn, Lincoln, LN5 0NL Tel: (01400) 272073 *Bar (Licensed) Hire*

John Chapman, 77 Hilliard Road, Northwood, Middlesex, HA6 1SL Tel: (01923) 824201 *Specialised cabinet makers*

Chapman Marsden Partnership, 1 West Street, Welford, Northampton, NN6 6HU Tel: (01858) 575123 *Computer consultants*

Chapman & Mellor, 20 Hockley Hill, Birmingham, B18 5AQ Tel: 0121-554 3778 Fax: 0121-554 7931 E-mail: sales@foilprinters.co.uk *Foil printing & embossing*

Chapman & Smith Ltd, Safir Works, South Street, East Hoathly, Lewes, East Sussex, BN8 6EW Tel: (01825) 840323 Fax: 01825 840827 E-mail: sales@chapman-smith.co.uk *Protective clothing & equipment manufrs*

Chapman Stevens, 21 Wintersells Road, Byfleet, West Byfleet, Surrey, KT14 7LF Tel: (01932) 334140 Fax: (01932) 351238 *Insurance brokers*

Tony Chapman Electronics Ltd, Hayleys Manor, Epping Upland, Epping, Essex, CM16 6PQ Tel: (01992) 578231 Fax: (01992) 576139 E-mail: sales@tceltd.co.uk *Distributors of microwave components.*

Chapman Ventilators Ltd, 9 Bridge Gate Centre, Martinfield, Welwyn Garden City, Hertfordshire, AL7 1JG Tel: (01707) 372858 Fax: (01707) 325001 *Ventilation & air conditioning contractors. Tender or design and build projects considered up to £500,000*

▶ Chapman Watson & Co. Ltd, 25 Rodney Street, Edinburgh, EH7 4EL Tel: 0131-556 6275 Fax: 0131-556 8105

Chapman Woodcraft Ltd, Gravelly Bottom Road, Kingswood, Maidstone, Kent, ME17 3NU Tel: (01622) 844599 Fax: (01622) 844818 E-mail: chapmangates@hormail.co.uk *Wooden gates manufrs*

▶ Chapman's, 21-29 Beechway, Scunthorpe, South Humberside, DN16 2HF Tel: (01724) 862585 Fax: (01724) 270096 *Fishing tackle sales*

Chapmore Controls Ltd, 64 Junction Road, Northampton, NN2 7HS Tel: (01604) 714431 Fax: (01604) 714431 E-mail: info@chapmore.co.uk *Experts in motion control*

Chappell Associates, Westfield House, Bratton Road, Westbury, Wiltshire, BA13 3EP Tel: (01373) 826506 Fax: (01373) 824952 E-mail: sales@chappellassociates.co.uk *Chartered accountants*

▶ Chappell & Dix Ltd, The Barns, Huntingford, Wotton-under-Edge, Gloucestershire, GL12 8EX Tel: (01453) 843504

Chappell Machine Tools Ltd, Poultry Farm, New Road, Lambourne End, Romford, RM4 1AJ Tel: (020) 8500 6111 Fax: (020) 8500 6888 *Machine tool merchants*

Chappell & Tibbert Ltd, 50 Stamford Road, Easton on the Hill, Stamford, Lincolnshire, PE9 3PA Tel: (01780) 751014 Fax: (01780) 751014 *Electric motors rewinds & sales*

Philip Chapper & Co. Ltd, Unit 1, Orbital 25 Business Park, Dwight Road, Watford, WD18 9DA Tel: (01923) 235179 Fax: (01923) 242278 *Hospital equipment suppliers*

▶ Chapter Eight Ltd, Medius House, 2 Sheraton Street, Soho, London, W1F 8BH Tel: (020) 7788 9861 Fax: (020) 7788 9862 *Web designers, search engine optimisation, e-commerce & custom software*

Chapway Fabrications, Charlton Mead Lane, Hoddesdon, Hertfordshire, EN11 0DJ Tel: (01992) 468028 Fax: (01992) 479720 *Steel fabricators & welders*

Characteristic Promotional Items Ltd, Unit 2 Trenant Industrial Estate, Wadebridge, Cornwall, PL27 6HB Tel: (01208) 813813 Fax: (01208) 813168 E-mail: sales@cxnet.co.uk *Promotional products manufrs*

Characters Signs, Aston Bury, Aston, Stevenage, Hertfordshire, SG2 7EG Tel: (01438) 880181 Fax: (01438) 880182 E-mail: info@characterssigns.com *Graphic sign manufrs*

Charapak Ltd, Meadow Lane, Alfreton, Derbyshire, DE55 7EZ Tel: (01773) 835735 Fax: (01773) 520148 E-mail: sales@charapak.co.uk *Corrugated cardboard box manufrs*

Charcon Tunnels, Southwell Lane, Kirkby In Ashfield, Nottingham, NG17 8GQ Tel: (01623) 754493 Fax: (01623) 759825 E-mail: sales@tarmacprecast.co.uk *Concrete tunnel & shaft lining manufrs*

Charcroft Electronics Ltd, Pump House Dol Y Coed, Llanwrtyd Wells, Powys, LD5 4TH Tel: (01591) 610408 Fax: (01591) 610385 E-mail: sales@charcroft.com *Suppliers of electronic components*

Chard, 521 Lytham Road, Blackpool, FY4 1RJ Tel: (01253) 343081 Fax: (01235) 408058 E-mail: enquiries@24carat.co.uk *Jewellery retailers*

▶ Chard Ltd, Hurtham Farm, Chilson Common, South Chard, Chard, Somerset, TA20 2NT Tel: (01460) 221399 Fax: (01460) 221399 *Stainless steel & aluminum fabricators*

▶ Chard Construction Ltd, Unit 9, Block 2 Blantyre Industrial Es, Glasgow, G72 0UD Tel: (01698) 820333

Chard Stone Co. Ltd, 14 Millfield, Chard, Somerset, TA20 2BB Tel: (01460) 63824 Fax: (01460) 61849 *Concrete manufrs*

Chardec Consultants Ltd, 3 Hyde Close, The Street, Kingston, Lewes, East Sussex, BN7 3PA Tel: (01273) 483800 Fax: (01273) 483900 E-mail: rich@chardec.co.uk *Electronic design consultants*

Chardstock Joinery, Chubbs Yard, Chardstock, Axminster, Devon, EX13 7BT Tel: (01460) 221148 Fax: (01460) 221148 *Joiners*

Charger Bay Solutions, 7 Fitton Road, St. Germans, King's Lynn, Norfolk, PE34 3AU Tel: 07723 391485 Fax: (01553) 617619 E-mail: info@chargerbaysolutions.co.uk *UK distributor for AquaPro battery topping system. *European distributor for Liquid Precision deionisers and auto shut off topping guns. Suppliers of flooded and gel batteries and chargers for material handling, EV, access, mobility and leisure.*Battery changing equipment and charger bay design and installation.*National service and maintenance for all makes and types of battery and charger.*

▶ Charig Associates Ltd, 24 Honister Gardens, Stanmore, Middlesex, HA7 2EH Tel: (020) 8933 0917 E-mail: info@charig-associates.co.uk *Technical writing for marketing, sales, engineering*

Charion Spares Ltd, Unit 7 Paper Mill End Industrial Estate, Birmingham, B44 8NH Tel: 0121-344 4540 Fax: 0121-344 3017 E-mail: charionspares@yahoo.co.uk *Fork lift truck spare parts*

Charisma, 44 Broomhead Park, Dunfermline, Fife, KY12 0PT Tel: (01383) 732183 *Blinds manufrs*

Charisma, Sligo Road, Enniskillen, County Fermanagh, BT74 7JY Tel: (028) 6632 7111 Fax: (028) 6632 7999 *Blinds manufrs*

Charisma Blinds, 3 Manitoba Place, Chapel Allerton, Leeds, LS7 4LU Tel: 0113-228 7193 Fax: 0113-262 1626 E-mail: charismablindswetherby@yahoo.co.uk *Window blinds fitting & installation*

Charisma Design, 15 Juniper Close, Bridgwater, Somerset, TA6 4ER Tel: (01278) 427179 E-mail: sales@charismadesign.co.uk *Website design engineers*

Charisma Sound & Light, 31e Redwood Drive, Brant Road Waddington, Lincoln, LN5 9BN Tel: (01522) 881212 Fax: (01522) 881515 *Electricial contractors*

▶ Charity T Shirts, 3 Staple Hill Road, Bristol, BS16 5AA Tel: 0117-965 6320 Fax: 0117 9656320 E-mail: janine@charityt-shirts.co.uk *We supply printed t-shirts, mugs, polo shirts, school uniforms, workwear and much much more. Hen and stag t-shirts a speciality*

J.P. Charles [Binding Systems] Ltd, Units 11-12, 6 Old Church Road, London, E4 6ST Tel: (020) 8801 4222 Fax: (020) 8529 6464 *Ring binder manufrs*

Chas A Blatchford & Sons Ltd, Wella Road, Basingstoke, Hampshire, RG22 4AH Tel: (01256) 316600 Fax: (01256) 329256 E-mail: sales@blatchford.co.uk *Artificial limb specialists* Also at: Branches throughout the U.K.

▶ Chas A Blatchford & Sons Ltd, Royal National Orthopaedic Hospital, Brockley Hill, Stanmore, Middlesex, HA7 4LP Tel: (020) 8954 5024 Fax: (020) 8954 0182

▶ Chas A Blatchfords, 11 Atlas Way, Sheffield, S4 7QQ Tel: 0114-263 7900 Fax: 0114-263 7901 *Manufacture orthopedic & prosthetic medical goods*

A.S. Charles, RMC Aggregates Eastern Counties, Mentmore Rd, Leighton Buzzard, Beds, LU7 7PA Tel: 01525 381042 *Moulded concrete products manufr*

Charles Andrews, The Corner House, Fourth Avenue, Trafford Park, Manchester, M17 1DB Tel: 0161-848 9955 Fax: 0161-848 9966 E-mail: info@charlesandrews.co.uk *Consulting engineers*

CHAS Appliance Spares, 36 Tynewydd Road, Rhyl, Clwyd, LL18 3SP Tel: (01745) 355066 Fax: (01745) 355077 *Plumbing & heating spares*

▶ Ashley Charles Residential Sales & Letting Agents, 98 Whitley Street, Reading, RG2 0EQ Tel: 0118-975 2211 E-mail: info@ashleycharles.com *Ashley Charles Estates is an Independent Estate Agent offering an exceptional service in Residential Sales, Rentals and Property Management in the Reading, Tilehurst, Caversham, Twyford and Earley areas of Berkshire. **The principal aim of Ashley Charles Estate Agents is to provide all customers with a highly professional, personal and courteous service. Our proactive approach to selling and letting properties ensures that our customersâ interests are our main priority. **We have utilised the latest computer technology to improve our services and the property details on our website are updated daily. Whether you are searching for a new home, selling or letting your own or wanting to rent, our website enables you to make your own choices at any time, day or night. ***

Charles Barr Furniture, 72 Sunderland Road, Sandy, Bedfordshire, SG19 1QY Tel: (01767) 681444 Fax: (01767) 681397 E-mail: enquiries@charlesbarr.com *Traditional furniture manufrs*

Charles Bell 1963 Ltd, 344 Oldpark Road, Belfast, BT14 6QE Tel: (028) 9074 7244 Fax: (028) 9074 7248 *Window blind manufrs*

▶ Charles Bentley & Son, 1 Monarch Way, Loughborough, Leicestershire, LE11 5XG Tel: (01509) 232757 Fax: (01509) 233861 E-mail: sales@bentleybrushware.co.uk *Brush manufacturers, horse grooming brushes and equipment, decorating and household equipment, broom handles*

Charles Building Services Ltd, 6 Viewpoint, Hyatt Trading Estate, Stevenage, Hertfordshire, SG1 2EQ Tel: (01438) 750371

Charles Church Developments Ltd, Charles Church House, Knoll Road, Camberley, Surrey, GU15 3TQ Tel: (01276) 808080 Fax: (01276) 808030 *Property developers*

Charles Church Western, Churchward House, Churchward Road, Yate, Bristol, BS37 5NN Tel: (01454) 333800 Fax: (01454) 327123 *House builders & executive homes*

▶ Charles Day Steels Ltd, Downgate Drive, Sheffield, S4 8BT Tel: 0114-244 5544 Fax: 0114-244 5588 E-mail: sales@daysteel.co.uk *Specialists in laser cutting & flame cutting. Established 25 years. Fully ISO approved. Machining, grinding, bending & shotblasting available. Lage in house stocks for rapid turnaround. Laser cut steel art a speciality*

Chas E Prossor & Co. Ltd, 14 Dryden Street, Liverpool, L5 5HD Tel: 0151-207 1832 Fax: 0151-298 1101 E-mail: richard.prossor@prossor.com *Protective clothing importers & distributors*

Charles F Stead & Co. Ltd, Tannery, Sheepscar Street North, Leeds, LS7 2BY Tel: 0113-262 8643 Fax: 0113-262 6309 E-mail: suede@cfstead.com *Leather & suede manufrs* Also at: York

▶ Charles Footman, Alltwalis Road, Pontarsais, Carmarthen, Dyfed, SA32 7DU Tel: (01267) 253443 Fax: (01267) 253545

Charles Gregory & Sons Ltd, Nottingham Road, Tansley, Matlock, Derbyshire, DE4 5FR Tel: (01629) 582376 Fax: (01629) 57112 *Timber merchants*

▶ Charles H Coward Ltd, 540 Ecclesfield Road, Sheffield, S5 0DJ Tel: 0114-257 7666 Fax: 0114-257 7565 E-mail: ccsltd@btconnect.com *Foundry manufacturing of castings & supply conservatory trade*

Charles Hawkins, The Offices, Glaston Road, Uppingham, Oakham, Leicestershire, LE15 9EU Tel: (01572) 823030 Fax: (01572) 823040 E-mail: info@charleshawkinsandpartners.com *Wine agents*

▶ Charles Hewitt Ltd, Merton Farm, Merton Lane, Canterbury, Kent, CT4 7BA Tel: (01227) 464386

Chas Hunt & Co. Ltd, Unit 2 Senlan Industrial Estate, Rhymney River Bridge Road, Cardiff, CF23 9AF Tel: (029) 2048 4476 Fax: (029) 2048 9092 E-mail: hunt.chas@virgin.net *Commercial printers*

▶ J. Charles (Auto Advantage) Ltd, 1 Shallcross Mill Road, Whaley Bridge, High Peak, Derbyshire, SK23 7JQ Tel: (0845) 3303545 Fax: (0845) 3303543 E-mail: virgin.surfer@virgin.net *Car leasing*

▶ Charles James Homes, Chanctonbury Walk, Storrington, Pulborough, West Sussex, RH20 4LT Tel: (01903) 741155 Fax: (01903) 745599

John Charles, Unit 1, Foundry La, Leicester, LE1 3WU Tel: 0116-251 8565 Fax: 0116-251 8565 *Knitwear manufrs*

▶ Charles Keith & Sons, Station Road, Cults, Aberdeen, AB15 9NP Tel: (01224) 868144 *Joiners*

Charles Kendrew Metal Workers Ltd, 33-35 Tower Street, Harrogate, North Yorkshire, HG1 1HS Tel: (01423) 502025 Fax: (01423) 531028 E-mail: enquiries@kendrews.co.uk *Architectural metalwork, balustrades staircases & sheet metalwork*

Charles Kirk & Co. Ltd, Horton Buildings, Goring Street, Goring-by-Sea, Worthing, West Sussex, BN12 5AD Tel: (01903) 244863 Fax: (01903) 700577 E-mail: sales@charleskirk.co.uk *School knitwear & sweatshirt manufrs*

Charles L Warren Ltd, Station Approach, Pasture Road, Wirral, Merseyside, CH46 8SF Tel: 0151-677 2368 Fax: 0151-677 1910 E-mail: clwarrenltd@aol.com *Civil engineering contractors*

▶ Chas Lavery & Sons Ltd, 12 Kilmaine Street, Lurgan, Craigavon, County Armagh, BT67 9AL Tel: (028) 3832 6282

▶ Charles Lawrence Surfaces plc, Newbridge Industrial Estate, Newbridge, Midlothian, EH28 8PJ Tel: 0131-333 3030 Fax: 0131-333 4154

Charles Letts Group Ltd, Thornybank Industrial Estate, Dalkeith, Midlothian, EH22 2NE Tel: 0131-663 1971 Fax: 0131-660 3225 E-mail: diaries@letts.co.uk *Diary publishers*

Charles Lighting Ltd, Priestlands Lane, Sherborne, Dorset, DT9 4HL Tel: (01935) 817444 Fax: (01935) 816778 *Lighting equipment manufrs*

▶ Chas Long & Son, Woodside, Great North Road, Brompton, Richmond, North Yorkshire, DL10 7JL Tel: (01748) 811359

Charles Lucas & Marshall, Eastcott House, 4 High Street, Swindon, SN1 3EP Tel: (01793) 511055 Fax: (01635) 570275 *Solicitors*

Charles Lucas & Sons, 72-74 Camden Street, Birmingham, B1 3DR Tel: 0121-265 6410 *Stone set dress rings*

Charles M Willie & Co (Shipping) Ltd, Celtic House, Brittania Road, Roath Basin, Cardiff, CF10 4SF Tel: (029) 2047 1000 Fax: (029) 2047 5799 E-mail: mail@williegroup.co.uk *Ship owners* Also at: Liverpool

Chas Mathews Lapidaries Ltd, 5 Hatton Garden, London, EC1N 8AA Tel: (020) 7405 7333 Fax: (020) 7405 3827 *Gemstone cutting*

Charles Millward Partnership Ltd, Old Angel Cottage, Main Road, Flax Bourton, Bristol, BS48 3QQ Tel: (01275) 464868 Fax: (01275) 464868 E-mail: cmp.ltd@btinternet.com *Advertising & marketing consultancy practice*

Chas Newens Marine Co. Ltd, The Boathouse, Embankment, London, SW15 1LB Tel: (020) 8788 4587 Fax: (020) 8780 2339 E-mail: sales@chastheboat.co.uk *Boats & marine equipment suppliers*

Charles Owen & Co (Bow) Ltd, Royal Works, Croesfoel Industrial Estate, Rhostyllen, Wrexham, Clwyd, LL14 4BJ Tel: (01978) 317777 Fax: (01978) 317778 E-mail: charles.owen@ukonline.co.uk *Military & uniform cap & hat makers & equestrian hat manufrs*

Chas Paisley & Sons, 2 Caroline Street, Langholm, Dumfriesshire, DG13 0AF Tel: (01387) 380308 Fax: (01387) 381048 *Fellmongers*

▶ Charles & Patricia Lester Ltd, Old Workhouse, Union Road West, Abergavenny, Gwent, NP7 7RL Tel: (01873) 853559 Fax: (01873) 858666

Charles Pearson (Hull) Ltd, New Works, Spyvee Street, Hull, HU8 7JU Tel: (01482) 329602 Fax: (01482) 325860 E-mail: keith@cpgltd.com *Chain test & lifting gear inspectors & maintenance repair services*

Charles Pugh, Millmarsh Lane, Enfield, Middlesex, EN3 7QG Tel: (020) 8805 5222 Fax: (020) 8805 2251 E-mail: sales@pughs.co.uk *Automotive windscreens, distributors & wholesalers*

Charles Raper, 255 Amhurst Road, London, N16 7UN Tel: (020) 7254 7877 E-mail: charlesraper@btconnect.com *Commercial printers*

▶ Charles Russell International Ltd, Walton Hill Farm, Tewkesbury Road, Gloucester, GL19 4BN Tel: (01242) 680678 Fax: (01242) 680078

▶ Charles Scott & Partners, 9 Park Quadrant, Glasgow, G3 6BS Tel: 0141-332 2873 Fax: 0141-332 2873

Charles Stanley & Co. Ltd, 25 Luke Street, London, EC2A 4AR Tel: (020) 7739 8200 Fax: (020) 7739 7798 E-mail: finance@charles-stanley.co.uk *Stock brokers*

Charles Swan Walsall Ltd, Old Landywood Lane, Essington, Wolverhampton, WV11 2AP Tel: (01922) 408152 Fax: (01922) 711350 *Wholesale coal merchants*

▶ Charles Sweetland & Sons Ltd, Cher, Minehead, Somerset, TA24 5EL Tel: (01643) 703085 Fax: (01643) 707256

Charles Taylor Consulting, International House, 1 St.Katherines Way, London, E1W 1UT Tel: (020) 7759 4955 Fax: (020) 7481 9545 E-mail: info@charlestaylorconsulting.com *Marine surveyors*

Chas Tennant & Co., 81 Lochburn Road, Glasgow, G20 9AE Tel: 0141-946 1833 Fax: 0141-946 5752 E-mail: enquiries@tennantsdistribution.com *Plastics container & blow moulders*

▶ Charles Tennant & Co., Craighead, Whistleberry Road, Blantyre, Glasgow, G72 0TH Tel: (01698) 717900 Fax: (01698) 717910 E-mail: tennants.scot@dial.pipex.com *Chemicals suppliers*

Charles W Michie Ltd, 54 Park Road, Aberdeen, AB24 5PA Tel: (01224) 632281 Fax: (01224) 649012 E-mail: carolyn@michietransport.co.uk *Road haulage & storage services*

Charles Walker Ltd, 22-24 John Brannan Way, Bellshill, Lanarkshire, ML4 3HD Tel: (01698) 327600 Fax: (01698) 327602 E-mail: se.scotland@charleswalker.co.uk *Conveyor belting manufrs*

▶ Charles Wilson Ltd, 317 Bromford Lane, Washwood Heath, Birmingham, B8 2SH Tel: 0121-325 8686 Fax: 0121-328 7475

Charlestown Electrical Co. Ltd, Collier Street, Glossop, Derbyshire, SK13 8LS Tel: (01457) 852134 Fax: (01457) 852134 *Industrial & domestic contractors*

Charlestown Engineering Services Ltd, Rayner House, Bayley Street, Stalybridge, Cheshire, SK15 1PZ Tel: 0161-338 7300 Fax: 0161-338 4884 E-mail: sales@charlestown1.com Principal Export Areas: Worldwide *Building engineers*

Charlestown Joinery Ltd, West Haul Park, Par Moor Road, St. Austell, Cornwall, PL25 3RF Tel: (01726) 812666 Fax: (01726) 812666 *Joinery manufrs*

Charleswater Ltd, Unit C, 4th Dimension, Fourth Avenue, Letchworth Garden City, Hertfordshire, SG6 2TD Tel: (01462) 672005 Fax: (01462) 670440 E-mail: sales@vermason.co.uk *Manufacturers electrostatic & nti-static control products*

A.E. Charlesworth & Co.Ltd, Rugby St, Leicester, LE3 5FG Tel: 0116-251 0552 Fax: 0116-251 8629 *Dyers & finishers*

Charlesworth China Ltd, 254 Deighton Road, Huddersfield, HD2 1JJ Tel: (01484) 517077 Fax: (01484) 517068 E-mail: mail@charlesworth.com *Lithographic printers & electronic publishers*

▶ Charlesworth Electrical Services, 46 Park Street, Worksop, Nottinghamshire, S80 1HF Tel: (01909) 476722 Fax: (01909) 476722 *Domestic & industrial electrical instalation & maintainance*

Charlesworth & Son Ltd, Wishaw Lane, Curdworth, Sutton Coldfield, West Midlands, B76 9EL Tel: (01675) 470382 E-mail: sales@charlesworth-son.co.uk *Plastic moulding engineers*

Charlesworth & Valentine, 34 Bridgnorth Road, Aqueduct Village, Telford, Shropshire, TF3 1BZ Tel: (01952) 592012 Fax: (01952) 270121 *Photographers & electronic imaging*

▶ Charlie the copywriter, 33 Malvern Way, Croxley Green, Rickmansworth, Hertfordshire, WD3 3QQ Tel: 01923 775554 E-mail: charlie@charlie-the-copywriter.co.uk *offers professional, friendly, affordable copywriting services to small and medium-size businesses in the UK and abroad.*

▶ Charlies Pine, 2 Narborough Road, Leicester, LE3 0BQ Tel: 0116-247 1474 *Pine furniture manufrs*

Charlotte Street Joinery, Unit A1 New Normanton Mills, Charlotte Street, Derby, DE23 6QG Tel: (01332) 367962 Fax: (01332) 748452 E-mail: charlottestreet@hotmail.com *Joinery manufrs*

▶ Charlton Doors Ltd, Unit C & D Rearing Site, Odbury Lane, Oldbury-on-Severn, Bristol, BS35 1RF Tel: (01454) 417567 Fax: (01454) 417311 E-mail: sales@charltondoors.co.uk *Suppliers, manufacturers & installers of all types of industrial doors*

Matthew Charlton Ltd, Station Road, Hexham, Northumberland, NE46 1HB Tel: (01434) 604911 Fax: (01434) 604147 *Builders & DIY merchants* Also at: Morpeth

Matthew Charlton & Sons (Slaters) Ltd, Chareway Lane, Hexham, Northumberland, NE46 3HW Tel: (01434) 606177 Fax: (01434) 601679 E-mail: slaters@matthewcharlton.com *Slate contractors* Also at: Penrith

▶ Charlwood Ltd, Old Park, Whitfield, Dover, Kent, CT16 2HQ Tel: (01304) 822411 Fax: (01304) 822401

Charlwood Aquatics, Horley Road, Charlwood, Horley, Surrey, RH6 0BJ Tel: (01293) 776377 Fax: (01293) 786730 *Aquatic wholesalers*

Charlwood Copiers, 60 The Street, Charlwood, Horley, Surrey, RH6 0DF Tel: (01293) 862743 Fax: (0870) 8032291 E-mail: info@charlwoodcopiers.co.uk *Suppliers & repairers photocopiers*

Charm Managaement Specialists Ltd, 13 High Street, Ruddington, Nottingham, NG11 6DT Tel: 0115-984 7760 Fax: 0115-921 1887 E-mail: resources@charmhrm.co.uk *Learning resource centre, workshop delivery & design specialists*

Charmans Joinery, Dean Lane, Bristol, BS3 1DD Tel: 0117-966 2781 Fax: 0117-966 2781 E-mail: sales@charmansjoinery.co.uk *Joinery manufrs*

▶ Charmed Cards & Crafts, 22 Somerville Road, London, SE20 7NA Tel: 0208 6590737 E-mail: sales@charmedcardsandcrafts.co.uk *Handmade crafts suppliers*

▶ Charmeldon Air Conditioning Equipment, Unit B Roe Cross Industrial Park, Mottram, Hyde, Cheshire, SK14 6NB Tel: (01457) 764666 Fax: (01457) 764999 E-mail: n-shenton@charmeldon.com *Air conditioning designers*

▶ Charming Invitations, 170 Erskinefauld Road, Linwood, Paisley, Renfrewshire, PA3 3QH Tel: (01505) 353353 E-mail: charminginvitations@yahoo.co.uk *Beautiful handmade wedding stationery & favours, free bespoke service we offer the complete stationery package including Save the Date Magnets RSVP Cards Thank-you cards Menus Place Cards OOS Table Plans & Guest books to match your chosen Invitation*

Charmouth Village Bakery Ltd, Barrs Lane, Charmouth, Bridport, Dorset, DT6 6PS Tel: (01297) 560213 *Bakers*

Charnley Joinery, 2 Concorde House, Charnley Road, Blackpool, FY1 4PP Tel: (01253) 752820 Fax: (01253) 752820 *Joinery manufrs*

Charntec Electronics Ltd, PO Box 477, Eastleigh, Hampshire, SO5 0AR Tel: (01962) 735718 Fax: (01962) 736756 E-mail: charntec@btinternet.com *Semiconductor manufacturing equipment distributors*

Charnvel Ltd, Charnvel House, Canterbury Road, Nottingham, NG8 1PQ Tel: 0115-985 4000 Fax: 0115-985 5558 E-mail: info@charnvel.co.uk *Switchgear manufrs*

Charnwood, Cedar Court, Walker Road, Bardon Hill, Coalville, Leicestershire, LE67 1TU Tel: (01530) 516925 Fax: (01530) 516929 E-mail: sales@charnwood.net *Woodworking machine merchants*

Charnwood Cabling Ltd, Ark Business Centre, Gordon Road, Loughborough, Leicestershire, LE11 1JP Tel: (01509) 236200 Fax: (01509) 236211 E-mail: kevin@charnwoodcabling.co.uk *Cabling & telecommunications*

Charnwood Fasteners Ltd, F27-30 Trading Estate, Cumberland Road, Loughborough, Leicestershire, LE11 5DF Tel: (01509) 237280 Fax: (01509) 262428 *Fastener, bolt & nut sales*

Charnwood Forest Brick Ltd, Old Station Close, Shepshed, Loughborough, Leicestershire, LE12 9NJ Tel: (01509) 503203 Fax: (01509) 507566 E-mail: sales@charnwoodforest.com *Handmade facing brick manufrs*

Charnwood Furniture Ltd, Whitebridge Lane, Stone, Staffordshire, ST15 8LQ Tel: (01785) 815000 Fax: (01785) 815002 E-mail: *Charnwood is a Staffordshire-based company offering a range of quality furniture to the leisure industry. A range of tables, chairs, stools, cast iron bases and fixed seating, We also supply Fixed Seating, made to measure by experienced craftsmen. A spraying service is also available should a colour be required other than light oak, dark oak or raw. Upholstery can be choosen from our fabric ranges and samples can be supplied. Tax efficient finance can be arranged. We Deliver anywhere in the UK*

▶ Charnwood Healthcare Ltd, Unit B7, 46 Holton Heath Training Park, Holton Road, Poole, Dorset, BH16 6LT Tel: (01202) 620839 Fax: (01202) 620839 E-mail: charnwood.healthcare@virgin.net *Medical products manufrs*

Charnwood Instrumentation Services, 81 Park Road, Coalville, Leicestershire, LE67 3AF Tel: (01530) 510615 Fax: (01530) 510950 E-mail: graham@instrumentationservices.net *Distributors & agents of gauges*

▶ Charnwood Lifts Ltd, Orchard House 20 Narborough Wood Park, Desford Road, Enderby, Leicester, LE19 4XT Tel: 0116-239 1670 Fax: 0116-239 4638 E-mail: admin@charnwoodlifts.com *Lift installations & manufrs*

Charnwood Management Centre Ltd, 175 Birchwood Lane, Somercotes, Alfreton, Derbyshire, DE55 4NF Tel: (01773) 606606 Fax: (01773) 606606 E-mail: sales@thecharnwoodgroup.com *Management training & consultants*

Charnwood Publishing Co. Ltd, Vaughan Street, Coalville, Leicestershire, LE67 3GG Tel: (01530) 832288 Fax: (01530) 510390 E-mail: chardwoodp@aol.com *Photocopying services, printing & commercial stationery*

Charnwood Ties Ltd, 91 Farndale Drive, Loughborough, Leicestershire, LE11 2RG Tel: (01509) 215378 Fax: (01509) 215378 E-mail: mail@charnwoodties.co.uk *Necktie designers & manufrs*

Charnwood Video Productions, 11 Endor Grove, Burley in Wharfedale, Ilkley, West Yorkshire, LS29 7QJ Tel: (01943) 863393 *Video production services*

▶ Chars Display London Ltd, 28 Redchurch Street, London, E2 7DP Tel: (020) 7739 3604 Fax: (020) 7739 1962

Chart Engineering Ltd, Pivington Works, Pluckley, Ashford, Kent, TN27 0PG Tel: (01233) 840555 Fax: (01233) 840687 E-mail: sales@chartengineering.com *Formwork & mould manufrs*

Chart Right Ltd, Units 34, Aston Fields Trading Estate, Bromsgrove, Worcestershire, B60 3DW Tel: (01527) 571500 Fax: (01527) 571516 E-mail: sales@chartright.com *Paper recording chart manufrs*

Charter P.L.C., 52 Grovenor Gardens, London, SW1W 0AU Tel: (020) 7881 7800 Fax: (020) 7259 9338 E-mail: investor-relations@charterplc.com *Industrial engineering company*

Charter Building Services Ltd, Mayplace Road East, Bexleyheath, Kent, DA7 6EJ Tel: (01322) 558011 Fax: (01322) 520282 E-mail: mail@charter.uk.com *Building maintenance & lift consultants*

Charter Business Forms Ltd, Harris Industrial Estate, Hanbury Road, Stoke Prior, Bromsgrove, Worcestershire, B60 4AD Tel: (01527) 575166 Fax: (01527) 579152 *Books, pads, business forms printers & manufrs*

Charter Castings Ltd, Bagnall Street, Great Bridge, Tipton, West Midlands, DY4 7BS Tel: 0121-557 9831 Fax: 0121-520 4761 E-mail: mail@chartercastings.co.uk *Gravity die casters & sand manufrs*

▶ Charter Commercial Windows & Doors, Hoo Farm Industrial Estate, Worcester Road, Kidderminster, Worcestershire, DY11 7RA Tel: (01562) 745940 Fax: (01562) 66596 E-mail: info@chartercommercial.com *Aluminium framed windows & doors*

Charter Crate, Berwick Barns, Terling Hall Road, Hatfield Peverel, Chelmsford, CM3 2EY Tel: (01245) 382001 Fax: (01245) 382999 *Crate hire*

Charter Engineering Services, 6 Sycamore Centre, Sycamore Road, Eastwood Trading Estate, Rotherham, South Yorkshire, S65 1EN Tel: (01709) 836822 Fax: (01709) 836955 E-mail: sales@chartmach.co.uk *Machine tool engineers*

Charter Health Care, Unit 1, The Links, Bakewell Road, Orton Southgate, Peterborough, PE2 6BJ Tel: 0800 132787 *Surgical appliance fitters & dispensers*

Charter Litho Plates Ltd, Charter Ho, 51-53 Bickersteth Rd, London, SW17 9SH Tel: 020-8767 3513 Fax: 020-8767 7128 E-mail: printing@charterlitho.co.uk *Lithographic plate makers*

Charter Precision Engineering, Unit 25-26, Enfield Industrial Estate, Redditch, Worcestershire, B97 6BY Tel: (01527) 584187 Fax: (01527) 584187 *Precision engineers*

▶ Charter Print Group, Leicester Road Kingsway House, Lutterworth, Walcote, Lutterworth, Leicestershire, LE17 4JN Tel: (01455) 203600 Fax: (01455) 557979 E-mail: sales@chartergrp.co.uk

▶ Charter Self Drive Ltd, Charter House, Forge Way Cleveland Street, Darlington, County Durham, DL1 2PB Tel: (01325) 481814 Fax: (01325) 484636 E-mail: Info@charterselfdrive.co.uk *The hire of Cars, People carriers and the Rental of vans including Transits, Lutons, Minibus and LCV for daily, weekly or long term hire at excellents rates*

Charter Tech Ltd, Leanne Business Centre, Sandford Lane, Wareham, Dorset, BH20 4DY Tel: (01929) 553000 Fax: (01929) 550022 E-mail: paul.burns@charter-tech.com *Process control system design*

▶ CHARTER WISE LTD., 21a High Street, Lyndhurst, Hampshire, SO43 7BB Tel: 023 80284459 Fax: 023 80283888 E-mail: dick@charterwise.wanadoo.co.uk *Providing a service to any company trading in, or involved with trading in, bulk commodities; that covers all aspects of problems relating to "The International Sale of Goods Carried by Sea". To include disptes under the Sale Contract, Bills of Lading, Charterparties, Insurance Policies & Letters of Credit. Handling trade and maritime arbitrations for Traders and their Underwriters.*

Charterbrae Ltd, Unit 3 Coneygre Industrial Estate, Tipton, West Midlands, DY4 8XP Tel: 0121-520 5353 Fax: 0121-522 2018 E-mail: sales@cbbeds.u-net.com *Contract metal framed beds manufrs*

Charterbrook Signs, 1 Acorn Court, Clarion Close, Swansea Enterprise Park, Swansea, SA6 8QU Tel: (01792) 799888 Fax: (01792) 795400 E-mail: nigel.hillman@charterbrook.co.uk *Sign manufrs*

The Chartered Institute Of Logistics And Transport, 11-12 Buckingham Gate, London, SW1E 6LB Tel: (01536) 740100 Fax: (020) 7592 3111 E-mail: enquiry@iolt.org.uk *Charity organisation*

Chartered Institute of Logistics & Transport (UK), Logistics & Transport Centre, Earlstrees Road, Corby, Northamptonshire, NN17 4AX Tel: (01536) 740100 Fax: (01536) 740101 E-mail: enquiry@ciltuk.org.uk *Professional associates*

Chartered Institute Of Marketing, Moor Hall, The Moor, Cookham, Maidenhead, Berkshire, SL6 9QH Tel: (01628) 427500 Fax: (01628) 427499 E-mail: marketing@cim.co.uk *Marketing & sales training services*

Chartered Institute Of Purchasing & Supply, Easton House, Church Street, Easton on the Hill, Stamford, Lincolnshire, PE9 3NZ Tel: (01780) 756777 Fax: (01780) 751610 E-mail: sales@cips.org *International professional body*

Chartered Institute Of Taxation, 12 Upper Belgrave Street, London, SW1X 8BB Tel: (020) 7235 9381 Fax: (020) 7838 9958 E-mail: info@att.org.uk *Professional body & taxation consultants*

Chartered Management Institute, Management House, Cottingham Road, Corby, Northamptonshire, NN17 1TT Tel: (01536) 204222 Fax: (01536) 201651 E-mail: member@inst-mgt.org.uk *Professional association services*

Charterhouse Development Capital Ltd, 5 Paternoster Square, London, EC4M 7DX Tel: (020) 7334 5300 Fax: (020) 7334 5333 E-mail: recept@charterhouse.co.uk *Venture capital*

▶ Charterhouse Group International Plc, 2nd Floor, 37 Lombard Street, London, United Kingdom, EC3V 9BQ Tel: 0800 634 4848 Fax: 0800 634 4849 E-mail: sales@charterhouseplc.com

Charterhouse Muller plc, Little Johns Lane, Reading, RG30 1RA Tel: 0118-958 8700 Fax: 0118-958 4444 E-mail: sales@pcbroker.co.uk *Computer agents*

▶ Charteris, 85 Southdown Road, Harpenden, Hertfordshire, AL5 1PR Tel: (01582) 716100 Fax: (01582) 469051 *Computer maintenance services*

Charter-Kontron Ltd, Avant BSNS Centre, Avant Business Centre, First Avenue, Bletchley, Milton Keynes, MK1 1DL Tel: (01908) 646070 Fax: (01908) 646030 E-mail: sales@charter-kontron.co.uk *Medical electronic equipment distributors*

Charters Ltd, 6 Centre Way, Claverings Industrial Estate, London, N9 0AP Tel: (020) 8345 6999 Fax: (020) 8345 5837 E-mail: sales@chartershire.com *Catering equipment hire*

Chartex Systems, Ashdene House, Langton Road, Langton Green, Tunbridge Wells, Kent, TN3 0HL Tel: (01892) 862024 Fax: (01892) 863437 E-mail: info@chartexsystems.com *Photocopiers sales & service*

Chartland Electronics Ltd, Chartland House Old Station Approach, Randalls Road, Leatherhead, Surrey, KT22 7TE Tel: (01372) 363666 Fax: (01372) 363833 E-mail: sales@chartlandelectronics.co.uk *Transducers*

▶ Chartley Coffee Co., Drointon, Stafford, ST18 0LX Tel: (01889) 500308 Fax: (01889) 500771 E-mail: enquiries@chartleycoffee.co.uk *Rancilio espresso coffee machines & drury tea & coffee suppliers*

▶ Charttape Ltd, 14 Witt Road, Fair Oak, Eastleigh, Hampshire, SO50 7FR Tel: (07836) 671676 Fax: (023) 8069 6743 E-mail: charttape@btinternet.com *Hvac CAD design*

▶ Chartus, 5 Gratton Road, Cheltenham, Gloucestershire, GL50 2BT Tel: (01242) 701014 Fax: (01242) 701014 E-mail: info@chartus.co.uk *Specialists in internet solutions & consultancy services*

Chartway Industrial Services Ltd, Faraday Drive, Bridgnorth, Shropshire, WV15 5BA Tel: (01746) 764900 Fax: (01746) 768770 E-mail: sales@chartway.co.uk Purchasing Contact: J Clark *Precision engineers, turning (centre lathe) services, machinists (engineers')/ general machining services & machinists, precision machining services*

Chartway Janitorial Supplies, Great Tong Farm, Great Tong, Headcorn, Ashford, Kent, TN27 9PP Tel: (01622) 890220 Fax: (01622) 890991 *Janitorial supplies distributors*

Chartwell Learning & Development Ltd, Old Orchard, Bickley Road, Bromley, BR1 2NE Tel: (020) 8467 1956 Fax: (020) 8467 1754 E-mail: info@chartwell-learn.co.uk *Management training*

▶ The Chartwell Practice Ltd, St. Pauls Square, Burton-on-Trent, Staffordshire, DE14 2EF Tel: (01283) 741400 Fax: (01283) 741417 E-mail: info@chartwellpractice.com *Chartered Accountants and Business Advisers offering a friendly proactive service. Our fees are always fixed in advance so that there are no nasty surprises during your time with us. We are passionate about delivering what our clients really want, helping them to tackle issues that really matter to their business.*

Chartwell Systems, Malens, Beacon Gardens, Crowborough, East Sussex, TN6 1BG Tel: (01892) 669597 Fax: (01892) 669597 E-mail: chartwell.sys@btconnect.com *Computer software manufrs*

Charvo Finishing Ltd, Snaygill Industrial Estate, Keighley Road, Skipton, North Yorkshire, BD23 2QR Tel: (01756) 795028 Fax: (01756) 798473 E-mail: sales@charvo.co.uk *Chocolate wholesalers*

Charvo Finishing Ltd, Snaygill Industrial Estate, Keighley Road, Skipton, North Yorkshire, BD23 2QR Tel: (01756) 795028 Fax: (01756) 798473 E-mail: sales@charvo.co.uk *Clear & anti reflective hardcoats*

Charybdis Ltd, The Cowshed Strelley Hall, Main St, Strelley, Nottingham, NG8 6PE Tel: 0115-942 6962 *Software devlopers*

Chase AV Ltd, Unit 10, Upper Gamma, West Road, Ransomes Europark, Ipswich, IP3 9SX Tel: (01473) 279992 Fax: (01473) 279993 E-mail: sales2@chaseavdirect.co.uk *Audio visual accessories*

Chase Business Service, 14 Elton Avenue, Greenford, Middlesex, UB6 0PW Tel: (020) 8864 0701 Fax: (0870) 0518485 E-mail: chase@greenford.demon.co.uk *Translation service (most languages)*

▶ Chase Colour Ltd, 2 The Sidings, Station Road, Guiseley, Leeds, LS20 8BX Tel: (01943) 874110 Fax: (01943) 870350 E-mail: info@chasecolour.com

▶ Chase Construction Group, 2 Camborne Mews, London, SW18 5ED Tel: (020) 8871 1828 Fax: (020) 8871 0108

▶ Chase Consulting, 17 The Chase, Crowthorne, Berkshire, RG45 6HT Tel: (0845) 4501946 Fax: (08454) 501947 E-mail: mail@chaseconsulting.biz *Executive & management recruitment consultancy*

Chase De Vere Mortgage Management Ltd, St James House, 23 Kings Street, London, SW1Y 6QY Tel: (020) 7930 7242 Fax: (020) 7930 3691 E-mail: simon.tyler@cdvmm.co.uk *Financial & mortgage brokers*

Chase Design & Print, White Cottage Works, Rumer Hill Road, Cannock, Staffordshire, WS11 8EX Tel: (01543) 462334 Fax: (01543) 505707 E-mail: chasedesign2000@hotmail.com *Printers*

Chase Diamond Tools International Ltd, 10 Shieling Court, Corby, Northamptonshire, NN18 9QD Tel: (01536) 461133 Fax: (01536) 461144 E-mail: sales@chasediamond.com *Diamond tipped tools manufrs*

Chase Equipment Ltd, 53A Wellington Industrial Estate, Coseley, Bilston, West Midlands, WV14 9EE Tel: (01902) 675835 Fax: (01902) 674998 E-mail: sales@chaseequipment.com *Material handling & storage manufrs*

Chase Group Printing & Stationery Ltd, Unit 11 Heston Industrial Mall, Church Rd, Hounslow, TW5 0LD Tel: (020) 8577 1930 Fax: (020) 8572 3065 E-mail: info@chasegrp.co.uk *General printers*

Chase Heating Ltd, Somerfield Stores, Racecourse Road, Pinvin, Pershore, Worcestershire, WR10 2EY Tel: (01386) 553542 Fax: (01386) 552269 E-mail: chasehtg@gxn.co.uk *Wood burning stoves suppliers*

▶ Chase International, Dunfermline Business, Learning & Conference Centre, Halbeath, Dunfermline, Fife, KY11 8DY Tel: (01383) 559050 Fax: (01383) 559052 *It training*

Chase Manufacturing Ltd, Unit 52 Enterprise Way, Newport, Gwent, NP20 2AQ Tel: (01633) 841088 Fax: (01633) 243087 E-mail: sales@chaseladders.co.uk *Ladder manufrs*

▶ Chase Marketing, 26 Pine Walk, Cobham, Surrey, KT11 2HJ Tel: (01932) 586960 *Chase Marketing provide telemarketing services for companies in the UK from their base in Surrey.*

▶ Chase Of Milford, The White House, Main Road, Milford, Stafford, ST17 0UW Tel: (01785) 660939 Fax: (01785) 660914 E-mail: caseofmillford@aol.com *Retailer of fires & stoves*

Chase Mouldings Ltd, 5 Swaffield Park, Hyssop Close, Cannock, Staffordshire, WS11 7FU Tel: (01543) 572425 Fax: (01543) 572451 E-mail: chase@chasemouldings.fsnet.co.uk *Polyurethane moulding services*

Chase Perrin Ltd, 7 Littleton House, Littleton Road, Ashford, Middlesex, TW15 1UU Tel: (01784) 250200 Fax: (01784) 257283 E-mail: printmail@lineone.net *Direct mail printing services*

Chase Pine, Vine Cottage, Winchester Road, Waltham Chase, Southampton, SO32 2LX Tel: (01329) 832366 E-mail: chasepine@yahoo.co.uk *Furniture restoration & pine manufrs*

Chase Precision Engineering Ltd, 10 7 Blackmoor Road, Ebblake Industrial Estate, Verwood, Dorset, BH31 6AX Tel: (01202) 813237 Fax: (01202) 813734 *CNC, milling engineering & precision turned parts manufrs*

Chase Saddlery, 76 Chase Side, Enfield, Middlesex, EN2 6NX Tel: (020) 8363 7238 Fax: (020) 8367 8190 E-mail: sales@chase-saddlery.co.uk *Saddlery distributor*

Chase Timber Products Ltd, Twickenham Avenue, Brandon, Suffolk, IP27 0PD Tel: (01842) 810690 Fax: (01842) 812987 E-mail: mail@chasetimberproducts.co.uk *Fencing manufrs*

Chaselink UK Ltd, New Street, Chase Terrace, Burntwood, Staffordshire, WS7 1BS Tel: (01543) 459655 Fax: (01543) 459949 E-mail: sales@chaselink.co.uk *Garden products suppliers & manufrs*

Chasmood Ltd, Unit 8 Weydown Industrial Estate, Haslemere, Surrey, GU27 1DW Tel: (01428) 641655 Fax: (01428) 641654 E-mail: info@chasmood.com *Architectural ironmongers*

Chasmors Weighing Equipment, 18 Camden High Street, London, NW1 0JH Tel: (020) 7387 2060 Fax: (020) 7387 2060 *Scale manufrs*

Chassis Development Ltd, 16 Botley Road, Park Gate, Southampton, SO31 1AJ Tel: (01489) 885738 Fax: (01489) 570227 *Wheelchair transport specialist*

Chassis Developments Ltd, Grovebury Road, Leighton Buzzard, Bedfordshire, LU7 4SL Tel: (01525) 374151 Fax: (01525) 370127 E-mail: david.brain@chassisdevelopments.co.uk *Commercial chassis alterations*

Chateau Papillon Estates, C7 Boston Trade Park, Norfolk Street, Boston, Lincolnshire, PE21 9HG Tel: (0845) 8381790 Fax: (0870) 1313172 E-mail: info@chateau-papillon.com *International Distributors, UK importers and wholesalers of fine organic, biodynamic & vegetarian wine, champagne, port and cider*

▶ Chater Bros Windows Ltd, 26-38 Jubilee Street, Rugby, Warwickshire, CV21 2JJ Tel: (01788) 540245 Fax: (01788) 547617 E-mail: chaterbrosltd@btconnect.com *Manufacture of double glazing windows & doors*

▶ Chatham Windows Ltd, Chatham Mill, Chatham Street, Wigan, Lancashire, WN1 3DB Tel: (01942) 492137 Fax: (01942) 323994

Chatsworth Forge Ltd, Woods Way, Goring-by-Sea, Worthing, West Sussex, BN12 4RE Tel: (01903) 502221 Fax: (01903) 700002 E-mail: sales@chatsworthforge.co.uk *Balustrade manufrs*

A.M. & B.J. Chattaway, Meriden Mill Farm, Meriden, Coventry, CV7 7LJ Tel: (01675) 442564 Fax: (01675) 443120 E-mail: info@waterinthegarden.co.uk *Agricultural engineers & water garden specialists*

Chattem UK Ltd, Ringway Centre, Edison Road, Basingstoke, Hampshire, RG21 6YH Tel: (01256) 844144 Fax: (01256) 844145 *Sell cosmetics & toiletries*

▶ Chatterbox Magazine, Head Office, 2 Alpine Rise, Styvechale Grange, Coventry, CV3 6NT Tel: (024) 7641 4458 Fax: (024) 76414458 E-mail: enquiries@chatterbox-magazine.co.uk *Chatterbox is a free quality magazine covering the UK including the Coventry area. It is produced bi-monthly with extremely competitive rates and is the obvious choice to advertise your business!*

Chaucer Foods, Uppermoor Road, Allenton, Derby, DE24 9BY Tel: (01332) 362311 Fax: (01332) 295387 E-mail: derby@chaucerfoods.com *Food manufrs*

Chaucer Group, 67 Preston Street, Faversham, Kent, ME13 8PB Tel: (0845) 0724500 Fax: (0845) 0724510 E-mail: sales@chaucer-group.com *Project management consultants*

Chaucer Hotel, Chantry House, 63 Ivy Lane, Canterbury, Kent, CT1 1TU Tel: (01227) 464427 Fax: (01227) 450397 E-mail: sales@heritage-hotel.com *Conference facilities & hotel*

Chaucer Solutions Ltd, Leycourt Farm, Etisley Road, Great Gransden, Sandy, Bedfordshire, SG19 3AS Tel: (01480) 476202 Fax: (01480) 356162 *Janitorial suppliers*

▶ Chauffeur Driven, 68 High Street, Witney, Oxon, OX28 6HJ Tel: 0800 5876646 E-mail: info@chauffeurdriven.net *Top of the class Mercedes makes travelling with Chauffeur Driven comfortable and luxurious. Relax and travel to your destination with one of our fully trained and friendly chauffeurs*

Chauvin Arnoux UK Ltd, Waldeck House, Waldeck Road, Maidenhead, Berkshire, SL6 8BR Tel: (01628) 788888 Fax: (01628) 628099 E-mail: sales@chauvin-arnoux.co.uk *Electronic measuring equipment*

▶ CHC Scotia Ltd, CHC House Howe Moss Drive, Kirkhill Industrial Estate, Dyce, Aberdeen, AB21 0GL Tel: (01224) 846000 Fax: (01224) 771632 E-mail: sales@chc.ca

Cheadle Glass Co. Ltd, Adswood Road, Cheadle Hulme, Cheadle, Cheshire, SK8 5QA Tel: 0161-486 9333 Fax: 0161-486 9335 *Glass processors*

Cheadle Royal (Industries) Ltd, Wilmslow Road, Cheadle, Cheshire, SK8 3US Tel: 0161-428 4101 Fax: 0161-428 1764 E-mail: sales@cri-ltd.net *Novelty hat manufrs*

Cheadle Snooker, 11 Carrs Road, Cheadle, Cheshire, SK8 2EE Tel: 0161-491 0868 *Maintenance & repair of snooker tables*

Cheam Bedding, 34 The Broadway, Cheam, Sutton, Surrey, SM3 8BD Tel: (020) 8642 2232 Fax: (020) 8288 0785 E-mail: sales@cheambedding.co.uk *Beds & furniture retailers*

Joseph Cheaney & Sons Ltd, PO Box 1 69 Rushton Road, Kettering, Northamptonshire, NN14 2RZ Tel: (01536) 760383 Fax: (01536) 761354 E-mail: info.cheaney@cheaney.co.uk *Boot & shoe manufrs*

▶ Cheap Formations Ltd, 19 Moulton Park Office Village, Scirocco Close, Northampton, NN3 6AP Tel: (01604) 491031 Fax: (0870) 4325545 E-mail: enquiries@quickformations.com *Register office*

Cheap-IT, 338 City Road, Angel, London, EC1V 2PY Tel: (01582) 600883 E-mail: sales@cheap-it.com *New & used laptops retailers*

▶ CheapSoftwareOnline, PO BOX 5786, Southend-on-Sea, SS1 9DA Tel: 01702 300801 E-mail: support@cheapsoftwareonline.co.uk *Buy bargain software for accounts, antivirus, graphics, education, operating systems & more!*

Check Communications Ltd, The Haven Communications House, 40 Chester Road West, Queensferry, Deeside, Clwyd, CH5 1SA Tel: (01244) 834800 Fax: (01244) 831606 E-mail: solutions@checkcomm.comm *Telecommunications services & consultancy*

▶ Check Computer Services Ltd, Unit 7, Globe Park, Moss Bridge Road, Rochdale, Lancashire, OL16 5EB Tel: (01706) 651555 Fax: (01706) 651666 E-mail: Gareth@check.co.uk *IT hardware distributor*

Check Equipment, 2 Spencer Drive, Melbourn, Royston, Hertfordshire, SG8 6HP Tel: (01763) 261971 Fax: (01763) 262995 E-mail: Sales Contact: R.R. Pedder Principal Export Areas: Middle East, Central/East Europe & West Europe *Cleaning (industrial) equipment/washing/ cleaning pressure equipment, working within 100 mile radius.*

Check Tek Ltd, 38-42 Newport Street, Swindon, SN1 3DR Tel: (01793) 480222 Fax: (01793) 480066 E-mail: sales@check-tek.co.uk *IT consultants*

▶ Check Your Security Ltd, Grange, Cottage Road, West Somerton, Great Yarmouth, Norfolk, NR29 4DL Tel: (01493) 393333 Fax: (0870) 4797149 E-mail: info@checkyoursecurity.co.uk *Security specialists*

Checker Leather Ltd, The Station, Crosshouse Road, Kilmaurs, Kilmarnock, Ayrshire, KA3 2TU Tel: (01563) 541709 Fax: (01563) 537819 E-mail: sales@glenroyal.com Purchasing Contact: P.W. Pattison Sales Contact: P.W. Pattison Principal Export Areas: Asia Pacific, Central/East Europe, West Europe & North America *We are manufacturers of a wide variety of leather products ranging from instrument cases to luggage tags. We have a wide variety of machinery and processes which are combined with traditional craftsmanship. Our services & products include: Brace Ends, Industrial leather Components, Leather Instrument Cases, Leather Cutting Services, Leather Strapping, Leather Luggage Tags, Leather Thonging, Leather Straps, Leather, Leather Goods to Specification, Leather Clothing Components, Leather Elbow Patches, Leather Kilt Straps, Leather Goods Made Up, Buckles, Kilt Pins, and much more*

Checkfire, Unit 12, Pontygwindy Industrial Estate, Caerphilly, Mid Glamorgan, CF83 3HU Tel: (029) 2086 8333 Fax: (029) 2085 0627 E-mail: sales@checkfire.co.uk Purchasing Contact: B. Robins Sales Contact: A. Robins *Fire protection equipment distributors or agents. Also fire constructors/contractors. In addition, fire extinguishers (reconditioned) rebuilders, fire extinguisher refills, fire fighting equipment, fire seals (cable/pipe penetration) distributors or agents. Also safety signs & fire stopping materials*

Checkland Kindleysides Ltd, Charnwood Edge, Syston Road, Cossington, Leicester, LE7 4UZ Tel: 0116-264 4700 Fax: 0116-264 4701 E-mail: info@checkind.com *Design consultants*

Checkley & Co., Broad St House, 212 Broad Street, Birmingham, B15 1AY Tel: 0121-643 8538 Fax: 0121-643 7416 E-mail: mailbox@checkleys.co.uk *Chartered surveyors*

Checkmate Designs, New Road, Sheerness, Kent, ME12 1PZ Tel: (01795) 580333 Fax: (01795) 668280 E-mail: sales@checkmateuk.com *Lifting sling & PPE products manufrs* Also at: Ipswich & Southampton

Checkmate Devices Ltd, Gore Cross Business Park, Corbin Way, Bradpole, Bridport, Dorset, DT6 3UX Tel: (01308) 423871 Fax: (01308) 458276 E-mail: checkmate@ackerman-eng.com *Vehicle safe Sales & Manufacture*

Checkmate Industries Ltd, Bridge House, 12 Bridge Street, Halstead, Essex, CO9 1HT Tel: (01787) 477272 Fax: (01787) 476334 E-mail: checkmatecarpets@btconnect.com *Manufacture of contract carpet tiles & broad-loom*

▶ Checkmate Passive Fire Protection Ltd, B Honley Business Centre, New Mill Road, Honley, Holmfirth, HD9 6QB Tel: (01484) 664028 Fax: (01484) 665320

Checkmate Products Ltd, 64 Lindsell Road, West Timperley, Altrincham, Cheshire, WA14 5NX Tel: 0161-928 0046 Fax: 0161-286 3729 E-mail: checkprod@aol.com *Pressure gauge manufrs*

Checkpoint Computing Ltd, 2 Millfield, Lambourn, Hungerford, Berkshire, RG17 8YQ Tel: (01488) 71467 Fax: (01488) 71467 *Computer databases*

Checkpoint Meto, 43 Western Road, Bracknell, Berkshire, RG12 1RF Tel: (01344) 701200 Fax: (01344) 701333 E-mail: lfardell@eur.checkpt.com *Anti-shoplifting systems manufrs*

Checo 2000, Brailwood Road, Bilsthorpe, Newark, Nottinghamshire, NG22 8UA Tel: (01623) 871976 Fax: (01623) 871964 E-mail: info@checo200.co.uk *Steam cleaning equipment manufrs*

▶ Cheddar Chocolate Co., 3 Saxon Place, Station Road, Cheddar, Somerset, BS27 3AG Tel: (01934) 741777 Fax: (01934) 741666 *Confectionery suppliers*

▶ Cheeky Brats, 470 Coventry Road, Small Heath, Birmingham, B10 0UG Tel: (0870) 2467605 Fax: (0870) 1318974 E-mail: sales@cheekybrats.co.uk *Supplier of Full range of Baby furnitures & baby products*

▶ Cheeky Legs Wholesale Tights and Hosiery, Unit 10 Coombe Park, Ashprington, Totnes, Devon, TQ9 7DY Tel: (0845) 2576847 E-mail: admin@cheekylegs.co.uk *Manufacturers of tights, stockings, opaques, sheers & patterns for kids to adults*

▶ CheekyTiki Ltd, Unit E, 2 Leswin Place, Stoke Newington, London, N16 7NJ Tel: (020) 7241 0742 Fax: (020) 7241 0742 E-mail: info@cheekytiki.com *Purveyors of exotic arts & decor, ceramic bar ware & tiki carvings*

▶ Cheerful Promotions Ltd, 38 Ferncroft Avenue, London, NW3 7PE Tel: (020) 7431 6293 Fax: (020) 7431 2060 E-mail: sales@cheerfulpromotions.co.uk *Promotional clothing distributors*

▶ Cheese Shed, 8 Shepherds Business Park, Norwich Road, Lenwade, Norwich, NR9 5SG Tel: (01603) 879802 Fax: (01603) 879802 *Cheese wholesaler*

Cheese Wedge, Chester Market Hall, Princess Street, Chester, CH1 2HH Tel: (01244) 325458 *Cheese & eggs suppliers*

Cheeses Cheese Makers, 13 Fortis Green Road, London, N10 3HP Tel: (020) 8444 9141 *Cheese makers & suppliers*

Cheesework Cheese Makers, 1 Folly Hill Cottages, Folly Hill, Cranbrook, Kent, TN17 2LT Tel: (01580) 892021 Fax: (01580) 890774 *Cheese wholesalers*

Cheetham Hill Construction Ltd, Woodhill Road, Bury, Lancashire, BL8 1AR Tel: 0161-761 5109 Fax: 0161-761 1300 E-mail: enquiries@cheethamhillconstruction.co.uk *Civil engineering contractors & landfill development*

Chef Call Ltd, 44 Barr Common Road, Walsall, WS9 0SY Tel: (01922) 452508 Fax: (01922) 452543 E-mail: chefcall@aol.com *Chef Call based in Walsall are recruitment consultants for the catering and hospitality industries.*

Chef De La Maison Ltd, Winslow Road, Netherton, Peterborough, PE3 9RE Tel: (01733) 332122 Fax: (01733) 332122 E-mail: charis@chefdelamaison.co.uk *Outside caterers*

Chefmate Ltd, Sunnydale Road, Bakers Field, Nottingham, NG3 7GG Tel: (07770) 663314 Fax: 01623 797997 *Catering equipment engineers*

Chekemcolour Ltd, Smithfield Works, South Lane, Elland, West Yorkshire, HX5 0HQ Tel: (01422) 378221 Fax: (01422) 310074 E-mail: enquiries@chekem.co.uk *Dyestuff & fluorescent brightening agents*

▶ Chela Cleaning Materials, 78 Bilton Way, Enfield, Middlesex, EN3 7LW Tel: (020) 8805 2150 Fax: (020) 8443 1868 E-mail: sales@chela.co.uk *Supplier of cleaning chemicals*

Chelburn Precision Ltd, 2 Plot 7-9 Trans Pennine Trading Estate, Gorrells Way, Rochdale, Lancashire, OL11 2PX Tel: (01706) 644538 Fax: (01706) 861733 E-mail: chelburn@zen.co.uk *Precision & CNC engineers*

Chelford Farm Supplies Ltd, 2 Chelford Farm Supplies Ltd, Knutsford Road, Chelford, Macclesfield, Cheshire, SK11 9AS Tel: (01625) 861588 Fax: (01625) 861235 E-mail: sales@chelfordfarmsupplies.fsbusiness.co.uk *Agricultural suppliers*

Chelford Joinery Co. Ltd, Boundary Cottage, Chelford Road, Ollerton, Knutsford, Cheshire, WA16 8TA Tel: (01565) 751012 Fax: (01565) 652087 *Joinery manufrs*

▶ Chell Instruments Ltd, Folgate House, Folgate Road, North Walsham, Norfolk, NR28 0AJ Tel: (01692) 500555 Fax: (01692) 500088 E-mail: info@chell.co.uk *Engineering*

Chello Chemicals, Homme Castle, Shelsley Walsh, Worcester, WR6 6RR Tel: (01886) 812877 Fax: (01886) 812899 E-mail: sales@chellochemicals.co.uk *Chemical aerosols & degreasers*

Chelma Graphics, Unit 17 Brymau 4 Estate, River Lane, Saltney, Chester, CH4 8RF Tel: (01244) 674969 Fax: (01244) 677081 E-mail: sales@chelmagraphics.co.uk *Graphic designers & printers*

Chelmer Food Machinery, Stone Cottage Farm, Ipswich Road, Dedham, Colchester, CO7 6HS Tel: (01206) 321222 Fax: (01206) 321221 E-mail: sales@cfmsupplies.com *Fish and Chip shop catering equipment sales, service and repairs of Lincat, Bold, IMC, Hobart, Crypto and other major manufacturers of potato peelers, potato chippers, steamers, microwaves, fryers, refrigeration units, beverage & bottle coolers, griddles, ranges, ice makers and much more covering Bedfordshire, Cambridgeshire, Norfolk, Suffolk, Essex, and London*

Chelmer Pneumatics, Unit 8, Moss Rd, Freebournes Industrial Estate, Witham, Essex, CM8 3UQ Tel: (01376) 500595 Fax: (01376) 501589E-mail: sales@chelmerpneumatics.co.uk *Air compressor & pneumatics distribs*

Chelmer Precision Welding, Marks Hall, Marks Hall Lane, Margaret Roding, Dunmow, Essex, CM6 1QT Tel: (01245) 231269 Fax: (01245) 231842 E-mail: cpweld@aol.com *Welders & engineering services*

Chelmer Surgical Supply, PO Box 1424, Braintree, Essex, CM77 8XH Tel: (01376) 550501 Fax: (01376) 550501 E-mail: chelmer@talk21.com *Medical equipment manufrs*

Chelmix Concrete Ltd, 2 Kendrick Trading Estate, Galton Way, Swindon, SN2 2DU Tel: (01793) 610420 Fax: (01793) 610420 *Concrete manufrs*

▶ Chelmsford Dental Laboratories Ltd, 65 Victoria Road, Chelmsford, CM1 1PA Tel: (01245) 287535 Fax: (01245) 600008 *Dental laboratory*

Chelmsford Precision Services, 29 The Westerings, Great Baddow, Chelmsford, CM3 3UY Tel: (01245) 474901 *Calibrating services & inspection equipment manufacturers*

Chelmsford Safety Supplies, 10 Marlborough Road, Chelmsford, CM2 0JR Tel: (01245) 355243 Fax: (01245) 290660 *Safety equipment suppliers*

Chelsea Financial Services plc, St James Hall, Moore Park Road, London, SW6 2JS Tel: (020) 7384 7300 Fax: (020) 7384 7320 E-mail: info@chelseafs.co.uk *Investment & pensions consultants*

Chelsea Foods Ltd, Ferry Lane Industrial Estate, Lamson Road, Rainham, Essex, RM13 9YY Tel: (01708) 521378 Fax: (01708) 525662 E-mail: sales@chelseafoods.co.uk *Tea merchants, confectionery packers & wholesalers*

Chelsea Glass Ltd, 650 Portslade Road, London, SW8 3DH Tel: (020) 7720 6905 Fax: (020) 7978 2827 *Glass merchants & mirror specialists*

Chelsea Health Store, 402 Kings Road, London, SW10 0LJ Tel: (020) 7352 4663 Fax: (020) 7532 4663 E-mail: enquiries@chelseahealthstore.com *Chelsea Health Store provides natural and organic products, alternative remedies, vitamins, minerals, herbs and supplements for a wide range of common ailments and sicknesses. We also offer professional advice, a beauty clinc and a colonics facility.*

Chelsea Hire, 54-58 Bunting Road, Northampton, NN2 6EE Tel: (01604) 722255 E-mail: enquiries@chelseahire.co.uk *Marquee & Catering Equipment Hire. Weddings, Corporate, Parties, Festivals.*

Chelsea Technologies Group, 55 Central Avenue, West Molesey, Surrey, KT8 2QZ Tel: (020) 8941 0044 Fax: (020) 8941 9349 E-mail: sales@chelsea.co.uk *Sonar equipment manufrs*

Chelsea Yacht & Boat Co. Ltd, Anchor House, 106 Cheyne Walk, London, SW10 0DG Tel: (020) 7352 1427 Fax: (020) 7352 1428 *Boat moorings & repairs services*

Cheltape Engineering Company Ltd, Stoneville Street, Cheltenham, Gloucestershire, GL51 8PH Tel: (01242) 245121 Fax: (01242) 224345 E-mail: sales@cheltape.co.uk *CNC sub contract machinists*

Cheltec Ltd, Unit B2B, Horsted Keynes Industrial Estate, Horsted Keynes, Haywards Heath, West Sussex, RH17 7BE Tel: (01342) 811303 Fax: (01342) 811802 E-mail: mike@cheltec.co.uk *Manufacturers of plastic mouldings*

Cheltenham Auto Security, 22 Oak Av, Charlton Kings, Cheltenham, Glos, GL52 6JG Tel: 01242 239283 *Car security distributors*

Cheltenham Bouncy Castles, Unit 8, Mead Park, Mead Road, Cheltenham, Gloucestershire, GL53 7EF Tel: (01242) 235273 Fax: (01242) 235273 *Inflatable suppliers*

Cheltenham Ceiling Co. Ltd, 81-85 Calton Road, Gloucester, GL1 5DT Tel: (01452) 411740 Fax: (01452) 527368 *Suspended ceiling manufrs*

Cheltenham Cheese, 147 Fairview Road, Cheltenham, Gloucestershire, GL52 2EX Tel: (01242) 584212 Fax: (01242) 577834 *Cheese distributors*

Cheltenham Clocks, 16a Lansdown Place Lane, Cheltenham, Gloucestershire, GL50 2LB Tel: (01242) 516022 *Antique clock restoration*

Cheltenham College Enterprises Ltd, Cheltenham College, Bath Road, Cheltenham, Gloucestershire, GL53 7LD Tel: (01242) 513540 Fax: (01242) 513540 E-mail: higley.helen@cheltcoll.gloucs.sch.uk *Educational electronic suppliers*

Cheltenham Controls, 183 Westgate Street, Gloucester, GL1 2RN Tel: (01452) 503390 Fax: (01452) 503630 E-mail: info.cheltcontrols@dis-ltd.co.uk *Switchboard distributors & control panel manufrs*

▶ Cheltenham Decorators Ltd, Galena Becketts Lane, Greet, Cheltenham, Gloucestershire, GL54 5NX Tel: (01242) 602649 E-mail: kevin@cheltenhamdecorators.co.uk *A painting and paperhanging service for both homes and businesses. You are assured of quality, reliability and value for money."If we say we'll be there, we'll be there" is our motto and we live and breathe it.*

Cheltenham Fencing & Landscaping Supplies, Hayden Road, Cheltenham, Gloucestershire, GL51 0SN Tel: (01242) 526946 Fax: (01242) 526480 E-mail: info@cheltenhamfencing.co.uk *Wood fencing & gate manufrs*

Cheltenham Induction Heating Ltd, Saxon Way, Cheltenham, Gloucestershire, GL52 6RU Tel: (01242) 222204 Fax: (01242) 224146 E-mail: sales@cihinduction.com Principal Export Areas: Worldwide *Manufacturers of brazing equipment/machinery, induction heat application equipment/heaters, induction heating (brazing/ soldering) equipment & induction heating equipment. Also furnaces, heat treatment; furnaces, billet heating; furnaces, melting & furnaces, induction. In addition heat treatment services, case hardening & induction heat treatment services*

Cheltenham Induction Heating Ltd, Saxon Way, Cheltenham, Gloucestershire, GL52 6RU Tel: (01242) 222204 Fax: (01242) 224146 E-mail: sales@cihinduction.com *Induction heating equipment manufrs*

Cheltenham Insurance Brokers Ltd, Herriot House, North Place, Cheltenham, Gloucestershire, GL50 4DS Tel: (01242) 517787 *Insurance brokers*

Cheltenham Laminating Company Ltd, Unit 10, Bamfurlong Indust Park, Staverton, Cheltenham, Gloucestershire, GL51 6SX Tel: (01452) 713098 Fax: 01452 715114 E-mail: murray.derek@sky.com *Glass fibre moulding manufrs.*GRP production and design.*Composite Eng**

Cheltenham Patterns 1983 Ltd, Gloucestershire Airport, Staverton, Cheltenham, Gloucestershire, GL51 6SP Tel: (01452) 713037 Fax: (01452) 713270 E-mail: mike@cheltpatts.fsnet.co.uk *Engineers & pattern makers*

Cheltine Ltd, 16 Suffolk Parade, Cheltenham, Gloucestershire, GL50 2AE Tel: (01242) 253243 Fax: (01242) 253243 E-mail: mail@cheltine.co.uk *Property owners & managers*

Chelton Ltd, 4th Avenue, Chelton Centre Fieldhouse Lane, Marlow, Buckinghamshire, SL7 1TF Tel: (01628) 472072 Fax: (01628) 482255 E-mail: mkt@chelton.co.uk *Aircraft component manufrs* Also at: Leominster

Chelton Desant Comunications Ltd, Emblem House, Pynes Hill, Exeter, EX2 5BA Tel: (01392) 667777 Fax: (01392) 667778 E-mail: info@whiskyalpha.com *Systems & software engineering for defence industry*

Chelton Radomes Witney Ltd, Avenue One, Station Lane, Witney, Oxfordshire, OX28 4XS Tel: (01993) 778881 Fax: (01993) 776089 E-mail: sales@radomeswitney.co.uk Principal Export Areas: Worldwide *Aerospace component manufrs*

Chelwood Brick Ltd, Eurolink Industrial Estate, Castle Road, Sittingbourne, Kent, ME10 3TN Tel: (01795) 421651 Fax: (01795) 426489 *Brick manufrs*

Chelwood Group, Adswood Road, Cheadle Hulme, Cheadle, Cheshire, SK8 5QY Tel: 0161-485 8211 Fax: 0161-486 1968 E-mail: marketing@chelwood.co.uk *Makers & sellers of bricks* Also at: Aldridge & Denton

Chem Products Ltd, 5 Poplar Place, Hayes, Middlesex, UB3 2DS Tel: (020) 8797 0567 Fax: (020) 8797 0567 E-mail: chemproducts@myisp.co.uk *Industrial & hygiene chemicals*

Stan Chem International Ltd, Gapton Hall Industrial Estate, Viking Road, Great Yarmouth, Norfolk, NR31 0NU Tel: (01493) 419904 Fax: (01493) 442241 E-mail: yarmouth@stanchem.co.uk *Import & export industrial chemical suppliers*

Chema UK Ltd, Station Road, Cheddleton, Leek, Staffordshire, ST13 7EF Tel: (01538) 369000 Fax: (01538) 361330 E-mail: *Fatty acid & acetate ester manufrs*

Chemaide Ltd, Unit 8 Gilmans Industrial Estate, Billingshurst, West Sussex, RH14 9EZ Tel: (01403) 780638 Fax: (01403) 780639 E-mail: info@chemaide.co.uk *Industrial chemical suppliers, cleaners & manufs*

Chemcolloids Ltd, Tunstall Road, Bosley, Macclesfield, Cheshire, SK11 0PE Tel: (01260) 223284 Fax: (01260) 223589 E-mail: dennis.quinn@chemcolloids.com *Manufacturers & stockists of natural gums*

▶ Chemdry Ki, 8 Harvest Close, Stilton, Peterborough, PE7 3FF Tel: (01733) 245763 Fax: (01733) 240426 E-mail: chemdryki@btconnect.com *Carpet, upholstery, rug cleaning specialists*

Chemence Ltd, 13 Princewood Road, Earlstrees Industrial Estate, Corby, Northamptonshire, NN17 4XD Tel: (01536) 402600 Fax: (01536) 400266 E-mail: sales@chemence.com Principal Export Areas: Worldwide *Adhesives manufrs*

Chemex Environmental International Ltd, Unit J, Broad Lane, Cottenham, Cambridge, CB4 8SW Tel: (01954) 252519 Fax: (01954) 251764 E-mail: analysis@chemex.co.uk *Environmental laboratory, consultancy & eco toxicology*

▶ Chemi Craft, 112 Newhall Street, Willenhall, West Midlands, WV13 1LQ Tel: (01902) 631531

Chemi Supply Cleaning & Hygiene Ltd, Ewell House, Brunel Road, Earlstrees Industrial Estate, Corby, Northamptonshire, NN17 4JW Tel: (01536) 402522 Fax: (01536) 401341 *Janitorial supply services*

Chemical Corporation UK Ltd, Atlas House Unit 9, Bedwas Business Centre, Bedwas, Caerphilly, Mid Glamorgan, CF83 8DU Tel: (029) 2088 0222 Fax: (029) 2088 0676 E-mail: sales@chemicalcorporation.co.uk *Oil suppliers*

Chemical & Industrial Consultants Association, 6 Church Bank, Richmond Rd, Bowdon, Altrincham, Cheshire, WA14 3NW Tel: 0161-928 6681 Fax: 0161-929 8544 *Consulting chemists*

Chemical Innovations Ltd, 217 Walton Summit Road, Walton Summit Centre, Bamber Bridge, Preston, PR5 8AQ Tel: (01772) 322888 Fax: (01772) 315853 E-mail: sales@polycil.co.uk *Polyurethane elastomer manufrs*

▶ Chemical Plant, PO Box 16, Wirral, Merseyside, CH47 3EH Tel: 0151-625 4796 Fax: 0151-625 4805

Chemical Reactor Services, Unit 5 Lyon Road Industrial Estate, Kearsley, Bolton, BL4 8TG Tel: (01204) 862777 Fax: (01204) 577484 *PTFE gaskets glass steel equipment manufrs*

Chemical Recoveries, Rockingham Works Smoke Lane, Bristol, BS11 0YA Tel: 0117-982 0303 Fax: 0117-982 0301E-mail: info@chemrec.co.uk *Solvent recovery services & manufrs*

Chemical Release Co. Ltd, 5 Cheltenham Mount, Harrogate, North Yorkshire, HG1 1DW Tel: (01423) 569715 Fax: (01423) 563384 E-mail: crc@releaseagents.co.uk *Release agent distributors & rubber production industry chemicals*

Chemical Services Boulting Group P.L.C., Presentation House, Atkin Street, Walkden, Manchester, M28 3DG Tel: 0161-703 7434 Fax: 0161-703 7426 E-mail: enquiries@chemserv.co.uk *Pipework erection & installation contractors*

Chemical Solutions, 474 Reigate Road, Epsom, Surrey, KT18 5XA Tel: (01737) 351777 Fax: (01737) 371606 *Analytical & consulting chemists*

Chemigraphic Ltd, 2 Fleming Centre, Fleming Way, Crawley, West Sussex, RH10 9NF Tel: (01293) 543517 Fax: (01293) 552859 E-mail: sales@chemigraphic.co.uk *Electronic contract manufacturing services*

Chemi-Kal Ltd, Powerforce House, Rowland Way, Hoo Farm Industrial Estate, Kidderminster, Worcestershire, DY11 7RA Tel: (01562) 755884 Fax: (01562) 825319 E-mail: chemi-kal@globalnet.co.uk *Industrial chemicals, industrial & automotive lubricants specialists*

Chemineer Ltd, 7 Cranmer Road, West Meadows Industrial Estate, Derby, DE21 6XT Tel: (01332) 363175 Fax: (01332) 290323 E-mail: sales@chemineer.com *Chemical industry mixer manufrs*

Chemipetro Ltd, Plant A Peartree Indust Park, Pear Tree Lane, Dudley, West Midlands, DY2 0UW Tel: (01384) 239441 Fax: (01384) 238430 E-mail: sales@chemipetro.com Principal Export Areas: Worldwide *CNC engineers*

Chemische Fabrik Tubingen UK Ltd, 6 Newby Road Industrial Estate, Levens Road, Hazel Grove, Stockport, Cheshire, SK7 5DA Tel: 0161-456 3355 Fax: 0161-456 4153 E-mail: dbyrne@chtuk.co.uk *Bleaching & dyeing chemical manufrs*

Chemisphere, 3, Trafford Park, Manchester, M17 1RE Tel: 0161-874 7200 Fax: 0161-874 7201 *Detergent manufrs*

▶ Chemist On Call Ltd, 11 Queensway, Hemel Hempstead, Hertfordshire, HP1 1LS Tel: (0871) 2240740 Fax: (020) 8287 8007 E-mail: sales@chemist-on-call.com *A dedicated web database and 24 hour helpline service that enable employers to check their staff are safe to take over the counter and prescribed medication eg when driving, operating machinery or working in a safety critical environment.*

Chemix Ltd, Vauxhall Industrial Estate, Greg Street, Stockport, Cheshire, SK5 7BR Tel: 0161-480 3487 Fax: 0161-480 2394 *Plastic compound manufrs*

Chemodex Chemicals, Canal Road, Worksop, Nottinghamshire, S80 2EH Tel: (01909) 473301 Fax: (01909) 500961 E-mail: sales@chemodex.co.uk *Lubricant distributors*

Chemox Ltd, Sussex House 11 The Pines Trading Estate, Broad Street, Guildford, Surrey, GU3 3BH Tel: (01483) 450660 Fax: (01483) 450770 E-mail: chemox@tbase.co.uk *Chemical importers & distributors*

Chempact (Yorkshire) Ltd, Wayside Units, Darley, Harrogate, North Yorkshire, HG3 2QQ Tel: 01423 780848 *Hygiene product manufrs*

Chempak Products, Unit 40 Hillgrove Business Park, Nazeing Road, Nazeing, Waltham Abbey, Essex, EN9 2BB Tel: (01992) 890770 Fax: (01992) 890660 *Fertiliser production*

Chempix Ltd, Vantage Way, Erdington, Birmingham, B24 9GZ Tel: 0121 380 0100 Fax: 0121 359 3313 E-mail: sales@precisionmicro.com *Photo etching*

Chemquest Ltd, Springfield House, Water Lane, Wilmslow, Cheshire, SK9 5BG Tel: (01625) 528808 Fax: (01625) 527557 E-mail: enquiries@chemquest.co.uk *Chemical suppliers third party procurement healthcare, agriculture*

Chemring Ltd, Alchem Works, Rodney Road, Southsea, Hampshire, PO4 8SX Tel: (023) 9273 5457 Fax: (023) 9281 7509 *Electronic counts manufrs*

Chemsafe Containers Ltd, Higher Merley Lane, Corfe Mullen, Wimborne, Dorset, BH21 3EG Tel: (01202) 881502 Fax: (01202) 841282 E-mail: chemsafe@iswgroup.co.uk *Chemical waste container distribs*

Chemsearch, Landchard House, Victoria Street, West Bromwich, West Midlands, B70 8ER Tel: 0121-525 1666 Fax: 0121-500 5386 E-mail: patrick.toye1@btinternet.com *Hygiene chemical manufrs*

Chemson Ltd, Hayhole Works, Northumberland Dock Road, Wallsend, Tyne & Wear, NE28 0PB Tel: 0191-259 7000 Fax: 0191-259 7001 E-mail: sales@chemson.co.uk *Lead oxide producers or suppliers*

Chemspeed Ltd, Unit 20, Helix Business Park, Camberley, Surrey, GU15 2QT Tel: (01276) 670668 Fax: (01276) 709907 E-mail: chemspeed@chemspeed.com *Make automated machines to do with science*

Chemsquad Ltd, 23 Izons Industrial Estate, Oldbury Road, West Bromwich, West Midlands, B70 9BS Tel: 0121-553 1340 Fax: 0121-525 2077 *Paint stripping, derusting & descaling specialists*

Chemtec UK Ltd, PO Box 3, Beith, Ayrshire, KA15 1JQ Tel: (01505) 502206 Fax: (01505) 502545 E-mail: sales@chemtecuklimted.co.uk Principal Export Areas: Worldwide *Heat exchangers*

Chemtech International Ltd, 448 Basingstoke Road, Reading, RG2 0LP Tel: 0118-986 1222 Fax: 0118-986 0028 E-mail: sales@chemtechinternational.com *Process plant equipment manufrs*

Chemtechno Ltd, 49 Queens Gardens, London, W2 3AA Tel: (020) 7723 2323 Fax: (020) 7724 9297 E-mail: chemtechno@dial.pipex.com *Export & importers*

Chem-Trend (UK) Ltd, Hough Mills, Bradford Road, Halifax, West Yorkshire, HX3 7BN Tel: (0870) 3504708 Fax: (0870) 3509427 E-mail: uksales@chemtrend.com *Release products for rubber mouldings*

Chemtrol Valve Manufacturers, Clerk Green Street, Batley, West Yorkshire, WF17 7SE Tel: (01924) 475481 Fax: (01924) 473579 *Valve reconditioners*

Chemtura Manaufacturing UK Ltd, Tenax Road, Trafford Park, Manchester, M17 1WT Tel: (01407) 830451 Fax: (01407) 830001 E-mail: *Industrial & fine chemical manufrs*

Chemviron Carbon Ltd, 434 London Road, Grays, Essex, RM20 4DH Tel: (01375) 381711 Fax: (01375) 389644 E-mail: info@chemvironcarbon.com *Activated carbon manufrs* Also at: Grays

Chenalord Ltd, Unit 3 Turnoaks Lane, Chesterfield, Derbyshire, S40 2HA Tel: (01246) 211296 Fax: (01246) 277227 E-mail: chenalord@btconnect.com *General & precision engineers*

Cheneler Products Ltd, Bonehill Farm, Bonehill Road, Tamworth, Staffordshire, B78 3HP Tel: (01827) 65740 Fax: (01827) 59755 *Brick cutters*

Chenies Aquatics Ltd, The Van Hage Garden Co, Chenies, Rickmansworth, Hertfordshire, WD3 6EN Tel: (01494) 764549 Fax: (01494) 765783 *Aquatics*

Chenko Kurtev, 21 Hastingwood Court, Pembroke Road, London, E17 9NQ Tel: (07810) 158794 Fax: (020) 8509 2955 E-mail: g_chenks@yahoo.co.uk *We Will Design, Supply & Fit What You Have Dreamt Of! 078 158 794 Experienced in all types of work: Kitchens, Bathrooms and Carpentry Etc. Visit us on www.G-Chenks.co.uk*

Chep, Unit 2,, Weybridge Business Park, Addlestone Road, Addlestone, Surrey, KT15 2UP Tel: (01932) 850085 Fax: (01932) 850144 *Pallet & container hire*

▶ Chep UK Ltd, Dales Industrial Estate, Peterhead, Aberdeenshire, AB42 3JF Tel: (01779) 491007 Fax: (01779) 491008

Chepstow Pharmaceuticals Ltd, Unit 11 Severn Link Distribution Centre, Newhouse Farm Industrial Es, Mathern, Chepstow, Gwent, NP16 6UN Tel: (01291) 624499 Fax: (01291) 624566 *Pharmaceutical distributors*

▶ Chequers Personnel, Wiltshire House, 121 High Street, Marlborough, Wiltshire, SN8 1LZ Tel: (01672) 519194 Fax: 01672 519195 E-mail: info@chequers-personnel.co.uk *Recruitment, Employment, Consultants, Senior Management, Middlemanagement, Sales & Marketing/PR, Engineering, HR, Finance & Accounts, Logistics, Purchasing, IT, Legal, Office Support*

Chequers UK Ltd, 78 Ponders End Industrial Estate, East Duck Lees Lane, Enfield, Middlesex, EN3 7SR Tel: (020) 8805 8855 Fax: (020) 8805 9318 *Instrument & fascia panel manufrs*

Chera Marine, 3 Overmoor Fold, Idle, Bradford, West Yorkshire, BD10 8UT Tel: (07976) 741327 Fax: (01274) 619663 *Marine engine parts*

▶ Cherith Press Ltd, 4 Craggs Industrial Park, Morven Street, Creswell, Worksop, Nottinghamshire, S80 4AJ Tel: (01909) 722411 Fax: (01909) 722811

Cherlyn Electronics Ltd, Brookmount Court, Kirkwood Road, Cambridge, CB4 2QH Tel: (01223) 424169 Fax: (01223) 426543 E-mail: mail@cherlyn.co.uk *Electronic weighing systems distributors*

Cherox Precision Engineering Co., Unit 1A, Pope Iron Road, Barbourne, Worcester, WR1 3HB Tel: (01905) 21425 Fax: (01905) 25921 E-mail: john@cherox.connectfree.co.uk *Subcontract machinists*

Cherrie Adhesive Coatings Ltd, Unit 14 Raikes Clough Industrial, Estate Raikes Lane, Bolton, BL3 1RP Tel: (01204) 371645 Fax: (01204) 371645 *Adhesive application & coating services*

M.A. Cherrington Ltd, Haydown House, Wildhern, Andover, Hampshire, SP11 0JE Tel: (01264) 738224 Fax: (01264) 738382 *Building contractors & developers*

Cherry Creek Gallery, 7 Station Road East, Oxted, Surrey, RH8 0BD Tel: (01883) 734755 Fax: (01883) 734755 *Original & limited edition art sales*

Cherry Fashions, 25 Sanvey Gate, Leicester, LE1 4EP Tel: 0116-262 8420 Fax: 0116-242 5485 *Women clothing & fabric manufrs*

Cherry Hinton Catering Supplies, 8 Home End, Fulbourn, Cambridge, CB21 5BS Tel: (01223) 506005 Fax: (01223) 506386 *Disposable catering supplies*

Cherry Lewis Ltd, Brindley Road, Hinckley, Leicestershire, LE10 3BY Tel: (01455) 610386 Fax: (01455) 631296 E-mail: cherry@cherrylewis.demon.co.uk *Knitwear manufrs*

Cherry Security Co., 53 Cherry Garden Rd, Eastbourne, E. Sussex, BN20 8HG Tel: (01323) 641759 Fax: (01323) 641759 E-mail: andy@cherrysecurity.co.uk *Shutter (rolling) manufrs & repair services*

▶ Cherry & Son Ltd, Crimea Yard, Great Tew, Chipping Norton, Oxfordshire, OX7 4AQ Tel: (01608) 683666 Fax: (01608) 683176

Cherry Tree Machines Ltd, Imperial House, Gorse Street, Blackburn, BB1 3EU Tel: (01254) 671155 Fax: (01254) 671144 E-mail: sales@cherrytreemachines.co.uk *Industrial laundry equipment*

▶ Cherry Tree Pet Crematorium, Cherry Tree Farm, Pot Kiln Road, High Halden, Ashford, Kent, TN26 3HJ Tel: (01233) 850929 Fax: (01233) 850316 E-mail: cherrytree@petcrem.fsnet.co.uk *pet and equine cematorium in kent.*horse cremation*equine cremation*individual cremation*WHEN THE TIME COMES WE CARE.*

Cherry Tree Products Ltd, Barn Meadow House, Barnmeadow Lane, Great Harwood, Blackburn, BB6 7AB Tel: (01254) 882544 Fax: (01254) 882550 *Mop manufrs*

Cherry Valley Farms Ltd, Rothwell, Market Rasen, Lincolnshire, LN7 6BJ Tel: (01472) 371271 Fax: (01472) 362422 E-mail: admin@cherryvalley.co.uk *Duck processing*

Cherry Woodworkers Ltd, Village Road, Denham, Uxbridge, Middlesex, UB9 5BH Tel: (01895) 832056 Fax: (01895) 834219 *Taper fit wood cross grain pellet manufacturers*

Cherrymill Ltd, 23 Hoylake Road, Scunthorpe, South Humberside, DN17 2AZ Tel: (01724) 867244 Fax: (01724) 858509 E-mail: cherrymill.co.uk@amserve.net *Steel fabricators*

▶ Cherrysource Ltd, Unit 14 Rother View, Burwash, East Sussex, TN19 7BN Tel: 07005 805594 Fax: 07005 802296 E-mail: sales@cherrysource.co.uk *Manufacturers of rubber washers, sleeves, bushes and speciality rubber bands.*

Chertsey Marine Ltd, Penton Hook Marina, Mixnams Lane, Chertsey, Surrey, KT16 8QR Tel: (01932) 565195 Fax: (01932) 571668 *Chandlers*

Chertsey Tool Hire Ltd, 149 Upper Weybourne Lane, Farnham, Surrey, GU9 9DD Tel: (01252) 333122 Fax: (01252) 333155 E-mail: farnhamsales@chertseytoolhire.co.uk *Tool hire & sales to trade & diy customers*

▶ Cherwell Logistics Ltd, The Freight Terminal, Bicester Road, Enstone, Chipping Norton, Oxfordshire, OX7 4NP Tel: (01608) 677112 Fax: (01608) 677162 E-mail: info@cherwell-logistics.com

Cherwell Packaging Ltd, Southfield Road, Kineton Road Industrial Estate, Southam, Warwickshire, CV47 0FB Tel: (01926) 817585 Fax: (01926) 817806 E-mail: sparkle@cleaningnet.co.uk *Cleaning materials distributors*

Cherwell Valley Silos Ltd, Twyford, Banbury, Oxfordshire, OX17 3AA Tel: (01295) 811441 Fax: (01295) 811228 E-mail: cvs@cherwellvalleysilos.co.uk *Haulage, storage & animal feed ingredient manufrs*

▶ Chesham Amalgamations & Investments Ltd, 19 Woodsyre, London, SE26 6SS Tel: (0870) 9032748 Fax: (020) 7060 4462 E-mail: confidential@chesham.ltd.uk *Merger brokers*

Chesham Glass Co., 1 Broad Street, Chesham, Buckinghamshire, HP5 3EA Tel: (01494) 792266 Fax: (01494) 782377 *Glass merchants*

Chesham Speciality Ingrediants Ltd, Cunnigham House, Westfield Lane, Kenton, Harrow, Middlesex, HA3 9ED Tel: (020) 8907 7779 Fax: (020) 8927 0686 E-mail: sales@cheshamchemicals.co.uk *Chemical raw materials distributors*

Cheshire Adhesives Tapes & Packaging, New Road, Winsford, Cheshire, CW7 2NU Tel: (01606) 863228 Fax: (01606) 863139 E-mail: bullfinchgroup@freeuk.com *Adhesive tape distributors or agents*

▶ Cheshire Beds & Pine, 86 Wellington Road North, Stockport, Cheshire, SK4 1HW Tel: 0161-477 7712 Fax: 0161-477 7712 *Beds retailers*

Cheshire Bespoke, 1-2 Lancaster Fields, Crewe, CW1 6FF Tel: (01270) 587002 Fax: (01270) 216952 Principal Export Areas: Worldwide *Suits & jackets manufrs*

▶ Cheshire Brickworks, 150 Park Road, Timperley, Altrincham, Cheshire, WA15 6QE Tel: 0161-495 9121 E-mail: cheshire@cheshirebrickworks.co.uk *Bricklayers*

Cheshire Concrete Products Ltd, Road Beata, Middlewich, Cheshire, CW10 0QF Tel: (01606) 837364 Fax: (01606) 837365 E-mail: ccp@cheshireconcrete.co.uk *Concrete products manufrs*

Cheshire Contracts Shopfitting Ltd, Imperial Works, 151 Bennett Street, Manchester, M12 5BH Tel: 0161-273 6253 Fax: 0161-274 3454 E-mail: enquiries@cheshire-contracts.co.uk *Shop & bank fitting specialists*

Cheshire Crane Hire, 12 Nant Road, Connah's Quay, Deeside, Clwyd, CH5 4AL Tel: (01244) 814164 Fax: (01244) 815265 *Crane hire*

Cheshire Curtainsiders, Second Avenue, Crewe, CW1 6BZ Tel: (01270) 766131 Fax: (01270) 255798 *Vehicle trailer repair services*

Cheshire Dairy Products, Congleton Road, Arclid, Sandbach, Cheshire, CW11 2UJ Tel: (01477) 500480 Fax: (01477) 500480 *Dairy products*

Cheshire Demolition & Excavation Contractors Ltd, 72 Moss Lane, Macclesfield, Cheshire, SK11 7TT Tel: (01625) 424433 Fax: (01625) 611094 E-mail: sales@cheshiredemolition.co.uk *Reclaim materials & demolition, Cast iron, Slate and Marble Fireplaces, New and Old York Stone, Slate Paving, Stone and Granite Setts. Roofing Tiles, Ridge and Finial Tiles. Reclaimed Bricks, Beams, Gates, Railway Sleepers. Garden Ornaments.*

Cheshire Drapes Ltd, Chichister Road, Romley, Stockport, Cheshire, SK6 4BL Tel: 0161-430 4110 Fax: 0161-406 6327 *Soft furnishing manufrs*

▶ Cheshire Engraving Services Ltd, Fifth Avenue, Dukinfield, Cheshire, SK16 4PP Tel: 0161-344 5558 Fax: 0161-330 9766 *Anilox rollers manufrs*

Cheshire Fabrications, Villa Farm, Sound Lane, Sound, Nantwich, Cheshire, CW5 8BE Tel: (01270) 780707 Fax: (01270) 780707 *Steel fabrication manufrs*

▶ Cheshire Industrial Doors, 8 Dalton Court, Astmoor Industrial Estate, Runcorn, Cheshire, WA7 1PU Tel: (01928) 500530 Fax: (01928) 500531 E-mail: sales@cheshireindustrialdoors.com *Industrial door manufrs*

▶ Cheshire Interiors, 75 Shepperton Close, Appleton, Warrington, WA4 5JZ Tel: 01925 213339 E-mail: tamara@cheshireinteriors.com *All aspects of commercial and residential inteior design covered. From basic colour advice to full project management.*

▶ Cheshire IT Services, 7 Holmes Chapple Road, Sproston, Crewe, CW4 7LW Tel: (01606) 841577 Fax: (01606) 841577 *Computer maintenance consultancy*

Cheshire Leathers UK Ltd, 3 Cobden Industrial Centre, Quakers Coppice, Crewe, CW1 6FA Tel: (01270) 251556 Fax: (01270) 251557 E-mail: cheshireleather@aol.com *Heavy duty leather manufacturer specialising in leather seals and straps and all industrial leather applications.*

Cheshire Lock & Safe Co., Unit 3 Fence Avenue Industrial Estate, Macclesfield, Cheshire, SK10 1LT Tel: (01625) 614178 Fax: (01625) 617898 E-mail: sales@cheshirelock.co.uk *Locksmiths*

▶ Cheshire Marble Industries Ltd, Unit 6 Atlantic Point, Atlantic St, Broadheath, Altrincham, Cheshire, WA14 5DE Tel: 0161-926 8775 Fax: 0161-926 9381 E-mail: info@chesiremarble.co.uk *Manufacturers & installation of marble*

▶ Cheshire Metalcraft, 17 Atterburys Park Estate, Attenburys Lane, Timperley, Altrincham, Cheshire, WA14 5QE Tel: 0161-962 3838 Fax: 0161-962 3838 *Wrought ironworkers*

Cheshire Packaging Ltd, Unit B2 Talbot Road, Newton Business Park, Hyde, Cheshire, SK14 4UQ Tel: 0161-367 8331 Fax: 0161-367 8417 *Print finishers & carton manufacturers*

▶ Cheshire Pine Co., Sealand Farm, Sealand Road, Sealand, Chester, CH1 6BS Tel: (01244) 881320 Fax: (01244) 881322 *Furniture*

▶ Cheshire Plastics, 1d Wellington Street, Clayton le Moors, Accrington, Lancashire, BB5 5HU Tel: (01254) 384222 Fax: (01254) 382555 E-mail: geoff@cheshireplastics.co.uk *Compression moulding*

Cheshire Polythene Film Co. Ltd, 3 Lawnhurst Trading Estate, Ashurst Drive, Stockport, Cheshire, SK3 0SD Tel: 0161-428 4251 Fax: 0161-428 8329 E-mail: trevor@polythene-films.com *Polythene film manufrs*

Cheshire Portable Buildings, 214c Manchester Road, Altrincham, Cheshire, WA14 5LU Tel: 0161-941 6631 Fax: 0161-927 7693 E-mail: sales@cheshireportablebuildings.co.uk *For 50 years, Compton has built an enviable reputation with thousands of customers for manufacturing top quality concrete garages and sectional buildings at outstanding value for money prices. Our vast product range includes:- Banbury Concrete Garages Apex Spar Concrete Garages Flat Spar Concrete Garages Apex Brick Concrete Garages Apex Rockstone Concrete Garages Timber Garages Motorcycle Concrete Garages Concrete Sheds Concrete Workshops & Buildings Compton's ranges of both domestic and commercial Concrete Buildings include:- Extra High Concrete Garages (Suitable for Minibuses, Vans and other High Vehicles etc) Secure Stores Battery Garages Clubhouses Bin Stores Semi Industrial Buildings Workshop & Offices*

Cheshire Pressings, Road Five, Winsford, Cheshire, CW7 3QX Tel: (01606) 863557 Fax: (01606) 869483 *Pressing & manufacturers & welding fabricators*

Cheshire Refrigeration Ltd, Unit E6, Ford Street, Chestergate, Stockport, Cheshire, SK3 0BT Tel: 0161-480 4084 Fax: 0161-480 7355 E-mail: cheshire.refrig@cwcom.net *Refrigeration engineers*

Cheshire Ribbon Manufacturing Co., Kingston Mills, Manchester Road, Hyde, Cheshire, SK14 2BZ Tel: 0161-368 2048 Fax: 0161-367 8193 E-mail: sales@cheshirerib.co.uk *Thermal insulating material manufrs*

▶ Cheshire Roofix, 6 St. Augustines Road, Stockport, Cheshire, SK3 0JN Tel: (01614) 771449 Fax: (01614) 771449 E-mail: john.h.carroll@btinternet.com *all roofing work undertaker, professional service at competitive prices*

Cheshire Scaffolds Ltd, Haigh Avenue, Whitehall Trading Estate, Stockport, Cheshire, SK4 1NU Tel: 0161-476 2223 Fax: 0161-476 2227

▶ Cheshire Spas & Pools, Buildwas Road, Clayhill Light Industrial Park, Neston, CH64 3RU Tel: 0151-336 3417 Fax: 0151-336 8671

Cheshire Specialist Engineering, L & M Business Park, Norman Road, Altrincham, Cheshire, WA14 4ES Tel: 0161-928 6138 Fax: 0161-928 6139 E-mail: sales@cseng.co.uk *Precision engineers*

Cheshire Textiles Ltd, 11 Ruskin Way, Knutsford, Cheshire, WA16 6TJ Tel: (01565) 633535 Fax: (01565) 653152 E-mail: cheshiretex@aol.com *Yarn merchants*

Cheshire Training Centre, 41 Hightown, Crewe, CW1 3BZ Tel: 01270 500886 Fax: 01270 582 036 *Computer training*

Cheshire Vehicle Windows Ltd, Unit 3 Phoenix Centre, Road One Winsford Indust Estate, Winsford Industrial Estate, Winsford, Cheshire, CW7 3PZ Tel: (01606) 557114 Fax: (01606) 861250 E-mail: cvwindows@ukonline.co.uk *Commercial window manufrs*

Cheshire Water Life, Blakemere Craft Centre, Chester Road, Sandiway, Northwich, Cheshire, CW8 2EB Tel: (01606) 882223 Fax: (01606) 889964 E-mail: sales@cheshire-waterlife.co.uk *Aquatic & falconry centre*

▶ Cheshires Jewellers, 95 Spencer Street, Birmingham, B18 6DA Tel: 0121 5231124 Fax: 0121 523 1222 E-mail: info@cheshiresjewellers.co.uk *Jewellery - diamond and gemstone rings bracelets and pendants all fine handcrafted certified jewellery. Buy online or visit our shops. Commissions also undertaken.*

Cheshires Of Nottingham, Concorde House, Dabell Avenue, Nottingham, NG6 8WA Tel: 0115-977 0278 Fax: 0115-979 4085 E-mail: cheshires@mcd.co.uk *Floor distributors*

Chesim Engineering Ltd, 7 Brunel Way, Fareham, Hampshire, PO15 5TX Tel: (01489) 885994 Fax: (01489) 885931 E-mail: sales@chesim.co.uk *Design & development engineers*

Chess Logistics Technology, Commerce Way, Trafford Park, Manchester, M17 1HW Tel: 0161-888 2580 Fax: 0161-888 2590 E-mail: info@chess.uk.com *Warehouse management software*

Chess Plastics Ltd, 2 George Baylis Road, Berry Hill Industrial Estate, Droitwich, Worcestershire, WR9 9RB Tel: (01905) 794405 Fax: (01905) 794495 E-mail: genmail@chessplastics.co.uk *Plastics injection moulders*

Chesser Engineering Ltd, 6-8 West Gorgie Parks, Edinburgh, EH14 1UT Tel: 0131-443 4943 Fax: 0131-443 4943 E-mail: enquiries@chesserengineering.ltd.uk *Precision engineers*

Chessington Tyres Ltd, Unit 19 Beeching Park Industrial Services, Wainwright Road, Bexhill-on-Sea, East Sussex, TN39 3UR Tel: (01424) 223365 *Tyre & exhaust retailers*

Chessington Tyres Ltd, 95 Norman Road, St. Leonards-on-Sea, East Sussex, TN38 0EG Tel: (01424) 437415 *Tyre distributors* Also at: Branches throughout the U.K.

▶ Chester Cash Registers, Unit 6 Eastwood Court, Manor Lane, Hawarden, Deeside, Clwyd, CH5 3QB Tel: (01244) 528999 Fax: (01244) 528998 E-mail: cashregisters@fsbdial.co.uk *Cash register sales*

Chester Chain Company Ltd, Broughton Mills Road, Bretton, Chester, CH4 0BY Tel: (01244) 663580 Fax: (01244) 663587 E-mail: admin@chesterchain.co.uk *Lifting gear hire*

Chester Chain Co. Ltd, 19 Greys Court, Kingsland Grange, Woolston, Warrington, WA1 4SH Tel: (01925) 838899 Fax: (01925) 811416 E-mail: warrington@chesterchain.co.uk *Lifting equipment manufacturers & distributors*

Chester Chronicle, Chronicle House, Commonhall Street, Chester, CH1 2AA Tel: (0870) 7021234 *Regional newspapers publishers*

Chester Jefferies Ltd, Buckingham Road, Gillingham, Dorset, SP8 4QE Tel: (01747) 822629 Fax: (01747) 824092 E-mail: enquiries@chesterjefferies.co.uk *Glove manufrs*

▶ Chester Security Systems, 32 Church Road, Saughall, Chester, CH1 6EN Tel: (01244) 881399 Fax: (01244) 880935 E-mail: info@chestersecurity.co.uk

Chesterfield Auto Electrical Ltd, Storforth La Trading Estate, Hasland, Chesterfield, Derbyshire, S41 0QL Tel: (01246) 554404 Fax: (01246) 554404 E-mail: sales@cae-auto-electrical.co.uk *Auto electrical suppliers*

Chesterfield Crane Co., Whittington House, South St North, New Whittington, Chesterfield, Derbyshire, S43 2BP Tel: (01246) 454521 Fax: (01246) 260815 *Electrical engineers*

▶ Chesterfield Electric Motors, South St North, New Whittington, Chesterfield, Derbyshire, S43 2BP Tel: (01246) 456778 Fax: (01246) 456252

▶ Chesterfield Equipment Sales, Lancaster House Common Bank Industrial Estate, Ackhurst Road, Chorley, Lancashire, PR7 1NH Tel: (01257) 266656 *Equipment rental for the construction industry*

Chesterfield Plastics, 61 Foljambe Avenue, Chesterfield, Derbyshire, S40 3EY Tel: (01246) 540670 Fax: (01246) 540106 E-mail: clive.cooper1@virgin.net *Plastic materials distributors*

Chesterman Marketing Ltd, 3 Kenworthy Road, Stafford, ST16 3DY Tel: (01785) 250341 Fax: (01785) 250345 E-mail: enquiries@chestermanmarketing.com *Tool distributors*

▶ Chesterman & Matthews, 28a Old Parish Lane, Weymouth, Dorset, DT4 0HY Tel: (01305) 781939 Fax: (01305) 781939

▶ Chestminster Ltd, Bridgefields, Welwyn Garden City, Hertfordshire, AL7 1RX Tel: (01707) 391390 Fax: (01707) 391394

▶ Chestnut Horse Feeds, Newnham Fields Farm, Willey, Rugby, Warwickshire, CV23 0SL Tel: (01455) 558808 Fax: (01455) 559401 E-mail: sales@anifeed.co.uk *Horse feed services*

Chestnut Products Ltd, Unit 15 Gaza Trading Estate, Scabharbour Road, Hildenborough, Tonbridge, Kent, TN11 8PL Tel: (01732) 463777 Fax: (01732) 454636 E-mail: sales@chestnutproducts.fsnet.co.uk *Fencing contractors*

Cheswell Engineering Ltd, Waldeck House, Waldeck Road, Maidenhead, Berkshire, SL6 8BR Tel: (01628) 624726 Fax: (01628) 773907 *Tool & press tool manufrs*

Chettle Timber Impregnation Co., Chettle House, Chettle, Blandford Forum, Dorset, DT11 8DB Tel: (01258) 830380 Fax: (01258) 830380 *Fencing stakes manufr*

Chettleburgh International Ltd, Temple House, 20 Holywell Row, London, EC2A 4XH Tel: (020) 7377 0381 Fax: (020) 7377 0381 E-mail: info@chettleburghs.co.uk *Company registration agents*

▶ Chetwynd Computers, 38 Chetwynd Road, Edgmond, Newport, Shropshire, TF10 8HL Tel: (01952) 811402 Fax: (01952) 811402 E-mail: info@chetwyndcomputers.co.uk *Computer repairers*

Chevin Computer Systems Ltd, East Mill, Bridge Foot, Belper, Derbyshire, DE56 2UA Tel: (01773) 821992 Fax: (01773) 829910 E-mail: sales@chevincomputers.com *Fleet management software suppliers*

Chevin Computer Systems Ltd, East Mill, Bridge Foot, Belper, Derbyshire, DE56 2UA Tel: (01773) 821992 Fax: (01773) 829910 E-mail: sales@chevincomputers.com *Computer hardware & consumables distributors*

Cheviot Farmers Trading Co. Ltd, Greensfield Park, Willowburn Avenue, Alnwick, Northumberland, NE66 2DD Tel: (01665) 603117 Fax: (01665) 603119 *Agricultural merchants*

▶ Cheviot Trees Ltd, Newton Brae, Berwick-upon-Tweed, TD15 1UL Tel: (01289) 386755 Fax: (01289) 386750 E-mail: katherine@cheviot-trees.co.uk *Growers & suppliers of cell grown trees & shrubs for forestry*

▶ Chevler Packaging Ltd, Tir Y Berth Industrial Estate, Hengoed, Mid Glamorgan, CF82 8AU Tel: (01443) 865900 *Paperboard or cardboard manufrs*

Chevron Associates Ltd, P O Box 3092, Milton Keynes, MK17 9AN Tel: 01525 290600 Fax: 01525 290600 *Uniform manufrs*

Chevron Lifts Ltd, The I O Centre, Barn Way, Lodge Farm Industrial Estate, Northampton, NN5 7UW Tel: (01604) 750080 Fax: (01604) 750081 E-mail: email@chevron-lift.com *Lift service & installation services*

▶ Chevron London Ltd, 9b High Road, Seddington, Sandy, Bedfordshire, SG19 1NU Tel: (01767) 699011 Fax: (01767) 699012 E-mail: sales@chevrontraffic.co.uk

Chevron Oronite Sa, St. Marks House, St. Marks Road, Windsor, Berkshire, SL4 3BD Tel: (01753) 844301 Fax: (01753) 844300 *Chemical manufrs*

Chevron Technical Services Ltd, Beta Court, 2 Harper Road, Sharston Industrial Area, Manchester, M22 4QE Tel: 0161-902 9029 Fax: 0161-945 0945 E-mail: info@chevrontechnicalservices.com *Recruitment consultants services*

Chevron & Texaco Ltd, 1 Westferry Circus, Canary Wharf, London, E14 4HA Tel: (020) 7719 3000 Fax: E-mail: *Natural gasses, lubricating oil producers, oil & gas explorers*

▶ Chevrontexaco Europe, Seafield House, Hill of Rubislaw, Aberdeen, AB15 6XL Tel: (01224) 334000

Chew Valley Hire Ltd, Woodwick Farm, Bristol Road, Compton Martin, Bristol, BS40 6NQ Tel: (01761) 221105 Fax: (01761) 221121 E-mail: hans@cvhire.force9.co.uk *Portaloo hire*

▶ Chi Storm Ltd, 76 Broadway Plaza, 19 Francis Road, Birmingham, B16 8SU Tel: (07795) 467314 E-mail: enquiries@chistorm.com *Website design*

▶ Chic Costume Jewellery, 27 Lawrence Avenue, Letchworth Garden City, Hertfordshire, SG6 2EY Tel: (01462) 678288 E-mail: sales@chic-costume-jewellery.co.uk *Affordable up to date fashionable jewellery & accessories manufrs*

Chicago Clothing Co., 77 London Street, Leicester, LE5 3RW Tel: 0116-276 4004 Fax: 0116-276 4004 *Clothes manufrs*

Chicago Coating Co., Manchester Road, Mossley, Ashton-under-Lyne, Lancashire, OL5 9QA Tel: (01457) 832046 Fax: (01457) 838697 *Powder coaters & shot blasters*

Chicago Mercantile Exchange Inc, Mark Douglas Blundell, Chicago Mercantile Exchange Inc., London, EC3R 8HN Tel: (020) 7623 2550 Fax: (020) 7623 2565 E-mail: cme@cmeurope.co.uk *Futures & options exchange services*

Chichester Armoury, 43 West Street, Chichester, West Sussex, PO19 1RP Tel: (01243) 774687 Fax: (01243) 778865 *Gun shop retailers*

▶ Chichester Canal Trading Ltd, Canal Society HQ, Canal Basin Canal Wharf, Chichester, West Sussex, PO19 8DT Tel: (01243) 576701 Fax: (01243) 671051 E-mail: jco37ja@aol.com

Chichester Canvas, Chichester Road, Sidlesham Common, Chichester, West Sussex, PO20 7PY Tel: (01243) 641164 Fax: (01243) 641888 E-mail: sales@chicanvas.co.uk *Based in West Sussex, Chichester Canvas are a leading supplier of inspirational marquees and framed structures to the South. The company specialises in dealing with marquees for events, corporate hospitality, wedding receptions and outdoor parties. It has been long established for over 60 years and provides expert knowledge in the field as well as excellent customer service.*

Chichester Caravans, Worcester Road, Upton Warren, Bromsgrove, Worcestershire, B61 7EX Tel: (01527) 831515 Fax: (01527) 870315 E-mail: chichester123@yahoo.co.uk *Caravan retailers* Also at: Branches throughout the U.K.

Chichester Caravans, Main Road, Nutbourne, Chichester, West Sussex, PO18 8RL Tel: (01243) 377441 Fax: (01243) 377442 *Caravan distributors* Also at: Birmingham, Stourport-on-Severn & Uckfield

Chichester Joinery Ltd, Unit 12 Quarry Lane Industrial Estate, Gravel Lane, Chichester, West Sussex, PO19 8PQ Tel: (01243) 784723 Fax: (01243) 533382 E-mail: michaelcarter3@btconnect.com *Joinery manufacturers/contractors/suppliers*

Chichester Paper Bag Co., 5 St. James Industrial Estate, Westhampnett Road, Chichester, West Sussex, PO19 7JU Tel: (01243) 773742 Fax: (01243) 538898 E-mail: martin@chipack.co.uk *Paper bag wholesalers*

Chi-Chi Style, The Old Schoolhouse, Church Street, Netherseal, Swadlincote, Derbyshire, DE12 8DF Tel: (01283) 763604 E-mail: sales@chi-chi-style.com *Sale of exclusive jewellery, handbags & accessories*

Chick Master UK Ltd, Unit 2 Express Park, Bristol Road, Bridgwater, Somerset, TA6 4RN Tel: (01278) 411000 Fax: (01278) 451213 E-mail: sales@chickmaster.com *Poultry incubator manufrs*

Chick Plastics Ltd, 42 Kenilworth Drive, Oadby, Leicester, LE2 5LG Tel: 0116-271 3377 *General plastic injection moulders*

Chicken Joes, Empire Industrial Estate, Brickyard Road, Aldridge, Walsall, WS9 8UR Tel: (0870) 0601240 E-mail: mail@chickenjoes.net *Chicken kebab manufrs*

Chidlow & Cheshire Ltd, Steward Street, Birmingham, B18 7AE Tel: 0121-454 1003 Fax: 0121-456 3935 *Battery clips & booster cables manufrs*

Chidlow Decorators, Unit 33 Business Resource Centre, Admin Road, Knowsley Industrial Park, Liverpool, L33 7TX Tel: 0151-546 7754 Fax: 0151-546 7754 E-mail: admin@chidlowdecorators.co.uk *It is our policy to give to you the highest level of customer service that you have come to expect from a long established Painting and Decorating Contractor. We will provide a full Painting and Decorating Service to any potential customer of ours, across Liverpool, Manchester, Merseyside, North West England, North Wales and further afield (UK). If you are looking for a professional Painting and Decorating Contractor, which prides itself in the quality of service and value for money it constantly gives to its customers, then please spend a little time in browsing our site. If*

continued

you require any further information from us or you would like a quotation for any Painting and Decorating Work, then please do not hesitate to Contact Us.

Chieftain Contracts Ltd, 33 Broomhill Road, Bonnybridge, Stirlingshire, FK4 2AL Tel: (01324) 812911 Fax: (01324) 814927 *Steel fabricators*

▶ Chiene & Taite CA, 61 Dublin Street, Edinburgh, EH3 6NL Tel: 0131-558 5800 Fax: 0131-558 5899

Chiffon Engineering Services Ltd, 11 Almond Rd, Bermondsey, London, SE16 3LR Tel: (020) 7231 8831 Fax: (020) 7231 1997 *Metal fabricators*

Chilburne Spring Ltd, Acre House, Kilburn, York, YO61 4AL Tel: (01347) 868181 Fax: (01347) 868151 *Water coolers services*

Child Rewinds, Fairfield Road, Downham Market, Norfolk, PE38 9ET Tel: (01366) 382946 Fax: (01366) 383299 *Electric motor repairs & rewinds*

Childrens Bed Centres, Unit 3, Saltney Business Centre, High Street, Saltney, Chester, CH4 8SE Tel: (08448) 007772 Fax: (01244) 675637 E-mail: enquiries@childrensbedcentres.co.uk *Childrens Bed Centres is a dedicated family run business based in the UK, with over 25 years experience in bedroom furniture manufacture. *Their new e-commerce website launched in autumn 2008 offers not only kids furniture, but also children's bedding and bedroom accessories that have been carefully sourced from respectable suppliers. **CBC's furniture range is practical and durable, yet fun and includes; children's storage beds, bunk beds, tent beds, four-poster beds, sleepover beds and study units, as well as wardrobes, chests of drawers, bedside cabinets, toy boxes, desks, shelves and more. The majority of CBC beds come with storage and are available in a choice of two widths, three lengths and six colours; natural ash, blue, pink, red, yellow and white. **Delivery is available throughout mainland UK, please see their website for details. Beds are assembled in your home by their trained staff free of charge. **

Childrens Entertainment Service, Brookview, Knights Road, Oxford, OX4 6DQ Tel: (01865) 775906 Fax: 01865775906 *Entertainment karaoke discos*

▶ The Children's Playground Co. Ltd, 1 George Street, Wolverhampton, WV2 4DG Tel: (01902) 422515 Fax: (028) 9032 7614 E-mail: sales@thechildrensplayground.com *Supplier of creative play-equipment & safety surface*

Chilfen Joinery Ltd, 1 Flint Road, Letchworth Garden City, Hertfordshire, SG6 1HJ Tel: (01462) 705390 Fax: (01462) 674327 E-mail: michelled@chilfen.co.uk *Joinery contractors, suppliers & manufrs*

Chilham Darts, Station Approach, Chilham, Canterbury, Kent, CT4 8EG Tel: (01227) 730310 Fax: (01227) 730630 *Gun cover & bag manufrs*

Chill Factor, 71 Ellenborough Cl, Bishop's Stortford, Herts, CM23 4HT Tel: (01279) 506543 Fax: (01279) 506543 *Air conditioning service*

Chill The World Ltd, Myler Court, 156-158 Marsh Road, Leagrave, Luton, LU3 2QL Tel: (01582) 593377 Fax: (01322) 436238 E-mail: sales@chilloutaircon.com *Air conditioning engineers & installers*

Chillaire Ltd, Unit 1, Veasey Close, Attleborough Fields Industrial Estate, Nuneaton, Warwickshire, CV11 6RT Tel: (024) 7632 0300 Fax: (024) 7632 0400 E-mail: g.fowler@chillaire.co.uk *Chillaire Ltd offer commercial air conditioning repairs, air conditioning servicing, air conditioning maintenance and air con installations locally in Leicester, Coventry and Nuneaton and nationwide throughout the UK. We provide commercial air conditioning air con installations to shops, offices and other public buildings. We also provide dedicated Air conditioning repairs with our 24hr emergency call out service for our customers. Find out more about air conditioning or please contact us for more air con information.*

Chillaire-Isis, 4b Black Bourton Road, Carterton, Oxfordshire, OX18 3EZ Tel: (01993) 841527 Fax: (01993) 841846 E-mail: sales@chillaire-isis.co.uk *Refrigeration & air conditioning contractors*

Chiller Box Ltd, Unit 6, Carbery Enterprise Park, 36 White Hart Lane, Tottenham, London, N17 8DP Tel: (0800) 8491188 E-mail: mail@chillerbox.com *As one of the UK's leading equipment specialists for the hospitality, restaurant and catering industry, we have a proven reputation for successfully delivering our products and services. We provide an extensive range of quality equipment from all leading brands offering a convenient one stop shop for new openings, refurbishments and established businesses Our comprehensive kitchen planning & design service allows us to work closely with executive chefs, architects, management and new business owners, to create the best solution for any kitchen and budget. We can offer expert advice and full project management as well as sales & installation, service, repair and spares*

Chiller Rental Services, Wigan Road, Leyland, PR25 5XW Tel: (01772) 643040 Fax: (01772) 643041 E-mail: info@chiller-rental.com *Industrial air conditioning suppliers & heating*

▶ CHILLFREEZE DIRECT LTD, UNIT 6C BASSET COURT, LOAKE CLOSE, GRANGE PARK, NORTHAMPTON, NN4 5EZ Tel: 0870 2407998 Fax: 0870 7202733 E-mail: enquires@chillfreezedirect.co.uk *Temperature Controlled Couriers Services. 24/7, 365 days a year. Chilled/Frozen/Ambient. Uk and European Collections & Deliveries carried out SameDay /NextDay you decide.*

Chilli Group, Station Road Industrial Estate, Mauchline, Ayrshire, KA5 5EU Tel: (01290) 550362 Fax: (01290) 552677 E-mail: mail@chilliref.co.uk *Air conditioning & refrigeration contractors*

▶ Chilli Sound, 8 Albert Road, Finsbury Park, London, N4 3RW Tel: (07973) 500651 Fax: (01273) 679416 E-mail: info@chillisound.co.uk *Sound system hire, design & installation services*

Chillington Wolverhampton Ltd, Chillington Fields, Wolverhampton, WV1 2BY Tel: (01902) 451326 Fax: (01902) 452010 *Furniture manufrs*

Chilstone, Fordcombe Road, Fordcombe, Tunbridge Wells, Kent, TN3 0RD Tel: (01892) 740866 Fax: (01892) 740249 E-mail: office@chilstone.com *Stone producers, processors, merchants & suppliers*

Chiltern Agricultural Services, Blackhorse, Checkendon, Reading, RG8 0TE Tel: (01491) 682456 *Agricultural engineers*

Chiltern Air Services, 6 Pleckspool Cottage, Henton, Chinnor, Oxfordshire, OX39 4AE Tel: (01844) 351486 Fax: (01844) 351486 *Air compressor maintenance & distributors*

Chiltern Airfreight, Poyle Road, Colnbrook, Slough, SL3 0AY Tel: (01753) 680845 Fax: (01753) 681094 *Chiltern Air Freight Ltd undertake freight forwarding, logistics, shipping, air cargo transport, sea freight, road haulage, charter flights, aog, excess baggage and project cargo services to most global locations specialising in freight forwarding to Nigeria, China, Australia, Canada and the USA.*

Chiltern Batteries, 44 Camford Way, Luton, LU3 3AN Tel: (01582) 585231 Fax: (01582) 491964 *Battery sales*

Chiltern Cam Service Ltd, Unit 2a Watlington Industrial Estate, Cuxham Road, Watlington, Oxfordshire, OX49 5LU Tel: (01491) 614422 Fax: (01491) 613813 E-mail: enquiries@chilterncam.com *Machinery re-conditioning manufrs*

Chiltern Cargo Services Ltd, Willen Works, Willen Road, Newport Pagnell, Bucks, MK16 0DG Tel: (01908) 611222 Fax: (01908) 612221 E-mail: admin@chiltern.cargo.co.uk *International freight forwarders*

Chiltern Circuits Ltd, 51 Poppy Road, Princes Risborough, Buckinghamshire, HP27 9DB Tel: (01844) 343437 Fax: (01844) 347102 E-mail: chiltnccts@aol.com *Printed circuit board manufacturers*

▶ Chiltern Coffee, 18 Shenley Hill Road, Leighton Buzzard, Bedfordshire, LU7 3BT Tel: (01525) 853691 Fax: (01525) 853691 E-mail: info@chilterncoffee.co.uk *Suppliers of coffee and coffee machines and dispensers for loan, rent, lease or sale, filter coffee, coffee beans, tea, chocolate, water dispensers*

Chiltern Colour Services, Unit 23 Titan Court, Laporte Way, Luton, LU4 8EF Tel: (01525) 385184 Fax: (01582) 482888 *Printing industry suppliers*

Chiltern Concrete & Stone Ltd, Faldo Road, Barton-le-Clay, Bedford, MK45 4RF Tel: (01582) 881414 Fax: (01582) 881855 E-mail: info@chilternprecast.co.uk *Concrete product manufrs*

Chiltern Connections Ltd, 2 Hithercroft Court, Lupton Road, Wallingford, Oxfordshire, OX10 9BT Tel: (01491) 824788 Fax: (01491) 824799 E-mail: sales@chilternconnections.co.uk *PCB contract services*

Chiltern Electrical Services, 1 Shenstone Drive, Burnham, Slough, SL1 7HJ Tel: (01628) 665090 Fax: (01628) 665090 E-mail: miketerry@chilelecserv.freeserve.co.uk *Welding consultants, welding equipment services & welding supplies*

Chiltern Foil Printing Co., 6 Acorn Business Centre, Cublington Road, Wing, Leighton Buzzard, Bedfordshire, LU7 0LB Tel: (01296) 682299 Fax: (01296) 682299 E-mail: plucas@fsbdial.co.uk *Foil blocking & blind embossing services*

▶ Chiltern Games & Puzzles, PO Box 5, Llanfyllin, Powys, SY22 5WD Tel: (01691) 648864 *Producers & retailers of handcrafted wooden games & puzzles*

▶ Chiltern Handiman Services, Forest Lodge, Christmas Common, Watlington, Oxfordshire, OX49 5HN Tel: (01491) 613074 E-mail: enquiries@chilternhandiman.co.uk *Property maintenance*

▶ Chiltern Handyman Service, 123 Waterside,, Chesham, Buckinghamshire, HP5 1PE Tel: 07958 967549 E-mail: mike@chilternhandyman.com *Professional handyman service*

Chiltern Hills Watercoolers Ltd, Toms Hill, Aldbury, Tring, Hertfordshire, HP23 5SD Tel: (0870) 1678899 Fax: (01442) 851538 *Mineral water manufrs*

▶ Chiltern Invadex Ltd, Unit A2 Acorn Industrial Park, Crayford Road, Dartford, DA1 4AL Tel: (01322) 524358 Fax: (01322) 554252

Chiltern Labels, Bassetsbury Lane, High Wycombe, Buckinghamshire, HP11 1HT Tel: (0845) 2239450 Fax: (0845) 2239460 *Self-adhesive label printers & manufrs*

▶ The Chiltern Lift Company Ltd, 8 Furlong Road, Bourne End, Buckinghamshire, SL8 5DG Tel: (01628) 529247 Fax: (01628) 810821

Chiltern Mills, Enterprise House, Belle Isle Road, Leeds, LS10 2DG Tel: 0113-277 6226 Fax: 0113-277 6220 *Soft furnishings*

Chiltern Plastics Ltd, Unit 31, Jubilee Trade Centre, Jubilee Road, Letchworth Garden City, Hertfordshire, SG6 1SP Tel: (01462) 676262 Fax: (01462) 481075 E-mail: carrol@chilternplastics.co.uk *Manufacturers of drum liner (circular base); polyethylene/polythene bag/carrier/sack.*

Chiltern Seeds, Bortree Stile, Ulverston, Cumbria, LA12 7PB Tel: (01229) 581137 Fax: (01229) 584549 E-mail: info@chilternseeds.co.uk *Small retail packets of fresh horticultural seeds, mail-order & online*

▶ Chiltern Shed Co, Unit 9b Chiltern Trading Estate, Earl Howe Road, Holmer Green, High Wycombe, Buckinghamshire, HP15 6QT Tel: (01494) 712230 Fax: (01494) 712230

Chiltern Telecom, 61 Union Street, Dunstable, Bedfordshire, LU6 1EX Tel: (01582) 604040 Fax: (0871) 2230230 E-mail: sales@chilterntelecom.co.uk *Telephone systems sales & installation*

Chiltern Thrust Bore Ltd, Unit 1 The Barn, Firs Farm, Stagsden, West End, Bedford, MK43 8TB Tel: (01234) 825948 Fax: (01234) 824147 E-mail: chiltern@onweb.co.uk *Trenchless specialist using Horizontal Directional Drilling,*

continued

Guided Auger boring, Pipe Ramming, Bursting, Impact Moling, Rock Drilling. Installing Products such as, clay, mdpe, hdpe, steel, grp pipes.

Chiltern Transmission, 11 Britannia Industrial Park, Dashwood Avenue, High Wycombe, Buckinghamshire, HP12 3ES Tel: (01494) 534806 *Reconditioned gear boxes repair & services*

Chiltern UK Ltd, 64 Waterloo Road, Manchester, M8 8GJ Tel: 0161-832 3206 Fax: 0161-832 7844 *Luggage, handbags & small leather goods*

Chiltern Water Management Services, 1 Inkerman Drive, Hazlemere, High Wycombe, Buckinghamshire, HP15 7JJ Tel: (01494) 712831 Fax: (01494) 712831 E-mail: rh@chilternwater.co.uk *Water sampling & analysis services*

Chilton Joinery Ltd, 3 Chilton Industrial Estate, Martins Road, Sudbury, Suffolk, CO10 2FT Tel: (01787) 378667 Fax: (01787) 880632 E-mail: lee@chiltonjoinery.co.uk *Joiners*

Chilworth Communications, 106 Star Street, London, W2 1QF Tel: (020) 7706 1014 Fax: (020) 7258 3852 E-mail: enquiries@chilworthcommunications.com *Direct marketing & advertising agency*

Chilworth Manor Ltd, Chilworth Manor, Chilworth, Southampton, SO16 7PT Tel: (023) 8076 7333 Fax: (023) 8070 1743 E-mail: general@chilworth-manor.co.uk *Conference centre & hotel*

Chilworth Technology Ltd, Beta House Enterprise Road, Chilworth Science Park, Chilworth, Southampton, SO16 7NS Tel: (023) 8076 0722 Fax: (023) 8076 7866 E-mail: info@chilworth.co.uk *Experts in process safety*

Chimera C M T Ltd, 9 Blenheim Court, Lustleigh Close, Marsh Barton Industrial Estate, Exeter, EX2 8PW Tel: (01392) 667444 Fax: (01392) 667440 *Computer solutions provider*

▶ Chimney Co., 39 Crescent Road, Warley, Brentwood, Essex, CM14 5JR Tel: (0800) 7319570 Fax: (01277) 204322

Chimo Holdings, White Rose Works, 61 Eyre Lane, Sheffield, S1 3GF Tel: 0114-272 4656 Fax: 0114-249 0922 E-mail: sales@chimoholdings.co.uk *Advertising business gift manufrs*

Chimo Holdings, White Rose Works, 61 Eyre Lane, Sheffield, S1 3GF Tel: 0114-272 4656 Fax: 0114-249 0922 E-mail: sales@chimoholdings.co.uk *Cutlers & silversmiths*

▶ China Bandwagon, Invest House, Bruce Road, Fforestfach Industrial Estate, Swansea, SA5 4HS Tel: (01792) 412882 Fax: (01792) 587046 E-mail: import@chinabandwagon.com *Sourcing products from China*

China Industrial Materials Ltd, Unit 29 Phoenix International Industrial Estate, Charles Street, West Bromwich, West Midlands, B70 0AY Tel: 0121-520 3050 Fax: 0121-601 8039 E-mail: marketing@cimukltd.com *Industrial material importers & exporters*

▶ China Interface, 39 Middlepark Drive, Northfield, Birmingham, B31 2FL Tel: 0121-476 0845 Fax: (0845) 2803140 E-mail: info@china-interface.co.uk *Specialise in chinese translation*

China Millers Ltd, 409 King Street, Stoke-on-Trent, ST4 3EF Tel: (01782) 313291 Fax: (01782) 599494 *Waterground calcined bone & stone*

▶ China Project Management Ltd, 1 Lady Place, Livingston, West Lothian, EH54 6TB Tel: (01506) 411866 E-mail: info@chinapro.co.uk *Specialising in Engineered Products, ChinaPro provides an outsourcing service for companies who are looking for a competitive edge and improved margins.*

China Repairers, King Street Mews, London, N2 8DY Tel: (020) 8444 3030 E-mail: enquiries@chinarepairers.co.uk *China repairers*

▶ China Company Research Services Ltd, Catherinefield House, Catherinefield Business Park, Dumfries, DG1 3PQ Tel: (01387) 247588 Fax: (01387) 257143 E-mail: info@ccrs.info *Provides detailed information on private and listed Chinese and Asian companies using local research and Western analysis.*

China Trade Direct Ltd, 26b Sydney Road, Cradley Heath, West Midlands, B64 5BA Tel: (07909) 662093 Fax: 01384 565466 E-mail: chinatradedirect@btinternet.com *Consultancy, direct trade, organised sourcing trips, sourcing, sampling, advice, supplier introductions and screening, advice on China Business (new or existing)*

China Trading Co., 42 Winchgrove Road, Bracknell, Berkshire, RG42 2EL Tel: (01344) 428866 Fax: (01344) 428866 *Catering equipment hire services*

Chinal Management Services, King Charles House, 2 Castle Hill, Dudley, West Midlands, DY1 4PS Tel: (01384) 234234 Fax: (01384) 456183 E-mail: info@chinal.co.uk *Consultants business, management & productivity* Also at: Coatbridge, Egham, Manchester, Nottingham & Swansea

▶ Chinaventure, 25 Orchard Estate, Twyford, READING, RG10 9JY Tel: 08703 210018 Fax: 08701 383878 E-mail: sally@chinaventure.co.uk *We import from and trade with China. We also offer consultancy to UK and EU companies sourcing in China, for example made-to-design manufacturing projects or wholesale purchasing.*

Chindwell Co. Ltd, Hyde House, The Hyde, London, NW9 6JT Tel: (020) 8208 0808 Fax: (020) 8205 8800 E-mail: chindwell_co_ltd@compuserve.com *Importers & distributors*

Chinese Carpet Co. Ltd, 1st Floor Building C, 105 Eade Rd, London, N4 1TJ Tel: (020) 8802 2323 Fax: (020) 8802 0560 *Carpet importers & exporters*

Chinese Marketing & Communications, 16 Nicholas Street, Manchester, M1 4EJ Tel: (0870) 0181298 Fax: (0870) 0181299 E-mail: support@chinese-marketing.com *Translation*

▶ Chingford Dental Laboratories, 118 Chingford Mount Road, London, E4 9AA Tel: (020) 8531 1212 Fax: (020) 8926 2685 E-mail: mandy@chingford.com *Dental laboratory*

J.S. Chinn Engineering Co. Ltd, Faraday Road, Harrowbrook Industrial Estate, Hinckley, Leicestershire, LE10 3DE Tel: (01455) 238333 Fax: (01455) 890585 E-mail: enquiries@jschinn.com *Fabricating engineers*

J.S. Chinn Project Engineering Ltd, Coventry Road, Exhall, Coventry, CV7 9FT Tel: 0117-958 4600 Fax: 0117-958 4601 E-mail: jschinn@internet-uk.net *Project design & systems engineering & aerospace consultants*

▶ Chint Europe, Unit 5 Bracken Trade Park, Dumers Lane, Bury, Lancashire, BL9 9QP Tel: 0161-762 9333 Fax: 0161-762 9898 E-mail: sales@chint.co.uk *Electrical component manufrs*

Chiorino (London) (UK) Ltd, Unit 1 Seven House, 36-40 Town End, Caterham, Surrey, CR3 5UG Tel: (01883) 336748 Fax: (01883) 330868 E-mail: sales@chiorino.co.uk *Supplier & fitters of conveyor & transmission belts*

Chiorino UK, Phoenix Avenue, Featherstone, Pontefract, West Yorkshire, WF7 6EP Tel: (01977) 691880 Fax: (0870) 6065061 E-mail: sales@chiorino.co.uk *Transmission & conveyor belt manufrs* Also at: Croydon & Solihull

▶ Chip Ltd, 46a Grahams Road, Falkirk, FK1 1HR Tel: (01324) 628853

Chippindale Plant Hire & Sales Ltd, Gas Works Road, Keighley, West Yorkshire, BD21 4LY Tel: (01535) 606135 Fax: (01535) 690303 E-mail: general@chippindale-plant.co.uk *Contract plant hire* Also at: Keighley

▶ Chippington Derrick Consultants Ltd, 1 Carlton Close, Camberley, Surrey, GU15 1DS Tel: (01276) 508949 *Specialist consultants for advanced planning systems*

▶ Chips, 15 Heywood Street, Brimington, Chesterfield, Derbyshire, S43 1DB Tel: (01246) 200214 E-mail: info@chips-pc.co.uk *A high quality Computer sales serive, selling all types of systems and parts.*we also sell software and computer related products*

Chips Computers, Stall 29, Duke Street, Barrow-in-Furness, Cumbria, LA14 1HU Tel: (01229) 822115 Fax: (01229) 822115 *Computer retailers & upgraders*

▶ ChipsAway (AshBruch) Ltd, 1 Kingfisher Business Park, London Road, Bedford, MK42 0NY Tel: (01234) 360300 Fax: (01234) 360300 E-mail: lucie@chips-away.com *Mobile car body & trim repairers*

▶ ChipsAway Leamington Spa, 8 Markham Drive, Leamington Spa, Warwick, CV31 2PP Tel: 01926 330561

▶ Chirnside Sawmills Ltd, Chirnside, Duns, Berwickshire, TD11 3XJ Tel: (01890) 818213 Fax: (01890) 818698 *Sawn & planed wood services*

Chiromart, Suite 3, 36 Sea Road, Bexhill-on-Sea, East Sussex, TN40 1ED Tel: (01424) 731432 Fax: (01424) 225836 E-mail: chiromart@tiscali.co.uk *Chiropody equipment suppliers*

Chiropody Appliance Service, P O Box 32, Colyton, Devon, EX24 6YR Tel: (01297) 553818 Fax: (01297) 553818 *Chiropody appliances manufrs*

Chirus Ltd, Park House, 15-19 Greenhill Crescent, Watford, WD18 8PH Tel: (01923) 212744 Fax: (01923) 244751 *Medical diagnostic equipment manufrs*

▶ Chisholme & Co., Lulham, Madley, Hereford, HR2 9JW Tel: (01981) 250642

Chislett Hire, Enterprise Way, Pinchbeck, Spalding, Lincolnshire, PE11 3YR Tel: (01775) 725778 Fax: (01775) 767523 E-mail: sales@chislett.co.uk *Tool hire*

Chisnall Environmental Services, 63 Vernon Road, Poynton, Stockport, Cheshire, SK12 1YS Tel: (01625) 858567 Fax: (01625) 858856 *Water treatment servicing*

Chistlehurst Bar Seating, 1 Redhill, Chislehurst, Kent, BR7 6DB Tel: (020) 8467 7138 Fax: (020) 8467 7138 *Pub furniture manufrs*

▶ Chiswell Fireplaces Ltd, 192 Watford Road, St. Albans, Hertfordshire, AL2 3EB Tel: (01727) 859512 Fax: (01727) 836343 E-mail: sales@chiswellfireplaces.com *Air conditioning sales & installation service*

Chiswick Lane Glass Ltd, 44 Chiswick Lane, London, W4 2JQ Tel: (020) 8994 5779 Fax: (020) 8742 1467 E-mail: sales@chiswickglass.co.uk *Glass merchants* Also at: London SW14

Chitter Chatter Telecom Ltd, 92 North End, Croydon, CR0 1UJ Tel: (020) 8688 2616 Fax: (020) 8688 5523 E-mail: info@chitter-chatter.co.uk *Telecommunication*

▶ Chivas Brothers Ltd, 111-113 Renfrew Road, Paisley, Renfrewshire, PA3 4DY Tel: 0141-531 1800 Fax: 0141-531 1816 *Scotch whiskey & gin makers*

Frank Chivers & Son, 1 Estcourt Street, Devizes, Wiltshire, SN10 1LQ Tel: (01380) 723411 Fax: (01380) 728078 *Commercial vehicle repair services & retail coal merchants*

▶ Chivers Period Book Binders, Aintree Avenue, White Horse Business Park, Trowbridge, Wiltshire, BA14 0XB Tel: (01225) 752888 Fax: (01225) 752666 E-mail: info@chivers-period.co.uk *Craft book binders & paper conservators*

Chiviott Machine Tools Ltd, Unit C1 Rudford Industrial Estate, Ford Road, Ford, Arundel, West Sussex, BN18 0BD Tel: (01903) 721281 Fax: (01903) 730868 E-mail: sales@chiviott.co.uk *Supply new & used machine tools*

▶ Chloes Caravan Holidays, 31 Templars Field, Canley, Coventry, CV4 8FR Tel: (024) 7647 3580 E-mail: frank@leach60.fsnet.co.uk *Caravan holidays*

Chloride Group plc, Third Floor, 23 Lower Belgrave Street, London, SW1W 0NR Tel: (020) 7881 1440 Fax: (020) 7730 5085 E-mail: info@chloridegroup.com *Holding company*

Chloride Power Ltd, Kempston Court, Manor Road, Kempston Hardwick, Bedford, MK43 9PQ Tel: (01234) 840282 Fax: (01234) 841156 *Electronic power suppliers*

Chloride Power Protection, Unit C George Curl Way, Southampton, SO18 2RY Tel: (023) 8061 0311 Fax: (023) 8061 0852 E-mail: uk.sales@chloridepower.com *Uninterruptible power supply sales*

Chloride UK, George Curl Way, Southampton, SO18 2RY Tel: (023) 8061 0311 Fax: (023) 8061 2039 *Generator & ups maintenance services & design installation*

Chloroxy-Tech Ltd, Powke Lane Industrial Estate, Powke La, Blackheath, Birmingham, B65 0AH Tel: 0121-559 4141 Fax: 0121-559 2503 E-mail: chloroxy.tech@virgin.net Principal Export Areas: Africa *Water treatment (legionella control) & chloride dioxide sterilisation services. Also manufacturing of water (portable) treatment plants & equipment & water purification systems*

CHN Gas Services & Maintenance, Paper Mill End Industrial Estate, Birmingham, B44 8NH Tel: 0121-344 4789

▶ Chocolate Events, 71 High Street, Buckden, St. Neots, Cambridgeshire, PE19 5TA Tel: (01480) 819338 E-mail: chocolateevents@hotmail.co.uk *Party and event organisers, whatever the occasion we are experienced in handling all aspects of your special day.*

▶ Chocolate Factory Hutton Le Hole, Chocolate Factory, Hutton-le-Hole, York, YO62 6UA Tel: (01751) 417084 E-mail: sales@the-chocolate-factory.co.uk *Chocolate retailers & manufrs*

▶ Chocolate Fountains from Hot Chocolate Lunch Ltd, St Hilda Close, Deepcar, Sheffield, S36 2TH Tel: 0784 0685595 E-mail: info@hotchocolatelunch.com *Chocolate Fountain Hire of the highest standard. Free illuminated surround. Let us bring that WOW factor to your event.*

▶ Chocolate Graphics, Hawthorn Road, Skegness, Lincolnshire, PE25 3TD Tel: (01754) 896668 Fax: (01754) 896668 E-mail: info@chocolategraphics.co.uk *Manufacturers of quality personalised chocolate and chocolate novelties.**

▶ Chocolate Paradise, 122 Station Road, Shotts, Lanarkshire, ML7 4BQ Tel: 01501 821958 E-mail: bookings@chocolate-paradise.co.uk *Chocolate Fountain Hire in Scotland - Lanarkshire, West Lothian, Borders, North Scotland.**Providing chocolate fondue of belgian chocolate and dipping foods.*

▶ Chris Choi, Unit 3, Alexandra Court, Alexandra Road, Yeovil, Somerset, BA21 5AL Tel: (01935) 478175 *Sign writing*

▶ Choice Computers, 32 Buckingham Drive, Dukinfield, Cheshire, SK16 5BZ Tel: (0870) 7776755 *Computer maintained & suppliers*

Choice Saddlery, 1 Broad Street, Knighton, Powys, LD7 1BL Tel: (01547) 528385 Fax: (01547) 528385 *Saddle manufacturers & retailers*

Choice Technical Recruitment Ltd, 8 West Alley, Hitchin, Hertfordshire, SG5 1EG Tel: (01462) 442929 Fax: (01462) 442828 E-mail: choicetec@ctr.uk.com *Engineering & IT recruitment agents*

▶ Choicedomains.Co.Uk, 30a Wings Road, Farnham, Surrey, GU9 0HW Tel: (01252) 820863 Fax: (01252) 821001 E-mail: admin@choicedomains.co.uk *Premium quality internet domain names*

▶ Choices, Masada, Highbury Road, Anna Valley, Andover, Hampshire, SP11 7LU Tel: (01264) 365697 Fax: (08707) 628127 E-mail: choices@anna-valley.demon.co.uk *Choices provide equipment hire for any event at any venue. We offer event management, advice, equipment, platters, linen, disposable products, crockery, cutlery, spit roast, bbq, gas, gas items, platters, Bouncy castles, refrigerated trailers. New to Choices is the much aclaiamed CHOCOLATE FOUNTAIN we also offer much more. We also offer a craft service for hire or purchase and deal with Fiskars, Sizzix, Makeower, Personal Impressions, Medallion Stamps.*

Cholcroft Ltd, 7 Dane Drive, Ferndown, Dorset, BH22 8LX Tel: (01202) 874455 Fax: (01202) 874003 E-mail: trevor@cholcroft-ltd.freeserve.co.uk *Enclosures & power cods*

Chomerics, Unit 6 Century Point, Cressex Business Park, High Wycombe, Buckinghamshire, HP12 3SL Tel: (01628) 404000 Fax: (01628) 404091 E-mail: chomerics_europe@parker.com *Manufacturers of gaskets , insulating materials & el shielding*

Chomette Ltd, 307 Merton Road, London, SW18 5JS Tel: (020) 8877 7000 Fax: (020) 8874 8627 E-mail: paulb@chomettedornberger.co.uk *Cookware & tableware importer & distributors*

Choose At Home Window Blinds, 36 Sackville Gardens, East Grinstead, West Sussex, RH19 2AH Tel: (01342) 328364 *Blind Suppliers*

▶ Chord Co., Boscombe Down Business Park, Mills Way, Amesbury, Salisbury, SP4 7RX Tel: (01980) 625070 Fax: (01980) 625070 E-mail: chord@chord.co.uk *Electronic component manufrs*

▶ Chord Land Ltd, 13a St. Pauls Square, Birmingham, B3 1RB Tel: 0121-200 8090 Fax: 0121-200 8091 E-mail: webmaster@chordhomes.co.uk *Chord Homes is a Birmingham-based developer. Passionate about our schemes, we go the extra mile to ensure our developments are of high quality and meet customer needs. Our range covers affordable studio apartments for first-time buyers, prestigious city-centre apartments and luxury detatched homes. Chord's developments are concentrated in the West Midlands, in particular in Birmingham's exciting and evolving Jewellery Quarter.*

Chord Reprographic Services, 19-20 Britton Street, London, EC1M 5NQ Tel: (020) 7253 3340 Fax: (020) 7253 5371 *Litho printers*

John Chorley & Co. Ltd, Dallam Lane, Warrington, WA2 7PZ Tel: (01925) 636552 Fax: (01925) 415812 E-mail: sales@johncholey.co.uk *Steel stockholders*

Chortex Ltd, Victoria Mills, Chorley New Road, Horwich, Bolton, BL6 6ER Tel: (01204) 695611 Fax: (01204) 696680 E-mail: mark.tuley@coats-viyella.com *Towel manufrs*

Chorus Application Software Ltd, Devonshire House, Riverside Road, Pottington Business Park, Barnstaple, Devon, EX31 1SW Tel: (01271) 346738 Fax: (01271) 379250 *Develop computer software applications*

Chowart Ltd, 58 Heming Road, Redditch, Worcestershire, B98 0EA Tel: (01527) 501601 Fax: (01527) 510217 E-mail: admin@chowart.co.uk *Kitchen, shower & bathroom fittings manufrs*

Chown Dewhurst L L P, 51 Lafone Street, London, SE1 2LX Tel: (020) 7403 0787 Fax: (020) 7403 6693 E-mail: info@chowndewhurst.com *International economic & tax consultants*

CHP Consulting Ltd, Augustine House, 6a Austin Friars, London, EC2N 2HA Tel: (020) 7588 1800 Fax: (020) 7588 1802 E-mail: info@chp.co.uk *IT consultants*

▶ CHR Commercial Cleaning Services Ltd, Unit 12 Union Bridge Mills, Roker Lane, Pudsey, West Yorkshire, LS28 9LE Tel: 0113-257 7893 Fax: 0113-236 0916 E-mail: brendan@chrservices.co.uk *Commercial cleaning specialists**

Chr. Hansen (UK) Ltd, 2 Tealgate, Charnham Park, Hungerford, Berkshire, RG17 0YT Tel: (01488) 689800 Fax: (01488) 685436 E-mail: contactus-gb@gb.chr-hansen.com Principal Export Areas: Worldwide *Natural food colorings suppliers*

▶ Chris Allsop Ltd, Covert Farm, Langar Road, Colston Bassett, Nottingham, NG12 3FT Tel: (01949) 81945 Fax: (01949) 81785 E-mail: allsopcranes@aol.com *Scrap metal specialists*

Chris Appleby Engineering, Homestead Farm, Great Burches Road, Benfleet, Essex, SS7 3NG Tel: (01268) 776642 Fax: (01268) 776645 E-mail: enquiries@applebee.co.uk *Motorcycle, jet ski & marine engineers*

Chris Bennett Heavy Haulage Ltd, Arden Hall, Castle Hill, Bredbury, Stockport, Cheshire, SK6 2RY Tel: 0161-406 8466 Fax: 0161-406 8335 E-mail: sales@chrisbennett.co.uk *Heavy haulage contractors*

▶ Chris Booth Associates, Hilltop, Shirenewton, Chepstow, Gwent, NP16 6RP Tel: (01291) 641934 Fax: (08700) 940849 E-mail: info@chris-booth.com *Finite element analysis, bridge and temporary works design*

▶ Chris Bowker Ltd, Whitegate, White Lund Industrial Estate, Morecambe, Lancashire, LA3 3BS Tel: (01524) 36353 Fax: (01524) 841683

▶ Chris Hanley, 2 Wellfield Road, Stockport, Cheshire, SK2 6AS Tel: 0161-487 1217 E-mail: info@chrishanleyphotography.co.uk *Creative contemporary photography and digital artistry, specialising in reportage weddings, portraiture and picture restorations*

Chris Hardy Tyres, The Tyre Station, Hortonwood 8, Telford, Shropshire, TF1 7GR Tel: (01952) 270009 Fax: (01952) 605892 *Truck tyre repair & retread services*

▶ Chris Hatcher & Son Ltd, 33 High Street, Seaford, East Sussex, BN25 1PL Tel: (01323) 890100 Fax: (01323) 891400

▶ Chris Hayter Transport Ltd, Northwood Road, Witney, Oxfordshire, OX29 7HB Tel: (01993) 771551 Fax: (01993) 773139

Chris Hodgson Engineering Ltd, Seven Acres, Hollocombe, Chulmleigh, Devon, EX18 7QH Tel: (01769) 520422 Fax: (01769) 520544 *Structural steel fabricators*

Chris Jack Toolmaking, Block 6, Upper Mills Trading Estate, Bristol Road, Stonehouse, Gloucestershire, GL10 2BJ Tel: (01453) 826852 Fax: (01453) 826852 *Press tool manufrs*

Chris Lewis, Faraday House, 38 Poole Road, Bournemouth, BH4 9DW Tel: (01202) 751599 Fax: (01202) 759500 E-mail: sales@chrislewissecurity.co.uk *Security system installers*

▶ Chris Precious Ltd, Fox Lane, Wakefield, West Yorkshire, WF1 2AJ Tel: (01924) 382500 Fax: (01924) 382037

▶ Chris Support, 55 Balmoral Gardens, North Shields, Tyne & Wear, NE29 9BB Tel: 0191 257 3607 E-mail: support@chrissupport.co.uk *Freelance web developer and IT Support consultant. I use css, xhtml, asp, asp.NET and php. The databases I use are PostGreSQL, MySQL, MS SQL and InterBase.*

Chris Topp & Company Ltd, Lyndhurst, Carlton Husthwaite, Thirsk, North Yorkshire, YO7 2BJ Tel: (01845) 501415 Fax: (01845) 501072 E-mail: enquiry@realwroughtiron.com *Supplier of genuine wrought iron*

▶ Chris Williams Photography, 31 Manor House Road, Glastonbury, Somerset, BA6 9DF Tel: 01458 835946 *Commercial photographer specialising in brochure and Web images of industrial and retail products.*

▶ Chris Wright Road Planning Ltd, Hollins Hill, Baildon, Shipley, West Yorkshire, BD17 7QB Tel: (01274) 533905 Fax: (01274) 530045

▶ Chrisalis Ltd, 19 Mount House Close, Formby, Liverpool, L37 3LH Tel: (01704) 870942 E-mail: kellysearch@chrisalis-uk.com

▶ Christchurch Blinds, 328 Wimborne Road, Bournemouth, BH9 2HH Tel: (01202) 535577 *Blind manufrs*

Christchurch Blinds, 58 Bargates, Christchurch, Dorset, BH23 1QL Tel: (01202) 478363 Fax: (01202) 485054 *Blind manufrs*

Christchurch Computer Centre, 2-4 Fairmile Parade, Fairmile Road, Christchurch, Dorset, BH23 2LP Tel: (01202) 486338 Fax: (0845) 8622661 E-mail: sales@c-c-c.co.uk *Computer systems & software developers*

Christeyns UK Ltd, Rutland Street, Bradford, West Yorkshire, BD4 7EA Tel: (01274) 393286 Fax: (01274) 309143 E-mail: headoffice@christeyns.co.uk *Detergent manufrs*

▶ Christian Bits, 5 Underwood Road, Haslemere, Surrey, GU27 1JQ Tel: (01428) 653853 E-mail: enquiries@christianbits.co.uk *Christian books, CDs, videos, Bibles, software and gifts available by mail order or internet shopping.*

▶ Clive Christian, 10 Phoenix Place, Lewes, East Sussex, BN7 2QJ Tel: (01273) 483080 Fax: (01273) 483639 E-mail: sales@clivechristian.com *Furnace designers & builders*

Christian Day, 2 Phoenix Building, Rushock Trading Estate, Rushock, Droitwich, Worcestershire, WR9 0NR Tel: (01299) 250385 Fax: (01299) 250335 E-mail: sales@christianday.co.uk *Glass fibre moulding manufrs*

Christian Education Europe Ltd, Marantha House, Northford Close, Shrivenham, Swindon, SN6 8HL Tel: (01793) 783783 Fax: (01793) 783775 E-mail: info@christian-education.org *Educational supplies distributors*

Christian Fabrications Ltd, 5 Chase Side Crescent, Enfield, Middlesex, EN2 0JA Tel: (020) 8482 2082 Fax: (020) 8364 6488 *Install sound systems in churches*

▶ Christian Garnett Partners, 195 High Holborn, London, WC1V 7BD Tel: (020) 7404 7677 Fax: (020) 7404 6648 E-mail: sales@christiangarnett.com *Architect services*

▶ Christian I D Coachworks, Russell Hill Place, Purley, Surrey, CR8 2LH Tel: (020) 8660 6444 Fax: (020) 8668 0116 E-mail: ian@idcoachworks.fsnet.co.uk *Car body repairs & accident repair specialists*

Christian Marcus Fashions (Nottingham), Iremonger Road, Nottingham, NG2 3HU Tel: 0115-986 7056 Fax: 0115-985 0916 E-mail: cmd@christianmarcus.co.uk *Ladies fashion wholesalers*

▶ Christian Salvesen plc, Regional Distribution Centre, Melford Road, Righead Industrial Estate, Bellshill, Lanarkshire, ML4 3QD Tel: (01698) 844050 Fax: (01698) 842845

▶ Christian Salvesen plc, Pilsworth Road, Bury, Lancashire, BL9 8RD Tel: 0161-796 5900 Fax: 0161-796 5007

▶ Christian Salvesen plc, Easton, Grantham, Lincolnshire, NG33 5AU Tel: (01476) 515000 Fax: (01476) 515011

Christian Salvesen plc, Easton, Grantham, Lincolnshire, NG33 5AU Tel: (01476) 515000 Fax: (01476) 515011 *Frozen food manufacturer, storage & transport*

Christian Salvesen plc, Salvesen Buildings, Ladysmith Road, Grimsby, South Humberside, DN32 9SL Tel: (01472) 327200 Fax: (01472) 327210 *Cold storage & vegetable processors* Also at: Branches throughout the U.K.

▶ Christian Salvesen plc, Flex Meadow, Harlow, Essex, CM19 5TX Tel: (01279) 626444 Fax: (01279) 441291

▶ Christian Salvesen plc, Stakehill Industrial Estate, Touchet Hall Road, Middleton, Manchester, M24 2GZ Tel: 0161-654 4000 Fax: 0161-654 4040

▶ Christian Salvesen plc, 2 Roundhead Road, Heathfield Industrial Estate, Newton Abbot, Devon, TQ12 6UE Tel: (01626) 835560 Fax: (01626) 835540 E-mail: info@salversan.co.uk

Christian Salvesen P.L.C., Salvesen House, Lodge Way, Lodge Farm Industrial Estate, Northampton, NN5 7SL Tel: (01604) 737100 *Logistic distributors* Also at: Branches throughout the U.K.

▶ Christian Salvesen plc, Beaufort House Beaufort Court, Sir Thomas Longley Road, Medway City Estate, Rochester, Kent, ME2 4FB Tel: (01634) 731700 Fax: (01634) 731748

▶ Christian Salvessen Industrial Division, Swift House, Lodge Way Industrial Estate, Duston, Northampton, NN5 7TU Tel: (01604) 759900 Fax: (01604) 590323

Christian Salvessen Industrial Division, Swift House, Lodge Way Industrial Estate, Duston, Northampton, NN5 7TU Tel: (01604) 759900 Fax: (01604) 584101 E-mail: sales@salvesen.com *Industrial haulage* Also at: Birmingham, Coventry, Gloucester, Maidstone, Manchester, Motherwell, Stoke-on-Trent & Wakefield

Andrew Christie Junior Ltd, 3 Riverside Business Centre, North Esplanade West, Aberdeen, AB11 5RJ Tel: (01224) 590327 Fax: (01224) 580763 E-mail: office@achristiejnr.com *Fish processors*

▶ Christie Catering Co., Tillwicks Road, Harlow, Essex, CM18 6EN Tel: (01279) 433888 Fax: (01279) 433888

Christie & Grey Ltd, Morley Road, Tonbridge, Kent, TN9 1RA Tel: (01732) 371100 Fax: (01732) 359666 E-mail: sales@christiegrey.com *Antivibration mounting, rubber/metalbonded products & control (architectural) materials/ products manufacturers. Also antivibration services/consultants/designers/installation engineers*

Christie Intruder Alarms Ltd, Security House, 212-218 London Road, Waterlooville, Hampshire, PO7 7AJ Tel: (023) 9226 5111 Fax: (023) 9226 5112 E-mail: enquiries@ciaalarms.co.uk *Security systems installers & maintenance services*

▶ Christie & Son (Metal Merchants) Ltd, Lobnitz Dock, Meadowside Street, Renfrew, PA4 8SY Tel: 0141-885 1253 Fax: 0141-885 1937 E-mail: info@christieandson.com *Scrap metal merchants*

▶ Christie Turner Ltd, Knightsdale Road, Ipswich, IP1 4LE Tel: (01473) 742325 Fax: (01473) 462 773 E-mail: info@christyhunt.co.uk *Manufacturers of pulverisers, hammer mills & laboratory grinding equipment/mills.*

Christies Ltd, Cloyfin Road, Coleraine, County Londonderry, BT52 2RA Tel: (028) 7035 4911 Fax: (028) 7035 1601 E-mail: christiesltd@btinternet.com *Builders merchants*

Christies Agencies Ltd, Symal House, Edgware Road, London, NW9 0HU Tel: (020) 8200 9584 Fax: (020) 8200 6592 E-mail: info@christiesagencies.com *Menswear clothing agents*

▶ Christie's Emergency Glazing, 2 Trafalgar Road, Dartford, DA1 1NS Tel: (01322) 229874 Fax: (0845) 4309391 E-mail: john@glassforhome.com *Window specialists*

Christies International P.L.C., 8 King Street, St. James's, London, SW1Y 6QT Tel: (020) 7839 9060 Fax: (020) 7839 1611 E-mail: info@christies.com *Fine art estimators & auctioneers*

Christie-Tyler Ltd, Abergaroo Road, Brynmenyn, Bridgend, Mid Glamorgan, CF32 9LN Tel: (01656) 726200 Fax: (01656) 726233 *Furniture manufrs*

Christina May, Rotherdale, Fir Toll Road, Mayfield, East Sussex, TN20 6NB Tel: (01435) 873673 Fax: (01435) 873673 E-mail: bob@christinamay.com *Speciality soap makers*

▶ Christine Elcombe Voice Over Artist, 3 Elizabeth Drive, Capel-le-Ferne, Folkestone, Kent, CT18 7NA Tel: 0207 558 8269 Fax: 0870 137 8050 E-mail: webmaster@moneyspiderwebdesign.co.uk *Christine Elcombe is a well-spoken and well-modulated speaker with good emphasis and based in the UK.*

Christine's Cane Furniture, 2a Watson Road, Worksop, Nottinghamshire, S80 2BB Tel: (01909) 483790 Fax: (01909) 483790 E-mail: christinestevens30@virgin.com *Cane & wicker furniture retailers*

Christison Technology Group Ltd, Albany Road, Gateshead East Industrial Estate, Gateshead, Tyne & Wear, NE8 3AT Tel: 0191-478 8120 Fax: 0191-490 0549 E-mail: sales@christison.com *Scientific laboratory equipment distributors & manufrs*

Christmas Stockholders Ltd, Ainsdale Drive, Shrewsbury, SY1 3TL Tel: (01743) 462515 Fax: (01743) 464430 *Steel cutters & stockholders*

Christo Trophies, 49 Broad Street, Banbury, Oxfordshire, OX16 5BT Tel: (01295) 262330 Fax: (01295) 262330 *Trophies engravers*

Christopher Beale Associates Ltd, 14 Queen Anne's Gate, London, SW1H 9AA Tel: (020) 7976 7701 Fax: (020) 7976 7265 *Management & executive search consultancy*

Christopher Dyer & Co., 36 School Road, Finstock, Chipping Norton, Oxfordshire, OX7 3DJ Tel: (01993) 705001 Fax: (01993) 705741 E-mail: info@cabinetmaker.co.uk *Cabinet makers*

Christow Consultants Ltd, 21 Bloomsbury Square, London, WC1A 2NS Tel: (020) 7631 0990 Fax: (020) 7631 0102 E-mail: christow@christow.com *Corporate public relations consultants*

Christy Group, Wood Street, Barnsley, South Yorkshire, S70 1NB Tel: (01226) 730226 Fax: (01226) 771234 *Advertising headwear & children's dress up manufrs*

Christy Lighting Ltd, 8 Northumberland Court, Chelmsford, CM2 6UW Tel: (01245) 451212 Fax: (01245) 451818 *Flood lighting installation & manufrs*

William Christy & Son Ltd, 1 Mopack Business Complex, Ballycolman Avenue, Strabane, County Tyrone, BT82 9AF Tel: (028) 7188 5566 Fax: (028) 7188 6746 *Leisure wear manufacturers, school wear*

Chrisym Leisure Wear, Ferndale House, Mill Hill Road, Arnesby, Leicester, LE8 5WG Tel: 0116-247 8303 Fax: 0116-247 8303 *Leisure wear manufrs*

Chroma Visual, 61 Leyland Trading Estate, Wellingborough, Northamptonshire, NN8 1RS Tel: (01933) 443737 Fax: (01933) 271770 E-mail: cvl@globalnet.co.uk *CCTV systems installation specialists*

Chromacol Ltd, Unit 3, Little Mundells, Mundells Industrial Estate, Welwyn Garden City, Hertfordshire, AL7 1EW Tel: (01707) 394949 Fax: (01707) 391311 E-mail: chromacol@easynet.co.uk Principal Export Areas: Worldwide *Chromatographic column & instrument suppliers*

Chromalloy Metal Tectonics Ltd, Bramble Way, Clover Nook Industrial Park, Somercotes, Alfreton, Derbyshire, DE55 4RH Tel: (01773) 521522 Fax: (01773) 521482 *Gas turbines repairers*

Chromalloy Prestwick, Liberator House, Glasgow Prestwick Intnl Airport, Prestwick, Ayrshire, KA9 2PT Tel: (01292) 678400 Fax: (01292) 474989 *Aircraft repairs*

Chromalock Ltd, Beechwood House, Falkland Close, Charter Avenue Industrial Estate, Coventry, CV4 8HQ Tel: (024) 7646 6277 Fax: (024) 7646 5298 E-mail: admin@chromalock.com *Custom built electronic equipment contractors*

Chromalox (U K) Ltd, Eltron House, 20-28 Whitehorse Road, Croydon, CR0 2JA Tel: (020) 8665 8900 Fax: (020) 8689 0571 E-mail: uksales@chromalox.com *Chromalox Ltd manufacture a full & comprehensive range of both standard & custom engineered electric heating equipment associated control systems. Immersion heaters, line/flow heaters, boilers, air warmers, fan heaters, rod elements,, cartridge, controls all for use in safe or hazardous ATEX certified areas.*

Chromatechnic Ltd, 35 Princes Street, Ulverston, Cumbria, LA12 7NQ Tel: (01229) 581551 E-mail: edavidson@chromatechnic.com *Opto & photoelectronic components*

▶ Chromavision CCTV & Video Equipment, 88 Judd Road, Tonbridge, Kent, TN9 2NJ Tel: (01732) 771999 Fax: (01732) 771888 E-mail: john@chroma-vision.co.uk *CCTV & integrated systems suppliers, installations & maintenance*

▶ Chrome Consulting Ltd, 26 Fitzroy Square, London, W1T 6BT Tel: 020 7323 1610 E-mail: enquiries@chromeconsulting.com *Tangible results.**That's the business we are in. You may not know our name, but if you read newspapers, watch TV or listen to the radio you have almost certainly seen and heard our work.**From healthy eating in schools to global warming, a brilliant new pomegranate juice to Vodka Shots confectionery, rarely a day goes by* continued *without high profile, targeted coverage for our clients.**How do we do it? By understanding clients' marketing objectives and planning the right media relations routes for them. And that comes from years of dealing with (and for some of us, being) journalists while being bang up to date on media opportunities now. Of course, there is more to PR than just getting you into (or keeping you out of) the media. Anything from a complete communications strategy and its implementation to a quick project designed to give a brand a boost is within our remit.**So if you want to talk to PR people that live in the real world give us a call.*

▶ Chrome Molly Publications, 10A Pilot Road, Corby, Northamptonshire, NN17 5YH Tel: (01536) 268968 Fax: (01536) 401489 E-mail: chromemolly@hotmail.com *Book publishers*

Chronos Richardson Ltd, Unit 1 Centurion Business Centre, Dabell Avenue, Nottingham, NG6 8WN Tel: 0115-935 1351 Fax: 0115-935 1353 E-mail: info@chronos-richardson.com *Weighing systems manufrs*

Chrysalis Clothes Ltd, L Harlow House Shelton Road, Willowbrook East Industrial Estate, Corby, Northamptonshire, NN17 5XH Tel: (01536) 269034 Fax: (01536) 269034 E-mail: blackmor@btconnect.com *Outerwear manufrs*

▶ Chrysalis Conservatories Windows & Doors Ltd, 95 Bridgwater Road, Bristol, BS13 8AE Tel: 0117-935 8580

Chrystal & Hill Ltd, 14-30 Woodhead Road, South Nitshill Industrial Estate, Glasgow, G53 7WA Tel: 0141-880 6600 Fax: 0141-880 6611 E-mail: sales@chrystal-hill.co.uk *Office equipment suppliers*

▶ Chubb Electronic Security Ltd, 120 Gower Road, Sketty, Swansea, SA2 9BT Tel: (0870) 2418680 Fax: (0870) 2418681

Chubb Emergency Response, 5 Repton Court, Repton Close, Basildon, Essex, SS13 1LN Tel: (01268) 522066 Fax: (01268) 273070 E-mail: andrew.vaccari@chubb.co.uk *Chubb Emergency Response is the leading provider of Keyholding, Mobile Patrol and Response Services in the U.K. Our intruder alarm response service ensures a prompt response by our trained personnel to your premises on notification of alarm activations. This ensures that incidents occuring whilst your premises are unoccupied are investigated and provides for the co-ordination of the police, alarm engineers or repair contractors, where required.* Also at: Enfield

Chubb Fire Ltd, Chubb House, Staines Road West, Sunbury-on-Thames, Middlesex, TW16 7AR Tel: (01932) 785588 Fax: (01932) 776673 E-mail: info@chubb.co.uk *PREVENT Fire Fire Risk Assessment Fire Risk Management Fire Training Service Videos & CDs Gas Detection DETECT Fire Fire Detection Systems Design & Installation Service & Maintenance Fire Alarm Monitoring CONTAIN Fire Fire Extinguishers Health & Safety Hose Reels Extinguishing Systems System Maintenance Room Integrity Testing Dry and Wet Risers Marine Extinguisher Rental Fire Safety Equipment Chubb Dorgard Ensure ESCAPE from Fire Voice Alarms Fire Safety Signage Emergency Lighting Fire Training*

Chubb Fire Scotland Ltd, South Deeside Road, Maryculter, Aberdeen, AB12 5GB Tel: (01224) 735605 Fax: (01224) 735604 E-mail: gfp.limited@btinternet.com *Fire protection equipment distributors*

Brian Chubb Insurance, Salt Quay House, Sutton Harbour, Plymouth, PL4 0RA Tel: (01752) 312680 Fax: (01752) 226727 E-mail: brianchubb@virginbus.co.uk *Insurance brokers*

Chubb Locks Custodial Services Ltd, Well Lane, Wednesfield, Wolverhampton, WV11 1TB Tel: (01902) 867730 Fax: (01902) 867789 *High security lock system manufrs*

▶ Chubb Securities Ltd, 18 & 19 Lionel Street, Birmingham, B3 1AQ Tel: 0121-200 3311

Chubb Security Personnel Ltd, 2nd Floor The Brooke Building, Shepcote Lane, Sheffield, S9 1QT Tel: 0114-272 6552 Fax: 0114-242 5641

▶ Chuck Mccall Highland Wear, 36 South Street, Elgin, Morayshire, IV30 1JX Tel: (01343) 542743 Fax: (01343) 542743 E-mail: kilts@chuckmccall.com *We are a local company who specialise in hand sewn kilts and all the associated accesories including jackets, sporrans, belts, buckles, sgian duhb"s, and much more.*

Chuckle Shoes, 3 New Bridge Street, Exeter, EX4 3JW Tel: (01392) 270321 Fax: (01392) 207003 *Footwear manufrs*

Chudleigh Second Hand Shop, 30 Fore Street, Chudleigh, Newton Abbot, Devon, TQ13 0HX Tel: (01626) 853309 *Metal detector distributors*

Chugai Pharma Europe Ltd, Mulliner House, Flanders Road, London, W4 1NN Tel: (020) 8987 5600 Fax: (020) 8987 5660 *Pharmaceutical product distributors*

Chum Engineering Ltd, Churchill Way, Trafford Park, Manchester, M17 1BS Tel: 0161-872 3253 Fax: 0161-872 0484 E-mail: info@chumengineering.co.uk *Sheet metalworkers & fabricators*

▶ Chunkichilli Knitwear, Unit 4, St Arvans Court, Evesham Road, Cheltenham, Gloucestershire, GL52 3AA Tel: (07724) 625469 *Designer knitwear for retail, wholesale and OEM. Website at www.chunkichilli.com.*

Chunkies Knitwear & Textiles, Tabernacle Street, Aberaeron, Dyfed, SA46 0BN Tel: (01545) 570144 Fax: (01545) 570144 E-mail: sueholder@hotmail.com *Knitwear manufrs*

Church & Dwight (U K) Ltd, Wear Bay Road, Folkestone, Kent, CT19 6PG Tel: (01303) 850661 Fax: (01303) 858701 E-mail: sales@carterwallace.co.uk Principal Export Areas: Worldwide *Toiletries & personal care suppliers*

Church & Co (Footwear Ltd), St James, Northampton, NN5 5JB Tel: (01604) 593333 Fax: (01604) 754405 E-mail: sales@church-footwear.com *Quality shoe & slipper manufrs*

Church Hill Systems Ltd, Unit 4h Hinckley Business Centre, Burbage Road, Burbage, Hinckley, Leicestershire, LE10 2TP Tel: (01455) 890685 Fax: (01455) 891341 E-mail: sales@churchhillsystems.co.uk *Electrical storage boiler manufrs*

Church Of Ireland Ace Ventures, The Old Rectory, 217 Holywood Road, Belfast, BT4 2DH Tel: (028) 9065 1135 Fax: (028) 9067 2126 E-mail: aceventures@btconnect.com *New deal UD25 plus & computer training providers*

Church Lane Restorations, 1 Church La, Teddington, Middx, TW11 8PA Tel: (020) 8977 2526 *Furniture restoration services*

Church Micros, Causeway Side, 1 High Street, Haslemere, Surrey, GU27 2JZ Tel: (01428) 644122 Fax: (01428) 656300 E-mail: churchmicros@haslemere.com *Computer hardware suppliers*

Churches Fire Security Ltd, Fire House, Mayflower Cose, Chandler's Ford, Eastleigh, Hampshire, SO53 4AR Tel: (0870) 6084350 Fax: (08706) 084351 E-mail: sales@churchesfire.com *Fire fighting equipment distributors*

▶ Churchfayre (UK) Ltd, 26 St. Davids Drive, Leigh-On-Sea, Essex, SS9 3RF Tel: (07946) 505105 E-mail: churchfayre@churchfayre.co.uk *Amusement machines suppliers*

Churchill Controls Ltd, Unit 12 Station Industrial Estate, Oxford Road, Wokingham, Berkshire, RG41 2YQ Tel: 0118-989 2200 Fax: 0118-989 2007 E-mail: sales@churchill-controls.co.uk *Telemetry equipment manufrs*

Churchill Fine Bone China (Holdings) Ltd, Marlborough Works, High Street, Stoke-on-Trent, ST6 5NZ Tel: (01782) 577566 Fax: (01782) 810318 E-mail: churchill@churchillchina.plc.uk *Ceramic manufrs*

Churchill Fine Bone China (Holdings) Ltd, Marlborough Works, High Street, Stoke-on-Trent, ST6 5NZ Tel: (01782) 577566 Fax: (01782) 810318 E-mail: churchill@churchillchina.com *China manufrs*

Churchill Recruitment Consultants Ltd, Arodene House, 41-55 Perth Road, Ilford, Essex, IG2 6BX Tel: (020) 8518 6969 Fax: (020) 8518 6970 E-mail: recruit@churchillrecruitment.com *Security recruitment*

Churchill & Sim Group Ltd, Ashdown Court, Lewes Road, Forest Row, East Sussex, RH18 5EZ Tel: (01342) 826333 Fax: (01342) 825103 E-mail: sales@churchillsim.com *Timber agents* Also at: Hull

Churchill Tool Co. Ltd, Empress Street, Old Trafford, Manchester, M16 9EN Tel: 0161-848 9539 Fax: 0161-872 9234 E-mail: info@churchill-grinders.co.uk *Precision grinding services*

Churchill Windows, Unit 18 Northbrook Trading Estate, Northbrook Road, Worthing, West Sussex, BN14 8PN Tel: (01903) 230918 Fax: (01903) 823091 E-mail: sales@churchill-windows.co.uk *Replacement windows*

Churchills, 55 Hazell Close, Clevedon, Avon, BS21 5DW Tel: (01275) 341325 Fax: (01275) 341325 *Snack foods*

Churchills Cleaning Contractors, Unit 45, Woolsbridge Industrial Park, Three Legged Cross, Wimborne, Dorset, BH21 6SZ Tel: (01202) 825284 Fax: (01202) 828229 *Industrial cleaning contractors*

Churchills Handmade Sandwich Co Ltd, 2-3 Robin Hood Industrial Estate, Alfred St South, Nottingham, NG3 1GE Tel: 0115-941 9789 *Sandwich manufrs*

Church's Pork Butchers Ltd, 224 High Street, Epping, Essex, CM16 4AQ Tel: (01992) 573231 Fax: (01992) 561525 *Retail of meat products*

Churchtown Ltd, 18A London Street, Southport, Merseyside, PR9 0UE Tel: (01704) 227826 Fax: (01704) 220247 E-mail: cabins@churchtown.co.uk *Custom design of portable offices & modular buildings*

Churngold Construction Ltd, St. Andrews House, St. Andrews Road, Avonmouth, Bristol, BS11 9DQ Tel: 0117-900 7100 Fax: 0117-900 7111 E-mail: construction@churngold.co.uk *Construction services*

▶ Churwell Art Stone, Hill Top Farm, Rooms Lane, Gildersome, Morley, Leeds, LS27 7NJ Tel: 0113-252 3855 *Manufacture stone products*

▶ Chy Garth Guest House, P.O. Box 4, St. Ives, Cornwall, TR26 2JX Tel: (01736) 795677

Cia, 1 Paris Garden, London, SE1 8NU Tel: (020) 7633 9999 Fax: (020) 7803 2001 *Advertising agency*

Ciat Ozonair Ltd, 5 Byfleet Technical Centre, Canada Road, Byfleet, Surrey, KT14 7JX Tel: (01932) 354955 Fax: (01932) 342998 E-mail: sales@ciat.co.uk *Air conditioning equipment & systems manufrs*

Ciba Additives, Charter Way, Macclesfield, Cheshire, SK10 2NX Tel: (01625) 421933 Fax: (01625) 619637 *Chemicals manufrs*

▶ Ciba Speciality Chemicals Colours plc, Hawkhead Road, Paisley, Renfrewshire, PA2 7BG Tel: 0141-887 1144 Fax: 0141-840 2283 *Manufacturers of pigments*

Ciba Specialty Chemicals plc, Charter Road, Macclesfield, Cheshire, SK10 2NX Tel: (01625) 665000 Fax: (01625) 619637 *Pigment manufrs*

Ciba Specialty Chemicals plc, Charter Road, Macclesfield, Cheshire, SK10 2NX Tel: (01625) 665000 Fax: (01625) 619637 *Chemical manufrs*

Ciba Specialty Chemicals P.L.C., Ashton New Road, Clayton, Manchester, M11 4AP Tel: 0161-223 1391 Fax: 0161-223 4315 *Chemicals & dyes manufrs*

CIBA Vision (UK) Ltd, Flanders Road, Hedge End, Southampton, SO30 2LG Tel: (01489) 785580 Fax: (01489) 786802 E-mail: parkwest.reception@cibavision.com *Contact lens optical manufrs*

Ciber (U.K.) Ltd, 101 Wigmore Street, London, W1U 1QU Tel: (020) 7355 1101 Fax: (020) 7355 9000 E-mail: info.uk@ciber.com *Computer services*

Ciber UK Ltd, Sketchley Meadows Business Park, 2 Watling Drive, Hinckley, Leicestershire, LE10 3EY Tel: (01455) 898800 Fax: (0870) 0000205 E-mail: enquiries@c.co.uk *IT solutions suppliers*

▶ cibsfacilities.com, Unit 1, 20-22 Union Road, London, SW4 6JP Tel: (0800) 0757515 Fax: (0870) 3452428 E-mail: sales@ci-bs.com *Making work a better place*With 20 years" experience, we"re London"s leading office services supplier, specialising in:**commercial cleaning*pest control*tropical plants*Our many high-profile clients enjoy award-winning service and customer care.**WINNERS Kimberly-Clark Golden Service Awards 2007*Capita Group Plc GOLD ACCREDIATION 2006*BUYING FORCE Preferred Supplier Status 2006*Our green credentials**At cibsfacilities.com:**cutting chemicals and water use with microfibre cleaning technology*cutting emissions by using company vans that run on Liquefied Petroleum Gas (LPG)*recycling - and helping your business to do the same*aiming for even higher environmental standards - we"ve already achieved ISO 9001 and we"re working towards ISO 14001*using advanced SAP software for e-billing and e-credit control to lower our carbon footprint.*

▶ cibshygiene.com, Unit 1, 20-22 Union Road, London, SW4 6JP Tel: (0800) 0757890 Fax: (0870) 3452511 E-mail: sales@ci-bs.com *Welcome to cibs*your complete hygiene service*To ensure your company operates in an environment that is safe, clean and fully compliant with UK legislation we offer a comprehensive range of hygiene products and services delivered nationwide.**Customer care and quality service**88% of our customers would recommend us as a service provider, according to a recent survey. Our contract retention rate is 95%.*

▶ Cibshygiene.com, 211 Picadilly, London, W1J 9HF Tel: (0800) 0757890 Fax: (0870) 3452511 E-mail: sales@ci-bs.com *Washroom solutions provider*

▶ Cic Omec Ltd, Moor Lane Trading Estate, Sherburn In Elmet, Leeds, LS25 6ES Tel: (01977) 682966

▶ Cicada Interiors Limited, 64 Knightsbridge, London, United Kingdom, SW1X 7JF Tel: (020) 7590 3095 Fax: (020) 7590 9601 E-mail: peter@cicadainteriors.com

Cicero Languages Ltd, 42 Upper Grosvenor Road, Tunbridge Wells, Kent, TN1 2ET Tel: (01892) 547077 Fax: (01892) 522749 E-mail: info@cicero.co.uk *Translation & interpretation services*

Cid Lines, The Old Stable, Mawbrook, Scalford, Melton Mowbray, Leicestershire, LE14 4UB Tel: (01664) 444505 Fax: (01664) 444370 E-mail: dick@cidlines.be *Hygiene specialists & disinfectant distributors*

Cifer Data Systems Ltd, 1 Main Street, West Wilts Trading Estate, Westbury, Wiltshire, BA13 4JU Tel: (01373) 824129 Fax: (01373) 824127 E-mail: sales@cifer.co.uk *Computer systems maintenance services*

▶ CIFF - Credit Insurance, Factoring & Finance., Cliff House, 75 Hill Top, Bolsover, Derbyshire, S44 6NJ Tel: 01246 241002 Fax: 0845 127 4385 E-mail: ciff1@holroydr.plus.com *Credit Insurance Consultants & brokers, also dealing in credit reports, finance, debt collection.*registered with the FSA (financial services authority).*

Cigarette Bin.Co.Uk, 118 Woodside Business Park, Birkenhead, Merseyside, CH41 5LB Tel: (0870) 1212388 E-mail: info@ciggybins.co.uk *Manufacturers & retailers of cigarette bins*

Cigarette Bins, 57 Bowden Road, Liverpool, L19 1QN Tel: (0870) 7605666 Fax: (0870) 7605666 E-mail: info@ciggybins.co.uk *Safety Cigarette Lighters /Safe Area Cigarette Lighter*

Cigna Health Care & Group Life, Cigna House, 1 Knowe Road, Greenock, Renfrewshire, PA15 4RJ Tel: (01475) 492222 Fax: (01475) 492326 E-mail: sales@cigna.co.uk *Group life healthcare insurance services*

▶ Cilix Ltd, Dell Cottage Menin Way, Farnham, Surrey, GU9 8DY Tel: (01252) 711532 Fax: (01252) 719612 E-mail: sean.connolly@cilix.co.uk *We are an IT services company combining the flexibility, responsiveness and close customer relationships offered by a small business with the high standards of professionalism and quality of the best large organisations.*

Cima, 26 Chapter Street, London, SW1P 4NP Tel: (020) 7663 5441 Fax: (020) 7663 5442 E-mail: marketing@cimaglobal.com *Accountants*

▶ Cimc, City House, Murraysgate Industrial Estate, Whitburn, Bathgate, West Lothian, EH47 0LE Tel: (0870) 4438280 Fax: (0870) 4438281 E-mail: mail@cimc-lighting.co.uk *Home furnishings suppliers*

▶ Cim-Team UK Ltd, PO Box 133, Stockport, Cheshire, SK12 1NS Tel: (0870) 4211252 Fax: (0870) 4211253 E-mail: info@cim-team.co.uk *CIM-TEAM develops and sells design products and services to the engineering sector. Our products cover many disciplines of engineering design, including; Electrical Control Schematics and Panel Layout, Electronic Schematic and Board Layout, Harness Design and Formboard Layout.*

Cimtech, College Lane, Hatfield, Hertfordshire, AL10 9AB Tel: (01707) 281060 Fax: (01707) 281061 E-mail: c.cimtech@herts.ac.uk *Consultancy & publishing*

Cinch Connectors Ltd, Shireoaks Road, Worksop, Nottinghamshire, S80 3HA Tel: (01909) 474131 Fax: (01909) 478321 E-mail: sales@cinchuk.com *Cinch is a supplier of reliable, high quality interconnect devices for use in a variety of industries. The main markets are, Transportation, Telecommunication & Electronics for which Cinch Designs & manufactures a number of leading edge products including the CIN:APSE solderless interconnect system which is the perfect solution for achieving high data throughput in a small form factor in rugged environments. Cinch is also a major supplier of products to the Mil/Aero Market with a significant presence in the Commercial & Military Aviation market, Navel & Land vehicles, Missile's & Satellite Communications segments. Designing & manufacturing custom solutions, whilst offering a wide range of standard products*

Cincinnati Machine Ltd, PO Box 505, Birmingham, B24 0QU Tel: 0121-351 3821 Fax: 0121-313 5379 E-mail: info@cinmach.co.uk *CNC machining centre & lathe manufrs*

Cincom Systems UK Ltd, 1 Grenfell Road, Maidenhead, Berkshire, SL6 1HN Tel: (01628) 542300 Fax: (01628) 542310 *Computer software publishers, call centre solutions & e-commerce*

▶ Cinderella Elegance Chair Covers, Apartment 8, 5 Bewley Street, Wimbledon, London, SW19 1XF Tel: (020) 8540 8161 E-mail: info@cinderellaelegance.co.uk *Cinderella Elegance is a family run business based in South West London. After planning our own wedding, we realised how stressful and expensive it can be hiring Chair Covers for that special occasion. Having first hand experience our aim is take the stress away from you and make your day whatever the occasion a day to remember. We specialise in weddings but also provide hire for Christenings, Engagements, Celebrations, Graduations and even dinner parties.*

▶ Cinderford Design, 27 Victoria Street, Cinderford, Gloucestershire, GL14 2T Tel: 07780 971730 Fax: 0709 2182233 E-mail: f15_her@hotmail.com *Affordable Spreadsheet & Database design for the small business user*

Cine Engineering Services, 99 Gander Green Lane, Sutton, Surrey, SM1 2ES Tel: (020) 8643 7152 Fax: (020) 7770 7275 *Precision engineers*

▶ Cinecosse Presentation Services, Unit 4 North Meadows, Oldmeldrum, Inverurie, Aberdeenshire, AB51 0GQ Tel: (01651) 873311 Fax: (01651) 873300

▶ Cinema Beds & Sofa Store, Court Ash, Yeovil, Somerset, BA20 1HG Tel: (01935) 413413 Fax: (01935) 423344

Ci-Net, Langford Locks, Kidlington, Oxfordshire, OX5 1GA Tel: (01865) 856000 Fax: (01865) 856001 E-mail: info@ci-net.com *IPS business, global roaming provider*

Cinetic Landis Grinding Ltd, Skipton Road, Cross Hills, Keighley, West Yorkshire, BD20 7SD Tel: (01535) 633211 Fax: (01535) 635493 E-mail: sales@cinetic-landis.co.uk *Precision grinding machine manufrs*

Cing Technologies Ltd, 3 Malt House Cottages, 31 Byfield Road, Chipping Warden, Banbury, Oxfordshire, OX17 1LE Tel: (01295) 660682 E-mail: nigel.galletly@cingtech.com *IT & computer consultants services*

Cinmech Services Ltd, 63 Colvilles Place, Kelvin Industrial Estate, Glasgow, G75 0XE Tel: (01355) 244544 Fax: (01355) 248717 E-mail: cinmech@cinmech.com *Sheet metalworking machinery merchants & engineers*

Cinnamond Plant Ltd, Cinnamond House, Baldwins Lane, Croxley Green, Rickmansworth, Hertfordshire, WD3 3RT Tel: (01923) 235225 Fax: (01923) 229220 E-mail: contracts@cinnamond.co.uk *Established in 1970 Cinnamond provide a first class contracting service in the following fields.*Demolition; Site Clearance; Earthworks; Groundworks; Roadworks; Land Reclamation; Landscaping; Landfill.*

Cinque Ports Pottery, The Monastery, Conduit Hill, Rye, East Sussex, TN31 7LE Tel: (01797) 222033 Fax: (01797) 222400 E-mail: cppottery@aol.com *Pottery manufrs*

Cinque Ports Water Ltd, 4 Walton Road, Folkestone, Kent, CT19 5QR Tel: (01303) 223773 Fax: (01303) 221675 *Water coolers hire & supply*

Cinque Products Ltd, Harbour Road, Rye, East Sussex, TN31 7TE Tel: (01797) 223561 Fax: (01797) 224530 E-mail: longproducts@aol.com *Corrosion control & waterproofing manufrs*

Cinro Plastics Ltd, Garden Street, Stockport, Cheshire, SK2 7PP Tel: 0161-483 0696 Fax: 0161-483 0696 *Plastic injection moulders*

Cintech International, 11 Gold Tops, Newport, Gwent, NP20 4PH Tel: (01633) 246614 Fax: (01633) 246110 E-mail: cintec@aol.com *Cementitious reinforcement & anchors manufrs*

Cintel International Ltd, Watton Road, Ware, Hertfordshire, SG12 0AE Tel: (01920) 463939 Fax: (01920) 460803 E-mail: sales@cintel.co.uk *Film scanning equipment manufrs*

Cintex Ltd, Featherstone Road, Wolverton Mill, Milton Keynes, MK12 5TH Tel: (01908) 629200 Fax: (01908) 579824 *Metal detecting food process machines manufrs*

Cintique Ltd, 43 Andrews Road, London, E8 4RN Tel: (020) 7254 1262 Fax: (020) 7254 6774 E-mail: sales@cintique.co.uk *Chair manufrs*

Cirbo Ltd, 16 Normandy Way, Bodmin, Cornwall, PL31 1EX Tel: (01208) 74174 Fax: (01208) 76801 *Carbide drill & router manufrs*

Circadia, 4 Deer Park Road, London, SW19 3GY Tel: (020) 8254 3100 Fax: (020) 8540 7430 E-mail: circadia@compass-group.co.uk *Food manufrs*

▶ Circatex, Eldon Street, South Shields, Tyne & Wear, NE33 5BU Tel: 0191-403 1000 Fax: 0191-456 4387 E-mail: fastrax@circatex.com *Circatex Fastrax offers 2 - 36 layer boards and flexi rigids, 2,3 and 5 day quick turn service options, a range of surface finish early DFM involvement from customer centered engineers who really understand PCB's. Included co-ordinated manufacture of solder paste stencils combined with a dedicated fastrax team managing the process from initial enquiry to delivery.*

Circle Control & Design Systems Ltd, Unit 8 The Poplars Industrial Estate, Wetherby Road, Boroughbridge, York, YO51 9HS Tel: (01423) 323900 Fax: (01423) 323304 *Control Panel manufrs*

Circle Security, 170 Lanark Road West, Currie, Midlothian, EH14 5NY Tel: (0800) 0723712 Fax: 0131-476 9578 *Security equipment installation services*

Circle Technical Services Ltd, Turulus Way, Midmill Business Park, Kintore, Aberdeenshire, AB51 0TG Tel: (01467) 632020 Fax: (01467) 632022 E-mail: info@circletechnical.co.uk *Dredging & cold cutting services*

Circles, A Summer Place, Golf Course Road, Hunstanton, Norfolk, PE36 6JG Tel: (01485) 533132 *Jewellery manufacturers & repairers*

Cir-Comm Systems Ltd, Bailey Brook House, Amber Drive, Langley Mill, Nottingham, NG16 4BE Tel: (01773) 761999 *Computer maintenance*

Circor Instrumentation Ltd, Frays Mill Works, Cowley Road, Uxbridge, Middlesex, UB8 2AF Tel: (01895) 206780 Fax: (020) 8423 5933 E-mail: aratna@circor.co.uk *Valve fitting sales*

▶ Circuit Coatings Ltd, Old Walsall Road, Hampstead Industrial Estate, Birmingham, B42 1EA Tel: 0121-357 9365 Fax: 0121-358 7524

Circuit Coatings Ltd, Marlow Street, Walsall, WS2 8AQ Tel: (01922) 635589 Fax: (01922) 638444 E-mail: mail@circuit-coating.co.uk *Powder coating services*

Circuit Dynamics Ltd, 112 Beckenham Road, Beckenham, Kent, BR3 4RH Tel: (020) 8650 0723 Fax: (020) 8650 0921 E-mail: cirtcuitdynamics@businessserve.co.uk *Printed circuit manufrs*

Circuit Engineering Marketing Co. Ltd, 1 Silverthorne Way, Waterlooville, Hampshire, PO7 7XB Tel: (023) 9226 2120 Fax: (023) 9226 2089 E-mail: sales@cemco.com *Printed circuit production equipment manufrs*

Circuit Hydraulics Ltd, Unit 16 Kensington Industrial Park, Kensington Road, Southport, Merseyside, PR9 0RY Tel: (01704) 546288 Fax: (01704) 546313 E-mail: circuit.hyd@btinternet.com Principal Export Areas: Worldwide *Hydraulic components, fittings distributors & hose manufrs*

Circuit Supplies & Engineering Ltd, Unit 4 High Street, Wollaston, Wellingborough, Northamptonshire, NN29 7QF Tel: (01933) 663663 Fax: (01933) 674788 *PVC fabricators*

Circularising Ltd, 6 Landor Road, London, SW9 9PP Tel: (020) 7733 3177 Fax: (020) 7978 9059 E-mail: ross@circularising.freeserve.co.uk *Direct mail fulfilment & print*

▶ Circulate, 11 Reverdy Road, London, SE1 5QE Tel: (020) 7237 6042 Fax: (020) 7237 6042 E-mail: info@circulateonline.com *We provide the complete Virtual Viewing experience with advanced navigation tools as standard. *We enable the virtual Viewer the opportunity to look around the entire property as if they were *there in person.Save everyones time and circulate it. We deliver high quality & low prices everytime.*Offers include up to 6 tours for £300.*

Cirencester Civil Engineering Ltd, 4 Esland Place, Love Lane, Cirencester, Gloucestershire, GL7 1YG Tel: (01285) 652020 Fax: (01285) 651007 E-mail: sales@cirencestercivilengineering.co.uk *Civil engineering & specialist surfacing*

▶ Cirencester Composites Ltd, Unit 8 Crudwell, Malmesbury, Wiltshire, SN16 9SH Tel: (01666) 577888 Fax: (01666) 577888 *Specialist moulders of glass reinforced plastics (GRP) manufrs*

▶ Cirencester Plastics Ltd, Wilkinson Road, Love Lane Industrial Estate, Cirencester, Gloucestershire, GL7 1YR Tel: (01285) 655995 Fax: (01285) 885243 E-mail: mail@cirencesterplastics.co.uk *Backing formers*

Ciretech Ltd, Unit 4 Huffwood Trading Estate, Billingshurst, West Sussex, RH14 9UR Tel: (01403) 784855 Fax: (01403) 783000 *Control panel manufrs*

Ciro Pearls Ltd, C/o, 26-36 Silver St, Bedford, MK40 1SX Tel: 01234 327363 Fax: 01234 269703 *Costume jewellery*

Ciro Pearls Ltd, Welsh Designer Outlet Village, Bridgend, Mid Glamorgan, CF32 9SU Tel: (01656) 655916 *Costume jeweller distribution*

▶ Cirris Solutions Ltd, 4 Commerce Way, Stanbridge Road, Leighton Buzzard, Bedfordshire, LU7 4RW Tel: (01525) 374466 Fax: (01525) 374468 E-mail: sales@cirris.co.uk *Cable & harness test equipment manufacturers and suppliers. Range includes basic continuity to high voltage systems. Patented easy-change interface adapters.*

Cirrus Communication Systems Ltd, Hampton Lovett Industrial Estate, Lovett Road, Hampton Lovett, Droitwich, Worcestershire, WR9 0QG Tel: (01905) 827252 Fax: (01905) 827253 E-mail: info@coltronic.co.uk *Security specialists*

▶ Cirrus Environmental Solutions Ltd, Business & Innovation Centre, Sunderland Enterprise Park Estate, Wearfield, Sunderland, SR5 2TA Tel: 0191-516 6960 Fax: 0191-516 6961 E-mail: info@cirrusenvironmentalsolutions.co.uk *Environmental consultancy, emission monitoring*

Cirrus Event Management, 34 Foxhurst Road, Ash Vale, Aldershot, Hampshire, GU12 5DY Tel: (01252) 337373 Fax: (01252) 337374 E-mail: sales@cirrus-events.com *Event or exhibition service stand design & construction*

▶ Cirrus Information Technology, 101 Bourges Boulevard, Peterborough, PE1 1NG Tel: (01733) 425930 E-mail: sales@cirrusit.com *IT consultancy specialising in payroll & hr systems*

Cirrus Plastics, Esky Drive, Carn Industrial Area, Portadown, Craigavon, County Armagh, BT63 5WD Tel: (028) 3835 0001 Fax: (028) 3835 0002 E-mail: sales@cirrusplastics.co.uk *Polythene bag manufrs*

Cirrus Technologies Ltd, Heming Road, Washford Industrial Estate, Redditch, Worcestershire, B98 0DN Tel: (01527) 527882 Fax: (01527) 502074 E-mail: sales@cirrustesting.com *Automation special purpose equipment & systems*

Cirteq Ltd, Hayfield, Colne Road, Keighley, West Yorkshire, BD20 8QP Tel: (01535) 633333 Fax: (01535) 632966 E-mail: sales@cirteq.com *Cir clips, retaining rings & automotive industry fasteners manufrs*

▶ CIS Aberdeen Ltd, 16 Bon Accord Crescent, Aberdeen, AB11 6DE Tel: (01224) 593366

Cit Realisations Ltd, 6 Wedgwood Road, Bicester, Oxfordshire, OX26 4UL Tel: (01869) 327173 Fax: (01869) 247214 E-mail: sales@chilterninvadex.co.uk *Shower units for disabled persons*

Cita Furniture, 36 Seein Road, Sion Mills, Strabane, County Tyrone, BT82 9NJ Tel: (028) 8165 9744 Fax: (028) 8165 9744 *Furniture manufrs*

Citadel Engineering Supplies Ltd, 14 Marlow Street, Rowley Regis, West Midlands, B65 0AY Tel: 0121-561 5557 Fax: 0121-561 5558 E-mail: sales@citadel-eng.co.uk *Power transmission equipment agents*

Citadel Retail Systems, 62 Portman Road, Reading, RG30 1EA Tel: 0118-959 8020 *Sales & maintenance of cash registers*

Citibase Ltd, 100 Wellington Street, Leeds, LS1 4LT Tel: 0113-242 2444 Fax: 0113-242 2433 E-mail: leeds.ws@citibase.co.uk *Office services*

Citigate Public Affairs, 26 Grosvenor Gardens, London, SW1W 0GT Tel: (020) 7838 4800 Fax: (020) 7838 4801 *Public relations*

Citisigns Ltd, 2a Church Lane, Dinnington, Sheffield, S25 2LY Tel: (01909) 567474 Fax: (01909) 564141 E-mail: mail@citysigns.co.uk *Sign manufrs*

▶ Cititec Building Services Ltd, Little Hyde Farm, Little Hyde Lane, Ingatestone, Essex, CM4 0DU Tel: (01277) 350730 Fax: (01277) 350731

Citrikem Ltd, 2 Cameron Court, Winwick Quay, Warrington, WA2 8RE Tel: (01925) 234707 Fax: (01925) 234693 E-mail: info@klenzan.co.uk *Chemical manufrs*

Citrix Systems Research and Development Ltd, Venture House, Cambourne Business Park, Cambourne, Cambridge, CB23 6DW Tel: (01954) 283600 Fax: (01954) 283601 *Computer research & development*

Citroen Birmingham, Small Heath Highway, Birmingham, B10 0BT Tel: 0121-766 7060 Fax: 0121-766 7042 E-mail: sisav@supanet.com *Commercial & passenger vehicle leasing*

Citroen UK Ltd, 221 Bath Road, Slough, SL1 4BA Tel: (0870) 6069000 Fax: (01753) 748100 *Car manufrs*

Citrus Lime Ltd, County Square, Ulverston, Cumbria, LA12 7AL Tel: (01229) 588628 Fax: (0870) 7065088 E-mail: sales@citrus-lime.com *Computer consultants*

▶ Citrus Media Ltd, Trivarden House, Milton Road, Shipton-under-Wychwood, Chipping Norton, Oxfordshire, OX7 6BD Tel: (01993) 830955 Fax: (01993) 831906 E-mail: info@citrus-media.co.uk *Multi media development services*

Citrus Training Ltd, 16 Bentley Court, Finedon Road Industrial Estate, Wellingborough, Northamptonshire, NN8 4BQ Tel: (0870) 8503505 Fax: (01933) 228876 E-mail: develop@citrustraining.com

City Air Conditioning Ltd, 6 Palace Industrial Estate, Bircholt Road, Maidstone, Kent, ME15 9XU Tel: (01622) 692338 Fax: (01622) 672377 E-mail: cityair@cityairltd.co.uk *Air conditioning installation & maintenance services*

City Air Express Ni Ltd, West Bank Drive, Belfast, BT3 9LA Tel: (028) 9078 1878 Fax: (028) 9078 1788 E-mail: sales@cityairexpress.com *International air couriers*

▶ City Associates, Centre Gate, Colston Avenue, Bristol, BS1 4TR Tel: 0117-317 8133 Fax: 0117-317 8134 E-mail: sales@city-associates.co.uk *South West accountancy recruitment consultancy owned and run by accountants. Temporary, contract and permanent recruitment in all industries and at all levels from ledger clerk to Finance Director.*We account for your success.*

City Assurance Services Ltd, First Floor Gatton Place, St Matthews, Redhill, RH1 1TA Tel: (01737) 854440 Fax: (01737) 854445 E-mail: inquires@cityassurance.com *Independent financial advisors*

▶ City Bakeries Ltd, Unit 5 Enterprise Close, Medway City Estate, Rochester, Kent, ME2 4LY Tel: (01634) 718075 Fax: (01634) 291201 *Bakeries*

▶ City Bakers Ltd, 111 Dundas Spur, Portsmouth, PO3 5NX Tel: (023) 9263 9800

City Blinds, 1 Primacy Road, Bangor, County Down, BT19 7PQ Tel: (028) 9127 2949 Fax: (028) 9143 9101 E-mail: sales@cityblindsni.co.uk *Blinds manufrs*

City Blinds Blind Manufacturers, Fairbairn Street, Dundee, DD3 7JZ Tel: (01382) 877788 Fax: (01382) 737635 E-mail: km@city-blinds.co.uk *Blind manufrs*

City Cash Registers, 35 Leachfield Road, Galgate, Lancaster, LA2 0NX Tel: (01524) 751051 Fax: (01524) 752672 *Sales & repairs of cash registers*

City Catering Equipment (London) Ltd, Railway Arch, 7-8 Commercial Street, London, E1 6NU Tel: (020) 7247 4620 *Catering trade suppliers*

▶ City Centre Maintenance Services, 13 Duke Street, Glasgow, G4 0UL Tel: 0141-552 2419 Fax: 0141-552 4010

City Ceramics, Quarry Lane, Chichester, West Sussex, PO19 8NY Tel: (01243) 775613 Fax: (01243) 776863 *Ceramic tile distributors & importers*

City Clean, 67-69 Richardson Street, Wallsend, Tyne & Wear, NE28 7PS Tel: 0191-263 6218 Fax: 0191-262 1172 E-mail: Richard@cityclean77freeservce.uk *Cleaning contractors*

City Conference Centre, 80 Coleman Street, London, EC2R 5BJ Tel: (020) 7382 2626 Fax: (020) 7382 2670 E-mail: info@cityconferencecentre.com *Conference centre*

▶ City Construction Longcroft Ltd, Chislet Park, 12, Chislet, Canterbury, Kent, CT3 4BY Tel: (01227) 719559 Fax: (01227) 719558

City County Screen Print, 7 Adco Business Centre, Bobbers Mill, Nottingham, NG8 5AH Tel: 0115-970 1130 Fax: 0115-970 4557 E-mail: paul@ccsigns.co.uk *Sign makers & screen printers*

City & County Signs, 209 Pinhoe Road, Exeter, EX4 8AB Tel: (01392) 434366 Fax: (01392) 434366 *Sign manufrs*

City Deco Centre, 113-115 Kenton Road, Harrow, Middlesex, HA3 0AN Tel: (020) 8907 9494 Fax: (020) 8907 9062 E-mail: info@citydeco.co.uk *Paint & hardware shop dealers*

City Digital East Midlands Ltd, Samson House, Samson Road, Coalville, Leicestershire, LE67 3FP Tel: (01530) 815581 Fax: (01530) 815262 *Photocopier specialists*

▶ City Digital Technology, 29 Cressex Enterprise Centre, Lincoln Road, Cressex Business Park, High Wycombe, Buckinghamshire, HP12 3RL Tel: (01494) 532222 Fax: (01494) 538787 E-mail: nigel@cdt-group.com *Sale, rental, lease & hire of photocopiers*

City Electrical Factors Ltd, 19 Bedford Business Centre, Mile Road, Bedford, MK42 9TW Tel: (01234) 212444 Fax: (01234) 268081 E-mail: sales.bedford@cef.co.uk *Electrical wholesalers*

City Electrical Factors Ltd, Units 4-6, St Nicholas Road, Beverley, North Humberside, HU17 0QT Tel: (01482) 869861 Fax: (01482) 866297 *Electrical wholesalers*

City Electrical Factors Ltd, 2 Blackstone Road, Stukeley Meadows Industrial Estate, Huntingdon, Cambridgeshire, PE29 6EF Tel: (01480) 456456 Fax: (01480) 457457 E-mail: sales.huntingdon@cef.co.uk *Electrical wholesaler & distributor*

City Electrical Factors Ltd, Tritton Road, Lincoln, LN6 7QY Tel: (01522) 682548 Fax: (01582) 694512 E-mail: info.lincoln@cef.co.uk *Electrical equipment suppliers*

City Electrical Factors Ltd, Unit N6 Riverside Industrial Estate, Bridge Road, Littlehampton, West Sussex, BN17 5DF Tel: (01903) 723801 Fax: (01903) 730361 *Electrical wholesalers*

City Electrical Factors Ltd, Unit 6 Dunbeath Court, Elgin Industrial Estate, Swindon, SN2 8QF Tel: (01793) 535256 Fax: (01793) 513287 E-mail: sales.swindon@cef.co.uk *Electrical goods suppliers*

▶ City Electrical Installations Cobridge Ltd, 36 Woodbank Street, Stoke-on-Trent, ST6 3BD Tel: (01782) 812217

City Engineering Ltd, 9 Cygnus Business Centre, Dalmeyer Road, London, NW10 2XA Tel: (020) 8451 4930 Fax: (020) 8459 1120 E-mail: roul@cityengineering.fsnet.uk *Air conditioning engineers*

City Fax Ltd, 1 Cronin Road, Weldon South Industrial Estate, Corby, Northamptonshire, NN18 8AQ Tel: (01536) 402242 Fax: (01536) 402201 E-mail: cityfax.corby@cityfaxltd.com *Neckwear manufrs*

▶ City Fire Protection Ltd, 30 Ansdell Drive, Brockworth, Gloucester, GL3 4BU Tel: (0800) 0730250 Fax: (01452) 530669 E-mail: info@cityfireprotection.co.uk *Service installation & supplier*

City Gate Automation, 32 Hetherington Road, Shepperton, Middlesex, TW17 0SP Tel: (01932) 786464 Fax: (01932) 766199 *Gates manufrs*

▶ City Goldsmiths, 3-5 Carts Lane, Leicester, LE1 5FL Tel: 0116-253 1636 Fax: 0116-253 1655 E-mail: sales@citygoldsmiths.co.uk *Goldsmiths in Leicester.*Quality Jewellery.*

City Guardian Electrical Ltd, Vision House, 182 Landells Road, London, SE22 9PP Tel: (020) 8299 5120 Fax: (020) 8299 5130 E-mail: reception@caivision.com *Electrical contractors*

City Hardware Electrical Ltd, 6-10 Goswell Road, London, EC1M 7AA Tel: (020) 7253 4095 Fax: (020) 7490 2654 E-mail: sales@cityhardware.co.uk *Builders' & electrical suppliers*

City Insulation Contractors Ltd, City House, Horspath Industrial Estate, Pony Road, Cowley, Oxford, OX4 2RD Tel: (01865) 715173 Fax: (01865) 770547 E-mail: info@cityins.co.uk *Asbestos removal specialists*

▶ City Irrigation Ltd, Bencewell Granary, 39 Oakley Road, Bromley, BR2 8HD Tel: (020) 8462 4630 Fax: (020) 8462 3810 E-mail: sales@cityirrigation.co.uk *City Irrigation Ltd are distributors for equipment from Philmac, Orbit, Holman,Irritrol, Kulker,Rolland, Antelco, Hozelock, Wolf Tools, etc supllying both trade and retail customers*

City Leather Co Leicester Ltd, 47 Kenilworth Drive, Oadby, Leicester, LE2 5LT Tel: 0116-271 3322 Fax: 0116-272 0828 *Shoe component manufrs*

City Lifting, Purfleet Industrial Park, Aveley, South Ockendon, Essex, RM15 4YA Tel: (01708) 805550 Fax: (01708) 805558 E-mail: hire@citylifting.co.uk Purchasing Contact: T. Jepson Sales Contact: B. Jones *Mobile, lorry mounted crane hire, tower cranes including hire/leasing/rental*

City Mastic Asphalt Ltd, 315a Weston Road, Stoke-on-Trent, ST3 6HA Tel: (01782) 311249 Fax: (01782) 311249 *Roofing contractors*

City Moving & Storage Ltd, Canada House Business Centre, 272 Field End Road, Ruislip, Middlesex, HA4 9NA Tel: (020) 8582 0420 Fax: (020) 8582 0421 E-mail: info@citymoving.co.uk *Removal contractors*

City Mutual Ltd, PO Box 521, Taunton, Somerset, TA3 6YB Tel: (01460) 281775 Fax: (01460) 281853 E-mail: edu@citymutual.com *Electronic publishers*

City Office Audio London Ltd, Superstore, 303-309 Camberwell New Road, London, SE5 0TF Tel: (020) 7703 6032 Fax: (020) 7703 5500 E-mail: grm@cityoffice.co.uk *Office supplies,stationery and*equipment. Large Superstore,Car park. Free local & international deliveries.*

City Office Interiors Ltd, Albany House, 31 Hurst Street, Birmingham, B5 4BD Tel: 0121-622 4811 Fax: 0121-622 5756 E-mail: contact@cityofficeinteriors.co.uk *Office refurbishment*

City Office Interiors Ltd, 1 Duchess Street, London, W1W 6AN Tel: (0870) 2203772 Fax: (020) 7079 5929 E-mail: sales@cityofficeinteriors.co.uk *Office designers & builders* Also at: Birmingham

City Office Ni Ltd, 67 Boucher Cresent, Belfast, BT12 6HU Tel: (028) 9038 1838 Fax: (028) 9038 1954 E-mail: info@cityofficni.com *Business machine distributors*

City Office Services Ltd, Templeworks, Brett Passage, Brett Road, London, E8 1JR Tel: (020) 8510 0555 Fax: (020) 8510 0666 *Office partitioning contractors*

▶ City Office - Virtual Office Services, 12 St. James Square, St. James's, London, SW1Y 4RB Tel: (020) 7692 0608 Fax: (020) 7692 0607 E-mail: Sales@YourCityOffice.com *City Office offer Phone Answering, Mail Forwarding solutions with Meeting Rooms and Fax2Email facilities. Call now 0207 692 06 08*

City Paper Ltd, Xerox House, Maylands Avenue, Hemel Hempstead, Hertfordshire, HP2 7DE Tel: (0870) 2410472 Fax: (0870) 2410473 E-mail: sales@citypaper.com *Wholesale paper merchants*

City Partitions, 13 Chesterfield Road, Ashford, Middlesex, TW15 2NB Tel: (01784) 255552 *Office refurbishment partitioning*

▶ City Plant Services Ltd, 12 Craigmore Road, Newry, County Down, BT35 6PL Tel: (028) 3082 5522 Fax: 02830 825533 E-mail: sales@cpsnewry.com *HOSE BURST SAFETY VALVES*HAMMER PIPEWORK**SHEAR/PULVERISER/GRAB CIRCUITS**ROTATE/MAGNET/TILT BUCKET CIRCUITS**HEIGHT, SLEW & DIPPER LIMITERS**Plant Repairs*Japanese Plant Spares & Accessories*Hydraulic Hoses & Fittings*Excavator Buckets, Teeth, Pins, Bushes & Linkages*Track & Undercarriage Parts*Hydraulic Cylinder Seal Kits Supplied & Fitted*Oil & Grease Products*Hydraulic, Air, Fuel & Oil Filters*

City Plumbing Supplies Ltd, 1 Faraday Street, Dryburgh Industrial Estate, Dundee, DD2 3QQ Tel: (01382) 825625 Fax: (01382) 826926 *Plumbers' merchants* Also at: Branches throughout the U.K.

City Plumbing Supplies Ltd, Unit 1a Roundwood Drive, Sherdley Road Industrial Estate, St. Helens, Merseyside, WA9 5JD Tel: (01744) 453874 Fax: (01744) 27482 E-mail: andrew.ormerod@city-plumbing-supplies.co.uk *Plumbers merchants* Also at: Warrington & Widnes

City Plumbing Supplies Ltd, 159 Stanley Road, London, Teddington, Middlesex, TW11 8UF Tel: (020) 8943 3933 Fax: (020) 8943 2873 *Heating & plumbing merchants* Also at: Godalming, Mitcham & Walton-on-Thames

City Plumbing Supplies plc, 27 Aston Road, Waterlooville, Hampshire, PO7 7XJ Tel: (023) 9226 7341 Fax: (023) 9225 5698 E-mail: ian@city-plumbingsupplies.co.uk *Heating & plumbing equipment stockists* Also at: Chard, Cheltenham, Edinburgh, Glasgow, Poole, Salisbury, Southampton & Swindon

City Plumbing Supplies Ltd, George Cayley Drive, York, YO30 4XE Tel: (01904) 690088 Fax: (01904) 692990 *Builders' merchants*

City Pluming Supplies, 65-67 Kelvin Avenue, Hillington Industrial Estate, Glasgow, G52 4LP Tel: 0141-882 7700 Fax: 0141-882 9390 *Plumbing merchants services*

City Press, The Old Courthouse, 1 The Paddock, Chatham, Kent, ME4 4RE Tel: (01634) 832820 Fax: (01634) 818741 *Printers & lithographers*

City Press Knives, 101 Weymouth Street, Leicester, LE4 6FR Tel: 0116-266 0709 Fax: 0116-266 0711 *Knife manufrs*

▶ City Press Leeds Ltd, St Anns Mill, Commercial Road, Leeds, LS5 3AE Tel: 0113-278 4286 Fax: 0113-278 6066

City Print Milton Keynes Ltd, 17 Denbigh Hall Industrial Estate, Denbigh Hall, Bletchley, Milton Keynes, MK3 7QT Tel: (01908) 377085 Fax: (01908) 649335 E-mail: sales@cityprint.net *Commercial printers*

▶ City Renovations Ltd, 10 Bond Avenue Bletchley, Bletchley, Milton Keynes, MK1 1SW Tel: (01908) 366936

City Response Ltd, 19 Cross Keys Street, Manchester, M4 5ET Tel: 0161-832 8325 Fax: 0161-834 2260 *Building refurbishment contractors*

▶ City Restaurants Guide, 4 Oak Close, Measham, Swadlincote, Derbyshire, DE12 7JY Tel: (01530) 274830 Fax: 01530 274823 E-mail: info@cityrestaurantsguide.com *The City Restaurants Guide is a complete on-line magazine covering city restaurants both in the UK and internationally. It is designed specifically for clients to search for restaurants easily using multiple criteria and also book online for free. The magazine further provides suppliers, jobs and for sale repositories for the restaurant industry.*

City Roofing & Asphalt Services Ltd, 3a Pennyburn Industrial Estate, Londonderry, BT48 0LU Tel: (028) 7126 9648 Fax: (028) 7136 7016 *Roofing & flooring contractors*

▶ City Scaffolding Ltd, City House, 124a Chesterfield Road, Barlborough, Chesterfield, Derbyshire, S43 4TT Tel: (01246) 819125 Fax: (01246) 819060 E-mail: city@scaffoldingm1.fsnet.co.uk

City Screen Print Ltd, Unit 2 Sextant Park Neptune Close, Medway City Estate, Rochester, Kent, ME2 4LU Tel: (01634) 297779 Fax: (01634) 294264 E-mail: info@cityscreenprint.co.uk *Screen printers*

City Screen Printers (UK) Ltd, Unit 9, Earls Way, Earls Way Industrial Estate, Thurmaston, Leicester, LE4 8DL Tel: 0116-260 2484 Fax: 0116-264 0261 E-mail: info@cityscreen.fsnet.co.uk *Fabric rotary printers*

City Seals & Bearings Ltd, Stevenson Road, Sheffield, S9 3XG Tel: 0114-244 3030 Fax: 0114-244 0044 E-mail: info@cityseals.co.uk *Engineering distributors & agents*

City Self Drive, Swallowdale Lane, Hemel Hempstead Industrial Estate, Hemel Hempstead Industrial Estate, Hemel Hempstead, Hertfordshire, HP2 7EA Tel: (01442) 419419 Fax: (01442) 419201 E-mail: info@citygroup.com *Retail interior fixtures & fittings*

City Sign Centre, Ockley Road, Bognor Regis, West Sussex, PO21 2HW Tel: (01243) 774833 Fax: (01243) 539114 E-mail: info@cmlsigns.co.uk *Sign manufrs*

City Signs, Darley Abbey Mills, Darley Abbey, Derby, DE22 1DZ Tel: (01332) 349772 Fax: (01332) 341164 *Sign manufrs*

City Signs Midlands Ltd, 34 Jasper Street, Stoke-on-Trent, ST1 3DA Tel: (01782) 281069 Fax: (01782) 281609 E-mail: citysignuk@netscapeonline.co.uk *Sign manufacturers & installers*

City Space Services Ltd, 37-39 Holmesdale Road, North Holmwood, Dorking, Surrey, RH5 4HS Tel: (0800) 592058 Fax: (01306) 884552 *Archival document storage & self-stores*

City Sprints, 58-62 Scrutton Street, London, EC2A 4PH Tel: (020) 7880 1100 Fax: (020) 7466 4901 *Security courier services*

▶ City Of Stirling Media Ltd, Suite 1, Castle House, 1 Baker Street, Stirling, FK8 1AL Tel: 0845 226 1896 E-mail: hello@cos-media.co.uk *Marketing, Graphic Design, Print, Advertising, Web, Media Solutions*

▶ City Storage Vault, The Pentagon Centre, 30 Washington Street, Glasgow, G3 8AZ Tel: (0845) 8500400 Fax: 0141-226 3944 E-mail: info@citystoragevault.com

City Styles Leicester Ltd, 150 St Nicholas Circle, Leicester, LE1 4JJ Tel: 0116-251 5411 *Leisure clothing manufrs*

City of Sunderland, Civic Centre, Sunderland, SR2 7DN Tel: 0191-553 1171 Fax: 0191-553 1180 E-mail: business.investment@sunderland.gov.uk *City business & investment team services*

City Tayloring, 219 Bow Road, London, E3 2SJ Tel: (020) 8981 1450 Fax: (020) 8983 1728 *Clothing manufrs*

City Technical Services UK Ltd, 38 Southcroft Road, Rutherglen, Glasgow, G73 1UG Tel: 0141-643 2248 Fax: 0141-613 4432 *Refrigeration repairers & sellers*

City Technology Ltd, City Technology Centre, Walton Road, Portsmouth, PO6 1SZ Tel: (023) 9232 5511 Fax: (023) 9238 6611 E-mail: sensors@citytech.co.uk *Gas detection equipment manufrs*

City Telecom, 36 Golders Gardens, London, NW11 9BU Tel: (0870) 9502750 Fax: (0870) 0118330 E-mail: sales@citytelecom.co.uk *Telecommunications providers & maintainers*

City Tiles Contracts Ltd, 73 Dean Court Road, Rottingdean, Brighton, BN2 7DL Tel: (01273) 390777 Fax: (01273) 390888 *Ceramic tiling sub contractors*

City Transair, 58 Loughborough Road, Mountsorrel, Loughborough, Leicestershire, LE12 7AT Tel: 0116-230 0070 Fax: 0116-230 0075 *Bearings & transmission equipment suppliers*

▶ City & Urban, Loubond House, 2 Denham Road, Canvey Island, Essex, SS8 9HB Tel: (01268) 685800 Fax: (01268) 685544

▶ City Walls Ltd, Aztec House, 137a Molesey Avenue, West Molesey, Surrey, KT8 2RY Tel: (01444) 417030 Fax: (020) 8481 7289 E-mail: londonsales@brokhouse.net *Folding partitions installers*

City Water Pre-Com Ltd, Maidenhead Yard, The Wash, Hertford, SG14 1PX Tel: (01992) 505353 Fax: (01992) 554852 E-mail: enquiries@city-water.com *Risk Assessment to ACOP L8, Independent Audit of Risk Management Schemes, Water Hygiene Programme Monitoring, Supply and Monitoring of Water Treatment Chemical Programmes, Operator Training in Water Treatment Application, Customised In House Courses, Water Storage Tank Refurbishment.*

City Wholefoods, 67 Magdalen Road, Exeter, EX2 4TA Tel: (01392) 252295 *Health food retailers*

City Wrought Iron Centre, 2 Erskine Street, Liverpool, L6 1AL Tel: 0151-260 0550 Fax: 0151-260 0550 *Wrought iron manufrs*

Cityarch Ltd, 3 Potters Lane, Kiln Farm, Milton Keynes, MK11 3HE Tel: (01908) 265557 Fax: (01908) 265400 E-mail: cityarch.limited@virgin.net *Fabricators of fume extractors*

Citybeds Ltd, 17-39 Gibbins Road, London, E15 2HU Tel: (020) 8503 1503 Fax: (020) 8519 8450 E-mail: sales@citybeds.co.uk *Bed retailers*

Citycare, Mile Cross Road, Norwich, NR3 2DY Tel: (01603) 484868 Fax: (01603) 496725 *Buildings service & maintenance*

Citygate Dewe Rogerson Ltd, 3 London Wall Buildings, London, EC2M 5SY Tel: (020) 7638 9571 Fax: (020) 7628 3444 *Public relations consultants*

▶ CityJobs, Langstone technology park, Langstone road, Havant, Hampshire, PO9 1SA Tel: 0870 774 8847 E-mail: Kelly@receptional.com *Search and apply for current vacancies in the banking, finance and accountancy sectors from the top City companies and recruitment agencies. Register for CityJobs' jobs by email service and upload your CV.*

Citymain Insurance, 18 Church Road, Fleet, Hampshire, GU51 3RH Tel: (01252) 819504 Fax: (01252) 626440 E-mail: citymain@citymain-insurance.co.uk *Insurance consultants*

Cityown Ltd, Unit M Charlwoods Business Centre, East Grinstead, West Sussex, RH19 2HH Tel: (01342) 327787 Fax: (01342) 324289 *Hydraulic system manufrs*

▶ Citysafe Wholesale Ltd, Unit 1-4 Mortimers Farm Industrial Estate, Romsey Road, Ower, Romsey, Hampshire, SO51 6AF Tel: (023) 8081 4181 Fax: (023) 8081 2771 E-mail: admin@citysafe.co.uk *Security wholesaler*

▶ cityview printers, 7a Bakers Yard, Alphinbrook Road, Marsh Barton Trading Estate, Exeter, EX2 8SS Tel: 01392 410222 E-mail: andy@cityviewprinters.co.uk *Free estimates, Fast & friendly service, Business cards to Brochures, Single to Full Colour,*Quality Heidelberg Presses,*In House Mac design studio*

Civic Alarms Ltd, 79 Main Rd, Long Hanborough, Witney, Oxon, OX29 8JX Tel: 01993 883448 Fax: 01993 883661 *Electronic security*

Civic Security Ltd, Vision House, 182 Landells Road, London, SE22 9PP Tel: (020) 8299 5150 Fax: (020) 8299 5160 E-mail: sales@civicsecurity.com *Closed Circuit Television & security contractors*

Civica Financial Systems Ltd, Plain Tree Crescent, Feltham, Middlesex, TW13 7DT Tel: (020) 8844 2141 Fax: (020) 8751 4386 E-mail: enquiries@civica.co.uk *Computer systems house operating for local government & higher education* Also at: Branches throughout the UK

Civica It Systems Ltd, Regent Court, Laporte Way, Luton, LU4 8SP Tel: (01582) 644444 Fax: (01582) 644446 Principal Export Areas: Worldwide *Computer consultants*

Civica UK Ltd, Castlegate House, Castlegate Drive, Dudley, West Midlands, DY1 4TD Tel: (01384) 453400 Fax: (01384) 453600 *Computer systems consultants & software for the public sector* Also at: Leeds

Civil Aviation Authority, 45-59 Kingsway, London, WC2B 6TE Tel: (020) 7379 7311 Fax: (020) 7453 6028 E-mail: sales@caa.co.uk *Civil aviation authority*

Civil Engineering Dynamics Ltd, 11 Oak Walk, Wallington, Surrey, SM6 7DE Tel: (020) 8647 1908 Fax: (020) 8395 1556 E-mail: sales@environmental.co.uk *Noise & vibration consultants*

Civil & Environmental Project Services Ltd, 1 Port Street, Evesham, Worcestershire, WR11 3LA Tel: (01386) 424007 Fax: (01386) 424007 E-mail: info@civenv.co.uk *Civil & Environmental offer a comprehensive range of products & services in the specialist field of water & wastewater engineering*

Civil & Marine Slag Cement Ltd, 7 Sinclair Road, Belfast, BT3 9LY Tel: (028) 9074 1690 Fax: (028) 9035 7127 *Cement distributors & manufrs*

Civil & Marine Slag Cement Ltd, London Road, Grays, Essex, RM20 3NL Tel: (01708) 864813 Fax: (01708) 865907 E-mail: enquiries@civilmarine.co.uk *Slag cement*

Civil & Marine Slag Cement Ltd, Llanwern Works, Llanwern, Newport, Gwent, NP19 4QX Tel: (01633) 278708 Fax: (01633) 277017 *Cement additive manufrs*

▶ The Civils, 500 Pavilion Drive, Northampton, NN4 7YJ Tel: (01604) 664200 Fax: (01604) 708373 E-mail: glyn.holt@birse.co.uk *Civil engineering, highways & land remediation contractors*

▶ CJ Carpets & Lighting, 53 Scotgate, Stamford, Lincolnshire, PE9 2YQ Tel: (01780) 754825 Fax: (01780) 754825 *Carpet retailers*

▶ CJ Interactif UK, 02 Palace Street, Burnley, Lancashire, BB12 6EA Tel: 08707 432150 E-mail: sales@cj-interactif.co.uk *Providers of basic-bespoke website design, low cost web hosting, logo design, search engine marketing consultations and online home/office business opportunities. Call now for a quote or fill out our information request form and we will call you back.*

CK Industrial Engineers Ltd, Units 4-6 Enterprise Way, Wickford Business Park, Wickford, Essex, SS11 8DH Tel: (01268) 561471 Fax: (01268) 764891 E-mail: enquiries@ck-ind.com *Automotive industry jigs & fixtures manufrs*

▶ Cka Signs, 61 High Street, Felling, Gateshead, Tyne & Wear, NE10 9LU Tel: 0191-469 3555 Fax: 0191-469 3555 E-mail: ckasignsandgraphics@blueyonder.co.uk *Sign services & manufrs*

CKC Engineering Services, 31 Bowlers Croft, Honeywood Road, Basildon, Essex, SS14 3DZ Tel: (01268) 273188 Fax: (01268) 273199 *Machining & engineering services*

CKF Systems Ltd, Unit 10 St Albans Road, Empire Way, Gloucester, GL2 5FW Tel: (01452) 424565 Fax: (01452) 423477 E-mail: sales@ckf.co.uk *Industrial conveyor manufrs*

▶ CL Automotive, Unit 111 B M K Industrial Estate, Wakefield Road, Liversedge, West Yorkshire, WF15 6BS Tel: (01924) 404040 Fax: (01924) 404050 *Gasket manufrs*

Claas UK Ltd, Saxham, Bury St. Edmunds, Suffolk, IP28 6QZ Tel: (01284) 763100 Fax: (01284) 769839 E-mail: info-uk@claas.com *Agricultural engineers*

▶ Clachan Construction Ltd, Ruthvenfield Road, Inveralmond Industrial Estate, Perth, PH1 3EE Tel: (01738) 620221 Fax: (01738) 630734

Clad Safety Products, PO Box 123, Harrogate, North Yorkshire, HG1 4PT Tel: (01423) 881266 *Safety equipment distributors*

Cladburn Engineering Co., C Block 17 South Avenue, Blantyre Industrial Estate, Blantyre, Glasgow, G72 0XB Tel: (01698) 822550 Fax: (01698) 825130 *Profile cutters*

Cladding Components Ltd, 17 Trinity Street, Leamington Spa, Warwickshire, CV32 5RH Tel: (01926) 420825 Fax: (01926) 313927 E-mail: clad.comp@ic24.net *Wall, floor tiling contractors & suppliers*

▶ Cladswell House Systems Ltd, The Old Fishery, Holborrow Lodge, Holberrow Green, Redditch, Worcestershire, B96 6SF Tel: (01386) 793377 Fax: (01386) 793376 E-mail: sales@chs.eu.com *Computer hardware suppliers & maintenance*

Claire Clifford Stationery & Office Products, 48 Watt Road, Hillington Park, Hillington Industrial Estate, Glasgow, G52 4RY Tel: 0141-882 6789 Fax: 0141-882 7777 E-mail: mail@claire-clifford.co.uk *Stationery & cleaning supply manufrs*

Claire Fabrications, 1 Abbey Street, Birkenhead, Merseyside, CH41 5JG Tel: 0151-647 3399 *Steel fabricators*

▶ claire gray floral designs, 57 Clement Way, Upminster, Essex, RM14 2NX Tel: 07800 918615 E-mail: claire.gray57@ntlworld.com *I am a freelance florist, with 15 years experience. Let me come to you to discuss your needs. I specialise in weddings and corporate events.*

Claire International Ltd, 29 The Bank, Barnard Castle, County Durham, DL12 8PL Tel: (01833) 637325 Fax: (01833) 690880 *Knitwear suppliers*

▶ Clairegodwincoaching.co.uk, 33 Yew Tree Gardens, Denmead, Waterlooville, Hampshire, PO7 6LH Tel: (023) 9225 5232 *Life and Corporate Coaching**We have no choice of what color we"re born or who our parents are or whether we"re rich or poor. **What we do have is some choice over what we make of our lives once we"re here. **-Mildred Taylor*

▶ Clairglow Heating Ltd, Bourne Enterprise Centre, Wrotham Road, Borough Green, Sevenoaks, Kent, TN15 8DG Tel: (01732) 885822 Fax: (01732) 886117

Clairtex Gwent, Merthyr Road, Tredegar, Gwent, NP22 3AY Tel: (01495) 711226 Fax: (01495) 718124 *Soft furnishing manufrs*

Clairtronic Ltd, Shuttleworth Road, Elm Farm Industrial Estate, Bedford, MK41 0EP Tel: (01234) 330774 Fax: (01234) 330775 E-mail: sales@clairtronic.co.uk *Transformers manufrs*

Clamason Industries Ltd, Gibbons Industrial Park, Dudley Road, Kingswinford, West Midlands, DY6 8XG Tel: (01384) 400000 Fax: (01384) 400588 E-mail: sales@clamason.co.uk *General presswork & pressings, non-ferrous metal*

Clam-Brummer Ltd, London Road, Spellbrook, Bishop's Stortford, Hertfordshire, CM23 4BA Tel: (020) 7476 3171 Fax: (020) 7474 0098 E-mail: sales@brummer.co.uk *Woodfillers, adhesives & diy product manufrs*

Clamcleats Ltd, Watchmead, Welwyn Garden City, Hertfordshire, AL7 1AP Tel: (01707) 330101 Fax: (01707) 321269 E-mail: sales@clamcleat.com *Rope cleats for boats & plastic moulding manufrs*

▶ Clampco, Unit 6, Hammond Avenue, Stockport, Cheshire, SK4 1PQ Tel: 0161-476 3600 Fax: 0161-476 3600 E-mail: sales@Clampcouk.ltd.uk *Exhaust & Workshop consumables distributors*

▶ Clan Albanach Kiltmakers, 24 High Street, South Queensferry, West Lothian, EH30 9PP Tel: 0131-331 2221 Fax: 0131-319 2221 *Kilt makers*

▶ Clan Distribution, Seabegs Road, Bonnybridge, Stirlingshire, FK4 2BT Tel: (01324) 812914

Clancast Contracts Ltd, 48 Shaw Street, Glasgow, G51 3BL Tel: 0141-440 2345 Fax: 0141-440 2488 E-mail: info@clancast.co.uk *Architectural detailing*

Clanchatton Birmingham Ltd, Bell Way House, 7 Worcester Road, Bromsgrove, Worcestershire, B61 7DL Tel: (01527) 879000 Fax: (01527) 870071 *Credit control consultants*

Clancy Docwra/Vws UK Jv Ltd, Clare House Coppermill Lane, Harefield, Uxbridge, Middlesex, UB9 6HZ Tel: (01895) 823711 Fax: (01895) 825263 E-mail: admin@theclancygroup.co.uk *Contractors' plant hirers*

Clandrex Cleaning Ltd, PO Box 14, Grantham, Lincolnshire, NG31 9BL Tel: (01476) 577972 Fax: (01476) 590862 *Floor & carpet cleaning equipment distributors & cleaning contractors*

Clanpress (Kings Lynn) Ltd, 1 Dundee Court, Hamburg Way, King's Lynn, Norfolk, PE30 2ND Tel: (01553) 772737 Fax: (01553) 768403 E-mail: clanpress@aol.com *Colour printing services*

▶ Clanroots, Braeside, 162 High Street, Gardenstown, Banff, AB45 3YW Tel: (01261) 851059 E-mail: nda@clanroots.co.uk *In the small North East Scottish coastal village of Gardenstown, Clanroots produces Hand Carved Clan Crests, cold cast in bronze, then mounted on a Scottish Hardwood Sheild with a brass plaque displaying the clan name. Unique and limited editions of 500.*

Clansey Communications Ltd, 68-70 Market Street, Cannock, Staffordshire, WS12 1AY Tel: (01543) 424485 Fax: (01543) 422256 E-mail: sales@clansey.co.uk *Telecommunications*

Clansman Dynamics Ltd, The Stephenson Building, Nasmyth Avenue, Scottish Enterprise Technology Park, East Kilbride, Glasgow, G75 0QR Tel: (01355) 579900 Fax: (01355) 579901 E-mail: info@clansmandynamics.com Principal Export Areas: Worldwide *Mechanical handling equipment*

Clanville Sawmills Ltd, Clanville, Castle Cary, Somerset, BA7 7PQ Tel: (01963) 350881 Fax: (01963) 351562 E-mail: admin@clanvillsawmills.co.uk *Pallet & case manufrs*

Clapham & Woolley Ltd, 3 Mandale, South Street, Keighley, West Yorkshire, BD21 1DB Tel: (01535) 665143 Fax: (01535) 691893 *Valve re-furbishment specialists*

Clapro Ltd, 2 Sussex Road, New Malden, Surrey, KT3 3PY Tel: (020) 8949 4963 Fax: (020) 8949 7517 *Pet food & horticultural products importers & distributors*

Clare Instruments, Dominion Way, Worthing, West Sussex, BN14 8NW Tel: (01903) 233314 Fax: (01903) 216089 E-mail: sales@clareinstruments.com *Safety electrical equipment & safety test solutions manufrs*

Clare Lallow, 3 Medina Road, Cowes, Isle of Wight, PO31 7BU Tel: (01983) 292112 Fax: (01983) 281180 E-mail: lallows@lallowsboatyard.com *Yacht, launch builder & repairers*

Clare Sewing Machine Shop, 13 Great Darkgate Street, Aberystwyth, Dyfed, SY23 1DE Tel: (01970) 617786 *Domestic sewing machine suppliers*

▶ Clare Window Centre, St. Johns Bridge Road, Plymouth, PL4 0JJ Tel: (01752) 670400 Fax: (01752) 228284

Clarehill Plastics Ltd, New Building, 21 Clarehill Road, Moira, Craigavon, County Armagh, BT67 0PB Tel: (028) 9261 1077 Fax: (028) 9261 2672 E-mail: info@clarehill.co.uk *Tank stockholders & distributors*

Claremont Automatics Ltd, 40 Oakley Road, Chinnor, Oxfordshire, OX39 4ES Tel: (01844) 353635 Fax: (01844) 352750 *Amusement machine hire*

Claremont Business Environment, Design Studio 2 Quay Side Commerce Centre, Lower Quay, Fareham, Hampshire, PO16 0XR Tel: (01329) 220123 Fax: (01329) 221322 E-mail: info@claremontgi.com *Office interior specialists*

Claremont Catering Engineers, 69-71 Lower Bents Lane, Bredbury, Stockport, Cheshire, SK6 2NL Tel: 0161-406 6464 Fax: 0161-406 6383 E-mail: info@claremontengineers.co.uk *Catering equipment sales & services*

Claremont Controls Ltd, Suite 4 Wansbeck Business Centre, Rotary Parkway, Ashington, Northumberland, NE63 8QZ Tel: (01670) 819000 Fax: (01670) 857886 E-mail: honet@claremont-controls.co.uk *Computer software development services*

▶ Clarendon Apartments, Wraysbury Hall, Ferry Lane, Wraysbury, Staines, Middlesex, TW19 6HG Tel: (01784) 489200 Fax: (01784) 489201 E-mail: info@clarendonuk.com *Fully serviced accommodation from Clarendon Apartments, all Clarendon"s locations provide excellent accessibility to motorways, airports & London, & are handy for amenities, leisure facilities, schools & visitor attractions*

Clarendon Engineering Ltd, 30 High Street, Earl Shilton, Leicester, LE9 7DG Tel: (01455) 841200 Fax: (01455) 841110 E-mail: sales@clarendoneng.co.uk *Motorsport fastener distributors*

Clarendon Fabrications, 25 Morris Road, Leicester, LE2 6AL Tel: 0116-244 8057 Fax: 0116-270 9214 E-mail: sales@clarendonfab.co.uk *Solid surface/surface material manufacterers.*

▶ Clarendon Haulage Ltd, New Trees Garage, Myerscough Road, Mellor Brook, Blackburn, BB2 7LB Tel: (01254) 814997 Fax: (01254) 814049 E-mail: info@aaisecurity.co.uk

Clarendon Southern, 4-5 Toll Gate Estate, Stanbridge Earls, Romsey, Hampshire, SO51 0HE Tel: (01794) 517649 Fax: (01794) 515968 *Carpet manufrs*

Clares Of Croydon Ltd, 54 Tamworth Road, Croydon, CR0 1XW Tel: (020) 8688 7952 Fax: (020) 8688 1867 *Locksmiths*

Clareville Communications, 315-317 New Kings Road, London, SW6 4RF Tel: (020) 7736 4022 Fax: (020) 7736 3504 E-mail: johnstar@clareville.co.uk *Public relations*

▶ Claric Design & Build Ltd, 30 Holly Road, Golborne, Warrington, WA3 3JR Tel: (01942) 731384 Fax: (01942) 731384 · *Full Design Planning & Build Service **· Full design Service.**· Submissions for Planning to Local Authority**· Estimating Service providing Bills of quantities, material list etc..**· Building and Civil Engineering Contractors**· Barn & Loft Conversions**· Plant & Eqipment Hire**· As built drawings**· Land Surveys**· Setting out Engineers**

▶ Clarich Ltd, Building 25, Leicester Road, Rugby, Warwickshire, CV21 1BD Tel: (01788) 554433 Fax: (01788) 554434 E-mail: andy.clarke@clarichltd.com *World leaders in the manufacture of AC & DC electrical windings*

Claridge Presswork Co. Ltd, 11 Bolton Road, Reading, RG2 0NH Tel: 0118-986 0114 Fax: 0118-931 3842 E-mail: sales@springsandwireforms.co.uk *Springs & Wireforms manufacture coil springs, flat springs, wireforms & pressed components to customer specification in a range of materials including spring steel,stainless steel,phosphor bronze & beryllium copper*****

Clarifoil, PO Box 5, Derby, DE21 7BP Tel: (01332) 661422 Fax: (01332) 660178 E-mail: info@clarifoil.com *Cellulose diacetate film manufrs*

▶ Clarion Flooring & Blinds Ltd, Whitstable Park, Widnes, Cheshire, WA8 9AS Tel: 0151-420 0714 Fax: (0870) 705 1304 E-mail: info@cfab.co.uk *Blinds & flooring retailers /installers*

Clarion G B Ltd, Unit 1-2 & 14, Marshall Road, Hillmead, Swindon, SN5 5YU Tel: (01793) 870400 Fax: (01793) 875747 E-mail: enquiries@clarion.co.uk *Car audio company*

▶ Clarion Loss Prevention Ltd, Oak House, 103 Manchester Road, Audenshaw, Manchester, M34 5PY Tel: 0161-371 1888 Fax: (0870) 4448348

▶ Clarisol, 1 Holme Lane, Spondon, Derby, DE21 7BP Tel: (01332) 681210 Fax: (01332) 660178 E-mail: info@clarifoil.com *Manufacturers of water soluble products*

Claritas Ltd, 2 Earlswood Street, London, SE10 9ES Tel: (020) 8858 2411 Fax: (020) 8305 2875 E-mail: claritasltd@amstrad.co.uk *Optical wholesalers*

Clarity, Forge Road, Willenhall, West Midlands, WV12 4HD Tel: (01902) 638340 Fax: (01902) 637594 *Printers*

Clarity Communications, Barley Mow Passage, London, W4 4PH Tel: 0845 355 1178 Fax: 0870 706 4834 E-mail: enquiries@claritycomms.com *Clarity can provide PR coverage at trade, local and national levels, including TV news. Our rates are highly competitive and you can test the water with a low-cost trial period. Why not get in touch and talk directly to one of our consultants?*

▶ Clarity Computing, 33 Fryent Grove, London, NW9 7HE Tel: (020) 8205 4242 Fax: (020) 8205 4242 E-mail: jon@clarity-computing.com *Suppliers of hardware & software*

Clarity Copiers Cornwall & Co, Unit 5d 5d Carminnow Road Industrial Estate, Bodmin, Cornwall, PL31 1EP Tel: (01208) 78201 Fax: (01208) 75916 *Office equipment retailers*

Clarity Copiers Sheffield, 126 Handsworth Road, Sheffield, S9 4AE Tel: 0114-244 8844 Fax: 0114-244 9944 *Photocopier services & maintenance*

Clark, Regent Buildings, Tuttle Hill, Nuneaton, Warwickshire, CV10 0HU Tel: (024) 7638 2686 Fax: (024) 7638 8812 E-mail: sales@clarkmachinery.com *Machine tools sales, machine tool engineers, maintenance, installation*

Arnold Clark Automobiles Ltd, 527 Queensferry Road, Edinburgh, EH4 7QD Tel: 0131-312 4444 Fax: 0131-312 4445 E-mail: barnton@arnoldclark.co.uk *Car repair & sales service, financial products*

Clark Associates U.K, 57 Selby Lane, Keyworth, Nottingham, NG12 5AQ Tel: 0115-937 6136 *Personal computer suppliers*

Clark Business Products Ltd, Old Ferry Road, Lower Bristol Road, Bath, BA2 1ES Tel: (01225) 337600 Fax: (01225) 337206 E-mail: info@clarkbusinessproducts.co.uk *Office machinery & copiers*

C. & J. Clark International Ltd, 40 High Street, Street, Somerset, BA16 0YA Tel: (01458) 443131 Fax: (01458) 447547 E-mail: john.keery@clarks.com *Boot & shoe exporters & manufrs*

Clark Commercials (Aberdeen) Ltd, Wellheads Drive, Wellheads Industrial Estate, Dyce, Aberdeen, AB21 7GQ Tel: (01224) 725412 Fax: (01224) 793319 E-mail: sales@clarkcommercials.co.uk *Vehicle sales & rental*

Clark Computer & Management Services Ltd, 6-8 High Street, Shoreham-by-Sea, West Sussex, BN43 5DA Tel: (01273) 454064 Fax: (01273) 440515 *Software system services & reinsurance systems*

Clark Construction Ltd, Lancaster Approach, North Killingholme, Immingham, South Humberside, DN40 3JZ Tel: (01469) 540004 Fax: (01469) 540426 E-mail: info@clarkconstruction.co.uk *Civil engineering & building services*

Clark Contracting, Brentford Grange Farm, Beaconsfield Road, Coleshill, Amersham, Buckinghamshire, HP7 0JU Tel: (01494) 431871 Fax: (01494) 431872 E-mail: sales@clark-contracting.co.uk *Land fill farming property developers*

▶ Clark Contracts Ltd, Unit 2 East Main Industrial Estate, Broxburn, West Lothian, EH52 5AB Tel: 0131-551 3551 Fax: 0141-884 6211

Clark Electrical Industries Ltd, 1e North Crescent, London, E16 4TG Tel: (020) 7474 7404 Fax: (020) 7473 1961 E-mail: enquries@ceiltd.co.uk *Electrical engineers & contractors*

Clark Electrical Services, 78 Milnrow Road, Shaw, Oldham, OL2 8ER Tel: (01706) 290837 Fax: (01706) 290837 E-mail: electricalspurs@aol.com *Electrical services*

Clark Electro-Plating (Wrexham) Ltd, The Old Foundry, Hill Street, Rhostyllen, Wrexham, Clwyd, LL14 4AT Tel: (01978) 355803 Fax: (01978) 291321 *Zinc, nickel & electroplating services*

Clark Engineering, 6 Cranborne Industrial Estate, Cranborne Road, Potters Bar, Hertfordshire, EN6 3JN Tel: (01707) 651393 Fax: (01707) 644094 *Display unit installation services*

Clark & Fenn Skanska Ltd, Unit 19 Mitcham Industrial Estate, Streatham Road, Mitcham, Surrey, CR4 2AP Tel: (020) 8685 5000 Fax: (020) 8640 1986 E-mail: clark.and.fenn@skanska.co.uk *Suspended ceiling designers & installers*

Clark Fixings Ltd, Unit 1, Crescent Works Industrial Estate, Willenhall Road, Darlaston, Wednesbury, West Midlands, WS10 8JJ Tel: 0121-568 6968 Fax: 0121-568 8719 E-mail: clarkfixings@btconnect.com *U bolt distributors*

Clark Handling Ltd, Hobson Industrial Estate, Hobson, Newcastle upon Tyne, NE16 6EA Tel: (01207) 270825 Fax: (01207) 271393 E-mail: sales@clarkhandling.co.uk *Material handling equipment suppliers & manufrs*

Clark International Machinery Ltd, PO Box 58, Stratford-upon-Avon, Warwickshire, CV37 7YF Tel: (01789) 263636 Fax: (01789) 263637 E-mail: sales@clarkintmachinery.co.uk *Machine tool merchants or agents*

▶ James Clark, 30 Glenlyon Place, Leven, Fife, KY8 4QY Tel: (01333) 426484 Fax: (01333) 426686

Clark & Kemp Joinery Ltd, Units 8-10 Baddow Park, West Hanningfield Road, Great Baddow, Chelmsford, CM2 7SY Tel: (01245) 476667 Fax: (01245) 474857 E-mail: clark@clark-kemp.freeserve.co.uk *Joiners*

Kenneth Clark Ceramics, The North Wing, Southover Grange, Southover Road, Lewes, East Sussex, BN7 1TP Tel: (01273) 476761 Fax: (01273) 479565 *Ceramic tiles producers (hand decorated)*

Martin Clark Consultants, Trendle Cottage, Trendal Street, Sherborne, Dorset, DT9 3NT Tel: (01935) 815777 Fax: (0870) 1360933 E-mail: victor@cahor.plus.com *Digital mapping services & software for agriculture*

Clark Masts Teksam Ltd, 18 Ringwood Road, Binstead, Ryde, Isle Of Wight, PO33 3PA Tel: (01983) 563691 Fax: (01983) 566643 E-mail: sales@clarkmasts.co.uk *Radio mast manufrs*

▶ Clark Motor Engineering, 1 & 2 Charlwood Park Cottages, Charlwood Road, Horley, Surrey, RH6 0AJ Tel: 01293 772202 E-mail: recovery@clarkmotorengineering.co.uk *24 hour breakdown recovery, cars commercials ,buses, coaches mobile cranes plant heavy winching*

Clark Office Electronics, 18 Willoughby Road, Tamworth, Staffordshire, B79 8NH Tel: (01827) 53520 Fax: (01827) 58557 E-mail: clark.office@ntlworld.com *Fax & electronic machine repairers*

Clark Office Furniture Ltd, Unit 8, Cannock Chase Enterprise Centre, Walkers Rise, Hednesford, Staffordshire, WS12 0QW Tel: (01543) 423456 Fax: (01543) 426565 E-mail: sales@clarkofficefurniture.com *Office furniture suppliers*

P.H. Clark (Tiers Cross) Ltd, Freshmoor Road, East Moors, Cardiff, CF24 5HS Tel: (029) 2047 3737 Fax: (029) 2048 1132 E-mail: sales@clarkmodualer.co.uk *Portable building hire & sales*

Robert Clark & Sons (Steel Fabricators) Ltd, Wallace Road, Sheffield, S3 9UA Tel: 0114-273 7233 Fax: 0114-272 3532 *Steel fabricators*

▶ Clark & Rose, Barclayhill Place, Portlethen, Aberdeen, AB12 4LH Tel: (0845) 2301906 Fax: (01224) 782822

Clark & Terry, Unit 25-26-Newhaven Business Park, Barton Lane, Eccles, Manchester, M30 0HH Tel: 0161-787 7898 Fax: 0161-787 7728 E-mail: clarkandterry@talk21.com *Fabric importers & exporters*

Clark Transmissions, Watermill House, 2 Restmor Way, Wallington, Surrey, SM6 7AH Tel: (020) 8647 0570 *Gear box, unit & clutches manufrs*

William Clark & Sons Ltd, Upperlands, Maghera, County Londonderry, BT46 5RZ Tel: (028) 7964 2214 Fax: (028) 7954 7207 E-mail: sales@wmclark.co.uk *Textile manufrs*

▶ Clark-Drain, Station Works, Station Road, Yaxley, Peterborough, PE7 3EQ Tel: (01733) 765315 Fax: (01733) 246923

Clarke, 25-26 Kenyon Street, Birmingham, B18 6AR Tel: 0121-236 4642 Fax: 0121-455 6430 E-mail: efc@jeweler.co.uk *General gold jewellery*

A.J. Clarke (Automatic Machinists) Ltd, Unit 7, Wessex Industrial Estate, Bourne End, Buckinghamshire, SL8 5DT Tel: (01628) 521301 Fax: (01628) 819142E-mail: sales@ajclarke.info *Precision turned parts manufrs*

Clarke Associates, The Old School House, Chapel Lane, Wythall, Birmingham, B47 6JX Tel: 0121-702 2525 Fax: 0121-702 2085 E-mail: pr@clarke-associates.co.uk *Public relations consultants*

▶ Clarke Automation, Quarles, Elm Lane, Roxwell, Chelmsford, CM1 4NJ Tel: (01245) 231234 Fax: (01245) 231270 E-mail: sales@clarkeautomation.com *Audio visual equipment suppliers*

Clarke Bros Auto Factors Ltd, 161/163 Cromac Street, Belfast, BT2 8JE Tel: (028) 9024 8444 Fax: (028) 9023 8094 *Clutch specialists*

C.H. Clarke & Co. (Engineers) Ltd, Griffin Industrial Estate, Penncricket Lane, Rowley Regis, West Midlands, B65 0SP Tel: 0121-561 1111 Fax: 0121-559 6027 E-mail: sales@chc-machining.co.uk *Machinery services subcontract machinist*

▶ Clarke Chapman Services, Unit 15 Planetary Industrial Estate, Planetary Road, Willenhall, West Midlands, WV13 3XA Tel: (01902) 728844 Fax: (01902) 728822 E-mail: info@clerkchapman.co.uk *Crane hire designers, & manufrs*

▶ Clarke Chapman Syncrolift Division, H M N B Clyde, Faslane, Helensburgh, Dunbartonshire, G84 8HL Tel: (01436) 810001

Clarke Computer Systems, 43 Cannock Road, Burntwood, Staffordshire, WS7 0BL Tel: (01543) 670756 Fax: (01543) 670756 E-mail: info@clarkecomputers.co.uk *Computer systems for businesses*

Clarke Contracts, 89 Bann Road, Rasharkin, Ballymena, County Antrim, BT44 8SZ Tel: (028) 2954 0191 Fax: (028) 2954 0401 E-mail: sales@clarkecontracts.com *Plastering & flooring contractors*

Clarke Cutters, 17 Offerton Industrial Estate, Hempshaw Lane, Stockport, Cheshire, SK2 5TH Tel: 0161-477 6440 Fax: 0161-477 8090 E-mail: sales@clarkecutters.co.uk *Cutter & creasing form manufrs*

Clarke Designs Ltd, Imberhorne Lane, East Grinstead, West Sussex, RH19 1RJ Tel: (01342) 321021 Fax: (01342) 321021 *Engineering designers & consultants*

Clarke Energy Ltd, C Senator Point, South Boundary Road, Knowsley Industrial Park, Liverpool, L33 7RR Tel: 0151-546 4446 Fax: 0151-546 4447 E-mail: info@clarke-energy.com *Gas engine distributors*

Clarke Engineering Company Ltd, P.O. Box 76, Bodmin, Cornwall, PL30 5PJ Tel: (01637) 881112 Fax: (01637) 880598 *Power transmission engineering*

Clarke Engineering & Construction Co. Ltd, 13 Sydenham Road, Belfast, BT3 9DH Tel: (028) 9045 8337 Fax: (028) 9073 2382 E-mail: mail@ceccltd.co.uk *Building & construction engineers*

Clarke Instruments Ltd, Distloc House, Old Sarum Airfield, Old Sarum, Salisbury, SP4 6DZ Tel: (01722) 323451 Fax: (01722) 335154 E-mail: sales@clarke-inst.com *Providers of total access control*

Clarke International Ltd, Hemnall Street, Epping, Essex, CM16 4LG Tel: (01992) 565300 Fax: (01992) 561562 E-mail: sales@clarkeinternational.com *Generator & air compressor manufrs*

Clarke Joinery, Dairy Works, Normans Road, Sutton, St. Helens, Merseyside, WA9 4JQ Tel: (01744) 815399 *Joinery manufrs*

▶ Alan Clarke Joinery Works Ltd, 18 8 Meadowbank Road, Carrickfergus, County Antrim, BT38 8YF Tel: (028) 9336 8129 Fax: (028) 9336 8129

Clarke Lane Engineering Ltd, 6 Belgrave Industrial Estate, Belgrave Road, Southampton, SO17 3EA Tel: (023) 8067 1564 Fax: (023) 8067 6774 E-mail: clarke-lane@supernet.com *Sheet metalworkers & fabricators*

M. Clarke Engineering, 566 Attercliffe Road, Sheffield, S9 3QP Tel: 0114-244 7234 Fax: 0114-244 7234 *General engineers*

Clarke Nicholls & Marcel, Galena House, 8-30 Galena Road, London, W6 0LT Tel: (020) 8748 8611 Fax: (020) 8741 8171 E-mail: cnm@cnmlondon.com *Structural engineers*

Peter Clarke, 52 Southey Avenue, Sheffield, S5 7NL Tel: 0114-232 3381 Fax: 0114-233 7602 *Glasses & cleaning material suppliers*

John Clarke Productions, 3 Alma Studios, 32 - 34 Stratford Road, London, W8 6QF Tel: (020) 7937 4373 E-mail: jsc@jscprods.com *Commercial productions*

Clarke Rendall Business Furniture Ltd, 12 Denbigh Hall Industrial Estate, Denbigh Hall, Bletchley, Milton Keynes, MK3 7QT Tel: (01908) 391600 Fax: (01908) 391601 E-mail: salessupport@clarkerendall.com *Designers and manufacturers of bespoke and standard ranges of office reception desks, boardroom, meeting room, presentation room tables and executive/management furniture. Full design and sales support backed up by nationwide delivery and installation service.*

Clarke Rubicon Ltd, Telford Way, Stephenson Industrial Estate, Coalville, Leicestershire, LE67 3HE Tel: (01530) 513700 Fax: (01530) 513701 E-mail: info@clarke-rubicon.co.uk *Rigid presentation packaging manufrs based in the heart of the UK. We design & produce for a wide range of markets in our modern, purpose built premises.*

Clarke S.J Company Ltd, Caxton Park, Caxton Road Elm Farm Indusrial Estate, Elm Farm Industrial Estate, Bedford, MK41 0TY Tel: (01234) 346513 Fax: (01234) 364047 E-mail: sales@sjclarke.co.uk *Curtains & soft furnishings manufrs*

Clarke & Spears International Ltd, Knaphill Nursery, Barrs Lane, Knaphill, Woking, Surrey, GU21 2JW Tel: (01483) 485800 Fax: (01483) 485801 E-mail: sales@clarkandspears.co.uk *Glass fibre plant container manufrs*

Clarke W R Signs Ltd, Scholars Lane, Stratford-upon-Avon, Warwickshire, CV37 6HE Tel: (01789) 292898 Fax: (01789) 414653 *Sign makers*

Clarke Web Ltd, 9 Poplar Industrial Estate, Redditch Road, Studley, Warwickshire, B80 7AY Tel: (01527) 857335 Fax: (01527) 857315 E-mail: clarkeweb@btconnect.com *Plastics converting machinery manufrs*

▶ Clarkelift, 16 Sir William Wallace Wynd, Old Aberdeen, Aberdeen, AB24 1UW Tel: (0784) 0261931 Fax: (0871) 6619106 E-mail: john@clarkelift.com *Materials Handling and Manual Handling Products thoughout Scotland*

Clarkeprint Ltd, 45-47 Stour Street, Birmingham, B18 7AJ Tel: 0121-454 7117 Fax: 0121-454 8404 E-mail: sales@clarkeprint.co.uk *Litho printers*

Clarke's Contracts, 71 Kings Road, Tyseley, Birmingham, B11 2AX Tel: 0121-707 6968 Fax: 0121-680 8108 E-mail: sales@clarkescontracts.co.uk *Contract furnishing suppliers*

▶ Clarkes Electrical Services, 127-128 Windmill Street, Gravesend, Kent, DA12 1BL Tel: (01474) 322948 Fax: (01474) 329988

Clarkes International, Natland Road, Kendal, Cumbria, LA9 7LS Tel: (01539) 815021 Fax: (01539) 815139 E-mail: john.keery@clarkes.com *Warehouse* Also at: Branches throughout the U.K.

Clarkes Metal Merchants, 39 Livingstone Place, Newport, Gwent, NP19 8EW Tel: (01633) 259178 E-mail: iancl2@aol.com *Metal merchants*

Clarkewear Ltd, Marshall House, West Street, Glenfield, Leicester, LE3 8DT Tel: 0116-287 1661 Fax: 0116-232 0568 E-mail: nail@clarkewear.co.uk *mens wear wholesalers*

Clarkin Electronics, 1 50 Lakes Road, Derwent Howe Industrial Estate, Workington, Cumbria, CA14 3YP Tel: (01900) 64576 Fax: (01900) 872475 E-mail: clarkin46@aol.com *Electronic cable assemblers*

Clarks Catering Hire, Tatchbury Lane, Winsor, Southampton, SO40 2GZ Tel: (023) 8081 3219 *Catering equipment hire services*

Clarks Garage (Walkern) Ltd, 107 High Street, Walkern, Stevenage, Hertfordshire, SG2 7NU Tel: (01438) 861634 E-mail: clarksgarage@hotmail.com *Workshop, petrol & second hand cars specialists*

Clark's Of Headingley, 14-16 Clifton Green, Leeds, LS9 6EW Tel: 0113-249 7793 *Joinery manufrs*

▶ Clarks Home Bakery Ltd, Algernon Industrial Estate, New York Road, Shiremoor, Newcastle upon Tyne, NE27 0NB Tel: 0191-251 3772 Fax: 0191-251 3772 *Bakery*

Clarks Signs Ltd, Alchorn Place, Portsmouth, PO3 5QL Tel: (023) 9282 6411 Fax: (023) 9266 9991 E-mail: sales@clarks-signs.co.uk *Sign manufrs*

▶ Clarks (Wantage) Ltd, Town Mills, Wantage, Oxfordshire, OX12 9AB Tel: (01235) 768991 *Food factory & food products*

Clarkson Knitting Ltd, Western Industrial Estate, Lon-Y-Llyn, Caerphilly, Mid Glamorgan, CF83 1XJ Tel: (029) 2086 1411 Fax: (029) 2086 0127 E-mail: paulslevin@clarksonknitting.com *Manufacture of synthetic knitted fabrics in warp, weft and weft insertion. Providing high quality leading edge fabrics in Sportswear, Intimate Apparel, Furnishings, Clinical and much more. We work with our customers to design and develop the properties and functionality they require.*

Clarkwood Engineering Ltd, 7 Blackenhall Industrial Estate, Sunbeam Street, Wolverhampton, WV2 4PF Tel: (01902) 710868 Fax: (01902) 712840 E-mail: enquiries@clarkwood.co.uk *Special bolt & nut manufacturers & engineers*

Clarman Joinery, Ferry Road, Fiskerton, Lincoln, LN3 4HW Tel: (01522) 751988 Fax: (01522) 751988 *Joinery manufrs*

Claron Hydraulic Seals Ltd, Station Road, Cradley Heath, West Midlands, B64 6PN Tel: 0121-559 9711 Fax: 0121-559 1036 E-mail: sales@claron-seals.co.uk Principal Export Areas: Worldwide *Hydraulic & pneumatic seals & packings manufrs*

Claron Hydraulic Services, Alders Way, Yalberton Industrial Estate, Paignton, Devon, TQ4 7QL Tel: (01803) 528852 Fax: (01803) 525134 E-mail: sales@claron.co.uk Principal Export Areas: Worldwide *Manufacturers of PTFE seals, Spiral Back-up Rings, Bearing Tape and Custom PTFE components*

Claron Plastics Ltd, Alders Way, Yalberton Industrial Estate, Paignton, Devon, TQ4 7QL Tel: (01803) 528677 Fax: (01803) 525134 E-mail: services@claron.co.uk Principal Export Areas: Worldwide *Semi-Finished PTFE Tube and Rod manufacturers*

Clarrie Jackson Photography, 18 Whites Road, Cleethorpes, South Humberside, DN35 8RP Tel: (01472) 696979 *Commercial photographer*

Class 1 Signs Ltd, 69 Breck Road, Anfield, Liverpool, L4 2QS Tel: 0151-264 0003 Fax: 0151-263 5996 E-mail: sales@class1signs.co.uk *Signs, posters & nameplate engravers*

Class 100 Ltd, Units 32-33 London Road Industrial Estate, Baldock, Hertfordshire, SG7 6NG Tel: (01462) 893336 Fax: (01462) 893377 E-mail: cadcam@class100.co.uk *Engineering & bureau services*

▶ Class A, 14 Mccoy's Arcade, Fore Street, Exeter, EX4 3AN Tel: (01392) 494988 Fax: (01392) 496335 E-mail: sales@classadistribution.co.uk *Musical instrument suppliers*

Class Business Systems Ltd, 77 Yew Tree Road, Ormskirk, Lancashire, L39 1RY Tel: (01695) 579988E-mail: enquiries@classbusiness.uk.com *Computer software & systems development*

▶ Class Creations Ltd, The Lippiatt, Cheddar Gorge, Cheddar, Somerset, BS27 3QP Tel: (01934) 740240 Fax: (01934) 740234 E-mail: mail@classcreations.co.uk *Class Creations is a Traditional Toy Shop offering Quality Wooden Toys as well as a large selection of Constuction Toys, Games, Puzzles, Books and Soft Toys for all ages.*

Class Instrumentation Ltd, 837 Garratt Lane, London, SW17 0PG Tel: (020) 8333 2288 Fax: (020) 8944 0141 E-mail: info@classltd.com *Ultrasonic instrumentations manufrs*

Class Panel Ltd, Colder Wharfe Works, Huddersfield Road, Ravensthorpe, Dewsbury, West Yorkshire, WF13 3JW Tel: (01924) 430034 Fax: (01924) 430596 E-mail: enquiries@qm-architectural.co.uk *Aluminium structure fabricators*

▶ Class Pools, 50 Penderry Road, Penlan, Swansea, SA5 7EB Tel: (07903) 591450 E-mail: classpools@ntlworld.com *Swimming pools manufrs*

▶ Class Sheet Metal, Ynyshir Road, Porth, Mid Glamorgan, CF39 0AT Tel: (01443) 682277 Fax: (01443) 682285 *Sheet metal work and general fabrication*

Class (UK) Ltd, 9 Harvest Road, Newbridge, Midlothian, EH28 8PN Tel: 0131-333 3237 Fax: 0131-333 4845 *Agricultural machinery wholesalers*

Classcoat, 21 High Street, Upper Heyford, Bicester, Oxfordshire, OX25 5LE Tel: (01869) 232793 Fax: (01869) 233625 E-mail: classcoat7921718@aol.com *Protective coating distributors*

Classic, Hildersley, Ross-on-Wye, Herefordshire, HR9 7NW Tel: (01989) 769191 Fax: (01989) 769191 *Car & motorcycle classic spare parts manufrs*

Classic Alarms Ltd, 337 Holyhead Road, Coventry, CV5 8LD Tel: (024) 7659 4204 Fax: (024) 7659 4204 *Security supply & installation*

Classic Blinds, Unit 35b Abbeycentre, Longwood Road, Newtownabbey, County Antrim, BT37 9UH Tel: (028) 9086 2872 Fax: (028) 9081 3052 E-mail: sales@classic-blinds.com *Blinds manufrs*

▶ Classic Carrieage Co., Risdon Farm, Boasley Cross, Okehampton, Devon, EX20 4JQ Tel: (0845) 6441581 Fax: *Chauffeur driven executive classic car hire wedding*

Classic Cash Register Finance Ltd, Victory Works, Northam Road, Stoke-on-Trent, ST1 6DA Tel: (01782) 283333 Fax: (01782) 204261 E-mail: info@classic-retail.co.uk *Cash registers distributors*

▶ Classic Chambers, 6 Penny Lane, Easingwold, York, YO61 3RR Tel: (07767) 776927 *Portable toilet suppliers*

Classic Closures Ltd, 12a Eton Grove, London, SE13 5BY Tel: (020) 8852 3874 Fax: (020) 8318 2111 *Plastics injection moulders*

Classic Components UK Ltd, Unit 1A, Stratford Court, Cranmore Boulevard, Shirley, Solihull, West Midlands, B90 4QT Tel: 0121-746 5300 Fax: 0121-746 5344 E-mail: sales@classicuk.co.uk *Electronic components suppliers*

Classic Curtains Blinds & Upholstery, 22 Mercia Dr, Mynydd Isa, Mold, Clwyd, CH7 6UH Tel: 01352 756267 *Curtains & blinds*

Classic Design & Build (UK) Ltd, Lode Lane Industrial Estate, Vulcan Road, Solihull, West Midlands, B91 2JY Tel: 0121-709 2040 Fax: 0121-709 2044 E-mail: info@classicdb.co.uk *Exhibition stand contractors*

▶ Classic Desserts, Unit 10, Blencathra Business Centre, Threlkeld, Keswick, Cumbria, CA12 4TR Tel: (01768) 779043

Classic Doors, 10-12 Cheapside, Morley, Leeds, LS27 9DQ Tel: 0113-238 0220 E-mail: sales@classic-doors.co.uk *Doors retailers*

Classic Engravers, 6 Old Bridge Street, Truro, Cornwall, TR1 2AQ Tel: (01872) 241960 Fax: (01872) 241960 *Trophy engraving*

Classic Excel, William Jones House, Cambois, Blyth, Northumberland, NE24 1QY Tel: (01670) 530550 Fax: (01670) 531452 E-mail: info@classicceilings.co.uk *Construction services*

Classic Finish, Midseat Cott, Bathgate, West Lothian, EH47 8AA Tel: (01501) 763185 Fax: (01501) 763171 *Powder coatings*

Classic Fireplaces & Furniture, Unit F Weddington Industrial Estate, Nuneaton, Warwickshire, CV10 0AP Tel: (024) 7634 3407 Fax: (07070) 711475 *Wooden cabinet manufrs*

▶ Classic Folios Ltd, Unit 15a Vicarage Farm Business Park, Winchester Road, Fair Oak, Eastleigh, Hampshire, SO50 7HD Tel: (023) 8060 2787 Fax: (0870) 7444785 E-mail: sales@classicfolios.com *Specialises in leather & man-made binders, files, folios*

Classic Foods, Gratwicke Road, Worthing, West Sussex, BN11 4BH Tel: (01903) 231760 Fax: (01903) 231760 *Dairy produce suppliers*

Classic Fork Trucks Ltd, 1 Durbar Avenue Industrial Estate, Durbar Avenue, Coventry, CV6 5QF Tel: (024) 7663 7467 Fax: (024) 7663 7600 *Sales hire & repair of fork lift trucks*

▶ Classic Formai, Crofton House, Lindal Road, London, SE4 1EJ Tel: (020) 8469 2340 Fax: (020) 8694 8020

▶ Classic Formai, Crofton House, Lindal Road, London, SE4 1EJ Tel: (020) 8469 2340 Fax: (020) 8694 8020 E-mail: sales@classicformi.com *Stone & architectural masons*

Classic Glass, 6 Hillview Industrial Estate, Castle Road, Randalstown, Antrim, BT41 2ED Tel: (028) 9447 2920 Fax: (028) 9447 2964 E-mail: sales@classicglass.com *Glass & mirrors distributors & manufrs*

Classic Graphics, Standard Way Industrial Estate, Standard Way Industrial Estate, Northallerton, North Yorkshire, DL6 2XA Tel: (01609) 761060 Fax: (01609) 761060 *Sign manufrs*

▶ Classic Heating Services, 103 Station Road, Sutton Coldfield, West Midlands, B73 5LA Tel: 0121-355 1782 E-mail: ian@walklett.freeserve.co.uk *Central Heating Installation and Repair. Corgi Registered, all types of Gas installation and servicing carried out. Emergency callout service. Also General plumbing and bathroom refitting.*

Classic Holdings, 55 Cradley Road, Cradley Heath, West Midlands, B64 7BB Tel: (01384) 637825 Fax: (01384) 564079 E-mail: classicholdings@aol.com *Joinery shop fitting & construction manufrs*

▶ Classic Home Improvements Ltd, 4 362b Spring Road, Southampton, SO19 2PB Tel: (023) 8044 7744 Fax: (023) 8044 0033 E-mail: sales@classichome.co.uk *Windows, doors & conservatories suppliers*

▶ Classic Hot Air Ballooning, Home Farm Cottage, Lenham Heath Road, Sandway, Maidstone, Kent, ME17 2HX Tel: (01622) 858956 Fax: (01622) 853817 E-mail: glen@ballooning.fsnet.co.uk *Balloons hot air & promotions supplier*

Classic Images Ltd, Oakcroft Works, Oakcroft Road, Chessington, Surrey, KT9 1RH Tel: (020) 8391 1133 Fax: (020) 8397 5040 E-mail: classicimages@ukonline.co.uk *Joiners*

Classic Interiors Malvern Ltd, 47 Worcester Road, Malvern, Worcestershire, WR14 4AD Tel: (01684) 573734 Fax: (01684) 892519 E-mail: classicinteriors@btopenworld.com *Carpet retailers*

Classic Joinery, Castle Hotel, Jewel Street, Barry, South Glamorgan, CF63 3NQ Tel: (01446) 722335 Fax: (01446) 722335 *Joinery manufrs*

Classic Joinery, 91 Ballylough Road, Castlewellan, County Down, BT31 9JG Tel: (028) 4377 0556 Fax: (028) 4377 0556 *Joiners*

Classic Joinery, 324 Guildford Road, Bisley, Woking, Surrey, GU24 9AE Tel: (01932) 354333 Fax: (01483) 797713 E-mail: john@classicjoinery.co.uk *Joiners*

▶ Classic Joinery Northwest Ltd, Unit 3 Albert Street, Droylsden, Manchester, M43 7BA Tel: 0161-371 0031 Fax: 0161-371 9840 *Joiners*

Classic Joinery Products, Unit G, 6 The Roundel, Falkirk, FK2 9HG Tel: (01324) 670066 Fax: (01324) 670065 *Joinery manufrs*

The Classic Label Company Ltd, Unit 9-14 Whitehall Properties, Town Gate, Wyke, Bradford, West Yorkshire, BD12 9JQ Tel: (01274) 690217 Fax: (01274) 690046 E-mail: info@classiclabels.co.uk *Label designers & manufrs*

Classic Legal Services Ltd, Suite 3a & 3b, Britannia House, Cowbridge, South Glamorgan, CF71 7EG Tel: (0800) 389 4137 Fax: (01446) 774000 E-mail: alun@weeks4444.fslife.co.uk *National specialists for legal services, wills, enduring power of attorney, executor help, advanced directive, conveyancing, document storage, probate, property trusts & personal life plans'*

▶ Classic Lifts Ltd, Jubilee House, Altcar Road, Formby, Liverpool, L37 8DL Tel: (01704) 833255 Fax: (01704) 833880 E-mail: dave.markman@lift-engineers.co.uk *Install & repairs lifts*

Classic Loo's, Litnnets, Ogdens, Fordingbridge, Hampshire, SP6 2PY Tel: (01725) 513130 Fax: (01425) 650634 *Mobile toilet hirers*

▶ Classic Masonry Ltd, Church Hall, Albion Road, North Shields, Tyne & Wear, NE30 2RQ Tel: 0191-257 6666 Fax: 0191-258 4411 E-mail: info@classicmasonry.co.uk

Classic Miniatures Ltd, 8 Heathlands Close, Twickenham, TW1 4BP Tel: (020) 8892 3686 Fax: (020) 8744 1142 E-mail: sales@classicminiatures.co.uk *Medals, badges & sign manufrs*

Classic & Modern & Paint & Bodywork, Unit 2 Manor Park, Windsor Road, Bedford, MK42 9HW Tel: (01234) 341410 *Vehicle repairs*

▶ Classic Motoring Ltd, Smilers Cottage, Brimpsfield, Gloucester, GL4 8LD Tel: (01452) 864050 E-mail: info@classicmotoring.co.uk *Specialist hire of Jaguar E-Type convertibles for self-drive. Situated in the heart of the Cotswolds.*

▶ Classic Paving Services, Classic House, Hollands Road, Northwich, Cheshire, CW9 8AU Tel: (01606) 350800 Fax: (01606) 352800

Classic Pen Advertising, 23 Cradle Hill Industrial Estate, Seaford, East Sussex, BN25 3JE Tel: (01323) 890873 *Promotional gift printers*

Classic Performance Ltd, 7 Trent Industrial Estate, Wetmore Road, Burton-on-Trent, Staffordshire, DE14 1QY Tel: (01283) 531122 Fax: (01283) 531328 E-mail: sales@classicperformance.co.uk *Specialist care of classic & performance cars*

Classic Plaster Moulds, 19 Tame Road, Lawson Industrial Estate, Middlesbrough, Cleveland, TS6 6LL Tel: (01642) 246535 Fax: (01642) 246535 *Plaster mould manufrs*

Classic Portable Buildings Ltd, Gordleton Farm, Silver Street, Sway, Lymington, Hampshire, SO41 6DJ Tel: (01590) 683193 Fax: (01590) 683193 E-mail: mail@classic-pb.co.uk *Portable building manufrs*

Classic Powder Coating Ltd, Bridge Works, Iver Lane, Uxbridge, Middlesex, UB8 2JG Tel: (01895) 270616 Fax: (020) 8892 4048 *Powder coating services*

Classic Precision Engineering Ltd, Unit 2, New Line Road, Kirkby-In-Ashfield, Nottingham, NG17 8JQ Tel: (01623) 720402 Fax: (01623) 720353 E-mail: russ@cpeng.freeserve.co.uk *Precision engineers*

Classic Printed Bag Co. Ltd, Unit 5, Silver Business Park, Airfield Way, Christchurch, Dorset, BH23 3TA Tel: (01202) 488144 Fax: (01202) 481341 E-mail: bags@classicbag.co.uk *Carrier bags retail & promotional manufrs*

▶ Classic Printers (Peterborough) Ltd, 3 Crowland Business Centre, Crease Drove, Crowland, Peterborough, PE6 0BN Tel: (01733) 210789

Classic Rewinds Ltd, 50a Park Road, Nottingham, NG7 1JG Tel: 0115-947 3758 Fax: 0115-947 3758 *Electric motor specialists*

Classic Signs, 52 Cardigan Road, Bridlington, North Humberside, YO15 3HQ Tel: (01262) 673131 Fax: (01262) 673131 E-mail: sales@classic-signs.co.uk *Sign maker*

▶ Classic Signs Of London, 11 Redburn Industrial Estate, Woodall Road, Enfield, Middlesex, EN3 4LQ Tel: (020) 8805 4649 Fax: (020) 8805 1847

▶ CLASSIC SPICES, 30 KINGSLEY DRIVE, CHORLEY, LANCASHIRE, PR7 2NE Tel: 01257 233891 Fax: 01257 233891 E-mail: sales@classicspicesuk.com *we are specalist suppliers of herbs, spices, and nuts.*

▶ Classic Stained Glass Designers, Unit 9-10 Drakemire Drive, Linnpark Industrial Estate, Glasgow, G45 9SS Tel: 0141-634 7532 Fax: 0141-634 7504

Classic Steels Stockholding Ltd, The Old Press House, Irwell Vale Road, Rossendale, Lancashire, BB4 6LF Tel: (01706) 244880 Fax: (01706) 219331 E-mail: classicsteels@lineone.net *Steel stockholders*

▶ Classic Trade Frames Ltd, Unit 7 Priestley Road, Worsley, Manchester, M28 2LY Tel: 0161-793 1166 Fax: 0161-793 1177 *Pvc window & doors manufrs*

Classic Trophies UK, 27 Roman Road, Middlesbrough, Cleveland, TS5 6EA Tel: (01642) 881040 Fax: (01642) 881035 *Trophy engraving service*

▶ Classic Upholstery Ltd, Unit 1, Stanford Street, Amblecote, Stourbridge, West Midlands, DY8 4HR Tel: (01384) 444546

Classic Video Productions Ltd, 19 Waterloo Street, Glasgow, G2 6BT Tel: 0141-248 3882 Fax: 0141-204 1535 *Video production services*

Classic Windows, Construction House, Callywhite Lane, Dronfield, Derbyshire, S18 2XR Tel: (0800) 2980591 Fax: (01246) 413321 *Windows & conservatories installers & manufrs*

Classic Windows Ne Ltd, Unit 95 Tanfield Lea Industrial Estate North, Tanfield Lea, Stanley, County Durham, DH9 9NX Tel: (01207) 284707 Fax: (01207) 237062 E-mail: classicwindows1@btconnect.com *Window & door installers*

Classic Windsors, Coventry Street, Coventry, CV2 4LZ Tel: (024) 7665 0907 Fax: (024) 7665 0907 *Furniture manufrs*

Classic Wrought Iron, Jorista, Top Road, Ilketshall St. Andrew, Beccles, Suffolk, NR34 8NN Tel: (01986) 781214 Fax: (01986) 781214 *Wrought iron manufrs*

▶ Classical Bathrooms Ltd, Little Lane, Ilkley, West Yorkshire, LS29 8EA Tel: (01943) 601118 Fax: (01943) 609354

Classical Conveniences, 2 The Pleasance, Harpenden, Hertfordshire, AL5 3NA Tel: (01582) 841143 Fax: (01582) 849354 E-mail: sales@luxuryloos.co.uk *Luxury mobile toilet supplier to events*

Classical Lighting, R/O 499 High Rd, Leytonstone, London, E11 4PG Tel: (020) 8556 3056 Fax: (020) 8556 4242 E-mail: sales@classical-lighting.freeserve.co.uk *Traditional & period lighting manufrs*

▶ Classical Location Recording Services, Hope Cottage, 10 Middle Road, Berkhamsted, Hertfordshire, HP4 3EQ Tel: 01442 877698 E-mail: jules@julesmusic.co.uk *Located in Hertfordshire, I specialise mainly (but not exclusively) in classical music location recording, in churches, halls or wherever clients whish to work. I also offering complete audio post production and mastering services."*

Classical Toilet Hire Ltd, Unit 19 Shepherds Grove Industrial Estate, Stanton, Bury St. Edmunds, Suffolk, IP31 2AR Tel: (01359) 253556 Fax: (01359) 253557 *Toilet hire agents*

▶ Classique Conservatories, 1-3 Christleton Road, Chester, CH3 5UF Tel: (01244) 345355 Fax: (01244) 345255 E-mail: sales@classique.co.uk

Classique Window Blinds, Unit 2 River Place, Kilbirnie, Ayrshire, KA25 7EN Tel: (01505) 684441 Fax: (01505) 684333 *Window blind manufrs*

Classroom Video, Northavon Business Centre, Dean Road, Yate, Bristol, BS37 5NH Tel: (01454) 324222 Fax: (01454) 325222 E-mail: sales@classroomvideo.co.uk *Educational videos*

▶ CLASS-UK, 12 Tadcaster Road, Dringhouses, York, YO24 1LH Tel: (01904) 709091 E-mail: steve@class-uk.com *Sales, repairs & installations of dj, disco, & karaoke equipment*

Classy Clobber, The Croft, Chapel Lane, Lower Withington, Macclesfield, Cheshire, SK11 9DE Tel: (01477) 571999 *Corporate uniform suppliers*

Claud Hamilton Electrical Services Ltd, 24 Ellon Road, Bridge Of Don, Aberdeen, AB23 8BX Tel: (01224) 822685 Fax: (01224) 826200 E-mail: hq@ches-group.co.uk *Electrical contractors*

Claude Fenton, Arrowhead Road, Reading, RG7 4AE Tel: 0118-929 8900 Fax: 0118-930 6734 E-mail: reading@fentonplant.co.uk *Building & public works contractors*

▶ Claude Fenton (Plant Hire) Ltd, Unit 1 Kennet Weir Business Park, Arrowhead Road, Theale, Reading, RG7 4AE Tel: 0118-930 3066 Fax: 0118-930 3041 E-mail: reading@fentonplant.co.uk *Plant hire*

Claude Fenton (Plant Hire) Ltd, Unit 1 Kennet Weir Business Park, Arrowhead Road, Theale, Reading, RG7 4AE Tel: 0118-930 3066 Fax: 0118-930 3411 *Contractors plant hire*

Claude Systems Ltd, 4 Bellman Way, Donibristle Industrial Park, Hillend, Dunfermline, Fife, KY11 9JW Tel: (01383) 820011 Fax: (01383) 820093 E-mail: sales@claudesystems.com *Audio communication & security manufrs*

▶ Claudy Tackle & Sports, 630 Baranailt Road, Claudy, Londonderry, BT47 4EA Tel: (028) 7133 7323 *Fishing tackle retailers*

Claughton Office Equipment Ltd, 53 Beverley Road, Hull, HU3 1XL Tel: (01482) 323235 Fax: (01482) 224201 E-mail: sales@claughtons.com *Office equipment manufrs*

Cla-Val (UK) Ltd, Dainton House, Goods Station Road, Tunbridge Wells, Kent, TN1 2DH Tel: (01892) 514400 Fax: (01892) 543423 E-mail: info@cla-val.co.uk *Valve manufacturers & distributors*

▶ Clave & Barford Ltd, Plot 6, Village Farm Industrial Estate, Pyle, Bridgend, Mid Glamorgan, CF33 6BJ Tel: (01656) 743231

Claverbury Ltd, 11 Tindale Cl, South Croydon, Surrey, CR2 0RT Tel: (020) 8651 5265 Fax: (020) 8651 6037 *Heating & ventilating engineers*

Claverham Ltd, Bishops Road, Claverham, Bristol, BS49 4NF Tel: (01934) 835224 Fax: (01934) 835337 E-mail: reception@claverham.com *Actuator manufrs*

Claw Scaffold Ltd, Arrowhead Road, Theale, Reading, RG7 4AE Tel: 0118-930 6688 Fax: 0118-930 6713 E-mail: royclarke@clawscaffold.co.uk *Scaffolding contractors*

Claxton Blinds Ltd, Beaumont Works, Sutton Road, St. Albans, Hertfordshire, AL1 5HH Tel: (01727) 840001 Fax: (01727) 840004 E-mail: claxton-blinds@btconnect.com *Internal & external window blinds*

Claxton Engineering Co., 1 Buckminster Lane, Skillington, Grantham, Lincolnshire, NG33 5EY Tel: (01476) 860870 Fax: (01476) 861681 E-mail: claxtonsprayers@lineone.net *Agricultural spraying equipment manufrs*

Claxton International Services, Sarankot House Gell Farm, Kinnerton Road, Lower Kinnerton, Chester, CH4 9AE Tel: (01244) 661000 Fax: (01244) 660240 E-mail: claxtoninter@aol.com *Crane services*

Clay & Abbott Ltd, Unit 2 Beauchamp Industrial Park, Watling Street, Wilnecote, Tamworth, Staffordshire, B77 5BZ Tel: (01827) 288093 Fax: (01827) 288764 E-mail: clayandabbott@btconnect.com *Laundry engineers*

Noel Clay Buildbase, Gin Close Way, Awsworth, Nottingham, NG16 2TA Tel: 0115-938 2283 Fax: 0115-938 5229 E-mail: nottingham@buildbase.co.uk *Buildbase is one of the UK's fastest growing builders merchants. All of our branches are long established companies which have been serving local trades people for many years, with knowledge and experience to match. We believe strongly in understanding the needs of trades professional and our business has been developed specifically to meet those demands. Massive stocks, top quality products, competitive pricing, reliable delivery, specialist staff and exceptional customer service*

Robin Clay Ltd, 31 St. Leonards Road, Bexhill-on-Sea, East Sussex, TN40 1HP Tel: (01424) 730302 Fax: (01424) 730291 E-mail: sarah@ashbuscent.co.uk *Business & secretarial services*

▶ Clay Shooters Supplies, 32 St Marys Road, Market Harborough, Leicestershire, LE16 7DU Tel: (01858) 466616 Fax: (01858) 466616 E-mail: shaun@shooterssupplies.co.uk *Retail gun smiths*

Claybrook Computing Holdings Ltd, Sutherland House, Russel Way, Crawley, West Sussex, RH10 1UH Tel: (01293) 604028 Fax: (01293) 604029 *Pensions administration software*

Claybrooke Mill, Frolesworth La, Claybrooke Magna, Lutterworth, Leics, LE17 5DB Tel: (01455) 202443 Fax: (01455) 202443 E-mail: claybrookmill@yahoo.co.uk *Stone grow flour distribs*

Claydon Architectural Ltd, 11-12 Claydon Industrial Park, Great Blakenham, Ipswich, IP6 0NL Tel: (01473) 831000 Fax: (01473) 832154 E-mail: sales@cam-ltd.co.uk *Metal designers & manufrs*

Claydon Associates Ltd, Edison Road, Rabans Lane Industrial Area, Aylesbury, Buckinghamshire, HP19 8TE Tel: (01296) 434611 Fax: (01296) 436334 E-mail: associates@claydon-group.co.uk *Building contractors*

R.H. Claydon Ltd, Saxham Industrial Estate, Saxham, Bury St. Edmunds, Suffolk, IP28 6RZ Tel: (01284) 700748 Fax: (01284) 754833 E-mail: raa@rhc.co.uk *Tyre tube & wheel wholesalers*

Claygate Digital Services Ltd, Airport House, Purley Way, Croydon, CR0 0XZ Tel: (020) 8288 3588 Fax: (020) 8288 3599 E-mail: sales@claygate.com *Scanning conversion & reprographics*

Clayman Electronics Ltd, 91 Stour View Gardens, Corfe Mullen, Wimborne, Dorset, BH21 3TL Tel: (01202) 849777 *Security systems engineers*

▶ Claymate Trap Controllers, Silver Willows, The Croft, Bures, Suffolk, CO8 5JL Tel: (01787) 228143 Fax: (01787) 227503 E-mail: info@claymate.co.uk *Range of clay counting trap control systems for shooting grounds*

Claymore Carpets, 48 Brown Street, Dundee, DD1 5DT Tel: (01382) 229414 Fax: (01382) 229414 E-mail: claymorecarpetscts.co.uk *Tufted carpet & tile manufrs*

▶ Claymore Dairies Ltd, 4a Dochcarty Road, Dingwall, Ross-Shire, IV15 9UG Tel: (01349) 863120 Fax: (01349) 861921

Claymore Graphics Ltd, 63 Cotton Street, Aberdeen, AB11 5EG Tel: (01224) 576176 Fax: (01224) 584431 E-mail: mail@claymoregraphics.co.uk *Commercial printers*

▶ Claymore Lock & Alarm Co., 3 Hardgate, Haddington, East Lothian, EH41 3JW Tel: (01620) 829550 Fax: (01620) 829751 *Locksmiths*

Claymore Lubricants (Midlands) Ltd, 48 Heming Road, Washford, Redditch, Worcestershire, B98 0EA Tel: (01527) 502252 Fax: (01527) 502253 E-mail: sales@claymore-lubricants.co.uk *Lubricant manufrs*

Claymore Plastics, Hegdon, Pencombe, Bromyard, Herefordshire, HR7 4SL Tel: (01885) 400278 Fax: (01885) 400616 E-mail: claymore278@aol.com *PVC products & raw materials stockholders*

Claymore Signs, 498 Knutsford Road, Warrington, WA4 1DX Tel: (01925) 573091 Fax: (01925) 630900 E-mail: claymoresigns@aol.com *Photocopying services*

Clays Ltd, St Ives House, Lavington Street, London, SE1 0NX Tel: (020) 7928 8844 Fax: (020) 7902 6436 E-mail: sales@st-ives.co.uk *Book printers*

Company Information

▶ Clays Lane Advise & Training Centre, High Meads, Temple Mill Lane, London, E15 2EW Tel: (020) 8522 0088 Fax: (020) 8522 0088

▶ Clayson Country Homes Ltd, 447 Wellingborough Road, Northampton, NN1 4EZ Tel: (01604) 604033 Fax: (01604) 604762

Claystyle Technology & Design, Mica Close, Tamworth, Staffordshire, B77 4DR Tel: (01827) 316696 Fax: (01827) 316697 *Case moulds & bathroom equipment manufrs*

▶ Clayton Cabinets Ltd, The Barn, Langdale, Sampford Courtenay, Okehampton, Devon, EX20 2SY Tel: (01837) 82788 Fax: (01837) 82788 E-mail: nick@claytoncabinets.co.uk *Furniture suppliers in both contemporary & traditional styles*

Clayton Commercials Ltd, Langley Road, Burscough Industrial Estate, Ormskirk, Lancashire, L40 8JR Tel: (01704) 894244 Fax: (01704) 894226 E-mail: sales@claytoncommercials.com *Road tanker manufrs*

Clayton Contracts, 6 Beverley Close, Penkridge, Stafford, ST19 5SS Tel: (01785) 716133 Fax: (01785) 716166 E-mail: kelly@claytoncarcontracts.co.uk *Contract hire & leasing of cars & vans*

Clayton Engineering Co., Church Street, Belper, Derbyshire, DE56 1EY Tel: (01773) 828955 Fax: (01773) 828243 E-mail: claytonenguk@aol.com *Repetition work machinists production & precision engineers*

Clayton Equipment Ltd, Unit 2a, Second Avenue, Centrum One Hundred, Burton-on-Trent, Staffordshire, DE14 2WF Tel: (01283) 524470 Fax: (0870) 1129192 E-mail: info@claytonequipment.com *Mining & tunneling locomotive manufrs*

J.M. Clayton & Co. Ltd, Unit 3 Phoenix Court, Hammond Avenue, Stockport, Cheshire, SK4 1PQ Tel: 0161-474 0061 Fax: 0161-474 0071 E-mail: omar@jmclayton.co.uk *Fabric merchants*

Clayton & Co Penistone Ltd, Westhorpe Works, Halifax Road, Sheffield, S36 7EY Tel: (01226) 763130 Fax: (01226) 370145 *Mechanical, electrical contractors & project engineers*

Clayton Thermal Processes Ltd, 2 Summerton Road, Oldbury, West Midlands, B69 2EL Tel: 0121-511 1203 Fax: 0121-511 1192 E-mail: claytonthermal@claytonholdings.com *Fluidised bed furnace sales*

▶ Clayton Transport D A Ltd, Granville Way, Bicester, Oxfordshire, OX26 4JT Tel: (01869) 253897 Fax: (01869) 245666

Clayton (Twickenham) Precision Engineering Co. Ltd, Clock Tower Road, Isleworth, Middlesex, TW7 6DT Tel: (020) 8568 9527 Fax: (020) 8569 9526 E-mail: claytonprecision@aol.com *Precision engineers*

Clayton UK Ltd, 12 Little Lane, Calverton, Nottingham, NG14 6JU Tel: 0115-965 5009 Fax: 0115-965 2333 E-mail: graham.clayton@claytonukltd.co.uk *Textile agents*

Claytons, 28 Main Street, Whittington, Lichfield, Staffordshire, WS14 9JS Tel: (01543) 433038 *Fencing contractors*

CLC Contractors Ltd, 212 Manchester Road, Warrington, WA1 3BD Tel: (01925) 417200 Fax: (01925) 417201 *Painting contractors*

▶ Cleaford Services Ltd, 46 Hazell Road, Farnham, Surrey, GU9 7BP Tel: (01252) 717166 Fax: (01252) 717137 E-mail: sales@cleaford.co.uk Principal Export Areas: Central/East Europe & Central America *Software development*

▶ Clean 4 You, 7 Rosina Way, Penwithick, St. Austell, Cornwall, PL26 8TS Tel: 01726 851418 Fax: 01726 851418 E-mail: cleanforyou@btinternet.com *Local domestic cleaning service. Regular and one off appointments. All cleaning supplies are brought with us and are included in price. Reliable and convenient service. Fully insured and for key hold.*

▶ Clean Air Power, 1 Aston Way, Moss Side, Leyland, PR26 7UX Tel: (01772) 624499 Fax: (01772) 436495 *Commercial vehicle repairers*

▶ Clean Air Services Ltd, Conway Road, Mochdre, Colwyn Bay, Clwyd, LL28 5HL Tel: (01492) 546063 Fax: (01492) 544076 E-mail: cleanair@poppleton.co.uk *Ventilation sheet metal duck worth*

Clean Air Technologies, Unit B11 Laser Quay, Culpeper Close, Medway City Estate, Rochester, Kent, ME2 4HU Tel: (01634) 725295 Fax: (01634) 713929 E-mail: sales@catltd.com *Air handling & clean room facilities & anti-contamination services*

Clean Approach Ltd, 86 Sydney Road, Watford, WD18 7QX Tel: (01923) 210009 Fax: (01923) 210065 *Cleaning supplies*

Clean Card Systems Ltd, Unit 3 Spring Gardens, Middleton, Manchester, M24 6DQ Tel: 0161-654 6611 Fax: 0161-643 1040 E-mail: info@cleancardsystems.co.uk *Cleaning cards, cleaning credit cards service*

▶ Clean Drains Services, Fryers Lane, High Wycombe, Buckinghamshire, HP12 3AN Tel: (01494) 437164 Fax: (01494) 510596 E-mail: sales@cleandrains.com *Drain maintenance & repair services*

Clean Heat & Engineering Co. Ltd, Southbank House, Black Prince Road, London, SE1 7SJ Tel: (020) 7793 4002 Fax: (020) 7735 7253 E-mail: email@cleanheat.co.uk *Heating & ventilation engineers*

▶ Clean I.T. Services Ltd., 70, Brookfield Avenue, Glasgow, G33 1SX Tel: 0141 558 5496 E-mail: info@cleanitservices.co.uk *Computer Cleaning and sanitization service. Computer & IT cleaning services, PC"s terminals & other electronic office eqpt cleaned. Faxes, printers, telephones & VDU"s. Out of hours working to minimize down time. **

▶ Clean Image, The Car Valet Centre, Unit 1 Court Industrial Estate, Chelmsford, CM2 6ND Tel: (01245) 350035 Fax: (01245) 265626 E-mail: info@clean-image.co.uk *Silver car care services*

▶ Clean Impact, 103 Junction Road, Burgess Hill, West Sussex, RH15 0JL Tel: (07811) 107268 E-mail: sales@cleanimpact.ws *we offer general cleaning including window cleaning via pole washing upto 6 floors high*office cleaning and more please see website*

Clean It All, Keepers Cottage, Alston Lane, Churston Ferrers, Brixham, Devon, TQ5 0HT Tel: (01803) 842249 Fax: (01803) 842249 *Domestic & commercial cleaning agency*

Clean Linen Services Ltd, 54 Furze Platt Road, Maidenhead, Berkshire, SL6 7NL Tel: (01628) 645900 Fax: (01628) 674099 E-mail: info@cleanservices.co.uk *Clean Linen Services Ltd (CLEAN) is one of the largest privately owned laundry service providers in the UK. Our 5 sites in the South of England support thousands of clients with their both linen and garment requirements with our Maidenhead garment facility being one of the most advanced and 'food trade' - compliant laundries in the UK.*

Clean Machine Garage & Industrial Services Ltd, Bridge Industrial Centre, Wharf Road, Tovil, Maidstone, Kent, ME15 6RR Tel: (01622) 688115 Fax: (01622) 688054 E-mail: sales@clean-machine.com *Garage equipment services, distributors & manufrs*

Clean Modules Ltd, Unit 3, Hawthorne Road, Castle Donington, Derby, DE74 2QR Tel: (01332) 696970 Fax: 01332 696963 E-mail: enquiries@cleanmodules.co.uk *Clean Modules Ltd. designs, manufactures & installates clean rooms, clean air systems, containerised & mobile clean rooms in a modular way of building, clean room equipment, laminar flow systems, glove boxes, isolators & mini-environments. Also clean room trial facilities.*

Clean Plastic Mouldings Ltd, Unit 6, Kenfig Industrial Estate, Margam, Port Talbot, West Glamorgan, SA13 2PE Tel: (01656) 740102 Fax: (01656) 745354 E-mail: cpm@bryncae.fsbusiness.co.uk Principal Export Areas: Worldwide *Plastics injection mouldings manufacturers including small batch. Also injection mould (plastic) toolmakers & hot foil stamping services.*

Clean Room Installation Services Ltd, 9 The Metro Centre, Ronsons Way, St. Albans, Hertfordshire, AL4 9QT Tel: (01727) 840594 Fax: (01727) 843368 E-mail: cleanrooms@stodec.co.uk *Manufacturers of clean rooms (environmental) & clean room wall systems. Also clean room installation/service contractors clean room constructors/assembly services*

Clean Solutions, Unit 1 Kenwood Road, Stockport, Cheshire, SK5 6PH Tel: 0161-947 9947 Fax: 0161-947 9940 E-mail: enquiries@cleansolutions.co.uk *Cleansing materials distributors*

Clean Surface Ltd, 14 Highmeres Road, Leicester, LE4 9LZ Tel: 0116-224 0072 Fax: 0116-224 0074 E-mail: sales@cleansurface.co.uk *Dry ice blast cleaning equipment*

Clean Tech, Corporate House, Carmarthen Road, Kilgetty, Dyfed, SA68 0UG Tel: (01834) 813827 Fax: (01834) 811962 *Janitorial supplies*

▶ Clean Tech, 35 Church Close, Grimston, King's Lynn, Norfolk, PE32 1BN Tel: (01485) 609223 Fax: (01485) 600475 E-mail: mikebarrett@genie.co.uk *Carpet & upholstery cleaning services*

Clean & Tidy (UK), 351 Cambridge Heath Road, London, E2 9RA Tel: (020) 7739 4194 Fax: (020) 7739 2072 E-mail: cleanandtidyuk@yahoo.co.uk *Commercial & industrial cleaning contractors*

Cleanacres Machinery Ltd, Hazleton, Cheltenham, Gloucestershire, GL54 4DX Tel: (01451) 860721 Fax: (01451) 860139 E-mail: info@cleanacres.co.uk *Crop sprayer manufrs*

▶ Clean-A-Home Leeds, Suite A, 43 Cardinal Grove, Leeds, LS11 8HG Tel: 0113 2171248 E-mail: denise.cleanahome@ntlworld.com *Domestic cleaning company*

Cleanair Group Ltd, Technology House, 5 Newton Close, Drayton Fields, Daventry, Northamptonshire, NN11 5RR Tel: (01327) 301383 Fax: (01327) 301384 E-mail: info@cleanair.com *Air conditioning, heating, ventilation & filtration installation services*

▶ Cleanceil, 46 Owen Road, Kirkdale, Liverpool, L4 1RW Tel: 0870 910 1602 E-mail: enquiries@cleanceil.co.uk *A suspended ceiling cleaning specialist based in Merseyside catering for the small to medium business. No minimum charge.*

▶ Cleancut Ltd, 4 Tripps Mews, Manchester, M20 2JT Tel: 0161-448 8090 Fax: 0161-448 8033

▶ The Cleaner Co., 8 Acomb Court, Front Street, Acomb, York, YO24 3BJ Tel: (01904) 787485 Fax: (01904) 789424 E-mail: chris@hsyork.co.uk *Cleaner offices*

▶ Cleaner Systems Ltd, 108 Preston Road, Birmingham, B26 1TQ Tel: (0800) 7561331 Fax: (0800) 7569821 E-mail: info@cleaner-systems.co.uk *Computer cleaning products & services*

Cleanforce Contracting Ltd, Force Group House, 31-33 Albion Street, Stoke-on-Trent, ST1 1QF Tel: (01782) 213333 Fax: (01782) 284555 E-mail: info@clean-force.biz *Cleaning contractors*

▶ Cleanhire UK, 148 Hinckley Road, Laffak, St. Helens, Merseyside, WA11 9JY Tel: (01744) 633738 Fax: (01744) 633738 E-mail: enquiries@cleanhire.co.uk *Specialists in the hire, sales, service*

▶ Cleaninc., 88 Kilmaurs Road, Kilmarnock, Ayrshire, KA3 1QF Tel: (01563) 539556 E-mail: rthass@ukonline.co.uk *Construction service, estate agent service, commercial, office & domestic cleansing*

Cleaning Contractors Services Group Ltd, 253 Alcester Road South, Kings Heath, Birmingham, B14 6DT Tel: 0121-444 4232 Fax: 0121-443 1117 E-mail: contractcleaning@kingsheathb14. wannadoo.co.uk *Office cleaning contractors, window cleaners*

▶ Cleaning Equipment Supplies Ltd, Unit 5 Caldicot Way, Avondale Industrial Estate, Cwmbran, Gwent, NP44 1UF Tel: (01633) 868866 Fax: (01633) 862286 E-mail: admin@ces-ltd.uk.com *Repair, sell, hire cleaning machine, equipment*

Cleaning & Hygiene Distributors, Sandbach Road, Stoke-on-Trent, ST6 2DU Tel: (01782) 825222 Fax: (01782) 825200 *Cleaning & hygiene products distribution*

Cleaning Machinery K E W Ltd, Whiteball Garage, Whiteball, Wellington, Somerset, TA21 0LT Tel: (01823) 672069 Fax: (01823) 672200 E-mail: kew.cleaning@virgin.net *Pressure washers & floor cleaning*

Cleaning & Packaging Supplies (Worcester), A Perrywood Trading Park, Wylds Lane, Worcester, WR5 1DZ Tel: (01905) 763500 Fax: (01905) 763363 E-mail: cps.worcs@btinternet.com *Janitorial supply services*

Cleaning Rag Supply Co. Ltd, 28 Brearley Street, Hockley, Birmingham, B19 3NR Tel: 0121-333 4446 Fax: 0121-333 4442 E-mail: enquiries@cleaningragsupply.co.uk *Cleaning & wiping rags*

▶ Cleaning Supplies 2U, Unit 3, Wallace Court, Road Three, Winsford, Cheshire, CW7 3PD Tel: (0800) 0725282 Fax: (01606) 552288 E-mail: info@cleaningsupplies2u.co.uk *Janitorial & hygiene products suppliers*

Cleaning Supplies Direct, 424 Portswood Road, Southampton, SO17 3SD Tel: (023) 8043 4139 Fax: (023) 8090 0556 E-mail: sales@cleaningsuppliesltd.co.uk *Janitorial supplies*

Cleaning Supplies UK, Lovet House, Lovet Road, The Pinnacles, Harlow, Essex, CM19 5TB Tel: (01279) 459345 Fax: (01279) 772376 E-mail: websupport@cleaningsuppliesuk.com *Businesses throughout the UK and around the globe have come to rely on Cannon to provide a range of services that are essential to their operations. From the provision of specially selected Consumable products to Washroom Hygiene and Textile Care, Pest Control to Horticulture, attention to detail and a desire to exceed customer expectations is foremost in the minds of all our staff. **By listening to our customers and understanding the business needs, we can tailor each service to best suit their requirements or integrate all our services to offer a complete solution. As part of the UK's leading independently owned provider of Property Support Services, Cannon are uniquely positioned to offer help and advice to anyone involved in facilities management or building maintenance.*

Cleaning & Wiping Supplies Ltd, 23 Colvilles Road, East Kilbride, Glasgow, G75 0RS Tel: (01355) 245065 Fax: (01355) 227421 E-mail: cleaningandwiping@lineone.net *Paper products & janitorial supplies*

Cleankill Environmental Services Ltd, P O Box 2087, Kenley, Surrey, CR8 5LU Tel: (020) 8668 5477 Fax: (020) 8668 4446 *Pest controllers*

Cleanline Engineering Co. Ltd, 27 Acacia Grove, New Malden, Surrey, KT3 3BJ Tel: (07909) 983648 E-mail: c.mence@cleanline-eng.co.uk *Stainless steel pipework contractors*

Cleanline Installations Ltd, Terminal House, Station Approach, Shepperton, Middlesex, TW17 8AS Tel: (01932) 260490 Fax: (01932) 227037 E-mail: cleanline@compuserve.com *Telecommunication consultants*

Cleanrite Property Services Ltd, 10 Nab Hill Avenue, Leek, Staffordshire, ST13 8EE Tel: (01538) 386857 E-mail: clean.rite@btopenworld.com *Commercial & domestic contract cleaners*

▶ Cleanrock Civil Engineers, 46 Armitage Way, Cambridge, CB4 2UE Tel: (01223) 302921 Fax: (01223) 302927

Cleanroom Supplies Ltd, Violet House, Cumrew, Carlisle, CA8 9DD Tel: (01768) 896800 Fax: 01228 830100 *One Stop Shop for Cleanroom and Laboratory Consumables, Cleanroom Clothing and Cleanroom Furniture. Contamination Control. Protective Clothing*

▶ Cleansafe, Unit 111, Bradley Hall Trading Estate, Bradley Lane, Standish, Wigan, Lancashire, WN6 0XQ Tel: (01257) 422200 Fax: (01257) 472555 E-mail: sales@cleansafe.co.uk *Specialised cleaning for plasma, lcd & tft screens*

▶ Cleansave Cleaning Material Suppliers, 6 Fairview Close, Tonbridge, Kent, TN9 2UU Tel: (0845) 2267275 Fax: E-mail: mail@cleansave.co.uk *Cleaning and janitorial supplies including: cleaning chemicals, paper towels, toilet paper, floor care, waste sacks,and much much more.*

Cleanscreen Computer Services, 6 Woodmere Avenue, Croydon, CR0 7PA Tel: (020) 8656 7114 Fax: (020) 8406 4931 E-mail: enquiries@cleanscreen.co.uk *Specialist computer cleaning*

Cleansing Service Group Ltd, Botley Road, Hedge End, Southampton, SO30 2HE Tel: (01489) 785856 Fax: (01489) 789821 E-mail: enquiries@csgwasteman.co.uk *The UK's largest waste management company, specialising in waste collection, waste treatment and waste disposal for liquid, dry, hazardous, commercial and household waste products.* Also at: Aylsford, Bournemouth, Bristol, Newbury & Oxford

▶ Cleansmart Carpet Cleaning Machines & Equipment, W12 Lenton Business Centre, Lenton Boulevard, Lenton, Nottingham, NG7 2BY Tel: (0845) 8620209 *Providing equipment machinery & chemicals to carpet cleaners*

Cleanwell High Pressure Washers Ltd, Unit 12a Apsley Industrial Estate, Kents Avenue, Hemel Hempstead, Hertfordshire, HP3 9XH Tel: (01442) 263552 Fax: (01442) 266871 E-mail: sales@cleanwell.co.uk *Cleaning equipment manufrs*

▶ Cleanwright Ltd, Ings farm, West Torrington, Market Rasen, Lincolnshire, LN8 5SQ Tel: (01673) 857454 Fax: (01673) 857456 E-mail: sales@cleanwrightltd.co.uk *Importers & manufacturers of high pressure cleaning equipment, *UK agents for bertolini pumps, udor pumps & HPP pumps**

continued

Clear Brook Water Treatment, 8 Hollow Hill Road, Ditchingham, Bungay, Suffolk, NR35 2QZ Tel: (01986) 893076 Fax: (01986) 893076 *Water treatment*

Clear Cube Consulting Ltd, 145-157 St. John Street, London, EC1V 4PY Tel: (020) 8776 8788 Fax: (020) 7253 9040 E-mail: info@asimex-consulting.co.uk *Business consulting & emerging market specialists*

▶ Clear Cut Mortgages, St. James House, St. James Square, Cheltenham, Gloucestershire, GL50 3WD Tel: (0845) 0698000 E-mail: info@clearcutmortgages.com *Most refreshing Independent Mortgage broker in the UK.*

▶ Clear Design Services, 44 Seaford Road, Wokingham, Berkshire, RG40 2EL Tel: 0118 9894455E-mail: info@cleardesignservices.co.uk *Graphic & website designers*

▶ Clear Drains UK Ltd, Beaconsfield House, Fieldhouse Lane, Marlow, Buckinghamshire, SL7 1LW Tel: (01628) 484995 Fax: (01628) 890434 E-mail: helpdesk@cleardrainsnet-revenue.com *Drain clearance services*

▶ Clear Flow Environmental Technologies Ltd, 30 Ainsley Grove, Darlington, County Durham, DL3 0GD Tel: (01325) 460624 E-mail: sales@fatstrippa.info *Authorised Dealer & Instalers Of Fatstrippa Products.**

Clear Hedge Forestry, Chiddingly Road, Horam, Heathfield, East Sussex, TN21 0JJ Tel: (01435) 812202 Fax: (01435) 812202 *Fencing equipment manufrs*

▶ Clear I T, 328 Meanwood Road, Leeds, LS7 2JE Tel: 0113-200 7500 Fax: 0113-200 7508 *Computer systems consultant services & software*

▶ Clear Packaging Ltd, 215 Torrington Avenue, Coventry, CV4 9AP Tel: (024) 7646 4566 Fax: (024) 7642 2299 E-mail: info@clearpkgltd.co.uk *Manufacturer of pvc, pet polypropylene cartons & lids*

Clear Polishing, Unit 7 Brandon Way Industrial Estate, Brandon Way, West Bromwich, West Midlands, B70 9PW Tel: 0121-580 4744 Fax: 0121-580 4744 *Polishers of all metals*

Clear Print Office Equipment, 18-22 Prior Deram Walk, Coventry, CV4 8FT Tel: (024) 7671 6123 Fax: (024) 7671 7427 *Photocopier suppliers*

Clear Waste Services, Meridian Centre, King Street, Oldham, OL8 1EZ Tel: 0161-628 3215 Fax: 0161-633 3215 E-mail: info@clearws.co.uk *Provide a waste to landfill minimization consultancy service*

Clear Water Interiors, 69 Anglesmede Crescent, Pinner, Middlesex, HA5 5ST Tel: (020) 8863 1732 *Interior Design for offices*

Clear Water Koi Direct, Unit 10 Acaster Industrial Estate, Acaster Malbis, York, YO23 2TX Tel: (01904) 705536 Fax: (01904) 705536 E-mail: sales@koikeeping.com *Japanese ponds specialists*

Clear Wise, 41 Cresswell Road, Newbury, Berkshire, RG14 2PQ Tel: (01635) 48196 Fax: (01635) 48196 *Waste tank disposal services - septic tanks*

The Clearance Store Ltd, 74 Oakfield Road, London, E17 5RP Tel: (0800) 7312689 Fax: (020) 8503 2600 *Computer mail-order sales*

Clearex Plastics Ltd, Dubmire Trading Estate, Houghton le Spring, Tyne & Wear, DH4 5RF Tel: 0191-385 2880 Fax: 0191-385 2855 *Plastics moulding manufrs*

Clearflow Southern, 10 Laxton Gardens, Redhill, RH1 3NJ Tel: (01737) 644625 *Water treatment equipment agents*

Clearol Pest Control, 29 Nant Y Gaer Road, Llay, Wrexham, Clwyd, LL12 0SH Tel: (01978) 852975 Fax: (01978) 855108 *Pest & vermin control services*

▶ Clearpeople Ltd, 17 Heathmans Road, London, SW6 4TJ Tel: (0870) 1999910 Fax: (0709) 2163189 E-mail: info@clearpeople.com *Web services & solutions*

Clearpoint Print Services Ltd, Park Lane, Nottingham, NG6 0DT Tel: 0115-979 7925 Fax: 0115-979 7958 E-mail: sales@clearpoint-print.com *Promotional colour screen & litho printers*

Clearprint, 99 East Road, Sleaford, Lincolnshire, NG34 7EH Tel: (01529) 303176 Fax: (01529) 303172 E-mail: sales@clearaprint.com *Offset litho printers & stationers*

Clearprint Labels Ltd, 1-2 Essex Street, Preston, PR1 1QE Tel: (01772) 258185 Fax: (01772) 256622 E-mail: sales@clearprint.co.uk *Self adhesive label manufrs*

▶ Cleartech Water Solutions, 1 Howard Court, East Kilbride, Glasgow, G74 4QZ Tel: (01355) 267199 Fax: (01355) 267109 E-mail: info@cleartechwater.co.uk *Water treatment supplies*

Cleartone Telecomms Ltd, Unit 15 Pontyfelin Industrial Estate, New Inn, Pontypool, Gwent, NP4 0DQ Tel: (01495) 752255 Fax: (01495) 752323 E-mail: admin@cleartone.co.uk *Communications equipment*

▶ Cleartron Computers, 636 First Floor, Southchurch Road, Southend-on-Sea, SS1 2PT Tel: (01702) 602436 Fax: (01702) 602429 E-mail: sales@cleartron.co.uk *Computer support & maintenance sales accountancy software solutions*

▶ Clearview Commercial Contractors, Old Farm Road, Hampton, Middlesex, TW12 3QU Tel: (0800) 7311332 E-mail: clearview@talk21.com *We specialise in high level & high access window cleaning to commerical offices, units & blocks. We use high rise water purification Reach & Wash systems & cherry pickers. health & Safety accredited & approved*

Clearview Computers, 1A Parklands Avenue, Billingham, Cleveland, TS23 1DZ Tel: (01642) 868690 Fax: (01642) 868691 E-mail: clearviewcomputers@hotmail.co.uk *Computer repair & distribution*

▶ ClearView Ladderless Window Cleaning, 21 Lightfoot Road, Uttoxeter, Staffordshire, ST14 7HA Tel: 01889 560119 *Window cleaning services*

▶ Clearview Pvcu, Hospital Road, Ellon, Aberdeenshire, AB41 9AW Tel: (01358) 722202 E-mail: lawrence.muirhead@btopenworld.com *PVCu windows & frame suppliers*

Clearview Stoves, More Works, Bishops Castle, Shropshire, SY9 5HH Tel: (01588) 650401 Fax: (01588) 650493 *Stove manufrs*

Clearview Stoves, Dinham House, Dinham, Ludlow, Shropshire, SY8 1EH Tel: (01584) 878100 Fax: (01584) 872010 E-mail: info@clearviewstoves.com *Stove manufrs*

▶ Clearview Window Cleaning Services, PO Box 4117, Hornchurch, Essex, RM12 4ER Tel: (0800) 7311332 Fax: (01708) 502899 E-mail: mail@clearviewwindowcleaners.co.uk *Window cleaning contractors services*

▶ Clearview Window Cleaning Services Ltd, 216 City Road, London, EC1V 2PH Tel: (0800) 7311332 Fax: (01708) 502899 E-mail: info@clearviewwindowcleaners.co.uk *Clear view window cleaning services*

▶ Clearview (Yorkshire) Limited, Unit 4, Sullivan Business Park, West Dock Street, Hull, HU3 4TG Tel: 01482 609310 Fax: 01482 218444 E-mail: sales@conservatoryroofskits.co.uk *BBA Approved Fabricator and Supplier of K2 Conservatory Roof Systems and components*

▶ Clearwater Business Consulting Ltd, 28 Clearwater, Londonderry, BT47 6BE Tel: (028) 7131 3660 E-mail: peter@clearwaterconsulting.org *We are a specialist Employment and Human Resource Consultancy and Advisory Service, based in Northern Ireland, offering expert personnel management support to small and medium sized organisations.*

Clearwater Consultancy Ltd, 18 St Georges Street, Chorley, Lancashire, PR7 2AA Tel: (01257) 272730 Fax: (01257) 272731 E-mail: info@clearwater-consultancy.co.uk *Bespoke software developers*

▶ Clearwater D C, Carnbroe Road, Bellshill, Lanarkshire, ML4 1RS Tel: (01698) 844771 Fax: (01698) 844723

Clearwater Process Control Ltd, Clearwater House, Clearwater Industrial Park, Bristol Road, Bridgwater, Somerset, TA6 4AW Tel: (01278) 433443 Fax: (01278) 453653 *Water, sewage & treatment plant manufrs*

Clearwater Swimming Pools Ltd, The Studio, 81 Langley Close, Headington, Oxford, OX3 7DB Tel: (01865) 766112 Fax: (01865) 741373 E-mail: sales@clearwater-pools.co.uk *Indoor pool construction & design service*

Clearway Disposals Ltd, 41 Dobbin Road, Portadown, Craigavon, County Armagh, BT62 4EY Tel: (028) 3833 7333 Fax: (028) 3833 6716 E-mail: info@clearwaypordesign.ffs.uk *Scrap metal merchants*

Clearway Distribution, Triumph Road, Nottingham, NG7 2GA Tel: 0115-924 8484 Fax: 0115-942 3148 *Storage & distribution services*

▶ Clearway Sales & Promotional Products, PO Box 2779, Faringdon, Oxfordshire, SN7 7BZ Tel: (01367) 242400 Fax: (01367) 244299 E-mail: enquiry@clearwaykeyrings.co.uk *Manufacture of promotional goods*

Clearwell Pest Control Services, 26 Chapel Street, Bradford, West Yorkshire, BD1 5DL Tel: (01274) 371577 Fax: (01274) 743173 E-mail: office@clearwell.biz *Pest control services*

▶ Cleckheaton Construction Ltd, Crossland House, Northgate, Cleckheaton, West Yorkshire, BD19 3NB Tel: (01274) 873344 Fax: (01274) 876850

Cleckheaton Holdings Ltd, P O Box 24, Cleckheaton, West Yorkshire, BD19 3LN Tel: (01274) 863704 Fax: (01274) 863705 E-mail: cleckhol@globalnet.co.uk *Motor dealers*

Cledwyn Saunders & Son Ltd, Rhigos Road, Rhigos, Aberdare, Mid Glamorgan, CF44 9YR Tel: (01685) 813613 *Welding fabricators*

▶ Clee Hill Plant Ltd, 41 Downiebrae Road, Rutherglen, Glasgow, G73 1PW Tel: 0141-647 0067 Fax: 0141-647 7600 E-mail: glasgow@cleehill.co.uk *Contractors plant hire*

▶ Clee Hill Plant Ltd, Turner Crescent, Newcastle, Staffordshire, ST5 7JZ Tel: (01782) 566017 Fax: (01782) 565858 E-mail: stoke@cleehill.co.uk *Road surfacing & plant hire*

Clee Hill Plants, Mansfield Road, Corbriggs, Chesterfield, Derbyshire, S41 0JW Tel: (01246) 551637 Fax: (01246) 551639 E-mail: sales@cleehill.co.uk *Plant hire & rental* Also at: Chesterfield

Cleen Flo Manchester Ltd, 5 Lower Chatham Street, Manchester, M1 5QL Tel: 0161-237 3880 Fax: 0161-236 9388 *Dust fume collection equipment manufrs*

▶ Cleenol Group Ltd, Neville House, Beaumont Road, Banbury, Oxfordshire, OX16 1RB Tel: (01295) 251721 Fax: (01295) 269561 E-mail: sales@cleanol.co.uk *Janitorial chemicals manufacturers*

Cleethorpes Angling Centre, 291 Brereton Avenue, Cleethorpes, South Humberside, DN35 7QX Tel: (01472) 602002 Fax: (01472) 602002 *Fishing tackle suppliers*

Cleeve Engineering Ltd, 38 Evesham Rd, Bishops Cleeve, Cheltenham, Glos, GL52 8SA Tel: (01242) 673223 Fax: (01242) 677282 *Mechanical engineering*

Cleftbridge Coatings Ltd, Unit 8a, Lower Road Trading Estate, Ledbury, Herefordshire, HR8 2DH Tel: (01531) 633771 Fax: (01531) 633719 E-mail: enquiries@cleftbridge.co.uk *Powder coating & paint finishing services*

Brian Clegg Educational Products Ltd, Regent Mill, Regent Street, Rochdale, Lancashire, OL12 0HQ Tel: (01706) 666620 Fax: (01706) 666621 E-mail: office@brianclegg.co.uk *Art & craft material manufrs*

▶ Clegg Food Projects, Bishops House, 42 High Pavement, Nottingham, NG1 1HN Tel: 0115-941 9531 Fax: 0115-841 3122 E-mail: ann.clarke@declegg.co.uk *A one stop shop for all your food project needs. Feasibility, Design Project Management, Construction, Equipment Installation and Commissioning are all part of the service*

Cleggys Electrics, 3 Sharpe Close, Barton-upon-Humber, South Humberside, DN18 5TL Tel: (01652) 636066 E-mail: jrclegg147@aol.com *Closed circuit television (CCTV) equipment installers*

▶ Clehonger Plant Hire Ltd, Unit 4-5 Beech Business Park, Tillington Road, Hereford, HR4 9QJ Tel: (01432) 277366 Fax: (01432) 277366

▶ Cleland Construction Ltd, Greenside Depot, Biggar Road, Newarthill, Motherwell, Lanarkshire, ML1 5SS Tel: (01698) 860890

M.S.O. Cleland Ltd, The Linenhall Press, 399 Castlereagh Road, Belfast, BT5 6QP Tel: (028) 9040 0200 Fax: (028) 9070 5446 E-mail: info@mso.com *Carton & label printers*

Clelland Engineering Ltd, 25 Lawmoor Road, Dixons Blazes Industrial Estate, Glasgow, G5 0UG Tel: 0141-429 5585 Fax: 0141-420 1045 E-mail: clelleng@aol.com *Precision engineers*

M. Wallace Clelland & Co. Ltd, Burnside Industrial Estate, Kilsyth, Glasgow, G65 9JY Tel: (01236) 823015 Fax: (01236) 823256 *Green waste, compost hire & contractors*

Clement Clarke International Ltd, Unit A Cartel Business Estate, Edinburgh Way, Harlow, Essex, CM20 2TT Tel: (01279) 414969 Fax: (01279) 456339 E-mail: info@c3headsets.com *Communications equipment*

Clement John Son Glazing, Unit 4 Broadmoor Park, Forest Vale Indust Estate, Dean, Cinderford, Gloucestershire, GL14 2YF Tel: (01594) 822081 Fax: (01594) 825897 *Window manufrs*

▶ Clementine Oakley, 259 Water Road, Wembley, Middlesex, HA0 1HX Tel: (020) 8922 4567 Fax: (020) 8922 4568

Clements Engineering (St. Neots) Ltd, Unit 120 Westgate, Airfield Industrial Park, Little Staughton, Bedford, MK44 2BN Tel: (01234) 378814 Fax: (01234) 376779 E-mail: sales@clementsmarine.co.uk *Manufacturers and suppliers of high performance marine propulsion assemblies for the light commercial and motor boat industries. We cast all of our own propellers and gear, provide engineering design and propeller specification and supports worldwide customers with local dealer network and carries out boat performance optimisation by attending sea trials.*

Clements & Street Ltd, Hanbury Road, Stoke Prior, Bromsgrove, Worcestershire, B60 4AA Tel: (01527) 835777 Fax: (01527) 873061 E-mail: sales@clementsandstreet.co.uk *Full service exhibition stand contractor*

William Clements (Chemicals) Ltd, 38a Witham Street, Belfast, BT4 1HP Tel: (028) 9073 8395 Fax: (028) 9045 0532 *Distributors & manufacturers of soap, detergent & disinfectant*

Clemmitt Nick Joinery Contracts, Ghyll Crest, Over Silton, Thirsk, North Yorkshire, YO7 2LJ Tel: (01609) 883636 Fax: (01609) 883111 E-mail: sales@timbergates.co.uk *Wooden gates manufrs*

Clena Supplies, St. Albans Road, Stafford, ST16 3DP Tel: (01785) 229229 Fax: (01785) 229030 *Cleaning equipment supplier*

Clenal Ware Systems, Farnham Trading Estate, Farnham, Surrey, GU9 9NN Tel: (01252) 712789 Fax: (01252) 723719 E-mail: info@clenalware.com *Catering equipment manufrs*

▶ Cleopatra Palace, Lady Lane, Blunsdon, Swindon, SN25 4DN Tel: (01793) 876796 Fax: (01793) 876796 E-mail: cleopatra.enquiries@apexmail.com *Berenguer Dolls UK,Antonio Juan Dolls UK,Baby Dolls,Reborn Dolls, Baby Beau and Belle,Kirks Folly, Italian babywear,Biocol Swindon,*Special occassion babywear*

Cle-Pol Manufacturing Co. Ltd, PO Box 5, Barking, Essex, IG11 0TL Tel: (020) 8532 6900 Fax: (020) 8532 6940 *Chemical manufrs*

Clerical Medical Forestry Ltd, 33 Old Broad Street, London, EC2N 1HZ Tel: (020) 7321 1941 Fax: (020) 7321 1423 *Assurance company* Also at: Dranches throughout the U.K.

▶ Clerici Associates, Pemberley, Ricksons Lane, West Horsley, Leatherhead, Surrey, KT24 6HU Tel: (01483) 283573 E-mail: enquiries@clerici.co.uk *Clerici Associates - Architecture and Design*

Clerkdrive Ltd, 3 Tolliday Close, Wivenhoe, Colchester, CO7 9SL Tel: (01206) 827676 *It consultants*

▶ Clerkenwell Bathrooms, 266 Hackney Road, London, E2 7SJ Tel: (020) 7729 6698 Fax: (020) 7729 6698 *Bathroom designers & installers*

Clerkenwell Screws Ltd, 107-109 Clerkenwell Road, London, EC1R 5BY Tel: (020) 7405 1215 Fax: (020) 7831 3057 *Screw distributors*

Clesse (UK) Ltd, Unit 8, Planetary Industrial Estate, Wednesfield, Wolverhampton, WV13 3XQ Tel: (01902) 383233 Fax: (01902) 383234 E-mail: sales@clesse.co.uk *Distributors of LP gas regulators & equipment*

Clestra Cleanrooms, Hamilton House, 3 North Street, Carshalton, Surrey, SM5 2HZ Tel: (020) 8773 2121 Fax: (020) 8260 6814 *Cleanroom environment manufrs*

Clevedon Fasteners Ltd, Reddicap Trading Estate, Sutton Coldfield, West Midlands, B75 7BU Tel: 0121-378 0619 Fax: 0121-378 3186 E-mail: sales@clevedon-fasteners.co.uk *Rivet manufrs*

Cleveland Biotech Ltd, 3 Vanguard Court, Preston Farm Business Pk, Stockton-on-Tees, Cleveland, TS18 3TR Tel: (01642) 606606 Fax: (01642) 606040 E-mail: bugs@clevebio.com *Growth of micro-organisms & formulation of biologically active products to treat industrial, commercial & municipal wastes*

Cleveland Bridge, PO Box 27, Darlington, County Durham, DL1 4DF Tel: (01325) 469735 Fax: (01325) 382320 E-mail: info@clevelandbridge.com *Steel bridge builders*

▶ Cleveland Circuits Ltd, Skelton Industrial Estate, Skelton-in-Cleveland, Saltburn-by-the-Sea, Cleveland, TS12 2LQ Tel: (01287) 651991 Fax: (01287) 652898 E-mail: sales@pcb.co.uk *Printed circuit board manufacturers. Bare and populated. Full range from conventional to surface mount. Manual, semi and fully automatic*

continued

assembly options. Prototype and testing service. Also inter-connection wiring and sub-assembly available. ISO & UL accredited.

Cleveland Crop Sprayers Ltd, Platform 1, Station Road, Duns, Berwickshire, TD11 3EJ Tel: (01361) 883418 Fax: (01361) 882082 E-mail: info@gambetti.co.uk *Crop sprayer manufacturers & suppliers*

Cleveland Electrical Co. Ltd, 50 Park Lane, Liverpool, L1 8HE Tel: 0151-709 6883 Fax: 0151-709 8861 E-mail: enquiries@cleveland-electrical.co.uk *Armature & electrical motor rewinding & repair*

▶ Cleveland Gas Service Engineers, 151 York Road, Hartlepool, Cleveland, TS26 9EQ Tel: (01642) 615232 Fax: (01642) 868336

Cleveland Joinery Ltd, Cleveland Place, Farncombe Street, Godalming, Surrey, GU7 3LP Tel: (01483) 415522 Fax: (01483) 861103 *Joinery manufrs*

Cleveland Joinery East Anglia Ltd, Joinery Works, Lake View Road, Lowestoft, Suffolk, NR33 9NE Tel: (01502) 501917 Fax: (01502) 585044 *Joinery manufrs*

Cleveland Potash Ltd, Boulby Mine, Loftus, Saltburn-by-the-Sea, Cleveland, TS13 4UZ Tel: (01287) 640140 Fax: (01287) 640934 E-mail: jan.hunton@clevelandpotash.co.uk *Muriate potash potassium & salt manufrs*

Cleveland Refrigeration Co. Ltd, Unit 5, Leven Road, Lawson Industrial Estate, Middlesbrough, Cleveland, TS3 6LG Tel: (01642) 242592 Fax: (01642) 226020 E-mail: agcrl@cdnscustomers.com *Commercial refrigerators & air conditioning*

Cleveland Sitesafe, Dockside Road, Middlesbrough, Cleveland, TS3 8AT Tel: (01642) 244663 Fax: (01642) 244664 E-mail: info@cleveland-sitesafe.ltd.uk *Portable high security storage units & modular steel buildings manufrs*

Cleveland Steel & Tubes Ltd, Dalton Airfield, Dalton, Thirsk, North Yorkshire, YO7 3JN Tel: (01845) 577789 Fax: (01845) 578373 E-mail: admin@cleveland-steel.com *Steel tube distributors*

▶ Clever Air Conditioning Sales Ltd, 26 York Street, London, W1U 6PZ Tel: (0845) 0573097 Fax: (020) 7206 9432 E-mail: sales@cleverengineering.co.uk *Energy management products suppliers*

▶ Clever Little Things, PO Box 598, Addlestone, Surrey, KT15 2WU Tel: (01932) 841481 Fax: (01932) 820316 E-mail: afsheen@cleverlittlethings.co.uk *Innovative and smart baby products for smarter parents*

▶ Ian Clews, B8 Parkside Commercial Centre, Terry Avenue, York, YO23 1JP Tel: (01904) 629182 *Jewellery manufrs*

CLF Technologies Ltd, Sawpit Lane, Tibshelf, Alfreton, Derbyshire, DE55 5NH Tel: (01773) 876333 Fax: (01773) 876301 E-mail: info@clf.co.uk *Sub contract engineer services & motor vehicle component manufrs*

Click Display Systems Ltd, Unit 1a Goodson Industrial Mews, Wellington Street, Thame, Oxfordshire, OX9 3BX Tel: (01844) 212574 Fax: (01844) 211899 E-mail: click@netherfield.com *Manufacture display cases for international museums*

Click Here Ltd, Globe Ii Business Centre, 128 Maltravers Road, Sheffield, S2 5AZ Tel: 0114-281 4477 Fax: 0114-281 4478 E-mail: info@clickhere.co.uk *Computer training*

▶ click4it.co.uk, Unit 2, Hope House Farm, Martley, Worcester, WR6 6QF Tel: 0845 2303084 E-mail: sales@click4it.co.uk *Computer web sales business*

▶ Click4PC Ltd, Station House, 150 New Road, Bromsgrove, Worcestershire, B60 2LG Tel: (0800) 0852143 Fax: (01527) 576611 E-mail: enquiries@click4pc.co.uk *PC 24 hour callout services*

▶ Clickbooks Accountancy Services, Rowe Leyes Furlong, Rothley, Leicester, LE7 7LS Tel: 0116-230 1173 Fax: 0116-230 1173 E-mail: info@clickbooksaccountancy.co.uk *Accountancy and Payroll solutions for the small business. VAT, PAYE, Tax Returns, Management Accounts. Sole-traders, Partnerships, Limited Companies.*

Clicks Media Studios, Amp House, Grove Road, Strood, Rochester, Kent, ME2 4BX Tel: (01634) 723838 E-mail: pjstv@blueyonder.co.uk *Video maintenance & repair services*

Clicksoftware Europe Ltd, 65 New Cavendish Street, London, W1G 7LS Tel: (01753) 701066 Fax: (01753) 553127 *Software development*

Clico Sheffield Tooling Ltd, 7 Fell Road, Sheffield, S9 2AL Tel: 0114-243 3007 Fax: 0114-243 4158 E-mail: info@clico.co.uk *Router cutter manufrs*

▶ Client Appeal, 13 Crutchley Road, Wokingham, Berkshire, RG40 1XA Tel: 0118-977 6775 E-mail: sales@clientappeal.co.uk *Client Appeal is a marketing and p.r. consultancy offering advice and support to professional firms such as solicitors, lawyers, and accountants.*

Client Management Solutions, Avonmore, Wilmslow Road, Alderley Edge, Cheshire, SK9 7QW Tel: (01625) 585050 *Physiotherapists*

Client Management Systems, Holmes Chapel Rd, Sproston, Crewe, CW4 7LW Tel: 01606 738080 Fax: 01606 837540 *Computer software designers*

Client Services, 66 Portland Place, London, W1B 1AD Tel: (020) 7307 3700 Fax: (020) 7436 9112 E-mail: cs@inst.riba.org *Trade associations*

Clifda Steels Ltd, Northwick Corner, Canvey Island, Essex, SS8 0PS Tel: (01268) 510066 Fax: (01268) 683815 E-mail: clifdasteels@yahoo.com *Steel stockholders & processors*

Cliff Hotel, Cliff Hill, Gorleston, Great Yarmouth, Norfolk, NR31 6DH Tel: (01493) 662179 Fax: (01493) 653617 E-mail: cliffhotel@aol.com *Conference organizers*

Cliff Madden Angling, 5 Church Street, Staveley, Chesterfield, Derbyshire, S43 3TL Tel: (01246) 472410 *Wallpaper & angling distributors*

Cliff Technologies, Pentlandfield Business Park, Roslin, Midlothian, EH25 9RE Tel: 0131-448 2006 Fax: 0131-448 2006 *Computer consultants*

▶ Cliffe Industrial Packaging Ltd, Marshfield Bank Employment Park, Marshfield Bank, Crewe, CW2 8UY Tel: (01270) 212136 Fax: (01270) 212145 *Polythene products, including pallet covers & sacks*

▶ Cliffe Veterinary Group, 70 Springett Avenue, Ringmer, Lewes, East Sussex, BN8 5QX Tel: (01273) 814590 Fax: (01273) 815310 *Veterinary medicine suppliers*

Clifford Packaging Ltd, Network 65 Business Park, Bentley Wood Way, Hapton, Burnley, Lancashire, BB11 5ST Tel: (01282) 458550 Fax: (01282) 410650 E-mail: enquires@clifford.packaging.com *Corrugated case manufrs*

Clifford Packaging Ltd, Bradbourne Drive, Tilbrook, Milton Keynes, MK7 8AQ Tel: (0870) 1226333 Fax: (01908) 270429 E-mail: enquiries@cliffordpackaging.com *Corrugated & fibreboard cases*

Clifford Thames Ltd, Springfield Lyons House, Chelmsford Business Park, Chelmsford, CM2 5TH Tel: (01245) 236600 Fax: (01245) 236611 E-mail: sales@clifford-thames.com *Parts cataloguing, menu pricing & marketing*

▶ Clifford Whittaker Ltd, Britannia New Mill, Queen Street, Mossley, Ashton-under-Lyne, Lancashire, OL5 9AL Tel: (01457) 833461 Fax: (01457) 835644

Cliffridge Ltd, 83 Kempston Street, Liverpool, L3 8HE Tel: 0151-207 2770 Fax: 0151-207 2770 *Wholesale clothing merchants*

Cliffsend Ltd, Falconer Road, Haverhill, Suffolk, CB9 7XU Tel: (01440) 762664 Fax: (01440) 762428 E-mail: mail@ccsheetmetal.co.uk *Subcontract sheet metal engineers*

Cliffside Joinery, Cliff Side, Wakebridge, Matlock, Derbyshire, DE4 5HD Tel: (01773) 853077 Fax: (01773) 853077 *Joinery manufrs*

Cliffstar Ltd, Unit 2 Stafford Mill Trading Estate, London Road, Thrupp, Stroud, Gloucestershire, GL5 2AZ Tel: (01453) 750057 Fax: (01453) 757448 *Trade pinters, all types of labels. Manufacturers of self adhesive labels, computer labels, laser sheets, roll labels, clock cards, Tyvek self adhesive or Tyvek film and piggyback labels attached to business forms either plain or printed.*

Clift Controls Ltd, Unit 5 2 Perry Way, Witham, Essex, CM8 3SX Tel: (01376) 512604 Fax: (01376) 518187 *Electrical control systems manufrs*

▶ Clifton, 28 Sugarbrook Road, Finstall, Bromsgrove, Worcestershire, B60 3DW Tel: (01527) 835355 Fax: (01527) 835355 E-mail: mark@cliftoncleaningservices.co.uk *Midlands based commercial window cleaners. Our trained and insured operatives can competently do any kind of glass cleaning in mainland UK, from straightforward low-level shop windows to high-level all-glass office blocks using either a harness, cradle, cherry-picker or abseiling techniques.*

▶ Clifton Engineering Ltd, Old Road, Clifton-on-Teme, Worcester, WR6 6DR Tel: (01886) 812224 Fax: (01886) 812706 *Manufacture & sales of gas & electric patio heaters*

Clifton Enterprises Ltd, Clifton House, 32 Cavendish Road, Sheffield, S11 9BH Tel: 0114-258 7229 Fax: 0114-250 0239 E-mail: vanasyl@aol.com *Hygienic valves & sampling equipment suppliers*

Clifton Litho, 29-31 Richmond Road, Staines, Middlesex, TW18 2AA Tel: (01784) 458127 Fax: (01784) 465744 *Litho & letterpress printers*

Clifton Packaging Group P.L.C., Maridian Business Park, Centurion Way, Leicester, LE19 1WH Tel: 0116-289 3355 Fax: 0116-289 1113 E-mail: info@cliftonpackaging.co.uk *Flexible packaging materials printers & converters.*

Clifton Paints Ltd, 92-100 North Street, Bedminster, Bristol, BS3 1HF Tel: 0117-966 0321 Fax: 0117-963 1301 E-mail: sales@dacrylate.co.uk *Paint merchants*

Clifton Partners Co. Ltd, 18a Shaw Road, Newhey, Rochdale, Lancashire, OL16 4LT Tel: (01706) 848224 Fax: (01706) 881441 E-mail: clifton.partners@jtemail.co.uk *Structural steel manufrs*

Clifton Precision Tools Ltd, Cakemore Road, Rowley Regis, West Midlands, B65 0QW Tel: 0121-559 3096 Fax: 0121-561 5661 E-mail: p.clifton@cliftonprecision.com *Press tool design & manufrs*

Clifton Rubber Co. Ltd, 5 Edison Road, St. Ives, Cambridgeshire, PE27 3FF Tel: (01480) 496161 Fax: (01480) 484700 E-mail: sales@cliftonrubber.co.uk Purchasing Contact: P. Holt Sales Contact: C. Wright Principal Export Areas: Central/East Europe & West Europe *Manufacturers of roller covering (rubber), rubber mouldings, rubber products (industrial), rubber/metal bonded products, rubber liner/lining systems, polyurethane products, rollers (polyurethane), gaskets, antivbration mountings, silicone products, silicone rubber mouldings or extrusions, polyurethane components (industrial). Also polyurethane moulding services, polyurethane elastomer products, roller cover services or processors, rubber rollers industrial rollmakers & rubber mould toolmakers.*

Clifton Services, 18 Donegall Street, Belfast, BT1 2GP Tel: (028) 9024 2396 *General engravers*

Clifton & Son Ltd, Uplands Business Park, Blackhorse Lane, London, E17 5QJ Tel: (020) 8523 1133 Fax: (020) 8531 1341 E-mail: tim@clifton.org *Specialist print finishers & binders*

Clifton Steel Ltd, 122 Fazeley Industrial Estate, Fazeley Street, Birmingham, B5 5RS Tel: 0121-603 4000 Fax: 0121-603 4001 E-mail: sales@cliftonsteel.co.uk *Steel & steel coil stockholders*

Cliftonair Ltd, 48 High Street, Newport Pagnell, Buckinghamshire, MK16 8AQ Tel: (01908) 216416 Fax: (01908) 616732 E-mail: brian@cliftonair.co.uk *Dust & fume extraction engineers*

Cliftongrade Ltd, 262 Newport Road, Cowes, Isle of Wight, PO31 8PE Tel: (01983) 292261 Fax: (01983) 292612 *Scrap metal merchants*

Cliftonville Intruder Alarms, 2 Alkali Row, Margate, Kent, CT9 1DB Tel: (01843) 297353 Fax: (01843) 297353 E-mail: cia.kent@btclick.com *Intruder alarm installers*

Clik Ltd, The Tobacco Factory, Raleigh Road, Bristol, BS3 1TF Tel: 0117-902 2012 Fax: 0117-902 2010 Principal Export Areas: Central/East Europe & West Europe *Computer bespoke software writing suppliers*

Climate Center, 63 Pritchett Street, Birmingham, B6 4EX Tel: 0121-333 3636 Fax: 0121-359 8497 E-mail: gk.aston@wolseley.co.uk *Heating & control wholesalers* Also at: Manchester

Climate Centers Ltd, Unit 8 Brickyard Business Park, Excelsior Road, Off Western Avenue, Cardiff, CF14 3AT Tel: (029) 2062 0033 Fax: (029) 2069 1155 *Refrigeration wholesale*

Climate Centre, Unit 17, Durham Street, Kenning Park Way Estate, Glasgow, G41 1BS Tel: 0141-427 6899 Fax: 0141-427 4680 *Refrigeration equipment suppliers*

Climate Centre, Unit 428, Oak Shop Place, Walton Summit Centre, Bamberbridge, Preston, PR5 8AT Tel: (01772) 628608 Fax: (01772) 628599 E-mail: preston.gl@wolseley.co.uk *Refrigeration services*

▶ Climate Cooling, East Malling Enterprise Centre, New Road, West Malling, Kent, ME19 6SJ Tel: (0783) 6385567 Fax: (01732) 874598

Climate Parts Ltd, Unit 3 Jack Lane Industrial Estate, Jack Lane, Leeds, LS11 9NP Tel: 0113-243 1339 Fax: 0113-234 0262 *Refrigeration supplier*

Climate Services, Unit 1 Bold Street, Sheffield, S9 2LQ Tel: 0114-261 0111 Fax: 0114-261 8949 *Air conditioning & refrigeration services*

▶ Climate Services Ltd, Haigh Park, Haigh Avenue, Stockport, Cheshire, SK4 1QR Tel: 0161-480 4625 Fax: 0161-476 5423

▶ Climate Services Ltd, 4 Swan Wharf Business Centre, Waterloo Road, Uxbridge, Middlesex, UB8 2RA Tel: (01895) 812280 Fax: (01895) 234136

Climate Services, Intersection House, 110-120 Birmingham Road, West Bromwich, West Midlands, B70 6RP Tel: 0121-524 8825 Fax: 0121-524 8823 E-mail: mail@climate-services.co.uk *Air conditioning engineers* Also at: Bristol, Glasgow, London, Sheffield & Stockport

Climatec Ltd, Unit 23 Empire Centre Imperial Way, Watford, WD24 4YH Tel: (01923) 237178 Fax: (01923) 237403 E-mail: robert_livingstone@talk21.com *Environmental test equipment servicing & manufr*

Climatec Systems Ltd, Unit 6 Dymock Road Indust Estate, Dymock Road, Parkway, Ledbury, Herefordshire, HR8 2JQ Tel: (01531) 631161 Fax: (01531) 631165 E-mail: climatec@climatec.co.uk *Environmental control systems manufrs*

▶ Climater Center, Unit 10, Stockton Close, Minworth Industrial Park, Minworth, Sutton Coldfield, West Midlands, B76 1DH Tel: 0121-351 7777 Fax: 0121-351 5835 *Control systems manufrs*

Climatic Engineering, 1 Cannon Road, Heathfield Industrial Estate, Newton Abbot, Devon, TQ12 6SG Tel: (01626) 203686 Fax: (01626) 203687 E-mail: sales@climaticengineering.co.uk *Air conditioning services supply & installation*

Climatic Services Ltd, 41 Cavendish Way, Glenrothes, Fife, KY6 2SB Tel: (01592) 771254 Fax: (01592) 775626 E-mail: webmail@climaticservices.co.uk *Environmental chamber services*

Climavent Systems Ltd, Units 1-3 Cairngorm Business Park, Liverpool Road, Ashton-in-Makerfield, Wigan, Lancashire, WN4 0YU Tel: (01942) 726164 Fax: (01942) 722300 E-mail: info@climavent.co.uk *air movement systems, air knives, air cannon, bespoke extraction systems, dust and fume hazards, ductwork, turn key installations, compressed, design, installation, dust extraction, collection, fume exhaust systems, fume hoods and cupboards, warm circulation, cabinets, ovens, paint spray booths, exhaust, filtration, pulse jet dust collector, micronisation plant, micronisation waste, particulate classifiers, furnace covers, shot blast machinery, pneumatically driven extraction fans, vehicle exhaust fumes, coshh testing, lev testing, cost effective solutions, foundry, foundry, Specialists, design, installation, movement, control, Wallsend, Newcastle, Tyne & Wear*

Climavent Systems Ltd, Units 1-3 Cairngorm Business Park, Liverpool Road, Ashton-in-Makerfield, Wigan, Lancashire, WN4 0YU Tel: (01942) 726164 Fax: (01942) 722300 E-mail: info@climavent.co.uk *Dust & fume extraction unit manufrs*

Climax Molybdenum UK Ltd, Needham Road, Stowmarket, Suffolk, IP14 2AE Tel: (01449) 674431 Fax: (01449) 675972 E-mail: climax@phelpsdodge.com *Ferro-molybdenum & molybdenum product manufrs* Also at: London EC2

Climax Pro Squash, 3 St. Marys Drive, Greenfield, Oldham, OL3 7DT Tel: (01457) 829966 E-mail: headoffice@cxprosport.com *Squash equipment suppliers*

▶ Climitize Upvc Windows, Shady Lane, Birmingham, B44 9ER Tel: 0121-325 1792 Fax: 0121-325 1799 *Window frame installers & manufrs*

Climpson & Co Ltd, 8 St. Albans Place, London, N1 0NX Tel: (020) 7226 4414 Fax: (020) 7226 4414 *Carpet contractors*

Clingbrook Ltd, Unit 10 Lakes Industrial Park, Lower Chapel Hill, Braintree, Essex, CM7 3RU Tel: (01376) 327206 Fax: (01376) 330755 *Rubber mouldings manufrs*

Clingfoil Ltd, Unit 1 Second Avenue, Poynton, Stockport, Cheshire, SK12 1ND Tel: (01625) 878953 Fax: (01625) 859005 E-mail: sales@clingfoil.co.uk *Packaging materials suppliers*

Clinical Engineering Consultants Ltd, 2 Harlow House, Dukes Road, Newdigate, Dorking, Surrey, RH5 5BY Tel: (01306) 631681 Fax: (01306) 631688E-mail: cec.co@lineone.net *Disabled & handicapped persons chair manufrs*

▶ Clinical Hypnotherapy, St Mark's Clinic, 47 St Mark's Road, Teddington, Middlesex, TW11 9DE Tel: 01483 825649 E-mail: info@hypno-clinic.com *Dr Tig Calvert PhD is a Clinical Hypnotherapist and Chartered Psychologist with a clinic in Teddington. She specialises in rapid, effective treatment for weight-loss, stopping smoking, sports performance and injury, IBS, ME/CFS, anxiety, phobias and fears, pain, childbirth and relationship issues.*

▶ Clinical Support Services LLP, CSS House, The Dens, Wadhurst, East Sussex, TN5 6NJ Tel: (0800) 3289231 Fax: (0870) 0523000 E-mail: info@ukcss.com *Experts in controlled waste management. Specialising in medical waste removal from Doctors, Dentists, Vets and all manner of private practices.*

▶ CliniServ, Harley Street, London, UK, W1G 9PF Tel: 0845 6100670 Fax: 0845 6100671 E-mail: customerservice@cliniserv.com *CliniServ offers corporate health screening and blood testing. Based in London.*

Clino Ltd, 54 Britten Drive, Malvern, Worcestershire, WR14 3LG Tel: (01684) 561525 Fax: (01684) 561721 E-mail: sales@clino.co.uk *Tilt sensors & inclinometers*

Clint Hill Engineering, Newton Road, Hinckley, Leicestershire, LE10 3DS Tel: (01455) 239239 Fax: (01455) 238559 E-mail: clinthill@wanadoo.co.uk *High precision turned parts*

Clin-Tech Ltd, Unit G Perram Works, Merrow Lane, Guildford, Surrey, GU4 7BN Tel: (01483) 301902 Fax: (01483) 301907 E-mail: info@clin-tech.co.uk *Laboratory reagents manufrs*

Clinton Conservatories, 153 Cumbernauld Road, Chryston, Glasgow, G69 9AF Tel: 0141-779 4423 *Conservatory design & manufrs*

Clip Ltd, Athena, 210 Bristol Business Park, The Close, Bristol, BS16 1FJ Tel: 0117-937 5700 Fax: 0117-931 4561 E-mail: info@clipdisplay.com *Display kits to conference sets & fully serviced exhibition stands*

Clip International Ltd, Avon Works, Church Road, Bristol, BS30 5RD Tel: 0117-937 2636 Fax: 0117-937 3172 E-mail: info@clipdisplay.com *Display modular systems & graphics manufrs*

Clipfast, Lancaster House, Lancaster Fields, Crewe, CW1 6FF Tel: (01270) 585959 E-mail: info@clipfast.co.uk *Hog rings pliers & fencing clips manufrs*

Clippa Safe Ltd, Lanthwaite Road, Nottingham, NG11 8LD Tel: 0115-921 1899 Fax: 0115-984 5554 E-mail: sales@clippasafe.co.uk *Children's safety products manufrs*

Clipper Components Ltd, 3 Ministry Wharf, Wycombe Road, Saunderton, High Wycombe, Buckinghamshire, HP14 4HW Tel: (01296) 432067 Fax: (01296) 487272 E-mail: ccompo6494@aol.com *Cable assembly & harness manufrs*

Clipper Tech Ltd, 1 Oakley Industrial Estate, Carnock Road, Oakley, Dunfermline, Fife, KY12 9QB Tel: (01383) 851133 Fax: (01383) 851144 E-mail: sales@clippertech.co.uk *Service & support for control engineers*

▶ Clipperlight Nautical Books, Albrighton, Wolverhampton, WV7 3WL Tel: (01902) 373217 E-mail: clipperuk@aol.com *Suppliers of nautical books & gifts*

Clipvalve Ltd, 88 Stonefield Road, Hastings, East Sussex, TN34 1QA Tel: (01424) 425682 Fax: (01424) 438789 E-mail: enquiries@clipvalve.co.uk *Kitchen & bathroom fittings & accessories distributors*

▶ Clitheroe Lighting Centre, 14 Moor Lane, Clitheroe, Lancashire, BB7 1BE Tel: (01200) 423757 Fax: (01200) 423757 E-mail: lights@clitheroelightingcentre.co.uk *Wholesale & retail of lighting & lightbulbs*

▶ Clive Durose Ltd, Newstead Industrial Trading Es, Stoke-On-Trent, ST4 8HX Tel: (01782) 646222

▶ Clive Hurt Ltd, 31 Talbot Road Industrial Centre, Leyland, PR25 2ZF Tel: (01772) 432475 Fax: (01772) 622398 E-mail: clivehurt@btinternet.com *Plant hire*

Clive Leyland Music Ltd, 4 Newmeadow, Lostock, Bolton, BL6 4PB Tel: (01204) 845459 Fax: (01204) 496767 E-mail: clive.leyland@btinternet.com *IT consultancy*

Clive Palmer, 5 Fettiplace Close, Appleton, Oxford, OX2 4HW Tel: (01865) 864662 Fax: (01865) 865436 *Two way radio supply & hire*

Clive Powell & Co, Franksbridge, Llandrindod Wells, Powys, LD1 5SA Tel: (01982) 570297 *Agricultural contractors*

▶ Clive View Engineering Ltd, Block 5, New Albion Industrial Estate, Halley St Yoker, Glasgow, G13 4DT Tel: 0141-952 3186 *General engineering & fabrication*

Clive Walton Engineering, Rivendell Cottage, Cumrew, Brampton, Cumbria, CA8 9DD Tel: (01768) 896232 Fax: (01768) 896451 E-mail: waltoneng@tiscali.co.uk *Engineers machining manufrs*

Cliveden House, Taplow, Maidenhead, Berkshire, SL6 0JF Tel: (01628) 668561 Fax: (01628) 661837 E-mail: reservations@clivedenhouse.co.uk *Conference centres*

▶ Clive's Light Removals, 4 Coastguard Cottages, Isle of Grain, Rochester, Kent, ME3 0DS Tel: 0777 8872492 E-mail: clive@fsmail.net *light removal,s also parcel,s small pallet,s no job too small any thing considerd distance no problem *mobile 07778872492*

Clives Tyre & Exhaust Co. Ltd, Unit1 Hampers Common, Petworth, West Sussex, GU28 9NN Tel: (01798) 343441 Fax: (01798) 343441 *Fitters of tyres & exhausts*

Clivet Aircon Ltd, Unit F5 Railway Triangle, Walton Road, Portsmouth, PO6 1TG Tel: (023) 9238 1235 Fax: (023) 9238 1243 E-mail: info@clivetaircon.co.uk *Air conditioning engineers*

Clivet UK, Unit 4 Kingdom Close, Segenworth East, Fareham, Hampshire, PO15 5TJ Tel: (01489) 550621 Fax: (01489) 573033 E-mail: info@clivet-uk.co.uk *Air conditioning equipment distribs*

Clivnars Ltd, Pindar Road, Hoddesdon, Hertfordshire, EN11 0EA Tel: (01992) 467710 Fax: (01992) 467866 E-mail: sales@clivnars.co.uk *UPVC & aluminium window manufrs*

CLM Engineering Services Ltd, 711 Banbury Avenue Trading Estate, Slough, SL1 4LR Tel: (01753) 743000 Fax: (01753) 811256 E-mail: lisa.perryman@clm-group.co.uk *General engineers*

▶ Cloburn Quarry Co Ltd, Pettinain, Lanark, ML11 8SR Tel: (01555) 663444 Fax: (01555) 664111

▶ Clockhouse Computer Trading, Ascot, Berkshire, SL5 0ZN Tel: (01344) 872868 Fax: (01344) 872869 *Computer suppliers*

Clocktower Scaffolding, 17 Parkway, Romford, RM2 5NT Tel: (01708) 731781 Fax: (01708) 742112 *Scaffolding contractors*

▶ Clockwork Components Ltd, 6 Network Point, Range Road, Witney, Oxfordshire, OX29 0YN Tel: (01993) 775767 Fax: (01993) 892313

▶ Clockwork Removals Ltd, 2 Armoury Way, London, SW18 1SH Tel: (020) 8870 6176 Fax: (020) 8870 6054

▶ Clockwork Removals & Storage, 38-40 West Harbour Road, Edinburgh, EH5 1PU Tel: 0131-551 5800 Fax: 0131-657 2624

▶ Clockworkz Leisure Ltd, 9 Phillips Chase, Off Bradford Street, Braintree, Essex, CM7 9BH Tel: (01376) 349542 E-mail: bookings@clockworkz.co.uk *Bouncy Castle Hire and sales of party products, party bags and garden games*

Clogau Gold Of Wales Ltd, Unit 5 Kinmel Park, Abergele Road, Bodelwyddan, Rhyl, Clwyd, LL18 5TX Tel: (0845) 6068877 Fax: (01745) 536191 E-mail: sales@clogau.co.uk *Jewellery suppliers & wholesalers*

Clomac Ltd, 4 Hills House, Wellington Road, Wavertree, Liverpool, L15 4JN Tel: 0151-734 5400 Fax: 0151-734 2333 E-mail: info@clomac.co.uk *Foam conversions*

Clonshall Ltd, Whiteacre House, 97 Whiteacre Road, Ashton-under-Lyne, Lancashire, OL6 9PJ Tel: 0161-339 9637 Fax: 0161-343 1036 E-mail: adrian.young@clonshall.co.uk *Roofing contractors*

Close Invoice Finance Ltd, 25 Bartholomew Street, Newbury, Berkshire, RG14 5LL Tel: (01635) 31517 Fax: (01635) 521180 E-mail: sales@closeinvoice.co.uk *Finance services*

Cloud Communications Ltd, 58 Broadoak Road, Langford, Bristol, BS40 5HB Tel: (01934) 853900 Fax: (01934) 853909 E-mail: brian@cloud-isdn.com *Telecommunications*

Cloud Electronics Ltd, 140 Staniforth Road, Sheffield, S9 3HF Tel: 0114-244 7051 Fax: 0114-242 5462 E-mail: info@cloud.co.uk *Electronic audio suppliers*

Cloud Ten, Tadlow, Royston, Hertfordshire, SG8 0EP Tel: (01767) 631810 Fax: (01767) 631811 E-mail: office@cloud-ten.co.uk *Web interface design & programming*

▶ Clouds Hill Imaging Ltd., Rock House, Curland, Taunton, Somerset, TA3 5SB Tel: 01823 481894 E-mail: david@cloudshillimaging.co.uk *Specialised film and photography work including scanning electron microscopy, macro, time-lapse, motion control and light microscopy. Large still & video library of science, medical, natural history and scientific images*

Clough & Farmer Ltd, 89 Granville Road, Sidcup, Kent, DA14 4BT Tel: (020) 8300 1436 Fax: (020) 8308 0468 E-mail: cloughandfarmer@btconnect.com *Gymnasium equipment manufrs*

Cloughcor House Furnishings, 33 Townhall Street, Enniskillen, County Fermanagh, BT74 7BD Tel: (028) 6632 4805 Fax: (028) 6632 8828 *Teak furniture reproduction*

David Clouting Ltd, 7B Perry Road, Witham, Essex, CM8 3UD Tel: (01376) 518037 Fax: (01376) 500104 E-mail: sales@davidclouting.co.uk *Solvent recovery machine & vinyl distributors*

Harold Cloutt Associates Ltd, PO Box 87, Battle, East Sussex, TN33 9XR Tel: (01424) 838829 Fax: (0870) 1365618 E-mail: cloutt.hr@bcs.org.uk *Computer consultants*

Clovelly Contractors, Huntshaw Barton, Huntshaw, Torrington, Devon, EX38 7HH Tel: (01805) 623255 Fax: (01805) 625225 *Agricultural contractors*

Clovelly Engineering Ltd, Unit 59, Lunsford Road, Leicester, LE5 0HW Tel: 0116-246 1831 Fax: 0116-246 1474 E-mail: clovellyt@aol.com *Engineering subcontract & CNC milling engineering services.*

▶ Clovemead Ltd, Telford House, 105 Parker Drive, Leicester, LE4 0JP Tel: 0116-234 2800

Clovemead, Stephenson House, Howley Lane, Warrington, WA1 2DN Tel: (01925) 411221 Fax: (01925) 418496 E-mail: clovemead@brunelhouse.u-net.com *Building contractors*

Clover Consultancy, 21 The Crescent, Taunton, Somerset, TA1 4EB Tel: (01823) 336220 Fax: (01823) 270105 E-mail: info@cloveruk.net *Computer consultants*

Clover Controls, Princesway, Team Valley Trading Estate, Gateshead, Tyne & Wear, NE11 0TU Tel: 0191-442 8000 Fax: 0191-442 8010 E-mail: clover@clover-controls.co.uk *Building management system design*

Clover Systems, 7 Endsleigh Gardens, Long Ditton, Surbiton, Surrey, KT6 5JL Tel: (020) 8399 1822 Fax: (020) 8770 0556 E-mail: cloversystems@btconnect.com *Embedded microprocessor systems manufrs*

Clover Technical Services, 4 Valiant Way, Lairdside Technology Park, Birkenhead, Merseyside, CH41 9HS Tel: 0151-650 1551 Fax: 0151-650 1213 E-mail: sales@cloveruk.com *Air conditioning & refrigeration services*

Cloverbrook, Peel Mill, Gannow Lane, Burnley, Lancashire, BB12 6JJ Tel: (01282) 712000 Fax: (01282) 457723 E-mail: info@cloverbrook.co.uk *Double & single jersey fabrics manufrs*

▶ Cloverleaf Press Ltd, 243 Felixstowe Road, Ipswich, IP3 9BN Tel: (01473) 274777

Clovertone Ltd, 9 Canal Walk, London, N1 5SA Tel: (020) 7923 0300 Fax: (020) 7923 0266 E-mail: sales@clovertone.co.uk *Direct mail & laser printers*

Clovis Lande Associates, 104 Branbridges Road, East Peckham, Tonbridge, Kent, TN12 5HH Tel: (01622) 872581 Fax: (01622) 873903 E-mail: sales@clovis.co.uk *Steel fabricators*

Clow Group Ltd, Garratts Lane, Cradley Heath, West Midlands, B64 5AW Tel: 0121-559 5222 Fax: 0121-559 0330 E-mail: clowgroup@btconnect.com *Manufacturers of access platforms & equipment*

Clow Group Ltd, 185 Broad Street, Glasgow, G40 2QR Tel: 0141-554 1739 Fax: 0141-551 0813 E-mail: clow@ladders-direct.co.uk *Ladder & brush manufrs* Also at: Belfast, Dublin & Walsall

Clow Group Ltd, 90 Camlachie Street, Glasgow, G31 4AD Tel: 0141-556 6324 Fax: 0141-551 9087 E-mail: engineering@clowgroup.co.uk *Conveyor manufacturers, stainless steel, mild steel & *aluminium metal fabricators**

Clower & Son Ltd, 48-52 Nottingham Road, Ripley, Derbyshire, DE5 3AT Tel: (01773) 742351 Fax: (01773) 744610 *Builders & plumbers merchants* Also at: Langley Mill

Arthur W. Clowes Ltd, Unit 2 Pepper Road Hazel Grove, Hazel Grove, Stockport, Cheshire, SK7 5BW Tel: 0161-483 1827 Fax: 0161-483 1827 E-mail: sales@clowesprinters.co.uk *Specialist packaging printers*

William Clowes Ltd, Copland Way, Ellough, Beccles, Suffolk, NR34 7TL Tel: (01502) 712884 Fax: (01502) 717003 E-mail: william@clowes.co.uk *Book manufrs*

The Club, 35 Bedfordbury, London, WC2N 4DU Tel: (020) 7759 7100 Fax: (020) 7379 5210 E-mail: bill@theclubpc.co.uk *Television post producers*

Club Copying Co. Ltd, 10-18 Sandgate Street, London, SE15 1LE Tel: (020) 7635 5252 Fax: (020) 7635 5714 E-mail: jacquidalton@clubcopying.co.uk *Photocopier & fax machine suppliers*

Club First Ltd, Unit 51, Milmead Industrial Centre, Mill Mead Road, London, N17 9QU Tel: (020) 8493 9611

Club Sports Trophies, Unit 6A Bombay Street, Bermondsey, London, SE16 3UX Tel: (020) 7639 5401 Fax: (0870) 7059029 E-mail: marc@munichtrophies.co.uk *Club sports trophies*

Club Systems (International) Ltd, Club House, 34-36 Fairacres Road, High Lane, Stockport, Cheshire, SK6 8JQ Tel: (01663) 766999 Fax: (01663) 762499 E-mail: sales@club2000.co.uk *Computer systems & software development consultants*

Club Ties, Brook Street Studios, 60 Brook Street, Glasgow, G40 2AB Tel: 0141-554 3066 Fax: 0141-554 4581 E-mail: clubties@hotmail.com *Club neckties, scarf & t-shirt manufrs*

▶ Club Together Ltd, 31 Strathmore Road, Teddington, Middlesex, TW11 8UJ Tel: (020) 8943 2682 E-mail: dave.weston@teddingtontennis.org *Club Together is a software consultancy specialising in Web site design, implementation and management.*

Clubsafe Case Mnfrs, 1 Spinners End Industrial Estate Oldfields, Corngreaves, Cradley Heath, West Midlands, B64 6BS Tel: (01384) 411311 Fax: (01384) 411311 E-mail: enquiries@cslclubsafe.co.uk *Flight case & speaker enclosure manufrs*

Clugston Distribution Services, Brigg Road, Scunthorpe, South Humberside, DN16 1BB Tel: (01724) 855029 Fax: (01724) 270240 E-mail: andrew.hansed@clugston.co.uk *Steel haulage*

Clugston Estates Ltd, St Vincent House, Normanby Road, Scunthorpe, South Humberside, DN15 8QT Tel: (01724) 843491 Fax: (01724) 281714 E-mail: group@clugston.co.uk *Holding company*

Cluine Group Ltd, 15 Lochside Street, Oban, Argyll, PA34 4HP Tel: (01631) 562572 Fax: (01631) 565286 E-mail: info@officesupplies-printing.co.uk *Stationers & office suppliers*

Clumber Pets, 1 Clumber Street, Warsop, Mansfield, Nottinghamshire, NG20 0LR Tel: (01623) 842652 *Pet supplies retailer*

▶ Clunie Group Ltd, 15 Lochside St, Oban, Argyll, PA34 4HP Tel: (01631) 565485

Cluny Lace Co. Ltd, Belper Street Works, Ilkeston, Derbyshire, DE7 5FJ Tel: 0115-932 5031 Fax: 0115-944 0590 E-mail: sales@clunylace.co.uk *Lace manufrs*

Cluson Engineering Ltd, Unit 6, Bedford Road, Petersfield, Hampshire, GU32 3LJ Tel: (01730) 264672 Fax: (01730) 260475 E-mail: sales@clulite.co.uk *High powered rechargeable lamps manufrs*

Clutch Direct, Adrian Avenue, London, NW2 1LX Tel: (020) 8450 5040 *Clutch care*

Clutch Master, Boundary Road, Buckingham Road Industrial Estate, Brackley, Northamptonshire, NN13 7ES Tel: (01280) 704838 Fax: (01280) 705204 E-mail: admin@clutchmaster.com *Commercial clutch rebuilders & manufrs*

Clutton Agricultural Ltd, Bedwell Road, Marchwiel, Wrexham, Clwyd, LL13 0TS Tel: (01978) 661871 Fax: (01978) 661756 *Incineration services*

Cluttons P.L.C., Portman House, 2 Portman Street, London, W1H 6DU Tel: (020) 7408 1010 Fax: (020) 7629 3263 E-mail: ph@cluttons.co.uk *Office agents & surveyors*

Clwyd Agricultural, Terfyn Farm, Caerwys Road, Cwm Dyserth, Rhyl, Clwyd, LL18 6HT Tel: (01745) 571018 Fax: (01745) 571002 *Agricultural dealers*

Clwyd Blinds Direct, Unit 5 Pistyll Farm, The Long Barn Pistyll Farm, Mold, Clwyd, CH7 4EW Tel: (01352) 757474 Fax: (01352) 758034 *Window blind manufrs*

Clwyd Communications, 1 Llewelyn Drive, Bryn-y-Baal, Mold, Clwyd, CH7 6SW Tel: (01352) 700352 Fax: (01352) 759724 E-mail: sales@cymrucomms.co.uk *Telephone systems installation*

Clwyd Compounders Ltd, Gardden Industrial Estate, Ruabon, Wrexham, Clwyd, LL14 6RG Tel: (01978) 810551 Fax: (01978) 810740 E-mail: sales@clwydcompounders.com Principal Export Areas: Central/East Europe & West Europe *Rubber & silicone compounds, industrial rubber products manufrs*

Clwyd Concrete Co. Ltd, Varis Works, Bodfari, Denbigh, Clwyd, LL16 4DA Tel: (01745) 710277 Fax: (01745) 710303 *Pre cast concrete manufrs*

Clwyd Precision Engineering, Bridge Road, Wrexham Industrial Estate, Wrexham, Clwyd, LL13 9PS Tel: (01978) 660259 Fax: (01978) 661069 E-mail: cpe@bytecraft.net *Sub-contract mechanical engineers*

Clwyd Re Inforcements Ltd, Rhosddu Industrial Estate, Main Road, Rhosrobin, Wrexham, Clwyd, LL11 4YL Tel: (01978) 354454 Fax: (01978) 291373 E-mail: sales@clwyd-reinforcements.co.uk *Reinforcing steel manufrs*

Clwyd Refractory Fibres Ltd, Spencer Industrial Estate, Liverpool Road, Buckley, Clwyd, CH7 3LY Tel: (01244) 548308 Fax: (01244) 541121 E-mail: info@gasglo.co.uk *Ceramic fibre radiant manufrs*

▶ Clwyd Refrigeration Ltd, Conwy Morfa Enterprise Park, Parc Caer Seion, Conwy, Gwynedd, LL32 8FA Tel: (01492) 572323 Fax: (01492) 582626 E-mail: sevice@clwydrefrigeration.com *Commercial refrigeration suppliers*

Clwyd Tool & Die, 35 Greenfield Business Park, Bagillt Road, Greenfield, Holywell, Clwyd, CH8 7HJ Tel: (01352) 715515 Fax: (01352) 715515 *Toolmakers & tool making services*

Clwyd Welding Services Ltd, Clwyd Close, Hawarden Industrial Park, Hawarden, Deeside, Clwyd, CH5 3PZ Tel: (01244) 531667 Fax: (01244) 531842 E-mail: clwydweld@aol.com *Welding & engineering supplies*

Clyde Air Conditioning Ltd, 72 North Vennel, Lanark, ML11 7PT Tel: (01555) 661366 Fax: (01555) 661367 *Air conditioning installers & manufrs*

Clyde Associated Engineers Ltd, Block 5, 76 Beardmore Way, Clydebank Industrial Estate, Clydebank, Dunbartonshire, G81 4HT Tel: 0141-951 1331 Fax: 0141-951 3460 E-mail: lac@caeltd.co.uk *Pump distributors, fluid handling engineers*

Clyde Bergenann Ltd, 47 Broad Street, Glasgow, G40 2QR Tel: 0141-550 5400 Fax: 0141-550 5401 E-mail: icarruthers@clydebergemann.co.uk *Soot blower manufrs*

Clyde Broadcast Products Ltd, 2 Rutherford Court, 15 North Avenue, Clydebank Business Park, Clydebank, Dunbartonshire, G81 2QP Tel: 0141-952 7950 Fax: 0141-941 1224 E-mail: mail@clydebroadcast.com *Radio studio & system equipment installation services*

Clyde Building Group plc, 161-181 Whitefield Road, Glasgow, G51 2SD Tel: 0141-445 1242 Fax: 0141-440 5375 *Property developers*

Clyde Cash Registers Ltd, 909 Dumbarton Road, Glasgow, G11 6NB Tel: 0141-337 6199 Fax: 0141-337 6199 E-mail: clydecashregisters@hotmail.com *Cash registers suppliers*

Clyde Computers Southern Ltd, Lovelace Works, High Street, Ripley, Woking, Surrey, GU23 6AF Tel: (01483) 225930 Fax: (01483) 225931 E-mail: sales@clydecomputers.co.uk *Computer hardware distributors or agents*

▶ Clyde Demolition, Trump House, 15 Edison Street, Hillington Industrial Estate, Glasgow, G52 4JW Tel: 0141-883 2233 Fax: 0141-882 3840

Clyde Energy Solutions Ltd, Unit 10, Lion Park Avenue, Chessington, Surrey, KT9 1ST Tel: (020) 8391 2020 Fax: (020) 8397 4598 E-mail: info@clyde-nrg.com *Boiler & radiator distributors*

Clyde Fasteners Ltd, Hawbank Road, East Kilbride, Glasgow, G74 5ET Tel: (01355) 225451 Fax: (01355) 263191 E-mail: info@clydefasteners.com *Socket screws & fastener products* Also at: Birmingham

▶ Clyde Kilts Ltd, 71 James Street, Glasgow, G40 1BZ Tel: 0141-554 4649

Clyde Leather Co., Broadlie Works, Neilston, Glasgow, G78 3AB Tel: 0141-881 4558 Fax: 0141-881 0522 *Tannery, suede & leather for handbags, shoes & belts*

Clyde Optical Co. Ltd, Optics House, Seath Road, Rutherglen, Glasgow, G73 1RW Tel: 0141-643 0639 Fax: 0141-643 1219 *Opticians*

Clyde Process Solutions plc, Carolina Court, Lakeside, Doncaster, South Yorkshire, DN4 5RA Tel: (01302) 321313 Fax: (01302) 554400 E-mail: solutions@clydematerials.co.uk Principal Export Areas: Worldwide *Dense phase, medium phase, lean phase, positive pressure & vacuum specialists*

Clyde Recycling Ltd, 1650 London Road, Glasgow, G31 4QG Tel: 0141-554 8778 Fax: (0141) 554 6717 *Textile waste processors*

▶ Clyde Space Ltd, 6.01 Kelvin Campus, West of Scotland Science Park, Glasgow, G20 0SP Tel: 0141-946 4440 Fax: 0141-945 1591 E-mail: enquiries@clyde-space.com *Clyde Space is a provider of high reliability hardware for extreme environments. Our main product is the supply subsystem solutions for small satellites, including power and battery subsystems. The Clyde Space team has extensive experience in the design and manufacture of high reliability systems having worked on more than 25 spacecraft missions.**Clyde Space has expertise in:*- Power electronics design and test (e.g. DC-DC converters & motor control).*- Solar cell array maximum power point tracking.*- Battery chargers.*- High reliability primary and secondary batteries.**Our expertise is applicable to a number of additional applications, including:*- The safe interfacing of batteries, fuel cells, solar cell arrays, wind turbines and other power sources.*- Renewable energy systems electronics (wind energy, wave energy, solar cell arrays, hydro).*- Unmanned arial and under water vehicles.*High pressure, high temperature applications (e.g. oil drilling apparatus).**

Clyde Valley Hawks, Glasgow Zoo, Hamilton Rd, Uddingston, Glasgow, G71 7RZ Tel: 0141-781 1712 *Pest control*

▶ Clydebank Post, 88 Dumbarton Road, Clydebank, Dunbartonshire, G81 1UG Tel: 0141-952 1345 Fax: 0141-952 7267 E-mail: editorial@clydebankpost.co.uk

Clydefab Fabricators, Upper Ingleston, Greenock, Renfrewshire, PA15 3AD Tel: (01475) 888918 Fax: (01475) 888918 *Welding & fabricators*

Clydeforth Engineers & Contractors Ltd, Barclay Curle Complex, 739 South Street, Glasgow, G14 0BX Tel: 0141-958 0628 Fax: 0141-959 0912 E-mail: louise@clydeforth.fsnet.co.uk *Fabrication of pipework*

Clydesdale Ltd, 3 Sunbeam Road, Woburn Road Industrial Estate, Kempston, Bedford, MK42 7BZ Tel: (01234) 855855 Fax: (01234) 856845 E-mail: david@clydesdale.ltd.uk Principal Export Areas: Worldwide *Cable laying, overhead line fitting & electricians equipment suppliers*

▶ Clydesdale Double Glazing Ltd, 18-20 Netherdale Road, Netherton Industrial Estate, Wishaw, Lanarkshire, ML2 0ER Tel: (01698) 355424 Fax: (01698) 355425 E-mail: sales@scottishconservatories.com

Clydesdale Engineering Services Ltd, Belvoir Way, Fairfield Industrial Estate, Louth, Lincolnshire, LN11 0LQ Tel: (01507) 605991 Fax: (01507) 605991 E-mail: info@clydesdale.fsbusiness.co.uk *Pump repair & balancing services*

Clydesdale Forge Co., Marriott Road, Dudley, West Midlands, DY2 0LA Tel: (01384) 252587 Fax: (01384) 231005 E-mail: sales@clydesdale-forge.co.uk *Forgings*

Clydeside Galvanizers Ltd, 96 Eastvale Place, Glasgow, G3 8QG Tel: 0141-334 9678 Fax: 0141-337 1830 E-mail: sales@clydegalv.co.uk *Galvanized coating services*

Clydeside Steel Fabrications Ltd, 180 Hardgate Road, Glasgow, G51 4TB Tel: 0141-445 2898 Fax: 0141-445 6964 E-mail: fabs@bmsteel.co.uk *Steel fabricators*

Clydeview Engineering Cleland Ltd, 24 Bellside Road, Cleland, Motherwell, Lanarkshire, ML1 5NP Tel: (01698) 860287 Fax: (01698) 861866 E-mail: clydeview@btconnect.com *Milling & turning engineers* Also at: Clydebank

Clydeview Precision Engineering & Supplies Ltd, 197a Dumbarton Road, Clydebank, Dunbartonshire, G81 4XJ Tel: 0141-941 1873 Fax: 0141-951 1928 *Engineering subcontract services*

▶ Clydewide Taxis, 99 High Street, Lanark, ML11 7LN Tel: (01555) 663813 Fax: (01555) 678937 E-mail: taxis@clydewide.co.uk *Taxi & coach hire*

▶ Clymac Ltd, Unit 1 Cloudway Court, Belton Road, Loughborough, Leicestershire, LE11 1LW Tel: (01509) 232651 Fax: (01509) 232665 E-mail: sales@clymac.co.uk *Install fire alarm systems*

Clynderwen & Cardiganshire Farmers Ltd, Glanrhyd Stores, Glanrhyd, Cardigan, Dyfed, SA43 3NX Tel: (01239) 612057 Fax: (01239) 615295 *Cattle feed*

Clynderwen & Cardiganshire Farmers Ltd, Main St, Clynderwen, Dyfed, SA66 7NW Tel: (01437) 563441 Fax: (01437) 563745 E-mail: info@ccfagri.co.uk *Merchants co-operative society*

Clynderwen & Cardiganshire Farmers Ltd, Hermon Road, Crymych, Dyfed, SA41 3QE Tel: (01239) 831203 Fax: (01239) 831363 *Co-operative farmers*

Clynderwen & Cardiganshire Farmers Ltd, Station Road, Letterston, Haverfordwest, Dyfed, SA62 5SY Tel: (01348) 840208 Fax: (01348) 841030 *Agricultural feeds suppliers*

Clynderwen & Cardiganshire Farmers Ltd, Heol Maengwyn, Machynlleth, Powys, SY20 8EA Tel: (01654) 702448 Fax: (01654) 703685 *Agricultural merchants*

Clynderwen & Cardiganshire Farmers Ltd, Spring Gardens, Narberth, Dyfed, SA67 7BT Tel: (01834) 860369 Fax: (01834) 869185 *Agricultural wholesale merchants*

Clynderwen & Cardiganshire Farmers Ltd, Hebron, Whitland, Dyfed, SA34 0XP Tel: (01994) 419238 Fax: (01994) 419238 *Agricultural merchants*

CM Yuill, Cecil House, Loyalty Road, Hartlepool, Cleveland, TS25 5BD Tel: (01429) 266620 *House building contractors*

Cma Tools Burnley Ltd, Belle Vue Mill, Westgate, Burnley, Lancashire, BB11 1SD Tel: (01282) 423619 Fax: (01282) 427944 E-mail: cmatools@airtime.co.uk *Press tool, jigs & fixtures manufrs*

Cmac Electronics Systems, Rashieburn, Fintray, Aberdeen, AB21 0YX Tel: (01651) 806888 Fax: (01651) 806696 E-mail: info@cmac-sys.co.uk *Installation & maintenance of telecommunications & broadcast systems*

▶ C-MAC MicroTechnology, Station Road, Crewkerne, Somerset, TA18 8AR Tel: 01460 270200 Fax: 01460 72578 E-mail: info@cmac.com *C-MAC MicroTechnology has a 70-year pedigree in designing and manufacturing high-performance oscillators and quartz crystals. Our frequency control product range encompasses AT and SC cut crystals, simple packaged crystal oscillators (XOs or SPXOs), voltage controlled crystal oscillators (VCXOs), temperature compensated crystal oscillators (TCXOs), oven controlled crystal oscillators (OCXOs), and rubidium oscillators and clocks. Particular specializations include patented ASIC-based high-stability TCXOs, ultrastable OCXOs and SDH/SONET reference oscillators.*

Cmaine Shipping Ltd, 22 Ruther Park, Haverfordwest, Dyfed, SA61 1DH Tel: (01437) 769922 Fax: (01437) 766797 E-mail: cmaine@btinternet.com *Shipping agents*

CMAssociates Limited, 23 Rhosleigh Avenue, Sharples Park, Bolton, BL1 6PP E-mail: enquires@cmassociates.co.uk *Change management, business transformation, transition, growth, survival, efficiency, effectiveness, performance management, Organisational development, design, learning, Profit improvement, Customer satisfaction competitiveness, Central, local government, public sector services, funding SME financial investments, Relationship management, effective leadership, risk management, Brand development, strategic partnership development, Corporate governance ICT, Enterprise relationship management, EFQM PR public relations balance*

C-Matic Systems Ltd, Warren Court, Park Road, Crowborough, East Sussex, TN6 2QX Tel: (01892) 665688 Fax: (01892) 667515 E-mail: info@cmatic.co.uk *Electrical power monitoring agents*

C-Max Ltd, Unit B1 Roman Hill Business Park, Broadmayne, Dorchester, Dorset, DT2 8LY Tel: (01305) 853005 Fax: (01305) 852136 E-mail: mail@cmaxsonar.com Principal Export Areas: Worldwide *Marine electronic manufrs*

▶ CMB Fylde Engineering, 3 Skyways Commercial Campus, Amy Johnson Way, Blackpool, FY4 2RP Tel: (01253) 298366 Fax: (01253) 298377

CMB International Ltd, Little Alton Farm, Ashby Road, Ravenstone, Coalville, Leicestershire, LE67 2AA Tel: (01530) 563600 Fax: (01530) 563900 E-mail: sales@cmb.uk.com *Quarry machinery maintenance & repair*

CMC Consulting, 2 Progress Business Centre, Whittle Parkway, Slough, SL1 6DQ Tel: (01628) 600870 Fax: (01628) 660688 E-mail: jason@sian-consulting.com *Telecommunications consultancy encompassing recruitment, educational training & professional services*

▶ CMC Joinery, 3 Radnor Close, Congleton, Cheshire, CW12 4PT Tel: (01260) 297348 *Joinery*

CMGsoftfurnishings, 46, The Haystack, Daventry, Northamptonshire, NN11 0NZ Tel: (01327) 703063 E-mail: info@cmgsoftfurnishings.co.uk *CMG Soft Furnishings offer highly experienced seamstress skills, trained in an extensive range of soft furnishing and fashion clothes manufacture. CMG Soft Furnishings have established a reputation for high quality soft furnishings to meet exacting client requirements whilst devoting ourselves to the highest standards of product quality, on-time delivery and customer care.*

CMJ Mould Tools, 22 Benfield Way, Braintree, Essex, CM7 3YS Tel: (01376) 347776 Fax: (01376) 347776 E-mail: sales@cmjmouldtools.co.uk *Injection mould toolmakers - Engineering die cast tools, plastic injection mould tools*

CML Alloys, Buildings 8 9, 8 First Avenue, Pensnett Trading Estate, Kingswinford, West Midlands, DY6 7TG Tel: (01384) 282400 Fax: (01384) 270800 E-mail: sales@amari-international.com Principal Export Areas: Worldwide *Stockholders of nickel alloy flanges & fittings manufrs*

▶ CML Group, Bluebell Farm, Hewitts Road, Orpington, Kent, BR6 7QR Tel: (01959) 533833 Fax: (01689) 821893 E-mail: alyson@ah-design.co.uk

▶ CMP Support, 46 Freshwater Drive, Poole, Dorset, BH15 4JE Tel: (01202) 245318 Fax: 01202 245318 E-mail: enquiries@cmpsupport.co.uk *Online secretarial assistance including audio typing, copy/digital typing, CVs, dissertations, reports, minutes, manuscripts, data entry.*

CMR Catering Equipment, 27 Queen Street, Ashford, Kent, TN23 1RF Tel: (07773) 885556 *Commercial catering equipment distributors, suppliers & manufacturers, supplying to the food & beverage industry, hotels, local authorities. RIBA /barbour index /interior design handbook -listed suppliers, product information available to architects, quantity surveyors & specifiers*

CMR Catering Equipment, 27 Queen Street, Ashford, Kent, TN23 1RF Tel: (07773) 885556 Fax: (0871) 2301318 E-mail: info@cmr-catering-equipment.co.uk *Catering equipment suppliers nationwide*

CMR Controls, 22 Repton Court, Repton Close, Basildon, Essex, SS13 1LN Tel: (01268) 287222 Fax: (01268) 287099 E-mail: sales@cmr.co.uk *Controls & sensor equipment manufrs*

CMS Broadband Ltd, Conchieton, Twynholm, Kirkcudbright, DG6 4TA Tel: (01557) 870256 Fax: (01557) 870400 E-mail: info@thinkcms.co.uk *Computer resellers & web designers*

▶ CMS Construction, 118 Longcauseway, Farnworth, Bolton, BL4 9BL Tel: (01204) 576558 Fax: (01204) 706116

CMS Industries, Downsview Road, Wantage, Oxfordshire, OX12 9FF Tel: (01235) 773370 Fax: (01235) 773371 E-mail: sales@cmsindustries.com *Suppliers of office seating & desk components*

CMS International Ltd, Crowborough, East Sussex, TN6 1XU Tel: (01892) 669966 Fax: (01892) 669977 E-mail: info@cmsinternational.com *Promotional gifts & website designers*

CMS Lift Trucks Ltd, 9 Michelin Road, Newtownabbey, County Antrim, BT36 4PT Tel: (028) 9084 2537 Fax: (028) 9084 2947 E-mail: colin@cmslifttrucks.com *Fork lift services*

▶ CMS Partnership, MILRIG, 56 Prestwick Road, Ayr, KA8 8JR Tel: 01292 260393 Fax: 01292 281214 E-mail: rob@cms-partnership.com *We provide coaching and mentoring services to business and individuals. CMS-Partnership is an approved centre to deliver coaching and mentoring qualifications through the Institute of Leadership and Management at all levels from supervisory to senior executive.*

▶ CMT Industrial Powdercoaters, 27 Dencora Way, Luton, LU3 3HP Tel: (01582) 575494 Fax: (01582) 584297 E-mail: cmtpowdercoaters@aol.com *Powder coating suppliers*

CMT (Testing) Ltd, Prime Park Way, Prime Enterprise Park, Derby, DE1 3QB Tel: (01332) 383333 Fax: (01332) 602607 E-mail: testing@cmt-ltd.co.uk *Building industry testing laboratory*

▶ CNA Electronic Systems, Unit 25, Furnace Industrial Estate, Shildon, County Durham, DL4 1QB Tel: (01388) 778051 E-mail: info@talking-alarms.co.uk *Electronic manufrs*

CNC Doors, Premier Partnership Estate, Leys Road, Brierley Hill, West Midlands, DY5 3UP Tel: (01384) 78833 Fax: (01384) 78867 E-mail: cncdoors@btconnect.com *Industrial doors suppliers & manufrs*

CNC Precision, Unit 15 Enfield Industrial Estate, Redditch, Worcestershire, B97 6BG Tel: (01527) 596727 Fax: (01527) 585049 E-mail: sales@c-n-c.co.uk *Precision engineers*

▶ CNC Router Project Ltd, 76-77 Brunner Road, London, E17 7NW Tel: (020) 8223 0639 Fax: (020) 8223 0663 E-mail: cnc@netcomuk.co.uk *Manufacturer of wooden components*

CNC Support Ltd, Advance Factory Site, Skipton Road, Trawden Colne, Colne, Lancashire, BB8 8BJ Tel: (01282) 859122 Fax: (01282) 859144 E-mail: sales@cncsupport.co.uk *CNC machinery service & woodworking machinery*

cnc-it Ltd, Unit 4, Craven Court, Canada Rd, Byfleet, Surrey, KT14 7JL Tel: 01932 331333 Fax: 01932 350370 E-mail: sales@cnc-it.co.uk *We specialise in fast turnaround CNC and laser cutting/engraving for a wide range of materials, we offer a fast friendly service with flexible lead times, we work closely with Film/Exhibition & Construction companies and many other industries.**

CNS Computer Networks Ltd, Transport Hall, Gloucester Road, Avonmouth, Bristol, BS11 9AQ Tel: (0870) 7771650 Fax: (0870) 7771655 E-mail: sales@c-n-s.co.uk *Computer*

▶ Coach House Communications Ltd, The Coach House, Sherridge Road, Leigh Sinton, Malvern, Worcestershire, WR13 5DB Tel: (0870) 4440888 Fax: (0844) 8440124 E-mail: enquiries@coachhousecommunications.co.uk *Telecommunications provider*

Coach Trimming Coventry, Sutton Stop, Longford, Coventry, CV6 6DF Tel: (024) 7664 5488 Fax: (024) 7636 2545 *Contract furnishers & upholsterers*

▶ Coaching Unlimited, Orchard Holding, The Croft, East Hagbourne, Didcot, Oxfordshire, OX11 9LS Tel: (01235) 813370 E-mail: ianclancy@coachingunlimited.co.uk *Coaching Unlimited - Life, Performance, Business, Executive Coaching - Work/Life balance - Coaching Helps people and businesses to remove obstacle that are getting in the way of the path to success; Help to become more productive and focused; Build effective processes and teams that get results; Solve problems by identifying the source and preventing them from happening again; Get more (clients), Plan time to enable people to lead a more balanced life AND Grow the business or Life balance AND have time for fun*

▶ Coaching With Soul - Modern VOCAL COACH, Trentham, Stoke-on-Trent, ST4 8TU Tel: (07957) 127348 E-mail: thesessionsinger@tiscali.co.uk *Experienced modern vocal coach, with special interest in Rock, Pop, Soul, R&B. If you want to be taken seriously in the industry, you need to work with serious industry professionals. Excellent tuition, great rates, packages, even gift vouchers.*

Coachman Caravan Co. Ltd, Amsterdam Road, Hull, HU7 0XF Tel: (01482) 839737 Fax: (01482) 878143 E-mail: info@coachman.co.uk *Touring caravan manufrs*

▶ Co-active Ltd, 25 Wolseley Close, Plymouth, PL2 3BY Tel: 01752 500888 Fax: 01752 500444 E-mail: contact@co-active.org.uk *Business support for social enterprises (co-operatives, community businesses, social firms, credit unions, community development trusts etc) in the South West of England. We provide business advice, training and diagnostic services.*

▶ Coady Consultants Ltd, 87 The Straits Lower Gornal, Dudley, West Midlands, DY3 3AL Tel: (01902) 664837 Fax: (01902) 664837 E-mail: enquiries@coadyconsultants.co.uk *Coady Consultants will provide purpose designed packages designed to increase the abilities of all team members. Participants will recognise and learn how to deal with Anger, Aggression, Bullying and Stress in themselves and others by developing and using high quality inter and intra-personal skills*

Coalesence, 9-10 St. Andrews Square, Edinburgh, EH2 2AF Tel: (0870) 0439901 Fax: 0131-718 6100 E-mail: info@edincc.co.uk *IT consultants*

Coalite Smokeless Fuels, PO Box 21, Chesterfield, Derbyshire, S44 6AB Tel: (01246) 822281 Fax: (01246) 240044 E-mail: enquiries@coalite.co.uk *Smokeless fuel manufrs*

▶ Coalition Computer Systems, 1 Newhams Row, London, SE1 3UZ Tel: (020) 7234 0312 Fax: (020) 7504 8233 *Computer software development*

Coalville Signs, Units 2 3 Stephenson Indust Estate, Stephenson Way, Coalville, Leicestershire, LE67 3HB Tel: (01530) 811398 Fax: (01530) 830958 *Sign manufrs*

▶ Coalville Trophy Centre, 42 Belvoir Road, Coalville, Leicestershire, LE67 3PN Tel: (01530) 810100 *Sports trophy manufrs*

Coar Agricultural Services, Settle Road, Newsholme, Clitheroe, Lancashire, BB7 4JF Tel: (01200) 445187 Fax: (01200) 445187 *Agricultural engineers*

Coast & County Engineering, Enterprise Road, Mablethorpe, Lincolnshire, LN12 1NB Tel: (01507) 473170 Fax: (01507) 473170 *Steel fabricators*

continued

continued

Coast To Coast Boot Co. Ltd, Lower Fold, Marple Bridge, Stockport, Cheshire, SK6 5DU Tel: (01663) 745461 Fax: (01663) 741433 *Safety & work footwear*

Coastal Ltd, D'Oriel House, Holton Heath Trading Park, Poole, Dorset, BH16 6LE Tel: (01202) 624011 Fax: (01202) 622465 E-mail: sales@coastalwindows.co.uk *Manufacturers of conservatories & PVCu doors & windows*

▶ Coastal Cottage, 26 North Road, Kingsdown, Deal, Kent, CT14 8HP Tel: 01304 367585 *Self-Catering Holiday Cottage by the Sea.*

Coastal Fire, 799 Foxhall Road, Ipswich, IP4 5TJ Tel: (01473) 714708 Fax: (01473) 714708 *Fire extinguisher distributors service*

Coastal Grains Ltd, Station Road, Belford, Northumberland, NE70 7DT Tel: (01668) 213609 Fax: (01668) 213609 E-mail: terence@coastalgrains.fsnet.co.uk *Agricultural grain merchants*

▶ Coastal Leisure, Unit 14 College Close, Sandown, Isle of Wight, PO36 8EH Tel: (01983) 401234 E-mail: steph@coastalleisure.org.uk *Amusement machines & equipment suppliers*

▶ Coastal Leisure Derby Ltd, 17 Mason Crescent, Swadlincote, Derbyshire, DE11 8JP Tel: (01283) 551133 *Amusement machines & equipment hire services*

Coastal Leisure UK Ltd, Eagle House, Richmond Road, Southampton, SO15 3FT Tel: (023) 8022 3555 Fax: (01983) 401088 E-mail: steph@coastalleisure.org.uk *Amusement machines*

Coastal Marine (Boatbuilders) Ltd, Browns Bank, Eyemouth, Berwickshire, TD14 5DQ Tel: (01890) 750328 Fax: (01890) 751325 *Boat builders services*

Coastal Sheds, Alpha Works, Common Road, Gorleston, Great Yarmouth, Norfolk, NR31 0QG Tel: (01493) 650050 *Shed manufrs*

Coastel Groundworks Ltd, 5 Somerset Road, Walmer, Deal, Kent, CT14 7TD Tel: (01304) 361126 Fax: (01304) 361126 *Groundwork consultants*

Coastground Ltd, Morton Peto Road, Harfreys Industrial Estate, Great Yarmouth, Norfolk, NR31 0LT Tel: (01493) 650455 Fax: (01493) 655047 E-mail: coastground@rjt.co.uk *Protective coating contractors*

Coastguard Kites, Outwood, Redhill, RH1 5QB Tel: (0870) 2401018 E-mail: info@coastguard-kites.com *Kite shop & power kites*

Coastline Adhesive Tapes Ltd, 8 Skye Road, Shaw Farm Industrial Estate, Shawfarm Industrial Estate, Prestwick, Ayrshire, KA9 2TA Tel: (01292) 470289 Fax: (01292) 671287 E-mail: sales@coastlinetapes.co.uk *Adhesive tape distributors*

Coastline Business Computers Northern Ltd, 10-11 Avenue Cresent, Seaton Delaval, Whitley Bay, Tyne & Wear, NE25 0DN Tel: 0191-237 4000 Fax: 0191-237 7788 E-mail: sales@cbcnorthern.com *Stationary suppliers*

▶ Coat & Fry Technology Ltd, 18 Cotton Brook Road, Derby, DE23 8YJ Tel: (01332) 367136 Fax: (01332) 372006 E-mail: sales@coatandfry.co.uk *Fryers seasoning, flavouring systems & batter coating equipment suppliers*

Coatapart Ltd, 58 Arthur Street, Redditch, Worcestershire, B98 8JY Tel: (01527) 528851 Fax: (01527) 517186 *Powder coaters*

Coated Screens Ltd, Unit 4 218 Purley Way, Croydon, CR0 4XG Tel: (020) 8256 1500 Fax: (020) 8256 1515 E-mail: enquiries@coated-screens.co.uk *Screens process manufrs*

Coates Bros, Manor Farm, Watlington Road, Runcton Holme, King's Lynn, Norfolk, PE33 0EJ Tel: (01553) 810463 Fax: (01553) 811549 E-mail: enquiries@coates-bros.co.uk *Agricultural contractors*

Coates Consulting, Lower Flat, 126 Main Street, Lower Largo, Leven, Fife, KY8 6BP Tel: (01333) 329118 Fax: (01333) 329118 *Computer consultants*

Coates Engineering International Ltd, Millfold, Whitworth, Rochdale, Lancashire, OL12 8DN Tel: (01706) 852122 Fax: (01706) 853629 E-mail: info@bchltd.com *Process design & chemical production plant*

Coates Fencing Ltd, Unit 3 Barham Close, Bridgwater, Somerset, TA6 4DS Tel: (01278) 423577 Fax: (01278) 427760 E-mail: info@coatesfencing.co.uk *Steel, wood fencing suppliers & manufrs*

Coates Holdings Ltd, 3 Brindley Road, Cardiff, CF11 8TX Tel: (029) 2034 4554 Fax: (029) 2034 4545 E-mail: coates-co@fsmail.net *Sheet metalwork precision fabricators*

Coates Lorilleux, Cray Avenue, St. Mary Cray, Orpington, Kent, BR5 3PP Tel: (01689) 894000 Fax: (01689) 894020 *Printing ink manufrs*

Coates Optical Supplies, Gretton Road, Winchcombe, Cheltenham, Gloucestershire, GL54 5EE Tel: (01242) 603888 Fax: (01242) 603828 E-mail: info@coates-optical.demon.co.uk *Optical instruments & machinery*

▶ Coates & Parker Ltd, 36 Market Place, Warminster, Wiltshire, BA12 9AN Tel: (01985) 213030 Fax: (01985) 217680 E-mail: sales@coatesandparker.co.uk *Commercial printers & newspaper printers*

Coates & Shaw, Unit 23 Moss La Industrial Estate, Moss Lane, Royton, Oldham, OL2 6HR Tel: (01706) 840238 Fax: (01706) 881633 *Welding fabricators*

Coates Signs, 84 Holme Lane, Sheffield, S6 4JW Tel: 0114-234 4834 Fax: 0114-234 4834 E-mail: info@coatesigns.co.uk *Sign manufrs*

Coating Applications Group, Newhouse Road, Huncoat Business Park, Accrington, Lancashire, BB5 6NT Tel: (01254) 391769 Fax: (01254) 393519 E-mail: sales@coatingapplications.co.uk *Coated fabric manufrs*

Coating & Converting Solutions Ltd, Bloomfield Park, Bloomfield Road, Tipton, West Midlands, DY4 9AP Tel: 0121-557 1155 Fax: 0121-557 9997 E-mail: sales@coatingconverting.co.uk

continued

Adhesive tape manufacture, custom, coating & converting

Coating Repair Specialists, 2 Somerset Road, Springwell Estate, Sunderland, SR3 4EB Tel: 0191- 522 9577 Fax: 0191- 522 9577 E-mail: j.collier40@ntlworld.com *We repair and respray damaged cladding panels dented or scratched doors, mullions , transons, flashings and colour changes. Our mobile unit is equipped with a professional paint mixing scheme to enable efficient mixing and tinting to all RAL and BS colour codes on site. For personal attention ring Jim Collier mob: 07714 333513*

Coatings & Safe Access Ltd, PO Box 11, York, YO41 5YP Tel: (01759) 380804 Fax: (01759) 380329 E-mail: casalyork@aol.com *Refurbish industrial & commercial roofs*

Coats Crafts U.K, Lingfield, McMullen Road, Darlington, County Durham, DL1 1YQ Tel: (01325) 394394 Fax: (01325) 394200 E-mail: consumer.services@coats.com *Hand knitting yarn manufrs* Also at: Alloa

Coats UK Ltd, Netherplace, Newton Mearns, Glasgow, G77 6PP Tel: 0141-616 1000 Fax: 0141-616 1060 E-mail: coats@coatsviyella.com *Industrial thread manufrs* Also at: Belfast, Gateshead, Haringey & Leicester

Cobal Cranes Ltd, Doctor Lane, Sheffield, S9 5AP Tel: 0114-261 8003 Fax: 0114-261 9003 E-mail: steven.hides@btconnect.com *Overhead cranes, lifting gear repairs, site installation & manufrs*

Cobal Sign Systems Ltd, Brookway Industrial Estate, Brookway, Hambridge Lane, Newbury, Berkshire, RG14 5PE Tel: (01635) 570600 Fax: (01635) 32432 E-mail: info@cobal.co.uk *Sign manufrs*

Cobalt NDT Ltd, 2 Eccleston Park Trade Centre, Prescot Road, St. Helens, Merseyside, WA10 3BZ Tel: (01744) 734321 Fax: (01744) 734321 *Non-destructive testing services*

▶ Cobault Computer Systems, 29 Great George Street, Bristol, BS1 5QT Tel: 0117-920 0123 Fax: 0117-920 0124 E-mail: info@cobault.com *Customer relationship management consultants*

Cobb Group Exhibition Services Ltd, PO Box 37, Luton, LU1 1YW Tel: (01582) 453308 Fax: (01582) 417528 E-mail: info@cobbgroup.co.uk *Manufacturers of modular exhibition display systems*

Cobban Environmental Development & Remediation Ltd, 93 Clifton Street Roath, Cardiff, CF24 1LT Tel: (029) 2040 7330 Fax: (029) 2040 7330 *Project management of remediation projects. Services include insitu and exsitu remediation, filling station decommissioning, site clearance of hazardous wastes, treatment of ecological contaminants including Japanese knotweed.*

▶ Cobbett & Keen Events, Unit 8 Billet Lane, Berkhamsted, Hertfordshire, HP4 1DP Tel: (01442) 878122 Fax: (01442) 878461 E-mail: info@ckfg.co.uk *providing catering and event management services for corporates, weddings and other occassions*

Cobble Blackburn Ltd, Gate Street, Blackburn, BB1 3AH Tel: (01254) 55121 Fax: (01254) 671125 E-mail: info@cobble.co.uk *Tufting machinery manufrs*

▶ Cobblers Bench, 128a Central Drive, Blackpool, FY1 5DY Tel: (07890) 307647 E-mail: cobblersbench@fsmail.net *Cobblers*

Cobblers Den, 11 St.Davids Road South, Lytham St. Annes, Lancashire, FY8 1TF Tel: (01253) 714391 E-mail: thecobblersden@hotmail.com *Sports trophies & engraving,also leather & shoe repairs & key cutting.*

Cobbs Country Store, Barrow House Farm, Woodcoates Lane, Darlton, Newark, Nottinghamshire, NG22 0TH Tel: (01777) 228260 Fax: (01777) 228160 E-mail: sales@cobbscountrystore.co.uk *Animal food retailers*

Cobbs Health Foods, Unit 7 Brunel Shopping Centre, Somerton, Somerset, TA11 7PY Tel: (01458) 274066 Fax: (01458) 274190 *Health foods & products sales*

Cobb-Slater Ltd, Cosim Works, Church Road, Darley Dale, Matlock, Derbyshire, DE4 2GG Tel: (01629) 732344 Fax: (01629) 733446 E-mail: technical@cobb-slater.co.uk *Plastic injection moulding manufrs*

▶ Cobden, 4-5 Laundry Street, Salford, M6 6WJ Tel: 0161-745 7744 Fax: 0161-745 9027 E-mail: info@cobdensupplies.co.uk Principal Export Areas: Worldwide *Packaging material merchants*

Cobham Composites Ltd, Davey House, Gelders Ha, Shepshed, Loughborough, Leicestershire, LE12 9NH Tel: (01509) 504541 Fax: (01509) 507563 *Manufacturers of aircraft components & composites*

Cobham Computer Systems Ltd, 56-58 Smithbrook Kiln, Cranleigh, Surrey, GU6 8JJ Tel: (01483) 275515 Fax: (01483) 277067 E-mail: sales@cobhamsystems.co.uk *Software sales*

Coblands Landscapes Ltd, South Farm Barn, South Farm Lane, Langton Green, Tunbridge Wells, Kent, TN3 9JN Tel: (01892) 863535 Fax: (01892) 863778 E-mail: info@coblandslandscapes.co.uk *Landscape contractors to commercial and public authority sectors in London and South East of England. Specialising in prestige amenity landscape and sportsfield construction and maintenance including historic gardens restoration. Ecological and environmental contractors for habitat restoration,hibernacula construction wetland management. Regional multi-site maintenance of amenity landscape for public utilities, business parks.*Founder member British Association Landscape Industries. *Accreditation by Constructionline.*

Cobolt Systems Ltd, Mill Road, Reedham, Norwich, NR13 3TL Tel: (01493) 700172 Fax: (01493) 701037 E-mail: cobolt@compusreve.co.uk *Blind products sales & manufrs*

Coborn Beds, 100 Coborn Road, London, E3 2DG Tel: (020) 8981 7530 *Beds & Blankets*

Coborn Engineering Co. Ltd, Chesham Close, Romford, RM7 7PJ Tel: (01708) 744666 Fax: (01708) 725187 E-mail: coborneng@aol.com Sales Contact: G. Hornsby Principal Export Areas: Worldwide *Manufacturers of dynamic balancing machines, carbide, CBN & diamond tool grinding machines & precision spindles*

Cobra Computers, 220 Birmingham New Road, Wolverhampton, WV4 6NF Tel: (01902) 679555 Fax: (01902) 663508 E-mail: sales@cobra-computers.co.uk *Computer suppliers & manufrs*

▶ Cobra Electronics Ltd, 1 Greenacres, Bordon, Hampshire, GU35 0EX Tel: (01420) 479830 Fax: (01420) 479860 E-mail: sales@cobra4coax.com *Coaxial cable assemblies & RF manufrs*

Cobra Engineering, 34 Tenby Street, Birmingham, B1 3ES Tel: 0121-233 1724 Fax: 0121-236 3731 *Auto & capstan repetition work*

Cobra Engineering UK Ltd, Redmoor Lane, Wisbech, Cambridgeshire, PE14 0RN Tel: (01945) 860578 Fax: (01945) 860914 *Stainless steel fabricators*

Cobra Machinery, Riverdane Road, Eaton Bank Trading Estate, Congleton, Cheshire, CW12 1PL Tel: (01260) 279326 Fax: (01260) 299017 E-mail: sales@cobrabraids.co.uk *Cobra manufacturers braiding machinery & braiding machines. These are used in a variety of worldwide markets which include automotive, aerospace, medical, engineering & narrow fabrics companies*

▶ Cobra Pest Control, 57 Severn Way, Bletchley, Milton Keynes, MK3 7QG Tel: (0800) 1078769 E-mail: vermin.biz@tesco.net *Cobra Pest Control for all your pest solutions*Wasps fleas mice rats and many others*

Cobra Seats Ltd, Units D1-D2 Halesfield 23, Telford, Shropshire, TF7 4NY Tel: (01952) 684020 Fax: (01952) 581772 E-mail: enquiries@cobraseats.com *Replacement motor car seat manufrs*

Cobra Security Systems Ltd, 155 Station Road, London, E4 6AG Tel: (020) 8529 0179 Fax: (020) 8529 0091 E-mail: keith@cobra-security.fsnet.co.uk *Security systems, equipment engineers & installers*

Cobra Systems, 5 Morven Park, Glenrothes, Fife, KY6 3PX Tel: (01592) 620067 Fax: (01592) 620067 E-mail: info@cobra-systems.com *Computer consultants & retailer*

Cobra Therapeutics Ltd, The Science Park, University of Keele, Keele, Newcastle, Staffordshire, ST5 5SP Tel: (01782) 714181 Fax: (01782) 714168 *Gene therapy research*

Cobsen-Davies Roofing Leicester Ltd, 20 Sompting Road, Worthing, West Sussex, BN14 9EP Tel: (01903) 821616 Fax: (01903) 208044 E-mail: info@cobsen-davies.co.uk *Roofing contractors*

Coburg Engineering Ltd, Unit 22F, Wincombe Business Park, Shaftesbury, Dorset, SP7 9QJ Tel: (01747) 855022 Fax: (01747) 854744 E-mail: info@coburg.co.uk *Machine tool importers & exporters*

Coburn Electronics, A3 Faraday Road, Newbury, Berkshire, RG14 2AD Tel: (01635) 35133 Fax: (01635) 36350 E-mail: sandra@newstart-electronics.co.uk *Sub-contract assembly services*

Coburn Fasteners, Unit 1-3 Brunel Way, Stroudwater Business Park, Stonehouse, Gloucestershire, GL10 3SX Tel: (01453) 828515 Fax: (01453) 791040 E-mail: andy@coburnfasteners.co.uk *Packaging services*

Cobweb Computers, 471 Buxton Road, Stockport, Cheshire, SK2 7HE Tel: 0161-484 0100 *Computer resellers manufrs*

Cobweb Crafts, The Old School, Cadney Road, Howsham, Market Rasen, Lincolnshire, LN7 6LA Tel: (01652) 678761 Fax: (01652) 678710 *Furniture manufrs*

Cobweb Furniture, The Old Chapel Workshop, West Street, West Butterwick, Scunthorpe, South Humberside, DN17 3JZ Tel: (01724) 783888 *Antique restoration & furniture manufrs*

Cobweb Solutions Ltd, Delme Place, Cams Hall Estate, Fareham, Hampshire, PO16 8UX Tel: (0845) 2239000 Fax: (0845) 2493310 E-mail: sales@cobweb.co.uk *Internet service provider*

Cobwebs Pine, The Quadrant, St. Ives, Cambridgeshire, PE27 5PE Tel: (01480) 386187 Fax: (01480) 386187 *Pine furniture supplier retailer*

Coca Cola Enterprises Ltd, Cray Road, Sidcup, Kent, DA14 5DF Tel: (020) 8302 2600 Fax: (020) 8565 3309 *Soft drinks manufrs*

Coca Cola GB & Ireland, 1 Queen Caroline Street, London, W6 9HQ Tel: (020) 8237 3000 Fax: (020) 8237 3700 *Soft drink manufrs*

Coca-Cola Bottlers Ulster, The Green, Lambeg, Lisburn, County Antrim, BT27 5SS Tel: (028) 9267 4231 Fax: (028) 9267 1049 *Soft drink manufrs*

Coca-Cola Enterprises Europe Ltd, Charter Place, Vine Street, Uxbridge, Middlesex, UB8 1EZ Tel: (01895) 231313 *Soft drink manufrs*

Cochrane & Watt Ceilings, Sonas, Forth, Lanark, ML11 8HD Tel: (01555) 811934 Fax: (01555) 811934 *Suspended ceilings services*

Cochranes of Oxford Ltd, Grove Farm Barns, High Street, Shipton-under-Wychwood, Chipping Norton, Oxfordshire, OX7 6DG Tel: (01993) 832868 Fax: (01993) 832578 E-mail: cochranes@mailbox.co.uk *Education equipment manufrs*

Cocina Ceramics, Unit 5 Knighton Hill Business Centre, Knighton Hill, Wembury, Plymouth, PL9 0ED Tel: (01752) 863663 Fax: (01752) 863663 E-mail: cocinaceramics@ffmail.net *Spanish terracotta pots importers*

▶ Cockett's Bespoke Beds, 32-34 High Street, Herne Bay, Kent, CT6 5LH Tel: (0870) 7552343 E-mail: mail@cockets.com *Bed & mattresses manufrs*

Cocklestorm Fencing Co., Cross Lane, Radcliffe, Manchester, M26 2RF Tel: 0161-724 9595 Fax: 0161-724 9595 E-mail: sales@cocklestorm.co.uk *Domestic fencing services*

Cockney Trophies & Darts Centre, 1 Waterloo Road, Stoke-on-Trent, ST6 2EH Tel: (01782) 838404 Fax: (01782) 817791 *Trophies & darts distributors*

▶ Cocksedge Building Contractors, 25 Hampstead Avenue, Mildenhall, Bury St. Edmunds, Suffolk, IP28 7AS Tel: (01638) 713694 Fax: (01638) 713588

Cockx Sudbury Ltd, Unit A Woodhall House Drury Drive, Woodhall Business Park, Sudbury, Suffolk, CO10 1WH Tel: (01787) 880511 Fax: (01787) 378102 E-mail: info@cockx.co.uk *Screen-printing agents services*

▶ Coco Aura, Unit 5 Quayside Business Centre, Lowestoft Enterprise Park, Lowestoft, Suffolk, NR33 9NW Tel: (01502) 500520

Cocoa Tree, Chillington, Kingsbridge, Devon, TQ7 2LA Tel: (01548) 580009 Fax: (01548) 580009 *Confectionery manufrs*

▶ Cococda, 61 London Road, Woolmer Green, Knebworth, Herts, SG3 6JE Tel: 01438 810999 Fax: 01438 817193 E-mail: mail@cococda.biz *Marketing, distribution and import/export of specialist confectionery*

Cocon Construction Ltd, North Shore Builders Yard, Holyhead, Gwynedd, LL65 3AG Tel: (01407) 742222 Fax: (01407) 769347 E-mail: cocon@btinternet.com *Construction, civil engineering & concrete repairs*

▶ Coconut House Ltd, Hall Street, Long Melford, Sudbury, Suffolk, CO10 9JQ Tel: (01787) 312922 E-mail: chrisandgina@coconuthouse.co.uk *A very special shop based in Long Melford, Suffolk specialising in the sale of exquisite lighting and decorative furniture and furnishings.*

▶ Coconut Island, 43 Enys Road, Eastbourne, East Sussex, BN21 2DH Tel: (01323) 641757 E-mail: smaas@btinternet.com *Your UK source for supreme 0% pure Virgin Coconut Oil for Health and Beauty; Light and white, a pure delight!*

Cod Steaks, 2 Cole Road, St Philips, Bristol, BS2 0UG Tel: 0117-980 3910 Fax: 0117-972 8999 E-mail: mail@codsteaks.com *Model retailers*

Coda P.L.C., Cardale Park, Beckwith Head Road, Harrogate, North Yorkshire, HG3 1RY Tel: (01423) 509999 Fax: (01423) 530525 E-mail: info@coda.com *Computer software house*

Coda Plastics Ltd, Folgate Road, North Walsham, Norfolk, NR28 0AJ Tel: (01692) 501020 Fax: (01692) 501030 E-mail: admin@coda-plastics.co.uk *Manufactures of plastic caps & closures*

Coda Systemforms Ltd, Harbour House, Coldharbour Lane, Rainham, Essex, RM13 9YA Tel: (01708) 520100 Fax: (01708) 550073 E-mail: neilcook@codasystemforms.co.uk *Continuous stationery manufrs*

Codan UK Ltd, Gostrey House, Union Road, Farnham, Surrey, GU9 7PT Tel: (01252) 717272 Fax: (01252) 717337 E-mail: sales@codanuk.com.au *HF land & mobile radio & satellite manufrs*

CodaOctopus Products Ltd, Admiral House, 29-30 Maritime Street, Edinburgh, EH6 6SE Tel: 0131-553 1380 Fax: 0131-554 7143 E-mail: info@codaoctopus.com *Technology, under water*

Coday Sheet Metal Fabrications Great Yarmouth Ltd, Salmon Road, Great Yarmouth, Norfolk, NR30 3QS Tel: (01493) 857566 Fax: (01493) 331446 E-mail: stevegraham@codaygy.co.uk *Sheet metalwork fabricators*

▶ Code Blue Imaging Ltd, Unit 3A, Herald Industrial Estate, Hedge End, Southampton, SO30 2JW Tel: (01489) 790088 E-mail: benm@codeblueimaging.co.uk

Code Computing, Global House, Berry Hill, Berry Hill Industrial Estate, Droitwich, Worcestershire, WR9 9AB Tel: (01905) 775566 Fax: (01905) 621676 *Computer software & solutions*

Code Masters Software Co. Ltd, Lower Farm, Stoneythorpe, Southam, Warwickshire, CV47 2DL Tel: (01926) 814132 Fax: (01926) 817595 E-mail: enquiries@codemasters.com *Design & publish computer games*

Code-A-Weld, Units 5-10, Bessemer Way, Harfreys Industrial Estate, Great Yarmouth, Norfolk, NR31 0LX Tel: (01493) 602844 Fax: (01493) 653331 E-mail: codeaweld@btinternet.com *Steel fabricators*

Code-A-Weld, 2nd Avenue, Westfield Trading Estate, Midsomer Norton, Radstock, BA3 4BE Tel: (01761) 410410 Fax: (01761) 418388 E-mail: info@codeaweld.com *Weld testing services*

Codebyte Ltd, 9 Belleisle, Purley on Thames, Reading, RG8 8AP Tel: 0118-941 6244 *Computer consultants*

Codegate Ltd, Unit 3 The Sapphire Centre, Fishponds Road, Wokingham, Berkshire, RG41 2QL Tel: 0118-977 0808 Fax: 0118-989 2187 E-mail: sales@codegate.co.uk *Bar code products systems supplier*

▶ Code-IT, Unit 11, Lea Green Business Park, Eurolink, St. Helens, Merseyside, WA9 4TR Tel: (01744) 811564 Fax: (01744) 811395 E-mail: code.it@virgin.net *Printers*

Codel Computer Systems, 71 St. Helens Road, Swansea, SA1 4BG Tel: (01792) 654154 Fax: (01792) 644392 E-mail: info@codelsoftware.com *Computer consultants & software developers*

Codel International Ltd, Station Yard, Station Road, Bakewell, Derbyshire, DE45 1GE Tel: (01629) 814351 Fax: (0870) 0566307 E-mail: sales@codel.co.uk *Stack emission monitors*

▶ Codelog Logistic Support Solutions Ltd, Unit 22B, Progress Business Park, Orders Lane, Kirkham, PR4 2TZ Tel: (01772) 672080 E-mail: info@codelog.com *Integrated Logistic Support (ILS). Specialising in Logistic Support Analysis (LSA) and Logistic Support Analysis Record (LSAR)*Project Management*Product Support*Life Cycle Mangement*Engineering Support**Technical Authoring*

Codemark Developments Ltd, 8 West Lodge Lane, Sutton, Ely, Cambridgeshire, CB6 2NX Tel: (01353) 775153 Fax: (07932) 231525 E-mail: sales@codemark.co.uk *Barcode & labeling equipment suppliers*

▶ Codepack Solutions Ltd, Woodhorn Lane, Oving, Chichester, West Sussex, PO20 2BX Tel: (01243) 792445 Fax: (01243) 792108 E-mail: sales@codepack.co.uk *Barcode scanners, label printers & data collection services*

▶ CodeStorm, CodeStorm House, Walton Road, Portsmouth, PO6 1TR Tel: (023) 9238 3999 Fax: (023) 9238 3444 E-mail: services@codestorm.co.uk *Direct mail & fulfilment*

▶ Codestrata Ltd, 21 Melbourn Road, Royston, Hertfordshire, SG8 7DE Tel: (01763) 222876 E-mail: codestrata@ntlworld.com *A first-class, internationally renowned translation company, run by Paul Boulter.*

Codeway Ltd, 13 Telford Way, Severalls Industrial Park, Colchester, CO4 9QP Tel: (01206) 756738 Fax: (01206) 756705 E-mail: sales@codeway.com *Bar code systems manufrs*

Codi International Ltd, Abbey Lodge, Tintern, Chepstow, Gwent, NP16 6SF Tel: (01291) 689427 Fax: (01291) 689999 E-mail: info@codi-international.com *Garage equipment & lifts suppliers*

▶ Codina Group, 11 Scriven Road, Knaresborough, North Yorkshire, HG5 9EQ Tel: (01423) 541133 Fax: (01423) 541144 E-mail: fsengineering@ntlworld.com *Manufacture woven wire products*

Coding & Handling, 52 Meeting Lane, Burton Latimer, Kettering, Northamptonshire, NN15 5LS Tel: (01536) 721026 Fax: (01536) 725056 E-mail: inkjets@codinghandling.co.uk *Inkjet printing & product manufrs*

Codis Ltd, 38-44 St Anns Road, Harrow, Middlesex, HA1 1LA Tel: (020) 8861 0610 Fax: (020) 8515 7049 E-mail: codis@codis.co.uk *IT consultants*

▶ Codnor Angling, 21 Market Place, Codnor, Ripley, Derbyshire, DE5 9QA Tel: (01773) 743411 *Fishing tackle suppliers*

▶ Codoc, 12 George Street, Falkirk, FK2 7EY Tel: (01324) 628206

Codringtons Ltd, 38 Crawley Road, London, N22 6AG Tel: (020) 8889 8494 Fax: (020) 8889 6731 E-mail: admin@codringtons.com *Lock & padlock suppliers*

Coercive Group Ltd, Beta House, Laser Quay, Rochester, Kent, ME2 4HU Tel: (01634) 713053 Fax: (01634) 712541 E-mail: csl@coercive.com *Electric motor manufrs*

Coexistence Ltd, 288 Upper Street, London, N1 2TZ Tel: (020) 7354 8817 Fax: (020) 7354 9610 *Contract furnishers*

▶ Cofathec Heatsave Ltd, E Ryedale Court, London Road, Riverhead, Sevenoaks, Kent, TN13 2DN Tel: (01732) 744870 Fax: (01732) 469986 *Commercial installations*

Coffee Bay, 67A Holly Rd, Twickenham, TW1 4HF Tel: 020 87442363 Fax: 020 88928110 *Food wholesale*

Coffee Craft, 30 Industrial Estate, Old Church Road, East Hanningfield, Chelmsford, CM3 8AB Tel: (01245) 403301 Fax: (01245) 403306 E-mail: mail@coffeecraft.co.uk *Free Loan Fuly Automatic Hot Drinks Equipment, Free Servicing & Repairs. Next Day Delivery For Ingedient and Sundry Supplies.*

The Coffee Exchange (Birmingham) Ltd, 654 Holly Lane, Erdington, Birmingham, B24 9PD Tel: 0121-682 2093 Fax: 0121-682 0008 *Despatch coffee manufrs*

▶ Coffee Merchants, Rathdown Road, Lissue Industrial Estate, Lisburn, County Antrim, BT28 2RE Tel: (028) 9262 2733 Fax: (028) 9262 2734 E-mail: stuart@coffeemerchantsltd.com *Coffee roasters*

Coffee People, Unit 9 Watford Enterprise Centre, 25 Greenhill Crescent, Watford, WD18 8XU Tel: (01923) 242022 Fax: (01923) 242044 E-mail: coffe.people@hotmail.co.uk *Coffee machines & ingredients manufrs*

▶ Coffee Point plc, Henfield Road, Small Dole, Henfield, West Sussex, BN5 9XH Tel: (01903) 879102 Fax: (01903) 879642 *Vending machines suppliers*

Coffee Supply Co., 3 Sunnylaw Road, Bridge of Allan, Stirling, FK9 4QD Tel: (01786) 834242 Fax: (01786) 833988 *Office drinks wholesalers & distributors*

Coffee Trade Federation, 63a Union Street, London, SE1 1SG Tel: (020) 7403 3088 Fax: (020) 7403 7730 E-mail: coffeetradefed@compuserve.com *Trade association*

▶ Coffee Warehouse, Reform Street, Hull, HU2 8EF Tel: (01482) 216061 Fax: (01482) 221225

▶ The Coffee Works, Unit 19a, Solway Industrial Estate, Maryport, Cumbria, CA15 8NF Tel: (01900) 819090 E-mail: info@thecoffeeworks.co.uk *Any type of private or corporate catering undertaken, from small buffets to large functions inside or out The Coffee Works can provide just what you need.*

Coffeeman Disposables, Unit 5 Endeavour Park, 11 Witney Road, Poole, Dorset, BH17 0GJ Tel: (01202) 684111 Fax: (01202) 685111 E-mail: sales@coffeeman.co.uk *Catering disposables suppliers*

▶ Coffeenetonline, 118 High Street, Bloxwich, Walsall, WS3 2DG Tel: (01922) 409007

▶ Coflex Films Ltd, Westfields Trading Estate, Hereford, HR4 9NS Tel: (01432) 276555 Fax: (01432) 279898 E-mail: sue.mohan@coflexfilms.co.uk *Coextruded flew wrapping film manufrs*

Cofra UK Ltd, PO Box 154, Horsham, West Sussex, RH12 3PJ Tel: (01403) 754422 Fax: (01403) 754433 E-mail: cofra.uk@cofra.com *Installation of geo-synthetics for geotechnical engineering*

Cofton Ltd, Firswood Road, Birmingham, B33 0ST Tel: 0121-628 4000 Fax: 0121-628 1398 E-mail: admin@cofton.co.uk *Civil engineering contractors*

Cogan & Shackleton, 35 Railway Road, Coleraine, County Londonderry, BT52 1PE Tel: (028) 7034 4036 Fax: (028) 7035 7028 E-mail: admin@coshack.co.uk *Mechanical & electrical engineering consultants*

Cogent Contracts Ltd, Limekiln Lane, Birmingham, B14 4SP Tel: 0121-474 2500 Fax: 0121-474 6163 E-mail: cogentcontracts@hotmail.com *Metal & aluminium alloy fabricators*

▶ Cogent Electrical Services Ltd, Unit 16 Sulivan Enterprise Centre, Sulivan Road, London, SW6 3DJ Tel: (020) 7736 5666 Fax: (020) 7736 4666

Cogent Orb Electrical Steels, PO Box 30, Newport, Gwent, NP19 0XT Tel: (01633) 290033 Fax: (01633) 294592 E-mail: sales@cogent-power.com Principal Export Areas: Worldwide *Electrical steel manufrs*

Cogent Passenger Seating Ltd, 12 Prydwen Road, Fforestfach, Swansea, SA5 4HN Tel: (01792) 585444 Fax: (01792) 588191 E-mail: enquiries@cogentseating.co.uk *Manufactures vehicle seats & covers*

Cogent Sankey Scott Laminations (Bilston), Bankfield Works, Greenway Road, Bilston, West Midlands, WV14 0TJ Tel: (01902) 401140 Fax: (01902) 409710 E-mail: sll@cogent-power.com Principal Export Areas: Worldwide *Manufacturers of laminated metal lamination/assembly, including electric motor. In addition, electrical industry stampings*

Cogent Technology Ltd, Dock Lane, Melton, Woodbridge, Suffolk, IP12 1PE Tel: (01394) 387444 Fax: (01394) 380604 E-mail: sales@cogent-technology.co.uk *Electronic design services & contract manufrs*

Coglan Air Conditioning, Church Lane, Worting, Basingstoke, Hampshire, RG23 8PX Tel: (01256) 464158 Fax: (01256) 811876 E-mail: clive@coglanaircon.com *Air conditioning suppliers*

Cognex UK, Sunningdale House, Caldecotte Lake Drive, Caldecotte, Milton Keynes, MK7 8LF Tel: (0800) 0180018 Fax: (01908) 392463 E-mail: sales@cognex.co.uk Principal Export Areas: Asia Pacific, Middle East, Africa, Central/ East Europe, West Europe & North America *Cognex is the world leader in machine vision technology with over 275,000 systems installed worldwide. Applications include automated inspection, error proofing, guidance, gauging, identification and traceability in a wide range of industries including automotive, medical, pharmaceutical, aerospace, packaging, food and beverage, consumer products, semiconductor and electronics.*

Cognis Performance Chemicals Ltd, Hardley, Hythe, Southampton, SO45 3ZG Tel: (023) 8089 4666 Fax: (023) 8024 3113 E-mail: *Chemicals*

Cognitech Ltd, City Cloisters, 188-194 Old St, London, EC1V 9FR Tel: (020) 7251 9316 Fax: (020) 7251 9317 *Computer systems & software development*

Cognitive Network Solutions Ltd, High Street, Lye, Stourbridge, West Midlands, DY9 8LX Tel: (01384) 340666 Fax: (01384) 350666 *Consultants & computer storage*

Cognitronics Ltd, Claylands Avenue, Worksop, Nottinghamshire, S81 7DJ Tel: (01909) 477272 Fax: (01909) 486260 E-mail: sales@cognitronics.co.uk *Data Capture Solutions, Counterfeit Note Detectors, Banknote Counters, Data Capture Repair Centre.*

Cognos Ltd, Adlington Court Greencourts Business Park, Styal Road, Manchester, M22 5LG Tel: 0161-436 8888 Fax: 0161-436 6918 *Software manufrs*

Jack Cohen & Sons, 107 Fairfield Street, Manchester, M1 2WG Tel: 0161-273 3788 Fax: 0161-273 3788 *Rag merchants*

Cohen Packaging Ltd, Unit 15 Clayton Court, Castle Avenue Industrial Estate, Invergordon, Ross-Shire, IV18 0SB Tel: (01349) 853880 Fax: (01349) 853964 *Rigid box manufrs*

Cohen & Wilks International Ltd, Aquatite House, Mabgate, Leeds, LS9 7DR Tel: 0113-245 0804 Fax: 0113-391 7858 E-mail: reception@cwil.co.uk *Fashion wear designers & import agents*

Coherent Technologies Ltd, Vyne House, 2 Hardwicks Way, London, SW18 4AJ Tel: (020) 8871 3515 Fax: (020) 8877 3683 E-mail: sales@coherent-tech.co.uk *Development of modems, ISDN, & modem chips*

Coherent Technology Ltd, 33 Belgrade Road, London, N16 8DH Tel: (020) 7690 7075 Fax: (020) 7923 0110 *Computer systems consultants*

Coherent UK Holdings Ltd, 28 St Thomas Place, The Cambridge Business Park, Ely, Cambridgeshire, CB7 4EX Tel: (01353) 658800 Fax: (01353) 659110 E-mail: sales.uk@coherent.com Purchasing Contact: A. Marley Sales Contact: F. Colville *Laser systems manufrs*

Cohn & Wolfe Ltd, 30 Orange St, London, WC2H 7LZ Tel: (020) 7331 5300 Fax: (020) 7331 9083 *Public relations company*

Cohort Manufacturing, PO Box 6368, Kettering, Northamptonshire, NN14 4YZ Tel: (01933) 626062 Fax: (01933) 626562 *Industrial spare parts suppliers*

Coil Products Ltd, Evington Valley Road, Leicester, LE5 5LU Tel: 0116-249 0044 Fax: 0116-249 0033 *Manufacturers & suppliers of heat pipes*

Coilcolor Ltd, Docks Way, Newport, Gwent, NP20 2NW Tel: (01633) 254382 Fax: (01633) 243219 E-mail: sales@colorgroup.co.uk *Coil coaters*

Coilcraft (U K), 21 Napier Place, Wardpark North, Cumbernauld, Glasgow, G68 0LL Tel: (01236) 730595 Fax: (01236) 730627 E-mail: sales@coilcraft-europe.com *Manufacturers of surface mounted assembly & components*

Coilmech Transformer Mnfrs, 1 Barratt Industrial Park, Whittle Avenue, Fareham, Hampshire, PO15 5SL Tel: (01489) 885309 Fax: (01489) 885309 *Coil winding designers & manufrs*

▶ Coils & Cables Ltd, Unit 29, Siddons Factory Estate, Howard Street, West Bromwich, West Midlands, B70 0SU Tel: 0121-556 0500 Fax: 0121-556 0600 *Induction furnace repairers*

Coin Acceptors Europe Ltd, 4 The Felbridge Centre, Imberhorne Lane, East Grinstead, West Sussex, RH19 1XP Tel: (01342) 315724 Fax: (01342) 313850 E-mail: sales@coinco.com *Coin acceptor manufrs*

Coin & Leisure, Unit 1, Station Enterprises, Station Road, Abergavenny, Gwent, NP7 5HY Tel: (01873) 853360 *Amusement machines hire*

Coinage (Bristol) Ltd, 91 Mayflower Street, Plymouth, PL1 1SB Tel: (0870) 1600992 Fax: (01364) 73799 E-mail: sales@coinage.co.uk *Vending machine manufrs*

Coincraft Coins, PO Box 112, London, WC1B 3PH Tel: (020) 7636 1188 Fax: (020) 7323 2860 E-mail: info@coincraft.com *Coins & medal suppliers*

▶ Coker Systems, 7 Fosters Business Park, Old School Road, Hook, Hampshire, RG27 9NY Tel: (01256) 768178 Fax: (01256) 766234 E-mail: sales@cokerexpo.co.uk *Exhibition stands, banner stands, pop up displays suppliers*

Colamet Manufacturing Ltd, 870 South St, Whiteinch, Glasgow, G14 0SY Tel: 0141-959 1183 Fax: 0141-958 1173 E-mail: info@booth-muirie.co.uk *Architectural claddings & cladding*

Colanders, Unit 15 Martinfield Business CNT, Martinfield, Welwyn Garden City, Hertfordshire, AL7 1HG Tel: (01707) 320757 Fax: (01707) 335131 E-mail: sales@colanders.demon.co.uk *Sale of cookware*

Colart Fine Art & Graphics Ltd, Whitefriars Avenue, Harrow, Middlesex, HA3 5RH Tel: (020) 8427 4343 Fax: (020) 8863 7177 E-mail: initial.surname@colart.co.uk *Artists' materials manufrs*

Colas Ltd, Wallage Lane, Rowfant, Crawley, West Sussex, RH10 4NF Tel: (01342) 711000 Fax: (01342) 711198 E-mail: info@colas.co.uk *Civil engineering, road construction & maintenance* Also at: Branches throughout the U.K.

▶ Colas Ltd, Tan Lane, Exeter, EX2 8EG Tel: (01392) 207201 Fax: (01392) 201530 E-mail: sales@cola.co.uk *Emulsion paint for road surfaces etc*

Colas (I O M) Ltd, Balthane Industrial Estate, Ballasalla, Isle Of Man, IM9 2AQ Tel: (01624) 823360 Fax: (01624) 825604 *Civil engineers*

Colbear Ltd, 45 Lady Lane Industrial Estate, Hadleigh, Ipswich, IP7 6BQ Tel: (01473) 823722 Fax: (01473) 827466 E-mail: info@colbearuk.com *Heating engineers*

Colbear Advertising Ltd, Unit 8, Durham Lane, Armthorpe, Doncaster, South Yorkshire, DN3 3FE Tel: (01302) 302414 Fax: (01302) 836171 E-mail: emma@colbear.co.uk *Marketing, advertising, design, media*

Henry Colbeck Ltd, Seventh Avenue, Team Valley Trading Estate, Gateshead, Tyne & Wear, NE11 0HG Tel: 0191-482 4242 Fax: 0191-491 0357 E-mail: sales@colbeck.co.uk *Edible oils & frozen food suppliers*

Colborne Ltd, Park Road, Trowbridge, Wiltshire, BA14 8AP Tel: (01225) 764101 Fax: (01225) 762009 E-mail: sales@awards.uk.com *Glass engraving & sports trophy manufrs*

Colbree Precision Ltd, Units 10-12 Beacon Court, Pitstone Green Business Park, Quarry Road, Pitstone, Leighton Buzzard, Bedfordshire, LU7 9GY Tel: (01296) 664200 Fax: (01296) 664201 E-mail: sales@colbree.com *Precision engineering services*

Colchester Accident Repairs, 105 Gosbecks Road, Colchester, CO2 9JT Tel: (01206) 578242 Fax: (01206) 762616 *Motor body repairers*

Colchester Bait & Tackle, 243a Harwich Road, Colchester, CO4 3DQ Tel: (01206) 860649 Fax: (01206) 860649 *Fishing equipment retailers*

Colchester Business Transfer Agents, Suite 3 Hadleigh Business Centre, 351 London Road, Hadleigh, Benfleet, Essex, SS7 2BT Tel: (01206) 767147 Fax: (01702) 554253 E-mail: sales@cbta.co.uk *Business transfer agents*

Colchester Fuel Injection Ltd, Haven Road, Colchester, CO2 8HT Tel: (01206) 862049 Fax: (01206) 861771 E-mail: info@colchesterfuelinjection.co.uk *Diesel inject equipment suppliers for the auto, construct, rail & marine industries*

Colchester Lathe Co. Ltd, P O Box 20, Heckmondwike, West Yorkshire, WF16 0HN Tel: (01924) 412603 Fax: (01924) 412604 E-mail: sales@colchester.co.uk Principal Export Areas: Worldwide *Machine tool manufrs*

Colchester Motor Factors, 3a Hawkins Road, Colchester, CO2 8JY Tel: (01206) 799503 Fax: (01206) 790915 *Motor parts suppliers*

Colchester Rewind & Repairs Ltd, Moss Road, Stanway, Colchester, CO3 0LE Tel: (01206) 768886 Fax: (01206) 768915 E-mail: sales@colchesterrewinds.co.uk *Electrical & mechanical engineers*

Colchester Shooting Centre, 27a North Station Road, Colchester, CO1 1RE Tel: (01206) 763336 *Gunsmiths*

▶ Colco Scientific Enterprises Ltd, 6 Peatmore Close, Pyrford, Woking, Surrey, GU22 8TQ Tel: (01932) 349141 E-mail: sales@colco.co.uk *Medical equipment brokers*

Colcrete Eurodrill, Tower Business Park, Derby Road, Clay Cross, Chesterfield, Derbyshire, S45 9AG Tel: (01246) 868700 Fax: (01246) 868701 E-mail: info@colcrete-eurodrill.co.uk *Drilling equipment manufrs*

Cold Box Ltd, 28 Benson Road, Nuffield Industrial Estate, Poole, Dorset, BH17 0GB Tel: (01202) 667667 Fax: (01202) 667666 E-mail: ian@coldbox.co.uk *Cooler & industrial cooling systems*

Cold Chain Instruments Ltd, 1 Martlets Way, Goring-by-Sea, Worthing, West Sussex, BN12 4HF Tel: (01903) 249000 Fax: (01903) 248740 E-mail: sales@transcan.co.uk *Temperature recorder manufrs*

▶ Cold Formed Products Ltd, 24 St. Mary's Road, London, E13 9AD Tel: (020) 8471 2727 Fax: (020) 8470 1706 E-mail: sales@cfp.biz Principal Export Areas: Worldwide *Manufacturers of aluminum extrusion*

▶ Cold Move Ltd, Glovers Meadow, Maesbury Road Industrial Estate, Oswestry, Shropshire, SY10 8JN Tel: (01691) 677404 Fax: (01691) 677404

Cold Service Ltd, Avonside House, Kingfisher Park, Blashford, Ringwood, Hampshire, BH24 3NX Tel: (01425) 485700 Fax: (01425) 485701 E-mail: enquiries@coldservice.co.uk *Refrigeration & air conditioning suppliers*

Cold Start Ltd, Little Tennis St South, Nottingham, NG2 4EU Tel: 0115-950 5095 Fax: 0115-950 5096 E-mail: sue@coldstart.freeserve.co.uk *Refrigeration & air conditioning installation*

Cold Temp Refrigeration Service, Vicarage Lane, Skirlaugh, Hull, HU11 5HE Tel: (01964) 562773 Fax: (01964) 563350 E-mail: sales@coldtemp.co.uk *Refrigerators manufrs*

Coldhams Of East Anglia Ltd, 23 Kingsway, Norwich, NR2 4UE Tel: (01603) 629531 Fax: (01603) 632686 *Hairdressing product suppliers*

▶ Coldhold Systems Ltd, Albright Road, Widnes, Cheshire, WA8 8FY Tel: 0151-423 0023 Fax: 0151-423 0043 E-mail: info@coldhold.com *UK based manufacturer and installer of insulated panels and doors used to form coldrooms and cold stores*

Coldlink, 18 Wellesley Road, Tharston, Norwich, NR15 2PD Tel: (01508) 532277 Fax: (01508) 532377 *Transport refrigeration & air conditioning service engineers*

Coldon Engineering Co. Ltd, 7 Wates Way, Ongar Road, Brentwood, Essex, CM15 9TB Tel: (01277) 231717 Fax: (01277) 262799 E-mail: sales@coldonengineering.co.uk *Precision engineering services*

Coldstore, Coldstore Road, Felixstowe, Suffolk, IP11 8SF Tel: (01394) 604786 *Cold storage*

Coldstore Hire UK, Unit 6 Morley Street, Daybrook, Nottingham, NG5 6JX Tel: 0115-926 5965 Fax: 0115-926 5963 E-mail: sales@coldstorehire.co.uk *Refrigeration & catering equipment hire*

▶ Coldstream, 21 Wingate Road, Gosport, Hampshire, PO12 4DR Tel: (0870) 8501568 Fax: (023) 9252 9272 *Refrigeration equipment manufrs*

Coldstream (Engineering) Ltd, Olympus House, Mill Green Road, Haywards Heath, West Sussex, RH16 1XQ Tel: (01444) 440091 Fax: (01444) 472329 E-mail: sales@adelphi.uk.com *Suppliers of high quality stainless steel products*

Coldwater (Aberdeen) Ltd, Craigshaw Street, West Tullos Industrial Estate, Aberdeen, AB12 3AE Tel: (01224) 878099 Fax: (01224) 878438 *Fish processors*

Coldwater Seafood UK Ltd, Estate Road 2, South Humberside Industrial Estate, Grimsby, South Humberside, DN31 2TG Tel: (01472) 321100 Fax: (01472) 321220 E-mail: reception@coldwater-seafood.co.uk *Frozen food processors & products manufrs*

▶ Cole, 209 Upper Road, Carrickfergus, County Antrim, BT38 8PN Tel: (028) 9036 5650 Fax: (028) 9036 5660

Cole, 24 Station Parade, Hornchurch, Essex, RM12 5AB Tel: (01708) 444279 Fax: (01708) 705003 *Furniture manufrs*

D. & J. Cole (Joinery), Palmers Yard, London Road, Newbury, Berkshire, RG14 2BA Tel: (01635) 49748 Fax: (01635) 528413 *Joinery manufrs*

Cole Fabrics plc, 3 Ludlow Hill Road, West Bridgford, Nottingham, NG2 6HF Tel: 0115-923 5251 Fax: 0115-923 3274 E-mail: info@colefabrics.com *Ribbon & decorative manufrs*

Cole Jarman Associates, John Cree House, 24b High Street, Addlestone, Surrey, KT15 1TN Tel: (01932) 829007 Fax: (01932) 829003 E-mail: info@colejarman.com *Acoustic consultants*

Cole Joinery, Unit H, 8 Park Avenue Estate, Sundon Park Road, Luton, LU3 3BP Tel: (01582) 584740 Fax: (01582) 494605 E-mail: nigel.cole@btconnect.com *Cole Joinery is a Luton Joinery Manufacturers and Joiners, specialising in Wood Staircases and Wooden Staircase Manufacture and Wood Staircase Joinery, as well as Bespoke Wooden Furniture Making, including Wooden Cabinets. As Wood Staircase Joiners and Wood Cabinet Makers based in Luton, covering Herts (Hertfordshire), Beds (Bedfordshire) and Bucks (Buckinghamshire), but also the WHOLE UK for Major Work, Cole Joinery has been trading since 1970, and would be delighted to receive your genuine enquiry for Wooden Staircases, Wood Banisters (bannisters) and Wood Handrails and Wooden Balustrades or Wooden Furniture Cabinets, including Wooden Audio Visual (AV) Cabinets and Bespoke Wood AV Furniture. As CNC Joiners, Cole Joinery serve: Major Work (5k - 500k) entire UK, also Joinery Luton, Joiners Bedford, Staircase Joiners Milton Keynes, Stevenage, Staircase Joiners London, Birmingham, Northampton, Watford, St. Albans, Flitwick, Ampthill, Buckingham, Leighton Buzzard, Hemel Hempstead.*

Cole & Mason Ltd, Bridge House, Eelmoor Road, Farnborough, Hampshire, GU14 7UE Tel: (01252) 522322 Fax: (01252) 522542 E-mail: customer.service@coleandmason.co.uk *Wood turners & kitchenware manufrs*

Cole Parmer Instrument Company Ltd, 3 River Brent Business Park, Trumpers Way, London, W7 2QA Tel: (020) 8574 7556 Fax: (020) 8574 7543 E-mail: sales@coleparmer.co.uk *Cole-Parmer offers an online ordering catalogue featuring detailed technical specifications, current pricing, and availability on over 100,000 products. We are a leading distributor of process equipment, control instrumentation, fluid handling products, personal safety items, and supplies for the laboratory, industrial, chemical, and water quality markets. We specialise in fluid handling and offer an extensive range of flowmeters, mixers, pH and conductivity meters and controllers, tubing and fittings, MASTERFLEX® peristaltic pumps, metering pumps for chemical dosing, and general liquid transfer pumps. Compare and buy online or call our Application Specialists at 0500-345-300 for technical assistance or to arrange a site visit.*

Company Information

▶ W. & D. Cole Ltd, Ashford Road, Bethersden, Ashford, Kent, TN26 3AT Tel: (01233) 820240 Fax: (01233) 820805 E-mail: emailus@wdcole.com *Steel railings, guardrails balustrades & gates manufrs*
Cole & Wilson Ltd, Nabbs Lane Chemical Works, Slaithwaite, Huddersfield, HD7 5AT Tel: (01484) 842353 Fax: (01484) 843598 E-mail: sales@colewilson.co.uk *Dry cleaning chemicals*
Colebrand Ltd, Goodshawfeld Rd, Rossendale, Lancs, BB4 8QF Tel: (01706) 217226 Fax: (01706) 831712 *Protective coating suppliers, distributors & agents*
Colebrook Bosson & Saunders Products Ltd, 18 Bowden Street, London, SE11 4DS Tel: (020) 7587 5283 Fax: (020) 7587 5275 E-mail: sales@cbsproducts.co.uk *Design & manufacture of office ergonomic computer accessories*
Colecraft Engineering Ltd, The Old Timber Yard, Southam Road, Long Itchington, Southam, Warwickshire, CV47 9QL Tel: (01926) 817070 Fax: (01926) 815124 E-mail: sales@colecraft.co.uk *Boat builders & repairers*
▶ Coleface Marketing, 6 Gaveller Road, Redhouse, Swindon, SN25 2DQ Tel: 07887 574527 Fax: 01793 724267 E-mail: info@coleface-marketing.co.uk *Outsourced Marketing & Marketing Training.*Working with Coleface Marketing will transform the way you approach marketing. Instead of a series of techniques and activities, you will naturally start to follow a planned methodology, with an understanding of your customers and your business objectives at the core. Coleface Marketing will assist you in developing your own competition beating marketing function which really does make a positive difference to your business. We will show you the techniques that will enable you to deliver efficient and effective sales & marketing initiatives.*
Colefax Group plc, 39 Brook Street, Mayfair, London, W1K 4JE Tel: (020) 7493 2231 Fax: (020) 7355 4037 *Interior designers*
▶ Colega Limited, 5300 Lakeside, Cheadle Royal Business Park, Cheadle, Cheshire, SK8 3GP Tel: 0161 408 0505 E-mail: stephen@colega.co.uk *We are a specialist recruitment consultancy for the supply of Welders, Fabricators and allied skills*
▶ Coleherne Laser, Newton Moor Industrial Estate, Lodge Street, Hyde, Cheshire, SK14 4LE Tel: 0161-366 6603 Fax: 0161-367 8239 E-mail: brian@coleherneuk.com *White metal bearing manufacturers & laser & profile cutting services*
Coleman Bennett International P.L.C., 30 St. Mary Axe, London, EC3A 8AD Tel: (020) 7623 2000 Fax: (020) 7623 2001 E-mail: info@cbi-plc.com *IT systems consultants*
▶ Coleman Construction & Utilities Rail Division, 2 Bridgeway, St. Leonards-on-Sea, East Sussex, TN38 8AP Tel: (01424) 715743 Fax: (01424) 714870 E-mail: accounts@colemanconstruction.net
▶ Coleman F M Ltd, PO Box 2088, Rayleigh, Essex, SS6 8WB Tel: (0845) 2261756 Fax: (0845) 2261757 *Facilities management, commercial & office cleaning*
Coleman Fumigation Services, Wester Glentore, Greengairs, Airdrie, Lanarkshire, ML6 7TU Tel: (01236) 830700 Fax: (01236) 830703 *Fumigation, pest control & hygiene services*
Coleman Manufacturing Ltd, Graycar Business Park, Barton Turn, Barton under Needwood, Burton-on-Trent, Staffordshire, DE13 8EN Tel: (01283) 716688 Fax: (01283) 712370 E-mail: simon.denning@colemans.uk.net *Sheet metalwork fabricators*
Coleman Milne, Wigan Road, Westhoughton, Bolton, BL5 2EE Tel: (01942) 815600 Fax: (01942) 815115 E-mail: sales@woodall-nicholson.co.uk *Motor vehicle body builders & manufrs*
▶ Coleman Property Care Ltd, 29 Harley Street, London, W1G 9QR Tel: 0845 095 1280 Fax: 0845 095 1290 E-mail: info@colemanfm.com *Office cleaning*Specialist cleaning*Grounds Maintenance*Property Maintenance*
Coleman Signs, 44 Revell Road, Kingston upon Thames, Surrey, KT1 3SW Tel: (020) 8949 2693 E-mail: afcol@waitrose.com *Sign contractors, suppliers & installers*
▶ Coleman Taylor Graphic Design, Haven House, 10 Haven Close, Grasscroft, Saddleworth, Oldham, OL4 4DU Tel: (01457) 872666 E-mail: info@colemantaylor.co.uk *Graphic design services*
Coleman Tunnelling & Technology Services Ltd, Old Wolverton Road, Old Wolverton, Milton Keynes, MK12 5NL Tel: (01908) 312744 Fax: (01908) 220676 E-mail: ctil@btconnectaol.com *Pipe jacking, boring & tunnelling*
Colemans, 34-36 St Giles Street, Northampton, NN1 1JW Tel: (01604) 636708 Fax: (01604) 622533 *Office stationary & artist materials suppliers*
Colemans Blinds, 9a Bath Road, Bridgwater, Somerset, TA6 4PH Tel: (01278) 453008 Fax: (01278) 453008 *Blinds manufrs*
Colemans Kitchens & Bedrooms Ltd, 178 Victoria Road, Kirkby-in-Ashfield, Nottingham, NG17 8AT Tel: (01623) 751239 Fax: (01623) 754649 *Kitchen & bedroom manufrs*
Colemans Office Supplies, 8a Berrington Road, Leamington Spa, Warwickshire, CV31 1NB Tel: (01926) 451751 Fax: (01926) 450973 E-mail: info@colemansofficesupplies.co.uk *Office equipment distributors*
Colemans Removals & Storage, Unit 16, Garston Industrial Estate, Blackburne Street, Liverpool, L19 8JA Tel: 0151-494 3251 Fax: 0151-494 0034 *Removal & storage specialists*
Colenso Screen Services Ltd, Unit 2-3, Fairoak Court, Runcorn, Cheshire, WA7 3DX Tel: (01928) 701356 Fax: (01928) 713047 E-mail: sales@colenso.co.uk *Suppliers to screen printing industry*
Coleridge Business Supplies, Dollis Hill Estate, Brook Road, London, NW2 7BZ Tel: (020) 8208 7711 Fax: (020) 8208 7722 *Lithographic printers & lithographers*
Coles, Steam Mill Lane, Great Yarmouth, Norfolk, NR31 0HP Tel: (01493) 602100 Fax: (01493) 602100 *General engineers, welding & steel fabricators*
Coles Electroacoustics Ltd, Pindar Road, Hoddesdon, Hertfordshire, EN11 0BZ Tel: (01992) 466685 Fax: (01992) 446583 E-mail: sales@coleselectroacoustics.com *Loudspeaker & microphone manufrs*
Coles Traditional Foods Ltd, London Road, Great Chesterford, Saffron Walden, Essex, CB10 1PG Tel: (01799) 531053 Fax: (01799) 531140 E-mail: sales@colestrad.co.uk *Christmas puddings & fruit cakes manufrs*
Coleshill Alloy Sales Ltd, Gorsey Lane, Coleshill, Birmingham, B46 1JU Tel: (01675) 463170 Fax: (01675) 463748 E-mail: office@coleshill-aluminium.com *Aluminium ingot manufrs*
Coleshill Freight Services Ltd, Coleshill Freight Terminal, Station Road, Coleshill, Birmingham, B46 1JJ Tel: (01675) 463869 Fax: (01675) 465727 E-mail: john@coleshillfreight.com *Freight forwarders & packers*
Coleshill Laboratories Ltd, Gorsey Lane, Coleshill, Birmingham, B46 1JU Tel: (01675) 462313 Fax: (01675) 463748 *Metallurgical analysts*
Coleshill Metals, 234 Station Road, Nether Whitacre, Coleshill, Birmingham, B46 2BY Tel: (01675) 464533 *Scrap metal merchants*
Coleshill Tool Service Centre, 74 Birmingham Road, Water Orton, Birmingham, B46 1TH Tel: 0121-747 2357 Fax: 0121-747 2357 *Tool hire services*
Colets Piling Ltd, Old Village Hall, The Street, Effingham, Leatherhead, Surrey, KT24 5JS Tel: (01372) 452506 Fax: (01372) 452427 E-mail: mail@coletspiling.com *Piling & groundwork contractors*
Coletta Doors, Bulls Lane, North Mymms, Hatfield, Hertfordshire, AL9 7BB Tel: (01707) 665018 Fax: (01707) 665344 E-mail: office@colettadoors.com *Industrial door manufrs*
Colette Hill Associates, 18-20 Bromells Road, London, SW4 0BG Tel: (020) 7622 8252 Fax: (020) 7622 8253 E-mail: cha@chapr.co.uk *Public relations*
E.R. Coley (Steel) Ltd, James Scott Road, Off Park Lane, Halesowen, West Midlands, B63 2QT Tel: (01384) 567121 Fax: (01384) 411259 *Steel & cast iron merchants*
Coley Ian Gunsmith, 444 High Street, Cheltenham, Gloucestershire, GL50 3JA Tel: (01242) 522443 Fax: (01242) 226703 *Guns & country clothing distributors*
Coley Instruments Ltd, Burnside Industrial Estate, Kilsyth, Glasgow, G65 9JX Tel: (01236) 821533 Fax: (01236) 824090 E-mail: sales@stewarts-group.com *Instrument engineering services*
Coley Porter Bell Ltd, 18 Grosvenor Gardens, London, SW1W 0DH Tel: (020) 7824 7700 Fax: (020) 7824 7701 E-mail: brand-design@cpb.co.uk *Design consultants*
Colgijan Merault Ltd, PO Box 56, Evesham, Worcestershire, WR11 3FR Tel: (01386) 760009 Fax: (01386) 442779 *Air conditioning engineers*
Colin Almack Furniture, Beaver Lodge, Sutton, Thirsk, North Yorkshire, YO7 2PR Tel: (01845) 597420 Fax: (01845) 597420 E-mail: enquiries@beaverfurniture.co.uk *Cabinet manufrs*
▶ colin bowen, 80Quarrysprings, Harlow, Essex, CM20 3HS Tel: 07916 245161 Fax: 01279 869605 E-mail: stanstedtaxis@yahoo.co.uk *Taxi Service toand From Stansted Airport, bookings taken, Fully Insured. tel 07916 245161*Accommodation room only, £40 per person per night in one of our apartments tel 07916 226171*
Colin E J Bennett, Bridgend Works, Bridgend, Stonehouse, Gloucestershire, GL10 2BA Tel: (01453) 825090 Fax: (01453) 825868 *Road transport/warehousing services*
▶ Colin Laver, Riverside Buildings, Nile Road, Pontypridd, Mid Glamorgan, CF37 1BW Tel: (01443) 404516 Fax: (01443) 486048
Colin Mackenzie Engineering Ltd, 3 Murray Street, Paisley, Renfrewshire, PA3 1QG Tel: 0141-889 3031 Fax: 0141-889 3031 *Sub-contract precision engineers*
Colin Rayner Green, The Street, Beachamwell, Swaffham, Norfolk, PE37 8BD Tel: (01366) 328275 Fax: (01366) 328853 E-mail: colin@rayner-green.sfnet.co.uk *Agricultural merchants*
▶ Colin Tyzack / National Legal Services, 14 Cleveland Road, Aylesbury, Buckinghamshire, HP20 2 AZ Tel: (01296) 581300 E-mail: colin@colin-tyzack.co.uk *National Legal Services are an established legal company who pride themselves on providing a highly personal service through a network of local consultants. Together we specialise in Estate Planning services - helping people like yourself ensure that your assets are protected, and that your mind is at rest knowing that when the time comes, your wishes will be carried out. We recognise that our clients each have important issues to discuss when they consider putting their affairs in order, and we know that time and understanding are required in equal measure.*
Colin's Caravans of Berkshire Ltd, Bath Road, Aldermaston, Reading, RG7 5JD Tel: 0118-971 2424 Fax: 0118-971 3010 E-mail: sales@colinscaravans.com *Touring caravan distributors*
Colinton Manufacturing Ltd, 2 Lochend Road South, Musselburgh, Midlothian, EH21 6BD Tel: 0131-665 0371 Fax: 0131-665 9993 E-mail: sales@colintonfurniture.co.uk *Timber furniture*
▶ Colintonwigglys, 51 Redford Road, Colinton, Edinburgh, EH13 0AD Tel: 0131-441 2454 Fax: 0131-441 2454 E-mail: james@colintonwigglys.com *Logo designers corporate, schools, colleges, clubs or personal*
▶ Collage Trading Services, 81 Lower Manor Lane, Burnley, Lancashire, BB12 0EF Tel: (01282) 439993 Fax: (01282) 439993 *Soft furnishing manufrs*
▶ Collard Construction Ltd, 5 Belgrave Lane, Plymouth, PL4 7DA Tel: (01752) 309808 Fax: (01752) 309808
Collard Industrial Gloves Ltd, Portskewett Street, Newport, Gwent, NP19 0GJ Tel: (01633) 213471 Fax: (01633) 257696 *Industrial glove & workwear clothing manufrs*
▶ Colleague Ltd, Catherine House, Coventry Road, Hinckley, Leics, LE10 0JT Tel: (01455) 633233 Fax: (01455) 639404
Collease Ltd, Choats Road, Chequers Lane, Dagenham, Essex, RM9 6RJ Tel: (020) 8517 1171 Fax: (020) 8593 0300 *Trailer hirers* Also at: Felixstow & Wymondham
▶ Collectomania, 12 Hoghton Street, Southport, Merseyside, PR9 0TF Tel: (01704) 513913 Fax: (01704) 513913 E-mail: mike@kitis316.freeserve.co.uk *Collectables retailers*
▶ Collector Set Printers Ltd, Aylesford Mill, St Michaels Close, Aylesford, Kent, ME20 7BU Tel: (01622) 716636 Fax: (01622) 717515 E-mail: sales@collectorsetprinters.co.uk
Collectors Cellar, 11 Hencotes, Hexham, Northumberland, NE46 2EQ Tel: (01434) 601392 Fax: (01434) 601392 E-mail: sales@collectorscellar.co.uk *Train model retail & distributor*
Colledge & Morley (Gears) Ltd, Curriers Close, Charter Avenue, Canley, Coventry, CV4 8AW Tel: (024) 7646 2328 Fax: (024) 7669 4008 *Gear cutters & grinders manufrs*
College Computers, 169 Hollow Way, Cowley, Oxford, OX4 2NE Tel: (01865) 774410 Fax: (01865) 774410 E-mail: sales@college-computers.com *Computer repair maintenance & services*
College Engineering Supply, 2 Sandy Lane, Codsall, Wolverhampton, WV8 1EJ Tel: (01902) 842284 Fax: (01902) 842284 E-mail: enquiries@collegeengineering.co.uk *Education industry & model engineers*
College Gauge & Tool Co. Ltd, Unit 16 The Business Centre, 20 James Road, Tyseley, Birmingham, B11 2BA Tel: 0121-764 6433 Fax: 0121-764 6499 *Plate thickness gauge manufrs*
College Hill Associates Ltd, 78 Cannon Street, London, EC4N 6HH Tel: (020) 7457 2020 Fax: (020) 7248 3295 E-mail: pr@collegehill.co.uk *Financial public relations consultants*
College Hill Press Ltd, 37 Webber Street, London, SE1 8QW Tel: (020) 7633 0543 Fax: (020) 7633 0181 E-mail: sales@collegehillpress.co.uk *Litho printers*
▶ College Of Technology London, Bow House, 153-159 Bow Road, London, E3 2SE Tel: (020) 8980 7888 Fax: (020) 8983 4911 *Private college*
Barry Collen Ltd, 31 Northampton Road, Scunthorpe, North Lincolnshire, DN16 1UJ Tel: (01724) 867817 Fax: (01724) 877111 E-mail: info@barrycollen.co.uk *Roofing & cladding contractors*
Collen Brothers Quarries Ltd, Hanover Street, Portadown, Craigavon, County Armagh, BT62 3ET Tel: (028) 3833 4131 Fax: (028) 3884 0313 *Quarry & asphalt surfacing agents*
Colletex Ltd, Whitebirk Road, Blackburn, BB1 3JA Tel: (01254) 261768 Fax: (01254) 665425 E-mail: sales@colletex.co.uk *Fusible interlining manufrs*
▶ Colley Construction Ltd, Watling Street, Cannock, Staffordshire, WS11 8LX Tel: (01922) 415407 Fax: (01922) 413938
George Colliar Ltd, Middle Balado, Balado, Kinross, KY13 0NH Tel: (01577) 863173 Fax: (01577) 864768 E-mail: colliar@harleys.co.uk *Agricultural engineers*
Collier Castings, Raybar, Hooe, Battle, East Sussex, TN33 9EU Tel: (01424) 892248 Fax: (01424) 892248 *Brass casting manufrs*
Collier & Catchpole Ltd, 11 London Road, Stanway, Colchester, CO3 0NT Tel: (01206) 715500 Fax: (01206) 715517 E-mail: mail@colliercatchpole.co.uk *Building & civil engineers*
▶ David Collier Fitted Furniture, Unit 5 Stirling Industrial Estate, Off Chorley New Road, Horwich, Bolton, BL6 6DU Tel: (01204) 668899 Fax: (01204) 668899 E-mail: info@davidcollier.co.uk *Bedroom furniture manufrs*
F.G. Collier Kitchens & Bathrooms Ltd, 29-35 Edward Street, Westbury, Wiltshire, BA13 3BL Tel: (01373) 822227 Fax: (01373) 824704 E-mail: sales@fgcollier.com *Fitted kitchen, bathrooms & bedrooms designer*
Collier & Henry Concrete Floors Ltd, Unit 2 Mellors Road, Trafford Park, Manchester, M17 1PB Tel: 0161-872 8410 Fax: 0161-872 9875 *Pre-cast concrete floors & staircase manufrs*
Collier Industrial Waste Ltd, Nash Road, Trafford Park, Manchester, M17 1SX Tel: 0161-848 7722 Fax: 0161-872 9906 *Waste disposal agents*
Collier Insurance, 146 Bellegrove Road, Welling, Kent, DA16 3QR Tel: (020) 8303 4761 Fax: (020) 8301 6021 E-mail: info@collierinsurance.co.uk *Insurance brokers*
▶ Collier Plant Hire York Ltd, Station Yard, Temple Lane, Copmanthorpe, York, YO23 3RS Tel: (01904) 707851 Fax: (01904) 700447
R.H. Collier & Co. Ltd, 1-41 Sutton Road, Erdington, Birmingham, B23 6QH Tel: 0121-377 8888 Fax: 0121-377 6907 E-mail: fleetsales@rhcollier.co.uk *Car sales*
Colliers Cre, Broad Quay House, Broad Quay, Bristol, BS1 4DJ Tel: 0117-917 2000 Fax: 0117-917 2099 E-mail: sales@colliers.com *Commercial property services*
Colliers Cre, 39 George Street, Edinburgh, EH2 2HN Tel: 0131-240 7500 Fax: 0131-240 7599 E-mail: anglia.black@collierscre.co.uk *Charted surveyors*
Colliers Cre, 15-16 Park Row, Leeds, LS1 5HD Tel: 0113-200 1800 Fax: 0113-200 1840 E-mail: leeds@collierscre.co.uk Principal Export Areas: Worldwide *Chartered surveyors*
Colliers Cre, 9 Marylebone Lane, London, W1U 1HL Tel: (020) 7935 4499 Fax: (020) 7487 1894 E-mail: property@collierscre.co.uk *International property consultant*
Colliers Garage, 133b Upper Street, London, N1 1QP Tel: (0870) 7772757 Fax: (020) 7354 5106 *Citreon service & repair agents*
Colliers Truck Builders Ltd, Blackwater Trading Estate, The Causeway, Maldon, Essex, CM9 4GG Tel: (01621) 843109 Fax: (01621) 843047 E-mail: mainoffice@collierstruckbuilders.co.uk *Commercial vehicle builders*
▶ Collin Burrows Air Conditioning Ltd, 9 Josselin Court, Josselin Road, Burnt Mills Industrial Estate, Basildon, Essex, SS13 1QF Tel: (01268) 590369 Fax: (01268) 590370 *Installation, maintenance & repairing of air conditioning*
Collin Gladwell, Pencrennow, Tregye Road, Carnon Downs, Truro, Cornwall, TR3 6JH Tel: (01872) 864777 Fax: (01872) 870094 E-mail: cgmt@netcomuk.co.uk *Machine tool distribs*
Collinda Investments Ltd, 25 Ottways Lane, Ashtead, Surrey, KT21 2PL Tel: (01372) 278416 Fax: (01372) 278559 E-mail: info@collinda.co.uk *Industrial chemicals distributor*
Collings Bros Of Abbotsley Ltd, 3-5 Prospect Way, Chatteris, Cambridgeshire, PE16 6TZ Tel: (01354) 694169 Fax: (01354) 694218 E-mail: sales@collingbrothers.co.uk *Agricultural engineering services*
Collings Bros Of Abbotsley Ltd, Potton Road, Abbotsley, St. Neots, Cambridgeshire, PE19 6TZ Tel: (01767) 677316 Fax: (01767) 677451 E-mail: sales@collingsbrothers.co.uk *Agricultural engineers & dealers*
Collingwood, Sywell Aerodrome, Sywell, Northampton, NN6 0AW Tel: (01604) 495151 Fax: (01604) 495095 E-mail: sales@collingwoodgroup.com *Lighting component suppliers & distributors*
▶ Collingwood Consultancy, 20 Estcourt Road, Great Yarmouth, Norfolk, NR30 4JG Tel: (01493) 842022 Fax: (01493) 331955 *Industrial electronics designers*
Collingwood Engineering Lincs Ltd, Dam Road, Barton-upon-Humber, South Humberside, DN18 5AS Tel: (01652) 632388 Fax: (01652) 632388 *Precision engineers*
Collingwood Houses Services Ltd, Collingwood House, 367 Croydon Road, Wallington, Surrey, SM6 7NY Tel: (020) 8773 2411 Fax: (020) 8669 3013 E-mail: collingwoodhouse@btinternet.com *Office services*
Collins, Unit 5-6 Aultone Yard Industrial Estate, Aultone Way, Carshalton, Surrey, SM5 2LH Tel: (020) 8647 3123 Fax: (020) 8647 3123 *Chemical black oxidising services*
Collins & Chambers Ltd, 197-199 Mare Street, London, E8 3QF Tel: (020) 8985 9970 Fax: (020) 8985 3123 E-mail: nautilus@talk21.com *Diving & industrial safety equipment*
▶ Collins (Construction) Ltd, 2A Carlton Grove, London, SE15 2UE Tel: (020) 7732 0241
Collins Contractors Ltd, 31 Gillian Street, London, SE13 7AJ Tel: (020) 8690 0077 Fax: (020) 8690 4077 E-mail: info@collins-contractors.co.uk *Architectural decoration services*
Collins Debden, Westerhill Road, Bishopbriggs, Glasgow, G64 2QT Tel: 0141-300 8500 Fax: 0141-300 8600 E-mail: sales@collinsdebden.com *Diary & stationery publishers*
Collins Extrusions Ltd, Bidavon Industrial Estate, Waterloo Road, Bidford-on-Avon, Alcester, Warwickshire, B50 4JW Tel: (01789) 773536 Fax: (01789) 490225 E-mail: coltec1@yahoo.com *Plastic extrusions & fabricators*
Collins & Hayes Ltd, Menzies Road, Ponswood, St. Leonards-On-Sea, East Sussex, TN38 9XF Tel: (01424) 720027 Fax: (01424) 720270 E-mail: sales@collinsandhayes.com *Upholstered furniture manufrs*
Collins Re Inforcements Ltd, 5 Dobson Park Industrial Estate, 234 Manchester Road, Ince, Wigan, Lancashire, WN2 2ED Tel: (01942) 322210 Fax: (01942) 820380 E-mail: info@collins-reinforcements.co.uk *Steel reinforcement suppliers*
T. Collins, 20 Sugar House Lane, Stratford, London, E15 2QS Tel: (020) 8519 8476 Fax: (020) 8555 4076 *Scrap metal merchants*
Collins Walker Ltd, Unit 7a Nottingham South & Wilford Industrial Estate, Ruddington Lane, Nottingham, NG11 7EP Tel: 0115-981 8044 Fax: 0115-945 5376 E-mail: sales@collins-walker.co.uk Principal Export Areas: Worldwide *Manufacturer of electric steam & hot water boilers*
Collinson Ernest & Co. Ltd, Riverside Industrial Park, Tan Yard Road, Catterall, Preston, PR3 0HP Tel: (01995) 606451 Fax: (01995) 605503 E-mail: agri.sales@collinson.co.uk *Suppliers of silos in GRP, steel & fabric. Materials handling systems for bulk materials & ingredients. Prefabricated steel frame buildings with PVC cover, widespan up to 100m. Relocatable, temporary or permanent for warehouses, storage, hangars, sports halls etc.*
Collinson & Grainger Ltd, 77 Dixons Green, Dudley, West Midlands, DY2 7DJ Tel: (01384) 230318 Fax: (01384) 457418 *Electrical contractors*
Collinson Grant, Ryecroft, Aviary Road, Worsley, Manchester, M28 2WF Tel: 0161-703 5600 Fax: 0161-790 9177 E-mail: postmaster@collinsongrant.com *Management consultants*
▶ Collinsons Ceramics, 31 Rosebury Styreet, Edinburgh, EH12 5PE Tel: 0131-313 3577 E-mail: info@colllinson-ceramics.co.uk *Ceramic tiles suppliers*
Collinswood Joinery, 2 Rutherglen Road, Corby, Northamptonshire, NN17 1ER Tel: (01536) 201885 Fax: (01536) 409474 *Joinery manufrs*
▶ D. Collis, 51 Harehill Road, Grangewood, Chesterfield, Derbyshire, S40 2NG Tel: (01246) 540180 Fax: (01246) 540180 E-mail: david@dcollis.wanadoo.co.uk *Ground work paving services*

Collis Engineering Ltd, Salcombe Road, Alfreton, Derbyshire, DE55 7RG Tel: (01773) 833255 Fax: (01773) 836525 E-mail: sales@collis.co.uk *Railway equipment manufrs*

Sinclair Collis Ltd, Unit 4 & 5, Laches Close, Four Ashes, Wolverhampton, WV10 7DZ Tel: (01902) 797272 Fax: (01902) 797270 *Cigarette vending machines*

Collister & Glover (Pipeline Materials) Ltd, Tenth Avenue, Deeside Industrial Park, Deeside, Clwyd, CH5 2UA Tel: (01244) 288000 Fax: (01244) 289000E-mail: sales@colglo.co.uk *Supplier of tubes, valves, fittings, pumps, mechanical seals and ancillary products. Shop online now or telephone our sales team who are happy to offer free advice. We are trusted stockist of Effast, Lowara, DAB, Grundfos, Tracpipe, ABS, Ebara, Polypipe, Philmac and many more.**Our Pump Repair Facility is dedicated to Pump, Gearbox & Motor repairs and certified ISO 9001. As well as a fully equiped engineering workshop with machining, manufacturing and fabrication equipment, we also have specialised seal manufacture and repair equipment. All repairs are fully tested and certified on our Hydrostatic and Vacuum test rig and re-sprayed before they are released for despatch.**Our stock of New & Refurbished Seals and Seal Components is valued at over £0,000 and with fully automated Lapping & Polishing machines; we can repair and refurbish all makes of Cartridge & Single spring seals, providing you with a same day service if required.*

Colloid Treatment Technologies, Rovert House, Water Tower Road, Clayhill Light Industrial Park, Neston, CH64 3US Tel: 0151-336 7775 Fax: 0151-336 7733 E-mail: colltreat@aol.com *Effluent treatment services*

Collords Ltd, Kirkby Bank Road, Knowsley Industrial Park, Liverpool, L33 7SY Tel: 0151-546 9222 Fax: 0151-549 0489 E-mail: sales@colloids.co.uk Principal Export Areas: Worldwide *Masterbatch, colour compounders & manufrs*

Colmac Plastic Fabricators, Unit C1 South Way, Bounds Green Industrial Estate, London, N11 2UL Tel: (020) 8361 4807 Fax: (020) 8361 4670 *Plastics fabricators*

Joseph Colman & Son Ltd, The Coachyard, Dowry Square, Bristol, BS8 4SJ Tel: 0117-926 5141 Fax: 0117-925 3881 E-mail: colmansoffice@cs.com *Building contractors*

Colman Moducel, Oldfields Business Park, Birrell Street, Stoke-on-Trent, ST4 3ES Tel: (01782) 599995 Fax: (01782) 599220 E-mail: sales@eaton-williams.com *Air conditioning & heating equipment manufrs*

Colmart Marketing Ltd, Vulcan Rd, Lode Lane Industrial Estate, Solihull, W. Midlands, B91 2JY Tel: 0121-705 4645 Fax: 0121-711 2051 E-mail: sales@lslmarketing.co.uk *Air fresheners commercial*

Colmet Plus, The Morgans, Lower Road, Little Hallingbury, Bishop's Stortford, Hertfordshire, CM22 7RA Tel: (01279) 722400 Fax: (01279) 726901 E-mail: mr@colmetplus.co.uk *Badge design & medals manufrs*

Colmet Precision Ltd, Unit 15 Upper Wingbury Courtyard Business Centre, Leighton Road, Wingrave, Aylesbury, Buckinghamshire, HP22 4LW Tel: (01296) 681658 Fax: (01296) 681726 E-mail: sales@colmet.co.uk *Sheet metalwork engineering*

Colmi Ltd, The Brackens, London Road, Ascot, Berkshire, SL5 8BE Tel: (01344) 885050 Fax: (01344) 884141 *Computer consultants*

Colmil Plant & Equipment Co. Ltd, Abbotsford Road, Gateshead, Tyne & Wear, NE10 0LF Tel: 0191-469 4926 Fax: 0191-469 6084 E-mail: sales@colmil.fsnet.co.uk *Scaffolding hire & contractors* Also at: Birmingham & Wakefield

▶ Colmil Plant & Equipment Co. Ltd, High Street, Crigglestone, Wakefield, West Yorkshire, WF4 3HT Tel: (01924) 259411 Fax: (01924) 253427

Colne Anodising Co. Ltd, Calder Mill, Green Road, Colne, Lancashire, BB8 8AL Tel: (01282) 867300 Fax: (01282) 867407 E-mail: sales@colneanodising.co.uk *Hard & soft anodises*

Colne Pine Centre, Colne Lane, Colne, Lancashire, BB8 0EF Tel: (01282) 861978 *Sale room*

Colne Press Ltd, Unit 11-12, Eastman Way, Hemel Hempstead Industrial Estate, Hemel Hempstead, Hertfordshire, HP2 7DU Tel: (01442) 212922 Fax: (01442) 265967 E-mail: info@colne.co.uk *Lithographic printers*

Colne Saddlery, The Barn, Tewkesbury Road, Norton, Gloucester, GL2 9LH Tel: (01452) 731456 Fax: (01452) 731456 E-mail: sales@colnesaddlery.co.uk *Saddlery, riding wear & accessories*

Colne Valley Engineering, Unit 12 Olds Close, Watford, WD18 9RU Tel: (01923) 776212 Fax: (01923) 896587 E-mail: alanhughes@tesco.net *Steel & stainless steel fabricators*

Cologne & Cotton Ltd, 39 Kensington Church Street, London, W8 4LL Tel: (020) 7376 0324 Fax: (020) 7376 0373 *Bed linen retailer*

Colomer Professional International, 22-24 Claremont Road, Claremont House, Surbiton, Surrey, KT6 4QU Tel: (020) 8339 9080 Fax: (020) 8390 9853 *Professional hair care wholesalers*

Colomor Electronics Ltd, Unit 5 Huffwood Trading Estatw, Brookers Road, Billingshurst, West Sussex, RH14 9RZ Tel: (01403) 786559 Fax: (01403) 786560 *RF components & electronic tubes manufrs*

▶ Colonial Granite Ltd, Unit 4 The Sidings, Rhosddu Industrial Estate, Rhosddu, Wrexham, Clwyd, LL11 4YL Tel: (01978) 312000 Fax: (01978) 312002 E-mail: brymbolad@hotmail.com *Specialising in building, renovation or made to measure counter tops*

Colonnade UK, Unit 41 Hallmark Trading Estate, Fourth Way, Wembley, Middlesex, HA9 0LB Tel: (020) 8902 7722 Fax: (020) 8795 4187 E-mail: info@colonnadeuk.com *Metal finishers*

Colophon Corporate Ltd, 59 Churchfield Road, Acton, London, W3 6AU Tel: (020) 8992 2555 Fax: (020) 8993 4598 *Computer consultancy*

Colophon Press Printers Ltd, 17 Peterfield Road, Carlisle, CA3 0EY Tel: (01228) 524444 Fax: (01228) 590090 E-mail: colophon@btconnect.com *Printers*

Coloplast Ltd, Peterborough Business Park, Lynch Wood, Peterborough, PE2 6FX Tel: (01733) 392000 Fax: (01733) 233348 E-mail: gbcareteam@coloplast.com *Continence products manufrs*

Color Co. Ltd, C7 The Chambers, Chelsea Harbour, London, SW10 0XF Tel: (020) 7351 4310 Fax: (020) 7795 1419 *Reprographic services*

Color Communications Inc, Rowan House, 28 Queens Road, Hethersett, Norwich, NR9 3DB Tel: (01603) 813930 Fax: (01603) 813933 *Printing specialists*

Color Steels Ltd, Blackvein Industrial Estate, Cross Keys, Newport, Gwent, NP11 7YD Tel: (01495) 279100 Fax: (01495) 271456 *Steel stockholders*

Color-Board, Cartersfield Road, Waltham Abbey, Essex, EN9 1JD Tel: (01992) 714382 Fax: (01992) 714938 E-mail: liz@color-board.co.uk *Flat panel curtain coaters sprayers*

Colorcon Ltd, Flagship House Victory Way, Crossways, Dartford, DA2 6QD Tel: (01322) 293000 Fax: (01322) 627200 E-mail: info@colorcon.co.uk *Manufacturers of pharmaceutical colour*

Colordrives Ltd, 65 Knowle Wood Road, Dorridge, Solihull, West Midlands, B93 8JP Tel: (01564) 772755 Fax: (01564) 772755 E-mail: info@colordrives.co.uk *Tar macadam & block paving contractors*

▶ Colorfoto Lifestyle Portrait Studio, Image House, East Tyndall St, Cardiff Bay, Cardiff, CF24 5EF Tel: 029 20448222 E-mail: info@colorfotolifestyle.co.uk *A new digital photography studio,located in Cardiff, UK. For framed family photo portraits and high class photographic prints. Cheap prices on photos, excellent for interior design. Previewings available, professional photographers for professional prints and images.*

Colorgroup Ltd, Whitehead Estate, Docks Way, Newport, Gwent, NP20 2NW Tel: (01633) 223854 Fax: (01633) 253992 E-mail: dave.burston@colorgroup.co.uk *Steel stockholders*

▶ Colorite Paint Co. Ltd, 169 Boston Road, Hanwell, London, W7 3QJ Tel: (020) 8579 3381 Fax: (020) 8567 5158 E-mail: info@colorite.co.uk *Paint & aerosols manufacturer emulsion car paint leather*

Colorlites, Unit 23 Lordswood Industrial Estate, Revenge Road, Chatham, Kent, ME5 8UD Tel: (01634) 862839 Fax: (01634) 865285 E-mail: salesdesk@colorlites.com *Glass coating specialists, supply, colour & print*

▶ Colormatrix Europe Ltd, 9-11 Unity Grove, Knowsley Business Park, Prescot, Merseyside, L34 9GT Tel: 0151-632 8800 Fax: 0151-548 3800 E-mail: info@colormatrix.co.uk

Colormax Ltd, Unit 3, Stafford Park 12, Telford, Shropshire, TF3 3BJ Tel: (01952) 292101 Fax: (01952) 292761 E-mail: info@colormax.co.uk *Plastics colouring systems & materials handling*

Colorminium, 356-358 Prince Avenue, Westcliff-On-Sea, Essex, SS0 0NF Tel: (01702) 390091 Fax: (01702) 432840 *Double glazing installers*

▶ Coloroll Bedding & Blankets, 651 Rolston Road, Hornsea, North Humberside, HU18 1UT Tel: (01964) 534234 *Beds retailers*

Colorphaze, 73 Bunting Road, Northampton, NN2 6EE Tel: (01604) 792001 E-mail: sales@colorphaze.co.uk *Business stationery suppliers*

Colorprofile Printers, 4 Whitworth Road, Stevenage, Hertfordshire, SG1 4QS Tel: (01438) 724891 Fax: (01438) 720512 *Litho printers*

Colorscope Printers Ltd, Charlwoods Road, East Grinstead, West Sussex, RH19 2HF Tel: (01342) 311821 Fax: (01342) 315358 E-mail: sales@colorscope.co.uk *Graphic design, printing & artwork typesetting*

▶ Colortrac Ltd, Kings Hall, St Ives Business Park, Parsons Green, St. Ives, Cambridgeshire, PE27 4WY Tel: (01480) 464618

Colorway Blinds Ltd, Victoria Mills, 12-16 Elder Road, Leeds, LS13 4DL Tel: 0113-255 7637 Fax: 0113-255 8342 E-mail: sales@colorway-blinds.co.uk *Window blind manufrs*

Colour Anodising Ltd, Holland Street, Radcliffe, Manchester, M26 2RH Tel: 0161-723 2637 Fax: 0161-725 9252 E-mail: info@anodising.com *Anodising services*

Colour Assembly Ltd, 28 Thurrock Commercial Centre, Purfleet Industrial Park, Aveley, South Ockendon, Essex, RM15 4YA Tel: (01708) 891777 Fax: (01708) 891333 E-mail: info@colourassembly.co.uk *Lithographic plate manufrs*

Colour Blinds, ClaytonHeights, Bradford, West Yorkshire, BD13 1DT Tel: (01274) 415082 E-mail: blinds@colourblinds.co.uk *W*

Colour Coatings South East, Unit 19 Warsop Trading Estate, Hever Road, Edenbridge, Kent, TN8 5LD Tel: (01732) 866700 Fax: (01732) 865983 E-mail: info@colour-coatings.co.uk *Powder coating & metal finishing specialists*

▶ Colour Direct, G Arklow Trading Estate, Arklow Road, London, SE14 6EB Tel: (020) 8305 8205 Fax: (020) 8305 8206

Colour Film Services Ltd, 10 Wadsworth Road, Perivale, Greenford, Middlesex, UB6 7JX Tel: (020) 8998 2731 Fax: (020) 8997 8738 E-mail: johnward@colourfilmservices.co.uk *Film, video & tape facilities distributor*

▶ Colour Management by ColourPhil, White Hill Court, Berkhamsted, Hertfordshire, HP4 2PS Tel: (01442) 874937 *Colour Management consultancy to the Prepress, Printing and Photographic Industries. Fuji and Crosfield scanner expertise.*

Colour Powder Coatings Ltd, Westwood House, 10 Westwood Avenue, Colevalley Business Park, Birmingham, B11 3RF Tel: 0121-772 3878 Fax: 0121-772 2697 E-mail: stevemay@colourpodercoatings.co.uk *Powder coating services*

Colour Separations Ltd, 31-33 Woodford Road, Watford, WD17 1PB Tel: (01923) 245555 Fax: (01923) 241637 *Film separation*

Colourcode Cable Colouring Services, 243C Watford Road, Croxley Green, Rickmansworth, Hertfordshire, WD3 3RX Tel: (01923) 250767 Fax: (01923) 234772 *Wrought iron fabricators*

▶ Colourcraft Media, Unit 1 Primrose Works, Stour Road, London, E3 2NT Tel: (020) 8533 3385 Fax: (020) 8985 3894 *Printing design*

Colourfast, 2 The Arcade, Cwmbran, Gwent, NP44 1PQ Tel: (01633) 865586 Fax: (01633) 869434 E-mail: arcadecolour1@btconnect.com *Colour copying & printing services*

Colourgraphics Cambridge Ltd, 40 Clifton Road, Cambridge, CB1 7ED Tel: (01223) 213322 Fax: (01223) 212320 E-mail: colourgraphicscambridge@btconnect.com *Lithographic plate makers*

Colourite Anodisers Ltd, Selinas Lane, Dagenham, Essex, RM8 1ET Tel: (020) 8592 1172 Fax: (020) 8592 1171 E-mail: info@colourite.net *Metal finishing & anodising aluminium services*

▶ Colourite Building Services, The Leas, Minster on Sea, Sheerness, Kent, ME12 2NL Tel: (01795) 871077 E-mail: email@colourite.co.uk *Brick colouring services*

Colourmaster, Stock Lane, Peel St, Chadderton, Oldham, OL9 9EY Tel: 0161-624 9479 Fax: 0161-678 8877 E-mail: sales@colour-master.co.uk *Small lot distributor of masterbatches*

Colourpass Cartons Ltd, 52 Cressex Enterprise Centre, Lincoln Road, Cressex Business Park, High Wycombe, Buckinghamshire, HP12 3RL Tel: (01494) 452527 Fax: (01494) 463815 E-mail: mikewillard2211@aol.com *Carton manufrs*

▶ Colourplan Design & Print Ltd, 11 Waterside Court, St. Helens, Merseyside, WA9 1UA Tel: (01744) 612636

Colourplus Print & Design, Unit 28 Monument Business Park, Warpsgrove Lane, Chalgrove, Oxford, OX44 7RW Tel: (01865) 400040 Fax: (01865) 400040 E-mail: design@colourplus.co.uk *Litho & digital printing graphic design*

Colourprint Screen Printers, Moor Lane, North Hykeham, Lincoln, LN6 9BD Tel: (01522) 680254 Fax: (01522) 501052 *Screen printers*

▶ Colourprint UK Ltd, Unit Colchester Estate, Colchester Avenue, Penylan, Cardiff, CF23 9AP Tel: (029) 2046 5550 Fax: (029) 2048 2300

Colourscans Ltd, Unit 89 The Washford Industrial Estate, Heming Road, Redditch, Worcestershire, B98 0EA Tel: (01527) 500048 Fax: (01527) 526673 E-mail: info@lemonpress.co.uk *Printers colour separation service*

Colourscope Offset Ltd, 6 Beckenham Business Centre, Kent House Lane, Beckenham, Kent, BR3 1LB Tel: (020) 8778 3112 Fax: (020) 8776 8779 *Printers*

▶ Colourspec Ltd, 11 Cricketers Way, Chatteris, Cambridgeshire, PE16 6UR Tel: (01354) 696496 E-mail: sales@colourspec.co.uk *We print for business. Business Cards, Leaflets, Booklets, Flyers etc.. We have an in house design service for all artwork requirements. A Mailing servive is also available.*

Coloursped Ltd, Stacey House, Bushey Hall Drive, Bushey, WD23 2ER Tel: (01923) 211255 Fax: (01923) 211255 E-mail: coloursped@aol.com *Distributors of printing inks*

▶ Colourstream Litho Ltd, Riverside Court, Pride Park, Derby, DE24 8JN Tel: (01332) 224860 Fax: (01332) 224861 E-mail: sales@surrey-imaging.co.uk

Colourtec Powder Coatings, 23a Willow Road, Colnbrook, Slough, SL3 0BS Tel: (01753) 683820 Fax: (01753) 680020 *Stove enamelling/ powder coating services*

▶ Colourtech, Stafford Close, Unit 2-3, Ashford, Kent, TN23 4TT Tel: (01233) 642020 Fax: 01233 632040 E-mail: Sarah@colourtechgroup.com *Digital printers with xeikon 500 press providers*

Colourwise K C O Ltd, 1 Unifax, Woods Way, Goring-by-Sea, Worthing, West Sussex, BN12 4QY Tel: (01903) 242894 Fax: (01903) 506126 *Printing services*

Colpa Precision Engineering Ltd, 100 Cecil Street, Watford, WD24 5AQ Tel: (01923) 237596 Fax: (01923) 213326 E-mail: colpa.ltd@virgin.net *Precision engineering & CNC*

Colpac Ltd, Enterprise Way, Maulden Road, Bedford, MK45 5BW Tel: (01525) 712261 Fax: (01525) 718205 E-mail: sales@colpac.co.uk *Carton printed packaging manufrs.*

▶ Colprint Ltd, 2 Lower Trinity Street, Birmingham, B9 4AG Tel: 0121-766 7606 Fax: 0121-772 1350 E-mail: sales@colprint.com

Colsalake Ltd, 6 Eldon Road Industrial Estate, Attenborough, Beeston, Nottingham, NG9 6DZ Tel: 0115-943 1558 Fax: 0115-925 0990 E-mail: coleslakeltd@aol.com *Gear cutting services & precision engineers*

Colsec Ltd, Wassage Way, Hampton Lovett, Droitwich, Worcestershire, WR9 0NX Tel: (01905) 795070 Fax: (01905) 794013 E-mail: sales@colsec.co.uk *Manufacturers of cold rooms, freezer rooms & insulation panels. Also cold store installation & clean room installation/service contractors*

Colson Castors Ltd, Golds Green Works, Bagnall Street, Hill Top, West Bromwich, West Midlands, B70 0TZ Tel: 0121-556 7221 Fax: 0121-502 2658 Principal Export Areas: Worldwide *Castors to specification*

Colson Castors Ltd, Golds Green Works, Bagnall Street, West Bromwich, West Midlands, B70 0TS Tel: 0121-556 7221 Fax: 0121-502 6258 E-mail: info@colson-castors.co.uk *Manufacturers of castors*

Colson Engineering, 8 Headlands Trading Estate, Swindon, SN2 7JQ Tel: (01793) 526660 Fax: (01793) 513294 E-mail: sales@colsonengineering.com *Engineering services*

Colstan Profiles Ltd, Unit 4 Central Works, Peartree Lane, Dudley, West Midlands, DY2 0QU Tel: (01384) 861122 Fax: (01384) 861144 E-mail: info@colstanprofiles.co.uk *Profile cutting services*

Colston Forge, Colston Yard, Colston Street, Bristol, BS1 5BD Tel: 0117-927 3660 Fax: 0117-927 3660 *Wrought ironworks*

The Colston Manufacturing Engineering Company Ltd, Brunel Park, Vincients Road, Bumpers Farm, Chippenham, Wiltshire, SN14 6NQ Tel: (01249) 652652 Fax: (01249) 444684 E-mail: sales@colstonltd.co.uk *Food regeneration equipment design manufrs*

Colt Car Company Ltd, Watermoor, Cirencester, Gloucestershire, GL7 1LF Tel: (01285) 655777 Fax: (01285) 658026 E-mail: enquiries@mitsubishi-cars.co.uk *Car importers*

Colt Construction, Witty Street, Hull, HU3 4TT Tel: (01482) 581880 Fax: (01482) 215037 E-mail: info@colt-industrial.co.uk *Building contractors*

Colt Industrial Services Ltd, Colt Business Park, Witty Street, Hull, HU3 4TT Tel: (01482) 214244 Fax: (01482) 215037 E-mail: sales@colt.co.uk *Asbestos waste removal merchants*

Colt International Ltd, 13 Dormer Place, Leamington Spa, Warwickshire, CV32 5AA Tel: (01926) 450650 Fax: (01926) 450651 *Ventilation manufrs*

Colt Staplers, 10 Bunting Close, Mitcham, Surrey, CR4 4ND Tel: (020) 8687 5500 Fax: (020) 8687 5501 E-mail: sales@coltstaplers.co.uk *Packaging material suppliers & manufrs*

Coltan Electronics Ltd, Unit D16-17 Boston Industrial Centre, Norfolk Street, Boston, Lincolnshire, PE21 9HG Tel: (01205) 351027 Fax: (01205) 354296 E-mail: coltan@eletron.fsbusiness.co.uk *Control panel & system manufrs*

Coltec Parker Ltd, Unit 3 Royd Way, Keighley, West Yorkshire, BD21 3LG Tel: (01535) 608405 Fax: (01535) 669276 E-mail: sales@coltecparker.com *Lithographic printers*

Colter Products Ltd, Unit 7 Zone C Chelmsford Road Industrial Estate, Chelmsford Road, Dunmow, Essex, CM6 1HD Tel: (01371) 876887 Fax: (01371) 875638 E-mail: sales@coltergroup.co.uk *Specialists in industrial automation auto id electronic design & manufacture*

▶ Colter Steels Ltd, Unit 10 Owen Road Industrial Estate, Willenhall, West Midlands, WV13 2PY Tel: 0121-526 6066 Fax: 0121-526 3044 E-mail: sales@coltersteels.co.uk *Rolling,slitting,de-coiling,edge dressing suppliers*

Coltman Precast Concrete Ltd, London Road, Canwell, Sutton Coldfield, West Midlands, B75 5SX Tel: (01543) 480482 Fax: (01543) 481587 E-mail: sales@coltman.co.uk *Pre-cast concrete, floors, staircases manufrs*

Colton Electrical Equipment Ltd, Hainge Road, Tividale, Oldbury, West Midlands, B69 2NB Tel: 0121-522 4112 Fax: 0121-522 4174 E-mail: sales@coltonelectricalequipment.co.uk *Power systems supplier*

Colton Electrical Equipment Co. Ltd, 329 Front Lane, Upminster, Essex, RM14 1LW Tel: (01708) 224454 Fax: (01708) 221191 E-mail: sales@coltonelectricalequipment.co.uk *Crane conductor & electrical connector distributors*

Colton Packaging Ltd, 60-65 The Warren, East Goscote, Leicester, LE7 3XA Tel: 0116-264 1060 Fax: 0116-264 1066 *Packaging materials distributors*

Colton Signs, Castlegate Mills, Spa Mews, Harrogate, North Yorkshire, HG2 7LF Tel: (01423) 886461 Fax: (01423) 881141 E-mail: coltonsigns@harrogatespa.fsn.co.uk *Sign manufrs*

Colton Tooling Ltd, 4 Highmeres Road, Leicester, LE4 9LZ Tel: 0116-276 6225 Fax: 0116-276 6226 E-mail: colton@talk21.com *Suppliers of tooling for the woodworking industry*

Coltran Products Ltd, 17-31 Church Street, Mexborough, South Yorkshire, S64 0EW Tel: (01709) 584031 Fax: (01709) 584431 E-mail: sales@coltran.com *Coltran Products manufacture and coat steel wire and tube products in Plastic and Epoxy Paint Finishes.We specalise in Storage and POS Display for Retail and Industry. Product can be designed from a brief or we can work from a sample provided. Either way, a first class service is given.*

Columbia Metals Ltd, Union Street South, Halifax, West Yorkshire, HX1 2LA Tel: (01422) 343026 Fax: (01422) 346587 E-mail: export@columbiametals.co.uk *Metal stockholders & distributors, non- ferrous and stainless steel, super alloys, aerospace alloys, nickel copper alloys, aluminium bronze, brass, copper, nickel silver, copper alloys, NIBRON, TROJAN, COLSIBRO, COLPHOS-90, COLFIT-DZR, COLDUR-A, COLBRONZE, ENVIROBRASS, CHROMZIRC-328, AMAZON-256Cu, ZAMALLOY, BECOL-25, beryllium copper, aluminium nickel bronze, aluminium silicon bronze, metal export, metal supplier.*

Columbia Metals Ltd, 19 High Street, Earls Barton, Northampton, NN6 0JG Tel: (01604) 810317 Fax: (01604) 812494 E-mail: sales@columbiametals.co.uk *Metal stockholders & distributors, non- ferrous and stainless steel, super alloys, aerospace alloys, nickel copper alloys, aluminium bronze, brass, copper, nickel silver, copper alloys, NIBRON, TROJAN, COLSIBRO, COLPHOS-90, COLFIT-DZR, COLDUR-A, COLBRONZE, ENVIROBRASS, CHROMZIRC-328, AMAZON-256Cu, ZAMALLOY, BECOL-25, beryllium copper, aluminium nickel bronze, aluminium silicon bronze, metal export, metal supplier.*

▶ Columbia Precision Ltd, 125 Cheston Road, Birmingham, B7 5EA Tel: 0121-327 1500 Fax: 0121-327 1511 E-mail: enquires@columbia.uk.com *Computer software, hardware & networking services*

Columbia Ribbon Manufacturing Co. Ltd, Kangley Bridge Road, London, SE26 5AW Tel: (020) 8659 3659 Fax: (020) 8659 6270 *Chemicals printing Industry*

Columbia Saw Works Ltd, 120 Hackney Road, London, E2 7QL Tel: (01708) 550601 Fax: (020) 8281 1260 E-mail: kevin@columbia37.freeserve.co.uk *Saw services & blade manufrs*

Columbia Staver Ltd, Russell Gardens Industrial Estate, Wickford, Essex, SS11 8QR Tel: (01268) 733346 Fax: (01268) 735893 E-mail: info@columbia-staver.co.uk *Heat dissipater manufrs*

Columbian Press, 69 Lower Road, Kenley, Surrey, CR8 5NH Tel: (020) 8763 9088 Fax: (020) 8763 1053 E-mail: columbianpress@btinternet.com *Commercial & colour printers*

Colval Engineering, Unit 1a Bury Farm, Curbridge, Botley, Southampton, SO30 2HB Tel: (01489) 799100 Fax: (01489) 799100 *Sheet metal workers, welding fabricators & engineers*

Colvin Ltd, 34 Silverwing Estate, Croydon, CR0 4RR Tel: (01737) 771311 Fax: (01737) 773268 E-mail: tarbot@tarbot.co.uk *Computer consumables*

Colwick Instruments Ltd, PO Box 8268, Nottingham, NG3 6AJ Tel: 0115-962 2999 Fax: 0115-961 4582 E-mail: enquires@colwickinstruments.co.uk *Gas analyser manufrs*

Colwick Vale Coachworks Ltd, Colwick Road, Nottingham, NG2 4BG Tel: 0115-950 2670 Fax: 0115-941 4398 *Motor vehicle repairers*

Colwill Plant & Contracting, Ashlea, Main Street, Hatfield Woodhouse, Doncaster, South Yorkshire, DN7 6NF Tel: (01302) 840680 Fax: (01302) 351704 *Plant hire & contracting*

Com Development Europe Ltd, Unit 10 Triangle Business Park, Quilters Way, Stoke Mandeville, Aylesbury, Buckinghamshire, HP22 5SX Tel: (01296) 616400 Fax: (01296) 616500 E-mail: info@comdev.co.uk *Manufacturers of space parts*

▶ Com Pak Design Ltd, Units 3-4 Kestral Close, Quarry Hill Road, Ilkeston, Derbyshire, DE7 4DA Tel: 0115-944 2224 Fax: 0115-944 1433

Comack Upholstery Co., Farington Sawmill, Stanifield Lane, Farington, Leyland, PR25 4QA Tel: (01772) 424491 Fax: (01772) 621347 E-mail: comackuph@btinternet.com *Contract furnishers & manufrs*

Comainwells Ltd, Harfreys Road, Great Yarmouth, Norfolk, NR31 0LS Tel: (01493) 656444 Fax: (01493) 656444 E-mail: comwell@hotmail.co.uk *Suppliers of welding equipment & consumables & industrial gases*

Comair Rotron Europe Ltd, 9 The I O Centre, Nash Road, Redditch, Worcestershire, B98 7AS Tel: (01527) 520525 Fax: (01527) 520565 E-mail: info@comairrotron.com *Designers & manufacturers of custom fans, fan trays, heat exchangers & air conditioner units for cooling of telecommunications and other electronics equipment in accordance with CE, ETSI & ISO 9001 Standards*

▶ John Comaish Advertising Services, Unit 17, Sefton Lane Industrial Estate, Maghull, L31 8BX Tel: 0151-520 4330 E-mail: enquires@comaish.co.uk *Advertising consultants*

Comap Westco, Unit C6 Moss Industrial Estate, St. Helens Road, Leigh, Lancashire, WN7 3PT Tel: (01942) 603351 Fax: (01942) 607780 E-mail: sales@comap.co.uk *Brass foundry distributors*

Comapex, The Glebe, Culsalmond, Insch, Aberdeenshire, AB52 6UJ Tel: 01464 841209 Fax: 01464 841241 *Computer consultancy*

Comar Instruments, 70 Hartington Grove, Cambridge, CB1 7UH Tel: (01223) 245470 Fax: (01223) 410033 E-mail: mail@kyinstruments.com *Manufacturers & suppliers of optical equipment*

Comark Ltd, Comark House Gunnels Wood Park, Gunnels Wood Road, Stevenage, Hertfordshire, SG1 2TA Tel: (01438) 367367 Fax: (01438) 367400 E-mail: salesuk@comarkltd.com *Electronic instrument manufrs*

Comart ITM, Technology House, Ridge Road, Rotherham, South Yorkshire, S65 1NS Tel: (01709) 363418 Fax: (01709) 835369 E-mail: enquiries@comartplc.co.uk *Computer installation, maintenance & repairers*

Comau Estil Systems, Midland Road, Luton, LU2 0HR Tel: (01582) 817600 Fax: (01582) 817700 *Special purpose custom built machinery*

Combase Information Systems, 5 Buckingham Road, Cheadle Hulme, Cheadle, Cheshire, SK8 5EG Tel: 0161-283 1813 Fax: 0161-486 0779 E-mail: info@combase.co.uk *Systems & software manufrs*

Combass Ltd, Rotherham Close, Norwood Industrial Estate, Sheffield, S21 2JU Tel: 0114-248 0616 Fax: 0114-248 2684 E-mail: irmackie@aol.com *Manufacturers of polyurethane*

▶ Combat Trousers UK, Anchor Street, Tunstead, Norwich, NR12 E-mail: military_kit@btinternet.com *Online retail of mens clothing, combat trousers, camouflage & outdoor clothing & equipment.*

▶ Comber Model Makers, 6 Viewpoint, Boxley Road, Penenden Heath, Maidstone, Kent, ME14 2DZ Tel: (01622) 355850 Fax: (01622) 355860 *Model manufrs*

Combi Services Heating Ltd, 196 Whittington Road, London, N22 8YL Tel: (020) 8881 1941 Fax: (020) 8881 3740 *Heating engineers*

Combi Vent Engineering Ltd, Northumberland House, Emerald Street, Denton, Manchester, M34 3GQ Tel: 0161-336 5065 Fax: 0161-320 4218 E-mail: enquiries@combigroup.co.uk *Ventilation systems supply & installation*

Combidrive Ltd, Unit 6, Parc Menter, Meadows Bridge, Cross Hands, Llanelli, Carmarthenshire, SA14 6RA Tel: (01269) 834848 Fax: (01269) 834850 E-mail: sales@combidrive.com Principal

continued

Export Areas: Worldwide *Power transmission equipment specialists*

Combine Fabrications Ltd, Fen Lane, Long Bennington, Newark, Nottinghamshire, NG23 5ED Tel: (01400) 281506 Fax: (01400) 282100 E-mail: enquiries@combinefabs.co.uk *Agricultural engineers*

▶ Combine Pallets, Grove Road, Northfleet, Gravesend, Kent, DA11 9AX Tel: (01474) 363421 Fax: (01474) 353031 E-mail: ian@pallet.co.uk *Pallet manufrs*

▶ Combined Book Services Ltd, Units I-K, Paddock Wood Distribution Centre, Paddock Wood, Tonbridge, Kent, TN12 6UU Tel: (01892) 837171 Fax: (01892) 837272 E-mail: info@combook.co.uk *Independent book distributor with full distribution service for trade*

Combined Building Services Ltd, 7 Kennet Road, Dartford, DA1 4QN Tel: (01322) 520270 E-mail: combinedcbs@aol.com *Electrical Contractors, Mechanical Contractors available from Combined Building Services Ltd based in Dartford. Click the links below to visit our website or contact us via our profile page.*

▶ Combined Colour Solutions Ltd, 9 Holme Road, Ramsey, Huntingdon, Cambridgeshire, PE26 2SS Tel: (01733) 844285

Combined Communications Ltd, 19 Lodge Lane, Grays, Essex, RM17 5RY Tel: (01375) 392600 Fax: (01375) 392008 *Telephone installers*

▶ Combined Construction Ltd, 306 Glentanar Road, Balmore Industrial Estate, Glasgow, G22 7XS Tel: 0141-347 1800 Fax: 0141-347 1877

▶ Combined Electrical Engineering Services, 12 Wyvern Buildings, Grove Trading Estate, Dorchester, Dorset, DT1 1ST Tel: (01305) 251177 Fax: (01305) 250552 E-mail: sales@ceesltd.co.uk

Combined Frame Makers Ltd, Hopes Lane, Ramsgate, Kent, CT12 6RN Tel: (01843) 595846 Fax: (01843) 851831 *Wooden furniture manufrs*

Combined Insulations & Plastics Ltd, 6 Bedford Business Centre, Mile Road, Bedford, MK42 9TW Tel: 01234 211771 Fax: 01234 211771 Purchasing Contact: P. Todd Sales Contact: P. Todd *Plastic machinists & fabricators. Also manufacturers of retail displays & plastic vacuum formed products up to 0.25m*

Combined Office System Services, PO Box 31, Hemel Hempstead, Hertfordshire, HP3 0JA Tel: (01442) 834216 Fax: (01442) 831352 E-mail: info@combinedoffice.co.uk *Computer consultants*

▶ Combined Security, 79 Pickford Lane, Bexleyheath, Kent, DA7 4RW Tel: (020) 8304 6111 Fax: (020) 8304 6555 E-mail: info@combinedsecurity.co.uk *With a 15-30 minute response time in and around Greater London, Combined Security are the completesecurity solution for commercial and residential needs. Our Locksmiths and Engineers are ready to supply, fit and maintain your locks, safes, shutters, grilles, security doors and more from our vast range of services.*

Combined Services UK Ltd, 4 Marlborough Trading Estate, High Wycombe, Buckinghamshire, HP11 2LB Tel: (01494) 462262 Fax: (01494) 438707 E-mail: mailbox@combinedservices.co.uk *Building energy management services*

Combined Signs, 4 Carpenters Place, London, SW4 7TD Tel: (020) 7720 5797 Fax: (020) 7720 2318 E-mail: signs@combinedsigns.co.uk *Sign manufrs*

Combined Steel Services Ltd, 5 Boddis Industrial Park, Garratts Lane, Cradley Heath, West Midlands, B64 5SS Tel: 0121-559 3737 Fax: 0121-559 2500 E-mail: combinedsteels@btconnect.com *Steel stockholders*

Combined Trading (Garments) Ltd, 77-79 Great Eastern Street, London, EC2A 3HU Tel: (020) 7739 0551 Fax: (020) 7729 2556 *Textile manufrs*

Combserve Combustion Service Ltd, 1 Brookfield Works, Wood Street, Elland, West Yorkshire, HX5 9AP Tel: (01422) 370051 Fax: (01422) 377374 E-mail: combserve@hotmail.com *Combustion control systems*

Combustion Energy & Steam Specialists Ltd, 77-79 John Street, Stromness, Orkney, KW16 3AD Tel: (01856) 851177 Fax: (01856) 851199 E-mail: enquiries@cess.co.uk *Engineers*

Combustion Lining Ltd, Jacaidam Works, Walley Street, Stoke-on-Trent, ST6 2AH Tel: (01782) 822712 Fax: (01782) 823920 E-mail: info@combustionlinings.com *Suppliers & installers of refractory linings & boilers*

Comcare Technology Ltd, Anglo House, Chapel Road, Manchester, M22 4JN Tel: 0161-902 0330 Fax: 0161-946 0126 E-mail: info@comcare.co.uk *Computer networking specialists*

Comcen Computer Supplies Ltd, 1 York Place, Leeds, LS1 2DS Tel: 0113-234 5000 Fax: 0113-234 2757 E-mail: leeds@comcen.co.uk *Computer sales*

Comcir Radio Communications, 66 Goldstone Villas, Hove, East Sussex, BN3 3RU Tel: (01273) 779828 Fax: (01273) 204900 E-mail: info@comcir.co.uk *Radio equipment distributors*

Comco Combustion & Equipment Ltd, Building 50 Third Avenue, Pensnett Trading Estate, Kingswinford, West Midlands, DY6 7XD Tel: (01384) 297788 Fax: (01384) 297789 E-mail: comcoice@globalnet.co.uk *Industrial furnaces manufrs*

Comco Plastics UK Ltd, 27 Long Wood Road, Trafford Park, Manchester, M17 1PZ Tel: 0161-873 7080 Fax: 0161-873 7079 E-mail: steve.mitchell@vinkplastics.com *Vink Plastics offer semi-finished engineering plastics to industry.*Nylon PA6, Nylon PA66, POM Acetal, PEEK, Polypropylene, PVC, Acrylic, Polycarbonate, UHMWPE, PTFE, PETG, PETP, PET are all items that are offered on the Engineering Plastics range.*Most products are available in sheet, rod and tube format.*Machined Parts service available with very competitive lead times.*We can provide our service throughout the UK from our Manchester site.*

Comcount Ltd, Unit 16 Cranham Estate, Shipston Close, Worcester, WR4 9XN Tel: (01905) 454710 Fax: (01905) 455849 E-mail: mail@comcount.co.uk *Packaging machinery manufrs*

▶ Comcraft Computer Consultants, 57 Old Tye Avenue, Biggin Hill, Westerham, Kent, TN16 3NA Tel: (01959) 570798 Fax: (01959) 540047 E-mail: sales@comcraft.freeserve.co.uk *Databases, web site design & computer networks*

Comer Industries (UK) Ltd, Units 2-3, Heath Road, Merrylees Industrial Estate, Desford, Leicester, LE9 9FE Tel: (01530) 231504 Fax: (01530) 231503 E-mail: sales@comer.co.uk *Power transmissions equipment manufrs*

▶ Comery Hill & Co., The Poplars, Benthall Lane, Benthall, Broseley, Shropshire, TF12 5RR Tel: 01952 881056 Fax: 01952 881056 E-mail: comeryhillco@btinternet.com *Preparing Patent Drawings, Formal Drawings, Patent Draughting.*

Comet Catering Equipment Co. Ltd, 45 Brimsdown Industrial Estate, Lockfield Avenue, Brimsdown, Enfield, Middlesex, EN3 7XZ Tel: (020) 8804 4779 Fax: (020) 8804 9470 *Stainless steel catering equipment manufrs*

Comet Fluid Power, Horace Waller V C Parade, Shaw Cross Business Park, Dewsbury, West Yorkshire, WF12 7RF Tel: (01924) 455667 Fax: (01924) 456292 E-mail: comet@challenger-group.co.uk *Hose & fitting distributors*

▶ Comet Home Delivery, Unit 12 Severn Link Distribution Centre, Newhouse Farm Industrial Es, Mathern, Chepstow, Gwent, NP16 6UN Tel: (01291) 628866 Fax: (01291) 630757 *Electrical retailer*

▶ Comet Tankers Ltd, Hawkford Hall, 231 Uxbridge Road, Mill End, Rickmansworth, Hertfordshire, WD3 8DP Tel: (01923) 770261 Fax: (01923) 770277 E-mail: info@comettankers.co.uk *Drainage & plumbing services*

Comet-Pramesco Services, 30 Holywell Avenue, Folkestone, Kent, CT19 6JZ Tel: (01303) 255585 Fax: (01303) 243122 E-mail: steve_baxter@lineone.net *Packaging machinery*

▶ Comfit Computer Services, 37, Wackerfield Road, Rendlesham, Woodbridge, Suffolk, IP12 2UT Tel: (01394) 420166 Fax: (01394) 420166

▶ Comfortable Living, 1 The Close, Fulwood, Preston, PR2 5RY Tel: (0800) 0832558 Fax: (0800) 0832557 *We offer genuinely discounted off plan and stock property to the serious investor.*

▶ Comfy Graphics, 8 Metcalf Mews, Uppermill, Oldham, OL3 6DN Tel: (01457) 810734 E-mail: info@comfygraphics.co.uk *Corporate design solutions to businesses*

Comfy Quilts, Albany Mill, Old Hall Street, Middleton, Manchester, M24 1AG Tel: (0870) 7662324 Fax: (0870) 7662333 E-mail: info@comfyquilts.com *Bedspread & sleeping bag manufrs*

The Comfy Seat Co., George Baylis Road, Berry Hill Industrial Estate, Droitwich, Worcestershire, WR9 9RB Tel: (01905) 795955 Fax: (01905) 794683 E-mail: sales@comfyseating.co.uk *Seating sales*

Comhire P.L.C., Communications House, Vauxhall Road, Sheffield, S9 1LD Tel: (0800) 163778 Fax: (020) 8961 9687 E-mail: ccpl.comhire-comhire@btinternet.com *Radio communication equipment suppliers*

Comice Ltd, 12A Lower Church Street, Chepstow, Gwent, NP16 5HJ Tel: (01291) 628886 Fax: (01291) 628334 E-mail: comice@comice.co.uk *Computer software & services*

Comid Engineering Ltd, Greenacres Road, Oldham, OL4 2AB Tel: 0161-624 9592 Fax: 0161-627 1620 E-mail: sales@comid.co.uk *Industrial valves distributors & suppliers*

Comino Services P.L.C, 11th Floor Amp House, Dingwall Road, Croydon, CR0 2LX Tel: (08708) 466111 Fax: (08708) 466888 *Software systems*

Comlec Units Ltd, Northgate Way, Northgate, Aldridge, Walsall, WS9 8TH Tel: (01922) 456237 Fax: (01922) 455251 E-mail: sales@comlec.co.uk *Direct current motor specialists*

Alexander Comley Ltd, Pensnett Trading Estate, Kingswinford, West Midlands, DY6 7ND Tel: (01384) 401080 Fax: (01384) 273935 E-mail: sgwilliams@alexandercomley.co.uk *Steel flange & steel tube fittings manufrs*

Comm Systems Ltd, Unit 17 Martello Enterprise Centre, Courtwick Lane, Wick, Littlehampton, West Sussex, BN17 7PA Tel: (01903) 722222 Fax: (01903) 726000 E-mail: enquiries@commsys.biz *Telecommunications*

Comma Oil & Chemicals Ltd, Comma Works, Dering Way, Gravesend, Kent, DA12 2QX Tel: (01474) 564311 Fax: (01474) 333000 E-mail: sales@commaoil.com *Oil product suppliers*

Comma Tech Ltd, Carlyon Road, Atherstone, Warwickshire, CV9 1LW Tel: (01827) 714741 Fax: (01827) 718943 E-mail: sales@commatech.co.uk *Sub contract machinists & gear manufrs*

Command Alkon Ltd, 21 St Annes Road, St Annes Park, St. Annes Park, Bristol, BS4 4AB Tel: 0117-972 4777 Fax: 0117-972 4888 *Computer systems suppliers & installers*

Command Pest Control Ltd, College Farm Unit 4, The Street, Preston St. Mary, Sudbury, Suffolk, CO10 9NQ Tel: (01787) 248049 Fax: (01787) 247113 E-mail: sales@commandpestcontrol.co.uk *Pest control services*

▶ Command Software Services Ltd, Bassett Court, Newport Pagnell, Buckinghamshire, MK16 0JN Tel: (01908) 283580 Fax: (07002) 227374 E-mail: info@commandsoftware.plus.com *IT software developers*

Commando Fasteners Co. Ltd, 3 Canal Street, Stourbridge, West Midlands, DY8 4LU Tel: (01384) 393949 Fax: (01384) 393933 E-mail: info@comfast.co.uk *Bolts, screws & upset forgings*

Commando Knitwear Ltd, Countesthorpe Road, Wigston, Leicestershire, LE18 4PJ Tel: 0116-278 5288 E-mail: info@commando-knitwear.co.uk *Knitwear manufrs*

Commando Security Services Ltd, Black Friars House, West Street, Warwick, CV34 6AN Tel: (01926) 499495 Fax: (01926) 499802 *Industrial & commercial cleaning contractors*

Commark Air, Oaktrees, Little Warley Hall La, Little Warley, Brentwood, Essex, CM13 3EX Tel: (01277) 200309

▶ com,mas, 18 Sussex Mansions, 39-40 Sussex Square, Brighton, BN2 5AD Tel: (0845) 0095083 Fax: (0700) 3401419 E-mail: sales@com-mas.co.uk *Communication solutions for home office & small business. Telephone, Website, Internet, Computer Networking, Brighton, Sussex, South Coast*

Commbinary Ltd, Citrus House, Dale Street, Liverpool, L2 5SF Tel: 0151-255 2121 Fax: 0151-255 2122 E-mail: sales@telecom2l.co.uk *Telecommunications solutions*

Commerce International G B Ltd, 14 Dalston Gardens, Stanmore, Middlesex, HA7 1BU Tel: (020) 8206 1133 Fax: (020) 8204 6969 E-mail: commintl@aol.com *Bearing stockists*

▶ Commerce-Connections Ltd, 17-21 Wyfold Road, London, SW6 6SE Tel: (0845) 1279955 Fax: (0845) 1279944 E-mail: info@cc-ltd.com *Computer software*

Commercial Aerospace Services Co. Ltd, Aviation Centre, Star Estate, Horsham, West Sussex, RH13 8RA Tel: (01403) 711444 Fax: (01403) 711582 E-mail: judith@casco.aero *Aircraft components manufrs*

Commercial Bearings Ltd, Plume Street, Birmingham, B6 7RY Tel: 0121-322 2036 Fax: 0121-327 6926 E-mail: sales@commercialbearings.co.uk *Conveyor bearing manufrs*

▶ Commercial Bodies East Anglia, 9 Hurricane Way, Norwich, NR6 6EZ Tel: (01603) 484047 Fax: (01603) 417834 E-mail: mwcbea@freenet.co.uk *Specialists in commercial body building & repair*

Commercial Body Fittings, 80 Bridge Road East, Welwyn Garden City, Hertfordshire, AL7 1JY Tel: (01707) 371161 Fax: (01707) 372603 E-mail: sales@cbf.uk.com *Commercial body fittings distributors* Also at: Brierley Hill

Commercial Body Specialists, 2 Beresford Trading Estate, High Street, Stoke-on-Trent, ST6 5EU Tel: (01782) 832554 Fax: (01782) 832426 *Vehicle manufrs*

Commercial Body Works, Toseland Road, Graveley, St. Neots, Cambridgeshire, PE19 6PS Tel: (01480) 831821 Fax: (01480) 831322 *Body building & repairs*

Commercial Business Equipment Ltd, 1-3 Chorley Road, Walton-le-Dale, Preston, PR5 4JA Tel: 0151-495 2359 Fax: 0151-495 2827 *Photocopiers & faxes*

Commercial Catering Centre, 46b Grasmere Road, Blackpool, FY1 5HT Tel: (01253) 292976 Fax: (01253) 292977 E-mail: markconstantine@aol.com *Catering equipment services*

Commercial Catering Engineers Ltd, 13 Clarkson Road, Lingwood, Norwich, NR13 4BA Tel: (01603) 713679 *Catering engineering*

Commercial Catering Services, Station Business Park, Pensarn, Abergele, Clwyd, LL22 7PX Tel: (01745) 822166 Fax: (01745) 832656 E-mail: comcatering@btconnect.com *Catering equipment & laundry machines*

Commercial Ceiling Factors Ltd, Malvern Drive, Llanishen, Cardiff, CF14 5DR Tel: (029) 2076 3311 Fax: (029) 2075 5910 E-mail: sales@ccfltd.com *Suspended ceiling distributors*

Commercial Collection Services, 797 London Road, Thornton Heath, Surrey, CR7 6YY Tel: (020) 8665 4900 Fax: (020) 8683 2283 E-mail: stephen.durrant@ccscollect.co.uk *Debt collectors service* Also at: Birmingham

Commercial Colours Ltd, Zone 3 Link 56, Weighbridge Road, Deeside Industrial Park, Deeside, Clwyd, CH5 2LL Tel: (01244) 281352 Fax: (01244) 280936 E-mail: admin@commercialcolours.co.uk *Commercial vehicle bodybuilders & repairers*

Commercial Communications, Unit 25 Titan Court, Laporte Way, Luton, LU4 8EF Tel: (01582) 721884 Fax: (01582) 705073 E-mail: sales@commcomms.co.uk *Radio communication equipment*

Commercial Cooling Equipment Ltd, 57-59 Cross Street, Nelson, Lancashire, BB9 7NQ Tel: (01282) 604003 Fax: (01282) 720829 *Install fridges*

Commercial & Domestic Investigations Ltd, 7 The Esplanade, Sunderland, SR2 7BQ Tel: 0191-510 8474 Fax: 0191-514 4225 *Debt recovery services*

Commercial & Domestic Refrigeration, 1 Stansty Drive, Wrexham, Clwyd, LL11 2DG Tel: (01978) 352563 Fax: (01978) 352563 *Refrigeration engineers*

Commercial Engineering Metals Ltd, Unit 5 & 6, Shawbank Industrial Estate, Lakeside, Redditch, Worcestershire, B98 7YN Tel: (01527) 529145 Fax: (01527) 510236 *Aluminium scrap processors*

▶ Commercial Envelopes, 158 Lichfield Road, Sandhills, Walsall, WS9 9PF Tel: (01543) 452326 Fax: (01543) 821509 E-mail: denise@commercialenvelopes.co.uk *Office stationary suppliers*

Commercial Facilities & Logistics, 89 Park Road, Didcot, Oxfordshire, OX11 8QT Tel: (01235) 511054 Fax: (01235) 511056 E-mail: mhall@cfl-ltd.co.uk *Print paper storage, distributors & fulfillment*

▶ Commercial Factoring Ltd, Belle Grove House, Manor Court, Rogiet, Caldicot, Gwent, NP26 3TU Tel: (0845) 1235696 E-mail: admin@factoringadvice.com *Commercial finance brokers, specialising in factoring, commercial mortgages & leasing facilities.*

Commercial Finishes Ltd, Birmingham Road, Redditch, Worcestershire, B97 6DY Tel: (01527) 584244 Fax: (01527) 61127 E-mail: info@cfltd.co.uk *Bathroom accessory manufrs*

Commercial Graphics Ltd, 11 Greenway, Conlig, Newtownards, County Down, BT23 7SU Tel: (028) 9127 0431 Fax: (028) 9127 0137 E-mail: sales@commercialgraphics.co.uk *Book & brochure printing specialists*

Commercial & Industrial Electrical Services Ltd, Unit 70, Gravelly Indust Park, Birmingham, B24 8TQ Tel: 0121-328 1780 Fax: 0121-327 7589 *Electrical contractors*

Commercial & Industrial Gauges, Unit 7 Coed Aben Road, Wrexham Industrial Estate, Wrexham, Clwyd, LL13 9UH Tel: (01978) 661704 Fax: (01978) 660321 E-mail: info@cigltd.co.uk *Draper tool agent based in Wrexham but supplying the UK. Specialist suppliers of hydrant keys and all types of gauges*

▶ Commercial & Industrial Interiors Ltd, 1e Princess Court, Princess Way, Prudhoe, Northumberland, NE42 6PL Tel: (01661) 836304 Fax: (0845) 3454229 E-mail: john@ciinteriors.com *Specialists in internal office building & construction*

Commercial Injection Services, 2 Flowers Industrial Estate, Latimer Road, Luton, LU1 3XA Tel: (01582) 724072 Fax: (01582) 728043 *Diesel fuel injection services*

▶ Commercial Interior Specialists, Bowesfield Lane, Stockton-on-Tees, Cleveland, TS18 3HJ Tel: (01642) 611295 Fax: (01642) 611296 E-mail: sales@cis-interiors.co.uk *Ceilings, interior building work*

▶ Commercial Leasing Quote, 65 High Street, Hemel Hempstead, Hertfordshire, HP1 3AF Tel: (0800) 0198836 E-mail: inbox@commercialleasingquote.co.uk *Car & van leasing services*

▶ Commercial Lending Solutions Ltd, Longueville House, 10 Hawksmill Street, Needham Market, Ipswich, IP6 8AA Tel: (01449) 723272 Fax: 01449 723273 E-mail: phil@lending-solutions.co.uk *Commercial Mortgage broker specialising in property mortgages.*Sectors include retail, hotels, agriculture, industry and development finance.*

Commercial Lighting Systems Ltd, Unit 16-17, Park Gate Business Centre, Chandlers Way, Park Gate, Southampton, SO31 1FQ Tel: (01489) 581002 Fax: (01489) 576262 E-mail: sales@commercial-lighting.co.uk *Lightings fittings/equipment*

Commercial Microbiology Ltd, Kettock Lodge Campus 2 Aberdeen Science Park, Balgownie Drive, Bridge of Don, Aberdeen, AB22 8GU Tel: (01224) 706062 Fax: (01224) 706012 *Consultancy, Management Systems, Training, Production Microbiology, Health and Hygiene,Field Services related to - microbiologically influenced corrosion, reservoir souring, biocides, nitrates, bioflims, legionnella, audits, sampling and analyses,*

Commercial Microwave Repairs Ltd, Cobbetts Lane, Hill Farm, Blackwater, Camberley, Surrey, GU17 9LW Tel: (01252) 879752 Fax: (01252) 879307 *Microwave repairers*

Commercial Nameplate Manufacturing Co., Butt End Mills, Chadwick Fold Lane, Mirfield, West Yorkshire, WF14 8PW Tel: (01924) 498652 Fax: (01924) 491167 E-mail: sales@commercialnameplates.co.uk *Nameplate & sign manufrs*

Commercial Out Sourcing Ltd, 46 Starrs Mead, Battle, East Sussex, TN33 0UH Tel: (01424) 774287 Fax: (01424) 775876 E-mail: mail@cos-uk.com *Purchasing & contract consultants*

▶ Commercial Panels, Unit 28, Fort Industrial Park, Chester Road, Castle Vale, Birmingham, B35 7AR Tel: 0121-749 2877 *Insulated panels manufrs*

Commercial & Personal Relocations Ltd, Space Centre, Legg Brothers Industrial Estate, Spring Road, Wolverhampton, WV4 6JT Tel: (01902) 491001 Fax: (01902) 491002 E-mail: liz@cpr-uk.com *Commercial & domestic removals, containerised & storage*

▶ Commercial Property Maintenance Services, Victoria House, Mary Street, Johnstone, Renfrewshire, PA5 8BT Tel: (01505) 382333 Fax: (01505) 382338

Commercial Propshaft Services Ltd, 190 Kingsway South, Team Valley Trading Estate, Gateshead, Tyne & Wear, NE11 0SH Tel: 0191-482 1690 Fax: 0191-482 0582 *Manufacture propshafts*

Commercial Refurb Ltd, Unit 6 Orton Industrial Estate, London Road, Coalville, Leicestershire, LE67 3JA Tel: (01530) 810982 *Trailer refurbishment*

Commercial Repairs, Derber House Old Newton Road, Heathfield Industrial Estate, Heathfield, Newton Abbot, Devon, TQ12 6SL Tel: (01626) 834789 Fax: (01626) 835425 *Repair heavy goods vehicles*

Commercial Replacements, Unit L1 Blackpole Trading Estate East, Blackpole Road, Worcester, WR3 8SG Tel: (01905) 458052 Fax: (01905) 756078 *Commercial vehicle spares distributors*

Commercial Science, 11 Hylands Close, Crawley, West Sussex, RH10 6RX Tel: (01293) 446244 Fax: (01293) 446244 *Medical electronic equipment manufrs*

Commercial Signs & Displays Ltd, Commercial Road, Devizes, Wiltshire, SN10 1EH Tel: (01380) 721068 Fax: (01380) 721068 E-mail: commercialsigns@btconnect.com *Sign makers*

Commercial Software Management Ltd, Devereux House, Church Hill, Coleshill, Birmingham, B46 3AA Tel: (01675) 466731 Fax: (01675) 466734 E-mail: sales@csmltd.co.uk *Hardware & software suppliers*

▶ Commercial Systems (Fabrication) Ltd, 1 Queensway, Rochdale, Lancashire, OL11 2LA Tel: (01706) 644223 Fax: (01706) 644188 E-mail: atonyarmstrong@aol.com *Wall panelling fixing system manufacturer. Choice of finishes; polished, plain, anodised, powder coated, to most RAL or BS colours. Designed for fast & efficient assembly to save money & time*

▶ Commercial Telematics Group, Chantry House, Chantry Place, Harrow, Middlesex, HA3 6NY Tel: (020) 8428 7755 Fax: (020) 8428 4600 E-mail: Mark.Naldrett@commercialtelematics.com *Vehicle tracking and fleet management systems provider, utilising latest GSM and GPS technologies provide significant cost efficiences.*

Commercial Testing Services Ltd, Blackmore Street, Sheffield, S4 7TZ Tel: 0114-276 8758 Fax: 0114-272 0449 E-mail: cts@allvac.com *Mechanical & metallurgical testing services*

Commercial Trade Services Group Ltd, Lea Park Trading Estate, Warley Close, London, E10 7LF Tel: (020) 8558 9988 Fax: (020) 8558 1155 E-mail: services@comtrad.co.uk *Catering equipment & refrigeration retailers*

Commercial Trading, Bridge Road, Kingswood, Bristol, BS15 4PT Tel: 0117-961 0710 Fax: 0117-960 2933 E-mail: commercial.trading@btinternet.com *Manufacturers of cases, packing cases & wooden crates*

Commercial Trading Co. Ltd, Unit D6 Sandown Industrial Park, Mill Road, Esher, Surrey, KT10 8BL Tel: (01372) 468383 Fax: (01372) 468576 E-mail: admin@ctc.co.uk *Industrial & high tech removal & installation market service*

▶ Commercial Training, Training & Development Centre, Longfield, Hitchin Road, Stevenage, Herts, SG1 4AE Tel: 01438 847321 Fax: 01438 314031 E-mail: commercial.training@hertscc.gov.uk *The Commercial Training department of Hertfordshire Fire & Rescue provides a one stop fire and safety training solution, helping organisations maintain a safe working environment. Courses offered range from Fire Marshal and First Aid through to IOSH and Leadership Skills, all courses can be tailored to suit individual business requirements.*

Commercial Vehicle Bodies, Lady Pitt Farm, Fosse Road, Syerston, Newark, Nottinghamshire, NG23 5NQ Tel: (01636) 525874 Fax: (01636) 525874 *Commercial vehicle body repair & manufrs*

Commercial Vehicle Enterprises, Redhouse Industrial Estate, Middlemore Lane, Aldridge, Walsall, WS9 8DL Tel: (01922) 457992 *Commercial vehicle repairs*

Commercial Window Films, Unit 12 Parkside Industrial Estate, Edge La Street, Royton, Oldham, OL2 6DS Tel: 0161-627 5274 Fax: 0161-627 0533 E-mail: sales@commercialblinds.co.uk *Solar heat reflecting film distributors*

▶ Commercial Window Supplies, Unit 4 Little Fountain Street, Morley, Leeds, LS27 9EN Tel: 0113-252 5544 Fax: 0113-252 5544 *Horse box window manufrs*

▶ Commertech Ltd, 55 High Street, Leatherhead, Surrey, KT22 8AG Tel: (01372) 376427

▶ Commic International, Unit 9,, Phoenix Works, Willows Lane, Accrington, Lancashire, BB5 0RT Tel: (07984) 768938 Fax: (01254) 388422 E-mail: sales@commic-int.com *Surgical instruments*

▶ Commissum Computer Security, 142 Commercial Street, Edinburgh, EH6 6LB Tel: 0131-625 2730 Fax: 0131-476 6061 E-mail: sales@commisum.com *Information security consultancy*

Commodities Research Unit Ltd, 31 Mount Pleasant, London, WC1X 0AD Tel: (020) 7278 0414 Fax: (020) 7837 0976 *Research/ consultancy in metals/mining/chemicals*

Commodore Kitchens Ltd, Acorn House, Gumley Road, Grays, Essex, RM20 4XP Tel: (01375) 382323 Fax: (01375) 394955 E-mail: info@commodorekitchens.co.uk *Kitchen & bedroom unit manufrs*

Common Heard Productions Ltd, Elizabeth House, 40 Lagland Street, Poole, Dorset, BH15 1QG Tel: (01202) 679671 Fax: (01202) 691672 E-mail: mail@commonheard.com *Audio production services*

▶ Common Sense Solutions, 12 Mark Road, Hemel Hempstead Industrial Estate, Hemel Hempstead, Hertfordshire, HP2 7BN Tel: (01442) 260586 Fax: (01442) 397884 *Cash register sales*

Commonsense Computing Ltd, East Furlong Farmhouse, Littleham, Bideford, Devon, EX39 5HW Tel: (01237) 474795 Fax: (01237) 421216 *Computer consultants*

Commontime Ltd, 568 Burton Road, Derby, DE23 6DG Tel: (01332) 368500 Fax: (01332) 366880 E-mail: sales@commontime.com *Mobile computing & software solutions*

▶ Commprep Ltd, North Kelsey Road, Caistor, Market Rasen, Lincolnshire, LN7 6SF Tel: (01472) 852166

Comms Resources, 1 Sherman Road, Bromley, BR1 3JH Tel: (020) 8663 1999 Fax: (020) 8313 6601 E-mail: mail@commsresources.com *Telecommunications & it recruitment*

Commscare, 20 Norbury Crescent, Hazel Grove, Stockport, Cheshire, SK7 5PD Tel: 0161-482 4433 Fax: 0161-482 4777 E-mail: sales@headsetsolutions.co.uk *Telecommunications*

Commsplus Ltd, 51 Gazelle Road, Weston-super-Mare, Avon, BS24 9ES Tel: (01934) 882200 Fax: (01934) 411010 E-mail: julyanb@commsplus.co.uk *Telephone system sales*

Comm-Tec Ltd, 6 Danbury Court, Sunrise Parkway, Linford Wood East, Milton Keynes, MK14 6PL Tel: (01908) 550039 Fax: (01908) 696120 E-mail: sales@comm-tec.co.uk *Audio & visual equipment*

▶ Commtech Associates Ltd, 149 Melrose Avenue, London, SW19 8AU Tel: (020) 8944 9036 Fax: (020) 8944 9036 E-mail: ctassociates@btconnect.com *Welding & corrosion engineering & consultancy*

▶ Commtech It Solutions Ltd, 101 Lockhurst Lane, Godiva Trading Estate, Coventry, CV6 5SF Tel: (0871) 7112172 E-mail: sales@commtech-it.com *Cisco repairs, hardware repairs, cisco hardware, UPS Battery replacement, APC systems, Asset valuations, Site clearance*

Comm-Tech Martham Ltd, 2 Rollesby Road, Martham, Great Yarmouth, Norfolk, NR29 4RU Tel: (01493) 748274 Fax: (01493) 740185 E-mail: enquiries@comm-tech.co.uk *Telecommunications systems & vehicle security sales & services*

Commtech Trading Co. (Lancashire) Ltd, 5 Petre Road, Clayton Park Industrial Estate, Accrington, Lancashire, BB5 5JB Tel: (01254) 232638 Fax: (01254) 301197 E-mail: sales@commtechcomm.com *Cable distributors*

▶ Communicate, The Old Barn, East Hanningfield Road, Rettendon Common, East Hanningfield, Chelmsford, CM3 8EW Tel: 01245 400044 Fax: 01245 400469 E-mail: office@communicateuk.co.uk *Specialists in security & communications*

Communicating Ltd, Incom House, 370 Old Street, London, EC1V 9LT Tel: (020) 7613 4747 Fax: (020) 7353 4949 *Software development*

Communication Arts, Horsemans Hill Barn, Gore Lane, Uplyme, Lyme Regis, Dorset, DT7 3RJ Tel: (01297) 444707 Fax: (01297) 444934 E-mail: info@communicationarts.co.uk *Technical Author /Writer specialising in software user documentation, business process & procedure manuals, company newsletters, reports, data & product sheets, marketing & technical copywriting, and training manuals. *Extensive experience including the Pharmaceutical, Government, Financial, Medical, Police & ISP sectors. *Also specialist web design & creation consultancy focusing on usability, navigation, clarity of information and accessibility.*

Communication Centre (International) Ltd, 60 Riverside I I I, Sir Thomas Longley Road, Strood, Rochester, Kent, ME2 4BH Tel: (01634) 295295 Fax: (01634) 723895 E-mail: enquiries@commscentre.com *Fibre optics distributors & agents*

▶ Communication Eleven, Hill View, Mid-Holmwood Lane, Mid Holmwood, Dorking, Surrey, RH5 4HD Tel: (01306) 881137 Fax: (01306) 881137 E-mail: info@4x4cb.com *CB radio prm 446 suppliers*

▶ Communication In Print, 31 Ormside Way, Redhill, RH1 2LW Tel: (01737) 761987 Fax: (01737) 779188 E-mail: sales@ukcip.co.uk

Communication Skills Europe Ltd, 91 Charterhouse Street, London, EC1M 6HL Tel: (020) 7670 0500 Fax: (020) 7670 0515 E-mail: cse@cseltd.co.uk *Commercial & office training services*

Communication Systems, 82 Elm Grove, Worthing, West Sussex, BN11 5LJ Tel: (01903) 532323 Fax: (01903) 700238 *Second hand phone distributors*

Communication Technology 2000, Hardy Street, Eccles, Manchester, M30 7NB Tel: 0161-789 0222 Fax: 0161-788 0111 E-mail: sales@commtech2000.co.uk *Computer consultants*

▶ Communications Co., Pickwood Hall, Pickwood Avenue, Leek, Staffordshire, ST13 5BZ Tel: (01538) 372424 Fax: (01538) 388238 *Radio communications equipment manufrs*

▶ Communications Express Ltd, 7 Grafton Place, Dukes Park Industrial Estate, Chelmsford, CM2 6TG Tel: (01245) 459490 Fax: (0845) 2000257 E-mail: sales@comms-express.com *Computer network consultants*

Communications Software Airline Systems Ltd, 8 The Centre, Church Road, Colchester, CO5 0HF Tel: (01621) 817425 Fax: (01621) 817262 E-mail: info@commsoft.co.uk Principal Export Areas: Central America *Software house*

▶ Communications & Sound Systems Ltd, Unit 1, Sandhurst Barn, Sandhurst Lane, Bexhill-On-Sea, East Sussex, TN39 4RH Tel: (01424) 848400 Fax: (01424) 848300 E-mail: sales@commsandsound.com *Sales, installation & maintenance of professional electronics services*

Communications South Ltd, 284 Hayling Avenue, Portsmouth, PO3 6EF Tel: (023) 9283 3993 Fax: (023) 9283 3288 E-mail: sales@commsouth.co.uk *Telephone equipment agents distributors*

Communications & Surveillance Systems Ltd, 3 Portman Square, London, W1H 6LB Tel: (020) 7486 3885 Fax: (020) 7486 2655 E-mail: sales@spymaster.co.uk *Electronic surveillance*

Communications Systems Maintenance, 38 George V Avenue, Margate, Kent, CT9 5QA Tel: (01843) 231782 Fax: (01843) 224292 *Specialist mobile radio distributors & maintenance services*

Communications UK Ltd, Comms House, Collingwood Road, Wimborne, Dorset, BH21 6QF Tel: (01202) 894222 Fax: (01202) 892262 E-mail: sales@comms.uk.com *Install & maintain telecommunication systems*

▶ Communicopia Productions Ltd, 27, Foundry Street, Brighton, BN1 4AT Tel: (01273) 691333 Fax: (01273) 683399

Comm-Unique Aquarious Ltd, 3 Sillins Hall, Sillins Lane, Callow Hill, Redditch, Worcestershire, B97 5TP Tel: (01527) 404100 Fax: (01527) 404503 *Telecommunication agents*

Communique Print Services Ltd, 3-11 Little Peter Street, Manchester, M15 4PS Tel: 0161-274 0105 Fax: 0161-236 1251 E-mail: manchester@staniforth.co.uk *Commercial printers*

Communique Public Relations Ltd, Waterside, 2 Canal Street, Manchester, M1 3HE Tel: 0161-228 6677 Fax: 0161-228 7391 E-mail: info@communiquepr.co.uk *Public relations consultants*

Communisis Security Products Ltd, Trafford Wharf Road, Trafford Park, Manchester, M17 1HE Tel: 0161-869 1000 Fax: 0161-869 1010 Principal Export Areas: Worldwide *Direct mail printers*

Communisis Security Products Ltd, Trafford Wharf Road, Trafford Park, Manchester, M17 1HE Tel: 0161-869 1000 Fax: 0161-869 1010 *Security printers*

Communitis Chorleys Ltd, Manston Lane, Leeds, LS15 8AH Tel: 0113-225 5000 Fax: 0113-225 5400 E-mail: sales@chorleys-communisis.co.uk *Direct mail services & security printers*

▶ Community Network Services Ltd, 204-207 Berth, Western Docks, Southampton, SO15 1DA Tel: (023) 8079 9601 Fax: (023) 8079 9602 *Software developers*

▶ Community Resourcing Ltd, 5-11 Lavington Street, London, London, SE1 0NZ Tel: (020) 76330007 E-mail: info@resourcinggroup.co.uk *Recruitment Solutions, Career Progression and Opportunities within: **Housing Management*Homelessness*Supported Housing*Customer Services*Tenant Participation*Strategy & Policy*Estate Wardens & Caretakers*Community Development*Housing Advice*Tenancy Services**

Community Security Products Ltd, Frances Street, Crewe, CW2 6HG Tel: (01270) 502600 Fax: (01270) 502601 *Cheque printing services*

Community Training Services NHS Trust, Oaklands Road, Salford, M7 3QQ Tel: 0161-792 9545 Fax: 0161-792 9708 *Health care consultants*

Comonin Garage, Mitchel Troy, Monmouth, Gwent, NP25 4BL Tel: (01600) 740623 Fax: (01600) 740623 *Agricultural merchants*

Compac Services Ne Ltd, Compac House, 173 Victoria Road, South Shields, Tyne & Wear, NE33 4NW Tel: 0191-454 9090 Fax: 0191-454 1212 E-mail: sales@compac.co.uk *Heating, ventilation & air conditioning*

Compack Ltd, 1 Letham Road, Houstoun Industrial Estate, Livingston, West Lothian, EH54 5BY Tel: (01506) 438654 Fax: (01506) 433815 *Cardboard box manufrs*

▶ Compact Data Management Ltd, 6 Leons Way, Tollgate Drive, Tollgate Industrial Estate, Stafford, ST16 3HS Tel: (01785) 220846 Fax: (01785) 220876 E-mail: sales@compact.uk.com *Document scanning & archiving service, data conversion, microfilm scanning, microfiche scanning, paper scanning services*

Compact Fork Trucks Ltd, Unit 8B Blackbrook Business Park, Narrowboat Way, Dudley, West Midlands, DY2 0XQ Tel: (01384) 238000 Fax: (01384) 240300 E-mail: sales@thecompactgroup.co.uk *Fork lift trucks, fork lift truck hire, reconditioned, second hand, used, electric, servicing, spare parts, hoist hire, scaffold hoists, rack & pinion, gantry, cable , platform, winch, covering the Midland, Dudley & West Bromwich*

▶ Compact Group Ltd, 4 Deacon Industrial Estate, Forstal Road, Aylesford, Kent, ME20 7SP Tel: (01622) 719365 Fax: (01622) 718831 E-mail: litho@compactlitho.co.uk

Compact Group Ltd, 4 Deacon Industrial Estate, Forstal Road, Aylesford, Kent, ME20 7SP Tel: (01622) 719365 Fax: (01622) 718831 E-mail: directmail@compactgroup.co.uk *Direct mail suppliers*

Compact Instruments Ltd, 61-65 Lever Street, Bolton, BL3 2AB Tel: (01204) 532544 Fax: (01204) 522285 E-mail: info@compactinstruments.co.uk Principal Export Areas: Worldwide *Manufacturers of tachometers, (including hand), electronic stroboscopes & speed indicators*

Compact Lighting Ltd, Dundas Spur, Portsmouth, PO3 5RW Tel: (023) 9265 2999 Fax: (023) 9265 3053 E-mail: info@compact-lighting.co.uk *Low energy lighting manufrs*

Compact Orbital Gears Ltd, Unit A Brynberth Industrial Estate, Rhayader, Powys, LD6 5EW Tel: (01597) 811676 Fax: (01597) 811677 E-mail: info@compactorbitalgears.com Principal Export Areas: Worldwide *Gear box manufrs*

▶ Compact Tractor World, 3 Three Cocks Lane, Offenham, Evesham, Worcestershire, WR11 8RY Tel: (01386) 761166

Compair UK Ltd, Reavell House, 53-56 White House Road, Ipswich, IP1 5PB Tel: (01473) 242000 Fax: (01473) 745451 E-mail: sales.ipswich@compair.com *High performance air compressor manufrs*

CompAir UK Ltd, Claybrook Drive, Washford Industrial Estate, Redditch, Worcestershire, B98 0DS Tel: (01527) 525522 Fax: (01527) 521140 E-mail: sales@compair.com Sales Contact: M Sanford-Casey *CompAir - Your Air and Gas Solution Company CompAir is one of the world's leading manfacturers of compressed air and gas systems, our range of products and services include the most efficient range of compressors on the market today. CompAir's compressors, equipment and services are in use across the globe providing economical, clean, quality and reliable compressed air and gas for almost every conceivable application. From general industry, offshore, oil-free, construction, high pressure marine to gas compression, CompAir has a product range including rotary screw, oil-free, vane, piston, and portable compressors, ancillary products and services to satisfy all requirements.*

▶ Companyclean Ltd, Unit 2A 83 Prestbury Road, Cheltenham, Gloucestershire, GL52 2DR Tel: (01242) 572918 E-mail: sales@companyclean.co.uk *Commercial cleaning contractor*

Compaq Ltd, 50 The Highlands, Edgware, Middlesex, HA8 5HL Tel: (020) 8381 1180 Fax: (020) 8621 3050 E-mail: sales@netlineltd.co.uk *Hardware computer consultancy*

▶ Compass Inc Ltd, Regus House, Fairbourne Drive, Atterbury, Milton Keynes, MK10 9RG Tel: (01908) 487509 Fax: (01908) 787501 E-mail: info@compassinc.co.uk *Exhibition stands, design and build, UK and international, marketing support, graphics, design, web design and development specialising in corporate web sites, online catalogues, asset management and image libraries.*

▶ Compass Business Promotions Ltd, 16 Crosslee Gardens, Crosslee, Johnstone, Renfrewshire, PA6 7AF Tel: (01505) 613569 Fax: (01505) 612603

Compass Communications Northern Ltd, 3 Lewis Road, Sidcup, Kent, DA14 4NB Tel: (020) 8309 1400 Fax: (020) 8300 2062 E-mail: compass@compass-comm.co.uk *Data network support services*

Compass Components, Greta Lodge, Southey Hill, Keswick, Cumbria, CA12 5ND Tel: (01768) 772118 Fax: (01768) 772118 *Hand tool distributors*
Compass Group plc, Compass House, Guilford Street, Chertsey, Surrey, KT16 9BQ Tel: 0121-457 5555 Fax: (01932) 569956 *Contract foodservice* Also at: Branches throughout the U.K.
Compass Industrial Manufacturing, Units 26-27 Izons Industrial Estate, Oldbury Road, West Bromwich, West Midlands, B70 9BS Tel: 0121-553 1298 Fax: 0121-500 6452 *Screw & fastener manufrs*
▶ Compass Lift Truck Services Ltd, Unit 15b, Lowley Road, Pennygillam Industrial Estate, Launceston, Cornwall, PL15 7PY Tel: (01566) 777750 Fax: (01566) 777746 E-mail: info@compasslifttrucks.co.uk *Fork lift truck hire services sales*
▶ Compass Marine Services, 156 South Street, Lancing, West Sussex, BN15 8AU Tel: (01903) 761773 *Marine fitting & repair services*
Compass Marquees, East Oakdene, Headcorn, Ashford, Kent, TN27 9JF Tel: (01622) 892254 Fax: (01622) 891473 E-mail: tents@compass-marquees.co.uk *Tent & marquee hire services*
Compass Oilfield Supply Co. Ltd, James Watt Close, Great Yarmouth, Norfolk, NR31 0NX Tel: (01493) 667037 Fax: (01493) 653603 E-mail: intray@compass-hq.com Principal Export Areas: Worldwide *Instrumentation equipment distribs*
Compass Print Ltd, Hareness Road, Altens Industrial Estate, Aberdeen, AB12 3LE Tel: (01224) 875987 Fax: (01224) 896137 E-mail: info@compassprint.co.uk *Printers*
Compass Printing Packaging Ltd, 49-51 Bridgeman Place, Bolton, BL2 1DE Tel: (01204) 527130 Fax: (01204) 381629 E-mail: mail@compasslabels2002.freeserve.co.uk *Label manufacturers & printers*
▶ Compass Recruitment Solutions Ltd, Suite 37, Thamesgate House, 37 Victoria Avenue, Southend-on-Sea, SS2 6DF Tel: (01702) 431311 Fax: (01702) 431322 *IT & general office recruitment services*
Compass Relocation Ltd, 5a Oxenturn Rd, Wye, Ashford, Kent, TN25 5BH Tel: (01233) 813305 Fax: (01233) 812730 *Relocation consultants*
Compass Shipping & Trading Co. Ltd, Office No. 10, 34-35 Hatton Garden, London, EC1N 8DX Tel: (020) 7242 6116 Fax: (020) 7242 3143 *Ship repairs services*
▶ Compass Tractors Ltd, Manor Farm, Hele, Taunton, Somerset, TA4 1AH Tel: (01823) 462999 Fax: (01823) 462998 *Agricultural machinery retailers*
Compat Europe Ltd, 24 Harnham Trading Estate, Salisbury, SP2 8NW Tel: (01722) 326411 Fax: (01722) 326413 E-mail: compat@tesco.net *Packaging materials & adhesive tape printing manufrs*
Compatibility Ltd, Park Road, Crowborough, East Sussex, TN6 2QX Tel: (01892) 665326 Fax: (01892) 665607 E-mail: info@compatibility.co.uk *Computer supply & distributors*
Comp-Connection, 4 Park Grove, Belhelvie, Belhelvie, Aberdeen, AB23 8YG Tel: (07713) 508201 Fax: (01358) 743666 E-mail: sales@comp-connection.co.uk *Computer networking & security installers*
Compelsolve Ltd, Bishops Court, Solihull Parkway, Birmingham Business Park, Birmingham, B37 7YD Tel: 0121-329 0200 Fax: 0121-329 0201 E-mail: birmingham.reception@compelsolve.com *Corporate resellers*
Compere Systems Ltd, Ivy Street, Birkenhead, Merseyside, CH41 5EE Tel: 0151-647 7457 Fax: 0151-666 2569 E-mail: davidj@comperesystems.com *Control system designers*
Compete IT Ltd, 5 Watling Court, Attleborough Fields Industrial Estate, Nuneaton, Warwickshire, CV11 6GX Tel: (0870) 2202644 Fax: (0870) 2202643 E-mail: info@compete-it.co.uk *Business to business software*
▶ Competel Ltd, Old Skene Road, Kingswells, Aberdeen, AB15 8QA Tel: (01224) 742550
▶ Competitive Cleaning, 4 Haselden Crescent, Wakefield, West Yorkshire, WF2 8NW Tel: (01924) 382716 Fax: 07849 343175 E-mail: competitiveclean@yahoo.co.uk *Affordable and reliable home cleaning and ironing service throughout Wakefield and Leeds..*Flexible,trustworthy,fully insured,COSHH trained.Reduced rates for Senior Citizens.*
Compex Computer Services, Heritage Works, First Floor Winterstoke Road, Weston-super-Mare, Avon, BS24 9AN Tel: (01934) 645044 Fax: (01934) 645077 E-mail: sales@compexcomputers.com *Networking & computer engineers*
Compex Development & Marketing Ltd, Century House, The Lake, Northampton, NN4 7HD Tel: (01604) 233333 Fax: (01604) 233334 E-mail: sales@compexdm.co.uk *Computer systems & software services*
Compfix Enterprises Ltd, 119 Manchester Road, Chorlton cum Hardy, Manchester, M21 9PG Tel: 0161-881 2395 Fax: 0161-881 2395 E-mail: sales@compfixpc.co.uk *Computer repairs*
Complete, Midland House, London Road, Chesterton, Newcastle, Staffordshire, ST5 7JB Tel: (01782) 562249 Fax: (01782) 566612 *Installation distributors*
▶ Complete, Calcot Lane, Curdridge, Southampton, SO32 2BN Tel: (01489) 797979 Fax: (01489) 797978 E-mail: malcolm@completemaintenance.co.uk *Plumbing, heating & swimming pool maintenance services*
Complete Air Systems, Unit H & I Maybrook Industrial Estate, Maybrook Road, Walsall, WS8 7DG Tel: (01543) 361301 Fax: (01543) 372530 *Sheet metal fabrications & ductwork*
Complete Bookkeeping Payroll Services Ltd, 12 Hatherley Road, Sidcup, Kent, DA14 4BG Tel: (020) 8308 0317 Fax: (020) 8302 7421 *Specialists in payroll*
▶ Complete Business Logistics, Hill Farm, Fillongley Road, Coleshill, Birmingham, B46 2QU Tel: (01675) 467890
Complete Business Systems, Studio 3 Highfield Farm, Huncote Road, Stoney Stanton, Leicester, LE9 4DJ Tel: (01455) 271222 Fax: (01455) 271071 *Software developers*
▶ Complete Catering Advice, 7 Market Street, Kettering, Northants, NN16 0AH Tel: (01536) 481973 E-mail: Info@completecateringadvice.co.uk *Catering consultancy and advice.*Providing you with the information you require for your business to grow in the way you want it to, and not others. From small to large problems lets share it and put you back in control.*
Complete Catering & Engineering Services Ltd, 29-30 Milk Street, Birmingham, B5 5TR Tel: 0121-633 0110 Fax: 0121-633 0399 *Catering & engineering manufrs*
▶ Complete CCTV, Ty Crwn, Llangoed, Beaumaris, Isle of Anglesey, LL58 8NR Tel: (01248) 490575 E-mail: info@completecctv.co.uk *CCTV installer with particular expertise in mobile and temporary CCTV applications.*Independent CCTV Consultancy.*Clients include local authorities, police, international consulting engineers and traffic and transportation professionals acting as agents for major UK retailers.**
▶ Complete Cladding Co., 13 Roundmoor Drive, Cheshunt, Waltham Cross, Hertfordshire, EN8 9HZ Tel: (01992) 622299 Fax: 01992 622299 E-mail: wayne@thecompletecladdingcompany.com *The complete cladding company specialises in domestic and commercial replacement fascias, soffits, guttering and all aspects of roofing undertaken.Covering the M25 and home counties.*
Complete Cleaning Services Scotland, 6 Muriel Street, Barrhead, Glasgow, G78 1QB Tel: 0141-880 8118 Fax: 0141-880 6673 E-mail: info@completecleaningservices.com *Commercial cleaning contractors*
Complete Coffee Ltd, 1 Kentish Buildings, 125 Borough High Street, London, SE1 1NP Tel: (020) 7403 8787 Fax: (020) 7403 5276 E-mail: coffee@completecoffe.co.uk *Coffee merchants*
Complete Connections, 75 Milford Road, Reading, RG1 8LG Tel: 0118-959 4286 Fax: 0118-950 5263 E-mail: sales@cableshop.co.uk *Computer cable, point of sale & loom manufrs*
Complete Design Installations Ltd, 63 Austhorpe Road, Crossgates, Leeds, LS15 8EQ Tel: 0113-294 3909 Fax: 0113-294 3909 *Specialists in all work, i.e. all electrical work for domestic & business, refurbishment's from design, planning & installation,plumbing, building maintenance, all ground work building & maintenance. All in-house work fully approved & guaranteed*
Complete Engineering Systems Ltd, The Lower Barn, Tilburstow Hill Road, South Godstone, Godstone, Surrey, RH9 8LY Tel: (01342) 893788 Fax: (01342) 893988 *Systems engineering*
Complete Event Solutions, Lymington Bottom Road, Four Marks, Alton, Hampshire, GU34 5DL Tel: (01420) 561105 Fax: (01420) 561105 E-mail: info@completeeventsolutions.com *Corporate hospitality, event management & conference production*
▶ Complete Events, Events House Red Shute Hill Industrial Estate, Red Shute Hill, Hermitage, Thatcham, Berkshire, RG18 9QL Tel: (01635) 202466 Fax: (01635) 202467 E-mail: sales@completeevents.co.uk *Marquee hire*
Complete Fabrication Ltd, Unit B1, Faircharm Studios, 8-12 Creekside, London, SE8 3DX Tel: (020) 8694 9666 Fax: (020) 8694 9669 E-mail: mail@completefabrication.com *Art and design bespoke model making service. Work includes art facilitation, commercial and retail display, interior design fabrication, architectural features, lighting, bespoke objects.*
Complete Fire Protection Ltd, Unit 32, Moor Park Industrial Centre, Tolpits Lane, Watford, WD18 9SP Tel: (01923) 251446 Fax: (01923) 801170 E-mail: cfirep@tiscali.co.uk *Fire alarms supplier to businesses, fire extinguisher training*
Complete Gardeners Ltd, Timberyard, 2 Mile Lane, Highnam, Gloucester, GL2 8DW Tel: (01452) 523078 Fax: (01452) 309323 E-mail: cotswoldpools@aol.com *Swimming pool constructors*
▶ Complete Gas Maintenance, St James Business Centre, 10A Linwood Road, Linwood, Paisley, Renfrewshire, PA3 3AT Tel: 0141-887 3798
▶ Complete Health & Safety, 15-19 Norway Street, Portslade, Brighton, BN41 1GN Tel: (01273) 833919 Fax: (01273) 414199 E-mail: info@complete-hs.co.uk *Health & safety consultancy and training services for companies from all sectors in the South East. Accredited (IOSH and CIEH)and general H&S training courses are run in-house or as open courses in Sussex. Please see our website for more details about our services.*
Complete Home Security, 467 Liverpool Road, Southport, Merseyside, PR8 3BN Tel: (01704) 579844 Fax: (01704) 579844 *Burglar alarm manufrs*
▶ Complete Hydraulic Services Ltd, Unit 46 Weaver Industrial Estate, Blackburne Street, Liverpool, L19 8JA Tel: 0151-494 3887 Fax: 0151-494 2388
Complete Imaging plc, 62 Ravenhurst Street, Birmingham, B12 0EL Tel: 0121-766 2000 Fax: 0121-766 5404 E-mail: sales@completeplc.co.uk *Photocopier & facsimile supplies*
Complete Industrial Services Ltd, 63 Cromwell Road, Bushbury Wolverhampton, Wolverhampton, WV10 8UT Tel: (01902) 651795 Fax: (01902) 651795 E-mail: sales@ciservices.worldonline.co.uk *Automation services*
Complete Integrated Services, 4 Seville House, Wapping High Street, London, E1W 1NX Tel: (020) 7481 0943 *Computer trainers*
Complete Interior Contracts, Caxton Hall, 88-92 Chapel Street, Salford, M3 5DW Tel: 0161-834 1285 Fax: 0161-834 2170 *Partitioning & ceiling contractors*
Complete Interiors, Ansell Road, Inscape House, Dorking, Surrey, RH4 1QN Tel: (01306) 882198 Fax: (01306) 876427 E-mail: info@completeinteriors.co.uk *Office refurbishers*
Complete It, 3 The Courtyard, Furlong Road, Bourne End, Buckinghamshire, SL8 5AU Tel: (01628) 552850 Fax: (01628) 552851 E-mail: sales@complete-it.co.uk *Computer consultancy*
▶ Complete Joinery Services, Freeman Road, North Hykeham, Lincoln, LN6 9AP Tel: (01522) 509675 Fax: (01522) 509673 E-mail: info@completejoineryservices.co.uk *Joinery manufrs*
Complete Kitchens, 56-58 Springbank Road, London, SE13 6SN Tel: (020) 8852 5926 Fax: (020) 8244 0907 E-mail: completekitchens@talk21.com *Kitchen, bedroom & bathroom fitters*
▶ Complete Laboratory Installations, 5 Loughborough Technology Centre, Epinal Way, Loughborough, Leicestershire, LE11 3GE Tel: (01509) 611322 Fax: (01509) 611416 E-mail: sales@completelabs.co.uk *Complete laboratory design & installation service*
▶ Complete Leisure Ltd, 5 Spectrum Business Estate, Bircholt Road, Maidstone, Kent, ME15 9YP Tel: (01622) 683628 Fax: (01622) 683576 E-mail: sales@completebowling.co.uk *Bowling equipment & alley maintenance*
▶ Complete Packaging Ltd, Oaklands Business Park, Old Icknield Way, Benson, Wallingford, Oxfordshire, OX10 6PW Tel: (01491) 832222 Fax: (01491) 834222 E-mail: sales@completepackaging.co.uk
▶ Complete Packaging Solutions, 52-54 Hayhill Industrial Estate, Barrow upon Soar, Loughborough, Leicestershire, LE12 8LD Tel: (01509) 816262 Fax: (01509) 816488 E-mail: sales@completepackagingsolutions.com *Packaging manufrs*
▶ Complete Polythene Packaging, Hanney Road, Steventon, Abingdon, Oxfordshire, OX13 6AP Tel: (01235) 820610 Fax: (01235) 820710 E-mail: compolypack@tiscali.co.uk *Packaging supplies*
Complete Preservation Service Ltd, 4-5 Wyvern House, Harriers Trading Estate, Stadium Close, Kidderminster, Worcestershire, DY10 1NJ Tel: (01562) 69945 Fax: (01562) 69945 E-mail: complete.preservation@ukonline.co.uk *Building preservation*
Complete Projects CDM Ltd, 25 Cadman Street, Mosborough, Sheffield, S20 5BU Tel: 0114-251 4106 Fax: 0114-251 4106 E-mail: info@completeprojectscdm.co.uk *Health & safety consultants & construction design & management*
▶ Complete Property Maintenance Ltd, Broadcroft Business Centre, 24 Broadcroft, Kirkintilloch, Glasgow, G66 1HP Tel: 0141-775 2200 Fax: 0141-775 2063
Complete Sign Experience Ltd, 20 Fox Croft, Tibshelf, Alfreton, Derbyshire, DE55 5QR Tel: (01773) 590163 Fax: (01773) 590163 *Sign manufrs*
Complete Signs, 226 High Street, Croydon, CR9 1DF Tel: (0870) 8707331 Fax: (0870) 8707332 E-mail: sales@completesigns.co.uk *Sign contractors, suppliers, installers*
Complete Solution, 12 High Street, Newhall, Swadlincote, Derbyshire, DE11 0HX Tel: (01283) 229466 Fax: (01283) 229466 *Chemical manufrs*
Complete Support Group Ltd, The Garden House, Castle Bromwich, Chester Road, Birmingham, B36 9DE Tel: 0121-776 7766 Fax: 0121-776 7666 E-mail: enquiries@completesupport.co.uk *Conference organising services*
▶ Complete Technical Services Ltd, Hope Street, Rotherham, South Yorkshire, S60 1LH Tel: (01709) 821757 Fax: (01709) 385068 E-mail: gary.collinson@complete-tech.co.uk *Building maintenance contractors*
▶ Complete Telecoms Ltd, 132 Henwick Road, Worcester, WR2 5PB Tel: (0845) 4564110 Fax: (0870) 0528973 E-mail: enquiries@completetelecoms.co.uk *Suppliers of new & used telecoms equipment & spares*
▶ Complete Temperature Solutions Ltd, Unit 1, Gardners Business Park, Brent Road, Cossington, Bridgwater, Somerset, TA7 8LF Tel: (01278) 723744
Complete Tooling Solutions Ltd, Kinmel Park, Royal Welch Avenue, Abergele Road, Bodelwyddan, Rhyl, Denbighshire, LL18 5TY Tel: (01745) 583917 Fax: (01745) 584018 E-mail: darren.foster@completetoolingsolutions.com *Established in 2004, Complete Tooling Solutions provides clients with a package of tooling solutions, from product design to implementation. With decades of experience, our highly experienced team operate on a UK wide basis and through our excellent reputation for quality of service and speed of delivery among clients, we have become one of the leading tool-making organisations in the UK Complete Tooling Solutions have extensive experience in manufacturing precision components for a wide variety of engineering industries, from automotive and medical to white goods and transport.*
Complex Ltd, 1st Floor, 199 Cumberland Road, Stanmore, Middlesex, HA7 1EL Tel: (020) 8206 2067 Fax: (020) 8204 2294 E-mail: complex@jayaar.com *Export merchants*
▶ Complex Online, Rear of, 130 Handsworth Road, Sheffield, S9 4AE Tel: 0114-256 1010 Fax: 0114-256 1010 E-mail: sales@complexonline.co.uk *Computer software manufrs*
▶ Complexatools Precision Engineers, Railway Stables, Surrey Street, Glossop, Derbyshire, SK13 7AJ Tel: (01457) 864446 Fax: (01457) 861010 E-mail: enquiries@complexatools.co.uk
▶ Compliance Inspection Services Ltd, 16 Thistlewood Road Outwood, Wakefield, West Yorkshire, WF1 3HH Tel: (01924) 829411 E-mail: bill@compliance-is.co.uk *STATUTORY ENGINEERING INSPECTION*
Compliance Modules Ltd, Platts La Industrial Estate, Burscough, Ormskirk, Lancashire, L40 7TP Tel: (0791) 7407559 Fax: (01704) 891501E-mail: sales@compliancemodules.co.uk *Design, manufacture & installation of safety & acoustic enclosures*
Compliant Business Systems Ltd, PO Box 25, King's Lynn, Norfolk, PE30 4AR Tel: (01553) 660500 Fax: (01553) 660500 E-mail: mail@compliant.co.uk *Software house*
▶ Complicad Ltd, 75a Phyllis Avenue, Peacehaven, East Sussex, BN10 7RA Tel: (01273) 582347 Fax: (01273) 582347 E-mail: complicad@btopenworld.com *CAD consultancy in automotive & electrical fields suppliers*
Complus Teltronic Ltd, Sibleys Green, Thaxted, Dunmow, Essex, CM6 2NU Tel: (01371) 830326 Fax: (01371) 831096 E-mail: enquires@complusteltronic.co.uk *Intercom solutions*
▶ Comply at Work Health and Safety Consultancy &Training, 5 Vale Coppice, Horwich, Bolton, BL6 5RP Tel: (01204) 690851 Fax: (01204) 690851 E-mail: info@complyatwork.co.uk *Consultancy services*
Component Distributors Ltd, Blackwater Road, Newtownabbey, County Antrim, BT36 4UA Tel: (028) 9034 1900 Fax: (028) 9034 1977 E-mail: mail@cd-group.com *Vehicle spare part distributors*
▶ Component Erectors, 77 Main Road, East Wemyss, Kirkcaldy, Fife, KY1 4RQ Tel: (01592) 716600 Fax: (01592) 716237 E-mail: davecel@tiscali.co.uk *Sheet metalwork engineers, fabricators*
▶ Component Erectors Ltd, Levenmouth Business Centre, Hawkslaw Trading Estate, Riverside, Leven, Fife, KY8 4LT Tel: (01333) 429300
Component Forum Ltd, PO Box 20, Towcester, Northamptonshire, NN12 7XJ Tel: (01908) 543808 Fax: (01908) 543909 E-mail: enquiries@componentforum.co.uk *Electronic component distributors & sourcing*
Component Logistics Ltd, Milton Court Horsfield Way, Bredbury Park Industrial Estate, Bredbury, Stockport, Cheshire, SK6 2TD Tel: 0161-406 2800 Fax: 0161-406 2809 E-mail: cll@component-logistics.com *Component direct line logistic services*
Component Moulders, 4-5 Teville Industrials, Dominion Way, Worthing, West Sussex, BN14 8NW Tel: (01903) 235765 Fax: (01903) 212751 E-mail: sales@nordell.co.uk *COMPONENT MOULDERSare specialist injection moulders of technical & precision thermoplastic parts, with capacity up to 500 grams shot - 210 tonne lock. Virtually all thermoplastics & elastomers processed, including high-performance grades of LCP, PAA, PBT, PEEK, PEI, PPS, TPE, TPU, blends & specialist compounds. Services include mould-making, printing, insertion, ultra-sonic welding, product assembly, kanban & DLF deliveries - all with complete quality assurance. ISO9002 & Aerospace approvals.*
▶ Component One Europe Ltd, Knapp House, Howley, Chard, Somerset, TA20 3DU Tel: (01460) 234636 Fax: (01460) 234616 E-mail: info@componentone.co.uk *Computer software retailers*
▶ Component Solution, 3 Lyme Drive, Parklands, Stoke-on-Trent, ST4 6NW Tel: (01782) 610211 Fax: (01782) 715316
Component Source, 30 Greyfriars Road, Reading, RG1 1PE Tel: 0118-958 1111 Fax: 0118-958 9999 E-mail: sales@componentsource.com Principal Export Areas: Worldwide *Computer system suppliers*
▶ The Components Co. Ltd, Unit 30, Wem Business Park, New Street, Wem, Shrewsbury, SY4 5JX Tel: (01939) 235800 Fax: (01939) 233088 E-mail: dan@components-company.com *Custom led product solutions, rapid prototype development*
Components Automotive (73) Ltd, 4-6 Wulfrun Industrial Estate, Stafford Road, Wolverhampton, WV10 6HG Tel: (01902) 311499 Fax: (01902) 715213 E-mail: sales@comp.co.uk *Motor car wheel manufrs*
Components Direct, Nunn Brook Road, County Estate, Huthwaite, Sutton-In-Ashfield, Nottinghamshire, NG17 2HU Tel: (01623) 788400 Fax: (01623) 788488 E-mail: sales@comdirect.co.uk *Adhesive & fastener industrial) distributors*
Components Electronic & Lighting Ltd, 93 Chilton Way, Hungerford, Berkshire, RG17 0JF Tel: (01488) 684625 Fax: 01488 683184 E-mail: celclive@btconnect.com *Electronic component distributor*
Components & Products, P O Box 2053, Hockley, Essex, SS5 4WA Tel: (01702) 207247 Fax: (01702) 207224 *Systems engineers & transducer manufrs*
Components & Technology, Unit M Valley Way, Market Harborough, Leicestershire, LE16 7PS Tel: (01858) 439503 Fax: (01858) 466536 E-mail: sales@coldform.co.uk *Aluminium rivets & fasteners manufrs*
Components & Technology, Unit M Valley Way, Market Harborough, Leicestershire, LE16 7PS Tel: (01858) 439503 Fax: (01858) 466536 E-mail: sales@coldform.co.uk *Manufacturers of weld bolt, stud & nuts*
Composing Operations Ltd, Sheffield Road, Tunbridge Wells, Kent, TN4 0PD Tel: (01892) 511725 Fax: (01892) 511726 E-mail: compops@btconnect.com *Printing, scanning services & pre press bureau*
▶ Composing Room, 18 Leather Lane, London, EC1N 7SU Tel: (020) 7430 0861 Fax: (020) 7242 1854 E-mail: sales@thecomposingroom.com *Mac studio services*

Composite Cladding Systems Ltd, Eckington Business Park, Rotherside Road, Eckington, Sheffield, S21 4HL Tel: (01246) 434275 Fax: (01246) 434452 E-mail: mick.herbert@compclad.co.uk *Roofing contractors*

▶ Composite Entrance Doors Ltd, 7-9 Tannoch Drive, Cumbernauld, Glasgow, G67 2XX Tel: (01236) 739910 Fax: (01236) 782570

▶ Composite Integration, Unit 21f Saltash Industrial Estate, Saltash, Cornwall, PL12 6LF Tel: (01752) 849998 Fax: (01752) 849808 E-mail: info@composite-integration.co.uk *Closed mould processing services*

▶ Composite Systems, Gortrush Industrial Estate, Great Northern Road, Omagh, County Tyrone, BT78 5LU Tel: (028) 8224 8046 Fax: (028) 8224 8047 E-mail: info@compositedesign.ltd.uk *Metal deck flooring manufrs*

Composite Technology Ltd, Thruxton Airport, Thruxton, Andover, Hampshire, SP11 8PW Tel: (01264) 773361 Fax: (01264) 773980 E-mail: repairs@composite-technology.co.uk *Helicopter blade repairers*

Composite Tooling & Structures Ltd, Lola House, Clebe Road, Huntingdon, Cambridgeshire, PE29 7DS Tel: (01480) 459378 Fax: (01480) 455585 *Composite tooling & components for aerospace*

The Composites Centre, Imperial College, Prince Consort Road, London, SW7 2AZ Tel: (020) 7594 5084 Fax: (020) 7594 5083 E-mail: composites@imperial.ac.uk *Composite material testing services*

Compound Sections Ltd, Bond Avenue, Bletchley, Milton Keynes, MK1 1JS Tel: (01908) 622400 Fax: (01908) 622421 *Cold rolled metal sections*

Compre Group, 110 Fenchurch Street, London, EC3M 5JT Tel: (020) 7816 4400 Fax: (020) 7816 4401 E-mail: consult@compre-group.com *Outsourcing services for insurance industry* Also at: London EC3

Comprehensive Planning Associates (Overseas), Bromsash House, Bromsash, Ross-On-Wye, Herefordshire, HR9 7PL Tel: (01989) 750243 Fax: (01989) 750243 *Architects planners*

Compressed Air Contracts, 5b Alleysbank Road, Rutherglen, Glasgow, G73 1LX Tel: 0141-647 0007 Fax: 0141-647 9090 E-mail: glasgow@economatics.co.uk *Air compressor agents & distributors*

Compressed Air Management, 74a Regent Road, Bootle, Merseyside, L20 8DB Tel: 0151-933 7565 Fax: 0151-922 2962 E-mail: canb@btconnect.com *Compressor sales & service*

▶ Compressed Air Pipe Installations, 48 Leam Drive, Burntwood, Staffordshire, WS7 9JG Tel: (01543) 686258 E-mail: pipework@btopenworld.com *Compressor & Equiptment installations*

Compressed Air Services Ltd, Unit 22 Bordesley Trading Estate, Bordesley Green Road, Birmingham, B8 1BZ Tel: 0121-327 1700 Fax: 0121-322 0970 E-mail: pthomas@cas-ltd.uk.com *Repair & servicing of air tools*

Compressor & Air Equipment, Abbey Gate, Leicester, LE4 0AA Tel: 0116-251 4914 *Air compressor distributors*

Compressor Engineering Sales Ltd, Cunliffe Drive Industrial Estate, Cunliffe Drive, Kettering, Northamptonshire, NN16 8LD Tel: (01536) 520339 Fax: (01536) 310061 Purchasing Contact: Pulley Sales Contact: Green *Compressed air systems* Also at: Salford

▶ Compressor Maintenance Repair Services Ltd, Unit 24 Maybrook Industrial Estate, Maybrook Road, Walsall, WS8 7DG Tel: (01543) 453881 Fax: (01543) 453882 E-mail: sales@cmrs.co.uk *Supply & service of air compressors*

Compressor Service & Repairs Ltd, 9 Delph Road Indust Estate, Brierley Hill, West Midlands, DY5 1HD Tel: (01384) 480762 Fax: (01384) 480762 *Compressor sale & repairs service*

Compressor Specialists, 118 Alcester Road, Stratford-upon-Avon, Warwickshire, CV37 9DP Tel: (01789) 205635 Fax: (01789) 205635 E-mail: compressorspecialist@hotmail.com *Air compressor distributors & pipework services*

Compressor Systems South West Ltd, 5 Riverside Business Park, St Annes Road, St. Annes Park, Bristol, BS4 4ED Tel: 0117-977 4531 Fax: 0117-972 3650 E-mail: sales@compressorsystems.co.uk *Air compressor distributors & agents*

Compressor Valve Engineering Ltd, 4 Burnell Road, Ellesmere Port, CH65 5EX Tel: 0151-355 5937 Fax: 0151-357 1098 E-mail: sales@compvalve.co.uk *Compressor valve manufrs*

Compressors Ltd, 145 Nottingham Road, Alfreton, Derbyshire, DE55 7FL Tel: (01773) 836816 Fax: (01773) 520556 E-mail: compressors@fsbdial.co.uk *Compressor accessories & services*

Compressors & Systems Suppliers Ltd, Cane End Lane, Bierton, Aylesbury, Buckinghamshire, HP22 5BH Tel: (01296) 415000 Fax: (01296) 434363 E-mail: graham@cass-air.co.uk *Air compressor, pneumatic equipment & systems sales*

Compressors & Washers Ltd, James David Building, 134 Widemarsh Street, Hereford, HR4 9HN Tel: (01432) 268799 Fax: (01432) 279922 E-mail: sales@compressorsandwashers.co.uk *Pressure equipment suppliers & compressed air specialists*

▶ Compromitto, 151 West George St, Glasgow, G2 2JJ Tel: 0141 2284737 *Dispute Resolution & Mediation Service Provider To The UK Construction Industry*

Compserve Ltd, 130 Cowley Road, Cambridge, CB4 0DL Tel: (01223) 425777 Fax: (01223) 424387 E-mail: info@compserve.co.uk *Computer consultants suppliers*

Compsoft plc, Equinox House, Oriel Court, Alton, Hampshire, GU34 2YT Tel: (01420) 89545 Fax: (01420) 81444 E-mail: sales@compsoft.co.uk *Computer software house*

Compton Engineering Ltd, Cheapside, Bridgend Industrial Estate, Bridgend, Mid Glamorgan, CF31 3UN Tel: (01656) 654341 Fax: (01656) 669936 E-mail: comptoneng@aol.com *General engineers*

Compu Hut, 54 Union Street, Melksham, Wiltshire, SN12 7PR Tel: (01225) 708181 Fax: (01225) 708181 *Computer rebuilding & repairers*

Compuchange, 14 Parson Street, London, NW4 1QB Tel: (020) 8203 3363 Fax: (020) 8202 0860 *Computer support & maintenance*

Compucorp Ltd, Unit 37 Watford Metro Centre, Dwight Road, Watford, WD18 9SB Tel: (01923) 220121 E-mail: info@compucorp.co.uk *Software developers*

Compudos Computer Sales Accessories, York Street, Manchester, M1 7DE Tel: 0161-274 4100 E-mail: sales@compudos.co.uk *Computer services*

Compugraphics International Ltd, Unit F Newark Road North, Glenrothes, Fife, KY7 4NT Tel: (01592) 772557 Fax: (01592) 775359 E-mail: enquiries@cgi.co.uk *'Photomask' for electronics industry manufrs*

Compunet Technology Ltd, 14 Carolina Place, Finchampstead, Wokingham, Berkshire, RG40 4PQ Tel: 0118-973 0584 E-mail: sales@compunet-technology.co.uk *Computer network installers*

Compuprint 2000, Centrepoint, North Street, Rotherham, South Yorkshire, S60 1LG Tel: (01709) 373322 Fax: (01709) 373344 *Printed stationery*

Compurange Ltd, 337 Derby Street, Bolton, BL3 6LR Tel: (01204) 651212 Fax: (01204) 658060 E-mail: info@compurange.co.uk *Computer software & system suppliers*

▶ Compusence, 6, Market Street, Soham, Ely, Cambs, CB7 5JG Tel: (01353) 722759 Fax: (01353) 725185

Compuserve Ltd, Fourth Floor, Albany House, Hurst Street, Birmingham, B5 4BD Tel: 0121-622 5050 Fax: 0121-622 3931 E-mail: enquiries@compuserveuk.co.uk *Software developers*

▶ Computa Centre, Carrick Business Centre, 4-5 Bonville Road, Bristol, BS4 5NZ Tel: 0117-316 0344 Fax: 0117-316 0399 E-mail: computacentre@blitz-it.com *IT vendors services*

Computa Services & Consultants Ltd, 310 Broughty Ferry Road, Dundee, DD4 7NJ Tel: (01382) 450011 Fax: (01382) 450601 E-mail: admin@computa.co.uk *Computer software developers & consultants*

Computacare Services, 2 Williams Way, Dartford, DA2 7WF Tel: (01322) 310728 Fax: (01322) 310728 E-mail: sales@computacare.co.uk *Specialists in data centre cleaning (technical cleaning) and computer /PC cleaning - ensuring the uninterrupted operation of your computer equipment and IT infrastructure.Covering London and the south east.*

Computacenter Ltd, The Glover Pavillion, Aberdeen Science And Tecnology Park, Balgownie Road, Bridge Of Don, Aberdeen, AB22 8GH Tel: (01224) 825000 *Computer services*

Computacentre, 1 West Point Court, Great Park Road, Bradley Stoke, Bristol, BS32 4PS Tel: (01454) 614444 Fax: (01454) 620803 *Computer systems & software sales*

Computaclean Computer Cleaning, 3 Church Road, Cam, Dursley, Gloucestershire, GL11 5PJ Tel: (01453) 544442 Fax: (01453) 544442 *Computer cleaning services*

▶ Computafixit.Com, 49 Oxford Road, Acocks Green, Birmingham, B27 6DS Tel: (0845) 8900689 E-mail: sales@computafixit.com

Computaform, 4 Merivale Road, Harrow, Middlesex, HA1 4BH Tel: (020) 8423 5005 Fax: (020) 8422 7216 E-mail: mail@computaform.com *Computer consumables*

Computalabel International Ltd, 2ND Floor, 53A London Road, Leicester, LE2 0PD Tel: 0116-255 7898 Fax: 0116-255 7899 E-mail: info@computalabel.com *Bar code systems manufrs*

Computaphile Software Soltuions Ltd, 13 Surrey Close, Rugeley, Staffordshire, WS15 1JZ Tel: (01889) 579572 Fax: (01889) 579572 E-mail: brian@computaphile.com *IT consultants*

Computational Dynamics Ltd, Hythe House, 200 Shepherds Bush Road, London, W6 7NL Tel: (020) 7471 6200 Fax: (020) 7471 6201 *Computer systems & software developers*

Computeach International Ltd, University House, Jews Lane, Dudley, West Midlands, DY3 2AH Tel: (01384) 458515 Fax: (01384) 455650 E-mail: info@computeach.co.uk *The Uks leading provider of IT distance Training* Also at: Branches throughout the U.K.

Computec Computers, 67 Frog Lane, Wigan, Lancashire, WN6 7DU Tel: (01942) 493400 Fax: (01942) 736967 *Computer repairers*

Computec Solutions Ltd, 566 Streatham High Road, London, SW16 3QQ Tel: (020) 8679 1717 Fax: (020) 8679 5245 E-mail: mail@computecltd.com *Computer maintenance services*

▶ Computec UK Ltd, 28A Bath Road, Swindon, SN1 4BA Tel: (01793) 420333 Fax: (01793) 541911

▶ Compu-Tech, 11 Balmoral CR, Okehampton, Devon, EX20 1GN Tel: (01837) 659714 *We provide a complete range of IT services to Business and Home users throughout Devon, Cornwall and Somerset.**All of our engineers are fully trained and certified by Microsoft and the Computing Technology Industry Association (CompTIA), and will offer a minimum guarantee period of 1 year on most work carried out. Certain cable installations come with a fully comprehensive 10 year guarantee. All work is carried out in compliance with ESD prevention procedures and precautions.**

▶ Computek, 21 Harewood Road, Oakworth, Keighley, West Yorkshire, BD22 7NS Tel: (0845) 0094265 Fax: (0871) 5971154 E-mail: help@computek-ltd.co.uk *IT problems solved small local businesses & home users*

Computel, 13 The Broadway, Thatcham, Berkshire, RG19 3JA Tel: (01635) 847701 *Telecommunications*

Computential Computer Systems, 70 Norris Road, Sale, Cheshire, M33 3QR Tel: 0161-969 2663 *Computer operating system developers*

Computer Aid, 4 Hothfield Road, Rainham, Gillingham, Kent, ME8 8BJ Tel: (01634) 262534 Fax: (01634) 267215 E-mail: denise@computer-aid.co.uk *Computer support*

Computer Aided Business Systems Ltd, 8 Forum Place, Fiddlebridge Lane, Hatfield, Hertfordshire, AL10 0RN Tel: (01707) 258338 Fax: (01707) 258339 E-mail: sales@cabs-cad.com *Computer designers*

Computer Associates Ltd, First Floor, Lynnfield House, Church St, Altrincham, Cheshire, WA14 4DZ Tel: 0161-928 9334 Fax: 0161-929 0292 E-mail: sales@cai.com *Computer software*

Computer Associates UK plc, Ditton Park, Riding Court Road, Datchet, Slough, SL3 9LL Tel: (01753) 577733 Fax: (01753) 825464 *Software*

Computer Base Ltd, 21 Market Avenue, Plymouth, PL1 1PG Tel: (01752) 672128 Fax: (01752) 668490 E-mail: sales@computerbase.co.uk *Computer retailers*

The Computer Broker/Direct Stationery Ltd, 80 Cricklade Street, Cirencester, Gloucestershire, GL7 1JN Tel: (0870) 2860891 Fax: (0870) 0632949 E-mail: sales@directstationery.net *IT technicians*

Computer Builders, 42 Janson Cl, London, E15 1TF Tel: 020 82212424 *Computer manufrs*

Computer Care 2000, 14 St. Bryde Street, East Kilbride, Glasgow, G74 4HQ Tel: (01355) 241628 Fax: (01355) 573073 E-mail: sales@cc2000.co.uk *Computer builders*

Computer Care Centre, 890 Romford Rd, London, E12 5JP Tel: (020) 8478 4789 Fax: (020) 8478 5699 *Computer company distributors & manufrs*

▶ The Computer Centre, Belmont Road, Exeter, EX1 2HF Tel: (01392) 204690 Fax: (01392) 204128 E-mail: sales@cobrexcomputers.com *Repair & sales of computer equipment*

Computer Centre Direct, 56 Battersea Rise, London, SW11 1EJ Tel: (020) 7228 1888 Fax: (020) 7228 8881 E-mail: ccconnect@btconnect.com *Computer component sales & repair services*

Computer Chaos, 1 Brookfield Dirve, Cannock, Staffordshire, WS11 0JN Tel: (01543) 578579 Fax: (01543) 571218 *Computer systems & software sales*

Computer Clinic Ltd, 204 Rayleigh Road, Hutton, Brentwood, Essex, CM13 1PN Tel: (01277) 261597 Fax: (01277) 261599 E-mail: guy@clinic2.freeserve.co.uk *Computer repairsers*

▶ Computer Commodities, Pittman Court, Pittman Court, Fulwood, Preston, PR2 9ZG Tel: (01772) 707240 Fax: (01772) 888241 E-mail: sales@computercommodities.com *Supplier of computer hardware*

Computer Communications Systems Consulting Ltd, 35 Thurloe Street, London, SW7 2LQ Tel: (020) 7581 5400 Fax: (020) 7584 4319 E-mail: enq@compcom.co.uk *Computer consultancy*

Computer Connection Retail, Unit 25, Holden Industrial Estate, Wombwell, Barnsley, South Yorkshire, S73 8HA Tel: (01226) 732975 Fax: (01226) 238139 E-mail: sales@ccretail.co.uk *Computer sales & repair*

▶ Computer Connections, 191 Donegall Street, Belfast, BT1 2FJ Tel: (028) 9032 4633 Fax: (028) 9032 4644 E-mail: matthew@computer-connections.info *Computer repair, sales, web design, web hosting, networking*

Computer Consultancy Group Ltd, Cathedral House, Beacon Street, Lichfield, Staffordshire, WS13 7AA Tel: (01543) 410498 Fax: (01543) 254307 *Consultants*

Computer Consultants, 22a Bellside Road, Cleland, Motherwell, Lanarkshire, ML1 5NP Tel: (01698) 861849 Fax: (01698) 861326 *Computer consultants*

Computer Consultants Ltd, Guild Street, Stratford-upon-Avon, Warwickshire, CV37 6RP Tel: (01789) 261200 Fax: (01789) 262525 E-mail: sales@cclnet.co.uk *Computer consultants*

▶ Computer Craft, Unit 26 Shaftesbury Centre, 83 Barlby Road, London, W10 6BN Tel: (020) 8964 0734

Computer Doctor Services Ltd, 20a Portland Road, Kilmarnock, Ayrshire, KA1 2BS Tel: (01563) 537733 Fax: (01563) 537733 E-mail: kellyenquiry@computerdoctorservice.co.uk *Computer maintenance, repair & consultancy*

▶ Computer Doctors Ltd, Unit 12 Blackthorn Industrial Estate, 40 Blackthorn Road, Northampton, NN3 8PT Tel: (01604) 411444 Fax: (0871) 2519099 E-mail: sales@computerdoctors.uk.net *Computer maintenance services*

▶ Computer England, Quadro, Ivy Mill, Failsworth, Manchester, M35 9BD Tel: 0870 2201835 Fax: 0870 2201836 *Computer England; The Global Provider of New, Used and Volume computer related products from main line manufactures.*Computer England recognize and provide for consumers looking for extra margin, constraint product and real services.*Computer England is a specialist distributor geared to allow a company to connect, to store, to network and to create.*

▶ Computer Future, Training at 2nd Floor , St Clare House, St Clare House, 30-33 The Minories, London, EC3N 1DD Tel: (020) 7798 5648 E-mail: sarah@computerfuture.net *Customised IT training, IT training, one-to-one IT training, One-to-one training, 1-1 training, word, excel, powerpoint, dreamweaver , access database, HTML, javascripts, train-the-trainer, train-the-IT-trainer, web design training, frontpage, photoshops*

▶ Computer Geek, 16 Fowey Close, Wellingborough, Northamptonshire, NN8 5WW Tel: (01933) 401010 E-mail: sales@thecomputergeek.co.uk *Computer repairs & maintenance*

Computer Help, 4 Roslyn Gardens, Llandudno, Gwynedd, LL30 1BS Tel: (01492) 871290 Fax: (01492) 871997 E-mail: y2000pc@aol.com *Computer support*

▶ Computer Home Help, 14 West Park Cr, Inverbervie, Montrose, Angus, DD10 0TX Tel: (01561) 362902 E-mail: lincoln.callander@btinternet.com *Computer Home Help - home visiting computer PC repairs, upgrades, new system builds, troubleshooting, internet problems, broadband installation, Virus & Spyware fixes and affordable website design for the home user and small business in Aberdeenshire and Angus. We come to you. No callout charge.*

▶ Computer Home Help, The Vineyard, Welwyn Garden City, Hertfordshire, AL8 7PU Tel: (01707) 690468 *IT Support services*

▶ Computer Hospital, 100 Camlough Road, Bessbrook, Newry, County Down, BT35 7EE Tel: (028) 3083 9888 E-mail: newrycomputerhospital@yahoo.co.uk *Computer repairers*

Computer Hospital, 7 Kings Parade, King St, Stanford-le-Hope, Essex, SS17 0HR Tel: (01375) 643690 *Programming*

Computer Hotline, 7 Blossom Waye, Hounslow, TW5 9HB Tel: (020) 8570 8275 Fax: (020) 8570 1152 *Transport computers*

Computer Junction, 276 Arundel Street, Portsmouth, PO1 1NT Tel: (023) 9282 5210 Fax: (023) 9282 5210 E-mail: cjsolent@btconnect.com *Computer suppliers*

Computer Junk Shop, 10 Waterloo Road, Widnes, Cheshire, WA8 0PY Tel: 0151-420 6671 Fax: 0151-420 6671 E-mail: info@computer-junkshop.co.uk *Component reclamation services*

▶ Computer Lan Services Ltd, 42 Baird Avenue, Dryburgh Industrial Estate, Dundee, DD2 3TN Tel: (01382) 880444 Fax: (01382) 823951

▶ Computer & Laptop Centre, 3 Savoy Lane, Newcastle, County Down, BT33 0SJ Tel: (028) 4372 6668 Fax: (028) 4372 6999 E-mail: info@computerandlaptopcentre.com *Computer peripherals & printer accessory suppliers*

Computer Links Ltd, 7 Grange Road, Houston Industrial Estate, Houstoun Industrial Estate, Livingston, West Lothian, EH54 5DE Tel: (01506) 434811 Fax: (01506) 441997 E-mail: service@computer-links.co.uk *Data cabling contractors*

Computer Luggage The Company, London Road, Unit 6, Marlborough, Wiltshire, SN8 2AP Tel: (01672) 519933 Fax: (01672) 519966 E-mail: sales@tehair.co.uk *Computer luggage manufrs*

▶ Computer M8, 159 Hale Lane, Edgware, Middlesex, HA8 9QW Tel: (020) 8959 0088

Computer Maintenance Cost Control, Windsor Bridge Works, Windsor Bridge Road, Bath, BA2 3DT Tel: (01225) 426066 E-mail: mail@cmcc.co.uk *Computer consultancy*

Computer Maintenance Services, 11 Carvoza Road, Truro, Cornwall, TR1 1BA Tel: (01872) 241062 Fax: (01872) 241062 *Computer maintenance services*

Computer Move Ltd, Unit 1, Lakeside Industrial Estate, Colnbrook By Pass, Colnbrook, Slough, SL3 0ED Tel: (01753) 283260 Fax: (01753) 689004 *Computer transportation services*

Computer Optical Products, 45 Leaver Road, Henley-On-Thames, Oxfordshire, RG9 1UW Tel: (01491) 412055 Fax: (01491) 413006 E-mail: sales@sensortronic.co.uk *Optical encoder manufrs* Also at: Henley-on-Thames

▶ Computer Orbit Ltd, 36-44 West Road, Newcastle upon Tyne, NE4 9PY Tel: 0191-242 0120 *It retail support*

The Computer Partnership Ltd, Berwick House, 8-10 Knoll Rise, Orpington, Kent, BR6 0EJ Tel: (01689) 898000 Fax: (01689) 898089 E-mail: marketing@tcplifesystems.com Principal Export Areas: Central/East Europe *Software development*

Computer People Ltd, Anglo City House, 2-6 Shirley Road, Southampton, SO15 3EU Tel: (023) 8021 0400 Fax: (023) 8021 0410 E-mail: southampton@computerpeople.co.uk *Recruitment agents*

Computer People Midlands Ltd, Alpha Tower, Suffolk St Queensway, Birmingham, B1 1TT Tel: 0121-643 8501 Fax: 0121-632 5996 E-mail: cpbirmingham@computerpeople.co.uk *IT consultants*

Computer Performance International Ltd, Outwoods, Oxford Road, Gerrards Cross, Buckinghamshire, SL9 7PU Tel: (01753) 890808 Fax: (01753) 890918 E-mail: mail@cpiuk.co.uk *IT consultants*

Computer Plus, 14 Scarrots Lane, Newport, Isle of Wight, PO30 1JD Tel: (01983) 826555 Fax: (01983) 821222 *Computer accessories suppliers*

▶ The Computer Point, 19C East Princes Street, Helensburgh, Dunbartonshire, G84 7DE Tel: (01436) 676017 Fax: (01436) 670136 E-mail: sales@thecomputerpoint.co.uk *Computer maintenance & repair services*

Computer Power Protection, 6 Lynwood Road, Liverpool, L9 3AF Tel: 0151-525 1387 Fax: 0151-525 9044 E-mail: info@cppsales.com *Backup power systems for computers*

Computer Precision Ltd, 185 Upper Street, London, N1 1RQ Tel: (020) 7359 9797 Fax: (020) 7359 9507 E-mail: 185@cipi.co.uk *Computer dealers*

Computer Press, 1 Rowles Way, Kidlington, Oxfordshire, OX5 1LA Tel: (01865) 849158 Fax: (01865) 374007 E-mail: sales@cpdirect.co.uk *Computer stationery printing services*

Computer Print, 23 West View, Chirk, Wrexham, LL14 5HL Tel: 01691 778320 Fax: 01691 774849 *Sign manufr*

Computer Project Services Ltd, 16 Bank Street, Lutterworth, Leicestershire, LE17 4AG Tel: (01455) 558231 Fax: (01455) 554299 E-mail: cv@cps-euro.com *IT consultants*

Computer Repair Centre, 32 The Avenue, St. Pauls Cray, Orpington, Kent, BR5 3DJ Tel: (020) 8556 5331 Fax: (020) 8556 8890 *Computer repairer & retailer*

Company Information

▶ Computer Repair Shop, 141c High Road, Loughton, Essex, IG10 4LT Tel: (0845) 1342003 Fax: (020) 8502 5900 E-mail: sales@crs2004.com *Computers repairs, upgrades & sales services*

▶ Computer Repair Shop, Weedon Road, Northampton, NN5 5DA Tel: (0800) 0933072 Fax: (01604) 590160 *Computer maintenance & repairers*

Computer Resale, 4 Mill Road, Cambridge, CB1 2AD Tel: (01223) 305007 Fax: (01223) 305008 E-mail: info@computerresale.co.uk *Computer resellers*

▶ Computer Resale Brokers, High Pavement, Nottingham, NG1 1HF Tel: 0115-959 6464 Fax: 0115-959 6467

Computer Research Consultant, Bell House, Kingsland, Leominster, Herefordshire, HR6 9RU Tel: (01568) 709180 Fax: (08456) 008250 *Computer auditing*

Computer Research Consultants Ltd, 9 Duke Street, Alderley Edge, Cheshire, SK9 7HX Tel: (01625) 582228 Fax: (01993) 822701 E-mail: sales@crc-computeraudit.co.uk *Auditing & computer research*

Computer Resourcing, 1 Woodlea Grove, Northwood, Middlesex, HA6 2DW Tel: (01923) 828848 *Computer systems & software sales*

Computer Response, Response House, Foundry Street, Chesterfield, Derbyshire, S41 9AU Tel: (01246) 450540 Fax: (01246) 450483 E-mail: sales@computer-response.com *Computer, sales, servicing & training*

Computer Risk Management, 2 Davyhulme Circle, Urmston, Manchester, M41 0SS Tel: 0161-749 7250 Fax: 0161-747 2476 *Computer repairs & maintenance*

▶ Computer Salvage Specialist Ltd, 5 Abex Road, Newbury, Berkshire, RG14 5EY Tel: (01635) 552666 Fax: (01635) 582990 E-mail: enquiries@computersalvagespecialists.com *Waste & recycling contractors*

Computer Scene, 5 Kings Street, Mildenhall, Bury St. Edmunds, Suffolk, IP28 7EZ Tel: (01638) 717726 Fax: (01638) 510079 E-mail: sales@computerscene.co.uk *Computer systems building & sales*

Computer Sciences Corporation, Bristol Data Centre, Station Road, Kingswood, Bristol, BS15 4NR Tel: 0117-991 2600 Fax: 0117-991 2650 *Computer systems & development software*

Computer Sciences Corporation, Euxton House, Euxton Lane, Chorley, Lancashire, PR7 6FE Tel: (01257) 265507 Fax: (01257) 242609 *Computer systems & software developers*

▶ Computer Security Co., 79 London Road, Whitchurch, Hampshire, RG28 7LX Tel: (01256) 893662 E-mail: info@computersecuritycompany.co.uk *IT & information security services*

▶ Computer Services & Engineers, Unit 4a Stag Industrial Estate, Atlantic Street, Broadheath, Altrincham, Cheshire, WA14 5DW Tel: 0161-941 4555 Fax: 0161-941 6182 E-mail: sales@cselimited.co.uk *Computer service & support*

Computer Shack Ltd, 11 Church Street, Tewkesbury, Gloucestershire, GL20 5PA Tel: (01684) 275757 Fax: (01684) 275670 *Network installation & support*

The Computer Shop, 2 New Rents, Ashford, Kent, TN23 1JH Tel: (01233) 613113 *Computer distributors*

The Computer Shop, 8 South Mall, Frenchgate Centre, Doncaster, South Yorkshire, DN1 1TT Tel: (01302) 326111 Fax: (01302) 326222 *Computer distributors*

▶ The Computer Shop, 69 Brockhurst Road, Gosport, Hampshire, PO12 3AR Tel: (023) 9252 2777 E-mail: sales@coppcomm.com *IT services*

The Computer Shop, 1 Brewery Street, Grimsby, South Humberside, DN31 1EJ Tel: (01472) 268777 *Computer wholesalers*

Computer Shop, 15 Hencotes, Hexham, Northumberland, NE46 2EQ Tel: (01434) 600022 Fax: (01434) 609262 E-mail: info@600022.com *Computer consultants*

▶ Computer Shop, Unit 8 Bargate Shopping Centre, Southampton, SO14 2YB Tel: (023) 8023 2261 Fax: (023) 8023 6560 *Computer suppliers*

Computer Software Group Plc, Merchants House, Wapping Wharf, Bristol, BS1 4RW Tel: 0117-926 6281 Fax: 0117-925 1330 *Computer software house* Also at: Bristol

Computer Software Group, Pepper House, Market Street, Nantwich, Cheshire, CW5 5DQ Tel: (01270) 613800 Fax: (01270) 613801 E-mail: info@computersoftware.com *Computer software manufrs*

Computer Solutions Ltd, 1A New Haw Road, Addlestone, Surrey, KT15 2BZ Tel: (01932) 829460 Fax: (01932) 840603 E-mail: sales@computer-solutions.co.uk *Embedded micro processing development tools*

▶ Computer Solutions, 7 Sandringham Cresent, Harrow, Middlesex, HA2 9BW Tel: (020) 8422 7570 Fax: (020) 8248 0548 E-mail: info@1001solutions.co.uk *Computer repairs, maintenance & support services*

Computer Solutions, 38 Chingford Mount Rd, London, E4 9AB Tel: 020 85318880 Fax: 020 85392338 *Computer solutions, sales & services*

Computer Solutions, 83 Station Road, West Wickham, Kent, BR4 0PX Tel: (020) 8777 2228 Fax: (020) 8777 2276 E-mail: sales@thecomputersolution.co.uk *Computer dealers*

Computer Solutions Grimsby Ltd, Wellowgate, Grimsby, South Humberside, DN32 0RA Tel: (01472) 311777 Fax: (01472) 311778 *Computer maintenance, networking & repairs*

Computer Solutions & Networks, 315 Lichfield Road, Sutton Coldfield, West Midlands, B74 4BZ Tel: 0121-323 3450 Fax: 0121-323 3358 E-mail: tony.h@csnuk.net *IT consultants services*

▶ Computer Sos Gampian Ltd, Howford, Inverurie, Aberdeenshire, AB51 4DL Tel: (01467) 622766 E-mail: info@comp-sos.co.uk *Computer repairs, rebuilds & upgrades*

Computer Station Ltd, Station House, Station Road, Rayleigh, Essex, SS6 7HL Tel: (01268) 746746 Fax: (01268) 746747 E-mail: sales@computerstation.co.uk *Computer repairers & suppliers*

Computer Store, 16 Priory Street, Carmarthen, Dyfed, SA31 1NA Tel: (01267) 221661 Fax: (01267) 222214 E-mail: sales@perfectcomputers.com *Computer hardware suppliers*

▶ Computer Store, 82 Boothferry Road, Goole, North Humberside, DN14 6AA Tel: (01405) 720099 *Computer maintenance & repair services*

Computer Support Services, 8 Baker Street, Rochester, Kent, ME1 3DW Tel: (01634) 407462 Fax: (01634) 409568 E-mail: tony@pobgee.demon.co.uk *Computer consultants*

Computer Surgery, Apple Barn, Maidstone Road, Pembury, Tunbridge Wells, Kent, TN2 4AD Tel: (0845) 1303343 Fax: (0870) 0118128 E-mail: sales@computer-surgery.co.uk *Computer repair & support*

▶ Computer Surplus, 106 Walcot Street, Bath, BA1 5BG Tel: (01225) 470077 Fax: (01225) 471166 *Computer software distributors*

Computer Systems Ltd, 33 Malmesbury Close, Pinner, Middlesex, HA5 2NG Tel: (01895) 623555 Fax: (01895) 631541 E-mail: enquiries@computer.dircon.co.uk *Computer hardware*

Computer Systems For Distribution plc, Croughton Lodge, High Street, Croughton, Brackley, Northamptonshire, NN13 5LT Tel: (01869) 810913 Fax: (01869) 810993 E-mail: sales@csfd.co.uk *Computer software house*

Computer Systems (Ireland) Ltd, Old Crow Building, Glen Road, Comber, Newtownards, County Down, BT23 5EL Tel: (028) 9187 3700 Fax: (028) 9087 4421 E-mail: cfiltd@btconnect.com *Wholesalers for nintendo software & playstation*

Computer Systems Support, 74 Eglinton Avenue, Guisborough, Cleveland, TS14 7BX Tel: (01287) 610433 Fax: (01287) 610438 E-mail: info@computersystemssupport.co.uk *Computer consultants*

Computer Technocentre Ltd, 182 High Road Leytonstone, London, E11 3HU Tel: (020) 8519 9052 Fax: (020) 8519 9052 E-mail: isrealctc@aol.co *Computer trainers & services*

Computer Time Ltd, 363 Lugtrout Lane, Catherine-de-Barnes, Solihull, West Midlands, B91 2TN Tel: 0121-711 4006 Fax: 0121-711 2373 *Computer software services*

Computer Trade Shopper, Quadrant House, The Quadrant, Sutton, Surrey, SM2 5AS Tel: (020) 8652 3500 Fax: (020) 8652 3793 *Computer Trade Shopper is read by resellers, VARs, integrators & distributors who assemble PCs & s*

▶ Computer Trouble Shooters (South Warwickshire), The Laurels, Birmingham Road, Pathlow, Stratford-upon-Avon, Warwickshire, CV37 0ES Tel: (01789) 296642 E-mail: douglas@comptroub.com *Computer maintenance & repairers*

▶ Computer Troubleshooters, The Old Rectory, Lanreath, Looe, Cornwall, PL13 2NU Tel: (01503) 220135 E-mail: cedge@comptroub.com *Computer repair*

▶ Computer Troubleshooters, 44 Alberta Avenue, Sutton, Surrey, SM1 2LL Tel: (020) 8395 0182 E-mail: sales@cts-sutton.co.uk *Computer services maintenance & repairers*

Computer Two Thousand Ltd, Eclipse Court, 14B Chequer Street, St. Albans, Hertfordshire, AL1 3YD Tel: (01727) 868176 Fax: (01727) 831202 E-mail: mail@2000group.co.uk *IT recruitment services*

Computer Village, 76 Lorne Road, Bath, BA2 3BZ Tel: (01225) 405111 Fax: (01225) 466665 E-mail: sales@computervillage.biz *Computer systems & software suppliers*

Computer Warehouse, 61 Low Street, Keighley, West Yorkshire, BD21 3QP Tel: (01535) 691157 Fax: (01535) 691157 E-mail: sales@computer-warehouse.net *Computer suppliers*

Computer Weekly, Quadrant House The Quadrant, Brighton Road, Sutton, Surrey, SM2 5AS Tel: (020) 8652 8642 Fax: (020) 8652 8979 *Computer Weekly is the UK's leading publication for IT decision makers in end-user companies. Its award-winning editorial team consistently delivers news and analysis on the topics that matter - from the latest technical developments to winning management strategies.**Computer Weekly is recognised by the IT industry and by our readers, the UK's senior IT decision makers, as the leader in independent and authoritative business and technology journalism. Its award winning editorial team consistently delivers news and analysis on the topics that matter - from the latest technical developments to winning management strategies.**Computer Weekly consistently comes out top in independent research: it was named PPA Business Magazine of the Year 2000 and Campaigning Magazine of the Year in 2001, 2002 and 2004. In 2000 the Campaign Hall of Fame named Computer Weekly the most influential IT business magazine of the 20th century.*

Computer Wizard, 405 Hatfield Road, St. Albans, Hertfordshire, AL4 0XP Tel: (01727) 861010 E-mail: sales@computerwizard.co.uk *Computer suppliers & repairers*

▶ Computer World Cookstown, 11 James Street, Cookstown, County Tyrone, BT80 8AA Tel: (028) 8675 8177 Fax: (028) 8675 8188 E-mail: info@computerworlds.co.uk *Computer hardware suppliers*

Computeraid Ltd, Neptune Point, Nettlefold Road, Cardiff, CF24 5JQ Tel: (029) 2066 4285 Fax: (029) 2045 5515 E-mail: training@computeraidwales.com *Software trainers*

Computeraid Ltd, The Innovation Centre Swansea University, Singleton Park, Swansea, SA2 8PP Tel: (01792) 610550 Fax: (01792) 610560 E-mail: computeraid@computeraidwales.com *Computer consultants*

▶ ComputerDJ, Unit 5 The Shine, St. Marks Street, Hull, HU8 7FB Tel: (01482) 319700 Fax: (01482) 319701 E-mail: info@computerdj.net *Computer Based Background Music Instalations, within pubs, Clubs, Bars, Shops, you name it we do it. With remote administration, and music updates every month. Reliability is the key, and style is our Forte.*

▶ computer-doctor.uk.com, 40 Graham Road, Worthing, West Sussex, BN11 1TL Tel: (01903) 868010 E-mail: surgery@computer-doctor.uk.com *on-site computer services for worthing and brighton. New computers, repairs, upgrades, networks, backups, technical support, training.*

▶ Computerguard Ltd, Hazlewell House, Graffham, Petworth, West Sussex, GU28 0QA Tel: (01798) 867133 Fax: (01798) 867135 Principal Export Areas: Middle East *Access security systems manufrs*

Computerhire South West Ltd, 5 Kingsway, Kingswood, Bristol, BS15 8BF Tel: 0117-907 7101 Fax: 0117-907 7105 E-mail: sales@computerhire-sw.co.uk *Computer hardware & software hire & leasing*

Computerisation Ltd, Washington Chambers, Stanwell Road, Penarth, South Glamorgan, CF64 2AF Tel: (029) 2071 2664 Fax: (029) 2071 2997 E-mail: admin@computerisation.co.uk *Software house*

Computerised Engineering Co., Unit 2a High Pastures, Stortford Road, Hatfield Heath, Bishop's Stortford, Hertfordshire, CM22 7DL Tel: (01279) 739455 Fax: (01279) 739454 E-mail: james@computerisedengineering.com *CNC engineering services*

Computerised Engineering Services Ltd, 11 Alverton Close, Great Hampton, Malton, North Yorkshire, YO17 6RR Tel: (07767) 834329 Fax: (01653) 669083 E-mail: info@ces-ltd.co.uk *Software systems for engineering*

Computerised Engraving, 10 Waterloo Road, Widnes, Cheshire, WA8 0PY Tel: 0151-420 4590 Fax: 0151-495 1132 E-mail: info@computerisedengraving.com *Engravers*

Computerised Exhibition Services Badges Ltd, 31 Highbridge Road, Sutton Coldfield, West Midlands, B73 5QB Tel: 0121-354 9595 Fax: 0121-354 6227 E-mail: badgereg@aol.com *Badge suppliers*

Computerlinks, Suffolk House, Newmarket, Suffolk, CB8 7AN Tel: (01638) 569600 Fax: (01638) 569601 E-mail: info@computerlinks.co.uk *Software distribution services*

Computermarsters, 55 Plessey Road, Blyth, Northumberland, NE24 3BZ Tel: (0870) 3210112 Fax: (0870) 3210113 E-mail: info@webmarsters.co.uk *Computer upgrades & services*

Computerpower Consultants Ltd, 21 Mount Pleasant, Guiseley, Leeds, LS20 9EB Tel: (01943) 870070 Fax: (01943) 879186 *Uninterruptible power supply systems, power solutions & generators*

▶ Computers Doctor, 19 Bolton Walk, London, N7 7RW Tel: (0845) 3307881 E-mail: info@computersdoctor.com *PC maintenance, repairs and disaster recovery house-calls aimed at Small Office /Home Office users.*

Computers In Action, 30 The Spinney, Beaconsfield, Buckinghamshire, HP9 1SB Tel: (01494) 675202 E-mail: powers@systemsworld.net *Network installers*

Computers In Construction, 337 Brook Street, Broughty Ferry, Dundee, DD5 2DS Tel: (01382) 776733 Fax: (01382) 521438 *Computer hardware & software installation*

Computers In Personnel Ltd, Abbey House, 28-30 Chapel Street, Marlow, Buckinghamshire, SL7 1DD Tel: (01628) 814000 Fax: (0870) 3662346 E-mail: sales@ciphr.com *Human resources software*

Computers For Linguists, 45 Endwell Road, London, SE4 2PQ Tel: (020) 7732 1740 Fax: (020) 7358 9214 E-mail: sales@marguet-ball.net *IT consultants*

Computers North Ltd, Unit 1 Derwentside Business Centre, Consett Business Park, Villa Real, Consett, County Durham, DH8 6BP Tel: (01207) 583978 Fax: (01207) 508206 E-mail: info@durhamofficesystems.ltd.uk *Office equipment distributors*

Computers For Schools & Education, 21 Bramble Bank, Frimley Green, Camberley, Surrey, GU16 6PN Tel: (01252) 836463 E-mail: james.findlay@lineone.net *Computer software development of hardware & networking*

▶ Computersave.Co.Uk, 45 Windmill Road, Hampton Hill, Hampton, Middlesex, TW12 1QZ Tel: (07950) 412207 Fax: (0795) 0412207 E-mail: info@computersave.co.uk *Computer repairs, laptop repairs, PC repairs, notebook repairs, sales, spares & data recovery services for greater London. Onsite visits to work or home at reasonable rates. Network, Internet, Wireless and more...*

▶ Computersave.Co.Uk, 45 Windmill Road, Hampton Hill, Hampton, Middlesex, TW12 1QZ Tel: (07950) 412207

▶ Computersolutions-online, PO Box 24, Cardiff, CF23 0AA Tel: (08701) 999 630 Fax: (07092) 860228 E-mail: enquiries@cs-o.co.uk *We provide quality IT hardware and training for business and personal users at a price that suits your budget.**We deliver and install onsite at your request and will setup a network of computers to file,printer and internet share. We also provide website hosting, building and optimization. **Give us a call for a free quotation.***

▶ Computersurgeon, 3 High Copse, Farnham, Surrey, GU9 0BL Tel: (01252) 717096 Fax: (01252) 717096 E-mail: derek@computersurgeon.net *computer hardware/software instalations, web design and hosting*

Computertel Ltd, 53 Bath Street, Gravesend, Kent, DA11 0DF Tel: (01474) 561111 Fax: (01474) 561122 E-mail: sales@computertel.co.uk *Telecommunication suppliers & maintenance*

Computerworld Western, Unit 1 Fernhill Court, Fernhill, Almondsbury, Bristol, BS32 4LX Tel: (01454) 275400 Fax: (01454) 619931 E-mail: enquiries@computerworld.co.uk *Systems integrators & computer training service*

Computing Advisory Services, Unit 1b Kennedy Way Industrial Estate, Belfast, BT11 9DT Tel: (028) 9061 6287 Fax: (028) 9061 6287 *Computer consultants services*

Computing Matters, C M House, Bowers, Wimborne, Dorset, BH21 7DL Tel: (01202) 888990 Fax: (01202) 888383 E-mail: ian@computing-matters.com *IT consultancy & training*

Computing Needs Ltd, 9-11 Manor Road, Felixstowe, Suffolk, IP11 2EJ Tel: (01394) 278067 Fax: (01394) 458140 E-mail: sales@computingneeds.co.uk *Computer hardware & office software suppliers*

▶ Computing Solutions, Unit 3b North Castle Street, Banff, AB45 1JJ Tel: (01261) 815511 Fax: (01261) 815511 E-mail: sales@cseltham.co.uk *Computers Built to your spec.*Repairs & Upgrades.*Home Networking.*Realistic Charges.*Computer Components*

Computing Solutions, 14 Well Hall Parade, London, SE9 6SP Tel: (020) 8294 0090 Fax: (020) 8859 4562 E-mail: sales@cymc.com *Organisations it requirements services*

Computing (UK) Ltd, 7 London Stile, London, W4 3AU Tel: (020) 8742 3336 Fax: (020) 8995 3991 E-mail: info@computinguk.co.uk *Computer systems value added resellers*

▶ Computool, 5 Bilberry Close, Eaton Ford, St. Neots, Cambridgeshire, PE19 7GU Tel: (01480) 476670 Fax: (01480) 476670 E-mail: computool@ntlworld.com *Computer aided design & computer aided manufacturing services*

▶ Computopia, 7 Riverside, Port Talbot, West Glamorgan, SA13 1PH Tel: (01792) 410516 Fax: (01639) 899943 *Computer maintenance & repair services*

Computoy Computer Consultants, 151 Boundary Road, London, E13 9PT Tel: (020) 8552 1800 Fax: (020) 8470 0909 E-mail: stephen@computoy.co.uk *Bar code scanning solution services*

Computronic Controls Ltd, 41-46 Railway Terrace, Nechells, Birmingham, B7 5NG Tel: 0121-327 8500 Fax: 0121-327 8501 E-mail: sales@computroniccontrols.com *Manufacturers of battery chargers*

Computype Ltd, Oslo Road, Hull, HU7 0YN Tel: (01482) 835366 Fax: (01482) 822441 E-mail: enquiries@compu.co.uk *Bar code system manufrs*

Compuvision Computer Consultants, 25 Mucklets Court, Musselburgh, Midlothian, EH21 6SP Tel: 0131-665 6728 Fax: 0131-665 6728 *Computer services*

Alexander Comrie & Sons Ltd, Unit 8, Second Avenue Business Park, Millbrook, Southampton, SO15 0LP Tel: (023) 8070 2911 Fax: (023) 8070 2617 *Industrial rubber product & gasket manufrs*

Comsec, Unit 6-7 Manor Complex, Kirkby Bank Road, Knowsley Industrial Park, Liverpool, L33 7SY Tel: 0151-549 2300 Fax: 0151-549 2300 *Communication technology* Also at: Kirkby

Comserve Ltd, Comserve House, 54 Watling Street, Radlett, Hertfordshire, WD7 7NN Tel: (01923) 853269 Fax: (01923) 857370 E-mail: service@comserve.co.uk *Building engineering services*

Comset Ltd, Ilex Court, 94 Holly Road, Twickenham, TW1 4HF Tel: (020) 8831 7700 Fax: (020) 8831 7711 E-mail: sales@comset.co.uk *Computer consultants*

▶ Comsoft Computer Consultants, Edon Business Park, Thame Road, Wheatley, Oxford, OX33 1JN Tel: (01865) 297842 Fax: (01865) 297848

Comstock Electronics Ltd, Unit 6 Paycocke Road, Quatro Park, Basildon, Essex, SS14 3GH Tel: (01268) 295555 Fax: (01268) 523455 E-mail: celsales@comstock.co.uk *Electronic component distributors*

Comtec Cables, Unit 3 Cardinal Way, Godmanchester, Huntingdon, Cambridgeshire, PE29 2XN Tel: (01480) 415400 Fax: (01480) 454724 E-mail: sales@comtec-comms.com *Telecommunication systems & equipment suppliers*

Comtec Computers Ltd, 96-98 Merritt Road, Greatstone, New Romney, Kent, TN28 8SZ Tel: (01797) 366333 Fax: (01797) 366333 E-mail: stuart.sayer@comteccomputers.co.uk *Computer suppliers*

Comtec Precision Sheet Metal, 60 Loverock Road, Reading, RG30 1DY Tel: 0118-958 8050 Fax: 0118-958 8040 E-mail: sales@comtecsheet.softnet.co.uk *Precision sheet metal workers*

Comtech Computer Systems Ltd, 34 Hightown, Crewe, CW1 3BS Tel: (01270) 584572 Fax: (01270) 500933 E-mail: admin@comtechcsl.co.uk *Computer networks & telephone systems*

▶ Comtech Enterprises Ltd, 41 Leigh Road, Cobham, Surrey, KT11 2LF Tel: (01932) 589667 Fax: (01932) 862181 E-mail: office@comtech.eu.com *Copper traders & manufrs*

Comtech Holdings Ltd, Comtech House, 28 Manchester Road, Westhoughton, Bolton, BL5 3QJ Tel: (01942) 851800 Fax: (01942) 851808 E-mail: sales@comtech.uk.com *Telemetry solutions to remotely monitor & control equipment*

Comtech Networks Ltd, The Old Barn, Worton Park, Worton, Witney, Oxfordshire, OX29 4SX Tel: (01865) 880023 Fax: (08701) 288309 E-mail: info@comtechnetworks.co.uk *Computer networking*

Comtech Solutions, 2 Moor Allerton Gardens, Leeds, LS17 6QU Tel: 0113-269 1034 *Computer system suppliers*

Comtech Telecommunications Ltd, 30 Bradford Road, Stanningley, Pudsey, West Yorkshire, LS28 6DD Tel: 0113-255 3927 Fax: 0113-205 7567 E-mail: info@comtech-telecom.co.uk *Computer consultants*

► Com-Tek, 46 Welsh Row, Nantwich, Cheshire, CW5 5EJ Tel: (01270) 624300 Fax: (01270) 624300

Comtek Accounts Ltd, Venture House Venture Court, Boleness Road, Wisbech, Cambridgeshire, PE13 2XQ Tel: (01945) 464854 Fax: (01945) 465575 E-mail: accounts@comtekaccounts.com *Computer consultants service*

Comtek Computers Manchester, 12 Silver Street, Bury, Lancashire, BL9 0EX Tel: 0161-761 2200 Fax: 0161-761 2211 E-mail: kazpenash@comtekcomputersmanchester.co.uk *Computer maintenance & repair services*

Comtek Network Systems Ltd, Unit 108, Tenth Avenue, Deeside Industrial Park, Deeside, Clwyd, CH5 2UA Tel: (01244) 280390 Fax: (01244) 280374 E-mail: michael.williams@comtek.co.uk *Network product suppliers*

Comtel Communication Supplies Ltd, School Road, Great Yarmouth, Norfolk, NR30 1LA Tel: (01493) 851865 Fax: (01493) 851767 *Computer consumables & office suppliers*

Comtext Services Ltd, 2 Chatsworth Technology Park, Dunston Road, Whittington Moor, Chesterfield, Derbyshire, S41 8XA Tel: (01246) 260650 Fax: (01246) 260613 E-mail: info@comtextservices.co.uk *Sales & marketing services*

Comtherm Ltd, Comenco Works, Union Lane, Droitwich, Worcestershire, WR9 9AZ Tel: (01905) 775783 Fax: (01905) 794195 E-mail: sales@comtherm.co.uk *Gas burner manufrs*

Comtrol Europe, Unit 2, Stapleshurst Business Park, Howes Lane, Bicester, Oxfordshire, OX25 3QU Tel: (01869) 352740 Fax: (01869) 323211 E-mail: info@comtrol.co.uk *Computer hardware*

Comvek Engineering Ltd, Station Drive, Unit 1, Breener Industrial Estate, Brierley Hill, West Midlands, DY5 3JZ Tel: (01384) 571515 Fax: (01384) 262088 E-mail: clbradley@btconnect.com *Press brake facilities & services*

Comverse Infosys U K Ltd, Hertford Place, Rickmansworth, Hertfordshire, WD3 9XB Tel: (01923) 717300 Fax: (01923) 717301 *Telecommunications & voice mailing service*

Comverse Kenan UK, 1a Stoke Road, Slough, SL2 5AA Tel: (01753) 745300 Fax: (01753) 745304 *Software house*

Comwald Engineering, Unit 8 Bromag Industrial Estate, Minster Lovell, Witney, Oxfordshire, OX29 0SR Tel: (01993) 771478 Fax: (01993) 708220 *Welding & construction*

► Comz4biz, Lonsdale House, 52 Blucher Street, Birmingham, B1 1QU Tel: (0845) 3301589 Fax: (0845) 2805675 E-mail: sales@comz4biz.com *Advice, Supply, Install and Support of Business Communication Tools including Phone Systems, Data Networks, VoIP, IP Telephony, Mobile and Remote Working, Security, Video.*

► Comz4biz Mercia, 6 Teal Crescent, Kidderminster, Worcestershire, DY10 4ET Tel: 0845 130 1589 E-mail: nic.windley@comz4biz.com *Advice, Supply, Install and Support of Business Communication Tools including Phone Systems, VoIP, IP Telephony, Data Networks, Security, Video, Remote and Home Working, CRM.*

► Con Form Ltd, PO Box 4233, Maldon, Essex, CM9 8GX Tel: (01621) 843938 Fax: (01621) 843998 E-mail: sales@con-form.co.uk *Ground remediation, soil stabilisation modification services*

Con Mech Engineers, Hare Law Industrial Estate, Stanley, County Durham, DH9 8UR Tel: (01207) 230621 Fax: (01207) 290100 E-mail: sales@conmecheng.co.uk *Bread slicing machine blade manufrs*

Con Mech Group Ltd, Cleary Court, Church Street East, Woking, Surrey, GU21 6HJ Tel: (01483) 714024 Fax: (01483) 714343 *Earth moving equipment manufrs*

Con-a-crete Ltd, 52 Haghue Side Way, Rothwell, Leeds, LS26 0UG Tel: 0113-282 7310 Fax: 0113-282 0805 *Ready mixed concrete supplier & layers*

Conagra Resources Europe Ltd, 3rd Floor, London, SW1W 9TR Tel: (020) 7824 8595 Fax: (020) 7824 8504 *Blend fertiliser importers*

Conair Group Ltd, Prospect Court, 3 Waterfront Business Park, Fleet, Hampshire, GU51 3TW Tel: (01252) 813000 Fax: (01252) 813008 *Hair care appliances*

Conard Systems & Engineering Ltd, Unit 6d Lowick Close, Newby Road Industrial Estate, Hazel Grove, Stockport, Cheshire, SK7 5ED Tel: 0161-456 5285 *Control panel manufrs*

Conbury Consultants Ltd, Bowcombe Business Park, Bowcombe Road, Newport, Isle Of Wight, PO30 3HZ Tel: (01983) 532727 Fax: (01983) 532727 *Glass fibre mouldings manufrs*

Concentric Pumps Ltd, Unit 10 Gravelly Park, Tyburn Road, Birmingham, B24 8HW Tel: 0121-327 2081 Fax: 0121-327 6187 E-mail: general@concentric-pumps.co.uk *Oil & water pumps*

► Concept 2, 2B Mount Pleasant Road, London, SE13 6RB Tel: (020) 8690 3496

► Concept Automated Systems Ltd, Trinity House, 160 John Wilson Business Park, Chestfield, Whitstable, Kent, CT5 3RA Tel: (01227) 770677 Fax: (01227) 771392 E-mail: sales@conceptautomatedsystems.co.uk *Automation equipment manufrs*

Concept Balustrades Ltd, Unit 9, Papermill Road, Cardiff, CF11 8DH Tel: (029) 2022 0040 Fax: (029) 2034 4402 E-mail: enq@conceptbalustrades.co.uk *Concept Balustrades Ltd are based in Cardiff, South Wales. Steel fabrications, Balustrades, Architectural Metalwork, Steel Balconies*

Concept Card, Marsh Road, Lords Meadow Industrial Estate, Crediton, Devon, EX17 1EU Tel: (01363) 777567 Fax: (01363) 777553 E-mail: sales@conceptcard.co.uk *Plastic card printers*

Concept Computers, 390 High Street, Winsford, Cheshire, CW7 2DP

Concept Control Services, Robson House, Robson Street, Stoke-on-Trent, ST1 4ER Tel: (01782) 261111 Fax: (01782) 261111 E-mail: simon.f@conceptcontrolservices.com *Temperature control instruments servicing & suppliers*

Concept Covers Ltd, 1 Monarch Works, Balds Lane, Stourbridge, West Midlands, DY9 8TE Tel: (01384) 897101 Fax: (01384) 891171 E-mail: concept-covers@supanet.com *Garment cover manufrs*

Concept Creative Services Ltd, Unit 1, Baird House, Dudley Innovation Centre, Pensnett Trading Estate, Kingswinford, West Midlands, DY6 7YA Tel: (01384) 400161 Fax: (01384) 400190 E-mail: sales@concept-models.com *Architectural, model makers & contractors*

Concept (Design & Engineering), Unit 29, Palmerston Business Park, Palmerston Drive, Fareham, Hampshire, PO14 1DJ Tel: (023) 9250 3532 Fax: (023) 9260 2311 E-mail: cde.eng@virgin.net *Machinery manufrs*

Concept Engineering Ltd, 7 Woodlands Business Park, Woodlands Park Avenue, Maidenhead, Berkshire, SL6 3UA Tel: (01628) 825555 Fax: (01628) 826261 E-mail: info@concept-smoke.co.uk Principal Export Areas: Worldwide *Smoke generating & fire training equipment manufrs*

► Concept Environmental Services, Galton Court, Newton Road, Birmingham, B43 6BW Tel: (0800) 0192560 E-mail: draintester@hotmail.co.uk *Drainage. Blocked drains. Engineers, Drainage careers. Chat and industry news*

Concept Fire & Security Ltd, Unit 8 Canal Industrial Park, Dumballs Road, Cardiff, CF10 5FE Tel: (029) 2048 3148 Fax: (029) 2048 3149 E-mail: info@conceptcctv.com *Security installation*

Concept Flooring Suppliers Ltd, Unit 1, Corner Of Roebuck Lane, Dartmouth Road, Smethwick, West Midlands, B66 1BY Tel: 0121-580 1300 Fax: 0121-580 1180 *Flooring supply service providers*

Concept Group, 66 Carden Place, Aberdeen, AB10 1UL Tel: (01224) 648784 Fax: (01224) 636372 E-mail: enquiries@concept-group.co.uk *Photocopier maintenance services*

Concept Group, Concept House, Victoria Industrial Park, Victoria Road, Leeds, LS14 2LA Tel: 0113-265 0093 Fax: 0113-265 0132 E-mail: sales@concept-data.com *Concept Data, established in 1988, has grown to become one of the UK's market leaders in the manufacture and installation of display systems. They are designers and manufacturers of point of sale, display and merchandising systems for the retail trade, brands, shopfitters and supermarkets.*

Concept III Textiles International Ltd, 2 Marton Mills, Marton Street, Skipton, North Yorkshire, BD23 1TA Tel: (01756) 702100 Fax: (01756) 702101 E-mail: info@conceptiii.co.uk *Technical apparel fabric distributors*

Concept Interiors Neston Ltd, 10 High Street, Neston, CH64 9TY Tel: 0151-336 7042 Fax: 0151-336 7042 E-mail: info@conceptinteriors.co.uk *Soft furnishings suppliers*

Concept Labelling Solutions, The Old Sunday School, Bakes Street, Bradford, West Yorkshire, BD7 3EX Tel: (01274) 404400 Fax: (01274) 405599 E-mail: sales@concept-labelling.co.uk *Labelling specialists*

Concept Leasing & Finance, 123 Mile Stone Meadow, Euxton, Chorley, Lancashire, PR7 6FB Tel: (01257) 263171 Fax: (01257) 263171 E-mail: info@conceptleasing.co.uk *Computer financing service.*

Concept Media Ltd, 172 Tonbridge Road, Wateringbury, Maidstone, Kent, ME18 5NS Tel: (01622) 817177 Fax: (01622) 817178 E-mail: enquiries@concept-media.co.uk *Audio & visual production services*

► Concept Network Solutions, 17 Honours Mead, Bovingdon, Hemel Hempstead, Hertfordshire, HP3 0DA Tel: (0870) 9905495 Fax: (0870) 9905494 E-mail: info@conceptnetworksolutions.com *We offer Cat5e Network & Telecom cabling, Wireless Networking, PC & Laptop Repairs & supply everything you will need to get your network off the ground at low prices*

Concept Northern, 14 St Bryde Street, East Kilbride, Glasgow, G74 4HQ Tel: (01355) 573173 Fax: (01355) 573073 E-mail: louiset@cc2000.co.uk *Computer aids for visually impaired*

► Concept Sails, Unit B1, Romany Centre Business Park, Wareham Road, Holton Heath, Poole, Dorset, BH16 6JL Tel: (01202) 623355

Concept Security Systems, 21 Park Avenue, London, NW10 7EX Tel: (020) 8965 3657 Fax: (020) 8965 3657 *Security system installers*

Concept Signs, 40-42 Albert Road, Braintree, Essex, CM7 3JQ Tel: (01376) 329240 Fax: (01376) 331937 E-mail: signsconcept@aol.com *Banner & plastic sign manufrs*

Concept Signs Ltd, Unit 7, Collingwood Industrial Estate, Maidstone Road, Sutton Valence, Maidstone, Kent, ME17 3QS Tel: (01622) 844884 Fax: (01622) 843884 E-mail: signletters2003@yahoo.co.uk *Sign manufrs*

Concept Smoke Screens, North End, Swineshead, Swineshead, Boston, Lincolnshire, PE20 3LR Tel: (01205) 821111 Fax: (01205) 820316 E-mail: info@smoke-screen.co.uk *Suppliers of security smoke, smoke machines & burglar alarm systems*

Concept Staffing Ltd, 11 Boutport Street, Barnstaple, Devon, EX31 1RW Tel: (01271) 321666 Fax: (01271) 326280 E-mail: headoffice@conceptstaffing.co.uk *Recruitment agency*

Concept Stainless Ltd, Little Fields Way, Oldbury, West Midlands, B69 2BT Tel: 0121-552 8881 Fax: 0121-552 9981 E-mail: sales@concept-stainless.co.uk *Stainless steel tube stockholders*

Concept Systems, Unit 2, Wolsey Street, Leicester, LE4 0BS Tel: 0116-251 5181 Fax: 0116-251 5540 *Blind manufrs*

Concept Technical Services Ltd, Unit 8, Peartree Industrial Park, Dudley, West Midlands, DY2 0UW Tel: (01384) 241600 Fax: (01384) 243657 *CNC engineering consultants*

► Concept To Reality, Unit 2, The Factory, Lightsfield, Oakley, Basingstoke, Hampshire, RG23 7BY Tel: 01256 782764 Fax: 01256 782764 E-mail: enquiries@ctr-design.co.uk *Concepts To Reality is ideally placed to offer individuals & organisations a full mechanical design engineering & prototyping service*

Concept UK Building Systems, 63 Nevada Road, Canvey Island, Essex, SS8 8EY Tel: (01268) 512121 Fax: (01268) 512121 E-mail: conceptukltd@hotmail.com *Port cabin hire & sales services*

► Conception Design, 83 Alder Close, Leyland, PR26 7TU Tel: (01772) 434464 Fax: (0870) 6618883 E-mail: info@conceptiondesign.co.uk *Professional Web Site Design *E-Commerce*Internet, SMS & Fax Marketing Campaigns*Professional Photography *Industry Specific Solutions *Advertising Campaigns *Business Logo Design *Corporate Identities*

Concepts I T Training & Consultancy Ltd, 28 Norman Drive, Eastwood, Nottingham, NG16 3FJ Tel: (01773) 788907 Fax: (01773) 788907 E-mail: dorme@concepts-it.com *IT & management training*

► Concert Print & Display Ltd, Unit 7, Abbey Mead Industrial Park, Brooker Road, Waltham Abbey, Essex, EN9 1HU Tel: (01992) 650555

Conchango (UK) P.L.C., Heritage House, Church Road, Egham, Surrey, TW20 9QD Tel: (01784) 470448 Fax: (01784) 222200 E-mail: talktous@conchango.com *Computer consultants*

► Concise Electronic Engineering Ltd, Rhydybont Mill, Llanybydder, Dyfed, SA40 9QS Tel: (01570) 481344 Fax: (01570) 481495 E-mail: enquiries@concise-electronics.co.uk *Electronic engineering & development*

Conclusive Marketing Ltd, 76 The Downs, Harlow, Essex, CM20 3RF Tel: (01279) 303373 *Design Engineering*

Concord Computer Services, Meridian Centre, King St, Oldham, OL8 1EZ Tel: 0161-627 2370 Fax: 0161-628 9429 E-mail: enq@concordservices.co.uk *Computer consultants*

Concord Lifting Equipment Ltd, Unit 4, Buzzard Creek Ind Estate, River Road, Barking, Essex, IG11 0EL Tel: (020) 8594 7529 Fax: (020) 8594 8674 *Lifting equipment hire*

Concord Lifting Equipment Ltd, Unit 53/56, Wimbledon Stadium Business Centre, Riverside Road, London, SW17 0BE Tel: (020) 8946 7902 Fax: (020) 8946 7001 *Lifting equipment hire & sales*

Concord Marlin Ltd, Avis Way, Newhaven, East Sussex, BN9 0ED Tel: (01273) 515811 Fax: (01273) 512688 E-mail: info@concordmarlin.com *Lighting products manufrs*

Concord Motor Contracts Ltd, 10 Cambridge Road, Stansted, Essex, CM24 8BZ Tel: (01279) 813608 Fax: (01279) 813594 E-mail: sales@motorcontracts.com *Vehicle contract hire*

Concord Sportswear, 1 Ware Road, Hertford, SG13 7DY Tel: (01992) 583165 Fax: (01992) 553662 E-mail: sales@concordsportswear.co.uk *Trophy manufacturers & suppliers*

Concorde Agency, 28a High Street, Harpenden, Hertfordshire, AL5 2SX Tel: (01582) 715000 Fax: (01582) 461306 E-mail: sue.churchhouse@concord-agency.com *Typing & business services*

Concorde Blind Co., 12 Worsley Road, Woburn Road Industrial Estate, Kempston, Bedford, MK42 7TN Tel: (01234) 841535 Fax: (01234) 840682 E-mail: sales@concordeblinds.com *Blind & curtain manufrs*

► Concorde Blind & Curtain Co. Ltd, 45 Waterside Park, Old Wolverton Road, Old Wolverton, Milton Keynes, MK12 5NP Tel: (01908) 320600 Fax: (01908) 227338 *Blinds retailers*

Concorde Business Machines Ltd, 4 Dye House Lane, London, E3 2TB Tel: (020) 8983 0777 Fax: (020) 8983 0689 *Computer & office equipment repairs*

Concorde Chemicals P.L.C., Concorde Works, Bilton Way, Brimsdown, Enfield, Middlesex, EN3 7NH Tel: (020) 8804 7411 Fax: (020) 8805 6553 E-mail: dgoldberg@concordechemicals.co.uk *Cleaning chemicals sales & manufrs* Also at: Glasgow

Concorde Graphics Ltd, Units 21-23, Chiltonian Industrial Estate, Manor Lane, London, SE12 0TX Tel: (020) 8297 1115 Fax: (020) 8297 9755 E-mail: david.b@concordegraphics.co.uk *Lithographic printers & screen printers*

Concorde Hydraulics Ltd, Unit 10 Vastre Industrial Estate, Newtown, Powys, SY16 1DZ Tel: (01686) 624945 Fax: (01686) 624595 E-mail: sales@concord-hydraulics.co.uk *Hydraulic equipment & systems distributors*

Concorde Informatics Ltd, Stoneleigh, 39 Halifax Road, Brighouse, West Yorkshire, HD6 2AQ Tel: (01484) 405405 Fax: (01484) 405400 E-mail: info@concordeinf.com *IT solutions & consultants*

Concorde Nottingham & Leicester Flag Co., 48 School Lane, Woodhouse, Loughborough, Leicestershire, LE12 8UJ Tel: (01509) 891078 Fax: (01509) 891281 E-mail: sales@concordeflag.co.uk *Flag sales*

Concorde Precision Profile Ltd, Unit 86 Gibbons Industrial Park, Dudley Road, Kingswinford, West Midlands, DY6 8XF Tel: (01384) 400366 Fax: (01384) 402166 E-mail: carlconcorde@fsbdial.co.uk *Profilers*

Concorde Services Ltd, 42 Canham Road, London, W3 7SR Tel: (020) 8743 3106 Fax: (020) 8743 1010 E-mail: london@concorde-uk.com *Conference & exhibition organisers*

Concorde Trophies, 85 Victoria Street, Crewe, CW1 2JH Tel: (01270) 213753 Fax: (01270) 213753 *Trophies supplier*

Concorde Wireworking & Cleaning Co. Ltd, 175 Beckenham Road, Beckenham, Kent, BR3 4PT Tel: (020) 8658 8080 Fax: (020) 8658 8282 E-mail: info@concordetrolleys.co.uk *Supermarket trolleys repairers & refurbishers*

Concordia Co. Ltd, Derwent Street, Long Eaton, Nottingham, NG10 3LP Tel: 0115-946 7400 Fax: 0115-946 1026 *Cable manufacturers, distributors & agents*

The Concrete Ltd, Station Road, Thorney, Peterborough, PE6 0QE Tel: (01733) 270870 Fax: (01733) 270285 *Concrete supplies*

► Concrete Butterfly, 31 Albion Road, Edinburgh, EH7 5QJ Tel: 0131-661 9918

► Concrete Contractors (Bristol) Ltd, Long Acres, Redfield Hill, Bitton, Bristol, BS30 6NX Tel: 0117-932 3847

Concrete Cutters Sarum Ltd, 18 David Road, Colnbrook, Slough, SL3 0DG Tel: (01753) 689920 Fax: (01753) 689920 E-mail: info@concut.co.uk *Concrete sawing & drilling services*

Concrete Developments Great Barr Ltd, Baltimore Road, Great Barr, Birmingham, B42 1DD Tel: 0121-356 5575 Fax: 0121-344 3285 E-mail: james@concrete-developers.freeserve.co.uk *Concrete, ready mixed*

► Concrete Fabrications Ltd, Crewshole Road Off, Blackswarth Road, St George, Bristol, BS5 8AU Tel: 0117-955 7530 *Construction materials*

Concrete Garage Co Pudsey Ltd, Premier House, Vickers Place, Stanningley, Pudsey, West Yorkshire, LS28 6HN Tel: 0113-256 0011 Fax: 0113-256 9971 *Concrete garage manufrs*

► Concrete Gardens Patio & Garden Centre, Flour Square, Grimsby, South Humberside, DN31 3LS Tel: (01472) 352022

Concrete Machinery Systems Ltd, Unit 1A, Farrington Fields, Farrington Gurney, Bristol, BS39 6UU Tel: (01761) 450050 Fax: (01761) 453200 E-mail: sales@concretemachinerysystems.co.uk *Mould & concrete machinery manufrs*

Concrete Products Kirkcaldy Ltd, Hayfield Place, Hayfield Industrial Estate, Kirkcaldy, Fife, KY2 5DH Tel: (01592) 261326 Fax: (01592) 200498 *Paving slab & kerb manufrs*

Concrete Products (Lincoln) 1980 Ltd, Riverside Industrial Estate, Skellingthorpe Road, Saxilby, Lincoln, LN1 2LR Tel: (01522) 704158 Fax: (01522) 704233 E-mail: sales@bowlandlincoln.co.uk *Paving slab manufrs*

Concrete Repair & Grouting Ltd, 163 Sutton Road, Kidderminster, Worcestershire, DY11 6QN Tel: (01562) 748101 Fax: (01562) 829007 E-mail: enquiries@crg-ltd.co.uk *Concrete structural repair*

Concrete Repairs Ltd, Cathite House, 23a Willow Lane, Mitcham, Surrey, CR4 4TU Tel: (020) 8288 4848 Fax: (020) 8288 4847 E-mail: sales@concrete-repairs.co.uk Principal Export Areas: Worldwide *Concrete structural repair contractors.* Also at: Jersey, Manchester, Sheffield & Stirling

Concrete T S Ltd, Unit A8 Moss Industrial Estate, St. Helens Road, Leigh, Lancashire, WN7 3PT Tel: (01942) 261909 Fax: (01942) 261750 *Concrete repairers*

► Concrete Waterproofing, PO Box 864, Guildford, Surrey, GU2 9US Tel: (0870) 7621507 Fax: (0870) 7621507 E-mail: info@concretewaterproofing.co.uk

Concurrent UK Ltd, Chiltern House, Broad Lane, Bracknell, Berkshire, RG12 9GU Tel: (01344) 403280 Fax: (01344) 403283 *Mini computer manufrs*

Condale Construction Ltd, Millar Barn Lane, Rossendale, Lancashire, BB4 7AU Tel: (01706) 831100 Fax: (01706) 830990

Condat Ltd, Bancroft Farm, Bawtry Road, Misson Springs, Doncaster, South Yorkshire, DN10 6EZ Tel: (01302) 770088 Fax: (01302) 770776 E-mail: sales@condat.fsnet.co.uk *Lubricant suppliers*

The Conde Nast Publications, Vogue House, 1 Hanover Square, London, W1S 1JU Tel: (020) 7499 9080 Fax: (020) 7493 1345 *Publishers*

Conder Developments Ltd, 3rd Floor Royal Buildings, Victoria Street, Derby, DE1 1ES Tel: (01332) 299777 Fax: (01332) 299595 E-mail: info@conder.dev.fsnet.co.uk *Property developers* Also at: Winchester

Conder Products Ltd, Whitehouse Way, South West Industrial Estate, Peterlee, County Durham, SR8 2HZ Tel: 0191-587 8660 Fax: 0191-586 1274 E-mail: sales@conderproducts.co.uk *GRP tanks suppliers & manufrs*

Conder Structures Ltd, Wellington Road, Burton-on-Trent, Staffordshire, DE14 2AA Tel: (01283) 545377 Fax: (01283) 530483 E-mail: sales@conderstructures.co.uk *Specialist structural steelwork & fabricators*

Conditioned Environment Contracts Ltd, Ander House, 245 Acton Lane, London, NW10 7NR Tel: (020) 8453 1010 Fax: (020) 8965 8469 E-mail: sales@coolinguk.com *Air conditioning engineers*

Condor Cases, 7c Wendover Road, Rackheath Industrial Estate, Rackheath, Norwich, NR13 6LH Tel: (01603) 735900 Fax: (01603) 735901 E-mail: sales@condor-cases.co.uk *Manufacturer of custom designed & built flight cases*

Condor Group Ltd, 700 Great Cambridge Road, Enfield, Middlesex, EN1 3EA Tel: (020) 8370 4300 Fax: (020) 8370 4321 E-mail: sales@condorgrp.com *Watch strap, bracelets & watch batteries*

► Conductive Inkjet Technology, The Power House, Lumen Road, Royston, Hertfordshire, SG8 7AG Tel: (01223) 437933 Fax: (01763) 245400 E-mail: sales@rentit.net *IT consultants*

Conductix Ltd, 1 Michigan Avenue, Salford, M50 2GY Tel: 0161-848 0161 Fax: 0161-873 7017 E-mail: info@conductix.co.uk *Crane conductor systems manufrs*

Conec Electronic Equipment Component, Ringway House, Kelvin Road, Newbury, Berkshire, RG14 2DB Tel: (01635) 36929 Fax: (01635) 36925 E-mail: conec@conec.co.uk *Connector manufrs*

► indicates data change since last edition

Conex Data Communications Ltd, Connex House, Follingsby Close, Gateshead, Tyne & Wear, NE10 8YG Tel: 0191-416 5444 Fax: 0191-416 0707 E-mail: sales@conexdata.com *Network installers*

Conexant Systems UK Ltd, 1210 Parkview, Arlington Business Park, Theale, Reading, RG7 4TY Tel: 0118-965 7831 *PC modem chipset manufrs*

Confectionery Supplies, 31 Lower Cathedral Road, Cardiff, CF11 6LU Tel: (029) 2037 2161 Fax: (029) 2039 6632 *Cake decoration suppliers*

Confederation Of British Industry, 103 New Oxford Street, London, WC1A 1DU Tel: (020) 7379 7400 Fax: (020) 7240 1578 E-mail: information.centre@cbi.org.uk *Trade association for industry*

Confederation Of British Metal Forming Ltd, 37-47 Birmingham Road, West Bromwich, West Midlands, B70 6PY Tel: 0121-601 6350 Fax: 0121-601 6373 E-mail: info@britishmetalforming.com *Trade association for those who are engaged in hot & cold forging*

Confederation Of British Metal Forming Ltd, 37-47 Birmingham Road, West Bromwich, West Midlands, B70 6PY Tel: 0121-601 6350 Fax: 0121-601 6373 E-mail: info@britishmetalforming.com *Trade association metal casting industry*

Confederation Of Paper Industries, Papermakers House, Rivenhall Road, Westlea, Swindon, SN5 7BD Tel: (01793) 889600 Fax: (01793) 878700 E-mail: fedn@paper.org.uk *Trade association*

Confederation Of Shipbuilding & Engineering Unions, 140 Walworth Road, London, SE17 1JL Tel: (020) 7703 2215 Fax: (020) 7252 7397 E-mail: alanrobson@cseu.org.uk *Trade union*

Conference Business Ltd, The Priory, Syresham Gardens, Haywards Heath, West Sussex, RH16 3LB Tel: (01444) 416678 Fax: (01444) 441162 E-mail: enq@conferencebusiness.co.uk *Conference organisation*

Conference Centre, Lancaster University, Boland Avenue, Lancaster, LA1 4YT Tel: (01524) 592444 Fax: (01524) 843695 E-mail: conferenceoffice@lancaster.ac.uk *Conference halls*

Conference Contacts Ltd, 16a College Avenue, Maidenhead, Berkshire, SL6 6AX Tel: (01628) 773300 Fax: (01628) 621033 E-mail: enquiries@c-contacts.com *Event organisers venue finders*

Conference & Events Derbyshire, Innovation House East Service Road, Raynesway, Spondon, Derby, DE21 7BF Tel: (01332) 548000 Fax: (01332) 548088 *Business support organisation services*

▶ Conference Organisers & Event Management, Exhibition House, London Road, Macclesfield, Cheshire, SK11 7QX Tel: 0870 242 2305 Fax: (01625) 611699 E-mail: info@conference-event.co.uk *Apex are one of the UK"s leading specialists in conference organisation and event management. We have over 20 years experience and we can add significant value to your next conference, seminar or roadshow. We offer venue advice, delegate management, online payments, and full in house technical and AV support*

Conference Presentation Systems, 92 Vernon Drive, Stanmore, Middlesex, HA7 2BL Tel: (020) 8200 6222 Fax: (020) 8200 6322 *Audio-visual hire services*

Conference Search Ltd, 92 Church Lane, Marple, Stockport, Cheshire, SK6 7AR Tel: 0161-427 7057 Fax: 0161-427 2415 E-mail: sales@conferencesearch.co.uk *Conference organisers & venue-finders*

Conferex Communications, Inglewood, Copsewood Lane, Stone Allerton, Axbridge, Somerset, BS26 2NS Tel: (01934) 712824 Fax: (01934) 713004 E-mail: info@conferex.co.uk *Conference production hire & sales*

▶ Confetti Magic Ltd, Rocket Park, Pepperstock, Luton, LU1 4LL Tel: (01582) 723502 Fax: (01582) 485545 E-mail: ian@confettimagic.com *Special, theatrical effects equipment & confetti suppliers*

Confidential Communications Ltd, 344 Kilburn Lane, London, W9 3EF Tel: (020) 8968 0227 Fax: (020) 8968 0194 E-mail: info@spyestoreuk.com *Surveillance equipment manufrs*

▶ Confidential Couriers, The Willows, The Cadney, Bettisfield, Whitchurch, Shropshire, SY13 2LP Tel: (0800) 2983485 Fax: (01948) 710730 E-mail: confcouriers@aol.com *Sameday/ Nextday/Light Haulage*Flexible 24/7 deliveries.*

Confidential Destruction Services Ltd, Unit 2, Peterboat Close, Greenwich, London, SE10 0PX Tel: (020) 8293 1999 Fax: (020) 8293 5222 E-mail: admin@shredding.info *Secure waste disposal services*

Configuration Computer Services, 40 Surrey Technology Centre, Occam Road, Surrey Research Park, Guildford, Surrey, GU2 7YG Tel: (01483) 295796 Fax: (01483) 295797 E-mail: tony@configuration.co.uk *Network installations*

Configuration Management Services Ltd, 20 The Avenue, Crowthorne, Berkshire, RG45 6PG Tel: (01344) 761155 *Computer consultants*

Confluence Creative, Unit 23, Merryhills Enterprise Park, Park Lane, Wolverhampton, WV10 9TJ Tel: (01902) 862601 Fax: (01902) 862602 E-mail: contact@confluencecreative.co.uk *Exhibition, architectural, engineering & scale models*

Confoco International Ltd, Duncan House, High Street, Ripley, Woking, Surrey, GU23 6AY Tel: (01483) 211288 Fax: (01483) 211388 E-mail: info@confoco-food.com *Food ingredient distributors*

Conford Electronics, 1 Hillview, Conford, Liphook, Hampshire, GU30 7QW Tel: (01428) 751469 Fax: (01428) 751223 E-mail: contact@confordelec.co.uk *Audio equipment dealers & distributors*

▶ Conformance Services Ltd, 24 Tidnock Avenue, Congleton, Cheshire, CW12 2HW Tel: (01260) 270729 Fax: (01260) 270729 E-mail: enquiries@conformance-services.com

continued

EMC conformance testing, electrical & mechanical safety

▶ Conger Electrical, 18 Beatty Close, Poulner, Ringwood, Hampshire, BH24 1XR Tel: (01425) 477943

Congress Centre, Congress House, 23-28 Great Russell Street, London, WC1B 3LS Tel: (020) 7467 1200 Fax: (020) 7467 1313 E-mail: congress.centre@tuc.org.uk *Conference & banqueting venue*

Conibear Bros, Unit 2 Commercial Road Businness Park, Lords Meadow Industrial Estate, Crediton, Devon, EX17 1ER Tel: (01363) 772911 Fax: (01363) 772185 *Constructional engineers*

Coningsby International, 22 School Lane, Coningsby, Lincoln, LN4 4WX Tel: (01526) 342231 Fax: (01526) 344367 E-mail: info@coningsby.com *Educational equipment & suppliers*

Coningsby Metals Ltd, 47-49 Silver Street, Coningsby, Lincoln, LN4 4SG Tel: (01526) 342141 Fax: (01526) 343382 E-mail: sales@cml-gt.co.uk *Manufacturers of materials handling equipment*

Conisborough Furniture Components Ltd, Denaby Lane Industrial Estate, Denaby Main, Doncaster, South Yorkshire, DN12 4JS Tel: (01709) 863122 Fax: (01709) 865068 E-mail: components@conisborough.com *Injection mouldings manufrs*

Coniston Computers Ltd, Hylton Park, Wessington Way, Sunderland, SR5 3NR Tel: 0191-516 0088 Fax: 0191-516 0476 *Computer resellers*

Con-Lloyd Ltd, Chapter Street, Manchester, M40 2AY Tel: 0161-203 4660 Fax: 0161-205 4518 E-mail: info@con-lloyd.com *Export packing company*

Conlon Ltd, 6 Kendrick Trading Estate, Galton Way, Swindon, SN2 2DU Tel: (01793) 644956 Fax: (01793) 535116 E-mail: survey@conlon.co.uk *Groundworks, civil engineering, demolition, land reclamation, recycled aggregated, hardcore tipping, hardcore collection, site clearance, brownfield site regeneration, crusher hire, screener hire, dump truck hire, soft strip & dismantling works, asbestos removal, roll on roll off skips.*

▶ Conlon Construction, 20 Great Northern Way, Netherfield, Nottingham, NG4 2HD Tel: 0115-938 1800 Fax: 0115-938 1801 E-mail: office@conlonconstruction.co.uk

Conlon Construction Ltd, Charnley Fold Lane, Bamber Bridge, Preston, PR5 6BE Tel: (01772) 335268 Fax: (01772) 770200 E-mail: enquire@conlonconstruct.co.uk *Building contractors & property developers*

ConMac, Stoneyhill Industrial Estate, Whitchurch, Ross-On-Wye, Herefordshire, HR9 6BX Tel: (01600) 890401 Fax: (01600) 890934 E-mail: marksnell@conmac.co.uk *Concrete products*

Connaught Collections UK Ltd, Airport House, Purley Way, Croydon, CR0 0XZ Tel: (020) 8253 0350 Fax: (020) 8680 7661 E-mail: sales@connaught.uk.com *Debt recovery agents*

(Connaught Competition Engines) Ltd, Wormdale Farm, Wormdale Hill, Newington, Sittingbourne, Kent, ME9 7PX Tel: (01795) 843802 Fax: (01795) 841358 E-mail: info@hillclimb.freeserve.co.uk *Design & building of competition engines for all forms of motorsport*

Connaught Lithoservices Ltd, 129 Munster Road, London, SW6 6DD Tel: (020) 7731 0900 Fax: (020) 7731 0066 E-mail: info@connaught.net *Graphic & lithographic printers web design*

Connaught Partners Ltd, 111 Hagley Road, Birmingham, B16 8LB Tel: 0121-452 5117 Fax: 0121-452 5118 E-mail: sales@connaughtpartners.com *Executive search & selection (recruitment)*

▶ Connect 2, 49 Meads Street, Eastbourne, East Sussex, BN20 7RN Tel: (01323) 641644 Fax: (01323) 643904 E-mail: info@connect2sussex.com *Promotional business gifts & corporate clothing distributors*

Connect 2 Technology Ltd, Longbeck Road, Marske-by-the-Sea, Redcar, Cleveland, TS11 6HQ Tel: (01642) 492220 Fax: (01642) 492223 E-mail: sales@connect2t.co.uk Purchasing Contact: G. Burton Sales Contact: G. Nossiter *Connect-2 Technology is an ideal strategic manufacturing partner for the supply of cable assemblies, wiring harnesses & looms, wire kits, electronic sub-assemblies, small panels and box-builds. With a proven track record in the conversion of make-to-buy projects, our UK facilities provide prototype and low/ medium production volumes, whilst our Far East manufacturing provides medium/high volume batches to secure further cost reductions and provide a genuinely flexible service. Every OEM organisation must constantly look to reduce the product development cycle, control overhead cost and keep stock and work-in-progress under tight control. Increasingly, the outsourcing of manufacturing operations is recognised as an essential strategy in gaining and maintaining an edge over the competition. We are Specialists in the manufacture and supply of cable assemblies, wiring harnesses & looms, wire kits, electronic sub-assemblies, small panels and box-builds.*

Connect Building Systems Ltd, Barmston Road, Beverley, North Humberside, HU17 0LA Tel: (01482) 330430 Fax: (01482) 330431 *Re-Locators of port cabins*

▶ Connect Colour Ltd, Unit C, Northbridge Road, Berkhamsted, Hertfordshire, HP4 1EH Tel: (01442) 879701 Fax: (01442) 879702

Connect Colour Ltd, Unit C, Northbridge Road, Berkhamsted, Hertfordshire, HP4 1EH Tel: (01442) 879701 Fax: (01442) 879702 E-mail: sales@connektcolour.com *Commercial & general printers*

▶ Connect Computer Consultants Ltd, 6 Crumplins Business Court, Dunleys Hill, Odiham, Hook, Hampshire, RG29 1DU Tel: (01256) 704693 Fax: (01256) 702659 *Computer consultancy*

Connect Computers, 6 Durlston Parade, Durlston Drive, Bognor Regis, West Sussex, PO22 9DJ Tel: (01243) 830300 Fax: (01243) 830298 E-mail: trade@computers.uk.com *Computer hardware vendor*

Connect Distibution, Connect Business Park, Bordesley Green Road, Birmingham, B9 4UA Tel: (0870) 4423700 Fax: 0121-766 7138 *Electronic component distribs* Also at: Manchester

Connect Engineering Ltd, Thomas Brown House, Edwin Road, Manchester, M11 3ER Tel: 0161-273 6333 Fax: 0161-273 8351 E-mail: connectengineering@yahoo.co.uk *Sheet metalworkers, pipefitters & fabricators*

▶ Connect Exhibitions Ltd, 73 Lynton Road, Acton, London, W3 9HL Tel: (0845) 0170820 Fax: (020) 8896 2064 E-mail: info@connectexhibitions.com *Wall partitions for the art & exhibition world*

Connect It, Aizlewoods Mill, Nursery Street, Sheffield, S3 8GG Tel: 0114-282 3307 Fax: 0114-282 3302 *Suppliers of home entertainment solutions to house/home builders*

Connect Packaging, 6-8 Brunel Road, Manor Trading Estate, Benfleet, Essex, SS7 4PS Tel: (01268) 755206 Fax: (01268) 755206 E-mail: info@connectpackaging.com *Corrugated cardboard box manufrs*

Connect Support Services Ltd, South Quay Plaza 2, 183 Marsh Wall, London, E14 9SH Tel: (020) 7517 2000 Fax: (020) 7517 2099 E-mail: connect@connect.co.uk *IT support services*

▶ Connect Up Ltd, Westgold, 2 Barras Street, Leeds, LS12 4JS Tel: 0113-263 1904 Fax: 0113-231 9139 E-mail: sales@connect-up.co.uk *It company*

Connect Wall Systems, 26 Westcott Crescent, London, W7 1PA Tel: (020) 8578 2437 Fax: (020) 8578 2450 *Wall systems, sale & rental for exhibitions, venues & events*

▶ Connectafone Mobile Phones, 184 Brownhill Road, London, SE6 2DJ Tel: (020) 8244 6666 Fax: (020) 8698 9417 E-mail: enquiries@konnectafone.co.uk *Mobile phones & accessories sales*

Connected Tote Systems Ltd, 129 Sydenham Rd, Spark Brooke, Birmingham, B11 1DG Tel: 0121-753 3555 Fax: 0121-771 0906 E-mail: mail@toteuk.force9.co.uk *Pharmaceutical manufrs*

Connectic Synx Ltd, The Flarepath, Elsham Wolds Industrial Estate, Brigg, South Humberside, DN20 0SP Tel: (01652) 688908 Fax: (01652) 688928 E-mail: sales@synx.ltd.uk Principal Export Areas: Worldwide *Explosion proof equipment & television monitoring system manufrs*

Connection Aml Ltd, Unit 8-9 Newtown Business Park, Albion Close, Poole, Dorset, BH12 3LL Tel: (01202) 733510 Fax: (01202) 715455 E-mail: info@travisperkins.co.uk *Plumbers importers & distributors*

Connection Delivery Service Ltd, 6 Domingo Street, London, EC1Y 0TA Tel: (020) 7253 2211 Fax: (020) 7251 3381 *Courier, messenger & express parcel delivery services*

Connections Employment Agency Ltd, 182-186 Cross Street, Sale, Cheshire, M33 7AG Tel: 0161-962 9711 Fax: 0161-905 1413 E-mail: recruitment@connections.co.uk *Recruitment, executive appointments, connections financial & 50*

▶ Connections Properties Ltd, Phoenix House, 37 Palmer Street, Chippenham, Wiltshire, SN14 0DT Tel: (01249) 444715

▶ Connective Logic Projects, Paceycombe House, Paceycombe Way, Poundbury, Dorchester, Dorset, DT1 3WB Tel: (01305) 251123 Fax: (01305) 251123 *Software engineers*

Connectomatic Ltd, 31 Bretton Street, Dewsbury, West Yorkshire, WF12 9BJ Tel: (01924) 452444 Fax: (01924) 430607 E-mail: sales@connectomatic.co.uk Principal Export Areas: Worldwide *Manufacturers of hose couplings, irrigation equipment & plastic hoses. Also hose distributors or agents*

Connector & Terminal Supplies Ltd, Unit A3 Mountbatten Business Park, Jackson Close, Portsmouth, PO6 1US Tel: (023) 9237 5966 Fax: (023) 9237 5904 E-mail: sales@connectors-uk.com *Cables assembly, control system & component distributors*

Connectors & Switchgear Ltd, 25 Chacombe Road, Middleton Cheney, Banbury, Oxfordshire, OX17 2QS Tel: (01295) 710505 Fax: (01295) 712667 E-mail: sales@connectorandswitchgear.co.uk *Low & high voltage connectors manufrs*

▶ Connell Communications Ltd, 63 Brights Avenue, Rainham, Essex, RM13 9NW Tel: (01708) 521598 Fax: (01708) 521648 E-mail: doconnell@connellcommunications.com *Telecommunications and cabling specialists, structed cabling*

D & M Connell, Shay Dene, Shaw Lane, Queensbury, Bradford, West Yorkshire, BD13 2LD Tel: (01274) 881099 Fax: (01274) 881099 *Industrial model manufrs*

J.A. Connelly Fencing Ltd, Town Foot, Acre Lane, Preesall, Poulton-Le-Fylde, Lancashire, FY6 0HW Tel: (01253) 700017 Fax: (01253) 700017 *Garden fencing manufrs*

▶ Lucy Connelly Web Design, Guest Avenue, Branksome, Poole, Dorset, BH12 1JB Tel: (01202) 741243 E-mail: lucy@lucy-connelly.co.uk *Web design for small businesses & the self-employed*

Connelly Manton Printing Ltd, Albert Buildings, 49 Queen Victoria Street, London, EC4N 4SA Tel: (020) 7248 0404 Fax: (020) 7236 0353 *Direct mail services*

Connelly Security Systems, 100 Glentanar Road, Glasgow, G22 7XS Tel: 0141-336 3336 Fax: 0141-336 1456 *Security engineers*

Connevans Ltd Equipment For The Deaf, 54 Albert Road North, Reigate, Surrey, RH2 9YR Tel: (01737) 247571 Fax: (01737) 223475 E-mail: mail@connevans.com *Equipment for deaf & hearing impaired*

▶ Connexion Electrical Ltd, 9 Carlisle Road, London, NW9 0HD Tel: (020) 8200 5451 Fax: (020) 8205 3034

▶ Connexion World Cargo, Unit 3 Blackburn Trading Estate, Northumberland Close, Stanwell, Staines, Middlesex, TW19 7LN Tel: (01784) 263000 Fax: (01784) 263111 E-mail: info@connexcargo.com *We are a Freight Forwarding company with a wealth of knowledge and experience in all aspects of imports and exports by Air,Sea and Road.*

▶ Connexions 4 London, 22 St. Peters Road, Bournemouth, BH1 2LE Tel: (01202) 299799 Fax: (0870) 7061094 E-mail: matt@c4l.co.uk *Connexions4London provides an excellent range of business class internet services for large and small businesses. Clients can expect a highly professional technical and customer service team. Connexions4London are one of the UK's largest independent colocation providers.*With over 5 years experience and high profile companies such as BBC, Sony, Channel 4, Panasonic, Time Warner and many others relying on our network you can be assured your colocation is in good hands. We have over 7Gbps Internet connectivity ensuring you will never experience latency. We can provide anything from a simple fast 1U server up to full RAID 5, multi site distributed arrays.*Connexions4London also provide high quality business class Voice Over IP and other business internet services.**

Connextions Logistics, Link House, Bute Street, Stoke-on-Trent, ST4 3PR Tel: (01782) 339559 Fax: (01782) 339561 *Road transport, haulage & freight services*

Connoisseur Cashmere Ltd, 59 Huddersfield Road, Mirfield, West Yorkshire, WF14 8AA Tel: (01924) 490044 Fax: (01924) 492637 E-mail: sales@connoisseurcashmere.com *Cashmere knitwear manufrs*

David Connolly Ltd, 3 Stanley Mills Business Park, Britannia Road, Huddersfield, HD3 4QS Tel: (01484) 641832 Fax: (01484) 462011 E-mail: davidconnolly@btconnect.com *Office file & hand covered box manufrs*

Connolly Refrigeration Ltd, 13 Howlett Way, Thetford, Norfolk, IP24 1HZ Tel: (01842) 766655 Fax: (01842) 763497 E-mail: sales@connollyrefrigeration.co.uk *Refrigeration & air conditioning suppliers*

Connop & Son Ltd, Folley Farm, Eardisland, Leominster, Herefordshire, HR6 9BS Tel: (01544) 388489 Fax: (01544) 388926 *Concrete contractors*

▶ Connor Associates, 7 Grangewood Terrace, Stobswood, Morpeth, Northumberland, NE61 5QE Tel: (01670) 791997 E-mail: ian@doors-opened.co.uk *Connor Associates will find you new clients.*

Connor Innovations, 23a Pensilva Industrial Estate, St Ive Road, Pensilva, Liskeard, Cornwall, PL14 5RE Tel: (01579) 363067 Fax: (01579) 363581 *Trolley manufrs*

Connor Solutions Ltd, 1-2 Gadwall Road, Houghton le Spring, Tyne & Wear, DH4 5NL Tel: 0191-512 1555 Fax: 0191-512 1666 *Electronic manufacturing service provider*

Connor's Fuels Ltd, 48 Trench Road, Newtownabbey, County Antrim, BT36 4TY Tel: (028) 9084 8586 Fax: (028) 9084 3909 E-mail: post@maxol.ie *Petroleum distributors* Also at: Dublin

Connswater Graphics Ltd, 1 Dargan Court, Dargan Cresent, Belfast, BT3 9JP Tel: (028) 9077 7395 Fax: (028) 9077 7065 E-mail: info@connswatergraphics.com *Sign manufrs*

Conoco Phillips, Seal Sands, Middlesbrough, Cleveland, TS2 1UH Tel: (01642) 546411 Fax: (01642) 546096 *Oil terminal*

Conoco (UK) Ltd, Rubislaw House, Anderson Drive, Rubislaw Ho, Aberdeen, AB15 6FZ Tel: (01224) 205000 Fax: (01224) 205222 *Oil & gas exploration & production*

Conocophillips Ltd, 2 Portman Street, London, W1H 6DU Tel: (020) 7408 6000 Fax: (020) 7408 6660 *Oil & gas exploration*

Conoflex Ltd, 9 Sybron Way, Crowborough, East Sussex, TN6 3DZ Tel: (01892) 664388 Fax: (01892) 664178 E-mail: sales@conoflex.co.uk *Manufacturers of x-ray inspection systems*

Conoflow Ltd, 18 Brook Road, Wimborne, Dorset, BH21 2BH Tel: (01202) 888010 Fax: (01202) 842009 *Valve designers & manufrs*

Conport Structures Ltd, 1 Duke of York Square, London, SW3 4LY Tel: (020) 7730 9105 Fax: (020) 7730 5031 E-mail: sales@conport.com *Prefabricated building manufacturers & exporters*

Conqueror Industries Ltd, Units 3-9, Royston Trading Estate, South Close, Royston, Hertfordshire, SG8 5UH Tel: (01763) 249535 Fax: (01763) 247276 E-mail: info@c-i-ltd.co.uk *Conqueror Industries based in Royston, Hertfordshire are specialists in powder coating services including; polyester powder coating, epoxy polyester powder coating, nylon powder coating, zinc phosphate pre-treatment, and a range of coloured powder coating. Conqueror Industries are an Akzo Nobel Associated Quality Coater so you can be sure your products will be powder coated to a high standard. Conqueror Industries are also stove enamelling contractors, shot blast contractors, paint spraying contractors and metal finishing contractors. Specialising in the coating of galvanised steel, architecturally specified and items in excess of one tonne which are processed in our three large box ovens, two of which are 8m x3m x3m. Conqueror Industries can powder coat, spray or enamel most materials including steel, aluminium and plastic, we offer our services to a range of industries including automotive, construction and general manufacturing.*

Conqueror Manufacturing Ltd, Unit 1 William Street, West Bromwich, West Midlands, B70 0BG Tel: 0121-522 2300 Fax: 0121-522 2400 E-mail: conquerormanuf@aol.com *Bottle handling equipment manufrs*

Conquest Clothing Ltd, The Old Farm House, Amport, Andover, Hampshire, SP11 8JB Tel: (01264) 889566 Fax: (01264) 889371 E-mail: bob@conquestclothing.co.uk *Clothing manufrs*

Conquest Joinery Co. Ltd, Hacken Lane, Bolton, BL3 1SD Tel: (01204) 520201 Fax: (01204) 361484 *Pallets manufrs*

Conquest Products, 29 Whitley Street, Reading, RG2 0EG Tel: 0118-987 4635 Fax: 0118-987 4638 E-mail: phil@conquestproducts.co.uk *Promotional bag manufrs*

▶ Conran Homes Ltd, 25 King Street, Knutsford, Cheshire, WA16 6DW Tel: (01565) 650734 Fax: (01565) 650734

Conren Ltd, Astwith Close, Holmewood, Chesterfield, Derbyshire, S42 5UR Tel: (01246) 853900 Fax: (01246) 856348 E-mail: info@conren.com *Construction product manufrs*

W.J. Cons & Co., 20 Queensway, Enfield, Middlesex, EN3 4SA Tel: (020) 8443 4001 Fax: (020) 8804 0805 E-mail: info@berbo.com *Eyeletting machinery manufrs*

Consam Communications, 33 Highmeres Road, Leicester, LE4 9LZ Tel: 0116-276 0909 Fax: 0116-276 2141 E-mail: info@consam.com *Supply, rent & repair two way radio systems & vehicle fleet management*

Consarc Engineering Ltd, 12 North Road, Bellshill, Lanarkshire, ML4 1EN Tel: (01698) 748845 Fax: (01698) 747925 E-mail: sales@consarceng.com *Vacuum equipment manufrs*

Conseco International Security Ltd, 5 Manchester Square, London, W1U 3PD Tel: (020) 7486 3661 Fax: (020) 7487 4153 E-mail: marketing@pellfrischmann.com *Consulting engineers (civil)*

Consensus Research International Ltd, 61 Southwark Street, London, SE1 0HL Tel: (020) 7803 4050 Fax: (020) 7803 4051 E-mail: mail@consensus-research.com *Market research organisation*

Consent Services Ltd, 168 Repps Rd, Martham, Great Yarmouth, Norfolk, NR29 4QZ Tel: (01493) 748647 Fax: (01493) 748647 *Plumbing & heating engineers*

▶ Conserva-Care Ltd, 40 Main Street, Egginton, Derby, DE65 6HL Tel: (0845) 0098854 Fax: (0845) 0098853 E-mail: info@conserva-care.co.uk *Conservatory cleaning & repair, solar insert supplier & installations*

▶ Conservation By Design Ltd, 5 Singer Way, Woburn Road Industrial Estate, Kempston, Bedford, MK42 7AW Tel: (01234) 853555 Fax: (01234) 852334 E-mail: info@conservation-by-design.co.uk *Storage & archive filing service*

Conservation Resources (UK) Ltd, Unit 2 Ashville Way, Watlington Road, Cowley, Oxford, OX4 6TU Tel: (01865) 747755 Fax: (01865) 747035 E-mail: conservarts@aol.com *Archival storage materials manufrs*

▶ The Conservatory, Spitfire Studios, 63-71 Collier Street, London, N1 9BE Tel: (020) 7278 3222 E-mail: studio@theconservatory.co.uk *Magazine, logo, brand identity, brochure, leaflet & packaging design*

▶ Conservatory Accessories, Bidder Street, London, E16 4ST Tel: (0845) 1651658 Fax: (0845) 1651659 E-mail: info@conservatory-accessories.co.uk *Online shop for solar foils*

Conservatory Supplies Ltd, The Conservatory Centre, Leighsinton Road, Malvern, Worcestershire, WR14 1JP Tel: (01684) 575588 Fax: (01684) 576077 E-mail: sales@csltd.net *Fibreglass conservatory & components suppliers*

Conservatory & Window World Ltd, 149-151 Watling Road, Bishop Auckland, County Durham, DL14 9AU Tel: (01388) 458088 Fax: (01388) 810292

Conservatory World, Unit 1, Speedwell Unit, Nelson Road Industrial Estate, Dartmouth, Devon, TQ6 9SZ Tel: (01803) 839330 Fax: (01803) 835803 *Window distributors*

Conserve Ltd, 80 Priory Road, Kenilworth, Warwickshire, CV8 1LQ Tel: (01926) 512006 Fax: (01926) 864569 E-mail: martin@proserveltd.co.uk *Underwater concreting engineers*

Conserve Corporation plc, Hillview Road, East Tullos Industrial Estate, Aberdeen, AB12 3HB Tel: (01224) 873797 Fax: (01224) 871029 E-mail: enquiries@conserveplc.co.uk *Container hire service providers*

Consett Steel Services Ltd, Bradley Workshops, Consett, County Durham, DH8 6HG Tel: (01207) 590171 Fax: (01207) 592086 E-mail: sales@consett-steel.co.uk *Steel stockholders & processors*

▶ Consider It Done Lifestyle Management Ltd, The Courtyard, 4 Evelyn Road, London, W4 5JL Tel: (020) 8742 8718 Fax: (08712) 428362 E-mail: info@consider-it-done.co.uk *Consider it Done's lifestyle management services help transform the lives of time pressured people by supporting them with all the things that help to keep their home lives ticking over smoothly. Our clients avoid distractions while at work, and regain time and the freedom to focus where they need to. **Whether it"s researching a holiday, organising a house move or simply having some paperwork taken care of, we have a team of friendly professionals who can organise pretty much anything someone with a hectic lifestyle might need.**Each client has a single point of contact on the Consider it Done team to support them, with our prime aim to make things work as simply and easily as possible for you. **Clients quickly see results, and feel back in control. Sometimes it's the small things in life that make the biggest difference**

Consilium, The Old Stables, Onehouse Hall, Lower Road, Onehouse, Stowmarket, Suffolk, IP14 3BY Tel: (01449) 676435 Fax: (01449) 676436 E-mail: sb@exclusiveheritagevenues.co.uk *Heritage marketing consultants*

Consilium Marine UK Branch, 23 Saffron Court, Southfields, Laindon, Basildon, Essex, SS15 6SS Tel: (020) 8508 1702 Fax: (020) 8508 1703 *Marine electronics*

Consilium UK Ltd, 141 St. James Road, Glasgow, G4 0LT Tel: 0141-847 1545 Fax: (07020) 935560 E-mail: info@consilium-uk.com *IT consultants & software developers*

Consistent Cleaning Services Ltd, 78 North End Road, London, W14 9ES Tel: (020) 7602 6981 Fax: (020) 7602 1306 *Hotel recruitment specialists*

Consoil Geotechnical Instruments UK, Clark House, 3 Brassey Drive, Aylesford, Kent, ME20 7QL Tel: (01622) 882093 Fax: (0870) 0543915 E-mail: info@consoil.co.uk *Sales & hire of pipe & duct profiling & level measuring equipment. Measuring the difficult to access places.*

Consol Scotland Ltd, 176 St. Vincent Street, Glasgow, G2 5SG Tel: 0141-249 6610 Fax: 0141-249 6609 *Business consultancy*

Consolidare, 27 Kensington Road, Savile Park, Halifax, West Yorkshire, HX3 0HN Tel: 08701 417027 Fax: 08701 417027 E-mail: info@consolidare.co.uk *Consolidare are a computer cabling and network infrastructure specialist. Full telecommunication integration. Siemon listed installers. Copper, fibre and wireless technologies to the latest standards. CCTV, audio-visual, door entry and security systems. We welcome enquires from both public and private sectors, projects large and small.*

Consolidated Brick, Brindley Road, Cardiff, CF11 8TL Tel: (029) 2034 0168 Fax: (029) 2034 2466 *Brick manufrs*

▶ Consolidated Carriers Ltd, 27 Burnside Place, Troon, Ayrshire, KA10 6LZ Tel: (01292) 310510 Fax: (01292) 310810 E-mail: sales@ccl-logistics.com

Consolidated Cash Systems, 28 Springfield Road, Luton, LU3 2HF Tel: (01582) 494946 Fax: (01582) 494946 *Money counters distribution*

Consolidated Ceramic Products, Rotherham Close, Norwood Industrial Estate, Killamarsh, Sheffield, S21 2JU Tel: 0114-247 8251 Fax: 0114-247 8253 E-mail: ccp.uk@btinternet.com *Thermocouple manufrs*

Consolidated Diamond Products Ltd, Unit 9a2, Carcroft Enterprise Park, Carcroft, Doncaster, South Yorkshire, DN6 8DD Tel: (01302) 725553 Fax: (01302) 725523 E-mail: enquiries@consolidateddiamond.co.uk *Diamond tool manufrs*

Consolidated Laser Line Ltd, Fawcett House, Record Street, Ruthin, Clwyd, LL15 1DS Tel: (01824) 705807 Fax: (01824) 705816 E-mail: ruthincll@btconnect.com *Freight forwarders*

Consolidated Stainless Recycling Ltd, 5-6 Station Road, Warley, Rowley Regis, West Midlands, B65 0JY Tel: 0121-561 4282 Fax: 0121-561 4708 E-mail: enquiries@consolidateduk.com *Metal merchants*

Consolidated Supply Services, Unit 7, Hastingwood Business Centre, Hastingwood, Harlow, Essex, CM17 9GD Tel: (01279) 641131 Fax: (01279) 635438 *Hospital supply services*

Consort Ltd, 1-4 Export Drive, Huthwaite, Sutton-in-Ashfield, Nottinghamshire, NG17 6AF Tel: (01623) 440880 Fax: (01623) 440396 E-mail: info@consort.ltd.uk *UPVC windows, doors & conservatories manufrs*

Consort 1996 Ltd, Thornton Industrial Estate, Milford Haven, Dyfed, SA73 2RT Tel: (01646) 692172 Fax: (01646) 695195 E-mail: enquiries@consortepl.com *Manufacturers & suppliers of industrial, commercial & domestic electric space heating, air purifiers & crossflow fans and sheet metal fabrication.* Also at: Redditch

Consort Abrasives Products Ltd, Swallowfields, Welwyn Garden City, Hertfordshire, AL7 1JD Tel: (01707) 330319 Fax: (01707) 376697 E-mail: consortabrasives@btconnect.com *Abrasive products manufrs*

Consort Diamond Products Ltd, A1-A2 Unit, Tir Llwyd Industrial Estate, Kinmel Bay, Rhyl, Clwyd, LL18 5JA Tel: (01745) 343951 Fax: (01745) 342015 E-mail: info@consortprecision.co.uk *Diamond dresser manufrs* Also at: Coventry

Consort Engineering (Ashton-under-Lyne) Ltd, Commercial Brow, Hyde, Cheshire, SK14 2JR Tel: 0161-366 6883 Fax: 0161-366 9703 *Orthopaedic engineers design & precision*

Consort Glass Fibre, Brooke End Farm Buildings, Portleys Lane, Drayton Bassett, Tamworth, Staffordshire, B78 2AD Tel: (01827) 283775 Fax: (01827) 283775 *Glass fibre mouldings manufrs*

Consortium For Purchasing & Distribution Ltd, Hammond Way, Trowbridge, Wiltshire, BA14 8RR Tel: (01225) 777333 Fax: (01225) 775921 E-mail: sales@theconsortium.co.uk *Purchasing consortium*

Consortium Support Services Ltd, 99 Wheatcroft Grove, Gillingham, Kent, ME8 9JE Tel: (01634) 232343 Fax: (01634) 232365 E-mail: derekrainham@blueyonder.co.uk *Cleaning & security services*

▶ Consortium Systems, Lint House, Linthouse Lane, Wolverhampton, WV11 3EA Tel: (01902) 723327 Fax: (01902) 739886

▶ Conspare Ltd, Bestwood Road, Brookhill Industrial Estate, Pinxton, Nottingham, NG16 6NT Tel: (01773) 860796 Fax: (01773) 860055 E-mail: sales@conspare.com *Spare parts to the concrete producing industry*

Constable & Co. Ltd, 3 Lanchesters, 162-166 Fulham Palace Road, London, W6 9ER Tel: (020) 8741 3663 Fax: (020) 8748 7562 E-mail: enquiries@constablerobinson.com *Publishers*

Constables Curtain Services, Station House, Tarring Road, Worthing, West Sussex, BN11 4SR Tel: (01903) 533513 Fax: (01903) 505080 E-mail: info@ccscurtains.co.uk *Curtain makers to the trade*

James Constance & Sons Ltd, The Estate Office Longhope Industrial Estate, Church Road, Longhope, Gloucestershire, GL17 0LB Tel: (01452) 830297 *Manage industrial estate & woodland*

Constant Air Systems Ltd, Hillbottom Road, Sands Industrial Estate, High Wycombe, Buckinghamshire, HP12 4HJ Tel: (01494) 469529 Fax: (01494) 469549 E-mail: admin@constantair.co.uk *Heating & ventilating engineers*

Constant Aluminium Supplies Ltd, Unit B2 Junction 22 Business, Park Tweedale Way, Oldham, OL9 7LD Tel: 0161-681 9917 Fax: 0161-683 4182 E-mail: sales@constant-engineering.co.uk *Door protection plates*

Constant Cooling Services, 2 London Road Industrial Estate, London Road, Pampisford, Cambridge, CB2 4EE Tel: (01223) 834711 Fax: (01223) 837818 E-mail: constantcooling@hotmail.com *Refrigeration engineers*

Constant Instruments, Unit 8 Minster Court, Courtwick Lane, Wick, Littlehampton, West Sussex, BN17 7RN Tel: (01903) 739333 Fax: (01903) 739222 E-mail: sales@constant-ceia.com *Industrial metal detection & x-ray systems manufrs*

Constant Power Services Ltd (CPS), Units 3, Trust Industrial Estate, Wilbury Way, Hitchin, Hertfordshire, SG4 0UZ Tel: (01462) 422955 Fax: (01462) 422754 E-mail: sales@cps4ups.co.uk Principal Export Areas: Middle East, Africa, Central/East Europe & West Europe *Constant Power Services Ltd are a reliable source of service support & engineering in the field of Uninterruptible Power Supplies & Power Conditioning. CPS is well-established & part of an international manufacturing group enhancing product range & resources. UPS systems from CPS up to 160kVA are compact & efficient enough to be installed alongside sophisticated computer equipment. All designs are "true on-line" systems, employing double conversion techniques with static & manual bypass facilities up to 800kVA as single modules with parallel systems taking power capabilities to much higher levels. Onsite site load bank testing & demonstrations can be accommodated as well as full Witness testing at the Italian manufacturing plant. Stock is held at the Hitchin based factory, with units usually available from 3kVA up to 300kVA to meet urgent requirements. CPS support installations with a comprehensive spares holding, 24-7 emergency callout facilities & preventative maintenance agreements.*

Constant Precision, 5 Triumph Way, Woburn Road Industrial Estate, Kempston, Bedford, MK42 7QB Tel: (01234) 851131 Fax: (01234) 841265 E-mail: sales@constant-precision.co.uk *Engineering subcontractors, precision & CNC engineers*

▶ Constant Systems Ltd, Low March Industrial Estate, Low March, Daventry, Northamptonshire, NN11 4SD Tel: (01327) 314146 Fax: (01327) 314147 E-mail: sales@constantsystems.com

Constar International UK Ltd, Moor Lane Trading Estate, Sherburn in Elmet, Leeds, LS25 6ES Tel: (01977) 882000 Fax: (01977) 882092 E-mail: enquiries@constar.net *Plastic bottle & jar manufrs*

Constat Computer Supplies, The Cross, Worcester, WR1 3PX Tel: (01905) 616610 Fax: (01905) 616640 E-mail: sales@constat.co.uk *Computer consumables*

Constell Engineers Ltd, Nile Street, Rochdale, Lancashire, OL16 2JQ Tel: (01706) 646936 Fax: (01706) 647817 E-mail: office@constell.co.uk *Mould & die makers*

Constellation I X Ltd, Post Office House, Main Street, Leicester, LE9 2AL Tel: 0116-239 2300 E-mail: sales@conix.co.uk *Computer consultants*

Constitution Warehouse, 39-45 Constitution Hill, Birmingham, B19 3LE Tel: 0121-236 1910 Fax: 0121-236 6897 *Wholesale cash & carry*

▶ Constructall Ltd, The Old Granary, Thurley Farm, Pump Lane, Grazeley, Reading, RG7 1JN Tel: 0118-988 3322

Construction & Commercial Recycling Ltd, Century Business Centre, Century Business Park, Manvers, Rotherham, South Yorkshire, S63 5DA Tel: 01709 300090 Fax: 01709 300102 E-mail: Candcrecycling@aol.com *Company operates mini-crushers specialising in processing construction and demolition (C&D) waste nationwide. Available with or without operators.*

Construction Computer Software Ltd, Wester Kerse, Lochwinnoch, Renfrewshire, PA12 4DU Tel: (01505) 506118 Fax: (01505) 506117 E-mail: info@ccsuk.com *Software solutions for construction industry*

Construction Confederation, 55 Tufton Street, London, SW1P 3QL Tel: (020) 7227 4500 Fax: (020) 7227 4501 E-mail: bwf@bwf.org.uk *Trade association*

Construction Confederation, 56-64 Leonard Street, London, EC2A 4JX Tel: (020) 7608 5000 Fax: (020) 7631 3872 E-mail: enquiries@thecc.org.uk *Civil engineering trade associations*

▶ Construction Consultancy Services Ltd, 3 Wellington Park, Belfast, BT9 6DJ Tel: (028) 9092 3360 Fax: (028) 9038 2451 E-mail: info@ccsni.com *We provide technical support services to the construction industry in Northern Ireland***CCS RESOURCES- 'Recruitment with a difference'. We second Engineering Staff to the Construction Industry, Engineers, Project Managers, Site Supervision, AutoCAD, GIS and Environmental Technician Posts. Our professionals fulfil the need for temporary and project based expertise.**CCS SURVEYING - We provide GPS & GIS Data Capture Solutions to accurately record the location of Utility Network Assets. Topographical Surveys are also enhanced by the customisation of our GPS surveying solutions which incorporate Network Control. Our Field Data Collection solutions are tailored to suit the recording and mapping of asset inventories such as manholes, watermains and sewers.**CCS CONSTRUCTION MANAGEMENT- We provide performance measurement to monitor and record the improvement to the Construction Environment brought about by the development of Partnering Procurement and TQM**

Construction Cosmetics, Red Mill House Centurion Way Business Park, Alfreton Road, Derby, DE21 4AY Tel: (01332) 867740 Fax: (01332) 867741 E-mail: info@concos.co.uk *Brick & Mortar Tinting, Stone Repairs, Facade Cleaning, Graffiti Removal,*Anti Graffiti Treatments.*

D & J R Construction, 2 Farra Road, Portadown, Craigavon, County Armagh, BT62 1QZ Tel: (028) 3835 6450 Fax: (028) 3835 6450 *Building & construction contractors*

Construction Elliz Ltd, Chart House Farm, Bullen Road, Ryde, Isle of Wight, PO33 1QB Tel: (01983) 612317 Fax: (01983) 615600 E-mail: iow@mansell.plc.uk *Construction*

Construction Fastener Techniques, C F T House, Mill Race Lane, Stourbridge, West Midlands, DY8 1JN Tel: (01384) 442277 Fax: (01384) 442999 E-mail: sales@cftltd.co.uk *Roof fitting fastenings & self-drilling screws*

▶ Construction Industry Quality Assurance Ltd, 45 High Street, Walton-on-Thames, Surrey, KT12 1DH Tel: (01932) 231361 Fax: (01932) 222647 E-mail: mail@ciqa.eu.com *Quality Assurance services to construction and property professionals to ISO 9001:2000*

Construction Industry Solutions Ltd, Coins Buildings, The Grove, Slough, SL1 1QP Tel: (01753) 501000 Fax: (01753) 711010 E-mail: info@coins-global.com *Computer software services*

Construction Leads, Camargue Eagle Tower, Mometpellier Drive, Cheltenham, Gloucestershire, GL50 1TA Tel: (01242) 577277 Fax: (01242) 527277 *Project opportunities for consultants*

Construction Machinery Supplies (UK) Ltd, Dormers, Hawthorn Lane, Four Marks, Alton, Hampshire, GU34 5AU Tel: (01420) 587216 Fax: (01420) 588303 E-mail: douglas.bonham@virgin.net *Construction machinery*

Construction Management & Design, Ty Capel, Yr Henffordd, Nercwys, Mold, Clwyd, CH7 4DL Tel: (01352) 755522 Fax: (01352) 754656 E-mail: constmanagdesign@aol.com *Building consultants*

▶ Construction Plant Services (SW) Ltd, Nordic House, Longships Road, Cardiff, CF10 4RP Tel: (029) 2048 2002 Fax: (029) 2048 0876 E-mail: info@cpsltd.co.uk *Electrical dealership*

Construction Products & Services Ltd, 40 Rannoch Drive, Cardiff, CF23 6LQ Tel: (029) 2076 1176 Fax: (029) 2075 6179 E-mail: john.lowder@conprod.co.uk *Construction industry crash barrier suppliers*

Construction Profiles Ltd, Carriage House, Little Broom Street, Birmingham, B12 0EU Tel: 0121-766 6633 Fax: 0121-766 7792 E-mail: accounts@construction-profiles.co.uk *Roofing & cladding contractors*

Construction Sealants Ltd, 59 Warwick Road, Rainham, Essex, RM13 9XU Tel: (01708) 631421 Fax: (01708) 631407 *Application of mastic sealants*

Construction & Shopfitting Ltd, 117, Piccotts End, Hemel Hempstead, Hertfordshire, HP1 3AU Tel: (01442) 244117 Fax: (01442) 233274 E-mail: cs.co@virgin.net *Suspended ceiling systems constructors*

Construction Site Safety Training (CSST), 29a Market Square, Biggleswade, Beds, SG18 8AQ Tel: 07815 154157 E-mail: paul@csst-ltd.org *Construction Site Safety Training (CSST) was developed whilst working within the Health & Safety training environment and witnessing the lack of quality training and consultancy available to individuals at a fair price, throughout the construction industry. **Specialising in CSCS (Health & Safety) Card training and testing (all trades).**CSST aim to provided the highest standard of Training and Consultancy available to the Construction Industry**Training Centre in East/Central London but serving the whole of the South East**

Constructional Steel & Alloy, Unit 7 Salamons Way, Rainham, Essex, RM13 9UL Tel: (01708) 551967 Fax: (01708) 555453 *Scrap metal merchants & skip hire services*

▶ Constructional Steelwork, Unit 3, 204 Oldbury Road, West Bromwich, West Midlands, B70 9DE Tel: 0121-525 8766 *Steel fabricators*

Constructional Veneers Ltd, 2 Timberwharf Road, Stamford Hill, London, N16 6DB Tel: (020) 8802 1166 Fax: (020) 8802 4222 E-mail: veneers@talk21.com *Veneer & plywood merchants*

Constructiv Company Ltd, 1/St. Giles Business Park, Pool Road, Newtown, Powys, SY16 3AJ Tel: (01686) 610890 Fax: (01686) 610880 E-mail: enquiries@constructiv.co.uk *Embroidery manufrs*

▶ Constructive Approach, 6 Millside Industrial, Southmill Road, Bishop's Stortford, Hertfordshire, CM23 3DP Tel: (01279) 757225 Fax: (01279) 757427

▶ Consult TM Ltd, Avon Lodge, Watery Lane, Sherbourne, Warwick, CV35 8AL Tel: (0845) 4085960 Fax: (0845) 4085961 E-mail: tonym@consulttm.co.uk *Management consultancy*

▶ Consultancy People Ltd, Nelson House, 1a Church Street, Epsom, Surrey, KT17 4PF Tel: (0845) 0504657 E-mail: mail@consultpeople.com

▶ Consultancy Skills Training Ltd, 32 York Road, Sutton, Surrey, SM2 6HH Tel: (020) 8642 9568 Fax: (020) 8643 0443 E-mail: sales@cst-ltd.co.uk *Providing consultancy & training, internationally to prestigious clients, in a variety of European languages, to organisations and people who wish to develop their client engagement performance. Offering public and in-house training courses for consultants*

Consultant Gas Engineers, Peel Road, West Pimbo, Skelmersdale, Lancashire, WN8 9PT Tel: (01695) 727441 Fax: (01695) 729466 E-mail: sales@cgekilns.co.uk *Kiln & furnace manufrs*

▶ Consultants In Quality Assurance Ltd, 215 Staines Road, Lauham, Staines, Middlesex, TW18 2RS Tel: (01784) 460563 E-mail: rhoweles@ciqa.co.uk *Consultant in quality assurance*

J M P Consultants Ltd, 172 Tottenham Court Road, London, W1T 7NA Tel: (020) 7388 5331 Fax: (020) 7387 0078 E-mail: london@jmp.co.uk *Consulting civil engineers*

Consulting Engineers' Co-Partnership London Ltd, 1528 London Road, London, SW16 4EU Tel: (020) 8679 5621 Fax: (020) 8679 7922 E-mail: mail@cecp.co.uk *Structural & civil engineers*

▶ CONSUMABLES EXPRESS LTD, Unit 31 Brambles Enterprise Ctr, Waterberry Drive, Waterlooville, Hants, PO7 7TH Tel: 02392 256211 Fax: 02392 256211 E-mail: sales@consumablesexpress.co.uk *wholesaler of paper center feed rolls, dispensers, disposable gloves, dust masks, protective coveralls, specialist wipes, paint mixing cups,tacky cloths,paint strainers,plastic spreaders & aerosol adhesive.*

▶ Consumables Solutions Ltd, Safeguard House, Unit E, Hazleton Interchange, Lakesmere Road, Horndean, Waterlooville, Hampshire, PO8 9JU Tel: (0870) 7746500 Fax: (0870) 7746540 E-mail: sales@consumables-uk.com *Protective clothing, hygiene & janitorial products,*

Consumer Microcircuits Ltd, Ovel Park, Langford, Maldon, Essex, CM9 6WG Tel: (01621) 875500 Fax: (01621) 875600 E-mail: sales@cmlmicro.com *Integrated circuit design & manufrs*

Consumers Utility Costs Ltd, C U C House, Crawley, West Sussex, RH11 9BN Tel: (01293) 516521 Fax: (01293) 512030 E-mail: sales@consumers-utility-cost.co.uk *Client utility cost services*

▶ Consuming Passion, Arundel House, 22 The Drive, Hove, East Sussex, BN3 3JD Tel: (01273) 719160 E-mail: saragsanders@hotmail.com *Highly personalised catering service. We provide excellent food & flawless service. A company small enough to care about each individual event. Our passion for food means we source the best ingredients possible to create a delicious meal for a reasonable price, leaving you to relax and entertain your guests.*

Contact Attachments, Unit E, Mochdre Industrial Estate, Newtown, Powys, SY16 4LE Tel: (01686) 611200 Fax: (01686) 611201 E-mail: sales@forklift-attachments.co.uk *Contact Attachments: Forklift Attachments, Materials Handling, Lifting Attachments, Lifting Equipment, Crane Attachments, Lifting Beams, Access Equipment, Access Platforms, Forks, Fork Extensions, Load Stabilisers, Tines, Jibs, Hooks, Scoops, Snow Ploughs, Sweeping Broom, Yard Brush, Building Materials Handling, Waste Handling, Skips, Waste Container, Wheelie Bin Handling, Drum Handling, Drum Positioning, Drum Rotators.*

▶ Contact Building Services, Albert Street, Droylsden, Manchester, M43 7BA Tel: 0161-370 1200 Fax: 0161-371 9840

Contact Components Ltd, 5 Parkend, Harlow BSNS Park, Harlow, Essex, CM19 5QF Tel: (01279) 424211 Fax: (01279) 424213 *Electronic component distributors*

▶ Contact Construction, 76 Riverside Drive, Radcliffe, Manchester, M26 1HY Tel: (01204) 701510 E-mail: costellosteve@hotmail.com

Contact Copiers, 79 Commercial Street, Risca, Newport, Gwent, NP11 6AW Tel: (01633) 894488 Fax: (01633) 615566 *Photocopiers suppliers & services*

▶ Contact Electrical, Rackheath Industrial Estate, Rackheath, Norwich, NR13 6LH Tel: (01603) 720401 Fax: (01603) 720070

Contact Electronics Ltd, Unit 4 Westmead House, 123 Westmead Road, Sutton, Surrey, SM1 4JH Tel: (020) 8643 3000 Fax: (020) 8643 5777 E-mail: contact@contact-electronics.co.uk *Sub contractors & electronics manufrs*

▶ Contact Industrial Recruitment, Valley Farm Way, Leeds, LS10 1SE Tel: 0113-276 1010 Fax: 0113-276 1155 E-mail: info@contact4jobs.com

Contact Middle East (UK) Ltd, 106 Hammersmith Grove, London, W6 7HB Tel: (020) 8846 9255 Fax: (020) 8748 0844 *Journalism*

Contact Packaging, Unit 5-17, Prince Road, Kings Norton Business Centre, Birmingham, B30 3HB Tel: 0121-458 5060 *Packaging materials & products*

Contact Print & Packaging Ltd, Haigh Avenue, Stockport, Cheshire, SK4 1NU Tel: 0161-480 3568 Fax: 0161-480 8185 *Litho printed carton manufrs*

Contact Public Relations & Management, Unit 11 Hackford Walk, Hackford Road, London, SW9 0QT Tel: (020) 7582 2220 Fax: (020) 7820 0195 E-mail: contactpr@btconnect.com *Presenter publishers*

Contact Radio Communications Ltd, Unit 19 Leeway Court, Leeway Industrial Estate, Newport, Gwent, NP19 4SJ Tel: (01633) 270005 Fax: (01633) 271305 *Two-way radio equipment sales, servicing & hire*

Contact Services (W R) Ltd, Paddock Works, 149A Shay Lane, Halifax, West Yorkshire, HX3 6RR Tel: (01422) 349536 Fax: (01422) 349468 *Steel fabricators*

Contact Technical Services, Jarodale House, 7 Gregory Boulevard, Nottingham, NG7 6LB Tel: 0115-911 9230 Fax: 0115-911 9231 E-mail: admin@makecontact.co.uk *Recruitment services*

▶ Contact Training Ltd, Exmouth Business Support Centre, 27 Gibson Close, Exmouth, Devon, EX8 4BU Tel: (01395) 222174 E-mail: simon@contact-training.com *Imagine a training version of the "Crystal Maze". Then Imagine a company that brings the whole circus to you. NOW IMAGINE CONTACT TRAINING. For real training solutions look no further.*

Contacta Ltd, 11 Tower View, Kings Hill, West Malling, Kent, ME19 4UY Tel: (01732) 223900 Fax: (01732) 223909 E-mail: sales@contacta.co.uk *Communication equipment manufrs*

Contacta Engineering Ltd, Unit 21 Laurence Industrial Estate, Eastwoodbury Lane, Southend-on-Sea, SS2 6RH Tel: (01702) 511887 Fax: (01702) 420631 E-mail: info@contacta.co.uk *Precision engineers*

Contactum Ltd, Victoria Works, Edgware Road, London, NW2 6LF Tel: (020) 8452 6366 Fax: (020) 8208 3340 E-mail: general@contactum.co.uk *Electric wiring accessories manufrs*

Contactus Water Treatment Equipment, 227 Walsall Road, Sutton Coldfield, West Midlands, B74 4QA Tel: 0121-353 7208 Fax: 0121-352 0117 E-mail: contactus@fsmail.net *Water treatment plant*

Container Kitchen Systems Ltd, Henley Park, Normandy, Guildford, Surrey, GU3 2BL Tel: (0845) 812 0800 Fax: (0845) 812 0801 E-mail: mark.kingston@cksltd.co.uk *Container Kitchen Systems Ltd based in Guildford, Surrey offer the hire of portable kitchens. They provide container kitchens with temporary catering facilities.*

Container Printers (UK) Ltd, 248 Mackadown Lane, Kitts Green, Birmingham, B33 0JU Tel: 0121-789 7777 Fax: 0121-789 5539 E-mail: info@cprint.co.uk *Aerosols drums manufrs*

Container Products Ltd, Unit 7C, Castle Mill Works, Bimingham New Road, Dudley, West Midlands, DY1 4DA Tel: 01384 251391 Fax: 01384 251390 E-mail: info@containerproducts.co.uk *Container Products Ltd (West Midlands) are specialist in the manufacture of Corrugated Cartons, Timber Packing Cases,experienced Export Packers and supplies of Packaging Materials. We offer a complete in-house service to the exporter. From the manufacture of bespoke cases/crates or cartons, to export packing in accordance with BS1133 section 8 also to the Ministry of Defence DEF STAN specifications, to arranging Freight Forwarding. Contact us to day to discuss your requirements or see our website for further details (quoting Kellyseach).*

Containercare Ltd, Dock Road, Liverpool, L19 2JW Tel: 0151-427 1771 Fax: 0151-427 1772 E-mail: sales@concare.co.uk *Freight containers*

Containerships UK Ltd, Teesport Container Terminal, Teesport, Middlesbrough, Cleveland, TS6 7SA Tel: (01642) 468592 Fax: (01642) 770737 *Shipping agents*

Containment Technology Ltd, 9 Telford Road, Ferndown Industrial Estate, Wimborne, Dorset, BH21 7QW Tel: (01202) 870189 Fax: (01202) 870212 *Laboratory test & patient handling equipment*

Contak components Ltd, Unit A The Anderson Centre, Spitfire Close, Ermine Business Park, Huntingdon, Cambridgeshire, PE29 6XY Tel: (01480) 411022 Fax: (01480) 411082 E-mail: impakgroup@compuserve.com *Plastic foam converter & protective clothing*

Contamination Control Apparel Ltd, Northolt Drive, Bolton, BL3 6RE Tel: (01204) 528019 Fax: (01204) 361549 E-mail: cca@mikar.co.uk *Protective & safety clothing manufrs*

▶ The Contamination Investigation Co. Ltd, 60 Elan Avenue, Stourport-on-Severn, Worcestershire, DY13 8LX Tel: (01299) 877539 Fax: (0845) 2991523 E-mail: sales@contamination-investigation.co.uk

Contarnex Europe Ltd, 252 Martin Way, Morden, Surrey, SM4 4AW Tel: (020) 8540 1034 Fax: (020) 8543 3058 E-mail: enquiries@contarnex.com *Clock & clock system distributors & alarm systems suppliers*

Contarps North West Ltd, Unit D4 Newton Business Park, Talbot Road, Hyde, Cheshire, SK14 4UQ Tel: 0161-367 9341 Fax: 0161-367 9352 E-mail: sales@contarps.co.uk *PVC tarpaulin & interlocking sheets*

Contec & Co., Sub-Station Road, Felixstowe, Suffolk, IP11 3JB Tel: (01394) 674574 Fax: (01394) 674574 *Suppliers of spares to the container industry*

Contech Electronics Ltd, Unit C Mindenhall Court, High Street, Stevenage, Hertfordshire, SG1 3BG Tel: (01438) 315757 Fax: (01438) 313679 E-mail: sales@contech.co.uk *Computer keyboard distribution*

▶ Con-Tech Services Ltd, Oaks Lane, Hoyle Mill, Barnsley, South Yorkshire, S71 1HT Tel: (01226) 244051 *Concrete products & construction materials*

Contek Software Ltd, Camkins House, Risborough Road, Little Kimble, Aylesbury, Buckinghamshire, HP17 0UE Tel: (01296) 612121 E-mail: sales@anaclara.net *Computer consultants*

Contelec Engravings Ltd, Spring Lane, Willenhall, West Midlands, WV12 4JG Tel: (01902) 369307 Fax: (01902) 369309 E-mail: engrave@contelec.co.uk *Industrial engravers & mosaic mimic displays*

Contemporary Design Unit, Arlington Wharf, 12 Arlington Square, London, N1 7DR Tel: (020) 7226 2077 Fax: (020) 7359 7032 E-mail: info@cdu.co.uk *Exhibition designers & contractors*

▶ Contemporary Living, 25 Peaseland Road, Cleckheaton, West Yorkshire, BD19 3EZ Tel: (01274) 861855 Fax: (01274) 876529 E-mail: design@contemporaryliving.tv *Interior design company, domestic and commercial work. Specialising in bespoke textiles. Specialist curtain and blind making. "Styling and prop. buying for advertisers and photographers."Show homes "*

▶ Contemporary Music Design, 50 Washington Street, Brighton, BN2 9SR Tel: 07789 435036 E-mail: info@comd.co.uk *Composition and Arrangement for multimedia, advertising, private and corporate. Bespoke music production and score writing with professional studio facilities for editing, mastering and post production"*

▶ contemporaryart4all.co.uk, 14 West Park Crescent, Inverbervie, Montrose, Angus, DD10 0TX Tel: 01561 362902 E-mail: ros@contemporaryart4all.co.uk *Online Art gallery showcasing sunset paintings, seascape paintings, landscape paintings, portraits, fine art and abstract work by Scottish artist Ros C. Commissions accepted.*

Context Information Security Ltd, Blake House, Admirals Way, London, E14 9UJ Tel: (020) 7537 7515 Fax: (020) 7537 1071 E-mail: michael.leviseur@contextis.co.uk *Computer consultants*

▶ Contherm Ltd, 2 Union Lane, Droitwich, Worcestershire, WR9 9AZ Tel: (01905) 775783 Fax: (01905) 794195 *Manufacture combustion systems*

Conti Fibre UK Ltd, Hulley Road, Macclesfield, Cheshire, SK10 2LT Tel: (01625) 429636 Fax: (01625) 610974 *Nylon yarn manufrs*

Continental Ltd, Unit C2 Herrick Way, Staverton Technology Park, Staverton, Cheltenham, Gloucestershire, GL51 6TQ Tel: (01452) 855222 Fax: (01452) 856794 E-mail: sales@continental.co.uk *Computer services*

Continental Ltd, 229 East Street, London, SE17 2SS Tel: (020) 7703 6705 Fax: (020) 7701 6433 *Continental meat suppliers*

Continental Airlines, Beulah Court, Albert Road, Horley, Surrey, RH6 7HP Tel: (0845) 6076760 Fax: (01293) 773726 *Airline* Also at: London SW1

Continental Appliance Services Midlands Ltd, 5 Showell Lane, Wolverhampton, WV4 4TZ Tel: (01902) 894433 Fax: (01902) 894433 *Electrical contractors*

Continental Conveyor Ltd, West Quay Road, Sunderland Enterprise Park, Sunderland, SR5 2TD Tel: 0191-516 5353 Fax: 0191-516 5399 E-mail: sales@continental-conveyor.co.uk Principal Export Areas: Worldwide *Mining machinery manufrs*

▶ Continental Data Graphics Ltd, Gate House, Fretherne Road, Welwyn Garden City, Hertfordshire, AL8 6RD Tel: (01707) 392520 Fax: (01707) 371813 E-mail: sales@cdgl.com *Technical documentation to the aerospace & defence industry suppliers*

Continental Engineering (1986) Ltd, 24 Invincible Road, Farnborough, Hampshire, GU14 7QU Tel: (01252) 512122 Fax: (01252) 549291 E-mail: conteng86ltd@btinternet.com *Materials handling sales*

Continental Engravers Precision Ltd, Huxley Close, Newnham Industrial Estate, Plympton, Plymouth, PL7 4JN Tel: (01752) 344474 Fax: (01752) 342938 *Sign makers/engravers*

Continental Freight Forwarding Ltd, PO Box 11438, Ellon, Aberdeenshire, AB41 9NU Tel: (01358) 723418 Fax: (01358) 723613 E-mail: fgb@continental-freight.co.uk *Freight forwarding agents*

Continental Meat Products, 241 Radford Road, Nottingham, NG7 5GU Tel: 0115-978 4129 Fax: 0115-978 4129 *Importers & manufacturers of meat*

▶ Continental Medical, Ashby House, 64 High Street, Walton-on-Thames, Surrey, KT12 1BW Tel: (01932) 231733

Continental Pasta Ltd, Units 1-2, Locksbrook Court, Locksbrook Road, Bath, BA1 3EN Tel: (01225) 312300 Fax: (01225) 460343 E-mail: enquiries@cpastas.co.uk *Food manufrs*

Continental Polymers Ltd, PO Box 983, Swindon, SN5 5WJ Tel: (01793) 875161 Fax: (01793) 887281 E-mail: cpl@contpoly.co.uk *Plastic packaging consultants*

Continental Service Station Ltd, Brecon Road, Caerbont, Abercrave, Swansea, SA9 1SW Tel: (01639) 730279 Fax: (01639) 730282 E-mail: continentalss@aol.com *Car dealership*

▶ Continental Shooting Supplies, Blackstone Farm, Dalry, Ayrshire, KA24 5HN Tel: (01294) 833297 Fax: (01294) 833312 *Shooting equipment importers & wholesalers*

▶ Continental Soil Technology, The Old Dairy, Chavenage Estate, Tetbury, Gloucestershire, GL8 8XY Tel: (0845) 6034136 Fax: E-mail: info@continentalsoiltechnology.com *Bennett Soil Technology are the importers and distributors for a comprehensive and complimentary machinery range. From complete Soil Stabilisation systems to site re-instatement machinery and stone crushers it is our unique ability to offer the complete package.*

Continental Teves UK Ltd, Waun-Y-Pound Industrial Estate, Ebbw Vale, Gwent, NP23 6PL Tel: (01495) 350350 Fax: (01495) 350351 *Automotive industry backing parts manufrs*

Continental Tyre Group Ltd, Continental House, 191 High Street, Yiewsley, West Drayton, Middlesex, UB7 7XW Tel: (01895) 425900 Fax: (01895) 425982 *Tyre manufrs* Also at: Rugby

▶ Continental Wigs, 39 Granada Road, Southsea, Hampshire, PO4 0RD Tel: (01455) 559679 Fax: (01455) 559541 E-mail: continental.wigs@ntlworld.com *Mail order wigs for ladies*

Continuous Transfer Paper Printers Ltd, Lotti Works, Two Bridges Road, Newhey, Rochdale, Lancashire, OL16 3SR Tel: (01706) 299015 Fax: (01706) 841159 E-mail: sales@ctpp.co.uk *Continuous transfer paper manufrs*

▶ Continuum Blue Ltd, 10 Signal Court, Station Road, Lingfield, Surrey, RH7 6DY Tel: (01342) 837720 Fax: 07916 495348 E-mail: info@continuum-blue.com *Continuum Blue is a technology development company, with a strong focus on medical devices. We provide engineering solutions including: design, development, prototyping, finite element analysis, computational fluid mechanics and material selection.*

Contisteel (Southern) Ltd, Wyvols Court, Swallowfield, Reading, RG7 1WY Tel: 0118-988 0258 Fax: 0118-988 0348 E-mail: well.joshi@contisteelarcelor.com *Steel stockholders*

Contitrades Ltd, 348a Jersey Road, Isleworth, Middlesex, TW7 5PL Tel: (020) 8847 4411 Fax: (020) 8568 8239 E-mail: info@contitrade.com *Export traders & hotel owners*

▶ Contour Direct Ltd, Unit 40 The Metropolitan Centre, Halifax Road, Greenford, Middlesex, UB6 8XU Tel: (020) 8575 8989 Fax: (020) 8575 7553

▶ Contour Home Design Ltd, 23 Benson Road, Nuffield Industrial Estate, Poole, Dorset, BH17 0GB Tel: (01202) 680415 Fax: (01202) 667592 E-mail: sales@contourhomedesign.co.uk *Suppliers & manufacturers of furniture*

Contour Showers Ltd, Siddorn Street, Winsford, Cheshire, CW7 2BA Tel: (01606) 592586 Fax: (01606) 861260 E-mail: sales@contour-showers.co.uk Principal Export Areas: Worldwide *Disabled persons shower cabinets, cubicles manufrs*

▶ Contour Steel Fabrication Services, Paynes Business Park, Dereham Road, Beeston, King's Lynn, Norfolk, PE32 2NQ Tel: (01328) 701574 Fax: (01328) 701542

Contour Video Productions, 164 Ellerdine Road, Hounslow, TW3 2PX Tel: (020) 8737 6557 Fax: (020) 8737 6557 *Video producers*

Contra Vision Ltd, Victoria House, 19-21 Ack Lane East, Bramhall, Stockport, Cheshire, SK7 2BE Tel: 0161-439 9307 Fax: 0161-440 7934 E-mail: sales@contravision.com *Screen printed material suppliers & outdoor advertisers*

Contrac Computer Supplies North East, Pinetree Centre, Durham Road, Birtley, Chester le Street, County Durham, DH3 2TD Tel: 0191-492 2999 Fax: 0191-492 3011 E-mail: enquiries@contrac.co.uk *IT resellers*

Contract Blending & Packing Ltd, Heys Lane, Great Harwood, Blackburn, BB6 7UA Tel: (01254) 877870 Fax: (01254) 877871 *Contract packers*

Contract Ceilings, Unit 3c Firlands Mill, South Parade, Pudsey, West Yorkshire, LS28 8AD Tel: 0113-239 4614 Fax: 0113-239 3638 *Suspended ceilings*

Contract Chemicals Properties Ltd, Penrhyn Road, Knowsley Business Park, Prescot, Merseyside, L34 9HY Tel: 0151-548 8840 Fax: 0151-548 6548 E-mail: info@contract-chemicals.com *Pharmaceutical & fine chemical manufrs*

Contract Components, Unit 37 Pitcliffe Way, Bradford, West Yorkshire, BD5 7SG Tel: (01274) 721982 Fax: (01274) 306876 E-mail: sales@cclveloduct.co.uk *Duct fitting & ventilation products manufrs*

▶ Contract Design Northern Ltd, 9-11 St James Street, Newcastle upon Tyne, NE1 4NF Tel: 0191-232 2737 Fax: 0191-261 1219 E-mail: sales@contractdesign.co.uk *Recruitment*

Contract Diamond Drilling Ltd, Harvest Court, Harvest Drive, Lowestoft, Suffolk, NR33 7NB Tel: (01502) 566500 Fax: (01502) 585815 *Diamond cutters*

Contract Distributors, 7 Tansley Road, North Wingfield, Chesterfield, Derbyshire, S42 5JZ Tel: (01246) 859257 Fax: (01246) 853787 E-mail: somedayuk2000@yahoo.co.uk *Induction loops nursecall systems panic alarm systems*

▶ Contract Ecology and Landscapes, 84 Tulketh Crescent, Ashton-On-Ribble, Preston, PR2 2RJ Tel: 01772 731404 E-mail: enquiries@contractecology.co.uk *Licensed ecological surveyors*

Contract Engineering Ltd, Meadow Mill, Water Street, Stockport, Cheshire, SK1 2BY Tel: 0161-480 5673 Fax: 0161-477 2687 *General engineers*

Contract Fertiliser & Storage Ltd, Spaldington Airfield, Bubwith Road, Spaldington, Goole, East Yorkshire, DN14 7NG Tel: (01430) 431511 Fax: (01430) 432070 E-mail: cfs@jhbunn.co.uk *Fertiliser manufrs*

▶ Contract Flooring Magazine, 93 Northbank Road, Walthamstow, London, E17 4JY Tel: (020) 8531 4545 E-mail: pstuart40@ntlworld.com *Contract Flooring Magazine is a leading online magazine for the floor trade.**It provides a way of publishing press releases, floor product and project information at hardly any cost but with excellent market exposure.*

▶ Contract Foods Ltd, 16 Oxleasow Road, Redditch, Worcestershire, B98 0RE Tel: (01527) 514777 Fax: (01527) 516755

Contract (H/F) Electrode Supplies Ltd, Newhaven Industrial Estate, Barton Lane, Eccles, Manchester, M30 0HL Tel: 0161-707 4090 Fax: 0161-707 1314 E-mail: enquiries@contractelectrode.co.uk *PVC welders & advertising gift house*

▶ Contract & Home Blinds Ltd, Shelco House, Northgate, Aldridge, Walsall, WS9 8TH Tel: (01922) 454345 Fax: (01922) 454410 *Blind manufrs*

Contract Maintenance Team, 10 Promenade Terrace, Edinburgh, EH15 1DT Tel: 0131-657 5246 *Industrial engineers*

Contract Packers (Midlands) Ltd, Kiln Way, Woodville, Swadlincote, Derbyshire, DE11 8ED Tel: (01283) 224289 Fax: (01283) 224030 E-mail: barrypresscott@vitax.co.uk *Contract packers*

Contract Paper Ltd, Sovereign House, Rhosili Road, Brackmills, Northampton, NN4 7JE Tel: (0870) 6082374 Fax: (0870) 6082375 E-mail: marketing@hspg.com *Paper merchants* Also at: Leeds

▶ Contract Scaffolding Services Ltd, Carleton Depot, Carleton, Carlisle, CA1 3DS Tel: (01228) 549411 Fax: (01228) 810867

Contract Security Services Ltd, Challenger House, 125 Gunnersbury Lane, London, W3 8LH Tel: (020) 8752 0160 Fax: (020) 8992 9536 E-mail: cssltd1@aol.com *Security contractors*

▶ Contract Services Ltd, 28 Church Road, Baglan, Port Talbot, West Glamorgan, SA12 8ST Tel: (01639) 823789 Fax: (01639) 823987 E-mail: info@contractservicesgroup.co.uk

Contract Services, Madera House, 25 Brindley Road Hertburn Industrial Estate, Hertburn, Washington, Tyne & Wear, NE37 2SB Tel: 0191-416 2230 Fax: 0191-416 2366 *Woodwork machinery dealers*

Contract Services Renovation & Refurbishing Ltd, Lombardian House Liverpool Road, Cadishead, Manchester, M44 5DD Tel: 0161-777 8278 Fax: 0161-777 6298 E-mail: general@contracts-svcs.co.uk *Office design & refurbishment*

Contract Sign Services, The Old Chapel, Sandfield Road, Churchdown, Gloucester, GL3 2HD Tel: (01452) 857017 Fax: (01452) 713706 E-mail: sales@contractsignservices.co.uk *Displays, modular & sign manufrs*

Contract Sign Systems Ltd, John Davey Drive, Treleigh Industrial Estate, Redruth, Cornwall, TR16 4AX Tel: (01209) 313449 Fax: (0870) 8706929 E-mail: sales@contractsigns.co.uk *Signs manufrs*

Contract Trade And Professional Ltd, Duchy Business Centre, Wilson Way, Pool, Redruth, Cornwall, TR15 3RT Tel: (01209) 314644 Fax: (01209) 314944 E-mail: sales@cornish-steel.co.uk *Steel fabricators*

Contract Turning Ltd, Unit 27 Ventura Place, Poole, Dorset, BH16 5SW Tel: (01202) 625502 Fax: (01202) 625502 E-mail: info@contractturning.co.uk *Precision engineers*

Contractors Equipment Sales Ltd, 1 Harrier Way, Airport Industrial Estate, Norwich, NR6 6HY Tel: (01603) 404620 Fax: (01603) 429717 E-mail: ces@ces.demon.co.uk *Plant sales, service & repairs*

Contractors Plant Hire Ltd, 3 Green Gables, Tidmarsh Lane, Tidmarsh, Reading, RG8 8HG Tel: 0118-984 3123 Fax: 0118-984 1101 *Contractors plant hire was founded in 1997 and we have become the area's leading plant hire company. We are confident in our ability to provide the full spectrum of plant hire and associated services. From our purpose built operations centre in Tadley, we offer a combination of new quality equipment and knowledgeable and enthusiastic staff. We can confidently say we offer"the right equipment, on time and at the right price **Give us a call and you will not be disappointed with our service.*

Contracts Engineering Ltd, Chapel Park, Stadium Way, Sittingbourne, Kent, ME10 3RW Tel: (01795) 479284 Fax: (01795) 477812 E-mail: contracts@totalserve.co.uk *Precision sheetmetal workers*

Contracts Galleypearl, 382 Aston Lane, Aston, Birmingham, B6 6QN Tel: 0121-356 0135 Fax: 0121-344 3558 *Development & investment*

Contracut Cutting Services, Unit 19 Mill House Lane, Triangle, Sowerby Bridge, West Yorkshire, HX6 3LN Tel: (01422) 835313 Fax: (01422) 835320 E-mail: scott.thewlis@tiscali.co.uk *Metal & steel sawing services*

► Contradig, Bethania, Capel Garmon, Llanrwst, Conwy, LL26 0RL Tel: (01690) 710309 Fax: (01690) 710154 E-mail: info@contradig.com

Contraflow Ltd, Unit 2 Stirling Road Industrial Estate, Airdrie, Lanarkshire, ML6 7UD Tel: (01236) 770999 Fax: (01236) 770666 *Traffic management agents*

Contral Instrument Services Ltd, 6 Abbotsinch Road, Grangemouth, Stirlingshire, FK3 9UX Tel: (01324) 484080 Fax: (01324) 483654 E-mail: info@contral.co.uk *Industry instrument services*

Contrasound Ltd, Unit 15 Rye Industrial Park, Rye Harbour Road, Rye, East Sussex, TN31 7TE Tel: (01797) 227070 Fax: (01797) 225969 *Noise control & ductwork engineers*

► Contrast Media Solutions, Unit 7A, St. Martins House, St. Martins Gate, Worcester, WR1 2DT Tel: (01905) 330566 Fax: (01905) 330566

Contrast Signs, 135 Roxeth Green Avenue, Harrow, Middlesex, HA2 0QJ Tel: (020) 8864 9242 *Sign manufrs*

Contrast Upholstery, Cobden Mill, Whalley Road, Sabden, Clitheroe, Lancashire, BB7 9DZ Tel: (01282) 778122 Fax: (01282) 771925 *Furniture, fabric & leather manufrs*

Contrax Industrial Services, B11 46 Holton Road, Holton Heath Trading Park, Poole, Dorset, BH16 6LT Tel: (01202) 621681 Fax: (01202) 621618 *Screen printers*

Contrel Ltd, PO Box 4127, Sudbury, Suffolk, CO10 1AB Tel: (01787) 881292 Fax: (01787) 881926 E-mail: intray7@contrel.co.uk *Manufacturers & suppliers of industrial electronic controls*

Contrive Ltd, 32 Beresford Road, London, E4 6EE Tel: (020) 8529 8425 Fax: (020) 8281 5980 *Electronic engineers*

Control Ability, Unit 2, Ashworth Buildings, Heys Lane, Great Harwood, Blackburn, BB6 7BA Tel: (01254) 886685 Fax: (01254) 886068 E-mail: sales@controlability.com *Tachometer manufrs*

Control Applications Ltd, Unit 12, Steeton Grove, Steeton, West Yorkshire, BD20 6TT Tel: (01535) 650890 Fax: (01535) 658824 E-mail: info@controlapplications.co.uk *Control panel manufrs*

Control Centre NRS Ltd, 8 Kestrel Park, Tallon Road, Hutton, Brentwood, Essex, CM13 1TN Tel: (01277) 228060 Fax: (01277) 227970 *Refrigeration & air conditioning suppliers*

Control Design, Unit Z Paddock Wood Distribution Centre, Paddock Wood, Tonbridge, Kent, TN12 6UU Tel: (01892) 836350 Fax: (01892) 837292 E-mail: controldesign@btconnect.com *Heating & ventilation installation services*

► Control & Display Systems Ltd, 1570 Parkway, Whiteley, Fareham, Hampshire, PO15 7AG Tel: (01489) 571771 Fax: (01489) 571555 E-mail: sales@cdsrail.com *Railway monitoring systems suppliers*

Control Electrics Leicester Ltd, 30 Fowke Street, Rothley, Leicester, LE7 7PJ Tel: 0116-237 4233 E-mail: enquire@controlelectrics.co.uk *Electrical control system engineers*

Control Energy Costs Ltd, Tollers Farm, Drive Road, Coulsdon, Surrey, CR5 1BN Tel: (01737) 556631 Fax: (01737) 553601 E-mail: analysts@cec.uk.com *Utility auditing & contract negotiators*

Control Equipment Ltd, Tyco Park, Grimshaw Lane, Newton Heath, Manchester, M40 2WL Tel: 0161-455 4232 Fax: 0161-455 4441 E-mail: tycocontrolsystems.uk@tycoint.com *Safety & control systems*

Control Gear Distributors Ltd, 3 Farthing Road, Ipswich, IP1 5AP Tel: (01473) 741404 Fax: (01473) 240904 E-mail: sales@controlgear.co.uk *Electric motor control gear distributors*

Control Gear (EPS) Ltd, Unit 30 Stroud Business Centre, Oldends Lane, Stonehouse, Gloucestershire, GL10 2DG Tel: (01453) 828559 Fax: (01453) 791048 E-mail: garygriffiths@control-gear.com *Pneumatic equipment distributors*

Control Gear Fluid Power Ltd, Heol Groeaswen, Treforest Industrial Estate, Pontypridd, Mid Glamorgan, CF37 5YF Tel: (01443) 843126 Fax: (01443) 842997 E-mail: sales@control-gear.com *Pneumatic control systems distributors*

► Control & Machinery Services, Manor House, Ipswich Road, Cardiff, CF23 9AQ Tel: (029) 2046 2200 Fax: (029) 2048 5678

► Control Plant Ltd, Lansbury Estate, 102 Lower Guildford Road, Knaphill, Woking, Surrey, GU21 2EP Tel: (01483) 472571 Fax: (01483) 475618

Control & Power Engineering Ltd, Fox Covert Lane, Misterton, Doncaster, South Yorkshire, DN10 4ER Tel: (01427) 891256 Fax: (01427) 891307 E-mail: capeuk@aol.com *Motor control centre manufrs*

Control & Power Systems Ltd, 3D Burniston Industrial Estate, Willymath Close, Burniston, Scarborough, North Yorkshire, YO13 0HG Tel: (01723) 871112 Fax: (01723) 870625 E-mail: controlandpower@compuserve.com *Control panels*

Control Risks, Cottons Centre, Cottons Lane, London, SE1 2QG Tel: (020) 7970 2100 Fax: (020) 7970 2222 E-mail: enquiries@control.risks.com *Business risk consultants*

The Control Shop Ltd, 17 Bilton Industrial Estate, Stockmans Close, Birmingham, B38 9TS Tel: 0121-451 1030 Fax: 0121-459 1511 E-mail: sales@controlshop.co.uk *Temperature probe manufrs*

Control Solutions Ltd, Avon House, 82 Wellington Street, Thame, Oxfordshire, OX9 3BN Tel: (01844) 216988 Fax: (01844) 261466 E-mail: mail@control-solutions.co.uk *Electrical control systems manufrs*

Control Stockholders & Properties Ltd, Perry Road, Witham, Essex, CM8 3AS Tel: (01376) 513348 Fax: (01376) 513361 E-mail: mail@control-engineering.ltd.uk *Control panel manufrs*

Control System Supplies, Oaktrees, Croxton, Stafford, ST21 6PF Tel: (01630) 620355 Fax: (01630) 620377 *Electronic engineers*

Control Techniques, Business Development Centre, Stafford Park 4, Telford, Shropshire, TF3 3BA Tel: (01952) 213727 Fax: (01952) 213701 E-mail: uksales@controltechniques.com *Speed drives & systems manufrs*

Control Techniques Dynamics Ltd, South Way, Andover, Hampshire, SP10 5AB Tel: (01264) 387600 Fax: (01264) 356561 E-mail: sales@ctdynamics.com *Servo motor manufrs*

Control Technology International Ltd, Regal Chambers, 49-51 Bancroft, Hitchin, Hertfordshire, SG5 1LL Tel: (01462) 457700 Fax: (01462) 453377 E-mail: info@ctiweb.co.uk *Software electronic engineers*

Control & Traceability Systems, The Mistal Hagg Farm, Haggs Road, Follifoot, Harrogate, North Yorkshire, HG3 1EQ Tel: (01423) 810820 Fax: (01423) 810288 E-mail: info@ctsol.co.uk Principal Export Areas: Central/East Europe & West Europe *Supply of shop floor data capture systems/MRP software, traceability and tracking systems, thermal printers, bar code scanners, thermal/transfer labels and ribbons.*

Control Valve Maintenance (Staines) Ltd, 874 Plymouth Road, Slough Trading Estate, Slough, SL1 4LP Tel: (01753) 567744 Fax: (01753) 567799 E-mail: controlvalves@cvml.demon.co.uk *Valves & actuators over haulers & sellers*

► Control Valve Systems, Lower Coilentowie, Callander, Perthshire, FK17 8LW Tel: (01786) 841228 *Dealers in control valves*

Control Waterjet Cutting, Unit 18 Telford Crescent, Speedwell Industrial Estate, Staveley, Chesterfield, Derbyshire, S43 3PF Tel: (01246) 284000 Fax: (01246) 284003 E-mail: sales@controlwaterjet.co.uk *Water jet cutting & profiling services*

► Controldraw Ltd, 17 Wilberforce Road, Southsea, Hampshire, PO5 3DR Tel: (023) 9279 6719 Fax: (023) 9271 6858 E-mail: fl@controldraw.co.uk *Software & consulting service*

Controline Ltd, Crown Works, Dewsbury Road, Elland, West Yorkshire, HX5 9BG Tel: (01422) 311993 Fax: (01422) 311818 E-mail: info@controline.co.uk *Electrical drives & control panel engineers*

Controlla Covers Ltd, Brunswick Industrial Park, Hannah Street, Darwen, Lancashire, BB3 3HL Tel: (01254) 772020 Fax: (01254) 773030 E-mail: controlla@aol.com *Industrial covers manufrs*

Controlled Access Ltd, Treadaway Technical Centre, Treadaway Hill, High Wycombe, Buckinghamshire, HP10 2RS Tel: 0118-977 0667 Fax: (01628) 850251 *Photocopier control systems manufrs*

Controlled Access Storage Cabinets Ltd, Ford House, Dewing Road, Rackheath Industrial Estate, Rackheath, Norwich, NR13 6PS Tel: (01603) 722770 Fax: (01603) 722771 E-mail: sales@casc-ltd.com *Electronic designers, security cabinet manufrs*

► Controlled Construction, Unit 1a CCL House Station Road Industrial Estate, Station Road, Coleshill, Birmingham, B46 1HT Tel: (01675) 464460 Fax: (01675) 465646 E-mail: enquires@asbestos-ccl.com *Controlled Construction Limited are fully licensed, insured and equipped to undertake both large and small asbestos removal contracts inclusive of re-insulation as required. The company's current client list includes work for local authorities, the motor industry, shops, schools and councils. Controlled Construction Limited operate a strict Health and Safety policy and Environmental policy. Controlled Construction Limited will produce a full method statement and risk assessment on every contract. We offer a 24 hour service and will undertake contracts from one day to one year. References and site inspections available upon request. We are members of ARCA and have achieved accreditation to the Site Audit Accreditation Scheme.*

Controlled Equipment, 17 The Mead Business Centre, Mead Lane, Hertford, SG13 7BJ Tel: (01992) 584404 Fax: (01992) 500177 E-mail: sales@meltingtank.com *Process heating equipment manufrs*

Controlled Flame Boilers Ltd, Gorse Lane Industrial Estate, Brunel Road, Clacton-on-Sea, Essex, CO15 4LU Tel: (01255) 224500 Fax: (01255) 224555 E-mail: sales@steamboilers.co.uk *Steam boilers manufrs*

Controlled Repair Instruments Ltd, Controlled Repair Institute Ltd, 1-5 Dock Tavern Lane, Gorleston, Great Yarmouth, Norfolk, NR31 6PY Tel: (01493) 602060 Fax: (01493) 441782 E-mail: sales@controlvalverepairs.co.uk *Fisher approved valves, spares supply & repair services*

Controlled Speed Engineering Ltd, St Pegs House, Thornhills Beck Lane, Brighouse, West Yorkshire, HD6 4AH Tel: (01484) 721981 Fax: (01484) 721984 E-mail: info@controlledspeed.co.uk *Variable speed drive manufrs*

► Controlled Systems Ltd, Unit 1, Ryder Close, Swadlincote, Derbyshire, DE11 9EU Tel: (01283) 216231

Controlled Waste Ltd, Highview Works, New Years Green Lane, Harefield, Uxbridge, Middlesex, UB9 6LX Tel: (01895) 673069 Fax: (01895) 636068 *Waste disposal compactors*

► ControlLoop, 14 St. Davids, Newtongrange, Midlothian, EH22 4LG Tel: (0131) 4540499

Controls Center, 112a Warner Road, London, SE5 9HQ Tel: (020) 7733 0951 Fax: (020) 7370 7312 *Boiler parts & heating equipment*

Controls Testing Equipment Ltd, Icknield Way Industrial Estate, Icknield Way, Tring, Hertfordshire, HP23 4JX Tel: (01442) 828311 Fax: (01442) 828466 E-mail: sales@controlstesting.co.uk *Test equipment for the construction industry supplier & manufrs*

► Controls UK Ltd, Whithams Mill, Plumbe Street, Burnley, Lancashire, BB11 3AW Tel: (01282) 433380 Fax: (01282) 451807 E-mail: sales@controls-uk.co.uk

► ControlsEngineer, Graham Batchelor, 15 Burnt House Road, Turves, Whittlesey, PE7 2DP Tel: (01733) 840558 Fax: (07906) 632565 E-mail: graham@controlsengineer.co.uk *Control System Design and Development.**PLC / SCADA Software and Commissioning.* *Automation, Process Control and Motion Control.**Manufacturing and Process Metrics and Reliability Analysis.**Control System Upgrades and Refurbishment.*

Controlware Communications Systems Ltd, 2 The Vo-Tec Centre, Hambridge Lane, Newbury, Berkshire, RG14 5TN Tel: (01635) 584500 Fax: (01635) 584599 E-mail: info@controlware.co.uk *Controlware Communications Systems are specialist suppliers and distributors of digital IP CCTV surveillance solutions. We have extensive experience of IT communications networks and delivery of video transmission, management, recording, and video content analytics systems. Working with an expanding partner network Controlware provide distribution with a difference. As specialist suppliers of IP CCTV we work closely with installers, integrators and end users from all vertical markets to deliver not just products but award winning solutions. Our services range from product advice through to system design, integration, installation, commissioning and support*

Contromec Services Ltd, Beechcroft Farm Industrial Estate, Chapel Wood Road, Ash, Sevenoaks, Kent, TN15 7HX Tel: (01474) 871171 Fax: (01474) 871199 *HAVC control systems installations*

► Contron Computer Systems, Station House North, Mercer Road, Warnham, Horsham, West Sussex, RH12 3SR Tel: (01403) 261029 Fax: (01403) 261120 *Computer software development*

Contronics Ltd, Greenfield Farm Industrial Estate, Congleton, Cheshire, CW12 4TU Tel: (01260) 298383 Fax: (01260) 298387 E-mail: sales@contronics.co.uk *Electronic control instruments & temperature monitoring*

Convatec Ltd, Milton Road, Uxbridge, Middlesex, UB10 8EF Tel: (01895) 628400 Fax: (01895) 628456 *Medical production*

Convatec Ltd, Milton Road, Uxbridge, Middlesex, UB10 8EF Tel: (01895) 628400 Fax: (01895) 628456 *Medical & stoma care suppliers*

Convenience Co., Harvey Road, Basildon, Essex, SS13 1RP Tel: (0845) 1003330 Fax: (01268) 722313 E-mail: enq@luxurytoilethire.com *Luxury mobile toilets hire services*

Convenience Co., Cot Nab Farm, Bishop Wilton, York, YO42 1SY Tel: (01759) 369841 Fax: (01759) 368711 *Luxury mobile toilets*

Convenience Food Systems, Interchange Park, Newport Pagnell, Buckinghamshire, MK16 9PS Tel: (01908) 513500 Fax: (01908) 513555 *Food packaging manufrs*

The Convenience Co (Midlands), Canalside Industrial Park, Kinoulton Road, Cropwell Bishop, Nottingham, NG12 3BE Tel: 0115-989 0011 Fax: 0115-989 0022 E-mail: isabel@theconco.co.uk *Hire mobile toilet suppliers*

► Convenience Services Ltd, Unit 1, The Old Dairy, Manor Farm, Fulling Mill Lane, Easton, Winchester, Hampshire, SO21 1DG Tel: (01962) 867808 Fax: (01962) 841784 E-mail: enquiries@justloos.com *Hire & sales of luxury mobile toilets for a wide range of event*

Convergent Development Ltd, Wortham, Lewdown, Okehampton, Devon, EX20 4QJ Tel: (01837) 871544 Fax: (01837) 871558 *Business software sales services*

Converging Solutions Holdings Ltd, Unit 13, Waterloo Business Park, Bidford-on-Avon, Alcester, Warwickshire, B50 4JG Tel: (01789) 491144 Fax: (01789) 491155 E-mail: sale@convergingsolutions.co.uk *Converging equipment manufrs*

► Convergis Ltd, The Old School House, Castle Ashby, Northampton, NN7 1LF Tel: (01604) 696704 Fax: (01604) 696852 E-mail: sales@convergis.co.uk *Computer systems consultants*

Convergys Emea Ltd, Building 1020, Cambourne Business Park, Cambourne, Cambridge, CB3 6DN Tel: (01223) 705000 Fax: (01223) 705001 *Software developers*

► Convergys Emee Ltd, 4 Lochside View, Edinburgh, EH12 9DH Tel: 0131-200 5000 Fax: 0131-200 5001 *Soft wear manufacturer for telephone billing*

Conversion Co Ltd, Unit F9 St. Hildas Business Centre, The Ropery, Whitby, North Yorkshire, YO22 4ET Tel: (01947) 605859 Fax: (01947) 600023 *Software development & web design*

Conversion Engineering, 5 Dunsfold Rise, Coulsdon, Surrey, CR5 2ED Tel: (020) 8668 2898 Fax: (020) 8660 8656 *LED display & custom power suppliers*

Convert Recruitment Solutions Ltd, 127 Hillcroft Crescent, Oxhey, Watford, WD19 4PA Tel: (08700) 333370 Fax: (08700) 333371 E-mail: enquiry@convertrecruitment.co.uk *Convert Recruitment is a privately owned recruitment company that specialises in the provision of top calibre Health & Safety Professionals covering all industries throughout the UK and Europe. We are committed to providing bespoke, cost-effective business solutions for clients and candidates to achieve success.*

Converteam, Boughton Road, Rugby, Warwickshire, CV21 1BU Tel: (01788) 546600 Fax: (01788) 560767 *Steam turbine manufrs*

► Convert-E-Lite Ltd, Contech House, Rushington Business Park, Unit 2 Rushington Lane, Totton, Southampton, SO40 9LT Tel: (023) 8066 0987

Conveyco Ltd, 120 Fir Street, Cadishead, Manchester, M44 5AG Tel: 0161-777 9779 Fax: 0161-777 9770 E-mail: info@conveyco.co.uk *Conveyco Limited, has 35 years experience in the Bulk and Materials Handling Industry, we offer an unrivalled service to our Clients with personal attention and an intelligent approach to solutions. Whether it is a complex handling system or replacement spare parts, the right choice of design ultimately affects our Clients' profitability, therefore careful consideration is given to each application, big or small!*Screw Conveyors -*Screw elements- Spiral Blades - 'U' Troughs - Drive Trains etc.*Roller Conveyors - Powered - Accumulating - Zero Pressure - Gravity - Rollers etc. *Belt Conveyors - Horizontal - Inclined - Vehicle Loading / Unloading - Metering etc.*Chain Conveyors - Bailing - Drum - Pallet etc.*Slat Conveyors - Bottling - Canning - Bakery etc.*Process Equipment - Horizontal Batch Mixers - Vessels - Weigh Hoppers - Feeders etc.*Design - Installation - Commissioning - Full Documentation - Maintenance*

Conveyor Accesories Direct, 16 James Watt Close, Drayton Fields Industrial Estate, Drayton Fields Industrial Esta, Daventry, Northamptonshire, NN11 8RJ Tel: (01327) 311122 Fax: (01327) 314188 E-mail: sales@conveyor-accessories-direct.co.uk *Adjustable & conveyor levelling feet manufrs*

Conveyor Belt Systems Ltd, 19 Kewferry Road, Northwood, Middlesex, HA6 2NS Tel: (01923) 820121 Fax: (01923) 835699 *Conveyor belting distributors or stockholders*

Conveyor & Elevator Co., Grange Works, Wellington Street, Accrington, Lancashire, BB5 2NT Tel: (01254) 390727 Fax: (01254) 390521 *Mechanical handling equipment & bucket elevators manufrs*

Conveyor Engineering Co., Walsall Street, Wolverhampton, WV1 3LN Tel: (01902) 871254 Fax: (01902) 871254 E-mail: ce.goodall@btopenworld.com *General engineers*

► Conveyor Hire, Unit 15d Nuralite Industrial Centre, Canal Road, Higham, Rochester, Kent, ME3 7JA Tel: (01474) 824747 Fax: (01474) 824747 *Hire & sale of conveyors*

Conveyor Hire, Unit 15d Nuralite Industrial Centre, Canal Road, Higham, Rochester, Kent, ME3 7JA Tel: (01474) 824747 Fax: (01474) 824747 E-mail: mokempen@blueyonder.co.uk *Industrial conveyor hire & sales*

Conveyor Lines Ltd, Unit 11 Scotia Close, Brackmills Industrial Estate, Northampton, NN4 7HR Tel: (01604) 762672 Fax: (01604) 708827 E-mail: sales@conveyorlines.com Purchasing Contact: Goosey Sales Contact: Goosey *Conveyor systems manufrs*

Conveyor Lines Accessories Ltd, Unit 17 Millbrook Close, Northampton, NN5 5JF Tel: (01604) 592960 Fax: (01604) 592970 E-mail: sales@casrollers.com *Conveyor component manufrs*

Conveyor Units Ltd, Sandy Lane Industrial Estate, Titton, Stourport-On-Severn, Worcestershire, DY13 9PT Tel: 0845 5314049 Fax: (01299) 877921 E-mail: conveyorsales@conveyor-units.co.uk *Conveyor Units is the UK's largest Belt and Roller Conveyor manufacturer.*We offer an extensive range of Pallet, Gravity, Belt, Line shaft , Powered Roller, Aluminium, Stainless and Flexible Conveyors.**Our UNI-XU and UNI-FLEX brand of Conveyors has become known throughout the UK and Europe as a symbol of QUALITY.*Visit our website for more information on these products as well as our complete range of Conveyor Ancillaries.*

Conveyors Direct, Unit 6, Fishburn Industrial Estate, Fishburn, Stockton-on-Tees, Cleveland, TS21 4AJ Tel: 01740 623338 Fax: 01740 622504 E-mail: sales@conveyorsdirect.co.uk *Conveyor systems & materials handling*

► Convoys Ltd, Wardley Industrial Estate, Holloway Drive, Worsley, Manchester, M28 2LA Tel: 0161-727 8323 Fax: 0161-794 4435

Convoys Chatham Ltd Head Office, No 3 Basin, Chatham Docks, Chatham, Kent, ME4 4SR Tel: (01634) 892099 Fax: (01634) 895235 E-mail: enquiries@convoys.co.uk *Wharfingers & terminal operators* Also at: Glasgow & Manchester

► Conway Bailey Transport, Goonearl, Scorrier, Redruth, Cornwall, TR16 5EB Tel: (01209) 820283 Fax: (01209) 820284

M.J. Conway, Woodleigh, Stoke Row, Henley-On-Thames, Oxfordshire, RG9 5RB Tel: (01491) 681220 Fax: (01491) 681220 *Excavation & groundwork contractors*

Conway Packing Services Ltd, Central Works, Groveland Road, Tipton, West Midlands, DY4 7UD Tel: 0121-520 1144 Fax: 0121-520 2670 E-mail: admin@conwaypack.co.uk *Export packers*

▶ Paul Conway, Suites A, Floor 8, St. James's House, Pendleton Way, Salford, M6 5FW Tel: 0161-737 9898 Fax: 0161-737 8989 E-mail: paul.conway@pmctelecom.co.uk *Telecommunications services*

Conway Precision Engineering Group Ltd, 106 Tame Road, Birmingham, B6 7EZ Tel: 0121-327 8037 Fax: 0121-328 4885 E-mail: design@gauges.co.uk *Gauge designers & manufrs*

Conway Relf, 7 Apple Tree Yard, London, SW1Y 6LD Tel: (020) 7629 9100 Fax: (020) 7484 9250 E-mail: property@conwayrelf.com *Commercial property agents & surveyors*

Conway Security Products Ltd, Seymour House, Copyground Lane, High Wycombe, Buckinghamshire, HP12 3HE Tel: (01494) 461373 Fax: (01494) 531685 E-mail: sales@conway-cctv.co.uk *Closed circuit television equipment manufrs*

Conway Security Services Ltd, 18 Bridgegate, Retford, Nottinghamshire, DN22 6AA Tel: (01777) 706478 Fax: (01777) 706478 *Security services*

Arthur Conyers, 3 West Street, Blandford Forum, Dorset, DT11 7AW Tel: (01258) 452307 Fax: (01258) 452307 E-mail: jay@conyers.biz *Gunsmith, fishing tackle & country clothing*

Coo Var, Ellenshaw Works, Lockwood St, Hull, HU2 0HN Tel: (01482) 328053 Fax: (01482) 219266 E-mail: sales@coo-var.co.uk *Paint, varnish, special & matte coatings manufrs*

Coogan & Watts Ltd, Central Park, Newtownabbey, County Antrim, BT36 4FS Tel: (028) 9084 5800 Fax: (028) 9034 2739 E-mail: info@cooganwatts.co.uk *Packaging distributors*

Cook Associates Design Consultants Ltd, Unit 1 Casbrook Park, Bunny Lane, Timsbury, Romsey, Hampshire, SO51 0PG Tel: (01794) 367996 *Audio visual equipment consultants*

The Cook & The Butler Event Company Ltd, Blackfriars Foundry Annexe, 65 Glasshill Street, London, SE1 0QR Tel: (020) 7620 1818 Fax: (020) 7620 1820 E-mail: cookandbutler@btconnect.com *The Cook & The Butler is an outstanding London Catering company with over ten years London experience in the art of food service and professional hospitality management.*

Cook Contracting, Ednam West Mill, Ednam, Kelso, Roxburghshire, TD5 7QL Tel: (01573) 223840 Fax: (01573) 224995 *Agricultural contractors*

Cook Fabrications Ltd, Broomfield Works, Fernfield Lane, Hawkinge, Folkestone, Kent, CT18 7AW Tel: (01303) 893011 Fax: (01303) 893407 E-mail: info@cookfabrications.co.uk *Welding fabricators*

▶ Cook Facilities Ltd, Technology Centre, 20 Westgate, Morecambe, Lancashire, LA3 3LN Tel: (01524) 402090 Fax: (01524) 418269 E-mail: sales@cookfire.co.uk *Supply & install emergency lighting, door access & electrical systems*

Cook Hammond & Kell Ltd, Whittington House, 764-768 Holloway Road, London, N19 3JQ Tel: (020) 7281 2161 Fax: (020) 7281 4117 *Map makers, printers & sellers*

▶ Cook & Harris Ltd, Unit 36 Barnack Trading Centre, Novers Hill, Bedminster, Bristol, BS3 5QE Tel: 0117-966 4792 Fax: 0117-963 9007

▶ Cook & Hicks Reinforcements, Sunnydene, Gainsborough Road, Scotter, Gainsborough, Lincolnshire, DN21 3UB Tel: (01724) 762523 Fax: (01724) 764645

Ian Cook & Son, Tremoddrett Farm, Roche, St. Austell, Cornwall, PL26 8LP Tel: (01726) 890206 Fax: (01726) 890899 *Foam wholesaler & retailer*

Keith Cook Training Services, Madonna Villa, Oaks Road, Coalville, Leicestershire, LE67 5UN Tel: (01509) 506913 Fax: 01509 506913 E-mail: admin@kcts.me.uk *Your one stop shop for your health and safety requirements.**Providing operator training for agricultural - construction - quarry and industry.**Covering all types of lift truck or plant we are also an approved training centre for lantra, aitt, cpcs.**The quality of our training is second to none.*

▶ Cook & Lucas, 1 Prince Albert Gardens, Grimsby, South Humberside, DN31 3AG Tel: (01472) 340906 Fax: (01472) 359862 *Fish supplies*

P.C. Cook & Co., Unit D Woddeley Industrial Estate, Woddeley Road, Kirkinploch, Glasgow, G66 3UU Tel: 0141-776 0993 Fax: 0141-776 2442 *Joinery manufrs*

▶ Peter Cook Ltd, Wholeflats Road, Grangemouth, Stirlingshire, FK3 9UY Tel: (01324) 666089

Ron Cook Engineers, 48-50 Oxford Street, Hull, HU2 0QP Tel: (01482) 327187 Fax: (01482) 213658 *Industrial engineers*

Cookcraft Ltd, Welcome House, 21 High Street, Cheslyn Hay, Walsall, WS6 7AB Tel: (01922) 416555 Fax: (01922) 418844 *Cookware*

Cooke & Arkwright, 7-8 Windsor Place, Cardiff, CF10 3SX Tel: (029) 2034 6346 Fax: (029) 2034 6300 E-mail: sales@coark.com *Chartered surveyors*

Cooke Group, West Avenue, Wigston, Leicestershire, LE18 2FB Tel: 0116-288 1234 Fax: 0116-288 1238 E-mail: cookejohn@hotmail.com *Engineers pattern makers*

Cooke International, Unit 9 Ford La Business Park, Ford, Arundel, West Sussex, BN18 0UZ Tel: (01243) 555590 Fax: (01243) 551455 *Electronic test & measuring equipment*

Marshall Cooke Ltd, Burrell Way, Thetford, Norfolk, IP24 3RW Tel: (01842) 764312 Fax: (01842) 761033 E-mail: sales@marshallcooke.com *Waste disposal container manufrs*

Richard Cooke Engineering Steels Ltd, 38 Moorgate Road, Rotherham, South Yorkshire, S60 2AG Tel: (01709) 830214 Fax: (01709) 830216 E-mail: sales@rces.co.uk *Alloy powder manufacturers & steel stockholders*

W.A. Cooke & Sons Engineers (Est 1926) Ltd, Southern Street, Walkden, Worsley, Manchester, M28 3QN Tel: (01204) 574721 Fax: (01204) 861778 E-mail: admin@wacooke.co.uk *Structural engineers & steel fabricators*

Cookequip Ltd, Unit 4, Sumner Place, Addlestone, Surrey, KT15 1QD Tel: (01932) 841171 E-mail: sales@cookequip.co.uk *Innovative Cookware for home food smoking and a whole lot more - Including Camerons Stovetop Smokers, 10 Flavours of Wood Chips, Chicken Beeroaster, Baking & Grilling Planks, Maldon Salt, Salt & Pepper Mills*

▶ Cookerburra Oven Cleaning Services, 18 Monterey Street, Manselton, Swansea, SA5 9PE Tel: 01792 475551 Fax: 01792 467765 E-mail: neil.cox@cookerburra.co.uk *From Carmarthen to Cardiff. All types of cookers professionally cleaned, commercial and domestic - AGAs, Rayburns, ranges, microwaves, etc. We are fully trained and insured. No nasty smells in your kitchen - most of the parts are cleaned in the tank on our van. We guarantee amazing results!*

▶ Cookmate South West, 15 High Street, Barnstaple, Devon, EX31 1BG Tel: (01271) 373341 Fax: (01271) 373341 E-mail: cookmate@btconnect.com *Cookware retailers*

Cooknell Electronics Ltd, 17 Cambridge Road, Granby Industrial Estate, Weymouth, Dorset, DT4 9TJ Tel: (01305) 773744 Fax: (01305) 779527 E-mail: admin@cooknell-electronics.co.uk *Electronic instrument designers & manufrs*

Cooknell Optronics Ltd, 48 Lynch Lane, Weymouth, Dorset, DT4 9DN Tel: (01305) 781567 Fax: (01305) 759648 E-mail: sales@cooknelloptronics.co.uk *Cooknell Optronics have been established for over 10 years and are part of the Cooknell Group of companies which include Cooknell Electronics and Cooknell Computers. Situated in Weymouth, Dorset, UK, we occupy a 40000sq ft factory on the Lynch Lane Trading Estate. Cooknell Optronics supplies major customers such as Bookham Technology, Pi Photonics,Covega Corporation and Confluent Photonics with specialised fibre tails. As well as generic, (FC, SC, ST, LC, FSMA and angled variants) patchcords and pigtails which we supply to a variety of customers, our special products division produces fibre tails in ribbon, PM and 3M Volition Fibre. Our contract manufacturing division works for a variety of customers, many not associated with telecommunications. We design, and produce, within the Group much of the equipment used to produce specialised fibre tails. This enables us to react quickly to changes in customer preferences and to produce "one offs", prototypes and limited production runs.*

▶ Cookprior Associates Ltd, 6 High Street, Sutton-in-Craven, Keighley, West Yorkshire, BD20 7NX Tel: (01535) 635128 Fax: (0870) 0529845 E-mail: enquiries@cookprior.co.uk *CookPrior Associates Ltd provide process, audit, optimisation, and management services to water, chemical, process industries to give cost saving and environmental improvement. Registered as a centre of expertise in manufacturing.*

Cooks Brushes Ltd, 52 The Street, Old Costessey, Norwich, NR8 5DD Tel: (01603) 748339 Fax: (01603) 748339 E-mail: sales@cooks-brushes.co.uk *General, Domestic, Industrial and Agricultural Brushes. Janitorial Supplies and Chemicals, Houseware Wholesalers/Factors/distributors.*

▶ Cooks Of Cranleigh Ltd, North Street, Horsham, West Sussex, RH12 1RE Tel: (01403) 243000 Fax: (01403) 277141

Cooks Insulations, Holly Cottage, 74 New Road, Tadley, Hampshire, RG26 3AN Tel: (07711) 241365 Fax: 0118-981 2552 *Thermal insulation engineers & contractors*

Cookson Ltd, 16 Morris Road, Clarendon Industrial Estate, Leicester, LE2 6BR Tel: 0116-270 6288 Fax: 0116-270 6882 *Fabric embroiderers*

Cookson Bros, Hornby Boulevard, Bootle, Merseyside, L20 5DX Tel: 0151-922 3394 Fax: 0151-922 3014 *Steel fabricators*

Cookson & Clegg, PO Box 11, Blackburn, BB1 2WX Tel: (01254) 844544 Fax: (01254) 844545 E-mail: sales@cooksonclegg.com *Workwear & protective clothing manufrs*

Cookson Electronics, 3 Langlands Place, Kelvin South Business Park, East Kilbride, Glasgow, G75 0YF Tel: (01355) 276500 Fax: (01355) 264770 *PCB stencil manufrs*

Cookson Electronics, 2 Dunlop Square, Deans South West, Livingston, West Lothian, EH54 8SB Tel: (01506) 412812 Fax: (01506) 410571 *Printed circuit laminate distributors*

Cookson Precious Metals Ltd, 49-50 Hatton Garden, Theba House, London, EC1N 8YS Tel: (020) 7400 6500 Fax: (020) 7400 6511 E-mail: sales@cooksongold.com *Suppliers of precious metals*

Cookson & Zinn PTL Ltd, Station Road Works, Station Road, Hadleigh, Ipswich, IP7 5PN Tel: (01473) 825200 Fax: (01473) 828446 E-mail: info@czltd.com *Pressure vessel & chemical storage tank manufrs*

▶ Cookstown Rewinds, Derryloran Industrial Estate, Sandholes Road, Cookstown, County Tyrone, BT80 9LU Tel: (028) 8676 1070 *Electric motor manufrs*

Cool Air Co, 14 Seaforth Avenue, New Malden, Surrey, KT3 6JP Tel: (020) 8949 5259 Fax: (020) 8949 4490 E-mail: coolairco@aol.com *Air conditioning design & installation services*

Cool Cair, 34 Benview, Bannockburn, Stirling, FK7 0HY Tel: (01786) 815335 Fax: (01786) 815335 *Refrigeration & air conditioning suppliers*

Cool Chalis Ltd, 4 Tyne Road, Sandy, Bedfordshire, SG19 1SA Tel: (01767) 680930 Fax: (01767) 692053 E-mail: coolchalis@cs.com *Road transport, haulage & freight services*

▶ Cool Concerns Ltd, Unit 12, Priesthawes Farm, Hailsham Road, Polegate, East Sussex, BN26 6QU Tel: (01323) 768768 Fax: (01323) 768768

▶ Cool Heat Refrigeration, 10 Downpatrick Business Centre, Brannish Road, Downpatrick, County Down, BT30 6LL Tel: (07881) 807788 Fax: (028) 4484 2228 E-mail: coolheatrefrig@aol.com *Installation & maintenance of refrigeration equipment*

Cool Heat Services, 167 Hullbridge Road, South Woodham Ferrers, Chelmsford, CM3 5LN Tel: (01245) 321615 Fax: (01245) 328981 *Air conditioning & refrigeration quality controllers*

Cool Hire Services, Whittingham House, Hazel Road, Ash Green, Aldershot, Hampshire, GU12 6HR Tel: (01252) 333669 Fax: (01252) 310004 *Air conditioning hire*

Cool Rite Air Conditioning Ltd, 65 High Street, Winterbourne, Bristol, BS36 1RA Tel: (01454) 772011 Fax: (01454) 250687 E-mail: sales@coolrite.com *Refrigeration specialists*

Cool Running Rental, Blueberry Business Park, Wallhead Road, Off Kingsway, Rochdale, Lancashire, OL16 5AF Tel: (01706) 640055 Fax: (01706) 640067 E-mail: richard@rentruck.co.uk *Vehicle hire*

▶ Cool Temp Ltd, Unit 1+2 Bedford Park, Banbury Road, Scunthorpe, South Humberside, DN16 1UL Tel: (01724) 868300 Fax: (01724) 279439 E-mail: service@cooltemp.co.uk *Air conditioning & refrigeration designers*

Cool Therm (U K) Ltd, Unit 5, 121 London Road, Warmley, Bristol, BS30 5NA Tel: 0117-961 0006 Fax: 0117-947 8642 E-mail: sales@cooltherm.co.uk *Air condition & refrigeration, distributors maintenance services*

Cool Tools Ltd, 144 St James Road, Croydon, CR0 2UY Tel: (020) 8684 5663 E-mail: enquiries@cooltoolsuk.com *Software developers*

Coolair Equipment plc, Coolair House, Broadway, Dukinfield, Cheshire, SK16 4UR Tel: 0161-343 6000 Fax: 0161-339 1077 *Air conditioner installers*

Coolair UK Ltd, Kingsley Road, Lincoln, LN6 3TA Tel: (01522) 682288 Fax: (01522) 681197 *Automotive air conditioning unit installation, suppliers & manufrs*

Coolburn Air Conditioning Ltd, Betsoms, The Avenue, Westerham, Kent, TN16 2EE Tel: (01959) 563361 Fax: (01959) 562786 E-mail: coolburn@tiscali.co.uk *Air conditioning installation design hire*

▶ CoolClean Solutions Europe LTD, 86 Tilston Road, Aintree, Liverpool, L9 6AL Tel: 0151 2805172 E-mail: info@coolclean.co.uk

▶ COOLCLIMATE, 8 Turton Gardens, Feckenham, Redditch, Worcestershire, B96 6JD Tel: 01527 892823 Fax: 01527 892823 E-mail: sales@coolclimate.co.uk *Air Conditioning Installation.Redditch. Midlands, Birmingham. Evesham. Worcestershire. Hire, Service, Sales.*

Coolco Refrigeration Ltd, Unit 18 Green Lane Industrial Estate, Second Avenue, Small Heath, Birmingham, B9 5QP Tel: 0121-771 3373 Fax: 0121-771 3687 E-mail: coolcoltd@btconnect.com *Air conditioning & refrigeration engineers*

▶ Cooleasy.co.uk, Ixus House, Ogmore Terrace, Bridgend, Mid Glamorgan, CF31 1SU Tel: (0870) 4581818 Fax: (0870) 4581919 E-mail: info@cooleasy.co.uk *Air conditioning unit suppliers*

Cooler Co., Enterprise Road, Raunds, Wellingborough, Northamptonshire, NN9 6JE Tel: (01933) 461046 Fax: (01933) 624494 E-mail: info@coolercompany.co.uk *Water cooler distributors*

▶ COOLfreeze, Unit 12 Parsons Hall, High Street, Irchester, Wellingborough, Northamptonshire, NN29 7AB Tel: (08708) 508091 Fax: (01495) 750080 E-mail: info@coolfreeze.com *COOLfreeze - The Refrigeratin & Air Conditioning People for Sales, Servicing & Repairs to ALL Makes of Refrigeration & Air Conditing Systems.*

Coolheat Ltd, Dovedale House, 16 Butts Road, Alton, Hampshire, GU34 1NB Tel: (01420) 82410 Fax: (01420) 541747 E-mail: sales@coolheatltd.co.uk *Refrigeration & air conditioning engineers*

▶ Cooling Direct Ltd, Unit 10 Arrow Industrial Estate, Eelmoor Road, Farnborough, Hampshire, GU14 7QH Tel: (0871) 8712266 Fax: (01252) 511242 E-mail: sales@coolingdirect.com *Air conditioning equipment suppliers*

Cooling Equipment Hire Ltd, 1144 Manchester Road, Rochdale, Lancashire, OL11 2XX Tel: (01706) 643003 Fax: (01706) 643005 E-mail: info@cool-equip.co.uk *Air conditioning equipment hirers*

Cooling Heating Electrical Services, 18 Old Pawlett Road, West Huntspill, Highbridge, Somerset, TA9 3RH Tel: (07970) 565026 Fax: (01278) 795511 E-mail: sales@chesuk.com *Air conditioning services & cellar coolers*

Cooling Point Ltd, 12 Sheldrake Close, Dukinfield, Cheshire, SK16 5QG Tel: 0161-338 2629 Fax: 0161-338 2628 *Air conditioning contractors*

Cooling Tower Projects Ltd, Shortacres, Kineton, Warwick, CV35 0LH Tel: (01926) 642547 Fax: (01926) 647812 E-mail: ctprojects@aol.com *Cooling tower spare parts & design services & consultancy*

Coolings Nurseries Ltd, Rushmore Hill Nurseries, Rushmore Hill, Knockholt, Sevenoaks, Kent, TN14 7NJ Tel: (01959) 532269 Fax: (01959) 534092 *Retail garden centre services*

Coolmetal Steel Fabricators, 68-72 Bromley Street, Stourbridge, West Midlands, DY9 8JA Tel: (01384) 424424 Fax: (01384) 892810 E-mail: info@coolmetal.co.uk *Architectural steelwork, sheetmetal & fabrication, tig/mig welding, punching & lasering, st/st glass canopies, balustrade & handrails, furniture & any bespoke metalwork.*

Cool-Move, Nautilus Works, 2 Goldcroft, Yeovil, Somerset, BA21 4DQ Tel: (01935) 700777 Fax: (01935) 700723 E-mail: sales@cool-move.com *Cool Move was established in Yeovil, Somerset, to provide specialist services to all businesses requiring refrigerated transport at competitive rates. They offer a 'one stop shop' solution specifically for all your refrigerated vehicle needs.*

Coolrite Refrigeration Ltd, Unit 382H Jedburgh Court, 11th Avenue, Team Valley Trading Park, Gateshead, Tyne & Wear, NE11 0BQ Tel: (0191-491 0096 Fax: 0191-482 0514 *Refrigerator & air conditioning suppliers*

▶ Coolspan, 23 Botwell Lane, Hayes, Middlesex, UB3 2AB Tel: (020) 8842 3344 Fax: (020) 8842 3311 *Refrigeration equipment manufrs*

Cool-Tec Services, 17 Sandford La Industrial Estate, Sandford Lane, Wareham, Dorset, BH20 4DY Tel: (01305) 268881 Fax: (01929) 554786 E-mail: sales@cool-tec.co.uk *Refrigeration & air conditioning installers*

Coolus Services, 95 Front Lane, Upminster, Essex, RM14 1XN Tel: (01708) 641333 Fax: (01708) 641233 E-mail: sales@coolus-services.co.uk *Concept cooling from design to installation.Change the way you feel by calling FREE on 0800 731 1737.*

Coolwater (Essex) Ltd, Unit 9,Thurrock Business Centre, Breach Road, West Thurrock, Grays, Essex, RM20 3NR Tel: (01708) 252522 Fax: (01708) 862423 E-mail: info@coolwateressex.co.uk *Suppliers of natural mineral water & water cooler deliveries for monthly/annual rentals to the Essex, London, Kent, Surrey & surrounding areas within & around the M25. All E, EN, N, IG & RM postcodes.*

Coolwell Ltd, 87 Ribbleton Avenue, Preston, PR2 6DA Tel: (01772) 651144 Fax: (01772) 652025 E-mail: coolwellaircon@btconnect.com *Air conditioning suppliers*

Coombe Valley Fabrications, Coombe Valley, Sandford, Crediton, Devon, EX17 4EN Tel: (01363) 774290 *Farm buildings contractors*

Coombe Valley Transport Ltd, 16a Primrose Road, Dover, Kent, CT17 0JA Tel: (01304) 206498 Fax: (01304) 240059 E-mail: info@coombevalley.net *Road transport haulage & freight services*

Coomber Electronic Equipment Ltd, 1 Croft Walk, Worcester, WR1 3NZ Tel: (01905) 25168 Fax: (01905) 612701 E-mail: sales@coomber.co.uk *Audio equipment for education manufrs*

Coonan Concrete Pumping, 147 Western Road, Mitcham, Surrey, CR4 3EF Tel: (020) 8648 2088 Fax: (020) 8648 2088 *Concrete pumping services*

Cooneen Textiles Ltd, 23 Cooneen Road, Fivemiletown, County Tyrone, BT75 0NE Tel: (028) 8952 1401 Fax: (028) 8952 1488 E-mail: info@cooneen.co.uk *Childrens wear manufrs*

▶ Cooneen Textiles Ltd, Unit 1, Dark Lane, Manchester, M12 6FA Tel: 0161-273 5213 Fax: 0161-274 3713 *Childrens clothing retailers*

Cooney Marine Intl Ltd, Telford Way, Telford Way Industrial Estate, Kettering, Northamptonshire, NN16 8UN Tel: (01536) 484481 Fax: (01536) 411580 E-mail: sales@cooneymarine.co.uk *Stainless steel manufrs*

▶ Coopack, 12 Katmandu Road, Bromsgrove, Worcs, B60 2SP Tel: 0845 127 9877 Fax: 0845 257 0876 E-mail: sales@coopack.co.uk *We can provide a truly competitive packaging solution using a wide range of plain and printed (8 colour) polyethene, polypropylene, andlaminate flexibles from a range of UK and European manufacturers.We have over 20 years experience within the flexibles business. Products, Bags, Sacks, Films, Palletcovers, Pouches, and Minigrips.*

Cooper 2005 Ltd, Great Bridge Street, West Bromwich, West Midlands, B70 0DJ Tel: 0121-521 1500 Fax: 0121-521 1526 E-mail: stevet@coopercoated.co.uk *Aluminium & steel coil pre-coaters*

Cooper and Controls Ltd, Unit 13 Cornwall Business Centre, Cornwall Road, Wigston, Leicestershire, LE18 4XH Tel: 0116-277 9940 Fax: 0116-277 6503 *Tubular motor sale agents*

Cooper Armer International Co. Ltd, Unit 2C Fernfield Farm, Whaddon Road, Milton Keynes, MK17 0PR Tel: (01908) 503018 Fax: (01908) 503811 E-mail: info@caidata.co.uk *Cable contractors*

Cooper B Line Ltd, Commerce Way, Highbridge, Somerset, TA9 4AQ Tel: (01278) 783371 Fax: (01278) 789037 E-mail: mwatts@cooperbline.co.uk *Electrical & electronic cabinet manufrs*

Cooper Beal & Ross, 33 Shaw Road, Stockport, Cheshire, SK4 4AG Tel: 0161-442 9770 Fax: 0161-442 9775 E-mail: cooperbealross@aol.com *Consulting engineers* Also at: Stoke-on-Trent

Cooper Buckley Ltd, Third Avenue, Crewe, CW1 6XU Tel: (01270) 251458 Fax: (01270) 251460

Cooper Callas Ltd, 3c Gatwick Gate Industrial Estate, Lowfield Heath, Crawley, West Sussex, RH11 0TG Tel: (01293) 551921 Fax: (01293) 526106 *Sanitary ware wholesalers*

Cooper Callas Ltd, PO Box 32, Oxford, OX1 1LH Tel: (01865) 249931 Fax: (01865) 790561 *Bathroom fittings & kitchen furniture distributors*

Cooper Carriers Ltd, Tir Llwyd Industrial Estate, Kinmel Bay, Rhyl, Clwyd, LL18 5JA Tel: (01745) 362800 Fax: (01745) 362801 *Courier & freight services*

Cooper Clarke Civils & Lintels, Bloomfield Road, Farnworth, Bolton, BL4 9LP Tel: (01204) 862222 Fax: (01204) 795296 E-mail: farnworth@civilsandlintels.co.uk *Buildbase is one of the UK's fastest growing builders merchants. All of our branches are long established companies which have been serving local trades people for many years, with knowledge and experience to match. We believe strongly in understanding the needs of trades professional and our business has been developed specifically to meet those demands. Massive stocks, top quality products, competitive pricing, reliable delivery, specialist staff and exceptional customer service*

▶ Cooper Construction, 21 Commercial Road, Plymouth, PL4 0LE Tel: (01752) 665077 Fax: (01752) 225477 E-mail: office@cooperconstruction.uk.com

▶ John Cooper Construction Ltd, Cooper House, 25 Belmont Circle Kenton Lane, Harrow, Middlesex, HA3 8RF Tel: (020) 8907 8908 Fax: (020) 8907 8903 E-mail: info@johncooperconstruction.co.uk *Specialist concrete, groundworks, building & civil engineering contractors*

Cooper Control Ltd, 20 Greenhill Crescent, Watford Business Park, Watford, WD18 8XG Tel: (01923) 495495 Fax: (01923) 800190 E-mail: nelco@polaron-group.co.uk *Electric motor manufacturers, motor design drive system*

Cooper Craft Ltd, 17a Barclay Road, London, E11 3DQ Tel: (020) 8539 3067 E-mail: coopercraft@btopenworld.com *Plastics moulding services*

Cooper Electrical Services, Unit 4e Wistaston Road Business Centre, Wistaston Road, Crewe, CW2 7RP Tel: (01270) 589879 Fax: (01270) 589191 *Electrical contractors*

Cooper Electronics, Tenlons Road, Nuneaton, Warwickshire, CV10 7HT Tel: (024) 7632 0585 Fax: (024) 7632 0564 E-mail: enquiries@cooper-electronics.com *Electronic equipment manufrs & engineers*

Cooper Energy Services, Mondial House, 5 Mondial Way, Hayes, Middlesex, UB3 5AR Tel: (020) 8990 1900 Fax: (020) 8990 1911 *Oil & gas turbines merchants*

Frederick Cooper P.L.C., Great Bridge Street, West Bromwich, West Midlands, B70 0DJ Tel: 0121-521 1535 Fax: 0121-521 1536 E-mail: info@fredco.co.uk *Holding company*

Cooper Freer Ltd, Kenilworth Drive, Oadby, Leicester, LE2 5LG Tel: 0116-271 0401 E-mail: sales@cooperfreer.co.uk *Air compressor engineers & manufrs*

Cooper Gay & Co. Ltd, International Ho, 26 Creechurch La, London, EC3A 5JE Tel: (020) 7480 7322 Fax: (020) 7481 4695 *Insurance brokers*

Giles Cooper Trading Ltd, Hetherson Green Farm, Hetherson Green, Malpas, Cheshire, SY14 8EL Tel: (01829) 720155 Fax: (01829) 720166 *Dairy produce trade*

John Cooper & Sons Ltd, 74 Baddow Road, Chelmsford, CM2 7PJ Tel: (01245) 261909 Fax: (01245) 493109 E-mail: info@johncooperandsons.co.uk *Cookers sales & service*

Cooper Kitchen, 48 Southgate, Elland, West Yorkshire, HX5 0DQ Tel: (01422) 372577 Fax: (01422) 372577 *Retail ironmongers & locksmiths services* Also at: Yorkshire

Leonard Cooper Ltd, Balm Road, Leeds, LS10 2JR Tel: 0113-270 5441 Fax: 0113-276 0659 E-mail: sales@leonardcooperltd.co.uk *Structural engineering services*

Cooper Lighting & Security, Wheatley Hall Road, Doncaster, South Yorkshire, DN2 4NB Tel: (01302) 321541 Fax: (01302) 303220 E-mail: sales@cooper-ls.com *Emergency lighting & fire alarm systems manufrs*

Cooper M.E, Pantgwyn, Prengwyn, Llandysul, Dyfed, SA44 4LL Tel: (01559) 362399 E-mail: cooperplant@freenetname.co.uk *Plant hire*

Cooper Office Supplies Ltd, 61c Lord Avenue, Thornaby, Stockton-on-Tees, Cleveland, TS17 9JX Tel: (01642) 760414 Fax: (01642) 750991 E-mail: sales@cooperoffice.co.uk *Commercial stationers & office equipment suppliers*

Paul Cooper Transport Ltd, Top House Farm, High Street, West Cowick, Goole, North Humberside, DN14 9EB Tel: (01405) 860330 Fax: (01405) 862604 *Road transport, haulage & freight services*

Cooper Plastics Machinery, Unit 12 Harmill Industrial Estate, Grovebury Road, Leighton Buzzard, Bedfordshire, LU7 4FF Tel: (01525) 850610 Fax: (01525) 218008 E-mail: cooperplastics@btclick.com Principal Export Areas: Asia Pacific *Manufacturers of plastic machinery*

Cooper Printers, 43 Manse Street, Fraserburgh, Aberdeenshire, AB43 9JB Tel: (01346) 518831 Fax: (01346) 511311 E-mail: cooper.printers@virgin.net *Commercial printing*

Cooper Printing Machinery Ltd, 42 Coldharbour Lane, Harpenden, Hertfordshire, AL5 4UN Tel: (01582) 764431 Fax: (01582) 768608 E-mail: sales@cooperprint.co.uk *Printing equipment manufrs*

Cooper Rason Ltd, 30 Victoria Street, Irthlingborough, Wellingborough, Northamptonshire, NN9 5RG Tel: (01933) 650950 Fax: (01933) 652821 E-mail: sales@cooper-rason.co.uk Principal Export Areas: Africa *Conveyor handling equipment manufrs*

Cooper Roller Bearings Co. Ltd, Wisbech Road, King's Lynn, Norfolk, PE30 5JX Tel: (01553) 767677 Fax: (01553) 761113 E-mail: sales@cooperbearings.com *Split & solid roller bearings suppliers*

Cooper Security Systems Ltd, 11 Tenby Grove, Worksop, Nottinghamshire, S80 2PP Tel: (01909) 487411 *Intruder alarm & CCTV installation*

Cooper Slide Rails Ltd, Unit 12 Pedmore Road Industrial Estate, Pedmore Road, Brierley Hill, West Midlands, DY5 1TJ Tel: (01384) 75500 Fax: (01384) 79712 E-mail: coopersliderails@aol.com *Slide rail manufrs*

Cooper & Stolbrand Ltd, Cottenham House, 1 Cottenham Lane, Salford, M3 7LJ Tel: 0161-834 3062 Fax: 0161-834 7586 E-mail: mail@cooperstollbrand.co.uk *Rainwear manufrs*

T. Cooper & Co. (Macclesfield) Ltd, Hobson Street, Macclesfield, Cheshire, SK11 8BB Tel: 01625 422953 *Packaging materials suppliers*

Cooper Tools, Pennine House, Washington, Tyne & Wear, NE37 1LY Tel: 0191-419 7700 Fax: 0191-417 9421 E-mail: sales@coopertools.com *Soldering iron manufrs*

Cooper & Turner Ltd, Sheffield Road, Sheffield, S9 1RS Tel: 0114-256 0057 Fax: 0114-244 5529 E-mail: sales@cooperandturner.co.uk *Industrial fastener manufrs*

Cooper Tyre & Rubber Co UK Ltd, Bath Road, Melksham, Wiltshire, SN12 8AA Tel: (01225) 703101 Fax: (01225) 707880 *Car, truck & motorcycle tyres*

Cooper UK Ltd, Melton Road, Burton-on-the-Wolds, Loughborough, Leicestershire, LE12 5TH Tel: (01509) 882600 Fax: (01509) 882786 E-mail: eurosales@bussmann.co.uk *Fuse manufrs*

Cooper & West, 101 Clarence Road, Fleet, Hampshire, GU51 3RS Tel: (01252) 617873 Fax: (01252) 617873 *Electrical contractors*

Co-operative Insurance Society Ltd, Miller Street, Manchester, M60 0AL Tel: 0161-832 8686 Fax: 0161-837 5954 E-mail: cis@cis.co.uk *Insurance company* Also at: Branches throughout the U.K.

▶ Co-Operative Monumental Services, 217 Bogmoor Road, Glasgow, G51 4TH Tel: 0141-445 1886 Fax: 0141-440 5391 *Makers of head stones*

▶ Co-Operative Retail Logistics, 5 Wardpark Road, Cumbernauld, Glasgow, G67 3HW Tel: (01236) 458568 Fax: (01236) 731609

Cooperative Retail Logistics Ltd, Unit 24, Raleigh Hall Industrial Estate, Eccleshall, Stafford, ST21 6JL Tel: (01785) 850831 Fax: (01785) 851850 *Frozen & chilled food distributors & storage*

Co-Operative Society Ltd, 189 Hamilton Road, Felixstowe, Suffolk, IP11 7DT Tel: (01394) 283085 Fax: (01394) 279629 *Co-operative society*

Co-Operative Systems, 18-20 Miles Street, London, SW8 1SD Tel: (020) 7793 0395 Fax: (020) 7735 6472 E-mail: team@coopsys.net *IT solutions providers*

▶ Coopers Bathrooms & Heating, 8 Elvin Way, Sweet Briar Road Industrial Estate, Norwich, NR3 2BB Tel: (01603) 400134 Fax: (01603) 400134 *Bathroom & heating suppliers & installers*

Coopers Great Yarmouth Ltd, New Road, Fritton, Great Yarmouth, Norfolk, NR31 9HR Tel: (01493) 602204 Fax: (01493) 655620 E-mail: enquiries@supercoopers.co.uk *Builders merchants*

Coopers Needleworks Ltd, 261-265 Aston Lane, Handsworth, Birmingham, B20 3HS Tel: 0121-356 4719 Fax: 0121-356 3050 E-mail: sales@coopernw.com *Hypodermic needle manufrs*

Coopers Security Ltd, Security House, Xerox Business Park, Mitcheldean, Gloucestershire, GL17 0SZ Tel: (01594) 543343 Fax: (01594) 545401 E-mail: marketing@menviersecurity.co.uk *Burglar alarm & security systems*

▶ Coopland & Son Scarborough Ltd, Cooplands Bakery, Caxton Way, Eastfield, Scarborough, North Yorkshire, YO11 3YT Tel: (01723) 360477 Fax: (01723) 585706 *Bakery*

Cooplands (Doncaster) Ltd, Victoria Mill Business Park, Wharf Road Wheatley, Doncaster, South Yorkshire, DN1 2SX Tel: (01302) 361333 Fax: (01302) 329776 E-mail: info@cooplands.co.uk *Bakers & confectionery suppliers*

▶ Co-Ordinated Services, 24, Ullswater Crescent, Coulsdon, Surrey, CR5 2HR Tel: (020) 8763 8874

Co-ordination Catering Hire Ltd, Unit 4 Wallis Court, Fleming Way, Crawley, West Sussex, RH10 9NY Tel: (01293) 553040 Fax: (01293) 553020 E-mail: info@co-ordination.net *Catering equipment hire*

Co-ordinators Services (Engineering) Ltd, Hazel Lane, Great Wyrley, Walsall, WS6 6AA Tel: (01922) 413712 *Property management services*

Coorstek, 64-66 Cavendish Way, Glenrothes, Fife, KY6 2SB Tel: (01592) 773743 Fax: (01592) 774925 E-mail: sales@coorstek.co.uk *Industrial ceramics manufrs*

Coote & Hall Engineers Ltd, Spen Vale Street, Heckmondwike, West Yorkshire, WF16 0NQ Tel: (01924) 402854 Fax: (01924) 402854 E-mail: sales@coote-hall.co.uk *Sub-contract engineers*

Coote Lane Garage, Coote Lane, Whitestake, Preston, PR4 4LJ Tel: (01772) 335385 Fax: (01772) 335385 *Commercial vehicle engineers*

Coote Vibratory Co. Ltd, 10 The Apex Centre, Speedfields Park, Newgate Lane, Fareham, Hampshire, PO14 1TP Tel: (01329) 287841 Fax: (01329) 827451 E-mail: info@coote-vibratory.co.uk *Heat sealing machine manufrs*

Copa Ltd, Copa House, Crest Industrial Estate, Pattenden Lane, Marden, Tonbridge, Kent, TN12 9QJ Tel: (01622) 833900 Fax: (01622) 831466 E-mail: enquiries@copa.co.uk *Waste water equipment manufrs*

▶ Copa M B R Technology, Bradford Road, Trowbridge, Wiltshire, BA14 9AX Tel: (01225) 757800

Copa Waste Water Controls Ltd, Lisduff Industrial Estate, Newry, County Down, BT35 6QH Tel: (028) 3026 7996 Fax: (028) 3026 6777 E-mail: kieran@glv.com *Pumping & effluent treatment plant*

Copac, 14 Aylesbury Business Centre, Chamberlain Road, Aylesbury, Buckinghamshire, HP19 8DY Tel: (01296) 398844 Fax: (01296) 431153 *Polythene manufrs*

▶ Copas Traditional Turkeys Ltd, King Coppice Farm, Grubwood Lane, Cookham, Maidenhead, Berkshire, SL6 9UB Tel: (01628) 474678 Fax: (01628) 474679 E-mail: turkeys@copas.co.uk *Family-run specialist producer of Traditional Farmfresh Christmas turkeys since 1957. We maintain the highest welfare standards for all our turkeys. Our Free Range bronze and barn reared white-feathered turkeys are reared on a natural cereal-based diet, rich in oats, with no growth promoting additives. We still use centuries-old production methods, where turkeys are naturally reared to full maturity before being dry plucked by hand and game-hung to mature for at least twelve days, ensuring the finest taste for Christmas day. Turkey Crowns (turkey breast &* continued *wings) and Boneless Turkey Breast are also available.*

Cope Allman Plastic Packaging Ltd, Railway Triangle, Walton Road, Portsmouth, PO6 1TS Tel: (023) 9237 0102 Fax: (023) 9238 0314 E-mail: bridget.lambert@copeallman.com *Manufacturers of bottles, jars, vials & closures*

Cope Engineering (Radcliffe) Ltd, Sion St Works, Sion Street, Radcliffe, Manchester, M26 3SF Tel: 0161-723 6500 Fax: 0161-723 6501 E-mail: sales@cope-engineering.co.uk *General engineering & roll manufrs*

COPE Ergonomics, Unit 1, The Business Park, Technology Drive, Nottingham, NG9 2ND Tel: 0115-925 9222 Fax: 0115-925 2111 E-mail: nick.aubrey@copeohs.com *An Ergonomics Society Registered Consultancy, COPE specializes in the management of musculoskeletal risks in the working environment.*

Cope & Timmins Ltd, Innova House 4 Kinetic Crescent, Enfield, Middlesex, EN3 7XH Tel: (0845) 4588860 Fax: (0800) 0740078 E-mail: customerservice@copes.co.uk *Soft furnishing hardware manufrs*

Copeland Corporation Ltd, Unit 17, Theale Lakes Business Park, Moulden Way, Sulhamsted, Reading, RG7 4GB Tel: 0118-983 8000 Fax: 0118-983 8001 E-mail: uksales@ecopeland.com *Refrigeration equipment manufrs*

Copeland & Craddock Ltd, Radnor Park Trading Estate, Back Lane, Congleton, Cheshire, CW12 4PX Tel: (01260) 279641 Fax: (01260) 276987 E-mail: mail@copelandandcraddock.co.uk *Turning services, centreless* Also at: Bilston

▶ Copeland Industrial Park, 133 Copeland Road, London, SE15 3SN Tel: (020) 7635 0000 Fax: (020) 7635 0100

Copenhagen Reinsurance Co. (UK) Ltd, The London Underwriting Centre, 3 Minster Court, Mincing Lane, London, EC3R 7DD Tel: (020) 7369 0010 Fax: (020) 7369 0018 *Reinsurance company*

Copeplan Co., Neath Road, Landore, Swansea, SA1 2JG Tel: (01792) 799895 Fax: (01792) 776670 *Timber merchants & pallet manufrs*

Coperion Ltd, Victoria House, 19-21 Ack Lane East, Bramhall, Stockport, Cheshire, SK7 2BE Tel: 0161-925 6910 Fax: 0161-925 6911 E-mail: sandra.wyatt@coperion.com *Projects & sales of plastics & chemicals*

Copes-Vulcan, Road Two, Winsford Industrial Estate, Winsford, Cheshire, CW7 3QL Tel: (01606) 552041 Fax: (01606) 558275 E-mail: copes@processequipment.spx.com *Control valves manufrs*

▶ Copex UK, 30 Princes Avenue, Walsall, WS1 2DG Tel: (01922) 649990 Fax: (01922) 649750 E-mail: copex@tiscali.co.uk *Polythene foam maufrs*

Copi Stationers, Lower Cardiff Road, Pwllheli, Gwynedd, LL53 5BY Tel: (01758) 614364 Fax: (01758) 614364 *Office equipment suppliers & stationers*

Copier Maintenance Co. Ltd, 642 Warwick Road, Tyseley, Birmingham, B11 2HJ Tel: 0121-624 8484 Fax: 0121-708 2406 E-mail: sales@printersforbusiness.com *Photocopier sales, service & suppliers*

Copiers & Servicing Ltd, 46 Queensway, Wigan, Lancashire, WN1 2HR Tel: (01942) 233505 Fax: (01942) 324877 E-mail: info@copiersandservicing.com *Photocopiers distributor & service*

Copley Decor Ltd, 1 Leyburn Business Park, Harmby Road, Leyburn, North Yorkshire, DL8 5QA Tel: (01969) 623410 Fax: (01969) 624398 E-mail: mouldings@copleydecor.co.uk *Plastic mouldings manufrs*

Copley Marshall, Tunbridge Mills, Quay Street, Huddersfield, HD1 6QX Tel: (01484) 345320 Fax: (01404) 345321 E-mail: yarns@wm-white-hudd.co.uk *Yarn, fancy yarns, striping yarns manufrs*

Copley Motion Systems, Luckyn Lane, Basildon, Essex, SS14 3BW Tel: (01268) 287070 Fax: (01268) 293344 E-mail: sales@copleymotion.com *Linear electric motors*

Copley Scientific Ltd, Colwick Quays Business Park, Private Road Number 2, Colwick, Nottingham, NG4 2JY Tel: 0115-961 6229 Fax: 0115-961 7637 E-mail: sales@copleyscientific.co.uk *Pharmaceutical testing equipment manufrs*

Copper Cyl, E Bull Street Trading Estate, Bull Street, Brierley Hill, West Midlands, DY5 3RA Tel: (01384) 77357 Fax: (01384) 77357 E-mail: roger.child@btconnect.com *Copper cylinder & tank manufrs*

▶ Copper Fayre, 48 High Rd, Benfleet, Essex, SS7 5LH Tel: (01268) 566855 Fax: 01268 683311 E-mail: Copperfayre@hotmail.com *Copper Fayre is a copper jewellery, plaque, clock and hollow-ware manufacturer and distributor. We have been in business for over 25 years. We offer highly competitive prices, top quality copper and speedy delivery.*

Copper Mill Engineering, The Mill, Bath Road, Bitton, Bristol, BS30 6LW Tel: 0117-932 2614 Fax: 0117-932 9388 E-mail: russell@coppermillengineering.com *Precision engineers & small batch production*

Copper & Optic Terminations Ltd, 90 Town Road, Stoke-on-Trent, ST1 2LD Tel: (01782) 275810 Fax: (01782) 287820 E-mail: sales@copperandoptic.com *Copper & Optic Terminations Limited is a UK based sub contract assembly company manufacturing cable harness assembly and electronic unit assembly featuring fibre optic and copper cable wiring. Copper & Optic manage projects encompassing not only our core activity of cable harness assembly and unit electronic assembly but to configuration control manage the complete build programme of your product. All types of cable harness assembly and unit assembly are undertaken at our Stoke on Trent facility in the UK, eg. open wire harnesses, multicore, heatshrink & conduit cable harness assembly typical of the marine, defence, aerospace and professional electronics industries*

▶ Copper Ridges Systems Ltd, 154 Larne Road, Carrickfergus, County Antrim, BT38 7NL Tel: (028) 9335 1767 E-mail: info@copperridges.com *Roof constructors*

▶ Copperchase Ltd, 1 Ventura Centre, Ventura Place, Poole, Dorset, BH16 5SW Tel: (01202) 774500 Fax: (01202) 774540 E-mail: support@copperchase.co.uk *Air traffic control systems manufrs*

Coppercraft Of Edinburgh Collection, Newbattle Road, Dalkeith, Midlothian, EH22 3LL Tel: 0131-660 1020 Fax: 0131-660 1020 *Giftware manufrs*

Coppercraft Of Malton, Delamere House, Main Street, Scagglethorpe, Malton, North Yorkshire, YO17 8DT Tel: (01944) 758638 Fax: (01944) 758638 E-mail: coppercraft@btconnect.com *Giftware company*

Coppermill, 118-122 Cheshire Street, London, E2 6EJ Tel: (020) 7739 6102 Fax: (020) 7739 9400 E-mail: info@coppermill.ltd.uk *Cleaning cloth manufrs*

Coppice Alupack Ltd, Isfryn Industrial Estate, Blackmill, Bridgend, Mid Glamorgan, CF35 6EQ Tel: (01656) 840711 Fax: (01656) 841552 E-mail: enquiries@coppicealupack.com *Aluminium foil container manufrs*

Copras Specialities Ltd, Copperas House Terrace, Todmorden, Lancashire, OL14 7PU Tel: (01706) 817899 Fax: (01706) 813671 E-mail: copras@packing.fsbusiness.co.uk *Contract packers & dyestuff manufrs*

Copratec Mouldings Ltd, Unit 1-4 Cats Lane, King George Road, Minehead, Somerset, TA24 5JE Tel: (01643) 705843 Fax: (01643) 707979 *Resin mouldings manufrs*

Copsey Communication Consultants, Edgcott House, Edgcott, Aylesbury, Buckinghamshire, HP18 0QW Tel: (01296) 770552 Fax: (01296) 770423 E-mail: sales@copesy-coms.com *Communication consultants services*

Peter Copsey Engineering Ltd, 2 Wheaton Road, Witham, Essex, CM8 3UJ Tel: (01376) 518378 Fax: (01376) 515294 E-mail: sales@pcopseyuk.freeserve.co.uk *General & precision engineers*

Copthorne Furniture Co. Ltd, Copthorne Bank, Copthorne, Crawley, West Sussex, RH10 3RE Tel: (01342) 718886 Fax: (01342) 712802 *Pine furniture manufrs*

Copthorne Hotel Manchester, Clippers Quay, Salford, M50 3SN Tel: 0161-873 7321 Fax: 0161-873 7318 E-mail: manchester@mill-cop.com *Hotel & conference facilities*

▶ Copy Centre, 25 Rodney Street, Edinburgh, EH7 4EL Tel: 0131-556 3417 Fax: 0131-556 8105

Copy Centre, 70 Park Lane, London, N17 0JR Tel: (020) 8808 7275 Fax: (020) 8365 1430 *Printers*

Copy Prints Ltd, 1 Talbot Yard, London, SE1 1YP Tel: (020) 7407 2079 Fax: (020) 7403 5411 E-mail: sales@copyprintsltd.co.uk *Business centre*

▶ Copy Shop Newbury Ltd, Unit 1, Mill Lane, Newbury, Berkshire, RG14 5RE Tel: (01635) 49959 E-mail: sales@copyshopnewbury.co.uk *A Copy,Print & Finishing Company that offers a vast range of reprographic and printing services, everything from a single photocopy to a full colour A0 CAD plot...please see website for more details.*

▶ Copy Solutions, Unit 21 The Bell Centre, Newton Road, Crawley, West Sussex, RH10 9FZ Tel: (01293) 455035 Fax: (01293) 434484 E-mail: sales@copysolutions.org.uk *Photocopier, fax machine & printer sales, service & repair*

Copybest (Essex) Ltd, 172-174 Coggeshall Road, Braintree, Essex, CM7 9ER Tel: (01376) 550164 Fax: (01376) 552857 *Copy shop*

▶ Copycare Ltd, Unit 3, Chiltern Works, Chiltern Drive, Surbiton, Surrey, KT5 8LS Tel: (020) 8296 0202 Fax: (020) 8296 0596 E-mail: info@copycare.net *Service, sales, rental office equipment*

Copydoc Printers, Carlton Hill, Carlton, Nottingham, NG4 1FP Tel: 0115-940 4804 Fax: 0115-847 6941 E-mail: info@copydoc-copyshop.co.uk *Photocopier services & manufrs*

Copyfast Photocopiers, 57 Cecil Road, Romford, RM6 6LB Tel: (020) 8599 3033 Fax: (020) 8270 9869 *Photocopier suppliers*

Copyfax Ltd, Unit C, Burnham Trading Park, Burnley, Lancashire, BB11 4AA Tel: (01282) 453935 Fax: (01282) 416071 E-mail: sales@copifax.co.uk *Photocopier & fax machine retailers*

Copylogic Ltd, The Palmerston Centre, Oxford Road, Wealdstone, Harrow, Middlesex, HA3 7RG Tel: (020) 8863 4483 Fax: (020) 8861 1620 E-mail: mail@copylogic.co.uk *Office equipment re-sellers*

Copymaster International Ltd, 14 Lombard Road, Merton, London, SW19 3TZ Tel: (020) 8543 9223 Fax: (020) 8543 9299 E-mail: sales@copymaster.co.uk *CD & DVD, complete media replication & duplication services*

Copymatt Drawing Office Supplies Solihull, 25 Henley Cresent, Solihull, West Midlands, B91 2JD Tel: 0121-711 1112 Fax: 0121-711 4844 E-mail: sales@copymatt.co.uk *Plan printers*

▶ Copypoll Ltd, 9-11 Francis Court, Wellingborough Road, Rushden, Northamptonshire, NN10 6AY Tel: (01933) 411188 Fax: (01933) 411199

Copyprint UK Ltd, Ground Floor West Block Westminster Business Square, Durham Street, London, SE11 5JH Tel: (020) 7735 0956 Fax: (020) 7793 0519 E-mail: sales@copyprint.co.uk *Instant printing & duplicating manufrs* Also at: Bromley & Victoria SW1

Copyright Office Furniture & Equipment, 150 Conway Road, Colwyn Bay, Clwyd, LL29 7LR Tel: (01492) 534807 Fax: (01492) 534807 E-mail: sales@copyrite.net *Office equipment suppliers*

Copyright Promotions, 6th Floor, 3 Shortlands, London, W6 8PP Tel: (020) 8563 6400 Fax: (020) 8563 6465 E-mail: sales@cprg.com *Character licensing agents*

Copyrite Business Systems Ltd, Copyrite House, Pigot Road, Denbigh, Clwyd, LL16 3DG Tel: (01745) 816473 Fax: (01745) 815516 E-mail: sales@copyrite.com *Photocopier distributor*

Copyserve UK Ltd, 21 Kingswear Parade, Leeds, LS15 8LJ Tel: 0113-260 9026 Fax: 0113-264 0468 E-mail: sales@copyserve.co.uk *Photocopier service & supply*

Copystatic Midlands Ltd, Northern House, Moor Knoll Lane, East Ardsley, Wakefield, West Yorkshire, WF3 2EE Tel: (01924) 823455 Fax: (01924) 820433 E-mail: headoffice@eurocopy.co.uk *Photocopier distributors*

▶ Copytec, 104 Newark Road, North Hykeham, Lincoln, LN6 8NA Tel: (01522) 696111 Fax: (01522) 806828 *Photocopying suppliers*

Copytech Business Equipment, 3 Saxon Place, Station Road, Cheddar, Somerset, BS27 3AG Tel: (01934) 744093 Fax: (01934) 744611 *Office machinery servicing*

▶ Copytek Duplication, Unit 8B, Cromwell Centre, Roebuck Road, Ilford, Essex, IG6 3UG Tel: (020) 8500 3773 Fax: (020) 8500 3773 *Computer accessories suppliers*

Copytext Business Machines, 29 Irish Street, Dungannon, County Tyrone, BT70 1DB Tel: (028) 8772 9277 Fax: (028) 8775 3929 E-mail: copytext@hotmail.com *Photocopying services*

Copywise, Unit 6, Block A6, Coombswood Way, Halesowen, West Midlands, B62 8BH Tel: 0121-559 9998 *Fax, photocopier & printer equipment supplier*

Copyworld Duplicating Services, 6 Merville Garden Village, Newtownabbey, County Antrim, BT37 9TF Tel: (028) 9080 0500 Fax: (028) 9087 9087 E-mail: info@copyworld.co.uk *Plan printing photocopying, digital imaging, lamination & binding*

▶ Cor Blimey Creations, 21 Barley Crescent, Long Meadow, Worcester, WR4 0HW Tel: (07903) 824506 E-mail: georgiehome@yahoo.co.uk *Photographic restoration & arts services*

Coraff Ltd, 51 Market Place, London, NW11 6JT Tel: (020) 8731 7766 Fax: (020) 8209 0098 E-mail: sales@coraffcarpets.co.uk *Carpet, hardwood flooring & rug merchants*

Coral Ltd, The Forge, Grange Court, Tongham, Farnham, Surrey, GU10 1DW Tel: (01252) 781000 Fax: (01252) 781001 E-mail: sales@coral.ltd.uk *Computer consultants & services*

The Coral Bazaar Aquatic Centre, Queens Close, Chequers Lane, Walton On The Hill, Tadworth, Surrey, KT20 7SU Tel: (01737) 812475 Fax: (01737) 812722 *Aquariums & fisheries suppliers*

Coral Press Ltd, 115 Hatfield Road, St. Albans, Hertfordshire, AL1 4JS Tel: (01727) 854466 Fax: (01727) 851331 E-mail: sales@coralpress.co.uk *Stationers*

Coralfoam Ltd, 12 Petworth Industrial Estate, Petworth, West Sussex, GU28 9NR Tel: (01798) 342441 Fax: (0870) 9223485 E-mail: dave@coralfoam.com *Research & development*

Coram Showers Ltd, Stanmore Industrial Estate, Bridgnorth, Shropshire, WV15 5HP Tel: (01746) 766466 Fax: (01746) 764140 E-mail: sales@coram.co.uk *Shower enclosures & overbath screens*

Corbeau Seats Ltd, 17 Wainwright Close, St. Leonards-on-Sea, East Sussex, TN38 9PP Tel: (01424) 854499 Fax: (01424) 854488 E-mail: mat@corbeau'seats.co.uk *Car seat manufrs*

Corbett Engineering Ltd, Unit 1 2 Mercia Villas, Torwood Close Westwood Business Park, Coventry, CV4 8HX Tel: (024) 7646 9930 Fax: (024) 7642 0994 E-mail: info@celcat.com *Software developers & electrical engineering consultants*

Corbett Storage Solutions, Enterprise House, Enterprise Way, Edenbridge, Kent, TN8 6HF Tel: (0800) 3165656 Fax: (01732) 862430 E-mail: customerservice@paulcorbett.co.uk *Storage equipment manufrs*

W. Corbett & Co. (Galvanizing) Ltd, New Alexandra Works, Haldane Halesfield 1, Telford, Shropshire, TF7 4QQ Tel: (01952) 412777 Fax: (01952) 412888 E-mail: corbetthotdip@aol.com *Hot dip galvanisers*

▶ William Corbett & Co. Ltd, Pantyffynnon Road, Ammanford, Dyfed, SA18 3HN Tel: (01269) 593215 Fax: (01269) 591929 E-mail: sales@williamcorbett.co.uk *Tinplate sheet suppliers*

Corbin & Frost Ltd, 3 Stepfield, Witham, Essex, CM8 3DP Tel: (01376) 572202 Fax: (01376) 513921 E-mail: corbin.frost@macunlimited.net *Tool wholesalers & importers*

▶ Corbitt Greenwood Associates, 2 Phoenix Terrace, Hartley Witney, Hook, Hampshire, RG27 8RU Tel: (01252) 844567 Fax: (01252) 844567

Corby Aluminium Co. Ltd, Princewood Rd, Earlstrees, Corby, Northamptonshire, NN17 4AP Tel: (01536) 262437 Fax: (01536) 204216 E-mail: sales@alishapes.co.uk *Supplier of tight tolerance and standard aluminium profiles/ components with extensive internal fabrication capabilities which include long bed CNC machine centre, cut to length saws and punch facilities, with no minimum quantities! Aluminium Shapes offers the One stop aluminium profile/ component shop, from proto-type to production, and with our customer focused team we cannot be beaten. Why not try us and experience our exceptionally fast turnaround*

Corby Bottlers P.L.C., Clarke House, Brunel Road, Earlstrees Industrial Estate South, Corby, Northamptonshire, NN17 4JW Tel: (01536) 446000 Fax: (01536) 446001 *Bag-in-box & bottling specialist*

▶ Corby Chilled Northern Ltd, Strutherhill Industrial Estate, Larkhall, Lanarkshire, ML9 2PD Tel: (01698) 889542

▶ Corby Courier Services, 4 Lovap Way, Great Oakley, Corby, Northamptonshire, NN18 8JL Tel: (01536) 742412 Fax: (01536) 742412 E-mail: sales@corbycouriers.co.uk *A*

continued

sameday,nextday courier company giving a local, national and international service delivering anything from a parcel to a pallet based in Corby, Northamptonshire.

Corby & Fellas, First Floor, 284-5 Southtown Rd, Great Yarmouth, Norfolk, NR31 0JB Tel: (01493) 658800 Fax: (01493) 442308 E-mail: sales@corby-fellas.co.uk *Software house consultants*

Corby Hose & Hydraulics Ltd, Geddington Road, Corby, Northamptonshire, NN18 8AA Tel: (01536) 201534 Fax: (01536) 400986 *Hydraulic hose assemblies manufrs*

Corby Kilns Ltd, Corby, Northamptonshire, NN17 5WA Tel: (01536) 269229 Fax: (01536) 269229 E-mail: info@corbykilns.co.uk *Pottery kilns repairers*

Corby Mechanical Services Ltd, Unit C1 Priors Court, Priors Haw Road, Corby, Northamptonshire, NN17 5JG Tel: (01536) 408866 Fax: (01536) 408811 E-mail: sales@corby-mechanical.co.uk *Engineering*

▶ Corby Nameplates, 7 Wentin Close, Corby, Northamptonshire, NN18 8NJ Tel: (01536) 266288 Fax: (01536) 266370 E-mail: corbyetching@aol.com *Etched & engraved nameplates, plaques, chemical milling*

Corby Refrigeration & Mechanical Services, Gordon House, Dale Street, Corby, Northamptonshire, NN17 2BQ Tel: (01536) 265273 Fax: (01536) 205881 E-mail: enquiries@corbyrefrigeration.co.uk *Air conditioning engineers*

Corby Steel Supplies Ltd, Sondes House, Willowbrook East Industrial Estate, Corby, Northamptonshire, NN17 5XL Tel: (01536) 261164 Fax: (01536) 402971 *Steel stockholders*

▶ Corby Windows Ltd, Pywell Road, Willowbrook East Industrial Estate, Corby, Northamptonshire, NN17 5XJ Tel: (01536) 409100 Fax: (01536) 408757 E-mail: sales@cwg-uk.com

Corcoran Chemicals Ltd, Oak House, Oak Close, Wilmslow, Cheshire, SK9 6DF Tel: (01625) 532731 Fax: (01625) 539096 E-mail: info@corcoranchemicals.com *Chemical merchants*

Cord Controls Ltd, 29 Wigston Street, Countesthorpe, Leicester, LE8 5RP Tel: 0116-277 7396 Fax: 0116-277 7396 E-mail: cord.controls@btclick.com *Lift control panel repairers & manufrs*

Cord Electronics Ltd, The Pumphouse, Farley Bridge, Farley Lane, Maidstone, Kent, ME16 9NB Tel: (01622) 721444 Fax: (01622) 721555 E-mail: sales@chordelectronics.co.uk *Amplifier manufrs*

Cordatec, 22 Marlborough Road, Southend-on-Sea, SS1 2UA Tel: (01702) 613339 Fax: (01702) 613339 E-mail: sales@cordatec.co.uk *Tennis string suppliers*

Cordeal Ltd, 89 High Street, Cowes, Isle of Wight, PO31 7AW Tel: (01983) 298745 Fax: (01983) 291598 E-mail: jcboats@aol.com *Boat builders*

Cordell Engineering, 26-28 Elmtree Road, Teddington, Middlesex, TW11 8ST Tel: (020) 8943 8884 Fax: (020) 8943 8852 *Air conditioning engineers*

Cordell Group Ltd, 159-160 High Street, Stockton-on-Tees, Cleveland, TS18 1PL Tel: (01642) 662400 Fax: (01642) 662402 E-mail: enquiries@cordellgroup.com *Project management services*

Cordelle Precision Engineers, 76 Wharfdale Road, Birmingham, B11 2DE Tel: 0121-706 0525 Fax: 0121-706 3551 *Precision engineers*

▶ Corden Pattern & Tools Ltd, Oban Road, Longford, Coventry, CV6 6HH Tel: (024) 7636 2525 Fax: (024) 7664 4115

▶ Cordialav, 55 The Oaks, Abbeymead, Gloucester, GL4 5WP Tel: (01452) 616785 Fax: (01452) 616785 E-mail: enquiries@cordialav.co.uk *CD & DVD authoring & duplication, video & multimedia services. Short run & bulk CD & DVD duplication. Corporate & event video production & editing.*

▶ Cordiner, 5 Crombie Place, Aberdeen, AB11 9PJ Tel: (01224) 877611 Fax: (01224) 875510 *Timber merchants*

▶ James Cordiner & Son Ltd, Silverbank Sawmill, Banchory, Kincardineshire, AB31 5PY Tel: (01330) 823366 *Sawmill*

Cordingley Barnes Ltd, 5 The Courtyard, Hall Lane, Haughton, Tarporley, Cheshire, CW6 9RJ Tel: (01829) 260029 Fax: (01829) 261209 E-mail: karen@cordingleybarnes.com *Computer software resellers*

Cordon Insurance Ltd, Andil House, Court Street, Trowbridge, Wiltshire, BA14 8BR Tel: (01225) 775566 Fax: (01225) 775544 E-mail: info@cordoninsurance.co.uk *Commercial insurance brokers*

Cordstrap Ltd, Paddock Road, Skelmersdale, Lancashire, WN8 9PL Tel: (01695) 554700 Fax: (01695) 556644 E-mail: sales@cordstrap.net *Strapping manufacturers & suppliers*

Cordtape Energy Management Systems, Unit 13-15 Broxtowe Park Business Centre, Calverton Drive, Strelley, Nottingham, NG8 6QP Tel: 0115-975 6551 Fax: 0115-975 6559 E-mail: cems@cordtapeenviromental.co.uk *Manufacturers of insulation valve covers*

▶ Cordula Ltd, Unit 6, Vale Lane, Bristol, BS3 5SD Tel: 0117-902 0259 Fax: 0117-966 6216 E-mail: sales@cordula.co.uk *Remote control garage door suppliers* Also at: Bristol, Kenilworth, Manchester & Woking

Cordwallis Commercials (Maidenhead) Ltd, Cordwallis Street, Maidenhead, Berkshire, SL6 7BE Tel: (01628) 622264 Fax: (01628) 770446 *Commercial vehicle dealers*

Paul Cordwell Photography Ltd, Unit 3 Century Park, Garrison Lane, Birmingham, B9 4NZ Tel: (07831) 416477 E-mail: paul@paulcordwell.com *Architectural, industrial, commercial & advertising photographers*

Core Consultancy Ltd, 7 Kings Bench Street, London, SE1 0QX Tel: (020) 7928 3338 Fax: (0871) 6613393 E-mail: info@core-consultancy.com *IT consultants*

Core Cut Ltd, Bankhead, Winchburgh, Broxburn, West Lothian, EH52 6PP Tel: (01506) 854710 Fax: (01506) 853068E-mail: info@corecut.co.uk *Diamond drilling & grouting contractor* Also at: Stockport

▶ Core Drilling Specialist, Core Drilling House, Hardie Road, Livingston, West Lothian, EH54 8BA Tel: (01506) 414400

Core Estates Ltd, 3 Pendeford Place, Pendeford Industrial Estate, Wolverhampton, WV9 5HD Tel: (0870) 7014343 Fax: (01902) 557701 E-mail: sales@coresystems.co.uk *Estate agency software suppliers*

Core Facts, 68 Queensway, Mildenhall, Bury St Edmunds, Suffolk, IP28 7JY Tel: 01638 711931 Fax: 01638 711865 *Computer consultancy*

▶ Core IS Limited, Suite 12 Basepoint, Caxton Close, East Portway, Andover, Hampshire, SP10 3FG Tel: 0870 7653210 Fax: 01264 326471 E-mail: info@coreis.co.uk *CoreIS are leading providers of programme management training and project management training and consultancy. MSP, PRINCE2, MoR training, exceptional PRINCE2 Practitioner pass rates, supporting business skills, project health checks. No Nonsense PRINCE2 key facts book.*

Core Laboratories, 17 Howe Moss Drive, Kirkhill Industrial Estate, Dyce, Aberdeen, AB21 0GL Tel: (01224) 421000 Fax: (01224) 421003 E-mail: sales@corelab.co.uk *Production services*

▶ Core Technical Services Ltd, Howe Moss Drive, Kirkhill Industrial Estate, Dyce, Aberdeen, AB21 0GL Tel: (01224) 771118 Fax: (01224) 771112

Core Technology Systems UK Ltd, Holland House, 1-4 Bury Street, London, EC3A 5AW Tel: (020) 7626 0516 Fax: (020) 7953 3600 E-mail: sales@core.gb.com *Core Technology Systems Ltd. is a Microsoft® Gold Certified Partner functioning within the Information*Worker Solutions and Integrated EBusiness Solutions competencies.**Core has over 15 years experience delivering specialized solutions in the insurance and financial services industry. Unlike many of its competitors, Core is based in the City of London and has the in-depth knowledge, technical skills, and highly talented employees to ensure that it can provide customers with the global IT solutions they need. Core has 50 employees and concentrates on systems integration around solutions involving Microsoft® Office System applications.*

Core UK Ltd, Cellphone House, North Circular Road, London, NW10 7SH Tel: (020) 8961 9990 Fax: (020) 8961 4371 E-mail: info@core-business.com *IT software services*

▶ Corehard Ltd, 4 Viewpoint, Babbage Road, Stevenage, Hertfordshire, SG1 2EQ Tel: (01438) 225102 Fax: (01438) 213721 E-mail: info@corehard.com *Quality audits on Utility & Civil Engineering Projects.*Network Asset Management*GPS mapping and CAD services*Plant Protection*Core Sample Programs*NRSWA Inspection & Supervision*NRSWA Technical Assistance*Dispute Resolution*UKAS Test Laboratory Coring* Macro-texture depth*

▶ Corelogic Computer Systems, Studley Road, Redditch, Worcestershire, B98 7HR Tel: (01527) 503691 E-mail: sales@corelogic.co.uk *Computer software developers*

Corenso UK Ltd, Corenso House, 2 Patriot Drive, Rooksley, Milton Keynes, MK13 8LN Tel: (01908) 678111 Fax: (01908) 690067 *Cardboard tubes manufrs*

Corenso (UK) Ltd, North Tyne Industrial Estate, Whitley Road, Longbenton, Newcastle Upon Tyne, NE12 9SZ Tel: 0191-266 0222 Fax: 0191-270 1663 *Cardboard & paper tube*

Cores & Tubes Ltd, 42 Vulcan Way, New Addington, Croydon, CR0 9UG Tel: (01689) 848586 Fax: (01689) 841468 E-mail: info@coresandtubes.co.uk *Cardboard & paper tube manufrs*

▶ Corespec Ltd, Unit 7 Parkhead, Greencroft Industrial Park, Stanley, County Durham, DH9 7YB Tel: (01207) 529944 Fax: (01207) 529955 E-mail: core.spec@btconnect.com *Convert paper, make cardboard tubes*

▶ Coresys Ltd, Merlin Cottage, 23 Fore Street, Polruan, Fowey, Cornwall, PL23 1PQ Tel: (01726) 870775 E-mail: coresys@btinternet.com

▶ Coreware Ltd, Gosden Common, Tannery Lane, Bramley, Guildford, Surrey, GU5 0AB Tel: (01483) 894158 Fax: (01483) 898932 E-mail: debs@russellsharpe.com *Computer systems consultants*

Corewire Ltd, Poplars Farm, Station Road West, Ash Vale, Aldershot, Hampshire, GU12 5QD Tel: (01252) 517766 Fax: (01252) 515833 E-mail: info@corewire.com Principal Export Areas: Worldwide *Arc welding electrodes & wire manufrs*

Corex (UK) Ltd, Units B1-B3 Airport Industrial Park, Howe Moss Drive, Dyce, Aberdeen, AB21 0GL Tel: (01224) 770434 Fax: (01224) 771716 E-mail: mail@corex.co.uk *Core analysis consultants services* Also at: Watford

Corfield Auto Electrics Ltd, Short Acre Street, Walsall, WS2 8HW Tel: (01922) 623063 Fax: (01922) 621830 E-mail: ken@corfield-auto.freeserve.co.uk *Car, commercial vehicle & plant auto-electrician services*

Morris Corfield & Co. Ltd, Westington, Docklow, Leominster, Herefordshire, HR6 0SJ Tel: (01885) 488884 Fax: (01885) 483888 *Agricultural engineers*

Corfix Structures Ltd, No 3 Hoobrook Industrial Estate, Kidderminster, Worcestershire, DY10 1HY Tel: (01562) 60226 Fax: (01562) 60227 *Steel manufrs*

Corgi Hosiery Ltd, New Road, Ammanford, Dyfed, SA18 3DS Tel: (01269) 592104 Fax: (01269) 593220 E-mail: sales@corgihosiery.co.uk *Hosiery & knitwear manufrs*

Corina Cleaning Services, Unit M The Old Bakery, Bakery Lane, Bognor Regis, West Sussex, PO21 1UR Tel: (01243) 868302 Fax: (01243) 868302 E-mail: adrienne@corinacleaning.co.uk *Commercial cleaning company*

Corinium Building Services, 25 Cotswold Avenue, Cirencester, Gloucestershire, GL7 1XW Tel: (01285) 641200 Fax: (01285) 641200 E-mail: cbsciren@fsbdial.co.uk *Building services engineers*

▶ Corinium Language Associates, Wadham Close, Southrop, Lechlade, Gloucestershire, GL7 3NR Tel: (01367) 851100 E-mail: info@coriniumlanguage.co.uk *Language services for business. Highly tailored language and cultural training at our dedicated training centre or on clients premises, multilingual recruitment, translating and interpreting & special multilingual projects.*

▶ Corinne Dauncey, PO Box 2448, Slough, SL1 1ZB Tel: 0870 8701193 Fax: 0870 8701194 E-mail: coz.dauncey@theengineeringjob.com *TheENGINEERINGjob.com is a specialist job board for the engineering industry, part of The TipTopJob Group. The site deals with various engineering related jobs, such as, chemical, biological, civil and mechanical engineering. Job seekers can add a CV to the database, set up email alerts and search and apply for jobs for free online. To find your next engineering job or to use the site to advertise your vacancies or to find an employee, visit the website www.theENGINEERINGjob.com.*

Corintech Ltd, Ashford Mill, 118-122 Station Road, Fordingbridge, Hampshire, SP6 1DZ Tel: (01425) 655655 Fax: (01425) 652756 E-mail: info@corintech.co.uk *Hi-Density electronic solutions provider, contract electronics manufacturer, thick film hybrid, surface mount, chip & wire microcircuits on ceramic, steel & FR4 PCB, electronics design services & far east production facilities.*

▶ Corinthean Surgical, Mill, Unit B2f The Business Park, Pleasley Vale, Mansfield, Nottinghamshire, NG19 8RL Tel: (01623) 819741 Fax: (01623) 819742 *Medical equipment suppliers*

Corinthian Windows, Oak Street, Quarry Bank, Brierley Hill, West Midlands, DY5 2JQ Tel: (01384) 411033 *Window manufrs*

▶ Corio Signs & Printing, Unit 4, Hurlbutt Road, Heathcote Industrial Estate, Warwick, CV34 6TD Tel: (01926) 422262 Fax: (01926) 422262 E-mail: sales@corioprinting.co.uk *Signs & promotional printing*

Corkery Construction Ltd, 15 Linnet Avenue, Paddock Wood, Tonbridge, Kent, TN12 6XG Tel: (01892) 838097 Fax: (01892) 834030 E-mail: michcrkry@aol.com *Form work & steel fabrication*

▶ Corkill Datasafe, 39 Finch Road, Douglas, Isle of Man, IM1 2PW Tel: (01624) 666575 Fax: (01624) 661095

S. Corman (Calverton) Ltd, Mancor House, Bolsover Street, Hucknall, Nottingham, NG15 7TZ Tel: 0115-963 2268 Fax: 0115-963 2062 *Clothing retailers factory outlet*

Cormeton Fire Protection Ltd, Unit 12 Delaval Trading Estate, Seaton Delaval, Whitley Bay, Tyne & Wear, NE25 0QT Tel: 0191-237 0790 Fax: 0191-237 5143 E-mail: sales@cormeton.co.uk *Fire protection engineers*

Cormon Ltd, Unit 3 Robell Building, Chartwell Road, Lancing, West Sussex, BN15 8TU Tel: (01903) 854800 Fax: (01903) 854854 E-mail: sales@cormon.com *Corrosion & wear monitoring systems manufrs*

▶ Cormorant Communications Ltd, Unit 1, 14 Willow Tree Rise, Bournemouth, BH11 8EE Tel: (0845) 9000190 Fax: (0845) 9000191 E-mail: info@cormorantcomms.co.uk *Telecommunications services*

▶ Cormorant Information Systems, Leveret House, Manor Park Estate, Nailsea, Bristol, BS48 4DD Tel: (01275) 854455 Fax: (0871) 4338600 E-mail: sales@cormorant.co.uk *Software developers*

▶ Corn Dolly, Unit 4 Ballinacraig Way, Greenbank Industrial Estate, Newry, County Down, BT34 2QX Tel: (028) 3026 0525 Fax: (028) 3083 2818 E-mail: corndolly@btconnect.com *Bakery*

Cornelius Group plc, Woodside, Dunmow Road, Birchanger, Bishop's Stortford, Hertfordshire, CM23 5RG Tel: (01279) 714300 Fax: (01279) 714320 E-mail: sales.dept@cornelius.co.uk *Speciality chemical distributors*

Cornelly Sales, 207 North Approach, Garston, Watford, WD25 0ES Tel: (01923) 670884 Fax: (01923) 670883 E-mail: fredstrous@cornelly.co.uk *Agents for construction industry*

Corner House, Laverstock, Uttoxeter Road, Foston, Derby, DE65 5PX Tel: (01283) 812848 Fax: (01283) 814542 E-mail: sales@cornerhouse.uk.com *Exhibition stand designers*

Corner House Hotel, 78 High Street, Annan, Dumfriesshire, DG12 6DL Tel: (01461) 202754 Fax: (01461) 202193 E-mail: corner.house@btconnect.com *Hotel & conference facilities*

▶ Corner Post Fencing & Sheds, 1b Raynor Road, Wolverhampton, WV10 9QY Tel: (01902) 736444 Fax: (01902) 736444 *Fencing suppliers*

The Corner Shop, 47 Portland Street, Lincoln, LN5 7JZ Tel: (01522) 512600 Fax: (01522) 512600 *Furniture reproduction*

Cornercare Ltd, Unit 3-4 Walter Nash Road West, Birchen Coppice Trading Estate, Kidderminster, Worcestershire, DY11 7QY Tel: (01562) 515200 Fax: (01562) 864063 E-mail: cornercare@compuserve.com *Plasterers angle bead & expanded metals manufrs*

Corners Direct Ltd, Hillam Road, Bradford, West Yorkshire, BD2 1QL Tel: (01274) 733213 Fax: (01274) 721128 E-mail: peterwright@cornersdirect.co.uk *Printers manufrs*

▶ Cornerstone Computer Centre, 15 The Arcade, Bognor Regis, West Sussex, PO21 1LH Tel: (01243) 820082 *Computer software retailers*

▶ Cornerstone Projects Ltd, PO Box 182, Wirral, Merseyside, CH29 9AU Tel: 0151-632 4555 Fax: (0870) 7626172 E-mail: enquiries@cornerstoneprojects.co.uk *Underground service search*

Cornfield Law LLP, 47 Cornfield Road, Eastbourne, East Sussex, BN21 4QN Tel: (01323) 412512 Fax: (01323) 411611 *Cornfield Law LLP's offices stand opposite the War Memorial roundabout on Cornfield Road in Eastbourne. Our Lawyers provide a range of legal services and we have considerable experience and expertise in Company and Commercial matters, Residential and Commercial Conveyancing, Probate, Trusts and Wills and Litigation including all aspects of Personal Injury and Family and Divorce Litigation.**We are the only Solicitors in Eastbourne able to offer Insolvency Services, both personal and Corporate Insolvency. We have a large experienced Insolvency Department who are able to help and advise on Bankruptcy, Voluntary Arrangements and Liquidations. Contact us for a free half hour consultation if you are affected by Insolvency.**

Cornflower Wholefoods, 49 High Street, Brightlingsea, Colchester, CO7 0AQ Tel: (01206) 306679 Fax: (01206) 308515 E-mail: cornflowerbsea@aol.com *Health food shop*

Cornford Group, 56-57 Joseph Wilson Industrial Estate, Whitstable, Kent, CT5 3PS Tel: (01227) 280000 Fax: (01227) 771158 E-mail: info@cornfordrecords.com *Guitar amplifier manufrs*

▶ Corniche Estates, Campbell Park, Fernhurst Road, Liphook, Hampshire, GU30 7LU Tel: (01428) 741999 Fax: (01428) 741005 *Properties to let, relocating, development management & greek property specialists*

▶ Corning Ltd, Wear Glass Works, Sunderland, SR4 6EJ Tel: 0191-514 8800 Fax: 0191-514 8801 E-mail: thompsons@corning.com *Borosilicate Glass Manufacture:*Blown vessel - bottles, flask etc.*Pressed articles - Lenses, reflectors.*Rolled Sheet - 1/8" to 2 1/4" thick.****

▶ Cornish Concrete Products Ltd, Point Mills, Bissoe, Truro, Cornwall, TR4 8QZ Tel: (01872) 864808 Fax: (01872) 863606 *Concrete product manufrs*

Cornish Country Larder Ltd, The Creamery, Trevarrian, Newquay, Cornwall, TR8 4AH Tel: (01637) 860331 Fax: (01637) 860133 E-mail: enquiries@ccl-ltd.co.uk *Cheeses*

Cornish Cuisine, The Smoke House, Islington Wharf, Penryn, Cornwall, TR10 8AT Tel: (01326) 376244 Fax: (01326) 376244 *Traditional smoked foods*

Cornish Diving, Bar Road, Falmouth, Cornwall, TR11 4BN Tel: (01326) 313178 Fax: (01326) 311265 E-mail: info@cornishdiving.co.uk *Diving services teaching retail shop*

Cornish Engineering Ltd, Popham Street, Nottingham, NG1 7JD Tel: 0115-950 4944 Fax: 0115-950 4215 *Gear manufacturers & cutters including precision*

Cornish Farmhouse Bacon, West Balsdon Farm, Whitstone, Holsworthy, Devon, EX22 6LE Tel: (01288) 341171 Fax: (01288) 341075 E-mail: justin_uglow@btconnent.com *Meat producers*

Cornish Fishing Vessels Insurance Society Ltd, Fish Market, Newlyn, Penzance, Cornwall, TR18 5DS Tel: (01736) 360720 Fax: (01736) 331079 *Marine insurance*

▶ Cornish Lime Co., Brims Park, Old Callywith Road, Bodmin, Cornwall, PL31 2DZ Tel: (01208) 77287 Fax: (01208) 73744 E-mail: sales@cornishlime.co.uk *Building conservation materials & sustainable building products*

Cornish Linen Service, Dudnance Lane, Pool, Redruth, Cornwall, TR15 3RA Tel: (01256) 471311 Fax: (01209) 714133 E-mail: sales.camborne@cls-group.co.uk *Linen & garment rental*

Cornish Linen Services, The Praze, Penryn, Cornwall, TR10 8DJ Tel: (01326) 373539 Fax: (01326) 377194 E-mail: sales@cls-group.co.uk *Laundry services*

Cornish Maintenance Co, 4 Bilton Road, Perivale, Greenford, Middlesex, UB6 7FB Tel: (020) 8998 9247 Fax: (020) 8998 9149 E-mail: d.cornish@theshelvingcentre.co.uk *Shelving distributors*

Cornish Mutual, CMA House, Newham Road, Truro, Cornwall, TR1 2SU Tel: (01872) 277151 Fax: (01872) 223053 E-mail: enq@cornishmutual.co.uk *Insurance services*

Cornish Pasty Bakery, 54 Boar Lane, Leeds, LS1 5EL Tel: 0113-242 0121 Fax: 0113-242 0121 *Wholesale bakers*

Cornish Rosette Co., Higher Bofarnel, Lostwithiel, Cornwall, PL22 0LP Tel: (01208) 871001 Fax: (01208) 871001 E-mail: conishrosette@ukonline.co.uk *Rosette manufrs*

Cornish Stairways Ltd, Kernick Industrial Estate, Penryn, Cornwall, TR10 9DQ Tel: (01326) 374662 Fax: (01326) 376596 E-mail: mikejordan@cornishstairways.co.uk *Precast concrete spiral staircases, design & manufacture of feature*

Cornish Stone Co. Ltd, 10a Belle Vue, Bude, Cornwall, EX23 8JL Tel: (01288) 352356 Fax: (01288) 352356 *Jewellers*

Cornish Windbreaks, Treleigh Avenue, Redruth, Cornwall, TR15 1DB Tel: (01209) 214944 Fax: (01209) 214944 *Windbreak manufrs*

Cornpool Ltd, 174 Station Road, March, Cambs, PE15 8NG Tel: (01354) 655200 Fax: (01354) 656421 *Glazing contractors*

Cornpoppers Ltd, 40-42 Potters Lane, Wednesbury, West Midlands, WS10 0AT Tel: 0121-505 3311 Fax: 0121-505 3174 E-mail: sales@cornpoppers.co.uk *Popcorn manufrs*

John Cornthwaite Farm Machinery Ltd, The Auction Mart, Pilling, Preston, PR3 6AH Tel: (01253) 790771 Fax: (01253) 790839 E-mail: enquiries.pilling@cornthwaites.co.uk *News & used agricultural machinery suppliers*

Cornwall Battery Centre, 34 Threemilestone Industrial Estate, Threemilestone, Truro, Cornwall, TR4 9LD Tel: (01872) 270011 Fax: (01872) 264250 E-mail: sales@bristolbatteries.com *Battery distributors*

▶ Cornwall Bookkeeping Services, 57 Vyvyan Drive, Quintrell Downs, Newquay, Cornwall, TR8 4NF Tel: 01637 851949 Fax: 01637 851949 E-mail: mjd@cornwall-bookkeeping.co.uk *Self Assessment, Bookkeeping, Payroll, VAT Returns..........*

Cornwall Bros Ltd, 2a Tovil Hill, Maidstone, Kent, ME15 6QS Tel: (01622) 755066 Fax: (01622) 755066 *Plastering contractors*

Cornwall & Devon Transmissions Ltd, Old Ambulance Station, Pentewan Road, St. Austell, Cornwall, PL25 5BU Tel: (01726) 63666 Fax: (01726) 68898 *Gearbox reconditioning services*

▶ Cornwall Engineering Ltd, Unit 3, Millsboro House, Ipsley Street, Redditch, Worcestershire, B98 7AL Tel: (01527) 67850 Fax: (01527) 61984 E-mail: presswell@btconnect.com *Metal manufacturers of press work & wire work*

Cornwall Farmers Ltd, School Road, Praze, Camborne, Cornwall, TR14 0LB Tel: (01209) 831431 Fax: (01209) 832212 *Agricultural merchants*

Cornwall Farmers Ltd, Otterham Station, Otterham, Camelford, Cornwall, PL32 9SW Tel: (01840) 261235 Fax: (01840) 261369 *Agricultural merchants & contractors*

Cornwall Farmers Ltd, Station Yard, Liskeard, Cornwall, PL14 4DX Tel: (01579) 343446 Fax: (01579) 345645 E-mail: info@cornwallfarmers.co.uk *Agricultural services & fertilizers*

Cornwall Farmers Ltd, Three Milestone Industrial Estate, Truro, Cornwall, TR4 9LD Tel: (01872) 274301 Fax: (01872) 260484 E-mail: enquiries@cornwallfarmers.co.uk *Agricultural merchants*

Cornwall Scale & Equipment Co., 29 Mount Ambrose, Redruth, Cornwall, TR15 1NX Tel: (01209) 213413 Fax: (01209) 872902 E-mail: martin.jsanders@virgin.net *Cash registers, restaurant systems, bar systems, scanning & scales suppliers*

Cornwall Scale & Equipment Co., Wallasey, 29 Mount Ambrose, Redruth, Cornwall, TR15 1NX Tel: (01209) 213413 Fax: (01209) 213413 E-mail: martin.jsanders@virgin.net *Weighing machines, scales & cash registers suppliers*

Cornwall Trophies, Unit 7b Pool Industrial Estate, Pool, Redruth, Cornwall, TR15 3RH Tel: (01209) 313733 Fax: (01209) 313733 *Trophy engravers services*

▶ Cornwall Wood Treatment Services Ltd, 12, United Downs Industrial Park, St. Day, Redruth, Cornwall, TR16 5HY Tel: (01209) 820878 Fax: (01209) 822222 E-mail: sales@cornwallwood.co.uk *Retailers of timber, picnic tables, garden furniture, decking & fencing*

Cornwallis Ltd, Unit 42 Coneygre Industrial Estate, Tipton, West Midlands, DY4 8XP Tel: 0121-520 5552 Fax: 0121-520 3330 E-mail: sales@sandgroup.com *Beer dispenser equipment & cellar fittings*

▶ Cornwells, 65A High Street, Sawston, Cambridge, CB2 4BG Tel: (01223) 834533 Fax: (01223) 834533 E-mail: kevin.i.cornwell@btconnect.com *Computer maintenance & repairers*

Coronation Cables Ltd, Abbey Industrial Estate, Mount Pleasant, Wembley, Middlesex, HA0 1NR Tel: (020) 8900 1383 Fax: (020) 8903 7089 E-mail: details@coronationcables.co.uk *Cable & wire manufrs*

Coronation Travel & Tours Ltd, 108 Aldersgate Street, London, EC1A 4JQ Tel: (020) 7253 6666 Fax: (020) 7251 8240 E-mail: info@coronation-group.com *Confirming housing*

Coronet Hire Services, Parles Farm, Bank Lane, Warton, Preston, PR4 1TB Tel: (01772) 634771 Fax: (01772) 631092 E-mail: nikki.nye@tiscali.co.uk *Catering equipment hire services*

Coronet Medical Technologies Ltd, The Coach House, Phoenix Business Centre, Low Mill Road, Ripon, North Yorkshire, HG4 1NS Tel: (01765) 605551 Fax: (01765) 608476 *Medical device manufrs*

Coronet Rail Ltd, Castor Road, Sheffield, S9 2TL Tel: 0114-256 2225 Fax: 0114-261 7826 E-mail: sales@coronetrail.co.uk *Railway fishplate manufrs*

Coronhurst Ltd, Unit 16 Martindale Trading Estate, Martindale, Cannock, Staffordshire, WS11 7XL Tel: (01543) 577101 Fax: (01543) 571876 E-mail: info@coronhurst.co.uk *Ironmongers, industrial fasteners/turned parts*

Corpach Boatbuilding Co. Ltd, Corpach, Fort William, Inverness-Shire, PH33 7NN Tel: (01397) 772861 Fax: (01397) 772765 *Boat builders & repairers*

Corpak Film Converters, Unit 19 Dinting Lane Industrial Estate, Glossop, Derbyshire, SK13 7NU Tel: (01457) 860758 Fax: (01457) 856008 *Film, paper converting & shredding services*

▶ Corporate Business Contracts, 10 St Stephens Avenue, Rutherglen, Glasgow, G73 5LS Tel: 0141-634 0403 Fax: 0141-613 3479

Corporate Business Systems, 11 Shotts St, Glasgow, G33 4JB Tel: 0141-774 5000 Fax: 0141-774 2256 *Office equipment retail & manufrs*

Corporate Business Technology, Tileyard Road, Unit 31, London, N7 9AH Tel: (020) 7503 3000 Fax: (020) 7503 3072 E-mail: sales@corporategroup.co.uk *Telecommunication systems distributors*

Corporate Clothing, 5-7 Linkfield Corner, Station Road, Redhill, RH1 1BD Tel: (01737) 767912 Fax: (01737) 780666 E-mail: info@armawear.co.uk *Industrial overall manufrs*

Corporate CMT Ltd, 59 Featherstone Lane, Featherstone, Pontefract, West Yorkshire, WF7 6LS Tel: (01977) 792226 Fax: (01977) 795536 *Clothing manufrs*

▶ Corporate Communications Ltd, 45 Bank Street, Galashiels, Selkirkshire, TD1 1EP Tel: 0870 7460060 Fax: 0870 7460061 E-mail: info@corpcl.co.uk *Landline and mobile telecommunication specialists, covering the UK. **We offer comprehensive cost reduction analysis, with free reports and recommendations.**We supply non-geographic number services such as 0800"s, 0870"s, 0845"s, and related services such as fax to email conversion.**We specialise in corporate mobile telecom provision and account management for all mobile networks.*

▶ Corporate Computing UK Ltd, Unit 14 Miller 3, Southmill Road, Bishop's Stortford, Hertfordshire, CM23 3DH Tel: (01279) 755339 *Computer systems consultants*

Corporate Engineering Ltd, Culham Mill, Little London Road, Silchester, Reading, RG7 2PP Tel: 0118-970 1366 Fax: 0118-970 1566 E-mail: sales@corporateengineering.co.uk *Glass reinforced plastic*

▶ Corporate Executive Gifts Ltd, Unit K, Houndswood Gate, Harper Lane, Radlett, Hertfordshire, WD7 7HU Tel: (01923) 852330 Fax: (01923) 859946 E-mail: sales@corporateexecutivegifts.com *Importers & stockists of executive gifts*

Corporate Express, Tameside Drive, Birmingham, B6 7AY Tel: 0121-331 3400 Fax: 0121-331 3002 E-mail: dylan.jones@cexp.co.uk *Office equipment suppliers* Also at: Branches throughout the U.K.

Corporate Express, Brunel Road, Wakefield 41 Industrial Estate, Wakefield, West Yorkshire, WF2 0XG Tel: (0870) 4205359 Fax: (0870) 0660707 *Wholesale stationers*

▶ Corporate Food Co. Ltd, Unit 6 Queensferry Industrial Estate, Chester Road, Pentre, Deeside, Flintshire, CH5 2DJ Tel: (01244) 536273 Fax: (01244) 537999 E-mail: info@cfccaterers.co.uk *Caterers*

Corporate Health Ltd, 30 Bradford Road, Slough, SL1 4PG Tel: (01753) 781600 Fax: (01753) 517889 E-mail: enquiries@corporatehealth.co.uk *Occupational health & health safety services*

▶ Corporate Image, 41-45 Richmond Terrace, Carmarthen, Dyfed, SA31 1HG Tel: (01267) 233737

▶ Corporate Image Solutions Ltd, PO Box 698, Crawley, West Sussex, RH10 8AD Tel: (01293) 511200 E-mail: moreinfo@corporateimagesolutions.biz *Corporate image solutions & marketing consultants*

Corporate Promotions Ltd, 47 Morriston Park Drive, Cambuslang, Glasgow, G72 7LJ Tel: 0141-641 3166 Fax: 0141-641 3166 E-mail: sales@promotionsworld.co.uk *Gift house*

Corporate Telecom Systems Ltd, 3 College St Mews, Northampton, NN1 2QF Tel: (01604) 603009 Fax: (01604) 637838 E-mail: sales@corporate-telecom.co.uk *Radio telephone & cellular systems*

Corporate Trends, Rotherham Close, Norwood Industrial Estate, Killermarsh, Sheffield, S21 2JU Tel: 0114-251 3511 Fax: 0114-251 3399 E-mail: sales@corporatetrends.co.uk *Leisure wear suppliers*

▶ Corporate Turnaround Services, 30 Nicholds Close, Bilston, West Midlands, WV14 9JS Tel: (07813) 102014 Fax: (0870) 1681652 E-mail: paul_brindley@talk21.com *Company doctors specialising in turnaround, restructuring, re-financing, insolvency, divestitures, m&a, business planning and strategy. We help you negotiate with the Insolvency Practitioner on an equal par*

Corporate Upgrade Centre Ltd, Ornhams Hall, Boroughbridge, York, YO51 9JH Tel: (01423) 324777 Fax: (01423) 324113 *Computer upgrading & software developers*

▶ Corporate Wellbeing, The Office Millworks, 28 Field Road, Glasgow, G76 8SE Tel: 0141-644 8302 Fax: 0141-644 5753

▶ CorporateFX, 163 Eversholt Street, Euston, London, NW1 1BU Tel: 0207 3808400 *UK's Leading Foreign Currency Brokers Publicised regularly in CNBC, CNN, BBC and the FT.*

Corporatewear UK, 98-104 Constitution Hill, Birmingham, B19 3JT Tel: 0121-604 9898 Fax: 0121-604 6868 E-mail: info@corporatewearuk.co.uk *Supply & manufrs or all types of work wear & corporate clothing including personal protection*

▶ Corran Ferry, Ardgour, Fort William, Inverness-Shire, PH33 7AA Tel: (01855) 841243 Fax: (01855) 841243

▶ Corren Troen, 4 Buckingham Place, London, SW1 6HR Tel: (020) 7798 9344 Fax: (020) 7798 9349 E-mail: office@correntroen.com *Lawyers & solicitors*

Alistair Corrie, 3 Station Drive, Hurlford, Kilmarnock, Ayrshire, KA1 5AU Tel: (01563) 543315 Fax: (01563) 543315 *Skip hire service*

▶ Corrie Construction Ltd, North Road, Fort William, Inverness-Shire, PH33 6PP Tel: (01397) 700680 Fax: (01397) 703933 E-mail: sales@corrieconstruction.com *Civil engineering*

▶ Corrie Plumbing & Heating Ltd, 12-14 Seafield Road, Inverness, IV1 1SG Tel: (01463) 250883

▶ Corrieri's Cafe, 7-9 Alloa Road, Stirling, FK9 5LH Tel: (01786) 472089 Fax: (01786) 445176

Corrin Software Products Ltd, SATRA Innovation Park, Rockingham Road, Kettering, Northamptonshire, NN16 9JH Tel: (01536) 414633 Fax: (01536) 414655 *Computer software programmers*

Corrintec Ltd, Marine House, 18 Hipper Street South, Chesterfield, Derbyshire, S40 1SS Tel: (01246) 246700 Fax: (01246) 246701 E-mail: sales@corrintec.co.uk *Cathodic protection systems manufrs*

Corrocoat Services Ltd, 10 Forster Street, Leeds, LS10 1PW Tel: 0113-276 0760 Fax: 0113-276 0700 E-mail: enquiries@corrocoat.com *Corrosion prevention services*

Corroless Northern Ltd, Regent House, Regent Street, Oldham, OL1 3TZ Tel: 0161-624 4941 Fax: 0161-627 5072 E-mail: sales@kenyon-group.co.uk *Anti-corrosion systems manufrs*

Corrosion Solutions Ltd, 5 Kirkhill Place, Kirkhill Industrial Estate, Dyce, Aberdeen, AB21 0GU Tel: (01224) 772694 Fax: (01224) 775810 E-mail: info@corrsol.co.uk *Corrosion preventives & inhibitors installation manufrs*

Corroy Products Ltd, 25 Queen Street, Premier Business Park, Walsall, WS2 9NT Tel: (01922) 644884 Fax: (01922) 471370 E-mail: sales@corroy.co.uk *Building fixings & woodscrew suppliers*

Corrpro Companies Europe, 4 Mill Court, The Sawmills, Durley, Southampton, SO32 2EJ Tel: (01489) 861980 Fax: (01489) 861981 E-mail: ccel@onyxnet.co.uk *Cathodic protection system suppliers*

▶ Corrpro Companies Europe Ltd, 2 Adam Street, Stockton-on-Tees, Cleveland, TS18 3HQ Tel: (01642) 614106 Fax: (01642) 614100 E-mail: ccel@corrpro.co.uk

Corrpro Companies Europe Ltd, 2 Adam Street, Stockton-on-Tees, Cleveland, TS18 3HQ Tel: (01642) 614106 Fax: (01642) 614100 E-mail: ccel@corrpro.co.uk Principal Export Areas: Worldwide *Cathodic protection systems manufrs*

▶ Corrugated Box Supplies Ltd, Kelvin Way, West Bromwich, West Midlands, B70 7LG Tel: 0121-525 5555 Fax: 0121-553 2501 *Cartons manufrs*

Corrugated Case Co. Ltd, Unit 1, Pilsley Road, Danesmoor, Chesterfield, Derbyshire, S45 9BU Tel: (01246) 860990 Fax: (01246) 860991 E-mail: info@corrugatedcase.com *Corrugated packaging manufrs*

Corrugated Paper Sales Ltd, Crown Industrial Estate Canal Road, Timperley, Altrincham, Cheshire, WA14 1TF Tel: 0161-976 3000 Fax: 0161-975 3727 *Paper merchants & rewinding services*

J.P. Corry Co. Ltd, 648 Springfield Road, Belfast, BT12 7EH Tel: (028) 9024 3661 Fax: (028) 9026 2123 E-mail: info@jpcorry.co.uk *Builders merchants* Also at: Ballynahinch, Bangor, Downpatrick, Dublin, Lisburn & Swansea

Corsair Computer Systems Ltd, Fourth Floor 1, Old Hall Street, Liverpool, L3 9HF Tel: (0845) 3901001 Fax: 0151-255 1943 E-mail: info@Corsairsoftware.co.uk *Computer systems & software developers*

Corsair Manufacturing Ltd, Beaumont Close, Banbury, Oxfordshire, OX16 1SH Tel: (01295) 267021 Fax: (01295) 270396 E-mail: general@corsair-mfg.co.uk *Catering equipment manufrs*

Corsair Vacuum Systems Ltd, The Avenue, Endon, Stoke-On-Trent, ST9 9BY Tel: (01782) 504459 Fax: (01782) 504459 E-mail: corsair@vacpumps.co.uk *Roots & side channel blowers ejectors eductors tube shell specialists*

Corstat Containers Ltd, Unit 7 Whitehill Industrial Estate, Whitehill Lane, Swindon, SN4 7DB Tel: (01793) 855168 Fax: (01793) 855209 E-mail: enquiries@corstat.co.uk *Anti-static packaging manufrs*

Corstorphine Security Systems, 26 Saughton Road, Edinburgh, EH11 3PT Tel: 0131-444 0005 Fax: (0871) 4331212 *Security systems*

Cort Engineering, 27 Waidshouse Road, Nelson, Lancashire, BB9 0RZ Tel: (01282) 612938 Fax: (01282) 612938 *Engineers & general fabricators*

Robert Cort Ltd, Elgar Road, Reading, RG2 0DL Tel: 0118-987 4311 Fax: 0118-986 6592 E-mail: mail@robertcort.co.uk *Design, manufacturers & suppliers of valves, control systems & actuators*

Cort Surface Coating Ltd, 26 Britten Rd, Elgar Road South, Reading, RG2 0AU Tel: 0118-975 6338 Fax: 0118-975 6350 *Metal finishers & polishers*

Cortex Controllers Ltd, 50 St. Stephens Place, Cambridge, CB3 0JE Tel: (01223) 368000 Fax: (01223) 462800 E-mail: info@cortexcontrollers.com *Non contact measuring equipment suppliers*

Cortland Fibron B X Ltd, Unitc R D Park, Stephenson Close, Hoddesdon, Hertfordshire, EN11 0BW Tel: (01992) 471444 Fax: (01992) 471555 *Sub-sea & underwater cable manufrs*

Corton Bashforth Screenprint Ltd, 78 Catley Road, Sheffield, S9 5JF Tel: 0114-243 0240 Fax: 0114-261 1653 *Screen process printers*

Corton Sinclair Ltd, 36 Glenburn Road, East Kilbride, Glasgow, G74 5BA Tel: (01355) 222273 Fax: (01355) 263682 E-mail: sales@corstonsinclair.com *Protective clothing manufrs*

Corufix UK Ltd, 28 Sidney Street, Gloucester, GL1 4DB Tel: (01452) 551860 Fax: (01452) 551860 *Packaging nails*

Corus, Mossend Works, Main Street, Bellshill, Lanarkshire, ML4 1DJ Tel: (01698) 748424 Fax: (01698) 747191 *Steel stockholders*

Corus, Mossend Works, Main Street, Bellshill, Lanarkshire, ML4 1DJ Tel: (01698) 748424 Fax: (01698) 747191 *Steel stockholders*

Corus, Walker Industrial Estate, Walker Road, Guide, Blackburn, BB1 2QE Tel: (01254) 55161 Fax: (01254) 677505 *Steel stockholders*

Corus, Unit 2 Pullman Court, Bolton, BL2 1HL Tel: (01204) 370999 Fax: (01204) 396684 E-mail: chris.deacon@corusgroup.com *Steel stockholders*

Corus, Sengate, The Drove, Brandon, Suffolk, IP27 0JY Tel: (01842) 816200 Fax: (01842) 813019 *Steel stockholders*

Corus, Station Road, South Darenth, Dartford, DA4 9LD Tel: (01322) 227272 Fax: (01322) 864893 *Steel stockholders*

▶ Corus Ltd, West Wing Midland House, New Road, Halesowen, West Midlands, B63 3HY Tel: 0121-585 5522 Fax: 0121-585 5241

Corus Ltd, West Wing Midland House, New Road, Halesowen, West Midlands, B63 3HY Tel: 0121-585 5522 Fax: 0121-585 5241 E-mail: cdtl@corusgroup.com *We are the UK"s leading manufacturer of precision cold drawn seamless & cold drawn welded (DOM) steel tube. Product range includes skived and roller burnished tubes for hydraulic cylinders.* Also at: Corby

Corus, Park Road, Halesowen, West Midlands, B63 2RN Tel: (01384) 897377 Fax: (01384) 898018 *Steel stockholders, steel profiles*

Corus Ltd, 20 Inch Pipe Mill Tube Works, Hartlepool, Cleveland, TS25 2EG Tel: (01429) 266611 Fax: (01429) 527283 *Steel tube manufrs*

continued

Company Information

Corus, Hetton Lyons Industrial Estate, Hetton-le-Hole, Houghton le Spring, Tyne & Wear, DH5 0RD Tel: 0191-526 3288 Fax: 0191-517 0138 E-mail: paul.brown@corusgroup.com *Black bars & alloy steel stockholders* Also at: Bristol, Leicester & Ossett
Corus Ltd, Ashorne Hill Management College, Ashorne Hill, Leamington Spa, Warwickshire, CV33 9PY Tel: (01926) 488029 Fax: (01926) 488024 *Metal manufrs*
Corus, 11 Oldfield Lane, Leeds, LS12 4DH Tel: 0113-263 4242 Fax: 0113-231 0491 E-mail: angela.barnard@corusgroup.com *Steel stockholders*
Corus, Wakefield Road, Leeds, LS10 1AY Tel: 0113-276 0660 Fax: 0113-272 7197 *Steel stockholders*
Corus, 216a Moira Road, Lisburn, County Antrim, BT28 2SN Tel: (028) 9266 0747 Fax: (028) 9266 0748 *Steel stockholders* Also at: Dublin
Corus, 15 Great Marlborough Street, London, W1F 7HR Tel: (020) 7717 4444 Fax: (020) 7717 4455 *Metal products, processes & manufrs*
Corus Ltd, Brinsworth Strip Mills, Sheffield Road, Rotherham, South Yorkshire, S60 1BN Tel: (01709) 377113 Fax: (01709) 375250 *Steel stockholders*
Corus Ltd, PO Box 69, Rotherham, South Yorkshire, S60 1BN Tel: (01709) 377113 Fax: (01709) 375250 E-mail: info@corusgroup.com *Hot rolled steel strips manufrs*
Corus Ltd, PO Box 69, Rotherham, South Yorkshire, S60 1BN Tel: (01709) 377113 Fax: (01709) 375250 E-mail: bsmsales@corusgroup.com *Cold rolled steel strip manufrs*
Corus, Colndale Road, Colnbrook, Slough, SL3 0HL Tel: (01753) 683131 Fax: (01753) 684372 E-mail: customer-services@corusgroup.com *Steel stockholders*
Corus, 202 Solent Business Centre, 343 Millbrook Road West, Southampton, SO15 0HW Tel: (023) 8023 3094 Fax: (023) 8023 3096 *Mould steel stockholders*
Corus, 202 Solent Business Centre, 343 Millbrook Road West, Southampton, SO15 0HW Tel: (023) 8023 3094 Fax: (023) 8023 3096 *Steel stockholders*
Corus, 96 Stourbridge Road, Lye, Stourbridge, West Midlands, DY9 7DD Tel: (01384) 424151 Fax: (01384) 424073 *Steel stockholders*
Corus, Brockhurst Crescent, Walsall, WS5 4AX Tel: (01922) 629593 Fax: (01922) 648202 *Stainless steel coating services*
Corus, Steelpark Way, Wolverhampton, WV11 3SQ Tel: (01902) 631163 Fax: (01902) 484001 E-mail: enquiries@corus-servicecentres.co.uk *Steel manufrs*
Corus, Steelpark Way, Wolverhampton, WV11 3SQ Tel: (01902) 631163 Fax: (01902) 484001 E-mail: enquiries@corus-servicecentres.co.uk *Multi product steel stockholders*
Corus Ltd, PO Box 4, Wolverhampton, WV5 8AT Tel: (01902) 324444 Fax: (01902) 324204 E-mail: enquiries@corus.com *Steel stockholders*
Corus Bristol, Badminton Road Trading Estate, Yate, Bristol, BS37 5JU Tel: (01454) 316600 Fax: (01454) 321014 E-mail: info@corusgroup.com *Steel stockholders*
Corus Building Systems, Units 1-3 Fishwicks Industrial Estate, Kilbuck Lane, St. Helens, Merseyside, WA11 9SZ Tel: (01942) 295500 Fax: (01942) 272136 E-mail: info@kalzip.co.uk *Building merchants services*
Corus Cogifer Switches & Crossings, Hebden Road, Scunthorpe, South Humberside, DN15 8DD Tel: (01724) 862131 Fax: (01724) 295243 E-mail: info@coruscogifer.com *Railway track manufrs*
▶ Corus Construction & Industrial, Dalzell Works, Park St, Motherwell, Lanarkshire, ML1 1PU Tel: (01698) 266100
Corus Construction & Industrial UK Ltd, Brigg Road, Scunthorpe, South Humberside, DN16 1BP Tel: (01724) 404040 Fax: (01724) 402191 E-mail: andrew.page@corusgroup.com *Steel manufrs*
Corus Engineering Steels, Station Works, 680 Warwick Rd, Tyseley, Birmingham, B11 2HL Tel: 0121-706 1110 Fax: 0121-706 8459 E-mail: enquiries.ces@corusgroup.com *Scrap iron & steel merchants* Also at: Wolverhampton
Corus Engineering Steels, Coleford Road, Sheffield, S9 3QE Tel: 0114-244 7264 Fax: 0114-243 0941 E-mail: chris.deacon@corusgroup.com *Steel stockholders*
Corus Engineering Steels, PO Box 25, Wolverhampton, WV1 3DY Tel: (01902) 875000 Fax: (01902) 875011 E-mail: keith.grant@corusgroup.com *Black & bright steel bars*
Corus Engineering Steels Pension Scheme Trustee Ltd, PO Box 50, Rotherham, South Yorkshire, S60 1DW Tel: (01709) 371234 E-mail: christianname.surname@corusgroup.com *Carbon, alloy & freecutting steel*
Corus Group, Hampton House, 20 Albert Embankment, London, SE1 7TJ Tel: (020) 7975 8000 Fax: (020) 7975 8400 *Steel producers manufacture & distribution*
Corus Hotels Bristol, Beggar Bush Lane, Failand, Bristol, BS8 3TG Tel: (01275) 393901 Fax: (01275) 392104 E-mail: meetings.bristol@corushotels.com *Hotel services*
Corus Metal Centre, Fairfax Road, Heathfield Industrial Estate, Newton Abbot, Devon, TQ12 6UD Tel: (01626) 835008 Fax: (01626) 835009 E-mail: andrew.curtis@corusgroup.com *Steel stockholders*
Corus Panels Profiles, Llandeilo Road Industrial Estate, Llandybie, Ammanford, Carmarthenshire, SA18 3JG Tel: (01269) 850691 Fax: (01269) 851272 *Profile & composite panel sheet manufrs*
Corus Process Engineering, Old Frame RM, Derwent Howe, Workington, Cumbria, CA14 3YZ Tel: (01900) 68000 Fax: (01900) 601111 E-mail: cpe@corusgroup.com *Engineers & steel fabricators*
Corus Service Centre, Chainbridge Road Industrial Estate, Blaydon-On-Tyne, Tyne & Wear, NE21 5SS Tel: 0191-414 2181 Fax: 0191-414 2210 *Steel stockholders*
Corus Service Centre, Unit 4 Symondscliffe Way, Portskewett, Caldicot, Gwent, NP26 5PW Tel: (01291) 421732 Fax: (01291) 425085 *Steel stockholders*
Corus Service Centre, Garmouth Road, Mosstodloch, Fochabers, Morayshire, IV32 7LH Tel: (01343) 820606 Fax: (01343) 821295 *Steel stockholders*
Corus Service Centre, Spittlegate Industrial Estate, Grantham, Lincolnshire, NG31 7UP Tel: (01476) 565522 Fax: (01476) 562459 *Steel stockholders*
Corus Service Centre, The Steelpark, Steelpark Way, Wolverhampton, WV11 3SR Tel: (01902) 484200 Fax: (01902) 484049 *Steel stockholders*
▶ Corus Special Profiles Ltd, Skinningrove, Saltburn-By-The-Sea, Cleveland, TS13 4ET Tel: (01287) 640212 Fax: (01287) 643467 *Stainless steel fabricators*
Corus Tubes plc, PO Box 101, Corby, Northamptonshire, NN17 5UA Tel: (01536) 402121 Fax: (01536) 404111 *Welded steel tube manufrs*
Corus (U K) Ltd, Llanwern Works, Newport, Gwent, NP19 4QZ Tel: (01633) 290022 Principal Export Areas: Worldwide *Steel manufrs*
Corus UK Ltd, Glamorgan Works, Pontarddulais, Swansea, SA4 8SB Tel: (01792) 882548 Fax: (01792) 885196 *Aluminium coated steel*
Corus UK Ltd, Moss Bay Road, Workington, Cumbria, CA14 5AE Tel: (01900) 64321 Fax: (01900) 842237 E-mail: info@britishsteel.co.uk Principal Export Areas: Worldwide *Rail track & railway steel sleeper manufrs*
Corvette Marine Ltd, 19 Station Road, Reedham, Norwich, NR13 3TA Tel: (01493) 701260 Fax: (01493) 701455 E-mail: sales@corvettemarine.co.uk *Boat builders*
Corwell Cabinet Makers, Unit 6 Amners Farm, Burghfield, Reading, RG30 3UE Tel: 0118-983 3404 Fax: 0118-983 3404 E-mail: info@corwell.co.uk *Cabinet makers & restorers*
Corwen Farmers Ltd, Station Yard, Corwen, Clwyd, LL21 0EG Tel: (01490) 412272 Fax: (01490) 412431 E-mail: enquiries@corwenfarmers.co.uk *Agricultural foodstuffs*
▶ Corwoods Electrical Contractors, Unit 28 King Street Trading Estate, Middlewich, Cheshire, CW10 9LF Tel: (01606) 737395
Cory Bros Shipping Ltd, The Deep Business Centre, Tower Street, Hull, HU1 4BG Tel: (01482) 382840 Fax: (01482) 382841 E-mail: coryhull@cory.co.uk *Shipping agents*
Cory Environmental Municipal Services, Riverside, London, SE7 7SU Tel: (020) 8858 2008 Fax: (020) 8858 2107 *Barge repairers & waste disposal services*
Cory Logistics Ltd, 90 Giles Street, Leith, Edinburgh, EH6 6BZ Tel: 0131-554 6631 Fax: 0131-554 8504 E-mail: info@cory.co.uk *Shipping & forwarding agents* Also at: Grangemouth
Coryndon Ltd, Rainscombe Farm Buildings, Oare, Marlborough, Wiltshire, SN8 4HZ Tel: (01672) 562581 Fax: (01672) 563995 *Cabinet makers*
▶ Coryton Energy Co. Ltd, Coryton Power Station, The Manorway, Coryton, Stanford-le-Hope, Essex, SS17 9GN Tel: (01375) 645300 Fax: (01375) 645302
The Cos Group Ltd, Unit 6 Ty Verlon Industrial Estate, Cardiff Road, Barry, South Glamorgan, CF63 2BE Tel: (01446) 418000 Fax: (01446) 418009 E-mail: sales@cosgroup.co.uk *Office products & printers & business interiors*
Cosalt Ballyclare Ltd, Banner House, Greg Street, Stockport, Cheshire, SK5 7BT Tel: 0161-429 1100 Fax: (0870) 8502376 E-mail: info@cosalt-ballyclare.com *Suppliers of clothing, uniforms & workwear*
Cosalt Holiday Homes Ltd, Stoneferry, Hull, HU8 8EH Tel: (01482) 227203 Fax: (01482) 210481 E-mail: info@coshomes.co.uk *Chalet & static home manufrs*
Cosalt International Ltd, Fish Dock Road, Grimsby, South Humberside, DN31 3NW Tel: (01472) 504300 Fax: (01472) 504200 E-mail: sales@cosaltlighting.co.uk *Marine specialists*
Cosalt International Ltd, School Road, Lowestoft, Suffolk, NR33 9NB Tel: (01502) 516731 Fax: (01502) 500659 E-mail: lowestoft@cosalt.co.uk *Safety equipment manufrs*
Cosalt Sea-Dog Ltd, 4 Albert Road, Leith, Edinburgh, EH6 7DP Tel: 0131-554 8531 Fax: 0131-554 8061 *Marine safety engineers*
Cosalt Workwear Ltd, Banner House, Greg Street, Stockport, Cheshire, SK5 7BT Tel: (0800) 0188110 Fax: (0870) 8502378 E-mail: info@cosalt-workwear.com *Work wear manufrs*
Cosalt Young, 1 Liddell Street, North Shields, Tyne & Wear, NE30 1HE Tel: 0191-257 6121 Fax: 0191-296 1431 E-mail: northshields@cosalt.co.uk *Safety at sea manufrs*
Cosarnia (U K) Ltd, 8 Alpha Business Park, Deedmore Road, Coventry, CV2 1EQ Tel: (024) 7662 1369 Fax: (024) 7662 1346 E-mail: cosarnia@compuserve.com *Tooling plate suppliers*
▶ Cosco, Unit C2 Zenith, Paycocke Road, Basildon, Essex, SS14 3DW Tel: (01268) 643000 Fax: (01268) 643019
▶ Coscom (U K) Ltd, Unit 1, Dooley Road, Felixstowe, Suffolk, IP11 3HG Tel: (01394) 675404 Fax: (01394) 675424
Coselt Kenmore, Unit G3 Narvik Way, Tyne Tunnel Trading Estate, North Shields, Tyne & Wear, NE29 7XJ Tel: 0191-259 6644 Fax: 0191-258 6363 E-mail: sales@cosaltkenmore.co.uk *Service fire safety equipment*
Cosensa Learning & Development, 661 Lisburn Road, Belfast, BT9 7GT Tel: (028) 9066 4443 Fax: (028) 9066 5535 E-mail: enquiries@cosensa.co.uk *Cosensa Learning & Development Ltd provide General management and Health & Safety management training services to both the Public and Private sector on an in-house and public training courses basis.*
Sam Cosgrove, Greatstone, New Romney, Kent, TN28 8NR Tel: 07749 368792 E-mail: cozy297@hotmail.com *We are mobile caterers based in kent, and can cater for your event and give you % of our profits*
▶ Cosham Plant Hire & Construction, Gate 4, Southmoor Lane, Havant, Hampshire, PO9 1JW Tel: (023) 9247 6400 Fax: (023) 9245 1581 E-mail: info@coshamplant.co.uk
Cosi Ltd, Watersmead Business Park, Littlehampton, West Sussex, BN17 6LS Tel: (01903) 734734 Fax: (01903) 844552 E-mail: sales@cosiworld.com *Cosmetics & toiletries manufrs*
▶ Coslin Construction Ltd, 120 London Road, Gloucester, GL1 3PL Tel: (01452) 305055 Fax: (01452) 308735
▶ Cosmetica Manufacturing Ltd, Faraday Close, Eastbourne, East Sussex, BN22 9BH Tel: (01323) 506055 Fax: (01323) 520681 E-mail: sales@cosmetica.eu.com *Manufacturers of cosmetic products*
Cosmetochem UK Ltd, Cunningham House, Westfield Lane, Harrow, Middlesex, HA3 9ED Tel: (020) 8907 7779 Fax: (020) 8927 0686 E-mail: cosmetochem@cheshamchemicals.co.uk *Cosmetic raw materials*
▶ Cosmic Castles Ltd, 6 High Arcal Road, Dudley, West Midlands, DY3 3AP Tel: (01902) 883299 E-mail: inquiries@theportableskittlealley.co.uk *BOUNCY CASTLE & INFLATABLE HIRE.MANUFACTURE, SALES & HIRE OF SKITTLE ALLEYS & TRADITIONAL GAMES.*
Cosmo Ltd, PO Box 543, Peterborough, PE1 4FN Tel: (08707) 890110 Fax: (08707) 890110 E-mail: sales@cosmo.uk *Garden furnituers*
Cosmo Imaging Ltd, Systems House, Ocean Street, Altrincham, Cheshire, WA14 5DP Tel: 0161-928 6042 Fax: 0161-929 7327 E-mail: info@cgil.co.uk *Microfilm & document management*
Cosmo Services Ltd, 5 Rudolf Place, London, SW8 1RP Tel: (020) 7582 1144 Fax: (020) 7735 2400 E-mail: office@cosmogroup.co.uk *Catering equipment engineers*
Cosmographics, 1 Mowat Industrial Estate, Sandown Road, Watford, WD24 7UY Tel: (01923) 210909 Fax: (01923) 211657 E-mail: enquiries@cosmographics.co.uk *Mapping services*
Cosmos Decorators Ltd, 580 Lawmoor Street, Glasgow, G5 0TX Tel: 0141-429 8171 Fax: 0141-420 1143 E-mail: sales@cosmosdecorators.co.uk *Painting contractors*
Cosmos Motor Products Ltd, Unit 3A Neptune Industrial Estate, Neptune Road, Harrow, Middlesex, HA1 4HX Tel: (020) 8863 8666 Fax: (020) 8427 3689 E-mail: salescomopro@cs.com *Car seat cover manufrs*
▶ Coss Computer Consumables, Unit 10-10a Waterloo Industrial Park, Upper Brook Street, Stockport, Cheshire, SK1 3BP Tel: 0161-476 6633 Fax: 0161-476 6611 *Computer accessory & stationary suppliers*
Cost Index Ltd, 48 Meadow Rise, Barton under Needwood, Burton-on-Trent, Staffordshire, DE13 8DT Tel: 01283 716426 Fax: 01283 716426 E-mail: chris@costindex.co.uk *Cost Index is a business cost comparison service. Initially it will focus on business overhead areas and will empower buyers with relevant peer group cost comparisons to enable cost reduction to be achieved.*
Costa Cruises, Carnival House, 5 Gainsford Street, London, SE1 2NE Tel: (020) 7940 4499 Fax: (020) 7940 5378 E-mail: sales@costacruises.co.uk *Shipping line*
▶ Costain Ltd, Cardiff Business Park, 18 Lambourne Crescent, Llanishen, Cardiff, CF14 5GF Tel: (029) 2075 7755
Costain Ltd, Anchor Bay Wharf, Manor Road, Erith, Kent, DA8 2AW Tel: (01322) 397600 Fax: (01322) 397775 *Plant hire & maintenance services*
Costain Ltd, Costain House, 111 Westminster Bridge Road, London, SE1 7UE Tel: (020) 7705 8444 Fax: (020) 7705 8599 *Construction services* Also at: Branches throughout the U.K.
Costan UK Ltd, Unit 8 Haslemere Industrial Estate, The Pinnacles, Harlow, Essex, CM19 5SZ Fax: (01279) 415266 *Refrigerator distributors*
▶ Costco UK Ltd, Costkea Way, Loanhead, Midlothian, EH20 9BY Tel: 0131-440 4518 Fax: 0131-440 0390
▶ Costco Wholesale UK Ltd, Arnhall Business Park, Westhill, Aberdeenshire, AB32 6UF Tel: (01224) 745560 Fax: (01224) 745563
Costello London Ltd, Unit 8, 274 Queenstown Road, Battersea, London, SW8 4LP Tel: (020) 7720 4779 Fax: (020) 7498 7388 *Structural steelwork engineers*
Costello Security, 77 Nork Way, Banstead, Surrey, SM7 1HN Tel: (0845) 2608830 Fax: 01737 353742 E-mail: info@costellosecurity.co.uk *SUPPLY AND INSTALL FULL RANGE OF SECURITY PRODUCTS TO INSURANCE APPROVED STANDARDS.*
Coster Aerosols Ltd, Babbage Rd, Stevenage, Hertfordshire, SG1 2EQ Tel: (01438) 367763 Fax: (01438) 728305 E-mail: sales.uk@coster.com *Manufacturers of aerosol valves & atomisers/sprays (perfume or toiletry). Also aerosol filling equipment distributors or agents & dispensing pump (spray) manufacurers. In addition bottles, spray capped, plastic*
Coster Environmental Controls Ltd, Unit 5 Sir Francis Ley Indust Park, Derby, DE23 8XA Tel: (01332) 200555 Fax: (01332) 204181 *Temperature control distributors & agents*
Costerwise Ltd, Studio A Royalty Studios, 105 Lancaster Road, London, W11 1QF Tel: (020) 7221 0666 Fax: (020) 7229 7000 E-mail: costerwise@talk21.com *Packaging material manufrs*
▶ Cosy Home Furnishings Ltd, Premier House, Premier Road, Manchester, M8 8HE Tel: 0161-819 5145 Fax: 0161-819 5152 *Pillows & quilt manufrs*
Cotec Converting Machinery Ltd, Unit 20 St. Johns Industrial Estate, Lees, Oldham, OL4 3DZ Tel: 0161-626 5350 Fax: 0161-626 5450 E-mail: jackcotten@btconnect.com *Paper converting machine manufrs*
Cotec Technology Ltd, Sunwin Unit, Westgate, Guisborough, Cleveland, TS14 6AF Tel: (01287) 619196 Fax: (01287) 619195 E-mail: mail@cotectechniology.co.uk *Electronic design services*
Cotech Ltd, Unit 13-16, Tafarnaubach Industrial Estate, Tafarnaubach, Tredegar, Gwent, NP22 3AA Tel: (01495) 711970 Fax: (01495) 725765 E-mail: sales@cotech-uk.com *Manufacturers of lighting filters and interjet printable graphic film.*
Cotech Plastics Ltd, Unit 53 Sapcote Trading Centre, Powke Lane, Cradley Heath, West Midlands, B64 5QX Tel: (01384) 635508 Fax: (01384) 567267 *Plastic mouldings manufrs*
Cotech Software Consultants Ltd, 9 Drakefield Road, London, SW17 8RT Tel: (020) 8682 0123 Fax: (020) 8682 4550 E-mail: faisal@cotech.co.uk *Computer consultancy*
▶ Cotecna International Ltd, Hounslow Centre, Lampton Road, Hounslow, TW3 1JB Tel: (020) 8277 7700 Fax: (020) 8277 7809 E-mail: info@cotecna.co.uk *Inspection certification engineers*
Cotel, Unit 6 Dudnance Lane, Poole, Redruth, Cornwall, TR15 3QT Tel: (01209) 712376 Fax: (01209) 719331 *Radio communication equipment manufrs*
Cotesi Ltd, 5-7 Mill Fold, Sowerby Bridge, West Yorkshire, HX6 4DJ Tel: (01422) 821000 Fax: (01422) 821007 E-mail: enquiries@cotesi.co.uk *Rope & twine manufrs*
Cotleigh Engineering Co. Ltd, 586 Green Lanes, London, N8 0RP Tel: (020) 8802 0111 Fax: (020) 8809 5516 E-mail: j.markham@cotleigh.com *Design engineers & recruitment*
Cotrans International Ltd, Strathallen House, 197 Winchester Road, Chandlers Ford, Eastleigh, Hampshire, SO53 2DU Tel: (023) 8027 3222 Fax: (023) 8027 3244 E-mail: gary_m_turner@hotmail.co.uk *Haulage services*
Cotswald Design & Manufacture Ltd, The Daniel Gooch Building, Whitehill Lane, Wootton Bassett, Swindon, SN4 7DB Tel: (01793) 848007 Fax: (01793) 848526 E-mail: heather@ergotec-cdm.co.uk *Sheet metalwork engineers & fabricators*
Cotswold Architectural Products Ltd, Manor Park Industrial Estate, Manor Road, Cheltenham, Gloucestershire, GL51 9SQ Tel: (01242) 246624 Fax: (01242) 221146 E-mail: info@cotswold-windows.co.uk *Window hardware distributors & manufrs*
Cotswold Autoflo Ltd, Unit 2, Willow Park, Hinton Road, Childswickham, Broadway, Worcestershire, WR12 7HY Tel: (01386) 853284 Fax: (01386) 854636 E-mail: sales@autoflo.co.uk *A leading manufacturer of precision lock nuts & washers. We also provide subcontract machining services, including milling, turning, & drilling. Our expert team of engineers can manufacture to your own specification from your drawings. See our website & online catalogue for further information*
Cotswold Blast Cleaning, Linenfields, Old Boars Hill, Oxford, OX1 5JJ Tel: (07831) 705205 Fax: (01865) 326134 *Shot blasting contractors*
Cotswold Bouncy Castles, 35 Albemarle Gate, Cheltenham, Gloucestershire, GL50 4PH Tel: (01242) 231899 Fax: (01242) 525950 *Entertainment*
Cotswold Casement Co. Ltd, Cotswold Business Village, London Road, Moreton-in-Marsh, Gloucestershire, GL56 0PS Tel: (01608) 650568 Fax: (01608) 651699 E-mail: sales@cotswold-casements.co.uk *Steel windows manufrs*
Cotswold Chemicals & Lubricants, Unit 16-17, Ryeford Industrial Estate, Ryeford, Stonehouse, Gloucestershire, GL10 2LB Tel: (01453) 825292 Fax: (01453) 791451 E-mail: sales@cotswoldchemicals.co.uk *Cleaning materials & equipment suppliers*
The Cotswold Collection, 1 Babdown Airfield, Beverston, Tetbury, Gloucestershire, GL8 8TT Tel: (01666) 503555 Fax: (01666) 505288 *Pine furniture manufrs*
Cotswold Collections, 15 King Street, Ludlow, Shropshire, SY8 1AQ Tel: (01584) 875612 Fax: (01584) 875998 *Ladies clothing retailers*
Cotswold Crockery Hire, Well Cottage, Ewen, Cirencester, Gloucestershire, GL7 6BU Tel: (01285) 770212 Fax: (01285) 770212 E-mail: cotswoldcrockery@btopenworld.com *Crockery & catering equipment hire services*
Cotswold Dairy Equipment Ltd, Avenue Three, Witney, Oxfordshire, OX28 4BP Tel: (01993) 774567 Fax: (01993) 774567 E-mail: sales@cotswold-dairy.co.uk *Dairy equipment manufrs*
▶ Cotswold Decorative Ironworkers, Marsh Farm, Stourton, Shipston-on-Stour, Warwickshire, CV36 5HS Tel: (01608) 685134 Fax: (01608) 685135 E-mail: sales@cd-ironworkers.co.uk *Metalworking & fabrication service*
Cotswold Engine Reconditioners, Gloucester Road, Cheltenham, Gloucestershire, GL51 8NL Tel: (01242) 244496 Fax: (01242) 244496 E-mail: mjm1@btconnect.com *Engine reconditioners*
Cotswold Engineering, The Downs, Wickwar, Wotton-under-Edge, Gloucestershire, GL12 8JD Tel: (01454) 294609 Fax: (01454) 299427 *Sheet metalworkers & fabricators*
Cotswold Fasteners, Winterwell, Ampney Crucis, Cirencester, Gloucestershire, GL7 5EA Tel: (01285) 651711 Fax: (01285) 651096 E-mail: sales@cotsfast.com *Suppliers of fasteners to the distributor trade only*
Cotswold Fire Ltd, Cotswold House, Coldpool Lane Badgeworth, Cheltenham, Gloucestershire, GL51 4UP Tel: (01452) 713272 Fax: (01242) 227765 *Fire extinguishing services*

Cotswold Foam Products, 33 Morelands Trading Estate, Bristol Road, Gloucester, GL1 5RZ Tel: (01452) 521364 Fax: (01452) 310461 E-mail: cotswoldfoam@aol.com *Converters of foam products*

▶ Cotswold Forge, 2 Exmouth Street, Cheltenham, Gloucestershire, GL53 7NS Tel: (01242) 242754 Fax: (01242) 242754 E-mail: sales@cotswoldforge.com *Gate manufrs*

Cotswold Graphics Ltd, 10 Draycott Business Village, Draycott, Moreton-in-Marsh, Gloucestershire, GL56 9JY Tel: (01386) 701222 Fax: (01386) 701228 E-mail: johnl@cotswold-graphics.co.uk *Sign manufrs*

Cotswold Handmade Meringues, Newmarket, Nailsworth, Stroud, Gloucestershire, GL6 0RF Tel: (01453) 836611 Fax: (01453) 836622 E-mail: sales@meringues.co.uk *Bakery & confectionery suppliers*

▶ Cotswold Hygiene, 29 Davenport Road, Witney, Oxfordshire, OX28 6EL Tel: (01993) 704406 Fax: (01993) 700224 *Warm air hand dryers & stainless steel washroom hardware suppliers*

Cotswold Industrial Products, Westmead Drive, Westmead Industrial Estate, Swindon, SN5 7YT Tel: (01793) 610880 Fax: (01793) 616941 E-mail: sales@cpkgg.com *Packaging & strapping products*

Cotswold Industrial Products, Westmead Drive, Westmead Industrial Estate, Swindon, SN5 7YT Tel: (01793) 610880 Fax: (01793) 616941 E-mail: sales@cpkgg.com *Packaging retailers*

Cotswold Industrial & Welding Supplies, B Staverton Connection, Gloucester Road, Staverton, Cheltenham, Gloucestershire, GL51 0TF Tel: (01452) 855507 Fax: (01452) 859006 *Welding & industrial goods*

Cotswold Machinery Sales, 11 Isbourne Way, Winchcombe, Cheltenham, Gloucestershire, GL54 5NS Tel: (01242) 603907 Fax: (01242) 604059 E-mail: sales@cotswold-machinery-sales.co.uk *Machine tool importers*

Cotswold Outdoor Ltd, 13 Lower Northam Road, Hedge End, Southampton, SO30 4FN Tel: (01489) 799555 Fax: (01489) 790010 *Camping equipment retailers*

Cotswold Perfumery Ltd, Victoria Street, Bourton-on-the-Water, Cheltenham, Gloucestershire, GL54 2BU Tel: (01451) 820698 Fax: (01451) 821717 E-mail: sales@cotswold-perfumery.co.uk *Perfume compound*

▶ Cotswold Reclamation Co., 2 Sandy Lane Court, Upper Rissington, Cheltenham, Gloucestershire, GL54 2NF Tel: (01451) 820292 Fax: (01451) 822455 E-mail: info@cotswoldreclamation.com

Cotswold Recording Systems, 12 Rodbourne Road, Swindon, SN2 2AG Tel: (01793) 618874 Fax: (01793) 511874 E-mail: rodger@clockingmachine.co.uk *Time recorder systems agents & installers*

Cotswold Steel Stockholders Ltd, Unit 1m2 Babdown Industrial Estate, Babdown, Tetbury, Gloucestershire, GL8 8YL Tel: (01666) 504889 Fax: (01666) 504891 E-mail: james@cotswoldsteels.com *Steel stockholding & fabricators*

Cotswold Tool & Press, Bromag Industrial Estate, Minster Lovell, Witney, Oxfordshire, OX29 0SR Tel: (01993) 772923 Fax: (01993) 779615 E-mail: sales@ctap.co.uk *Press work & steel manufrs*

Cotswold Valves Ltd, Upper Mills Trading Estate, Stonehouse, Gloucestershire, GL10 2BJ Tel: (01453) 826612 Fax: (01453) 827505 E-mail: info@cotswoldvalves.co.uk *Distributors, agents & stockholders of valves*

Cott Beverages Ltd, Bondgate, Pontefract, West Yorkshire, WF8 2XA Tel: (01977) 601600 Fax: (01977) 708447 E-mail: sales@cott.co.uk *Manufacture soft drinks*

Cottage Blinds Of Sedgley Ltd, Old Nail Works, Brick Street, Dudley, West Midlands, DY3 1NT Tel: (01902) 661267 Fax: (01902) 884312 E-mail: info@cottageblinds.co.uk *Blind & awning manufrs*

Cottage Catering Hire Services, Redriff, Ethelbert Road, Rochford, Essex, SS4 3JS Tel: (01702) 204472 Fax: (01702) 204521 *Catering Equipment Hire*

▶ Cottage Conservatories, 12 Clooney Road, Londonderry, BT47 6TB Tel: (028) 7134 5571 Fax: (028) 7134 9400

Cottage Flooring, 5 Oakhurst Close, Barkingside, Ilford, Essex, IG6 2LT Tel: (020) 8551 8875 Fax: (020) 8551 8875 E-mail: cottageflooring@aol.com *Contract flooring specialists*

▶ Cottage Property Services, Cottage Farmhouse, Cottage Road, Wooler, Northumberland, NE71 6AD Tel: (01668) 281000 Fax: (01668) 281000 E-mail: brian@bpatterson3.wannado.co.uk *New, alter, repair, maintenance, to all houses, extensions*

Arthur Cottam & Co., Carrwood Road, Chesterfield, Derbyshire, S41 9QB Tel: (01246) 453672 Fax: (01246) 260274 E-mail: sales@cottamhorseshoes.com *Farriers tool & horse shoe manufrs*

▶ Brian Cottam Photography, 3 Morlais Street, Roath, Cardiff, CF23 5HQ Tel: (029) 20498675 E-mail: info@briancottam.co.uk *Comercial, industrial, Advertising, Corporate, portrait and aerial photography service available both UK and Internationally.*

Cottam Bros Ltd, Wilson Street North, Sheepfolds Industrial Estate, Sunderland, SR5 1BB Tel: 0191-567 1091 Fax: 0191-510 8187 E-mail: cottam.bros@dial.pipex.com *Manufacturers of brushes general, industrial*

▶ Cottam Parkinson Consulting Ltd, Unit 5, Thomas Street, Congleton, Cheshire, CW12 1QU Tel: (01260) 289229 Fax: (01260) 289221 E-mail: info@cottamparkinson.co.uk *Occupational hygiene, health & safety consultants*

Cottam & Preedy Ltd, 68 Lower City Road, Tividale, Oldbury, West Midlands, B69 2HF Tel: 0121-552 5281 Fax: 0121-552 6895 E-mail: enquiries@cottampreedy.co.uk *Ball valve distributors*

▶ Cottenden Ltd, 1 Oakfield Business Corner, Works Road, Letchworth Garden City, Hertfordshire, SG6 1FB Tel: (01462) 672179 E-mail: terry@cottenden.co.uk *Precision engineers & toolmakers*

Cotterell Light Centres, 28-30 Carnoustie Place, Glasgow, G5 8PH Tel: (0141) 429 5648 Fax: 0141-429 7853 E-mail: glasgow@cotterell-lightcentres.com *Lamp shade lighting distributors*

Cotterill Cook Printers Ltd, 40 St Clements Road, Nechells, Birmingham, B7 5AF Tel: 0121-327 1156 Fax: 0121-327 5203 E-mail: print@cotterillcook.fsnet.co.uk *Commercial & colour printers*

Cottesmore Press, Baxters Yard, Stuart Street, Grantham, Lincolnshire, NG31 9AF Tel: (01476) 405959 Fax: (01476) 405959 E-mail: fastrack@cottersmorepressfsbusiness.co.uk *General printers*

Cottingham Joinery Co. Ltd, Beckside North, Beverley, North Humberside, HU17 0PR Tel: (01482) 868145 Fax: (01482) 870728 E-mail: info@cottjoinery.co.uk *Joinery specialists services*

Cotton Conquest, 42-44 Heron Street, Stoke-on-Trent, ST4 3AS Tel: (01782) 312173 Fax: (01782) 593234 *Industrial sewing machines suppliers, repairers & rental*

Guy Cotton Ltd, Unit 1 Heathlands Road Industrial Estate, Station Road, Liskeard, Cornwall, PL14 4DH Tel: (01579) 347115 *Water proof clothing manufrs*

Cotton Mill Ltd, 2 Gourley Street, London, N15 5NG Tel: (020) 8802 2305 Fax: (020) 8802 2307 *Cotton manufrs*

▶ Cotton Transport & Sons Ltd, Church Street, Church Gresley, Swadlincote, Derbyshire, DE11 9NR Tel: (01283) 213777 Fax: (01283) 550408

▶ Cottrell Brickwork Ceramics Ltd, 729 Woodbridge Road, Ipswich, IP4 4NB Tel: (01473) 724842 Fax: (01473) 717639

Cottrell Electrical Services Ltd, 276-278 Smithdown Road, Liverpool, L15 5AJ Tel: 0151-733 5100 Fax: 0151-734 4457 E-mail: sales@cottrellelectrical.co.uk *Electrical contractors*

Coubrough & McKeracher (Printers) Ltd, 8 Falfield Street, Glasgow, G5 8HL Tel: 0141-429 0487 Fax: 0141-429 0515 E-mail: enquiries@cmckprinters.com *Stationery & printer manufrs*

Cougar Automation Ltd, Cougar House Parklands Business Park, Forest Road, Denmead, Waterlooville, Hampshire, PO7 6XP Tel: (023) 9226 9960 Fax: (023) 9226 9968 E-mail: info@cougar-automation.com *Control systems manufrs*

Cougar Designs, 6A Bart Street, Sparkhill, Birmingham, B11 4SA Tel: 0121-773 9491 Fax: 0121-771 0464 *Diary & gift publishers*

Cougar Developments Glanford Ltd, Sixth Avenue, Flixborough Industrial Estate, Flixborough, Scunthorpe, South Humberside, DN15 8SH Tel: (01724) 841111 Fax: (01724) 841144 E-mail: christine@cougardevelopments.co.uk Principal Export Areas: Worldwide *Temporary road sign frames, manufacturing & engineering*

Cougar Flex, 59 Rixon Road, Wellingborough, Northamptonshire, NN8 4BA Tel: (01933) 223354 Fax: (01933) 224522 E-mail: salescougarflex@btconnect.com *Hydraulic component suppliers*

Cougar Industries Ltd, 1 Riverpark, Billet Lane, Berkhamsted, Hertfordshire, HP4 1HL Tel: (01442) 860000 Fax: (01442) 864686 E-mail: sales@cougar-industries.co.uk Principal Export Areas: Worldwide *Pump distributors*

▶ Coul Plant Hire, Coul Road, Contin, Strathpeffer, Ross-Shire, IV14 9ES Tel: (01997) 421817

D.F. Coulam & Sons, Northfields Industrial Estate, 3 Stirling Way, Market Deeping, Peterborough, PE6 8LG Tel: (01778) 346518 Fax: (01778) 380495 E-mail: sales@dfcspares.com *Marine industrial diesel engines manufrs*

Sam Coulbeck (Refrigeration Rentals) Ltd, North Quay Fish Docks, Grimsby, South Humberside, DN31 3SY Tel: (01472) 345827 Fax: (01472) 358083 *Refrigeration rental, engineers, service & sales*

Couldridge Industrial Supplies, Crucible Close, Mushet Industrial Park, Coleford, Gloucestershire, GL16 8RE Tel: (01594) 833177 Fax: (01594) 837423 *Adhesive distributors & manufrs*

Coulling Brothers Ltd, Sandway Road, Sandway, Maidstone, Kent, ME17 2LX Tel: (01622) 858448 Fax: (01622) 850609 E-mail: mail@coullingbrothers.co.uk *Road transport, haulage & freight services*

Coulson, William James House, Cowley Road, Cambridge, CB4 0WX Tel: (01223) 423800 Fax: (01223) 420550 E-mail: group@coulson.co.uk *Masonry, decorating & restoration contractors*

▶ Coulson Construction Ltd, Woodbine Cottage Birtley, Birtley, Hexham, Northumberland, NE48 3HL Tel: (01434) 230612

▶ Coulsons Chartered Accountants, 2 Belgrave Crescent, Scarborough, North Yorkshire, YO11 1UB Tel: (01723) 364141 Fax: (01723) 376010 E-mail: postmaster@coulsons.co.uk *Audit, taxation, payroll, bookkeeping accountancy & advice services*

Coulter Claddings, 17 Lurgan Road, Banbridge, County Down, BT32 4LY Tel: (028) 4062 8855 Fax: (028) 4062 8866 E-mail: sales@coultercladdings.co.uk *Plastic products wholesaler*

Coulter Windows Ltd, 27 Dunavail Road, Kilkeel, Newry, County Down, BT34 4JT Tel: (028) 4176 3884 Fax: (028) 4176 4665 E-mail: neil@coulterwindows.co.uk *PVC windows, doors, conservatories*

William Coulthard & Co. Ltd, Stephenson Road, Durranhill Trading Estate, Carlisle, CA1 3NS Tel: (01228) 521418 Fax: (01228) 511310 E-mail: sales@wmcoulthard.com *Lubricating system manufrs*

Coulthard's Concrete Products, Blackdyke Industrial Estate, Silloth, Wigton, Cumbria, CA7 4WY Tel: (01697) 331324 Fax: (01697) 331418 *Concrete blocks & holding company*

Coulthards UK Ltd, Haydn Road, Nottingham, NG5 1DH Tel: 0115-924 6100 Fax: 0115-924 6796 *Ladies hosiery manufrs*

Inc Council Of Law Reporting For England & Wales, 119 Chancery Lane, London, WC2A 1PP Tel: (020) 7242 6471 Fax: (020) 7831 5247 E-mail: postmaster@iclr.co.uk *Printing & publishing of law reports*

Harry Counsell & Co., Cliffords Inn, Fetter Lane, London, EC4A 1LD Tel: (020) 7269 0370 Fax: (020) 7831 2526 E-mail: blandhc@aol.com *Law court & conference writers*

Countax Ltd, Countax House, Great Haseley Trading Estate, Great Haseley, Oxford, OX44 7PF Tel: (01844) 278800 Fax: (01844) 278792 E-mail: sales@countax.com *Garden lawnmower manufacturers & eco power tools distributors*

Countdown Clean Systems Ltd, Unit 2276, Dunbeath Road, Elgin Industrial Estate, Swindon, SN2 8EA Tel: (01793) 512505 Fax: (01793) 541884 E-mail: ais@countdown.com Principal Export Areas: Central/East Europe & West Europe *Clean room clothing manufrs*

Counter Corrosion, PO Box 18, Dewsbury, West Yorkshire, WF12 0JP Tel: (01924) 468559 Fax: (01924) 458019 *Corrosion specialists*

Counter Solutions Ltd, Lakeside Business Centre, Shipley, Heanor, Derbyshire, DE75 7JQ Tel: (01773) 530303 Fax: (01773) 530404 E-mail: sales@countersolutions.com *Counter Solutions offer a flexible product portfolio that incorporates a wide range of high performance business services and solutions specifically designed for the hospitality sector - from traditional Cashless Systems & Vending Systems to EPOS terminals & Stock Management Systems.* Making life simple doesn't have to be complicated. All it takes is a Counter Solutions single multi application cashless card with a high IQ. A Counter Solutions Cashless System with the intelligence to handle a multitude of services, no matter how challenging your requirements*.*

Counterhouse Systems Ltd, PO Box 381, Worcester, WR6 5YB Tel: (01886) 833044 Fax: (01886) 833152 E-mail: robert@counterhouse.co.uk *EPOS suppliers*

Countertops (Holdings) Ltd, Unit 4-5 Lymore Gardens, Bath, BA2 1AQ Tel: (01225) 424467 Fax: (01225) 448107 E-mail: worktops@btconnect.com *Laminated plastics fabricators*

Counties Barn Dance Agency, Derby Close, Broughton Astley, Leicester, LE9 6NF Tel: (0870) 240 1214 Fax: (0870) 240 1214 E-mail: countiesfolkagency@hotmail.com *We can provide various styles of barn dance bands to suit all tastes and budgets from private parties to large corporate events.*

Counting Solutions Ltd, 1-3 Bowling Green Road, Kettering, Northamptonshire, NN15 7QW Tel: (01536) 511010 Fax: (01536) 513653 E-mail: sales@counting-solutions.co.uk *People & vehicle counting specialists*

Countplace Ltd, PO Box 52, Littlehampton, West Sussex, BN17 5RZ Tel: (01903) 716802 Fax: (01903) 715896 E-mail: sales@nukey.co.uk *Replacement key & lock suppliers*

Countrose Bearings, PO Box 376, Birmingham, B42 2TB Tel: 0121-356 7220 Fax: 0121-356 7322 E-mail: c.bennett@tufnol.co.uk *Marine bearing manufrs*

Country Artists Ltd, Country Artists House, Loxley Road, Wellesbourne, Warwick, CV35 9JY Tel: (01789) 473000 Fax: (01789) 473001 E-mail: reception1@country-artists.co.uk *Ornaments manufrs*

Country Bake House Dorset, Unit 2 Ambassador Trade Park, Five Bridges, West Stour, Gillingham, Dorset, SP8 5SE Tel: (01747) 838877 Fax: (01747) 838876 *Bakers*

Country Boarding Kennels, Pitt Farm, Swettenham Lane, Swettenham, Congleton, Cheshire, CW12 2JY Tel: (01260) 224270 Fax: (01260) 224769 *Garden furniture manufrs*

▶ Country Colonial Ltd, 82-86 Seymour Place, London, W1H 2NQ Tel: (020) 7723 0465 Fax: (020) 7723 4430 E-mail: textilediva@countrycolonial.co.uk *Design & import specialising in fashion accessories*

Country Concept, Old Church School, Church Hill, Halkyn, Holywell, Clwyd, CH8 8BU Tel: (01352) 780749 Fax: (01352) 780769 E-mail: sales@countryconcept.co.uk *Knitwear, fleeces, leisure & country wear distributors*

Country Corner, Unit 15 Taverham Craft Centre, Fir Covert Road, Taverham, Norwich, NR8 6HT Tel: (01603) 261745 *Furniture retailers*

Country Corner, 25-27 High Street, Swanage, Dorset, BH19 2LS Tel: (01929) 421198 Fax: (01929) 421198 *Pine furniture retailers*

▶ Country Cross Stitch Kits, Standen Cottage, Lower Road, Thetford, Norfolk, IP25 7EB Tel: 01760 440091 E-mail: steve@countrycrossstitchkits.co.uk *Arts & crafts services*

Country Cures Pest Control Ltd, The Boundary, Coxford Down, Micheldever, Winchester, Hampshire, SO21 3BD Tel: (01962) 774342 Fax: (01962) 774342 E-mail: countrycures@aol.com *Pest controllers*

Country Custom Engineering, Units 11-13 Enterprise Units, 21-27 Hollands Road, Haverhill, Suffolk, CB9 8PU Tel: (01440) 763881 Fax: (01440) 763800 E-mail: countrycustom@hotmail.co.uk *General engineers & fabricators*

Country Estates Developments Ltd, 17 Albury Close, Loverock Road, Reading, RG30 1BD Tel: 0118-950 8366 Fax: 0118-959 5857 E-mail: sales@countryestates.co.uk *Industrial estate developers*

Country Fare Produce, Stall 7b-11b Fish Market, Market Place, Leicester, LE1 5HQ Tel: 0116-253 1432 Fax: 0116-288 0311 *Dairy product wholesale&retail*

Country Forge, Kidderminster Road, Dodford, Bromsgrove, Worcestershire, B61 9DU Tel: (01527) 575765 Fax: (01527) 575761 E-mail: sales@metalartproducts.co.uk *Gate manufrs*

Country Furniture, 36london Rd, Nantwich, Cheshire, CW5 7JR Tel: 01270 610543 Fax: 01270 610543 *Furniture manufrs*

Country Furniture Makers, Victoria Road, Yeovil, Somerset, BA21 5AZ Tel: (01935) 428404 Fax: (01935) 424261 *Furniture manufrs*

▶ Country Homes, 14-15 Axwell House, Westerton Road, East Mains Industrial Estate, Broxburn, West Lothian, EH52 5AU Tel: (01506) 852665

▶ Country Homes Anglia Ltd, Brome Industrial Park, Airfield Industrial Estate, Eye, Suffolk, IP23 7HN Tel: (01379) 871041 Fax: (01379) 870809

Country House Furniture Ltd, Inglenook, Sheep St, Stow on the Wold, Cheltenham, Glos, GL54 1AA Tel: (01451) 831525 Fax: (01451) 831527 *Readymade home & office furniture manufrs*

Country Kitchen, 84 Northern Rd, Portsmouth, PO6 3ER Tel: 023 92321148 *Chilled food distribution*

Country Lanes Garden Centre Ltd, Country Lanes Garden Centre, Exeter Road, Stockley, Okehampton, Devon, EX20 1QH Tel: (01837) 52489 Fax: (01837) 52489 *Aquarium suppliers & garden centre*

Country Leisure Ltd, Cholderton, Salisbury, SP4 0EQ Tel: (01980) 629555 Fax: (01980) 629501 E-mail: sales@countryleisure.co.uk *GRP fabricators*

Country Lines, 4 Alexandria Terrace, Bridge Street, Brigg, South Humberside, DN20 8NW Tel: (01652) 651650 Fax: (01652) 651650 E-mail: sales@gpmgroup.com *Fishing & angling equipment suppliers*

Country & Mineral Supplies, 5 Beeches Industrial Estate, Coedcae Lane, Pontyclun, Mid Glamorgan, CF72 9DY Tel: (01443) 224239 Fax: (01443) 224239 *Pre-pack animal feeds, pet foods & promotional clothing suppliers*

Country Pine, The Tithe Barn, Letheringsett Hill, Holt, Norfolk, NR25 6RY Tel: (01263) 711666 Fax: (01263) 711666 E-mail: sales@holt-country-pine.com *Pine furniture manufrs*

Country Pine, Hayton, Retford, Nottinghamshire, DN22 9LG Tel: (01777) 710001 Fax: (01777) 706967 *Pine furniture manufrs*

Country Pine Furniture Cowbridge Ltd, Duke of Wellington Mews, Church Street, Cowbridge, South Glamorgan, CF71 7BB Tel: (01446) 775491 Fax: (01446) 775040 *Interior design & wooden furniture suppliers to trade & retail*

Country Plastics Injection Moulding Services, 2 Weensland Mill, Weensland Road, Hawick, Roxburghshire, TD9 9PS Tel: (01450) 377583 Fax: (01450) 376065 *Plastic injection moulding*

Country Secrets, The Annex Downside House, Wells Road, Chilcompton, Radstock, BA3 4EU Tel: (01761) 233880 Fax: (01761) 233990 E-mail: countrysecrets@care4free.net *Giftware manufrs*

Country Signs, 4 Northern Road, Newark, Nottinghamshire, NG24 2EG Tel: (01636) 605505 Fax: (01636) 605522 *Manufacturer of signs*

▶ Country Style, 220 Moulsham Street, Chelmsford, CM2 0LS Tel: (01245) 252277

Country Supplies, Hundred House, Llandrindod Wells, Powys, LD1 5RY Tel: (01982) 570200 *Agricultural supplies distributors*

Country Theme, 12 South Street, Wareham, Dorset, BH20 4LT Tel: (01929) 553001 Fax: (01929) 553001 *Pine furniture retailers*

Country Upholstery, Unit 1 Kennet Enterprise Centre, Charnham La, Hungerford, Berks, RG17 0EY Tel: (01488) 682226 Fax: (01488) 682226 E-mail: paulcho@btinternet.com *Upholstered headboards*

Country Vale Products, Bath Road, Bridgwater, Somerset, TA6 4PW Tel: (01823) 271011 Fax: (01823) 431059 *Abattoir manufrs*

Country Vehicles Horse Box Manufacturer, Mount Pleasant Farm, Main St, Pymoor, Ely, Cambs, CB6 2DY Tel: (01353) 698075 *Horse box manufr*

Country Ways, 115 Holburn Street, Aberdeen, AB10 6BQ Tel: (01224) 585150 Fax: (01224) 581023 E-mail: sales@countryways.com *Horse saddler*

Country West Trading Ltd, Northgate, Barnstaple Street, Bideford, Devon, EX39 4AE Tel: (01237) 424373 Fax: (01237) 425054 *Agricultural engineers & merchants*

Country West Trading Ltd, Scarne Industrial Estate, Launceston, Cornwall, PL15 9HS Tel: (01566) 775488 Fax: (01566) 772434 E-mail: countrywest@excite.com *Animal feed merchants*

Country Wide Mobility Partners, Copenhagen Court, 32 New Street, Basingstoke, Hampshire, RG21 7DT Tel: (01256) 812700 Fax: (01256) 333420 E-mail: info@countrywidemobility.co.uk *Relocation*

▶ Country Window Systems Ltd, Unit 1 Hardys Monument Indus, 1 Blagdon Road, Dorchester, Dorset, DT1 2JN Tel: (01305) 889500

Country Window Systems Ltd, Flightway, Dunkeswell Industrial Estate, Dunkeswell, Honiton, Devon, EX14 4LN Tel: (01404) 891144 Fax: (01404) 891044 E-mail: info@countrywindows.com *PVC window & door manufrs*

Countrylife Stoves, Coopers Orchard, Brook Street, North Newton, Bridgwater, Somerset, TA7 0BL Tel: (01278) 662449 Fax: (01278) 662449 *Service & sales central heating*

The Countryside Agency, John Dower House, Crescent Place, Cheltenham, Gloucestershire, GL50 3RA Tel: (01242) 521381 Fax: (01242) 584270 E-mail: info@countryside.gov.uk *Government agents*

▶ Countryside Art, The Old Rectory, Alford, Lincolnshire, LN13 0BQ Tel: (01507) 480685

Countryside Cabinet Maker, 8 Wellsway Works, Wells Road, Radstock, BA3 3RZ Tel: (0781) 2688101 Fax: (01225) 840864 E-mail: scott.joyce@virgin.net *Furniture & cabinet manufrs*

The Countryside Centre, Chapel Lane, Ullenhall, Henley-In-Arden, West Midlands, B95 5RT Tel: (01564) 793244 *Educational equipment & suppliers*

Countryside Fencing, Capel Grove, Capel St. Mary, Ipswich, IP9 2JS Tel: (01473) 314230 Fax: (01473) 314052 E-mail: sales@countryside-gates.co.uk *Fencing contractor & gate manufrs*

Countryside Gates & Timber Products, Gressy Holme Farm, Bullpit Road, Balderton, Newark, Nottinghamshire, NG24 3LZ Tel: (01636) 679983 Fax: (01636) 703434 *Timber gate manufrs*

▶ CountrystoreDirect, Lodge Farm, Bowl Road, Charing, Ashford, Kent, TN27 0HB Tel: 01233 712948 Fax: 01233 713804 E-mail: sales@countrystoredirect.com *Electric fencing for horses, ponies & all livestock manufrs*

▶ Countrywide Electrical Service Ltd, 76 Summer Lane, Birmingham, B19 3NG Tel: 0121-248 1400 Fax: 0121-248 1401 E-mail: admin@ceslimited.uk.com *Electrical contractors*

Countrywide Farmers P.L.C., Brickhouse Lane, Stoke Prior, Bromsgrove, Worcestershire, B60 4LX Tel: (01527) 831663 Fax: (01527) 570290 E-mail: enquiries@countrywidefarmers.co.uk *Agricultural, equestrian & garden suppliers*

Countrywide Farmers plc, Church Street, Melksham, Wiltshire, SN12 6LS Tel: (01225) 701470 Fax: (01225) 702318 E-mail: info@countrywidefarmers.co.uk *Agricultural & animal feeds* Also at: Branches throughout the South West

Countrywide Farmers P.L.C., Lady Lane, Blunsdon, Swindon, SN2 4DN Tel: (01793) 722888 Fax: (01793) 706011 *Agricultural merchants*

Countrywide Fleet Services UK Ltd, West Mill House, 114 Carisbrooke Road, Newport, Isle of Wight, PO30 1DF Tel: (0870) 6080858 Fax: (0870) 6080859 E-mail: sales@countrywide-fleet.co.uk *Vehicle contract hire*

Countrywide Industrial Coatings, Thwaite Lodge, Thwaite Close, Erith, Kent, DA8 1DP Tel: (01322) 338639 Fax: (01322) 359060 *Protective coating services*

Countrywide Photographic, 116 Ellingham Industrial Centre, Ellingham Way, Ashford, Kent, TN23 6LZ Tel: (01233) 666868 Fax: E-mail: info@countrywidephotographic.co.uk *Photographers*

Countrywide Porter Novelli Ltd, 31 St. Petersburgh Place, London, W2 4LA Tel: (020) 7853 2222 Fax: (020) 7853 2244 E-mail: enquiries@countrywidepn.co.uk *Public relations consultants*

Countrywide Principal Services, Sovereign House, Hockliffe Street, Leighton Buzzard, Bedfordshire, LU7 1GT Tel: (01525) 383084 Fax: (01525) 850285 *Finance & estate agents services* Also at: Basildon, Basingstoke, Ipswich & Wellingborough

Countrywide Property Management, 760 Lea Bridge Road, London, E17 9DH Tel: (020) 8556 9211 Fax: (020) 8539 8543 *Commercial estate agents & property management services*

Countrywide Signs, Church Villa, 23 Brinkley Road, Dullingham, Newmarket, Suffolk, CB8 9UW Tel: (01638) 508077 Fax: (01638) 507880 E-mail: sales@countrywide-signs.com *Sign writing*

Countrywide Steel & Tubes, 326-328 Coleford Road, Sheffield, S9 5PH Tel: 0114-244 8444 Fax: 0114-244 8555 *Steel stockholders*

Countrywide Stores, Lower Monk Street, Abergavenny, Gwent, NP7 5LU Tel: (01873) 855180 Fax: (01873) 856299 *Animal feed manufrs*

Countrywide Stores, Old Gloucester Road, Thornbury, Bristol, BS35 3UH Tel: (01454) 260406 Fax: (01454) 260749 *Agricultural farming & suppliers*

Countrywide Stores, Hook Norton Road, Chipping Norton, Oxfordshire, OX7 5TE Tel: (01608) 642071 Fax: (01608) 645125 E-mail: enquiries@countrywidefarmers.co.uk *Agricultural merchants*

Countrywide Stores P.L.C., Station Road, Stockton, Southam, Warwickshire, CV47 8HA Tel: (01926) 812513 Fax: (01926) 815105 *Agricultural merchants*

Countrywide Stores, Grange Mill, Abergavenny Road, Raglan, Usk, Gwent, NP15 2AA Tel: (01291) 690056 Fax: (01291) 690378 *Agricultural retailers*

▶ Countrywise Spring Water, Dairycoates Industrial Estate, Wiltshire Road, Hull, HU4 6PA Tel: (01482) 351003 Fax: (01482) 358928 E-mail: info@countrywise.net *Water coolers rental, mineral water delivery & installing of plumbed in water coolers**

Countryworld Ltd, Common Lane, Culcheth, Warrington, WA3 4EH Tel: (01925) 765448 *Health food shop*

County Abrasive Supplies, 7 Bawden Road, Bodmin, Cornwall, PL31 1PT Tel: (01208) 75121 Fax: (01208) 76358 *Industrial abrasives resellers*

County Battery Services Ltd, Field Industrial Estate, Clover Street, Kirkby-in-Ashfield, Nottingham, NG17 7LJ Tel: (01623) 757377 Fax: (01623) 757347 E-mail: sales@countybattery.co.uk *Battery distributors & manufrs*

County Bearings, 76 Hart Road, Benfleet, Essex, SS7 3PF Tel: (01268) 758933 Fax: (01268) 755058 *Bearings retailers*

County Blinds & Awnings Ltd, 109 Worlds End Lane, Orpington, Kent, BR6 6AE Tel: (01689) 851093 Fax: (01689) 859779 *Window blind suppliers*

County Club Ltd, 244 Tolworth Rise South, Surbiton, Surrey, KT5 9NB Tel: (020) 8337 5050 E-mail: sales@countyclub.co.uk *Embroiderers & club clothing manufrs*

County Communications, Yew Tree, Walls Quarry, Brimscombe, Stroud, Gloucestershire, GL5 2PA Tel: (01453) 887594 Fax: (01453) 883428 *Voice data equipment*

County Computers, Aranway House, Dyserth Road, Rhyl, Clwyd, LL18 4DS Tel: (01745) 330663 Fax: (01745) 337515 E-mail: admin@countycomputers.co.uk *Computer systems*

County Conference & Banqueting Centre, Meadow Lane, Nottingham, NG2 3HJ Tel: 0115-955 7222 Fax: 0115-955 7238 E-mail: candb@nottscountysc.co.uk *Conference rooms & banqueting services*

▶ County Constructions Ltd, New Barn Farm, Tadlow, Royston, Hertfordshire, SG8 0EL Tel: (01767) 631063 Fax: (01767) 631083

County Consumables, Lower Common Road, West Wellow, Romsey, Hampshire, SO51 6BT Tel: (01794) 324032 Fax: (01794) 323646 E-mail: sales@countyconsumables.co.uk *Trucks & trolley specialists*

▶ County Contractors, Unit 17, Leeway Court, Leeway Industrial Estate, Newport, Gwent, NP19 4SJ Tel: (0870) 2434241 Fax: (01633) 270970 E-mail: info@countycontractors.co.uk

County Decorating, 134 Crossbrook Street, Cheshunt, Waltham Cross, Hertfordshire, EN8 8JH Tel: (01992) 628265 Fax: (01992) 628265 E-mail: countydecs_@cheshotmail.com *Building & painting suppliers*

County Engineering (Lincoln) Ltd, 23 Crofton Road, Allenby Industrial Estate, Lincoln, LN3 4NL Tel: (01522) 510753 Fax: (01522) 560497 E-mail: sales@county-engineering.co.uk *Catering equipment distributors*

County Engineering Southern Ltd, Unit 9, Annington Commercial Centre, Annington Road, Bramber, Steyning, West Sussex, BN44 3WA Tel: (01903) 879428 Fax: (01903) 815077 E-mail: ces@countyeng.demon.co.uk *Heat exchanger repairers*

County Engravers, 1 Newcombe Road, Northampton, NN5 7AZ Tel: (01604) 585565 Fax: (01604) 585565 E-mail: countyengrevers@supanet.com *Trophies & engraving service*

County Engravers & Signs, Unit 5 Trentview Court, Nottingham, NG2 3FX Tel: 0115-985 1171 Fax: 0115-986 1007 E-mail: sales@countyengravers-signs.co.uk *Industrial engravers & sign manufrs*

County Enterprises Sheltered Workshop, St Pauls Street, Worcester, WR1 2BA Tel: (01905) 23819 Fax: (01905) 27832 E-mail: countyentepriseS@worcestershire.gov.uk *General assembly work & packing*

County Fabrications Leicester Ltd, B1 Valley Way, Market Harborough, Leicestershire, LE16 7PS Tel: (01858) 433958 Fax: (01858) 410463 E-mail: contact@countyfabs.co.uk *Steel & stainless steel fabricators*

County Glass Ltd, Easton Lane, Winchester, Hampshire, SO23 7RU Tel: (01962) 869447 Fax: (01962) 841532 *Glass merchants*

County Glassware Ltd, 4 Faraday Court, Park Farm Industrial Estate, Wellingborough, Northamptonshire, NN8 6XY Tel: (01933) 402204 Fax: (01933) 400433 E-mail: sales@countyglassware.co.uk *Supplier of glassware & caterers*

County Heating Centre Ltd, 6-18 Dunstall Street, Scunthorpe, South Humberside, DN15 6LF Tel: (01724) 844872 Fax: (01724) 871197 *Builders merchants*

County Hire & Sales, Wymeswold Industrial Park, Wymeswold Road, Burton-on-the-Wolds, Loughborough, Leicestershire, LE12 5TY Tel: (01509) 881152 Fax: (01509) 889413 *Temporary accommodation sales*

County Hospital & Mortuary Equipment, 13 Westfield Crescent, Brighton, BN1 8JB Tel: (01273) 885441 Fax: (01273) 240954 E-mail: county@pavilion.co.uk *Mortuary refrigeration designers & suppliers*

County Industrial Supplies Ltd, County House, Chapel Street, Pontnewydd, Cwmbran, Gwent, NP44 1DL Tel: (01633) 872226 Fax: (01633) 864922 E-mail: cissales@aol.com *General engineering distributors* Also at: Merthyr

County Installations, 15 Moore Road, Church Crookham, Fleet, Hampshire, GU52 6JB Tel: (01252) 616093 Fax: (01252) 627755 E-mail: patlowe@countyinstallations.co.uk *Industrial door contractors & manufrs*

County Joinery, The Workshop, 13 Felpham Road, Bognor Regis, West Sussex, PO22 7AS Tel: (01243) 842714 E-mail: info@countyjoinery.co.uk *Joinery manufrs*

County Laboratories, 78 Sitwell Street, Spondon, Derby, DE21 7FG Tel: (01332) 678411 Fax: (01332) 678411 *Optical manufrs*

County Lifting Equipment & Safety Co Ltd, Unit 2 Telford Way, Telford Way Industrial Estate, Kettering, Northamptonshire, NN16 8UN Tel: (01536) 417878 Fax: (01536) 417877 *Fabricating lifting equipment hirers*

County Luxdon Laundry Ltd, 10 Wearfield, Sunderland Enterprise Park, Sunderland, SR5 2TZ Tel: 0191-548 7676 Fax: 0191-516 0648 E-mail: countyluxdonlaundry@tiscali.co.uk *Laundering & linen hire services*

County Offset, North Quays Business Park, Atlantic Street, Broadheath, Altrincham, Cheshire, WA14 5BF Tel: 0161-928 5333 Fax: 0161-927 7069 E-mail: sales@countyprint.com *Lithographic colour printers*

County Packaging Services Ltd, Unit 4, Adams Close, Heanor Gate Industrial Estate, Heanor, Derbyshire, DE75 7SW Tel: (01773) 535750 Fax: (01773) 535751 E-mail: info@countypack.co.uk *Suppliers of packaging & packaging machinery equipment*

County Pest Control, 54 Baxter Drive, Sheffield, S6 1GH Tel: 0114-285 3340 Fax: 0114-232 1977 *Pest control services*

County Pest Control, Greendale, East Allington, Totnes, Devon, TQ9 7RP Tel: (01548) 521388 Fax: (01548) 521326 *Pest control services*

County Pest Control Contracts, Thickthorn, Lower Shuckburgh, Daventry, Northamptonshire, NN11 6DX Tel: (01327) 705231 Fax: (01327) 878231 E-mail: cpc-contracts@mywebpage.net *Pest control & products*

▶ County Plumbimg and Heating, R/O, 33 High Street, Aveley, South Ockendon, Essex, RM15 4BE Tel: (01708) 861878

▶ County Plumbing & Heating, Unit 5 Norris Way, Norris Way Industrial Estate, Rushden, Northamptonshire, NN10 6BP Tel: (01933) 413055 Fax: (01933) 413002 E-mail: info@countyplumbingandheating.com *Installation, service & repair of f industrial heating equipment*

County Powder Coaters Ltd, Kemp House, Brunel Road, Earlstrees Industrial Estate, Corby, Northamptonshire, NN17 4AU Tel: (01536) 261082 Fax: (01536) 269163 *Powder coating services*

County Pre Cast Ltd, Sectional Building Centre, Maltings Industrial Estate, Maltings Road, Battlesbridge, Wickford, Essex, SS11 7RH Tel: (01268) 735261 Fax: (01268) 571575 E-mail: enquiries@countyprecast.co.uk *Sectional concrete garage manufrs*

County Press, County Press Buildings, Station Road, Bala, Gwynedd, LL23 7PG Tel: (01678) 520262 Fax: (01678) 521251 E-mail: budgerigarworld@msn.com *Printers & typesetters*

County Properties & Developments Ltd, 8-10 Hallcraig Street, Airdrie, Lanarkshire, ML6 6AH Tel: (01236) 757850 Fax: (01236) 757851 *Amusement machines distributors*

County Radiators Ltd, 21 Nobel Square, Burnt Mills Industrial Estate, Basildon, Essex, SS13 1LP Tel: (01268) 728314 Fax: (01268) 728314 *Radiator manufrs*

County Retail Services, 8 Grantham Road, Brighton, BN1 6EE Tel: (01273) 508858 Fax: (01273) 541853 *Cash registers*

County Ryan Ltd, Staveley Road, New Whittington, Chesterfield, Derbyshire, S43 2BZ Tel: (01246) 454649 Fax: (01246) 269033 *Conveyor belt supplier*

County Saddlery, New Street, Walsall, WS1 3DF Tel: (01922) 659080 Fax: (01922) 659089 E-mail: countysaddlery@btconnect.com *Saddle manufrs*

County Scales Ltd, Langley Business Park, Station Road, Langley Mill, NG16 4DG Tel: (0800) 7311774 Fax: (01773) 763222 *Industrial weighing specialists*

County Shopfitting Ltd, 7 Portsmouth Enterprise Centre, Quartermaine Road, Portsmouth, PO3 5QT Tel: (023) 9269 8365 Fax: (023) 9267 3647 E-mail: enquiries@countyshopfitting.co.uk *Shop equipment manufrs*

County Shutters & Grills Ltd, 8 Winstanley Way, Basildon, Essex, SS14 3BP Tel: (01268) 532048 Fax: (01268) 286161 E-mail: alison@countyshutters.com *Industrial door engineers & manufrs*

County Signs, Unit 13 Orchard Industrial Estate, Christen Way, Parkwood, Maidstone, Kent, ME15 9YE Tel: (01622) 672232 Fax: (01622) 752559 E-mail: mail@county-signs.co.uk *Sign manufrs*

County Windows, 22 Stephenson Road, St. Ives, Cambridgeshire, PE27 3WJ Tel: (01480) 461505 Fax: (01480) 494407 E-mail: enquiries@countywindows.com *Replacement window suppliers & installers*

County Windows (Winchester) Ltd, Units 3-4, Winchester, Hampshire, SO23 7RU Tel: (01962) 840780 Fax: (01962) 841532 E-mail: ian@county-glass.co.uk *Double glazed window manufrs*

▶ Countywide Entertainments, 63 Normandy Close, Exmouth, Devon, EX8 4PB Tel: (01395) 268263 E-mail: steve@countywideentertainments.co.uk *Karaoke, Disco & Pa equipment Hire,Laney Bear childrens parties,Wedding entertainments, Adult Entertainments, Strippers, Solo Acts, Duo''s Bands, Tribute Acts, Comedians, Hypnotists. If its entertainments then we can supply it.*

Clifford Coupe Ltd, 1 Royal Close, Worcester Park, Surrey, KT4 7JS Tel: (020) 8330 0660 Fax: (020) 8330 0660 *Food processing plant distributors*

▶ Coupe Construction, Station Lane, Birtley, Chester le Street, County Durham, DH2 1AW Tel: 0191-410 2177 Fax: 0191-410 6583 E-mail: general@coupeconst.plus.com

Coupe Foundry Ltd, The Foundry, Kittlingbourne Brow, Higher Walton, Preston, PR5 4DQ Tel: (01772) 338151 Fax: (01772) 627609 E-mail: reception@coupefoundry.co.uk *Iron founders*

Coupe Line Ltd, Hackworth Industrial Park, Shildon, County Durham, DL4 1HG Tel: (01388) 774040 Fax: (01388) 776010 *Whitelining*

Coupland Bell Ltd, Barclays Venture Centre University of Warwick, Science Park, Coventry, CV4 7EZ Tel: (01926) 777566 E-mail: info@couplandbell.com *Consulting engineers*

Courage & Co., Rye Hill Farm, Slaley, Hexham, Northumberland, NE47 0AH Tel: (01434) 673426 Fax: (01434) 673608 E-mail: info@consult-courage.co.uk *Computer consultants*

Courier Cars, 353 Norbury Avenue, London, SW16 3RW Tel: (020) 8764 4444 Fax: (020) 8679 5050 *Courier services*

▶ Courier Connect, McKean Road, Birmingham, B69 4BA Tel: (07813) 519 954 Fax: 0121-544 6231 E-mail: info@courierconnect.co.uk *As as established Sameday Nextday Birmingham courier service to many blue chip companies in the Birmingham, Wolverhampton, Walsall, Kidderminster, Solihull and midlands area, we have built a reputation based on quality of service and reliability to our customers as there preferred supplier*

▶ Courier Express, Unit 4, Blowick Business Park, Crowland Street, Southport, Merseyside, PR9 7RU Tel: (0870) 4644422 Fax: 0161-799 5940 E-mail: enquiries@refigeratedtransportuk.com

Courier Network Systems, K 301 Tower Bridge Business Complex, 100 Clements Road, London, SE16 4DG Tel: (020) 7231 9030 Fax: (020) 7231 9102 E-mail: yes@couriernetworks.co.uk *Couriers*

▶ Courier Please Ltd, Suite 44, 468 Walton Road, West Molesey, Surrey, KT8 8AE Tel: 07890 454428 Fax: 0208 3309859 E-mail: info@acourierplease.co.uk *Same day or Overnight Courier service covering all of UK and Europe at a resonable cost*

Coursamis Ltd, Unit 3 11 Tait Road, Croydon, CR0 2DP Tel: (020) 8684 7973 Fax: (020) 8684 6532 E-mail: sgv@csgroup.fsnet.co.uk *Traffic supplies & exporters*

Court Catering Equipment Limited, Units 1 & 2 Acton Vale Industrial Park, Cowley Road, London, W3 7QE Tel: (020) 8746 0808 Fax: (020) 8746 1116 E-mail: sales@courtcatering.co.uk *Court Catering equipment ltd have a wealth of experience in the design and project management of all types of commercial kitchens. Our range of products and services will meet your requirements whether you are looking to purchase individual items or as part of a complete kitchen design project. the range of catering equipment available includes gas and electric cooking appliances, servery counters, refrigeration and ventilation. Close associations with many manufacturers ensures that we can co-ordinate a scheme from design to completion, ensuring we furnish your kitchen to meet with your personal specifications. Services and maintenance contracts for both new and existing equipment can be arranged as required. Court Catering Equipment Ltd is a member of CEDACARE and is able to offer service nation-wide, when required.*

Court Consultancy Ltd, 5 Fairholme Avenue, Romford, RM2 5UP Tel: (01708) 704650 Fax: (01708) 438952 E-mail: ngs_tcc@yahoo.com *IT consultants*

The Court Hotel Bromley Ltd, Bromley Hill, Bromley, BR1 4JD Tel: (020) 8464 5011 Fax: (020) 8460 0899 E-mail: enquireys@bromleycourt.co.uk *Conference facilities restaurant licensed bar*

Court Management & Accounting Services, Court Ho, Hooe, Battle, East Sussex, TN33 9HJ Tel: (01424) 842600 Fax: (01424) 846161 *Computer consultants*

▶ Court Paving Ltd, 20 Princess Drive, Knaresborough, North Yorkshire, HG5 0AG Tel: (01423) 860641

Courtenay Stewart Ltd, 3 Hanover Square, London, W1S 1HB Tel: (0871) 2227616 Fax: (0871) 2227626 E-mail: sales@courtenayhr.com *Specialists in management selection*

Courtesy Cleaning Services Ltd, Courtesy House 35 Redburn Industrial Estate, Woodall Road, Enfield, Middlesex, EN3 4LQ Tel: (020) 8805 8586 Fax: (020) 8805 5868 *Contract cleaning services*

The Courthouse Project (Otley) Ltd, Courthouse Street, Otley, West Yorkshire, LS21 3AN Tel: (01943) 467216 Fax: (01943) 851033 E-mail: admin@courthousecredit.co.uk *Debt recovery & industrial collection services*

Courtney Bell Ltd, Lawson Road, Dartford, DA1 5BP Tel: (01322) 221833 Fax: (01322) 228581 *Mechanical & casting project engineers*

Courtney Contract Furnishers Ltd, J-K Unit Enterprise Centre, Paycocke Road, Basildon, Essex, SS14 3DY Tel: (01268) 531771 Fax: (01268) 271299 E-mail: sales@courtney-contracts.co.uk *Upholsterers & furniture manufrs*

Courtyard Consultants Ltd, 27 Lichfield St, Bilston, W. Midlands, WV14 0AQ Tel: 0121-609 7279 Fax: 0121-609 7001 E-mail: srudd@court.co.uk *Consultancy*

Courtyard Electronics Ltd, 13 Riverside Park, Dogflud Way, Farnham, Surrey, GU9 7UG Tel: (01252) 712030 Fax: (01252) 722060 E-mail: info@courtyard.co.uk *Manufacture broadcast television equipment*

▶ Cousins, 1 Towcester Road, London, E3 3ND Tel: (020) 7510 0037 *Metalwork fabrication services*

Cousins Dave, 42 The Roundway, Kingskerswell, Newton Abbot, Devon, TQ12 5BW Tel: (01803) 404431 Fax: (01803) 391998 E-mail: dcsigns@hotmail.com *Computer cut letters*

Cousins of Emneth Ltd, The Forge, Hungate Road, Emneth, Wisbech, Cambridgeshire, PE14 8DE Tel: (01945) 584600 Fax: (01945) 584616 E-mail: sales@cousinsofemneth.co.uk *Agricultural equipment manufrs*

Cousins Engineering, 23 Bunting Road, Northampton, NN2 6EE Tel: (01604) 712456 Fax: (01604) 719578 E-mail: sales@counsinsengineering.co.uk *CNC precision engineers*

Cousins & Wright, 5 The Halve, Trowbridge, Wiltshire, BA14 8SB Tel: (01225) 754242 *Photographic apparatus repairers*

Coutts & Findlater Ltd, 15-18 Hudson Road, Sunderland, SR1 2LL Tel: 0191-567 1291 Fax: 0191-564 0590 E-mail: john@jfwilsonshopfittersltd.fsnet.co.uk *Shop fitters & joinery manufrs*

Coutts Refrigeration, Blackhills, Peterhead, Aberdeenshire, AB42 3LJ Tel: (01779) 478074 Fax: (01779) 478074 *Refrigeration engineers*

Coutts Retail Communications Ltd, Golden House, Great Pulteney Street, London, W1F 9NN Tel: (020) 7534 8800 Fax: (020) 7534 8805 *Cardboard box & container manufrs*

▶ Couture Digital, Studio 12 & 13, 1b Darnley Road, London, E9 6QH Tel: (0870) 0429813 E-mail: info@couturedigital.com *Couture Digital specialise in bespoke design & installation of *home cinema, audio visual and automation systems in*residential and commercial properties throughout the UK.*

Cov Rad Heat Transfer, Canley Works, Sir Henry Parkes Road, Coventry, CV5 6BN Tel: (024) 7671 3316 Fax: (024) 7671 3316 E-mail: glen.hurst@covrad.co.uk *Heat exchanger manufrs*

Cov Tek Security Systems Ltd, 10 Captain Street, Coleraine, County Londonderry, BT52 2NJ Tel: (028) 7032 6166 Fax: (028) 7032 7225 E-mail: cctv@covtec.com *Security services*

Cova Products Ltd, Station Road, Cramlington, Northumberland, NE23 8AQ Tel: (01670) 718222 Fax: (01670) 590096 *Suppliers of PVC films*

Cove Ltd, 18 Invincible Road, Invinciblerial Road Industrial Estate, Farnborough, Hampshire, GU14 7QU Tel: (01252) 512919 Fax: (01252) 543384 E-mail: sales@cove-industries.co.uk *Manufacturers of plastic dip mouldings & handle grips. Also plastic coating services.*

Cove Workshop, 61 Gobbins Road, Islandmagee, Larne, County Antrim, BT40 3TY Tel: (028) 9335 3403 Fax: (028) 9335 3404 E-mail: sales@thechairmaker.com *Cabinet & chair makers*

Coveford Data Systems Ltd, Old Bank House, 59 High Street, Odiham, Hampshire, RG29 1LF Tel: (01256) 704333 Fax: (07031) 159754 E-mail: cds@coveford.com *Computer systems consultants & services*

▶ Covelec Electric Motor Sales, 1 171 Church Hill Road, Thurmaston, Leicester, LE4 8DH Tel: 0116-269 8111 Fax: 0116-269 8222 E-mail: enquires@covelec.co.uk *Electric motor manufrs*

▶ Covent Garden Connection, 18-20 York Buildings, London, WC2N 6JU Tel: 0207 8399700 Fax: 0207 8399720 E-mail: info@cgc.uk.com *Market Research Viewing Facility in the heart of the west end. 2 Studios and observation rooms. Also available for meeting hire.*

▶ Covent Garden Flower Emporium Ltd, 5 Thornhill Road, Cardiff, CF14 6PD Tel: (029) 2075 0750 Fax: (029) 2075 0757 E-mail: coventgardenfloweremporium@btconnect.com *Flowers & giftware retailers*

▶ Coventry Aquatics, 59, Winsford Avenue, Allesley Park, Coventry, CV5 9JG Tel: (024) 7667 7706 Fax: (024) 7667 5052 E-mail: sales@covaquatics.co.uk *Tropical & Cold Water Fish. All leading brand names & accessories. Aquariums & fully stocked showroom. Water testing and loads of free advice for the beginner or experianced fish keeper.*Pond pumps & filters plus loads of spares & accessories for all leading brand names.*

Coventry Boring & Metalling Co. Ltd, 3 Coniston Road, Coventry, CV5 6GU Tel: (024) 7667 2372 Fax: (024) 7667 9948 *Cylinder re-borers*

Coventry Building Supplies, 172a Holbrook Lane, Coventry, CV6 4BY Tel: (024) 7668 7172 Fax: (024) 7668 8172 *Builders' merchants*

Coventry Carbide Tools Ltd, 1 Telford Road, Bayton Road Industrial Estate, Coventry, CV7 9ES Tel: (024) 7636 5490 Fax: (024) 7636 5465 E-mail: asaptooling@btconnect.com *Tungsten carbide tool manufrs*

▶ Coventry Castings Ltd, Barlow Road, Aldermans Green Industrial Estate, Coventry, CV2 2LD Tel: (024) 7662 2092 Fax: (024) 7662 1917 E-mail: cast01@btconnect.com *Casting manufrs*

Coventry Chemicals Ltd, Woodhams Road, Siskin Drive, Coventry, CV3 4FX Tel: (024) 7663 9739 Fax: (024) 7663 9717 *Cleaning chemicals manufrs*

▶ Coventry Computer Repairs, 26 Canon Drive, Shilton, Coventry, CV7 9HJ Tel: (0870) 3834068 E-mail: info@coventrycomputerrepairs.co.uk *Computer Repairs, Computer Upgrades, Networking, Laptop Repairs*

Coventry Construction Ltd, Torrington Avenue, Coventry, CV4 9AP Tel: (024) 7646 2321 Fax: (024) 7669 4020 E-mail: info@covcon.co.uk *Structural engineers & steel fabricators*

Coventry Fencing, Castle Wynd, Auchterarder, Perthshire, PH3 1DA Tel: (01764) 662911 Fax: (01764) 664291 E-mail: c4fencing@aol.com *Fencing & industrial agricultural fencing suppliers*

Coventry Fencing, Carnwath Road, Carstairs Junction, Lanark, ML11 8RW Tel: (01555) 870494 Fax: (01555) 870941 *Fencing suppliers*

Coventry For Fencing, Station Yard, Oxton, Lauder, Berwickshire, TD2 6PR Tel: (01578) 750666 Fax: (01578) 750612 *Fencing manufrs*

Coventry Form Tools Ltd, 10 Cashs Lane, Coventry, CV1 4DS Tel: (024) 7622 2440 Fax: (024) 7622 8778 E-mail: coventryformtools@hotmail.co.uk *Form tool manufrs*

Coventry Grinders Ltd, 7 Alpha Business Park, Deedmore Road, Coventry, CV2 1EQ Tel: (024) 7660 4377 Fax: (024) 7660 4975 E-mail: info@coventry-grinders.co.uk *Steel stockholders*

Coventry Heat Treatment Ltd, Unit A-B, Brindley Road, Bayton Road Industrial Estate, Coventry, CV7 9EP Tel: (024) 7636 0099 Fax: (024) 7636 6222 E-mail: covheat@aol.com *Nitride hardening & heat treatment services*

Coventry Lifting Services Ltd, 19 Claverdon Road, Coventry, CV5 7HP Tel: (024) 7647 1972 Fax: (024) 7647 1972 *Lifting gear inspection, maintenance & repair service providers*

Coventry Nameplate Co., 5 Watercall Ave, Styvechale, Coventry, CV3 5AW Tel: (024) 7669 3212 Fax: (024) 7669 3288 E-mail: markcove@dsl.pipex.com *Manufacturers of nameplates (anodised aluminium) & labels including anodised aluminium & metal. Also nameplate production services*

Coventry Powder Coating, Unit 5-7 Bilton Industrial Estate, Humber Avenue, Coventry, CV3 1JL Tel: (024) 7645 4694 Fax: (024) 7645 4476 E-mail: info@cpc.co.uk *Powder coating contractors*

▶ Coventry Rewinds Ltd, Unit 3b Maguire Industrial Estate, 219 Torrington Avenue, Coventry, CV4 9HN Tel: (024) 7646 7960 Fax: (024) 7647 1460 E-mail: coventryrewinds@btopenworld.com *Rewinds to electric motors, pumps, transformers*

Coventry Toolholders Ltd, Grovelands Estate, Longford Road, Exhall, Coventry, CV7 9ND Tel: (024) 7664 5999 Fax: (024) 7664 4081 E-mail: info@coventrytoolholders.co.uk *CNC toolholding & machine tool manufrs*

▶ Coventry Trophy Centre, 4 Cedars Avenue, Coventry, CV6 1DR Tel: (024) 7659 2022 Fax: (024) 7659 2022 E-mail: coventrytrophies@yahoo.co.uk *Suppliers of trophies & corporate awards*

Coventry Turned Parts Ltd, Wedgenock Industrial Estate, Warwick, CV34 5PZ Tel: (01926) 491583 Fax: (01926) 410583 *Engineers*

David Cover & Son Ltd, Sussex House, Quarry Lane, Chichester, West Sussex, PO19 8PE Tel: (01243) 785141 Fax: (01243) 531151 E-mail: enquiries@covers-group.co.uk *Timber merchant*

Cover Press Ltd, Unit 119 J C Albyn Complex, Burton Road, Sheffield, S3 8BZ Tel: 0114-276 5867 Fax: 0114-276 5867 *General engineering & presswork*

Cover Up Clothing Ltd, 122-128 Arlington Road, London, NW1 7HP Tel: (020) 7267 9222 Fax: (020) 7267 8868 *Clothing manufrs*

Coverad Ltd, The Brows, Farnham Road, Liss, Hampshire, GU33 6JG Tel: (01730) 893393 Fax: (01730) 893696 *Radiator cover manufrs*

Covercat Spray Systems, 2 Whorlton Road, Riverside Park, Middlesbrough, Cleveland, TS2 1QJ Tel: (01642) 243844 Fax: (01642) 240343 E-mail: sales@covercat.com *Paint spraying equipment manufrs*

The Coverdale Organisation Ltd, Plestowes Farm, Hareway Lane, Barford, Warwick, CV35 8DD Tel: (01926) 625757 Fax: (01926) 625758 E-mail: info@coverdale.com *Management consultants*

Coverguard, 8 Flanders Park, Hedge End, Southampton, SO30 2FZ Tel: 01489 776 022 Fax: 01489 775 015 E-mail: info@coverguard.com *cover guard® is an integrated range of flame retardant products used to protect vertical and horizontal surfaces, and to wrap objects during construction, work activity, transportation and storage. It is extensively used in the construction industry, both marine and land based, during new build, refurbishment, refitting and maintenance.***

Coverite Air Conditioning Services Ltd, Unit 17 Coldart Business Centre, Dartford, DA1 2HZ Tel: (01322) 270989 Fax: (01322) 278203 E-mail: info@coverite-ac.co.uk *Air conditioning engineers* Also at: London SE25

Coverlite Blinds & Awnings, 9-11 Hanover Street, Bolton, BL1 4TG Tel: (01204) 364444 Fax: (01204) 397232 *Roller & shop blind manufrs*

Covers, Unit 1, Home Farm Business Centre Home Farm Road, Brighton, BN1 9HU Tel: (01273) 607044 Fax: (01273) 685208 *Timber & builders merchants* Also at: Burgess Hill, Chichester, Cooksbridge & Havant

Covershield Lighting Consultants, 10 Heatons Bridge Road, Scarisbrick, Ormskirk, Lancashire, L40 8JG Tel: (01704) 841073 Fax: (01704) 841362 E-mail: sales@covershield.co.uk *Specialised lighting for food*

▶ Covert Surveillance & Investigations, 107 Brookdale Road, Liverpool, L15 3JF Tel: 0151-222 1188 Fax: 0151-222 1188 E-mail: enquiries@csilimited.co.uk *Private investigators that operate throughout the whole of the UK. We offer the following services - Internal & Corporate Investigations, Process Serving, Matrimonial Surveillance, Debtor Tracing, Staff Absenteeism, Staff Training, Employee Background & Reference Checking and Security Consultations.*

▶ Covertec Wigan, Unit 3-4 Richard Street, Ince, Wigan, Lancashire, WN3 4JN Tel: (01942) 231377 Fax: (01942) 231377 *Tarpaulin manufrs*

Covertech Plastics, Springfield Commerical Centre, Bagley Lane, Farsley, Pudsey, West Yorkshire, LS28 5LY Tel: 0113-255 2288 Fax: 0113-255 2381 E-mail: enquiries@cover-techleeds.co.uk *Banner & industrial cover manufrs*

Coverthem Ltd, PO Box 47, Waterlooville, Hampshire, PO8 9TE Tel: (023) 9257 1612 Fax: (023) 9257 1612 E-mail: coverthem@btinternet.com *Print house & safety labels*

▶ The Coverworks, Dartside Quay, Galmpton Creek, Galmpton, Brixham, Devon, TQ5 0EH Tel: (01803) 844003 E-mail: james@thecoverworks.eclipse.co.uk *specialising in the manufacture and repair of marine and 4x4 covers. Call for a quote, or come down to the workshop for more information.*

▶ Coverworld UK Ltd, Mansfield Road, Bramley Vale, Chesterfield, Derbyshire, S44 5GA Tel: (01246) 454711 Fax: (01246) 858223 E-mail: sales@coverworld.co.uk *Cladding services*

Covflex Hydraulic & Engineering Co. Ltd, Rowleys Green Industrial Estate, Rowleys Green Lane, Coventry, CV6 6AN Tel: (024) 7668 8714 Fax: (024) 7668 8720 E-mail: sales@covflex.freeserve.co.uk *Hydraulic couplings & hose assemblies manufrs*

Cowal Mobility Aid Ltd, Cowal Court, Heath End Road, Great Kingshill, High Wycombe, Buckinghamshire, HP15 6HL Tel: (01494) 714400 Fax: (01494) 714818 E-mail: sales@cowalmobility.co.uk *Vehicle adaptations for disabled people*

Cowan Architects Ltd, 9-10 Old Stone Link, Ship Street, East Grinstead, West Sussex, RH19 4EF Tel: (01342) 410242 Fax: (01342) 313493 E-mail: info@cowan-architects.co.uk *Architectural & design services*

Cowan Bros, 11 Monnaboy Road, Eglinton, Londonderry, BT47 3AZ Tel: (028) 7181 0699 Fax: (028) 7181 1429 *Agriculture machinery suppliers*

▶ Cowan Construction Ltd, 144 Greaves Road, Lancaster, LA1 4UW Tel: (01524) 63954 Fax: (01524) 849118

▶ Cowan & Linn, 53 Morrison Street, Glasgow, G5 8LB Tel: 0141-429 2980

▶ Cowan Print, 23 Brougham Street, Edinburgh, EH3 9JS Tel: 0131-622 1000 Fax: 0131-622 2121

T.A. Cowap & Co. Ltd, Hazel Grove Works, Guy Edge, Linthwaite, Huddersfield, HD7 5TQ Tel: (01484) 851177 Fax: (01484) 648798 E-mail: lisa@tacowap.com *Fire protection engineers*

▶ Cowden Consulting Ltd, Ruthin House, Southgate, Eckington, Sheffield, S21 4FT Tel: (07786) 068477 Fax: (01246) 432237 E-mail: enquiries@cowdenconsulting.com *Strategic planning consultancy from idea development to bringing home the bacon. Cowden provides full accounting and financial systems implementation. Our aim is to put business owners in the driving seat of their business.*

Cowell Export, Marsh Green, Edenbridge, Kent, TN8 5QL Tel: (01732) 864211 Fax: (01732) 863106 E-mail: mail@bobcowell.co.uk *Cable installation & winch equipment exporters*

▶ Cowen Builders Ltd, 21 Benbow Drive, South Woodham Ferrers, Chelmsford, CM3 5FP Tel: (01245) 324276 Fax: (01245) 324174

Cowen Signs, 65 Old Chester Road, Birkenhead, Merseyside, CH41 9AW Tel: 0151-647 8081 Fax: 0151-666 1087 E-mail: sales@cowen-signs.co.uk *Signs, nameplate suppliers & manufrs*

Cowens Ltd, Ellers Mill, Dalston, Carlisle, CA5 7QJ Tel: (01228) 710205 Fax: (01228) 710331 E-mail: info@cowens.co.uk Purchasing Contact: J. Coulthard Sales Contact: J. Coulthard Principal Export Areas: Worldwide *Cowens Ltd provide expert solutions for all your health, safety and environmental issues Environmental: Pollution control hardware (booms, skimmers, pumps, separators, tanks, Oil detection, Portable bunds) and spill clean-up consumables. Cowens are also level 3 accredited oil spill response contractors. They have a contaminated land division for desk studies, intrusive site investigations and ground & groundwater remediation services. Safety: Fire barriers and fireproof fillings and linings; air/gas filter media; liquid filters and separators; protective waddings and felts; chemical storage and transfer equipment; personal protective equipment; intrinsically safe pumps; chemical absorbents; biological cleaning agents and solvent-free degreasers. Health: Medical, pharmaceutical, cosmetic and veterinary cotton wools, bandages and absorbents. NHS, wholesale and retail. Factory shop, mail order and export.*

▶ Cowern Transport, Unit 1-2 Building 13, Stanmore Industrial Estate, Bridgnorth, Shropshire, WV15 5HP Tel: (01746) 763848 Fax: (01746) 769760 E-mail: sales@clivecowerntransport.co.uk

▶ Cowes Floating Bridge, Ferry Office, Medina Road, Cowes, Isle of Wight, PO31 7BX Tel: (01983) 293041 Fax: (01983) 293041

Cowfold Precision Engineering, Oakendene Industrial Estate, Bolney Road, Cowfold, Horsham, West Sussex, RH13 8AZ Tel: (01403) 864945 Fax: (01403) 864945 E-mail: cowfold.precision@blueyonder.co.uk *Precision & sub-contract engineers*

Cowill Construction 1989 Ltd, The Mill, Congleton Road, Talke, Stoke-on-Trent, ST7 1NE Tel: (01782) 785319 Fax: (01782) 775404 E-mail: office@cowill89.freeserve.co.uk *Suspended ceilings contractors*

Cowley Components Ltd, Masons Road, Stratford-upon-Avon, Warwickshire, CV37 9NF Tel: 0117-963 7142 Fax: (01789) 415623 *Domestic appliance spare parts, LP & Natural gas & electric.*Cookers, boilers, fires, water heaters.*

Cowley Fire, 29 Arkwright Court, Blackpool & Fylde Industrial Estate, Blackpool, FY4 5DR Tel: (01253) 769666 Fax: (01253) 769888 E-mail: info@cowleyfire.co.uk *BAFE & ISO 9001:2000 registered, for the sales, rental, installation & maintenance of fire extinguishers, also suppliers of signage & all other associated fire protection products*

William Cowley, 97 Caldecote Street, Newport Pagnell, Buckinghamshire, MK16 0DB Tel: (01908) 610038 Fax: (01908) 611071 *Parchment & vellum makers*

Cowlin Construction Ltd, Stratton House, 39 Cater Road, Bristol, BS13 7UH Tel: 0117-983 2000 Fax: 0117-987 7758 E-mail: bristol@cowlin.co.uk *Building contractors & developers* Also at: Cardiff, Usk & Wincanton

Cowlin Construction, 5 Armtech Row, Houndstone Business Park, Yeovil, Somerset, BA22 8RW Tel: (01935) 423131 Fax: (01935) 847680 *Building contractors*

Henry Cowls & Sons, Gilly Gabben Industrial Estate, Mawgan, Helston, Cornwall, TR12 6BB Tel: (01326) 221514 Fax: (01326) 221382 *Horticultural, garden & fishing net manufrs*

Cowper Shaw Locksmiths Ltd, 33-34 Blandford Street, Sunderland, SR1 3JJ Tel: 0191-567 2882 Fax: 0191-564 0383 *Security installation contractors & locksmiths* Also at: Southwick

Cox Accommodation, Haydock Lane, Haydock Industrial Estate, Haydock, St. Helens, Merseyside, WA11 9UQ Tel: (01942) 727284 Fax: (01942) 271064 *Hire portable accommodation*

▶ Alan Cox Consultancy, 28 Hitchin Road, Letchworth Garden City, Hertfordshire, SG6 3LU Tel: (01462) 682080 E-mail: alan_cox_consultant@yahoo.co.uk

▶ Cox & Allen (Kendal) Ltd, Unit 3, Shap Road, Shap Road Industrial Estate, Kendal, Cumbria, LA9 6NZ Tel: (01539) 733533

Cox Auto Electrical, 10 Abeles Way, Holly Lane Industrial Estate, Atherstone, Warwickshire, CV9 2QZ Tel: (01827) 718484 Fax: (01827) 712097 E-mail: enquiries@coxautomotive.co.uk *Auto electricians*

Cox Braithwaite, Park House, Greyfriars Road, Cardiff, CF10 3AF Tel: (029) 2023 2148 Fax: (029) 2037 3687 E-mail: coxbr@coxbraithwaite.co.uk *Insurance brokers*

Cox Building Products Ltd, Shaw Road, Bushbury, Wolverhampton, WV10 9LA Tel: (01902) 371800 Fax: (01902) 371810 E-mail: sales@coxbp.com *Roof light & window*

Dave Cox, 43 Ingrave Road, Brentwood, Essex, CM15 8AZ Tel: (01277) 228240 Fax: (01277) 228240 *Blinds shutters & garage door services*

Cox Geo J Ltd, Westfield Road, Wellingborough, Northamptonshire, NN8 3HD Tel: (01933) 224181 Fax: (01933) 277892 E-mail: info@georgecox.co.uk *Men's footwear suppliers*

Cox Hire Centre, Cromwell Road, Bredbury, Stockport, Cheshire, SK6 2RP Tel: 0161-430 4324 Fax: 0161-494 5686 *Contractors' plant hire* Also at: St. Helens

Cox, John Car & Commercial, 23A Mansfield Road, Sheffield, S12 2AE Tel: 0114-239 8228 *Commercial body painters*

Cox Long Ltd, Airfield Industrial Estate, Hixon, Stafford, ST18 0PA Tel: (01889) 270166 Fax: (01889) 271041 E-mail: info@coxlong.com *Timber merchants & stockists*

Cox Orthopaedic, 108 Whitechapel Road, London, E1 1JD Tel: (020) 7247 1178 Fax: (020) 7247 0622 E-mail: enquiries@coxortho.com *Disabled orthopaedic appliances/aids* Also at: Coulsdon

Peter Cox Ltd, 53 Cuckoo Road, Birmingham, B7 5SY Tel: 0121-326 6434 Fax: 0121-326 7242 E-mail: petercox.birmingham@ecolab.com *Timber suppliers*

▶ Peter Cox Ltd, Suite 5, Keynes House, Alfreton Road, Derby, DE21 4AS Tel: (01332) 299222 Fax: (01332) 200066 *Damp proofing & pest repellant manufrs*

▶ Peter Cox Ltd, Unit 1, Marybank Lane, Dundee, DD2 3DY Tel: (01382) 400242 Fax: (01382) 400262 E-mail: petercox.dundee@ecolab.com *Preservation company*

▶ Peter Cox Ltd, John O Gaunts Trading Estate, Leeds Road, Rothwell, Leeds, LS26 0JB Tel: 0113-282 5316 Fax: 0113-393 4927 E-mail: petercox.leeds@ecolab.com *Preservations company*

▶ Peter Cox Ltd, Unit M, Orchard Business Centre, St. Barnabas Close, Allington, Maidstone, Kent, ME16 0JZ Tel: (01622) 750081 Fax: (01622) 750083 *Timber preservation & damp proofing*

Peter Cox Ltd, Unit 35, Viewforth Industrial Estate, The Loan, South Queensferry, West Lothian, EH30 9NS Tel: 0131-331 5030 Fax: 0131-319 1635 E-mail: peter.cox@ecolab.com *Providers of repair solutions*

Peter Cox Ltd, Falcon House, Oakhurst Drive, Stockport, Cheshire, SK3 0XT Tel: 0161-491 3181 Fax: 0161-428 8138

Cox & Plant Products Ltd, Monument Works, Balds Lane, Stourbridge, West Midlands, DY9 8SE Tel: (01384) 895121 Fax: (01384) 893611 E-mail: convey@cox-plant.com *Food Processing equipment manufacturer which can be supplied from a single vibratory conveyor through to a full bespoke turn key project to suit the customer needs*

▶ Cox Plastics, Unit 1, Brooklands Way, Boldon Business Park, Boldon Colliery, Tyne & Wear, NE35 9LZ Tel: 0191-537 7000

Cox Plastics, Kingfisher Way, Sowton Industrial Estate, Exeter, EX2 7LE Tel: (01392) 439701 Fax: (01392) 444017 E-mail: cox.southwest@coxplastics.co.uk *Plastic materials, products & components*

▶ Cox Plastics Technologies Ltd, Weedon Road Industrial Estae, Northampton, NN5 5AX Tel: (01604) 752200 Fax: (01604) 752266 E-mail: info@arkplastics.co.uk *Plastics injection mouldings, assembly services*

Ron Cox, 24 Shoebury Road, Great Wakering, Southend-on-Sea, SS3 0BW Tel: (01702) 218418 *Industrial furniture manufrs*

Cox Thermoforming Ltd, Unit 4, Icknield Way Industrial Estate, Tring, Herts, HP23 4JX Tel: (01442) 891055 Fax: (01442) 890967 E-mail: sales@cwpl.net Sales Contact: A.J. Mitchell *Technical thermoforming specialists, based in Wokingham, Berkshire, with additional manufacturing facility in Tring, Hertfordshire, covering the whole of the UK through our team of local sales engineers. The new company, name was born when "Wokingham Plastics Ltd" acquired "Cox Thermoforming Ltd". The new alliance of these two long-established companies forms an industry leading capability for vacuum forming, rotary forming, pressure forming, press forming, drape forming, free blown moulding, line bending, CNC machining, assembly and finishing. All carried out in our ISO 9001:2000 accredited factories, with comprehensive post moulding services such as printing, painting, distort screen printing and special coatings. With our comprehensive CAD/CAM facilities and in-house tooling design and manufacture we can offer a complete solution for all your thermoforming needs, from prototyping to production at cost-effective prices for high quality components with reliable service.*

Coxhire Ltd, Lower Walsall Street, Wolverhampton, WV1 2EX Tel: (01902) 351407 Fax: (01902) 453062 *Plant hire*

▶ Coxmoor Electrical Services Ltd, 14-16 Diamond Avenue, Kirkby-in-Ashfield, Nottingham, NG17 7GR Tel: (01623) 722366 Fax: (01623) 722365

Coxon E & J, 10 Park Road, Stonehouse, Gloucestershire, GL10 2DE Tel: (01453) 827100 Fax: (01453) 827100 E-mail: eric@ejcoxon.co.uk *Computer services*

Cox's Boatyard Ltd, Staithe Road, Barton Turf, Norwich, NR12 8AZ Tel: (01692) 536206 Fax: (01692) 536206 E-mail: info@coxsboatyard.co.uk *Boat builders & repairers & moorings*

▶ Coxs Tackle, Unit 120, 122 The Commercial Centre, Picket Piece, Andover, Hampshire, SP11 6LU Tel: (01264) 333170 Fax: (01264) 333170 *Fishing tackle retailers*

Coyle Fabrications, Culdee House, Culdee Drive, Armagh, BT61 7RJ Tel: (028) 3752 3753 Fax: (028) 3751 1526 E-mail: info@coylefabrications.com *Ironwork (ornamental)*

P.J. Coyne Ltd, Unit 4A Huckers Buildings, Long Acre Street, Walsall, WS2 8HP Tel: (01922) 646511 Fax: (01922) 639544 *Bridle & saddle manufrs*

▶ Coynet UK Ltd, 18 Argyle Street, Stonehouse, Larkhall, Lanarkshire, ML9 3LL Tel: (01698) 792711

▶ Cozeebee, Unit 49, Vinehall Business Centre, Vinehall Road, Robertsbridge, East Sussex, TN32 5JW Tel: 01424 871434 E-mail: sales@cozeebee.co.uk *Cozeebee provides nursing cushions for expectant mums and nursing mothers. Filled with thousands of tiny micro-beads our high quality positioning cushions provide comfort during pregnancy and assist breast feeding.*

Cozens & Cole Ltd, Spring Road, Ettingshall, Wolverhampton, WV4 6JT Tel: (01902) 405971 Fax: (01902) 497021 E-mail: sales@cozensandcole.co.uk *Transmission & conveyor belting manufrs*

Cozens Smith, The Common, Cranleigh, Surrey, GU6 8SB Tel: (01483) 273131 Fax: (01483) 268238 *Steel fabrications*

Cozier's Ltd, Littlebrook, Llangolman, Clynderwen, Dyfed, SA66 7XL Tel: (01437) 532660 Fax: (01437) 532670 E-mail: sales@coziers-ltd.co.uk Principal Export Areas: Worldwide *Heating element & thermocouple*

▶ Cozyslide, 208 Bruce Road, London, E3 3EU Tel: (07795) 967321 Fax: (020) 8981 3807 *Manufacturers & installers of fitted wardrobes*

▶ CP Computers, 21 The Inlands, Daventry, Northants, NN11 4DD Tel: 01327 702182 Fax: 0871 2398138 E-mail: c.palmer@lycos.co.uk *CP Computers offers new computers, repairs, maintenance, virus and spyware removals and tuition.*

CP Films Solutia UK Ltd, Chadwick Road, Astmoor Industrial Estate, Runcorn, Cheshire, WA7 1PW Tel: (01928) 580508 Fax: (01928) 580100 E-mail: sales.runcorn@cpfilms.co.uk *Specialised coating & laminating services*

CP Holdings Ltd, C P House, Otterspool Way, Watford, WD25 8HG Tel: (01923) 250500 Fax: (01923) 221628 E-mail: someone@cpholdingsltd.com *Holding company*

CPCR, The Charcoal, Blagdon Estate, Seaton Burn, Newcastle upon Tyne, NE13 6DB Tel: (01670) 785100 Fax: (01670) 785108 E-mail: people@cpcr.co.uk *Human resource consultants*

CPD Distribution, 8 Commerce Way, Trafford Park, Manchester, M17 1HW Tel: 0161-874 5311 Fax: 0161-874 5312 E-mail: mikejennion@cpdplc.co.uk *Interior supplies, ceilings & partitions contractors*

Cpio Ltd, Arden House The Courtyard, Gorsey Lane, Coleshill, Birmingham, B46 1JA Tel: (01675) 467046 Fax: (01675) 467682 E-mail: rcf@cpio.co.uk *Computer tetra resellers*

CPL Distibution, Holly House, Fen Road, Donington, Spalding, Lincolnshire, PE11 4XE Tel: (01775) 820403 Fax: (01775) 822396 *Coal merchants*

CPM Mobile Marketing, Unit 3 Newby Road Industrial Estate, Levens Road, Hazel Grove, Stockport, Cheshire, SK7 5DA Tel: 0161-483 5319 Fax: 0161-483 5375 E-mail: enquiries@mmcpm.co.uk *Mobile exhibition specialists, experiential specialists*

CPM Moulds Solutions Ltd, Pattison House, Addison Road, Chesham, Buckinghamshire, HP5 2BD Tel: (01494) 782131 Fax: (01494) 778542 E-mail: precision@chesham-moulds.co.uk *Plastic & injection mould toolmakers*

CPP-LM Ltd, 38 Swaisland Drive, Crayford, Dartford, DA1 4HS Tel: (01322) 551940 Fax: (01322) 550212 E-mail: info@cpp-lm.com *Injection moulders*

CPS Ltd, Unit 15D, Brackla Street Centre, Bridgend, Mid Glamorgan, CF31 1DD Tel: (01656) 662347 Fax: (01656) 662329 E-mail: sales@cps-uk.co.uk *Computer repairs & resellers*

CPS, 53 Bank Top Road, Rotherham, South Yorkshire, S65 3DY Tel: (01709) 543338 Fax: (01709) 543338 *Shelving & storage equipment services*

CPS Interiors Ltd, 1 Prince William Way, Loughborough, Leicestershire, LE11 5DD Tel: (01509) 230429 Fax: (01509) 610617 E-mail: cpsinteriors@btconnect.com *Partitioning contractors & interior contractors*

CPS Supply Co. Ltd, 5 Riverside Road, London, SW17 0BA Tel: (020) 8944 9016 Fax: (020) 8944 9018 *Disposable paper & glass products wholesalers & distributors*

Cpu Holders 4 U, Drury Lane, St. Leonards-on-Sea, East Sussex, TN38 9BA Tel: (01424) 439385 Fax: (01424) 718572 E-mail: sales@cpuholders4u.com *4U retails ergonomic cpu holders suppliers*

CPV Ltd, Woodington Mill, Woodington Road, East Wellow, Romsey, Hampshire, SO51 6DQ Tel: (01794) 322884 Fax: (01794) 322885 E-mail: sales@cpv.co.uk *Founded in 1948, CPV Ltd is an established specialist in processing thermoplastics and providing engineering solutions. CPV operates across a multitude of markets from industrial/process to civil and building services applications. **Product ranges include: **Chemflo - Polypropylene and PVDF pressure pipe systems*CPV-Zurn - Laboratory and chemical waste systems*Floway - Underground chemical drainage systems*CPV-Safeflo - Dual containment pipe systems*Hiline - Pre-insulated pipe systems*CPV-Bulk - Thermoplastic tanks, vessels and fabrications*Suncell - Solar heating for swimming pools*Custom thermoplastic extrusions, mouldings and fabrications.**In addition to CPV"s standard products, CPV can offer custom and bespoke solutions to many customer requirements.*

▶ CR Building Services Ltd, 24 Percival Lane, Runcorn, Cheshire, WA7 4UX Tel: (01928) 565069 Fax: (01928) 560297 *Engineering*

CR Smith, Gardeners Street, Dunfermline, Fife, KY12 0RN Tel: (01383) 732181 Fax: (01383) 739095 E-mail: admin@crsmith.co.uk *Windows, doors & conservatories manufrs*

▶ The CR Supply Co., 44 Chapelfield Way, Rotherham, South Yorkshire, S61 2TL Tel: (07967) 990598 E-mail: ralph@crsupply.co.uk *Electronic components*

▶ Crabb Engineering Ltd, 12 Aber Park, Aber Road, Flint, Clwyd, CH6 5EX Tel: (01352) 762121 Fax: (01352) 763040 E-mail: sales@crabbengineering.co.uk *Sub-contractors in engineering*

Crabtree Cottage Interiors, 24 Shore Road, Enniskillen, County Fermanagh, BT74 7EF Tel: (028) 6632 4333 Fax: (028) 6632 0819 *Furniture & gift manufrs*

Crabtree & Evelyn Trading Ltd, 9 The Podium, Northgate Street, Bath, BA1 5AL Tel: (01225) 481519 Fax: (01225) 329477 *Toiletries & fine food retailers*

Crabtree & Evelyn Trading Ltd, Bentalls Shopping Centre, Wood Street, Kingston upon Thames, Surrey, KT1 1TP Tel: (020) 8974 9610 *Toiletries*

Crabtree & Evelyn Trading Ltd, 134 Kings Road, London, SW3 4XB Tel: (020) 7589 6263 Fax: (020) 7584 7746 *Toiletries distributors & retailers*

Crabtree & Evelyn Trading Ltd, Kelso Place, London, W8 5QG Tel: (020) 7361 0499 Fax: (020) 7361 0498 E-mail: london@crabtree-evelyn.co.uk *Toiletries supplier & food distributors* Also at: Branches throughout the U.K.

Crabtree & Evelyn Trading Ltd, The Oracle Centre, Reading, RG1 2AG Tel: 0118-950 8843 Principal Export Areas: Worldwide *Toiletries suppliers*

Crabtree Sports & Leisure Ltd, Ebor Mills, Ebor Lane, Haworth, Keighley, West Yorkshire, BD22 8HS Tel: (01535) 640000 Fax: (01535) 640044 E-mail: info@acornsport.co.uk *Cycle & accessory distributor*

Crabtree Textile Machines Ltd, Norman Road, Oswaldtwistle, Accrington, Lancashire, BB5 4NF Tel: (01254) 304410 Fax: (01254) 304415 E-mail: info@crabtreelooms.com *Loom manufrs*

▶ T. Cracknell Haulage, Ashgrove Farm, Main Road, Nether Kellet, Carnforth, Lancashire, LA6 1EF Tel: (01524) 727602 E-mail: tcracknellhaulage@hotmail.co.uk *T cracknell Haulage operates weekly trailers to Belgium and Holland from the north west.*full loads/groupage service.Fast reliable service*

▶ Craddock Engineering Ltd, 7 Hall Lane, Walsall Wood, Walsall, WS9 9AS Tel: (01543) 454572 Fax: (01543) 454585

▶ Craddock Security Systems, 11 Daisy Close, Corby, Northamptonshire, NN18 8LD Tel: (01536) 741361 Fax: (01536) 741644 *Security services*

Cradle Access Services Ltd, PO Box 70, Erith, Kent, DA8 3WY Tel: (01322) 345999 Fax: (01322) 345999 E-mail: cradle.access@btconnect.com *Cradle systems installers & manufrs*

▶ Cradle & All, 28 Rockingham Road, Kettering, Northamptonshire, NN16 8JS Tel: (01536) 410006 Fax: (01536) 410006 E-mail: sales@cradleandall.ltd.uk *Nursery good suppliers*

▶ Cradley Digital Imaging, Chester Road, Cradley Heath, West Midlands, B64 6AB Tel: (01384) 414110

Cradley Heath Army Stores, 1 Upper High Street, Cradley Heath, West Midlands, B64 5HX Tel: (01384) 560796 Fax: (01384) 560796 *Work wear distribution*

Craemer UK Ltd, Craemer House, Hortonwood 1, Telford, Shropshire, TF1 7GN Tel: (01952) 641366 Fax: (01952) 607801 E-mail: sales@craemer.co.uk *Craemer, one of the first plastic pallet manufacturers in Europe, is now the leading plastic pallet provider internationally. Offering an extensive range of plastic pallets, Craemer have successfully supplied millions of plastic pallets to handling and storage systems worldwide. Craemer plastic pallets are the most durable plastic pallets available today.*

▶ Craft Bakers, 4 Empress Road, Newcastle upon Tyne, NE6 3NW Tel: 0191-234 2754 Fax: 0191-234 2764 E-mail: sales@craftbakery.co.uk *Wholesale bakers*

▶ Craft Corner, Velco House, The Square, Knottingley, West Yorkshire, WF11 8ND Tel: (01977) 607007 Fax: (01977) 607007

▶ Craft Daft, 9 Castle Parade, Bournemouth, BH7 6SH Tel: (01202) 488411 *Art material suppliers*

Craft Data, 92 Broad Street, Chesham, Buckinghamshire, HP5 3ED Tel: (01494) 778235 Fax: (01494) 773645 E-mail: sales@craftdata.co.uk *Craft Data Ltd. a family company, has been a distributor of electronic displays and thermal printers since 1982. We work with some of the worlds leading manufacturers of Passive Liquid Crystal, Colour TFT and OLED displays plus Thermal Printers and Touch Overlays.*

Craft Engineering, Unit 21 Huffwood Trading Estate, Billingshurst, West Sussex, RH14 9UR Tel: (01403) 784603 Fax: (01403) 784603 *General engineering*

Craft Engineering International Ltd, Lower Granby Street, Ilkeston, Derbyshire, DE7 8DJ Tel: 0115-932 2810 Fax: 0115-944 0048 E-mail: sales@craftex.co.uk *Machinery spare manufrs*

▶ Craft Fairy, 8 Park View, Coychurch, Bridgend, Mid Glamorgan, CF35 5HS Tel: (01656) 653796 E-mail: yvonne@craftfairy.co.uk *Suppliers of craft & card making materials*

Craft Kits UK Ltd, Hounslow, TW3 4RE Tel: (020) 8814 2227 Fax: (020) 8814 1367 *Craft & hobby suppliers*

▶ Craft Magic, Conduit Hill, Rye, East Sussex, TN31 7LE Tel: (01797) 226920 Fax: (01424) 755599 *Craft Magic offers one stop shopping for all of your crafting needs. From Card Making to Jewellery Making with so much in between! We also run studio classes for children and adults as well as hosting Childrens birthday parties!*

Craft Metal Products, Unit 18 Birksland Industrial Estate, Bradford, West Yorkshire, BD4 8TY Tel: (01274) 731531 Fax: (01274) 731531 *Precision machinists*

Craft Metal Spinning (Warrington) Ltd, Howley Tannery, Howley Lane, Warrington, WA1 2DN Tel: (01925) 630985 Fax: (01925) 235187 E-mail: craft@metalspinning.co.uk *Deep drawn pressings, light fabrication & welding services*

Craft Packs, Unit 3 Axis Park, Fort Fareham Industrial Site, Fareham, Hampshire, PO14 1FD Tel: (01329) 238282 Fax: (01329) 234550 E-mail: sales@craftpacks.co.uk *Educational equipment & supplies. Class room materials. Fete & Fundraisinf supplies.*

Craft Signs, 1 Hermitage Lane, Mansfield, Nottinghamshire, NG18 5HA Tel: (01623) 626166 Fax: (01623) 420977 *Sign makers*

Craft Supplies Ltd, Newburgh Works, Netherside, Bradwell, Hope Valley, Derbyshire, S33 9NT Tel: (01433) 622550 Fax: (01433) 622552 E-mail: sales@craft-supplies.co.uk *Exotic timbers & woodwork training services*

▶ Keith Crafter Agencies, 8 Cause End Road, Wootton, Bedford, MK43 9DA Tel: (01234) 766014 Fax: (01234) 766014 E-mail: jim@kcaclosures.co.uk *Specialists in closures*

Craftex Cleaning Supplies, 66-68 Priory Bridge Road, Taunton, Somerset, TA1 1QB Tel: (01823) 332696 *Carpet cleaning products manufrs*

▶ The Crafthouse, 118-120 Outram Street, Sutton-in-Ashfield, Nottinghamshire, NG17 4FT Tel: (01623) 550011 Fax: (01623) 550011 *Art & craft material suppliers*

▶ Crafting Mad, 14 Fulmar Brae, Livingston, West Lothian, EH54 6UY Tel: (01506) 414398 E-mail: angela@crafting-mad.co.uk *We are a UK only online mail order company, offering card-making supplies *at bargain prices. We sell all manner of card making supplies including *Decoupage, Stickers, Miniatures, Toppers, Embellishments, Die Cuts *and much, much more... * *We are committed to providing a high quality of service and aim to *dispatch orders the same day payment is received. * *AND BEST OF ALL.... * *We offer FREE P&P in the UK for orders of £5 and over. * * **

▶ CraftingCards.com, 75 Walsall Road, Darlaston, West Midlands, WS10 9JU Tel: 0121 531-8082 E-mail: chris@craftingcards.com *Rubber stamp manufrs*

▶ Craftsman Cladding, B Station Industrial Estate, Station Road, Mauchline, Ayrshire, KA5 5EU Tel: (01290) 551055 Fax: (01290) 551958 E-mail: sales@craftsmancladding.co.uk *uPVC roofline replacement including, fascias, soffits, bargeboards, gutters and downpipes. Scotlands number one indepéndent installer of plastic roofline products*

Craftsman Tools Ltd, Side Copse, Otley, West Yorkshire, LS21 1JE Tel: (01943) 466788 Fax: (01943) 850144 E-mail: r.johnson@craftsmantools.com *Tooling equipment*

Craftsmen Potters Association, 25 Fouberts Place, London, W1F 7QF Tel: (020) 7437 6781 Fax: (020) 7287 9954 *Studio ceramics*

Craftstones Europe, 52-54 Holmethorpe Avenue, Holmethorpe Industrial Estate, Redhill, RH1 2NL Tel: (01737) 767363 Fax: (01737) 768627 E-mail: craftstones@craftstones.co.uk *Semi precious gemstone & jewellery wholesalers*

Craftwork Industries Ltd, 98 Lower Richmond Road, London, SW15 1LN Tel: (020) 8780 1798 Fax: (020) 8780 1861 E-mail: sales@craftwork-interiors.co.uk *Total office refurbishment also storage & materials handling equipment. Office furniture distributors.*

▶ Crafty Individuals, 1 Sidelingtails, Yarm, Cleveland, TS15 9HT Tel: (01642) 789955 *Art & craft material suppliers*

▶ Crafty Patch, 24-28 South Street, Boston, Lincolnshire, PE21 6HT Tel: (01205) 311103 Fax: (01205) 311649 *Art craft material suppliers*

Craftye Fisherman, 13 Montagu Terrace, Edinburgh, EH3 5QX Tel: 0131-551 1224 Fax: 0131-551 1226 *Fishing tackle suppliers & manufrs*

Cragg's Of Conder Green, Thurnham, Thurnham, Lancaster, LA2 0BD Tel: (01524) 751946 Fax: (01524) 752378 E-mail: craggsofconder@tiscali.co.uk *Agricultural machinery suppliers*

Craig, Merton Bank Road, St. Helens, Merseyside, WA9 1HZ Tel: (01744) 25080 Fax: (01744) 26882 E-mail: enquiries@craigengineering.co.uk *Roller shutter manufrs*

Craig Bragdy Ltd, 7 Colomendy Industrial Estate, Rhyl Road, Denbigh, Clwyd, LL16 5TA Tel: (01745) 815656 Fax: (01745) 814488 E-mail: cbd@cbdmurals.co.uk Principal Export Areas: Worldwide *Ceramic murals & art work suppliers*

Craig & Buchanan Ltd, 23 Lochburn Road, Glasgow, G20 9AE Tel: 0141-946 2007 Fax: 0141-945 2100 E-mail: shona@craigbuchanan.co.uk *Steel fabricators*

▶ Craig Chalmers & Son, 6 Drumgelloch Street, Airdrie, Lanarkshire, ML6 7EW Tel: (01236) 756655 Fax: (01236) 749390

Craig Collier, Linney Lane, Shaw, Oldham, OL2 8HD Tel: (01706) 845800 Fax: (01706) 880877 E-mail: sales@craigcollier.co.uk *Safety barrier manufrs*

▶ Craig Generics Ltd, Thistle Building, 9 Cairn Court, East Kilbride, Glasgow, G74 4NB Tel: (01355) 576500 Fax: (01355) 576510 *Pharmaceutical distributors*

Craig International Supplies Ltd, 219 Albert Quay, Aberdeen, AB11 5QA Tel: (01224) 591555 Fax: (01224) 212558 E-mail: cis@craig-group.com Principal Export Areas: Worldwide *Oilfield suppliers*

▶ Craig Jones Video Jockey, Breckland House, Hanbury Road, Hanbury, Bromsgrove, Worcestershire, B60 4DA Tel: (01527) 821303 Fax: (01527) 821303 E-mail: craigjones@clubberuk.com *Live video jockey mixing visuals to music to enhance a venue*

▶ Peter Craig, Wallyford Industrial Estate, Wallyford, Musselburgh, Midlothian, EH21 8QJ Tel: 0131-665 4517 Fax: 0131-653 1969 *Shop fitting & joinery*

Robert Craig & Sons Ltd, Unit 10, Knock Moore Hill, Industrial Estate, Fergusion Drive, Lisburn, County Antrim, BT28 2OX Tel: (028) 9266 8500 Fax: (028) 9266 8550 E-mail: sales@craigs-products.co.uk *General engineers & engineering distributors*

Craig Specialist Services Ltd, Unit 3 Preston Enterprise Ctr, Salter St, Preston, PR1 1NT Tel: 01772 828585 Fax: 01772 827307 *Garage equipment manufrs*

▶ Craig Steven, 28 Mayburn Avenue, Loanhead, Midlothian, EH20 9EP Tel: 0131-440 0602 Fax: 0131 4400602 E-mail: info@sc-electrical-services.co.uk *All Domestic and Commercial work undertaken.*Rewires, showers, consumer unit upgrades, security lights etc*

continued

Craig Wyllie Plumbing & Heating, 20 Scott Court, Alva, Clackmannanshire, FK12 5LZ Tel: (07917) 033271 Fax: (01259) 769027 E-mail: craigwyllie@hotmail.co.uk

Craigavon Office Supplies, 1 Moores Lane, Lurgan, Craigavon, County Armagh, BT66 8DW Tel: (028) 3832 7231 Fax: (028) 3832 1801 E-mail: info@jameshamiltongroup.com *Office furniture distributors*

▶ CRAIGCAT UK LIMITED, P.O. BOX 131, LYMINGTON, HAMPSHIRE, SO41 9UG Tel: 07770 546250 Fax: 01590 610527 E-mail: enquiries@craigcat.co.uk *Distributors of the CraigCat for the UK & Europe*

Craigdon Business Gifts, Advertising House, Burghmuir Circle, Inverurie, Aberdeenshire, AB51 4FS Tel: (01467) 622943 Fax: (01467) 620286 E-mail: sales@craigdon.com *Promotional & advertising gift services*

▶ Craighead Building Supplies, 1 Block 8, 9 Clydesmill Drive, Clydesmill Industrial Estate, Glasgow, G32 8RG Tel: 0141-641 0077 Fax: 0141-641 0073 E-mail: sales@craighead-supplies.co.uk *Vesting & fastener suppliers*

▶ Craigie Engineering Ltd, Grainshore Road, Hatston, Kirkwall, Orkney, KW15 1FL Tel: (01856) 874680 Fax: (01856) 875255 *Engineering services*

Craigie & Scott, 3 Riverside, Station Road, Bruton, Somerset, BA10 0EH Tel: (01749) 812867 Fax: (01749) 812867 E-mail: craigiewoodworks@waitrose.com *Cabinet making services*

▶ Craigs Electrical Co., 203 Kersey Crescent, Speen, Newbury, Berkshire, RG14 1SW Tel: (07876) 550331 Fax: (01635) 820308 E-mail: craig@youhirewewire.co.uk *Craig"s Electrical Company only employs skilled and qualified electricians, to ofer a service you can depend on.***We use a fixed menu price bookto give you a precise and instant quotation with no call out /overtime charges or hourly rates.**

Craigton Packaging Ltd, 43 Scotts Road, Paisley, Renfrewshire, PA2 7AN Tel: 0141-887 0244 Fax: 0141-887 5462 E-mail: info@craigton.com *Contract packaging services*

▶ Craigvar Construction, Langhaugh Mill, Langhaugh, Galashiels, Selkirkshire, TD1 2AJ Tel: (01896) 752828 Fax: (01896) 758040

Crailcrest Ltd, Coach House, Birch Grove, Horsted Keynes, Haywards Heath, West Sussex, RH17 7DJ Tel: (01825) 740190 Fax: (01825) 740178 E-mail: sales@crailcrest.com *AC-DC electric motor & gearboxes sourcing & manufrs*

Craintern Ltd, 13-17 Haltwhistle Road, South Woodham Ferrers, Chelmsford, CM3 5ZA Tel: (01245) 322438 Fax: (01245) 328926 E-mail: mailbox@ctlmedical.co.uk *Product designers & manufrs*

▶ C-Ram Ltd, 126 Malvern Road, Leytonstone, London, E11 3DL Tel: (0845) 0589813 Fax: (0709) 2087787 E-mail: sales@c-ram.co.uk *C-RAM Ltd. is one of Londons cheapest suppliers of computer software and hardware. With experienced PC engineers*

Cramar Contracts Ltd, Unit 8 Clipstone Brook Industrial Park, Cherrycourt Way, Leighton Buzzard, Bedfordshire, LU7 4GP Tel: (01525) 850957 Fax: (01525) 851347 *Joinery manufrs*

Cramer Music Ltd, 23 Garrick Street, London, WC2E 9RY Tel: (020) 7240 1612 Fax: (020) 7240 2639 *Music publishers*

Cramlington & District Metals Ltd, Appleby Street, North Shields, Tyne & Wear, NE29 6TE Tel: 0191-257 2049 Fax: 0191-257 9907 *Scrap metal merchants*

▶ Crams People Coounting Systems, 6 Lee Road, Marton, Blackpool, FY4 4QS Tel: 01253 769675 E-mail: chris.hirst@candsdesign.co.uk *CRAMS is a people counting system aimed at entertainment venues. A range of systems are also available for other types of premises.**

Cranage E M C Testing Ltd, Stable Court, Oakley Hall, Market Drayton, Shropshire, TF9 4AG Tel: (01630) 658568 Fax: (01630) 658921 E-mail: info@cranage.co.uk *Cranage EMC & Safety specialise in EMC Testing, LVD Testing, EMF Testing, Machinery & Mechanical Testing, Surge Testing, Product Safety Testing, RFI Testing, Medical Device Testing and Electrical Safety Testing. We also offer a Calibration service along with technical problem solving and a range of related services to support technical professionals.*

▶ Cranbrook Loft Conversions Ltd, 732 Cranbrook Road, Ilford, Essex, IG6 1HU Tel: (0800) 525883 Fax: (020) 8551 1580 E-mail: admin@cranbrook.co.uk

▶ Cranbury's Removals & Storage, 25 Leigh Road, Eastleigh, Hampshire, SO50 9FF Tel: (023) 8065 2630 Fax: (023) 8061 7164

Cranden Diamond Products Ltd, Mounts Hill, Cranbrook Road, Benenden, Cranbrook, Kent, TN17 4ET Tel: (01580) 241013 Fax: (01580) 241838 E-mail: andrew.cranshaw@diamondtoolsuk.com *Diamond tool parts manufrs*

Crane Building Services & Utilities, Crane House, Epsilon Terrace, West Road, Ipswich, IP3 9FJ Tel: (01473) 277300 Fax: (01473) 270301 E-mail: enquiries@cranebsu.com *Tube fittings & valves manufrs*

Crane Care Ltd, 15 Avenue Road, Aston, Birmingham, B6 4DY Tel: 0121-333 3995 Fax: 0121-333 3996 E-mail: sales@cranecare.ltd.uk *Sole distribution for HBC radiomatic Industrial remote controls ideal for use with overhead travelling cranes, lifting machines, construction. When replacing any alternative products: Ikusi, Tele Crane, Flextronic, Jay, Dartek, Cattron, Commander, Scanreko, MBB Special "Cash Back" Discounts apply. Fully equipped service centre, to handle radio installation, conversion, repair warranty and service work*

Crane Catering Services, 6 The Crescent, Station Road, Woldingham, Caterham, Surrey, CR3 7DB Tel: (01883) 652045 Fax: (01883) 652097 *Catering equipment engineers service & supply*

The Crane Centre Ltd, Norton Way, Moss Lane Industrial Estate, Sandbach, Cheshire, CW11 3YT Tel: (01270) 753435 Fax: (01270) 759389 E-mail: info@cranecentre.co.uk *Crane repairers & hose assembly manufrs*

Crane Computers, Unit 4 Exter Road Industrial State, Okehampton, Devon, EX20 1UA Tel: 01837 55664 *Computer network sales*

Crane Electronics Ltd, Open House, 3 Watling Drive, Hinckley, Leicestershire, LE10 3EY Tel: (01455) 251488 Fax: (01455) 614717 E-mail: sales@crane-electronics.com *Torque control, measurement & analysis equipment*

Crane Enterprises, Brookhouse Road, Aston, Sheffield, S26 2AH Tel: 0114-287 5499 Fax: 0114-287 5388 *Crane test, inspection, maintenance & repair*

▶ Crane Force, 67 Haigh Moor Way, Swallownest, Sheffield, S26 4SW Tel: 0114-288 0909

Crane Foundry Ltd, PO Box 43, Wolverhampton, WV1 2QX Tel: (01902) 452731 Fax: (01902) 454895 *Iron casting manufrs*

Crane Hill Engineering Ltd, Harvey Reeves Road, St. James Mill Industrial Estate, Northampton, NN5 5JR Tel: (01604) 587656 Fax: (01604) 588341 E-mail: robinson@cranehill.sagehost.co.uk *Precision engineers*

▶ Hugh Crane Cleaning Equipment Ltd, Fishley Lane, South Walsham Road, Acle, Norwich, NR13 3ES Tel: (01493) 750072 Fax: (01493) 751854 E-mail: sales@hughcrane.co.uk *Manufacturer/distributor*

Crane Inspection & Lifting Services Ltd, Unit 17 Neptune Industrial Estate, Neptune Close, Medway City Estate, Rochester, Kent, ME2 4LT Tel: (01634) 290030 Fax: (01634) 730584 E-mail: cils@btconnect.com *Crane service & maintenance testing lifting equipment suppliers*

John Crane UK Ltd, Buckingham House, 361-366 Buckingham Avenue, Slough, SL1 4LU Tel: (01753) 224000 Fax: (01753) 224224 *Specialist seal manufrs* Also at: Manchester

Crane & Lifting Services Ltd, Evtol Trading Estate, Frederick Street, Newport, Gwent, NP20 2DR Tel: (01633) 265445 Fax: (01633) 265446 *Crane repairs, maintenance & lifting equipment*

Crane Plastic Fabrication, 127 Upper Thrift Street, Northampton, NN1 5HR Tel: (01604) 602224 Fax: (01604) 602214 E-mail: craneplastics@tiscali.co.uk *Plastic safety guards manufrs*

Crane Rail Installations UK Ltd, 9 Portersfield Road, Cradley Heath, West Midlands, B64 7BN Tel: (01384) 634466 Fax: (01384) 634277 E-mail: cri@btinternet.com *Crane track contractors*

Crane Scales Ltd, 21-23 Bagnall Street, Ocker Hill, Tipton, West Midlands, DY4 0EF Tel: 0121-556 4062 Fax: 0121-556 8217 E-mail: info@cranescales.co.uk *Scale distributors*

Crane Services Ltd, Platts Road, Stourbridge, West Midlands, DY8 4YR Tel: (01384) 370318 Fax: (01384) 440203 E-mail: sales@craneservices.co.uk *Crane & lifting gear manufrs*

Crane Spring Co., Frederick Street, Walsall, WS2 9NJ Tel: (01922) 625313 Fax: (01922) 723561 E-mail: sales@cranesp.co.uk *Spring manufrs*

Craneprint Ltd, Marshalls Industrial Estate, Sedgley Street, Wolverhampton, WV2 3AJ Tel: (01902) 450505 Fax: (01902) 450980 E-mail: sales@craneprint.co.uk *Commercial printers*

▶ Cranequip Ltd, Cattell Road, Cape Industrial Estate, Warwick, CV34 4JN Tel: (01926) 406900 Fax: (01926) 406910 E-mail: robert.shearsby@uk.gantry.com *Manufacturers of lifting magnets & crane rail installation*

Cranes Ltd, 14 Valley Side Parade, London, E4 8AJ Tel: (020) 8524 3928 Fax: (020) 8559 4459 E-mail: sales@cranescigarettevending.co.uk *Vending machine supplier*

Cranes Of Hollesley Ltd, The Street, Hollesley, Woodbridge, Suffolk, IP12 3QU Tel: (01394) 411687 Fax: (01394) 410238 E-mail: enquiries@cranesford.co.uk *Motor vehicle sales & services*

▶ Cranes (UK), Rockingham House, Wentworth Way, Tankersley, Barnsley, South Yorkshire, S75 3DH Tel: (0870) 0665466 Fax: (0870) 0665501 *Crane hire suppliers*

▶ Cranetech (Bristol) Limited, 467 Bath Road, Brislington, Bristol, BS4 3JU Tel: 0778 995 3837 Fax: 0117 904 7142 E-mail: crane-tech@blueyonder.co.uk

▶ Cranetek Services Ltd, Craigellachie, Golf Road, Ellon, Aberdeenshire, AB41 8UZ Tel: (01358) 723263 Fax: (01358) 722548 E-mail: sales@cranetek.co.uk *Crane services*

Cranfield Electrical Ltd, 2 Adams Close, Kempston, Bedford, MK42 7JE Tel: (01234) 853044 Fax: (01234) 853054 E-mail: sales@cranfieldelectrical.com *Manufacturers of electrical cable assemblies/ wiring harnesses & neon lamp assemblies. Mains cordsets, gas ignition & high current links made to customers' specifications. Provider of wire stripping & printed circuit board assembly ser vices. Supply of specialist cables & electrical components*

▶ Cranford Builders, Cranford, Gollanfield, Inverness, IV2 7UR Tel: (01667) 462457

Cranford Controls, 2 Waterbrook Estate, Waterbrook Road, Alton, Hampshire, GU34 2UD Tel: (01420) 592444 Fax: (01420) 592445 E-mail: sales@cranfordcontrols.com *Cranford Controls is an independently owned Company located in Alton, Hampshire, UK. Cranford fire alarm solutions are sold worldwide through a highly experienced distribution network. Focussing on Fire Alarm sounder and accessories, the Company has generated a research & development programme that creates future-proof solutions for our customers.**Cranford Controls is committed to Manufacturing, with a modern in-house SMT line coupled with an increasing level of automation.**The manufacturing and R&D facility is assessed to ISO 9001:2000 by the*

continued

*LPCB.**2004 saw Cranford Controls move to a new ,000 sq ft, purpose built headquarters on a greenfield site in Alton. With its main road and main line connections Cranford Controls is conveniently located to both London and all south coast ports.*

Cranford Controls Systems Ltd, Unit 3 Pattenden La Buis Centre, Marden, Tonbridge, Kent, TN12 9QS Tel: (01622) 833300 Fax: (01622) 833311 E-mail: sales@cranfordcontrol.co.uk *Electrical contractors & control panels manufrs*

Cranford Engineering, 13 Craddocks Parade, Ashtead, Surrey, KT21 1QL Tel: (01372) 272380 Fax: (01372) 273776 E-mail: craneng@aol.com *Injection mould toolmakers*

Cranford International Ltd, 10 Beech Waye, Gerrards Cross, Buckinghamshire, SL9 8BL Tel: (01753) 889831 Fax: (01753) 890892 E-mail: cranfd@aol.com *Food technology consultants & machinery suppliers*

Cranks & Bearings, 1A Rotherfield Road, Enfield, Middlesex, EN3 6AL Tel: (01992) 763279 Fax: (01992) 650840 *Engine reconditioning service*

Cranleigh Control Co., Unit 30 Hewitts Industrial Estate, Elmbridge Road, Cranleigh, Surrey, GU6 8LW Tel: (01483) 272663 Fax: (01483) 272663 E-mail: mail@cranleighcontrol.co.uk *Automatic control equipment manufrs*

Cranleigh Freight Services Ltd, Building 68 Dunsfold Park, Stovolds Hill, Cranleigh, Surrey, GU6 8TB Tel: (01483) 201330 Fax: (01483) 272124 E-mail: info@cranleigh.co.uk *We are one of the South of England's leading UK & European distribution companies. Specialist services include European & UK distribution, direct home delivery and supply chain solutions.*

Cranmer Signs, 117a Sutton Avenue North, Peacehaven, East Sussex, BN10 7QJ Tel: (01273) 583706 Fax: (01273) 583706 E-mail: terrysignman@dsl.pipex.com *Sign manufrs*

Cranmore Instant Print Ltd, Crompton Road Mill, Crompton Road, Macclesfield, Cheshire, SK11 8DS Tel: (01625) 615093 Fax: (01625) 613539 E-mail: copy@cranmoreprint.com *Copying services*

▶ Crannog Cruises Ltd, Town Pier, Fort William, Inverness-Shire, PH33 6TD Tel: (01397) 700714 Fax: (01397) 700134

Cransons, 55 Sherburn Terrace, Consett, County Durham, DH8 6ND Tel: (01207) 505621 *Wrought ironworking services*

Cranworth Farm Services, High Common, Cranworth, Thetford, Norfolk, IP25 7SX Tel: (01362) 820391 Fax: (01362) 820077 E-mail: sales@c-f-s.info *Agricultural machinery maintenance & repair services*

▶ Crash It, Kettles Wood Drive, Birmingham, B32 3DB Tel: 0121-421 7601 Fax: 0121-421 7601 E-mail: enquire@crash-it.org *Computer maintenance & repair services*

Crate Co. Ltd, Unit 7 Green Role Estate, Howe Moss Drive, Kirkhill Industrial Estate, Dyce, Aberdeen, AB21 0GL Tel: (01224) 771494 Fax: (01224) 775140 *Packing case manufrs*

Crauford Technology Ltd, 135B Edinburgh Avenue Trading Estate, Slough, SL1 4SW Tel: (01753) 531462 Fax: (01753) 552580 E-mail: davidd@craufurd.com *Mechanical engineers services* Also at: Slough

Craufurd Engineering Services Ltd, Unit 4-5 Lower Mount Farm, Cookham, Maidenhead, Berkshire, SL6 9EE Tel: (01628) 532288 Fax: (01628) 532424 *Structural steelwork engineers*

Cravelon Metal-Pack Ltd, 28 Hayes Street, Bromley, BR2 7LD Tel: (020) 8462 1197 Fax: (020) 8462 5282 *Tinplate importers & exporters*

Craven & Co. Ltd, Manse Lane, Knaresborough, North Yorkshire, HG5 8ET Tel: (01423) 796208 Fax: (01423) 869189 E-mail: sales@craven-solutions.com *A UK manufacturer of catering equipment. We design and manufacture high quality trolleys, shelving and POS display equipment.*

Craven Construction Ltd, Butts Works, High Bentham, Lancaster, LA2 7AN Tel: (01524) 261145 Fax: (01524) 262060 *Manufacturers of farm buildings & pre cast concrete*

Craven Fawcett Ltd, Elm Tree Street, Bellvue, Wakefield, West Yorkshire, WF1 5EQ Tel: (01924) 375444 Fax: (01924) 370928 E-mail: sales@cravenfawcett.com *Brick & tile machine manufrs*

Craven & Nicholas Engineering Ltd, St Johns Road, Boston, Lincolnshire, PE21 6BG Tel: (01205) 364004 Fax: (01205) 310798 E-mail: info@carven-nicholas.co.uk *General constructional engineers*

▶ Craven Plumbing & Electrical, 75 St. Johns Road, Dartford, DA2 6BE Tel: (01322) 276067 E-mail: julian@squash4.freeserve.co.uk *Instrumentation control & automation*

Craven Rambler, 19 Coach Street, Skipton, North Yorkshire, BD23 1LH Tel: (01756) 796166 Fax: (01756) 700213 E-mail: sales@penninecruises.com *Outdoor equipment retailers*

Craven Yarn Services, Milton House, Cononly, Keighley, West Yorkshire, BD20 8LL Tel: (01535) 630683 Fax: (01535) 630683 E-mail: john@cravenyarns.fsnet.co.uk *Textile processors*

Cravenplan Computers Ltd, Wilbury Barn, Swallowcliffe, Salisbury, SP3 5QH Tel: (01747) 858000 Fax: (01747) 858010 E-mail: info@cravenplan.co.uk *Website design management*

Crawford Ltd, Zetland Road, Hillington Industrial Estate, Glasgow, G52 4BW Tel: 0141-810 9900 Fax: 0141-810 9901

Crawford Amber, Units 5 Dedridge East Industrial Estate, Abbotsford Rise, Livingston, West Lothian, EH54 6QD Tel: (01506) 417237 Fax: (01506) 412726 E-mail: sales@crawfordamber.co.uk *Industrial door manufrs*

Crawford Bros (Walthamstow) Ltd, 1A-3A Hoe St, London, E17 4SD Tel: (020) 8520 3981 Fax: (020) 8509 3158 E-mail: crawfordj@btconnect.com *Glass merchants*

▶ Crawford Controls Ltd, Unit D7 Templeborough Business Park, Bow Bridge Close, Rotherham, South Yorkshire, S60 1BY Tel: (01709) 837201 Fax: (01709) 839109 E-mail: info@crawfordcontrols.com *Control panel manufrs*

Crawford Hansford & Kimber Ltd, 18 Farnborough Road, Farnborough, Hampshire, GU14 6AY Tel: (01252) 377077 Fax: (01252) 377228 E-mail: admin@crawfordhk.com *Industrial electronic equipment manufrs*

▶ John Crawford Artist/Signwriter, 120 Hundred Acre Road, Streetly, Sutton Coldfield, West Midlands, B74 2BJ Tel: 0121-353 1772 E-mail: john@jcrawford.fsnet.co.uk *Signwriting including gold leaf work, mural artist, interior decoration*

Crawford Joinery, 21 Creevery Road, Antrim, BT41 2JP Tel: (028) 9446 7711 Fax: (028) 9446 7710

Crawford Precision Engineering, Cross Court Industrial Estate, Kettering, Northamptonshire, NN16 9BN Tel: (01536) 417140 Fax: (01536) 524059 E-mail: cpeng@globalnet.co.uk *Bearings manufrs*

Crawford Reid Engineers, Reed Street, North Shields, Tyne & Wear, NE30 1DD Tel: 0191-259 5767 Fax: 0191-259 5767 *Precision engineers*

Crawford Scientific Ltd, Holm Street, Strathaven, Lanarkshire, ML10 6NB Tel: (01357) 522961 Fax: (01357) 522168 E-mail: enquiries@crawfordscientific.com *Scientific instrument distributors*

▶ Crawford Transport Services, Industrial Road, Hertburn, Washington, Tyne & Wear, NE37 2SD Tel: 0191-415 1771 Fax: 0191-419 0396

Crawford's Packaging, 1 Barton Street, North Tawton, Devon, EX20 2HN Tel: (01837) 82388 Fax: (01837) 82388 *Buy & sell new/used cartons*

Crawford-Swift, Rosemount Works, Huddersfield Road, Elland, West Yorkshire, HX5 0EE Tel: (01422) 379222 Fax: (01422) 379122 E-mail: mail@crawfordswift.co.uk *Centre/general purpose & CNC lathes. In addition, gas fire rapid heater manufrs*

Crawley Fire Protection, Hazelwick Mill Lane, Crawley, West Sussex, RH10 1SU Tel: (01293) 547654 Fax: (01293) 440295 *Service & maintenance of fire extinguishers*

▶ Crawley Office Cleaning Services, 69 Gatwick Road, Crawley, West Sussex, RH10 9RD Tel: (01293) 619975 Fax: (01293) 619975 E-mail: crawleyoffice@cleaningservices.net *Crawley Office Cleaning Services has been established in the Gatwick area for 30 years.In addition to office cleaning we also provide office maintenance, gardening and outside maintenance and window cleaning services.*

Crawley Patterns Ltd, Unit 17, Blackhouse Farm, Blackhouse Road, Colgate, Horsham, West Sussex, RH13 6HS Tel: (01293) 852744 *Engineering pattern makers*

Crawley Welding Supplies Ltd, Royce Road, Crawley, West Sussex, RH10 9NX Tel: (01293) 529761 Fax: (01293) 545081 E-mail: crawleywelding@btclick.co.uk *Welding suppliers, distributors & hire*

▶ Crawt Simpkins Partnership, 71 Loudoun Road, London, NW8 0DQ Tel: (020) 7372 1881 Fax: (020) 7372 1991

Cray Metal Finishers, D1-D2 Unit Riverside Industrial Estate, Riverside Way, Dartford, DA1 5BS Tel: (01322) 220662 Fax: (01322) 288032 E-mail: sales@craymetalfinishers.co.uk *Powder coating systems manufrs*

Cray Valley Ltd, Laporte Road, Stallingborough, Grimsby, South Humberside, DN41 8DR Tel: (01469) 572464 Fax: (01469) 572988 E-mail: martin.brewer@crayvalley.com *Manufacturers of resins*

Craychase Ltd, Alington Road, Eynesbury, St. Neots, Cambridgeshire, PE19 6HY Tel: (01480) 215196 Fax: (01480) 476723 *Precision machining*

Crayfield Computer Consultants, 64 Cuckfield Road, Hurstpierpoint, Hassocks, West Sussex, BN6 9SB Tel: (01273) 834999 Fax: (01273) 835550 E-mail: systems@crayfield.net *Computer consultants*

Crayford Ltd, The Old Fire Station, Christchurch St West, Frome, Somerset, BA11 1EH Tel: (01373) 474466 Fax: (01373) 474499 E-mail: roger@crayford.ltd.uk *Networking system consultants*

Crayford Sheet Metal Fabrications, Unit 37 Crayford Industrial Estate, Swaisland Drive, Crayford, Dartford, DA1 4HS Tel: (01322) 551555 Fax: (01322) 553124 *Sheet metalworkers*

Crayford Special Vehicle Ltd, Lyon Way, St. Albans, Hertfordshire, AL4 0LQ Tel: (01727) 851222 Fax: (01727) 859222 E-mail: sales@crayford.co.uk *The Crayford Group is mainly involved in import and sales of special purpose vehicles and marine equipment through a network of dealers in UK & EU. Our Vehicle division specializes in low ground pressure all terrain vehicles, utility & sports quad bikes from N.America, Bank tractors and ATV trailers. The Marine division offers two floating pontoon systems with boat hoists and storage platforms, a unique range of hydrofoil assisted catamaran RIB's (Rigid Inflatable Boats) and PWC's (Personal Water Craft) from S.Africa and we have developed a disc braked boat trailer to meet Euro regulations.*

Crayford Tubes Ltd, Unit 33 Acorn Industrial Park, Crayford Road, Dartford, DA1 4AL Tel: (01322) 526614 Fax: (01322) 559462 E-mail: info@crayford-tubes.co.uk *Cardboard tube manufrs*

Tony Craze Welding & Fabrication, 13 United Downs Industrial Park, St. Day, Redruth, Cornwall, TR16 5HY Tel: (01209) 821166 Fax: (01209) 821864 E-mail: steel@tonycraze.net *Steel fabricators*

Crazy Products Ltd, P O Box 170, Northwood, Middx, HA6 3SS Tel: (01923) 842222 Fax: (01923) 842233 *Distribution snack foods*

CRC Associates, 41 The Park, Stow on the Wold, Cheltenham, Gloucestershire, GL54 1DX Tel: (01451) 831048 Fax: (01451) 832297 *Computer software developers*

CRD Tool & Engineering Ltd, Station Road, Manningtree, Essex, CO11 1AA Tel: (01206) 394343 Fax: (01206) 391460 E-mail: merlyncrd@aol.com *Precision engineers*

▶ Cre-8 Communications, 28, Church Street, Kidderminster, Worcs, DY10 2AR Tel: (01562) 741160 Fax: (01562) 741170

▶ CRE8 Computer Systems, Unit K Chadwell Heath Industrial Park, Kemp Road, Dagenham, Essex, RM8 1SL Tel: (020) 8597 4400 Fax: (020) 8597 4400

▶ CreaCom Design, 181 High Street, Invergordon, Ross-Shire, IV18 0AL Tel: (01349) 853003 E-mail: info@creacomdesign.com *Web Design-Graphic Design-Print*

▶ Cream Computers UK Ltd, The Red House, Kingswood Park, Bonsor Drive, Tadworth, Surrey, KT20 6AY Tel: (01737) 377220 Fax: (01737) 377221 E-mail: ray@creamcomputers.com *IT hardware & software suppliers*

▶ Cream Interim, Hudson House, 8 Tavistock Street, London, WC2E 7PP Tel: (020) 7559 6767 Fax: (0870) 0941613 E-mail: info@creaminterim.co.uk *Interim management services*

▶ Crease Release, 53 Virginia Avenue, Stafford, ST17 4YA Tel: (01785) 223296 E-mail: iron@crease-release.co.uk *Ironing service covering Stafford and surrounding areas.*

▶ Create a Cake, Unit H, Maesteg Market Area, Maesteg, CF34 9DA Tel: (07976) 518649 E-mail: helen@createacake.co.uk *We supply wedding cakes in Wales and the rest of the UK. All prices include free delivery in the Maesteg, Bridgend, Cardiff, Swansea and Neath areas.*

Create Form International Ltd, Instone House, Instone Road, Dartford, DA1 2AG Tel: (01322) 279797 Fax: (01322) 279779 E-mail: info@createform.com *Software developers*

Create Real Estate, PO Box 48533, London, NW4 2XW Tel: (020) 8457 3200 Fax: (020) 8457 3202 E-mail: info@create-re.com *Estate agents*

Createability Ltd, 2 Woodlands Business Village, Coronation Road, Basingstoke, Hampshire, RG21 4JX Tel: (01256) 818915 Fax: (01256) 335704 E-mail: info@createability.co.uk *Building refurbishment consultants service leisure industry*

▶ Created, Newhouses Road, Broxburn, West Lothian, EH52 5MZ Tel: (01506) 853587 Fax: (01506) 856106

Creation Carriers, Vista Business Centre, 50 Salisbury Road, Hounslow, TW4 6JQ Tel: (020) 8538 0204 Fax: (020) 8538 0207 E-mail: creationcarriers@btconnect.com *Carrier bag & packaging merchants*

▶ Creation Greetings Ltd, Afton Road, Freshwater, Isle of Wight, PO40 9UH Tel: (01983) 758540 Fax: (01983) 758541 E-mail: sales@jarthurdixon.com

Creation Internet Services Ltd, 30 Broad Oak Way, Rayleigh, Essex, SS6 8JU Tel: (01268) 774415 Fax: (01268) 779159 E-mail: ian@creationinternet.co.uk *Web site design services*

▶ Creation Project Management Ltd, Becks Field House, Becks Field, Stoke-sub-Hamdon, Somerset, TA14 6PB Tel: 0845 3519922 Fax: 01935 829218 E-mail: sales@creationpm.com *Creation Project Management Ltd is a client focused project management company that specialises in turn key solutions for the design, build and construction of multi-million pound capital development projects, alterations or refurbishment of existing premises, technology transfers and high purity cleanroom environments for the optical and semiconductor industries within the UK and overseas.*

▶ Creations, 64 High Street, North Berwick, East Lothian, EH39 4HQ Tel: (01620) 890411 Fax: (01620) 890411 *Art material suppliers*

▶ Creative Air Express, Unit 8c Rainbow Industrial Estate, Trout Road, West Drayton, Middlesex, UB7 7XT Tel: (01895) 448072 Fax: (0870) 7777881 E-mail: operations@creativeair.co.uk *UK & worldwide time critical delivery services*

Creative Aluminium, 2 Tower View, Egremont, Cumbria, CA22 2BN Tel: (0778) 5950889 Fax: (0870) 2206938 E-mail: sales@creativealuminium.com *Aluminium extrusions*

▶ Creative Angels, 3 New Buildings, Gandy Street, Exeter, EX4 3LS Tel: (01392) 422720 E-mail: creative1angels@aol.com *Jewellery manufrs*

Creative Art Ltd, 56 Harrow Drive, Hornchurch, Essex, RM11 1NX Tel: (01708) 474644 Fax: (01708) 474 644 E-mail: kcreativeart@aol.com *Print posters, banners & canvas art suppliers*

Creative Art Products Ltd, Manor Lane, Holmes Chapel, Crewe, CW4 8AG Tel: (01477) 535868 Fax: (01477) 535996 E-mail: sales@scolaquip.go-plus.net *Educational art & craft material manufrs*

Creative Audio Design, 12 Harold Road, Hawley, Dartford, DA2 7SA Tel: (01322) 224998 E-mail: jbthecad@homecall.co.uk *Creative audio design and consultancy for any media.*Recording, scriptwritng, voice casting, music composition, soundscape creation.*

Creative Beadcraft Ltd, 20 Beak Street, London, W1F 9RE Tel: (01494) 778818 Fax: (01494) 718510 E-mail: sales@cb.co.uk *Costume jewellery*

▶ The Creative Business, 37 Deans Walk, Gloucester, GL1 2PX Tel: (01452) 545076 E-mail: davidn@thecreativebiz.com *The Creative Business is a creative marketing consultancy for businesses which like to think big, no matter what their size of operation or budget.**Our services include; marketing strategy - planning and development, advertising and design creative concepts, copywriting, direct marketing, sales promotion, web design/build, online marketing email marketing and search engine optimisation.*

Creative Canapes, Unit D12, Barwell Business Park, Leatherhead Road, Chessington, Surrey, KT9 2NY Tel: (0845) 3668811 E-mail: enquiries@creativecanapes.co.uk

continued

▶ indicates data change since last edition

continuation
Creative Canapes is a specialist small foods caterer, providing a personal service for any size of function in London, Surrey and Sussex. All canapes and finger foods are hand made to order and finished at your venue.

▶ Creative Celebration Cakes, 12 Church Close, East Huntspill, Highbridge, Somerset, TA9 3QF Tel: 01278 793216 E-mail: Elaine@creativecelebrationcakes.co.uk *Novelty cake decorator*

▶ Creative Cellular Solutions Ltd, Fox Covert Farm, South Cave Road, Riplingham, Brough, East Yorkshire, HU15 1QT Tel: (0845) 1298297 Fax: (01482) 652727 E-mail: info@creativecellular.co.uk *We are Master Distributors of SimplyTrak - the leading standalone vehicle tracking system in the UK and Europe.*

Creative Club Ties, The Whitehouse, 84 Cromley Road, High Lane, Stockport, Cheshire, SK6 8BU Tel: (01663) 762173 Fax: (01663) 810243 E-mail: karen9702@hotmail.co.uk *Necktie & ladies' scarf manufrs*

Creative Club Ties, The Whitehouse, 84 Cromley Road, High Lane, Stockport, Cheshire, SK6 8BU Tel: (01663) 762173 Fax: (01663) 810243 E-mail: julian.hyde@talk21.com *Promotional tie & clothing sales*

▶ Creative Colour Coatings, Lockhill Mills, Holmes Road, Sowerby Bridge, West Yorkshire, HX6 3LF Tel: (01422) 316066 *Metal finishers*

Creative Communications Recruitment, Leaf House, Bluebell Lane, Sharpthorne, East Grinstead, West Sussex, RH19 4PF Tel: (01342) 811572 Fax: (01342) 811572 E-mail: mick@ccrecruit.co.uk *recruiters for the creative industry. We place 2D, 3D and 4D designers, account managers, project managers, producers, new business developers in creative communications companies within the UK. design creative*

Creative Computers Ltd, 258 Old Christchurch Road, Bournemouth, BH1 1PS Tel: (01202) 775600 Fax: (01202) 775559 E-mail: sales@creativegroup.co.uk *Computer maintenance consultants*

Creative Computers UK Ltd, 65 West Main Street, Whitburn, Bathgate, West Lothian, EH47 0QD Tel: (01501) 742600 Fax: (01501) 742600 E-mail: sales@creativegroup.co.uk *Computer accessories suppliers*

Creative Computing Solutions Ltd, Bishops Gate, Station Road, Taplow, Maidenhead, Berkshire, SL6 0PA Tel: (01628) 660600 Fax: (01628) 605434 E-mail: sales@creative-computing.co.uk *Computer systems & software developers*

▶ Creative Conversions, 6 Bishop Street, Alfreton, Derbyshire, DE55 7EF Tel: (01773) 834508 Fax: (01773) 843508 E-mail: creativeconversions@hotmail.co.uk *We undertake garage,and loft conversions. we provide a complete service from planning to finished product.we also provide all aspects of building services from plumbing, plastering, electricals, landscaping and blockpaving, to windows doors and conservatories.*

▶ Creative Copy N Colour Ltd, Unit 14c, Raleigh Hall Industrial Estate, Stafford, ST21 6JL Tel: (01785) 851183 Fax: (01785) 850445 E-mail: info@creativecopyncolour.co.uk

Creative Cosmetics Ltd, 6-7 Riverside Industrial Park, Rapier Street, Ipswich, IP2 8JX Tel: (01473) 685599 Fax: (01473) 680727 E-mail: alan@creativecosmetics.com Principal Export Areas: Worldwide *Cosmetic & cosmetic colour manufrs*

▶ Creative Crafts Art3 Craft Gift, 38 Rainham Shopping Centre, Rainham, Gillingham, Kent, ME8 7HW Tel: (01634) 372200 Fax: (01634) 372200 E-mail: sales@justdoitcrafts.com *Art & craft material suppliers*

Creative Database Projects Ltd, Queens Wharf, Queen Caroline Street, London, W6 9RJ Tel: (020) 8600 2605 Fax: (020) 8600 2603 E-mail: enquiry@cdproj.com *Software developers*

▶ Creative Detail, 32 Thorncliffe Drive, Darwen, Lancashire, BB3 3QA Tel: 01254 773391 E-mail: val@creative-detail.co.uk *Craft suppliers*

Creative Display Group, Millersdale Close, Euroway Industrial Estate, Bradford, West Yorkshire, BD4 6RX Tel: (01274) 700690 Fax: (01274) 700699 E-mail: sales@creativedisplaygroup.co.uk *Screen printers & display makers*

Creative Displays (UK) Ltd, St Helens Way, Thetford, Norfolk, IP24 1HG Tel: (01842) 751503 Fax: (01842) 754060 E-mail: chris@creativedisplaysltd.co.uk *Point of sale purchase*

Creative Edge, P O Box 13492, Edinburgh, EH6 6YH Tel: 0131-226 3339 *Computer development*

▶ Creative Educationltd, 89 Sanderstead Road, South Croydon, Surrey, CR2 0PF Tel: (020) 8666 0234 Fax: (020) 8666 0414 E-mail: sales@creativeeducation.co.uk *Open and In-school training for teachers. Interim management. school consultancy. Inclusion Quality Mark. Special School Courses*

▶ Creative Fires UK Ltd, Unit 14, Arnside Road, Waterlooville, Hampshire, PO7 7UP Tel: (023) 9223 3030

Creative Flowers, 28 Highwalls Avenue, Dinas Powys, South Glamorgan, CF64 4AP Tel: (029) 2051 4754 Fax: (029) 2051 4754 E-mail: creflow@aol.com *Interior plant & floral designers*

▶ Creative Fusion, 1 Church Close, Todber, Sturminster Newton, Dorset, DT10 1JH Tel: (01258) 820702 Fax: 01258 820702 E-mail: hannah@creative-fusion.co.uk *IT support, website design, development & graphic design*

▶ Creative Gateway, 26 Market Place, Swaffham, Norfolk, PE37 7QH Tel: (01760) 336200 E-mail: roy@creativegateway.com *A management consultancy specialising in the strategic development of skills and technology within the creative and cultural industries sector.*

▶ Creative Graphics International, Unit 21, Weston Road Industrial Estate, Stratford-upon-Avon, Warwickshire, CV37 0AH Tel: (01789) 415141 Fax: (01789) 414160 *Exhibition graphic servicing*

Creative Image Signs & Displays Ltd, 8 Spibton Abbey, Bedford, MK41 0UQ Tel: (01234) 356588 Fax: (01234) 346898 E-mail: signsplusbeford@aol.com *Sign manufr*

▶ Creative Images, Garwin House, Romsey Road, East Wellow, Romsey, Hampshire, SO51 6BG Tel: (01794) 322026 Fax: (01794) 322026 E-mail: enquiries@creativeimages.uk.com *Promotion clothing & business gifts suppliers*

▶ Creative Images Wedding Photography, 68 hutton close, Crowther Industrial Estate, Washington, Tyne & wear, NE38 0AH Tel: (07905) 744304 E-mail: gainesuk@hotmail.com *Based in North East England serving Sunderland, Newcastle and County Durham. Provides information about wedding photography services. Includes sample wedding photographs and albums.*

▶ Creative Imaging (UK) Ltd, Waterside House, 60 Wharf Road, London, N1 7SF Tel: (020) 7251 6006

▶ Creative Impressions Ltd, 237 Oldfield Road, Walton Summit Centre, Bamber Bridge, Preston, PR5 8BG Tel: (01772) 335435 Fax: (01772) 335434 E-mail: sales@creative-impressions.com *Manufacturers and suppliers of tools and materials for PATTERN IMPRINTED CONCRETE. Polyurethane Texture Mats, Colour Hardeners, Liquid & Powder Releases, Sealers, Resinprint Overlay, Stencilcrete Stencils, Spraycrete, Plastiform, Deckdrain,and much much more.....*

Creative Interior Projects Ltd, 4 Denham Walk, Chalfont St. Peter, Gerrards Cross, Buckinghamshire, SL9 0EN Tel: (01494) 873347 Fax: (01494) 873353 E-mail: sales@creativeinteriorprojects.co.uk *Office interior designers & refurbishers services*

▶ Creative Joinery, 3 Gibson Street, Stoke-on-Trent, ST6 6AQ Tel: (01782) 825220 Fax: (01782) 825227 *Architectural joiners*

Creative Laser Services, The Bakehouse, 17b High Street, Lutterworth, Leicestershire, LE17 4AT Tel: (01455) 559229 Fax: (01455) 554712 E-mail: rob@creativelaserservices.co.uk *Laser cutting, engraving & etching of acrylic & wood*

Creative Lighting & Sound, 6 Spires Business Units, Mugiemoss Road, Bucksburn, Aberdeen, AB21 9NY Tel: (01224) 683111 Fax: (01224) 686611 E-mail: cls_aberdeen@btconnect.com Principal Export Areas: Worldwide *Oil field equipment*

Creative Logistics Ltd, Duncan Street, Salford, M5 3SQ Tel: 0161-873 7101 Fax: 0161-872 1447 E-mail: enquiries@creative-logistics.co.uk *Road transport, rail freight & warehousing*

▶ Creative Max Imports, 5 Fourth Avenue, Bluebridge Industrial Estate, Halstead, Essex, CO9 2SY Tel: (01787) 473249 Fax: (01787) 474118 E-mail: sales@creativemax.com *Manufacturers of unique hair accessory & fashion jewellery ranges*

▶ Creative Mind Skills Therapeutic Training, Holden House, Holden Road, Leigh, Lancashire, WN7 1EX Tel: 08704 323423 E-mail: info@cmst.co.uk *Creative Mind Skills Therapeutic Training, Clinical Hypnotherapy Consultant specialising in work based stress managment training, development and awareness*

Creative Packaging South Wales, 47a Millers Avenue, Brynmenyn, Bridgend, CF32 9TD Tel: (01656) 720444 Fax: (01656) 720769 E-mail: enquiries@creative-packaging.co.uk *Established in 1998, Creative Packaging offers innovative design development and manufacture of cardboard products. *Located along the M4 corridor Creative Packaging is ideally situated, to easily service Wales and the South West as well as the rest of the UK. *The core development team head up a tight unit and oversee both the cardboard engineering facility and the production unit. *Creative Packaging has had continued success in the cardboard engineering field. Some of the foremost reasons for this are:- *A strong empathy with designers concerns to preserve the integrity of the design. *We have a firm awareness on the consequence of construction of ease of use and manufacturing costs. *Our ability to successfully marry these sometimes conflicting issues, especially when tight budgets apply.*

▶ Creative Patternmaking by T J B Design, 5 Pinfold Close, Wheaton Aston, Stafford, ST19 9PF Tel: (01785) 840067 Fax: (01785) 840067 *We have over 30 years experience in GRP pattern, mould & model making, freeform shape generation using traditional methods is our speciality, visit our website for more details*

▶ Creative Photo Shop & Portrait Studio, Unit 16, 34 Gerard Street, Ashton-In-Makerfield, Wigan, Lancashire, WN4 9AE Tel: (01942) 725847 E-mail: info@creativephotoshop.co.uk *Portrait studio*

▶ Creative Place Ltd, 4 Millfield House, Woodshots Meadow, Watford, WD18 8SS Tel: (01923) 227272 Fax: (01923) 246556 E-mail: sales@thecreativeplace.co.uk *Design, print, exhibition, retail, display, signage*

Creative Play (U K) Ltd, P O Box 707, Mold, Clwyd, CH7 1FG Tel: (01244) 375627 Fax: (01244) 374990 E-mail: info@creativeplayuk.com *Children's playground manufrs*

▶ Creative Pod Ltd, Basepoint Business & Innovation Centre, Metcalf Way, Crawley, West Sussex, RH11 7XX Tel: (01293) 817228 Fax: (01293) 518201 E-mail: ideas@creative-pod.com *Creative design, print & marketing*

Creative Polymer Developments, 24 Brookfield Drive, Littleborough, Lancashire, OL15 8RH Tel: (01706) 374631 Fax: (01706) 370189 E-mail: michaelgooder@creativepolymer.co.uk *Polyurethane application consultants*

Creative Presentations, 5 The Square, Bagshot, Surrey, GU19 5AX Tel: (01276) 474182 Fax: (01276) 472982 E-mail: info@creative-presentations.com *We excel at graphic design, mixing expertise in*

continued

website design with marketing solutions involving brand identity through to exhibition stand graphics. We understand your needs for online marketing solutions that work, and are both affordable and timely. We are a friendly group of people always happy to discuss your needs. So, if you're looking for a fully interactive web-based learning solution, or your first e-commerce website, we're sure to be able to help you.

▶ Creative Print & Design Wales, Unit 27 Rassau Industrial Estate, Rassau, Ebbw Vale, Gwent, NP23 5SD Tel: (01495) 307007 Fax: (01495) 309572

Creative Promotions, 79 West Regent Street, Glasgow, G2 2AW Tel: 0141-332 7471 Fax: 0141-331 2801 E-mail: enquiries@creativepromotions.co.uk *Advertising gift distributors*

▶ Creative Rage Ltd, Wassell Wood House, Habberley Road, Bewdley, Worcestershire, DY12 1LD Tel: (01299) 409062 E-mail: contact@creativerage.co.uk *A complete media design agency*

Creative Retail Solutions Ltd, 33 - 35 Chapel Road, Parkstone, Poole, Dorset, BH14 0JU Tel: (01202) 710842 Fax: (01202) 710845 E-mail: mary@creativeretailsolutiuons.co.uk *Refrigeration & air conditioning*

Creative Signage, 60 Station Avenue, West Ewell, Epsom, Surrey, KT19 9UH Tel: (020) 8224 0056 E-mail: info@creativesignage.co.uk *Sign makers*

Creative Signs, 10 Worcester Road Industrial Estate, Chipping Norton, Oxfordshire, OX7 5XW Tel: (01608) 643557 Fax: (01608) 643557 E-mail: sales@creativepubsigns.co.uk *Sign manufrs*

Creative Signs, Sandbach Road, Stoke-on-Trent, ST6 2DG Tel: (01782) 214589 Fax: (01782) 214589 E-mail: creative.signs@btopenworld.com *Sign makers*

Creative Signwriting Co., 64 Englands Lane, Gorleston, Great Yarmouth, Norfolk, NR31 6BE Tel: (01493) 600742 Fax: (01493) 653984 E-mail: info@creativesign.co.com *Sign Manufacturer*

Creative Solutions, 197 Hagley Road, Birmingham, B16 9RD Tel: 0121-454 2222 Fax: 0121-456 2362 E-mail: pressoffice@prontaprint.com

Creative Solutions, 32 Ford Lane, Wrecclesham, Farnham, Surrey, GU10 4SF Tel: (01252) 724680 Fax: (01252) 724900 E-mail: production@cresol.co.uk *Conference organising services*

Creative Solutions, Swanston's Road, Great Yarmouth, Norfolk, NR30 3NQ Tel: (01493) 851899 Fax: (01493) 330178 E-mail: sales@creativesolutionsprinting.co.uk *Signs manufrs*

Creative Store Ltd, Studio House, 142 Merton Hall Road, London, SW19 3PZ Tel: (020) 8543 3855 Fax: (020) 8540 7367 E-mail: sales@thecreativestore.co.uk *Design, photography, colour printing & website design*

Creative Technology Management Solutions Ltd, Westall Centre, Holberrow Green, Redditch, Worcestershire, B96 6JY Tel: (01386) 791900 Fax: (0870) 0518715 E-mail: info@ctms-uk.com *Desk top support & asset management*

▶ Creative Timber Ltd, Unit 9A, Luton Business Park, Ilminster, Somerset, TA19 9DU Tel: (01460) 57915 Fax: (01460) 57903 *Shop fitting manufrs*

Creative Works UK Ltd, Unit 1 The Stable Block, Brewer Street Bletchingley, Bletchingley, Redhill, RH1 4QP Tel: (01883) 742999 E-mail: info@ckworks.net *Floral Designers, operating throughout London & South East. Wedding Flowers, Corporate & Event Flowers, Designer Bouquets, flowers for special occasions*

Creativeretouch, 29 Crossfell Road, Hemel Hempstead, Hertfordshire, HP3 8RG Tel: (07790) 850422 E-mail: simon@creativeretouch.co.uk *Creative & digital retouching*

Creaton Engineering Ltd, 6 Merse Road, Moons Moat North Industrial Es, Redditch, Worcestershire, B98 9HL Tel: (01527) 582900 Fax: (01527) 582909 E-mail: enquiries@creaton-engineering.co.uk *CNC machining sub-contractor*

▶ CreatorArt, The Mega Centre, Bernard Road, Sheffield, S2 5BQ Tel: 0114-253 5996 Fax: 0114-269 5882 E-mail: design@creatorart.com *Graphic design & printing services*

▶ Creatside Ltd, 1 Dover Road, Northfleet, Gravesend, Kent, DA11 9PH Tel: (01474) 361230 Fax: (01474) 564380

▶ Creavite Ltd, Colworth House, Sharnbrook, Bedford, MK44 1LQ Tel: (01234) 783720

▶ Creca Sawmills, Crece Camp, Creca, Annan, Dumfriesshire, DG12 6RP Tel: (01461) 500523 Fax: (01461) 500645

Credenhill Ltd, 10 Cossall Industrial Estate, Cossall Industrial Estate, Ilkeston, Derbyshire, DE7 5UG Tel: 0115-932 0144 Fax: 0115-944 0437 E-mail: sales@credenhill.co.uk *Distributor & retailers of medical or surgical supplies*

▶ Credes Solutions, 326 Molesey Road, Walton-on-Thames, Surrey, KT12 3PD Tel: (01932) 244599 Fax: (01932) 244955 E-mail: sales@credes.co.uk *CreDes Solutions is an innovative and creative design and marketing*agency offering our clients a high quality service to meet all design*requirements from the smallest project to a large integrated campaign. We have worked on a variety of projects, from bespoke flyers, corporate literature and identity to websites, direct mail campaigns, exhibitions and integrated campaigns! **Please contact us to request your copy of our promotion CD, containing portfolio samples and an introduction to CreDes Solution, or to speak to us about any of your advertising or marketing requirements. Further information can also be obtained from our website www.credes.co.uk.*See your business potential through creative design....*

Credit Card Keys Ltd, 37 Sovereign Road, Kings Norton Business Centre, Birmingham, B30 3HN Tel: 0121-451 3911 Fax: 0121-451 3133 E-mail: sales@cckeys.co.uk *Credit card key manufrs*

Credit Card Systems Ltd, 64 Walsworth Road, Hitchin, Hertfordshire, SG4 9SX Tel: (01462) 429400 Fax: (01462) 429401 E-mail: sales-ccs@fimak.com *Credit card systems & prepaid tele-phone cards*

▶ Credit Link U K, First Floor Nathaniel House, David Street, Bridgend Industrial Estate, Bridgend, Mid Glamorgan, CF31 3SA Tel: (01656) 767622 Fax: (01656) 669978 E-mail: enquiries@creditlink.co.uk *Creditlink is a well established family run business which was started in 1986 .we have helped thousands of customers all over the uk and are now one of the longest established credit brokers in the uk.*

Credit Protection Association plc, 350 King Street, London, W6 0RX Tel: (020) 8846 0000 Fax: (020) 8741 7459 E-mail: sales@cpa.co.uk *Debt collectors & factors*

Credit Recovery Systems, 345 City Road, London, EC1V 1AS Tel: (020) 8295 7220 Fax: (020) 7833 4832 *Debt recovery services*

Credit Solutions Ltd, Barlow House, 3 Butter Hill, Carshalton, Surrey, SM5 2TW Tel: (020) 8773 7111 Fax: (020) 8773 9919 E-mail: credsol@globalnet.co.uk *Commercial & consumer debt collectors*

▶ Credit Tel International, Network House, 45 Warwick Road, Thames Ditton, Surrey, KT7 0PR Tel: (020) 8398 9555 Fax: (020) 8398 7831 E-mail: info@credittel.com *Debt Recovery for Private Medical accounts. No success No fee. Trace and legal work undertaken.*

Crediton Milling Co. Ltd, Fordton Mill, Fordton, Crediton, Devon, EX17 3DH Tel: (01363) 772212 Fax: (01363) 775009 E-mail: cmc@creditonmilling.co.uk *Animal feed manufrs*

Credo Business Group, 146 Welling Way, Welling, Kent, DA16 2RS Tel: (020) 8856 1700 Fax: (020) 8856 9394 *Secretarial services*

Credowan Ltd, 148 Stocks Lane, East Wittering, Chichester, West Sussex, PO20 8NT Tel: (01243) 670711 Fax: (01243) 672907 E-mail: sales@credowan.co.uk *Microwave component manufrs*

▶ Creeds The Printers, The Gables, Broadoak, Bridport, Dorset, DT6 5NL Tel: (01308) 423411 Fax: (01308) 421511

The Creek Aquatic Garden Centre, 427 Walton Road, West Molesey, Surrey, KT8 2EJ Tel: (020) 8941 8758 E-mail: sales@koicarpuk.co.uk *Aquarium centre*

Creek Audio Ltd, 12 Avebury Court, Mark Road, Hemel Hempstead, Hertfordshire, HP2 7TA Tel: (01442) 260146 Fax: (01442) 243766 *Audio equipment manufrs*

Creekside Boatyard Ltd, Creekside Boatyard, Old Mill Creek, Dartmouth, Devon, TQ6 0HN Tel: (01803) 832649 *Boat repairers*

Creighton Developments Ltd, Unit 15 Enterprise Centre Two, Chester Street, Stockport, Cheshire, SK3 0BR Tel: 0161-480 0668 Fax: 0161-480 0668 *Compression moulders & consultants*

Creighton & Son Ltd, 2 Parr Road, Stanmore, Middlesex, HA7 1QA Tel: (020) 8952 8252 Fax: (020) 8951 1434 E-mail: metalman@btconnect.com *Steel fabricators & welding services*

Creightons P.L.C., Lincoln Road, Peterborough, PE4 6ND Tel: (01733) 281000 Fax: (01733) 281028 E-mail: sales@creightons.com *Toiletries & hair preparation manufrs*

▶ Creme22 Entertainments, Hockers Farm House, Hockers Lane, Detling, Maidstone, Kent, ME14 3JN Tel: 0845 607 6642 E-mail: info@creme22.com *Creme22 is a UK-wide entertainment booking service that prides itself on providing a professional, quality-assured service to all customers.**Creme22 is constantly building its reputation on ensuring tailor-made entertainment for each individual party, so that you get exactly the right act for your party, function or special occasion. We give our time, advice and commitment to guarantee you are happy with the service we offer.**Creme22 has a firm belief in making certain only the best of the UK's entertainment industry work with us. So you can be certain that all our acts - from bands to solo artistes, DJs to magicians - are of an extremely high standard**

▶ Cremyll Ferry, 1 Cremyll Quay Penhellis, Maker Lane, Cremyll, Torpoint, Cornwall, PL10 1HX Tel: (01752) 822105

▶ Crendon Timber Engineering Ltd, Drakes Drive, Long Crendon, Aylesbury, Buckinghamshire, HP18 9BA Tel: (01844) 201020 Fax: (01844) 201625 E-mail: sales@crendon.co.uk *Timber roof trusses*

▶ Creo Audio Equipment, 62 North Street, Leeds, LS2 7PN Tel: 0113-246 7373 Fax: 0113-242 5114 E-mail: sales@creo-designs.com *Audio visual equipment & accessories retailers*

▶ Creo Media, 21 Musters Road, West Bridgford, Nottingham, NG2 7PP Tel: 0115-981 5842 Fax: 0115-982 2238 E-mail: enquiries@creomedia.co.uk *Creo Media is a full service design agency offering creative and technical solutions for both print and the web.**Our services include Corporate Identity, Branding, Brochures, Sales Literature and Direct Mail, Logo Design, Advertising Website Design and Build (including dynamic data base driven, e-Commerce, e-Business and Flash animated sites), CD-ROMs Multimedia and Digital Video/ Animation.*

▶ Creole Trading Ltd, 47 Esplanade, St. Helier, Jersey, JE2 3QB Tel: (01534) 619647 *Aluminium specialists*

Crescent Audio Ltd, 5 Croydon Road, Penge, London, SE20 7TJ Tel: (020) 8778 3391 Fax: (020) 8778 2574 *In car entertainment & security products sales*

Crescent Automatics, 60 St. James St, London, W6 9RW Tel: (020) 8529 9477 *Bingo equipment manufrs*

▶ indicates data change since last edition

▶ Crescent Credit Control, PO Box 459, Walton-on-Thames, Surrey, KT12 2WE Tel: (01932) 706590 Fax: (01932) 706590 E-mail: info@credit-specialists.co.uk *Credit control, aged debt specialists, collection, invoicing, ledger management, account management advice for all sized companies.*

Crescent Draughting & Design, PO Box 914, Market Harborough, Leicestershire, LE16 9YJ Tel: (01858) 410320 Fax: (01858) 410320 E-mail: cresdesign@aol.com *Mechanical engineering design*

Crescent Engineering & Technical Services Ltd, Unit 5, Lee Smith Street, Hull, HU9 1SD Tel: (01482) 329625 Fax: (01482) 581130 *General engineers*

Crescent Glass Ltd, Derby Road, Burton-On-Trent, Staffordshire, DE14 1RX Tel: (01283) 563070 Fax: (01283) 566898 E-mail: info@longlifewindows.co.uk *Double glazed unit manufrs*

Crescent Group, Brunswick House, 8-13 Brunswick Place, Southampton, SO15 2AP Tel: (023) 8063 9777 Fax: (023) 8063 9888 E-mail: sales@crescentplc.com *Ship owners & operators*

Crescent Interiors, Sunnyside Road, Worcester, WR1 1RJ Tel: (01905) 619144 Fax: (01905) 619155 E-mail: sales@crescentinteriors.com *Interior design & manufacturer of fine furnishings*

Crescent Machinery Ltd, Unit 1 Moderna Business Park, Moderna Way, Mytholmroyd, Hebden Bridge, West Yorkshire, HX7 5QQ Tel: (01422) 884888 Fax: 01422 881338 E-mail: info@crescentmachinery.co.uk *Sheet metalwork machinery manufrs and specialist service engineers to the sheet metal and fabrication industries. On site repairs to Presses, Press Brakes, Guillotines, Folders, Band and Circular Saws and ancillary equipment used inthe production of Sheet Metal or Fabricated Steel products. Full workshop facilities for off site repairs and overhaul of machinery. Suppliers of GUILLOTINE SHEAR BLADES, Press Brake Tooling, Saw Blades and Steelworker Punches and Dies.*

Crescent Machinery Ltd, Unit 1 Moderna Business Park, Moderna Way, Mytholmroyd, Hebden Bridge, West Yorkshire, HX7 5QQ Tel: (01422) 884888 Fax: (01422) 881338 E-mail: info@crescentmachinery.co.uk *Metal cutting & metal forming machinery*

Crescent Office Ltd, 71-73 Beverley Road, Hull, HU3 1XL Tel: (01482) 224444 Fax: (01482) 213505 E-mail: user@crescent-office.com *Office furnishers & interiors*

▶ Crescent Plant Hire, South Street, Braintree, Essex, CM7 3QQ Tel: (01376) 344871

▶ Crescent Press Ltd, 9 Wainwright Street, Birmingham, B6 5TH Tel: 0121-326 9223 Fax: 0121-326 9224 E-mail: info@crescentpress.com *Printers*

Crescent Sewing Machines Centre, 3a Crescent East, Thornton-Cleveleys, Lancashire, FY5 3LJ Tel: (01253) 856894 *Sewing machines maintenance & sales haberdashery*

Crescent Sheet Metal Co., 6 Wood End No 2 Mill, Manchester Road, Mossley, Ashton-under-Lyne, Lancashire, OL5 9RR Tel: (01457) 836518 Fax: (01457) 833611 *Sheet metalwork & control panels*

Crescent Signs & Engraving, Unit 5q, Faraday Road, Newbury, Berkshire, RG14 2AD Tel: (01635) 528037 Fax: (01635) 49549 E-mail: enquiries@crescentsigns.co.uk *Interior and exterior Sign manufacturers. Vehicle graphics, display work, acid etching, laser engraving, routing and profiling, vinyl graphics, digital printing, awards. Please refer to our website for a complete range.*

Crescent Silver Repairs & Restoration, 85 Spencer Street, Birmingham, B18 6DE Tel: 0121-236 9006 Fax: 0121-212 1466 E-mail: mail@cresent-silver.co.uk *Silversmiths*

Crescent-Webb Ltd, 14-15 Weller Street, London, SE1 1LQ Tel: (020) 7407 0085 Fax: (020) 7403 0889 *Conveyor manufrs*

Cresco Industrial Supplies Ltd, Brunel Close, Harworth, Doncaster, South Yorkshire, DN11 8QA Tel: (01302) 750057 Fax: (01302) 752922 E-mail: sales@cresco.co.uk *Hose assemblies & pipeline fabrication*

Cress Security Co. Ltd, 6 Wolverhampton Road, Stafford, ST17 4BN Tel: (01785) 211014 Fax: (01785) 227711 *Burglar alarms, cctv systems & lock installers*

Cresswell & Co Birmingham Ltd, 85 New Summer Street, Birmingham, B19 3TE Tel: 0121-359 6311 Fax: 0121-359 5736 *Electroplaters*

Cresswell Morgan Associates, 41 Chobham Road, Woking, Surrey, GU21 6JD Tel: (01483) 776686 Fax: (01483) 730199 *Commercial property agents*

Crest Amusements, St. James Street, New Bradwell, Milton Keynes, MK13 0BL Tel: (01908) 320142 Fax: (01908) 320142 *Amusement machines suppliers*

▶ Crest Bathrooms Ltd, 9 Colquhoun Avenue, Hillington Industrial Estate, Glasgow, G52 4BN Tel: 0141-882 7799 Fax: 0141-882 2777

Crest Engineering, Malvern View Business Park, Stella Way, Bishops Cleeve, Cheltenham, Gloucestershire, GL52 7DQ Tel: (01242) 674687 Fax: (01242) 679315 E-mail: crest.engineering@virgin.net *Precision engineers*

Crest Erection Services, 44a Bristol Road, Keynsham, Bristol, BS31 2BE Tel: 0117-986 6111 Fax: 0117-986 6333 *Shelving & racking*

Crest Freight Forwarding Ltd, 76 High Street, Stony Stratford, Milton Keynes, MK11 1AH Tel: (01908) 307655 Fax: (01908) 307656 E-mail: sales@crestfreight.co.uk *International freight forwarders*

▶ Crest Home Improvements Ltd, Crown Trading Estate, Shepton Mallet, Somerset, BA4 5QQ Tel: (01749) 344211 Fax: (01749) 346376 *Suppliers & installers of windows & doors*

Crest Identity Ltd, Crest House, Stockton Road, Hartlepool, Cleveland, TS25 1TY Tel: (01429) 233533 Fax: (01429) 272400 *Embroideries & work wear suppliers*

Crest Nicholson P.L.C., Crest House, Thurcroft Road, Chertsey, Surrey, KT16 9GN Tel: (01932) 580555 Fax: (0870) 3363990 E-mail: info@crestnicholson.com *House building & construction*

▶ Crest Nicholson Residential (Eastern) Ltd, 1 The Progression Centre, Mark Road, Hemel Hempstead Industrial Estate, Hemel Hempstead, Hertfordshire, HP2 7DW Tel: (01442) 219921 Fax: (01442) 219829

▶ Crest Nicholson Residential South East Ltd, Crest House, 30 High Street, Westerham, Kent, TN16 1RG Tel: (01959) 564282 Fax: (01959) 564177

▶ Crest Nicholson Residential South East Ltd, Crest House, 30 High Street, Westerham, Kent, TN16 1RG Tel: (01959) 564282 Fax: (01959) 564177

▶ Crest Nicholson Residential SW Ltd, Crest House, Lime Kiln Close, Stoke Gifford, Bristol, BS34 8ST Tel: 0117-923 6600 Fax: 0117-969 5792

▶ Crest Plant Ltd, Portland House, 51 Colney Hatch Lane, London, N10 1LJ Tel: (020) 8444 4165 Fax: (020) 8444 1084

Crest Reprographics (Northern) Ltd, Crest House, Gibralter Row, Liverpool, L3 7HJ Tel: 0151-236 2642 Fax: 0151-236 2726 E-mail: info@crest-reprographics.co.uk *Office equipment services*

▶ Crest Scaffolding Ltd, 654 Liverpool Road, Irlam, Manchester, M44 5AD Tel: 0161-776 1055 Fax: 0161-775 9990

▶ Crest Technology, 5 East Glebe, Stonehaven, Kincardineshire, AB39 2HW Tel: (01569) 766662 Fax: (07876) 881265 E-mail: info@crest2000.com *Computing & engineering*

Crest Ultrasonics Ltd, Units 1 & 4 Italstyle Factory, Cambridge Road, Harlow, Essex, CM20 2HE Tel: (01279) 418942 Fax: (01279) 453926 E-mail: sales@cchydrosonics.com *Ultrasonic cleaning equipment manufacturers*

▶ Crest Windows Nottingham Ltd, Park Road East, Calverton, Nottingham, NG14 6LL Tel: 0115-965 5179 Fax: 0115-965 5102

Cresta Gems, 12 Victoria Street, Derby, DE1 1EQ Tel: (01332) 296666 Fax: (01332) 298888 *Jewellery manufrs & distributors*

Crestala Fencing Ltd, South Farm, Broom Lane, Langton Green, Tunbridge Wells, Kent, TN3 9JN Tel: (01892) 864366 Fax: (01892) 864366 *Fencing & gates suppliers*

▶ Crestbrook Heating Ltd, 9-11 Whitby Street, Hartlepool, Cleveland, TS24 7AD Tel: (01429) 263191 Fax: (01429) 861965

Crestline Printers Ltd, 1 Atlas Court, Coalville, Leicestershire, LE67 3FL Tel: (01530) 838761 Fax: (01530) 812582 E-mail: enquiries@crestline.co.uk *Design print & print management services*

Crete Shipping, 42 Battersea Rise, London, SW11 1EE Tel: (020) 7223 1244 Fax: (020) 7924 3895 E-mail: sales@creteshipping.co.uk *Freight forwarding agents*

Creteco Sales, 17 St. Martins Street, Wallingford, Oxfordshire, OX10 0EA Tel: (01491) 839488 Fax: (01491) 833879 E-mail: sales@creteco.co.uk *Reinforced concrete accessories* Also at: Stoke-on-Trent

Crew Stainless & Special Alloys, Unit 17 Coneygre Industrial Estate, Tipton, West Midlands, DY4 8XP Tel: 0121-520 1066 Fax: 0121-520 7600 E-mail: sales@crewstainless.co.uk *Stainless steel processors & plasma cutting*

Crewdson & Co. Ltd, Beck Mills, Shap Road, Kendal, Cumbria, LA9 6NY Tel: (01539) 730990 Fax: (01539) 725316 E-mail: crewco@btconnect.com *Effluence treatment agents*

Crewe Colour Printers Ltd, Millbuck Way, Sandbach, Cheshire, CW11 3SH Tel: (01270) 761113 Fax: (01270) 766386 *Lithographic colour printers*

Crewe Precision Engineering Ltd, Tricketts Lane, Willaston, Nantwich, Cheshire, CW5 6PY Tel: (01270) 661033 Fax: (01270) 664524 E-mail: chris@cpe-eng.fsnet.co.uk *Precision engineers*

Crewe Stove Enamelling Co. Ltd, Springvale Industrial Estate, Moston Road, Sandbach, Cheshire, CW11 3HL Tel: (01270) 769069 Fax: (01270) 768003 *Powder coating services & fabrications*

▶ Crewes Carp'In Centre, 122 West Street, Crewe, CW1 3HG Tel: (01270) 588466 Fax: (01270) 258825 *Fishing tackle retailers*

▶ Crewkerne Bouncy Castles, Court Dairy Farm, Clapton, Crewkerne, Somerset, TA18 8PU Tel: (01460) 77562 *Inflatable bouncy castle hire services*

▶ Crewkerne Carriers Ltd, 18 Buckland Road, Pen Mill Trading Estate, Yeovil, Somerset, BA21 5EA Tel: (01935) 477003 Fax: (01935) 477001

Crewkerne Concrete Products, Unit 12 Cropmead, Crewkerne, Somerset, TA18 7HQ Tel: (01460) 74415 Fax: (01460) 74415 *Pre cast concrete product suppliers*

Crewkerne Horticultural Engineers, North Street Trading Estate, North Street, Crewkerne, Somerset, TA18 7AW Tel: (01460) 72428 Fax: (01460) 75644 *Horticultural machinery sales & repairs*

Crewsaver Ltd, Clarence Square, Mumby Road, Gosport, Hampshire, PO12 1AQ Tel: (023) 9252 8621 Fax: (023) 9251 0905 E-mail: sales@crewsaver.co.uk *Marine lifesaving equipment manufrs*

▶ Cri Digital, 18 St Peters Street, Nottingham, NG7 3FF Tel: 0115-978 3337

Criag Mill Of Scotland, 17 Station Road, Biggar, Lanarkshire, ML12 6BS Tel: (01899) 220289 Fax: (01899) 221182 E-mail: calzeat@aol.com *Tie & scarf manufrs*

A.B. Crick (Printers) Ltd, 762 Ampthill, Bedford, MK45 2XH Tel: (01234) 742292 Fax: (01234) 742292 *Stationery printers*

▶ Crick House Interiors, Landscape House, Northampton Road, Weston-on-the-Green, Bicester, Oxfordshire, OX25 3TJ Tel: (01869) 343007 Fax: (01869) 343080 *Furniture manufrs*

▶ Crickhowell Joinery, Timbercraft Park, Llangattock, Crickhowell, Powys, NP8 1HW Tel: (01873) 810156 Fax: (01873) 810204

Cricklewood Electronics Ltd, 40-42 Cricklewood Broadway, London, NW2 3ET Tel: (020) 8452 0161 Fax: (020) 8208 1441 E-mail: sales@cricklewoodelectronics.com *CCTV & electronic component distributors*

Crieff Hydro Hotel, Sand Tower Road, Crieff, Perthshire, PH7 3LQ Tel: (01764) 655555 Fax: (01764) 653087 *Hotel services*

Crieff Pottery, Muthill Road, Crieff, Perthshire, PH7 4HQ Tel: (01764) 655081 Fax: (01764) 655081 E-mail: enquiries@crieff.co.uk *Pottery manufrs*

The Crier Media Group, 11 Station Road East, Oxted, Surrey, RH8 0BD Tel: (01883) 734582 Fax: (01883) 713640 E-mail: general@crier.co.uk Principal Export Areas: Worldwide *Business to business magazine publishers*

Crilco Confections Ltd, 15 Flagstaff Road, Cloughoge, Newry, County Down, BT35 8NR Tel: (028) 3026 4877 Fax: (028) 3025 6311 E-mail: crilco@utinternet.com *Confectionery manufrs*

Crime Beat Security, 388 High Road, Ilford, Essex, IG1 1TL Tel: (020) 8478 4999 Fax: (020) 8478 7722 E-mail: sales@crimebeatsecurity.co.uk *Burglar alarm installers*

Crimecure Burglar Alarm Systems, Enterprise House, 27a North Street, Crewkerne, Somerset, TA18 7AL Tel: (01460) 77582 Fax: (01460) 77582 E-mail: ken@crimecure.fsnet.co.uk *Security system installation, maintenance & monitoring services. SSAIB Approved*

Crimewatch Security Ltd, Magpie House, 57 Earle Street, Crewe, CW1 2AS Tel: (01270) 589627 Fax: (01270) 584087 E-mail: kevinvickers@crimewatch-security.co.uk *Security installation services*

▶ Crimewatch Video International, 89-91 Wellington Road North, Stockport, Cheshire, SK4 2LP Tel: 0161-480 5003 E-mail: sales@crimewatchcctv.com *Closed circuit television equipment suppliers*

Crimped Paper Works(M/C) Ltd, Bowden Park, Chapel-En-Le-Frith, High Peak, Derbyshire, SK23 0JX Tel: (01298) 812181 Fax: (01298) 815905 E-mail: sales@crimpedpaper.co.uk *Crimped paper goods & food packaging material manufrs*

Crimway, 17 County Road, Buckingham Road Industrial Estate, Buckingham Road Industrial Estate, Brackley, Northamptonshire, NN13 7AX Tel: (01280) 840005 Fax: (01280) 704440 *Lampshades manufrs*

Crinan Boatyard Ltd, Crinan, Lochgilphead, Argyll, PA31 8SW Tel: (01546) 830232 Fax: (01546) 830281 E-mail: info@crinanboatyard.co.uk *Boatyard & chandlers*

Cringate Engineering Ltd, 31-51 Blundell Street, Liverpool, L1 0AJ Tel: 0151-708 6082 Fax: 0151-708 5612 E-mail: cringate.eng.ltd@btconnect.com *Structural steelwork engineers*

Cripps Sears & Partners, Sardinia House, 52 Lincoln's Inn Fields, London, WC2A 3LZ Tel: (020) 7440 8999 Fax: (020) 7242 0515 E-mail: london@crippssears.com *Management consultants*

Crips Ltd, 40 Oxford Drive, Berdmonsey Street, London, SE1 2FB Tel: (020) 7403 1190 Fax: (020) 7407 4734 E-mail: enquiries@crips.co.uk *Asbestos removal contractors*

Criptic-Arvis Ltd, Croft Grange Works, Bridge Park Road, Thurmaston, Leicester, LE4 8BL Tel: 0116-260 9700 Fax: 0116-264 0147 E-mail: sales@arvis.co.uk Principal Export Areas: Worldwide *Design & manufacturers for assorted bearings*

Crisp Clean Services Ltd, Unit 17-18, Curry Rivel, Langport, Somerset, TA10 0PP Tel: (01458) 250385 Fax: (01458) 252515 E-mail: john@crispclean.demon.co.uk *Janitorial manufrs*

▶ Crisp Design, 5 Market Square, Winslow, Buckingham, MK18 3AB Tel: (01296) 712387 Fax: (01296) 715281 E-mail: sales@crispdesign.com *Contemporary & tradition engraved awards & trophies , name badges*

Crisp Marketing Associates Ltd, 45 Queen Street, Exeter, EX4 3SR Tel: (01392) 412582 Fax: (01392) 421942 E-mail: office@crisp-uk.com *Business development consultancy training* Also at: Exeter

▶ Crisp Solutions Ltd, Enterprise House, 5 Roundwood Lane, Harpenden, Hertfordshire, AL5 3BW Tel: 08456 120042 Fax: 08456 120043 E-mail: answers@crispsolutions.co.uk *Providing Enhanced Marketing Services to Industry*

▶ Crispins Services Ltd, 35-37 Pearson Street, London, E2 8JD Tel: (020) 7739 0303 Fax: (020) 7739 7757 E-mail: e-mail@crispins-removals.co.uk

Cristal Insulations Ltd, 48 Goodmayes Road, Ilford, Essex, IG3 9UR Tel: (020) 8597 0442 Fax: (020) 8597 0713 *Insulation contractors*

▶ Cristal Lighting, Priory Mill House, Leckhampstead Road, Akeley, Buckingham, MK18 5HG Tel: (01280) 860154 Fax: (01280) 860546 E-mail: sales@crystal-lighting-centre.com *Sales of Decorative Crystal Lighting by Swarovski for Domestic and Commercial use. Products include Crystal Recessed Downlights and Spots, Crystal Fibre Optics and Crystal Panels.*

Cristie Ltd, Cristie Mill, Chestnut Lane, Stroud, Gloucestershire, GL5 3EH Tel: (01453) 847000 Fax: (01453) 847001 E-mail: sales@cristie.com *Computer peripheral equipment*

Cristom Construction Ltd, Plot 10 Ryeford Indust Estate, Ryeford, Stonehouse, Gloucestershire, GL10 2LG Tel: (01453) 823847 Fax: (01453) 823847 *Civil engineering*

Critchley & Curtis, 7 Clegg Street, Liverpool, L5 3SP Tel: 0151-207 2437 Fax: 0151-207 2437 *Joinery manufrs*

Criterion Ices, The Manor Farm Creamery, Bird Green, Thurston, Bury St. Edmunds, Suffolk, IP31 3QJ Tel: 01359 230208 Fax: 01359 232838 E-mail: enquiries@criterion-ices.co.uk *Criterion has over 30 traditional and surprising fresh cream dairy ices, from Vanilla to Vintage*

continued

Marmalade. Yodel yogurt ice is a refreshing alternative in five tangy fresh fruit flavours plus Natural, which also makes a superb base for iced smoothies! Criterion also offers around a dozen full fruit sorbets and a deliciously different dark chocolate sorbet. These exclusive award-winning ices are all hand made at Criterion's family-run farm creamery in Suffolk from only natural ingredients. Scoop them straight from the freezer or serve in single portion tubs. Criterion delivers direct from its London depot and Suffolk creamery, and nationwide through Stratford Fine Foods. Find out more at www.criterion-ices.co.uk or call Jim Valenti on 07778 842090

▶ Critical Blue Ltd, The SMC, West Mains Road, Edinburgh, EH9 3JF Tel: 0131-650 7474

Critical Research Ltd, Crown Life House, 41-43 Alma Street, Luton, LU1 2PL Tel: (01582) 480588 Fax: (01582) 485015 E-mail: mail@critical.co.uk *Telephone market researchers*

Crittall Windows Ltd, Springwood Drive, Braintree, Essex, CM7 2YN Tel: (01376) 324106 Fax: (01376) 349662 E-mail: hq@crittall-windows.co.uk *Metal window manufrs* Also at: Glasgow

▶ CRM4Business Limited, Huntington House Business Centre, 278 - 290 Huntington Street, Nottingham, NG7 7FN Tel: (0870) 3501808 E-mail: james.bogue@crm4business.co.uk *CRM4Business provide small and medium sized business with sales, marketing and customer service software. Contact management and CRM solutions*

▶ Croaky Karaoke, 11 Perrylands, Charlwood, Horley, Surrey, RH6 0BL Tel: (01293) 863796 E-mail: taylormadeentertainment@btconnect.com *Karaoke*

Croan Seafoods Ltd, Units 5-10 Albert Street, Peterhead, Aberdeenshire, AB42 1ZW Tel: (01779) 471621 Fax: (01779) 472916 *Fish merchants*

Croboride Engineering Ltd, Little Burton West, Burton-on-Trent, Staffordshire, DE14 1PP Tel: (01283) 511188 Fax: (01283) 530845 E-mail: info@croboride.co.uk *Hardfacing, general machining & metal spraying*

Crochet Design, 11 North Street, Morecambe, Lancashire, LA4 5LR Tel: (01524) 831752 Fax: (01524) 833099 E-mail: paulineturner@crochet.co.uk *Provide teaching & instruction for crochet*

Jas Crockart & Son, 26 Allan Street, Blairgowrie, Perthshire, PH10 6AD Tel: (01250) 872056 Fax: (01250) 872168 E-mail: info@jamescrockartandson.co.uk *Gun makers & repairs*

Crocker Bros, 8-18 Station Road, Chellaston, Derby, DE73 5SU Tel: (01332) 700699 Fax: (01332) 705655 E-mail: sales@crockerbros.co.uk *Marquee & portable building manufrs*

Crockerhill Cars, Unit 10 Quarry Lane, Chichester, West Sussex, PO19 8QA Tel: (01243) 528731 Fax: (01243) 533343 E-mail: rbjervis@aol.com *Car & tyre repairers*

Crocket Equestrian & Outdoor, 3 Old Bridge Road, Ayr, KA8 9SX Tel: (01292) 286377 Fax: (01292) 610444 *Equestrian retailers*

Crockett Guitars, Nethersole Farm, The Street, Womenswold, Canterbury, Kent, CT4 6HE Tel: (01227) 832832 E-mail: info@crockettguitars.com *Guitar repairs & manufrs*

Crockett & Son, Aylesbury Road, Askett, Princes Risborough, Buckinghamshire, HP27 9LY Tel: (01844) 344175 Fax: (01844) 343509 *Gate makers & erectors*

▶ Crockford Lane Pet, Coal, Salt Supplies, Crockford Lane,, Chineham, Basingstoke, Hampshire, RG24 8NA Tel: (01256) 818051 E-mail: joanner@ntlworld.com *Supplies coal, salt, pet feeds & accessories*

Crocks Emporium, 63 Longrow, Campbeltown, Argyll, PA28 6ER Tel: (01586) 551344 Fax: (01586) 551277 *Household furniture suppliers*

Crocodilla Ltd, East Cottage, Hill View Road, Michelmersh, Romsey, Hampshire, SO51 0NN Tel: (01794) 367286 Fax: (01794) 367286 E-mail: info@crocodilla.co.uk *Crocodilla Ltd the company with the solution to your problems. We are a company which you can work with to reach your ultimate goal. With a team of dedicated staff ready to help answer any questions or queries you have to offer. We offer solutions for many applications including, reinforced prepunched door and window steels, steel framed enclosures, casement containers, safety storage systems, security grills and covers.*

Croda Chemicals Europe Ltd, Oak Road, Hull, HU6 7PH Tel: (01482) 443181 Fax: (01482) 341792 *Fatty acid & derivatives manufrs*

Croda Chemicals International Ltd, Cowick Hall, Snaith, Goole, North Humberside, DN14 9AA Tel: (01405) 860551 Fax: (01405) 861767 *Raw material suppliers*

Croda Europe Ltd, Foundry Lane, Widnes, Cheshire, WA8 8UB Tel: 0151-423 3441 Fax: 0151-423 3441 *Cosmetic proteins manufrs*

Croft plc, 74 Hounds Gate, Nottingham, NG1 6BA Tel: 0115-952 7551 Fax: 0115-952 7553 E-mail: sales@croftplc.com *Business development consultants*

Alan Croft Property Services, 48 Conduit Street, London, W1S 2YR Tel: (020) 7434 9799 Fax: (020) 7734 0217 *Surveyors & valuers*

Croft Architectural Hardware Ltd, 23 Lower Lichfield Street, Willenhall, West Midlands, WV13 1QQ Tel: (01902) 606493 Fax: (01902) 606933 E-mail: sales@croft-arch.co.uk *Builders hardware manufrs*

Croft Backstop Ltd, Winston Avenue, Croft, Leicester, LE9 3GQ Tel: (01455) 285600 Fax: (01455) 285909 E-mail: sales@croftbackstop.com *To help prevent accidents when reversing large vehicles, Backstop automatically applies the brakes when the sensing ONLY OPERATES IN REVERSE GEAR. The system becomes active as soon as reverse gear is selected.**Once the sensor has been activated, the brakes stay locked on until*

continued

Company Information

continuation
*reverse gear is de-selected.**LOWER COST...*Croft Backstop saves money for two good reasons:** It reduces the likelihood of damage to vehicles and property.* It can be a considerable asset when vehicle insurance premiums are reviewed.**EASY FITMENT AND MAINTENANCE*Backstop comes in kit form. It is simple to fit in three to four hours to almost any air braked rigid truck or trailer. Weekly maintenance checks only take minutes and damaged components are easily replaced.*

▶ Croft Bros UK Ltd, Unit D1 Riverside Way, Cowley, Uxbridge, Middlesex, UB8 2YF Tel: (01895) 850700 Fax: (01895) 270584 E-mail: info@croftbrothers.co.uk *Croft Brothers are specialists in Bedford Trucks, Bedford Spares and Bedford Parts as well as Isuzu Trucks and Isuzu Spares*

Croft Computer Supplies, 7 Croft Road, Kiltarlity, Beauly, Inverness-Shire, IV4 7HZ Tel: (01463) 741683 Fax: (01463) 741683 *Computer consumables supplier*

Croft Computer Systems, 124 Heath Lane, Croft, Warrington, WA3 7DS Tel: (01925) 764999 Fax: (01925) 765655 E-mail: croft.computers@virgin.net *Software development services*

Croft Diamond Tools (UK '91) Ltd, Plumpton House, Plumpton Road, Hoddesdon, Hertfordshire, EN11 0LB Tel: (01992) 447700 Fax: (01992) 447519 E-mail: rosecroft@btconnect.com *Optical equipment manufrs*

Croft Engineering Co. Ltd, Unit 7A, Parnall Road, Fishponds, Bristol, BS16 3JH Tel: 0117-958 3286 Fax: 0117-958 4390 *Precision engineers & machinists*

Croft Engineering, Green Croft, Oughterby, Carlisle, CA5 6JH Tel: (01228) 576336 Fax: (01228) 576155 *General engineers*

Croft Engineering UK Ltd, 4 The Omni Business Centre, Omega Park, Alton, Hampshire, GU34 2QD Tel: (01420) 590009 Fax: (01420) 590009 E-mail: sales@croft-eng.co.uk *Concrete drilling equipment & precision engineers*

▶ Croft Fuels Ltd, PO BOX 0, LIVERPOOL, L38 0WY Tel: 0151 929 2900 Fax: 0151 929 3050 E-mail: sales@croft-fuels.co.uk *Diesel fuel cards derv bunkering Keyfuels network. Low cost diesel.*

▶ Croft Impex Ltd, Unit 5 Henry Boot Way, Hull, HU4 7DY Tel: (01482) 351116 Fax: (01482) 351091 E-mail: sales@croftimpex.co.uk *Suppliers of fasteners,fixings & sealants to the UK distributor network*

Croft Joinery, Castle Garage Yard, Croft Road, Neath, West Glamorgan, SA11 1RW Tel: (01639) 633355 *Joinery manufrs*

Croft Mill, Croft Mill, Lowther Lane, Foulridge, Colne, Lancashire, BB8 7NG Tel: (01282) 869625 Fax: (01282) 870038 E-mail: info@croftmill.co.uk *Postal fabrics & sewing aids suppliers*

▶ Croft Networking, 20 Jardine Way, Dunstable, Bedfordshire, LU5 4AX Tel: (01582) 513234 *Pc building , home servicing , upgrading . computer training , Home and office network solutions . Web site building and hosting . Hardware and software retailer . in herts . beds and bucks*

Croft Printing, Label House, Wilford Road, Ruddington, Nottingham, NG11 6ES Tel: 0115-945 6065 Fax: 0115-945 6067 E-mail: info@croftprinting.co.uk *Flexographic & lithographic printers*

▶ Croft Sales, East Durran, Castletown, Thurso, Caithness, KW14 8TE Tel: (01847) 821405 Fax: (01847) 821153 E-mail: jim@jimmacmillan.co.uk *Land agents*

Croftbench Ltd, Pindar Road, Hoddesdon, Hertfordshire, EN11 0DA Tel: (01992) 444133 Fax: (01992) 445296 *Fibreboard corrugated containers*

▶ Crofters Commission, 6 Castle Wynd, Inverness, IV2 3EQ Tel: (01463) 663450 E-mail: sales@crofterscommission.org.uk

Crofton Conservatory Centre, 112 Stubbington Lane, Fareham, Hampshire, PO14 2PE Tel: (01329) 665025 Fax: (01329) 668526 E-mail: sales@croftonconservatorycentre.com *Conservatories suppliers & installers*

Crofton Engineering Ltd, Cambridge Road, Linton, Cambridge, CB21 4NN Tel: (01223) 892138 Fax: (01223) 893547 E-mail: info@crofton-eng.co.uk *Steel fabricators & finishers*

Crofton House Associates, Crofton House, The Moor, Hawkhurst, Cranbrook, Kent, TN18 4NN Tel: (01580) 752919 Fax: (01580) 754173 E-mail: info@crofton-house.co.uk *Industrial cleaning equipment suppliers & suspended ceiling restorers*

Crofton Micro Systems Ltd, Forest Hill Industrial Estate, Perry Vale, London, SE23 2LX Tel: (020) 8699 7575 E-mail: sales@crofton.co.uk *Computer systems manufrs*

▶ Crofton Pallets Ltd, Thorold Street, Grimsby, South Humberside, DN31 3AL Tel: (01472) 362677 Fax: (01472) 358857 E-mail: sales@crofton-pallets.co.uk *Pallet company*

Crofton Park Removals Ltd, Unit 8 Thurston Industrial Estate, Jerrard Street, London, SE13 7SH Tel: (020) 8318 5731 Fax: (020) 8318 5787 *Removal contractors*

Croftons Manufacturers, Unit A001-2 Faircharm Trading Estate, 8-12 Creekside, London, SE8 3DX Tel: (020) 8320 2083 Fax: (020) 8320 2084 E-mail: enquiries@croftonltd.com *Crofton Ltd, London, has been established since 1954. Crofton is a leading supplier of Patient Case Note Folders & Doctors Surgery Folders to The NHS. Crofton also specialise in manufacturing bespoke stationery products, including presentation, foolscap, conference folders & hotel stationery. Full lithographic printing and finishing services available.*

Crofts & Assinder, Standard Brass Works, Lombard Street, Deritend, Birmingham, B12 0QX Tel: 0121-622 1074 Fax: 0121-622 1074 E-mail: general@crofts.co.uk *Cabinet fittings & furniture manufrs*

Crolla Ice Cream Co. Ltd, 48 Jessie Street, Glasgow, G42 0PG Tel: 0141-423 1161 Fax: 0141-423 2596 E-mail: sales@crollaicecream.co.uk *Ice cream suppliers*

Cromac Smith Ltd, 34-40 Warwick Road, Kenilworth, Warwickshire, CV8 1HE Tel: (01926) 865800 Fax: (01926) 865808 E-mail: albatros@cromacsmith.com *International transportation, freight forwarding & shipping*

▶ Cromar Metal Products Ltd, Unit 3 Hill View Trading Estate, Guards Road, Coldstream, Berwickshire, TD12 4EE Tel: (01890) 882944 Fax: (01890) 882944 E-mail: info@cromarmp.freeserve.co.uk *Swarf conveyors, chip conveyors, swarf management systems - repairs/service*

▶ Cromar Solutions Ltd, 8 Chestnut Close Baltonsborough, Glastonbury, Somerset, BA6 8PH Tel: (01458) 851568 Fax: (01458) 851568 E-mail: martyn@cromarsolutions.co.uk *Cromar Solutions Ltd is a global technical consultancy with the emphasis on MAKING THE CHEMISTRY WORK. It offers a total commitment to the process of effective change and improving 'competitiveness' through encouragement of manufacturing excellence and Business Sustainability under "Lean Manufacturing" principles.*Specialists in the manufacture of Polyester polyols for the Polyurethanes polymer businesses.*Uniquely, specialising in the use of nIR (near Infra Red) analysis for process and product validation studies**

Cromartie Kilns Ltd, Park Hall Road, Longton, Stoke-On-Trent, ST3 5AY Tel: (01782) 313947 Fax: (01782) 599723 E-mail: enquiries@cromartie.co.uk *Kiln builders*

▶ Cromaston Ltd, 17 Swan Street, Sileby, Loughborough, Leicestershire, LE12 7NN Tel: (01509) 812840 Fax: (01509) 813494

▶ Cromb Electricians Crieff Ltd, Unit 7 Crioch Business Centre, Crioch Place, Crieff, Perthshire, PH7 3BW Tel: (01764) 653177

Crombie Computer Consultants, 28 Bolney Avenue, Peacehaven, East Sussex, BN10 8NA Tel: (01273) 583304 Fax: (01273) 575312 E-mail: ccc@crombies.freeserve.co.uk *IT consultants*

Crombie Office Equipment Ltd, Unit 9 Wellington Business Park, Wellington Circle, Nigg, Aberdeen, AB12 3JG Tel: (01224) 630082 Fax: (01224) 632168 E-mail: sales@gfofficesupplies.co.uk *Office equipment retailers*

▶ Cromer Portland Limited, 130 Shaftesbury Avenue, London, W1D 5EU Tel: (020) 7031 0877 Fax: (020) 7031 0879 E-mail: info@cromer.uk.com *DDA/Disabled Access Consultancy services and training, access audits and design appraisals, facilities planning, strategic relocation management.*

Crompton Controls Ltd, Monckton Road, Wakefield, West Yorkshire, WF2 7AL Tel: (01924) 368251 Fax: (01924) 367274 E-mail: sales@cromptoncontrols.co.uk *Speed drives manufrs*

Crompton Instruments Ltd, Freebournes Road, Witham, Essex, CM8 3AH Tel: (0870) 8707500 E-mail: crompton.info@tycoelectronics.com *An extensive range of products designed for the measurement, control, analysis and communication of power and energy consumption, and power quality data.* Also at: Branches throughout the U.K.

Crompton & Rathbone (Tools) Ltd, 111-117 Sydenham Road, Birmingham, B11 1DG Tel: 0121-773 7140 Fax: 0121-773 7140 *Press tool & jig manufrs*

Crompton Technology Group Ltd, Thorp Park Thorpe Way, Banbury, Oxfordshire, OX16 4SU Tel: (01295) 220130 Fax: (01295) 220138 E-mail: info@ctgltd.co.uk Principal Export Areas: Worldwide *Manufacturers of cryogenic composite materials*

▶ Cromwall Fabrications (Sayrank) Ltd, Unit 10A, Palatine Industrial Estate, Causeway Avenue, Warrington, WA4 6QQ Tel: (01925) 637665 Fax: (01925) 417979 *Metalworking & fabrication*

Cromwell Ltd, Station Road, North Hykeham, Lincoln, LN6 9AL Tel: (01522) 500888 Fax: (01522) 500857 E-mail: sales@cromwell.co.uk *Complete industrial suppliers*

Cromwell Basingstoke, Unit 5, Sherrington Way, Basingstoke, Hampshire, RG22 4DQ Tel: (01256) 355966 Fax: (01256) 477230 E-mail: info@cromwell.co.uk *Industrial supplies & tool distributors*

Cromwell (Birmingham), 217 Chester Street, Aston, Birmingham, B6 4AE Tel: 0121-380 1700 Fax: 0121-380 1710 E-mail: birmingham@cromwell.co.uk *Industrial Supplies & Tool Distributors*

Cromwell Bristol Ltd, Unit E St. Vincents Trading Estate, Bristol, BS2 0UY Tel: 0117-972 1127 Fax: 0117-972 4287 E-mail: bristol@cromwell.co.uk *Industrial Supplies & Tool Distributors*

Cromwell Group Ltd, B Great Fenton Business Park, Grove Road, Stoke-on-Trent, ST4 4LZ Tel: (01782) 746746 Fax: (01782) 414414 E-mail: stoke@cromwell.co.uk *Industrial suppliers & tool distributors*

Cromwell Industrial Supplies Ltd, Unit 11 Manton Centre, Manton Lane, Manton Industrial Estate, Bedford, MK41 7PX Tel: (01234) 716470 Fax: (01234) 211214 E-mail: bedford@cromwell-tools.co.uk *Industrial tool distributors*

Cromwell Industrial Supplies, Unit 2-3 Anthonys Way, Medway City Estate, Rochester, Kent, ME2 4DN Tel: (01634) 290586 Fax: (01634) 290589 E-mail: rochester@cromwell.co.uk *Industrial Supplies & Tool Distributors*

▶ Cromwell Industrials Supplies, 31 Alvis Road, Engineer Park, Sandycroft, Deeside, Clwyd, CH5 2QB Tel: (01244) 530400 Fax: (01244) 532100

Cromwell Manchester Ltd, 2 Brent Road, Green Lane Trading Estate, Stockport, Cheshire, SK4 2LD Tel: 0161-476 6666 Fax: 0161-476 4444 E-mail: cromwell@manchester.co.uk *Industrial supplies & tool distributors*

Cromwell Packers, 53A Milton Rd, Warley, Brentwood, Essex, CM14 5DS Tel: (01277) 213290 *Food processing*

Cromwell Plastics Ltd, 53-54 New Street, Quarry Bank, Brierley Hill, West Midlands, DY5 2AZ Tel: (01384) 564146 Fax: (01384) 561645 E-mail: sales@cromwell-plastics.co.uk *Compression & transfer moulding services*

Cromwell (Portsmouth), Unit 15, Admirals Park, Williams Road, Portsmouth, PO3 5NJ Tel: (023) 9266 8512 Fax: (023) 9269 9179 E-mail: portsmouth@cromwell-tools.co.uk *Industrial Supplies & Tool Distributors*

Cromwell Security & Fire Services Ltd, 72 Fortune Green Road, London, NW6 1DS Tel: (020) 7435 0334 Fax: (020) 7794 3384 *Commercial & residential security services*

Cromwell (Smethwick), Middlemore Road, Smethwick, West Midlands, B66 2DR Tel: 0121-558 1133 Fax: 0121-565 3530 E-mail: smethwick@cromwell.co.uk *Industrial Tool Distributors*

Cromwell Tools Ltd, 2 Murcar Industrial Estate, Denmore Road, Bridge of Don, Aberdeen, AB23 8JW Tel: (01224) 820851 Fax: (01224) 820877 E-mail: sales@kennedy-tools.co.uk *Industrial suppliers & tool distributors*

Cromwell Tools Ltd, Gorman House, James Street, Righead Industrial Estate, Bellshill, Lanarkshire, ML4 3LU Tel: (01698) 746974 Fax: (01698) 841988 E-mail: glasgow@cromwell-tools.co.uk *Industrial Tool Distributors*

Cromwell Tools Ltd, 3-4 Tollgate Close, Cardiff, CF11 8TN Tel: (029) 2034 5888 Fax: (029) 2034 5777 E-mail: cardiff@cromwell.co.uk *Industrial supplies & tool distributors*

Cromwell Tools Ltd, 27 Endemere Road, Coventry, CV6 5PY Tel: (024) 7666 4614 Fax: (024) 7666 6667 E-mail: coventry@cromwell-tools.co.uk *Industrial Supplies & Tool Distributors*

▶ Cromwell Tools Ltd, Thirsk Place, Derby, DE24 8JJ Tel: (01332) 360660 Fax: (01332) 204239 E-mail: derby@cromwell.co.uk *Complete industrial supplies & tooling distributors*

Cromwell Tools Ltd, Shaw Lane Industrial Estate, Ogden Road, Doncaster, South Yorkshire, DN2 4SQ Tel: (01302) 366600 Fax: (01302) 327556 E-mail: doncaster@cromwell-tools.co.uk *Industrial Tool Distributors*

Cromwell Tools Ltd, Estate Road 6, South Humberside Industrial Estate, Grimsby, South Humberside, DN31 2TG Tel: (01472) 358741 Fax: (01472) 241433 E-mail: grimsby@cromwell-tools.co.uk *Industrial supplies & tool distributors*

Cromwell Tools Ltd, St. James Street, Hull, HU3 2DH Tel: (01482) 326999 Fax: (01482) 213089 E-mail: hull@cromwell-tools.co.uk *Industrial supply company distributors*

Cromwell Tools Ltd, Gibraltar Island Road, Old Mill Business Park, Leeds, LS10 1RJ Tel: 0113-277 7730 Fax: 0113-277 7724 E-mail: leeds@cromwell.co.uk *Industrial supplies & tool distributors*

Cromwell Tools Ltd, Unit D 7 Bilton Way, Luton, LU1 1UU Tel: (01582) 484666 Fax: (01582) 726167 E-mail: luton@cromwell-tools.co.uk *Industrial Tool Distributors*

Cromwell Tools Ltd, The Tool Centre, 75 St James Mill Road, Northampton, NN5 5JP Tel: (01604) 752488 Fax: (01604) 753815 E-mail: northampton@cromwell-tools.co.uk *Industrial Tool Distributors*

Cromwell Tools Ltd, 19 Concorde Road, Norwich, NR6 6BJ Tel: (01603) 410939 Fax: (01603) 410939 E-mail: norwich@cromwell-tools.co.uk *Industrial Tool Distributors*

Cromwell Tools Ltd, 131 Queens Road, Beeston, Nottingham, NG9 2FE Tel: 0115-922 3311 Fax: 0115-925 1342 E-mail: nottingham@cromwell-tools.co.uk *Industrial Supplies & Tool Distributors*

Cromwell Tools Ltd, Westcombe Square, Royce Road, Peterborough, PE1 5YB Tel: (01733) 555524 Fax: (01733) 311103 E-mail: peterborough@cromwell-tools.co.uk *Industrial Tool Distributors*

Cromwell Tools Ltd, 770 Buckingham Avenue, Slough, SL1 4NL Tel: (01753) 696000 Fax: (01753) 696966 E-mail: slough@cromwell-tools.co.uk *Industrial Supplies & Tool Distributors*

Cromwell Tools Ltd, Ark Grove Industrial Estate, Ross Road, Stockton-on-Tees, Cleveland, TS18 2NH Tel: (01642) 673605 Fax: (01642) 671479 E-mail: stockton@cromwell.co.uk *Industrial suppliers & tool distributors*

Cromwell Tools Ltd, Kirkby Folly Road, Sutton-in-Ashfield, Nottinghamshire, NG17 5HN Tel: (01623) 551616 Fax: (01623) 552007 E-mail: mansfield@cromwell-tools.co.uk *Industrial Tool Distributors*

Cromwell Tools Ltd, PO Box 14, Wigston, Leicestershire, LE18 1AT Tel: 0116-288 8888 Fax: 0116-288 8222 E-mail: sales@cromwell.co.uk *Industrial Supplies, Tool Distributors & Manufacturers* Also at: Branches throughout the U.K.

Cromwells, Waverley House, Effingham Road, Sheffield, S4 7YR Tel: 0114-275 0631 Fax: 0114-275 4447 E-mail: sheffield@cromwell.co.uk *Industrial supplies & tool distributors*

Cromwells Fife, Unit 4 Woodgate Way South, Glenrothes, Fife, KY7 4PF Tel: (01592) 631632 Fax: (01592) 631641 E-mail: fife@cromwell.co.uk *Industrial suppliers & tool distributors*

Cronation Ltd, Carlton Business Centre, 104 Nechells Place, Birmingham, B7 5AB Tel: 0121-359 7567 Fax: 0121-359 5339 E-mail: sales@cronation.co.uk *Products & services for the sanitary ware & bathroom industries*

Croner Consulting, Croner House, Wheatfield Way, Hinckley, Leicestershire, LE10 1YG Tel: (01455) 897000 Fax: (01455) 897400 E-mail: info@cronerconsulting.co.uk *Health & safety, taxation & personnel management consultants*

Cronite Precision Castings Ltd, Blacknell Lane, Crewkerne, Somerset, TA18 7YA Tel: (01460) 270300 Fax: (01460) 72643 E-mail: cpc@cronite.co.uk *Precision casting manufrs*

Cronite Scomark Engineering, Church Street, Swadlincote, Derbyshire, DE11 9NR Tel: (01283) 218222 Fax: (01283) 226468 E-mail: tonyknight@scomark.com *Pressure vessel & pipework manifold manufrs*

Cronos Containers Ltd, The Ice House, Dean Street, Marlow, Buckinghamshire, SL7 3AB Tel: (01628) 405580 Fax: (01628) 405650 E-mail: bjp@cronos.com *Marine container leasing service*

Crop Chemicals Ltd, Drem Airfield, North Berwick, East Lothian, EH39 5AW Tel: (01620) 842170 Fax: (01620) 843596 E-mail: enquires@cropchemicals.co.uk *Agricultural services*

Crop Protection Association, Units 20, Culley Court, Bakewell Road, Orton Southgate, Peterborough, PE2 6WA Tel: (01733) 367213 Fax: (01733) 367212 E-mail: info@cropprotection.org.uk *Trade association*

Crop Services Ltd, Elie Road, Pitscottie, Cupar, Fife, KY15 5TE Tel: (01334) 828303 Fax: (01334) 828564 *Agricultural contractors*

Cropchem Wholesale (S.W.) Ltd, Tamar House, Thornbury Road, Estover, Plymouth, PL6 7TT Tel: (01752) 695363 Fax: (01752) 695969 *Agricultural chemical merchants*

▶ Cropco Ltd, 67 Nunnery Street, Halstead, Essex, CO9 3DP Tel: (01787) 460600 Fax: (01787) 460066 E-mail: sales@cropco.co.uk *Agricultural services*

Cropico Ltd, 15-18 Bracken Hill, South West Industrial Estate, Peterlee, County Durham, SR8 2SW Tel: 0191-586 3511 Fax: 0191-586 0227 E-mail: sales@seaward.co.uk *Cropico has over 50 years experience in the specialist precision instrument market, and over 70 testers, analysers and measurement instruments in its range. An ongoing commitment to research and development demonstrates Cropico's dedication to meeting customer requirements, and means that new applications such as highly accurate temperature measuring instruments have been identified. Used in a variety of industries from the manufacture of switches, relays and connectors, to resistance bonding in aircraft and military vehicles, Cropico's resistance measurement instruments provide high quality solutions for a large range of applications.*

Cropper & Jones, New Chester Road, Hooton, Ellesmere Port, CH66 6AQ Tel: 0151-327 2560 E-mail: sales@cjrad.cwc.net *Motor radiator repairers*

Cropwise Ltd, Saxelby Lodge, Saxelby Road, Old Dalby, Melton Mowbray, Leicestershire, LE14 3NA Tel: (01664) 823535 Fax: (01664) 823536 *Agricultural chemicals merchants*

Cropwise (North) Ltd, Unit 2a Greensfield Park Industrial Estate, Alnwick, Northumberland, NE66 2DD Tel: (01665) 510022 Fax: (01665) 510901 *Agricultural suppliers*

Crosbie Cain & Kennish, South Quay Industrial Estate, Douglas, Isle of Man, IM1 5AT Tel: (01624) 673156 Fax: (01624) 676354 *Motor body repairers*

Crosbie Casco Ltd, Wood Lane, Partington, Manchester, M31 4BT Tel: 0161-775 3025 Fax: 0161-777 9076 E-mail: sales@crosbie-casco.co.uk *Paint & protective coating manufrs*

Crosbie Coatings Ltd, Walsall Street, Wolverhampton, WV1 3LP Tel: (01902) 352020 Fax: (01902) 456392 E-mail: ccsales@crosbie-casco.co.uk *Paint manufrs*

▶ Crosby Electrical Services Ltd, 5 Sovereign Business Centre, Stockingswater Lane, Enfield, Middlesex, EN3 7JX Tel: (020) 8443 1212 Fax: (020) 8804 3259 E-mail: info@crosbyelectrical.com

Crosby Europe (U K) Ltd, Unit 10, Fallbank Industrial Estate, Dodworth, Barnsley, South Yorkshire, S75 3LS Tel: (01226) 290516 Fax: (01226) 240118 E-mail: sales@crosbyeurope.co.uk *Heavy lifting gear distributors*

▶ Crosby Homes (Yorkshire) Ltd, Mortech Park, York Road, Leeds, LS15 4TA Tel: 0113-265 2000

▶ Crosby Kitchens, 402 Petre Street, Sheffield, S4 8LU Tel: 0114-243 4701 Fax: 0114-243 0400

Crosby Plant Sales Ltd, Church Street, Bootle, Merseyside, L20 1AF Tel: 0151-933 9920 Fax: 0151-933 7735 *Shelving & racking*

Crosland Ltd, 502 Bradford Road, Batley, West Yorkshire, WF17 5JX Tel: (01924) 474625 Fax: (01924) 443554 E-mail: sales@crosland-electrical.com *Electrical suppliers*

Crosland Cutters Ltd, Nimmings Road, Halesowen, West Midlands, B62 9JE Tel: 0121-559 7915 Fax: 0121-561 3064 E-mail: sales@croslandcuttersltd.co.uk *Cutting & creasing form manufrs*

Crosland V K Ltd, Unit 4, Lyons Road, Trafford Park, Manchester, M17 1RN Tel: 0161-877 8668 Fax: 0161-876 5234 E-mail: sales@croslandvk.com *Carton & packaging equipment manufrs*

▶ Crosrol UK Ltd, Macart House, Farnham Road, Bradford, West Yorkshire, BD7 3JG Tel: (01274) 525937 Fax: (01274) 525945 E-mail: sales@crosrol.co.uk

Alan Cross Ltd, 15 Ludlow Hill Road, West Bridgford, Nottingham, NG2 6HF Tel: 0115-923 2223 Fax: 0115-923 2223 E-mail: enquiries@alancrossuk.com *Cabinet makers*

Colin Cross & Co. Ltd, Fitzwilliam House, Kimbolton Road, Higham Ferrers, Rushden, Northamptonshire, NN10 8HL Tel: (01933) 358966 Fax: (01933) 410327 E-mail: adrian-alasdaire@colincrossn10.fsnet.co.uk *Leather merchants or factors*

Cross Country Ltd, 4 Darby Gate, West Portway, Andover, Hampshire, SP10 3LF Tel: (01264) 351409 Fax: (01264) 333921 *Precision engineers*

▶ Cross Electrical Nottingham Ltd, Trace Works, Debdale Lane, Keyworth, Nottingham, NG12 5HN Tel: 0115-937 5121 Fax: 0115-937 5116 E-mail: heat@cross-electrical.co.uk *Trace heating & thermal insulation*

Cross Fire Protection, 413 Chichester Road, Bognor Regis, West Sussex, PO21 5BU Tel: (01243) 827168 Fax: (01243) 827168 *Supply & service fire extinguishers*

Cross Machine Components Ltd, 5 Mandervell Road, Oadby, Leicester, LE2 5LQ Tel: 0116-271 3315 Fax: 0116-272 0068 E-mail: kingsley.cross@tiscali.co.uk *General engineers*

Cross Manufacturing Co 1938 Ltd, Midford Road, Bath, BA2 5RR Tel: (01225) 837000 Fax: (01225) 834115 E-mail: mail@crossmanufacturing.com *Sealing rings*

Cross Pak Ltd, 14 Calow Brook Drive, Hasland, Chesterfield, Derbyshire, S41 0DR Tel: (01246) 200183 Fax: (01246) 200183 E-mail: crosspak@wyldboy.demon.co.uk *Cutting & greasing formers & packaging design services*

Cross Vetpharm Group UK Ltd, Unit 2 Bryn Cefni Industrial Park, Llangefni, Gwynedd, LL77 7XA Tel: (01248) 725400 Fax: (01248) 725416 E-mail: sales@bimeda.co.uk *Pharmaceutical veterinary products manufrs*

▶ Crossan Communications, 37 Bernard Street, Edinburgh, EH6 6SH Tel: 0131-553 1872 Fax: 0131-555 4255 E-mail: info@crossancom.co.uk

Crossbow Clothing Ltd, 31 Broadway Market, London, E8 4PH Tel: (020) 7923 9313 Fax: (020) 7923 9314 E-mail: sales@crossbowwear.co.uk *Uniform suppliers*

Crossbow Eductional, 1 Sawpit Lane, Brocton, Stafford, ST17 0TE Tel: (01785) 660902 Fax: (01785) 661431 E-mail: sales@crossboweducation.com *Educational equipment suppliers*

Crossbow Fashions Ltd, 4 Maryland Industrial Estate, 26 Maryland Road, London, E15 1JW Tel: (020) 8522 1652 Fax: (020) 8522 1752 E-mail: crossbowfashions@aol.com *Leather garment manufrs*

Crossbrook Furniture Ltd, 8 Marshgate Industrial Estate, 20 Marshgate Drive, Hertford, SG13 7AJ Tel: (01992) 557000 Fax: (01992) 501666 E-mail: sales@crossbrook.co.uk *Education furniture manufrs*

Crosse & Crosse Ltd, 14 Southernhay West, Exeter, EX1 1PL Tel: (01392) 258451 Fax: (01392) 278938 E-mail: mail@crosse.co.uk *Solicitors services*

Crossen Engineering Ltd, Maryland Industrial Estate, Crossnacrevey, Newtownards, County Down, BT23 6BL Tel: (028) 9044 8569 Fax: (028) 9044 8221 E-mail: paul@crossenengineering.co.uk *Press tools, press parts & injection mould manufrs*

Crossfield Engineering Co., Barrow Road, Sheffield, S9 1JZ Tel: 0114-243 8441 Fax: 0114-243 9266 E-mail: sales@crossfielduk.com *Mechanical handling equipment consultants & designers*

Crossfield Excalibur Ltd, Unit 21 Woolfold Trading Estate, Mitchell Street, Bury, Lancashire, BL8 1SF Tel: 0161-763 4377 Fax: 0161-763 4926 E-mail: enquiry@excalibur-rm.co.uk *Manufacturers of rotational moulding tools*

Crossford Oil & Tool Supplies Ltd, Unit 94 Springvale Industrial Estate, Cwmbran, Gwent, NP44 5BH Tel: (01633) 873612 Fax: (01633) 864884 E-mail: sales@crossfords.co.uk *Fasteners & power tools*

▶ Crossguard Trade Mark Agents, 4 Berkeley Road, Kenilworth, Warwickshire, CV8 1AP Tel: (0845) 0536675 Fax: (0870) 0468361 E-mail: mail@crossguard.info *Patent, Trade Mark & Copyright Attorneys*

Crosshall Engineering Ltd, 1 Wellington Street, Liverpool, L3 6JH Tel: 0151-207 4292 Fax: 0151-298 1447 E-mail: sales@crosshall.com *Electrical & mechanical engineers*

Crosskill Ventilation Ltd, Spar Road, Norwich, NR6 6BX Tel: (01603) 423028 Fax: (01603) 401136 E-mail: crosskill@btconnect.com *Ventilation, dust extraction & sheet metal fabrications*

Crossland Components Ltd, Unit L Tanfield Lea Industrial Estate South, Tanfield Lea, Stanley, County Durham, DH9 9XA Tel: (01207) 230269 Fax: (01207) 283849 E-mail: info@crossland.co.uk *Heat sensor, thermostats manufrs*

Crossle Car Co. Ltd, 217 Old Holywood Road, Holywood, County Down, BT18 9QS Tel: (028) 9076 3332 Fax: (028) 9076 0676 E-mail: arnie@crossle.fsnet.co.uk *Racing car manufrs*

Crossley & Bradley Ltd, Ulnes Walton Lane, Leyland, PR26 8NB Tel: (01772) 622800 Fax: (01772) 456859 E-mail: info@crossley-bradley.co.uk *Printed circuit laminates distributors*

Crossley Charles & Son Ltd, 9-11 Astley Street, Stockport, Cheshire, SK4 1AW Tel: 0161-480 2858 Fax: 0161-429 7353 E-mail: mail@charlescrossley.com *Fabrication engineers, metalworkers & welding services*

Crossley & Craven Halifax Ltd, Exmoor Street, Halifax, West Yorkshire, HX1 3QP Tel: (01422) 352027 Fax: (01422) 358122 *Non-ferrous metal scrap merchants*

Crossley's Shuttles Ltd, Woodbottom Mill, Hollins Road, Walsden, Todmorden, Lancashire, OL14 6PG Tel: (01706) 812152 Fax: (01706) 813767 E-mail: sales@crossleysshuttles.co.uk *Shuttle makers & textile machinery accessories*

Crossling, 2 Kingstown Broadway, Kingstown Industrial Estate, Carlisle, CA3 0HA Tel: (01228) 541101 Fax: (01228) 539288 E-mail: marketing@crossling.co.uk *Plumbers & engineers merchants*

Crossling Ltd, Coast Road, Heaton, Newcastle upon Tyne, NE6 5TP Tel: 0191-265 4166 Fax: 0191-276 4839 E-mail: marketing@crossling.co.uk *Plumbers' merchants* Also at: Sunderland, Stockton, Carlisle & Liverpool

Crossman Engineering Ltd, Downsview Road, Wantage, Oxfordshire, OX12 9FA Tel: (01235) 772885 Fax: (01235) 772886 E-mail: sales@crossmaneng.co.uk *Sheet metalwork engineers*

▶ Crossover Group Ltd, High Street, Ashwell, Baldock, Hertfordshire, SG7 5NT Tel: (01462) 742948 Fax: (01462) 743619 E-mail: sales@crossovergroup.com *CCTV access control & data cabling specialists*

Crossprint Ltd, Newport Business Park, 21 Barry Way, Newport, Isle of Wight, PO30 5GY Tel: (01983) 524885 Fax: (01983) 522878 E-mail: info@crossprint.co.uk *Design & print company*

▶ Crossroad Health & Safety Systems, Barn 6 Watsome Farm Development Wotton Road, Kingswood, Wotton-under-Edge, Gloucestershire, GL12 8SP Tel: (01453) 845108 Fax: (08700) 941122 E-mail: info@safetycrossroad.com *Health & safety policies*

Crossroads Commercials Group Ltd, Pheasant Drive, Birstall, Batley, West Yorkshire, WF17 9LR Tel: (01924) 425000 Fax: (01924) 441111 E-mail: info@crossroads.co.uk *Volvo commercial vehicle distributors* Also at: Hull, Malton, Rotherham & Thirsk

▶ Crossroads Design Ltd, 4 Sanctus Court, Stratford-upon-Avon, Warwickshire, CV37 6DL Tel: (01789) 551682 Fax: (01789) 551682 E-mail: info@crossroadsdesign.co.uk *Consultancy in areas of design, web & graphics to product design*

Crossroads Insurance Services, 261 Kingsland Road, London, E2 8AS Tel: (020) 7739 1189 Fax: (020) 7256 0403 E-mail: crossroadsinsurance@btconnect.com *Insurance agents*

Cross's, 20 Lower Bridge Street, Canterbury, Kent, CT1 2LG Tel: (01227) 458776 Fax: (01227) 760827 *Supply art equipment suppliers*

Cross's, Brenchley House, Week Street, Maidstone, Kent, ME14 1RF Tel: (01622) 677436 Fax: (01622) 752254 *Suppliers to art craft trade*

Crossways Tanks & Fabrications Ltd, Vanguard Road, Gapton Hall Industrial Estate, Great Yarmouth, Norfolk, NR31 0NT Tel: (01493) 661156 Fax: (01493) 661159 E-mail: sales@crossways-tanks.co.uk *Steel fabricators tank manufrs*

▶ Croston Conservatories, Unit 85 Bison Place, Moss Side Industrial Estate, Leyland, PR26 7QR Tel: (01772) 435353 Fax: (01772) 452525 E-mail: sales@crostonconservatories.com *Conservatory manufrs*

Croston Engineering Ltd, Tarvin Mill Barrow Lane, Tarvin Sands, Tarvin, Chester, CH3 8JF Tel: (01829) 741119 Fax: (01829) 741169 E-mail: admin@croston-engineering.co.uk *Bulk materials handling equipment manufrs*

Crouch Bros Engineering Ltd, The Britannia Centre, Langston Road, Loughton, Essex, IG10 3SQ Tel: (020) 8508 3622 Fax: (020) 8508 4481 *Sheet metalworkers & fabricators*

Crouch Engineering Co. (Burnham-on-Crouch) Ltd, 150 Station Rd, Burnham-on-Crouch, Essex, CM0 8HQ Tel: (01621) 782130 Fax: (01621) 782130 *Marine engineers*

Croucher, Reoch & Partners Ltd, 3rd Floor Babmaes Ho, 2 Babmaes St, London, SW1Y 6HD Tel: (020) 7839 5735 Fax: (020) 7930 4281 E-mail: fiztwilliamfinancial@compuserve.com *Independent financial advisers*

Croudace Services Ltd, Croudace House, 97 Godstone Road, Caterham, Surrey, CR3 6XQ Tel: (01883) 346464 Fax: (01883) 349927 E-mail: info@croudacehomes.co.uk *Building contractors*

Crouzet Ltd, Intec 3, Wade Road, Basingstoke, Hampshire, RG24 8NE Tel: (01256) 318900 Fax: (01256) 318901 E-mail: sales@crouzet.com *Temperature controllers electric motors & switch manufrs*

V.C. Crow & Co. Ltd, Unit F, Halesfield 19, Telford, Shropshire, TF7 4QT Tel: (01952) 686888 Fax: (01952) 686889 E-mail: info@cropac.co.uk *Printers of packaging*

F. Crowe & Sons Ltd, 50 Hurricane Way, Norwich, NR6 6JB Tel: (01603) 403349 Fax: (01603) 485164 E-mail: sales@crowes.co.uk *Commercial printers*

Crowe Plant Fabrication Ltd, 11-29 Groton Road, Earlsfield, London, SW18 4HT Tel: (020) 8870 5121 Fax: (020) 8877 9239 *Scaffolding erectors*

Ronnie Crowe Ltd, 63 Maldon Road, Great Baddow, Chelmsford, CM2 7DN Tel: (01245) 471246 *Shooting & fishing equipment retailers*

Crow-Electro Instruments Ltd, 9A Connors Yard, Crowborough Hill, Crowborough, East Sussex, TN6 2DA Tel: (01892) 662078 Fax: (01892) 663983 E-mail: crowelectro@fsbdial.co.uk *Audio transformer manufrs & sub-contract assemblers*

▶ Crowfoot Carriers Ltd, Gosforth Rd, Ascot Drive, Derby, DE24 8HU Tel: (01332) 372621 Fax: (01332) 346171

▶ Crowfoots Carriers (Manchester) Ltd, Park Street, Stalybridge, Cheshire, SK15 2BT Tel: 0161-303 7133 Fax: 0161-304 8226

E.B. Crowhurst & Co. Ltd, Building 50, Pensnett Trading Estate, Kingswinford, West Midlands, DY6 7XD Tel: (01384) 400100 Fax: (01384) 400455 E-mail: sales@crowhurst.cio.uk *Presentation box & carton manufrs*

Crowle Wharfe Engineers Ltd, Wharf Road, Ealand, Scunthorpe, South Humberside, DN17 4JW Tel: (01724) 710455 Fax: (01724) 711508 *Precision engineers*

Crown Agents Ltd, St Nicholas House, St Nicholas Road, Sutton, Surrey, SM1 1EL Tel: (020) 8643 3311 Fax: (020) 8643 9113 E-mail: enquiries@crownagents.co.uk *International development*

▶ Crown Aluminium Ltd, Stafford Mill, London Road, Thrupp, Stroud, Gloucestershire, GL5 2AZ Tel: (01453) 753222 *Aluminium doors & windows*

Crown Artist Brush Ltd, Crown Street West, Lowestoft, Suffolk, NR32 1SG Tel: (01502) 573142 Fax: (01502) 562272 *Brush manufrs*

Crown Brolac Decorator Centre, 5 London Road, Bedford, MK42 0PB Tel: (01234) 360541 Fax: (01234) 360551 E-mail: cdc406.bedford@dwn.akzonobel.com *Decorators merchants*

Crown Business Efficiency Consultants Ltd, 41 Parsonage Road, Horsham, West Sussex, RH12 4AW Tel: (01403) 259773 Fax: (01403) 254604 E-mail: crownbec@aol.com *Management & business consultants*

▶ Crown Ceramics, 8 Mill Lane, Codnor, Ripley, Derbyshire, DE5 9QF Tel: (01773) 749278 Fax: (01773) 749278 E-mail: info@crown-ceramics.co.uk

Crown Cleaning Equipment & Hygiene Supplies, 494 Calder Street, Glasgow, G42 0QD Tel: 0141-423 1022 Fax: 0141-423 0306 *Cleaning contractors equipment & suppliers*

▶ Crown Cleaning Management, 1 Silver Street, Lincoln, LN2 1DY Tel: (01522) 545400 Fax: (01522) 545403 E-mail: info@crown-cleaning.com *Suppliers of cleaning services to the commercial & industrial sectors*

▶ Crown Coaching, 11 Rookery Court, Marlow, Buckinghamshire, SL7 3HR Tel: (01628) 488042 E-mail: helen@crowncoaching.com *Business Coach specialist for SME Business owners, for Business Growth, Leadership skills and People development. Life Coach specialist for increased confidence & self esteem to enable to you be, do & have what YOU want. Coaching helps you to take control.*

▶ Crown Construction Contracting Ltd, 6 Benjamin Outram Business Centre, Whiteley Road, Ripley, Derbyshire, DE5 3QL Tel: (01773) 570044 Fax: (01773) 570121

Crown Conveyors Ltd, 8 Clamp Road, Wishaw, Lanarkshire, ML2 7XQ Tel: (01698) 254621 Fax: (01698) 261027 E-mail: sales@crownconveyors.co.uk *Converyor systems manufrs*

Crown Cruisers Ltd, Yacht Station, Somerleyton, Lowestoft, Suffolk, NR32 5QW Tel: (01502) 730335 Fax: (01502) 730310 *Boat builders*

The Crown Decorating Centre, Unit 2 Southsea Works, Rodney Road, Southsea, Hampshire, PO4 8SP Tel: (023) 9283 8201 Fax: (023) 9285 1736 E-mail: cdc706.portsmouth@dwn.akzonobel.com *Paint & wallpaper decorator's supplies* Also at: Branches throughout the U.K.

Crown Direct (Scotland) Ltd, 27-33 Tobago Street, Glasgow, G40 2RH Tel: 0141-554 1111 Fax: 0141-554 1303 E-mail: enquiries@crowndirect.co.uk *Amusement machine distributors*

Crown Engineering Co., Unit 9 Hedgend Industrial Estate, Shuart Lane, St. Nicholas at Wade, Birchington, Kent, CT7 0NB Tel: (01843) 845300 Fax: (01843) 848352 E-mail: enquiries@crownengineering.co.uk *Plastics & steel fabricating engineers & sheet metal workers*

Crown Exhibitions & Displays, 3 Partons Road, Kings Heath, Birmingham, B14 6TA Tel: 0121-441 2822 Fax: 0121-441 2772 E-mail: info@crownexhibition.co.uk *Exhibition & display contractors*

Crown Gold Blocking Co. Ltd, 63 Camden Street, Birmingham, B1 3DD Tel: 0121-233 1670 Fax: 0121-233 1670 *Hot foil stamping, gold blocking stamping & printing services*

Crown Graphic Sales Ltd, 77 Leonard Street, London, EC2A 4QS Tel: (020) 7739 7977 Fax: (020) 7739 3404 E-mail: crowngraph@aol.com *Lithographic plate makers*

Crown Hand Tools Ltd, Excelsior Works, Burnt Tree Lane, Hoyle Street, Sheffield, S3 7EX Tel: 0114-272 3366 Fax: 0114-272 5252 E-mail: info@crowntools.com *Hand tool manufrs*

Crown Hill Associates Ltd, Station House, Station Road, Wilburton, Ely, Cambridgeshire, CB6 3PZ Tel: (01353) 749990 Fax: (01353) 749991 E-mail: sales@crownhill.co.uk *Device programmers manufrs*

▶ Crown House Engineering, C/O N E C, Carnegie Road, Deans Industrial Estate, Deans, Livingston, West Lothian, EH54 8QX Tel: (01506) 410696

Crown House Technologies, Off Phoenix Way, Garngoch Industrial Estate, Gorseinon, Swansea, SA4 9WF Tel: (01792) 224100 Fax: (01792) 224101 *Electrical engineering services, data communication*

Crown House Technologies, Peal House, 50 Waterloo Road, Wolverhampton, WV1 4RU Tel: (01902) 428666 Fax: (01902) 428774 *Construction services*

Crown Joinery, Unit 6 Farthing Road, Ipswich, IP1 5AP Tel: (01473) 740030 Fax: (01473) 744231 E-mail: crownjoinery@aol.com *Joinery manufrs*

Kate Crown Ltd, Trinity Way, West Bromwich, West Midlands, B70 6NU Tel: 0121-500 6348 Fax: 0121-580 0749 E-mail: katecrown@fsmail.net *Powder coating services*

Crown Knitwear Ltd, 10-20 Grosvenor Street, Manchester, M1 7JJ Tel: 0161-274 3855 Fax: 0161-274 3855 *Knitwear manufrs*

▶ Crown Labels Ltd, 2 The I O Centre, Nash Road, Redditch, Worcestershire, B98 7AS Tel: (01527) 527444 Fax: (01527) 527565 *Label manufrs*

Crown Labels, 102 Walkley Rd, Sheffield, S6 2XP Tel: 0114-232 1152 Fax: 0114-232 1301 E-mail: sales@crownlabels.co.uk *Self adhesive labels manufacturer & distributor*

Crown Leisure Ltd, Gerrish Avenue, Whitehall, Bristol, BS5 9DG Tel: 0117-955 4044 Fax: 0117-955 4045 E-mail: sales@crownleisure.co.uk *Amusement machine operators*

Crown Lift Truck Ltd, Stirling Road, South Marston Park, Swindon, SN3 4TS Tel: (01793) 821090 Fax: (0845) 8509271 *Fork lift trucks retailers*

Crown Lift Trucks Ltd, Tollbridge House, 135 Windmill Road, Sunbury-on-Thames, Middlesex, TW16 7EF Tel: (01932) 777500 Fax: (0845) 8509277 E-mail: info@crown.com *Fork lifts sales, rental, leasing, service & manufacturing*

Crown Lift Trucks Ltd, The Quay Centre, West Quay Road, Winwick, Warrington, WA2 8TS Tel: (01925) 445777 Fax: (01925) 425656 E-mail: info@crown.com *Fork lift truck sales, rental, leasing, service & manufacturing*

Crown Lifts Ltd, Regancy House, 33-49 Farwig Lane, Bromley, BR1 3RE Tel: (020) 8464 5000 Fax: (020) 8290 7646 *Disabled & handicapped person lifts manufrs*

Crown Manufactory Rotherham Ltd, Chapel Walk, Masborough Street, Rotherham, South Yorkshire, S60 1EP Tel: (01709) 562957 Fax: (01709) 554728 *Photo mount manufacturers & trade distributors*

Crown Max Investments Ltd, Halesfield 19, Telford, Shropshire, TF7 4QT Tel: (01952) 581121 Fax: (01952) 588284 E-mail: info@crownmax.co.uk *Electronic consultants*

Crown Metal Fabrications, 24-26 Albert St West, Failsworth, Manchester, M35 0JN Tel: 0161-688 7571 Fax: 0161-688 7546 *Fabricators & wire workers*

Crown Nail Co. Ltd, 48 Commercial Road, Wolverhampton, WV1 3QS Tel: (01902) 351806 Fax: (01902) 871212 E-mail: sales@crown-nail.com Principal Export Areas: Worldwide *Steel cut & tack manufrs*

Crown Packaging (U K) Plc, Borland Avenue, Borland Avenue, Botcherby, Carlisle, CA1 2TL Tel: (01228) 811200 Fax: (01228) 811290 Principal Export Areas: Worldwide *Produce cans for beverage industry*

Crown Park Consultants Ltd, 343 Union Street, Aberdeen, AB11 6BS Tel: (01224) 588348 Fax: (01224) 584317 E-mail: info@crown-park.fsnet.co.uk *Property development consultants*

Crown Personnel Ltd, 2 St. Giles Square, Northampton, NN1 1DA Tel: (01604) 622244 Fax: (01604) 230825 E-mail: branch@crownjobs.com *Recruitment services*

Crown Pest Control & Environmental Services Ltd, Crown House, Thomas Street, Crewe, CW1 2BD Tel: (01270) 256444 Fax: (01270) 587024 *Pest control services*

Crown Photo Systems, East Portway, Andover, Hampshire, SP10 3LU Tel: (01264) 335334 Fax: (01264) 333349 E-mail: sales@dandfphoto.com *Suppliers of photographic equipment*

Crown Plastic Moulding Ltd, Broad Lanes, Bilston, West Midlands, WV14 0RY Tel: (01902) 496151 Fax: (01902) 493102 E-mail: sales@crown-plastic-mouldings.co.uk *Injection moulders & plastic moulding manufrs*

▶ Crown Polishing & Plating Co., Derry Street, Wolverhampton, WV2 1EY Tel: (01902) 870529 Fax: (01902) 830528 *Metal polisher & electro plating services*

Crown Products International Ltd, Innovation House, Cobnar Wood Close, Chesterfield, Derbyshire, S41 9RQ Tel: (01246) 451451 Fax: (01246) 260122 E-mail: sales@crownproducts.demon.co.uk *Screen printers & advertising product manufrs*

Crown Records Management Ltd, Marshgate Business Centre, 10-12 Marshgate Lane, London, E15 2NH Tel: (020) 8555 1880 Fax: (020) 8555 2110 *Document storage & record management*

Crown Securities UK Ltd, Security House, Bunsley Bank, Audlem, Crewe, CW3 0HS Tel: (01270) 812286 Fax: (01270) 812322 E-mail: mail@crownsecurities.co.uk *Burglar alarms & security installation*

Crown Security, 49a Cricklade Road, Swindon, SN2 1AA Tel: (01793) 433999 Fax: (01793) 434002 *Security sales & services*

Crown Speciality Packaging, Edgefield Avenue, Fawdon, Newcastle upon Tyne, NE3 3TS Tel: 0191-285 8168 Fax: 0191-284 7570 *Tinplate manufrs*

Crown Speciality Packaging U K Ltd, Rock Valley, Mansfield, Nottinghamshire, NG18 2EZ Tel: (01623) 622651 Fax: (01623) 624626 Principal Export Areas: Worldwide *Custom made promotional packaging*

Crown Speciality Packaging (UK), Heysham Road, Bootle, Merseyside, L30 6UR Tel: 0151-522 2222 Fax: 0151-522 2200 *Tin plate packaging custom makers*

Crown Steel Buildings, Green Park, Burnards House, Holsworthy, Devon, EX22 7JA Tel: (01409) 253315 Fax: (01409) 254224 *Agricultural buildings manufrs*

▶ Crown Structural Engineering, Burma Road, Blidworth, Mansfield, Nottinghamshire, NG21 0RT Tel: (01623) 490555 Fax: (01623) 490666 E-mail: enquiries@crownstructuralengineering.co.uk *Structural steelwork manufrs*

Crown Surveillance, 11 Huss's Lane, Long Eaton, Nottingham, NG10 1GS Tel: 0115-946 5422 Fax: 0115-946 5433 E-mail: info@crown-cctv.co.uk *CCTV, access control & network equipment installers*

Crown Trading Ltd, 26a Sidney Road, London, SW9 0TS Tel: (020) 7733 4607 Fax: (020) 7733 8100 *Paper exporters*

▶ Crown Trent China Ltd, Spring Garden Road, Longton, Stoke-On-Trent, ST3 2TE Tel: (01782) 332623 E-mail: sam@crowntrent.com *China*

Crown UK Ltd, Old Mill Road, Portishead, Bristol, BS20 7BX Tel: (01275) 818008 Fax: (01275) 818288 E-mail: mcross@crownukltd.com *Surveillance equipment manufrs*

Crown Water Heaters Ltd, Sunbeam Studios, Sunbeam Street, Wolverhampton, WV2 4PF Tel: (01902) 310678 Fax: (01902) 425707 E-mail: sales@crownheat.force9.co.uk *Suppliers of gas & electric water heaters*

Crown Windows Ltd, Manor Works, Brunel Road, Newton Abbot, Devon, TQ12 4PB Tel: (01626) 332288 Fax: (01626) 333440 E-mail: sales@crown-windows.co.uk *PVC-U, aluminum windows & door fabricators*

Crown Windows Hull Ltd, New Cleveland Street, Hull, HU8 7HA Tel: (01482) 329043 Fax: (01482) 39043 *Upvc window manufacturers & installers*

Crown Worldwide Ltd, Cullen Square, Deans Road, Deans Industrial Estate, Livingston, West Lothian, EH54 8SJ Tel: (01506) 468150 Fax: (01506) 468151 E-mail: general.gblob@crownworldwide.com *Export packers & removal contractors*

Crown Worldwide Movers Ltd, 1 Ninian Park, Ninian Way, Wilnecote, Tamworth, Staffordshire, B77 5ES Tel: (01827) 264100 Fax: (01827) 264101 E-mail: general@crownrelo.com *Shipping & overseas removals*

▶ Crown Worlwide Movers Ltd, 7 Lockwood Court, Middleton Grove Road, Leeds, LS11 5TY Tel: 0113-277 1000

Crowncast Ltd, Rushenden Road, Queenborough, Kent, ME11 5HD Tel: (01795) 662722 Fax: (01795) 666552 E-mail: crowncast@whsmithnet.co.uk *Grey & heavy iron castings manufrs*

Crowndale Associates Ltd, 3 St Marys Street, Worcester, WR1 1HA Tel: (01905) 452570 Fax: (01905) 21044 E-mail: pauld@crowndaleassociates.com *Business transfer services*

Crowne Plaza Manchester Airport, Ringway Road, Manchester Airport, Manchester, M90 3NS Tel: (0870) 4009055 Fax: 0161-436 2340 E-mail: manchesterairport@6c.com *Hotel with conference facilities*

Crownfield Engineering Ltd, Crownfield, Wycombe Road, Saunderton, Princes Risborough, Buckinghamshire, HP27 9NR Tel: (01844) 345746 Fax: (01844) 347225 E-mail: crownfield@nildram.co.uk *Precision engineers*

Crownham Ltd, Crownham House, Gladstone Street, Off Prospect Road, Cleckheaton, West Yorkshire, BD19 3DQ Tel: (01274) 855080 Fax: (01274) 855650 *Bespoke rug & carpet manufrs*

▶ Crownhill Consulting Ltd, 1 Lansbury Road, Halesworth, Suffolk, IP19 8SA Tel: (01986) 875814 Fax: (0870) 7058775 E-mail: kevin.holland@crownhill-consulting.com *IT support & consultancy services to small & medium sized businesses*

▶ Crownlea Group Ltd, Crownlea House, 247-253 Wood Street, London, E17 3NT Tel: (020) 8521 8812 Fax: (020) 8509 1914 E-mail: cfisher@crownlea.com *Bloc & mesh manufrs* Also at: Ilford

Crownmain Ltd, 19 Buxton Avenue, Gorleston, Great Yarmouth, Norfolk, NR31 6HG Tel: (01493) 663639 Fax: (01493) 669622 E-mail: crownmain@aol.com *Recruitment agency*

Peter Crownshaw, St. Michaels Forge, Tenbury Wells, Worcestershire, WR15 8TG Tel: (01584) 811371 Fax: (01584) 811094 *Architectural metalworkers*

Crownsway Insurance Brokers Ltd, 185 Holyhead Road, Birmingham, B21 0AS Tel: 0121-554 3566 Fax: 0121-523 2992 E-mail: crowns@btconnect.com *General insurance brokers & underwriters*

▶ Crowntec Computers Limited, Mayfield,, Claremont Road, Kingsdown, Deal, Kent, CT14 8BU Tel: 01304 239158 Fax: 01304 361003 E-mail: davidforester@crowntec.co.uk *Suppliers of computing equipment, networks and software. Provide maintenance and enhancement services to commercial entities and general public.*

Crowson Fabrics, Crowson House, Bellbrook Industrial Estate, Uckfield, East Sussex, TN22 1QZ Tel: (01825) 761044 Fax: (01825) 764283 E-mail: sales@crowsonfabrics.com *Soft furnishing fabric manufrs*

Crowther Clayton Associates, 31 Tennyson Road, London, NW7 4AB Tel: (020) 8959 7376 Fax: (020) 8959 6880 E-mail: info@crowther-clayton.com *Waste water & environmental consultants*

Crowther Engineering Ltd, 52 Hutton Close, Crowther, Washington, Tyne & Wear, NE38 0AH Tel: 0191-417 9916 Fax: 0191-415 5136 E-mail: nick@crowthereng.co.uk *General engineers*

▶ Frederick Crowther & Son Ltd, 4b High Level Way, Halifax, West Yorkshire, HX1 4PN Tel: (01422) 367788 Fax: (01422) 363802 E-mail: sales@cromar.co.uk *Swarf conveyor manufacturers repairs & service "*

Crowthorne Fencing Systems Ltd, Weston Road, Bretforton, Evesham, Worcestershire, WR11 7QA Tel: (01386) 831450 Fax: (01386) 831475 *Fencing suppliers*

Crowthorne Fencing & Timber Supplies, Cambridge Road, Bedford, MK42 0LH Tel: (01234) 273077 Fax: (01234) 217130 E-mail: sales@crowthornefencing.com *Fence retailers*

▶ Crowthorne Heating Co. Ltd, Devonshire House, 4 Dukes Ride, Crowthorne, Berkshire, RG45 6LT Tel: (01344) 772397

Crowthorne Numerical Control Ltd, 13 St Georges Industrial Estate, Wilton Road, Camberley, Surrey, GU15 2QW Tel: (01276) 20076 Fax: (01276) 685344 E-mail: info@crowthornenc.com *CNC engineering company that specialises in 3D machining.*

▶ Crox Tech, 48 Crompton Drive, Liverpool, L12 0JX Tel: 0151-222 4691 E-mail: sales@croxtech.com *IT support services, covering PC & server repairs*

Croxfords Joinery Manufacturers, Meltham Joinery Works, New Street, Meltham, Holmfirth, HD9 5NT Tel: (01484) 850892 Fax: (01484) 850969 E-mail: ralph@croxfords.demon.co.uk *Joiners*

Croxgrove Powder Coaters 1987 Ltd, Unit 10 11 The Hayes Trading Estate, Folkes Road, Stourbridge, West Midlands, DY9 8RG Tel: (01384) 423942 Fax: (01384) 423941 *Powder coating & metal finishing manufrs*

Croxley Alarm Systems, 4 Scots Hill, Croxley Green, Rickmansworth, Hertfordshire, WD3 3AD Tel: (01923) 771920 Fax: (01923) 772901 *Burglar alarm suppliers & fitters*

Croxson William & Son Ltd, Alpha Place, Garth Road, Morden, Surrey, SM4 4LX Tel: (020) 8337 2945 Fax: (020) 8337 6783 E-mail: exports@croxsons.com *Glass bottles,*

continued

jars & cap suppliers, UK & Worldwide exports from one pallet upwards. Offices in the UK, Australia & New Zealand

Croxton Power Ltd, Croxton Kerrial, Grantham, Lincolnshire, NG32 1QX Tel: (01476) 870386 Fax: (01476) 879377 E-mail: enquiries@croxtonpower.com *Croxton Power Ltd supply, manufacture and install LV or HV generating sets from 1kVA to 3000kVA. Fuelled by Petrol, Diesel or Gas, we offer any engine/alternator/control panel combination to meet your generator requirements*

Croy Glass Fibre Products, 3 Lower Dartmouth Street, Birmingham, B9 4LG Tel: 0121-773 8714 Fax: 0121-773 8714 *Glass fibre moulders*

Croydex Ltd, Central Way, Andover, Hampshire, SP10 5AW Tel: (01264) 365881 Fax: (01264) 356437 E-mail: admin@croydex.co.uk *Domestic hardware & bathroom accessories distributors*

Croydon Ceilings Ltd, 94-96 Drummond Road, Croydon, CR0 1TX Tel: (020) 8686 0500 Fax: (020) 8688 9229 *Ceiling product distributors*

Croydon Computer Supplies Ltd, Unit 4, Broadfield Close, Progress Way, Croydon, CR0 4XR Tel: (020) 8686 0046 Fax: (020) 8667 1552 E-mail: sales@croydoncomputersupplies.co.uk *Computer ancillaries & suppliers*

Croydon Cut & Strip, 105 Shirley Church Road, Croydon, CR0 5AG Tel: (020) 8656 4416 Fax: (020) 8656 6319 E-mail: ccs.stratford@virgin.net *Electrical wire (preparation) services*

Croydon Ductwork Ltd, 312 Lower Addiscombe Road, Croydon, CR0 7AF Tel: (020) 8654 7813 Fax: (020) 8654 9527 E-mail: richardwood@croydenductworkltd.co.uk *Ventilation & air conditioning ductwork*

Croydon Electroplaters Ltd, 2 Bridge Parade, Waddon Road, Croydon, CR0 4JH Tel: (020) 8688 4709 *Electroplating services*

Croydon Tool Hire Ltd, 87a Whitehorse Road, Croydon, CR0 2JJ Tel: (020) 8684 1751 Fax: (020) 8684 1811 *Industrial power tool hire services*

Crozet Alarms, PO Box 16, Oxted, Surrey, RH8 9YZ Tel: (01883) 723458 Fax: (01883) 730823 E-mail: sales@crozet.co.uk *Alarm installation*

▶ Croztech Electrical Engineers, Unit 18 Botany Business Park, Macclesfield Road, Whaley Bridge, High Peak, Derbyshire, SK23 7DQ Tel: (01663) 719977 Fax: (01663) 719900

CRP Print & Packaging Ltd, Cooks Road, Weldon North Industrial Estate, Corby, Northamptonshire, NN17 5JT Tel: (01536) 200333 Fax: (01536) 403329 E-mail: sales@crpprint.co.uk *Heavy cardboard boxes manufrs*

▶ CRS 24: 7, 6 Whitburn Road, Bathgate, West Lothian, EH48 1HH Tel: (0870) 7665 206 Fax: (01506) 637562 E-mail: gary@crs247.com

▶ CRS Debt Recovery Solicitors, 12 Park Place, Leeds, LS1 2RU Tel: 0113 2467887 Fax: 0113 2439822 E-mail: info@carrickread.com *Insolvency and Debt Recovery Solicitors*

Crucible Technologies, 11 Glaisdale Road, Northminster Business Park, York, YO26 6QT Tel: 01904 792211 Fax: 01904 780054 E-mail: seggy@tele-products.com *Telephone systems*

Cruddas Security Services Ltd, 1 Oak Street Industrial Park, Oak Street, Cradley Heath, West Midlands, B64 5JY Tel: (01384) 569307 Fax: (01384) 569307 *Ornamental iron gate & security bars manufrs*

▶ Cruden Building Ltd, 26 Orr Street, Glasgow, G40 2LQ Tel: 0141-551 0098

▶ Cruden Investments Ltd, Baberton House, Westburn Avenue, Edinburgh, EH14 3HN Tel: 0131-442 3862 Fax: 0131-442 4556

W. & J. Cruickshank & Co., Cunningholes Industrial Estate, Rathven, Buckie, Banffshire, AB56 4DA Tel: (01542) 832132 Fax: (01542) 835573 E-mail: cruickshank@wheenet.com *Alcohol & soft drinks distributors*

Cruise Controls, 18 Becconsall Drive, Crewe, CW1 4RU Tel: 0777 9265214 E-mail: info@cruisecontrols.co.uk *Cheap hire of Satnav and Dvd players for use within vehicles.*

▶ Cruiseline Models, 16 Winston Road, Barry, South Glamorgan, CF62 9SW Tel: (01446) 420901 *Model retailers*

▶ Crumlin Village Cabs Ltd, 28 Main Street, Crumlin, County Antrim, BT29 4UP Tel: (028) 9445 2829 E-mail: crumlinvillage@cabs.wannadoo.co.uk *Taxi, mini bus & couriers services*

▶ Crummles English Enamels, The Workshops, Weston Coyney Road, Stoke-on-Trent, ST3 5JT Tel: (01782) 599948 Fax: (01782) 599397 E-mail: sales@crummles.com *Enamel manufacturer*

▶ Crummock Scotland Ltd, Butlerfield Industrial Estate, Bonnyrigg, Midlothian, EH19 3JQ Tel: (01875) 823222 Fax: (01875) 823444

Crumpsall Plastics & Engineering Ltd, Pike Fold Works, Frenchbarn Lane, Blackley, Manchester, M9 6PB Tel: 0161-795 5000 Fax: 0161-721 4684 *Fabrications & machined parts*

▶ Crupron Construction Ltd, PO Box 50, Dinas Powys, South Glamorgan, CF64 4HE Tel: (029) 2051 5562

Crusader Ltd, Oxford House, Easthorpe Street, Ruddington, Nottingham, NG11 6LA Tel: 0115-940 5550 Fax: 0115-940 6660 E-mail: sales@crusaderltd.com *Computer consultants*

Crusader Abrasives Ltd, Unit 24 Crossfield Industrial Estate, Crossfield Road, Lichfield, Staffordshire, WS13 6RJ Tel: (01543) 263632 Fax: (01543) 415787 *Industrial diamond wheel manufrs*

Crusader Cleaning Services, 17 Bulmer Way, Cannon Park Industrial Estate, Middlesbrough, Cleveland, TS1 5JT Tel: (01642) 226403 Fax: (01642) 226403 *Cleaning services*

Crusader Industrial Doors, Unit 6, Bridge Court, Leeds, LS11 9TU Tel: 0113-243 9595 Fax: 0113-242 7992 *Door manufrs*

Crusader Plastics Ltd, Crown Street, Failsworth, Manchester, M35 9BD Tel: 0161-688 6466 Fax: 0161-683 5732 E-mail: geoffkay@crusader-ltd.co.uk *Display metal, tubular & wire equipment*

Crusader Sails, The Sail Loft, Cobbs Quay, Poole, Dorset, BH15 4EU Tel: (01202) 670580 Fax: (01202) 675578 E-mail: info@cruisadersails.com *Sail makers*

Crusader Technologies, 34 Northill Road, Cople, Bedford, MK44 3UD Tel: (01234) 838040 Fax: (01234) 838152 *IT support agents*

Cruse Control Ltd, 6 Wolsey Mansions, Main Avenue, Moor Park, Northwood, Middlesex, HA6 2HL Tel: (01923) 842295 Fax: (01923) 842698 E-mail: mail@crusecontrol.com *Database creators*

Crusely Trailer Engineering Ltd, Beacon Hill Industrial Estate, Botany Way, Purfleet, Essex, RM19 1SR Tel: (01708) 861144 Fax: (01708) 863308 *Road trailer refurbishment, repairs & mot's*

Crusher Electrical Engineers, 120 Yapham Road, Pocklington, York, YO42 2DY Tel: (01759) 302652 Fax: (01759) 302680 E-mail: brucelufc@aol.com *Specialists in industrial, agricultural & commercial design, installation & maintenance*

Crusherform Grinding Co., 30 Kennington Road, Nuffield Industrial Estate, Poole, Dorset, BH17 0GF Tel: (01202) 679363 Fax: (01202) 682970 *Precision engineers*

Crusoe Paper Ltd, D Banovallum Court, Holmes Way, Horncastle, Lincolnshire, LN9 6JW Tel: (01507) 524545 Fax: (01507) 524580 *Paper distributors & carbon paper manufrs*

Crusteel Ltd, Rutland Way, Sheffield, S3 8DG Tel: 0114-276 0651 Fax: 0114-273 9005 E-mail: Sales@crusteel.co.uk *Steel stockholders*

Crux Products Ltd, Paddock Wood, Carlton Road, South Godstone, Godstone, Surrey, RH9 8LE Tel: (01342) 892260 Fax: (01342) 893878 E-mail: mblandcrux@aol.com *Oil & gas field suppliers*

Cruz Yardy Engineering, Roundwell Works, Dereham Road, New Costessey, Norwich, NR5 0SQ Tel: (01603) 746774 Fax: (01603) 746774 *Sheet metalwork engineers or fabricators*

▶ CRx - Digital Audio Productions, 1 Kimble Court, Marsh Road, Little Kimble, Aylesbury, Buckinghamshire, HP22 5XS Tel: (07841) 115338 E-mail: cerrie1@hotmail.com *We can take care of almost every aspect of your event, need a venue location? need music there? need a Limo to get there? Just contact us and tell us what you need! or Choose a party "package" to suit you..*

Crymatics Ltd, Oakwood House, Bishop Thornton, Harrogate, North Yorkshire, HG3 3JN Tel: (01423) 771133 Fax: (01423) 770093 *Hand-held computer manufrs*

▶ Crynant Concrete Products, Unit 6, Crynant Business Park, Crynant, Neath, West Glamorgan, SA10 8PX Tel: (01639) 750850

Cryo Med Instruments Ltd, Cryomed House, Grove Way, Mansfield Woodhouse, Mansfield, Nottinghamshire, NG19 8BW Tel: (01623) 424200 Fax: (01623) 424777 *Medical cryosurgical equipment manufrs*

▶ Cryo Systems Ltd, Eaton House, Eaton Green Road, Luton, LU2 9LD Tel: (01582) 416699 Fax: (01582) 726840 *Super conductors*

Cryogenics International Ltd, 7 Brunel Way, Fareham, Hampshire, PO15 5TX Tel: (01489) 886722 Fax: (01489) 575229 E-mail: alan.rjones@cryogenicsinternational.co.uk *Provision of deep cryogenic treatment services, increasing operational life of production tooling, manufacture & supply of deep cryogenic treatment chambers*

Cryosonic UK Ltd, 11 Boundary Court Rathmore Road, Cambridge, CB1 7BB Tel: (01223) 720695 Fax: (0870) 1314500 E-mail: sales@cryosonic.co.uk *CryoSonic (UK) Ltd provides Dry Ice Blasting Machines sales and rental to the UK. We also offer dry ice blast cleaning service.*

Cryotec Air Conditioning, Unit 4 Wolf Business Park, Alton Road Industrial Estate, Ross-on-Wye, Herefordshire, HR9 5NB Tel: (0800) 3892369 Fax: (01989) 764401 E-mail: info@cryotec.co.uk *Air conditioning contractors*

Crypton Ltd, Bristol Road, Bridgwater, Somerset, TA6 4BX Tel: (01278) 436205 Fax: (01278) 450567 E-mail: sales@cryptontechnology.com *Motor vehicle engine test equipment*

Cryselco Lighting Ltd, 274 Ampthill Road, Bedford, MK42 9QJ Tel: (01234) 273355 Fax: (01234) 210867 E-mail: sales@cryselco.co.uk *Light fittings manufrs*

Crystal Ltd, Unit D Leswin Pl, London, N16 7NJ Tel: 020 72758322 Fax: 020 79231172 *Clothing manufrs*

Crystal Abrasive Products & Co. Ltd, Clamark House, 63 Stalker Lees Road, Sheffield, S11 8NP Tel: 0114-266 6281 Fax: 0114-268 5336 E-mail: info@crystal-abrasives.com *Manufacturers of diamond & borazon wheels & tooling*

Crystal Blinds Ltd, 6 Kirkstone Road North, Liverpool, L21 7NS Tel: 0151-525 3646 Fax: 0151-474 7733 *Blind manufrs*

Crystal Blinds, 166 Logan Street, Nottingham, NG6 9FU Tel: 0115-927 2025 Fax: 0115-916 1140 *Blinds manufrs*

Crystal Ceramics Ltd, Unit 14A Whitebridge Industrial Estate, Whitebridge Lane, Stone, Staffordshire, ST15 8LQ Tel: (01785) 811545 Fax: (01785) 811545 *Ceramic decorators*

Crystal Class, Unit 2b Mill Park Industrial Estate, Woodbury Salterton, Exeter, EX5 1EL Tel: (01395) 233362 Fax: (01395) 233362 *Engraving glass & trophies*

▶ Crystal Clean Southwest, Carrick Business Centre, Commercial Road, Penryn, Cornwall, TR10 8AR Tel: (01326) 377999 Fax: 01326 377999 E-mail: crystal_cleaning@btconnect.com *Professional Domestic and Office Cleaning, After Party Clean, Spring Clean, DOmestic Clean, Office Clean. Friendly reliable staff.*

Crystal Cleaning Supplies, 82 St James Way, Sidcup, Kent, DA14 5HF Tel: (020) 8309 0237 Fax: (020) 8308 0825 E-mail: sales@crystalcleaningsupplies.co.uk *Janitorial suppliers & distributors*

▶ Crystal Clear Contractors, 3 Earlston Road, Wallasey, Merseyside, CH45 5DX Tel: 0151-630 3339 E-mail: crystalclear007@hotmail.co.uk *WE ARE AN EXPERIENCED COMPANY , WHO ARE HIGHLY MOTIVATED, ALL ARE EMPLOYEES COME FULLY INSURED,WITH UNIFORM AND A TRUSTWORTHY PLEASENT MANNER.WE PROVIDE A PROFESSIONAL SERVICE .*

Crystal Clear Glass Engravers, 37A Lisburn Road, Belfast, BT9 7AA Tel: (028) 9032 9655 Fax: (028) 9032 9655 E-mail: info@crystal_engravers.com *Crystal & glass engravers & suppliers*

▶ Crystal Clear Manufacturing Ltd, 1-2 Lacerta Court, Letchworth Garden City, Hertfordshire, SG6 1FD Tel: (01462) 489900 Fax: (01462) 489909 *Double glazing manufrs*

▶ Crystal Clear Products 2000 Ltd, Grove Cottages, Wormingford Grove, Wormingford, Colchester, CO6 3AJ Tel: (01206) 243700 Fax: (01206) 241806 E-mail: sales@pure-watercoolers.co.uk *Suppliers of water coolers & bottled drinking water to offices*

▶ Crystal Consult, Barton Road, Nuneaton, Warwickshire, CV10 7BN Tel: (024) 7638 5371 Fax: (024) 7638 5371 E-mail: sales@crystal-consult.co.uk *Offering cost solutions for all types of carrier requirements and courier services, also offering packaging and stantionary reduction services.*

▶ Crystal Cut Drilling Services, Cannock Chase Enterprise Centre, Walkers Rise, Hednesford, Cannock, Staffordshire, WS12 0QW Tel: (01543) 876511 Fax: (01543) 877821 E-mail: crystalcutpl@aol.com *Construction*

Crystal Drinks (UK) Ltd, 14 Wakefield Road, Featherstone, Pontefract, West Yorkshire, WF7 5HJ Tel: (01977) 797171 Fax: (01977) 791753 E-mail: gmcgoldrick@crystaldrinks.co.uk *Soft drink manufrs*

▶ Crystal Employment Services Ltd, Gilbert Wakefield House, 67 Bewsey Street, Warrington, WA2 7JQ Tel: 01925 631300 Fax: 01925 638440 E-mail: info@crystalemp.com *Crystal is an employment agency and HR consultancy business that can assist and advise you with all your staffing needs whether temporary or permanent. Our friendly but competent approach together with our competitive prices make us stand out from our competitors.*

Crystal Finishes Ltd, Blackwater Way, Aldershot, Hampshire, GU12 4DP Tel: (01252) 325999 Fax: (01252) 330256 *Stove enamelling, powder coating & screen printers/printing services*

▶ Crystal Glass Innovations, Unit 4D/21, Goatsmoor Lane, Billericay, Essex, CM4 9RS Tel: (01277) 650867 Fax: (01277) 651587 E-mail: crystalglassinnovations@yahoo.co.uk *Shower enclosure suppliers & manufrs*

Crystal Leisure Ltd, Unit 6, Stadium Close, Cardiff, CF11 8TS Tel: (029) 2023 9740 Fax: (029) 2022 5845 E-mail: sales@crystal-leisure.co.uk *Fruit machine manufrs*

▶ Crystal Offset, Crystal House, 17 Tariff Road, London, N17 0DY Tel: (020) 8801 1733 Fax: (020) 8365 1826

Crystal Polishing Ltd, Century Park, Garrison Lane, Birmingham, B9 4NZ Tel: 0121-766 6733 Fax: 0121-766 6733 *Metal polishers*

Crystal Refrigeration, 4 Dolman Road, London, W4 5UY Tel: (020) 8994 9398 Fax: (020) 8994 1445 *Refrigeration contractors*

Crystal Spring Water Co. Ltd, 4050 Chander Court, Oxford Business Park South, Garsington Road, Oxford, OX4 2JY Tel: (01865) 848848 Fax: (01865) 847847 E-mail: customerservice@powwowwaters.com *Suppliers of cold & hot water for offices*

Crystal Structures Ltd, Crystal Park, Tunbridge Lane, Bottisham, Cambridge, CB25 9EA Tel: (01223) 811451 Fax: (01223) 811452 E-mail: sales@crystalstructures.co.uk Purchasing Contact: G.A. Wooster Sales Contact: G.A. Wooster Principal Export Areas: Worldwide *Established in 1947, we are specialist manufacturers of shaft position encoder (process control), special purpose custom built machinery, x-ray inspection (real-time) equipment. Also manufacturers of encoders including absolute & optical industrial. Subcontract surface/cylindrical grinding machines, spark eroding (EDM) & specialist measurement equipment*

Crystal Supplies, 4 Bessemer Road, Cardiff, CF11 8BA Tel: (029) 2022 4227 Fax: (029) 2039 0724 *Catering equipment suppliers*

Crystal Waters Spas UK Ltd, Island Road, Hersden, Canterbury, Kent, CT3 4JD Tel: (01227) 361163 Fax: (01227) 361163 E-mail: mike@crystalwatersspas.co.uk *Spas & pool retailers*

▶ Crystal Windscreens Ltd, Springvale Industrial Park, Bilston, West Midlands, WV14 0QL Tel: (01902) 405040 Fax: (01902) 405474 E-mail: sales@crystal-windscreens.com *Windscreen repair services*

Crystalclear Leisure, Woodside Centre, Southend Arterial Road, Rayleigh, Essex, SS6 7TR Tel: (01268) 776690 Fax: (01268) 775842 E-mail: accleisure@aol.com *Specialist supplier of swimming pools & spas*

Crystalink Jewellery Manufacturers, 32-35 Hall Street, Birmingham, B18 6BS Tel: 0121-233 2547 Fax: 0121-236 3203 E-mail: sales@crystalink.co.uk *Jewellery manufrs*

Crystalox Ltd, 1 Limborough Road, Wantage, Oxfordshire, OX12 9AJ Tel: (01235) 770044 Fax: (01235) 770111 E-mail: sales@crystalox.com *Crystal growing equipment manufrs*

Crystalware Ltd, Brook Street, Lakeside, Redditch, Worcestershire, B98 8NG Tel: (01527) 63746 Fax: (01527) 584549 E-mail: sales@crystalwareltd.co.uk *Plastic manufrs*

CS Blinds, 11 Merlin Court, Newton Industrial Estate, Carlisle, CA2 7NY Tel: (01228) 598646 *Vertical blind manufrs*

▶ CS Press Tools Ltd, Unit 23 Nutwood Trading Estate, Limestone Cottage Lane, Sheffield, S6 1NJ Tel: 0114-234 8563 Fax: 0114-234 6290 E-mail: david@cspresstools.co.uk *Press tools to specification*

CSB Engineering Services Ltd, 56 Roman Bank, Saracens Head, Spalding, Lincolnshire, PE12 8BB Tel: (01406) 425201 E-mail: csbeng@valves66.fsnet.co.uk *Valve & boiler services*

CSB Lifting & Marine Products, 3 Station Road Industrial Estate, Station Road, Rowley Regis, West Midlands, B65 0JY Tel: 0121-559 5112 Fax: 0121-559 4173 *Marine hardware & lifting gear distributors*

CSC, Alliance House Clayton Green Business Park, Library Road, Clayton-le-Woods, Chorley, Lancashire, PR6 7EN Tel: (01772) 323555 Fax: (01772) 318000 *Computer suppliers*

Csc Computer Sciences Ltd, Sovereign House, Vision Park Chivers Way, Histon, Cambridge, CB4 9BY Tel: (01223) 547000 Fax: (01223) 547158 *Computer software programmers*

▶ CSC Computer Sciences Corp, Prestwick Intl Airport, British Aerospace, Prestwick, Ayrshire, KA9 2RW Tel: (01292) 672514

CSC Crop Protection Ltd, Schoolcroft, Culbokie, Dingwall, Ross-Shire, IV7 8JH Tel: (01349) 877557 Fax: (01349) 877533 E-mail: enquiries@csccrop.com *Agri chemical distributors*

CSC Crop Protection Ltd, Gooseberry Farm, Whinney Hill, Stockton-on-Tees, Cleveland, TS21 1BQ Tel: (01642) 588585 Fax: (01642) 570597 E-mail: sales@csccrop.co.uk *Crop protection*

▶ CSC Forecourt Services Ltd, 6 Timon View, Heathcote, Warwick, CV34 6ES Tel: (01926) 882377 Fax: (01926) 882377 E-mail: info@cscspec.com *Petrol retail contractors*

C-Scope International Ltd, Kingsnorth Technology Park, Wotton Road, Ashford, Kent, TN23 6LN Tel: (01233) 629181 Fax: (01233) 645897 E-mail: info@cscope.co.uk *Metal detection equipment manufrs*

CSE Aviation, Langford Lane, Oxford Airport, Kidlington, Oxfordshire, OX5 1RA Tel: (01865) 844200 Fax: (01865) 840628 E-mail: jdg@cse-aviation.com *Engineering company*

Cse Citation Centre, Hanger 100 North West Sector, Bournemouth International Airpo, Hurn, Christchurch, Dorset, BH23 6NW Tel: (01202) 573243 Fax: (01202) 581579 E-mail: info@cse-aviation.com *Aircraft maintenance services*

Csea Services Ltd, 114 High Street, Gorleston, Great Yarmouth, Norfolk, NR31 6RE Tel: (01493) 444666 Fax: (01493) 444646 E-mail: martyn@csea.co.uk *Computer suppliers & manufrs*

▶ Csi, Harris Business Park, Hanbury Road, Stoke Prior, Bromsgrove, Worcestershire, B60 4BD Tel: (01527) 559900 Fax: (01527) 559901 *Partitioning & mezzanine floors installers*

▶ Csi Leasing, 2 Newton Business Centre Thorncliffe Park Estate, Newton Cham, Chapeltown, Sheffield, S35 2PH Tel: 0114-232 9200 Fax: 0114-232 9216 *Computer hire services*

CSL, Caxton Road, Newton Industrial Estate, Carlisle, CA2 7NS Tel: (01228) 544422 Fax: (01228) 544464 *Hygiene & maintenance chemical manufrs*

CSL Business Machines Ltd, 28/30 Hinckley Road, Leicester, LE3 0RA Tel: 0116-255 1000 Fax: 0116-233 3224 *Office machine & equipment sales & service*

Csm Computer Ltd, Lighthouse Farm, Main Road, Ashton, Helston, Cornwall, TR13 9SX Tel: (0845) 4561016 Fax: (0845) 4561621 E-mail: sales@csmcomputers.co.uk *Computer services*

▶ Csma Ltd, Queens Road, Stoke-on-Trent, ST4 7LQ Tel: (01782) 764440 Fax: (01782) 412331 E-mail: enquires@csma.ltd.uk *CSMA Limited is an independent laboratory in the United Kingdom offering specialist expertise in surface analysis and surface technology to many industry sectors*

CSS Ltd, Road Three, Winsford Industrial Estate, Winsford, Cheshire, CW7 3PD Tel: (01606) 861809 Fax: (01606) 559337 E-mail: sales@chemicalsupport.co.uk *Chemical dosing equipment manufrs*

▶ CSS Alarms Ltd, 4 Hambridge Road, Newbury, Berkshire, RG14 5SS Tel: (01635) 233033 Fax: (01635) 233044 E-mail: info@cssalarms.co.uk *Installment service of security systems*

▶ CST Automation, Unit B2 93-95 Turner Lane, Ashton-under-Lyne, Lancashire, OL6 8SS Tel: 0161-330 9287 Fax: 0161-330 9287 E-mail: sales@cstautomation.co.uk *Industrial electronic equipment manufrs*

CT Production Ltd, 32-40 Harwell Road, Nuffield Industrial Estate, Poole, Dorset, BH17 0GE Tel: (01202) 687633 Fax: (01202) 680788 E-mail: sales@ctproduction.co.uk *Quality electronics manufacturing services, prototype to volume Lead or lead-free, separate lines Fast turn prototypes, batches, high volume SMT build 3 automated lines, 0201, BGA, 35000 CPH Through hole assembly, wave solder Box build, test Materials procurement IPC 610 and ISO 9001/2000 standards*

CTD, Unit 2, CTD House, Summit Business Park, Hanworth Road, Sunbury-on-Thames, Middlesex, TW16 5BH Tel: 01932 771300 Fax: 01932 789229 E-mail: sales@ctdprinters.com *Specialists in printing Reports & Accounts, Brochures, fine art etc. Proud of being one of the best commercial Litho printers in the UK.*

Ctech 2000 Ltd, Royle Road, Rochdale, Lancashire, OL11 3ES Tel: (0870) 2004786 Fax: (0870) 9507755 E-mail: sales@ctech2000.co.uk *Leading supplier of computer components and peripherals.**The computer center, Computer center, computer repair center, computer hardware component, wholesale computer component, discount computer component, computer system components, computer component distributor, c2k, cheap computer and monitor, computer keyboard sale, best amd motherboard, usb external hard drive, graphic card driver, best graphic card, multiple sound card, laptop sound card,Small Form Factor, computer memory unit, clean computer memory, computer operating system software,the computer center in rochdale, c2k*

continued

▶ CTES Ltd, 1 Claremont Street, Aberdeen, AB10 6QP Tel: (01224) 588788 Fax: (01224) 588840 E-mail: uksales@ctes.com *Hardware & software manufrs*

▶ CTI, 12 Pemberton Valley, Ayr, KA7 4UH Tel: (01292) 445423

Cti Balloons Ltd, 6 Consul Road, Rugby, Warwickshire, CV21 1PB Tel: (01788) 546299 Fax: (01788) 546114E-mail: ctiballoon@aol.com *Balloon manufrs & distributors*

Cti Data Solutions Ltd, Nordic House, 120 High Street, Purley, Surrey, CR8 2AD Tel: (020) 8763 3888 Fax: (020) 8763 3863 E-mail: info@ctidata.co.uk *Call management software suppliers*

▶ CTL, Princes Business Centre, 26 Mostyn Road, Colwyn Bay, Clwyd, LL29 8PB Tel: (01492) 535986 Fax: (01492) 534958 E-mail: ian.mclaughlin3@btopenworld.com *Medical equipment suppliers*

▶ CTL Components, Falcon House, 19 Deer Park Road, London, SW19 3UX Tel: (020) 8543 0911 Fax: (020) 8540 0034 E-mail: info@ctl-components.com *Metalwork & electrical components specialists*

CTL/EDM Ltd, Green Street, Green Road, Mile End Green, Dartford, DA2 8EB Tel: (01474) 708621 Fax: (01474) 708948 E-mail: ctl.edm@lineone.net *Wire spark erosion subcontractors*

CTM Communications Ltd, Unit 15, Lamplight Way, Swinton, Manchester, M27 8UJ Tel: (0870) 0271122 Fax: 0161-925 0478 *Computer consultants*

CTM Contract Maintenance Ltd, Hawkins Road, Colchester, CO2 8JY Tel: (01206) 793479 Fax: (0870) 2402151 E-mail: enquiries@ctm-ltd.co.uk *Specialists in property maintenance & repairs*

CTR Engineering Ltd, Whitley Street, Bingley, West Yorkshire, BD16 4JH Tel: (01274) 562550 Fax: (01274) 551218 E-mail: ctrengltd@hotmail.com *Precision engineers*

C-Trak Ltd, 6 Greaves Indust Estate, Leighton Buzzard, Bedfordshire, LU7 4UB Tel: (01525) 850316 Fax: (01525) 854050 E-mail: sales@ctrak.fsnet.co.uk *Systems for food & packaging industry services*

Ctronix Ltd, New Druids, 41 Eastgate, Cowbridge, South Glamorgan, CF71 7EL Tel: (01446) 775252 Fax: (01446) 775262 E-mail: es@ctronix.com *CTRONIX specialises in the design, software & manufacture of Queue Management Systems & Nanotechnology displays.*

C-Tronix UK Ltd, 185a Lower Blandford Road, Broadstone, Dorset, BH18 8DH Tel: (01202) 695500 E-mail: ap9000mart@aol.com *Marine steering gear manufrs*

CTS, Curriers Close, Charter Avenue Industrial Estate, Coventry, CV4 8AW Tel: (0870) 7511400 Fax: (024) 7642 6401 E-mail: enquiries@ctsnet.co.uk *Event registration & badging contractor providing bespoke registration solutions to suit all events from large trade exhibitions to small product launches. Services include - registration systems, call centre services, database management, web services, research services, event staff, fulfilment house, badging systems & visitor badges*

CTS, 23 Belle Vue Road, London, E17 4DQ Tel: (020) 8527 2001 Fax: (020) 8527 1511 *Curtain track manufrs*

CTS, 7-9 Moorland Road, Stoke-on-Trent, ST6 1DP Tel: (01782) 836194 Fax: (01782) 814818 E-mail: sales@names.co.uk *Computer services*

CTS, 41 Forge Lane, Minworth Industrial Park, Minworth, Sutton Coldfield, West Midlands, B76 1AH Tel: 0121-351 4445 Fax: 0121-351 4442 E-mail: sales@centretank.com *Pumps, fuel, lubricating systems & equipment*

Cubby Construction Ltd, Unit H, Knights Drive, Kingmoor Park Central, Carlisle, CA6 4SG Tel: (01228) 521284 Fax: (01228) 591952 E-mail: info@cubby.co.uk *Roofing contractors*

▶ Cube Airconditioning Ltd, Hillcrest 2 Pirbright Road, Normandy, Guildford, Surrey, GU3 2AG Tel: (01483) 811169 E-mail: info@cubeacltd.com *Service & maintenance of most air conditioners*

Cube Arts Ltd, 14-18 Abbotsbury Road, Morden, Surrey, SM4 5LQ Tel: (020) 8685 9108 Fax: (020) 8085 9089 E-mail: info@cubearts.com *Shop fitting manufrs*

Cube Conversions Ltd, 10 Ravenswood Road, Bristol, BS6 6BN Tel: 0117-946 7036 Fax: 0117-946 7036 *Computer consultants*

▶ Cube Display Ltd, Downham Street, Bradford, West Yorkshire, BD3 9QY Tel: (01274) 746611 Fax: (01274) 746622 *Sign manufr*

▶ Cubed Creative, The London Business Innovation Centre 28 Innova Business Par, Enfield, Middlesex, EN3 7XU Tel: (020) 8350 1289 Fax: (020) 8350 1351 E-mail: sales@cubedcreative.co.uk *Cubed is an experienced company with the knowledge, ability and *creativity to deliver everythingyou require to promote your business; *whether you require a brochure, pop-up display or simplya vinyl sign. *Cubed was created to provide a complete design and print service *under one roof,with clients first and foremost in our minds, we aim *to produce realistic cost effective design solutions.*Specialising in graphic design, large format digital printing and *vinyl signage, we use our extensive*knowledge, traditional skills and the latest technology to offer *creative solutions that exceed our*clients expectations.*Put us to the test, and discover what we can do for you....**

Cubed Design, 30 North Grove Rise, Leeds, LS8 2NL Tel: 0113-265 5581 E-mail: cubeddesign@cubeddesign.co.uk *Cubed is a design studio based in Leeds. Our area of expertise is interior design, from consultancy and advice to full design packages. We also offer a range of graphic design and multimedia services, from catalogues to website design.*

Cubex Contracts Ltd, 8 Desborough Road, Rothwell, Kettering, Northamptonshire, NN14 6JG Tel: (01536) 712729 Fax: (01536) 418990 E-mail: sales@cubexcontracts.com *Stock & handling*

Cubic Design & Construction Ltd, Ventureforth House, South Denes Road, Great Yarmouth, Norfolk, NR30 3PT Tel: (01493) 332031

Cubic Modular Systems (UK) Ltd, Unit 8 Boston Court, Kansas Avenue, Salford, M50 2GN Tel: 0161-876 4742 Fax: 0161-876 4746 E-mail: info@cubic-uk.co.uk *Electrical enclosure equipment manufrs*

Cubic Transportation Systems Ltd, Honeycrock Lane, Redhill, RH1 5LA Tel: (01737) 782200 Fax: (01737) 789759 E-mail: cubicafc@cts-ltd.co.uk *Ticket issuing machine maintenance or repair*

Cubical Systems Ltd, Units 1-4 Nova Business Unit, Gore Road Industrial Estate, New Milton, Hampshire, BH25 6RP Tel: (01425) 615585 Fax: (01425) 628144 E-mail: sales@cubicalsystems.co.uk *Toilet cubicle manufrs*

Cubitt Theobald & Sons Ltd, St Catherines Road, Long Melford, Sudbury, Suffolk, CO10 9JU Tel: (01787) 371002 Fax: (01787) 880625 E-mail: cubitt-theobald@cubitt.co.uk *Building contractors*

Cubix Ltd, 34 Candlemas Lane, Beaconsfield, Buckinghamshire, HP9 1AF Tel: (01494) 678661 Fax: (01494) 678663 E-mail: sales@cubix.co.uk *Telecommunications services*

▶ Cuchulain Construction, 124 Kings Park Avenue, Glasgow, G44 4HS Tel: 0141-632 3020

Cudd Bentley Consulting, Ashurst Manor, Church Lane, Ascot, Berkshire, SL5 7DD Tel: (01344) 628821 Fax: (01344) 623448 E-mail: reception@ascot.cbp.co.uk *Building services consultants*

Cudd Bentley Consulting Ltd, Suite 1 Shelly Cresent Centre, 20 Farm House Way, Monkspath, Solihull, West Midlands, B90 4EH Tel: 0121-711 4343 Fax: 0121-711 3535 *Consulting engineers*

▶ Cuddles The Baby Shop, 59 Sweyn Road, Cliftonville, Margate, Kent, CT9 2DD Tel: (01843) 229929 Fax: (01843) 229929 E-mail: samgregory3@msn.com3 *Baby care equipment manufrs*

Cuddra Aquatic Nursery Wholesale, Cuddra Nursery, St. Austell, Cornwall, PL25 3JQ Tel: (01726) 76686 Fax: (01726) 76602 *Water gardening*

▶ Cuddy Demolition & Dismantling Ltd, Tank Farm Road, Llandarcy, Neath, West Glamorgan, SA10 6EN Tel: (01792) 321110 Fax: (01792) 321411 E-mail: info@cuddy-group.com

Cudlow Steel Services Ltd, Unit H4 Rudford Industrial Estate, Ford Road, Ford, Arundel, West Sussex, BN18 0BD Tel: (01903) 714545 Fax: (01903) 716151 E-mail: cudlow@fsbdial.co.uk *Steel stockholders & shearing facilities*

Cudworth Of Norden, Baitings Mill, Rochdale, Lancashire, OL12 7TQ Tel: (01706) 641771 Fax: (01706) 641771 *Retailers of cotton moleskin & corduroy cloth*

Cue Above The Rest, 5 Demontfort Rise, Ware, Hertfordshire, SG12 0DQ Tel: (01920) 484847 Fax: (01920) 484847 E-mail: queabovetherest@yahoo.co.uk *Snooker & pool table distributors & repairers*

Cue Doctor, 120 Prince Avenue, Westcliff-on-Sea, Essex, SS0 0NW Tel: (01702) 391323 Fax: (01702) 391323 E-mail: poolandsnooker@googlemail.co.uk *Snooker equipment manufacturers & retailers*

Cuecraft Ltd, Unit 3 Coach Close, Shireoaks, Worksop, Nottinghamshire, S81 8AP Tel: (01909) 474461 Fax: (01909) 483197 E-mail: sales@cuecraft.com *Snooker cue manufrs*

Cuerdale Fire Protection Systems Ltd, Chorley Road, Walton Le Dale, Preston, PR5 4JA Tel: (01772) 566210 Fax: (01772) 558165 E-mail: enquiries@cuerdalefire.co.uk *Fire extinguisher & fire alarms suppliers*

Jose Cuervo Ltd, 150 Brompton Road, London, SW3 1HX Tel: (020) 7591 1900 Fax: (020) 7589 7016 *Marketing for Jose Cuero, Mexico*

Cuesim Ltd, 2-4 Highfield Park, Highfield Road, Oakley, Bedford, MK43 7TA Tel: (01234) 828000 Fax: (01234) 828001 E-mail: sales@cuesim.com *Simulation products retailers*

Cuff Services Ltd, Unit 4 Elmham Enterprises, Billingford Road, North Elmham, Dereham, Norfolk, NR20 5HN Tel: (01362) 668684 Fax: (01362) 668684 *Electronic assembly & manufrs*

Cuffley Tool & Engineering, 6 Spurling Works, Pindar Road, Hoddesdon, Hertfordshire, EN11 0DB Tel: (01992) 478888 Fax: (01992) 478888 E-mail: cuffleytool@tiscali.co.uk *Tool & mould manufrs*

Cuisenaire Co., Unit 5, Feidr Castell, Fishguard, Dyfed, SA65 9BB Tel: (0845) 6122912 Fax: (0845) 6123912 E-mail: cuisenaire@cuisenaire.co.uk *Teaching systems*

▶ CUK Audio, Unit 4, Davieland Court, Ibrox Business Park, Glasgow, G51 2JR Tel: 0141-440 5333 Fax: 0141-440 1119 E-mail: sales@cuk-audio.com *Distribution of audio products*

▶ Culdaff Construction Co Ltd, 55 Hamilton Street, Glasgow, G42 0PL Tel: 0141-423 4230 Fax: 0141-424 4484

▶ Culex Ltd, 7 Telford Court, Chestergates Business Park, Chester, CH1 6LT Tel: (01244) 853838 Fax: (01244) 853800 E-mail: info@culex.co.uk *Computer systems consultants*

Culimetea Saveguard Ltd, Tame Valley Mill, Wainwright Street, Dukinfield, Cheshire, SK16 5NB Tel: 0161-344 2484 Fax: 0161-344 2486 E-mail: sales@culimetea-saveguard.com *Textiles manufrs*

Cullen Engineering Ltd, 51 Naysmith Rd, Southfield Industrial Estate, Glenrothes, Fife, KY6 2SD Tel: (01592) 771132 Fax: (01383) 771182 E-mail: sales@cullen-bp.co.uk *Building product manufrs*

▶ John Cullen Lighting, 585 Kings Road, London, SW6 2EH Tel: (020) 7371 5400 Fax: (020) 7371 7799 E-mail: design@johncullenlighting.co.uk *Lighting for both the contemporary & traditional house & garden*

▶ Cullen Packaging, 10 Dalsholm Avenue, Glasgow, G20 0TS Tel: 0141-945 2222 Fax: 0141-945 3567 E-mail: jamesg@cullen.co.uk *Cullen packaging manufrs*

Cullen Scholefield Ltd, Maxwelton House, 41 Boltro Road, Haywards Heath, West Sussex, RH16 1BJ Tel: (01444) 455052 Fax: (01444) 459221 E-mail: enquiries@csgconsult.com *Personnel, management & training consultants*

Culligan Interational Ltd, Culligan House, Outwood Lane, Coulsdon, Surrey, CR5 3NA Tel: (01737) 550087 Fax: (01737) 550092 E-mail: slcs@culligan.co.uk *Supply & distribute bottled water & water dispensers*

Culligan International UK Ltd, Daimler Drive, Cowpen Lane Industrial Estate, Billingham, Cleveland, TS23 4JD Tel: (01642) 373500 Fax: (01642) 373575 E-mail: brianaire@culligan.co.uk *Filter manufrs*

Culligan International UK Ltd, Culligan House, Coronation Road, High Wycombe, Buckinghamshire, HP12 3SU Tel: (01494) 436484 Fax: (01494) 523833 E-mail: enquires@culligan.co.uk *Water treatment plant manufrs*

Cullimore Hydraulic Engineering, C 14 Copt Elm Close, Charlton Kings, Cheltenham, Gloucestershire, GL53 8AD Tel: (01242) 241112 Fax: (01242) 241112 *Hydraulic engineers*

Moreton C. Cullimore Gravels Ltd, 47 London Road, Stroud, Gloucestershire, GL5 2AU Tel: (01453) 765381 Fax: (01453) 766491 *Gravel & sand producers*

Culloden Foods Ltd, Smithton Industrial Estate, Smithton, Inverness, IV2 7WL Tel: (01463) 792421 Fax: (01463) 794939 *Bakery*

Cullum & Clarke Joinery, Brackendale, Felthorpe Road, Attlebridge, Norwich, NR9 5TF Tel: (01603) 860564 Fax: (01603) 261084 E-mail: info@cullumclarke.co.uk *Joinery manufrs*

Cullum Detuners Ltd, Adams Close, Heanor Gate Industrial Park, Heanor, Derbyshire, DE75 7SW Tel: (01773) 717341 Fax: (01773) 760601 E-mail: sales.enquiries@cullum.co.uk *Noise control engineers*

Cullum Plant Hire & Sales Ltd, 11 Boleness Road, Wisbech, Cambridgeshire, PE13 2RB Tel: (01945) 463356 Fax: (01945) 463248 E-mail: cullumsales@btinternet.com *Plant hire services*

▶ Culm Environmental Pest Control, 26 Shortlands Road, Cullompton, Devon, EX15 1HJ Tel: (0800) 0232130

Culm Industrial Clothing, Saunders Way, Cullompton, Devon, EX15 1BS Tel: (01884) 32302 Fax: (01884) 38482 *Industrial clothing distributors*

Culm Print Ltd, Unit 2 Blundells Road, Tiverton, Devon, EX16 4BZ Tel: (01884) 258904 Fax: (01884) 242466 E-mail: andywestcote@ukonline.co.uk *Printers*

Culpeper Ltd, Pall Mall Deposit, Unit 47, 124-128 Barlby Road, London, W10 6BL Tel: (020) 8962 3010 Fax: (020) 8969 9247 E-mail: info@culpeper.co.uk *Herb merchants & producers*

Culpitt Ltd, Jubilee Industrial Estate, Ashington, Northumberland, NE63 8UQ Tel: (01670) 814545 Fax: (01670) 815248 E-mail: reception@culpitt.com *Cake board, decoration, frill & edible decorations*

Cultech Ltd, Unit 2/3, Christchurch Road, Baglan Industrial Park, Port Talbot, West Glamorgan, SA12 7BZ Tel: (01639) 825101 Fax: (01639) 825100 E-mail: sales@cultech.co.uk *Vitamins & health foods manufrs*

Cults Lime Ltd, Cults Hills, Cupar, Fife, KY15 7TF Tel: (01334) 652548 Fax: (01334) 657887 *Limestone producers*

▶ Culture Boats, Unit 43 Weaver Industrial Estate, Blackburne Street, Liverpool, L19 8JA Tel: 0151-494 1234 Fax: 0151-494 9494 *Steel boat builders*

Cultured Pearl Co. Ltd, 27 Hatton Garden, London, EC1N 8BR Tel: (020) 7405 3339 Fax: (020) 7405 5936 E-mail: info@theculturedpearl.co.uk *Pearl importers*

▶ Culwick & Co, 69 Southend Road, Hockley, Essex, SS5 4PZ Tel: (01702) 200939 Fax: (01702) 207258 E-mail: info@culwick.com *Culwick & Co.,chartered accountants,business advisors,professional *service,referral,satisfied clients,high level of professionalism,competence,major *firm,personal,individual,comprehensive range of services,accounting,Institute of Chartered Accountants,England,Wales,free consultation,year end accounts,limited companies,latest Computer software,presentation,law,Accounting standards,registered auditor,approved,audits,personal,corporate tax *inspector,planning,VAT,NIC,self-employed, partnerships,company *formation,formed,Registered office,company secretarial services,Payroll bureau *service,competitive rates,weekly,monthly*

Culwick Printers Ltd, 131 Long Street, Atherstone, Warwickshire, CV9 1AD Tel: (01827) 712618 Fax: (01827) 718527 E-mail: culwicks@anchorprint.co.uk *Printers*

▶ Cumberland Cathodic Protection, 4 Strand View, Liverpool Intermodal Freeport Terminal, Bootle, Merseyside, L20 1HA Tel: 0151-922 3041 Fax: 0151-922 4605 E-mail: sales@cumberlandcp.com *Cathodic protection system manufrs*

Cumberland Commercial Bodies, Unit 3 Peart Road, Derwent Howe Industrial Estate, Workington, Cumbria, CA14 3YT Tel: (01900) 606000 Fax: (01900) 606001
E-mail: ss@ccbodies.freeserve.co.uk
Commercial body builders

Cumberland Europe Ltd, Daniels Industrial Estate, 104 Bath Road, Stroud, Gloucestershire, GL5 3TJ Tel: (01453) 768980 Fax: (01453) 768990
E-mail: europeansales@cumberland-plastics.com *Plastic recycling & shredding machinery manufrs*

The Cumberland Hotel, Great Cumberland Place, Marble Art, London, W1A 4RF Tel: (020) 7262 1234 Fax: (0870) 3339281
E-mail: enquiries@thecumberland.co.uk
Conference centre, hotel, restaurant & bar

▶ Cumbernauld Pallets, Redding Road, Redding, Falkirk, FK2 9TX Tel: (01324) 711998 Fax: (01324) 719701

▶ Cumbria Access Services Ltd, Stonegarth, Crosthwaite, Kendal, Cumbria, LA8 8HT Tel: (01539) 568001 Fax: 015395 68002
E-mail: info@casaccess.co.uk *CAS Ltd are a specialist rope access company. Services provided include, high level cleaning,painting, inspection maintenance and repair. Based in the noth west of the country we are located close to the motorway system for mobilisation through out the country.*

Cumbria Bearings & Transmissions Ltd, 2 James St Workshop, James Street, Carlisle, CA2 5AH Tel: (01228) 512404 Fax: (01228) 512811
E-mail: info@cbtuk.co.uk *Supplier of bearings, transmissions & pneumatics*

Cumbria Blinds North West, 111 Corporation Road, Workington, Cumbria, CA14 2PN Tel: (01900) 605070 Fax: (01900) 605070 *Vertical blind manufrs*

Cumbria Chamber Of Commerce, Carlisle Enterprise Centre, James Street, Carlisle, CA2 5DA Tel: (01228) 534120 Fax: (01228) 515602
E-mail: sales@cumbriachamberofcommerce.co.uk *Enterprise agency*

Cumbria Communications 2000 Ltd, Westgate, Milburn, Penrith, Cumbria, CA10 1TW Tel: (01768) 361416 Fax: (01768) 362000 *Radio communications, telephone & data specialists*

▶ Cumbria Design Scaffold Ltd, Unit 3 North Lonsdale Road, Olverston, Ulverston, Cumbria, LA12 9DL Tel: (01229) 587804

Cumbria Extrusion Dies Ltd, Unit 4, Buddle Road, Clay Flatts Industrial Estate, Workington, Cumbria, CA14 3YD Tel: (01900) 66952 Fax: (01900) 66761 *Metal extrusion manufrs*

▶ Cumbria Joinery, 3 Chapel Street, Egremont, Cumbria, CA22 2DU Tel: (01946) 823300 Fax: (01946) 823300

Cumbria Kendal Scaffold Co., Mintsfeet Road North, Kendal, Cumbria, LA9 6LZ Tel: (01539) 722674 Fax: (01539) 730640 *Scaffolding contractors*

Cumbria Loos, Winscales, Workington, Cumbria, CA14 4JZ Tel: (01900) 607272 Fax: (01900) 602323 *Portable toilets hire*

Cumbria Minimix, Kendal Lime Works, Underbarrow Road, Kendal, Cumbria, LA9 5RT Tel: (01539) 735784 Fax: (01539) 735784 *Concrete manufacture & supplier*

Cumbria Pumps, Unit 8 Lake District Business Park, Mint Bridge Road, Kendal, Cumbria, LA9 6NH Tel: (01539) 735572 Fax: (01539) 735572 *Pump distributors*

▶ Cumbria Storage Systems Ltd, 52a Main Street, Cockermouth, Cumbria, CA13 9LU Tel: (01900) 827333 Fax: (01900) 827334
E-mail: sales@cumstore.co.uk *Shelving distributors*

▶ Cumbria Truck Centre Ltd, Leabank Road, Kingstown Industrial Estate, Carlisle, CA3 0HB Tel: (01228) 536405 Fax: (01228) 590300
E-mail: sales@warmstrong.co.uk *Sales, service & supply of commercial vehicles*

Cumbrian Implement Co. Ltd, 4 King Street, Aspatria, Wigton, Cumbria, CA7 3ET Tel: (01697) 320269 Fax: (01697) 322677
E-mail: newdale@btconnect.com *Agricultural building manufrs*

▶ Cumbrian Industrials Ltd, 150 Preston Road, Lytham St. Annes, Lancashire, FY8 5AT Tel: (01253) 741730 Fax: (01253) 796532

Cumbrian Industrials Ltd, 3 Cowper Road, Gilwilly Industrial Estate, Penrith, Cumbria, CA11 9BN Tel: (01768) 865571 Fax: (01768) 862380
E-mail: enquiries@cumbrian-industrials.co.uk
Civil engineers & road maintenance service

Cumbrian Mini-mix Concrete, Pittwood Road, Lillyhall Industrial Estate, Lillyhall, Workington, Cumbria, CA14 4JP Tel: (01900) 870601 Fax: (01900) 604426 *Ready mixed concrete suppliers*

Cumbrian Newspapers Ltd, Newspaper House, Newspaper House, Dalston Road, Carlisle, CA2 5UA Tel: (01228) 612600 Fax: (01228) 612601
E-mail: news@cumbrian-newspapers.co.uk
Newspaper publishers

Cumbrian Sea Foods, Whelpside, Whitehaven, Cumbria, CA28 8XX Tel: (01946) 63131 Fax: (01946) 63232 *Cold storage & fish processors*

▶ Cumbrian Windows, 3 Adams Road, Derwent Howe Industrial Estate, Workington, Cumbria, CA14 3YS Tel: (01900) 68337 Fax: (01900) 601592

▶ Cumming & Co. Ltd, 8 Whitefriars Street, Perth, PH1 1PP Tel: (01738) 567899 Fax: (01738) 567900

Cumming Fire & Security, 10 Loch Way, Kemnay, Inverurie, Aberdeenshire, AB51 5QZ Tel: (01467) 643917 Fax: (01467) 643917
E-mail: sales@cummingfireandsecurity.co.uk *Fire & security installer*

Cummings Bros, 5-7 Merridale Road, Wolverhampton, WV3 9RX Tel: (01902) 427000 Fax: (01902) 712247 *Security locks*

Cummins Diesel, Rutherford Drive, Park Farm South, Wellingborough, Northamptonshire, NN8 6AN Tel: (01933) 672200 Fax: (01933) 334198 E-mail: cduksales@cummins.com *Diesel engine distributors* Also at: Branches throughout the U.K.

Cummins Engine Co. Ltd, Royal Oak Way South, Royal Oak Industrial Estate, Daventry, Northamptonshire, NN11 8NU Tel: (01327) 886000 Fax: (01327) 886100 *Diesel engine manufrs*

Cummins Generator Technologies, Barnack Road, Stamford, Lincolnshire, PE9 2NB Tel: (01780) 484000 Fax: (01780) 484100
E-mail: info@cumminsgeneratortechnologies.com *Generator manufrs*

Cummins & Papyrus Ltd, Canal Road, Bradford, West Yorkshire, BD2 1AJ Tel: (01274) 533555 Fax: (01274) 533666
E-mail: sales@cummingspapyrus.co.uk
Envelope manufrs

▶ Cummins & Pope Ltd, 10 London Road, Horndean, Waterlooville, Hampshire, PO8 0BZ Tel: (023) 9259 5199

Cummins Power Generation Ltd, Manston Park, Columbus Avenue, Manston, Ramsgate, Kent, CT12 5BF Tel: (01843) 255000 Fax: (01843) 255902
E-mail: graham.n.baldock@cummins.com
Generating sets, diesel driven, emergency/ standby, mobile & silenced

Cummins Turbo Technologies Ltd, St. Andrews Road, Huddersfield, HD1 6RA Tel: (01484) 422244 Fax: (01484) 511680
E-mail: enquiries@cummins.co.uk *Automotive component engineers* Also at: Halifax

Cumulus Mattress Protectors, Selinas Lane, Dagenham, Essex, RM8 1ES Tel: (020) 8592 2233 Fax: (020) 8593 3787
E-mail: enquiries@abbey-quilting.co.uk
Purchasing Contact: D. Cadman Sales Contact: D. Cadman Principal Export Areas: Worldwide *Mattress cover & bed sheet manufrs*

Cundall Johnston & Partners, Horsley House, Regent Centre, Gosforth, Newcastle upon Tyne, NE3 3LU Tel: 0191-213 1515 Fax: 0191-213 1701 *Consulting engineers*

Cundell, Saffron House, 6-10 Kirby Street, London, EC1N 8TS Tel: (020) 7438 1600 Fax: (020) 7438 1601 E-mail: info@cundall.com *Consulting engineers*

Cuneiform, Coxford Abbey Farm, Coxford, King's Lynn, Norfolk, PE31 6TB Tel: (01485) 528050 Fax: (01485) 528380 *Medical equipment manufrs*

Cuneiform Medical Equipment Mnfrs, The Old Post Office, Weasenham Road, Great Massingham, King's Lynn, Norfolk, PE32 2EY Tel: (01485) 520309 Fax: (01485) 528380
E-mail: cuneiform@freenet.co.uk *Medical equipment manufrs*

W.L. Cunliffe (Southport) Ltd, Gratton Place, Skelmersdale, Lancashire, WN8 9UE Tel: (01695) 711800 Fax: (01695) 711811
E-mail: sales@wlcunliffe.com *We are world leaders in the manufacture of glass reinforced composites. Our objective is to provide our customers with a quality product, at an economic price, whilst offering the highest level of service. Specialising in advanced high quality composites, we combine the latest manufacturing technology with a highly experienced and skilled work force.*

Cunningham Coates Ltd, 19 Donegall Street, Belfast, BT1 2HA Tel: (028) 9032 3456 Fax: (028) 9023 1479
E-mail: info@cuncoates.com *Stockbrokers*

Cunningham Covers Ltd, 42 Tobermore Road, Maghera, County Londonderry, BT46 5DR Tel: (028) 7964 2638 Fax: (028) 7964 3511
E-mail: info@cunninghamcovers.co.uk *Tension curtain trailer systems & tarpaulins manufrs*

▶ Cunningham McLean Partnership, 4 Canniesburn Square, Bearsden, Bearsden, Glasgow, G61 1QW Tel: 0141-942 2221 Fax: 0141-942 3113

Cunninghams, 564-566 Kingston Road, London, SW20 8DR Tel: (020) 8946 3352 Fax: (020) 8540 1626 *Builders merchants & contractors*

▶ Cupboard Love, 181 Barrack Road, Christchurch, Dorset, BH23 2AR Tel: (01202) 479874 Fax: (01020) 470958
E-mail: sales@cupboardlovesouthern.co.uk
Furniture manufrs

Cupboards Direct Ltd, PO BOX 6788, Northampton, NN1 4WP Tel: (0870) 7661826 Fax: (0800) 1698127 E-mail: sales@cupboardsdirect.co.uk
Industrial mail-order

▶ CUPE Ltd, 48 Methuen Road, Charminster, Bournemouth, BH8 8ND Tel: (01202) 555711 Fax: (01202) 555722
E-mail: enquiries@cupe.co.uk *Project management training services & consultancy*

Francis Cupiss Ltd, The Wilderness, The Entry, Diss, Norfolk, IP22 4NT Tel: (01379) 642045 Fax: (01379) 642045
E-mail: mail@franciscupiss.co.uk *Horse medicine manufrs*

Robert Cupitt Ltd, 4 Joplin Court, Sovereign Business Park, Crownhill, Milton Keynes, MK8 0JP Tel: (01908) 563063 Fax: (01908) 562910 E-mail: sales@robertcupitt.co.uk *Robert Cupitt Limited based in Milton Keynes and established in 1954 is a stockist and distributor of specialist power transmission components, namely caliper disc brakes, right angle gear drives, variable speed drives, overhung load adaptors and torque limiters. We represent three US manufacturers, namely Tolomatic, Zero-Max and HB Performance Systems (formally Hayes Brake) selling components in the UK for the OEM, replacement and resale markets in a wide range of industry sectors. Our products are used in the industrial and off highway markets. Industries served for caliper disk brakes include construction, agriculture, rail maintenance, mining, groundcare, materials handing, buggies, karts and a variety of utility vehicles. Industrial applications include packaging, conveyors, filling food processing and special purpose machinery. Brakes can be used for static, holding, positioning as well as dynamic applications.*

Curaim (UK) Ltd, Units 11-12 Cockridden Farm Industrial Estate, Brentwood Road, Herongate, Brentwood, Essex, CM13 3LH Tel: (01277) 811003 Fax: (01277) 811522
E-mail: curaim@aol.com *Air conditioning engineers*

Curbridge Motor Co. Ltd, Unit 8a Bury Farm, Botley, Southampton, SO30 2HB Tel: (01489) 780782 Fax: (01489) 783982
E-mail: ian@curbridge-engineering.fsnet.co.uk
Sheet metalwork engineers & fabricators

Curle M J Ltd, Sunnymead Farm, Naird Lane, Shifnal, Shropshire, TF11 9PJ Tel: (01952) 460382 Fax: (01952) 463238
E-mail: mjcurle@netscapeonline.co.uk *Plant hire services, skip hire & haulage*

Curley Specialised Mouldings In Group, Weald House, Pattenden Lane, Marden, Tonbridge, Kent, TN12 9QJ Tel: (01622) 833181
E-mail: info@curleyuk.com *Glass fibre molding manufrs*

Currall Lewis & Martin Construction Ltd, 89-93 Broadwell Road, Oldbury, West Midlands, B69 4BL Tel: 0121-552 9292 Fax: 0121-544 9899 E-mail: office@clmconstruction.com *Civil engineering & concrete structural repair* Also at: Stoke-on-Trent

Curran Engineering Ltd, Unit 15 Valley Enterprise, Bedwas House Industrial Estate, Bedwas, Caerphilly, CF83 8DW Tel: (029) 2085 0800 Fax: (029) 2085 0800
E-mail: rjh@curranltd.co.uk *Aerospace design & project management*

Curran Packaging Co. Ltd, Thames Industrial Park, Princess Margaret Road, East Tilbury, Tilbury, Essex, RM18 8RH Tel: (01375) 857131 Fax: (01375) 856884
E-mail: sales@curran.co.uk Purchasing Contact: A. Coote Sales Contact: S. Blowes Principal Export Areas: Central/East Europe & West Europe *Manufacturers of cardboard & paper tubes.*

Currie Of Airdrie Ltd, Deanston Factory, 36 Glencraig Street, Airdrie, Lanarkshire, ML6 9AS Tel: (01236) 764218 Fax: (01236) 764218 *Steel fabricators*

▶ Currie Bros Ltd, Crowness Road, Hatston, Kirkwall, Orkney, KW15 1RG Tel: (01856) 877770 Fax: (01856) 876331

Currie & Brown, 44 Carden Place, Aberdeen, AB10 1UP Tel: (01224) 624484 Fax: (01224) 628369 E-mail: sales@curriebrown.com *Quantity surveyors & cost engineers* Also at: Glasgow

Currie & Brown, Osborne House, 1-5 Osborne Terrace, Edinburgh, EH12 5HG Tel: 0131-313 7020 Fax: 0131-313 7021

Currie Business Services Ltd, 244-252 Price Street, Birkenhead, Merseyside, CH41 3PS Tel: 0151-343 9196 Fax: 0151-647 7627
E-mail: cbssupply@aol.com *Office equipment distributors*

Currie European Transport Ltd, Heathhall, Dumfries, DG1 3NX Tel: (01387) 267333 Fax: (01387) 267339
E-mail: info@currie-european.com *Road transport, haulage & freight services*

▶ Currier Ltd, 48 Park Street, Shifnal, Shropshire, TF11 9BL Tel: (01952) 462200
E-mail: info@currier.co.uk *Website designers & search engine marketing*

Currock Engineering Co. Ltd, Industrial Buildings, Beehive Lane, Chelmsford, CM2 9TE Tel: (01245) 257785 Fax: (01245) 283287
E-mail: currock@compuserve.com *Precision engineers*

Curry & Bevans, Unit 1 Willow Row, Stoke-on-Trent, ST3 2PU Tel: (01782) 596109 Fax: (01782) 596356 *Control systems & electrical contractors*

Gilbert Curry Industrial Plastics Co. Ltd, 16 Bayton Road, Exhall, Coventry, CV7 9EJ Tel: (024) 7664 4645 Fax: (024) 7658 8389
E-mail: k-sales@gcip.co.uk *Stockholders & distributors of all engineering plastics, lexan polycarbonate sheet & perspex acrylic sheet & rod, range includes nylons, acetals, nylatron, polyethylene, polypropylene, tufnols, celazole, torlon, peek, cestilene, fluorosint, polyurethane*

▶ Currys Home Delivery Service, Unit 5, Walworth Road, Aycliffe Industrial Park, Newton Aycliffe, County Durham, DL5 6XF Tel: (01325) 320082 Fax: (01325) 300481

Cursey Technology Ltd, Siddington, Cirencester, Gloucestershire, GL7 6EU Tel: (01285) 650090 Fax: (01285) 650091
E-mail: sales@cursey.co.uk *Electronic equipment assemblers*

▶ Cursiter Quarry, Finstown, Kirkwall, Orkney, KW15 1TT Tel: (01856) 761295 *Quarry*

▶ Cursor Controls Ltd, Conroi House, Brunel Drive, Newark, Nottinghamshire, NG24 2EG Tel: (01636) 615600 Fax: (01636) 615601
E-mail: sales@cursorcontrols.com Principal Export Areas: Worldwide *Computer devices manufrs*

▶ Curtain & Blind, 39-41 Appleton Gate, Newark, Nottinghamshire, NG24 1JR Tel: (01636) 702102 Fax: (01609) 781669 E-mail: tony@hotmail.com *Window covering blinds or curtains*

Curtain & Blind Specialists, West Drive, Lancaster, LA1 5BY Tel: (01524) 383000 *Curtain & blind manufrs*

▶ Curtain Blinds: Custom Curtain Blinds, Redhouse Road, Moulton Park, Northampton, NN3 6AQ Tel: (01604) 497994 Fax: (01604) 497994 E-mail: blinds@saster.fsnet.co.uk *Curtain Blinds: UK Curtain Blinds Northampton- Custom Made Curtain Blinds- wooden Curtain Blinds and conservatory curtain blinds. *Venetion blinds: wooden venetion blinds- vertical venetioan blinds- Custom Made vertical blinds- Custom Made window blinds.*

▶ Curtain Calls, 6 Ambleside Close, Woodley, Reading, RG5 4JJ Tel: 0118-901 4632 Fax: 0118-901 4632
E-mail: studio@curtaincalls.co.uk *Curtains & soft furnishings.*

Curtain Couture, 281 Stockport Road, Ashton-under-Lyne, Lancashire, OL7 0NT Tel: 0161-339 2227 Fax: 0161-339 2227
E-mail: curtaincouture@hotmail.com *Curtain designer & manufrs*

▶ Curtain Genius, Eallisaid, Corsock, Castle Douglas, Kirkcudbrightshire, DG7 3DW Tel: (01644) 440264 Fax: (01644) 440253
E-mail: info@curtaingenius.co.uk *Curtain accessories retailers*

Curtain Studio, Unit 10, Swallow Mill, Swallow Street, Higher Hillgate, Stockport, Cheshire, SK1 3HJ Tel: 0161-480 6480 *Curtain & soft furnishing goods manufrs*

▶ Curtain Tek, Acre Workshop, Blackburn Road, Haslingden, Rossendale, Lancashire, BB4 5AZ Tel: (01706) 212303 Fax: (01706) 212303 *Tarpaulin repairs*

▶ Curtain Traders, 123 High Street, Marlborough, Wiltshire, SN8 1LZ Tel: (01672) 516994 Fax: (01672) 512400 *We sell high quality pre-loved designer curtains at a reasonalbe price. **We also offfer a bespoke curtain making service as well as full interior design.*

Curtains Plus, 6 Bridge Close, Horsell, Woking, Surrey, GU21 4PD Tel: (01483) 472121
E-mail: rose.austin@ntlworld.com *Curtain manufrs*

Curteis Ltd, Pant Lane, Dudleston, Ellesmere, Shropshire, SY12 9EG Tel: (01691) 690505 Fax: (01691) 690556 E-mail: info@curteis.com *Chain manufrs*

Curtins Consulting Engineers plc, 26-29 St. Cross Street, London, EC1N 8UH Tel: (020) 7213 9000 Fax: (020) 7213 9001
E-mail: london@curtins.com *Structural engineering consultants*

Alan Curtis Photography, 34 Church Hill, Belbroughton, Stourbridge, West Midlands, DY9 0DT Tel: (01562) 731222 Fax: (01299) 250122 E-mail: alancurtinphoto@btconnect.com *Industrial & commercial photographers*

Brian Curtis, 60 Park Avenue, Maidstone, Kent, ME14 5HL Tel: (01622) 757759 *Cash registers*

Curtis Holt (East Anglia) Ltd, Harford House, 50 White Lodge Business Estate, Hall Road, Norwich, NR4 6DG Tel: (01603) 671630 Fax: (01603) 671634
E-mail: publications@toolbank.com *Hand & power tool distributors*

Curtis Holt Southampton Ltd, Westwood Business Park, Nutwood Way, Totton, Southampton, SO40 3WW Tel: (023) 8086 1991 Fax: (023) 8066 4505 E-mail: sales@tallbank.com *Hand & power tool wholesalers*

Curtis Holt Southampton Ltd, Westwood Business Park, Nutwood Way, Totton, Southampton, SO40 3WW Tel: (023) 8086 1991 Fax: (023) 8066 4555 E-mail: sales@tallbank.com *Hand tool distributors*

Curtis Holt (St. Albans), Unit 10B Brick Knoll Park, Ashley Road, St. Albans, Hertfordshire, AL1 5UG Tel: (01727) 845095 Fax: (01727) 845082 E-mail: stalbons.sales@torbank.com *Hand & power tool distributors*

Curtis Instruments (U K) Ltd, Spencer Bridge Road, Northampton, NN1 2PT Tel: (01604) 629755 Fax: (01604) 629876
E-mail: barry.langsford@curtisinst.co.uk *Panel instrumentation manufrs*

Curtis Machine Tools Ltd, Martells Industrial Estate, Ardleigh, Colchester, CO7 7RU Tel: (01206) 230032 Fax: (01206) 231426
E-mail: cnt@douglascurtis.co.uk Principal Export Areas: Worldwide *Machine tool specialists*

▶ Curtis Plumbing & Heating, 2 Pollard Court, Pollard Road, Morden, Surrey, SM4 6EH Tel: (07020) 930940 Fax: 020 81506313
E-mail: sales@cphs.co.uk *Central heating servicing & installation services*

Curtis Power & Co. Ltd, Carter La Farm, 5 Carterhall Lane, Sheffield, S12 3XD Tel: 0114-239 8764 Fax: 0114-265 4441 *Mobile crane hire & skip contractors*

Curtis Screen Print, 26 Fairfax Road, Colchester, CO2 7EW Tel: (01206) 760666 Fax: (01206) 760666 E-mail: sales@curtisscreenprint.co.uk *Screen printers, sign makers, digital print*

Curtis & Shaw, Cowbeech, Hailsham, East Sussex, BN27 4JE Tel: (01323) 833441 Fax: (01323) 833072 E-mail: sales@curtisandshaw.co.uk *Agricultural machinery distributors*

Curtis Steel Ltd, Mill Road, Radstock, BA3 5TX Tel: (01761) 432841 Fax: (01761) 433919
E-mail: sales@unilockproducts.com *Industrial interior specialists*

Curtis Wright, Gore Cross Business Park, Corbin Way, Bradpole, Bridport, Dorset, DT6 3UX Tel: (01308) 422256 Fax: (01308) 427760
E-mail: sales@sp.curtisswright.com *Solent & Pratt is a manufacturer of High Performance and Triple Offset Butterfly Valves specializing in exotic materials large diameters and high pressure ratings in size ranges from 2" to 130" and available in metal, resilient. fire safe, and rubber lined seat and seals. Farris Engineering is a manufacturer of Spring Loaded and Pilot Operated Pressure Relief Valves in size ranges from 1/2" Npt through to 20" flanged. Sprague Products is a manufacturer of high pressure, air driven, pumps and gas boosters.*

▶ Curve It Ltd, Riverside Place, Bridgewater Road, Leeds, LS9 0RQ Tel: 0113-248 8080 Fax: 0113-249 4006 *Computer hardware re-sellers*

Curved Glass (UK) Ltd, 10 Marshgate Lane, London, E15 2NH Tel: (020) 8555 9660 Fax: (020) 8519 5934
E-mail: info@curvedglassuk.co.uk Principal Export Areas: Central/East Europe & West Europe *Glass bending services*

▶ Curvin Transport Ltd, 21 Cowley Road, Nuffield Industrial Estate, Poole, Dorset, BH17 0UJ Tel: (01202) 679369 Fax: (01202) 681228

Cusden's, 104 Arlington Road, London, NW1 7HP Tel: (020) 7424 0349 Fax: (020) 7324 0352
E-mail: cusdens@aol.com *Architectural ironmongers* Also at: London SW1

Cush In Co., Heald House Road, Leyland, PR25 4JA Tel: (01772) 621804 *Cushions fillers*

Cushendall Ornamental Concrete, 14 Tromra Road, Cushendall, Ballymena, County Antrim, BT44 0SS Tel: (028) 2177 2066 Fax: (028) 2177 2191 *Concrete ornament manufacturers & distributors*

▶ Cussen & Sons Mechanical Services Contractors, 3 Bowman Trading Estate, Bessemer Drive, Stevenage, Hertfordshire, SG1 2DL Tel: (01438) 728525

Custance & Thomson Blackheath Ltd, Meadowcourt Road, London, SE3 9DX Tel: (020) 8852 1545 Fax: (020) 8852 4352 *General engineers & precision engineers*

Custard It Ltd, Lake View Drive Unit 1, Innovate Mews, Annesley, Nottingham, NG15 0EA Tel: (01623) 687650 Fax: (0870) 4019960 E-mail: info@custardgroup.co.uk *Computer systems builders*

Custom Audio Design, Ridgeway Office Park, Bedford Road, Petersfield, Hampshire, GU32 3QF Tel: (01730) 269572 Fax: (0870) 7479878 E-mail: sales@customaudiodesigns.co.uk *Domestic & commercial soundproofing & industrial acoustic suppliers. Door seals, acoustic panels, acoustic doors, sound absorbers, basotect & acoustic foams, soundproofing for part E building regulations, underlays, screens, sealants & adhesives and many more sound insulation products.*

Custom Bags, Unit 2b 102 Throckley Way, Middlefields Industrial Estate, South Shields, Tyne & Wear, NE34 0NU Tel: 0191-427 7766 Fax: 0191-427 7755 E-mail: sales@custombags.co.uk Purchasing Contact: S. Wilkinson Sales Contact: P. Chaganis Principal Export Areas: Africa *Manufacturers of nylon, custom made & promotional/advertising bags. In addition, sports bag manufrs*

Custom Built Rods, 1c Valebridge Road, Burgess Hill, West Sussex, RH15 0RA Tel: (01444) 250930 Fax: 01444 250930 *Fishing rod manufrs*

Custom Candles Ltd, 12 Cross Lane, Coal Aston, Dronfield, Derbyshire, S18 3AL Tel: (01246) 414740 Fax: (01246) 290012 E-mail: sales@customcandles.co.uk *Decorative, printed & promotional candle manufrs*

Custom Card Services International Ltd, The Lennox, Lennox Road, Basingstoke, Hampshire, RG22 4AP Tel: (01256) 328883 Fax: (01256) 328884 E-mail: mike@ccsi.co.uk *Card bureau (imaging for id cards) supplier*

Custom Cartons & Packaging Ltd, Custom House, Shire Hill, Saffron Walden, Essex, CB11 3AQ Tel: (01799) 525000 Fax: (01799) 525001 *Carton & packaging manufrs*

Custom Coatings Ltd, 450 Blandford Road, Poole, Dorset, BH16 5BN Tel: (01202) 621155 Fax: (01202) 627622 E-mail: custom_coatings@hotmail.com *Stove enamelling finishes*

Custom Coils, Newgate Lane, Fareham, Hampshire, PO14 1AR Tel: (01329) 822222 Fax: (01329) 821238 E-mail: sales@custom-coils.co.uk *Manufacturers of air coolers, heat exchangers & transfer equipment*

Custom Components Ltd, Unit 3 Boxer Place, Leyland, PR26 7QL Tel: (01772) 455520 Fax: (01772) 436472 E-mail: sales@customcomponents.co.uk *Engravers, industrial screen printers & plastic fabricators*

Custom Composites Ltd, Hugo Street, Rochdale, Lancashire, OL11 2PH Tel: (01706) 526255 Fax: (01706) 350187 E-mail: mail@customcom.co.uk *Manufacturers of composite components*

Custom Computers UK Ltd, Custom House, Kenn Road, Clevedon, Avon, BS21 6EX Tel: (01275) 874233 Fax: (01275) 874235 *Computer consultants*

Custom Connections, Unit 1, Green Lane, Romiley, Stockport, Cheshire, SK6 3JG Tel: 0161-406 8600 Fax: 0161-406 9846 *Bedroom & kitchen manufrs*

Custom Control Sensors International, 13 Shrivenham Hundred Business Park, Majors Road, Watchfield, Swindon, SN6 8TZ Tel: (01793) 783545 Fax: (01793) 783532 E-mail: pswitch@ccsdualsnap.co.uk *Pressure & temperature switch manufrs*

Custom Covers 1984 Ltd, Quayside Road, Southampton, SO18 1AD Tel: (023) 8033 5744 Fax: (023) 8022 5581 E-mail: sales@customcovers.co.uk *Tarpaulin, canvas & PVC cover manufrs*

▶ Custom Creations, 1 Plot 120 Village Farm Road, Village Farm Industrial Estate, Pyle, Bridgend, Mid Glamorgan, CF33 6BL Tel: (01656) 749855 Fax: (01656) 749855 E-mail: customc@tiscali.co.uk *Wooden garden product manufrs*

Custom Design, Southview, Rhodes Minnis, Canterbury, Kent, CT4 6XU Tel: (01303) 862888 Fax: (0871) 7503757 E-mail: highbarn@globalnet.co.uk *Interior design consultants specialising in office design*

Custom Design Cables, Unit 4 Westwood Farm, Highcross Road, Southfleet, Gravesend, Kent, DA13 9PH Tel: (01474) 834893 Fax: (01474) 834595 E-mail: info@customdesigncables.com *Specialists in high quality short run cables etc*

Custom Design Mouldings Ltd, Unit 212-215, Springvale Industrial Estate, Cwmbran, Gwent, NP44 5BJ Tel: (01633) 861441 Fax: (01633) 876412 E-mail: sales@cdg-uk.com *Underwater cable & moulded cables manufrs*

Custom Diesels, Unit 10, Blackhill Road West, Holton Heath Trading Park, Poole, Dorset, BH16 6LW Tel: (01202) 621935 *Diesel engine reconditioners*

Custom Enclosures Ltd, Concorde House, Concorde Street, Luton, LU2 0JD Tel: (01582) 480425 Fax: (01582) 414372 E-mail: custom.enclosures@btconnect.com *Package handling equipment designers*

Custom Extruded Profiles, 35c Lysander Road, Bowerhill, Melksham, Wiltshire, SN12 6SP Tel: (01225) 791818 Fax: (01225) 791818 *Plastic extrusion manufrs*

Custom Filter Co., Bretfield Court, Bretton Street Industrial Estate, Dewsbury, West Yorkshire, WF12 9BG Tel: (01924) 468272 Fax: (01924) 464240 E-mail: sales@customfilter.co.uk *Filter manufrs*

▶ Custom Fitness LLP, 15 The New Poplars, Ash Street Ash, Aldershot, Hampshire, GU12 6LH Tel: (01252) 328837 E-mail: *Custom Fitness LLP are importers, manufacturers & suppliers of Commercial Fitness Equipment.*Our reputation is continuously growing as our services are sought after by Councils, Private Home Owners, Developers, Sports Centres, Privately owned Gyms and Corporations.*

Custom Fittings Ltd, Pavilion, Cleckheaton, West Yorkshire, BD19 3UD Tel: (01274) 852066 Fax: (01274) 852029 E-mail: sales@customfittings.co.uk *Hose fittings in stainless steel*

Custom Foams, Deans Rd, Wolverton Industry, Milton Keynes, MK12 5NA Tel: (01908) 312331 Fax: (01908) 220715 E-mail: sales@customfoams.co.uk Sales Contact: I. Day *Manufacturers of acoustic insulation materials, filter foam, filters, plastic foam converters/products, polyurethane foam converters/products, sound or acoustic insulating materials, industrial noise control polyurethane foam products & packaging materials/goods/ products. Explosion suppressant, foams & EZ-DR1 upholstery foam*

▶ Custom Glass Ltd, Unit 2, Custom Complex, Yardley Road, Liverpool, L33 7SS Tel: 0151-549 1264 E-mail: sales@customglass.co.uk *Glass company*

Custom Grafix, Knighton-On-Teme, Tenbury Wells, Worcestershire, WR15 8LZ Tel: (0800) 5421646 Fax: (01584) 781077 *Sign manufr*

Custom Grind Ltd, Unit 1c Brown Lees Road Industrial Estate, Forge Way, Knypersley, Stoke-on-Trent, ST8 7DN Tel: (01782) 518503 Fax: (01782) 522110 E-mail: sales@customgrind.com *Centreless grinding machine manufrs*

Custom Hose & Fitting, 194 Queens Road, Watford, WD17 2NT Tel: (01923) 225534 Fax: (01923) 818714 E-mail: sales@customhose.co.uk *Specialist hose suppliers & distributors of all types of pneumatic & hydraulic equipment**

▶ Custom Images Ltd, 12 Mill Brow, Armathwaite, Carlisle, CA4 9PJ Tel: (01697) 472522 E-mail: julie@customimages.co.uk

Custom IT Security UK Ltd, Custom Ho, Kenn Rd, Clevedon, Avon, BS21 6EX Tel: (01275) 874233 Fax: (01275) 874235 *IT security*

▶ Custom Joinery, 37 Roseburn Street, Edinburgh, EH12 5PE Tel: 0131-337 3003 Fax: 0131-346 0333

Custom Keyboards Electronics Ltd, Unit 11, Claylands Road, Claylands Park, Bishops Waltham, Southampton, SO32 1BH Tel: (01489) 891851 Fax: (01489) 893708 E-mail: alancoppini@custom-keyboards.co.uk *Electronic sub contract manufrs*

▶ Custom Made Shutters, Red House Lodge, Brick Kiln Lane, Limpsfield Common, Oxted, Surrey, RH8 0QZ Tel: 01883 722148 Fax: 01883 717173 E-mail: info@cms.gb.com *Suppliers and Installers of Interior Adjustable Louvered Shutters (Plantation Shutters), Premium range manufactured from Hardwood. Also available MDF shutters. Available in stain, paint or clear lacquer finishes.*

Custom Made (U K) Ltd, Oldends Hall, Oldends Lane, Stonehouse, Gloucestershire, GL10 3RQ Tel: (01453) 826884 Fax: (01453) 791259 E-mail: info@custommade.co.uk *Aluminium, uPVC window & door manufrs*

Custom Metalcraft Ltd, 36 Bennet Road, Reading, RG2 0QX Tel: 0118-986 8077 Fax: 0118-986 8078 *Precision machining services*

Custom Metalwork Co Ltd, Eagle House, Essex Road, Hoddesdon, Hertfordshire, EN11 0DN Tel: (01992) 445151 Fax: (01992) 441884 E-mail: info@custom-metalwork.co.uk *Architectural metalwork manufrs*

Custom Micro Products Ltd, 450 Blandford Road, Poole, Dorset, BH16 5BN Tel: (01202) 631733 Fax: (01202) 632036 E-mail: sales@custom-micro.com *Microprocessor product specialists*

Custom Mouldings Ltd, Woodside House, Plaistow Road Dunsfold, Godalming, Surrey, GU8 4PG Tel: (01483) 200492 Fax: 01483 200514 *Fibreglass mouldings*

Custom & Ornamental Iron Work, Glan Moelyn, Llanrug, Caernarfon, Gwynedd, LL55 4PG Tel: (01286) 677725 Fax: (01286) 677725 *Wrought ironwork manufrs*

Custom Packaging Ltd, Unit 1, Hortonwood 33, Telford, Shropshire, TF1 7EX Tel: (01952) 608270 Fax: (01952) 608041 E-mail: alantown@custom-pkg.co.uk *Contract packaging services*

Custom Packing Solutions Ltd, Unit 15, Shaw Wood Business Park, Shaw Wood Way, Doncaster, South Yorkshire, DN2 5TB Tel: (01302) 325242 Fax: (01302) 322061 E-mail: neils@custompackingsolutions.co.uk *Contract packing & fulfillment services with packing design*

Custom Pharmaceuticals Ltd, Gill House, Conway Street, Hove, East Sussex, BN3 3LW Tel: (01273) 323513 Fax: (01273) 729483 *Independent Contract pharmaceutical manufacturers*

Custom Plastics, Unit 24g, Tone Dale Business Park, Tonedale, Wellington, Somerset, TA21 0AW Tel: (01823) 667669 Fax: (01823) 667669 E-mail: sales@customplastics.co.uk *Plastic displays & engraving services*

Custom Powders Ltd, Gateway, Crewe, CW1 6YT Tel: (01270) 530000 Fax: (01270) 500250 E-mail: powders@custompowders.co.uk *Chemical, granulation & powder processing services*

Custom Power Transmission Ltd, 69 Garamonde Drive, Wymbush, Milton Keynes, MK8 8DD Tel: (01908) 563252 Fax: (01908) 563077 E-mail: custompower@btopenworld.com *Power transmission engineers*

Custom Print, 2 Ashvale Road, Tooting, London, SW17 8PW Tel: (020) 8672 3511 Fax: (020) 8682 2904 E-mail: sales@customprint.com *Screen printers & instrument dial manufrs*

▶ Custom Sign Co., 19 Meadow Way, Bracknell, Berkshire, RG42 1UE Tel: (01344) 456117 Fax: (01344) 456117 *Manufacture/supply/fit business signs*

▶ Custom Software Systems, 16 Auchengreoch Avenue, Johnstone, Renfrewshire, PA5 0RJ Tel: (01505) 358223 *Web design & custom software*

Custom Software Systems, 2 Undercliff Rd, Wemyss Bay, Renfrewshire, PA18 6AQ Tel: 01475 522541 Fax: 01475 522572 *Software development, epos systems & web design*

Custom Stainless Fabrication Ltd, Unit 20 Leyton Business Centre, Etloe Rd, London, E10 7BT Tel: (020) 8558 2596 Fax: (020) 8558 7650 E-mail: csfltd@talk21.com *Commercial catering equipment manufrs*

Custom Stock, 1 Rotherham Close, Norwood Industrial Estate, Killamarsh, Sheffield, S21 2JU Tel: 0114-247 6965 Fax: 0114-247 2947 *Gun stocks manufrs*

Custom Tanks & Designs, Unit 23a Pershore Trading Estate, Pershore, Worcestershire, WR10 2DD Tel: (01386) 554136 *Classic motorcycle services*

Custom Technology Ltd, Brooks Road, Lewes, East Sussex, BN7 2BY Tel: (01273) 479101 Fax: (01273) 486727 E-mail: sales@customtechnology.co.uk *Turnkey engine & vehicle test services*

Custom Tooling Ltd, Unit 65, Station Road Industrial Estate, Hailsham, East Sussex, BN27 2ED Tel: (01323) 641811 E-mail: custo@btconnect.com *Plastic mould toolmakers*

Custom Transformers Ltd, Unit 23, Whitewalls, Easton Grey, Malmesbury, Wiltshire, SN16 0RD Tel: (01666) 824411 Fax: (01666) 824413 E-mail: sales@custom-transformers.co.uk Purchasing Contact: C. Picter Sales Contact: K. Baldwin Principal Export Areas: Worldwide *Design & manufacture of laminated style transformers, chokes,wound components & ferrite core types for switch mode. Many transformer applications require custom solutions & our company has developed extensive experience in tailoring products to specific customer requirements. our range includes; ferrite transformers, frame mount transformers, ferrite core transformers, inductor transformers, laminated transformers, low profile transformer, low voltage transformers, toroidal transformer, open frame transformers, printed circuit board (pcb) transformers, pulse transformers, surface mounted transformers, switched mode transformers, ferrites transformer, fly back transformers, mains transformers, & much more. *Our range includes: ferrite transformers, frame mount transformers, ferrite core transformers, inductor transformers, laminated, low profile transformer, low voltage transformers, toroidal transformer, open frame transformers, printed circuit board (PCB) transformers, pulse transformers, surface mounted transformers, switched mode transformers, ferrites transformer, fly back transformers, mains transformers and much more.*

Custom Wytelyne Powder Coating Ltd, 88-90 Hopewell Drive, Chatham, Kent, ME5 7NL Tel: (01634) 819520 Fax: (01634) 819510 E-mail: info@custom-powder.co.uk *Powder coaters*

Customdesigntechnologies Ltd, Greatworth Park, Welsh Lane, Greatworth, Banbury, Oxfordshire, OX17 2HB Tel: (01280) 845530 Fax: (01295) 768888 E-mail: sales@customdesigntechnologies.com *Plastics enclosure*

▶ Customer Research Technology Ltd, Business Innovation Centre Binley Business Park, Harry Weston R, Coventry, CV3 2TX Tel: (024) 7643 0295 Fax: (024) 7643 0291 E-mail: info@opinionmeter.co.uk *Customer feedback & marketing service*

▶ Customgolf Co., 7 Mount Braddon Mews, Braddons Hill Road West, Torquay, TQ1 1BG Tel: (07860) 858485 E-mail: keith@simdean.com *golf club repair & customising*

▶ Customised Control panel Services, 3 York Close, Gillow Heath, Stoke-On-Trent, ST8 6SE Tel: 01782 523673 Fax: 01782 523673 E-mail: stuart.booth700@ntlworld.com

▶ Customised Formulations Ltd, 146 Elmsfield Avenue, Norden, Rochdale, Lancashire, OL11 5XA Tel: 07840 133339 Fax: 0845 8330945 E-mail: andy@customised-formulations.co.uk *Specialist formulator of technical coatings, adhesives and sealants.*Particular expertise in water-based coatings, PVC plastisols, PVC adhesives, Polyurethanes and PUR hot melt reactive systems.*Distributors for Foreco Srl, a manufacturer of sealing compounds for the food, beverage, aerosol and general line metal packaging markets.**

▶ Customplas Plastics, Castle Lane, Melbourne, Derby, DE73 8JB Tel: (01332) 865765 Fax: (01332) 864960 E-mail: mark@customplas.co.uk *Plastic extrusion manufrs*

Customworks Giftware Mnfrs, Unit 1-3 Bo'Mains Industrial Estate, Linlithgow Road, Bo'Ness, West Lothian, EH51 0QG Tel: (01506) 821910 Fax: (01506) 821911 E-mail: sales@customworks.co.uk *Gift products manufrs*

Cut Above, 7 Langham Road, Leicester, LE4 9WF Tel: 0116-246 1376 Fax: 0116-276 5275 E-mail: sales@cutaboveuk.com *Printing trade finishing services & carton manufrs*

▶ Cut N Cover, The Barn Workshop, Pamphill Dairy, Pamphill, Wimborne, Dorset, BH21 4ED Tel: (01202) 881122 E-mail: wayne@cutncover.fsnet.co.uk *Suppliers of tarpaulins, wedding marquees, boat covers etc*

Cut Price Blinds, Burleigh Street, Glasgow, G51 3LA Tel: 0141-445 2229 Fax: 0141-445 2229 *Blinds manufrs*

▶ Cutcost.Com, 200 Brook Drive, Reading, RG2 6UB Tel: (0870) 3518828 Fax: (0870) 3518829 E-mail: save@cutcost.com *The Cutcost system is based on 35 years experience in business procurement. No gimmicks or technical mumbo-jumbo just a straight forward, easy to use online system backed up by decades of money saving consultancy. The Cutcost solution provides seamless procurement, allowing you to order everything you need for your business through a single intelligent sourcing system, which automatically offers you the best price for each item. Trade prices mean big savings, over 90% of which go directly to your bottom line.*

Cutec Ltd, 19 Branson Court, Plymouth, PL7 2WU Tel: (0870) 3211801 Fax: (0870) 3211802 E-mail: sales@cutec.co.uk *IT consultants*

Cutec Ltd, 19 Branson Court, Plymouth, PL7 2WU Tel: (0870) 3211801 Fax: (0870) 3211802 E-mail: sales@cutec.co.uk *Computer consultants*

Cutform Holdings Ltd, 6 Phoenix Industrial Estate, North Street, Lewes, East Sussex, BN7 2PQ Tel: (01273) 480420 Fax: (01273) 483089 E-mail: sales@cutform.co.uk *Precision cold heading specialists*

Cuthbert Service & Jackson Ltd, 111 Bell Street, Glasgow, G4 0UA Tel: 0141-566 9651 Fax: 0141-566 9022 E-mail: mail@csjltd.co.uk *Insurance brokers*

Cuthbertson Maunsell Ltd, Dunedin House, 25 Ravelstone Terrace, Edinburgh, EH4 3TP Tel: 0131-311 4000 Fax: 0131-311 4090 E-mail: cml-edin@compuserve.com *Consulting engineers*

Cuthbertson & Rapson, 35 Wall Road, Gwinear, Hayle, Cornwall, TR27 5HA Tel: (01736) 850625 Fax: (01736) 850625 *Joinery manufrs*

Cutlass Fasteners Ltd, Dixon Close, Old Boston Trading Estate, Haydock, St. Helens, Merseyside, WA11 9SL Tel: (01942) 712387 Fax: (01942) 722306 E-mail: sales@cutlass-studwelding.com Principal Export Areas: Worldwide *Stud welding & industrial fastener manufrs*

Cutler Freight Forwarding Ltd, Car Shipping House, 2a South Gipsy Road, Welling, Kent, DA16 1JB Tel: (020) 8301 6626 Fax: (020) 8301 2580 E-mail: info@cutlerfreight.co.uk *Overseas car shippers*

Cutler & Maclean Ltd, Daimler Drive, Cowpen Industrial Estate, Billingham, Cleveland, TS23 4JD Tel: (01642) 564585 Fax: (01642) 371142 *Precision engineers*

Cutler & Woolf (Steel) Ltd, Unit 32, Jubilee Trade Centre, Jubilee Road, Letchworth Garden City, Hertfordshire, SG6 1SP Tel: (01462) 480420 Fax: (01462) 480430 E-mail: sales@cutlerandwoolfe.co.uk *Steel sheet stockholders*

Cutlery & Allied Trades Research Association, Henry Street, Sheffield, S3 7EQ Tel: 0114-276 9736 Fax: 0114-272 2151 E-mail: info@britishtools.com *Trade association*

Cutter Grinders Birmingham Ltd, Unit 1-2 Armoury Trading Estate, Armoury Road, Birmingham, B11 2RG Tel: 0121-772 6321 Fax: 0121-773 6819 E-mail: cuttergrinders@webleicester.co.uk *Tool & cutter grinding services*

Cutter Grinding Services, 22b Guildford Street, Luton, LU1 2NR Tel: (01582) 735626 Fax: (01582) 404164 E-mail: john.malia@tesco.net *Cutter grinding specialists*

Cutter Services Precision Engineers Ltd, 6 Glebe Road, Letchworth Garden City, Hertfordshire, SG6 1DR Tel: (01462) 671861 Fax: (01462) 670532 *Precision toolmaking services*

Cuttermate Ltd, 55 Walkenden Road, Worsley, Manchester, M28 3DA Tel: 0161-790 8426 Fax: 0161-790 8762 E-mail: cuttermate@btconnect.com *Label die cutter manufrs*

▶ Cutting Edge Ltd, Unit 6 Mosshall Industrial Estate, Blackburn, Bathgate, West Lothian, EH47 7LY Tel: (01506) 632000 Fax: (01506) 634000 *Subcontract precision machining*

▶ Cutting Edge Consulting, 16 Holford Way, Barton Hills, Luton, LU3 4EB Tel: (07973) 721097 E-mail: gian@cec08.com *IT consultants*

▶ Cutting Edge Food Equipment, 4C Station Yard, Thame, Oxfordshire, OX9 3UH Tel: (01844) 212120 Fax: (01844) 212550 E-mail: dhazel@aol.com *Catering equipment wholesalers*

Cutting Edge Services Ltd, Unit 362A Walton Summit Centre, Bamber Bridge, Preston, PR5 8AS Tel: (0870) 062 1030 Fax: (0870) 062 1024 E-mail: accounts@cuttingedgeservices.co.uk *Knife manufrs*

Cutting Edge Tooling Ltd, Unit 75, Trent Business Centre, Canal Street, Long Eaton, Nottingham, NG10 4HN Tel: (0870) 7667681 Fax: (0870) 4602353 E-mail: sales@cuttingedgetooling.co.uk *Cutting edge tooling suppliers*

Cutting Import & Distribution, 2 Arthur Street, Stanningley, Pudsey, West Yorkshire, LS28 6JY Tel: 0113-256 7111 Fax: 0113-274 4759 *Diamond cutting & drilling*

Cutting & Wear Resistant Development Ltd, Greasbrough Road, Rotherham, South Yorkshire, S60 1RW Tel: (01709) 361041 Fax: (01709) 374211 E-mail: sales@cwuk.com *Drill bit & drilling equipment manufrs*

Cutting & Welding Supplies Ltd, 15-16 Lower High Street, Cradley Heath, West Midlands, B64 5AB Tel: (01384) 567874 Fax: (01384) 567064 E-mail: cutweld@btconnect.com *Welders & cutting equipment suppliers*

Cutts Box Co. Ltd, Lion Works, Mowbray Street, Sheffield, S3 8EZ Tel: 0114-272 8673 Fax: 0114-276 5757 *Cardboard box manufrs*

Cutts Refrigeration Ltd, Rowbrook Farm, Ryton, Dorrington, Shrewsbury, SY5 7NR Tel: (01743) 718871 Fax: (01743) 718040 *Refrigeration & airconditioning installation services*

Cuxson Gerrard & Co., 125 Broadwell Road, Oldbury, West Midlands, B69 4BF Tel: 0121-544 7117 Fax: 0121-544 8616 E-mail: sales@cuxsongerrard.com *Consumable medical dressings for chiropody.*

CV Honesty Box, 64 Burghley Street, Bourne, Lincolnshire, PE10 9NG Tel: (01778) 420407 E-mail: info@cvhonestybox.co.uk *CV writing service*

▶ The CV People, 46 Woodhead Grove, Armadale, Bathgate, West Lothian, EH48 3HU Tel: (07981) 347380 *cv writing, cv preparation, cv assistance, cv advice, career advice, carrer, cv, cv help, help cv*

CV Precision Engineering, Unit 2 Rea Court, 40 Trent Street, Birmingham, B5 5NL Tel: 0121-643 7144 Fax: 0121-633 3680 E-mail: tomcross@cvprecision.co.uk *Toolmakers & general engineers*

CVH Fabrications, Unit 2a Crown Works, Little Poutney Street, Wolverhampton, WV2 4JH Tel: (01902) 426020 Fax: (01902) 425726 *Fabricators & general engineers*

CVT Ltd, 4-6 Carters Lane, Kiln Farm, Milton Keynes, MK11 3ER Tel: (01908) 563267 Fax: (01908) 568354 *Semi-conductor manufacturing systems*

▶ CVwriting.net, 29 Great George Street, Bristol, BS1 5QT Tel: 0870 766 9896 E-mail: enquiries@CVwriting.net *CV writing - We show you how to write the perfect CV in minutes. Professional CV writing at a fraction of the price. Full instructions and helpful tips. Telephone support and Web CV options for your complete CV writing solution. Free interview guide with every purchase.*

CW Concepts Ltd, Concept House, 6 Richard Lewis Close, Llandaff, Cardiff, CF5 2TB Tel: (0845) 0715056 Fax: (0845) 0715065 E-mail: info@cwconcepts.co.uk *Customer relationship management*

Cwmbran Electrical Services Ltd, Unit 34 Court Road Industrial Estate, Cwmbran, Gwent, NP44 3AS Tel: (01633) 483416 Fax: (01633) 874712 *Electrical contractors*

Cwmbran Engineering Services, Unit 38 John Baker Close, Llantarnam Industrial Park, Cwmbran, Gwent, NP44 3AX Tel: (01633) 871616 Fax: (01633) 861052 E-mail: sales@cesmoulds.co.uk *Aluminium & polystyrene mould manufrs*

Cwmbran Fire Protection (SW) Ltd, Unit 13, Oldbury Business Centre, Cwmbran, Gwent, NP44 3JU Tel: (01633) 863895 Fax: (01633) 869552 E-mail: rod@cfirep.co.uk *Fire service*

Cwmna Gro Ltd, Penybryn Farm, Sarnau, Bala, Gwynedd, LL23 7LH Tel: (01678) 530297 Fax: (01678) 530389 *Concrete, sand & gravel manufrs*

Cwmnant Calves Ltd, Cwmnant, Tregaron, Dyfed, SY25 6NL Tel: (01974) 298564 Fax: (01974) 298745 E-mail: cwmnant.calves@farmline.com *Livestock dealers*

▶ CWP, 37 38 The Old Woodyard, Hall Drive, Hagley, Stourbridge, West Midlands, DY9 9LQ Tel: (01562) 730066 Fax: (01562) 730066 E-mail: chris@cwppr.u-net.com *Strategic marketing & public relations*

CWT Services Ltd, Bridgend Wigsley Road, Thorney, Newark, Nottinghamshire, NG23 7DF Tel: (01522) 702477 Fax: (01522) 702477 *Pest control contractors*

Cwv Group Ltd, 1 The Beehive, Lions Drive, Shadworth Business Park, Blackburn, BB1 2QS Tel: (01254) 222800 Fax: (01254) 222960 *Wallcoverings manufrs*

▶ Cy 4 Or, Bury, Lancashire, BL8 9AG Tel: 0161-767 8123 Fax: 0161-797 8122 E-mail: info@cy4or.co.uk *Computer forensics analysts*

▶ Cyan Group Ltd, Regal House, 70 London Road, Twickenham, TW1 3QS Tel: (0870) 6088808 Fax: (0870) 6060270 E-mail: enquiries@cyan-group.com *Business & commercial printing services*

▶ Cyba Manufacturing Technology Ltd, Unit 5 Hattersely Industrial, Estate Stockport Road, Hyde, Cheshire, SK14 3QT Tel: 0161-367 8789 Fax: 0161-367 8785 E-mail: info@cybamantech.co.uk *CNC machine tool 3D machining systems suppliers*

▶ Cyber Networks, Stratford Road, Hall Green, Birmingham, B28 8AE Tel: 0121-778 6008 *IT consultants*

▶ Cybercut Laser Profiling Ltd, 7 Manford Industrial Estate, Manor Road, Erith, Kent, DA8 2AJ Tel: (01322) 344890 Fax: (01322) 344899 E-mail: sales@cybercut.co.uk *Laser profiling*

▶ Cyber-Eye, 45, Altom Street, Blackburn, BB1 7LJ Tel: (01254) 678879 Fax: (01254) 678558

▶ Cyberia Systems, 6 Broom Wynd, Shotts, Lanarkshire, ML7 4HP Tel: (0845) 4565329 Fax: (01501) 826868 E-mail: sales@cyberiasystems.co.uk *UK wide suppliers of custom AMD, Intel and ASUS desktop computer systems.*

▶ Cyberience Internet Solutions, 56 Willow Grove, Livingston, West Lothian, EH54 5NA Tel: 07764 494889 Fax: 07764 494889 E-mail: contact@cyberience.co.uk *Offering a comprehensive, professional web site design and development service to businesses, organisations and individuals within the Edinburgh and Livingston area.*

Cybernaut Solutions, 30 Little Newport St, Walsall, WS1 1SA Tel: 01922 645554 *Software & hardware reseller*

Cybernetic Applications Ltd, West Portway Industrial Estate, Andover, Hampshire, SP10 3LF Tel: (01264) 350093 Fax: (01264) 333771 *Robotic educational manufrs*

Cybernex Computers Ltd, Unit 17, Bingham Park Farm, Potten End Hill, Hemel Hempstead, Hertfordshire, HP1 3BN Tel: (01442) 288469 Fax: (01442) 255207 *High performance graphics workstations, servers & storage solutions*

▶ Cyberra.Com, Apartment 127, Ilex Mill, Bacup Road, Rawtenstall, Rossendale, Lancashire, BB4 7NQ Tel: (07799) 414044 *IT software, design & browsers*

▶ Cyberscape Solutions, 87 Shepherds Bush Road, London, W6 7LR Tel: (0845) 1260897 Fax: 0871 733 3545 E-mail: office@cyberscapesolutions.co.uk *Web design & development*

Cyberscience Corporation Ltd, Rawdon House, High Street, Hoddesdon, Hertfordshire, EN11 8BD Tel: (01992) 441111 Fax: (01992) 442740 E-mail: info@cyberscience.com *Report writers*

Cybersign, 1 Newtown Road, Camlough, Newry, County Down, BT35 8NN Tel: (028) 3083 7070 Fax: (028) 3083 7028 E-mail: sales@cybersign.co.uk *Sign makers*

Cybertronix Ltd, 110 London Street, Reading, RG1 4SJ Tel: 0118-958 5900 Fax: 0118-958 5911 E-mail: sales@cybertronics.co.uk *Multimedia software company*

▶ Cyberzia Ltd, PO Box 555, Stoke-on-Trent, ST11 9DY Tel: (01782) 631112 E-mail: mail@cyberzia.net *Web design and development, Web programming and database design, hosting, multimedia,search engine optimisation, marketing and advertising.*

▶ Cybi Electrical Contracting, Cybi Buildings, St. Cybi Street, Holyhead, Gwynedd, LL65 1DS Tel: (01407) 762244 Fax: (01407) 762255

Cybis Computer Systems, 34 Sudley Road, Bognor Regis, West Sussex, PO21 1ER Tel: (01243) 840000 Fax: (01243) 840084 E-mail: sales@cybis.co.uk *Computer services*

▶ Cyci Clothing Mnfrs, Southwick Place, London, W2 2TN Tel: (020) 7706 1020 Fax: (020) 7706 1040 *Clothing manufrs*

▶ Cycle Pods Ltd, Unit 5, Hortons Way, Westerham, Kent, TN16 1BT Tel: (01959) 562633 Fax: (0560) 1130219 E-mail: info@cyclepods.co.uk *Cyclepods has created a form of cycle parking, shelter and storage like nothing out there at the moment. It not only looks modern, novel and exciting, but it also maximises space allowing 8 bikes to be stored in a 2metre diameter. The Cyclepod offers shelter which not only compliments the design, but also offers the possibility of advertising. The new product is more secure than any other form of cycle parking as cyclists can lock both the frame of the bike and the wheel to the unit using almost any type of lock. The Cyclepod is very low maintenance and parts are easy to replace if vandalised. Cyclepods are user friendly and bikes can be easily rolled up the unit to fit into place.*

Cyclesport North, 464 Ranglet Road, Walton Summit Centre, Bamber Bridge, Preston, PR5 8AR Tel: (01772) 339220 Fax: (01772) 339290 E-mail: sales@cyclesportnorth.co.uk *Cycle component manufrs*

▶ Cycleurope UK Ltd, 21-23 Mill Street, Bedford, MK40 3EU Tel: (01234) 245929 Fax: (01234) 270562 E-mail: sales@bianchi.com *Cycle & bicycle parts distributors & importers*

▶ Cycle-works Ltd, 2 Rances Way, Winchester, Hampshire, SO22 4PN Tel: (023) 9281 5555 Fax: (023) 9281 5544 E-mail: info@cycle-works.com *Cycle-works are a specialist cycle parking company, who provide a wide range of quality bicycle parking. This includes lockers, shelters, and 2 tier racks, as well as individual "Sheffield" type racks.*

Cyclone Crane Services Ltd, Water Lane, Drayton St. Leonard, Wallingford, Oxfordshire, OX10 7BE Tel: (01865) 400253 Fax: (01865) 400254 E-mail: enquiries@cyclone-cranes.co.uk *Lifting gear specialists*

▶ Cyclone Holdings Ltd, PO Box 29, Tenbury Wells, Worcestershire, WR15 8HT Tel: (01584) 811467 Fax: E-mail: admin@cyclone-chieftain.co.uk *Software developers services*

Cyclops Signs, 76 London Road, Bexhill-on-Sea, East Sussex, TN39 3LE Tel: (0845) 1991814 Fax: (01424) 215025 E-mail: sales@cyclopssigns.co.uk *Sign manufrs*

Cyclops Technologies Ltd, Durban Road, Bognor Regis, West Sussex, PO22 9QT Tel: (01243) 841123 Fax: (01243) 829321 E-mail: sales@cyclopstech.co.uk *Boat safety equipment manufrs*

Cygma Manufacturing, Unit B7- B9 Greengate Industrial Estate, Greenside Way, Middleton, Manchester, M24 1SW Tel: 0161-654 9777 Fax: 0161-654 9181 E-mail: cygmaplc@aol.com *Computer consumables distributors*

▶ Cygma Partnership, Kings Court, 5 Waterloo Road, Stalybridge, Cheshire, SK15 2AU Tel: 0161-338 5000 Fax: 0161-304 9961 *Computer accessories & consumable suppliers*

Cygnet Solutions Ltd, Swan House, The Straith, Priestland, Darvel, Ayrshire, KA17 0LP Tel: (01560) 323444 Fax: (01560) 323432 *IT consultants*

Cygnus Automotive Ltd, Unit 10, Advance Business Park, Burdock Close, Cannock, Staffordshire, WS11 7SG Tel: (01543) 573912 Fax: (01543) 572812 E-mail: sales@cygnus-automotive.co.uk *Automotive systems*

Cygnus Marine Ltd, 6 Annear Road, Penryn, Cornwall, TR10 9ER Tel: (01326) 372970 Fax: (01326) 374585 E-mail: info@cygnusmarine.co.uk *GRP fishing boat builders*

Cylinder Repair Services, 168 Rede Court Road, Rochester, Kent, ME2 3TU Tel: (01634) 723366 Fax: (01634) 723388 E-mail: crs.hydraulics@ukonline.co.uk *Hydraulic sales & repairers*

▶ Cylinder Resurfacing Co UK Ltd, Harwood Street, Blackburn, BB1 3DW Tel: (01254) 697300 Fax: (01254) 697199

Cylinder Service Centre, W3/1 BENTALL BUSINESS PARK, WASHINGTON, TYNE & WEAR, NE37 3JD Tel: 0191 4166288 Fax: 0191 4160644 E-mail: gary@cylinder.co.uk *HYDRAULIC ENGINEERS *SPECIALISTS IN CYLINDER REPAIR & MANUFACTURE*

Cym Consulting Ltd, 14 Well Hall Parade, London, SE9 6SP Tel: (020) 8294 1622 Fax: (020) 8859 4562 E-mail: cym@cymc.com *IT consultancy & development services*

Cymac Damon, 3 West Bawtry Road, Canklow, Rotherham, South Yorkshire, S60 2XG Tel: (01709) 370213 Fax: (01709) 367705 *High pressure vehicle cleaning equipment*

Cymarc Engineering, 5 Bessemer Way, Sawcliffe Industrial Park, Scunthorpe, South Humberside, DN15 8XE Tel: (01724) 289222 Fax: (01724) 852504 E-mail: cymarcengineering@cwcom.net *Laser work, presswork & fabrication services*

▶ Cymbal Corporation, 22 Upper Grosvenor Street, London, W1K 7PE Tel: (020) 7629 4243 E-mail: sales@cymbal.com

▶ Cymitric, 5 The Brache, Maulden, Bedford, MK45 2DZ Tel: (01525) 404434 Fax: (0871) 4335545 E-mail: info@cymitric.net *Web site designs, support services, IT training & information management expertise*

Cymru Lifting Gear Ltd, Unit 31 Abenbury Way, Wrexham Industrial Estate, Wrexham, Clwyd, LL13 9UZ Tel: (01978) 661439 Fax: (01978) 661238 E-mail: rossgrp_cog@msm.com *Lifting equipment engineers*

Cynetix Group Ltd, Unit C1, Aven Industrial Park, Tickhill Road, Maltby, Rotherham, South Yorkshire, S66 7QR Tel: (01709) 819922 Fax: (01709) 798804 E-mail: sales@cynetix.co.uk *Computer resellers*

Cynflex Ltd, Highfield Street, Long Eaton, Nottingham, NG10 4GY Tel: 0115-973 5689 Fax: 0115-972 2149 E-mail: sales@cynflex.com *Industrial rubber product & silicone rubber moulding or extrusion manufrs*

Cyphermet Ltd, Bone Lane, Newbury, Berkshire, RG14 5SH Tel: (01635) 34099 Fax: (01635) 528623 E-mail: sales@cyphermet.co.uk *Manufacturers of metal cabinets & vending machines. Engineers & fabricators of sheet metalwork including precision fine limit. Contractors & services of paint spraying & powder coating. Also electromechanical assembly production*

▶ Cyprus Construction Ltd, Leeds Road, Idle, Bradford, West Yorkshire, BD10 8JH Tel: (01274) 621820 Fax: (01274) 615919

▶ Cyprus Ideal, 35 Micklethwaite Grove, Wetherby, West Yorkshire, LS22 5LA Tel: (0870) 4460010 Fax: 01937 583919 E-mail: sales@cyprus-ideal.com *Cyprus Ideal is a consulting agent for buying property in Cyprus our website is aimed at providing information about living in Cyprus, the benefits of investing in Cyprus and our properties for sale. Cyprus Ideal has developed relationships with builders and developers in Southern Cyprus. Primarily in the regions of Paphos, Larnaka, Limassol, Polis and Agia Napa, we have a wide range of properties and land available for sale.*

Cyptec UK Ltd, 134 Timbercroft Lane, London, SE18 2SG Tel: (020) 8855 6664 Fax: (020) 8855 1714 E-mail: sales@vellumfile.com *Computer main systems maintenance*

Cyril Isaacs & Co. Ltd, 1 Apex Way, Leeds, LS11 5LN Tel: 0113-245 4143 Fax: 0113-245 0486 *Glazing contractors*

Cyril Luff Metal Decorators Ltd, 57-58 Springvale Industrial Estate, Cwmbran, Gwent, NP44 5BD Tel: (01633) 869531 Fax: (01633) 865046 E-mail: info@cyrilluff.co.uk *Tinplate metal decorating*

Cyril W Bishop, 58a Shirley Road, Croydon, CR0 7EP Tel: (020) 8656 8234 Fax: (020) 8654 5459 E-mail: pipefreezing@bishop.co.uk *Shrink fitting services*

Cytec Computer Systems Ltd, Pishill Bank, Pishill, Henley-on-Thames, Oxfordshire, RG9 6HR Tel: (01491) 638477 Fax: (01491) 638374 E-mail: sales@cytec.uk.com *Computer hardware resellers*

Cytec Engineered Materials Ltd, Abenbury Way, Wrexham Industrial Estate, Wrexham, Clwyd, LL13 9UZ Tel: (01978) 665200 Fax: (01978) 665222 E-mail: info@cytec.com Principal Export Areas: Worldwide *Manufacturers of adhesives*

▶ Cytek Jersey, Petit Haut Du Rue, La Rue de la Clochette, St. Martin, Jersey, JE3 6HN Tel: (01534) 855263

▶ Cytyc UK Ltd, 2 Link 10, Napier Way, Crawley, West Sussex, RH10 9RA Tel: (01293) 522080 Fax: (01293) 528010 *Medical suppliers*

C. Czarnikow Sugar Ltd, 24 Chiswell Street, London, EC1Y 4SG Tel: (020) 7972 6600 Fax: (020) 7972 6699 E-mail: czarnikow@czarnikow.com *Commodity brokers*

Czech & Speake Ltd, 244-254 Cambridge Heath Road, London, E2 9DA Tel: (020) 8983 7400 Fax: (020) 8981 7232 E-mail: sales@czechspeake.com *Bathroom fittings & aromatics manufrs*

D 4 S Fabrications Ltd, 19 Morses Lane, Brightlingsea, Colchester, CO7 0SF Tel: (01206) 303668 Fax: (01206) 304835 E-mail: ab@d4sfabrication.co.uk *Noise control equipment & louver manufrs*

D & A, Conference Centre Aston Cross Business Park, 50 Rocky Lane, Aston, Birmingham, B6 5RQ Tel: 0121-706 6133 Fax: 0121-697 2700 E-mail: contactus@danda.co.uk *Retail opticians*

D A B Carnegie, 2nd Floor 24 Chiswell Street, London, EC1Y 4UE Tel: (020) 7216 4000 Fax: (020) 7417 9424 *Stock & share brokers*

D A B Engineering Co Ltd, 157 Dukes Road, London, W3 0SL Tel: (020) 8993 1771 Fax: (020) 8993 9048 *Fire fighting equipment suppliers*

D A Baldwin & Son, Head Office Pasford House, Chesterton Road, Pattingham, Wolverhampton, WV6 7DZ Tel: (01902) 700456 Fax: (01902) 700492 E-mail: watersoft@aol.com *Water softener manufrs*

▶ D A Bird Ltd, Camp Hill, Bugbrooke, Northampton, NN7 3PH Tel: (01604) 830455 Fax: (01604) 832369

D A Brockwell, Mancetter Road, Hartshill, Nuneaton, Warwickshire, CV10 0RT Tel: (024) 7639 2283 Fax: (024) 7639 8259 *Timber merchants*

D A C Air Conditioning Ltd, 4 Butler Way, Stanningley, Pudsey, West Yorkshire, LS28 6EA Tel: 0113-236 2101 Fax: 0113-236 2087 E-mail: info@dacairconditioning.co.uk *Air conditioning & refrigeration maintenance*

D A C Handling, Unit 1 Douglas Mill, Bradley Lane, Standish, Wigan, Lancashire, WN6 0XF Tel: (01257) 425050 Fax: (01257) 422080 *Fork lift trucks distributors*

▶ D A C Handling Solutions Ltd, Oxford Street Industrial Park, Vulcan Road, Bilston, West Midlands, WV14 7JG Tel: (0845) 6013529 Fax: (0870) 1662904 E-mail: drock@dac-handling.co.uk *Materials handling equipment suppliers*

D A C Services, 45 Ross Avenue, Dalgety Bay, Dunfermline, Fife, KY11 9YN Tel: (01383) 820700 Fax: (0871) 2421081 *Security installation services*

D A Cant Ltd, Unit 23 Lodge Lane, Langham, Colchester, CO4 5NE Tel: (01206) 231500 Fax: (01206) 231599 E-mail: d.a.cant@virgin.net *Civil engineer contractors*

▶ D A Clarke, Highfields Farm, Huncote Road, Stoney Stanton, Leicester, LE9 4DJ Tel: (01455) 272214 Fax: (01455) 273302

▶ D A Computers Ltd, 15 Bell Lane, Leicester, LE5 3BA Tel: 0116-299 9549 Fax: 0116-299 9545 E-mail: sales@dacomputers.com *Managed IT services provider. We provide a range of services for SME businesses:* *HARDWARE: computers, laptops, servers, peripherals, consumables, spares, upgrades.*INTERNET: email, connectivity, webdesign, e-commerce, security, firewalls, virus protection, content filtering. *NETWORK : Structured cable, wirless, VPN, remote, fibre optics, cat5/6, netwrok secutiry. *SOFTWARE: Bespoke software, office, accounts, CRM. SUPPORT: Maintenance, installation, remote access. *SECUTIRY: Network monitoring, Backup, Risk assemsment*

▶ D A Cooper & Sons Ltd, Fullerton Road, Rotherham, South Yorkshire, S60 1DH Tel: (01709) 828517 Fax: (01709) 828562 E-mail: sales@dacooper.co.uk

D & A Fabrications Ltd, Barn House, Red House Lane, Eccleston, Chorley, Lancashire, PR7 5RH Tel: (01257) 452181 *Steel fabrication*

D & A Fabrications, Unit 23 Landgate Industrial Estate, Wigan Road, Ashton-in-Makerfield, Wigan, Lancashire, WN4 0BW Tel: (01942) 717183 Fax: (01942) 719880 *Fabricators*

D A Green & Sons Ltd, High Road, Whaplode, Spalding, Lincolnshire, PE12 6TL Tel: (01406) 370585 Fax: (01406) 370766 E-mail: sales@dagreen.co.uk *Steel framed building manures*

▶ D A Harrison Ltd, Waverton, Wigton, Cumbria, CA7 0AE Tel: (01697) 342277 Fax: (01697) 342250 E-mail: shelly@daharrison.co.uk

D & A Health & Pet Foods, 94 Connaught Avenue, Frinton-on-Sea, Essex, CO13 9PT Tel: (01255) 679603 *Health & pet food retailers*

▶ D A Johnstone, Station Yard, Longhirst, Morpeth, Northumberland, NE61 3HZ Tel: (01670) 812244 Fax: (01670) 810088

D A K International, Unit 12 Ashmead Business Centre, Ashmead Road, Keynsham, Bristol, BS31 1SX Tel: 0117-986 6198 Fax: 0117-986 6704 *Decorative glass manufrs*

▶ D A Kennedy Construction Ltd, North Muirton Industrial Estate, Inchcape Place, Perth, PH1 3DU Tel: (01738) 632700 Fax: (01738) 630214

▶ D A Mcdonald, Kilmory, Lochgilphead, Argyll, PA31 8RR Tel: (01546) 603583 Fax: (01546) 602576

D A Marketing & Communications Ltd, Prince Consort House, 109-111 Farringdon Road, London, EC1R 3BW Tel: (020) 7841 0088 E-mail: enquiries@damarketing.co.uk *Marketing & design consultants*

D A & N D Towers, Spacey Houses Farm, Spacey Houses, Harrogate, North Yorkshire, HG3 1LD Tel: (01423) 879076 *Farmers*

D A N Toilet Hire, Dillybrook Farm, Poplar Tree Lane, Southwick, Trowbridge, Wiltshire, BA14 9NB Tel: (01373) 830110 Fax: (01373) 830110 *Portable toilet hire services*

D A P International Removals Ltd, 209 Manor Road, Erith, Kent, DA8 2AD Tel: (01322) 335621 Fax: (01322) 332518 E-mail: dapinternational@btinternet.com *Overseas relocation specialists*

D & A Plastics, Stubcroft Farm Studios, Stubcroft Lane, East Wittering, Chichester, West Sussex, PO20 8PJ Tel: (01243) 671588 Fax: (01243) 671588 *PTFE machinists*

D A Ramsay, Auchentoshan Estate, Clydebank, Dunbartonshire, G81 4SP Tel: (01389) 873391 Fax: (01389) 872287 *Fence & gate fitters*

D A S Air Cargo Ltd, North Elm Park Court Tilgate Forest Business Centre, Crawley, West Sussex, RH11 9BP Tel: (01293) 540303 Fax: (01293) 514036 E-mail: sales@dasair.com *Cargo airline services*

D A S Alarms, 34 Water Lane, Ashton-on-Ribble, Preston, PR2 2NL Tel: (01772) 728900 Fax: (01772) 728300 *Alarm services & installers*

D A Security Systems Ltd, 5 Cornfield Road, Lee-On-The-Solent, Hampshire, PO13 8HZ Tel: (023) 9255 0627 *Burglar alarm system installations*

D & A Steering Ltd, 27 Nursey Road, Hockley, Birmingham, B19 2XN Tel: 0121-523 8444 Fax: 0121-523 8136 *Motor vehicle steering specialists*

D A Stuart Ltd, Lincoln Street, Wolverhampton, WV10 0DZ Tel: (01902) 456111 Fax: (01902) 453764 E-mail: dastuart@dastuart.co.uk *Metal working lubricant manufrs*

D A T A Services, 1 Coates Place, Edinburgh, EH3 7AA Tel: 0131-225 7707 Fax: 0131-225 7708 *Data analysis distribution*

D & A Tackle, 242-244 Woodhouse Road, London, N12 0RU Tel: (020) 8368 8799 Fax: (020) 8368 8799 *Fishing tackle*

D A Wright Ltd, 13 Lowman Units Lowman Way, Tiverton Business Park, Tiverton, Devon, EX16 6SR Tel: (01884) 254474 Fax: (01884) 256479 E-mail: info@dawright.co.uk *Electrical & plumbing contractors*

▶ D Astin & Son, 16 Waddington Road, Clitheroe, Lancashire, BB7 2HJ Tel: (01200) 422315 Fax: (01200) 422315

▶ D B Boat Fitting Ltd, Braunston Marina Trade Centre, The Wharf, Braunston, Daventry, Northamptonshire, NN11 7JH Tel: (01788) 891727 Fax: (01788) 891727 E-mail: lyn@dbboatfitting.co.uk *Builder of high class narrow & wide beam steel boats*

D B Brooks Electrical Engineers Ltd, Sinclair Close, Heanor, Derbyshire, DE75 7SP Tel: (01773) 763444 Fax: (01773) 530332 E-mail: admin@dbbrooks.co.uk *Control panel manufrs*

D B C Food Services Ltd, Industrial Road, Hertburn Estate, Washington, Tyne & Wear, NE37 2SD Tel: 0191-416 2571 Fax: 0191-415 5739 *Food wholesaler*

▶ D B C M Web Design, 14 Wallacebrae Drive, Danestone, Aberdeen, AB22 8YB Tel: (01224) 825401 E-mail: info@dbcmtest.co.uk

D B C Tools Ltd, Jubilee Trading Estate, Jubilee Road, Letchworth Garden City, Hertfordshire, SG6 1NE Tel: (01462) 679905 Fax: (01462) 480219 E-mail: don.carter@dbctools.co.uk *Precision engineers*

▶ D B Consulting Ltd, 109 Blackthorn Road, Southampton, SO19 7LP Tel: (07717) 453409 E-mail: info@electricalconsultant.org *Building services, consultation, project management, on-site engineer*

D B Controls Ltd, 9 Station Road, Adwick-Le-Street, Doncaster, South Yorkshire, DN6 7BE Tel: (01302) 330837 Fax: (01302) 724731 E-mail: sales@dbcontrols.co.uk *Instrument & electrical engineers*

D B Crane Ltd, Unit 10 Sovereign Works, Deepdale Lane, Dudley, West Midlands, DY3 2AF Tel: (01384) 458763 Fax: (01384) 459766 *Crane & hoist specialists*

▶ D B Electrics, 3 Spartleton Place, Dundee, DD4 0UJ Tel: (01382) 739447 Fax: (01382) 739447 E-mail: dbelectrics@blueyonder.co.uk *Electrical contractor*

D B Grinders Ltd, Primrose Works, Primrose Bank, Oldham, OL8 1HQ Tel: 0161-626 4202 Fax: 0161-626 4210 E-mail: dbgrinders@btconnect.com *Textile machinery manufrs*

▶ D B H (Dorset) Ltd, Unit 14, 4-6 Abingdon Road, Nuffield Industrial Estate, Poole, Dorset, BH17 0UG Tel: (01202) 684899 Fax: (01202) 677429 *Marine engineering*

▶ D B Hair, 161 Brownroyd Hill Road, Bradford, West Yorkshire, BD6 1RU Tel: (01274) 690909 E-mail: info@dbhair.co.uk *Advanced Cutting and Colouring Order from db essentials, ghd and TIGI online, find out more about us or make a booking*

D B I, Marsh La, Burgh le Marsh, Skegness, Lincs, PE24 5AG Tel: (01754) 811777 Fax: (01754) 811555 *Agricultural machinery manufrs*

D B I Ailsa, 33-35 McFarlane Street, Paisley, Renfrewshire, PA3 1FE Tel: 0141-887 0666 Fax: 0141-889 8765 E-mail: into@dbigroup.co.uk *Industrial & environmental services*

D B I Associates Ltd, Stoneleigh Park Mews, Stonleigh Abbey, Kenilworth, Warwickshire, CV8 2DB Tel: (01926) 312481 Fax: (01926) 515616 E-mail: consultants@dbiconsulting.co.uk *Management consultants*

D B Industrial Fasteners Ltd, Q Gunnels Wood Road Industrial Estate, Gunnels Wood Road, Stevenage, Hertfordshire, SG1 2BH Tel: (01438) 728872 Fax: (01438) 740279 E-mail: salesdb@dbfasteners.com *Threaded fastener distributors & stockholders*

D B Industrial Services Ltd, Lyn Castle Way, Appleton, Warrington, WA4 4ST Tel: (01606) 597151 Fax: (01606) 597152 E-mail: sales@dbigroup.co.uk *Insulation & scaffolding removal service*

D & B Injection Moulders Ltd, Unit 3 Kiln Hill Industrial Estate, Slaithwaite, Huddersfield, HD7 5JS Tel: (0845) 5314194 Fax: (01484) 841214 E-mail: sales@dbmoulders.co.uk *We are a small company that has been trading for 18 years manufacturing plastic and nylon cable glands and associated plastic products. We also offer a trade moulding service from design to finished product. We offer a comprehensive range of metric and pg glands, and mould a large range of associated products eg. locknuts, brushes, blanking plugs, threaded reducer brushes etc. A growing part of our business offers a trade moulding service and we can assist with product concept through to final production, including in house CAD, our own tool room for mould manufacture, sampling, production, packing and despatch.*

▶ D B Installations, 4 Bridge Street, Newbridge, Midlothian, EH28 8SR Tel: (0800) 0377416 Fax: 0131-335 3770

D B Keighley Machinery Ltd, Vickers Place, Stanningley, Pudsey, West Yorkshire, LS28 6LZ Tel: 0113-257 4736 Fax: 0113-257 4293 E-mail: sales@dbkeighley.co.uk *Woodworking machinery distributors*

D B M Chemicals Ltd, 73 Ferry Lane South, Rainham, Essex, RM13 9YH Tel: (01708) 522151 Fax: (01708) 557546 E-mail: jrhornett@aol.com *Chemical trading company*

▶ D B M Engineering, Burnwood House, Rockley, Retford, Nottinghamshire, DN22 0QW Tel: (01777) 838100 Fax: (01777) 838710

▶ D B Mcintyre, Lochty Industrial Estate, Almondbank, Perth, PH1 3NP Tel: (01738) 582225 Fax: (01738) 582226

▶ D & B Mairs Car Trimmers, 734 Stockport Road West, Bredbury, Stockport, Cheshire, SK6 2EE Tel: 0161-494 8874 E-mail: dbmairs@ntlworld.com *family business established for over 30 years , fully trained llumar window tinting specialists*

D B Marine, Cookham Bridge, Cookham On Thames, Cookham, Maidenhead, Berkshire, SL6 9SN Tel: (01628) 526032 Fax: (01628) 520564 E-mail: sales@dbmarine.co.uk *Marine engineering services*

D B Prepared Vegetables, Bedford Street, Stoke-on-Trent, ST1 4PZ Tel: (01782) 207266 *Vegetable suppliers*

▶ D B Promotions UK, PO Box 3809, Sutton Coldfield, West Midlands, B74 4QY Tel: 0121-308 4551 Fax: 0121-323 3914 E-mail: info@dbpromotions.co.uk *Tickets manufrs*

▶ D B Russell (Construction) Ltd, Edward House, 18 Alexandra Road, Clevedon, Avon, BS21 7QE Tel: (01275) 876411 Fax: (01275) 875985

▶ D B S Engineering, Tilbury Docks Industrial Complex, Tilbury, Essex, RM18 7EH Tel: (01375) 842202 Fax: (01375) 844144

▶ D B S Engineers Ltd, Bankfield Works, Emlyn Street, Farnworth, Bolton, BL4 7EP Tel: (01204) 571705 *Fencing & gate manufrs*

D B Services, 19 Diamond Road, Dromore, County Down, BT25 1PH Tel: (028) 9269 2714 Fax: (028) 9269 9938 E-mail: del@dbservicesni.co.uk *Steel fabrication services*

▶ D B Services, 194 West Street, Fareham, Hampshire, PO16 0HF Tel: (01329) 288464 Fax: (01329) 825815 E-mail: southern@dbservices.co.uk *Cleaning & Facilities*Cleaning*Window Cleaning*Floor Care*Security & Concierge*Grounds Maintenance*Handy Person*Janitorial Supplies*

D B Sheetmetals, 1 Coopers Park, Cooper Drive, Braintree, Essex, CM7 2TN Tel: (01376) 552951 Fax: (01376) 552951 *Stainless steel sheet fabricators*

D B Shoes Ltd, Irchester Road, Rushden, Northamptonshire, NN10 9XF Tel: (01933) 359217 Fax: (01933) 410218 E-mail: denton@dbshoes.freeserve.co.uk *Footwear manufrs* Also at: Leicester & Northampton

D B Sign Associates Ltd, Dukeries Industrial Estate, Claylands Avenue, Worksop, Nottinghamshire, S81 7BQ Tel: (01909) 472922 Fax: (01909) 478698 E-mail: office@dbsigns.com *All types of signs contractors & suppliers*

D B Sign & Engraving Co., Unit 4, Windmill Lane Industrial Estate, Denton, Manchester, M34 3RB Tel: 0161-320 0068 Fax: 0161-320 6829 *Sign makers*

D B Springs Ltd, 1 Double Century Works, High Street, Astwood Bank, Redditch, Worcestershire, B96 6AR Tel: (01527) 893220 Fax: (01527) 893220 *Pressing springs & wire formed products manufrs*

D B T GB Ltd, Hallam Fields Road, Ilkeston, Derbyshire, DE7 4BS Tel: 0115-930 2603 Fax: 0115-932 9683 Principal Export Areas: Middle East, Africa, North America & Central America *Mining equipment manufrs*

D B T Medical Ltd, 14 The Crofts, Witney, Oxfordshire, OX28 4DJ Tel: (01993) 773673 Fax: (01993) 778267 E-mail: office@dbtmedical.co.uk *Rubber products small volume products made from sheet rubber*

D B Thomas & Son Ltd, 219 Bow Road, London, E3 2SJ Tel: (020) 8980 9743 Fax: (020) 8981 4979 *clothing manufacturers*

D & B Training Ltd, Sandy Court Moss Industrial Estate, St. Helens Road, Leigh, Lancashire, WN7 3PT Tel: (01942) 678986 Fax: (01942) 602566 E-mail: sales@db-training.net *Training HGV, FLT, Health & Safety, First Aid etc*

▶ D B Wilson & Co. Ltd, 1 Alleysbank Road, Rutherglen, Glasgow, G73 1AL Tel: 0141-647 0161 Fax: 0141-613 1795 E-mail: dbwilsonjr@aol.com *Battery manufrs*

D B Wilson & Co. Ltd, 1 Alleysbank Road, Rutherglen, Glasgow, G73 1AL Tel: 0141-647 0161 Fax: 0141-613 1795 E-mail: dbwilsonjr@aol.com *Motor battery manufrs*

▶ D Baff Joinery Ltd, The Rear Workshop, 138 Brookland Road, Bridlington, North Humberside, YO16 4HD Tel: (01262) 676946 Fax: (01262) 676946 E-mail: lorrainbaff@btconnect.com *Window frames manufrs*

D Beacock & Son, Colin Road, Scunthorpe, South Humberside, DN16 1TT Tel: (01724) 854370 Fax: (01724) 854370 *Joinery manufrs*

D Benson & Co. Ltd, Normanton Industrial Estate, Normanton, West Yorkshire, WF6 1QS Tel: (01924) 894162 Fax: (01924) 896518 E-mail: info@dbensoncontrols.co.uk *Control panel manufrs*

D Berry & Co. Ltd, Middlemoor Industrial Estate, Kentish Road, Middlemore Industrial Estate, Birmingham, B21 0AY Tel: 0121-558 4411 Fax: 0121-555 5546 E-mail: enquires@dberryandco.co.uk *Tube fitting distributors*

D Blowers Ltd, High Croft, London Road, Halesworth, Suffolk, IP19 8LR Tel: (01986) 872861 Fax: (01986) 873048 *Livestock hauliers*

D Brash & Sons Ltd, 37 Stamperland Crescent, Clarkston, Glasgow, G76 8LH Tel: 0141-638 2284 Fax: 0141-620 1842 E-mail: sales@dbrash.co.uk *Weighing machine service, repair & distributors* Also at: Potters Bar & Stockport

D Brash & Sons Ltd, 840 Chester Road, Stretford, Manchester, M32 0QJ Tel: 0161-865 0333 Fax: 0161-865 0444 E-mail: sales@dbrash.co.uk *Weighing & counting equipment*

D C A & Co. Ltd, The Old Chapel, Chapel Street, Taylor Hill, Huddersfield, HD4 6HL Tel: (01484) 510066 Fax: (01484) 467800 E-mail: sales@dca-ltd.com *D C A & Co. Ltd based in Huddersfield are hydraulic equipment distributors. They supply components and/or manufacture and install complete systems.*

▶ D C A Data Solutions, 17 Gayfield Square, Edinburgh, EH1 3NX Tel: 0131-556 7787 Fax: 0131-556 2856 *Software development services*

D C A Elect, Unit 3D, Herald Industrial Estate, Hedge End, Southampton, SO30 2JW Tel: (01489) 799927 Fax: (01489) 798770 E-mail: sales@flocking.biz *Electro static flock spraying*

▶ D C A Recruitment, 15a High Street, Godalming, Surrey, GU7 1AZ Tel: (01483) 422212 Fax: (01483) 418219 E-mail: vacancy@dcass.co.uk *Godalming based family run Recruitment Agency, local office support positions*

▶ D C Angling, 292 Charter Avenue, Coventry, CV4 8DA Tel: (024) 7647 1526 Fax: (024) 7647 4053

▶ D C Automatics, 3 Hammond Business Centre, Hammond Close, Attleborough Fields Industrial Estate, Nuneaton, Warwickshire, CV11 6RY Tel: (024) 7634 7606 Fax: (024) 7634 7606 *Amusement machine suppliers*

D C B Electronics, 702 Southchurch Road, Southend-on-Sea, SS1 2PS Tel: (01702) 304030 Fax: (01702) 305030 E-mail: sales@dcb-electronics.co.uk *Radio communications, TV Installation & repair*

D C Baxter Motors Ltd, The Garage, Rectory Road, Ruskington, Sleaford, Lincolnshire, NG34 9AB Tel: (01526) 832321 Fax: (01526) 833662 E-mail: peterbaxter4@btinternet.com *Motor trader*

D C Carter Ltd, Meadow Farm, Packards Lane, Wormingford, Colchester, CO6 3AH Tel: (01206) 243309 Fax: (01206) 242161 E-mail: dccarter@onetel.com *Manufacturers of Convex & Concave mirrors in glass & acrylic. Precision glass benders & silverers*

D C Contracts, Kennoway, Leven, Fife, KY8 5SG Tel: (01333) 352500 Fax: (01333) 352500 *Agricultural contractors*

D C Dalgleish Ltd, Dunsdale Mill, Dunsdale Road, Selkirk, TD7 5EB Tel: (01750) 20781 Fax: (01750) 20502 *Tartan specialists*

D C E Holne Ltd, Mardle Way Industrial Estate, Buckfastleigh, Devon, TQ11 0NS Tel: (01364) 643862 Fax: (01364) 643025 E-mail: enquiries@dce-holne.co.uk *Precision engineers*

D C Emergency Systems Ltd, Wharf Street, Dukinfield, Cheshire, SK16 4JG Tel: 0161-343 1189 Fax: 0161-343 2235 E-mail: sales@dc-emergency.com *Emergency lighting equipment manufrs*

D C Engineering, Steel Close, Eaton Socon, St. Neots, Cambridgeshire, PE19 8TT Tel: (01480) 216598 Fax: (01480) 473857 E-mail: melvyn@dcengineering.fsnet.co.uk *Sub-engineering services*

D & C Engineers Ltd, Unit 1, Mariner, Lichfield Road Industrial Estate, Tamworth, Staffs, B79 7UL Tel: (01827) 54824 Fax: (01827) 61203 E-mail: dandcengineers@compuseve.com Purchasing Contact: B. Dixson Sales Contact: G. Chatterley *Manufacturer, welding, general engineering & steel fabrication to the concrete, quarry & asphalt plant industries*

D C F M Quotas Ltd, 1 Bridge Street, Boston, Lincolnshire, PE21 8QF Tel: (01205) 310644 Fax: (01205) 310645 E-mail: post@dcfm.com *National quota agency*

D C Gardner Training, Nestor House, Playhouse Yard, London, EC4V 5EX Tel: (020) 7779 8917 Fax: (020) 7779 8786 *Training organisation*

▶ D C Group, Corsley, Corsley, Warminster, Wiltshire, BA12 7QH Tel: (01373) 832288 Fax: (01373) 832589 E-mail: stefen@dcgroup.uk.net *Advertise company literature, direct mail, exhibition & web design*

D C H Pest Control, 38 Fish Street, Ripley, Bransgore, Christchurch, Dorset, BH23 8EU Tel: (01425) 672866 *Pest controllers*

D C Hall Ltd, Woburn Lane, Aspley Guise, Milton Keynes, MK17 8JJ Tel: (01908) 583888 Fax: (01908) 582041 E-mail: ray@dchall.co.uk *Precision engineers & cnc machining*

D C I Precision Engineering, 5b1 Ramsden Road, Rotherwas Industrial Estate, Hereford, HR2 6LR Tel: (01432) 279555 Fax: (01432) 279777 *Rubber & plastic mould toolmakers*

▶ D C Lighting Services Ltd, Unit 2a Keillor Buildings, 34 Mains Loan, Dundee, DD4 7BT Tel: (01382) 818222 Fax: (01382) 825028

D C M Drillquip Ltd, Hazel Way, Bermuda Road, Nuneaton, Warwickshire, CV10 7QG Tel: (024) 7634 8328 Fax: (024) 7634 8329 E-mail: sales@drillquip.co.uk *Drilling & wellboring equipment*

D C M Group Ltd, Bayton Road Industrial Estate, 41 Bayton Road, Exhall, Coventry, CV7 9EL Tel: (024) 7636 1601 Fax: (024) 7636 7914 E-mail: sales@dcm.co.uk *Sheet metalwork engineers*

D C Materials Supply Ltd, Selham, Petworth, West Sussex, GU28 0PJ Tel: (01798) 861625 Fax: (01798) 461702 E-mail: sales@deepwater.demon.co.uk *Corrosion prevention materials*

D C Merrett, The Grain Store Castle Lane, Epney, Saul, Gloucester, GL2 7LN Tel: (01452) 740782 Fax: (01452) 741496 E-mail: info@dcmerrett.co.uk *New & used equipment sales servicing & hire, lorries*

D C Norris & Co Engineering Ltd, Sand Road Industrial Estate, Sand Road, Great Gransden, Sandy, Bedfordshire, SG19 3AH Tel: (01767) 677515 Fax: (01767) 677956 E-mail: mail@dcnorris.co.uk *Food processing equipment suppliers*

D C Ould, Mount Pleasant, Roche, St. Austell, Cornwall, PL26 8LH Tel: (01726) 890349 Fax: (01726) 890910 *New & secondhand steel stockholders*

D C P M Manuals, Rock Drive, Gelli, Pentre, Rhondda Cynon Taff, CF41 7NX Tel: (01443) 442029 Fax: (01443) 442199 E-mail: info@dcpmmanuals.com *Compilers of digital & hardcopy operation & maintenance manuals for the construction & other industries. UK wide service.*

D C Plastic Handrails Ltd, Unit 6, Cowen Road, Cowen Road Industrial Estate, Blaydon-On-Tyne, Tyne & Wear, NE21 5TW Tel: 0191-414 0034 Fax: 0191-414 0034 E-mail: davey@dchandrails.freeserve.co.uk *Supply of pvc handrail coverings*

D C Richards Farrier, 9 Mount Pleasant, Fairford, Gloucestershire, GL7 4BA Tel: (01285) 711025 Fax: (01285) 712097 *Farrier distributors*

D C S Associates, 50 High Street, Kingswood, Bristol, BS15 4AJ Tel: 0117-960 3242 Fax: 0117-960 3282 E-mail: sales@dcs-imago.com *IT support & consultancy*

D C S Automotive Ltd, Clarendon House, Clarendon Square, Leamington Spa, Warwickshire, CV32 5QJ Tel: (01926) 831401 Fax: (01926) 450183 E-mail: info@dcs-automotive.co.uk *Computer management systems & software*

D C S Door Systems, Unit 5 Whitehall Industrial Park, Whitehall Road, Great Bridge, Tipton, West Midlands, DY4 7JU Tel: 0121-520 5151 Fax: 0121-520 0535 E-mail: sales@irsp.co.uk *Automatic & industrial door manufrs*

D C S Telecom Ltd, Reculver Road, Herne Bay, Kent, CT6 6PB Tel: (01227) 741825 Fax: (01227) 361011 E-mail: sales@dcstelecom.co.uk *Telecommunication systems distributors*

D C Security, 3 Litherland Road, Sale, Cheshire, M33 2PE Tel: 0161-926 9955 Fax: 0161-286 1633 *Alarm system installators*

D C T Civil Engineering Ltd, Prospect House, George Street, Shaw, Oldham, OL2 8DX Tel: (01706) 842929 Fax: (01706) 882158 E-mail: info@dct-civils.co.uk *Civil engineers*

D C T Services, Summer Trees, Hawley Drive, Hale Barns, Altrincham, Cheshire, WA15 0DP Tel: 0161-621 0730 Fax: 0161-904 7392 *Reprographic consultants*

D C Thomson & Co. Ltd, Albert Square, Dundee, DD1 9QJ Tel: (01382) 223131 Fax: (01382) 225778 E-mail: amcintosh@dcthomson.co.uk *Publishers*

D C Trading, Copdock House, London Road, Copdock, Ipswich, IP8 3JW Tel: (01473) 730286 Fax: (01473) 730257 E-mail: info@dctrading.co.uk *IT support & network solutions for businesses*

D & C TV's, 152 Holdenhurst Road, Bournemouth, BH8 8AS Tel: (01202) 318708 Fax: (01202) 380280 *Computer repairers*

D C V Container Conversions, Mardyke Works, St Marys Lane, North Ockendon, Upminster, Essex, RM14 3PA Tel: (01708) 641169 Fax: (01708) 641192 E-mail: derek@containerconversions.freeserve.co.uk *Freight container conversion services*

D C W Accided Repairs Ltd, Cornhill Close, Lodge Farm Industrial Estate, Harlestone Road, Northampton, NN5 7UQ Tel: (01604) 753208 Fax: (01604) 759718 *Crash repairers*

▶ D C W Training Services, 63 Barnwell Street, Kettering, Northamptonshire, NN16 0JD Tel: (07947) 641457 Fax: (01536) 392137 E-mail: sedcwe17@ntlworld.com *Industrial training services*

D C Woodhead & Partners Ltd, Carlisle Drive, Pudsey, West Yorkshire, LS28 8QS Tel: 0113-257 2275 Fax: 0113-255 3224 E-mail: woodhdpl@dialstart.net *Engineers*

D Canavan, 66 Mountjoy Road, Dungannon, County Tyrone, BT71 5EF Tel: (028) 8774 7666 Fax: (028) 8774 7666 *Agricultural engineers*

D Cave Hydraulics Ltd, Rainford Road, Bickerstaffe, Ormskirk, Lancashire, L39 0HG Tel: (01695) 735888 Fax: (01695) 725511 *Hydraulic fitting distributors & plant installers*

▶ D Clarke, 2 Southfield Road, Hinckley, Leicestershire, LE10 1UB Tel: (01455) 618187 Fax: (01455) 233600

▶ D Cruikshanks & Son, 6A South Crescent Road, Ardrossan, Ayrshire, KA22 8DU Tel: (01294) 463410

D Cutler International Ltd, 148-150 Commercial Street, London, E1 6NU Tel: (020) 7377 8738 Fax: (020) 7377 2624 E-mail: d.cutler@hotmail.co.uk *Baby & children's clothing importers*

D D Blinds, 25 Craven Park, London, NW10 8SU Tel: (020) 8961 3972 *Suppliers of blinds*

D D C Control Systems Ltd, Unit 1 Broadwyn Trading Estate, Waterfall Lane, Cradley Heath, West Midlands, B64 6PS Tel: 0121-561 3312 Fax: 0121-561 3541 E-mail: ian.biddle@ddccontrolsystems.co.uk *Control panel manufrs*

D D C (U K) Ltd, Mill Reef House, 9-14 Cheap Street, Newbury, Berkshire, RG14 5DD Tel: (01635) 40158 Fax: (01635) 32264 *Electronic component distributors*

▶ D & D Computer Services, 2 Northfield Road, Narberth, Dyfed, SA67 7AA Tel: (01834) 869319 Fax: (01834) 860450 E-mail: enquiries@ddcs.co.uk *Computer maintenance & rebuilds repair services*

D D Concrete Ltd, Blaenant Industrial Estate, Brynmawr, Ebbw Vale, Gwent, NP23 4AZ Tel: (01495) 311253 Fax: (01495) 311253 *Concrete garden products*

D & D Conference & Event Management Ltd, 66a High Street, Egham, Surrey, TW20 9EY Tel: (01784) 432233 Fax: (01784) 430088 E-mail: dd@ddconfrence.com *Conference organising services*

D & D Construction Ringmer Ltd, 19-21 Cradle Hill Industrial Estate, Seaford, East Sussex, BN25 3JE Tel: (01323) 890403 Fax: (01323) 490140 E-mail: info@danddconstruction.co.uk *Steel agricultural buildings*

D D D Ltd, 94 Rickmansworth Road, Watford, WD18 7JJ Tel: (01923) 229251 Fax: (01923) 220728 *Medicine suppliers*

D D D Security Systems Ltd, Security House, Mile Lane, Coventry, CV1 2NL Tel: (024) 7652 5525 Fax: (024) 7652 5104 E-mail: admin@dddltd.com *DDD offer a professional design and advisory service supported by highly competent and experienced installation, service and maintenance departments to deliver customer confidence and excellence.**DDD is a NACOSS GOLD approved installer with quality assured BS EN ISO9001:2000 Certification, awarded by the National Security Inspectorate (NSI).*

D & D Dispersions Ltd, Unit G, St. Marks Road, St. James Industrial Estate, Corby, Northamptonshire, NN18 8AN Tel: (01536) 400488 Fax: (01536) 407365 E-mail: dispersion@dddispersions.co.uk Principal Export Areas: Worldwide *Printing Ink Manufr*

D & D Engineering Hull Ltd, Stockholm Road, Hull, HU7 0XW Tel: (01482) 879175 Fax: (01482) 838449 E-mail: info@ddeng.co.uk *Specialist manufacturers of conveyor equipment & conveyor systems*

D D Evans & Co Ltd, The Garage, New Road, Pontarddulais, Swansea, SA4 8TB Tel: (01792) 882637 *Garage service providers*

D D Fabrications, Blackdyke Road, Kingstown Industrial Estate, Kingstown, Carlisle, CA3 0PJ Tel: (01228) 536595 Fax: (01228) 536595 E-mail: enquiries@ddfabrications.co.uk *General & sheet metalwork engineers*

D & D Fabrications, Mariner, Tamworth, Staffordshire, B79 7UL Tel: (01827) 53159 Fax: (01827) 53597 *Steel fabricators*

D & D Fabrications Runcorn, Old Power Station, Percival Lane, Runcorn, Cheshire, WA7 4YR Tel: (01928) 569203 Fax: (01928) 569203 *Steel fabrication manufrs*

D & D Fine Limits, 2 St Clare Business Park, Holly Road, Hampton, Middlesex, TW12 1PZ Tel: (020) 8979 3545 Fax: (020) 8979 3545 E-mail: info@sheetmetalproduction.com *Sheet metalwork engineers*

D & D Flooring, 42 Colinward Street, Belfast, BT12 7EP Tel: (028) 9024 6060 Fax: (028) 9024 6047 E-mail: danddflooring@aol.com *Flooring contractors*

Company Information

D D Forklift Services, 318 Main Road, Walters Ash, High Wycombe, Buckinghamshire, HP14 4TH Tel: (01494) 563150 Fax: (01494) 563150 *Maintenance & repairers*

D D Group UK Ltd, 35 Bo'ness Road, Grangemouth, Stirlingshire, FK3 8AN Tel: (01324) 472442 Fax: (01324) 474002 E-mail: mailroom@dbgroup.uk.com *Consultant engineers*

D D Health & Safety Supplies Ltd, Unit 2, Kingsway, City Trading Estate, Norwich, NR2 4UE Tel: (01603) 628891 Fax: (01603) 764882 E-mail: bpuplett@dd-healthandsafetysupplies.co.uk *Safety equipment specialists*

D & D James, Bryn Myfyr, High Street, Coedpoeth, Wrexham, Clwyd, LL11 3UF Tel: (01978) 756611 Fax: (01978) 756611 *Steel fabricators*

D & D Leisure, Arcadia House, Glanmor Terrace, New Quay, Dyfed, SA45 9PX Tel: (01545) 560584 Fax: (01545) 561040 *Music arcades*

▶ D D Porter Ltd, 1 Walnut Business Park, Walnut Street, Halifax, West Yorkshire, HX1 5JD Tel: (01422) 362374 Fax: (01422) 343467

D D S A Pharmuceuticals Ltd, 310 Old Brompton Road, London, SW5 9JQ Tel: (020) 7373 7884 Fax: (020) 7370 4321 *Pharmaceutical manufrs*

▶ D & D Snack Foods Ltd, Orchard Works, Badsell Road, Five Oak Green, Tonbridge, Kent, TN12 6QU Tel: (01892) 838418 Fax: (01892) 838450

D & D Stainless, Unit 16 Nettlehill Road, Houstoun Industrial Estate, Livingston, West Lothian, EH54 5DL Tel: (01506) 434325 Fax: (01506) 435345 E-mail: sales@danddstainless.co.uk *Stainless steel stockholders*

▶ D D Thomson, Northraw, East Calder, Livingston, West Lothian, EH53 0ET Tel: (01506) 881588

D D Z Marine, Largs Yacht Haven, Irvine Road, Largs, Ayrshire, KA30 8EZ Tel: (01475) 686072 Fax: (01475) 672887 E-mail: sales@ddzmarine.com *Marine engineers & boat sales*

D Davies & Sons, Cornerswell Road, Penarth, South Glamorgan, CF64 2UZ Tel: (029) 2070 8524 Fax: (029) 2051 3189 *Joinery manufrs*

D Devine, 20 Kimpton Road, Luton, LU2 0SX Tel: (01582) 450567 *Building contractors*

D Donovan & Sons Carpet Services Ltd, 112 Blythe Road, London, W14 0HD Tel: (020) 7603 4161 Fax: (020) 7602 9929 *Carpet suppliers for exhibitions*

D Drill, 12 Hazel Road, Four Marks, Alton, Hampshire, GU34 5EY Tel: (020) 7355 4444 Fax: (01420) 560187 E-mail: info@d-drill.co.uk *Concrete drilling & sawing contractors & engineers services*

D Drill Master Drillers Ltd, Unit 5 Coity Cresent, Bridgend Industrial Estate, Bridgend, Mid Glamorgan, CF31 3RS Tel: (01656) 662321 Fax: (01656) 667779 *Concrete drilling, sawing contractors & engineers services*

D Drill Master Drillers Ltd, 4 Westover Industrial Estate, Ermington Road, Ivybridge, Devon, PL21 9ES Tel: (01752) 698890 Fax: (01752) 698891 E-mail: plymouth@d-drill.co.uk *Concrete drilling, sawing contractors & engineers*

▶ D Drill Master Drillers Ltd, Unit 7 Wood Street, Poulton Industrial Estate, Poulton-le-Fylde, Lancashire, FY6 8JY Tel: (01253) 894554 Fax: (01253) 893848

D Drill Master Drillers Ltd, 84 Clun Street, Sheffield, S4 7JS Tel: 0114-273 9199 Fax: 0114-276 5884 E-mail: sheffield@d-drill.co.uk *Diamond drilling contractors*

D Drill Master Drillers Ltd, Daleside Works, Craghead Colliery Industrial Estate, Stanley, County Durham, DH9 6HB Tel: (01207) 231671 Fax: (01207) 299541 E-mail: newcastle@d-drill.co.uk *Concrete drilling, sawing contractors & engineers*

D Dunkerley & Son, High Street, Hogsthorpe, Skegness, Lincolnshire, PE24 5ND Tel: (01754) 872371 Fax: (01754) 872361 E-mail: gary@dunkerleyjoiners.freeserve.co.uk *Joinery manufacturers & building contractors*

▶ D E A Associates, 154 Wickham Road, Croydon, CR0 8BF Tel: (020) 8654 0706 Fax: (020) 8654 0706 E-mail: collect@deaassociates.org.uk *Worldwide Debt Recovery Web Directory*

D E A Design, Suite 4 143-145 Yorkshire St, Oldham, OL1 3TH Tel: 0161-627 0724 Fax: 0161-622 1311 *Catering facility design & equipment distribs*

D E B Electronics Ltd, 2 Redbourn Industrial Centre, High St, Redbourn, St. Albans, Hertfordshire, AL3 7LG Tel: (01582) 794466 Fax: (01582) 792559 E-mail: admin@deb-electronics.co.uk *Printed circuit board manufrs*

▶ D & E Bouncy Castle Hire, 40 Winchelsea Road, Chatham, Kent, ME5 7LY Tel: (01634) 669880 Fax: (01634) 669880 E-mail: darren@d-and-e-bouncycastles.co.uk *Adult, kids bouncy castles, slides, ball pools, sumo suits, games suppliers*

D E C Rubber Co. Ltd, Unit 20, Fordhouse Road Industrial Estate, Fordhouses, Wolverhampton, WV10 9XD Tel: (01902) 780046 Fax: (01902) 780076 *Motor industry rubber products manufrs*

▶ D E Clegg Ltd, Bishops House, 42 High Pavement, Nottingham, NG1 1HN Tel: 0115-841 3121 Fax: 0115-841 3122 E-mail: info@declegg.co.uk

D E E Services, Ael Y Bryn, Llandinam, Powys, SY17 5BT Tel: (01686) 688025 Fax: (01686) 688025 E-mail: info@dee-dervices.co.uk *Domestic , comercial & industrial Electrical installations. Total design Engineers from concept to completion*

D & E Fabrications Ltd, Latteridge Road, Iron Acton, Bristol, BS37 9TL Tel: (01454) 228810 Fax: (01454) 228810 *Gates, railings & lights manufrs*

D E Fabrications, Unit 7e E Plan Estate, New Road, Newhaven, East Sussex, BN9 0EX Tel: (01273) 515876 Fax: (01273) 517963 E-mail: sales@defabrications.freeserve.co.uk *Precision engineers*

D E Fencing Ltd, Forthill Avenue, Jedburgh, Roxburghshire, TD8 6HJ Tel: (01835) 863623 Fax: (01835) 862113 *Security fencing suppliers & erectors*

D E G A Broadcast Systems, 1 Newton Court, Rankine Road, Basingstoke, Hampshire, RG24 8GF Tel: (01256) 816220 Fax: (01256) 843952 E-mail: david@dega.co.uk *Television studio equipment installers*

D E Horn Pneumatic Services, Air Centre, Park Street, Ivybridge, Devon, PL21 9DW Tel: (01752) 893531 Fax: (01752) 690449 E-mail: sales@dehorn.co.uk *Compressed air & tool specialists*

D E I Electrical Services, Edison House, Dunslow Road, Eastfield, Scarborough, North Yorkshire, YO11 3UT Tel: (01723) 581515 Fax: (01723) 585247 *Electrical contractors*

D E & J Levy, Dukes Court, 32 Duke Street, London, SW1Y 6DF Tel: (020) 7930 1070 Fax: (020) 7930 3028E-mail: info@dejlevy.co.uk *Chartered surveyors*

D E Jenkins, Brynawelon, Llanddarog Road, Carmarthen, Dyfed, SA32 8AP Tel: (01267) 275381 Fax: (01267) 275443 *Refrigeration sales & services*

D E L Industrial Fastenings Ltd, Elvetham Bridge, Fleet, Hampshire, GU51 1AE Tel: (01252) 626425 Fax: (01252) 811741 E-mail: info@delindustrial.co.uk *Rubber manufrs*

▶ D E M Transport, 30 Plume Street, Birmingham, B6 7RT Tel: 0121-328 2422 Fax: 0121-328 2422 *Commercial vehicle body builders*

▶ D & E Mackay Contractors Ltd, Craigearn Business Park, Midmills, Kintore, Inverurie, Aberdeenshire, AB51 0TH Tel: (01467) 633388 Fax: (01467) 633454

D E Montfort Packaging, De Montfort Place, 18 Slater St, Leicester, LE3 5ASY Tel: 0116-242 3900 Fax: 0116-253 9055 E-mail: raithbylawrence@btconnect.com *Cardboard box & printing firm manufrs*

D & E Optics Ltd, 163-164 Rolfe Street, Smethwick, West Midlands, B66 2AU Tel: 0121-565 2333 Fax: 0121-565 1658 *Optical manufrs*

D E P E Breaden Electrical Ltd, 396 Finchley Road, London, NW2 2HR Tel: (020) 7435 1304 Fax: (020) 7435 0194 *Commercial electrical contractors*

D & E Plastics Ltd, Ogilvie Road, High Wycombe, Buckinghamshire, HP12 3DS Tel: (01494) 463111 Fax: (01494) 461194 E-mail: enquiries@deplastics.co.uk *Injection mould toolmakers*

D E S Fabrications Ltd, Littleton Lane, Shepperton, Middlesex, TW17 0NF Tel: (01932) 563616 Fax: (01932) 570933 E-mail: denise@desgroupltd.co.uk *Steel fabricators*

▶ D E S Heating & Plumbing, 253 Fenwick Road, Giffnock, Glasgow, G46 6JQ Tel: 0141-638 9589

▶ D E S Operations Ltd, 3 Prospect Place, Westhill, Aberdeenshire, AB32 6SY Tel: (01224) 748460 *Oil & gas services*

D E Signs, Cartref, Chelmsford Road, Barnston, Dunmow, Essex, CM6 1LS Tel: (01371) 874011 Fax: (01371) 874011 E-mail: tim@de-signs.co.uk *Sign contractors, suppliers & installers*

D E Signs & Labels Ltd, Westbury Close Unit 26, Townsend Industrial Estate, Houghton Regis, Dunstable, Bedfordshire, LU5 5BL Tel: (01582) 699665 Fax: (01582) 661419 E-mail: sales@de-signsdunstable.co.uk *Sign manufrs*

D E Spencer & Sons, Nupend, Nupend, Stonehouse, Gloucestershire, GL10 3SS Tel: (01453) 822764 Fax: (01453) 792600 *Agricultural contractors*

▶ D & E Technical Services Ltd, 15 Whistler Road, Eaton Ford, St. Neots, Cambridgeshire, PE19 7RT Tel: (01480) 474430 Fax: (01480) 386474 E-mail: enquiries@de-techservices.co.uk *Design & installation of air conditioning & ventilation systems*

D & E Wilson & Sons Ltd, 60 Bold Street, Preston, PR1 7NX Tel: (01772) 254648 Fax: (01772) 203667 *Sausage manufrs*

▶ D Electrical, Valley Works, Bacup Road, Todmorden, Lancashire, OL14 7PJ Tel: (01706) 814854 Fax: (01706) 815023 *Industrial electrical contractors*

D Evans, The Poplars, Redhall Lane, Penley, Wrexham, Clwyd, LL13 0NA Tel: (01978) 710756 *Farm suppliers*

D F Barber, Bunwell Road, Besthorpe, Attleborough, Norfolk, NR17 2NZ Tel: (01953) 452422 Fax: (01953) 452422 *Racing motor cycle frame manufrs*

D F Bennett & Son (Plastics), Barkers Lane, Bedford, MK41 9RU Tel: (01234) 351017 Fax: (01234) 212941 *Laminated plastics fabricators*

▶ D F Blanchard Ltd, 12-14 Lower Road, Churchfields Industrial Estate, Salisbury, SP2 7QD Tel: (01722) 337331

D F C Ltd, 141-143 Drury Lane, London, WC2B 5TB Tel: (020) 7836 3424 Fax: (020) 7379 4931 E-mail: london@thedfcgroup.com *Financial consultants*

D F D Instruments, Northpoint House, 52 High Street, Knaphill, Woking, Surrey, GU21 2PY Tel: (01483) 799333 Fax: (01483) 480199 E-mail: tore@dfdinstruments.co.uk *Adhesion test equipment manufrs*

D F D S, Enterprise Point, Altrincham Road, Manchester, M22 4NY Tel: 0161-947 6592 Fax: 0161-947 6588 *Freight forwarders & agents*

D F D S Transport Ltd, Third Way, Avonmouth, Bristol, BS11 9HL Tel: 0117-982 2288 Fax: 0117-938 6793 E-mail: transport@dfdstransport.co.uk *Freight forwarders*

▶ D F D S Transport Ltd, Block 3, Bothwell Park Industrial Estate, Uddingston, Glasgow, G71 6NZ Tel: (01698) 811522 Fax: (01698) 810199

D F D S Transport Ltd, Kingsbury Link, Trinity Road, Piccadilly, Tamworth, Staffordshire, B78 2EX Tel: (01827) 871200 Fax: (01827) 871212 E-mail: transport@dfdstransport.co.uk *Freight forwarders*

D F Dickens Ltd, Little Tennis Street South, Nottingham, NG2 4EU Tel: 0115-950 4084 Fax: 0115-950 8425 *Food suppliers & wholesalers*

D F E Underwood, Holly Bush Farm, Cleedownton, Ludlow, Shropshire, SY8 3EH Tel: (01584) 823270 *Livestock dealer*

D F King Electroplating, 5-7 Sandhurst Close, Kings Road, Canvey Island, Essex, SS8 0QY Tel: (01268) 695672 Fax: (01268) 511014 *Nickel, chrome & brass electroplating*

D & F Party Ltd, Units 25-26 Walthamstow Business Centre, Clifford Road, London, E17 4SX Tel: (020) 8523 5555 Fax: (020) 8523 5554 E-mail: sales@dfparty.co.uk *Wholesalers of party goods & novelties*

▶ D F S Casket, Nelson House, Stapleton Road, Annan, Dumfriesshire, DG12 6JP Tel: (01461) 205114 Fax: (01461) 205512

▶ D F Smith & Co. Ltd, Unit 15 The Wallows Industrial Estate, Wallows Road, Brierley Hill, West Midlands, DY5 1QB Tel: (01384) 482958 Fax: (01384) 482958 *Wire & wire component suppliers*

D & F Steels Ltd, Valley Farm Road, Stourton, Leeds, LS10 1SD Tel: 0113-277 0951 Fax: 0113-276 0591E-mail: dandf@asdplc.co.uk *Steel stockholders & distributors*

D F T, The Flax Mill, 134 Townhill Road, Portglenone, Ballymena, County Antrim, BT44 8AW Tel: (028) 2582 2877 Fax: (028) 2582 2805 E-mail: info@dftfixings.com *Diamonds fixings & tool manufrs*

▶ D F Warehouses Ltd, Old Brighton Road South, Pease Pottage, Crawley, West Sussex, RH11 9NQ Tel: (01293) 540686 Fax: (01293) 536260

D F Wishart & Co. Ltd, St Clair St, Edinburgh, EH6 8LJ Tel: 0131-554 4393 Fax: 0131-553 7242 E-mail: sales@wishart.co.uk *Wholesale architectural ironmongers, tools & garden equipment*

D Fix Bridgend Ltd, Newton Yard, Cemetery Road, Bridgend, Mid Glamorgan, CF31 1NA Tel: (01656) 669609 Fax: (01656) 767584 E-mail: mikecoleman@datapowertool.co.uk *Structural fixing systems agents*

D G Booth, Scandinavia, Ash Terrace, Ashmore Green, Thatcham, Berkshire, RG18 9EU Tel: (01635) 862572 *Cabinet makers*

D G C Engineering Ltd, Sabhal Mor, Loan Dykes, Hillside, Montrose, Angus, DD10 9JN Tel: (01674) 830922

D G C Engineering UK Ltd, Unit 7 Building 6, Stanmore Industrial Estate, Bridgnorth, Shropshire, WV15 5HP Tel: (01746) 767133 Fax: (01746) 767133 *Based in Shropshire D G C Engineering Ltd have been manufacturers of aluminium foil container tooling since 1984. We manufacture foil tools for bakeries, general presswork, pressings, special purpose assembly machines, special purpose assembly systems, foil blocking tools, special purpose machine tools, foil packaging forming tools, foil packaging filling tools, presswork wire cutting, aluminium foil container tooling, foil packaging sealing tools, agricultural tools. D G C Engineering Ltd provides an excellent service in both the technical advice given and the supply of the correct product for your specific needs.*

D G Clifton & Son, High Street, Loxwood, Billingshurst, West Sussex, RH14 0RE Tel: (01403) 753337 E-mail: enquiries@dgclifton.com *D.G. Clifton & Son, established in Loxwood since 1955, is a Sussex joinery providing high quality, individually designed kitchens, bedroom, bathrooms, home offices and bespoke furniture.*

D G Collins, Hillcrest, Oughterby, Carlisle, CA5 6JH Tel: (01228) 576563 Fax: (01228) 576563 *Air conditioning & refrigeration services*

D G Colour Ltd, 15 Shrrington, Warminster, Wiltshire, BA12 0SN Tel: 01985 878185 Fax: 0207 149 9826 E-mail: info@dgcolour.co.uk *Industrial colour suppliers of Munsell soil charts, books of colour, colour checkers, plant tissue charts, USDA Color Food standards, educational student sets, Munsell Colour Trees, Metamerism Tesk Kits, Farnsworth-Munsell 100 Hue test, Farnsworth-Munsell Dichotomous D-15 Test, Ishihara Colour Blind Tests, Sol Source Daylight Desk Lamps Judge II Lighting cabinets*

D G Controls Ltd, Cadley Hill Road, Swadlincote, Derbyshire, DE11 9TB Tel: (01283) 550850 Fax: (01283) 550776 E-mail: mail@beaconlamps.com *UK Manufacturer and distributor of permanent and portable audible and visual warning indicators for use in Industrial, Marine, Vehicle (fixed and Mag-mount), Fire and Security and Explosionproof markets with a wide range of technologies available such as Rotating Mirror, Revolving LED, Pulsed filament and LED, Static filament and LED as well as High Intensity Xenon Strobe. The product range incorporates small individual indicators through to large-format beacons as well as modular multi-status displays including multi-module tower and stacking beacons. Applications such as Aircraft Obstruction Warning, Industry, Fire, Security, Automation, Telephone, Alarms, Health & Safety, Highway, Robotics, Bridges, Navigation, Law enforcement, and Traffic signals are catered for. We distribute directly and through a wide range of major UK stockists; deegee also exports world-wide through its network of over 32 international distributors and has customers in all 6 continents of the globe.*

D G Design & Graphics, 11 Industrial Centre, Gower Street, Ipswich, IP2 8EX Tel: (01473) 681077 Fax: (01473) 690604 E-mail: dgdesigngraphics@aol.com *Sign manufrs*

D & G Electrical Controls, 7a Weller Drive, Finchampstead, Wokingham, Berkshire, RG40 4QZ Tel: 0118-973 7123 Fax: 0118-973 0071 E-mail: dg.electrical@virgin.net *Electrical contractors*

▶ D & G Electrical Engineering Ltd, Unit Bs1 Junction 7 Business Park, Blackburn Road, Clayton le Moors, Accrington, Lancashire, BB5 5JW Tel: (01254) 398725 Fax: (01254) 398725

D & G Engineering, Unit 18 Lynx Cresent, Weston-super-Mare, Avon, BS24 9DJ Tel: (01934) 628476 Fax: (01934) 418410 *Precision engineers manufrs*

▶ D G Esaias Ltd, 5 Castle Garage, Croft Road, Neath, West Glamorgan, SA11 1RW Tel: (01639) 641700 Fax: (01639) 641824

D G Felts, Fox Street, Batley, West Yorkshire, WF17 5QA Tel: (01924) 471462 Fax: (01924) 471462 E-mail: philgibson@fsnet.co.uk *Felt & furniture filling manufrs*

D G H Security & Electrical Installations, 35 Lansdowne Road, Sevenoaks, Kent, TN13 3XU Tel: (01732) 464165 Fax: (01732) 464166 *Installers*

D G Howell (Hydraulic Engineers) Ltd, 78-84 Commercial St, Risca, Newport, Gwent, NP11 6BA Tel: (01633) 614326 Fax: (01633) 601581 E-mail: dghowell@aol.com *Hydraulic equipment & systems manufrs*

D G Jackson Industrial Supplies Ltd, Dukeries Way, Worksop, Nottinghamshire, S81 7DW Tel: (01909) 474085 Fax: (01909) 477201 *Engineers' suppliers*

D G M Cabinet Makers & Joiners, The Barns, Linden Road, Clenchwarton, King's Lynn, Norfolk, PE34 4EL Tel: (01553) 768335 Fax: (01553) 766172 E-mail: inquries@dgmjoinery.co.uk *Joinery manufrs*

D G Marketing, Ditchford Mill Farm, Todenham, Moreton-In-Marsh, Gloucestershire, GL56 9NU Tel: (01608) 650399 Fax: (01608) 650560 E-mail: graham@farmline.com *Livestock equipment suppliers*

D G N Design, Unit 7 270 Lakey Lane, Birmingham, B28 8RA Tel: 0121-778 6878 Fax: 0121-778 6878 *Architectural & engineering services*

▶ D G Owens Ltd, 34 Saxon Way, Old Windsor, Windsor, Berkshire, SL4 2PU Tel: (01753) 856762 Fax: 01753 856762 E-mail: jon@dgowens.co.uk *Accountant*For small businesses: limited companies, sole traders, partners.*Prepartion of accounts, bookkeeping, VAT, tax returns, payroll. Business planning and advice.*

▶ D G Pool & Leisure, Bines Green, Partridge Green, Horsham, West Sussex, RH13 8EH Tel: (01403) 711581 Fax: (01403) 713581

▶ D G S, Unit 3, Block 1, Watson Terrace, Drongan, Ayr, KA6 7AA Tel: (01292) 592266 Fax: (01292) 592266 *Shed builders*

▶ D G S Abrasives Division, 189-191 New Road, Portsmouth, PO2 7QU Tel: (023) 9266 1481 Fax: (023) 9267 3476 E-mail: south@dgsabrasives.co.uk *Specialist suppliers of all forms of abrasives*

D G S Grinding Wheels & Machines Ltd, 90-92 Dovedale Road, Wolverhampton, WV4 6RA Tel: (01902) 661111 Fax: (01902) 880311 E-mail: sales@dgsabrasives.co.uk *Abrasive distributors*

D G Scroggie Ltd, 11 Camden Street, Liverpool, L3 8JR Tel: 0151-207 2379 *Jewellery manufacturers & repairers*

▶ D & G Short, 19 Station Road, Flitwick, Bedford, MK45 1JT Tel: (01525) 753819 Fax: (01525) 716687 E-mail: info@dandgshort.com *D and G Short Locksmiths are experts in all aspects of physical and electronic security. We can supply, install and repair all types of key operated, digital and electronic locks. *As members of the Master Locksmiths Association you can be assured that all our work is carried out to the highest standard and integrity at a fair and competitive price. Access control swipe card or proximity and CCTV are the growing areas of security, we at Short's Locksmiths are also well placed as experts in this field. Ram raiding and other forms of violent attack on property are becoming an increasing problem we can supply and fit a wide range of Security Grilles, Shutters and anti ram posts. Plumbing, Electrical goods for trade and retail are also held in large ranges, along with Dulux paint, decorating tools and sundries and a vast range of DIY products.**

▶ D.G. Simpson Plant, Unit 2, Mill Lane, Littleburn Industrial Estate, Langley Moor, Durham, DH7 8HE Tel: 0191-378 3666 Fax: 0191-378 2333 E-mail: dgequipt@aol.com *International plant sales, plant hire, plant transport, storage and warehousing*

D G Spectro Oil Analysis Company Ltd, Palace Gate, High Street, Hook, Hampshire, RG29 1NP Tel: (01256) 704000 Fax: (01256) 704006 E-mail: enquiries@jet-care.com *Analytical chemists*

▶ D G Steel & Son Engineering Ltd, Gear Works, Brook Street, Bury, Lancashire, BL9 6AF Tel: 0161-764 4862

D & G Sullivan, 6 Sextant Park, Neptune Close, Medway City Estate, Rochester, Kent, ME2 4LU Tel: (01634) 730011 Fax: (01634) 730022 *Cleaning materials for transport industry*

D G T Precision Engineering, 9C, Corbin Way, Gore Cross Business Park, Bridpole, Bridport, Dorset, DT6 3UX Tel: (01308) 420024 Fax: (01308) 424007 E-mail: info@dgtpreceng.co.uk *Based in Bridport Dorset covering the Southern Counties DGT calls on it's vast technical and manufacturing experience to offer it's customers an unrivalled service in Precision Engineering & Tool Making. Our qualified staff have extensive experience in producing the high quality products our clients need. The company has many clients who have been with us during our 10 years of business, testament to our service an attention to detail. CNC Machining CAD-CAM Spark Erosion Plastic Injection Mould Tooling Plastic Extrusion Tools Lost Wax Tooling Press Tooling Jigs and Fixtures Special Purpose Machinery Plastic Injection Components Project Management Product Design and Development*

D G T Steel & Cladding Ltd, Atlas Works, Norwich Road, Lenwade, Norwich, NR9 5SW Tel: (01603) 308200 Fax: (01603) 308201 E-mail: sales@dgt-steelandcladding.co.uk *Steel fabricators*

▶ D G Tel Communications, Unit 10 Stammerham Business Centre, Capel Road, Rusper, Horsham, West Sussex, RH12 4PZ Tel: (01306) 710370 Fax: (01306) 710371 E-mail: dg.tel@btinternet.com *Installation of Panasonic, I.box Goldstar, LG, GDK, Meridian Compact*Also maintainers for the*

continued

continuation
above*Installation of Voice and Data Networks including Fibre with all work guarenteed*

D & G Toolmakers (Frome), Unit 13, Court Farm Trading Estate, Bishops Frome, Worcester, WR6 5AY Tel: (01885) 490714 Fax: (01885) 490380 *Plastics mould toolmakers*

▶ D Geddes (Contractors) Ltd, Swillburne, Colliston, Arbroath, Angus, DD11 3SH Tel: (01241) 890237

▶ D Gibson R D & Quarry Services Ltd, Unit 5, 211 Cambuslang Rd, Cambuslang, Glasgow, G72 7TS Tel: 0141-613 1919 Fax: 0141-613 1404 E-mail: sales@gibsonquarry.co.uk *Metal road signs*

D Glass, 9 Artillery Road, Lufton Trading Estate, Lufton, Yeovil, Somerset, BA22 8RP Tel: (01935) 471359 Fax: (01935) 420464 *Glass glazing, PVCU window & doors manufrs*

D Gurteen & Sons Ltd, Chauntry Mills, Haverhill, Suffolk, CB9 8AZ Tel: (01440) 702601 Fax: (01440) 703394 E-mail: sales@gurteen.co.uk *Mens clothing wholesalers*

D & H Allied Engineering Ltd, Purdy Road, Bilston, West Midlands, WV14 8UB Tel: (01902) 493331 Fax: (01902) 493241 *General engineers*

D H Bryant Ltd, 33 Station Road, Shalford, Guildford, Surrey, GU4 8HF Tel: (01483) 577721 Fax: (01483) 579888 E-mail: dhbryant.ltd@btconnect.com *Heating & mechanical services*

▶ D.H. Carpentry, 3 Tytherley Road, Southampton, SO18 5DW Tel: (023) 8034 4299 Fax: (023) 8034 0954 E-mail: d.hawkins50@ntlworld.com *Carpentry, small building works, staircases, garden projects*

D & H Concrete Products, Fernbank Avenue, Barnoldswick, Lancashire, BB18 5UX Tel: (01282) 812299 Fax: (01282) 812659 E-mail: info@dhconcrete.co.uk *Pre-cast concrete products*

D & H Display Ltd, Facet Road, Birmingham, B38 9PT Tel: 0121-451 3666 Fax: 0121-451 3666 *Shop fittings manufrs*

▶ D H Electrical Services Ltd, Unit 2 Eversley Way, Thorpe Industrial Estate, Egham, Surrey, TW20 8RG Tel: (01784) 479400 Fax: (01784) 479300

▶ D H Engineering, Butt Lane, Milton, Cambridge, CB24 6DQ Tel: (01223) 864000 *Metal working & fabrication*

D & H Equipment & Service, Unit 3, Linstock Way, Atherton, Manchester, M46 0RS Tel: (01942) 887557 Fax: (01942) 889800 *Garage equipment service, installers & suppliers*

▶ D H H Sprinklers, 123 Front Road, Drumbo, Lisburn, County Antrim, BT27 5JY Tel: (028) 9082 7008 Fax: (028) 9082 7012 E-mail: *Fire Protection Engineers*

D H Jones, Unit 10 Industrial Estate, Llanuwchllyn, Bala, Gwynedd, LL23 7NL Tel: (01678) 520666 Fax: (01678) 520666 *Forest & gardening equipment maintenance*

D H Keys & Sons Ltd, 45 Belvedere Road, Ipswich, IP4 4AB Tel: (01473) 728117 Fax: (01473) 729729 *Roofing & scaffolding contractors*

▶ D H L, Western Avenue, Western Docks, Southampton, SO15 0HH Tel: (023) 8077 2200 Fax: (023) 8078 1111

D H L Ltd, Pickerings Road, Halebank Industrial Estate, Widnes, Cheshire, WA8 0NH Tel: 0151-424 5441 Fax: 0151-423 2678 E-mail: d.a.welding9@msn.com *Suppliers of welding equipment & hand tools to the industry*

D H Load Control, Unit A & B Highway House, 250 Coombs Road, Halesowen, West Midlands, B62 8AA Tel: 0121-559 0484 Fax: 0121-559 0585 E-mail: sales@dhloadcontrol.co.uk *Lorry side curtains, lorry sheets, steel carries suppliers*

▶ D H Loveday & Son Ltd, 96 Cotterells, Hemel Hempstead, Hertfordshire, HP1 1JG Tel: (01442) 256254

D H M Marketing Services, Orchard House, Westbury Road, Warminster, Wiltshire, BA12 0AW Tel: (01985) 217950 Fax: (01985) 217950 E-mail: enquiries@dohelpme.co.uk *Business support & development, marketing services & training*

The D H M Partnership, Forge House, Hunton, Bedale, N. Yorkshire, DL8 1PX Tel: 0845 1235129 Fax: 0845 1235130 E-mail: dhmp@dhm-partnership.co.uk *Theatre, conference exhibition, presentation consultants & events organiser**

▶ D H Marrion Ltd, 220 Sheffield Road, Barnsley, South Yorkshire, S70 4PF Tel: (01226) 282576 Fax: (01226) 248354

D H Morris & Co, Bellfield Street, Dundee, DD1 5DY Tel: (01382) 229691 Fax: (01382) 202621 E-mail: dhmorris@dhmdundee.fsnet.co.uk *Electrical engineers & contractors*

▶ D H Morris Group, Omega House, 37 Telford Street, Inverness, IV3 5LD Tel: (01463) 237667

▶ D H Morris Group (Edinburgh), 4 Trinity Crescent, Edinburgh, EH5 3ED Tel: 0131-552 7644

▶ D H P, Bracewell House, Broughton, Skipton, North Yorkshire, BD23 3AG Tel: (01756) 702480 Fax: (01756) 702489 E-mail: info@optimaenergy.net *Energy management software suppliers*

▶ D H Potter & Co. Ltd, 9-11 Tower Street, Hartlepool, Cleveland, TS24 7HH Tel: (01429) 290800

D H S Communications, 421 Hertford Road, Enfield, Middlesex, EN3 5PT Tel: (020) 8482 4432 Fax: (020) 8482 4434 *Radio Communications*

D H S Tool Supply Co. Ltd, 61 St Modwen Road, Park Way Industrial Estate, Marsh Mills, Plymouth, PL6 8LH Tel: (01752) 223536 Fax: (01752) 222706 *Engineers suppliers*

▶ D H Structures Ltd, Tollgate Drive, Tollgate Industrial Estate, Stafford, ST16 3HS Tel: (01785) 246269 Fax: (01785) 222077 E-mail: enquiries@dhstructures.co.uk *Structural steel fabricators & erectors*

D H Systems Consultancy Ltd, Studio 107, Abbey Mill Business Centre, Paisley, Renfrewshire, PA1 1TJ Tel: 0141-561 0320 Fax: 0141-561 2136 *Software company producers*

D H Tools, Unit 9 Newlands End, Basildon, Essex, SS15 6DU Tel: (01268) 540633 Fax: (01268) 540742 E-mail: enquiries@dhtools.co.uk *Precision engineers*

▶ D H Welton, Corn Street, Failsworth, Manchester, M35 0UE Tel: 0161-682 1000 Fax: 0161-483 4113

D H Willis & Sons Ltd, Carrbeck House, Gilling West, Richmond, North Yorkshire, DL10 5LN Tel: (01748) 822714 Fax: (01748) 822714 *Agricultural engineers & plant hire*

▶ D Harker Fabrications, D.H.F. Ltd, Greeves Road, Dewsbury, West Yorkshire, WF13 1EP Tel: (01924) 457614 Fax: (01924) 462291 E-mail: sales@dhfltd.co.uk *Steel fabrications*

D Harper Non Ferrous Foundry, Airedale Works, New Works Road, Low Moor, Bradford, West Yorkshire, BD12 0QN Tel: (01274) 691842 Fax: (01274) 691842 E-mail: sales@dhfoundries.co.uk *Non ferrous castings*

D Harvey & Co., 4 Mill Park, Cannock, Staffordshire, WS11 7XT Tel: (01543) 573408 Fax: (01543) 462100 E-mail: sales@dharveyandco.co.uk *Toolmakers*

D Haynes Ltd, 9-11 Hanover Street, Bolton, BL1 4TG Tel: (01204) 382122 Fax: (01204) 397232 *Tarpaulin manufrs*

D Henderson, 12 Acomb Industrial Estate, Acomb, Hexham, Northumberland, NE46 4SA Tel: (01434) 601966 Fax: (01434) 601966 *Agricultural engineers*

D Highland, Salthill View, Clitheroe, Lancashire, BB7 1NY Tel: (01200) 423300 *Agricultural services*

D Hinds, Low Wood Farm, Bewerley, Harrogate, North Yorkshire, HG3 5BT Tel: (01423) 712065 Fax: (01423) 711984 *Agricultural tractor dealers*

▶ D Hughes Demolition, Coteman Heights Farm, Hill Top Lane, Delph, Oldham, OL3 5RW Tel: 0161-624 3460 Fax: 0161-620 6295

D Hurrell Joinery, Unit 3-4 Garden Mill Industrial Estate, Derby Road, Kingsbridge, Devon, TQ7 1SA Tel: (01548) 853513 Fax: (01548) 856652 *Joinery*

D & I Bridgman & Son Ltd, Down View, Newton St. Petrock, Torrington, Devon, EX38 8LS Tel: (01409) 261321 Fax: (01409) 261520 E-mail: mike@bridgmans.co.uk *Agricultural merchants*

D I G Corrugated Machinery Ltd, Masterlord Industrial Park, Station Road, Leiston, Suffolk, IP16 4JD Tel: (01728) 832755 Fax: (01728) 832764 E-mail: sales@dig-group.co.uk *Packaging machinery manufrs*

D I Gubb, Sunnymead, Culmbridge Road, Hemyock, Cullompton, Devon, EX15 3QP Tel: (01823) 680553 *Agricultural engineers*

D I K Bearings & Transmissions Ltd, J Hawkhill Court, Mid Wynd, Dundee, DD1 4JG Tel: (01382) 228711 Fax: (01382) 202559 E-mail: sales@dik.sol.co.uk *Engineering component suppliers*

▶ D I Recruitment, 8 Dig Street, Ashbourne, Derbyshire, DE6 1GF Tel: (01335) 342354 Fax: (01335) 300179 E-mail: info@direcruitment.co.uk *Recruitment specialists for temporary and permanent office staff.*

▶ D I S Electrical Contractors Ltd, Le Petit Catelet, La Route De St. Jean, St. John, Jersey, JE3 4EA Tel: (01534) 861488 Fax: (01534) 861487

D I S Group, Gainsborough House, 42-44 Bath Road, Cheltenham, Gloucestershire, GL53 7HJ Tel: (01242) 533120 Fax: (01242) 221187 *Building engineering services*

▶ D I S Sprinklers, 183 Westgate Street, Gloucester, GL1 2RN Tel: (01452) 330585 Fax: (01452) 306692 E-mail: sprinklers@dis-ltd.co.uk *Specialists in the design, installation & maintenance of Fire Sprinkler Systems.*

▶ D I T T Construction Ltd, Holmsgarth Road, Lerwick, Shetland, ZE1 0PW Tel: (01595) 692733 Fax: (01595) 695110

▶ D I Y Automation, 224 Spen Lane, Gomersal, Cleckheaton, West Yorkshire, BD19 4PJ Tel: (01274) 862201 Fax: (0870) 1164912

D Ibbotson & Son, 219a Wakefield Road, Barnsley, South Yorkshire, S71 3TP Tel: (01226) 206044 Fax: (01226) 244456 E-mail: sales@ibbotsonjoinery.ak.com *Joinery manufrs*

D J A Parry, Gorsgoch, Llanybydder, Dyfed, SA40 9TH Tel: (01545) 590215 *Agricultural contractors*

D & J Air Conditioning Services Ltd, 5 Long Wood Road, Trafford Park, Manchester, M17 1PZ Tel: 0161-872 1033 Fax: 0161-848 0587 E-mail: info@djaircon.co.uk *Air conditioning, hire & install service providers*

D J Automation Engineering Ltd, 11d Old Bridge Way, Shefford, Bedfordshire, SG17 5HQ Tel: (01462) 813703 Fax: (01462) 816810 E-mail: enquiries@djautomation.co.uk *Power transmission equipment manufrs*

D J B Associates Ltd, 4-6 Roman Court, Watling Street, Bridgtown, Cannock, Staffordshire, WS11 0BN Tel: (01543) 574162 Fax: (01543) 574282 *Industrial finishing plant designers & suppliers*

▶ D J B Ceramics Ltd, Beaufort Mill, Beaufort Road, Stoke-on-Trent, ST3 1RH Tel: (01782) 312121 Fax: (01782) 312121 E-mail: djb.ceramics@btinternet.com *Manufacturers bone china*

D J B Precision Engineering, 24 Chantry Road, Woburn Road Industrial Estate, Kempston, Bedford, MK42 7JF Tel: (01234) 840174 Fax: (01234) 855566 E-mail: djbeng@btconnect.com *Precision engineering services*

▶ D J Bryant, 59 Queen Victoria Avenue, Hove, East Sussex, BN3 6XA Tel: (01273) 707300 Fax: (01273) 541005

D J Circuits Ltd, Jubilee Works, Anchor Road, Harrogate, North Yorkshire, HG1 4TA Tel: (01423) 889055 Fax: (01423) 884912 E-mail: enquiries@djcircuits.com *Printed circuit manufrs*

▶ D J Construction Southern Ltd, Saxonwood, Springles Lane, Fareham, Hampshire, PO15 6RR Tel: (01329) 844253 E-mail: kaz@djfencing.co.uk *Security, commercial & domestic fencing suppliers*

D J Consultants, The Leas, Elsworth Road, Conington, Cambridge, CB3 8LW Tel: (01954) 267441 Fax: (01954) 267441 E-mail: enquiries@djinter.net *Computer consultants & internet services*

D J Contracts South Ltd, 7 Kent Close, Granby Industrial Estate, Weymouth, Dorset, DT4 9TF Tel: (01305) 780111 Fax: (01305) 761409 E-mail: mail@darrenholland.co.uk *Industrial & agricultural buildings*

D J Dickson Ltd, 127 Derryboy Road, Crossgar, Downpatrick, County Down, BT30 9DH Tel: (028) 4483 0434 Fax: (028) 4483 1492 E-mail: dickson.david@btconnect.com *Building contractors*

▶ D J Dunabie Ltd, Drummurran Garage, 51 Kirkoswald Road, Maybole, Ayrshire, KA19 8BW Tel: (01655) 883668 Fax: (01655) 883668

D J Eade, 93a Cavendish Place, Eastbourne, East Sussex, BN21 3TZ Tel: (01323) 731730 Fax: (01323) 731730 *Jewellery repairers*

▶ D J Electrical, Laramie, North Roskear Road, Tuckingmill, Camborne, Cornwall, TR14 8PX Tel: (01209) 711825 E-mail: dajo13496@lineone.net *Electrical contracting*

▶ D J Empire, 888 High Road, East London, Chadwell Heath, Romford, RM6 4HU Tel: (020) 8597 0119 Fax: (020) 8983 8852 E-mail: sales@djempire.co.uk *DJ mixing pro store for all dj equipment*

D J Engineering, 4 Camp Industrial Estate, Rycote Lane, Milton Common, Thame, Oxfordshire, OX9 2NP Tel: (01844) 278749 Fax: (01844) 278749 E-mail: djjjeff@aol.com *Architectural metalworkers*

▶ D & J Enterprises, Croftlands, Southstoke Lane, Bath, BA2 5SH Tel: (01225) 837837 Fax: (01225) 837507 E-mail: sales@dandjenterprises.co.uk

D & J Export Ltd, 33 Valkyrie Road, Westcliff-on-Sea, Essex, SS0 8BY Tel: (01702) 348340 Fax: (01702) 331080 E-mail: don@d-jexports.com *Exporters of automotive, industrial & construction equipment*

D & J Fabrications Atherton Ltd, 160 Elizabeth Street, Atherton, Manchester, M46 9JL Tel: (01942) 873393 Fax: (01942) 897967 E-mail: sales@dandjfabrications.co.uk *Fabricating engineers*

D J G Exhibition Freight Services Ltd, Unit 34 Grace Business Centre, Willow Lane, Mitcham, Surrey, CR4 4TQ Tel: (020) 8646 4200 Fax: (020) 8646 6090 E-mail: d.j.g.efsl@btinternet.com *Exhibition & general freight forwarders*

D J Garages, 46 St. Andrews Road, Carshalton, Surrey, SM5 2DY Tel: (020) 8669 2344 Fax: (020) 8669 2344 *MOT station & servicing*

D J Gardner (Joinery) Ltd, Forest Vale Industrial Estate, Cinderford, Gloucestershire, GL14 2YA Tel: (01594) 823030 Fax: (01594) 823030 *Joinery manufrs*

▶ D J Groundworkers Ltd, Robins Barn, Church Lane, Frampton, Dorchester, Dorset, DT2 9NL Tel: (01300) 320118 Fax: (01300) 321611 *Ground workers*

D J Hann Ltd, Aylesford Way, Thatcham, Berkshire, RG19 4NW Tel: (01494) 524422 Fax: (01494) 461670 E-mail: sales@djhann.com *Wholesale floor covering distributor*

▶ D J Hewer & Co., 39-41 Haverly Street, Gloucester, GL1 4PN Tel: (01452) 525854

D J Howe (Weston) Ltd, The Yard, Winterstoke Road, Weston-super-Mare, Avon, BS23 3YE Tel: (01934) 623228 Fax: (01934) 620074 *Scrap metal merchants*

D J Installations & Fabrications, The Cottage, Backworth, Newcastle upon Tyne, NE27 0AP Tel: 0191-268 4215 Fax: 0191-268 4215 *Steel fabricators & railings manufrs*

D J J Precision Engineering Ltd, Unit 14 Pontyfelin Avenue Industrial Estate, New Inn, Pontypool, Gwent, NP4 0DQ Tel: (01495) 760561 Fax: (01495) 756256 E-mail: sales@djjengineering.com *Jig & precision engineers*

D J Joinery, William Street, Cwm, Ebbw Vale, Gwent, NP23 7TH Tel: (01495) 370217 *Joinery manufrs*

D J K Machinery Supplies Ltd, 20 Midhurst Close, Northside, Sunderland, SR3 2QD Tel: 0191-528 6923 Fax: 0191-528 6936 E-mail: d.sirey@btopenworld.com *Foundry equipment distributors*

D J Lockhart Ltd, Ballycastle Road, Coleraine, County Londonderry, BT52 2DY Tel: (028) 7035 1121 Fax: (028) 7035 1124 *Wholesalers of motor parts*

▶ D J M Logistics UK Ltd, Road One, Winsford, Cheshire, CW7 3YZ Tel: (01606) 861972 Fax: (01606) 550540

D J M Music Ltd, Unit 2 Archers Park, Branbridges Road, East Peckham, Tonbridge, Kent, TN12 5HP Tel: 0845 4584581 Fax: 0845 4584581 E-mail: sales@djmmusic.com *Nationwide mail order suppliers of new and used musical instruments for sale and hire. Student and school specialists. Professional and friendly advice for beginners and more advanced players. www.djmmusic.com - Fast Online Store, UK delivery.*

D J Martin Joinery, 210 Springvale Road, Sheffield, S6 3NU Tel: 0114-268 6718 Fax: 0114-268 6718 *Joinery manufrs*

D J Mills, 23 Mead Road, Cheltenham, Gloucestershire, GL53 7DY Tel: (01242) 528633 Fax: (01242) 528633 *Machinery removal contractors & installers*

D J Morgan Engravers Ltd, 53 Warwick Street, Coventry, CV5 6ET Tel: (024) 7671 1232 Fax: (024) 7671 1232 E-mail: djmorgan@btconnect.com *General engravers*

D J N Signs, The Banks, Sileby, Loughborough, Leicestershire, LE12 7RE Tel: (01509) 813359 Fax: (01509) 814374 E-mail: sales@djn.co.uk *Sign makers*

D J Newson Ltd, 2 Bunkell Road, Rackheath Industrial Estate, Rackheath, Norwich, NR13 6PX Tel: (01603) 720904 Fax: (01603) 720756 *Spectacle & lens manufrs*

D J Price, Sleap, Harmer Hill, Shrewsbury, SY4 3HE Tel: (01939) 290894 Fax: (01939) 290894 E-mail: sales@davidjprice.co.uk *Fencing service, retail & manufrs*

▶ D J R Electrical Services, 6 Suffolk Close, Oldbury, West Midlands, B68 8RP Tel: 0121-541 1658 E-mail: djrelectrical@blueyonder.co.uk *Electrical Installation, Testing, Maintenance and Design. Industrial, Domestic, Commercial.**Part P registered company*

▶ D J R Engineering, 1 Station Road, Oldmeldrum, Inverurie, Aberdeenshire, AB51 0EZ Tel: (01651) 873377 Fax: (01651) 873388 E-mail: sales@djrengineering.com *General light engineering*

D J R Roof Trusses Ltd, Winnards Perch, St. Columb, Cornwall, TR9 6DE Tel: (01637) 881333 Fax: (01637) 881315 E-mail: andy@djr-roof-trusses.demon.co.uk *Timber roof trusses manufrs*

▶ D J R Services 2000 Ltd, Buntsford Park Road, Bromsgrove, Worcestershire, B60 3DX Tel: (01527) 833222

▶ D J Refrigeration & Air Conditioning, Woodland Works, Station Road, Pontnewydd, Cwmbran, Gwent, NP44 1NY Tel: (01633) 486260 Fax: (01633) 486292 *Installation of refrigeration & dispense equipment*

▶ D J Robinson Electrical Ltd, Moat Mill, Brewerton Street, Knaresborough, North Yorkshire, HG5 8AZ Tel: (01423) 865129 Fax: (01423) 868412

D J S Forktruck, Crowthers Crossing, Worcester Road, Summerfield, Kidderminster, Worcestershire, DY11 7RB Tel: (01299) 251182 Fax: (01562) 744888 *Fork truck repairs*

D J S Forktruck, Crowthers Crossing, Worcester Road, Summerfield, Kidderminster, Worcestershire, DY11 7RB Tel: (01299) 251182 Fax: (01562) 744888 *Fork lift truck repairers*

D J Sanders, Orchard Farm, Ockham Lane, Cobham, Surrey, KT11 1LP Tel: (01932) 866705 Fax: (01932) 860685 *Dairy products distributors*

▶ D & J Sibbald, Hardhill Garage, Bathgate, West Lothian, EH48 2HL Tel: (01506) 655711 Fax: (01506) 632449

D J Simons & Sons Ltd, 122-150 Hackney Road, London, E2 7QL Tel: (020) 7739 3744 Fax: (020) 7739 4452 E-mail: dsimons@djsimons.co.uk *Picture frame manufrs*

D & J Simpson, Eassie Smithy, Eassie, Forfar, Angus, DD8 1SG Tel: (01307) 840325 *Agricultural engineers*

D J Sportscars International Ltd, 2 Edinburgh Place, Harlow, Essex, CM20 2DJ Tel: (01279) 442661 Fax: (01279) 434956 E-mail: post@daxcars.co.uk *Replica car & grp manufrs*

D J Stanton Engineering Ltd, Station Road, Hook Norton, Banbury, Oxfordshire, OX15 5LS Tel: (01608) 737452 Fax: (01608) 737051 *Aluminium fabrications service*

D J T Engineering, Willenhall Lane, Bloxwich, Walsall, WS3 2XN Tel: (01922) 491919 Fax: (01922) 497332 E-mail: djtsales@btconnect.com Sales Contact: D. Thomas *DJT Engineering based in the West Midlands (UK) Specialise in manufacturing all types of industrial fasteners, connectors, turned parts and engineered products. Formally David J Thomas Engineering we have combined experience of over 30 years. Our systems are tailored to suit individual customer requirements. We offer competitive prices on our wide range of products form M3 to M64 internal thread. We also offer drilling and tapping services to suit your requirements. We work in a variety of metals including high tensile and stainless steel. Many items are available directly from stock. We look forward to being able to provide you with a highly competitive quote and quick delivery.*

▶ D J Thomas & Sons, Aurora, Llanarth, Dyfed, SA47 0NF Tel: (01545) 580213 Fax: (01545) 580053 E-mail: djtandsons@aol.com

D J Transmissions Ltd, Huxley Close, Newnham Industrial Estate, Plympton, Plymouth, PL7 4JN Tel: (01752) 342469 Fax: (01752) 348319 E-mail: admin@djtransmissions.co.uk *Transmission recondition specialist*

D J Trophies, 30 Fairfield Approach, Wraysbury, Staines, Middlesex, TW19 5DS Tel: (01784) 483483 Fax: (01784) 482563 *Trophy manufrs*

D J Williams & Son, H Peblig Mill, Llanbeblig Road, Caernarfon, Gwynedd, LL55 2SE Tel: (01286) 673254 Fax: (01286) 672007 *Steel fabricators & metalwork (art/decorative/ornamental) manufrs*

D K Associates Ltd, 26-34 Friar Lane, Nottingham, NG1 6DQ Tel: 0115-947 3500 Fax: 0115-985 9007 E-mail: office@dk-recruit.co.uk *Permanent and Temporary Staff for both Commercial and Industrial sectors within Nottinghamshire and Mansfield areas. Place a vacancy using this link and receive an automatic discount Trial our temporary workers for 4 hour free of charge Free replacement and extended rebate periods on permanent placements 24 hour on call service - 0115 9473500 and 07884 000958*

D K Computing Services, Kebbell House, Delta Gain, Watford, WD19 5EF Tel: (020) 8428 1000 Fax: (020) 8428 1111 E-mail: dennis@dkcomputing.co.uk *Computer software consultants*

D K Engineering Services, 7 Enterprise Industrial Estate, Enterprise Road, Waterlooville, Hampshire, PO8 0BB Tel: (023) 9259 3947 Fax: (023) 9259 3948 E-mail: sales@dkeltd.co.uk *Manufacturers of special purpose custom built machinery*

D & K (Europe) Ltd, Unit 38-40, Crossgate Road, Park Farm Industrial Estate, Redditch, Worcestershire, B98 7SN Tel: (01527) 520073 Fax: (01527) 524056 E-mail: info@dkeurope.co.uk *Encapsulating machine & systems manufrs*

D K Fibreglass Works, Montana Place, Rotterdam Road, Lowestoft, Suffolk, NR32 2EX Tel: (01502) 572562 Fax: (01502) 589119 *Fibreglass component manufrs*

Company Information

D K G Hobbies UK, 14 Princes Street, Southport, Merseyside, PR8 1EZ Tel: (01704) 500630 Fax: (01704) 500630 *Models merchants*

D K & K Ltd, Unit 29, 64 Hoyland Road, Sheffield, S3 8AB Tel: 0114-276 9766 Fax: 0114-276 9755 *Insulation contractors*

▶ D K L Metals Ltd, Avontoun Works, Linlithgow, West Lothian, EH49 6QD Tel: (01506) 847710 Fax: (01506) 848199 E-mail: sales@dklmetals.co.uk *Metalwork services*

D K M Sheet Metal Co. Ltd, Unit 9 Oldends Industrial Estate, Oldends, Stonehouse, Gloucestershire, GL10 3RQ Tel: (01453) 827661 Fax: (01453) 824094 E-mail: gill@dkmsheetmetal.co.uk *Precision sheet metalwork engineers*

D K Moriarty Ltd, Eastgates Industrial Estate, Moorside, Colchester, CO1 2TJ Tel: (01206) 867141 Fax: (01206) 867613 E-mail: sales@dk-moriarty.ltd.uk *Instrument transformer manufrs*

D K O Designs, 66 Georges Road, London, N7 8HX Tel: (020) 7607 2653 Fax: (020) 7607 0515 *Security grille manufrs*

D K S Packaging Ltd, 62-70 Litherland Road, Bootle, Merseyside, L20 3HZ Tel: 0151-922 2656 Fax: 0151-933 0547 E-mail: reception@dkspackaging.co.uk *Metal container suppliers*

D & K Singer, Fordoun, Fordoun, Laurencekirk, Kincardineshire, AB30 1JR Tel: (01561) 320639 Fax: (01561) 320690 E-mail: dksinger@freeserve.co.uk *Agricultural machinery dealers*

D & K Specialist Exhaust Centre Ltd, Unit 19 Halifax Industrial Centre, Marshway, Halifax, West Yorkshire, HX1 5RW Tel: (01422) 322141 Fax: (01422) 322939 *Wholesale exhaust systems distributors*

▶ D K T Group Ltd, Albany Court Blenheim Road, Airfield Industrial Estate, Ashbourne, Derbyshire, DE6 1HA Tel: (01335) 300222 Fax: (01335) 300353 *Metal street furniture*

D & K Wiring Services Ltd, Unit 1 Urban Hive, Sundon Park Road, Luton, LU3 3QU Tel: (01582) 492033 Fax: (01582) 565944 E-mail: sales@dkwiring.co.uk *Transformers & pcb manufrs*

D Kelleher Flooring Ltd, Unit 1 B Alexandria Park 1, Penner Road, Havant, Hampshire, PO9 1QY Tel: (023) 9247 1029 Fax: (023) 9245 3288 E-mail: mail@kelleherflooring.co.uk *Decorative flooring specialists*

D Kennedy & Son Ltd, 6 Ashcombe Drive, Radcliffe, Manchester, M26 3NL Tel: 0161-723 5136 Fax: 0161-723 5136 E-mail: j.kennedy33@ntlworld.com *Ground work & engineers*

▶ D Kerr & Sons, Helenslea, Castlecary Road, Cumbernauld, Glasgow, G68 0HQ Tel: (01324) 840337 Fax: (01324) 840885

D Kiddy, 28 Barton Road, Torquay, TQ1 4DP Tel: (01803) 293999 Fax: (01803) 201326 *Fishing tackle suppliers*

D L A Computers, 47 Southend Road, Hockley, Essex, SS5 4PZ Tel: (01702) 202655 Fax: (01702) 202540 E-mail: sales@dlacomputers.co.uk *IT consultants*

D & L Cash Registers, 67 North Street, London, E13 9HL Tel: (020) 8552 5294 Fax: (020) 8472 1654 *Cash registers & scales*

D & L Computer Services, The Crescent, Spalding, Lincolnshire, PE11 1AE Tel: (01775) 768287 Fax: (01775) 713591 E-mail: services@d-l.co.uk *Computer software developers*

▶ D & L Contractors, Manchester Road, Mossley, Ashton-under-Lyne, Lancashire, OL5 9AY Tel: (0870) 2422892 Fax: (0870) 2422893 Sales Contact: M Berry

D.L.D. Engineering, Foundry Yard, Hall La, Walton On The Naze, Essex, CO14 8HW Tel: (01255) 671722 Fax: (01255) 671722 E-mail: sales@dldeng.fsnet.co.uk *Steel fabricators*

D L D Rewinds Ltd, Unit 52 Westbrook Trading Estate, Westbrook Road, Trafford Park, Manchester, M17 1AY Tel: 0161-848 7601 Fax: 0161-876 0680 *Electric motor repair services*

▶ D L Design & Print, 23 Chisholm Road, Croydon, CR0 6UQ Tel: (020) 8686 8717 Fax: (020) 8680 2383 E-mail: ideas@dldesigns.wanadoo.co.uk *Complete graphic design service including advertising design*

D & L Diesel Ltd, 75 Scot Lane, Wigan, Lancashire, WN5 0TU Tel: (01942) 825545 Fax: (01942) 493890 E-mail: davidlong@dldiesels.co.uk *Supplier of spare parts*

D L Electrical Supplies (Mitcham) Ltd, 1A Totterdown Street, London, SW17 8TB Tel: (020) 8672 0064 Fax: (020) 8767 6372 E-mail: sales@dlelectrical.co.uk *Cable harness & assembly manufrs*

D L F Packaging Materials, 56 School Road, Shirley, Solihull, West Midlands, B90 2BB Tel: 0121-744 6101 Fax: 0121-744 9823 E-mail: sales@dlfpackaging.demon.co.uk *Suppliers of polythene & other packaging materials*

D L I Precision Engineering Ltd, Trimdon Grange Industrial Estate, Trimdon Grange, Trimdon Station, County Durham, TS29 6PA Tel: (01429) 880454 Fax: (01429) 880369 E-mail: info@dlipe.plus.com *Sub contract precision engineers*

D L K Ltd, 8 Stather Road, Burton-upon-Stather, Scunthorpe, South Humberside, DN15 9DH Tel: (01724) 720982 Fax: (01724) 720313 E-mail: sales@dlk.co.uk *Educational software developers*

▶ D L M Distribution, 54 Birch Avenue, Quarry Bank, Brierley Hill, West Midlands, DY5 1BG Tel: (01384) 820511 Fax: E-mail: davem65@hotmail.com *sameday nationwide delivery service*

D L Packing Ltd, Unit 4 Lawrence Trading Estate, Blackwell Lane, Greenwich, London, SE10 0AR Tel: (020) 8858 3713 Fax: (020) 8293 4578 E-mail: dlpacking@btconnect.com *Export packers*

D L Pugh Plant, Pentreclwyda House, Pentreclwyda, Resolven, Neath, West Glamorgan, SA11 4DU Tel: (01639) 720017 Fax: (01639) 721122 *Sale & hire of construction plant machinery*

D L S Plastics Ltd, Occupation Lane, Gonrby Moor, Grantham, Lincolnshire, NG32 2BP Tel: (01476) 564549 Fax: (01476) 567538 E-mail: sales@dlsplastics.co.uk *Injection moulders & product development*

D L S Services, Unit 2 Union Park Industrial Estate, Triumph Way, Kempston, Bedford, MK42 7QB Tel: (01234) 840104 E-mail: dls@kbnet.co.uk *Computer cable & connector distributors*

D & L Sheet Metal, 9 Whitehouse Enterprise Centre, Whitehouse Road, Newcastle upon Tyne, NE15 6EP Tel: 0191-275 0286 Fax: 0191-275 0286 *Sheet metalwork engineers*

D L Skerrett Ltd, 14-14a Unit, Palmerston Street, Joiners Square Industrial Estate, Stoke-on-Trent, ST1 3EU Tel: (01782) 281471 Fax: (01782) 202357 E-mail: sales@dlskerrett.co.uk *Engineering merchants*

D L Storage Handling Ltd, 20 Jessops Riverside, 800 Brightside Lane, Sheffield, S9 2RX Tel: 0114-244 0202 Fax: 0114-244 1222 E-mail: sales@thedlcompany.com *Partitioning & storage equipment suppliers*

D L Turner & Son Ltd, Underedge Farm, Rowland, Bakewell, Derbyshire, DE45 1NR Tel: (01629) 640305 Fax: (01629) 640684 *Haulage contractors*

D Lavington, Park Road, Crowborough, East Sussex, TN6 2QX Tel: (01892) 654227 Fax: (01892) 654227 *Joinery contractors*

D Leonardt & Co., New Road, Highley, Bridgnorth, Shropshire, WV16 6NN Tel: (01746) 861203 Fax: (01746) 862296 E-mail: sales@leonardt.com *Metal diary cornerspen nib manufrs*

D Littler, Chester Road, Backford, Chester, CH1 6PE Tel: (01244) 851635 Fax: (01244) 851363 *Concrete manufrs*

▶ D Lo UK Ltd, Select House, Popes Lane, Oldbury, West Midlands, B69 4PA Tel: 0121-544 6256 Fax: 0121-541 4264 E-mail: info@dlog.co.uk *Industrial software & hardware developer*

D Lycett & Sons Ltd, Long Street, Premier Business Park, Walsall, WS2 9DY Tel: (01922) 625393 Fax: (01922) 616761 E-mail: donshir@tiscali.co.uk *Lock & hardware manufrs*

▶ D M A Engineering, F Sams Lane, West Bromwich, West Midlands, B70 7EX Tel: 0121-553 7370 Fax: 0121-553 7626 *Steel fabricators & machinists*

D M A Signs, Unit 5-6 Bridge Works, Kingston Road, Leatherhead, Surrey, KT22 7SU Tel: (01372) 363808 Fax: (01372) 363801 E-mail: sale@dmasigns.co.uk *General sign manufrs*

D M Adams, Coombe Farm, Llanvair Discoed, Chepstow, Gwent, NP16 6LN Tel: (01291) 641792 Fax: (01291) 641792 *Agricultural contractors*

D M Anderton Ltd, First Floor 19, Bark St East, Bolton, BL1 2BQ Tel: (01204) 532618 Fax: (01204) 532619 E-mail: dmanderton@btconnect.com *Electrical contractors*

D M B Farm & Garden Ltd, Riverbank Indust Park, Downshire Road, Newry, County Down, BT34 1DX Tel: (028) 3026 2354 Fax: (028) 3026 2658 *Animal feed merchants & garden sundries*

D & M Barthorpe, Oxford Street, Boston, Lincolnshire, PE21 8TW Tel: (01205) 367612 Fax: (01205) 357932 *Electrical contractors*

D & M Builders Merchants, 73-81 Heath Road, Twickenham, TW1 4AW Tel: (020) 8892 3813 Fax: (020) 8744 1044 *DIY & home improvement products*

D & M Burgess, 2a City Walk, Pendlebury, Swinton, Manchester, M27 8SA Tel: 0161-794 6008 Fax: 0161-790 6153 *Joinery manufrs*

D & M Business Cards, 4 Foxley Court, Oakwood, Derby, DE21 2EU Tel: (01332) 668468 Fax: (01332) 668462 E-mail: sales@dmbusinesscards.co.uk *Plastic business card printers*

D M C Ltd, 7 Sherwood Court, Thurston Road, Lewisham, London, SE13 7SD Tel: (020) 8297 1001 Fax: (020) 8297 1002 *Ventilation ductwork manufrs*

D M C Products, P O Box 22, Derby, DE1 9ZU Tel: (01332) 205822 Fax: (01332) 205822 E-mail: info@dmc-systems.com *Computer components & networking*

D M Chainsaws, Walberton Place Farm, Yapton Lane, Walberton, Arundel, West Sussex, BN18 0AS Tel: (01243) 554065 Fax: (01243) 554065 *Garden machinery wholesale & retailer*

▶ D M Clarkson, Borderline Garage, Biggar, Lanarkshire, ML12 6JJ Tel: (01899) 220346 Fax: (01899) 221279

▶ D M Construction Ltd, Marriott Way, Melton Constable, Norfolk, NR24 2BT Tel: (01263) 862512 Fax: (01263) 861512

▶ D M D Contract Furnishings, 27B Harris Business Park, Hanbury Road, Stoke Prior, Bromsgrove, Worcestershire, B60 4DJ Tel: (01527) 821828 E-mail: dmdfurnishings@live.co.uk *curtains, blinds, beds, headboards, bedding, duvets, pillows, upholstery, carpets, safety flooring, furniture repairs & restoration, french polishing, pictures & bric-a-brac, reflective & safety window films.*

D M D Electronic Engineers Ltd, 2 Nags Head Road, Enfield, Middlesex, EN3 7AJ Tel: (020) 8805 5056 Fax: (020) 8443 4160 *Manufacture Steel decking panels*Sheetmetal and fabrications*

D & M Demolitions Ltd, Meek Street, Royton, Oldham, OL2 6HL Tel: 0161-652 2550 Fax: 0161-652 5203 E-mail: sales@dandmdemolitions.ltd.uk *Demolition contractors*

D M Design Ltd, 1 Deerdykes Place, Cumbernauld, Glasgow, G68 9HE Tel: (01236) 739200 Fax: (01236) 728862 E-mail: dmdesigns@ukonline.co.uk.*Built-in & fitted furniture manufrs*

D & M Design Bedrooms, 99 Neilston Road, Paisley, Renfrewshire, PA2 6ES Tel: 0141-889 0336 Fax: 0141-848 7908 *Designers & manufacturers of bedrooms & kitchens*

▶ D M E U K, Carrwood Road, Chesterfield Trading Estate, Chesterfield, Derbyshire, S41 9QB Tel: (020) 7133 0037 Fax: (020) 7133 0036 E-mail: dme_uk@dmeeu.com *Manufacturers of parts for plastic injection mold bases*

D M F Ltd, 2 Dewsbury Road, Wakefield, West Yorkshire, WF2 9BS Tel: (01924) 370685 Fax: (01924) 360404 E-mail: sales@dmfwakefield.ltd.uk *Compressed air garage equipment specialists*

D & M Fashions Scotland Ltd, Block 3 Units 1 & 2 Riverbank Industrial Estate, Ward Street, Alloa, Clackmannanshire, FK10 1ET Tel: (01259) 721400 Fax: (01259) 720170 *Garment manufrs*

D M G Control Systems Ltd, Unit 9, Bridgewater Road, Hertburn Industrial Estate, Washington, Tyne & Wear, NE37 2SG Tel: 0191-417 9888 Fax: 0191-415 1965 E-mail: sales@dmgcsl.co.uk *Electrical control systems manufrs*

D.M.G. Profile, 25 Oak St, Quarry Bank, Brierley Hill, W. Midlands, DY5 2JH Tel: (01384) 561448 Fax: (01384) 561448 *Profile cutting services*

▶ D M G Security Systems, Knowler Hill, Liversedge, West Yorkshire, WF15 6DY Tel: (01924) 400927 E-mail: sales@dmgsecuritysystems.co.uk *Alarms, cctv & access installation*

D M G UK Ltd, Unitool House, 151 Camford Way, Luton, LU3 3AN Tel: (01582) 570661 Fax: (01582) 593700 E-mail: sales@gildemeister.com *Lathe & tool distributors*

D M G World Media, Westgate, 120-130 Station Road, Redhill, RH1 1ET Tel: (01737) 855000 Fax: (01737) 855475 E-mail: pamelatiernan@uk.dmgworldmedia.com *Directory publishers & magazine publishers*

▶ D M Guitars, 2 37 Brook Road, Rayleigh, Essex, SS6 7XJ Tel: (01268) 777356 E-mail: sales@dm-guitars.co.uk *Stringed instrument makers & repairers*

▶ D M H Blacksmiths, 5 Carsegate Road, Inverness, IV3 8EX Tel: (01463) 233736 Fax: (01463) 236650 *Metalworking & fabrication services*

▶ D M Harris Ltd, 51 Eastmuir Street, Glasgow, G32 0HS Tel: 0141-763 2309 Fax: 0141-763 2373

▶ D M Homes Ltd, 37 Hartwood Road, Shotts, Lanarkshire, ML7 5BY Tel: (01698) 292321

D M Hughes Ltd, 31 Weardale Lane, Glasgow, G33 4JJ Tel: 0141-774 2898 Fax: 0141-774 2251 *Ceramic wall & floor tile fixers*

D M Interiors Ltd, 37 Enstone Road, Uxbridge, Middlesex, UB10 8EZ Tel: (01895) 674479 Fax: (01895) 621383 *Adjustable shelving manufrs*

D M K Chemical Process Plant Ltd, Unit 7B, Riverside Industrial Estate, Fiddlers Ferry, Warrington, WA5 2UL Tel: (01925) 727227 Fax: (01925) 652075 E-mail: dmk@netcentral.co.uk *Chemical plant glassware suppliers & installers*

D M Kent Electronics Ltd, 8 Hedge End Industrial Estate, Shuart Lane, St. Nicholas at Wade, Birchington, Kent, CT7 0NB Tel: (01843) 846755 Fax: (01843) 848008 E-mail: sales@dmkent.co.uk *Electronic designers & manufrs*

D M L Contracting, 29-31 North Cross Road, London, SE22 9HZ Tel: (020) 8693 0416 Fax: (020) 8693 6221 E-mail: info@dml.co.uk *General builders, refurbishment contractors & decorating services*

D M Lloyd & Son, Workshop 43a, Castle Street, Oswestry, Shropshire, SY11 1JZ Tel: (01691) 670254 *Joinery manufrs*

D M Mcclurg, Blakeley Hill Farm, North Bitchburn, Crook, County Durham, DL15 8AP Tel: (01388) 603608 Fax: (01388) 603608 *Farming contractors*

▶ D M R Engineering, Somerton Industrial Park, Newport Road, Cowes, Isle of Wight, PO31 8PB Tel: (01983) 209030 Fax: (01983) 209060 *Industrial fasteners manufrs*

D M R Engineering Services Ltd, 64 Regent Road, Kirkdale, Liverpool, L5 9SY Tel: 0151-207 4451 Fax: 0151-207 5627 E-mail: dmr1966@hotmail.co.uk *Power transmission equipment*

D M Resources Ltd, 10 Slimbridge Rd, Burgess Hill, W. Sussex, RH15 8QE Tel: (01444) 246391 *Photographic services*

D M S Engineering Services, 32 Beverley Road, Oakengates, Telford, Shropshire, TF2 6SD Tel: (01952) 409836 Fax: (01952) 410873 E-mail: mikesarchet@blueyonder.co.uk *Fabrication services & architectural metalworkers*

▶ D M S Stainless Fabrications Ltd, 1 St Peters Works, St Peters Road, Maidenhead, Berkshire, SL6 7QU Tel: (01628) 777391 Fax: (01628) 777396 E-mail: sales@dmslaserprofiles.co.uk *Laser profiling services*

D M S Stainless Fabrications Ltd, 1 St Peters Works, St Peters Road, Maidenhead, Berkshire, SL6 7QU Tel: (01628) 777391 Fax: (01628) 777396 E-mail: sales@stainless.demon.co.uk *Stainless steel fabricators*

D M S 2000 Ltd, 4 Doynton Mill, Mill Lane, Doynton, Bristol, BS30 5TQ Tel: 0117-937 2136 Fax: 0117-937 4756 E-mail: dms2k@fsmail.net *Garage doors,roller shutters, grilles,gates closers & locks.*

D & M Systems Ltd, 28 Langdale Avenue, Chichester, West Sussex, PO19 8JQ Tel: (01243) 781950 Fax: (01243) 784478 E-mail: info@dandmsystems.co.uk *Computer consultants*

D M W Copier Services, 431 Oakleigh Road North, London, N20 0RU Tel: (020) 8361 4833 Fax: (020) 8368 6229 *Office equipment retailers*

D M W Motor Cycles Ltd, Tynesbank Works, Walkden, Manchester, M28 0SF Tel: 0161-790 5277 Fax: 0161-703 8170 E-mail: dctomkinson@hotmail.com *Villiers motor cycle component suppliers*

D M Welsh, West Quay, Gourdon, Montrose, Angus, DD10 0PQ Tel: (01561) 361454 Fax: (01561) 361441 *Fish merchants*

▶ D Mcauley & Sons, Unit 1b Edenderry Industrial Estate, 326 Crumlin Road, Belfast, BT14 7EE Tel: (028) 9074 9797 Fax: (028) 9074 9398 E-mail: info@mcauleys.net *Design supply & installation of terrazzo marble granite & ceramics*

D Mcconnell & Sons, Muiredge, Coaltown of Burnturk, Cupar, Fife, KY15 7TR Tel: (01337) 830246 Fax: (01337) 830246 *Agricultural contractors*

▶ D Macdonald & Co, Balivanich, Isle of Benbecula, HS7 5LA Tel: (01870) 602396 Fax: (01870) 603298

D Mcinnes, Clayslap, Kilmarnock, Ayrshire, KA1 5LN Tel: (01563) 522774 Fax: (01563) 571530 E-mail: enquires@duncanmcinnes.com *Welding engineers*

▶ D Malloch & Co., Walk Mill, Coupar Angus, Blairgowrie, Perthshire, PH13 9DG Tel: (01828) 627452

D Martindale Ltd, Crosse Hall Street, Chorley, Lancashire, PR6 0QQ Tel: (01257) 263504 Fax: (01257) 263504 E-mail: info@donaldmartindale.co.uk *Used commercial vehicle dealers & spares*

D Midgley & Sons Ltd, Holmfield Industrial Estate, Holdsworth Road, Holmfield, Halifax, West Yorkshire, HX2 9TN Tel: (01422) 247185 Fax: (01422) 247234 E-mail: dmidleyandsons@aol.com *Machine tools manufrs*

▶ D Moffatt & Son Ltd, 3 Newbattle Road, Newtongrange, Dalkeith, Midlothian, EH22 4RA Tel: 0131-663 4732

D Morgan Ltd, Chester Road, Great Sutton, New Hay, Ellesmere Port, CH66 2LS Tel: 0151-339 8113 Fax: 0151-347 1254 E-mail: ibyrne@dmorgan.co.uk *Contractors plant hire*

D Morris, 5 The Laurels, Bedworth, Warwickshire, CV12 0PW Tel: (024) 7631 0762 Fax: (024) 7631 0385 E-mail: d.g.morris@talk21.com *General security system suppliers*

▶ D Munro & Son, 8 Cornwall Street, Glasgow, G41 1AQ Tel: 0141-427 2633

D Murrie & Son, 42 Main Street, Methven, Perth, PH1 3PU Tel: (01738) 840477 Fax: (01738) 840477 *Agricultural engineers*

D N A Computers, Lamorna Haven, 17 Rosebery Avenue, Eastbourne, East Sussex, BN22 9QB Tel: (01323) 508810 Fax: (01323) 521228 *Computer development*

▶ D N A Insurance Services Ltd, New Enterprise House, 149-151 High Road, Chadwell Heath, Romford, RM6 6PJ Tel: (020) 8548 7300 Fax: (0870) 7872365 E-mail: mail@dnainsurance.co.uk *DNA Insurance cater for all your insurance needs ranging from car insurance to liability insurance. Find out more!*

D N A UK Ltd, Bighton Hill, Ropley, Alresford, Hampshire, SO24 9SQ Tel: (01962) 772666 Fax: (01962) 772660 E-mail: info@dnacap.com *Capacitor distributors*

D N Brettle Cabinet Makers, 2 Burgage Garden Workshop, Burgage, Southwell, Nottinghamshire, NG25 0EP Tel: (01636) 816036 *Cabinet maker*

D N C Machine Tools Ltd, 31 Kent End, Ashton Keynes, Swindon, SN6 6PU Tel: (01285) 869199 Fax: (01285) 869199 E-mail: russ@dabsons.org *Machine tools services*

D N Consultancy Services, 60 Southover, London, N12 7ES Tel: (020) 8446 6001 Fax: (020) 8445 3711 E-mail: chains@dnconsultancy.com *Mooring systems*

D N D Ltd, Billington Road, Leighton Buzzard, Bedfordshire, LU7 9HH Tel: (01525) 370888 Fax: (01525) 851619 E-mail: traffic@dnd.co.uk *General haulage services*

▶ D N Decorations, 22 Germander Way, Bicester, Oxfordshire, OX26 3WB Tel: (0800) 0192733 Fax: (0870) 7575045 E-mail: sales@dndltd.co.uk *Painting & decorating*

D & N Design, 2 Weston Road, Thames Ditton, Surrey, KT7 0HN Tel: (020) 8398 9639 Fax: (020) 8398 9639 *Advertising gift engravers*

D N H Worldwide Ltd, 31 Clarke Road, Mount Farm, Bletchley, Milton Keynes, MK1 1LG Tel: (01908) 275000 Fax: (01908) 275100 E-mail: dnh@dnh.co.uk Purchasing Contact: K. Golds Sales Contact: C. Evans Principal Export Areas: Worldwide *Manufacturers of public address systems, voice alarm systems, loudspeaker (flameproof) systems, loudspeaker systems, sound reproduction equipment, intercommunication equipment/systems & voice evacuation (PA) systems. Also public address systems background music suppliers*

▶ D & N Hall & Sons Ltd, 1a Retreat Place, London, E9 6RH Tel: (020) 8985 2877 Fax: (020) 8533 1574

D N R Services (Dudley) Ltd, Bay 4, 84 Pensnett Trading Estate, First Avenue, Kingswinford, West Midlands, DY6 7FN Tel: (01384) 400800 Fax: (01384) 298042 E-mail: dnrservices@tiscali.co.uk *Electronic motor repair/rewind*

▶ D N S Auto Electrical, Phoenix Way, Gorseinon, Swansea, SA4 9WF Tel: (01792) 896600 *Electrical Quotation Specification has been developed by electrical engineers to simplify the task of tender compilation for electrical control panels. Electrical quotations for electrical control panels*

D N S Fencing, Station Road, West Hallam, Ilkeston, Derbyshire, DE7 6HB Tel: 0115-944 4280 Fax: 0115-944 4280 *Fencing erection & manufrs*

▶ D N Traffic Management Ltd, 21 Waxlow Road, London, NW10 7NU Tel: (020) 8963 0880 Fax: (020) 8963 0996

D & N Transport, Unit 4b Arrow Trading Estate, Corporation Road, Audenshaw, Manchester, M34 5LR Tel: 0161-336 3024 Fax: 0161-320 3124 E-mail: dntransport@nippinet.co.uk *Road transport, haulage & freight services*

D N W Ceramics Of Staffordshire, Wood Street, Longton, Stoke-on-Trent, ST3 1EA Tel: (01782) 598949 Fax: (01782) 598949 *Pottery Manufacturers*

D O A Terminators Ltd, 23 Gorof Road, Lower Cwmtwrch, Swansea, SA9 1EH Tel: (01639) 842501 Fax: (01639) 849899 *Pest control*

D O J Pipe Welding Services, 6 Pear Tree Close, Little Billing, Northampton, NN3 9TH Tel: (01604) 404010 Fax: (01604) 408636 E-mail: welding@pipewelding.co.uk *Pipework & welding onsite fabricators*

D & P Bingham, 40 Ballymartin Road, Templepatrick, Ballyclare, County Antrim, BT39 0BS Tel: (028) 9443 2452 *Agricultural contractors*

▶ D P Builders Ltd, Coquet Enterprise Park, Amble, Morpeth, Northumberland, NE65 0PE Tel: (01665) 710315 Fax: (01665) 712385

D P Connect, Garrard House, 2-6 Homesdale Road, Bromley, BR2 9LZ Tel: (020) 8466 5666 Fax: (020) 8313 1716 E-mail: info@dpconnect.co.uk *IT recruitment*

D P Controls Ltd, Giles Farm Oast, Pluckley, Ashford, Kent, TN27 0SY Tel: (01233) 840900 Fax: (01233) 840900 E-mail: sales@dpcontrols.com *Instrumental engineers*

D & P D Upton, Park Farm, Six Hills Road, Six Hills, Melton Mowbray, Leicestershire, LE14 3PR Tel: (01509) 880284 Fax: (01509) 889222 E-mail: roy@sixhills.freeserve.co.uk *Agricultural & horticultural engineers services*

D & P Data Systems Ltd, 15 Carnarvon Street, Manchester, M3 1HJ Tel: 0161-832 6969 Fax: 0161-832 6970 E-mail: sales@dpdata.co.uk *Computer hardware distributors*

D P Dental, 85 Seaward Street, Glasgow, G41 1HJ Tel: 0141-420 1111 Fax: 0141-420 3338 E-mail: mary@dpdental.co.uk *Dental laboratories*

The D P Design Co. Ltd, 31 Warwick Row, Coventry, CV1 1EY Tel: (024) 7622 3390 Fax: (024) 7622 0740 Principal Export Areas: Central/East Europe *Graphic design, technical illustration, model making, brochures, full exhibition service*

D P Dyers Ltd, Thirstin Dye Works, Thirstin Road, Honley, Holmfirth, HD9 6JL Tel: (01484) 661215 Fax: (01484) 665591 *Piece dyers*

D P Energy Services, Unit 5 & 6, Heron Avenue, Wickford, Essex, SS11 8DL Tel: (01268) 560040 Fax: (01268) 560261 E-mail: sales@drakepower.com Principal Export Areas: Worldwide *DC Power supplies up to 1MW for Electrochemical, Metal Finishing, Water treatment, Electrochlorination, Cathodic protection, Electrophorectic processes. Transformers from 1VA to 500KVA, single and three phase, mains, audio, valve output, standard range 3VA to 200VA. UK based technical support staff available for prompt response to maintain power supply systems world wide*

▶ D P Engineering, Treleigh Industrial Estate, Jon Davey Drive, Redruth, Cornwall, TR16 4AX Tel: (01209) 217400 Fax: (01209) 217480 *Precision engineering*

D P Fabrications Ltd, Chantry Road, Woburn Road Industrial Estate, Kempston, Bedford, MK42 7HU Tel: (01234) 840166 Fax: (01234) 840177 E-mail: sales@dpfabs.co.uk *Control panel cabinet manufrs*

D P Furniture Express, 15 King Street, Blackburn, BB2 2DH Tel: (01254) 691004 Fax: (01254) 691106 *Pine furniture retailer*

D P Furniture Express, 18-20 Silver Street, Doncaster, South Yorkshire, DN1 1HQ Tel: (01302) 365535 Fax: (01302) 365535 *Pine furniture retailers*

D P H, Whitburn Road, Bathgate, West Lothian, EH48 2HR Tel: (01506) 630887 Fax: (01506) 633845 *Commercial vehicle contract hire & leasing*

▶ D P H Electrical, 77 Birchtree Avenue, Peterborough, PE1 4HP Tel: (01733) 701254 E-mail: sales@dphpat.co.uk *Specialists in portable appliance testing*

▶ D & P Haulage, Tower House Lane, Saltend, Hull, HU12 8EE Tel: (01482) 890073 Fax: (01482) 890624

▶ D P I Ltd, Printing House, Church Lane, Norton, Worcester, WR5 2PS Tel: (0845) 0700750 Fax: (0845) 0700751 E-mail: dclover@dpi4xerox.co.uk *Authorised xerox, copiers, printers, faxes & digital colour products suppliers*

D P I Systems Ltd, L C S House, Ainleys Industrial Estate, Huddersfield Road, Elland, West Yorkshire, HX5 9JP Tel: (01422) 375444 Fax: (01422) 370037 E-mail: elland@dpisystems.co.uk *Computer consumables*

D P Instrumentation Ltd, 2 Ainslie Street, West Pitkerro Industrial Estate, Broughty Ferry, Dundee, DD5 3RR Tel: (01382) 731200 Fax: (01382) 731201 E-mail: sales@dpil.co.uk *Instrumentation suppliers*

D & P Joinery Manufacturers, 32a George Road, Carlton, Nottingham, NG4 3AE Tel: 0115-987 0128 Fax: 0115-956 0095 E-mail: dpjoinery@ntlworld.com *Joinery*

D P L, Elliott Works, Elliott Road, Bromley, BR2 9NT Tel: (020) 8460 2147 Fax: (020) 8313 3072 E-mail: sales@dplaw.co.uk *Steel & sheet metal fabricators*

D P M (Padding) Ltd, Glover Centre, Egmont Street, Mossley, Ashton-under-Lyne, Lancashire, OL5 9PY Tel: (01457) 833899 Fax: (01457) 837931 *Shoulder pad manufrs*

D P Marine Services, The Boat Yard, Hordern Road, Wolverhampton, WV6 0HT Tel: (01902) 755951 *Boat services & repairers*

D P Mouldings, 4 Station Hill, Maesteg, Mid Glamorgan, CF34 9AE Tel: (01656) 737033 *Plaster moulders*

D P Passmore Ltd, Hunts Lane, London, E15 2QE Tel: (020) 8555 7676 Fax: (020) 8534 4470 *Plasters merchants*

D P R Engineering, Unit 11 Prospect Business Park, Longford Road, Cannock, Staffordshire, WS11 0LG Tel: (01543) 577910 Fax: (01543) 572306 *Sub-contract machining & hydraulic jacks*

D P S Birmingham Ltd, 46 Hallam Street, Birmingham, B12 9PS Tel: 0121-440 3203 Fax: 0121-440 5220 *Textile embroidery services*

D P S Fabrications Ltd, East Hanningfield Industrial Estate, Chelmsford, CM3 5BX Tel: (01245) 400161 Fax: (01245) 400435 *Steel fabrications*

D P S Integro, Unit 1 Langley House Business Park, Wykeham, Scarborough, North Yorkshire, YO13 9QP Tel: (01723) 866700 Fax: (01723) 865705 E-mail: info@dps-integro.co.uk *Computer software design & services*

D P Security, Ryecroft House, Green St Green Road, Dartford, DA2 8DX Tel: (01474) 707030 Fax: (01474) 707313 E-mail: info@dpsecurity.co.uk *Security system installers & manufrs*

D & P Services, 2 Ceres Street, Liverpool, L20 8PZ Tel: 0151-922 2071 Fax: 0151-922 2425 *Hydraulic engineers*

▶ D & P Shop, 76 Huddersfield Road, Elland, West Yorkshire, HX5 9AA Tel: (01422) 310552 Fax: (01422) 310552 E-mail: sales@dandpshop.co.uk *D and P Shop stock a wide range of products from household essentials, personal hygiene, car, mother and baby, stationery and party products*

D P Systems Ltd, 85 Longbridge Road, Barking, Essex, IG11 8TB Tel: (020) 8594 2244 Fax: (020) 8594 2777 E-mail: sales@d-p-systems.com *Computer consultants*

▶ D P Valve Spares Ltd, Unit 51B Port Street, Evesham, Worcestershire, WR11 3LF Tel: (01386) 760033 Fax: (01386) 760099 E-mail: sales@dpvalvespares.co.uk *Control valve spare parts*

D Perkins, 3 Maltings Industrial Estate, Derby Road, Burton-on-Trent, Staffordshire, DE14 1RN Tel: (01283) 510451 Fax: (01283) 517977 E-mail: info@cncmetalproducts.co.uk *CNC engineers*

D Pither, Cirencester Road, Brockworth, Gloucester, GL3 4TN Tel: (01452) 864714 Fax: (01452) 864714 *Agricultural contractors*

D Q R Precision Ltd, Unit 11 Colchester Business Centre, 1 George Williams Way, Colchester, CO1 2JS Tel: (01206) 766116 Fax: (01206) 766117 E-mail: sales@dqr.co.uk *Offering a comprehensive range of high quality products for the protection of linear slideways & ballscrews. These include bespoke bellow covers in various profiles & fabrics, steel telescopic covers, 'Samurai' bellows with the addition of stainless steel lamellas, ballscrew spiral covers, roller blinds in steel & fabric & aluminium apron covers. Also offering rectangular bellow covers for lift table applications*

D & R, Unit 4 Long Furrow, East Goscote, Leicester, LE7 3ZL Tel: 0116-260 6530 Fax: 0116-269 7283 *Steel fabricators*

D R B Power Transmission, First Avenue, Deeside Industrial Park, Deeside, Clwyd, CH5 2QR Tel: (01244) 280280 Fax: (01244) 288367 E-mail: sales@drbgroup.co.uk *Valve distributors & stockholders*

D R B Precision Ltd, Unit H, Bowen Industrial Estate, Aberbargoed, Bargoed, Mid Glamorgan, CF81 9EP Tel: (01443) 828940 Fax: (01443) 879133 E-mail: sales@drbprecision.com *CNC machine fire access & contract tool room*

D R Blinds, 1d Linden Place, Trowbridge, Wiltshire, BA14 9AU Tel: (01225) 777385 Fax: (01225) 753754 *Blinds*

D R C Computer Services, 66 Snipe Street, Ellon, Aberdeenshire, AB41 9FW Tel: (01358) 722007 Fax: (01358) 721628 E-mail: info@drc-ellon.co.uk *Business software supplies & supporters*

D R C Polymer Products Ltd, 1 Regal Lane, Soham, Ely, Cambridgeshire, CB7 5BA Tel: (01353) 720989 Fax: (01353) 624668 E-mail: info@drc-polymers.com *Innovators & processors of thermoplastics*

D R Case & Son, 5 Lady Bee Marina Industrial Units, Albion Street, Southwick, Brighton, BN42 4EG Tel: (01273) 870850 Fax: (01273) 870855 E-mail: colin.case@btconnect.com *Wire erosion specialists*

D R Chemicals Ltd, Viking Way, Winch Wen Industrial Estate, Winch Wen, Swansea, SA1 7DA Tel: (01792) 701135 Fax: (01792) 771797 E-mail: chemics@btconnect.com *Industrial chemicals suppliers*

▶ D R Clothing, 17 Parkburn Court, Parkburn Industrial Estate, Hamilton, Lanarkshire, ML3 0QQ Tel: (01698) 712693 Fax: (01698) 712693 *Clothing distributors*

D R Cooker Hoods Ltd, 2 Alpha Road, Aldershot, Hampshire, GU12 4RG Tel: (01252) 351111 Fax: (01252) 311608 E-mail: sales@drcookerhoods.co.uk *Cooker hood & ducting distributors*

▶ D & R Couriers, Building 2, 47 Skelwith Road, Marton, Blackpool, FY3 9UL Tel: 01253 312713 Fax: 01253 312713 E-mail: richard@dandrcouriers.co.uk

▶ D R Diesel, 1 Harbour Road, Fraserburgh, Aberdeenshire, AB43 9TB Tel: (01346) 517444 Fax: (01346) 517222 *Diesel engineering services*

▶ D & R Electrical, 6 Rayners Crescent, Northolt, Middlesex, UB5 6PB Tel: (020) 8841 2520 Fax: (020) 8723 3213 E-mail: sales@drelectricalservices.co.uk *Electrical Installation, Repairs, Maintainance, Portable appliance testing. 3 phase works, Domestic, Factory, Office, Shop works*

D & R Fabrications Ltd, Mill Farm Yard, Darnhall, Winsford, Cheshire, CW7 4DG Tel: (01270) 528105 Fax: (01270) 528109 E-mail: info@drfabrications.co.uk *Steel fabrication manufrs*

D R Fox, Grange Farm, Stillingfleet Road, Escrick, York, YO19 6EB Tel: (01904) 728668 *Agricultural engineers*

D R Garments Ltd, 39 Spalding Street, Leicester, LE5 4PH Tel: 0116-276 3550 Fax: 0116-276 3570 E-mail: dr@drgarments.com *Garments manufrs*

D R H Screens Ltd, 3 The High Cross Centre, Fountayne Road, London, N15 4QN Tel: (020) 8885 5504 Fax: (020) 8365 1108 E-mail: sales@drhscreens.co.uk *Projection screen manufrs*

D R Harrod, 79 Denford Road, Ringstead, Kettering, Northamptonshire, NN14 4DF Tel: (01933) 626260 Fax: (01933) 460072 *Agricultural engineers*

D & R James Engineering Services Ltd, 16 Benson Road, Nuffield Industrial Estate, Poole, Dorset, BH17 0GB Tel: (01202) 678679 *Engine re-conditioning/re-manufacturing*

D R L Systems Ltd, Woodside House, Woodside, Chilworth, Southampton, SO16 7LB Tel: (023) 8076 0808 Fax: (023) 8076 7900 E-mail: sales@drlsystems.co.uk *Computer systems sales & consultants*

D R Labelling Systems Ltd, 12 Westgarth Place, College Milton Industrial Estate, East Kilbride, Glasgow, G74 5NT Tel: (01355) 221200 Fax: (01355) 221737 E-mail: sales@drlabelling.co.uk *Label printers*

▶ D R Macleod, 9 Henderson Road, Inverness, IV1 1SN Tel: (01463) 715217 Fax: (01463) 715232

D R P Group, 252 Ikon Industrial Estate, Droitwich Road, Hartlebury, Kidderminster, Worcestershire, DY10 4EU Tel: (01299) 250531 Fax: (01299) 250173 E-mail: sales@drp.co.uk *Video producers event management services*

D R Precision, 8 Shell Corner Industrial Estate, Long Lane, Halesowen, West Midlands, B62 9LD Tel: 0121-561 1874 Fax: 0121-561 1874 *Die & tool manufrs*

▶ D & R Removals, 245 St. Levan Road, Plymouth, PL2 1JJ Tel: (01752) 606949 Fax: (01752) 561777 *Removals company, domestic, commercial*

D R S Cases Ltd, Unit 17, Forest Business Park, Argall Avenue, London, E10 7FB Tel: (020) 8520 7500 Fax: (020) 8520 9385 *Export packers*

D R S Legal Services, Tradewinds House, Otterham, Camelford, Cornwall, PL32 9SL Tel: (01840) 261136 Fax: (0871) 4339159 E-mail: mail@debtrecovery.me.uk *Debt recovery services*

D R S Press Tools, Unit 18 Oldfields, Corngreaves Road, Cradley Heath, West Midlands, B64 6BS Tel: (01384) 410711 Fax: (01384) 410711 *Press tool manufacturers & precision engineers*

D R S Rugged Systems (Europe) Ltd, Lynwood House, The Trading Estate, Farnham, Surrey, GU9 9NN Tel: (01252) 734488 Fax: (01252) 730530 *Rugged computer equipment*

D & R Scaffold Eastern, Archers Fields, Burnt Mills Industrial Estate, Basildon, Essex, SS13 1DH Tel: (01268) 525678 Fax: (01268) 284478 *Scaffolding hire/leasing/rental*

D R Security Systems, 96 Osborne Road, London, E7 0PL Tel: (020) 8534 7130 Fax: (020) 8519 5147 E-mail: info@drsecurity.co.uk *Security systems & electrical installation*

D & R Services, 36 Eastfield Road, Wellingborough, Northamptonshire, NN8 1QU Tel: (01933) 278921 Fax: (01933) 278921 *Office cleaning contractors & window cleaners*

D & R Structures Ltd, 7 Lidsey Road, Woodgate, Chichester, West Sussex, PO20 3SU Tel: (01243) 544838 Fax: (01243) 544840 *Steel fabricators*

D R V, Lower Tregenna, Newquay, Cornwall, TR8 4HS Tel: (01637) 875824 Fax: (01637) 876082 E-mail: mail@drv.com *Audio visual installers*

D R Ventilation Ltd, 14 Bishop Close, Leighton Buzzard, Bedfordshire, LU7 4ST Tel: (01525) 630730 Fax: (01525) 630730 E-mail: dr.ventilation@ntlworld.com *Ductwork, heat recovery, central vacuum installation & suppliers*

D R Warehouse Ltd, 60-64 Great Hampton Street, Birmingham, B18 6EL Tel: 0121-551 4920 Fax: 0121-551 6504 *Knitwear wholesalers*

D Ramply, High Street, Great Paxton, St. Neots, Cambridgeshire, PE19 6RG Tel: (01480) 475979 Fax: (01480) 403555 *Grain traders*

D Reed & Son, Churchill Road, Cheltenham, Gloucestershire, GL53 7EG Tel: (01242) 523637 *Car body repairers & sprayers*

D Reynolds Agricultural Engineers, 7 High Street, Bromyard, Herefordshire, HR7 4AA Tel: (01885) 483241 Fax: (01885) 483409 *Agricultural engineers*

D S A, 4-5 Edison Road, Rabans Lane Industrial Area, Aylesbury, Buckinghamshire, HP19 8TE Tel: (01296) 486911 Fax: (01296) 334335 E-mail: hq@gforcemotorsport.co.uk *Porsche & japanese performance specialists*

D & S Air Conditioning Ltd, 5-6 Millbrook Close, Northampton, NN5 5JF Tel: (01604) 586482 Fax: (01604) 586477 E-mail: admin@dandsairconditioning.co.uk *Air conditioning & insulation suppliers*

D S B Offshore Ltd, Eden House, 59 Fulham High Street, London, SW6 3JJ Tel: (020) 7384 2882 Fax: (020) 7731 8163 E-mail: sales@dsboffshore.com *Offshore marine & tug brokers*

D & S Blinds, 177 Stamford St Central, Ashton-under-Lyne, Lancashire, OL6 7PS Tel: 0161-339 5755 Fax: 0161-339 5755 E-mail: sales@kcblinds.co.uk *Curtain fitters, blind & sunblind manufrs*

D S C Associates, Chester Court Chester Park, Alfreton Road, Derby, DE21 4AB Tel: (01332) 204144 Fax: (01332) 200344 E-mail: info@derwentsafetycentre.co.uk *Training & safety consultants*

D S C Controls Ltd, 8 Lea Green Business Park, Eurolink, St. Helens, Merseyside, WA9 4TR Tel: (01744) 820777 Fax: (01744) 820707 E-mail: derek@dsc-control.freeserve.co.uk *Automation & control systems*

D S Callards Ltd, 2 Station Yard, Ashburton, Newton Abbot, Devon, TQ13 7EF Tel: (01364) 654222 Fax: (01364) 652288 E-mail: ray.kemp@developersolutions.co.uk *Software development & consultants services*

▶ D S Carriers, Lyon Road, Linwood Industrial Estate, Linwood, Paisley, Renfrewshire, PA3 3BQ Tel: (01505) 337520 Fax: (01505) 331418 E-mail: info@dscarriersandsons.co.uk

D S Controls, Sleekburn Business Centre, Cambois, Blyth, Northumberland, NE24 1QQ Tel: (01670) 520022 Fax: (01670) 520033 E-mail: sales@dscontrolvalves.com *Valves suppliers & manufrs*

D S F Refractories & Minerals Ltd, Friden, Newhaven, Buxton, Derbyshire, SK17 0DX Tel: (01629) 636271 Fax: (01629) 636892 E-mail: dsf@dsf.co.uk *Refractory materials manufrs*

D & S Factors Ltd, 1 Pinder Lane, Donington, Spalding, Lincolnshire, PE11 4SN Tel: (01775) 820309 Fax: (01775) 821263 E-mail: dsfactor@globalnet.co.uk *Wheel manufacturers & distributors*

D S Fashions, Units 8-9, Albert Road, Darlington, County Durham, DL1 2PD Tel: (01325) 357144 Fax: (01325) 357144 *Big sized clothing manufrs*

D S Fasteners Ltd, Unit 7, Hill Fort Close, Fison Way Industrial Estate, Thetford, Norfolk, IP24 1HS Tel: (01842) 763000 Fax: (01842) 764055 *Self-locking nut distributors*

D S G Auto Contracts, Bredbury Park Way, Bredbury, Stockport, Cheshire, SK6 2SN Tel: (0870) 7875418 Fax: (0870) 7875419 E-mail: sales@dsgvans.com *Van hire & leasing*

D S G Canusa GmbH & Co., Sales Bergstrand House, Parkwood Close, Roborough, Plymouth, PL6 7SG Tel: (01752) 209880 Fax: (01752) 209850 E-mail: info@dsgcanusa.com *Heat shrinkable sleeving manufrs and distributors*

D S Gear Company Ltd, Knights Bridge, Kirton Holme, Boston, Lincolnshire, PE20 1TH Tel: (01205) 290601 Fax: (01205) 290601 E-mail: ds.gears@virgin.net *Precision engineers*

D S H Electronics Ltd, 206 Idle Road, Bradford, West Yorkshire, BD2 4JT Tel: (01274) 626261 Fax: (01274) 626299 E-mail: sales@dsh-electronics.co.uk *Computer supplies, maintenance support & consultants*

▶ D S I Heating Installations Ltd, Olde Byre, Stoke Street, Rodney Stoke, Cheddar, Somerset, BS27 3UP Tel: (01749) 870192 Fax: (01749) 870811 E-mail: sfoster@dsiheating.freeserve.co.uk

▶ D & S Kitching, Camwal Road, Harrogate, North Yorkshire, HG1 4PT Tel: (01423) 885632 Fax: (01423) 884800 E-mail: mai@dskplant.co.uk *Vertical mast forklifts & dumpers plant hire*

D S Logan, 25 Duneoin Road, Cullybackey, Ballymena, County Antrim, BT42 1PL Tel: (028) 2588 0297 Fax: (028) 2588 1041 E-mail: kuhn@dslogan.wanadoo.co.uk *Agricultural machinery suppliers*

D S M Automation Ltd, Eel Street, Oldbury, West Midlands, B69 2BX Tel: 0121-541 1335 Fax: 0121-511 1298 *Power press repairers*

▶ D S M Geodata Ltd, 3 Hope Street, Bo'Ness, West Lothian, EH51 0AA Tel: (01506) 518000 Fax: (01506) 517777 E-mail: info@dsmgeodata.com *Geographical information systems (GIS) services, maps, databases*

D S M Industrial Engineering Ltd, Nottingham Road, Beeston, Nottingham, NG9 6DP Tel: 0115-925 5927 Fax: 0115-925 8456 E-mail: dsmengineering@tiscali.co.uk *Catering equipment manufrs*

D S P G Ltd, 253a Kilburn Lane, London, W10 4BQ Tel: (020) 8964 0774 Fax: (020) 8964 0720 E-mail: info@dspg.co.uk Principal Export Areas: Worldwide *Telecommunication designers & manufrs*

D & S & P Humphrey, New House Farm, Newhouse Lane, East Dean, Chichester, West Sussex, PO18 0NJ Tel: (01243) 811685 Fax: (01243) 773676 *Farm plant contractors*

▶ D & S Pottery Ltd, Unit 14 Chemical Lane, Stoke-on-Trent, ST6 4PB Tel: (01782) 813535 Fax: (01782) 813535 E-mail: sales@dandspottery.co.uk *Pottery manufrs*

D S Print & Redesign, 7 Jute Lane, Enfield, Middlesex, EN3 7JL Tel: (020) 8805 9585 Fax: (020) 8805 2044 E-mail: re-info@ds-redesign.co.uk *Mailing design & printing services*

D & S Services, Unit H2 & Unit H3 Rudford Industrial Estate, Ford Road, Ford, Arundel, West Sussex, BN18 0BD Tel: (01903) 732732 Fax: (01903) 716151 E-mail: sales@dandsservices.co.uk *Manufacturers & distributors of tanks including oil storage & steel*

D & S Shopfitters, 103 Brinksway Trading Estate, Stockport, Cheshire, SK3 0BZ Tel: 0161-477 3142 Fax: 0161-477 3142 *Nationwide shop fitters*

▶ D & S Sloanes, 24 Alexandra Park, Sunderland, SR3 1XJ Tel: 0191-522 6610 Fax: 0191-549 1345 E-mail: dandasloanes@btconnect.com

D S Smith, First Avenue, Royal Portbury Dock, Portbury, Bristol, BS20 7XR Tel: (01275) 375311 Fax: (01275) 374939 *Fireboard corrugated box manufrs*

▶ D S Smith, Block 13, Vale of Leven Industrial Estate, Dumbarton, G82 3PD Tel: (01389) 721102 Fax: (01389) 721060 E-mail: sales@dumbartondssp.com *Manufacturers of packaging*

D S Smith, Paper Mill Road, Rawcliffe Bridge, Goole, North Humberside, DN14 8SL Tel: (01405) 837400 Fax: (01405) 837192 *Corrugated carton manufrs*

D S Smith, Mareham Road, Horncastle, Lincolnshire, LN9 6NG Tel: (01507) 523434 Fax: (01507) 523431 *Sacks & bag manufrs*

D S Smith, Scarne Industrial Estate, Launceston, Cornwall, PL15 9HN Tel: (01566) 777700 Fax: (01566) 774489 E-mail: sales@launceston.dssp.com *Corrugated packaging manufrs*

D S Smith, Muir Road, Houstoun Industrial Estate, Livingston, West Lothian, EH54 5DP Tel: (01506) 432841 Fax: (01506) 438347 *Packaging materials manufrs*

D S Smith, Muir Road, Houstoun Industrial Estate, Livingston, West Lothian, EH54 5DP Tel: (01506) 432841 Fax: (01506) 438347 *Cardboard box manufrs*

D S Smith, Windsor Road, Louth, Lincolnshire, LN11 0YG Tel: (01507) 609393 Fax: (01507) 600478 *Trade sheet feeders*

D S Smith, Fordham Road, Newmarket, Suffolk, CB8 7TX Tel: (01638) 722100 Fax: (01638) 722101 *Corrugated fibreboard containers* Also at: Ely, Launceston, Livingstone & Monmouth

D S Smith Celtic, 5 Rush Drive, Pen-Y-Fan Industrial Estate, Crumlin, Newport, Gwent, NP11 3EJ Tel: (01495) 248255 Fax: (01495) 247675 *Corrugated cardboard box manufrs*

D S Smith Packaging, Common Side Lane, Featherstone, Pontefract, West Yorkshire, WF7 5DF Tel: (01977) 791121 Fax: (01977) 780356 *Manufacturer cardboard boxes*

D S Smith Packaging Wessex, 86 Livingstone Road, Andover, Hampshire, SP10 5NS Tel: (01264) 350753 Fax: (01264) 353315 E-mail: sales@danisco.com *Cardboard box manufrs*

D S T, Afinity House, Beaufort Court, Rochester, Kent, ME2 4FD Tel: (01634) 292292 Fax: (01293) 554600 *Billing & finance computer software support services*

D S T International Ltd, DST House, St. Marks Hill, Surbiton, Surrey, KT6 4QD Tel: (020) 8390 5000 Fax: (020) 8390 7000 E-mail: webmaster@dstintl.com *Investment management software systems*

D & S Tarpaulins, Evergreen, Groves Farm Road, Eastchurch, Sheerness, Kent, ME12 3SY Tel: (01795) 880956 *Tarpaulin manufrs*

▶ D S Technology Ltd, 43-45 Phoenix Park, Avenue Close, Nechells, Birmingham, B7 4NU Tel: 0121-359 3637 Fax: 0121-359 1135 E-mail: info@ds-technology.co.uk *Suppliers to the Aerospace industry, General Engineering, Power Industry and Automotive Industries.Dörries Scharmann Technologie GmbH delivers machine tools from Dörries, Droop + Rein, Scharmann and Berthiez with well proven outstanding performances for drilling, turning, boring, milling and grinding of medium and large size components. We deliver the machining technologies for you to solve your machining tasks in an economical way.*

▶ D S Traditional Drawings, Birmingham, B44 8ET Tel: 0121-382 5544 *Measuring equipment suppliers*

D S W Engineering Co. Ltd, 6 Chester Hall Lane, Basildon, Essex, SS14 3BG Tel: (01268) 523185 Fax: (01268) 534325 E-mail: admin@dsw.biz *Precision engineers & toolmakers services*

▶ D S Watson, 19-21 Ravensmere, Beccles, Suffolk, NR34 9DX Tel: (01502) 470700 Fax: (01502) 470777

D Sankey, 15 Lewes Road, Haywards Heath, West Sussex, RH17 7SP Tel: (01825) 763159 Fax: (01825) 769736 *Pest control*

D Sankey Pest Control Services, 39 Sackville Road, Hove, East Sussex, BN3 3WD Tel: (01273) 203055 Fax: (01825) 769736 *Pest control*

D Sankey Pest Control Services, 39 Sackville Road, Hove, East Sussex, BN3 3WD Tel: (01273) 203055 Fax: (01825) 769736 *Pest control services*

▶ D Selby, Newcastle Street, Bulwell, Nottingham, NG6 8AW Tel: 0115-927 5103 Fax: 0115-927 4159

D Shackleton, 19 High Street, Snainton, Scarborough, North Yorkshire, YO13 9AE Tel: (01723) 859577 *Cabinet manufrs*

D Simmons, 4 Devonshire House, North Street, North Tawton, Devon, EX20 2EX Tel: (01837) 82564 Fax: (01837) 82564 *Plant hire & ground work*

D Steer Fabrication, 4 Riverside Avenue West, Lawford, Manningtree, Essex, CO11 1UN Tel: (01206) 391767 Fax: (01206) 391767 E-mail: thesteers@virgin.net *Stainless steel fabricators*

D Stephens & Co. Ltd, The Woodlands, New Haden Road, Cheadle, Stoke-on-Trent, ST10 1UF Tel: (01538) 753399 *Joiners & building maintenance services*

D Stewart, Brocks Way, East Mains Industrial Estate, Broxburn, West Lothian, EH52 5NB Tel: (01506) 858282 Fax: (01506) 858465 *Security fencing manufrs*

D Stretton, High Barns, Isley Walton, Castle Donington, Derby, DE74 2RL Tel: (01332) 810757 *Agricultural engineers*

▶ D Sturrock, 37 Ravensby Road, Carnoustie, Angus, DD7 7NH Tel: (01241) 410286

D Sutherland & Son Ltd, Union Street, Wick, Caithness, KW1 5ED Tel: (01955) 602101 Fax: (01955) 602917 *Timber merchants*

▶ D Swinley Engineering Ltd, 1 Midfield Road, Mitchelston Industrial Estate, Kirkcaldy, Fife, KY1 3NL Tel: (01592) 650300 Fax: (01592) 651469 E-mail: mail@dse.me.uk *Light engineering services*

D T A Computer Systems Ltd, 58 Norbiton Avenue, Kingston upon Thames, Surrey, KT1 3QR Tel: (020) 8974 5114 Fax: (07092) 314906 E-mail: info@dta.co.uk *Bespoke software producers*

▶ D & T Campbell (Meigle) Ltd, Forfar Road Garage, Meigle, Blairgowrie, Perthshire, PH12 8RS Tel: (01828) 640261

D T Donan & Co., 8 Abercorn Commercial Centre, Manor Farm Road, Wembley, Middlesex, HA0 1YA Tel: (020) 8903 8288 Fax: (020) 8900 1533 *Textiles manufrs*

▶ D & T Electronics, Woodfield Road, Broadheath, Altrincham, Cheshire, WA14 4EU Tel: 0161-926 9149 Fax: (0870) 4445945 E-mail: sales@dandt.co.uk *Residential audio equipment sales & services*

D & T Engineering, Unit 12d Thorn Business Park, Rotherwas, Hereford, HR2 6JT Tel: (01432) 355433 Fax: (01432) 355519 E-mail: d.t.eng@btopenworld.com *Engineering, mechanical & electrical installations*

D T I Action Hardware Ltd, West Farm, Popham, Micheldever, Winchester, Hampshire, SO21 3BH Tel: (01892) 511753 Fax: (01892) 530294 E-mail: action.hardware@virgin.net *Electronic component importers & exporters*

D T I (Department of Trade and Industry), 1 Victoria Street, London, SW1H 0ET Tel: (020) 7215 5000 Fax: (020) 7215 3529 E-mail: dti.enquiries@dti.gsi.gov.uk *Government department for trade & industry*

D & T Industrial Finishers Ltd, 9 Commerce Way, Stanbridge Road, Leighton Buzzard, Bedfordshire, LU7 4RW Tel: (01525) 376135 Fax: (01525) 217595 E-mail: info@dtindustrialfinishings.co.uk *Stove enamelling & powder coating*

D T Industries Ltd, Unit 10, Coulman Road Industrial Estate, Doncaster, South Yorkshire, DN8 5JU Tel: (01405) 740313 Fax: (01405) 817903 E-mail: sales@dtindustries.co.uk *Plastic mouldings specialising in thermoplastic bearings*

D T Jones & Son, Plas Yn Rhal, Llanbedr Dyffryn Clwyd, Ruthin, Clwyd, LL15 2UY Tel: (01824) 702955 Fax: (01824) 704585 *Farmers*

▶ D T L Training & Recruitment, Unit 1, Dunstall Hill Industrial Estate, Gorsebrook Road, Wolverhampton, WV6 0PJ Tel: (01902) 422722 Fax: (01902) 422711 E-mail: info@d-t-l.co.uk

D T P Services, 39 Bridle Road, Croydon, CR0 8HN Tel: (020) 8777 2735 Fax: (020) 8777 0299 E-mail: sales@dtp-services.co.uk *Computer consultants*

D.T.P. Supplies, 242 Whitworth Rd, Rochdale, Lancashire, OL12 0SA Tel: 0845 8550605 Fax: (01706) 648180 E-mail: jon@dtpsupplies.com *DTP Supplies have been established for over 25 years and are one of the leading distributor of eyelets. Made from a variety of metals and plastic, our range covers sizes from 1mm to 66mm hole diameter and are suitable for all industries including curtains, banner and sign making, electronics, marine, automotive, clothing, heavy textiles, pattern book and stationery. Our selection of eyelet setting equipment covers inexpensive hand tools through foot presses to fast powered semi and fully automatic machines.**We also stock a range of fasteners including rivets (two part, semi-tubular and bifurcated), buckles, press-fasteners, cord locks and ends, turnbuttons, webbing and bungee cord. Our range of products specifically for the sign maker include the Holdon clip, hinge handle (an inexpensive alternative to A frames), H901 self-piercing eyelet system and sign link.**Our friendly and knowledgeable staff are happy to help.*

D T R Newnham, Unit C5 Oakendene Industrial Estate, Bolney Road, Cowfold, Horsham, West Sussex, RH13 8AZ Tel: (01403) 864014 Fax: (01403) 864054 *Plastics fabricators*

▶ D T S Process Technologies Ltd, 5 Glen Lyon Crescent, Kilmarnock, Ayrshire, KA2 0LJ Tel: (01563) 534713

D T S Raeburn Ltd, Moor Lane, Witton, Birmingham, B6 7HG Tel: 0121-344 3826 Fax: 0121-344 4754 E-mail: enquiries@dts-raeburn.co.uk *Geotechnical & environmental consultants*

D T Signs Ltd, Willow Court, Bracewell Avenue, Poulton Industrial Estate, Poulton-le-Fylde, Lancashire, FY6 8JF Tel: (01253) 892410 Fax: (01253) 899802 E-mail: admin@dtsigns.co.uk *Sign manufrs*

D T Wright, Herald Way, Binley Industrial Estate, Binley Industrial Estate, Coventry, CV3 2RQ Tel: (024) 7643 1055 Fax: (024) 7663 5730 E-mail: info@wrightjoinery.sage-host.co.uk *Joinery manufrs*

D T Z Debenham Tie Leung, 30 Throgmorton Street, London, EC2N 2BQ Tel: (020) 7710 8000 Fax: (020) 7710 8080 *Property development consultants*

D T Z Pieda Consulting, 1 Edinburgh Quay, 133 Fountainbridge, Edinburgh, EH3 9QG Tel: 0131-222 4500 Fax: 0131-222 4501 *Economic consultants*

D Tec, Unit 2 Whitegate Business Center, Chadderton, Oldham, OL9 9QL Tel: 0161-627 3988 Fax: 0161-627 0194 E-mail: enquiries@dtec-elec.co.uk *Electrical contractors*

D Tech Computers, 31 Fore Bondgate, Bishop Auckland, County Durham, DL14 7PE Tel: (01388) 662891 Fax: (01388) 665702 E-mail: dtech@nildram.co.uk *Computer hardware*

D Theakstone, Lawrence Cottage, Beningbrough, York, YO30 1BZ Tel: (01904) 470550 Fax: (01904) 470566 *Agricultural engineers*

D Tipton, Kinston Elms, Church Road, North Leigh, Witney, Oxfordshire, OX29 6TX Tel: (01993) 881651 Fax: (01993) 883424 *Service catering equipment engineers*

D Tobias Ltd, 50 Rogart Street, Glasgow, G40 2AA Tel: 0141-554 2348 Fax: 0141-550 1090 *Blacksmiths & fabricators*

D Tox, Bramble Lane, Burntwood, Staffordshire, WS7 9AU Tel: (01543) 670707 Fax: (01543) 673110 *Portable toilet hire*

D Train, 43-45 Fisher Street, Stranraer, Wigtownshire, DG9 7LH Tel: (01776) 702357 Fax: (01776) 702357 *Plumber & plumbing contractors*

D Trippier, The Mill, Mill Lane, Bury, Lancashire, BL8 1TB Tel: 0161-764 4050 Fax: 0161-764 5050 *Motor trade consumables*

D U O Plastics Ltd, Vickers Street, Manchester, M40 8PU Tel: 0161-203 5767 Fax: 0161-203 5663 E-mail: duoplastics@btconnect.com *Polythene product manufrs*

D Urquhart, Glenglassaugh, Portsoy, Banff, AB45 2SQ Tel: (01261) 842594 Fax: (01261) 842860 *Joiners & funeral directors*

▶ D V D Videobox, Askew Road, London, W12 9AS Tel: (020) 8811 1449 *Computers services*

D & V Engineering, 17 Browning Avenue, Sutton, Surrey, SM1 3QU Tel: (020) 8642 5127 Fax: (020) 8770 1992 *Engineering & welding suppliers*

D V M Pigments & Additives, 45 Judeland, Chorley, Lancashire, PR7 1XJ Tel: (01257) 270311 Fax: (01257) 265509 E-mail: sales@dvmpigments.co.uk *Pigment pastes distributors*

D V R Electrical Wholesale Ltd, Unit 1 Dawson Road, Bletchley, Milton Keynes, MK1 1LH Tel: (01908) 271555 Fax: (01908) 271367 E-mail: info@dvr.co.uk *Electrical supply wholesale distribs*

D V R Fabrications, Unit 10 Winster Grove Industrial Estate, Winster Grove, Birmingham, B44 9EG Tel: 0121-325 0087 Fax: 0121-325 0087 *Welded fabrication manufrs*

▶ D W B Anglia Ltd, Mapledean Industrial Estate, Maldon Road, Latchingdon, Chelmsford, CM3 6LG Tel: (01621) 744455 Fax: (01621) 744976 E-mail: info@dwbgroup.co.uk *Roof trusses manufrs*

D W Begal & Son, Vulcan Works, Malta Street, Manchester, M4 7AP Tel: 0161-273 3296 Fax: 0161-273 3293 *Cleaning & polishing cloth manufrs*

D W Cases, Inveresk Mills Industrial Park, Musselburgh, Midlothian, EH21 7UQ Tel: 0131-665 4645 Fax: 0131-665 0792 *Corrugated case manufrs*

D W Cassell & Co., The Belper, Dudley, West Midlands, DY1 3AH Tel: (01384) 234321 *Electrical contractors*

D W Direct, 4 Merivale Road, Harrow, Middlesex, HA1 4BH Tel: (020) 8423 2030 Fax: (020) 8422 7216 E-mail: sales@computaform.force9.co.uk *Computer consumables retailers*

D & W Electrics West Bromwich, 29 Colshaw Road, Stourbridge, West Midlands, DY8 3AS Tel: (01384) 378289 Fax: (01384) 378289 E-mail: dw-electrics@blueyonder.co.uk *Electrical contractors*

D W Engineering, Unit A1 Industrial Estate, Watling Street, Consett, County Durham, DH8 6TA Tel: (01207) 505608 Fax: (01207) 505608 *Fabricators, sheet metalworkers & machinists services*

▶ D W Fabrications Ltd, Charles Street, Bury, Lancashire, BL9 5AJ Tel: 0161-761 6731 Fax: 0161-761 6731 E-mail: dwfabs@aol.com *Fabrication*

D W General Wood Machinists Ltd, 855 High Road, Tottenham, London, N17 8EY Tel: (020) 8801 1127 Fax: (020) 8808 1215 E-mail: sales@dw-group.co.uk *General wood machinists & CNC routering* Also at: Sandy

D W Group Ltd, Unit 7 Peverel Drive, Milton Keynes, MK1 1NL Tel: (01908) 642323 Fax: (01908) 640164 E-mail: sales@dw-view.com *Photo library systems manufacturers & cd rom manufrs*

▶ D W Hargreaves Electrical Contractors, 92-94 Buttermarket Street, Warrington, WA1 2NZ Tel: (01925) 414884 Fax: (01925) 573748

D W Hire, 41 Home Rule Road, Locks Heath, Southampton, SO31 6LH Tel: (01489) 581269 Fax: (01489) 559321 E-mail: dwhireaccess@aol.com *Hydraulic Access Platform Hire*

D W Industrial Doors, Unit 27 Farset Enterprise Park, Springfield Road, Belfast, BT12 7DY Tel: (028) 9023 7723 Fax: (028) 9023 7723 *Industrial steel doors manufrs*

D W Jones (Printers) Ltd, Beverley St, Port Talbot, West Glamorgan, SA13 1DY Tel: (01639) 883228 Fax: (01639) 882725 E-mail: sales@dwjones.com *Reprographics colour printing*

▶ D W M Productions, 83 Stonelaw Drive, Rutherglen, Glasgow, G73 3PA Tel: 0141-647 4221 E-mail: webdesign@dwmproductions.co.uk *Websites designed & maintained*Accessibility standards met*Reasonable prices*All in one package deals*Various Third Party products*All enquiries welcome*

D W Mouldings Ltd, 58 Sunderland Road, Sandy, Bedfordshire, SG19 1QY Tel: (01767) 683400 Fax: (01767) 692296 E-mail: info@dwmouldings.co.uk *Hardwood timber merchants & suppliers*

D W O'Brien Ltd, 64 Trafalgar Road, Kettering, Northamptonshire, NN16 8DD Tel: (01536) 484495 Fax: (01536) 410976 E-mail: sales@dwobrien.co.uk *Sheet metal pressings manufrs*

D W Precision Engineering, 9 Sopwith CR, Hurricane Way, Wickford, Essex, SS11 8YU Tel: (01268) 571616 Fax: (01268) 571626 E-mail: dwp@netcomuk.co.uk *Mould tool manufrs*

D W Precision Engineers, Studio 8 Building 56 Magnet Road, East Lane, Wembley, Middlesex, HA9 7RG Tel: (020) 8904 4038 Fax: (020) 8984 8802 E-mail: sales@dwprecision.freeserve.co.uk *Small component precision engineers*

▶ D W Supplies, PO Box 4139, Wolverhampton, WV4 6WZ Tel: (01902) 674407 Fax: (01902) 676808 E-mail: sales@dwsupplies.co.uk *Cleaning supplies*

D W Systems, 19 Cleveland Close, Highwoods, Colchester, CO4 9RD Tel: (01206) 842711 *domestic aerial installation. freeview digital upgrades, dtt, high gain aerials, storm damage repairs, new home installation, extra tv points, telephone points: Area covered; colchester, mersea, tiptree, maldon, kelvedon, witham, hatfield peverel, chelmsford, braintree, great dunmow, halstead, sible hedingham, yeldham. (post codes CO & CM)idsc member*

D W W Fencing Ltd, Gorseinon Road, Penllergaer, Swansea, SA4 1GE Tel: (01792) 874222 Fax: (01792) 874222

▶ D W Weaver Ltd, Blenheim Road, Airfield Industrial Estate, Ashbourne, Derbyshire, DE6 1HA Tel: (01335) 344182

D W Weaver Ltd, Park Farm, Park Lane, Endon, Stoke-on-Trent, ST9 9JB Tel: (01782) 503186 Fax: (01782) 504998 *Road transport, haulage & freight services*

D W Windsor Ltd, Pindar Road, Hoddesdon, Hertfordshire, EN11 0DX Tel: (01992) 474600 Fax: (01992) 474601 E-mail: sales@dwwindsor.co.uk *Street Lighting Manufacturing*

▶ D Wise Ltd, Parkfields, Nomansheath, Malpas, Cheshire, SY14 8DY Tel: (01948) 820418 Fax: (01948) 820452 *Producers of pasteurised egg products.*

D Wynn, 15 Kennington Road, Nuffield Industrial Estate, Poole, Dorset, BH17 0GF Tel: (01202) 677741 Fax: (01202) 667769 E-mail: david.wynn@lineone.net *Engineers*

▶ D X G Media Ltd, Abc House, Latham Close, Bredbury, Stockport, Cheshire, SK6 2SD Tel: 0161-612 3030 Fax: 0161-612 7001

D X Imaging, Units 19 & 20, Watford Enterprise Centre, Watford, WD18 8EA Tel: (01923) 227644 Fax: (01923) 816896 E-mail: dximaging@dximaging.co.uk *Digital printers*

D X L Parcels, Unit 5 Oakfield Trading Estate, Oakfield Road, Altrincham, Cheshire, WA14 5PR Tel: 0161-941 6277 Fax: 0161-941 7383 E-mail: operations@dxlparcels.co.uk *Sameday* *continued* *Couriers. Express Document and Parcel Deliveries Nationwide to and from Manchester Sameday, Nextday and Timed Services. International Courier Services, Warehousing, Storage*

D X Telecommunications Systems, Unit 14, Beaumont Business Centre, Beaumont Close, Banbury, Oxfordshire, OX16 1TN Tel: (01295) 672700 Fax: (01295) 672707 E-mail: info@dxts.co.uk *Data networkers*

D Young & Co., 120 Holborn, London, EC1N 2DY Tel: (020) 7269 8550 Fax: (020) 7269 8555 E-mail: mail@dyoung.co.uk *Chartered patent agents & trademark agents* Also at: Southampton & Windsor

D&B, Unit 3 Birds Industrial Estate, Risca, Newport, Gwent, NP11 6EW Tel: (01633) 619030 Fax: (01633) 619030 *Sheds & fencing distributors & manufrs*

D&B Tracks & Blinds, 1 Caistor Close, Calcot, Reading, RG31 7AY Tel: 0118-943 2757 *Curtain Fitters*

D&R, 36 Dale Street, Chilton, Ferryhill, County Durham, DL17 0HQ Tel: (01388) 721125 *Pest control services*

▶ D2, 23 High East St, Dorchester, Dorset, DT1 1HD Tel: 01305 252112 Fax: 01305 251908 E-mail: info@d2email.net *Digital Print Services : Personalised data handling and printing; Short run high quality printing;Print on waterproof materials*

D2 Information Solutions, Law Street, Cleckheaton, West Yorkshire, BD19 3QR Tel: (01274) 866006 Fax: (01274) 875549 E-mail: info@d2.com *Business information systems services*

D3 Display, 1 Cyril Road, Small Heath, Birmingham, B10 0SS Tel: 0121-772 1815 Fax: 0121-766 6052 E-mail: info@d3display.co.uk *Signwriting & screen printers*

▶ D4 Design, 295 Fortenay House, 14A Ongar Road, Brentwood, Essex, CM15 9GB Tel: (07974) 705032 E-mail: gary@d4design.co.uk *Specialists in providing a personal, professional, reliable and inexpensive Computer Aided Design service for all requirements ranging from office space planning to electrical schematics, including Licensing application plans and General Application packs. A full CAD design service is available from initial concept to final hand over or from any stage in-between.*We provide a convenient space planning service for office refurbishment companies, as well as CAD work for data & electrical businesses, and to FM services providing a convenient in-house facility for clients requiring a freelance CAD operator.*D4"s freelance service can be a huge benefit to companies where budgets are tight and the ability to employ a full time designer is limited. A freelance CAD operator gives flexibility should staff take holiday, maternity or sick leave.*If you think D4's services can benefit you then please don't hesitate to contact us, we look forward to hearing from you to discuss your requirements*

Da Ltd, Bridge House, Marsh Lane, Shepley, Huddersfield, HD8 8AE Tel: (01484) 609609 Fax: (01484) 609600 E-mail: sales@dacreative.com *Marketing consultants specialising in graphic design*

▶ DA Internet, 128 Peckover Drive, Pudsey, Leeds, LS28 8EG Tel: 078216 11939 E-mail: sales@dainternet.net *Cheap Internet at Low Cost*

▶ Da Media Ltd, 8 Fallowfield, Sittingbourne, Kent, ME10 4UT Tel: (01795) 559456 E-mail: info@da-media.co.uk *Bespoke software development & consultancy*

Da Plating Jigs & Light Fabrications, 16 Cornwall Road Industrial Estate, Smethwick, West Midlands, B66 2JS Tel: 0121-555 8687 Fax: 0121-555 8688 E-mail: david@daplating.wannadoo.co.uk *Engineering services*

▶ DA Taylor Consultants Ltd, Finny Bank Road, Sale, Cheshire, M33 6LR Tel: 0161-976 5138 E-mail: info@taylorconsultants.co.uk *IT consultants*

▶ Dab Handling, 42-50 Tannoch Drive, Cumbernauld, Glasgow, G67 2XX Tel: (01236) 453331 Fax: (01236) 452653 E-mail: arthur@dabhandling.co.uk *Forklift trucks & accessories*

Dab Pumps Ltd, 4 Stortford Hall Industrial Park, Dunmow Road, Bishop's Stortford, Hertfordshire, CM23 5GZ Tel: (01279) 652776 Fax: (01279) 655147 E-mail: info@dabpumps.com *Pump manufrs*

▶ Dab Systems Ltd, White Meadow Farm, Parwich, Ashbourne, Derbyshire, DE6 1QY Tel: (01335) 390320 Fax: (01335) 390633 E-mail: info@dabsystems.co.uk

Dab Valves Ltd, White Meadow Farm, Parwich, Ashbourne, Derbyshire, DE6 1QY Tel: (01335) 390572 Fax: (01335) 390633 E-mail: sales@dabsystems.co.uk *Valves manufrs*

The Dabarr Group Ltd, The Packhouse, Parsonage Farm Heath Road, Boughton Monchelsea, Maidstone, Kent, ME17 4JB Tel: (01622) 747450 Fax: (01622) 746812 E-mail: info@dabarr.co.uk *New & reconditioned packaging machinery*

▶ Dabbrook Power Systems, Unit 23, Bells Marsh Rd, Gorleston, Great Yarmouth, Norfolk, NR31 6PT Tel: (01493) 441711 Fax: (01493) 440322 E-mail: info@dabbrook.com Principal Export Areas: Asia Pacific, Central Asia, Middle East, Africa, Central/East Europe, West Europe & South America *As approved distributors for BP Solar, Dabbrook Power Systems designs, supplies and installs renewable energy systems that can either provide power to remote locations or help supplement mains electricity supplies.*

Dabro Precast Concrete Ltd, The Old Colliery Yard, Pensford, Bristol, BS39 4BU Tel: (01761) 490664 Fax: (01761) 490758 *Pre-cast concrete manufrs*

▶ Dac Air Conditioning, Carrington Business Park, Manchester Road, Carrington, Manchester, M31 4DD Tel: 0161-776 4484 Fax: 0161-776 4485

Dac Handling Solutions, 10 Kestrel Park, Tallon Road, Hutton, Brentwood, Essex, CM13 1TN Tel: (01277) 223055 Fax: (01277) 222472 E-mail: info@dac-handling.co.uk *Container handling/fork lift trucks*

Dac Handling Solutions, 7 Eldon Way, Bristol, BS4 3PZ Tel: (01264) 772012 Fax: (01264) 771083 E-mail: drock@dac-handling.co.uk *Distributors of forklifts, trucks, hire sales, exchange repairs*

▶ Dac Systems, 4 Balloo Drive, Bangor, County Down, BT19 7QY Tel: (028) 9185 7711 Fax: (028) 9185 7722 E-mail: sales@dacsystems.co.uk *IT consultants*

Dachser Transport UK Ltd, Oxwich Close, Brackmills Industrial Estate, Northampton, NN4 7BH Tel: (01604) 666222 Fax: (01604) 666239 E-mail: dachser.northampton@dachser.com *Freight forwarders & shipping agents* Also at: Doncaster

Dacoll Ltd, Gardners Lane, Bathgate, West Lothian, EH48 1TP Tel: (01506) 815000 Fax: (01506) 656012 E-mail: sales@dacoll.co.uk *Computer systems consultants*

▶ Dacom (UK) Ltd, 115A Brunswick Park Road, London, N11 1EA Tel: (020) 8361 6560

Dacon P.L.C., 1 Enterprise Way, Hemel Hempstead, Hertfordshire, HP2 7YJ Tel: (01442) 233222 Fax: (01442) 219656 E-mail: info@dacon.co.uk *Telecommunications system manufrs*

Dacon Fabrications Ltd, Dukesway, Team Valley Trading Estate, Gateshead, Tyne & Wear, NE11 0PZ Tel: 0191-482 5464 Fax: 0191-482 5463 E-mail: info@daconfab.co.uk *Control panel cabinet manufrs*

Dacre Agriculture Ltd, Astwood Road, Cranfield, Bedford, MK43 0AT Tel: (01234) 751591 Fax: (01234) 750745 E-mail: sales@dacreag.co.uk *Agricultural engineering*

Dacrylate Ltd, Lime Street, Kirkby-In-Ashfield, Nottingham, NG17 8AL Tel: (01623) 753845 Fax: (01623) 757151 E-mail: sales@dacrylate.co.uk *Paint manufrs*

Dacs Electrical Ltd, Old Fire Station, Church Street, Connah's Quay, Deeside, Clwyd, CH5 4AS Tel: (01244) 834100 Fax: (01244) 831858 E-mail: sales@dacselectrical.co.uk *Control panel manufrs* Also at: Branches throughout the UK

▶ dae illustrations, 31 westby avenue, Blackpool, FY4 3QL Tel: 07900 532083 E-mail: abyllez@yahoo.com *Darren Elwell is a contemporary illustrator working in a variety of media, including digital, to create eye-catching work to satisfy any brief.*

▶ Daedalus Industrial Design Studio, Bloxwich, Walsall, WS3 2AB Tel: 01922 400374 E-mail: info@daedalusdesign.co.uk *Design & illustration services*

Daejan Holdings P.L.C., 158-162 Shaftesbury Avenue, London, WC2H 8HR Tel: (020) 7836 1555 Fax: (020) 7379 6365 *Property management services*

Daemon Fire & Security Ltd, 41-42 Albert Road, Tamworth, Staffordshire, B79 7JS Tel: (01827) 69266 Fax: (01827) 53584 E-mail: sales@daemonfire.co.uk *Fire detection & alarm systems*

Daewoo Electronics UK Ltd, Rathenraw Industrial Estate, 62-82 Greystone Road, Antrim, BT41 1NU Tel: (028) 9442 5117 Fax: (028) 9442 5100 *Electronic goods manufacturer*

Daewoo International Ltd, 10TH Floor C I Tower, St. Georges Square, New Malden, Surrey, KT3 4HH Tel: (020) 8336 9130 Fax: (020) 8949 3783 E-mail: kelliedodds@daewoo.co.uk *International trading*

Daf Trucks Ltd, Eastern By Passage, Thame, Oxfordshire, OX9 3FB Tel: (01844) 261111 Fax: (01844) 217111 E-mail: info@daftrucks.com *HGV hire & sales*

Daften Ltd, Trevilling Quay, Wadebridge, Cornwall, PL27 6EB Tel: (01208) 812148 Fax: (01208) 814092 E-mail: diecasting@daften.co.uk *Diecasting manufrs*

Dagar Tools Ltd, 6 Providence Industrial Estate, Providence Street, Stourbridge, West Midlands, DY9 8HQ Tel: (01384) 893344 Fax: (01384) 422996 *Engineers, suppliers & fastener stockist*

Dagenham Construction Ltd, 3 Ardmore Road, South Ockendon, Essex, RM15 5TH Tel: (01708) 851631 Fax: (01708) 852247 E-mail: dagenhamcon@btconnect.com *Roofing contractors*

Dagless Ltd, Brigstock Road, Wisbech, Cambridgeshire, PE13 3JL Tel: (01945) 583826 Fax: (01945) 582673 E-mail: info@shiregb.co.uk *Timber merchants*

▶ Dagmar Courier Services, 18 St. Rumbold Street, Lincoln, LN2 5AP Tel: (01522) 567588 Fax: (01522) 567588 E-mail: dagmarcouriers@fsmail.net *Courier & light removals services*

Dagnall Electronics Ltd, 3 Shuttleworth Road, Elm Farm Industrial Estate, Bedford, MK41 0EP Tel: (01234) 330077 Fax: (01234) 330088 E-mail: sales@dagnall.co.uk *Transformer manufrs*

▶ Daifuku Co. Ltd, 3 Waterside Drive, Langley, Slough, SL3 6EZ Tel: (01753) 581000 Fax: (01753) 582210 E-mail: sales@daifuku.co.uk *Manufacturer of automotive equipment*

Daihatsu Diesel (Europe) Ltd, 5th Floor, Devon House, 58 St. Katharines Way, London, E1W 1LB Tel: (020) 7977 0280 Fax: (020) 7626 6020 E-mail: daihatsu@ddeuk.com *Diesel engine manufrs*

▶ Daihatsu Entrance Systems Ltd, Unit E8 Kingfisher Business Park, Hawthorne Road, Bootle, Merseyside, L20 6PF Tel: 0151-933 9443 Fax: 0151-933 9447

Daihatsu Vehicle Distributors, Ryder Street, West Bromwich, West Midlands, B70 0EJ Tel: 0121-520 5000 Fax: (01304) 206317 *Motor vehicle importers*

Daiichi Sankyo UK Ltd, Sankyo House, Repton Place, Amersham, Buckinghamshire, HP7 9LP Tel: (01494) 766866 Fax: (01494) 766557 E-mail: info@sankyo.co.uk *Pharmaceutical sales & marketing*

Daikin Air Conditioning East Ltd, The Old Stable, Station Road, Arlesey, Bedfordshire, SG15 6RG Tel: (01462) 834999 Fax: (01462) 731208 *Air conditioning distributors*

Daikin Airconditioning UK Ltd, The Heights, Brooklands, Weybridge, Surrey, KT13 0NY Tel: (0845) 6419000 Fax: (0845) 641009 E-mail: sales@daikin.co.uk *Daikin Airconditioning UK Ltd is the country's leading supplier of air conditioning equipment and solutions and has gained an established reputation for excellence in product design and engineering. This, combined with the company's extensive network of highly professional installers and D1 Partners makes for a winning combination in design, installation, supply and service of modern and energy efficient air conditioning systems*

Daikin Airconditioning UK Ltd, The Heights, Brooklands, Weybridge, Surrey, KT13 0NY Tel: (0845) 6419000 Fax: (0845) 6419009 E-mail: marketing@daikin.co.uk *Air conditioning*

Dail Design Products, St Mary Church, Cowbridge, South Glamorgan, CF71 7LT Tel: (01446) 773123 Fax: (01446) 773123 *Fibreglass consultants*

Dailly Glazing & Interiors, 15 Mains Road, Dundee, DD3 7RH Tel: (01382) 825400 Fax: (01382) 832978 E-mail: dailly.glazing@btconnect.com *Glazing contractors*

Daily Office Cleaning, 30 West Gorgie Parks, Edinburgh, EH14 1UT Tel: 0131-455 7364 Fax: 0131-455 7364 E-mail: info@scotdoc.co.uk *Office cleaning contractors*

▶ Dailycer Chestergate, Unit 14, Fourth Avenue, Deeside Industrial Park, Deeside, Clwyd, CH5 2NR Tel: (01244) 289188 *Breakfast cereals*

Daines & Hathaway, Shelton House, Bridgeman Street, Walsall, WS2 9PG Tel: (01922) 621823 Fax: (01922) 623393 E-mail: sales@dainesandhathaway.com *Leather good manufrs*

Dainippon Screen UK Ltd, Michigan Drive, Tongwell, Milton Keynes, MK15 8HT Tel: (01908) 848500 Fax: (01908) 848501 E-mail: sales@screeneurope.co.uk *Printing trade suppliers & services*

▶ Dainton Portable Buildings Ltd, Dainton Business Park, Newton Abbot, Devon, TQ12 5TZ Tel: (01626) 835547 Fax: (01626) 830407 E-mail: info@dainton.com *Storage & container suppliers*

Dairi Pak, Platt Bridge, Ruyton XI Towns, Shrewsbury, SY4 1LS Tel: (01939) 260342 Fax: (01939) 260275 E-mail: sales@dairi-pak.co.uk *Corrugated board manufrs*

Dairy Crest Ltd, Pelton Road, Basingstoke, Hampshire, RG21 6XD Tel: (01256) 321329 Fax: (01256) 810833 *Milk delivery service*

▶ Dairy Crest Ltd, 4 Alexandra Road, Epsom, Surrey, KT17 4BJ Tel: (01372) 726551 Fax: (01372) 747231 E-mail: epson.depot@dairycrest.co.uk *Customer services in regards to retail sales*

▶ Dairy Crest Ltd, 10 George Edwards Road, Fakenham, Norfolk, NR21 8NL Tel: (01328) 862025 Fax: (01328) 855704 *Milk retailers*

▶ Dairy Crest Ltd, Stenner House, Brinell Way, Great Yarmouth, Norfolk, NR31 0LU Tel: (01493) 660400 Fax: (01493) 657289

▶ Dairy Crest Ltd, Barn Hawe, Church Hill, Orpington, Kent, BR6 0HE Tel: (01689) 827511

Dairy Crest Ltd, Dudnance Lane, Pool, Redruth, Cornwall, TR15 3QT Tel: (01209) 713238 Fax: (01209) 612126 *Dairy distributors*

▶ Dairy Crest Ltd, Tavistock Road, West Drayton, Middlesex, UB7 7QX Tel: (01895) 443611

Dairy Crest, Units 1B, Weir Lane, Worcester, WR2 4AY Tel: (01905) 748100 Fax: (01905) 748483 *Dairies for milk*

Dairy Industry Association, 93 Baker Street, London, W1U 6RL Tel: (020) 7486 7244 Fax: (020) 7487 4734 E-mail: mailbox@dif.org.uk *Trade association*

Dairy Pipe Lines Ltd, Commercial Centre, Ashdon Road, Saffron Walden, Essex, CB10 2NH Tel: (01799) 520188 Fax: (01799) 520183 E-mail: dairypipelines@dpluk.co.uk *Stainless steel valves & fittings manufrs*

Dairyborn Foods Ltd, Eaton Green Road, Luton, LU2 9XF Tel: (01582) 457979 Fax: (01582) 400957 *Cheese suppliers*

Dairyland Ices (East Anglia) Ltd, Little Plumstead, Norwich, NR13 5BY Tel: (01603) 720317

▶ Daisy Galore, Nutfield House, Eyre Street, Stanley, County Durham, DH9 7AF Tel: (01207) 299290

▶ Daisyfield Foods Ltd, Wellington Street, Bury, Lancashire, BL8 2XX Tel: 0161-797 1100 Fax: 0161-797 1100

Daiwa Sports Ltd, Netherton Industrial Estate, Wishaw, Lanarkshire, ML2 0EY Tel: (01698) 355723 Fax: (01698) 372505 E-mail: info@diawasports.co.uk *Manufacturers of fishing rods*

Dakar Cars Ltd, Stanhill Farm, Birchwood Road, Dartford, DA2 7HD Tel: (01322) 614044 Fax: (01322) 668500 E-mail: sales@dakar.co.uk *Garage workshop*

▶ Dakin-Flathers Ltd, Dakin-Flathers Ltd Boothroyds, Way, Featherstone, Pontefract, West Yorkshire, WF7 6RA Tel: (01977) 705600 Fax: (01977) 705700 E-mail: sales@dakin-flathers.com *Bandsaws, bandknife, bandsaw blade, bandknives, bandknife blades*

Dako Ltd, Denmark House, Angel Drove, Ely, Cambridgeshire, CB7 4ET Tel: (01353) 669911 Fax: (01353) 668989 *Diagnostic kit & system manufrs*

Daks Simpson Ltd, 10 Old Bond Street, London, W1S 4PL Tel: (020) 7409 4000 Fax: (020) 7499 4494 *Clothing manufrs*

▶ DAL Utilities Ltd, 2 Westcliff Park Drive, Westcliff-on-sea, Essex, SS0 9LP Tel: 01702 304849 Fax: 01702 304849 E-mail: dal_ltd@btinternet.com *Repair and renew water pipes*

▶ Dalair Ltd, Southern Way, Wednesbury, West Midlands, WS10 7BU Tel: 0121-556 9944 Fax: 0121-502 3124 E-mail: sales@dalair.co.uk *Air handling & packaged air conditioning equipment manufrs*

▶ Dalatek Ltd, Junction Road, Sutton-in-Ashfield, Nottinghamshire, NG17 5GS Tel: (01623) 440077 Fax: (01623) 440954 E-mail: sgreen@techtube.co.uk *Molding & packaging company*

Dalbeattie Finance Co. Ltd, Maxwell Street, Dalbeattie, Kirkcudbrightshire, DG5 4AJ Tel: (01556) 610243 Fax: (01556) 611717 E-mail: info@dalbeattiefinance.co.uk *Financial services*

Dalblair of Ayr Ltd, 127 Prestwick Road, Ayr, KA8 8ND Tel: (01292) 269123 Fax: (01292) 280290 E-mail: dalblair@yahoo.com *Motor car dealers*

Dalbrook Ltd, Box Cottage, West Kington Wick, Chippenham, Wiltshire, SN14 7JD Tel: (01249) 782146 Fax: (01249) 782948 *Computer systems for television*

Dalby Consultants Ltd, High Dalby House, Dalby, Pickering, North Yorkshire, YO18 7LP Tel: (01751) 460020 *Timber framed building contractors*

Harry Dalby Engineering Incoporating Dalby Sheetmetal, Gloucester Crescent, Wigston, Leicestershire, LE18 4YQ Tel: 0116-291 6000 Fax: 0116-291 6001 E-mail: enquiries@dalby.co.uk Principal Export Areas: Worldwide *Manufacturer of Automotive and Industrial Paint Spray Booths and a subcontract sheet metal manufacturer. Offering CNC Laser cutting, CNC plasma cutting, CNC punching, CNC Press Brake folding, Welding (MIG, TIG, Gas and Spot), General Fabrication, Painting and Plating**

Dale, Herriot Way, Scunthorpe, South Humberside, DN15 8XU Tel: (01724) 855645 Fax: (01724) 278278 E-mail: sales@daleuk.co.uk *Chemical manufacturers/safety wear distributors, paint distributors, oil and greases.*

Alan Dale Pumps Ltd, 75 Clockhouse Lane, Ashford, Middlesex, TW15 2HA Tel: (01784) 421114 Fax: (01784) 421092 E-mail: info@alandalepumps.wanadoo.co.uk *Manufacturers & distributors of high pressure water jetting pumps*

Dale Carnegie Training, 1200 Century Way, Thorpe Park, Leeds, LS15 8ZA Tel: 0113-251 5116 *Training services*

▶ Dale Electronics Ltd, Dale House, Wharf Road, Frimley Green, Camberley, Surrey, GU16 6LF Tel: (01252) 832600 Fax: (01252) 837010 E-mail: june@uk.minicircuits.com *European distribution of mini circuits rf & if microwave products*

Dale Engineering Co. Ltd, Wolverhampton Road, Wedges Mills, Cannock, Staffordshire, WS11 1SN Tel: (01543) 503265 Fax: (01543) 505475 *Wire cloth manufrs*

Dale Engineering Services, 20 Manor Road, Scunthorpe, South Humberside, DN16 3PA Tel: (01724) 858748 Fax: (01724) 858748 *General engineers*

Dale Express Transport Ltd, Dale House, 232 Selsdon Road, Croydon, CR2 6PL Tel: (020) 8760 5000 Fax: (020) 8760 0202 E-mail: service@daleexpress.co.uk *Couriers & express delivery services*

Dale Farm Ice Cream Ltd, 15 Dargan Road, Belfast, BT3 9LS Tel: (028) 9037 2200 E-mail: info@utdni.co.uk *Dale Farm is part of the United Dairy Farmers Group, a UK dairy farmer co-operative owned by 2500 dairy farmers who supply it with fresh milk. Dale Farm has operations throughout the UK and Ireland producing and distributing a wide range of dairy products which it sells across the UK and Ireland as well as exporting to over 45 countries world wide. The Group's consumer brands - Dale Farm, Spelga, Dromona, Rowan Glen and Loseley - encompass every dairy need from milk, cream, cheese, butter, and dairy spreads to yogurts, probiotic drinks, ice-cream and desserts and are synonymous with natural, wholesome and quality dairy goodness.*

Dale Farm Ingredients Ltd, Dargan Road, Belfast, BT3 9JU Tel: (028) 9037 0903 Fax: (028) 9077 1442 E-mail: k.lyons@halib.co.uk *Manufacturers of dairy produce*

Dale Fencing Ltd, 834 London Road, North Cheam, Sutton, Surrey, SM3 9BJ Tel: (020) 8641 2367 Fax: (020) 8641 1838 E-mail: dale@fences.fsbusiness.co.uk *Fencing contractors*

Dale Heating Services (U.K.) Ltd, Unit 2, Rookery Lane, Thurmaston, Leicester, LE4 8AU Tel: 0116-264 0055 Fax: 0116-269 7007 *Heating & ventilation engineers* Also at: Birmingham, Northampton & Nottingham

▶ Jo Dale Consulting Ltd, 90 Stourvale Road Southbourne, Bournemouth, BH6 5JB Tel: (01202) 248731 E-mail: mail@jodaleconsulting.com *Jo Dale Consulting"s work focuses on helping organisations to maximize employee performance by ensuring it is aligned to the business strategy. We work with you to create alignment and engagement and to maximise the performance of your employees. **Our work focuses on 4 main areas, Succession and Talent Management, Motivation and Reward, Change Management and Recruitment and Retention, all supported by understanding what your particular organisation needs to achieve its goals.*

Dale Joinery Lichfield Ltd, Europa Way, Britannia Enterprise Park, Lichfield, Staffordshire, WS14 9TY Tel: (01543) 414223 Fax: (01543) 255538 *Joiners*

Dale Lifting and Handling, 2 Kelbrook Road, Manchester, M11 2QA Tel: 0161-223 1990 Fax: 0161-223 6767 E-mail: ingfo@dale_lifiting.com *Lifting gear manufrs*

Dale Mansfield Ltd, Rotherham Road, New Houghton, Mansfield, Nottinghamshire, NG19 8TF Tel: (01623) 810659 Fax: (01623) 811660 E-mail: enquiry@dale-mansfield.co.uk Principal Export Areas: North America & South America *Hydraulic cylinder/ram manufrs*

Dale Power Solutions Ltd, Salter Road, Eastfield, Scarborough, North Yorkshire, YO11 3DU Tel: (01723) 583511 Fax: (01723) 581231 E-mail: sales@dalepowersolutions.com *Generator service & maintenance*

Dale Products Plastics Ltd, Barnsley Road, Hoyland, Barnsley, South Yorkshire, S74 0QW Tel: (01226) 742511 Fax: (01226) 350496 E-mail: dale.products@fsbdial.co.uk *Flexible products & specialised packaging manufrs*

Dale R Contractors, 2 Mereside Avenue, Congleton, Cheshire, CW12 4JZ Tel: (01260) 270776 Fax: (01260) 270776 *Groundwork contractors*

Dale Sailing Co Ltd, Brunel Quay, Neyland, Milford Haven, Dyfed, SA73 1PY Tel: (01646) 601061 Fax: (01646) 601061 E-mail: enquiries@dale-sailing.co.uk *Marine industry, builders & repairers*

Dale Signs, 19 Woodhouse Road, Sheffield, S12 2AY Tel: 0114-253 1461 Fax: 0114-239 8127 *Sign manufrs*

Daleba Electronics, 49 Tamworth Road, Hertford, SG13 7DJ Tel: (01992) 582232 Fax: (01992) 582222 E-mail: sales@daleba.co.uk *Printed circuit board manufrs*

Dalebrook Supplies Ltd, Eastways Industrial Estate, Witham, Essex, CM8 3UA Tel: (01376) 510101 Fax: (01376) 510153 E-mail: sales@dalebrook.com *Dalebrook Supplies is a leading designer and manufacturer of melamine tableware. Our products are sold internationally to supermarkets, hotels, contract caterers, delicatessens and many more. Our range of melamine products include bowls, trays, dishes, plates, gastro products and buffet ware. We also sell a range of melamine dinner and tableware perfect for children and babies. This range includes fun characters and designs available in plates, bowls, meal trays, cups and beakers. These melamine products are ideal for serving children's food in restaurants or for retail merchandise. Our melamine products are 100% food grade, extremely durable and dishwasher safe. We also have a design and customisation service where we can make a unique product just for you. All of our products can be viewed on www.dalebrook.com or if you would like to see just our children's items then check out www.dalebrookdirect.co.uk.*

Dalehall Mills Ltd, Newport Lane, Stoke-on-Trent, ST6 3PJ Tel: (01782) 837055 Fax: (01782) 577782 E-mail: dalehallmills@tiscali.co.uk *Pottery suppliers*

Dalen Ltd, Garretts Green Trading Estate, Valepits Road, Birmingham, B33 0TD Tel: 0121-783 3838 Fax: 0121-784 6348 E-mail: sales@top-tec.co.uk *TV stands & computer security cages manufrs*

▶ Dalepak, Caswell Road, Brackmills Industrial Estate, Northampton, NN4 7PW Tel: (01604) 676246 Fax: (01604) 767606 E-mail: sales@dalepak.ltd.uk *Dalepak Ltd - Total Logistics Services based in Northampton, including, storage and distribution, contract packing, warehousing, field marketing and frieght forwarding*

▶ Dalepak Packing, The Business Centre, Ross Road, Weedon Road Industrial Estate, Northampton, NN5 5AX Tel: (01604) 580777 Fax: (01604) 756600

Dales Broadcast Ltd, Unit 4, Oaks Industrial Estate, Coventry Road, Narborough, LE19 2GF Tel: 0116-272 5190 Fax: 0116-272 5196 E-mail: sales@dalesbroadcast.co.uk *TV post production services*

Dales Contractors Ltd, Rough Heys Farm, Rough Heys Lane, Henbury, Macclesfield, Cheshire, SK11 9PF Tel: (01625) 501529 Fax: (01625) 501403 E-mail: dales@farmline.com *Agricultural contractors*

Dales Engineering Ltd, Dales Industrial Estate, Peterhead, Aberdeenshire, AB42 3JF Tel: (01779) 478778 Fax: (01779) 471846 E-mail: sales@dalesgroup.co.uk *Engineering fabricators* Also at: Aberdeen

Dales Fabrication Ltd, Crompton Road, Ilkeston, Derbyshire, DE7 4BG Tel: 0115-930 1521 Fax: 0115-930 7625 E-mail: technical@dales-eaves.co.uk *Rainwater & fascia soffit system suppliers*

▶ Dales Sports Surfaces Ltd, Sharpes Lane, Sheepgate, Leverton, Boston, Lincolnshire, PE22 0AR Tel: (01205) 761066 Fax: (01205) 760856

Dalescraft Art & Craft Materials, 26a Bondgate Green, Ripon, North Yorkshire, HG4 1QW Tel: (01765) 692053 Fax: (01765) 692053 E-mail: colin@dalescraft.com *Woodware manufrs*

▶ Daleside Group Shopfitters Ltd, Park Road East, Calverton, Nottingham, NG14 6LL Tel: 0115-965 6696 Fax: 0115-965 6328 E-mail: info@dalesidegroup.com *Shop fitting service*

Daleside Welding, Gowrey Farm, Wandales Lane, Kirkby Lonsdale, Carnforth, Lancashire, LA6 2JN Tel: (01524) 272312 Fax: (01524) 273123 *Steel fabricators*

▶ Dalesman Fabrications Ltd, 3 Astley Way, Astley La Industrial Estate, Swillington, Leeds, LS26 8XT Tel: 0113-287 5732 Fax: 0113-287 2319

▶ Dalestone Concrete Products & Patio Laying, Whisby Garden Centre, Whisby Road, Whisby Moor, Lincoln, LN6 9BY Tel: (01522) 689530 Fax: (01522) 684040 E-mail: dalestone01@aol.com *Possibly the widest selection of patio slabs in Lincolnshire,Manufacturing our own delightful ranges as well as being agents for Tarmac Paving products,Livingstone,Natural paving and Grange fencing.*Also suppliers of local gravels, decorative gravels, hardcore,sand and topsoil. Fence Panels concrete Posts and gravel boards also in stock. we have an inhouse Hard landscaping team for all fitting requirementst and guarantee to beat any genuine quote. Can arrange to have over 12 pallet loads of Tarmac paving producs or block pavers delivered anywhere in england at amazing bulk buy prices- ask for a quote.*

Daleswear, Dales Business Park, New Road, Ingleton, Carnforth, Lancashire, LA6 3HL Tel: (01524) 241477 Fax: (01524) 241047 E-mail: sales@daleswear.co.uk *Outdoor Clothing manufrs*

Daletech Electronics Ltd, Regency House, Valley Road, Pudsey, West Yorkshire, LS28 9EN Tel: 0113-239 4220 Fax: 0113-255 3583 E-mail: sales@daletech.co.uk *Electronic product regulatory compliance service, design & manufrs*

Dalewood Designs, Greenhill Lane, Riddings, Alfreton, Derbyshire, DE55 4EX Tel: (01773) 604384 Fax: (01773) 604384 *Wooden cabinet manufrs*

Dalewood Designs, Skirlaugh Road, Old Ellerby, Hull, HU11 5AN Tel: (01964) 563242 Fax: (01964) 563242 *Furniture*

Dalgarno Chemicals & Oils, Newton of Thainstone, Kintore, Inverurie, Aberdeenshire, AB51 0YG Tel: (01467) 632673 Fax: (01467) 633016 E-mail: dalgarnochemicals@btconnect.com *Agricultural merchants*

▶ Dalgarven Homes Ltd, Dalgarven House, 55 Maryborough Road, Prestwick, Ayrshire, KA9 1SW Tel: (01292) 478288 Fax: (01292) 478288

Dalgety Arable Ltd, Throws Farm, Stebbing, Dunmow, Essex, CM6 3AQ Tel: (01371) 856431 Fax: (01371) 856616 E-mail: throws.farm@dalgety.co.uk *Arable trials & researchers*

▶ Dalkeith Demolition Ltd, Mayfield Industrial Estate, Newtongrange, Dalkeith, Midlothian, EH22 4AH Tel: 0131-660 1939

▶ Dalkeith Demolition Ltd, Unit 27 Mayfield Industrial Estate, Newtongrange, Dalkeith, Midlothian, EH22 4AD Tel: 0131-660 1939 Fax: 0131-663 8138 E-mail: iwmg@btconnect.com

▶ Dalkeith Transport & Storage Ltd, Westerton Road, East Mains Industrial Estate, Broxburn, West Lothian, EH52 5AU Tel: (01506) 858544 Fax: (01506) 855862

▶ Dalkeith Transport & Storage Co Ltd, Lady Victoria Business Centre, Newtongrange, Dalkeith, Midlothian, EH22 4QN Tel: 0131-663 2451 Fax: 0131-654 0284

Dalkia, The Connect Centre, Kingston CR, Portsmouth, PO2 8AD Tel: (0800) 0853208 Fax: (023) 9262 9656 E-mail: enquiries@dalkia.co.uk *Building services, energy & technical services* Also at: Branches throughout U.K.

▶ Dalkia Energy & Technical Services Ltd, 506-510 Old Kent Road, London, SE1 5BA Tel: (020) 7231 1338

Dalkia Utilities plc, Oakenshaw Lane, Crofton, Wakefield, West Yorkshire, WF4 1SE Tel: (01924) 258331 Fax: (01924) 259585 *Contract energy management* Also at: Staines

Dalkia Utilities Services plc, 12 London Road, Nottingham, NG2 3AB Tel: 0115-950 2816 Fax: 0115-953 6646 *Energy management services*

Dallas Wear, 11 Vallance Road, London, E1 5HS Tel: (020) 7247 6435 Fax: (020) 7247 8824 E-mail: sales@dallsawear.com *Wholesale clothing distributors*

Dallmac Precision Engineering, Hardley Industrial Estate, Hythe, Southampton, SO45 3NQ Tel: (023) 8084 9211 Fax: (023) 8084 9211 *Precision engineers*

Dalman & Narborough Ltd, 38-40 Lombard Street, Birmingham, B12 0QN Tel: 0121-772 2008 Fax: 0121-771 4182 E-mail: sales@dalman-narborough.co.uk *Highland regalia manufrs*

Dalman Technical Services, Unit 36 Walworth Enterprise Centre Duke Close, West Way, Andover, Hampshire, SP10 5AP Tel: (01264) 357580 Fax: (01264) 351325 E-mail: sales@dalmants.co.uk *Electronic systems to specification*

Dalmec Ltd, Quebec Street, Elland, West Yorkshire, HX5 9BX Tel: (01422) 376899 Fax: (01422) 379802 E-mail: sales@dalmecltd.co.uk *Industrial manipulators*

Dalmek Ltd, 2 Ringway Centre, Edisin Road, Basingstoke, Hampshire, RG21 6YH Tel: (01256) 814420 Fax: (01256) 814434 E-mail: info@dalmecltd.co.uk *Pick & place systems manufrs*

▶ Dalmore Distillery, Dalmore, Alness, Ross-Shire, IV17 0UT Tel: (01349) 882362 Fax: (01349) 883655

▶ Dalmuri Community Concierge Service, 455 Dumbarton Road, Clydebank, Dunbartonshire, G81 4DT Tel: 0141-952 4666 Fax: 0141-952 5114

Dalon International Ltd, 12 The Spire Green Centre, Harlow, Essex, CM19 5TR Tel: (01279) 453823 Fax: (01279) 453824 E-mail: longdalon@aol.com *Laboratory & scientific suppliers*

Dalroad Distribution Ltd, Bramingham Business Park, Enterprise Way, Luton, LU3 4BU Tel: (01582) 505252 Fax: (01582) 560060 E-mail: sales@dalroad.com *Specialist distributors electromechanical components*

▶ Dalrymple (Construction) Ltd, Randolph Place, Randolph Industrial Estate, Kirkcaldy, Fife, KY1 2YX Tel: (01592) 652635 Fax: (01592) 652461 E-mail: enquiries@dalrympleconstruction.co.uk *Steel construction*

▶ Dalston Mill Fabrics, 69-73 Ridley Road, London, E8 2NP Tel: (020) 7249 4129 E-mail: info@dalstonmillfabrics.co.uk *We strive to be a reliable and varied stockist of low cost and high quality fabric products from all over the World.* *

Dalton & Ditcham Agencies Ltd, Brent House, 3rd Floor Kenton Road, Harrow, Middlesex, HA3 8BT Tel: (020) 8909 3996 Fax: (020) 8909 2686 E-mail: dalton.ditcham@btinternet.com *China & glass agents*

Dalton ID Systems Ltd, Dalton House, Newtown Road, Henley-on-Thames, Oxfordshire, RG9 1HG Tel: (0800) 838882 Fax: (0800) 7311957 E-mail: sales@dalton.co.uk *Livestock eartags, electronic identification systems & animal ID systems manufrs*

Dalton Joinery, Glendale Works, Dacre, Penrith, Cumbria, CA11 0HL Tel: (01768) 486684 Fax: (01768) 486684 E-mail: radjoinery@aol.com *Joiners*

Dalton Joinery Ltd, The Old Malt Kiln, Westfield Road, Tockwith, York, YO26 7PY Tel: (01423) 358005 Fax: (01423) 358019 *Joinery specialists*

▶ Dalton Label International Ltd, Dalton Airfield, Dalton, Thirsk, North Yorkshire, YO7 3HE Tel: (01845) 577926

Dalton Power Products Ltd, Unit 19 Autumn Park Industrial Estate, Dysart Road, Grantham, Lincolnshire, NG31 7DD Tel: (01476) 576666 Fax: (01476) 577127 E-mail: dppask@daltonpowerproducts.co.uk *Ford & Iveco power product dealers* Also at: Manchester & Washington

Dalton & Co Printers Ltd, Oxford Court, Oxford Street, Accrington, Lancashire, BB5 1QX Tel: (01254) 871666 Fax: (01254) 871148 E-mail: info@daltons-printers.com

Dalton Printers, Dalton House, Thesiger Street, Cardiff, CF24 4BN Tel: (029) 2023 6832 Fax: (029) 2066 6516 E-mail: daltonprinters@dial.pipex.com *Printers*

▶ Dalton Transport, Eling Terminal, 26 High Street, Totton, Southampton, SO40 9HN Tel: (023) 8086 0844 Fax: (023) 8086 0901

▶ Dalton Transport, Eling Terminal, 26 High Street, Totton, Southampton, SO40 9HN Tel: (023) 8086 0844 Fax: (023) 8086 0901

Dalton Transport Ltd, Dalton Lane, Dalton, Thirsk, North Yorkshire, YO7 3HR Tel: (01845) 577479 Fax: (01845) 577344 *Dalton Transport & storage are based in Thirsk, North Yorkshire. The ideal location for your warehousing requirements. Please call for more details*

Daltrade P.L.C., 16 Devonshire Street, London, W1G 7AF Tel: (020) 7436 5454 Fax: (020) 7436 1445 E-mail: info@daltrade.co.uk *Importers of chemicals from Poland*

▶ Dalwhinnie Distillery, Dalwhinnie Distillery, Dalwhinnie, Inverness-Shire, PH19 1AB Tel: (01540) 672200 Fax: (01540) 672201 *Distilling*

Daly Catering & Bakery Maintenance, Unit 4 Lennox Industrial Mall, Lennox Road, Basingstoke, Hampshire, RG22 4AP Tel: (01256) 364500 Fax: (01256) 814069 E-mail: sarah.daly@daly-electrical.co.uk *Daly CBM are a family owned business offering a first class service in the UK and are renowned for a fast, friendly and reliable service. Over 20 years we have developed a reputation for reliable and technically advanced electrical maintenance and repair services for many companies in the UK including supermarkets, fast food outlets and hotels. We provide specialist services in bakery, catering and refrigeration; all geared towards keeping your electrical and gas equipment functioning at peak efficiency at all times.*

▶ Daly Engineering Services Ltd, 19 Falkland House, Falkland Close, Coventry, CV4 8AG Tel: (024) 7646 5281 Fax: (024) 7669 4156

Daly (Painting Contractors) Ltd, Decor House Terracotta Drive, Clay Lane, Coventry, CV2 4LG Tel: (024) 7665 0033 Fax: (024) 7665 0056 E-mail: sales@dalypaintings.co.uk *Painting & decorating contractors*

Daly Telecom, The Point, Granite Way, Mountsorrel, Loughborough, Leicestershire, LE12 7TZ Tel: (01509) 410400 Fax: (0870) 2407755 E-mail: info@dalytelecom.co.uk *Telecommunication equipment distributors*

▶ Dalzell Precast, 4 Somerset Place, Glasgow, G3 7JT Tel: 0141-332 5345

Dalzell Window Cleaning Service, 23 Polwarth Gardens, Edinburgh, EH11 1JT Tel: 0131-229 3874 E-mail: dpark@window-cleaning-in-edinburgh.com *Window cleaning contractors*

Dalziel Ltd, Belgowan St, Bellshill North Ind Estate, Bellshill, Lanarkshire, ML4 3NS Tel: (01698) 749595 Fax: (01698) 740503 *Butcher supply manufrs*

Dalziel Ltd, Unit 11 Hunslet Trading Estate, Low Road, Leeds, LS10 1QR Tel: 0113-277 7662 Fax: 0113-271 4954 *Food industry meat & sundries suppliers*

Dalziel Ltd, Afon Aboo Road, Rogerstone, Newport, Gwent, NP10 9HZ Tel: (01633) 898150 Fax: (01633) 898160 E-mail: claire.warren@dalziel..co.uk *Frozen meat equipment*

Dalziel Ltd, 100 New Greenham Park, Greenham, Thatcham, Berkshire, RG19 6HN Tel: (01635) 265160 Fax: (01635) 38559 *Food packaging distributors*

Dalziel Packaging, Unit C3 Drumhead Road, Chorley North Business Park, Chorley, Lancashire, PR6 7DE Tel: (01257) 226010 Fax: (01257) 226019 E-mail: chorley@dalziel.co.uk *Serving the food industry*

▶ Damac Transporters Ltd, Mariners Street, Goole, North Humberside, DN14 5BW Tel: (01405) 766979 Fax: (01405) 782612

Damar Advertising Ltd, 32 Cogan Street, Barrhead, Glasgow, G78 1EJ Tel: 0141-881 3733 Fax: 0141-881 0430 E-mail: enquiries@damar-printing.co.uk *Screen printers*

Damar Ceilings Ltd, Owl House, Chathan Street, Macclesfield, Cheshire, SK11 6EE Tel: (01625) 511323 Fax: (01625) 610475 E-mail: damarceilings@btconnect.com *Suspended ceilings & partition installations*

Damar Group Ltd, Unit 15-19, Mill Road, Radstock, BA3 5TX Tel: (01761) 439111 Fax: (01761) 439123 E-mail: info@damarnet.com *Civil mechanical electrical engineers*

Damar Industrial Machinery Ltd, Clipper Road, Troon Industrial Estate, Leicester, LE4 9JE Tel: 0116-276 4144 Fax: 0116-246 0663 E-mail: sales@damar.biz *Hand tool & cutter suppliers*

Damar Webbing Products Ltd, Unit 3 Cobnar Wood Close, Chesterfield, Derbyshire, S41 9RQ Tel: (01246) 269969 Fax: (01246) 269946 E-mail: sales@damarwebbingproducts.com *Lifting sling manufrs*

Damartex UK Ltd, Bowling Green Mills, Bingley, West Yorkshire, BD97 1AD Tel: (0870) 8330000 Fax: (01274) 551024 E-mail: infouk@damart.com *Thermal underwear importers* Also at: Croydon & Hounslow

Damax Electrical Laminations Ltd, Unit C Amyco Works, Doris Road, Bordesley Green, Birmingham, B9 4SJ Tel: 0121-771 3857 Fax: 0121-771 1913 E-mail: info@damaxlams.co.uk *Motor laminators & general pressworkers*

Dambi UK Ltd, Units 24-25, Rassau Industrial Estate, Rassau, Ebbw Vale, Gwent, NP23 5SD Tel: (01495) 350855 Fax: (01495) 350074 E-mail: enquiries@dambi.co.uk *Manufacturers feminine hygiene & tissue products*

Damco Sea & Air Ltd, Suite 20 Orwell House, Ferry Lane, Felixstowe, Suffolk, IP11 3QP Tel: (01394) 675989 Fax: (01394) 674208 E-mail: sales@damcomar.com Principal Export Areas: Worldwide *Shipping & forwarding agents* Also at: Bradford, Birmingham, Felixstowe, Glasgow ,Manchester & Newcastle

▶ Damco Solutions Ltd, 23 Clayton Road, Hayes, Middlesex, UB3 1AN Tel: +44 (0) 208 817 1047 Fax: (020) 8573 9072 E-mail: sales@damcosoft.co.uk *Wide range of data processing services- Data Entry, Data Capture, Document Scanning, Forms/Survey Processing, Digitisation, data conversion, mailing lists creation/cleansing, data conversion, proof reading/typesetting and so on*

Dame Catering, 49 Milton Road, Westcliff-on-Sea, Essex, SS0 7JP Tel: (01702) 354541 Fax: (01702) 431775 E-mail: catering@uktraders.com *Catering equipment manufrs*

Damers Blinds & Awnings, 117a Radipole Lane, Weymouth, Dorset, DT4 9SS Tel: (01305) 784601 Fax: (01305) 789625 E-mail: sales@damers.com *Blind manufrs*

Damixa Ltd, Edison Courtyard, Brunel Road, Earlstrees Industrial Estate, Corby, Northamptonshire, NN17 4LS Tel: (01536) 409222 Fax: (01536) 400144 E-mail: uksales@damixa.com *Shower & shower accessory manufrs*

Damixa Ltd, The Case Building, Watford Business Park, Caxton Way, Watford, WD18 8ZF Tel: (01923) 690100 Fax: (01923) 690101 E-mail: damixa@damixa.com *Kitchen & bathroom brassware suppliers*

▶ Damm Builders, 43 Watt Road, Hillington Industrial Estate, Glasgow, G52 4RY Tel: 0141-810 2460

Dammit Ltd, 11 Glenthorne Road, London, N11 3HU Tel: (020) 8361 7769 Fax: (07070) 800473 *Audio services*

▶ Dammy Air Ltd, 43 Old Farm Close, Hounslow, TW4 7AB Tel: (020) 8572 9841 Fax: (020) 8230 0937

Dampco (U.K.) Ltd, 21 Lythalls Lane, Coventry, CV6 6FN Tel: (0800) 626925 Fax: (024) 7668 7683 E-mail: info@dampco.org *Damp proofing timber treatment contractors* Also at: Leicester & Northampton

Dampcoursing Ltd, 10-12 Dorset Road, London, N15 5AJ Tel: (020) 8802 2233 Fax: (020) 8809 1839 E-mail: dampcoursingltd@london.com *Damp proofing contractors* Also at: East Molesey

Dampcure Luton Co., 1 Ashton Road, Luton, LU1 3QE Tel: (01582) 735650 *Damp proofing contractors*

▶ Dampcure Woodcure 30 Ltd, 41 Merton Road, Watford, WD18 0WJ Tel: (01923) 663322 Fax: (01923) 223842 E-mail: admin@dampcurewoodcure.com *We specialise in all aspects of Timber Treatment, Damp Proofing, Damp Course Installation. Tanking of Basements, either with Membrane System or Sika Systems. Condensation Control*

▶ Dams Of Craigie Farm Ltd, Dams of Craigie, Whitecairns, Aberdeen, AB23 8XE Tel: (01651) 862274 Fax: (01651) 862078

Dams International Ltd, Gores Road, Knowsley Industrial Park, Liverpool, L33 7XS Tel: 0151-548 7111 Fax: 0151-548 7071 *Office furniture manufrs*

▶ Dams International, 29-35 Great Portland Street, London, W1W 8QF Tel: (020) 7637 9520 Fax: (020) 7436 8696 *Office furniture manufrs*

DAMS International (Office Equipment) Ltd, Sefton Retail Park, Dunnings Bridge Road, Bootle, Merseyside, L30 6YL Tel: 0151-525 7222 Fax: 0151-530 1164 *Furniture manufrs*

Damstahl Stainless Ltd, Halesfield 4, Telford, Shropshire, TF7 4AP Tel: (01952) 583999 Fax: (01952) 583958 E-mail: stainless@damstahl.com *Stainless steel stockholders*

Dan Display & Imaging Ltd, Harlequin House, Coedcad Lane, Pontyclun, Mid Glamorgan, CF72 9EW Tel: (01443) 225656 Fax: (01443) 226544 E-mail: info@dandisplay.co.uk *Illuminated sign manufacturers for the catering industry*

▶ Dan Lee Cleaning & Hygiene Supplies Ltd, Elliott Road, Plymouth, PL4 0SG Tel: (01752) 665838 Fax: (01752) 226361

Dan (UK) Ltd, Unit 1, Mucklow Hill 1 Trading Estate, Mucklow Hill, Halesowen, West Midlands, B62 8DF Tel: 0121-585 7171 Fax: 0121-585 7272 E-mail: sales@danlyuk.com *Press & die set manufrs*

▶ Dan Wood Group Ltd, 5 The Courtyards, Wyncolls Road, Severalls Industrial Park, Colchester, CO4 9PE Tel: (01206) 754744 Fax: (01206) 754743 E-mail: sales@danwoods.co.uk *Photo copying & IT solution services*

Dana Spicer Axle Europe Ltd, Birch Road, Witton, Birmingham, B6 7JR Tel: 0121-249 2500 Fax: 0121-249 2599 E-mail: pete.yale@dana.com Principal Export Areas: Asia Pacific, Middle East, Africa, Central/ East Europe, West Europe & North America *Axle manufrs*

Danagri - 3 S Ltd, Wenlock Road, Bridgnorth, Shropshire, WV16 4QR Tel: (01746) 762777 Fax: (01746) 764777 E-mail: info@danagri-3s.com *Agricultural machinery & equipment distributors*

Danaher Motion, Fishleigh Road, Roundswell Business Park, Barnstaple, Devon, EX31 3UD Tel: (01271) 334500 Fax: (01271) 334502 E-mail: information@tiblmail.com *Bearings, ball screw & linear guide manufrs*

Danaher & Rolls Ltd, Rufus Centre, Steppingley Road, Flitwick, Bedford, MK45 1AH Tel: (01525) 721900 Fax: (01525) 721800 E-mail: office@danaherandrolls.co.uk *Commercial building contractors*

Danatrol Ltd, Canal Bank, Loughborough, Leicestershire, LE11 1QA Tel: (01509) 217516 Fax: (01509) 230886 E-mail: graham@danatrol.com *Precision engineering*

Danbury Electronics, 20 Cutlers Road, Saltcoats Industrial Estate, South Woodham Ferrers, Chelmsford, CM3 5XJ Tel: (01245) 328174 Fax: (01245) 328963 E-mail: danburyelectx@aol.com *Industrial Customer Base. We supply transformers to a range of equipment manufacturers in the UK electrical and electronic industries, for example:- Manufacturers of Audio Amplifiers (Stage and Hi-Fi), Sound Systems, Loudspeakers, Security Systems, Power Supplies and Electronic Distributors etc. Many of our products are exported within our customer's equipment and we have supplied many of our loyal customers since 1983. We provide close technical liaison from prototypes through to production, and always endeavour to meet customer's specific requirements. We are designers and manufacturers of transformers (size 1VA - 750VA).*

Danbury Plant Hire, 2 Maldon Road, Danbury, Chelmsford, CM3 4QJ Tel: (01245) 223483 Fax: (01245) 226067 E-mail: danburyplanthire@aol.com *Operated & self drive hire*

▶ Dancap Electronics, 24 Trent Crescent, Thatcham, Berkshire, RG18 3DN Tel: (01635) 866394 Fax: (01635) 869589 E-mail: dancap@btinternet.com *Hakko soldering & desoldering equipment*

▶ Dancemania, 431-441 Wimborne Road, Poole, Dorset, BH15 3EE Tel: (01202) 681801 E-mail: support@dancemania.biz *International dance shop based in Poole selling clothing and footwear for dance, gymnastics, trampolining and the performing arts. Secure friendly service.*

Dancerace plc, 2 Brock Street, Bath, BA1 2LN Tel: (0870) 7773033 Fax: (0870) 7772022 E-mail: info@dancerace.com *Computer systems & software*

Dancing Octopus Ltd, 2 Millers Gate, Stone, Staffordshire, ST15 8ZF Tel: (01889) 505691 Fax: (01889) 505691 E-mail: webmaster@dancingoctopus.com *Fast access to travel information, focused on Europe*

▶ Dancourt Ltd, Davron Court, Whitehouse Place, Bristol, BS3 4BL Tel: 0117-953 9766 Fax: 0117-953 9767 E-mail: info@dancourt.co.uk

Danda UK Packaging Ltd, 8 Drury Way Industrial Estate, Laxcon Close, London, NW10 0TG Tel: (020) 8459 5500 Fax: (020) 8459 2351 *Packaging material merchants*

Dandelion Natural Foods, 120 Northcote Road, London, SW11 6QU Tel: (020) 7350 0902 Fax: (020) 7350 0902 *Health foods*

Dandf Garden Products Ltd, Unit 6, Onward Business Park, Wakefield Road, Ackworth, Pontefract, West Yorkshire, WF7 7BE Tel: (01977) 624200 Fax: (01977) 624201 E-mail: sales@dandf.co.uk *Timber garden product manufrs*

▶ Dando Drilling International Ltd, Old Customs House, Wharf Road, Littlehampton, West Sussex, BN17 5DD Tel: (01903) 731312 Fax: (01903) 730305 E-mail: info@dando.co.uk *Drilling rig equipment & water well drilling equipment manufrs*

▶ Dandys Topsoil, Yew Tree Farm, Sealand Road, Sealand, Chester, CH1 6BS Tel: (0845) 4563089 Fax: (01244) 881922 E-mail: adam@dandys.org *Topsoil & garden materials suppliers*

Dane Architectural Ltd, Viking Works, Hamsterley, Newcastle Upon Tyne, NE17 7SY Tel: (01207) 565000 Fax: (01207) 565010 E-mail: info@danearchitectural.co.uk *Aluminium fabricators*

▶ Dane Crafts, Havyatt Farm, Glastonbury, Somerset, BA6 8LF Tel: (01458) 835105 Fax: (01458) 832627

Dane Paper Products Ltd, Rushenden Road, Queenborough, Kent, ME11 5HL Tel: (01795) 669933 Fax: (01795) 669909 E-mail: suenightingale@dane-paper.co.uk *Paper converter*

▶ Dane Valley Haulage, Wood Flour Mills, Tunstall Road, Bosley, Macclesfield, Cheshire, SK11 0PE Tel: (01260) 223284 Fax: (01260) 223746

Danecroft Consultants Ltd, The Old Station House, Off Wilson Close, Compton, Newbury, Berkshire, RG20 6QT Tel: (01635) 579596 E-mail: danecroft@consultant57.fsnet.co.uk *Systems consultancy*

Daneplast Ltd, 6 Gunby Road, Sewstern, Grantham, Lincolnshire, NG33 5RD Tel: (01476) 860081 Fax: (01476) 861401 E-mail: sales@daneplast.co.uk *Plastic injection mouldings manufacturers & toolmakers*

Daner Ltd, 36 Walsall Road, Willenhall, West Midlands, WV13 2EG Tel: (01902) 368788 Fax: (01902) 637584 E-mail: info@daner.co.uk *Hosiery & underwear wholesaler*

Daneside Boxes, 5 Albany Mill, Canal Street, Congleton, Cheshire, CW12 3AE Tel: (01260) 273959 Fax: (01260) 273959 *Cardboard products*

▶ Daneswood Solutions Ltd, The Studio, 40/41 Monmouth Street, Topsham, Exeter, EX3 3AJ Tel: 0845 257 1102 Fax: 0871 994 3169 E-mail: info@daneswood.co.uk Sales Contact: P. Weeks *Daneswood Solutions aim to be able to provide you with all the internet solutions your business will need, including bespoke website design, low cost websites, intranets, email marketing , e-commerce, multimedia, website audit, content management, online marketing and online backup.*

Danetech Glass Fibre Mnfrs, 2b The CR, Witney, Oxfordshire, OX28 2EL Tel: (01327) 311011 Fax: (01327) 300216 E-mail: sales@danetech.co.uk *GRP Fabricators*

Danfast, English Street, Hull, HU3 2DZ Tel: (01482) 599333 Fax: (01482) 599321 E-mail: enquiries@danfast.co.uk *Caravan, marine suppliers & manufrs*

continued

Danfield Ltd, St. Helens Road, Leigh, Lancashire, WN7 3PF Tel: (01942) 675316 Fax: (01942) 670063 E-mail: info@danfield.co.uk *Quilting thread manufacturers which has been established over 40 years*

Danfoss Ltd, Capswood Business Centre, Oxford Road, Denham, Uxbridge, Middlesex, UB9 4LH Tel: (0870) 6080008 Fax: (0870) 6080009 *Industrial controls manufrs*

Danfoss Bauer, Unit 1, Natlane Business Park, Winsford, Cheshire, CW7 3BS Tel: (01606) 868600 Fax: (01606) 868603 E-mail: sales@danfoss.com Principal Export Areas: Worldwide *Electric geared motors manufrs*

Danfoss Randall Ltd, Ampthill Road, Bedford, MK42 9ER Tel: (0845) 1217400 Fax: (0845) 1217515 E-mail: danfossrandall@randall.com *Domestic & commercial heating controls*

Danfusion Image Library, The Old Bridge Inn, High Street, Bidford-on-Avon, Alcester, Warwickshire, B50 4BG Tel: (01789) 491304 E-mail: info@danfusion.co.uk

Danglo Components Ltd, Unit 9-10, Wedgewood Way, Stevenage, Hertfordshire, SG1 4QB Tel: (01438) 735616 Fax: (01438) 735625 E-mail: sales@danglo.co.uk *Manufacturers of eyelets, rivets & tubes*

▶ Daniel, Unit 1, 25 Carnarvon Road, Huthwaite, Sutton-in-Ashfield, Nottinghamshire, NG17 2JQ Tel: (01623) 556700 E-mail: futurefascias@hotmail.co.uk

▶ Daniel Campbell & Son (Contractors) Ltd, 57-59 Kirk Street, Strathaven, Lanarkshire, ML10 6LB Tel: (01357) 520394

Daniel Chilled Food, Biddenden Road, Headcorn, Ashford, Kent, TN27 9LW Tel: (01622) 892800 Fax: (01622) 892829 *Food product manufrs*

Daniel Englender Furniture Projects Ltd, 37 Hopefield Avenue, London, NW6 6LJ Tel: (020) 7289 0000 Fax: (020) 7289 0303 E-mail: sales@englender.com *Contract furniture manufrs* Also at: London

Daniel J Morgan & Son, Merydd Bakery, Llandissilio, Clynderwen, Dyfed, SA66 7TG Tel: (01437) 563297 *Bakers*

Daniel Lewis & Son Ltd, 493-495 Hackney Road, London, E2 9ED Tel: (020) 7739 8881 Fax: (020) 7739 2136 E-mail: daniellewis@ad.com *Steel & Aluminium Stockists*

Daniel Paper & Packaging, 133 Old Lane, Manchester, M11 1DD Tel: 0161-301 4710 Fax: 0161-370 9753 *Paper converters & merchants*

Daniel Pipework Services, Unit 44 Owen Road Industrial Estate, Willenhall, West Midlands, WV13 2PX Tel: 0121-526 5311 Fax: 0121-526 6900 E-mail: enquiries@danielpipework.co.uk *Industrial pipework suppliers*

▶ Daniel Prince Of London, 24 Hatton Garden, London, EC1N 8BQ Tel: (0845) 1083684 Fax: (020) 8944 8418 E-mail: sales@danielprince.co.uk *Fine bespoke handmade diamond jewellery in platinum & gold. Specialists in commissioned one-off pieces.*

▶ Daniel Sims, 2 Cheriton High Street, Folkestone, Kent, CT19 4ER Tel: (01303) 277211 Fax: (01303) 270370 E-mail: sales@danielsims.co.uk *Whether you are experienced buyers or looking for the first time, DanielSims Estate Agents is the place to seek fully independent advise on all issues relating to purchasing your home.*

Daniels, 27-29 Cross Green Lane, Leeds, LS9 8LJ Tel: 0113-245 4020 Fax: 0113-245 5528 *Sign installers*

Daniels Fans Ltd, Heol Gors, Dafen Indust Estate, Felinfoel, Llanelli, Dyfed, SA14 8QR Tel: (01554) 752148 Fax: (01554) 741109 E-mail: sales@danielsfans.ltd.uk *High temperature & industrial fans manufrs*

Daniels Healthcare, Unit 14 Station Field Industrial Estate, Kidlington, Oxfordshire, OX5 1JD Tel: (01865) 371841 Fax: (01865) 841869 E-mail: info@daniels.co.uk *Plastic bins manufrs* Also at: London W1

Daniels Precision Engineering, Queens Road, Southall, Middlesex, UB2 5AY Tel: (020) 8574 3037 *Precision turned parts manufrs*

Daniel's Sweet Herring, Achnagonlin Industrial Estate, Grantown-on-Spey, Morayshire, PH26 3TA Tel: (01479) 870072 Fax: (01479) 870077 *Fish curers*

Danielson Ltd, Commercial House, 52 Perrymount Road, Haywards Heath, West Sussex, RH16 3DT Tel: (01444) 883430 Fax: (01444) 440469 *Membrane switches manufrs*

The Danielson Group Ltd, 29 Pembroke Road, Aylesbury, Buckinghamshire, HP20 1DB Tel: (01296) 319000 Fax: (01296) 392141 E-mail: sales@danielson.co.uk *Manufacturer and supplier of membrane switches, touch screens, nameplates, labels, decals, front panels, enclosures, electroluminescent lamps*

Danisco, Denington Road, Wellingborough, Northamptonshire, NN8 2QJ Tel: (01933) 304200 Fax: (01933) 304224 Principal Export Areas: Worldwide *Flavouring essence suppliers*

▶ Danisco Beaminster, 6 North Street, Beaminster, Dorset, DT8 3DZ Tel: (01308) 862216 Fax: (01308) 863630 *Natural preservative services*

Danisco Beaminster, 6 North Street, Beaminster, Dorset, DT8 3DZ Tel: (01308) 862216 Fax: (01308) 863630 *Food preservatives manufrs*

Danisco Pack Rhondda Ltd, Ynyshir Road, Ynyshir, Porth, Mid Glamorgan, CF39 0RF Tel: (01443) 683121 Fax: (01443) 685856 E-mail: stephen.ridley@dssp.com *Corrugated packaging manufrs*

Danish Bacon Co. P.L.C., Manors Industrial Estate, Manors Avenue, Ilkeston, Derbyshire, DE7 8EF Tel: 0115-932 5041 Fax: 0115-930 7854 *Foods suppliers*

Danka (UK) P.L.C., Parkfield House, Moss Lane, Altrincham, Cheshire, WA15 8FH Tel: 0161-927 8500 Fax: 0161-927 8519 *Photocopiers & reprographics*

Danka (UK) P.L.C., Carlisle, CA4 8LL Tel: (01228) 562935 Fax: (01228) 562936 E-mail: bcowen@danka.co.uk *Office equipment suppliers*

Danka UK P.L.C., 1ST Floor, Holvorn Gate, 330 Higher Holvorn, London, WC1B 7QT Tel: (020) 7716 5634 Fax: (020) 7716 5750 *Photocopier suppliers & manufrs*

Dankfern Ltd, 11 Tait Road, Croydon, CR0 2DP Tel: (020) 8683 2748 Fax: (020) 8665 6627 *Heating element manufrs*

Dankroy Ltd, 129 Mayfield Avenue, London, N12 9HY Tel: (020) 8445 2157 Fax: (020) 8445 0538 *Precision engineers*

▶ K Danks, 3 St. Aidans Terrace, Prenton, Merseyside, CH43 8ST Tel: 0151-653 6598 E-mail: ken@thestrapshop.co.uk *Watch retail*

Danline International Ltd, Nebo Road, Llanrwst, Gwynedd, LL26 0SE Tel: (01492) 640651 Fax: (01492) 641601 E-mail: sales@danline.co.uk Principal Export Areas: Worldwide *Brush manufrs* Also at: Colwyn Bay

Danly UK Ltd, 2 Aintree Road, Perivale, Greenford, Middlesex, UB6 7LA Tel: (020) 8998 5381 Fax: (020) 8991 2461 E-mail: sales@danleyuk.com *Engineering*

Danoil Ltd, 94 Owl Lane, Ossett, West Yorkshire, WF5 9AU Tel: (01924) 263128 Fax: (01924) 264078 *Lubricant manufrs*

▶ Danoli Solutions Ltd, 116 Yew Tree Road, Ormskirk, Lancashire, L39 1NX Tel: (01695) 579442 E-mail: enquiries@danoli.co.uk *Computer repairs & maintenance in your home or business*

Danor Circuits, 82 Cannock Street, Leicester, LE4 9HR Tel: 0116-274 0312 Fax: 0116-274 0879 E-mail: sales@danorcircuits.com *Printed circuit manufrs*

Danor Engineering Ltd, 465 Hornsey Road, London, N19 4DR Tel: (020) 7281 0182 Fax: (020) 7263 0154 E-mail: danor.uk@btinternet.com *Ironing press manufrs*

Danro Ltd, 68 Station Road, Earl Shilton, Leicester, LE9 7GA Tel: (01455) 847061 Fax: (01455) 841272 E-mail: info@danroltd.co.uk *Labelling machine systems manufrs*

Dansac Ltd, Victory House, Vision Park, Histon, Cambridge, CB4 9ZR Tel: (01223) 235100 Fax: (01223) 235145 E-mail: dansac.ltd@dansac.com *Medical supply services*

Danscot Print Ltd, 8 Kinnoull Street, Perth, PH1 5EN Tel: (01738) 635228 Fax: (01738) 638805

▶ Danscot Prints Ltd, Bute House, Arran Road, Perth, PH1 3DZ Tel: (01738) 622974 Fax: (01738) 620536

Danson Steel Ltd, C Kingsbridge Wharf, Kingsbridge Road, Barking, Essex, IG11 0BD Tel: (020) 8507 8921 Fax: (020) 8507 8746 E-mail: danson@barking57.fsnet.co.uk *Steel stockholders*

▶ Dante Fire & Security, Houghton Enterprise Centre, Lake Road, Houghton Le Spring, Tyne & Wear, DH5 8BJ Tel: (0870) 4447073 Fax: (0870) 4447078 *Fire & security system suppliers*

Dantec Ltd, Tarran Way, Tarran Industrial Estate, Wirral, Merseyside, CH46 4TL Tel: 0151-678 2222 Fax: 0151-606 0188 E-mail: sales@dantec.ltd.uk Principal Export Areas: Asia Pacific, Middle East, Africa, Central/ East Europe, West Europe, North America & South America *Manufacturers of hoses, including oil, gasket & seal manufrs*

Dantec Dynamics Ltd, Unit 16 Garonor Way, Portbury, Bristol, BS20 7XE Tel: (01275) 375333 Fax: (01275) 375336 E-mail: scientific@dantecdynamics.com *Anemometers, flow measurement systems & particle size analyser manufrs*

Dantech UK Ltd, Burlington House, Crosby Road North, Liverpool, L22 0LG Tel: 0151-920 9080 Fax: 0151-920 9083 E-mail: sales@dantech.info *Food processing equipment suppliers*

Danter Automatics, 11a Copse Cross Street, Ross-on-Wye, Herefordshire, HR9 5PD Tel: (01989) 563604 Fax: (01989) 563604 *Game & amusement machine suppliers*

Dantex Graphics Ltd, Danon House, 5 Kings Road, Bradford, West Yorkshire, BD2 1EY Tel: (01274) 777788 Fax: (01274) 777766 E-mail: dillion.c@dantex.com *Graphic art suppliers*

Dantherm Filtration Ltd, Limewood Approach, Seacroft, Leeds, LS14 1NG Tel: 0113-273 9400 Fax: 0113-265 0735 E-mail: info.uk@danthermfiltration.com Principal Export Areas: Worldwide *Dantherm filtration ltd is a leading supplier of dust, fume & chip extraction solutions for a wide range of industries all over the world. Dantherm filtration takes care of everything from design & engineering, through feasibility studies, installation & commissioning, to lifetime service & maintenance. On top of this we also offer a comprehensive spares department & a full range of ductwork.*

Dantom Production Solutions Ltd, 18 Cameron Court, Winwick Quay, Warrington, WA2 8RE Tel: (01925) 657400 Fax: (01925) 657006 E-mail: davecoyne@danton.freeserve.co.uk *Subcontract manufrs*

Danum Supplies, Kelham Street, Doncaster, South Yorkshire, DN1 3RE Tel: (01302) 344475 *Hiring of paint spraying equipment*

Danum Tools & Equipment, Great North Road, Doncaster, South Yorkshire, DN5 7UN Tel: (01302) 390080 Fax: (01302) 390081 *Engineering consultants*

▶ Danvac Ltd, 3 Jaras Drive, The Bridleways, Baschurch, Shrewsbury, SY4 2DH Tel: (01939) 260403 Fax: (01939) 260403 E-mail: sales@danvac.co.uk *Vacuum Lifting Equipment Sales & Services*

▶ Danwood Group, 14 The Courtyard, Buntsford Drive, Bromsgrove, Worcestershire, B60 3DJ Tel: (01527) 571571 Fax: (01527) 571572 E-mail: sales@englands.co.uk *Printing & copying company*

Danwood Group, Seymour House, Little Money Road, Loddon, Norwich, NR14 6JD Tel: (01508) 521300 Fax: (01508) 521319 E-mail: mail@danwood.co.uk *Office equipment suppliers*

Danzas AEI Intercontinental, 18-32 London Road, Staines, Middlesex, TW18 4BP Tel: (01784) 871118 Fax: (01784) 871158 E-mail: mark.oxtoby@gb.danzas.com *Freight forwarders & forwarding agents*

Dapp Hydraulics, Bentley Mill Close, Walsall, WS2 0BN Tel: (01922) 632885 Fax: (01922) 721980 E-mail: sales@dapp.co.uk *Hydraulic power pack manufrs*

Dappat Engineering Ltd, Hodgson Street, Hull, HU8 7JB Tel: (01482) 328872 Fax: (01482) 223265 *Steel & sheet metalwork fabricators*

Dapro Ltd, PO Box 194, Hitchin, Hertfordshire, SG4 0TY Tel: (01462) 432021 E-mail: daprosonics@talktalk.net *Ultrasonic welding of plastics*

Dar Al-Handasah Consultants Shair & Partners UK Ltd, Darpen House, 3 Waterlane, Richmond, Surrey, TW9 1TJ Tel: (020) 8334 7676 Fax: (020) 8334 2701 E-mail: darlondon@darlondon.com *Consulting engineers*

▶ Dar Interiors, 11 Arches, Miles Street, London, SW8 1RZ Tel: (020) 7720 9678 Fax: (020) 7627 5129 E-mail: enquiries@darinteriors.com *Design, manufacturers & suppliers of handmade gardens & interiors*

Dar Lighting Ltd, Wildmere Road, Banbury, Oxfordshire, OX16 3JZ Tel: (01295) 672200 Fax: (01295) 271743 E-mail: sales@darlighting.co.uk *Domestic lighting fittings manufrs*

Darac, 37 The Meadway, Shoreham-by-Sea, West Sussex, BN43 5RN Tel: (01273) 455607 Fax: (01273) 441631 E-mail: sales@darac.com *Rubber & plastic moldings & stainless steel*

Daray Lighting Ltd, Unit 6A, Commerce Way, Stanbridge Road, Leighton Buzzard, Bedfordshire, LU7 4RW Tel: (01525) 376766 Fax: (01525) 216519 E-mail: info@daray.com *Dental & medical light fitters*

Darby Design & Print, 6 Kerry Close, Ancells Park, Fleet, Hampshire, GU51 2UF Tel: 01252 669948 E-mail: designandprint@ntlworld.com *Graphic design and printing for stationery, leaflets, brochures and posters.*Door to door distribution throughout Hampshire, Berksire and Surrey.*

▶ Darby Express, Ocean House, Dundas Lane, Portsmouth, PO3 5ND Tel: (023) 9269 9752 Fax: (023) 9267 7235

Darby Glass Ltd, Darby House, Sunningdale Road, Scunthorpe, South Humberside, DN17 2SS Tel: (01724) 280044 Fax: (01724) 868295 *Glass processors*

Darby Groundworks, Salamons Way, Rainham, Essex, RM13 9UL Tel: (01708) 521100 Fax: (01708) 525533 E-mail: admin@emerald-hse.com *Civil engineers*

Darby Rosettes & Trophies, 5 Goulburn Road, Norwich, NR7 9UX Tel: (01603) 440694 Fax: (01603) 440687 *Rosette & trophy manufrs*

▶ Darby Scotland Ltd, Block 2 Lochshore Industrial E, Caledonia Place, Glengarnock, Beith, Ayrshire, KA14 3BB Tel: (01505) 682962

Darchem Engineering Ltd, Iron Masters Way, Stillington, Stockton-on-Tees, Cleveland, TS21 1LB Tel: (01740) 630461 Fax: (01740) 630529 E-mail: sales@darchem.co.uk *High temperature insulation systems*

▶ D'arcy Diggers, Hitcham Road, Walthamstow, London, E17 8HL Tel: (020) 8923 6062 *Garden maintenance and clearance professional service in East London, owned and run by women. The services we offer include all forms of hard and soft landscaping, such as decking, patios, fencing, paths, laying lawns, planting etc.*

Darent Wax Co., Horton Road, South Darenth, Dartford, DA4 9AA Tel: (01322) 865892 Fax: (01322) 864598 E-mail: mail@darentwax.com *Speciality wax packers*

Darenth Weighing Services Ltd, 75 Campbell Road, Maidstone, Kent, ME15 6PS Tel: (0870) 4436670 Fax: (0870) 4436671 *Weighing systems (industrial) manufrs*

Darfen Durafencing, 15-21 Speedwell Road, Yardley, Birmingham, B25 8HU Tel: 0121-772 8666 Fax: 0121-772 8648 E-mail: central@darfen.co.uk *Fencing contractor, supply & installation of security, access control*

Darfen Durafencing, Herons Way, Carr Hill, Doncaster, South Yorkshire, DN4 8WA Tel: (01302) 360242 Fax: (01302) 364359 E-mail: mail@darfen.co.uk *Security, perimeter & sports fencing & access solutions suppliers*

Darfen Durafencing, Bradman Road, Knowsley Industrial Park, Liverpool, L33 7UR Tel: 0151-547 3626 Fax: 0151-549 1205 E-mail: northwest@darfen.co.uk *Fencing contractor*

Darfen Steelhoard, Herons Way, Balby, Doncaster, South Yorkshire, DN4 8WA Tel: (0845) 7023878 Fax: (01302) 327135 E-mail: sales@steelhoard.co.uk *Fencing contractors*

Darjon Mouldings, 7 Dock Road, Tilbury, Essex, RM18 7DB Tel: (01375) 857505 Fax: (01375) 857505 E-mail: info@darjon-mouldings.co.uk *Design engineers of glass fibres mouldings*

▶ Dark Blue, Unit K, Trecenydd Industrial Estate, Caerphilly, Mid Glamorgan, CF83 2RZ Tel: (0870) 8736800 Fax: (0870) 8736802 *Computer systems consultants*

▶ Dark Sensations, Chapel Works, East Street, Cannock, Staffordshire, WS11 0BU Tel: (01543) 437555 Fax: (01543) 437444 E-mail: info@darksensations.com *The UK's leading manufacturer of high class bondage gear*

Darke & Taylor Ltd, Langford Locks, Kidlington, Oxfordshire, OX5 1LH Tel: (01865) 290000 Fax: (01865) 290029 E-mail: darke.taylor@btinternet.com *Electrical contractors*

▶ Darkside Industries Ltd, 4 Hare Lane, Pudsey, West Yorkshire, LS28 9LH Tel: 0113-255 7191 Fax: 0113- 257 9799 E-mail: info@riggingsupplies.co.uk *The One Stop Shop for all theatrical rigging supplies and lifting equipment to the entertainment industry.**Supply of Lifting Equipment, Load Monitoring Equipment, Wire Ropes, Roundslings and all other equipment*

▶ Darlac Ltd, Deseronto TRDG Estate, Slough, SL3 7WW Tel: (01753) 547790 Fax: (01753) 580524 E-mail: sales@darlac.com *Garden tool suppliers*

Darlaston Diecast Alloys Ltd, Ashmore Lake Way, Willenhall, West Midlands, WV12 4LF Tel: (01902) 606436 Fax: (01902) 609405 E-mail: darlastondiecast@btconnect.com *Pressure die castings*

▶ Darlaston Printers Ltd, Reeves Street, Walsall, WS3 2DL Tel: (01922) 710671 Fax: (01922) 495652

Darley Ltd, Wellington Road, Burton-on-Trent, Staffordshire, DE14 2AD Tel: (01283) 564936 Fax: (01283) 545688 E-mail: mailbox@darley.co.uk *Business forms & continuous stationery*

Darley Couches, Unit 5 Restormel Industrial Estate, Lostwithiel, Cornwall, PL22 0HG Tel: (01208) 873200 Fax: (01208) 872772 *Beauty equipment suppliers*

A.J. Darling & Sons Ltd, Unit 1, Mereway Road, Twickenham, TW2 6RF Tel: (020) 8898 5555 Fax: (020) 8898 9874 E-mail: darlingsigns@aol.com *Sign contractors & sign makers*

Darlington Alarm Centre, 78 Heathfield Park, Middleton St. George, Darlington, County Durham, DL2 1LW Tel: (01325) 354500 E-mail: sales@darlingtonalarmcentre.co.uk *Installing, servicing & repairing all types of alarms*

Darlington Farmers Auction Mart Co. Ltd, Clifton Road, Darlington, County Durham, DL1 5DU Tel: (01325) 464529 Fax: (01325) 384282 *Livestock auctioneers*

▶ Darlington Group plc, Bankfields Drive, Wirral, Merseyside, CH62 0AZ Tel: 0151-328 5600 Fax: 0151-328 5605

▶ Darlington Group plc, Bankfields Drive, Wirral, Merseyside, CH62 0AZ Tel: 0151-328 5600 Fax: 0151-328 5605 E-mail: martin@darlingtons-group.co.uk *Salt merchants & road haulage, storage services*

▶ Darlington Scaffolding Ltd, Lingfield Way, Darlington, County Durham, DL1 4GD Tel: (01325) 480450 Fax: (01325) 354565

▶ Darlingtonantqiue Pine Warehouse, 12 Union Street, Darlington, County Durham, DL3 6JE Tel: (01325) 361575 *Bespoke kitchen services*

Darlow Medals & Rosettes, 8 Verney Close, Butlers Marston, Warwick, CV35 0NP Tel: (01926) 640050 Fax: (01926) 640050 E-mail: darlowro@supanet..com *Rosette manufrs*

Darncrest Recycling & Commodities, Unit 11 Lyon Industrial Estate, River Road, Barking, Essex, IG11 0JS Tel: (020) 8594 4779 Fax: (020) 8591 3998 *Scrap metal merchants*

Darnell Consultants Ltd, 14a Kenworthy Lane, Manchester, M22 4EJ Tel: 0161-945 6996 Fax: 0161-945 6997 E-mail: bernard@darnellconsultants.com *Telecommunication & data communication consultants*

Darnells Ltd, Oakfield Industrial Estate, Eynsham, Witney, Oxfordshire, OX29 4TH Tel: (01865) 883996 Fax: (01865) 883986 E-mail: mail@darnells.ltd.uk *Heating, plumbing & ventilation engineers*

Darnton Elgee Architects, Monk Fryston Hall, Monk Fryston, Leeds, LS25 5DU Tel: (01977) 681001 Fax: (01977) 681006 E-mail: email@darntonelgee.com *Architects & project managers*

Daro Engineering Stafford Ltd, Unit 7a & 7b Dewick Depot, Cannock Road, Brocton, Stafford, ST17 0SU Tel: (01785) 660391 Fax: (01785) 665347 E-mail: office@daroengineering.co.uk *General industrial fabrications & stud weldings*

Daro Factors Ltd, 80-84 Wallis Road, London, E9 5LW Tel: (020) 8510 4000 Fax: (020) 8510 4001 E-mail: sales@daro.com *Metal fitting distributors*

Daro Products Ltd, Churfield Road, Churchfield Industrial Estate, Sudbury, Suffolk, CO10 2YA Tel: (01787) 881191 Fax: (01787) 374291 E-mail: sales@daroproducts.co.uk *East Anglia's Premier Complete Product Manufacturers. We are unique in the services we currently provide from our manufacturing site in Sudbury. Sheet Metal Work, Powder-Coating, Plastic Vacuum Forming and Electrical Assembly. The Complete Service.*

Darpan Controls Ltd, Sandford Works, Cobden Street, Long Eaton, Nottingham, NG10 1BL Tel: 0115-973 2672 Fax: 0115-972 0682 *Electronic control apparatus manufrs*

▶ DARRAN PRYCE, 23 DARKWOOD WAY, SHADWELL, LEEDS, LS17 8BQ Tel: 0113 2669639 Fax: 0113 2669639 E-mail: darran@surf4amove.com *THE new site for advertising residential and commercial lettings in West Yorkshire!**Why surf4amove?**From a student to a business person, looking for a home to an office to rent, searching multitudes of letting agents who have hundreds, even thousands of properties each can be a daunting project. **Enter what you are looking for and let surf4amove find properties that match your criteria, from all landlords and agents in West Yorkshire. One needn't look anywhere else! **Landlord, letting agent, residential or commercial, YOU can have your properties on our website.**Surf4amove will list as many properties in the West Yorkshire area as you want, there's no limit.**Based only in the West Yorkshire area, our aim is to provide a more personal service to our clients. **

Darrell Fieldhouse, Victoria Road, Rushden, Northamptonshire, NN10 0AS Tel: (01933) 410458 *Engineers pattern & model makers manufrs*

Darren Sbo, Canklow Meadows Industrial Estate, Rotherham, South Yorkshire, S60 2XL Tel: (01709) 722600 Fax: (01709) 722657 E-mail: pspeechley@darron.co.uk *Hollow bored steel bar manufrs*

Darren Sbo, Canklow Meadows Industrial Estate, Rotherham, South Yorkshire, S60 2XL Tel: (01709) 722600 Fax: (01709) 722657 E-mail: info@darron-sbo.com *Oil drilling tool manufrs* Also at: Aberdeen & Great Yarmouth

Company Information

Darrenpalm Ltd, 33 Highmeres Road, Leicester, LE4 9LZ Tel: 0116-276 9872 *Stove enamellers & powder coaters*
Darrow Farm Supplies Ltd, Darrow Wood Farm, Shelfanger Road, Diss, Norfolk, IP22 4XY Tel: (01379) 640331 Fax: (01379) 641331 *Agricultural & equestrian services*
Dart Computers (Wales) Ltd, 26B Wellington Road, Rhyl, Clwyd, LL18 1BN Tel: (01745) 330128 Fax: (01745) 330128 E-mail: emquiries@dart-computers.com *Computer systems consultants*
▶ Dart Distribution Ltd, Plot 5, Sub-Station Road, Felixstowe, Suffolk, IP11 3JB Tel: (01394) 600420 Fax: (01394) 676062
Dart Fire Protection Ltd, Dart Fire Protection Centre, Plymouth Road, Totnes, Devon, TQ9 5PH Tel: (01803) 862416 Fax: (01803) 867183 E-mail: sales@dartfire.co.uk Principal Export Areas: Worldwide *Fire prevention services*
▶ Dart Jerry Ltd, Unit 10 Barton Hill Trading Estate, Maze Street, Bristol, BS5 9TQ Tel: 0117-955 9911 Fax: 0117-955 9922
▶ Dart Meet Services, Pipers Close, Pennygillam Industrial Estate, Launceston, Cornwall, PL15 7PJ Tel: (01566) 777488 Fax: (01566) 777488 *Steel fabricators*
Dart Mobile Welding, 1 Pembroke Road, Paignton, Devon, TQ3 3UR Tel: (01803) 522877 *Mobile welding*
▶ Dart Pleasure Craft Ltd, 5 Lower Street, Dartmouth, Devon, TQ6 9AJ Tel: (01803) 834488 Fax: (01803) 835248 E-mail: sales@riverlink.co.uk
Dart Precision Engineering, 41 Eton Wick Road, Eton Wick, Windsor, Berkshire, SL4 6LU Tel: (01753) 831110 Fax: (01753) 831110 *Sub-contractor proto type precision & production engineering*
▶ Dart Resourcing, Mda House, The Grove, Slough, SL1 1RH Tel: (01753) 828900 Fax: 0870 8700299 E-mail: slo@mdarg.com *A recruitment agency specialising in contract and permanent IT jobs and engineering vacancies. We have offices throughout the UK and in Europe servicing a wide range of National and International blue chip clients drawn from all sectors of industry and commerce.*
Dartex Office Furniture, Unit 6 Crayside Industrial Estate, Thames Road, Crayford, Dartford, DA1 4RF Tel: (01322) 521545 Fax: (01322) 558685 E-mail: sales@dartexofficefurniture.co.uk *New & used office furniture wholesalers*
Dartford Engraving Ltd, 4 Power Works Estate, Slade Green Road, Erith, Kent, DA8 2HY Tel: (01322) 340194 Fax: (01322) 347819 E-mail: mail@desp.co.uk *Engravers & silk screen printers*
Dartford Metalcrafts Ltd, Priory Road, Rochester, Kent, ME2 2EG Tel: (01634) 296123 Fax: (01634) 296129 E-mail: dmc@dartfordmetalcrafts.co.uk Principal Export Areas: Central/East Europe & West Europe *Refuse system stainless steel manufrs*
Dartford Rebore Ltd, 15 Overy Street, Dartford, DA1 1UP Tel: (01322) 220634 Fax: (01322) 220634 *Engine reconditioners*
Darthaven Marina Ltd, Brixham Road, Kingswear, Dartmouth, Devon, TQ6 0SG Tel: (01803) 752733 Fax: (01803) 752722 *Boat repairers & marine engineers*
▶ Darthuizer Ltd, Unit 2, Vicarage Farm, Winchester Road, Fair Oak, Eastleigh, Hampshire, SO50 7HD Tel: (023) 8069 6956 Fax: (023) 8069 6958 E-mail: sales@darthuizer.co.uk *Floral suppliers*
Dartington Crystal Ltd, Town Park, Torrington, Devon, EX38 7AN Tel: (01805) 626262 Fax: (01805) 626263 E-mail: enquiries@dartington.co.uk *Crystal & glassware manufacturers & retailers*
▶ Dartmoor, Moor Cottages, Middlemoor, Tavistock, Devon, PL19 9DY Tel: (01822) 617316 Fax: (01822) 617316 E-mail: frank.fields2@btopenworld.com *Website designer*
Dartmoor Hardwoods, Duchy Yard, Station Road, Princetown, Yelverton, Devon, PL20 6QX Tel: (01822) 890559 Fax: (01822) 890559 *Timber supplies & hard wood product manufrs*
▶ Dartmoor Memorials, Westbridge Trading Centre, Westbridge Indust Estate, Tavistock, Devon, PL19 8DE Tel: (01822) 617700 Fax: (01822) 617702 E-mail: enquiries@dartmoor-memorials.com *Lettering in stone & granite stonemasons*
Dartmoor Windows & Conservatories Ltd, 1 Mill Road, Okehampton, Devon, EX20 1PS Tel: (01837) 54543 Fax: (01837) 54192 *PVCU system installation service*
Dartmouth Associates Ltd, 43 Baltimore Road, Great Barr, Birmingham, B42 1DD Tel: 0121-358 0422 Fax: 0121-358 1334 E-mail: dartmouth@dartmouth-associates.co.uk *Precision machining services & machinists*
Dartmouth Boating Centre, South Embankment, Dartmouth, Devon, TQ6 9BH Tel: (01803) 832093 Fax: (01803) 835135 *Boat retail clothing & safety equipment retailers*
Darton Longman & Todd Ltd, 140-142 Wandsworth High Street, London, SW18 4JJ Tel: (020) 8875 0155 Fax: (020) 8875 0133 E-mail: tradesales@darton-longman-todd.co.uk *Publishing religious books & bibles*
Dartpoint Ltd, Unit 1b Kitewell Lane, Lydd, Romney Marsh, Kent, TN29 9LP Tel: (01797) 320910 Fax: (01797) 320571 E-mail: sales@dartpoint.co.uk *Manufacturer of battery chargers for standby power*
Dartsoft Ltd, Noland Park, South Brent, Devon, TQ10 9DE Tel: (01364) 646000 Fax: (01364) 646002 E-mail: kevin@dartsoft.co.uk *Internet consultants*
Dar-Val Engineering Ltd, Ground Floor Unit B, 443-449 Holloway Road, London, N7 6LJ Tel: (020) 7263 7017 Fax: (020) 7263 7003 *General engineers*
Darvill Engineering, 2 Bilston Street, Willenhall, West Midlands, WV13 2AW Tel: (01902) 605872 Fax: (01902) 605872 *Industrial fastener manufrs*
▶ Darwill Fabrications, Arnold Works, Stevenson Road, Sheffield, S9 3XG Tel: 0114-256 2244 Fax: 0114-256 2243
▶ Darwin Press, Unit B Pier Road, Feltham, Middlesex, TW14 0TW Tel: (020) 8844 3780 Fax: (020) 8844 3795
Darwins Holdings Ltd, Fitzwilliam Works, Sheffield Road, Sheffield, S9 1RL Tel: 0114-244 8421 Fax: 0114-256 1775 *Stainless steel & alloy casting manufrs*
▶ Das Business Furniture Ltd, 12 Appold Street, London, EC2A 2AW Tel: (020) 7655 4933 Fax: (020) 7247 3613
▶ Das Engineering Services Ltd, 5 Aire & Calder Industrial Park, Lock Lane, Castleford, West Yorkshire, WF10 2JA Tel: (01977) 559955 Fax: (01977) 520777
Das Fabrications Ltd, Ajax Works, Whitehill Street, Stockport, Cheshire, SK4 1NT Tel: 0161-476 1222 Fax: 0161-476 1333 E-mail: dave@dasfabs.fsbusiness.co.uk *Steel farbications*
Das Legal Expenses Insurance Co. Ltd, D A S House Quay Side, Temple Back, Bristol, BS1 6NH Tel: 0117-934 2000 Fax: 0117-934 2109 E-mail: sales@das.co.uk *Legal expense insurance services*
▶ Dasca Cornmill Ingredients, Crosby Road South, Seaforth, Liverpool, L21 4PF Tel: 0151-922 6261 Fax: 0151-933 8208 *Corn based food ingredients suppliers*
Dash Associates, 50 Binswood Avenue, Leamington Spa, Warwickshire, CV32 5RX Tel: (01926) 315862 Fax: (01926) 315854 E-mail: sales@dashoptimization.com *Software manufacturer & distributor*
Dash Consulting, 4 Friars Cottage, off Copyground Lane, High Wycombe, Bucks, HP12 3XB Tel: (01923) 256655 Fax: (01923) 222494 E-mail: duncan@dashconsulting.com *Computer consultancy.*
▶ Dash Energy Services, 32 Ash Lane, Hale, Altrincham, Cheshire, WA15 8PD Tel: 0161-980 0018 Fax: 0161-980 0018 *Boiler distributors*
Dashdoctor Plastic & Leather Repair, 112 Dukes Brow, Blackburn, BB2 6DJ Tel: 01254 698783 Fax: 01254 698783 *Service provider*
▶ Dashtech Services (UK), Delta Street, New Basford, Nottingham, NG7 7GJ Tel: (07980) 213377 E-mail: m_ali1972@hotmail.com *Car electronics*
Dashwood Finance Co. Ltd, Georgian House, 63 Coleman Street, London, EC2R 5BB Tel: (020) 7588 3215 Fax: (020) 7588 4818 E-mail: dashwood.group@virgin.net *International finance*
Dashwood Metal Products, PO Box 23, St. Neots, Cambridgeshire, PE19 8UZ Tel: (01480) 477339 *Storage & handling equipment suppliers*
Dasic International Ltd, Winchester Hill, Romsey, Hampshire, SO51 7YD Tel: (01794) 512419 Fax: (01794) 522346 E-mail: sales@dasicinter.com *Oil dispersant & cleaning chemicals services*
Dask Timber Products Ltd, Meenan Mill, Dublin Road, Banbridge, County Down, BT32 3PB Tel: (028) 3831 8696 Fax: (028) 3831 8698 E-mail: info@dasktimber.co.uk *Joiners*
▶ Dass Manufacturing Ltd, Sutton Business Centre, Restmor Way, Wallington, Surrey, SM6 7AH Tel: (020) 8669 8012 Fax: (020) 8669 9529
Dassett Process Engineering Ltd, Daimler Close, Royal Oak Industrial Estate, Woodford Halse, Daventry, Northants, NN11 8QJ Tel: (01327) 312914 Fax: (01327) 314162 E-mail: info@dassett.com Purchasing Contact: I Pantling Sales Contact: A.R. Pantling *Manufacturers & refurbishers of plastic processing equipment. Maintenance & repair services of plastic processing equipment. (Injection moulding equipment, blow moulding equipment & bottle handling systems)*
Data Base Unlimited, The Old School, Bagwell Lane, Winchfield, Hook, Hampshire, RG27 8DB Tel: (01256) 393050 Fax: (01256) 393051 E-mail: techsupport@dbu.co.uk *Database consultants*
Data Business, 1-4 Bankside, Kidlington, Oxfordshire, OX5 1JE Tel: (01865) 848574 Fax: (0870) 766 5210 E-mail: sales@databiz.com *Format Conversion & Video Digitisation; DVD/CD Editing, Encoding & Authoring; Replication; Express DVD-R & CD-R Duplication; Printing; Packaging; Fulfilment; Blank Media.*
Data Cabling Ltd, 6 Farrier Road, Lincoln, LN6 3RU Tel: (01522) 500699 Fax: (01522) 500882 E-mail: sales@data-cabling.co.uk *Designers & suppliers of data cabling*
▶ Data Capture & Apply Technology Ltd, PO Box 164, Brough, East Yorkshire, HU15 1AU Tel: (01482) 662626 Fax: (01482) 662626 E-mail: info@dcatonline.co.uk *Bar code systems equipment manufrs*
▶ Data Cars, 101 Eltham High Street, London, SE9 1TD Tel: (020) 8850 1111 Fax: (020) 8850 1000 E-mail: mail@datacars.com *Data Cars is one of the largest Private Hire taxi companies in the UK. With a fleet of 200 vehicles we provide a fast, efficient and reliable service. Our Call Centre currently handles over 1 million calls per year. **The company was formed in July 1999 and has continued to expand to its current size and now has over 30 staff working in the Call Centre. Our aim is to provide the people of South East London with a fast and efficient taxi service. **Local/long distance journeys, airport and hotel transfers, Meet & Greet at Airports. Driver & Car for daily hire. **
Data Clinic, Unit 9 The Pavilions, Bridge Hall Lane, Bury, Lancashire, BL9 7NY Tel: 0161-764 3060 E-mail: customer.services@dataclinic.co.uk *Data recovery*
Data Collection Systems Ltd, 6 Station Court, Station Approach, Borough Green, Sevenoaks, Kent, TN15 8AD Tel: (01732) 780456 Fax: (01732) 780445 E-mail: sales@dcs-sol.com *Software house*
Data Communication Services Ltd, 447-449 Manchester Road, Stockport, Cheshire, SK4 5DJ Tel: 0161-443 0800 Fax: 0161-443 1336 E-mail: sales@data-comms.com *Radio communication equipment suppliers*
▶ Data Compliance Equipment Ltd, 28 Poplar Avenue, Sherwood, Nottingham, NG5 1DJ Tel: 01159 858600 Fax: 01159 858660 E-mail: info@dce-uk.com *Manufactures & Distributors of CCTV Data Compliant Equipment.*CCTV Signs, Anpr Signs, Computer Security, Data Safes, Fuji Starter Kits, Fuji Digital Starter kits, CCTV bespoke signs, Desktop Computer Security,* CCTV Flytipping Signs, CCTV Data Protection Code of Practice, CCTV Warning Signs, CCTV Awareness Signs, CCTV Security Signs* ***
Data Connection Ltd, 100 Church Street, Enfield, Middlesex, EN2 6BQ Tel: (020) 8366 1177 Fax: (020) 8363 1468 E-mail: recruit@dataconnection.com *Software house*
Data Consultants, 49 Leander Crescent, Bellshill, Lanarkshire, ML4 1JA Tel: (01698) 834343 Fax: (01698) 834343 *Printers & stationers*
▶ Data Creative Ltd, 9 Elm Grove, Toddington, Dunstable, Bedfordshire, LU5 6BJ Tel: (01525) 877911 Fax: (01525) 877921 E-mail: enquiries@data-creative.com *Data related services*
Data Crown Ltd, Bearnshaw Tower Farm, Carr Road, Todmorden, Lancashire, OL14 7ES Tel: (01706) 817885 Fax: (01706) 817165 *Computer consultancy*
Data Day It Ltd, The Old Stack Yard, Shrawardine, Shrewsbury, SY4 1AH Tel: (01743) 851188 Fax: (01743) 850088 *Computer consultants*
▶ Data Day Supplies, 8, Halesowen Drive, Elstow, Bedford, MK42 9GG Tel: (01234) 245923 Fax: (01293) 782277
Data Development Services Ltd, Blythe Valley Innovation Centr, Central Boulevard, Blythe Valley Park, Solihull, West Midlands, B90 8AJ Tel: 0121-506 9310 *Computer programmers*
Data Discovery Solutions LRD, 2 Venture Road, Chilworth, Southampton, SO16 7NP Tel: (023) 8076 7678 Fax: (023) 8076 7665 E-mail: sales@activenavigation.com *Software production*
Data Encryption Systems Ltd, Silver Street House, Silver Street, Taunton, Somerset, TA1 3DL Tel: (01823) 352357 Fax: (01823) 352358 E-mail: enquiries@des.co.uk *Design computer security systems*
Data Engineering, Pindar Road, Hoddesdon, Hertfordshire, EN11 0DE Tel: (01992) 462610 Fax: (01992) 450953 E-mail: scherry@dataeng.freeserve.co.uk *Press tool manufrs*
▶ Data Global Services Ltd, 6 Old Bath Road, The Lawns, Colnbrook, Slough, SL3 0NH Tel: (0776) 5788244 Fax: E-mail: dataglobalservices@yahoo.com *Data Recovery, *Recuperação De Dados, *Recuperación De Datos.*- Recovering any deleted or lost data or photos from Hard Drives, Floppy Discs, any Memory Card, CDs, DVDs.*- Recuperamos qualquer dados que tenham sidos apagados or perdidos em Disco Duros, Cartoes de Memoria, Disquetes, CDs, DVDs.*--------*other professional areas at*Data Global Services Ltd:*-Brazilian Coffee Importer;*-Recruitment /Employment for Data Entry;*-Translation /Interpreting: Portuguese, Spanish, English.*
Data Graphic Application Ltd, 26 Felpham Road, Bognor Regis, West Sussex, PO22 7AZ Tel: (01243) 861621 Fax: (01243) 869326 E-mail: info@dga-ltd.co.uk *Computer systems & software developers*
Data Harvest Group Ltd, 1 Eden Court, Eden Way, Leighton Buzzard, Bedfordshire, LU7 4FY Tel: (01525) 373666 Fax: (01525) 851638 E-mail: sales@data-harvest.co.uk *Data acquisition systems manufrs*
▶ The Data Imaging & Archiving Co. Ltd, Unit A, Kennetside, Bone Lane, Newbury, Berkshire, RG14 5PX Tel: (01635) 550006 Fax: (01635) 550010 E-mail: enquiry@imagingandarchiving.co.uk *Document scanning & microfilming, archive storage & scanner & software*
Data Impex Ltd, 58 Beakes Road, Smethwick, West Midlands, B67 5RU Tel: (01902) 456619 Fax: 0121-533 0154 E-mail: sales@dataimpex.com
▶ Data & Information Technology Ltd, Technology House, Normanton Lane, Bottesford, Nottingham, NG13 0EL Tel: (01949) 843757 Fax: (01949) 843758
Data Loop Ltd, Beare Green Court, Dorking, Surrey, RH5 4SL Tel: +44 (0) 1306 711088 Fax: +44 (0) 1306 713108 E-mail: sales@data-loop.co.uk *Export distributor of electronic equipment for security, traffic monitoring, environmental & industrial monitoring to central & eastern Europe, including Poland, Czech Republic, Slovakia, Hungary, Romania, Croatia, Macedonia, Albania, Bulgaria, Bosnia & Herzegovina, Serbia & Montenegro & Kosovo. Our main products are: Video Spectral Comparator (VSC), Electrostatic Detection Apparatus (ESDA), Forgery Detector, Micro spectrophotometer (QDI), UV Lamp, Raman Spectrometer (Foram), Forensic Lamp (Crime-Lite), Digital Fingerprint Imaging System (DCS), Cyanoacrylate Fuming Cabinet (MVC), CO2 Detector, Drug Test Kit, Contraband Detector, Narcotic Detector, Explosive Detector, Flexible and Rigid Endoscope, Fibrescope, Inspection Mirror, Torch, Search Tool Kit, IR Thermal Imaging Camera, Night Vision Goggles, Body Armour, Protective Clothing, Vehicle Traffic Counter and Classifier, Vehicle Weighbridge and Weighpads, Sound Level Meter, Personal Air Sampling Pump, Laboratory Balance & Bath*
▶ Data Medik Systems Ltd, PO Box 3807, Sheffield, S25 9AH Tel: (0845) 4568958 Fax: (07092) 351812 E-mail: info@datamediksystems.co.uk *IT equipment sales, maintenance & installations*
Data One Ltd, Unit 12 Loughborough Technology Centre, Epinal Way, Loughborough, Leicestershire, LE11 3GE Tel: (01509) 215662 Fax: (01509) 212571 E-mail: danny@dataone.ltd.uk *Primary software developers*
Data Physics (UK) Ltd, South Rd, Hailsham, East Sussex, BN27 3JJ Tel: (01323) 846464 Fax: (01323) 847550 E-mail: sales@dataphysics.com *Data Physics designs, manufactures, and markets high performance solutions in signal processing for applications in noise and vibration test. The Dynamic Signal Analyser range is based on the SignalCalc® family of software which is common across all analyser products to address requirements from low cost 2 channel up to high specification 1000+ channel analysis. The Vibration Controller range is based on the SignalStar® family of software. With a range spanning entry level, through to High Capability and on through to sophisticated multi-Axis applications, the systems exceed expectation. The entire range is based on Network able Abacus DSPCentric hardware with 130+dB dynamic range and frequency ranges up to 20kHz for control. The Data Physics SignalForce® range of electrodynamic shaker systems covers all requirements from table-top to more than 200kN. In addition, a range of more specialised systems for modal test and inertial excitation is available.*
Data Plastics, Avenue Three, Witney, Oxfordshire, OX28 4BP Tel: (01993) 700777 Fax: (01993) 700555 E-mail: sales@dataplastics.co.uk *Injection moulders, Class 7 cleanroom moulders, toolmakers, designers, assembly facility*
Data & Power Solutions, Unit 1 The Monarch Centre, Venture Way, Priorswood Industrial Estate, Taunton, Somerset, TA2 8DE Tel: (01823) 275100 Fax: (01823) 275002 E-mail: sales@dataandpower.com *Data & Power Solutions are a manufacturing company based in the UK. We supplying a complete portfolio of 19" mounted power distribution units, fan trays and accessories. Design, punch, fold, powder coat, assemble, test and dispatch all from under one roof.*
▶ Data Practical Application Protection Ltd, 60 The CR, Bredbury, Stockport, Cheshire, SK6 2DX Tel: 0161-494 6073 Fax: 0161-494 6163
Data Print, 11A West Way, Oxford, OX2 0JB Tel: (01865) 243624 Fax: (01865) 243624 E-mail: info@dataprintoxford.co.uk *Printers*
Data Radio Ltd, 5-7 Falkland Street, Liverpool, L3 8HB Tel: 0151-298 2150 Fax: (0870) 0940005 E-mail: admin@dataradio.co.uk *Radio communications*
Data & Research Services plc, Sunrise Parkway, Linford Wood, Milton Keynes, MK14 6LR Tel: (01908) 666088 Fax: (01908) 607668 E-mail: enquiries@drs.co.uk *Data entry equipment manufrs*
▶ Data Results, Suite 10, Sackville Place, 44-48 Magdalen Street, Norwich, NR3 1JU Tel: (01603) 768465 Fax: (07092) 155445
Data Room Supplies, Conbar House, Mead Lane, Hertford, SG13 7AP Tel: (01992) 558737 Fax: (01992) 558714 E-mail: sales@dataroomsupplies.co.uk *Communications cabling*
▶ Data Run, 2 Quebec Way, London, SE16 7LF Tel: (020) 7232 1616 Fax: (020) 7252 0315
▶ Data Services 24/7, 124 Harborough Road, Rushden, Northamptonshire, NN10 0LP Tel: 08701 660724 Fax: (08709) 162101 E-mail: support@dataservices247.com *Data recovery & password recovery*
Data Set Ready, 25 Leygreen Close, Luton, LU2 0SQ Tel: (01582) 618080 Fax: (01582) 618081 E-mail: datatasteready@ntlworld.co.uk *Computer terminal repairs*
Data Shred Ltd, Bradfield Road, London, E16 2AX Tel: (020) 8450 6282 Fax: (020) 7476 2548 *Security shredding agents*
Data Shredding Services Ltd, 38 Pound Lane, Upper Beeding, Steyning, West Sussex, BN44 3JD Tel: (01903) 814949 Fax: (01903) 813925 E-mail: info@datashreddingservices.com *Security shredding services*
Data Spectrum, Sycamore House, Wendlebury, Bicester, Oxfordshire, OX25 2PB Tel: (01869) 325266 E-mail: enquiries@dataspectrum.co.uk *IT centre furniture manufrs*
Data Strategy Ltd, 44 Kingswood Road, London, SW19 3NE Tel: (020) 8296 0643 E-mail: info@datadtrategy.com *Computer consultants*
Data Systems & Solutions, Unit 14 Princes Park Princes Way, Team Valley Trading Estate, Gateshead, Tyne & Wear, NE11 0NF Tel: 0191-499 4000 Fax: 0191-499 4001 E-mail: tomsimpson@ds-s.com *Power station software*
▶ Data Systems UK, Data House, Kirton Lane, Thorne, Doncaster, South Yorkshire, DN8 5RJ Tel: (01405) 815848 Fax: (01405) 815848 E-mail: glynn@datasystemsuk.com *Database Designer, Data Management Database software systems consultants*
▶ Data Techniques, Unit 7, Farnborough Business Centre, Eelmoor Road, Farnborough, Hampshire, GU14 7XA Tel: (01252) 375566 Fax: (01252) 375577 E-mail: info@datatechniques.co.uk *Data Cabling*
Data Technology Group Ltd, Unit 3-4 The Long Room, Coppermill Lock, Uxbridge, Middlesex, UB9 6JA Tel: (01895) 829300 Fax: (01895) 820555 E-mail: general.information@datatechnology.co.uk *Business management IT solutions*
Data Teknologies Ltd, Seneca House, Buntsford Business Park, Buntsford Park Road, Bromsgrove, Worcestershire, B60 3DX Tel: (01527) 559411 Fax: (01527) 559258 E-mail: mail@datateknologies.com *Bar code system resale*
Data Time Systems Time Recorders Systems, 5 Lowlands Drive, Keyworth, Nottingham, NG12 5HG Tel: 0115-937 3368 Fax: 0115-937 6611 E-mail: info@datatime.co.uk *Time recorders*
Data Tooling & Enginering Services Ltd, Unit 1-2 Paddock Farm, Bethersden Road, Hothfield, Ashford, Kent, TN26 1EP Tel: (01233) 620805 Fax: (01233) 620889 E-mail: info@datatooling.co.uk *General engineers & fabricators*

Data Track Process Instruments Ltd, 153 Somerford Road, Christchurch, Dorset, BH23 3TY Tel: (01425) 271900 Fax: (01425) 271978 E-mail: dtpi.sales@dtrack.com *Data Track design & manufacture the Tracker range of instrumentation. This includes digital panel meters, PID controllers, signal conditioners, remote data acquisition modules and large number displays. A Tracker can be used in simple measurement only applications, or in more complex and demanding situations requiring digital communications, alarms, maths functions and complex signal conditioning.*

Data Track Services Ltd, Unit 38 Basepoint Enterprise Centre, Basingstoke, Hampshire, RG24 8UP Tel: (01256) 406616 Fax: (01256) 406617 E-mail: sales@datatrackservices.co.uk *DLT REPAIR LTO REPAIR TAPE DRIVE REPAIR DATA STAORAGE LIBRARY REPAIR FAST TURN AROUND AND LOAN EQUIPMENT AVAILABLE.**

Data Track Technology P.L.C., 153 Somerford Road, Christchurch, Dorset, BH23 3TY Tel: (01425) 270333 Fax: (01425) 270433 E-mail: sales@dtrack.com Sales Contact: Staddon *Design, manufacture, markets & supports software & hardware products for the management of both legacy & IP voice & data systems under the ISO 9001:2000 quality standard*

▶ Data Voice & Fibre Installations, 22 Eastways, Bishops Waltham, Southampton, SO32 1EX Tel: (01489) 894894

Data Works Ltd, Priory House, 25 St. Johns Lane, London, EC1M 4HD Tel: (020) 7553 7800 Fax: (020) 7553 7801 E-mail: info@strategicdataworks.co.uk *Computer software developers*

▶ Data2Wisdom Ltd t/a Business for Breakfast, 51 Grangeway, Handforth, Wilmslow, Cheshire, SK9 3HY Tel: 0870 742 3090 Fax: 0871 433 5478 E-mail: Gez@BforB.co.uk *Creating Business communities in West Cheshire through Business Forums. Forums of up to 30 different businesses meet fortnightly to build co-operation as they get to know like and trust each other. The aim is simple MORE BUSINESS for us all.*MEETINGS curently at*De Vere St. David"s Park Ewloe Chester on Fridays of Odd weeks*Grosvenor Pulford Chester on Thursdays of Even weeks. De vere Daresbury Park Warrington on Tuesdays of Even weeks.*Rookery Hall Nantwich on Fridays of Even weeks. Wheatsheaf Hotel Sandbach on Wednesdays of odd weeks. Floatel Northwich on Thursdays of Odd weeks.Meetings 6.45 for 7.00 ending at 8.30 a.m. Chester meetings 7.00 to 8.45am*Call Gez Mason on 077 369 66 369 to reserve your place or ask about NEW venues.*

Databac Group, 1 The Ashway Centre, Elm CR, Kingston upon Thames, Surrey, KT2 6HH Tel: (020) 8546 9826 Fax: (020) 8547 1026 E-mail: info@databac.com *Card manufrs*

▶ Database Design Solutions, 21 Carrholm Road, Leeds, LS7 2NQ Tel: (07786) 963562 Fax: 0113-228 6859 E-mail: sales@databasedesignsolutions.net *We provide MS Access database solutions for small to medium companies at an affordable price*

▶ Database Development, 34 St. Edmunds Avenue, Thurcroft, Rotherham, South Yorkshire, S66 9QL Tel: (07713) 166938 E-mail: sales@databasedevelopment.co.uk *It consultants*

Database Developments Ltd, 2 South Street, Uley, Dursley, Gloucestershire, GL11 5SS Tel: (01453) 861155 Fax: (01453) 861166 E-mail: sales@databasedevelopments.com *Database development,computer & software services*

The Database Group Ltd, Colston Tower, Colston Street, Bristol, BS1 4UH Tel: 0117-918 3500 Fax: 0117-918 3501 E-mail: sales@databasegroup.co.uk *Database marketing* Also at: London

Database Workshop Ltd, 11b Church Street, Tamworth, Staffordshire, B79 7DH Tel: (01827) 52233 Fax: (01827) 52234 E-mail: alison@dbw.net *Software development*

Datacom Communication Systems Ltd, Unit 11 Towngate Business Centre, Durham, DH7 8HG Tel: 0191-378 3409 Fax: 0191-378 3402 *Telephone equipment & installation*

Datacore Consultants, 319 Broomfield Road, Chelmsford, CM1 4DU Tel: (01245) 261578 Fax: (01245) 356146 E-mail: pstevdata@aol.com *Computer consultants*

Datacourt Computer Systems, 198 Knutsford Road, Warrington, WA4 1AU Tel: (01925) 243898 Fax: (01925) 243732 *Data processing*

Dataday Computer Services, Chalfont House, Hampden Road, Chalfont St. Peter, Gerrards Cross, Buckinghamshire, SL9 9RY Tel: (01753) 891222 Fax: (01753) 892113 *Software house*

Dataday Computer Services Ltd, 3-5 Waterloo Road, Uxbridge, Middlesex, UB8 2QX Tel: (01895) 257980 Fax: (01895) 239696 E-mail: info@dataday.uk.com *Computer reseller*

Datadean Ltd, 60 Tinney Drive, Truro, Cornwall, TR1 1AQ Tel: (01872) 264008 Fax: (01872) 263972 E-mail: david.dawkins@quivivre.com *IT Consultancy*

▶ Datadesk Computer Services Ltd, 21 Anniesdale Avenue, Stepps, Glasgow, G33 6DW Tel: 0141-779 9162 Fax: 0141-779 9083 E-mail: info@datadesk.it *IT support consultants, sage reseller*

Dataflair Systems Ltd, PO Box 271, Fleet, Hampshire, GU51 3FD Tel: (01252) 812221 Fax: (01252) 819337 *Software business system services*

Dataflex Design Communications Ltd, 2Nd Floor Chancery House, St. Nicholas Way, Sutton, Surrey, SM1 1JB Tel: (020) 8710 1700 Fax: (020) 8710 1705 *Telephone communications*

Dataflow I T Ltd, 26 George Street, Richmond, Surrey, TW9 1HY Tel: (020) 8332 7733 Fax: (020) 8332 7456 E-mail: info@dataflowit.com *I T services*

Dataforce Group Ltd, Moulton House, 10 Pond Wood Close, Moulton Park Industrial Estate, Northampton, NN3 6DF Tel: (01604) 673800 Fax: (01604) 673801 E-mail: dfreception@dataforce.co.uk *Direct marketing*

Datag Ltd, Holly Farm, Somerford Booths, Congleton, Cheshire, CW12 2JX Tel: (01260) 224794 Fax: (01260) 224794 E-mail: enquiries@datag.co.uk *Agricultural software supplies*

Datagraphic UK Ltd, Cottage Leap, Butler's Leap, Rugby, Warwickshire, CV21 3XP Tel: (01788) 535383 Fax: (01788) 535351 E-mail: sales@datagraphic.co.uk *Computer stationery printing suppliers*

▶ DataInterpreters, 276 West Park Drive West, Leeds, LS8 2BD Tel: 07886 847024 *IT support services & home repairs*

Dataline Northern Ltd, 160-162 Cross Street, Sale, Cheshire, M33 7AQ Tel: 0161-905 1200 Fax: 0161-905 3001 E-mail: dataline@btconnect.com *Telecommunication equipment resellers*

Datalink Software UK Ltd, Unit 61 Old Market Court, George Street, Glastonbury, Somerset, BA6 9LT Tel: (01458) 830134 Fax: (01458) 830135 E-mail: info@datalinklpg.co.uk *Software suppliers to building industries*

Datalogic Scanning, Datalogic House, Dunstable Road, Redbourn, St. Albans, Hertfordshire, AL3 7PR Tel: (01582) 791700 Fax: (01582) 791705 E-mail: uk.scanning@datalogic.com *Bar code systems manufrs*

Datamach Ltd, Falkland Close, Charter Avenue Industrial Estate, Coventry, CV4 8AU Tel: (024) 7647 0707 Fax: (024) 7646 4059 E-mail: enquiries@datamach.co.uk *Machine tool merchants*

Datamail Business Forms Ltd, 141 Kinghorn Road, Burntisland, Fife, KY3 9JW Tel: (01592) 872346 Fax: (01592) 874839 *Computer business forms manufrs*

Datamaster Training Services Ltd, Unit 4 Crescent Court, 51 High Street, Billericay, Essex, CM12 9AQ Tel: (01277) 624007 Fax: (01277) 630044 E-mail: enquiries@datamaster.uk.com *Computer training, software & sales*

▶ Datamate Computers, 37 Darkes Lane, Potters Bar, Hertfordshire, EN6 1BJ Tel: (01707) 664499 Fax: (01707) 649964 *Computer hardware retailers*

Datamirror UK Ltd, Elizabeth House, 39 York Road, London, SE1 7NQ Tel: (020) 7633 5200 Fax: (020) 7633 5210 *Software development*

Datamore, 7 Lake View, Alsager, Kidsgrove, Stoke-on-Trent, ST7 2FY Tel: (01270) 878552 *Computer software*

▶ Datapa Ltd, Midlothian Innovation Centre, Roslin, Midlothian, EH25 9RE Tel: 0131-440 9075 Fax: 0131-445 3941 E-mail: info@datapa.com *Business intelligence software*

Datapact Ltd, 188 St. John Street, London, EC1V 4JY Tel: (020) 7336 7511 E-mail: sales@datapact.co.uk *Computer dealers & repair services*

Datapaq Ltd, Deanland House, 160 Cowley Road, Cambridge, CB4 0GU Tel: (01223) 423141 Fax: (01223) 423306 E-mail: sales@datapaq.co.uk *Temp profilms equipment for industry & monitoring equipment manufrs*

Dataplex Computers Ltd, 129 Bath Road, Slough, SL1 3UW Tel: (01753) 676333 Fax: (01753) 811127 E-mail: info@dataplex.co.uk *Computer repairers & manufrs*

Dataplex Systems Ltd, Orbit House, Albert Street, Eccles, Manchester, M30 0BL Tel: 0161-707 3355 Fax: 0161-707 3344 E-mail: sales@dataplex-systems.com *Computer consultants*

▶ Dataplus Print & Design, 13 Hill Street, Dunmurry, Belfast, BT17 0AD Tel: (028) 9030 1717 Fax: (028) 9061 1292

Datapro Software Ltd, North Street, Portslade, Brighton, BN41 1DH Tel: (01273) 886000 Fax: (01273) 886066 E-mail: sales@datapro.co.uk *Software house*

Dataproof, The Bond, 180-182 Fazeley Street, Birmingham, B5 5SE Tel: 0121-753 7930 Fax: 0121-753 7939 E-mail: office@dataproof.biz *Computer business form printers*

▶ Dataquest Solutions Ltd, 41 Clifton Road, Henlow, Bedfordshire, SG16 6BL Tel: (01462) 857877 Fax: (01462) 811492 E-mail: info@dqsolutions.co.uk *Computer instrumentation*

Dataracks, Stagwood House, Beach Road, Cottenham, Cambridge, CB4 8FP Tel: (01954) 252229 Fax: (01954) 251461 E-mail: sales@dataracks.co.uk *Enclosures manufrs*

Datareason Ltd, College View, Hollington, Stoke-on-Trent, ST10 4HH Tel: (01889) 507348 E-mail: jslim@datareason.co.uk *Computer consultancy*

Dataroll Ltd, Knightcott Industrial Estate, Banwell, Avon, BS29 6JN Tel: (01934) 823253 Fax: (01934) 822990 E-mail: mail@dataroll.co.uk *Rubber manufrs*

Datarota Ltd, High Street, Denford, Kettering, Northamptonshire, NN14 4EQ Tel: (01832) 733671 Fax: (01832) 734188 E-mail: peter@datarota.com *Software development*

Datascan Solutions Group Ltd, 424 Kingtson Road, Raynes Pk, London, SW20 8LL Tel: (020) 8542 5151 Fax: (020) 8544 0108 E-mail: enqiures@imagingandarchiving.co.uk *Microfiche bureau services*

Datascan Systems Ltd, Harris Business Park, Hanbury Road, Stoke Prior, Bromsgrove, Worcestershire, B60 4BD Tel: (01527) 839010 Fax: (01527) 839011 E-mail: sales@datascansystems.com *DataScan Systems Limited was established with a focus on developing barcode scanning solutions utilising barcode and RFID equipment from barcode and RFID manufacturers including DataLogic, renowned for their range of fixed position barcode readers, Hand Held Products Ltd and Escort Memory Systems, a leading*

continued

*manufacturer of LF/HF Radio Frequency Identification equipment (RFID). DataScan Systems supply a wide range of Auto-ID, barcode scanning systems and data capture equipment and barcode solutions including: * Handheld Barcode readers and scanners for industrial and commercial environments * Portable barcode Data Terminals and barcode reading PDA's * Fixed position laser barcode scanners from Datalogic * 2 D code readers and scanner systems * RFID solutions and systems including RFID tags and RFID antennas * Interface and control modules * Barcode label validation systems - The VeriBox system * Barcode label Printers*

▶ Datascape Online Ltd, 24 Waters Edge Business Park, Modwen Road, Salford, M5 3EZ Tel: (0870) 0621200 Fax: (0870) 0621203 *Remote back up, data protection solutions & disaster recovery services*

Datashare Solutions Ltd, 10 Chandler Court, Tolworth Rise South, Surbiton, Surrey, KT5 9NN Tel: (020) 8337 2700 Fax: (020) 8337 2701 E-mail: info@datasharesolutions.com *IT design consultancy & support services*

▶ Datasharp, 43 Cork Lane, Glen Parva, Leicester, LE2 9JS Tel: (0845) 4505034 Fax: (0870) 7705589

Datasharp 2000, Hoggington Lane, Southwick, Trowbridge, Wiltshire, BA14 9NR Tel: (01225) 756910 Fax: (01225) 756911 E-mail: sales@datasharp2000.co.uk *Telephone systems installation & suppliers*

Datasharp Independent Solutions, The Old Stockyard, Farleigh Road, Cliddesden, Basingstoke, Hampshire, RG25 2JS Tel: (01256) 811519 Fax: (01256) 818211 E-mail: sales@datasharp.uk.com *Office equipment suppliers*

▶ Datasharp Telecom (Chiltern), Linton House, The Rowans, Gerrards Cross, Buckinghamshire, SL9 8SE Tel: (0870) 7702670 Fax: (0870) 7702680 E-mail: info@dstelecom.co.uk *Office telecommunications*

Datasharp Telecom (Eastern) Ltd, 78 Chapel Street, King's Lynn, Norfolk, PE30 1EF Tel: (01553) 666111 Fax: (01553) 666112 E-mail: sales@datasharptelecom.com *Business telephone systems suppliers*

▶ Datasharp Voice & Data Ltd, 3 Snaresbrook Drive, Stanmore, Middlesex, HA7 4QN Tel: (020) 8958 8179 Fax: (0870) 0505929 E-mail: info@dsvd.co.uk *Sales and support of Phone Systems and services. Exceptional service, advice and proactive local support for small, medium & large businesses. London and south east England."*

Datasharp Voice Solutions, 50 Lonsdale Road, Notting Hill, London, W11 2DE Tel: 0207 565 9895 Fax: 0207 221 6600 E-mail: info@datasharpvoice.co.uk *London based B2B telephone system supplier, installer and maintainer.*

Datasharp Wales, Unit 5b, Llangan, Bridgend, Mid Glamorgan, CF35 5DR Tel: (01656) 869999 Fax: (01656) 869990 E-mail: info@datasharpwales.com *Supplier of Complete Telecommunication Systems, Hi-Speed Broadband, Voice over IP, IPTV, Movies On Demand, Hotel Multimedia Systems*

▶ Datashred, Units 1-2, Rennys Lane Industrial Estate, Gilesgate, Durham, DH1 2RW Tel: 0191-386 4966 Fax: 0191-370 9850 E-mail: sales@securishred.com *Shredding services*

Datasights Ltd, 228-234 Alma Road, Enfield, Middlesex, EN3 7BB Tel: (020) 8805 4151 Fax: (020) 8805 8084 E-mail: sales@datasights.com *Optical component manufrs*

Datasmith Ltd, 30 Helen Street, Golborne, Warrington, WA3 3QR Tel: (01942) 700828 Fax: (01942) 516572 E-mail: tony@datasmith.co.uk *Computer software consultants*

Datasouth UK, 5 Chevron Business Park, Limekiln Lane, Holbury, Southampton, SO45 2QL Tel: (023) 8089 0800 Fax: (023) 8089 0875 E-mail: info@datasouth.co.uk *Web sites from new concepts*

▶ Datasphere, 25 St. Mary Street, Chepstow, Gwent, NP16 5EU Tel: (01291) 621628 E-mail: sales@data-sphere.co.uk

Datastart (Wales) Ltd, Unit 1 Dolphin Court, Brunel Quay, Neyland, Milford Haven, Dyfed, SA73 1PY Tel: (01646) 602770 Fax: (01646) 602721 *Software company*

Datastor Systems Ltd, 74 Manchester Road, Congleton, Cheshire, CW12 2HT Tel: (01260) 277025 Fax: (01260) 270334 E-mail: sales@datastorsystems.com *Automation & process control engineers*

Datastor Technology Ltd, Old Mushroom Farm, Heathend, Wotton-under-Edge, Gloucestershire, GL12 8AX Tel: (01454) 299399 Fax: (01454) 299400 E-mail: sales@datastor.co.uk *Computer repair services*

Datatec, 31 Bollington Road, Stockport, Cheshire, SK4 5ER Tel: 0161-432 4245 Fax: 0161-442 1375 E-mail: datatec@tiscali.co.uk *Mail order hand held computers*

Datatec Computer Services West Midlands Ltd, 121 Brownswall Road, Dudley, West Midlands, DY3 3NS Tel: (01902) 666144 Fax: (01902) 666146 E-mail: mail@datateclimted.co.uk *Computer services accountancy*

▶ Datatec Online, Market House, 2 Marlborough Road, Swindon, SN3 1QY Tel: 01793 694777 E-mail: doug@datateconline.com *Website design*

▶ Datatech DTP, First Floor Offices, 16 Mere Street, Diss, Norfolk, IP22 4AD Tel: (01379) 742772 *Traditional & electronic publishers*

▶ Datatray System Ltd, Bridge Works, Bridgefields, Welwyn Garden City, Hertfordshire, AL7 1RX Tel: (01707) 332239 Fax: (01707) 331912 E-mail: sales@datatray.co.uk *Cable containment systems*

Datavalley Sales Ltd, 32 London Road, Southborough, Tunbridge Wells, Kent, TN4 0QA Tel: (01892) 514545 Fax: (01892) 518282 E-mail: sales@datavalley.co.uk *Software house*

Datawright Computer Services Ltd, Parsons House, Parsons Road, Washington, Tyne & Wear, NE37 1EZ Tel: 0191-419 4190 Fax: 0191-419 5800 E-mail: sales@datawright.co.uk *Computer systems manufrs*

Date Electronic Supplies Ltd, Lilleshall Street, Newport, Gwent, NP19 0FB Tel: (01633) 259666 Fax: (01633) 266939 E-mail: alwin.treharne@pavecost.com *Electronic equipment, industrial manufrs*

▶ Datec Electronic Holdings, Cromwell House, 142 High Street, Stevenage, Hertfordshire, SG1 3HN Tel: (01438) 360300

Datech Scientific Ltd, Unit 13 Step Business Centre, Wortley Road, Deepcar, Sheffield, S36 2UH Tel: (0870) 7469810 Fax: (0870) 7469811 E-mail: sales@datech-scientific.co.uk *Sample preparation equipment agents*

Datel Direct Ltd, Stafford Road, Stone, Staffordshire, ST15 0DG Tel: (01785) 810800 Fax: (01785) 810820 E-mail: sales@datel.co.uk *Computer software*

Datel Products Ltd, Morgan Rushford Trading Estate, Providence Street, Stourbridge, West Midlands, DY9 8HS Tel: (01384) 893589 Fax: (01384) 893589 *Steel fabricators*

Datel Solutions, 71 Elgin Street, Dunfermline, Fife, KY12 7SA Tel: (01383) 742752 Fax: (01383) 432223 E-mail: info@datel-solutions.co.uk *Suppliers of telecommunications equipment*

Datel UK Ltd, 15 Campbell Court, Bramley, Tadley, Hampshire, RG26 5EG Tel: (01256) 880444 Fax: (01256) 880706 E-mail: datel.ltd@datel.com *Manufacturers of DC to DC converters, data acquisition boards, converters, analogue to digital & meters, panel, digital*

Datex Ohmeda Ltd, 71 Great North Road, Hatfield, Hertfordshire, AL9 5EN Tel: (01707) 263570 Fax: (01707) 260065 *Medical equipment manufacturers & suppliers*

▶ Datex Systemcare Ltd, 6, Leeholme Road, Billingham, Cleveland, TS23 3TA Tel: (01642) 371033 Fax: (01642) 373461

Dathan Tool & Gauge Co. Ltd, Mean Lane, Meltham, Holmfirth, HD9 5RU Tel: (01484) 851207 Fax: (01484) 852271 E-mail: sales@dathan.co.uk *Gear shaper cutters manufrs*

Datona Ltd, Unit 1 Addington Park Industrial Estate, Irthlingborough Road, Little Addington, Kettering, Northamptonshire, NN14 4AS Tel: (01933) 651561 Fax: (01933) 411873

Datona Ltd, Unit 1A, Lawton Rd, Rushden, Northants, NN10 0DX Tel: (01933) 411616 Fax: (01933) 411873 *General engineers, welders, fabricators*

Datone Joiners, Cemetery Road, Pudsey, West Yorkshire, LS28 7LW Tel: 0113-255 5532 Fax: 0113-255 5532 *Joinery manufrs*

Dats (Holdings) Ltd, 1 Springfield Street, Palmyra Square, Warrington, WA1 1BB Tel: (01925) 428559 Fax: (01925) 403801 E-mail: dats@dats.co.uk *Design engineers & contractors & recruitment services* Also at: Stockport, Warrington & Workington

▶ Dats Print Services Ltd, Victoria House, 30 Victoria Street, Irthlingborough, Wellingborough, Northamptonshire, NN9 5RG Tel: (01933) 650623 Fax: (01933) 650698 E-mail: sales@datsprint.co.uk

Datum Automation Ltd, 18 Aston Road, Waterlooville, Hampshire, PO7 7XG Tel: (023) 9224 1154 Fax: (023) 9224 1156 E-mail: sales@datum-automation.com *Manufacturers of identity & credit card systems*

Datum Dynamics, Thistle Business Park South, Craigens Road, Cumnock, Ayrshire, KA18 3AL Tel: (01290) 426200 Fax: (01290) 426212 E-mail: beth@globaldatum.com *PCB tooling engineers*

Datum Engine Services, Yard Mead, Egham, Surrey, TW20 0AB Tel: (01784) 470878 *Vehicle engine recondition services*

Datum Engineering, Nedham St, Leicester, LE2 0HE Tel: 0116-251 9102 Fax: 0116-253 7538 E-mail: datum@2211.com *General engineers*

Datum Fabrications, 66 Redhill Road, Yardley, Birmingham, B25 8EX Tel: 0121-753 0119 Fax: 0121-753 0272 *Sheet metalwork & general metal fabricators*

Datum Products Ltd, Blatchford Road, Horsham, West Sussex, RH13 5QR Tel: (01403) 253453 Fax: (01403) 272687 E-mail: info@datumporductshorsham.co.uk *Precision engineers*

Datum Tools Ltd, Mardens Hill, Crowborough, East Sussex, TN6 1XL Tel: (01892) 667800 Fax: (01892) 667900 *Woodworking machine manufrs*

▶ Datumpress Ltd, 87 Great North Road, Hatfield, Hertfordshire, AL9 5DA Tel: (01707) 251222 Fax: (01707) 251444 *Datumpress handles a wide*range of packaging and publishing portfolios for a number of blue chip clients*

Dau Components Ltd, 70-74 Barnham Road, Barnham, Bognor Regis, West Sussex, PO22 0ES Tel: (01243) 553031 Fax: (01243) 553860 E-mail: sales@dau-components.co.uk *Passive component distributors*

Daub & Wattle Ceramics Ltd, 50 High Street, Bromsgrove, Worcestershire, B61 8EX Tel: (01527) 574004 *Manufacture ceramics*

▶ Daubeneys, Daubeneys High Street, Colerne, Chippenham, Wiltshire, SN14 8DB Tel: (01225) 745732 Fax: (01225) 744384 *Computer system consultants*

Dauphin Museum Services, PO Box 602, Oxford, OX44 9LU Tel: (01865) 343542 Fax: (01865) 343307 E-mail: sales@dauphin.co.uk *Museum services*

C.T.P. Davall Ltd, Durham Lane Industrial Park, Eaglescliffe, Stockton-On-Tees, Cleveland, TS16 0RB Tel: (01554) 749000 Fax: (01642) 790779 E-mail: paul.caldwell@carclo-plc.com *Plastics mouldings manufrs*

Davall Stock Gears, Travellers Lane, North Mymms, Hatfield, Hertfordshire, AL9 7JB Tel: (01707) 283100 Fax: (01707) 283111 E-mail: dsg@davall.co.uk *Gears, gearboxes, couplings pulleys, timing drives*

Davalow Metal Finishing Co. Ltd, Landport Road, Wolverhampton, WV2 2QJ Tel: (01902) 455562 Fax: (01902) 351268 E-mail: davalow@btopenworld.com *Metal finishing, zinc platers and electroplating services.*

Davan Caravans & Motor Homes Ltd, Goosey Lane, St. Georges, Weston-super-Mare, Avon, BS22 7XA Tel: (01934) 510606 Fax: (01934) 516025 E-mail: info@davan.co.uk *Caravan & motor home distributors*

Davand Lables Ltd, Unit 19 Offerton Industrial Estate, Hempshaw Lane, Stockport, Cheshire, SK2 5TJ Tel: 0161-474 7133 Fax: 0161-429 9265 E-mail: davandlabels@tiscali.co.uk *Self-adhesive label manufrs*

Davand Plastics Ltd, Units 33/34, Mill St East, Dewsbury, West Yorkshire, WF12 9AH Tel: (01924) 466248 Fax: (01924) 430148 *Fiberglass moldings manufrs*

Davant Products Ltd, Davant House, Jugs Green Business Park, Staplow, Ledbury, Herefordshire, HR8 1NR Tel: (01531) 630068 Fax: (01531) 640827 E-mail: info@davant.co.uk *Plumbing & insulation*

Davart Fasteners, Unit 10 Honeybourne Airfield Trading Estate, Honeybourne, Evesham, Worcestershire, WR11 7QF Tel: (01386) 833784 Fax: (01386) 833002 E-mail: sales@davart.co.uk *Industrial fastener manufrs*

▶ DAVCAD CAD Draughting Services, 16 Bodmin Close, Eastbourne, East Sussex, BN20 8HZ Tel: 01323 730829 Fax: 01323 730829 E-mail: david.j.saunders@davcad.co.uk *Draught services*

Dave Casey & Co., 1 Raeburn Street, Hartlepool, Cleveland, TS26 8PT Tel: (01429) 261510 Fax: (01429) 274950 *Electrical contractors*

Dave Cooper PCT Environmental Services, Imex Business Centre, Shobnall Road, Burton-on-Trent, Staffordshire, DE14 2AU Tel: (01889) 570430 Fax: (01889) 570430 *Pest control consultants*

Dave Hunt Flooring NW Ltd, 1 Laskey Lane Farm, Laskey Lane, Thelwall, Warrington, WA4 2TF Tel: (01925) 757505 Fax: (01925) 754467 *Commercial flooring specialists*

Dave Mac Supplies, 1-3 Northey Road, Coventry, CV6 5NF Tel: (024) 7668 3239 Fax: (024) 7658 1852 *Motor engineers*

Dave Prior Tiling Co., 40 Kingsley Road, London, E17 4AU Tel: (020) 8531 7221 Fax: 020 85317221 *Tile installation & manufacturer*

▶ Dave Quirk Washing Machine, Unit 4 St. Michaels Industrial Estate, Widnes, Cheshire, WA8 8TL Tel: 0151-424 0539 E-mail: info@davequirkwashingmachines.com *Sell new & reconditioned washing machines spare parts, repair*

▶ Dave Upton, Walnut View, Brook Street, Moreton Pinkney, Daventry, Northamptonshire, NN11 3SL Tel: (01295) 760745 Fax: (01295) 760858

Dave Vickers, Thame Station Industrial Estate, Thame, Oxon, OX9 3UH Tel: (01844) 260100 Fax: (01844) 260900 *Distributors and stockholders of rivets, bolts & nuts*

Davel Technology, Woodlands, Branksome Avenue, Wickford, Essex, SS12 0JD Tel: (01268) 763336 Fax: (01268) 763305 E-mail: davtech@onetel.com *Computer maintenance & repair services*

▶ Davella Transport Ltd, 21 Bradfield Close, Finedon Road Industrial Estate, Wellingborough, Northamptonshire, NN8 4RQ Tel: (01933) 273946 Fax: (01933) 225896

▶ Davemont Reproduction Ltd, 118-122 Cheshire Street, London, E2 6EJ Tel: (020) 7613 3505 Fax: (020) 7256 0366

Davenheath, Unit 3 Kingfisher House, Trinity Business Park, London, E4 8TD Tel: (020) 8531 2003 Fax: (020) 8531 9105 *Security & fire engineers*

Davenport Burgess, 47 Wednesfield Road, Willenhall, West Midlands, WV13 1AL Tel: (01902) 366448 Fax: (01902) 602472 E-mail: sales@davenport-burgess.com *Key & lock wholesalers*

▶ Davenport Control & Instrumentation Ltd, Rowland House, 2 Thundersley Park Road, Benfleet, Essex, SS7 1ET Tel: (01268) 566330 Fax: (01268) 566778

Davenport House, Worfield, Bridgnorth, Shropshire, WV15 5LE Tel: (01746) 716221 Fax: (01746) 716021 *Caterers & wedding services*

Lloyd Davenport Ltd, Unit 10 Kingfisher Court, Hambridge Road, Newbury, Berkshire, RG14 5SJ Tel: (01635) 529191 Fax: (01635) 524278 *Plastering & dry lining contractors*

Davenport Western Ltd, Oxford Road, Pen Mill Trading Estate, Yeovil, Somerset, BA21 5HR Tel: (01935) 425311 Fax: (01935) 432816 *Saw services & manufrs*

▶ Daventry Guarding, 3 Siddeley Way, Royal Oak, Daventry, Northamptonshire, NN11 8PA Tel: (01327) 312880 Fax: (01327) 312881 E-mail: gareth@dglfabs.com *Metal work fabricator, service & repairs*

Daventry Refrigeration, 4 Cross Lane, Braunston, Daventry, Northamptonshire, NN11 7HH Tel: (01788) 890469 Fax: (01788) 891453 *Air conditioning & refrigeration contracting services*

Daventry Thermoforming UK Ltd, West March Industrial Estate, West March, Daventry, Northamptonshire, NN11 4SA Tel: (01327) 878273 Fax: (01327) 300424 E-mail: diane@davthermoforming.demon.co.uk *Thermoforming plastic manurfs*

Daver Steels Ltd, 395 Petre Street, Sheffield, S4 8LN Tel: 0114-261 1999 Fax: 0114 261 1888 E-mail: sales@daversteels.co.uk *Stainless & carbon steel fabrications*

Davern Work Wear Ltd, Elliott Road, March, Cambridgeshire, PE15 8QU Tel: (01354) 654001 Fax: (01354) 658274 E-mail: info@davern.co.uk *Workwear manufrs*

▶ Daves, 215 Freeman Street, Grimsby, South Humberside, DN32 9DW Tel: (01472) 267325 *Guns & gunsmiths*

Daves Peg, Corner Shop, 1 London Road, Sleaford, Lincolnshire, NG34 7LF Tel: (01529) 415896 *Fishing tackle suppliers*

Dave's Trophies, Unit 29 Lewisham Centre, Riverdale, London, SE13 7EP Tel: (020) 8852 7013 Fax: (020) 8852 7013 *Trophies medals & rosette manufrs*

A. & H. Davey (Roadways) Ltd, Shelton New Road, Cliffe Vale, Stoke-on-Trent, ST4 7DL Tel: (01782) 847691 Fax: (01782) 747181 E-mail: ahdavey@btclick.com *Road transport, haulage & freight services*

Davey & Jordan, 3 Jennings Road, Kernick Industrial Estate, Penryn, Cornwall, TR10 9AA Tel: (01326) 372282 Fax: (01326) 376596 *Blacksmiths & general engineers*

Davey & Co London Ltd, 1 Commerce Way, Colchester, CO2 8HR Tel: (01206) 500945 Fax: (01206) 500949 E-mail: chandlery@davey.co.uk *Marine chandlery & lighting suppliers*

Davey Motor Engineering, High Street, Hawkesbury Upton, Badminton, Avon, GL9 1AU Tel: (01454) 238294 *Garage general motor repairs*

Daveys Bakery & Confectionery Supplies, 1-2 Westside Centre, London Road, Stanway, Colchester, CO3 8PH Tel: (01206) 213333 Fax: (01206) 213335 *Bakers*

Davey's Livestock Transport Ltd, Council Houses, Tregadillett, Launceston, Cornwall, PL15 7EX Tel: (01566) 774251 Fax: (01566) 774251 *Cattle haulage*

Davian Designs, 81 Main Road, Waterside, Kilmarnock, Ayrshire, KA3 6JU Tel: (01563) 550091 Fax: (01563) 550091 E-mail: mark@davian79.fsnet.co.uk *manufacture double glazed sealed units,stained glass and leaded mirrors also supply and fit upvc windows doors conservatories supply glass and do repair on upve windows locks handels stays*

Davian Systems, c/o The Punch Hotel, 25, Chapels, Darwen, Lancashire, BB3 0EE Tel: 07792 287416 E-mail: info@daviansystems.co.uk *We are a computer services company specialising in new and reconditioned PC sales, repair and upgrades. We also do website creation and maintence, network design and installation plus much more!*

Davian Systems, 46 Bank Road, Dawley Bank, Telford, Shropshire, TF4 2BB Tel: (01952) 507377 Fax: (01952) 507377 E-mail: info@daviansystemsltd.co.uk *Distributor for lockers,seating, cabinets, shelving, racking,cubicles, SALTO access control equipment. CAD draughting service in Autocad and Genes1s.*

Davicon Structural Engineers, The Wallows Industrial Estate, Fens Pool Avenue, Brierley Hill, West Midlands, DY5 1QA Tel: (01384) 572851 Fax: (01384) 265098 E-mail: sales@davicon.com *Established for over 25 years, we are the UK's leading mezzanine floor manufacturer; we design, manufacture and install mezzanine floors for commercial, industrial & retail applications. We also manufacture/supply raised platforms, balustrades, hand rails, staircases, pallet gates and steel structures.*

Davics Construction Ltd, 154 College Road, Liverpool, L23 3DP Tel: 0151-932 9007 Fax: 0151-931 2196 .

David A Clifford, 118 Maescader, Pencader, Dyfed, SA39 9HR Tel: (01559) 384891 Fax: (01559) 384891 *Agricultural contractors*

▶ David Archibald, 3 Queen Charlotte Lane, Edinburgh, EH6 6AY Tel: 0845 0110184 E-mail: info@contactfoundry.com *Contact Foundry is one of the UK"s leading specialist sales support and lead generation companies.**We deliver highly qualified, exclusive prospect profiles and sales leads to our diverse client base across the UK. We can assist companies in many areas of OUTBOUND telesales work including:**Sales lead generation *Prospect generation *Market research *Interim sales staff *Projects range from as little as £250.00 up to £250,000+, either on a monthly or "one off" project basis. All projects are underwritten by our customer service agreement.*"

▶ David Avery Ltd, 34 Cheriton Road, Folkestone, Kent, CT20 1BZ Tel: (01303) 850288 Fax: (01303) 850289

David B Harries, Maesyronnen, Llangeitho, Tregaron, Dyfed, SY25 6TT Tel: (01974) 821682 Fax: (01974) 821682 E-mail: enquiries@dbhtranspoters.co./uk *Commercial vehicle repairers & horse box builders*

▶ David Baggaley, 79 West Bar, Sheffield, S3 8PS Tel: (07877) 162431 E-mail: david.baggaley1@btinternet.com *Specialists In Hand crafted Jewellery & Giftitems and Jewellery Repair*

David Ball Group plc, Huntingdon Road, Cambridge, CB23 8HN Tel: (01954) 780687 Fax: (01954) 782912 E-mail: sales@davidballgroup.com *Industrial sands & cementations systems division*

David Band Metals Ltd, Friarton Road, Perth, PH2 8BB Tel: (01738) 634991 Fax: (01738) 628439 *Scrap metal merchants*

David Barnett Associates, The Studio, 84 Park Street, St. Albans, Hertfordshire, AL2 2JR Tel: (01727) 872481 Fax: (01727) 875587 E-mail: design@dbassociate.co.uk *Design consultants*

David Bedlington Ltd, Flemingate Works, Flemingate, Beverley, North Humberside, HU17 0NZ Tel: (01482) 867590 Fax: (01482) 866472 *Pump distributors agents & stockists*

David Birch Milking Equipment, Milliganton Farm, Auldgirth, Dumfries, DG2 0JX Tel: (01387) 740219 Fax: (01387) 740667 *Milking equipment installation, retail & maintenance*

David Blane, 66A Station Road, Petersfield, Hampshire, GU32 3ET Tel: (01730) 263202 *Burglar alarm installation services*

David Bowler & Sons Ltd, Hardley Industrial Estate, Hardley, Hythe, Southampton, SO45 3YQ Tel: (023) 8084 3109 Fax: (023) 8084 0034 E-mail: bowler.group@virgin.net *General presswork manufrs*

David Brown Hydraulics Ltd, 32 Factory Road, Poole, Dorset, BH16 5SL Tel: (01202) 627500 Fax: (01202) 627555 E-mail: info@dbh.textron.com *Hydraulic component manufrs*

David Burns, 44-46 Riding House Street, London, W1W 7EX Tel: (020) 7580 1422 Fax: (020) 7436 3046 E-mail: david@davidburnsinttex.com *Textile agents*

▶ David C Osborne Ltd, 2-4 Park Avenue, Deal, Kent, CT14 9AL Tel: (01304) 381999

David Chapman, Lynn House, Mill Lane, Sutton St. James, Spalding, Lincolnshire, PE12 0EJ Tel: (01945) 440273 Fax: (01945) 440273 *Agricultural contractor suppliers*

David & Charles Publishers Ltd, Brunel House, Forde Close, Newton Abbot, Devon, TQ12 4PU Tel: (01626) 323200 Fax: (01626) 323291 E-mail: postmaster@dcpublishers.co.uk *Publishers*

David Charles Whitaker, Killatree Farm, Holsworthy, Devon, EX22 6LP Tel: (01409) 253539 Fax: (01409) 253539 *Agricultural machinery distributors*

David Colwell, Llawr-Y-Glyn, Llawr-y-Glyn, Caersws, Powys, SY17 5RH Tel: (01686) 430434 E-mail: info@davidcolwell.com *Furniture design*

David Cover & Son Ltd, Chatfields Yard, Cooksbridge, Lewes, East Sussex, BN8 4TJ Tel: (01273) 476133 Fax: (01273) 400164 E-mail: sales@covers-group.co.uk *Timber merchants & builders merchants*

▶ David Craig Ltd, The Mill Industrial Estate, Langley Moor, Durham, DH7 8JE Tel: 0191-378 1211 Fax: 0191-378 0411 E-mail: info@davidcraigtractors.co.uk

▶ David Cruikshank, River View Business Park, Friarton Road, Perth, PH2 8BB Tel: (01738) 449944

David Etchells Signs, Unit 5 Brassey Close, Peterborough, PE1 2AZ Tel: (01733) 347847 Fax: (01733) 311242 E-mail: sales@etchells-signs.co.uk *Sign makers, installers & engravers services*

▶ David Evans Ltd, Unit 2 The Old Saw Mill, Clitheroe, Lancashire, BB7 1LY Tel: (01200) 428460 Fax: (0870) 4601595 E-mail: david@evansaccountants.com *Chartered Accountants and Business Advisers. Providing a professional, efficient and friendly service to owner managed businesses in the North West (England), and to actors, authors and musicians throughout the UK.*

David Evans & Co, Bourne Road, Crayford, Dartford, DA1 4BP Tel: (01322) 557521 Fax: (01322) 550476 E-mail: sales@davidevans.co.uk *Silk printers*

David & Co. Financial Advisers, Old Croft, Bogmoor, Spey Bay, Fochabers, Morayshire, IV32 7PB Tel: (01343) 829290 Fax: (01343) 821257 *Advice on all personal debt problems & help with reducing debt*

▶ David Fox (Transport) Ltd, Stora Terminal, Immingham Dock, Immingham, South Humberside, DN40 2NT Tel: (01469) 577380 Fax: (01469) 577014 E-mail: traffic@davidfox.co.uk

▶ David Frank Hair & Beauty, 18 Dalton Square, Lancaster, LA1 1PL Tel: (01524) 843434 Fax: *Retailers of ladies accessories*

David G Alker, The Quern, Chapel Lawn, Bucknell, Shropshire, SY7 0BW Tel: (01547) 530344 Fax: (01547) 530844 E-mail: davequern@aol.com *Central heating installation*

David Gerrard Fisheries Ltd, 4 Mid Shore, Pittenweem, Anstruther, Fife, KY10 2NJ Tel: (01333) 311551 Fax: (01333) 312286 *Refrigerated transport providers*

▶ David Gregory Building & Roofing Contractors Ltd, Greaves Bakery, Townfoot, Rothbury, Morpeth, Northumberland, NE65 7SP Tel: (01669) 620064

▶ David Hansford Photography, 17 Casterbridge Way, Gillingham, Dorset, SP8 4FG Tel: 01747 831 082 Fax: 0870 124 6166 E-mail: david@davidhansfordphoto.co.uk *Photographer. Photographic images, digital and film based photography, scanning, large format digital printing, greetings cards, framed and mounted prints of Dorset, Wiltshire, Blackmore Vale and Stourhead. Stock photography*

▶ David Harber, Valley Farm, Turville, Henley-on-Thames, Oxfordshire, RG9 6QU Tel: (01491) 576956 Fax: (01491) 413524 E-mail: sales@davidharbersundials.com *Handmade sundials, tailored to individual locations. Armillary spheres, egyptian obelisks and more.*

▶ David Harrison, Stone Gables, 58 Langton Rd, Norton, Malton, North Yorkshire, YO17 9AE Tel: (01653) 693097

▶ David Hathaway Ltd, Westerleigh Business Park, 30 Woodward Avenue, Yate, Bristol, BS37 5YS Tel: (01454) 334500 Fax: (01454) 334550 E-mail: contact@davidhathaway.co.uk *Complete solution to companies requiring storage & distribution*

▶ David Heeps (Haulage) Ltd, 5 Hugh Place, Lochgelly, Fife, KY5 9DN Tel: (01592) 780393

▶ David Hilton, Orchard Cottage, Littledown Farm, Brighton Road, Lewes, East Sussex, BN7 3JJ Tel: 01273 479799 Fax: 01273 239999 E-mail: david.hilton@ambulanceservice.gb.com *Private ambulance service based in Sussex, UK specialising in the movement of ill and injured patients by ambulance nationally and worldwide.*

David Hobdell Building Ltd, Cheltenham House, Grange Road, London, N17 0ER Tel: (020) 8801 5244 Fax: (020) 8885 2876 *Painting contractors*

David Huggett Commercial Motor Factors Ltd, D Brittania Road, Waltham Cross, Hertfordshire, EN8 7NH Tel: (01992) 762519 Fax: (01992) 718472 *Commercial vehicle parts distributors*

David Huish, 1-2 Rectors Way, Weston-super-Mare, Avon, BS23 3NP Tel: (01934) 636584 Fax: (01934) 636584 *Joinery manufrs*

David Hunt Castings, Romsey Industrial Estate, Budds La, Romsey, Hants, SO51 0HA Tel: (01794) 511259 Fax: (01794) 518325 E-mail: davidhunt.castings@btopenworld.com *Castings manufacturers, including aluminium/ alloy*

David Hunt Lighting Ltd, Tilemans Lane, Shipston-on-Stour, Warwickshire, CV36 4HP Tel: (01608) 661590 Fax: (01608) 662951 *Lighting manufrs*

David J Haddock, Rope Farm, Mapperton Hill, Milton on Stour, Gillingham, Dorset, SP8 5QG Tel: (01747) 860016 Fax: (01747) 860221 *Cabinet makers*

David J Tremain, Millside, Bridge, St. Columb, Cornwall, TR9 6BE Tel: (01637) 880352 *Agricultural contractors*

David John Houlston, 62 Haygate Drive, Wellington, Telford, Shropshire, TF1 2BZ Tel: (01952) 244905 Fax: (01952) 244905 E-mail: enquiries@houlstonphotography.co.uk *Industrial photographers*

David Johnson Lutterworth Ltd, Upper Bruntingthorpe, Lutterworth, Leicestershire, LE17 5QZ Tel: 0116-247 8349 Fax: 0116-247 8349 *Agricultural engineers*

▶ David Kinns Joinery, 23 San Remo Road, Aspley Guise, Milton Keynes, MK17 8JY Tel: (01908) 582678 Fax: (01908) 586898 *Timber merchants*

▶ David Kirk Ltd, Rock Head House, Cowdale, Buxton, Derbyshire, SK17 9SE Tel: 01298 78413 Fax: 01298 78429 E-mail: davidkirkltd@btconnect.com *Chartered accountants*Chartered tax advisers*We specialise in tax advice for non-specilaist accountants, high net worth individuals and owner-managed businesses*

▶ David Lancaster, 23 Borrowdale Road, Lancaster, LA1 3HF Tel: (01524) 66913 Fax: 01524 66913 E-mail: david@davidlancaster.co.uk *Stylish entertainment company for private parties & businesses*

▶ Lawrence David Ltd, Maxwell Road, Peterborough, PE2 7JR Tel: (01733) 397600 Fax: (01733) 397601 E-mail: sales@lawrencedavid.co.uk *Commercial vehicle builders*

Lawrence David Ltd, Maxwell Road, Peterborough, PE2 7JR Tel: (01733) 397600 Fax: (01733) 397601 E-mail: sales@lawrencedavid.co.uk *Commercial vehicle body builders*

David Lee Photography, George Street, Barton-upon-Humber, South Humberside, DN18 5ES Tel: (01652) 632451 Fax: (01652) 637481 E-mail: enquiries@davidleephotography.co.uk *Industrial, commercial & aerial photographers*

David Lewis & Co., 21 Gloucester Place, London, W1U 8HR Tel: (020) 7486 2277 Fax: (020) 7224 5173 *Consultant surveyors & estate agents*

David Lewis Consultancy Ltd, 31b High Street, Tunbridge Wells, Kent, TN1 1XL Tel: (01892) 542825 Fax: (01892) 708700 E-mail: sales@dlcltd.com *Market researchers*

David Lloyd Associates, 35 Victor Road, Harrow, Middlesex, HA2 6PT Tel: (020) 8728 2421 Fax: (020) 8728 2421 E-mail: david_lloyd_a@compuserve.com *Training & development consultancy*

▶ David Lowder Electrical Contractors Ltd, 55a Hercus Loan, Musselburgh, Midlothian, EH21 6AU Tel: 0131-665 7895 Fax: 0131-665 4577

▶ David Luke Ltd, 4 Midland Street, Manchester, M12 6LB Tel: 0161-272 7474 Fax: 0161-272 6363 E-mail: sales@davidluke.com *School & scout wear wholesalers*

▶ David M Blyth, 153 Commercial Street, Kirkcaldy, Fife, KY1 2NS Tel: (01592) 263378 Fax: (01592) 263378

David M Petherick, Higher Thorne Farm, Down St. Mary, Crediton, Devon, EX17 6EB Tel: (01363) 82487 Fax: (01363) 82487 *Farming*

David Mcclure Ltd, Mersey Dynamo Works, Range Road, Stockport, Cheshire, SK3 8EF Tel: 0161-474 7362 Fax: 0161-429 0251 E-mail: mail@david-mcclure.co.uk *Electric motors & control equipment manufrs*

David Mckay Brown (Gunmakers) Ltd, 32 Hamilton Road, Bothwell, Glasgow, G71 8NA Tel: (01698) 853727 Fax: (01698) 854207 E-mail: info@mckaybrown.com *Sporting shotguns & rifles manufrs*

David Maddox Ltd, 53-55 Gatwick Road, Crawley, West Sussex, RH10 9RD Tel: (01293) 452830 Fax: (01293) 452830 E-mail: david.maddox@virgin.net *Printed circuit assembly services*

▶ David Mellor Ltd, Sandybrook Garage, Buxton Road, Ashbourne, Derbyshire, DE6 1EX Tel: (01335) 343840 Fax: (01335) 343816

▶ David Morin Builders Ltd, 5 Saltcoats Road, Gullane, East Lothian, EH31 2AQ Tel: (01620) 843232 Fax: (01620) 844007

▶ David Murray N M P Ltd, Woodhead Road, Chryston, Glasgow, G69 9JD Tel: 0141-779 3535 Fax: 0141-779 3956

David Newman Camshafts & Co., Farnborough Way, Orpington, Kent, BR6 7DH Tel: (01689) 857109 Fax: (01689) 855994 E-mail: info@newman-cams.com *Camshaft & rocker arm manufrs*

▶ David Nightingale, 20 Gastard Lane, Gastard, Corsham, Wiltshire, SN13 9QN Tel: (01249) 701271 Fax: (01249) 701271 E-mail: david.nightingale@coachtrimming.co.uk *Coachtrimming. Restoration of car interiors, trimming aircraft cockpits. Restoration of car hoods, carpets, seats, panels, headlinings.*

▶ David Paterson, 18 Linkwood Way, Linkwood Industrial Estate, Elgin, Morayshire, IV30 1HY Tel: (01343) 545190 Fax: (01343) 540444 *Engineering*

▶ David Patton & Sons (N I) Ltd, Woodside Road, Ballymena, County Antrim, BT42 4PT Tel: (028) 2564 2141

David Payne & Son Coachbuilders Ltd, Beddow Way, Aylesford, Kent, ME20 7BT Tel: (01622) 718645 Fax: (01622) 716365 *Refrigerated trailer repairs*

▶ David Petyt Exclusive Menswear, 8-12 Hanover Street, Keighley, West Yorkshire, BD21 3QJ Tel: (01535) 604853 Fax: (01535) 610408 E-mail: sales@petyt.co.uk *Corporate clothing suppliers, tuxedo & suit hire, dinner & wedding*

▶ David Price Property Services, Meadow View, Low Cotehill, Carlisle, CA4 0EL Tel: 01228 562632 E-mail: david@priceps.wanadoo.co.uk *Building Repair, Renovation and Restoration*

continued

continuation
*Specialist.**David has been involved with building restoration for over 20 years and offers a comprehensive set of skills. Whether it's renovation of an historic building or refitting and upgrading a more modern house, David has a reputation for quality and reliability. **As well as a direct hands-on approach, David Price Property Services also undertakes project management and advisory roles from initial planning to completion of project.**Previous customers include:**The Church of England Diosecan Parsonages Board*Ministry of Defence (PSA)*Solway Aviation Museum*Cumbria County Council (Schools)*Impact Housing*CASS*Cumberland Building Society*Reeds Rains**David Price Property Services also offers insurance work to fire, flood and weather damaged buildings.*****

David R Howells, Maes Y Gelli, Penybont, Carmarthen, Dyfed, SA33 6QA Tel: (01994) 484257 *Agricultural contractors*

David Richards Ltd, 1-2 The Deacon Estate, Cabinet Way, London, E4 8QF Tel: (020) 8523 2051 Fax: (020) 8523 2746 E-mail: enquiries@davidrichards.co.uk *Business forms management*

David S Smith, Prickwillow Road, Queen Adelaide, Ely, Cambridgeshire, CB7 4TZ Tel: (01353) 660000 Fax: (01353) 660011 *Corrugated litho-laminated cartons manufrs*

David S Smith, Prickwillow Road, Queen Adelaide, Ely, Cambridgeshire, CB7 4TZ Tel: (01353) 660000 Fax: (01353) 660011 E-mail: steve.wills@ely.dssp.com *Corrugated box manufrs*

▶ David South, 15 High Street, Pateley Bridge, Harrogate, North Yorkshire, HG3 5AP Tel: (01423) 712022 Fax: (01423) 712412 E-mail: sales@davidsouth.co.uk *Suppliers of period & antique upholstered furniture. Upholstery workshop, curtain making, loose covers etc. Contract service for interior designers. Suppliers of prestige designer furniture & gilded upholstered furniture. Large range of fabrics, wallpapers.*

▶ David South Ltd, Southdale House Holloway Drive, Wardley Industrial Estate, Worsley, Manchester, M28 2LA Tel: 0161-279 8020 Fax: 0161-279 8021

▶ David Stagg & Associates Ltd, 49 Watchouse Road, Chelmsford, CM2 8PU Tel: (01245) 492491 Fax: 01245 269690 E-mail: brian@davidstagg.co.uk *Portable Appliance Testing*Electrical Contracting *Electrical Safety testing*

▶ David Stanley, Vulcan Court, Vulcan Way, Coalville, Leicestershire, LE67 3FW Tel: (01530) 831200 Fax: (01430) 814143

▶ David Sykes (Whitley Bridge) Ltd, The Maltings Industrial Estate, Doncaster Road, Whitley Bridge, Goole, North Humberside, DN14 0HH Tel: (01977) 661351

▶ David Taylor Garages (Filling Stations) 2000 Ltd, Granada Park Motors, Llangattock, Crickhowell, Powys, NP8 1HW Tel: (01873) 810304 Fax: (01873) 811320 E-mail: davidtaylorgarages@compuserve.co.uk *Petrol stations & car retailers*

▶ David Tervet, Glaichbea, Beauly, Inverness-Shire, IV4 7HR Tel: (01463) 741293

▶ David Turner, 55 Easthouses Road, Easthouses, Dalkeith, Midlothian, EH22 4EB Tel: 0131-663 2900 Fax: 0131-663 2900

▶ David Tyrrell Catering & Hospitality, 481 Chessington Road, Epsom, Surrey, KT19 9JH Tel: (020) 8397 3030 Fax: (020) 8397 4747 E-mail: davidtyrrell@btconnect.com *Specialise in weddings & hospitality services*

▶ David White Associates, Craven House, 14-18 York Road, Wetherby, West Yorkshire, LS22 6SL Tel: (01937) 589113 Fax: (01937) 589744 E-mail: info@dwa-ltd.com *quantity surveying and project management consultancy to the construction industry.*

David Williams Llandudno Ltd, 4 Builder Street, Llandudno, Gwynedd, LL30 1DR Tel: (01492) 876869 Fax: (01492) 870664 *Oxy-acetylene welders & steel fabricators*

▶ David Wilson Homes Ltd, Barfield House, Britannia Road, Morley, Leeds, LS27 0DT Tel: 0113-252 9900

David Wilson's Trailers, Hillsdown Farm, Birch Grove, Horsted Keynes, Haywards Heath, West Sussex, RH17 7DH Tel: (01825) 740696 Fax: (01825) 740260 E-mail: info@dwt-exhibitions.co.uk *Exhibit display services & organisers*

▶ Davids Driving School, 46 London Road, Ramsgate, Kent, CT11 0DN Tel: (01843) 851148 *Approved Driving Instructor.*Driving Standards Agency *AA driving School Franchise.*Thanet Area.*Not Instructor Training.*No listing for Normal Teaching.**

Davidson & Co. Ltd, 92 Harwood Street, Sheffield, S2 4SE Tel: 0114-272 4584 Fax: 0114-279 7309 *Marking device manufrs*

Davidson Bros Shotts Ltd, Gray Street, Shotts, Lanarkshire, ML7 5EZ Tel: (01501) 820048 Fax: (01501) 822926 E-mail: info@davidsonsfeeds.co.uk *Animal feed company manufrs*

Davidson & Hardy (Lab Supplies) Ltd, 453-459 Antrim Road, Belfast, BT15 3BL Tel: (028) 9078 1611 Fax: (028) 9077 2801 E-mail: info@dhlab.com *Laboratory supply services*

John Davidson Pipes Ltd, Townfoot, Longtown, Carlisle, CA6 5LY Tel: (01228) 791503 Fax: (01228) 791682 E-mail: jdpcentral@jdpipes.co.uk Principal Export Areas: Worldwide *PVC pipes distributors* Also at: Birtley, Bolton, Bristol, Broxburn, Cambridge, Carlisle, Glasgow, Inverurie, Longton, Maidstone, Northampton & Warley

▶ Davidson Pre Press Graphics Ltd, 116 Elderslie Street, Glasgow, G3 7AW Tel: 0141-248 1222 Fax: 0141-248 7589

Davidson Sheet Metal, Bourtree House, Minto Drive, Altens, Aberdeen, AB12 3LW Tel: (01224) 897676 Fax: (01224) 895199 E-mail: enquiry@hutcheon-services.ltd.uk *Sheet metal fabricators*

▶ Davidson & Wilson Ltd, Sclattie Quarry Industrial Estate, Bankhead, Bucksburn, Aberdeen, AB21 9EG Tel: (01224) 716588 Fax: (01224) 716170

▶ Davidsons, Seagate, Peterhead, Aberdeenshire, AB42 1JP Tel: (01779) 474455 Fax: (01779) 475218 *Engineering services*

Davies, Sunningdale, Great North Road, Bawtry, Doncaster, South Yorkshire, DN10 6DF Tel: (01302) 719341 Fax: (01302) 711181

Andrew Davies Construction Ltd, The Manor House, High Street, Buntingford, Hertfordshire, SG9 9AB Tel: (01763) 274334 Fax: (01763) 274335 *Civil engineers*

▶ Ashley Davies Livery & Competition Yard, Ysgubor Fach Farm, Crwbin, Kidwelly, Carmarthenshire, SA17 5EB Tel: (01269) 870831 *FULL LIVERY SERVICE, OFF SEASON STABLING FOR RACE HORSES,SCHOOLING,BREAKING IN SERVICE,BUYING AND SELLING HORSES, SAND BOX.CAN COLLECT HORSES*

Davies Associates Ltd, 95 York Street, London, W1H 4QG Tel: (020) 7258 0701 Fax: (020) 7724 0106 E-mail: hq@dapr.com *Public relations consultants*

Davies Brook & Co Ltd, Moreton-on-Lugg, Hereford, HR4 8DY Tel: (01432) 760666 Fax: (01432) 761477 *Mineral water manufrs*

▶ Davies Bros, 5 Holborn Square, Birkenhead, Merseyside, CH41 9HQ Tel: 0151-647 3002 Fax: 0151-647 3002 E-mail: dvsbrn@aol.com *Davies Brothers, polyurethane specialists, are based on the Wirral in Cheshire. Davies Brothers manufacture a wide range of polyurethane products to meet customer requirements for polyurethane commodities using innovative and practical approaches to achieve the final polyurethane products in the required time scale. Davies Brothers can produce polyurethane material as soft as flesh (35 shore D) to a rigid impact resistant polyurethane material of 95 shore A. Our range of products include polyurethane products, polyurethane mouldings, polyurethane elastomer products, polyurethane moulding services etc. Please feel free to give us a call or view our website.*

Davies Bros (Metal Finishers), 123-127 Western Road, Hockley, Birmingham, B18 7QD Tel: 0121-554 3148 Fax: 0121-554 3148 E-mail: sales@british-fireside.co.uk *Brass ware manufrs*

▶ Clive Davies, 4 Crispin Centre, Street, Somerset, BA16 0HP Tel: (01458) 441001 Fax: (01458) 441001 E-mail: sales@clivedaviesfurnishings.co.uk *Beds retailers*

Davies Control Systems, Unit 20 South Pontypool Industrial Park, Panteg Way, New Inn, Pontypool, Gwent, NP4 0LS Tel: (01495) 764094 Fax: (01495) 756237 E-mail: info@daviescontrolsystems.co.uk *Control panel manufacturers.*PLC Programming.*Control System Design.*Fully Automated Systems.*HMI.*

Davies Crane Hire Ltd, Pensarn Road, Carmarthen, Dyfed, SA31 2BS Tel: (01267) 234660 Fax: (01267) 232346 E-mail: enquiries@daviescranehire.co.uk *Mobile crane hires*

Davies Crane Hire Ltd, Phoenix Wharf, Harbour Road, The Docks, Port Talbot, West Glamorgan, SA13 1RA Tel: (01639) 883474 Fax: (01639) 897028 E-mail: enquiries@daviescrane.co.uk *Mobile crane hire* Also at: Carmarthen

David Davies & Sons, 1 Waylands Upper Church Street, Oswestry, Shropshire, SY11 2AA Tel: (01691) 653116 Fax: (01691) 650702 E-mail: hugh@daviddaviesandsons.co.uk *Funeral directors & glazing contractors & joinery contractors services*

Davies & Davies, 22 Lower Street, Rode, Frome, Somerset, BA11 6PU Tel: (01373) 831331 Fax: (01373) 831331 *Catering equipment hire*

▶ Davies Edward Construction)Ltd, Tremorfa Foreshaw, Ocean Park, Cardiff, CF10 4LJ Tel: (029) 2049 8798 E-mail: admin@edav.co.uk

Davies Envelope, Foxwood Industrial Park, Chesterfield, Derbyshire, S41 9RN Tel: (020) 8368 4236 Fax: (01246) 572270 *Envelope suppliers & printers*

Gerald Davies Ltd, Kenfig Industrial Estate, Margam, Port Talbot, West Glamorgan, SA13 2PE Tel: (01656) 745525 Fax: (01656) 746270 E-mail: enquiries@geralddavies.co.uk *Landscape Gardening*

Davies Implements Ltd, Blaenteg, Llwynderi, Trevaughan, Carmarthen, Dyfed, SA31 3QN Tel: (01267) 237726 Fax: (01267) 238696 E-mail: davies@implements.preserve.co.uk *Agricultural, horticultural & forestry equipment retailers*

▶ Davies International Transport Ltd, 21 Brunel Way, Fareham, Hampshire, PO15 5SD Tel: (01489) 579957 Fax: (01489) 575728

Islwyn Davies, 120 Glynhir Road, Pontarddulais, Swansea, SA4 8PY Tel: (01792) 883149 *Mobile shop*

Davies & Co. (Kettering), Beatrice Road, Kettering, Northamptonshire, NN16 9QS Tel: (01536) 513456 Fax: (01536) 310080 E-mail: david@davieskett.co.uk *Horse & cow mats manufrs*

Davies Machinery, 21 Harris Road, Lostock Gralam, Northwich, Cheshire, CW9 7PE Tel: (01606) 48683 Fax: (01606) 48683 *Bag stitches & heat sealers*

Davies Precision Grinding Ltd, 282 Upper Balsall Heath Road, Birmingham, B12 9DR Tel: 0121-440 4400 Fax: 0121-440 1414 *Universal grinding specialists*

Davies Products Liverpool Ltd, Alsol House, Laburnum Place, Bootle, Merseyside, L20 3NE Tel: 0151-922 4246 Fax: 0151-944 1901 *Fancy goods distributors*

Davies Riding Boots, 6 Blaenant Industrial Estate, Blaenavon Road, Brynmawr, Ebbw Vale, Gwent, NP23 4BX Tel: (01495) 313045 Fax: (01495) 313045 E-mail: sales@daviesridingboots.co.uk *Riding boots manufrs*

▶ Davies & Robson Logistics Ltd, The Coach House, Watling Street, Weedon, Northampton, NN7 4QG Tel: (01327) 349090 Fax: (01327) 349820 E-mail: sales@daviesrobson.co.uk *Logistics Consultancy*

▶ Stephen J. Davies, 43 Curtis Avenue, Abingdon, Oxfordshire, OX14 3UL Tel: (01235) 200869 *Furniture repair & restoration services*

Davies (Stove Enamellers) Ltd, Unit M Cradock Road Industrial Estate, Cradock Road, Luton, LU4 0JF Tel: (01582) 572582 Fax: (01582) 594703 E-mail: tom@lth.co.uk *Stove enamelling & engineering services*

Davies Timber Ltd, Wythall Saw Mills Alcester Road, Wythall, Birmingham, B47 6JG Tel: (01564) 826861 Fax: (01564) 823505 E-mail: davistimber@davistimber.fsnet.co.uk *Timber merchants*

Davies Turner & Co. Ltd, Dartford Freight Terminal, Edison's Park, Dartford, DA2 6QJ Tel: (01322) 277558 Fax: (01322) 289063 E-mail: webmaster@daviesturner.co.uk *Freight forwarding agents*

Davies Turner & Co. Ltd, Unit C16 Taylors Court, Parkgate, Rotherham, South Yorkshire, S62 6NU Tel: (01709) 529709 Fax: (01709) 529710 E-mail: paulknight@daviesturner.co.uk *Freight forwarders* Also at: Bedfont, Ilford & Liverpool

Davies Turner & Co. Ltd, 184 Portswood Road, Southampton, SO17 2NJ Tel: (023) 8055 5955 Fax: (023) 8055 5644 E-mail: mikerees@davisturner.co.uk *Freight forwarders*

Davies Turner & Co. Ltd, London House, Hide Street, Stoke-on-Trent, ST4 1NF Tel: (01782) 413617 Fax: (01782) 744063 *Freight forwarding company*

Davies Turner Worldwide Movers Ltd, 49 Wates Way, Mitcham, Surrey, CR4 4HR Tel: (020) 7622 4393 Fax: (020) 7720 3897 E-mail: removals@daviesturner.co.uk *International removers & antiques packing services*

W.G. Davies (Landore) Ltd, Unit 11, St. Davids Road, Morriston, Swansea, SA6 8QL Tel: (01792) 795705 Fax: (01792) 797823 E-mail: wgdavies@telnet.co.uk *Heavy goods repair services*

Davies Wise Design Co., 14 Spring Mill, Avening Road, Nailsworth, Stroud, Gloucestershire, GL6 0BS Tel: (01453) 839192 Fax: (01453) 839193 E-mail: sales@dwdc.co.uk *Design consultants*

Davies Woven Wire Ltd, Unit 38 Cradley Heath Factory Centre, Woods Lane, Cradley Heath, West Midlands, B64 7AQ Tel: (01384) 411991 Fax: (01384) 410999 E-mail: sales@davieswovenwire.co.uk *Manufacture & supply woven wire conveyor belting*

Davin Fowler, 15 Queens Square, Leeds, LS2 8AJ Tel: 0113 2255517 E-mail: info@giant-systems.co.uk *A specialist provider of custom built Ecommerce solutions based in Leeds, West Yorkshire.*

Davin Optronics Ltd, Creycaine Road, Watford, WD24 7GW Tel: (01923) 206800 Fax: (01923) 234220 E-mail: sales@davinoptronics.com *Optical systems & components manufrs*

Davis Co. Ltd, 45-49 Mortimer Street, London, W1W 8HL Tel: (020) 7323 6696 Fax: (020) 7323 6697 E-mail: marketing@davisrecruitment.co.uk *Recruitment consultancy*

Davis, Old Wesley Hall, Bridge Street, Newbridge, Newport, Gwent, NP11 5FE Tel: (01495) 243619 Fax: (01495) 243619 *Joinery manufrs*

Davis Architects Services Ltd, Units 1 & 2 Ropery Business Park, Anchor & Hope Lane, London, SE7 7RX Tel: (020) 8853 5997 Fax: (020) 8853 4137 *Architectural fittings manufrs*

Beryl Davis, 1 Primrose Mill, Friday Street, Chorley, Lancashire, PR6 0AA Tel: (01257) 272121 Fax: (01257) 268033 E-mail: sales@beryl-davis.co.uk *Protective clothing manufrs*

Davis Cash & Co. Ltd, Alexandra Road, Enfield, Middlesex, EN3 7EN Tel: (020) 8804 4028 Fax: (020) 8805 2896 E-mail: sales@daviscash.co.uk *Electric light fittings manufrs*

Davis Decade Ltd, 30 Spring Lane, Birmingham, B24 9BX Tel: 0121-377 6292 Fax: 0121-377 6645 E-mail: dmg@decade.co.uk *Load monitoring systems manufrs*

Davis Emblems, Unit 3 David Cuthbert Business Centre, Ashton Old Road, Manchester, M11 2NA Tel: 0161-231 7300 E-mail: davisembroidery@aol.com *Emblems & printers*

F. Davis & Co., 64 London Road, Bexhill-On-Sea, East Sussex, TN39 3LE Tel: (01424) 211248 Fax: (01424) 730568 *Scrap metal merchants*

Davis Fishing Tackle, 75 Bargates, Christchurch, Dorset, BH23 1QE Tel: (01202) 485169 Fax: (01202) 474261 E-mail: mail@davistackle.co.uk *Fishing tackle suppliers*

Davis Freight Forwarding Ltd, Manby Road Bypass, Immingham, South Humberside, DN40 2DW Tel: (01469) 572556 Fax: (01469) 571287 *Freight forwarders & forwarding agents*

Davis Group, 48 Watersfield Way, Edgware, Middlesex, HA8 6RZ Tel: (020) 8951 4264 Fax: (020) 8951 4342 E-mail: rdavis7054@aol.com *Manufacturers of packaged goods*

▶ Davis Haworth Jacob, A 449 Holloway Road, London, N7 6LJ Tel: (020) 7263 7744 Fax: (020) 7263 6644 E-mail: clive@davishowarthjacob.com *Furniture manufrs*

Davis & Hill, 56 Pritchett Street, Birmingham, B6 4EY Tel: 0121-359 4091 Fax: 0121-333 3163 E-mail: sales@davisandhill.co.uk *Aluminium & non ferrous casting manufrs*

Davis Hudson & Co. Ltd, 17 Bickford Road, Birmingham, B6 7EE Tel: 0121-327 0020 Fax: 0121-328 5649 E-mail: electricians@davishudson.co.uk *Electrical engineers & contractors*

Davis Industrial (Filters) Ltd, 21d Holmethorpe Avenue, Redhill, RH1 2NB Tel: (0845) 2735025 Fax: (0845) 2735026 E-mail: sales@davisfilters.co.uk *Air filtration equipment manufrs*

Davis International Banking Consultants (UK) Ltd, 42 Brook Street, London, W1K 5DB Tel: (020) 7958 9008 Fax: (020) 7958 9275 E-mail: dibc@dibc.co.uk *Financial consultants*

J.W. Davis (Plymouth) Ltd, 14 Stonehouse Street, Plymouth, PL1 3PE Tel: (01752) 664756 Fax: (01752) 660720 E-mail: jwdavisltd@aol.com *Electric motor repair & rewind specialists services*

Mark Davis Engineering Co. Ltd, Hayes Lane, Lye, Stourbridge, West Midlands, DY9 8RA Tel: (01384) 424404 Fax: (01384) 424707 E-mail: enquiries@markdavis.co.uk Principal Export Areas: Africa, Central/East Europe, West Europe & North America *General presswork & fittings manufrs*

Davis Memorials, 56a Station Road, Cradley Heath, West Midlands, B64 6NU Tel: (01384) 566958 Fax: (01384) 569708 *Stone masons & merchants*

Davis Memorials, 1 Park Street, Kidderminster, Worcestershire, DY11 6TN Tel: (01384) 566958 Fax: (01562) 861160 *Stone masons*

Mick Davis Rewinds Ltd, Unit 27 Marlow Road Industrial Estate, Marlow Road, Leicester, LE3 2BQ Tel: 0116-282 6956 *Motor rewind manufrs*

Davis & Moore, 5 Bute Street, Salford, M50 1DU Tel: 0161-737 1166 Fax: 0161-736 4038 *Adhesive & masking tape distributors*

▶ Davis Ornamental Ironwork, Hoghton Road Business Centre, Hoghton Road, St. Helens, Merseyside, WA9 3HS Tel: (01744) 821400 Fax: (01744) 821400 E-mail: daviesornamental@merseymail.com *Wrought iron workers*

Davis Pneumatic Systems Ltd, Units C-E Huxley Close, Newnham Industrial Estate, Plympton, Plymouth, PL7 4BQ Tel: (01752) 336421 Fax: (01752) 345828 E-mail: sales@davispneumatic.co.uk *Designer & manufacturer of specialised pneumatic components & systems*

Davis Rubin Associates Ltd, PO Box 15, Towcester, Northamptonshire, NN12 8DJ Tel: (01327) 830999 Fax: (01327) 831000 E-mail: btrubin@davisrubin.com *DVD & CD replication duplication & production service*

Davis & Samson Contractors, Billet Lane, Berkhamsted, Hertfordshire, HP4 1DP Tel: (01442) 878800 Fax: (01442) 878801 E-mail: sales@davisandsamson.co.uk *Demolition & site clearance contractors*

Davis Scientific Treatments Ltd, Delta Drive, Tewkesbury, Gloucestershire, GL20 8HB Tel: (01684) 296601 Fax: (01684) 274239 E-mail: davis.scientific@btconnect.com *Vacuum heat treatment & brazing services*

Davis Shipping Ltd, Enterprise Industrial Estate, Bolina Road, London, SE16 3LF Tel: (020) 7231 9340 Fax: (020) 7231 1120 E-mail: bevan@davis-se1.freeserve.co.uk *Freight forwarders*

Stanley Davis Group Ltd, 41 Chalton Street, London, NW1 1JD Tel: (020) 7554 2222 E-mail: info@stanleydavis.co.uk *Company registration & secretarial consultants*

▶ Steve Davis, 25 Camross Drive, Shrewsbury, SY1 3XH Tel: (01743) 242116

William Davis Ltd, Forest Field, Forest Road, Loughborough, Leicestershire, LE11 3NS Tel: (01509) 231181 Fax: (01509) 239773 E-mail: post@williamdavis.co.uk *Building contractors*

Davislangdon, Mid City Place, 71 High Holborn, London, WC1V 6QS Tel: (020) 7061 7000 Fax: (020) 7061 7061 *Chartered surveyors* Also at: Branches throughout the U.K.

Davison Chemographics Ltd, 28 Woolmer Way, Bordon, Hampshire, GU35 9QF Tel: (01420) 487275 Fax: (01420) 488041 E-mail: sales@davchemo.demon.co.uk *Printing ink research & development services*

▶ Davison Electrical, 6c Ridley Road, Bournemouth, BH9 1LD Tel: (01202) 530260 Fax: (01202) 538341

Davison Fork Lift, Ablow Street, Wolverhampton, WV2 4ER Tel: (01902) 420123 Fax: (01902) 429013 *Fork lift truck hire & sales*

Davison Highley Ltd, Old Oxford Road, Piddington, High Wycombe, Buckinghamshire, HP14 3BE Tel: (01494) 883862 Fax: (01494) 881572 E-mail: magic@davisonhighley.co.uk *Upholstery furniture designers & manufrs*

Davison Tyne Metal Ltd, Davison Tyne Works, Bridge End, Hexham, Northumberland, NE46 4JL Tel: (01434) 604211 Fax: (01434) 602733 E-mail: sales@davisontynemetal.co.uk *Iron founders & general engineers*

Davlec Ltd, Unit 16, Severn Farm Industrial Estate, Welshpool, Powys, SY21 7DF Tel: (01938) 555791 Fax: (01938) 555792 E-mail: sales@davlec.com *Subcontract assembly*

Davley Fabrications Ltd, Drakes Indust Estate, Shay Lane, Ovenden, Halifax, West Yorkshire, HX3 6RL Tel: (01422) 355982 Fax: (01422) 355984 E-mail: sales@davleyfabrications.co.uk *Aluminium & stainless steel fabricators*

Davmar Machine Tool Services, Unit D1 Whitemoor Business Park, Cliff Common, Selby, North Yorkshire, YO8 7EG Tel: (01757) 289714 Fax: (01757) 704432 *Engineering machine tools buy, sell & repairs*

Davmar Workwear, 1 Centenary Court, Earlsway, Team Valley Trading Estate, Gateshead, Tyne & Wear, NE11 0RQ Tel: 0191-487 2249 Fax: 0191-491 4237 E-mail: contact@davmarworkwear.com *Workwear suppliers & distributors*

Davmark Ltd, 63 Keats Way, West Drayton, Middlesex, UB7 9DU Tel: (07824) 638853 Fax: (01895) 905902 E-mail: david.slade@davmark.co.uk *Civil engineerins*

Davrek Engineering, Finmere Road, Eastbourne, East Sussex, BN22 8QL Tel: (01323) 643788 Fax: (01323) 431266 *Fine limit sheet metalworkers*

Company Information

Davro Iron & Steel Co. Ltd, Ridgewell Works, Stourbridge Road, Wootton, Bridgnorth, Shropshire, WV15 6ED Tel: (01746) 780242 Fax: (01746) 780930 E-mail: mikenielen@davrodeal.co.uk *Steel sheet stockholders & slit coils*

Davroc Ltd, Ibroc House, Essex Road, Hoddesdon, Hertfordshire, EN11 0QS Tel: (01992) 441672 Fax: (01992) 708308 E-mail: info@davroc.co.uk *Shower & brassware distributors*

Davron, 21 Beechfield Road, Davenport, Stockport, Cheshire, SK3 8SF Tel: 0161-483 5678 Fax: 0161-483 5678E-mail: sales@davron.co.uk *Suppliers of rotary selector switches*

Davron Finishing Industries Ltd, 18 Tanners Drive, Blakelands, Milton Keynes, MK14 5BW Tel: (01908) 210799 Fax: (01908) 217211 E-mail: sales@davronfinsihing.co.uk *Anodising & plating services*

▶ Davroy Contracts Ltd, 510 Queslett Road, Great Barr, Birmingham, B43 7EJ Tel: 0121-325 0899 Fax: 0121-360 6840 E-mail: post@davroy.co.uk *Supply and installation of metal stud partitions, drylining, fire protection, aluminium framed office partitioning complete with decoration, glass and integral blinds, all types of suspended ceilings including tiled ceilings, feature plasterboard ceilings with curved work incorporated. Also the supply and installation of Mezzanine Floors, single and double sided steel partitioning*

Davrus Technology Ltd, 34 Townend Lane, Deepcar, Sheffield, S36 2TN Tel: 0114-288 8889 Fax: 0114-290 3605 E-mail: david@davrus.co.uk *Website design & search engine optimization*

Davsons Mouldings Ltd, 20-22 Woodall Road, Redburn Industrial Estate, Enfield, Middlesex, EN3 4LE Tel: (020) 8805 3117 Fax: (020) 8443 4773 E-mail: sales@davsons.co.uk *Plastics mouldings manufrs*

Davtex UK Ltd, Link House, Bute Street, Fenton, Stoke-on-Trent, ST4 3PR Tel: (01782) 318000 Fax: (01782) 319000 E-mail: davtexuk@netscapeonline.co.uk *Wire mesh distributors, agents & stockholders*

Davtrend Ltd, 7a Fitzherbert Spur, Farlington, Portsmouth, PO6 1TT Tel: (023) 9237 2004 Fax: (023) 9232 6307 E-mail: sales@davtrend.co.uk *Electronic design & manufacturing services & solutions*

Davy Process Technology, The Technology Centre, Princeton Drive, Thornaby, Stockton-On-Tees, Cleveland, TS17 6PY Tel: (01642) 853800 Fax: (01642) 853801 E-mail: davy@davyprotech.com *Chemical engineers*

The Davy Roll Co. Ltd, P O Box 21, Gateshead, Tyne & Wear, NE8 3DX Tel: 0191-477 1261 Fax: 0191-477 8096 E-mail: enquiries@davyroll.co.uk Principal Export Areas: Worldwide *Rolling mill plant*

Daw Refrigeration Equipment, Lake Barton, Newton St. Cyres, Exeter, EX5 5AU Tel: (01392) 851613 Fax: (01392) 851909 E-mail: info@dawref.com *Refrigeration & air conditioning & milk tanks supply & service*

Daw Signs Ltd, Unit 7 Edgefauld Avenue, Glasgow, G21 4UR Tel: 0141-557 2223 Fax: 0141-558 9333 E-mail: sales@dawsigns.com *Sign manufrs*

Dawber Williamson (Lincs) Ltd, Torrington House, Torrington Street, Grimsby, South Humberside, DN32 9QH Tel: (01472) 347532 Fax: (01472) 344223 *Suspended ceilings, partitions installers*

Dawcul Ltd, 42 West St, Marlow, Buckinghamshire, SL7 2NB Tel: (01628) 472737 Fax: (01628) 890055 E-mail: sales@dawcul.co.uk *Engineering exporters (europe)*

Dawes Cycles, 35 Tameside Drive, Castle Vale, Birmingham, B35 7AG Tel: 0121-748 8050 Fax: 0121-748 8060 *Cycles distributors*

▶ Mairead Dawes, 7 Frogmore Lane, Stanford in the Vale, Faringdon, Oxfordshire, SN7 8LG Tel: (020) 7870 6230 Fax: (08712) 426796

S. Dawes Weaving Ltd, Manor Mill Hallam Road, Nelson, Lancashire, BB9 8DN Tel: (01282) 612325 Fax: (01282) 690466 E-mail: info@sdawesweaving.co.uk *Textile manufrs*

Dawes Security Systems, 74 Hulme Hall Road, Cheadle Hulme, Cheadle, Cheshire, SK8 6LF Tel: 0161-485 8100 Fax: 0161-486 6500 E-mail: sales@dawessecurity.co.uk *Fit security systems*

Dawk Trimmers, Crown Mill, 1 Crown Street, Salford, M3 7DH Tel: 0161-832 3262 Fax: 0161-834 4704 E-mail: fpinetex@aol.com *Distributors, merchants & agents of hook & loop fasteners, haberdashery ribbons, zip fasteners, plastic buckles & reflective materials*

▶ Dawn Construction Ltd, Eldo House, Prestwick Road, Monkton, Prestwick, Ayrshire, KA9 2PB Tel: (01292) 670000 Fax: (01292) 671199 E-mail: info@dawn-group.co.uk *The Dawn Group are one of Scotland's largest privately owned companies operating in construction, property development and house building. Dawn Construction Limited is the Group's founding company and over the last 32 years the company has steadily grown into one of the country's leading construction specialists having gained a wealth of experience over the entire spectrum of market sectors including retail, commercial, industrial, leisure, health and education. With extensive experience in both the private and public sector, we lead the way in design and build, traditional tender, management and development led contracts.*

Dawn Fire Engineers Ltd, 26 Wooburn Industrial Park, Wooburn Green, High Wycombe, Buckinghamshire, HP10 0PF Tel: (01628) 526531 Fax: (01628) 526634 E-mail: sales@dawnfire.co.uk *Precision engineers & fire protection manufrs*

Dawn Foods Ltd, Worcester Road, Evesham, Worcestershire, WR11 4QU Tel: (01386) 760800 Fax: (01386) 443608 E-mail: uk@dawnfoods.com *Frozen and Ambient American Bakery Goods as Muffins, Donuts, Cookies and Brownies, as well as Bakery Ingredients/Mixes*

▶ Dawn Group Ltd, 220 West George Street, Glasgow, G2 2PG Tel: 0141-285 6700

Dawndeal Ltd, 7 Hunsdon Drive, Sevenoaks, Kent, TN13 3AX Tel: (01732) 455386 Fax: (01732) 740002 E-mail: bdl@fsbdial.co.uk Principal Export Areas: Africa *International marketing consultants-rubber industry*

Dawnfresh Projects Ltd, Bothwell Park Industrial Estate, Uddingston, Glasgow, G71 6LS Tel: (01698) 810008 Fax: (01698) 810088 E-mail: sales@dawnfresh.co.uk *Frozen food processors/products manufrs*

Dawnlight Ltd, 56 Lindsay Drive, Harrow, Middlesex, HA3 0TD Tel: (020) 8204 3828 Fax: (020) 8204 3420 *Exporters of plastics*

▶ Dawnthrive, Unit 7 Belbins Business Park, Cupernham Lane, Romsey, Hampshire, SO51 7JF Tel: (01794) 830352 Fax: (01794) 523539 E-mail: info@dawnthrive.com *Procurement house & sourcing agents*

Daws Engineering Ltd, Curtis Road, Dorking, Surrey, RH4 1XD Tel: (01306) 881546 Fax: (01306) 740407 E-mail: rob.collinson@dawseng.co.uk *Precision machining services*

Dawson, Muirfield, Overthickside, Jedburgh, Roxburghshire, TD8 6QX Tel: (01835) 863003 Fax: (01835) 863003

▶ Dawson, Unit 1 Colquhoun Street, Stirling, FK7 7PX Tel: (01786) 446882 Fax: (01786) 446882

Dawson, Stephenson Way, Thetford, Norfolk, IP24 3RU Tel: (01842) 753505 Fax: (01842) 753508 E-mail: sales@bwi-dawson.com *Bottle handling equipment manufrs*

Dawson Bowman Ltd, 16 Flakefield, College Milton, East Kilbride, Glasgow, G74 1PF Tel: (01355) 229445 Fax: (01355) 264744 E-mail: sales@dawsonbowman.co.uk *Engineering merchants*

Dawson Bros, Gauntlet Road, Bicker, Boston, Lincolnshire, PE20 3AU Tel: (01775) 820273 Fax: (01775) 821691 *Road transport, haulage & freight services*

Dawson Bros Timber Ltd, Blowers Green Cresent, Dudley, West Midlands, DY2 8XQ Tel: (01384) 253816 Fax: (01384) 457248 E-mail: sales@dawsontimber.co.uk *High quality hardwood & softwood importers*

Colin Dawson Windows Ltd, Chapel Works, John Kennedy Road, King's Lynn, Norfolk, PE30 2AA Tel: (01553) 775191 Fax: (01553) 760639 *PVC windows, doors & conservatory installation*

Dawson Construction Plant Ltd, Chesney Wold, Bleak Hall, Milton Keynes, MK6 1NE Tel: (01908) 240300 Fax: (01908) 240222 E-mail: dawson@dcpuk.com Principal Export Areas: Worldwide *Pile driving equipment manufrs*

▶ Dawson Design, Number 6, 27 Whitworth Street West, Manchester, M1 5ND Tel: 0161-236 0735 E-mail: robert@dawsondesign.com *Graphic design & marketing communications agency*

Dawson, Downie, Lamont, 31 Rutherford Road, Glenrothes, Fife, KY6 2RT Tel: (01592) 775577 Fax: (01592) 775517 E-mail: sales@ddl-ltd.com *Reciprocating Pumps Manufacturing*

Dawson Fur Fabrics Ltd, Saville Road, Skelmanthorpe, Huddersfield, HD8 9EE Tel: (01484) 863433 Fax: (01484) 865635 Principal Export Areas: Worldwide *Fur & fleece fabric manufrs*

Dawson & Gibbond Ltd, 55 Red Lion St, Holborn, London, WC1R 4PD Tel: (020) 7242 6014 Fax: (020) 7242 2630 E-mail: admin@d-n-g.co.uk *Electrical contractors industrial, domestic & commercial industries*

Dawson International plc, Lochleven Mills, Kinross, KY13 8GL Tel: (01577) 867000 Fax: (01577) 867010 E-mail: enquiries@dawson-international.co.uk *Specialist textile group*

James Dawson & Son Ltd, Tritton Road, Lincoln, LN6 7AF Tel: (01522) 531821 Fax: (01522) 510029 E-mail: sales@james-dawson.co.uk *Reinforced rubber products*

James Dawson & Son Ltd, Unit 7, 2ND Avenue, Poynton Industrial Estate, Poynton, Cheshire, SK12 1ND Tel: (01625) 879494 Fax: (01625) 879555 E-mail: indico@indico-europe.co.uk *Industrial rubber products*

Dawson Marketing P.L.C., The Arena, Stafferton Way, Maidenhead, Berkshire, SL6 1AY Tel: (01628) 628777 Fax: (01628) 789634 E-mail: sales@dawsonmarketing.co.uk *Computer applications designers*

▶ Dawson Peebles Ltd, 5 Morris Road, Leicester, LE2 6BR Tel: 0116-274 5270 Fax: 0116-274 5271

Dawson Plant Hire Ltd, 79 Middle Watch, Swavesey, Cambridge, CB24 4RW Tel: (01954) 200400 E-mail: info@dawsonplanthire.co.uk *Contractors' plant & earth mover & skip hire*

Dawson Rentals Ltd, Aberford Road, Garforth, Leeds, LS25 2ET Tel: 0113-287 4874 Fax: 0113-286 9158 E-mail: info@dawsongroup.co.uk *Materials handling equipment suppliers*

Dawson Reproductions, 74 Church Street, Leatherhead, Surrey, KT22 8ER Tel: (01372) 375383 Fax: (01372) 362975 *Cabinet maker, bespoke furniture*

Robert Dawson Joinery, Back Square Workshop, The Square, Ingleton, Carnforth, Lancashire, LA6 3EG Tel: (01524) 242474 Fax: (01524) 241474 *Joiners*

Dawson Shanahan Ltd, Cranborne Industrial Estate, Cranborne Road, Potters Bar, Hertfordshire, EN6 3JN Tel: (01707) 602000 Fax: (01707) 602049 E-mail: postmaster@dawson-shanahan.co.uk *Precision machining services*

Dawson Signs, 19 Lime Street, Waldridge, Chester Le Street, County Durham, DH2 3SG Tel: 0191-388 0513 Fax: 0191-388 0513 E-mail: info@dawsonsigns.co.uk *Sign Makers*

Dawson & Son Ltd, Clayton Wood Rise, West Park Ring Road, Leeds, LS16 6RH Tel: 0113-275 9321 Fax: 0113-275 2761 E-mail: sales@dawsonbrush.co.uk *Brush manufrs*

Dawson & Son Ltd, Clayton Wood Rise, West Park Ring Road, Leeds, LS16 6RH Tel: 0113-275 9321 Fax: 0113-275 2761 E-mail: sales@dawsonbrush.co.uk Principal

continued

Export Areas: Worldwide *Brush designers & consultants*

Stan Dawson Ltd, Kirkley Sawmills, Kirkley, Newcastle upon Tyne, NE20 0BD Tel: (01661) 860413 Fax: (01661) 822352 *Timber merchants & steel stockholders*

Dawsongroup P.L.C., Delaware Drive, Tongwell, Milton Keynes, MK15 8JH Tel: (01908) 218111 Fax: (01908) 218444 E-mail: contactus@dawsongroup.co.uk *Commercial vehicle rentals* Also at: Branches throughout the U.K.

Dawsons, Unit 22 Victoria Spring Business Park, Wormald Street, Liversedge, West Yorkshire, WF15 6RA Tel: (01924) 414620 Fax: (01924) 414601 E-mail: customerservice@dawson-uk.com Principal Export Areas: Worldwide *Filling conveyors*

Dawsons Marketing Services, 200 Milton Park, Abingdon, Oxfordshire, OX14 4TB Tel: (01235) 824200 Fax: (01235) 824304 E-mail: sales@dawson-marketing.co.uk *Promotional handling services*

Dawson's Pattern Works Ltd, Westland Square, Leeds, LS11 5SS Tel: 0113-270 5142 Fax: 0113-276 1335 *Engineers pattern makers*

▶ Dawson's Trailers, Sunny-Vale, Far Westhouse, Ingleton, Carnforth, Lancashire, LA6 3NR Tel: (01524) 241372 E-mail: sydney@dawsonstrailers.f9.co.uk *A Unique trailer business that is open when the others are closed, new and used trailers always in stock. Also - Wooden Sheds, Workshops, Kennels, Hen huts and Stables, all of outstanding quality, supplied to your requirements."*

Dawton Engineers Ltd, Unit 11-12, Waleswood Road, Wales Bar, Sheffield, S26 5PY Tel: (01909) 515313 Fax: (01909) 515499 E-mail: enquiries@dawton.co.uk *Specialist precision machinist engineers*

Dax Printing Co. Ltd, Free Street, Bishops Waltham, Southampton, SO32 1EE Tel: (01489) 891006 Fax: (01489) 891699 E-mail: general@daxprinting.co.uk *Full printing services*

Day & Coles Agricultural Ltd, Newton Close, Park Farm, Wellingborough, Northamptonshire, NN8 6UW Tel: (01933) 673900 Fax: (01933) 675858 *Agricultural engineers*

Day Environmental Engineering, 7 Nash Meadows, South Warnborough, Hook, Hampshire, RG29 1RJ Tel: (01256) 862467 Fax: (01256) 862967 *Industrial plant suppliers*

Gary Day Associates, 7 Unity Court, Broadmead Lane, Keynsham, Bristol, BS31 1ST Tel: 0117-986 9911 Fax: 0117-986 9944 *Software writing for scaffolding industry*

Day Group Ltd, Transport Avenue, Great West Road, Brentford, Middlesex, TW8 9HF Tel: (01483) 725100 Fax: (020) 8380 9700 E-mail: email@daygroup.co.uk *Aggregates, recycled aggregates & filter bedmedia*

Day Impex Ltd, Station Road, Earls Colne, Colchester, CO6 2ER Tel: (01787) 223232 Fax: (01787) 224171 E-mail: general@day-impex.co.uk *Glass component manufrs*

Day International Ltd, Balgray Street, Dundee, DD3 8HN Tel: (01382) 422200 Fax: (01382) 832310 E-mail: bill_crowe@day-intel.com *Manufacturers of printing blankets, rubber compound*

J. Day & Son Ltd, Station Road, Bishop's Stortford, Hertfordshire, CM23 3BJ Tel: (01279) 653450 Fax: (01279) 503637 E-mail: jdayandson@tiscali.co.uk *Monumental masons in stone*

John Day Engineering Ltd, Welford Works, Easton, Newbury, Berkshire, RG20 8EA Tel: (01488) 608666 Fax: (01488) 608781 *Agricultural & car sales services*

Day Lewis Medical Supplies, 54 Springfield Road, Gorleston, Great Yarmouth, Norfolk, NR31 6AD Tel: (01493) 602673 Fax: (01493) 651106 E-mail: albanoffshore@daylewisplc.com *First aid equipment suppliers*

Nigel Day, Manor Farm Buildings, Stoke Road, Martock, Somerset, TA12 6AF Tel: (01935) 824287 Fax: (01935) 825442 *Fashion material suppliers*

Day Paper Sales Ltd, 15 Silverwell Street, Bolton, BL1 1PP Tel: (01204) 398222 Fax: (01204) 362370 E-mail: sales@daypapersales.co.uk *Packaging agents & suppliers*

Day Plant Hire Co. Ltd, 43-45 Brookhill Road, New Barnet, Barnet, Hertfordshire, EN4 8SE Tel: (020) 8441 4422 Fax: (020) 8447 0193 *Plant hire services*

Day Print Photocopiers, 55 Pitt Avenue, Witham, Essex, CM8 1JQ Tel: (01376) 510716 Fax: (01376) 510716 *Photocopiers*

Day Signs, 1 Ford Road, Totnes, Devon, TQ9 5LQ Tel: (01803) 865880 Fax: (01803) 868466 E-mail: sales@daysigns.net *Sign manufrs*

Day Wellington, 32 Collum End Rise, Leckammpton, Cheltenham, Glos, GL53 0PB Tel: 01242 570584 *Heating & plumbing engineers*

Dayboard Ltd, Unit 6 Ravenstone Road Industrial Estate, Coalville, Leicestershire, LE67 3NB Tel: (01530) 813279 Fax: (01530) 510602 E-mail: richard@dayboard.co.uk *Pool & snooker tables*

Daybury Electrical Services Ltd, Coppice Trading Estate, Kidderminster, Worcestershire, DY11 7QY Tel: (01299) 822070 Fax: (01562) 829747 E-mail: sales@daybury.co.uk *Electrical engineers*

Dayfold Ltd, Unit 4-6 27 Black Moor Road, Ebblake Industrial Estate, Verwood, Dorset, BH31 6BE Tel: 01202 827401 Fax: (01202) 825841 E-mail: enquiries@dayfold.com *We specialise in binding machines to all market's, for all your printing requirements including brochures, catalogues, presentation folders, laminating machines & services, conference folders. Contact us now for a first class service and prices.* Also at: Cheddar

Dayford Designs Ltd, The Chaple, Brimscombe Port, Brimscombe, Stroud, Gloucestershire, GL5 2QG Tel: (01453) 732820 Fax: (01453) 732830 E-mail: accounts@dayford.co.uk *Printed circuit designers*

Dayla Liquid Packing Ltd, Netherton Road, Overross Industrial Estate, Ross-on-Wye, Herefordshire, HR9 7QQ Tel: (01989) 760400 Fax: (01989) 760414 E-mail: dayla@dayla.co.uk *Fruit juice producers & manufrs*

Daylight Insulation Ltd, Brandleside, Dunlop, Kilmarnock, Ayrshire, KA3 4BJ Tel: (01560) 486688 Fax: (01560) 486699 *Architectural glass product suppliers*

Daylock Marine Services, Banks End, Wyton, Huntingdon, Cambridgeshire, PE28 2AA Tel: (01480) 455898 Fax: (01480) 455898 *Boat hire service*

Dayman Display Ltd, Sidney House, 262 Aylestone Lane, Wigston, Leicestershire, LE18 1BD Tel: 0116-288 3338 E-mail: sales@daymandisplay.fsnet.co.uk *Shop fitters*

Daymark Ltd, Unit 70 Hartlebury Trading Estate, Hartlebury, Kidderminster, Worcestershire, DY10 4JB Tel: (01299) 251365 Fax: (01299) 251386 E-mail: sales@labelsandtags.com *Self-adhesive label printers*

Days Buildbase, Burrfields Road, Portsmouth, PO3 5NA Tel: (023) 9266 2261 Fax: (023) 9266 6497 E-mail: portsmouth@buildbase.co.uk *Buildbase is one of the UK's fastest growing builders merchants. All of our branches are long established companies which have been serving local trades people for many years, with knowledge and experience to match. We believe strongly in understanding the needs of trades professional and our business has been developed specifically to meet those demands. Massive stocks, top quality products, competitive pricing, reliable delivery, specialist staff and exceptional customer service*

Days Health, North Road, Bridgend Industrial Estate, Bridgend, Mid Glamorgan, CF31 3TP Tel: (01656) 657495 Fax: (01656) 767178 E-mail: info@dayshealthcare.com *Day's Medical Aids is one of the UK's foremost manufacturers and distributors of mobility and rehabilitation products for the elderly and the disabled. Our exciting range of products, for both indoor and outdoor use, to aid mobility and assist in daily living, are stylish, modern and specifically designed to make your life easier at prices you can afford and with a support and service network you can trust.*

Days Inn, Port Road, Rhoose, Barry, South Glamorgan, CF62 3BT Tel: (01446) 710787 Fax: (01446) 719318 *Hotel & conference facilities*

▶ Days Precision Thermoplastics, Unit 2 Bradley House, Moston Road, Middleton, Manchester, M24 1SE Tel: 0161-655 4955 Fax: 0161-655 4955 E-mail: sales@daysprecisionthermoplastics.com *Injection moulding specialists*

Daystar, Daystar House, 102 Burnage Lane, Manchester, M19 2NG Tel: 0161-248 8088 Fax: 0161-224 2522 *Computer consultants*

Day-Timers Europe Ltd, Chene Court, Poundwell Street, Modbury, Devon, PL21 0QJ Tel: (08705) 143583 Fax: (08705) 143580 Principal Export Areas: Worldwide *Business incentive designers*

Dayton Engineering Ltd, Unit 1-4 Tir Llwyd Industrial Estate, Kinmel Bay, Rhyl, Clwyd, LL18 5JA Tel: (01745) 336457 Fax: (01745) 354247 E-mail: info@dayton-engineering.co.uk *Steel fabricators*

Daytona Visual Marketing Ltd, Amber Close, Tamworth, Staffordshire, B77 4RP Tel: (01827) 54551 Fax: (01827) 63159 E-mail: info@daytonavisual.com *Screen printers*

Dayworth Packaging, Unit Q1, Trecenydd Industrial Estate, Caerphilly, Mid Glamorgan, CF83 2RZ Tel: (029) 2085 4860 Fax: (029) 2085 4861 E-mail: enquiries@dayworthpackaging.co.uk *Corrugated, polythene, labelling & packaging systems.*

Dazer International, 16 Thorpe Meadows, Peterborough, PE3 6GA Tel: (01733) 315888 E-mail: enquires@dazer.com *Ultra sonic pest control suppliers*

▶ Dazer (International), PO Box 456, Altrincham, Cheshire, WA14 5WP Tel: 0161-927 4508 Fax: 0161-927 4502

▶ Dazone Construction, 28 Creevagh Road, Londonderry, BT48 9XB Tel: (028) 7136 6292 Fax: (028) 7136 6293

▶ dB Acoustics, The Old School, Ipswich Road, Gosbeck, Ipswich, IP6 9SN Tel: 01449 760689 E-mail: gordon@10db.co.uk *Provider of acoustics consultancy services including environmental noise assessments, PPG24 investigations, noise at work, BS4142 assessments.*

DB Audio & Electronic Services Ltd, 5 East Point, High Street, Seal, Sevenoaks, Kent, TN15 0EG Tel: (01732) 760877 Fax: (01732) 760977 *Audio visual services*

DB Graphics, 162 Blackstock Road, London, N5 1HA Tel: (01438) 261305 Fax: (020) 7226 6217 E-mail: sales@dbgraphics.co.uk *Computer reseller & maintenance*

DBC Agriculture Supplies, 3 Old Jewson Yard, Edenwall, Coalway, Coleford, Gloucestershire, GL16 7HN Tel: (01594) 835625 Fax: (01594) 835625 *Agricultural supplies (seeds)*

DBC Foodservice Ltd, Denmark House, Parkway, Welwyn Garden City, Hertfordshire, AL8 6JN Tel: (01707) 323421 Fax: (01707) 320143 E-mail: info@dbc.foodservice.co.uk *D B C Foodservice's range of over 8,000 products offers caterers a real 'one stop shop' solution to their foodservice needs. A product portfolio combining leading brands with our own 'd'brand range ensures we have the right products at the right price for all your requirements.*

Dbi Plastics, Cottage La Industrial Estate, Broughton Astley, Leicester, LE9 6PD Tel: (01455) 283380 Fax: (01455) 283384 E-mail: info@dbiplastics.com Principal Export Areas: Central/East Europe & West Europe *Plastic injection moulder manufrs*

DBK Technitherm Ltd, 11 Llantrisant Business Park, Llantrisant, Pontyclun, Mid Glamorgan, CF72 8LF Tel: (01443) 237927 Fax: (01443) 237867 E-mail: info@dbktechnitherm.ltd.uk Principal Export Areas: Africa *Manufacturers of heating elements*

DBL Software Ltd, Tytherley Road, Winterslow, Salisbury, SP5 1PY Tel: (01980) 863505 Fax: (0845) 2269028 E-mail: sales@dbl.co.uk *Computer software developers*

DBM Electrical Supplies Ltd, Unit B6 Halesfield 8, Telford, Shropshire, TF7 4QN Tel: (01952) 588800 Fax: (01952) 588822 E-mail: DMASON@DBMELECTRICAL.CO.UK *Electrical wholesalers*

▶ DBS Brand Factors, Unit 5, Haydock Lane, Haydock, St. Helens, Merseyside, WA11 9UY Tel: (01942) 276657 Fax: (01942) 722067 E-mail: enquiries@dbsbrandfactors.co.uk *Forklift trucks*

▶ DBSconsultants ltd, 44 osborne rd, Palmers Green, London, UK, N13 5PS Tel: 07940 379 935 E-mail: kingsley_ijomah@yahoo.com *IT, computers, networking,dbs, london, liverpool, kingsley,database,webdesign,office, flash, best flash sites,html,computer graphics, elegance,recruitment,pc, laptop*

DBTS LIMITED, Meeting Lane, Needingworth, Huntingdon, Cambridgeshire, PE27 4SN Tel: (01480) 300601 Fax: (01480) 465058 E-mail: dbtrans@btopenworld.com *Hydraulic services*

▶ DC Voltage Gradient Technology & Supply Ltd, Corbett House, Swan Lane, Hindley Green, Wigan, Lancashire, WN2 4EY Tel: (01942) 522180 Fax: (01942) 522179 E-mail: dcvg@fsbdial.co.uk *Manufacturers of Pipeline survey Equipment, DCVG and CIPS. Also Software for ECDA. Designers of Cathodic Protection Systems.*

DC Welding Fabrication, Pegs Farm, Staplow, Ledbury, Herefordshire, HR8 1NQ Tel: (01531) 640779 Fax: (01531) 640779 E-mail: dc.welding@btinternet.com *Stainless steel manufrs*

DCB Abrasives & Industrial Ltd, Unit 12 Vale Business Park, Llandow, Cowbridge, South Glamorgan, CF71 7PF Tel: (01446) 772902 Fax: (01446) 775863 *Industrial products & abrasives distributors*

DCC Electronics Ltd, 1 Newmarket Drive, Derby, DE24 8SW Tel: (01332) 757733 Fax: (01332) 572229 E-mail: reception@dcc-electronics.co.uk *Electronic contract manufrs*

DCN Bearings & Engineering, The Old Foundary, Wood Street, Lye, Stourbridge, West Midlands, DY9 8RX Tel: (01384) 896528 Fax: (01384) 896534 E-mail: sales@dcnbearings.com *Bearing manufrs*

DCS, 2-4 Watt Road, Hillington Industrial Estate, Glasgow, G52 4RR Tel: 0141-883 8629 Fax: 0141-883 6436 E-mail: info@dcsuk.com *Industrial Drain cleaning contractors, Jetting, HPWJ, Aquavac, CCTV Surveys, Civil excavation works, 24 hour service all year.*

▶ DCS Europe plc, Timothy Bridge Road, Stratford-upon-Avon, Warwickshire, CV37 9YL Tel: (01789) 298000 Fax: (01789) 208030 E-mail: info@dcseurope.com *UK's No 1 distributor of toiletries and household brands - including Gillette, P&G, Lever, Cussons, Colgate, Sara Lee, SC Johnson and Coty.*

DDB Ltd, 12 Bishops Bridge Road, London, W2 6AA Tel: (01446) 795264 Fax: (020) 7402 4871 E-mail: sales@bmpddb.com *Advertising & marketing services*

DDF Computer Systems, Horsham Road, Walliswood, Dorking, Surrey, RH5 5QD Tel: (01306) 627155 Fax: (01306) 627166 E-mail: info@ddf.co.uk *Computer maintenance & writers*

D-Drill (Master Drillers) Ltd, Unit 1 Rosebridge Way, Ince, Wigan, Lancashire, WN1 3DP Tel: (01942) 824724 Fax: (01942) 829944 E-mail: wigan@d-drill.co.uk *Concrete drilling, diamond drilling & sawing engineers*

▶ DD's Kosher Sandwiches Ltd, 54a Minerva Road, London, NW10 6HJ Tel: (020) 8810 4321 Fax: (020) 8963 0828

DDSM Tools, Cartersfield Road, Waltham Abbey, Essex, EN9 1JD Tel: (01992) 651607 Fax: (01992) 701105 E-mail: ddsm@netcomuk.co.uk *Abrasive manufrs*

De Agositini, Griffin House, 161 Hammersmith Road, Griffin House, London, W6 8SD Tel: (020) 8600 2000 Fax: (020) 8600 2002 *Publishers*

▶ DE AR International, 20 Bidwell Close, Letchworth Garden City, Hertfordshire, SG6 1QR Tel: 07772 258128 Fax: (01462) 641839 E-mail: enquiries@dearinternational.com *We are manufacturer, exporter, importer & supplier of all kind of Inflatable Balls like Football, Volleyball, Rugbyballs etc. Our prices are very competitive. please contact us if you have any query"""""s.*

De Dietrich Process Systems Ltd, Tollgate Drive, Tollgate Industrial Estate, Stafford, ST16 3HS Tel: (01785) 609900 Fax: (01785) 609899 E-mail: reception@qvf.co.uk *Process plant & pipeline equipment*

De Facto Communications Ltd, 1 London Bridge, London, SE1 9BG Tel: (020) 7940 1000 Fax: (020) 7940 1001 E-mail: info@hccdefacto.com *Healthcare & life science services*

De Facto Software Ltd, The Rutherford Centre, 8 Dunlop Road, Ipswich, IP2 0UG Tel: (01473) 230202 Fax: (01473) 230247 E-mail: sales@defactosoftware.com *Accountancy software developers*

De Icers M H G Ltd, 11 Hamilton Street, Charlton Kings, Cheltenham, Gloucestershire, GL53 8HN Tel: (01242) 573321 Fax: (01242) 573543 *Heater element for aerospace industry*

Keith De La Plain Ltd, The Street, Smarden, Ashford, Kent, TN27 8NA Tel: (01233) 770555 Fax: (01233) 770666 *Furniture import & sales*

De La Rue Cash Systems, 7-8 Wolfe Close, Parkgate Industrial Estate, Knutsford, Cheshire, WA16 8XJ Tel: (01565) 654662 Fax: (01565) 658657 E-mail: robert.clark@uk.delarue.com *Customer service solutions specialists*

De La Rue Holdings plc, De Lane Rue House, Jays Close, Basingstoke, Hampshire, RG22 4BS Tel: (01256) 329122 Fax: (01256) 351323 E-mail: sales@delarue.com *Security printers* Also at: Dunstable & London

De Luxe Media Services Ltd, Phoenix Park, Great West Road, Brentford, Middlesex, TW8 9PL Tel: (020) 8232 7600 Fax: (020) 8232 7601 *Video tape duplication services & packers*

De Maeyer International, Office, 77 Winchester Road, Four Marks, Alton, Hampshire, GU34 5HR Tel: (01420) 562776 Fax: (01420) 562874 E-mail: admin@demaeyer.co.uk *Cosmetic glass suppliers*

De Montfort Tool Co. Ltd, 4 Mandervell Road, Oadby, Leicester, LE2 5LQ Tel: 0116-271 3223 Fax: 0116-272 0847 E-mail: dmt@btclick.com *Precision engineers & mould manufrs*

De Rijke Intermodal UK Ltd, 1 Aston Lane N Preston Brook, Preston Brook, Runcorn, Cheshire, WA7 3GE Tel: (01928) 755400 Fax: (01928) 759816 *Road transport, haulage & freight services*

▶ De Sandosse Ltd, Hillside Mill, Quarry Lane, Swaffham Bulbeck, Cambridge, CB25 0LU Tel: (01223) 811215 Fax: (01223) 810020 E-mail: david@desangosse.co.uk *Agricultural wholesaler*

De Smet Rosedowns Ltd, Cannon Street, Hull, HU2 0AD Tel: (01482) 329864 Fax: (01482) 325887 E-mail: info@rosedowns.co.uk *Oil extraction & effluent engineers*

De Tech, Unit 36e The Lingfield Estate, Mcmullen Road, Darlington, County Durham, DL1 1RW Tel: (01325) 489001 Fax: (01325) 489001 E-mail: sales@detech.fsnet.co.uk *Transformers*

De Vere Belton Woods, Belton, Grantham, Lincolnshire, NG32 2LN Tel: (01476) 593200 Fax: (01476) 574547 E-mail: belton.woods@belvere-hotels.com *Hotel & conference facilities*

De Vere Daresbury Park Hotel, Daresbury, Warrington, WA4 4BB Tel: (01925) 267331 Fax: (01925) 601496 *Conference centre & hotel services*

De Vere Venues Ltd, Wokefield Park, Mortimer, Reading, RG7 3AE Tel: 0118-933 4000 Fax: 0118-9334001 *Hotel conference centres*

De Witt Floors, The Green, Boughton Monchelsea, Maidstone, Kent, ME17 4LT Tel: (01622) 744886 Fax: (01622) 747461 *Flooring contractors*

Deacon Bros Printers Ltd, Old Mill Park, Kirkintilloch, Glasgow, G66 1SW Tel: 0141-776 5272 Fax: 0141-776 1094 E-mail: sales@deacon-brothers.com *Printers & stationers*

▶ Deacon Cad Consultancy Ltd, Unit 17, Gosport Business Centre Aerodro, Gosport, Hampshire, PO13 0FQ Tel: (01329) 848725 Fax: 01329 848722 E-mail: john@deaconcad.co.uk *The UK''s leading independant and impartial Computer Aided Design services company. Providing CAD Design, CAD Training, CAD Support and CAD Contractors to industry.*

▶ Deacon Construction, 2a Maritime Close, Medway City Estate, Medway City Estate, Rochester, Kent, ME2 4DJ Tel: (01634) 717445 Fax: (01634) 717445 E-mail: sales@deaconconstruction.co.uk

Ernest Deacon Ltd, Victoria Road, Kington, Herefordshire, HR5 3BY Tel: (01544) 230403 Fax: (01544) 231740 E-mail: ernestdeacon@freeuk.com *Building contractors* Also at: Leominster

Deacon Products Ltd, Unit 1, Penn Industrial Estate, Providence Street, Cradley Heath, West Midlands, B64 5DJ Tel: (01384) 416931 Fax: (01384) 635172 E-mail: info@chain-fittings.co.uk *We are a centrally located family run business that has been established for over 33 years. We offer UK wide delivery. Our products include: Chains, Shackles, Hooks, Tensioners, Eye bolts, Linch pins, R clips, Round Rings, Dee Rings, Wire rope assemblies, Tow pins, Key rings, Spring pins, stainless steel fittings, Cleats, Pulleys, Carbine hooks, Rope slings, Springhooks, Winch cables, Dee shackles, Eye nuts, U bolts, J Bolts, Hook bolts, S Hooks, Wire formed Components, Threaded fasteners, Oval links, Triangular links, Rings on plates, Spring bolts, Turned parts, Lashing links, Chain assemblies, Rope Hooks, Webbing strap assemblies, Hold back chains, Trigger hooks, Thimbles, Wire rope lanyards, Connecting links, Lifting Chains, Chain slings, Quick links.*

Deacon & Sandys, Apple Pie Farm, Cranbrook Road, Benenden, Cranbrook, Kent, TN17 4EU Tel: (01580) 243331 Fax: (01580) 243301 E-mail: sales@deaconandsandys.co.uk *English oak furniture & interiors manufrs*

Deacons, Bridge Road, Bursledon, Southampton, SO31 8FR Tel: (023) 8040 2253 Fax: (023) 8040 5665 E-mail: info@deaconsboatyard.co.uk *Moorings & brokerage boatyard*

Deadman Confidential, 17 Golf Side, Sutton, Surrey, SM2 7HA Tel: (020) 8642 3600 Fax: (020) 8642 8378 E-mail: info@deadmanconfidential.co.uk *Confidential document destruction*

▶ Deago Audio Visual Solutions Ltd, 8 Stoney Lane, Quinton, Birmingham, B32 1AN Tel: 0121-422 3777 Fax: 0121-423 2223 E-mail: deagoavs@hotmail.com *Audio visual equipment hire services*

Deakins Packing Co., 3 Osman House, Prince Street, Bolton, BL1 2NP Tel: (01204) 393211 Fax: (01204) 381282 E-mail: deakinspackaging@yahoo.co.uk *Packaging material merchants*

Deal Bros, 5 East Street, Leigh-on-Sea, Essex, SS9 1QF Tel: (01702) 710983 Fax: (01702) 472620 *Fish merchants*

▶ Deal Detective, Knavesmire House, 4 Campleshon Road, York, YO23 1PE Tel: (01904) 632615 Fax: (01904) 629825 E-mail: deals@thedealdetectives.com *We guarantee to beat your dealers price on New cars.**Status and Non status *Finance, Contract Hire, Bank Accounts, Business Plans.*

Deal Rentals Ltd, 46 Gillender Street, London, E14 6RN Tel: (020) 7537 1257 Fax: (020) 7537 1257 E-mail: info@dealref.co.uk *We hire out all commercial refrigeration for shows, exhibitions &*

continued

*events**Comprehensively maintained monthly rental is also available at very competitive prices, there is also a selection of ex-rental equipment for sale or we can sell new**All service and maintenance work undertaken by out qualified, experienced engineers.**Come and visit our showroom, located on the A12 in Poplar. **Call us on 0207 537 1257*

Dealer Consultancy, 12 Crofton Close, Christchurch, Dorset, BH23 2JN Tel: (01202) 478600E-mail: dealer-consultancy@hotmail.com *Software consultants*

Dealer Systems, 11 Market Hill, Southam, Warwickshire, CV47 0HF Tel: (01926) 815792 Fax: (01926) 813395 *Computer consultants*

▶ Dealmead Ltd, Knen Hall, Knenhall, Stone, Staffordshire, ST15 8TJ Tel: (01782) 373708 Fax: (01782) 373569

Dealogic, 231-232 The Strand, London, WC2R 1DA Tel: (020) 7379 5650 Fax: (020) 7379 7505 *Software manufrs*

Dealpage Ltd, Station Road, Uppingham, Rutland, Leicestershire, LE15 9TX Tel: (01572) 823198 Fax: (01572) 823199 *Sheet metalwork fabricators & engineers*

▶ Deals On Wheels, 22 Bruce Street, Dunfermline, Fife, KY12 7AG Tel: (01383) 728108 Fax: (01383) 730077 E-mail: info@premierfrenchparts.com *Fishing tackle suppliers*

Dean, Wester Clockeasy, Urquhart, Elgin, Morayshire, IV30 8LP Tel: (01343) 842210 Fax: (01343) 843198 *Agricultural contractor*

Charles Dean Partnership Ltd, Brasted Lodge, Westerham Road, Westerham, Kent, TN16 1QH Tel: (01959) 565909 Fax: (01959) 565606 E-mail: sales@charlesdean.co.uk *Building & office interiors*

Dean Dismantlers, Springhall Works, 28 West Lane, Thornton, Bradford, West Yorkshire, BD13 3HX Tel: (01274) 832600 Fax: (01274) 832566 *Asbestos removal*

Dean & Dyball Developments Ltd, Endeavour House, Crow Arch Lane, Ringwood, Hampshire, BH24 1PN Tel: (01425) 470000 Fax: (01425) 472724 E-mail: enquiries@deandyball.co.uk *Construction engineers*

▶ Dean Edward, Unit C3 Horsted Keynes Industrial Park, Cinder Hill Lane, Horsted Keynes, Haywards Heath, West Sussex, RH17 7BA Tel: (01342) 811183 Fax: (01342) 811193

Dean Foods Ltd, Stocks Lane, Duckmanton, Chesterfield, Derbyshire, S44 5HZ Tel: (01246) 822161 Fax: (01246) 826717 *Food product manufrs*

Dean Head Services, 167 Cold Bath Road, Harrogate, North Yorkshire, HG2 0HN Tel: (01423) 564626 Fax: (01423) 564626 *Alarm systems installers*

Dean Konrad Plant Sales, 78 Moira Road, Crumlin, County Antrim, BT29 4JL Tel: (028) 9442 3787 Fax: (028) 9445 4144 E-mail: sales@kdplant.com *Construction equipment suppliers*

Dean Microcomputers Ltd, 1 Abenhall Technolgy Centre, Abenhall Road, Mitcheldean, Gloucestershire, GL17 0DT Tel: (01594) 542116 Fax: (01594) 542643 E-mail: mary@deanmicros.co.uk *Computer software engineers*

Dean Smith & Grace Ltd, PO Box 15, Keighley, West Yorkshire, BD21 4PG Tel: (01535) 605261 Fax: (01535) 680921 E-mail: mail@deansmithandgrace.co.uk *Lathe manufrs*

Stan Dean (Jig-Boring Service) Ltd, Boodle Street, Ashton-Under-Lyne, Lancashire, OL6 8NF Tel: 0161-344 2352 Fax: 0161-339 7165 E-mail: satndeanltd@yahoo.co.uk *Precision machinists*

Dean & Tranter, Rockbourne Road, Sandleheath, Fordingbridge, Hampshire, SP6 1RA Tel: (01425) 654011 Fax: (01425) 654141 E-mail: office@deantranter.co.uk *Manufacturers and suppliers of minerals for industry including mica powder, granules and flakes. Manufacturers of mica products (electrical) for commercial applications. Manufacturers of wire formings including springs, stainless steel and nickel pressings.. Suppliers of nautral slate for flooring and roofs.*

Dean & Wood Ltd, Unit 1, Camwal Road, St. Philips, Bristol, BS2 0UZ Tel: 0117-971 7413 Fax: 0117-972 1561 *Refrigerator components & air conditioning distributors*

Dean & Wood Ltd, Mole Business Park, Randalls Road, Leatherhead, Surrey, KT22 2BA Tel: (01372) 378788 Fax: (01372) 386239 E-mail: dw@dean-wood.co.uk *Refrigeration & air conditioning wholesalers* Also at: Birmingham, Bristol, Glasgow, Leeds, London E1, Manchester, Newcastle, Norwich & Southampton

Deandi Building Services Ltd, Crown House, Union Street, Willenhall, West Midlands, WV13 1UZ Tel: (01902) 609715 Fax: (01902) 634383 *Mechanical & electrical engineers & building services*

Deandray, 5 Monmouth Street, Lyme Regis, Dorset, DT7 3PX Tel: (01297) 445632 Fax: (01297) 445464 E-mail: deandray@btinternet.com *Computer peripheral wholesalers*

Deane & Amos Aluminium Systems Ltd, Queens Park Indust Estate, Studland Road, Northampton, NN2 6NA Tel: (01604) 718708 Fax: (01604) 717170 *Shop fittings manufrs*

Deane & Amos Group Ltd, South Portway Close, Round Spinney, Northampton, NN3 8RH Tel: (01604) 790990 Fax: (01604) 644644 E-mail: mail@deane-amos.co.uk *Shop fitters & joiners*

Deane Austin Associates, PO Box 274, Aldershot, Hampshire, GU11 1TT Tel: (01252) 333727 Fax: (01252) 337266 E-mail: daa@tacitus.co.uk *Providing noise control consultancy around the world*

Deane Public Works Ltd, Irvinestown, Enniskillen, County Fermanagh, BT94 1RE Tel: (028) 6862 1555 Fax: (028) 6862 8523 E-mail: sales@deanepublicworks.co.uk *Civil engineers & public works*

Deanestor Ltd, Deanestor Building, Warren Way, Forest Town, Mansfield, Nottinghamshire, NG19 0FL Tel: (01623) 420041 Fax: (01623) 420061 E-mail: sales@deanestor.co.uk *Healthcare furnishers*

Deanprint Ltd, Cheadle Heath Works, Stockport Road, Stockport, Cheshire, SK3 0PR Tel: 0161-428 2236 Fax: 0161-428 0817 E-mail: sales@deanprint.co.uk *Bookbinders & litho printers*

Deans Blinds & Awnings UK Ltd, 4 Haslemere Industrial Estate, Ravensbury Terrace, London, SW18 4SE Tel: (020) 8947 8931 Fax: (020) 8947 8336 E-mail: info@deansblinds.co.uk *Blind & awning manufrs*

▶ Deans Carpets, 28c Sherwood Street, Warsop, Mansfield, Nottinghamshire, NG20 0JW Tel: (01623) 846655 Fax: (01623) 846655 *Carpets suppliers*

Deans Engineering Livingston Ltd, Royston Road, Deans Industrial Estate, Deans, Livingston, West Lothian, EH54 8AH Tel: (01506) 419797 Fax: (01506) 413849 E-mail: enquiries@deansengineering.com *Precision engineers*

Deans Engineering Supplies, E M S House, Rossfield Road, Ellesmere Port, CH65 3BS Tel: 0151-357 1030 Fax: 0151-357 1990 *Pipeline fittings & flanges distributors*

Deans Feeds, Finmere Mill, Chetwode, Buckingham, MK18 4JS Tel: (01280) 848551 Fax: (01280) 847812 *Animal feed suppliers & manufrs*

Deans Foods Ltd, The Moor, Bilsthorpe, Newark, Nottinghamshire, NG22 8TS Tel: (01623) 870384 Fax: (01623) 870657 *Egg product suppliers* Also at: Monmouth, Norwich, Thornton, Walsall & Warrington

Dean's Of Huntly Ltd, Depot Road, Huntly, Aberdeenshire, AB54 8JX Tel: (01466) 792086 Fax: (01466) 792895 E-mail: sales@deans.co.uk *Shortbread biscuit manufrs*

Deans Marine, Conquest Drove, Farcet, Peterborough, PE7 3DH Tel: (01733) 244166 Fax: (01733) 244166 E-mail: deansmarine@yahoo.co.uk *Boat kit manufrs*

Deans Systems Ltd, Borwick Drive, Grovehill, Beverley, North Humberside, HU17 0HQ Tel: (01482) 868111 Fax: (01482) 881890 E-mail: info@deanssystems.com *Coach door & handrail fittings manufrs*

▶ Deans Telford Ltd, Unit 1 & 24 Shifnal Industrial Estate, Lamledge Lane, Shifnal, Shropshire, TF11 8SD Tel: (01952) 462877 Fax: (01952) 463047

Deansfield Metal Finishing Co. Ltd, Colliery Road, Wolverhampton, WV1 2RD Tel: (01902) 351811 Fax: (01902) 458165 E-mail: admin@deansfield.fsbusiness.co.uk *Metal finishers services*

Deanson Wilkes Forms & Systems Ltd, 1 Cramp Hill, Wednesbury, West Midlands, WS10 8ES Tel: 0121-568 7123 Fax: 0121-568 7122 E-mail: sales@deansonwilkes.co.uk *Print & supply business stationery manufrs*

▶ Dearden Formwork & Steelfixing, Hunters Farm, Hunters Lane, Tarleton, Preston, PR4 6JL Tel: (01772) 811150 Fax: (01772) 811788

Dearing Plastics Ltd, Unit 12 National Avenue, Hull, HU5 4HT Tel: (01482) 348588 Fax: (01482) 470255 E-mail: sales@dearingplastics.com *Plastic injection moulding solutions for Industry including Design & manufacture, contract assembly & packing, insert moulding,& full in-house tool making facilities. We undertake general trade moulding and sub-contract work for organisations operating in areas as diverse as Automotive Engineering, Caravan manufacture, Electronics, Leisure, Packaging, Printing & Petrol chemicals.*

Dearneside Fabrications, Trafalgar Works, Wallace Road, Sheffield, S3 9SR Tel: 0114-241 9540 Fax: 0114-278 7681 *Metal work fabricators*

T. Deas & Sons Ltd, 27-29 Wilder Street, Bristol, BS2 8QA Tel: 0117-924 6967 *Mens & boys clothes wholesalers*

Deb Ltd, 108 Spencer Road, Belper, Derbyshire, DE56 1JX Tel: (01773) 596700 Fax: (01773) 822548 E-mail: enquiry@deb.co.uk *Deb Ltd, experts in cleaning, hygiene and occupational skin safety produce a comprehensive range of highly professional hand cleaners, soaps and soap dispensing units, janitorial and general cleaning products to suit the requirements of a wide range of locations and industries.**Deb has been at the forefront of research and development into skincare and cleaning products for over 60 years and it's brands which include Cutan, Florafree, Odex, Swarfega, Janitol and Deb itself, are recognised as leading names within their sectors, each synonymous with quality products. ****

▶ Debach Enterprises Ltd, Blue Stem Road, Ransomes Industrial Estate, Ipswich, IP3 9RR Tel: (01473) 270207 Fax: (01473) 719939 E-mail: sales@debach.co.uk

Debaer Incorperating Rimac, 7 Langley Business Centre, Station Road, Langley, Slough, SL3 8DS Tel: (01753) 710071 Fax: (01753) 572772 E-mail: sales@rimac.co.uk *Design, manufacture, supply & manage company clothing for the city, industry & local authorities*

Debaff Developments Ltd, Unit 2a Forest Row Business Park, Station Road, Forest Row, East Sussex, RH18 5DW Tel: (01342) 822106 Fax: (01342) 824198 *Building contractors*

Debanks Engineering, C3-C4 Unit, Grovelands Avenue Workshops, Winnersh, Wokingham, Berkshire, RG41 5LB Tel: 0118-977 3008 Fax: 0118-977 0903 *Precision engineers*

Debbage Yachting Services, New Cut West, Ipswich, IP2 8HN Tel: (01473) 601169 Fax: (01473) 603184 *Yachting services*

Debdale Metal Powders Ltd, Waterhouse Road, Manchester, M18 7HZ Tel: 0161-231 1504 Fax: 0161-223 2763 E-mail: info@debdale.com *Bronze, metal & aluminium powder manufrs*

Deben Buildbase, 15-17 Pickford Lane, Bexleyheath, Kent, DA7 4RD Tel: (020) 8304 3567 Fax: (020) 8298 0201 E-mail: bexleyheath@buildbase.co.uk *Buildbase is one of the UK's fastest growing builders merchants. All of our branches are long*

continued

continuation
established companies which have been serving local trades people for many years, with knowledge and experience to match. We believe strongly in understanding the needs of trades professional and our business has been developed specifically to meet those demands. Massive stocks, top quality products, competitive pricing, reliable delivery, specialist staff and exceptional customer service.

Deben Buildbase, 10/14 Crossway, Stoke Newington, London, N16 8HX Tel: (020) 7254 1117 Fax: (020) 7249 4535 E-mail: stokenewington@buildbase.co.uk *Buildbase is one of the UK's fastest growing builders merchants. All of our branches are long established companies which have been serving local trades people for many years, with knowledge and experience to match. We believe strongly in understanding the needs of trades professional and our business has been developed specifically to meet those demands. Massive stocks, top quality products, competitive pricing, reliable delivery, specialist staff and exceptional customer service.*

Deben Cruises, The Quay, Waldringfield, Woodbridge, Suffolk, IP12 4QZ Tel: (01473) 736260 Fax: (01473) 736260 *Boat yard & river trips*

Deben Group Industries Ltd, Gore Cross Business Park, Corbin Way, Bradpole, Bridport, Dorset, DT6 3UX Tel: (01308) 423576 Fax: (01308) 425912 E-mail: johnp@deben.com *Manufacturing of field sports*

▶ Deben Print Co., 1 Bailey Close, Hadleigh Road Industrial Estat, Ipswich, IP2 0UD Tel: (01473) 210244 Fax: (01473) 217299 E-mail: sales@debenprint.co.uk *Screen printers & printing services*

▶ Deben Transport Southampton Ltd, Oyster House, Andes Road, Nursling, Southampton, SO16 0YZ Tel: (023) 8073 5566 Fax: (023) 8073 5567

Deben UK, Brickfields Business Park, Old Stowmarket Road, Woolpit, Bury St. Edmunds, Suffolk, IP30 9QS Tel: (01359) 244870 Fax: (01359) 244879 E-mail: web@deben.co.uk *Scientific equipment manufrs*

▶ Debitz Book Keeping, 38 Charminster Avenue, Bournemouth, BH9 1SA Tel: 01202 523469 E-mail: debitz_bkeeper@yahoo.co.uk *Affordable Book Keeping and Office Services for self employed and small business.*

Graham Debling Precision Engineering Ltd, 3A-4 Booth Place, Margate, Kent, CT9 1QN Tel: (01843) 298804 Fax: (01843) 298858 E-mail: gdebling@gdpe.co.uk *CNC engineering services*

Deboiz Equestrian Supplies, Roman Castle Barn, Pickhill, Thirsk, North Yorkshire, YO7 4JR Tel: (01845) 567840 Fax: (01845) 567840 E-mail: sales@deboiz.com *Horse wear products manufrs*

Debonair, Anchor House, 4 Bridgeman Street, Walsall, WS2 9NW Tel: (01922) 649399 Fax: (01922) 648091 E-mail: salesdebonair@aol.com *Uniform designers & manufrs*

▶ Deborah Mather, Woodseaves, Upper North Wraxall, Chippenham, Wiltshire, SN14 7AG Tel: (01225) 891379 Fax: (0870) 0516263 E-mail: info@matherwood.co.uk *Designer & maker of crochet hats, scarves, sweaters & jackets*

Deborah Services Ltd, Souter Head Industrial Centre, Souter Head Road, Altens Industrial Estate, Aberdeen, AB12 3LF Tel: (01224) 878529 Fax: (01224) 897927 E-mail: aberdeen.hire@deborahservices.co.uk *Scaffolding hire services*

▶ Deborah Services Ltd, Quarry Lane, Chichester, West Sussex, PO19 8NY Tel: (01243) 782345 Fax: (01243) 527581

▶ Deborah Services Ltd, 23, Maple Road, Saddlebow, King's Lynn, Norfolk, PE34 3AH Tel: (01553) 771465 Fax: (01553) 773010 E-mail: kingslynn.hire@deborahservices.co.uk *Scaffolding hire services*

Deborah Services Ltd, 137 Gelderd Road, Leeds, LS12 6BZ Tel: 0113-244 4629 Fax: 0113-242 0475 *Scaffolding suppliers*

Deborah Services Ltd, 731-761 Harrow Road, London, NW10 5NY Tel: (020) 8969 1191 Fax: (020) 8968 1301 E-mail: harrow.contracts@deborahservices.co.uk *Scaffolding contractors*

Deborah Services Ltd, 227-231 Selbourne Road, Luton, LU4 8NR Tel: (01582) 491000 Fax: (01582) 493384 E-mail: luton.hire@deborahservices.co.uk *Scaffolding hire*

Deborah Services Ltd, Thornes Moor Road, Wakefield, West Yorkshire, WF2 8PT Tel: (01924) 378222 Fax: (01924) 366250 E-mail: enquiries@deborahservices.co.uk *Scaffolding erectors non mechanical access equipment* Also at: Branches throughout the U.K.

Debro Engineering & Presswork, Stourvale Trading Estate, Banners Lane, Halesowen, West Midlands, B63 2AX Tel: (01384) 633004 Fax: (01384) 633746 *Pipework supports & brackets manufrs*

▶ Debt Aid, Chatton Mill, Chatton, Alnwick, Northumberland, NE66 5RA Tel: (01668) 215505 Fax: (01668) 215000 E-mail: marketing@debtaid.ltd.uk *We offer advice and management for people in debt. Free phone line 08000 722 332. Free information packs can be requested.*

Debt Busters (Universal), Communications House, 9 St Johns Street, Colchester, CO2 7NN Tel: (01206) 761777 Fax: (01206) 763444 E-mail: info@debtbustersuniversal.com *Debt management services*

Debt Collect, Baltic Chambers, 50 Wellington Street, Glasgow, G2 6HJ Tel: (0845) 1202935 Fax: (0845) 1302936 E-mail: enquiries@debtcollectuk.com *Free debt collection in the UK, pre-litigation reports, worldwide debt collection, tracing services*

▶ Debt Collection Services UK Ltd, 1 Queen Street, Mirfield, West Yorkshire, WF14 8AH Tel: (01924) 499824 Fax: (0870) 7581125 E-mail: colette.rhodes@btconnect.com *"No Collection No Fee" debt collection service.*

▶ Debt Free Direct Ltd, York House Ackhurst Park, Foxhole Road, Chorley, Lancashire, PR7 1NY Tel: (0800) 9775985

▶ Debt Sentinel, Acorn House, Nailsworth Mills Estate, Avening Road, Nailsworth, Stroud, Gloucestershire, GL6 0BS Tel: (0870) 3501870 Fax: (0870) 3501871 E-mail: info@debtsentinel.co.uk *Commercial debt collection*

Debtsave, Palmerston House, 814 Brighton Road, Purley, Surrey, CR8 2BR Tel: (020) 8655 8484 Fax: (020) 8655 8501 E-mail: debtsave@palmerston.co.uk *Debt collection & credit management*

▶ Debut Publications Ltd, Creative Industries Centre, Wolverhampton Science Park, Glaisher Drive, Wolverhampton, WV10 9TG Tel: 01902 561600 Fax: 01902 837401 E-mail: info@debutpublications.co.uk *Debut Publications, publishers of high quality Art and Design books, catalogues and promotional literature, for students and established artists. Debut's publications offer all Art and Design creatives the opportunity to showcase their work to national and international creatives, galleries, buyers of imagery, employers and industry decision makers. Debut Publications also run regular briefs and competitions alongside the chance for established artists to publish their work in themed publications.*

▶ Deca Freelance Couriers Ltd, 240 Burton Road, Lincoln, LN1 3UB Tel: (01522) 851612 Fax: (01522) 851613 E-mail: deca.couriers3@ntlworld.com *We are specialists in the sameday courier industry as we only take on 1 job at a time "NO MULTI DROPPING" this means we can give 100% customer care at all times. For a specialist quote please call Andy today on 07841679121*

Deca Materials Handling Ltd, 13 Adkin Way, Wantage, Oxfordshire, OX12 9HN Tel: (01235) 770022 Fax: (01235) 770027 E-mail: sales@deca-mh.co.uk *Fork lift truck hire services*

▶ Decade Electronics Ltd, Ivy House Farm, Marston On Dove, Hilton, Derby, DE65 5GB Tel: (01283) 810044 Fax: (01283) 810077 *Electronic component distributors*

Decantae Mineral Water Ltd, Trofarth Farm, Llangernyw, Abergele, Clwyd, LL22 8RF Tel: (01745) 860340 Fax: (01745) 860552 *Mineral water manufrs*

Decco, Crabtree Manor Way North, Belvedere, Kent, DA17 6LJ Tel: (0870) 9506565 Fax: (020) 8310 4665 *Horticultural sundries merchants*

Deceuninck Ltd, Stanier Road, Porte Marsh Industrial Estate, Calne, Wiltshire, SN11 9PX Tel: (01249) 816969 Fax: (01249) 815234 E-mail: deceuninck.ltd@deceuninck.com *Insulator foam products*

▶ Decipher Design, 107, Boundary Rd, London, NW8 0RG Tel: (020) 7328 2545 E-mail: info@decipherdesign.co.uk *Graphic & web design*

▶ Decision Systems Ltd, St. Mary'S Studio, St. Mary'S Road, Bowdon, Altrincham, Cheshire, WA14 2PL Tel: 0161-928 2244 Fax: 0161-929 0087 E-mail: info@decisionsystems.co.uk *Computer software services*

Decisions Express Ltd, 15 17 Hatherley House, Wood Street, Barnet, Hertfordshire, EN5 4AT Tel: (020) 8441 9800 Fax: (020) 8449 9597 E-mail: info@decisions.co.uk *Computer consultants*

Decke Newcastle Ltd, 244 Park View, Whitley Bay, Tyne & Wear, NE26 3QX Tel: 0191-251 2606 Fax: 0191-251 4880 E-mail: decke.newcastle@contactbox.co.uk *Suspended ceilings, partitions & dry lining installation*

Deckel Grinders Ltd, Pasture Lane Business Centre, Pasture Lane, Rainford, St. Helens, Merseyside, WA11 8PU Tel: (01744) 886651 Fax: (01744) 885201 E-mail: sales@deckel-grinders.com *CNC milling retailers*

Decking (NI) Ltd, 75 Coole Road, Dungannon, County Tyrone, BT71 5DR Tel: (028) 8774 1199 Fax: (028) 87749140

▶ Decking Style, 19 Manor Road, East Grinstead, West Sussex, RH19 1LP Tel: (01342) 303120 E-mail: info@deckingstyle.co.uk *Decking suppliers*

▶ Declaration Ltd, The Bearings, Bowbridge Road, Newark, Nottinghamshire, NG24 4BZ Tel: (01636) 708330 Fax: (01636) 708331 E-mail: rcihard@declaration.co.uk *PR agency, distribute press releases*

Deco Bishop Auckland Ltd, Roman Way Industrial Estate, Bishop Auckland, County Durham, DL14 9AW Tel: (01388) 604590 Fax: (01388) 604590 *Machine & hand engravers & sign makers*

Decomatic, Unit 6, Robins Drive, Bridgwater, Somerset, TA6 4DL Tel: (01278) 444151 Fax: (01278) 422411 E-mail: sales@decomatic.com *Polythene bag manufrs*

Decon Laboratories Ltd, Conway Street, Hove, East Sussex, BN3 3LY Tel: (01273) 739241 Fax: (01273) 722088 E-mail: sales@decon.co.uk *Manufacturers of cleaning fluids*

▶ Deconsys Technology Ltd, Macart House, Farnham Road, Bradford, West Yorkshire, BD7 3JG Tel: (01274) 521700 Fax: (01274) 521700 E-mail: info@deconsys.co.uk *Steel fabrication*

Decor Blindmakers, 111 High Street, Ecclesfield, Sheffield, S35 9XA Tel: 0114-246 8311 Fax: 0114-246 8311 *Blind manufrs*

Decor Centre, North Quay, Pwllheli, Gwynedd, LL53 5YR Tel: (01758) 612562 Fax: (01758) 704999 E-mail: sales@decorcentrewales.com *DIY & car accessories*

Decor Iron, Mill Street, Darlaston, Wednesbury, West Midlands, WS10 8TH Tel: 0121-526 7498 Fax: 0121-568 6778 *Gates & railings manufrs*

Decor Signs, Unit 22 Oldbury Business Centre, Oldbury Road, Cwmbran, Gwent, NP44 3JU Tel: (01633) 866349 Fax: (01633) 866349 E-mail: marketing@decorsigns.co.uk *Sign writing contractors*

Decora Blinds, 79-81 Andersonstown Road, Belfast, BT11 9AH Tel: (028) 9060 4646 Fax: (028) 9060 4646 *Blinds manufrs*

▶ Decorative Flooring Services, 1501 Nitshill Road, Thornliebank, Glasgow, G46 8QG Tel: 0141-621 2990 Fax: 0141-621 2991 E-mail: sales@decorativeflooringservices.co.uk *Flooring retailers*

Decorative Resin Floors, PO Box 26, Hengoed, Mid Glamorgan, CF82 7YD Tel: 0870 950 3037 Fax: 0871 434 6732 E-mail: info@decorativeresinfloors.com *Resin flooring installers*

Decorative Sleeves, Unit 6 Pioneer Way, Castleford, West Yorkshire, WF10 5QU Tel: (01977) 510030 Fax: (01977) 521240 *PVC sleeve printers*

Decorative Sleeves Holdings, Rollesby Road, Hardwick Industrial Estate, King's Lynn, Norfolk, PE30 4LS Tel: (01553) 769319 Fax: (01553) 767097 E-mail: mktg@decorativesleeves.co.uk *Packaging material manufrs*

Decorative Specialist Ltd, 14 Kensington Church Street, London, W8 4EP Tel: (020) 7937 3483 Fax: (020) 7376 2182 *Painting contractors*

▶ Decorbuild & Co., Premier House, 50-52 Cross Lances Road, Hounslow, TW3 2AA Tel: (020) 8577 3773 Fax: (020) 8577 4547 E-mail: service@decorbuild.com

Decorfix, Halstow Lane, Upchurch, Sittingbourne, Kent, ME9 7AB Tel: (01795) 843124 Fax: (01795) 842465 *Suspended ceilings*

Decorflair Ltd, Chaddock Lane, Worsley, Manchester, M28 1DL Tel: 0161-790 2551 Fax: 0161-702 8665 E-mail: sales@decorflair.co.uk *Engravers to wall coverings*

Decoritalia UK Ltd, 198 Moorland Road, Stoke-on-Trent, ST6 1EB Tel: (01782) 832662 Fax: (01782) 832651 E-mail: sales@decoritialia.co.uk *Sales ceramic transfers*

Decorlight, B 68 Pier Avenue, Clacton-on-Sea, Essex, CO15 1NH Tel: (01255) 421818 Fax: (01255) 474147 *Decorative lighting agents*

Decorshades LLP, 5 Brewery Mews Business Centre, St Johns Road, Isleworth, Middlesex, TW7 6PH Tel: (020) 8847 1939 Fax: (020) 8847 1939 E-mail: martin@decshade.demon.co.uk *Textile laminators*

▶ Decorum, 209 Tedco Business Works, Henry Robson Way, South Shields, Tyne & Wear, NE33 1RF Tel: 0191-456 7667 Fax: 0191-427 4508 *Sports goods equipment accessory manufrs*

▶ DECT Phones, Thorp Arch Trading Estate, Thorp Arch, Wetherby, West Yorkshire, LS23 7RR Tel: (0870) 7775777 Fax: (0870) 7776665 E-mail: stuart.moffatt@evocal.co.uk *A UK-based supplier of discount telephones, fax machines and other home/office telecommuncations equipment.*

Dectek Ltd, Unit 29 Business Development Centre, Main Ave, Treforest Industrial Estate, Pontypridd, M. Glam, CF37 5UR Tel: (01443) 841840 Fax: (01443) 842815 E-mail: sales@dectek.co.uk *Based in South Wales, DecTek is a leading manufacturer of Polyurethane Resin Domed Badges, Domed Labels, Domed Stickers and Fabric Doming supplying throughout the UK and Europe. We provide instant telephone quotations, 48 hr sampling, 24hr online order tracking, 7-10 day production, 3/5 day express services, spot/full colour vinyl print and spot/full colour metallic print with a minimum order quantity of 100. Employing state-of-the art digital print equipment and CNC resin application machines, DecTek's products are produced for a multitude of industries including it's renown trade service to Screen Printers, Label Printers and Print Brokers. Applications include: Computer Badges, Promotional Badges, Furniture Badges, Point-of-Sale Badges, Corporate Badges and Product Branding. Other names for these products include: Gel Badges, Gel Stickers, Resin Badges, Resin Labels, Domed Decals and Polydomes. During 2006, DecTek opened it's first European Sales Office in Malaga, Spain which will aid the company's expansion plans throughout Europe.*

▶ Dectel Ltd, 105 Horse St, Chipping Sodbury, Bristol, BS37 6DE Tel: (01454) 883300 Fax: (01454) 883300 E-mail: dectel@blueyonder.co.uk *Telephone and data network repairs & installations*

Dectel Information Systems, Swinbourne Road, Burnt Mills Industrial Estate, Basildon, Essex, SS13 1EF Tel: (01268) 727586 Fax: (01268) 591422 E-mail: sales@dectel.co.uk Principal Export Areas: Africa, Central/East Europe & West Europe *Security company & document management*

▶ Dectelonline, Swinborne Road, Burnt Mills, Basildon, Essex, SS13 1EF Tel: 01268 727884 Fax: 01268 591422 *Photographic media supplier*

DED Ltd, Mill Road, Lydd, Romney Marsh, Kent, TN29 9EJ Tel: (01797) 320636 Fax: (01797) 320273 E-mail: sales@ded.co.uk *Specialists for over 25 years in a wide range of hardware products for Hospitality applications, DED offer plastic card printers for ID, membership, discount & loyalty, pos receipt, label, barcode, ticket & lottery printers, kiosk printers, touchscreen terminals, barcode printers and scanners, data collection terminals, cash drawers, printer mechanisms, panel & portable printers, magnetic, smart & proximity card reader & writers alongside a comprehensive range of supporting consumables and accessories. DED also offer a unique card based customer loyalty software system and a bureau service for plastic card printing.* Servicing wide reaching markets across the UK, DED sell through a network of regional and vertical market dealers who have a specific understanding of leisure, retail and hospitality industries. DED are accredited by NQA to the BS EN ISO 9001:2000 Quality*
continued

Standard and offer unrivalled product knowledge and technical support which is second to none.

Dedicated Micros Ltd, Aegon House, Daresbury Park, Daresbury, Warrington, WA4 4HS Tel: (01928) 706400 Fax: (01928) 706350 E-mail: customerservice@dmicros.com *Security systems manufrs*

Dedicated Systems Ltd, 12 Thurman Street, System House, Ilkeston, Derbyshire, DE7 4AQ Tel: 0115-944 2944 Fax: 0115-932 6336 *Software designers & development*

Dee Bee Foams Ltd, 19-20 Pulloxhill Business Park, Greenfield Road, Pulloxhill, Bedford, MK45 5EU Tel: (01525) 718111 Fax: (01525) 718112 E-mail: sales@deebeefoams.co.uk *Foam converters*

Dee Communications, 453 Brook Lane, Birmingham, B13 0BT Tel: 0121-702 2552 Fax: 0121-778 3633 E-mail: sales@deecomms.co.uk *Two way radio system distribs*

Dee Communications Ltd, Dutton Green, Stanney Mill, Chester, CH2 4SA Tel: 0151-356 5955 Fax: 0151-356 5944 E-mail: sales@deecommunications.co.uk *Radio communications distributors*

John Dee Humane Traps, 4 Russett Cottage, Greendale Barton, Woodbury Salterton, Exeter, EX5 1EW Tel: (01395) 233340 Fax: (01395) 233548 E-mail: desmo1@btopenworld.com *Vermin trap manufrs*

Dee Kay Knitwear, 227-229 Belgrave Gate, Leicester, LE1 3HT Tel: 0116-253 7560 Fax: 0116-253 7852 *Knitwear manufrs*

▶ Dee Safety & Embroidery, Unit B1 Evans Easyspace, Deeside Industrial Park, Deeside, Clwyd, CH5 2JZ Tel: (01244) 280090

▶ Dee Tech Services Ltd, 5 Jackson Court, Manor Lane, Hawarden, Deeside, Clwyd, CH5 3QP Tel: (01244) 530100 Fax: (01244) 530101

Dee Valley Water plc, Packsaddle, Wrexham Road, Rhostyllen, Wrexham, Clwyd, LL14 4EH Tel: (01978) 846946 Fax: (01978) 846888 E-mail: contact@deevallygroup.com *Water company suppliers*

Deebees Ltd, 4 Mayne Avenue, Bridge of Allan, Stirling, FK9 4RA Tel: (01786) 832014 Fax: (01786) 832825 *Building maintenance*

Deebridge Electrical Engineers, Craigshaw Road, West Tullos Industrial Estate, Aberdeen, AB12 3AR Tel: (01224) 871548 Fax: (01224) 899910 E-mail: info@deebridge.co.uk *Electrical machinery repair services*

Deeco Lighting, Highfield, Bryn Awelon, Mold, Clwyd, CH7 1LT Tel: (01352) 700380 Fax: (01352) 700380 *Flood lighting equipment & outdoor lighting erectors*

Deedman Tropical Plant Hire Co., 3k Longcauseway, Farnworth, Bolton, BL4 9BS Tel: (01204) 577000 Fax: (01204) 577770 E-mail: sales@deedman.co.uk *Tropical plant hire*

Deegee Systems Ltd, 15 Hawksley Rise, Oughtibridge, Sheffield, S35 0JB Tel: 0114-286 4400 Fax: 0114-286 4400 E-mail: sales@deegee.co.uk *Computer systems & software developers*

▶ Deejay Solutions, 101 Upper Queen Street, Rushden, Northamptonshire, NN10 0BS Tel: (01933) 411777 Fax: (01933) 358721

▶ Deejays, Unit 74 Haydon Industrial Estate, Radstock, BA3 3RD Tel: (01761) 437866 *Water products for the waters services*

Deeley Precision Engineering Ltd, Unit 1 Aston Fields Industrial Estate, Aston Road, Bromsgrove, Worcestershire, B60 3EX Tel: (01527) 870001 Fax: (01527) 579101 *CNC, milling, turning & welded fabricators*

Deeleys Ltd, Unit 43 Belgrave Industrial Estate, Highgate Place, Birmingham, B12 0DD Tel: 0121-693 0740 Fax: 0121-693 0741 E-mail: info@deeleysdisplays.co.uk *Exhibition & display graphic panels manufrs*

Deeleys Castings Ltd, Leamore Lane, Walsall, WS2 7BY Tel: (01922) 476898 Fax: (01922) 493507 E-mail: deeleys@fsmail.net *Grey iron & malleable iron founders*

Deeleys Fencing, The Stables, Ford Lane, Chorley, Lichfield, Staffordshire, WS13 8BY Tel: (01543) 682361 *Fencing contractors*

John Deeny Ltd, 123 Learmount Road, Claudy, Londonderry, BT47 4AL Tel: (028) 7133 8229 Fax: (028) 7133 8039 *Animal health & agricultural products*

Deeny Manufacturing, 4 Arcadia Avenue, Sale, Cheshire, M33 3SA Tel: 0161-976 3976 Fax: (0161) 976397 *Corporate wear manufrs*

Dee-Organ, Signature House, 4 Newmains Avenue, Inchinnan, Paisley, Renfrewshire, PA4 9RR Tel: 0141-812 5121 Fax: 0141-812 5125 E-mail: signs@dee-organ.co.uk *Manufacturers road signs*

Deep Blue Systems Ltd, Unit 1, Lawrence Parade, Lower Square, Isleworth, Middlesex, TW7 6RG Tel: (020) 8541 4131 Fax: (020) 8569 9691 E-mail: sales@deepbluesystems.com *Computer system consultants*

Deep Sea Electronics plc, Hunmanby Industrial Estate, Hunmanby, Filey, North Yorkshire, YO14 0PH Tel: (01723) 890099 Fax: (01723) 893303 E-mail: marketing@deepseaplc.com *Electronics manufacturers of control systems for generators*

Deep Sea Seals Ltd, 4 Marples Way, Havant, Hampshire, PO9 1NX Tel: (023) 9249 2123 Fax: (023) 9249 2470 *Marine shaft seal manufrs*

▶ Deepbluemedia, Flat 3, 375 Union Street, Aberdeen, AB11 6BT Tel: (01224) 592572 E-mail: info@deepbluemedia.co.uk *Multi media services*

Deepdale Technical Services Ltd, 33A Scalbie Road, Scarborough, North Yorkshire, YO12 5PZ Tel: (0870) 2201486 Fax: (01723) 377571 E-mail: info@deepdale.co.uk *Computer repairers & suppliers*

▶ Deeproot Europe UK Ltd, Stone, Staffordshire, ST15 9AD Tel: (01782) 551865 Fax: (01782) 551862 E-mail: info@deeprooteurope.com *aims and comitment, DeepRoot is committed to helping trees survive in the harsh urban environment for almost thirty years.Deeproots unique guiding barriers with anti lift locks,double top edge prevents tree roots from damaging roads,pavements also protects cables,pipes and infrastructure,root block barriers create a root*
continued

continuation
free zone.consultation and advice is always available we also manafacture tree protecting products.ArbGuard,ArborTie

Deer Management & Vermin Control, 2 Browns Farm Cottages, Church St, Belchamp St Paul, Sudbury, Suffolk, CO10 7DQ Tel: 01787 278126 Fax: 01787 278126 *Deer management & vermin control*

John Deere Ltd, Harby Road, Langar, Nottingham, NG13 9HT Tel: (01949) 860491 Fax: (01949) 860490 *Agricultural machinery manufrs*

Deering Agri-Supplies Ltd, Cortrasna, Roslea, Rosslea, Enniskillen, County Fermanagh, BT92 7FU Tel: (028) 6775 1232 Fax: (028) 6775 1987 *Farm suppliers*

Deerite Partitions, 9 Eastway, Sale, Cheshire, M33 4DT Tel: 0161-969 5216 Fax: 0161-905 1774 E-mail: birddeerite@btinternet.com *Ceilings & partitions installers to business*

Deerness Rubber Co. Ltd, Coulson Street, Spennymoor, County Durham, DL16 7RS Tel: (01388) 420301 Fax: (01388) 420284 E-mail: sales@deerness-rubber.co.uk *Manufacturers of rubber mouldings & seals (including industrial). In addition, hydraullic/fluid seal, silicone rubber compound & non-standard o-ring manufacturers. Also, silicone rubber moulding or extrusion services*

▶ Dee's Bridalwear, Melbourne Road, Grantham, Lincolnshire, NG31 9RH Tel: 0773 6469276 E-mail: info@deesbridalwear.co.uk *We sell wedding, bridesmaid and evening dresses along with accessories. All my dresses are made to measure and come at amazing prices making them perfect for any shape size and best of all budget.*

Deeside Electrical Ltd, Central Point, Brunswick Road, Buckley, Clwyd, CH7 2EH Tel: (01244) 547707 Fax: (01244) 550616

Deeside Engineering Services, Park Road, Rhosymedre, Wrexham, Clwyd, LL14 3YR Tel: (01978) 824335 Fax: (01978) 810696 E-mail: johnevans@deesideengineeringfsnet.co.uk *Sheet metalwork engineers service*

▶ Deeside Homes, 8 Spurryhillock Industrial Estate, Broomhill Road, Stonehaven, Kincardineshire, AB39 2NH Tel: (01569) 767123 Fax: (01569) 767766

▶ Deeside Marine Ltd, Dee Walk, Kirkcudbright, DG6 4DR Tel: (01557) 331407

Deeson Group Ltd, Ewell House, Graveney Road, Goodnestone, Faversham, Kent, ME13 8UP Tel: (01795) 535468 Fax: (01795) 535469 E-mail: enquiries@deeson.co.uk *Public relations consultants* Also at: London

Deetronic Fire Systems Ltd, 41 Hope Street, Chester, CH4 8BU Tel: (01244) 659300 Fax: (01244) 659551 E-mail: info@deetronic.com *Fire alarms & smoke detectors installation*

Deeva Productions, 174 Singlewell Road, Gravesend, Kent, DA11 7RB Tel: (01474) 350300 Fax: (01474) 353931 *Corporate video producers*

▶ Defence Estates, Building Moss, HMNB Devonport, Plymouth, PL2 2BG Tel: (01752) 554952 Fax: (01752) 554740 E-mail: plymouth@gdpmod.co.uk *Marine safety channel sips, defence sector & commercial businesses*

Defence Fasteners Ltd, Brighton Road, Pease Pottage, Crawley, West Sussex, RH11 9AD Tel: (01293) 525811 Fax: (01293) 525814 E-mail: sales@defencefasteners.com *Fasteners for defence & aerospace industries*

Defence Group Ltd, 411 Petre Street, Sheffield, S4 8LL Tel: 0114-244 1178 Fax: 0114-244 7710 E-mail: sales@defencegroup.co.uk *Roller shutter manufrs*

▶ Defence Imaging, 17 Lyndhurst Road, Exeter, EX2 4PA Tel: 01392 403316 E-mail: info@defenceimaging.com *Marine & medical s[ecialists*

▶ Defence Security Systems Ltd, 119 Kelvin Way, West Bromwich, West Midlands, B70 7LD Tel: 0121-457 9550 Fax: 0121-457 9551 E-mail: info@defencesecurity.co.uk *Security systems installers for home & business*

Defensor Fire Detection Systems, 11-15 Kingsley Street, Leicester, LE2 6DY Tel: 0116-244 8689 Fax: 0116-244 8884 *Fire alarm installation services*

Defiant Alarms Ltd, 45 Hornby Street, Wigan, Lancashire, WN1 2DR Tel: (01942) 248872 Fax: (01942) 248872 *Burglar alarm engineers*

Definite Software P.L.C., 3 Waterloo Road, Stockport, Cheshire, SK1 3BD Tel: (0870) 7406575 Fax: (0870) 7406576 *Linux distribution*

▶ Definitive Consulting, Parkfield Business Centre, Park Street, Stafford, ST17 4AL Tel: (01785) 226430 Fax: (01785) 222217 E-mail: info@definitiveuk.com *Web design graphic design & design consultancy & pr*

Defontaine Ltd, Hinnegar Lodge, Didmarton, Badminton, Avon, GL9 1DN Tel: (01454) 238831 E-mail: janice@ukdefontaine.com Sales Contact: J. Walker *Rotary bearings, hygienic valves distributors*

Defra Design, Bradley Farm, Cumnor, Oxford, OX2 9QU Tel: (01865) 863937 Fax: (01865) 865878 E-mail: design@defra.co.uk *Computer aided design*

Degussa Ltd, Winterton House, Winterton Way, Lyme Green Business Park, Macclesfield, Cheshire, SK11 0LP Tel: (01625) 503050 Fax: (01625) 502096 *Chemicals*

Degussa Ltd, Tego House, Chippenham Drive, Kingston, Milton Keynes, MK10 0AF Tel: (0870) 1262250 Fax: (0845) 1289579 *Plexiglas's manufrs*

Degussa Knottingley Ltd, Common Lane, Knottingley, West Yorkshire, WF11 8BN Tel: (01977) 673321 Fax: (01977) 607032 *Intermediate chemical suppliers*

Dehavilland, 10 Stonehouse Commercial Centre, Bristol Road, Stonehouse, Gloucestershire, GL10 3RD Tel: (01453) 828272 Fax: (01453) 821945 *Subcontract fabricators*

Dehumidifier Co., Langsford Farm, Peter Tavy, Tavistock, Devon, PL19 9LY Tel: (01822) 810638 Fax: (01822) 810638 E-mail: mike@pidsley.com *Dehumidifiers distributors*

Deighton Manufacturing UK Ltd, Gibson Street, Bradford, West Yorkshire, BD3 9TR Tel: (01274) 668771 Fax: (01274) 665214 E-mail: sales@deightonmanufacturing.co.uk *Manufacturers of food processing equipment*

Deimos Ltd, Simmonds Road, Wincheap Industrial Estate, Canterbury, Kent, CT1 3RA Tel: (01227) 472822 Fax: (01227) 768597 E-mail: info@zincsmart.com *Manufacturer of cathodic protection*

Deister Electronic UK, Camel Gate, Spalding, Lincolnshire, PE12 6ET Tel: (01775) 717100 Fax: (01775) 717101 E-mail: info@deister.co.uk *Security access control systems*

Deith Leisure Ltd, Unit 2, Block 5, Tweedbank, Galashiels, Selkirkshire, TD1 3RS Tel: (01896) 758342 Fax: (01896) 758059 *Amusement machines distributors*

Deja Vu Computer Cleaners, 149 Bramley Close, London, E17 6EG Tel: (020) 8523 4661 Fax: (020) 8523 4661 *Computer cleaners*

Dek Printing Machines Ltd, 11 Albany Road, Granby Industrial Estate, Weymouth, Dorset, DT4 9TH Tel: (01305) 760760 Fax: (01305) 760123 E-mail: marketing@dek.com *Screen printing machine manufrs*

Deka Capital Advisors, 56-58 Clerkenwell Road, London, EC1M 5PX Tel: (020) 7566 0020 Fax: (020) 7566 0050 E-mail: davidcookarch@aol.com *Architects*

Dekkertoys Ltd, 16 Innovation Way, Orton Wistow, Peterborough, PE2 6FL Tel: (01733) 397400 Fax: (01733) 370241 E-mail: sales@dekkertoys.co.uk *Toy manufrs*

▶ Dek-Tec UK Ltd, 2 Quayside Nantwich Marina, Basin End, Acton, Nantwich, Cheshire, CW5 8LB Tel: (01270) 628076 Fax: (01270) 626716 E-mail: info@dek-tec.co.uk *Suppliers of "Dri-Dek" tiling/flooring system*

Dekton Components Leicester Ltd, All Saints Road, Leicester, LE3 5AB Tel: 0116-251 8387 Fax: 0116-253 2824 E-mail: mouldmakers@dekton.co.uk *Plastic tool manufrs*

Dekura, 19-26 Bracken Hill, South West Industrial Estate, Peterlee, County Durham, SR8 2LS Tel: 0191-586 2379 Fax: 0191-586 1581 E-mail: sales@dekura.co.uk *UPVC plastic scrap, waste recycling & disposal*

Del Monte Europe Ltd, Del Monte House, London Road, Staines, Middlesex, TW18 4JD Tel: (01784) 447400 Fax: (01784) 465301 *General canned food manufrs*

▶ Del Monte Fresh Produce, Kingsway North, Team Valley Trading Estate, Gateshead, Tyne & Wear, NE11 0JH Tel: 0191-487 2700 Fax: 0191-487 6787

▶ Del Norte Technology Ltd, Unit 20 Hunts Rise, South Marston Industrial Estate, Swindon, SN3 4TG Tel: (01793) 827982 Fax: (01793) 827984 E-mail: lsmith@del-norte.co.uk *Hydrographic positioning systems consultants service*

Del Tarpaulins Ltd, Unit 39, Millers Bridge Industrial, Bootle, Merseyside, L20 8AB Tel: 0151-922 9461 Fax: 0151-922 9908 E-mail: sales@r-lunt.co.uk *Tarpaulin manufrs*

▶ Delabole Slate Co. Ltd, Pengelly Road, Delabole, Cornwall, PL33 9AZ Tel: (01840) 212242 Fax: (01840) 212948 E-mail: sales@delaboleslate.com *Slate quarry, manufacturer & supplier of Cornish slate building products*

▶ Delaceys Of Huddersfield, Royd Business Park, Dye House Lane, Brighouse, West Yorkshire, HD6 1LL Tel: (01484) 401011 Fax: (01484) 401447 E-mail: enquires@delaceys.co.uk *distinctive,BMW,Mercedes,BMWs,Mercedes, model,vehicle,car,cars,vehicles,sale and *servicing,repair,rigorous selection process,low mileage,single owner,full service history,thoroughly *examined,full hpi check,specific requirements,comprehensive warranty,road tax,12 months mot *certificate,new,used,uk supplied,european imports,imported,importer,fair price,under *£5000,recommendation,satisfied customers,letters,comments,excellent, exceptional,luxury,valet,purpose *built facility,high performance and reliability,genuine manufacturers parts at prices,free collection *and delivery,Replacement of broken glass,CD,stereo fitment,Fitting alarms,immobilisers,Curing *automatic gearbox problems,air-conditioning systems,electric windows,balancing,alloy*

▶ Delaney Ditchfield Recruitment, 17 Shires Mead, Verwood, Dorset, BH31 6LD Tel: 01202 825676 E-mail: info@delaneyditchfield.co.uk *We are an independent recruitment consultancy specialising in sales marketing, administration and engineering vacancies across the UK.*

Delaney Plant, Beckside Works, Old Corn Mill Lane, Bradford, West Yorkshire, BD7 2LB Tel: (01274) 579224 Fax: (01274) 503372 *Heavy plant hire*

Delavan Ltd, Gorsey Lane, Widnes, Cheshire, WA8 0RJ Tel: 0151-424 6821 Fax: 0151-495 1043 E-mail: sales@delavan.co.uk Principal Export Areas: Worldwide *Industrial spray nozzle manufactures. Also rotary wash head tank cleaning & spray drying equipment*

Delbanco Meyer & Co. Ltd, Portland House, Ryland Road, London, NW5 3EB Tel: (020) 7468 3000 Fax: (020) 7468 3094 *Bristle & linen distributors*

Delcam, Talbot Way, Birmingham, B10 0HJ Tel: 0121-766 5544 Fax: 0121-766 5511 E-mail: marketing@delcam.com *Toolmakers & toolmaking services*

Delcor Furniture Ltd, 80-82 Whiteladies Road, Clifton, Bristol, BS8 2QN Tel: 0117-973 0932 Fax: 0191-237 6892 *Upholstered furniture manufrs* Also at: Seaton Delaval

Delcor Furniture Ltd, Double Row, Seaton Delaval, Whitley Bay, Tyne & Wear, NE25 0PR Tel: 0191-237 2395 Fax: 0191-237 6892 *Furniture manufrs*

▶ Deleka Group, 55 Pitairlie Road, Newbigging, Broughty Ferry, Dundee, DD5 3RH Tel: 01382 370608 *Drainage service*

Delen Tooling, Lansbury Estate, 102 Lower Guildford Road, Knaphill, Woking, Surrey, GU21 2EP Tel: (01483) 487033 Fax: (01483) 487033 E-mail: info@delentooling.co.uk *Toolmakers*

Delenco Foods Ltd, Unit 6 Heybridge Way Lea Bridge Road, London, E10 7NQ Tel: (020) 8558 3278 Fax: (020) 8558 6585 *Sausage manufrs*

Delf Freezer Wear Ltd, Delf House, Pool Close, West Molesey, Surrey, KT8 2HW Tel: 020 89412802 Fax: (020) 89417201 E-mail: david.barker@delf.co.uk *Manufacturers & suppliers of industrial clothing including thermo insulated cold store, chill room & work wear & safety footwear*

Delf Technology, Carrington Business Park, Manchester Road, Carrington, Manchester, M31 4QQ Tel: 0161-776 4802 Fax: 0161-776 4803 E-mail: info@delftechnology.com *Data storage manufrs*

Delfield Precision Engineering Co. Ltd, Apex House, Stonefield Close, Ruislip, Middlesex, HA4 0XT Tel: (020) 8842 0527 Fax: (020) 8845 7796 *Precision engineers & nuclear lead shielding manufrs*

Delfinware, Pennypot Industrial Estate, Pennypot, Hythe, Kent, CT21 6PE Tel: (01303) 266061 Fax: (01303) 261080 E-mail: sampsonwwp@aol.com *Wire products manufrs*

A.E.W. Delford, Main Road, Dovercourt, Harwich, Essex, CO12 4LP Tel: (01255) 241000 Fax: (01255) 241155 E-mail: sales@delford.co.uk *Industrial weighing systems manufrs*

▶ Deli Solutions, Salt Hill Industrial Estate, Salthill Road, Clitheroe, Lancashire, BB7 1NU Tel: (01200) 420790 Fax: (01200) 427782 *Supply retail ready meals (tappas) bespoke packaging*

Delian Systems, 21 Lakin Close, Springfield, Chelmsford, CM2 6RU Tel: (01245) 450012 Fax: (01245) 602533 *Database developers*

Delice De France plc, Opal Way, Stone Business Park, Stone, Staffordshire, ST15 0SS Tel: (01785) 811200 Fax: (01785) 812233 *Bread & cake distributors*

▶ Delichon Ltd, Kings Yard, Sillen Lane, Martin, Fordingbridge, Hampshire, SP6 3LB Tel: (01725) 519405 Fax: (01725) 519406

▶ Delicious Moments, Marston Park Industrial Estate, Tytherington, Frome, Somerset, BA11 5BS Tel: (01373) 457080 Fax: (01373) 467877 *Desserts manufrs*

Delivered On Time, 4 Mercury Centre, Central Way, Feltham, Middlesex, TW14 0RN Tel: (020) 8890 5511 Fax: (020) 8890 5533 E-mail: sales@shand.co.uk *Air cargo agents import & export* Also at: Gatwick

Delivery Service Ltd, Stoke Hall Road, Ipswich, IP2 8EJ Tel: (01473) 601564 Fax: (01473) 602789 E-mail: sales@ipswichdeliveryservice.co.uk *Removal & storage contractors*

Delkor Ltd, Unit C, First Avenue, Midsomer Norton, Radstock, BA3 4BS Tel: (01761) 417079 Fax: (01761) 414435 *Engineers*

Dell Inc, Technology House Dell Campus, Cain Road, Bracknell, Berkshire, RG12 1BF Tel: (01344) 860456 Fax: (01344) 372767 *Portable computer suppliers*

▶ Delmar Corporation Ltd, 167 Watling Road, Castleford, West Yorkshire, WF10 2QY Tel: (01977) 519529 E-mail: brian@delmar-cleaning.co.uk *Daily Cleaning, Factory, Retail, Office ATM"s, Computers, Washrooms, Canteen & Kitchen, One-off Cleans Bars & Clubs, Castleford, Normanton, Pontefract, Featherstone, Garforth, Wakefield. **

Delmark Engineering, Unit 26 V I P Trading Estate, 50 Anchor & Hope Lane, London, SE7 7TE Tel: (020) 8305 1919 Fax: (020) 8853 1509 E-mail: sales@delmark.co.uk *Lifting equipment*

Delmex Cleaning Materials, Ghyll Industrial Estate, Heathfield, East Sussex, TN21 8AW Tel: (01435) 868520 Fax: (01435) 864838 E-mail: mikethompson@airvert.freeserve.co.uk *Hand cleansers supply services*

Delmore, Chiswick Avenue, Mildenhall, Bury St. Edmunds, Suffolk, IP28 7AY Tel: (01638) 714805 Fax: (01638) 713043 *Plastic, textile product & hospital slippers manufrs*

Deloitte, Stonecutter Court, 1 Stonecutter Street, London, EC4A 4TR Tel: (020) 7936 3000 Fax: (020) 7583 1198 *Chartered accountants* Also at: Branches throughout the U.K.

Delomac Ltd, 1b Orchard Street, Kempston, Bedford, MK42 7JA Tel: (01234) 851222 Fax: (01234) 840864 E-mail: delomac@aol.com *Roofing contractors*

Delonghi Ltd, 15-16 Bridle Close, Finedon Road Industrial Estate, Wellingborough, Northamptonshire, NN8 4RN Tel: (01933) 442040 Fax: (01933) 441891 E-mail: marketing@delonghi.co.uk *Electrical product distributors*

Deloro Stellite UK (Director) Ltd, Cheney Manor Industrial Estate, Swindon, SN2 2PW Tel: (01793) 498500 Fax: 01793 498501 E-mail: sales@delorostellite.co.uk Principal Export Areas: Worldwide *Precision engineers*

Delph Developments Ltd, 55 Bamford Street, Clayton, Manchester, M11 4FE Tel: 0161-231 6444 Fax: 0161-231 8555 E-mail: stan@delph-uk.com *Fabrication of metal products*

Delph Electrical Lifting Services Ltd, 3 The Wallows Industrial Estate, Fens Pool Avenue, Brierley Hill, West Midlands, DY5 1QA Tel: (01384) 76222 Fax: (01384) 75524 *Overhead crane manufrs*

Delphi Diesel Systems, Courteney Road, Gillingham, Kent, ME8 0RU Tel: (01634) 224000 Fax: (01634) 374725 E-mail: paul.turner@dds.delphiauto.com Principal Export Areas: Worldwide *Diesel equipment manufrs*

Delphi Floral Display Hire, Studio 4, The Business Village, Broomhill Road, London, SW18 4JQ Tel: (020) 8871 5146 Fax: (020) 8871 5079 E-mail: studio@freshflower.co.uk *Flowers distributors*

Delphi Food Products Ltd, 14 Grenville Road, London, N19 4EH Tel: (020) 7281 2206 Fax: (020) 7281 4390 *Food manufrs*

Delphic Computer Services Ltd, White House, Preston Wynne, Hereford, HR1 3PB Tel: (01432) 820220 Fax: (01432) 820456 E-mail: sdent@delphic.uk.com *Computer brokers*

Delphorge 83 Ltd, Overend Road, Corngreaves Trading Estate, Cradley Heath, West Midlands, B64 7DD Tel: (01384) 636279 Fax: (01384) 636279 *Manufacturers of equipment for foundries*

Delpro Ltd, Peakdale Road, Glossop, Derbyshire, SK13 6XE Tel: (01457) 862776 Fax: (01457) 862433 E-mail: sales@delpro.co.uk *Manufacturers & designers of converters*

Delrac Acs, Fairman Law House, 1-3 Park Terrace, Worcester Park, Surrey, KT4 7JZ Tel: (020) 8335 3141 Fax: (020) 8337 5539 E-mail: enquiries@delrac-acs.co.uk *Air conditioning equipment distributors. Maintenance and servicing of all building services*

Delron Services Ltd, Carlton House, Hall Road, Aylesford, Kent, ME20 7HR Tel: (01622) 790111 Fax: (01622) 792170 *Fabricating engineers*

▶ Delsey Service Centre, Unit 4, Sharp House, Laindon, Basildon, Essex, SS15 6DR Tel: (01268) 541100 Fax: (01268) 541110 *Mail order suppliers*

Delsol Air Systems Ltd, Bankfield Mills, Huddersfield Road, Mirfield, West Yorkshire, WF14 9DD Tel: (01924) 498971 Fax: (01924) 499554 E-mail: enquiries@delsolairsystems.co.uk *Industrial & commercial heating engineers*

▶ Delson Contracts Ltd, Orchardbank Industrial Estate, Forfar, Angus, DD8 1TD Tel: (01307) 468666

Delstar Engineering Ltd, Homefield Road, Haverhill, Suffolk, CB9 8QP Tel: (01440) 762518 Fax: (01440) 703820 E-mail: general@delstar.co.uk *Hydraulic cylinder manufacturers & general engineers*

Delta, 15 Brook Road, Kimbolton, Huntingdon, Cambridgeshire, PE28 0LR Tel: (01480) 861154 Fax: (01480) 861134 E-mail: info@deltafabrications.com *Steel fabricators*

Delta Adhesives Ltd, 2 Lakeside Industrial Estate, Lakeside Road, Leeds, LS12 4QP Tel: 0113-279 6966 Fax: 0113-231 0828 E-mail: info@delta-adhesives.co.uk *Industrial adhesive manufacturers & distributors*

Delta Air Conditioning (Reading) Ltd, 20-22 Richfield Avenue, Reading, RG1 8EQ Tel: (020) 8893 4700 *Install & maintaining air conditioners*

Delta Aviation, Newton Hall, Town Street, Newton, Cambridge, CB22 7ZE Tel: (01223) 874343 Fax: (01223) 873702 E-mail: info@newtonhall.co.uk *Precision engineers*

▶ Delta Balloons, OAKLEIGH, BROADWAY, Sandown, Isle of Wight, PO36 9BY Tel: (01983) 400321 E-mail: info@deltaballoons.demon.co.uk *Wholesalers, suppliers & distributors of Latex balloons, gas & accessories in the South East of England.*

▶ Delta Balustrades, Millbuck Way, Sandbach, Cheshire, CW11 3JA Tel: (01270) 753383

Delta Balustrades, Belpher Road, Stockport, Cheshire, SK4 3QW Tel: 0161-947 4747 *Balustrade & handrail manufrs*

Delta Biotechnology Ltd, 59 Castle Boulevard, Nottingham, NG7 1FD Tel: 0115-955 3355 Fax: 0115-955 1299 *Pharmaceuticals*

Delta Business Equipment, Unit G3 Meadow Mill, Water Street, Stockport, Cheshire, SK1 2BY Tel: 0161-480 1222 Fax: 0161-480 0022 E-mail: sales@deltaoffice.co.uk *Business equipment suppliers*

Delta Communications, 6 Knockbreda Park, Belfast, BT6 0HB Tel: (028) 9049 1212 Fax: (028) 9049 1833 *Access control system suppliers*

Delta Components, The Courtyard, Sevenacres, Smallfield Road, Horne, Horley, Surrey, RH6 9JP Tel: (01342) 844555 Fax: (01342) 844552 E-mail: sales@deltacomponents.com *Transformers (including toroidal) & inductors agents*

Delta Comtech Ltd, Artillery House, Gunco Lane, Macclesfield, Cheshire, SK11 7JL Tel: (01625) 430055 Fax: (0870) 2200568 E-mail: sales@delta-comtech.co.uk *Computer management services*

Delta Design, 1 Kings Park Industrial Estate, Primrose Hill, Kings Langley, Hertfordshire, WD4 8ST Tel: (01923) 269522 Fax: (01923) 260167 E-mail: sales@deltadesign.co.uk *Vehicle hazard lights manufrs*

Delta Designs Systems Ltd, The Green, Tendring, Clacton-on-Sea, Essex, CO16 0BU Tel: (01255) 830355 Fax: (01255) 830356 E-mail: info@deltadesignsystems.co.uk Principal Export Areas: Worldwide *Diesel generators & control panels service & providers*

▶ Delta Distributors, Unit 10 Win Business Park, Canal Quay, Newry, County Down, BT35 6PH Tel: (028) 3026 7555 Fax: (028) 3026 8814 E-mail: sales@deltadistributors.co.uk *Suppliers specialising in in-car entertainment systems*

▶ Delta Electrical Ltd, Queen Anne Battery, Plymouth, PL4 0LP Tel: (01752) 225225 Fax: (01752) 256357

Delta Environmental Ltd, Delta House Stanney Mill Industrial Park, Dutton Green, Little Stanney, Chester, CH2 4SA Tel: 0151-357 1121 Fax: 0151-357 2480 E-mail: sales@deltaenvironmental.net *Industrial & commercial air conditioning services*

Delta Equipment Ltd, Laurel Street, Bradford, West Yorkshire, BD3 9TP Tel: (01274) 778855 Fax: (01274) 666028 E-mail: sales@deltaforktrucks.co.uk *Forklift trucks hire, sales & repairers*

Delta Equipment Ltd, Laurel Street, Bradford, West Yorkshire, BD3 9TP Tel: (01274) 778855 Fax: (01274) 666028 E-mail: sales-hire-del@btconnect.com *Fork trucks services*

Delta Fire Ltd, 8 Mission Road, Rackheath Industrial Estate, Rackheath, Norwich, NR13 6PL Tel: (01603) 735000 Fax: (01603) 735009 E-mail: sales@deltafire.co.uk *Fire fighting equipment distributors*

Company Information

Delta Fire Systems Ltd, Jews Lane, Dudley, West Midlands, DY3 2AV Tel: (01902) 664181 Fax: (01902) 665538 *Fire extinguisher services & sign manufrs*

Delta Flags Ltd, 37 Weathercock Lane, Woburn Sands, Milton Keynes, MK17 8NP Tel: (01908) 582883 Fax: (01908) 582552 E-mail: info@deltaflags.co.uk *Flag manufacturers & printers, flagstaff/pole contractors/producers/suppliers, bunting manufactuers & banner manufacturers or printers*

Delta Fluid Products Ltd, Delta Road, St. Helens, Merseyside, WA9 2ED Tel: (01744) 611811 Fax: (01744) 611818 E-mail: enquiries@deltafluidproducts.com *Sight glass manufrs*

Delta G B N Ltd, 115 Lodgefield Road, Halesowen, West Midlands, B62 8AX Tel: 0121-602 1221 Fax: 0121-602 3222 E-mail: rogerw@deltagbn.co.uk *Anti-corrosion surface treatment services*

▶ Delta Galil, 6 Gambrel Road, Westgate Industrial Estate, Northampton, NN5 5BB Tel: (01604) 594600 Fax: (01604) 594610

Delta GBM, Unit 4 P D H Industrial Estate, Western Way, Moxley, Wednesbury, West Midlands, WS10 7DQ Tel: 0121-556 6262 Fax: 0121-556 6264 *Corrosion prevention & protective coating services*

▶ Delta Green (Tianjin) Industries Co., Ltd, 1 Redwood Court, Peel Park, East Kilbride, Glasgow, G74 5PF Tel: (01355) 588888 Fax: (01355) 588889

Delta Hygiene Supplies, P O Box 126, Rotherham, South Yorkshire, S66 2TP Tel: (01709) 533040 Fax: (01709) 540425 *Chemical cleaning blockages*

Delta Joiners Ltd, Brewsters Corner, Pendicke Street, Southam, Warwickshire, CV47 1PN Tel: (01926) 815253 Fax: (01926) 811040 E-mail: mail@deltajoiners.co.uk *High quality architectural joinery manufacturers. Delivery and installation throughout the UK.*

▶ Delta Labelling, Unit A Apollo Park Apollo, Litchfield Road Industrial, Lichfield Road Industrial Estate, Tamworth, Staffordshire, B79 7TA Tel: (01827) 302862 Fax: (01827) 300891 E-mail: enquiries@delta-labelling.co.uk *Label & badge manufrs*

Delta Light, Gresham House 2a Unicorn Trading Estate, Weydown Lane, Haslemere, Surrey, GU27 1DN Tel: (01428) 651919 Fax: (01428) 644506 E-mail: sales@deltalight.co.uk *Lighting manufrs*

Delta Manufacturing Co., 28f Park View West Industrial Estate, Hartlepool, Cleveland, TS25 1PE Tel: (01429) 276895 Fax: (01429) 865766 E-mail: info@brushmaster.com *DIY products manufrs*

▶ Delta Membrane Systems Ltd, Hurricane Way, North Weald Airfield, North Weald, Epping, Essex, CM16 6AA Tel: (01992) 523811 Fax: (01992) 524046 E-mail: info@deltamembranes.com *Basement, cellar, sumps, pumps & drainage system manufrs*

▶ Delta Motorsport, Litchlake Barns, Buckingham Road, Silverstone, Towcester, Northamptonshire, NN12 8TJ Tel: (01327) 858200 Fax: (01327) 858134 E-mail: enquiries@delta-motorsport.com *Engineering designers, manufacturers & suppliers*

▶ Delta Neu Ltd, Newby Road Industrial Estate, Newby Road, Hazel Grove, Stockport, Cheshire, SK7 5DR Tel: 0161-456 5511 Fax: 0161-456 2460 *Design industrial ventilation, dust control, process waste*

Delta Pattern & Tool Co. Ltd, Unit 32, Llantarnum Industrial Estate Park, Cwmbran, Gwent, NP44 3AX Tel: (01633) 838108 Fax: (01633) 838108 E-mail: carl@deltapattern.fsnet.co.uk *Machining engineers & pattern manufrs*

▶ Delta PC, 2 Camelot Court, Bancombe Road, Somerton, Somerset, TA11 6SB Tel: (01458) 270060 Fax: (01458) 270080 E-mail: sales@deltapc.co.uk *Microsoft small business server installation & support services*

Delta Pc Services Ltd, Bridge House, Bridge Street, Walton-On-Thames, Surrey, KT12 1AL Tel: (01932) 252514 Fax: (01932) 252818 *PC services*

▶ Delta Pipelines, Redwither Road, Wrexham Industrial Estate, Wrexham, Clwyd, LL13 9RD Tel: (01978) 661221

Delta Pipework Services Ltd, 17 Hazel Road, Southampton, SO19 7GA Tel: (023) 8068 5411 Fax: (023) 8042 2435 *Industrial pipefitting & welders*

▶ Delta Plumbing & Heating Supplies, Duchy Road, Heathpark Industrial Estate, Honiton, Devon, EX14 1YD Tel: (01404) 47040 Fax: (01404) 42237

Delta Point Computers Ltd, Oakley House, Pinfold Lane, Ashampstead, Reading, RG8 8SH Tel: (01635) 579059 Fax: (020) 7691 9601 *Communication software- resale and installation*

Delta Power Services, Newby Road Industrial Estate, Newby Road, Hazel Grove, Stockport, Cheshire, SK7 5DR Tel: 0161-456 6588 Fax: 0161-456 6686 E-mail: cdyas@deltarib.u-net.com *Inflatable & rigid boat manufrs*

Delta Precision Engineering Ltd, 87-89 Sterte Avenue West, Poole, Dorset, BH15 2AW Tel: (01202) 661166 Fax: (01202) 661166 E-mail: sales@deltaprecision.freeserve.co.uk *Precision engineers & specialists in milling & turning*

▶ Delta Precision Engineering, Site 3 Unit 1, Cold Hesledon Industrial Estate, Cold Hesledon, Seaham, County Durham, SR7 8ST Tel: 0191-513 1026 Fax: 0191-513 1027 E-mail: sales@deltaprecision-eng.co.uk *Engineering*

Delta Press Ltd, Cameron House, North Bridge Road, Berkhamsted, Hertfordshire, HP4 1EH Tel: (01442) 877794 Fax: (01442) 877828 E-mail: deltap98@aol.com *Technical books publishers*

Delta Print, 19 Potters Lane, Kiln Farm, Milton Keynes, MK11 3HF Tel: (01908) 568020 Fax: (01908) 261383 E-mail: sales@deltaprint.fsworld.co.uk *Commercial printers*

Delta Print & Packaging Ltd, Factory No. 10, Kennedy Way Industrial Estate, Belfast, BT11 9DT Tel: (028) 9062 8626 Fax: (028) 9030 1505 E-mail: info@deltapack.com *Carton manufrs*

Delta Refrigeration Services, 10 The Moor, Melbourn, Royston, Hertfordshire, SG8 6ED Tel: (01763) 263060 Fax: (01763) 263207 E-mail: info@deltarefrig.com *Main distributor of Costan cabinets in the UK (Formerly Costan UK) buy Costan cases from the people who really know the product. *Technical data and spare parts for Costan equipment all available.*

Delta Resin Products Ltd, 77 Torkington Road, Hazel Grove, Stockport, Cheshire, SK7 6NR Tel: 0161-483 4513 Fax: 0161-426 0329 E-mail: info@deltaresins.co.uk *Resin formulators & manufrs*

Delta Scales, Kalena Cottage, Higher Tremar, Liskeard, Cornwall, PL14 5HP Tel: (01579) 344832 Fax: (01579) 344832 *Weighing machines manufrs*

Delta Scientific Corporation UK Ltd, Delta House, 70 South View Avenue, Caversham, Reading, RG4 5BB Tel: 0118-948 1133 Fax: 0118-948 1122 E-mail: deltascuk@aol.com *High security crash rated vehicle control systems*

Delta Software Ltd, Whitwood Lodge, Whitwood Lane, Whitwood, Wakefield, West Yorkshire, WF10 5QD Tel: (01204) 529171 Fax: (01977) 668378 E-mail: info@deltasoftware.co.uk *Computer software manufrs*

Delta Styling.co.uk, Unit 12, Carlton Industrial Estate, Albion Road, Carlton, Barnsley, South Yorkshire, S71 3HW Tel: (01226) 722761 *Fibre glass manufrs*

Delta Systems Electrical, 65 Boleness Road, Wisbech, Cambridgeshire, PE13 2RB Tel: (01945) 466866 Fax: (01945) 466108 E-mail: sales@deltasystems-uk.co.uk *Stainless steel fabricators*

Delta T Trace Heating Ltd, 7 Alston Works, Alston Road, Barnet, Hertfordshire, EN5 4EL Tel: (020) 8441 9499 Fax: (020) 8441 4459 E-mail: enquiries@deltat.co.uk *Electric trace heating systems manufrs*

Delta Textiles London Ltd, 4-10 North Road, London, N7 9EY Tel: (020) 7316 7200 Fax: (020) 7316 7276 *Textile manufrs*

Delta Watch Co., 12-13 Greville Street, London, EC1N 8SB Tel: (020) 7405 0784 Fax: (020) 7404 8200 *Jewellary importers*

Deltaband Ltd, 2280 Coventry Road, Sheldon, Birmingham, B26 3JR Tel: 0121-742 9922 Fax: 0121-742 9933 E-mail: enquiries@deltaband.co.uk *Sign makers*

Deltace Systems Ltd, Pierremont Hall, Pierremont Avenue, Broadstairs, Kent, CT10 1JX Tel: (01843) 861888 Fax: (01843) 865006 *Computer systems*

Deltaflash Angling Equipment, 40 Broom Road, Ferryhill, County Durham, DL17 8AF Tel: (01740) 652360 Fax: (01740) 652360 *Fishing tackle suppliers*

Deltagroom Beauty Products, 13 Dodnor Park, Newport, Isle of Wight, PO30 5XE Tel: (01983) 522004 Fax: (01983) 522004 *Hairdressers sundries*

Deltamove Ltd, Clare Terrace, Carterton, Oxfordshire, OX18 3ES Tel: (01993) 845020 Fax: (01993) 843023 E-mail: andy@deltamove.co.uk *Removals & container storage*

Deltaprint Printers, 5 Warner Industrial Park, Warner Way, Sudbury, Suffolk, CO10 2GG Tel: (01787) 370714 Fax: (01787) 881065 E-mail: info@delta-print.co.uk *General & commercial printers*

Deltawaite Ltd, Old Dairy, Roose Road, Barrow-in-Furness, Cumbria, LA13 0EP Tel: (01229) 821959 Fax: (01229) 820377 E-mail: sales@deltawaite.co.uk *Protective clothing distributors*

▶ Deltec Maintenance Ltd, Unit R Taywood Enterprise Centre, Duchess Place, Rutherglen, Glasgow, G73 1DR Tel: 0141-647 6676 Fax: 0141-647 6643

Deltex Medical Ltd, Terminus Road, Chichester, West Sussex, PO19 8TX Tel: (01243) 774837 Fax: (01243) 532534 E-mail: info@deltexmedical.com *Medical equipment manufrs*

Delton Central Services Ltd, 62-70 Camden Street, Birmingham, B1 3DP Tel: 0121-233 1051 Fax: 0121-236 6178 E-mail: sales@deltongroup.co.uk *Control panel & coil winder manufrs*

Deltor Communications Ltd, Unit C Long Acre, Saltash, Cornwall, PL12 6LZ Tel: (01752) 841717 Fax: (01752) 850450 E-mail: enquiries@deltor.uk *Printer equipment suppliers*

Deltra Electronics Ltd, Deltra House, Heather Park Drive, Wembley, Middlesex, HA0 1SS Tel: (020) 8795 3000 Fax: (020) 8795 0700 E-mail: tony@deltra.co.uk *Merchants components*

Deltronics Electronic Engineers, Unit 15 Church Road Industrial Estate, Gorslas, Llanelli, Dyfed, SA14 7NN Tel: (01269) 843728 Fax: (01269) 845527 E-mail: sales@deltronics.co.uk *Educational electronic equipment suppliers*

▶ Delux Packaging, 16 Broomknowe Drive, Kincardine, Alloa, Clackmannanshire, FK10 4QL Tel: (01259) 730576 Fax: (01259) 731412

Delver Construction, Queens Road, Barnet, Hertfordshire, EN5 4HE Tel: (020) 8440 1993 *Contract excavation & plant hire*

Delyn Packaging Ltd, Delyn House, Acacia Avenue, Hengoed, Mid Glamorgan, CF82 7JR Tel: (01443) 815512 Fax: (01443) 815512 E-mail: mike.knight@delynpackaging.co.uk *Packaging manufrs*

DEM Industrial Weighing Systems, 3 Hill Rise, Measham, Swadlincote, Derbyshire, DE12 7NZ Tel: (01530) 272704 Fax: (01530) 272704 E-mail: sales@demmachines.co.uk

Demack Company Chartered Accountants, 120 Towngate, Leyland, PR25 2LQ Tel: (01772) 491769 Fax: (01772) 622935 E-mail: info@demacks.com *Chartered accountants*

Demag Cranes & Components Ltd, Beaumont Rd, Banbury, Oxfordshire, OX16 1QZ Tel: (01295) 676100 Fax: (01295) 226106 E-mail: help@demagcranes.com *Based in Banbury, Oxfordshire, Demag Cranes & Components Ltd are the UK Subsidiary of Demag Cranes AG, Germany. We're an international supplier of industrial cranes & crane components for material flow, logistics & industrial drive applications. Providing specialist handling solutions to all types of industries such as aerospace, automotive, steel & waste, our products include: electric overhead travelling cranes, automated handling systems, electric hoists, modular light track systems, slewing jib cranes, pendant & infra-red control handsets, drives & gearboxes. 24/7 spare-parts availability & service packages ensure the economical use of Demag products & lasting customer satisfaction. In addition we provide a material handling consultancy & design service. Complete control of our own products & understanding the customer's processes, speaking the customer's language & finding the best solutions together, are the commitment resulting from a company history dating more than 180 yrs.*

Demand It, Units 19-21, Deacon Way, Tilehurst, Reading, RG30 6QG Tel: 0118-945 8600 Fax: 0118-945 3737 E-mail: sales@demand-it.co.uk *Computer rentals, solutions & sales*

Demand Solutions (Europe) Ltd, Mid-Day Court, 30 Brighton Road, Sutton, Surrey, SM2 5BN Tel: (020) 8770 9320 Fax: (020) 8770 9303 E-mail: info@demandmanagement.com *Software reseller*

▶ Demar Ltd, Era House, Weir Lane, Worcester, WR2 4AY Tel: (01905) 422688 Fax: (01905) 422610 E-mail: sales@demarvan.co.uk *Manufacture & supply light commercial vehicles & security products*

Demarchi Engineering, Vincients Road, Bumpers Farm, Chippenham, Wiltshire, SN14 6NQ Tel: (01249) 448860 Fax: (01249) 445496 E-mail: sales@demarchi.co.uk *Fabricating engineers*

Dematic Ltd, Beaumont Rd, Banbury, Oxon, OX16 1QZ Tel: (01295) 274600 Fax: (01295) 274808 E-mail: sd.uk.ma-marketing@siemens.com *Supplier of integrated logistics software and solutions incorporating storage/retrieval, conveying, sortation, order picking and robotic handling. Industry experience covers retail, manufacturing, postal, parcels, airport and automotive.*

Dematic Ltd, Sir William Siemens House, Princess Road, Manchester, M20 2UR Tel: 0161-446 5292 Fax: 0161-446 5214 E-mail: sfmpost@plcman.siemens.co.uk *Automation drives*

Demco, Grange House, 2 Geddings Road, Hoddesdon, Hertfordshire, EN11 0NT Tel: (01992) 454500 Fax: (01992) 448989 E-mail: direct@gresswell.co.uk *Library equipment & furniture*

▶ Demenex Plant Hire Ltd, Wick Lane, London, E3 2TB Tel: (020) 8981 7711 Fax: (020) 8983 1080

Louis Demery & Sons Ltd, 67a Newcastle Avenue, Worksop, Nottinghamshire, S80 1LX Tel: (01909) 500358 Fax: (01909) 500637 E-mail: ldsltd@btconnect.com *Machine tool merchants*

Demeter Windings, Beehive Lane, Chelmsford, CM2 9TE Tel: (01245) 344544 Fax: (01245) 265344 E-mail: demeterw@lycos.co.uk *Transformer manufrs*

C.P. Demetriades & Son, 7 Beech Close, Ollerton, Knutsford, Cheshire, WA16 8TD Tel: (01565) 652488 Fax: (01565) 652588 *Exporters & export agents*

Demo Fences, 4 Garden Close, London, SW15 3TH Tel: (020) 8785 1078 *Fencing contractors*

Demolition By Trojan, 116 Knutsford Road, Grappenhall, Warrington, WA4 2PW Tel: (01925) 860039 Fax: 01925 860084 *Leather belt manufrs*

Demolition & Salvage Ltd, Ackworth Road, Portsmouth, PO3 5NS Tel: (023) 9267 7890 Fax: (023) 9267 0644 E-mail: sales@demolitionandsalvage.co.uk *Demolition contractors*

Demon International Ltd, Abbots Close, Lee Mill Industrial Estate, Ivybridge, Devon, PL21 9GA Tel: (01752) 690690 Fax: (01752) 690919 E-mail: sales@demon-pressure-washers.com *Manufacture of Industrial Pressure Washers.*

Demon Internet Ltd, Gateway House, 322 Regents Park Road, Finchley, London, N3 2QQ Tel: (020) 8371 1000 Fax: (020) 8371 1150 E-mail: sales@demon.net *Internet service & solution provider*

▶ Demontford Color Tech, 18 Slater Street, Leicester, LE3 5AY Tel: 0116-262 5151

▶ Demopad Software Ltd, Midwest House, Canal Road, Timperley, Cheshire, WA14 1TF Tel: 08700 551100 Fax: 08707 062171 E-mail: sales@sentrypad.com *DemoPad Software Ltd for Business Automation and Innovative CCTV and Security Solutions.*

Demountable Partitions Ltd, 4 Twin Bridges Business Park, 232 Selsdon Road, South Croydon, Surrey, CR2 6PL Tel: (020) 8410 3800 Fax: (020) 8239 0083 E-mail: sales@demountables.co.uk *Office interior refurbishment services*

B.P. Dempsey Ltd, Units 6 & 8, March Street, Sheffield, S9 5DQ Tel: 0114-242 1900 Fax: 0114-243 2232 *Heating plumbing & electrical services*

Dempson Packaging, Hermitage Mills, Hermitage Lane, Maidstone, Kent, ME16 9NP Tel: (01622) 727027 Fax: (01622) 720768 E-mail: sales@dempson.co.uk Sales Contact: J. Katzauer Principal Export Areas: Africa *Manufacturers of paper bags and carriers,*

continued

polythene carriers and serviettes made primarily for the catering industry.

▶ Den Caney, 182 Stonehouse Lane, Quinton, Birmingham, B32 3AH Tel: 0121-427 2693 Fax: 0121-427 8905 E-mail: dencaneycoaches@blueyonder.co.uk *Providing coach travel and tours in the west midlands for 50 years call now for a competitve quotation NOW*

Den Mark Tools, 4 Queensway Link Industrial Estate, Stafford Park, Telford, Shropshire, TF3 3DN Tel: (01952) 200633 Fax: (01952) 200133 E-mail: mrowlands@den-mark.freeserve.co.uk *Injection & plastic mould toolmakers*

Denall Engineering Co. Ltd, 55 Bridgewater Street, Little Hulton, Manchester, M38 9ND Tel: 0161-799 2600 Fax: 0161-703 8342 *General fabricators*

Denbar Fabrications, Archers Yard, Springwell Lane, Northallerton, North Yorkshire, DL7 8QJ Tel: (01609) 770658 Fax: (01609) 770658 *Stainless steel fabricators*

Denber Trading Co., Unit H3 Rudford Industrial Estate, Ford Road, Ford, Arundel, West Sussex, BN18 0BD Tel: (01903) 723155 Fax: (01903) 733160 E-mail: denberint.rubber@virgin.net *Industrial rubber product manufrs*

Denbridge Marine Ltd, Cammell Lairds Waterfront Park, Campbell Town Road, Birkenhead, Merseyside, CH41 9HP Tel: 0151-649 4080 Fax: (0870) 0518953 E-mail: info@denbridgemarine.com *Vessel traffic systems*

Denby Ltd, Denby, Ripley, Derbyshire, DE5 8NX Tel: (01773) 740700 Fax: (01773) 570211 *Tableware manufrs*

Denby Dale Cast Products Ltd, 230 Cumberworth Lane, Lower Cumberworth, Huddersfield, HD8 8PR Tel: (01484) 863560 Fax: (01484) 865597 *Cast concrete products manufrs*

Denby Dale Shirt Co. Ltd, The Old School House, Spark Lane, Mapplewell, Barnsley, South Yorkshire, S75 6AB Tel: (01226) 390211 Fax: (01226) 388192 E-mail: charles@denbydaleshirt.co.uk *Shirt & blouse manufrs*

▶ Denby Display Ltd, Unit 9, Stewart Close, Penarth Road, Cardiff, CF11 8QF Tel: (029) 2022 3446 E-mail: t.tribe@sky-hook.com *Hire of exhibition & event display-equipment & furniture*

Denby Industrial Supplies Ltd, Chandos Pole Street, Derby, DE22 3BA Tel: (01332) 332831 Fax: (01332) 371206 *Industrial suppliers*

▶ Denby Training, Sadler Road, Lincoln, LN6 3JR Tel: 01522 503902 Fax: 01522 686372 E-mail: terry.rose@denbytransport.co.uk *Training provider offering forklift truck, LGV driver, and health and safety training. Also can access funding for businesses for apprenticeships and NVQs.*

Denby Transport Ltd, 73 Sadler Road, Lincoln, LN6 3JR Tel: (01522) 503900 Fax: (01522) 686372 E-mail: sales@denbytransport.co.uk *Road transport, haulage & freight services*

Alan Dench Photography, Carringtons, Pond Hall Road, Ipswich, IP7 5PQ Tel: (01473) 828343 Fax: (01473) 828864 *Commercial photographers*

Denco, Unit 19 Langlands Avenue, Kelvin South Business Park, East Kilbride, Glasgow, G75 0YG Tel: (01355) 271020 Fax: (01355) 271039 *Air conditioning (AC) system maintenance*

Denco Air Ltd, Unit 1, Clifton Lane, Sutton Weaver, Runcorn, Cheshire, WA7 3EZ Tel: (01928) 713240 Fax: (01928) 719762 *Air conditioning & maintenance*

Denco Air Conditioning, Dolphin House, Morton On Legg, Hereford, HR4 8DS Tel: (01432) 277277 Fax: (01432) 268005 Principal Export Areas: Worldwide *Cooling water systems manufrs*

▶ Denco Lubrication Ltd, Ramsden Court, Ramsden Road, Rotherwas Industrial Estate, Hereford, HR2 6LR Tel: (01432) 365000 Fax: (01432) 365001 E-mail: info@delimon.co.uk *Cooling systems, chillers suppliers*

Dencora Property Developers, Dencora Court, Meridian Way, Norwich, NR7 0TA Tel: (01603) 433100 Fax: (01603) 433800 E-mail: admin@dencora.com *Property developers & investors*

▶ Dencowear Ltd, 48 Barkston House, Croydon Street, Leeds, LS11 9RT Tel: 0113-244 4267 Fax: 0113-243 4534 E-mail: info@dencowear.co.uk *Work wear manufrs*

▶ Dendale Ltd, New Street, Holbrook, Sheffield, S20 3GH Tel: 0114-248 0055 Fax: 0114-248 0460

Dendrite Europe Ltd, 2 Windsor Dials, Arthur Road, Windsor, Berkshire, SL4 1RS Tel: (01753) 834200 Fax: (01753) 834399 E-mail: denuk@dendrite.co.uk *Pharmaceutical computers*

▶ Dendrite Fabrications, 18 Gordon Close, Leek, Staffordshire, ST13 8NZ Tel: (07785) 325342 Fax: (01538) 384789 E-mail: jasonbanks@worldonline.co.uk *Fabrication, welding & engineers*

Dene Spring UK Ltd, Bridge Works, Allum Lane, Borehamwood, Hertfordshire, WD6 3LT Tel: (020) 8953 6888 Fax: (020) 8207 5872 E-mail: deor@denespringuk.co.uk *Spring manufacturers & distribs*

Denebank Engineering UK Ltd, 108 Windmill Road, Sunbury-on-Thames, Middlesex, TW16 7HB Tel: (01932) 788180 Fax: (01932) 788150 E-mail: paulgoldthorpe@denebank.co.uk *Tool manufrs*

Denford Ltd, Birds Royd, Brighouse, Brighouse, West Yorkshire, HD6 1NB Tel: (01484) 712264 Fax: (01484) 722160 E-mail: sales@denford.co.uk *Machine tool manufrs*

▶ DENHAM BROTHERS LTD, 122 ANNS HILL RD, GOSPORT, HANTS, PO12 3JZ Tel: 07754 210523

Denham Wine Ltd, 1-3 Law Lane, Halifax, West Yorkshire, HX3 9QU Tel: (01422) 356146 Fax: (01422) 380224 *Wine wholesalers*

Denhaolm Oilfield Services, Greenbank Place, East Tullos Industrial Estate, Aberdeen, AB12 3BT Tel: (01224) 249424 Fax: (01224) 249496 *Pump manufrs*

Denholm Barwil, Avonmouth Dock, Bristol, BS11 9DN Tel: 0117-982 5836 Fax: 0117-982 6272 E-mail: agency.brf@denholm-barwil.com *Shipping services*

Denholm Fish Selling Co., 119 Shore Street, Fraserburgh, Aberdeenshire, AB43 9BR Tel: (01346) 513211 Fax: (01346) 517649 E-mail: fraserburgh.fishselling@denholm-fishsell.co.uk *Fish selling agents*

Denholm Forwarding Ltd, 1 First Way, Avonmouth, Bristol, BS11 9EF Tel: 0117-982 5313 Fax: 0117-982 5885 *Freight forwarders*

Denholm Glove Co., Eastgate, Denholm, Hawick, Roxburghshire, TD9 8NQ Tel: (01450) 870597 Fax: (01450) 870597 *Glove manufrs*

▶ Denholm Industrial Services, King George V Dock, Renfrew Road, Glasgow, G51 4SP Tel: 0141-445 3939 Fax: 0141-445 3020 *Scaffolding specialists*

▶ Denholm Industrial Services Ltd, Hoe Gate Farm, Hoe Street, Hambledon, Waterlooville, Hampshire, PO7 4RD Tel: (023) 9263 2828 E-mail: paulfoskett@denholmindustrial.co.uk

Denholm Industrial Services Ltd, Boundary Way, Lufton Trading Estate, Yeovil, Somerset, BA22 8HZ Tel: (01935) 420081 Fax: (01935) 427383 *Scaffolding contractors*

Denholm Rees & O'Donnell Ltd, 116 Albany Road, Walton, Liverpool, L9 0HB Tel: 0151-525 1663 Fax: 0151-525 1618 E-mail: sales@denholms.co.uk *Turning services, CNC & engineers*

Denholm Shipping Company Ltd, Liner House, Test Road, Eastern Docks, Southampton, SO14 3GE Tel: (023) 8071 3100 Fax: (023) 8071 3129 E-mail: finadmin@denshipsouth.co.uk *Shipping agents importers & exporters* Also at: Aberdeen, Avonmouth, Felixstowe, Glasgow, Grangemouth, Greenock, London, Poole & Rochester

Denholme Velvets Ltd, Halifax Rd, Denholme, Bradford, West Yorkshire, BD13 4EZ Tel: (01274) 832185 Fax: (01274) 832646 E-mail: sales@denholme-velvets.co.uk Sales Contact: T. Roberts Principal Export Areas: Worldwide *Denholme Velvets specialises in the manufacture and supply of velvet cloth for the fashion industry, Textile dress fabric, soft furnishing fabric, textile fashion fabric & velvet manufacturers. Additionally velvet is converted into ribbon for use in 35mm film cassettes in the photographic Industry.*

Deniet & Son Ltd, Finchley Avenue, Mildenhall, Bury St. Edmunds, Suffolk, IP28 7BG Tel: (01638) 713442 Fax: (01638) 712783 E-mail: bob@deniet.flexnet.co.uk *Shop fittings manufrs*

Denimex, Northdown Business Park, Ashford Road, Lenham, Maidstone, Kent, ME17 2DL Tel: (01622) 850057 Fax: (01622) 850097 E-mail: sales@denimex.co.uk *Wholesaler animal health products*

Denios Ltd, Unit 1 - 3, Audley Avenue Enterprise Park, Newport, Shropshire, TF10 7DW Tel: (01952) 811991 Fax: (01952) 825687 E-mail: sales@denios.co.uk *Environmental Protection, chemical and oil storage and containment*

▶ Denis Brinicombe Ltd, Fordton Trading Estate, Crediton, Devon, EX17 3BZ Tel: (01363) 775115 Fax: (01363) 776761 E-mail: sales@brinicombe.co.uk *Agricultural merchants*

▶ Denis Brinicombe Ltd, Fordton Trading Estate, Crediton, Devon, EX17 3BZ Tel: (01363) 775115 Fax: (01363) 776761 E-mail: info@brinicombe-equine.co.uk *Animal health service*

Denis Grimshaw Machinery Ltd, PO Box 64, Droitwich, Worcestershire, WR9 0JR Tel: (01905) 621789 Fax: (01905) 621384 E-mail: sales@grimshaw.co.uk *Machine tool merchants*

Denis R Robinson & Associates, 169 Sherwood Avenue, Northampton, NN2 8TB Tel: (01604) 843807 Fax: (01604) 843807 E-mail: denis-rr@skynet.co.uk *Acoustic & noise control consultants & designers*

Denis Welch Motors Ltd, Sudbury Road, Yoxall, Burton-on-Trent, Staffordshire, DE13 8NA Tel: (01543) 472214 Fax: (01543) 472339 E-mail: sales@bighealey.co.uk *Classic car restoration services*

Denley Engineering, Bayton Road, Exhall, Coventry, CV7 9EJ Tel: (024) 7636 1943 Fax: (024) 7664 4315 *Engineering subcontract services*

Denley Hydraulics Ltd, Spen Vale Street, Heckmondwike, West Yorkshire, WF16 0NQ Tel: (01924) 413400 Fax: (01924) 410109 E-mail: sales@denleyhydraulics.co.uk Principal Export Areas: Asia Pacific, Central Asia, Middle East, Africa, Central/East Europe & West Europe *Designers & manufacturers of complete hydraulic & electrical control systems, power units,cylinders,manifold assemblies,test rigs,special valves,special purpose machines,servo systems,installation,servicing.*

Denleys Agricultural & Motor Engineers, Awliscombe, Honiton, Devon, EX14 3PU Tel: (01404) 841237 Fax: (01404) 841311 E-mail: info@agricultural-parts.co.uk *Agricultural engineers & supply of parts*

▶ Denline plc, Crown House, Home Gardens, Dartford, DA1 1DZ Tel: (01322) 424543 Fax: (01322) 424567

Denman Group Ltd, Wolvers Home Farm, Ironsbottom, Sidlow, Reigate, Surrey, RH2 8QG Tel: (01293) 863100 Fax: (01293) 863808 E-mail: info@denmanrest.co.uk *Provide facilities management & building maintenance solutions*

Denman International Ltd, Clandeboye Road, Bangor, County Down, BT20 3JH Tel: (028) 9146 2141 Fax: (028) 9145 1654 *Denman hairbrushes & contract custom plastics manufrs*

Denmans Electrical Wholesalers Ltd, Unit 10 Pages Industrial Park, Eden Way, Leighton Buzzard, Bedfordshire, LU7 4TZ Tel: (01525) 374666 Fax: (01525) 852662 E-mail: denmans@theleightonbuzzard.freeserve.co.uk *Electrical wholesalers*

Denmans Electrical Wholesalers Ltd, Hickman Avenue, Wolverhampton, WV1 2XD Tel: (01902) 453551 Fax: (01902) 456666 E-mail: wolverhampton@denmans.co.uk *Electrical wholesalers*

Denmans Of Whitchurch, Highgate, Whitchurch, Shropshire, SY13 1SD Tel: (01948) 666611 Fax: (01948) 667723 E-mail: denmanmovers@aol.com *Removal contractors & light haulage*

Denmark Signs, 150 London Road, Bedford, MK42 0PS Tel: (01234) 269025 Fax: (01234) 269025 E-mail: sales@denmarksigns.co.uk *Sign manufr*

Denmay Steel & Hire Co., 137 Wellington Road, Portslade, Brighton, BN41 1DN Tel: (01273) 430399 Fax: (01273) 430799 *Steel stockholders & steel fabricators*

Denmead Aquatic Nursery, Soake Road, Waterlooville, Hampshire, PO7 6HY Tel: (023) 9225 2671 Fax: (023) 9225 2671 *Aquatic plant growers & suppliers, ponds*

Denmic Engineering Ltd, 7 Linburn Close, Royston, Barnsley, South Yorkshire, S71 4NB Tel: (01226) 701887 Fax: (01226) 701096 *Engineering & steel fabrication*

▶ Denn UK Ltd, 22 Hither Mead, Bishops Lydeard, Taunton, Somerset, TA4 3NT Tel: (01823) 432893 Fax: (01823) 430037 E-mail: dennuk@btopenworld.com *CNC machinery to deform plate & tube by rotation*

Dennard Ltd, 55 Fleet Road, Fleet, Hampshire, GU51 3PN Tel: (01252) 614884 Fax: (01252) 626013 E-mail: sales@dennard-cctv.com *Television closed circuit equipment*

▶ Denne Building Services Ltd, Bramling House, Bramling, Canterbury, Kent, CT3 1NB Tel: (01227) 723000 Fax: (01227) 723001

▶ Denne Group, Denne Court, Hengist Field, Borden, Sittingbourne, Kent, ME9 8FH Tel: (0870) 6001803 Fax: (01795) 434800 E-mail: info@denne.co.uk

Denne Group, Denne Court, Hengist Field, Borden, Sittingbourne, Kent, ME9 8FH Tel: (0870) 6001803 Fax: (01795) 434800

Denner Kelford Grinding Ltd, D3 Seedbed Centre, Avenue Road, Nechells, Birmingham, B7 4NT Tel: 0121-359 7728 Fax: 0121-359 0255 *Precision engineers*

Dennett & Parker Ltd, Sydney Nursery, Dover Rd, Sandwich, Kent, CT13 0DA Tel: 01304 613240 *Horse boxes & transportation*

Denney Diving, Esplanade Garage, 50-55 Esplanade, Redcar, Cleveland, TS10 3AG Tel: (01642) 486666 Fax: (01642) 483507 *Diving retail & motor vehicle services*

Alexander Dennis Ltd, 91 Glasgow Road, Camelon, Falkirk, FK1 4JB Tel: (01324) 621672 Fax: (01324) 632469 E-mail: enquiries@alexander-dennis.com *Bus manufrs* Also at: Newtonabbey

▶ Dennis Cox Electrical Contractors, 5 Portland Business Centre, Manor House Lane, Datchet, Slough, SL3 9EG Tel: (01753) 580400 Fax: (01753) 549820

Dennis Eagle Ltd, Heathcote Way, Heathcote Industrial Estate, Warwick, CV34 6TE Tel: (01926) 316000 Fax: (01926) 316550 *Refuse collecting vehicles*

Fred Dennis Ltd, Eastern Avenue, Lichfield, Staffordshire, WS13 6UY Tel: (01543) 419700 Fax: (01543) 419755 E-mail: sales@freddennis.co.uk *Door bolt manufrs*

▶ Dennis Gordon Electrical, 68 High Street, Fraserburgh, Aberdeenshire, AB43 9HP Tel: (01346) 518561 Fax: (01346) 519229

▶ John Dennis & Co. Ltd, 68 Lothian Street, Bonnyrigg, Midlothian, EH19 3AQ Tel: 0131-663 3275

Dennis Johns Electrical Ltd, 94a Rendlesham Road, London, E5 8PA Tel: (020) 8985 7668 Fax: (020) 8533 7356 E-mail: dennisjohns.elek@btconnect.com *Electrical contractors*

▶ Dennis King, Unit 7 Middlethorpe Grange, Sim Balk Lane, Bishopthorpe, York, YO23 2UE Tel: (01904) 700334 Fax: (01904) 700390

Dennis Motor Mowers, Howardson Works, Ashbourne Road, Kirk Langley, Ashbourne, Derbyshire, DE6 4NJ Tel: (01332) 824777 Fax: (01332) 824525 E-mail: sales@dennisuk.com *Professional motor mower manufrs*

Dennis & Robinson Ltd, Blenheim Road, Lancing, West Sussex, BN15 8UH Tel: (01903) 755321 Fax: (01903) 750679 E-mail: sales@manhattan.co.uk Principal Export Areas: Middle East *Manhattan kitchen furniture*

Dennis Shingler & Son, Agricultural Service Station, Cyfronydd, Welshpool, Powys, SY21 9EW Tel: (01938) 850270 Fax: (01938) 850387 *Agricultural machinery distributors*

Dennison Commercials Ltd, 16 Carewamean Road, Killeavy, Newry, County Down, BT35 8JQ Tel: (028) 3026 5425 Fax: (028) 3026 3807 E-mail: sales@dennisons.co.uk *Commercial vehicle spares & repairs services*

Denny Brothers Ltd, Kempson Way, Bury St. Edmunds, Suffolk, IP32 7AR Tel: (01284) 701381 Fax: (01284) 705575 E-mail: denny.bros@dennybros.com *Specialist printers*

Denny Engineering, Titley Bawk Avenue, Earls Barton, Northampton, NN6 0LA Tel: (01604) 811403 Fax: (01604) 812514 *Precision engineers*

Denny Engineering Ltd, 10 Morgan Way, Bowthorpe Employment Area, Norwich, NR5 9JJ Tel: (01603) 747066 Fax: (01603) 748421 E-mail: dennengltd@aol.com *Toolmaking & mould making manufrs*

Denny Engraving, 1 Manse Place, Falkirk, FK1 1JN Tel: (01324) 634900 Fax: (01324) 634900 *Trophies & engraving*

Denormo Technics Ltd, 8 Teal Business Pk, Dudwell Bridge, Hinckley, Leics, LE10 3BZ Tel: (01455) 250153 Fax: (01455) 617061 *Tube manipulators*

▶ Denovo Interiors, Units 1-2, Lock Way, Dewsbury, West Yorkshire, WF13 3SX Tel: (01924) 491887 Fax: (01924) 496591 E-mail: lcameron@denovo-int.co.uk *Office furniture & furnishings*

Denray Cables & Controls, Edwards House, 327 Whapload Road, Lowestoft, Suffolk, NR32 1UL Tel: (01502) 516971 Fax: (01502) 537045 *Cable suppliers*

Denray Machine Tools & Automation Ltd, Westwood House, Westwood Road, Earlsdon, Coventry, CV5 6GF Tel: (024) 7667 8916 Fax: (024) 7669 1478 *Machine tool agents, merchants & manufrs*

Denroyd Ltd, Lockhill Mills, Holmes Road, Sowerby Bridge, West Yorkshire, HX6 3LD Tel: (01422) 833147 Fax: (01422) 833615 E-mail: sales@denroyd.co.uk *Plastic injection mouldings*

▶ Densit Wear Protection UK Ltd, Oasis Building, 17 Lisle Avenue, Kidderminster, Worcestershire, DY11 7DE Tel: (01562) 515195 Fax: (01562) 515094 E-mail: enquiries@densit.co.uk *Furnish lining of pipe work & heat treatment metal*

Densitron Technologies P.L.C., 145 Cannon Street, London, EC4N 5BP Tel: (020) 7648 4200 Fax: (020) 7648 4201 E-mail: sales@densitron.com Principal Export Areas: Worldwide *LCD display manufrs*

Denso Manufacturing (Midlands) Ltd, Shaftsmoor Lane, Hall Green, Birmingham, B28 8SW Tel: 0121-777 3232 Fax: 0121-777 7232 *Automotive parts manufrs*

Denso Manufacturing UK Ltd, Queensway Campus, Hortonwood, Telford, Shropshire, TF1 7FS Tel: (01952) 608400 Fax: (01952) 675222 *Motor vehicle heating & air-conditioners*

Denson Marston Ltd, Otley Road, Baildon, Shipley, West Yorkshire, BD17 7JR Tel: (01274) 582266 Fax: (01274) 597165 E-mail: enquiries@denso.co.jp *Vehicle radiator manufrs*

Dent Ltd, 191-195 Sturton St., Cambridge, CB1 2QH Tel: (01223) 350038 Fax: (01223) 300996 E-mail: dentsecur@aol.com *Lock repairs & suppliers*

Benjamin Dent & Co. Ltd, 33 Bedford Place, London, WC1B 5JU Tel: (020) 7637 2211 Fax: (020) 7637 2248 *Printing & publishers*

Dent Instrumentation Ltd, Enterprise Way, Whitewalls Industrial Estate, Colne, Lancashire, BB8 8LY Tel: (01282) 862703 Fax: (01282) 862037 E-mail: sales@dentsensors.com *Yarn break detection*

Dent Steel Services (Yorkshire) Ltd, Unit 17, Chapel Lane, Airdrie, Lanarkshire, ML6 6GX Tel: (01236) 439511 Fax: (01744) 439512 *Steel stockholders*

Dent Steel Services Yorkshire Ltd, New Works Road, Low Moor, Bradford, West Yorkshire, BD12 0QN Tel: (01274) 607070 Fax: (01274) 672979 E-mail: enquiries@dentsteel.co.uk *Steel stockholders*

Dentacast Of Exeter Ltd, PO Box 21, Exeter, EX2 9BE Tel: (01392) 273489 Fax: (01392) 423036 E-mail: info@dentacast.co.uk *Dental laboratories*

▶ Dentafix UK Ltd, Unit 11-13, Helix Business Park, Camberley, Surrey, GU15 2QT Tel: (01276) 691821 Fax: (01276) 23490 E-mail: info@dentafix.co.uk

Dental Channel Ltd, 128 Woodward Road, London, SE22 8UT Tel: (020) 8299 9742 Fax: (020) 8399 4554 *Dental software house*

Dental Style, Neroche House, Factory Lane, Bason Bridge, Highbridge, Somerset, TA9 4RN Tel: (01278) 789119 Fax: (01278) 781825 E-mail: sales@castleneroche.com *Dental cabinet manufrs*

Den-Tal-Ez Dental Products (GB) Ltd, Cleveland Way, Hemel Hempstead, Hertfordshire, HP2 7DY Tel: (01442) 269301 Fax: (01442) 217594 E-mail: contact@dentalez.co.uk *Dental equipment wholesalers*

▶ Dentastic Paintless Dent Repairs, 1 Delamere Road, Urmston, Manchester, M41 5GL Tel: (07958) 573 234 E-mail: richard@dentastic.co.uk *paintless dent repairs for cars &vans.repairs carried out your home or place of work.*

Dentocare Ltd, 7 Cygnus Business Centre, Dalmeyer Road, London, NW10 2XA Tel: (020) 8459 7550 Fax: (020) 8451 0063 E-mail: sales@dentocare.co.uk *Dental care products manufrs*

Denton Aquatics, 98 Denton Street, Carlisle, CA2 5EN Tel: (01228) 526651 Fax: (01228) 526651 *Aquarium & pond supplies*

Denton Engineering Co. Ltd, The Bearing Shop, 194 Talbot Road, Hyde, Cheshire, SK14 4HJ Tel: 0161-368 2097 Fax: 0161-368 0881 *Ball bearing stockists*

Denton & Gibson, Parkside House, 6 Headley Road, Woodley, Reading, RG5 4JB Tel: 0118-944 8558 Fax: 0118-944 8668 E-mail: graham.denton@dentonandgibson.com *Commercial & residential property developers*

John Denton Services, Unit 6 Heron Industrial Estate, Cooks Rd, Stratford, London, E15 2PW Tel: (020) 8519 3969 Fax: (020) 8519 3695 *Packaging, mailing services/data capture*

Denton's Catering Equipment Ltd, 2-4 Clapham High Street, London, SW4 7UT Tel: (020) 7622 7157 Fax: (020) 7622 5546 E-mail: sales@dentons.co.uk *Catering equipment distributors*

Dents, Fairfield Road, Warminster, Wiltshire, BA12 9DL Tel: (01985) 212291 Fax: (01985) 216435 E-mail: dents@dents.co.uk *Gloves & accessories* Also at: Bolton

▶ Dents UK Car Body Repairs, 490 High Road, Ilford, Essex, IG1 1UE Tel: (020) 8478 7356 Fax: (020) 8478 7356 E-mail: sales@dentsuk.com *Car body repairs service*

Dentsply Ltd, Hamm Moor Lane, Addlestone, Surrey, KT15 2SE Tel: (01932) 853422 Fax: (01932) 840168 E-mail: sales.weybridge@dentsply-gb.com *Dental materials supplies* Also at: Blackpool, Exeter & Plymouth

▶ Denver Construction Services Ltd, Construction House, Dumballs Road, Cardiff, CF10 5FE Tel: (029) 2049 7441

Denvic Ltd, Greenhill Industrial Estate, Kidderminster, Worcestershire, DY10 2RN Tel: (01562) 755274 Fax: (01562) 755274 E-mail: denvic@btconnect.com *Pipework & steel stockholding*

▶ Denwal Press, Park House, Warren Row, Reading, RG10 8QS Tel: (01628) 824071 Fax: (01628) 825844

▶ Deodrant Stone, Caerdelyn, Pencader, Dyfed, SA39 9BX Tel: (01559) 384856 Fax: (01559) 384771 E-mail: info@deodorant-stone.co.uk *Natural body deodorants distributors*

Dep Supplies Ltd, Units 2-3 Maressa Building, Icknield Way, Letchworth Garden City, Hertfordshire, SG6 1EX Tel: (01462) 484595 Fax: (01462) 484580 E-mail: sales@depsupplies.co.uk *Plastic fabricators & distributors*

▶ Department of Automatic Control & Systems Engineering, Mappin Street, Sheffield, S1 3JD Tel: 0114-222 5250 Fax: 0114-222 5661 E-mail: z.c.fletcher@shef.ac.uk *Training services for undergraduate & post-graduate degrees*

Department Of Continuing Education, Lonsdale College, Bailrigg, Lancaster, LA1 4YN Tel: (01524) 592624 Fax: (01524) 592448 E-mail: managementlearning@lancaster.ac.uk *Management consultants*

DePe Gear Co. Ltd, Unit 1 Grove Road Industrial Estate, Grove Road, Fenton, Stoke-On-Trent, ST4 4LG Tel: (01782) 594114 Fax: (01782) 594115 E-mail: sales@depe.co.uk *Gearboxes & refurbishment specialists*

Depeche Mode Laboratories, 8 Chestnut Close, Maidenhead, Berkshire, SL6 8SY Tel: (01628) 674644 Fax: (01628) 789640 E-mail: info@depeche-mode.co.uk *Health care product developing & manufrs*

Dependable Diamond Drilling, 4 Parkway House Ashley Industrial Estate, Wakefield Road, Ossett, West Yorkshire, WF5 9JD Tel: (01924) 265646 Fax: (01924) 267217 E-mail: d.d.drilling@btconnect.com *Concrete drilling contractors*

Depicton Ltd, Units 3-5 Maer Lane Industrial Estate, Market Drayton, Shropshire, TF9 1QX Tel: (01630) 655800 Fax: (01630) 653258 E-mail: sales@depicton.com *Plastics printing services*

Deplynn Engineering Ltd, 3 Thornham Grove, London, E15 1DN Tel: (020) 8519 6028 Fax: (020) 8519 6028 Sales Contact: B. Kirk *Welded fabrication manufacturers & welding services*

Depo FHT, Lion House, Welsh Road East, Southam, Warwickshire, CV47 1NE Tel: (01926) 813969 Fax: (01926) 817722 E-mail: sales@fht-uk.com *Cutting, carbide tools & thread rolling*

▶ Depotbuild Ltd, The Old Sawmill, 105 Hague Lane, Renishaw, Sheffield, S21 3UR Tel: (01246) 436727

Depuy International Holdings Ltd, St Anthonys Road, Beeston, Leeds, LS11 8DT Tel: 0113-270 0461 Fax: 0113-272 4101 E-mail: depuy@dpygb.jnj.com *Orthopedic implant services*

▶ Dera Food Technology Ltd, Derby Road Business Park, Clay Cross, Chesterfield, Derbyshire, S45 9AG Tel: (01246) 250626 Fax: (01246) 250638 E-mail: callygreen@foodology.co.uk *Food colouring & additives manufrs*

Derbrich Fabrications, Estate Road 7, South Humberside Industrial Estate, Grimsby, South Humberside, DN31 2TP Tel: (01472) 885888 Fax: (01472) 884965 E-mail: fabrications@derbrich.freeserve.co.uk *Engineers & fabricators of sheet metal work*

Derby Electronics, 41 St Thomas Road, Derby, DE23 8RF Tel: (01332) 774825 Fax: (01332) 270127 E-mail: derbyelectronics@btinternet.com *Radio communications equipment & accessories suppliers*

Derby Foam & Upholstery Supplies, 10 Becket Street, Derby, DE1 1HT Tel: (01332) 345059 *Foam distribution & retailers*

▶ Derby Just Lets, 2 Foxfields Drive, Oakwood, Derby, DE21 2ND Tel: 0870 027 3654 Fax: 0870 1334836 E-mail: derby@justlets.com *Derby & Nottingham lettings agency - we provide a quality letting service for landlords and tenants in Nottingham and Derby*

Derby Laminates, 1 The Old Boatyard, Church Broughton Lane, Foston, Derby, DE65 5PW Tel: (01283) 521183 Fax: (01283) 521183 *Glass fibre & custom moulders*

▶ Derby Lets, 18 Maidenshaw Road, Epsom, Surrey, KT19 8HE Tel: (0845) 6023008 E-mail: office@derbylets.wanadoo.co.uk *Epsom Accomodation - Flats and Houses for rental. Various terms available*

Derby Office Machines Ltd, 16 Prime Enterprise Park, Prime Park Way, Derby, DE1 3QB Tel: (01332) 371500 Fax: (01332) 385001 E-mail: sales@derbyofficemachines.co.uk *Office equipment manufrs*

Derby Optical Co. Ltd, 18 Agard Street, Derby, DE1 1YS Tel: (01332) 349527 Fax: (01332) 292462 *Wholesale & manufacturing opticians*

Derby Plating Services Ltd, 148 Abbey Street, Derby, DE22 3SS Tel: (01332) 382408 Fax: (01332) 382408 *Polishers & electroplaters*

▶ Derby Polythene Ltd, Unit 1 Osmaston Park Road, Derby, DE24 8BT Tel: (01332) 331955 Fax: (01332) 361355 E-mail: sales@derbyplastics.co.uk *Polythene & polypropylene bags, all types, plain & printed manufrs*

Derby Polythene Ltd, Unit 1 Osmaston Park Road, Derby, DE24 8BT Tel: (01332) 331955 Fax: (01332) 361355 E-mail: sales@doninggroup.aol.com *Polythene film & bag manufrs*

Derby Unitex Ltd, Derbyshire Business Development Centre, Beaufort Street, Derby, DE21 6AX Tel: (01332) 298988 Fax: (01322) 295696 E-mail: derby@unitex.co.uk *Protective clothing manufrs*

Derbybeech Ltd, Swinemoor Industrial Estate, Barmston Road, Beverley, North Humberside, HU17 0LA Tel: (01482) 868993 Fax: (01482) 872109 E-mail: info@derbybeech.com *Derbybeech Limited are one of the market leaders in the development and manufacture of modular buildings both in permanent and temporary installations, working in partnership*

continued

continuation
with you, we will design a building that meets all your specifications and needs.

Derbyshire Building Supplies Ltd, Woodside Farm, Stanton Hill, Ticknall, Derby, DE73 7LA Tel: (01332) 865373 Fax: (01332) 865534 E-mail: sales@derbyshirebuildingsupplies.co.uk *Builders merchant*

Derbyshire Castings Ltd, Churchill Road, Altrincham, Cheshire, WA14 5LT Tel: 0161-928 1764 Fax: 0161-927 7623 E-mail: roger@derbyshirecastings.com *Non-ferrous & ferrous foundry manufrs*

Derbyshire Chamber Of Commerce & Industry, Commerce Centre, Canal Wharf, Chesterfield, Derbyshire, S41 7NA Tel: (01246) 211277 Fax: (01246) 203173 E-mail: chamber@derbyshire.org *Chambers of commerce*

Derbyshire Commercial Bodybuilders Ltd, 8 Derby Road, Denby, Ripley, Derbyshire, DE5 8RA Tel: (01332) 781498 Fax: (01332) 781498 *Commercial vehicle body builders*

Derbyshire Hose & Fittings Ltd, Calow Lane, Hasland, Chesterfield, Derbyshire, S41 0AL Tel: (01246) 477707 Fax: (01246) 222251 E-mail: dhfhyds@aol.com *Stockists & distributors of hydraulic equipment*

Derbyshire Industrial Sales Ltd, Unit 17 Vanguard Trading Estate, Britannia Road, Chesterfield, Derbyshire, S40 2TZ Tel: (01246) 208963 Fax: (01246) 277139 *Abrasive products agents or distributors & power tools*

Derdon Design & Development (Electronics) Ltd, Livingstone Road, Foleshill, Coventry, CV6 5AR Tel: (024) 7668 9302 Fax: (024) 7666 4146 *Sub contract electronic assembly*

Dereham Industrial Engravers Ltd, 63 Spitalfields, Norwich, NR1 4EY Tel: (01603) 622634 Fax: (01603) 622534 *Machine engravers*

▶ Derek Anthony Ltd, Units 4-5 White Swan Industrial Estate, Derker Street, Oldham, OL1 3LY Tel: 0161-627 4200 Fax: 0161-627 3616 E-mail: derekanthony@talk21.com *Sheet metal & welding*

▶ Derek C Miles Fire & Safety Consultants, 502 Fulwood Road, Sheffield, S10 3QD Tel: 0114-230 2200 Fax: 0114-230 7700 E-mail: info@dcmfiresafe.co.uk *Fire & safety consultants*

Derek Cooper, Turnpike Road, Red Lodge, Bury St. Edmunds, Suffolk, IP28 8LB Tel: (01638) 751974 Fax: (01638) 751665 *Road transport contractor* Also at: Enstone, Kings Lynn, Norwich, Siblehedingham & Tuxford

▶ Derek Cooper Transport Ltd, Yarmouth Road, Blofield, Norwich, NR13 4DS Tel: (01603) 715888 Fax: (01603) 715424

Derek De'Ath Ltd, New Line, Bacup, Lancashire, OL13 9RY Tel: (01706) 879456 Fax: (01706) 878080 E-mail: office@derekd.co.uk *Building & joinery manufrs*

Derek E Dye, 33 Station Road, Long Sutton, Spalding, Lincolnshire, PE12 9BP Tel: (01406) 363107 Fax: (01406) 363107 *Agricultural contractors & farmers*

Derek Horton, Rollingmill Street, Walsall, WS2 9EG Tel: (01922) 621909 Fax: (01922) 634829 *Road transport, haulage & freight services*

▶ Derek Mitchell, 2 Station Yard Industrial Estate, Oakwell Road, Castle Douglas, Kirkcudbrightshire, DG7 1LA Tel: (01556) 503150 Fax: (01556) 504411

Derek Raphael, 6 York Street, London, W1U 6PL Tel: (020) 7535 1690 Fax: (020) 7535 1691 *Metal merchants*

▶ Derek Smith Electrical Ltd, 5C Jefferson Avenue, Bournemouth, BH1 4NX Tel: (01202) 751508

Derek Stacey, 21 Great Bank Road, Rotherham, South Yorkshire, S65 3BT Tel: (01709) 837352 Fax: (01709) 837352 *Blinds, awnings distributors & installers*

▶ Derek Waller, The Old Bus Garage, Harborne Lane, Selly Oak, Birmingham, B29 6SN Tel: 0121-472 3571 Fax: 0121-472 4171 E-mail: derek@derekwaller.co.uk *Fenestration surveyors*

Derek Walmsley & Co Ltd, Lyons Street, Sheffield, S4 7QS Tel: 0114-243 0142 Fax: 0114-244 2870 E-mail: sales@derekwalmsley.com *Cutting tool distributors*

Derek Wilkinson, Winfield Road, Nuneaton, Warwickshire, CV11 5AZ Tel: (024) 7637 5198 Fax: (024) 7637 5198 E-mail: derekw@enta.net *Engineering consultant*

Dereve Flow Control Ltd, Park Lane, Handsworth, Birmingham, B21 8LE Tel: 0121-553 7021 Fax: 0121-525 5664 E-mail: dc.controls@btinternet.com *Flow control valve manufrs*

Dereve Flow Control Ltd, Park Lane, Handsworth, Birmingham, B21 8LE Tel: 0121-553 7021 Fax: 0121-525 5664 E-mail: sales@dereve.co.uk *Bell chime manufrs*

Deritend, Shoolbred Works, Cumberland Street, Luton, LU1 3BP Tel: (01582) 729301 Fax: (01582) 729977 E-mail: luton@deritend.co.uk *Industrial motors repair services*

Deritend, Rollingmill Street, Walsall, WS2 9EN Tel: (01922) 621664 Fax: (01922) 723128 E-mail: walsall@deritend.co.uk *Electro-mechanical services & induction heating*

The Deritend Group Ltd, Armstrong Street, West Marsh Industrial Estate, Grimsby, North East Lincolnshire, DN31 1XD Tel: (01472) 242870 Fax: (01472) 242863 E-mail: grimsby@deritend.co.uk *Electrical coil winder services & repairers*

Derivity Ltd, Chiltern House, 45 Station Road, Henley-on-Thames, Oxfordshire, RG9 1AT Tel: (01491) 845345 Fax: (01491) 845501 E-mail: info@derivity.com *Financial market software*

Dermal Laboratories Ltd, Singer Way, Woburn Road Industrial Estate, Kempston, Bedford, MK42 7AG Tel: (01234) 841555 Fax: (01234) 840498 E-mail: info@dermal.co.uk *Pharmaceutical contract manufrs*

Dermal Laboratories Ltd, Tatmore Place, Preston Road, Gosmore, Hitchin, Hertfordshire, SG4 7QR Tel: (01462) 458866 Fax: (01462) 420565 *Pharmaceutical manufrs*

Dernier & Hamlyn Ltd, Unit 5 Jaycee House, 214 Purley Way, Croydon, CR0 4XG Tel: (020) 8760 0900 Fax: (020) 8760 0955 E-mail: info@dernier-hamlyn.com *Spoke lighting manufacturers & restoration specialists*

Dero Fabrication Ltd, Unit 67, Blackpole Trading Estate West, Blackpole Road, Worcester, WR3 8TJ Tel: (01905) 455199 Fax: (01905) 754152 E-mail: sales@dero.co.uk *Sheet metalwork fabrication services*

Deroma UK Ltd, Quedgeley Trading Estate East, Haresfield, Stonehouse, Gloucestershire, GL10 3EX Tel: (01452) 725520 Fax: (01452) 725521 *Terracotta pots distributor*

Derriclean, 12 Lakeside Close, St Johns, Woking, Surrey, GU21 8UN Tel: (01483) 824010 Fax: (01483) 824010 E-mail: gr.derrick@ntlworld.com *NCCA trained carpet & upholstery cleaners*

Derry Journal Newspapers Ltd, 22 Buncrana Road, Londonderry, BT48 8AA Tel: (028) 7127 2200 Fax: (028) 7127 2218 E-mail: editorial@jerryjernonal.com *Newspaper printers*

Kevin Derry Agrochemicals, 10 West Mount, Tadcaster, North Yorkshire, LS24 9LB Tel: (01937) 832037 *Agrochemical suppliers*

Derrywood Display, 3-6 Tuxford Road, Leicester, LE4 9TZ Tel: 0116-276 0006 Fax: 0116-276 0007 E-mail: info@derrywooddisplay.co.uk *Point of sale display & shop fitting manufrs*

▶ Derw Glass, Pantyderi, Blaenffos, Boncath, Dyfed, SA37 0JB Tel: (01239) 841596 Fax: (01239) 841670

Derwent Cast Stone Co. Ltd, Eden Works, Old Malton, Malton, North Yorkshire, YO17 6SD Tel: (01653) 692860 Fax: (01653) 600129 E-mail: dcs@cast-stone.co.uk *Manufacturer of precast concrete & cast stone*

Derwent Castings Ltd, Derwent Foundry, Derby Road, Whatstandwell, Matlock, Derbyshire, DE4 5HG Tel: (01773) 852173 Fax: (01773) 856632 E-mail: info@derwent-foundry.co.uk *Iron works manufrs*

Derwent Koi & Tropicals, Hope Road, Bamford, Hope Valley, Derbyshire, S33 0AL Tel: (01433) 650029 Fax: (01433) 650029 *Fish suppliers*

Derwent Lighting, Derwent Road, York Road Business Park, Malton, North Yorkshire, YO17 6YB Tel: (01653) 696444 Fax: (01653) 696965 E-mail: enquiries@derwentlighting.co.uk *Table lamps & lamp shades manufrs*

Derwent Lynton Co. Ltd, Siddals Road, Derby, DE1 2QD Tel: (01332) 365121 Fax: (01332) 343173 E-mail: info@derwentlynton.co.uk *Confectionery manufrs*

Derwent Patterns & Models Ltd, Sandown Road, Derby, DE24 8SR Tel: (01332) 349555 Fax: (01332) 349555 *Engineers pattern makers*

Derwent Stone Products Ltd, Unit 16 Greencroft Industrial Estate, Stanley, County Durham, DH9 7XP Tel: (01207) 521482 Fax: (01207) 521455 E-mail: derwentstone@aol.com *Manufacturers of decorative stone wall claddings*

▶ Derwent Systems Ltd, Derwent House Unit 41A, Colbourne Crescent, Nelson Park, Cramlington, Northumberland, NE23 1WB Tel: (01670) 730187 Fax: (01670) 730188 *Closed circuit television*

▶ Derwent Systems Technology, 8 Hugh Parke Close, Loughton, Milton Keynes, MK5 8FG Tel: (01908) 678686 E-mail: rsapk@espuk.com *Software developers*

Derwent Upholstery Ltd, Amber Business Centre, Greenhill Lane, Riddings, Alfreton, Derbyshire, DE55 4BR Tel: (01773) 604121 Fax: (01773) 540813 E-mail: sales@derwentupholstery.com *Furniture manufrs*

▶ Derwentside Cottage, Unit 3 Bradley Workshops, Consett, County Durham, DH8 6HG Tel: (01207) 509895 Fax: (01207) 509895 *Timber garden furniture manufrs*

Derwentside Precision Gears Ltd, Morrison Industrial Estate, Stanley, County Durham, DH9 7XW Tel: (01207) 231274 Fax: (01207) 231274 *Engineers*

Derwick Ltd, 14 Westwood Close, Potters Bar, Hertfordshire, EN6 1LH Tel: (01707) 645855 Fax: (01707) 857291 E-mail: m.anjarwalla@btconnect.com *Surgical export merchants*

Derwood & Abel Ltd, Imperial Trading Estate, Lambs La North, Rainham, Essex, RM13 9XL Tel: (01708) 554611 Fax: (01708) 559726 *Polishing & buffing services*

Des Computers, Cardiff University, Senghennydd Road, Cardiff, CF24 4AG Tel: (029) 2025 0000 Fax: (029) 2025 9600 E-mail: sales@descom.co.uk *Computer maintenance*

▶ DES Group Ltd, Unit 9, Shield Drive, West Cross Centre, Great West Road, Brentford, Middlesex, TW8 9EX Tel: (020) 8560 8787 Fax: (020) 8758 2184 E-mail: jo.chambers@d-e-s.co.uk *Machinery removal & relocation, process system for food & chemical industry*

Desal Supplies, Unit 4 Fletcher Street, Rochdale, Lancashire, OL11 1AE Tel: (01706) 869777 Fax: (01706) 713095 E-mail: sales@desal.co.uk *Desalination, membranes, chemicals & ancillaries*

Descalite Supply Co. Ltd, Unit 2 Loaland Business Centre, Maritime Close, Medway City Estate, Rochester, Kent, ME2 4AZ Tel: (01634) 294455 Fax: (01634) 294494 E-mail: descalite@aol.com *Descaling products distributors*

Descant Ltd, Inchcross, Bathgate, West Lothian, EH48 2HT Tel: (01506) 653252 Fax: (01506) 631362 E-mail: sales@descantltd.co.uk *Joinery manufrs*

Desch Plantpak Ltd, Varey Road, Eaton Bank Trading Estate, Congleton, Cheshire, CW12 1HD Tel: (01260) 279432 Fax: (01260) 280856 E-mail: sales@desch-plantpak.co.uk *Horticultural product manufrs*

Desch Plantpak Ltd, Burnham Road, Mundon, Maldon, Essex, CM9 6NT Tel: (01621) 745500 Fax: (01621) 745525 E-mail: sales@desch-plantpak.co.uk Principal Export Areas: Africa *Horticultural plastic products & plastic mouldings manufrs*

Descon Ltd, Graphic House, Otley Road, Guiseley, Leeds, LS20 8BH Tel: (01943) 877721 Fax: (01943) 870247E-mail: info@descon.co.uk *Engineering design services*

Describe Video Services, 21 Lesley Avenue, Canterbury, Kent, CT1 3LF Tel: (01227) 464265 Fax: (01227) 464265 *Video production*

Design 4 Plastics Ltd, Unit 402 Thorp Arch Trading Estate, Thorp Arch, Wetherby, West Yorkshire, LS23 7BJ Tel: (01937) 845176 Fax: (01937) 845419 E-mail: enquiries@design4plastics.com *Product design & development consultants*

▶ Design 5, 17 Crimp Hill Road, Old Windsor, Windsor, Berkshire, SL4 2QY Tel: (01753) 620000 Fax: (01753) 622522 E-mail: mail@design5.co.uk *Professional design services, interior & furniture design*

▶ Design & Analysis Ltd, The Green, Stathern, Melton Mowbray, Leicestershire, LE14 4HH Tel: (0771) 8866630 E-mail: sale@design-and-analysis.co.uk *Cost effective design and analysis services to general engineering industries. Core experience in Rail and Military Vehicles.*

▶ Design Analysis Solutions, Bramling Cross Barns, Beauchamp Lane, Worcester, WR2 4UQ Tel: (01905) 830608 Fax: (0870) 7062737 E-mail: info@das4pcbs.co.uk *Designers PCB & CAD*

▶ Design Blinds, Rear of, 1346 Stratford Road, Hall Green, Birmingham, B28 9EH Tel: 0121-777 0403 Fax: (0871) 4332309 *Sell & manufacture blinds*

Design Bridge Ltd, 18 Clerkenwell Close, London, EC1R 0QN Tel: (020) 7814 9922 Fax: (020) 7814 9024 E-mail: info@designbridge.co.uk *Brand designers*

Design Built Exhibitions Ltd, 46 Enfield Industrial Estate, Redditch, Worcestershire, B97 6DE Tel: (01527) 69132 Fax: (01527) 65692 *International exhibition contractors*

Design Cabinet Makers, Unit 1 Clapham North Business Centre, 26-32 Voltaire Road, London, SW4 6DH Tel: (020) 7627 1440 Fax: (020) 7627 1440 *Design cabinets*

Design & Care Cleaning Services Ltd, 89 Walcot Square, London, SE11 4UB Tel: (020) 7261 1502 Fax: (020) 7820 0032 E-mail: design.care@virgin.net *Office cleaning contractors*

Design Channel, 107 Warwick Street, Leamington Spa, Warwickshire, CV32 4QZ Tel: (01926) 435789 Fax: (01926) 430799 E-mail: sales@thedesignchannel.co.uk *Patient communication services*

Design Clinic, Unit 5-7 Wheal Vor, Breage, Helston, Cornwall, TR13 9NW Tel: (01736) 762813 Fax: (01736) 762813 *Giftware manufrs*

Design Communications UK Ltd, Breckenwood Road, Ash House, Fulbourn, Cambridge, CB21 5DQ Tel: (01223) 882488 Fax: (01223) 882499 E-mail: sales@designcom.co.uk *Telecommunications & cabling installations*

Design Computer, 16A Littleway, Exeter, EX2 9PB Tel: (01392) 435340 E-mail: mousepad@eurobell.co.uk *Computer designers*

Ltd Design Consultants, 54 Warwick Square, London, SW1V 2AJ Tel: (020) 7931 7607 Fax: (020) 7931 7608 E-mail: enquiries@ltddesign.co.uk *Design consultants*

▶ Design Craft Furnishings Cleveland Ltd, 63 Gilkes Street, Middlesbrough, Cleveland, TS1 5EH Tel: (01642) 247483

▶ Design Distillery Ltd, 12 Northgate, Chichester, West Sussex, PO19 1BA Tel: (01243) 537837 Fax: (01243) 839448 E-mail: leslie@design-distillery.co.uk *Graphic design marketing & design*

▶ The Design Division, 7TH Floor Silkhouse Court, Tithebarn Street, Liverpool, L2 2LZ Tel: 0151-515 3002 Fax: 0151-515 3001 E-mail: info@thedivision.co.uk *Design & marketing solutions for your business*

Design Drafting Services, 4 Carr Street, Ramsbottom, Bury, Lancashire, BL0 9AE Tel: (01706) 823331 Fax: (01706) 827910 *Printed circuit board design & manufrs*

Design Engineering, 169 Railway Arches, Midland Road, London, E10 6JT Tel: (020) 8925 3003 Fax: (020) 8925 3013 *Furniture engineering fabricators*

Design Engineering & Fabrications International Ltd, 14 Newbridge Way, Pennington, Lymington, Hampshire, SO41 8BH Tel: (01590) 671411 Fax: (01590) 676021 E-mail: info@defint.com *Stainless steel fabricators*

▶ Design Extreme Ltd, Wood Hill, Squirrel's Jump, Alderley Edge, Cheshire, SK9 7DR Tel: (01625) 586522 Fax: (01625) 586533 E-mail: info@designextremelimited.co.uk *Graphic design services, advertising agency, photographic services, printing services*

▶ Design Forte, Harewood Cottage, Main Street, Weeton, Leeds, LS17 0AY Tel: (01423) 734856 E-mail: chris@designforte.co.uk *Designers of company stationery/brochures, packaging and websites.*

Design Group, 2nd Floor Quay House, 7 The Quay, Poole, Dorset, BH15 1HA Tel: (01202) 669090 Fax: (01202) 669930 E-mail: sales@designgroup.co.uk *Graphic designers specialising in branding, stationery design, brochures, leaflets, direct mail, exhibition design and advertising.*

▶ Design Heat Winchester Ltd, 5 Bar End Road, Winchester, Hampshire, SO23 9NT Tel: 01962 867564

Design House, 2 Borough Road, Buckingham Road Industrial Estate, Brackley, Northamptonshire, NN13 7BE Tel: (01280) 840451 Fax: (01280) 840454 E-mail: enquiries@linearpro.ltd.uk *Blind manufrs*

Design House, 52 Hollins Lane, Marple Bridge, Stockport, Cheshire, SK6 5BD Tel: 0161-427 1426 Fax: 0161-427 9316 E-mail: siddesigns@aol.com *Creative design consultants*

▶ design indeed, Top flat, 80 Cavendish Road, London, N4 1RS Tel: 0794 4231340 E-mail: info@design-indeed.co.uk *Graphic design and Multimedia services,we provide high standard design for logos, corporate identity,*

continued

packaging, leaflets, catalogues, websites... contact us to discuss your needs.

Design Initiative Ltd, The Old Granary, The Street, Glynde, Lewes, East Sussex, BN8 6SX Tel: (01273) 858525 Fax: (01273) 858531 E-mail: info@designit.eu.com *Design development & manufacture weighing equipment*

▶ The Design Initiative, Unit 2 Mowbray Street, Stockport, Cheshire, SK1 3EJ Tel: 0161-474 1314 Fax: 0161-474 1314 E-mail: info@designinitiative.co.uk *Graphic design studio*

Design Installation Service Electrical Ltd, P O Box 137, Cheltenham, Gloucestershire, GL53 7ZF Tel: (01242) 533100 Fax: (01242) 221187 *Heating & ventilation consultants*

▶ Design Interface Ltd, Thurston Grange, Thurston End, Hawkedon, Bury St. Edmunds, Suffolk, IP29 4LQ Tel: (01284) 789608 Fax: (01284) 789617 E-mail: enquiries@design-interface.com *Electronic product development service*

Design International Ltd, Unit 8, Clwydfro Business Centre, Lon Parcwr Industrial Estate, Ruthin, Clwyd, LL15 1NJ Tel: (01824) 704327 Fax: (0871) 2215698 E-mail: sales@designinternational.ltd.uk *Security systems manufrs*

Design Lighting Ltd, 9 Eagles Wood Business Park, Woodlands Lane, Bradley Stoke, Bristol, BS32 4EU Tel: (01454) 616100 Fax: (01454) 618518 E-mail: sales@designlighting.co.uk *Lighting designers & suppliers*

Design Line, G/3, Unit Joseph Adamson Industrial Estate Croft Street, Hyde, Cheshire, SK14 1EE Tel: 0161-368 0713 Fax: 0161-368 0713 E-mail: vbirley@hotmail.com *Built-in & fitted furniture manufrs*

Design Masters Ltd, 2 Marlows Court, Marlows, Hemel Hempstead, Hertfordshire, HP1 1LE Tel: (01442) 256756 Fax: (01442) 260602 E-mail: designmasters@aol.com *Storage equipment distributors*

Design & Materials Ltd, Lawn Road, Carlton-In-Lindrick, Worksop, Nottinghamshire, S81 9LB Tel: (01909) 730333 Fax: (01909) 730605 *Self build houses*

Design & Media Solutions, Tovil Hill, Maidstone, Kent, ME15 6QS Tel: (01622) 681366 Fax: (01622) 688928 E-mail: craftsmencolour@craftsmencolour.co.uk *Design Type setting, reprographics & plate making*

Design For Modern Living, 43 High St, Wing, Leighton Buzzard, Bedfordshire, LU7 0NS Tel: (01296) 682994 Fax: (01296) 682995 E-mail: graham@mancha.demon.co.uk *Furniture suppliers & manufrs*

▶ Design One For Me, Gorseway, Coventry, CV5 8BL Tel: (07779) 713543 E-mail: contact@designoneforme.com *Web design & search engine manufrs*

▶ Design Ontap, 200 Brook Drive, GreenPark, Reading, RG2 6UB Tel: 0845 644 7782 Fax: 0845 644 7783 E-mail: glen.richardson@design-ontap.co.uk *Advertising & graphic designers*

Design packaging Solutions Ltd, Grove Farm, The Grove, Moulton, Northampton, NN3 7UF Tel: (01604) 645334 Fax: (01604) 644920 E-mail: suden@fsbdial.co.uk *Corrugated fibre packaging design & production*

Design Pattern & Tool Co. Ltd, Unit 31A, Central Industrial Estate, Cable Street, Wolverhampton, WV2 2RL Tel: (01902) 872777 Fax: (01902) 872778 E-mail: sales@designpattern.co.uk *Utilising full CAD/CAM design & manufacture of jigs fixtures & mould tools for automotive & trade P.U., rotational & forming tools. Full prototype & production service available. Full turnkey project management*

Design & Print Partnership, 7 Rivermead South, Rivermead Industrial Estate, Chelmsford, CM1 1PD Tel: (01245) 290516 Fax: (01245) 265137 E-mail: designandprintpartnership@btconnect.com *Lithographic printers & designers*

Design & Reprographic Supplies, Repro House, Liverpool Road, Newcastle, Staffordshire, ST5 9HD Tel: (01782) 712024 Fax: (01782) 713083 E-mail: sales@drs-paper.com *Office equipment suppliers*

Design Research Shopfittings Ltd, 7 Cam Centre, Wilbury Way, Hitchin, Hertfordshire, SG4 0TW Tel: (01462) 420725 Fax: (01462) 421196 *Joinery manufrs*

▶ Design Services, 2/2fl Marchmont Street, Edinburgh, EH9 1EJ Tel: 0131-339 0793

Design Services NW Ltd, 42 Long Street, Middleton, Manchester, M24 6UQ Tel: 0161-643 0088 Fax: 0161-643 6254 E-mail: info@designservicesltd.co.uk *Technical staff & draughting agency*

▶ Design Signs, 8 Queen Mary Works, Queen Marys Avenue, Watford, WD18 7JR Tel: (01923) 497087 E-mail: design_signs@hotmail.com *Watford based company offering a fast efficient service specialising in: Vinyl Graphics - Vehicle Liveries - Shop Fascias & Windows - PVC Banners - Magnetics - General Sign Boards etc.*

▶ The Design Station Ltd, 9 Turnstone Drive, Featherstone, Wolverhampton, WV10 7TA Tel: (01902) 722192 E-mail: jackie@thedesignstation.co.uk *Wax seal stamps, gifts manufrs*

Design Systems, The Old School, Exton St, London, SE1 8UE Tel: 020 79289275 *Sign designers*

▶ Design & Visual Concepts Ltd, 4 Keston Showmans Park, Layhams Road, Keston, Kent, BR2 6AR Tel: (01959) 571071 Fax: (01959) 577150 E-mail: info@designandvisual.com *"Design and Visual Concepts specialise in GRG internal cladding and suspended ceilings of high architectural demand where the manufacture and installation of specially formed GRG units are required.*

Design of Walton, 3 Lyln Road, Hersham Trading Estate, Walton-on-Thames, Surrey, KT12 3PU Tel: (01932) 240376 Fax: (01932) 241110 E-mail: signs@designofwalton.co.uk *Sign makers*

▶ Design Wise, Matrix House, Constitution Hill, Leicester, LE1 1PL Tel: 0116-262 8678 Fax: 0116-262 8678 E-mail: info@designwise.org.uk *Promotional & personalised products*

Design Woodworking, 7 Vernon Place, Northern Court, Nottingham, NG6 0DE Tel: 0115-977 0302 *Joinery specialists*

▶ Design Works, 18 High Street, Swindon, SN1 3EP Tel: (01793) 421900 Fax: (01793) 421901 E-mail: enquiries@designswindon.com *Sign service, from design & manufacture of bespoke signage, full installation in any location*

▶ Design4business, Design 4 Business, Prestwick Hall Farm, Ponteland, Newcastle upon Tyne, NE20 9TU Tel: 01661 820769 *Design4business is a network for your business to take shape. Inspiring, practical, fun and creative interior design presentations. We supply mood boards, concept layouts, sketch ideas, visuals and scaled plans.*

▶ De-signage, Briarwood House, 32, Briarwood Gardens, Woodlaithes Village, Rotherham, South Yorkshire, S66 3XR Tel: 01709 700309 Fax: 01709 700309 E-mail: sales@de-signage.com

▶ Designasausage, 12 Hibel Road, Macclesfield, Cheshire, SK10 2AB Tel: (01625) 611888 Fax: (01625) 611956 E-mail: sausages@sausagemaking.co.uk *Suppliers of sausage making machinery & accessories*

Designation Ltd, Newark Road, Peterborough, PE1 5YD Tel: (01733) 893333 Fax: (01733) 314889 E-mail: sales@desihose.com *Import & export of hoses*

▶ Designbern, 31 Yorkland Avenue, Welling, Kent, DA16 2LE Tel: (07855) 856529 E-mail: bern@designbern.com *Graphic design studio*

▶ DesignCambridge, Jesus Lane, Cambridge, CB5 8BA Tel: (01223) 367206 E-mail: chris@designcambridge.com *Chris is a Chartered Designer and Fellow of the Chartered Society of Designers, Trained in Interior Architecture at London College of Furniture, remodelling space from single rooms to whole premises are mainstay activities. Furniture and furnishings and total project management for Homes, Retail Outlets and Commercial Office Premises where best use of space, attention to detail and alternative, fresh approach are important call for a free no obligation surgery to discuss your project*

Designcode Ltd, 5 Merseyton Road, Ellesmere Port, CH65 2JE Tel: 0151-355 9172 Fax: 0151-357 2868 E-mail: designcode@tinyworld.co.uk *Refractory steel work service manufrs*

Designed Architectural Lighting Ltd, 6 Conqueror Court, Spilsby Road, Harold Hill, Romford, RM3 8SB Tel: (01708) 381999 Fax: (01708) 381585 *Lighting designers & manufrs*

▶ Designer Appliances, Candidus Court, Peterborough, PE4 5DB Tel: (01733) 755510 Fax: (0871) 6613572 E-mail: info@peterboroughappliances.co.uk *Kitchen appliances, integrated appliances, built in appliances*

Designer Blinds, 45a Commercial Street, New Tredegar, Gwent, NP24 6AA Tel: (01443) 830003 *Blinds manufrs*

▶ Designer Blinds & Awnings, 56 Beam Street, Nantwich, Cheshire, CW5 5LJ Tel: (01270) 611161 Fax: (01270) 611161 *Blind & awning retailers*

Designer Bounce Ltd, St Asaph Avenue, C C I Business Park, Kinmel Bay, Rhyl, Clwyd, LL18 5HA Tel: (01745) 345462 Fax: 01745 344196 *Inflatables manufr*

Designer Browbands, Great Dunham, King's Lynn, Norfolk, PE32 2FE Tel: (01328) 700808 Fax: (01328) 700505 E-mail: sales@seignewrbrowbands.co.uk *Equestrian accessories manufrs*

Designer Carpets, 2 Ham Street, Richmond, Surrey, TW10 7HT Tel: (020) 8332 6006 Fax: (020) 8332 0660 E-mail: info@designercarpets.co.uk *Carpet agents*

Designer Logo Matting, 56 Southbury Road, Enfield, Middlesex, EN1 1YB Tel: (020) 8342 2020 Fax: (020) 8342 2021 *Promotional coir mat manufrs*

▶ Designer Metal Products, 40 Cromwell Industrial Estate, Staffa Road, London, E10 7QZ Tel: (020) 8558 9239 *Steel fabricators*

Designer Mirrors, Unit 11, Slingsby Close, Attleborough Fields Industrial Estate, Nuneaton, Warwickshire, CV11 6RP Tel: (024) 7664 1206 Fax: (024) 7664 1260 *Mirror & picture framing agents*

The Designer Sign Company Ltd, Unit 11 Ebblake Enterprise Park, Black Moor Road, Ebblake Industrial Estate, Verwood, Dorset, BH31 6YS Tel: (01202) 813575 Fax: (01202) 813606 *Sign manufrs*

Designer Systems, 15 Andrew Place, Truro, Cornwall, TR1 3HZ Tel: (01872) 223306 Fax: (01872) 223306 E-mail: sales@designersystems.co.uk *Electronic hardware designers*

▶ Designer Time, High Street, Bridgnorth, Shropshire, WV16 4DX Tel: (01746) 768444 Fax: (01746) 780870 E-mail: info@Designer-Time.Com *Designer-Time.Com - Designer Watches, Jewellery, Gifts and Gadgets*

▶ Designer Vision Ltd, Unit 75, Capitol Industrial Park, Capitol Way, London, NW9 0EW Tel: (020) 8200 1515 Fax: (020) 8200 0022 *Audio visual suppliers*

Designex Ltd, Caxton House, Hopewell Drive, Chatham, Kent, ME5 7NP Tel: (01634) 844644 Fax: (01634) 831519 E-mail: info@designex.co.uk *Creative digital designers*

Designex Cabinets Ltd, Unit 10, Button Mill Industrial Estate, Lower Mill, Bridgend, Stonehouse, Gloucestershire, GL10 2BB Tel: (01453) 826868 Fax: (01453) 826868 E-mail: sales@designex-cabinets.co.uk *Designers & manufacturers of glass display cabinets*

Designplan Lighting Ltd, 6 Wealdstone Road, Sutton, Surrey, SM3 9RW Tel: (020) 8254 2000 Fax: (020) 8644 4253 E-mail: info@designplan.co.uk *Vandal resistant lighting fittings*

▶ Designplus Kent, 59 Marshall Crescent, Broadstairs, Kent, CT10 2HR Tel: (01843) 602218 E-mail: designpluskent@btinternet.com

Designs, 53 Middleton Road, Banbury, Oxfordshire, OX16 3QR Tel: (01295) 254777 Fax: (01295) 254541 E-mail: david@designs-uk.com *Sign manufrs*

Designs To Print, 15 Devonshire Rd, London, W4 2EU Tel: (020) 8995 5155 Fax: (020) 8995 5156 *Typing & printing services*

▶ Designvan, 23 Wiltshire Drive, Wokingham, Berkshire, RG40 1TQ Tel: 0118-989 1295 E-mail: rob@designvan.com *Bathroom design & installation*

Designwrights Ltd, Unit 18 Liss Business Centre, Station Road, Liss, Hampshire, GU33 7AW Tel: (01730) 890050 Fax: (01730) 890051 E-mail: info@designwrights.co.uk *Electronic product development*

▶ Desire, Whitehedge Road, Liverpool, L19 1RZ Tel: 0151-427 4002 *Clothing manufrs*

Desiree Boutique, 26 High Street, Rottingdean, Brighton, BN2 7HR Tel: (01273) 303444 Fax: (01273) 303444 *Swimwear*

Desk Depot Ltd, 276 Queenstown Road, London, SW8 4LP Tel: (020) 7627 3897 E-mail: sales@deskdepot.co.uk *The desk depot cabinet makers,*established in battersea, london in 1985, design & make a vast*range of reproduction antique style & contemporary office furniture at highly competitive prices**

▶ The Desk Warehouse, Beersbridge Road, Belfast, BT5 5DX Tel: (028) 9058 0900 Fax: (028) 9058 0900 E-mail: sales@deskwarehouse.co.uk *Office equipment retailers & rentals*

Desktop Associates Ltd, Unit 1, 6 Putney Common, London, SW15 1HL Tel: (020) 8789 2250 Fax: (020) 8789 2249 E-mail: info@desktop-associates.co.uk *Software training & event organisers*

Desktop Design & Draughting Ltd, 27 Hall Drive, Lincoln, LN6 7SW Tel: (01522) 531861 Fax: (01522) 546795 *Software developers*

▶ Desktop Network Systems Ltd, 8 Croydon Road, Nottingham, NG7 3DS Tel: (07710) 394296 Fax: 0115-841 3761 E-mail: sales@dns-direct.com *Computer system consultants services*

Desktop Security Solutions, 14 Penrose Avenue, Watford, WD19 5AD Tel: (020) 8386 1624 Fax: (020) 8386 1624 E-mail: sales@desktopsecuritysolutions.co.uk *Computer security*

Desman Engineering Ltd, Burma Road, Blidworth, Mansfield, Nottinghamshire, NG21 0RT Tel: (01623) 490086 Fax: (01623) 490087 E-mail: sales@desman-engineering.com *Precision engineers*

Desmi Ltd, Unit 6A, Rosevale Business Park, Parkhouse Industrial Estate West, Newcastle, Staffordshire, ST5 7UB Tel: (01782) 566900 Fax: (01782) 563666 E-mail: desmi_ltd@desmi.com *Marine pump manufrs*

Desoutter Ltd, Eton Road, Hemel Hempstead, Hertfordshire, HP2 7DR Tel: (01442) 344300 Fax: (01442) 344600 *Manufacturers of industrial power tools*

Desoutter Ltd, Eton Road, Hemel Hempstead, Hertfordshire, HP2 7DR Tel: (01442) 344300 Fax: (01442) 344600 *Power tools distributors*

Desoutter Ltd, Eton Road, Hemel Hempstead, Hertfordshire, HP2 7DR Tel: (01442) 344300 Fax: (01442) 344600 E-mail: desoutter.sales@cp.com *Manufacturers of pneumatic tools, industrial power tools & hand tools*

Dessian Products Ltd, Boucher Business Centre, Apollo Road, Belfast, BT12 6HP Tel: (028) 9038 1118 Fax: (028) 9066 0741 E-mail: dessian@dessian.co.uk *PVC windows frame manufrs*

Destec Engineering Ltd, Five Mile Lane, Washingborough, Lincoln, LN4 1AF Tel: (01522) 791721 Fax: (01522) 790033 E-mail: sales@destec.co.uk *Clamp connectors & flange manufrs*

Destec Systems, 21 Grovelands Avenue, Swindon, SN1 4ET Tel: (01793) 496217 Fax: (01793) 610739 E-mail: info@destecsystems.co.uk *UK Distributors for SeKure Controls range of anti-shoplifting and anti-theft products*

Destech UK Ltd, 3 Millbrook Business Park, Hoe Lane, Nazeing, Waltham Abbey, Essex, EN9 2RJ Tel: (01992) 899002 Fax: (01992) 899003 E-mail: sales@destech-uk.co.uk *Destech offer electrical safety testing.*

▶ Destiny Entertainments, Unit 9 Bankside Park, 28 Thames Road, Barking, Essex, IG11 0HZ Tel: (0870) 3501079 *Discotheque equipment suppliers*

Destrodent Pest Control, Mill House, 165 Powder Mill Lane, Twickenham, TW2 6EQ Tel: (020) 8894 3249 *Pests & vermin services*

▶ Desworx Ltd, 2 Allan Close, Stourbridge, West Midlands, DY8 4BB Tel: (01384) 832832 E-mail: info@desworx.com *Desworx Ltd offers affordable solutions for your Internet presence. With experience in web site design, website management, web site development, graphic design, logo design, and Internet marketing.**We will work closely with you to assure your business needs and specifications are exceeded. Whether you're looking for a basic presence on the Internet, or a fully customized, interactive e-commerce web site, Desworx Ltd will meet all your expectations.*

Deta Electrical Co. Ltd, Kingsway House, Laporte Way, Luton, LU4 8RJ Tel: (01582) 544544 Fax: (01582) 544501 E-mail: sales@detaelectrical.co.uk *Electrical wholesalers*

Detail Design, 2d Metropolitan Wharf, Wapping Wall, London, E1W 3SS Tel: (020) 7488 1669 Fax: (020) 7488 2524 E-mail: gorden@detail.co.uk *Interior design architects*

Detail Sheet Metal Ltd, Unit 26 Fawkes Avenue, Questor, Dartford, DA1 1JQ Tel: (01322) 222122 Fax: (01322) 291794 E-mail: sales@kentech.co.uk *Sheet metalworkers*

Detailed Plastic Components Ltd, 8 Rutherford Way, Thetford, Norfolk, IP24 1HA Tel: (01842) 764414 Fax: (01842) 762715 E-mail: sales@dpc.uk.com Principal Export Areas: Africa & North America *Plastic mouldings & injection mouldings manufrs*

▶ Detect International Ltd, Hulmes Bridge House, North Moor Lane, Halsall, Ormskirk, Lancashire, L39 8RF Tel: (0870) 3007201 Fax: (0870) 3007202 E-mail: Info@dik9.com *Providers of specialist search dogs and handlers*explosive{BOMB} and narcotics{DRUGS}private or commercial*all dogs and handlers trained to home office standards and fully insured*

Detection Instruments (Northern) Ltd, Unit 5-6 Bonnyton Industrial Estate, Munro Place, Kilmarnock, Ayrshire, KA1 2NP Tel: (01563) 525525 Fax: (01563) 542350 E-mail: info@di-northern.com Principal Export Areas: Worldwide *Fire & gas detection equipment sales, service & manufrs*

Detection Supplies, 14 Fordingbridge Business Park, Ashford Road, Fordingbridge, Hampshire, SP6 1BD Tel: (01425) 658239 Fax: (0870) 2430305 E-mail: sales@detectionsupplies.co.uk *Fire alarms*

▶ DetectUpet Ltd, Argyle Suite, Leek New Road, Stoke-on-Trent, ST6 2LB Tel: (01782) 274171 Fax: (01782) 287828 E-mail: martin@detectupet.co.uk *Take the Trauma out of Locating your Lost Pet. *DetectUpet is 'The 1st Emergency Service for Lost Pets' which is a unique fee-based pet re-unification service, available 24hrs that maintains up to date contact details of both you and your pet.*

Detek Ltd, 27 Granby Street, Loughborough, Leicestershire, LE11 3DU Tel: 0116-235 0244 Fax: 0116-235 8750 E-mail: detek@lineone.net *CNC machinists specialising in high quality turned & milled components*

Detrra Fabrications Ltd, Unit 12 Droicon Industrial Estate, Portway Road, Rowley Regis, West Midlands, B65 9BY Tel: 0121-559 1152 Fax: 0121-559 6909 E-mail: derekk@btconnect.com *Cold rolled section manufrs*

Deublin Ltd, Royce Close, Andover, Hampshire, SP10 3TS Tel: (01264) 333355 Fax: (01264) 333304 E-mail: deublin@deublin.co.uk *DEUBLIN are the world leader in rotating unions for water, steam, air, oil and coolant service. Covering standard products available from our extensive stocks to one off custom unions we encompass the whole range of rotary unions and rotary joints. Deublin also manufacture steam Joints and syphon systems specifically for the paper industry where we also offer steam systems engineering and technical support.*At DEUBLIN reliable products at competitive prices and on time deliveries are standard.*Deublin manufacture rotating unions for numerous industry sectors, including: - Rubber and plastics processing machinery - Machine tool through spindle coolant, air and hydraulic - Continuous steel casting and coil winding - Papermaking and corrugating machinery - Printing & packaging machinery*

Deutsch Ltd, 4 Stanier Road, St. Leonards-on-Sea, East Sussex, TN38 9RF Tel: (01424) 852721 Fax: (01424) 851532 E-mail: sales@deutsch.co.uk *Electrical connector manufrs*

Deutsche Asset Management Group Ltd, 1 Appold Street, London, EC2A 2HE Tel: (020) 7545 6000 Fax: (020) 7545 7700 *Financial services*

Deutz AG - UK, Willow Park, Burdock Close, Cannock, Staffordshire, WS11 7FQ Tel: (01543) 438900 Fax: (01543) 438932 *Diesel engine manufrs* Also at: Hull

Deva Cores Ltd, Stephen Gray Road, Bromfield Industrial Estate, Mold, Clwyd, CH7 1HE Tel: (01352) 751777 Fax: (01352) 700066 E-mail: info@devacores.com *Manufacturers cardboard tubes*

Deva Dog Ware Ltd, 320 Witton Road, Birmingham, B6 6PA Tel: 0121-327 1108 Fax: 0121-328 2699 E-mail: info@devadogware.com *Dog chain & lead manufrs*

Deva Electronic Controls Ltd, Unit 52 Woodside Business Park, Birkenhead, Merseyside, CH41 1EL Tel: 0151-647 3222 Fax: 0151-647 4511 E-mail: sales@deva.co.uk *Electronic hardware & software designers*

Deva Forge Fabrication, Hoole Bank, Hoole Village, Chester, CH2 4ES Tel: (01244) 301730 Fax: (01244) 300421 *Metal fabricators*

Deva Hawarden Board & Display, Kus Industrial Estate, Manor Lane, Hawarden, Deeside, Clwyd, CH5 3PJ Tel: (01244) 532312 Fax: (01244) 520858 E-mail: enquiries@hawarden.co.uk *Paper & board converters*

Deva Manufacturing Services, Unit 3 Chester Gates, Dunkirk, Chester, CH1 6LT Tel: (01244) 851183 Fax: (01244) 851187 E-mail: sales@deva-uk.com *Manufacturer of stainless steel nuclear waste containers*

Deva Paper & Board Co. Ltd, KUS Industrial Estate, Manor Lane, Hawarden, Deeside, Flintshire, CH5 3PJ Tel: (01244) 534302 Fax: (01244) 520858 E-mail: reception@devaboard.co.uk *Laminating manufrs*

Deval Ltd, Unit 6 Hamilton Way, New Milton, Hampshire, BH25 6TQ Tel: (01425) 620772 Fax: (01425) 638431 E-mail: sales@deval-ltd.co.uk *Manufacturers of cable assemblies*

▶ T.W. Devanney & Sons Ltd, Knowsthorpe Way, Leeds, LS9 0SW Tel: 0113-235 1875 Fax: 0113-235 1876 E-mail: stephendevanney@yahoo.co.uk *UK & international haulage*

▶ Devant Ltd, 298 Hyde End Road, Spencers Wood, Reading, RG7 1DN Tel: 0118-988 9670 E-mail: info@devant.co.uk *Commercial contract & negotiation training & consultancy services*

Devco Fireworks Ltd, 8 Fauconberg Road, London, W4 3JY Tel: (020) 8994 0714 Fax: (020) 8994 6305 E-mail: info@devecofireworks.co.uk *Fireworks importer & wholesalers*

▶ Develop IT Ltd, Springfield House, Springfield Business Park, Springfield Road, Grantham, Lincolnshire, NG31 7BG Tel: 01476 514670 Fax: 01476 514679 E-mail: info@develop-it.com *IT training and database development. Offering an extensive range of customisable IT courses, both on-site and off-site. Database developers in MS Access and SQL Server. Application development and IT project management and support.*

▶ Developing People, The Old Vicarage, Onecote, Leek, Staffordshire, ST13 7SD Tel: (01538) 304186 Fax: (01538) 304564 E-mail: davebentley@developingpeople.co.uk *We are a broad based coaching,training and management development company who provides tailored solutions to suit our clients needs*

Developlant Ltd, Unit 37, Clocktower Business Centre, Works Road, Hollingwood, Chesterfield, Derbyshire, S43 2PE Tel: (01246) 471982 Fax: (01246) 471886 E-mail: sales@developlant.co.uk *Process plant & machinery manufrs*

Development Associates Group Ltd, Blenheim House, Fitzalan Court, Cardiff, CF24 0TN Tel: (029) 2049 2773 Fax: (029) 2026 4505 *Management training & development consultants*

▶ Development Capital Exchange, PO Box 75, Leominster, Herefordshire, HR6 8RG Tel: 01568 611196 E-mail: dcxworld@aol.com *The market place for entrepreneurial investment in early-stage enterprises. We release the deal-flow between fund-seekers, investors and advisers.*

▶ Development Design Detailing Services Ltd, Tonge Bridge Way, Bolton, BL2 6BD Tel: (01204) 396606 Fax: (01204) 396634 E-mail: sales@3dsltd.co.uk *Designers*

Development Dimensions International Ltd, B Sefton Park, Bells Hill, Stokes Poges, Slough, SL2 4JS Tel: (01753) 616000 Fax: (01753) 616099 E-mail: info@ddi-europe.com *Management consultants*

▶ Development Solutions, The Needlemakers, West Street, Lewes, East Sussex, BN7 2NZ Tel: 07971 390522 Fax: 01273 486974 E-mail: michael@developmentsolutions.co.uk *Consultancy, training coaching and mentoring in management, marketing and individual development.*

▶ Development Through Change, 3 Jubilee Close, Long Buckby, NN6 6NP Tel: 01327 844634 E-mail: info@brianperry.co.uk *DEVELOPMENT THROUGH CHANGE *helps organisations, teams and individuals to improve their performance by establishing not just what needs to change and why, but how the changes need to be effected.*DEVELOPMENT THROUGH CHANGE *works with organisations to identify their vision for the future and to help bring that vision into reality.**One of the hallmarks of the organisation's reputation with clients, is its ability to transfer skills to the client's team throughout the implementation process.**

Devenish Nutrition Ltd, 96 Duncrue Street, Belfast, BT3 9AR Tel: (028) 9035 7900 Fax: (028) 9074 8820 E-mail: info@devenishnutrition.com *Animal feed suppliers*

▶ Deverall Services Ltd, S1 Unit Rudford Industrial Estate, Ford Road, Ford, Arundel, West Sussex, BN18 0BD Tel: (01903) 725123 Fax: (01903) 725456

Deverill plc, Itec House, 34-40 West Street, Poole, Dorset, BH15 1LA Tel: (01202) 785000 Fax: (01202) 785001 E-mail: marketing@deverill.co.uk *Complete IT solutions & services* Also at: London & Southampton

▶ David Deverill, 172 Spendmore Lane, Coppull, Chorley, Lancashire, PR7 5BX Tel: (01257) 793196 Fax: (01257) 793196 *Adhesive & coatings manufrs*

▶ Deveron Homes, Clashmach View, Huntly, Aberdeenshire, AB54 8PW Tel: (01466) 794300 Fax: (01466) 794600

▶ Deveron Homes, Clashmach View, Huntly, Aberdeenshire, AB54 8PW Tel: (01466) 794300 Fax: (01466) 794600 E-mail: homes@deveronhomes.co.uk

▶ Deverse Ltd, Leeds Innovation Centre, 103 Clarendon Road, Leeds, LS2 9DF Tel: 0113-245 0400 Fax: 0113-245 9304 *E-Learning Courses in Diversity*Age,Gender, Race, Sexual Orientation,Religion or Belief, Valuing Diversity*

Colin Devey Clearance Fabrics, 139 Blacker Lane, Netherton, Wakefield, West Yorkshire, WF4 4EZ Tel: (01924) 275087 Fax: (01924) 275087 *Wholesale fabric & textiles*

DeVille & Lear Ltd, Mill Lane Works, Mill Lane, Roston, Ashbourne, Derbyshire, DE6 2EE Tel: (01335) 324302 Fax: (01335) 324568 E-mail: info@devilleandlear.co.uk *Constructional engineers, fabrication of steel framed buildings*

▶ DevilWear Ltd, The Fashion House, Seaside Lane, Easington Colliery, Peterlee, County Durham, SR8 3PF Tel: (0870) 3217353 Fax: (0870) 7652757 E-mail: karl@devilwear.co.uk *Clothing retailers*

▶ Billy Devine, PO Box 16272, Glasgow, G13 9AW Tel: (07903) 303307 E-mail: info@thedevinesite.com *Web design, graphic design, logo design & creative services*

▶ Devine Wines, Main Road, Gwaelod-y-Garth, Cardiff, CF15 9HJ Tel: (029) 2081 1200 Fax: (029) 2081 4080 E-mail: info@devinewine.co.uk *Bespoke wine & crystal ware & labels services*

Devol Engineering Ltd, 13 Clarence Street, Greenock, Renfrewshire, PA15 1LR Tel: (01475) 720934 Fax: (01475) 787873 E-mail: sales@devol.com *Design & manufacture of thermoplastic components*

Devol Moulding Services Ltd, Edgefield Industrial Estate, Loanhead, Midlothian, EH20 9TB Tel: 0131-440 4367 Fax: 0131-440 3328 *Plastic injection moulding*

Devon Computers Ltd, 39 Totnes Road, Paignton, Devon, TQ4 5LA Tel: (01803) 526303 Fax: (01803) 663289 *Microcomputer dealers*

Devon Contractors Ltd, Clyst Court, Hill Barton Business Park, Clyst St. Mary, Exeter, EX5 1SA Tel: (01395) 234280 Fax: (01395) 234281 E-mail: office@devoncontractors.co.uk *Building contractors civil engineers*

▶ Devon & Cornwall Fire Protection Ltd, 2 Church Street, South Brent, Devon, TQ10 9AB Tel: (01364) 728220 Fax: (01364) 728220 E-mail: paul@dcfire.entadsl.com *Fire & Security Protection, Extinguishers, Alarms, Signs, Training Courses, Sprinkler Systems, Nurse Call, Intruder Alarms, Access Systems*

Devon & Cornwall Wools, Lamellion, Liskeard, Cornwall, PL14 4JT Tel: (01579) 342422 Fax: (01579) 340517 *Wool merchants* Also at: South Molton

Devon Desserts Ltd, Minerva Way, Brunel Rd, Newton Abbot, Devon, TQ12 4PJ Tel: 01626 366166 Fax: 01626 361400 *Produce chilled & frozen desserts*

Devon Forklift Services, Merribrocke, Station Road, Broadclyst, Exeter, EX5 3AR Tel: (01392) 462754 Fax: 01392 462754 *Fork lift services*

The Devon Marquee Co., Fairview, Murchington, Chagford, Newton Abbot, Devon, TQ13 8HJ Tel: (01647) 433530 Fax: (01647) 433530 *Marquee hire services*

Devon Metalcrafts Ltd, 2 Victoria Way, Exmouth, Devon, EX8 1EW Tel: (01395) 272846 Fax: (01395) 276688 E-mail: info@devonmetalcrafts.co.uk *Investment casting manufrs*

▶ Devon Print Proof plc, 15 Abbey Gate, Leicester, LE4 0AA Tel: 0116-251 4711 Fax: 0116-253 7984 *Printing*

Devon Rubber Co. Ltd, Central Avenue, Lee Mill Industrial Estate, Ivybridge, Devon, PL21 9PE Tel: (01752) 894695 Fax: (01752) 690794 E-mail: drubber@bandvulc.co.uk *Rubber compound manufrs*

Devon Signs Exmouth, The Old Dairyworks, New North Road, Exmouth, Devon, EX8 1RU Tel: (01395) 276618 Fax: (01395) 276618 *Sign manufrs*

Devon & Somerset Engineering Co. Ltd, 2A-2B Brunel Way, Mart Road, Minehead, Somerset, TA24 5BJ Tel: (01643) 707169 Fax: (01643) 705008 E-mail: enquiries@desoengineering.co.uk *Plastic tank manufrs*

DEVON STONE Ltd, 8 Pilot Wharf, Pierhead, Exmouth Marina, Exmouth, Devon, EX8 1XA Tel: 01395 222525 E-mail: mail@devonstone.com *Discounted natural stone tiles. Devon Stone specialises in the supply and installation of limestone, travertine, marble, sandstone and slate. NEW natural stone LANDSCAPING service now available.*

▶ Devon Truck Centre, Woodbury Salterton, Exeter, EX5 1EL Tel: (01395) 239399 Fax: (01395) 239399 *Vehicle body repairs & vehicle recovery services*

Devondale Electrical Distributors, Unit 3 24 Marsh Green Road West, Marsh Barton Trading Estate, Exeter, EX2 8PN Tel: (01392) 667474 Fax: (01392) 420037 E-mail: sales@devondale.net *Electrical supplies wholesalers* Also at: Barnstaple, Taunton & Torquay

▶ Devonia Water, Lipton Farm, Totnes, Devon, TQ9 7RN Tel: (01548) 521506 Fax: (01548) 521321 *Mineral water distributors*

Devons Catering Equipment, 1589-1593 London Road, London, SW16 4AA Tel: (020) 8679 8585 Fax: (020) 86796633 E-mail: info@devonscatering.co.uk

Devonshire Coffee Shop, 68 Spring Gardens, Buxton, Derbyshire, SK17 6BZ Tel: (01298) 23405 Fax: 01298 25551 *Bakery*

Devonshire House Associates Ltd, Gainsborough Trading Estate, Rufford Road, Stourbridge, West Midlands, DY9 7ND Tel: (01384) 442322 Fax: (01384) 440949 *Exhibition stand designers*

Devonshire Made, 6 Bitton Park Road, Teignmouth, Devon, TQ14 9BU Tel: (01626) 776893 *Confectioners*

Devonshire Pine Ltd, Caddsdown Industrial Park, Clovelly Road, Bideford, Devon, EX39 3DX Tel: (01237) 421900 Fax: (01237) 470070 *Pine goods manufrs*

Devontech Ltd, 6 Sandygate Business Park, Strap Lane, Kingsteignton, Newton Abbot, Devon, TQ12 3XF Tel: (01626) 333886 Fax: (01626) 333815 E-mail: roland.gardner@devontech.co.uk *Electrical control panels*

Devonvale Ltd, 2 Duchy Road, Heathpark Industrial Estate, Honiton, Devon, EX14 1YD Tel: (01404) 549980 Fax: (01404) 549981 E-mail: enquiries@devonvale.com *Bakery food manufrs*

Devoran Metals, Devoran Joinery Works, Greenbank Road, Devoran, Truro, Cornwall, TR3 6PQ Tel: (01872) 863376 Fax: (01872) 862123 E-mail: sales@devoran-metals.co.uk *Building contractors & woodworking services*

Devoran Metals, Devoran Joinery Works, Greenbank Road, Devoran, Truro, Cornwall, TR3 6PQ Tel: (01872) 863376 Fax: (01872) 862123 E-mail: richard@devoran-joinery.demon.co.uk *PVCU windows & door manufrs*

Devro plc, Gartferry Road, Chryston, Glasgow, G69 0JE Tel: (01236) 872261 Fax: (01236) 811005 E-mail: mail.plc@devro-casing.com *Sausage casing manufrs* Also at: Bellshill

Devro-teepak Ltd, 5 Belgrave Street, Bellshill Industrial Estate, Bellshill, Lanarkshire, ML4 3LD Tel: (01236) 878699 Fax: (01698) 746273 E-mail: male.plc@devro-casings.com *Manufacture sausage casings*

▶ Dev-Soft Ltd, 125 Thomas Street, Abertridwr, Caerphilly, Mid Glamorgan, CF83 4AY Tel: (029) 20 830339 E-mail: enquiries@dev-soft.co.uk *Specialist rent accounting and monitoring software for housing associations and special needs housing projects.*

Devway Marketing Ltd, 86 Oatlands Drive, Weybridge, Surrey, KT13 9HS Tel: (01932) 252699 Fax: (01932) 220972 *Chemical distributors service*

Dew Construction Ltd, Featherstall Road South, Oldham, OL9 6HH Tel: 0161-624 5631 Fax: 0161-678 0289 E-mail: admin@dewconstruction.co.uk *Civil engineering contractors*

▶ Dew Group, Carron Works, Stenhouse Road, Carron, Falkirk, FK2 8DR Tel: (01324) 627905 Fax: (01324) 633944

DEWA Moving Signs, 140 Heanor Road, Ilkeston, Derbyshire, DE7 8TB Tel: 0115-932 1577 Fax: 0115-930 3976 *Electronic message sign manufrs*

Dewalt, 210 Bath Road, Slough, SL1 3YD Tel: (01753) 567055 Fax: (01753) 521312 E-mail: sales@dewalt.co.uk *Professional power tool manufrs*

Dewar Bros Ltd, Cleuch Mills, Lower Mill Street, Tillicoultry, Clackmannanshire, FK13 6BP Tel: (01259) 750669 Fax: (01259) 750573 E-mail: email@dewarbrothers.com *Packaging manufrs*

▶ John Dewar & Son Ltd, Royal Brackla Distillery, Nairn, IV12 5QY Tel: (01667) 402002 Fax: (01667) 402004 *Whiskey specialists*

▶ John Dewar & Sons Ltd, Aultmore Distillery, Keith, Banffshire, AB55 6QY Tel: (01542) 881800 Fax: (01542) 881804 E-mail: rfullerton@bacardi.com *Whiskey distillers*

Dewatering Service Ltd, The Triangle, Hambridge Lane, Newbury, Berkshire, RG14 5TZ Tel: (01635) 33313 *Ground water lowering services*

Dewert Motorised Systems, Phoenix Mecano House, 1 Faraday Road, Aylesbury, Buckinghamshire, HP19 8TX Tel: (01296) 398855 Fax: (01296) 398866 E-mail: dewertgb@phoenix-mecano.com *Actuators, electromechanical & actuators, linear*

Dewey Automatics, Unit 12 The Rope Walk, Station Road, Ilkeston, Derbyshire, DE7 5HX Tel: 0115-930 8397 Fax: 0115-944 2397 *Amusement machines*

Dewhirst Accessories Ltd, Kitty Brewster Industrial Estate, Blyth, Northumberland, NE24 4RG Tel: (01670) 368587 Fax: (01670) 365773 *Manufacture of childrens car seat cover*

Dewhirst Childrenswear Ltd, Amsterdam Road, Hull, HU7 0XF Tel: (01482) 835373 Fax: (01482) 824377 *Children's clothing manufrs*

Dewhirst Corporate Clothing, 3 Burdon Drive, North West Industrial Estate, Peterlee, County Durham, SR8 2JH Tel: 0191-518 1888 Fax: 0191-586 3167 Principal Export Areas: Worldwide *Corporate clothing*

Dewhirst Group Ltd, Dewhirst House, Westgate, Driffield, North Humberside, YO25 6TH Tel: (01377) 252561 Fax: (01377) 253814 E-mail: technical.support@dewhirst.com *Clothing & shirt manufrs* Also at: Branches thorughout the U.K.

▶ Dewhirst Group, 204 Great Portland Street, London, W1W 5HU Tel: (020) 7388 7631 Fax: (020) 7383 4997

Dewhirst Group Ltd, Road Five, Winsford Industrial Estate, Winsford, Cheshire, CW7 3PN Tel: (01606) 555600 Fax: (01606) 555601 E-mail: linda.bradbury@dewhirst.com *Clothing manufrs*

Dewhirst Toiletries Ltd, Sunderland Road, Sandy, Bedfordshire, SG19 1QY Tel: (01767) 691990 Fax: (01767) 691908 E-mail: teresa.waller@mellerbeauty.co.uk *Toiletries manufrs*

Edward Dewhurst Ltd, Grierson House, Chain Call Way, Preston Riversway Docklands, Preston, PR2 2DG Tel: (01772) 761777 Fax: (01772) 761666 E-mail: pad@edewhurst.com *Electrical engineers*

James Dewhurst Ltd, Altham Lane, Altham, Accrington, Lancashire, BB5 5YA Tel: (01282) 775311 Fax: (01282) 774717 E-mail: sales@james-dewhurst.co.uk *Industrial fabric manufrs*

Dewhurst Trophies, 101 Norfolk Street, King's Lynn, Norfolk, PE30 1AQ Tel: (01553) 773355 Fax: (01553) 773355 *Sports trophy supplier*

Dewi A Jones, 9 Groesffordd, Llanddoged, Llanrwst, Gwynedd, LL26 0UA Tel: (01492) 640399 Fax: (01492) 641905 E-mail: sales@burtech-daj-trailers.co.uk *Garage service & trailer manufrs*

Dewric Ltd, St Lawrence Street, Great Harwood, Blackburn, BB6 7QZ Tel: (01254) 884855 Fax: (01254) 884855 E-mail: neil.dewhurst@tesco.net *Wirework fabricators*

Dews, Yew Green Road, Huddersfield, HD4 5EN Tel: (01484) 304060 Fax: (01484) 304477 E-mail: traffic@dews-haulage.co.uk *Road transport, haulage & freight services*

Dewsbury Dyeing Co. Ltd, Oaklands Mill, Netherfield Road, Dewsbury, West Yorkshire, WF13 3JY Tel: (01924) 463321 Fax: (01924) 460899 E-mail: dews.dyeing@btclick.com *Loose fibre dyers*

Dewsbury Lifting Services, 12 Brown La West, Leeds, LS11 0DN Tel: 0113-272 3586 Fax: 0113-272 3575 E-mail: sales@dewsburyliftingservices.co.uk *Lifting equipment suppliers*

▶ Dewsbury Plastering, 48 Valley Road, Dewsbury, West Yorkshire, WF12 0HZ Tel: (01924) 511773 E-mail: sapmaddox@hotmail.com *Building & plastering services*

Dewsbury & Proud Ltd, Biddings Lane, Bilston, West Midlands, WV14 9NN Tel: (01902) 405553 Fax: (01902) 354420 E-mail: operations@cranehiremidlands.com *Mobile crane hire services* Also at: Birmingham

Dewsbury & Proud, Cedar House, Kingsbury Road, Marston, Sutton Coldfield, West Midlands, B76 0DS Tel: (01675) 443048 *Crane hire*

Dewshurst Menswear Ltd, 3 Stephenson Road, North East Industrial Estate, Peterlee, County Durham, SR8 5AA Tel: 0191-518 6699 Fax: 0191-518 0445 *Menswear distributors*

Peter Dewson, Chequers Hill, Doddington, Sittingbourne, Kent, ME9 0BN Tel: (01795) 886869 Fax: (01795) 886426 *Foam product suppliers*

▶ Dex Tamar Marine, 3, The Mews, Chapeldown Road, Torpoint, Cornwall, PL11 2NW Tel: (01752) 812214 Fax: (01752) 812666

Dexdyne Ltd, Oakley House, Tetbury Road, Cirencester, Gloucestershire, GL7 1US Tel: (01285) 658122 Fax: (01285) 655644 E-mail: sales@dexdyne.com *Remote monitoring solutions design & manufrs*

Dexion Storage Centre Anglia Ltd, 43 Hurricane Way, Norwich, NR6 6HE Tel: (01603) 418121 Fax: (01603) 418124 E-mail: sales@dexion-anglia.co.uk *Storage equipment suppliers*

Dexmore Co Ltd, Hartshill Road, Stoke-on-Trent, ST4 7NF Tel: (01782) 846376 Fax: (01782) 414769 E-mail: sales@dexmore.co.uk *Bakery equipment manufrs*

Dexter & Gordon, Priory Farm, Andwell, Hook, Hampshire, RG27 9PA Tel: (01256) 765951 Fax: (01256) 765608 E-mail: sales@printedfootballs.co.uk *Sports, promotional clothing & printed ball manufrs*

▶ Dexter Graphics Ltd, 4-5 Sandpit Road, Dartford, DA1 5BU Tel: (01322) 288880 Fax: (01322) 287333 E-mail: enquiries@dextergraphics.com

Dexter Paints Ltd, Albert Works, Trafalgar Street, Burnley, Lancashire, BB11 1RE Tel: (01282) 423361 Fax: (01282) 414573 *Paint manufrs* Also at: Atherton, Blackburn, Blackpool, Grimsby, Keighley, Lancaster, Nelson, Preston & Telford

▶ Dexter-IT, 11 Babylon Lane, Bishampton, Pershore, Worcestershire, WR10 2NN Tel: 0845 6442414 Fax: 0870 1328311 E-mail: enquiries@Dexter-IT.co.uk *IT consultancy providing cost efficient IT services to Small and Medium businesses - in IT strategy, design, usability & processes. Making your IT your business ally.*

Dextra Lighting Systems plc, 17 Brickfields Business Park, Gillingham, Dorset, SP8 4PX Tel: (01747) 826096 Fax: (01747) 858119 E-mail: sales@dextralighting.co.uk *Lighting manufrs*

Deycom Ltd, I T Solution Centre, 35-37 Esther Road, London, E11 1JB Tel: (020) 8988 7700 Fax: (020) 8988 7701 E-mail: sales@deycom.co.uk *IT resellers*

Deyn Plastics Ltd, Netherwood Road, Rotherwas Industrial Estate, Hereford, HR2 6JU Tel: (01432) 359763 Fax: (01432) 351928 E-mail: enquires@deynplastics.co.uk *Injection moulders*

Deyron Ltd, 32 Southgate Avenue, Mildenhall, Bury St. Edmunds, Suffolk, IP28 7AT Tel: (01638) 716340 Fax: (01638) 515707 *Net curtain manufrs*

▶ Dezac Group, Site F, Forest Vale Road, Forest Vale Industrial Estate, Cinderford, Gloucestershire, GL14 2PH Tel: (01594) 820900

▶ Dezigned4U Embroidery & Printing Services, 164 Newport Road, Caldicot, Monmouthshire, NP26 4AA Tel: (01291) 423724 Fax: (01291) 423724 E-mail: info@dezigned4u.com *Embroidery & printing onto work wear school wear sports kits*

▶ D-Face Design, Studio, 104 Kensal Road, Kensal Rise, London, W10 5BZ Tel: (020) 8959 3125 Fax: (020) 8959 3125 E-mail: design@d-face.co.uk *Logo, Brochure, Leaflet, Web, DVD, CD Design. We specialise in all apects of the design process from artwork to print.*

DFDS Seaways, International Ferry Terminal, Royal Quays, North Shields, Tyne & Wear, NE29 6EE Tel: 0871 882 0885 E-mail: travel.sales@dfds.co.uk *Passenger ferry services to Holland, Denmark, Norway and Beyond*

▶ DFDS Transport Ltd, 10 Brunel Way, Fareham, Hampshire, PO15 5TX Tel: (01489) 563170 Fax: (01489) 563198

▶ Dfire Media Ltd, Shed Studios, 67 Larkhill Road, Abingdon, Oxfordshire, OX14 1BJ Tel: (01235) 559053 E-mail: damian@dfiremedia.com *Produce corporate business films*

▶ DFS Ltd, Buywell Shopping Centre, Thorp Arch Trading Estate, Thorp Arch, Wetherby, West Yorkshire, LS23 7BJ Tel: (01937) 842039 Fax: (01937) 541493

DFS Trading Ltd, 1 Rockingham Way, Adwick-le-Street, Doncaster, South Yorkshire, DN6 7NA Tel: (01302) 330365 Fax: (01302) 330880 *Upholstery manufrs*

▶ DG Stone, 33 Farm Crescent, Wexham, Slough, SL2 5TQ Tel: 01753 524316 Fax: 01753 524316 E-mail: dgstone@hotmail.co.uk *We are Stone, Marble, Granite & Ceramic Tile Suppliers & Fixers.A London Based Contractor, we undertake various size contracts in the south east of england for Main Building Contractors, Managing Agents and Surveyors.**Supply & Fix Natural Stone, Granite and Marble (Internal/ External)*Supply & fix Ceramic Tiles & Mosaic*Stone steps /staircase*Stone, Granite & Marble Repair & Cleaning*Stone /Brick paving**

▶ D-Grease UK Ltd, Unit 3 North Gawber Industrial Park, Blacker Road, Mapplewell, Barnsley, South Yorkshire, S75 6BS Tel: (01226) 230890 Fax: (01226) 381100 E-mail: enquiries@dgrease.fsnet.co.uk *Parts, washers suppliers*

DGS, 7 New Albion Estate, Halley Street, Glasgow, G13 4DJ Tel: 0141-941 3553 Fax: 0141-941 3777 *Clothing manufrs*

▶ DH Electrical, 1 Rosemary Cresent, Tiptree, Colchester, CO5 0XA Tel: (01621) 817827 E-mail: dh.electrical@btopenworld.com *Electrical contractors*

▶ DH.Services UK & European Pilots Ltd, 4 Kingsway, Heanor, Derbyshire, DE75 7QU Tel: 07966 795477 Fax: 01773 710850 E-mail: info@dhservicesltd.co.uk *ABNORMAL LOAD ESCORT SPECIALIST,BASED IN THE EASTMIDLANDS SUPPLYING ESCORTS,STEERSMAN AND ROUTE SURVEYS THROUGHOUT THE UK AT REASONABLE RATES*

Dhap Ltd, The Headlands, Downton, Salisbury, SP5 3HT Tel: (01725) 513639 Fax: (01725) 513698 *Aerospace fabricators*

▶ DHL P.L.C., West Bay Road, Western Docks, Southampton, SO15 1AW Tel: (023) 8022 1835

DHL Express (UK) Ltd, Orbital Pk, 178-188 Great South West Rd, Hounslow, TW4 6JS Tel: (08701) 100300

DHL Global Forwarding Ltd, Danzas House, Dawley Park, Kestrel Way, Hayes, Middlesex, UB3 1HJ Tel: (020) 8754 5000 Fax: (020) 8754 5154 E-mail: penny.darnbrook@dhl.com *Air & ocean freight global network*

DHL Global Mail Ltd, Mills Road, Quarry Wood, Aylesford, Kent, ME20 7WZ Tel: (01622) 792111 Fax: (01622) 792333 *Mailing services*

▶ Di Rollo Of Musselburgh, 8-14 South Street, Musselburgh, Midlothian, EH21 6AT Tel: 0131-665 3002 Fax: 0131-653 2908

▶ Diack & Macaulay Ltd, 7 Gartferry Road, Chryston, Glasgow, G69 0LY Tel: (01236) 875166 Fax: (01236) 875488

▶ Diadora (UK) Ltd, Sovereign Court, King Edward Street, Macclesfield, Cheshire, SK10 1AA Tel: (01625) 421212 *Sporting goods specialists*

Diafade Ltd, 4 Norfolk Road, Buntingford, Hertfordshire, SG9 9AN Tel: (01763) 273379 E-mail: mailroom@diafade.co.uk *Web site designers*

▶ Diageo, Benrinnes Distillery, Aberlour, Banffshire, AB38 9NN Tel: (01340) 872600 Fax: (01340) 872603 *Distiller*

▶ Diageo Ltd, Dailuaine Distillery, Carron, Aberlour, Banffshire, AB38 7RE Tel: (01340) 872500 Fax: (01340) 872504

▶ Diageo Ltd, Cardow Distillery, Knockando, Aberlour, Banffshire, AB38 7RY Tel: (01340) 872550 Fax: (01340) 872554 *Whiskey distillery*

▶ Diageo Ltd, Blackgrange Bond, Blackgrange, Alloa, Clackmannanshire, FK10 2PH Tel: (01259) 722093 Fax: (01259) 766657

▶ Diageo Ltd, Carsebridge Road, Alloa, Clackmannanshire, FK10 3BB Tel: (01259) 216811 Fax: (01259) 766670 *Spirits manufrs*

▶ Diageo Ltd, Blackgrange Bond, Blackgrange, Alloa, Clackmannanshire, FK10 2PH Tel: (01259) 722093 Fax: (01259) 766657 *Distilling spirit specialists*

▶ Diageo Ltd, Clynelish Distillery, Brora, Sutherland, KW9 6LR Tel: (01408) 623000 Fax: (01408) 623004 *Spirits*

▶ Diageo Ltd, Millburn, Linkwood Distillery, Elgin, Morayshire, IV30 8RD Tel: (01343) 553800 Fax: (01343) 553802

▶ Diageo Ltd, Longmorn, Elgin, Morayshire, IV30 8SL Tel: (01343) 862100 Fax: (01343) 862102

▶ Diageo Ltd, Glendullan Distillery, Dufftown, Keith, Banffshire, AB55 4DJ Tel: (01340) 822311 Fax: (01340) 822319 *Distilling company*

▶ Diageo Ltd, 18-20 Hill Street, Kilmarnock, Ayrshire, KA3 1HF Tel: (01563) 575000 Fax: (01563) 536744 *Blenders & bottling whiskey specialists*

▶ The Diageo, Stafford Street, Oban, Argyll, PA34 5NH Tel: (01631) 572000 Fax: (01631) 572006 *Distilling services*

▶ The Diageo, Stafford Street, Oban, Argyll, PA34 5NH Tel: (01631) 572000 Fax: (01631) 572006 *Malt whiskey distillers*

▶ Diageo Ltd, Argyll Avenue, Renfrew, PA4 9EB Tel: 0141-885 6300 *Spirits supplier*

▶ Diageo Distillers Plc, Mortlach Distillery, Dufftown, Keith, Banffshire, AB55 4AQ Tel: (01340) 820318 *Distillant*

Diageo Global Supply, Banbeath Industrial Estate, Leven, Fife, KY8 5HD Tel: (01333) 424000 Fax: (01333) 425037 E-mail: marketing@diageo.com *Scotch whisky bottlers & blenders*

▶ Diagnostic Monitoring Systems Ltd, The Teacher Building, 14 St Enoch Square, Glasgow, G1 4DB Tel: 0141-572 0840

Diagnostic Solutions Ltd, Unit 1, Rossett Business Village, Rossett, Chester, LL12 0AY Tel: (01244) 571411 Fax: (01244) 571977 E-mail: office@diagnosticsolutions.co.uk *Maintenance management & electronic data collection methods*

Diagnostic Sonar Ltd, Baird Road, Kirkton Campus, Livingston, West Lothian, EH54 7BX Tel: (01506) 411877 Fax: (01506) 412410 E-mail: sales@diagnosticsonar.com *Ultrasonic medical equipment*

▶ Diagnostic Ultrasound UK Ltd, The Granary, Aston Sandford, Aylesbury, Buckinghamshire, HP17 8LP Tel: (01844) 299207 Fax: (01844) 299218

Diagnostics Social & Market Research Ltd, 109 Gloucester Road, London, SW7 4SS Tel: (020) 7373 7111 Fax: (020) 7370 2580 E-mail: reception@diagnostics.co.uk *Market researchers*

▶ Diagraph Advertising & Display Products, Croydon Road, Nottingham, NG7 3DS Tel: 0115-924 9111 Fax: 0115-924 9222

Diak Technical Export Ltd, Diak House, Romsey, Hampshire, SO51 6AE Tel: (01794) 518808 Fax: (01794) 519960 E-mail: sales@diak.com *Engineering equipment exporters*

▶ Dial a Box Ltd, 35 Riverside Close, Warrington, WA1 2JD Tel: (01925) 650964 Fax: (0800) 7316769 E-mail: sales@dial-a-box.co.uk *Supplier of Removal and Storage Boxes and Accessories*

▶ Dial A Roti, 582 Great Horton Road, Bradford, West Yorkshire, BD7 3EU Tel: (01274) 522722

Dial A Sign, Bessemer Road, Cardiff, CF11 8BA Tel: (029) 2039 8208 Fax: (029) 2039 8209 E-mail: signs@dialasign.fsnet.co.uk *Signs manufrs*

Dial Art (PC) Ltd, 3 Airfield Way, Christchurch, Dorset, BH23 3PE Tel: (01202) 486486 Fax: (01202) 488988 E-mail: sales@dialart.com *Printed circuit manufrs*

▶ Dial Direct Travel, 18 Abbey Fields, Telford, Shropshire, TF3 2AL Tel: (01952) 274636 Fax: (01952) 274636 E-mail: sales@dialdirecttravel.co.uk *Cruise Holidays, late holidays deals & last minute flights to Canary Islands, Egypt. Nile cruises, Dominican Republic, Caribbean. last minute travel, hotels with bed & breakfast, half board, full board or all inclusive*

Dial Marketing Ltd, 68 Dial Hill Road, Clevedon, Avon, BS21 7EW Tel: (01275) 875876 Fax: (01275) 340899 E-mail: dialmarketing@btconnect.com *Corporate merchandising producers*

Dial Patterns Ltd, 5 Bridge Road Business Centre, Bridge Road, Ashford, Kent, TN23 1BB Tel: (01233) 663073 Fax: (01233) 643775 E-mail: sales@dialpatterns.co.uk *Foundry Pattern and Model Makers for General Engineering, Automotive and Tooling Requirements. Specialists of Investment Castings and Rapid Prototyping.*

Dial Precision Engineering Ltd, Dial House Dutton Green, Stanney Mill Industrial Park, Little Stanney, Chester, CH2 4SA Tel: 0151-357 2016 Fax: 0151-355 0751 E-mail: warren@dial-eng.co.uk *Precision engineers & steel fabricators*

Dial Solutions Ltd, PO Box 84, Leeds, LS15 8UZ Tel: 0113-294 5111 Fax: (0870) 0517288 *Computer software developer & consultants*

Dialcrown Ltd, 90 Tollington Way, London, N7 6RY Tel: (020) 7281 8130 Fax: (020) 7281 8809 *Ladies clothing & dress manufrs*

Dialight B L P Ltd, Exning Road, Newmarket, Suffolk, CB8 0AX Tel: (01638) 665161 Fax: (01638) 660718 E-mail: sales@blpcomp.com Principal Export Areas: North America *Solenoid manufrs*

▶ Dialog Global Trade, 655 North Circular Road, London, NW2 7AY Tel: (020) 8830 9555 Fax: (020) 8830 9800 E-mail: pyramidgroup@dg-trade.co.uk *We are specializing in Refurbishment and Construction for Listed Buildings, our expertise enables us to carry out work such as Dry Rot Eradication, Water&Damp Proofing in partnership with BIOKILCRWON**

Dialog Semiconductor UK Ltd, Windmill Hill Business Park, Whitehill Way, Swindon, SN5 6PJ Tel: (01793) 875327 Fax: (01793) 875328 E-mail: mixed_signal@diasemi.com *Microcircuit designers*

▶ Dialogue Commercial Interiors Ltd, New Farm Buildings, Northampton Road, Stoke Bruerne, Towcester, Northants, NN12 7XU Tel: (01604) 864401 Fax: (01604) 862519 *Shop fitting manufrs*

Dialrack Ltd, 8 Bilton Industrial Estate, Bilton Road, Basingstoke, Hampshire, RG24 8LJ Tel: (01256) 810907 Fax: (01256) 810942 E-mail: sales@dialrack.co.uk *Racking & storage systems distributors*

Dialstat Office Supplies, 1 Sovereign Business Park, 46-48 Willis Way, Poole, Dorset, BH15 3TB Tel: (01202) 774400 Fax: (01202) 666818 E-mail: info@dialstat.co.uk *Office suppliers, office furniture & interiors*

Diam Software Ltd, 4 Lincoln Avenue, Canterbury, Kent, CT1 3YD Tel: (01227) 479333 E-mail: enquiries@diam.co.uk *Computer consultants*

Diamant Precision Engineering Ltd, Unit 1 Marcus Close, Tilehurst, Reading, RG30 4EA Tel: 0118-945 1222 Fax: 0118-945 1077 E-mail: quality@damantltd.co.uk *Subcontract engineers*

▶ Diamanttek Ltd, Unit 12 Raikes Clough Industrial Estate, Raikes Lane, Bolton, BL3 1RP Tel: (01204) 366435 Fax: (01204) 366437

Diamar Fabrications Ltd, Unit 6 North St Trading Estate, Brierley Hill, West Midlands, DY5 3QF Tel: (01384) 480528 Fax: (01384) 480528 *Steel fabrication*

Diametric Metal Fabrications Ltd, The Brookland, Blithbury Road, Rugeley, Staffordshire, WS15 3HQ Tel: (01889) 577243 Fax: (01889) 584672 E-mail: sales@diametricmetalfabrications.co.uk *Tubular & sheet metalwork engineers or fabricators*

Diametric Technical Manufacturing Ltd, 26-28 Manners View, Newport, Isle of Wight, PO30 5FA Tel: (01983) 826611 Fax: (01983) 826622 E-mail: tad.james@diemetric-manufacturing.co.uk *Badge label & nameplate manufrs*

Diamik Solutions Ltd, A W Nielsen Road, Goole, North Humberside, DN14 6UE Tel: (0845) 1300690 Fax: (0845) 1300691 E-mail: sales@diamikbymorris.co.uk *Educational furniture manufrs*

Diamond Accumulator Co. Ltd, The Chase, Bournemouth Park Road, Southend-on-Sea, SS2 5LW Tel: (01702) 467083 *Lead acid battery manufrs*

Diamond Aircraft UK Ltd, Gamston Airfield, Gamston, Retford, Nottinghamshire, DN22 0QL Tel: (01777) 839200 Fax: (01777) 839300 E-mail: diamond@diamondair.co.uk *Aircraft service supplier*

Diamond Alarm Systems, 106 Crwys Road, Cardiff, CF24 4NQ Tel: (029) 2045 1789 Fax: (029) 2037 2505 *Security alarms*

▶ Diamond Auto Parts, Brookbank Garage, Scotland Road, Carnforth, Lancashire, LA5 9JZ Tel: 01524 734200 Fax: 01524 734200 E-mail: sales@diamondautoparts.co.uk *Car parts internet retailers*

▶ Diamond Business Solutions, PO Box 184, Ashford, Middlesex, TW15 2ZQ Tel: (0871) 8714605 Fax: (0871) 2773138 E-mail: admin@diamondbusinesssolutions.com *Information consultancy services*

Diamond Ceilings Ltd, 227 Southborough Lane, Bromley, BR2 8AT Tel: (020) 7232 2122 Fax: (020) 8295 5941 *Ceiling fixing & partitioning contractors*

Diamond Chain Co., Unit 7-9 Blaydon Industrial Park, Chainbridge Road, Blaydon-on-Tyne, Tyne & Wear, NE21 5AB Tel: 0191-414 8822 Fax: 0191-414 8877 E-mail: sales@diamondchain.co.uk *Drive chain distributors*

▶ Diamond Coatings, 11 Lodge Forge Trading Estate, Cradley Road, Cradley Heath, West Midlands, B64 7RW Tel: (01384) 566222 Fax: (01384) 562826 E-mail: enquires@diamondcoatings.co.uk *Indium tin oxide coaters*

▶ Diamond Compresser Services, 23 Mayfield Road, Chaddesden, Derby, DE21 6FX Tel: (01332) 677835 Fax: (01332) 677835 E-mail: ap@diamondcompressor.fsnet.co.uk *Suppliers of refrigeration equipment*

▶ Diamond Computers Ltd, 36 New England Road, Brighton, BN1 4GG Tel: (01273) 625032 Fax: (01273) 711504 *Computer software suppliers*

Diamond Corrugated Cases Ltd, 12-13 Pennyburn Industrial Estate, Londonderry, BT48 0LU Tel: (028) 7126 2957 Fax: (028) 7126 7094 E-mail: mail@diamondcorr.com *Fibreboard manufrs*

Diamond Cutters Herts Ltd, 10 Silk Mill, Brook Street, Tring, Hertfordshire, HP23 5EF Tel: (01442) 891313 Fax: (01442) 890751 E-mail: diamond.cutters@virgin.net *Concrete drilling contractors*

Diamond Cutting Formes, 2 Monks Brook Industrial Park, School Close, Chandler's Ford, Eastleigh, Hampshire, SO53 4RA Tel: (023) 8026 7326 Fax: (023) 8027 5187 E-mail: dcformes@izrmail.com *Cutting form services*

Diamond Diesels Ltd, Unit 4 Blackburn Industrial Estate, Enterprise Way, Sherburn In Elmet, Leeds, LS25 6NA Tel: (0844) 4996373 Fax: (0844) 4996383 E-mail: sales@diamonddiesels.co.uk *Industrial & marine diesel engines & spare parts importers* Also at: Sherburn-in-Elmet

Diamond Distributors, 2 Loughgall Road, Armagh, BT61 7NH Tel: (07802) 903300 Fax: (028) 3752 6464 E-mail: sales@automaintain.co.uk *Motor products suppliers*

Diamond Edge Ltd, 126 Gloucester Road, Brighton, BN1 4BU Tel: (01273) 605922 Fax: (01273) 625074 E-mail: diamondedge@btclick.com *Dog grooming & hairdressing equipment, sharpening & repair service available for scissors, blades, clippers & dryers.*

▶ Diamond Engineers Ltd, PO Box 014, Halesowen, West Midlands, B63 3HY Tel: (0870) 1630019 Fax: (0870) 1630021 E-mail: mandi@dimondengineers.co.uk *IT & cabling engineers*

▶ Diamond Event Security Ltd, 60 Heol Collen, Cardiff, CF5 5TX Tel: (029) 2059 1340 Fax: (029) 2059 6091 E-mail: info@diamondeventsecurity.co.uk *Diamond Event Security Ltd are suppliers of licensed and experienced stewards and security personnel to the entertainment and leisure industry.*

Diamond Glass Works, Brown Street, Bolton, BL1 1TY Tel: (01204) 527853 Fax: (01204) 527853 *Glass merchants*

▶ Diamond Glaze Ltd, Fen Road, Ruskington, Sleaford, Lincolnshire, NG34 9TH Tel: (01526) 832228 Fax: (01526) 832228 *UPVC manufrs*

Diamond Graphics, Norton House, 61a High Street, Wordsley, Stourbridge, West Midlands, DY8 5SD Tel: (01384) 572878 Fax: (01384) 481975 *Plastic labels, nameplates & badges manufrs*

Diamond Ground Products Ltd, Blackstone Road, Stukeley Meadows Industrial Estate, Huntingdon, Cambridgeshire, PE29 6EF Tel: (01480) 459706 Fax: (01480) 453649 E-mail: sales@diamondground.co.uk *Welding electrodes specialists*

Diamond Group, 145 Willington Street, Maidstone, Kent, ME15 8QX Tel: (01622) 688817 Fax: (01622) 670212 E-mail: sales@diamondgroup.org.uk *Computer value added resellers*

Diamond H Controls Ltd, Vulcan Road North, Norwich, NR6 6AH Tel: (01603) 425291 Fax: (01603) 424907 E-mail: sales@diamond-h-controls.co.uk *Manufacturers of electrical, electronic & gas controls*

▶ Diamond Industrial, 10 Carrock Road, Croft Business Park, Bromborough, Wirral, Merseyside, CH62 3RA Tel: 0151-343 0303 Fax: 0151-343 0303 E-mail: diamondindustrial@yahoo.co.uk *Pneumatic equipment distribution*

Diamond Instrumentation Ltd, 46 Swan Road, Swan Industrial Estate, District 9, Washington, Tyne & Wear, NE38 8JJ Tel: 0191-417 8911 Fax: 0191-419 1426 *Electronic engineers*

Diamond Interior Design, Century Street, Stoke-on-Trent, ST1 5HT Tel: (01782) 212242 Fax: (01782) 202375 E-mail: sales@diamond-interior-design.co.uk *Interior design, bathrooms, kitchens, bedrooms, tiles, living rooms*

▶ Diamond Linen Services, Coventry Street, Birmingham, B5 5NH Tel: 0121-631 1626 Fax: 0121-631 1627 E-mail: jam158@hotmail.com *Supplying linen to the hotel & restaurant catering industry*

Diamond Logistics, 8 The Elms Centre, Glaziers Lane, Normandy, Guildford, Surrey, GU3 2DF Tel: (01483) 812020 Fax: (01483) 811500 E-mail: sales@thegcg.com Principal Export Areas: Central/East Europe, West Europe & North America *Courier services*

Diamond Management Services Ltd, Diamond House, 149 Frimley Road, Camberley, Surrey, GU15 2PS Tel: (01276) 691415 Fax: (01276) 692903 E-mail: info@dms-management.com *Computer software developers*

The Diamond Metal Finishing Company Ltd, 6 Newfields Industrial Estate, High Street, Stoke-on-Trent, ST6 5PD Tel: (01782) 822442 Fax: (01782) 839125 E-mail: stevependo@aol.com *Electroplating specialists*

Diamond Mine Jewellery, Marr House, Copley Hill, Leeds, LS12 1HY Tel: 0113-243 4950 Fax: 0113-242 3478 E-mail: dgm@dmj.co.uk *Jewellery manufrs*

Diamond Offshore, Howe Moss Drive, Kirkhill Industrial Estate, Dyce, Aberdeen, AB21 0GL Tel: (01224) 727500 Fax: (01224) 722873 *Offshore drilling contractors*

Diamond Paste & Mould Co., 78 Battle Road, St. Leonards-on-Sea, East Sussex, TN37 7AG Tel: (01424) 201505 Fax: (01424) 421359 E-mail: sales@sugarcity.co.uk *Cake craft business manufrs*

Diamond People Ltd, The Chestnuts, Munderfield, Bromyard, Herefordshire, HR7 4JT Tel: (01885) 490480 Fax: (01885) 490484 E-mail: enquiries@diamondpeople.co.uk *Computer software development services*

Diamond Point International, Unit 9 North Point Business Estate, Enterpise Close, Medway City Estate, Rochester, Kent, ME2 4LX Tel: (01634) 722390 Fax: (01634) 722398 E-mail: sales@dpie.com *Industrial & embedded computer dealers & distributors service*

Diamond Power Service, 1a Clarke Street, Farnworth, Bolton, BL4 9JH Tel: (01204) 793303 Fax: (01204) 403804 E-mail: diamondpsi@aol.com *Diamond cutting service & repairers*

Diamond Power Specialty Ltd, Glasgow Road, Dumbarton, G82 1ES Tel: (01389) 744000 Fax: (01389) 762669 E-mail: sales@diamondpower.co.uk *Soot blower manufrs*

Diamond Precision Engineering, 4 Kelvin Park, Dock Road, Birkenhead, Merseyside, CH41 1LT Tel: 0151-647 9050 Fax: 0151-647 9186 E-mail: sales@diamondprecisionengineering.co.uk *Press tools jigs, fixtures & special purpose machinery*

Diamond Printed Products Plastic Printers, Maidstone Road, Nettlestead, Maidstone, Kent, ME18 5HP Tel: (01622) 871666 Fax: (01622) 872628 E-mail: info@diamondprinted.com *Screen printing services*

Diamond Seal Ltd, Bowling Back Lane, Bradford, West Yorkshire, BD4 8SX Tel: (01274) 303400 Fax: (01274) 303401 *Industrial door & window manufrs*

Diamond Software Ltd, Ryecroft Hall, Manchester Road, Audenshaw, Manchester, M34 5ZJ Tel: 0161-301 3888 Fax: 0161-371 7337 E-mail: info@diamondsoftware.co.uk *Computer systems & software developers*

Diamond Styles, 13 Melton Street, Leicester, LE1 3NB Tel: 0116-251 2745 Fax: 0116-251 2745 *Clothing & fabric manufrs*

The Diamond Stylus Company Ltd, Council Street West, Llandudno, Gwynedd, LL30 1ED Tel: (01492) 860880 Fax: (01492) 860653 E-mail: sales@diamondstylus.co.uk *Audio & visual equipment accessories distributors*

▶ Diamond Wheels, 6 Brighton Road, Stockport, Cheshire, SK4 2BE Tel: 0161-442 7474 Fax: 0161-442 7474 *Wheels & castors refurbishment*

Diamond Wildwater, Northolt Drive, Bolton, BL3 6RE Tel: (01204) 528225 Fax: (01204) 361549 E-mail: diamondwild-water@mikar.co.uk *Wet & dry water sport suit manufrs*

Diamond Windows, 25 The Fairways, New River Trading Estate, Cheshunt, Waltham Cross, Hertfordshire, EN8 0NL Tel: (01992) 635162 Fax: (01992) 623300 *Aluminum & wood frame window installers*

Diamondjack Ltd, 16 Huntsmead, Alton, Hampshire, GU34 2SE Tel: (01420) 542932 Fax: (01420) 542608 *Diamond cutting blades distributors*

Diamonds Andrew Ltd, 11 Hatton Garden, London, EC1N 8AH Tel: (020) 7405 4402 Fax: (020) 7831 4807 E-mail: info@arlington.co.com *Jewellery*

▶ Diamould Ltd, 10 Peter Green Way, Furness Business Park, Barrow-in-Furness, Cumbria, LA14 2PE Tel: (01229) 825888 Fax: (01229) 825950 E-mail: sales@diamould.com

▶ Diane's Dolls! Antique Dolls & Collectable Dolls, 4 Dowland Gardens, High Green, Sheffield, S35 4GQ Tel: 0114-284 6582 Fax: 0114-284 7813 E-mail: dolls@dmcginley.com *Antique dolls & collectable dolls including bisque retailer*

Dia-Nielsen UK Ltd, Enfield Lock, South Ordnance Road, Enfield, Middlesex, EN3 6JG Tel: (01992) 787110 *Marking device manufrs*

Diaploy Ltd, Manners Avenue, Manners Industrial Estate, Ilkeston, Derbyshire, DE7 8EF Tel: 0115-944 2272 Fax: 0115-944 2272 *CNC punching & bending*

Diaquip Sales & Service, 1 Whitefield Road, Bredbury, Stockport, Cheshire, SK6 2QR Tel: 0161-406 0609 Fax: 0161-406 0211 *Professional diamond cutting products manufrs*

Diatest UK Ltd, 18 Avondale Avenue, Hinchley Wood, Esher, Surrey, KT10 0DA Tel: (020) 8398 1100 Fax: (020) 8398 9887 E-mail: sales@diatest.co.uk *Precision engineering measuring equipment (metrology)*

▶ Diatherm & Ancillary Equipment, Gresham Works, Mornington Road, London, E4 7DR Tel: (020) 8524 9546 Fax: (020) 8524 9546 E-mail: diatherm@talk21.com *Enamelling suppliers*

Diaward Equipment (UK) Ltd, Firmin House, 82-86 New Town Row, Birmingham, B6 4HU Tel: 0121-359 6666 Fax: 0121-359 3292 E-mail: enquiries@firmin.co.uk *Uniform clothing manufrs*

Dibbin's Removals & Storage, Nicholson Road, Ryde, Isle of Wight, PO33 1BQ Tel: (01983) 566425 Fax: (01983) 566211 E-mail: sales@dibbensremovals.com *Removals & container storage, local, national, european, Worldwide shipping and air freight, on-line quotations, members of the national guild of removers & storers*

Dibro Ltd, Unit 2, Bechers Drive, Aintree Racecourse Retail & Business Park, Liverpool, L9 5AY Tel: 0151-525 0365 Fax: 0151-525 0342 E-mail: tom@dibro.com *Vacuum coated plastic product manufrs*

Dichtomatik Ltd, Donington House, Riverside Road, Pride Park, Derby, DE24 8HY Tel: (01332) 202121 Fax: (01332) 524404 E-mail: mail@dichtomatik.co.uk *Manufacturers of industrial rubber, hydraulic & oil seals*

Alan Dick & Co. Ltd, The Barlands, London Road, Charlton Kings, Cheltenham, Gloucestershire, GL52 6UT Tel: (01242) 518500 Fax: (01242) 510191 E-mail: contact@uk.alandickgroup.com *Antenna & tower manufrs*

Alan Dick Engineering Ltd, Middleton Road, Heysham, Morecambe, Lancashire, LA3 2SE Tel: (01524) 855011 Fax: (01524) 859158 E-mail: adeheysham@btclick.com *Sub-contract engineers* Also at: Cleator Moor & Heysham

▶ Dick Fleming Communications, The Riverside Drive Arches, 33-37 South College Street, Aberdeen, AB11 6LE Tel: (01224) 588844 Fax: (01224) 212538 E-mail: sales@dfcommunications.com *Telecommunications services*

Dick Freecast Inverness, Dores Road, Inverness, IV2 4RP Tel: (01463) 237556 Fax: (01463) 222871 *Concrete product manufrs*

Dick Lovett Bristol Ltd, Laurel Court, Cribbs Causeway, Bristol, BS10 7TU Tel: 0117-905 0000 Fax: 0117-905 0090 *Car servicing, parts & accessories*

Dick Precast Ltd, Taymouth Engineering Works, Anderson Street, Carnoustie, Angus, DD7 7LZ Tel: (01241) 858687 Fax: (01241) 858535 *Pre-cast concrete products manufrs*

Dick Ropa, Carrstone Lodge, Pullover Road, Tilney All Saints, King's Lynn, Norfolk, PE34 4SG Tel: (01553) 692035 E-mail: info@dickropa.com *Entertainment suppliers*

Dick Thomas York Ltd, Hallfield Road, York, YO31 7XQ Tel: (01904) 430920 Fax: (01904) 430911 *Commercial stationery suppliers*

Dick Thompson & Co., Unit 91a Blackdyke Road, Kingstown Industrial Estate, Carlisle, CA3 0PJ Tel: (01228) 549000 Fax: (01228) 521200 *Window manufrs*

Dickens Bros Ltd, 69-71 Kettering Road, Northampton, NN1 4AP Tel: (01604) 636537 Fax: (01604) 636537 E-mail: dickensbrothers@btinternet.com *Leather dressers & merchants*

Dickerman Overseas Contracting Co. Ltd, Unit 3 Adam Business Centre, Henson Way, Telford Way Industrial Estate, Kettering, Northamptonshire, NN16 8PX Tel: (01536) 525131 Fax: (01536) 412031 E-mail: info@dickermangroup.com *Corrosion prevention & protection services*

M. Dickerson Ltd, Ely Road, Waterbeach, Cambridge, CB5 9PG Tel: (01223) 860000 Fax: (01223) 440378 E-mail: reception@m-dickerson.co.uk *Sand & gravel suppliers*

▶ Dickfisher Ltd, 5 Harland Close, Little Haywood, Stafford, ST18 0JY Tel: (01889) 881159 E-mail: dick@dickfisher.com *Video production services*

▶ Dickie Construction, Burnfield Avenue, Glasgow, G46 7TY Tel: 0141-633 1234

Dickies, Garth Road, Bangor, Gwynedd, LL57 2SE Tel: (01248) 363414 Fax: (01248) 354169 E-mail: info@dickies.co.uk *Yacht chandlers & brokers, boat distributors & facilities for repairs*

Dickies Workwear, Second Avenue, Westfield Trading Estate, Midsomer Norton, Radstock, BA3 4BH Tel: (01761) 410041 Fax: (01761) 414825 E-mail: uksales@dickies.com *Dickies (UK) Ltd *With over 80 years' experience in workwear manufacturing, generations of workers have found Dickies to be a brand they can trust From oil fields around the world to major construction sites Dickies workwear has been tested to the limit, gaining a reputation for quality and performance. *Our range includes Coverall's, Redhawk Workwear, Chef's Workwear, Painters Workwear, Deluxe Workwear, Eisenhower Workwear, Delta Workwear, Flame Retardant Workwear especially designed for the off shore industry, High Visibility workwear our range includes highway safety trousers, jackets & waistcoats. We have a waterproof range, including trousers, jackets etc. We also stock safety and non safety footwear, rigger boots, executive safety footwear. *Utilising the best of both modern and traditional construction techniques the Dickies range is made to last. *Great value, hardwearing, functional workwear. Dickies - the preferred choice for workers worldwide.*

Dickinson Catering Equipment, 7 Stalbridge Road, Crewe, CW2 7LR Tel: 0800-977 5325 Fax: (01270) 215213 E-mail: menderman@aol.com *Dickinson Catering Equipment based in Crewe are catering equipment suppliers and engineers.*

Dave Dickinson & Associates Ltd, Ahed House, Sandbeds Trading Estate, Ossett, West Yorkshire, WF5 9ND Tel: (01924) 265757 Fax: (01924) 275117 E-mail: enquiries@ddaltd.co.uk *Consultant engineers*

Dickinson Legg Ltd, Moorside Road, Winchester, Hampshire, SO23 7SS Tel: (01962) 842222 Fax: (01962) 840567 E-mail: sales@dickinson.com *Tobacco & tea processing machinery manufrs*

Dickinson & Morris, P O Box 580, Leicester, LE4 1ZN Tel: 0116-235 5900 Fax: 0116-235 5711 *Bakery & confectionery suppliers & retailers*

Dickinson Philips & Co., Snaygill Industrial Estate, Keighley Road, Skipton, North Yorkshire, BD23 2QR Tel: (01756) 700359 Fax: (01756) 700360 E-mail: sales@dickinsonphilips.com *Injection mould toolmakers & plastic injection mouldings.*

Dickinson Shoe Services Ltd, 345 Shields Road, Newcastle upon Tyne, NE6 2UD Tel: 0191-265 4858 Fax: 0191-224 2245 E-mail: westgaterubbers@aol.com *Safety & non safety footwear manufrs*

Dicks Electrical Installation Ltd, Winnall Valley Road, Winchester, Hampshire, SO23 0LR Tel: (01962) 841441 Fax: (01962) 840730 *Electrical contractors*

Ian Dickson Ltd, 22a Kemball Street, Ipswich, IP4 5EE Tel: (01473) 714750 Fax: (01473) 727923 *Cabinet makers*

W. Dickson (Blinds & Shutters) Ltd, 25 Sunnyside, Easter Road, Edinburgh, EH7 5RA Tel: 0131-661 8877 Fax: 0131-661 5922 *Blind & shutter manufrs*

Dicol Co. Ltd, Colchester Road, Tendring, Clacton-on-Sea, Essex, CO16 9AA Tel: (01255) 830119 Fax: (01255) 831362 E-mail: sales@dicol.com *Hydraulic cylinder & ram manufrs*

Dicom Ltd, Lydford Road, Alfreton, Derbyshire, DE55 7RQ Tel: (01773) 520565 Fax: (01773) 520881 E-mail: sales@dicom.ltd.uk *Waste compaction systems manufrs* Also at: Derby

▶ Dicsmart Disc Services, 25a Caxton Avenue, Blackpool, FY2 9AP Tel: (01253) 508670 Fax: (01253) 508670 *Suppliers of cd & dvd services*

▶ indicates data change since last edition

Dictacliff Ltd, Burywater Barn, Burywater Lane, Newport, Saffron Walden, Essex, CB11 3TZ Tel: (01799) 542242 Fax: (01799) 542322 E-mail: john@dictacliff.co.uk *Furniture manufrs*

Dictating Machine Co Ltd, 22 Broadway, London, SW1H 0BH Tel: (020) 7222 2626 Fax: (020) 7222 6680 *Dictating machine distributors*

▶ Diddimix Concrete, 53 Bradgate Street, Leicester, LE4 0AW Tel: 0116-253 2653 Fax: 0116-253 7779

Didsbury Engineering, Unit 1b Lower Meadow Road, Brooke Park, Handforth, Wilmslow, Cheshire, SK9 3LP Tel: 0161-486 2200 Fax: 0161-486 2211E-mail: sales@didsbury.com *Precision lifting & handling manufrs*

▶ Didsbury Plant Hire Ltd, Limefield House, Limefield Brow, Bury, Lancashire, BL9 6QS Tel: 0161-764 2580 Fax: 0161-763 9511

Die Max Engineering, 1-2 Mid Wynd, Dundee, DD1 4JG Tel: (01382) 224481 Fax: (01382) 224481 *Precision engineers*

Die Technology Ltd, Corbrook Road, Chadderton, Oldham, OL9 9SD Tel: 0161-626 3827 Fax: 0161-627 2341 E-mail: info@ditech.co.uk *Microelectronic distributors*

▶ Diedesign Emblems, Unit 16 Magreal Industrial Estate, Freeth Street, Birmingham, B16 0QZ Tel: 0121-455 0505 Fax: 0121-455 8484 E-mail: info@diedesign.co.uk *Die sinkers*

▶ Diego Co., Carbost, Isle Of Skye, IV47 8SR Tel: (01478) 614308 Fax: (01478) 614302 E-mail: dorothymorrison@diagio.co.uk *Distillers*

▶ Diego Distillers Ltd, Blair Athol Distillery, Perth Road, Pitlochry, Perthshire, PH16 5LY Tel: (01796) 482000

Diehl Sales UK, 2 West Street, Bradford, West Yorkshire, BD2 3BS Tel: (01274) 632227 Fax: (01274) 632059 *Non ferrous metal manufrs*

Dielife Actheron, 30 Commercial Street, Middlesbrough, Cleveland, TS2 1JW Tel: (01642) 241516 Fax: (01642) 245171 *Welding services*

Diemaster Associates Ltd, 63 Kenilworth Road, Sale, Cheshire, M33 5DA Tel: 0161-973 1414 Fax: 0161-905 1466 *Tungsten carbide dyes & tools manufrs*

Diemould Service Co. Ltd, 11 Blenheim Road, Cressex Business Park, High Wycombe, Buckinghamshire, HP12 3RS Tel: (01494) 523811 Fax: (01494) 452898 E-mail: sales@dms-diemould.co.uk *Diecasting mould & die toolmakers*

Die-Pat Holdings Ltd, The Die-Pat Centre, Broad March, Daventry, Northamptonshire, NN11 4HE Tel: (01327) 311144 Fax: (01327) 871821 E-mail: sales@die-pat.co.uk *Specialised hardware for the food service industry*

Diepress Refresherator Ltd, 27-31 Cato St North, Birmingham, B7 5AP Tel: 0121-333 3139 Fax: 0121-359 1729 E-mail: diepress@birmingham.co.uk *Heating & ventilating grille manufrs*

Dies To Die For, Unit 1, Low Bank Garage, Ashton-in-Makerfield, Wigan, Lancashire, WN4 9RN Tel: (01942) 711063 Fax: (01942) 711063 E-mail: kirstywiseman@hotmail.com *Mail order craft supplier with everything a cardmaker and scrapbooker could want. New premises with small shop open to customers too!. Our range increases weekly with stock arriving from the US, Australia and the far east. We pride ourselves in finding little bits not commonly available and if we cannot supply what you are looking for then we will try so hard to find somewhere that does. Customer service and satisfaction is our speciality. Come and see us and look up some of our workshops and crops on the website - we would love to meet you. We now also provide cutting and creasing services including business card and promotion campaign literature.*

Diesel Industrial Electrical Spares & Equipment (London), Units 19-20 Thurrock Commercial Park, Purfleet Industrial Park, London Road, Aveley, South Ockendon, Essex, RM15 4YA Tel: (01708) 890011 Fax: (01708) 862111 E-mail: dieseluk@aol.com Principal Export Areas: Worldwide *Diesel engine component manufrs*

Diesel Injection (Aylesbury) Ltd, Unit 20, Edison Road, Rabans Lane, Aylesbury, Buckinghamshire, HP19 8TE Tel: (01296) 487400 Fax: (01296) 422343 *Bosch diesel injection engineers*

Diesel Injector Services, 8 Staveley Way, Brixworth Industrial Estate, Brixworth, Northampton, NN6 9EU Tel: (01604) 880546 Fax: (01604) 880704 E-mail: info@dieselinjectors.co.uk *Injector & fuel pump suppliers*

Diesel Marine International Ltd, Gloucester Road, North Shields, Tyne & Wear, NE29 8RQ Tel: 0191-257 5577 Fax: 0191-258 6398 E-mail: david.murray@dmiuk.co.uk *Electroplating services*

Diesel Marine International Ltd, Gloucester Road, North Shields, Tyne & Wear, NE29 8RQ Tel: 0191-257 5577 Fax: 0191-258 6398 E-mail: sales@dmiuk.co.uk *Diesel & marine engine components & surface coatings suppliers*

Diesel Power Ltd, Unit 12 Mitcham Industrial Estate, 85 Streatham Road, Mitcham, Surrey, CR4 2AP Tel: (020) 8648 0041 Fax: (020) 8640 8471 E-mail: info@dpdirect.net *Mailing house*

Diesel Recon, 2 Napier Place, Wardpark North Cumbernauld, Dullatur, Glasgow, G68 0BP Tel: (01236) 505600 Fax: (01236) 724517 Principal Export Areas: West Europe *Diesel engine restoration services*

Diesel Service Centre, Mount Pleasant, Peterborough, PE2 8HW Tel: (01733) 558600 *Vehicle repairers*

Diespark Precision Engineers, Phillips Street Industrial Estate, 99 Phillips Street, Birmingham, B6 4PT Tel: 0121-359 5800 Fax: 0121-359 5800 *Spark erosion machining services*

Dietary Foods Ltd, Cumberland House, Brook Street, Soham, Ely, Cambridgeshire, CB7 5BA Tel: (01353) 720791 Fax: (01353) 721705 E-mail: info@dietaryfoods.co.uk *Food packaging & manufrs*

Dietiker Metals (UK) Ltd, 89-91 Freckleton Rd, Eccleston Hill, St. Helens, Merseyside, WA10 3AS Tel: (01744) 454141 Fax: (01744) 453535 E-mail: dietikermetals@ic24.net *Metal dealers*

Diffusion Alloys Ltd, 160-162 Great North Road, Hatfield, Hertfordshire, AL9 5JW Tel: (01707) 266111 Fax: (01707) 276669 *Surface protection of metals*

Diffusion Environmental Systems Ltd, Unit 14 Sherrington Way, Basingstoke, Hampshire, RG22 4DQ Tel: (01256) 352250 Fax: 01256 817815 *Air conditioning specialist*

Digby & Nelson Ltd, 8 Deer Park Road, London, SW19 3UU Tel: (020) 8543 1141 Fax: (020) 8543 5408 *Cheese cutting equipment manufrs*

Digi Europe Ltd, Digi House, Rookwood Way, Haverhill, Suffolk, CB9 8DG Tel: (01440) 712176 Fax: (01440) 712173 *Weighing scales (industrial & retail) manufrs*

Digi International Ltd, Ashwood House, Almondsbury Business Park, Bradley Stoke, Bristol, BS32 4QH Tel: (01454) 643444 Fax: (01454) 619048 *Computer hardware suppliers*

▶ Digi Source (UK) Ltd, Chalmers Square, Deans Industrial Estate, Deans, Livingston, West Lothian, EH54 8RJ Tel: (01506) 463046

▶ Digi Tech Ltd, Unit 7 Plantation Business Park, Stadium Road, Wirral, Merseyside, CH62 3RN Tel: 0151-343 9595 Fax: 0151-343 9575 *Closed circuit television equipment specialists*

Digica Ltd, Phoenix House, Colliers Way, Nottingham, NG8 6AT Tel: 0115-977 1177 Fax: 0115-977 7000 E-mail: niki_torrance@digica.com *IT outsourcing & desktop services*

Digicad Designs, Martens Business Centre, Coney Lane, Keighley, West Yorkshire, BD21 5JE Tel: (01535) 691763 Fax: (01535) 691763 E-mail: digicad@hotmail.com *Website designers*

▶ Digicore, Sage House, 319 Pinner Road, Harrow, Middlesex, HA1 4HF Tel: (020) 8515 2900 Fax: (020) 8861 3888 E-mail: mark.naldrett@digicore.co.uk *Tracking systems manufrs*

▶ Digilution, 1 The Hoppits, Park Lane, Puckeridge, Ware, Hertfordshire, SG11 1SG Tel: (01920) 822936 E-mail: stephen@digilution.co.uk *Digilution UK stockists of La Crosse RS900 and Ansmann NiMH battery chargers,rechargable batteries and Wine and window thermometers*

▶ DiGi-Masters.Com, 24 Franche Road, Wolverley, Kidderminster, Worcestershire, DY11 5TP Tel: (01562) 636213 E-mail: info@digi-masters.com *Internet services*

▶ Digimode IT Ltd, 5 Boxworth Close, London, N12 9HJ Tel: (020) 8446 2642

▶ Digiscans, 66 High Street, Hoddesdon, Hertfordshire, EN11 8ET Tel: (01992) 441516 Fax: 01992 450159 E-mail: admin@digiscans.co.uk *AutoCAD Plotting*Large Format Scanning*Plan Printing*CAD Printing*

▶ Digit Computers, PO Box 47761, London, NW10 5UN Tel: (08700) 420490 Fax: (070) 92844761 E-mail: info@digitcomputers.co.uk *Computer services*

▶ Digit Info Tec, Unit 1a Victoria Business Park, Roche, St. Austell, Cornwall, PL26 8LX Tel: (01726) 890546 Fax: (01726) 890597 E-mail: sales@digit-info-tec.co.uk *Computer support services*

Digita International Ltd, Liverton Business Park, Exmouth, Devon, EX8 2NR Tel: (01395) 270273 Fax: (01395) 268893 E-mail: info@digita.com *Computer software manufacturers & suppliers*

▶ Digital Aerials, H/O, 19 Cleveland Close, Colchester, CO4 9RD Tel: 01206 842711 E-mail: daniboy28@hotmail.co.uk *sky digital, sky plus, freesat, sky, multiroom, free dish and box, freeview reception specialist, high gain aerial installs, digital aerials, dab aerials, fm aerials, installation of multipoints, telephone extensions,. Upgrade my tv aerial for freeview, digital signals. wind damage repairs, free quotes, local comapany. covering: North East Essex, suffolk, ipswich, east bergholt, brantham, hintlesham, sproughton, bramford, chantry, kesgrave,ip1, ip2, ip3, ip4, ip8, ip5, ip9, (aerial, digital, dtt, freeview, upgrade, install, highgain), idsc member*

▶ Digital Amulet Computer Solutions, 100 Gordon Road, London, E18 1RD Tel: (0845) 2573019 E-mail: andy.williams@digitalamulet.com *Computer solutions provider*

Digital Applications International Ltd, Axtell House, 24 Warwick Street, London, W1B 5NQ Tel: (020) 7292 7500 Fax: (020) 7439 2077 E-mail: enquiries@dai.co.uk *Computer consultants* Also at: Aberdeen & Manchester

▶ Digital Copier Systems, Bristol Courtbetts Avenue Martlesham Heath Business Park, Martlesham Heath, Ipswich, IP5 3RH Tel: (01473) 636000 Fax: (01473) 614400 E-mail: sales@digitalcopyprint.co.uk *Photocopying machine distributor*

▶ Digital Cubed, The Hive, Nottingham, NG1 4BU Tel: (0870) 8148333 Fax: 0115-848 4612 E-mail: nicholas.timms@digitalcubed.co.uk *Multi media services*

Digital Depot, 13 High Street, Stevenage, Hertfordshire, SG1 3BG Tel: (01438) 367619 Fax: (01438) 359020 E-mail: sales@digitaldepot.co.uk *Digital camera equipment retailers*

▶ Digital Design Canvas UK, 10, churchbury rd, enfield, middx, EN1 3HR Tel: 0208 3646205 E-mail: enquiries@digitaldesignuk.co.uk *High quality contemporary art and photos*on canvas at great prices from £60**

Digital Development, The Old School, East Baldwin, Isle Of Man, IM4 5EP Tel: (01624) 851482 Fax: (01624) 851482 *Electronic design consultants*

Digital Dispatch Ltd, 38-39 Bar Hill Business Park, Saxon Way, Bar Hill, Cambridge, CB23 8SL Tel: (01954) 780888 Fax: (01954) 781612 E-mail: sales@digitaldispatch.com *Mobile IT data specialists*

▶ Digital Error, 6a High Street, Wincanton, Somerset, BA9 9JP Tel: (0845) 2266432 Fax: (0845) 2266432 E-mail: sales@digitalerror.co.uk *Computer repairs*

▶ The Digital Eye (London) Ltd, Camden Park Studios, Camden Park Road, London, NW1 9AY Tel: (020) 7485 0658 *Digital photographers*

▶ Digital Fix, Millbank Cottages, Moneymore, Magherafelt, County Londonderry, BT45 7XT Tel: (028) 8672 6092 E-mail: info@digitalfix.co.uk *Cheap restoration and repair of old or damaged photos. Enhancement, manipulation, "beauty airbrushing" and more. Prices start at just £5 /$. Receive restored photos either by email or in print. UK-based.**

▶ Digital Freedom Ltd, 109 Trent Road Shaw, Oldham, OL2 7QH Tel: (01706) 847772 *Promotional work*

▶ Digital Imaging Services & Photography, 8 Odense Court, East Kilbride, G75 0SA Tel: 07855 669213 E-mail: alex_disp@yahoo.co.uk

Digital Lift Controls Ltd, 14 Gresley Close, Drayton Fields Industrial Esta, Daventry, Northamptonshire, NN11 8RZ Tel: (01327) 311816 Fax: (01327) 706636 *Electronic lifts manufrs*

▶ Digital Media Music, 61 Birkbeck Road, Mill Hill, London, NW7 4BP Tel: 020881 67775 E-mail: info@digitalmediamusic.co.uk *Music for film, television and advertising.*

Digital Metal Ltd, The Church Gatehouse, Skinner Lane, Pontefract, West Yorkshire, WF8 1HG Tel: (01977) 706121 Fax: (01977) 705226 *Mechanical design*

Digital Networks Ltd, PO Box 24402, London, W5 4WQ Tel: (020) 8998 7293 Fax: (020) 8998 0216 E-mail: sales@dignet.co.uk *Web site design*

▶ Digital Office Solutions, 2 Hyders Farm, Bonnetts Lane, Ifield, Crawley, West Sussex, RH11 0NY Tel: (01293) 537827 Fax: (01293) 619934 E-mail: sales@digital-office-solutions.co.uk *Office equipment suppliers*

Digital Office Supplies, Bentalls, Basildon, Essex, SS14 3BS Tel: (01268) 532100 Fax: (01268) 532411 E-mail: sue.brochem@winstonmead.co.uk *Cannon dealer photocopiers*

Digital Office Systems Ltd, 6 Brookside, Ashby-de-la-Zouch, Leicestershire, LE65 1JW Tel: (01530) 414409 Fax: (01530) 414380 E-mail: sales@digital-os.co.uk *Office equipment supplies, copiers & networking*

▶ Digital Office Systems, Unit 424 Parkers House, 48 Regent Street, Cambridge, CB2 1FD Tel: (0870) 7655565 Fax: (08707) 654565 *Computer maintenance services*

Digital Peninsula Network, 1 Brewery Yard, Penzance, Cornwall, TR18 2SL Tel: (01736) 333700 Fax: (01736) 366700 E-mail: office@digitalpeninsula.com *Digital network services*

Digital Print Factory, 12-12a Rosebery Avenue, London, EC1R 4TD Tel: (020) 7837 8666 Fax: (020) 7404 4762 E-mail: t.harding@colyer.co.uk *Exhibition stand contractors*

The Digital Printed Word Ltd, 19 Briset Street, London, EC1M 5NR Tel: (020) 7250 1404 Fax: (020) 7253 4675 E-mail: printedword@btconnect.com *Digital printers*

▶ Digital Printing Services, 24 Carre Street, Sleaford, Lincolnshire, NG34 7TR Tel: (01529) 300452 Fax: (01529) 300452 E-mail: matt@dpsfineart.co.uk *Print & design*

▶ Digital Products, 59 Imperial Way, Croydon, CR0 4RR Tel: (0845) 1306251 E-mail: sales@dmcplc.co.uk *Suppliers & wholesalers of business machines*

▶ Digital Progression, 123 Old Christchurch Road, Bournemouth, BH1 1EP Tel: (01202) 316660 Fax: (01202) 311185 E-mail: mail@digitalprogression.co.uk *Digital illustration & animation*

Digital Read Out Centre, Unit 1 53a Third Avenue, Pensnett Trading Estate, Kingswinford, West Midlands, DY6 7XG Tel: (01384) 270022 Fax: (01384) 270022 *Pressure die tool & plastic mould manufs*

Digital Repro, Cambridge Road Industrial Estate, Milton, Cambridge, CB4 6AZ Tel: (01223) 420444 Fax: (01223) 420783 *Digital printing & pre-press services*

Digital Sales, Chip House, Byron CR, Coppull, Chorley, Lancashire, PR7 5BE Tel: (01257) 471204 Fax: (01257) 793525 E-mail: sales@digitalsales.co.uk Principal Export Areas: Worldwide *Satellite specialist suppliers*

Digital & Screen Printing Association (UK) Ltd, Association House, 7A West Street, Reigate, Surrey, RH2 9BL Tel: (01737) 240792 Fax: (01737) 240770 E-mail: info@spauk.co.uk *Trade association agents*

▶ Digital Secretary, Feldwicke Cottage, Ardingly Road, West Hoathly, East Grinstead, West Sussex, RH19 4RA Tel: (01342) 716137 Fax: (01342) 716137 E-mail: info@digital-secretary.co.uk *Digital Secretary provides transcription, typing and virtual secretarial services via the Internet. We specialise in legal and medical secretarial work, but also provide services for small and medium sized businesses. We provide a Web based account for the upload and retrieval of work orders (audio files and completed documents).*

Digital Systems, Solutions House Derby Road, Sandiacre, Nottingham, NG10 5HU Tel: 0115-849 9984 Fax: 0115-849 9993 *Computers system manufrs*

▶ Digital Systems Com Ltd, 3 Sidney Robinson Business Park, Ascot Drive, Derby, DE24 8EH Tel: (0870) 7439867 Fax: (0870) 0007039

Digital Telecom Ltd, Llanthony Industrial Estate, Llanthony Road, Hempsted, Gloucester, GL2 5HL Tel: (01452) 382382 Fax: (01452) 876406 E-mail: sales@digital-telecom.co.uk *Telecommunication installation*

▶ Digital Typeline Publications Ltd, 2d West Telferton, Edinburgh, EH7 6UL Tel: 0131-657 1001 Fax: 0131-669 0049

Digital Video Interview Services, The City Arc, Curtain Court, 7 Curtain Road, London, EC2A 3LT Tel: 0207 1009270 Fax: 0207 1009310E-mail: info@digitalvideointerview.co.uk *Provide digital video interview services to job seekers and recruiters. Services include video interviews, cv writing and personalised webpages. Offices in Essex and London.*

Digital Video Solutions, Unit K6 South Point, Foreshore Road, Cardiff, CF10 4SP Tel: (029) 2045 5512 Fax: (029) 2045 5513 E-mail: sales@dvs.uk.co.uk *Premier distributors of CCTV & access control products*

Digital Village, St. Mary Street, Southampton, SO14 1NR Tel: (023) 8023 3444 Fax: (023) 8023 3266 *Retail music technology supplies*

▶ Digital Vision Technologies Ltd, Langdale House, Gadbrook Business Centre, Rudheath, Northwich, Cheshire, CW9 7TN Tel: (01606) 331234 Fax: (01606) 338640 E-mail: info@dutl.co.uk *Tech company*

Digital Workshop, 42-44 North Bar Street, Banbury, Oxfordshire, OX16 0TH Tel: (01295) 258335 Fax: (01295) 254590 *Computer systems & software development manufrs*

▶ Digitalarkitec Ltd, 121 Eastern Avenue, Lichfield, Staffordshire, WS13 6RL Tel: (01543) 251123 E-mail: enquiries@digitalarkitec.co.uk *IT & business consultancy*

▶ Digital-Canvas-Print Ltd, 69 Enid Street, London, SE16 3RA Tel: (020) 7237 9333 Fax: (020) 7237 9444 E-mail: angus@superchrome.co.uk *Specialists in large format canvas printing, banners, billboards*

▶ Digitalis, Llangoed Hall, Llyswen, Brecon, Powys, LD3 0YP Tel: (01874) 754631 Fax: (01874) 754588 E-mail: simon@digitalis.uk.com *Digital textile printers, finishers, home furnishing & apparel*

▶ Digitalzone UK Ltd, 28 William Street, Ystrad, Pentre, Mid Glamorgan, CF41 7QR Tel: (01443) 422322 Fax: (01443) 422327 E-mail: sales@digitalzone.co.uk *P C sales & repairers*

▶ Digitata Ltd, Old Academy, Back Road, Stromness, Orkney, KW16 3AW Tel: (01856) 851740 Fax: (0870) 0518821 E-mail: info@digitatadesign.co.uk *Designs & produces a range of luxury woven & screen printed fabrics*

▶ Digitax Electronics UK Ltd, The Smoke House, 31 Tanners Bank, North Shields, Tyne & Wear, NE30 1JH Tel: 0191-296 1294 E-mail: digitax2@aol.com *Taxi meters suppliers*

Digitec Installations Ltd, 2 Massey Walk, Manchester, M22 5JY Tel: 0161-437 9357 Fax: 0161-613 2769 *Alarm system services*

Digitel Europe Ltd, Ivy Street, Birkenhead, Merseyside, CH41 5EE Tel: 0151-650 0065 Fax: 0151-650 1162 *Communication*

Digitel Technology Ltd, 7 Cross Street, Barnstaple, Devon, EX31 1BA Tel: (01271) 311913 E-mail: sales@digitel.uk.net *Electronic equipment retailer*

Digitimer Ltd, 37 Hydeway, Welwyn Garden City, Hertfordshire, AL7 3BE Tel: (01707) 328347 Fax: (01707) 373153 E-mail: bcooper@digitimer.com *Electronic contract manufacturing services*

Digitrol Ltd, Coronet Way, Swansea Enterprise Park, Swansea, SA6 8RH Tel: (01792) 796000 Fax: (01792) 701600 E-mail: info@digitrol.com *Industrial computers manufrs*

Digitron Translift Ltd, Hallcroft Road, Retford, Nottinghamshire, DN22 7PT Tel: (01777) 707511 Fax: (01777) 860778 *Overhead Monorail & floor conveyor systems designers*

▶ Digits Industries Ltd, Office 4 Universal Marina, Crableck Lne, Sarisbury Green, Southampton, SO31 7ZN Tel: (01489) 564845 Fax: (01489) 564846 E-mail: sales@digits.co.uk *Specializing in internet-intranet design & e learning development*

▶ Digiwave Technologies, 198 Slade Road, Birmingham, B23 7RJ Tel: 0121-386 4678 *Computer components retailers*

▶ Dijon Exhibition Design Co., 1 Castle Farm, Clifton Road, Deddington, Banbury, Oxfordshire, OX15 0TP Tel: (01869) 337311 Fax: (01869) 337322 E-mail: sales@dijondesigns.com *Exhibition designs & services*

Diktron Developments Ltd, Griptight House Unit 19, Spitfire Road, Castle Bromwich, Birmingham, B24 9PR Tel: 0121-382 4938 Fax: 0121-747 3009 E-mail: diktron@btconnect.com *Fire fighting safety equipment*

▶ Dilectus, Century Business Centre, Century Park, Manvers, Rotherham, South Yorkshire, S63 5DA Tel: (01709) 300216 Fax: (0870) 4602601 E-mail: kelly@dilectus.com *We specialise in the recruitment of Commercial and Sales Staff in and around the Yorkshire Area. We offer a tailor made, professional and trustworthy service to all our clients and candidates.*

▶ Dili, 2-4 Tottenham Road, London, N1 4BZ Tel: (020) 7923 4888 *Clothing retailers*

Diligencia Ltd, The Maltings, 100 Wilderspool Causeway, Warrington, WA4 6PU Tel: (01925) 241444 Fax: (01925) 241666 E-mail: info@diligencia.co.uk *Strategic management support services*

R. Dillon (Clacton) Ltd, Ford Road Industrial Estate, Clacton-On-Sea, Essex, CO15 3DT Tel: (01255) 423059 Fax: (01255) 222836 *Shop fitters & joinery contractors*

▶ Dillon's Ltd, Hardres Court, Canterbury, Kent, CT4 6EN Tel: (01227) 700236 E-mail: info@dillonsspirits.com *Distributors of dillon's spirits*

Di-Log, Unit 28 Wheel Forge Way, Trafford Park, Manchester, M17 1EH Tel: 0161-877 0322 Fax: 0161-877 1614 E-mail: sales@dilog.co.uk *Multimeters, voltmeters & test equipment suppliers*

Dilworth & Morris Engineering Ltd, Hyde Bank Road, New Mills, High Peak, Derbyshire, SK22 4BP Tel: (01663) 746383 Fax: (01663) 744230 E-mail: dillworth.morris@btconnect.com *Industrial processing rollmakers*

Dimanco Ltd, 24 Henlow Industrial Estate, Henlow, Bedfordshire, SG16 6DS Tel: (01462) 813933 Fax: (01462) 817407 E-mail: dimanco@ltdhenlow.fsbusiness.co.uk *Diagnostic kits distributors & manufrs*

Dimension Data Advanced Infrastructure, Thelwall Industrial Estate, Thelwall New Road, Warrington, WA4 2LY Tel: (01925) 602942 Fax: (01925) 267464 E-mail: sales@uk.didata.com *Data communication integration systems*

Dimension Development, Komet Works, Sawday Street, Leicester, LE2 7JW Tel: 0116-255 3090 Fax: 0116-255 3092 E-mail: dimensiondev@btconnect.com *Plastic vacuum formed products*

Dimension Engineering, Unit 21 The Business Village, Wexham Road, Slough, SL2 5HF Tel: (01753) 538166 Fax: (01753) 518966 *Sheet metalwork engineering or fabricators*

▶ Dimension Furniture, Church Lane, OXTED, Surrey, RH8 9LH Tel: 07860 809104 E-mail: martin.parsons@dimensionfurniture.co.uk *Bespoke handmade furniture built to order by Designer and Cabinet Maker Martin Parsons, based in Surrey, UK.*

Dimension Graphics, 43 Hergest Road, Kington, Herefordshire, HR5 3EL Tel: (01544) 231887 E-mail: dimensions@btinternet.com *Computer programmers software development services*

Dimensional Design Ltd, 3-5 Park Street, Fleckney, Leicester, LE8 8BB Tel: 0116-240 4242 Fax: 0116-240 4488 *Plastic product manufrs*

Dimensional Inspection Services, Unit 19 Wombourne Enterprise Park, Bridgnorth Road, Wombourne, Wolverhampton, WV5 0AL Tel: (01902) 326225 Fax: (01902) 326225 E-mail: sales@diserv.free-online.co.uk *Engineering inspection testing & metrology consultants*

▶ Dimensionize Ltd, 145-157 St. John Street, London, EC1V 4PY Tel: (0870) 7538485 Fax: (0870) 7538483 E-mail: contact@dimensionize.com *Dimensionize Ltd, import, export company with global reach*

Dimill Engineering Ltd, Doric Works, Church Street, Studley, Warwickshire, B80 7LG Tel: (01527) 854672 Fax: (01527) 853683 E-mail: info@dimill.co.uk *Toolmakers*

Dimmock Engineering, Unit 6 Westbury Close, Houghton Regis, Dunstable, Bedfordshire, LU5 5BL Tel: (01582) 602588 Fax: (01582) 602588 E-mail: sjdimmock1@aol.com *Plastics mould toolmakers*

▶ Dimor Plumbing Ltd, 15 Acorn Business Centre, Livingstone Way, Taunton, Somerset, TA2 6BD Tel: (01823) 331405 Fax: (01823) 352911

▶ Dince Hill Property Ltd, Manor Mill, South Brent, Devon, TQ10 9JD Tel: (01364) 72779

Dinefwr Gates, Cwmcib Ganol, Ffairfach, Llandeilo, Dyfed, SA19 6TE Tel: (01558) 822833 Fax: (01558) 824612 *Sawmill & timber & gates manufr*

Dingbro Ltd, Unit 7 Whitemyres Avenue, Aberdeen, AB16 6HQ Tel: (01224) 692842 Fax: (01224) 693881 E-mail: filter@dingbro.com *Supplier for filtration equipment & filter elements*

Dingbro Ltd, 1 Merchant Place, Mitchelston Industrial Estate, Kirkcaldy, Fife, KY1 3NJ Tel: (01592) 652400 Fax: (01592) 653989 *Car parts supplies & service*

The Dinghy Store, Sea Wall, Whitstable, Kent, CT5 1BX Tel: (01227) 274168 Fax: (01227) 772750 E-mail: sales@thedinghystore.co.uk *Marine supplies, yacht & boat equipment, yacht & dinghy fittings*

Dingle Star Ltd, Unit 27 Metro Centre, Britannia Way, Coronation Road, London, NW10 7PR Tel: (020) 8965 8060 Fax: (020) 8453 0885 *Broadcasting equipment suppliers*

Dingley Dell Enterprises, Kidderminster, Worcestershire, DY14 9ZE Tel: (01905) 621636 Fax: (01905) 620311 *Stove & garden heater & large plant pots manufrs*

Dining 4 You, 8 Saunders Street, Gillingham, Kent, ME7 1ET Tel: 07804 325697 E-mail: info@dining4you.co.uk *Personal Chef providing a personalised service, food is prepared and cooked in the customers own kitchen. From planning and preparation through to the final clearing away, a dinner party can be provided allowing hosts and guests to relax.*

Dining in Style Group Limited, 18 High Street, Pinner, Middlesex, HA5 5PW Tel: (020) 8866 7856 Fax: (020) 8866 1033 E-mail: paul@dininginstyle.co.uk *Caters for corporate & private catering in London and the home counties, Weddings, parties & all events catered**

▶ Dinks, Winchester Road, Burghclere, Newbury, Berkshire, RG20 9LE Tel: (01635) 278556 Fax: (01635) 278709 E-mail: info@dinksltd.co.uk *Promotional bags, tote bags, personalised items, promotional gifts*

Dinnages Car Dealers, Brougham Road, Worthing, West Sussex, BN11 2NR Tel: (01903) 820505 Fax: (01903) 212523 E-mail: marketing@dinnages.co.uk *Car mechanics, bodywork repairs, car sales & servicing providers*

Gerald Dinnis Ltd, Tedburn Road, Whitestone, Exeter, EX4 2HF Tel: (01392) 811581 Fax: (01392) 811722 E-mail: info@whitehorsemotors.co.uk *4 x 4 suppliers & services*

S.T.A. Dinnis, 25 Meadow Drive, Bude, Cornwall, EX23 8HZ Tel: (01288) 355006 Fax: (01288) 355006 *Agricultural contractors*

Dins Technologies Ltd, 45 Commerce Street, Glasgow, G5 8AD Tel: 0141-420 3735 Fax: 0141-429 1914 *Computer components distribution*

▶ Dinsdale Embroideries, 13 Castle Close, Middleton St. George, Darlington, County Durham, DL2 1DE Tel: (01325) 332592 Fax: (01325) 335704 E-mail: info@dinsdaleembroideries.co.uk *Embroidery suppliers*

Dinsley Devices Ltd, Ivy House, Streatlam, Barnard Castle, County Durham, DL12 8TZ Tel: (01388) 710734 Fax: (01833) 637971 E-mail: dinsearch@hotmail.com *Non destructive testing equipment*

Francis Dinsmore Ltd, 25 Greenfield Road, Kells, Ballymena, County Antrim, BT42 3JL Tel: (028) 2589 1203 Fax: (028) 2589 2295 E-mail: info@dinsmore.co.uk *Textile importers, bleachers, dyers & finishers*

Dinsmores Ltd, Westgate, Aldridge, Walsall, WS9 8EX Tel: (01922) 456421 Fax: (01922) 455791 E-mail: dinsmoresmft@aol.com *Fishing tackle manufrs*

Dinstock Ltd, Unit C1, Hortonwood row 10, Telford, Shropshire, TF1 7ES Tel: (01952) 676700 Fax: (01952) 676800 *Manufacturers of bolts & nuts*

Dinting Metric, 8 Hadfield Industrial Estate, Waterside, Hadfield, Glossop, Derbyshire, SK13 1BS Tel: (01457) 855510 Fax: (01457) 838609 E-mail: sales@dintingmetric.com *Bottling plant manufrs*

Diomed Ltd, Diomed House 2000 Cambridge Research Park, Beach Road, Waterbeach, Cambridge, CB5 9TE Tel: (01223) 729300 Fax: (01223) 729329 E-mail: info@diomed-lasers.com *Medical laser system manufrs*

Dionach Ltd, Greenford House, London Road, Wheatley, Oxford, OX33 1JH Tel: (01865) 877830 Fax: (01865) 877850 *Computer security system suppliers*

Dione P.L.C., Dione House, Oxford Road, Stokenchurch, High Wycombe, Buckinghamshire, HP14 3SX Tel: (01494) 486000 Fax: (01494) 486050 E-mail: info@dionecorp.com *Electronic fund transfer systems designers*

▶ Diotte Consulting & Technology Ltd, The Conifers 36 Bishops Wood, Nantwich, Cheshire, CW5 7QD Tel: (01270) 627129 Fax: 01270 610358 E-mail: ranj@diotte.co.uk *Diotte is a consultancy company based in Nantwich, Cheshire.*We specialised in Aseptic Technology & food product innovations. Our activities include design & supply of commercial & laboratory scale food process plants, design & supply of aseptic systems, development of on farm production & mini dairies, process engineering & instrumentation.*Expert in trouble shooting in the food & dairy industries.*We also offer training (Plant operation, hygeine, cream manufacture etc) & seminars (Aseptic technology & awareness, yellow fat technology etc).*Experience in international consultancy work (via EU, UNFAO, EBRD)**

Dipcoat Plastics, Beoley Mill, Marlfield Lane, Redditch, Worcestershire, B98 8PU Tel: (01527) 60342 Fax: (01527) 60342 E-mail: dipcoat@amserve.com *Plastics coating services*

Diplomat Extrusions Ltd, Dukesway, Gateshead, Tyne & Wear, NE11 0PZ Tel: 0191-482 8800 Fax: 0191-482 0571 E-mail: info@diplomat-extrusions.co.uk *PVCu window profile manufrs*

Dippon Label Co. Ltd, 125 Dartmouth Middleway, Aston, Birmingham, B7 4UA Tel: 0121-359 8183 Fax: 0121-359 2749 E-mail: sales@dippon.co.uk *Label manufrs*

Dipsticks Calibration Services, Westacre, Belton Road, Portishead, Bristol, BS20 8DR Tel: (01275) 843651 Fax: (01275) 844784 *Dip-stick & dip rod manufrs*

Diptec Computer Systems Ltd, 80 Cleveland Avenue, Long Eaton, Nottingham, NG10 2BT Tel: 0115-946 4773 Fax: 0115-946 4719 *Software solutions manufrs*

Direct Air Supplies Ltd, 4 Brocklebank Industrial Estate, Brocklebank Road, London, SE7 7SX Tel: (020) 8853 2186 Fax: (020) 8293 5539 E-mail: direct.air@virgin.net *Air-conditioning suppliers*

Direct Alarm, 10 Limetree Avenue, Grimsby, South Humberside, DN33 2BB Tel: (01472) 278816 *Alarms installation services*

Direct Alarms, 11 Croft House Drive, Morley, Leeds, LS27 8NU Tel: 0113-289 7897 Fax: 0113-255 6919 *Alarm installation*

Direct Auto Electrics, 126 Myton Drive, Shirley, Solihull, West Midlands, B90 1HH Tel: (07966) 398848 Fax: 0121-436 6235 E-mail: sales@directautoelectrics.co.uk *Car alarm & satellite navigation installation*

▶ Direct Bathrooms, 1 Wallis Road, Skippers Lane Industrial Estate, Middlesbrough, Cleveland, TS6 6DU Tel: (01642) 430066 *Bathroom suppliers*

Direct Blinds, 21 Kaimes View, Danderhall, Dalkeith, Midlothian, EH22 1QZ Tel: 0131-660 2622 Fax: 0131-660 6622 *Blinds, awnings & canopies*

Direct Blinds, 6 Oswald Road, Oswestry, Shropshire, SY11 1RE Tel: (01691) 670257 Fax: (01691) 679078 *Blind manufrs & suppliers*

Direct Building Maintenance Services Ltd, 1 Nelmes Close, Hornchurch, Essex, RM11 2QA Tel: (01708) 447373 Fax: (01708) 445888 *Air conditioning unit maintenance & installers*

▶ Direct Building Services, 502 Lickey Road, Rednal, Birmingham, B45 8UU Tel: 0121-460 1777 Fax: 0121-460 1555

Direct Business Supplies, 7 Terry Dicken Industrial Estate, Station Road, Stokesley, Middlesbrough, Cleveland, TS9 7AE Tel: (01642) 714715 Fax: (01642) 714715 E-mail: sales@dbsupplies.net *Adhesive labels, office stationery, cash registers, till rolls**

Direct Business Systems, Reema Road, Bellshill, Lanarkshire, ML4 1RY Tel: (01698) 740074 Fax: (01698) 741074 *Photocopier & fax retailers & repairs*

▶ Direct Cartons, Unit2, Mountain View, Holmfield, Halifax, West Yorkshire, HX2 9SL Tel: 0796 8070597 Fax: 01422 242347 E-mail: DIRECT.CARTONS@BTINTERNET.COM *New & once used boxes distributors & manufrs*

Direct Catering Supplies, Unit 16, Mornington Road, Smethwick, Birmingham, B66 2JE Tel: 0121-558 4200 Fax: 0121-565 3132 E-mail: sales@directcateringsupplies.co.uk

Direct Chemicals & Detergents Ltd, Unit 17 Eagle Trading Estate, 29 Willow Lane, Mitcham, Surrey, CR4 4UY Tel: (020) 8687 6679 *Cleaning chemicals manufrs*

▶ Direct Chilled Ltd, Edward Street, Redditch, Worcestershire, B97 6HA Tel: 0845 6010348 E-mail: dcdsredditch@aol.com *Same day express temperature controlled specialist chilled couriers.*

Direct Commissioning Services, 8 Ashfields, Loughton, Essex, IG10 1SB Tel: (020) 8418 9996 Fax: (020) 8418 9914 E-mail: directcommissioning@btinternet.com *Commissioning engineers*

Direct Computer Supplies Ltd, Kenmar House, 2 Wesley Drive, Newcastle upon Tyne, NE12 9UP Tel: 0191-270 2020 Fax: 0191-270 0404 E-mail: info@directbp.co.uk *Office suppliers*

Direct Computer Training Ltd, Argyle Ho, 29-31 Euston Rd, London, NW1 2SD Tel: (020) 7837 4800 Fax: (020) 7837 1090 *Computer training*

Direct Cooling & Heating Services Ltd, 1 Northbank Avenue, Cambuslang, Glasgow, G72 7TG Tel: 0141-641 7788 Fax: 0141-641 8333 *Air conditioning sales, repair & services*

Direct Copiers plc, Former Royal Mail Building, Horseley Road, Tipton, West Midlands, DY4 7DB Tel: 0121-521 0200 Fax: 0121-521 0220 *Photocopier services*

Direct Despatch International Ltd, D D I House, 1-21 Elkstone Road, London, W10 5NT Tel: (020) 7724 4000 Fax: (020) 8964 8244 E-mail: sales@ddi.co.uk *International couriers*

▶ Direct Dialogue, 1 Call Flex Business Park, Golden Smithies Lane, Wath-upon-Dearne, Rotherham, South Yorkshire, S63 7ER Tel: 07917 811057 Fax: 01709 384372 E-mail: keir.woolhouse@directdialogue.co.uk *Direct Dialogue is an FSA-regulated "Loyalty Engine".**We take customer data as our input and output new or additional revenue streams together with greater knowledge of those customers on behalf of our customers.**Loyalty Engine is sophisticated and where our intellectual property lies. In essence it brings together data, data analytics and products, which fuel an expert team of relationship staff.**This fine-tuned team converts knowledge to revenue and general consumers to customers who have a positive disposition towards our clients. It gets customers to opt in to our clients" marketing programmes and therefore counters the effect of the closing TPS door.*

Direct Diary Planner, 111 Brecon Road, Hirwaun, Aberdare, Mid Glamorgan, CF44 9NS Tel: (01685) 810217 Fax: (01685) 810217 *Diary manufrs*

▶ Direct Distribution, Unit 7 Forties Commercial Campus, Rosyth, Dunfermline, Fife, KY11 2XB Tel: (01383) 420867 Fax: (01383) 420869

▶ Direct Doorpanels, Busk Road, Oldham, OL9 6QZ Tel: 0161-626 5539 Fax: 0161-626 4355 *Door manufrs*

▶ Direct Electrical Services, 27 Broadmeadow Close, Totton, Southampton, SO40 8WB Tel: (023) 8066 0859 Fax: (023) 8066 0932 E-mail: sales@deslamps.co.uk *Lamp, light bulb & fluorescent tube suppliers*

Direct Engineering, Regent Road, Countesthorpe, Leicester, LE8 5RF Tel: 0116-278 0416 Fax: 0116-247 7731 *General & precision engineers*

Direct Fabrications (Banbury) Ltd, Unit 2, Bridge Wharf, Lower Cherwell Street, Banbury, Oxfordshire, OX16 5AY Tel: (01295) 270808 Fax: (01295) 270808 E-mail: info@directfabrications.co.uk *Steel fabricators*

▶ Direct Fabrics, Rolleston Road, Skeffington, Leicester, LE7 9YD Tel: 0116-259 9700 *Rugby shirts fabric manufrs*

▶ Direct Factory Bathrooms, Unit 5 Selby Business Park, Oakney Wood Road, Selby, North Yorkshire, YO8 8NB Tel: (01757) 291122 Fax: (01757) 241144 *Bathroom designers & installers*

Direct Farm Marketing Ltd, Saxon Way, Melbourn, Royston, Hertfordshire, SG8 6DN Tel: (01763) 263031 Fax: (01763) 262504 *Seed suppliers*

▶ Direct Farming & Rural Solutions Ltd, Newton House, Birch Way, Easingwold, York, YO61 3FB Tel: (01347) 822776 Fax: 01347 822776 E-mail: nola@dfrs.co.uk *Agricultural Consultancy*

Direct Fencing Supplies, 58 Gateford Road, Worksop, Nottinghamshire, S80 1EB Tel: (01909) 475928 Fax: (01909) 475928 *Fencing suppliers*

Direct Fire Protection, 52 Watling Street, Gillingham, Kent, ME7 2YN Tel: (01634) 855600 Fax: (01634) 570571 *Fire extinguishing services*

Direct Fuel Services Ltd, Sandy Lane, Titton, Stourport-on-Severn, Worcestershire, DY13 9PN Tel: (01299) 828449 Fax: (01299) 828435 E-mail: sales@directfuelservices.co.uk *Liquid fuel haulage*

Direct Garden Services, 23 Orched Road, South Croydon, CROYDON, CR2 9LY Tel: (07900) 687013 E-mail: sales@directgardenservices.co.uk *Gardening services*

Direct Generation, Newstead Industrial Trading Estate, Stoke-on-Trent, ST4 8HX Tel: (01782) 646767 Fax: (01782) 646868 E-mail: sales@directgeneration.co.uk *Supply, installation, commissioning & service of power generators. Diesel & gas powered alternators for standby & prime power. Authorised Caterpillar power generation dealer. Bespoke generator solutions based on Caterpillar products*

▶ Direct Imaging Ltd, Demmings House, Brookfield Road, Cheadle, Cheshire, SK8 2PE Tel: 0161-491 2121

Direct It Distribution Ltd, 12 The Markham Centre, Station Road, Theale, Reading, RG7 4PE Tel: 0118-912 6400 Fax: 0118-912 6444 E-mail: sales@direct-it.co.uk *Computer hardware dealers*

Direct Know How, 17 St. Annes Court, London, W1F 0BQ Tel: (020) 7734 3532 Fax: (020) 7734 1779 E-mail: postmaster@tsm-direct.co.uk *Marketing & sales promotions services*

Direct Labels, Unit 2c Allans Indust Park, Coulman Street, Thorne, Doncaster, South Yorkshire, DN8 5JS Tel: (01405) 741111 Fax: (01405) 741112 E-mail: sales@directlabelsonline.co.uk *Labels manufrs*

▶ Direct Laboratories, Woodthorne, Wergs Road, Wolverhampton, WV6 8TQ Tel: (01902) 743222 Fax: (01902) 746183 E-mail: angeliki.chrevatidis@directlabs.co.uk *Microbiological analysis, chemical analysis, laboratory, analytical testing, consultancy, research.*

▶ Direct Lighting Distributors Ltd, Gibbs Marsh Trading Estate, Stalbridge, Sturminster Newton, Dorset, DT10 2RY Tel: (01963) 362697 Fax: (01963) 363445

Direct Line Group Ltd, 3 Edridge Road, Croydon, CR9 1AG Tel: (020) 8686 3313 Fax: (020) 8681 0512 *General insurance* Also at: Glasgow

▶ Direct Line Timber Ltd, 122 Liff Road, Dundee, DD2 2TL Tel: (01382) 624533 Fax: (01382) 400186 E-mail: sales@directlinetimber.co.uk *Timber merchants, importers & saw millers & in house timber treatment service*

Direct Link South, 38 Millbrook Road East, Southampton, SO15 1HY Tel: (023) 8033 1541 E-mail: louis.roe@dirlinks.freeserve.co.uk *Express courier service*

Direct Locks Ltd, 145-157 St John Street, London, EC1V 4PY Tel: 0870 6091682 Fax: 0870 6091682 E-mail: Sales@directlocks.co.uk *Direct Locks Ltd UK online supplies door locks and other security products direct to residential/ commercial clientele.**

Direct Machine Tools Ltd, Unit 4a Tame Valley Industrial Estate, Wilnecote, Tamworth, Staffordshire, B77 5DQ Tel: (01827) 260272 Fax: (01827) 260838 E-mail: leroy1@easynet.co.uk *Machine tool builders & rebuilders*

Direct Machine Tools Ltd, Unit 4a Tame Valley Industrial Estate, Wilnecote, Tamworth, Staffordshire, B77 5DQ Tel: (01827) 260272 Fax: (01827) 260838 E-mail: stevedmt@aol.com *Machine tool sales & services*

Direct Mail Advertising & Marketing Services Ltd, 3 Wallis Court, Fleming Way, Crawley, West Sussex, RH10 9DA Tel: (01293) 541511 Fax: (01293) 562996 E-mail: reception@dmams.co.uk *Direct mail services*

Direct Mail Publicity Birmingham Ltd, PO Box 581, Birmingham, B6 7ER Tel: 0121-327 1172 Fax: 0121-326 6139 E-mail: sales@dmpb.co.uk *Direct mail advertising*

Direct Manufacturing Supply Co., 19 Anne Road, Smethwick, West Midlands, B66 2PJ Tel: 0121-558 4591 Fax: 0121-565 7513 E-mail: admin@slemcka.co.uk *Brass & copper giftware manufrs*

Direct Marketing Lists, Tapton Park Innovation Centre, Brimington Road, Chesterfield, Derbyshire, S41 0TZ Tel: (01246) 297179 E-mail: info@direct-marketing-lists.co.uk *If you want to generate new leads, build mailing lists, or run a direct mail campaign - Our Business and Consumer databases have the comprehensive information required to meet these objectives.*

Direct Metal Services Ltd, 2 Swan Business Park, Sandpit Road, Dartford, DA1 5ED Tel: (01322) 287878 Fax: (01322) 287567 E-mail: info@directmetalservices.co.uk *Non-ferrous metal stockholders*

Direct Paper Agents, Amy Johnson Way, Blackpool, FY4 2RP Tel: (01253) 402502 Fax: (01253) 405872 E-mail: info@direct-paperagentsltd.sagenet.co.uk *Paper merchants*

▶ Direct Parcel Services, 1 Purley Chase Estate, Pipers Lane, Nuneaton, Warwickshire, CV10 0RH Tel: (024) 7639 5750 Fax: (024) 7639 5756

▶ Direct Parking Glasgow Airport, 67 Murray Street, Paisley, Renfrewshire, PA3 1QW Tel: 0141-840 1234 Fax: 0141-840 1236 *Secure car parking for glasgow airports*

▶ Direct Passport & Visa Company Ltd, 12 Chepstow Road, London, W2 5BD Tel: (029) 1412 2072 E-mail: directvisas@e3internet.com

Direct Plastics Ltd, Unit 12 Portland Business Park, Richmond Park Road, Sheffield, S13 8HS Tel: 0114-256 0889 Fax: 0114-256 0809 E-mail: paul@directplastics.co.uk *Plastics materials, products & components distributors*

▶ Direct Response Ltd, 3 Angel Walk, London, W6 9HX Tel: (0870) 4149000 Fax: (0870) 4149001 E-mail: sales@drltd.com *Voice, data & call centre services*

▶ Direct Response Employment Services, 43 Roundstone Street, Trowbridge, Wiltshire, BA14 8DE Tel: (01225) 776500 Fax: (01225) 753931 E-mail: sales@direct-response.biz *We are a local reputable employment agency supplying staff to west wiltshire.*

▶ Direct Route Collections Ltd, Tong Hall, Tong Lane, Bradford, West Yorkshire, BD4 0RR Tel: 0113-287 9123 Fax: 0113-287 9153 E-mail: rdavy@directroute.co.uk *ZERO COST DEBT RECOVERY ON SUMS UP TO £3000.*TRADITIONAL DEBT RECOVERY*CREDIT REPORTING*FAST EFFICIENT SERVICE*

Direct Sales Agency Ltd, 4 Bankside, Hanborough Business Park, Long Hanborough, Witney, Oxfordshire, OX29 8SP Tel: (01993) 883606 Fax: (01993) 882733 E-mail: sales@direct.co.uk *Computer reseller*

Direct Salt Supplies Ltd, Runcorn, Cheshire, WA7 4JE Tel: (0845) 6030444 Fax: (0845) 6030333 E-mail: direct.salt@ineofenterprises.com *Salt manufrs*

Direct Security Systems Midlands Ltd, 7 Doctors Piece, Willenhall, West Midlands, WV13 1PZ Tel: (01902) 602042 Fax: (01902) 602888 E-mail: service@direct-security.co.uk *Electronic alarms installation*

Direct Signs, 31 Vale Avenue, Horwich, Bolton, BL6 5RF Tel: (01204) 669209 Fax: (01204) 669676 *Sign manufrs*

▶ Direct Sound Hire, Unit 52 Imex Business Park, Ormonde Street, Fenton, Stoke-on-Trent, ST4 3NP Tel: (01782) 596666 E-mail: info@directsoundhire.co.uk *Direct Sound Hire Local P.A equipment hire to Stoke on Trent. Quality service low prices. Microphones, mixers,*

continued

Company Information

continuation
disco/DJ hire, bands, theatres/schools. Sound equipment for all events.

Direct Specialist Recruitment, 8-10 North Street, Barking, Essex, IG11 8AW Tel: (020) 8591 6787 Fax: (020) 8591 6787 E-mail: info@dsrecruitment.com *BASED IN EAST LONDON/ESSEX OFFERING A WIDE RANGE OF STAFF ON OUR BOOKS FROM PROJECT MANAGERS AND QS THROUGH TO LABOURERS FOR IMMEDIATE START.*

Direct Sports Leisurewear Ltd, 6 Chartmoor Road, Leighton Buzzard, Bedfordshire, LU7 4WG Tel: (01525) 853344 Fax: (01525) 858600 E-mail: sales@directsportswear.co.uk *Sportswear manufr*

Direct Staff & Direct Calculating Ltd, 40 Goodmayes Road, Ilford, Essex, IG3 9UR Tel: (020) 8590 0074 Fax: (020) 8590 8432 E-mail: info@direct-staff.co.uk *Recruitment & calculating services*

Direct Telecom Services Ltd, 17 Bessemer Way, Harfreys Industrial Estate, Great Yarmouth, Norfolk, NR31 0LX Tel: (01493) 440000 Fax: (01493) 440063 E-mail: tim@direct-telecom-svs.co.uk *Telecommunication system agents*

Direct Telecommunications Systems Ltd, Direct House, 16 Commercial Road, Skelmanthorpe, Huddersfield, HD8 9DA Tel: (01484) 867867 Fax: (01484) 867860 E-mail: info@direct-telecom.co.uk *Telecommunication equipment installation services*

▶ Direct Traffic Management Ltd, Unit 26 Frontier Works, King Edward Road, Thorne, Doncaster, South Yorkshire, DN8 4HU Tel: (01405) 817733 Fax: (01405) 813007 E-mail: info@direct-traffic.co.uk *Traffic control & management services*

▶ Direct Transportation Ltd, Swan Street, Chappel, Colchester, CO6 2EE Tel: (01787) 223301

▶ Direct Tube Automation Ltd, 1 Block A, Wednesbury Trading Estate, Wednesbury, West Midlands, WS10 7JN Tel: 0121-505 6388 E-mail: p.mcevoy@dta-ltd.co.uk *Tube bending forming machinery*

▶ Direct Vehicle Leasing (Coventry) Ltd, Sovereign Court, 230 Upper Fifth Street, Milton Keynes, MK9 2HR Tel: (0870) 2424628 Fax: (0870) 0514667 E-mail: sales@dvl-coventry.net *Time is money and by using our services to source your vehicles for business or personal use you will save both. We can supply anything from a Smart Car to a Mercedes to a Transit, new or pre-owned on any type of finance contract. We specialise in smaller fleets.*

▶ Direct Vehicles Logistics Ltd, Standhill, Inchcross, Bathgate, West Lothian, EH48 2HS Tel: (01506) 655800

Direct Visual Group, Unit 39-42, Batley Business & Technology, Batley, West Yorkshire, WF17 6ER Tel: (01924) 500433 Fax: (01924) 500434 E-mail: enquiries@direct-visual.co.uk *Suppliers of video conferencing technology*

Direct Water Services UK Ltd, 2 Woodford Road, Barnby Dun, Doncaster, South Yorkshire, DN3 1BN Tel: (01302) 883838 Fax: (01302) 883838 *Water treatment plant engineers*

Direct Weigh, 14 Milldown Avenue, Goring, Reading, RG8 0AS Tel: (01491) 872042 Fax: (01491) 873782 E-mail: sales@flintec.net *Load specialists*

▶ Direct Works, Unit 1 Union Park, Bircholt Road, Maidstone, Kent, ME15 9XT Tel: (01622) 757111 Fax: (01622) 757222 E-mail: sales@direct-works.com *Direct mail*

▶ Direct2workwear, Limlow House, Royston Road, Litlington, Royston, Hertfordshire, SG8 0RS Tel: (0845) 3454550 Fax: (0800) 174137 E-mail: martin@direct2workwear.com *Supplying specialist, generic & promotional work wear to businesses*

▶ Direct-Inks, 18 The Island, Midsomer Norton, Radstock, BA3 2HQ Tel: (01761) 410222 *Retail general office supplies*

Direction Fire Ltd, 5 First Quarter, Blenheim Road, Epsom, Surrey, KT19 9QN Tel: (01372) 744499 Fax: (01372) 741188 E-mail: angellinaw@directionfire.co.uk *Fire suppression engineers*

▶ Direction International P.L.C., Hildenbrook House, The Slade, Tonbridge, Kent, TN9 1HR Tel: (01732) 366351

▶ Directorpower Ltd, The Quarries, Almondsbury, Bristol, BS32 4HL Tel: (01454) 202909 Fax: (01454) 202929 E-mail: info@directorpower.co.uk *Business and management advice and support to SME"s.*

Directory Publishers Association, PO Box 23034, London, W6 0RJ Tel: (020) 8846 9707 E-mail: rosemarypettit@onetel.net *Protects, represents & promotes the interest of directory & database publishers*

▶ Directspares, 56 Vale Road, Rhyl, Clwyd, LL18 2BY Tel: (01745) 343926 E-mail: tech@directspares.co.uk *Spares & repairs*

Dirk European Holdings Ltd, Dirk House, 29-31 Woodchurch Lane, Prenton, Birkenhead, Merseyside, CH42 9PJ Tel: 0151-608 8552 Fax: 0151-608 7579 E-mail: gdirk@dirkgroup.com *Sewage treatment services*

Dirt Drifters Ltd, Windmill Road, Markyate, St. Albans, Hertfordshire, AL3 8LP Tel: (01582) 842244 E-mail: dirtdrifters@btconnect.com *Corporate or leisure extreme driving activies, off road driving experience centre in Hertfordshire. Quad bikes, Rage off road buggies, extreme 4x4 Land Rover driving. The most fantastic and demanding tracks with lots of water and mud. Casual arrive and drive available most weekends. Corporate bookings welcome.*

▶ Dirt Master Services, 37 Hillside Crescent, Edinburgh, EH6 8NP Tel: (07835) 627741 E-mail: info@dirtmaster.co.uk *Carpet cleaning, disinfecting, odorize stain removal*

Disability Access Co, 16-18 Chapel Street, Glossop, Derbyshire, SK13 8AT Tel: (01457) 868547 Fax: (08717) 335071 E-mail: sales@disabilityaccessco.com *Disability access lifts, goods lifts, disabled toilet access & dumb waiters*

▶ Disc To Print, Unit 1 Lydd Road Industrial Estate, Lydd Road, New Romney, Kent, TN28 8HD Tel: (01797) 367755 Fax: (01797) 364884 E-mail: sales@disctoprint.co.uk *Printing services*

Disc Wizards, 3 Oakleigh Court, Edgware, Middlesex, HA8 5JB Tel: (020) 8931 0001 Fax: (020) 8931 0001 E-mail: info@discwizards.com *CD & DVD replication & duplication service*

Disc Wizards, 33-35 Daws Lane, Mill Hill, London, NW7 4SD Tel: (020) 8931 0001 Fax: (020) 8931 0001 E-mail: info@discwizards.com *Lowest Price CD & DVD replication & duplication. Call us on 0845-045-4550 for a FREE product brochure & quote. We can beat any price in the UK.*

Discain Project Services Ltd, Crow Lane, Little Billing, Northampton, NN3 9BZ Tel: (01604) 787276 Fax: (01604) 407290 E-mail: discain@discain.co.uk *Structural steel manufrs*

▶ Discburner CD Duplication, 11 Sunnyhill, Witley, Godalming, Surrey, GU8 4UH Tel: 0800 0508449 E-mail: info@discburner.co.uk *CD duplication, DVD duplication. Printing and packaging for CD duplication projects. Short run specialists.*

▶ Disccity Ltd, Unit 12, Westbrook Road, Westbrook Trading Estate, Trafford Park, Manchester, M17 1AY Tel: 0870 166 0757 Fax: 0870 166 0759 E-mail: enqs@disccity.co.uk *Suppliers of Blank CD-R, DVD-R, Compatible Ink Cartridges and Computer Consumables. Call at our showroom or order online.*Trade Enquiries Welcome.*

Disclaw Publishing Ltd, The Royal Hunting Lodge, York, YO30 1BD Tel: (01904) 471492 E-mail: info@emplaw.co.uk *Electronic legal publishing*

Disc-Lock Europe Ltd, PO Box 134, Sittingbourne, Kent, ME9 7TF Tel: (01795) 844332 Fax: (01795) 843986 E-mail: info@disc-lock.com *Fastener suppliers*

▶ Disco Dog, 23 Spittal Street, Edinburgh, EH3 9DZ Tel: 0131-622 0556 E-mail: info@discodog.co.uk *Web development*

Disco Drives (Kings Lynn) Ltd, Oldmedow Road, Hardwick Trading Estate, King's Lynn, Norfolk, PE30 4LE Tel: (01553) 761331 Fax: (01553) 692137 E-mail: enquiries@discodrives.co.uk *Variable speed drive subcontract machinists manufrs*

Disco Equipment Hire, 214 High Road, Romford, RM6 6LS Tel: (020) 8597 4575 Fax: (020) 8590 4125 *Disco equipment distributors*

Disco Hi-Tec, Second Floor, 151 London Road, East Grinstead, West Sussex, RH19 1ET Tel: (01342) 313165 Fax: (01342) 313177 E-mail: sales.uk@discoeurope.com *Dicing & slicing saw manufrs*

Discon Concrete Products, Mearcloth Road, Sowerby Bridge, West Yorkshire, HX6 3LF Tel: (01422) 833776 *Concrete products & landscape product manufrs*

▶ Discontinued Color Ltd, 30 Chandler's Walk, Dalgety Bay, Dunfermline, Fife, KY11 9FE Tel: (01383) 822335 Fax: (01383) 823800 E-mail: enquiries@discontinuedcolor.co.uk *Suppliers of bathrooms*

▶ Discord Distribution, 64 High Street, Rusthall, Tunbridge Wells, Kent, TN4 8SD Tel: (01892) 511522 Fax: (01892) 511526 E-mail: post@discord.co.uk *DVD titles & spoken word catalogues of music*

▶ Discos Occasions, 12 Park Meadow, Westhoughton, Bolton, BL5 3UZ Tel: (01942) 817292 Fax: E-mail: info@occasionsdiscos.co.uk *Mobile disco entertainment service*

▶ Discos Online, 29 Oaken Copse Crescent, Hawley, Farnborough, Hants, GU14 8DS Tel: 01252 661674 E-mail: andy@discosonline.co.uk *Professional DJ's For the Corporate Market*

Discotechnology Ltd, 479a Wakefield Road, Liversedge, West Yorkshire, WF15 6BL Tel: (01924) 400700 Fax: (01924) 400700 E-mail: discotechnololgy@btconnect.com *Disco equipment retailer*

▶ Discount Appliance Centre Ltd, Cook House, Brunel Drive, Newark, Nottinghamshire, NG24 3FB Tel: (0870) 0671420 Fax: (01636) 707737 E-mail: info@thedac.co.uk *Retailers of kitchen*

▶ Discount Baby Brands, 8 High Street, Galashiels, Selkirkshire, TD1 1SD Tel: (01896) 753308 *Big discounts in the UK on Mamas & Papas Cots, Prams, Highchairs, furniture, bedding, baby clothes and more Mamas and Papas products*

▶ Discount Baby Goods, 4 Mellowmead, Manaton, Newton Abbot, Devon, TQ13 9UE Tel: (01647) 221480 Fax: (01647) 221480 E-mail: sales@discountbabygoods.co.uk *Baby goods /nursery equipment, cots, Grobags, feeding, changing and bathing equipment all below makers rrp*

Discount Blind Centre, 11 Centurion Street, Belfast, BT13 3AS Tel: (028) 9033 3606 Fax: (028) 9024 5724 *Blinds manufrs*

Discount Cars & Exhaust, Deverill Road Trading Estate, Deverill Road, Sutton Veny, Warminster, Wiltshire, BA12 7BZ Tel: (01985) 840110 Fax: (01985) 841317 *Sutton Veny Warminster Discount Tyres and Exhaust Garage Services Vehicle Repair Repairs Breakdown Service*

Discount Computer Supplies, 58 Copley Road, Doncaster, South Yorkshire, DN1 2QW Tel: (01302) 364155 Fax: (01302) 366062 E-mail: sales@dcs.uk.com *Computer systems & software development*

▶ Discount Computer Warehouse Ltd, Unit 5 Bordesley Trading Estate, Bordesley Green Road, Birmingham, B8 1BZ Tel: (0800) 1804599 Fax: 0121-327 9521 *Computer maintenance & repair services*

▶ Discount Computers, 7 Canvey Road, Canvey Island, Essex, SS8 0LL Tel: (01268) 511716 Fax: (01268) 511716

Discount Desk Centre, Kilsyth Road, Longcroft, Bonnybridge, Stirlingshire, FK4 1HD Tel: (0870) 2407817 Fax: (0870) 2407814 E-mail: sales@discountdeskcentre.co.uk *Office furniture manufrs*

▶ Discount Double Glazing Ltd, 844 Romford Road, London, E12 5JP Tel: (020) 8514 0819 E-mail: info@discountdoubleglazing.co.uk *UPVC & aluminium windows & door manufrs*

▶ Discount DVDs & Videos, 11 Craighead Drive, Huntly, Aberdeenshire, AB54 8LG Tel: (01466) 799142 E-mail: cheapstock@tiscali.co.uk *we have hundreds of dvds and videos films childrens plus lots more see our web site for full info*

▶ Discount Equestrian Ltd, 197/199 Barnsley Road, Wombwell, Barnsley, South Yorkshire, S73 8DR Tel: 01226 270555 E-mail: sales@discountequestrian.co.uk *Retailer of all equestrian equipment for horse and rider. Brands include John Whitaker, Shires, Gorringe, FAL, Just Togs, Fieldhouse, Equitector and more. All at prices well below RRP.*

▶ Discount Floor Heating Ltd, Studio 24, Torfaen Business Centre, Gilchrist Thomas Industrial Estate, Blaenavon, Gwent, NP4 9RL Tel: (0845) 6581511 Fax: (0845) 6613557 E-mail: info@discountfloorheating.co.uk *Electric under floor heating manufrs*

Discount Furniture Co., Riverdale Business Park, Wheatley Hall Road, Doncaster, South Yorkshire, DN2 4PF Tel: (01302) 340049 Fax: (01302) 340049 *Furniture retailers*

Discount Furniture Manufacturing, Wilford Road, Nottingham, NG2 1EB Tel: 0115-986 6868 Fax: 0115-986 6868 E-mail: dfm_ltd@yahoo.co.uk *Kitchen & bedroom & bathroom manufrs*

Discount Label Suppliers Ltd, 25-31 Hill Street, Brierfield, Nelson, Lancashire, BB9 5AT Tel: (01282) 696061 Fax: (01282) 696122 *Label manufrs*

Discount Security Wholesalers Ltd, 217 Manchester Road, Oldham, OL8 4QY Tel: 0161-682 6869 Fax: 0161-682 8787 *Burglar alarm equipment retailers*

▶ Discount Sheds, Bowdell Farm, Brenzett, Romney Marsh, Kent, TN29 9RP Tel: (01797) 343991

▶ Discount Store, 53 Westmuir Street, Glasgow, G31 5EL Tel: 0141-556 7321 Fax: 0141-556 7188

Discount Toiletries, 340 Woodstock Road, Belfast, BT6 9DP Tel: (028) 9045 7303 *Toiletries suppliers*

Discount Tool Supplies Ltd, 66 St. Johns Lane, Bristol, BS3 5AF Tel: 0117-977 8076 Fax: 0117-971 7991 E-mail: info@harryneill.com *Woodworking machinery, powertools & welding machines*

▶ discount tower scaffolding, Unit 24, Carlisle, CA6 4RH Tel: 01228 547374 *tower scaffolding brand new 6x4 21ft working height pre-galvanised steel comes with tie bars & safety rails, lockable caster wheels availble, contact us to see what special offer's we are currently offering when replying Quoto kelly to receive special offer price!!!!!!*

▶ Discount-Line Ltd, 5 Witches Linn, Ardrossan, Ayrshire, KA22 8NP Tel: (0845) 1223110 E-mail: discount.line@btinternet.com *Discount-Line is the web site where businesses, including Engineering, Trades, Manufacturing, and Retail - advertise their Sales, Deals and Discounts.**Discount-line provides the cheapest advertising available in Scotland.*

▶ Discovery Childcare Training, 7 Union Street, Plymouth, PL1 3HQ Tel: (01752) 492363 Fax: (01752) 492363 E-mail: info@discoverychildcaretraining.co.uk *Provides inspirational training and learning experiences in Early Years Care and Education in Plymouth. NVQ's, Bespoke and Consultancy Services.*

Discovery Computer Services Ltd, Burnham Business Park, Springfield Road, Burnham-on-Crouch, Essex, CM0 8TE Tel: (01621) 786860 Fax: (01621) 786861 E-mail: info@buy-it-back.com *Computer networking equipment sales & recycling services*

▶ Discovery Computing Group, 228 Blackness Road, Dundee, DD2 1RG Tel: (01382) 908262

Discovery Electronics, 2 Newark Road South, Glenrothes, Fife, KY7 4NS Tel: (01592) 771755 Fax: (01592) 771758 E-mail: enquiries@discoveryltd.com *Process control equipment manufrs*

▶ Discovery Initiatives, The Travel House, 51 Castle Street, Cirencester, Gloucestershire, GL7 1QD Tel: (01285) 643333

▶ Discovery Media Direct, 1 Brookhampton Lane, Kineton, CV35 0JA Tel: 0871 474 2724 *Media catalogue with a fantastic range of music CDs, DVDs, Karaoke & entertainment to suit everyone. Music CDs & DVD Collector boxed gift sets*

Discovery Workshops, 516A Burnley Road, Accrington, Lancashire, BB5 6JZ Tel: (01254) 237649 Fax: (01254) 237649 E-mail: mail@dicoveryworkshops.co.uk *Scientific instrument manufrs*

Discreet, Ingeni, 15-17 Broadwick Street, London, W1F 0DE Tel: (020) 7851 8000 Fax: (020) 7851 8001 *IT software developers*

Discreet Pest Control, 85 Grinstead Lane, Lancing, West Sussex, BN15 9DT Tel: (01903) 751048 Fax: (01903) 750544 *Pest & vermin control services*

Discspeed Computer Consultants, Farley Common, Westerham, Kent, TN16 1UB Tel: (01959) 562117 *Computer consultants*

Diset Engineering, Units 46-48 Hotchkiss Way, Binley Indust Estate, Coventry, CV3 2RL Tel: (024) 7644 9607 *Precision engineers*

Diskel Ltd, 212-214 Farnham Road, Slough, SL1 4XE Tel: (01753) 821091 Fax: (01753) 512438 E-mail: sales@diskel.co.uk *Computer software dealers*

Disking International, 5 South Street, Farnham, Surrey, GU9 7QU Tel: (01252) 719719 Fax: (01252) 719819 E-mail: farnhamshop@disking.co.uk *Computer suppliers*

Diskovery Business Services, 123 Bournemouth Road, Poole, Dorset, BH14 9HR Tel: (01202) 733620 Fax: (01202) 737184 E-mail: dbs@diskovery.co.uk *IT support*

Diskovery Systems, 123 Bournemouth Road, Poole, Dorset, BH14 9HR Tel: (01202) 746353 Fax: (01202) 737184 E-mail: sales@diskovery.co.uk *Computer dealers*

▶ Disney Flooring, Albert Avenue, Weston-super-Mare, Avon, BS23 1YJ Tel: (01934) 628320 Fax: (01934) 615006 E-mail: enquiries@disney-flooring.com *Specialists in the supply & installation*

Di-Soft Research, Little Frankley, Hook Heath Road, Woking, Surrey, GU22 0QL Tel: (01483) 727906 Fax: (01483) 727906 E-mail: colin.howard@comdaq.net *Software consultants*

Di-Spark Ltd, Unit 3B Wessex Gate, Portsmouth Road, Horndean, Waterlooville, Hampshire, PO8 9LP Tel: (023) 9259 6338 Fax: (023) 9259 4077 E-mail: sales@dispsrks.co.uk *Spark erosion services*

Dispatchit Bath Ltd, 58 Claude Avenue, Bath, BA2 1AG Tel: (01225) 444443 Fax: (01225) 461123 E-mail: dispatchit@btconnect.com *LARGEST SAMEDAY AND NEXTDAY COURIERS BATH ENGLAND FREEPHONE* 0800 195 6356*

Dispec Anodizing Ltd, Unit 4 Sough Bridge Mill, Colne Road, Barnoldswick, Lancashire, BB18 6UH Tel: (01282) 841341 Fax: (01282) 841341 E-mail: dispec@ic24.net *Specialists in decorative/protective aluminium anodizing*

Dispense Technology Services Ltd, 19a Watts Road, Studley, Warwickshire, B80 7PT Tel: (01527) 853014 Fax: (01527) 853014 E-mail: j_pickering@btconnect.com *Beer dispense equipment suppliers*

▶ Disperse, G 7 Academy Apartments, Elmbank Avenue, Kilmarnock, Ayrshire, KA1 3BT Tel: (01563) 574062 E-mail: info@disperse-distribution.com *We offer a simple and cost effective advertising service which includes DOOR TO DOOR DISTRIBUTION, STREET MARKETING and DESIGN AND PRINT ASSISTANCE.*

Dispersion Technology Ltd, Factory Lane, Brantham, Manningtree, Essex, CO11 1NJ Tel: (01206) 395000 Fax: (01206) 392872 E-mail: christine@dispersion-technology.co.uk *Ink & paint toll manufrs*

▶ Dispirito Design Ltd, Tump House Studio, Dingestow, Monmouth, Gwent, NP25 4DX Tel: (01600) 740432 E-mail: info@dispirito.co.uk *Design consultants*

Displad Ltd, Eton Hill Works, Eton Hill Road, Radcliffe, Manchester, M26 2DL Tel: 0161-723 3125 Fax: 0161-723 3125 E-mail: carpetdisplay@ukonline.co.uk *Display equipment for floor coverings & textiles*

Display, Unit 1 White Road, Off Charfleets Road, Canvey Island, Essex, SS8 0PQ Tel: (01268) 696509 Fax: (01268) 696587 E-mail: display.uk@virgin.co.uk *Signs manufrs*

Display Array Ltd, Unit 4 Britannia Industrial Estate, Cherry Holt Road, Bourne, Lincolnshire, PE10 9LA Tel: (01778) 423400 Fax: (01778) 423444 E-mail: display2u@aol.com *Point of sale & display manufrs*

The Display Centre UK Ltd, 2 The Avenue, Westside Fareham Railway Station, Fareham, Hampshire, PO14 1NP Tel: (01329) 231333 Fax: (01329) 823262 E-mail: sales@displaycentre.co.uk *Shop fittings*

Display Containers Ltd, 19b Moor Road, Broadstone, Dorset, BH18 8AZ Tel: (01202) 658838 Fax: (01202) 698284 E-mail: sales@displaycontainers.co.uk *Information display products suppliers*

Display Ideas Ltd, 30 White Ladies Road, Clifton, Bristol, BS8 2LG Tel: 0117-970 6400 Fax: 0117-970 6401 E-mail: design@displayideas.co.uk *Interiors & design display specialists*

Display Maintenance Ltd, Old Bank Mills, Old Bank Road, Earlsheaton, Dewsbury, West Yorkshire, WF12 7AA Tel: (01924) 469664 Fax: (0870) 8508511 E-mail: enquiries@displaymaintenance.co.uk *Exhibition stand contractors*

Display Matrix, Unit 14, Dixon Business Centre Dixon Road, Bristol, BS4 5QW Tel: 0117-300 9925 Fax: 0117-977 2457 E-mail: info@displaymatrix.co.uk *Display stand & equipment manufrs*

Display Promotions London Ltd, 17 Station Parade, Whitchurch Lane, Edgware, Middlesex, HA8 6RW Tel: (020) 8951 0088 Fax: (020) 8381 3229 E-mail: snb@display.freeserve.co.uk *Promotions & display suppliers*

Display Services International, Unit 3 Victoria Wharf Victoria Industrial Park, Victoria Road, Dartford, DA1 5AJ Tel: (01322) 222474 Fax: (01322) 276328 E-mail: info@handsie-display.co.uk *Handsie Display offers a full range of equipment for all your display requirements, from exhibition and outdoor event stands, temporary bar units, barrier systems, shop fitting, shell schemes, seminars and promotional events. Purchase or hire it's up to you*

Display System Fabrications Ltd, Dunsteads Farm, Trueloves Lane, Ingatestone, Essex, CM4 0NJ Tel: (01277) 352700 Fax: (01277) 352766 E-mail: dsfdisplay@aol.com *Marketing display designers & manufrs*

Display Works (Scotland) Ltd, Unit 2, Polbeth Industrial Estate, Polbeth, West Calder, West Lothian, EH55 8TJ Tel: (01506) 872010 Fax: (01506) 873010 E-mail: sales@display-works.co.uk *Designers & producers of window & interior display systems*

Display-Corr, Unit 3 4 & 6 Elms Yard, Stevenage Road, Little Wymondley, Hitchin, Hertfordshire, SG4 7HY Tel: (01438) 747498 Fax: (01438) 747461 E-mail: sales@displaycor.co.uk *Point of sale display manufrs*

▶ Displayer, 30 Rosedale Way, Forest Town, Mansfield, Nottinghamshire, NG19 0QR Tel: (01623) 628309 Fax: 01623 628309 E-mail: alanmarshall@displayer.co.uk *Suppliers of portable display equipment suitable for exhibitions*

▶ Displaymania, Back Grove Farm Estate, Bulls Lane, Wishaw, Sutton Coldfield, West Midlands, B76 9QN Tel: 0121-313 1313 Fax: 0121-313 1212 E-mail: sales@displaymania.co.uk *National Suppliers of Portable Exhibition Display and*

continued

continuation
Digital graphics. Huge format print, Corporate Identity signs, lightboxes, poster units, pos/pop.

Displaysia Exhibitions Ltd, Unit 49 Longshot Industrial Estate, Longshot Lane, Bracknell, Berkshire, RG12 1RL Tel: (01344) 487220 Fax: (01344) 487221 *Design & building exhibition stands*

▶ Display-Stands.uk.com, Barton Hall, Hardy Street, Eccles, Manchester, M30 7NN Tel: 0161-609 0262 Fax: 0161-609 0252 E-mail: sales@panelwarehouse.com *Manufacturer & supplier of display & exhibition stands*

Displex Display & Exhibition Ltd, Graphex House, Adcroft Street, Stockport, Cheshire, SK1 3HZ Tel: 0161-480 4626 Fax: 0161-474 1875 E-mail: sales@displex.co.uk *Exhibition stand contractors*

Dispo Products Ltd, 2 Carrakeel Drive, Maydown Industrial Estate, Maydown, Londonderry, BT47 6UQ Tel: (028) 7186 1086 Fax: (028) 7186 0170 E-mail: dispo-products@91.net *Hygiene products suppliers*

Disposable Supplies, Movement House Soho Mills, London Road, Wallington, Surrey, SM6 7HN Tel: (020) 8773 2692 Fax: (020) 8669 1907 E-mail: sales@disposablesupplies.co.uk *Disposable & janitorial suppliers*

Disposables & Catering Supplies, Haltwhistle House, Haltwhistle Road, South Woodham Ferrers, Chelmsford, CM3 5ZA Tel: (01245) 320839 Fax: (01245) 322256 E-mail: sales@dcs-swf.co.uk *Catering suppliers*

Diss Fasteners Ltd, A8 Gilray Road, Diss, Norfolk, IP22 4EU Tel: (01379) 643506 Fax: (01379) 651121 E-mail: sales@dissfasteners.co.uk *Industrial fasteners*

Distinction Computer Training, 273 Liverpool Road, Eccles, Manchester, M30 0QN Tel: 0161-788 7560 Fax: 0161-788 7560 E-mail: enquires@go2dct.co.uk *Computer training*

▶ Distinctive Design, Oldmill Street, Stoke-on-Trent, ST4 2RP Tel: (01782) 844629 Fax: (01782) 849334 *General fabricators iron works*

Distinctive Developments, 1 East Parade, Sheffield, S1 2ET Tel: 0114-281 2208 Fax: 0114-281 2207 E-mail: info@distdevs.co.uk *Video game writers for mobile phones*

▶ Distinctive Gates & Railings, Enterprise House, 260 Chorley New Road, Horwich, Bolton, BL6 5NY Tel: (01204) 699675 Fax: (01204) 668300 E-mail: enquiries@bendtube.co.uk *Design, manufacture & installation of cast iron gates & railings*

Distinctive Iron Work, Forge House, Tewkesbury Road, Uckington, Cheltenham, Gloucestershire, GL51 9SX Tel: (01242) 680453 Fax: (01242) 680453 *Blacksmiths*

Distinctive Systems Ltd, Amy Johnson Way, York, YO30 4XT Tel: (01904) 692269 Fax: (01904) 690810 E-mail: sales@distinctive-systems.com *Computer software for motor coach operators*

▶ Distress Services, Thurne, Norwich, NR6 6DW Tel: (01692) 672173 *Distress Services have specialised in Lie Detector Testing (Polygraph Testing) since being established in the UK in 1999. Our professionally trained lie detector examiners are available to carry out polygraph tests on a variety of issues*

Distributed Technology Ltd, Howard House, Amy Road, Oxted, Surrey, RH8 0PW Tel: (01883) 716161 Fax: (01883) 716865 E-mail: mail@dtl-connectors.co.uk *Electronic component distributors*

▶ Distributor Recruitment - Kleeneze Europe, 26 Westbury Gardens, Farnham, Surrey, GU9 9RN Tel: 01252 715426 E-mail: info@k-eze.com *Kleeneze - The Home Based Business. Distributors required on a full-time or part-time basis. Full support & training given.*

District Tooling Co., 7 Harolds Road, Harlow, Essex, CM19 5BJ Tel: (01279) 424302 Fax: (01279) 451186 *Press tools & special purpose machines manufrs*

Distrupol, 119 Guildford Street, Chertsey, Surrey, KT16 9AL Tel: (01932) 566033 Fax: (01932) 560363 E-mail: info@distrupol.com *Thermoplastics distributors*

Distrupol Ltd, Distrupol, Marston Road, Wolverhampton, WV2 4LN Tel: (01902) 426839 Fax: (01902) 426852 E-mail: info@distrupol.com *Plastic distributors & compounders*

Disys Technologies Ltd, 24-25 Cross Hands Business Centre, Heol Parc Mawr, Cross Hands, Llanelli, Dyfed, SA14 6RE Tel: (01269) 842496 Fax: (01269) 844708 E-mail: info@disystechnologies.com *Control solutions.*

Ditac Ltd, 1 Latton Bush Business Centre, Southern Way, Harlow, Essex, CM18 7BH Tel: (01279) 427779 Fax: (01279) 427103 *Self adhesive label printers manufrs*

Ditchling Press, Consort Way, Burgess Hill, West Sussex, RH15 9YS Tel: (01444) 243253 Fax: (01444) 242198 *Litho printers*

▶ Ditech Metal Products, 17 Alrewas Road, Kings Bromley, Burton-on-Trent, Staffordshire, DE13 7HW Tel: (01543) 473633 Fax: (01543) 473634 E-mail: info@ditechltd.co.uk *Plastic & metal fabricators*

Ditone Labels, Harvard Industrial Estate, Kimbolton, Huntingdon, Cambridgeshire, PE28 0NJ Tel: (01480) 862600 Fax: (01480) 862623 E-mail: enquire@ditone.co.uk *Self adhesive labels supplier*

Ditra Systems Ltd, Unit 14 Albury Close, Reading, RG30 1BD Tel: 0118-958 5489 Fax: 0118-959 6343 E-mail: info@ditra-systems.co.uk *Electronic systems manufrs*

▶ Diva Cosmetics Ltd, 25 Bourne Valley Road, Poole, Dorset, BH12 1DZ Tel: (01202) 540045 Fax: (01202) 540066

▶ Divebitz, The Shop, High Street, Brasted, Westerham, Kent, TN16 1JA Tel: (01959) 569960 Fax: (01959) 562353 E-mail: info@divebitz.com *Probably The Smallest Scuba Diving Shop in Kent!**DiveBitz is a friendly Scuba Diving and Snorkelling Equipment shop in the picturesque village of Brasted in Kent.**We offer a wide range of*

continued

diving equipment from some of the best manufacturers including Cressi-sub, Ralf Tech, Apeks, Poseidon and Seemann Sub among many others. We sell Masks, Snorkels, Fins, BCD"s, Wet Suits, Dry Suits, Bags, Clips, Buckles, Dive Computers, Dive Watches, Dive Knives, Scuba Glue, Scuba Wax, Scuba Cylinders and many other Scuba related products.

▶ DiveLife, 151 Bury New Road, Whitefield, Manchester, M45 6AA Tel: 0161 7960300 E-mail: info@divelife.co.uk *Scuba diving training, equipment sales, servicing and diving gas suppliers*

Diverco Ltd, 4 Bank Street, Worcester, WR1 2EW Tel: (01905) 23383 Fax: (01905) 613523 *Company sales & acquisitions* Also at: Branches throughout the U.K.

A Divers JNR, 6 Russell Road, Aberdeen, AB11 5RB Tel: (01224) 580830 Fax: (01224) 580830 *Fish merchants*

▶ Diverse Book-Keeping Services, Unit 2C East Gores Farm, Salmons Lane, Coggeshall, Colchester, CO6 1RZ Tel: (01376) 564922 Fax: (01376) 564923 E-mail: diverseaccounts@yahoo.co.uk *We offer the following services for small business"s at very competitive prices:-*Monthly book-keeping*VAT Returns*Payroll*Tax Returns***

Diverse Products (Scotland) Ltd, Unit 34 Govan Workspace, 6 Harmony Row, Glasgow, G51 3BA Tel: 0141-445 3263 Fax: 0141-445 4668 E-mail: sales@diverseproducts.com *Engineers suppliers*

Diverse Yacht Services, Unit 12 Hamble Yacht Services, Port Hamble, Hamble, Southampton, SO31 4NN Tel: (023) 8045 3399 Fax: (023) 8045 5288 E-mail: phil@diverseyachts.com *Yacht equipment suppliers*

Diversey Lever Equipment Ltd, 4 Finway, Dallow Road, Luton, LU1 1TR Tel: (01582) 702100 Fax: (01582) 702171 *Liquid soap dispenser manufrs*

Diversified Agency Services Ltd, 239 Old Marylebone Road, London, NW1 5QT Tel: (020) 7298 7000 Fax: (020) 7724 8292 E-mail: sales@dasglobal.com *Holding company*

Diversified Software Systems Europe Ltd, Unit 110, Wharfedale Road, Winnersh, Wokingham, Berkshire, RG41 5RB Tel: 0118-944 4000 Fax: 0118-944 4030 E-mail: elisabeth.hager@diversifiedsoftware.com *Computer systems & software developers*

▶ Diversity Solutions Ltd, 18 Westminster Palace Gardens, Artillery Row, London, SW1P 1RR Tel: (0870) 7606227 Fax: (07092) 228007 *IT Consultants*

Divex Ltd, Enterprise Drive, Westhill Industrial Estate, Westhill, Aberdeenshire, AB32 6TQ Tel: (01224) 740145 Fax: (01224) 740172 E-mail: info@divex.co.uk *Diving equipment*

Divided Space Ltd, Old Station Yard, Cawston, Norwich, NR10 4BB Tel: (01603) 872935 Fax: 01603 872920 *Office partition suppliers & manufrs*

Dividers Ltd, Unit 1, Llanelli Gate, Dafen, Llanelli, Dyfed, SA14 8LQ Tel: (01269) 844877 Fax: (01269) 831112 E-mail: sales@esperowalls.com *Partition contractors*

Diving Services Anglesey, Heather Cliffe, Ravenspoint Road, Trearddur Bay, Holyhead, Gwynedd, LL65 2AQ Tel: (01407) 860318 Fax: (01407) 860318 *Diving equipment suppliers*

Division 5 Builders, 15-17 Arcola Street, London, E8 2DJ Tel: (020) 7241 1555 *Building contractors.*

Dix & Sons Ltd, Havelock Street, Kettering, Northamptonshire, NN16 9QA Tel: (01536) 512827 Fax: (01536) 512827 *General & steam heating engineers*

Walter Dix & Co., 1 Stirling Court, Team Valley Trading Estate, Gateshead, Tyne & Wear, NE11 0JF Tel: 0191-482 0033 Fax: 0191-491 1488 E-mail: sales@wdix.co.uk *Cooker distributors*

Dixey Instruments, 5 High Street, N Hykeham, Northampton, NN6 9DD Tel: (01522) 683152 Fax: (01604) 882488 E-mail: info@dixeyinstruments.com *Ophthalmic instrument manufrs* Also at: Hailsham

Dixi & Associates, Unit 3 Riverstone Middlemarch Business Park, Coventry Tradin, Middlemarch Business Park, Coventry, CV3 4FJ Tel: (024) 7688 2108 Fax: (024) 7688 2115 *Precision machinists*

Dixon, Unit C, 3 Fen End, Astwick Road, Stotfold, Hitchin, Hertfordshire, SG5 4BA Tel: (01462) 834911 Fax: (01462) 834911 E-mail: sales@dixontechnologies.com *Coating & laminating machinery manufrs*

▶ Andy Dixon, PO Box 164, Hertford, SG13 7ZJ Tel: (0845) 3308770 Fax: (0870) 6611554 E-mail: andy@scene2.co.uk *theatrical event design - specialists in 3Dimensional set, prop and costume for conference, promotional event marketing, exhibition, retail display, product launch and decorative dressing.*

▶ Dixon Block Paving, Long Lane, Attenborough, Beeston, Nottingham, NG9 6BG Tel: 0115-925 9511 E-mail: iandixon01@hotmail.com *Block paving suppliers for driveways*

▶ Dixon Contractors, 143 Tullaghans Road, Dunloy, Ballymena, County Antrim, BT44 9EA Tel: (028) 2765 7310

Dixon Hall & Co. Ltd, Grafton Street, Batley, West Yorkshire, WF17 6AR Tel: (01924) 476166 Fax: (01924) 471667 E-mail: sales@dixonhall.co.uk *Industrial ironmongers* Also at: Bradford, Dewsbury & Wakefield

Dixon Hurst Kemp Ltd, Station House, Bepton Road, Midhurst, West Sussex, GU29 9RE Tel: (01243) 787888 Fax: (01243) 787180 E-mail: chichester@dhk.co.uk *Consulting structural & civil engineers*

▶ Martin Dixon, 5B Julien Road, Ealing, London, W5 4XA Tel: (020) 8354 0510 E-mail: martin@m-dixon.com *Website design & internet consultancy,*

Dixon Signs, Stratford Rd, Drayton, Banbury, Oxon, OX15 6EE Tel: (01295) 730707 Fax: (01295) 730026 E-mail: mail@dixonsigns.co.uk *Signs manufrs*

Dixon Steelstock, Unit 2a Southgate, White Lund Industrial Estate, Morecambe, Lancashire, LA3 3PB Tel: (01524) 67241 Fax: (01524) 382641 E-mail: morcambe@bmsteel.co.uk *Steel stockholders*

Dixon & Stell Ltd, 21-25 Main Street, Cross Hills, Keighley, West Yorkshire, BD20 8TX Tel: (01535) 632138 Fax: (01535) 635983 E-mail: sales@dixontarget.com *Colour offset & screen printers*

▶ Dixon Timber Products Ltd, Roberts Road, Balby, Doncaster, South Yorkshire, DN4 0JT Tel: (01302) 341833 Fax: (01302) 341839 E-mail: dixontimber@btconnect.com *Office, medical & reception furniture desks*

Dixon Webb, Palmyra Square Chambers, 15 Springfield Street, Warrington, WA1 1BJ Tel: (01925) 577577 Fax: (01925) 579679 E-mail: warrington@dixonwebb.com *Surveyors & commercial agents* Also at: Chester, Warrington & Whitehaven

Dixon-PureFill Ltd, 65 Rainford Road, Billinge, Wigan, Lancashire, WN5 7PG Tel: (01744) 892555 E-mail: sales@dixonpurefill.co.uk *Powder handling equipment manufrs*

Dixons Blinds Manufacturers Ltd, Customes House, Ridley Street, Blyth, Northumberland, NE24 3AG Tel: (01670) 355011 Fax: (01670) 355011 *Blind manufrs*

Dixons Clothing Co., Berwick Street Mills, Berwick Street, Halifax, West Yorkshire, HX1 1QL Tel: (01422) 322284 Fax: (01422) 364068 E-mail: sales@dixons-clothing.fsnet.co.uk *Sportswear manufrs*

Dixons Of Darlington, North Road, Middlesbrough, Cleveland, TS2 1DD Tel: (01642) 244995 Fax: (01642) 249359 *Butchers equipment suppliers*

Dixons Forge, Unit 47 Salthouse Mills Industrial Estate, Barrow-in-Furness, Cumbria, LA13 0DH Tel: (01229) 431618 Fax: (01229) 431618 *Forgings & stamping manufrs*

▶ DIY Sash Windows, Unit 2 Whitworth Drive, Aycliffe Industrial Park, Newton Aycliffe, County Durham, DL5 6SZ Tel: (01325) 308888 Fax: (01325) 316002 E-mail: sales@diysashwindows.co.uk *Suppliers of sliding sash windows to diy & trade*

▶ DIY Tool Hire Ltd, 5 Enterprise Court, Gapton Hall Road, Great Yarmouth, Norfolk, NR31 0ND Tel: (01493) 669911 Fax: (01493) 661133 E-mail: info@diytoolhire.com *Equipment hire*

▶ DIY Tracking Ltd, Brooklands House, 3 Kingdom Close, Fareham, Hampshire, PO15 5TJ Tel: (01489) 571600 Fax: (01489) 571010 E-mail: sales@diytracking.com *Vehicle tracking systems suppliers*

▶ DIYdeals.com, 6 The Shaw, Glossop, Derbyshire, SK13 6DE Tel: (01457) 855259 E-mail: timber@diydeals.com *Suppliers of decking & other outdoor timbers*

▶ DIYproperty4sale.co.uk, Carlton Business Centre, 3 Horsford Walk, Bysingwood Estate, Faversham, Kent, ME13 7RW Tel: 01795 590996 E-mail: dan@121evangint.org *To enable Property Sellers to choose to sell their own property and save thousands of pounds on Estate Agent"s commission.*

▶ Diyses, Bowmore, Fintry, Turriff, Aberdeenshire, AB53 5PS Tel: (01888) 551778 Fax: (01888) 551784

Diytools Com Ltd, 20 Market Street, Watford, WD18 0PD Tel: (01923) 250295 Fax: (01923) 818219 E-mail: mur@diytools.com *Portable power tool distributors*

▶ DJ Hodgy! . Ltd, 54 Haig Street, Grangemouth, Falkirk, FK3 8QF Tel: (07043) 346349 Fax: (07043) 346349 E-mail: care@dj-hodgy.com *Scotlands Best Mobile Disoc Services, In Association with Real Radio (Scotland) & First Scotrail*

DJ & Music Shop, Dyffryn Orion, Saron Road, Pentrecwrt, Llandysul, Carmarthenshire, SA44 5DL Tel: (01559) 362957 E-mail: info@djandmusicshop.co.uk *Online shop selling Dj, Sound & Lighting equipment for dj"s as well as the professional end of the market. Top names at great prices. Based in West Wales we also hire marquees, staging, PA & lighting equipment for events large & small & we"re always willing to give friendly & helpful if requested.*

▶ DJ Services, 44 Melbourne Street, Worcester, WR3 8AX Tel: (01905) 745339 E-mail: sales@djservicesuk.net

DJ Supplies Sound & Lighting, 149 Greatfield Road, Kidderminster, Worcestershire, DY11 6PP Tel: (01562) 865353 Fax: (01562) 865353 E-mail: sales@djsupplies.co.uk *Disco equipment retail & hire*

▶ DJB Recycling Machinery Ltd, 37 Cotswold Road, Sheffield, S6 4QY Tel: 0114-233 3058 Fax: 01142 333058 *Whatever your waste processing needs we have the solution for you.We manufacture all types of recycling machinery but specialise in Waste Compactors,Baling Presses and Drum Crushers.All our products are manufactured in the UK to the highest possible standard.We would be happy to visit and carry out site surveys to make an assessment of the equipment suitable to the customer"""""s needs.All our products carry a 12 month full parts and labour warranty.WE ALSO HAVE A SELECTION OF REFURBISHED MACHINES AVAILABLE.*

▶ DJB Tools, Unit 10 Oak Street Industrial Park, Oak Street, Cradley Heath, West Midlands, B64 5JY Tel: (01384) 567292 Fax: (01384) 567292

DJD Components Wolverhampton, 2 Showell Road, Wolverhampton, WV10 9LN Tel: (01902) 426228 Fax: (01902) 424706 E-mail: steve@djd.co.uk *Springs, circlips & wireforming*

DJH Engineering Ltd, Consett Business Park, Consett, County Durham, DH8 6BP Tel: (01207) 500050 Fax: (01207) 599757 E-mail: sales@djhpewterworks.co.uk *Advertising gift, business incentive & souvenir designers & producers*

DJM Engineering, The Courtyard, Warkworth, Banbury, Oxfordshire, OX17 2AG Tel: (01295) 712424 E-mail: djm.eng@btconnect.com *Injection mould, plastic mould & precision toolmakers. In addition injection mould tools services*

▶ Djo UK Ltd, 7 The Pines Business Park, Broad Street, Guildford, Surrey, GU3 3BH Tel: (01483) 452964 Fax: (01483) 459470 *Orthopedic bracing manufrs*

DJR Executive Resourcing Ltd, Canal House, Kennet Road, Newbury, Berkshire, RG14 5JB Tel: (01635) 584111 Fax: (01635) 584129 E-mail: info@djr.co.uk *Recruitment agency*

DJS Engineering, 11-12 Benedict Square, Peterborough, PE4 6GD Tel: (01733) 328214 Fax: (01733) 328214 *Precision engineering*

DJS Welding Services & R & J Pipe Work, Norwich Road, Brooke, Norwich, NR15 1HJ Tel: (01508) 550177 Fax: (01508) 558011 E-mail: mike@rjpipe.demon.co.uk *Industrial pipe work & steel fabricators services*

DK Assemblies Ltd, Unit 2 Corbin Way, Gorecross Business Park, Bridport, Dorset, DT6 3UX Tel: (01308) 424095 Fax: (01308) 421490 E-mail: info@dkassemblies.com *Toroidal windings & transformers for electronic industries manufrs*

▶ DK Property Maintenance, 28 Springbourne Court, Beckenham, Kent, BR3 5ED Tel: 020 84606857 Fax: 0845 3309318 E-mail: dkpm@btconnect.com *We offer a complete property maintenance service from building to finishing.*Competitive Rates, free estimates and advice.*Fully insured and all work fully guaranteed.*Honest, reliable, and clean workmanship.*Commercial and residential.*Insurance work undertaken.**

▶ DKF Iinteriors, Royce Road, Peterborough, PE1 5YB Tel: (0845) 6443145 Fax: (0845) 6443146 E-mail: info@dkfiinteriors.com *Commercial interior design & refurbishment services*

▶ DKM Graphics Ltd, 132a Raceview Road, Ballymena, County Antrim, BT42 4HY Tel: (028) 2564 9239 Fax: (028) 2564 0192 E-mail: info@dkmprint.co.uk

▶ Dko Consulting Ltd, Caladh, Rock Road, Storrington, Pulborough, West Sussex, RH20 3AH Tel: (01903) 891528 Fax: (01903) 891528 E-mail: sales@dko-consulting.com *We provide ERP software selection and implementation, accounting and auditing services. Production Engineering and Manufacturing Management services.*

DKS, 32 Fir Trees Cresent, Lostock Hall, Preston, PR5 5SL Tel: (01772) 312466 *Trophies & engravers*

DKSH Great Britain, Wimbledon Hill Road, London, SW19 7PA Tel: (020) 8879 5500 Fax: (020) 8879 5501 E-mail: info.lon@dksh.com *Specialist chemicals suppliers* Also at: Selby

DKW Engineering, Bolde Close, Portsmouth, PO3 5RD Tel: (023) 9267 7747 Fax: (023) 9269 4335 E-mail: sales@dkwengineering.co.uk *CNC precision milling & turning engineers*

DL Plastics Ltd, 9-11 Commerce Way, Lawford, Manningtree, Essex, CO11 1UT Tel: (01206) 396646 Fax: (01206) 396602 E-mail: enquiries@dlplastics.co.uk *Injection moulding & hot blocking*

Dli Seals Ltd, Unit A-D Trimdon Court, Trimdon Grange Industrial Estate, Trimdon Grange, Trimdon Station, County Durham, TS29 6PE Tel: (01429) 881660 Fax: (01429) 882299 E-mail: sales@dliseals.co.uk *Hydraulic seal manufrs*

DLS UK, Water Lane, Wirksworth, Matlock, Derbyshire, DE4 4AA Tel: (01629) 822185 Fax: (01629) 825683 E-mail: sales@dls-uk.co.uk *Motor vehicle accessories suppliers*

DLT Shop Front & Shutter Systems Ltd, Shaw Road, Dudley, West Midlands, DY2 8TS Tel: (01384) 455277 Fax: (01384) 458847 E-mail: sales@weatherite-group.co.uk *Shutters & shop front systems manufrs*

▶ D-LUX UPVC Wigan, 20 Cloughwood Crescent, Shevington, Wigan, Lancashire, WN6 8EP Tel: (01257) 251631 E-mail: jm001j3373@blueyonder.co.uk *PVC double glazed windows, doors & conservatories*

DLW Computing, 1 Crowley Crescent, Croydon, CR0 4EE Tel: (020) 8686 8484 Fax: (020) 8239 0024 *Computer consultants*

▶ DM tiling, 27 Harris Road, Carnoustie, Angus, DD7 7NS Tel: 01241 855580 E-mail: contact@dmtiling.com *Located in Angus and Tayside, DM tiling offers a high quality, comprehensive tile fixing service for floors and walls, both indoor and outdoor.*

▶ DM Tyre Supplies, In2Connect house, Acton Road, Nottingham, NG10 1NJ Tel: 07779 765614 Fax: 0115 9284912 E-mail: dmtyrsupplies@btopenworld.com *supplier of all tyre maintainance products from TECH, TRAX & SCHRADER*

DMC Creative World, 62 Pullman Road, Wigston, Leicestershire, LE18 2DY Tel: 0116-281 1040 Fax: 0116-281 3592 E-mail: salesandmarketing@dmc.com *Handicraft & needlework suppliers*

▶ DMC Glass & Glazing, 36 Marbles Way, Tadworth, Surrey, KT20 5LG Tel: (01737) 212687 Fax: (01737) 212687 E-mail: dmcglazingservices@hotmail.co.uk *24hr Boarding-up Service...All Glass,Safety Glass,Mirrors,Pattern,Leaded Lights fitted & Replaced...Shop Fronts Fitted/Repaired...Double Glazing Installed Doors Windows Conservatories,All Double Glazing Repairs units,Rollers,Locks,Handles Hinges*

DMF Ltd, Deighton Mills, Leeds Road, Huddersfield, HD2 1TY Tel: (01484) 429889 Fax: (01484) 420445 *Textile furnishing manufrs*

▶ DMG Freight Services, Mead Park Industrial Estate, Harlow, Essex, CM20 2SE Tel: (01279) 452468 Fax: (01279) 415810 E-mail: info@dmg-freight.com

DMG World Media, Equitable House, Lyon Road, Harrow, Middlesex, HA1 2EW Tel: (020) 8515 2000 Fax: (020) 8515 2080 E-mail: sales@dmgworldmedia.com *Exhibition organisation*

▶ Dmi Fabrications, 2 Derby Works, Derby Road, Bootle, Merseyside, L20 8LQ Tel: 0151-922 4015 Fax: 0151-922 4019 *Metal fabrication*

▶ Dmi Technical Services Ltd, 5 Harwich Road, Great Bromley, Colchester, CO7 7UH Tel: (01206) 250734 E-mail: enquiries@dmitechnicalservices.co.uk *DMI Technical Services has over 20 years experience in the service of, supply and installation of all types of marine instrumentation and process controls. We can also offer other technical services for the marine industry, through our partners, such as navigational equipment, communications equipment and security systems. We can also offer state of the art alarm/monitoring and control systems including power management.*

DMI Young & Cunningham Ltd, West Chirton Industrial Estate, Gloucester Road, North Shields, Tyne & Wear, NE29 8RQ Tel: 0191-270 4690 Fax: 0191-270 4691 E-mail: newcastle@yandc.co.uk *Special purpose valve manufrs*

▶ DMJ Computer Services, 55 Home Close, Chiseldon, Swindon, SN4 0ND Tel: (01793) 740964 E-mail: martinj@dmjcomputerservices.com *We supply Software, Project Management, Website Design and Development solutions to small and medium-sized companies. Our Web Marketing solution is becoming very popular with business wishing to drive more traffic to their websites in a cost effective manner.*

DMK Leisure Ltd, 5 Alexander Drive, Unsworth, Bury, Lancashire, BL9 8PF Tel: 0161-705 2282 E-mail: sales@ukbouncers.co.uk *Bouncy castle & inflatable manufacturer & sales*

▶ DML International Limited, 6 Grebe Close, Poynton, Stockport, Cheshire, SK12 1HU Tel: 01625 850055 Fax: 01625 850055 E-mail: enquiries@dml.uk.com *DML provide Search, Planning & Acquisition Services for Mobile Telecommunications Sites. Site Management Services to Landlords and Landowners.Negotiation Services*

▶ DMMI, 745 Antrim Road, Templepatrick, Ballyclare, County Antrim, BT39 0AP Tel: (028) 9443 9449 Fax: (028) 9443 9446 E-mail: info@dmmi.co.uk *Factory removal or relocation contractors*

DMP, 49 High Street, Thornbury, Bristol, BS35 2AR Tel: (01454) 419900 Fax: (01454) 419156 E-mail: sales@dmpbestlicensedvals.co.uk *Cookseys DMP is a firm of Chartered Surveyors operating from offices in Bristol, Reading, London and Cardiff that has an established nationwide reputation. We are a professional practice of Chartered Surveyors that have been able to identify and fulfill a truly specialist role, tailor-made to client requirements. Remarkably few other professional practices offer a comparable and comprehensive depth of experience and quality throughout the stated specialisations.**We specialise in pub rent reviews, expert evidence, business planning, building surveys and business valuations for pubs, public houses, restaurants, night clubs, hotels, casinos, tied houses and freehouses.*

DMP Group, Unit 5F Canal Estate, Station Road, Langley, Slough, SL3 6EG Tel: (01753) 580101 Fax: (01753) 542685 E-mail: sales@dmpgroup.co.uk *Based in Langley, Berkshire, DMP Group offer presswork services to industry including compound presswork, pick & place multi operation services and sheet metal fabrication.*

DMS Flow Measurement & Control Ltd, The Lodge, 9 Mansfield Rd, Eastwood, Nottingham, NG16 3AQ Tel: (01773) 534555 Fax: (01773) 534666 E-mail: sales@dmsltd.com Sales Contact: Heidi Scannell *Based centrally in Nottinghamshire covering the whole of the UK, DMS Limited was formed in 1999 to service the Building Services market sector. The product ranges that DMS have secured and represent from around Europe mean that we have a very strong presence in the Heating/Cooling Energy Metering markets. These are markets where the company's principals have over 20 years experience. As well as Heat /Cooling Meters we also supply a comprehensive range of Water Meters, Natural Gas & LPG Meters, Oil Meters, Electricity Meters, Gas Governors, Gas Detectors and Safety Valves. All the products we supply are backed up by an experienced technical team, who will ensure that your enquiry is responded to the same day wherever possible. Fast and efficient "ex-stock" availability is offered on most of the products we supply so therefore you can order with confidence knowing your goods will be there next day!*

DMS Metal Spinning, 6 Grafton Road, Birmingham, B11 1JP Tel: 0121-773 8885 Fax: 0121-773 3141 E-mail: adriandms@aol.com *Metal spinning & polishing services, powder coating*

DMS Systems, Ivel Road, Shefford, Bedfordshire, SG17 5JU Tel: (01462) 857955 Fax: (01462) 819168 *Printer repairs & maintenance*

Dna Computer Services Ltd, 64d Sutton Court Road, London, W4 3EG Tel: (020) 8742 3524 Fax: (020) 8995 8312 E-mail: info@dnacomputers.co.uk *Computer engineers*

Dna Engineering, 36 Gainsford Road, Southampton, SO19 7AU Tel: (020) 8692 4567 Fax: (023) 8044 1226 E-mail: dna.engineering@btconnect.com *DNA ENGINEERING LTD HAVE OVER 30 YEARS EXPERIENCE IN SOURCING VEE & WEDGEBELTS,BEARINGS,*ELECTRIC MOTORS,TOOLS,CHAINS & SPROCKETS,TIMING BELTS,COUPLINGS,CASTORS AND LUBRICANTS AND ANY OTHER PRODUCT YOU NEED TO KEEP INDUSTRY MOVING.**

▶ Dna Logistics, Unit 5 Chariot Way, Glebe Farm Industrial Estate, Rugby, Warwickshire, CV21 1DA Tel: (01788) 535111 Fax: (01788) 567117 E-mail: dnalogistics@btconnect.com *Business support services including document archiving, confidential waste destruction, bulk storage, distribution, direct courier services and specialist in-night deliveries.*

▶ DND, 25 Ackworth Road, Portsmouth, PO3 5NS Tel: (023) 9265 2866 Fax: 023 92652866 E-mail: enquiries@dnd.co.uk *French polishers*

DNS Midlands Ltd, 1 Bridge Street, Derby, DE1 3HZ Tel: (01332) 363187 Fax: (01332) 371615 E-mail: enquiries@dnsmidlands.co.uk *DNS has built an enviable reputation for delivering a professional service that's second to none. With over 40 years experience, we have establish many long standing relationships with our clients. Who we feel appreciate our considerable expertise and total commitment to deliver high quality work at all times. If you would like to discuss any future project, please access our details by using the link provided.*

▶ DNS Security Alarms, 154 Sandy Road,, Seaforth,, Liverpool, L21 1AQ Tel: 0151 7225505

DNS Windows Ltd, Daniels Way, Hucknall, Nottingham, NG15 7LL Tel: 0115-963 6361 Fax: 0115-968 0183 *Steel window installers & manufrs*

DNV, Cromarty House, Regent Quay, Aberdeen, AB11 5AR Tel: (01224) 335000 Fax: (01224) 593311 *Certification & verification services*

LEARN>DO London0" corp="00222477" new="N" rule=" " type="NORM"> Do>Learn>do, 21 Cantelowes Road, London, NW1 9XR Tel: 020 7267 8228 Fax: 020 7267 8228 E-mail: info@do-learn-do.com *Training & software skills specialists*

Dobbie McInnes, 42 Methil Street, Glasgow, G14 0AN Tel: 0141-959 2247 Fax: 0141-954 1172 E-mail: dobbie@yandc.co.uk *Instrument control equipment manufrs*

Dobbin Refrigeration Services Ltd, 93 Creevy Road, Boardmills, Lisburn, County Antrim, BT27 6UL Tel: (028) 9263 8814 Fax: (028) 9263 9233 *Refrigeration installation*

Dobbindale Foods, Armagh Business Centre, Loughgall Road, Armagh, BT61 7NH Tel: (028) 3751 0501 Fax: (028) 3751 0501 *Butchery & sandwich manufrs*

▶ Dobbs, Unit 5 Wainer Close, Lincoln, LN6 3RY Tel: (01522) 500100 Fax: (01522) 500110 *Blind manufacturers & distributors*

Dobbs Logistics Ltd, 23 Hawthorn Road, Eastbourne, East Sussex, BN23 6QA Tel: (08708) 518770 Fax: (01323) 641539 E-mail: services@dobbslogistics.co.uk *Road transport, haulage & freight services*

Dobie Johnston Ltd, 151 Poplin Street, Glasgow, G40 4LW Tel: 0141-550 2345 Fax: 0141-550 1115 *Suspended ceilings contractors*

Dobie Wyatt Ltd, Old School, Cadley, Marlborough, Wiltshire, SN8 4NE Tel: (01672) 512563 Fax: (01672) 516948 E-mail: dobiewyatt@cwcom.net *Tarpaulin manufrs*

Dobson & Beaumont Ltd, Appleby Street, Blackburn, BB1 3BH Tel: (01254) 53297 Fax: (01254) 676121 E-mail: philip@dobsonandbeaumont.co.uk *Stud & stud-bolt manufrs*

Dobson & Crowder Ltd, Berwyn Works, Holyhead Road, Llangollen, Clwyd, LL20 8AE Tel: (01978) 862100 Fax: (01978) 860410 *Litho printers & envelope manufrs*

Dobson Welding, 69 Carlisle Street, Leicester, LE3 6AH Tel: 0116-254 1675 Fax: 0116-254 1675 *Gates & fences fitters & manufrs*

Dobsons, 104-106 Stoke Road, Slough, SL2 5AP Tel: (01753) 520978 Fax: (01753) 823821 E-mail: dobsons@hotmail.com *DIY materials & timber distributors*

Doby Ltd, Doby Ltd, Hare Law Industrial Estate, Stanley, County Durham, DH9 8UJ Tel: (01207) 299861 Fax: (01207) 283563 E-mail: sales@dobyverrolec.com *Cold rolled metal sections*

▶ Doccombe European Transport Ltd, Unit 19, Sandleheath Industrial Estate, Fordingbridge, Hampshire, SP6 1PA Tel: (01425) 654753

Dochart Packaging & Hygiene Supplies Ltd, 46-48 Maurice Gaymer Road, Attleborough, Norfolk, NR17 2QZ Tel: (01953) 456040 Fax: (01953) 455144 *Packaging materials wholesalers*

▶ Docherty, 139 Stirling Road, Kilsyth, Glasgow, G65 0PT Tel: (01236) 826438 Fax: (01236) 826475

Docherty Chimney Group, 15 Alfred St South, Nottingham, NG3 2AD Tel: 0115-958 4734 Fax: 0115-950 2899 E-mail: sales@docherty.co.uk *Chimney & flue suppliers*

DocIndexer, St. Martins House, 16 St. Martins le Grand, London, EC1A 4EN Tel: (0870) 7668440 Fax: (0871) 2884087 E-mail: kellysearch@tickboxdb.com *DocIndexer is an internet hosted Document Management System (DMS) where you can instantly upload your version-controlled Office, PDF"s and any other documents or files for your staff to securely access - to and from any internet connection without special software installation or licensing issues. DocIndexer is a system from Tickbox Databased Systems Ltd - a database, website and secure hosting company offering CMS and DMS based in London, UK.*

Dockdale Ltd, 30 Lower Dartmouth Street, Birmingham, B9 4LG Tel: 0121-771 4681 Fax: 0121-773 7783 *Pressing fabricators*

Dockerills Brighton Ltd, 3abc Church Street, Brighton, BN1 1UJ Tel: (01273) 607434 Fax: (01273) 679771 E-mail: dockerills@dockerills.demon.co.uk *Locksmiths, ironmongery, hardware, engraving & timber services*

Docklands Light Railway Ltd, PO Box 154, London, E14 0DX Tel: (020) 7363 9898 Fax: (020) 7363 9708 *Transport services*

▶ Dockright Ltd, Forest Vale Road, Forest Vale Industrial Estate, Cinderford, Gloucestershire, GL14 2PH Tel: (01594) 822591 Fax: (01594) 823544 E-mail: service@dockright.co.uk *Dock loading equipment manufrs*

▶ Docman Solutions Ltd, Charter House, Pittman Way, Preston, PR2 9ZD Tel: (01772) 907087 Fax: (01772) 707114 E-mail: enquiries@docmansolutions.co.uk *Document management solution provider*

Docscan Ltd, 23 Cater Road, Bishopsworth, Bristol, BS13 7TW Tel: 0117-935 9818 Fax: 0117-935 9828 E-mail: docscan@servicepointuk.com *Document scanning & microfilm bureau*

Doctor, Quadrant House, The Quadrant, Sutton, Surrey, SM2 5AS Tel: (020) 8652 3500 Fax: (020) 8652 3793 *General publishers*

Doctor, Quadrant House, The Quadrant, Sutton, Surrey, SM2 5AS Tel: (020) 8652 3500 Fax: (020) 8652 3793 E-mail: hospital.doctor@rbi.co.uk *Publishers of magazine for doctors who work in hospitals*

▶ Doctor Software, Suite 3, Stanta Business Centre, 3 Soothouse Spring, St. Albans, Hertfordshire, AL3 6PF Tel: (01727) 869806 Fax: (0871) 4742864 E-mail: chris.beere@doctorsoftware.co.uk *Software support for home & small office computers*

Doctor's Laboratory plc, 60 Whitfield Street, London, W1T 4EU Tel: (020) 7460 4800 Fax: (020) 7460 4848 Principal Export Areas: Worldwide *Laboratory test analytical services*

Documation Software Ltd, Wessex House, Market Street, Eastleigh, Hampshire, SO50 9FD Tel: (023) 8064 7776 Fax: (023) 8064 7775 E-mail: info@documatation.co.uk *Software developer of document management*

▶ Documation Software Ltd, Wessex House, Market Street, Eastleigh, Hampshire, SO50 9FD Tel: (023) 8064 7776 Fax: (023) 8064 7775 E-mail: info@documation.co.uk *Software developers*

Documedia, Northern Way, Bury St. Edmunds, Suffolk, IP32 6NR Tel: (01284) 762201 Fax: (01284) 764033 E-mail: sales@documedia.co.uk *Printers*

Document Control Services Ltd, 10 Stapledon Road, Orton Southgate, Peterborough, PE2 6TB Tel: (01733) 366800 Fax: (01733) 366801 E-mail: dcs@sapasolutions.co.uk *Document management solutions & services*

Document House, Viscount House Queensway Court Business Park, Arkwright Way, Scunthorpe, South Humberside, DN16 1AD Tel: (01482) 370470 Fax: (01724) 271041 E-mail: sherralee.thompson@documenthouse.co.uk *Office suppliers*

Document Imaging Services Ltd, Image House, Radford Way, Billericay, Essex, CM12 0BT Tel: (01277) 625000 Fax: (01277) 624999 E-mail: sales@document-imaging.co.uk *Document imaging & microfilm services*

Document Plus Ltd, The Station House, Hever, Edenbridge, Kent, TN8 7ER Tel: (01732) 867792 Fax: (01732) 865585 E-mail: sales@chamnet.com *Software house*

Document Co. Xerox Ltd, Bridge House, Oxford Road, Uxbridge, Middlesex, UB8 1HS Tel: (01895) 251133 Fax: (01895) 254095 Principal Export Areas: Worldwide *Office equipment manufrs*

Dodd Anderson Ltd, Graphic House, Mylord Cresent, Camperdown Industrial Estate, Newcastle upon Tyne, NE12 5UJ Tel: 0191-268 9993 Fax: 0191-268 6667 E-mail: doddanderson@btconnect.co.uk *Promotional product suppliers*

▶ Dodd Group, Unit 1 Rabone Lane, Smethwick, West Midlands, B66 3JH Tel: 0121-565 6000 Fax: 0121-565 6038

▶ Dodd Group, Unit 8-9 Gate Centre, Bredbury Park Way, Bredbury, Stockport, Cheshire, SK6 2SN Tel: 0161-406 1720 Fax: 0161-406 1729

▶ Dodd Group South Western Ltd, 17-25 Hoopern Street, Exeter, EX4 4LU Tel: (01392) 426345 Fax: (01392) 426446

Doddgroup Eastern Ltd, Oldmedow Road, King's Lynn, Norfolk, PE30 4LB Tel: (01553) 772423 Fax: (01553) 691343 E-mail: kings-lynn@doddgroup.com *Electrical contractors, mechanical installation engineers*

Dodds Ltd, Mansfield Road, Aston, Sheffield, S26 2BS Tel: 0114-287 4187 Fax: 0114-287 2251 E-mail: traffic@dodds.co.uk *Road transport/haulage/freight services*

Dodgsons Of Preston Ltd, 143-155 Fylde Road, Preston, PR1 2XP Tel: (01772) 258353 Fax: (01772) 555937 *Motor spares factors*

Dods Of Haddington Ltd, Backburn, Haddington, East Lothian, EH41 4NN Tel: (01620) 823305 Fax: (01620) 824406 *Seed merchants*

▶ Dodson Shop Fitters, Loders Cottage, Gaunts, Wimborne, Dorset, BH21 4JJ Tel: (01258) 840509 E-mail: info@dodsonshopfitters.co.uk

Ernest Doe & Sons Ltd, Wilbraham Road, Fulbourn, Cambridge, CB21 5EX Tel: (01223) 880676 Fax: (01223) 880775 *Ford tractor dealership*

Ernest Doe & Sons Ltd, Whempstead Road, Benington, Stevenage, Hertfordshire, SG2 7BZ Tel: (01438) 869251 Fax: (01438) 869302 E-mail: ernestdoe@benington.com *Agricultural, construction & horticulture service*

Ernest Doe & Sons Ltd, Industrial Estate, Valleyside, Wymondham, Norfolk, NR18 0NN Tel: (01953) 602982 Fax: (01953) 601270 E-mail: rossjohnson@ernestdoe.com *Agriculture engineers*

W.R. Doe Engineering Ltd, The Boat House, Timsway, Staines, Middlesex, TW18 3JY Tel: (01784) 461408 Fax: (01784) 461408 *Woodworking machinery engineers & tool spares sales & service*

Doeflex Vitapol, Unit 64 Boswell Way, Stakehill Industrial Estate, Middleton, Manchester, M24 2FL Tel: 0161-655 3265 Fax: 0161-655 3735 *PVC granules manufrs*

Doeflex Vitapol, Hawksworth Trading Estate, Swindon, SN2 1DX Tel: (01793) 442442 Fax: (01793) 442443 E-mail: info@doeflex-vitapol.co.uk *PVC compound manufrs*

Doel Engineering Ltd, 5 Europa Park, Croft Way, Witham, Essex, CM8 2FN Tel: (01376) 515515 Fax: (01376) 500015 E-mail: info@doelengineering.com *Doel Engineering Ltd is firmly established as a leader in the design and manufacture of Web Converting Machines, Sheeters, Coaters, Laminators, Unwinds, Rewinds and other Special Purpose Custom Built Machinery [info@doelengineeing.com].*

Doepke UK Ltd, Unit 19, Woodlands Business Park, Woodlands Park Avenue, Maidenhead, Berkshire, SL6 3UA Tel: (01628) 829133 Fax: (01628) 829149 E-mail: sales@doepke.co.uk *Earth leakage & circuit breakers equipment*

▶ Doepud Web Design, PO Box 16263, Glasgow, G13 9AJ Tel: 0141-954 8671 E-mail: info@doepud.co.uk *Makers of websites design*

Dog Lane Blockworks Ltd, Dog Lane, Horsford, Norwich, NR10 3DH Tel: (01603) 898676 Fax: (01603) 891649 *Building block manufrs*

Dog World Ltd, Somerfield House, Wotton Road, Ashford, Kent, TN23 6LW Tel: (01233) 621877 Fax: (01233) 645669 E-mail: info@dogworld.co.uk *Newspaper publisher*

▶ DogEgg Ltd, Network House, Bolton Road, Pendlebury, Swinton, Manchester, M27 8BB Tel: 0161-728 4666 Fax: (07869) 078013 E-mail: sales@dogegg.net *Sales of mobile telecommunications products*

▶ Doggie Coats, 59 Headroomgate Road, Lytham St. Annes, Lancashire, FY8 3BD Tel: (01253) 714713 Fax: (01253) 714713 E-mail: anne@doggiecoats.co.uk *Manufacturers and suppliers of high quality designer dog coats*

▶ Doggie Solutions, Hazel Edge, Scotts Grove Road, Chobham, Woking, Surrey, GU24 8DX Tel: (01276) 488119 E-mail: info@doggiesolutions.co.uk *Dog training equipment retailers*

Doherty It Solutions Ltd, Doherty House, 2 Heathfield Terrace, London, W4 4JE Tel: (020) 8742 3338 Fax: 0845 6010597 E-mail: info@doherty.co.uk *Doherty Associates specialise in providing outsourced IT support to small and medium sized businesses in London and the South East. We also offer a range of IT consultancy services including project management, network design, network implementation and disaster recovery as well as business solutions such as mobile working and software development.*

▶ Doidge Fastenings, George Baylis Road, Berry Hill Industrial Estate, Droitwich, Worcestershire, WR9 9RB Tel: (01905) 779448 Fax: (0845) 0780334 E-mail: sales@doidge.com Sales Contact: P. Heim *Manufacturer and Supplier of Rivets - Semi-Tubular, Solid, Bifurcated, Self-Piercing, Eyelets and Blind Fasteners (Blind Rivets, Rivet Nuts, hankbushes). A full range of manual and semi-automatic machinery always available.*

Doig Springs, Unit 1 Fairview Estate, Beech Road, Wycombe Marsh, High Wycombe, Buckinghamshire, HP11 1RY Tel: 01494 556700 Fax: 01494 511002 E-mail: enquiries@springs.co.uk *Spring manufrs*

Doity Engineering Ltd, Isherwood Street, Rochdale, Lancashire, OL11 1JF Tel: (01706) 345515 Fax: (01706) 640454 E-mail: sales@doity.com *Electric crane distributors, mechanical handling & mezzanine flooring*

Dokic Joinery Ltd, Porte Marsh Road, Calne, Wiltshire, SN11 9BN Tel: (01249) 811133 Fax: (01249) 811144 *Joinery manufrs*

Dolby Laboratories Inc, Interface Business Park, Binknoll Lane, Wootton Bassett, Swindon, SN4 8QJ Tel: (01793) 842100 Fax: (01793) 842101 E-mail: website@dolby.com *Noise reduction & signal processors*

Dold Industries, 11 Hamberts Road, Blackall Industrial Estate, South Woodham Ferrers, Chelmsford, CM3 5UW Tel: (01245) 324432 Fax: (01245) 325570 E-mail: admin@dold.co.uk *Motor control products & safety relays*

B.S. Dollamore, Burton Rd, Castle Gresley, Swadlincote, Derbyshire, DE11 9HA Tel: (01283) 217905 Fax: (01283) 550119 E-mail: bsdollamore@aol.com *Quilters, extruders & binding manufrs*

Dolland & Aitchison Ltd, 35 Wigmore Street, London, W1U 1PW Tel: (020) 7580 4343 Fax: (020) 7580 3966 *Opticians*

Dollar Rae Ltd, 47 Haggs Road, Glasgow, G41 4AR Tel: 0141-649 9331 Fax: 0141-632 9882 E-mail: sales@dollarrae.co.uk *Shop fitters*

▶ Dolly Dolittle Ltd, 23 High Street, Market Harborough, Leicestershire, LE16 7NJ Tel: (01858) 466262 Fax: (01536) 770160 E-mail: ray@dollydolittles.co.uk *Greeting card suppliers*

Dolman, 10 Rouse Mill Lane, Batley, West Yorkshire, WF17 5QB Tel: (01924) 445577 Fax: (01924) 443222 E-mail: sales@jamesdolman.co.uk Principal Export Areas: Worldwide *Manufacturers of gaskets, cork/rubber & cork neoprene products, pressed felt & electrical-switchboard matting. In addition, rubber moulding , extrusion, matting/ mat & rubber industrial product manufrs*

H.F.A. Dolman Ltd, Ajax Works, Potters Way, Temple Farm Industrial Estate, Southend-On-Sea, SS2 5SJ Tel: (01702) 461155 Fax: (01702) 464177 *Demolition, dismantling & plant hire services*

Dolphin Bathrooms, Dolphin House, Springvale Industrial Park, Bilston, West Midlands, WV14 0QL Tel: (01902) 407000 E-mail: dolphin_reception@dolphin-mail.co.uk *Shower & bathroom distributors* Also at: Branches throughout the U.K.

Dolphin Bell Securities, PO Box 288, Guernsey, GY1 3RN Tel: (01481) 736682 Fax: (01481) 729910 E-mail: chris.brock@brewin.co.uk *Stock brokers & investment managers*

▶ Dolphin Computer Upgrades Ltd, 30 Arlington Gardens, Brighton, BN2 8QE Tel: (01273) 248871 Fax: (01273) 245717 E-mail: sales@dolphinupgrades.com *Computer upgrade & repair consultants*

Dolphin Design, 17 Invincible Road, Farnborough, Hampshire, GU14 7QU Tel: (01252) 518028 Fax: (01252) 518351 E-mail: thomas-frear@btconnect.com *Specialists in art work for printing*

Dolphin Drilling Ltd, Howe Moss Drive, Kirkhill Industrial Estate, Dyce, Aberdeen, AB21 0GL Tel: (01224) 411411 Fax: (01224) 723627 *Oil well drilling engineers/contractors*

Dolphin Drilling Ltd, Howe Moss Drive, Kirkhill Industrial Estate, Dyce, Aberdeen, AB21 0GL Tel: (01224) 411411 Fax: (01224) 723627 *Borehole measurement specialists* Also at: Great Yarmouth

Dolphin Enterprises, 4 Eddington Drive, Newton Mearns, Glasgow, G77 5AX Tel: 0141-639 4551 Fax: 0141-639 4551 E-mail: dolphinenterprizes@btconnect.com *Air-conditioning & water & dust extraction services*

▶ Dolphin Enviromental Services, Unit 1, Dolphin Business Park, 58D Arthur Street, Redditch, Worcestershire, B98 8JY Tel: (01527) 525505 Fax: (01527) 527622 *Water treatment services*

Dolphin Maritime & Aviation Services Ltd, 16 The Broadway, Stanmore, Middlesex, HA7 4DW Tel: (020) 8954 8800 Fax: (020) 8954 8844 E-mail: intfo@dolphin-maritime.com *Ship & air brokers*

Dolphin Movers, Unit 2 Haslemere Business Centre, Lincoln Way, Enfield, Middlesex, EN1 1DX Tel: (020) 8804 7700 Fax: (020) 8804 3232 E-mail: sales@dolphinmovers.com *Export & import agents*

▶ Dolphin Stairlifts, Unit 10b Airport Industrial Estate, Newcastle upon Tyne, NE3 2EF Tel: 0191-271 2600 Fax: 0191-286 3773

▶ Dolphin Stairlifts, 37 Chertsey Road, Chobham, Woking, Surrey, GU24 8PD Tel: (01276) 856060 Fax: (01276) 858689 E-mail: christian@dolphinlifts.co.uk *Mobility accessories supply & installation services*

Dolphine Ventilation, The Green, Barrow, Bury St. Edmunds, Suffolk, IP29 5AA Tel: (01284) 810563 Fax: (01284) 811119 E-mail: dolphineventilation@btinternet.com *Agricultural machinery equipment & distribs*

Doltons Silos & Storage Ltd, Water Eaton, Oxford, OX2 8HA Tel: (01865) 552914 *Agricultural merchants*

Domain 2000 Ltd, Old Rectory, Church Lane, Whaddon, Gloucester, GL4 0UE Tel: (01452) 306410 Fax: (01452) 306530 *Specialist software developers & suppliers*

Domain Powder Coating, Mayfair Industrial Estate, Maldon Road, Latchingdon, Chelmsford, CM3 6LF Tel: (01621) 742779 Fax: (01621) 742779 *Metal powder coating services*

Domain Selfstorage, 21-31 Shacklewell Lane, London, E8 2DA Tel: (020) 7923 3003 Fax: (020) 7923 7799 E-mail: info@domainselfstorage.co.uk *Self storage services*

▶ Domain Technologies Ltd, 284 Upper Richmond Road West, London, SW14 7JE Tel: (020) 8878 4994 Fax: (020) 8878 1554 E-mail: info@domtech.co.uk *IT consultancy software*

Domainrage.com, 1353 Dumbarton Rd, Glasgow, G14 9UZ Tel: (07020) 970206 Fax: (07020) 970208 E-mail: info@domainrage.com *Domain names for sale & under auction, web site development*

Dome Cosmetics, 30 West Hill, Epsom, Surrey, KT19 8JD Tel: (01372) 745577 Fax: (01372) 747274 E-mail: press@domeltd.freeserve.co.uk *Manufacturers of own brand cosmetics*

Dome Products Ltd, Burnside Business Centre, Burnside Road, Boddam, Peterhead, Aberdeenshire, AB42 3AW Tel: (01779) 481964 Fax: (01779) 481965 *Computer services & web site designers*

Domestic & General Insulation Ltd, 9 Bridges Business Park, Bridge Road, Horsehay, Telford, Shropshire, TF4 3EE Tel: (01952) 507777 Fax: (01952) 501111 E-mail: office@dgitelford.co.uk *Insulation contractors*

▶ Domestic Perfection, 4 Speldhurst Road, Tunbridge Wells, Kent, TN4 0DP Tel: (07743) 933171 E-mail: d.perfection@btinternet.com *High specification bespoke cleaning service. Suppliers of residential, contract, end of tenancy & one-off cleans.*

▶ Domestic Plumbing & Heating, 7 Fairfield Street, Dundee, DD3 8HX Tel: (01382) 880030

Domglade Ltd, 1a Desborough Avenue, High Wycombe, Buckinghamshire, HP11 2RS Tel: (01494) 437771 Fax: (01494) 462357 *Ductwork custom builders, general steel fabricators heat & vent*

Domian Electronics Ltd, The Bungalow, Portland Road, Burgess Hill, West Sussex, RH15 9RL Tel: (01444) 254583 Fax: (01444) 254584 E-mail: domianelec@aol.com *Computer repairers, suppliers & manufrs*

Domic Welding Services, Unit 8, Victor Business Centre, Arthur St, Redditch, Worcestershire, B98 8JY Tel: (01527) 510041 Fax: (01527) 510403 E-mail: paul@pjwelding.fsnet.co.uk *Conveyor systems manufrs*

Domic Welding & Sheetmetal Ltd, Unit 8 Victor Business Centre, Arthur Street, Redditch, Worcestershire, B98 8JY Tel: (01527) 515445 Fax: (01527) 510403 E-mail: touv@domic-pjwelding.fsnet.co.uk *Sheet metalwork engineers & welding services*

Dominic Evans Electronics, Woodhall Farm, Fox Lane, Kempsey, Worcester, WR5 3QD Tel: (01905) 820860 *Electronic control systems manufrs*

Dominion Business Supplies Ltd, Dominion House, Medway City Industrial Estate, Medway City Estate, Rochester, Kent, ME2 4DU Tel: (01634) 716666 Fax: (01634) 290620 E-mail: sales@dominion-group.com *Stationery print furniture suppliers*

Dominion (England) Ltd, 6 Strathmore Court, 143 Park Rd, London, NW8 7HY Tel: (020) 7483 2117 Fax: (020) 7586 6974 E-mail: dominionengland@cs.com *Manufacture & distribution of hydraulic pumps & components*

Dominion Shutters, 8 Argall Avenue, London, E10 7QD Tel: (020) 8558 6572 Fax: (020) 8556 6956 E-mail: dominionshutters@btconnect.com *Security products manufrs*

Dominion Software Ltd, 63 Parkside, London, SW19 5NL Tel: (020) 8947 4059 *Computer systems & software development*

Domino Equipping Solutions, Ashmead Close, Newcastle Upon Tyne, NE12 6GB Tel: 0191-268 1171 Fax: 0191-268 1171 *Hospital equipment consultancy*

Domus Ventilation Ltd, Bearwalden Industrial Park, Royston Road, Wendens Ambo, Saffron Walden, Essex, CB11 4JX Tel: (01799) 541175 Fax: (01799) 541143 E-mail: info@domusventilation.co.uk *Domestic & commercial ventilation ducting & fans manufrs*

Don Bur Service Ltd, Boothen Old Road, Stoke-on-Trent, ST4 4EE Tel: (01782) 749333 Fax: (01782) 749191 E-mail: sales@donbur.co.uk *Commercial vehicles repairers*

Don Construction Products, Station Road, Churnetside Business Park, Cheddleton, Leek, Staffordshire, ST13 7RS Tel: (01538) 361799 Fax: (01538) 361899 E-mail: info@donconstruction.co.uk *Manufacturers of products for building industry*

Don Controls Ltd, Low Lane, Horsforth, Leeds, LS18 5NY Tel: 0113-258 4286 Fax: 0113-239 0056 E-mail: mail@don.co.uk *Electric control panel manufrs*

▶ Don Greenwood & Partners, Main Road, Nether Broughton, Melton Mowbray, Leicestershire, LE14 3HB Tel: (01664) 823000 Fax: (01664) 823408 *Corrugated packaging services*

Don Heating, Osprey Road, Sowton Industrial Estate, Exeter, EX2 7JG Tel: (01392) 444070 Fax: (01392) 444804 E-mail: donsales@gazco.com *Oil conversion kit manufrs*

▶ Don Hoods Trimming Co. Ltd, 2a Hampton Road, Erdington, Birmingham, B23 7JJ Tel: 0121-373 1313 Fax: 0121-377 7631 E-mail: sales@donhoods.com *Man*

Don Industrial Supplies Ltd, Unit 17 Guildhall Industrial Estate, Sandall Stones Road, Kirk Sandall Industrial Estate, Doncaster, South Yorkshire, DN3 1QR Tel: (01302) 884086 Fax: (01302) 887458 E-mail: donindust@aol.com *Industrial fastener distributors*

Don & Low, Glamis Road, Forfar, Angus, DD8 1FR Tel: (01307) 452249 Fax: (01307) 452201 E-mail: sales@donlow.co.uk *Fabric & yarn manufrs*

▶ Don Quijote, 2-4 Stoneleigh Park Road, Epsom, Surrey, KT19 0QT Tel: (020) 8786 8081 Fax: (020) 8786 8086 E-mail: info@donquijote.org *High quality In-country Spanish language courses in Spain and Mexico. Weekends, intensive, super-intensive and long duration. Fully guaranteed.*

▶ Don Rogers Ltd, 29 Faringdon Road, Swindon, SN1 5AR Tel: (01793) 527378 Fax: (01793) 527378 *Sports & Trophies Retailer.*

Don Ruffles, 53 Bell Street, Reigate, Surrey, RH2 7AQ Tel: (01737) 245755 Fax: (01737) 244095 E-mail: sales@rufflesstationery.com *Office equipment & stationery*

Don Springs (Sheffield) Ltd, 340 Coleford Road, Sheffield, S9 5PH Tel: 0114-244 1545 Fax: 0114-243 5291 E-mail: tony@donsprings.co.uk Principal Export Areas: Worldwide *Specialist manufacturer of Springs from one off prototypes to full production runs. Our product range includes extension, compression, torsion, Clock type, Leaf and disc springs for all aspects of industry from Automotive to Aerospace, all our work is Accredited to ISO 9001/2000.*

Don Valley Engineering Co. Ltd, Sandall Stones Road, Kirk Sandall Industrial Estate, Doncaster, South Yorkshire, DN3 1QR Tel: (01302) 881188 E-mail: info@donvalleyeng.com *Coal preparation plant manufrs*

▶ Don Valley Signs, Unit 4, Valley Works, Grange Lane, Sheffield, S5 0DQ Tel: 0114-246 6111 Fax: 0114-240 1928 E-mail: sales@donvalleysigns.co.uk *Sign makers*

Don Valley Sports, Littleworth Lane, Rossington, Doncaster, South Yorkshire, DN11 0HJ Tel: (01302) 868408 Fax: (01302) 868286 E-mail: sales@donvalleysports.co.uk *Camping equipment retailers*

▶ Don Wood Double Glazing Ltd, Shields Road, Gateshead, Tyne & Wear, NE10 0HW Tel: 0191-438 6558 Fax: 0191-495 0370

Donaghmore Construction Ltd, 3 Savings Bank Street, Dungannon, County Tyrone, BT70 1DT Tel: (028) 8772 6500 Fax: (028) 8772 4138 *Building contractors*

▶ Donaghy Civil Engineers, 42 Loanbank Quadrant, Glasgow, G51 3HZ Tel: 0141-440 1122 Fax: 0141-440 1133

Donald Bros, Arrol Road, West Gourdie Industrial Estate, Dundee, DD2 4TH Tel: (01382) 618488 Fax: (01382) 618488 E-mail: sales@donald-bros.com *Furnishing fabric manufrs*

▶ Donald C Mcrobert & Son, Millbank, Lochfoot, Dumfries, DG2 8NN Tel: (01387) 730250 Fax: (01387) 730500

Donald C Speakman, Brendon, Monkland, Leominster, Herefordshire, HR6 9DB Tel: (01568) 720235 Fax: (01568) 720235 *Agricultural engineers*

Donald Cope & Co., 1 Cheadle Shopping Centre, Cheadle, Stoke-on-Trent, ST10 1UY Tel: (01538) 755646 Fax: (01538) 750717 E-mail: sales@donaldcopeandco.com *Building society & insurance brokers*

Donald Engineering Services Ltd, 131 Walmley Road, Sutton Coldfield, West Midlands, B76 1QL Tel: 0121-351 4057 E-mail: donaldengser@aol.com *Welding engineers*

Donald Heath Cartons, Unit 22b Calder Trading Estate, Huddersfield, HD5 0RS Tel: (01484) 432900 Fax: (01484) 515800 *Paper merchants*

Donald Humberstone & Co. Ltd, Brackenborough Road, Louth, Lincolnshire, LN11 0AG Tel: (01507) 603003 Fax: (01507) 603003 *Decorative & industrial painting contractors*

▶ Donald Mackenzie, Park House, Dunvegan, Isle of Skye, IV55 8GU Tel: (01470) 521434

Donald Murray, 211 Maclellan Street, Glasgow, G41 1RR Tel: 0141-427 1271 Fax: 0141-427 6999 E-mail: sales@donald-murray-paper.co.uk *Paper merchants* Also at: Aberdeen, Belfast, Bristol, Edinburgh & Newcastle

▶ Donald Smith Model Makers Ltd, Coply Industrial Estate, Old Meldrum, Oldmeldrum, Inverurie, Aberdeenshire, AB51 0NT Tel: (01651) 873043 Fax: (01651) 872008 E-mail: sales@dsmodelmakers.co.uk *Model makers*

▶ Donald's Cream Ices, 5 Tarbet Street, Gourock, Renfrewshire, PA19 1UF Tel: (01475) 633191 Fax: (01475) 637618

Donaldson Filter Components Ltd, Oslo Road, Hull, HU7 0YN Tel: (01482) 835213 Fax: (01482) 835411 E-mail: info@donaldson.com *Air filtration manufacturers & distrbutors*

Donaldson Filtration (GB) Ltd, Humberstone Lane, Thurmaston, Leicester, LE4 8HP Tel: 0116-269 6161 Fax: 0116-269 3028 E-mail: peter.cowing@emea.donaldson.com *Dust collection equipment & fume extraction plant & equipment manufrs*

Donaldson Filtration (GB) Ltd, Humberstone Lane, Thurmaston, Leicester, LE4 8HP Tel: 0116-269 6161 Fax: 0116-269 3028 E-mail: peter.cowing@emea.donaldson.com *Compressed air & filter manufrs*

▶ Donaldson Group Ltd, 2230 London Road, Glasgow, G32 8YG Tel: 0141-778 5533

Donaldson & Mcconnell Ltd, Grangemouth Road, Bo'Ness, West Lothian, EH51 0PU Tel: (01506) 828891 Fax: (01506) 829070

▶ Donaldson Timber Engineering, Brunswick Road Cobbswood Industrial Estate, Brunswick Road, Ashford, Kent, TN23 1ED Tel: (01233) 895222 Fax: (01233) 895220

Donaldson & Weir Graphics Ltd, Unit 6a Maryland Industrial Estate, Moneyrea, Newtownards, County Down, BT23 6BL Tel: (028) 9044 8048 Fax: (028) 9044 8014 *Art material suppliers*

▶ Donaldsons, 48 Warwick Street, London, W1B 5NL Tel: (020) 7534 5000 Fax: (020) 7424 0045 *Chartered surveyors/shop property agents*

Donalds Of St Andrews Ltd, 21 Crossgate, Cupar, Fife, KY15 5HA Tel: (01334) 656433 Fax: (01334) 653729 *Bakers & confectioners*

Donarm Construction Ltd, Viewfield Industrial Estate, Glenrothes, Fife, KY6 2RS Tel: (01592) 775201 Fax: (01592) 771751 E-mail: donarm_construction@compuserve.com *Marine engineering & diving contractors*

Donart Engineering Co., Station Street, Bromsgrove, Worcestershire, B60 2BS Tel: (01527) 879722 Fax: (01527) 879722 *Jigs, fixtures & general toolmakers*

Donatantonio plc, Lupa House, York Way, Borehamwood, Hertfordshire, WD6 1PX Tel: (020) 8236 2222 Fax: (020) 8236 2288 E-mail: lupa@donatantonio.com *Food importer & distributors, also edible oil & fat producers*

Donatel Freres Ltd, The Vintage House, 42 Old Compton Street, London, W1D 4LR Tel: (020) 7437 2592 Fax: (020) 7734 1174 E-mail: vintagehouse.co@virgin.net *Wine, spirit & cigar merchants*

Donau Express Services, 52 Factory Lane, Croydon, CR0 3RL Tel: (020) 8256 5000 Fax: (020) 8256 5001 E-mail: donau@donau.co.uk *Cleaning contractors*

Doncaster Chamber, Enterprise House, White Rose Way, Hyde Park 45, Doncaster, South Yorkshire, DN4 5ND Tel: (01302) 341000 Fax: (01302) 328382 E-mail: chamber@doncaster-chamber.co.uk *Chamber of commerce*

Doncaster Computer Exchange, 250 Great North Road, Woodlands, Doncaster, South Yorkshire, DN6 7HP Tel: (01302) 728737 Fax: (01302) 725129 E-mail: dceexchange@aol.com *Building & resale of computer components*

Doncaster Packaging Ltd, Units 4/5 Shaw Lane Indust Estate Ogden Road, Long Sandall, Doncaster, South Yorkshire, DN2 4SQ Tel: (01302) 365334 Fax: (01302) 329012 *Packaging box manufrs*

Doncaster (Shrewsbury) Ltd, Whitchurch Road, Shrewsbury, SY1 4DP Tel: (01743) 445181 Fax: (01743) 450125 E-mail: mparry@doncasters.com *Gas turbine component repair services*

Doncasters Amtech, Weycroft Avenue, Axminster, Devon, EX13 5HU Tel: (01297) 34567 Fax: (01297) 631110 E-mail: dgage@doncasters.com *Mechanical engineers*

Doncasters Blaenavon Ltd, Forge Side, Blaenavon, Pontypool, Gwent, NP4 9XG Tel: (01495) 790345 Fax: (01495) 791565 E-mail: rhudson@doncasters.com *Special metalworkers*

Doncasters F B C Ltd, PO Box 160, Sheffield, S4 7QY Tel: 0114-243 1041 Fax: 0114-243 1358 *Stainless steel & centrishape tube manufrs*

Donelan Trading Ltd, Tower Road, Darwen, Lancashire, BB3 2DU Tel: (01254) 873873 Fax: (01254) 873065 E-mail: sales@donelan-trading.co.uk *Transport services*

Doner Cardwell Hawkins, 26 Emerald Street, London, WC1N 3QS Tel: (020) 7405 4611 Fax: (020) 7437 3961 E-mail: doner@donermail.co.uk *Advertising agencies*

▶ Donika, Parkside House, 17 East Parade, Harrogate, North Yorkshire, HG1 5LF Tel: (0845) 8381773 Fax: (0845) 8381774 E-mail: info@donika.co.uk *Industrial maintenance chemicals manufrs*

Donington Aviation Engineering, East Midlands Airport, Castle Donington, Derby, DE74 2SA Tel: (01332) 812694 Fax: (01332) 812726 *Air craft maintenance company*

Donington Plastics Ltd, Unit 1 Spiral Tube Works, Derby, DE24 8BT Tel: (01332) 363313 Fax: (01332) 361355 E-mail: sales@doningtongroup.co.uk *Manufacturers of low density polythene film and bags, which can be plain or printed. Printers and converters of high density polythene and polypropylene and printers of oriented polypropylene, pearlised and metallic films.*

Donisthorpe, PO Box 137, Leicester, LE4 1BF Tel: 0116-234 7920 Fax: 0116-234 7901 E-mail: sales@amann.com *Sewing threads, including polyester & nylon suppliers*

Donland Engineering Southern Ltd, Foundation House, Stoneylands Road, Egham, Surrey, TW20 9QR Tel: (01784) 436151 Fax: (01784) 436038 E-mail: e@donlandeng.co.uk *Boiler specialist services*

▶ Donna Chapman & Co., Daisy Hill, Knarr Barn Lane, Dobcross, Oldham, OL3 5RF Tel: (01457) 871533 Fax: (01457) 871533 E-mail: sales@donnachapman.com *Donna Chapman is an independent HR practitioner/ management consultant with specialism in direct hire strategy with skills and experience across a universal range of industries.*Her services have succeeded in reducing clients' recruitment spend by several million in one year.**

▶ Donnell & Ellis, 24 Beltany Road, Omagh, County Tyrone, BT78 5NA Tel: (028) 8224 7015 Fax: (028) 8225 0545

R.R. Donnelley UK, Flaxby Moor, Knaresborough, North Yorkshire, HG5 0XJ Tel: (01423) 796500 Fax: (01423) 796501 *Directory printers*

P.J. Donnelly Rubber, 15 Cornwall Road Industrial Park, Smethwick, West Midlands, B66 2JT Tel: 0121-565 0988 Fax: 0121-565 0976 *Manufacturers of rubber extrusions*

Donner Oswald & Co, 11-15 Jarrom Street, Leicester, LE2 7DH Tel: 0116-254 8210 Fax: 0116-247 0338 E-mail: sales@oswalddonner.com *Specialists in and suppliers of security seals, cable ties, fastenings & textile accessories**

Donovan Data Systems Ltd, 7 Farm Street, London, W1J 5RX Tel: (020) 7255 7222 Fax: (020) 7255 7171 E-mail: ukinfo@dds.co.uk *Computer software retailers*

Donovan Diesel Engine Equipment, St. Bartholomew Building, Nelson Street, Bolton, BL3 2AH Tel: (01204) 527520 Fax: (01204) 524348 E-mail: donovanandson@aol.com *Marine engine spare parts*

Donovan Kendell Ltd, 18-20 Catherine Street, St. Albans, Hertfordshire, AL3 5BY Tel: (01727) 841717 Fax: (01727) 860859 *Panel beaters & sprayers*

Donside Plastics Welding Ltd, Drill Hall, Upper Platts, Ticehurst, Wadhurst, East Sussex, TN5 7HA Tel: (01580) 200663 Fax: (01580) 200464 *Manufacturers of clear PVC report or document covers and pockets for comb or wire binding, also folders, ring binders and self-adhesive pockets.*

Dontaur Engineering Ltd, C1 Wakehurst Road, Ballymena, County Antrim, BT42 3AZ Tel: (028) 2565 9886 Fax: (028) 2564 2487 E-mail: info@dontaur.co.uk *Precision engineers*

Donyal Holdings Ltd, Unit 7 Hobson Industrial Estate, Hobson, Newcastle upon Tyne, NE16 6EA Tel: (01207) 270909 Fax: (01207) 270333 *Steel fabricators*

Dooa Wholesalers Ltd, Dooa House, 55-61 North Acton Road, London, NW10 6PH Tel: (020) 8961 7978 Fax: (020) 8961 8767 E-mail: info@dooa.co.uk *Cosmetics wholesalers*

▶ Doodle & Construct, Port Medway Marina, Station Road, Cuxton, Rochester, Kent, ME2 1AB Tel: (01634) 727599 Fax: (01634) 295070 E-mail: info@fastracconstruction.co.uk *Construction services*

▶ Doodlebugz, Marton, Marton cum Grafton, York, YO51 9QE Tel: (01347) 830100 Fax: (01347) 830100 E-mail: info@doodlebugz.co.uk *Manufacture, wholesale & retail of children's colour in poster art kits*

Doon Trading Co., 55 Westfield Road, Smethwick, West Midlands, B67 6AW Tel: 0121-555 5398 Fax: 0121-555 5398 *Casual & country wear*

Doon Valley (Heat Treatment) Ltd, Unit 6, Block 7 Chapelhall Industrial Estate, Stirling Road, Airdrie, Lanarkshire, ML6 8QX Tel: (01236) 756668 Fax: (01236) 756646 E-mail: doon.valley@talk21.com *Heat treatment services*

▶ Doonin Plant Ltd, New Road, Cambuslang, Glasgow, G72 7PU Tel: 0141-641 3731 Fax: 0141-641 3761

The Door Canopy Company Ltd, 65 Coronation Road, Motherwell, Lanarkshire, ML1 4JF Tel: (01698) 733465 *Joiners, door canopies*

Door Care & Security Ltd, 86-88 Edward Street, Glossop, Derbyshire, SK13 7AE Tel: (01457) 868711 Fax: (01457) 852464 *Automatic door manufrs*

Door Centre, Eastfield Industrial Estate, Penicuik, Midlothian, EH26 8HA Tel: (01968) 671680 Fax: (01968) 671684 E-mail: sales@thedoorcentre.co.uk *Wood & uPVC door & window manufrs*

Door Entry Systems Ltd, Belgrave Business Centre, 45 Frederick Street, Edinburgh, EH2 1EP Tel: (01905) 799110 Fax: 0131-220 3550 *Club security systems supplier & installer*

Door Handles UK, 9 Meadow Vale, Oakdale, Blackburn, BB2 4UA Tel: (01254) 692908 E-mail: sales@doorhandlesuk.com *Door furniture & accessories*

Door Maintenance Co. Ltd, Unit 8, Curran Industrial Estate, Curran Road, Cardiff, CF10 5DF Tel: (029) 2066 5539 Fax: (029) 2066 8207 E-mail: rpickford@harlechdoors.net *Door Maintenance Ltd, based in South Wales covering the UK have been established over 30 years specialising in the repair & maintenance of Roller Shutter Doors, Industrial Doors, Security Doors Commercial Doors, Door Grilles, Sectional, Fire Doors, Hinge & Sliding, Bar Shutters, Rapid Doors, Folding & Sliding. Our fully qualified installation teams, with their friendly, helpful and professional service, compliment our manufacturing base. Repair, Maintenance & Installations are normally U.K. wide, however Europe and beyond can be arranged for larger contracts with sufficient notice. Each repair & installation team has one member with a minimum of 10 years experience in order to iron out any possible queries the customer may have on site, combined with the back-up of regional area managers and representatives. All Works carried out by Door Maintenance Ltd. are covered by our comprehensive 12 month warranty. We offer 24 hour call out service Nationwide. Call 02920 665539*

Door Repair Service, 5a Hilton Drive, Prestwich, Manchester, M25 9NN Tel: 0161-773 6370 Fax: 0161-773 2145 *Industrial door repairers*

Door Services, Severnside Trading Estate, St. Andrews Road, Avonmouth, Bristol, BS11 9YQ Tel: 0117-949 4919 Fax: 0117-938 1711 E-mail: doorservices@free-online.co.uk *Industrial door manufrs*

Door Spring Supplies Co, 25 Knox Road, Wellingborough, Northamptonshire, NN8 1HW Tel: (01933) 222431 Fax: (01933) 222531 E-mail: tony@autodoorsprings.co.uk *Door & window specialist*

Door Stop, 1 Park Lane, St. Clement, Truro, Cornwall, TR1 1SX Tel: (01872) 261260 Fax: (01872) 262260 *Window manufacturer & distributor*

▶ Door System UK Ltd, 450a Bradford Road, Batley, West Yorkshire, WF17 5LW Tel: (01924) 471801 Fax: (01924) 471828 *Fabricators of doors*

Doorco Ltd, Phoenix Works, Whitefield Road, Bredbury, Stockport, Cheshire, SK6 2QR Tel: 0161-406 8660 Fax: 0161-406 8433 E-mail: info@doorco.co.uk *Suppliers of industrial doors & loading bay equipment*

▶ Dooria UK Ltd, 22 Glenburn Road, East Kilbride, Glasgow, G74 5BA Tel: (01355) 243918 Fax: (01355) 244137 E-mail: sales@doorian.co.uk *Door manufrs*

Doorman Long Tech, The Charles Parker Building, Midland Road, Higham Ferrers, Rushden, Northamptonshire, NN10 8DN Tel: (01933) 319133 Fax: (01933) 319135 E-mail: dlt@dormanlong.com *Heavy lifting equipment specialists*

▶ Doormatic Garage Doors, Clasford Farm House, Clasford Farm, Aldershot Road, Guildford, Surrey, GU3 3HQ Tel: (0808) 1551287 Fax: (01483) 237278 E-mail: marc@doormatic.co.uk *Garage door supply, installation & automation*

Doors & Hardware Ltd, Taskmaster Works, Maybrook Road, Minworth, Sutton Coldfield, West Midlands, B76 1AL Tel: 0121-351 5276 Fax: 0121-313 1228 E-mail: sales@doors-and-hardware.com *Steel doorsets & fire screen manufrs*

▶ Door-Tech Solutions Ltd, 4 Kean Close, Lichfield, Staffordshire, WS13 7EL Tel: (01543) 252374 Fax: (01543) 256845 E-mail: sales@doortechsolutions.co.uk *Suppliers of equipment for the door industry*

▶ Doosanbabcock, Porterfield Road, Renfrew, PA4 8DJ Tel: 0141-886 4141 *Thermal power, nuclear, petrochemical, oil & gas industry pipes*

Doppelgangers Ltd, 3 Fountain Cottages, South Park Lane, Bletchingley, Redhill, RH1 4NH Tel: (01883) 743324 Fax: (01883) 743324 E-mail: doppelgangers@btclick.com *Company clothing suppliers*

▶ Dor Rely Garage Doors, 21 Lydlynch Road, Totton, Southampton, SO40 3DW Tel: (023) 8066 6574 Fax: (023) 8066 6574 E-mail: info@dor-rely.co.uk *Door manufrs*

Dor Tech, 3 Cala Trading Estate, Ashton Vale Road, Bristol, BS3 2HA Tel: 0117-963 9014 Fax: 0117-953 3462 E-mail: online@vortech.fsnet.co.uk *Industrial door supply & installers*

▶ Dora Mouse, 8 Thorley Crescent, Peterborough, PE2 9RF Tel: (01733) 892026 *Manufacturers of doorstops*

Dora Wirth Languages Ltd, 86-87 Campden Street, London, W8 7EN Tel: (020) 7229 4552 Fax: (020) 7727 0744 E-mail: sales@dwlanguages.com *Medical translation agency*

Doran Engineering Co Holdings Ltd, Planetary Industrial Estate, Planetary Road, Willenhall, West Midlands, WV13 3XW Tel: (01902) 866000 Fax: (01902) 866222 *Special bolt & nut manufrs*

I.G. Doran & Partners, Malone Exchange, 226 Lisbon Road, Belfast, BT9 6GE Tel: (028) 9038 1321 Fax: (028) 9066 3255 *Civil engineering & public works*

Dorcas Engineering Ltd, Howard Road, Eaton Socon, St. Neots, Cambridgeshire, PE19 8ET Tel: (01480) 213316 Fax: (01480) 216319 *Precision engineers*

Dorchester Fabrications, Unit 32 Casterbridge Industrial Estate, Casterbridge, Dorchester, Dorset, DT1 1PL Tel: (01305) 267733 *Steel fabricators*

▶ Dorchester Ledbetter Photographers Ltd, The Studio, 54 North Street, Leeds, LS2 7PN Tel: 0113-245 1718 Fax: 0113-245 0737 E-mail: simon@hyltonphotography.co.uk *Commercial & industrial photography*

Dorchester Typesetting Group Ltd, Bridport Road, Dorchester, Dorset, DT1 1UA Tel: (01305) 262038 Fax: (01305) 260886 E-mail: dorchtype@btconnect.com *Filmsetting, page make-up, type setting & design* Also at: Bournemouth & Southampton

Dorcom Ltd, Unit 3, St Joseph's Business Park, St Joseph's Close, Hove, East Sussex, BN3 7HG Tel: 01273 202851 Fax: 01273 220108 E-mail: info@dorcom.co.uk *Door entry systems & cctv surveillance installers*

Dordon Brick Ltd, Unit 41 Fourways, Carlion Industrial Estate, Atherstone, Warwickshire, CV9 1LH Tel: (01827) 714123 Fax: (01827) 715343 E-mail: cutbricks@aol.com *Manufacturers of special bricks*

▶ Dore IT Consultants Ltd, 24 Bonners Field, Bentley, Farnham, Surrey, GU10 5LH Tel: (01420) 520542 *Computer software developers*

Dore Metal Services Ltd, Unit 2 Dolphin Park Cremers Road, Sittingbourne, Kent, ME10 3HB Tel: (01795) 473551 Fax: (01795) 429473 E-mail: ian@doremetals.co.uk *Aluminium stockholders*

▶ Doree Bonner International, Unit 21 Leafield Industrial Estate, Leafield Way, Corsham, Wiltshire, SN13 9SW Tel: (01225) 811992 Fax: (01225) 812536

▶ Dorelbury Ltd, 1 Crompton Way, Segensworth West, Fareham, Hampshire, PO15 5SS Tel: (01489) 885388 Fax: (01489) 885893

Doreth Engineering Co. Ltd, 1514 Pershore Road, Stirchley, Birmingham, B30 2NW Tel: 0121-458 3178 Fax: 0121-458 3178 *Hydraulic equipment repair, service & sales*

Dorey's Ltd, 13-15 Oakford, Kingsteignton, Newton Abbot, Devon, TQ12 3EQ Tel: (01626) 361200 Fax: (01626) 361205 E-mail: dorey's@btconnect.com *Diamond grinding tools*

Dorfell Textiles, 50 Cambrian Street, Manchester, M40 7EG Tel: 0161-273 7747 Fax: 0161-274 3862 *Sheet & quilt cover manufrs*

Dorgrove Floors Ltd, 9 Causeway Green Road, Oldbury, West Midlands, B68 8LA Tel: 0121-544 7877 Fax: 0121-511 1386 E-mail: dorgrove@aol.com *Flooring specialists & suppliers*

Doric Anderton, Fifth Avenue, Trafford Park, Trafford Park, Manchester, M17 1TN Tel: 0161-848 0156 Fax: 0161-872 1652 E-mail: info@doricanderton.com *Paper & board merchants*

▶ Doric Ceilings & Plastic Ltd, 1 Station Parade, South Street, Lancing, West Sussex, BN15 8AA Tel: (01903) 762953 Fax: (01903) 756228 E-mail: dceilings@aol.com *Ceilings specialists*

Doric Productions Ltd, 6-8 Kellner Road, London, SE28 0AX Tel: (020) 8316 0222 Fax: (020) 8316 0316 E-mail: sales@doricsigns.co.uk *Signs & displays*

Dorking Autos Ltd, 6 Reading Arch Road, Redhill, RH1 1HG Tel: (01737) 780040 Fax: (01737) 779986 *Garage mechanical & bodyshop*

Dorking & District Chamber of Commerce, 156 High Street, Dorking, Surrey, RH4 1BQ Tel: (01306) 880110 Fax: (01306) 502283 *Chamber of commerce*

Dorling Kindersley Holdings P.L.C., 80 The Strand, London, WC2R 0LR Tel: (020) 7010 3000 Fax: (020) 7010 6060 *Publishers*

Dorling Print Ltd, Dorling House, 44 Wates Way, Mitcham, Surrey, CR4 4HR Tel: (020) 8685 9399 Fax: (020) 8685 9140 E-mail: info@dorling.co.uk *Colour & commercial printers*

Dorling Signs Ltd, 66-74 Virgil Street, Liverpool, L5 5BY Tel: 0151-298 1511 Fax: 0151-298 1512 E-mail: info@dorling-signs.co.uk *Sports sign promotions*

Dorma Group Ltd, Newtown Mill Lees Street, Pendlebury, Swinton, Manchester, M27 6DB Tel: 0161-251 4400 Fax: 0161-251 4417 E-mail: info@dorma.co.uk *Household linen manufrs*

Dorma UK Ltd, Unit 3 Cala Trading Estate, Ashton Vale Road, Ashton, Bristol, BS3 2HA Tel: 0117-963 9014 Fax: 0117-953 3462 *Aluminium product manufrs*

Dorma UK, Wilbury Way, Hitchin, Hertfordshire, SG4 0AB Tel: (01462) 477602 Fax: (01462) 477603 E-mail: info@dorma-uk.co.uk *Door controls manufrs*

Dorma UK, Wilbury Way, Hitchin, Hertfordshire, SG4 0AB Tel: (01462) 477602 Fax: (01462) 477603 E-mail: info@dorma-uk.co.uk *Door repairers*

Dorman Machinery, 4 Percy Street, Coventry, CV1 3BY Tel: (024) 7622 6611 Fax: (024) 7622 6560 E-mail: dormansale@aol.com *Machine tool suppliers*

Dormar Fabrications Bilston Ltd, Jubilee House, Halesfield 2, Telford, Shropshire, TF7 4QH Tel: (01952) 585736 Fax: (01952) 684526 *Fire escape, balustrade installation & general steel fabricators*

Dormy Ltd, Battersea Road, Heaton Mersey, Stockport, Cheshire, SK4 3EN Tel: 0161-432 9451 Fax: 0161-431 8442 E-mail: sales@dormy.co.uk *Stamp manufrs*

Dormy Custom Products, 144 Neilston Road, Paisley, Renfrewshire, PA2 6QH Tel: 0141-884 6441 Fax: 0141-884 7819 *Rubber stamp manufrs*

Dorplan Architectural Ironmongers, 434-436 Mutton Lane, Potters Bar, Hertfordshire, EN6 3AT Tel: (01707) 647647 Fax: (01707) 647378 *Architectural ironmongers & security fittings*

Peter Dorrell & Co., PO Box 14, Malvern, Worcestershire, WR13 5AS Tel: (01684) 567504 Fax: (01684) 563101 E-mail: sales@peterdorrell.freeserve.co.uk *Sanding contractors*

Dorset Aluminium Products Ltd, Poundbury West Industrial Estate, Dorchester, Dorset, DT1 2PG Tel: (01305) 265235 Fax: (01305) 260882 E-mail: sales@dorsetaluminium.com *Metal spinnings & spinners, aluminium fabricators & manufrs*

▶ Dorset Cake Co. Ltd, 50 Dorchester Road, Weymouth, Dorset, DT4 7JZ Tel: (01305) 786252 Fax: (01305) 777487 E-mail: office@dorsetcakeco.sagehost.co.uk *Bakery wholesale & retail, sandwiches & corporate buffets*

▶ Dorset Catering Equipment Co., 9, Chettle, Blandford Forum, Dorset, DT11 8DB Tel: (01258) 830624 E-mail: m3wvh@hotmail.com *dorset catering equipment company 01258 830624 www.billynet.zapto.org/cateringappliance/*

▶ Dorset Cottage Foods, Gallop Cottages, Spetisbury, Blandford Forum, Dorset, DT11 9ED Tel: (01258) 857300 E-mail: jdwwatt@aol.com *Winners of 8 Awards from 2001 to 2004 - Manufacturer of Homemade Preserves from Spetisbury in Dorset.*Gluten Free and Award Winning. inc Banana Jam, Chocolate and Banana Jam, Plum and Ginger, Garlic Chutney, TJ"s Chilli Sauce and many more.*TRADE ENQUIRIES WELCOME.**We used to make the Preserves at our Home in Poole, but have been bought by Erika Watt, who continues to make the Preserves at Spetisbury*

Dorset Diving Services, Unit 6 & 7 West Howe Industrial Estate, Elliott Road, Bournemouth, BH11 8JX Tel: (01202) 580065 Fax: (01202) 593529 E-mail: mail@dorsetdiving.co.uk *Diving equipment & services*

▶ Dorset Ductings, 2 Edward Street, Dunstable, Bedfordshire, LU6 1HE Tel: (01582) 600007

Dorset Enterprises, Elliott Road, Bournemouth, BH11 8JP Tel: (01202) 577966 Fax: (01202) 570049 E-mail: dorsetenterprises@bournemouth.gov.uk *continued*

Wooden garden furniture, toys & deck chairs manufrs

Dorset Food Machinery, 29c St. Catherines Road, Bournemouth, BH6 4AE Tel: (01202) 423754 Fax: (01202) 434583 *Food machinery suppliers*

Dorset Glass Co. Ltd, 51 Nuffield Road, Nuffield Industrial Estate, Poole, Dorset, BH17 0RJ Tel: (01202) 673926 Fax: (01202) 684394 E-mail: duncan@dorsetglass.co.uk *Wholesale glass merchants window manufrs* Also at: Weymouth

▶ Dorset Kitchen & Bathroom Studio, Unit 14 Jubilee Enterprise Centre, 15 Jubilee Close, Weymouth, Dorset, DT4 7BS Tel: (01305) 766776 Fax: (01305) 766776 *Kitchen & bathroom showroom,supply and fit, or supply of goods only.corgi reg.*

▶ Dorset Larder, 23a Hambledon Road, Bournemouth, BH6 5PJ Tel: (01202) 467837 Fax: (01202) 467837

▶ Dorset Lowloader Hire Plant Movers, 9 Chettle, Blandford Forum, Dorset, DT11 8DB Tel: (0770) 3177521 E-mail: m3wvh@hotmail.com *dorset heavy lowloader haulage company 0770 3177521 call now for a qoute*

▶ Dorset Marine Services Ltd, Unit C51, Block B, Winfrith Technology Centre, Winfrith, Dorchester, Dorset, DT2 8DH Tel: (0845) 3452493 Fax: (0845) 3452494 E-mail: sales@dorsetmarineservices.co.uk *Suppliers of marine equipment*

Dorset Mechanical Services, 28 Gravel Hill, Wimborne, Dorset, BH21 1RR Tel: (01202) 841241 *Forklifts repairers*

Dorset Merc, 851 Wimborne Road, Bournemouth, BH9 2BG Tel: (01202) 775566 E-mail: david.bridgewater@dorset-merc.net *Computer training, network installation, web hosting & design*

Dorset Metal Spinning Services, Blue Zone Aviation Park West, Bournemouth International Airport, Hurn, Christchurch, Dorset, BH23 6NW Tel: (01202) 593670 Fax: (01202) 593670 *Metal spinners manufrs*

▶ Dorset Networking, The Enterprise Pavilion, Fern Barrow, Poole, Dorset, BH12 5HH Tel: (0845) 7337374 Fax: (0845) 2008360 E-mail: info@dorsetnetworking.co.uk *Online networking forum for the Dorset business community. Discussion includes grants, training, sales & marketing, legal issues, Internet, technology and real world networking events. Free registration.*

▶ Dorset Nursing Supplies Co., 3 Wickham Road, Bournemouth, BH7 6JX Tel: (01202) 425070 Fax: (01202) 418332 E-mail: sales@dorsetnursing.co.uk *Nursing supplies (DNS) is a medical supply*

dorset rancilio espresso machine engineer repairs, Espressocity, 9 Chettle Village, Blandford Forum, Dorset, DT11 8DB Tel: (01258) 830624 E-mail: sales@espressocity.co.uk *Dorset rancilio coffee machine engineer 01258 830 624*

Dorset Stainless, 39 Balena Close, Poole, Dorset, BH17 7EB Tel: (01202) 697469 Fax: (01202) 658899 E-mail: solutions@robton.co.uk *Stainless steel fabricators*

Dorset Technical Mouldings, Unit C20-24, Holton Road, Holton Heath Trading Park, Poole, Dorset, BH16 6LT Tel: (01202) 624790 Fax: (01202) 623761 E-mail: sales@dtm-poole.fsnet.co.uk *Plastic mouldings*

Dorset Tube, Thrush Road, Poole, Dorset, BH12 4NT Tel: (01202) 725000 Fax: (01202) 725025 E-mail: sales@dorsettubes.co.uk *Manufacturers of copper & cupro-nickel tube*

Dorset Water Centre Ltd, 9 Pomeroy Buildings, Grove Trading Estate, Dorchester, Dorset, DT1 1ST Tel: (01305) 265548 Fax: (01305) 269404 E-mail: tim@dorset-water.co.uk *Water filter system distributors*

Dorset Waterlily Co., Dorset Water Lilies, Yeovil Road, Halstock, Yeovil, Somerset, BA22 9RR Tel: (01935) 891668 Fax: (01935) 891946 *Pond supplies*

Dorset Weather Vanes, 284 Bournemouth Road, Charlton Marshall, Blandford Forum, Dorset, DT11 9NG Tel: (01258) 453374 Fax: (01258) 453374 E-mail: enquiries@weathervanes-direct.co.uk Principal Export Areas: Worldwide *Weather vane manufrs*

Dorset Yacht Co., Lake Drive, Poole, Dorset, BH15 4DT Tel: (01202) 674534 Fax: (01202) 677518 E-mail: sales@bostonwhaler.co.uk *Yacht repairers & brokerage*

Dortrend International Ltd, Riverside Business Centre, Worcester Road, Stourport-on-Severn, Worcestershire, DY13 9BZ Tel: (01299) 827837 Fax: (01299) 827094 E-mail: sales@dortrend.co.uk *Door & window furniture manufrs*

Dorval Construction Ltd, Tudwick Road, Tolleshunt Major, Maldon, Essex, CM9 8LW Tel: (01621) 860310

Dorvic Engineering Co. Ltd, New Street, Holbrook Industrial Estate, Holbrook, Sheffield, S20 3GH Tel: 0114-248 5633 Fax: 0114-251 0654 E-mail: sales@dorvic.com Principal Export Areas: Worldwide *Dorvic Engineering Company Limited are a leading manufacturer and supplier of material handling and lifting equipment, including heavy load moving skates, machinery movers, roller dollies, heavy moving systems, roller crowbars, hydraulic and ratchet toe jacks.*

Dorwin Ltd, Unit 1 Forge Works, Mill Lane, Alton, Hampshire, GU34 2QG Tel: (01420) 84217 Fax: (01420) 541648 E-mail: linden.ransley@dorwin.co.uk *UPVC windows & doors manufrs*

Dorwingear, 107 Hospital Street, Birmingham, B19 3XA Tel: 0121-359 1744 Fax: 0121-333 3475 E-mail: dorwingearltd@btconnect.com *Manufacturers of doors & rolling shutters*

Dosco Overseas Engineering Ltd, Dosco Industrial Estate, Ollerton Road, Tuxford, Newark, Nottinghamshire, NG22 0PQ Tel: (01777) 870621 Fax: (01777) 871580 E-mail: sales@dosco.co.uk *Mining machinery manufrs*

Dot Copiers Distribution Ltd, Unit 35, Brickyard Road, Aldridge, Walsall, WS9 8XT Tel: (01922) 455359 Fax: (01922) 455316 E-mail: dotcopiers@lineone.net *Dot Copiers* *continued*

Distribution specialise in the distribution of Canon Photocopiers throughout the U.K. Mono Photocopiers, Colour Digital Photocopiers, High Volume Digital Photocopiers.

Dot Hill Systems Europe Ltd, Network House, Basing View, Basingstoke, Hampshire, RG21 4HG Tel: (01256) 840600 Fax: (01256) 814462 E-mail: uk@dothill.com *Computer hardware manufrs*

▶ Dotrix, PO Box 3972, Tipton, West Midlands, DY4 9ZS Tel: 0121- 530 0814 E-mail: contact@dotrix.co.uk *Website design & multimedia solutions, basic sites, flash sites, ecommerce/shopping carts & self updatable sites*

Dotted Eyes Ltd, Hanbury Court Harris Business Park, Hanbury Road, Stoke Prior, Bromsgrove, Worcestershire, B60 4JJ Tel: (01527) 556920 Fax: (01527) 556939 E-mail: info@dottedeyes.com *Digital mapping consultants*

Double D Bakery Engineering Ltd, 6 Simpson Road, East Mains Industrial Estate, Broxburn, West Lothian, EH52 5NP Tel: (01506) 857112 Fax: (01506) 852232 E-mail: sales@double-d.co.uk *Manufacturers of cookers & ovens for the food industry & bakery ovens*

Double D Electronics Ltd, 6 Robins Wharf, Grove Road, Northfleet, Gravesend, Kent, DA11 9AX Tel: (01474) 333456 Fax: (01474) 333414 E-mail: sales@ddelec.co.uk *Custom electronic system suppliers*

Double Dean Ltd, Fallowfields, Dummer, Basingstoke, Hants, RG25 2AG Tel: (01256) 398550 *IT consultants*

Double Glazing Supplies Group plc, Sycamore Road, Castle Donington, Derby, DE74 2NW Tel: (01332) 811611 Fax: (01332) 812650 E-mail: reception@dgsgroup.co.uk *Friction stay manufrs*

▶ Double Jay Furniture Transport Ltd, Unit 3C, Garston Industrial Estate, Blackburn Street, Liverpool, L19 8JB Tel: 0151-427 6686

Double K J Textiles Ltd, Cameron Road, Derby, DE23 8RT Tel: (01332) 773699 Fax: (01332) 773699 *Clothing manufrs*

Double M Nottingham Ltd, Nunn Brook Road, County Estate, Huthwaite, Sutton-in-Ashfield, Nottinghamshire, NG17 2HU Tel: (01623) 515904 Fax: (01623) 515929 *Hydraulic cylinder manufrs*

Double M Transport Ltd, The Courtyard, Warkworth, Banbury, Oxfordshire, OX17 2AG Tel: (01295) 712828 Fax: (01295) 711886 E-mail: stuartdoublem@aol.com *Courier & express parcel delivery*

▶ Double Plas, 1 Babington Park, Grange Park, Swindon, SN5 6EZ Tel: (01793) 875171 Fax: (01793) 878389 *Double glazing manufrs*

Double R Consol Ltd, Broadfield Distribution Park, Pilsworth Road, Heywood, Lancashire, OL10 2TA Tel: (01706) 623625 Fax: (01706) 366881 E-mail: sales@drc.co.uk *Bespoke engineers*

Double R Labels Ltd, 17-21 Redhills Road, South Woodham Ferrers, Chelmsford, CM3 5UL Tel: (01245) 325455 Fax: (01245) 325001 E-mail: info@doublerlabels.co.uk *Self-adhesive label printing services*

Double Sided Tapes, 47 Copland Medows, Totnes, Devon, TQ9 6ES Tel: (01803) 863022 Fax: (01803) 863022 *Adhesive tapes re-salers services*

Double Two Ltd, Thornes Wharf Lane, Wakefield, West Yorkshire, WF1 5RQ Tel: (01924) 375651 Fax: (01924) 290096 E-mail: double2@wsg.co.uk *Shirt & blouses*

▶ Double V Design & Support Services, Langarth, Stoke Road, Westbury sub Mendip, Wells, Somerset, BA5 1HD Tel: (01749) 871104 Fax: (01749) 871105 *Computer consultants & software designers*

▶ Doubledrive Ltd, PO Box 363, Pinner, Middlesex, HA5 3ZR Tel: (020) 8429 5304 Fax: (020) 8429 0418 E-mail: info@translectrix.co.uk *Auto electrical equipment services.*

Doublescale, Beili Glas Uchaf, Gwaun Cae Gurwen, Ammanford, Dyfed, SA18 1PR Tel: (01269) 822440 Fax: (01269) 822440 E-mail: sales@doublescale.ltd.uk *Fabrication engineers*

Doubletex Leathers Ltd, Stervon House, 1 Seaford Road, Salford, M6 6AS Tel: 0161-737 1000 Fax: 0161-737 7555 E-mail: dtxleather@aol.com *Leather merchants & distributors*

Doublewood Engineering, 4 Enterprise Court, Station Road, Witham, Essex, CM8 2TJ Tel: (01376) 517337 Fax: (01376) 517337 *Milling & steel fabricators*

Doughty Cakes, 3 Greetwell Hollow, Crofton Drive, Lincoln, LN3 4NR Tel: (01522) 543434 Fax: (01522) 543434 E-mail: doughtycakes@btconnect.com *Wholesale cake distributors*

Doughty Pressings Ltd, Stewart Street, Wolverhampton, WV2 4JW Tel: (01902) 426264 Fax: (01902) 772245 E-mail: info@doughty.uk.com *General presswork. Pressings & welded assemblies*

Dougland Holdings Ltd, Little Park Farm, Segensworth West Industrial Estate, Fareham, Hampshire, PO15 5SN Tel: (01489) 574234 Fax: (01489) 576104 E-mail: margaret@dougland.co.uk *Cleaning & support services*

Douglas Acheson, Navan Fort Road, Armagh, BT60 4PN Tel: (028) 3752 2667 *Concrete product manufrs*

▶ Douglas Bates, Suite 8 Phoenix House, 63 Campfield Road, St. Albans, Hertfordshire, AL1 5FL Tel: 01727 736690 E-mail: dougbates@intelligentpeople.co.uk *Intelligent People are a recruitment consultancy who specialise in placing teams and individuals with Technology Companies, including Software Vendors, VARs, IT Consultancies, Solutions Providers, Systems Integrators, Service Providers, and Hardware Manufacturers. **

Douglas Buildings, Syke Road, Wigton, Cumbria, CA7 9NG Tel: (01697) 478690 Fax: (01697) 349073 *Steel framed building manufrs*

Douglas Deakin Young Ltd, 22-25a Sackville Street, London, W1S 3HQ Tel: (020) 7439 3344 Fax: (020) 7439 3402 E-mail: enquiries@ddy.co.uk *Financial consultants*

▶ Douglas Electronic Industries Ltd, 55 Eastfield Road, Louth, Lincolnshire, LN11 7AL Tel: (01507) 603643 Fax: (01507) 600502 E-mail: sales@douglas-transformers.co.uk Purchasing Contact: D. Goodwin Sales Contact: L. Goodwin *Douglas Electronic Industries Ltd are DC to AC inverter manufacturers. In addition, custom built, emergency, industrial, linear & uninterruptible power supply manufacturers. Also audio, constant voltage & isolating transformers*

▶ Douglas F Mitchell Ltd, Archgrove, Station Road, Laurencekirk, Kincardineshire, AB30 1BE Tel: (01561) 377741 Fax: (01561) 378035

Douglas Fraser & Sons (London) Ltd, 4 Clifton Hill, London, NW8 0QG Tel: (020) 7328 9393 Fax: (020) 7247 5379 *Jute goods merchants*

▶ Douglas Gauld & Co. (Tayside) Ltd, Shanwell Court Industrial Esta, Shanwell Road, Tayport, Newport-On-Tay, Fife, DD6 9EA Tel: (01382) 553494

Douglas & Grahame Ltd, Wellington House, 322 Donegall Road, Belfast, BT12 6FX Tel: (028) 9056 7777 Fax: (028) 9032 7700 E-mail: sales@douglasandgrahame.com *Menswear distributors*

Douglas & Grahame UK Ltd, Shenstone Business Park, Lynn Lane, Shenstone, Lichfield, Staffordshire, WS14 0SB Tel: (0870) 8507777 Fax: (0870) 2077700 *Menswear clothing manufrs*

Douglas Knight Sunblinds Ltd, 31b Station Road, Park Gate, Southampton, SO31 7GJ Tel: (01489) 575507 Fax: (01489) 575507 *Sunblind manufrs*

Douglas Marine Ltd, Becconsall Lane, Hesketh Bank, Preston, PR4 6RR Tel: (01772) 812462 Fax: (01772) 812462 E-mail: ray@douglas-marine.co.uk *Boat repairers & builders*

Oliver Douglas Ltd, Amberley Works, Chelsea Close, Leeds, LS12 4HP Tel: 0113-279 7373 Fax: 0113-279 1014 E-mail: admin@oliverdouglas.com *Industrial washing machines manufrs*

Douglas Co Services Ltd, Regent House, 316 Beulah Hill, London, SE19 3HF Tel: (020) 8761 1176 Fax: (020) 8761 7486 E-mail: enquiries@douglas-cs.co.uk *Company registration agents*

Douglas Signs Ltd, Unit 1 Moorings Close, Lower Hollin Bank Street, Blackburn, BB2 4AH Tel: (01254) 694284 Fax: (01254) 694292 E-mail: sales@douglas-signs.co.uk *Sign manufrs*

Douglas Storrie Labels Ltd, Tudor Works, Tudor Rd, Lytham St. Annes, Lancashire, FY8 2LA Tel: (01253) 643000 Fax: (01253) 643001 E-mail: sales@storrielabels.com *Douglas Storrie Labels based in Lytham St Annes, Lancashire are a manufacturer and supplier of bespoke printed self adhesive labels. We specialise in printing to your requirements in any size or shape using our in house design and reprographics facilities. We have been in business for over 50 years and combined with our experienced staff and printing machinery we offer a service to a wide range of industries including food, manufacturing, retail and distribution. Our custom self adhesive labels can be printed in up to 8 spot colours, process print, flexographic, rotary letterpress, A4 sheets, variable bar code labels, thermal transfer, digitally printed labels, computer labels, electrical labels, hot foil and many more with short turn around times. Please see our website or call for more information.*

Douglas Supplies, Brunton Quarry, North Gosforth, Newcastle upon Tyne, NE13 6PH Tel: 0191-236 5196 Fax: 0191-236 2777 *Chemical cleaning equipment supplier*

Douglas Transport Ltd, Baker House, The Hayes, Lye, Stourbridge, West Midlands, DY9 8RS Tel: (01384) 424489 Fax: (01384) 893754 *Haulage contractors*

Douglas W Standring, 20 Cae Gwastad, Harlech, Gwynedd, LL46 2GY Tel: (01766) 780483 Fax: (01766) 780483 E-mail: timberframestructures@btinternet.com *Timber frame suppliers & erectors*

Doulos, Church Hatch Centre, 22 Market Place, Ringwood, Hampshire, BH24 1AW Tel: (01425) 471223 Fax: (01425) 471573 E-mail: info@doulos.com *Computer software consultants*

▶ Doust Decor, 5 Lonsdale Road, Leamington Spa, Warwickshire, CV32 7EP Tel: (01926) 771736 Fax: (01926) 771736 E-mail: vicki@doustfamily.co.uk *Curtain, blind & accessories make-up service*

J. Douthwaite & Sons Ltd, Forest Street, Blackburn, BB1 3BB Tel: (01254) 675115 Fax: (01254) 297255 E-mail: info@jdstrucks.co.uk *Commercial vehicle distributors*

Douthwaite Signs, 14 Lumley Street, Castleford, West Yorkshire, WF10 5LB Tel: (01977) 603605 Fax: (01977) 603605 E-mail: chris@chrisarcher.wanadoo.co.uk *Sign manufrs*

▶ Dove Anodising Ltd, 14-16 Kelvin Place, Thetford, Norfolk, IP24 3RR Tel: (01842) 753908 Fax: (01842) 766007 E-mail: sales@doveanodising.co.uk *Anodising contractors*

▶ Dove Computer Solutions, Oak Cottage, Dove Street, Ellastone, Ashbourne, Derbyshire, DE6 2GY Tel: (0845) 2260522 Fax: (01335) 324317 E-mail: info@dovecomputers.com *Computer maintenance and support for SMEs. Complete IT Solutions from backup, training to onsite maintenance and repairs.*

▶ Dove Despatch Ltd, 83 Essington Road, Willenhall, West Midlands, WV12 5DT Tel: (01922) 404857 Fax: (01922) 408803 E-mail: sales@dovedespatch.co.uk *We offer a same day and next day delivery service covering England, Wales and Scotland.*

Dove Furniture, 1 Nursery Buildings, York Road, Riccall, York, YO19 6QQ Tel: (01757) 249171 Fax: (01757) 249278 E-mail: craigandkim@btinternet.com *Pine furniture manufrs*

Dove Heating Ltd, 227 Kingston Road, New Malden, Surrey, KT3 3SZ Tel: (020) 8241 0141 Fax: (020) 8942 9992 *Electrical & heating engineers*

Dove Interious, Unit 6, Fairfield Road, Downham Market, Norfolk, PE38 9ET Tel: (01366) 383684 Fax: (01366) 387429 E-mail: simon@doveinteriers.com *Upholstery & furniture manufrs*

Dove Tail Joinery, 7 Field Barn Lane Industrial Estate, Field Barn Lane, Cropthorne, Pershore, Worcestershire, WR10 3LY Tel: (01386) 861123 Fax: (01386) 860975 *Joinery manufrs*

Dove Technology UK Ltd, 8 London Road, Worcester, WR5 2DL Tel: (01905) 353153 Fax: (01905) 352863 E-mail: sales@dovetech.co.uk *Radio paging systems & solutions services*

Dovedale Confectionery Ltd, Vernon St Industrial Estate, Shirebrook, Mansfield, Nottinghamshire, NG20 8SS Tel: (01623) 742277 Fax: (01623) 743020 E-mail: dovedale@o2.co.uk *Confectioners*

▶ Dovedale Fleet Deliveries, 34 Woodmans Croft, Hatton, Derby, DE65 5QQ Tel: (01283) 520445 Fax: (01283) 520445

Dover District Chamber Of Commerce, White Cliffs BSNS Park, Honeywood Road, Whitfield, Dover, Kent, CT16 3EH Tel: (01304) 824955 Fax: (01304) 822354 E-mail: mail@doverchamber.co.uk *Chamber of commerce*

Dover Marquee Co. Ltd, 30 Mayfield Avenue, Dover, Kent, CT16 2PL Tel: (01304) 215315 Fax: (01304) 202086 E-mail: sales@dover-marquee.co.uk *Corporate, industrial & domestic marquee hirers*

Dover Yacht Co. Ltd, Custom House Quay, Dover, Kent, CT17 9DG Tel: (01304) 201073 Fax: (01304) 207458 E-mail: peter.butler6@btinternet.com *Boat repairs & maintenance*

Dovercourt Ford Ltd, 30 Robjohns Road, Widford Industrial Estate, Chelmsford, CM1 3AQ Tel: (01245) 706600 E-mail: simon.beament@dovercourt.com *Motor vehicle repairers*

▶ Dovetail Contract Furniture, 1 St. Georges Court, St. Georges Road, Bristol, BS1 5UG Tel: 0117-930 4442 Fax: 0117-976 0014 E-mail: info@dovetail.com *Office furniture suppliers*

Dovetail Enterprises Ltd, Dunsinane Avenue, Dunsinane Industrial Estate, Dundee, DD2 3QN Tel: (01382) 810099 Fax: (01382) 814816 E-mail: enquiries@dovetailenterprises.co.uk *Bedding, furniture & fire doors manufrs*

Dovetail Human Resource Services, 19 The Broadway, Newbury, Berkshire, RG14 1AS Tel: (01635) 43100 Fax: (01635) 550743 E-mail: sales@dovetailhrs.co.uk *Employment recruitment*

Dovetail UK Ltd, 16 Hill Crescent, Dudleston Heath, Ellesmere, Shropshire, SY12 9NA Tel: (01691) 690407 Fax: (01691) 690419 *Agricultural merchants*

Dovetail Woodcraft, The Old Bakery, 8 Edward Street, Bridgwater, Somerset, TA6 5ET Tel: (01278) 424021 Fax: (01278) 424021 *Cabinet manufrs*

▶ Dovetails, Shay Lane Works, Shay Lane, Ovenden, Halifax, W. Yorkshire, HX3 6SF Tel: (01422) 329988

Dovetails, Browns Marsh, North Molton, South Molton, Devon, EX36 3HQ Tel: (01769) 574027 Fax: 01769 574027 *Cabinet makers*

Dovey Estates Ltd, Suffolk House, Trade Street, Cardiff, CF10 5DQ Tel: (029) 2034 4150 Fax: (029) 2034 4170 E-mail: dovey@estatesltd.fsnet.co.uk *Property developers*

▶ Dovidio Brothers Ltd, Worth House Farm, Worth, Wookey, Wells, Somerset, BA5 1LW Tel: (01749) 673984

Dow Agro Sciences Ltd, Latchmore Court, Brand Sreet, Hitchin, Hertfordshire, SG5 1NH Tel: (01462) 457272 Fax: (01462) 426605 E-mail: dowagrosciencesuk@dow.com *Insecticide manufrs*

Dow Chemical, 2 Heathrow Boulevard, 284 Bath Road, West Drayton, Middlesex, UB7 0DQ Tel: (020) 8917 5000 Fax: (020) 8917 5400 *Industrial chemical manufrs* Also at: Barry, Kings Lynn & Wilmslow

Dow Chemicals Ltd, PO Box 54, Middlesbrough, Cleveland, TS90 8JA Tel: (01642) 543000 Fax: (01642) 374192 Purchasing Contact: Kearns Sales Contact: Kearns *Industrial chemical manufrs*

Dow Corning, Copse Drive, Coventry, CV5 9RG Tel: (01676) 528000 Fax: (01676) 528001 *Silicone producers*

▶ Dow Group Ltd, 23 Lenziemill Road, Cumbernauld, Glasgow, G67 2RL Tel: (01236) 730730 Fax: (01236) 730555 E-mail: sales@wmdow.com *Plant hire & contractors*

Dow Mirfield, Steanard Lane, Mirfield, West Yorkshire, WF14 8HZ Tel: (01924) 493861 Fax: (01924) 490972 E-mail: enquiries@dow.com Principal Export Areas: Worldwide *Manufacturers of pharmaceutical intermediates & insecticides*

Albert Dowd & Son, 27 Derrycarne Road, Portadown, Craigavon, County Armagh, BT62 1PT Tel: (028) 3833 5471 Fax: (028) 3833 5471 *Horsebox window manufrs*

Dowding & Mills plc, Camp Hill, Birmingham, B12 0JJ Tel: 0121-766 6161 Fax: 0121-773 2345 E-mail: group.birmingham@dowdingandmills.com *Electrical & mechanical services*

Dowding & Mills Calibration, The Service Centre Watchmoor Point, Watchmoor Road, Camberley, Surrey, GU15 3AD Tel: (01276) 701717 Fax: (01276) 700245 E-mail: calibration.camberley@dowdingandmills.com *Calibration services & repairs*

Dowding & Mills Calibration, Fulwood Road South, Sutton-in-Ashfield, Nottinghamshire, NG17 2JZ Tel: (01623) 555110 Fax: (01623) 555022 E-mail: calibration.nottingham@dowdingandmills.com *Calibration service & repairers*

Dowding & Mills Engineering Services Ltd, Unit 14 Maple Business Park, Walter Street, Birmingham, B7 5ET Tel: 0121-326 6306 Fax: 0121-326 9379 E-mail: electronics.birmingham@dowdingandmills.com *Industrial electronic repairs.*

Dowding & Mills Engineering Services Ltd, Third Way, Avonmouth, Bristol, BS11 9HL Tel: 0117-938 1188 Fax: 0117-938 0066 *Electrical mechanical instrumentation services*

Dowding & Mills Engineering Services Ltd, 71b Whitecraigs Road, Glenrothes, Fife, KY6 2RX Tel: (01592) 773008 Fax: (01592) 772877 E-mail: calibration.glenrothes@dowdingandmills.com *Calibrating services*

Dowding & Mills Engineering Services Ltd, Colwall Street, Sheffield, S9 3WP Tel: 0114-244 6661 Fax: 0114-243 6782 E-mail: engineering.sheffield@dowdingandmills.com Principal Export Areas: Worldwide *Electrical & mechanical repairers* Also at: Branches throughout the U.K.

Dowding & Mills Southern Ltd, 24-26 White Post Lane, London, E9 5EP Tel: (020) 8985 8351 Fax: (020) 8985 9615 E-mail: engineering.london@dowdingandmills.com *Electrical & mechanical repairs* Also at: Ashford, Bristol, Hemel Hempstead, Ipswich, Kingston, Poole & Southampton

Dowds Electrical Ltd, 2-4 Milltown Road, Ballymoney, County Antrim, BT53 6LE Tel: (028) 2766 2789 Fax: (028) 2766 5905 E-mail: info@dowdselectrical.com *Electrical contractors*

Dowelhurst Ltd, 1 Hawkes Drive, Heathcote Industrial Estate, Warwick, CV34 6LX Tel: (01926) 461600 Fax: (01926) 461626 *Pharmaceutical distributors or agents*

Dowell Enterprises Ltd, Unit 6 & 7, 549 Eskdale Road, Uxbridge, Middlesex, UB8 2RT Tel: (01895) 811422 Fax: (01895) 811423 E-mail: sales@glue-4u.co.uk *Dowell Enterprises (UK) Limited are manufacturers, consultants, and distributors of a variety of adhesives, coatings and ancillary products. Our range of products include: Hot melt adhesives (granular, slugs, glue sticks, pillows) based on EVA, PSA, PA and Polyurethane chemistry as well as water based emulsions and polymers based on PVAs, VAEs, We supply adhesives to a variety of Industries including: Self seal adhesives and PSA grades for PP and PE bags and envelopes Bookbinding spine and side glues Adhesives for laminated and varnished boards to make folders and point of sales PSA labeling adhesives Hot melt adhesive sticks and slugs for hand packers Carton manufacturers, Carton gluers and for carton sealing , All our products are certified by EU industry standards and where applicable are FDA approved where necessary*

▶ Dowhigh Ltd, Park La West, Bootle, Merseyside, L30 3SU Tel: 0151-523 4372 Fax: 0151-525 6074

Dowling & Fransen (Engineers) Ltd, North End Road, Wembley, Middlesex, HA9 0AN Tel: (020) 8903 2155 Fax: (020) 8903 2158 E-mail: dowling@fransen.fsbusiness.co.uk *General engineers*

▶ Keith Dowling, 35 Harris Road, Bexleyheath, Kent, DA7 4QD Tel: (020) 8303 0162 Fax: (020) 8303 0162 E-mail: homeplan2001@yahoo.com *Kitchens manufrs*

Dowling Stoves, 3 Bladnoch Bridge Industrial Estate, Bladnoch, Wigtown, Newton Stewart, Wigtownshire, DG8 9AB Tel: (01988) 402666 Fax: (01988) 402666 E-mail: enquiries@dowlingstoves.com *Stove manufrs*

William Dowling Ltd, 71-73 Grand Street, Hilden, Lisburn, County Antrim, BT27 4TX Tel: (028) 9266 6444 Fax: (028) 9262 9678 E-mail: info@williamdowlingpreserve.co.uk *Building contractors*

▶ Dowlings Ltd, Duttons Farm, Bangors Road South, Iver, Buckinghamshire, SL0 0AY Tel: (01753) 630653 Fax: (01753) 630653 E-mail: sales@dowlingsltd.co.uk *Suppliers of hand crafted & automated gates, railings & metal products*

Dowlings Ltd, Duttons Farm, Bangors Road South, Iver, Buckinghamshire, SL0 0AY Tel: (01753) 630653 Fax: (0870) 2201684 E-mail: dowlingsltd@aol.com *Metal gate & railing manufrs*

Dowlings Sewing Machines, Unit 3, Orwell Court, Hurricane Way, Wickford, Essex, SS11 8YJ Tel: (01268) 570248 Fax: (01268) 562023 E-mail: sales@dowlings-sew.co.uk *Sewing machines, parts, needles, accessories & technical advice for Home, Industry and Education.Specialist suppliers to bed and matress manufacturers.*

Down & Francis Industrial Products Ltd, Ardath Road, Kings Norton, Birmingham, B38 9PN Tel: 0121-433 3300 Fax: 0121-433 3325 E-mail: reception@downandfrancis.co.uk *Structural steelwork engineers*

Down Recorder, 2-4 Church Street, Downpatrick, County Down, BT30 6EJ Tel: (028) 4461 3711 Fax: (028) 4461 4624 E-mail: advertis@downrecorder.uk *Publishers & commercial printers*

Stephen Down Furniture, Unit 5 Whitehouse Centre, Stannington, Morpeth, Northumberland, NE61 6AW Tel: (01670) 789727 Fax: (01670) 789418 *Furniture manufrs*

Down To Earth, 406 Sharrow Vale Road, Sheffield, S11 8ZP Tel: 0114-268 5220 *Health foods retailers*

Downend Fencing, Cuckoo Lane, Winterbourne Down, Bristol, BS36 1AG Tel: 0117-951 8582 *Fencing manufrs*

Downes C.R Agricultural Engineer, Lower House, Llandrinio, Llanymynech, Powys, SY22 6SH Tel: (01691) 830407 *Agricultural engineers*

Downes & Duncan, Unit 2, Ashley Drive, Bothwell, Glasgow, G71 8BS Tel: (01698) 803088 Fax: (01698) 803087 E-mail: sales@downsduncan.co.uk *Catering distributors*

▶ Downey & Co., Castle Street, Abergavenny, Gwent, NP7 5EE Tel: (01873) 859569 Fax: (01873) 855461 E-mail: huwdowney@btconnect.com *Downey & Co. are a firm of Chartered Secretaries in Public Practice, offering company secretarial support and advice to a range of companies both on on-going and specific project bases.*

Downey & Co. Ltd, Unit 1 Peterley Business Centre, 472 Hackney Road, London, E2 9EG Tel: (020) 7739 8696 Fax: (020) 7739 9877 E-mail: orders@downey.co.uk *Copperplate engraving services* Also at: Great Yarmouth

Downey Engineering, Pontrilas, Hereford, HR2 0BB Tel: (01981) 240427 Fax: (01981) 240953 *Specialist blacksmiths services*

Downham Components, Church Lane, Whittington, King's Lynn, Norfolk, PE33 9TG Tel: (01366) 500737 Fax: (01366) 501156 *Environmental services*

Downham Door Services, 16 Woodward Close, Shouldham, King's Lynn, Norfolk, PE33 0DE Tel: (01366) 347669 Fax: (01366) 347669 *Industrial door manufrs*

Downhill Enterprises Ltd, 62 Skegoneill Avenue, Belfast, BT15 3JQ Tel: (028) 9037 0165 Fax: (028) 9037 0204 *Building contractors*

Downhurst Engineering, 15 Aintree Road, Keytec 7 Business Park, Pershore, Worcestershire, WR10 2JN Tel: (01386) 554195 Fax: (01386) 561195 E-mail: downhurst@lineone.net *Precision engineers*

▶ Downie Allison Downie Bookbinders Ltd, Unit H, Purdon Street, Partick, Glasgow, G11 6AF Tel: 0141-339 0333 Fax: 0141-337 1113 E-mail: mail@dadbookbinders.com *Bookbinding*

Downland Bedding Co. Ltd, 23 Blackstock Street, Liverpool, L3 6ER Tel: 0151-236 7166 Fax: 0151-236 0062 E-mail: sales@downlandbedding.co.uk *Pillow, duvet, mattress & divan manufrs*

Downland Contractors, The Old Poorhouse, Graffham, Petworth, West Sussex, GU28 0NS Tel: (01798) 867297 Fax: (01798) 867297 *Excavation & groundwork contractors*

Downland Printing Services Ltd, Unit 1 Kingley Centre, Downs Road, Weststoke, Chichester, West Sussex, PO18 9HJ Tel: (01243) 576576 Fax: (01243) 576577 E-mail: studio@downlandrepro.demon.co.uk *Lithographic printers*

Downpatrick Farm & Garden Supplies Ltd, Ballydugan Industrial Estate, Ballydugan Road, Downpatrick, County Down, BT30 6TE Tel: (028) 4461 3719 Fax: (028) 4461 3719 *Agricultural equipment & garden machinery*

Downs Insulation & Electrical Ltd, Unit 16 Poulton Close, Dover, Kent, CT17 0HL Tel: (01304) 214473 Fax: (01304) 214473 E-mail: downselectrical@hotmail.com *Insulation & electrical contractors services*

▶ Downs Stone Co. Ltd, Lower Buildings, Sarsden, Chipping Norton, Oxfordshire, OX7 6PN Tel: (01608) 658357 Fax: (01608) 658882 E-mail: sales@downstone.com *Quarry & stone processing services*

Downshire Camping & Caravan Centre, 12 Newry Road, Banbridge, County Down, BT32 3HN Tel: (028) 4062 3378 Fax: (028) 4062 9295 E-mail: sales@downshirecaravans.net *Caravan & camping equipment suppliers*

Downshire Interiors, The Cottage, 18 Townsend Street, Banbridge, County Down, BT32 3LF Tel: (028) 4066 2317 Fax: (028) 4062 6500 *Interior designers*

Downsoft Ltd, Downsway House, Epsom Road, Ashtead, Surrey, KT21 1LD Tel: (01372) 272422 Fax: (01372) 276122 E-mail: sales@downsoft.co.uk *CD & cassette duplicators & manufrs*

Dowty Aerospace Propellers, Anson Business Park, Cheltenham Road East, Gloucester, GL2 9QN Tel: (01452) 716000 Fax: (01452) 716001 Principal Export Areas: Worldwide *Aircraft engine components*

Dowty Engineered Seals Ltd, Ashchurch, Tewkesbury, Gloucestershire, GL20 8JS Tel: (01684) 299111 Fax: (01684) 852210 Principal Export Areas: Worldwide *Rubber & plastics seals manufrs*

John Dowty Ltd, Kidderminster Road, Ombersley, Droitwich, Worcestershire, WR9 0JH Tel: (01905) 620404 Fax: (01905) 621016 E-mail: n.dowty@ombersleygolfclub.co.uk *Horticultural packaging & sundries*

Doxford Design Engineering Ltd, 3 Fellside, Ponteland, Newcastle upon Tyne, NE20 9JW Tel: 0191-519 1433 *Drawing office services*

Doyen (Cleveland) Ltd, Phonix Centre, Wilton, Redcar, Cleveland, TS10 4RG Tel: (01642) 463344 Fax: (01642) 463355 E-mail: doyen_personnel@btconnect.com *Employment agents*

J. Doyle Ltd, Manchester Road, Chequerbent, Westhoughton, Bolton, BL5 3JA Tel: (01942) 813231 Fax: (01942) 840505 E-mail: louise@holtgordon.co.uk *Scrap iron & steel merchants*

John Doyle Construction Ltd, John Doyle House, 2-3 Little Burrow, Welwyn Garden City, Hertfordshire, AL7 4SP Tel: (01707) 329481 Fax: (01707) 328213 E-mail: admin@john-doyle.co.uk *Building & refurbishment construction*

Doyle Partnership, 5 Waverley Road, Huddersfield, HD1 5NA Tel: (01484) 516977 Fax: (01484) 516958 *Consulting structural & civil engineers*

DP World, 16 Palace Street, London, SW1E 5JQ Tel: (020) 7930 4343 Fax: (020) 7901 4015 *International logistics & transport services*

DPAC UK Ltd, Unit 14a, E Space North, 181 Wisbech Road, Littleport, Ely, Cambridgeshire, CB6 1RA Tel: (0845) 2576380 Fax: (0845) 2576375 E-mail: sales@dpacuk.co.uk *Official sole UK distributors and marketing agents for De'Longhi S.p.A professional air conditioning.*

Company Information

▶ DPC Ltd, Unit 29, Spring Road Industrial Estate, Lanesfield Drive, Wolverhampton, WV4 6UB Tel: (0845) 8380801 Fax: 0121-559 6688 E-mail: sales@custom-finish.com *Powder coated finishes*

▶ Dpge Rebuilds, Unit 11 Martor Industrial Estate, Tormarton Road, Chippenham, Wiltshire, SN14 8LJ Tel: (01225) 892226 Fax: (01225) 892129 E-mail: sales@dpge-rebuilds.co.uk *Repair & refurbishment services*

DPI 21 Ltd, 10 Heaton Street, Blackburn, BB2 2EF Tel: (07903) 243666 Fax: (01254) 694485 E-mail: studio@dpi21.com *DPI 21 is a specialist web design & graphic design company offering practical solutions to suit your business needs. Take advantage of our skills & competitive rates to create a website & corporate identity that will stand you out from the crowd. Whether it's simple & effective, or complex & dynamic, we can offer a wide range of services to create the perfect website for you.*

▶ DPM Systems Ltd, Suite 4, Cornerstone House, Stafford Park 13, Telford, Shropshire, TF3 3AZ Tel: (01952) 504400 Fax: (01952) 504500 E-mail: info@dpmsys.com *Based in Shropshire and the Caribbean, we are an Independent Software Supplier based around the IBM iSeries (formerly AS/400) and a set of software applications. These include, but not limited to, Business Intelligence solutions; Accounting software solutions; Distribution Software solutions and CRM Software solutions. We have embraced the Web and have applications for Portals and web integration available immediately. We specialise in identifying business process improvements through a tried and tested, benefits driven, methodology. DPM Systems Ltd has been providing an excellent service for over 15 years to over 250 companies.*

DPR Services, 171 Ranworth Avenue, Hoddesdon, Hertfordshire, EN11 9NU Tel: (01992) 470654 Fax: (0871) 6613985 E-mail: info@dprservices.co.uk *Providing computer training, support, development & web design*

▶ DPS Computer Shop, 69 Market Hall, Scotch Street, Carlisle, CA3 8QX Tel: 01228 528333 E-mail: david.prentice@tiscali.co.uk *Computer repairs, cartridges, cables, media, accessories & parts*

▶ DPS Fine Art, 14 Hermes Way, Sleaford, Lincolnshire, NG34 7WH Tel: 01529 300452 Fax: 01529 300452 E-mail: matt@dpsfineart.co.uk *Canvas printing and stretching services, any size from your artwork or pictures. Competitive prices.*

DPS Tableware Ltd, 11-12 Beacon Road, Walton Industrial Estate, Stone, Staffs, ST15 0NN Tel: (01785) 826333 Fax: (01785) 826330 E-mail: sales@dpstableware.co.uk *Specialists in supplying the catering industry with quality porcelain tableware*

DPT Wear Ltd, 17-20 Martinfield Business Centre, Martinfield, Welwyn Garden City, Hertfordshire, AL7 1HG Tel: (01707) 373838 Fax: (01707) 332288 E-mail: admin@dptwear.com *Necktie manufrs*

Dpus Plus Ltd, Flotta Oil Terminal, Flotta, Stromness, Orkney, KW16 3NP Tel: (01856) 702000 Fax: (01856) 701473 E-mail: admin@opusplus.co.uk *Environmental engineering & laboratory services*

Dr Burns, Craigton Frant Road, Grantown-on-Spey, Morayshire, PH26 3LB Tel: (01479) 872297 *Doctor*

▶ Dr Security & Electrical, De Beauvoir Road, London, N1 4EN Tel: (020) 7241 1001 E-mail: marketing@drsecurity.co.uk *DR Security & Electrical have been supplying, installing and maintaining security and electrical equipment since 1988. Our aim is to provide a high-quality installation, tailored to your needs, and conscientious after-sales service. At DR Security & Electrical we take pride in reliability, both in the equipment we supply and in the performance of our installation team. We have an unblemished record for punctuality, conscientious workmanship and friendly co-operation with clients. Please don''t hesitate to contact us to discuss your electrical and security requirements, to ask any questions or to request a quote.*

Draco Gas Springs, 26 Waterloo Park, Bidford-on-Avon, Alcester, Warwickshire, B50 4JG Tel: (01789) 490030 Fax: (01789) 490904 *Springs, gas operated manufrs*

Dracup (UK) Ltd, Lane Close Mills, Bartle Lane, Bradford, West Yorkshire, BD7 4QQ Tel: (01274) 571071 Fax: (01274) 501209 E-mail: email@dracupuk.com *General engineers*

▶ Draeger Ltd, 2 The Willows, Mark Road, Hemel Hempstead Industrial Estate, Hemel Hempstead, Hertfordshire, HP2 7BN Tel: (01442) 211110 Fax: (01442) 240327 *Medical equipment*

Draford Optical Ltd, Abford Works, 12 Crittall Road, Industrial Estate West, Witham, Essex, CM8 3AT Tel: (01376) 512040 Fax: (01376) 515817 *Optical lens manufrs*

Dragon, 72-74 Heol Tawe, Abercrave, Swansea, SA9 1XR Tel: (01639) 730031 Fax: (01639) 730020 *Caving equipment*

Dragon Alfa Cement Ltd, The Docks, Sharpness, Berkeley, Gloucestershire, GL13 9UX Tel: (01453) 819098 Fax: (01453) 811953 *Cement suppliers*

Dragon Blockworks Ltd, Concrete Works, Alltwalis, Carmarthen, Dyfed, SA32 7EE Tel: (01559) 384317 Fax: (01559) 384175 E-mail: dragonconcreteworksltd@hotmail.com *Concrete blocks manufacturing*

Dragon Cash Registers Wales Ltd, 110 High Street, Swansea, SA1 1LZ Tel: (01792) 460168 Fax: (01792) 460493 E-mail: sales@dragon-cashregisters.co.uk *Cash register sales*

Dragon Crane Services, Unit 18 Lamby Workshops, Lamby Way, Rumney, Cardiff, CF3 2EQ Tel: (029) 2077 7444 Fax: (029) 2077 7404 E-mail: email@dragoncraneservices.co.uk *Crane repairs & manufrs*

▶ Dragon Design, 14a Cambridge Road, Granby Industrial Estate, Weymouth, Dorset, DT4 9TJ Tel: (01305) 750777 Fax: (01305) 784555 E-mail: info@dragondesignltd.com *Electronics design & manufacture*

▶ Dragon Engines Ltd, Henry Street, Chesterfield, Derbyshire, S41 9BT Tel: (01246) 456123 Fax: (01246) 453666 *Engine suppliers to fleet companies*

Dragon Fire & Security Ltd, Dragon House, Norwich Road, Cardiff, CF23 9AB Tel: (029) 2048 5555 Fax: (029) 2048 4400 *Alarm system installers*

Dragon Machines, 122 Trehafod Road, Pontypridd, Mid Glamorgan, CF37 2LY Tel: (01443) 683219 Fax: (01443) 684425 *Amusement machine distributors*

Dragon Rising Publishing, 18 Marlow Avenue, Eastbourne, East Sussex, BN22 8SJ Tel: (01323) 729666 Fax: E-mail: info@dragonrising.com *E-publishing & traditional publishers*

Dragon Signs Of North Wales, Unit 1-2 Plot 11 Llandegai Industrial Estate, Llandygai, Bangor, Gwynedd, LL57 4YH Tel: (01248) 352286 Fax: (01248) 352286 *Sign manufrs*

Dragon Solutions UK Ltd, 55 Valley Road, Bramhall, Stockport, Cheshire, SK7 2NJ Tel: 0161-439 0610 Fax: 0161-439 9252 E-mail: sales@dragon-solutions.com *Bar code technology products*

▶ Dragon Supplies, Unit 3, Enterprise Way, Newport, Gwent, NP20 2AQ Tel: 01633 216035 Fax: 01633 216035

Dragon Systems, Gyllellog, Pennal, Machynlleth, Powys, SY20 9DU Tel: (01654) 791642 Fax: (01654) 791277 E-mail: dragoncom@aol.com *Computer systems*

Dragon Workshop, 47 Princess Victoria Street, Bristol, BS8 4BX Tel: 0117-973 2656 *Goldsmiths & silversmiths*

▶ Dragoncad, 9 St. Maughans Close, Monmouth, Gwent, NP25 5BU Tel: (07920) 054495 E-mail: info@dragoncad.co.uk *Drawing & graphical services*

Dragonfly Saddlery, Ditchling, Hassocks, West Sussex, BN6 8UQ Tel: (01273) 844606 *Saddlery*

▶ Drain & Able, 124 Grovelands Road, Reading, RG30 2PD Tel: 0118-957 6244 Fax: 0118-956 7416 E-mail: drainandable1105@btinternet.com *All Blockages Cleared, 24 Hours a Day, 365 Days a Year. Sinks/Urinals/Toilets/Baths/ Soakaways/Storm Drains/Foul Water Drains/ Downpipes. Public Liability Insurance. No Call-Out Charge/No VAT. Full Drain Repair Service. Call Kevin for a honest and reliable service.*

Drain Brain Ltd, Meadowlands, Bibury, Cirencester, Gloucestershire, GL7 5LZ Tel: (01285) 740682 Fax: (01285) 740638 E-mail: enquiries@dbigroup.co.uk *Drain, pipe & sewer cleaning & repair*

▶ Drain Brain Offshore, Unit 5 Dales Industrial Estate, Peterhead, Aberdeenshire, AB42 3JF Tel: (01779) 471536 Fax: (01779) 473694 E-mail: enquiries@dbigroup.co.uk *Specialist industrial cleaning services*

Drain Center Ltd, Lincoln Road, Cressex Business Park, High Wycombe, Buckinghamshire, HP12 3RB Tel: (01494) 462351 Fax: (01494) 444923 *Plastic stockholders*

Drain Center Ltd, 20 Cosgrove Way, Luton, LU1 1XL Tel: (01582) 414140 Fax: (01582) 451488 E-mail: gary.gillingham@wolseley.co.uk *Pipeline specialists services for utilities market*

Drain Center, Unit 20, West Churton Industrial Estate, Alder Road, North Shields, Tyne & Wear, NE29 8SD Tel: 0191-257 8125 Fax: 0191-257 8819 *Plastic pipe distributors*

Drain Center Civils, 248 Gosport Road, Fareham, Hampshire, PO16 0SS Tel: (01329) 232129 Fax: (01329) 822368 E-mail: p16.fareham@wolseley.co.uk *Thermoplastic pipework distributors*

Drain Center Civils, 386 Coleridge Road, Sheffield, S9 5DD Tel: 0114-244 0926 Fax: 0114-243 5990 E-mail: sheffield.p24@wolsley.co.uk *Plastic pipe work distributors*

Drain Centre, Stenplas Works, Grecian Crescent, Bolton, BL3 6QS Tel: (01204) 388388 Fax: (01204) 389411 *PTFE hose stockholders*

Drain Centre, A Axis One, Brunel Way, Severalls Industrial Park, Colchester, CO4 9QX Tel: (01206) 853853 Fax: (01206) 855228 E-mail: colchester@wolseley.co.uk *Plastic fabrications & assemblies*

Drain Centre, 19 Bank Head Drive, St. Hillndustrial Estate, St.Hill, Edinburgh, EH11 4DW Tel: 0131-552 8181 Fax: 0131-453 2008 E-mail: edinbr@capperplastics.com *Plastics stockists*

Drain Centre, Heron Works, Heron Road, Sowton Industrial Estate, Exeter, EX2 7LL Tel: (01392) 445588 Fax: (01392) 445599 *Plastic products distributors*

Drain Centre, 115 Clyde Place, Cambuslang, Glasgow, G32 8RF Tel: 0141-425 2720 E-mail: glasgow.p28@wolsley.co.uk *Plastic tube distributors*

Drain Centre, Cinderhill Industrial Estate, Weston Coyney Road, Longton, Stoke-On-Trent, ST3 5JT Tel: (01782) 311311 Fax: (01782) 343400 E-mail: p23.stoke@wolseley.co.uk *Plastic stockholders*

▶ Drain Cure Services, 6 Strathmore Street, Perth, PH2 7HP Tel: (01738) 449300 Fax: (01738) 634167

▶ Drain Doctor Plumbing, 1 East School Road, Dundee, DD3 8NU Tel: (01382) 811899

▶ Drain Doctor Plumbing, Station House, Macnaghten Road, Southampton, SO18 1GG Tel: (023) 8033 3312 Fax: (023) 8033 2600 E-mail: j-rook@btconnect.com *Drainage services*

Drain Maintenance Services, 3 Astwick Avenue, Hatfield, Hertfordshire, AL10 9LB Tel: (01707) 261709 Fax: (01707) 261121 E-mail: dmsgroup@talk21.com *Drain cleaning & maintenance*

Drainage Center Ltd, 116 London Road, Hailsham, East Sussex, BN27 3AL Tel: (01323) 442333 Fax: (01323) 847488 E-mail: sales@drainagecenter.co.uk *Builders merchants*

Drainage Spares & Pipework Supplies Ltd, Fairy Farm Wethersfield, Wethersfield, Braintree, Essex, CM7 4EP Tel: (01371) 850808 Fax: (01371) 850120 E-mail: adam.dsps@btinternet.com *Drain pipe, sell sewage treatment & sewage handling services*

▶ Draincare Services Ltd, Unit 2, Batford Mill, Lower Luton Road, Harpenden, Hertfordshire, AL5 5BZ Tel: (01582) 467111

Draincare Services, 23 Faraday Court, Park Farm Industrial Estate, Wellingborough, Northamptonshire, NN8 6XY Tel: (01933) 679292 Fax: (01933) 676161 E-mail: info@draincare.com *Sewer cleaning contractors*

▶ Drains 4U, The Copse, Common Road, Ightham, Sevenoaks, Kent, TN15 9DY Tel: (01732) 884949 Fax: (01732) 884949 E-mail: info@drains4u.com *Drainage and sewer clearance, cctv surveys, homebuyers reports, high pressure water jetting, sewer clearance, repairs, call 07831 319275*

Drains Centre, Unit 2B, St. Georges Trading Estate, Avonmouth, Bristol, BS11 9HS Tel: 0117-916 2700 Fax: 0117-982 6820 E-mail: bristol.p11@wolseley.co.uk *PTFE hose stockists*

▶ Drainserve.com Ltd, 8 Scott Grove, Solihull, West Midlands, B92 7LJ Tel: 0121-707 7489

▶ Drainway Services, 1 Industria House Offices, La Route Des Genets, St. Brelade, Jersey, JE3 8LD Tel: (01534) 742846 Fax: (01534) 745116

Drainways Ltd, 108 Summer Road, Erdington, Birmingham, B23 6DY Tel: 0121-377 6583 Fax: 0121-377 7769 E-mail: sales@drainways.com *Drain clearance contractors*

Draka Comteq Cables Ltd, Crowther Road, Washington, Tyne & Wear, NE38 0AQ Tel: 0191-415 5000 Fax: 0191-415 8278 *Manufacture of data communication*

Draka Wire, Coastal Link Road, Llanelli, Dyfed, SA15 2NH Tel: (01554) 750121 Fax: (01554) 783808 E-mail: wiresales@draka.com *Copper wire manufrs*

Drake Educational Associates Ltd, 89 St. Fagans Road, Fairwater, Cardiff, CF5 3AE Tel: (029) 2056 0333 Fax: (029) 2055 4909 E-mail: info@drakeav.com *Educational publishers*

Drake Pneumatics, 138 Oyster Lane, Byfleet, West Byfleet, Surrey, KT14 7JQ Tel: (01932) 355239 Fax: (01932) 354954 E-mail: info@drakepneumatics.co.uk *Pneumatic tools repairs & fittings services*

Drake & Scull Engineering Ltd, Drake Scull Ho, 86 Talbot Rd, Old Trafford, Manchester, M16 0QD Tel: 0161-874 4800 Fax: 0161-874 4900 *Building services engineers* Also at: Branches throughout the U.K.

Drake Tooling & Abrasives Ltd, Unit 12 Chantry Park, Cowley Road, Nuffield Industrial Park, Poole, Dorset, BH17 0UJ Tel: (01202) 666467 Fax: (01202) 666468 E-mail: drake@poolebranch.co.uk *Abrasive product distributors & engineering wholesalers*

▶ Drakeloe Press Ltd, 7 James Way, Bletchley, Milton Keynes, MK1 1SU Tel: (01908) 271866

▶ Drakemire Dairy Ltd, 1 Argyle Crescent, Hillhouse Park Industrial Estate, Hamilton, Lanarkshire, ML3 9BQ Tel: (01698) 423236

Drakes Display & Shop Aids, 45 Wessex Trade Centre, Ringwood Road, Poole, Dorset, BH12 3PG Tel: (01202) 735858 Fax: (01202) 733979 E-mail: sales@drakesdisplay.co.uk *Shop fittings & display equipment*

Drakes Plumbing Supplies Ltd, 3 Independent Business Park, Imberhorne Lane, East Grinstead, West Sussex, RH19 1TU Tel: (01342) 319123 Fax: (01342) 319136 *Plumbers merchants* Also at: Sevenoaks & Uckfield

Drakes Pride Bowls Co., 128 Richmond Row, Liverpool, L3 3BL Tel: 0151-298 1355 Fax: 0151-298 2988 E-mail: drakespride@eaclare.co.uk *Lawn & crown green bowls manufrs*

Drakeset Ltd, 3 Tansey Green Road, Brierley Hill, West Midlands, DY5 4TL Tel: (01384) 79487 Fax: (01384) 70143 E-mail: drakeset@btconnect.com *Electrical contractors*

▶ Drakesridge, 25 Dale Close, Hitchin, Hertfordshire, SG4 9AS Tel: (01462) 631900 E-mail: enquiries@drakesridge.co.uk *Landscaping & Gardening:*Whatever your needs, whether it''''s realising a design, or the maintenance of your garden, we are here to help. From cosy town gardens to a rambling country pile, your every garden requirement can be left in our capable hands.**Homeowners:*Whatever the job & no matter how small YOU consider it to be we will be pleased to assist and accommodate you. *If it's simply advice you need prior to works commencing please get in touch with us via the 'Contact us' page.* *Commercials:*We provide maintenance contracts specifically tailored to your business needs. Whether you own or manage one or several properties, have a single office or a multi-national site network, we can deliver the services required during hours that suit YOUR business needs.* *************************

▶ Draks Shutters, Unit 316 Heyford Park, Camp Road, Upper Heyford, Bicester, Oxfordshire, OX25 5HA Tel: (01869) 232989 Fax: (01869) 232989 E-mail: sales@draksonline.co.uk

Drallim Industries, Drury Lane, St. Leonards-on-Sea, East Sussex, TN38 9BA Tel: (01424) 205140 Fax: (01424) 202140 E-mail: sales@drallim.com

Drallim Industries, Drury Lane, St. Leonards-on-Sea, East Sussex, TN38 9BA Tel: (01424) 205140 Fax: (01424) 202140 E-mail: sales@drallim.com *Cable pressurisation unit manufrs*

Dramex Expanded Metal Ltd, Unit 24-26, Crossgate Road, Park Farm Industrial Estate, Redditch, Worcestershire, B98 7SN Tel: (0800) 1804454 Fax: (01527) 501725 E-mail: uksales@dramex.com Principal Export Areas: Worldwide *Manufacturers & stockholders of expanded metal products based in Redditch supplying accross the UK and Europe.**Our extensive range of stock products is complemented by our ability to manufacture non-standard meshes and sheet sizes to meet your individual requirements.**We stock a comprehensive range of expanded metals that are available for immediate shipment in alloys such as Mild steel, Galvanized Steel, Aluminium and Stainless Steel grades 304, 316 and 430.**Contact our experienced sales team for prices or technical assistance.*

Dramicom, 14 Mooside Lane, Neston, Parkgate, Neston, CH64 6QP Tel: 0151-336 5107 Fax: 0151-336 5107 *Refractory distributor*

Dransfield Novelty Co. Ltd, Dransfield House, Mill Street, Leeds, LS9 8BP Tel: 0113-244 4555 Fax: 0113-234 3948 *Amusement machine distributors* Also at: Byker & Nottingham

Dransfields Engineering Services Ltd, Cotswold Avenue, Chadderton, Oldham, OL9 8PJ Tel: 0161-624 4142 Fax: 0161-627 5127 E-mail: sales@dransfields.co.uk *Precision engineers*

Albert Draper & Son Ltd, Black 5 Works, Ravenstreet, Hull, HU9 1PP Tel: (01482) 320712 Fax: (01482) 585312 E-mail: info@adraper.co.uk *Scrap metal merchants*

Draper Party Products, 30 Comberton Hill, Kidderminster, Worcestershire, DY10 1QN Tel: (01562) 754973 *Carnival, novelty & fancy goods distributors*

Draper Tools Ltd, Hursley Road, Chandler's Ford, Eastleigh, Hampshire, SO53 1YF Tel: (023) 8026 6355 Fax: (023) 8026 0784 E-mail: sales@draper.co.uk *Tool distributors*

Drapers Air Gun Centre, 122-128 Hartley Road, Nottingham, NG7 3AJ Tel: 0115-970 2525 Fax: 0115-970 2525 *Air gun sales*

▶ Drapers Developments Ltd, Black Five Works, Raven Street, Hull, HU9 1PP Tel: (01482) 323223 Fax: (01482) 585312 *Metal recycling services*

Drapes & Blinds, 289 Ashley Road, Poole, Dorset, BH14 9DZ Tel: (01202) 742042 Fax: (01202) 742042 *Blinds manufrs*

The Draughtsmans Centre Ltd, 819 Hagley Road West, Birmingham, B32 1AD Tel: 0121-423 1412 Fax: 0121-423 1812 *Drawing office equipment suppliers*

Draw Write, 72-74 Sandgate, Ayr, KA7 1BX Tel: (01292) 610735 Fax: (01292) 263877 E-mail: dwrite7274@aol.com *Art & craft stockists & stationers*

▶ The Drawing Co. Ltd, 8 Morton Close, Ely, Cambridgeshire, CB7 4FE Tel: (01353) 669952 Fax: (01353) 669952 E-mail: wc@thedrawingcompany.co.uk *2D & 3D CAD draughting.3D modelling & rendering services*

The Drawing Group Ltd, 3-9 West St, Hull, HU1 3UR Tel: (01482) 324263 Fax: (01482) 325176 E-mail: sales@drawgroup.co.uk *Drawing office & design suppliers*

Drawing Office Supplies & Photocopying South Wales Ltd, 4 North Point, Western Avenue, Bridgend Industrial Estate, Bridgend, Mid Glamorgan, CF31 3RX Tel: (01656) 654744 Fax: (01656) 646609 E-mail: drawing.os@btconnect.com *Stationery suppliers service*

Drawing Office Systems, 160 Congleton Road, Talke, Stoke-on-Trent, ST7 1LT Tel: (01782) 774817 Fax: (01782) 782143 E-mail: drawingofficesys@aol.com *Drawing office systems & stationery suppliers*

Drawn Metal Ltd, 50 Swinnow Lane, Leeds, LS13 4NE Tel: 0113-256 5661 Fax: 0113-239 3194 E-mail: sales@drawnmetal.co.uk *Stainless steel doors & entrances manufrs*

▶ Drawtrend Ltd, 95 Mains Lane, Poulton-le-Fylde, Lancashire, FY6 7LD Tel: (01253) 882158 Fax: (01253) 882158 E-mail: sales@drawtrend.com *System Integration*Software, Hardware Distribution*

Draycast Foundries Ltd, Bellingdon Road, Chesham, Buckinghamshire, HP5 2NR Tel: (01494) 786077 Fax: (01494) 791337 E-mail: sales@draycast.co.uk *Non-ferrous casting suppliers*

▶ Draycote Continental Transport Ltd, Glebe Farm Road, Rugby, Warwickshire, CV21 1GF Tel: (01788) 579060

▶ Drayfords Of Chesterfield, 4 Shap Close, Chesterfield, Derbyshire, S40 4NB Tel: (01246) 205914 *Specialist suppliers in hand made feather fascinators*

Drayfords Silk Wedding Flowers, 198, Derby Road, Chesterfield, Derbyshire, S40 2EP Tel: (01246) 205914

Drayton Data Ltd, 28 Old Forge Road, Fenny Drayton, Nuneaton, Warwickshire, CV13 6BD Tel: (01827) 715214 Fax: (01827) 713858 *Computer consultants*

Drayton Data Ltd, 4 Willow Park, Upton Lane, Stoke Golding, Nuneaton, Warwickshire, CV13 6EU Tel: (01455) 213075 Fax: (01455) 213075 E-mail: draytondata@aol.com *Microfilm services*

Drayton Fencing, 93 Park View Road, Uxbridge, Middlesex, UB8 3LN Tel: (01895) 444727 Fax: (01895) 431054 *Fencing suppliers & erectors*

Drayton Recycling Ltd, Old Mill Sidings, Thorney Mill Road, West Drayton, Middlesex, UB7 7EZ Tel: (01895) 442612 Fax: (01895) 422174 *Scrap metal merchants*

▶ Dream, Unit 1 Boucher CR, Belfast, BT12 6HU Tel: (028) 9066 8596 Fax: (028) 9066 9765 E-mail: sales@therockinghorse.co.uk *Bed retailers*

Dream Design, Hinton Old Sawmill, A35 Lyndhurst Road, Hinton, Christchurch, Dorset, BH23 7DU Tel: (01425) 279525 Fax: (01425) 273550 *Furniture manufrs*

▶ Dream Designs, 11 Cove Way, Cove Bay, Aberdeen, AB12 3DW Tel: (07971) 522186 E-mail: sales@dream-designs.co.uk *Website design & creation*

▶ Dream Doors Glasgow Ltd, 25 New Endrick Road, Killearn, Glasgow, G63 9QT Tel: (0845) 6009232 Fax: (0845) 6009232 *Kitchen furniture fitters*

continued

Dream Loaf Hot Bread Kitchen Ltd, 39A Market Place, Swaffham, Norfolk, PE37 7LA Tel: (01760) 722707 Fax: (01760) 725539 *Bakery suppliers*

Dream Merchants, Canal Mill, Botany Bay, Chorley, Lancashire, PR6 9AF Tel: (01257) 270172 Fax: (01257) 270172 *Furniture retail*

Dream Sleeper, The Lingfield Estate, Mcmullen Road, Darlington, County Durham, DL1 1RW Tel: (01325) 283105 Fax: (01325) 488502 *Headboard & sofa bed manufrs*

▶ dream4avilla, 11 Underwood Road, Southampton, SO16 7BZ Tel: (023) 8058 1520 Fax: (023) 8058 1520 E-mail: info@dream4avilla.com

▶ Dreamcrafts Ltd, 107 Thistledene, Thames Ditton, Surrey, KT7 0YW Tel: (020) 8873 2893 Fax: (020) 8873 2893 E-mail: sales@dreamcraftstore.co.uk *Online stationary*

Dreamlight, 599a Prescot Road, Old Swan, Liverpool, L13 5XA Tel: 0151-228 7770 Fax: 0151-228 8612 *Lighting manufrs*

▶ Dreamprint, Unit 36, Royds Enterprise Park, Future Fields, Buttershaw, Bradford, West Yorkshire, BD6 3EW Tel: (01274) 355661 Fax: (01274) 355662 E-mail: bob@dreamprint.co.uk *Garment printers, sign makers, engravers, pad printers & stationery*

▶ Dreams plc, Waterton Industrial Estate, Bridgend, Mid Glamorgan, CF31 3YN Tel: (01656) 668166 Fax: (01656) 662101 *Beds & bedroom suppliers*

▶ Dreams plc, Point West Waterfront West, Dudley Road, Brierley Hill, West Midlands, DY5 1LL Tel: (01384) 572568 Fax: (01384) 262616 *Retailer of beds*

▶ Dreams plc, Wyrley Brook Retail Park, Walkmill Lane, Cannock, Staffordshire, WS11 0XA Tel: (01543) 570606 Fax: (01543) 570764 *Bed retailers*

▶ Dreams plc, Unit 4a Cwmbran Retail Park, Cwmbran Drive, Cwmbran, Gwent, NP44 3JQ Tel: (01633) 480899 Fax: (01633) 480839

▶ Dreams plc, Southgate Retail Park, Normanton Road, Derby, DE23 6UQ Tel: (01332) 208989 Fax: (01332) 208124 *Bed suppliers*

▶ Dreams plc, 452-458 High Road, Ilford, Essex, IG1 1UT Tel: (020) 8478 5888

▶ Dreams plc, Unit 2a Crossley Retail Park, Carpet Trades Way, Kidderminster, Worcestershire, DY11 6DY Tel: (01562) 744144 Fax: (01562) 743022 *Bed retailers*

Dreams plc, Lonsdale House, 7-11 High Street, Reigate, Surrey, RH2 9AA Tel: (01737) 242451 Fax: (01737) 242452 *Retail beds*

Dreams plc, 11-12 High Street, Wraysbury, Staines, Middlesex, TW19 5DB Tel: (01784) 491174 Fax: (01784) 491175 *Bed retailer* Also at: Hayes

Dreams plc, 5 The Forum, Stevenage, Hertfordshire, SG1 1EH Tel: (01438) 759999 Fax: (01438) 749999 E-mail: enquiries@dreamsplc.co.uk *Bed retailers*

▶ Dreamweaver Weddings, 113 Cleethorpe Road, Grimsby, South Humberside, DN31 3ES Tel: (01472) 355001 Fax: (01472) 238742 E-mail: shirley@dreamweaverweddings.co.uk *Everything but the groom, everything for weddings*

Dredging International UK Ltd, Greenstede House Wood Street, Station Road, East Grinstead, West Sussex, RH19 1UZ Tel: (01342) 323000 Fax: (01342) 326000 E-mail: diuk@dredging.com *Dredging & land reclamation services*

Dreelside Engineering Ltd, Station Road, Anstruther, Fife, KY10 3JA Tel: (01333) 311060 Fax: (01333) 312197 *Hydraulic engineers*

Dreh Ltd, Duncombe Road, Bradford, West Yorkshire, BD8 9TB Tel: (01793) 533262 Fax: (01793) 619510 E-mail: sales@dreh.co.uk *Pipe workers*

Dremm Packaging Ltd, Erewash Court, Manners Avenue, Manners Industrial Estate, Ilkeston, Derbyshire, DE7 8EF Tel: 0115-930 7555 Fax: 0115-930 7618 E-mail: sales@dremm.co.uk *Plastic bottle manufrs*

Drenagh Sawmills Ltd, 89 Dowland Road, Limavady, County Londonderry, BT49 0HR Tel: (028) 7776 5611 Fax: (028) 7776 5984 E-mail: mark@drenagh.co.uk *Timber sawmills manufrs*

Drennan Transport Ltd, 103 Main Street, Tobermore, Magherafelt, County Londonderry, BT45 5PP Tel: (028) 7964 2116 Fax: (028) 7964 3570 E-mail: sales@drennan-transport.co.uk *Road transport, haulage & freight services*

Drent (UK) Ltd, 6 Blackburn Industrial Estate, Enterprise Way, Sherburn In Elmet, Leeds, LS25 6NA Tel: (01977) 685098 Fax: (01977) 681040 E-mail: duk@drentuk.com *Printing equipment distributors*

▶ Dressed by Scotland, 57 Main Street, Pathhead, Edinburgh, EH37 5WT Tel: 0131-467 7508 Fax: 0131-467 7508

Dresser Flow Control, Unit 4 Suite 1.1 Nobel House The Grand Union Office Park, Packe, Uxbridge, Middlesex, UB8 2GH Tel: (01895) 454900 Fax: (01895) 454919 E-mail: sales@dresser-valve.co.uk *Valve manufrs*

Dresser Rand UK Ltd, Hareness Circle, Altens Industrial Estate, Aberdeen, AB12 3LY Tel: (01224) 879445 Fax: (01224) 894616 E-mail: geoff_king@dresser-rand.com *Gas compressor repair services*

Dresser Roots-Holmes Operations, PO Box B7, Huddersfield, HD1 6RB Tel: (01484) 422222 Fax: (01484) 422668 E-mail: dmd_roots@dresser.co.uk *Rotary air blowers, vacuum pumps & gas compressor manufrs*

Dresser Valve Ltd, Gillibrands Road, Skelmersdale, Lancashire, WN8 9TU Tel: (01695) 52600 Fax: (01695) 52676 E-mail: dennis_alsancak@dresser.com *Valve repair centre*

Dresser-Rand (U K) Ltd, C I Tower St. Georges Square, High Street, New Malden, Surrey, KT3 4DN Tel: (020) 8336 7300 Fax: (020) 8336 0773 *Steam turbine manufrs*

Dressy Styles Ltd, 35 Hall Street, Birmingham, B18 6BS Tel: 0121-212 3499 Fax: 0121-212 3499 E-mail: dressystyles1@activemail.co.uk *Ladies fashion wholesalers*

Alan Drew Ltd, 8 Caxton Way, The Watford Bussiness Park, Watford, WD18 8JX Tel: (01923) 817933 Fax: (01923) 237824 E-mail: alandrew@onet.co.uk *Access specialists* Also at: London SE18, Loughborough & Milton Keynes

Drew Brady & Co. Ltd, Dove Mill, Dove Road, Bolton, BL3 4ET Tel: (01204) 854800 Fax: (01204) 854854 E-mail: drewbrady@ruia.co.uk *Hosiery manufrs*

▶ Drew & Co Electrical Contractors Ltd, Fellowes Court The Millfields, Plymouth, PL1 3JB Tel: (01752) 204415 Fax: (01752) 201684

Drew Forsyth & Co. Ltd, Beehive Mills, Hebble End, Hebden Bridge, West Yorkshire, HX7 6HJ Tel: (01422) 842206 Fax: (01422) 844828 E-mail: info@drewforsyth.co.uk *Wooden kitchen furniture manufrs*

Drew Scientific Group plc, Unit 4 Peter Green Way Furness Business Park, Barrow-in-Furness, Cumbria, LA14 2PE Tel: (01229) 432089 Fax: (01229) 432096 E-mail: sales@drew-scientific.com *Blood diagnosis equipment distributors*

▶ Drew & Sons, Venton Bungalow, Drewsteignton, Exeter, EX6 6PG Tel: (01647) 231306 Fax: (01647) 231306

▶ Drew Warren Building & Roofing Contractors, Coriander Cottage, Yelford, Witney, Oxfordshire, OX29 7QX Tel: (01865) 300977

Drew Wylie Building Services, 352 Saintfield Road, Belfast, BT8 7SJ Tel: (028) 9081 7170 Fax: (028) 9079 3443 E-mail: drewwylie@hotmail.com *Suspended ceilings & access flooring*

Drews of Dinton Ltd, Dinton, Salisbury, SP3 5EH Tel: (01722) 716377 Fax: (01722) 716489 *Agricultural engineers*

Drey Precision Ltd, 11-12 Priestley Way, Crawley, West Sussex, RH10 9NT Tel: (01293) 542695 Fax: (01293) 553703 E-mail: sales@drey.net *Precision engineers & manufrs*

Dri Pak Ltd, Furnace Road, Ilkeston, Derbyshire, DE7 5EP Tel: 0115-932 5165 Fax: 0115-944 0297 E-mail: sales@dripak.co.uk *Salt merchants & packers*

Dri Pool Accessories, 3 Westwood Court, Brunel Road, Totton, Southampton, SO40 3WX Tel: (023) 8066 3131 Fax: (023) 8066 3232 E-mail: sales@dripool.co.uk *Swimming pool covers manfurs*

Driffield Hardware Centre, Cranwell Road, Driffield, North Humberside, YO25 6UH Tel: (01377) 241399 Fax: (01377) 241252 *Ironmongers & DIY suppliers*

Driffield Refrigeration, Acorns, Ruston Parva, Driffield, North Humberside, YO25 4DG Tel: (01377) 254527 Fax: (01377) 254527 *Refrigeration service & repairers*

Driftgate 2000 Ltd, Little End Road, Eaton Socon, St. Neots, Cambridgeshire, PE19 8JH Tel: (01480) 470400 Fax: (01480) 470401 E-mail: sales@dg2k.co.uk *Mobile power supply unit manufrs*

▶ Drill Core Wednesbury Ltd, Ward House, Leabrook Road, Wednesbury, West Midlands, WS10 7NW Tel: 0121-556 3377 Fax: 0121-556 3382

Drill Cut Ltd, 3 Verulam Court, St. Albans Road, Stafford, ST16 3DT Tel: (01785) 240045 Fax: (01952) 820822 E-mail: info@drill-cut.freeserve.co.uk *Diamond drilling & sawing manufrs*

Drill Service Horley Ltd, 23 Albert Road, Horley, Surrey, RH6 7HR Tel: (01293) 774911 Fax: (01293) 820463 E-mail: sales@drill-service.co.uk *Cutting tool manufrs, small drilling specialists & CNC drilling machine manufrs*

Drill Sharp, Unit 22a Orgreave Crescent, Handsworth, Sheffield, S13 9NQ Tel: 0114-269 1664 Fax: 0114-288 0266 E-mail: rog@moorlandeng.co.uk *Mining & rock drilling tool manufrs*

Drill Supply Ltd, 41 Green Lane, Lower Kingswood, Tadworth, Surrey, KT20 6TJ Tel: (01737) 832820 Fax: (01737) 833025 E-mail: drillsupply@onetel.com *Drilling equipment suppliers*

▶ Drillcut Ltd, Unit 4b Cadleigh Close, Lee Mill Industrial Estate, Ivybridge, Devon, PL21 9GB Tel: (01752) 691992 Fax: (01752) 691993

▶ Drillcut Ltd, 3 The Galloway Centre, Express Way, Newbury, Berkshire, RG14 5TL Tel: (01635) 49090 Fax: (01635) 49091

Drillfield Engineering Co. Ltd, Scott Works, Unit 1, Mannor Road, Mancetter, Atherstone, Warwickshire, CV9 1RG Tel: (01827) 712468 Fax: (01827) 714252 *Pipework fabricators*

Drilling Systems UK Ltd, Hurnview House, Bournemouth International Airport, Hurn, Christchurch, Dorset, BH23 6EW Tel: (01202) 582255 Fax: (01202) 582288 E-mail: info@drillingsystems.com *Drilling simulator manufrs*

Drillserve Ltd, Roscroggan Mill, Roscroggan, Camborne, Cornwall, TR14 0BA Tel: (01209) 710079 Fax: (01209) 717139 *Drill rig manufacturers & drilling contractors*

▶ Drilltec Ltd, Diamond House, Dencora Way, Sundon Park, Luton, LU3 3HP Tel: (01582) 564455 Fax: (01582) 847016 E-mail: fiona@drilltec.co.uk Sales Contact: N. Goss *Drilltec Ltd provides contracting services for diamond drilling, concrete sawing, diamond floor/wall sawing, rotary percussive drilling, chemical anchoring, silent/specialist demolition services, chasing. Drilltec Ltd based in Luton are a member of Drilling and Sawing Association.*

Drilltec International Ltd, Margarethe House, Eismann Way, Corby, Northamptonshire, NN17 5ZB Tel: (01536) 262877 Fax: (01536) 200580 E-mail: jane@drilltec-int.co.uk *Tubular protection goods manufrs*

Drillturn Engineering Ltd, Victoria Road West, Hebburn, Tyne & Wear, NE31 1UB Tel: 0191-483 5871 Fax: 0191-428 0391 E-mail: sales@drillturnengineering.co.uk *Precision & general engineers*

Dril-Quip (Europe) Ltd, Stoneywood Park, Stoneywood Road, Dyce, Aberdeen, AB21 7DZ Tel: (01224) 727000 Fax: (01224) 727070 *Drilling equipment manufrs*

James Dring Power Plant Ltd, 8 Eagle Road, Quarry Hill Industrial Estate, Ilkeston, Derbyshire, DE7 4RB Tel: 0115-944 0072 Fax: 0115-944 0235 E-mail: enquiries@jamesdring.co.uk *Manufacturers of control panels; frequency converters(rotary/dynamic/motor generator); generating sets, diesel driven; generators/ generating sets & pumps. Also distributors of diesel engine components/spare parts, electromechanical equipment/machinery spare parts & generating set spare parts. In addition, welding equipment, electric*

▶ Drink to Industry Ltd, Forrester House, 24 Oaktree Road, Fen Drayton, Cambridge, CB4 5SS Tel: 0845 22 11 343 E-mail: liz@drinktoindustry.co.uk *Marketing and business services for the drinks and industrial/ manufacturing sectors.*Marketing agency, marketing consultancy, public relations, drinks marketing, manufacturing marketing, industrial marketing, marketing, PR, marketing communications, website design, marketing strategy, marketing plan.*

Drinkmaster Holdings Ltd, Plymouth Road, Liskeard, Cornwall, PL14 3PG Tel: (01579) 342082 Fax: (01579) 342591 E-mail: info@drinkmaster.co.uk *Vending machine suppliers & ingredients*

Driscoll Bros Group Ltd, 59 Grasmere Road, Gatley, Cheadle, Cheshire, SK8 4RS Tel: 0161-428 2109 Fax: (01625) 548466 E-mail: glynn@driscollbros.co.uk *Exhibition stand fitters*

Driscoll & Crowley Ltd, 496a Barking Road, London, E13 8QB Tel: (020) 7511 9287 Fax: (020) 7473 3019 E-mail: info@driscoll-crowley.co.uk *Plumbing & heating contractors*

Drivall Ltd, Narrow Lane, Halesowen, West Midlands, B62 9PA Tel: 0121-423 1122 Fax: 0121-422 9498 E-mail: sales@drivall.com *Agricultural fencing tools manufrs*

▶ Drive Inc Ltd, 1 Rose Lane, Ripley, Woking, Surrey, GU23 6NE Tel: (01483) 211200 E-mail: info@drivein.co.uk *Design development studio, for product, automotive, transportation and packaging industries. Our services include concept development through to production data. We also provide photo realistic images and animations for design review, marketing and advertising material.**

Drive Design Ltd, Clayton Lodge, Clayton Lane, Clayton, Bradford, West Yorkshire, BD14 6RF Tel: (01274) 883070 Fax: (01274) 883061 E-mail: sales@drivedesignltd.co.uk *Bearings & castors distributors*

▶ Drive 'n' Shine, 427 Leatherhead Road, Chessington, Surrey, KT9 2NQ Tel: (0796) 0781193 E-mail: info@driveandshine.co.uk *Mobile Valeting Service, covering Surrey, Middx, SW London, NE Berkshire*

Drive Technics Ltd, 1 Langley Terrace Industrial Park, Latimer Road, Luton, LU1 3XQ Tel: (01582) 486679 Fax: (01582) 486676 *Conveyor belting manufrs*

Drive Technology Ltd, Bibsworth Lane, Broadway, Worcestershire, WR12 7LW Tel: (01386) 852089 *Computer software developers*

Drive Way Alarm, 15 West Street, Hothfield, Ashford, Kent, TN26 1ET Tel: (0870) 2240315 Fax: (0870) 7625903 E-mail: sales@drivewayalarm.co.uk *Electronics manufrs*

▶ Drivebuddy Ltd, Unit 3, Waterhouse Mill, Albert Street, Huddersfield, HD1 3PR Tel: (0870) 1657218 Fax: (0870) 0117748

Drivelink UK Ltd, 190 Kingsway South, Team Valley Trading Estate, Gateshead, Tyne & Wear, NE11 0SH Tel: 0191-491 3666 Fax: 0191-487 1255 E-mail: enquiries@drivelink.com *Automotive components manufrs*

▶ Driver Development UK Ltd, 3 Euston Close, Forest Park, Lincoln, LN6 0XG Tel: (01522) 839317 E-mail: driverdevelopment@yahoo.co.uk *Driver development (UK)ltd. offers defensive driver training, in association with RoSPA,by department of transport approved driving instructors. Training is available in cars, light goods vehicles, minibuses and coaches.Most of our training stafff are former emergency service instructors.*

Driver Hire, Swan Street, Leicester, LE3 5AW Tel: 0116-251 6700 E-mail: leicester@driverhire.co.uk *Recruitment agents*

Driver Hire, Unit 16 Enterprise House, Dalziel Street, Motherwell, Lanarkshire, ML1 1PJ Tel: (01698) 275444 Fax: (01698) 276555 E-mail: southampton@driver-hire.co.uk *Supplying workforce to transport industry*

Driver Hire, 476 Broadway, Chadderton, Oldham, OL9 9NS Tel: 0161-683 4333 Fax: 0161-683 8888 *Driver hire services*

Driver Hire, 108 Town Street, Stanningley, Pudsey, West Yorkshire, LS28 6EZ Tel: 0113-229 9400 Fax: 0113-229 9500 *Driver hire services*

Driver Hire, 4/Maple House, Wykeham Road Northminster Business Park, Upper Poppleton, York, YO26 6QW Tel: (01845) 6023652 Fax: (01904) 557647 E-mail: york@driver-hire.co.uk *Supplying workforce to transport & industry*

Driver Hire Group Services, Progress House, Castlefields Lane, Bingley, West Yorkshire, BD16 2AB Tel: (01274) 551166 Fax: (01274) 551165 E-mail: info@driver-hire.co.uk *Specialist temporary labour supplier* Also at: Branches throughout the U.K.

Driver Hire Nationwide, Moulton Park Business Centre, Redhouse Road, Moulton Park Industrial Estate, Northampton, NN3 6AQ Tel: (01604) 670199 Fax: (01604) 644872 E-mail: enquires@driver-hire.co.uk *Driver hire service providers*

Driver Southall Ltd, Unit 18 Maybrook Industrial Estate, Maybrook Road, Walsall, WS8 7DG Tel: (01543) 375566 Fax: (01543) 375979 E-mail: email@driversouthall.co.uk *Driver*

continued

Southall designs and manufactures Checkweighers, Vibratory Weighers and Vibratory Conveyors for the food packaging and processing industry, pharmaceutical packaging, direct mailing and security mailing. Driver Southall Checkweighers have been developed to enable manufacturers to ensure their products remain within specification and provide accuracy and reliability in the harshest of environments. Our checkweighers can be supplied as, part of a complete line or interfaced with existing equipment to handle various pack types, including envelopes, bags, trays and cartons.

▶ Driver Training (Central Scotland) Limited, Fir Park, Tillicoultry, Clackmannanshire, FK13 6PL Tel: (01259) 753600 Fax: (01259) 753600 E-mail: driver.training.ltd@hotmail.co.uk *LGV, Trailer Towing and Fleet Driver Training across Scotland. Qualified and Registered DSA & IAM LGV and Fleet Driver Instructors.*

Driveshield Ltd, Stockton Business Centre, 70-74 Brunswick Street, Stockton-on-Tees, Cleveland, TS18 1DW Tel: (01642) 608464 Fax: (07092) 077805 *Specialist vehicle electronics installation*

▶ Driveway Design, 2 Randolph Court, Randolph Industrial Estate, Kirkcaldy, Fife, KY1 2YY Tel: (01592) 654300 Fax: (01592) 654390

▶ Driveway Co Scotland Ltd, 69 Buchanan Street, Glasgow, G1 3HL Tel: 0141-314 3839 Fax: 0141-314 3738

▶ Driveways Scotland, Morningside Road, Edinburgh, EH10 4BF Tel: (0800) 0191139 Fax: 0131-331 4001 E-mail: info@drivewaysscotland.com *Leading designer & installer of monoblock driveways & patios*

▶ Driveways Stirling, 44 Morningside Road, Morningside, Edinburgh, EH10 4QN Tel: (0800) 0191139 E-mail: info@drivewaysdirectscotland.co.uk *Leading designer & installer of mono block & natural stone driveways*

DRM Laminates, Unit B11, Sywell Airport Business Park, Wellingborough Road, Sywell, Northampton, NN6 0BN Tel: (01604) 790377 Fax: (01604) 790266 *Engineering plastics, thermoplastics fabrications & machining*

▶ Droicon P.L.C, Trow Way, Diglis, Worcester, WR5 3BX Tel: (01905) 763445 Fax: (01905) 356423 E-mail: sales@droicon.co.uk *Civil engineers electrical*

▶ Droitwich Fabrication & Installation Services Ltd, 10 North St Industrial Estate, Droitwich, Worcestershire, WR9 8JB Tel: (01905) 775096 Fax: (01905) 775880 E-mail: droitwich.fabs@virgin.net *Ventilation equipment*

▶ Droitwich Glass Fibre Mouldings Ltd, Hangar 5, Long Lane, Throckmorton, Pershore, Worcestershire, WR10 2JH Tel: (01386) 555787 Fax: (01386) 555748 E-mail: glassfibres@btconnect.com *We undertake a range of projects from all around the country, from concept to completion we are able to help. We manufacture glassfibre products for all industries including GRP and hand sprayed applications. We also manufacture and supply a complete range of truck tops. Save money, call us now!!*

Droitwich Plastics Ltd, Wassage Way, Hampton Lovett, Droitwich, Worcestershire, WR9 0NX Tel: (01905) 796709 Fax: (01905) 796067 *Plastic injection mouldings manufrs*

Droitwich Road Aquatics, Droitwich Road, Claines, Worcester, WR3 7SW Tel: (01905) 757376 Fax: (01905) 452242 *Aquatic centre*

▶ Drom UK Ltd, Trackside Business Centre, Abbot Close, Byfleet, West Byfleet, Surrey, KT14 7JN Tel: (01932) 355655 Fax: (01932) 250351 E-mail: info@dromuk.com *Sauna retailers*

▶ Dron & Dickson Ltd, Cumberland Place, Lowestoft, Suffolk, NR32 1UQ Tel: (01502) 539991 Fax: (01502) 584719 E-mail: info@drondickson.co.uk *Hazardous & industrial area electrical equipment consultants*

▶ Dron & Dickson, Unit 203 Vale Enterprise Centre, Hayes Road, Sully, Penarth, South Glamorgan, CF64 5SY Tel: (01446) 741310 Fax: (01446) 741312 E-mail: info@drondickson.co.uk *Industrial electrical equipment suppliers, installers, service*

▶ Dron & Dickson, The Innovation Centre, Vienna Court, Kirkleatham Business Park, Redcar, Cleveland, TS10 5SH Tel: (01642) 777990 Fax: (01642) 777990 E-mail: info@drondickson.co.uk *Hazardous & electrical equipment contractors*

Dron & Dickson Group, Craigshaw Road, West Tullos Industrial Estate, Aberdeen, AB12 3AR Tel: (01224) 874554 Fax: (01224) 895220 E-mail: info@drondickson.co.uk *Hazardous & industrial area electrical equipment service engineers*

John Dron Ltd, 43 Blundells Road, Bradville, Milton Keynes, MK13 7HD Tel: (01908) 311388 Fax: (01908) 222200 E-mail: sales@johndron.co.uk *Hotel textiles & linens*

Dron & Wright, 80 Cannon Street, London, EC4N 6HL Tel: (020) 7891 2300 Fax: (020) 7891 2300 E-mail: droncity@dronwright.co.uk *Surveyors/estate agents & valuers*

▶ Dronfield Storage Centre, Rosemarie House, Wreakes Lane, Dronfield, Derbyshire, S18 1PN Tel: (01246) 290290 Fax: (01246) 290348

D-Room Ltd, 14 Bark Street East, Bolton, BL1 2BQ Tel: (01204) 382599 Fax: (01204) 382461 E-mail: info@d-room.co.uk *Graphic design & marketing consultants services*

Drop In The Ocean, 17 City Arcade, Coventry, CV1 3HX Tel: (024) 7622 5273 Fax: (024) 7622 5273 *Health food merchants*

Droveleigh Ltd, Murray Street, Grimsby, South Humberside, DN31 3RD Tel: (01472) 352131 Fax: (01472) 240956 *Fish salesmen, agents & chandlers*

Drs Technoli UK Ltd, Lynwood House, Farnham Trading Estate, Farnham, Surrey, GU9 9NN Tel: (01252) 730500 Fax: (01252) 730530 E-mail: helpdesk@drs-tsl.com *Rugged computing manufrs*

Company Information

▶ indicates data change since last edition

▶ Druckers Vienna Patisserie, 100 Great Western Arcade, Birmingham, B2 5HU Tel: 0121-236 6292 Fax: 0121-236 6292 *Baking ingredient manufrs*

Druckers Vienna Patisserie, 940a Stratford Road, Sparkhill, Birmingham, B11 4BU Tel: 0121-777 3427 Fax: 0121-777 3427 *Patisserie*

▶ Drug & Alcohol Training, 15 Eilean Rise, Ellon, Aberdeenshire, AB41 9NF Tel: (01358) 729547 Fax: (01358) 729547 E-mail: les@datacservices.co.uk *Datac Services provides a UK wide consultancy service for companies and employers to advise on workplace substance misuse policy development and implementation, and provides drug and alcohol awareness training for managers and staff*

Drum Closures Ltd, Borwick Rails, Millom, Cumbria, LA18 4JT Tel: (01229) 772101 Fax: (01229) 774972 E-mail: sales@drum-closures.co.uk Principal Export Areas: Worldwide *Manufacturers of drum closures*

Drum Interior Systems Ltd, 2 Thatchers Close, Horley, Surrey, RH6 9LE Tel: (01293) 774422 Fax: (01293) 775204 E-mail: isiparts@aol.com *Office partitioning suppliers*

Drum International Ltd, Springmill Street, Bradford, West Yorkshire, BD5 7YH Tel: (01274) 718100 Fax: (01274) 718101 E-mail: sales@eu.gardnerdenver.com *Compressor & pump manufrs*

Drum Technology, 2 Green Lane, Hull, HU2 0HG Tel: (01482) 223824 Fax: (01482) 223824 E-mail: user@drumtech.karoo.co.uk Principal Export Areas: Worldwide *Manufacturers of drum & industrial washing equipment*

▶ Drumbow Homes Ltd, Drumbow Farm, Caldercruix, Airdrie, Lanarkshire, ML6 7RX Tel: (01236) 842296

▶ Drumderg Joinery, 1a Lismacloskey Road, Antrim, BT41 3RA Tel: (028) 7965 0198 Fax: (028) 7965 9106

▶ Drumland UK, Langney Road, Eastbourne, East Sussex, BN21 3JP Tel: (01323) 636142 Fax: (01323) 649100 *Drum retailers*

▶ Drummond Associates, 37 Duffryn Avenue, Cardiff, CF23 6LE Tel: (029) 2076 4555 Fax: (029) 2076 4555 E-mail: info@drummondassociates.co.uk *Marketing & IT consultants*

▶ Drummond Distribution, Eastmains Freight Centre, 1 Bathgate Road, Armadale, Bathgate, West Lothian, EH48 2PE Tel: (01501) 730221 Fax: (01501) 732981 E-mail: sales@drummond-distribution.co.uk

Drummond Parkland Of England, Park Valley Mills, Meltham Road, Huddersfield, HD4 7BH Tel: (01484) 668400 Fax: (01484) 668570 *Piece dye & colour woven fabrics* Also at: Huddersfield

▶ Drummond Security Ltd, 44 The Broadway, Darkes Lane, Potters Bar, Hertfordshire, EN6 2HW Tel: (01707) 644454 Fax: (01707) 651314 E-mail: enquiries@drummondsecurity.com *General security services*

Drummond Of York, Bloom House, Intake Lane, Dunnington, York, YO19 5NY Tel: (01904) 488978 Fax: (01904) 488046 *Machine tool stockists*

▶ Drummonds Kitchens & Bedrooms, 116 New Road Side, Horsforth, Leeds, LS18 4QB Tel: 0113-258 8588 Fax: 0113-258 8588 E-mail: eddie.drummond@btconnect.com *Designers & installers of bespoke farmhouse country kitchens*

▶ Drummotors & More, 49 Cyprus Road, Leicester, LE2 8QT Tel: 0116-283 8344 Fax: 0116-283 1544 E-mail: sales@drummotorsandmore.com *Power transmission equipment distributors*

Drumstar Ltd, Omega House, 17a Dereham Road, Mattishall, Dereham, Norfolk, NR20 3AA Tel: (01362) 858888 Fax: (01362) 858884 E-mail: sales@drumstar.fsnet.co.uk *Vehicle export specialists*

Drury Adams Ltd, New Hey Mill, Newchurch Road, Bacup, Lancashire, OL13 0BH Tel: (01706) 874000 Fax: (01706) 874747 E-mail: sales@druryadams.co.uk *Foam converters*

Drury Casement Co. Ltd, Blakemore Road, West Bromwich, West Midlands, B70 8JF Tel: 0121-553 2198 Fax: 0121-553 2301 E-mail: garry.jones@btclick.com *Metal & PVC window manufrs*

F. Drury Ltd, 5 Gilleyfield Avenue, Sheffield, S17 3NS Tel: 0114-236 7907 Fax: 0114-236 7907 *Silversmiths manufrs*

▶ Drury P S M Ltd, Ashfield House, Stewart Close, Bradford, West Yorkshire, BD2 2EE Tel: (01274) 626200 Fax: (01274) 626222 E-mail: info@drurypsm.com *Health & safety & other training services*

Drury Smart, 148 Brierley Road, Walton Summit Centre, Bamber Bridge, Preston, PR5 8AH Tel: (01704) 533243 Fax: (01772) 318400 *Packaging & storage contractors*

Drurys Engineering Ltd, 21 Knowl Piece, Wilbury Way, Hitchin, Hertfordshire, SG4 0TY Tel: (01462) 420123 Fax: (01462) 420124 E-mail: info@drurys.co.uk *Precision engineers*

Dry Cleaning & Laundry Services, 34 Mayfield Industrial Estate, Dalkeith, Midlothian, EH22 4AD Tel: 0131-663 5956 Fax: 0131-654 2102 E-mail: info@dlsdls.co.uk *Cleaning appliance distributors*

▶ Dry Riser Services, Ashdown House, Well Hill Lane, Orpington, Kent, BR6 7QJ Tel: (01959) 533838 Fax: (01959) 534848 *Test firefighting equipment suppliers*

Dry Transfers Ltd, 1 Jubilee Street, Melton Mowbray, Leicestershire, LE13 1ND Tel: (01664) 565785 Fax: (01664) 410344 E-mail: sales@dry-transfers.co.uk *Screen printers & sign manufrs*

▶ Drya UK Ltd, 33 Goodrich Close, Muxton, Telford, Shropshire, TF2 8SN Tel: (01952) 605932

Drymat Supplies, Top Lodge, 3 Decker Hill, Decker Hill, Shifnal, Shropshire, TF11 8QW Tel: (01952) 463747 Fax: (01952) 463905 *Plastic engineers*

▶ Drymen Pottery, Main Street, Drymen, Glasgow, G63 0BJ Tel: (01360) 660458 Fax: (01360) 660211 *Cafe, pub*

▶ DRY-OFF (UK) LTD, 23 Castalia Square, Docklands, London, UK, E14 3NG Tel: 0207 5441474 Fax: 0207 5441499 E-mail: EDWARD@DRY-OFF.COM *import and export of different products.*

Drysdale Brothers (Larbert) Ltd, 346 Main Street, Stenhousemuir, Larbert, Stirlingshire, FK5 3JR Tel: (01324) 562447 Fax: (01324) 556726 E-mail: enquiries@drysdalebrothers.com *Drysdale Brothers is a fully automated foundry and engineering company. We specialise in complex finished machined, pressure tight castings produced in Gunmetal and Aluminium Bronze.*

▶ Drysdale Freight, The Courtyard Tower Farm, Cockburnspath, Berwickshire, TD13 5YU Tel: (01368) 830640 Fax: (01368) 830730

Drysdale Timber & Mouldings Ltd, 36-38 River Road, Barking, Essex, IG11 0DN Tel: (020) 8594 6004 Fax: (020) 8594 1089 E-mail: sales@blumsom.co.uk *Timber importers & moulding manufrs*

Drytec Contract Processing Ltd, Unit K3, 46 Morley Road, Tonbridge, Kent, TN9 1RA Tel: (01732) 362611 Fax: (01732) 770776 E-mail: drytecltd@aol.com *Contract dryers*

Drywite Ltd, PO Box 1, Halesowen, West Midlands, B63 2RB Tel: (01384) 569556 Fax: (01384) 410583 E-mail: enquiries@drywite.co.uk *Manufacturers of peeled potato preservative & catering equipment*

▶ D's Auto Electrical, Unit 15 Orchard, Newbury Road, Kingsclere, Newbury, Berkshire, RG20 4SY Tel: (07796) 268848 E-mail: maria@dsauto.co.uk *Auto Electrical, Toad,Sigma and Autowatch Alarm Systms, RAC Tracking, Sat Navigation, Thatcham Cat 1, Thatcham Cat 2, VSIB approved, ICE, Hands free Phone Kits, Reverse Parking sensors, Reversing Cameras,Tow bars, Multi Media, Honda CRX Transtop roof specialist, Lexus LS400 flickering dash light repairs, Trade and public*

DS Developments, Unit 41a Hobbs Industrial Estate, Newchapel, Lingfield, Surrey, RH7 6HN Tel: (01342) 835444 Fax: (01342) 832277 E-mail: sales@dsdevelopments.co.uk *Manufacturers of water proof communications systems*

▶ DS Digital Video, The Corner Cot, Guildford Road, Chertsey, Surrey, KT16 9RU Tel: 08709 220032 Fax: 08707 601171 E-mail: admin@dsdigitalvideo.co.uk *Video production, editing, dvd authoring & duplication services*

▶ DSB Cleaning Services, Park Court Offices, 43-45 Rhosddu Road, Wrexham, Clwyd, LL11 2NS Tel: (01978) 352900 Fax: (01978) 355027 E-mail: info@dsbcleaningservices.co.uk *Family run business, windows, general cleaning*

▶ DSC Showcases, Merrill Ville, Enborne Row, Wash Water, Newbury, Berkshire, RG20 0LX Tel: (01635) 34656 Fax: (01635) 34656 E-mail: admin@dscshowcases.co.uk *Builders of display cabinets*

DSD Construction Ltd, Robert Street, Carlisle, CA2 5AN Tel: (01228) 594969 Fax: (01228) 598588 E-mail: admin@dsdconstruction.com *Civil engineers & surfacing contractors*

▶ DSF Delmec Ltd, Unit 2 Harrison Street, Blackburn, BB2 2JN Tel: (01254) 279271 Fax: (01254) 279274

Dsi, Empire Centre, Imperial Way, Watford, WD24 4YH Tel: (01923) 800430 Fax: (01923) 800556 *Computer systems consultants*

Dsi Business Support Ltd, 73 Whitby Road, Slough, SL1 3DR Tel: (01753) 714000 Fax: (01753) 714005 *Mailings lists*

DSI International Ltd, Unit 6, Abbey Road Enterprise Park, Neath, West Glamorgan, SA10 7DN Tel: (01639) 645400 Fax: (01639) 644664 E-mail: sales@aquapur950.com *Manufacture & supply water purification tank*

▶ D-Signs, Unit 44-45 51 Dungannon Road, Coalisland, Dungannon, County Tyrone, BT71 4HP Tel: (028) 8774 7844 Fax: (0870) 0469435 E-mail: info@d-signsonline.com

▶ DSL - installations, Unit , Farnborough Business Center, Eelmoor Road, Farnborough, Hampshire, GU14 7XA Tel: 01252 514228 Fax: 01252 547732 E-mail: info@dsl-installations.co.uk *We are experts at fitting wet floor showers, level access, low level and low step-in shower trays. We have specialist knowledge specifically in designing bathrooms where there is a special need, We use the best available products to transform any bathroom into the bathroom of your dreams.*

DSL Systems Holdings Ltd, Adbolton Hall Adbolton Lane, West Bridgford, Nottingham, NG2 5AS Tel: 0115-981 3700 Fax: 0115-813702 E-mail: mail@dsl-systems.com *Process engineering consultants & designers*

DSM, Delves Road, Heanor Gate Industrial Estate, Heanor, Derbyshire, DE75 7SG Tel: (01773) 536500 Fax: (01773) 536600 *Chemicals*

DSM, Riverside Works, Huddersfield Road, Mirfield, West Yorkshire, WF14 9DL Tel: (01924) 490781 Fax: (01924) 491128 E-mail: sales@dsm-group.co.uk *Rope & webbing strap manufrs*

DSM UK Ltd, D S M House, Paper Mill Drive, Redditch, Worcestershire, B98 8QJ Tel: (01527) 590590 Fax: (01527) 590555 E-mail: sales@dsm.com *Polymer raw materials suppliers*

DSSR, 9 Crown Terrace, Glasgow, G12 9EY Tel: 0141-334 6161 Fax: 0141-357 1993 E-mail: glasgow@dssr.co.uk *Mechanical & electrical engineering consultants* Also at: Aberdeen, Bristol, London W5 & Manchester

DST Engineering Ltd, 17 Chapmans Brae, Bathgate, West Lothian, EH48 4LH Tel: (01506) 631196 Fax: (01506) 634873 *Dust extraction system suppliers & installation services*

Dsys Plus Ltd, Swan Business Centre, Fishers Lane, London, W4 1RX Tel: (020) 8994 5050 Fax: (020) 8994 0510 *PC support*

Dtas Ltd, Low Common Road, Dinnington, Sheffield, S25 2RJ Tel: (01909) 552470 Fax: (01909) 552472 E-mail: info@dtas-diamonds.co.uk *DTAS is the home of the DURO ranges of diamond tools, used every day by construction professionals throughout the UK. For details of where to purchase our tools visit our website*

continued

DTC Surfacing, Birchmere, Balmedie, Aberdeen, AB23 8YS Tel: (01358) 742368 Fax: (01358) 742020 E-mail: info@dtcsurfacing.co.uk *Civil engineers*

Dtec Computers, White Ox Building, Inglewood Road, Penrith, Cumbria, CA11 8QN Tel: (01768) 895600 Fax: (01768) 895700 *Build computers (hardware)*

Dtech Catering Ltd, Wedgwood Works, Ravensdale, Stoke-On-Trent, ST6 4NU Tel: (01782) 817521 Fax: (01782) 817520 *Catering equipment manufrs*

DTM Olympic, Unit 10a Griffin Industrial Estate, Rowley Regis, West Midlands, B65 0SN Tel: 0121-559 8431 Fax: 0121-559 7551 *Metal fabricators*

D-trak Ltd, 8 Becket Way, Laverstock, Salisbury, SP1 1PZ Tel: (01722) 415144 Fax: (01722) 415143 E-mail: info@d-trak.com *Computer consultants*

DTS Computer Print Ltd, Adams Street, Birmingham, B7 4LT Tel: 0121-359 5551 Fax: 0121-359 7300 E-mail: sales@dts-ltd.com *Continuous stationery manufrs*

DTS Process Technologies Ltd, Meiklewood Business Park, Glasgow Road, Kilmarnock, Ayrshire, KA3 6AG Tel: (01563) 534713 Fax: (01563) 532543 E-mail: info@dtsprocess.com *DTS distribute a range of production consumables and equipment, cleaning products and special lubricants into various industry sectors*

Du Pont UK Ltd, Wedgewood Way, Stevenage, Hertfordshire, SG1 4QN Tel: (01438) 734000 Fax: (01438) 734836 E-mail: enquiries@dupontpharma.com Principal Export Areas: Worldwide *Chemical manufrs*

Du Pre plc, Unit 3-4 The Vo-Tec Centre, Hambridge Lane, Newbury, Berkshire, RG14 5TN Tel: (01635) 555555 Fax: (01635) 555533 E-mail: sales@dupre.co.uk *Telecommunications, IT, LAN, WAN, Calls, Lines, supply, installation and support.*

Dual Brown, Ross Road, Stockton-on-Tees, Cleveland, TS18 2NH Tel: (01642) 602226 Fax: (01642) 602227 *Metal fabricators*

Dual Metallising Ltd, Units 12-14 The Business Centre, James Rd, Tyseley, Birmingham, B11 2BA Tel: 0121-708 2748 Fax: 0121-708 2256 E-mail: sales@dual-metallising.co.uk *Based in Birmingham, covering the whole of the UK, we are an independent supplier of most types of injection mouldings, vacuum metallising, paint spraying, including: decorative mouldings, plastic mouldings, point of sale items, fashion jewellery mouldings, Trophy mouldings, Mining Reflectors, beacon reflectors, automotive prototypes, Decorative embellishments, plastic curtain accessories, paint spraying finishing, and much more. Dual Metallising Ltd provides an excellent service in both the technical advice given and the supply of the correct product for your specific needs.*

Dualit Ltd, County Oak Way, Crawley, West Sussex, RH11 7ST Tel: (01293) 652500 Fax: (01293) 652555 E-mail: sales@dualit.com *Electric toaster makers*

Dub Clothing Mnfrs, Thurland Chambers, 4-6 Thurland Street, Nottingham, NG1 3DR Tel: 0115-924 3166 Fax: 0115-924 3166 E-mail: sales@dubclothing.com *Garment producers*

Dubb Bros Ltd, 121 Soho Hill, Birmingham, B19 1AX Tel: 0121-554 6492 Fax: 0121-554 6759 *Clothing manufrs*

Dubb Fashions, 1-3 Rawlings Road, Smethwick, West Midlands, B67 5AD Tel: 0121-420 2707 Fax: 0121-434 4050 *Clothing manufrs*

Dubilier Electronic Component Distributors, Station House Station Yard Industrial Park, Station Road, Dunmow, Essex, CM6 1XD Tel: (01371) 875758 Fax: (01371) 875075 E-mail: sales@dubilier.co.uk *Electronic component distributors*

Dubois Ltd, Arkwright Road, Willowbrook North Industrial Estate, Corby, Northamptonshire, NN17 5AE Tel: (01536) 274800 Fax: (01536) 274902 E-mail: huw.lewis@uk.ag.media.com Principal Export Areas: Worldwide *Manufrs of plastic mouldings*

▶ Ducane Europe, 7 The Avenue, Sunbury-on-Thames, Middlesex, TW16 5HT Tel: (01932) 770002 Fax: (01932) 770015 *Barbecues distributors*

Ducatt Heating Co. Ltd, Platts Road, Stourbridge, West Midlands, DY8 4YT Tel: (01384) 394641 Fax: (01384) 440455 E-mail: info@ducattheating.co.uk *Air conditioning, heating & ventilation engineers*

T.M. Duche & Sons Ltd, 16A Hall Road, Wilmslow, Cheshire, SK9 5BN Tel: (01625) 538530 Fax: (01625) 538540 E-mail: info@tmduche.com *Commodity merchants*

▶ Duchess China Ltd, Uttoxeter Road, Stoke-on-Trent, ST3 1NX Tel: (01782) 313061 Fax: (01782) 314589

Duchy Alarms, Silverwell, Blackwater, Truro, Cornwall, TR4 8JG Tel: (01872) 560560 Fax: (01872) 560041 E-mail: irg@duchyalarms.co.uk *Security system services*

▶ Duck - Feet, Elm Cottagewinchester Rdkings Somborne, Kings Somborne, Stockbridge, Hampshire, SO20 6NZ Tel: (01794) 388672 E-mail: andrea@duck-feet.com *web design and graphic design specialists providing highly creative and practical solutions. From Logos and brochures to large ecommerce websites. Personal service and highly competitive rates, based near winchester*

Duckworth & Kent Ltd, Terence House, 7 Marquis Business Centre, Royston Road, Baldock, Hertfordshire, SG7 6XL Tel: (01462) 893254 Fax: (01462) 896288 E-mail: info@duckworth-and-kent.com *Titanium instrument manufrs*

Duckworth & Kent Reading Ltd, 113 Armour Road, Tilehurst, Reading, RG31 6HB Tel: 0118-942 9828 Fax: 0118-945 1191 E-mail: duckworth.kent@btconnect.com *Precision engineers*

Duco Ltd, Nelson Road, Newcastle upon Tyne, NE6 3NL Tel: 0191-295 0303 Fax: 0191-295 0842 E-mail: ducosbd@uk.coflexip.com *Umbilical systems designers & manufrs*

Duco International Ltd, Eastbourne Road, Slough, SL1 4SF Tel: (01753) 522274 Fax: (01753) 691952 E-mail: info@duco.co.uk *Printers blanket manufrs* Also at: Swindon

Duct Com Ltd, 94 Shrewsbury Lane, London, Greater London, SE18 3JL Tel: 0208 3172563 Fax: 0208 3174554 E-mail: info@ductcom.com *Designers, suppliers and installers of commercial and industrial air-conditioning and ventilation systems. Restaurant kitchen extract systems and canopies. Specialist ductwork suppliers and contractors.*

Duct Engineering Luton Ltd, Cradock Industrial Estate, Cradock Road, Luton, LU4 0JF Tel: (01582) 562626 Fax: (01582) 583046 E-mail: ductengineering@aol.com *Manufacturers of fire dampers, damper regulators & controlling dampers*

Duct Products, 2 Greenway, Conlig, Newtownards, County Down, BT23 7SU Tel: (028) 9147 1121 Fax: (028) 9147 9252 E-mail: postbox@ductproducts.com *Ventilation equipment manufrs*

Ductair Electrics Ltd, Unit 10c Castle Vale Industrial Estate, Maybrook Road, Castle Vale Industrial Estate, Sutton Coldfield, West Midlands, B76 1AL Tel: 0121-351 5742 Fax: 0121-313 1018 *Electric heater manufrs*

Ductaire Fabrications Ltd, G Marmi Works, 23 Grafton Road, Croydon, CR0 3RP Tel: (020) 8688 5188 Fax: (020) 8681 2606 E-mail: sales@ductaire.co.uk *Sheet metalwork engineers*

Ductavent Ltd, Gerrard Place, Skelmersdale, Lancashire, WN8 9SG Tel: (01695) 720368 Fax: (01695) 50618 E-mail: ductavents@aol.com *Steel fabricators*

Ducted Air Systems Ltd, 101 Sadler Road, Lincoln, LN6 3RS Tel: (01522) 682239 Fax: (01522) 883002 E-mail: nev@ductedair.com *Sheet metal ductwork contractors*

Ductile Castings Ltd, Trent Foundary, Dawes Lane, Scunthorpe, South Humberside, DN15 6UW Tel: (01724) 862152 Fax: (01724) 280461 E-mail: info@ductile.co.uk Principal Export Areas: Worldwide *Manufacturers of castings (alloy iron), iron castings*

Ductile Steel Processors, Planetary Industrial Estate, Planetary Road, Willenhall, West Midlands, WV13 3XP Tel: (01902) 303230 Fax: (01902) 303231 *Laboratory testing services*

Ductile Stourbridge Cold Mills Ltd, PO Box 13, Willenhall, West Midlands, WV13 1HQ Tel: (01902) 365400 Fax: (01902) 365444 E-mail: info@dscm.co.uk *Cold rolled steel strip producers*

Ductmann Ltd, Withy Road Industrial Estate, Withy Road, Bilston, West Midlands, WV14 0RX Tel: (01902) 492292 Fax: (01902) 408199 E-mail: sales@ductmann.co.uk *General sheet metal work& dust extraction plant manufrs*

Ductmate (Europe) Ltd, Arrol Road, Wesker Gourdie Industrial Estate, Dundee, DD2 4TH Tel: (01382) 622111 Fax: (01382) 621444 E-mail: sales@ductmate.co.uk *Duct jointing systems & accessories*

Ductwork Accessories Ltd, Haldon House, 385 Brettell Lane, Brierley Hill, West Midlands, DY5 3LQ Tel: (01384) 571767 Fax: (01384) 571767 *Flexible connection manufrs*

Ductwork By Design Ltd, Unit 7, 193 Garth Rd, Morden, Surrey, SM4 4LZ Tel: (020) 8330 0091 Fax: (020) 8330 0103 E-mail: info@dbdltd.com *Ductwork manufrs*

Ductwork & Fabrication Ltd, Dashwood Avenue, High Wycombe, Buckinghamshire, HP12 3DP Tel: (01494) 523935 Fax: (01494) 461970 E-mail: enquiries@cas-hw.demon.co.uk *Ductwork manufrs*

Ductwork Projects Ltd, Unit 303-305 Woolsbridge Industrial Park, Woolsbridge Industrial Estate, Three Legged Cross, Wimborne, Dorset, BH21 6SX Tel: (01202) 823621 Fax: (01202) 823744 E-mail: enquiries@dpl-kvd.co.uk *Air conditioning & ductwork contractors services*

Ductwork Wolverhampton Ltd, Unit 10-11, Spring Road, Ettingshall, Wolverhampton, WV4 6JT Tel: (01902) 353984 Fax: (01902) 353985 *Ductwork contractors & manufrs*

Duddon Tyres, Hindpool Road, Barrow-in-Furness, Cumbria, LA14 2ND Tel: (01229) 838537 Fax: (01229) 870757 *Tyre wholesalers*

Edward Dudfield Ltd, 4 Whilems Works, Forest Road, Ilford, Essex, IG6 3HJ Tel: (020) 8500 4455 Fax: (020) 8500 4488 E-mail: sales@dudfields.co.uk *Commercial colour printers*

Dudley College Of Technology, The Broadway, Dudley, West Midlands, DY1 4AS Tel: (01384) 363363 Fax: (01384) 363311 E-mail: christine.richards@dudleycol.ac.uk *College of further education*

Dudley Factory Doors Ltd, Unit G6, Grice Street, West Bromwich, West Midlands, B70 7EZ Tel: 0121-555 8989 Fax: 0121-558 4616 *Industrial door manufrs*

Frank Dudley Ltd, Unit 2 Wiggin Street, Hockley, Birmingham, B16 0AH Tel: 0121-523 0742 Fax: 0121-452 8159 E-mail: sales@frankdudley.com *Metal pressings manufrs*

Dudley H B S Ltd, Suite 1 Beaufighter House, Alpha 319, Chertsey Road, Chobham, Surrey, GU24 8HW Tel: (0870) 4442884 Fax: (0870) 4442885 E-mail: steve@howarine.co.uk *Office furniture distributors*

▶ Dudley Hunt, Unit 7, Blair Atholl Sawmill Yard, Blair Atholl, Pitlochry, Perthshire, PH18 5TL Tel: (01796) 482105 Fax: (01796) 481493 *Tablet dispensers*

Dudley Industries, Preston Road, Lytham St. Annes, Lancashire, FY8 5AT Tel: (01253) 738311 Fax: (01253) 794393 E-mail: dudley@cyberscape.net *Hygienic environment display system manufrs*

Dudley Inkwell, Howerine House, 5-6 Empire Way, Wembley, Middlesex, HA9 0XA Tel: (0870) 4442882 Fax: (0870) 4442883 E-mail: sales@dudley.co.uk *Stationers & office suppliers*

Dudley Iron & Steel Co. Ltd, Unit 8, Tividale, Oldbury, West Midlands, B69 3HU Tel: 0121-601 5000 Fax: 0121-601 5001 E-mail: sales@dudley-iron-steel.co.uk *Steel tube stockholders*

Dudley Jenkins List Broking, City Bridge House, 57 Southwark St, London, SE1 1RU Tel: (020) 7871 9070 Fax: (020) 7871 9071 E-mail: broking@djlb.co.uk *Direct mail list brokers*

Dudley Machine Tool Centre Ltd, High Street, Cleobury Mortimer, Kidderminster, Worcestershire, DY14 8DS Tel: (01299) 270474 Fax: (01299) 271342 E-mail: sales@dudleymachine.co.uk *Machine tool merchants*

Dudley Mixed, Peartree Lane, Dudley, West Midlands, DY2 0UU Tel: (01384) 242474 Fax: (01384) 242499 *Ready mixed concrete producers*

Dudley Office Products Ltd, 5-6 Empire Way, Wembley, Middlesex, HA9 0XA Tel: (020) 8980 7199 Fax: (0870) 4442883 E-mail: sales@dudley.co.uk *Office stationary suppliers*

▶ Peter Dudley Exhibitions & Displays, Uttoxer Road, Blithbury, Rugeley, Staffordshire, WS15 3JG Tel: (01889) 504284 Fax: (01889) 504284 *Sign & display manufrs*

Dudley Print, 2 The Sling, Dudley, West Midlands, DY2 9AJ Tel: (01384) 455316 Fax: (01384) 457519 E-mail: dudley.print@virgin.net *General printing & design*

Dudley Safes Ltd, Unit 17 Deepdale Works, Deepdale Lane, Upper Gornal, Dudley, West Midlands, DY3 2AF Tel: (01384) 239991 Fax: (01384) 455129 E-mail: sales@dudleysafes.com *Fire resistant safe manufrs*

Dudley Surgical Appliances Ltd, Horseley Heath, Tipton, West Midlands, DY4 7AA Tel: 0121-557 4204 Fax: 0121-520 1283 E-mail: dudsurg@aol.com *Footwear & orthopaedic specialists*

Dudley Tool & Engineering Co. Ltd, Mill Street, Wordsley, Stourbridge, West Midlands, DY8 5SX Tel: (01384) 571181 Fax: (01384) 265435 E-mail: info@dudley-tool.co.uk *General pressworkers & toolmakers*

Dudley Tubes Ltd, Meadow Lane, Bilston, West Midlands, WV14 9NQ Tel: (01902) 671747 Fax: (01902) 354049 E-mail: dudleytubes@btconnect.com *Steel tube stockholders*

Dudson Ltd, 200 Scotia Road, Stoke-on-Trent, ST6 4JD Tel: (01782) 819337 Fax: (01782) 813230 E-mail: info@dudson-group.co.uk *Hotel chinaware & earthenware manufrs*

Due Diligence Advice Ltd, 83 Heavitree Road, Exeter, EX1 2ND Tel: (01392) 431222 Fax: (01392) 422691 *Food analysis consultants*

▶ Duel, Unit 1 Parkers Yard, Marlborough Road, Ilfracombe, Devon, EX34 8JP Tel: (01271) 863397 Fax: (01271) 863024 E-mail: enquiries@duel-investigations.com *General Investigations, Matrimonial matters, serving of legal documents, people tracing, event security, premises security.*

Duerden, Lindal Moor Abbatior, Lindal In Furness, Ulverston, Cumbria, LA12 0LT Tel: (01229) 465619 Fax: (01229) 467218 *Abattoir distributors*

F. Duerr & Sons Ltd, Float Road, Roundthorn Industrial Estate, Manchester, M23 9DR Tel: 0161-226 2251 Fax: 0161-945 0143 E-mail: admin@duerrs.co.uk Principal Export Areas: West Europe *Jam manufrs*

Duferco UK Ltd, Buntsford Park Road, Bromsgrove, Worcestershire, B60 3DX Tel: (01527) 570509 Fax: (01527) 575274 *Steel distributors & manufrs*

M.G. Duff International Ltd, Unit 1 Timberlane Industrial Estate, Gravel Lane, Chichester, West Sussex, PO19 8PP Tel: (01243) 533336 Fax: (01243) 533422 E-mail: sales@mgduff.co.uk *Cathodic protection systems & hygienic cladding systems*

Duffield Printers Ltd, 421 Kirkstall Road, Leeds, LS4 2HA Tel: 0113-279 3011 Fax: 0113-231 0098 E-mail: info@duffieldprinters.co.uk *Printers*

Duffields Business Forms Ltd, 4 Nunn Brook Road, Huthwaite, Sutton-in-Ashfield, Nottinghamshire, NG17 2HU Tel: (01623) 440140 Fax: (01623) 440124 *Business form printers*

Dugard Logistics Ltd, 2 Sherwood Road, Bromsgrove, Worcestershire, B60 3DU Tel: (01527) 575947 Fax: (01527) 576100 E-mail: richardshowell@msn.com *Material handling equipment engineers*

Dugdale plc, Valley Mill, Holmes Road, Sowerby Bridge, West Yorkshire, HX6 2AA Tel: (01422) 832501 Fax: (01422) 833401 E-mail: sales@dugdaleplc.com Principal Export Areas: Central/East Europe *PVC compound manufrs*

▶ Dugdales, Skipton Auction Mart, Gargrave Road, Skipton, North Yorkshire, BD23 1UD Tel: (01756) 793530

Dugdales Electrical Engineers, Kirkgate, Settle, North Yorkshire, BD24 9DX Tel: (01729) 822337 Fax: (01729) 822785 E-mail: sales@dugdaleseuropean.com *Agricultural & electrical engineers* Also at: Skipton

Duggan Transport Ltd, Church Road, Shilton, Coventry, CV7 9HX Tel: (024) 7661 2871 Fax: (024) 7661 2871 *Road transport, haulage & freight services*

James Duke, Little Ham Barn, Ham Road, Ham, Chichester, West Sussex, PO20 7NY Tel: (01243) 641441 Fax: (01243) 641708 E-mail: dairytec@dircon.co.uk *Agriculture engineers*

Duke Street Textiles, 65 St Marys Road, Garston, Liverpool, L19 2NL Tel: 0151-427 4080 Fax: 0151-427 5000 E-mail: dukestreettextiles@virginnet.com *Clothing merchants*

Dukerswell Engineers Ltd, 52 Buckland Road, Maidstone, Kent, ME16 0SH Tel: (01622) 757710 Fax: (01622) 755516 E-mail: dukerswell@skynow.net *Cold casting stitching bars & tools*

Dulevo UK Ltd, Royds House Royds Mill, Leeds Road, Ossett, West Yorkshire, WF5 9YA Tel: (01924) 277026 Fax: (01924) 262074 E-mail: dulevo@dial.pipex.com *Floor cleaning & sweeping machine suppliers*

Dulex Decorators Ltd, 117-119 Hillingdon Hill, Uxbridge Road, Uxbridge, Middlesex, UB10 0JE Tel: (01895) 234523 Fax: (01895) 814359 E-mail: debcosales@zoom.co.uk *Decorators' merchants*

Dulux Ltd, Manchester Road, West Timperley, Altrincham, Cheshire, WA14 5PG Tel: 0161-968 3000 Fax: 0161-973 4202 *Wholesale decorators merchants*

Dulux Ltd, 60-72 New Town Row, Birmingham, B6 4HP Tel: 0121-359 5511 Fax: 0121-359 3537 *Decorators merchants* Also at: Branches throughout the U.K.

Dulux Ltd, Swansey Mill, Swansey Lane, Clayton-le-Woods, Chorley, Lancashire, PR6 7HY Tel: (01257) 269570 Fax: (01257) 269564 *Decorators merchants* Also at: Morecambe & Preston

Dulux Ltd, 66 Burleys Way, Leicester, LE1 3BD Tel: 0116-262 9471 Fax: 0116-251 2985 *Interior decoration & supply*

Dulux Ltd, Anglian House, Claydons Lane, Rayleigh, Essex, SS6 7UP Tel: (01268) 773891 Fax: (01268) 770314 *Decorators' supplies to the trade & retail*

R.L. Dumelow & Son, St. Matthews Street, Burton-On-Trent, Staffordshire, DE14 3DE Tel: (01283) 564292 Fax: (01283) 564292 *Stove enamellers*

▶ Dumfries Carriers, 12 Mosspark Road, Dumfries, DG1 4EE Tel: (01387) 266100 Fax: (01387) 266100 E-mail: samedaycourier@tiscali.co.uk *Dumfries Carriers are an independant Courier firm established and based in Dumfries since 1992. We only accept assignments we are confident we can undertake successfully within the agreed timescale. 24/7. Locally and Nationwide.*

Dun Fab Engineering Company Ltd, Coulman Street, Thorne, Doncaster, South Yorkshire, DN8 5JS Tel: (01405) 812165 Fax: (01405) 740333 E-mail: dunfabengineering@aol.com *Precision engineers*

Dunasfern Cable & Wire Suppliers, 24 Peverel Drive, Bletchley, Milton Keynes, MK1 1NW Tel: (01908) 647144 Fax: (01908) 270106 E-mail: dunasfern.sales@virgin.net *Telecom data & fibre optic specialists*

Alan Dunbar, Old Hall, Tough, Alford, Aberdeenshire, AB33 8ES Tel: (01975) 562664 Fax: (01975) 562741 *Vehicle body builders*

Dunbar & Boardman, 91-93 Great Eastern Street, London, EC2A 3HZ Tel: (020) 7739 5093 Fax: (020) 7739 5403 E-mail: mail@dunbarboardman.com *Lift consultants*

Dunbar Turning Ltd, 11 Tullykevin Road, Greyabbey, Newtownards, County Down, BT22 2QE Tel: (028) 4275 8231 Fax: (028) 4275 8193 E-mail: info@jhe-group.com *Precision engineering*

Dunblane Light Engineering Ltd, Stirling Road, Fallin, Stirling, FK7 7JB Tel: (01786) 818757 Fax: (01786) 818767 E-mail: john.swan@dle-eng.co.uk *Sub-contract machining & fabricators*

▶ Duncan, Glenfield Industrial Estate, Perth Road, Cowdenbeath, Fife, KY4 9HT Tel: (01383) 610956

Duncan & Associates, Jeeves Bank, Fernleigh Road, Grange-over-Sands, Cumbria, LA11 7HT Tel: (01539) 533857 Fax: (01539) 534963 E-mail: info@duncanandassociates.co.uk *Water sampling equipment suppliers*

▶ Duncan Bathroom Centre, 22-24 Auchmill Road, Bucksburn, Aberdeen, AB21 9LD Tel: (01224) 713330 Fax: (01224) 713310 E-mail: sales@dbc.demon.co.uk

▶ Duncan Collier Haulage, Block 1, Woodend Industrial Estate, Cowdenbeath, Fife, KY4 8HW Tel: (01383) 510329

Duncan Galliers, Corporation Lane, Shrewsbury, SY1 2PB Tel: (01743) 353981 Fax: (01743) 353981 *Upholstery manufrs*

Duncan Lynch Precision Tools Ltd, Unit E Weller Drive, Finchampstead, Wokingham, Berkshire, RG40 4QZ Tel: 0118-973 4845 Fax: 0118-973 0381 E-mail: sales@duncan-lynch.co.uk *Tool designers*

P. & C.A. Duncan, Stapleton Farm, Langtree, Torrington, Devon, EX38 8NP Tel: (01805) 601414 Fax: (01805) 601620 E-mail: sales@stapletonfarm.co.uk *Yogurt manufrs*

▶ Duncan Plant Hire Ltd, Gatehead Farm, Mansefield Road, New Cumnock, Cumnock, Ayrshire, KA18 4NU Tel: (01290) 338206 Fax: (01290) 338206

▶ Duncan Pryde, Cartmore Industrial Estate, Lochgelly, Fife, KY5 8LL Tel: (01592) 783130

▶ Duncan & Son Southwold Ltd, Unit 20 Southwold Business, Centre St Edmunds Road, Southwold, Suffolk, IP18 6JU Tel: (01502) 723636

Fred Duncombe Ltd, Progress Drive, Cannock, Staffordshire, WS11 0JE Tel: (01543) 578661 Fax: (01543) 570050 E-mail: sales@fredduncombe.co.uk *Emergency exit door furniture*

▶ Dundas UPVC, 1D Payne Street, Port Dundas Trading Estate, Glasgow, G4 0LE Tel: 0141 353 1996 *Glasgow"s newest " one stop" Roofline warehouse supplying quality UPVC Fascias, Soffits, Bargeboards, Cladding, Guttering, Uni-Dry Verge Cones,Silicone Sealants etc. Trade Counter open from 7am Weekdays, 9.30am Saturday.Installers and Public welcome.*

▶ Dundee City Council Property Support Services Section Education, 28 Crichton Street, Tayside House, Dundee, DD1 3RA Tel: (01382) 433749

The Dundee Perth & London Shipping Company Ltd, 26 East Dock Street, Dundee, DD1 9HY Tel: (01382) 203111 Fax: (01382) 200575 E-mail: agency@dpandl.co.uk *Freight forwarders & ships' agents*

Dundee Plant Co. Ltd, Longtown Street, Dundee, DD4 8LF Tel: (01382) 507506 Fax: (01382) 507550 *Scaffold contractors, demolition & civil engineering*

Dunedin Contract Cleaning Services, 2 Pitt Street, Edinburgh, EH6 4BU Tel: 0131-554 9879 Fax: 0131-554 9879 *Contract cleaners*

▶ Dunedin Stone Ltd, 3 Lower, London Road, Edinburgh, EH7 5TL Tel: 0131-661 0130 *Stone suppliers*

Dunelm Office Interiors, 149 Kells Lane, Gateshead, Tyne & Wear, NE9 5HR Tel: 0191-491 5080 Fax: 0191-420 0197 *Office refurbishers*

Dunelm Optical Co Ltd, 9 Enterprise Way, Spennymoor, County Durham, DL16 6YP Tel: (01388) 420420 Fax: (01388) 810102 *Manufacturer & distributors of optical products*

Dunelm Public Relations Ltd, Gun Court, 70 Wapping Lane, London, E1W 2RD Tel: (020) 7480 0600 Fax: (020) 7480 0606 E-mail: info@dunelmpr.co.uk *Public relations consultants*

Dunelm Supplies Ltd, Netherset Lane, Madeley, Crewe, CW3 9PF Tel: (01782) 750884 Fax: (01782) 751305 E-mail: dunelmpete@aol.co.uk *Manufacturers of cheese cutting equipment*

Dunelm Testing Service Ltd, 3 Phoenix Road, Crowther Industrial Estate, Washington, Tyne & Wear, NE38 0AD Tel: 0191-417 9911 Fax: 0191-419 3070 E-mail: dunelmtest@btconnect.com *Metallurgist & metallurgical analysts*

▶ Dunglass Designs, Old School, School Brae, West Barns, Dunbar, East Lothian, EH42 1UD Tel: (01368) 863590 Fax: (01368) 863590 *Builders*

Dunham Engineering, 48-49 Greenhey Place, Skelmersdale, Lancashire, WN8 9SA Tel: (01695) 729031 Fax: (01695) 555876 E-mail: alan@dunhameng.com *Excavator & undercarriage engineers*

Dunham Engineering Services Ltd, The Burton Business Park, Hudson Road, Leeds, LS9 7DN Tel: 0113-248 4422 Fax: 0113-235 0809 E-mail: info@dunhamengineering.co.uk *Mechanical & electrical services*

Dunham Water Treatment, 17 Bracken Road, Long Eaton, Nottingham, NG10 4DA Tel: 0115-972 7812 Fax: 0115-877 6238 E-mail: bob@dunhamwater.co.uk *Water treatment plant manufrs*

Dunhams Of Norwich, Hellesdon Park Road, Drayton High Road, Norwich, NR6 5DR Tel: (01603) 424855 Fax: (01603) 413336 *Laminated plastic product manufrs*

Alfred Dunhill Ltd, 27 Knightsbridge, London, SW1X 7YB Tel: (020) 7838 8000 Fax: (020) 7838 8333 *Mens luxury goods manufrs* Also at: Brentford & Walthamstow

Duni Ltd, Chester Road, Preston Brook, Runcorn, Cheshire, WA7 3FR Tel: (01928) 712377 Fax: (01928) 754580 *Disposable paper product suppliers*

Dunkelman & Son Ltd, 15 Jermyn Street, London, SW1Y 6LT Tel: (020) 7734 7340 Fax: (020) 7287 0933 E-mail: info@dunkelman.com *'Dasco' shoe care products manufrs* Also at: London

Dunkenhalgh Hotel, Blackburn Road, Clayton Le Moors, Accrington, Lancashire, BB5 5JP Tel: (01254) 398021 Fax: (01254) 872230 E-mail: reception.dunkenhalgh@mcdonald-hotels.co.uk *Hotel with conference facilities*

▶ Dunkin Rushton Ltd, Hood House, 19 Lower Church Street, Ashby-De-La-Zouch, Leicestershire, LE65 1AB Tel: (01530) 412059 E-mail: nr@dkrs.com *Property developers*

▶ Dunlap Sunbrand International, Unit 9 Taber Place, Crittall Road, Witham, Essex, CM8 3YP Tel: (01376) 516333 Fax: (01376) 516332 E-mail: denisekemp@dsinternational.co.uk *Spare parts, needles & accessories suppliers for industrial sewing*

▶ Dunlaw Engineering, Axis Business Centre, Thainstone Business Centre, Inverurie, Aberdeenshire, AB51 5TB Tel: (01467) 641183 Fax: (01467) 641185 E-mail: sales@dunlew.com *Offshore engineering*

Dunlop Aftrica Marketing UK Ltd, 40 Fort Parkway, Birmingham, B24 9HL Tel: 0121-384 8800 Fax: 0121-377 7150 E-mail: datlsales@compuserve.com *Aircraft tyres manufrs*

Alan Dunlop, 2 Killyleagh Road, Killinchy, Newtownards, County Down, BT23 6TA Tel: (028) 9754 1440 Fax: (028) 9754 1644 E-mail: bill_dunlop@btinternet.com *Agricultural machinery manufrs*

Dunlop Design Engineering, 1 Sackville Street, Lisburn, County Antrim, BT27 4AB Tel: (028) 9267 2333 Fax: (028) 9267 2383 E-mail: info@dnet.co.uk *Design & installation of laundry textile systems*

▶ Dunlop Extrusions, Nufox Rubber Ltd, Bentley Avenue, Middleton, Manchester, M24 2GP Tel: 0161-655 0170 Fax: 0161-655 0171 E-mail: sales@dunlopextrusions.com *Rubber extrusions, gaskets, moulding & fabrication services*

▶ Dunlop G R G Holdings Ltd, Unit 62, Touchet, Hall Road, Stakehill Industrial Estate, Middleton, Manchester, M24 2RW Tel: 0161-653 5964 Fax: 0161-643 0184 E-mail: sales@dunlopgrg.co.uk *Flexible fuel & water tanks manufrs*

Dunlop & Hamilton, 9 Prince Regent Road, Belfast, BT5 6SH Tel: (028) 9079 9399 Fax: (028) 9079 3251 *Electrical wholesalers*

Dunlop Hi Flex Fluidpower Ltd, Unit 59 Holly Court, St. Modwen Road, Plymouth, PL6 8LG Tel: (01752) 262268 Fax: (01752) 664722 E-mail: dunlophiflex@shelmerdined.freeserve.co.uk *Hydraulic hose manufrs*

Dunlop Hiflex Fluid Power Ltd, Howley Park Road, Morley, Leeds, LS27 0BN Tel: 0113-238 1547 Fax: 0113-238 3391 E-mail: leeds@dunlophiflex.com *Hydraulic equipment suppliers*

Dunlop Hiflex Fluid Power Ltd, Unit 31-32 Church Road Business Centre, Church Road, Sittingbourne, Kent, ME10 3RS Tel: (01795) 429807 Fax: (01795) 420423 E-mail: sales@dunlophiflex.xom *Hydraulic hose & pipe manufrs* Also at: Branches throughout the U.K.

Dunlop Slazenger International Ltd, Wakefield 41 Business Park, Wakefield, West Yorkshire, WF2 0XB Tel: (01924) 880000 Fax: (01924) 888287 E-mail: info@dsil.co.uk *Sports equipment distributors*

▶ Dunloy Quarry, 93 Bridge Road, Dunloy, Ballymena, County Antrim, BT44 9EG Tel: (028) 2765 7512

▶ Dunloy Tool Hire & Sales, 3 Pulloxhill Business Park, Greenfield Road, Pulloxhill, Bedford, MK45 5EU Tel: (01525) 716715 Fax: (01525) 720795 E-mail: dunloy@btconnect.com *suppliers of ppe to the rail & construction industries*

Dunmar Packaging Ltd, Kus Industrial Estate, Manor Lane, Hawarden, Deeside, Clwyd, CH5 3PJ Tel: (01244) 526872 Fax: (01244) 537396 *Carton manufacturers/die cutting services*

▶ Dunmor International Ltd, 56 Victoria Street, Perth, PH2 8JT Tel: (01738) 447808

Dunn Printing Co., 10a Beechings Way, Alford, Lincolnshire, LN13 9JE Tel: (01507) 463416 Fax: (01507) 463416 E-mail: dunnprintingco@lineone.net *Litho & letter press printing*

Dunn & Webster, 4 Hever Close, Dudley, West Midlands, DY1 2SY Tel: (07850) 750089 Fax: (01384) 233224 *Vehicle delivery & collection services*

Dunn & Wilson International Ltd, Glasgow Road, Camelon, Falkirk, FK1 4HP Tel: (01324) 621591 Fax: (01324) 611508 E-mail: info@rdw.co.uk *Library bookbinders & expert conservators*

▶ Dunne Building & Civil Engineering Ltd, Whitehill Industrial Estate, Bathgate, West Lothian, EH48 2EP Tel: (01506) 657777 Fax: (01506) 639810 E-mail: sales@dunne-group.com

▶ Dunne Roberts, Unit 3 Freemantle Business Centre, 152 Millbrook Road East, Southampton, SO15 1JR Tel: (023) 8082 9200 Fax: (023) 8082 9201 E-mail: contactus@dunneroberts.co.uk *Printed circuit consultancy services*

Dunnes Stores (Bangor) Ltd, Unit 31 The Concourse, Skelmersdale, Lancashire, WN8 6LN Tel: (01695) 50233 Fax: (01695) 50577 *Clothing retailer*

▶ Dunnett Hook Aluminium Ltd, Hill Street, Ashton-under-Lyne, Lancashire, OL7 0PZ Tel: 0161-339 2639 Fax: 0161-343 1634 *Architectural aluminium fabricators & fixers*

Dunnetts Ltd, 170 Kings Road, Tyseley, Birmingham, B11 2AS Tel: 0121-706 9180 Fax: 0121-706 6169 E-mail: dunnetts@dunnetts.co.uk *Bakeware manufrs*

Dunninghams Ltd, 16 Manor Road Dovercourt, Harwich, Essex, CO12 4DU Tel: (01255) 502497 Fax: (01255) 241707 E-mail: sales@g-dunningham.co.uk *Steel fabrication manufrs*

▶ Dunns Food & Drink Ltd, 32 Glasgow Road, Blantyre, Glasgow, G72 0JY Tel: (01698) 727700 Fax: (01698) 727770 E-mail: sales@dunnsfoodanddrinks.co.uk *Food & drink supplier*

Dunns Imaging Group Ltd, Chester Road, Cradley Heath, West Midlands, B64 6AA Tel: (01384) 564770 Fax: (01384) 637165 E-mail: enquiries@dunns.co.uk *Professional photographic laboratory* Also at: Birmingham

Dunnsprint Ltd, Clarence Works, Clarence Road, Eastbourne, East Sussex, BN22 8HJ Tel: (01323) 410902 Fax: (01323) 410573 E-mail: sales@dunnsprint.co.uk *Commercial printers*

Dunoon Ceramics Ltd, 5 Walton Industrial Estate, Beacon Road, Stone, Staffordshire, ST15 0RY Tel: (01785) 817414 Fax: (01785) 812322 E-mail: sales@dunoonmugs.co.uk *China & stone products manufrs*

Dunrave Precision Engineers Ltd, Oldbury Road, Cwmbran, Gwent, NP44 3JU Tel: (01633) 873838 Fax: (01633) 871477 E-mail: info@dunrave.co.uk *Precision engineering services*

Dunraven Manufacturing Ltd, Village Farm Industrial Estate, Pyle, Bridgend, Mid Glamorgan, CF33 6BJ Tel: (01656) 745035 Fax: (01656) 745918 *Window & door manufrs*

▶ Dunsire Associates Electrical Ltd, Unit 10 Phoenix Lane, Dunfermline, Fife, KY12 9EB Tel: (01383) 723583 Fax: (01383) 621216

Dunsley Heat Ltd, Bridge Mills, Holmfirth, HD9 3TW Tel: (01484) 682635 Fax: (01484) 688428 E-mail: sales@dunsleyheat.co.uk *Domestic heating apparatus manufrs*

Dunsmore Blinds, 69 Lawford Lane, Rugby, Warwickshire, CV22 7JS Tel: (01788) 811517 Fax: (01788) 811517 *Blinds retailers*

Dunsmore Products Ltd, 10 Avon Industrial Estate, Rugby, Warwickshire, CV21 3UY Tel: (01788) 571600 Fax: (01788) 541382 E-mail: dunsmoreprodltd@btconnect.com *Precision engineers services*

Dunstable Glass Co. Ltd, 87-91 High St North, Dunstable, Bedfordshire, LU6 1JJ Tel: (01582) 663277 Fax: (01582) 699907 *Large mirror showroom & emergency glazier service*

Dunstable Laminates, 47 Edward Street, Dunstable, Bedfordshire, LU6 1HE Tel: (01582) 668973 Fax: (01582) 608227 E-mail: sales@dunstablelaminates.co.uk *Laminating fabricators & worktop specialists & toilet cubicles*

Dunstable Waste Group Ltd, Townsend Farm Indust Estate, Blackburn Road, Houghton Regis, Dunstable, Bedfordshire, LU5 5DD Tel: (01582) 476600 Fax: (01582) 664117 E-mail: admin@dwg.uk.com *Waste management & recycling services*

Dunster House, Caxton Road, Bedford, MK41 0LF Tel: (01234) 272445 Fax: (01234) 272588 E-mail: enquiries@garden-buildings-uk.co.uk *UPVC window & door double glazing*

Dunster & Morton, 92 London Street, Reading, RG1 4SJ Tel: 0118-955 1700 Fax: 0118-955 1725 E-mail: info@dunsterandmorton.co.uk *Chartered surveyors*

▶ Dunston Printers Sheepbridge Ltd, Dunston Road, Chesterfield, Derbyshire, S41 9QD Tel: (01246) 454335 Fax: (01246) 260480

Company Information

▶ indicates data change since last edition

Dunston Ship Repaires Ltd, William Wright Dock, Hull, HU3 4PG Tel: (01482) 326774 Fax: (01482) 226815 E-mail: sales@dunstons.co.uk *Ship builders*

Dunstonian Holdings Ltd, 28a Station Square, Petts Wood, Orpington, Kent, BR5 1LS Tel: (01689) 832545 Fax: (01689) 878258 E-mail: enquiries@dunstonian.co.uk *Motor repair garage & sales services*

Dunton Bros Ltd, Blackwell Hall Lane, Chesham, Buckinghamshire, HP5 1TN Tel: (01494) 783730 Fax: (01494) 791255 E-mail: sales@duntons.com *Brick manufrs*

Dunwoody Airline Services Ltd, East Midlands International Airport, 70 Argosy Road, Castle Donington, Derby, DE74 2SA Tel: (01332) 811967 Fax: (01332) 850405 E-mail: accounts@baregionalcargo.com *Air freight forwarders*

▶ Duo Marketing Services, Primmers Green Cottages, Primmers Green, Wadhurst, East Sussex, TN5 6DU Tel: (01892) 783017 Fax: (01892) 783017 E-mail: enquiries@duomarketing.co.uk *Marketing support services*

Duoflex Ltd, Trimmingham House, 2 Shires Road, Buckingham Road Industrial Estate, Brackley, Northamptonshire, NN13 7EZ Tel: (01280) 701366 Fax: (01280) 704799 E-mail: sales@duoflex.co.uk *Upholstery specialists & coach retrimming*

Duoguard Burglar Alarm Systems, 15 Llandaff Road, Beaufort, Ebbw Vale, Gwent, NP23 5RL Tel: (01495) 304931 *CCTV equipment & security systems distributors*

Dupaul Engineering, Unit 5a Bone Lane, Newbury, Berkshire, RG14 5SH Tel: (01635) 31770 Fax: (01635) 521048 E-mail: dupaul@dupaul-eng.co.uk *Precision engineers*

Duplas, Diamond Business Park, 7 Thornes Moor Road, Wakefield, West Yorkshire, WF2 8PT Tel: (01924) 298298 Fax: (01924) 377101 E-mail: sales@duplas.co.uk *Specialist machine builders*

Duplex Cleaning Machines UK Ltd, Unit 27 Joseph Wilson Industrial Estate, Millstrood Road, Whitstable, Kent, CT5 3PS Tel: (01227) 771276 Fax: (01227) 770220 E-mail: info@duplex-cleaning.com *Industrial cleaner distributors*

Duplex Engineering (Scotland) Ltd, 34-36 Napier Court, Wardpark North, Cumbernauld, Glasgow, G68 0LG Tel: (01236) 612757 Fax: (01236) 612757 E-mail: enquiries@duplex-engineering.co.uk *Fabrication of sheet & tubular products in particular*

Duplex Telecom Ltd, The Widford Hall, Widford Hall Lane, Chelmsford, CM2 8TD Tel: (0870) 7481408 Fax: (0870) 7481407 E-mail: sales@duplex.co.uk *Telephone call management logging equipment*

Duplus Architectural Systems Ltd, 370 Melton Road, Leicester, LE4 7SL Tel: 0116-261 0710 Fax: 0116-261 0539 E-mail: sales@duplus.co.uk *Architectural glazing systems suppliers & manufrs*

DuPont Animal Health Solutions, Windham Road, Chilton Industrial Estate, Sudbury, Suffolk, CO10 2XD Tel: (01787) 377305 Fax: (01787) 310846 E-mail: biosecurity@gbr.dupont.com *Disinfectants producers*

Dupont Liquid Packaging Systems LB Europe Ltd, Oakwood Road, Romiley, Stockport, Cheshire, SK6 4DZ Tel: 0161-406 8880 Fax: 0161-406 8881 *Liquid packaging manufrs*

Dupont Powder Coatings UK Ltd, Whessoe Road, Darlington, County Durham, DL3 0XH Tel: (01325) 355371 Fax: (01325) 380092 *Powder coatings manufrs*

Dura Automotive Body & Glass Systems, Unit A, Castle Bromwich Business Park, Tameside Drive, Castle Bromwich, Birmingham, B35 7AG Tel: 0121-776 7733 Fax: 0121-749 6850 *Automotive parts manufrs*

Dura Beds, Moorebank Mills, Artillary Street, Heckmondwike, West Yorkshire, WF16 0NT Tel: (01924) 400066 Fax: (01924) 404071 *Bed manufrs*

Dura Hose & Fittings Ltd, Unit 8, Mountheath Industrial Park, Prestwich, Manchester, M25 9WB Tel: 0161-798 8665 Fax: 0161-773 3048 E-mail: sales@dura-hose.com *Suppliers of industrial rubber hose, hose assembly service & fittings*

▶ Dura Manufacturing, 101 Commercial Road, London, E1 1RD Tel: (020) 7247 5820 Fax: (020) 7247 5676

Dura Shifter Systems Ltd, Yspitty Road, Llanelli, Carmarthenshire, SA14 9TF Tel: (01554) 772445 Fax: (01554) 756808 E-mail: sales@duraauto.com *supplies of Automotive, Aerospace & Industrial cables systems. **Accelerator, clutch, Handbrake, Gear Change, openners, and special purpose/ applications requiring linear movement.*

▶ Durable, 1 498 Reading Road, Winnersh, Wokingham, Berkshire, RG41 5EX Tel: (0870) 2402480 Fax: 0118-989 5209 E-mail: mail@durable.co.uk *Supply and installation of window films for security, safety and solar control. Supply and installation of manifestations and window graphics.*

Durable, 1 498 Reading Road, Winnersh, Wokingham, Berkshire, RG41 5EX Tel: (0870) 2402480 Fax: 0118-989 5209 E-mail: mail@durable.co.uk *Window film manufrs*

▶ Durable Coatings Ltd, 21-29 Napier Court, Wardpark North, Cumbernauld, Glasgow, G68 0LG Tel: (01236) 860450 Fax: (01236) 781356

Durable Contracts Ltd, Durable House, Crabtree Manorway, Belvedere, Kent, DA17 6AB Tel: (020) 8311 1211 Fax: (020) 8310 7893 E-mail: sales@durable-online.com *Roofing contractors* Also at: Sandleheath

Durable UK Ltd, East Dorset Trade Park, 10 Nimrod Way, Wimborne, Dorset, BH21 7SH Tel: (01202) 897071 Fax: (01202) 873381 E-mail: marketing@durable-uk.com *Office stationary distributors*

▶ Durabuild Glazed Structures Ltd, Carlton Road, Coventry, CV6 7FL Tel: (024) 7666 9169 Fax: (024) 7666 9170 E-mail: enquiries@durabuild.co.uk *Conservatories, pool enclosures & roof light manufrs*

Duracell Wrexham, Unit 11 Ash Road North, Wrexham Industrial Estate, Wrexham, Clwyd, LL13 9JT Tel: (01978) 221000 Fax: (01978) 221001 *Hearing aid battery manufrs*

Duradiamond Ltd, Kingfisher House, Auld Mart Road, Milnathort, Kinross, KY13 9FR Tel: (01577) 863028 Fax: (01577) 866704 E-mail: enquiries@duradiamond.com *Diamond drilling bit manufrs*

Duraflex Ltd, Severn Drive, Tewkesbury Business Park, Tewkesbury, Gloucestershire, GL20 8TX Tel: (0870) 5351351 Fax: (0870) 0772663 E-mail: sales@duraflex.co.uk *Suppliers of PVC-u window & door systems, fabricators & installers*

Duraframe Structures Ltd, 4 Springhead Way, Crowborough, East Sussex, TN6 1LR Tel: (01892) 610534 Fax: (01892) 611643 *Building contractors*

Duram Ltd, Duram House, Cemetery Road, Bradford, West Yorkshire, BD8 9RZ Tel: (01274) 542603 Fax: (01274) 548526 E-mail: sales@duram.co.uk *General wholesalers shopfittings*

Duraplay, 3 Craigburn Ct, Dumfries, DG1 4QQ Tel: 01387 248892 *Childrens playground equipment*

Durasak, Stansfeld Street, Blackburn, BB2 2NG Tel: (01254) 51733 Fax: (01254) 51833 E-mail: sales@durasat.co.uk *Polythene bags bespoke services*

Duraseal, 7 27 Black Moor Road, Ebblake Industrial Estate, Verwood, Dorset, BH31 6BE Tel: (01202) 826911 Fax: (01202) 813811 *Duraseal print finishers*

Durastic, 47 Cuthbert Court, Bede Trading Estate, Jarrow, Tyne & Wear, NE32 3EG Tel: 0191-483 2299 Fax: 0191-483 2295 *Marine decking contractors* Also at: Branches throughout the UK

Duration Windows, Charfleets Road, Canvey Island, Essex, SS8 0PQ Tel: (01268) 681612 Fax: (01268) 510058 E-mail: sales@duration.co.uk *Aluminium windows & doors manufrs*

Duravac Products Ltd, 170 John Wilson Business Park, Chestfield, Whitstable, Kent, CT5 3RA Tel: (01227) 770828 Fax: (01227) 770878 E-mail: sales@duravac.co.uk *Vacuum oil, grease producers & refiners*

Durbin P.L.C., Unit 5, Redlands Business Centre, Redlands, Coulsdon, Surrey, CR5 2UN Tel: (020) 8660 2220 Fax: (020) 8668 0751 E-mail: catalogesales@durbin.co.uk *Supply overseas hospitals*

Durbin Metal Industries Ltd, Unit 0, Lawrence Drive, Stover Trading Estate, Bristol, BS37 5PG Tel: (01454) 322668 Fax: (01454) 317415 E-mail: sales@durbinmetals.co.uk *Non-ferrous metal stockholders*

Durbin (U.K.) Ltd, 180 Northolt Road, South Harrow, Harrow, Middlesex, HA2 0LT Tel: (020) 8869 6500 Fax: (020) 8869 6565 E-mail: durbin@durbin.co.uk *Wholesale chemists & pharmaceutical exporters*

Duresta Upholstery Ltd, Fields Farm Road, Long Eaton, Nottingham, NG10 3FZ Tel: 0115-973 2246 Fax: 0115-946 1028 *Upholstery manufrs*

Durey Castings Ltd, Shell Garage, Hawley Road, Dartford, DA1 1PU Tel: (01322) 272424 Fax: (01322) 288073 E-mail: sales@dureycastings.co.uk *Manhole & grating specialists*

Durga Sweets, 173-175 Ilford Lane, Ilford, Essex, IG1 2RT Tel: (020) 8478 3466 Fax: (020) 8514 7280 *Restaurant services*

Durham Computer Centre Ltd, 6 New Elvet, Durham, DH1 3AQ Tel: 0191-386 8989 Fax: 0191-384 4556 E-mail: info@durhamcomputercentre.co.uk *Build, repair & setup networks*

Durham Filtration Engineers Ltd, Victoria Industrial Estate, Victoria Road West, Hebburn, Tyne & Wear, NE31 1UB Tel: 0191-428 4111 Fax: 0191-428 4226 E-mail: sales@durhamfiltration.co.uk *Filter distributors*

Durham Foundry (Sheffield) Ltd, Durham Foundry, Harleston Street, Sheffield, S4 7QB Tel: 0114-249 4977 Fax: 0114-249 4910 E-mail: castings@durhamfoundry.com *Iron casting manufrs*

Durham Lifting Ltd, Britannia Testhouse, Forty Foot Road, Middlesbrough, Cleveland, TS2 1HB Tel: (01642) 240672 Fax: (01642) 247709 *Lifting equipment manufrs*

Durham Lifting Ltd, Unit 12 Thames Centre, Gurney Way, Aycliffe Industrial Park, Newton Aycliffe, County Durham, DL5 6UJ Tel: (01325) 318844 Fax: (01325) 318844 *Lifting gear manufacturers & suppliers*

Durham Sheet Metal Works Ltd, Progress House, Templetown, South Shields, Tyne & Wear, NE33 5TE Tel: 0191-455 3558 Fax: 0191-456 8837 E-mail: paul@durhamsheetmetal.co.uk *Sheet metal & light fabricators*

Durham Systems Management Ltd, PO Box 38, Washington, Tyne & Wear, NE38 9YX Tel: 0191-492 0429 E-mail: sales@dunelmsystems.co.uk *Computer consultants*

Durham Throphies UK, 69 Buckinghamshire Road, Durham, DH1 2BE Tel: 0191-386 9045 *Trophies suppliers & engraving*

Durham Tissue Supplies, Unit 1l The Dairies, Durham Road, Annfield Plain, Stanley, County Durham, DH9 7SR Tel: (01207) 237476 Fax: (01207) 237476 E-mail: durhamtissuesupplies@btinternet.com *Tissue suppliers*

Duright Engineering Co., Portway Road, Wednesbury, West Midlands, WS10 7DZ Tel: 0121-556 7718 Fax: 0121-556 7745 E-mail: sales@duright.co.uk *Cutting services*

Durkan Properties Ltd, Durkan House, 214-224 High Street, Waltham Cross, Hertfordshire, EN8 7DU Tel: (01992) 781400 Fax: (01992) 781500 E-mail: info@durkan.co.uk *Building contractors*

Durkin & Sons Ltd, Amex House, North End Road, Wembley, Middlesex, HA9 0UU Tel: (020) 8900 0203 Fax: (020) 8903 4754 E-mail: michaeldurkin@ndirect.co.uk Purchasing Contact: M. Durkin Sales Contact: F. Reeves *Civil engineers*

Durleigh Display Systems, 6 Symons Way, Bridgwater, Somerset, TA6 4DR Tel: (01278) 447447 Fax: (01278) 456376 *Display unit manufrs*

J.W. Durman, Greenway Farm, Moon Lane, North Petherton, Bridgwater, Somerset, TA7 0DS Tel: (01278) 662656 *Food product manufrs*

Durnbury Ltd, 30 First Avenue, Halstead, Essex, CO9 2EX Tel: (01787) 475351 Fax: (01787) 477821 E-mail: durnburyltd@aol.com *Garage equipment & fume extraction systems*

Durodata, 5 Castle Street, Canterbury, Kent, CT1 2FG Tel: (01227) 781037 Fax: (01227) 762416 E-mail: info@durodata.co.uk *Database design*

Durose Ltd, 33-35 Adams Street, Birmingham, B7 4LT Tel: 0121-333 3096 Fax: 0121-359 6408 E-mail: sales@durose.co.uk *Steel fabricators*

Durotan Ltd, 20 West Street, Buckingham, MK18 1HE Tel: (01280) 814048 Fax: (01280) 817842 E-mail: general@durotan.ltd.uk *Pre-insulated pipework supply & installation*

Durr Ltd, Broxell Close, Warwick, CV34 5QF Tel: (01926) 418800 Fax: (01926) 400679 E-mail: sales@durr.com *Manufacturers of paint shops*

Durr Technik (UK) Ltd, Unit 5, Ashmead Business Centre, Ashmead Road, Keynsham, Bristol, BS31 1SX Tel: 0117-986 0414 Fax: 0117-986 0416 E-mail: info@durrtechnik.co.uk *Air compressors & vacuum pumps manufrs*

James Durrans & Sons Ltd, Phoenix Works, Thurlstone, Sheffield, S36 9QU Tel: (01226) 370000 Fax: (01226) 370336 E-mail: enquiries@durrans.co.uk *Foundry blacking manufrs*

▶ Durrants English Wedding Collection, 6 Trevitt Close, Sleaford, Lincolnshire, NG34 8BT Tel: (01529) 302530 Fax: (01529) 302530 E-mail: info@englishweddingcollection.co.uk *Wedding stationary suppliers*

Durrants Press Cuttings Ltd, Discovery House, 28-42 Banner Street, London, EC1Y 8QE Tel: (020) 7674 0200 Fax: (020) 7674 0222 E-mail: contact@durrants.co.uk *Press cutting agency*

Durst (UK) Ltd, 9 Blenheim Road, Longmead Industrial Estate, Epsom, Surrey, KT19 9AR Tel: (01372) 726262 Fax: (01372) 740761 E-mail: info@durstuk.co.uk *Photographic & inkjet suppliers*

Durston Garden Products, Avalon Farm, Sharpham, Street, Somerset, BA16 9SE Tel: (01458) 442688 Fax: (01458) 448327 E-mail: info@durstongardenproducts.co.uk *Growing media (compost) manufrs*

▶ Durty Blinds, Unit 13-315 Drakemire Drive, Linnpark Industrial Estate, Glasgow, G45 9SS Tel: 0141-630 1222 Fax: 0141-630 1222 *Cleaning services*

Duscovent Engineering Ltd, 86 Wellington Road North, Stockport, Cheshire, SK4 1HT Tel: 0161-480 4811 Fax: 0161-480 6503 E-mail: sales@duscovent.co.uk *Industrial air systems manufrs*

▶ Dusk Crafts, 6 Sherwood, Uplyme Road, Lyme Regis, Dorset, DT7 3LS Tel: 01297 445033 E-mail: info@duskcrafts.co.uk *Dusk Crafts creates and supplies handcrafted and aromatic goods with a touch of magick. Online or mail order to UK customers, we offer an efficient service at generous prices. Products include: handcrafted jewellery, handmade soaps, gift baskets, greeting cards, incense, essential oils, crystalware, herbal goods and much more. We supply goods both retail and wholesale - new outlets sought, please get in touch for trade prices.*

Duskpoint Ltd, 27 Hockley Road, Poynton, Stockport, Cheshire, SK12 1RW Tel: (01625) 871102 Fax: (01625) 871102 *Computer consultants*

Dust Control, 1b Pury Business Park, Alderton Road, Paulerspury, Towcester, Northamptonshire, NN12 7LS Tel: (01327) 811510 Fax: (01327) 811413 E-mail: sales@dustcontrol.co.uk *Dust & fume extraction & equipment manufrs*

Dust Control Services Ltd, Brocus House, Parkgate Road, Dorking, Surrey, RH5 5AH Tel: (01306) 631505 Fax: 01306 631751 E-mail: sales@dustextraction.co.uk *Dust extraction services*

Dust Control Systems Ltd, Churwell Vale, Shaw Cross Business Park, Dewsbury, West Yorkshire, WF12 7RD Tel: (01924) 482500 Fax: (01924) 482530 E-mail: sales@dcslimited.co.uk *Dust extraction engineers*

Dust Plant Services, 87 Lothair Road, Leicester, LE2 7QE Tel: 0116-244 0150 *Dust extraction equipment suppliers*

Dust Pollution Systems Ltd, 2 Premacto Works, Queensmead Road, Loudwater, High Wycombe, Buckinghamshire, HP10 9XA Tel: (01494) 462333 Fax: (01494) 463777 E-mail: info@dustpollution.co.uk *Dust extraction systems manufrs*

▶ Dustacco Engineering Ltd, 83 Carron Place, Kelvin Industrial Estate, East Kilbride, Glasgow, G75 0YL Tel: (01355) 229191 *Pipe fitting, fabrication & manufrs*

Dustcheck Ltd, Environmental House, Galveston Grove, Stoke-on-Trent, ST4 3PE Tel: (01782) 599454 Fax: (01782) 599478 E-mail: sales@dustcheck.co.uk *Air filtration & industrial dust control*

▶ Dustdees Domestic Cleaning, 4 Hartland Road, Reading, RG2 8BN Tel: 0118-986 0254 E-mail: djs180671@yahoo.co.uk *Domestic cleaning*

Dustolex Ltd, Ebor Street, Littleborough, Lancashire, OL15 9AS Tel: (01706) 377344 Fax: (01706) 377332 E-mail: sales@dustolex.co.uk *Dust fume control equipment manufrs*

Duston Engineering Ltd, 50 Ivy Road, Northampton, NN1 4QT Tel: (01604) 233178 Fax: (01604) 233178 *Precision engineering services*

Distraction Ltd, Mandervell Road, Oadby, Leicester, LE2 5ND Tel: 0116-271 3212 Fax: 0116-271 3215 E-mail: steve.matuska@dustraction.co.uk Principal Export Areas: Africa *During the last 50 years Dustraction have become firmly established as a leading name for design manufacture and installation of dust extract equipment. The reputation has been based on providing a comprehensive service from initial enquiry through to a fully commissioned dust collection system suited to your site, machines and process We have an extensive product range including: -Cyclo filters -Shaker filters -Cartridge filters -Cyclones -Sanding benches -Spray booths -Woodwaste burning systems -Chipping systems All equipment tailor made to suit your requirements For further information contact Steve Matuska Sales Director*

▶ Dusty Sweeps, 3 Bridge End Road, Swindon, SN3 4PD Tel: 01793 326188 E-mail: dustysweeps@hotmail.co.uk *Chimney Sweep Services: *Thorough inspection, brush & vacuum. Bird nests & blockages removed. Friendly, helpful & reliable service. Clean & tidy. Fully insured on all work. **

Jack Dusty's Stores, 400 Sandwell Road, Kingswood, Bristol, BS15 1JJ Tel: 0117-949 6686 Fax: 0117-949 6495 E-mail: enquiries@jackdusty.co.uk *Janitorial retailers*

Dutch Engineering Services Ltd, Dutch House, Pentney Lane, West Bilney, Pentney, King's Lynn, Norfolk, PE32 1JE Tel: (01760) 339111 Fax: (01760) 339112 E-mail: enquiries@dutchengineering.co.uk *Suppliers of specialist high pressure valves & actuators*

Graham Dutnall, Unit 5 Shawbarn, Whitesmith, Lewes, East Sussex, BN8 6JD Tel: (01825) 872181 *Cabinet makers*

▶ Dutton Ltd, 2 Ocean Mews, 10 Fore Street, Budleigh Salterton, Devon, EX9 6NG Tel: (01395) 445092 E-mail: info@paritor.co.uk *Software house*

Dutton & Gavin Textiles Ltd, 62-66 Bermondsey Street, London, SE1 3UD Tel: (020) 7403 6388 Fax: (020) 7407 5814 E-mail: sales@dutgav.fsnet.co.uk *Textile merchants*

Dutton Glass & Mirrors Ltd, 66 Holloway Head, Birmingham, B1 1NG Tel: 0121-622 1221 Fax: 0121-643 5520 *Mirror & glass manufrs*

J.S. Dutton Ltd, Cale Street, Cale Green, Stockport, Cheshire, SK2 6SW Tel: 0161-480 2346 Fax: 0161-480 0728 E-mail: studio@jsdutton.co.uk *Lithographic printers*

▶ Dutton Simulation Ltd, 32 Lindsey Crescent, Kenilworth, Warwickshire, CV8 1FL Tel: (01926) 732147 Fax: (01926) 732147 E-mail: enquiries@duttonsimulation.com *Engineering simulation services*

Duval Products Ltd, Dexion Storage Centre, Armoury Way, London, SW18 1EU Tel: (020) 8870 7541 Fax: (020) 8870 2657 E-mail: sales@duvalproducts.co.uk *Steel shelving & ancillary products*

Duvatex Mytholmroyd Ltd, 8 Sunderland Street, Halifax, West Yorkshire, HX1 5AF Tel: (01422) 363534 Fax: (01422) 320335 *Clothing manufrs*

▶ Duxbury Builders Ltd, Brook Street, Adlington, Chorley, Lancashire, PR6 9LE Tel: (01257) 481683 Fax: (01257) 474603

Duxiana, 46 George Street, London, W1U 7DX Tel: (020) 7486 2363 Fax: (020) 7935 8080 *Bed distributors*

Dva Controls, 1 Sunningdale Grove, Colwyn Bay, Clwyd, LL29 6DG Tel: (01492) 534937 E-mail: info@dva-controls.co.uk *Printed circuit consultancy or design or production services*

▶ DVB Audio Ltd, 14 Saffron Road, Biggleswade, Bedfordshire, SG18 8DJ Tel: (01767) 317642 E-mail: info@dvbcaraudio.co.uk *Discount car audio products supplies with top brand names*

▶ Dvds4us.co.uk, PO Box 14375, Cowdenbeath, Fife, KY4 9YP Tel: (01383) 512005 Fax: (01383) 512005 E-mail: admin@dvds4us.co.uk *Rent Dvds Online from £1.50 for 7 nights. Postage and packing is Free. No need to sign up for monthly subscriptions. Just rent what you want - when you want.*

▶ Dvdsmart, 16 Boundary Street, Leyland, PR25 4ST Tel: 01772 451978 E-mail: info@dvdsmart.co.uk *Dvdsmart provides Top Quality Home Entertainment at a fantastically low price. All Dvd's are packaged and posted free of charge to any U.K. address.*

▶ DVH Design, 75 Bedells Avenue, Black Notley, Braintree, Essex, CM77 8NA Tel: 01376 322782 E-mail: request@dvhdesign.co.uk *Web Site Design Maintenance & Promotion.*

D'Vision Ltd, Market Place, Chipping Norton, Oxfordshire, OX7 5NA Tel: (01608) 648948 Fax: (01608) 648949 E-mail: info@d-vision.co.uk *Multimedia & video production*

DVS Computers, Unit 5 Gabalfa Workshops Clos Menter, Excelsior Industrial Estate, Cardiff, CF14 3AY Tel: (029) 2069 5020 E-mail: sales@dvscomputers.co.uk *Computer networks & systems installations*

DVS Leisure, 9 High Street, Timsbury, Bath, BA2 0HT Tel: (01761) 472100 Fax: (01761) 472666 E-mail: dvsleisureuk@aol.com *Amusement & gaming machines suppliers*

▶ DWC Services Ltd, 62 Nelson Street, Heanor, Derbyshire, DE75 7QR Tel: (01773) 531802 Fax: 01773 765112 E-mail: admin@dwcservices.co.uk *Industrial and Commercial Window Cleaners.*

A.W.D. Dwight & Sons (Engineers) Ltd, Delamare Road, Cheshunt, Waltham Cross, Hertfordshire, EN8 9UD Tel: (01992) 634255 Fax: (01992) 626672 E-mail: sales@imperialengineering.co.uk *Bus & commercial vehicle product remanufrs*

Dwyer Instruments Ltd, Unit 16 The Wye Estate, London Road, High Wycombe, Buckinghamshire, HP11 1LH Tel: (01494) 461707 Fax: (01494) 465102 E-mail: sales@dwyer-inst.co.uk *Flow meter & level indicator distributors*

Dwyers Business Management Services, Belton Ho, 15 Belton Drive, West Bridgford, Nottingham, NG2 7SJ Tel: 0115-984 2642 Fax: 0115-984 2642 *Business management consultants*

▶ Dxui Ltd, Unit 5 Autumn Park Industrial Estate, Dysart Road, Grantham, Lincolnshire, NG31 7DD Tel: (01476) 564387 Fax: (01476) 564448 E-mail: admin@dxui.net *National horticultural distributors, sundries retailers*

▶ Dyas Electrical, 225 Cleethorpe Road, Grimsby, South Humberside, DN31 3BE Tel: (01472) 312999

Dyce Carrier, Kirkton Avenue, Dyce, Aberdeen, AB21 0BF Tel: (01224) 723571 Fax: (01224) 770328 E-mail: info@dycecar.fsbuisiness.co.uk *Freight forwarders*

▶ Dyce Carriers Ltd, 18 Holton Road, Holton Heath Trading Park, Poole, Dorset, BH16 6LT Tel: (01202) 820829 Fax: (01202) 620829 E-mail: lunddyce@aol.com

Dyco Engineering, 3 Chancel Place, Boyer Street, Derby, DE22 3SH Tel: (01332) 372266 Fax: (01332) 372266 *Precision engineers*

Dyer Bros Marine Ltd, 129 St. Denys Road, Southampton, SO17 2JY Tel: (023) 8055 5406 *Marina & boat repairs*

Dyer Engineering Ltd, Unit 3-5 Morrison Industrial Estate North, Stanley, County Durham, DH9 7RU Tel: (01207) 234355 Fax: (01207) 282834 E-mail: sales@dyer-engineering.ltd.uk *Machining fabrications & special services*

Dyer Fastners, 31 Rodway Close, Brierley Hill, West Midlands, DY5 2NA Tel: (01384) 895588 Fax: (01384) 836032 E-mail: gilldyer@blueyonder.co.uk *Special stainless steel fasteners*

J.D. & C.W. Dyer, Penrock, Llandovery, Dyfed, SA20 0DZ Tel: 01550 720956 *Agricultural services*

Dyer Welding Services Ltd, West Bank Terminal, Wherstead Road, Ipswich, IP2 8NB Tel: (01473) 602101 Fax: (01473) 680459 E-mail: enquiries@dyerwelding.com *Fabricating, engineering & welding services*

▶ Dyfed Industrial Developments, Graig, Burry Port, Dyfed, SA16 0BJ Tel: (01554) 832777 Fax: (01554) 832777 E-mail: did@draenog.freeserve.co.uk *Pallet racking, shelving, warehouse equipment retailers & installers*

Dyfed Seeds Ltd, Old Llangunnor Rd, Carmarthen, Dyfed, SA31 2BJ Tel: (01267) 237309 Fax: (01267) 238400 E-mail: mail@dyfedseeds.freeserve.co.uk *Seed merchants*

Dyform Jenkins Dunn Ltd, Moland Forge, Central Trading Estate, Shaw Road, Dudley, West Midlands, DY2 8QX Tel: (01384) 232844 Fax: (01384) 455628 *Forging fabrication manufrs*

Dyglen Engineering Ltd, 68 Cavendish Way, Glenrothes, Fife, KY6 2SB Tel: (01592) 774881 Fax: (01592) 774871 E-mail: admin@dyglen.co.uk *Toolmakers manufrs*

Dyke Engineering, Unit 4, Vastre Industrial Estate, Newtown, Powys, SY16 1DZ Tel: (01686) 624412 Fax: (01686) 623236 E-mail: dykeengineering@mid-wales.net *Subcontract engineers*

Robert Dykes & Son, Burnside Works, Westend, Thornhill, Stirling, FK8 3PS Tel: (01786) 850242 Fax: (01786) 850740 *Agricultural engineers*

Dylan Thomas, Railway Yard, Boncath, Dyfed, SA37 0JW Tel: (01239) 841888 Fax: (01239) 841663 *General fabrication work, crane & plant hire*

▶ Dymond Engineering & Metal Products Ltd, Combrew Lane, Bickington, Barnstaple, Devon, EX31 2ND Tel: (01271) 372662 Fax: (01271) 322077 E-mail: sales@dymondengineering.co.uk *Office furniture*

Dyn Metal Ltd, 25-29 Chase Road, London, NW10 6TA Tel: (020) 8961 0656 Fax: (020) 8961 8820 E-mail: info@dynmetal.co.uk *Bronze casting manufrs*

▶ Dynacast UK Ltd, 10 Tything Road, Kinwarton, Alcester, Warwickshire, B49 6EP Tel: (01789) 400100 Fax: (01789) 400999 E-mail: info@dynacast.co.uk

Dynacast (UK) Ltd, Precision House, Arden Road, Alcester, Warwickshire, B49 6HN Tel: (01789) 400100 Fax: (01789) 761058 E-mail: lthomas@dynacast.co.uk *Dynacast is the world's leading precision zinc die-casting supplier to customers worldwide, producing complex three dimensional parts from proprietary high speed machines. Aiming at Zero defect through state of the art CAD, total design solutions and advanced production techniques.*

Dynafluid Ltd, Units D1-D2, Halesfield 21, Telford, Shropshire, TF7 4NX Tel: (01952) 580946 Fax: (01952) 582546 E-mail: enquiries@dynafluid.com *Valves manufrs*

Dynamic Access, Dairy Bungalow, Sodom Lane, Dauntsey, Chippenham, Wiltshire, SN15 4JA Tel: (01249) 891878 Fax: (01249) 891878 E-mail: storm@pgen.net *Nationwide industrial rope access company with over 10 years experience. We can deal with any difficult access projects including building maintenance, repair and painting, banner installations, safety netting, bird netting, electrical installation, glazing replacement and window cleaning.*

Dynamic Balancing Services, Hughenden Avenue, High Wycombe, Buckinghamshire, HP13 5SQ Tel: (01494) 462977 Fax: (01494) 462916 E-mail: sales@dynamicbalancing.co.uk *Balancing (dynamic) services, couplings, power transmission, electric motor repair/rewind specialist services & fan (industrial) maintenance/repair services*

Dynamic Cassette (International) Ltd, Marsh Lane, Boston, Lincolnshire, PE21 7TX Tel: (01205) 355555 Fax: (01205) 354823 E-mail: sales@dci.co.uk *Printing machine consumable manufrs*

Dynamic Construction Ltd, Rose Cottage, 73 Main Road, Kempsey, Worcester, WR5 3NB Tel: (01684) 594763 Fax: 01905 821858 E-mail: hayley.southall@virgin.net *Rental of construction units*

Dynamic Controls Ltd, Union Street, Royton, Oldham, OL2 5JD Tel: 0161-633 3933 Fax: 0161-633 4113 E-mail: sales@dynamiccontrols.co.uk *High pressure valve designers & manufrs*

▶ Dynamic Customer Solutions Ltd, 92 Sandgate Road, Hall Green, Birmingham, B28 0UL Tel: 0121-733 6672E-mail: liz@dynamiccs.co.uk *Specialists in customer relationship management*

▶ Dynamic Developer, Thamley, Mardyke Park, Purfleet, Essex, RM19 1GB Tel: (07956) 992072 E-mail: jomo@dynamicdeveloper.co.uk *Web design, databases, ecommerce & logo*

Dynamic Die & Steel (Sheffield) Ltd, 136 Savile Street East, Sheffield, S4 7UQ Tel: 0114-276 1100 Fax: 0114-275 0752 *General engineering & CNC engineering services*

Dynamic Fashion World, 2A Marlborough Road, Nuneaton, Warwickshire, CV11 5PG Tel: (024) 7664 2003 Fax: (024) 7664 2003 E-mail: razwan-amin@hotmail.com *Baby wear manufrs*

Dynamic Graphix, 8 Quarry Street, Hamilton, Lanarkshire, ML3 7AR Tel: (01698) 891172 Fax: (01698) 337449 E-mail: dynamicgrafix@btconnect.com *custom printed t shirts, polo shirts, workwear and high vis clothing.*

Dynamic Imaging Ltd, 9 Cochrane Square, Brucefield Industrial, Livingston, West Lothian, EH54 9DR Tel: (01506) 415282 Fax: (01506) 410603 E-mail: marketing@dynamicimaging.co.uk *Ultrasound scanning systems design manufrs*

Dynamic Load Monitoring UK Ltd, 3 Bridgers Farm, Nursling Street, Nursling, Southampton, SO16 0YA Tel: (023) 8074 1700 Fax: (023) 8074 1701 E-mail: info@dynaload.co.uk *Load cell manufrs*

Dynamic Packaging Ltd, 18-20 Cater Road, Bishopworth, Bristol, BS13 7TW Tel: 0117-978 1222 Fax: (0117) 978 1333 E-mail: sales@dymanicpackaging.co.uk *Commercial packers packaging service*

▶ Dynamic Packaging, St. Davids Close, Stevenage, Hertfordshire, SG1 4UZ Tel: (01438) 313161 Fax: (01438) 313161

Dynamic Positioning Services Ltd, Unit 2, Denmore Place, Bridge Of Don, Aberdeen, AB23 8JS Tel: (01224) 226850 Fax: (01224) 226851 E-mail: egrant@dynamic-positioning.co.uk *Dynamic positioning system suppliers*

Dynamic Pump Services Ltd, Unit 11 Loomer Road Industrial Estate, Loomer Road, Newcastle, Staffordshire, ST5 7LB Tel: (01782) 566116 Fax: (01782) 566556 E-mail: sales@dynamicpumps.co.uk *Hydraulic engineers, pump & component suppliers*

Dynamic Test Systems, 1 High Street, Puckeridge, Ware, Hertfordshire, SG11 1RN Tel: (01920) 821095 Fax: (01920) 822797 E-mail: dtsinfo98@aol.com *Shock test & measurement equipment*

▶ Dynamic Visions, Unit 6 Whittle Road, Ferndown Industrial Estate, Wimborne, Dorset, BH21 7RU Tel: 01202 890404

Dynamic Water Systems, Central Boulevard, Blythe Valley Park, Shirley, Solihull, West Midlands, B90 8AG Tel: (01564) 711034 Fax: (01564) 711302 E-mail: enquiries-uk@windriver.com *Embedded software company*

Dynamica Ltd, Enterprise Road, Mablethorpe, Lincolnshire, LN12 1NB Tel: (01507) 473052 Fax: (01507) 478832 *Security cabinet manufrs*

Dynamics, Berwicks Trading Estate, Terling Hall Road, Hatfield Peverell, Chelmsford, CM3 2EY Tel: 0870 1620130 Fax: 0870 1688707 E-mail: sales@dynospill-dynamics.com *Dyno Spill Absorbents, Dyno Spill Containments & Accessories. For all of your Oil, Chemical & Emergency Spill requirements, Dyno Spill has got it covered. We offer on-site Spill Risk Surveys and bespoke Spill Kits tailored to your individual needs.*

Dynamics (Bristol) Ltd, 1 Evercreech Way, Walrow Industrial Estate, Highbridge, Somerset, TA9 4AN Tel: (01278) 780222 Fax: (01278) 781824 E-mail: info@dynamicsbristol.co.uk *Transformer rectifier manufrs*

▶ Dynamite Pictures, 8 Wilkinson Terrace, Stutton, Tadcaster, North Yorkshire, LS24 9BP Tel: (07816) 319195 E-mail: richard.ball@lycos.co.uk *Video editing & web design*

Dynamotive Calibration Services, Whitwick Business Park, Stenson Road, Coalville, Leicestershire, LE67 4JP Tel: (01530) 277930 Fax: (01530) 277931 E-mail: sales@dynamotive.co.uk *Automotive test equipment manufrs*

▶ Dynaseq Monitoring Group, Unit 79 Greenfield Business Centre, Greenfield Road, Greenfield, Holywell, Clwyd, CH8 7GR Tel: (01352) 710600 Fax: (01352) 710703 E-mail: sales@dynaseq.co.uk *Vibration analysis consultancy*

Dynasurf, Millbuck Way, Sandbach, Cheshire, CW11 3HT Tel: (01270) 763091 Fax: (01270) 766564 E-mail: dynasurf@btconnect.com *Hard chrome depositors & precision grinders*

Dynatork Air Motors Ltd, Merchant Drive, Hertford, SG13 7BL Tel: (01992) 501900 Fax: (01992) 509890 E-mail: dynatork@huco.com *Dynatork air motors have manufactured a technically unique range of air motors for over 30 years and are in operation worldwide. The air motors are used in all industries on a whole host of applications which include the following; Air motors, pneumatic components, gearbox, wormwheel gearbox, planetary gearbox, piston motor, stirring, indexing, conveying, transmission, drive control, pneumatic motors, conveyor drums, control valve, belt drive, chain drives, pressure drives, high torque drives, speed control systems, pump drives, pumps, plastic motors, material handling, storage systems, mechanical handling, machining, textile drives, agitators, variable speed drives, variable torque drives, torque limiters, valve modulation, metering drives, positional control systems, oil industry drives, filter drives, opening and closing door systems, louvre drive systems, labelling machine drives, packaging machine drives, filling machine drives, heavy vehicle drive system,*

continued

trolley drives, coiling drives, uncoiling drives, winding drives, tension drives, marine drive, clamping drives, sealing drives, valve drives, modulating control, petrochemical drives, pharmaceutical drive, tablet brushing drives, emergency shut down drives, clutch actuator, bucket conveyor drives, submerged drives, marine drive.

▶ Dynawest Plastics Ltd, Jaylyn House, Elton Park Hadleigh Road, Ipswich, IP2 0DG Tel: (01473) 230248 Fax: (01473) 230256 E-mail: sales@dynawest.co.uk *Manufacturers of plastic palettes matting, environmental products*

Dyne Technology Ltd, PO Box 9593, Tamworth, Staffordshire, B78 3NU Tel: (01827) 284244 Fax: (01827) 286311 E-mail: info@dynetechnology.co.uk *Sales & marketing company*

Dynea UK Ltd, Alyn Works, Denbigh Road, Mold, Clwyd, CH7 1BF Tel: (01352) 757657 Fax: (01352) 758914 E-mail: sales@dynea.com *Synthetic resin specialists*

Dynex Semi Conductor Ltd, Doddington Road, Lincoln, LN6 3LF Tel: (01522) 500500 Fax: (01522) 500550 *Semi conductor manufrs*

Dynex-Rivett Inc, Unit C5, Steel Close, Eaton Socon, St. Neots, Cambridgeshire, PE19 8TT Tel: (01480) 213980 Fax: (01480) 405662 E-mail: sales@dynexhydraulics.co.uk *High pressure hydraulics distribution & sales services*

Dynis Ltd, The Chequers, St. Marys Way, Chesham, Buckinghamshire, HP5 1LL Tel: (01494) 777666 Fax: (01494) 777555 E-mail: sales@dynix.com *Automated library systems*

Dynisco (UK) Ltd, Unit 2B Crowood House, Gipsy Lane, Swindon, SN2 8YY Tel: (01527) 577077 Fax: (01527) 577070 E-mail: dyniscouk@dynisco.com *Pressure transducer manufrs*

Dyno-Locks, 143 Maple Road, Surbiton, Surrey, KT6 4BJ Tel: (020) 8481 2200 Fax: (020) 8481 2288 E-mail: postmaster@dyno.com *Lock repair, installation & security*

▶ Dynoptic Systems Ltd, Furlong House, Crowfield, Brackley, Northamptonshire, NN13 5TW Tel: (01280) 850521 Fax: (01280) 850568 E-mail: contact@dynoptic.com *Range of opacity and particulate monitors and sensors capable of measurements including mg/m3, opacity percentage, Ringleman, MOR - meteorological optical range - extinction and transmission suitable for boilers, incinerators, crematoria, power stations, furnaces, cement processing, bag houses, air filtration plant and tunnel monitoring.*

Dy-rect Services Ltd, Unit 8 Hikers Way, Crendon Industrial Park, Long Crendon, Aylesbury, Buckinghamshire, HP18 9RW Tel: (01844) 202233 Fax: (01844) 208748 E-mail: info@dy-rect.co.uk *Ductwork contractors*

▶ Dyrlaga Thompson Print, 1c Anchor Bridge Way, Dewsbury, West Yorkshire, WF12 9QS Tel: (01924) 456655 Fax: (01924) 460986

▶ Dysk Air Conditioning Equipment, Unit 3 40 Coldharbour Lane, Harpenden, Hertfordshire, AL5 4UN Tel: (01582) 463420 *Air Conditioning equipment distributors*

Dyson Ltd, Tetbury Hill, Malmesbury, Wiltshire, SN16 0RP Tel: (01666) 827200 Fax: (01666) 827299 E-mail: james.ross-smith@dyson.com *Vacuum cleaner manufrs*

Dyson Diecastings Ltd, Denbigh Industrial Estate, Second Avenue, Bletchley, Milton Keynes, MK1 1EA Tel: (01908) 279200 Fax: (01908) 279219 E-mail: dyson@alumascprecision.co.uk *Quality zinc suppliers*

Dyson Fork Truck Services, Unit 1 Lawn Court, Lawn Road Industrial Estate, Carlton-in-Lindrick, Worksop, Nottinghamshire, S81 9ED Tel: (01909) 732040 Fax: (01909) 732073 *Fork truck repairing services*

Dyson Group plc, 381 Fulwood Road, Sheffield, S10 3GB Tel: 0114-230 3921 Fax: 0114-230 8583 *Steel factory materials*

▶ Dyson Industries Ltd, Griffs Works, Stopes Road, Stannington, Sheffield, S6 6BW Tel: 0114-234 8663 Fax: 0114-232 2519 E-mail: enq@dyson-holloware.com *Refractories & industrial materials*

Dyson Insulations Ltd, Unit 16H, Sollingsby Park, Gateshead, Tyne & Wear, NE10 8YF Tel: 0191-416 5969 Fax: 0191-417 3817 *Insulation contractors & distributors* Also at: Halifax

James Dyson Ltd, Hoyle Ing Dyeworks, Linthwaite, Huddersfield, HD7 5RU Tel: (01484) 842456 Fax: (01484) 847253 E-mail: enquiries@jamesdyson.co.uk *Commission dyers*

Peter Dyson & Son Ltd, 3 Cuckoo Lane, Honley, Holmfirth, HD9 6AS Tel: (01484) 661062 Fax: (01484) 663709 *Gunsmiths*

Dyson Precision Ceramics, Low Road, Earlsheaton, Dewsbury, West Yorkshire, WF12 8BU Tel: (01924) 468201 Fax: (01924) 459429 *Glass shapes manufrs*

Dyson Presswork Ltd, Moor St Industrial Estate, Brierley Hill, West Midlands, DY5 3TS Tel: (01384) 77252 Fax: (01384) 480429 E-mail: gbh26@dial.pipex.com *General presswork manufrs*

Dyson Products, Moor St Industrial Estate, Moor Street, Brierley Hill, West Midlands, DY5 3ST Tel: (01384) 77833 Fax: (01384) 263724 *Electric conduit fittings manufrs*

Dytech Corporation Ltd, Stubley Lane, Dronfield, Derbyshire, S18 1LS Tel: (01246) 299700 Fax: (01246) 299720 E-mail: sales@hi-por.com *Ceramic products*

Dytecna Ltd, Spring Lane, Malvern, Worcestershire, WR14 1AL Tel: (01684) 892320 Fax: (01684) 892320 E-mail: info@dytecna.co.uk *Communications equipment*

Dywidag Systems International Ltd, Northfield Road, Kineton Road Industrial Estate, Southam, Warwickshire, CV47 0FG Tel: (01926) 813980 Fax: (01926) 813817 E-mail: sales@dywidag.co.uk *Specialist geotechnical system suppliers*

DZD Blyco Ltd, Lower Ground Floor, 145 Tottenham Court Road, London, W1T 7NE Tel: (020) 7388 7488 Fax: (020) 7388 7499 E-mail: enquiries@dzd.co.uk *Merchandise design company*

E A B Associates, 3 Craven Court, Craven Road, Broadheath, Altrincham, Cheshire, WA14 5DY Tel: 0161-926 9077 Fax: 0161-927 7718 E-mail: eaball@eabassoc.co.uk *Foaming agents & roof coating manufrs*

E A Bell Ltd, 45a Church Road, Kells, Ballymena, County Antrim, BT42 3JU Tel: (028) 2589 2164 *Agricultural merchants*

E A C Ltd, PO Box 6023, Solihull, West Midlands, B93 0JN Tel: (01564) 770359 Fax: (01564) 774025 E-mail: eaccomps@aol.com *Pressure switches manufrs*

▶ E A C Group Of Companies, Jubilee House, Broadway, Silver End, Witham, Essex, CM8 3RQ Tel: (01376) 585855 Fax: (01376) 587910 E-mail: mail@eacgroup.net *Suspended ceiling system suppliers*

E A Combs Ltd, Quantum House Station Estate, Eastwood Close, London, E18 1BY Tel: (020) 8530 4216 Fax: (020) 8530 1310 E-mail: sales@eacombs.co.uk *Clock importers & manufrs*

E A E Polishing Services Ltd, Green Street, Oldham, OL8 1TA Tel: 0161-678 8273 Fax: 0161-628 5144 E-mail: sales@eaepolishingservices.co.uk *Metal finishing & polishing services*

E A Ellison & Co. Ltd, Crondal Road, Bayton Industrial Estate, Exhall, Coventry, CV7 9NH Tel: (024) 7636 1619 Fax: (024) 7637 9183 E-mail: sales@ellisons.co.uk *Hairdressing & beauty suppliers.* Also at: Birmingham & Leicester

E A Foulds Ltd, Clifton Street, Colne, Lancashire, BB8 9AE Tel: (01282) 861500 Fax: (01282) 869655 E-mail: info@fouldslifts.co.uk *Supply service repair & refurbishment of lifts*

E A & H Sandford Lifting Ltd, Albion Parade, Gravesend, Kent, DA12 2RN Tel: (01474) 365361 Fax: (01474) 569036 *Lifting gear manufrs*

▶ E A P International Ltd, Junction 19 Industrial Park, Green Lane, Heywood, Lancashire, OL10 1NB Tel: (01706) 624422 Fax: (01706) 624455 E-mail: sales@eapseals.com Sales Contact: S. Glover *As a "Specialist Distributor" of industrial sealing products, with one of the largest stockholdings in Europe, we are able to offer a unique and personal service to all of our customers. If you have not previously dealt with us we can open a credit account for you instantly with minimal formalities, and we can do this whatever part of the world you are in. We have been stockists and worldwide distributors of ERIKS Seals and Gaskets and associated items for over 30 years.* Also at: Romford

E A S E, Mill Farm Business Park, Mill Field Road, Hounslow, TW4 5PY Tel: (020) 8893 9121 E-mail: wilma@ease.co.uk *Computer software development & hardware*

E A Signs, 25 New Street, Oadby, Leicester, LE2 5EB Tel: 0116-271 0474 Fax: 0116-271 7708 E-mail: enquiries@easwindows.co.uk *Sign & window manufrs*

▶ E & A Site Services, 34 Kingsman Road, Stanford-le-Hope, Essex, SS17 0JW Tel: (01375) 644400 Fax: (01375) 644400 E-mail: eass@approvedtrading.com *Thermal Insulation Specialists; With over 35 years experience in the trade, we are proficient in providing the following non-exhaustive list of services;** Ducting Insulation* Boiler Insulation* Pipework Insulation * Vessels Insulation**Work can be completed to all specifications, including:** Metal cladding* Polyisobutylene (PIB) * Isogenopak**We would be pleased to offer a quotation for any of the abovementioned services.***

E A Sowter Ltd, Old Boatyard, Cullingham Road, Ipswich, IP1 2EG Tel: (01473) 219390 Fax: (01473) 236188 E-mail: sales@sowter.co.uk *Audio transformers designers & manufrs*

E A Tailby Ltd, Bath Road, Kettering, Northamptonshire, NN16 8NL Tel: (01536) 512639 Fax: (01536) 414816 *Manufacturers of heels & pre-fabricated soles*

E A Technology Ltd, Capenhurst Lane, Capenhurst, Chester, CH1 6ES Tel: 0151-339 4181 Fax: 0151-347 2404 E-mail: john.hutchinson@eatechnology.com *Research, development & consultants service to the utility industry*

E & A Wates Ltd, 82-84 Mitcham Lane, London, SW16 6NR Tel: (020) 8769 2205 Fax: (020) 8677 4766 E-mail: sales@eandawates.co.uk *House furnishers & removal contractors* Also at: London SW17

E A West, Pyewipe, Grimsby, South Humberside, DN31 2SW Tel: (01472) 232000 Fax: (01472) 232020 E-mail: hmats_uk@huntsman.com *Water & sewage & effluent treatment chemicals*

E Abrahams & Co. Ltd, 1 Crown Close, London, E3 2JH Tel: (020) 8980 1937 Fax: (020) 8980 3762 E-mail: info@abrahamscases.co.uk *Packing & plywood box case manufrs*

E Anderson, 29 South Esplanade West, Aberdeen, AB11 9AA Tel: (01224) 877609 *Fish processors*

E Aston & Son Ltd, Dale Street, Bilston, West Midlands, WV14 7JY Tel: (01902) 402418 Fax: (01902) 493546 *Haulage contractors*

▶ E B A Consulting Ltd, PO Box 14, Kidwelly, Dyfed, SA17 4YH Tel: (01554) 890300 Fax: (01554) 891508 E-mail: info@ebassociates.co.uk *Business support & advice services*

E B Balmforth Ltd, The Old Forge, Sproxton, York, YO62 5EF Tel: (01439) 770568 Fax: (01437) 770618 *Leather manufrs*

E B Bright Engineering Sales, Unit 1 Tennis Court Industrial Estate, Nottingham, NG2 4EW Tel: 0115-950 6570 Fax: 0115-959 0921 E-mail: brightbearings@supanet.com *Bearing distributors, stockists & agents*

E B C Asset Management Ltd, East India House, 109-117 Middlesex Street, London, E1 7JF Tel: (020) 7621 0101 Fax: (020) 7626 7915 *Investment management services*

E B C Brakes, EBC Building, Countess Road, Northampton, NN5 7EA Tel: (01604) 583344 Fax: (01604) 583744 E-mail: info@ebcbrackesuk.com *Car components manufr*

E B C Computers, The Orchard, The Highway, Croesyceiliog, Cwmbran, Gwent, NP44 2NH Tel: (01633) 869670 Fax: (01633) 485547 *Computer software*

E B C Corporate Consultants Ltd, East India Ho, 109-117 Middlesex St, London, E1 7JF Tel: (020) 7621 0101 Fax: (020) 7626 7915 E-mail: sales@ebcam.co.uk *Corporate finance advisers*

E B D Computing Solutions Ltd, 57 Woodside, Ponteland, Newcastle upon Tyne, NE20 9JB Tel: (01661) 820389 Fax: (01661) 820389 E-mail: akeogh@excellencebydesign.co.uk *Computer solutions consultants*

E B Engineering, 17 All Saints Industrial Estate, All Saints Street, Birmingham, B18 7RJ Tel: 0121-551 3274 Fax: 0121-551 3274 *Precision engineers*

▶ E & B Engineering Services Special Works Ltd, 71-77 Brighton Road, Horley, Surrey, RH6 7HL Tel: (01293) 783344

E B Equipment Ltd, Barugh Green Road, Redbrook, Barnsley, South Yorkshire, S75 1HR Tel: (01226) 730037 Fax: (01226) 738101 E-mail: info@eb-equipment.com *Livestock feeding systems*

E B Hayward & Co., Sheet Metal Works, Nupend, Ashleworth, Gloucester, GL19 4JJ Tel: (01452) 700384 Fax: (01452) 700740 E-mail: simon@ebhayward.demon.co.uk *Sheet metalwork fabricators*

E B Mason & Son, 38 Breckhill Road, Woodthorpe, Nottingham, NG5 4GP Tel: 0115-926 4265 Fax: 0115-967 1537 *Electrical contractors*

E B R Ltd, West Quay Road, Enterprise Park, Sunderland, SR5 2TE Tel: 0191-501 1777 Fax: 0191-501 1700 E-mail: info@ebr.co.uk *Flexographic printers & converters services*

E B Service, 45 Bennett Road, Ipswich, IP1 5HU Tel: (01473) 421370 Fax: (01473) 421370 E-mail: eb.service@ntlworld.com *Cash registers & catering equipment suppliers*

E B V Elektronik, Thames House, 17 Marlow Road, Maidenhead, Berkshire, SL6 7AA Tel: (01628) 770707 Fax: (01628) 783811 *Semiconductor distributors*

E Bacon & Co. Ltd, Hutton Road, Grimsby, South Humberside, DN31 3PS Tel: (01472) 350267 Fax: (01472) 250987 E-mail: info@baconengineering.com *General engineers & welders*

E Binns & Sons Ltd, Stainland Road, Greetland, Halifax, West Yorkshire, HX4 8BD Tel: (01422) 372347 Fax: (01422) 377938 *Steelwork manufrs*

E Bowden & Sons, Little Woodland, Old Newton Road, Bovey Tracey, Newton Abbot, Devon, TQ13 9DT Tel: (01626) 833374 Fax: (01626) 832144 E-mail: ebowden@btconnect.com *Agricultural implement engineers*

E Bundock, 172 Parrock Street, Gravesend, Kent, DA12 1ER Tel: (01474) 327191 *Jewellery manufrs*

E Burke, Dock Road Industrial Estate, Connah's Quay, Deeside, Clwyd, CH5 4DS Tel: (01244) 831952 *Plant repairs*

▶ E C A, The Brackens, London Road, Ascot, Berkshire, SL5 8BE Tel: (01344) 882240 Fax: (01344) 882219 *Systems integrator services*

E C Cables Ltd, Unit 4B, Waymills Industrial Estate, Waymills, Whitchurch, Shropshire, SY13 1TT Tel: (01948) 660950 Fax: (01948) 660959 E-mail: ec.cables@virgin.net *Electric wire & cable distributors*

E C Computers Ltd, Mead Court, Cooper Road, Thornbury, Bristol, BS35 3UW Tel: (01454) 281500 Fax: (0870) 7776444 E-mail: info@eccomputers.co.uk *Computer sales, repairs & support*

▶ E C Creative Services Ltd, 1 Lansdowne Road, Chadderton, Oldham, OL9 9EF Tel: 0161-628 7723 Fax: 0161-284 6654

E C De Witt & Co Ltd, Tudor Road, Manor Park, Runcorn, Cheshire, WA7 1SZ Tel: (01928) 756800 Fax: (01928) 579712 *Toiletry manufrs*

E C E Environmental Control Equipment Ltd, Harvel Works, Harvel, Meopham, Gravesend, Kent, DA13 0BT Tel: (01474) 814432 Fax: (01474) 812488 E-mail: richardbarnes@ece.uk.com *Air conditioning equipment manufrs*

▶ E C E Systems Turnkey Ltd, Wendover Road, Rackheath, Norwich, NR13 6LH Tel: (01603) 721200 Fax: (01603) 721232 E-mail: info@ecesystems.co.uk *Electrical & mechanical services*

E C Electricals Ltd, 16C Wincombe Business Park, Warminster Road, Shaftesbury, Dorset, SP7 9QJ Tel: (01747) 853861 Fax: (01747) 855274 E-mail: enquiries@ecelectricals.co.uk *Electrical contractors*

E & C Engineering Services Ltd, Bargate House Woodside Park, Catteshall Lane, Godalming, Surrey, GU7 1LG Tel: (01483) 426766 Fax: (01483) 426708 E-mail: info@ecengineering.co.uk *Electrical goods test services*

▶ E C F Special Alloys Ltd, Lawn Road, Carlton-in-Lindrick, Worksop, Nottinghamshire, S81 9LB Tel: (01909) 540520 Fax: (01909) 540522

▶ E C Farrell (Transport) Ltd, Ashton Lane, Chester, CH3 8AA Tel: (01829) 751558

E C Gulbrandsen Ltd, Water Lane, Ancaster, Grantham, Lincolnshire, NG32 3QS Tel: (01400) 230700 Fax: (01400) 230601 *Chemical production*

E C H M, 43 Eagle Street, London, WC1R 4AT Tel: (020) 7304 9000 Fax: (020) 7304 9001 *Financial recruitment agency*

E C Hallam Engineering Leicester Ltd, Beaufield Smeeton Road, Kibworth, Leicester, LE8 0LG Tel: 0116-279 2330 E-mail: carey@hallam-eng.freeserve.co.uk *Aviation tow tractors*

E C Hodge MF Ltd, Norton Road, Stevenage, Hertfordshire, SG1 2BB Tel: (01438) 357341 Fax: (01438) 361408 E-mail: echodgemflimited@aol.com *Kitchen furniture manufrs*

E C Hopkins Ltd, Barton Industrial Estate, Mount Pleasant, Bilston, West Midlands, WV14 7LH Tel: (01902) 401755 Fax: (01902) 495097 E-mail: bhopkins@echopkins.co.uk *Automotive component suppliers & flocked cable manufrs*

E C Hopkins, Unit 34 Stretford Motorway Estate, Stretford, Manchester, M32 0ZH Tel: 0161-866 9122 Fax: 0161-866 9121 E-mail: sales@echopkins.com *Suppliers to engineering & metal finishing industries & woodworking*

E C I Europe Ltd, The Coach House, 52a Priory Street, Colchester, CO1 2QB Tel: (01206) 864600 *Computer outsourcers*

E C I Telecom, Isis House, Gastons Wood, Chineham, Basingstoke, Hampshire, RG24 8TW Tel: (01256) 388000 Fax: (01256) 388143 *Network service providers*

E C I Ventures, Brettenham House, Lancaster Place, London, WC2E 7EN Tel: (020) 7606 1000 Fax: (020) 7240 5050 *Venture capital*

▶ E C L Integrated Solutions, E Wrexham Road, Basildon, Essex, SS15 6PX Tel: (01268) 540926 Fax: (01268) 415326

E C Landamore & Co. Ltd, Elanco Works, Marsh Road, Hoveton, Norwich, NR12 8UH Tel: (01603) 782212 Fax: (01603) 784166 *Boat builders*

E C Logistics, Swallowfield Way, Hayes, Middlesex, UB3 1DQ Tel: (020) 8569 1918 Fax: (020) 8813 6564 E-mail: helpdesk@eclogistics.co.uk Principal Export Areas: Worldwide *Mailing & fulfillment services*

E C M Electronics Ltd, Penmaen House, London Road, Ashington, Pulborough, West Sussex, RH20 3JR Tel: (01903) 892810 Fax: (01903) 892738 E-mail: ecm@ecmelectronics.co.uk *Electronic component manufrs*

▶ E C M Fleet Wash, 148 Station Road, Whittlesey, Peterborough, PE7 2HA Tel: (01733) 206749 Fax: (01733) 206992 *Industrial cleaning equipment & chemicals also pressure washer manufrs*

E C M (UK) Ltd, The Old Yard, Rectory Lane, Brasted, Westerham, Kent, TN16 1JP Tel: (01959) 569999 Fax: (01959) 563333 *Utility consultants*

▶ E C M Vehicle Delivery Service Ltd, Carlisle Airport, Carlisle, CA6 4NW Tel: (01228) 573491 Fax: (01228) 573390

E C N (UK) Ltd, Mambury Moor Estate, Buckland Brewer, Bideford, Devon, EX39 5NL Tel: (01237) 451002 Fax: (01237) 451002 *Agricultural & industrial buildings*

E C O Manufacturing Ltd, St. Marys Road, Ramsey, Huntingdon, Cambridgeshire, PE26 2SJ Tel: (01487) 710800 Fax: (01487) 710900 E-mail: sales@ecomanufacturing.com *Office screen divider manufrs*

▶ E C P S, 1 Clooney Road, Londonderry, BT47 6TB Tel: (028) 7186 1174 Fax: (028) 7186 1179

▶ E C R Concepts, Unit 28, Hirwaun Industrial Estate, Hirwaun, Aberdare, Mid Glamorgan, CF44 9UP Tel: (01685) 810222 Fax: (01685) 810333

E C R Retail Systems Ltd, 297-303 Edgware Road, London, NW9 6NB Tel: (020) 8205 7766 Fax: (020) 8205 1493 E-mail: sales@ecr-systems.co.uk *EPOS terminals suppliers*

E C Reese Agricultural Ltd, Rose Brook, Pwlltrap, St. Clears, Carmarthen, SA33 4AR Tel: (01994) 230560 Fax: (01994) 230133 *Agricultural machinery repairs & sales*

E C S Business Forms Ltd, Harbour House, Coldharbour Lane, Rainham, Essex, RM13 9YA Tel: (01708) 555241 Fax: (01708) 525244 *Computer stationery suppliers*

E C S Computers Ltd, 98-99 London Road, King's Lynn, Norfolk, PE30 5HA Tel: (01553) 692727 Fax: (01553) 764564 E-mail: support@ecscomputers.co.uk *Computers sales & support*

E C S (Nottingham) Ltd, Unit 17 Hazelford Way, Newstead Village, Nottingham, NG15 0DQ Tel: (01623) 720444 Fax: (01623) 720445 E-mail: sales@ecsnotts.co.uk *Emulsion coating & graphic supplies*

E C S Phillips Lighting Controls, Phillips Centre, Guildford Business Park, Guildford, Surrey, GU2 8XH Tel: (01483) 293235 Fax: (01483) 575534 E-mail: ecs.phillips@phillips.com Principal Export Areas: Worldwide *Energy light saving controls manufrs*

▶ E C Saines & Co. Ltd, 417 New Cross Road, London, SE14 6TA Tel: (020) 8692 4443

E C Signs, Unit 33, Leyton Ind Village, Argall Ave, London, E10 7QP Tel: (020) 8556 7222 Fax: (020) 8518 7676 *Sign makers*

E C Snaith & Son Ltd, 20 Vale Street, Denbigh, Clwyd, LL16 3BE Tel: (01745) 812218 Fax: (01745) 816367 *Military tailors*

E C T Commercial Ltd, 112 Burcott Road, Severnside Trading Estate, Avonmouth, Bristol, BS11 8AF Tel: 0117-982 3825 Fax: 0117-982 4666 E-mail: commercial@ectrecycling.co.uk *Recycling*

▶ E C Tooling Systems Ltd, 1 Havant Business Centre, Harts Farm Way, Havant, Hampshire, PO9 1HU Tel: (023) 9248 0481 Fax: (023) 9248 0482 E-mail: info@ectooling.com *Manufacturers of high quality products on a subcontract basis*

E C Walton & Co. Ltd, Old North Road, Sutton-on-Trent, Newark, Nottinghamshire, NG23 6QN Tel: (01636) 821215 Fax: (01636) 822027 E-mail: waltons@waltons.co.uk *Timber garden building manufrs*

E C Williams Ltd, 17 Spencer Street, Birmingham, B18 6DN Tel: 0121-236 2524 Fax: 0121-233 4931 E-mail: plating@ecwilliams.co.uk *Electroplating services*

E C Y (Holdings) Ltd, Barley Castle Lane, Appleton, Warrington, WA4 4RB Tel: (01925) 860000 Fax: (01925) 861111 E-mail: sales@ecyltd.co.uk *Construction equipment hire*

E Chambers Mechanical Engineering Ltd, 32 Regal Drive, Soham, Ely, Cambridgeshire, CB7 5BE Tel: (01353) 624126 Fax: (01353) 624127 E-mail: info@ecl-ductwork.co.uk *Ductwork manufrs*

▶ E Cocoon, Gaddesden Place, Great Gaddesden, Hemel Hempstead, Hertfordshire, HP2 6EX Tel: (01442) 231000 Fax: (01442) 231600

E Cook Iron & Steel Ltd, 11 Monmore Road, Wolverhampton, WV1 2TZ Tel: (01902) 404740 *Scrap iron merchants*

E Crowley & Sons Ltd, Bentalls, Pipps Hill Industrial Estate, Basildon, Essex, SS14 3BY Tel: (01268) 293605 Fax: (01268) 285452 E-mail: sales@crowleysaws.com *Tungsten carbide tipped saw manufrs*

E.D.C. International Ltd, Brook House Station Road, Pangbourne, Reading, RG8 7AN Tel: 0118-984 2040 Fax: 0118-984 5300 E-mail: sales@edcinternational.com *Electronic control, condensate pumps & low ambient control manufrs*

E D C Technology, Suite 24, Mountbatten House, Hillcrest, Highgate, London, N6 4HJ Tel: (020) 8341 2689 *Electronic sign manufrs*

E D G S B Ltd, The Mews, 70 London Road, Burgess Hill, West Sussex, RH15 8NB Tel: (01444) 248691 Fax: (01444) 248721 E-mail: sales@edg.co.uk *Consulting & contracting engineers*

E D L Packaging, Oswald Street, Burnley, Lancashire, BB12 0BY Tel: (01282) 429305 Fax: (01282) 429350 E-mail: sales@johnquinn.co.uk *Packaging machine manufrs*

E D M Group Ltd, Woden Road, Wolverhampton, WV10 0AY Tel: (01902) 459907 Fax: (01902) 351243 E-mail: docman@edm.co.uk *Document management*

E D S, 57 Castle Street, Aberdeen, AB11 5BB Tel: (01224) 595705 Fax: (01224) 595705 E-mail: finnieseds@dsl.pipex.com *Graphic designers*

E D S, Matrix House, Northern Boulevard, Matrix Park, Swansea Enterprise Park, Swansea, SA6 8RE Tel: (01792) 785500 Fax: (01792) 785555 *Computer systems & software developers*

▶ E D S Developments Ltd, Unit 20, Saltash Business Park, Forge Lane, Moorlands Trading Estate, Saltash, Cornwall, PL12 6LX Tel: (01752) 847900 Fax: (01752) 837251 E-mail: info@edsdevelopments.com *Design & build of special purpose machines for automated industry*

E D S Roofing Supplies (Midlands) Ltd, Unit 3, Bilton Way, Lutterworth, Leicestershire, LE17 4JA Tel: (01455) 558877 Fax: (01455) 550116 E-mail: sales@eds-midlands.co.uk *Roofing material suppliers*

▶ E D S Systems North Wales Ltd, Heathfield, Padeswood Road, Buckley, Clwyd, CH7 2JL Tel: (01244) 541056 Fax: (0870) 7052350 E-mail: admin@edssystems.com *structured cableing installers CAT 5e CAT 6,Fibre Optic installers, fault findinf/repairs terminationand testing, CCTV, access control,Telephone systems*

E Darley, Darfield House, Hull Road, Hemingbrough, Selby, North Yorkshire, YO8 6QJ Tel: (01757) 638233 *Agricultural engineering*

▶ E Design House, 20 Elm Street, Blackburn, BB1 5NL Tel: (0871) 2221406 Fax: (0871) 2221407 E-mail: info@e-designhouse.co.uk *e-designhouse is a creative renaissance in graphic & website design. Our services include web site development, graphic design, multimedia, ecommerce solutions, animation and corporate identity.*

E Dobson & Co Gaskets Ltd, Oakworth Road, Keighley, West Yorkshire, BD21 1QQ Tel: (01535) 607257 Fax: (01535) 608171 E-mail: sales@dobsongasket.com *Manufacturers of asbestos-free packing*

E & E Engineering Ltd, Unit 74 Blackpole Trading Estate West, Worcester, WR3 8TJ Tel: (01905) 453527 Fax: (01905) 457395 E-mail: enquiries@e-and-e.co.uk *Precision machining engineers*

E E F, Broadway House, Cothill Street, London, SW1H 9NQ Tel: (020) 7222 7777 Fax: (020) 7343 3190 E-mail: enquires@eef-fed.org.uk *Trade association*

E E F Yorkshire & Humberside, Field Head, Sandhills, Thorner, Leeds, LS14 3DN Tel: 0113-289 2671 Fax: 0113-289 3170 E-mail: mtaylor@eef-yandh.org.uk *Employment law, employment tribunals, employee relations, HR, health & safety, environment, training & development, information & statistics, publications*

E E Moss, 3 26 Maryland Road, London, E15 1JJ Tel: (020) 8519 4227 Fax: (020) 8502 7087 *Cabinet makers & joiners*

E E Olley & Sons Ltd, Dartford Trade Park, Dartford, DA1 1PE Tel: (01322) 227681 Fax: (01322) 289724 E-mail: sales@eeolley.co.uk *Specialist timber importers services*

E E P Electrical, Crondal Road, Exhall, Coventry, CV7 9NH Tel: (024) 7636 3010 Fax: (024) 7636 5182 *Electrical contractors*

E E S Bristol Ltd, 62 Shirehampton Road, Bristol, BS9 2DL Tel: 0117-968 4002 Fax: 0117-968 3536 E-mail: kit@ees-group.co.uk *Supply & install lightning protection systems*

E E S Data, 41 George Street, Wakefield, West Yorkshire, WF1 1LW Tel: (01924) 200103 Fax: (01924) 200104 E-mail: info@ees-data.co.uk *Computer software developers services*

E E S London Ltd, 79 Croydon Road, Caterham, Surrey, CR3 6PD Tel: (01883) 341166 Fax: (01883) 341133 *Lightning conductor installers*

E & E Workwear, Church Lane, Marple, Stockport, Cheshire, SK6 7AR Tel: 0161-427 6522 Fax: 0161-426 0906 E-mail: eeworkwear@hotmail.com *Work wear manufrs*

E F C Fencing, Estate Yard, Lawnhead, Stafford, ST20 0JQ Tel: (01785) 284477 Fax: (01785) 284825 E-mail: andy@efcfencing.com *Fencing and gate manufrs. concrete timber and steel fencing stockists. Nationwide delivery service*

E & F Composites Ltd, Graythorp Industrial Estate, Hartlepool, Cleveland, TS25 2DF Tel: (01429) 272356 Fax: (01429) 861571 E-mail: sales@eandf-composites.co.uk *PU foam moulders, glass fibre reinforced plastics & fabricators*

E F D International, Unit 14 Apex Business Centre, Boscombe Road, Dunstable, Bedfordshire, LU5 4SB Tel: (01582) 666334 Fax: (01582) 664227 E-mail: sales@efd-inc.com *Fluid dispensing equipment distributors*

E F E & G B Nets, Bodmin, Cornwall, PL31 1YJ Tel: (01208) 873945 Fax: (01208) 873945 E-mail: sales@efe-uk.com *Field survey equipment manufrs*

▶ E F F, Haw Road, Londonderry, BT47 6XT Tel: (028) 7186 5050

▶ E F I Ltd, 46 Melbourne Road, Lowestoft, Suffolk, NR32 1ST Tel: (01502) 518397 Fax: (01502) 566692 E-mail: sales@efisystems.co.uk *Manufacturer & supplier of hot runner controllers*

▶ E & F Joinery Ltd, Unit 14, Apex Park, Diplocks Way, Hailsham, East Sussex, BN27 3JU Tel: (01323) 445500

E F M A, 4 Northgate Close, Rottingdean, Brighton, BN2 7DZ Tel: (01273) 495002 Fax: (01273) 495022 E-mail: sales@efma.co.uk *Reproduction furniture manufrs*

E F Moy Ltd, Elstree Film Studios, Shenley Road, Borehamwood, Hertfordshire, WD6 1JG Tel: (020) 8324 2634 Fax: (020) 8324 2336 *Precision engineers*

E F R Refrigeration, 695 High Road, Ilford, Essex, IG3 8RH Tel: (020) 8590 0022 Fax: (020) 8599 2870 E-mail: danney535@fsmail.net *Air conditioning & refrigeration suppliers*

E F S Manufacturing, 1 Newmarket Road, Stow-cum-Quy, Cambridge, CB5 9AQ Tel: (01223) 813848 Fax: (01223) 813848 *Printed circuit assembly services*

E & F Services Ltd, 10 Westleigh Business Park, Winchester Avenue, Blaby, Leicester, LE8 4EZ Tel: 0116-247 7450 Fax: 0116-247 7487 E-mail: info@eandfservices.com *Manufacturers of air filtration & dust collecting equipment*

E Farrington & Co. Ltd, Regent Engineering Works, Robert Street, Hyde, Cheshire, SK14 1BN Tel: 0161-368 1675 Fax: 0161-367 8868 E-mail: info@farringtons.fsbusiness.co.uk *Sheet metalworkers & light engineers*

E Felman Ltd, Barking Industrial Park, Alfreds Way, Barking, Essex, IG11 0TJ Tel: (020) 8594 0643 Fax: (020) 8594 0659 *Clothing wholesalers & distributors*

E Flat Minor Ltd, 1 Sheppy Race, Long Street, Croscombe, Wells, Somerset, BA5 3QL Tel: (01749) 343484 E-mail: info@eflatminor.co.uk *Musical Instruments & Accessories, Music Recordings, Event Management & Photography*

▶ E Fletcher Chesterfield, Burley Close, Chesterfield, Derbyshire, S40 2UB Tel: (01246) 545601 Fax: (01246) 545600 E-mail: admin@efletcher.co.uk

▶ E Francis & Son, Highgate, Leverton, Boston, Lincolnshire, PE22 0AW Tel: (01205) 870341 Fax: (01205) 871447

▶ E Fraser Electrical Orkney Ltd, The Store, Finstown, Orkney, KW17 2EL Tel: (01856) 761762

▶ E Fraser Electrical Orkney Ltd, The Store, Finstown, Orkney, KW17 2EL Tel: (01856) 761762 Fax: (01856) 761777

E G Brown Bristol Ltd, 63 Quarrington Road, Bristol, BS7 9PJ Tel: 0117-951 3215 Fax: 0117-935 4250 *General printers*

E G Carter & Co. Ltd, Bybrook House, Lower Tuffley Lane, Gloucester, GL2 5EE Tel: (01452) 529194

E G Coles & Son, Station Yard, Station Road, Semley, Shaftesbury, Dorset, SP7 9AN Tel: (01747) 854777 Fax: (01747) 855610 E-mail: sales@candotractors.co.uk *Agricultural dealers & spares*

E & G Engineering, The Street, Gooderstone, King's Lynn, Norfolk, PE33 9BS Tel: (01366) 328424 Fax: (01366) 328424 E-mail: mariko@supanet.com *Welders & fabricators*

▶ E G Hicks, Monks Hall Hanger, Bowsers Lane, Little Walden, Saffron Walden, Essex, CB10 1XQ Tel: (01799) 521559 Fax: (01799) 528339

E G Hingston & Son, Wilburton Farm, Ivybridge, Devon, PL21 9LB Tel: (01752) 880416 *Agricultural contractors*

E G Jenkinson, West Road, Filey, North Yorkshire, YO14 9HA Tel: (01723) 512039 Fax: (01723) 341665 *Fish merchants wholesalers*

E G L Vaughan Ltd, Brook St, Glossop, Derbyshire, SK13 8BG Tel: (01457) 866614 Fax: (01457) 869364 E-mail: egl.vaughan@virgin.net *CNC engineers*

E G Lewis & Co. Ltd, Tank Farm Road, Llandarcy, Neath, West Glamorgan, SA10 6EN Tel: (01792) 323288 Fax: (01792) 323255 E-mail: timl@eglewis.com *Painting & decorating service providers*

E G Rackham & Co. Ltd, 6 Jubilee Avenue, London, E4 9JD Tel: (020) 8531 9225 Fax: (020) 8531 0426 E-mail: sales@rackhams.co.uk *Carpet wholesalers*

E G Recruitment Ltd, 56 Meldon Terrace, Newbiggin-by-the-Sea, Northumberland, NE64 6XH Tel: (01670) 858834 Fax: (01865) 400166 E-mail: eddie@egrecruitment.co.uk *Specialist marketing & public relations recruitment*

E G Reeve & Sons Ltd, Burton Road, Norwich, NR6 6AT Tel: (01603) 427228 Fax: (01603) 789548 E-mail: alan@egreeve.co.uk *Steel industrial tank & chimney manufrs*

E G S Gauging Ltd, The Atrium, 18-21 Church Gate, Thatcham, Berkshire, RG19 3PN Tel: (01635) 861117 Fax: (01635) 273249 E-mail: info@egsgauging.com *Industrial process controls*

E G S (International) Ltd, 27 Woolmore Way, Bordon, Hampshire, GU35 9QE Tel: (01420) 489329 Fax: (01420) 489434 E-mail: info@egssurvey.co.uk *Geophysical & hydrographic surveyors*

E G S Technologies, 17 Lea Hall Enterprise Park, Wheelhouse Road, Rugeley, Staffordshire, WS15 1LH Tel: 01889 583220 Fax: 07092 012948 E-mail: p.evans@egstec.co.uk *Specialised computer equipment manufrs*

E G Steele & Co. Ltd, 25 Dalziel Street, Hamilton, Lanarkshire, ML3 9AU Tel: (01698) 283765 Fax: (01698) 891550 E-mail: egsteel@tiscalli.co.uk *Railway rolling stock supplies*

▶ E & G Websales Ltd, Delfryn, Lixwm, Holywell, Flintshire, CH8 8NQ Tel: (01352) 781944 E-mail: enquiries@digital-scales-company.co.uk *Supplier of digital scales to homes & businesses*

E Gandolfi Ltd, Mill Road, Wellingborough, Northamptonshire, NN8 1PR Tel: (01933) 224007 Fax: (01933) 227009 E-mail: gandolfisports@btconnet.com *Ballet dance shoe manufrs*

E George & Sons, Pontdolgoch, Caersws, Powys, SY17 5JE Tel: (01686) 688231 Fax: (01686) 688811 E-mail: info@egeorge.co.uk *Agricultural merchants*

E Gillies, 21 Seafield Road, Inverness, IV1 1SG Tel: (01463) 233023 Fax: (01463) 712353 *General building contractors*

E Gilligan & Sons Ltd, 25 Allcock Street, Birmingham, B9 4DY Tel: 0121-766 7666 Fax: 0121-766 7601 E-mail: gilligan@btconnect.com *Electroplating specialists services*

E H Advertising Ltd, Castlethorpe Court, Castlethorpe, Brigg, North Lincolnshire, DN20 9LG Tel: (01652) 650100 Fax: (01652) 650035 E-mail: eh.advertising@virgin.net *Business gift & incentive specialities*

E H Crack & Sons Ltd, High Mill, Shaw Mills, Harrogate, North Yorkshire, HG3 3HY Tel: (01423) 770226 Fax: (01423) 770188 *Leather goods manufrs*

▶ E H D London Number 1 Bond, Unit 1-2 Twickenham Trading Estate, Rugby Road, Twickenham, TW1 1DQ Tel: (020) 8744 3856 Fax: (020) 8744 2647

E H Hornsby Electrical Engineers Ltd, Kings Hall Works, Kings Hall Road, Beckenham, Kent, BR3 1LN Tel: (020) 8778 7900 Fax: (020) 8778 4058 E-mail: ehhltd@btconnect.com *Industrial electrical engineers*

E H Humphries Norton Ltd, Great Western House, 35 Martindale, Cannock, Staffordshire, WS11 7XN Tel: (01543) 466766 Fax: (01543) 504845 E-mail: enquiries@ehhumphries.co.uk *Electrical contractors*

E H Jones Ltd, Irlam Road, Bootle, Merseyside, L20 4TU Tel: 0151-922 6454 Fax: 0151-922 5425 *Paint manufrs*

E H L Networks Ltd, 13 Stevenson Court, Priory Park, Frazer Road, Bedford, MK44 4WH Tel: (01234) 831888 Fax: (01234) 832501 E-mail: sales@ehl.co.uk *Computer network consultants*

E H Lee Ltd, Sleaford Road, Bracebridge Heath, Lincoln, LN4 2NL Tel: (01522) 520251 Fax: (01522) 512239 E-mail: enquiries@ehleeatpeterborough.co.uk *Road transport, haulage & freight services*

E H M Ltd, Unit 10 Eagle Industrial Estate, Bagnall Street, Great Bridge, Tipton, West Midlands, DY4 7BS Tel: 0121-557 0626 Fax: 0121-557 0646 *Hard chrome plated bar stockholders*

E H Morgan & Son Ltd, 105 Cricklade Street, Cirencester, Gloucestershire, GL7 1JF Tel: (01285) 883100 Fax: (01285) 883111 E-mail: ehm@ehmorgan-insurance.co.uk *Insurance brokers*

E H P Technical Services Ltd, 6 Lincoln Road, Northborough, Peterborough, PE6 9BL Tel: (01733) 252428 Fax: (01733) 252674 E-mail: rayevans@ehpltd.freeserve.co.uk *High voltage test equipment distributors*

E H Penny, Fowl Ing Works, Fowl Ing Lane, Kendal, Cumbria, LA9 6PH Tel: (01539) 721605 Fax: (01539) 721605 *Horticultural machinery suppliers*

E H Roberts & Co Southend Ltd, 251-255 Church Road, Benfleet, Essex, SS7 4QP Tel: (01268) 752811 Fax: (01268) 793416 *Contractors' plant hire including fork lift trucks & air compressors*

E H S International Ltd, E H S House, Lyons Road, Trafford Park, Manchester, M17 1RN Tel: 0161-872 4541 Fax: 0161-872 5491 E-mail: enquiries@ehs-intl.co.uk *Air conditioning distributors*

E H Smith Builders Merchants Ltd, Leyhill Road, Bovingdon, Hemel Hempstead, Hertfordshire, HP3 0NW Tel: (01442) 833888 Fax: (01442) 834110 E-mail: sales@ehsmith.co.uk *Builders merchants*

E H Smith Builders Merchants Ltd, Mill Hill, Enderby, Leicester, LE19 4AJ Tel: 0116-275 0999 Fax: 0116-275 0135 E-mail: leicester@ehsmith.co.uk *Builders merchants*

E Hague Furnace Compounds, 31 Chorley Drive, Sheffield, S10 3RQ Tel: 0114-230 2707 Fax: 0114-230 2707 *Paint suppliers*

E Hammond Case & Pallets Ltd, Noose Lane, Willenhall, West Midlands, WV13 3AZ Tel: (01902) 606391 Fax: (01902) 604331 E-mail: sales@ehammond.co.uk *Packing case manufrs*

E Haste, Stoneleigh Farm, Shebbear, Beaworthy, Devon, EX21 5QT Tel: (01409) 281230 Fax: (01409) 281880 E-mail: haste@stoneleighsfnet.co.uk *Farmers*

E Hubert Agricultural Contractors Ltd, Dunt Avenue, Hurst, Reading, RG10 0SY Tel: 0118-934 1114 Fax: 0118-934 1114 *Agricultural contractors*

E Hughes, Bryn Eden, Caeathro, Caernarfon, Gwynedd, LL55 2SG Tel: (01286) 675401 Fax: (01286) 672816 *Agricultural contractors*

E Hughes, 28 Old Moy Road, Dungannon, County Tyrone, BT71 6RY Tel: (028) 8775 2030 Fax: (028) 8772 2060 *Furniture frame manufrs*

E I B M Electronics Ltd, Unit B2 Greengate Industrial Estate, Greenside Way, Middleton, Manchester, M24 1SW Tel: 0161-653 8181 Fax: 0161-653 8282 E-mail: jacki.eibm@boltblue.net *Electronic engineers*

E I D Ltd, 12 St Cross Street, London, EC1N 8UB Tel: (020) 7405 6594 Fax: (020) 7831 0372 E-mail: eidlondon@aol.com *Industrial diamond merchants*

E & I Hire Ltd, Newspaper House, Tannery Lane, Penketh, Warrington, WA5 2UD Tel: (01925) 726677 Fax: (01925) 725544 E-mail: sales@eihire.co.uk *Hire, calibration & supply of electrical & instrument test equipment. 16th edition to 3 phase relay test sets, AC & DC injection to 75/80kv resp, 100amp scits to 3000amp pcits etc process control calibration equipment druck calibrato rs, heat blocks, D.W.T.'s, test gauges, decade boxes etc calibration & supply of same items*

▶ E I S Ltd, Mckean Street, Paisley, Renfrewshire, PA3 1QP Tel: 0141-887 7888 Fax: 0141-887 2887 E-mail: sales@electricaltrade.co.uk

▶ E I S Axon Ltd, Unit 2, Crusader Industrial Estate, Stirling Road, Cressex Business Park, High Wycombe, Buckinghamshire, HP12 3ST Tel: (01494) 511558 Fax: (01494) 449351 E-mail: paul@eis-axon.co.uk *Electrical engineers & control panel specialists*

▶ E I S (Midlands) Ltd, Canterbury Business Centre, Suit 5, 18 Ashchurch Road, Tewkesbury, Gloucestershire, GL20 8BT Tel: (0870) 1430023 Fax: (0870) 1430024

▶ E I S (North) Ltd, Block 7 Unit 2 Larkhall Indust Estate, Dunedin Road, Larkhall, Lanarkshire, ML9 2QS Tel: (01698) 884110 E-mail: enquiries@eisnorth.co.uk

▶ E I S (South) Ltd, Maxwelton Industrial Estate, Glasgow Road, Dumfries, DG2 0NW Tel: (01387) 255231

E I W H S, 69-72 High Street, Croydon, CR0 1PA Tel: (020) 8680 7071 Fax: (020) 8680 9818 E-mail: eiwhs@davishouse.co.uk *Electrical contractors, mechanical & instrumentation engineers* Also at: Coventry & Derby

▶ E I W H S, Unit 23g The Avenues, Team Valley Trading Estate, Gateshead, Tyne & Wear, NE11 0JY Tel: 0191-487 9486 Fax: 0191-487 8048

E & I Williams, High View, The Doward, Whitchurch, Ross-on-Wye, Herefordshire, HR9 6DZ Tel: (01600) 890474 Fax: (01600) 890327 *Concrete products manufrs*

▶ E J C, PO Box 103, Aylesbury, Buckinghamshire, HP17 8WL Tel: (0845) 3510603 E-mail: enquiries@essenjay.com *We specilaise in Security Consultancy & Training, including SITO BJT's. **We employ experts with skills in providing anti and counter terrorism advice and training.**We undertake Crime Prevention Surveys of all types of premises, utilising qualified ex police officers.*We currently are undertaking multi agency senior command training focusing upon major incidents.***We are discreet, reliable and cost effective.*

E J Churchill, Fall Farm, Stanford Bridge, Worcester, WR6 6SJ Tel: (01886) 853240 *Farmer*

E J Churchill Shooting Ground, Park Lane, Lane End, High Wycombe, Buckinghamshire, HP14 3NS Tel: (01494) 883227 Fax: (01494) 883215 E-mail: sales@ejchurchill.com *Shooting ground*

E J Collins & Son, 57 Addington Village Road, Croydon, CR0 5AS Tel: (01689) 843059 *Wrought ironworkers*

E & J D Alderson, The Old Power House Garage, Wensley Station, Preston under Scar, Leyburn, North Yorkshire, DL8 4AQ Tel: (01969) 624160 *Agricultural engineers*

▶ E J Ditton & Co., 41 Longfield Road, Dover, Kent, CT17 9QR Tel: (01304) 205141 Fax: (01304) 215047

E & J Fire Protection, 5 Rice Bridge Industrial Estate, Station Road, Thorpe-le-Soken, Clacton-on-Sea, Essex, CO16 0HH Tel: (01255) 860645 Fax: (01255) 860156 E-mail: julie@ejfire.co.uk *Sales & services of fire extinguishers*

▶ E J Fleming Ltd, 19a Larkfield Road, Sevenoaks, Kent, TN13 2QH Tel: (01732) 453679 Fax: (01732) 740299

E J Harmer & Co. Ltd, 19a Birkbeck Hill, London, SE21 8JS Tel: (020) 8670 1017 Fax: (020) 8766 6026 E-mail: info@ejharmer.co.uk *Suppliers of fibrous plaster*

E J Harris & Sons Ltd, 18-25 Queen Victoria Street, Bristol, BS2 0QR Tel: 0117-955 7023 *Joinery manufrs*

E J Herok Ltd, Charlton Mead Lane, Hoddesdon, Hertfordshire, EN11 0DJ Tel: (01992) 462943 Fax: (01992) 464792 E-mail: info@herok.com *Educational furniture manufrs*

E J M Engineered Systems Ltd, Unit 1 Thornley Station Industrial Estate, Shotton Colliery, Durham, DH6 2QA Tel: (01429) 836161 Fax: (01429) 838034 E-mail: sales@ejmrefrigeration.co.uk *Refrigeration & air conditioning engineers*

E J M Engineering Ltd, Regent Road, Countesthorpe, Leicester, LE8 5RF Tel: 0116-278 7020 Fax: 0116-278 7020 E-mail: eric@ejm-engineering.co.uk *Turned parts manufrs*

E J Mansbridge (Engineering) Ltd, Lancaster Road, High Wycombe, Buckinghamshire, HP12 3NN Tel: (01494) 437325 Fax: (01494) 471736 E-mail: office@ejmansbridge.com *Precision engineers*

E J Masters Ltd, Railway Terrace, Kings Langley, Hertfordshire, WD4 8JA Tel: (01923) 265757 Fax: (01923) 267827 *Overnight parcel carriers*

E J Miller Nottingham Ltd, 539 Woodborough Road, Nottingham, NG3 5FR Tel: 0115-960 4232 Fax: 0115-955 2552 *Electrical contractors*

▶ E J Morgan & Son, School House, Sennybridge, Brecon, Powys, LD3 8TT Tel: (01874) 636766 Fax: (01874) 636766

E J P Tooling Co. (Coventry) Ltd, Unit 27 Lythalls Lane Industrial Estate, Lythalls Lane, Coventry, CV6 6FL Tel: (024) 7668 6810 *Toolmakers & Toolmaking Services*

E J Parkinson & Son Ltd, Kirk Lane, Yeadon, Leeds, LS19 7ET Tel: 0113-250 9111 Fax: 0113-250 0223 *Small plant & power tool hire*

E J Payne Ltd, 1-3 Belgrave Road, Stoke-on-Trent, ST3 4PR Tel: (01782) 312534 Fax: (01782) 599868 E-mail: sales@ejpayne.com Sales Contact: A. Payne Principal Export Areas: Worldwide *Swimming pool water treatment consultants & ceramic testing equipment distributors or agents*

E J Rawlins & Co. Ltd, Unit 6 Croydon Street, Leeds, LS11 9RT Tel: 0113-245 5450 Fax: 0113-245 2649 E-mail: sales@rawlinspaints.com *Paint manufacturers & distributors*

E J & S Y Barnard, 21 Nethermoor Road, Middlezoy, Bridgwater, Somerset, TA7 0PG Tel: (01823) 698536 *Basket manufrs*

E J Soper Ltd, 51 Ormside Way, Redhill, RH1 2LW Tel: (01737) 762230 *Made-up leather goods manufrs*

▶ E J Taylor & Sons Ltd, Mill Works, Burnham Road, Hazeleigh, Chelmsford, CM3 6QT Tel: (01621) 828661 Fax: (01621) 828066 E-mail: mail@ejtaylor.co.uk *Building & civil engineering contractor*

E J Tools (Press Toolmakers) Ltd, 112 Middlemore Industrial Estate, Smethwick, Warley, West Midlands, B66 2EP Tel: 0121-558 4154 Fax: 0121-558 4154 E-mail: richard_webb@btconnect.com *Press tool manufrs*

E J Wicks, Newbury Street, Lambourn, Hungerford, Berkshire, RG17 8PB Tel: (01488) 71766 Fax: (01488) 71707 E-mail: sales@ejwicks.co.uk *Saddlery repair services & country clothing suppliers*

E J Woollard Ltd, Fieldings Road, Cheshunt, Waltham Cross, Hertfordshire, EN8 9TY Tel: (01992) 623232 Fax: (01992) 641278 E-mail: sales@ejwoollard.co.uk *Irrigation equipment supply & installation services*

E Jeffries & Sons, Unit 32 New Firms Centre, Fairground Way, Walsall, WS1 4NU Tel: (01922) 642222 Fax: (01922) 615043 E-mail: sales@ejeffries.co.uk *Saddlery distributors & manufrs*

E Jones Engineering, Gweldir, Bancyffordd, Llandysul, Dyfed, SA44 4SD Tel: (01559) 384941 Fax: (01559) 384941 *Steel fabricators*

▶ E Jones & Son, Bronallt, Clawddnewydd, Ruthin, Clwyd, LL15 2NA Tel: (01824) 750604 Fax: (01824) 750402

▶ E Jordon Refrigeration Ltd, Refrigeration House, Quebec Street, Oldham, OL9 6QL Tel: 0161-622 9700 Fax: 0161-622 9709 E-mail: sales@jordon.co.uk *Specialists in refrigeration, air conditioning & shop fitting*

E Just & Son, Waterlog Farm, Spondon Road, Dale Abbey, Ilkeston, Derbyshire, DE7 4PQ Tel: (01332) 662994 Fax: (01332) 662994 *Agricultural Contractors*

E K C Systems Ltd, Walkley Works, Walkley Lane, Heckmondwike, West Yorkshire, WF16 0PH Tel: (01924) 411604 Fax: (01924) 403822 E-mail: info@ekcsystems.co.uk *Specialist supplies to the pre-stressing/pre-cast concrete industry. Services include pre-stressing equipment, safety training, calibration, fittings & accessories, lifting equipment (hire & sale) for the concrete industry*

E K C Technology Ltd, 19 Law Place, Nerston, East Kilbride, Glasgow, G74 4QL Tel: (01355) 244652 Fax: (01355) 595444 E-mail: sales@ekctech.co.uk *Printed circuit cleaning manufrs*

E K Motor Factors Ltd, Lansil Way, Caton Road, Lancaster, LA1 3QY Tel: (01524) 32361 Fax: (01524) 64423 E-mail: ekslancs@globalnet.co.uk *Car parts distributors*

E K W Fabrications Ltd, Coppice Side Industrial Estate, West Coppice Road, Walsall, WS8 7HB Tel: (01543) 378181 Fax: (01543) 361012 *Steel fabricators & machinists*

E Klein & Co., 122-126 Westferry Road, London, E14 3SG Tel: (020) 7987 1171 Fax: (020) 7538 0477 *Plastics, textile raw material & waste exporters*

E L B Engineering 91, Meekings Road, Sudbury, Suffolk, CO10 2XE Tel: (01787) 373055 *General engineers & engine reconditioners*

E L C International, 5 Five Mile Drive, Oxford, OX2 8HT Tel: (01865) 513186 E-mail: snyderbub@aol.com *Directory publishers*

▶ E L Chaplain & Co., 33 Frederick Street, Birmingham, B1 3HH Tel: 0121-236 3065

E L F Electric (London) Ltd, 511 Garratt Lane, London, SW18 4SW Tel: (020) 8874 2952 Fax: (020) 8874 2952 E-mail: elfelectric@tiscali.co.uk *Electrical motor maintenance services*

E L G Haniel Metals Ltd, Heath Road, Darlaston, Wednesbury, West Midlands, WS10 8LU Tel: 0121-526 2444 Fax: 0121-526 4831 E-mail: info@elgdarlaston.co.uk *Scrap metal merchants*

E & L Instruments Ltd, Aerial Road, Llay, Wrexham, Clwyd, LL12 0TU Tel: (01978) 853920 Fax: (01978) 854564 E-mail: info@eandl-group.com *Electronic teaching aids*

▶ E L Johnson Sons & Mowatt, Charter House 7th Floor, 450 High Road, Ilford, Essex, IG1 1UF Tel: (020) 8514 2456 Fax: (020) 8478 5760 E-mail: surveys@elj.co.uk *Marine Cargo Surveyors and Adjusters, also at Liverpool, Bristol and Antwerp*

E L Schofield & Son, 49 New Street, Pudsey, West Yorkshire, LS28 8PE Tel: 0113-256 5308 Fax: 0113-255 0052 E-mail: schofieldandson@aol.com *Furniture manufrs*

E L Shopfitters, 45 Huntly Road, Hillington Industrial Estate, Glasgow, G52 4DZ Tel: 0141-882 9979 Fax: 0141-882 9979 *Shop fitters*

E L Sibbles Ltd, Woolbloch House, Bolling Road, Bradford, West Yorkshire, BD4 7BT Tel: (01274) 729433 Fax: (01274) 370611 E-mail: sales@elsibbles.com *Forwarding agents*

E Lodge, Catherine House, 1 Albert Drive, Gateshead, Tyne & Wear, NE9 6EH Tel: 0191-482 6392 Fax: 0191-482 6392 E-mail: simplyimpressive@aol.com *Interior landscaping*

E M B Diecasting Machines Ltd, Unit 1 Oldbury Road Industrial Estate, 132 Oldbury Road, Smethwick, West Midlands, B66 1JE Tel: 0121-565 3199 Fax: 0121-555 5275 E-mail: emba@embdiecast.fsbusiness.co.uk *Diecasting machine services*

E & M Brennan Plant Hire Ltd, Unit 3, Crossley Industrial Estate, Manchester, M18 8BA Tel: 0161-231 2583 Fax: 0161-231 2792 E-mail: embrennan@btconnect.com *Excavation & groundwork contractors*

E M C Component Handling, Priors Mead, Alcester Road, Inkberrow, Worcester, WR7 4HN Tel: (01386) 793471 Fax: (01386) 793471 E-mail: EMCmail@componenthandling.co.uk *Companies can increase productivity by running machines unmanned*

▶ E M C E Ltd, 133 Dean Road, Scarborough, North Yorkshire, YO12 7JH Tel: (01723) 364083 Fax: (01723) 364083 E-mail: quotes@emceltd.co.uk

E M C Hire Ltd, Ivel Road, Shefford, Bedfordshire, SG17 5JU Tel: (01462) 817111 Fax: (01462) 817444 E-mail: sales@emchire.co.uk *EMC test instrumentation*

E M C O Estates Ltd, Emco House, 5-7 New York Road, Leeds, LS2 7PJ Tel: 0113-244 4236 Fax: 0113-244 0449 E-mail: henry@cityfusion.co.uk *Property investors & developers*

E M C Plastics UK Ltd, Wychwood Business Centre, Shipton-Under-Wychwobusiness, Chipping Norton, Oxfordshire, OX7 6XU Tel: (01993) 832000 Fax: (01993) 831444 E-mail: sales@emc-uk.com *EMC RFI shielded & contrast enhancement windows manufrs*

E M Cable Service North Sea Ltd, Unit 4c Wellheads Terrace, Wellheads Industrial Estate, Aberdeen, AB21 7GF Tel: (01224) 771791 Fax: (01224) 724335 E-mail: em.cables@virgin.net Principal Export Areas: Worldwide *Wireline cable suppliers*

E & M Composites Ltd, Unit Y1 Blaby Industrial Park, Winchester Avenue, Blaby, LE8 4GZ Tel: 0116-278 8954 Fax: 0116-278 9313 *Timber mould supplier*

E M Computers Ltd, 13 Victoria Street, Wigston, Leicestershire, LE18 1AJ Tel: 0116-288 1088 *Computer software developers*

▶ E M E, 8 Robert Frazer Industrial, Station Road, Hebburn, Tyne & Wear, NE31 1BD Tel: 0191-428 4500 Fax: 0191-428 2767

E M E Electrical & Mechanical Engineering Ltd, 25 The Mead Business Centre, Mead Lane, Hertford, SG13 7BJ Tel: (01992) 552151 E-mail: sales@emeltd.com *Electronic & mechanical design, development & manufrs*

E M E (Electro Medical Equipment) Ltd, 60 Gladstone Pl, Brighton, BN2 3QD Tel: (01273) 654100 Fax: (01273) 654101 E-mail: info@eme-med.co.uk *Electro-medical equipment manufrs*

E & M Engineering Services, Riverside, Thurso, Caithness, KW14 8BU Tel: (01847) 893702 Fax: (01847) 896511 *Marine engineers & fabricators*

▶ E M F Electronics, 146 Portsmouth Road, Lee-on-the-Solent, Hampshire, PO13 9AE Tel: (023) 9255 6225 E-mail: sales@emf-electronics.co.uk *Electronic consultants*

E & M Glass Ltd, Sarn Glass Studio, Sarn, Malpas, Cheshire, SY14 7LN Tel: (01948) 770464 Fax: (01948) 770592 E-mail: info@emglass.co.uk *Hand blown glass retailers & manufrs*

E M Hunt, Whitehirst Park Works, Kilwinning, Ayrshire, KA13 6PF Tel: (01294) 552682 Fax: (01294) 557949 *Metal fabricators*

E M & I (Marine) Ltd, 18 Fairburn Terrace, Dyce, Aberdeen, AB21 7DT Tel: (01224) 771077 Fax: (01224) 771049 E-mail: info@emiall.co.uk *Ultrasonic inspection services asset integrity management services*

E M I S, 77 Back Lane, Horsforth, Leeds, LS18 4RF Tel: 0113-259 1122 Fax: 0113-239 0162 E-mail: emis@e-mis.com *Computer software suppliers for the medical profession*

E M Inspection Co Ltd, 11-18 Victoria Street, Wigston, Leicestershire, LE18 1AJ Tel: 0116-288 3974 *Non-destructive test services*

E M J Management Ltd, Aspen House, Airport Service Road, Portsmouth, PO3 5RA Tel: (023) 9243 4650 Fax: (023) 9243 4681 E-mail: info@cjsltd.co.uk Sales Contact: A. Eggett *EMJ offer a "one stop shop" for all your workwear and corporate clothing requirements. From help in deciding on the correct garments to the designing of your logo, EMJ have the expertise. Offering a man-packing and embroidery service keeps EMJ ahead of many of its competitors.*

E M J Plastics Ltd, Clarence Drive, Filey, North Yorkshire, YO14 0AA Tel: (01723) 512224 Fax: (01723) 515512 E-mail: support@emjplastics.com *Plastic products manufrs*

E M & J R Evans, Priddbwll Mawr, Llangedwyn, Oswestry, Shropshire, SY10 9JZ Tel: (01691) 791203 Fax: (01691) 791203 *Dairy engineering services*

E M M UK Ltd, Old Road, Southam, Warwickshire, CV47 1RA Tel: (01926) 812419 Fax: (01926) 817425 E-mail: sales@emm.co.uk *Manufacturers of filters including air & spray booth air. Also motor vehicle body refinishing/ spraying products factors/distributors/agents*

E M Morgan, Nantybwla, Pentremeurig Road, Carmarthen, Dyfed, SA31 3QS Tel: (01267) 237905 Fax: (01267) 237905 *Cheese makers*

E M Natt Ltd, 45-47 Friern Barnet Road, London, N11 3EG Tel: (020) 8361 4649 Fax: (020) 8361 4145 E-mail: info@silencer.com *Dental & chiropody supplies, anti-storing systems*

E & M Office Equipment Ltd, 94 Gray's Inn Road, London, WC1X 8AD Tel: (020) 7713 1591 Fax: (020) 7242 0239 E-mail: sales@emofficeequipment.co.uk *Computer hire & repairers*

E M P Chefs, 12 Hidings Court Lane, Morecambe, Lancashire, LA4 4QJ Tel: (07834) 364732 E-mail: info@emp-chefs.com *emp-chefs website is aimed at chefs throughout the uk to provided an online job board with direct access to*

continued

▶ indicates data change since last edition

continuation
employers and recruiters. Search for positions by job type, location and award rating.

E M R Ltd, Tynedale Works, Factory Road, Blaydon-On-Tyne, Tyne & Wear, NE21 5RZ Tel: 0191-414 3618 Fax: 0191-414 0751 E-mail: info@amrltd.com *Scrap metal merchants & processors* Also at: Leeds

E M R Sliverthorn Ltd, 4 Abercorn Commercial Centre, Manor Farm Road, Wembley, Middlesex, HA0 1AN Tel: (020) 8903 1390 Fax: (020) 8903 9092 E-mail: emrsilverthorn@ndirect.co.uk *Electric motor supply & repairers*

E M R Windings Ltd, Units 5 & 6, Kiln Park Industrial Park, Searle Crescent, Weston-super-Mare, Somerset, BS23 3XP Tel: (01934) 631374 Fax: (01934) 622698 E-mail: lee.graham@emrelectronics.co.uk *Electronics manufrs*

E M Richford Ltd, Curzon Road, Sudbury, Suffolk, CO10 2XW Tel: (01787) 375241 Fax: (01787) 310179 E-mail: sales@richstamp.co.uk *Manufacturers of data machines*

E M S Ltd, 15-29 Eyre Street Hill, London, EC1R 5LB Tel: (020) 7837 4707 Fax: (020) 7833 8299 E-mail: enquiries@ems-maintenance.co.uk *Air conditioning engineers*

E M S Cargo Ltd, Unit 5, Ringway Trading Estate, Manchester, M22 5LH Tel: 0161-499 1344 Fax: 0161-499 0847 E-mail: man@ems-cargo.co.uk *Export & import freight agents*

▶ E M S Electrical & Mechanical Services, Unit 21 Eastbourne Road, Westham, Pevensey, East Sussex, BN24 5NH Tel: (01323) 765365 Fax: (01323) 765015

E M S Euroweld Ltd, 203 Strathmartine Road, Dundee, DD3 8PH Tel: (01382) 858947 Fax: (01382) 832359 *Engineers & welding suppliers*

E M S Radio, Fire & Systems Ltd, Unit 11, Herne Bay West Trading Estate, Herne Bay, Kent, CT6 8JZ Tel: (01227) 369570 Fax: (01227) 740041 E-mail: sales@emsgroup.co.uk *Radio fire security & fire systems manufrs*

E M T Healthcare Ltd, 4 Padge Road, Boulevard Industrial Park, Beeston, Nottingham, NG9 2JR Tel: 0115-849 7700 Fax: 0115-849 7701 E-mail: info@emthealthcare.com *Wholesale chemists supplies*

E M T Steels Ltd, 5 Gleneld Drive, Stourbridge, West Midlands, DY8 2PF Tel: (01384) 373888 Fax: (01384) 395712 E-mail: ajroden@btconnect.com Principal Export Areas: Middle East & Western Europe *Carbon & alloy steel tube stockholders*

▶ E M Treece, 42 South Road, Kirkby Stephen, Cumbria, CA17 4SN Tel: (01768) 371221 Fax: (01768) 371221 E-mail: edtreece@tiscali.co.uk *Stonework & restoration specialists*

E M Worts & Son, Little Mill, Disserth, Builth Wells, Powys, LD2 3TN Tel: (01982) 551426 Fax: (01982) 551601 *Agricultural merchants*

E Mckinney, 154 Ballycastle Road, Coleraine, County Londonderry, BT52 2EH Tel: (028) 7034 3927 *Bakery services*

E Media Ltd, Ember House, Pleasant Place, Walton-on-Thames, Surrey, KT12 4HR Tel: (01932) 254787 Fax: (01932) 254786 E-mail: info@e-media.co.uk *Software & internet developers*

E Mesrie & Sons Ltd, 3 Brazil Street, Manchester, M1 3PJ Tel: 0161-236 6274 Fax: 0161-236 8086 E-mail: yarns@mdmresourcing.com *Yarn merchants*

E Meyer & Co Mentor Ltd, Unit 15 Abbey Industrial Estate, Mount Pleasant, Wembley, Middlesex, HA0 1QX Tel: (020) 8902 5471 Fax: (020) 8900 1398 E-mail: sales@emeyer.co.uk *Precision turned parts manufrs*

▶ E Moorhouse & Son, Park House, Springfield Road, Bigrigg, Egremont, Cumbria, CA22 2TL Tel: (01946) 811152 Fax: (01946) 811052 *Stone products*

E N I UK Ltd, 10 Ebury Bridge Road, London, SW1W 8PZ Tel: (020) 7344 6000 Fax: (020) 7344 6044 E-mail: sales@eni.co.uk *Oil exploration company*

E.N.L Audio Visual, Alfreton Road, Nottingham, NG7 3NR Tel: 0115-924 8305 Fax: 0115-924 8329 E-mail: sales@hotkit.co.uk *Audio visual retail & services*

▶ E N Suiter & Sons Ltd, 31 North Everard Street, King's Lynn, Norfolk, PE30 5HQ Tel: (01553) 763195 Fax: (01553) 767694

▶ E Net Europe, Heathrow Boulevard, Bath Road, Sipson, West Drayton, Middlesex, UB7 0DQ Tel: (020) 8754 7894 Fax: (020) 8754 0862

E Nicholson & Sons, 445 Balmore Road, Glasgow, G22 6NX Tel: 0141-336 6065 Fax: 0141-336 5229 E-mail: sales@enicholson.co.uk *Scrap metal processors*

▶ E Nixon & Son Ltd, Morley Bridge Works, Chester Road, Bridge Trafford, Chester, CH2 4JS Tel: (01244) 300641 Fax: (01244) 300489

E O Burton, Thorndon Sawmills, The Avenue, Brentwood, Essex, CM13 3RZ Tel: (01277) 260810 Fax: (01277) 262823 E-mail: timber@eoburton.com *Hardwood merchants & importers*

E O Culverwell Ltd, Station Road, Robertsbridge, East Sussex, TN32 5DG Tel: (01580) 880567 Fax: (01580) 881022 E-mail: cars@eo-culverwell.ltd.uk *Agricultural machinery & implements* Also at: Haywards Heath & Robertsbridge

E O G B Energy Products Ltd, Howard Road, Eaton Socon, St. Neots, Cambridgeshire, PE19 8ET Tel: (01480) 477066 Fax: (01480) 477022 E-mail: sales@eogb.co.uk *Manufacturers and distributors of oil, gas and dual fuel burners for domestic and industrial applications.**Major distributor to the heating industry for all types of spare parts for oil, gas and dual fuel burners.*

E O S International Ltd, On Site Lodge, 9 Mansfield Road, Eastwood, Nottingham, NG16 3AR Tel: (01773) 766936 Fax: (01773) 767555 E-mail: general@eosintl.co.uk *Computer software consultants*

▶ E P Ltd, 86-88 Lower Lichfield Street, Willenhall, West Midlands, WV13 1QE Tel: (01902) 366533 Fax: (01902) 366550

E & P Associates Ltd Ltd, 52 Berwick Street, London, W1F 8SL Tel: (020) 7278 4272 Fax: (020) 7437 8176 E-mail: info@ep-associates.com *Television production designers*

E P C, PO Box 2229, London, W14 0JA Tel: (020) 7602 2979 Fax: (020) 7371 6431 E-mail: aboi@bmec.org.uk *Offshore consultants*

▶ E P Electrical, Unit 1, Block 14, 82 Clydesmill Drive, Clydesmill Industrial Estate, Glasgow, G32 8RG Tel: 0141-646 2535

E & P Engineering Services, 16 St Nicholas Road, Littlestone, New Romney, Kent, TN28 8PT Tel: (01797) 366724 *Steel fabricators*

E P I Service Ltd, Witan Park, Avenue Two, Station Lane, Witney, Oxfordshire, OX28 4FH Tel: (01993) 708855 Fax: (01993) 708850 E-mail: admin@epi-uk.com *UPS manufrs*

E P L Medical Ltd, 4 Yardley Road, Knowsley Industrial Park, Liverpool, L33 7SS Tel: 0151-548 1494 Fax: 0151-549 2046 E-mail: info@eplmedical.com *Plastic fabricators*

E P Laboratories Ltd, Amersham Road, Chesham, Buckinghamshire, HP5 1NE Tel: (01494) 791585 Fax: (01494) 771853 E-mail: sales@eplabs.com *Solvent & degreasing agent suppliers*

E P Oakes & Son, 113 Middlemore Road, Middlemore Industrial Estate, Smethwick, West Midlands, B66 2EP Tel: 0121-558 4145 Fax: 0121-555 5623 *Presswork & general engineers*

E P P Magnus Ltd, Ashbourne Estate, 174 Mile Cross Lane, Norwich, NR6 6RY Tel: (01603) 400861 Fax: (01603) 788496 E-mail: welcome@magnus-int.co.uk *Hydraulic pumps & cylinders manufrs*

E P Packaging Ltd, Queensway Industrial Estate, Queensway, Wrexham, Clwyd, LL13 8YR Tel: (01978) 346600 Fax: (01978) 290259 *Plastics vacuum products manufrs*

E & P Plastics Ltd, Gore Road Industrial Estate, New Milton, Hampshire, BH25 6TB Tel: (01425) 611026 Fax: (01425) 615500 *Trade moulders & injection moulding manufrs*

▶ E P Rothwell & Sons Ltd, Farnham Common Nurseries, Crown Lane, Farnham Royal, Slough, SL2 3SF Tel: (01753) 646012 Fax: (01753) 644087

E P S Ltd, 8 Bakers Park, Cater Road, Bishopsworth, Bristol, BS13 7TT Tel: 0117-964 9777 Fax: 0117-964 9888

E P S Logistics Technology Ltd, Staplehurst Road, Sittingbourne, Kent, ME10 1XS Tel: (01795) 424433 Fax: (01795) 426970 E-mail: sales@epslt.co.uk Principal Export Areas: Worldwide *Container designers*

E P S Page Ltd, Riverside House Unit, 1 New Mill Road, Orpington, Kent, BR5 3QA Tel: (020) 7407 6701 Fax: (0845) 6080354 E-mail: epspage@epsplc.com *Engineering services*

E P S Products Ltd, Units 5-6, Govan Road, Fenton Industrial Estate, Stoke-on-Trent, ST4 2RS Tel: (01782) 749662 Fax: (01782) 749757 *Expanded polystyrene products manufrs*

E P S Services, Ford Road, Wiveliscombe, Taunton, Somerset, TA4 2RE Tel: (01984) 624273 Fax: (01984) 623204 E-mail: info@eps-services.co.uk *Precision saw manufrs*

E P Services, Unit 1, Central Industrial Estate, Cable Street, Wolverhampton, WV2 2RJ Tel: (01902) 452914 Fax: (01902) 871547 E-mail: enquiries@ep-services.co.uk *Commercial marine tractor & vintage automobile water pump manufrs*

▶ E P Specialised Fluids & Lubricants, York Street, Radcliffe, Manchester, M26 2GL Tel: 0161-766 2664 Fax: 0161-766 4778 *Lubricant distributors*

E P Systems Ltd, Media House, 21 East Ways Industrial Estate, Witham, Essex, CM8 3YQ Tel: (01376) 531380 Fax: (01376) 531361 E-mail: neil-rowe@epsystems.co.uk *Manufacturers of electrical switchgear & control panels*

E Partridge & Sons Ltd, Maypole Fields, Halesowen, West Midlands, B63 2QH Tel: (01384) 566667 Fax: (01384) 410211 *Gas soldering iron manufacturers & spot welding electros*

▶ E Pawson & Son Ltd, Field Houses, Ashton Lane, Braithwell, Rotherham, South Yorkshire, S66 7RL Tel: (01709) 813901 Fax: (01709) 814330

▶ E Pilling Printers Ltd, Rose Mill, Union Street, Middleton, Manchester, M24 6DD Tel: 0161-653 9850 Fax: 0161-655 3804

E Platt & Sons, Waterloo Street, Bolton, BL1 8HU Tel: (01204) 526304 Fax: (01204) 526330 *Scrap metal merchants*

E Play Ltd, 62 The Elmsleigh Centre, Staines, Middlesex, TW18 4QF Tel: (01784) 451222 Fax: (01784) 451444 *Computer distribution*

E Poppleton & Son Ltd, Conway Road, Mochdre, Colwyn Bay, Clwyd, LL28 5HL Tel: (01492) 546061 Fax: (01492) 544076 E-mail: sales@poppleton.co.uk *Sheet metalworkers & ductwork manufrs*

E Preston Electrical Ltd, Unit 28 Broadway, Globe Lane, Dukinfield, Cheshire, SK16 4UU Tel: 0161-339 5177 Fax: 0161-343 1935 E-mail: sales@epreston.co.uk *Based in Cheshire, E. Preston Electrical is located six miles east of Manchester, covering the whole of the UK. We are a Specialist Electrical Distributor and Supplier of Electrical and Electronic Equipment, including Switch Components, Rocker, Toggle, Pushbutton, Proximity & Limit Switches, Microswitches, Indicators, LED's, Neons, Lighting Solutions, Control Gear, Contactors, Starters, Programmable Controllers, Circuit Breakers, Timers, Fuses, Fuseholders, Filters, Relays, Thermostats, Sensors, Inlets & Connectors. Our Manufacturing Partners include, ABB, Arcolectric, Bulgin, Burgess, Bussman, CAL, Chint, CML, Crouzet, Crydom, Eaton, Entrelec, ETA, Finder, Honeywell, Kraus & Naimer, Littelfuse, Moeller, Pepperl & Fuchs, Saia, Schaffner, Schurter, Sunon, Werma and Wieland. We recognize that business is carried out between people, not companies, so always*

continued

endeavor to build upon the personal relationships we have established with both customers and suppliers.

E Preston & Sons Ladybank Sawmills Ltd, Cupar Road, Ladybank, Cupar, Fife, KY15 7LS Tel: (01337) 830307 Fax: (01337) 830307 *Timber saw mill*

E Q Consultants, Allt-A-Fhionn, St. Fillans, Crieff, Perthshire, PH6 2NG Tel: (01764) 685220 Fax: (01764) 685241 E-mail: biz@eqc.co.uk *Computer hardware repairs*

E R A Rodman Bros Ltd, 20 Lower Park Road, London, N11 1QD Tel: (020) 8361 8553 Fax: (020) 8245 6389 *Rodman Brothers powder coaters offer powder coating services across North London including polyester, epoxy, epoxy/ polyester and hybrid powder coating finishes.*

E R Burgess Macclesfield Ltd, Brunswick Works, Lowe Street, Macclesfield, Cheshire, SK11 7NJ Tel: (01625) 423735 Fax: (01625) 502025 *Engineers, fabricators & suppliers to the baking industries*

E R D C Group Ltd, 20 Harvest Road, Newbridge, Midlothian, EH28 8LW Tel: 0131-333 1100 Fax: 0131-335 4300 E-mail: info@erdc.co.uk *Public works contractors*

E R Edwards & Sons Ltd, Blatchford Road, Horsham, West Sussex, RH13 5QR Tel: (01403) 224400 Fax: (01403) 224401 E-mail: sales@eredwards.com *Precision engineers*

E R F Strathclyde Ltd, Dalgrain Industrial Estate, Grangemouth, Stirlingshire, FK3 8EB Tel: (01324) 473700 Fax: (01324) 665323 *Commercial vehicle garage*

E R I Ltd, Bridge Road, Great Bridge, Tipton, West Midlands, DY4 0HR Tel: 0121-520 8171 Fax: 0121-522 2330 E-mail: sales@eritpltd.fsnet.co.uk *Precision turned parts manufrs*

▶ E R Jenkin & Sons, St. James Street, Penzance, Cornwall, TR18 2BT Tel: (01736) 361188 Fax: (01736) 361188

E & R Joinery Ltd, Old Laughton Sawmills, Park Lane, Laughton, Lewes, East Sussex, BN8 6BP Tel: (01323) 811190 Fax: (01323) 811191 E-mail: sales@er-joinery.com *Contract joiners*

E R L Ltd, Iroko House, Bolney Avenue, Peacehaven, East Sussex, BN10 8HF Tel: (01273) 581007 Fax: (01273) 581555 E-mail: erl@fastnet.co.uk *Power supply & water injection unit manufrs*

E R M Risks, 8 Cavendish Square, London, W1G OER Tel: (020) 7465 7349 Fax: (020) 7465 7270 E-mail: tawg@ermuk.com *Risk managemant consultants*

E R P Engineering Ltd, Barton Forge, Alexandra Road, Enfield, Middlesex, EN3 7EH Tel: (020) 8805 7289 Fax: (020) 8443 5786 *General engineers*

▶ The E R P Group, Bliss House, 251 Dewsbury Road, Ossett, West Yorkshire, WF5 9QF Tel: (0870) 3339032 Fax: (01924) 280117 E-mail: sales@theerpgroup.co.uk *We are unique...**in offering a range of Enterprise Resource Planning (ERP) solutions from some of the worlds leading IT companies.**Complimentary IT solution providers. Call us for a FREE IT consultation.*

E R P Power Products Ltd, Cannon House, Reform Street, Hull, HU2 8EF Tel: (01482) 227479 Fax: (01482) 588556 E-mail: enquries@erpuk.com *Industrial air compressor sets manufrs*

▶ E & R S Engineering Services, Park Road South, Havant, Hampshire, PO9 1HB Tel: (023) 9236 7777 Fax: (023) 9236 7776 E-mail: sales@e-r-s.com *3d modelling, engineering designers & special purpose machinery*

E R Varney (Tools) Ltd, Botsford Street, Sheffield, S3 9PF Tel: 0114-272 7650 Fax: 0114-272 7030 *Garage tool manufrs*

E R Wright & Son, 53 Millbrook Road East, Southampton, SO15 1HN Tel: (023) 8022 3334 Fax: (023) 8063 1956 E-mail: erwrightandson@tiscalli.co.uk *Glazing specialists contractors*

E Rand & Sons Ltd, Chapel Lane, Great Blakenham, Ipswich, IP6 0JY Tel: (01473) 832833 Fax: (01473) 832834 E-mail: sales@rand.uk.com *Diesel engineers, service, installaton, maintenance & generating sets*

▶ E Rankin, 178 Highmoor Road, Cross, Londonderry, BT47 3HS Tel: (028) 7130 1875 Fax: (028) 7130 1961

▶ E Reg Coatings, 4 Trans Britannia Industrial Estate, Farrington Road, Burnley, Lancashire, BB11 5SW Tel: (01282) 838378 Fax: (01282) 838015 E-mail: eregcoatings@aol.com *Powder coatings service*

E Reg Sheet Metal Fabricators, Unit 7 Kirby Road, Lomeshaye Industrial Estate, Nelson, Lancashire, BB9 6RS Tel: (01282) 697748 Fax: (01282) 697749 *Sheet metalwork fabricators*

▶ E Robson & Son, Crowle Street, Hull, HU9 1RH Tel: (01482) 226038 Fax: (01482) 325467

E & S B Davis Ltd, West View, Brighton Road, Tadworth, Surrey, KT20 6SU Tel: (01737) 833286 Fax: (01737) 832770 *Waste disposal contractors* Also at: Sutton

E S B Environmental, 126 Hillcroft Crescent, Watford, WD19 4NZ Tel: (01923) 800852 Fax: (01923) 229003 E-mail: jbird@moose.co.uk *Fire protection material manufrs*

▶ E S C Ltd, Unit 14 Impresa Park, Pindar Road, Hoddesdon, Hertfordshire, EN11 0DL Tel: (01992) 462307 Fax: (01992) 443237 E-mail: sales@escutters.co.uk *Steel Rule Dies/ *Laser-cutFormes /*Cutting and Creasing Dies/ *High Rule Cutters/*Laser-cut Custom Parts*

E S Engineering, Unit 13, Rowleys Green Lane Industrial Estate, Coventry, CV6 6AN Tel: (024) 7666 2038 Fax: (024) 7663 8946 *Reconditioned gear boxes & units*

E & S Forklift Sales, Malting Lane, Donington, Spalding, Lincolnshire, PE11 4XA Tel: (01775) 822022 Fax: (01775) 822009 E-mail: info@e-s-forklifts.co.uk *Forklift sales & hire*

E S Hadley, Foundry Yard, Hall Lane, Walton on the Naze, Essex, CO14 8HW Tel: (01255) 679913 Fax: (01255) 850932 E-mail: efhadleyeng@aol.com *Steel fabricators*

E S Harrison & Sons, The Willows, Haven Bank, New York, Lincoln, LN4 4XR Tel: (01205) 280336 Fax: (01205) 280336 *Farming & agricultural contractors*

E S Harverson & Son Transport Ltd, Unit 3 Abbey Industrial Estate, Mitcham, Surrey, CR4 4NA Tel: (020) 8648 5553 Fax: (020) 8646 7009 E-mail: bharverson@aol.com *New & reconditioned pallet suppliers*

▶ E S I Process Ltd, 2 Hill Street, Ty Coch Industrial Estate, Cwmbran, Gwent, NP44 7PG Tel: (01633) 877505 Fax: (01633) 877605 E-mail: sales@esitechnologies.co.uk *Valve manufrs*

E S I T Computer Consultancy, Suite A, Loughborough Technology Centre, Epinal Way, Loughborough, Leicestershire, LE11 3GE Tel: (01509) 235544 Fax: (01509) 260661 E-mail: info@esit.co.uk *Computer consultants & software developers*

E & S J Pearson, Felstead, Low Bentham Road, Bentham, Lancaster, LA2 7BP Tel: (01524) 261766 Fax: (01524) 263271 *Aluminum cattle truck containers & horse boxes*

▶ E & S J Walpole Ltd, 64 Causeway Road, Earlstrees Industrial Estate, Corby, Northamptonshire, NN17 4DU Tel: (01536) 201221 Fax: (01536) 406098

▶ E & S J Walpole Ltd, Greens Road, Dereham, Norfolk, NR20 3TG Tel: (01362) 655410 Fax: (01362) 655419

E S L Ltd, 301-303 Kennington Lane, London, SE11 5QU Tel: (020) 7820 7718 Fax: (020) 7820 7754 E-mail: ind-esl@msn.com *Computer systems suppliers & manufrs*

E S L Displays & Graphics, Units 3-5 Hillside Mews, Riding Barn Hill, Wick, Bristol, BS30 5PA Tel: 0117-937 4777 Fax: 0117-937 4550 E-mail: info@eslgroupuk.co.uk Principal Export Areas: Worldwide *Divine consultancy coffee machine importers & exporters*

E S L Engineers (Basildon) Ltd, Woolaston Way, Basildon, Essex, SS13 1DJ Tel: (01268) 727777 Fax: (01268) 728866 E-mail: sales@eslengineers.co.uk *Aerospace engineers & gear manufrs*

▶ E S L Healthcare Ltd, Sandown Court, Station Road, Glenfield, Leicester, LE3 8BT Tel: 0116-231 8900 Fax: 0116-233 1000 E-mail: uksales@pressalitcare.com *Manufacturing medical or surgical supplies*

▶ E S M Ltd, Unit C5, Imperial Business Estate, Westmill, Gravesend, Kent, DA11 0DL Tel: (01474) 536360 *ESM offer an integrated and creative design, planning and project management service for exhibitors. We provide exhibition and display services to many of the UK's leading brands at events across the globe. The core values of ESM are quality and customer service. ESM uses only the very latest materials available throughout our constructions and our excellent finishes are renowned throught the industry. **Click the links below to visit our website or contact us via our profile page.*

E S M (U K) Ltd, PO Box 47, Bredbury, Cheshire, SK6 2FN Tel: 0161-406 3888 Fax: 0161-406 3889 E-mail: bshaw@satake-esm.co.uk Principal Export Areas: Worldwide *Retailers of electronic & plastics sorting & processing equipment*

E & S Metals, Cadwell Lane, Hitchin, Hertfordshire, SG4 0SA Tel: (01462) 455171 Fax: (01462) 453037 *Scrap metal merchants*

E S P Colour, Elgin Drive, Swindon, SN2 8XU Tel: (01793) 438400 Fax: (01793) 530403 E-mail: firstinitial.surname@espcolour.co.uk *Printers*

E S P Plastics Ltd, Prospect Road, Crook, County Durham, DL15 8JL Tel: (01388) 765400 Fax: (01388) 765300 E-mail: sales@esp-plastics.co.uk *Plastic vacuum forming services*

E S P Technologies Group Ltd, 2 Euroway, Wood Close, Quarry Wood, Aylesford, Kent, ME20 7UB Tel: (01622) 715000 Fax: (01622) 797000 E-mail: sales@esptech.co.uk *Screen & digital printers manufrs*

E S P Technologies Group Ltd, 2 Euroway, Wood Close, Quarry Wood, Aylesford, Kent, ME20 7UB Tel: (01622) 715000 Fax: (01622) 797000 E-mail: sales@esptech.co.uk *Sign creators*

E S Plummer & Son, 82 High Street, Markyate, St. Albans, Hertfordshire, AL3 8LE Tel: (01582) 840611 Fax: (01582) 840611 E-mail: djp1947@ukgateway.net *Carpentry & joinery specialists*

▶ E S S Safety Services, Essential House, Vaux Road, Finedon Road Industrial Estate, Wellingborough, Northamptonshire, NN8 4TG Tel: (01933) 443442 Fax: (01933) 442635 E-mail: info@ess-safety.com *ESS Safety Services supplies a full range of safety equipment for individuals working in safety-critical environments, mainly construction , civil engineering, utilities and general industry. For more information please contact a member of our sales team on 0870 443 5044 or visit our website at www.ess-safety.com.*

E S Safety Supplies, Unit 33, 10 Barley Mow Pass, London, W4 4PH Tel: (020) 8575 8127 Fax: (020) 8944 1533 *Firefighting equipment supplier*

E S T Electrical Contractors Ltd, 18 Kenchester Close, Redditch, Worcestershire, B98 0BT Tel: (01527) 529050 Fax: (01527) 510550 *Portable appliance testing*

▶ E Saunders Ltd, 241 Northdown Road, Margate, Kent, CT9 2PL Tel: (01843) 228546 Fax: (01843) 228290

E Signs, 118 Piccadilly, Mayfair, London, W1J 7NW Tel: (0800) 7312259 Fax: (0845) 0042259 E-mail: info@e-signs.co.uk *Sign makers*

E Smith & Co, Albion Street, Hull, HU1 3TE Tel: (01482) 324599 Fax: (01482) 588266 *Surgical truss manufacturers & rehabilitation equipment suppliers*

E Stokes, 55 Wharf Road, Tyseley, Birmingham, B11 2DX Tel: 0121-707 2615 Fax: 0121-707 2615 *Metal heat treatment services*

E Stubbs Press Tools Ltd, Ann Street, Willenhall, West Midlands, WV13 1EN Tel: (01902) 608589 Fax: (01902) 608589 *Press tool manufrs*

E.Surv, 53 Bothell Street, Glasgow, G2 6TS Tel: 0141-847 0987 Fax: 0141-847 0579 *Residential surveyors*

E Sutton & Son Ltd, Riverside, Bacup, Lancashire, OL13 0DT Tel: (01706) 874961 Fax: (01706) 879268 E-mail: firstname@esutton.co.uk *Ladies & girls shoe manufacturers & importing*

E T B Instruments Ltd, Unit 15 Brookside, Sumpters Way Temple Farm, Temple Farm Industrial Estate, Southend-on-Sea, SS2 5RR Tel: (01702) 601055 Fax: (01702) 601056 E-mail: info@etbinstruments.com *Car instruments manufrs*

E T B Services Ltd, 7 James St Workshops, James Street, Carlisle, CA2 5AH Tel: (01228) 594747 Fax: (01228) 594665 E-mail: etb@btclick.com *Domestic appliance services*

E T C, 250 Queensferry Road, Edinburgh, EH4 2BR Tel: 0131-332 1616 Fax: 0131-343 6161 E-mail: etclocks@aol.com *Locksmith corporate sign specialist*

E T C Global Solutions Ltd, 75 Woodside Road, Amersham, Buckinghamshire, HP6 6AA Tel: (01494) 720600 Fax: (01494) 720601 E-mail: mail@etcgs.com *Computer software developers*

E T C Sawmills Ltd, Elson, Ellesmere, Shropshire, SY12 9EU Tel: (01691) 622441 Fax: (01691) 623468 E-mail: info@etcsawmills.co.uk *Timber & fencing suppliers*

E T C (UK) Ltd, Unit 4A, Barking Business Centre, 25 Thames Road, Barking, Essex, IG11 0JP Tel: (020) 8477 4490 Fax: (020) 8594 1243 E-mail: info@etclondonparis.com *Conference & events organizers*

E T Flower & Co. Ltd, 26-30 Theobald Street, Borehamwood, Hertfordshire, WD6 4SG Tel: (020) 8953 2343 Fax: (020) 8905 1845 *Metal polishing services*

E T H Ltd, 17 Pilrig Street, Edinburgh, EH6 5AN Tel: 0131-553 2721 *Music production manufrs*

E T H Metals Ltd, Unit 2B, 2 Bowyer Street, Birmingham, B10 0SA Tel: 0121-753 1673 Fax: 0121-753 1674 E-mail: zircon@onetel.net.uk *Opthalmic scalpel blade manufrs*

E T & Lee Roberts, 1b Graeme Road, Enfield, Middlesex, EN1 3UU Tel: (020) 8363 6452 Fax: (020) 8804 1102 *Hand & tenon saw manufrs*

E T Marine & Industrial Engineering Co Ltd, Manor Way, Grays, Essex, RM17 6BJ Tel: (01375) 378282 Fax: (01375) 385804 E-mail: works@etmarine.com *Marine & industrial engineering services*

E T Martin & Son Edmonton Ltd, Unit 21 Landmark Commercial Centre, Commercial Road, London, N18 1UB Tel: (020) 8884 2060 Fax: (020) 8807 7046 E-mail: sales@etmartinson.co.uk *Metal spinners & spinnings manufrs*

▶ E T Morris & Sons Ltd, King George Dock, Hull, HU9 5PR Tel: (01482) 786818 Fax: (01482) 782284

▶ E T Morris & Sons Ltd, Boston Road, New York, Lincoln, LN4 4XH Tel: (01205) 280345 Fax: (01205) 280445

E T S Maintenance, Bridge Works, Hall Green, Little Hallingbury, Bishop's Stortford, Hertfordshire, CM22 7RP Tel: (01279) 730022 Fax: (01279) 731777 E-mail: etsltd@btinternet.com *Broadcasting & communications & maintenance services*

▶ E T S Technical Sales, Phoenix House, Phoenix Way, Cirencester, Gloucestershire, GL7 1QG Tel: (0870) 0702246 E-mail: mark@ets-technical-sales.co.uk

E T Tucker Ltd, 87 Severn Road, Cardiff, CF11 9EA Tel: (029) 2022 9842 *Motor engineers services*

E U (Colchester) Ltd, Unit B1 Cowdray Centre, Cowdray Avenue, Colchester, CO1 1BL Tel: (01206) 548582 Fax: (01206) 579584 *Motor vehicle factors*

▶ E V Automotive Ltd, Padstow Road, Coventry, CV4 9XB Tel: (024) 7649 6666 Fax: (024) 7649 6677 E-mail: info@evukcarpanels.co.uk

E V O Instrumentation Ltd, 31a Coppice Trading Estate, Kidderminster, Worcestershire, DY11 7QY Tel: (01562) 741212 Fax: (01562) 741666 E-mail: sales@evoinstrumentation.co.uk *Pressure and vacuum gauges, pressure and temperature switches, pressure transducers and diaphragm seals for all industries. Onsite repair and calibrations and filling service for diaphragm seals. UK Nuova Fima agent and stockist. Thermometers and temperature switches for the industrial market. Bi Metal, Switch and Dial thermometers available. Thermometers for range cookers and woodburners.*

E V Wood Anodising Ltd, 421 Tyburn Road, Birmingham, B24 8HJ Tel: 0121-328 7646 Fax: 0121-327 1854 E-mail: carolyn@ebwood.co.uk *Anodising processors or services*

E W Allen, Hallgarth Garage, High Pittington, Durham, DH6 1AT Tel: 0191-372 0313 Fax: 0191-372 2440 E-mail: ewallentractors@fsmail.net *Agriculture goods & ground care equipment suppliers & manufrs*

E W Contracting Ltd, East Wick Farm, Wootton Rivers, Marlborough, Wiltshire, SN8 4NS Tel: (01672) 810255 Fax: (01672) 810884 *Agricultural contractors*

E.W. Creaser (Burnby) Ltd, Partridge Hall Quarry, Burnby, York, YO42 1RD Tel: (01430) 873428 Fax: (01430) 873428 *Quarry operators*

E W D Hair & Beauty Supplies Ltd, Units 1-3, Rainbow Street, Crewe, CW1 2AU Tel: (01270) 581307 Fax: (01270) 581307 *Wholesale hair & beauty products*

E W Equipment, 11 Worcester Road, Cheadle Hulme, Cheadle, Cheshire, SK8 5NW Tel: 0161-485 8730 Fax: 0161-485 6745 E-mail: sales@ewequipment.co.uk *Workshop & general tool supplier*

▶ E & W Fullertons, Stephenson Street, Hillington Industrial Estate, Glasgow, G52 4NX Tel: 0141-810 1588

E W H Support Services, Edwards House, 327 Whapload Road, Lowestoft, Suffolk, NR32 1QY Tel: (01502) 516971 Fax: (01502) 516970 E-mail: enquire@lecmarine-low.co.uk *Agencies*

E W Hoe Export Packers Ltd, Violet Road, London, E3 3QH Tel: (020) 7987 2444 Fax: (020) 7987 0497 E-mail: sales@ewhoe.co.uk *Packing case manufacturers & export packers*

E & W Hopkins Ltd, 32-33 Hatton Garden, London, EC1N 8BR Tel: (020) 7405 6354 Fax: (020) 7405 1170 E-mail: ew_hopkins@hotmail.com *Precious stone importers*

▶ E W L Ltd, 2A Newman Terrace, Gateshead, Tyne & Wear, NE8 3XA Tel: 0191-477 3330

E W Moore & Son Ltd, 39-43 Plashet Grove, London, E6 1AD Tel: (020) 8472 0521 Fax: (020) 8472 4702 E-mail: sales@wallposters.org.uk *Plumbers & decorators*

▶ E W Rayment & Co. Ltd, 3 Water End Road, Potten End, Berkhamsted, Hertfordshire, HP4 2SJ Tel: (01442) 864422 Fax: (01442) 877247

E W Taylor & Co Forwarding Ltd, Dunbar House Eurolink Industrial Centre, Castle Road, Sittingbourne, Kent, ME10 3RN Tel: (01795) 410110 Fax: (01795) 410111 E-mail: sharonlambert@ewtaylorgroup.com *Shipping warehousing distribution haulage* Also at: Dover, Felixstowe, Portsmouth, Sheerness & Tilbury

E W Turner & Co. Ltd, Tame Street, West Bromwich, West Midlands, B70 0QP Tel: 0121-556 1141 Fax: 0121-556 3911 E-mail: accounts@ewturner.co.uk *Export packing case & pallet manufrs*

▶ E Walters UK, Southern Avenue, Leominster, Herefordshire, HR6 0LY Tel: (01568) 613344 Fax: (01568) 610860 E-mail: reception@ewalters.co.uk *Manufacturing garments*

E White, Watling Street, Clifton upon Dunsmore, Rugby, Warwickshire, CV23 0AQ Tel: (01788) 860526 Fax: (01788) 860150 E-mail: sales@ericwhite.co.uk *Metallurgists, testing & inspection engineers*

▶ E Wilkinson Plumbing & Heating Contractors Ltd, 120d Milton Park, Milton, Abingdon, Oxfordshire, OX14 4SA Tel: (01235) 835070 Fax: (01235) 832033

E.Wiltshire & Son (Torquay) Ltd, Walls Hill Quarry, Babbacombe Road, Torquay, TQ1 3TA Tel: (01803) 327706 Fax: (01803) 327793 E-mail: info@wiltshires-babbacombe.co.uk *Ready mixed concrete, concrete blocks manufactures,dumpy bags sand & gravels, cement, paving, decorative gavels collected or deleivered throughout Devon.*

E Witten & Son, 7 Riverbank Business Centre, Old Shoreham Road, Shoreham-by-Sea, West Sussex, BN43 5FL Tel: (01273) 441255 Fax: (01273) 441264 *Saw & cutter sharpening services*

▶ E Wood Ltd, Standard Way Industrial Estate, Northallerton, North Yorkshire, DL6 2XA Tel: (01609) 778907 Fax: (01609) 783762 E-mail: copon@ewood.co.uk *High performance protective coatings for industry*

E Wood Ltd, Standard Way Industrial Estate, Northallerton, North Yorkshire, DL6 2XA Tel: (01609) 778907 Fax: (01609) 783762 E-mail: thortex@ewood.co.uk *Anti-corrosion chemical manufrs*

E X B Ltd, Unit 15 Eldonwell Trading Estate, Eldon Way, Bristol, BS4 3QQ Tel: 0117-972 8380 Fax: 0117-972 3615 *Brake lining & automotive components*

E X Heat Ltd, Threxton Road Industrial Estate, Watton, Thetford, Norfolk, IP25 6NG Tel: (01953) 886200 Fax: (01953) 886222 E-mail: sales@exheat.com *Manufacturer of electric heaters & control systems*

E X Stock Steel Ltd, Units 2-4, Isca Foundary, Millman St, Newport, Gwent, NP20 2JL Tel: (01633) 253111 Fax: (01633) 264333 *Steel stockholders*

E X X Projects, 72 Rivington Street, London, EC2A 3AY Tel: (020) 7684 8200 Fax: 0845-630 1282 E-mail: exx@plax.co.uk *Portfolio & planschest manufrs*

▶ E Z Credit, 34 Sudley Road, Bognor Regis, West Sussex, PO21 1ER Tel: (01243) 841818 Fax: (01243) 840180 *Specialists in providing vehicle finance for the subprime market.*

E Z Rect Ltd, Witan Park, Avenue Two, Witney, Oxfordshire, OX28 4FH Tel: (01993) 779494 Fax: (01993) 704111 E-mail: sales@e-z-rect.com *Boltless shelving systems manufrs*

E2 Systems Ltd, Broadway House, 21 Broadway, Maidenhead, Berkshire, SL6 1NJ Tel: (01628) 418128 E-mail: e2web@e2systems.co.uk *Computer consultants*

▶ E2S European Safety Systems Ltd, Impress House, Mansell Road, London, W3 7QH Tel: 020 8743 8880 Fax: 020 8740 4200 E-mail: sales@e2s.com Sales Contact: B. Isard *Specialising in the design, development and manufacture of high performance electronic sounders, intelligent voice annunciators and flash alarms for industrial, heavy duty, marine and hazardous environments, E2S is now the worlds leading independent signalling manufacturer. The company's wide range of intrinsically safe and explosion proof units are designed and manufactured at its West London offices and production facility. All the senior management have extensive experience of the sounder industry, gained with a number of other manufacturers. A close and pro-active relationship with a valued network of distributors and system integrators, strategically located throughout Europe, Australasia and the USA, ensures worldwide product availability and local technical support.*

▶ Ea Higginson & Co., 1 Carlisle Road, London, NW9 0HD Tel: (020) 8200 4848 Fax: (020) 8200 8249 E-mail: sales@higginson.co.uk *Distributors of italian spiral stairs in timber, steel & cast iron*

▶ Ea Scaffolding & Systems, Unit 16 North Luton Industrial Estate, Sedgewick Road, Luton, LU4 9DT Tel: (01582) 575200 Fax: (01582) 599254

▶ E-active Marketing, PO Box 332, Bushey, WD23 3XZ Tel: 07092 369840 Fax: 07092 369840 E-mail: john@e-active.co.uk

▶ Eaden Homes Ltd, Berwyn Porthdafarch Road, Holyhead, Gwynedd, LL65 2SA Tel: (01407) 765603

Eadie & Kanai Co. Ltd, 19 Scotts Road, Paisley, Renfrewshire, PA2 7AN Tel: 0141-889 4126 Fax: 0141-848 1290 E-mail: sales@ekcl.co.uk *Ring & ring traveller manufrs*

Eadie Refrigeration Ltd, 4 Old Perth Road, Cowdenbeath, Fife, KY4 9DR Tel: (01383) 513657 Fax: (01383) 611480 *Transport refrigeration*

▶ eaga Insulating, 23B Cherry Way, Dubmire Industrial Estate, Houghton Le Spring, Tyne & Wear, DH4 5RJ Tel: 0191-385 9266 Fax: 0191-385 9288E-mail: dubmire@eaga.com *The UK's leading installer of cavity wall and loft insulation. Varied products and services available, please call for details.*

▶ Eaga Insulation, 4B Cooper Drive, Springwood Industrial Estate, Braintree, Essex, CM7 2RF Tel: 01376 334044 Fax: 01376 331101 E-mail: essex@eaga.com *The UK's leading installer of cavity wall and loft insulation. Varied products and services available, please call for details.*

▶ eaga Insulation, Typhoon House, Oakcroft Road, Chessington, Surrey, KT9 1RH Tel: (020) 8391 3620 Fax: (020) 8391 2588 E-mail: chessington@eaga.com *The UK's leading installer of cavity wall and loft insulation. Varied products and services available, please call for details.*

▶ Eaga Insulation, Epsom House, Malton Way, Chase Park, Adwick Le Street, Doncaster, South Yorkshire, DN6 7FE Tel: (01302) 332100 Fax: (01302) 332157 *The UK's leading installer of cavity wall and loft insulation. Varied products and services available, please call for details.*

▶ Eaga Insulation, 4 Monks Way, Lincoln, LN2 5LN Tel: (01522) 563550 Fax: (01522) 563551 E-mail: lincoln@eaga.com *The UK's leading installer of cavity wall and loft insulation. Varied products and services available, please call for details. **

▶ Eaga Insulation Ltd, 34 Morgan Way, Bowthorpe Employment Area, Norwich, NR5 9JJ Tel: (01603) 734110 Fax: (01603) 734111 E-mail: norwich@eaga.com *The UK's leading installer of cavity wall and loft insulation. Varied products and services available, please call for details.*

▶ Eaga Insulation, Unit 8 Oldbury Point, Rood End Industrial Estate, Rood End Road, Oldbury, West Midlands, B69 4HT Tel: (01709) 830713 Fax: 0121-541 1991 E-mail: oldbury@eaga.com *The UK's leading installer of cavity wall and loft insulation. Varied products and services available, please call for details.*

▶ Eaga Insulation, Unit 14, Seaway Drive, Seaway Parade Industrial Estate, Port Talbot, West Glamorgan, SA12 7BR Tel: (01639) 825770 Fax: (01639) 825778 E-mail: porttalbot@eaga.com *The UK's leading installer of cavity wall and loft insulation. Varied products and services available, please call for details.*

▶ eaga Insulation, E1 Explorer, Portfield Road, Voyager Park, Portsmouth, PO3 5FL Tel: (023) 9262 3030 Fax: (023) 9262 3049 E-mail: portsmouth@eaga.com *The UK's leading installer of cavity wall and loft insulation. Varied products and services available, please call for details.*

▶ Eaga Insulation, Unit 12 Scotts Industrial Park, Fishwick Street, Rochdale, Lancashire, OL16 5NA Tel: (01706) 717470 Fax: (01706) 650057 E-mail: rochdale@eaga.com *The UK's leading installer of cavity wall and loft insulation. Varied products and services available, please call for details.*

▶ eaga Insulation, 61a Osbaldwick Lane, York, YO10 3AY Tel: (01904) 430122 Fax: (01904) 431467 E-mail: york@eaga.com *The UK's leading installer of cavity wall and loft insulation. Varied products and services available, please call for details.*

Eagland Machine Tools Ltd, The Studio, Hill Road, Lyme Regis, Dorset, DT7 3PG Tel: (01297) 446000 Fax: (01297) 446001 E-mail: info@eagland.co.uk *Machinery merchants*

Eagle Aerials, Mount Pleasant, Chapel Lane, Cannock Wood, Rugeley, Staffordshire, WS15 4SE Tel: (01543) 684558 Fax: (01543) 684558 *Aerial Installation company*

Eagle Airfield Equipment Ltd, Nebo Road, Llanrwst, Gwynedd, LL26 0SE Tel: (01492) 642201 Fax: (01492) 641992 E-mail: eagle@downline.co.uk *Ice detection equipment manufrs*

Eagle Controls International Ltd, PO Box 42, Letchworth Garden City, Hertfordshire, SG6 1HQ Tel: (01462) 670566 Fax: (01462) 673992 E-mail: info@eaglecontrols.co.uk *Temperature controller, timer & counter manufrs*

▶ Eagle Corrugated Ltd, Kayley Industrial Estate, Richmond Street, Ashton-Under-Lyne, Lancashire, OL7 0AU Tel: 0161-343 1722

Eagle Couriers Scotland, 1b Payne Street, Glasgow, G4 0LE Tel: 0141-332 1115 Fax: 0141-332 2567 *Couriers services*

Eagle Direct Marketing, Unit 1 Axis, Hawkfield Business Park, Whitchurch, Bristol, BS14 0BY Tel: 0117-902 0073 Fax: 0117-902 8220 E-mail: sc@eaglemailing.co.uk *Direct mail services*

Eagle Enterprises, The Retreat, Harby La, Eagle Moor, Lincoln, LN6 9DS Tel: 01522 696278 *Game machines supplier*

Eagle Envelopes Ltd, Bloxwich Road, Walsall, WS2 7BD Tel: (01922) 613888 Fax: (01922) 613999 E-mail: walsall@eagle-envelopes.com *Envelope printers & manufrs*

Eagle Fire Systems, 100 Liverpool Street, Salford, M5 4LP Tel: 0161-745 9578 Fax: 0161-745 9578 E-mail: eaglfirsys@aol.com *Fire protection system & equipment manufrs*

Eagle Global Logistics, 20 Leacroft Road, Birchwood, Warrington, WA3 6PJ Tel: (01925) 250500 Fax: (01925) 250585 *Freight container operators services & freight forwarders* Also at: Offices throughout the U.K.

Eagle Hydraulic Systems Ltd, 14 Chartwell Road, Lancing, West Sussex, BN15 8TU Tel: (01903) 751494 Fax: (01903) 751522 *Hydraulic equipment systems manufrs*

▶ Eagle Lcs, Innovation House, Unit 3 Linton Business Park, Gourdon, Montrose, Angus, DD10 0NH Tel: (01561) 360068

Eagle Ottawa Warrington Ltd, 254 Thelwall Lane, Warrington, WA4 1NQ Tel: (01925) 650251 Fax: (01925) 655547 *Leather manufrs*

Eagle Packaging, Unit 8A Churchfield Business Park, Clensmore Street, Kidderminster, Worcestershire, DY10 2JY Tel: (01562) 862254 Fax: (01562) 862308 E-mail: eaglepackaginguk@aol.com *Polythene bag manufrs*

Eagle Power, Johnson Bridge Road, Off Church Lane, West Bromwich, West Midlands, B71 1DG Tel: 0121-580 3222 Fax: 0121-525 4796 E-mail: eagle@kw1.com Principal Export Areas: Worldwide *Suppliers of new & used diesel generators*

Eagle Scientific Ltd, Regent House, Lenton Street, Sandiacre, Nottingham, NG10 5DJ Tel: 0115-949 1111 Fax: 0115-939 1144 E-mail: equip@eagle-scientific.co.uk *Supply & distribute scientific & lab equipment*

Eagle Security Solutions Ltd, 162 Trafalgar Road, London, SE10 9TZ Tel: (0845) 9002950 E-mail: info@eaglesecuritysolutions.co.uk *Based in London, covering the whole of England, Eagle Security Solutions provide sales, installation & maintenance of home security systems, including: burglar alarms, wireless alarm, smoke alarm, CCTV and door entry system. We also provide business security systems, such as security alarm, monitored intruder alarm, redcare, closed circuit television (CCTV), video entry system and access control. Our security systems comply with current British & European standards and meet police & insurance requirements. Eagle Security Solutions offers free quotation, fast track installation and security system upgrade/repair in London, Middlesex, Surrey, Cambridge,*Bedfordshire, Hertfordshire, Hampshire, Kent and Essex.*

Eagle Security Systems, 14 Station Approach, Birchington, Kent, CT7 9RD Tel: (01843) 845444 Fax: (01843) 845592 *Alarm installation*

▶ Eagle Service & Machinery Ltd, 5 Clare Road, Taplow, Maidenhead, Berkshire, SL6 0LH Tel: (01753) 790799 Fax: (01753) 672680 E-mail: ps@eagleservice.co.uk *Silk screen printing engineers*

Eagle Signs Ltd, 56 Oreston Road, Pomphlett, Plymouth, PL9 7JQ Tel: (01752) 402559 Fax: (01752) 481126 E-mail: info@eaglesigns.co.uk *Sign manufrs*

Eagle Specialist Vehicles Ltd, 105 Manchester Road, West Houghton, Bolton, BL5 3QH Tel: (01942) 850200 Fax: (01942) 819745 E-mail: eaglespecial@aol.com *Coach builders*

Eagle Structural Ltd, The Maples, Lordship Road, Great Carlton, Louth, Lincolnshire, LN11 8JS Tel: (01507) 450081 Fax: (01507) 450981 *Structural steel & cladding contractors*

Eagle Technologies Ltd, Unit 17, The Western Centre, Western Road, Bracknell, Berkshire, RG12 1RW Tel: (01344) 303700 Fax: (01344) 303701 E-mail: sales@eagletechnologies.co.uk *Printers & ID card printing specialists*

Eagle Tools & Fixings, The Willows, Eardisland, Leominster, Herefordshire, HR6 9BN Tel: (01544) 388830 Fax: (01544) 388830 *Power tool & fixings stockists*

Eagle Trailers, 241A Blandford Road, Hamworthy, Poole, Dorset, BH15 4AZ Tel: (01202) 671057 Fax: (01202) 671057 *Trailers*

▶ Eagleburgmann Industries UK, Welton Road, Warwick, CV34 5PZ Tel: (01926) 417600 Fax: (01926) 417617 E-mail: sales@burgmann.co.uk *Mechanical seals manufrs*

Eaglecrest Computer Systems Ltd, Brytirion, Chapel Street, Llanarmon-yn-Ial, Mold, Clwyd, CH7 4QE Tel: (01824) 780565 Fax: (01824) 780375 E-mail: mike.wheeler@eaglecrest-cs.com *Computer consultants & internet shop*

Eagledale Gate Mnfrs, Unit H Cavans Way, Binley Industrial Estate, Coventry, CV3 2SF Tel: (024) 7663 6064 Fax: (024) 7645 5378 *Gate manufrs*

Eaglemoss Publications Ltd, Beaumont House, Kensington Village, London, W14 8TS Tel: (020) 7590 8300 Fax: (020) 7590 8301 E-mail: sales@eaglemoss.co.uk *Part work publishers*

William Eagles Ltd, 100 Liverpool Street, Salford, M5 4LP Tel: 0161-736 1661 Fax: 0161-745 7765 E-mail: sales@william-eagles.co.uk *Manufacturing fire-fighting equipment*

Eakins Plant Hire & Ground Work Ltd, Manor Farm, Prestwood Lane, Ifield Wood, Crawley, West Sussex, RH11 0LA Tel: (01293) 871311 Fax: (01293) 871770 *Groundwork & civil engineering services*

S.W. Eakins, Ravensbank Stables, Icknield Street, Redditch, Worcestershire, B98 9AD Tel: (01527) 597354 *Farriers*

Samuel Eales Silverware Ltd, 26 Douglas Road, Sheffield, S3 9SA Tel: 0114 2720885 *Table cutlery manufrs*

▶ Ealing Fabrics, 131 Uxbridge Road, Hanwell, London, W7 3ST Tel: (020) 8579 0740 E-mail: zubiedyat@web.de *We sell dress fabrics, curtain material & do alterations*

▶ Ealing Hammersmith & West London College, Southall Library, Osterley Park Road, Southall, Middlesex, UB2 4BL Tel: (020) 8574 1472 *Educational publishers*

▶ Ealing Life Magazine, P O Box 54909, London, W3 9WP Tel: (020) 8932 8302 *Local lifestyle and community magazine delivered free to residents of Ealing and Acton.*

Eames Motor Repairs, 18 St James Industrial Estate, Westhampnett Road, Chichester, West Sussex, PO19 7JU Tel: (01243) 775968 Fax: (01243) 775968 *Motor repair services*

Company Information

▶ indicates data change since last edition

Eao Ltd, Albert Drive, Burgess Hill, West Sussex, RH15 9TN Tel: (01444) 236000 Fax: (01444) 236641 E-mail: sales.euk@eao.com *Electronic component distributors* Also at: Dunfermline

F. Eardley (Potteries) Ltd, Foley Works, Brocksford Street, Fenton, Stoke-on-Trent, ST4 3HF Tel: (01782) 313871 Fax: (01782) 325057 *China glass earthware merchants*

▶ Eardley International, Ecclefechan, Lockerbie, Dumfriesshire, DG11 3JD Tel: (01576) 300500 Fax: (01576) 300555

Earhtech Engineering Ltd, Unit 1, Grovebury Place Estate, Grovebury Road, Leighton Buzzard, Bedfordshire, LU7 4SH Tel: (01525) 374362 Fax: (01525) 377304 *Precision engineers*

Earl Plastics Ltd, Albert Works, St Huberts Street, Great Harwood, Blackburn, BB6 7BE Tel: (01254) 887494 Fax: (01254) 876355 E-mail: earlplastics@aol.com *Plastic injection moulding services*

Earl Road Sweepers Ltd, Shardlowes Farm, Hedingham Road, Gosfield, Halstead, Essex, CO9 1PL Tel: (01787) 273777 Fax: (01787) 273777 E-mail: office@ersweepers.wanadoo.co.uk *We are specialists in the following areas: Cleaning of: Car Parks, Factory Roads/Perimeters, Quarry Roads /Access , Wash Down Bays, Spillages (Non-Toxic), Forecourts, Gullies, White Lining, Leaves, Warehouse /Factory Interiors, Footpaths, Bus Shelters, Cattle Grids, Surface Dressing - Pre and Post Industries Covered: Construction, House Building, Factories & Agricultural Operations, Road Surfacing Contractors, Landfill Sites & Local Authorities. Our fleet includes 5 Johnston 600 series Road Sweepers, 1 Whale Tanker and 1 Jet Vac. The Jet Vac is designed with the more difficult and specialised job in mind. 24 Hour Emergency Work Undertaken. Telephone 07973 191116*

Earl Road Sweepers Ltd, Shardlowes Farm, Hedingham Road, Gosfield, Halstead, Essex, CO9 1PL Tel: (01787) 273777 Fax: (01787) 273777 E-mail: office@ersweepers.wanadoo.co.uk *Drain Jetting,path,patio and forecourt cleaning.Drain empting,Bubble gum removing and stain removal(ie paint ect)*

Earl & Thompson Marketing Ltd, The Creative Centre, 1 Hucclecote Road, Gloucester, GL3 3TH Tel: (01452) 627100 Fax: (01452) 627101 E-mail: info@earl-thompson.co.uk *Marketing & design & public relations consultants services*

▶ Earle & Ludlow, 77 Victoria Road, Cirencester, Gloucestershire, GL7 1ES Tel: (01285) 653599 Fax: (01285) 640286 E-mail: sales@earle-ludlow.co.uk

Earlex Ltd, Opus Park Moorfield Road, Slyfield Industrial Estate, Guildford, Surrey, GU1 1SZ Tel: (01483) 454666 Fax: (01483) 454548 E-mail: enquiries@earlex.co.uk *Paint rollers & steam cleaners equipment manufrs*

Earls Court & Olympia Group Ltd, Exhibition Centre, Warwick Road, London, SW5 9TA Tel: (020) 7370 8078 Fax: (020) 7370 8390 E-mail: sales@eco.co.uk *Exhibition halls & conference centres*

Earlsdon Technology Properties Ltd, Unit 11 Spitfire Close, Coventry Business Park, Coventry, CV5 6UR Tel: (024) 7671 7062 Fax: (024) 7671 7062 E-mail: sales@e-tech.co.uk *Special purpose machine suppliers*

Earlsmere Id Systems Ltd, Earlsmere House, Doncaster Road, Barnsley, South Yorkshire, S71 5EH Tel: (01226) 204096 Fax: (01226) 244169 E-mail: sales@earlsmere.co.uk *Bar coding systems & self adhesive labeling distributors*

Earlswood Supplies, Thatchems Farm, Williamscot, Banbury, Oxfordshire, OX16 3JR Tel: (01295) 758734 Fax: (01295) 758011 E-mail: sales@earlswoodsupplies.com *Rubber flooring suppliers*

Early Days, 15B Mandervell Road, Oadby, Leicester, LE2 5LQ Tel: 0116-271 6944 Fax: 0116-271 9869 E-mail: sales@earlydays.ltd.uk *Infants shoe manufrs*

▶ Early Match Ltd, Unit 10 Osborne Trading Estate, Osborne Street, Oldham, OL9 6QQ Tel: 0161-626 6798 Fax: 0161-628 2307

▶ Early Riser Disco Centre, 50-52 Beulah Road, London, E17 9LQ Tel: (020) 8520 3401 Fax: (020) 8520 1073 E-mail: sales@earlyriser.co.uk *DJ & karaoke equipment sales, service, installation & hire*

▶ Early Years, 2 City Arcade, Coventry, CV1 3HW Tel: (024) 7663 4242 *Baby wear & accessory retailers*

Earney Contracts, 221 Comber Road, Lisburn, County Antrim, BT27 6XY Tel: (028) 9263 8269 Fax: (028) 9263 9009 E-mail: s.earney@btconnect.com *Civil engineering contractors*

▶ Earnshaw Engineering Ltd, Unit 2 Barton Park Industrial Estate, Eastleigh, Hampshire, SO50 6RR Tel: (023) 8061 3137 Fax: (023) 8062 9151 *Manufacturing & fabrication of architectural tiles*

Earnvale Tractors Ltd, Townhead, Balbeggie, Perth, PH2 6ET Tel: (01821) 640444 Fax: (01821) 640525 E-mail: earnvale.tractors@btinternet.com *Agricultural machinery suppliers*

Earsdon Engineering Ltd, Euroseas Centre, Albert Street, Blyth, Northumberland, NE24 1LZ Tel: (01670) 545500 Fax: (01670) 546103 *Supply, treatment & installation of high specification stainless steel*

Earsham Hall Pine, 6 St Benedicts Street, Norwich, NR2 4AG Tel: (01603) 615710 Fax: (01603) 615710 E-mail: sales@earshamhallpine.co.uk *Pine furniture manufrs*

Earth 1st Hire, 198 Cannock Road, Westcroft, Wolverhampton, WV10 8QP Tel: (01902) 861333 Fax: (01902) 864400 *Construction, industrial & general equipment hire*

Earth Anchors Ltd, 15 Campbell Road, Croydon, CR0 2SQ Tel: (020) 8684 9601 Fax: (020) 8684 2230 E-mail: enquiries@earth-anchors.com *Park & street furniture suppliers*

▶ Earth Crimp Connectors Ltd, 79 Atherstone Road, Measham, Swadlincote, Derbyshire, DE12 7EG Tel: (01530) 273137 Fax: (01530) 273137 E-mail: colin@earthcrimp.co.uk *60% time saving, invented by plumbers. the worlds fastest earth bonding system. Invented by plumbers.*UK Distributor.Hayes UK Ltd**

▶ Earth Force Ltd, Park Chambers, 10 Hereford Road, Abergavenny, Monmouthshire, NP7 5PR Tel: (01873) 851953 Fax: (01873) 851951 E-mail: info@earthforce.com *Health food supplement importers & distributors*

Earthfair International, Cromwell House, Elland Road, Brighouse, West Yorkshire, HD6 2RG Tel: (01422) 374119 Fax: (01422) 374386 E-mail: enquiries@earthfair.co.uk *Road making & asphalt equipment suppliers*

Earthing Equipment Supplies Southern Ltd, Lavender House, Church Lane, Arborfield, Reading, RG2 9JA Tel: 0118-976 0239 Fax: 0118-976 0076 E-mail: sales@earthingequip.com *Lightning protection & earthing installation supporters*

Earthly Goods, 8 Field Close, Grafham, Huntingdon, Cambridgeshire, PE28 0AY Tel: (01480) 812004 Fax: 01480 812004 E-mail: timbers85@hotmail.com *Suppliers of domestic water purification systems.**Offers a supply and install service, with on going support including replacement of filters as required.*

▶ Earthworks & Contracting Ltd, The Walfe, Main Street, Hickling, Melton Mowbray, Leicestershire, LE14 3AH Tel: (01664) 823789 Fax: (01664) 823382

▶ Earthy Industrial Systems Ltd, Unit D, Wylds Road, Bridgwater, Somerset, TA6 4BH Tel: (01278) 455877

Eas Windows, 25 New Street, Oadby, Leicester, LE2 5EB Tel: 0116-271 0120 Fax: 0116-271 7708 E-mail: enquiries@easwindows.co.uk *Manufacturers & distributors of windows & doors*

▶ Easaway Drain Care UK Ltd, Four Seasons House, Railway Road Cross Gates, Leeds, LS15 8EL Tel: 0113-260 6767 Fax: 0113-260 3939 E-mail: enquiries@easawaydraincare.com *Provide a 24 hour plumbing & drainage service, commercial & domestic*

▶ EASB, 1st Floor, High Howden Social Club, Tynemouth Road, Howden, Wallsend, Tyne & Wear, NE28 0EA Tel: 0191 262 4333 Fax: 0191 262 4344 E-mail: simon.smith147@virgin.net *EASB - English Association for Snooker & Billiards.*Official National Governing Body for Snooker & Billiards in England.*

Easby Electronics Ltd, Mercury Road, Gallowfields Trading Estate, Richmond, North Yorkshire, DL10 4TQ Tel: (01748) 850555 Fax: (01748) 850556 E-mail: sales@easby.co.uk *Electronic component distributors*

Easdale Labels Ltd, Unit 1 Enterprise Way, Sherburn in Elmet, Leeds, LS25 6NA Tel: (01977) 686300 Fax: (01977) 681971 E-mail: sales@reflexlabels.co.uk *Self-adhesive label manufrs*

▶ Ease & Co Banquet Seating Ltd, 47a Hawks Road, Kingston upon Thames, Surrey, KT1 3DS Tel: (020) 8541 4471 E-mail: contact@easeco.co.uk *-Bar design & manufacture*-Seating design & manufacture*-Bar interior design*-Carpet fitting*-Complete Interior Refurbishment*

Ease-E-Load Trolleys Ltd, Saunders House, Moor Lane, Birmingham, B6 7HH Tel: 0121-356 2228 Fax: 0121-356 2220 E-mail: info@ease-e-load.co.uk *Truck & trolley makers*

Easeserve Ltd, 3 The Mill, Durham Street, Droylsden, Manchester, M43 6DT Tel: 0161-370 9580 Fax: 0161-370 6746 *Gate & fencing manufacturing*

▶ Easi Care Mobility, 18 Village Farm Industrial Estate, Pyle, Bridgend, Mid Glamorgan, CF33 6NU Tel: (01656) 670472 Fax: (01656) 670492 *Medical equipment suppliers*

Easi Uplifts (Aerials) Ltd, 16 Johnstone Street, Bellshill, Lanarkshire, ML4 1DE Tel: (01698) 308899 Fax: (01698) 308800 E-mail: ronan.maclennen@heightforhire.ie *Access platforms*

Easiclean Products, 10 East House Farm, Atherstone Lane, Merevale, Atherstone, Warwickshire, CV9 2HT Tel: (01827) 874787 Fax: (01827) 874745 E-mail: info@easicleanwipersl.com Principal Export Areas: Worldwide *All types of wipers, new woven polishers & micro fibre cloths manufrs*

▶ Easiclear, Atlas Transport Estate, Lombard Road, London, SW11 3RE Tel: (02077) 389555 E-mail: info@easiclear.co.uk *Offering Services like House Clearance, Removals, Rubbish Clearances, Antiques & Modern, Free Probate Valuations, Contract Furnishing, Carpet Fitting, Storage Maintenance & Gardening, Collectables, Second Hand Furniture and Collectables.*

▶ Easicook Microwave Ltd, Unit 23 Cardiff Business Park, Lambourne Cresent, Llanishen, Cardiff, CF14 5GF Tel: (029) 2074 7567 Fax: (029) 2021 4100 E-mail: info@easicook.co.uk *Microwave oven, glasswasher, dishwasher & ice maker specialists also catering equipment sales & repairs**

Easicut Grinding Co. Ltd, Leestone Road, Sharston Industrial Area, Manchester, M22 4RN Tel: 0161-428 3265 Fax: 0161-428 3267 E-mail: w.kilbride@virgin.net *Knife grinding services*

Easifall International Ltd, Unit 4 Booth Road, Sale Motorway Estate, Sale, Cheshire, M33 7JS Tel: 0161-969 5009 Fax: 0161-969 5009 E-mail: enquiries@easifall.com *Surfacing play & sports equipment suppliers*

Easiflo Engineering Ltd, Providence Street, Stourbridge, West Midlands, DY9 8HR Tel: (01384) 894811 Fax: (01384) 422447 E-mail: easiflo.eng@btconnect.com *Storage tank manufrs*

Easiflo Fabrications, 4 Building 64, Third Avenue, Pensnett Trading Estate, Kingswinford, West Midlands, DY6 7XX Tel: (01384) 279245 Fax: (01384) 400030 *Welded & steel fabrication manufrs*

Easifloor Ltd, Cranes Close, Basildon, Essex, SS14 3JB Tel: (01268) 288744 Fax: (01268) 532305 E-mail: tiles@easifloor.fsnet.co.uk *Wall & floor tile contractors*

▶ Easiglide, 21 Newtimber Avenue, Goring-by-Sea, Worthing, West Sussex, BN12 6NF Tel: (07941) 273680 Fax: (01903) 537392 E-mail: info@easiglide.co.uk *Upvc window timber windows*

Easilift Loading Systems Ltd, Spring Grove, Penistone Road, Kirkburton, Huddersfield, HD8 0PL Tel: (01484) 601400 Fax: (01484) 601401 E-mail: sales@easilift-loading-systems.co.uk *Safe loading system manufrs*

▶ Easily .Co.Uk, Prospero House, 241 Borough High Street, London, SE1 1GA Tel: (020) 7015 9241 E-mail: helpdesk@easily.co.uk *Web hosting specialists*

▶ Easingwold Bathroom Centre, Unit 2 Easingwold Business Park, Easingwold, York, YO61 3FB Tel: (01347) 824777 Fax: (01347) 824221 *Bathroom fittings or accessories suppliers*

Easirider Co. Ltd, S2 Nene Centre, Freehold Street, Northampton, NN2 6EF Tel: (01604) 714103 Fax: (01604) 714106 E-mail: info@easirider.com *Sheepskin manufrs*

Easiserv.Com, Suite C70 The Business Centre, Chapel Place, Northampton, NN1 4AQ Tel: (01604) 467930 Fax: (01604) 259749 E-mail: neil@easiserv.com *Website designers*

Easistore, Enterprise House, Enterprise Way, Edenbridge, Kent, TN8 6HF Tel: (0800) 3162323 Fax: (01732) 868087 E-mail: customerservice@easistore.co.uk *Self storage service*

Easiways Bermondsey Ltd, 138 Burnt Ash Road, Lee, London, SE12 8PU Tel: (020) 8852 2984 Fax: (020) 8852 2985 *Builders' merchants*

Easiweigh Ltd, Unit 1b Shrub Hill Industrial Estate, Worcester, WR4 9EL Tel: (01905) 28075 Fax: (01905) 22229 E-mail: sales@easiweigh.co.uk *Weighing & packaging machine manufrs*

Eason & Son Ni Ltd, 21-25 Boucher Road, Belfast, BT12 6QU Tel: (028) 9038 1200 Fax: (028) 9068 2544 E-mail: accountsreceivable@eason.co.uk *Wholesale stationery suppliers* Also at: Antrim, Ballymena, Coleraine, Craigavon, Lisburn & Newry & Newtonards

▶ Easons Ice Cream, Freckleton Road, Kirkham, Preston, PR4 3RB Tel: (01772) 684446 Fax: (01772) 683535

East Anglia Blinds Ltd, 6 Barrow Close, Sweet Briar Road Industrial Estate, Norwich, NR3 2AT Tel: (01603) 404040 Fax: (01603) 418398 E-mail: enquires@eablinds.co.uk *Blind manufrs*

East Anglia Cleaning & Safety Supplies, Langton Green, Eye, Suffolk, IP23 7HL Tel: (01379) 871110 Fax: (01379) 871160 E-mail: workwearunderstoreeastanglia@hotmail.com *Cleaning material & safety suppliers (janitorial)*

▶ East Anglia Leather, Rushmere Cottage, The Green, Wickham Skeith, Eye, Suffolk, IP23 8LX Tel: (01449) 766722 Fax: (01449) 766722 E-mail: sales@leather-furniture-repairs.com *Leather furniture repair services*

East Anglian Bearing Service Ltd, 19-21 Great Whip Street, Ipswich, IP2 8EY Tel: (01473) 602525 Fax: (01473) 688274 E-mail: sales@eabs.co.uk *Ball bearing components suppliers to the industry*

East Anglian Fine Weld Ltd, Unit 1, St. Margarets Way, Stukeley Meadows Industrial Estate, Huntingdon, Cambridgeshire, PE29 6EB Tel: (01480) 453412 Fax: (01480) 434952 E-mail: sales@eafw.co.uk *Heats sealing element manufrs*

East Anglian Galvanising Ltd, Wareley Road, Peterborough, PE2 9PF Tel: (01733) 346664 Fax: (01733) 310663 E-mail: east.anglian@wedge-galv.co.uk *Hot dip galvanizing organisation, part of nation-wide Wedge Group, for anything from large structural steelwork to consignments of small pieces, provide a free advisory service about coating requirements & steelwork design, so that you can make an informed choice about your individual needs* Also at: Bradford

East Anglian Galvanising Ltd, Wareley Road, Peterborough, PE2 9PF Tel: (01733) 346664 Fax: (01733) 310663 *Galvanizing services*

East Anglian Motor & Sheet Metal Co. Ltd, 10 Garden Street, Norwich, NR1 1QX Tel: (01603) 625664 Fax: (01603) 760545 E-mail: sales@ea-arc.co.uk *Vechicle body repair centre*

East Anglian Pharmaceuticals Ltd, Pinetrees Business Park, Pinetrees Road, Norwich, NR7 9BB Tel: (01603) 300336 Fax: (01603) 433274 *Wholesale pharmaceuticals*

▶ East Anglian Radio Services, 4 High Beech, Lowestoft, Suffolk, NR32 2RY Tel: (01502) 568021 Fax: (01502) 600176 E-mail: office@eastanglianradio.com *Theatre sound & lighting suppliers*

East Anglian Sealing Co. Ltd, Units 4 & 5, Goldingham Hall, Bulmer, Sudbury, Suffolk, CO10 7ER Tel: (01787) 880433 Fax: (0871) 4338858 E-mail: sales@easeals.co.uk *Manufacturer of gaskets, seals & all associated materials*

East Anglian Shelving Ltd, 20/21 Denny Rd, Hardwick Industrial Estate, King's Lynn, Norfolk, PE30 4HG Tel: (01553) 765205 Fax: (01553) 768464 E-mail: sales@eais-shelving.co.uk *Steel shelving manufrs*

East Anglian Tractors Ltd, Arkesden Road, Clavering, Saffron Walden, Essex, CB11 4QU Tel: (01799) 550268 Fax: (01799) 550874 E-mail: sales@eatractors.co.uk *Agricultural tractor export merchant agents*

East Anglian Wire Works, Wright Road, Ipswich, IP3 9RN Tel: (01473) 270820 *Manufacturers of wire goods*

East Antrim Mini Mix, 64 Larne Road, Whitehead, Carrickfergus, County Antrim, BT38 9TF Tel: (028) 9336 7771 Fax: (028) 9336 6949 E-mail: ronnie@eastantrimminimix.co.uk *Ready mixed concrete suppliers*

East Bros Holdings Ltd, The Sawmills, West Dean, Salisbury, SP5 1JA Tel: (01794) 340270 Fax: (01794) 341317 E-mail: mail@eastbros.co.uk *Timber merchants*

East Burn Pine, Unit 16 Eastburn Mills, Main Road, Eastburn, Keighley, West Yorkshire, BD20 7SJ Tel: (01535) 656297 Fax: (01535) 657717 E-mail: info@eastburnpine.co.uk *Restoring & selling antique furniture*

East Cheshire Trailers, Sandy Lane Garage, Sandy Lane, Macclesfield, Cheshire, SK10 4RJ Tel: (01625) 611550 Fax: (01625) 611550 *Trailer builders & hirers*

East Coast Castings Co. Ltd, The Foundry, Norwich Road, Carbrooke, Thetford, Norfolk, IP25 6TL Tel: (01953) 881741 Fax: (01953) 884769 E-mail: ecc@fsbdial.co.uk *Ferrous & non ferrous foundry*

East Coast Construction, 78 Grange Ave, Filey, North Yorkshire, YO14 0AT Tel: 01723 516558 E-mail: posborne@ic24.net *small building firm operating on the East Coast, Scarborough and area, from new build to renovation.*

▶ East Coast Controls Ltd, Acre House, Stirling Road, Kilsyth, Glasgow, G65 0PT Tel: (01236) 825490 Fax: (01236) 822307 *Test & measurement instrumentation suppliers*

East Coast Design, 23 Sidmouth Street, Hull, HU5 2LB Tel: (07811) 437205 E-mail: dave@eastcoastdesign.co.uk *Brand management agency*

East Coast Fittings, Gaddesby Lane, Rearsby, Leicester, LE7 4YH Tel: (01664) 424288 Fax: (01664) 424243 E-mail: sales@eastcoastfittings.co.uk *Furniture manufrs*

▶ East Coast Music, 71-72 Norfolk Street, King's Lynn, Norfolk, PE30 1AD Tel: (01553) 769006 E-mail: info@eastcoastmusic.co.uk *East Coast Music's Online Shop provides an extensive rangeof musical instruments and accessories including; guitars, keyboards, amplifiers, brass & woodwind, music lessons, local gig listings and much more. Excellent Quality, Fast Delivery & Great Service + Support*

East Coast Sales Limited, Woolverstone Marina, Woolverstone, Ipswich, IP9 1AS Tel: (01473) 780007 Fax: (01473) 780007 *Sail repairs & marine upholstery retailers*

East Coast Storage (Handling) Ltd, Clenchwarton Road, West Lynn, King's Lynn, Norfolk, PE34 3LW Tel: (01553) 772689 Fax: (01553) 691578 E-mail: ecoast@globalnet.co.uk *Storage & distribution contractors*

East Coast Surfacing, Europa Way, Atherton Way, Brigg, South Humberside, DN20 8AR Tel: (01652) 657651 Fax: (01652) 659636 E-mail: js.brown@btconnect.com *Tarmacadam & surfacing contractors*

East Dorset Trading Ltd, Central House, 4 Christchurch Road, Bournemouth, BH1 3LT Tel: (01202) 551212 Fax: (01202) 559090 E-mail: sales@tefcote.co.uk *Hygienic surface coatings suppliers & installers*

East Down Farmers Ltd, 20 Tullynaskeagh Road, Downpatrick, County Down, BT30 7EU Tel: (028) 4484 1463 Fax: (028) 4484 1463 *Agricultural merchants*

East Durham Business Service, 1 Palmer Road, South West Industrial Estate, Peterlee, County Durham, SR8 2HU Tel: 0191-586 3366 Fax: 0191-518 0332 E-mail: sales@edbs.co.uk *Development agency*

East Durham Manufacturing & Engineering Co. Ltd, Moreland Street, Hartlepool, Cleveland, TS24 7NL Tel: (01429) 869688 Fax: (01429) 222082 E-mail: derek.wheatley@btconnect.com *Machine builders & manufrs*

E. East & Son Ltd, 43-47 Chiltern Avenue, Amersham, Buckinghamshire, HP6 5AF Tel: (01494) 433936 Fax: (01494) 728366 *Builders merchants*

East End Foods (Midlands) Ltd, P S W Buildings, 58-66 Darwin Street, Birmingham, B12 0TY Tel: 0121-772 5201 Fax: 0121-772 4079 *Cash & Carry*

▶ East Of England Developments Ltd, Felixstowe Road, Nacton, Ipswich, IP10 0DE Tel: (01473) 659911 E-mail: dairy@eastofengland.coop *Dairy services*

East Essex Dental Laboratory Ltd, Ford Road Industrial Estate, Clacton-on-Sea, Essex, CO15 3DT Tel: (01255) 424071 Fax: (01255) 424071 *Dental laboratory*

East Ferry Timber Co., Shoemaker Lodge, 3 Brigg Road, Scotter, Gainsborough, Lincolnshire, DN21 3HU Tel: (01724) 762626 Fax: (01724) 762629 *Fencing manufrs*

East Finchley Electrical, 115 High Road, London, N2 8AG Tel: (020) 8883 9098 Fax: (020) 8444 3458 E-mail: dloizou@yahoo.co.uk *Electrical contractors*

East Fresh & Frozen, Trimmers Court, Broad Street, Portsmouth, PO1 2EE Tel: (023) 9282 9696 Fax: (023) 9287 3236 *Fish merchants*

East Goscote Fabrications 1992 Ltd, 2 The Warren, East Goscote, Leicester, LE7 3XA Tel: 0116-260 6161 Fax: 0116-264 0759 *Steel fabricators*

▶ East Goscote Plumbers Ltd, East Goscote Industrial Estate, East Goscote, Leicester, LE7 3SL Tel: 0116-260 7766

East Grinstead Tyre Service Ltd, 213-217 London Road, East Grinstead, West Sussex, RH19 1HD Tel: (01342) 324127 Fax: (01342) 317582 *Motor tyre factors & servicing*

East Herts Signs & Engraving, 3 Old Cross, Hertford, SG14 1HX Tel: (01992) 553004 Fax: (01992) 501165 *Producers of signs & engravings*

The East India Shipping Co., 7 Norfolk Cottages, Kings Cross Lane, South Nutfield, Redhill, RH1 5NG Tel: (07866) 638288 E-mail: theeastindiashippingcompany@yahoo.co.uk *We import certified organic fruit and veg for the European and US market.*

East Joinery, Unit 2 Willow Lane, Rugby, Warwickshire, CV22 5LX Tel: (01788) 568427 Fax: (01788) 574252 E-mail: r.ingram@ntlworld.com *Joinery*

▶ East Kent Carton Manufacturers Ltd, Unit 8 Lysander Close, Pysons Road Industrial Estate, Broadstairs, Kent, CT10 2YJ Tel: (01843) 600033 Fax: (01843) 600055 E-mail: sales@ekcartons.co.uk *Manufacturer of*

continued

continuation
custom-designed printed or plain folding carton boxes

▶ East Kent Carton Manufacturers Ltd, Unit 8 Lysander Close, Pysons Road Industrial Estate, Broadstairs, Kent, CT10 2YJ Tel: (01843) 600033 Fax: (01843) 600055 E-mail: sales@ekcartons.co.uk *Printed cartons manufrs*

East Kent Coatings Ltd, Westwood Industrial Estate, Margate, Kent, CT9 4JG Tel: (01843) 293343 Fax: (01843) 293343 *Powder coating suppliers*

▶ East Kent Plumbing & Heating Sevices, 5 Pinewood Close, Ramsgate, Kent, CT12 6DH Tel: (01843) 586864 Fax: (01843) 586864 E-mail: Eastkent@msn.com *Plumbing and Heating Domestic**Site Work including new builds and*flat conversion relating to plumbing and drainage as well as Gas*

▶ East Kent Storage, Bysing Wood Road, Faversham, Kent, ME13 7UE Tel: (01795) 532227 Fax: (01795) 590056

East Kilbride Industrial Plastics, 25-27 Langlands Place, Kelvin South Business Park, East Kilbride, Glasgow, G75 0YF Tel: (01355) 236231 Fax: (01355) 235182 E-mail: ek.plastics@btinternet.com *Plastics fabricators & engineers*

▶ East Kirkby Engineering Co Lincs Ltd, International House, Lealand Way, Boston, Lincolnshire, PE21 7SW Tel: (01205) 366833 Fax: (01205) 353811

East Kirkby Refrigeration & Air Conditioning Ltd, The Retreat, Station Road, Sibsey, Boston, Lincolnshire, PE22 0SB Tel: (01205) 353351 Fax: (01205) 750910 *Refrigeration, air conditioning installers & retailers*

East Lancashire Box, Spring Street, Rishton, Rishton, Blackburn, BB1 4LL Tel: (01254) 889820 Fax: (01254) 889927 *Packaging manufrs*

East Lancashire Chamber Of Commerce & Industry, Red Rose Court, Clayton Business Park, Clayton le Moors, Accrington, Lancashire, BB5 5JR Tel: (01254) 356400 Fax: (01254) 388900 E-mail: info@chamberelancs.co.uk *Chamber of commerce* Also at: Burnley

East Lancashire Chemical Co. Ltd, Edge Lane, Droylsden, Manchester, M43 6AU Tel: 0161-371 5585 Fax: 0161-301 1990 E-mail: info@eastlancschemical.com *Chemical blenders & manufrs*

▶ East Lancashire Fabrications Ltd, Unit 5-6 Springhill, Edleston Street, Accrington, Lancashire, BB5 0HG Tel: (01254) 871734 Fax: (01254) 872379 *Steel metal fabrication*

East Lancashire Platers Ltd, Oxford Mill, Oxford Road, Burnley, Lancashire, BB11 3BA Tel: (01282) 425621 Fax: (01282) 433618 *Electroplaters*

▶ East Lancashire Refrigeration Ltd, Clarendon Road, Blackburn, BB1 9SS Tel: (01254) 262787 Fax: (01254) 661576

East Lancashire Towel Co. Ltd, Park Mill, Halstead Lane, Barrowford, Nelson, Lancashire, BB9 6HJ Tel: (01282) 612193 Fax: (01282) 697736 *Towel manufrs*

▶ East Lancs Recruitment Services, 81 York Street, Heywood, Lancashire, OL10 4NR Tel: (01706) 627662 Fax: (01706) 365912 E-mail: enquiries@elservices.co.uk *Employment Agency supplying temporary and permanent Office,Industrial, Driving and Skilled staff*

East London Graphics, 86-88 Upton Lane, London, E7 9LW Tel: (020) 8470 1028 Fax: (020) 8470 0898 *Office stationary*

East London Print Finishers, Unit 7 Lockwood Way, London, E17 5RB Tel: (020) 8527 5448 Fax: (020) 8527 0635 *Printing trade finishing services*

East London Transmissions, Billet Road, London, E17 5DL Tel: (020) 8531 8390 Fax: (020) 8503 2182 *Gearbox manufrs*

▶ East Manufacturing, Pixmore Centre, Pixmore Avenue, Letchworth Garden City, Hertfordshire, SG6 1JG Tel: (01462) 675656 Fax: (01462) 481781 *Electronic components suppliers*

East Midland Water Co., 3 Cannock Street, Leicester, LE4 9HR Tel: 0116-276 3334 Fax: 0116-276 3335 E-mail: sales@emwc.uk.com *Water treatment equipment manufacturers & distributors*

East Midland Welding Supply Co. Ltd, Baker Brook Industrial Estate, Wigwam Lane, Hucknall, Nottingham, NG15 7SZ Tel: 0115-964 2000 Fax: 0115-964 1651 E-mail: sales@eastmidwelding.freeserve.co.uk *Welding equipment distributors*

East Midlands Aquatics Ltd, 1 Nottingham Road, Trowell, Nottingham, NG9 3PA Tel: 0115-930 0921 Fax: 01159 300921 E-mail: tim@emaconline.co.uk *Pet shop*

East Midlands Ceilings, Dinnington Lane, Moorwood Moor, South Wingfield, Alfreton, Derbyshire, DE55 7NW Tel: (01629) 534845 Fax: (01629) 534811 E-mail: info@emceilings.com *Suspended ceiling manufrs*

East Midlands Ceramics Ltd, Unit 1 Cowlairs, Nottingham, NG5 9RA Tel: 0115-977 0155 Fax: 0115-977 0710 E-mail: sales@east-midlands-ceramics.co.uk *Ceramic tiles suppliers*

East Midlands Fastener, 101 Sanders Road, Finedon Road Industrial Estate, Finedon Road Industrial Estate, Wellingborough, Northamptonshire, NN8 4NL Tel: (01933) 229110 Fax: (01933) 271600 E-mail: sales@emfast.co.uk *Fastener, bolt, nut & screw distributors*

East Midlands Instrument Co. Ltd, Laughton Lane, Morton, Gainsborough, Lincolnshire, DN21 3ET Tel: (01427) 616721 Fax: (01427) 810804 E-mail: emi@eminst.co.uk *Electrical contractors & steel fabricators*

East Midlands Micro Imaging, 46 Tenter Road, Moulton Park Industrial Estate, Northampton, NN3 6AX Tel: (01604) 644665 Fax: (01604) 643673 E-mail: sales@em-micro-imaging.co.uk *East Midlands Micro-Imaging are specialists with over 25 years experience in document imaging, including the conversion of paper documents & microfilms to scanned images on CD & DVD.*

continued

Retrieval software is supplied free on every disc together with the complete index. Discs will operate on any PC or server running at least Windows 95. Images can also be stored & accessed on a secure web site. Secure fire proof storage of back-up discs, tapes films etc. is also provided

East Midlands Mobile Communications, 44 High Street, Stanton Hill, Sutton-in-Ashfield, Nottinghamshire, NG17 3GA Tel: (01623) 555276 Fax: (01623) 558197 *Radio communication*

East Midlands Technologies, 54 Beeston Fields Drive, Barmcote, Beeston, Nottingham, NG9 3DD Tel: 0115-922 3874 Fax: 0115-922 3874 E-mail: bob@bramcote.demon.co.uk *Business management consultancy*

▶ East Neuk Technology, 21 Rodger Street, Anstruther, Fife, KY10 3DU Tel: (01333) 313300 Fax: (01333) 313067 *Computer repairs & computer wholesalers*

▶ East Riding Electrical Ltd, Unit 4b Colt Business Park Havelock Street, Hull, HU3 4TU Tel: (01482) 326553 Fax: (01482) 326553 E-mail: enquires@e-r-e.co.uk *Electrical contracting company emergency lighting & fire alarms*

East Riding Sacks Ltd, Full Sutton Industrial Estate, Stamford Bridge, Full Sutton, York, YO41 1HS Tel: (01759) 371366 Fax: (01759) 372125 E-mail: sales@eastridingsacks.co.uk *Paper sack manufrs*

East Of Scotland Farmers Ltd, Forfar Road, Coupar Angus, Blairgowrie, Perthshire, PH13 9AW Tel: (01828) 627264 Fax: (01828) 627002 E-mail: r.barron@eosf.co.uk *Farming suppliers*

▶ East Services Ltd, 69 Scarletts Road, Colchester, CO1 2HA Tel: 01206 792103 Fax: 01206 792157 E-mail: a.stoddart@eastservices.net *Health and Safety consultancy & training.*First Aid courses*Health and Safety for Managers and operatives*Risk Assessment*Working at Height*Site Supervisors Safety Management*COSHH*

▶ East Sussex Press Ltd, Crowborough Hill, Crowborough, East Sussex, TN6 2EE Tel: (01892) 654074

▶ East Technology Integrators, Lyndhurst, Seer Mead, Seer Green, Beaconsfield, Buckinghamshire, HP9 2QL Tel: 0845 0560245 E-mail: sales@east-ti.co.uk *Home Automation Systems Integrator utilising Teletask domotics system.*Whole home automation including Lighting, HVAC, Security, Audio/Visual, Access control, Garden/conservatory irrigation etc.*

East Yorkshire Engineering, Unit B 133 Marfleet Avenue, Hull, HU9 5SA Tel: (01482) 788008 Fax: (01482) 788008 *Engineers*

East Yorkshire Glazing Co. Ltd, Wiltshire Road, Hull, HU4 6QQ Tel: (01482) 561101 Fax: (01482) 565307 E-mail: eygsales@eygsales.com *Double glazing system manufrs* Also at: Scarborough

East Yorkshire Glazing Co. Ltd, Wiltshire Road, Hull, HU4 6QQ Tel: (01482) 561101 Fax: (01482) 565307 E-mail: eygsales@ukonline.co.uk *Industrial door manufrs*

East Yorkshire Polymers Ltd, Unit E, Londesborough Business Centre, Hull, HU3 1DR Tel: (01482) 211110 Fax: (01482) 581898 E-mail: pbmcm@eypoly.freeserve.co.uk *Thermoplastic compound manufrs*

Eastar-solutions Ltd, 123 Bath Row, Birmingham, B15 1LS Tel: 0121-643 5500 Fax: 0121 6337537 *Software house & value added reseller*

Eastbourne Borough Council, Town Hall, Grove Road, Eastbourne, East Sussex, BN21 4UG Tel: (01323) 415000 Fax: (01323) 410322 E-mail: film@eastbourne.gov.uk *Conference centre*

Eastbourne Tyre Co. Ltd, Fort Road, Eastbourne, East Sussex, BN22 7SE Tel: (01323) 720222 Fax: (01323) 720018 *Motor tyre distributors*

▶ Eastend Bakery, 1 Ardgowan Street, Port Glasgow, Renfrewshire, PA14 5DG Tel: (01475) 746242 Fax: (01475) 741121

Easter Road Plastics Signs Division, 289 Easter Road, Edinburgh, EH6 8LQ Tel: 0131-555 6446 Fax: 0131-553 3975 *Sign manufrs*

Eastern Air Executive Ltd, Sturgate Airfield, Heapham, Gainsborough, Lincolnshire, DN21 5PA Tel: (01427) 838280 Fax: (01427) 838416 *Air taxi, charter, maintenance & paint spray shop*

Eastern Business Systems Ltd, Systems House, Chippenham Hill, Moulton, Newmarket, Suffolk, CB8 7PL Tel: (01638) 552633 Fax: (01638) 552892 *Photocopying services*

Eastern Communications, Cavendish House, Happisburgh, Norwich, NR12 0RU Tel: (01692) 650077 *Telecommunication services*

Eastern Compressors Ltd, 1-9 Drapers Road, South Woodham Ferrers, Chelmsford, CM3 5UH Tel: (01245) 320624 Fax: (01245) 328700 E-mail: enquiries@easterns.co.uk *Compressors & air tools manufrs*

▶ Eastern Concrete Ltd, Barrells House, Wattisham Road, Hitcham, Ipswich, IP7 7LU Tel: (01449) 744276 Fax: (01449) 722093 E-mail: tom@captonconcrete.fsnet.co.uk *Concrete manufrs*

Eastern Counties Contracting, Panton Groveange, Wirehill Lane, Wragby, Market Rasen, Lincolnshire, LN8 5LD Tel: (01673) 857755 Fax: (01673) 857766

▶ Eastern Counties Pumps, 3 Burrell Road, Ipswich, IP2 8AD Tel: (01473) 400101 Fax: (01473) 400103 E-mail: sales@ecpgroup.com *ECP Group has over 35 years proven experience in the pumping and irrigation industry. ECP Group carries a wide range of pump and irrigation equipment to suit every kind of project via our online store or over the telephone. ECP Group also offers a nationwide mail order service. ECP Group can also offer a full installation service for sinking wells, drilling boreholes, installing water treatment equipment and full irrigation systems. Our advice is readily available, should you have any enquiries don't hesitate to contact us.*

▶ Eastern Electric Scotland Ltd, 4 New Broompark, Edinburgh, EH5 1RS Tel: 0131-551 4100 Fax: 0131-551 4200

Eastern Farm Implements Ltd, Bourne Road, Carlby, Stamford, Lincolnshire, PE9 4LW Tel: (01778) 590215 Fax: (01778) 590282 *Agricultural machinery distributors, engineers & groundcare*

Eastern Fluid Power Ltd, Gapton Hall Road, Great Yarmouth, Norfolk, NR31 0NL Tel: (01493) 441353 Fax: (01493) 440757 E-mail: sales@efphyd.co.uk *Hydraulic equipment distributors*

Eastern Forge Agriculture Ltd, Eastern Forge, Stockwell Gate, Whaplode, Spalding, Lincolnshire, PE12 6UE Tel: (01406) 422731 Fax: (01406) 424245 E-mail: eforge@nippymail.co.uk *Agricultural merchants*

Eastern Garage Equipment, 24 Orchard Bank, Drayton, Norwich, NR8 6RN Tel: (01603) 262523 Fax: (01603) 262523 *Garage equipment sales & service*

Eastern Glazed Ceramics Ltd, Tile House, Eversley Road, Norwich, NR6 6TA Tel: (01603) 423391 Fax: (01603) 789040 E-mail: enquiries@egctiles.co.uk *Ceramic tile distributors*

Eastern Glazed Ceramics Ltd, 1270 Lincoln Road, Peterborough, PE4 6LE Tel: (01733) 324074 Fax: (01733) 321909 E-mail: peterborough@egctiles.co.uk *Ceramic tiles distributor*

Eastern Hardware Co. Ltd, Hamilton Road, Lowestoft, Suffolk, NR32 1XF Tel: (01502) 573257 Fax: (01502) 586235 E-mail: eastern_hardware@btconnect.com *Sheet metalworkers*

Eastern Hydraulic Systems Ltd, Unit 10 Brookhouse Business Park, Brunel Road, Hadleigh Road Industrial Estate, Ipswich, IP2 0EF Tel: (01473) 289529 Fax: (01473) 289529 E-mail: ehs@ukf.net *Supplier of hydraulic & pneumatic components. Specialising in industrial applications. Repair services available*

Eastern Hydraulics, Unit 7 Wennington Hall Farm, Wennington Road, Rainham, Essex, RM13 9EF Tel: (01708) 558144 Fax: (01708) 555919 E-mail: janetgiles@onetel.com *Security systems, gates, barriers & maintenance*

Eastern Mediterranean Maritime (London) Ltd, Fountain House, 130 Fenchurch Street, London, EC3M 5DJ Tel: (020) 7283 9591 Fax: (020) 7444 1909 *Ship brokers*

Eastern Plastics Machinery Ltd, Eastern House, Priors Way, Coggeshall, Colchester, CO6 1TW Tel: (01376) 562288 Fax: (01376) 561385 E-mail: info@easternplastics.co.uk *Plastics machinery importers*

▶ Eastern Security, 172 North Avenue, Southend-on-Sea, SS2 4EU Tel: (01702) 354836 Fax: (01702) 460178 *Electronic security systems installers & maintainers*

Eastern Shop Equipment Ltd, Anson Road, Airport Industrial Estate, Norwich, NR6 6ED Tel: (01603) 424294 Fax: (01603) 405106 E-mail: sales@easternshopequipment.co.uk *Shop fitting suppliers*

Eastern Telephones, 2 Bowthorpe Workshops, Bowthorpe Hall Road, Norwich, NR5 9AA Tel: (01603) 743388 Fax: (01603) 743388 E-mail: webenquiries@eastern-telephones.co.uk *Telecommunications retailers & maintainers*

Eastern Transformer Ltd, Overland Industrial Park, Sudbury Road, Little Whelnetham, Bury St. Edmunds, Suffolk, IP30 0UL Tel: (01284) 388033 Fax: (01284) 386969 E-mail: info@ete.co.uk *Transformer manufrs*

Eastfield Engineering Ltd, PO Box 232, Stafford, ST19 5QY Tel: (01785) 714794 Fax: (01785) 711373 E-mail: sales@eastfield-engineering.com *Manufacture a variety of metal fabricated product*

Eastfield Joinery, Shavington House Farm, Crewe Road, Shavington, Crewe, CW2 5AH Tel: (01270) 664769 Fax: (01270) 665327 E-mail: sales@eastfieldjoinery.sagenet.co.uk *Building contractors & joinery manufrs*

Easthill Ltd, 1 Martinfield Business Centre, Martinfield, Welwyn Garden City, Hertfordshire, AL7 1HG Tel: (01707) 377355 Fax: (01707) 377358 E-mail: sales@easthill.co.uk *Control panel & switchgear manufrs*

▶ Eastlake Group Ltd, Unit 1, Philipshill Industrial Estate, East Kilbride, Glasgow, G74 5PG Tel: (01355) 593200 Fax: (01355) 593201 E-mail: info@eastlakegroup.com *Office furniture manufrs*

Eastland Compounding Ltd, Bank Street, Manchester, M11 4AS Tel: 0161-223 3241 Fax: 0161-223 3240 *Rubber & plastic compound manufrs*

Eastleigh Domestic Appliance Services, 53 Twyford Road, Eastleigh, Hampshire, SO50 4HH Tel: (023) 8064 4984 Fax: (023) 8061 2799 E-mail: sales@eastleigh-services.co.uk *Air conditioning services & gas corgi registered*

Eastleigh Power Plant, PO Box 199, Southampton, SO30 0WZ Tel: (023) 8040 7507 Fax: (01489) 780478 E-mail: epower@fpcad.com *Diesel driven, emergency standby, CHP & marine generating sets, generator/generating set hire, leasing, rental, maintenance & repair services. Also generating set spare parts distributors & power supply (uninterruptible) (computer) systems/unit manufrs*

Eastman Car Alarm & Sounds, 428 Green Lane, Ilford, Essex, IG3 9LD Tel: (020) 8597 8000 E-mail: eastman@onetel.com *Vehicle accessories installer & supplier*

Eastman Leather Clothing, 5 Whiteoaks Industrial Unit, Filham, Ivybridge, Devon, PL21 0DW Tel: (01752) 896874 Fax: (01752) 690579 *Leather clothing manufrs*

▶ Eastman Staples Ltd, 131 Lockwood Road, Huddersfield, HD1 3QW Tel: (01484) 888888 Fax: (01484) 888800 E-mail: enquiries@eastman.co.uk *Retailers & manufacturers to the clothing industry* Also at: Branches throughout the U.K.

Eastman & Co Timber Ltd, Princess Street, Bedminster, Bristol, BS3 4AG Tel: 0117-966 1596 Fax: 0117-907 3354 E-mail: andy@eastmantimber.wanadoo.co.uk *Timber merchants*

▶ Eastman (UK) Ltd, Suite 1, Wesley House, Unit 2 Chapel Lane, Birstall, Batley, West Yorkshire, WF17 9EJ Tel: (0870) 7503003 Fax: (0870) 7503004 E-mail: sales@eastmanuk.copm *Importers & distributors of gloves & safety equipment*

L.R. Easton & Co. Ltd, 5 & 7 Hollytree Parade, Sidcup Hill, Footscray, Sidcup, Kent, DA14 6JR Tel: (020) 8300 3955 Fax: (020) 8302 2562 *Glazing contractors*

Easton Masonry UK Ltd, 99 Easton Street, Portland, Dorset, DT5 1BP Tel: (01305) 861020 Fax: (01305) 820401 *Masonry contractors*

▶ Easton Sheet Metal Ltd, 31-38 South Road, Harlow, Essex, CM20 2AR Tel: (01279) 427842 Fax: (01279) 450761 E-mail: info@eastonsheetmetal.co.uk *Sheet metal*

▶ Eastside Consulting, 91 Brick Lane, London, E1 6QL Tel: 020 77706144 E-mail: trevor@eastsideconsulting.co.uk *Eastside Consulting aims to support entrepreneurs and managers expand and build their businesses into sustainable organisations.**We advise on strategy, business performance and market potential, prepare business plans and raise finance.***

Eastside Freight Services Ltd, Stratford St North, Birmingham, B11 1BY Tel: 0121-766 8333 Fax: 0121-766 8361 E-mail: efs.services@virgin.net *Export packers & freight forwarders*

▶ Eastside Surface Coatings Ltd, 18 Eastmuir Street, Glasgow, G32 0HS Tel: 0141-778 6541 Fax: 0141-764 0882

▶ Eastwick Engineering Services, 1 Gladwin Industrial Prk, Charles Street, Kilnhurst, Mexborough, South Yorkshire, S64 5TG Tel: (01709) 589044 Fax: (01709) 591752 E-mail: sales@eastwickengineeringservices.co.uk *Garage equipment supplies & repairs*

Eastwood Air Conditioning Ltd, Eastwood House, Hubert Street, Aston, Birmingham, B6 4BA Tel: 0121-380 0555 Fax: 0121-359 8152 E-mail: sales@eastwoodgroup.co.uk *Air conditioning & refrigeration manufrs*

▶ Eastwood Anglo European Investments Ltd, Burnell Arms, Winkburn, Newark, Nottinghamshire, NG22 8PQ Tel: (01636) 636132 Fax: (01636) 636643 E-mail: tom@eastwoodanglo.com *Corporate finance services*

Eastwood Automatics Cce Video Ltd, 19 James Street, Cookstown, County Tyrone, BT80 8AA Tel: (028) 8676 6100 Fax: (028) 8676 3412 *Amusement machine manufrs*

Eastwood Construction, Burns Lane, Warsop, Mansfield, Nottinghamshire, NG20 0QG Tel: (01623) 842581 Fax: (01623) 847955 E-mail: enquiries@adameastwood.co.uk *Builders & contractors*

Eastwood & Dickinson Ltd, Mayflower Works, Gladstone Road, Seaforth, Liverpool, L21 1DE Tel: 0151-928 2316 Fax: 0151-474 6224 E-mail: info@eastwood-dickinson.co.uk *Lifting gear suppliers*

Eastwood Die & Tool, 6 Morpeth Street, Sheffield, S3 7JL Tel: 0114-276 0454 Fax: 0114-276 0454 *Press tool manufrs*

▶ Eastwood Electricial, 27 James Watt Place, East Kilbride, Glasgow, G74 5HG Tel: (01355) 228484 Fax: (01355) 228484

Eastwood Park Joinery, 9 Eastwood Road, Penryn, Cornwall, TR10 8LA Tel: (01326) 376119 *Joinery manufrs*

▶ Easy Air Con, Unit A6 Churcham Business Park, Churcham, Gloucester, GL2 8AX Tel: 0845 0751002 Fax: 0845 0751040 E-mail: Sales@easyaircon.co.uk *Portable air conditioning suppliers*

Easy Cool Refrigeration Ltd, 30 Eleanor Crescent, Newcastle, Staffordshire, ST5 3SA Tel: (01782) 628750 Fax: (01782) 628750 E-mail: info@rsm-reallycool.co.uk *Air conditioning engineers*

▶ Easy Devices.Company Co .Uk, 14 New Lairdship Yards, Edinburgh, EH11 3UY Tel: (0871) 7000156 Fax: 0871 7000159 E-mail: sales@easydevices.co.uk *Specialist suppliers in handheld pcs & gps satellite navigation*

Easy Excavations Ltd, PO Box 33, Bolton, BL1 2QS Tel: (01204) 383838 Fax: (01204) 364002 *Building & civil engineering contractors*

Easy (Ez) Revenue Management Solutions Ltd, 2nd Floor, New Liverpool House, 15 Eldon Street, London, EC2M 7LD Tel: (020) 7495 0773 Fax: (020) 7495 7725 E-mail: hdq@easyrms.com *Easy (Ez) Revenue Management Solutions Ltd based in London provide Internet Revenue and Yield Management Solutions and independent consultancy services.*

▶ Easy Fix, N Prospect Court, Nottingham Road, Ripley, Derbyshire, DE5 3AY Tel: (01773) 570400 Fax: (01773) 570400 *Tool hire services*

▶ Easy Life GM Ltd, Dairy House Farm, Chester Road, Oakmere, Northwich, Cheshire, CW8 2HB Tel: (01606) 889833 Fax: (01606) 882090 *Garden machinery*

▶ The Easy P C Store, 114 Moorfield Road, Widnes, Cheshire, WA8 3HX Tel: 0151-424 5671 Fax: 0151-424 5671 E-mail: info@easypcstore.co.uk *Computer services, repairs & upgrades*

▶ Easy Parcel Worldwide, Lawlor House, Cawley Hatch, Harlow, Essex, CM19 5AN Tel: (0800) 1804995 Fax: (01279) 433326 E-mail: sales@easyparcelworldwide.com *Easy Parcel Worldwide is a new brokering system for sending documents and parcels Worldwide, We have accounts with most major carriers and are able to offer our customers fantastic rates which we receive from our carriers making you the ultimate winner!*

▶ Easy Parcel Worldwide, Mercury House, Russell Gardens, Wickford, Essex, SS11 8BH Tel: (0800) 180 4995 Fax: (01268) 570621 E-mail: sales@easyparcel.net *Easy Parcel*

continued

Company Information

continuation
Worldwide offer document and parcel services across the globe. We offer Sameday, Next day, European and International Services by road, air and sea, we also offer our customers a unique points scheme where the customer will gain points for vouchers from over 120 UK Outlets!

▶ Easy PC, 2 Margaret Road, Whitley Bay, Tyne & Wear, NE26 2PQ Tel: 0191-252 4534 Fax: 0191-252 4534

Easy PC'S, 38 Abbotsbry Road, Weymouth, Dorset, DT4 0AE Tel: (01305) 760350 Fax: (0870) 0940321 *Computer consumables suppliers*

Easy Peasy, 1 Winder Gate, Frizington, Cumbria, CA26 3QS Tel: (01946) 813065 *Computer software developers*

▶ Easy Plumbing, 451 Hinckley Road, Leicester, LE3 0WD Tel: 0116-255 3435 E-mail: easyplumbing@tiscali.co.uk *Plumbing services*

Easy Pools Ltd, PO Box 425, Haywards Heath, West Sussex, RH16 2YR Tel: (01825) 791122 Fax: (01825) 791128 *Swimming pool building & equipment manufrs*

Easy Rider (Europe) Ltd, Wright Street, Stafford, ST16 3AY Tel: (01785) 250353 Fax: (01785) 257048 E-mail: info@easyridereurope.co.uk *Motorcycle distributors*

▶ Easy Stages School, 121 Manor Hall Road, Southwick, Brighton, BN42 4NL Tel: (01273) 593691 Fax: 01273 593691 E-mail: magihall@btopenworld.com *Training in acting, public speaking, coaching for interviews, auditions, wedding speeches. Private lessons, group workshops for individuals, schools, business, organisations. Qualified Teacher of Speech and Drama(LLAM, MSTSD) CRB clearance. LAMDA examinations, RADA Shakespeare certs. Member of the British Voice Association and Voice Care network UK. VCN approved Voice Tutor.*

▶ Easy Tiger Creative Ltd, 25-27 Greenwich Market, Greenwich, London, SE10 9HZ Tel: (020) 8305 9292 E-mail: studio@easytigercreative.com *Creative solutions suppliers to graphic, exhibition & marketing needs*

▶ Easy Typing, 16 Burn View, Bude, Cornwall, EX23 8BZ Tel: 01288 355587 E-mail: easytyping@hotmail.co.uk *Virtual Assistant providing transcription services together with wordprocessing and spreadsheet work at great prices. Check it out.*

Easy Web, 10 St Andrews Cresent, Cardiff, CF10 3DD Tel: (029) 2034 4006 Fax: (029) 2034 4008 E-mail: enquiries@eazyweb.co.uk *Multi media & web designers*

Easy2name Labels & Tags, 2 Malthouse Cottages, Ecchinswell, Newbury, Berkshire, RG20 4UA Tel: (01635) 298326 Fax: (01635) 298352 *Label printers*

Easycleaning-London Ltd, Unit 5, Egerton Court, Old Brompton Road, London, SW7 3HT Tel: (0800) 7312341 E-mail: easycleaning-london@lycos.com *Easycleaning-London ltd. provides professional cleaning services in London, house cleaners london, office cleaners london,carpet cleaning london.Choose your own house cleaner london by calling 08007312341.all our house cleaners london are security checked.we also offer upholstery cleaning london,steam cleaning London,curtains cleaning london.call the professional cleaning company london and have your house cleaner and office cleaner London,domestic cleaner London,domestic cleaning service london,**

▶ Easycroft, 7, Bromham Mill, Giffard Park, Milton Keynes, MK14 5QP Tel: (01908) 617272

Easyfeel Clothing Co., 7-9 Sebert Road, London, E7 0NG Tel: (020) 8522 0100 Fax: (020) 8522 1500 E-mail: easyfeel@mtlworld.com *Clothing manufrs*

▶ Easyfile Ltd, Global House, Shottery Brook Industrial Estate, Timothys Bridge Road, Stratford-upon-Avon, Warwickshire, CV37 9NR Tel: (0870) 2424974 Fax: (0870) 0404799 E-mail: info@easyfile.com

▶ Easyinkz, 15 Lockyer Close, Newton Aycliffe, County Durham, DL5 7QZ Tel: (01325) 310608 E-mail: sales@easyinkz.co.uk *DVD accessories authoring & inkjet laser printer cartridges*

Easylearn, Trent House, Rolleston Road, Fiskerton, Southwell, Nottinghamshire, NG25 0UH Tel: (01636) 830240 Fax: (01636) 830162 E-mail: enquiry@easylearn.co.uk *Learning material retailers*

▶ EasyLeaseTrader Ltd, Walton Lodge, Hill Cliffe Rd, Walton, Warrington, WA4 6NU Tel: 01925 217250 Fax: 01925 217251 E-mail: allan.bromley@easyleasetrader.com *The Uk''s marketplace for transfering out of your lease,here you can take over a lease or exit a lease -NO PENALTIES -CLICK TO TERMINATE YOUR LEASE!*

▶ easylighting.co.uk, The Street, Long Stratton, Norwich, NR15 2XJ Tel: (0870) 3507440 E-mail: info@easylighting.co.uk *Lighting retailer*

▶ Easyline Ltd, 46 Northampton Street, Birmingham, B18 6DX Tel: 0121-233 1279 Fax: 0121-233 0706 *Jewellery manufrs*

▶ Easymove (Bristol) Ltd, Albert Crescent, Bristol, BS2 0SU Tel: 0117-977 1460

▶ easyonlineshop, 68 Monument Road, Talke Pits, Stoke-on-Trent, ST7 1SJ Tel: (01782) 771592 E-mail: lisahughesann@yahoo.co.uk *wiccan,gothic supplies body jewellrey*

Easypack Ltd, Unit 1, The Io Centre, Arlington Business Park, Stevenage, Hertfordshire, SG1 2BD Tel: (0845) 8380168 Fax: (0845) 8380160 E-mail: info@easypack.net *Paper based packaging systems suppliers*

▶ Easypack Corrugated Cases Ltd, Finchley Avenue, Mildenhall, Bury St. Edmunds, Suffolk, IP28 7BG Tel: (01638) 715922 Fax: (01638) 712836 E-mail: sales@easypack.uk.com *Brown box & pop manufrs*

▶ Easyrider Motorcycle Training School, rear of Stafford Cricket Club Riverway, Stafford, ST18 9BH Tel: (01785) 254542 Fax: (01785) 254542 E-mail: antonionarcisi@tiscali.co.uk *we offer a proffessional freindly service for all your needs to do with bike training. eg CBT,DIRECT ACCESS,REFRESHER COURSES and back to Biking*

▶ Easysearchandbook, 15A, Braemar Ave, London, Middlesex, N22 7BY Tel: 0785 5338295

▶ Easysoft Webdesign, 27 Holbeck Avenue, Scarborough, North Yorkshire, YO11 2XH Tel: (01723) 374713 *Web design services for static websites (hotels)*

▶ Easystands Ltd, Orford Farm, Mission Road, Iron Acton, Bristol, BS37 9XR Tel: (01454) 227170 Fax: (01454) 227171 E-mail: Kelly@easystands.com *Manufacturer and trade-only supplier of VERY Portable Graphic Display Exhibit Systems, such as pop-ups, roll-ups, banner stands and literature stands to graphics printing companies.*

Easystore, Church Close, Chedgrave, Norwich, NR14 6NH Tel: (01508) 520579 *Self storage*

▶ EasyVision Camera Systems, 82 St Benedict Rd, Brandon, Suffolk, IP27 0UN Tel: 01842 811985 E-mail: sales@easy-vision.co.uk *Reversing camera systems for any large vehicle including Campervans, lorries, caravans etc.*Eliminate that dangerous blind spot for safer reversing.*

▶ Eat Out Cornwall, Chiverton Lodge, The Saltings, Lelant, St. Ives, Cornwall, TR26 3DL Tel: (01736) 755113 Fax: (01736) 759413 E-mail: admin@eatoutcornwall.com *A comprehensive directory of places to eat out at restaurants bars and pubs in Cornwall.**

Eathornes Mica Hardware, 2 Drygate St, Larkhall, Lanarkshire, ML9 2AJ Tel: (01698) 881523 Fax: (01698) 882337 *Builders' merchants*

▶ Eaton, Tay House, 300 Bath Street, Glasgow, G2 4NA Tel: 0141-331 7000 Fax: 0141-331 7001

Eaton Aerospace Ltd, Abbey Park, Southampton Road, Titchfield, Fareham, Hampshire, PO14 4QA Tel: (01329) 853000 Fax: (01329) 853797 *Aircraft fuel control system manufrs*

Eaton Automotive Fluid Connectors Operations, P O Box 12, Brierley Hill, West Midlands, DY5 2LB Tel: (01384) 424911 Fax: (01384) 426300 *Plastics injection mouldings manufrs*

Eaton Berry Ltd, Bridge Farm, Reading Road, Arborfield, Reading, RG2 9HT Tel: 0118-976 1076 Fax: 0118-976 0479 E-mail: info@eatonberry.com *Agricultural retail & sales*

Eaton Clutch Transmission, Norfolk Street, Worsley Estate North, Worsley, Manchester, M28 3GJ Tel: (01204) 797077 Fax: (01204) 797090 *Truck components manufrs*

Eaton Corporation, 2 Broad Ground Road, Redditch, Worcestershire, B98 8YS Tel: (01527) 517555 Fax: (01527) 517556 E-mail: paulsmith@eaton.com *Aircraft component manufrs*

Eaton Electric Ltd, Reddings Lane, Tysley, Birmingham, B11 3EZ Tel: 0121-685 2100 Fax: 0121-706 2012 *Manufacturers of switchboards to specification*

Eaton Electric Ltd, Reddings Lane, Tyseley, Birmingham, B11 3EZ Tel: 0121-685 2100 Fax: 0121-706 2012 E-mail: meminfo@eaton.com Principal Export Areas: Asia Pacific, Central Asia, Middle East, Africa, Central/East Europe & West Europe *Residential, commercial & industrial circuit protection & control equipment.*

Eaton Environmental Services Ltd, Bradley Farm, Cumnor, Oxford, OX2 9QU Tel: (01865) 864488 Fax: (01865) 865855 E-mail: info@eatonenvironmental.co.uk *Water treatment equipment & service*

Eaton Fluid Power Group, Thorns Road, Brierley Hill, West Midlands, DY5 2BQ Tel: (01384) 426320 Fax: (01384) 891506 E-mail: mark.ward@aeroquip.com *Flexible hose assembly services*

Eaton Hydralics Ltd, 46 New Lane, Havant, Hampshire, PO9 2NB Tel: (023) 9248 6451 Fax: (023) 9248 7110 E-mail: barryking@eaton.com *Hydraulic equipment manufrs*

Eaton MEM, Grimshaw Lane, Middleton, Manchester, M24 1GQ Tel: 0161-655 8900 Fax: 0161-626 1709 E-mail: ukcommorders@eaton.com *Domestic switchgear manufrs*

Eaton Power Solutions Ltd, Heath Place, Ashgrove Industrial Park, Bognor Regis, West Sussex, PO22 9SJ Tel: (01243) 810500 Fax: (01243) 868613 *Power systems & telecommunications*

Eaton Socon Engineering, Renhold Road, Ravensden, Bedford, MK44 2RH Tel: (01234) 772145 Fax: (01234) 771881 E-mail: eaton-socon@tiscali.co.uk *Sub-contract precision engineers*

Eaton Tractors Ltd, High Street, Little Paxton, St. Neots, Cambridgeshire, PE19 6HD Tel: (01480) 473121 Fax: (01480) 404585 *Agricultural & Industrial engineers*

Eaton-Williams Holdings Ltd, Station Road, Edenbridge, Kent, TN8 6EG Tel: (01732) 866055 Fax: (01732) 863461 E-mail: peter.dewdney@eaton-williams.com *Air conditioning engineers*

▶ Eau Coolers Ltd, Unit 6 Woolmer Way, Bordon, Hampshire, GU35 9QF Tel: (01420) 488600 Fax: (01420) 488691 E-mail: eaucoolers@drinkingwater.co.uk *Drinking water coolers distributors*

Eaves Engineering Hyde Ltd, Unit F Adamsons Industrial Estate, Hyde, Cheshire, SK14 1EF Tel: 0161-368 9828 Fax: 0161-367 8143 E-mail: stan-feerick@yahoo.com *Medium & sub contract heavy machining*

Eawex International Trading Co. Ltd, Rear of 12 Burley Road, Oakham, Leicestershire, LE15 6DH Tel: (01572) 756322 Fax: (01572) 756322 E-mail: kimwahng@hotmail.com *Eawex International Trading was founded in 1997 with the design and distribution of the Keep Warm Bag®, an innovative brand designed for home delivery of hot meals and food transportation. The bags are now used throughout the United Kingdom and Ireland by businesses in the catering industry.*

▶ EB Marketing, 3 House Plat Court, Church Crookham, Fleet, Hampshire, GU52 6XW Tel: 01252 689308 E-mail: info@ebonybailey.co.uk *EB Marketing is an outbound telemarketing company. You can find all our services at our website, and can also contact us through the site.*We will speak directly to decision makers for you!!!*

▶ ebale.co.uk, Sales & Marketing Offices, 14 Crown Street, Brentwood, Essex, CM14 4BA Tel: (01277) 375759 Fax: (01277) 261588 E-mail: info@ebale.co.uk *Bale-it Sell-it Prof-it. Suppliers of balers and other waste handling equipment. Free Delivery, Free Installation, Free on-site Training. Buy or Rent online and start turning your trash into cash!*

Ebara Scotland, 4 Adam Square, Brucefield Industrial Estate, Livingston, West Lothian, EH54 9DE Tel: (01506) 460232 Fax: (01506) 460222 *Vacuum pump manufrs*

▶ e-bay-trader, 18 Saville Road, Radcliffe, Manchester, M26 4JX Tel: 0161-764 2962 E-mail: mail@e-bay-trader.co.uk *Internet service*

▶ John Ebbage Seeds Ltd, The Stable Yard, Ryston Hall, Ryston, Downham Market, Norfolk, PE38 0AA Tel: (01366) 387877 Fax: (01366) 384285 E-mail: info@ebbageseeds.co.uk *Seed wholesaler*

Ebbfix Ltd, Lancaster Road, Carnaby Industrial Estate, Carnaby, Bridlington, North Humberside, YO15 3QY Tel: (01262) 603714 Fax: (01262) 400510 E-mail: info@ic-systems.co.uk *Aluminium window frame manufrs*

Ebbs & Dale Ltd, Unit 27 Austin Fields, King's Lynn, Norfolk, PE30 1PH Tel: (01553) 765554 Fax: (01553) 769140 E-mail: sales@ebbsanddale.com *General engineers*

Ebbs & Dale Ltd, Unit 27 Austin Fields, King's Lynn, Norfolk, PE30 1PH Tel: (01553) 765554 Fax: (01553) 769140 E-mail: sales@ebbsanddale.com *Sheet metal fabricators*

EBC Group, 80-82 Dudley Road, Lye, Stourbridge, West Midlands, DY9 8ET Tel: (01384) 266666 Fax: (01384) 266661 E-mail: info@ebcgroup.co.uk *Cannon & Kyrocera office equipment dealer*

Ebc International Ltd, 7 Grovebury Place Estate, Leighton Buzzard, Bedfordshire, LU7 4SH Tel: (01525) 217217 Fax: (01525) 373772 E-mail: sales@ebcint.co.uk *Bearings suppliers*

Ebc UK Ltd, PO Box 28, Ross-on-Wye, Herefordshire, HR9 6YD Tel: (01989) 762051 Fax: (01989) 762052 *Supply equipment for concrete industry*

Ebdon Studios, 276 Broadway, Bexleyheath, Kent, DA6 8BE Tel: (020) 8303 1052 E-mail: sales@ebdon.co.uk *Commercial photographers* Also at: Chatham & Dartford

Ebdy Electrical, Acorn House, Acorn Close, Five Oak Green, Tonbridge, Kent, TN12 6RH Tel: (01892) 833000 Fax: (01892) 833311 E-mail: sales@ebdy.co.uk *Electrical contractors*

▶ Eben Staircase Manufacturers, 4 Murieston Lane, Edinburgh, EH11 2LX Tel: 0131-477 3566 Fax: 0131-622 7759

Ebene Hall Plant Care Ltd, Widbury Hill Nursery, Widbury Hill, Ware, Hertfordshire, SG12 7QE Tel: (01920) 460368 Fax: (01920) 461488 E-mail: sales@ebanyhall.co.uk *Interior & exterior landscaping*

Ebeniste Pine Ltd, Maunside, Green Line Industrial Estate, Mansfield, Nottinghamshire, NG18 5GU Tel: (01623) 421090 Fax: (01623) 632430 E-mail: info@ebenistepine.co.uk *Pine bed manufrs*

▶ Eberhardt Signs Ltd, Victory Trading Estate, Kiln Road, Portsmouth, PO3 5LP Tel: (023) 9266 5466 Fax: (023) 9266 5681 E-mail: sales@eberhardtsigns.com *Sign manufrs*

Eberspacher UK Ltd, Unit 10 Headlands Business Park, Salisbury Road, Blashford, Ringwood, Hampshire, BH24 3PB Tel: (01425) 480151 Fax: (01425) 480152 E-mail: enquiries@eberspacher.com *Independent heaters*

▶ Ebm UK Ltd, 16 Comely Park, Dunfermline, Fife, KY12 7HU Tel: (01383) 729920 Fax: (01383) 731366 *Product design consultants*

Ebm-Papst, The Barn, Sheepdown, East Ilsley, Newbury, Berkshire, RG20 7ND Tel: (0870) 7665170 Fax: (08707) 665180 E-mail: aanddsales@uk.ebmpapst.com *Retailers of electric motors*

▶ eboot auctions, 42a Stoke Road, Gosport, Hampshire, PO12 1JQ Tel: 02392 511909 E-mail: foo1952@hotmail.com *Online Auction bootsale site for buyers and sellers*

Ebor Concretes Ltd, Ripon, North Yorkshire, HG4 1JE Tel: (01765) 604351 Fax: (01765) 690065 E-mail: sales@eborconcrete.co.uk *Concrete fencing & municipal street furniture manufrs*

Ebor Machine Tools Ltd, 5 Kimberlow Woods Hill, York, YO10 5HF Tel: (01904) 431611 Fax: (01904) 431622 *Machine tools hire & repairs*

▶ Ebor Nannies Ltd, No 1 Ebor House, Dike Ray Close, Haxby, York, YO32 3WJ Tel: (01904) 767777 Fax: (01904) 767700 E-mail: jane@ebornannies.co.uk *Nanny agency. Professional providers of Nannies, Au Pairs, Mother''s Help, Maternity Help, Babysitters. Serving the needs of families, Nurseries, Schools and Corporates*

Eborcraft Ltd, 11-12 Chessingham Park Common Road, Dunnington, York, YO19 5SE Tel: (01904) 481020 Fax: (01904) 481022 E-mail: sales@eborcraft.co.uk *Office & boardroom furniture manufrs*

Ebs Panels, 144b Leek Road, Endon, Stoke-on-Trent, ST9 9EW Tel: (01782) 503386 Fax: (01782) 502265 E-mail: ebspanels@btconnect.com *Control panel manufrs*

Ebtrade Ltd, Albion Dockside Works, Bristol, BS1 6UT Tel: 0117-927 9204 Fax: 0117-929 8193 E-mail: enquiries@seetru.com *Engineering*

▶ Ebulbshop Lighting Retailers, 42 44 High Street, Hythe, Kent, CT21 5AT Tel: (01303) 264400 Fax: (01303) 264664 E-mail: andrew@ebulbshop.com *ebulbshop.com - the easy way to save money on all types of lighting - light bulbs, energy saving, halogen, dichroic and fluorescent. Order online for fast delivery to your door. **Whether itäs lighting for your business, shop, office, building, warehouse or home ebulbshop can supply the light bulbs you need direct to your premises quickly and efficiently. All our products are manufactured to the very highest safety and relevant IEC standards and you will be delighted with their quality and value for money.**

Ec Advantage Ltd, 30 Marsh Lane, Hemingford Grey, Huntingdon, Cambridgeshire, PE28 9EN Tel: (01480) 355034 Fax: (01480) 355036 E-mail: enquiries@call.uk.com *IT consultancy*

Ec Display Associates Ltd, Unit 1 Winsor, 50 Windsor Avenue, London, SW19 2TJ Tel: (020) 8545 0505 Fax: (020) 8545 0042 E-mail: info@ecdisplay.com *Modular display & exhibition consultants*

EC Testing, 6 Breeze Avenue, Aylsham, Norwich, NR11 6WF Tel: (01263) 732748 Fax: (01263) 732748 E-mail: info@ectesting.co.uk *Electrical installations inspection & testing*

Eca Contracts Ltd, 3 Fortnum Close, Kitts Green, Birmingham, B33 0LG Tel: 0121-785 4100 Fax: 0121-783 3596 E-mail: info@e-c-a.co.uk *Electrical contractors*

Eca Tool Fast, 26 Oswin Road, Leicester, LE3 1HR Tel: 0116-247 0402 *Tools & fixings* Also at: Coventry

▶ eCad Solutions - AutoCAD Electrical Design, 37 Ridgeway East, Sidcup, Kent, DA15 8RY Tel: (020) 8850 4217 Fax: (020) 8331 6893 E-mail: design@ecad-solutions.co.uk *Electrical AutoCAD Design Services. Located in London eCad Solutions are AutoCAD Design Engineers preparing electrical AutoCAD drawings for electrical contractors and consultants located within the UK*

▶ Ecado Ltd, 29 Lindley Street, Holgate, York, YO24 4JG Tel: (01904) 332214 E-mail: neil.ferguson@ecado.co.uk *Ecado provide specialist CAD development and draughting services for Microstation users in the UK Rail Industry.*

Ecam Engineering Ltd, Tower Crane Drive, Stoke-on-Trent, ST10 4DB Tel: (01538) 757166 Fax: (01538) 755857 E-mail: nick@ecam.co.uk *General fabricators*

▶ Ecatenate, 37 Otago Street, Top Floor, Glasgow, G12 8JJ Tel: 0141-334 6043 Fax: 0141-334 6044 *Computer software & hardware*

Eccles UK Foundries Ltd, Portland Street, Walsall, WS2 8AA Tel: (01922) 613222 Fax: (01922) 613444 *Manhole cover manufacturers & distributors*

Eccles Wing & Radiator Company Ltd, 3 Chadwick Road, Eccles, Manchester, M30 0NZ Tel: 0161-789 1126 Fax: 0161-789 1126 *Accident repair specialists*

▶ Ecclesall Woods Saw Mill, Abbey Lane, Sheffield, S7 2QZ Tel: 0114-262 0025 Fax: 0114-262 1470 E-mail: sales@logga.co.uk *Supplier of a wide range of Timber related garden products including:- Sheds, Summerhouses, Garden Furniture, Bark Chippings, Landscape Timber, Winter Fuel, Fencing Panels, and more..*

Ecclesiastical Insurance Group, Beaufort House, Brunswick Road, Gloucester, GL1 1JZ Tel: (01452) 528533 Fax: (01452) 423557 E-mail: marketing@eigmail.com *Insurance brokers* Also at: Belfast, Birmingham, Bristol, Cambridge, Cardiff, Dublin, East Grinstead, Edinburgh, Harrogate & Southampton

Ecclesiastical Insurance Group, 19-21 Billiter Street, London, EC3M 2RY Tel: (020) 7528 7364 Fax: (020) 7528 7365 *Investments & insurance services*

Ece Engineering Dundee Ltd, Unit 12 Faraday Street, Dryburgh Industrial Estate, Dundee, DD2 3QQ Tel: (01382) 811978 Fax: (01382) 812058 E-mail: ece.engineering@btinternet.com *General engineers*

Ecentric Media Ltd, PO Box 473, Horsham, West Sussex, RH12 5YL Tel: (01403) 253022 Fax: 01403 253022 E-mail: enquiries@ecentricmedia.co.uk *An independent multi-channel CRM systems integration consultancy with expertise in Chordiant, Ab-Initio and e-business-CTI application software solutions.*

▶ Ecg Resins Ltd, 48 Ashcroft Drive, Old Whittington, Chesterfield, Derbyshire, S41 9PD Tel: (01246) 454983 Fax: 01246 454983 E-mail: ecg@fsmail.net *Epoxy resin Suppliers*Resin bound aggregate drives,paths,and patio's. Floor, roof and wall sealers. wear-resistant lining engineers.*

Echem Ltd, 147 Kirkstall Road, Leeds, LS3 1JN Tel: 0113-245 7471 Fax: 0113-244 5082 E-mail: info@echem.co.uk *Industrial chemical distributors & manufrs*

▶ Echo, 2 Sloefield Drive, Carrickfergus, County Antrim, BT38 8GX Tel: (028) 9335 8165 Fax: (028) 9335 8154 E-mail: info@echosigns.co.uk *Specialist sign consultants*

Echo Ltd, 85 Greenwood Rd, London, E8 1NT Tel: 020 724 94796 *Clothing manufacturer*

Echo Engineering Southern Ltd, Chapel Land Farm, Ashford Road, New Romney, Kent, TN28 8TH Tel: (01797) 367670 Fax: (01797) 367671 E-mail: sales@echo-eng.com *Metal fabrication specialists*

▶ Echobeach Ltd, Manor Farm, Compton Durville, South Petherton, Somerset, TA13 5EX Tel: (01460) 240222 Fax: (01460) 240122 E-mail: sales@echobeachltd.co.uk *DIN rail & pcb terminals distributor*

Echopilot Ltd, 1 Endeavour Park, Crow Arch Lane, Ringwood, Hampshire, BH24 1SF Tel: (01425) 476211 Fax: (01425) 474300 E-mail: info@echopilot.com *Marine electronics manufrs*

Ecieurope, Buckingway Business Park, Rowles Way, Swavesey, Cambridge, CB24 4UG Tel: (01954) 278000 Fax: (01954) 278001 E-mail: sales@ipuk.com *Computer software developers*

▶ ECITechnical Services, Unit 1, Poole Hall Industrial Estate, Ellesmere Port, CH66 1ST Tel: 0151-357 2200 Fax: 0151-357 2235 E-mail: sales@ecitec.co.uk *Assett management company*

Eckart UK, Unit C The Sidings, Station Road, Ampthill, Bedford, MK45 2QY Tel: (01525) 409520 Fax: (01525) 409521 E-mail: sales@eckart.co.uk *Metal powder distributors*

Eckersley Joinery Ltd, Dawson Street, Swinton, Manchester, M27 4FJ Tel: 0161-794 5812 Fax: 0161-794 8586 *Joinery manufacturers*

ECL Chemicals Ltd, Impex House, Leestone Road, Sharston, Manchester, M22 4RN Tel: 0161-491 6744 Fax: 0161-491 6774 E-mail: info@eclchem.com *We supply mould release agents, pigment dispersions, in-mould paints, and ancillary products to manufacturers of moulded polyurethane components. Founded in 1982, we are in our 26th year, and have a reputation for excellence in service, technical support and customer care. Our UK based manufacturing and distribution operations are located at Sharston in Manchester. We offer ex stock supply of our frontline products. Technical support is available immediately by phone, or at your premises by appointment. We are an experienced, knowledgeable team with a friendly "can do" attitude. Our bespoke colouring facility for pigments and in-mould paints is second to none, guaranteeing a completed sample within 5 working days.*

Eclipse, Long Rock, Penzance, Cornwall, TR20 8LD Tel: (01736) 719170 Fax: (01736) 710872 *Equestrian leisure & agricultural services*

▶ Eclipse Automotive Technology Ltd, Clay House,, Horninglow Street, Burton-on-Trent, Staffordshire, DE14 1NG Tel: (0845) 4666699 Fax: 0845 4665986 E-mail: Sales@eclipseautomotivetechnology.com *Suppliers of inovative Diagnostic Test equipment for Car and Truck.Texa Car and Truck Diagnostic Equipment*

Eclipse Blind Systems Ltd, 10 Fountain Crescent, Inchinnan Business Park, Renfrew, PA4 9RE Tel: 0141-812 3322 Fax: 0141-812 5253 E-mail: orrd@eclipseblinds.co.uk *Blind system manufrs*

▶ Eclipse Colour Print Ltd, Riley Road, Telford Way Industrial Estate, Kettering, Northamptonshire, NN16 8NN Tel: (01536) 483401 Fax: (01536) 481102 E-mail: sales@eclipsecolourprint.co.uk

Eclipse Colours, Hillam Road, Bradford, West Yorkshire, BD2 1QN Tel: (01274) 731552 Fax: (01274) 738118 E-mail: sales@eclipsecolours.co.uk *Eclipse Colours Ltd produces colouration and additive solutions for the Plastics Industry and other related areas.**A wide range of Colour Masterbatch, Additives and Liquid Colourants are manufactured to each individual customer's requirements and specifications.**Polymers coloured include Polypropylenes, Polyethylenes, Polyamides, Styrenics, ABS & SAN, Polycarbonate, PBT, Acrylics, & PVC.**

Eclipse Computer Supplies Ltd, 106 St. Nicholas Street, Coventry, CV1 4BT Tel: (024) 7650 0100 Fax: (0870) 7436000 E-mail: sales@eclipse-computers.com *Computer part suppliers*

▶ Eclipse Corporate Communications, 111 Hagley Road, Birmingham, B16 8LB Tel: 0121-452 5070 Fax: 0121-452 5071 *Corporate communication company*

Eclipse Displays, Unit 20 Portland Business Park, 130 Richmond Park Road, Sheffield, S13 8HS Tel: 0114-242 2601 Fax: 0114-242 2629 E-mail: sales@eclipsedisplays.co.uk *Exhibition contractors & installation services*

Eclipse Energy Controls Ltd, Unit 4, Wombourne Enterprise Park, Bridgnorth Road, Wombourne, Wolverhampton, WV5 0AL Tel: (01902) 897760 Fax: (01902) 897613 E-mail: sales@eclipse-energy.co.uk *Software developers, electronic consultants or designers*

Eclipse Joinery, Castle View Works, High Street, Harriseahead, Stoke-On-Trent, ST7 4JS Tel: (01782) 510148 Fax: (01782) 510100 *Joinery*

Eclipse Motor Transport Co. Ltd, Clay Street, Hull, HU8 8HD Tel: (01482) 320066 Fax: (01482) 586617 *Warehousing & distribution services*

▶ Eclipse PC's, Suite 221, 26-32 Oxford Road, Bournemouth, BH8 8EZ Tel: (01202) 311052 Fax: (01202) 314513 E-mail: eclipsepcs@btinternet.com *Computer reseller*

▶ Eclipse Petroleum Technology, Salvesen Tower, Blaikies Quay, Aberdeen, AB11 5PW Tel: (01224) 588355 Fax: (01224) 588356

▶ Eclipse Presentations Ltd, 5 Chaffinch Business Park, Croydon Road, Beckenham, Kent, BR3 4AA Tel: (020) 8662 6444 Fax: (020) 8650 4635 E-mail: info@eclipse-presentations.co.uk *Audio-visual hire services*

Eclipse Tanning, 5 St. Johns Way, Corringham, Stanford-le-Hope, Essex, SS17 7NA Tel: (01375) 673397 *Tanning salon services*

Eclipse Telecom 99, 36 Hertford Drive, Tyldesley, Manchester, M29 8LU Tel: (01942) 889900 Fax: (01942) 878060 *Phone system installers*

▶ Eclipse Vehicle Management, Unit 15 Rectory La Trading Estate, Kingston Bagpuize, Abingdon, Oxfordshire, OX13 5AS Tel: (01865) 823113 Fax: (01865) 823115

▶ Eclipse Wedding Services, Woodruffe, Bagshot Road, Knaphill, Woking, Surrey, GU21 2SG Tel: (01483) 475554 Fax: (01483) 475554 E-mail: pamlawrence-eclipse@supanet.com *Professional wedding photographer*

▶ Eco Build Developments Ltd, 17 Wyche Avenue, Kings Heath, Birmingham, B14 6LG Tel: 0121-441 4434 Fax: 0121-441 4434 E-mail: brettecobuild@aol.com *Environmentally friendly building contractors*

▶ Eco Control Systems Ltd, Studio Centre, Wiston Road, Colchester, CO6 4LT Tel: (01206) 263390 Fax: (01206) 262899 *H & d controls*

▶ Eco European Ltd, Unit 1, Langlands Gate, East Kilbride, Glasgow, G75 0ZY Tel: (01355) 900159

Eco Health & Grainstore, 50 Hillfoot Street, Dunoon, Argyll, PA23 7DT Tel: (01369) 705106 *Health food retailers*

Eco Solutions Ltd, Summerleaze, Church Road, Winscombe, Avon, BS25 1BH Tel: (01934) 844484 Fax: (01934) 844119 E-mail: info@ecosolutions.co.uk *Developed & patented range of paint stripping services*

Eco Therm Insulation UK Ltd, Unit 3 Cabinet Way, Eastwood, Leigh-on-Sea, Essex, SS9 5LP Tel: (01702) 520166 Fax: (01702) 420636 E-mail: info@ecotherm.co.uk *Insulation manufrs*

Ecoat (Ireland) Ltd, Unit 13, Blaris Industrial Estate, Altona Road, Lisburn, County Antrim, BT27 5QB Tel: (028) 9260 4798 Fax: (028) 9260 4798 E-mail: info@ecoat.co.uk *Electrophoretic painters*

Ecobug Ltd, Llanteg, Narberth, Dyfed, SA67 8PY Tel: (07000) 326284 Fax: (01834) 831842 E-mail: phil@ecobug.com *Waterless urinals manufacturers & bacterial treatments*

▶ Ecoclean Environmental Services, 7 Lynn Road, Swaffham, Norfolk, PE37 7AY Tel: (01760) 336028 Fax: (01760) 725752 E-mail: info@ecocleanltd.co.uk *Cleaning & restoration services*

▶ Eco-Dec, 27a Northgate, Cleckheaton, West Yorkshire, BD19 3HH Tel: (07974) 683111 *Ecological decorating service domestic & commercial work*

▶ Ecoflam UK Ltd, 12 Goodwood Road, Pershore, Worcestershire, WR10 2JL Tel: (01386) 556092 Fax: (01386) 553789 E-mail: sales@ecoflam.co.uk

▶ Ecoflue Ltd, Copperfields, Beach Road, Kessingland, Lowestoft, Suffolk, NR33 7RW Tel: (01502) 741388 Fax: 07900 606241 E-mail: blojus@aol.com *Covering Norfolk and Suffolk, Ecoflue Ltd provide services such as: CCTV chimney camera inspections and surveys, Chimney Sweeping & certificates issued, Chimney Lining, Stove and Fireplace Sales & installation, Cowls and Bird /Rain guards fitted, Chimney repairs, Chimney pots fitted. A complete service. Ecoflue Ltd are HETAS and National Association of Chimney Sweeps registered. Visit our website at www.ecoflue.co.uk*

▶ EcoFuels UK Ltd, Smalleys Garage (Thorne), Selby Road, Thorne, Doncaster, South Yorkshire, DN8 4JD Tel: (0773) 0552832 Fax: (0784) 1399828 E-mail: info@EcoFuelsUK.com *LPGA (LPGas Association) Approved Autogas Conversions; Special Service, Support, Maintenance & Offers; Clients Visited, Prompt Service. Member of a National Network.*

Ecokem Ltd, 4 Trafalgar Court, Widnes, Cheshire, WA8 0SZ Tel: 0151-420 0172 Fax: 0151-510 5455 E-mail: dclarkson@ecokem.co.uk *Engineering chemical manufrs*

▶ Ecoknowlogy International Ltd, 26 York Street, London, W1U 6PZ Tel: (0870) 7777420 Fax: (0870) 7777421 E-mail: info@ecoknowlogy-intl.com *Environmentally sound non-toxic sealers & biodegradable oil cleaners*

Ecolab Ltd, Caerphilly Business Park, Caerphilly, Mid Glamorgan, CF83 3ED Tel: (029) 2085 2000 Fax: (029) 2086 5969 *Pest control services*

Ecolab Ltd, Stanley Green Trading Estate, Duke Avenue, Cheadle Hulme, Cheadle, Cheshire, SK8 6RB Tel: 0161-485 6166 Fax: 0161-488 4127 E-mail: inge.van.der.linden@ecolab.com *Disinfectant & detergents manufrs*

Ecolab Ltd, David Murray John Building, Swindon, SN1 1NH Tel: (01793) 511221 Fax: (01793) 618552 E-mail: sales.uk@ecolab.co.uk *Ecolab based in Swindon is the world's leading provider of cleaning, food safety and health protection products and services for the hospitality, foodservice, healthcare and industrial markets.* Also at: Bristol & Slough

▶ Ecolab Pest Control Ltd, Falcon House, Lawnhurst Industrial Estate, Stockport, Cheshire, SK3 0XT Tel: 0161-491 3855 Fax: 0161 491 6088

▶ Ecolab Pest Prevention, Unit 47 Clifton Industrial Estate, Cherry Hinton Road, Cambridge, CB1 7ED Tel: (01223) 211303 Fax: (01223) 215151 *Pest control services*

Ecolab Pest Prevention, John O Gaunts Trading Estate, Leeds Road, Rothwell, Leeds, LS26 0JB Tel: 0113 288 7787 Fax: 0113 282 1298

▶ Ecolab Pest Prevention, Unit 5, Waterside Court, Bone Lane, Newbury, Berkshire, RG14 5SH Tel: (01635) 524780 Fax: (01635) 524761

▶ Ecolab Pest Prevention, 146 Moor Lane, Preston, PR1 1JR Tel: (01772) 563303 Fax: (01772) 561106

▶ Ecolab Services Ltd, Unit 11 Prideaux Close, Tamar View Industrial Estate, Saltash, Cornwall, PL12 6LD Tel: (01752) 841842 Fax: (01752) 840700

▶ Ecologic Systems Ltd, Brook House, Birmingham Road, Henley-in-Arden, West Midlands, B95 5QR Tel: (0870) 2863730 Fax: (0870) 2863731 E-mail: info@ecologicsystems.co.uk *EcoLogic's unique cleaning system is both environmentally-friendly and non-abrasive while having the cleaning technology that delivers results - every time*

▶ Ecomiser, Cliftonville Chambers, 46 Billing Road, Northampton, NN1 5DB Tel: 01604 516750 Fax: 01604 516109 E-mail: info@ecomiser.co.uk *Promote and install energy efficiency products. Reducing heating costs for offices,hotels,care homes.*

▶ Ecommnet Ltd, Aidan House Tynegate Precinct, Sunderland Road, Gateshead, Tyne & Wear, NE8 3HU Tel: 0191-478 8315 Fax: 0191-478 9466 E-mail: robert.campbell@ecommnet.co.uk *Website support*

▶ Ecomould Ltd, Park Farm Road, Foxhill Industrial Estate, Scunthorpe, South Humberside, DN15 8QP Tel: (01724) 280495 Fax: (01724) 280496 *Automotives manufrs*

Econ Construction Ltd, Old Maidstone Road, Sidcup, Kent, DA14 5AZ Tel: (020) 8302 4691 Fax: (020) 8308 0483 E-mail: econconstruction@aol.com *Asbestos removal & demolition*

Econ Engineering Ltd, Boroughbridge Road, Ripon, North Yorkshire, HG4 1UE Tel: (01765) 605321 *Winter maintenance equipment manufrs*

Econintel Treasury Systems Ltd, The Octagon, 27 Middleborough, Colchester, CO1 1TG Tel: (01206) 760033 Fax: (01206) 760133 E-mail: colchester@econintel.com *Treasury Management System Software*

Econocom UK Ltd, Merevale House, Parkshot, Richmond, Surrey, TW9 2RG Tel: (020) 8948 8377 Fax: (020) 8948 8481 E-mail: lisa.dyne@econocom.be *Computer leasing*

Econogard Services Ltd, Econogard House, 1 Halifax Road, Cambridge, CB4 3QB Tel: (01763) 261970 Fax: (01223) 352494 *Fire protection equipment manufacturers & installers*

Econology Ltd, 4 Norsted Lane, Pratts Bottom, Orpington, Kent, BR6 7PG Tel: (01689) 860686 E-mail: cmaier@btconnect.com *Technical information & media services*

▶ Economatics, Victoria Industrial Estate, Victoria Road West, Hebburn, Tyne & Wear, NE31 1UB Tel: 0191-428 7070 Fax: 0191-414 9312 E-mail: mail@marshall-branson.co.uk *Compressor distributor & servicing pneumatics*

Economatics Industrial Ltd, 145 Leycroft Road, Leicester, LE4 1ET Tel: 0116-234 0555 Fax: 0116-234 0467 E-mail: leicester@economatics.co.uk *Pneumatic tool manufrs*

Economatics Industrial Ltd, Epic House, Darnall Road, Sheffield, S9 5AA Tel: 0114-281 3344 Fax: 0114-243 9306 E-mail: group@economatics.co.uk *Air compressor & pneumatic equipment distributors* Also at: Branches throughout the U.K.

Economatics (Industrial) Ltd, Unit 6 Alders Court, Watchmead, Welwyn Garden City, Hertfordshire, AL7 1LT Tel: (01707) 322622 Fax: (01707) 330724 E-mail: ailsford@economatics.co.uk *Pneumatic & compressed air distributors* Also at: Branches throughout the U.K.

▶ Economed First Aid Supplies, Station Road, Long Sutton, Spalding, Lincolnshire, PE12 9BP Tel: (01406) 364242 Fax: (01406) 364676 E-mail: sales@econo-med.com *Welcome to Econo-Med 24 hour on-line shopping. For the very best savings on quality medical and beauty products to anywhere in the united kingdom. Secure ordering and fast delivery. During normal office hours you can also contact a member of our sales team to place your order. Telephone 01406 36 42 42*

Economic Cutting Ltd, 1 Orgreave Crescent, Sheffield, S13 9NQ Tel: 0114-254 9222 Fax: 0114-254 9333 E-mail: sales@economiccutting.co.uk *Metal sawing engineers & services*

Economic Development Service, Gloucester City Council, 75-81 Eastgate Street, Gloucester, GL1 1PN Tel: (01452) 544911 Fax: (01452) 396994 *Economic development*

The Economist Intelligence Ltd, 15 Regent St, London, SW1Y 4LR Tel: (020) 7930 8763 Fax: (020) 7830 1023 E-mail: info@economist.com *Business report services*

Economist Newspaper Ltd, 25 St. James's Street, London, SW1A 1HG Tel: (020) 7576 8000 Fax: (020) 7839 2968 *Newspaper publishers*

Economy Auto Paint, 81a Main Street, Bainsford, Falkirk, FK2 7NZ Tel: (01324) 620002 Fax: (01324) 620002 *Car paint suppliers*

Economy Heating Services Ltd, Economy House, Hardley Industrial Estate, Hardley, Hythe, Southampton, SO45 3YQ Tel: (023) 8084 6646 Fax: (023) 8084 4479 E-mail: dick@economyservices.co.uk *Specialising in commercial portable boiler room to specification*

Economy Hire (Dorset) Ltd, 10 Parkside Industrial Estate, Ringwood, Hampshire, BH24 3SQ Tel: (01425) 474593 Fax: (01425) 479964 E-mail: jclark@economyhire.co.uk *Vehicle sales & hire commercial services*

Economy Pest Control, 10 Pier Street, Plymouth, PL1 3BS Tel: (01752) 265337 Fax: (01752) 265337 E-mail: sales@pestcontrol4u.com *Pest control & carpet cleaning services*

▶ Economy Windows & Conservatories, Churchgate Way, Terrington St. Clement, King's Lynn, Norfolk, PE34 4PG Tel: (01553) 827318 Fax: (01553) 827369 E-mail: enquiries@economywindows.co.uk

Econoprint Ltd, Unit 20 Castlebrae Business Centre, Peffer Place, Edinburgh, EH16 4BB Tel: 0131-652 6052 Fax: 0131-652 6026 *Printers*

Econoprint UK Ltd, Cooper Drive, Springwood Industrial Estate, Braintree, Essex, CM7 2RF Tel: (01376) 349955 Fax: (01376) 346853 E-mail: sales@econoprint.co.uk *Business forms distributors*

▶ Econorod, 6 Brownfields, Welwyn Garden City, Hertfordshire, AL7 1AN Tel: (01707) 333573 Fax: (01707) 333574

▶ Econowall, Church Street, Wellingborough, Northamptonshire, NN8 4PD Tel: (0800) 0431002 Fax: (0800) 0431004 E-mail: belinda@econowall.co.uk *Manufacturer of slatted panels and shopfittings*

▶ E-Consultancy.Com Publishing, 85 Clerkenwell Road, London, EC1R 5AR Tel: (020) 7681 4052 Fax: (020) 7681 4031 E-mail: ashley@e-consultancy.com *Information, training & events on best practice online marketing*

Ecopac Power, Unit 7 Field End, Crendon Industrial Area, Long Crendon, Aylesbury, Buckinghamshire, HP18 9EJ Tel: (01844) 204420 Fax: (01844) 204421 *Power supplies*

Ecophon Ltd, Old Brick Kiln, Ramsdell, Tadley, Hampshire, RG26 5PP Tel: (01256) 850989 Fax: (01256) 851550 E-mail: sales@ecophon.co.uk *Suspended ceilings manufrs*

▶ Ecopro Ltd, Lingwood House, Angel Hill, Earl Stonham, Stowmarket, Suffolk, IP14 5DP Tel: (01449) 710066 Fax: (01449) 710066 E-mail: steve.austen@ecopro.co.uk *Pest controllers*

Ecoro Ltd, 3 Rowanside Close, Headley Down, Bordon, Hampshire, GU35 8HH Tel: (01428) 717070 E-mail: info@ecoro.co.uk *Computer consultants*

Ecos Environmental, Low Moor Industrial Estate, Common Road, Low Moor, Bradford, West Yorkshire, BD12 0NB Tel: (01274) 691122 Fax: (01274) 608100 E-mail: info@ecos.co.uk *Environmental analysis*

▶ Ecosse Unique, Lilliesleaf, Melrose, Roxburghshire, TD6 9JD Tel: (01835) 870779 Fax: (01835) 870417 E-mail: mark@uniquescotland.com *letting company specialising in traditional self catering holiday accommodation all over Scotland in beautiful locations.*

▶ Ecostat Thermostats, Unit 20 Beehive Workshops, Parkengue, Penryn, Cornwall, TR10 9LX Tel: (01326) 378654 Fax: (01326) 378539 E-mail: ecostat@btconnect.com *Birds incubation specialists*

Tim Ecote, 31 Warner Drive, Springwood Industrial Estate, Braintree, Essex, CM7 2YW Tel: (01376) 528112 Fax: (01376) 528114

Ecotec Research & Consulting Ltd, 12-26 Albert Street, Birmingham, B4 7UD Tel: 0121-616 3600 Fax: 0121-616 3699 E-mail: welcome@ecotec.co.uk *Environmental researchers*

▶ Ecotechnics (UK) Ltd, 11 Storey Street, Leicester, LE3 5GR Tel: 0116-262 0200 Fax: 0116-251 0800 E-mail: daniel@dpelectronics.co.uk *Manufacture & distributor of horticultural products, supplier to garden centres*

▶ Ecotrax, Plaitford, Romsey, Hampshire, SO51 6YZ Tel: (01794) 324772 Fax: (01794) 324420 E-mail: ns@m977.com *Plant & machinery dealers*

▶ Ecourier.Co.Uk, Cityside House, 40 Adler Street, London, E1 1EE Fax: (020) 7877 6501 E-mail: mybigquestion@ecourier.co.uk *eCourier.co.uk offers same day & next day delivery service to local, national & international delivery points. You can book your eCourier online & track your delivery from pickup to dropoff address. Click for more information on eCourier.co.uk's express courier delivery services.*

Ecowater Systems Ltd, 1 Independent Business Park, Mill Road, Stokenchurch, High Wycombe, Buckinghamshire, HP14 3TP Tel: (01494) 484000 Fax: (01494) 484396 E-mail: sales@ecowater.co.uk *Water treatment equipment suppliers*

▶ e-craft, info@e-craft.co.uk, Irthlingborough, Wellingborough, Northants, NN9 5EP Tel: 07905 759109 E-mail: info@e-craft.co.uk *We specialise in individually hand-made Masks, Figurines, Sculptures, Walking Sticks, and Wall Adornments.*

▶ ECRE8, 4 Highlands Drive, Daventry, Northamptonshire, NN11 8ST Tel: (01327) 310808 Fax: (01327) 310808 E-mail: stuart@ecre8.co.uk *ECRE8 specialise in local web development and design for the Daventry area.*

E-CRM Solutions Ltd, 115 Church Road, Bath, BA2 5JJ Tel: (01225) 840490 Fax: (8701) 643582 E-mail: richardhill@e-crm.co.uk *Do you want your business or organization to have more customers that stay longer and so have better cash flow and be more profitable?. E-CRM helps you have more customers that stay longer and so have better cash flow and be more profitable. Those are the things we help you to achieve by working with you. E-CRM helps you to translate your ambitious goals into rapid, practical actions and results, cost effectively. We offer business advice, marketing support, direct marketing and interactive marketing services as well as intranets, extranets and web conferencing.*

▶ Ecruit UK Ltd, 41 Convent Road, Ashford, Middlesex, TW15 2HJ Tel: (08718) 714605 Fax: (08712) 773138 E-mail: admin@ecruit-direct.co.uk *Fully managed online recruitment services including job advertising and cv search. Plus job search, cv writing, cv marketing and career advice*

▶ Ecs Air Conditioning, 17 Station Road, London, SE20 7BE Tel: (020) 8778 9661 Fax: (020) 8778 9514

(ECSO) Express Computer Services, 636 Cathcart Road, Crosshill, Govanhill, Glasgow, G42 8AA Tel: (0871) 7890247 Fax: (0871) 7890248 E-mail: info@ecso.co.uk *CCTV electrical contractors & it services*

ECT, Pangbourne, Reading, RG8 8TX Tel: 0118-984 1141 Fax: 0118-984 1847 E-mail: adam@ect-av.com *Projection screens manufrs*

Ectron Ltd, Knap Close, Letchworth Garden City, Hertfordshire, SG6 1AQ Tel: (01462) 682124 Fax: (01462) 481463 E-mail: ectronltd@btconnect.com *Medical electronic equipment*

Ecu Castings, Claytons Meadow, Bourne End, Buckinghamshire, SL8 5DQ Tel: (01628) 524672 Fax: (01628) 850914 E-mail: robinecu@aol.com *Castings, aluminium alloy*

▶ EDA Ltd, c/o Sims Croft, Middleton, Milton Keynes, MK10 9GF Tel: 01908 393294 E-mail: info@eda-ltd.co.uk *Electronc Data Archives Ltd. Advanced document scanning and data archiving, serving clients around the Beds, Bucks and Herts area. Specialist in financial and legal compliance quality scanning and document storage.*

Edale Instruments (Cambridge) Ltd, Gresley House, Station Road, Longstanton, Cambridge, CB4 5DS Tel: (01954) 260853 Fax: (01954) 260894 *Electronic thermometer manufrs*

Edbro plc, Nelson Street, Bolton, BL3 2JJ Tel: (01204) 528888 Fax: (01204) 531957 E-mail: sales@edbro.co.uk *Hydraulic lifting equipment*

Edda Supply Ships UK Ltd, Seaforth Centre, 30 Waterloo Quay, Aberdeen, AB11 5BS Tel: (01224) 587788 Fax: (01224) 583276 E-mail: info@eddasupplyships.com *Shipping lines, ship owners*

▶ Eddies Autos Ltd, Buckrose Street, Huddersfield, HD1 6HB Tel: 078 76498676 E-mail: edward@eddiesautos.co.uk *Quality Used Autos at great prices!*

Eddingbrook Ltd, Valley Works, Bacup Road, Todmorden, Lancashire, OL14 7PJ Tel: (01706) 814854 Fax: (01706) 815023 E-mail: info@eddingbrook.co.uk *Sheet metalworkers*

Eddison & Wanless Ltd, Unit 1, Mallard Industrial Estate, Horbury, Wakefield, West Yorkshire, WF4 5QH Tel: (01924) 271128 Fax: (01924) 271251 E-mail: info@eddisonwanless.co.uk Principal Export Areas: Worldwide *Manufacturer Of Heavy Duty Fabrications*Transformer tank manufrs*

▶ Eddy Hosie, Chapel Road, Cuminestown, Turriff, Aberdeenshire, AB53 5ZA Tel: (01888) 544747 Fax: (01888) 544847

A.M. Ede Technical Services Ltd, Conger Cottage, Market Square, Dunstable, Bedfordshire, LU5 6BP Tel: (01525) 873890 Fax: (01525) 873890 *Woodworking, tanning machinery & coach building*

Ede Powder Coatings Ltd, Annie Reed Road, Beverley, North Humberside, HU17 0LF Tel: (01482) 865957 Fax: (01482) 864922 E-mail: info@edepc.com *Powder coatings*

▶ Ede & Ravenscoft, 9 Henry Crabb Road, Littleport, Ely, Cambridgeshire, CB6 1SE Tel: (01353) 862973 Fax: (01353) 863590 *Academic gowns manufrs*

▶ Eden, Field Road, Mildenhall, Bury St. Edmunds, Suffolk, IP28 7AR Tel: (0870) 7258826 Fax: (0870) 7258827 E-mail: fiona.diviney@eden-industries.co.uk *Design installation of shop fitting*

Eden, 1 Little Dockray, Penrith, Cumbria, CA11 7HL Tel: (01768) 869000 Fax: (01768) 865578 E-mail: david@edengraphics.co.uk *Graphic designers & sign printers*

Eden AngloFrench Ltd, 26 Uplands Business Park, Blackhorse Lane, London, E17 5QJ Tel: (020) 8503 2121 Fax: (020) 8503 2122 E-mail: sales@eaf.demon.co.uk *Veneer merchants*

Eden Catering Services Ltd, Ferndown Middle School, Peter Grant Way, Church Road, Ferndown, Dorset, BH22 9UP Tel: (01202) 876216 *School catering services*

▶ Eden Engineering, Tanfield Lea Industrial Estate, Stanley, County Durham, DH9 9QS Tel: (01207) 235811 *Engineering*

Eden Fabrication Ltd, Primrose Hall, Green End, Threeholes, Wisbech, Cambridgeshire, PE14 9JD Tel: (01354) 638446 Fax: (01354) 638467 *Metal fabricators*

▶ Eden Floor Store,The, 64 Wyle Cop, Shrewsbury, SY1 1UX Tel: 01743 340077 E-mail: sales@theedenfloorstore.com *Oak and Other Hardwwod Supply and Installation. Members of Guild of Master Craftsmen. Free quote within 30miles Shrewsbury. Showroom on Wyle Cop, Shrewsbury. Friendly and experienced staff.*

Eden Garage, Temple Sowerby, Penrith, Cumbria, CA10 1RS Tel: (01768) 361212 Fax: (01768) 361550 E-mail: enquire@eden-garage.co.uk *Motor repairs, hire & recover*

▶ Eden Group, 43 Ellens Glen Road, Edinburgh, EH17 7QJ Tel: 0131-664 3906 Fax: 0131-658 1038 E-mail: Lynne@edengroup.co.uk *Aerial Installations and repairs*Door Entry System installations and repairs*CCTV repairs*SKY television installations*SKY Plus Installations*and other ad-hoc installations i.e fire alarms when possible*

Eden House, 1 St Katharines Way, London, E1W 1UT Tel: (020) 7488 3490 E-mail: edenhouse@dialpipex.com *Eden House is a luxury designer villa on the West Indian Island of St Barths. Fully staffed and within reach of award-winning restaurants and beaches, it is the ultimate luxury destination*

Eden Material Services (UK) Ltd, Unit 42A No 1 Industrial Estate, Medomsley Road, Consett, County Durham, DH8 6TT Tel: (01207) 590055 Fax: (01207) 590059 E-mail: sales@edenmaterials.co.uk *Stainless steel stockholders* Also at: Birmingham

Eden Park Ltd, Crown Quay Lane, Sittingbourne, Kent, ME10 3JJ Tel: (01795) 471583 Fax: (01795) 428011 E-mail: sales@edenpark.co.uk *Compost manufrs*

Eden Plastics & Media Ltd, 6 Prince Georges Road, London, SW19 2PX Tel: (020) 8646 5556 Fax: (020) 8640 0475 E-mail: general@edenplastics.co.uk *Injection mouldings manufrs*

Eden River Press Ltd, Units C-D, Charlwoods Business Centre, East Grinstead, West Sussex, RH19 2HH Tel: (01342) 313577 Fax: (01342) 324125 E-mail: mail@edenriverpress.co.uk *Commercial printers*

Samuel Eden & Son Ltd, Station Road, Sutton-in-Ashfield, Nottinghamshire, NG17 5FQ Tel: (01623) 553521 Fax: (01623) 552115 E-mail: sales@samueleden.co.uk *Hosiery manufrs*

▶ Eden Steam Showers., 5 Bagshot Road, Chobham, Surrey, GU24 8BP Tel: 01276 856240 Fax: 0118-979 4565 E-mail: contact@edensteamshowers.co.uk *Steam showers, steam rooms & massage spa bath retailers*

Eden Valley Wholefoods, 34 The Market, Scotch Street, Carlisle, CA3 8QX Tel: (01228) 546853 *Retailers of fruit & dried food & pulses*

William T. Eden Ltd, PO Box 3, Barking, Essex, IG11 0DU Tel: (020) 8477 8006 Fax: (020) 8477 8010 E-mail: headoffice@edens.co.uk *Panel products specialists* Also at: Corsham, Coventry, Frindsbury, Liskeard, Luton, New Milton & Norwich

Eden Wood Structures, 81 Ashgrove Road, Newry, County Down, BT34 1QJ Tel: (028) 3026 6863 Fax: (028) 3026 2599 *Steel fabricators*

Edenaire Ltd, Station Road, Edenbridge, Kent, TN8 6EG Tel: (01732) 866066 Fax: (01732) 866653 *Air conditioning unit manufrs*

Edenbrook Furniture Ltd, Unit Merchant, Mitchelston Industrial Estate, Kirkcaldy, Fife, KY1 3NJ Tel: (01592) 655185 Fax: (01592) 655185 *Kitchen & bedrooms manufrs*

Edenhall Concrete Ltd, Evergreen, Hale Purlieu, Fordingbridge, Hampshire, SP6 2NN Tel: (01725) 510174 Fax: (01725) 512824 *Concrete suppliers*

Edenway Contractors Ltd, Brent Terrace, Staples Corner, London, NW2 1AL Tel: (020) 8450 8474 Fax: (020) 8450 5903 E-mail: mike@edenwaycontractors.co.uk *Groundworks and Civil Engineering to New build Residential and Commercial projects*

▶ Edesix Computer Systems, 24 Canning Street, Edinburgh, EH3 8EG Tel: 0131-272 2709 Fax: 0131-272 2809

Edeva Solutions Ltd, 73 Queensway, Taunton, Somerset, TA1 4NJ Tel: (01823) 279702 Fax: (01823) 352292 *Computer services*

Edexcel, Stewart House, 32 Russell Square, London, WC1B 5DN Tel: (0870) 2409800 Fax: (020) 7393 4445 E-mail: enquiries@edexcel.org.uk *Quality assurance consultants*

▶ The Edg, 22 King Street, Lancaster, LA1 1JY Tel: (01524) 66029 Fax: (0871) 4337840 *Art gallery*

Edgar Allen Ltd, PO Box 42, Sheffield, S9 1QW Tel: 0114-244 6621 Fax: 0114-242 6826 Principal Export Areas: Worldwide *Railway track switches & fastener manufrs*

Edgar Bros, Heather Close, Lyme Green Business Park, Macclesfield, Cheshire, SK11 0LR Tel: (01625) 613177 Fax: (01625) 615276 E-mail: admin@edgar-brothers.co.uk *Importers & distributors of firearms & shooting accessories*

▶ David Edgar Kitchen Designs, 228 Spearing Road, High Wycombe, Buckinghamshire, HP12 3LA Tel: (01494) 472247 E-mail: daveedgar@rock.com *Made to measure kitchen doors and drawer fronts. Choose from 19 designs and 27 colours,any size. Free survey and 75%Discount 5 year guarantee.Call for colour brosure*

Edgar Engineering Co., Woods Way Industrial Estate, Goring-By-Sea, Worthing, West Sussex, BN12 4QY Tel: (01903) 505056 Fax: (01903) 506456 E-mail: edgareng@btconnect.com *Electrical industry enclosure construction systems manufrs*

Edge Ltd, Unit 3 Falcon Close, Burton-on-Trent, Staffordshire, DE14 1SG Tel: (01283) 511177 Fax: (01283) 511941 E-mail: enquiries@edgecleaning.co.uk *Cleaning equipment distributors*

The Edge, 3 Wolseley Terrrence, Cheltenham, Gloucestershire, GL50 1TH Tel: (01242) 580365 Fax: (01242) 261816 E-mail: design@theedge.co.uk *Design & marketing*

Edge Designs Ltd, Enterprise House, Courtaulds Way, Coventry, CV6 5NX Tel: (024) 7666 7337 Fax: (024) 7666 7657 E-mail: sales@edgedesigns.co.uk *IT consultancy*

Edge Engineering, Unit 8 Mantra Ho, South St, Keighley, W. Yorkshire, BD21 1SX Tel: (01535) 606258 *Precision engineers*

Edge Hill Transport, Wilkinsons Yard, Ardleigh Road, Liverpool, L13 2BD Tel: 0151-228 7029 Fax: 0151-228 9477 *Road transport, haulage & freight service providers*

Edge Independent, Bridge Works, Fontley Road, Titchfield, Fareham, Hampshire, PO15 6QZ Tel: (01329) 842029 Fax: (01329) 842029 *Fork lift truck services & hire*

Edge Performance, 231 Shawfield Road, Ash, Aldershot, Hampshire, GU12 5DL Tel: (01252) 331888 Fax: (01252) 331888 E-mail: sales@edge-performance.co.uk *We offer a complete service that includes expert fitting and installation. Enthusiasts can visit our shop in Ash Vale, Aldershot and purchase a finished product complete with car parts and car accessories without needing any technical knowledge. Our staff have years of experience in fittings and installations, and as such our customers can buy with confidence. No matter how unusual your idea, we can turn your dreams into reality. We also offer a complete range of services such as window tinting, body styling, audio installation and custom graphics. The car parts and car accessories we sell and fit include: - Audio - Body Styling - Exhausts - Wheels - Lighting - Suspension - Interior Styling - Performance Parts - Alarms - Tyres*

▶ The Edge Software Consultancy Ltd, 13 Upper St Michael'S Road, Aldershot, Hampshire, GU11 3HA Tel: (023) 8041 1098 E-mail: info@edgesoftwareconsultancy.com *Professional services company specialising in software consultancy and business process re-engineering for Pharmaceutical and Biotechnology companies.*

Edge Tool Co. Ltd, Unit 2a Dronfield, Callywhite Lane, Dronfield, Derbyshire, S18 2XR Tel: (01246) 415111 Fax: (01246) 415222 E-mail: sales@etmblades.co.uk *Manufacturers of machine knives & blades*

Edge9 Design and Image Solutions, Liverpool Road, Eccles, Manchester, M30 Tel: 0161-707 1311 *Manchester based website designers, specialising in professional, high quality web design. Services include hosting, unique design, site maintenance and web graphics. Visit website at www.edge9.com for affordable prices and portfolio.*

Edgefine Ltd, Unit C1 3 Forum Drive, Rugby, Warwickshire, CV21 1NT Tel: (01788) 537920 Fax: (01788) 537911 E-mail: martin@edgefine.co.uk *Precision engineers*

▶ Edgeform Fabrications Ltd, 106a Pond Park Road, Lisburn, County Antrim, BT28 3QR Tel: (028) 9260 4426 Fax: (028) 9260 4416 E-mail: edgfab@edgeform.com *Metal fabrication*

▶ Edgemere Saddlery & Riding Wear, Clifford House, Hampton Heath Industrial Estate, Hampton, Malpas, Cheshire, SY14 8LU Tel: (01948) 820720 Fax: (01948) 820720 *Saddlery & harnesses distributors*

Edgerton Gears Ltd, Park Square, Ossett, West Yorkshire, WF5 0JS Tel: (01924) 273193 Fax: (01924) 275560 *Precision engineers & gear cutters services*

Edgewest Plastics Ltd, Malvern View Business Park, Stella Way, Bishops Cleeve, Cheltenham, Gloucestershire, GL52 7DQ Tel: (01242) 679000 Fax: (01242) 679011 E-mail: info@edgewestplastics.co.uk *Injection moulding manufrs*

Edghurst Ltd, Cowden Close, Horns Rd, Hawkhurst, Cranbrook, Kent, TN18 4QT Tel: (01580) 752330 Fax: (01580) 752892 E-mail: info@edghurst.demon.co.uk *Export sales & buying services*

▶ Edgley Distribution Express Ltd, 11 Acer Road, Saddlebow Industrial Estate, King's Lynn, Norfolk, PE34 3HN Tel: (01553) 761513

Edgley Joinery Ltd, River Lane, Fordham, Ely, Cambridgeshire, CB7 5PF Tel: (01638) 720245 Fax: (01638) 721582 *Joinery manufrs*

Edgley Sailplanes Ltd, Furzelease Farm, Tisbury Row, Tisbury, Salisbury, SP3 6RZ Tel: (01747) 870509 Fax: (01747) 870509 E-mail: edgleysailplanes@argonet.co.uk *Aeronautical engineers*

Edgware Motor Accessories, 33 Albany Close, Bushey, WD23 4SG Tel: (020) 8950 4694 Fax: (020) 8950 6557 E-mail: enquiries@rubbertrim.co.uk *Rubber manufrs*

Edi Telecommunications Equipment, 2 Church Road, Cholsey, Wallingford, Oxfordshire, OX10 9PP Tel: (01491) 652145 Fax: (01491) 652214 *Electrical services*

Edible Oils Ltd, Crabtree Manorway South, Belvedere, Kent, DA17 6BB Tel: (020) 8311 7171 Fax: (020) 8310 7505 E-mail: name@edible-oils.co.uk *Edible oil merchants*

Edicon Ltd, 39 Bucknalls Drive, Bricket Wood, St. Albans, Hertfordshire, AL2 3XJ Tel: (020) 7692 7050 E-mail: info@edicon.co.uk *Edicon is the UK"s leading product design and prototyping consultancy providing expertise to allow companies bring their products, ideas or services to market in a timely and costly fashion."*

Edicos Ltd, Unit 8-9 Cromwell Industrial Estate, Staffa Road, London, E10 7QZ Tel: (020) 8539 6102 Fax: (020) 8539 8061 *Edible oil & fat wholesalers*

Edimatrix Ltd, 411-413 High Road, Woodford Green, Essex, IG8 0XG Tel: (020) 8559 2454 Fax: (020) 8559 2497 E-mail: sales@edimatrix.co.uk *Software consultants*

Edinburgh Business Development, 27 Melville Street, Edinburgh, EH3 7JF Tel: 0131-477 7000 Fax: 0131-477 8051 E-mail: events@ecce.org *Business development consultants*

Edinburgh Camcorder Centre, 78 Haymarket Terrace, Edinburgh, EH12 5LQ Tel: 0131-313 5166 Fax: 0131-313 5182 E-mail: steven@camcordercentre.com *Camcorder suppliers*

▶ Edinburgh Canal Centre, Baird Road, Ratho, Newbridge, Midlothian, EH28 8RA Tel: 0131-333 1320 Fax: 0131-333 3480

Edinburgh Ceramics, 46 Balcarres Street, Edinburgh, EH10 5JQ Tel: 0131-452 8145 Fax: 0131-452 8145 E-mail: sales@tiles-by-artists.co.uk *Design manufacturers & retailers of ceramic tiles*

▶ Edinburgh Cleaning Services Ltd, Unit 5A, Whitehill Industrial Estate, Dalkeith, Midlothian, EH22 2QB Tel: 0131-660 0220 E-mail: sales@cleanse.uk.com *Carpet, upholstery & curtain cleaning & restoration services*

Edinburgh Designs Ltd, 27 Ratcliffe Terrace, Edinburgh, EH9 1SX Tel: 0131-662 4748 Fax: 0131-662 9156 E-mail: enquiries@edesign.co.uk *Scientific instrument distributors*

Edinburgh Embroidery Services, Unit 11 North Peffer Place, Edinburgh, EH16 4UZ Tel: 0131-621 7222 Fax: 0131-539 7374 E-mail: embroidery@forthsector.org.uk *Industrial embroidery*

▶ Edinburgh Event Production Services, 5/6 Broughton Place Lane, Edinburgh, EH1 3RS Tel: 0131-558 3824 E-mail: eeps@warpro.co.uk *Edinburgh based professional event production & event management company operating throughout Scotland.*

▶ Edinburgh Iron Works, 189 West Main Street, Broxburn, West Lothian, EH52 5LH Tel: (01506) 856334 Fax: (01506) 856334 *Blacksmiths & metal fabricators*

Edinburgh Painting Contractors, 30 Christiemiller Avenue, Edinburgh, EH7 6ST Tel: (0131) 669 4691 Fax: (0131) 669 4691 *Painting contractors*

▶ Edinburgh Plumbing & Drainage Co. Ltd, Unit 4, Fisherrow Industrial Estate, Newhailes Road, Musselburgh, Midlothian, EH21 6RU Tel: 0131-665 9090

Edinburgh Sensors Ltd, 2 Bain Square, Livingston, West Lothian, EH54 7DQ Tel: (01506) 425300 Fax: (01506) 425320 E-mail: sales@edinst.com *Gas centre*

The Edinburgh Smoked Salmon Company 1992 Ltd, 1 Strath View, Dingwall Business Park, Dingwall, Ross-Shire, IV15 9XD Tel: (01349) 860600 Fax: (01349) 840606 E-mail: essco@jwsaefoods.co.uk *Smoked salmon*

Edinburgh Solutions, 6 York Place, Basement Flat 2, Edinburgh, EH1 3EP Tel: 0131-557 1001 E-mail: graeme.thomas-green@virgin.net *Computer productivity consultants*

▶ Edison Consultancy, PO Box 6479, Brackley, Northamptonshire, NN13 5YU Tel: 01280 841500 E-mail: work@edison-consultancy.com *Edison Consultancy is a specialist recruitment consultancy, dealing with Productivity, Change, Re-engineering, Work Measurement, Industrial Engineering, Project Management and Programme Management vacancies. We deal wwith permanent and contract or temporary staff*

Edit, Unit 13 Govan Workspace, 6 Harmony Row, Glasgow, G51 3BA Tel: 0141-445 4847 Fax: 0141-445 4463 E-mail: info@edit-ltd.com *Document management, scanning services*

▶ Editorial Excellence, 29 Ewlyn Road, Cheltenham, Gloucestershire, GL53 7PB Tel: (01242) 576451 Fax: (01242) 576451 E-mail: andrea@editorialexcellence-ad.co.uk *Editorial Excellence offers editorial and copywriting services, as well as PR and media relations. Editorial services include writing, editing, proofreading and writing, editing and designing newsletters. Director Andrea Darby*

continued

has more than 15 years" experience in journalism and media relations.

Editt Group, 2 White Hart Fold, Todmorden, Lancashire, OL14 7BD Tel: (01706) 818271 Fax: (01706) 818271 *Computer consultants*

▶ Edivorp Ltd, 4 Bowland Rise, Chandlers Ford, Chandler's Ford, Eastleigh, Hampshire, SO53 4QW Tel: (023) 8025 2600 E-mail: enquiries@edivorp.co.uk *Edivorp provides supply chain and procurement solutions through interim management and consultancy. Also specialists in strategic planning, project management and process improvements.*

▶ EDL Group, Little Braxted Hall, Little Braxted, Witham, Essex, CM8 3EU Tel: (01376) 518840 Fax: (01376) 518860 E-mail: asbestos@edlgroup.com *Asbestos on line meets all current regulations. Asbestos surveys can be carried out using PDA's with Asbestos Template for uploading on to Asbestos Online.*

William Edleston, Moorbrook Mills, New Mill, Holmfirth, HD9 1JZ Tel: (01484) 690600 Fax: (01484) 690601 E-mail: email@william-edleston.co.uk *Fine hair accessories & piece goods*

Edlon, Riverside, Leven, Fife, KY8 4RT Tel: (01333) 426222 Fax: (01333) 426314 E-mail: sales@edlon.co.uk *PTFE fabricators & services*

Edm, Daisyfield Business Centre, Appleby Street, Blackburn, BB1 3BL Tel: (01254) 722033 Fax: (01254) 583003 *Computer system consultants*

EDM Ltd, Brunel House, 1 Thorp Road, Newton Heath, Manchester, M40 5BJ Tel: 0161-203 3150 Fax: 0161-202 2500 E-mail: reception@edm.ltd.uk *Model makers, museum designers & simulators*

Edm Ceco Holdings Ltd, 1 Carryduff Business Park, Comber Road, Carryduff, Belfast, BT8 8AN Tel: (028) 9081 5303 Fax: (028) 9081 5449 E-mail: sales@edmspanwall.com *Manufacturing company*

Edme Ltd, Edme House, High Street, Mistley, Manningtree, Essex, CO11 1HG Tel: (01206) 393725 Fax: (01206) 396699 E-mail: info@edme.com Sales Contact: S. Clayton-Bovill Principal Export Areas: Worldwide *Bakers' ingredient/prepared material producers/ suppliers. Also manufacturers of bakery mixes & concentrates supplied through wholesalers for the small user*

Edmiston & Mitchells, Haypark Business Centre, Marchmont Avenue, Polmont, Falkirk, FK2 0NZ Tel: (01324) 718728 Fax: (01324) 718738 E-mail: edmitch@compuserve.com *Timber plywood agents*

Edmo, Netherton Road, Overross Industrial Estate, Ross-on-Wye, Herefordshire, HR9 7QQ Tel: (01989) 564215 Fax: (01989) 564644 E-mail: sales@edmoengineering.co.uk *Powder coating services*

Edmo, Netherton Road, Overross Industrial Estate, Ross-on-Wye, Herefordshire, HR9 7QQ Tel: (01989) 564215 Fax: (01989) 564644 E-mail: sales@edmoengineering.co.uk Principal Export Areas: Africa *Aluminum fabricators*

Edmond Shipway & Partners, 42 Frederick Rd, Edgbaston, Birmingham, B15 1HN Tel: 0121-454 3515 Fax: 0121-454 3241 E-mail: edmond@shipway.co.uk *Quantity surveyors & project management consultants* Also at: Branches throughout the U.K.

▶ Edmonds Cabinet Makers, Edmonds Cabinet Makers, Buscott Farm, Ashcott, Bridgwater, Somerset, TA7 9QP Tel: 01458 210359 Fax: 01458 211005 E-mail: info@edmondscabinetmakers.co.uk *Edmonds Cabinet Makers specialise in high quality bespoke carpentry. We make cabinets, beds, chests, panelling, lynhays, tables, staircases, conservatories, carts, doors, windows and even candlesticks.*

Edmont Joinery Ltd, Hyde Road, Swindon, SN2 7RB Tel: (01793) 825765 Fax: (01793) 825725 E-mail: admin@edmont.co.uk *Joinery fitters & furnishers*

Edmonton Machines Ltd, Units 14-15, Great Cambridge Industrial Estate, Enfield, Middlesex, EN1 1SH Tel: (020) 8344 4777 Fax: (020) 8344 4700 *Amusement machines repairs service*

▶ EDMS Ltd, Suite 2, 135 London Road, Sevenoaks, Kent, TN13 1UP Tel: (01732) 455100 Fax: (01732) 742574 E-mail: brian.mudge@edms.eu.com *EDMS (European Data Management Services) provides Consultancy and Distribution facilities for VAS, VPN-IP, VOIP, Voice,WLAN, Satellite, Microwave, WLL, Wi-Fi, Broadband plus many other disciplines in the Telecommunication spectrum*

▶ Edmund Nuttall Ltd, Cambrian Buildings, Mount Stuart Square, Cardiff, CF10 5FL Tel: (029) 2046 2838 Fax: (029) 2048 9946

▶ Edmund Nuttall Ltd, Allbrook Depot, Allbrook Hill, Eastleigh, Hampshire, SO50 4LY Tel: (023) 8061 1333 Fax: (023) 8062 9186

▶ Edmund Nuttall Ltd, Glasgow Road, Kilsyth, Glasgow, G65 9BL Tel: (01236) 467050 Fax: (01236) 467072 *Metals & chemicals*

▶ Edmund Nuttall Ltd, Tenacre Court, Ashford Road, Harrietsham, Maidstone, Kent, ME17 1AH Tel: (01622) 852000 Fax: (01622) 851600

▶ Edmund Nuttall Ltd, 1 Eagle House, Asama Court, Newcastle Business Park, Newcastle upon Tyne, NE4 7LN Tel: 0191-273 7000 Fax: 0191-273 7002

Edmund Robson & Co Ltd, West Side, Tyne Dock, South Shields, Tyne & Wear, NE34 9PJ Tel: 0191-489 8134 Fax: 0191-489 0696 E-mail: timber@edmundrobson.co.uk *Timber merchants & importers*

▶ Edmunds Designs Ltd, 12 Wyndham Terrace, Risca, Newport, Gwent, NP11 6QN Tel: (01633) 264323 E-mail: wayne@edmunds-designs.co.uk *Engineering design prototype manufrs*

John Edmunds, Buscott Farm, 23 Station Road, Ashcott, Bridgwater, Somerset, TA7 9QP Tel: (01458) 210359 *Cabinet makers*

▶ Edmunds Webster Ltd, 2 Quarry Road, Treboeth, Swansea, SA5 9DJ Tel: (01792) 772475 Fax: (01792) 781652

Wilfred Edmunds Ltd, 37 Station Road, Chesterfield, Derbyshire, S41 7XD Tel: (01246) 504500 Fax: (01246) 504580 E-mail: editorial@derbyshiretimes.co.uk *Newspaper group*

Edmundson Electrical Ltd, 6 Springlakes Estate, Deadbrook Lane, Aldershot, Hampshire, GU12 4UH Tel: (01252) 343443 Fax: (01252) 328104 *Electrical wholesaler* Also at: Branches throughout the U.K.

▶ Edmundson Electrical Ltd, Hubert Road, Brentwood, Essex, CM14 4QQ Tel: (01277) 221338 Fax: (01277) 263531

Edmundson Electrical Ltd, 15 Lister Lane, Halifax, West Yorkshire, HX1 5AS Tel: (01422) 359428 Fax: (01422) 330291 E-mail: halifax.139@eel.co.uk *Electrical products suppliers*

Edmundson Electrical Ltd, 2 Portland Road Industrial Estate, Portland Road, Hove, East Sussex, BN3 5NT Tel: (01273) 430789 Fax: (01273) 430650 E-mail: brighton.122@eel.co.uk *Electrical wholesalers* Also at: St. Albans

Edmundson Electrical Ltd, 2 Bilton Way, Luton, LU1 1UU Tel: (01582) 728811 Fax: (01582) 418508 E-mail: luton.015@eel.co.uk *Electrical equipment suppliers*

Edmundson Electrical Ltd, 31C Ganton Way, Techno Trading Estate, Swindon, SN2 8ES Tel: (01793) 522241 Fax: (01793) 524504 E-mail: swindon.274@eel.co.uk *Control products distributors*

Edmundson Export Services, Unit 1 Skyport Drive, Harmondsworth, West Drayton, Middlesex, UB7 0LB Tel: (020) 8283 0820 Fax: (020) 8283 0821 E-mail: enquiries@edmundsonexport.com *Export of electrical equipment*

Edmundson Rickards Electrical, 30 Garrett Road, Lynx Trading Estate, Yeovil, Somerset, BA20 2TJ Tel: (01935) 472727 Fax: (01935) 472010 E-mail: mail@spectrumelectrical.co.uk *Electrical contractors*

Edmundson Rickards Electrical, 30 Garrett Road, Lynx Trading Estate, Yeovil, Somerset, BA20 2TJ Tel: (01935) 472727 Fax: (01935) 472010 E-mail: mail@spectrumelectrical.co.uk *Electrical & industrial contractors*

Edn Insurance Services Ltd, Standeven House, 27 Union Street, Oldham, OL1 1XS Tel: 0161-624 3801 Fax: 0161-627 4045 E-mail: enquiries@edaviesnorthern.freeserve.co.uk *Insurance brokers*

Edo MBM Technology Ltd, Emblem House, Home Farm Business Park, Brighton, BN1 9HU Tel: (01273) 810500 Fax: (01273) 810565 E-mail: info@edombmtech.co.uk *Manufacture & design*

Edoni Refrigeration Ltd, 100 Strathmore Road, Glasgow, G22 7TS Tel: 0141-336 7641 Fax: 0141-336 5302 *Ice cream*

Edos Microfilm, Audit Drive, Abingdon, Oxfordshire, OX14 3NJ Tel: (01235) 550505 Fax: (01235) 536719 E-mail: enquiries@edos.co.uk *Scanning bureau*

▶ Edotek Ltd, Silver Birches Water Lane, Fewcott, Bicester, Oxfordshire, OX27 7NX Tel: (01869) 345386 Fax: 0871 243 9813 E-mail: info@edotek.co.uk *Edotek is a scientific consultancy specialising in chemical and materials technology. We can advise on the selection of materials for particular applications, perform laboratory testing and failure analysis. Existing Clients include the UK Ministry of Defence and the European Space Agency.*

▶ Edp Consulting Engineers, Munro House, Quarrywood Court, Livingston, West Lothian, EH54 6AX Tel: (01506) 497200 Fax: (01506) 497949

▶ Edrington Distillers, Muirhall, West Calder, West Lothian, EH55 8NT Tel: (01506) 873433 Fax: (01506) 873438

▶ Edryd Jenkins, Units 43-44, Glan Yr Afon Industrial Estate, Llanbadarn Fawr, Aberystwyth, Dyfed, SY23 3JQ Tel: (01970) 626650 Fax: (01970) 611112

Eds, 4 Roundwood Avenue, Stockley, Uxbridge, Middlesex, UB11 1BQ Tel: (020) 8848 8989 Fax: (020) 8535 3484 E-mail: info@eds.com *Computer systems & services* Also at: Branches throughout the U.K.

▶ Ed's Beds, 26A Front Street, Framwellgate Moor, Durham, DH1 5EJ Tel: 0191-375 7275 Fax: 0191-375 7275 *Bed & bedroom furniture suppliers*

▶ EDS Global Field Services, D I A N House, 2 Aegean Road, Atlantic Street, Altrincham, Cheshire, WA14 5UW Tel: 0161-929 7889 Fax: (0870) 6067491

Edscha (U K) Manufacturing Ltd, Middlemarch Business Park, Coventry, CV3 4FJ Tel: (024) 7651 6900 Fax: (024) 7630 2299 E-mail: enquiries@edscha.co.uk *Automotive hinges & convertible roofs manufrs*

EDSCO, 118 Featherbed Lane, Hillmorton, Rugby, Warwickshire, CV21 4LQ Tel: 01788 331530 Fax: 01788 336858 E-mail: e.scholey@ntlworld.com *Cleaning & janitorial supplies*

Edsol Ltd, Edsol House, Meanwood Road, Buslingthorpe Green, Leeds, LS7 2HG Tel: 0113-262 1122 Fax: 0113-262 3957 E-mail: info@edwardsofleeds.com *Manufacturers of disposable paper products & table stationary*

Edson Electronics Ltd, Unit 2, Coquet Enterprise Park, Amble, Morpeth, Northumberland, NE65 0RB Tel: (01665) 710393 Fax: (01665) 711021 E-mail: sales@edsonelectronics.co.uk *Consumable products to the electronics industries*

Edson Machinery Co. Ltd, Unit 5 Snowhill Business Centre, Snow Hill, Copthorne, Crawley, West Sussex, RH10 3EZ Tel: (01342) 719719 Fax: (01342) 719718 E-mail: sales@edson.co.uk *Coil winding machine suppliers*

▶ The Education Furniture Co. Ltd, Education House, 22A Cobbet Road, Burntwood, Staffordshire, WS7 3GL Tel: (01543) 495086 Fax: (01543) 495089 *Educational equipment supplies*

▶ The Education Shop, Meekings Road, Sudbury, Suffolk, CO10 2XE Tel: (01787) 466207 Fax: (01787) 312302 E-mail: sales@the-education-shop.co.uk *Retailers of educational dice, counters, movers & pattern blocks*

Educational Co. Ltd, 47-49 Queen Street, Belfast, BT1 6HP Tel: (028) 9032 4687 Fax: (028) 9043 8115 E-mail: theshop@edco.co.uk *Educational supplies*

Educational Co. Ltd, High Park House, 54 Mallusk Road, Newtownabbey, County Antrim, BT36 4WU Tel: (028) 9084 4023 Fax: (028) 9084 0705 *Art & educational equipment suppliers*

Educational Aids (London) Ltd, 25 Bradfield Close, Finedon Road Industrial Estate, Wellingborough, Northamptonshire, NN8 4RQ Tel: (01933) 274434 Fax: (01933) 274313 E-mail: edaids@aol.com *School equipment supplies*

Educational Furniture Manufacturers, Pottery Lane West, Chesterfield, Derbyshire, S41 9BN Tel: (01246) 455191 Fax: (01246) 456506 E-mail: sales@efmchesterfield.co.uk *Educational furniture manufacture*

Educational & Municipal Equipment Scotland, Blackaddie Road, Sanquhar, Dumfriesshire, DG4 6DE Tel: (01659) 50404 Fax: (01659) 50107 E-mail: sales@emescotland.co.uk *Educational & office furniture suppliers*

▶ Educational Printing Services Ltd, Albion Mill, Water Street, Great Harwood, Blackburn, BB6 7QR Tel: (01254) 882080 Fax: (01254) 882010

Educational & Scientific Products Ltd, Unit A2 Dominion Way, Rustington, Littlehampton, West Sussex, BN16 3HQ Tel: (01903) 773340 Fax: (01903) 771108 E-mail: sales@espmodels.co.uk *Educational aids manufrs*

Educational Technology Ltd, Locomotion Way, Camperdown Industrial Estate, Newcastle upon Tyne, NE12 5US Tel: 0191-268 2222 Fax: 0191-268 1137 E-mail: sales@edtech.co.uk *Educational equipment suppliers*

Edulan Ltd, Unit M North Stage, 92 Broadway, Salford, M50 2UW Tel: 0161-876 8040 Fax: 0161-876 8041 E-mail: sales@edulan.com *Plastic foam production machinery & equipment, polyurethane foam raw materials, polyurethane foam structural/insulating systems & packaging material/goods products manufrs*

▶ Edvic Ltd, 9a Burrell Way, Thetford, Norfolk, IP24 3RW Tel: (01842) 754333 Fax: (01842) 754411 *Timber products*

Edw Controls, Birch Park, Huntington Road, York, YO31 9BL Tel: (01904) 643908 Fax: (01904) 623494 E-mail: info@edwcontrols.co.uk *Electronics design & manufrs*

Edward Drummond & Co Ltd., Westpoint 78 Queens Road, Clifton, Bristol, BS8 1QX Tel: 0117 9858755 E-mail: info@edwarddrummond.com

▶ Edward Duckett & Son, Milnthorpe Road, Holme, Carnforth, Lancashire, LA6 1PS Tel: (01524) 781232 Fax: (01524) 782353 E-mail: office@duckett.ltd.uk *Manufacturers of joinery products*

Edward Foster & Son Bradford Ltd, Benton House, Nelson Street, Bradford, West Yorkshire, BD5 0DP Tel: (01274) 733511 Fax: (01274) 730227 *Plumbers merchants*

Edward Green & Co., Cliftonville Road, Northampton, NN1 5BU Tel: (01604) 626880 Fax: (01604) 626889 E-mail: enquiries@edwardgreen.com Principal Export Areas: Worldwide *Boots & shoe manufrs*

Edward Henthorne & Co Ltd, 10-20 Chorley Road, Blackpool, FY3 7XQ Tel: (01253) 300006 Fax: (01253) 399969 E-mail: edwardhenthorne@aol.com *Building merchants*

Edward J Bows, South View, Oxhill, Warwick, CV35 0QU Tel: (01295) 680771 Fax: (01295) 688191 E-mail: 100127.1650@compuserve.com *Management consultants*

Edward J Wood & Co Printers Ltd, 31-37 Rosslyn Cresent, Harrow, Middlesex, HA1 2SA Tel: (020) 8427 6418 Fax: (020) 8861 2126 E-mail: jonengland@compuserve.com *Carton printing services, carton, cardboard box, case, container manufrs*

▶ Edward Mackay Ltd, Rosslyn Yard, Rosslyn Street, Brora, Sutherland, KW9 6NY Tel: (01408) 621223

Edward Robert Saddlery Ltd, 10 Berkeley Close, Moor Lane, Staines, Middlesex, TW19 6ED Tel: (01784) 460248 *Saddlery manufrs*

▶ Edward Sinclair By Mail Order, 9A Farncombe Street, Farncombe, Godalming, Surrey, GU7 3BA Tel: (01483) 860270 E-mail: sales@edwardsinclair.co.uk *Printers*

Edward Thompson International Ltd, Richmond Street, Sheepfolds Industrial Estate, Sunderland, SR5 1BQ Tel: 0191-514 4199 Fax: 0191-567 7510 E-mail: info@edward-thompson.com *Printers*

Edward Turner & Son Ltd, The Limes, 14 Crowgate, South Anston, Sheffield, S25 5AL Tel: (01909) 550097 Fax: (01909) 560544 *Manufacturers of industrial knives*

Edward W Mason Ltd, 14 Brownfields, Welwyn Garden City, Hertfordshire, AL7 1AN Tel: (01707) 331911 Fax: (01707) 331911 E-mail: craig@masonsbrushes.fsbusiness.co.uk *Specialist brush manufrs*

Edwardian Bedding Co., 44 Bank Street, Mexborough, South Yorkshire, S64 9LL Tel: (01709) 589673 Fax: (01709) 589673 *Bed mantel retailers & manufrs*

Edwards, Strathmore Avenue, Luton, LU1 3NZ Tel: (01582) 730256 Fax: (01582) 730256 *Removal & storage contractor*

Edwards' Analytical, Rose Cottage, Walker Hall, Winston, Darlington, County Durham, DL2 3PN Tel: (01325) 730766 Fax: (01325) 730911 E-mail: davidjhe@aol.com *Analysis of plastics & packaging* Also at: Durham

Edwards Brighouse Ltd, Vine Industrial Estate, Elland Road, Brookfoot, Brighouse, West Yorkshire, HD6 2QS Tel: (01484) 713335 Fax: (01484) 713335

continued

E-mail: sales@edwardstowbars.co.uk *Towing equipment fitting services & suppliers*

Edwards Bros, Unit J1 Dominion Way, Rustington, Littlehampton, West Sussex, BN16 3HQ Tel: (01903) 787184 Fax: (01903) 787184 *Precision engineers*

Edwards Buildbase, 28 Elm Road, Wisbech, Cambridgeshire, PE13 2TB Tel: (01945) 584491 Fax: (01945) 475121 E-mail: wisbeck@billbase.co.uk *Buildbase is one of the UK's fastest growing builders merchants. All of our branches are long established companies which have been serving local trades people for many years, with knowledge and experience to match. We believe strongly in understanding the needs of trades professional and our business has been developed specifically to meet those demands. Massive stocks, top quality products, competitive pricing, reliable delivery, specialist staff and exceptional customer service.*

Edwards Building Services Ltd, Craig Lelo Works, Bryn Saith Marchog, Corwen, Clwyd, LL21 9RY Tel: (01824) 750400 Fax: (01824) 750403 E-mail: info@craiglelo.co.uk *Prefabricated buildings*

▶ D.J. Edwards, Boduan, Pwllheli, Gwynedd, LL53 6DT Tel: (01758) 720815 Fax: (01758) 720881 *Agricultural merchants & animal feeds*

Edwards & Edwards Ltd, 385 Holywood Road, Belfast, BT4 2LS Tel: (028) 9047 1727 Fax: (028) 9047 1153 E-mail: sales@edwardsandedwards.co.uk *Wholesale electrical dealers*

Edwards Elite Engineering Ltd, 8 Dunkirk Trading Estate, Bypass Road, Dunkirk, Chester, CH1 6LZ Tel: (01244) 851311 Fax: (01244) 851411 E-mail: stuartedwards@btconnect.com *Pipework contractors*

Edwards Engineering (Liverpool) Ltd, Lipton Close, St. Johns Road, Brasenose Industrial Estate, Bootle, Merseyside, L20 8PU Tel: 0151-933 5242 Fax: 0151-922 3383 E-mail: edseng@edwardsenglpoolltd.freeserve.co.uk *Gravure printing cylinder manufrs*

Edwards Engineering (Perth) Ltd, Glenearn Road, Perth, PH2 0NJ Tel: (01738) 627101 Fax: (01738) 630769 E-mail: mail@edwardsengineering.co.uk *General engineers*

Edwards Excavations Ltd, 6 Woodman Works, South Lane, Elland, West Yorkshire, HX5 0PA Tel: (01422) 377829 Fax: (01422) 310082 *Excavation contractors*

Edwards & Farmer Ltd, Chatford, Bayston Hill, Shrewsbury, SY3 0AY Tel: (01743) 658669 Fax: (01743) 718126 *Agricultural engineers*

Edwards & Farndon, Lower Dartmouth Street, Birmingham, B9 4LG Tel: 0121-766 6255 Fax: 0121-766 8875 *Building & plumbing suppliers*

Edwards, Glyn Office Equipment Ltd, 4 Charles Street, Milford Haven, Dyfed, SA73 2AJ Tel: (01646) 698833 Fax: (01646) 698837 E-mail: mark@gedwards-office.demon.co.uk *Office equipment dealers & stationers*

Edwards & Godding Reading Ltd, 9d Loverock Road, Reading, RG30 1DZ Tel: 0118-939 3046 Fax: 0118-959 0294 E-mail: aga@edgod.globalnet.co.uk *Aga cooker suppliers*

Gordon Edwards & Sons, Fferm, Llanfwrog, Ruthin, Clwyd, LL15 2DB Tel: (01824) 702822 Fax: (01824) 702822 E-mail: edwfferm1@freeserve.co.uk *Farmers & cattle dealers*

H.N. Edwards & Partners Ltd, Field House Barn, Chineham Lane, Sherborne St. John, Basingstoke, Hampshire, RG24 9LR Tel: (01256) 473601 Fax: (01256) 841402 E-mail: bdd@hnep.co.uk *Building contractors*

▶ Edwards & Hampson Ltd, 194 Rimrose Road, Bootle, Merseyside, L20 4QS Tel: 0151-922 9122 Fax: 0151-922 4127 *Joinery contractors*

Edwards & Hope, 5 New Road, Brighton, BN1 1UF Tel: (01273) 775166 Fax: (01273) 746610 *Electrical suppliers* Also at: Worthing

Ian Edwards, The Old Chapel, 282 Skipton Road, Harrogate, North Yorkshire, HG1 3HE Tel: (01423) 500442 Fax: (01423) 705200 E-mail: enquiries@iansbespokefurniture.co.uk *Cabinet manufrs*

J. & M. Edwards Precision Engineers Ltd, Lefevre Way, Gapton Hall Industrial Estate, Great Yarmouth, Norfolk, NR31 0NW Tel: (01493) 604312 Fax: (01493) 655719 E-mail: sales@jmedwards.co.uk *Sheet metal & precision engineers*

Edwards Jeffery, Unit 57, The Enterprise Centre, Bridgend, Mid Glamorgan, CF32 9BS Tel: (0870) 2424 662 Fax: (0870) 2424 663 E-mail: enquiries@edwardsjeffery.co.uk *Edwards Jeffery is the UK's leading automotive recruitment consultancy. We recruit across a number of disciplines, which include UK & Export Sales Management, Marketing & Product Management, Branch, Logistics & Operational Staff through to Engineering and Manufacturing. Whether you are a client or a candidate, our emphasis is placed on working closely with you at every stage of the recruitment process to ensure your long-term goals are achieved. Our success is due to an ability to deliver a cost effective and high quality service, allied to our personal knowledge of the automotive industry.*

John Edwards Refrigeration, 4 Portland Grange, Hucknall, Nottingham, NG15 6RS Tel: 0115-963 5257 *Refrigeration services*

Edwards Logisitcs, PO Box 107, Hull, HU5 4JJ Tel: (01482) 492194 Fax: (01482) 473620 E-mail: info@edwards-logistics.com *Road transport, haulage & freight services*

▶ Edwards Logistics Ltd, Unit 5, James Street, Righead Industrial Estate, Bellshill, Lanarkshire, ML4 3LU Tel: (01698) 849977

Lyndon Edwards Ltd, Marlers, Pye Corner, Gilston, Harlow, Essex, CM20 2RD Tel: (01279) 414801 Fax: (01279) 450736 *Specialist plant & machinery removals*

Edwards Metals Ltd, Unit 37 Birch Road East Industrial Estate, Birch Road East, Birmingham, B6 7DA Tel: 0121-322 2366 Fax: 0121-326 9369 *Non-ferrous metal stockholders*

Edwards Modular Controls Ltd, 25 Freehold Terrace, Brighton, BN2 4AB Tel: (01273) 688285 Fax: (01273) 570657 E-mail: sales@emc4controls.co.uk *Control panels to specification*

Edwards Office Furniture, Twentypence Road, Cottenham, Cambridge, CB4 8PS Tel: (01954) 250949 Fax: (01954) 250949 *Office furniture manufrs*

Edwards Of Oldham Ltd, Shaw Road, Royton, Oldham, OL2 6EF Tel: 0161-665 2001 Fax: 0161-624 9300 *Service & recondition catering equipment*

Patrick Edwards, Langley Farm, Langley Lane, Little Clanfield, Bampton, Oxfordshire, OX18 2RZ Tel: (01367) 810259 Fax: (01367) 810545 *Agricultural*

▶ Edwards Photography, 16 The Vale, London, W3 7SB Tel: (020) 8749 8887 E-mail: studio@edwardsphotography.co.uk *Catalogue photography specialists*

▶ Edwards Photography, 16 The Vale, London, W3 7SB Tel: (020) 8749 8887 Fax: E-mail: studio@edwardsphotography.co.uk *Photography*

Edwards Precision Engineering Ltd, 173-179 Tyburn Road, Erdington, Birmingham, B24 8NQ Tel: 0121-327 7828 Fax: 0121-327 7987 E-mail: enquiries@edwards-precision.co.uk *Precision engineers*

Edwards Product, 2 Birkbeck Road, Beckenham, Kent, BR3 4SN Tel: (020) 8778 0918 Fax: (020) 8778 0918 *Kitchen & bedroom manufrs*

R. & K. Edwards Co. Ltd, 21 St. James Parade, Bath, BA1 1UL Tel: (01225) 421255 Fax: (01225) 469900 *Amusement machine distribs*

Richard Edwards Fabrications Ltd, 15 Broadfield Close, Croydon, CR0 4XR Tel: (020) 8686 8616 Fax: (020) 8686 5313 *We specialise in steel supports and fixings to the building and construction industry. We are able to provide Steel fabrications to your specifications.*

▶ Edwards Roofing, 1 Jacksonville Farm, Towyn Way West, Towyn, Abergele, Clwyd, LL22 9LG Tel: (01745) 339411 Fax: (01745) 369232 E-mail: sales@edwards-roofing.co.uk

Edwards S M Building Contractors, 77 Old Coach Road, Kelsall, Tarporley, Cheshire, CW6 0RA Tel: (01829) 752028 Fax: (01829) 751559 *Building maintenance services*

Edwards Sports Products Ltd, Unit 8 & 9 Hounsell Building, North Mills, Bridport, Dorset, DT6 3BE Tel: (01308) 424111 Fax: (01308) 455800 E-mail: sales@edsports.co.uk *Sports netting & posts equipment manufrs*

Steven Edwards Engineering Ltd, 3A Linden Road, Dunstable, Bedfordshire, LU5 4NZ Tel: (01582) 609411 Fax: (01582) 609411 E-mail: steven.edwards347@ntlworld.com *Platform repairing services*

Edwin Blyde & Co. Ltd, Little London Road, Sheffield, S8 0UH Tel: 0114-249 1930 Fax: 0114-249 1950 E-mail: pewter@edwinblyde.co.uk *Renowned manufacturers of quality pewterware, Edwin Blyde (established 1798) have one of the finest ranges of designed & crafted giftware. Edwin Blyde is ones of the largest manufacturers of pewterware supplying leading jewellers, department stores & gift shops worldwide. All the products are made by skilled craftsmen trained by the company*

Edwin Clarke, Francis House, George Street, Lincoln, LN5 8LG Tel: (01522) 530912 Fax: (01522) 510929 *Metal staircase manufrs*

Edwin Woodhouse & Co. Ltd, Unit 2a Sunnybank Mills, 83-85 Town Street, Farsley, Pudsey, West Yorkshire, LS28 5UJ Tel: 0113-257 4331 Fax: 0113-239 3228 E-mail: sales@edwin-woodhouse.co.uk *Worsted manufrs*

Eel Pie Island Slipways Ltd, Eel Pie Island, Twickenham, TW1 3DY Tel: (020) 8891 4481 Fax: (020) 8891 4481 *Boat builders & repairers*

Eemech Ltd, Unit 1 Kenn Court Business Park, Roman Farm Road, Bristol, BS4 1UL Tel: 0117-964 4497 Fax: 0117-964 4487 E-mail: eemech@hotmail.com *Mechanical electrical maintenance engineers*

Ees Engineering Ltd, Sheddingdean Industrial Estate, Marchants Way, Burgess Hill, West Sussex, RH15 8QY Tel: (01444) 244733 Fax: (01444) 236939 *Precision engineers & precision turned parts manufrs*

▶ EESSIS, 1 Wellgreen, Killearn, Glasgow, G63 9RT Tel: (01360) 449468 Fax: (0871) 9940715 E-mail: info@eessis.co.uk *Computer services*

Eet UK, Unit 4 Service Road, Cornwall Road, Pinner, Middlesex, HA5 4UH Tel: (020) 8421 0101 Fax: (020) 8421 3364 E-mail: sales@romtronics.co.uk *Computer parts resellers*

E-Exchange Ltd, 32 Ludgate Hill, London, EC4M 7DR Tel: 020 72486060 Fax: 020 72486060 *Computer software systems*

▶ EEZY Business Services, Great Brook Park, 69 Brook Lane, Warsash, SOuthampton, SO31 9FF Tel: (0845) 6442571 Fax: (07092) 047281 E-mail: ray@eezy.co.uk *Online, fax or email payroll services, Computer Disaster Recovery, Backup and Restore, Website Design*

▶ Efamol Ltd, Unit 14, Mole Business Park, Randalls Road, Leatherhead, Surrey, KT22 7BA Tel: (01372) 379828 Fax: (01372) 376599 E-mail: vitamins@wassen.com *Food supplements suppliers*

Efco Group Ltd, 29 Avro Way, Brooklands Business Park, Weybridge, Surrey, KT13 0YZ Tel: (01932) 350534 Fax: (01932) 350543 Principal Export Areas: Worldwide *Furnace consultants or designers*

Effectech Ltd, Dovefields Road, Dovefields Industrial Estate, Uttoxeter, Staffordshire, ST14 8HU Tel: (01889) 569220 Fax: (01889) 569220 E-mail: sharon.foster@effectech.co.uk *Specialists in gas measurement technology*

▶ Effectivate Ltd., Brinkworth House, Brinkworth, Swindon, SN15 5DF Tel: 0870 1993867 Fax: 07005 801602 E-mail: info@effectivate.co.uk *Effectivate can help increase the effectiveness of the HR departments recruitment programs. Offering a*

continued

continuation
wide range of training and consulting services, and now the revolutionary pre-employment assessment platform 'SavvyRecruiter', it provides a range of products and services to enable companies of all sizes turn each one of their employees into a star performer.

Effective Case Management Ltd, The Depository, Lewes Road, Lindfield, Haywards Heath, West Sussex, RH16 2LE Tel: (01444) 483968 Fax: (01444) 484852 E-mail: sales@casedocs.co.uk *Document scanning & image management services*

Effective Multimedia, 1107 Evesham Road, Astwood Bank, Redditch, Worcestershire, B96 6EB Tel: (01527) 892394 E-mail: sales@effectivemultimedia.co.uk *Multimedia services, web design & CD-Rom*

Effective Presentations & Events Ltd, Viking Court, Shepshed Road, Hathern, Loughborough, Leicestershire, LE12 5LZ Tel: (01509) 844444 Fax: (01509) 844104 E-mail: enquiries@thepresentationgroup.co.uk *Conference production company*

▶ Effective Screen & Photographic, 11 Malborough Way, Yardley Gobion, Towcester, Northamptonshire, NN12 7TU Tel: (01908) 543547 Fax: 01908 542536 *Sign manufrs*

Effective Screen & Photographic, 11 Malborough Way, Yardley Gobion, Towcester, Northamptonshire, NN12 7TU Tel: (01908) 543547 E-mail: 40quatro@tesco.net *Screen printers & sign writers*

Effective Solutions For Business, Acquest Ho, 183 Kingston Rd, London, SW19 1LH Tel: (020) 8395 6472 Fax: (020) 8241 2502 E-mail: sales@effects.co.uk *Computer consultants*

▶ Effectual Storage Services, 5 Benfield Way, Braintree, Essex, CM7 3YS Tel: (01376) 551234 Fax: (01376) 551515 E-mail: sales@effectualstorage.co.uk *Product procurement & sourcing specialists*

▶ EFFICENS RESOURCING LTD, EFFICENS HOUSE, 25 DENBROOK AVENUE, TONG, BRADFORD, WEST YORKSHIRE, BD4 0QJ Tel: 01274 681762 E-mail: career.management@efficens-resourcing.co.uk *Efficens Resourcing Ltd is a national and international Search and Selection Recruitment Consultancy specialising in the recruitment of sales and marketing, manufacturing, production, operations, supply chain, engineering and technical roles. These take in many disciplines and levels ranging from administrative support, through manufacturing and engineering positions to senior boardroom appointments across these and other market sectors.*Our ethos is simple; attract, retain and develop the very best people for our clients' businesses in a timely and efficient manner, at a cost effective and competitive price.***POUR NOTRE CLIENTS FRANCAIS.*Si peut-etre vous avez besoin de recruter quelqu''un en France ou en Angleterre, parlant couramment l''anglais, contactez-nous pour discuter de votre besoin au numero si-dessous ou visiter notre web.*

Efficiency Print Ltd, Engine Lane, Stourbridge, West Midlands, DY9 7AQ Tel: (01384) 891986 Fax: (01384) 893437 E-mail: colin@effprint.u-net.com *General printers*

Effigy, 4 Station Road, Thames Ditton, Surrey, KT7 0NR Tel: (020) 8972 9779 Fax: (020) 8972 9779 E-mail: info@effigy.uk.com *Design & manufacture of display mannequins*

Effingham Steel Services Ltd, Butterthwaite Lane, Ecclesfield, Sheffield, S35 9WA Tel: 0114-246 8977 Fax: 0114-245 4272 E-mail: sales@effinghamsteel.co.uk *Grinding & metal sawing services*

Effisoft Ltd, 69 King William Street, London, EC4N 7HR Tel: (020) 7626 5166 Fax: (020) 7626 5177 *Software developers*

Effluent Engineering Contracts Ltd, 16 The Promenade, Mayland, Chelmsford, CM3 6AR Tel: (01621) 740729 Fax: (01621) 744033 E-mail: paulbrinson@effluenteng.co.uk *Sewer contractors & drainers*

▶ Effpark Limited, Ground Floor Offices, Haverfield House, 4 Union Place, Worthing, West Sussex, BN11 1LG Tel: 01903 601240 Fax: 01903 601239 E-mail: admin@effpark.co.uk *Import and distribution of Marbo metalisation products including lacquers and bases to the UK.*

Efi Ltd, Little Park Farm, Wootton Bassett, Swindon, SN4 7QW Tel: (01793) 852185 Fax: (01793) 848580 E-mail: sales@jumpershorseline.com *Saddlery wholesales*

▶ Efnarc Building Refurbishment, 99 West Street, Farnham, Surrey, GU9 7EN Tel: (01252) 739147 Fax: (01252) 739140 E-mail: sales@efnarc.org *Represents National Trade Associations and major European manufacturing companies involved in the protection and repair of concrete structures, sprayed concrete and industrial flooring.*

▶ Eft Systems Ltd, 39a Cobden Road, Southport, Merseyside, PR9 7TR Tel: (01704) 229662 Fax: (01704) 505391

Eftec Ltd, Rhigos, Aberdare, Mid Glamorgan, CF44 9UE Tel: (01685) 815400 Fax: (01685) 813997 *Car engineers*

Eftee Metal Bodies Ltd, Glencraig Street, Airdrie, Lanarkshire, ML6 9AS Tel: (01236) 765975 Fax: (01236) 747415 E-mail: mail@efteetmetals.co.uk *Hydraulics & tipping gear installation & manufrs*

▶ EG Coding, 9 Lochans Mill Avenue, Lochans, Stranraer, Wigtownshire, DG9 9BZ Tel: (07979) 692580 Fax: (07092) 870019 E-mail: ellisgaston@hotmail.com *Sales & service of industrial coding*

▶ Eg Technology, 12 Kings Parade, Cambridge, CB2 1SJ Tel: (01223) 710799 Fax: (08707) 877021 E-mail: info@egtechnology.co.uk *eg technology is a product and process development resource that delivers cost-effective engineering problem solving services. We focus on the medical, biosciences, instrumentation and consumer goods industries. The founders, Andrew Ede and Danny Godfrey, have substantial experience of developing products and custom automation solutions for leading companies in these sectors.**eg technology apply this experience to work with smaller companies who require a long term relationship with an outsourced development resource.**

Egan Reid Stationery Co. Ltd, Horsfield Way, Bredbury Park Industrial Estate, Bredbury, Stockport, Cheshire, SK6 2SU Tel: 0161-406 6000 Fax: 0161-406 6591 E-mail: sales@eganreid.co.uk *Commercial stationers*

Egbert H Taylor & Co. Ltd, Oak Park, Rylands Lane, Elmley Lovett, Droitwich, Worcestershire, WR9 0QZ Tel: (01299) 251333 Fax: (01299) 254142 E-mail: custserv@taylor-ch.co.uk *Waste disposal container manufrs*

Egemin UK Ltd, 369 Wellingborough Road, Northampton, NN1 4EU Tel: (01604) 234994 Fax: (01604) 234483E-mail: info@egemin.co.uk Principal Export Areas: Worldwide *Handling equipment, auto guided vehicle & warehouse systems manufrs*

Egerton Consulting Ltd, The Green, Minety, Malmesbury, Wiltshire, SN16 9PL Tel: (01666) 860993 Fax: (0870) 7622911 E-mail: enquiries@egertonconsulting.co.uk *Reliability engineering and statistical analysis consultants, also offering training courses in these areas.*

Egerton Narrow Boats Ltd, Edge Lane, Stretford, Manchester, M32 8HW Tel: 0161-864 1066 Fax: 0161-864 1066 E-mail: sales@egertonnarrowboats.co.uk *Boat repairers*

Johnny Egg, 32 Clarendon Road, Borehamwood, Hertfordshire, WD6 1BJ Tel: (020) 8207 1333 Fax: (020) 8207 1333 E-mail: johnnyegg@ntlworld.com *Contemporary furniture designers & radiator cover manufrs*

Eggar Forrester Group, Rodwell House, Middlesex Street, London, E1 7HJ Tel: (020) 7377 1077 Fax: (020) 7247 2144 *Shipping & ship owners*

Eggbeers Transport Ltd, Greenhill Way, Kingsteignton, Newton Abbot, Devon, TQ12 3SB Tel: (01626) 352562 Fax: (01626) 333119 *Haulage contractors*

Egger Turo Pumps (U.K.) Ltd, Fountain House, Cleeve Road, Leatherhead, Surrey, KT22 7NH Tel: (01372) 377688 Fax: (01372) 373587 E-mail: info.uk@eggerpumps.com *Pump manufrs*

Egger UK Holdings Ltd, Anick Grange Road, Hexham, Northumberland, NE46 4JS Tel: (01434) 602191 Fax: (01434) 605103 E-mail: info@egger.co.uk *Wood based panel manufrs* Also at: Weybridge

Egginton Bros Ltd, 25-31 Allen Street, Sheffield, S3 7AW Tel: 0114-276 6123 Fax: 0114-273 8465 E-mail: steve@eggintongroup.co.uk Principal Export Areas: Worldwide *Specialist manufacturers of sharpening steels & equipment for the food processing industry. In addition, pocket knife manufacturers for a wide variety of uses*

Eggleston Bros Ltd, Centurion Way Business Park, Alfreton Road, Derby, DE21 4AY Tel: (01332) 341536 Fax: (01332) 295715 E-mail: info@egglestonbros.co.uk *Steel stockholders*

Eglen Engravers Ltd, 12 Lord Street, Halifax, West Yorkshire, HX1 5AE Tel: (01422) 365556 Fax: (01422) 365564 E-mail: sales@eglenengravers.co.uk *Machine engraving services*

Eglinton Wood Turners, Mid Lodge Cottage, Eglinton, Irvine, Ayrshire, KA12 8TA Tel: (01294) 558145 Fax: (01294) 558145 *Manufacturer of staircase components & other wood turned items*

Ego Computers Ltd, Salisbury Hall, London Colney, St. Albans, Hertfordshire, AL2 1BU Tel: (01727) 828400 Fax: (01727) 824141 E-mail: rdrinkwater@ego-computers.ltd.uk *Computer manufrs*

▶ Egolight Computer Consultants, 2.2 Queens Bridge Road, Nottingham, NG2 1NB Tel: 0115-986 4555 E-mail: egolight@mac.com *Internet application developers*

Egon Publishers Ltd, Royston Road, Baldock, Hertfordshire, SG7 6NW Tel: (01462) 894498 Fax: (01462) 894660 E-mail: information@egon.co.uk *Publishers*

Egyptair, 296 Regent Street, London, W1B 3PH Tel: (020) 7580 5477 Fax: (020) 7637 4328 E-mail: habib@egyptair.com.eg *Airline agents*

▶ Ehge, 58 Station Approach, South Ruislip, Ruislip, Middlesex, HA4 6SA Tel: (020) 8839 2640 Fax: (020) 8839 2641

▶ Ehl, Unit G2 Morton Park Way, Darlington, County Durham, DL1 4PJ Tel: (01325) 488533 Fax: (01325) 488533 E-mail: info@ehluk.co.uk *Installation, design, maintenance engineers to industry & commerce*

Ehs Roofing, Delta View 2309, 2311 Coventry Road, Sheldon, Birmingham, B26 3PG Tel: 0121-742 5799 Fax: (0845) 6343130 *Industrial roofing & cladding contractors*

Ei WHS, Staveley House, Fort Street, Blackburn, BB1 5EG Tel: (01254) 670261 Fax: (01254) 680832 E-mail: blackburn@eiwhs.co.uk *Electrical, instrumentation & mechanical engineers*

Eibe Play Ltd, Eibe House, Home Farm, A3 By-Pass Road, Hurtmore, Godalming, Surrey, GU8 6AD Tel: (01483) 813834 Fax: (01483) 813851 E-mail: eibe@eibe.co.uk *Playground equipment design manufrs*

▶ Eic Scotland Ltd, Dryden Road, Loanhead, Midlothian, EH20 9LZ Tel: 0131-440 0456 Fax: 0131-440 4546 *Electrical contractors*

▶ E-Id.Co.Uk, 52A Denton Road, Twickenham, TW1 2HQ Tel: (020) 8538 9898 Fax: (020) 8538 9898

Eiffel Steelworks Ltd, Studio 2 D Power Road Studios, 114b Power Road, London, W4 5PY Tel: (020) 8747 5990 Fax: (020) 8747 5991 E-mail: mail@eiffel-uk.co.uk *Steel & glass construction*

Eifionydd Farmers Association Ltd, Station Road, Penygroes, Caernarfon, Gwynedd, LL54 6NW Tel: (01286) 880234 Fax: (01286) 880234 *Agricultural merchants*

Eifionydd Farmers Association Ltd, Station Road, Tywyn, Gwynedd, LL36 9BG Tel: (01654) 710233 Fax: (01654) 712009 *Building merchants*

Eiger Torrance Ltd, 253 Europa Boulevard Westbrook, Westbrook, Warrington, WA5 7TN Tel: (01925) 232455 Fax: (01925) 237767 E-mail: sales@eiger-torrance.com *Chemical & process equipment manufrs*

Eiger (UK) Ltd, Unit 12, Landsdown Industrial Estate, Cheltenham, Gloucestershire, GL51 8PL Tel: (01242) 245678 Fax: (01242) 224643 E-mail: valform@aol.com *Glass fibre moulding manufrs*

Eight By Four Ltd, Eight By Four, 6A Kings Yard, Carpenters Road, London, E15 2HD Tel: (020) 8985 6001 Fax: (020) 8533 5372 E-mail: sales@eightbyfour.co.uk *Furniture Designers & bespoke makers*

▶ Eight Technology, 6 Park Fire Business Centre, Harrier Way, Exeter, EX2 7HU Tel: (0870) 3501888 *Computer systems consultants*

▶ Eikon Creations, 5 Black Lake Industrial Estate, Black Lake, West Bromwich, West Midlands, B70 0PG Tel: 0121-525 6876 Fax: 0121-525 6577 E-mail: sales@eikoncreations.co.uk *Metal furniture manufacturers & distributors*

Eildon Refractories Ltd, 26 Abbotsford Terrace, Darnick, Melrose, Roxburghshire, TD6 9AD Tel: (01896) 823853 Fax: (01896) 823880 *Foundry products supplies*

Eildon Systems, 27 St. Ronans Terrace, Innerleithen, Peeblesshire, EH44 6RB Tel: (01896) 831742 Fax: (01896) 831911

EilisOg Handknits, 11 Stewartstown Avenue, Belfast, BT11 9GE Tel: (028) 9062 3763 Fax: (028) 9062 3763 E-mail: john_savage@hotmail.com *Knitwear merchants*

Eim Northern Ltd, 1 Adcroft Street, Off Higher Hillgate, Stockport, Cheshire, SK1 3HZ Tel: 0161-476 3303 Fax: 0161-476 4010 E-mail: sales@eimnorthern.co.uk *Gas stack monitoring equipment hire distributors*

Eimskip UK Ltd, Middleplatt Road, Immingham, South Humberside, DN40 1AH Tel: (01469) 550200 Fax: (01469) 550394 E-mail: info@eimskip-uk.co.uk *Haulage & freight services*

▶ Einw Ltd, 12a Leicester Road, Blaby, Leicester, LE8 4GQ Tel: 0116-278 7066 Fax: 0116-278 7355 E-mail: sales@einwltd.co.uk

Eip Metals, Rabone Lane, Smethwick, West Midlands, B66 3JH Tel: 0121-555 1199 Fax: 0121-555 1188 E-mail: Purchasing Contact: E. Layton Sales Contact: P. West Principal Export Areas: Worldwide *EIP Metals Ltd is the UK''s largest supplier of precision rolled copper, phosphor bronze and brass strip. First established over 0 years ago, EIP Metals Ltd today has an outstanding reputation for product quality and customer service to our home and export customers. ***

▶ EIS Computing Ltd, Robin Hood Cottage, Epping New Road, Loughton, Essex, IG10 4AA Tel: (020) 8508 3695 Fax: (020) 8508 3695 E-mail: info@eis-computing.co.uk *Computer hardware, software maintenance & support, install networks*

Eiwhs, 1 London Road, Great Shelford, Cambridge, CB22 5DB Tel: (01223) 845776 Fax: (01223) 842910 E-mail: cambridge.eiwhs@staveley.co.uk *Electrical, instrumentation & mechanical engineers*

Eiwhs, 23 Dunlop Way, Queensway Industrial Estate, Scunthorpe, South Humberside, DN16 3RN Tel: (01724) 282328 Fax: (01724) 282321 E-mail: rchallis.eiwhs@staveley.co.uk *Electrical, instrumentation & mechanical engineers services*

Eiwhs, Unit 10, President Buildings Savile St East, Sheffield, S4 7UQ Tel: 0114-275 0012 Fax: 0114-276 1402 E-mail: sheffield.eiwhs@staveley.co.uk *Electrical instrumentation & mechanical engineers*

Eiwhs, 21 Allensway, Thornaby, Stockton-on-Tees, Cleveland, TS17 9HA Tel: (01642) 769085 Fax: (01642) 761137 E-mail: eiwhs.thornaby@staveley.co.uk *Electrical, instrumentation & mechanical engineers*

Ek Machine Tools Ltd, 14 Singer Road, Kelvin Industrial Estate, East Kilbride, Glasgow, G75 0XS Tel: (01355) 234600 Fax: (01355) 265979 E-mail: info@ekomat.co.uk *Lapping services & precision engineers*

Ek Partitions & Ceilings Ltd, 15 Arden Business Centre, Arden Road, Alcester, Warwickshire, B49 6HW Tel: (01789) 400404 Fax: (01789) 400505 E-mail: sales@ekpartitions.com *Demountable partitioning manufrs*

Ekaton Ltd, Jubilee House, Altcar Road, Formby, Liverpool, L37 8DL Tel: (01704) 870107 Fax: (01704) 831269 E-mail: colinmackay@ekaton.ltd.uk *Switchgear manufacturers & refurbishment*

Ekaw Projects Ltd, Link House, Church Street, Haxey, Doncaster, South Yorkshire, DN9 2HY Tel: (01427) 752006 Fax: (01427) 753581 *Buried utilities survey & mapping services & computer services*

Eker & Albert Ltd, 293-295 Old Street, London, EC1V 9LA Tel: (020) 7739 0158 Fax: (020) 7739 7402 *Textile merchants*

▶ Ekhaya Foods Ltd, 66 Potters Lane, Send, Woking, Surrey, GU23 7AL Tel: (01483) 773534 E-mail: info@ekhayafoods.co.uk *Manufacture and supply of quality South African foods and confectionary. Milk Tarts, Koeksisters, Banana Bread, Fudge, Date Dainties.*

▶ e-Kit, Field Cottage, Goadby Marwood, Melton Mowbray, LEICS, LE14 4LW Tel: 01664 464373 E-mail: Enquiries@e-Kit.co.uk *e-Kit specialises in designing and developing functional web solutions for small, medium and new businesses. We focus on your business throughout the design, development and launch stages to ensure that every aspect of your new site is what you and your customers need.**Our experience with database systems, graphic design and online marketing will help promote and grow your business in the digital age. We work in and with the visual arts and design industry to make your printed media, website and business stand out from the crowd.*

▶ Ekota Printers, 114 Brick Lane, London, E1 6RL Tel: (020) 7377 2626 Fax: (020) 7377 0666

Ekp Ltd Discount Tools, 142-143 Parrock Street, Gravesend, Kent, DA12 1EY Tel: (01474) 564829 Fax: (01474) 535266 *Power tools retail*

El Al Israel Airlines, 16 Upper Woburn Place, London, WC1H 0AF Tel: (020) 7121 1560 Fax: (020) 7121 1470 *International airline*

Elaflex Ltd, Riverside House, Plumpton Road, Hoddesdon, Hertfordshire, EN11 0PA Tel: (01992) 452950 Fax: (01992) 452911 E-mail: info@elaflex.co.uk *Aviation, petroleum & chemical industry hoses, ZVA fuel nozzels, hose end fittings. dry break - disconnect couplings. Rubber bellows, add blue. Stage II vapour recovery.*

▶ Elaine Scaife Consultancy, Mercury House,, Shipstones Business Centre, Northgate, New Basford, Nottingham, NG7 7FN Tel: 0870 0131700 E-mail: info@elainescaifeconsultancy.co.uk *Elaine Scaife Consultancy offers a variety of business focussed training courses to individuals and organisations who want to improve their perfomance and achieve the best outcome for their business in any situation.*

▶ Elan, 38 Bloomgate, Lanark, ML11 9ET Tel: (01555) 665777 Fax: (01555) 673888 *Party gift shop*

▶ Elan Consulting, 52 St Marks Road, Henley-on-Thames, Oxfordshire, RG9 1LW Tel: 07920 112909 E-mail: nick@elanconsulting.co.uk *IT Consultancy Services for support, projects and installations.*

Elan Dragonair Ltd, 162 Southampton Road, Portsmouth, PO6 4RY Tel: (023) 9237 6451 Fax: (023) 9237 0411 *Manufacturers of heating equipment & fittings*

Elan Electronics Ltd, 26 Bellfield Street, Dundee, DD1 5JA Tel: (01382) 206106 Fax: (01382) 206906 *Audio visual specialists*

Elan I T Computing, St Johns House, Barrington Road, Altrincham, Cheshire, WA14 1JY Tel: 0161-924 3900 Fax: 0161-924 3901 E-mail: info.alt@elanit.co.uk *IT recruitment agency*

Elan Industries, Unit 1 Townfield Industrial Estate, Townfield Street, Oldham, OL4 1XF Tel: 0161-627 2300 Fax: 0161-627 1899 E-mail: elanind@aol.com *Cold room manufrs*

▶ Elan Networks Ltd, The Mews, 12 Fortrose Street, Glasgow, G12 0TB Tel: 0141-337 6540 Fax: 0141-337 2244 E-mail: enquiries@elannetworks.co.uk *Designs & delivers wired & wireless networking systems*

Elan Pharma Ltd, Six Hills Court, Norton Green Road, Stevenage, Hertfordshire, SG1 2BA Tel: (01438) 742700 Fax: (01438) 765000 E-mail: operations@elan.com Principal Export Areas: Worldwide *Pharmaceutical suppliers*

Elan Polymers Ltd, 176 Leigh Road, Atherton, Manchester, M46 0PJ Tel: (01942) 889525 Fax: (01942) 873422 *Plastic reclaiming*

Elan Recruitment, Grampian House, Meridian Gate, Marsh Wall, Docklands, London, E14 9XT Tel: (020) 7537 4114 Fax: (020) 7537 3927 E-mail: enquiries@elanrecruitment.com *Employment agency*

Elan Support Services, Allerton Bywater Business Park, Newton Lane, Allerton Bywater, Castleford, West Yorkshire, WF10 2AL Tel: (01977) 604384 Fax: (01977) 604021 E-mail: evahorbury@elansupports.co.uk *Computer service maintenance,network support, installation of IT systems, network cableing installations*

Elanco Animal Health Ltd, Lilly House, Priestly Road, Basingstoke, Hampshire, RG24 9NL Tel: (01256) 315000 Fax: (01256) 315081 E-mail: elancouk@lilly.com *Animal Health Care Products Sales & marketing*

▶ Eland Business Services Ltd, 57 Eland Way, Cherry Hinton, Cambridge, CB1 9XQ Tel: (0800) 4589941 E-mail: contact@ebslfinance.co.uk *We are Business Finance Brokers offering Bridging Loans, Factoring, Invoice Discounting, Letters of Credit, Commercial Loans, Property Development Finance, Equipment & Vehicle Leasing plus much more.*

▶ Eland Cables Ltd, 120 Highgate Studios, 53-79 Highgate Road, London, NW5 1TL Tel: (020) 7241 8787 Fax: (020) 7241 8700 E-mail: sales@eland.co.uk Principal Export Areas: Middle East, Africa, Central/East Europe, West Europe, North America, Central America & South America *Why choose Eland Cables?*Eland Cables, a leading international cable supplier, is focussed on understanding the industries it serves and the needs of its customers. Designed as a one-stop-cable-shop, customers come expecting everything from control, coaxial, instrumentation, tri-rated and industrial cables to bespoke, high temperature, rail and telecom cables (in fact, if it's not in stock, Eland will source it, fast). They leave, however, having experienced a great deal more. Expect a different experience from Eland Cables.**

Eland Engineering Company, 29 Lyon Road, Walton-on-Thames, Surrey, KT12 3PU Tel: (01932) 252666 Fax: (01932) 252583 E-mail: info@elandeng.co.uk *Test equipment engineers & hydraulic*

Eland Fixings, Tree Tops, Broadshard, Crewkerne, Somerset, TA18 7NF Tel: (01460) 72219 Fax: (01460) 72219 *Fixings supplier to building trade*

Elanders UK Ltd, 32 Kings Road, Harrogate, North Yorkshire, HG1 5JW Tel: (01423) 530362 Fax: (01423) 530610 E-mail: sales@elanders.co.uk *Directory printers*

Elap Engineering Ltd, Fort Street, Accrington, Lancashire, BB5 1QG Tel: (01254) 871599 Fax: (01254) 389992 E-mail: mail@elap.co.uk *Manufacturer of disabled aids*

Elastic Berger Ltd, Jubilee Road, Newtownards, County Down, BT23 4XW Tel: (028) 9181 3046 Fax: (028) 9181 3140 E-mail: berger@globalnet.co.uk *Narrow fabric webbing manufrs*

Elastogran UK Ltd, Wimsey Way, Somercotes, Alfreton, Derbyshire, DE55 4NL Tel: (01773) 607161 Fax: (01773) 602089 E-mail: elastogran-uk@elastogran.co.uk

continued

continuation
Principal Export Areas: Worldwide *Polyurethane chemical manufrs*

Elastomerics Ltd, Summit House, 48a Bramhall Lane South, Bramhall, Stockport, Cheshire, SK7 1AH Tel: 0161-439 9116 Fax: 0161-440 8035 E-mail: info@elastomerics.com *Industrial chemical distributors services*

Elatech Polyurethane Mouldings & Castings Ltd, 34 London Road, Hailsham, East Sussex, BN27 3BW Tel: (01323) 845100 Fax: (01323) 846894 *Polyurethane moulding services*

Elateral Trustees Ltd, Elateral House Unit 4, Crosby Way, Farnham, Surrey, GU9 7XX Tel: (01252) 740740 Fax: (01252) 740741 *Internet marketing services*

▶ Elba Flooring & Bed Centre, 23-24 Mill Street, Gowerton, Swansea, SA4 3ED Tel: (01792) 879555 Fax: (01792) 879555 *Flooring specialists*

Elbee Traders, 839 Harrow Road, London, NW10 5NH Tel: (020) 8969 9423 Fax: (020) 8969 2611 E-mail: sales@elbee-traders.co.uk *Brass art importers, exporters & fragrance products*

Elbesee Products, Cotswold Works, London Road, Chalford, Stroud, Gloucestershire, GL6 8DT Tel: (01453) 883014 Fax: (01453) 882987 *Embroidery hoop & frame manufrs*

Elbmar Ltd, 5 Oppenheimer Centre, Greenbridge Road, Greenbridge Industrial Estate, Swindon, SN3 3JD Tel: (01793) 644155 Fax: (01793) 513170 E-mail: elbmar@aol.com *Plastic injection moulding manufrs*

Elbon Blinds, 961 London Road, Leigh-on-Sea, Essex, SS9 3LB Tel: (01702) 713107 Fax: (01702) 713107 *Blind retailer & manufrs*

▶ Elbow Grease Cleaners, Kestrel House, Gurnell Grove, West Ealing, London, W13 0AD Tel: 020 82211300 Fax: 020 85030400 E-mail: info@elbowgreasecleaners.co.uk *Professional cleaning company*

▶ Elbow Grease Mobile Valeting, 23 Bolyfant Crescent, Whitnash, Leamington Spa, Warwickshire, CV31 2RH Tel: (07863) 219378 *Car valeting services*

ELC North West, 31 Harrier Court, Fenton Street, Lancaster, LA1 1AE Tel: 01524 720604 Fax: 01524 33362 E-mail: sales@elc-barriers.co.uk *We Hire a unique high quality water filled plastic barrier. For use on Road works, construction sites and events. Full delivery and collection service covering the north west of England. Any information or related products needed please do not hesitate to contact us.*

▶ Elcadant Ltd, Lea Mills, Lea Road, Batley, West Yorkshire, WF17 8BB Tel: (01924) 479973 Fax: (01924) 443368

Elcef Fibre, 9 Oundle Road, Chesterton, Peterborough, PE7 3UA Tel: (01733) 233293 Fax: (01733) 235351 E-mail: info@spillshop.co.uk *Spill control products manufrs*

Elco Europe, Exning Road, Newmarket, Suffolk, CB8 0AT Tel: (01638) 675000 Fax: (01638) 675001 *Electronic components manufrs*

Elcom ITG Ltd, Elcom House, 203 Bedford Avenue, Slough, SL1 4RY Tel: (01753) 442500 Fax: (01753) 442501 E-mail: info@elcom.co.uk *Specialist online re-seller for IT products*

Elcome Ltd, The Engine Shed, Overtown Farm, Wroughton, Swindon, SN4 0SH Tel: (01793) 845144 Fax: (01793) 845177 E-mail: sales@elcome.ltd.co.uk *Data management software*

Elcometer Instruments Ltd, Edge Lane, Droylsden, Manchester, M43 6BU Tel: 0161-371 6000 Fax: 0161-371 6010 E-mail: sales@elcometer.com *Inspection equipment for surface coatings manufrs*

Elcometer Instruments Ltd, Edge Lane, Droylsden, Manchester, M43 6BU Tel: 0161-371 6000 Fax: 0161-371 6010 E-mail: sale@elcometer.com *Design & manufacture high quality portable industrial metal detectors, cover metals & rebar locators*

Elcomponent Ltd, Unit 5 Southmill Trading Centre, Southmill Road, Bishop's Stortford, Hertfordshire, CM23 3DY Tel: (01279) 503173 Fax: (01279) 654441 E-mail: sales@elcomponent.co.uk *Metering & monitoring suppliers*

Elcon Products International, 7 Merlin Court, Gatehouse Close, Gatehouse Industrial Area, Aylesbury, Buckinghamshire, HP19 8DP Tel: (01296) 331855 Fax: (01296) 331856 E-mail: elcon.sales@tycoelectronics.com *Power connectors & interconnection systems*

Elcontrol Ltd, 5 Regulus Works, 79 Lynch Lane, Weymouth, Dorset, DT4 9DW Tel: (01305) 773426 Fax: (01305) 760539 E-mail: sales@elcontrol.co.uk *Burner controls & flame sensors.*

▶ Elcosystems Computer Systems, Unit 54 Imex Business Centre, Shobnall Road, Burton-on-Trent, Staffordshire, DE14 2AU Tel: (01283) 544582 Fax: (01283) 544582 E-mail: dh@elcocad.com *Software developers & providers*

Eldapoint Ltd, Sub-Station Road, Felixstowe, Suffolk, IP11 3JB Tel: (01394) 613110 Fax: (01394) 613218 E-mail: sales@eldapoint.co.uk *Container refrigeration manufrs*

Eldapoint Ltd, Charleywood Road, Knowsley Industrial Park, Liverpool, L33 7SG Tel: 0151-548 9838 Fax: 0151-548 7357 E-mail: control.liverpool@eldapoint.co.uk *Container repair & storage*

Eldec Electronics Ltd, Whittle Close, Drayton Fields Industrial Estate, Daventry, Northamptonshire, NN11 8YE Tel: (01327) 307200 Fax: (01327) 307230 *Power supplies design & manufrs*

▶ Eldencross Ltd, Park Bridge, Ashton-under-Lyne, Lancashire, OL6 8AW Tel: 0161-330 3446 E-mail: info@eldencross.co.uk

▶ Elder Homes Ltd, 10-16 Cluny Drive, Edinburgh, EH10 6DP Tel: 0131-447 3411

Elder Repetition Sheet Metal Ltd, 30 Oxford Road, Denham, Uxbridge, Middlesex, UB9 4DQ Tel: (01895) 258968 Fax: (01895) 252651 E-mail: sales@eldersheetmetal.co.uk *Sheet metalwork light fabricators*

Elderkin & Son Gunmakers Ltd, 17 Broad Street, Spalding, Lincolnshire, PE11 1TG Tel: (01775) 722919 Fax: (01775) 760556 E-mail: william@elderkin.co.uk *Gun repairers, retailers & manufrs*

▶ Elder's Engineers, 9 Park CR, Edinburgh, EH16 6JD Tel: 0131-664 5176 Fax: 0131-664 5643 *Consulting engineers or designers for buildings*

▶ Elders Walker Glass Ltd, Glasscraft House, Mcnay Street, Darlington, County Durham, DL3 6SP Tel: (01325) 465343 Fax: (01325) 489232 E-mail: peterkelly5@netscape.net *Glass Merchants, Glazing Contractors, 24 Hour Boarding Up Service, PVCu Replacement Windows, Doors and Conservatories*

Eldis Electrical Distributors, 239-242 Great Lister Street, Birmingham, B7 4BS Tel: 0121-359 4521 Fax: 0121-333 1432 E-mail: eldis@eldis.co.uk *Electrical distribution stocks*

Eldon Electric Ltd, Rother Way, Hellaby, Rotherham, South Yorkshire, S66 8QN Tel: (01709) 701234 Fax: (01709) 701209 E-mail: info.uk@eldon.com *Manufacturers of electronic console*

Eldon Laboratories Ltd, 4 Pooley Close, Newcastle upon Tyne, NE5 2TF Tel: 0191-286 0446 Fax: 0191-286 0455 E-mail: orders@eldon-specials.co.uk *Pharmaceutical manufrs*

Eldred Geotechnics, Veitchii Barn, Newbarn Road, Swanley, Kent, BR8 7PW Tel: (01322) 663222 *Consulting engineers*

Eldridge Electrical Ltd, Binders Industrial Estate, Cryers Hill Road, Cryers Hill, High Wycombe, Buckinghamshire, HP15 6LJ Tel: (01494) 715956 Fax: (01494) 716176 E-mail: info@eldridgeelectricalltd.co.uk *Street lighting contractors*

▶ S. Eldridge Design & Draughting, 37 Hazelwood Close, Honiton, Devon, EX14 2XA Tel: (01404) 45054 E-mail: stephen.eldridge@btinternet.com *Engineering design consultancy*

Eldwick Ltd, Bentley Buildings, Glaisdale, Whitby, North Yorkshire, YO21 2QY Tel: (01947) 897337 Fax: (01947) 897660 *Ground works services*

Ele Flex Ltd, Quarry Lane, Chichester, West Sussex, PO19 8NY Tel: (01243) 782205 Fax: (01243) 532416 E-mail: eleflex@btconnect.com *Powder coaters, silk screeners & all 2 pack wet spraying services*

Ele International, Chartmoor Road, Leighton Buzzard, Bedfordshire, LU7 4WG Tel: (01525) 249200 Fax: (01525) 249249 E-mail: ele@eleint.co.uk *Environmental agricultural monitoring equipment manufacturers & civil engineering manufrs*

Eleco plc, 15 Gentlemens Field, Westmill Road, Ware, Hertfordshire, SG12 0EF Tel: (01920) 443830 Fax: (01920) 469681 E-mail: mail@eleco.com *Building products & construction software suppliers*

Eleco Timber Frame Ltd, Oaksmere Business Park, Eye Airfield Industrial Estate, Yaxley, Eye, Suffolk, IP23 8BW Tel: (01379) 783465 Fax: (01379) 783659 E-mail: stramit@eleco.com *Partitioning manufacturing services*

Elecon Ltd, Wharf Road, Hawkins Lane Industrial Estate, Burton-on-Trent, Staffordshire, DE14 1PZ Tel: (01283) 537575 Fax: (01283) 511227 *Chain manufrs*

Elecon Sheet Metal, Ravensfield Industrial Estate, Charles Street, Dukinfield, Cheshire, SK16 4SD Tel: 0161-339 6210 Fax: 0161-343 1006 *General sheet metalwork fabricators*

▶ Elecref Ltd, 20 Wilton Road, Humberston, Grimsby, South Humberside, DN36 4AW Tel: (01472) 211666 Fax: (01472) 810019

▶ Elecro Engineering Ltd, Unit 14 Leyden Road, Stevenage, Hertfordshire, SG1 2BW Tel: (01438) 749474 Fax: (01438) 361329 E-mail: info@eleco.co.uk *Manufacturer of electric heaters for swimming pools & aquatic heaters*

Elecsis Ltd, Yeo Road, Bridgwater, Somerset, TA6 5NA Tel: (01278) 453198 Fax: (01278) 453198 E-mail: chris.pratt@elecsis.com *Switchgear panel designers & manufrs*

Elect Computer Systems, 257 Wick Rd, London, E9 5DG Tel: (020) 8986 8014 Fax: (020) 8986 8180 *Computer maintenance & repairs*

▶ Electcetra Ltd, 25 The Walk, Kilburn, Belper, Derbyshire, DE56 0PP Tel: (01332) 881320 E-mail: info@electcetra.com *Portable electrical appliance testing services*

▶ Electec Services Edi Ltd, 19 Anstey Lane, Leicester, LE4 0FF Tel: 0116-251 7234

Elec-Tech Services, 132 Northfield Lane, Wickersley, Rotherham, South Yorkshire, S66 2HW Tel: (01709) 543211 Fax: (01709) 543211 *Electrical Service Mobile Cranes*

▶ ElecTech Solutions (East) Ltd, The Old Bakery, Keswick Road, Bacton, Norwich, NR12 0HE Tel: (07831) 107578 Fax: (0870) 7065369 E-mail: info@electechsolutions.co.uk *Marine electronics instillations*

Electic, 40 Thorneyfields Lane, Stafford, ST17 9YS Tel: (01785) 229330 Fax: (01785) 229330 *PAT, electrical inspection, wiring inspections, rewiring & remedial*

Electra Caddie, 99 Main Road, Bolton le Sands, Carnforth, Lancashire, LA5 8EQ Tel: (01902) 823300 Fax: (01524) 822382 E-mail: enquiries@kaddy.co.uk *Electric vehicle & batteries, motor vehicle (automotive) manufrs*

Electra Controls Ltd, 20 Acorn Close, Enfield, Middlesex, EN2 8LX Tel: (020) 8366 1433 *Vehicle access control*

Electra Holdings Ltd, Roughway Mill, Tonbridge, Kent, TN11 9SG Tel: (01732) 811118 Fax: (01732) 811119 E-mail: info@electrapolymers.com *Chemical & polymer products suppliers*

Electra Partners Europe Ltd, 65 Kingsway, London, WC2B 6QT Tel: (020) 7831 6464 Fax: (020) 7404 5388 E-mail: info@electraeurope.com *Investment consultants*

Electra Switch Ltd, Unit 4 Colne Way Court, Colne Way, Watford, WD24 7NE Tel: (01923) 246154 Fax: (01923) 246482 E-mail: esl@electra-switch.co.uk *Switchgear manufrs*

Electract, Walker Road, Bardon Hill, Coalville, Leicestershire, LE67 1TU Tel: (01530) 510011 Fax: (01530) 811224 E-mail: enquiries@electract.co.uk *Electrical contractors*

Electrak Holdings Ltd, Number One Industrial Estate, Medomsley Road, Consett, County Durham, DH8 6SR Tel: (01207) 503400 Fax: (01207) 501799 E-mail: sales@electrak.co.uk *Cable management systems manufrs*

Electranets Ltd, 31 Westfield Avenue, Brockworth, Gloucester, GL3 4AU Tel: (01452) 617841 Fax: (01452) 617841 E-mail: roy@electranets.fsnet.co.uk *Electrified net fencing manufrs*

Electraspec Control Panel Mnfrs, 4 Shell Corner Industrial Estate, Long Lane, Halesowen, West Midlands, B62 9LD Tel: 0121-559 9335 Fax: 0121-559 9362 *Technical engineering contractors*

Electraweld Ltd, Unit 1, Lowlands Bus Estate, Rochester, Kent, ME2 4AZ Tel: (01634) 291000 Fax: (01634) 291004 E-mail: dale@theweld.fsnet.co.uk *Welding equipment & accessory suppliers*

Electrex World Ltd, Units 44-45 Vanalloys Business Park, Stoke Row, Henley-On-Thames, Oxfordshire, RG9 5QW Tel: (01491) 682369 Fax: (01491) 682286 E-mail: electrex@btinternet.com *Motorcycle electrical components manufrs*

The Electric Elements Co., Tokenhouse Yard, Nottingham, NG1 2HH Tel: 0115-950 5253 Fax: 0115-958 8283 *Manufacture of electric elements*

The Electric Gate Shop LLP, Stoneycourt Cottage, Midhopestones, Sheffield, S36 4GP Tel: (01226) 370549 Fax: (01405) 785300 E-mail: gary@theelectricgateshop.co.uk *Suppliers of electric gates and automatic gate systems.*

Electric Lift Truck Services, 6 Village Way, Farndon, Newark, Nottinghamshire, NG24 4SX Tel: (01636) 701573 *Fork truck engineers*

▶ The Electric Man Ltd, Glascoed, Ger-y-Nant, Llangunnor, Carmarthen, SA31 2NY Tel: (07778) 463217 E-mail: gary@theelectricman.net *ELECTRICAL CONTRACTING IN AND AROUND THE CARMARTHEN AREA.FROM AN EXTRA SOCKET TO A FULL WIRING PROJECT UNDERTAKEN*

Electric Marketing, 22 John Street, London, WC1N 2BY Tel: (020) 7419 7999 Fax: (020) 7419 7282 E-mail: lists@electricmarketing.co.uk *UK mailing lists provider of senior business*

Electric Mobility Euro Ltd, Canal Way, Ilminster, Somerset, TA19 9DL Tel: (01460) 258100 Fax: (01460) 258125 E-mail: sales@electricmobility.co.uk *Electric scooters & power chair manufrs*

Electric Motor Rewinds, 114 Islingword Road, Brighton, BN2 9SG Tel: (01273) 685925 Fax: (01273) 685925 E-mail: sales@electricmotorrewinds.co.uk *Specialists in repair & servicing electric motors & sales*

Electric Motor Rewinds, 6 Upper Wharf, Fareham, Hampshire, PO16 0LZ Tel: (01329) 233154 Fax: (01329) 280679 *Electric motor repair services*

Electric Motor Sales Birmingham Ltd, Unit 39 Rovex Business Park, Hay Hall Road, Birmingham, B11 2AG Tel: 0121-765 4899 Fax: 0121-706 5080 *Electric motor repair services*

Electric Motor Services, Unit C, Lyttleton Road, Northampton, NN5 7ET Tel: (01604) 587700 Fax: (01604) 580073 E-mail: sales@elemoto.com *Electric motor repair & rewind specialists services*

Electric Power & Equipment Co., 619 Stretford Road, Manchester, M16 0QA Tel: 0161-872 1619 Fax: 0161-876 4160 *Power tool distributors*

Electric Software, Stream House, Castle Hill, Rotherfield, Crowborough, East Sussex, TN6 3RU Tel: (01825) 830388 *Computer systems*

Electric Vehicle Systems Ltd, 11 Glover Network Centre, Spire Road, Washington, Tyne & Wear, NE37 3HB Tel: 0191-416 1286 Fax: 0191-419 3746 E-mail: info@evsystems.co.uk *Electric vehicle control systems*

Electric Water Heating Co., 2 Horsecroft Place, Harlow, Essex, CM19 5BT Tel: (0845) 0553811 Fax: (0845) 0553822 E-mail: sales@ewh.co.uk *suppliers of electric water heating and parts*

Electrical & Acoustic Services Ltd, 105 Fermor Way, Crowborough, East Sussex, TN6 3BH Tel: (01892) 661950 *Audio visual equipment installation contractors*

Electrical Affairs Ltd, 151 Broad Lane, London, N15 4QX Tel: (020) 8808 7887 Fax: (020) 8801 5513 *Lightning protection services*

Electrical & Alarm Services, Colebrook Road, Plympton, Plymouth, PL7 4AA Tel: (01752) 337271 Fax: (01752) 337271 E-mail: easdale@eurobell.co.uk *CCTV installations & fire alarms-security alarm installers*

▶ Electrical Appliance Testing, PO Box 120, Richmond, North Yorkshire, DL10 7XW Tel: (0871) 8710098 Fax: (0871) 8710096 E-mail: sales@e-a-t.co.uk *Inspectors & testers of portable electrical equipment & appliances*

▶ Electrical Bitz, 62 St Helens Road, Hastings, East Sussex, TN34 2LN Tel: 01424 434981 Fax: 01424 433332 *Electrical Bitz offers a huge range of electrical products, parts and accessories including indoor and out door lighting. UK home delivery. Secure on-line ordering.*

Electrical Cabinets (Bradford) Ltd, 2 Essex Street, Wakefield Road, Bradford, West Yorkshire, BD4 7PG Tel: (01274) 729076 Fax: (01274) 732297 *Sheet metal fabricators*

▶ Electrical Concepts, 55 Aylands Road, Enfield, Middlesex, EN3 6PW Tel: (01992) 700825 Fax: (01992) 700825 E-mail: electrician74@tiscali.co.uk *We serve the North, East & West London Areas and the home counties**We are NIC EIC domestic installers *Have a fast and Efficient service *Have very reasonable prices *Fully insured *Preferential*

continued

*rates for repeat customers*Have over 12 years experience **For More information please see our website **

▶ Electrical Connections Ltd, Everik Business Centre, Prospect Way, Hutton, Brentwood, Essex, CM13 1XA Tel: (01277) 231414 Fax: (01277) 230617 E-mail: enquiries@electricalconnections.net

Electrical & Contractors Supplies, 177 Meanwood Road, Leeds, LS7 1JP Tel: 0113-242 9295 Fax: 0113-242 5021 E-mail: sales@ecs-electrical.com *Electrical suppliers*

▶ Electrical Control Panels Ltd, Unit 17 Midway Centre Bridge St Industrial Estate, Bridge Street, Clay Cross, Chesterfield, Derbyshire, S45 9NU Tel: (01246) 865770 Fax: (01246) 865770 *Control panel manufrs*

Electrical Control Systems, Cliff Nook Lane, Newark, Nottinghamshire, NG24 1LY Tel: (01636) 707309 Fax: (01636) 640003 E-mail: sales@ecscontroll.co.uk *Building control panels manufrs*

Electrical Control Systems, 89 Queslett Road East, Sutton Coldfield, West Midlands, B74 2AH Tel: 0121-353 1231 E-mail: info@ecscontrol.co.uk *Electrical control systems manufrs*

Electrical Design & Automation Ltd, The Old Bakery, Main Road, Pontesbury, Shrewsbury, SY5 0RR Tel: (01743) 791986 Fax: (01743) 791555 E-mail: eda1987@aol.com *Design automation systems*

Electrical Design & Manufacturing Co. Ltd, Station Street, Whetstone, Leicester, LE8 6JS Tel: 0116-286 2165 *Control panels, insulation monitoring equipment manufrs*

▶ Electrical & Electronic Services, 5 St Josephs Park, Downpatrick, County Down, BT30 7EN Tel: (028) 4484 1631 E-mail: aidenmoore@hotmail.com *Specialising in Inspection and Testing of: Electrical installations, Fire alarm systems, Emergency lighting systems, Petrol filling stations, Quarry installations. Also Portable appliance testing.*

Electrical Electronic Services, Sotherby Road, Middlesbrough, Cleveland, TS3 8BS Tel: (01642) 241600 *Custom built electronic equipment manufrs*

Electrical Elements Hinckley Ltd, 1 Willow Park Industrial Estate, Upton Lane, Stoke Golding, Nuneaton, Warwickshire, CV13 6EU Tel: (01455) 213171 Fax: (01455) 213614 E-mail: enquiries@electricalelements.co.uk *Industrial heating elements manufrs*

▶ Electrical Engineering Services (UK) Ltd, 33 Gresham Road, Middlesbrough, Cleveland, TS1 4LU Tel: (01642) 230024 *Electrical contractor's, Niceic approved. Domestic & Commercial. PAT testing,Inspecting and Certification.*

▶ Electrical Installations Ltd, Parker House, Suite 18, Parker Center, Mansfield Road, Derby, DE21 4SZ Tel: (01332) 200166

Electrical Installations North West Ltd, Lawsons Road, Thornton-Cleveleys, Lancashire, FY5 4PW Tel: (01253) 822626 Fax: (01253) 827846 E-mail: sales@einw.co.uk *Electrical contractors*

▶ Electrical Insulators & Supports Ltd, Unit 3 Albert Street, Little Lever, Bolton, BL3 1JH Tel: (07092) 122440 E-mail: sales@electricalinsulators.co.uk *Insulators busbar systems*

▶ Electrical Manufactured Solutions Ltd, Paragon House, Gatehouse Close, Aylesbury, Buckinghamshire, HP19 8DE Tel: (01296) 393375 Fax: (01296) 395608 E-mail: info@emsltd.org.uk *Manufacturers of switchgears, starters & isolators*

Electrical & Mechanical Controls Ltd, 8 Europa Way, Martineau Lane, Norwich, NR1 2EN Tel: (01603) 625535 Fax: (01603) 625030 E-mail: emc@norwichlife.co.uk *Control panel manufrs*

Electrical Mechanical Instrument Services (UK) Ltd, Central Equipment Base, Greenwell Road, East Tullos Industrial Estate, Aberdeen, AB12 3AX Tel: (01224) 894494 Fax: (01224) 894929 E-mail: info@emis-uk.com Sales Contact: J. O'Neil *EMIS, established in 1992 and based in Aberdeen support the oil and gas industry by the provision of calibration and repair services for test and metering instrumentation. The company is UKAS accredited and also supports ISO 9001:2000. With JV's in Qatar and Abu Dhabi services are also provided in Azerbaijan, Libya, Nigeria and Algeria. Calibration training has also been provided for several Middle East companies.*

Electrical Power Ltd, PO Box 115, Bingley, West Yorkshire, BD16 1WQ Tel: (01274) 510970 Fax: (01274) 511109 E-mail: epsrec@hotmail.com Principal Export Areas: Worldwide *Manufacturers of rectifiers (electrical) & electroplating plant & equipment*

Electrical Power Specialists Reading Ltd, 1 Blenheim Road, Reading, RG1 5NG Tel: 0118-935 1933 Fax: 0118-935 2373 E-mail: info@epsdirect.co.uk *Electrical contractors*

Electrical Repairs & Rewind Service Ltd, 2 Charlotte Street, Wakefield, West Yorkshire, WF1 1UL Tel: (01924) 365117 Fax: (01924) 200268 *Motor repairers*

Electrical Safeguards, Charlwoods Road, East Grinstead, West Sussex, RH19 2HR Tel: (01342) 325100 Fax: (01342) 327115 E-mail: enquiries@insulatedtools.co.uk *Insulated tools supplier*

▶ Electrical Services (Cornwall) Ltd, Pargolla Road, Newquay, Cornwall, TR7 1RP Tel: (01637) 872700

Electrical Services (Nelson) Ltd, 43 Belgrave St., Nelson, Lancashire, BB9 9HS Tel: (01282) 696317 Fax: (01282) 611632 E-mail: david@electricalsales.co.uk *Electrical contractors*

▶ Electrical Site Services, 111 Seaview Road, Wallasey, Merseyside, CH45 4NZ Tel: 0151-638 8444 Fax: 0151-639 5996 *Electrical engineers.Approved electrical contractor.Generator installation.Construction site power. cable,transformer and distribution board hire. Part P approved.*

Company Information

Electrical Supplies Ltd, 7 The Broadway, Hampton Court Way, Thames Ditton, Surrey, KT7 0LX Tel: (020) 8398 9377 Fax: (020) 8398 8093 *Lighting wholesalers & distributors*
Electrical Supplies Bolton Ltd, 68 Chorley Old Road, Bolton, BL1 3AE Tel: (01204) 362959 Fax: (01204) 362503 *Electrical wholesalers*
▶ Electrical Testing Surveyors Ltd, 1 Merlin Business Park, Fair Oak Close, Clyst Honiton, Exeter, EX5 2UL Tel: (01392) 444200 Fax: (01392) 444201 E-mail: ets.uk@virgin.net *Equipment testing services*
Electrical Wholesale Specialists, Unit12a Marshfield Avenue Village Farm Indust Estate, Pyle, Bridgend, Mid Glamorgan, CF33 6BJ Tel: (01656) 741133 Fax: (01656) 749957 E-mail: ewssalesteam@btconnect.com *Wholesale electrical*
Electricare, 21 Shepherds Lane, Bracknell, Berkshire, RG42 2BN Tel: (01344) 452648 Fax: (01344) 640098 E-mail: c.onions@ntlworld.com *Domestic appliance repairs*
▶ Electricare Services, 33 The CR, Urmston, Manchester, M41 5QR Tel: 0161-202 9499 E-mail: office@electricareservices.co.uk *Commercial, domestic & industrial electrical installations, repairs & maintenance*
Electricars Ltd, 15 Carlyon Road, Atherstone, Warwickshire, CV9 1LQ Tel: (01827) 716888 Fax: (01827) 717841 E-mail: electricars@lineone.net *Electric vehicle manufrs*
▶ Electricity 4 Business Ltd, 3 Radian Court, Knowlhill, Milton Keynes, MK5 8PJ Tel: (0800) 3160518 Fax: (0870) 1630832 E-mail: sales@electricity4business.co.uk *Business electricity supplier.*
Electricold Refrigeration, 13 Hillbury Road, Whyteleafe, Surrey, CR3 0ER Tel: (020) 8660 4641 Fax: (020) 8668 2358 *Refrigeration servicing*
Electrium Ltd, Lichfield Road, Brownhills, Walsall, WS8 6JZ Tel: (01543) 455000 *Electrical accessory manufrs*
Electrium Sales Ltd, Walkmill Business Park, Walkmill Way, Cannock, Staffordshire, WS11 0XE Tel: (01543) 455000 Fax: (01543) 455001 E-mail: darren.garbett@electrium.co.uk *Electrical installation equipment manufrs*
Electrium Sales Ltd, Sharston Road, Wythenshawe, Manchester, M22 4RA Tel: 0161-998 5454 Fax: 0161-945 1587 *'Wylex electrical product manufrs*
Electrix International Ltd, 1a-1b Dovecot Hill, South Church Enterprise Park, Bishop Auckland, County Durham, DL14 6XP Tel: (01388) 774455 Fax: (01388) 777359 E-mail: enquiries@electrix.co.uk *Perforated cable tray manufrs*
Electro Arc Co. Ltd, The Wallows Industrial Estate, Fens Pool Avenue, Brierley Hill, West Midlands, DY5 1QA Tel: (01384) 263426 Fax: (01384) 79017 E-mail: sales@electroarc.co.uk *Spark eroding machines manufrs*
Electro Avionics, D Burnham Road, Dartford, DA1 5BN Tel: (01322) 288698 Fax: (01322) 277520 E-mail: colin@electroavionics.co.uk *Electronic sub-contractors*
Electro Cables Ltd, Unit 2 Alliance Close, Attleborough Fields Industrial Estate, Nuneaton, Warwickshire, CV11 6SD Tel: (024) 7632 0066 Fax: (024) 7632 0122 E-mail: sales@electrocables.co.uk *Special purpose cables*
Electro Cal Ltd, 4 Bridge End Business Park, Park Road, Milnthorpe, Cumbria, LA7 7RH Tel: (01539) 564202 Fax: (01539) 564203 E-mail: sales@electro-cal.co.uk *Welding equipment suppliers*
Electro Control Systems, Backlands, Church Way, Guilsborough, Northampton, NN6 8QF Tel: (01604) 740305 Fax: (01604) 740305 *Variable speed drive consultants*
▶ Electro Entertainments (Karaoke & Disco), 6 Flintsham Grove, Hanley, Stoke-on-Trent, ST1 5QS Tel: (01782) 204152 E-mail: ianmaddock@wolfieselectro.co.uk *Electro entertainments (Stoke on Trent. Specialists in mobile disco & karaoke*
Electro Furnace Products Ltd, Hull Road, Saltend, Hull, HU12 8ED Tel: (01482) 899141 Fax: (01482) 890196 E-mail: sales@efp-hull.co.uk *Manufacturers of electro-fused magnesia*
Electro Graph Ltd, 177 Lower High Street, Stourbridge, West Midlands, DY8 1TG Tel: (01384) 378436 Fax: (01384) 392542 E-mail: sales@eguk.com *Health & safety sign & specialist label manufrs*
Electro Hire & Supply LLP, The Paddock, Off Wharf Road, Biddulph, Stoke-On-Trent, ST8 6AL Tel: (01782) 518322 Fax: (01782) 515960 E-mail: sales@ehireandsupply.co.uk *Heating & ventilation specialty hire services*
Electro Inductors, 19-25 Neville Road, Croydon, CR0 2DS Tel: (020) 8684 6100 Fax: (020) 8684 6109 E-mail: sales@aluminium-inductors.co.uk *Manufacturers of inductors & transformers & coils*
Electro Mech Agri Ltd, 7 Tulnagall Road, Dungannon, County Tyrone, BT70 3LR Tel: (028) 8776 7376 Fax: (028) 8776 7034 *Milking parlour manufrs*
Electro Mech Industrial Services Ltd, Stanthope, Adsett, Westbury-on-Severn, Gloucestershire, GL14 1PH Tel: (01452) 760441 Fax: (01452) 760441 *Mechanical services*
Electro Mechanical Installations Ltd, 7 Mackenzie Industrial Estate, Bird Hall Lane, Stockport, Cheshire, SK3 0SB Tel: 0161-428 7800 Fax: 0161-428 8999 E-mail: office@emiltd.co.uk *Thermowell manufrs*
Electro Mechanical Services Ltd, 24B Portman Road, Reading, RG30 1EA Tel: 0118-956 1222 Fax: 0118-956 1220 E-mail: info@emssolutions.co.uk *Engineering & fabrication services*
Electro Metal Depositors Ltd, 66 Bower Street, Roker Industrial Estate, Oldham, OL1 3LT Tel: 0161-624 8639 Fax: 0161-627 1575 E-mail: tmcpartland@btlink.com *Stove enamellers*
Electro Motion, Barkby Road, Leicester, LE4 9LX Tel: 0116-276 6341 Fax: 0116-274 3048 E-mail: sales@electromotion.co.uk *Machine tool merchants*
Electro Plating Services Ltd, 22 Bates Road, Romford, RM3 0JH Tel: (01708) 342761 Fax: (01708) 381168E-mail: epsessex@aol.com *Electroplaters*
Electro Power Engineering, Brian Royd Lane, Greetland, Halifax, West Yorkshire, HX4 8PE Tel: (01422) 379570 Fax: (01422) 370612 E-mail: enquiries@electropowerengineering.co.uk *Specialists in rotating machines*
Electro Refrigeration Services, Unit 5, Ashfield Close, Whitehall Industrial Estate, Leeds, LS12 5JB Tel: 0113-279 7000 Fax: 0113-279 4100 *Refrigeration contractors & air conditioning*
Electro Replacement Ltd, 1 Moor Park Industrial Centre, Tolpits Lane, Watford, WD18 9EU Tel: (01923) 255344 Fax: (01923) 255829 *Electrical distributors service*
Electro Serigraphic Products Ltd, Unit 8 Collers Way, Reepham, Norwich, NR10 4SW Tel: (01603) 871227 Fax: (01603) 871237 E-mail: esp@membrane-switches.co.uk *Membrane switches & key pads*
Electro Services Ltd, 14 Pulloxhill Business Park, Greenfield Road, Pulloxhill, Bedford, MK45 5EU Tel: (01525) 719994 Fax: (01525) 719995 E-mail: electrogbr@aol.com *Electronic engineers & civil engineering services*
Electro Signs Ltd, 97 Vallentin Road, London, E17 3JJ Tel: (020) 8521 8066 Fax: (020) 8520 8127 E-mail: info@electrosigns.co.uk *General sign designers/installers/manufrs* Also at: Birmingham, Manchester & Southampton
Electro Soft Development, 15 Sterndale Road, Long Eaton, Nottingham, NG10 3HQ Tel: 0115-973 2284 Fax: 0115-973 2284 *Industrial control software services*
Electro Technik Ltd, 10-12 Shaw Lane, Stoke Prior, Bromsgrove, Worcestershire, B60 4DT Tel: (01527) 831794 Fax: (01527) 574470 E-mail: electro.technik@virgin.net *Cable assembly, harness & lighting manufrs*
Electro Wind Scotland Ltd, Units 3, Station Road, Kinghorn, Burntisland, Fife, KY3 9RA Tel: (01592) 890990 Fax: (01592) 891153 *Transformers manufrs*
Electrobase RP Ltd, 7 Maxim Road, Dartford, DA1 4BG Tel: (01322) 555938 Fax: (01322) 555099 E-mail: sales@electrobaserp.co.uk *Sheet metalwork engineers*
▶ Electrocal Group Ltd, 7 Alfred Court Saxon Business Park, Hanbury Road, Stoke Prior, Bromsgrove, Worcestershire, B60 4AD Tel: (01527) 878222 Fax: (01527) 878111
Electrochemical Machining Services Ltd, High Street, Oadby, Leicester, LE2 5DE Tel: 0116-271 8022 Fax: 0116-271 8023 E-mail: ivan@electrochemical.co.uk *Electrochemical debarring equipment & machinery services*
Electrochemical Supplies Ltd, Chamberlain Road, Aylesbury, Buckinghamshire, HP19 8DY Tel: (01296) 428011 Fax: (01296) 392375 E-mail: info@echemsupplies.co.uk *Electroplating equipment manufrs*
Electrocoin Manufacturing Ltd, Phoenix Estate, Caerphilly Road, Cardiff, CF14 4QF Tel: (029) 2061 4000 Fax: (029) 2061 8400 E-mail: info@electrocoin.co.uk *Amusement machine manufrs* Also at: London NW10
Electrocomponents U K Ltd, 5000 John Smith Drive, Oxford Business Park South, Oxford, OX4 2BH Tel: (01865) 204000 Fax: (01865) 207400 E-mail: sales@electrocomponents.com *Electrical engineers*
Electroconnect Ltd, Unit 1, Riverside Avenue, Riverside Business Park, Irvine, Ayrshire, KA11 5DL Tel: (01294) 221360 Fax: (01294) 221272 E-mail: sales@electroconnect.co.uk Principal Export Areas: Central/East Europe *Printed circuit board*
▶ The Electrode Co., Llangwm, Usk, Gwent, NP15 1HJ Tel: (01291) 650279 E-mail: keltic@electo.co.uk *Medical electronics*
Electro-Discharge Ltd, Unit 14, Bagley Industrial Pk, Northfield Rd, Netherton, Dudley, West Midlands, DY2 9DY Tel: (01384) 238451 Fax: (01384) 245971 E-mail: ron@electro-discharge.co.uk *We are precision wire & spark erosion engineers based in Dudley, however we cover the rest of the UK and Europe. We have been established for over 25 years and are specialists in the satellite antennae and aerospace industries. Our services include; Spark Erosion Machining including On Site, CNC Wire Erosion Machining Services, Spark Eroding, Small Hole Drilling Services, Drilling Services Electrical Discharge Machining (EDM), Wire Erosion Machining Computer Aided Manufacturing (CAM), Spark Erosion Wire, Spark Erosion Tooling, Wire Erosion Machining including On Site, Wire Erosion Machining, Four Axis, CNC, Spark Erosion Machines, High Speed Drilling.*
Electroflock Ltd, Unit 7-8 Building 33, Second Avenue, Pensnett Trading Estate, Kingswinford, West Midlands, DY6 7UG Tel: (01384) 402660 Fax: (01384) 402662 E-mail: electroflock@btinternet.com *Flock spraying services*
Electroflora Ltd, The Old Transmitter House, The Baulk, Clapham, Bedford, MK41 6AA Tel: (01234) 262745 Fax: (01234) 262753 *Ventilating equipment manufacturer for glass houses*
Electro-Flow Controls Ltd, Unit 3 Souter Head Industrial Centre, Souter Head Road, Altens, Aberdeen, AB12 3LF Tel: (01224) 249355 Fax: (01224) 249339 E-mail: efcltd@attglobal.net *Electronic systems manufrs*
▶ Electro-Freeze Ltd, Summerhill Quarry, Douglas, Isle of Man, IM2 4PF Tel: (01624) 673921 Fax: (01624) 662312 E-mail: sales@electrofreeze.4mg.com
▶ Electrogate Ltd, Unit 4, Ahed Trading Estate, Dewsbury Road, Ossett, West Yorkshire, WF5 9ND Tel: (01924) 283322 Fax: (01924) 283344 E-mail: info@electrogate.co.uk *Automatic gates & traffic barriers services*
Electrogenerators Ltd, 14 Australia Road, Slough, SL1 1SA Tel: (01753) 522877 Fax: (01753) 824653 *Foundry machinery manufacturers & shot blasters*
Electroglass Ltd, 4 Brunel Road, Manor Trading Estate, Benfleet, Essex, SS7 4PS Tel: (01268) 565577 Fax: (01268) 565594 E-mail: info@electroglass.co.uk *Glass industry consultants*
Electrolab Ltd, Unit E2 Northway Trading Estate, Northway Lane, Tewkesbury, Gloucestershire, GL20 8JH Tel: (01684) 291007 Fax: (01684) 291006 E-mail: sales@electrolab.co.uk *Fermentation industrial equipment manufrs*
Electrolube, Midland Road, Swadlincote, Derbyshire, DE11 0AN Tel: (01283) 222111 Fax: (01283) 550177 E-mail: el_sales@hkw.co.uk *Lubrication, protection & cleaning distributors & manufrs*
Electrolux Ltd, Cornwall House, 55-57 High Street, Slough, SL1 1DZ Tel: (01753) 872500 Fax: (01753) 872501 *Fridges, freezers & washing machines*
Electrolux, Merrington Lane Trading Estate, Spennymoor, County Durham, DL16 7UU Tel: (01388) 814141 Fax: (01388) 812753 E-mail: graham.metcalfe@electrolux.co.uk *Domestic appliance manufrs*
Electrolux Outdoor Products, Preston Road, Aycliffe Industrial Park, Newton Aycliffe, County Durham, DL5 6UP Tel: (01325) 300303 Fax: (01325) 310339 *Lawn mower manufrs*
Electrolux Professional, Crystal Court, Aston Cross Business Park, Rocky Lane, Aston, Birmingham, B6 5RQ Tel: 0121-220 2800 Fax: 0121-220 2801 E-mail: foodservice@electrolux.co.uk *World leader in the production and distribution of food service solutions.* We have more than 200 exclusive patents.* Hundreds of thousands of kitchen appliances produced in the world's largest factories.* More than 1,000 sales agencies and 1,200 certified service centres. 60,000 hours of operator trainings per year in 52 training centres worldwide.* Electrolux Food Service makes life more enjoyable for consumers eating out of home, applying the most advanced technologies to guarantee always tasty and safe food, maximizing operators' revenues.*
Electrolytic Plating Co. Ltd, Crown Works, Wednesbury Road, Walsall, WS1 4JJ Tel: (01922) 627466 Fax: (01922) 723844 E-mail: sales@electrolytic.co.uk *Electroplating services*
Electromagnetic Testing Services, Pratts Field, Lubberhedges Lane, Stebbing, Dunmow, Essex, CM6 3BT Tel: (01371) 856061 Fax: (01371) 856144 E-mail: info@etsemc.co.uk *Electromagnetic testing*
Electromatic Scientific Instruments Ltd, Orchard House, Jubilee Bank Road, King's Lynn, Norfolk, PE34 4BJ Tel: (01553) 775526 Fax: (01553) 691023 *Peristaltic pump manufrs*
Electromec Access, Unit 11 Buslingthorpe Green, Leeds, LS7 2HG Tel: 0113-239 2818 Fax: 0113-237 4088 E-mail: sales@electromec-access.co.uk Principal Export Areas: Worldwide *External maintenance cradle system manufrs*
Electro-mec (Reading) Ltd, 28 Portman Road, Reading, RG30 1EA Tel: 0118-958 2035 Fax: 0118-950 5049 E-mail: info@electromec.co.uk *Manufacturers of aircraft components*
Electromech Engineering Services, 174 Manchester Road, Astley, Tyldesley, Manchester, M29 7FB Tel: (01942) 888181 Fax: (01942) 888802 E-mail: sales@electromech.org *Diesel generating equipment specialists*
▶ Electromech Packaging Services, 93 Sherrards Way, Barnet, Hertfordshire, EN5 2BP Tel: (020) 8440 9564 Fax: (020) 8440 0176 *End of Line Packaging M/C *Specialists in Pallet Wrappers, *Shrink Wrappers,*for Service/Sales/Hire *www.eps-packaging.com*
▶ Electro-Mechanical Assembly Ltd, Zetland Road, Hillington Industrial Estate, Glasgow, G52 4BW Tel: 0141-883 4875 Fax: 0141-883 0158 E-mail: dave.stark@emaglasgow.co.uk *Electronics sub contractor*
Electro-Medical Supplies Greenham, Grove Street, Wantage, Oxfordshire, OX12 7AD Tel: (01235) 772272 Fax: (01235) 763518 E-mail: info@emslimited.co.uk *Electro-therapy equipment manufrs*
Electron Beam Engineering, 49a Mill Corner, Soham, Ely, Cambridgeshire, CB7 5HT Tel: (01353) 624196 Fax: (01353) 624196 E-mail: ebengineering@btinternet.com *Electron beam welding engineers & services*
Electron Systems Ltd, Unit 5b Drum Industrial Estate, Chester le Street, County Durham, DH2 1SS Tel: 0191-492 2007 Fax: 0191-492 2009 E-mail: sales@electronsystems.com *Industrial automated control specialists*
Electron Technical Solutions Ltd, 14-15 Arkwright Road, Astmoor Industrial Estate, Runcorn, Cheshire, WA7 1NU Tel: (01928) 567474 Fax: (01928) 580516 E-mail: info@electron-ts.co.uk *Spray painting of plastic & rubber components, and subsequent assembly operations.*
Electron Technologies Ltd, Bury Street, Ruislip, Middlesex, HA4 7TA Tel: (01895) 630771 Fax: (01895) 635953 E-mail: info@electron-tubes.co.uk *Electron Tubes designs, develops, and manufactures high sensitivity, low noise photomultipliers for the measurement of very low light levels. *Most recently we have been developing new business with the our X-ray detection and data acquisition modules and with the LINX linear X-ray system.*We can also offer customised light detector modules and a complete instrument design-to-manufacture service.*Take a look at our website www.electrontubes.com and contact as by e-mail: info@electron-tubes.co.uk to discuss your requirements.**
Electronic Archive Solutions Ltd, 14 The Briars, Waterberry Drive, Waterlooville, Hampshire, PO7 7YH Tel: (023) 9223 3833 Fax: (023) 9223 8577 E-mail: info@e-asl.com *Computer software consultants*
▶ Electronic Business Services Ltd, Cavalry Park, Peebles, EH45 9BU Tel: (01721) 724881 Fax: (01721) 724882 E-mail: info@ebs-europe.com *Website design services*
Electronic Business Solutions, Business Centre West Letchworth Business Centre, Avenue One, Letchworth Garden City, Hertfordshire, SG6 2HB Tel: (01462) 483868 *Internet based business applications design & developers*
Electronic Business Systems Ltd, 852 Tyburn Road, Birmingham, B24 9NT Tel: 0121-384 2513 Fax: 0121-377 6014 E-mail: info@e-b-s.co.uk *Office equipment manufrs*
Electronic Data Processing P.L.C., Beauchief Hall, Beauchief, Sheffield, S8 7BA Tel: 0114-262 1621 Fax: 0114-262 1126 *Computing services* Also at: Halesowen, Livingstone, London N12, Milton Keynes & Woking
Electronic Data Processing Group P.L.C., Sunrise Parkway, Linford Wood, Milton Keynes, MK14 6LJ Tel: (01908) 665522 *Computer systems & software sales*
▶ Electronic Design Associates, 20 Greenock Road, Streatham, London, SW16 5XG Tel: 020 86796355 Fax: 020 86796355 E-mail: bill@electronicdesignassociates.co.uk *Suppliers of Electronic Monitoring Equipment.*Specialist repair of Veterinary electronics, hardware and lighting.*
Electronic Design Services Ltd, Stewart Street, Bury, Lancashire, BL8 1SP Tel: 0161-705 2117 Fax: 0161-763 6940 *Industrial printed circuit designers, assemblers & repairs*
The Electronic Development Co. Ltd, 26 Beckett Road, Worcester, WR3 7NH Tel: (01905) 759609 Fax: (01905) 453273 E-mail: jonathan@the-electronic-development.co.uk *Electronic product designers*
▶ Electronic Document Services Ltd, 54 Bankhead Crossway South, Edinburgh, EH11 4EP Tel: 0131-442 3000
Electronic & General Services Ltd, 3 Hitchs Yard, Church Street, Ware, Hertfordshire, SG12 9ES Tel: (01920) 468991 Fax: (01920) 469938 E-mail: klick@egs.co.uk *Computer maintenance services*
▶ Electronic Imaging Solutions, Fulmer House, Ocean Way, Cardiff, CF24 5HF Tel: (029) 2025 0900 Fax: (029) 2025 0901 *Business equipment suppliers*
▶ Electronic Lighting, 77-78 Fore Street, Buckfastleigh, Devon, TQ11 0BS Tel: (01364) 642111 Fax: (01364) 642111 *Electronics equipment suppliers*
Electronic Media Services, Lynchborough Road, Passfield, Liphook, Hampshire, GU30 7SB Tel: (01428) 751655 Fax: (01428) 751654 E-mail: info@ems-uk.com *Computer software consultants*
Electronic Metal Work Services Ltd, Hampstead Avenue, Mildenhall, Bury St. Edmunds, Suffolk, IP28 7AS Tel: (01638) 712054 Fax: (01638) 713832 E-mail: info@emws.co.uk *Metalwork manufrs*
Electronic Modular Solutions Ltd, Kendal House, 20 Blaby Road, Wigston, Leicestershire, LE18 4SB Tel: 0116-277 5730 Fax: 0116-277 4973 E-mail: sales@video-captures.com *Digital video & multimedia products*
▶ The Electronic Page Co., 218-219 Springvale Industrial Estate, Cwmbran, Gwent, NP44 5BJ Tel: (01633) 875555 Fax: (01633) 871990 E-mail: sales@electronicpage.co.uk
Electronic Payments & Commerce Ltd, 139 Tankerton Road, Whitstable, Kent, CT5 2AW Tel: (01227) 273000 E-mail: epaycom@compuserve.com *Computer consultants*
Electronic Print Systems, 51 Bells Road, Gorleston, Great Yarmouth, Norfolk, NR31 6AN Tel: (01493) 664204 Fax: (01493) 440241 E-mail: gabform@gtyarmouth.co.uk *Continuous stationery suppliers*
▶ Electronic Product Supplies Ltd, 7 Hillview Road, Irby, Wirral, Merseyside, CH61 4XH Tel: 0151-648 6736 E-mail: enquiries@electronicproductsupplies.co.uk *Electronic design services*
Electronic Production Services, Lansbury Estate, 102 Lower Guildford Road, Knaphill, Woking, Surrey, GU21 2EP Tel: (01483) 487644 Fax: (01483) 486347 E-mail: epswoking@btconnect.com *Electronic production services & product assembly*
Electronic Products & Industrial Control Systems Ltd, Unit 2 Bailey Drive, Sheffield, S21 2JF Tel: 0114-251 0801 Fax: 0114-248 8197 E-mail: epicsystemsltd@btinternet.com *Electronic batch weighers*
▶ Electronic Products Realisation, 6 Grant Street, Brighton, BN2 9UN Tel: (01273) 674757 E-mail: enqs@epritd.co.uk *Electronic Product Realisation Ltd - Designers and Consultant Engineers - Electronic Products, IT and Web.EPR are specialists in the design, development and manufacturing of electronic products for sale with all design and legal requirements*
Electronic Reading Systems Ltd, 14 Wolsdon Business Park, Woburn Road Industrial Estate, Kempston, Bedford, MK42 7PW Tel: (01234) 855300 Fax: (01234) 855446 E-mail: sales@ersltd.co.uk *ERS is a leading specialist in the field of data capture, information control and auto-ID, majoring in barcode, magnetic stripe and smart card technologies. Providing the complete data capture solution from a single scanner to a fully integrated and networked system.*
Electronic Recording Systems, Dundridge Lane, Bishops Waltham, Southampton, SO32 1GD Tel: (01489) 896682 Fax: (01489) 896682 *Dictating machine repairers*
Electronic Repair Technology, Signal Works, Talbot Road, Wellingborough, Northants, NN8 1QH Tel: (01933) 228866 Fax: (01933) 443623 E-mail: dave@autocontrol.freeserve.co.uk *Repairers of electronic equipment*
Electronic & Security Services Ltd, 50 Boucher Place, Belfast, BT12 6HT Tel: (028) 9066 3510 Fax: (028) 9066 1995 E-mail: info@ess-security.co.uk *Electric security systems installers & retailers*

► Electronic Security Systems & Fire Protection Ltd, Roman Road, Kirkintilloch, Glasgow, G66 1DY Tel: 0141-776 0999 Fax: 0141-776 4225

Electronic Services, 15 Cherry Tree Road, Wakefield, West Yorkshire, WF2 6LJ Tel: (01924) 256397 Fax: (01924) 256397 E-mail: john@jelecserv.wanadoo.co.uk *Microwave oven suppliers sales & service*

Electronic Storage Ltd, Endeavour House, Queens Road, Sunninghill, Ascot, Berkshire, SL5 9AF Tel: (01344) 874477 Fax: (01344) 871720 E-mail: sales@electronicstorage.co.uk *IT specialist*

Electronic & Technical Services Ltd, Unit 32, Price St Business Centre, Birkenhead, Merseyside, CH41 4JQ Tel: 0151-670 1897 Fax: 0151-652 9941 *Control systems manufrs*

Electronic Terminations Ltd, High Street, Wickham Market, Woodbridge, Suffolk, IP13 0RF Tel: (01728) 748111 Fax: (01728) 748222 E-mail: etl@grouproland.com *Electronic equipment manufrs*

Electronic Theatre Controls Ltd, Unit 26-28 Victoria Industrial, Estate Victoria Road, London, W3 6UU Tel: (020) 8896 1000 Fax: (020) 8896 2000 E-mail: mail@etcconnect.com *Lighting equipment manufrs*

Electronic Vision International Ltd, 39-43 Newarke Street, Leicester, LE1 5SP Tel: 0116-222 0919 Fax: 0116-222 1964 *Computer consultants*

Electronic Visuals Ltd, 20 Ferry Lane, Wraysbury, Staines, Middlesex, TW19 6HG Tel: (01784) 483311 Fax: (01784) 483918 E-mail: info@electronic-visuals.com *Test equipment.*

Electronic Weighing Services Ltd, Lytton Street, Stoke-On-Trent, ST4 2AG Tel: (01782) 416322 Fax: (01782) 413660 E-mail: sales@electronicweighing.co.uk *Weighing systems service*

Electronics 2000 Ltd, Grafton House, Grafton Street, High Wycombe, Buckinghamshire, HP12 3AJ Tel: (01494) 444044 Fax: (01494) 470499 E-mail: sales@e2000.com Principal Export Areas: Central/East Europe & West Europe *Electronic component distributors or agents* Also at: Dublin

Electronics Boutique, 6 Castle La, Belfast, BT1 5DA Tel: (028) 9024 8386 Fax: (028) 9024 7545 *Computer software*

Electronics Boutique Ltd, 39 Princess Square, Bracknell, Berkshire, RG12 1LS Tel: (01344) 305500 *Computer games retailer*

Electronics Boutique, 9 Havelock Square, Swindon, SN1 1LE Tel: (01793) 436946 Fax: (01793) 436946 *Computer games retailers*

Electronics Weekly, Quadrant House, The Quadrant, Sutton, Surrey, SM2 5AS Tel: (020) 8652 3500 Fax: (020) 8652 8938 *Electronics Weekly is the UK's leading magazine for electronics professionals, and together with ElectronicsWeekly.com offers news, analysis, features, business stories and hundreds of jobs.**ElectronicsWeekly.com is the online arm of Electronics Weekly, for over 40 years the leading source of information in the UK electronics industry.**Electronics Weekly brings you the best news and technology coverage in the industry, accessing stories from around the world via our partners in the Reed Electronics Group including Electronic News, EDN and EPN.*

► Electron-X Ltd, 20 Burners Lane, Kiln Farm, Milton Keynes, MK11 3HB Tel: (01908) 566794 Fax: 01908 305062 E-mail: sales@electron-x.co.uk *Industrial x-ray engineering consultants and project managers.*Designers and suppliers of purpose built x-ray cabinets, enclosures or rooms. Rental of micro-focus inspection systems*

Electropak Ltd, Bushell Street Mill, Bushell Street, Preston, PR1 2SP Tel: (01772) 251444 Fax: (01772) 251555 E-mail: info@electropak.net *Electronic enclosures manufacturers & engravers* Also at: Rossendale

Electropatent International Ltd, 30-32 Blyth Road, Hayes, Middlesex, UB3 1BY Tel: (020) 8867 3500 Fax: (020) 8573 9090 E-mail: sales@electropatent.co.uk *Electrical power voice data cable management systems*

► Electroplan Contracting Ltd, 2-4 St. James Road, Brentwood, Essex, CM14 4LF Tel: (01277) 210893 Fax: (01277) 849193

Electrosembly Co., 35-37 Haviland Road, Ferndown Industrial Estate, Wimborne, Dorset, BH21 7SA Tel: (01202) 893392 Fax: (01202) 893378 *Electronic contract manufacturing*

Electroserv Control Panel Mnfrs, Unit A Wentworth Industrial Court, Goodwin Road, Slough, SL2 2ER Tel: (01753) 539606 Fax: (01753) 539606 *Control panel manufrs*

Electroserv International, 30a Townley Street, Macclesfield, Cheshire, SK11 6HZ Tel: (01625) 615626 Fax: (01625) 617559 *Temperature control & thermocouple manufrs*

Electroserv (T C & S) Ltd, PO Box 163, Macclesfield, Cheshire, SK11 6JY Tel: (01625) 618526 Fax: (01625) 500746 E-mail: dh@electroserv.co.uk *Manufacturers of process controllers control instrumentation*

Electroserve Mechanical Handling Equipment, 8 Lemmington Way, Horsham, West Sussex, RH12 5JG Tel: (01403) 273335 Fax: (01403) 249803 *Forklift truck sales, rental & service*

Electrosite UK Ltd, Easton Lane, Bozeat, Wellingborough, Northamptonshire, NN29 7NN Tel: (01933) 665022 Fax: (01933) 665520 E-mail: electrosite@kbnet.net *Electrical equipment manufrs*

► Electrospect Ltd, 240 Queensferry Road, Edinburgh, EH4 2BP Tel: 0131-443 1692

Electrostatic Solutions Ltd, 13 Redhill Crescent, Southampton, SO16 7BQ Tel: (023) 8090 5600 E-mail: jeremys@static-sol.com *Electrostatic consultants*

Electrotech Files Ltd, 1 Stanley Buildings, Back Reads Road, Blackpool, FY1 4QL Tel: (01253) 628111 Fax: (01253) 628999 *Commercial cleaning equipment repairers*

Electrotech Maintenance Services, Clarkswell House, Sugarswell Business Park, Shennington, Banbury, Oxon, OX15 6HW Tel: (01295) 688429 Fax: (01295) 680005

continued

E-mail: admin@electrotech-cds.co.uk *Manufacturers of automatic & environmental control systems*

► Electrotech Solutions, Unit 2 Swan Park, Kettlebrook Road, Tamworth, Staffs, B77 1AG Tel: 01827 63989 Fax: 01827 64910 E-mail: mark@electrotech-solutions.co.uk *Electronic & Specialist Electronic Repair*System Integrators*Software Design & De-bug*Electro-mechanical Repair & Service*

Electrotechnical Engineering Ltd, Unit 3 The Rose Estate, Osbourne Way, Hook, Hampshire, RG27 9UT Tel: (01256) 766914 Fax: (01256) 766915 E-mail: sally-ottaway@eteltd.co.uk *Radio frequency power consultants*

Electrothermal Ltd, North Norfolk Ho, Pitmedden Road, Dyce, Aberdeen, AB21 0DP Tel: (01224) 722888 Fax: (01224) 772103 E-mail: eric.florence@rigblast.com *Electric surface heating contractors*

Electrothermal Engineering Ltd, 419 Sutton Road, Southend-on-Sea, SS2 5PH Tel: (01702) 612211 Fax: (01702) 619888 E-mail: sales@electrothermal.co.uk *Laboratory equipment manufrs*

Electroustic Ltd, 1 Eaglesfield Industrial Estate, Main Street, Leire, Lutterworth, Leicestershire, LE17 5HF Tel: (01455) 202364 Fax: (01455) 209043 E-mail: sales@electroustic.co.uk *Electric connectors distributors*

Electroversal Ltd, Units 4-9 Ribocon Way, Off Toddington Road, Luton, LU4 9UR Tel: (01582) 582023 Fax: (01582) 582087 E-mail: sales@electroversal.com *Electronic equipment repair & refurbishment*

Electrovision Ltd, Lancots Lane, St. Helens, Merseyside, WA9 3EX Tel: (01744) 745000 Fax: (01744) 745001 E-mail: sales@electrovision.co.uk *Industrial electronic distributors*

Elegance In Glass Ltd, Hill Lane Close, Markfield, Leicestershire, LE67 9PY Tel: (01530) 243838 Fax: (01530) 249122 E-mail: sales@eing.co.uk *Make decorative stain glasses*

Elegant, Estate House, 143 Connaught Avenue, Frinton-on-Sea, Essex, CO13 9AB Tel: (01255) 679559 Fax: (01255) 679825 E-mail: elegantltd@btconnect.com *Garden furniture wholesalers*

► Elegant Bathroom Interiors, Unit 29 G L S Depot, Mill Mead Road, London, N17 9QQ Tel: (020) 8885 5404

► Elegant IT Ltd, PO Box 381, Northampton, NN4 6WL Tel: (01604) 420001 Fax: (01604) 420002 E-mail: ian.jenkins@elegant-it.co.uk *Information technology consultancy*

► Elegant Lacing, 28 Longlands Road, Halesowen, West Midlands, B62 0AZ Tel: 0121-422 6476 Fax: 0121-422 3298 E-mail: barbara@elegantlacing.co.uk *From England's finest corsetieres - vollers, axfords & velda lauder - we are proud to offer traditional, modern, authentic steel boned tightlacing corsets, featuring both overbust & underbust designs in a wide variety of fabrics & colors that are both desirable & delectable, including softest satins, beautiful brocades, gorgeous velvet, luxurious Chinese silk & sumptuous leather & suede - for that discerning hourglass figure*

Elegant Plaster Mouldings, 1 Talbots La Trading Estate, Talbots Lane, Brierley Hill, West Midlands, DY5 2YX Tel: (01384) 263000 Fax: (01384) 262792 E-mail: die.tech@virgin.net *Plastic vacuum forming toolmakers*

Elegant Textile, 93 Commerce Street, Glasgow, G5 8EP Tel: 0141-420 1533 Fax: 0141-420 1533 E-mail: eleganttextiles@hotmail.com *Hosiery manufrs*

Elegant Window Systems Ltd, 1b St Vincent Street, Barrow-in-Furness, Cumbria, LA14 2NT Tel: (01229) 813066 Fax: (01229) 431933 *PVC fittings*

Eleganti Ltd, 3 Derby Road, Eastwood, Nottingham, NG16 3PA Tel: (01773) 534700 Fax: (01773) 534700 *Hosiery*

► Elektrek Services Ltd, 19 Manning Road, Felixstowe, Suffolk, IP11 2AY Tel: (01394) 270777 Fax: 01394 670189 E-mail: mail@elektrek.com *Electrical Engineers, specialising in marine repairs, servicing & installations. Authorised Agents for Kidde Graviner Oil Mist Detectors*

Elektrek Services Ltd, 19 Manning Road, Felixstowe, Suffolk, IP11 2AY Tel: (01394) 270777 Fax: (01394) 387177 E-mail: enquire@elektrek.com *Electrical engineers & contractors*

Elektro Magnetix Ltd, Sussex Innovation Centre, Science Park Square, Falmer, Brighton, BN1 9SB Tel: (01273) 704471 Fax: (01273) 704472 E-mail: elektro@elektro.co.uk *Electric motor & actuator designers*

► Element A V, 59 St. Michaels Close, Aveley, South Ockendon, Essex, RM15 4SY Tel: (01708) 402977 Fax: (01708) 402977 E-mail: andy@elementav.com *Audio visual installation services*

Elemental Microanalysis Ltd, Okehampton Business Park, Okehampton, Devon, EX20 1UB Tel: (01837) 54446 Fax: (01837) 54544 E-mail: info@microanalysis.co.uk *Microanalytical reagents suppliers, instrument suppliers*

Elemental Technology, PO Box 167, Petersfield, Hampshire, GU32 3LS Tel: (01730) 269857 Fax: (0870) 7065719 E-mail: enquiries@etluk.com *IT consultancy & support*

Elementis Chromium, Urlay Nook Road, Eaglescliffe, Stockton-on-Tees, Cleveland, TS16 0QG Tel: (01642) 780682 Fax: (01642) 791866 E-mail: chromium.uk@elementis-eu.com *Producers of chromium chemicals*

Elementis Specialties, Birtley, Chester le Street, County Durham, DH3 1QX Tel: 0191-410 5522 Fax: 0191-410 6005 E-mail: specinfo.uk@elemantis.com *Chemical manufrs*

Elementis UK Ltd, Nettlehill Road, Houston Industrial Estate, Livingston, West Lothian, EH54 5DL Tel: (01506) 430331 Fax: (020) 7398 1401 E-mail: info@elementis.com *Gellant chemical suppliers*

► Elena, Lingo24 Ltd, 31 Chelsea Park Gardens, London, SW3 6AF Tel: (0870) 7654646

Elephant Boatyard Ltd, Lands End Road, Bursledon, Southampton, SO31 8DN Tel: (023) 8040 3268 Fax: (023) 8040 5085 *Boat builders*

► Elephant Removals, Unit 1 53 Wandle Way, London, SW18 4UJ Tel: (020) 8877 9263 Fax: (0845) 0091801 E-mail: info@elephantremovals.co.uk *London Removals, UK Removals & International, Free Estimate - 30% Discount - Any Distance - Single Items, Home or Office - Delivery or Collection - Packing Materials or Services - Fully Insured - Storage - 7 Days - Short Notice, No Problems*

Elero UK Ltd, Foundry Lane, Halebank, Widnes, Cheshire, WA8 8TZ Tel: (0870) 2404219 Fax: (0870) 2404086 E-mail: sales@elerouk.co.uk *Innovators of motors & controls for blinds, shutters & awnings*

► Elesta UK Building Automation, PO Box 3418, Slough, SL1 0BR Tel: (01628) 664441 Fax: (01628) 664441 E-mail: info@elesta.co.uk *Building automation manufrs*

Elevation, 66 Patcham Terrace, London, SW8 4BP Tel: (020) 7622 5433 *Cabinet makers*

► Elevation Rigging Ltd, 3 Duchess Place, Edgbaston House, Birmingham, B16 8NH Tel: 0121 456 7949 Fax: 0121 789 6190 E-mail: mail@elevationrigging.com *Elevation is a provider of rigging services to the event and exhibition industry. We supply aluminium trussing and ground supported systems for the suspension of lighting, sound and AV equipment to "soft" solutions such as theatre drapes and bespoke cloths for venue dressing.*

► Elevations Roofing Specialists (UK) Ltd, The Ridings, Biggin Hill, Westerham, Kent, TN16 3LE Tel: (0800) 5877765 Fax: (01959) 572462 E-mail: info@elevationsroofing.co.uk *Roofing service*

Eley Ltd, Selco Way Off First Avenue, Minworth Industrial Estate, Minworth, Sutton Coldfield, West Midlands, B76 1BA Tel: 0121-313 4567 Fax: 0121-331 4173 E-mail: sales@eleyhawkltd.com *Ammunition cartridge manufrs*

► Eley Metrology Ltd, Beaufort House Beaufort Court Industrial Estate, Mansfield Road, Derby, DE21 4FS Tel: (01332) 367475 Fax: (01332) 371435 E-mail: email@eleymet.com *Metrology services*

Elf Ltd, Unit 1, Forest Close, Ebblake Industrial Estate, Verwood, Dorset, BH31 6DE Tel: (01202) 822206 Fax: (01202) 823382 E-mail: sales@elf.co.uk *Computer components*

► Elf Forktrucks, Alder Street, Huddersfield, HD1 6JY Tel: (01484) 511101 Fax: (01484) 432764 E-mail: sales@elfforktrucks.co.uk *Fork lift truck sales & services*

Elf Productivity, The Stables, Skull House Lane, Appley Bridge, Wigan, Lancashire, WN6 9DJ Tel: (01257) 256000 Fax: (01257) 256010 E-mail: sales@elf.uk.com *Computer software, monitoring systems & people management*

► Elf Software, Whitchurch Road, Wellington, Telford, Shropshire, TF1 3DS Tel: (01952) 249900 Fax: (01952) 249907 E-mail: info@elf-soft.co.uk *Software developing services*

Elfab Ltd, Alder Road, North Shields, Tyne & Wear, NE29 8SD Tel: 0191-293 1269 Fax: 0191-293 1200 E-mail: sales@elfab.com Principal Export Areas: Central Asia, Middle East, Africa, Central/ East Europe & West Europe *Manufacturer of Pressure Relief Safety Devices including bursting discs, explosion panels and detecting devices*

Elg Haniel Metals Ltd, Templeborough Works, Sheffield Road, Sheffield, S9 1RT Tel: 0114-244 3333 Fax: 0114-256 1742 E-mail: enquiries@elg.co.uk *Stainless steel re-processors*

Elga Welding Consumables, Unit 102 Rivington House, Horwich Business Park, Chorley New Road, Horwich, Bolton, BL6 5UE Tel: (01204) 473020 Fax: (01204) 473039 E-mail: sales@itw-welding.co.uk *Welding supplies distributors*

Elgamec, Unit 9-11 Enterprise Industrial Estate, Station Road West, Ash Vale, Aldershot, Hampshire, GU12 5QJ Tel: (01252) 518177 Fax: (01252) 541331 E-mail: info@elgamec.com *Elgamec Ltd founded in 1979 is one of the leading metal finishing companies in South East England. Elgamec provide a high quality professional service across a wide range of industries including the Automotive industry, Aircraft Furnishing industry, Stainless Steel industry & the Glass industry as well as producing specialised surface finishing now widely used in the seat manufacturing trade.Elgamec are ISO registered and offer a range of hand cabinets for specialist work & blast rooms for larger projects. Other services include: specialised surface finishing, reconditioning, surface enhancing, bead blasting, grit blasting, shot blasting, alumini blasting, shot peening, glass bead peening, chemical free etching (including window etching, glass etching & mirror etching), rust removal, surface bond preparation, hard anodising, electroplating, chromate conversion & stove enamelling.*

Elgate Products, Unit 1 Patricia Way, Pysons Road Industrial Estate, Broadstairs, Kent, CT10 2LF Tel: (01843) 609200 Fax: (01843) 866234 E-mail: sales@elgate.co.uk *Fancy goods distribs*

Elgee Plastics Ltd, Wilson Road, Reading, RG30 2RS Tel: 0118-957 5430 Fax: 0118-958 8782 *Plastic fabricators*

Elgin Refrigeration Services Ltd, Unit 1, Linkwood Industrial Estate, Elgin, Morayshire, IV30 1HY Tel: (01343) 543116 Fax: (01343) 549910 *Refrigeration & air conditioning manufrs*

Elgood Industrial Flooring Ltd, Yeoman Street, London, SE8 5DU Tel: (020) 7237 1144 Fax: (020) 7237 1629 E-mail: nigel@elgood.com *Industrial floor manufrs*

Eli Lilly Holdings Ltd, Kingsclere Road, Basingstoke, Hampshire, RG21 6XA Tel: (01256) 315000 Fax: (01256) 315858 *Pharmaceutical & marketing*

Elif Fashions Ltd, 2 Leswin Place, London, N16 7NJ Tel: (020) 7923 7469 Fax: (020) 7923 7469 E-mail: enquiries@eliffashions.com *Clothing manufrs*

► E-Linc Technologies Ltd, 3 Farrington Crescent, Lincoln, LN6 0YG Tel: (01522) 567765 E-mail: neil@elinc.co.uk

Elite, Forest Row, East Sussex, RH18 5ES Tel: (01342) 822292 E-mail: info@elitespage.co.uk *Song writer, vocalist, backing vocalist/keyboard player for studio and live work (including touring), producer, composer, music teacher - piano, keyboard, singing, computer production for children and adults.*

Elite Blinds, 160 Vernon Road, Nottingham, NG6 0AD Tel: 0115-942 0898 Fax: 0115-942 3442 *Blinds manufrs*

Elite Blinds & Tracks Ltd, Unit 10 Chitterley Workshops, Silverton, Exeter, EX5 4DB Tel: (01392) 860141 Fax: (01392) 860141 E-mail: eliteblindsdevon@btconnect.com *Blind manufrs*

Elite Blinds UK, 39 Whalley New Road, Blackburn, BB1 6JY Tel: (01254) 674263 Fax: (01254) 261935 E-mail: sales@eliteblindsuk.com *Blind manufrs*

► Elite Body Supplements, Sharma Park Industrial Estate, Grant Avenue, Leeds, LS7 1QB Tel: 0113-244 4959 Fax: 0113-244 4962

Elite Cables & Components Ltd, 5 Smiths Forge, North End Road, Yatton, Bristol, BS49 4AU Tel: (01934) 876661 Fax: (01934) 876646 E-mail: sales@elitecables.co.uk *Distributors & manufacturers of electrical cables*

Elite Caravans Ltd, 7 Signet Court, Swans Road, Cambridge, CB5 8LA Tel: (01223) 361433 Fax: (01223) 312010 *Caravan distributors* Also at: Blisworth

► Elite Ceiling Manufacturers Ltd, Ridgeway Industrial Estate, Iver, Buckinghamshire, SL0 9HU Tel: (01753) 654411 Fax: (01753) 630002 E-mail: henry@ecmuk.com *Suspended ceiling systems manufrs*

Elite Contract Security Ltd, Elite House, 83-85 Badsley Moor Lane, Rotherham, South Yorkshire, S65 2PH Tel: (01709) 382120 Fax: (01709) 376000 E-mail: ecs2004@aol.com *Security services*

Elite Contract Services Ltd, 6 Petsworth Lane, Great Notley, Braintree, Essex, CM77 7XS Tel: (0845) 2262796 E-mail: enquiries@ecsit.co.uk *Computer maintenance*

Elite Control Systems Ltd, Elite House, Starlaw Business Park, Livingston, West Lothian, EH54 8SF Tel: (01506) 597900 Fax: (01506) 597919 E-mail: admin@elitecontrols.co.uk *Control systems distributors*

Elite Cutters Ltd, Oakfield Works, Branksome Hill Road, College Town, Sandhurst, Berkshire, GU47 0QE Tel: (01276) 32991 Fax: (01276) 600146 E-mail: kriswatling@elitecutters.fsnet.co.uk *Printing trade finishing services*

► Elite Dental Studios, 30 West Street, Burgess Hill, West Sussex, RH15 8NX Tel: (01444) 245145 Fax: (01444) 245145

Elite Electric Gates, Unit 16 Bottesford Lane, Orston, Nottingham, NG13 9NX Tel: (01949) 831113 Fax: *Electric gate suppliers & installers*

► Elite Electrical Services Ltd, 2 Fieldings Road, Cheshunt, Waltham Cross, Hertfordshire, EN8 9TL Tel: (01992) 642000 Fax: (01992) 642959

Elite Electronic Systems Ltd, Lackaghboy Industrial Estate, Lackaghboy, Enniskillen, County Fermanagh, BT74 4RL Tel: (028) 6632 7172 Fax: (028) 6632 5668 E-mail: sales@elitees.com *Electronic contract manufacturing services*

► Elite Elevators, Gwynfa House, 663-675 Princes Road, Dartford, DA2 6EF Tel: (01322) 628100 Fax: (01322) 628101 *Elevator & lift suppliers*

Elite Engineering, 9 Neptune Works, Upper Trinity Street, Birmingham, B9 4EG Tel: 0121-772 8070 Fax: 0121-772 2230 *Bolt & screw manufrs*

Elite Engineering Ltd, 1 Davis Way, Fareham, Hampshire, PO14 1JF Tel: (01329) 231435 Fax: (01329) 822759 E-mail: sales@elite-eng.co.uk *PCB assembly production machinery*

Elite Engineering, Enterprise Road, Mablethorpe, Lincolnshire, LN12 1NB Tel: (07931) 404413 E-mail: colin@eliteengineering.org.uk *Elite Engineering (Mablethorpe) steel products manufacturing***Our aim is to provide you with all your Welding & Fabrication Needs From Automotive to Structural, all done to a high quality and at a competitive price. Our staff have over 20 year"s of experience.**We also design construct and hire trailers of all shapes and sizes. we also buy second-hand trailers. please contact us. ***We are A small and enterprising company based in Mablethorpe on the east coast of Lincolnshire uk.**Telephone: *01507 4771 **Mobile: *07931 4044 **Email colin@eliteengineering.org.uk**WEB www.eliteengineering.org.uk*

Elite Engraving, 6 Park Road, Kingswood, Bristol, BS15 1QU Tel: 0117-967 0034 Fax: 0117-967 0043 E-mail: eliteengraving@btconnect.com *General & process engraving services*

► Elite Estate Planning, West Midlands House, Gipsy Lane, Willenhall, West Midlands, WV13 2HA Tel: (0800) 4589188 E-mail: jon@eliteestateplanning.co.uk *Did you know that the U.K government took over 2.4 billion pounds last year in inheritance tax from people who never had the correct estate planning provision. Passing your wealth on to your heirs through your estate requires more than just a will, especially if your goal is to protect your assets from estate taxes*

► Elite Foods, Unit 3g Aireworth Mills, Aireworth Road, Keighley, West Yorkshire, BD21 4DH Tel: (01535) 661188 Fax: (01535) 661188 *Meat products, processed & cooked suppliers*

Elite Greenhouses Ltd, Bent Spur Road, Kearsley, Bolton, BL4 8PD Tel: (01204) 791488 Fax: (01204) 862412 E-mail: enquiries@elite-greenhouses.co.uk *Greenhouse manufrs*

Elite Group Computer Systems (UK) Ltd, Units 1-3, Newmarket Court, Kingston, Milton Keynes, MK10 0AG Tel: (01908) 481830 Fax: (01908) 481831 *Computer components*

▶ Elite Homes North West, Redwood House Woodlands Park, Ashton Road, Newton-le-Willows, Merseyside, WA12 0ZW Tel: (0870) 3503535 Fax: (0870) 3503536 E-mail: reception@elitehomes.co.uk

Elite Industrial Services, 41 Mafeking Road, Walderslade, Chatham, Kent, ME5 9HG Tel: (01634) 683334 Fax: (01634) 683334 *Silicone rubber product manufrs*

▶ Elite Landscapes, Penarth, London Road, Crays Hill, Billericay, Essex, CM11 2UY Tel: (01268) 526633 Fax: (01268) 526633 E-mail: sales@elitelandscapes.org

Elite Lockers Ltd, Daniel Street, Oldham, OL1 3NS Tel: 0161-620 4787 Fax: 0161-620 4733 E-mail: info@elitelockers.co.uk *Lockers & shelving manufrs*

Elite Metal Polishing Services, 81 Bunting Road, Northampton, NN2 6EE Tel: (01604) 712191 Fax: (01604) 712191 *Metal polishing & buffing services*

Elite Metalcraft, 9 Walmgate Road, Perivale, Greenford, Middlesex, UB6 7LH Tel: (020) 8810 5555 Fax: (020) 8810 5133 E-mail: sales@elitemetalcraft.co.uk *Architectural metalworkers & fabricators*

Elite Mobile Toilets, Owls End Farm, Brook Lane, Himbleton, Droitwich, Worcestershire, WR9 7LF Tel: (01905) 391204 *Portable toilet hire service*

Elite Office Supplies, 74 Bookerhill Road, High Wycombe, Buckinghamshire, HP12 4EX Tel: (01494) 473632 Fax: (01494) 440937 *Office stationery suppliers*

Elite Plastics Ltd, Twyford Road, Rotherwas Industrial Estate, Hereford, HR2 6JR Tel: (01432) 357337 Fax: (01432) 343175 E-mail: sales@eliteplastics.co.uk *Polythene extrusions manufrs*

Elite Promotions Personnel Ltd, 6 Park Lane, Whitefield, Manchester, M45 7PB Tel: 0161-272 1400 Fax: 0161-272 1401 E-mail: sales@elitepromo.co.uk *Event management & product launching services*

▶ Elite Removals, Dane Road, Margate, Kent, CT9 2AF Tel: (01843) 226736 E-mail: bernie@eliteremovalsmargate.co.uk *Flats, house, bungalows, all sizes of moves catered for. Local and long distance. Over 25 years experience within the moving industry. Removals in Margate Westgate Broadstairs Ramsgate Canterbury Herne Bay.*

Elite Safe & Security Services, Stanmore Industrial Estate, Bridgnorth, Shropshire, WV15 5HP Tel: (01952) 684855 E-mail: epicsafes@lineone.net *Security door & safes & other security manufrs*

Elite Screen Printing & Embroidery Ltd, 45 Sartoris Road, Rushden, Northamptonshire, NN10 9TL Tel: (01933) 315930 Fax: (01933) 418364 E-mail: elitetex@aol.com *Clothing printers & embroiderers*

▶ Elite Security, 27 James Clements Close, Kilwinning, Ayrshire, KA13 6PW Tel: (01294) 550155 Fax: (01294) 550170 *Burglar alarm system suppliers*

Elite Security, 168 Crowmere Road, Shrewsbury, SY2 5LA Tel: (01743) 441010 Fax: (01743) 341739 *Alarm installers*

Elite Security Services Ltd, Suite 1 2 Bateman Business Centre, Bateman Street, Derby, DE23 8JQ Tel: (01332) 383630 Fax: (01332) 299981 E-mail: sales@elite-derby.co.uk *Security installation services*

Elite Service Personnel, Suite 6 St. Georges House, St. Georges Road Industrial Estate, Donnington, Telford, Shropshire, TF2 7AS Tel: (01952) 616002 Fax: (01952) 612006 E-mail: info@elite-services.co.uk *Recruitment service consul, section & containment measurement automotive industry*

▶ Elite Services Ltd, Unit 3 & 6 Adswood Industrial Estate, Adswood Road, Stockport, Cheshire, SK3 8LF Tel: 0161-480 0617 Fax: 0161-480 3099 E-mail: sam_nickson@hotmail.com *We are a medium sized coach operator in Manchester, North West. We offer coaches from 35- 75 seats all of which are fully seatbelt complaint. We operate our coaches on most types of work, anything from school contracts to trips abroad. We also have Elite Seatbelts inside our group which supplys and fits seatbelts to almost any kind of vehicle. All of our fitments have been crash tested at MIRA and our work is insured. We offer 24 Roadside assitance to Coaches in the North West and also replacement coaches. We can also arrange recovery. If calling for roadside assitance out of normal office hours, please call the mobile number which is (07812964371)*

Elite Signs, 8 Cavendish Road, Salford, M7 4WW Tel: 0161-792 0232 Fax: 0161-792 0232 E-mail: elitesignsprint@aol.com *Sign makers & self-adhesive labels*

Elite Signs, Albemarle Rd, Taunton, Somerset, TA1 1BE Tel: (01823) 366219 Fax: (01823) 251095 E-mail: signs@elitecameron.com *Computer cut vinyl lettering*

Elite Signs & Clothing, 50 Trinity Street, Gainsborough, Lincolnshire, DN21 1HS Tel: (01427) 811800 Fax: (01427) 610444 *Sign installation & manufrs*

Elite Storage Ltd, New Holder Street, Bolton, BL1 4SN Tel: (01204) 522930 Fax: (01204) 366985 *Office partitions & ceilings services*

Elite Supplies, 19l Solway Trading Estate, Maryport, Cumbria, CA15 8NF Tel: (01900) 810111 Fax: (01900) 810222 E-mail: sales@elite-supplies.com *Suppliers of workwear & non slip over shoes*

▶ Elite Taxis Ltd, Unit 2, 400 Roding Lane South, Woodford Green, Essex, IG8 8EY Tel: (020) 8531 2292 Fax: (020) 8550 6718 E-mail: dave@elitelondontaxis.co.uk *Taxi & private hire industry*

Elite Tiles Ltd, Elite House, The Broadway, London, NW9 7BP Tel: (020) 8202 1806 Fax: (020) 8202 8608 E-mail: info@elitetiles.co.uk *Tiles & kitchens bathrooms manufrs*

Elite Training & Consultancy Services Ltd, Thomas House, 14-16 James Street South, Belfast, BT2 7GA Tel: (028) 9031 6840 Fax: (028) 9031 6841 E-mail: sales@elitetraining.com *Computer training centre & computer consultants*

▶ Elite Transport Services Ltd, Containerbase, Barton Dock Road, Urmston, Manchester, M41 7BQ Tel: 0161-755 0022 Fax: 0161-755 0011

Elite Vending Services Ltd, East Street, Grantham, Lincolnshire, NG31 6QW Tel: (01476) 591703 Fax: (01476) 576422 E-mail: neville@elitevending.freeserve.co.uk *Coffee vending machine distributors*

Elitebliss Ltd, Gingerbread Mill, Haincliffe Road, Keighley, West Yorkshire, BD21 5BU Tel: (01535) 691056 Fax: (01535) 602818 E-mail: sales@elitebliss.com *Plumbing services*

▶ Elitex UK Ltd, Unit 10, Sextant Park, Neptune Close, Medway City Estate, Rochester, Kent, ME2 4LU Tel: (01634) 727771 Fax: (01634) 727771 *Shop fixture manufrs*

Elixair International Ltd, Unit F2, Roman Hill Trading Estate, Broadmayne, Dorchester, Dorset, DT2 8LY Tel: (01305) 854735 Fax: (01305) 852060 E-mail: elixair.int@virgin.net *Chemical research & manufrs*

Elixirs Of Life, PO Box 2085, Canvey Island, Essex, SS8 9WZ Tel: (01268) 680832 E-mail: elixirsoflife@blueyonder.co.uk

Elizabeth Greenwood Equestrian Products Ltd, Unit 1-3 Stoney Spring Mill, Stoney Spring, Luddendenfoot, Halifax, West Yorkshire, HX2 6HP Tel: (01422) 884866 Fax: (01422) 885796 *Manufacturer of equestrian products*

Elizabeth Hotel, Ferriby High Road, North Ferriby, North Humberside, HU14 3LG Tel: (01482) 645212 Fax: (01482) 643332 E-mail: elizabeth.hull@elizabethhotels.co.uk *Hotel & conference facilities*

▶ Elizabeth-Anne Childrens Wear, Unit 21 D Vale Business Park, Llandow, Cowbridge, South Glamorgan, CF71 7PF Tel: (01446) 776877 Fax: (01446) 776877 E-mail: info@elizabeth-anne.co.uk *Wholesalers of children's clothing*

Eljays Spark Erosion Services Ltd, 6 Kirby Estate, Trout Road, West Drayton, Middlesex, UB7 7RU Tel: (01895) 448380 Fax: (01895) 420977 E-mail: sales@eljays.co.uk *Precision engineers & toolmakers*

Elkay Laboratory Products UK Ltd, PO Box 6004, Basingstoke, Hampshire, RG24 8HL Tel: (01256) 811118 Fax: (01256) 811116 E-mail: sales@elkay-uk.co.uk *Laboratory plasticequpment distributors*

Elkington Bros Ltd, 53-69 Baltimore Road, Birmingham, B42 1DD Tel: 0121-358 2431 Fax: 0121-358 7527 E-mail: lawrence.kelly@elkingtonbrothers.net *Engineers pattern makers & toolmakers*

Elkington & Fife, Beacon House, 113 Kingsway, London, WC2B 6PN Tel: (020) 7405 3505 Fax: (020) 7405 1508 E-mail: elkfife@elkfife.co.uk *Patent agents*

Elkington & Fife, Prospect House, 8 Pembroke Road, Sevenoaks, Kent, TN13 1XR Tel: (01732) 458881 Fax: (01732) 450346 E-mail: elkfife@elkfife.co.uk *Chartered patent agents* Also at: London WC1

Elkins Engineering Ltd, Unit 1 Enterprise Park, Ebblake Industrial Estate, Verwood, Dorset, BH31 6YS Tel: (01202) 825322 Fax: (01202) 823971 E-mail: sales@elkinsengineering.co.uk *Precision engineering services*

ElkinTatic, Hammond House, Holmestone Road, Poulton Close, Dover, Kent, CT17 0UF Tel: (01304) 203545 Fax: (01304) 215001 E-mail: acp@gaticdover.co.uk *Drainage & access cover manufrs*

Ellacombe Joinery Manufacturers, 26 Berachah Road, Torquay, TQ1 3AX Tel: (01803) 293416 Fax: *Joinery*

▶ Ellahi Servo Specialists, 34 Collingwood Court, Riverside Park Industrial Estate, Middlesbrough, Cleveland, TS2 1RP Tel: (01642) 249678 Fax: (01642) 249678 *Electric motor repairers*

▶ Ellament Limited, Manor Farm, Ashton, Chester, CH3 8DG Tel: 0870 2426995 E-mail: info@ellament.com *Organic and natural skincare from the planet"s purest natural brands*

Elland Metal Finishers, Woodman Works, South Lane, Elland, West Yorkshire, HX5 0PA Tel: (01422) 375974 Fax: (01422) 375974 *Stove enameling services*

▶ Elland Steel Structures Ltd, Philmar House, Gibbet Street, Halifax, West Yorkshire, HX2 0AR Tel: (01422) 380262 Fax: (01422) 380263 E-mail: sales@ellandsteel.com *Constructional steelwork engineers*

Ellard Ltd, Dallimore Road, Roundthorn Industrial Estate, Manchester, M23 9NX Tel: 0161-945 4561 Fax: 0161-945 4566 E-mail: sales@ellard.co.uk *Doors installation services*

Ellaway Bros, Mill House, Hawford, Worcester, WR3 7SE Tel: (01905) 458704 Fax: (01905) 754143 *Liquid waste removal service providers*

Ellco UK Ltd, Nile Street, Stoke-on-Trent, ST6 2AZ Tel: (01782) 837160 Fax: (01782) 837160 *Steel fabricators*

▶ Ellemby Ltd, 4 Market Place, Chalfont St. Peter, Gerrards Cross, Buckinghamshire, SL9 9EA Tel: (01753) 482465

▶ Ellenby Construction Co. Ltd, Stirling Industrial Estate, Chorley New Road, Horwich, Bolton, BL6 6DU Tel: (01204) 699316 Fax: (01204) 668431

Ellenell Promotions Ltd, 1b Shrubbery Road, London, N9 0QQ Tel: (020) 8887 0000 Fax: (020) 8887 0001 E-mail: sales@ellenell.com *Advertising giftware producers*

Ellerby & Webster Saddlers, Northfield Lane, Upper Poppleton, York, YO26 6QF Tel: (01904) 798532 Fax: (01904) 798532 E-mail: ewsaddlers@yahoo.co.uk *Saddlers & repairers*

Ellesmere Engineering Co. Ltd, Pennington Street, Worsley, Manchester, M28 3LR Tel: 0161-799 7626 Fax: 0161-703 8254 E-mail: marion@ellesmereeng.com *Heating & ventilation*

Ellesmere Farm Machinery, Cambrian House, Frankton, Ellesmere, Shropshire, SY12 9HE Tel: (01691) 690307 Fax: (01691) 690307 *Agriculture machinery dealers*

Ellesmere Port Lifting Gear, Portside North, Ellesmere Port, CH65 2HQ Tel: 0151-355 5091 Fax: 0151-357 2108 *Lifting equipment suppliers*

Ellgee Hydraulics Ltd, 103 Perry Road, Nottingham, NG5 3AL Tel: 0115-962 4126 Fax: 0115-969 2890 E-mail: ellgee@btconnect.com *Hydraulic cylinder ram repairers & manufrs*

Ellidge Ltd, Henderson Street, Littleborough, Lancashire, OL15 8DT Tel: (01706) 378400 Fax: (01706) 378400 *Catering equipment manufrs*

Ellidge & Fairley, New Line Industrial Estate, The Sidings, Bacup, Lancashire, OL13 9RW Tel: (01706) 875175 Fax: (01706) 875120 E-mail: info@ellidgefairley.co.uk *Catering equipment manufrs*

Sion Elliiott Ltd, 124A High Street, Nailsea, Bristol, BS48 1AH Tel: (01275) 851460 E-mail: info@sioncomputers.co.uk *Computer engineers & hardware development services*

▶ Ellingham Grain Store, Geldeston Road, Ellingham, Bungay, Suffolk, NR35 2ER Tel: (01508) 518763 Fax: (01508) 518528 E-mail: rknight@elgrain.com *Exporters of quality English green, yellow & maple peas, whole & split victor beans. Agricultural merchants, grain traders & seed suppliers*

Elliot & Black Ltd, Red Lonning Indust Estate, Moresby, Whitehaven, Cumbria, CA28 6SJ Tel: (01946) 67139 Fax: (01946) 67139 *Blinds, curtains & shutters manufrs*

G. Elliot Engineering Services Ltd, Bircotes, Doncaster, East Yorkshire, DN11 8WR Tel: (0844) 8002989 Fax: (01302) 745071 E-mail: sales@elliotteng.co.uk *System maintenance or repair hydraulic engineers services*

Elliot Scientific Ltd, 3 Allied Business Centre, Coldharbour Lane, Harpenden, Hertfordshire, AL5 4UT Tel: (01582) 766300 Fax: (01582) 766340 E-mail: sales@elliotscientific.com *Laser component distributors*

Elliot Technology Ltd, Unit 35 Earith Business Park, Meadow Drove, Earith, Cambridgeshire, PE28 3QF Tel: (01487) 841626 Fax: (01487) 841553 E-mail: ipcroft@hotmail.com *Woodworking machine suppliers*

Elliott & Co, Sherborne, Cheltenham, Gloucestershire, GL54 3DW Tel: (01451) 844448 Fax: (01451) 844695 E-mail: info@outofthewood.co.uk *Cabinet makers*

Elliott Baxter & Company Ltd, Central Way, North Feltham Trading Estate, Feltham, Middlesex, TW14 0RX Tel: (020) 8893 1144 Fax: (020) 8893 2167 E-mail: sales@ebbpaper.co.uk *Paper merchants*

▶ Elliott Box Co, 24 Brookfield Road, Thornton-Cleveleys, Lancashire, FY5 4DT Tel: (01253) 851929 Fax: (01253) 851929 E-mail: elliottboxco@yahoo.co.uk *Boxes, cartons, poly coated paper and board, foil coated board, solid board packaging divisions/ dividers*

Elliott Bros Ltd, Millbank Wharf, Northam, Southampton, SO14 5AG Tel: (023) 8022 6852 Fax: (023) 8023 2041 E-mail: donnac@elliott-brothers.co.uk *Builders merchants*

Elliott Electrical Supplies, 39 Margetts Road, Kempston, Bedford, MK42 8DT Tel: (01234) 857800 Fax: (01234) 857800 *Electrical wholesalers*

▶ G Elliott Engineering Services Ltd, Unit 2, Butterthwaite Lane, Ecclesfield, Sheffield, S35 9WA Tel: 0114-257 0704 Fax: 0114-257 0941 E-mail: sales@elliotteng.co.uk *Hydraulic, Mechanical, and Electronic Engineers.*

▶ Elliott Environmental, Unit 10, Brympton Way, Lynx West Trading Estate, Yeovil, Somerset, BA20 2HP Tel: (01935) 413700 Fax: (01935) 413722 E-mail: jim@e-e-s.co.uk *Heating & air conditioning equipment suppliers*

Elliott Gamble Kitchen Rental Ltd, St. Georges House, Gaddesby Lane, Rearsby, Leicester, LE7 4YH Tel: (01664) 424888 Fax: (01664) 424955 E-mail: enquiries@gamble-kr.co.uk *Elliott Gamble Kitchen Rental Limited is the UK's leading supplier of event hire catering equipment and portable kitchens. Whether your needs are for refurbishments, emergencies, special events, marquees, temporary structures or existing buildings - we have a solution. With our massive modern range of gas and electric equipment including production, servery, preparation, refrigeration, cold rooms and dish washing appliances, we are the leading force in catering equipment rental to the events industry and most prestigious events in the country. For excellent temporary solutions, we believe our bespoke 'Moduflex' portable kitchens with a wider than average 3m design, are perfect to complement your reputation and help maximise your working conditions. Whether you require production, preparation, dish washing, or dining facilities, our unique 'Moduflex' system enables us to join two units or as many as you require, creating complete flexibility. We also provide a complete planning, installation, servicing and a 24hr breakdown service giving you added peace of mind whether you hire for one day or five years plus.*

Elliott Group Ltd, Mill Lane, Congresbury, Bristol, BS49 5JD Tel: (01934) 832103 Fax: (01934) 876198 *Build & manufacture transportable buildings*

Elliott Group Ltd, Braemar House, Snelsins Lane, Cleckheaton, West Yorkshire, BD19 3UE Tel: (01274) 863221 Fax: (01274) 861582 E-mail: fastrack@elliott-algeco.com *Elliott Fastrack specialises in providing Fast Track Design and Build solutions for all accommodation requirements.*

Elliott Group Ltd, Ashley Drive, Bothwell, Glasgow, G71 8BS Tel: (01698) 811707 Fax: (01698) 811708 E-mail: info@elliotthire.co.uk *Suppliers of portable accommodation & secure storage*

▶ Elliott Group Ltd, Oliver Road, Grays, Essex, RM20 3ED Tel: (01708) 681500 Fax: (01708) 681519 E-mail: info@elliotthire.co.uk *Suppliers of portable accommodation & secure storage*

▶ Elliott Group Ltd, Oliver Road, Grays, Essex, RM20 3ED Tel: (01708) 681500 Fax: (01708) 681519 E-mail: info@elliotthire.co.uk *Suppliers of portable accommodation & secure storage*

Elliott Group Ltd, Littlewell Lane, Stanton-by-Dale, Ilkeston, Derbyshire, DE7 4QW Tel: 0115-944 8380 Fax: 0115-944 3728 E-mail: info@elliotthire.co.uk *Suppliers of portable accommodation & secure storage*

Elliott Group Ltd, Chaddock Lane, Worsley, Manchester, M28 1DP Tel: 0161-790 3721 Fax: 0161-703 8294 E-mail: info@elliotthire.co.uk *Suppliers of portable accommodation & secure storage*

Elliott Group Ltd, Chesney Wold, Bleak Hall, Milton Keynes, MK6 1LS Tel: (01908) 231361 Fax: (01908) 677262 E-mail: info@elliotthire.co.uk *Suppliers of portable accommodation & secure storage*

▶ Elliott Group Ltd, King Charles Business Park Old Newton Road, Heathfield Industrial Estate, Heathfield, Newton Abbot, Devon, TQ12 6UT Tel: (01626) 834377 Fax: 0117-982 2832 E-mail: info@elliotthire.co.uk *Suppliers of portable accommodation and secure storage*

Elliott Group Ltd, Manor Drive, Peterborough, PE4 7AP Tel: (01733) 298700 Fax: (01733) 573543 E-mail: hirediv@elliott-group.co.uk *Hire & sell re-locatable buildings*

▶ Elliott Group Ltd, Normandy Way, Marchwood, Southampton, SO40 4PB Tel: (023) 8087 3819 Fax: (023) 8087 3820 E-mail: info@elliotthire.co.uk *Suppliers of portable accommodation & secure storage*

Elliott Group Ltd, Seckar Wood Industrial Park, Barnsley Road, Newmillerdam, Wakefield, West Yorkshire, WF2 6QW Tel: (01924) 254420 Fax: (01924) 241959 E-mail: info@elliotthire.co.uk *Suppliers of portable accommodation & secure storage*

Elliott Group Fineline, Commissioners Road, Strood, Rochester, Kent, ME2 4ET Tel: (01634) 719701 Fax: (01634) 716394 E-mail: fineline.windows@virgin.net *PVC frame window manufrs*

▶ Elliott Hire, Victoria Road, Avonmouth, Bristol, BS11 9DB Tel: 0117-916 3400 Fax: 0117-982 2832 E-mail: info@elliotthire.co.uk *Suppliers of portable accommodation & secure storage*

Elliott Hire, Victoria Road, Avonmouth, Bristol, BS11 9DB Tel: 0117-916 3400 Fax: 0117-982 2832 E-mail: info@elliotthire.co.uk *Suppliers of portable accommodation & secure storage*

Elliott Hire Ltd, Oliver Road, Grays, Essex, RM20 3ED Tel: (01708) 862709 Fax: (01708) 861471 E-mail: sales@workspace.co.uk *Suppliers of portable accommodation & secure storage*

▶ Elliott Hire, Yard 1, 2, 3, 4, Camp Industrial Estate, East Calder, Livingston, West Lothian, EH53 0EP Tel: (01698) 801580 Fax: (01698) 811708 E-mail: info@elliotthire.co.uk *Suppliers of portable accommodation & secure storage*

Elliott Hire, Manor Drive, Peterborough, PE4 7AP Tel: (01733) 298600 Fax: (01733) 573543 E-mail: info@elliotthire.co.uk *Elliott Hire is the UK's largest supplier of portable accommodation and secure storage including cabins and site storage containers available to hire or buy. From a small office for a single worker to an office complex for a large workforce our portable buildings are instantly available for delivery nationwide .and with Elliott having the largest number of hire centres in the UK we're never far away from you. If you need instant secure storage we have thousands of secure steel containers with the best integral locking system of any UK container offering you complete peace of mind. Many sizes are available with a choice of options including racking, access ramps and alarm systems. Elliott Hire is a division of Elliott, the UK leader in relocatable accommodation and a subsidiary of Algeco which operates the largest fleet of rental accommodation facilities in the world employing over 5,200 people in 19 countries.*

Elliott Independent Ltd, 28 Spring Lane, Great Horwood, Milton Keynes, MK17 0QW Tel: (01296) 714745 Fax: (01296) 711957 E-mail: ann@elliottindependent.com *Marketing consultant specialising in service sectors*

Elliott Marshall Signs, Morven Road, Morven Studio, St. Austell, Cornwall, PL25 4PP Tel: (01726) 72863 Fax: (01726) 72863 E-mail: sales@elliottmarshall.com *Silk screen printers & sign makers*

Martin Elliott, The Laurels, Sling, Coleford, Gloucestershire, GL16 8JJ Tel: 01594 836758 *Sliding door installer & manufrs*

Elliott Musgrave Ltd, Jackson Street, Bradford, West Yorkshire, BD3 9SJ Tel: (01274) 731115 Fax: (01274) 722691 E-mail: sales@elliott-musgrave.co.uk *Textile engineers & pattern makers services*

Elliott Nationwide Transport Ltd, Elliott House, Greg Street, Stockport, Cheshire, SK5 7BS Tel: 0161-429 9485 Fax: 0161-429 9094 *Road transport, haulage & freight services*

Elliott Property & Leisure Group Ltd, Lee House, 109 Hammersmith Road, London, W14 0QH Tel: (020) 7371 2244 Fax: (020) 7371 2424 E-mail: edl@elliotgroup.co.uk *Holiday property developers*

Elliott Redispace, Valletta Street, Hull, HU9 5NP Tel: (01482) 781202 Fax: (01482) 712157 E-mail: hirediv@elliott-group.co.uk *Relocatable building system manufrs* Also at: Branches throughout the U.K.

Elliott Services, Seven Oaks, School Lane, Moffat, Dumfriesshire, DG10 9AX Tel: (01683) 220584 Fax: (01683) 221984 E-mail: mfelliott@aol.com *Supplier of secretarial & printing services*

Thomas Elliott Ltd, Oakley Road, Bromley, BR2 8HG Tel: (01732) 866566 Fax: (020) 8462 5599 *Fertilizer*

Elliott Turbo Machinery Ltd, 120 Thorneycroft Industrial Estste, Worting Road, Basingstoke, Hampshire, RG21 8BJ Tel: (01256) 354334 Fax: (01256) 322464 *Compressor & turbine services*

Elliott & Wragg Ltd, Elliott & Wragg, Buxton Road, Tideswell, Buxton, Derbyshire, SK17 8PQ Tel: (01298) 871582 Fax: (01298) 871785 *Steel fabricators & structural engineers*

Elliotthire, Chittening Industrial Estate, Avonmouth, Bristol, BS11 0YB Tel: 0117 916 3400 Fax: 0117 982 2832 E-mail: info@elliotthire.co.uk *Suppliers of portable accommodation & secure storage*

Elliotthire, Bowburn South Industrial Estate, Bowburn, Durham, DH6 5AD Tel: 0191-377 8788 Fax: 0191-377 8770 E-mail: info@elliotthire.co.uk *Suppliers of portable accommodation & secure storage*

Elliotthire, Scotter Road South, Bottesford, Scunthorpe, South Humberside, DN17 2BW Tel: (01724) 279660 Fax: (01724) 848384 E-mail: info@elliotthire.co.uk *Suppliers of portable accommodation & secure storage*

Elliotthire Hire Centres, Shaw Street, West Bromwich, West Midlands, B70 0TX Tel: 0121-506 1060 Fax: 0121-556 5081 E-mail: info@elliotthire.co.uk *Suppliers of portable accommodation & secure storage*

▶ Elliotthire Portable Accom Hire, Charville Lane, Hayes, Middlesex, UB4 8PD Tel: (020) 8845 6958 Fax: (020) 8841 1138 E-mail: info@elliotthire.co.uk *Suppliers of portable accommodation & secure storage*

▶ Elliotthire Portable Accom Hire, Charville Lane, Hayes, Middlesex, UB4 8PD Tel: (020) 8845 6958 Fax: (020) 8841 1138 E-mail: info@elliotthire.co.uk *Suppliers of portable accommodation & secure storages*

▶ Elliotts, Unit 8 Goodwood Road, Eastleigh, Hampshire, SO50 4NT Tel: (023) 8062 3960 Fax: (023) 8062 3965 E-mail: insulation@elliott-brothers.co.uk *Building materials suppliers*

Elliotts Tool Warehouse, 10 Winchester Trade Park, Easton Lane, Winchester, Hampshire, SO23 7FA Tel: (01962) 827610 Fax: (01962) 827611 E-mail: winchester@elliott-brothers.co.uk *Retail hand & power tools selection for professional trades*

Ellipse Design, 45 Marsh Lane, Crosspool, Sheffield, S10 5NN Tel: 0114-268 2961 Fax: 0114-268 2961 E-mail: enquiries@ellipsedesign.co.uk *Training, consultancy services & specialists in database driven website design, e-commerce*

Ellipsis Media Ltd, 82-86 Albany House, South End, Croydon, CR0 1DQ Tel: (020) 8239 1146 Fax: (020) 8239 1147 E-mail: sales@ellipsis-media.co.uk *Providing internet & Intranet*

▶ Elliptica Computers, Maylite Business Centre, Berrow Green Road, Martley, Worcester, WR6 6PQ Tel: (01886) 887712 Fax: (01886) 887731

▶ Ellis, 5 Macdougall Street, Greenock, Renfrewshire, PA15 2TG Tel: (01475) 888561

Ellis Dawe & Son, The Forge, Rye Street, Birtsmorton, Malvern, Worcestershire, WR13 6AS Tel: (01684) 833235 Fax: (01684) 833840 E-mail: sales@ellisdawe.co.uk *Agricultural engineers & blacksmiths*

▶ Ellis Developments, Bestwood Business Park, Park Road, Bestwood Village, Nottingham, NG6 8TQ Tel: (01636) 812100 E-mail: sales@ellisdevelopments.co.uk *Advanced Textile Technology*

▶ Ellis Electrical Ltd, Unit E6 Fareham Heights, Standard Way, Fareham, Hampshire, PO16 8XT Tel: (01329) 829333 Fax: (01329) 829555

Ellis Engineering & Welding Services, Salmon Road, Great Yarmouth, Norfolk, NR30 3QS Tel: (01493) 842690 Fax: (01493) 842690 E-mail: ellisengineering@btconnect.com *Factory maintenance services*

Ellis & Everard (Chemicals) P.L.C, 75 Bugsbys Way, Greenwich, London, SE10 0QD Tel: (020) 8858 5806 Fax: (020) 8858 1499 *Industrial chemical suppliers*

Ellis Fairbank P.L.C., Ellis Fairbank House, 2 Manor Road, Horsforth, Leeds, LS18 4DX Tel: 0113-259 3000 Fax: (0870) 0110883 E-mail: contactus@ellisfairbank.co.uk *Recruitment search & selection*

Ellis (Faull), Kemys Way, Swansea Enterprise Park, Swansea, SA6 6QA Tel: (01792) 797722 Fax: (01792) 792974 *Steel stockholders*

Ellis Furniture, Dormers, Main Road, Ashbocking, Ipswich, IP6 9JX Tel: (01473) 890309 Fax: (01473) 890309 E-mail: iroko@tinyonline.co.uk *Furniture manufrs*

Jack Ellis, Marshall House, West Street, Glenfield, Leicester, LE3 8DT Tel: 0116-232 0022 Fax: 0116-232 0032 E-mail: admin@jackellis.co.uk *Equestrian body protection wear & body armour manufrs*

Ellis Joshua & Co., Grange Valley Road, Grange Road, Batley, West Yorkshire, WF17 6LW Tel: (01924) 350070 Fax: (01924) 350071 E-mail: genoffice@joshuaellis.co.uk *Woollen manufrs*

▶ Ellis Motors, 6 Sheddingdean Business Centre, Marchants Way, Burgess Hill, West Sussex, RH15 8QY Tel: (01444) 480606 Fax: (01444) 480606 E-mail: fixit@ellismotors.co.uk *Full range of garage services for cars & light commercial vehicles*

Ellis Rees & Co., The Old Foundry, Grove Road, Northfleet, Gravesend, Kent, DA11 9AX Tel: (01474) 567861 Fax: (01474) 537056 *Cast metal nameplate manufrs*

Ellis Signs, Dunstan Road Railway Street, Gateshead, Tyne & Wear, NE11 9EE Tel: 0191-477 1600 Fax: 0191-460 4460 E-mail: bernerd@ellisssigns.fsnet.co.uk *Sign engravers & manufrs*

▶ Ellis & Sons Vehicle Builders Ltd, Hawkbrand House, Longbrooks Farm, Knowle Road, Brenchley, Tonbridge, Kent, TN12 7DJ Tel: (01892) 725720 Fax: (01892) 725728 E-mail: sales@ellisandson.com *Commercial vehicle body builders*

▶ Ellis Timlin & Co. Ltd, Stubbins Lane, Ramsbottom, Bury, Lancashire, BL0 0PT Tel: (01706) 823176 Fax: (01706) 827711

Ellis Welding & Fabrications, Ollershaw Lane, Marston, Northwich, Cheshire, CW9 6ES Tel: (01606) 45405 Fax: (01606) 40237 E-mail: sales@e-w-l.com *Welders & fabricators*

Ellison Bros, 24 Donegall Street, Belfast, BT1 2GP Tel: (028) 9032 5320 Fax: (028) 9032 8143 E-mail: sales@ellisonbrothers.co.uk *Diamond merchants*

J.W. Ellison & Co. Ltd, 677-681 Little Horton Lane, Bradford, West Yorkshire, BD5 9DQ Tel: (01274) 571943 Fax: (01274) 571943 *Worsted cloth manufrs*

Ellison Metal Finishing Ltd, 8 Acorn Business Park, Keighley Road, Skipton, North Yorkshire, BD23 2UE Tel: (01756) 796805 Fax: (01535) 630942 E-mail: sales@ellisonmf.co.uk *Electroplating & metal finishing*

Ellison Metal Products Ltd, Darley Abbey Mills, Darley Abbey, Derby, DE22 1DZ Tel: (01332) 340002 Fax: (01332) 383128 E-mail: enquiries@ellisonmetalproducts.co.uk Principal Export Areas: Africa *Oven furniture & pans support services*

Ellison Sensors International Ltd, Sensor House, Wrexham Technology Park, Wrexham, Clwyd, LL13 7YP Tel: (01978) 262255 Fax: (01978) 262233 E-mail: info@esi-tec.com Principal Export Areas: Worldwide *Transducers, pressure, transmitter (temperature & pressure) suppliers*

Ellison Switchgear, Mounts Road, Wednesbury, West Midlands, WS10 0DU Tel: 0121-505 2000 Fax: 0121-556 1981 E-mail: enquiries@ellison.co.uk *Substations bus & bar trunking manufrs*

Elliston Steady & Hawes (Aluminium) Ltd, Chapel Lane, Great Blakenham, Ipswich, IP6 0JT Tel: (01473) 830626 Fax: (01473) 832170 E-mail: esh@net.dii.co.uk *Building contractors*

▶ Ellita Ltd, 6 Rushout Avenue, Harrow, Middlesex, HA3 0AR Tel: (020) 8446 7401 Fax: (020) 8445 6335 E-mail: info@ellita.co.uk *Suppliers of base oils & additives for production of lubricants*

▶ Elljay Clothing Mnfrs, Unit 18 Enterprise Centre, Ray Street, Huddersfield, HD1 6BL Tel: (01484) 518488 Fax: (01484) 545422 *Ladies wear design & manufrs*

▶ Ellon Plant & Machinery Hire, Unit 1 Castle Street, Castlepark Industrial Estate, Ellon, Aberdeenshire, AB41 9RF Tel: (01358) 720991 Fax: (01358) 722417 E-mail: sales@ellon-plant-hire.co.uk

▶ Ellon Plant & Machinery Hire, Unit 1 Castle Street, Castlepark Industrial Estate, Ellon, Aberdeenshire, AB41 9RF Tel: (01358) 720991 Fax: (01358) 722417 E-mail: sales@ellon-plant-hire.co.uk

Ellrod Engineering, 6A Stone Road, Coal Aston, Dronfield, Derbyshire, S18 3AH Tel: (01246) 415436 Fax: (01246) 416494 *Steel erectors*

Ells Machinery (Spark Erosion), 49 The Rise, Partridge Green, Horsham, West Sussex, RH13 8JB Tel: (01403) 710609 Fax: (01403) 710609 *Spark erosion machine distributors*

Ellson Environmental Ltd, 263 Edinburgh Road, Newhouse, Motherwell, Lanarkshire, ML1 5RU Tel: (01698) 831234 Fax: (01698) 834148 E-mail: sales@ellson-env.com *Ventilation & air conditioning units distributors*

Ellsworth Adhesives Ltd, 2 Kelvin South BSNS Park, Glasgow, G75 0YG Tel: (01355) 231122 Fax: (01355) 235266 E-mail: info@ellsworthadhesives.co.uk *Distributor of adhesives & sealants for leading global companies, distributor of dispensing & mixing equipment***

Ellwood Steel Ltd, Unit 2 Park Lane, Halesowen, West Midlands, B63 2NT Tel: (01384) 564935 Fax: (01384) 410577 *Steel stockists & shearers*

Elm Alarms, 14 St. Vincent Road, Clacton-on-Sea, Essex, CO15 1NA Tel: (01255) 475017 Fax: (01255) 475017 *Intruder alarms service, supply & installation*

▶ Elm Bank, 22 Claypotts Road, Broughty Ferry, Dundee, DD5 1BW Tel: (01382) 477782 Fax: (01382) 477782 E-mail: mail@elmbanktowing.co.uk *Supplying & fitting tow bars*

Elm Leisure, Hitherford, Over, Cambridge, CB24 5NY Tel: (01954) 230230 Fax: (01954) 231775 E-mail: info@elmleisure.com *Swimming pool installers & manufrs*

Elma Electronic UK Ltd, Premier Business Centre, Speedfields Park, Fareham, Hampshire, PO14 1TY Tel: (01329) 289100 Fax: (01329) 289101 E-mail: info@elma-electronic.co.uk *Manufacturers of enclosure systems, back planes & rotary components*

Elmac Services, PO Box 111, Chichester, West Sussex, PO19 4ZS Tel: (01243) 533361 Fax: (01243) 790535 *Electromagnetic compatibility consultants*

▶ Elmar Graphics, Unit 3, 8 Becket Road, Montague Industrial Estate, London, N18 3PN Tel: (020) 8807 2350 Fax: (020) 8803 0370 E-mail: elmarhmg@globalnet.co.uk *Printers*

Elmar Services Ltd, Westhill Industrial Estate, Westhill, Aberdeenshire, AB32 6TQ Tel: (01224) 740261 Fax: (01224) 743138 E-mail: sales@elmar.co.uk *Wire-line & logging equipment manufrs*

Elmatic (Cardiff) Ltd, Wentloog Road, Rumney, Cardiff, CF3 1XH Tel: (029) 2077 8727 Fax: (029) 2079 2297 E-mail: sales@elmatic.co.uk Principal Export Areas: Asia Pacific, Central Asia, Middle East, Africa, Central/East Europe, West Europe & North America *Generator load frames, maintenance or testing*

Elmbank Hotel, The Mount, York, YO24 1GE Tel: (01904) 610653 Fax: (01904) 627139 E-mail: elmbank@hotmail.com *Hotel*

▶ Elmbank Logistics, Lodge Road, Sandbach, Cheshire, CW11 3HP Tel: (01270) 758840 Fax: (01270) 758848

Elmbridge Pump Co., 6a Shepherd Road, Gloucester, GL2 5EQ Tel: (01452) 501102 Fax: (01452) 303691 E-mail: sales@elmbridgepump.com *Pump distributors/agents/stockholders including centrifugal & electric motor driven. Also seal (mechanical) distributors or agents. Also pumps, booster sets.*

▶ Elmbronze Ltd, PO Box 8361, Largs, Ayrshire, KA30 8YA Tel: (01475) 689274 *manufacturer of fresh herbal skincare & cosmetic products, insect repellent including a midge repellant, insect bite, wasp & bee sting sprays, foot sprays, gifts & other herbal products.*

Elmbrook Computer Services Ltd, Alpha Place, Garth Road, Morden, Surrey, SM4 4TS Tel: (020) 8410 4444 Fax: (020) 8410 4445 *Computer reseller & installers*

Elmcroft Consulting Ltd, 156 Frimley Green Road, Frimley Green, Camberley, Surrey, GU16 6NA Tel: (01252) 838177 *Management consultants*

Elmdale Welding & Engineering Supplies Ltd, 100b Lady Lane Industrial Estate, Hadleigh, Ipswich, IP7 6BQ Tel: (01473) 827722 Fax: (01473) 828080 E-mail: hadleighsales@btconnect.com *Welding supplies distributors*

Elmdale Welding & Engineering Supplies Ltd, 25-27 Brook Road, Rayleigh, Essex, SS6 7XR Tel: (01268) 779011 Fax: (01268) 745192 E-mail: barry.cecil@elmdale.co.uk *Welding supplies distributors* Also at: Lowestoft

▶ Elmec Systems Ltd, Bowbridge La, New Balderton, Newark, Nottinghamshire, NG24 3BY Tel: (01636) 676666 Fax: (01636) 676667

Elmer Wallace Plansee, 30 Nasmyth Road South, Hillington Industrial Estate, Glasgow, G52 4RE Tel: 0141-810 5530 Fax: 0141-810 5539 E-mail: alex@elmerwallace.co.uk *Wholesalers of welding supplies*

Elmet Fascia Design Ltd, Unit 3 Blackburn Industrial Estate, Enterprise Way, Sherburn In Elmet, Leeds, LS25 6NF Tel: (01977) 681441 Fax: (01977) 681428 *Manufacturers of panels*

Elmgate Engineering Co. Ltd, Cattedown Road, Plymouth, PL4 0RW Tel: (01752) 222285 Fax: (01752) 222285 *Metal fabrication*

Elmill Products Ltd, 139a Engineer Road, West Wilts Trading Estate, Westbury, Wiltshire, BA13 4JW Tel: (01373) 864267 Fax: (01373) 858266 E-mail: sales@elmill.co.uk Principal Export Areas: Worldwide *Mechanical cables manufrs*

Elmlead Services Ltd, Unit 1, Riverside Court, Colne Road, Huddersfield, HD1 3ER Tel: (01484) 425565 Fax: (01484) 425418 E-mail: elmlead@yahoo.co.uk *Assemblers & contract packers*

Elmleigh Electrical Systems Ltd, Elmleigh House, Dawsons Lane, Barwell, LE9 8BE Tel: (01455) 847045 Fax: (01455) 844045 E-mail: belinda.jones@elmleigh.co.uk

Elmor Supplies Ltd, 104 Branbridges Road, East Peckham, Tonbridge, Kent, TN12 5HH Tel: (01622) 871870 Fax: (01622) 872024 *Fastener distributors & manufrs*

Elmpark Engineering Services Ltd, Washington Street Industrial Estate, Halesowen Road, Dudley, West Midlands, DY2 9RE Tel: (01384) 239301 Fax: (01384) 457378 E-mail: anything@elmparkeng.co.uk *Machinery dismantling, erecting & installing*

Elmrep Ltd, Elmrep House, Eastern Avenue, Gloucester, GL4 6QS Tel: (01452) 300959 Fax: (01452) 300988 *Photocopier & fax repair service*

Elms & Elms, 6-8 Brookfield Road, Cheadle, Cheshire, SK8 2PN Tel: 0161-428 8383 Fax: 0161-428 8855 E-mail: info@elmsandelms.co.uk *Distributors of leisure wear*

Elmstok, 4-6 Algores Way, Wisbech, Cambridgeshire, PE13 2TQ Tel: (01945) 463434 Fax: (01945) 582598 E-mail: sales@elmstok.co.uk *Reprographic materials suppliers*

Elmtree Signs, 62 Empress Road, Southampton, SO14 0JU Tel: (023) 8023 0903 Fax: (023) 8023 0904 E-mail: rod@elmtreesigns.co.uk *Sign manufrs*

Elmwood Design Ltd, 40-44 Thistle Street, Edinburgh, EH2 1EN Tel: 0131-225 1181 Fax: 0131-718 0390 E-mail: enquiries@elmwood.co.uk

Elmwood Fencing Ltd, 10 Sheen Lane, London, SW14 8LL Tel: (020) 8878 0993 Fax: (020) 8878 2332 *Fencing contractors & suppliers*

Elmwood (Glasgow) Ltd, 25 Eagle Street, Craighall Business Park, Glasgow, G4 9XA Tel: 0141-332 3086 Fax: 0141-331 1590 E-mail: mail@elmswoods.com *Joinery manufrs*

Elmwood Joinery, Unit 9 Blackmore Park Road, Hanley Swan, Worcester, WR8 0EF Tel: (01684) 569097 Fax: (01684) 569097 *Joinery manufrs*

Elnor Engineering, Checkley, Nantwich, Cheshire, CW5 7QA Tel: (01270) 520282 *General engineers*

Elof Hansson Pulp & Paper Ltd, Unit 22 Carlson Court, 116 Putney Bridge Road, London, SW15 2NQ Tel: 0845 5314057 Fax: (020) 8871 4689 E-mail: info@uk.elofhansson.com *Disposable paper goods distributors*

▶ E-Logic Computer Services Ltd, 15 Wades Croft Freckleton, Preston, PR4 1SU Tel: (01772) 634446 Fax: (0870) 4869123 E-mail: mark.cooper@e-logic.co.uk *Computer services*

Elonex P.L.C., 2 Apsley Way, London, NW2 7LF Tel: (020) 8452 4444 Fax: (020) 8452 6422 E-mail: sales@elonex.co.uk *IT solutions provider & PC manufrs*

Elopak UK, Meadway, Rutherford Close, Stevenage, Hertfordshire, SG1 2PR Tel: (01438) 847400 Fax: (01438) 741324 E-mail: elopak.hq@elopak.com *Liquid packaging suppliers*

Elopak UK, Meadway, Rutherford Close, Stevenage, Hertfordshire, SG1 2PR Tel: (01438) 847400 Fax: (01438) 741324 E-mail: elopak.hq@elopak.no *Liquid packaging suppliers* Also at: Dublin & Dumfries

Elpeeko Ltd, Wrightsway, Outer Circle Road, Lincoln, LN2 4JY Tel: (01522) 512111 Fax: (01522) 541796 E-mail: sales@elpeeko.com *General printers & designers*

▶ Elphinstone & Howarth, Baillister, Tingwall Airport, Gott, Shetland, ZE2 9XJ Tel: (01595) 840222 Fax: (01595) 840505

Elphis Engineering Ltd, 6 St Andrews Park, Princes Road, Wells, Somerset, BA5 1TE Tel: (01749) 676424 Fax: (01749) 675501 *Paper making machinery & general engineering services*

▶ Elpress UK, Unit 4 Carraway Road, Gillmoss Ind Est, Liverpool, L11 0EE Tel: 0151-547 2666 Fax: 0151-547 1444 E-mail: sales@e-tech-components.co.uk *Distributors of Elpress range of Crimp Terminals and Tooling, also Cable Glands, Cable Joints and Cable Ties.*

Elro UK Ltd, 3 Furzton Lake, Shellwell Crescent, Furzton, Milton Keynes, MK4 1GA Tel: (01908) 526444 Fax: (01908) 526449 E-mail: info@elro-uk.ltd.uk *Catering equipment suppliers*

Elsa Waste Paper Ltd, Unit 1 Station Road, Reddish, Stockport, Cheshire, SK5 6YZ Tel: 0161-432 3984 Fax: 0161-442 3105 *Recycling wastepaper, cardboard & plastic*

Elsam Cross & Co., 5-6 London Road, Spalding, Lincolnshire, PE11 2TA Tel: (01775) 723758 Fax: (01775) 768575 E-mail: geoff.hemsil@virgin.net *General printers*

Elsdon Mailing Ltd, Unit 16 Nonsuch Industrial Estate, Kiln Lane, Epsom, Surrey, KT17 1DH Tel: (01372) 720613 E-mail: elsdonmailing@lineone.net *House & direct mail services*

Else Refining & Recycling Ltd, Unit 7-8 Pole Hanger Farm, Shefford Road, Meppershall, Shefford, Bedfordshire, SG17 5LH Tel: (01462) 812000 Fax: (01462) 817117 E-mail: enquiries@elserefining.co.uk *Computer system refining & recyclers*

Elsenham Quality Foods Ltd, Elsenham, Bishop's Stortford, Hertfordshire, CM22 6DT Tel: (01279) 818307 Fax: (01279) 812715 *Gift foods, preserves & perium manufrs*

Elsevier Science, Belway House, 32 Jamestown Road, London, NW1 7BY Tel: (020) 7424 4200 Fax: (020) 7424 4431 E-mail: sales@elsevierscience.com *Book & journal publishers* Also at: Footscray

Elsome Engineering Ltd, Welby Road, Asfordby Hill, Melton Mowbray, Leicestershire, LE14 3RD Tel: (01664) 813234 Fax: (01664) 813341 E-mail: sales@elsomes.com *Steel fabricators*

Elson & Co. Ltd, Crown Industrial Estate, Anglesey Road, Burton-On-Trent, Staffordshire, DE14 3NX Tel: (01283) 500001 Fax: (01283) 517178 E-mail: elson@elson.co.uk *Brewers engineers*

▶ Elspeth Reid Coaching, 102 Clarence Road, London, SW19 8QD Tel: (020) 8879 7676 E-mail: coach@elspethreid.com *Is it time to sort your life out? We offer personal coaching to enable you to: discover the kind of work you enjoy, improve existing relationships or make new ones, build your self-confidence, and increase physical wellbeing (weight loss, fitness). We will help you to live a positive, balanced and fulfilled life. Our coaching service is confidential and the initial consultation is free.*

Elstar Manufacturing Ltd, Unit A & B, Newbold Drive, Castle Donington, Derby, DE74 2NP Tel: (01332) 850090 Fax: (01332) 853173 E-mail: matthew.trotter@elstar.co.uk *Refrigerated cabinet manufrs*

Elston & Hopkin, Unit 3a, Heapham Road Industrial Estate, Sandars Road, Gainsborough, Lincolnshire, DN21 1RZ Tel: (01427) 839271 Fax: (01427) 839271 E-mail: info@elstonandhopkin.co.uk *Cuesports specialists since 1938.*Tables & Accessories supplied , Tables recovered , renovated, dismantles , transported.*

Elston Manufacturing Wolverhampton Co., 30 Mander Street, Wolverhampton, WV3 0JZ Tel: (01902) 422159 Fax: (01902) 429465 *Sheet metalworkers*

Elston Profiles Ltd, Unit G2 Bullock Street, West Bromwich, West Midlands, B70 7HE Tel: 0121-553 6292 Fax: 0121-553 6707 *Profile cutting services*

Elston Profiles and Compnents Ltd, St. Annes Road, Cradley Heath, West Midlands, B64 5BH Tel: (01384) 566919 Fax: (01384) 569684 *Profile cutting services*

Elstone Engineering Co., Earlsway, Teesside Industrial Estate, Stockton-on-Tees, Cleveland, TS17 9JU Tel: (01642) 769442 Fax: (01642) 763068 *Steel fabricators*

Elstree Precision Co. Ltd, 26 Theobald Street, Borehamwood, Hertfordshire, WD6 4SF Tel: (020) 8953 3348 Fax: (020) 8207 1636 *Precision engineers*

J.E. Elsworth Ltd, 59 Hall Road, Clenchwarton, King's Lynn, Norfolk, PE34 4AS Tel: (01553) 769200 Fax: (01553) 769222 *Mixing machine manufrs*

Elsy & Gibbons Ltd, Simonside, South Shields, Tyne & Wear, NE34 9PD Tel: 0191-427 0777 Fax: 0191-427 0888 E-mail: info@elsonhotwater.co.uk *Hot water tank manufrs*

Elta Fans, 17 Barnes Wallis Road, Fareham, Hampshire, PO15 5TT Tel: (01489) 583044 Fax: (01489) 566555 E-mail: mailbox@eltafans.co.uk *Fan manufrs*

Eltek Energy (UK) Ltd, Eltek House, Maxted Road, Hemel Hempstead, Hertfordshire, HP2 7DX Tel: (01442) 219355 Fax: (01442) 245894 E-mail: uksales@eltekenergy.com Principal Export Areas: Worldwide *AC to DC power supply converters manufrs*

Eltek Semiconductors Ltd, Nelson Road, Townstal Industrial Estate, Dartmouth, Devon, TQ6 9LA Tel: (01803) 834455 Fax: (01803) 833011 E-mail: sales@eltek-semi.com *Semi-conductor chip supplies*

Eltek Systems Ltd, Eltek House, Nene Valley Business Park, Oundle, Peterborough, PE8 4HN Tel: (01832) 277590 Fax: (01832) 273941 E-mail: info@eltek-systems.com Principal Export Areas: Africa *Electrical control panel manufrs*

Eltham Executive Charter, Crown Woods Way, London, SE9 2NL Tel: (020) 8850 2011 Fax: (020) 8850 5210 E-mail: eec@cwcom.net *Minicoach hire, car sales & repairers*

Eltham Export Ltd, Crown House, Home Gardens, Dartford, DA1 1DZ Tel: (01322) 424600 Fax: (01322) 424601 E-mail: sales@elthamexport.com *Eltham Export is a London-based exporting company, specialising in single and multi-sourcing of electrical, welding, engineering and other equipment, site safety, catering, measurement, testing and much more. In these and other areas we aim to supply a quality export service to ISO 9001 standards, backed up by extensive experience in shipping, export documentation and technical support*

continued

Eltham Park Information Technology Services, 16 Glenlyon Rd, London, SE9 1AJ Tel: 020 88596958 *Computer consultants*
Eltham Welding Supplies Ltd, 7 Mill Road, Portslade, Brighton, BN41 1PD Tel: (01273) 414381 Fax: (01273) 424603 E-mail: ews.sussex@dial.pipex.com *Welding consumables & equipment sales hire service*
Eltham Welding Supplies Ltd, 2-12 Parry Place, London, SE18 6AN Tel: (020) 8854 1226 Fax: (020) 8854 2720 E-mail: sales.woolwich@elthamweldingsupplies.co.uk *Welding suppliers* Also at: Portslade
▶ Eltherington Group Ltd, Dansom Lane, Hull, HU8 7LA Tel: (01482) 320336 Fax: (01482) 317824 E-mail: info@eltherington.co.uk *Aluminium fabricators*
Eltime Ltd, 10-14 Hall Road, Heybridge, Maldon, Essex, CM9 4NF Tel: (01621) 859500 Fax: (01621) 855335E-mail: sales@eltime.co.uk *Electric measuring instrument manufrs*
Elton Fabrications Ltd, 21A Cemetery Road, Southport, Merseyside, PR8 6RH Tel: (01704) 537853 Fax: (01704) 530100 E-mail: david.hodge@eltongames.com *Amusement machine manufrs*
▶ Eltons Essential Office Products, 69 Old Woking Road, West Byfleet, Surrey, KT14 6LF Tel: (01932) 345075 Fax: (01932) 336176 E-mail: sales@eltons.demon.co.uk *Stationery, office supplies, art & craft*
Eltonsford Ltd, 106 Palmerston Road, Southsea, Hampshire, PO5 3PT Tel: (023) 9282 6926 Fax: (023) 9282 4338 *Ship & mooring equipment manufrs*
Elumatec UK Ltd, 2 Europa Business Park, Maidstone Road, Kingston, Milton Keynes, MK10 0BD Tel: (01908) 580800 Fax: (01908) 580825 E-mail: sales@elumatec.co.uk *Aluminium & PVCU products machinery distributors*
Elva Wholesale Ltd, 406 Long St, London, E2 8HG Tel: (020) 7739 5622 Fax: (020) 7739 8128 E-mail: elvawholesale@ukbusiness.com *Reproduction furniture wholesalers*
▶ Elvele Images Ltd, 13 Westland Road, Kirk Ella, Hull, HU10 7PH Tel: (01482) 650674 E-mail: info@elvele.com *Photographic services*
Elvet Structures Ltd, Low Willington Industrial Estate, Willington, Crook, County Durham, DL15 0UH Tel: (01388) 747120 Fax: (01388) 745861 E-mail: gordan.pearson@elvetstructures.co.uk *Joinery manufrs*
Elwell Sections Ltd, Phoenix Street, West Bromwich, West Midlands, B70 0AQ Tel: 0121-553 4274 Fax: 0121-553 4272 E-mail: sales@elwellsections.com *Cold formed metal sections & frames manufrs*
Elwen Eos Ltd, PO Box 261, Shefford, Bedfordshire, SG17 5PW Tel: (01462) 814708 Fax: (01462) 814708 E-mail: elweneos@aol.com *Optical instrument manufrs*
▶ Stephen Elwis, The Oaklands, Barton Street, Laceby, Grimsby, South Humberside, DN37 7LF Tel: (01472) 750700 Fax: (01472) 885949 E-mail: sales@globalstockuk.com *we are always looking to purchase surplus and unwanted stock, salvage, end of lines , closing down stock Y damaged stock. Give us a call whatever you have we are interested. Thank you for looking*
▶ Ely Boat Chandlers, 21 Waterside, Ely, Cambridgeshire, CB7 4AU Tel: (01353) 663095 Fax: (01353) 664514 E-mail: sales@elyboatchandlers.co.uk *A very well stocked inland chandlery who cater for both cruisers and Narrowboats. Specifics are: Honda outboard main dealers, specialists in fit-out sanitary & galley equipment, everything you"d expect in stock and MORE.*
Ely Concrete Products Ltd, Wisbech Road, Littleport, Ely, Cambridgeshire, CB6 1RA Tel: (01353) 861416 Fax: (01353) 862165 E-mail: sales@histonconcrete.co.uk *Concrete precast product manufrs*
▶ Elygra Ltd, 6 The Quad, Mercury Court, Chester, CH1 4QP Tel: (01244) 399900 Fax: (01244) 399904 E-mail: mail@elygra.co.uk
▶ Elyo Services, Manor House, 52 London Road, Blackwater, Camberley, Surrey, GU17 0AA Tel: (01276) 607360 Fax: (01276) 607361
Elyo Services, Apian House, Selinas Lane, Dagenham, Essex, RM8 1TB Tel: (020) 8252 2929 Fax: (020) 8270 7379 *Boiler repair services*
Elyo UK Ltd, 1 Sampson Road North, Birmingham, B11 1BL Tel: 0121-773 8421 Fax: 0121-773 2082 *Air conditioning specialists*
Elyo UK Ltd, Walker Office Park, Walker Road, Guide, Blackburn, BB1 2QE Tel: (01254) 662323 Fax: (01254) 664084 *Heating & ventilation engineers*
Elyo UK Industrial Ltd, Unit 3-4 Sheffield Airport Business Park, Europa Link, Sheffield, S9 1XU Tel: 0114-280 0000 Fax: 0114-280 0099 E-mail: sheffield@elyo.co.uk *Building services & air conditioning engineers* Also at: Birmingham, Bristol, Glasgow, London, Manchester & Newcastle upon Tyne
▶ Elysium Natural Products Ltd, Unit 12, Moderna Business Park, Moderna Way, Mytholmroyd, Hebden Bridge, West Yorkshire, HX7 5QQ Tel: (01422) 885523 Fax: (01422) 884629 E-mail: elysiumproducts@aol.com *Importers & distributors of organic products*
Elyzium, 12 Queensbrook, Bolton, BL1 4AY Tel: (01204) 528628 Fax: (01204) 534678 E-mail: sales@elyzium.co.uk *IT consultants*
Em Secure, 3 Rolleston Close, Market Harborough, Leicestershire, LE16 8BZ Tel: (07891) 340168 Fax: (01858) 432756 E-mail: info@emsecure.co.uk *Locksmiths*
Ema Technology, 15 Stevens Lane, Breaston, Derby, DE72 3BU Tel: (01332) 875657 Fax: (01332) 875658 E-mail: info@ema-tech.co.uk *Computer consultancy*
Emag (U.K.) Ltd, Chestnut House, Kingswood Business Park, Albrighton, Wolverhampton, WV7 3AU Tel: (01902) 373121 Fax: (01902) 376091 E-mail: sales@emag-vsc.co.uk *Machine tool sales & service*
Emak UK Ltd, Unit A1 Chasewater Industrial Estate, Burntwood Business Park, Burntwood, Staffordshire, WS7 3XD Tel: (01543) 687660 Fax: (01543) 670721 E-mail: sales@emak.co.uk *Saw & chain saw distributors*
Emanuel Bros Ltd, Wexham Road, Slough, SL1 1RW Tel: (01753) 524153 Fax: (01753) 530775 E-mail: sales@emanuelbrothers.co.uk *Crash repair specialist services*
Emanuel Whittaker Ltd, 400 Rochdale Road, Oldham, OL1 2LW Tel: 0161-624 6222 Fax: 0161-785 5510 E-mail: mail@emanuel-whittaker.co.uk *Joinery manufacturers & contractors*
Emap, Bowling Green Lane, London, EC1R 0DA Tel: (020) 7812 3700 E-mail: claire.jenkinson@ebc.emap.com *Publishers*
EMAP Communications, Greater London House, Hamstead Road, London, NW1 7EJ Tel: (020) 7874 0200 Fax: (020) 7874 0201 E-mail: lgc@lgc.emap.com *Publishers*
Emap Communications, 2ND Floor Scriptor Court, 155 Farringdon Road, London, EC1R 3AD Tel: (020) 7841 6600 Fax: (020) 7841 6605 E-mail: claire.jenkinson@emap.com *Journal publisher*
Emap Construct Ltd, 151 Roseberry Avenue, London, EC1R 4GB Tel: (020) 7505 6600 Fax: (020) 7505 6889 *Publishing company*
Emap Glenigan, 41-47 Seabourne Road, Bournemouth, BH5 2HU Tel: (0800) 373771 Fax: (01202) 431204 E-mail: info@glenigan.emap.com Sales Contact: K. Wilson *Suppliers of business information, including company information, building informationt, on-line information, technological development engineering services, direct mail services, marketing information services & sales lead information services*
Emap TPS Ltd, 19Th Floor Leon House, 233 High Street, Croydon, CR0 9XT Tel: (020) 8277 5000 Fax: (020) 8277 5887 E-mail: info@emap.com *Exhibition organisers*
Emapsite Com Ltd, Masdar House, 1-3 Reading Road, Eversley, Hook, Hampshire, RG27 0RP Tel: 0118-973 6883 Fax: 0118-973 0002 E-mail: justin.saunders@emapsite.com *Digital mapping*
Embassy Labels, Church Road, Tonge, Sittingbourne, Kent, ME9 9AP Tel: (01795) 473988 Fax: (01795) 420249 *Label manufrs*
▶ Embassy Press London Ltd, 341 Battersea Park Road, London, SW11 4LS Tel: (020) 7622 4522 Fax: (020) 7498 0173 E-mail: sales@embassypress.co.uk
Embassy Signs Ltd, 83 Bellenden Road, London, SE15 4QJ Tel: (020) 7732 1055 Fax: (020) 7732 4163 E-mail: sales@embassysigns.co.uk *Sign manufrs*
Embassy Suite, 2 Balkerne Hill, Colchester, CO3 3AA Tel: (01206) 575910 Fax: (01206) 763042 *Conference & banqueting centre*
Embedded Controls Ltd, Loyal Cottage, Alyth, Blairgowrie, Perthshire, PH11 8JG Tel: (01828) 633554 Fax: (01828) 633554 *Electronics design*
Embee Builders Merchants Ltd, 31-45 Mount Pleasant Road, Wallasey, Merseyside, CH45 5LA Tel: 0151-639 6127 Fax: 0151-630 2171 E-mail: sales@embeeltd.co.uk *Bathroom showrooms & plumbing supplies*
Ember J D Insurance, Belhaven House, 67 Walton Road, East Molesey, Surrey, KT8 0DP Tel: (020) 8941 2204 Fax: (020) 8979 9796 E-mail: ember1970@hotmail.com *Insurance brokers*
Embercay, Units 1 & 2 Sadler Road, Doddington Road Industrial Estate, Lincoln, LN6 3RS Tel: (01522) 500551 Fax: (01522) 500551 *Timber merchants & importers*
Emberheat, 295 Aylestone Road, Leicester, LE2 7PB Tel: 0116-287 8300 *Heating designers & service engineers*
▶ Embers Fireplaces, 221 Frimley Green Road, Frimley Green, Camberley, Surrey, GU16 6LA Tel: (01252) 837837 Fax: (01252) 837837 E-mail: steve@fireplaces.co.uk *Fireplaces suppliers*
▶ Embimed, 11 Highlands Road, Cosham, Portsmouth, PO6 1HL Tel: (023) 9237 9080 Fax: (023) 9237 9080 E-mail: martin-becker@embimed.co.uk *Embimed Ltd provides specialist design and project management solutions to health professionals and the healthcare industry allowing them to develop first class medical equipment and devices.*
Embiricos Ship Brokers Ltd, Commonwealth House, 1-19 New Oxford Street, London, WC1A 1NU Tel: (020) 7404 0420 Fax: (020) 7400 0887 *Ship brokers*
Emblem Die Sinking, 32 Hylton Street, Birmingham, B18 6HN Tel: 0121-554 8028 Fax: 0121-554 8028 *Die sinkers & engravers*
Emblem Furniture Ltd, Unit 1-2 Twickenham Trading Estate, Rugby Road, Twickenham, TW1 1DQ Tel: (020) 8892 3611 Fax: (020) 8892 5368 E-mail: enquiries@emblemfurniture.co.uk *Emblem Furniture provide furniture rental, show home furniture and design, home staging and property marketing, as well as furniture packages for buy-to-let property investors.*
▶ Emblem Print Products Ltd, 17 North Parade, Derby, DE1 3AY Tel: (01332) 362536 E-mail: sales@emblemprint.co.uk
Emblematic Embroiderers, Unit 26b North Tyne Industrial Estate, Whitley Road, Benton, Newcastle upon Tyne, NE12 9SZ Tel: 0191-270 1449 Fax: 0191-270 1449 E-mail: gmewett@emblematic.force9.co.uk *Embroidery manufrs*
▶ Embleton Services Ltd, 5 Freeland Way, Erith, Kent, DA8 2LQ Tel: (01322) 335373 Fax: (01322) 333510
Embley Business Unit, 41 Warwick Road, Solihull, West Midlands, B92 7HS Tel: 0121-707 8666 Fax: 0121-708 2858 *Industrial property agents*
Emc, Stevenage Business Park, Eastman Way, Stevenage, Hertfordshire, SG1 4SZ Tel: (01438) 748899 Fax: (01438) 728828 E-mail: sales@2k1.co.uk *Electronic components*
▶ Emc Advertising Gifts, Derwent House, 1064 High Road, London, N20 0YY Tel: (020) 8492 2200 Fax: (0845) 3451065 E-mail: sales@emcadgifts.co.uk
Emc Computer Systems, E M C Tower, Great West Road, Brentford, Middlesex, TW8 9AN Tel: (0870) 6087777 Fax: (0870) 6087788 E-mail: sales@uk.emc.com *Computer manufrs*
Emc Partner UK Ltd, 1a Golf Link Villas, The Common, Downley, High Wycombe, Buckinghamshire, HP13 5YH Tel: (01494) 444255 Fax: (01494) 444277 E-mail: sales@emcpartner.co.uk *EMC instrumentation manufrs*
Emcel Filters Ltd, Blatchford Road, Horsham, West Sussex, RH13 5RA Tel: (01403) 253215 Fax: (01403) 259881 E-mail: filtration@emcelfilters.co.uk *Air filter manufrs*
Emco Education Ltd, Unit 4 Hayling Billy Business, Furniss Way, Hayling Island, Hampshire, PO11 0ED Tel: (023) 9263 7100 Fax: (023) 9263 7660 *Computer aided engineers for education & training*
Emco Packaging Systems, The Coach House, Deal Road, Worth, Deal, Kent, CT14 0BD Tel: (01304) 620400 Fax: (01304) 614422 E-mail: info@emcouk.com *Oxygen & gas analysis equipment manufrs*
Emco (UK) Ltd, Unit 65, Atcham Business Park, Upton Magna, Shrewsbury, SY4 4UG Tel: (0870) 1611617 Fax: (0870) 1611618 E-mail: enquiries@emcouk.co.uk *Emco Auk Ltd manufactures, supplies and installs a high quality structured entrance mat from it's Shropshire based production facility. Emco are Europe's market leader in providing a high functional clean off system combined with an aesthetic appearance which would complement existing architectural integrity*
Emco Wheaton UK Ltd, Enterprise Road, Westwood Industrial Estate, Margate, Kent, CT9 4JR Tel: (01843) 221521 Fax: (01843) 295444 E-mail: sales@emcowheaton.co.uk *Tanker discharge & load equipment manufrs*
▶ Emcor Drake & Scull Ltd, 51 Great North Road, Hatfield, Hertfordshire, AL9 5EN Tel: (01707) 630300 Fax: (01707) 630333 *Mechanical & electrical constructions specialists*
Emcor Facilities Services Ltd, 1 Thameside Centre, Kew Bridge Road, Brentford, Middlesex, TW8 0HF Tel: (020) 8380 6700 Fax: (020) 8380 6701 *Building services engineers* Also at: Branches throughout the U.K.
EMD Plus Ltd, 190 Fletchamstead, Highway, Canley, Coventry, CV4 7BB Tel: (024) 7667 8888 Fax: (024) 7671 2059 E-mail: info@edmplus.co.uk *EDM consumable sales*
▶ Emea International Consulting, 500 Chiswick High Road, Chiswick, London, W4 5RG Tel: (020) 8995 8903 E-mail: info@praeda.co.uk *Management Consultancy focusing on delivering tangible business advantage. Specialising in delivering coherent commercial strategies to all business sectors.*
▶ eMedCareers, Jobsite UK (Worldwide) Ltd., Langstone Technology Park, Havant, Hampshire, PO9 1SA Tel: 0870 774 8732
Emefco Time Recorders, 5 The Briars, Harlow, Essex, CM18 7DG Tel: (01279) 419694 Fax: (01279) 419694 E-mail: p.hill@virgin.net *Repair, maintenance & suppliers of time recorders*
▶ Emeg Electrical Ltd, 3 Dunston Place, Dunston Road, Chesterfield, Derbyshire, S41 8NL Tel: (01246) 268678 Fax: (01246) 268679
▶ Emenex (Financial) Ltd, Fen Drayton House, Park Lane, Fen Drayton, Cambridge, CB4 5SW Tel: (01954) 232078 E-mail: julianredman@emenex.com *Emenex is a Cambridge based company whose management has considerable experience in Financial Planning, Financial Management and Financial Protection. Our name is derived from Empowering you with tools to craft your financial strategy, Enrich you through the provision of relevant information, and Execute your instructions cost efficiently.*
▶ Emerald Bay Ltd, 50 Gorsey Lane, Warrington, WA1 3PS Tel: (01925) 243366 Fax: (01925) 243377
▶ Emerald Bears, Carthall Road, Coleraine, County Londonderry, BT51 3LP Tel: (07929) 247710 E-mail: carol@emerald-bears.com *Irish Bear Artist. Hand made and designed , fully jointed Adult Collector Bears Direct From The Emerald Isles. Real and Faux Fur Available*
▶ Emerald Careers, 43 Temple Row, Birmingham, B2 5LS Tel: (0845) 2265857 Fax: (020) 8318 3222 E-mail: muyiwa@emeraldcareers.com *Recruitment consultancy*
Emerald Cleaning Supplies, Unit 21 Branxholme Industrial Estate, Bradford Road, Brighouse, West Yorkshire, HD6 4EA Tel: (01484) 400635 Fax: (01484) 711616 E-mail: emeraldsupplies@btinternet.com *Industrial cleaning equipment suppliers*
▶ Emerald Packaging Ltd, Ravenhead Road, St. Helens, Merseyside, WA10 3LR Tel: (01744) 755352 Fax: (01744) 750120
Emerald Sportswear, 47 Ballykine Road, Ballynahinch, County Down, BT24 8JE Tel: (028) 9756 1982 Fax: (028) 9756 4669 E-mail: sales@emerald-sportswear.co.uk *Sportswear manufrs*
Emerald Weld PVC Stationery Manufacturer, 101 Station Road, Reddish, Stockport, Cheshire, SK5 6ND Tel: 0161-432 7200 Fax: 0161-442 1248 E-mail: info@emweld.com *PVC welded goods manufrs*
▶ Emerge Communications, 5 Cults Business Park, Station Road, Cults, Aberdeen, AB15 9PE Tel: (0870) 0500152 E-mail: sales@emerge-comms.co.uk *Telecoms equipment supply, installation & support*
▶ Emergence Communications, Commercial Centre, Exchange Street, Colne, Lancashire, BB8 0SQ Tel: 0845 8381401 Fax: 0870 1342929 E-mail: info@emergence.biz *Emergence Communications provides a range of IT solutions for your business. With services ranging from Website Design & Hosting, eCommerce, VOIP telecoms, Network Security, and IT Support we*

continued

feel we can help you give your business the edge it needs to compete.
▶ Emergency Five, 186 Dalry Road, Edinburgh, EH11 2EP Tel: 0131-337 5151 Fax: 0131-337 5151 E-mail: sales@emergency5.com *IT repairs, hardware & software*
Emergency One UK Ltd, Block 4, Caponacre Industrial Estate, Cumnock, Ayrshire, KA18 1SH Tel: (01290) 424200 Fax: (01290) 423834 E-mail: mmadsen@emergencyone.co.uk *Fire engine & fire appliance manufrs*
Emergency Power Services Ltd, Maple House, Lingwood Close, Southampton, SO16 7GE Tel: (023) 8076 6464 Fax: (01487) 834111 E-mail: eps-cambs@cyberware.co.uk *Emergency lighting*
Emergency Power Systems, Suite 16 Enterprise House, Strathkelvin Place, Kirkintilloch, Glasgow, G66 1XQ Tel: 0141-775 1815 Fax: 0141-775 1609 E-mail: sales@emergencypowersystems.co.uk *Standby power specialists*
Emergency Power Systems P.L.C., Carley Drive Business Area, Westfield, Sheffield, S20 8NQ Tel: 0114-247 8369 Fax: 0114-247 8367 E-mail: sales@emergencypowersystems.co.uk *Power systems & converter manufrs*
Emergent Crown Contract Office Furnishings Ltd, 59 Pellon Lane, HX, Halifax, West Yorkshire, HX1 5BE Tel: (01422) 349119 Fax: (01422) 206033 E-mail: sales@emergent-crown.co.uk Principal Export Areas: Africa *Office furnisher distributors or agents*
Emergent Systems Solutions Ltd, 9 Briarwood, Finchampstead, Wokingham, Berks, RG40 4XA Tel: 0118-973 6077 Fax: 0118-973 6088 E-mail: consult@emergent.co.uk *Automatic identification & computer consultants*
Emerson Developments Holdings Ltd, Emerson House, Heyes Lane, Alderley Edge, Cheshire, SK9 7LF Tel: (01625) 588400 Fax: (01625) 585791 E-mail: info@emerson.co.uk *Building contractors*
Emerson Embedded Power, Astec House, Waterfront Business Park, Merry Hill, Dudley, West Midlands, DY5 1LX Tel: (01384) 842211 Fax: (01384) 843355 E-mail: sales@astec-europe.com *Power supply manufrs*
▶ Emerson Flow Computer Division, Outgang Lane, Pickering, North Yorkshire, YO18 7JA Tel: (01751) 471800 Fax: (01751) 471801 E-mail: sales@emersonprocess.com
Emerson Joinery, 50a Durham Road, Blackhill, Consett, County Durham, DH8 8NP Tel: (01207) 507805 Fax: (01207) 507805 *Joiners*
Emerson Process Management, Meridian East, Leicester, LE19 1UX Tel: 0116-282 2822 Fax: 0116-289 2896 *Electronic & optical instruments distribution*
Emerson Process Management, Horsfield Way, Bredbury, Stockport, Cheshire, SK6 2SU Tel: 0161-430 7100 Fax: (0870) 2404389 *Flow measurement systems manufrs*
Emerson & Renwick Ltd, Peel Bank Works, Peel Bank, Church, Accrington, Lancashire, BB5 4EF Tel: (01254) 872727 Fax: (01254) 871109 E-mail: sales@eandr.com *Paper printing & converting machinery supplier*
▶ Emerson Willis Ltd, Romford Road, Aveley, South Ockendon, Essex, RM15 4XD Tel: (01708) 861044 Fax: (01708) 861066
Emerthames Ltd, City Cloisters, 196 Old Street, London, EC1V 9FR Tel: (020) 7253 7900 Fax: (020) 7017 3901 *Computer consultants*
▶ Emery Electrical Ltd, Riverside Business Park, Stoney Common Road, Stansted, Essex, CM24 8PL Tel: (01279) 647799
Geoff Emery, Unit 4, 171 Bryants Hill, St. George, Bristol, BS5 8RQ Tel: 0117-975 9111 Fax: 0117-907 7675 *Die cutting services*
Emes Building Services, 128-130 Grange Road, Ramsgate, Kent, CT11 9PT Tel: (01843) 850260
Emetco Lighting Ltd, 81 Ellingham Industrial Centre, Ellingham Way, Ashford, Kent, TN23 6JZ Tel: (01233) 663333 Fax: (01233) 663366 E-mail: sales@emetco.co.uk *Electric meter repair services*
Emexco Ltd, Unit 1, 46B Bulkington, Devizes, Wiltshire, SN10 1SL Tel: (01380) 828900 Fax: (01380) 828999 E-mail: sales@emexco.co.uk *Emergency door hardware manufrs*
Emfec, Robins Wood House, Robins Wood Road, Aspley, Nottingham, NG8 3NH Tel: 0115-854 1616 Fax: 0115-854 1617 E-mail: enquiries@emfec.co.uk *Vocational education & training*
Emhart Fastening Technology Ltd, Walsall Road, Perry Barr, Birmingham, B42 1BP Tel: 0121-331 2408 Fax: 0121-356 1598 E-mail: uk.marketing@bdk.com Principal Export Areas: Worldwide *Manufacturers of rivets, blind & fixing systems*
Emi Mec, 23 Avern Close, Tipton, West Midlands, DY4 7ND Tel: 0121-522 4823 Fax: 0121-522 4823 E-mail: sales@emi-mec.co.uk *Sales spares and technical info available for EMI-MEC AUTOMATIC PROGRAM LATHES 24/7*
Emi Records UK, E M I House, 43 Brook Green, London, W6 7EF Tel: (020) 7605 5000 Fax: (020) 7605 5050 E-mail: enquiries@emirecordedmusic.co.uk *Pop & classical records & tapes producers* Also at: Hayes
▶ Emily May Productions Ltd, Slaney Place, Staplehurst, Kent, TN12 0DT Tel: (01580) 893209 Fax: (01580) 893209 E-mail: doug@emilymayproductions.com *Emily May Productions offers a full image creation and brand development service to the corporate & private sectors.*Letterheads, cards & stationary. *Integrated web development. *Promotional films & adverts. *Office accommodation addresses. *Let us take over your public appearance, while you concentrate on your own productivity.**
Emily's Cottage, Unit 21 Hatton Country World, Hatton, Warwick, CV35 7LD Tel: (01926) 843781 *Pine furniture & gifts wares*
Emi-Mec, Unit E2 Doulton Road Trading Estate, Doulton Road, Rowley Regis, West Midlands, B65 8JQ Tel: (01384) 633968 Fax: (01384) 633946 E-mail: sales@emi-mec.eu *Automatic lathe, spurs & services*

Eminox Ltd, Brick Kiln Lane, Stoke-On-Trent, ST4 7BS Tel: (01782) 206300 Fax: (01782) 283800 E-mail: dawn.day@eminox.com *Exhaust system manufrs*

▶ Emission Europe Ltd, 18c High Street, Battle, East Sussex, TN33 0AE Tel: 01435 872889 E-mail: info@emissioneurope.co.uk *Specialist Flat Panel Displays distributor covering latest*developments in Display Technology.*

Em-Jay Appointments, 17 Manor Road, Reigate, Surrey, RH2 9LA Tel: (01737) 224411 Fax: (01737) 224410 E-mail: recruitment@tinyonline.co.uk *Technical personnel consultants services*

▶ Emkay Plastics Ltd, 11 Charles Watling Way, Bowthorpe Employment Area, Norwich, NR5 9JH Tel: (01603) 746000 Fax: (01603) 746001 E-mail: stevenking@emkayplastics.co.uk *Distribution of Rohacell IG Foam in the UK*

Emkay Screw Supplies, 74 Pepys Way, Strood, Rochester, Kent, ME2 3LL Tel: (01634) 717256 Fax: (01634) 717256 E-mail: emkaysupplies@talktalk.net *Suppliers of precision fasteners to the model & light engineer*

Emlux Holdings Ltd, The Industrial Estate, Black Bourton Road, Brize Norton, Carterton, Oxfordshire, OX18 3LY Tel: (01993) 841574 Fax: (01993) 843186 E-mail: info@walraven.com *Structural, building & construction fixing systems*

Emlyn Canvas & Cordage Co. Ltd, George Street Conservatory Centre, Granville Square, Newport, Gwent, NP20 2AB Tel: (01633) 262262 Fax: (01633) 222420 *Tarpaulin manufrs*

Emma Bridgewater, 739 Fulham Road, London, SW6 5UL Tel: (020) 7371 5264 Fax: (020) 7384 2457 Principal Export Areas: Worldwide *Pottery retailers, wholesalers & pottery manufrs*

▶ Emma Pettifer Richardson, Cavenagh House, The Square, Sheriff Hutton, York, YO60 6QX Tel: (01347) 878173 Fax: (01347) 878176 E-mail: info@abouthouse.co.uk *We offer a friendly and personal design service, from a metre of fabric to a complete design scheme. We specialise in the creation of comfortable, timeless interiors with an emphasis on quality and attention to detail. Residential and commercial projects undertaken.*

Emma Services Ltd, 20 De Lisle Road, Bournemouth, BH3 7NF Tel: (01202) 522058 Fax: (01202) 522049 E-mail: sales@emmaservices.co.uk *Electronic manufrs*

Emmco Ltd, The Old Stables, Cork Lane, 19 West Bar Street, Banbury, Oxfordshire, OX16 9SA Tel: (01295) 262826 Fax: (01295) 709091 E-mail: info@emmcolimited.co.uk *Sales, Service, Hire of industrial process monitoring equipment, endoscopes, videoendoscopes, high speed video, data loggers and environmental , endescopes hire,fibre scope,fiber scope,fibrescope,fiberscope,pid hire,photoironiser hire,land fill monitors, landfill monitor hire,landfill monitor hire.*

Emmerich (Berlon) Ltd, Kingsnorth Industrial Estate, Wotton Road, Ashford, Kent, TN23 6JY Tel: (01233) 622684 Fax: (01233) 645801 E-mail: emmerick@emir.co.uk *Work bench manufrs*

Emmerson Industrial Doors Ltd, Enterprise Way, Sherburn in Elmet, Leeds, LS25 6NA Tel: (01977) 685566 Fax: (01977) 681981 E-mail: sales@emmerson-doors.co.uk *Industrial door manufrs* Also at: Nottingham

Emmerson Process Management Ltd, Heath Place, Bognor Regis, West Sussex, PO22 9SH Tel: (01243) 867554 Fax: (01243) 867554 *Manufacturers of process controllers*

Emmerson Process Management Bettis UK Division, 3 Furz Court, Wickham Road, Fareham, Hampshire, PO16 7SH Tel: (01329) 848900 Fax: (01329) 848901 E-mail: bettisuk_sales@msn.com Principal Export Areas: West Europe, North America, Central America & South America *Pneumatic & hydraulic actuators*

Emo Oil Ltd, Greenwich Road, Cliff Quay, Ipswich, IP3 0BZ Tel: (01473) 232931 Fax: (01473) 213126 *Fuel distributors*

▶ Emo Oil Ltd, Derwent Valley Industrial Estate, Dunnington, York, YO19 5PD Tel: (0800) 685685 E-mail: info@emooil.co.uk *Home heating oil & agricultural fuel /lubricants sales* Also at: York

Emo Oils Ni Ltd, Airport Road West, Belfast, BT3 9ED Tel: (028) 9045 4555 Fax: (028) 9046 0921 E-mail: enquiries@emooil.com *Independent oil importer & distributors*

▶ EMobilesdirect, 892 Chester Road, Stretford, Manchester, M32 0PA Tel: 0161-283 8727 E-mail: info@e-mobilesdirect.co.uk *Suppliers of Sim Free Mobile Phones, Mobile Accessories, Bluetooth Headsets and Contract Phones*

▶ E-Module, 7 Legion Court, Bennochy Road, Kirkcaldy, Fife, KY2 5JE Tel: (01592) 644744 E-mail: sales@e-module.co.uk *Small business consultants,advisors,resource,*

Emoos Consultants Ltd, 8 Battery Green Road, Lowestoft, Suffolk, NR32 1DE Tel: (01502) 587696 Fax: (01502) 589159 E-mail: navtronicks@rya-online.net *Sales of marine electronics*

Emp Tooling Services Ltd, Brockhampton Lane, Havant, Hampshire, PO9 1LU Tel: (023) 9249 2626 Fax: (023) 9249 2582 E-mail: info@e-m-p.biz *Plastics mould & tool polishing & manufacturers & repairers*

Empee Silk Fabrics, 31 Commercial Road, London, N18 1TP Tel: (020) 8887 6000 Fax: (020) 8887 6045 E-mail: empee@wholesalefabrics.co.uk *Wholesale textile merchants*

▶ Emperor Leisure Services Ltd, Lavenham Business Centre, Parsons Street, Oldham, OL9 7AN Tel: 0161-652 6048 E-mail: sales@empreor.co.uk *Catering equipment suppliers*

Emperor Tropicals & Water Garden Centre, 9 St Erth Road, Plymouth, PL2 3SW Tel: (01752) 706633 Fax: (01752) 313461 E-mail: sales@emperortropicals.co.uk *Aquarium suppliers*

▶ Empetus, Cleveland House, 39 Old Station Road, Newmarket, Suffolk, CB8 8QE Tel: (01638) 669440 Fax: (0870) 1299246

Empexion Ltd, Falcon House, 19 Deer Park Road, London, SW19 3UX Tel: (020) 8543 0911 Fax: (020) 8540 0034 E-mail: info@ctl-components.com *Sales of electronic components*

▶ Emphasis Photography, 517 Hagley Road, Birmingham, B66 4AX Tel: 0121-558 8733 Fax: 0121-558 8755 E-mail: richard@emphasis.biz *Architectural, interiors and advertising photographer based in the West Midlands offering a nationwide service. We are also leadinging practitioners of QTVR virtual images (360 degree images) and virtual tours.*

▶ Empire, 4 Rose Cottages, Station Road, Claygate, Esher, Surrey, KT10 9DJ Tel: (07010) 714766 Fax: (01372) 466158 *Locksmith*

Empire Alarms, 38 Kenmore Road, Prenton, Merseyside, CH43 3AS Tel: 0151-608 9919 Fax: 0151-608 9919 E-mail: enquiries@empirealarms.co.uk *Alarm system services*

Empire Auctions, 27 Old Gloucester Street, London, WC1N 3AF Tel: (020) 7419 5059 E-mail: enquiries@empireauctions.co.uk *Auctions & valuation of plant & machinery*

Empire Computers, Northern Ho, Moss Street East, Ashton-under-Lyne, Lancs, OL6 7BX Tel: 0161-330 1544 Fax: 0161-330 1616 *Computer hardware supplier*

▶ Empire Computers, 6 Manchester Road, Haslingden, Rossendale, Lancashire, BB4 5ST Tel: (01706) 212255 Fax: (01706) 212215 E-mail: marc@empirecoms.co.uk *Empire Computers specialise in supplying high quality Compatible Ink & Toner cartridges. ISO 9001 Certified Cartridges from £2. 56. FULL MONEYBACK GUARANTEE. MASSIVE RANGE! !*

Empire Games Ltd, Unit 5-7 New Street, Bridgend Industrial Estate, Bridgend, Mid Glamorgan, CF31 3UD Tel: (01656) 663300 Fax: (01656) 662200 E-mail: steve.brown@empiregames.co.uk *Fruit machines*

Empire Glass Co. Ltd, Unit 17, Saville Rd, Peterborough, PE3 7PR Tel: (01733) 260880 Fax: (01733) 262458 *Glass merchants*

Empire Process Engineers Ltd, Ryder Close, Swadlincote, Derbyshire, DE11 9EU Tel: (01283) 226599 Fax: (01283) 210160 *Dairy industry engineers*

▶ Empire Tinting, 1050 Manchester Road, Rochdale, Lancashire, OL11 2XJ Tel: (01706) 868435 E-mail: sales@empire-tinting.co.uk *Window tinting specaist for your car home or office*

Empire Travel & Insurance Services Ltd, 349 King Street, London, W6 9NH Tel: (020) 8748 1033 Fax: (020) 8748 1034 E-mail: empireti@hotmail.com *Travel & insurance services*

Emplas Ltd, Saddington Road, Fleckney, Leicester, LE8 8AW Tel: 0116-240 3407 *Plastic tube & extrusion manufrs*

▶ Employee Development Forum, Unit 11a Lyons Farm Estate, Lyons Road, Slinfold, Horsham, West Sussex, RH13 0QP Tel: (01403) 791292 Fax: (01403) 791293 E-mail: sales@theedf.com *Independent training provider delivering apprenticeships to engineering manufacturing sectors, training courses, forklift training and management courses.*

Employee Management, Stone Cross Place, Stone Cross La North, Lowton, Warrington, WA3 2SH Tel: (01942) 727200 Fax: (01942) 727225 E-mail: sales@employeemanagement.co.uk *Human resource, health & safety consultants*

▶ Employment Enjoyment Ltd, 6 Shurdington Road, Cheltenham, Gloucestershire, GL53 0DJ Tel: 01242 252337 Fax: 01242 580451 E-mail: info@employment-enjoyment.co.uk *Cheltenham based recruitment agency supplying permanent staff. Office Services, Managerial, Marketing, Industrial, Financial and Retail positions throughout Gloucestershire and the South West.*

Employment Service, Upper Holloway ESJ, North Star Ho, 554-556 Holloway Rd, London, N7 6JP Tel: (020) 7301 3700 Fax: (020) 7301 3752 *Recruitment services*

▶ Employment4students, 16 Spicers Field, Oxshott, Leatherhead, Surrey, KT22 0UT Tel: 01483 855528 Fax: 01483 855528 E-mail: nick.thompson@e4s.co.uk *Employment4students - dedicated to finding you the best staff for all your job vacancies. An effective way of advertising, we combine a first class service with excellent value for money. Visit Employment4students to fill your job vacancies now.*

Empower Dynamics Ltd, Moor Park House, Moor Park Lane, Farnham, Surrey, GU10 1QP Tel: (0870) 2435701 Fax: (0870) 2435702 E-mail: general@empdyna.com *Computer consultants & data migrati on specialists*

Empresa Ltd, 160 Northumberland Street, Norwich, NR2 4EE Tel: (01603) 623030 Fax: (01603) 623525 E-mail: sales@empresa.co.uk *IT solution providers, software, hardware & training consultants*

▶ Empress Electrical Ltd, 69 Plantation Street, Accrington, Lancashire, BB5 6RZ Tel: (01254) 871661

Empress Fencing Ltd, Empress Sawmills, Clitheroe Road, Chatburn, Clitheroe, Lancashire, BB7 4JY Tel: (01200) 441215 Fax: (01200) 449931 E-mail: sales@empressfencing.co.uk *Timber & fencing suppliers*

▶ Empress Foil Blocking, The Old Ebenezer Chapel, Sweetshouse, Bodmin, Cornwall, PL30 5AL Tel: (01208) 871487 Fax: (01208) 871487 E-mail: sales@empressfoilblocking.co.uk *Empress Foil Blocking is a cornwall based Hot Foil Blocking company, specialising in business cards, stationary and promotional items.*

Empress Mills (1927) Ltd, Glen Mill, North Valley Road, Colne, Lancashire, BB8 9DT Tel: (01282) 863181 Fax: (01282) 870935 E-mail: chris@empressmill.co.uk *Sewing thread manufrs*

Empress Promotions Ltd, 6 Holkham Road, Orton Southgate, Peterborough, PE2 6TE Tel: (01733) 391133 Fax: (01733) 370738 E-mail: sales@empresspromo.com *Magazine promotional finishing*

▶ Empress Timber, 48 Empress Way, Euxton, Chorley, Lancashire, PR7 6QB Tel: (01257) 269596 Fax: (01257) 269596 E-mail: philwalsh@empresstimber.co.uk *Agent for bulk sales of Hardwoods, Door Blanks, Plywood, Veneers, Trailer Flooring, Laminated Panels, and most other timber related products.*

▶ Emprima Limited, The Oracle Building, Blythe Valley Park, Solihull, West Midlands, B90 8AD Tel: 0121 506 9600 Fax: 0121 506 9601 E-mail: mail@emprima.co.uk *Project Management, Financial Management and Risk Management for Clients in the Construction Industry.*

▶ Empson Engineering, Unit 60, Sherwood Road, Bromsgrove, Worcestershire, B60 3DR Tel: (01527) 873020 Fax: (01527) 873020 E-mail: stevenbeckemp@aol.com *Machining components*

Empteezy Ltd, Alpha House, 4 Muir Road, Houstoun Industrial Estate, Livingston, West Lothian, EH54 5DR Tel: (01506) 430309 Fax: (01506) 441466 E-mail: sales@empteezy.co.uk *ISO 9001, 14001 & 18001 accredited manufacturers of drum/IBC fully bunded steel storage units, polyethylene sump pallets, spill kits, absorbents, waste handling containers and flammable liquid storage solutions*

Emr, Manor Road, Erith, Kent, DA8 2AD Tel: (01322) 336970 Fax: (01322) 331581 *Scrap iron merchants* Also at: Newmarket

Emr Brackley Ltd, County Road, Buckingham Road Industrial Estate, Brackley, Northamptonshire, NN13 7AX Tel: (01280) 701321 Fax: (01280) 701327 E-mail: sales@emreng.co.uk *Gear manufacturers, electric motor rewinds, general engineering, grinding, gearbox repairs/ manufacturing, CNC milling, CNC turning, anodising, plating*

Emr North East Ltd, 5c Bowes Road, Middlesbrough, Cleveland, TS2 1LU Tel: (01642) 226096 Fax: (01642) 245471 E-mail: duncan.mcneill@onyxnet.co.uk *Electrical & mechanical repairs*

▶ Emre Import & Export, 128 Malvern Road, Cherry Hinton, Cambridge, CB1 9LH Tel: (01223) 245028 Fax: (01223) 414862 E-mail: atitrade@btinternet.com *Castor & wheel manufacturer & importer*

Emreco International Ltd, 69 Springkell Avenue, Glasgow, G41 4NU Tel: 0141-424 1914 Fax: 0141-423 2997 E-mail: info@emreco.co.uk *Ladies' separates distributors*

▶ Ems Ltd, Grimshaw Street, Burnley, Lancashire, BB11 2AZ Tel: (07986) 782978 Fax: (01282) 860638 E-mail: mtools@btinternet.com *Supply used machine tools, lathes & milling machines*

Ems, 18-22 Queen Street, Leicester, LE1 1QR Tel: 0116-262 2588 Fax: 0116-251 1429 E-mail: emsleister@rexelscnete.co.uk *Wholesale electrical supplies* Also at: Branches throughout the U.K.

Ems Ltd, Sentinal House, 11a High Street, Long Buckby, Northampton, NN6 7RE Tel: (01327) 844848 Fax: (01327) 844849 E-mail: duncan@ environmental-mechanical-services.co.uk *Water sterilisation, treatment chemicals & equipment suppliers*

EMS Ship Management Ltd, 3 Commercial Quay, 80 Commercial Street, Edinburgh, EH6 6LX Tel: 0131-554 4466 Fax: 0131-554 3843 E-mail: admin.uk@ems-asa.com *Shipping lines*

Ems Synthesizers, Trendeal Vean Barn, Trendeal, Ladock, Truro, Cornwall, TR2 4NW Tel: (01726) 883265 Fax: (01726) 883283 E-mail: enquiries@ems-synthi.demon.co.uk *Sound equipment manufrs*

▶ Emsar Polymers UK Ltd, 2 The Court Stanley Green Business Park, Earl Road, Cheadle Hulme, Cheadle, Cheshire, SK8 6GN Tel: 0161-485 7772 Fax: 0161 485 7773 E-mail: info@emsarpolymers.co.uk *Suppliers of commodity and speciality masterbatches, creating masterbatch solutions to improve process or performance of our customers manufactured products.*

EMS-CHEMIE (UK) Ltd, Darfin House, Priestly Court, Stafford Technology Park, Stafford, ST18 0AR Tel: (01785) 283739 Fax: (01785) 283722 E-mail: welcome@uk.emsgrivory.com *Granules for plastic suppliers*

Emsley Crane Hire Of Harrogate, Unit 1-2 Claro Park, Harrogate, North Yorkshire, HG1 4BB Tel: (01423) 561929 Fax: (01423) 509772 *Mobile crane hire*

Emslie Industrial Engraving Co., 62 West Harbour Road, Edinburgh, EH5 1PW Tel: 0131-552 9944 Fax: 0131-552 1093 *Machine engravers*

Emstrey Timber Products, 2a Emstrey, Emstrey, Atcham, Shrewsbury, SY5 6QP Tel: (01743) 761131 Fax: (01743) 761825 *Timber manufrs*

Emsworth Shipyard Ltd, Thorney Road, Emsworth, Hampshire, PO10 8BP Tel: (01243) 375211 Fax: (01243) 377259 E-mail: sales@tarquin-boats.com *Boat builders & repairers*

Emtrol LLC, Davey House, Eaton Ford, St. Neots, Cambridgeshire, PE19 7BA Tel: (01480) 475071 Fax: (01480) 475046 E-mail: technical@emtrolcorp.co.uk *Dust collecting equipment & designer*

Emuge (UK) Ltd, 2 Claire Court, Rawmarsh Road, Rotherham, South Yorkshire, S60 1RU Tel: (01709) 364494 Fax: (01709) 364540 E-mail: sales@emuge-uk.co.uk *Engineers clamp manufrs*

Emulation Technology UK Ltd, 78 Asheridge Road, Chesham, Buckinghamshire, HP5 2PY Tel: (01494) 791336 Fax: (01494) 792336 *Adapters, sockets & test accessories providers*

Emulex Corporation, 7-8 Forest Court, Oaklands Park, Wokingham, Berkshire, RG41 2FD Tel: 0118-977 2929 Fax: 0118-977 3237 E-mail: enquire.europe@emulex.com *Computer products sales & service*

Emwood Co., 43 Broom Hill Road, Rochester, Kent, ME2 3LF Tel: (01634) 719242 Fax: (01634) 719242 *Catering tableware distributors*

En Aid Design Workshop, Wassage Way, Hampton Lovett, Droitwich, Worcestershire, WR9 0NX Tel: (01905) 451501 Fax: (01905) 771771 E-mail: enaid@btclick.com *Model manufrs*

En Mach Services, Unit 11 Lythalls Lane Industrial Estate, Lythalls Lane, Coventry, CV6 6FJ Tel: (024) 7668 1403 Fax: (024) 7668 1403 E-mail: yanhunt@tiscali.co.uk *Chemical black oxidising services*

▶ En Press Ltd, Unit 16-18 Home Farm Rural Industries, East Tytherley Road, Lockerley, Romsey, Hampshire, SO51 0JT Tel: (01794) 341425 Fax: (01794) 341424

Enable Access Disabled Access Equipement, 16 Plantagenet Road, Barnet, Hertfordshire, EN5 5JG Tel: (020) 8275 0375 Fax: (020) 8449 0326 *Disabled lifts & ramps manufrs*

▶ Enable Enterprises Ltd, 24 Treforest Road, Coventry, CV3 1FN Tel: (024) 7644 3830 Fax: 0800 358 8484 E-mail: simon.stevens@enableenterprises.com

▶ Enableit Technologies Ltd, Foxwood House, Dobbs Lane, Kesgrave, Ipswich, IP5 2QQ Tel: (01473) 618980 Fax: (01473) 618989 E-mail: david@e-nableit.com *IT support & training company*

Enabling Communications Group Ltd, Unit 3 Wareley Yard, Wareley Road, Peterborough, PE2 9PF Tel: (01733) 892031 Fax: (01733) 891197 E-mail: sales@ecgcomms.co.uk *Telephone communication services*

Enabling Computer Supplies Ltd, Castlefields, Stafford, ST16 1BU Tel: (01785) 243111 Fax: (01785) 243222 E-mail: sales@enablingtechnology.net *Computer hard & software distributors*

▶ Enact Services, 25 Park Road, London, N11 2QE Tel: (0870) 1657403 E-mail: salestraining@enact-services.com *Enact provides organisations with professional sales training and coaching services to ensure they can maximise client relationships and develop new business.*

Enalon Ltd, Vale Rise, Tonbridge, Kent, TN9 1RR Tel: (01732) 358500 Fax: (01732) 770463 E-mail: office@enalon.co.uk *Plastics injection moulders*

Enba NI Ltd, The Old Mill, Drumaness, Ballynahinch, County Down, BT24 8LS Tel: (028) 9756 1574 Fax: (028) 9756 1576 E-mail: sales@enbani.com *Oil recycling services & tank cleaners*

Enbray Cooper (UK) Ltd, Derwent Drive, Derwent Howe Industrial Estate, Workington, Cumbria, CA14 3YW Tel: (01900) 68173 Fax: (01900) 68189 E-mail: sales@enbray.co.uk *Contactors*

Encapsulated Print Services, Unit 3a Prince William Way, Loughborough, Leicestershire, LE11 5DD Tel: (01509) 230892 Fax: (01509) 230877 E-mail: encapprintmids@aol.com *Print finishers & encapsulation*

Encapsulating Co. Ltd, 3-11 Pensbury Place, London, SW8 4TP Tel: (020) 7498 6700 Fax: (020) 7498 6749 E-mail: admin@encapsulating.co.uk *Encapsulating & binding services*

Encapsulation Technology, 147 Tadcaster Road, Dringhouses, York, YO24 1QJ Tel: (01904) 705254 Fax: (01904) 705254 E-mail: alangeorge@encapsulationtechnology.co.uk *Engineering consultancy, design & development services*

EncapSulite International Ltd, 17 Chartwell Business Park, Chartmoor Road, Leighton Buzzard, Bedfordshire, LU7 4WG Tel: (01525) 376974 Fax: (01525) 850306 E-mail: reply@encapsulite.co.uk *Specialist safety & fluorescent lighting manufrs*

Encase Ltd, Beaumont Road, Banbury, Oxfordshire, OX16 1RE Tel: (01295) 250971 Fax: (01295) 752910 *Corrugated fibre board manufrs*

Encase Northern Ltd, 2 Yeadon Airport Industrial Estate, Harrogate Road, Yeadon, Leeds, LS19 7WP Tel: 0113-250 5616 Fax: 0113-239 1145 E-mail: operations.northern@encase.co.uk *Corrugated container manufrs*

Encase Packers Ltd, Scout Hill Mills, Broad Street, Dewsbury, West Yorkshire, WF13 3SA Tel: (01924) 502030 Fax: (01924) 520062 *Full storage facility including container de-stuffing*

▶ Encase Scotland Ltd, 9 Hawbank Road, East Kilbride, Glasgow, G74 5EG Tel: (01355) 246716 Fax: (01355) 264406

▶ Enchanted Heaven Fancy Dress & Party Supplies, 111 Cornwall Road, Herne Bay, Kent, CT6 7SZ Tel: (01227) 283933 E-mail: enchantedheaven1@yahoo.co.uk *We supply gorgeous fancy dress costumes for adults and children,together with party supplies including our unique parties in a box available in various themes and price ranges*

▶ Enclosed Solutions Ltd, 7a The Mall, Ealing Broadway, London, W5 2PJ Tel: 0208 7990900 Fax: 0208 799 0910 E-mail: paul@enclosed.co.uk *We specialise in virtual office space, call centre logistics and all aspects of administrative support.*

Enclosure Systems Ltd, Platt Industrial Estate, Maidstone Road, Borough Green, Sevenoaks, Kent, TN15 8JA Tel: (01732) 886552 Fax: (01732) 886443 E-mail: sales@enclosures.co.uk *Enclosure designers & manufrs*

Enco Design & Engineering Co. Ltd, 2 Birch Close, Allesley Green, Coventry, CV5 7PW Tel: (024) 7640 4509 E-mail: johnross@encodesign.co.uk *Jigs, fixtures & gauges*

Enco Engineering (Hants) Ltd, Block C, Stirling Business Park, Nimrod Way, Ferndown Industrial Estate, Ferndown, Dorset, BH21 7SH Tel: (01202) 875200 Fax: (01202) 866160 E-mail: sales@encoengineering.com *Precision*

Encon, 1 Rippleside Commercial Estate, Ripple Road, Barking, Essex, IG11 0RJ Tel: (020) 8595 2121 Fax: (020) 8595 9003 E-mail: info@encon.co.uk *Sound or acoustic & thermal insulating material*

Encon Ltd, Langage Science Park, Western Wood Way, Plympton, Plymouth, PL7 5BG Tel: (01752) 333720 Fax: (01752) 348938 *Sound or acoustic & thermal insulating materials suppliers*

Company Information

Encon Insulation Ltd, Unit F1-F2, St. Michaels Close, Aylesford, Kent, ME20 7BU Tel: (01622) 713400 Fax: (01622) 713403 E-mail: maidstone@encon.co.uk *Sound or acoustic & thermal insulation materials suppliers*

Encon Insulation Ltd, Unit 2 Elmbank, Channel Commercial Park, Queens Road, Belfast, BT3 9DT Tel: (028) 9045 4646 Fax: (028) 9045 4656 E-mail: t.patterson@encon.co.uk *Sound or acoustic & thermal insulating materials*

Encon Insulation Ltd, 3-4 Tamebridge Industrial Estate, Aldridge Road, Perry Barr, Birmingham, B42 2TX Tel: 0121-356 0606 Fax: 0121-356 4828 *Sound or acoustic & thermal insulating materials*

Encon Insulation Ltd, 3-4 Tamebridge Industrial Estate, Aldridge Road, Perry Barr, Birmingham, B42 2TX Tel: 0121-356 0606 Fax: 0121-356 4828 *Sound or acoustic & thermal insulating materials suppliers*

Encon Insulation Ltd, Buchanans Warehouse, Chittening Industrial Estate, Chittening, Bristol, BS11 0YB Tel: 0117-980 2100 Fax: 0117-980 2101 *Thermal insulating materials*

Encon Insulation Ltd, 23 Nettlefold Road, Cardiff, CF24 5JQ Tel: (029) 2089 5040 Fax: (029) 2089 5044 *Sound, acoustic & thermal insulating materials*

Encon Insulation Ltd, Unit 500, Fareham Reach, 166 Fareham Road, Gosport, Hampshire, PO13 0FP Tel: (01329) 230555 Fax: (01329) 230615 E-mail: fareham@encon.co.uk *Sound or acoustic & thermal insulating materials distributors*

Encon Insulation Ltd, Unit 9-10, Gelderd Road, Morley, Leeds, LS27 7JN Tel: 0113-289 7666 Fax: 0113-289 7555 E-mail: leeds@encon.co.uk *Sound or acoustic & thermal insulating materials*

Encon Insulation Ltd, Unit E2, High Flatworth, Tyne Tunnel Trading Estate, Northshields, Newcastle Upon Tyne, NE29 7UZ Tel: 0191-293 1090 Fax: 0191-293 1099 *Sound or acoustic & thermal insulation materials*

Encon Insulation Ltd, Brunswick House, Deaghton Close, Wetherby, West Yorkshire, LS22 7GZ Tel: (01937) 524200 Fax: (01937) 524222 *Insulating material, including sound, acoustic & thermal, distributors* Also at: Branches throughout the U.K.

Encon Insulation Ltd, Unit 3, Industrial Estate, Stanton Harcourt, Witney, Oxfordshire, OX29 5UX Tel: (01865) 734500 Fax: (01865) 734518 *Sound or acoustic & thermal insulation materials distributors*

Encon Insulation Materials, Unit 17-19, Bloomsgrove Industrial Estate, Nottingham, NG7 3JB Tel: 0115-978 0040 Fax: 0115-942 0264 *Sound, acoustic & thermal insulating material distributors*

Encon Insulation Northampton, 21 Saddleback Road, Westgate Industrial Estate, Northampton, NN5 5HL Tel: (01604) 580580 Fax: (01604) 580585 E-mail: info@encon.co.uk *Sound or acoustic & thermal insulation material specialists*

Encon Insulation Scotland, 80 Cambuslang Road, Cambuslang, Clydesmill Industrial Estate, Glasgow, G32 8NB Tel: 0141-641 0011 Fax: 0141-641 5170 *Sound, acoustic & thermal insulating material*

Encon Insulations, Unit 13 Studlands Park Industrial Estate, Newmarket, Suffolk, CB8 7AU Tel: (01638) 667292 Fax: (01638) 664081 E-mail: northampton@encon.co.uk *Sound or acoustic & thermal insulating materials*

Encon Manchester Ltd, Chaddock Lane, Worsley, Manchester, M28 1DR Tel: 0161-703 7400 Fax: 0161-703 7411 E-mail: manchester@encon.co.uk *Insulation distributors*

▶ Encon Special Contracts Ltd, Encon House Astin Court, Tenter Road Moulton Park, Moulton Park Industrial Estate, Northampton, NN3 6PZ Tel: (01604) 648200

▶ Encore Catering, Blair Court, Port Dundas Business Park, 100 Borron Street, Glasgow, G4 9XE Tel: 0141-353 9148 Fax: 0141-353 9145 *Catering services*

Encore Encapsulation Ltd, Swallow Mill, Swallow Street, Stockport, Cheshire, SK1 3HJ Tel: 0161-476 2646 Fax: 0161-476 2646 E-mail: sales@encoreencapsulation.co.uk *Encapsulation for print industry*

▶ Encore Entertainment Ltd, 44 Churchfield Road, Walton-on-Thames, Surrey, KT12 2SY Tel: 01932 253273 E-mail: Encore_info@yahoo.co.uk *Childrens entertainment corporate entertainment, bouncy castle hire. face painting, pamper parties, gladiators, sumos, in surrey and hertforshire*

Encore Of Gloucester Ltd, 5 Francis Woodcock Trading Estate, 277 Barton Street, Gloucester, GL1 4JE Tel: (01452) 503079 Fax: (01452) 310177 E-mail: j-mckee@btconnect.com *Exhibition & display contractors*

Encore International Limited, 26 York Street, London, W1U 6PZ Tel: 020 7788 7772 Fax: 020 7788 7773 E-mail: enquiries@encore-international.net *Encore International is an FSA approved independent advisor specialising in price risk management. Acknowledged as the leading provider of energy price risk management to some of the world's most successful global corporations we are regularly called upon for our unique expertise and insight into the energy markets.* Our risk management approach delivers a comprehensive range of measures beyond just price controls. Services include risk policies and procedures, compliance audits, investment management, regulatory impact assessments, environmental auditing and reporting. Physical supply contracts can be tendered and negotiated to maximise your ability to control your costs and then complimented by analytical support to simplify and optimise decision making.*

▶ Encore Personnel, 2 Plough Road, Wellington, Telford, Shropshire, TF1 1ET Tel: (01952) 262970 Fax: (01952) 641880 E-mail: sales@encorepersonnel.co.uk *Specialist supplier of Technical, Driving and Industrial staff.*

▶ Encore Personnel Services, Market Chambers, Shelton Square, Coventry, CV1 1DG Tel: (024) 7623 8330 Fax: (024) 7625 6475 E-mail: coventry@encorepersonnel.co.uk *Specialist supplier of Technical, Industrial and Driving staff*

Encyclopaedia Britannica UK Ltd, Unity Wharf, 13 Mill Street, London, SE1 2BH Tel: (020) 7500 7800 Fax: (020) 7500 7878 E-mail: enquiries@britannica.co.uk *E-commerce solutions*

End Design Ltd, Unit 37, Bookham Industrial Park, Church Road, Leatherhead, Surrey, KT23 3EU Tel: (01372) 458080 Fax: (01372) 450592 E-mail: sales@end-design.co.uk *Cable assembly manufrs*

End O Line Services, 1-3 Station Road, Maldon, Essex, CM9 4LQ Tel: (01621) 843535 Fax: (01621) 843534 E-mail: sales@eols.co.uk *IT disposal & data security services*

End To End Labels Ltd, Vale Road, Spilsby, Lincolnshire, PE23 5HE Tel: (01790) 753475 Fax: (01790) 752979 E-mail: sales@endtoendlabels.co.uk *Self-adhesive label manufrs*

Endaim, 3rd Floor Phoenix House, Christopher Martin Road, Basildon, Essex, SS14 3HG Tel: (01268) 270022 Fax: (01268) 285050 E-mail: sandie.lorkins@headoffice.endaim.com *Modern apprenticeship work based training to young people in retail, hair, customer service, call handling, business admin, estate agency & hospitality*

Endcape, Po Box 26, Pickering, North Yorkshire, YO18 7JL Tel: (01751) 476370 Fax: (01751) 474918 E-mail: sales@endcape.com *Specialists in the design, manufacture and supply of bespoke and standard product for the power generation industry.*

Endeavor Woodcrafts Ltd, 71 Darlington Road, Ferryhill, County Durham, DL17 8EX Tel: (01740) 657676 Fax: (01740) 657676 *Disabilities woodcraft co-operative promoters & manufrs*

Endecotts Ltd, 9 Lombard Road, London, SW19 3UP Tel: (020) 8542 8121 Fax: (020) 8543 6629 E-mail: sales@endecotts.com *Laboratory test sieve manufrs*

Endless Supply Ltd, Unit 31, Darlaston Centre Estate, Salisbery Street, Darlaston, West Midlands, WS10 8BQ Tel: 0121-568 7676 Fax: 0121-568 6787 E-mail: sales@endlessupply.co.uk *Stainless steel & aluminium fabrications for the food & pharmaceutical industries*

Endoline Machinery Ltd, Stratton Business Park, London Road, Biggleswade, Bedfordshire, SG18 8QB Tel: (01767) 316422 Fax: (01767) 318033 E-mail: info@endoline.co.uk *Packaging machinery manufrs*

Endon Group, Cross Green Industrial Park, Felnex Road, Leeds, LS9 0SS Tel: 0113-249 2755 Fax: 0113-248 4519 E-mail: sales@endon.co.uk *Lighting fittings suppliers*

▶ Endor Learning & Development, Normanby Gateway, Lysaghts Way, Scunthorpe, North Lincolnshire, DN15 9YG Tel: (01724) 275190 Fax: (01724) 275285 E-mail: info@endor.co.uk *Behaviourally based business services, training & development*

▶ Endorfin TV, Lower Green Road, Tunbridge Wells, Kent, TN4 8TE Tel: (01892) 533577 Fax: (01892) 515183 E-mail: mark@endorfin.tv *endorfin.tv provide cost effective test campaigns to get you on television quickly and affordably.*Direct response television advertising & production from start to finish.*marketing, advertising, commercials, media, tv commercials, video production, direct marketing, production companies, tv infomercials, direct response marketing, as seen on tv, infomercial products, direct response television advertising agency, direct response advertising, media, drtv**

Endoscan Ltd, 58 Acacia Road, St. Johns Wood, London, NW8 6AG Tel: (020) 7483 2300 Fax: (020) 7483 2900 E-mail: sales@endoscan.co.uk *Endoscopes & introscopes manufacturers industrial*

Endoscopic Manufacturing & Services Ltd, Unit 14 Alliance Court, Alliance Road, London, W3 0RB Tel: (020) 8896 1002 Fax: (020) 8752 1030 E-mail: info@endoscopiclondon.com *Medical equipment manufrs*

▶ Endoserve UK Ltd, 1a Stringer House Lane, Emley, Huddersfield, HD8 9SU Tel: (01924) 849150 Fax: (01924) 849150 E-mail: endoserve@btinternet.com *Sterile sheaths for rigid & flexible endoscopes sales*

Endress & Hauser Ltd, Floats Road, Roundthorn Industrial Estate, Manchester, M23 9NF Tel: 0161-286 5000 Fax: 0161-998 1841 E-mail: info@uk.endress.com *Endress+Hauser is a global supplier of process instrumentation, engineered solutions and added value services. We work closely with customers to increase plant efficiency, productivity and profitability. We offer comprehensive process control and automation solutions in level, pressure, flow, temperature, analysis, data acquisition and digital communications across a wide range of industries.*

Endress & Hauser, Unit 30 Northfield Way, Aycliffe Industrial Park, Newton Aycliffe, County Durham, DL5 6UF Tel: (01325) 329801 Fax: (01325) 300840 E-mail: sales@systems.endress.com *Tank gauging system manufrs*

The Ener G Group, Ener G House, Daniel Adamson Road, Salford, M50 2DT Tel: 0161-745 7450 Fax: 0161-745 7457 E-mail: sales@cpsl.co.uk *Power supply systems repair services*

Enercom Ltd, 122 High Street, Earl Shilton, Leicester, LE9 7LQ Tel: (01455) 840100 Fax: (01455) 840200 E-mail: mike.garlick@enercom.co.uk *Electrical metering*

Enercon Industries Ltd, 64 Edison Road, Rabans Lane Industrial Area, Aylesbury, Buckinghamshire, HP19 8UX Tel: (01296) 330542 Fax: (01296) 432098 E-mail: info@enerconind.co.uk *Induction heat sealing suppliers*

▶ ENERG P.L.C., ENER-G House, Daniel Adamson Road, Salford, M50 1DT Tel: 0161-745 7450 Fax: 0161-745 7457 E-mail: info@energ.co.uk *Energy efficiency consultants*

Energas Ltd, Westmorland Street, Hull, HU2 0HX Tel: (01482) 329333 Fax: (01482) 212335 E-mail: sales@energas.co.uk *Industrial gas producers & suppliers service*

Energas Ltd, Soho Street, Smethwick, West Midlands, B66 2RH Tel: 0121-555 5050 Fax: 0121-565 3830 E-mail: engweld@smethwick.fslife.co.uk *Welding plant & equipment suppliers*

▶ Energema Ltd, 77 Nicholas Gardens, High Wycombe, Buckinghamshire, HP13 6JG Tel: (01494) 465394 E-mail: info@energema.co.uk *Training consultants for computers*

Energen Ltd, Brunel Science Park, Kingston Lane, Uxbridge, Middlesex, UB8 3PQ Tel: (01895) 271000 Fax: (01895) 272000 E-mail: mikeharbord@energen.co.uk *Energy management consultancy*

Energizer Ltd, Unit 2 Tanfield Lea Industrial Park, Tanfield Lea, Stanley, County Durham, DH9 9QF Tel: (01207) 290900 Fax: (01207) 292016 E-mail: pam.holder@energiser.com *Battery component manufrs*

Energizer Group Ltd, Eveready House, 93 Burleigh Gardens, Southgate, London, N14 5AQ Tel: (020) 8882 8661 Fax: (020) 8882 1938 *Battery manufrs* Also at: Dunstable & Manchester

▶ Energo Limited, 3 The Square, Ellon, Aberdeenshire, AB41 9JB Tel: 01358 725139 E-mail: info@implement.it *Our innovative ICT solutions will have you communicating and collaborating with your colleagues, customers, suppliers and partners in no time.*

Energy Advisers Ltd, Beech Hedges, 1 Wishing Stone Way, Matlock, Derbyshire, DE4 5LU Tel: (01629) 581400 Fax: (01629) 57313 E-mail: energy@breathe.co.uk *Energy consultants*

Energy Alloys, Chesterfield Trading Estate, Carrwood Road, Sheepbridge, Chesterfield, Derbyshire, S41 9QB Tel: (01246) 264500 Fax: (01246) 264550 E-mail: imsuk.energy@ims-group.com *Steel stockholders*

Energy Alloys UK Ltd, Canklow Meadows Industrial Estate, West Bawtry Road, Rotherham, South Yorkshire, S60 2XN Tel: (01709) 788000 Fax: (01709) 788030 E-mail: uksales@ealloys.com *A key supplier to the oil industry with a special range of alloy, stainless and nickel alloy grades supported by a large machine shop with sawing, deephole boring and machining capabilities. Distributor of API and premium coupling stock & CRA materials**Carbon & alloy engineering steels **austenitic|martensitic|duplex stainless steels***Mill Representation**DMV Stainless|Valtimet|Sidenor Reinosa|CFR and offering seamless stainless steel tube, titanium tube and forgings**Sites**Rotherham|Chesterfield| Birmingham|England*Arbroath|Bellshill|Scotland* Houston|Lafayette|Tulsa|USA*Edmonton|Calgary| Canada*Dubai|Middle East**Specs**AISI40|4140|4145|8630|4330| 4340|18|4|420|LF2| Super Cr9Cr-1Mo|17-4PH|F51|F55|2205|ASTM A5|625|718|925|K500*API|NACE|NORSOK**304| 316|321|347|416|431|FV520B**070M20|080M40| 070M55|230M07|655M|835M15|605M36| 708M40|709M40|817M40|826M40|722M24**

Energy Chemical & Equipment Co, Southwell Business Park, Crew Lane, Southwell, Nottinghamshire, NG25 0TX Tel: (01636) 816600 Fax: (01636) 816602 E-mail: energypumps@aol.com *Pump manufrs*

▶ Energy Economisers Ltd, 1 Ewhurst Avenue, Birmingham, B29 6EY Tel: 0121-471 3038 Fax: 0121-471 3039 E-mail: sales@energyeconomisers.co.uk

▶ Energy Efficiency Advice Centre, 20 George Hudson Street, York, YO1 6WR Tel: (01904) 554406 Fax: (01904) 554412 E-mail: owen@4sustainable-energy.co.uk *Advice on energy efficiency within small business sector, management of local grant programs for small businesses*

▶ The Energy Helpline, Unit 8, Great Guildford House, 30 Great Guildford Street, London, SE1 0HS Tel: (020) 74018943 *Price comparison services*

Energy Industries Council, Newcombe House, 45 Notting Hill Gate, London, W11 3LQ Tel: (020) 7221 2043 Fax: (020) 7221 8813 E-mail: sales@the-eic.com Sales Contact: M. Freeman *Trade associations.*

Energy Institute, 61 New Cavendish Street, London, W1G 7AR Tel: (020) 7467 7100 Fax: (020) 7255 1472 E-mail: info@energyinst.org.uk *Energy consultants* Also at: Branches throughout the U.K.

▶ Energy Integration Ltd, The Lodge, Nettlestead Place, Maidstone Road, Nettlestead, Maidstone, Kent, ME18 5HA Tel: (07752) 539887 E-mail: info@energy-integration.com *Energy Management Systems, Power Quality monitoring, Energy Monitoring, Optimization of Corporate Energy*

Energy Services Ltd, Utility Management Centre, Mucklow Hill, Halesowen, West Midlands, B62 8DR Tel: 0121-585 4000 Fax: 0121-585 4103 E-mail: simon.steed@energy-services.co.uk *Energy management*

Energy Solutions, 33 Kyle Crescent, Dunfermline, Fife, KY11 8GU Tel: (01383) 732088 Fax: (0870) 1341377 E-mail: info@energybrokers.co.uk *We provide free advice and brokerage for gas and electricity to SME customers.*

▶ Energy Solutions International Ltd, Hastings House, Falcon Court, Preston Farm Industrial Estate, Stockton-on-Tees, Cleveland, TS18 3TS Tel: (01642) 677755 Fax: (01642) 606655 E-mail: sales@energy-solutions.com *Computer software development*

Energy Solutions UK Ltd, Property Services House, George Summers Close, Medway City Estate, Rochester, Kent, ME2 4NS Tel: (01634) 290772 Fax: (01634) 290773 E-mail: mail@energy-solutions.co.uk *Marine electrical equipment distributors*

Energy Systems Ltd, Unit 5 Nevis Business Park, Balgownie Road, Aberdeen, AB22 8NT Tel: (01224) 822580 Fax: (01224) 707153 E-mail: sales@nangall.co.uk *Well logging equipment manufrs*

Energy Systems, Systems House, Rotherside Road, Eckington, Sheffield, S21 4HL Tel: (01246) 439862 Fax: (01246) 431444 E-mail: websales@aeceuro.co.uk *Suppliers & installers of uninterruptible power supplies*

Energy Technique plc, 47 Central Avenue, West Molesey, Surrey, KT8 2QZ Tel: (020) 8941 2199 Fax: (020) 8783 0140 E-mail: sales@energytechniqueplc.co.uk *Manufacturers of heating, ventilating & air conditioning*

Energy Technology & Control Ltd, 25 North Street, Lewes, East Sussex, BN7 2PE Tel: (01273) 480667 Fax: (01273) 480652 E-mail: sales@energytechnologycontrol.com *Boiler controls manufrs*

▶ Energyfactor, Chichester Way, Maldon, Essex, CM9 6YY Tel: (01621) 874801 E-mail: energyfactor@tiscali.co.uk *Provision of consultancy advice to energy suppliers based on over 30 years experience. Energy audits for non-domestic sites. Registered with the Carbon Trust for free energy assessments.*Registered verifier for EU Emissions Trading Scheme.*Registered SAP assessor for existing domestic dwellings.*

Enerpac Ltd, PO Box 33, Darlaston, West Midlands, WS10 8LQ Tel: (01527) 598900 Fax: 0121-505 0799 E-mail: info@enerpac.com *Hydraulic tools manufrs*

Enertron Ltd, 32 New Forest Enterprise Centre, Chapel La, Totton, Southampton, SO40 9LA Tel: (023) 8087 3522 Fax: (023) 8087 3522 E-mail: bob@enertronltd.co.uk *Electrical & electronic measurement & control*

Enfield Roller Shutter Co., Unit 10 Kimberley Road Works, Billet Road, London, E17 5DT Tel: (020) 8527 2406 Fax: (01708) 750900 E-mail: ersco@lineone.net *Roller shutter & grill manufrs*

Enfield Safety Supplies, 40 Queensway, Enfield, Middlesex, EN3 4SP Tel: (020) 8805 1015 Fax: (0870) 3800077 *Safety equipment distributors*

▶ Enfield Speciality Doors, Alexandra Road, Enfield, Middlesex, EN3 7EH Tel: (020) 8805 6662 Fax: (020) 8443 1290 E-mail: sales@infodoors.co.uk *Door manufrs*

Enfield Timber Co., 1-23 Hertford Road, Enfield Highway, Enfield, Middlesex, EN3 5JD Tel: (020) 8804 1800 Fax: (020) 8443 4569 *Timber merchants service*

▶ Engage Av, 19 Cardiff Business Park, Lambourne Crescent, Llanishen, Cardiff, CF14 5GF Tel: (029) 2076 6873 Fax: (029) 2076 5847 E-mail: info@engage-av.com *Specialising in conference production & technical staging, hire, sales and installation of audio visual, data, video, sound & lighting equipment.*

▶ Engage Surveys, 5 Howbridge Close, Ellenbrook, Worsley, Manchester, M28 7XZ Tel: 0161-799 8992 E-mail: craig@engage-surveys.com *There are now three steps to maximising your vital business information with Engage:***Design & build your own surveys**Launch & collect responses**Analyse & take action**Engage Surveys are based in Manchester, operate nationally & our team of consultants can provide:***Help with your own surveys**Training**Consulting assistance **

Engel Workwear, Carters Yard, 30 Carters Lane, Kiln Farm, Milton Keynes, MK11 3HL Tel: (01908) 561560 Fax: (01908) 563805 E-mail: sales@f-engel.co.uk

Engelmann & Buckham Ltd, Buckham House, 25 Lenten Street, Alton, Hampshire, GU34 1HH Tel: (01420) 82421 Fax: (01420) 89193 E-mail: hrashleigh@buckham.co.uk *Sales agent supplying machinery to the packaging, processing, converting & plastics industries, ancillary equipment to the plastics & converting industries, & raw materials& finished products to the packaging industry.*

Engels, 1 Kingley Centre, Downs Road, West Stoke, Chichester, West Sussex, PO18 9HJ Tel: (01243) 576644 Fax: (01243) 576644 E-mail: sales@engels.co.uk *Windows & door importers & distributors*

Engine Developments, Leigh Road, Swift Valley Industrial Estate, Rugby, Warwickshire, CV21 1DS Tel: (01788) 541114 Fax: (01788) 546303 E-mail: sales@engdev.com *Racing engine design services*

Engine Power, 7 Bryant Road, Bayton Road Industrial Estate, Coventry, CV7 9EN Tel: (024) 7664 4660 Fax: (024) 7664 4634 *Diesel engine rebuilders*

Engine Services (Croydon) Ltd, 173 Handcroft Road, Croydon, CR0 3LF Tel: (020) 8665 1952 Fax: (020) 8665 1952 *General engineers*

▶ Engine Spares, 82 Mitcham Road, London, SW17 9NG Tel: (020) 8767 5990 Fax: (020) 8767 5991 E-mail: smithaustin01@btconnect.com *Import / export*

Engine & Truck (N I) Ltd, M2 Trade Centre, Duncrue Crescent, Belfast, BT3 9BW Tel: (028) 9077 1411 Fax: (028) 9077 5085 E-mail: sales@enginetruck.co.uk *Engine component distributors*

▶ The Engineer, St Giles House, 50 Poland Street, London, W1F 7AX Tel: (020) 7970 4114 Fax: 0207 9704193 E-mail: matt.comley@centaur.co.uk *The Engineer Jobs provides a comprehensive list of the latest engineering opportunities within the UK. Dedicated to engineering professionals ranging from mechanical, electrical, electronic, design, process and production, to name but a few! Functionalities include a searchable database of recruiters and CVs, as well as daily email alerts.*

Engineered Composites Ltd, 41 Hope St., Chester, CH4 8BU Tel: (01244) 676000 Fax: (01244) 677267 E-mail: info@engineered-composites.co.uk Purchasing Contact: B. Martin Sales Contact: B. Martin *One of the UK's largest distributor of GRP pultruded profiles. Full product range of structural profiles in stock. Other products include GRP scaffolding plank & tube, flat & corrugated sheet, chequer plate, open mesh grid & solid flooring*

▶ Engineered Piping Products, 36 Southweald Drive, Waltham Abbey, Essex, EN9 1PP Tel: (01992) 719595 Fax: (01992) 787002 E-mail: info@engineered-piping-products.com Purchasing Contact: S. O'Donnell Sales Contact: S. O'Donnell *Penstock installation services*

Engineered Solutions, Unit 2, North Court, Armstrong Road, Maidstone, Kent, ME15 6JZ Tel: (01622) 750650 Fax: (01622) 355199 E-mail: sales@engsolutions.co.uk *Control systems*

Engineered Systems (Electrical) Ltd, Systems House, Unit 1, Waterside Industrial Park, Waterside Road, Leeds, LS10 1RW Tel: 0113-272 1222 Fax: 0113-272 1333 E-mail: mick@eselimited.co.uk *Engineered Systems (Electrical) Ltd are a Leeds based company that designs/installs and commissions the complete high voltage electrical distribution system. In addition to this ESE Ltd also provides HV/LV switchgear both new and fully re-furbished, new and fully re-furbished distribution transformers, Maintenance agreements to look after HV distribution systems, emergency call out, cable installation/ jointing and fault finding up to and including 33000v inc all necessary trench work and support systems.*

Co Engineering Ltd, Unit 57 Coleshill Industrial Estate, Station Road, Coleshill, Birmingham, B46 1JT Tel: (01675) 464252 Fax: (01675) 467318 E-mail: coeng@tiscali.co.uk *Engineering company*

Engineering Appliances Ltd, 11 Brooklands Close, Sunbury-on-Thames, Middlesex, TW16 7DX Tel: (01932) 788888 Fax: (01932) 761263 E-mail: info@engineering-appliances.com *Rubber & metal bellows manufrs*

Engineering Design Partnership, 2 Barnet Road, Barnet, Hertfordshire, EN5 3LJ Tel: (020) 8449 9696 Fax: (020) 8449 6100 E-mail: edp@e-dp.co.uk *Building services consulting engineers*

Engineering & Design Plastics Ltd, 84 High Street, Cherry Hinton, Cambridge, CB1 9HZ Tel: (01223) 249431 Fax: (01223) 411803 E-mail: sales@edplastics.co.uk *Distributors of plastics to industry*

Engineering Designs With It Solutions, 17 Parkfield Drive, Sowerby Bridge, West Yorkshire, HX6 3PJ Tel: (01422) 834893 Fax: (01422) 835723 E-mail: sales@editsltd.co.uk *HVAC engineering design services complemented by CAD, Information Technology including supply, design and maintenance of bespoke systems, project management systems both design and supply, web design and other such services*

Engineering & Development Consultants Ltd, Keruing Cedar, Chess Hill, Loudwater, Rickmansworth, Hertfordshire, WD3 4HU Tel: (01923) 776567 Fax: (01923) 721438 E-mail: gmcrook@lineone.net *Aviation property consultants*

Engineering & Developments Lymington Ltd, Gosport Street, Lymington, Hampshire, SO41 9BB Tel: (01590) 673729 Fax: (01590) 675778 E-mail: sales@engdev.co.uk *Aluminium & alloy casting manufrs*

Engineering & Electrical Products Ltd, Bayton Road, Exhall, Coventry, CV7 9EL Tel: (024) 7636 3565 Fax: (024) 7664 4414 *General engineers*

Engineering Electrics (Wilmslow) Ltd, 67 Oldfield Road, Sale, Cheshire, M33 2AP Tel: 0161-973 8230 Fax: 0161-962 8648 *Control system design consultants*

Engineering Equipment Centre Ltd, 27 St Margarets Road, Bournemouth, BH10 4BG Tel: (01202) 528249 Fax: (01202) 528979 *CNC machinery distributors*

Engineering Equipment & Materials Users Association, 20 Long Lane, London, EC1A 9HL Tel: (020) 7796 1293 Fax: (020) 7796 1294 E-mail: sales@eemua.co.uk *Trade association*

Engineering & Factory Supplies Ltd, Algores Way, Wisbech, Cambridgeshire, PE13 2TQ Tel: (01945) 466644 Fax: (01945) 466232 *Engineer's supplies*

▶ Engineering & Foundry Supplies Colne Ltd, Phillips Lane, Colne, Lancashire, BB8 9PQ Tel: (01282) 868411 Fax: (01282) 867545 E-mail: mainoffice@ef-supplies.co.uk *Safety equipment suppliers*

Engineering & General Equipment Ltd, Eley Estate, Edmonton, London, N18 3BB Tel: (020) 8807 4567 Fax: (020) 8884 2229 E-mail: sales@centralube.com *Manufacturers & distributors of lubricating systems*

Engineering Installation Teesside Ltd, Owens Road, Middlesbrough, Cleveland, TS6 6HX Tel: (01642) 452471 Fax: (01642) 462005 E-mail: sales@enginst.co.uk *Electrical & mechanical engineers*

Engineering & Lifting Services, Unit B Drypool Way, Hull, HU9 1NL Tel: (01482) 323812 Fax: (01482) 320550 *Lifting equipment hire*

Engineering Light Assembly Co., Unit 1 Lower Road Trading Estate, Ledbury, Herefordshire, HR8 2DJ Tel: (01531) 632547 Fax: (01531) 634790 E-mail: engineering-light@btconnect.com *Sub-contract machinists*

Engineering & Maintenance Services, Unit 75a Gibbons Industrial Park, Dudley Road, Kingswinford, West Midlands, DY6 8XF Tel: (01384) 400147 Fax: (01384) 400148 *Machinery maintenance & repairs*

Engineering & Maintenance Services Ltd, Unit 12 St. Davids Industrial Estate, St. Davids Road, Swansea Enterprise Park, Swansea, SA6 8RX Tel: (01792) 797579 Fax: (01792) 772490 E-mail: ems@swanseauk.fsworld.co.uk *Heat exchanger & transfer equipment manufrs*

Engineering Metal Services Ltd, 4 Bradley Fold Trading Estate, Radcliffe Moor Road, Bradley Fold, Bolton, BL2 6RT Tel: (01204) 361811 Fax: (01204) 523697 E-mail: emslimited@emslimited.free-online.co.uk *Aluminium fabricators*

P.M.J. Engineering Co. Ltd, 5 & 6 Brunswick Road, Birmingham, B12 8NP Tel: 0121 4406760 *Precision machinists*

Engineering Co Partnership plc, Units 16-17 Metro Business Centre, Kangley Bridge Road, London, SE26 5BW Tel: (020) 8776 8070 Fax: (020) 8776 7372 E-mail: info@ecp.co.uk *Consulting engineers*

Engineering Patterns, Salford Trading Estate, Salford Street, Birmingham, B6 7SH Tel: 0121-327 0226 Fax: 0121-327 0226 *Pattern makers*

▶ Engineering Pipework Services Ltd, Unit 4 Derwent Howe Industrial Estate, Adams Road, Workington, Cumbria, CA14 3YS Tel: (01900) 603376 Fax: (01900) 65514

Engineering Plastic Products Ltd, Unit 6, Shaw Road, Dudley, West Midlands, DY2 8TS Tel: (01384) 235881 Fax: (01384) 255260 Purchasing Contact: R Kelly Sales Contact: R Kelly *Manufacturers of injection mouldings, plastic blow mouldings & plastic mouldings*

Engineering Plastic Services, 23a Eliot Street, Bootle, Merseyside, L20 4PD Tel: 0151-922 3243 Fax: 0151-922 6306 *Specialising in the fabrication & machining of all plastic materials.*

▶ The Engineering Practice, Gunnery House, Gunnery Terrace, Leamington Spa, Warwickshire, CV32 5PE Tel: (01926) 436010 Fax: (01926) 470326

Engineering Products & Services Ltd, Unit 10 Newporte Business Park, 9 Cardinal Close, Lincoln, LN2 4SY Tel: (01522) 544218 Fax: (01522) 510720 E-mail: phil@epsltd.karoo.co.uk *Generator controls & associated equipment manufrs*

▶ Engineering Resolutions, The Old Forge, Luckwell Bridge, Wheddon Cross, Minehead, Somerset, TA24 7EG Tel: (01643) 841183 E-mail: nic.wigley@engineeringresolutions.co.uk *Freelance Engineering Consultant specialising in problem solving and process improvement. Engineering support available also includes project management, product quality, and supplier management.*

Engineering Safety & Testing Ltd, P O Box 3, Saffron Walden, Essex, CB10 1RX Tel: (01799) 531040 Fax: (01799) 530917 E-mail: safety@sirdi.demon.co.uk *Crane & lifting equipment suppliers & repairers*

Engineering Service Co. Ltd, Albion Works, Bridgeman Street, Bolton, BL3 6BS Tel: (01204) 525647 Fax: (01204) 391705 E-mail: cad@eng-service.co.uk *Electrical contractors*

Engineering Services, 5 Gavin Road, Widnes, Cheshire, WA8 8RE Tel: 0151-495 1317 Fax: 0151-495 1559 E-mail: sales@engineering-services.co.uk *Bearing stockists*

Engineering Services Electrical Ltd, Century House, Enterprise Crescent, Lisburn, County Antrim, BT28 2BP Tel: (028) 9266 4583 Fax: (028) 9266 3700 E-mail: info@electroautomation.co.uk *Automatic gates, doors & car parking equipment suppliers*

▶ Engineering Services Fasteners Ltd, Parson Street, Keighley, West Yorkshire, BD21 3HD Tel: (01535) 665414 Fax: (01535) 608377 E-mail: sales@engservfast.co.uk *Distributors of fasteners, fixings tools & abrasives*

Engineering Services (Paisley) Ltd (ESL), 65 Espedair Street, Paisley, Renfrewshire, PA2 6RL Tel: 0141-889 1316 Fax: 0141-887 5344 E-mail: info@eslpaisley.co.uk *Specialist contractor providing liquid storage and handling installations, includes tanks, pipework, pumping and measuring equipment for fuels, solvents, liquid chemicals, water and effluent. Installations carried out in copper, steel, stainless and plastics.*

▶ Engineering Solutions 2000 Ltd, 32 Butterton Road, Rhyl, Denbighshire, LL18 1RF Tel: 07850 511707 Fax: (01745) 353184 E-mail: machinerepairs@yahoo.co.uk *REPAIRS TO ALL TYPES OF ENGINEERING AND SHEET METAL MACHINERY*MECHANICAL*ELECTRICAL* HYDRAULIC PNEUMATIC*FANUC CONTROL SYSTEMS*DNC LINKING*

Engineering Supplies Peterborough Ltd, Papyrus Road, Peterborough, PE4 5BH Tel: (01733) 577899 Fax: (01733) 321975 E-mail: engsupp@aol.com *Machine tool suppliers*

Engineering Supply Co., 5 Block 3, Thornliebank Industrial Estate, Thornliebank, Glasgow, G46 8TU Tel: 0141-638 7905 Fax: 0141-638 9714 E-mail: sales@scottishtools.co.uk *Engineers merchants*

Engineering Systems Ltd, Lifford Way, Binley Industrial Estate, Binley Industrial Estate, Coventry, CV3 2RN Tel: (024) 7645 7555 Fax: (024) 7645 7888 E-mail: engsysltd@tiscali.co.uk *Ductwork ventilation, fume extraction, contractors & builders*

Engineering Systems Nottm, 1 Loach Court, Radford Bridge Road, Nottingham, NG8 1NA Tel: 0115-928 8708 Fax: 0115-928 8715 E-mail: info@engsys.co.uk *Test materials equipment manufrs*

Engineering Tech Pgp Ltd, Unit 5 Harbour Road Industrial Estate, Lowestoft, Suffolk, NR32 3LZ Tel: (01502) 515768 Fax: (01502) 563211 E-mail: pete@eng-tech.co.uk *Precision engineers & fabricators*

Engineering Test Services Ltd, Tofts Farm Industrial Estate West, Brenda Road, Hartlepool, Cleveland, TS25 2BQ Tel: (01429) 233951 Fax: (01429) 865447 E-mail: inspection@engtestservicesltd.fsnet.co.uk *Non-destructive test services*

Engineering & Training Solutions, 46 Rosehill Road, Burnley, Lancashire, BB11 2JL Tel: (01282) 453620 Fax: (01282) 453620 E-mail: info@training-industry.com *Electrical & mechanical skills training for manufacturing*

Engineering UK Ltd, Dale View Works, Martin Lane, Blacker Hill, Barnsley, South Yorkshire, S74 0RX Tel: (01226) 742738 Fax: (01226) 350806 E-mail: enquiries@engineeringukltd.co.uk *General & precision engineering specialists*

Engineerstore Ltd, East Street, Prittlewell, Southend-On-Sea, SS2 5EQ Tel: (01702) 611711 Fax: (01702) 600048 *Power tool distributors & hirers*

Enginewise Corrosion Prevention, 3 Venture Business Park, Grimsby, South Humberside, DN31 2UW Tel: (01472) 347400 Fax: (01472) 267647 E-mail: sales@enginewise.co.uk *Anti-corrosion products for car, motorcycle, marine, and light aero engines and gearboxes. Vapour phase corrosion inhibitors. Rust inhibiting maintenance products for preserving metal surfaces and chrome-plated parts on tools, guns, machines and vehicles. Rust prevention emitters for restoration of classic, vintage and veteran motors.*

▶ Enginite Ltd, 25 & 26 College Street, Kempston, Bedford, MK42 8LU Tel: (01234) 344710

Engis UK Ltd, Unit 9 Centenary Business Park, Station Road, Henley-on-Thames, Oxfordshire, RG9 1DS Tel: (01491) 411117 Fax: (01491) 412252 E-mail: sales@engis.uk.com *Manufacturers of diamond lapping compound*

England Brothers Ltd, Higham Mead, Chesham, Buckinghamshire, HP5 2AH Tel: (01494) 792633 Fax: (01494) 793633 E-mail: info@englandbro.co.uk *Manufacturers of shop fittings & joinery*

John England (Textiles) Ltd, Portside Business Park, Airport Road West, Belfast, BT3 9ED Tel: (028) 9073 6990 Fax: (028) 9073 6989 E-mail: sales@johnenglandtextiles.com *Linen manufrs*

England Joinery, Holehouse Lane, Glue Hill, Sturminster Newton, Dorset, DT10 2AA Tel: (01258) 472846 Fax: (01258) 472846 E-mail: info@englandjoinery.co.uk *Joinery*

England Signs, The Malthouse, Main St, Offenham, Evesham, Worcs, WR11 8QD Tel: (01386) 442712 Fax: (01386) 442977 *Sign, panel, label engravers & manu frs*

England Worthside Ltd, Hope Mills, South Street, Keighley, West Yorkshire, BD21 1AG Tel: (01535) 682222 Fax: (01535) 682223 E-mail: enquiries@worthside.co.uk *Supply drinks dispensing equipment*

English Art Works Ltd, 175-176 New Bond Street, London, W1S 4RN Tel: (020) 7493 0807 Fax: (020) 7409 7594 *Jewellery repairers & manufrs*

English Bros Ltd, Salts Road, Walton Highway, Wisbech, Cambridgeshire, PE14 7DU Tel: (01945) 587500 Fax: (01945) 582576 E-mail: customerservices@englishbrothers.co.uk *Timber frame housing*

▶ English Chain Co Ltd, Chain House, Brighton Road, Godalming, Surrey, GU7 1NS Tel: (01483) 428383 Fax: (01483) 861931 E-mail: sales@englishchain.co.uk *Established in 1923, we are the UK's specialist supplier of Chains & Accessories in Steel, Stainless Steel, Brass & Plastic; Chain Assemblies; Security Chains, Cables & Locks; Wire Rope, Rope Grips & Thimbles, Ironmongery and Snowchains. We have the most comprehensive range in our industry, assured product quality & a minimum 98% stockholding, enabling the sourcing of all your chain products reliably, quickly & competitively from one supplier. Orders are processed and despatched within 24hrs. We also offer a unique chain assembly design & production service - from small prototype batches to high volume production runs. We are committed to the highest level of customer service - at the centre is our sales team with many years experience in the chain industry, able to offer technical help and advice in this very specialised market. For comprehensive product and technical information visit www.englishchain.co.uk and view our website's online catalogue.*

English Cleaning Co., 272 Latimer Industrial Estate, Latimer Road, London, W10 6RQ Tel: (020) 8960 0000 Fax: (020) 8969 7077 E-mail: info@english-cleaning.co.uk *Cleaning contractors*

English Corrugating Paper Co. Ltd, Wilson Place, Bristol, BS2 9HL Tel: 0117-955 2002 Fax: 0117-955 4004 E-mail: sales@english-corrugating.co.uk *Corrugated container suppliers & manufrs*

▶ English Country Pottery Ltd, Wickwar Trading Estate, 61 Station Road, Wickwar, Wotton-under-Edge, Gloucestershire, GL12 8NB Tel: (01454) 299100 Fax: (01454) 294053 E-mail: sales@ecpdesign.co.uk *Pottery manufrs*

English Ford, 1 Yarrow Road, Poole, Dorset, BH12 4QA Tel: (01202) 715577 Fax: (01202) 715973 E-mail: brettsanstleben@evanshalshaw.com *Cars & motor accessories suppliers*

▶ English Hardwood Design, Kellet Road, Carnforth, Lancashire, LA5 9XP Tel: (01524) 735077 Fax: (01524) 736526 E-mail: sales@englishhardwood.co.uk *Kitchen design & manufrs*

English Hurdle, Curload, Stoke St. Gregory, Taunton, Somerset, TA3 6JD Tel: (01823) 698418 Fax: (01823) 698859 E-mail: hurdle@enterprise.net *Garden accessories manufrs*

▶ English MeterCo, 9 Atherton Lane, Rastrick, Brighouse, West Yorkshire, HD6 3TJ Tel: (01484) 710073 Fax: (01484) 710073 E-mail: Geoff.English@Blueyonder.co.uk *Flowmeter manufacturer, calibration and hire service. Water, Oil, Gas, Steam*

▶ English Pewter Co., 1 Blackmore Street, Sheffield, S4 7TZ Tel: 0114-273 0584 Fax: 0114-276 1416 E-mail: sales@englishpewter.co.uk *Manufacturer of pewter ware tankards, flasks, sports trophies etc*

English Stamp Co., French Grass Quarry, Kingston Road, Worth Matravers, Swanage, Dorset, BH19 3JP Tel: (01929) 439117 Fax: (01929) 439150 E-mail: sales@englishstamp.com *Manufacturers of rubber stamps*

English Village Cellars Ltd, Camblesforth Grange, Brigg Lane, Camblesforth, Selby, North Yorkshire, YO8 8ND Tel: (01757) 618084 Fax: (01757) 614159 *Salad produce buyers & sellers*

Engravamet Engraving, Dock Meadow Drive, Wolverhampton, WV4 6LE Tel: (01902) 401666 Fax: (01902) 490129 E-mail: sales@engravamet.co.uk *ENGRAVAMET offers Engraving materials BRASS - RIGID & FLEXIBLE PLASTICS - ANODISED ALUMINIUM - STAINLESS STEEL.*Superior surface quality combined with high performance characteristics & exacting specifications - whatever the application we have the solution. SHEET - BLANKS - DISCS - STRIP*

Engraving Services, 102 Chester Road, Talke, Stoke-on-Trent, ST7 1SD Tel: (01782) 782270 Fax: (01782) 787020 E-mail: engravingservices@tinyworld.co.uk *Identification & marking services*

Engraving Tools Ltd, Unit 44 Stakehill Industrial Estate, Touchet Hall Road, Middleton, Manchester, M24 2FL Tel: 0161-653 8103 Fax: 0161-655 4061 E-mail: engrtools@aol.com *Embossing, printing, applicator & coating rolls*

Engravings Services Ltd, 21 Radnor Street, Hulme, Manchester, M15 5RD Tel: 0161-226 1197 Fax: 0161-227 9554 E-mail: studio@engraving.pennine.net *Colour printer services*

Enham Garden Centre, Enham Alamein, Andover, Hampshire, SP11 6JS Tel: (01264) 345800 Fax: (01264) 333638 E-mail: info@enham.co.uk *Engineering contract manufacturing services*

Enhance Designs Ltd, 125 Maner Green Road, Epsom, Surrey, KT19 8LW Tel: (01372) 812159 E-mail: stev_turpin@ntlworld.com *Graphic designers*

▶ Enhanced Business Solutions Ltd, Wrest Park, Silsoe, Bedford, MK45 4HR Tel: (01525) 862555 Fax: (01525) 862500 E-mail: enquiries@retail-services.co.uk *Internet payment & loyalty solutions & charity donation processing*

Enhurst Ltd, 65-69 County Street, London, SE1 4AD Tel: (020) 7403 0630 Fax: (020) 7407 5940 E-mail: office@enhurst.freeserve.co.uk *Building contractors*

▶ Enigma Signs, Unit 3 21a Sussex Road, Southport, Merseyside, PR9 0SS Tel: (01704) 545644 Fax: (01704) 536663 E-mail: info@enigmasigns.com *Sign making company*

▶ Enigma Software Solutions Ltd, 9 Carden Place, Aberdeen, AB10 1UR Tel: (01224) 631101 Fax: (01224) 586678 *Develop software for retail*

▶ Enigmathica Consulting, 64 Ampthill Road, Maulden, Bedford, MK45 2DH Tel: (01525) 403872 E-mail: sales@enigmathica.demon.co.uk *Research quality statistical analysis services*

Enigmex Ltd, Kestrel House, 14 Lower Brunswick Street, Leeds, LS2 7PU Tel: 0113-244 9969 Fax: 0113-244 9411 *Light manufrs*

▶ Enilow Engineers Ltd, Astley Way, Astley Lane Industrial Estate, Swillington, Leeds, LS26 8XT Tel: 0113-286 8091 Fax: 0113-286 6560

▶ Enitial, Enterprise Drive, Four Ashes, Wolverhampton, WV10 7DF Tel: (01902) 798798 Fax: (01902) 798711 *Environmental management service*

Enjay Marine, 10 Somerset Road, Christchurch, Dorset, BH23 2ED Tel: (01202) 481286 Fax: (01202) 481286 *Diving equipment suppliers*

Enlight Ltd, Suite 308 Third Floor, Whiteleys Centre, Queensway, London, W2 4YN Tel: (020) 7792 9065 Fax: (020) 7792 9089 E-mail: info@enlight.net

Enlight Uk Ltd, 53 Church Rd, London, NW4 4DU Tel: (020) 8830 6479 Fax: (020) 8830 6480 *PC casing*

Enline P.L.C., Newchase Court, Hopper Hill Road, Scarborough, North Yorkshire, YO11 3YS Tel: (0870) 5502015 Fax: (0870) 5673018 E-mail: marketing@enline.com *Computer solutions house*

Ennis Labels & Print, Tower Studios, Market Street, Darwen, Lancashire, BB3 1AZ Tel: (01254) 826138 Fax: (01254) 702135 E-mail: sales@ennislabels.co.uk *Label distributors*

Ennstone Building Products Ltd, Stainton Quarry, Barnard Castle, County Durham, DL12 8RB Tel: (01833) 690444 Fax: (01833) 690377 E-mail: ennstone@ukonline.co.uk *Natural stone products*

▶ Ennstone Thistle Ltd, Ethiebeaton Quarry, Broughty Ferry, Dundee, DD5 3RB Tel: (01382) 537600 Fax: (01382) 534778

▶ Ennstone Thistle Ltd, Cloddach Quarry, Elgin, Morayshire, IV30 8TW Tel: (01343) 559830 *Road servicing*

▶ Ennstone Thistle Ltd, Craigenlow Quarry, Dunecht Westhill, Skene, Aberdeenshire, AB32 7ED Tel: (01330) 833361 *Granite quarry*

Ennstone Thistle Ltd, Quarry Road, Balmullo, St. Andrews, Fife, KY16 0BH Tel: (01334) 870208 Fax: (01334) 870893 *Dry stone producers* Also at: Leven

Enodis plc, Washington House, 40-41 Conduit Street, London, W1S 2YQ Tel: (020) 7312 2500 Fax: (020) 7304 6001 E-mail: contact@enodis.com *Holding company*

Enodis Ltd, Provincial Park, Nether Lane, Ecclesfield, Sheffield, S35 9ZX Tel: 0114-257 0100 Fax: 0114-257 0251 E-mail: geremy.hobbs@enodis.co.uk *Catering & refrigeration equipment suppliers*

Enodis (UK) Food Service Ltd, Unit 5E, Langley Business Centre, Station Road, Langley, Slough, SL3 8DS Tel: (01753) 485900 E-mail: enodis.uk.sales@enodis.com *Catering equipment manufrs*

▶ Enotec UK Ltd, PO Box 9026, Dumfries, DG1 3YH Tel: (0870) 3500102 Fax: (0870) 3500302 E-mail: enotec.uk@enotec.com *Flue gas/oxygen analyser manufacturers*

Enpar Special Alloys Ltd, Station Road, Ecclesfield, Sheffield, S35 9YR Tel: 0114-219 3002 Fax: 0114-219 1145 E-mail: sales.esa@firthrixson.com *Nickel, titanium, alloys & stainless steel stockholders, manufrs*

Enquire Within, 1 North Road, Reigate, Surrey, RH2 8LY Tel: (01737) 243938 Fax: (01737) 243938 *Trophies & engravers*

Enraf Fluid Technology Ltd, 6 Pennant Park, Standard Way, Fareham, Hampshire, PO16 8XU Tel: (01329) 825823 Fax: (01329) 825824 E-mail: info@enraf.com *Additive injection equipment manufrs*

▶ Enricosmog Ergonomics, 21 Tisbury Row, Tisbury, Salisbury, SP3 6RZ Tel: (01747) 871868 Fax: (01747) 871868 E-mail: info@enricosmog.com *Ergonomic risk assessment service*

Enright Cabinets, Botany Bay Lane, Chislehurst, Kent, BR7 5PT Tel: (020) 8295 0539 *Cabinet makers*

Enright Engineering Services, Unit 8 Team Valley Business Centre, Earlsway, Team Valley Trading Estate, Gateshead, Tyne & Wear, NE11 0QH Tel: 0191-482 0002 Fax: 0191-482 0027 E-mail: info@enrightengineering.co.uk *Industrial & commercial heating & ventilation engineers*

▶ Enrogen Ltd, PO Box 240, York, YO42 2WL Tel: (01430) 879565 Fax: (01430) 879566 E-mail: gavin@enrogen.com *Generator sales & repairs*

▶ Ensafe Consultants Ltd, 9 Ladys Lane, Northampton, NN1 3AH Tel: (01604) 636436 Fax: (01604) 745339

▶ Ensco Offshore UK Ltd, Badentoy Avenue, Badentoy Industrial Estate, Portlethen, Aberdeen, AB12 4YB Tel: (01224) 780400 Fax: (01224) 780444

▶ Enseal Systems, 5 Meadow Court, High Street, Witney, Oxfordshire, OX28 6ER Tel: (01993) 770770 Fax: (01993) 776939 E-mail: enseal@enseal.com *Security software developers*

▶ Enserve, Metro House, 57 Pepper Road, Leeds, LS10 2RU Tel: (0800) 0377817 E-mail: sales@enserve.co.uk *Enserve - Low Cost Pest Control, Bird Control (BPCA members). Also Installers of Safety Netting (FASET trained)*

Enserve Corporation, Parkway House, Worth Way, Keighley, West Yorkshire, BD21 5LD Tel: (0800) 0377817 E-mail: info@enserve.co.uk *Pest Controllers in Bradford and Leeds West Yorkshire - also bird controllers and general vermin exterminators*

Ensiform Type Products Ltd, 2 Nafcot Street, Watford, WD17 4RB Tel: (01923) 442020 Fax: (0800) 838097 *Commercial stationers suppliers*

Ensign, Wakefield Place, Sandgate, Kendal, Cumbria, LA9 6HT Tel: (01539) 724433 Fax: (01539) 724499 E-mail: anne@sunsigns.co.uk *This Kendal based, family run Sign Making Business has recently invested in the latest state-of- the-art machinery and technology. They now offer wide format full colour printing of banners, displays and corporate advertising. **The Kendal workshop also boasts a huge flat bed router, which offers CNC routing /cutting. This versatile machine, which cuts 3D shapes in many different materials, will be of interest to joiners, kitchen fitters and other trades requiring computer controlled routing and cutting.****Full colour design & manufacture:**Posters *Banners *Point of sale signs *Window graphics *Vehicle graphics*Vehicle Wraps *Shop Fascias *Hotel/ Guest house signage *Illuminated signs *Digital printing *A boards *Directory systems *Health and safety signage *And Much more . . . call with your requirements.**"A Business with a good sign, is the sign of a good business"***

Ensign, 5 Cannon Park Road, Cannon Park Industrial Estate, Middlesbrough, Cleveland, TS1 5JP Tel: (01642) 800222 Fax: (01642) 241239 E-mail: info@ensign.co.uk *Sign manufrs*

Ensign, 44 Nelson Avenue, Minster on Sea, Sheerness, Kent, ME12 3SE Tel: (01795) 873993 Fax: (01795) 874720 *Signs & nameplates manufrs*

Ensign, 9 Station Road, Wokingham, Berkshire, RG40 2AD Tel: 0118-978 6272 Fax: 0118-978 6272 E-mail: ensign@btinternet.com *Sign maker*

Ensign Advanced Systems Ltd, 56 Regent Road, Leicester, LE1 6YD Tel: 0116-254 9444 E-mail: ensignsys@aol.com *Software estimating*

Ensign Associates, 75 Bourn Lea, Houghton le Spring, Tyne & Wear, DH4 4PF Tel: 0191-385 5188 Fax: 0191-385 5188 *CCTV installation*

Ensign Communications Ltd, Unit 20-21 Sandford La Industrial Estate, Sandford Lane, Wareham, Dorset, BH20 4DY Tel: (01929) 556553 Fax: (01929) 554516 E-mail: call@ensign-net.co.uk *Voice data communications system*

Ensign Engineering Co., Station Road, Baldock, Hertfordshire, SG7 5BT Tel: (01462) 892931 Fax: (01462) 893667 *Motor body repairers*

Ensign Flag, 42 Dunes Way, Liverpool, L5 9RJ Tel: 0151-298 1007 Fax: 0151-298 1006 E-mail: enquiries@ensignflags.com *Manufacturers & printers of flags*

Ensign Plastic Moulders Ltd, 8 Woodfield Road, Welwyn Garden City, Hertfordshire, AL7 1JQ Tel: (01707) 886795 Fax: (01707) 882566 E-mail: ensignplastic.moulders@ntlbusiness.com *Plastics mouldings manufrs*

Ensign Plastics Ltd, PO Box 55, Leatherhead, Surrey, KT22 7TD Tel: (01372) 377827 Fax: (01372) 377828 E-mail: sales@ensign-uk.com *Condenser tube protective insert manufrs*

▶ Ensign Property Management Ltd, Botany Way, Ensign Estate, Arterial Road, Purfleet, Essex, RM19 1TB Tel: (01708) 868844 Fax: (01708) 868278 E-mail: en@mckellargroup.com

▶ Ensign Signature Ltd, Ensign House, Green Lane, Gateshead, Tyne & Wear, NE10 0QH Tel: 0191-438 1177

Ensign UK Ltd, A5 Faraday Road, Newbury, Berkshire, RG14 2AD Tel: (0870) 0113436 Fax: (0845) 6431882 E-mail: info@ensign-water.co.uk *Water softener manufrs*

▶ Ensign UK, 21 Polesworth Close, Redditch, Worcestershire, B98 0EE Tel: (07791) 381048 E-mail: ensign-uk@blueyonder.co.uk *Banners, vehicle graphics,vinyl lettering, signs to industrial units,schools & shops*

Ension Technologies Ltd, Unit 14 The Capricorn Centre, Cranes Farm Road, Basildon, Essex, SS14 3JJ Tel: (01268) 795579 Fax: (01268) 461525 *Telecommunication systems & equipment manufrs*

Ensol Ltd, 344 St Helens Road, Bolton, BL3 3RP Tel: (01204) 660064 Fax: (01204) 660043 E-mail: sales@ensol.co.uk *Heating ventilation & air-conditioning installation services*

Ensor Lifting Services, 3 Park Road, Thurnscoe, Rotherham, South Yorkshire, S63 0TG Tel: (01709) 881908 Fax: (01709) 881908 E-mail: grahamensor-els@hotmail.com *Lifting gear manufrs*

▶ Enspec Power Ltd, Stanfield Business Centre, Addison Street, Sunderland, SR2 8BL Tel: 0191-514 2090 Fax: 0191-514 2151 E-mail: info@enspecpower.com *Electrical engineers*

ENSR UK, Portwall Place, Portwall Lane, Bristol, BS1 6NB Tel: (0845) 8630880 Fax: (0845) 8630880 E-mail: bgordon@ensr.aecom.com *Environmental consultants & testing services*

Enstec Services, 141 Queen Ediths Way, Cambridge, CB1 8PT Tel: (01223) 566471 Fax: (01223) 413800 E-mail: ss_ens@netcomuk.co.uk *Environmental engineering & monitoring services*

▶ Enstil & Thistle, Banavie Quarry, Banavie, Fort William, Inverness-Shire, PH33 7LX Tel: (01397) 772267 Fax: (01397) 772389

▶ Enstone Thistle Ltd, Dunecht, Westhill, Aberdeenshire, AB32 7ED Tel: (01330) 833361 Fax: (01330) 833565 *Quarry*

▶ Ensuite Solutions, 34-41 High Street, Newmarket, Suffolk, CB8 8NA Tel: (01638) 560566 *Installers of prefabricated ensuite bathrooms*

▶ Ensygn Ltd, 127 Barkby Road, Leicester, LE4 9LG Tel: 0116-246 0102 Fax: 0116-246 0321 *Structural steel*

▶ EnSynch Environmental Consultancy, North End, Hale Road, Woodgreen, Fordingbridge, Hampshire, SP6 2AN Tel: (07855) 581132 E-mail: peter.carpenter@ensynch.co.uk *Project and contract management in nature conservation and habitat management. GIS mapping, survey, management plan, farm environment plan (FEP), land drainage consent (LDC) applications. Liaison with EN, EA, Defra etc. Grassland, heathland, woodland, wetland, water meadow and riverine habitats particularly. (CEnv - MIEEM)*

Ensys Ltd, Unit 10 Rivermead, Thatcham, Berkshire, RG19 4EP Tel: (01635) 872227 Fax: (01635) 872206 E-mail: sales@ensys.co.uk *Ensys Ltd are specialist contractors in air conditioning, heating and ventilation. We carry out the design, installation and maintenance of systems in: offices, shops, factories, computer rooms, server rooms and also telecom"s sites.*

Entaco Ltd, Royal Victoria Works, Birmingham Road, Studley, Warwickshire, B80 7AP Tel: (01527) 852306 Fax: (01527) 857447 E-mail: sales@entaco.com *Hand sewing needles*

Entaprint Ltd, 1 Penfold Road Woodcote, Cranleigh, Surrey, GU6 8NZ Tel: (01483) 273173 *Printers*

▶ Entec Computer Systems, Ic2 Building Keele University, Science Park, Keele, Newcastle, Staffordshire, ST5 5NH Tel: (01782) 740900 Fax: (01782) 740600 *IT security agents*

Entec International Ltd, B Belfont Trading Estate, Mucklow Hill, Halesowen, West Midlands, B62 8DR Tel: 0121-585 8800 Fax: 0121-585 8899 E-mail: info@entec-int.com *Procurement & export agency*

Entech Precision Engraving, 4 Old Forge Cottage, Pearson Road, Sonning, Reading, RG4 6UH Tel: 0118-927 2499 Fax: 0118-927 2499 E-mail: ejak@btclick.com *General engraver services*

▶ Entech Usb, 24/26 Aire Street, Leeds, LS1 4HT Tel: 0113-234 4048 Fax: 0113-234 3383 E-mail: info@entech.usb.co.uk *Provide internet based data management solutions*

Entecon UK Ltd, Stanhope Road, Yorktown Industrial Estate, Camberley, Surrey, GU15 3BW Tel: (01276) 414540 Fax: (01276) 414544 E-mail: enquiries@entecon.co.uk *Specialists in the Bulk Powder and granular handling industry. Manufacturers of the Aeromec product range which includes, Aero Mechanical Conveyors, dust contained Sack Tip Stations, FIBC Discharging and filling Stations and automatic Sack Openers. http://www.aeromec.co.uk*

Entee Global Services Ltd, 2morrow Court, Appleford Road, Sutton Courtenay, Abingdon, Oxfordshire, OX14 4FH Tel: (01235) 845100 Fax: (01235) 845108 E-mail: mail@entee.co.uk *E-commerce computer consultants*

Entegra Ltd, Entergra House, Woodside Lane, Lymington, Hampshire, SO41 8FJ Tel: (01590) 671700 E-mail: sales@entegra.co.uk *Signal processing solutions*

▶ Enteleki Change Consultants Ltd, 37 Marston Street, Oxford, OX4 1JU Tel: (01865) 247003 E-mail: hazeldouglas@enteleki.co.uk *Management training & organisational development consultancy; action learning, coaching & facilitation*

▶ Entents Ltd, 1 Sycamore Close, Ross-on-Wye, Herefordshire, HR9 5UA Tel: (01989) 563783 *Racing Car Simulator Hire and Sales, UK and European coverage.*Giant Scalextric set s and a wide range of Giant Games and Casino Table hire.*

Enterasys Networks Ltd, Nexus House Newbury Business Park, London Road, Newbury, Berkshire, RG14 2PZ Tel: (01635) 580000 Fax: (01635) 810300 *Data communication services*

Enterprise plc, Lancaster House, Lancashire Enterprise Business Park, Leyland, PR26 6TX Tel: (01772) 819000 Fax: (01772) 819001 E-mail: headoffice@enterprise.plc.uk *Suppliers in water, gas & electric utilities & local authority maintenance*

Enterprise A B Ltd, 9 St. Albans Enterprise Centre, Long Spring, Porters Wood, St. Albans, Hertfordshire, AL3 6EN Tel: (01727) 751445 Fax: (01727) 759507 E-mail: admin@eab.co.uk *Internet services, web design & online application development*

continued

Enterprise Centre, Greenacre Court, Station Road, Burgess Hill, West Sussex, RH15 9DS Tel: (0845) 2301054 Fax: (0845) 2301058 E-mail: info@sussexenterprise.co.uk *Management consultants*

▶ Enterprise Cleaning Co, Enterprise House, 9 Martinfield, Welwyn Garden City, Hertfordshire, AL7 1HG Tel: (01707) 373111 Fax: (01707) 323842 E-mail: sales@entss.com *ISO9001:2000 accredited, we service offices and industrial sites throughout London and the South East for daily and specialist cleaning. Contact us today for a free no obligation quote!*N.B. We do not do domestic cleaning - sorry!*

Enterprise Data Systems, Enterprise House, 130-134 Bristnall Hall Road, Oldbury, West Midlands, B68 9TX Tel: (0845) 6444774 Fax: (0871) 2205363E-mail: andy@edsuk.co.uk *Computer repairers*

▶ Enterprise Electrical Services Ltd, Unit 7 129 Western Road, Hockley, Birmingham, B18 7QD Tel: 0121-507 0602 Fax: 0121-507 0605

Enterprise Engineering, Unit 23 Tweedale Court, Tweedale North, Madeley, Telford, Shropshire, TF7 4JR Tel: (01952) 583179 *Precision engineering services*

Enterprise Engineering Gloucester Ltd, Units D5-D6 Innsworth Technology Park, Innsworth Lane, Gloucester, GL3 1DL Tel: (01452) 731881 Fax: (01452) 731887 E-mail: dave@honing.co.uk *Honing specialists & precision engineers*

Enterprise Engineering Services Ltd, Craigshaw Drive, West Tullos Industrial Estate, Aberdeen, AB12 3TH Tel: (01224) 288400 Fax: (01224) 871327 E-mail: sales@eesl.com *Steel fabricators & steelwork engineers*

Enterprise Fabrication Co., Virginia Street, Southport, Merseyside, PR8 6RZ Tel: (01704) 541544 Fax: (01704) 544260 E-mail: enterprise@e-fabs.co.uk *Sheet metalworkers*

Enterprise Garage, Units 1 & 2, Fitzalan Road, Arundel, West Sussex, BN18 9JS Tel: (01903) 882278 E-mail: sales@enterprisegarage.com *Car repairs & servicing*

Enterprise Gates & Railings, 2 Herbert Road, Stoke-on-Trent, ST3 4QR Tel: (01782) 593122 Fax: (01782) 593122 *Gate manufrs*

Enterprise Graphics Ltd, 1 Earls Close, Earls Close Industrial Estate, Thurmaston, Leicester, LE4 8FZ Tel: 0116-260 0879 Fax: 0116-269 7729 E-mail: fiona@enterprisegraphics.wannado.co.uk *Design screenprint & display*

Enterprise Grinding Ltd, 58 Sapcote Trading Centre, Powke Lane, Cradley Heath, West Midlands, B64 5QX Tel: (01384) 413598 Fax: (01384) 413599 *Surface grinders*

Enterprise International UK Ltd, Whitbourne Lodge, 137 Church Street, Malvern, Worcestershire, WR14 2AN Tel: (01684) 566953 Fax: (01684) 560018 E-mail: info@ei-europe.com *IT applications & solutions suppliers*

Enterprise Liner Agencies Ltd, Unit 20 Trafalgar Business Centre, River Road, Barking, Essex, IG11 0JU Tel: (020) 8591 8787 Fax: (020) 8591 1502 E-mail: elaltd@elaltd.demon.co.uk *Freight forwarders*

▶ Enterprise Manage Services, Unit 12 Ashville Way, Whetstone, Leicester, LE8 6NU Tel: 0116-284 8005 Fax: 0116-284 1512

Enterprise Management Consulting Ltd, Crystal Palace Park Road, London, SE26 6EF Tel: (020) 8659 2000 Fax: (020) 8778 0101 E-mail: info@emcuk.com *Computer consultants*

▶ Enterprise Marketing Services Ltd, The Coach House, 1 Dunstall Road, Barton under Needwood, Burton-on-Trent, Staffordshire, DE13 8AX Tel: (01283) 713185 Fax: (01283) 716172 E-mail: info@enterprise-marketing.co.uk *Marketing & PR agents*

Enterprise Metals, Kemys Way, Swansea Enterprise Park, Swansea Enterprise Park, Swansea, SA6 8QF Tel: (01792) 796774 Fax: (01792) 792974 E-mail: sales@ellissteelgroup.co.uk *Non-ferrous stockholders* Also at: Bristol

Enterprise Motors, Dean Street, Bedford, MK40 3EQ Tel: (01234) 302230 Fax: (01234) 302230 E-mail: colindm@hotmail.com *Car repair services*

Enterprise Q Ltd, 1 Tallow Way, Fairhills Industrial Park, Irlam, Manchester, M44 6RJ Tel: 0161-777 4888 Fax: 0161-777 4899 E-mail: info@enterprise-q.co.uk Principal Export Areas: Worldwide *Suppliers & fabricators of quartz & silica fused products*

Enterprise Software Systems, Enterprise House, Atlantic Street, Broadheath, Altrincham, Cheshire, WA14 5EN Tel: 0161-925 2400 Fax: 0161-925 2401 E-mail: sales@essl.co.uk *Software for logistics, manufrs*

Enterprise Storage & Removals, 118-120 Garratt Lane, London, SW18 4DJ Tel: (020) 8874 6673

▶ Enterprise Systems UK Ltd, 303-305 King Street, Aberdeen, AB24 5AP Tel: (01224) 339815 Fax: 01224 339801 E-mail: jm@enterprisesystems.co.uk *Enterprise Systems provides all of the IT services that growing SMEs need in order to compete in an increasingly technical market.*

Enterprise Tackle, 6 Darlington Close, Sandy, Bedfordshire, SG19 1RW Tel: (01767) 691231 Fax: (01767) 691231 *Plastics injection moulders*

▶ Enterprise Technology Solutions Ltd, 19 Paxton Crescent, Shenley Lodge, Milton Keynes, MK5 7PX Tel: (01908) 395500 Fax: (01908) 395499 E-mail: info@etsl.net *IT solution provider*

▶ Enterprise Tyre Service, Unit 36-37, Neath Abbey Business Park, Neath Abbey, Neath, West Glamorgan, SA10 7DR Tel: (01792) 816731 Fax: (01792) 816503 E-mail: sales@entsuk.com *Discotheque equipment suppliers*

▶ Enterprise Works, Beach Road, Newhaven, East Sussex, BN9 0BX Tel: (01273) 511560 Fax: (01273) 611345 E-mail: info@enterpriseworks.co.uk *Enterprise Works is a unique Incubation Centre catering for early stage or start-up manufacturing businesses in the Newhaven (East Sussex) area. We are privately funded, set up as a not-for-profit company. **We aim to provide as much support as we can to Client Companies, providing assistance with administration, as well as providing Mentoring support.**The cost for Client Companies is kept low, and is inclusive of rates, power, broadband and use of communal facilities such as meeting rooms.**Enterprise Works owns and manages 22,000 square feet of good quality refurbished factory space in Newhaven, UK - which is available to accommodate up to 30 manufacturing companies who are in the early stages of development.*

continued

Enterpriseforce Metal Pressing, Unit 3c-Unit 3d Canal Estate, Station Road, Langley, Slough, SL3 6EG Tel: (01753) 585018 Fax: (01753) 542685 E-mail: david@dmpgroup.co.uk *Presswork, sheet metalwork, assembly work, toolmaking*

Entertainment Seating UK Ltd, 562-564 Lawmoor Street, Dixon Blazes Industrial Estate, Glasgow, G5 0TY Tel: 0141-420 1016 Fax: 0141-429 4661 E-mail: sales@entertainmentseating.co.uk *New seating and on-site refurbishment for the Entertainment Industry. Tubs, chairs, stools and tables. Soft furnishings and fittings. Servicing bingo halls, casinos, theatres, cinemas, bars and restaurants.*

▶ Entire Computers, Riverside Avenue East, Lawford, Manningtree, Essex, CO11 1US Tel: (01206) 396413 Fax: (01206) 396413 *Pc suppliers*

▶ Entropy Internet Designs, 35A Britania Row, London, N1 8QH Tel: (07815) 141091 E-mail: info@entropyid.com *Website design or creation services*

Entrus Automatic Solutions, 16 Bordon Road, Stockport, Cheshire, SK3 0UW Tel: (07971) 835277 Fax: 0161-283 9260 E-mail: entrus@hotmail.co.uk *Repair of all automatic & manual doors systems inc locks, pivots*

Entrust Technologies Ltd, Apex Plaza, Forbury Road, Reading, RG1 1AX Tel: 0118-953 3000 Fax: 0118-953 3001 *Computer software*

Entryphone Company Ltd, 23 Granville Road, London, SW18 5SD Tel: (020) 8870 8635 Fax: (020) 8874 0066 *Internal telephone systems manufrs*

Entwisle Paddon Ltd, 11 King Street West, Stockport, Cheshire, SK3 0DX Tel: 0161-480 2879 Fax: 0161-476 1325 *Office furniture suppliers*

Entwistle Thorpe & Co. Ltd, 18 St Nicholas Street, Bristol, BS1 1UB Tel: 0117-927 3467 Fax: 0117-925 1579 *Graphic art consumables suppliers*

Envair Ltd, Envair House, York Avenue, Haslingden, Rossendale, Lancashire, BB4 4HX Tel: (01706) 228416 Fax: (01706) 229577 E-mail: sales@envair.co.uk *Clean air equipment manufrs*

Envec Automotive Ltd, Halton Green West, Halton, Lancaster, LA2 6PA Tel: (01524) 811100 Fax: (01524) 811152 *Rubber & plastic product manufrs*

▶ Envelope Structures Ltd, The Old Mill, Wallops Wood Farm, Sheardley Lane, Droxford, SO32 3QY Tel: (01489) 878101 Fax: (0871) 6617326 E-mail: enquiries@envelopestructures.co.uk *Envelope Structures Ltd manufacture temporary inflatable buildings. Inflatables are perfect for use at outdoor events such as festivals - we produce marquees, emergency structures, construction and marine covers and much more. Quick and easy to put up - inflatables are the answer.*

Envelopes Wholesale Ltd, 37 Blythswood Drive, Paisley, Renfrewshire, PA3 2ES Tel: 0141-840 5210 Fax: 0141-840 5211 E-mail: sales@envelopeswholesale.co.uk *Stationery*

Envetron Standby Power Ltd, 28 Wash Road, Hutton, Brentwood, Essex, CM13 1TB Tel: (01277) 214455 Fax: (01277) 227341 E-mail: enquiry@nvtools.co.uk *Battery chargers, power supply units & tool manufrs*

Enviro Technology Services plc, Unit B1 Kingfisher Business Park, London Road, Thrupp, Stroud, Gloucestershire, GL5 2BY Tel: (01453) 733200 Fax: (01453) 733201 E-mail: sales@et.co.uk *Environmental monitoring instrumentation suppliers*

Envirocare Services Ltd, 5 Stratfield Park, Elettra Avenue, Waterlooville, Hampshire, PO7 7XN Tel: (023) 9264 4700 Fax: (023) 9264 4677 E-mail: info@envirocare-services.com *Filters & air filtration equipment*

Envirochem Technologists Ltd, Holt Lodge Farm, Hugmore La, Llan Y Pwll, Wrexham, Clwyd, LL13 9YE Tel: 01978 661933 Fax: 01978 661611 *Water, soil & microbiological testing kit manufrs*

Enviroclean Ltd, Spratton Grange Farm, Welford Road, Spratton, Northampton, NN6 8LA Tel: (01604) 846378 *Cleaning materials*

Enviroclean Services Ltd, Unit A 5 Colville Road, London, W3 8BL Tel: (020) 8896 0088 Fax: (020) 8896 2676 *Office cleaning contractors*

Envirocoat Industrial Paints, Northumberland Avenue, Fountain Road, Hull, HU2 0LN Tel: (01482) 585162 Fax: (01482) 327273 E-mail: envirocoat@aol.com *Industrial paint sales*

Envirodoor Ltd, Viking Close, Willerby, Hull, HU10 6BS Tel: (01482) 659375 Fax: (01482) 655131 E-mail: sales@envirodoor.com *Industrial door manufrs*

▶ Envirofield, 7 Barn Field, Chevington, Bury St. Edmunds, Suffolk, IP29 5QN Tel: (01284) 850473 Fax: (01284) 851028 E-mail: iain@envirofield.co.uk *Soil sampling to 90 cms for Nitrogen and sulphur status.*Field trials and research on all crops across th UK*

▶ Envirogreen Special Waste Services, 765 Henley Road, Slough, SL1 4JW Tel: (0845) 7125398 Fax: (01753) 537314 E-mail: info@envirogreen.co.uk *Envirogreen is a registered waste disposal contractor specialising in hazardous waste disposal including chemical waste, toxic waste and other difficult waste.*

Envirogroup Installation, 34 Osier Road, Spalding, Lincolnshire, PE11 1UU Tel: (01775) 761344 Fax: (01775) 766011 E-mail: kevin.savage@virgin.net *Air conditioning design and consultancy*

Envirohold Ltd, Viking Close, Willerby, Hull, HU10 6BS Tel: (01482) 651090 Fax: (01482) 651002 E-mail: sales@envirodoor.com *Specialist doors*

▶ Envirolite Ltd, Shore Road, Perth, PH2 8BH Tel: (01738) 630731 Fax: (01738) 637150 *Lamp recycling*

▶ Enviro-mech Systems Ltd, Briars House, Vicarage Lane, Hordle, Lymington, Hampshire, SO41 0HS Tel: (01425) 627799 Fax: (01425) 629076 E-mail: info@enviro-mech.co.uk *Air conditioning & refrigeration*

Enviromental Research Institute, Castle Street, Thurso, Caithness, KW14 7JD Tel: (01847) 889589 Fax: (01847) 890014

Environ International Ltd, Environ International Ltd, Ernesettle Lane, Plymouth, PL5 2EY Tel: (01752) 360070 Fax: (01752) 360172 E-mail: enquiries@envproduct.com *Non-metallic pipe work manufrs*

The Environ & Process Engineering Ltd, Monza House, Unit 4, Milbrook Trading Estate, Southampton, SO15 0LD Tel: (023) 8070 3344 Fax: (023) 8070 2679 E-mail: wel@workingenvironments.co.uk *Refrigeration contractors*

Environair Systems Ltd, The Old Foundery, Norwich Road, Great Yarmouth, Norfolk, NR29 5QD Tel: (01692) 678123 Fax: (01692) 678124 E-mail: kelly@environair.co.uk *Sheet metal fabricators & air conditioning manufrs*

▶ Environment Exchange, 41 Charlotte Square, Edinburgh, EH2 4HQ Tel: 0131-220 4870 Fax: 0131-220 4847

Environment Measures, East Forest Byre, Morpeth, Northumberland, NE61 3ET Tel: (01670) 786079 Fax: (01670) 786079 E-mail: info@enviromentmeasure.co.uk *Environmental monitoring equipment service & supply*

Environment Saving Supplies Ltd, 25-27 Dugdale Street, Nuneaton, Warwickshire, CV11 5QJ Tel: (024) 7638 6544 Fax: (024) 7664 1865 E-mail: info@envirocleanse.co.uk *Cleaning product manufrs*

▶ The Environment Shop Ltd, 25 Daggett Road, Cleethorpes, South Humberside, DN35 0EP Tel: (01472) 200023 E-mail: barrie_davis@hotmail.com *Energy consultancy*

Environmental Cleaning Technologies Ltd, Unit 65 North Mersey Bus Centre, Woodward Road, Knowsley Industrial Park, Liverpool, L33 7UY Tel: 0151-548 4015 Fax: 0151-548 4122 E-mail: sales@ect-ltd.co.uk *Degreasing plant manufrs*

Environmental Commissioning & Services Ltd, 6-8 Godstone Road, Whyteleafe, Surrey, CR3 0EA Tel: (020) 8763 1888 Fax: (020) 8763 1884 *Air conditioning manufrs*

▶ Environmental Control Services Ltd, Liberty Centre, Mount Pleasant, Wembley, Middlesex, HA0 1TX Tel: (020) 8902 1901

Environmental Control Systems (Anglia) Ltd, Pinelands Industrial Estate, Holt Road, Horsford, Norwich, NR10 3EB Tel: (01603) 890632 Fax: (01603) 891186 E-mail: enquiries@ecs-anglia.co.uk *Control panels*

Environmental Cooling Systems, PO Box 652, Aylesbury, Buckinghamshire, HP22 5XD Tel: (01296) 633315 Fax: (01296) 633316 *Air conditioning engineers*

Environmental Elements (UK) Ltd, Unit 2 Moor Street, Burton-on-Trent, Staffordshire, DE14 3SU Tel: (01283) 740536 Fax: (01283) 563969 E-mail: dcormack@eec1.com *Manufactuers & suppliers of air pol lution control eqiupment and maintenance services to the power, cement, steel, chemical and industrial makers*

Environmental Engineering Ltd, Floor 3 Aspen Building, Vantage Point Business Village, Mitcheldean, Gloucestershire, GL17 0DD Tel: (01594) 546334 Fax: (01594) 546342 *Environmental consultants & testing services*

▶ Environmental Engineering (UK) Ltd, Riverside Bridge Street, Dukinfield, Cheshire, SK16 4RX Tel: 0161-339 7100 Fax: 0161-339 7211 E-mail: email@envenguk.co.uk *Engineering services*

Environmental Equipments Ltd, 12, Eleanor House, Kingsclere Park, Kingsclere, Newbury, Berkshire, RG20 4SW Tel: (01635) 298502 Fax: (01635) 296499 E-mail: sales@e-equipments.com *Vibration test equipment manufrs*

▶ Environmental Fabrications, Unit 26 Manor Development Centre, Alison CR, Sheffield, S2 1AS Tel: 0114-278 8777 Fax: 0114-254 4974 E-mail: info@watertankrefurbishment.com *Water tank refurbishment, polypropylene lining system, tank lids etc*

Environmental Health Solutions Ltd, 17 Carrongrange Grove, Stenhousemuir, Larbert, Stirlingshire, FK5 3DX Tel: (01324) 562871 Fax: (01324) 562871 *Pest control services*

▶ Environmental Hygiene Products Ltd, Unit 1 & 3, & 8 Blairlaith Industrial Estate, Tain, Ross-Shire, IV19 1EB Tel: (01862) 893978 Fax: (01862) 894455

▶ Environmental Hygiene Services, 66a North Street, Wetherby, West Yorkshire, LS22 6NR Tel: (01937) 589220 Fax: (01937) 587999 E-mail: info@ehs-uk.co.uk

Environmental Lighting Ltd, P O Box 542, Altrincham, Cheshire, WA15 8ZU Tel: (0871) 2233320 Fax: (0871) 2233321 E-mail: envlighting@btconnect.com *Lighting manufrs*

Environmental Lining Systems Ltd, Westland Square, Leeds, LS11 5SS Tel: 0113-277 5635 Fax: 0113-277 5454 E-mail: sales@environmentallinings.co.uk *Installer & supplier of geomembranes & geotextiles*

Environmental Maintenance Services, Hyde Pk, London, W2 2UH Tel: 020 74021510 Fax: 020 74021510 *Electrical work contractors*

Environmental Management Consulting, Unit 8, Fountain Drive, Mead Lane Industrial Estate, Hertford, SG13 7UB Tel: (01992) 535445 Fax: (01992) 531111 E-mail: tina.hackett@emsgroup.org *Asbestos Surveying, Testing and Consultancy.*

Environmental Measurements Ltd, Business & Innovation Centre, Wearfield, Sunderland Enterprise Park, Sunderland, SR5 2TA Tel: 0191-501 0064 Fax: 0191-501 0065 E-mail: sales@emltd.net *Weather monitoring equipment manufrs*

▶ Environmental Noise Solutions Ltd, Suite 15 Doncaster Business Innovation Centre, Ten Pound WK, Doncaster, South Yorkshire, DN4 5HX Tel: (01302) 644001 Fax: (01302) 644002 E-mail: sales@environmental-noise-solutions.co.uk *Acoustic consultants*

Environmental Performance Technologies, Clarendon House, 52 Cornmarket Street, Oxford, OX1 3EJ Tel: (01865) 304060 Fax: (01865) 304001 E-mail: st@eptuk.com *Waste water & effluent solutions*

▶ Environmental Practice At Work Ltd, 10 Mayville Road, Brierfield, Nelson, Lancashire, BB9 5RP Tel: (01282) 602829 E-mail: info@epaw.co.uk *Environmental consultants*

Environmental Process Systems Ltd, 32 Mere View Industrial Estate, Yaxley, Peterborough, PE7 3HS Tel: (01733) 243400 Fax: (01733) 243344 E-mail: sales@epsltd.co.uk *Thermal energy storage equipment manufrs*

▶ Environmental Projects UK Ltd, 1 Cottered Road, Throcking, Buntingford, Hertfordshire, SG9 9RR Tel: (01763) 281400 Fax: (01763) 281500 E-mail: dave@environmentalprojectsuk.com *Environmental contractors*

Environmental & Remediation Services, Unit 11 12 Mercia Business Village, Torwood Close, Westwood Business Park, Coventry, CV4 8HX Tel: (024) 7642 6600 Fax: (024) 7642 6610 E-mail: ears@cel-international.com *Environmental & process consultants*

Environmental Services, 48 Shillingford Road, Exeter, EX2 8UB Tel: (01392) 438251 Fax: (01392) 435623 E-mail: tmayne@environmentuk.com *Occupational hygiene consultants*

Environmental Services Design, Inglewood House, Unit 8a, Inglewood, Alloa, Clackmannanshire, FK10 2HU Tel: (01259) 729545 Fax: (01259) 729545 *Geographical information systems software developers*

Environmental Silencing Ltd, D5 Fleming Road, Hinckley, Leicestershire, LE10 3DU Tel: (01455) 617067 Fax: (01455) 615633 E-mail: contact@enviromental-silencing.fsnet.co.uk *Manufacturers of noise control equipment & systems engineers*

▶ Environmental Street Furniture, 67 Valley Business Centre, Church Road, Newtownabbey, County Antrim, BT36 7LS Tel: (028) 9055 2876 Fax: (028) 9055 1661 E-mail: sales@streetfurniture-uk.com *Street lighting, benches, litter bins, cycle parking, signs & bollards suppliers*

Environmental Supply Co. Ltd, Unit 1, 10 Prince Regent Road, Belfast, BT5 6QR Tel: (028) 9040 2100 Fax: (028) 9040 2123 E-mail: environmental@btconnect.com *Fans & blower distributors*

Environmental Technology Ltd, Entech House, London Road, Woolmer Green, Knebworth, Hertfordshire, SG3 6JR Tel: (01438) 812812 Fax: (01438) 814224 E-mail: admin@etl-entech.co.uk *Architectural metalworkers*

▶ Environmental Waste Controls P.L.C., Laurel House, Kitling Road, Knowsley Business Park, Prescot, Merseyside, L34 9JA Tel: (0845) 4562456 Fax: (0845) 4563998 E-mail: enquiry@ewc.eu.com *Waste management & recycling services*

▶ Environmental Water Systems (UK) Ltd, Charwell House, Cheddar Business Park, Wedmore Road, Cheddar, Somerset, BS27 3EB Tel: (01934) 741782 Fax: (01934) 741783 E-mail: helent@reverseosmosis.co.uk *Design, supply, install, water purification, resource recovery*

▶ Enviropanel, Albright Road, Widnes, Cheshire, WA8 8FY Tel: 0151 423 0023 Fax: 0151 423 0043 E-mail: info@enviropanel.com *Enviropanel engineer and supply a UK, BBA accredited structural insulated panel (SIP) building system. - SIPs offer design flexibility, energy efficiency, installation ease and cost effectiveness.*

▶ enviro-pc.com, Unit2 Duncote Mill, Walcot, Telford, Shropshire, TF6 5ER Tel: (01952) 740200 *Recycler of waste computer equipment*

▶ Enviropest Control Services, Prince of Wales House Yardley, Wood 62 Prince of Wales Lane, Birmingham, B14 4JY Tel: 0121-693 6616 Fax: 0121-693 6617 E-mail: laurence@enviropest.co.uk *Pest control service commercial, residential , 24 hour call out*

Enviroplas Services, Unit 2 Shepherd Cross St Industrial Estate, Bolton, BL1 3DE Tel: (01204) 844744 Fax: (01204) 841500 E-mail: sales@enviroplas.co.uk *Designers in corrosion resistant plastic, plastic fabricators*

▶ Enviroquest U K Ltd, Derwent Business Centre, Clarke Street, Derby, DE1 2BU Tel: (01332) 362492 Fax: (01332) 345477

Enviros, Shrewsbury Business Park, Shrewsbury, SY2 6LG Tel: (01743) 284800 Fax: (01743) 245558 E-mail: marketing@enviros.com *Environmental management consultants*

Enviros Consulting Group, Waterfront Quay, Salford, M50 3XW Tel: 0161-874 3600 Fax: 0161-848 0181 E-mail: paul.bromley@enviros.com *Management & environmental consultants*

Enviroserve, 1 Croft Cottages, Dolgarrog, Conwy, Gwynedd, LL32 8JR Tel: (01492) 660490 Fax: (01492) 660490 E-mail: greg@enviroserve.co.uk *Pest control services. Hygiene Services. Emergency call outs Domestic and commercial contracts*

Envirosol Ltd, Unit 28 Thornleigh Trading Estate, Dudley, West Midlands, DY2 8UB Tel: (01384) 241808 Fax: (01384) 237519 E-mail: sales@envirosol.co.uk *Waste disposal services*

Envirosound Ltd, 8 Murrell Green Business Park, London Road, Hook, Hampshire, RG27 9GR Tel: (01256) 760775 Fax: (01256) 760754 E-mail: sales@envirosound.co.uk *Industrial noise control & test call equipment suppliers*

Envirotec Ltd, Desborough Park Road, High Wycombe, Buckinghamshire, HP12 3BX Tel: (01494) 525342 Fax: (01494) 440889 E-mail: sales@envirotec.co.uk *Air-conditioning equipment manufrs*

▶ Envirotec Group, St. James Business Centre Junction 29, Linwood Road, Linwood, Paisley, Renfrewshire, PA3 3AT Tel: 0141-889 9303 Fax: 0141-889 5394

Envirotec Support Services, Cornwall House, London Road, Purfleet, Essex, RM19 1PS Tel: (01708) 685230 Fax: (01708) 861862 *Carpet cleaning, jet washing & specialised cleaning service*

▶ Envirotech Pump Systems, Crompton Road, Ilkeston, Derbyshire, DE7 4BG Tel: 0115-932 8300 Fax: 0115-932 8360 E-mail: sales@envirotech-pumpsystems.com *Pump manufrs*

Envirotech Services Ltd, Envirotech House, 1 Main Road, Edenbridge, Kent, TN8 6JE Tel: (01732) 865171 Fax: (01732) 865057 E-mail: info@esl.gb.com *Air conditioning contractors*

▶ Envirotek Scot Ltd, 102 Millersneuk Crescent, Millerston, Glasgow, G33 6PH Tel: 0141-770 9816 Fax: 0141-770 9386 E-mail: jamie@envirotek-scotland.com *Pest & vermin control*

▶ Envirotek Services, 307, Bolton Rd, Edgworth, Bolton, BL7 0AW Tel: 01204 853415 Fax: 07968 136695 E-mail: sales@envirotekservices.co.uk *UK suppliers of garage and light industrial roller doors.*Manual and electric.*Choice of 15 colours.*Free delivery.*

Envirovent Fife, Strathore Road, Thornton, Kirkcaldy, Fife, KY1 4DF Tel: (01592) 774301 Fax: (01592) 630853 *Ventilation manufrs*

▶ Envisage Design Ltd, Brick Kiln Lane, Basford, Stoke-on-Trent, ST4 7BS Tel: (01782) 219922 Fax: (01782) 289580 E-mail: info@enviz.co.uk *Graphic Design, Large Format Print, Exhibition Design, Multimedia, Web*

▶ Envision Online, 6 Cockpit Hill, Cullompton, Devon, EX15 1DF Tel: 07740 778082 E-mail: info@Envision-Online.co.uk *Envision Online is a Microsoft OEM System Builder, and Ebay Power seller.**We are in partnership with Microsoft, and have been building computer since 1996, and well respected amongst clients.*

Envogen UK Ltd, Greetby Place, Skelmersdale, Lancashire, WN8 9UL Tel: (01695) 724414 Fax: (01695) 713279 *Instrument repair services*

Envoprint, Penry Avenue, Cadishead, Manchester, M44 5ZE Tel: 0161-775 7272 Fax: 0161-776 0067 *Envelope printing services*

Envy Designs Ltd, 88 Eltham High Street, London, SE9 1BW Tel: (020) 8850 3444 *Knitwear manufrs*

▶ Enzcom Solutions, 4 Maple Industrial Estate, Maple Way, Feltham, Middlesex, TW13 7AW Tel: (020) 8751 3108 Fax: (020) 8893 7082 *Telecommunication suppliers*

▶ Enzyme Process UK, 4 Broadgate House, Westlode Street, Spalding, Lincolnshire, PE11 2AF Tel: (01775) 761927 Fax: (01775) 761104 E-mail: enquiries@enzymepro.com *Healthcare nutritional remedies to healthcare professionals*

Eoin Technology Ltd, 35 Warwick Terrace, East Street, Olney, Buckinghamshire, MK46 4BU Tel: (07775) 935422 Fax: (0871) 2564641 E-mail: postbox@eointech.co.uk *Custom built machinery design services*

▶ Eon Media, Thomas Street, Hull, HU9 1EH Tel: (01482) 339650 Fax: (01482) 339701 E-mail: tevison@eon-media.com *Multimedia production company specialising in visual corporate communications*

▶ Eoss, 1 Ryelands Close, Market Harborough, Leicestershire, LE16 7XE Tel: (01858) 434555 Fax: (01858) 440009 E-mail: sales.eoss@ntlworld.com *Supplier of bearings and power transmission products*

▶ Epac, Unit 8, Burnmill Industrial Estate, Burnmill Road, Leven, Fife, KY8 4RA Tel: (01333) 428956

▶ epc photography, 6 Trafalgar Mews, London, E9 5JG Tel: 07956 194599 E-mail: epcphotography@aol.com *Chris Edgcombe photography, Architectural photography and model photography, studio near the City of London. Architectural clients as well as design, interior design and presentation companies.*

▶ EPC Services UK Ltd, 38 Skylines Village, Limeharbour, Docklands, London, E14 9TS Tel: (0845) 4584986 Fax: (0845) 4584987 E-mail: admin@epcservices-uk.com *Telecommunications specialists*

Epcot Systems Ltd, PO Box 114, Pinner, Middlesex, HA5 1TQ Tel: (020) 8537 0395 Fax: (020) 8931 5218 *Computer systems consultants*

Epelsa UK Ltd, Unit 10, Wroslyn Road Industrial Estate, Freeland, Witney, Oxfordshire, OX29 8HZ Tel: (01993) 882786 Fax: (01993) 883594 E-mail: epelsauk@bulkblue.com *Electronic weighing equipment distributors*

▶ Epic Blinds & Awnings, 10 Moor Park Place, Prestwick, Ayrshire, KA9 2NH Tel: (01292) 678193 Fax: (01292) 678193 E-mail: sales@epicawnings.co.uk *Epic Awnings, formed in 1999 is the leading Scottish company for supplying, installing, and maintaining high quality awning systems for commercial and domestic sun protection including Awnings, Canopies and Patiolas, and offer a professional design and installation service.*

Epic Computers Ltd, 4 Sybron Way, Crowborough, East Sussex, TN6 3DZ Tel: (01892) 667770 Fax: (01892) 665777 E-mail: sales@epicpc.co.uk *Computer manufrs*

Epic Engineering, 7 Crest Industrial Estate, Pattenden Lane, Marden, Tonbridge, Kent, TN12 9QJ Tel: (01622) 831327 Fax: (01622) 833085 *Steel fabrications*

Epic Marketing Services, Point Road, Canvey Island, Essex, SS8 7RT Tel: (01268) 514290 Fax: (01268) 695891 E-mail: sales@epictelemarketing.co.uk *Telemarketing services*

▶ Epic Printing Services, Epic House, Alington Avenue, Dorchester, Dorset, DT1 1EX Tel: (01305) 266055

▶ Epic Software Ltd, 105 Hanover Street, Edinburgh, EH2 1DJ Tel: 0131-477 2545 Fax: 0131-624 0071 E-mail: sales@epicsoftware.co.uk *Provide software solutions for recreation health & golf*

Epik Incentives, Unit 13 Silver End Business Park, Brettell Lane, Brierley Hill, West Midlands, DY5 3LG Tel: (01384) 77310 Fax: (01384) 481975 E-mail: sales@epik.co.uk *Advertising gifts*

▶ Epis Services, Mexborough Business Centre, College Road, Mexborough, South Yorkshire, S64 9JP Tel: (01709) 577736 Fax: (01709) 577764 E-mail: enquiries@epis-services.co.uk *Cctv security suppliers*

▶ Episys Group Ltd, Newark Close, York Way, Royston, Hertfordshire, SG8 5HL Tel: (01763) 248866 Fax: (01763) 246000 *Technology solutions provider*

▶ Epoint Ltd, Unit 6, Hillfoots, Business Villlage, Alva, Clackmannanshire, FK12 5DQ Tel: (01259) 763920 *Provide smart technology*

▶ Epoq IT Ltd, 57 London Road, Loudwater, High Wycombe, Buckinghamshire, HP11 1BF Tel: (01494) 444065 E-mail: sales@epoq-it.co.uk *It solutions provider*

Epos Cash Registers, 38 Prince Charles Road, Exeter, EX4 7EF Tel: (01392) 276688 Fax: (01392) 276688 E-mail: dave@eposcashregister.co.uk *Cash register repairers & suppliers*

Epos Computing Services Ltd, Demby West Business Park, Third Avenue, Milton Keynes, MK1 1DH Tel: (01908) 802345 Fax: (0845) 0450546 *Computer consultants*

Epoxy Products, 7 Haviland Road, Ferndown Industrial Estate, Wimborne, Dorset, BH21 7RZ Tel: (01202) 891899 Fax: (01202) 896983 E-mail: sales@epoxyproducts.co.uk *Industrial Floor maintenance supply services*

Epr Architects Ltd, 30 Millbank, London, SW1P 4WY Tel: (020) 7630 9027 Fax: (020) 7630 9027 E-mail: architects@epr.co.uk Principal Export Areas: Africa *Architects*

Eproduction Solutions Ltd, Viking Road, Great Yarmouth, Norfolk, NR31 0NU Tel: (01493) 652611 Fax: (01493) 444598 E-mail: andrew.williment@ep-solutions.com *Control systems distributors & manufrs*

▶ Eps Maintenance Ltd, Unit A The Homesdale Centre, 216 - 218 Homesdale Road, Bromley, BR1 2QZ Tel: (020) 8460 0960 Fax: (020) 8313 3550

▶ EPS Warehousing & Distribution, Euro House, St John Street, Leicester, LE1 3WL Tel: 0116-233 4545 Fax: 0116-233 8028 E-mail: g.hothi@europressing.com *STORAGE, TRANSPORT, RE-WORK, PACKING, LABEL PRINTING, QUALITY CONTROL AND MANY OTHER SERVICES. OUR SISTER COMPANY, EURO PRESSING SERVICES LTD OFFERS A FULL PRE-RETAIL GARMENT HANDLING SOLUTION SERVICE.*

Epsilon Test Services Ltd, Epsilon House, The Square, Gloucester Business Park, Gloucester, GL3 4AD Tel: (0845) 2336600 Fax: (0845) 2336633 E-mail: enquiries@epsilontsl.co.uk *Electrical safety test services*

▶ Epson Scotland Design Centre, The Alba Campus, Rosebank, Livingston, West Lothian, EH54 7EG Tel: (01506) 605040 Fax: (01506) 605041

▶ Epthorn Ltd, Units 19-20, Hayleys Manor, Epping Upland, Epping, Essex, CM16 6PQ Tel: (01992) 560956 Fax: (01992) 561956

Epwin Group plc, Alders Way, Paignton, Devon, TQ4 7QE Tel: (01803) 697197 Fax: (01803) 697196 E-mail: info@epwin.co.uk *Windows & doors suppliers & manufrs*

▶ Eqi Insurance, 11a The Cross, Lymm, Cheshire, WA13 0HR Tel: 01925 751758 Fax: 01925 751538 E-mail: greg@eqi-insurance.co.uk *General Insurance Brokers*

Equanet Ltd, Red Lion Road, Surbiton, Surrey, KT6 7RG Tel: (020) 8974 2321 Fax: (020) 8974 2982 *Computer systems & software suppliers*

Equation Audiovisual Ltd, Boston House, Downsview Road, Wantage, Oxfordshire, OX12 9FF Tel: (01235) 771144 Fax: (01235) 770404 *Audiovisual systems installation, distribution & hire*

▶ Equestrian Originals, 57 Severn Way, Bletchley, Milton Keynes, MK3 7QG Tel: (01908) 647555 E-mail: info@equestrian-originals.co.uk *We sell Libbys webbing tack, customised personalised poloshirts, sweatshirts, fleeces and baseball caps, we now have a SALE section and a wide range of english and imported bridles at discounted prices. We also custom make lambswool lined saddlecloths. Take a look at www.equestrian-originals.co.uk*

Equestrian World UK Ltd, Peppard Common, Henley-on-Thames, Oxfordshire, RG9 5LA Tel: (01491) 628548 Fax: (01491) 628968 *Saddlery*

▶ Equi Brief Ltd, Pinmore Mains, Pinmore, Girvan, Ayrshire, KA26 0TD Tel: (01465) 841161 Fax: (01465) 841161 *Equestrian clothing supply & manufrs*

Equibale Pet Foods, Sutton Lane, Langley Burrell, Chippenham, Wiltshire, SN15 4LW Tel: (01249) 721500 *Haulage suppliers*

▶ Equicentric Ltd, Tower Road, Little Downham, Ely, Cambridgeshire, CB6 2TD Tel: (01353) 699909 Fax: (01353) 699910 E-mail: sales@equicentric.com *Equestrian equipment retailers*

Equicraft, 42 Rodney Road, Backwell, Bristol, BS48 3HW Tel: (01275) 463933 Fax: (01275) 794414 *Riding wear*

Equifax P.L.C., Capital House, 25 Chapel Street, London, NW1 5DS Tel: (020) 7298 3000 Fax: (020) 7723 7555 E-mail: info@equifax.co.uk *Direct mail & credit information services*

Equifor, Barton House, Oake, Taunton, Somerset, TA4 1DR Tel: (01823) 400123 Fax: (01823) 400126 *Harness manufrs*

Equiform, Newday House, First Avenue, Crewe, CW1 6BE Tel: (01270) 530930 Fax: (01270) 251197 E-mail: sales@equiformnutrition.co.uk *Animal nutritional suppliers*

▶ Equilibrium Complementary Health Centre, 16 Station Street, Lewes, East Sussex, BN7 2DB Tel: (01273) 470955 E-mail: info@equilibrium-clinic.com *Complementary medicine & alternative healthcare centre*

Equilift Ltd, 8 Barrington Park, Leycroft Road, Leicester, LE4 1ET Tel: 0116-234 4310 Fax: 0116-234 4360 E-mail: info@equilift.com Principal Export Areas: Worldwide *Suppliers & installers of platform lifts*

Equimix Feeds & Saddlery, Sandy Lane, Titton, Stourport-on-Severn, Worcestershire, DY13 9QA Tel: (01299) 827744 Fax: (01299) 879470 E-mail: info@equimix.co.uk *Feeds, saddlery & riding clothing distributors*

▶ Equine, Hawes Hill Court, Drift Road, Winkfield, Windsor, Berks, SL4 4QQ Tel: (01344) 891695

Equine Affairs, Orchard Close, Gravenhurst, Bedford, MK45 4JF Tel: (01462) 713849 Fax: (01462) 713848 *Competition & trading guides*

▶ The Equine Shop, CWRT Y Draenog, Porthyrhyd, Carmarthen, Dyfed, SA32 8PG Tel: (01267) 275586 Fax: (01267) 275911 E-mail: sales@equineshopwales.co.uk *Equine services*

▶ Equine Wear, Unit 7 Lower Rectory Farm, Great Brickhill, Milton Keynes, MK17 9AF Tel: (01908) 271615 *Saddlery & harnesses manufrs*

Equinomic Products Ltd, Passfield House Farm, Headley Lane, Passfield, Liphook, Hampshire, GU30 7RN Tel: (01428) 751110 Fax: (01428) 751140 *Saddle pads manufrs*

Equinox Business Solutions Ltd, Technology House, Commerce Business Centre, West Wilts Trading Estate, Westbury, Wiltshire, BA13 4JB Tel: (01373) 825664 Fax: (01373) 859318 E-mail: enquiries@equinox-solutions.co.uk *Computer services consultants*

Equinox Design Ltd, Equinox Park, 100 Jack Lane, Leeds, LS10 1BW Tel: 0113-244 1300 Fax: 0113-242 4533 E-mail: equinoxdesign@compuserve.com *Full service exhibition contractors*

▶ Equinox Financial Search & Selection, Unity House, Clive Street, Bolton, BL1 1ET Tel: (0870) 9192457 Fax: (0870) 9192458 E-mail: iwright@equinox-financial.co.uk *Specialists in the recruitment of Senior Finance professionals in the North West.*

Equinox International Ltd, 1 Castle Gate Business Park, Old Sarum, Salisbury, SP4 6QX Tel: (01722) 415709 Fax: (01722) 424001 E-mail: sales@eqx.com *Stainless steel plates & bars manufrs*

Equinox Meridian, 18 Haycroft Road, Surbiton, Surrey, KT6 5AU Tel: (020) 8397 7347 Fax: (020) 8397 2652 E-mail: sales@equinoxmeridian.com *Buy & sell computer hardware*

Equinox Precision Engineering, Station Road, Great Harwood, Blackburn, BB6 7BB Tel: (01254) 888009 Fax: (01254) 885550 *General & precision engineering*

Equinox Training Solutions Ltd, 6 Darwin House Corby Gate Business Park, Priors Haw Road, Corby, Northamptonshire, NN17 5JG Tel: (01536) 409666 Fax: (0870) 7065600 E-mail: mick@equinoxac.co.uk *Control systems training specialist, PLCs, SCADA, Servos, fault diagnostics*

Equip (Midlands) Ltd, Byron Street, Buxton, Derbyshire, SK17 6NT Tel: (01298) 22233 Fax: (01298) 72097 *Suppliers to metal finishing industry*

Equip4work Ltd, 1st Floor, 1 St. Michael Street, Dumfries, DG1 2QD Tel: (0844) 4999222 Fax: (0844) 4999322 E-mail: sales@equip4work.co.uk *Equip4work are a family business with a huge range of office furniture items including office desks, office chairs, computer desks, cupboards, filing cabinets, lockers, reception desks and boardroom furniture. With free nationwide delivery, a professional installation service and over 150,000 office furniture items available on our website, Equip4work offer great choice and service at low prices. If you are looking to expand, refurbish or move office, our expert sales team are on hand to provide friendly professional advice from which range of office furniture will suit your needs best, down to space planning your office and managing your delivery and installation to fit in with your requirements. With six ranges of office furniture to choose from and the newest office furniture items from around the UK being added all the time, Equip4work pride themselves on being able to supply the office furniture products you require, at the lowest possible prices.*

Equiphire Northern, Bradford Road, Cleckheaton, West Yorkshire, BD19 5YR Tel: (01274) 871817 Fax: (01274) 851224 *Contractors hire plant*

Equiphire Northern Ltd, Morley Hire Centre, West Street, Morley, Leeds, LS27 9EU Tel: 0113-252 5320 Fax: (01274) 851224 *Contractors plant hire* Also at: Barnsley, Cleckheaton, Geole & Pudsey

▶ Equipment Leasing, 12 Theale Lakes Business Park, Station Park, Sulhamstead, Reading, RG7 4GB Tel: (0845) 4560047 Fax: 0118-983 8030 E-mail: info@equipmentleasing.co.uk *UK specialists in equipment & business leasing & finance solutions*

▶ Equipment Planthire Ltd, 6 Hydepark Road, Newtownabbey, County Antrim, BT36 4PY Tel: (028) 9034 2150 Fax: (028) 9083 6941 E-mail: info@eplhire.com

Equipment Supply Co.Ltd, Unit 21, Kirkhill Place, Kirkhill Industrial Estate, Dyce, Aberdeen, AB21 0GU Tel: (01224) 772555 Fax: (01224) 723681 *Hydraulic hose & pipe fittings distributors*

Equipment For You, PO Box 6, Cheltenham, Gloucestershire, GL51 9NJ Tel: (01242) 241822 Fax: (01242) 222994 E-mail: sales@3dsports.co.uk *Honing machines & accessories*

Equipu, Unit M1, The Maltings, Lodway Business Centre, Pill, Bristol, BS20 0DH Tel: (01275) 813838 Fax: (01275) 813122 E-mail: equipu@eurocopy.co.uk *Photocopier suppliers* Also at: Branches throughout the U.K.

Equisport Saddlery & Riding Wear, 54 Walsall Street, Willenhall, West Midlands, WV13 2DU Tel: (01902) 630083 Fax: (01902) 609389 E-mail: pjequest@aol.com *Equestrian equipment manufrs*

▶ Equity PC, Heath Road, Woolpit, Bury St. Edmunds, Suffolk, IP30 9RL Tel: (07774) 768172 E-mail: services@equitypc.co.uk *Computers and associated support services in Mid and West Suffolk, United Kingdom. We undertake all manner of projects for both businesses and private individuals, and strive to provide a truly reliable and personal service to every one of our clients, whether large or small.*

Equity Shoes Ltd, Western Road, Leicester, LE3 0GQ Tel: 0116-254 9313 Fax: 0116-255 3769 E-mail: equity@equityshoes.com *Shoe manufrs*

▶ Equus Enterprises, Speddyd, Llandyrnog, Denbigh, Clwyd, LL16 4LE Tel: (01824) 790687 Fax: (01824) 790338 E-mail: equusenterprises@i12.com *Retailers of horse boxes & trailers*

Equus Partnership Ltd, Park House, 15-19 Greenhill CR, Watford, WD18 8PH Tel: (01923) 213625 Fax: (01923) 213863 E-mail: acoustix@equuspartnership.co.uk *Noise & acoustic control assessment (consultants)*

Era Hydraulics & Pneumatics Ltd, Unit 5 Loaland Business Centre, Maritime Close Medway City, Estate Rochester, Rochester, Kent, ME2 4AZ Tel: (01634) 717499 Fax: (0845) 2412446 E-mail: erahydraulice@btconnect.com *Suppliers of pneumatic & hydraulic components*

Era Products Ltd, Straight Road, Willenhall, West Midlands, WV12 5RA Tel: (01922) 490049 Fax: (01922) 494420 E-mail: bevans@era-security.com *Architectural ironmongery locks etc manufrs*

Era Technology Ltd, Cleeve Road, Leatherhead, Surrey, KT22 7SA Tel: (01372) 367000 Fax: (01372) 367099 E-mail: info@era.co.uk *Electronic engineers*

Eram UK Ltd, 110 Malvern Avenue, Nuneaton, Warwickshire, CV10 8NB Tel: (024) 7632 7184 Fax: (024) 7634 2607 E-mail: eramuk@ntlworld.com *Precision turned parts manufrs*

▶ Erasmus Foundation, Moat House, Banyards Green, Laxfield, Woodbridge, Suffolk, IP13 8ER Tel: (01986) 798682 E-mail: julia@erasmus-foundation.org *Spiritual teaching & healing centre*

Eravision Lighting Design & Advertising, 8C Carrmere Road, Leechmere Industrial Estate, Sunderland, SR2 9TW Tel: 0191-523 5781 E-mail: info@eravision.co.uk *Sign making*

Ercol Furniture, Summerleys Road, Princes Risborough, Buckinghamshire, HP27 9PX Tel: (01844) 271800 Fax: (01844) 271888 E-mail: sales@ercol.com *Furniture manufrs*

Ercon Group Ltd, Midacre Willenhall Trading Estate, Willenhall, West Midlands, WV13 2JW Tel: (01902) 603763 Fax: (01902) 605081 E-mail: mail@ercongroup.com *Powder coating, sprays, dip treatment & complete finishing services*

Ercon Powder Coating Ltd, Unit 16-17, Spring Vale Business Park, Bilston, West Midlands, WV14 0QL Tel: (01902) 491011 Fax: (01902) 492032 *Powder coating services*

Erdington Aquatic Centre, 97 Church Road, Erdington, Birmingham, B24 9BE Tel: 0121-373 1100 Fax: 0121-373 1100 *Aquarium & pond supplies*

▶ Erea UK Ltd, 6 Carew Court, Dawlish Business Park, Dawlish, Devon, EX7 0NH Tel: (01626) 865551 Fax: (01626) 862434 *Transformer manufrs*

Erect A Scaffold Ltd, Crewe Bank Yard, Castle Foregate, Shrewsbury, SY1 2EB Tel: (01743) 360314 Fax: (01743) 272565 E-mail: info@erectascaffold.co.uk *Scaffolding contractors*

Erecting & Dismantling Services Ltd, 15 Chatsworth Road, Eccles, Manchester, M30 9DZ Tel: 0161-789 1216 Fax: 0161-787 8120 *Industrial machinery services*

Ereira & Matthews Ltd, 2 13-15 Sunbeam Road, London, NW10 6JP Tel: (020) 8965 8567 Fax: (020) 8965 8567 *Manufacturing upholsterers*

Eres Ltd, 264 Maybank Road, London, E18 1ES Tel: (020) 8504 1188 Fax: (020) 8504 1192 *Auto-electrical engineers*

Erf Electrical Wholesalers Ltd, Salop Street, Daybrook, Nottingham, NG5 6HD Tel: 0115-920 3960 Fax: 0115-967 3866 E-mail: sales.nottingham@erfelectrical.co.uk *Electrical equipment distributors* Also at: Bilston, Brierley Hill, Grantham, Ilkeston, Leicester, Mansfield & Nuneaton

Erg Energy, Church House, Misterton, Lutterworth, Leicestershire, LE17 4JP Tel: (01455) 558236 Fax: (01455) 558237 E-mail: RGriff7944@aol.com *Energy consultants*

ERG Transit Systems (UK) Ltd, Unit 1 Riverside, Waters Meeting Road, The Valley, Bolton, BL1 8TT Tel: (01204) 384709 Fax: (01204) 384806 *Fare collection system distributors & manufrs*

▶ Ergix Data Communications Ltd, 39 Rotherham Road, Dinnington, Sheffield, S25 3RG Tel: (07970) 264144 E-mail: scott@cawthorne962.fsnet.co.uk *Specialists manufacturers in structured cabling cat 5, cat 5e & cat 6*

Ergo Computer Accessories Ltd, 5 Pipers Industrial Estate, Pipers Lane, Thatcham, Berkshire, RG19 4NA Tel: (01635) 877979 Fax: (01635) 877676 E-mail: sales@ergo-consumables.co.uk *Retail sales computer consumables*

Ergonom Ltd, Whittington House, 19-30 Alfred Place, London, WC1E 7EA Tel: (020) 7323 2325 Fax: (020) 7323 2032 E-mail: enquiry@ergonom.com *Office furniture distributors*

Ergonomos Ltd, 11 St. Johns Road, Richmond, Surrey, TW9 2PE Tel: (020) 8940 7939 Fax: (020) 8940 7939 E-mail: info@ergonomos.co.uk *Publisher of ergonomic information for computer users*

Ergotech Scientific Apparatus, 8 Cae FFWT Business Park, Pendraw'R Llan, Glan Conwy, Colwyn Bay, Clwyd, LL28 5SP Tel: (01492) 592684 Fax: (01492) 592685 E-mail: sales@ergotech.co.uk *Scientific consultants & supply scientific equipment*

▶ Ergotron UK Ltd, Suite 3 The Carlton Centre, Outer Circle Road, Lincoln, LN2 4WA Tel: (01522) 523034 Fax: (01522) 523280 E-mail: info.uk@ergotron.com *Computer accessories & consumables suppliers, flat panel monitor arms*

Ergro Mechanical Services, Wallgrove House, Hooley Lane, Redhill, RH1 6DG Tel: (01737) 770001 Fax: (01737) 771900 E-mail: info@ergro.co.uk *Heating, mechanical & electrical engineers*

Erhard Valves Ltd, Unit 4, Buckingham Close, Bermuda Industrial Estate, Nuneaton, Warwickshire, CV10 7JT Tel: (024) 7635 4470 Fax: (024) 7635 0225 E-mail: sales@erhardvalves.co.uk *Valves manufacturers & distributors*

▶ Erhardt & Leimer, Russell Court, 9 Wool Gate, Cottingley, Bingley, West Yorkshire, BD16 1PE Tel: (08707) 559773 Fax: (08707) 559774 E-mail: info-uk@erhardt-leimer.com Sales Contact: J. Brau *Worldwide Manufacturers / Installers - Web Inspection Equipment, Surface Inspection Equipment, Web Guides, Fault Detection Systems. Quality Control for Continuous Manufacturing Processes. Bespoke Web Inspection Systems - Turnkey Solutions Specialists for all Machine Vision requirements. Serving all UK.*

Eric B Milner Ltd, Unit 106f The Big Peg, Vyse Street, Hockley, Birmingham, B18 6NE Tel: 0121-236 6821 Fax: 0121-236 6821 *Jewellery repair & manufrs*

Eric Banks Associates Ltd, 136 Victoria Road, Walton-le-Dale, Preston, PR5 4AU Tel: (01772) 465213 Fax: (01772) 466252 E-mail: enquiries@dba-uk.com *Timber frame design drawing*

▶ Eric Boam, 20 Meadowbank, Passage Hill, Mylor, Falmouth, Cornwall, TR11 5SW Tel: (01326) 375915 Fax: (01326) 375915 E-mail: eric@electricianscornwall.co.uk *Domestic electrical installations*

Eric C Flower Ltd, 413 Petre Street, Sheffield, S4 8LL Tel: 0114-243 1221 Fax: 0114-243 7196 E-mail: johnwilliams@ericcflowers.co.uk *Contract plumbers & heating engineers*

▶ Eric Carnaby & Son, Holton Farm, Town Street, South Killingholme, Immingham, South Humberside, DN40 3DA Tel: (01469) 540329 Fax: (01469) 541074

Eric Delo Ltd, Padstow Road, Coventry, CV4 9XB Tel: (024) 7669 5011 Fax: (024) 7669 4303 E-mail: eric.delo@virgin.net *Removal contractors*

Eric J Pothan, Worcester Road, Torton, Kidderminster, Worcestershire, DY11 7RR Tel: (01299) 250449 *Agricultural*

Eric Johnson Of Northwich Ltd, Ash House, Ash House Lane, Little Leigh, Northwich, Cheshire, CW8 4RG Tel: (01606) 892444 Fax: (01606) 892442 E-mail: irj@johnson42.fsnet.co.uk *Electrical contractors, data cable & cable network installation*

Eric Kinder, 66 Mallusk Enterprise Park, Mallusk Drive, Newtownabbey, County Antrim, BT36 4GN Tel: (028) 9034 2454 Fax: (028) 9034 2454 *Sale of food processing equipment*

Eric Potter Clarkson LLP, Park View House, 58 The Ropewalk, Nottingham, NG1 5DD Tel: 0115-955 2211 Fax: 0115-955 2201 *Registration of patents, trademarks and registered designs. Validity and infringement opinions. Searches for infringement clearance or validity. Regular watches.* Also at: Reading

Eric Thacker Industrial Control Ltd, 110 Lichfield Road, Bloxwich, Walsall, WS3 3LY Tel: (01922) 475865 Fax: (01922) 711770 *Electrical manufrs*

Eric Twigg Foods Ltd, 33-43 Aldwarke Road, Parkgate, Rotherham, South Yorkshire, S62 6BZ Tel: (01709) 523333 Fax: (01709) 523537 E-mail: info@erictwiggfoods.com *Food distributors*

Erico Europa GB Ltd, 52 Milford Road, Reading, RG1 8LJ Tel: 0118-958 8386 Fax: 0118-959 4856 *Electrical product distributors*

Ericsson Ltd, Maplewood Crockford Lane, Chineham Business Park, Chineham, Basingstoke, Hampshire, RG24 8YB Tel: (01256) 707874 Fax: (01256) 774373 *Cellular radios telephone equipment manufrs*

Ericsson Ltd, Midleton Gate, Guildford Business Park, Guildford, Surrey, GU2 8SG Tel: (01483) 303666 Fax: (01483) 303537 E-mail: info@sonyericsson.com *Telecommunications services*

Ericsson Ltd, Midleton Gate, Guildford Business Park, Guildford, Surrey, GU2 8SG Tel: (01483) 303666 Fax: (01483) 303537 *Telecom systems infrastructure suppliers* Also at: Scunthorpe, Surbiton & Warrington

▶ Ericsson Architects Ltd, Anfield House, Eskbank Toll, Dalkeith, Midlothian, EH22 3DY Tel: 0131-654 0101 Fax: 0131-654 1271

Erif UK Ltd, Prospect House, 6 Archipelago, Lyon Way, Frimley, Camberley, Surrey, GU16 7ER Tel: (0845) 8877999 Fax: (01276) 601337 E-mail: tim@erif.co.uk *Fire alarm suppliers*

Erik Johnson Products, Unit 3, Klondyke Industrial Estate, Rushden Road, Queenborough, Kent, ME11 5HH Tel: (01795) 662266 Fax: (01795) 669990 *Automatic gate manufrs*

ERIKS UK, Industrial Distribution Service Centre, Greenwell Place, East Tullos, Aberdeen, AB12 3AY Tel: (01224) 877523 Fax: (01224) 879645 E-mail: mcw.aberdeen@wyko.co.uk *Engineers merchants & agents*

ERIKS UK, Industrial Distribution Service Centre, 5 Perth House, Corby Gate Business Park, Priors Haw Road, Corby, Northamptonshire, NN17 5JG Tel: (01536) 204444 Fax: (01536) 400803 E-mail: corby@eriks.co.uk *Bearings distributors* Also at: Coventry, Leicester, Melton Mowbray & Rugby

ERIKS UK, 8 Brunel Gate, Brunel Industrial Estate, Harworth, Doncaster, South Yorkshire, DN11 8QB Tel: (01302) 752161 Fax: (01302) 752163 E-mail: couplings.drives@eriks.co.uk *Industrial & mechanical equipment distributors*

ERIKS UK, Industrial Distribution Service Centre, Unit 2-1 Festival Court, Govan, Glasgow, G51 1AR Tel: 0141-419 0112 Fax: 0141-419 0444 E-mail: glasgow@eriks.co.uk *Hydraulic hose & accessory distributors* Also at: Aberdeen & Edinburgh

ERIKS UK, Industrial Distribution Service Centre, Unit 3 Old Meadow Road, Hardwick Industrial Estate, King's Lynn, Norfolk, PE30 4JL Tel: (01553) 774961 Fax: (01553) 769159 E-mail: kings-lynn@erics.co.uk *Bearing & power transmission distribs*

ERIKS UK, Industrial Distribution Service Centre, Unit 12 Robin Hood Industrial Estate, Alfred Street South, Nottingham, NG3 1GE Tel: 0115-958 1312 Fax: 0115-958 1279 E-mail: nottingham@eriks.co.uk *Power transmission, bearing & gearbox distributors*

Eriks UK Ltd, Industrial Distribution Service Centre, Unit 16C, Pool Industrial Estate, Redruth, Cornwall, TR15 3RH Tel: (01209) 216839 Fax: (01209) 219793 E-mail: redruth@eriks.co.uk *Bearings & power transmission distributors & manufrs* Also at: Branches throughout the U.K.

Eris Technical Support Ltd, 21 Helen Road, Hornchurch, Essex, RM11 2EW Tel: (01708) 453997 E-mail: makkywebb@ec2uz.com *Computer consultants*

▶ Erith Concrete Co., Landau Way, Darent Industrial Park, Erith, Kent, DA8 2LF Tel: (01322) 333263

Erith Contractors Ltd, Riverside House, Maypole Crescent, Darent Industrial Park, Erith, Kent, DA8 2JZ Tel: (01322) 346811 Fax: (01322) 341978 E-mail: info@erith.net *Demolition contractors & asbestos removal*

▶ Erleback engineering Itd, Dixies Barns, High Street, Ashwell, Baldock, Hertfordshire, SG7 5NT Tel: (0870) 7407481 Fax: (0870) 7407482 E-mail: michael@erlebach.freeserve.co.uk *Electrical engineers*

Erlson Engineering Ltd, 4 Priorswood Place, Skelmersdale, Lancashire, WN8 9QB Tel: (01695) 720149 Fax: (01695) 556426 E-mail: sales@erlson.co.uk *Hydraulic components & fittings manufrs*

Ermine Engineering Company Ltd, Francis House Silver Birch Park, Great Northern Terrace, Lincoln, LN5 8LG Tel: (01522) 510977 Fax: (01522) 510929 E-mail: info@ermineengineering.co.uk *Steel fabricators*

Erne Lifting Services, Lisnaskea Road, Derrylin, Enniskillen, County Fermanagh, BT92 9LD Tel: (028) 6774 8214 Fax: (028) 6774 8813 E-mail: ernelifting@btopenworld.com *Lifting equipment & tools retailers*

▶ Ernest Bennett (Sheffield) Ltd, Main Street, North Anston, Sheffield, S25 4BD Tel: (01909) 567801

▶ Ernest Bond Printing, 4 Kingside, Ruston Road, London, SE18 5BX Tel: (020) 8855 7788 Fax: (020) 8855 7799

▶ Ernest Cooper Ltd, Unit 43 Lidgate CR, South Kirkby, Pontefract, West Yorkshire, WF9 3NR Tel: (01977) 642191 Fax: (01977) 649994

▶ Ernest Cummins Ltd, 385 Canal Road, Bradford, West Yorkshire, BD2 1AW Tel: (01274) 582555 Fax: (01274) 582666

Ernest Doe & Sons Ltd, Ulting, Maldon, Essex, CM9 6QH Tel: (01245) 380311 Fax: (01245) 381194 E-mail: info@ernestdoe.com *Horticultural equipment manufrs*

Ernest Draper & Co., 4 Crawford Avenue, Northampton, NN5 5PA Tel: (01604) 752609 *Protective clothing distributors*

Ernest H Hill Ltd, Unit 10-12, Meadowbrook Park, Halfway, Sheffield, S20 3PJ Tel: 0114-248 4882 Fax: 0114-248 9142 E-mail: sales@hillpumps.com *Fluid transfer systems, hose clips & lubricating system manufrs*

Ernest Leng & Son, Friars Hill Farm, Friars Hill, Sinnington, York, YO62 6SL Tel: (01751) 431774 Fax: (01751) 431774 *Agricultural building fabricators*

Ernest Morrison & Co., Unit 13 Loughside Industrial Estate, Dargan CR, Belfast, BT3 9JP Tel: (028) 9077 7093 Fax: (028) 9077 6299 *Filtration engineering*

Ernest Platt Bury Ltd, Whalley Road, Ramsbottom, Bury, Lancashire, BL0 0DE Tel: (01706) 282200 Fax: (01706) 821464 *Engineering gaskets & joints manufrs*

Ernex Group, P O Box 53967, London, SW15 3UY Tel: (020) 7731 6707 Fax: (020) 7731 6703 E-mail: ties@ernex.co.uk *Corporate and Club Neckties and scarf manufactures in both pure silk and polyester. We also offer hand embroidered blazer badges in gold and silver plus silk. Enameled Lapel badges, cufflinks and tie-pins.*

Ernst & Young Ltd, George House, 50 George Square, Glasgow, G2 1RR Tel: 0141-626 5000 Fax: 0141-626 5001 *Charter accountants*

Ernst & Young Ltd, 1 More London Place, London, SE1 2AF Tel: (020) 7951 2000 Fax: (020) 7951 1345 *Chartered accountants* Also at: Branches throughout the U.K.

Erodatools Ltd, Unit 4 Laurence Works, Sheffield Road, Penistone, Sheffield, S36 6HF Tel: (01226) 763725 Fax: (01226) 767139 E-mail: krolfe@aol.com Principal Export Areas: Worldwide *Spark & wire erosion machining specialists. In addition, press tool manufacturers, plastic mould toolmakers.*

Erode All, Queens Road, High Wycombe, Buckinghamshire, HP13 6AQ Tel: (01494) 521038 Fax: (01494) 531700 E-mail: sales@erode-all.com *Precision engineers services*

Erodex (UK) Ltd, Tipper Industrial Estate, Park Road, Halesowen, West Midlands, B63 2RH Tel: (01384) 892011 Fax: (01384) 897162 E-mail: sales@erodex.com *Graphite filters, spark erosion machines & carbon components manufrs*

Erodex UK Ltd, 42 Station Street, Wednesbury, West Midlands, WS10 8BW Tel: 0121-526 7368 Fax: 0121-526 6582 E-mail: sales@afshaw.com *Specialists in grinding graphite*

Eroga Die Co. Ltd, 6a Eastbrook Road Trading Estate, Eastbrook Road, Gloucester, GL4 3DB Tel: (01452) 524039 Fax: (01452) 500615 E-mail: mail@erogadie.com *Extrusion die manufrs*

Errington Reay & Co. Ltd, Tyneside Pottery Works, Bardon Mill, Hexham, Northumberland, NE47 7HU Tel: (01434) 344245 Fax: (01434) 344041 E-mail: sales@erringtonreay.co.uk *Pottery manufrs*

Ers, 21 Upton Cresent, Basingstoke, Hampshire, RG21 5SW Tel: (01256) 465604 Fax: (01256) 473737 *Air conditioning & refrigeration services*

Erskine Environmental Engineering Ltd., 16 Lady Lane, Paisley, Renfrewshire, PA1 2LJ Tel: 0141-887 7784 Fax: 0141-889 4338 *Heating, ventilation & dust extraction*

Erskine Systems Ltd, Salter Road, Eastfield Industrial Estate, Scarborough, North Yorkshire, YO11 3DU Tel: (01723) 583511 Fax: (01723) 581231 E-mail: sales@erskine-systems.co.uk *Battery charger manufrs*

Erste Technik Ltd, 1 Grange Close, Clover Nook Industrial Park, Somercotes, Alfreton, Derbyshire, DE55 4QT Tel: (01773) 521180 Fax: (01773) 521190 E-mail: info@erste-technik.co.uk *Veneer panel manufrs*

▶ Ertone Plastics Ltd, Unit 3 Telford Close, Aylesbury, Buckinghamshire, HP19 8DS Tel: (01296) 431482 Fax: (01296) 486299 *Man*

Ervin Amasteel Ltd, George Henry Road, Tipton, West Midlands, DY4 7BZ Tel: 0121-522 2777 Fax: 0121-522 2927 E-mail: info@ervinamasteel.com *Abrasive metallic/shotblasting material manufrs* Also at: Aberdeen

ES Repairs, Buckhurst Ave, Carshalton, Surrey, SM5 1PF Tel: (020) 8395 1536 E-mail: electrosysrep@blueyonder.co.uk *General electronic repairs to Public Address equipment, small CCTV systems, wireless microphones and Printed circuit boards. Sale of the above equipment. We can be contacted seven days a week between 0900hrs and 1800hrs.*

▶ Es Tech Network Solutions Ltd, 4 Avon Crescent, Bicester, Oxfordshire, OX26 2LZ Tel: (01869) 356018 Fax: (01869) 253005 E-mail: support@es-tech.co.uk *Computer networking consultants & services*

Esa Mcintosh Ltd, Mitchelston Drive, Mitchelston Industrial Estate, Kirkcaldy, Fife, KY1 3LX Tel: (01592) 656200 Fax: (01592) 656299 E-mail: sales@esamcintosh.co.uk *Educational & health care furniture manufrs*

Esab Group UK Ltd, Hanover House Britannia Road, Queens Gate, Waltham Cross, Hertfordshire, EN8 7TF Tel: (01992) 768515 Fax: (01992) 715803 E-mail: info@esab.co.uk *Welding products suppliers*

Escada UK Ltd, 6 Cavendish Place, London, W1G 9NB Tel: (020) 7580 6066 Fax: (020) 7637 8749 *Ladies fashion distributor & retailer*

Escadean, Baltimore Road, Birmingham, B42 1DP Tel: 0121-356 1001 Fax: 0121-356 7411 *Rubber moulding & control cable manufrs*

Escafeld Alloys Ltd, Bacon Lane, Sheffield, S9 3NH Tel: 0114-276 1091 Fax: 0114-273 9433 *Industrial fastener distributors*

▶ Escafeld Art Metalwork, Novo Works, Bessemer Road, Sheffield, S9 3XN Tel: 0114-256 2868 Fax: 0114-256 2898 E-mail: geoff@escafeld-art-metalwork.co.uk *Metal fabrication*

▶ E-ScanShop Ltd, 25a Harris Business Park, Hanbury Road, Stoke Prior, Bromsgrove, Worcestershire, B60 4BD Tel: (0845) 6121282 Fax: (0845) 6121292 E-mail: sales@e-scanshop.com *RFID & bar-coding equipment suppliers*

Escape, 29 Emscote Road, Warwick, CV34 5QH Tel: (01926) 493929 Fax: (01926) 492626 E-mail: shop@escape2.co.uk *Camping & outdoor leisure equipment suppliers*

▶ Escape Business Technologies, 5 Carden Place, Aberdeen, AB10 1UT Tel: (01224) 630600 Fax: (01224) 652969 E-mail: sales@escape-tech.co.uk *Computer support services*

▶ Escape Systems, 9 Salamanca Crescent, Penicuik, Midlothian, EH26 0LT Tel: (07764) 304166 *PC and Laptop repairs and upgrades, virus removal, data backup and recovery, network setup and configuration and web design in the Edinburgh and Lothian area.*

Escape-net UK, Hexham, Northumberland, NE46 3YP Tel: (01434) 603938 E-mail: hexham666@aol.com *Fire escape & fire safety*

Escol Products Ltd, Windover Road, Huntingdon, Cambridgeshire, PE29 7EB Tel: (01480) 454631 Fax: (01480) 411626 E-mail: info@escolproducts.co.uk *Vitreous enamel & electrostatic powder manufrs*

▶ Escombe Lambert Ltd, London Road, Barking, Essex, IG11 8BB Tel: (020) 8709 1600

Escor Toys, Elliott Road, Bournemouth, BH11 8JP Tel: (01202) 591081 Fax: (01202) 570049 E-mail: escortoys@bournemouth.gov.uk *Wooden toy & deckchair manufrs*

Escotex International Ltd, 38-40 Eastcastle Street, London, W1W 8DT Tel: (020) 7580 4237 Fax: (020) 7436 5327 *Textile agents*

Escott Signs Ltd, Princesway, Team Valley Trading Estate, Gateshead, Tyne & Wear, NE11 0TU Tel: 0191-487 1010 Fax: 0191-491 0762 E-mail: sales@escottsigns.co.uk *Sign makers*

▶ Escutcheon Limited, Suite 20, The Cavendish Centre, Winchester, Hampshire, SO23 0LB Tel: 0870 2250995 Fax: 0870 2250996 E-mail: answers@helpmybusiness.co.uk *Common sense, impartial business advice and pragmatic, practical solutions to problems old and new, whether in business management, finance, sales, marketing, troubleshooting or project management, from ad hoc projects to zero based budgets and beyond, from manufacturing to service and sectors in between... let us help your business.*

ESD Ltd, 68 - 71 Chapel Street, Netherton, Dudley, West Midlands, DY2 9PN Tel: (01384) 572699 Fax: (01384) 572698 E-mail: sales@esdltd.com *Why Choose the ESD Ltd group With the 3 main business activities of Distribution, Manufacturing and Power Solutions, ESD can offer you the both logistical and technical solutions to enable quick time to market allowing flexibility at a competitive price. Over 25 years experience in procurement and logistical solutions means that you are assured both expert knowledge and refined customer service. Over 20 years experience in the design and manufacture of power supplies AC-DC, DC-DC, PFC, ESD Power Solutions offer a "design and deliver" service unique to your needs. With its in house through hole and surface mount automated manufacturing facility ESD are able to manufacture small to high volume production quantities at competitive prices. Our dedicated staff and Hi Tech facilities are all geared to make things happen.*

▶ Esd Simulation Training Ltd, Craigearn Business Park, Morrison Way, Kintore, Inverurie, Aberdeenshire, AB51 0TH Tel: (01467) 634934 Fax: (01467) 634949 *Training company*

Esdale Plastics Ltd, 32 Union Street, Heckmondwike, West Yorkshire, WF16 0HH Tel: (01924) 401921 Fax: (01924) 401923 *Toolmakers*

Esdu International Ltd, 27 Corsham Street, London, N1 6UA Tel: (020) 7490 5151 Fax: (020) 7490 2701 E-mail: esdu@esdu.com *Engineering design data service*

ESE (Scotland) Ltd, 3 Dunlop Court, Deans Industrial Estate, Deans, Livingston, West Lothian, EH54 8SL Tel: (01506) 413313 Fax: (01506) 416550 E-mail: info@ese-scotland.co.uk *Ceiling constructors*

Esen Group, Heywood House, High Street, Bolton, BL3 6SR Tel: (01204) 386363 Fax: (01204) 386365 E-mail: industrialhose@esengroup.co.uk *Industrial hose manufrs*

▶ Esendee Construction Ltd, 16 Enderby Road, Luton, LU3 2HQ Tel: (01582) 579812 Fax: (01582) 598783

▶ Eserve It Ltd, Dealtree House, Blackmore Road Hook End, Brentwood, Essex, CM15 0DS Tel: (01277) 822005 Fax: (0870) 1166422 E-mail: info@eserve.it *Computer services, maintenance, support, recycling*

Eservglobal UK Ltd, 7th Floor East Gate House, Carr Street, Ipswich, IP4 1HA Tel: (01473) 289900 Fax: (01473) 289944 *Computer developers*

▶ ESF Lighting, National Sales Office, Broadway House, 149 - 151 St Neots Road, Hardwick, Cambridge, CB3 7QJ Tel: 0845 6066095 Fax: 0845 0725510 E-mail: sales@streetfurniture-uk.com *Supplier of all types of street lighting, exterior lighting, lighting columns in steel, stainless steel and aluminium as well as passively safe columns. Specialists on High Mast and stadium lighting as well as amenity and floodlighting systems.*

Esh Trace Heating, A Station Road, Guiseley, Leeds, LS20 8BX Tel: (01943) 884044 Fax: (01943) 884041 E-mail: enquiries@eshltd.com Principal Export Areas: Worldwide *Trace heating manufacturers, suppliers & installations*

▶ Eshenda Moda Ltd, Unit 23, Cygnus Business Centre,, Dalmeyer Road, London, NW10 2XA Tel: (020) 8200 3560 Fax: (020) 8200 6623 E-mail: shinyi_j@yahoo.co.uk *wedding gown manufacturer and wholesaler*

Esher Angling Centre, Pond House, Weston Green, Thames Ditton, Surrey, KT7 0JX Tel: (020) 8398 2405 *Fishing tackle manufrs*

ESI Ltd, Ochil House, Springkerse Business Park, Stirling, FK7 7XE Tel: (01786) 407000 Fax: (01786) 407003 E-mail: info@endat.com *Industrial process & environmental directories*

▶ ESI: Electrical Safety Inspections Ltd, 5 Chulkhurst, Sissinghurst Road, Biddenden, Ashford, Kent, TN27 8DG Tel: (0870) 4860351 Fax: (0870) 4860353 E-mail: jamie@esielectrical.co.uk *Electrical safety engineer specialists*

▶ ESI: Electrical Safety Inspections Ltd, Unit G32 Atlas Industrial Park, Rye Harbour Road, Rye, East Sussex, TN31 7TE Tel: (01797) 227741 Fax: (0870) 4860353 E-mail: rye@esi-team.co.uk *Periodic Wiring Inspections - PAT Testing - Electrical Testing - Emergency Lighting Inspections - Microwave Safety Testing.**We provide a full nationwide service to our clients from our operational bases in Kent, Sussex and Surrey.*

Esk Hygeine Supplies Ltd, Saffron Way, Leicester, LE2 6UP Tel: 0116-283 9362 E-mail: sales@eskgroup.co.uk *Disposable & cotton handwipes distributors & manufrs*

▶ Eskbank Control Panels, Lochlands Industrial Estate, Larbert, Stirlingshire, FK5 3NS Tel: (01324) 885556 Fax: (01324) 885559

Eskdale Harness, Craigshaws, Eaglesfield, Lockerbie, Dumfriesshire, DG11 3AH Tel: (01461) 600224 Fax: (01461) 600224 *Saddlery*

Eskdale Saddlery, 4 High Street, Longtown, Carlisle, CA6 5UE Tel: (01228) 792040 *Saddlery suppliers*

Esker, Durham House, Wyvern Business Park, Chaddesden, Derby, DE21 6BF Tel: (01332) 548181 Fax: (01332) 548160 E-mail: sam.townsend@esker.co.uk *Software manufrs*

▶ Eskhill & Co., Eskhill House, 15 Inveresk Village, Musselburgh, Midlothian, EH21 7TD Tel: 0131-271 4000 Fax: 0131-271 7000

Eskimo Express, Unit 8, Penton Hook Marina, Staines Road, Chertsey, Surrey, KT16 8PQ Tel: (01932) 560222 Fax: (01932) 569723 E-mail: sales@eskimoexpress.co.uk *ESKIMO EXPRESS OPERATE A TIME CRITICAL SAME DAY TEMPERATURE CONTROLLED COURIER SERVICE FOR THE EXPRESS MOVEMENT OF FOOD SAMPLES OR URGENT ORDERS OF FROZEN, CHILLED OR AMBIENT FOOD. CAN CARRY UP TO 1,250KG OR UP TO 3-4 PALLETS IN BOX VANS DOWN TO TEMPERATURES OF -25 DEGREES IF REQUIRED. COMPLETE SATELITE TRACKING OF VEHICLES AND TEMPERATURE AND DUAL COMPARTMENTS AVAILABLE FOR MIXED TEMPERATURE DELIVERIES.*

Eskimo Knitwear, Vinola Ho, Bruin St, Leicester, LE4 5AB Tel: 0116-266 3895 Fax: 0116-266 5280 *Knitted outerwear manufrs*

Esl Engineering, 11a Farrenlester Road, Coleraine, County Londonderry, BT51 3QR Tel: (028) 7035 6145 Fax: (028) 7035 4606 E-mail: eslengineering@btconnect.com *Design & manufacturing engineers*

Esl Healthcare Ltd, 9 Eastbourne Road, Westham, Pevensey, East Sussex, BN24 6EP Tel: (01323) 465800 Fax: (01323) 460248 E-mail: sales@eslindustries.co.uk *Shower cubicle manufrs*

Esmalglass (UK) Ltd, Eastfields Road, Dovefields Industrial Estate, Uttoxeter, Staffordshire, ST14 8AL Tel: (01889) 567277 Fax: (01889) 567892 E-mail: davidjohnson@esmalglass.co.uk *Ceramic glazes manufrs*

Esmanco Engineering Ltd, Hadfield Industrial Estate, Waterside, Hadfield, Glossop, Derbyshire, SK13 1BS Tel: (01457) 861673 Fax: (01457) 864044 E-mail: esmanco@btconnect.com *Structural & mechanical engineers*

Esmerk, Thames Tower, Station Road, Reading, RG1 1LX Tel: 0118-956 5820 Fax: 0118-956 5850 E-mail: response@esmerk.com *Business information consultants*

Esmil Process Systems Ltd, 30 Abbey Barn Road, High Wycombe, Buckinghamshire, HP11 1RW Tel: (01494) 474515 Fax: (01494) 474515 E-mail: info@esmil.co.uk *Water & effluent treatment manufrs*

Esograt Ltd, Caldervale Works, River Street, Brighouse, West Yorkshire, HD6 1JS Tel: (01484) 716228 Fax: (01484) 400107 E-mail: info@esograt.com *PVC window profile distributors*

▶ Esolutions Media Ltd, Unit 26, 140 Battersea Park Road, London, SW11 4NB Tel: (0870) 7477548 Fax: (0870) 7477549

ESP Coatings Ltd, Units A5-E13, Hastingwood Trading Estate, Harbet Road, Edmonton, London, N18 3HT Tel: (020) 8803 1115 Fax: (020) 8035 567 E-mail: espcoatings@btconnect.com *Powder coating service providers*

Esp Music Ltd, Ladywood Lodge, Spondon Road, Dale Abbey, Ilkeston, Derbyshire, DE7 4PS Tel: 0115-944 4140 Fax: 0115-944 4150 E-mail: sales@espmusic.co.uk *Providers of music software*

Espi Ltd, Network House, St. Neots Road, Dry Drayton, Cambridge, CB3 8AY Tel: (01954) 213999 Fax: (01954) 213998 E-mail: sales@espi.net *Accounting software developers*

▶ Espiner Medical Products, Unit 8, Carey Development, Tweed Road, Clevedon, Somerset, BS21 6RR Tel: (01275) 341072 Fax: (01275) 341073 E-mail: mail@espenermedical.com *Laparoscopic surgery suppliers*

F. Espley & Sons Ltd, Foregate House, 70A Foregate Street, Stafford, ST16 2PX Tel: (01785) 602040 Fax: (01785) 606566 E-mail: info@espleys.co.uk *Building & civil engineers*

▶ Espressocare, 12 Gordon Street, Colne, Lancashire, BB8 0NE Tel: 01282 710651 Fax: 01282 710651 E-mail: sales@espressocare.co.uk *Espresso machine cleaning products and accessories, descale tablets, milk cleaning liquid, coffee cleaning tablets*

Esprit Automation Ltd, Croft Mills, Church Drive, Sandiacre, Nottingham, NG10 5EE Tel: 0115-939 1888 Fax: 0115-939 1999 *Cnc plasma cutting machinery*

Esprit Communications, Supreme House, 300 Regents Park Road, London, N3 2JX Tel: (020) 8346 4499 Fax: (020) 8346 6969 E-mail: beter@espritcommunications.com *Sign manufrs*

▶ Esprit People Ltd, Unit 18 Pavilion Business Park, Royds Hall Road, Leeds, LS12 6AJ Tel: 0113-220 5530 Fax: 0113-220 5503 E-mail: tom.liptrot@esprit-people.co.uk *Esprit People Limited was formed in 1993 as a division of Esprit Systems Limited, with the objective of providing a flexible, high quality Engineering, Industrial, Driving and Production Recruitment Service to clients throughout the North of England. Esprit rapidly became the dominant force in our market sector, achieving year on year growth well above the industry average. Recent months have also seen the successful launch of our Commercial Division.*

▶ Esprit Solutions Ltd, 105 Boundary Street, Liverpool, L5 9YJ Tel: 0151-548 5900 Fax: (0870) 1417005 E-mail: sales@espritsolutions.info

Esr Electronic Components, Station Road, Cullercoats, North Shields, Tyne & Wear, NE30 4PQ Tel: 0191-251 4363 Fax: 0191-252 2296 E-mail: sales@esr.co.uk *Electronic component distributors*

Esri UK Ltd, Prebendal House, Parsons Fee, Aylesbury, Buckinghamshire, HP20 2QZ Tel: (01296) 745500 Fax: (01296) 745544 E-mail: info@esriuk.com *Computer software developers*

Ess, 12 Millcroft Road, Rutherglen, Glasgow, G73 1EN Tel: 0141-613 1714 Fax: 0141-613 1715

Ess Tee United Traders London Ltd, Northumberland House 11 The Pavement, Popes Lane, London, W5 4NG Tel: (020) 8566 3636 Fax: (020) 8566 1831 *Confirming house & export agents*

Essanti Textiles, Waterloo Road, Llandrindod Wells, Powys, LD1 6BH Tel: (01597) 825825 Fax: (01597) 825281 E-mail: sales@slippers.co.uk *Slipper manufrs*

▶ Essence Design, 125 Upper Holland Road, Sutton Coldfield, West Midlands, B72 1RD Tel: (0800) 0076914 Fax: (0871) 6612445 E-mail: info@essence-design.co.uk *Print & web design*

▶ Essential Business Services, 10 Woodland Road, Birmingham, B31 2HS Tel: 0121-478 1816 Fax: 0121 478 1816 E-mail: essentialserve@hotmail.com *Contract Cleaning, specialising in Offices and the common area's of apartment blocks.Each site is visited and supervised by one of our directors at least once a week without fail.*

Essential Computing Ltd, PO Box 49, Clevedon, Avon, BS21 7NB Tel: (01275) 343199 Fax: (01275) 340974 E-mail: sales@essential.co.uk *Software distributors*

▶ Essential Deliveries Ltd, 12 Seymour Court, Runcorn, Cheshire, WA7 1SY Tel: (01928) 579001 Fax: (0871) 2215400 E-mail: peter@essentialdeliveries.co.uk *Sameday courier service 24 hours a day, 7 days a week. Available at short notice to deliver throughout the UK and Europe. Emergency couriers for any urgent deliveries big or small in Warrington Runcorn Widnes St Helens Frodsham Helsby Northwich Storage available*

▶ Essential Dressings Ltd, 21 Eston Avenue, Malvern, Worcestershire, WR14 2SR Tel: (01684) 576150 E-mail: mail@essentialdressings.co.uk *Salad dressing suppliers*

Essential Equipment Ltd, Unit 24 Planetary Industrial Estate, Planetary Road, Willenhall, West Midlands, WV13 3XA Tel: (01902) 725055 Fax: (01902) 862684 E-mail: enquiries@essentialequipment.co.uk *Moulded rubber & plastic components*

▶ Essential Graphics, Graphics House, Heyford Park, Upper Heyford, Bicester, Oxfordshire, OX25 5HA Tel: (01869) 233435 Fax: (01869) 232287 E-mail: essentialsigns@btconnect.com *Sign makers*

▶ Essential Health Ltd, 2-3 Tabernacle Lane, Yeovil, Somerset, BA20 1QA Tel: (0845) 4085444 Fax: (01935) 476668 E-mail: sales@privatesurgery.info *Leading Health Insurance specialists**

The Essential Housewares Co. Ltd, 9 Foster Avenue, Woodside Park, Dunstable, Bedfordshire, LU5 5TA Tel: (01582) 475577 Fax: (01582) 690575 E-mail: sales@essentialhousewares.co.uk *Paper product importers & distributors*

Essential Hygiene & Workwear Services Ltd, 14 The Rowans, Leeds, LS13 1BD Tel: 0113-257 4411 Fax: 0113-256 2151 *Work wear rental services*

Essential Information Systems Ltd, 166 Station Road, Addlestone, Surrey, KT15 2BD Tel: (01932) 700370 Fax: (01932) 700380 *Computer repairs, retail & distribution*

Essential Ingredients Ltd, 25 Church Road, East Huntspill, Highbridge, Somerset, TA9 3PQ Tel: (01278) 783231 Fax: (01278) 783231 *Bulk food product manufrs*

Essential Karaoke, 58 Newport Road, Exeter, EX2 7EE Tel: (01392) 875865 Fax: (01392) 875865 E-mail: info@essentialballoons.co.uk *Suppliers of balloon decorations*

Essential Medical, 2 Lynfield Road, Lichfield, Staffordshire, WS13 7BS Tel: (01543) 301726 Fax: (01543) 301725 *Nebulae services for asthma*

Essential Motor Services Ltd, 5 Sugarbrook Road, Aston Fields Industrial Estate, Bromsgrove, Worcestershire, B60 3DN Tel: (01527) 870757 Fax: (01527) 870757 *Mechanical & accident repair centre*

Essex & Anglia Preservation Ltd, 24 Church End Lane, Runwell, Wickford, Essex, SS11 7JQ Tel: (0800) 0851695 Fax: (0800) 0851695 E-mail: info@essexandanglia.co.uk *Woodworm, dry rot & rising damp specialist*

▶ Essex Awnings, Unit 1, Claire Road, Kirby Cross, Frinton-On-Sea, Essex, CO13 0LY Tel: (01255) 850510 Fax: (01255) 862059 E-mail: info@essex-awnings.co.uk *Specialists in awnings, domestic blinds & commercial blinds*

▶ Essex Bedding Centres, Thornton Road Industrial Estate, Peall Road, Croydon, CR9 3EX Tel: (020) 8689 4430 Fax: (020) 8689 4430 *Beds retailers*

Essex Beds Ltd, Time Square, Southern Hay, Basildon, Essex, SS14 1DJ Tel: (01268) 522209 Fax: (01268) 530809 *Beds retailers*

Essex Blinds & Shutters, Brook Farm, Murthering Lane, Navestock, Romford, RM4 1HL Tel: (01277) 374100 Fax: (01277) 374100 E-mail: essexblinds@talk21.com *Blinds & resolving shutters manufrs*

Essex Bodybuilders Ltd, Arterial House, Claydons Lane, Rayleigh, Essex, SS6 7UP Tel: (01268) 778326 Fax: (01268) 774988 *Commercial vehicle body builders*

Essex Calabration Services, Five Tree Works Industrial Estate, Bakers Lane, West Hanningfield, Chelmsford, CM2 8LD Tel: (01277) 841410 Fax: (01277) 841418 E-mail: info@essexcal.demon.co.uk *Calibrating laboratory*

Essex Cleaning Services Ltd, 6 Alderman Avenue, Barking, Essex, IG11 0LX Tel: (020) 8594 2155 E-mail: ecsltd@arfoster.fsnet.co.uk *OFFICE CLEANING*WINDOW CLEANING*CARPET CLEANING*ONE OFF CLEANS*WASHROOM SUPPLIES*JANITORIAL SUPPLIES*FEMININE HYGIENE*COMPUTER CLEANING*TELEPHONE SANITIZING*ENTRANCE MATTING*STRIP &*

continued

Company Information

continuation
*POLISHING OF HARD FLOORS*CIS REGISTERED*WASTE MANAGEMENT*

▶ Essex Communications, Unit 11, Olympic Business Centre, Paycocke Road, Basildon, Essex, SS14 3EX Tel: (01268) 287575 Fax: (01268) 287585

▶ Essex Computer Services, 42 Brooklyn Road, Harwich, Essex, CO12 3QF Tel: (01255) 243235 *Computer maintenance & one on one training*

▶ Essex Counselling Practice, 442 Ipswich Road, Colchester, CO4 0EY Tel: 01206 842459 E-mail: brenda@essex-counselling-practice.co.uk *Person Centred Counselling for help coping with bereavement, stress, anxiety, depression, low self esteem, being elderly, adoption issues, relationship problems.*

Essex Demolition Contractors Ltd, 1 Navigation Road, Chelmsford, CM2 6ND Tel: (01245) 258333 Fax: (01245) 266911 *Demolition site clearance & contractors services*

▶ Essex Drums Ltd, Unit 3, Charles Street, London, E16 2BY Tel: (020) 7511 2785 Fax: (020) 7473 3975 *Barrel, cask, & keg dealers, reconditioners & suppliers*

Essex Electric Ltd, 46 Hanbury Road, Chelmsford, CM1 3TL Tel: (01245) 251291 Fax: (01245) 354051 *Air conditioning engineers*

Essex Engineering Works Wanstead Ltd, 12 Nelson Road, London, E11 2AX Tel: (020) 8989 2012 Fax: (020) 8530 1117 E-mail: enquiries@essexengineering.co.uk *Coin acceptor mechanism manufrs*

Essex Fixing & Abrasives Supplies Ltd, Unit 12 Featherby Way, Purdey's Industrial Estate, Rochford, Essex, SS4 1LD Tel: (01702) 549222 Fax: (01702) 541465 *Abrasives, adhesives & fixings*

Essex Graphic Signs, Cobwebs, 26 Scarletts, Basildon, Essex, SS14 2HZ Tel: (01268) 293293 Fax: (01268) 452525 E-mail: sign.sales@virgin.net *Sign manufrs*

Essex Heat Treatments Ltd, Unit C2, Perry Road, East Industrial Estate, Witham, Essex, CM8 3UX Tel: (01376) 515229 Fax: (01376) 518701 E-mail: eht@withamcm83ux.fsnet.co.uk *Heat treatment of metals*

Essex Injection Mouldings Ltd, 15 Temple Farm Industrial Estate, Craftsman Square, Temple Farm Industrial Estate, Southend-on-Sea, SS2 5RH Tel: (01702) 461160 Fax: (01702) 600805 E-mail: ed@essexinjectionmouldings.co.uk *Plastic injection moulding manufrs*

Essex Laser Job Shop Ltd, Unit D4, Frogmore Industrial Estate, Motherwell Way, Grays, Essex, RM20 3XD Tel: (01708) 689658 Fax: (01708) 865433 E-mail: sales@essexlaser.co.uk *Laser, profile & stainless steel profile cutting services*

▶ Essex Mechanical Services, 3 Peartree Business Centre, Peartree Road, Stanway, Colchester, CO3 0JN Tel: (01206) 368821 Fax: (01206) 368826

Essex Nexans UK Ltd, Ellis Ashton Street, Liverpool, L36 6BW Tel: 0151-443 6000 Fax: 0151-443 6025 E-mail: sales@essexgroup.co.uk *Copper, enamelled & insulated wire manufrs*

Essex Optical Co. Ltd, 172 Enterprise Court, Eastways, Witham, Essex, CM8 3YS Tel: (01376) 512630 Fax: (01376) 515154 E-mail: enquiries@essexoptical.co.uk *Optical lens manufrs*

Essex Pallet Truck Services, 16 Fennel Close, Tiptree, Colchester, CO5 0TF Tel: (07949) 091271 Fax: (01621) 810867 E-mail: essexpallettrucks.services@virgin.net *Materials handling services*

▶ Essex Parking Solutions, PO Box 5741, Southend-on-Sea, SS1 1AB Tel: 01702 332105 E-mail: andrew@eps0.wanadoo.co.uk *Essex Parking Solutions provides the following services;*Car Park Monitoring,Car Park Management,Car Park Tickets Issued,Wheel Clamping etc.*

Essex Partners Flange, 73 Park Lane, Liverpool, L1 5EX Tel: 0151-709 6636 Fax: 0151-709 2109 *Flange manufrs*

▶ Essex Power Tools & Fixings, Unit 1 Bramerton Road, Hockley, Essex, SS5 4AZ Tel: (01702) 207209 Fax: (01702) 203228

Essex Pyrotechnics Ltd, 6 Wicken Road, Newport, Saffron Walden, Essex, CB11 3QG Tel: (01799) 541414 Fax: (01799) 541415 *Fireworks business*

Essex Refractory Ltd, Unit 1 Middleton Hall, Brentwood, Essex, CM13 3LX Tel: (01277) 812282 Fax: (01277) 811185 *Boilers & furnace rebuilders*

Essex Replica Castings (Basildon) Ltd, 108-112 Westmoor Street, Charlton, London, SE7 8NQ Tel: (020) 8858 6110 Fax: (020) 8305 0907 E-mail: nicktownsend@jardineinternational.com *Castings manufrs*

▶ Essex Rodent Control, 3 Fleet Hall Road, Rochford, Essex, SS4 1NF Tel: (01702) 544777 Fax: 01702 54999 E-mail: richlunn@btinternet.com *We are a large distributor of pest control products for the trade. We provide a range of products for rodent control, insect control, bird control, PPE, and application equipment.*

▶ Essex Safety Glass Ltd, Moss Road, Witham, Essex, CM8 3UQ Tel: (01376) 520061 Fax: (01376) 521176 E-mail: graeme.brouder@essexsafetyglass.co.uk *Glass manufrs*

▶ Essex Security Services Ltd, 154 Church Hill, Loughton, Essex, IG10 1LJ Tel: (020) 8502 1360 Fax: (020) 8502 2700 E-mail: all@essexsecurity.co.uk *Install security systems*

▶ Essex Specialised Joinery, Essexquay House, Quayside Industrial Estate, Maldon, Essex, CM9 5FA Tel: (01621) 843384 Fax: (01621) 843411 *Bespoke joinery*

Essex Stairs & Joinery, Holmewood Farm, Brookhall Road, Fingringhoe, Colchester, CO5 7DG Tel: (01206) 728716 Fax: (01206) 729587 *Stairs & joinery manufrs*

▶ Essex Tape, 45 Canvey Road, Leigh-on-Sea, Essex, SS9 2PA Tel: (01702) 479729 E-mail: john@essextape.co.uk *Supplying quality adhesive tapes throughout Essex & along the Thames Corridor into the Olympic City Complex*

Essex Tractor Co. Ltd, Birchwood Road, Cock Clarks, Chelmsford, CM3 6RF Tel: (01621) 828880 Fax: (01621) 828944 E-mail: sales@tractor.net *Agricultural machinery & spares supply worldwide*

Essex Valves Engineering Services, Unit 13 Newlands End, Basildon, Essex, SS15 6DU Tel: (020) 8595 8749 Fax: (020) 8595 8749 *Valve repairers*

Essex Wirework Company Ltd, PO Box 1, Hockley, Essex, SS5 5LD Tel: (01702) 205022 Fax: (01702) 207678 *Steel fabricators & wireworkers*

Essex Woodcraft, Commerce Way, Colchester, CO2 8HJ Tel: (01206) 795464 Fax: (01206) 796596 E-mail: sales@essexwoodcraft.co.uk *Joinery manufrs*

Essie Carpets, 62 Piccadilly, London, W1J 0DZ Tel: (020) 7493 7766 Fax: (020) 7495 3456 E-mail: essiesakhai@compuserve.com *Carpet importers & exporters*

Essig Products Ltd, 4 Courtyard 3, Wentworth Road, Mapplewell, Barnsley, South Yorkshire, S75 6DT Tel: (01226) 383384 Fax: (01226) 390880 E-mail: sales@essig.co.uk *Manufacturers of ipm moles*

Essilor Ltd, Cooper Road, Thornbury, Bristol, BS35 3UW Tel: (01454) 417100 Fax: (01454) 281282 *Optical lens & equipment manufrs*

Esspee Fabrications Ltd, 149 Merton Bank Road, St. Helens, Merseyside, WA9 1DZ Tel: (01744) 28304 Fax: (01744) 28826 E-mail: sales@esspee.co.uk *Electrical insulating material suppliers*

Estate Computer Systems, 4-6 Dukes Road, London, WC1H 9AD Tel: (020) 7388 3400 Fax: (020) 7388 6006 E-mail: info@qubeglobal.com *Software house consultants*

Estate & Country Sports Equipment Ltd, 25 Five Acres Cl, Lindford, Bordon, Hants, GU35 0SJ Tel: (01420) 473395 Fax: (01420) 473395 *Angling & fishing equipment manufrs*

▶ Estate Lettings (Telford & Newport), 119A Trench Road, Trench, EstateLettings.co.uk, Telford, Shropshire, TF2 7DP Tel: 01952 603355 Fax: 08717 312962 E-mail: contact@estatelettings.co.uk *We Guarantee to beat all other Management fees**Landlords, we have a huge number of quality Tenants awaiting property. We offer a No Let No Fee system with our management fee being only 5% Let yours Today!**

Estate Signs, 176 Christchurch Road, Ringwood, Hampshire, BH24 3AS Tel: (01425) 475574 Fax: (01425) 479906 E-mail: sales@estate-signs.co.uk *Sign manufrs*

Estates Gazette, 147-151 Wardour Street, London, W1F 8BN Tel: (020) 7437 0141 Fax: (020) 7411 2874 *Property consultants*

Estera Scales Ltd, Europa House, Dorking Business Park, Dorking, Surrey, RH4 1HJ Tel: (01306) 740785 Fax: (01306) 740786 *Weigh, price & label system manufrs*

Esterform Packaging Ltd, Boraston Lane, Tenbury Wells, Worcestershire, WR15 8LE Tel: (01584) 810600 Fax: (01584) 810213 E-mail: paulw@esterform.com Principal Export Areas: Worldwide *Plastic bottle manufrs*

Estil Ltd, Charlotte Street, Dudley, West Midlands, DY1 1TD Tel: (01384) 243643 Fax: (01384) 243644 E-mail: sales@estil.co.uk *Electrical contractors*

Estimation Ltd, Highland House, Stirling Road, Shirley, Solihull, West Midlands, B90 4NE Tel: 0121-704 3221 Fax: 0121-711 2664 E-mail: info@estimation.co.uk *Computer software development services*

▶ Esto Perpetua Ltd, 447-449 South Ordnance Road, Enfield, Middlesex, EN3 6HR Tel: (01992) 761422 Fax: (01992) 711391

Estrade Ltd, 38-40 Eastcastle Street, London, W1W 8DT Tel: (020) 7580 4237 Fax: (020) 7436 5327 *Fabric importers*

Estuary Automation Ltd, 40 Shoebury Avenue, Shoeburyness, Southend-on-Sea, SS3 9BH Tel: (01702) 293901 Fax: (01702) 297318 E-mail: estaut@aol.com *Special purpose machinery design services & manufrs*

Estuary Engineering Co Ltd, Hamlin Way, King's Lynn, Norfolk, PE30 4NG Tel: (01553) 773678 Fax: (01553) 769121 E-mail: tony@estuary.demon.co.uk *Power transmission, hydraulic, pneumatic suppliers & services*

Estuary Fine Foods Ltd, Unit 3 Station Yard, Duddon Road, Askam-in-Furness, Cumbria, LA16 7AL Tel: (01229) 466828 Fax: (01229) 462343 *Meat fish & poultry*

Estuary Personal Computers, 318 Chartwell North, Victoria Plaza, Southend-on-Sea, SS2 5SR Tel: (01702) 543300 *Computer software development*

ESW Solutions, Penny Stone Farm, Westerland, Maldon, Paignton, Devon, TQ3 1RU Tel: (01803) 522522 Fax: (0871) 4338777 *PA hire & installation & conference equipment suppliers*

▶ Esynco Computer Services, 109 Park Court, London, SW11 4LE Tel: (0845) 6652897 E-mail: pcproblems@esynco.co.uk *Esynco is a computer company, specialising in computer*services for home & business users. We guarantee fast &*professional service at minimum cost.**Our overriding commitment to competitive prices, quality*personal service and excellent value for money has firmly*established Esynco Computers in London and the South East.**We value our customers, and constantly strive to improve our *service to them.*

▶ Esys Plc, 1 Occam Court, Occam Road, Surrey Research Park, Guildford, Surrey, GU2 7HJ Tel: (01483) 304545 Fax: (01483) 303878 E-mail: info@esys.co.uk *Consultancy*

Et Environmental Ltd, 47 Central Avenue, West Molesey, Surrey, KT8 2QZ Tel: (020) 8783 0033 Fax: (020) 8783 0140 E-mail: diffusion@etenv.co.uk *Air conditioning & heating equipment suppliers*

▶ Eta Fixing Systems Ltd, Fixings House, Crowcroft, Leigh Sinton, Malvern, Worcestershire, WR13 5ED Tel: (01886) 833600 Fax: (01886) 833477

▶ Eta Process Plant, King Street, Fenton, Stoke-on-Trent, ST4 2LT Tel: (01782) 744561 Fax: (01782) 602293 E-mail: tracey.bagley@etapp.com *Design, supply, installation & commissioning of chemical engineering*

Eta-Com UK Ltd, Unit 15 City Business Centre, Brighton Road, Horsham, West Sussex, RH13 5BB Tel: (01403) 265767 Fax: (01403) 254131 E-mail: busduct@etacom-uk.com Principal Export Areas: Worldwide *Busbar distribution systems manufrs*

▶ ETA-enclosures UK Ltd, Unit 4, Kea Park Close, Hellaby Industrial Estate, Rotherham, South Yorkshire, S66 8LB Tel: (01709) 730111 E-mail: info@eta-enclosures.co.uk *Enclosures stainless & enclosures steel*

Etas, 1 Lancaster Close, Winsford, Cheshire, CW7 1PS Tel: (01606) 551555 Fax: (01606) 862733 *Burglar alarm installation & services*

Etb, Cardiff Road, Barry, South Glamorgan, CF63 2QW Tel: (01446) 733167 Fax: (01446) 733167 *Fast fit tyre & auto centre*

▶ Etc Design Ltd, 2 Carriers Fold, Church Road, Wombourne, Wolverhampton, WV5 9DH Tel: (01902) 898282 Fax: (01902) 898283 E-mail: enquiries@etcarchitects.co.uk *Architects*

▶ ETC Embroidery, Enterprise House, 94 David Street, Bridgeton, Glasgow, G40 2UH Tel: 0141-550 1188 Fax: 0141-550 2999 *Wholesaler embroidery consumables*

Etch Components, Unit 3 58 Caroline Street, Birmingham, B3 1UF Tel: 0121-233 4409 Fax: 0121-233 9282 *Chemical engraving service*

Etch Mark Ltd, 5 Romford Road, Stafford, ST16 3DZ Tel: (01785) 253143 Fax: (01785) 223282 E-mail: info@etchmark.co.uk *Electrochemical etching equipment manufrs*

E-Tech Group (HVAC Div), The E-Tech Centre, Boundary Road, Great Yarmouth, Norfolk, NR31 0LY Tel: 01493 419800 Fax: 01493 419805 E-mail: etech-hvac@etechcentre.com *Building services. piping and heating engineers*

Eterna Lighting Ltd, Eterna Lighting Huxley Close, Park Farm South, Wellingborough, Northamptonshire, NN8 6AB Tel: (01933) 404140 Fax: (01933) 678083 E-mail: sales@eterna-lighting.co.uk *Lighting manufrs*

Eternal Clothing Ltd, 275a Ley Street, Ilford, Essex, IG1 4BN Tel: (020) 8514 3544 Fax: (020) 8514 1786 E-mail: ecuk@aol.com Principal Export Areas: Central/East Europe & West Europe *Ladies clothing & club wear wholesalers*

Etherington Air Conditioning Ltd, 44 Potternewton Mount, Leeds, LS7 2DR Tel: 0113-262 1112 Fax: 0113-262 5075 E-mail: graham@etheringtonac.co.uk *Air conditioning contracts engineers. HVAC solutions for Air Conditioning Installation, Service and Maintenance. Leeds based. REFCOM registered. Daikin D1, Mitsubishi Business Solutions Partner, Toshiba Registered.*

Charles Etherington Ltd, Hallgarth Field, Millington, York, YO42 1TX Tel: (01759) 302204 *Blacksmiths & manufacturers of products for farmers*

▶ Ethigen Pharmaceutical Distributors, 15 Springburn Place, East Kilbride, Glasgow, G74 5NU Tel: (01355) 598150 Fax: (01355) 598159

Ethnic Cuisine Ltd, Viking Way, Winch Wen Industrial Estate, Winch Wen, Swansea, SA1 7DE Tel: (01792) 772064 Fax: (01792) 773334 *Preparing packed food*

Ethos Candles Ltd, Quarry Fields, Mere, Warminster, Wiltshire, BA12 6LA Tel: (01747) 860960 Fax: (01747) 860934 E-mail: sales@charlesfarris.co.uk *Candle manufrs*

Ethos Partnership Limited, Suite E8, Business & Innovation Centre, Wearfield, Sunderland, SR5 2TP Tel: 0191-516 6251 Fax: (01892) 528433 E-mail: kym@ethospartnershipltd.co.uk *A specialist organisation offering Quality, Environmental and Health and Safety Management and Consultancy, combining over 30 years experience of international standards, legislation and organisational change, to bring fully integrated management systems and strategies. Southern Office: 16 Southridge Road, Crowborough, East Sussex, TN6 1LT, Tel: 01892 665336, Fax: 01892 528433*

Etma Engineering Ltd, Victoria Road, Halesowen, West Midlands, B62 8HY Tel: 0121-559 5333 Fax: 0121-559 2236 E-mail: sales@etma.co.uk *Zinc pressure die casters*

Eton M E M Low Voltage Products Ltd, Grimshaw Lane, Middleton Farm, Manchester, M24 1GQ Tel: 0161-655 8900 Fax: (0870) 0507525 E-mail: ukresiorders@eton.com *Switchgear manufrs*

Eton Racing Boats, Brocas Street, Eton, Windsor, Berkshire, SL4 6BW Tel: (01753) 671294 Fax: (01753) 671293 *Racing boat manufrs*

▶ E-Trade Enterprises Ltd, 21 Betchworth Road, Ilford, Essex, IG3 9JF Tel: (020) 8599 5259 E-mail: fismail@gadgetscene.co.uk *Computer & Peripherals reseller*

Etrali UK Ltd, Piercy House, 7-9 Copthall Avenue, London, EC2R 7NJ Tel: (020) 7628 2795 Fax: (020) 7628 4972 E-mail: enquiries@aircharlie.com *Telecommunications system contractors*

Etrinsic, 473 Stratford Road, Shirley, Solihull, West Midlands, B90 4AD Tel: (0870) 4646131 Fax: (0870) 4646040 *Computer stationery manufacturers & printing services*

Ets, Newton Brae, Foulden, Berwick-upon-Tweed, TD15 1UL Tel: (01289) 386664 Fax: (01289) 386750 E-mail: sales@etsluk.com

ETS Distribution Services, Logistics House, 175 Meadow Lane, Loughborough, Leicestershire, LE11 1NF Tel: (01509) 615050 Fax: (01509) 615067 E-mail: info@etsltd.co.uk *ETS Distribution Services, Loughborough, Leicestershire, East Midlands UK ETS provides quality, tailored logistics solutions in storage, handling and transportation and B2C direct marketing support services. In brief, services offered include 100,000 sq ft of secure, dry warehousing for client's goods, import and export freight, cross docking, electronic inventory, fulfilment, pick and pack, repackaging, bulk store, high-bay pallet racking, nationwide pallet transport network, part and full load deliveries using a combination of company vehicles and approved sub-contractors.*

Ets UK Ltd, Northside Industrial Park, Whitley Bridge, Goole, North Humberside, DN14 0GH Tel: (01977) 662910 Fax: (01977) 661797 E-mail: sales@ets-uk.co.uk *Torque converters & power transmission equipment repairers*

Etsgap Electrical Wholesalers, Energy House, Falkland Close, Charter Avenue Industrial Estate, Coventry, CV4 8AU Tel: (024) 7646 8259 Fax: (024) 7669 4090 E-mail: ets.gap@btconnect.com *Electrical supplies agents & distributors* Also at: Willenhall

Euchner (U K) Ltd, Unit 2, Petre Drive, Sheffield, S4 7PZ Tel: 0114-256 0123 Fax: 0114-242 5333 E-mail: info@euchner.co.uk *Control, limit & proximity switch manufrs*

Euclid Ltd, Euclid House, Parklands Business Park, Waterlooville, Hampshire, PO7 6XP Tel: (023) 9226 6333 Fax: (023) 9226 6555 E-mail: sales@euclid.ltd.uk *Equipment systems plastic card manufrs*

Eukero Controls Ltd, Unit 7 Worton Court, Worton Road, Isleworth, Middlesex, TW7 6ER Tel: (020) 8568 4664 Fax: (020) 8568 4115 E-mail: info@eukero.co.uk *Temperature controls limit switches, proximity switches, panel meters, interfaces timer & counters manufrs*

Eular Hermes Collections UK Ltd, 36 Floor, 1 Canada Square, Canary Wharf, London, E14 5DX Tel: (020) 7512 9333 *Debt recovery services*

Euler Hermes Guarantee plc, Surety House, Lyons Cresent, Tonbridge, Kent, TN9 1EN Tel: (01732) 770311 Fax: (01732) 770361 *Bond services*

Euler Hermes UK plc, 1 Canada Square, London, E14 5DX Tel: (0800) 0565452 Fax: (0207) 8602455 E-mail: creditinfo@eulerhermes.com *As the UK's leading credit insurer, Euler Hermes UK helps most companies of all sizes, wherever they trade to safeguard and grow their business. Our extensive range of credit management products is supported by our uniquely powerful knowledge of financial strength of companies and markets.*

▶ Euracess Ltd, Unit 6, Trubodys Yard, 121 London Road, Warmley, Bristol, BS30 5NA Tel: 0117-960 9497 Fax: 0117-960 9497

Euram Chemicals Ltd, PO Box 346, Marlow, Buckinghamshire, SL7 1WH Tel: (01628) 472848 Fax: (01628) 890095 E-mail: sales@euramchemicals.co.uk *Industrial chemicals distributors & manufrs*

Euramax Coated Products Ltd, Brunel Road, Earlstrees Industrial Estate, Corby, Northamptonshire, NN17 4JW Tel: (01536) 400800 Fax: (01536) 400101 *Aluminium coil coaters*

Euramco Ltd, The Quadrant, Newark Close, Royston, Hertfordshire, SG8 5HL Tel: (01763) 244490 Fax: (01763) 247733 E-mail: info@euramco.co.uk *Electrical cable distributors*

▶ Eurasia Education Consultancy, 2-4 Chepstow Road, Newport, Gwent, NP19 8EA Tel: 01633 216899

Eureka Direct, Unit 5, Sterte Road Industrial Estate, Sterte Road, Poole, Dorset, BH15 2AF Tel: (0800) 3580085 Fax: (0800) 3580095 E-mail: sales@eurekadirect.co.uk *Suppliers of first aid & safety equipment*

Eureka Products, 35 Norfolk Street, Nelson, Lancashire, BB9 7SY Tel: (01282) 615661 Fax: (01282) 699542 *Floor sanding & planning machine manufrs*

▶ Eureka Solutions (Scotland) Ltd, James Watt Building, Scottish Enterprise Technology Park, East Kilbride, Glasgow, G75 0QD Tel: (01355) 813500 Fax: (0870) 224730 E-mail: enquiries@eurekasolutions.co.uk *Developers of integrated solutions*

▶ Eurekastep, Exchange House, Worthing Road, Horsham, West Sussex, RH12 1SQ Tel: (01403) 219600 Fax: (01403) 273679 E-mail: info@eurekastep.co.uk *Technology, consulting, marketing, websites,*

Euremica Ltd, Instrument House, Morgan Drive, Guisborough, Cleveland, TS14 7DG Tel: (01287) 204020 Fax: (01287) 204021 E-mail: sales@euremica.com *Industrial & test measurement equipment*

Eurest, 47-51 Kingston Crescent, Portsmouth, PO2 8AA Tel: (023) 9266 0088 Fax: (023) 9266 5590 *Caterers*

Eurgent Ecspress, Unit 1b, Charnwood Park, Bridgend, Mid Glamorgan, CF31 3PL Tel: (01656) 645555 Fax: (01656) 656534 E-mail: enq@eurgent.co.uk *Freight forwarding services*

Euro Acoustics Holdings Ltd, 54 Trevean Way, Newquay, Cornwall, TR7 1TW Tel: (01637) 852172 Fax: (01637) 853960 E-mail: alan@euro-acoustics.com *Noise control equipment, systems engineers & acoustic insulation services*

▶ Euro Air, 118 Claverham Road, Yatton, Bristol, BS49 4LE Tel: (01934) 835662 Fax: (01934) 835662

Euro Aluminium Systems Ltd, Bradley Junction Industrial Estate, Leeds Road, Huddersfield, HD2 1UR Tel: (01484) 429987 Fax: (01484) 429937 E-mail: info@euroalisys.freeserve.co.uk *Aluminium fabricators & window frame manufrs*

Euro Asia Exports Ltd, 25 Uxendon Hill, Wembley, Middlesex, HA9 9RX Tel: (020) 8904 2575 Fax: (020) 8904 9187 E-mail: euro@euasia.demon.co.uk *Steel merchants*

Euro Baguettes (UK) Ltd, 21 Timberlaine Trading Estate, Decoy Road, Worthing, West Sussex, BN14 8JH Tel: (01903) 205825 Fax: (01903) 206666 E-mail: sales@euro-mouldinds.co.uk *Distributors to picture framing market*

Euro Blinds UK, King Street, Newton Abbot, Devon, TQ12 2LG Tel: (01392) 824225 Fax: (01626) 369005 E-mail: info@euroblindsdevon.co.uk *Blinds, awning manufrs & installers*

continued

▶ indicates data change since last edition

Euro Carb Ltd, 256 Kentwood Hill, Tilehurst, Reading, RG31 6DR Tel: 0118-943 1180 Fax: 0118-943 1190E-mail: sales@dellorto.co.uk *Carburettor distributors*

▶ Euro Circuitboards Ltd, 6 Diamond Industrial Centre, Works Road, Letchworth Garden City, Hertfordshire, SG6 1LW Tel: (01462) 481010 Fax: (01462) 480978 E-mail: sales@eurocircuitboards.com *Printing circuit*

Euro Clad Ltd, Wentloog Corparate Park, Wentloog Road, Rumney, Cardiff, CF3 2ER Tel: (029) 2079 0722 Fax: (029) 2079 3149 E-mail: sales@euroclad.com *Profiled cladding manufrs*

Euro Claddings Ltd, 9 Heathfield Road, Kings Heath, Birmingham, B14 7BT Tel: 0121-444 0375 Fax: 0121-441 1134 E-mail: eurocladdings@lineone.net *Decorative tile retailers*

▶ Euro Construction Corporation Ltd, 57 Crowhill Road, Waringstown, Craigavon, County Armagh, BT66 7SS Tel: (028) 3888 1867 Fax: (028) 3888 2262

Euro Conveying Equipment, Shepley Street, Failsworth, Manchester, M35 9DY Tel: 0161-682 6966 Fax: 0161-688 4942 E-mail: trev@beltman.co.uk *Conveyer belts suppliers*

Euro Diesel, Vulcan Road South, Norwich, NR6 6AF Tel: (01603) 406525 Fax: (01603) 484046 E-mail: rayradford@btconnect.com *Diesel engineers*

Euro Direct Database Marketing Ltd, 1 Park Lane, Leeds, LS3 1EP Tel: 0113-242 4747 Fax: 01132 424646 E-mail: Info@eurodirect.co.uk *EuroDirect and consultancy division GMAP Consulting are recognised as leading suppliers of targeted mailing lists, international consumer classifications, advanced GIS, strategic modeling and network planning solutions and consultancy services for some of the worldâs largest Organizations.*

▶ Euro Dividers Co. Ltd, Unit 3, Brookfield Industrial Estate, Leacon Road, Ashford, Kent, TN23 4TU Tel: (01233) 649500 Fax: (01233) 649509 E-mail: sales@eurodividers.co.uk *Manufacturer of cardboard dividers*

Euro DPC Ltd, Glyn Rhonwy, Llanberis, Caernarfon, Gwynedd, LL55 4EL Tel: (01286) 871871 Fax: (01286) 871802 E-mail: euro@dpconline.com Principal Export Areas: Worldwide *Scientific instrument manufrs*

▶ EURO Driveshafts & Hydraulics, Tannahill, Kilmaurs, Kilmarnock, Ayrshire, KA3 2LN Tel: (01563) 538011 Fax: (01563) 572389 *Driveshaft industrial manufrs*

Euro Environmental Containers, The Court House, Denmark Street, Wokingham, Berkshire, RG40 2AY Tel: (0845) 0094287 Fax: 0709 231 0266 E-mail: Enquiries@euroenvironmentalcontainers.co.uk *WASTE COOKING OIL COMPLIANT STORAGE CONTAINERS, 0 LTRS.**

Euro Fibres Ltd, 76 Forkhill Road, Newry, County Down, BT35 8QY Tel: (028) 3084 8912 Fax: (028) 3084 8179 *Springs & upholstery wholesalers*

Euro Filter, Hare Park Mills, 46 Hare Park Lane, Liversedge, West Yorkshire, WF15 8EP Tel: (01623) 412412 Fax: (01274) 869956 E-mail: info@ecsfiltration.com *Dust & fume controllers*

Euro Filter, Hare Park Mills, 46 Hare Park Lane, Liversedge, West Yorkshire, WF15 8EP Tel: (01623) 412412 Fax: (01623) 412455 E-mail: sales@eurofilter.co.uk Purchasing Contact: S Horrocks Sales Contact: M Mitchell *Air filter manufrs*

Euro Fire Guard Ltd, PO Box 95, Cirencester, Gloucestershire, GL7 5YX Tel: (01285) 850720 Fax: (01285) 850605 E-mail: carol@euro-fire-guard.co.uk *Fire extinguishers, alarms retailers & service providers*

Euro Fluid Power Ltd, St. Marys Works, Brierley Street, Stoke-on-Trent, ST6 1LB Tel: (01782) 575306 Fax: (01782) 575534 E-mail: eurofluid@aol.com *Hydraulic accessories distributors* Also at: Ashton-under-Lyne

Euro Food Machinery Ltd, Station Road Industrial Estate, Elmswell, Bury St. Edmunds, Suffolk, IP30 9HR Tel: (01359) 241971 Fax: (01359) 242092 E-mail: info@eurofood.co.uk *Food machinery equipment manufrs*

Euro Forklifts Ltd, St. Michaels Road, Sittingbourne, Kent, ME10 3DN Tel: (01795) 425536 Fax: (01795) 476192 *Forklift truck services*

▶ Euro Guard Technical Services, 129-130 Windmill Street, Gravesend, Kent, DA12 1BL Tel: (01474) 334888 Fax: (01474) 364111 E-mail: sales@euro-guard.co.uk *Pest controllers*

▶ Euro Hair Fashion UK Ltd, 4 North Cresent Business Park, Diplocks Way, Hailsham, East Sussex, BN27 3JF Tel: (01323) 842288 Fax: (01323) 449211 E-mail: info@eurohair.co.uk *Hair care products distributors*

Euro Hydraulics Ltd, Unit 4 Park Parade Industrial Estate, Welbeck St South, Ashton-under-Lyne, Lancashire, OL6 7PP Tel: 0161-308 2624 Fax: 0161-343 1926 E-mail: info@eurohydraulics.com *Hydraulic accessories distributors* Also at: Stoke-on-Trent

Euro Industrial Engineering, 161 Fog Lane, Manchester, M20 6FJ Tel: 0161-438 0438 Fax: 0161-438 2538 E-mail: info@eieuk.com *Hygienic pumps & butterfly valve manufacturers & electric motors*

Euro Industrial Plastics Ltd, Chamberlain Road, Aylesbury, Buckinghamshire, HP19 8DY Tel: (01296) 482252 Fax: (01296) 425482 E-mail: enquiries@euroindustrialplastics.co.uk *Industrial plastics distributors*

▶ Euro Lab Environmental Ltd, Peartree House, 1 Britannia Road, Warley, Brentwood, Essex, CM14 5LD Tel: (01277) 210022 Fax: (01277) 233049 E-mail: eurolab@btconnect.com *Asbestos surveying & consultancy, property management & registers*

Euro Lab Supplies Ltd, 43-44 Fourways, Carlyon Road Industrial Estate, Atherstone, Warwickshire, CV9 1LH Tel: (01827) 721781 Fax: (01827) 721781

continued

E-mail: kay.cauldwell@eurolabsupplies.co.uk *Laboratory supply services & scientific glassware*

Euro Laminations Ltd, Cromwell Road, Ellesmere Port, CH65 4DT Tel: 0151-356 1791 Fax: 0151-356 1806 E-mail: gls@cogent-power.com Purchasing Contact: D.C. Pugh Sales Contact: W.L. Johnson Principal Export Areas: Worldwide *Manufacturers of laminated metal lamination/ assembly, including electric motor. In addition, electrical industry stampings*

Euro Matic Ltd, Clauson House Perryvale Industrial Park, Horsenden Road South, Greenford, Middlesex, UB6 7QE Tel: (020) 8991 2211 Fax: (020) 8997 5074 E-mail: sales@euro-matic.com Principal Export Areas: Worldwide *Plastic ball manufrs*

Euro Medicon Ltd, 9 New Street, Sandwich, Kent, CT13 9AB Tel: (01304) 617769 Fax: (01304) 611547 E-mail: sales@euro-medicon.com *Hospital consumables & furniture, medical consumables & instruments, laboratory consumables*

Euro Moulds Ltd, Units 5 & 10 Borers Yard, Borers Arms Road, Copthorne, Crawley, West Sussex, RH10 3LH Tel: (01342) 712113 Fax: (01342) 717571 E-mail: euromoulds@btinternet.com *Injection mould toolmakers*

Euro Norfolk Foods Ltd, 34 Surrey Street, Norwich, NR1 3NY Tel: (01603) 760123 Fax: (01603) 760124 *Frozen food bulk national distribution & products manufrs*

Euro Office Supplies Ltd, 11 Bluebell Grove, Up Hatherley, Cheltenham, Gloucestershire, GL51 3BJ Tel: (01242) 227169 E-mail: customers@euro-supplies.com *Our Euro slot products produce the universal euro slot shape to enable the retail display of goods on hooks of various shapes and sizes in your shop. The shape is variously described as euroslot, euro-slot or euro slot.*

Euro Pack, Common Lane North, Beccles, Suffolk, NR34 9BP Tel: (01502) 716540 Fax: (01502) 716814 E-mail: europacksales@gei-int.com *Packaging equipment manufrs*

Euro Packaging plc, 118 Amington Road, Yardley, Birmingham, B25 8JZ Tel: 0121-706 6181 Fax: 0121-706 6514 E-mail: info@europackaging.co.uk *Polythene & paper bag specialists*

Euro Packaging plc, Unit 14 Elderpark Workspace, 100 Elderpark Street, Glasgow, G51 3TR Tel: 0141-445 3003 Fax: 0141-445 5111 E-mail: info@europackaging.co.uk Principal Export Areas: Worldwide *Packaging equipment manufs*

▶ Euro Polishing Technology, 83 Moorhey Street, Oldham, OL4 1JE Tel: 0161-628 4466 Fax: 0161-628 4477 E-mail: europolishing@hotmail.co.uk *Stainless steel polishing & finishing services*

▶ Euro Pools plc, 423 Hillington Road, Hillington Industrial Estate, Glasgow, G52 4BL Tel: 0141-810 1313 Fax: 0141-810 1414 *Building design & construction, swimming pools*

Euro Products Ltd, Yardley House, Yardley Street, Stourbridge, West Midlands, DY9 7AT Tel: (01384) 895000 Fax: (01384) 897000 E-mail: sales@europroducts.co.uk *Hardness testing accessories manufrs*

Euro RSCG Biss Lancaster, 6 Briset Street, London, EC1M 5NR Tel: (020) 7022 4000 Fax: (020) 7022 4100 *Public relations consultants*

Euro RSDG Riley, Hanover House, Queen Charlotte Street, Bristol, BS1 4LG Tel: 0117-925 7777 Fax: 0117-925 7001 E-mail: nick.brian@eurorscg-riley.co.uk *Advertising agency & personnel & sales recruitment services*

Euro Rubber Lines, Red Marsh Drive Industrial Estate, Red Marsh Industrial Estate, Thornton-Cleveleys, Lancashire, FY5 4HP Tel: (01253) 850929 Fax: (01253) 850064 E-mail: eurorubberlines@aol.com Principal Export Areas: Worldwide *Rubber & plastic machinery merchants*

Euro Safety & Abrasives, Unit 3, 13 Cobham Road, Ferndown Industrial Estate, Wimborne, Dorset, BH21 7TE Tel: (01202) 870661 Fax: (01202) 870095 *Abrasive & adhesive products distributors*

Euro Scaffolding, Unit 1 Heathfield Way, Kings Heath Industrial Estate, Northampton, NN5 7QP Tel: (01604) 583334 Fax: (01604) 583336 *Scaffolding Contractors or Erectors available from Euro Scaffolding Ltd based in Northampton. Click the links below to visit our website or contact us via our profile page.*

Euro Screws, 16 Whitchurch Lane, Edgware, Middlesex, HA8 6JZ Tel: (020) 8381 2675 Fax: (020) 8381 2674 *Fasteners distributors*

▶ Euro Seals & Gaskets Limited, PO BOX 1139, Luton, LU2 0WU Tel: (01582) 895459 Fax: (01582) 895469 E-mail: sales@eurosealsandgaskets.co.uk *We Supply Parking Posts and speed ramps, and gaskets, seals, Cork, Rubber and PTFE Plus many more.*

Euro Services Ltd, Unit 2C Rugby Road, Twickenham Trading Estate, Twickenham, TW1 1DG Tel: (020) 8744 1122 Fax: (020) 8744 0099 E-mail: eslceramics@aol.com *Ceramic tile distributors*

Euro Sheet Metal Ltd, 6 Aintree Road, Perivale, Greenford, Middlesex, UB6 7LA Tel: (020) 8810 5026 Fax: (020) 8991 5008 E-mail: info@eurosheetmetal.co.uk *Sheet metal engineers & fabricators*

Euro Shopfitting Ltd, Unit 3 Bilton Way, Lutterworth, Leicestershire, LE17 4JA Tel: (01455) 559999 Fax: (01455) 559898 E-mail: info@euroshopfitting.co.uk *Shop fittings services*

Euro Shutter Engineers Ltd, Woodside, Thornwood, Epping, Essex, CM16 6LJ Tel: (01992) 570044 Fax: (01992) 561176 E-mail: office@euroshutters.co.uk *Industrial door & rolling grilles manufrs*

Euro Signs, 70 Lower Dock Street, Newport, Gwent, NP20 1EH Tel: (01633) 216486 Fax: (01633) 216486 *Signs & nameplates*

Euro Signs UK Ltd, 92 Cato Street, Hartlands, Birmingham, B7 4TS Tel: 0121-359 5566 Fax: 0121-359 5354 E-mail: sales@europlate.com *Safety signs & number plates manufrs*

Euro Spec, Unit 7 Drakes Lane, Boreham, Chelmsford, CM3 3BE Tel: (01245) 362551 Fax: (01245) 360522 E-mail: sales@euro-spec.co.uk *Steel fabricators*

Euro Springs, Unit 58 Dungannon Enterprise Centre, 2 Coalisland Road, Dungannon, County Tyrone, BT71 6JT Tel: (028) 8772 6169 Fax: (028) 8772 6524 E-mail: matt@eurosprings.co.uk *Spring manufrs*

▶ Euro Steel Products Ltd, Floor 5,24, Chiswell Street, London, EC1Y 4TY Tel: (020) 7248 5473 Fax: (020) 7248 3069 E-mail: eurosteel@uk.stemcor.com *International steel traders*

Euro Steer Ltd, Shay La Industrial Estate, Shay Lane, Longridge, Preston, PR3 3BT Tel: (01772) 786022 Fax: (01772) 786237 *Steering gear systems*

Euro Supply & Trading Co., Canal Side, 3 Tattenhall Road, Tattenhall, Chester, CH3 9BD Tel: (01829) 771500 Fax: (01829) 771505 *Packaging materials suppliers*

Euro Tanks, 4 Heritage Way, Corby, Northamptonshire, NN17 5XW Tel: (01536) 201006 Fax: (01536) 400140 E-mail: sales@eurotanks.co.uk *Transformer tanks manufrs*

Euro Test, Lennox Mall, Shirley Avenue, Vale Road, Windsor, Berkshire, SL4 5LH Tel: (01753) 867267 Fax: (01753) 867847 E-mail: southern.analytical@bodycote-mt.com *Analytical & consultant chemists*

Euro Trading Ltd, Shepperton Marina, Felix Lane, Shepperton, Middlesex, TW17 8NS Tel: (01932) 246153 Fax: (01932) 226711 E-mail: eurotrading.co@virgin.net *Pipeline fittings stockholders services*

▶ Euro Trucks Direct Ltd, Terminus Road, Chichester, West Sussex, PO19 8TX Tel: (01243) 788415 Fax: (01243) 839436 E-mail: enquiries@eurotrucksdirect.co.uk *Fork lift truck distributors*

Euro Tube West Midlands Ltd, Navigation Road, Worcester, WR5 3DE Tel: (01905) 767833 Fax: (01905) 764305 E-mail: sales@eurotube.biz *Steel tube manipulators*

Euro Water Systems, 26 Hartwell Gardens, Harpenden, Hertfordshire, AL5 2RW Tel: (01582) 766062 Fax: (01582) 621756 E-mail: sales@clemsoft.co.uk *Water treatment & softening*

Eurobait, Pte Road No 4, Colwick Industrial Estate, Nottingham, NG4 2JT Tel: 0115-987 4888 Fax: (0115) 9875553 *Largest breeder of maggots for the fishing industry. Next Day delivery available! **www.eurobait.co.uk*

Eurobake Ltd, Bee Hive Industrial Estate, Crescent Road, Lostock, Bolton, BL6 4BU Tel: (01204) 669980 Fax: (01204) 696665 E-mail: sales@eurobake.co.uk *Bakery machinery suppliers*

Eurobelts.com, 8 Stuart Close, Darwen, Lancashire, BB3 1DP Tel: (01254) 704395 Fax: (01254) 704395 E-mail: roy@eurobelts.com *Online Sales of:*Leather Belts,Buckles,Small Leather Goods,Pewter Buckles*

Euroblinds Blinds & Awnings, 36-38 Clune Brae, Port Glasgow, Renfrewshire, PA14 5PA Tel: (01475) 744905 Fax: (01475) 744905 E-mail: sales@euroblinds.co.uk *Window blinds manufrs*

Eurobung Ltd, Roe Head Mill, Far Common Road, Mirfield, West Yorkshire, WF14 0DG Tel: (01924) 496671 Fax: (01924) 480257 E-mail: sales@eurobung.co.uk *Plastic injection mouldings manufrs*

Eurobuns Holdings Ltd, 80 South Audley Street, London, W1K 1JH Tel: (020) 7491 9002 Fax: (020) 7491 9005 *Manufacturers of bakery products*

Eurocare Impex Services Ltd, Units 9-10 Holme Industrial Estate, Ballplay Road, Moffat, Dumfriesshire, DG10 9JU Tel: (01683) 221336 Fax: (01683) 221335 *Retail toiletries, packaging services*

Eurocastors Ltd, Dalton Road, Southfield Industrial Estate, Glenrothes, Fife, KY6 2SS Tel: (01592) 774770 Fax: (01592) 772736 E-mail: sales@eurocastors.co.uk *Castor & wheel manufrs*

Eurocater, Suite 201 - 205 Grosvenor Gardens House, 35 - 37 Grosvenor Gardens, Victoria, London, UK, SW1W 0BS Tel: 0207 630 4880 Fax: 0207 630 4890 E-mail: info@eurocater.co.uk *Eurocater is an international distributor of premium quality catering equipment, specifically designed for user-demanding environments such as Restaurants, Hotels, Cafes and Food Processing. Our equipment is compatible with both British Industry Standard regulations and Health & Safety guidelines.**All of our products are sourced exclusively from specialist suppliers, who have a reputation for quality, precision and durability. **Eurocater understands the complexities of today's competitive market, which is why we are confident our products will offer you the quality required to keep one step ahead.**All of our products are delivered and installed free of charge.**We offer a financially sound, professional and reliable service complete with a one year guarantee and an on-site technician, if ever a problem should occur.**For an informal chat, a one to one consultation or a complete refit, please contact us.**

Eurocell Building Plastics Ltd, 1 Valley Buildings, Brunel Road Industrial Eatate, Newton Abbot, Devon, TQ12 4PB Tel: (01626) 335585 Fax: (01626) 336161 E-mail: sales@eurocellbuildingplastics.co.uk *Plastic products distributors*

Eurocell Building Plastics Ltd, 1 Sterling Park, York, YO30 4WU Tel: (01904) 479201 Fax: (01904) 475440 *Plastic raw & basic material manufrs*

▶ Eurochem Automotive Chemicals, Unit1 Bridgeholme Mill, Charley Lane, Chinley, High Peak, Derbyshire, SK23 6DX Tel: (01938) 555754 Fax: (01938) 555754 E-mail: support@eurochem.co.uk *Manufacture of auto, aviation & marine cleaning chemicals*

Euroclip 2000 Ltd, 2 Barrington Court, Ward Road, Brackley, Northamptonshire, NN13 7LE Tel: (01280) 840900 Fax: (01280) 840904 E-mail: sales@euroclip.fsnet.co.uk *Sheep handling & shearing machine manufrs*

Eurocoils Ltd, Unit D3, Bonham Drive, Eurolink Commercial Park, Sittingbourne, Kent, ME10 3RX Tel: (01795) 475275 Fax: (01795) 422210 E-mail: ecoils@globalnet.co.uk Principal Export Areas: Africa *Heat exchanger/transfer equipment manufrs*

Eurocold, Unit 7, Blackmoor Farm, New Road, Maulden, Bedford, MK45 2BG Tel: (01525) 406666 Fax: (01525) 403838 E-mail: sales@eurocold.co.uk *Manufacturer of insulated doors for use in coldstores, chillers, freezers food processing areas. Supply, installation and repair service available.*

▶ Eurocom Components Ltd, 22 Amhurst Parade, Amhurst Park, London, N16 5AA Tel: (020) 8802 7300 Fax: (020) 8802 7349

Eurocontinental Logistics Ltd, Unit 7, Everitt Close, Denington Industrial Estate, Wellingborough, Northamptonshire, NN8 2QE Tel: (01933) 223851 Fax: (01933) 272630 E-mail: info@eurocontinental-logistics.co.uk *Freight forwarding agents*

Eurocopy GB P.L.C., 30 Blacks Road, London, W6 9DT Tel: (020) 8741 7281 Fax: (020) 8741 5068 *Photocopiers*

▶ Eurocraft Distributors Ltd, Coxwell Avenue, Wolverhampton Science Park, Wolverhampton, WV10 9RT Tel: (01902) 718020 Fax: (01902) 718021

Eurocraft Trustees Ltd, Cinderbank, Netherton, Dudley, West Midlands, DY2 9AE Tel: (01384) 230101 Fax: (01384) 256883 E-mail: sales@eurocraft.co.uk *Manufacturers of metal enclosures for the telecommunications industry*

▶ Eurocup, 7 Paddock Road, Skelmersdale, Lancashire, WN8 9PL Tel: (01695) 550820 Fax: (01695) 558550 E-mail: sales@eurocup.co.uk

▶ Eurocush Cane Goods, 1 Dereham Road, Norwich, NR2 4HX Tel: (01603) 663686 Fax: (01603) 664604 *Furniture wholesaler*

Eurodata Computer Services Ltd, 8 Westmead Corner, Carshalton, Surrey, SM5 2NZ Tel: (020) 8643 0933 Fax: (020) 8643 1886 E-mail: eurodatacs@aol.com *Market research & data preparation*

Euro-Diesel (U K) Ltd, Stato House, Somerford Road, Cirencester, Gloucestershire, GL7 1TW Tel: (01285) 640879 Fax: (01285) 652509 E-mail: info@euro-diesel.co.uk *UPS diesel rotary maintenance service*

Eurodisc UK Ltd, Station Approach, Bridgnorth, Shropshire, WV16 5DP Tel: (01746) 764400 Fax: (01746) 764400 *Tachograph charts & accessories*

▶ Eurodyne, Unit 7 Alnat Industrial Park, Lindale, Grange-over-Sands, Cumbria, LA11 6PQ Tel: (01539) 536830 Fax: (01539) 536751 E-mail: sales@eurodyne.co.uk *Manufacturer of bearings & balances*

Euroeda Ltd, Britannia House, 29 Station Road, Kettering, Northamptonshire, NN15 7HJ Tel: (01536) 517657 Fax: (01933) 676372 E-mail: info@euro-eda.com *Electronic design automation software suppliers*

Eurofab Sheffield Ltd, Hudson Street, Sheffield, S6 3AW Tel: 0114-272 9339 Fax: 0114-278 6686 *Steel fabricators*

Eurofast Petrochemical Supplies Ltd, Unit 30 Planetary Industrial Estate, Planetary Road, Willenhall, West Midlands, WV13 3TA Tel: (01902) 307788 Fax: (01902) 307744 E-mail: eps-sales@eurofast.co.uk *Worldwide manufacturer, stockholder and supplier of bolting and fasteners to the oil, gas and petrochemical industries*

Eurofayre Ltd, Hudds Mill Ho, Edington, Westbury, Wilts, BA13 4NH Tel: 01380 831323 *Cheese producer*

Eurofill Ltd, Unit 1 Old Allen Barn, Old Allen Road, Bradford, West Yorkshire, BD13 3RY Tel: (01535) 270590 Fax: (01535) 270590 E-mail: eurofill@btopenworld.com *Bottle capping & filling machine manufrs*

Eurofire Firefighting Equipment, Mallusk Enterprise Park, Mallusk Drive, Newtownabbey, County Antrim, BT36 4GN Tel: (028) 9034 2991 Fax: (028) 9084 3414 E-mail: info@eurofire-ni.com *Fire protection & allied services*

Eurofire UK, 12 Fontwell Drive, Alton, Hampshire, GU34 2TN Tel: (01420) 542424 Fax: (01420) 82287 *Fire alarm & extinguisher suppliers & installers*

Euroforest Ltd, Mead House, Bentley, Farnham, Surrey, GU10 5HY Tel: (01420) 23030 Fax: (01420) 23774 *Tree harvesting & marketing services*

▶ Eurofreight Shipping Agencies Ltd, Pioneer House, Birmingham Street, Halesowen, West Midlands, B63 3HN Tel: 0121-585 0303 Fax: 0121-585 0636 *Eurofreight Shipping Agencies are an expanding and friendly company established in 1990. We offer very competitive export and import groupage/full load services to and from Europe, including express and also an expert deep-sea department. We Pride ourselves on high standards of customer service and have maintained long standing relationships with large companies such as Vauxhall Motors, Corus Steels, Little Tykes and Michelin Group.*

Eurofriction Ltd, Cessnock Road, Hurlford, Kilmarnock, Ayrshire, KA1 5DD Tel: (01563) 546000 Fax: (01563) 546039 *Brake pads manufrs*

Eurofusion Ltd, Ituri, Darcy Rise, Little Baddow, Chelmsford, CM3 4SN Tel: (01245) 221235 Fax: (0870) 4296791 E-mail: glass@eurofusion.co.uk Purchasing Contact: P. Scully Sales Contact: P. Scully *Engineering Consultants to the Glass*

continued

continuation
*Industry.*Process Technology for Float Glass, Hollow Glass & Technical Glasses.*Glass Furnace Design.*Glass Melting Technology.*

Eurogate International Forwarding Co. Ltd, Garret Green Freight Depot, Bannerley Road, Birmingham, B33 0SL Tel: 0121-785 0270 Fax: 0121-785 0271 E-mail: birmingham@eurogate.co.uk *Central eastern european freight forwarders*

Eurogel Ltd, PO Box 45, Swadlincote, Derbyshire, DE11 0ZX Tel: (01283) 210055 Fax: (01283) 215130 E-mail: eurogel@ic24.net *Refrigeration & air conditioning engineers*

Eurogloss Ltd, Units 3 & 5 Greyhound Commercial Centre, Greyhound Way, Dartford, DA1 4HF Tel: (01322) 557777 Fax: (01322) 555277 E-mail: production@eurogloss.co.uk *Ultra violet varnishing & laminating*

Eurograde Plant Ltd, 3 Viscount Industrial Estate, Horton Road, Colnbrook, Slough, SL3 0DF Tel: (020) 8606 0420 Fax: (01753) 681452 E-mail: david@eurograde.com *Gas & oil burner manufrs*

Eurograv Ltd, Sprint Industrial Estate, Chertsey Road, Byfleet, West Byfleet, Surrey, KT14 7BD Tel: (01932) 336262 Fax: (01932) 336271 E-mail: sales@eurograv.co.uk *Printing machine distributors*

Eurogreen Machinery, The Tythe Barn, North Barn Farm, Titnore Lane, Worthing, West Sussex, BN12 6NZ Tel: (01903) 700678 Fax: (01903) 247585 E-mail: admin@eurogreenuk.com *Recycling equipment sales*

Eurogrid (Incorp) B I E Ltd, Halesfield 18, Telford, Shropshire, TF7 4JS Tel: (01952) 581988 Fax: (01952) 586285 E-mail: sales@eurogrid.co.uk *Open steel flooring*

Euroguns Gunsmiths, School House, Main Street, Mattersey, Doncaster, South Yorkshire, DN10 5DZ Tel: (01777) 817809 Fax: (01777) 817809 E-mail: sales@euroguns.co.uk *We are stockists of quality shotguns, rifles & air rifles - Browning, Beretta, Tikka, Sako, Air Arms, Webley, Weihrauch. County clothing & footwear by Aigle, Barbour, Dubarry, Hunter, Musto, Schö ffel - skeet vests, moleskins, overtrousers, camo wear, tweeds. Shooting accessories for game, clay or rough shooting - cartridge bags & belts, decoys, hearing & eye protection, gundog & ferreting equipment, gun care, gunslips, gun cabinets, pellets, silencers, targets, books, videos, DVDs & shooting gifts.*

Euroheat Distributors (HBS) Ltd, Unit 2, Court Farm Business Park, Bishops Frome, Worcester, WR6 5AY Tel: (01885) 491100 Fax: (01885) 491101 E-mail: info@euroheat.co.uk *Import & distribution heating appliances*

Eurohill Labels Ltd, 195 Vale Road, Tonbridge, Kent, TN9 1SU Tel: (01732) 770700 Fax: (01732) 770779 E-mail: sales@eurohill.com *Labelling machine systems & label manufrs*

Eurohill Traders Ltd, 195 Vale Road, Tonbridge, Kent, TN9 1SU Tel: (01732) 770777 Fax: (01732) 770757 E-mail: sales@apac.co.uk *Labels & packaging*

Eurojet Aviation Ltd, Belfast Int Airport, Belfast, BT29 4AB Tel: (028) 9442 2888 Fax: (028) 9442 2640 E-mail: engineering@eurojet.co.uk *Aircraft charter services*

▶ Eurojet Scotland Ltd, 22 Taxi Way, Hillend, Dunfermline, Fife, KY11 9JT Tel: (01383) 825324

Eurolace Ltd, 9 New Road, Stapleford, Nottingham, NG9 8GS Tel: (01332) 780042 Fax: 0115-949 1691 *Lace manufrs*

EuroLAN Research, Peter Thompsom House, Market Close, Poole, Dorset, BH15 1NE Tel: (01202) 670170 Fax: (01202) 670456 E-mail: info@erolanresearch.com *Industry analysis*

Eurolec Components Midlands, Northmoor Industrial Park, Moor Street, Brierley Hill, West Midlands, DY5 3SU Tel: (01384) 70972 Fax: (01384) 74552 E-mail: eurolec@dial.pipex.com *Auto electrical components re-manufrs*

▶ Eurolifting Lifting Equipment, 15 Mountfield Road, New Romney, Kent, TN28 8LH Tel: (01797) 369494 Fax: (01797) 369151 *Lifting & engineering services*

▶ Euroline Time Critical Freight Ltd, 30 Inkerman Street, Birmingham, B7 4SB Tel: 0121-333 3900 Fax: 0121-333 3868

Eurolink Corporation Ltd, The Annexe Feildings, 11 Rosken Grove, Farnham Royal, Slough, SL2 3DZ Tel: (01753) 642500 Fax: (01753) 642999 E-mail: info@eurolinkcorp.com *Import & export agents*

▶ Eurolink Hardware, 5 Halesowen Industrial Park, Chancel Way, Halesowen, West Midlands, B62 8SE Tel: 0121-501 2800 Fax: 0121-434 6989 E-mail: info@eurolinkhardware.co.uk *Door furniture, hinges, hardware, ironmongery, distribute & manufrs*

Eurolink Telecom Ltd, Exeter Road, Bournemouth, BH2 5AR Tel: (01202) 558228 Fax: (01202) 558227 E-mail: enq@eurolinltelecom.com *Supply & installation of business telephone systems*

Eurolok Ltd, Tame Park, Vanguard, Wilnecote, Tamworth, Staffordshire, B77 5DY Tel: (01827) 287439 Fax: (01827) 287485 E-mail: sales@eurolok.com *Cable tie manufacturers/stockholders & general plastic moulders*

Eurolux Plastics Ltd, Unit 7 Station Road, Tolleshunt D'Arcy, Maldon, Essex, CM9 8TQ Tel: (01621) 868787 Fax: (01621) 868857 E-mail: euroluxplastic@ukonline.co.uk *Plastic fabricator & manufacturer of plastic formed products. Also point of sale services, marketing display designers & acrylic fabricators*

Euromachine Ltd, Laund House, Beamsley, Skipton, North Yorkshire, BD23 6AW Tel: (01756) 710588 Fax: (01756) 710234 E-mail: sales@euro-machine.com *Machine tool import merchants*

▶ Euromech, Unit 4, Stewart House, Kingsway East, Dundee, DD4 7RE Tel: (01382) 454447 Fax: (01382) 454088 *Fabrication engineers*

Euromix UK Ltd, 56 Alexandra Road, Enfield, Middlesex, EN3 7EH Tel: (020) 8805 8224 Fax: (020) 8805 8228 E-mail: mail@euromixltd.co.uk *Bakery machinery manufrs*

Euromoney Institional Invester P.L.C., Nestor House, Playhouse Yard, London, EC4V 5EX Tel: (020) 7779 8658 Fax: (020) 7779 8867 *Publishers*

Euromonitor plc, 60-61 Britton Street, London, EC1M 5UX Tel: (020) 7251 0985 Fax: (020) 7608 3149 E-mail: info@euromonitor.com *Market research services*

Euromotor Ltd, 5 Bolney Grange Business Park, Stairbridge Lane, Bolney, Haywards Heath, West Sussex, RH17 5PB Tel: (07000) 226276 Fax: (07002) 668677 E-mail: sales@euromotor.net *Electric motor distributors*

▶ Euronet-networks, 270 Castle Lane West, Bournemouth, BH8 9TU Tel: (01202) 248029 E-mail: euronet.steve@ntlworld.com *Computer network services*

Euronetwork Ltd, 1 Horwood Court, Bletchley, Milton Keynes, MK1 1RD Tel: (01908) 371909 Fax: (01908) 378239 E-mail: info@euronetwork.co.uk *Manufacturer and supplier of audio visual cables, hdmi cables, scart cables, computer cables & AV cables*

Euro-News Computer Consultants, 13 Trinity Road, Ilford, Essex, IG6 2BQ Tel: (020) 8550 6458 E-mail: euronews@ingamells.biz *Computer consultants*

Europa Ltd, Belvue Road, Northolt, Middlesex, UB5 5HX Tel: (020) 8841 0272 *Jewellery manufrs*

Europa Bearings (1976) Ltd, Empire Centre, Imperial Way, Watford, WD24 4YH Tel: (01923) 255166 Fax: (01923) 234069 E-mail: sales@europabearings.freeserve.co.uk *Power transmission equipment & bearing distributors*

▶ Europa Components, Europa House, Airport Way, Luton, LU2 9NH Tel: (01582) 692440 Fax: (01582) 692450 E-mail: sales@europacomponents.com *Suppliers of electrical control gear components, fuses*

Europa Computers Ltd, 11-13 Edward Street, Salford, M7 1SN Tel: 0161-279 0000 Fax: 0161-832 9104 E-mail: sales@europacomputers.com *Computer components*

Europa Conservatories Ltd, Unit 35 Tolpits Lane Industrial Centre, Watford, WD1 8SP Tel: (01923) 212700 Fax: (01923) 212727 E-mail: sales@europaconservatories.co.uk *Bespoke conservatories, conservatory roofs & roof lights manufrs*

Europa Electrical Ltd, Unit 22c Parker Industrial Estate, Mansfield Road, Derby, DE21 4SZ Tel: (01332) 295439 Fax: (01332) 383593 E-mail: sales@europalec.co.uk *Control panels & contracting services*

Europa Engineering, Bay 3 Ruscon Works, Rotherham Road, Parkgate, Rotherham, South Yorkshire, S62 6EZJ Tel: (0845) 129 5060 Fax: (0845) 129 5064

Europa Express Freight, Second Avenue, Trafford Park, Manchester, M17 1EE Tel: 0161-872 8094 Fax: 0161-873 8258 E-mail: manchester@europa-worldwide.co.uk *Freight services*

Europa Fastenings, Unit 5D, Leaton Industrial Estate, Bomere Heath, Shrewsbury, SY4 3AP Tel: (01939) 291199 Fax: (01939) 291299 E-mail: stephen@europafastenings.co.uk *Screw & washer assembly manufrs*

Europa Import Export, 3-8 Porchester Gate, Bayswater Road, London, W2 3HP Tel: (020) 7221 3449 Fax: (020) 7221 7461 E-mail: eie@compuserve.com *Steel import & export*

▶ Europa Leisure Equipment, 1 Croft Way, Eastways, Witham, Essex, CM8 2FB Tel: (01376) 517717 Fax: (01376) 518018 E-mail: sales@europa-leisure.co.uk *Heat presses sublimation & other heat transfer application products*

Europa Publications Ltd, 11 New Felter La, London, EC4P 4EE Tel: (020) 7589 9855 Fax: (020) 7842 2249 E-mail: sales@europapublications.co.uk *Reference book publishers*

Europa Rubber Stamps, 8 Mill Lane, Horsford, Norwich, NR10 3ET Tel: (01603) 898225 Fax: (01603) 893276 *Rubber stamp manufrs*

▶ Europa Security, 68 Privett Road, Fareham, Hampshire, PO15 6SP Tel: (0709) 2111588 Fax: (0709) 2376783 E-mail: admin@europasecurity.co.uk *CCTV & intruder alarm supplier*

Europa Shop & Office Fitting, 3 Maxted Road, Hemel Hempstead Industrial Estate, Hemel Hempstead, Hertfordshire, HP2 7DX Tel: (01442) 213412 Fax: (01442) 267672 E-mail: postmaster@europa-shopfitting.co.uk *Specialist joinery interior fitout contractors.*

Europa Sofabeds Ltd, Grindon Way, Heighington Lane Business Park, Newton Aycliffe, County Durham, DL5 6SH Tel: (01325) 318871 Fax: (01325) 300492 *Sofa bed manufrs*

Europa Trimmings Ltd, 13-15 Lever Street, London, EC1V 3QU Tel: (020) 7250 1663 Fax: (020) 7253 4309 *Trimmings merchants*

▶ Europa Worldwide, Unit 2 Building 110, Castle Donington, Derby, DE74 2SA Tel: (01332) 815900 Fax: (01332) 815909 E-mail: sales@europa-worldwide.co.uk *Groupage & express freight operator*

Europa Worldwide Logistics, Europa House, 68 Hailey Rd, Erith, Kent, DA18 4AU Tel: (020) 8311 5000 Fax: (020) 8310 4805 E-mail: sales@europa-worldwide.co.uk *Next day express & standard worldwide distribution servicesby road, sea or air. Courier & parcel services, UK distribution, warehousing, logistics, Eastern European division & pallet distribution & full load services*

▶ Europa Worldwide Services, Europa House, 46 Tilton Road, Birmingham, B9 4PP Tel: 0121-766 8000 Fax: 0121-771 4669 E-mail: sales@europa-worldwide.co.uk *Freight services*

Europa Worldwide Services, Europa House Unit 3 Severnside Trading Estate, St. Andrews Road, Avonmouth, Bristol, BS11 9AG Tel: 0117-982 1000 Fax: 0117-923 5741 E-mail: bristol@europa-worldwide.co.uk *European & worldwide freight forwarders*

Europace Ltd, 3 London Road, Stanmore, Middlesex, HA7 4PA Tel: (020) 8958 9333 Fax: (020) 8958 9333 E-mail: warshawron@aol.com *Import & export wood products services*

▶ Europalite Ltd, Eastfield Side, Sutton-In-Ashfield, Nottinghamshire, NG17 4JW Tel: (01623) 528760 Fax: (01623) 510955 E-mail: sales@europalite.co.uk *Plastic products manufrs*

▶ Europalm Services Ltd, Unit B Bouverie Mews, London, N16 0AE Tel: (020) 8211 7555 Fax: (020) 8211 7666 E-mail: sales@europalm.co.uk

Europanel UK Ltd, 1 Gerrards Place, East Gillibrands, Skelmersdale, Lancashire, WN8 9SU Tel: (01695) 731033 Fax: (01695) 727489 E-mail: europaneluk@btconnect.co.uk *Melamine faced chipboard manufrs*

European After Market Management Ltd, 22 The Parchments, Newton-le-Willows, Merseyside, WA12 0DY Tel: (01925) 223515 Fax: (01925) 223515 E-mail: phil@pjwipers.co.uk *Consultant for car components manufrs*

European Army Surplus, 14 Nobel Square, Burnt Mills Industrial Estate, Burnt Mills Industrial Estate, Basildon, Essex, SS13 1LS Tel: (01268) 591552 Fax: (01268) 591553 E-mail: email@europeanarmysurplus.co.uk *Wholesaler of authentic military surplus & new military style clothing*

European Asbestos Removals Ltd, 3 Norden Court, Alan Ramsbottom Way, Great Harwood, Blackburn, BB6 7UR Tel: (01254) 876686 Fax: (01254) 877000 E-mail: sales@asbestos-removers.co.uk *Asbestos removal*

European Automation Intelligence Ltd, 124 Warwick Street, Leamington Spa, Warwickshire, CV32 4QY Tel: (01926) 889393 Fax: (01926) 888378 *Analysis software developers*

European Autoparts Ltd, 5 Kimber Road, London, SW18 4NR Tel: (020) 8640 9335 Fax: (020) 8877 0359 *Motor car parts importers*

European Aviation Air Charter Ltd, European House, Bournemouth Int Airport, Hurn, Christchurch, Dorset, BH23 6EA Tel: (01202) 581111 Fax: (01202) 578333 E-mail: sales@eaac.co.uk *Aviation engineers*

European Blinds, 10 Oakdale Avenue, Peterborough, PE2 8TA Tel: (01733) 347978 *Domestic vertical blinds suppliers & fitters*

European Chemical News, Quadrant House, The Quadrant, Sutton, Surrey, SM2 5AS Tel: (020) 8652 3500 Fax: (020) 8652 8297 *European Chemical News is the leading international business title for the global chemical industry.*

European Circuit Solutions Ltd, Impress House, Mansell Road, London, W3 7QH Tel: (020) 8743 8880 Fax: (020) 8740 4200 E-mail: sales@ecsamplifiers.co.uk *Electronics engineering contractors*

European CNC Turned Parts Ltd, Unit 101 Telsen Industrial Centre, Thomas Street, Birmingham, B6 4TN Tel: 0121-359 2812 Fax: 0121-359 3520 E-mail: mick@europeancnc.com *CNC turned parts manufrs*

European Coatings Ltd, Sandwich Industrial Estate, Ramsgate Road, Sandwich, Kent, CT13 9LY Tel: (01304) 621121 Fax: (01304) 621535 *Steel fabrication & shot blasting contractors*

European Corrosion Ltd, Meadow Mill Industrial Estate, Dixon Street, Kidderminster, Worcestershire, DY10 1HH Tel: (01562) 820288 Fax: (01562) 515594 *Corrosion control monitoring systems manufrs*

European Drives & Motor Repairs Ltd, 9 Mansion Close, Moulton Park Industrial Estate, Northampton, NN3 6RU Tel: (01604) 499777 Fax: (01604) 492777 E-mail: sales@edmr.co.uk *Established in 1988 EDMR is the UKs leading servo motor & drive repairer. Providing repairs, spares and new equipment 24 hours-a-day, 7 days-a-week. Our mission is quite simply to provide the most cost effective, responsive and quality repair service in the UK. We are able to repair and service electric motors and drives products from ABB, Baldor, Baumuller, Bosch, Contraves, Control Techniques, Electrocraft, Fanuc, Indramat, Isoflux, Kollmorgen, Lenze, Oemer, Pacific Scientific, Powertec, SEM, Servomac, Siemens, Vascat and many more.*

▶ European Electrical Contractors UK Ltd, Unit 2, Sinfin Central Business Park, Derby, DE24 9HL Tel: (01332) 272225

European Electronique Ltd, Forward House, Oakfield Industrial Estate, Eynsham, Witney, Oxfordshire, OX29 4TT Tel: (01865) 883300 Fax: (01865) 883371 E-mail: sales@euroele.com *Computers - networking, modems specialists*

European Emc Products Ltd, Unit 8, Saffron Business Centre, Elizabeth Close, Saffron Walden, Essex, CB10 2BL Tel: (01799) 523073 Fax: (01799) 521191 E-mail: info@euro-emc.co.uk Purchasing Contact: I. King Sales Contact: I. King *The design, manufacture, installation and testing of RF (Radio Frequency) shielded enclosures and components. Enclosures from full size test facilities, MRI (Magnetic Resonance Imaging) suites, military EMPP (Electro-Magnetic Pulse Protection) bunkers to cabinets and desk top test boxes. The supply of RF shielded components from doors and vents to electrical filters for installation into new or refurnished RF shielded enclosures. The design, supply and testing of magnetic field shielding. Shielding of power frequency fields from sub-stations and power distribution systems. EMF (Electro-Magnetic fields) surveys from DC to Gigahertz. Shielding of DC magnetic fields from MRI magnets. The supply of a wide range of EMC (Electro-Magnetic Compatibility) gaskets and materials from conductive elastomers, gasket over foam, wire knit-mesh gasket to copper beryllium contacts. Official distributors for Chomerics product range.*

European Foods plc, Venton Orchard, Weare Giffard, Bideford, Devon, EX39 4QY Tel: (01237) 422000 Fax: (01237) 421011 E-mail: sales@europeanfoods.co.uk *Cheese manufrs*

European Friction Industries, 6-7 Bonville Road, Bristol, BS4 5NZ Tel: 0117-977 7859 Fax: 0117-971 0573 E-mail: sales@efi.compulink.co.uk *Brake & clutch lining manufrs*

European Handling Equipment Ltd, 43 Steward Street, Birmingham, B18 7AE Tel: 0121-585 7333 Fax: 0121-585 7444 E-mail: enquiries@european-handling.com *Material handling equipment*

European Infopoint Ltd, Premier House, 11 Marlborough Place, Brighton, BN1 1UB Tel: (01273) 608311 Fax: (01273) 609040 E-mail: kelly@premier-house.com *Rent offices, secretarial support & meeting rooms*

European Instruments, Shotover Kilns, Headington, Oxford, OX3 8ST Tel: (01865) 750375 Fax: (01865) 769985 E-mail: balances@euroinst.co.uk *New Products :*Balances, Scales, Calibration weights, test weights, calibration software, ductless fume enclosures.**Service :*Balance and scale service & Calibration*Pipette Service & Calibration*Weight /Mass Calibration*We are also UKAS accredited for the above.*Maintenance and filter replacement of Ductless Fume enclosures**

▶ European International, Unit 5 6 Skitts Manor Farm, Moor Lane, Marsh Green, Edenbridge, Kent, TN8 5RA Tel: (01732) 860330 Fax: (01732) 860331 E-mail: info@european-intl.com *Global exhibition freight project management, providing effective freight solutions for both exhibition organisers and exhibitors throughout the world*

European Lamp Group Lighting Specialists, Allenby House, Knowles Lane, Bradford, West Yorkshire, BD4 9AB Tel: (01274) 473400 Fax: (0870) 4450001 E-mail: sales@europeanlamp.co.uk *Lamp & lighting distributors*

▶ European Marine & Machinery Agencies, Nutsey House, Nutsey Lane, Totton, Southampton, SO40 3NB Tel: (023) 8058 0020 Fax: (023) 8058 0021 E-mail: sales@europeanmarine.co.uk *Marine equipment suppliers*

European Metal Recycling Ltd, Stoney Stanton Road, Coventry, CV1 4FF Tel: (024) 7668 9051 Fax: (024) 7663 8827 *Metal merchants*

European Metal Recycling Ltd, Harvey Reeves Road, Northampton, NN5 5JR Tel: (01604) 752257 Fax: (01604) 754885 *Scrap iron & metal merchants*

European Metal Recycling Ltd, Kingston Wharf, Brighton Road, Shoreham-by-Sea, West Sussex, BN43 6RN Tel: (01273) 462064 Fax: (01273) 440666 E-mail: info@emrltd.com *Scrap metal merchants & processors*

European Metal Recycling Ltd, Sirius House, Delta CR, Westbrook, Warrington, WA5 7NS Tel: (01925) 715400 Fax: (01925) 713480 *Ferrous & non ferrous metal recycling* Also at: Swindon

European Metals Recycling Ltd, Willows, Station Road, East Tilbury, Tilbury, Essex, RM18 8QR Tel: (01375) 856902 Fax: (01375) 843880 *Metal recycling*

European Oat Millers Ltd, Mile Road, Bedford, MK42 9TB Tel: (01234) 327922 Fax: (01234) 353892 E-mail: sales@oatmillers.com *Oat millers*

European Pipeline Ltd, Waterton House, Stoneywood, Bucksburn, Aberdeen, AB21 9HX Tel: (01224) 715554 Fax: (01224) 716079 E-mail: sales@europipe.co.uk *Pipe fittings & flange distributors*

▶ European Plastic Technology Solutions Ltd, Techno Parts Ltd, Heathfield Street, Elland, West Yorkshire, HX5 9AU Tel: (01354) 650789

European Printing Inks Ltd, Precision House, Ring Road, Seacroft, Leeds, LS14 1NH Tel: 0113-273 8333 Fax: 0113-265 0223 *Printing ink manufrs*

European Printing Inks Ltd, Unit 38 Phoenix International Industrial Estate, Charles Street, West Bromwich, West Midlands, B70 0AY Tel: 0121-520 2471 *Printing ink & suppliers*

European Process Plant Ltd, Epsom Business Park, Epsom, Surrey, KT17 1JF Tel: (01372) 745558 Fax: (01372) 745097 E-mail: sales@eppltd.co.uk *Bakers machinery agents*

European Research & Investigations Ltd, 52 Upper Brook Street, Mayfair, London, W1K 5BB Tel: (020) 7499 9822 Fax: (020) 7493 4220 E-mail: sipinternational@aol.com *Detective agency*

European Rivet Supplies, Uynit 4b Sovereign Park Industrial Estate, Market Harborough, Leicestershire, LE16 9EG Tel: (01858) 469191 Fax: (01858) 469190 E-mail: sales@eurorivet.co.uk *Industrial fastening systems*

▶ European Site Services Ltd, Unit 5, Harbour Industrial Estate, Ardrossan, Ayrshire, KA22 8EG Tel: (01294) 467360

European Spectrometry Systems, Genesis House, Denton Drive, Northwich, Cheshire, CW9 7LU Tel: (01606) 49400 Fax: (01606) 330937 E-mail: service@essco.u-net.com *Spectrometer services*

European Springs Ltd, 1 Indian Queens Industrial Estate, Lodge Way, Indian Queens, St. Columb, Cornwall, TR9 6TF Tel: (01726) 861444 Fax: (01726) 861555 E-mail: cornwallsales@europeansprings.com *SPRING MANUFACTURER. ISO 9001 ACCREDITED. Compression Springs, Extension Springs, Torsion Springs, Conical Compression Springs, Wave Springs, Die Springs, Disc Springs, Gas & Stock Springs, Clips, Circlips, Pressings. Laser Cutting & Prototypes. Assemblies. Toolroom Technology. For Industrial use, Automotive & Aerospace use. Such as Garage Door Springs, Shock Absorber Springs, Suspension Springs, Valve Springs, Damper Springs, Anti-Vibration Springs, Scallop Dredge Springs, Air Rifle Springs, Verge Roof Clips, Wireforms, Hooks, Clay Pigeon Trap Springs, Antenna Springs, Aerial Springs, Compressor*

continued

continuation
Springs, Mining Equipment Springs, Crusher Springs, Oil Filter Springs, Air Filter Springs, Heating /Boiler Springs, Hydraulic Pump Springs, Water Pump Springs, Piston Motor Springs, Braking System Springs, Trampoline Springs, Horsebox Springs, Trailer Springs, Ramp Tail Lift Springs, Railway Carriage /bogie Springs, Marine Springs, Diving Springs, Medical Device Springs.

European Springs & Pressings Ltd, Chaffinch Business Park, Croydon Road, Beckenham, Kent, BR3 4DW Tel: (020) 8663 1800 Fax: (020) 8663 1900 E-mail: sales@europeansprings.com Principal Export Areas: Worldwide *Spring & pressing equipment manufrs*

European Steel Sheets Ltd, Doris Road, Bordesley Green, Birmingham, B9 4SJ Tel: 0121-766 7677 Fax: 0121-766 7864 E-mail: dan.broadhurst@europeansteelsheets.com *Steel Stockholders*

▶ European Technology Services Emea Ltd, Anglo City House 13 Lansdowne, Road Bournemouth, Bournemouth, BH1 1RZ Tel: (01202) 200920 Fax: 01202 311549 E-mail: EMEA.Office@ets-tele.com *Founded in 1992, ETS is a European consulting organisation with Asia-Pacific and Americas regional offices established in Australia and Canada. ETS has been proactive principally within the converging IT, Communications (Telecom & Radio) and Broadcasting sectors supporting R&D, testing, standardisation, compliance, certification, type approval and deployment of products and services in more than 80 countries worldwide. With specific emphasis on emerging economies throughout Eastern and Central Europe, Commonwealth of Independent States, the Middle-East, Africa, Asia, Caribbean and South America. Areas of interest: Intelligent Homes & Buildings, Virtual Office Solutions, Next Generation Networks and Services ...*

European Trade & Exhibition Services Ltd, 9-11 High Street, Staines, Middlesex, TW18 4QY Tel: (01784) 880890 Fax: (01784) 880892 E-mail: enquiries@etes.co.uk *Organisers of engineering & manufacturers exhibitions*

European Truck Parts Ltd, Junction Two Industrial Estate, Demuth Way, Oldbury, West Midlands, B69 4LT Tel: 0121-544 1222 Fax: 0121-544 9500 E-mail: rob@etp-uk.com *Commercial vehicle underbody parts distributors* Also at: Leeds & Newcastle

▶ European Van Lines International Ltd, Unit 3 100 Church Street, Staines, Middlesex, TW18 4YA Tel: (01784) 466117 Fax: (01784) 464484 E-mail: info@evl.co.uk *EVL provides an international removal service for individuals, companies and agencies with commitment to quality and customer service.*

European WaterCare Systems, Regal House, South Road, Harlow, Essex, CM20 2BL Tel: (01279) 780250 Fax: (01279) 780268 E-mail: info@watercare.co.uk *European WaterCare has more than 20 years' experience of solving water related problems and is a leading supplier of water treatment systems including calcium treatment units (CTU), water filters, hot and cold water softeners, reverse osmosis and demineralisation systems. European WaterCare is the UK's leading manufacturer of water treatment products designed to meet the needs of caterers - available nationwide through most good catering equipment distributors.*

Europian Metal Recycling Ltd, Longbeck Trading Estate, Marske-By-The-Sea, Redcar, Cleveland, TS11 6HB Tel: (01642) 482386 Fax: (01642) 243566 *Ferrous & non-ferrous scrap metal merchants*

Europix Designs Ltd, Westgate Mill, Wiseman Street, Burnley, Lancashire, BB11 1RU Tel: (01282) 459031 Fax: (01282) 459031 E-mail: europix@shoemolds.com *Mold manufrs*

▶ Europlas Coatings Ltd, Pool Road Industrial Estate, Pool Road, Nuneaton, Warwickshire, CV10 9AE Tel: (024) 7632 7257

Europlaz Ltd, Hucknall Industrial Park, Daniels Way, Hucknall, Nottingham, NG15 7LL Tel: 0115-968 1888 Fax: 0115-968 0286 E-mail: info@europlaz.co.uk *Medical supplies & plastic moulds*

Europlaz Technologies Ltd, The Maltings Industrial Estate, Southminster, Essex, CM0 7EH Tel: (01621) 773471 Fax: (01621) 773792 E-mail: enquiries@europlaz.co.uk *Plastics Injection Moulders with fully integrated technical support for 3D CAD Design, Prototyping, Tool Manufacture, Injection Moulding, Decoration and Assembly. We will also design and outsource associated mechanical components for the complete product manufacturing service.*

▶ Europlex Technologies (UK) Ltd, Trent House, University Way, Cranfield Technology Park, Bedford, MK43 0AN Tel: (01234) 757100

Europlus Mouldings, Unit 1a Bilston Key Industrial Estate, Oxford Street, Bilston, West Midlands, WV14 7DW Tel: (01902) 404852 Fax: (01902) 409354 E-mail: nick@euro-plas.com *Disposable tableware manufacturers & importers*

Europress Printers, 15-17 Green Lane, Hull, HU2 0HG Tel: (01482) 224993 Fax: (01482) 211486 E-mail: info@europresshull.co.uk *Lithographic printers services*

▶ Europrint Ltd, Pigeon House Lane, Swindon, SN3 4QH Tel: (01793) 838800 Fax: (01793) 824696

▶ Europrint Games Ltd, Unit 9-10 Laneside Metcalf Drive, Altham Industrial Estate, Accrington, Lancashire, BB5 5TU Tel: (01282) 774333 Fax: (01282) 688701

Europrocessing Ltd, Euro Vent Ltd, Govan Road Fenton Industrial, Fenton Industrial Estate, Stoke-on-Trent, ST4 2RS Tel: (01782) 744242 Fax: (01782) 744475 E-mail: sales@eurovent.com *Pharmaceutical granulation & drying manufrs*

EuroProperty, 1 Proctor Street, London, WC1V 6EU Tel: (020) 7911 1700 Fax: (020) 7911 1730 E-mail: customer.services@europroperty.com *Magazine & property brochure publishing*

Europtronic Group, 5 Kerry Avenue, Stanmore, Middlesex, HA7 4NJ Tel: (020) 8954 9798 Fax: (020) 8954 8918 E-mail: evelina.huang@europtronic.com *Capacitors & electronic component manufrs*

Europump Services Ltd, Unit B Stover Trading Estate, Millbrook Road, Yate, Bristol, BS37 5PB Tel: (01454) 323415 Fax: (01454) 273022 E-mail: sales-uk@europump.co.uk *Pump & pipework suppliers*

▶ Europump Services, 3b Fleming Road, Kirkton Campus, Livingston, West Lothian, EH54 7BN Tel: (01506) 425440 Fax: (01506) 425444 E-mail: dbarrowcliffe@europump.co.uk *Mechanical & electrical contracting company*

Euroquartz Ltd, Blacknell Lane, Crewkerne, Somerset, TA18 7HE Tel: (01460) 230000 Fax: (01460) 230001 E-mail: sales@euroquartz.co.uk *Quartz crystals & oscillator manufrs*

▶ Euroquipment Ltd, Mallard House, Avon Way, Newbury Business Park, Newbury, Berkshire, RG14 2RF Tel: (0870) 1630077 Fax: (0870) 1630099 E-mail: sales@euroquipment.co.uk Principal Export Areas: Central/East Europe & West Europe *Distributors or agents of materials handling equipment, storage equipment systems, truck/trolley (industrial) & roll container* Also at: Rotherham

Eurorail Crash Barriers 2000, Unit 5, Joiners Court, Bawtry Road, Torworth, Retford, Nottinghamshire, DN22 8NW Tel: (01777) 817700 Fax: (01777) 817272 E-mail: enquiries@cpceurorail.co.uk *Vehicle safety barriers*

Eurorealm Consultants Ltd, 29 Ivanhoe Road, Finchampstead, Wokingham, Berkshire, RG40 4QQ Tel: 0118-973 2977 Fax: 0118-973 4470 E-mail: sales@eurorealm.co.uk *Computer software house*

Euroresins UK Ltd, Cloister Way, Ellesmere Port, CH65 4EL Tel: 0151-356 3111 Fax: 0151-355 3772 E-mail: sales@euroresins.com *Synthetic resin & GRP material suppliers*

Euroresins UK Ltd, 2 First Avenue, Halstead, Essex, CO9 2EX Tel: (01787) 472300 Fax: (01787) 473686 *GRP industrial suppliers*

▶ Euroresource International Ltd, Kitchener House, Warwick Road, West Drayton, Middlesex, UB7 9BS Tel: (0845) 1562152 E-mail: enquiries@my-resource.co.uk *Euroresource International Ltd. is a UK based construction recruitment agency placing construction workers from around the world with clients worldwide.**UK based it is represented in China, India, Hungary, India, Lithuania, Poland, Slovenia and the Ukraine; their web site is in Russian, Polish, Ukrainian & English.**It has a very large database of workers willing to relocate to anywhere in the world, currently over 30,000 and has c. 1,000 job vacancies at any time.**Search and selection procedures as well as all other procedures it employs are in strict conformity with exacting quality management and quality assurance practices under ISO 9001:2000.**Pipeline construction companies in Canada are amongst its more recent clients.*

Euroscales Holdings Ltd, Queens Court, Queens Avenue, Macclesfield, Cheshire, SK10 2BN Tel: (01625) 619554 Fax: (01625) 613295 E-mail: sales@euroscales.com *Weighing equipment manufrs*

Euro-Scot Design Ltd, James Watt Avenue, East Kilbride, Glasgow, G75 0QD Tel: (01355) 272300 Fax: (01355) 272153 *Engineering design consultants*

Euroscot Engineering Ltd, 427 Hillington Road, Hillington Industrial Estate, Glasgow, G52 4UJ Tel: 0141-883 2218 Fax: 0141-883 8970 E-mail: office@euroscotengineering.co.uk *Precision engineers*

Euroscot Seafood Services, The Fish Market, Milford Haven, Dyfed, SA73 3AT Tel: 01646 697733 Fax: 01646 694001 *Fishing vessel agents*

Euroscreen UK Ltd, Unit 3 Butts Court, Leigh, Lancashire, WN7 3AW Tel: (01942) 673333 Fax: (01942) 673344 *Road safety sign manufrs*

Euroseals (Wirral), 26 Carrock Road, Bromborough, Wirral, Merseyside, CH62 3RA Tel: 0151-343 1020 Fax: 0151-343 1020 E-mail: euroseals@btconnect.com *Repairers of mechanical seals*

Eurosecurity Alarms, 5 Harvine Walk, Stourbridge, West Midlands, DY8 3BQ Tel: (01384) 370717 Fax: (01384) 370717 *Elliptical contractors*

▶ Euroship Logistics Ltd, PO Box 515, Grimsby, South Humberside, DN37 9QD Tel: (01472) 353333 Fax: (01472) 595695 E-mail: dchristie@euroshiplogistics.co.uk *Freight forwarding,express loads next day deliveries to main land Europe.**

Eurosimm Ltd, Unit 9 Pilsworth Road, Heywood Distribution Park, Heywood, Lancashire, OL10 2TA Tel: (01706) 360000 Fax: (01706) 620000 E-mail: sales@eurosimm.com *Computer dealers*

Eurosis Ltd, 35 Rothschild Street, London, SE27 0JN Tel: (020) 8670 9351 Fax: (020) 8761 7954 E-mail: eurosis@dial.pipex.com *Interpreting services*

Eurosmart Ltd, 192 Clarendon Pk Rd, Leicester, LE2 3AF Tel: 0116-270 7440 Fax: 0116-270 7440 *Coffee machine sales & service*

Eurosoft (Leeds) Ltd, Howcroft House, 919 Bradford Road, Birstall, Batley, West Yorkshire, WF17 9JX Tel: (01924) 474732 Fax: (01924) 475729 E-mail: sales@eurosoft-leeds.co.uk *Labels for chemical industry manufrs*

Eurosoft (U K) Ltd, 3 St Stephens Road, Bournemouth, BH2 6JL Tel: (01202) 297315 Fax: (01202) 558280 E-mail: info@eurosoft-uk.com *Computer software developers including diagnostics*

Eurosonic Communications, 11 Sherborne Street, Manchester, M3 1JS Tel: 0161-831 7879 Fax: 0161-835 2125 E-mail: eurosonic@europasonic.com *Electrical electronics manufrs*

Eurosource Electronics Ltd, Parkway House, Sheen Lane, London, SW14 8LS Tel: (020) 8878 5355 Fax: (020) 8878 5733 E-mail: sales@eurosource.co.uk *Frequency control product distributors*

▶ Eurospan Engineering Ltd, 5 Wheatmoor Rise, Sutton Coldfield, West Midlands, B75 6AW Tel: 0121-378 1596 Fax: 0121-329 2542 E-mail: eurospan@blueyonder.co.uk *Expansion joint/bellows/connector (metal), ball joint, flexible metallic hose/tubing & pipeline fittings (threaded NPT) manufacturers. Also flow meters, venturi*

Eurospark Cutting Tools, Ashby Road, Stapleton, Leicester, LE9 8JE Tel: (01455) 292002 Fax: (01455) 293002 E-mail: sales@eurospark.co.uk *Experts in spark and wire erosion machines. Specialists in lathes, machining centres and grinding machines. Providers of spark and wire erosion turning and milling sub-contract, including tooling, robotic auto load systems and total turnkey projects from design to manufacture. Eurospark is a supplier of most machines within the 600 group and is a main distributor for the well know Harrison lathe range.*

▶ Euro-sport.co.uk, Monteagle Lane, Yateley, Hampshire, GU46 6NB Tel: (01252) 660670 E-mail: enquiries@euro-sport.co.uk *Designers and manufacturers of high quality sports equipment.*Martial arts equipment, destruction board holders, breaking board holders etc.*

▶ Eurospray Ltd, 2 Crompton Road, Glenrothes, Fife, KY6 2SF Tel: (01592) 770055 Fax: (01592) 770066 E-mail: admin@eurospray.sol.co.uk *Powder coat & robotic painting*

▶ Eurostationers, Talbot House, 204-226 Imperial Drive, Harrow, Middlesex, HA2 7HH Tel: (0845) 2020051 Fax: (0845) 2020052 E-mail: sales@eurostationers.com *Office stationery suppliers*

Eurosteel & Allied Ltd, 61 Washford Road, Sheffield, S9 3XW Tel: 0114-242 0066 Fax: 0114-242 0077 E-mail: frank@gsbaceroltd.co.uk *Steel & alloy steel producers*

▶ Eurostove Ltd, Littlemoor Road, Mark, Highbridge, Somerset, TA9 4NG Tel: (01278) 641367 Fax: (01278) 641419 E-mail: info@eurostove.co.uk *Wood heating appliances distributors*

Eurosurgical Ltd, Merrow Business Centre, Guildford, Surrey, GU4 7WA Tel: (01483) 456007 Fax: (01483) 456008 E-mail: sales@eurosurgical.co.uk *Medical & surgical supplies*

Eurotec Distribution Ltd, Church Croft House, Station Road, Rugeley, Staffordshire, WS15 2HE Tel: (01889) 503100 Fax: (01889) 503101 E-mail: sales@media-resources.co.uk *Magnetic media & computer consumables*

Eurotec Hydraulics Ltd, 173 Ashby Road, Moira, Swadlincote, Derbyshire, DE12 6DW Tel: (01283) 225224 Fax: (01283) 819921 E-mail: euroteclelcs@aol.com *On site hydraulic service & supply of hydraulic components*

Eurotec Industries Ltd, Unit 3 Stanley Centre, Kelvin Way, Crawley, West Sussex, RH10 9SE Tel: (01293) 846000 Fax: (01293) 613600 E-mail: sales@pdrsmt.com *Soldering equipment manufrs*

Eurotech Computer Services Ltd, Cambridge House, Cambridge Road, Walton-on-Thames, Surrey, KT12 2DP Tel: (01932) 260470 Fax: (01932) 260471 E-mail: sales@eurotech-computers.com *Computer re-seller*

Eurotech Electrical Services Ltd, Green Acres, Hilton Road Seamer, Middlesbrough, Cleveland, TS9 5LX Tel: (01642) 713804 Fax: (01642) 713804 E-mail: eurotechelectricalservices@greenacres110.fsnet.co.uk *Electrical lightening protection & earthing installations*

Eurotech Environmental Ltd, Northern Road, Newark, Nottinghamshire, NG24 2EU Tel: (0800) 0281786 Fax: (01636) 611727 E-mail: sales@eurotechenvironmental.com *Hazardous waste specialists*

Eurotech Filtration Ltd, 15 Furlong Lane, Stoke-on-Trent, ST6 3LE Tel: (01782) 836667 Fax: (01782) 834830 *Filter manufrs*

Eurotech Group plc, Dinan Way, Exmouth, Devon, EX8 4RZ Tel: (01395) 279393 Fax: (01395) 279902 E-mail: sales@eurotech-group.co.uk *Printed circuit board manufrs*

The Eurotech Group Plc, Sittingbourne Industrial Park, Crown Quay Lane, Sittingbourne, Kent, ME10 3JH Tel: (01795) 431637 Fax: (01795) 431638 E-mail: eurotech@sittingbourne92.fsnet.co.uk *Printed circuit manufrs*

Eurotech Mouldings Ltd, Unit E Underwood Business Park, Wells, Somerset, BA5 1AF Tel: (01749) 676298 Fax: (01749) 670089 *Plastic mouldings manufrs*

Eurotech Office Direct Ltd, Unit 11 The Sidings, Station Road, Guiseley, Leeds, LS20 8BX Tel: (01943) 870909 Fax: (01943) 871204 E-mail: peter@eurotechuk.co.uk *Distributors of consumables & spares for copiers, fax & printers*

Eurotech Precision Engineering Ltd, 4-5 Bergen Way, North Lynn Industrial Estate, King's Lynn, Norfolk, PE30 2JG Tel: (01553) 770426 Fax: (01553) 774726 E-mail: epelltd@kingslynn20.fsnet.co.uk *Precision engineers*

▶ Eurotech-NI, 11 Navan Manor, Armagh, BT61 7AP Tel: (028) 3751 1603 E-mail: info@eurotech-ni.com

Eurotecno Spraybooths, 120a Green Road, Bournemouth, BH9 1EF Tel: (01202) 549286 E-mail: sales@eurotecno.co.uk *Spray booths & equipment distributors*

Eurotek Designs Ltd, 9-10 Bessemer Close, Cardiff, CF11 8DL Tel: (029) 2066 6550 Fax: (029) 2066 7399 E-mail: eudeltd@aol.com *Amusement machines manufrs*

Eurotek Engineering Ltd, Eurotek House, Aylsham, Norwich, NR11 6RR Tel: (01263) 733499 Fax: (01263) 733899 E-mail: sales@eurotek-eng.co.uk *Freezing equipment design & manufrs*

Eurotek HSM, Manor Drive, Aylesbury, Buckinghamshire, HP20 1EW Tel: (01296) 435036 Fax: (01296) 431967 E-mail: james@eurotekhsm.co.uk *Computer resellers*

Eurotek Industrial Tyres Ltd, 313-315 Whapload Road, Lowestoft, Suffolk, NR32 1UL Tel: (01502) 532200 Fax: (01502) 508273 E-mail: colinlong@eurotektyres.com *Tyres for fork lift trucks*

Eurotel Ltd, Empire House, Mulcture Hall Road, Halifax, West Yorkshire, HX1 1SP Tel: (01422) 864000 Fax: (01422) 864100 E-mail: sales@eurotel.com *Telephone systems installation*

Eurotel Communications Ltd, Foleshill Enterprise Park, Courtaulds Way, Coventry, CV6 5NX Tel: (024) 7686 7400 Fax: 0870 750334 E-mail: sales@hbtcommunications.com *Communications & data specialists*

Eurotex Children & Babywear, 105 Warren Street, Dewsbury, West Yorkshire, WF12 9AS Tel: (01924) 461293 Fax: (01924) 460707 E-mail: enquirie@eurotexltd.com *Childrens & ladies clothing manufrs*

Eurotex International Ltd, Unit 20 Shipyard Estate, Brightlingsea, Colchester, CO7 0AR Tel: (01206) 304063 Fax: (01206) 304026 E-mail: terry.kershaw@virgin.net *Diesel engineers & marine engineering services*

Eurothane Ltd, Warndon Business Park, Prescott Drive, Worcester, WR4 9NE Tel: (01905) 458503 Fax: (01905) 456643 E-mail: sales@eurothane.com *Thermoplastics & polyurethane manufrs*

Eurotherm, Faraday Close, Durrington, Worthing, West Sussex, BN13 3PL Tel: (01903) 268500 Fax: (01903) 265982 E-mail: info@eurotherm.co.uk *Manufacturers & designers of temperature indicators, process controllers, data acquisition & recording equipment*

Eurotime Systems Ltd, 101 Blandford Avenue, Birmingham, B36 9JB Tel: 0121-776 6860 Fax: (0871) 9942954 E-mail: sales@eurotime.co.uk *Time recorders & access control manufrs*

▶ Eurotrade Global Ltd, 4 Julian Place, Docklands, London, E14 3AT Tel: (020) 7515 5499 Fax: (020) 7531 1412 E-mail: etguk@btinternet.com *Importers & exporters*

Eurotronix, 19, Telford, Shropshire, TF6 6HD Tel: (01952) 541873 Fax: (01952) 541874 E-mail: sales@eurotronixgb.co.uk *Industrial electronic repair services*

Eurotruck (Truck Trailer Spares) Ltd, 263 Derby Road, Bramcote, Nottingham, NG9 3JA Tel: 0115-939 7660 Fax: 0115-939 6428 *Truck & trailer spares distributors* Also at: Derby, Lincoln & Mansfield

Eurovac Aegeus Ltd, Unit 6-7 Lee Mills Industrial Estate, Scholes, Holmfirth, HD9 1RT Tel: (01484) 689055 Fax: (01484) 689042 E-mail: sales@csgeurovac.com *Hire pressure jetting & vacuum tanker manufrs*

Eurovib Acoustic Products Ltd, Goodwood House, 86 Holmethorpe Avenue, Redhill, RH1 2NL Tel: (01737) 779577 Fax: (01737) 779537 E-mail: sales@eurovib.co.uk *Anti-vibration mounting manufrs*

Eurowales Cable Accessories, Atlantic Trading Estate, Barry, South Glamorgan, CF63 3RF Tel: (01446) 739965 Fax: (01446) 739966 E-mail: sales@eurowales-cable-accessories.com *Suppliers and Manufactures of Brass Items and Cable Glands*

Eurowindows Ltd, 12 Poley Road, Stanford-Le-Hope, Essex, SS17 0JJ Tel: (01375) 641935 Fax: (01375) 672461 E-mail: reception@euro-windows.co.uk *Aluminium windows & doors installers & manufrs*

▶ Eurowire Containers Ltd, Maypole Fields, Cradley, Halesowen, West Midlands, B63 2QB Tel: (01384) 561786 Fax: (01384) 564044 E-mail: support@eurowirecontainers.com *Custom manufacturing specialists*

Euroxpress Delivery Services, 6e Arndale Road, Wick, Littlehampton, West Sussex, BN17 7HD Tel: (01903) 732733 Fax: (01903) 732734 E-mail: sales@euro-xpress.com *International couriers & freight forwarders*

Eurpa Silos Ltd, Unit 15, Prydwen Road, Swansea West Industrial Estate, Swansea, SA5 4HN Tel: (01792) 410450 Fax: (01792) 410455 *Silo systems manufrs*

Eurstyle Ltd, Park House, 19-20 Bright Street, Wednesbury, West Midlands, WS10 9HX Tel: 0121-526 2973 Fax: 0121-526 2061 E-mail: sales@vtex.co.uk *Promotional clothing & baseball caps*

Eutectic Co. Ltd, Moons Moat North Industrial Estate, Redditch, Worcestershire, B98 9HL Tel: (01527) 582200 Fax: (01527) 582201 E-mail: sales@eutectic.com *Welding products manufrs*

Eutectic Alloy Castings Wolverhampton Ltd, Units 25-26, Wood Street, Park Village, Wolverhampton, WV10 9DS Tel: (01902) 726699 Fax: (01902) 726692 *Die castings aluminium & alloy manufrs*

Evadx Ltd, Tir Llwyd Enterprise Park, Kinmel Bay, Rhyl, Clwyd, LL18 5JZ Tel: (01745) 336413 Fax: (01745) 339639 E-mail: sales@evadx.com *Structural steel fabricators*

Evak Ltd, Brentwood Grove, Wallsend, Tyne & Wear, NE28 6PT Tel: 0191-263 5843 Fax: 0191-234 1065 *General engineers*

▶ Evaluation Centre, 15 Chiltern Business Centre, 63-65 Woodside Road, Amersham, Buckinghamshire, HP6 6AA Tel: (0870) 9088767 Fax: (0870) 1340931 E-mail: info@pmp.co.uk *IT procurement & interactive services*

▶ Evan Coating Ltd, Unit 31, Garston Industrial Estate, Blackburn Street, Liverpool, L19 8JB Tel: 0151-427 8000 Fax: 0151-427 5000 *Powder coating suppliers*

Evan Rees Dyfed Ltd, Station Road, St. Clears, Carmarthen, SA33 4BP Tel: (01994) 230511 Fax: (01994) 231444 *Butter & egg merchants*

Evans Ltd, 11 St James Industrial Estate, Westhampnett Road, Chichester, West Sussex, PO19 7JU Tel: (07976) 444316 Fax: (01243) 530828 E-mail: john@evanswelding.com *Engineering*

▶ Evans & Co., Barras Lane, Vale, Guernsey, GY6 8EJ Tel: (01481) 253277 Fax: (01481) 253287 E-mail: sales@evansandco.com *Office furniture suppliers*

Company Information

Aaron Evans Architects Ltd, 3 Argyle Street, Bath, BA2 4BA Tel: (01225) 466234 Fax: (01225) 444364 E-mail: aea@aearchitects.co.uk *Architects*

Evans Bellhouse Ltd, South 3, Huskisson Dock, Regant Road, Liverpool, L3 0AT Tel: 0151-707 0000 Fax: 0151-922 7356 E-mail: james@evansbellhouse.co.uk *Timber importers & merchants*

▶ Evans Bliss, 5 St. James Terrace, Suffolk Parade, Cheltenham, Gloucestershire, GL50 2AA Tel: (01242) 704074 E-mail: jonathan@evansbliss.co.uk *Search Engine Optimisation and Web Marketing services for the small business.*

▶ Evans Boatwork, Unit 5 Havens Head Business Park, The Docks, Hakin, Milford Haven, Dyfed, SA73 3LD Tel: (07815) 075585 Fax: (07967) 303639 E-mail: info@evansboatwork.com *Wooden boats builders & repair services*

Evans Bros Ltd, 2a Block 2 Portman Mansions, Chiltern Street, London, W1U 6NR Tel: (020) 7935 7160 Fax: (020) 7487 0921 E-mail: sales@evansbooks.co.uk *Childrens book publishers*

Evans Bros, 6 High Street, Menai Bridge, Gwynedd, LL59 5ED Tel: (01248) 712388 Fax: (01248) 712388 *Wholesale ironmongers & building merchants*

Evans Bros Agriparts, Agricultural Parts, Cefn Mabws, Llanrhystud, Dyfed, SY23 5BD Tel: (01974) 272260 Fax: (01974) 272537 *Agricultural parts machinery repairs & distributors*

Evans Bros (Southport) Ltd, 69 Upper Aughton Road, Southport, Merseyside, PR8 5ND Tel: (01704) 566155 Fax: (01704) 562088 *Building contractors*

Evans Buildings, Little Acre, Cwmffrwd, Carmarthen, Dyfed, SA31 2LT Tel: (01267) 232478 Fax: (01267) 230588 E-mail: evans.buildings@virgin.net *Agricultural, industrial erectors & Sheeters*

D. Evans Electrical Ltd, Stretton Way, Wilson Road, Huyton Industrial Estate, Liverpool, L36 6JF Tel: 0151-489 1232 Fax: 0151-480 1496 E-mail: drowley@d-evans.co.uk *Cable harness & wiring assemblers*

Dennis D. Evans & Co. Ltd, 391 Holywood Road, Belfast, BT4 2LS Tel: (028) 9065 2220 E-mail: materials@devans.co.uk *Rubber stamp manufrs*

Geraint Evans A'i Fabion, Fronhaul, Llanpumsaint, Carmarthen, Dyfed, SA33 6LX Tel: (01267) 253244 Fax: (01267) 253244 *Agricultural contractors*

▶ Evans & Graham Heating Co. Ltd, 108 Westmead Road, Sutton, Surrey, SM1 4JD Tel: (020) 8661 1712 Fax: (020) 8642 3755

Evans Graphics Ltd, G Boyn Valley Industrial Estate, Boyn Valley Road, Maidenhead, Berkshire, SL6 4EJ Tel: (0870) 7773630 Fax: (0870) 7773632 E-mail: sales@evansgraphics.co.uk *Screen & digital printers & engravers*

Evans Gwyn Plant Ltd, Brackla Industrial Estate, Bridgend, Mid Glamorgan, CF31 2AN Tel: (01656) 655393 Fax: (01656) 655393 *Plant hire*

Evans Hallshaw Newport Ltd, Turner Street, Newport, Gwent, NP19 7XH Tel: (01633) 244442 Fax: (01633) 243041 *Vauxhall car retailer*

Evans Halshaw Ltd, Estate Garage, Treforest Industrial Estate, Pontypridd, Mid Glamorgan, CF37 5YA Tel: (01443) 842376 Fax: (01443) 842687 E-mail: justin.brown@pendragon.uk.com *Vehicle sales*

Evans Halshaw Motors Ltd, The Vauxhall Centre, Crownhill, Milton Keynes, MK8 0AE Tel: (01908) 568601 Fax: (01908) 261020 E-mail: vauxhallcentre@crownhillgm.demon.co.uk *Vauxhall motor sales*

I.N. Evans & Son, Tegfan Garage, 30 Carmarthen Road, Llandeilo, Dyfed, SA19 6RS Tel: (01558) 822542 Fax: (01558) 822337 *Agricultural suppliers*

J.A. Evans, 10 Underdale Avenue, Shrewsbury, SY2 5DY Tel: (01743) 236598 *Central heating engineers*

L. Evans & Son (Hereford) Ltd, Crown House, Canon Pyon, Hereford, HR4 8PE Tel: (01432) 830285 Fax: (01432) 830285 *Agricultural engineers*

Evans Mechanical Services Ltd, Derby House, 29 Castle Street, Caergwrle, Wrexham, Clwyd, LL12 9AD Tel: (01978) 760000 Fax: (01978) 761082 E-mail: enquiries@evans-mech.co.uk *Heating engineers & plumbers services*

Evans & Mondon Ltd, Bassett Road, Halesowen, West Midlands, B63 2RE Tel: (01384) 564224 Fax: (01384) 637305 E-mail: evansmillshaw@compuserve.com *Metal recyclers & industrial dismantlers*

Peter Evans & Associates Ltd, 52 The Parade, Roath, Cardiff, CF24 3AB Tel: (029) 2040 2200 Fax: (029) 2040 2213 E-mail: info@peterevans.com *Computer software developers*

Evans Peter Light Engineering, Bromyard Road Industrial Estate, Unit 12, Ledbury, Herefordshire, HR8 1NS Tel: (01531) 634177 Fax: (01531) 634177 *Reconditioned auger fillers & vibratory weighers. Machines for hire or sale.*

Evans & Reed Alloys Ltd, Anchor Road, Bilston, West Midlands, WV14 9NA Tel: (01902) 354776 Fax: (01902) 354856 E-mail: sales@evansandreid.com *High grade aluminium ingot manufrs*

Evans & Reid Coal Co. Ltd, Empire House, Cardiff, CF10 5QZ Tel: (029) 2048 8111 Fax: (029) 2049 1130 E-mail: evansandreid@btinternet.com *Coal importers & exporters*

Evans & Shea Ltd, 37 Collier Row Lane, Romford, RM5 3BD Tel: (01708) 741055 Fax: (01708) 764289 *Electrical contractors*

Evans Skip Hire, Park Lane, Halesowen, West Midlands, B63 2RA Tel: (01384) 412289 Fax: (01384) 412289 E-mail: sales@evansskips.com *Skip hire contractors*

Stanley Evans Ltd, Sandy Lane, Wildmoor, Bromsgrove, Worcestershire, B61 0QT Tel: 0121-366 7300 Fax: 0121-460 1397 *Foundry sand producers*

Evans Textile Sales Ltd, 22 Piccadilly Trading Estate, Manchester, M1 2NP Tel: 0161-274 4147 Fax: 0161-274 4070 E-mail: sales@evans-textiles.com *Textile merchant-converters*

Evans Transport, Braunton Road, Barnstaple, Devon, EX31 1LE Tel: (01271) 326632 Fax: (01271) 326616 E-mail: evanstransport@btconnect.com *Road transport contractors*

Evans Transport Ltd, Peamore Truck Centre, Alphington, Exeter, EX2 9SL Tel: (01392) 833030 Fax: (01392) 833540 E-mail: sales@palletforce.com *A member of the PalletFORCE distribution network- palletised distribution, timed, next day, economy, tail loft, Ireland and services to mainland Europe. Through its expanding shareholder member depot network, full and part loads, warehouse and logistics services are available.*

Evans Turner Finishes Ltd, 200 Manor Road, Erith, Kent, DA8 2AD Tel: (01322) 346911 Fax: (01322) 332706 E-mail: sales@evans-turner.com *Architectural metalworkers & fabricators specialist engineers services*

W.H. Evans & Sons Ltd, Sealand Industrial Estate, 5 Knutsford Way, Chester, CH1 4NS Tel: (01244) 383456 Fax: (01244) 381822 E-mail: print@whevans.co.uk *Commercial & colour printers*

Evans & White Manufacturing Ltd, Canal Street, Stourbridge, West Midlands, DY8 4LU Tel: (01384) 394731 Fax: (01384) 442603 E-mail: sandra@evansandwhite.co.uk *Horizontal boring services & precision engineering specialists*

William Evans Ltd, 67a St James's Street, London, SW1A 1PH Tel: (020) 7493 0415 Fax: (020) 7499 1912 E-mail: salew@willa.com *Retailers & manufacturers of guns & rifles*

Evans Windows Ltd, Cambrian Place, Pool Road, Newtown, Powys, SY16 1DH Tel: (01686) 626465 Fax: (01686) 627695 *Portable buildings & windows manufrs*

Evante Fitness Ltd, 71-73 High Street North, Dunstable, Bedfordshire, LU6 1JF Tel: (01582) 477600 Fax: (01582) 471366 *Electrical & communication*

▶ Eva-Pro Heating Services, Unit 7A, Pant Industrial Estate, Dowlais, Merthyr Tydfil, Mid Glamorgan, CF48 2SR Tel: (01685) 722467

▶ Eva-Pro Heating Services, Unit 1, Old Rediffusion Buildings, Merthyr Tydfil, Mid Glamorgan, CF47 0AX Tel: (01685) 379969

Evasafe Products Ltd, Farren Court, Cowfold, Horsham, West Sussex, RH13 8BP Tel: (01403) 864486 Fax: (01403) 864873 E-mail: info@evasafe.co.uk *Alarm & control system designers & installers*

Evb Ltd, 48-52 Barking Industrial Park, Alfreds Way, Barking, Essex, IG11 0TJ Tel: (020) 8507 8088 Fax: (020) 8591 2419 E-mail: alanevb@f2s.com *Steel fabricators & Security entrance screens*

Evc Compounds Ltd, Chester Road, Helsby, Frodsham, WA6 0DF Tel: (01928) 762700 Fax: (01928) 725101 E-mail: ken_goodwin@evc-int.com *PVC compound manufrs*

▶ Eveho Computer Systems, Horizon House Baldock Industrial Estate, London Road, Baldock, Hertfordshire, SG7 6NG Tel: (01462) 893800 Fax: 01462 894800 E-mail: gglen@eveho.com *Supplier of high quality remanufactured toner cartridges, savings of up to 50%. Also supplies the complete range of original branded printer consumables at competitive prices, all nextday delivery, online ordering.*

▶ Evelogic Ltd, Centaur House, Ancells Road, Fleet, Hampshire, GU51 2UJ Tel: (0870) 1203148 Fax: (0870) 1203149 E-mail: sales@evelogic.com *IBM iSeries Systems Management software. A complete range from traditional job scheduling, message management and back up and recovery through to areas such as LPAR management to report management*

Evencray Ltd, Unit 8, Welbeck Way, Woodston, Peterborough, PE2 7WH Tel: (01733) 371700 Fax: (01733) 361065 E-mail: ashley_young@btclick.com *Electric appliance spares & dealers*

Evendale Blinds, Indoor Market, 62-72 Titchfield Street, Kilmarnock, Ayrshire, KA1 1PH Tel: (01563) 573767 Fax: (01563) 573767 *Blinds suppliers & installers*

Evendine College, 227 Tottenham Court Road, London, W1T 7QF Tel: (020) 7580 1989 Fax: (020) 7580 1959 E-mail: evendine@evendine.com *School of English/business administration*

Evenort Ltd, Houghton Road, North Anston, Sheffield, S25 4JJ Tel: (01909) 569361 Fax: (01909) 550631 E-mail: sales@evenort.co.uk *Stainless steel flange manufacturers & bar blanks*

▶ Event & Electrical Services, 32 Southfields Rise, North Leverton, Retford, Nottinghamshire, DN22 0AY Tel: 01427 880802 E-mail: info@eventelectricalservices.co.uk *Electrical Contractor*

▶ Event Energy, Russet Knowle, Wild Duck Lane, Cleasby, Darlington, County Durham, DL2 2RB Tel: (01325) 467684 *Hire of road towable generator sets for private parties, music events etc... Please call for futher details.*

Event Hire, Stuart Road, Bredbury Park Industrial Estate, Bredbury, Stockport, Cheshire, SK6 2SR Tel: 0161-494 5213 Fax: 0161-494 5213 E-mail: info@mcmeventhire.co.uk *Catering equipment & hire services*

Event Lighting, 10 Palmerston Close, Kibworth, Leicester, LE8 0JJ Tel: 0116-279 3851 *Lighting contractors*

▶ Event Outpost Ltd, 5 Empire Crescent, Hanham, Bristol, BS15 3GG Tel: (0845) 3312521 Fax: 0117-981 6050 E-mail: info@eventoutpost.co.uk *Online event product suppliers*

▶ Event Plant & Access., Events House, Braye Road, Vale, Guernsey, GY3 5PB Tel: (01481) 243334 Fax: (01481) 243899 E-mail: admin@eventsci.com *Hire of Powered Access, on-site power, Generators and Site Accommodation units.*

▶ Event Prop Hire, Unit 1, Green Park Business Centre, Eastmoor, Sutton on the Forrest, York, YO61 1ET Tel: (01347) 811713 Fax: (0845) 0940817 E-mail: enquiries@eventprophire.com *Prop hire & bespoke props*

▶ Event Services Ltd, The Old Foundry, Brow Mills Industrial Estate, Brighouse Road, Halifax, West Yorkshire, HX3 8EF Tel: (01422) 204114 Fax: (01422) 204431 E-mail: sales@event-services.co.uk *Hire of event equipment crowd control barriers*

Eventemp (Midlands) Ltd, Carrwood Road, Chesterfield Trading Estate, Sheepbridge, Chesterfield, Derbyshire, S41 9QB Tel: (01246) 453685 Fax: (01246) 260359 E-mail: enquiries@eventempmidland.ltd.uk *Air conditioning engineers services*

▶ Eventous, Unit 26B, 8-10 Glasgow Road, Kirkintilloch, Glasgow, G66 1SH Tel: (0845) 1679565 E-mail: info@eventous.com *Events planner*

▶ Eventsi Marquees Ltd., 8 Silvermead Road, Sutton Coldfield, West Midlands, B73 5SR Tel: 0121-240 1470 E-mail: enquiries@eventsimarquees.co.uk *Marquee hire specialists*

Eventsigns Sign Makers, Unit 6 Poplar Drive, Witton, Birmingham, B6 7AD Tel: 0121-344 3141 Fax: 0121-344 3181 E-mail: eventsignsgb@aol.com *Banners & signs manufrs*

▶ Event-tech Exhibition Services Ltd, Drybridge Park, Shewalton Road, Drybridge, Irvine, Ayrshire, KA11 5AL Tel: (01294) 312537 Fax: (01294) 273691

▶ Eventurous, The Water front, West Midlands Water Ski centre, Tamworth, Staffordshire, B78 2DL Tel: (0870) 6071258 E-mail: sales@eventurous.co.uk *Team Building and corporate event specialists*

Evenwood Engineering Ltd, Evenwood, Bishop Auckland, County Durham, DL14 9NJ Tel: (01388) 832556 Fax: (01388) 832966 *Light to medium steel fabricators*

Eveque Leisure Equipment Ltd, 8 Duttons Business Centre, Dock Road, Northwich, Cheshire, CW9 5HJ Tel: (01606) 45611 Fax: (01606) 421517 E-mail: info@eveque.co.uk *Signs & leisure equipment manufrs*

▶ Ever Cal, Citadel Trading Park, Citadel Way, Hull, HU9 1TQ Tel: (01482) 610601 Fax: (01482) 610602 E-mail: sales@ever-cal.com *Mobile calibration services*

▶ Ever Cool Ltd, 38 Devon Close Perivale, Middx, Greenford, Middlesex, UB6 7DP Tel: (020) 8997 0395 Fax: (020) 8997 0395 E-mail: info@rapidservice.co.uk *Air conditioning & refrigeration suppliers, installation & services*

Ever Ready Health Care Ltd, 13 Sentinel Square, Hendon, London, NW4 2EL Tel: (020) 8202 3171 Fax: (020) 8203 9083 E-mail: david@everreadyhealthcare.com *Toiletries manufrs*

Ever Ready Tools & Plastics Co. Ltd, Unit H, Chesham Close, Romford, RM7 7NA Tel: (01708) 762262 Fax: (01708) 723006 E-mail: everreadytools@btconnect.com *Precision mould toolmakers*

F.T. Everard & Sons Ltd, Blake House, Admiral Park, Crossway, Dartford, DA2 6QQ Tel: (01322) 394500 Fax: (01322) 311943 *Ship owners*

Everard Shipping Companies, Peninsular House, 36 Monument Street, London, EC3R 8LJ Tel: (020) 7398 4450 Fax: (020) 7398 4480 *Ship management or managing agents*

Everbright Stainless, Brimington Road North, Chesterfield, Derbyshire, S41 9BE Tel: (01246) 451600 Fax: (01246) 451611 E-mail: everbright.sales@infast.com *Fastener distributors* Also at: Bradford & Coventry

Everbright Stainless, Brimington Road North, Chesterfield, Derbyshire, S41 9BE Tel: (01246) 451600 Fax: (01246) 451611 E-mail: everbright.sales@infast.com *Fasteners engineers & distributors*

▶ Everest Ltd, Cwmsaerbren Street, Treherbert, Treorchy, Mid Glamorgan, CF42 5HY Tel: (01443) 771382 Fax: (01443) 777046 *Manufacturers of windows & doors*

▶ Everest Cooling Services, 11 Brunshaw Avenue, Burnley, Lancashire, BB10 4LT Tel: (01282) 685223 Fax: (01282) 685223 E-mail: info@everestcooling.com *Air conditioning & refrigeration equipment sales, service & repairs*

Everest Dairies Ltd, L Vulcan Business Centre, Vulcan Road, Leicester, LE5 3EB Tel: 0116-253 0909 *Dairy products*

Everest Packaging, 52 Wellington Road, Edgbaston, Birmingham, B15 2ER Tel: 0121-236 3573 *Packaging machine manufrs*

Everest VIT (UK) Ltd, 18 Tannery Yard, Witney Street, Burford, Oxfordshire, OX18 4DW Tel: (01993) 822613 Fax: (01993) 822614 E-mail: sales.office-hswuk@btinternet.com *Distributors remote visual inspection equipment*

Alex Everett Ltd, 34 Victoria Road, Writtle, Chelmsford, CM1 3PA Tel: (01245) 421198 Fax: (01245) 422433 E-mail: aelconnectors@btclick.com *Miniature connectors & cables ribbon*

Everett Charles, Fence Avenue Indust Estate, Fence Avenue, Macclesfield, Cheshire, SK10 1LT Tel: (01625) 500303 Fax: (01625) 500306 *Advanced technology board test products*

Everetts, 691 Holderness Road, Hull, HU8 9AN Tel: (01482) 374201 Fax: (01482) 788801 *Fishing equipment distributors*

▶ Everfast Products, Unit 47 Barkston House, Croydon Street, Leeds, LS11 9RT Tel: 0113-242 5835 Fax: 0113-242 5836 E-mail: sales@everfastproducts.co.uk *Nametape & adhesive products manufrs*

▶ Everglade Windows Ltd, 22 Wadsworth Road, Greenford, Middlesex, UB6 7JD Tel: (020) 8998 8775 Fax: (020) 8997 0300 E-mail: sales@everglade.co.uk *PVC & aluminium doors & windows manufrs*

Everglades International Ltd, The Old Station, Station Road, Cheddar, Somerset, BS27 3AH Tel: (01934) 744051 Fax: (01934) 743184 *Manufacture & distributors of craft products*

▶ Everglaze, Corner Farm, Ashbourne, Derbyshire, DE6 4LY Tel: (01332) 824367 Fax: (01332) 824483 *Joiners*

Evergreen, Clare Park, Unit 2, Farnham, Surrey, GU10 5DT Tel: (01252) 851849 Fax: (01252) 851849 *Joinery*

Evergreen Blinds, 2 Llanwenarth Road, Govilon, Abergavenny, Gwent, NP7 9PN Tel: (01873) 830112 Fax: (01873) 830112 *Window blind manufrs*

▶ Evergreen Computing Ltd, 42 Woodlands Road, Charfield, Wotton-under-Edge, Gloucestershire, GL12 8LS Tel: (01454) 269087 Fax: (0870) 7515596 E-mail: info@evergreencomputing.com *Website design hosting & maintenance*

▶ Evergreen Gallery, 12 Sheaf Street, Daventry, Northamptonshire, NN11 4AB Tel: (01327) 878117 E-mail: info@evergreengallery.co.uk *Fine art suppliers & picture framing experts*

Evergreen Irrigation Ltd, 50a High Street, Wing, Leighton Buzzard, Bedfordshire, LU7 0NR Tel: (01296) 688317 Fax: (01296) 688332 E-mail: sales@evergreen-irrigation.co.uk *Irrigation services*

Evergreen UK Ltd, Evergreen House, 160 Euston Road, London, NW1 2DX Tel: (020) 7559 8000 Fax: (020) 7559 8103 *Shipping company* Also at: Birmingham, Dublin, Felixstowe, Glasgow & Manchester

▶ Everhot Ltd, Coaley Mill, Coaley, Dursley, Gloucestershire, GL11 5DS Tel: (01453) 890018 Fax: (01453) 890598 E-mail: sales@everhot.co.uk *A superb electric heat storage range which has the good looks, durability and reliability of a traditional range without the usual installation and operational hassles. Requiring no flue and built to a standard 600mm wide to fit any kitchen size, the Everhot still comprises two capacious ovens, two large hotplates and a radiant grill, all with independent temperature adjustment.*

Everitt Bros Short Heath, 11a Pooles Lane, Willenhall, West Midlands, WV12 5HH Tel: (01922) 479123 Fax: (01922) 479216 E-mail: everittconstruction@btconnect.com *Building contractors*

▶ William Stephen Everitt, 2 Highfield Road, Woodford Green, Essex, IG8 8JA Tel: (020) 8491 6994 E-mail: william.everitt@ntlworld.com *All types of lead roofing*

Everlac (GB) Ltd, Hawthorn House, Helions Bumpstead Road, Haverhill, Suffolk, CB9 7AA Tel: (01440) 766360 Fax: (01440) 768897 E-mail: admin@everlac.co.uk *Paint manufrs*

Evermore Carpets, 148 Westpole Avenue, Cockfosters, Barnet, Hertfordshire, EN4 0AR Tel: (020) 8449 7362 *Carpet contactors*

▶ Everquip Garage Equipment Ltd, Tex Works, Wyke St, Hull, HU9 1PA Tel: (01482) 226699 Fax: (01482) 211184 E-mail: info@everquip.co.uk *Fabricated commercial inspection pits & garage equipment manufrs*

Everrett Charles Technology, Homer House, Sibthorp Street, Lincoln, LN5 7SL Tel: (01522) 548220 Fax: (01522) 568419 *Semiconductor testing*

Evershed Robotics Ltd, Unit D1 Hortonwood 10, Telford, Shropshire, TF1 7ES Tel: (01952) 608020 Fax: (01952) 608388 E-mail: sales@evershedrobotics.com *Robots & factory automation integrators*

Evertaut, Lions Drive, Shadsworth Business Park, Blackburn, BB1 2QS Tel: (01254) 297880 Fax: (01254) 274859 E-mail: sales@evertaut.co.uk *Office furniture*

Evertile Ltd, 6 Moresby Road, London, E5 9LF Tel: (020) 8806 3167 Fax: (020) 8806 7434 E-mail: sales@evertile.com *Industrial floor tile manufrs* Also at: Manchester

Everton Water Gardens, Newlands Manor, Everton, Lymington, Hampshire, SO41 0JH Tel: (01590) 644405 Fax: (01590) 642343 E-mail: sales@water-garden-workshop.com *Water gardening services*

Everts International Ltd, Second Avenue, Flixborough Industrial Estate, Flixborough, Scunthorpe, South Humberside, DN15 8SD Tel: (01724) 282525 Fax: (01724) 282526 E-mail: info@evertsballoon.co.uk *Balloon & party ware distributors*

▶ Everwell Occupational Health Ltd, The Rowans, Holmes Chapel Road, Somerford, Congleton, Cheshire, CW12 4SP Tel: (01477) 544306 E-mail: enquiries@everwelloh.co.uk *Occupational health service*

Every Body's Display, Scrubs Lane, London, W10 6AH Tel: (020) 8960 6121 Fax: (020) 8960 9894 E-mail: info@universaldisplay.co.uk *Mannequins & retail displays*

▶ Every Occasion, 464 Blackburn Road, Bolton, BL1 8PE Tel: (01204) 595100 *Suppliers of balloons & ribbons for parties & weddings*

▶ Everyday Essentials, 2 Cranford Crescent, Kilfennan, Londonderry, BT47 5QN Tel: (028) 7129 1478 E-mail: everyday_essentials@hotmail.com *New Shopping Company. Everyday Essentials are a catalogue company rapidly expanding throughout the UK. We sell quality everyday products such as traditional sweets, Ecover, HG, Orangeglo, Compatiable Printer Cartridges, Own Brand Coffee's and much more.**If you join our company, you will not be disappointed. Our commission is one of the best in the business, so why not contact me and take the risk!!.*

Everything Equestrian, Westerton Avenue, Clarkston, Glasgow, G76 8JU Tel: 0141-644 2698 Fax: 0141-423 5733 *Horse maintenance & saddlery*

Everything X-Ray Ltd, Mill End Road, High Wycombe, Buckinghamshire, HP12 4JN Tel: (01494) 510911 Fax: (01494) 510914 E-mail: office@evexray.co.uk *X-ray accessory suppliers & manufrs*

Eves Joinery, Edwards Lane, Liverpool, L24 9HX Tel: (0151-486 1896 Fax: (0151-448 1548 *Joinery services.*

Russell Eves Electrical Ltd, Unit 7 Oxen Industrial Estate, Oxen Road, Luton, LU2 0DX Tel: (01582) 732766 Fax: (01582) 726147 E-mail: evesrussell@aol.com *Electrical contractors*

W. & H. Eves Ltd, Unit 5 The Aviary, Woodgate, Crawley Lane, Kings Bromley, Burton-on-Trent, Staffordshire, DE13 7JF Tel: (01543) 473444 Fax: (01543) 472152 E-mail: info@wheves.com *Index table manufrs*

Evesham Ltd, 5 Glisson Road, Cambridge, CB1 2HA Tel: (01223) 323898 Fax: (01223) 322883 *Computer reseller*

Evesham Alarm Co., Summer Place, Blacksmiths Lane, Cropthorne, Pershore, Worcestershire, WR10 3LX Tel: (01386) 861386 E-mail: chris.tunstill@freenet.co.uk *Alarm engineer*

Evesham Technology Ltd, Vale Park, Evesham, Worcestershire, WR11 1TD Tel: (01386) 769600 Fax: (01386) 769795 *Computer suppliers*

Evesham Technology, 1 Gloucester Court, Gloucester Terrace, Leeds, LS12 2ER Tel: 0113-203 2000 Fax: 0113-203 2001 E-mail: leeds.showroom@evesham.com *Purveyors of hand crafted quality PC's to business & home users*

▶ Evesham Technology, 27-29 Cursitor Street, London, EC4A 1PB Tel: (020) 7611 1800

Evesons Fuels Ltd, 456 Station Road, Dorridge, Solihull, West Midlands, B93 8EX Tel: (01564) 778877 Fax: (01564) 770655 E-mail: sales@evesons.co.uk *Oil, lubricant & petroleum distributors* Also at: Droitwich & Eastleigh

Evobush UK Ltd, Ashcroft Way, Crosspoint Business Park, Coventry, CV2 2TU Tel: (024) 7662 6000 Fax: (024) 7662 6010 *Complete coach distributors & repair services*

▶ Evocal Ltd, Thorp Arch, Wetherby, West Yorkshire, LS23 7RR Tel: (0870) 7775777 Fax: (0870) 7776665 E-mail: sales@evocal.co.uk *Telecommunication distributors*

Evolution Automotive Components Ltd, 17 Lythalls Lane, Coventry, CV6 6FN Tel: (024) 7663 7337 Fax: (024) 7663 7351 E-mail: sales@eacparts.com Principal Export Areas: Asia Pacific, Middle East, Africa, Central/ East Europe, West Europe, North America & South America *Motor vehicle component & motor vehicle trade merchants*

Evolution Computers, 135 Bradford Road, Shipley, West Yorkshire, BD18 3TB Tel: (01274) 773394 Fax: (01274) 778788 E-mail: info@evolutiondirect.com *Computer consultants*

▶ Evolution Electronic Security Systems, 1 Lancaster Court, Coronation Road, Cressex Business Park, High Wycombe, Buckinghamshire, HP12 3TD Tel: (01494) 539880 Fax: (01494) 539881 E-mail: rs@evoloutionsecurity.com *Security installation services*

Evolution Power Tools Ltd, Venture 1, Long Acre Close, Holbrook Industrial Estate, Sheffield, S20 3FR Tel: 0114-251 1022 Fax: 0114-247 3339 E-mail: bill@evolutionpowertools.com *Power tools supplier*

Evolution Training & Development, 3 Whitebeam Road, Oadby, Leicester, LE2 4EA Tel: 0116-271 4616

▶ Evolve, 35 Townfield Road, Mobberley, Knutsford, Cheshire, WA16 7HG Tel: (01565) 872683 Fax: (01565) 872534 *Graphic design, print & advertising services*

▶ Evolve Print Solutions, Unit 8 Woodcock Hill Estate, Harefield Road, Rickmansworth, Hertfordshire, WD3 1PQ Tel: (01923) 774111

Evotec UK Ltd, 151 Milton Park, Milton, Abingdon, Oxfordshire, OX14 4SD Tel: (01235) 441200 Fax: (01235) 863139 E-mail: sales@evotecoai.com *Chemical services*

Evox Rifa Uk, 20-21 Cumberland Drive, Granby Industrial Estate, Weymouth, Dorset, DT4 9TE Tel: (01305) 830737 Fax: (01305) 760670 *Capacitors, electric/electronic interference suppressors & inductors electrical, general purpose*

EVR Commercial Ltd, Priory Goods Yard, St. Johns Road, Dover, Kent, CT17 9SE Tel: (01304) 211011 Fax: (01304) 214885 E-mail: evrandeec@yahoo.co.uk *Road transport/ haulage/freight services*

Evridge Precison Engineering Ltd, Holmesdale Works, Holmesdale Road, South Darenth, Dartford, DA4 9JP Tel: (01322) 868961 Fax: (01322) 868962 E-mail: mailbox@evridgeengineering.com Principal Export Areas: Worldwide *Precision engineers services*

Ewab Engineering Ltd, Stafford Park 16, Telford, Shropshire, TF3 3BS Tel: (01952) 239200 Fax: (01952) 239258 E-mail: pam.berry@ewab.net *EWAB Engineering Ltd supply automation for manufacturing cells worldwide, which includes, conveyors, gantires, pick & places, docking stations, lift units and industrial robots. We can also provide and manage turnkey solutions. Additional Services: Project Management, project coordination, simultaneous engineering, layout coordination, installation and after sales service.*

▶ Ewan Associates Ltd, 8 Boleyn Court, Manor Park, Runcorn, Cheshire, WA7 1SR Tel: (01928) 571025 Fax: (01928) 571026

▶ Ewan Group plc, Canterbury House Stephensons Way, Wyvern Business Park, Chaddesden, Derby, DE21 6LY Tel: (01332) 680066 Fax: (01332) 680080 *Water cleaners*

▶ Ewan Group P.L.C., Beta Centre, Stirling University Innovation Park, Stirling, FK9 4NF Tel: (01786) 449131 Fax: (01786) 449 852 E-mail: stirling@ewan.co.uk *Water & environmental consultancy*

Ewart Chain Ltd, Colombo Street, Derby, DE23 8LX Tel: (01332) 345451 Fax: (01332) 371753 E-mail: sales@ewartchain.co.uk *Conveyor drive & plastic chain manufrs*

Ewart Engineering Ltd, Gretna Industrial Estate, Gretna, Dumfriesshire, DG16 5JN Tel: (01461) 337081 Fax: (01461) 337962 E-mail: info@ewart-eng.co.uk *Engineering subcontract services*

Ewen Engineering, Roscoe Road, Sheffield, S3 7DZ Tel: 0114-273 0327 Fax: 0114-275 1955 E-mail: sales@ewenengineering.co.uk *CNC engineering & grinding services*

▶ Ewenny Angling Supplies, 11b Ewenny Road, Bridgend, Mid Glamorgan, CF31 3HN Tel: (01656) 662691 Fax: (01656) 662691 E-mail: keith@reelfishing.co.uk *Fishing tackle retail*

▶ Ewing & Reeson, 38 Broadway, St. Ives, Cambridgeshire, PE27 5BN Tel: (01480) 469295 Fax: (01480) 495367 E-mail: sales@commercial-photography.co.uk *Commercial photography for business and industry. Pack shots and catalogue photography. Magazine features, technical photography of equipment. Digital manipulation in Adobe Photoshop. Public Relations photography on location. Architecture and landscape. Model portfolios in B/W and colour.*

Ewood Products, Barnmeadow House, Barnmeadow Lane, Great Harwood, Blackburn, BB6 7AB Tel: (01254) 882550 Fax: (01254) 882550 *Mops & mop fittings*

Ewos Ltd, Westfields, Westfield, Bathgate, West Lothian, EH48 3BP Tel: (01506) 633966 Fax: (01506) 632730 E-mail: ian.carr@ewos.com *Manufacturers of animal feed supplements*

EWS Railways, Channel Gate Rd, London, NW10 6TY Tel: 020 89636587 Fax: 020 89636582 *Railway freight*

The Ex Mill Envelope & Paper Company Ltd, 5-9 City Garden Row, London, N1 8DW Tel: (020) 7253 8312 Fax: (020) 7251 5336 E-mail: sales@exmill.co.uk *Envelope stockists*

Ex Pressed Steel Panels Ltd, Ickornshaw Mill, Ickornshaw, Cowling, Keighley, West Yorkshire, BD22 0DB Tel: (01535) 632721 Fax: (01535) 636977 E-mail: sales@steelpanels.co.uk *Car body panel manufacturer*

▶ Exa Networks, 27-29 Mill Field Road, Cottingley Business Park, Cottingley, Bingley, West Yorkshire, BD16 1PY Tel: (0845) 1451234 Fax: (01274) 567646 E-mail: sales@exa-networks.co.uk *Providing quality in reliable internet services for business, support*

Exact Air Ltd, 39 Horton Drive, Middleton Cheney, Banbury, Oxfordshire, OX17 2LN Tel: (01295) 710831 Fax: (01295) 711892 E-mail: sales@exactair.co.uk *Air conditioning equipment & systems services*

▶ Exact Designs Ltd, Neep Cottage, Pencaitland, East Lothian, EH34 5DE Tel: (01875) 340859

Exact Engineering Ltd, 1-4 Burke Road, Totnes, Devon, TQ9 5XL Tel: (01803) 866464 Fax: (01803) 866385 E-mail: sales@exact-eng.co.uk Principal Export Areas: Worldwide *Distributor of hose & fittings for the motorsport industry*

Exact Engineering Thompson Ltd, Kingsway South, Team Valley Trading Estate, Gateshead, Tyne & Wear, NE11 0JS Tel: 0191-482 6622 Fax: 0191-482 1602 E-mail: john.martin@exact-engineering.com *Precision engineers*

Exact Pest Control Ltd, 18 Becketts Avenue, St. Albans, Hertfordshire, AL3 5RU Tel: (01727) 865922 *Pest control services*

▶ Exact Property Services, Unit B10 Moss Industrial Estate, St. Helens Road, Leigh, Lancashire, WN7 3PT Tel: (01942) 684466 Fax: (01942) 671918

Exact Weld (GB) Ltd, Unit 8E, Charlwoods Road, East Grinstead, West Sussex, RH19 2HG Tel: (01342) 311595 Fax: (01342) 326526 *Welding contractors*

Exactaform Cutting Tools Ltd, G2 Little Heath Industrial Estate, Old Church Road, Coventry, CV6 7ND Tel: (024) 7666 5823 Fax: (024) 7663 8251 E-mail: sales@exactaform.co.uk *Engineering services*

▶ Exair, 10 Creek Road, Greenwich, London, SE8 3BN Tel: (020) 8691 9000 Fax: (020) 8691 9300 E-mail: cary@exair.co.uk *Sale & rental of air purifiers for photocopiers & printers*

Exallot Ltd, Patent Drive, Moorcroft Business Park, Wednesbury, West Midlands, WS10 7XD Tel: 0121-506 7330 Fax: 0121-506 7333 *Glass fibre products manufrs*

▶ Example Courier Services, 4 Hayfield Close, Baildon, Shipley, West Yorkshire, BD17 6TY Tel: (01274) 585321 Fax: (01274) 583609 E-mail: office@exsamplecourierservices.com *Exsample Courier Services. Professional same day courier service based *in Bradford, Leeds and West Yorkshire, specialising in Nationwide and European *deliverie*

▶ Exant Software, West Midland House, Gipsy Lane, Willenhall, West Midlands, WV13 2HA Tel: 0121-609 7102

▶ EXBG, 16 Altamont, Westview Road, Warlingham, Surrey, CR6 9JD Tel: (01883) 620070 E-mail: info@exbg.co.uk *Central heating system maintenance*

▶ Excalibur Exhibitions Ltd, 4 Stowe Close, Buckingham, MK18 1HY Tel: (01280) 815093 Fax: (01280) 822022 E-mail: info@excaliburexhibitions.com *Ex:calibur Exhibitions are specialists in exhibition stand design, construction,project management and consultancy.*

Excalibur Glass & Windows Ltd, 137 Ringwood Road, Poole, Dorset, BH14 0RH Tel: (01202) 743144 Fax: (01202) 716449 E-mail: sales@glassandwindows.co.uk *Glass merchants*

Excalibur Group Holdings, Excalibur House, First Avenue, Crewe, CW1 6UG Tel: (01270) 252405 Fax: (01270) 581010 E-mail: mark@radwayeng.co.uk *Steel fabricators*

▶ Excalibur Screwbolts Ltd, 10 Aldermans Hill, Hockley, Essex, SS5 4RW Tel: (01702) 206962 Fax: (01702) 207918 E-mail: charles.bickford@screwbolt.com *Fixing systems manufrs*

Excalibur Textiles, Unit 3, 71-77 Stoney Stanton Road, Coventry, CV1 4FW Tel: (024) 7655 5330 Fax: (024) 7655 5360 *Clothing manufrs*

▶ Exceed Cleaning Ltd, PO Box 8781, Stansted, Essex, CM24 8AN Tel: 01279 814990 Fax: 01279 814551 E-mail: info@exceedcleaning.com *Exceed Cleaning Limited is now one of the most exciting new and experienced cleaning contractors within the South East.**Our depth of expertise comprises of over 15 years experience within the soft services sector, yet we remain bright, innovative and competitive.*.*We pride ourselves on providing value for money, consistently high standards and full operational support to both our clients and our staff**Office buildings*Healthcare establishments*Educational premises*Retail outlets*Industrial sites*Commercial properties**

Excel Adhesives, 18 Low Farm Place, Moulton Park Industrial Estate, Northampton, NN3 6HY Tel: (01604) 648484 Fax: (01604) 790370 *Adhesive & shoe mercury distributors*

▶ Excel Audio Systems Ltd, Highfield Road, Acton, London, W3 0AJ Tel: (020) 8354 0820 Fax: (020) 8354 0834 E-mail: sales@excelaudio.co.uk *Audio equipment retailers & manufrs*

Excel Automation Ltd, Gregorys Bank, Worcester, WR3 8AB Tel: (01905) 721500 Fax: (01905) 613024 E-mail: information@excel-automation.co.uk *Conveyor systems manufrs*

▶ Excel Chauffeur Services, Warrington Business Park, Long Lane, Warrington, WA2 8TX Tel: (0871) 2881433 Fax: (0871) 2881433 E-mail: enquiries@xl-cars.co.uk *Airport transfers, Road shows, Corporate Entertainment & Leisure.*What ever the event or requirments of our clients we will ensure the safe transfer to required destination.*

Excel Computer Systems, Bothe Hall, Tamworth Road, Long Eaton, Nottingham, NG10 3XL Tel: 0115-946 0101 Fax: 0115-946 0606 E-mail: sales@exel.co.uk *Computer software developers*

Excel Consultants Ltd, 10 Laburnham Road, Maidenhead, Berkshire, SL6 4DB Tel: (01628) 631991 *Computer chip designers*

▶ Excel Couriers UK, 11 St. Johns Road, Peterborough, PE2 8BL Tel: (07786) 128197 Fax: (0870) 7625282 E-mail: pete@excel-couriers.co.uk *An efficient and professional Same-day Courier service to meet all your needs throughout the UK 'Delivering First Time, On Time'*

▶ Excel Cutting Formes Ltd, Unit 39, Horndon Industrial Park, West Horndon, Brentwood, Essex, CM13 3XD Tel: (01277) 811116 Fax: (01277) 812778 E-mail: info@excelsf.com *Printing machine services*

Excel Embroidery, 12 Argyll Road, Rosneath, Helensburgh, Dunbartonshire, G84 0RP Tel: (01436) 831850 Fax: (01436) 831028 E-mail: sales@excel-embroidery.com *Embroidered garment suppliers*

Excel Glass Ltd, Musgrave Park Industrial Estate, Stockmans Way, Belfast, BT9 7ET Tel: (028) 9038 2121 Fax: (028) 9038 1951 E-mail: bg@excel.dnet.co.uk *PVCu door manufrs*

Excel Graphics Ltd, Unit 20 Finch Drive, Braintree, Essex, CM7 2SF Tel: (01376) 551199 Fax: (01376) 322899 *Prestige sign systems manufrs*

Excel Heat, Oak St Trading Estate, Oak Street, Quarry Bank, Brierley Hill, West Midlands, DY5 2JQ Tel: (01384) 560713 Fax: (01384) 411742 E-mail: excelheat@freeuk.com *Furnaces & heat treatment*

Excel I T Ltd, Trafalgar House, 712 London Road, Grays, Essex, RM20 3JT Tel: (01708) 865855 Fax: (01708) 866856 E-mail: enquiries@excelit.com *Computer cable installation services*

Excel Industrial Systems Ltd, Unit 4, Beeston Court, Stuart Road, Manor Park, Runcorn, Cheshire, WA7 1SS Tel: 01928 597834 Fax: 01928 579308 E-mail: sales@xlg.co.uk *Control systems manufrs*

Excel Industries, Maerdy Industrial Estate, Rhymney, Tredegar, Gwent, NP22 5PY Tel: (01685) 845200 Fax: (01685) 844106 E-mail: info@excelfibre.com *Recycled insulating material manufrs*

▶ Excel Installations, Little Hyde Farm, Little Hyde Lane, Ingatestone, Essex, CM4 0DU Tel: (01277) 356438 Fax: (01277) 356441 *Shop fitting service*

Excel Kids' Club & Chilcare Services Ltd, 9 Holliday Square, Battersea, London, SW11 2HR Tel: (020) 8672 3800 Fax: (020) 8767 5139 E-mail: admin@excelservices.co.uk *Cleaning & childcare services*

Excel Labels Ltd, 9 Crown Road, Kings Norton Business Centre, Birmingham, B30 3HY Tel: 0121-486 3300 Fax: 0121-486 3330 E-mail: enquiries@excellabels.co.uk *Label manufrs*

Excel Laces & Fabrics Ltd, 13 Rancliffe Avenue, Keyworth, Nottingham, NG12 5HY Tel: 0115-937 5030 Fax: 0115-937 6619 E-mail: clive-johnson@lineone.net *Lace exporters & manufrs*

Excel London, 6-16 Arbutus Street, London, E8 4DT Tel: (020) 7241 2100 Fax: (020) 7923 0098 E-mail: info@excellondon.co.uk *Ladies wear suppliers*

Excel Marketing, Excel House, 6 The Crescent, Abbots Langley, Hertfordshire, WD5 0DS Tel: (01923) 261003 Fax: (01923) 266899 E-mail: adrianclarke@excelmarketing.co.uk *Internet marketing consultants specialists*

Excel Office Equipment, 24 Mannamead Road, Plymouth, PL4 7AA Tel: (01752) 660151 Fax: (01752) 225778 E-mail: sales@exeloffice.co.uk *Office equipment distributors*

Excel Packaging & Insulation Co. Ltd, Unit 9, Woodcock Hill Estate, Harefield Road, Rickmansworth, Hertfordshire, WD3 1PQ Tel: (01923) 770247 Fax: (01923) 770248 E-mail: enquiries@excelpackaging.co.uk *Located in Greater London, Excel Packaging & Insulation*

continued

Co Ltd is a specialist manufacturer of custom made protective packaging, foil insulation panels (Profoil) for use with warm water underfloor heating systems and insulated polystyrene cold boxes (FerriBox) for the distribution of temperature sensitive goods. A leading converter of industrial foams including flexible polyurethane foam (PU), expanded polystyrene (EPS), extruded polystyrene (XPS), and both cross-linked and non cross-linked polyethylene foams (PE), we manufacture high performance products for protective packaging, thermal insulation, medical, pharmaceutical, laboratory, building, construction and civil engineering, film, television, theatre, exhibition and display produced by manufacturing processes ranging from diecutting and laminating to hot-wire cutting, cnc contour cutting, profile cutting and routing.

▶ Excel packaging Machinery Limited, Unit 24b Monument Business Park, Warpsgrove Lane, Chalgrove, Oxford, OX44 7RW Tel: (01865) 400489 Fax: (01865) 890356 E-mail: info@excel-packagingmachinery.com *Excel Packaging Machinery Ltd is focused on supplying Packaging Machinery within the Cosmetic, Personal Care, Pharmaceutical and Healthcare industries.*Our team has nearly 50 years of experience collectively within design, manufacture, service work, troubleshooting, project management and sales and marketing of Packaging Machinery.**Our Principle lines of Supply and Service include:-** Unscrambling of bottles/containers* Bottle cleaning machines. * Semi-automatic and Automatic Liquid filling lines including: - Hot filling and Cream Filling.* Semi-automatic and Automatic Capping.* Labelling of bottles.* Tube filling and sealing of tubes, using Metal jaw, Hot jaw, Hot air, High frequency and Ultrasonic closure.* Cartoning machines for tubes.* Special purpose filling lines*

Excel Partnership, 25 Silverthorn Drive, Hemel Hempstead, Hertfordshire, HP3 8BX Tel: (01442) 242929 Fax: (01442) 216057 E-mail: training@excellpartnership.co.uk *Quality & environmental training consultancy*

Excel Plastering Ilford Ltd, 1 Natal Road, Ilford, Essex, IG1 2HA Tel: (020) 8553 2244 Fax: (020) 8553 4489 E-mail: excelplastering1@btopenworld.com *Plastering & flooring contractors*

Excel Powder Coating Ltd, 15 Chiswick Avenue, Mildenhall, Bury St. Edmunds, Suffolk, IP28 7PU Tel: (01638) 510993 Fax: (01638) 515089 E-mail: excel.sales@btopenworld.com *Powder coating services*

Excel Precision Engineering Ltd, 32 High St, Drayton, Abingdon, Oxon, OX14 4JW Tel: (01235) 538333 Fax: (01235) 538303 E-mail: neiltyler@btconnect.com *Precision engineers & engineering subcontract services. Also machinists, prevision machining services; milling engineering & CNC engineering services/ machinists*

Excel Precision Engineering Services Ltd, Unit 16, Trostra Industrial Estate, Llanelli, Dyfed, SA14 9UU Tel: (01554) 751935 Fax: (01554) 778804 E-mail: debbie@excel-eng.co.uk *Precision toolmakers*

Excel Precision Wse Ltd, Unit 2 Woodrow Way, Gloucester, GL2 5DX Tel: (01452) 419743 Fax: (01452) 307135 E-mail: sales@excel-precision.co.uk *Spark & wire erosion machining services*

▶ Excel Refrigeration, Unit 2, Angel Park, Chester Le Street, County Durham, DH2 1AQ Tel: 0191-492 1929 *Heating ventilation & air conditioning manufrs*

Excel Security Systems, 63 Vicars Hall Gardens, Worsley, Manchester, M28 1HW Tel: 0161-702 0500 Fax: 0161-702 0522 E-mail: sales@excelcctv.co.uk *Closed circuit television installation*

Excel Steel Stock, Harbour Road Trading Estate, Portishead, Bristol, BS20 7AT Tel: (01275) 847997 Fax: (01275) 849855 *Steel stockholders*

Excel Water, Unit 441a Thorp Arch Trading Estate, Thorp Arch, Wetherby, West Yorkshire, LS23 7BJ Tel: (01937) 844211 Fax: (01937) 844101 E-mail: sales@excelwater.co.uk *Water treatment equipment service providers*

Exceldee Ltd, Unit 120 Culham No1 Site, Station Road, Culham, Oxford, OX14 3DA Tel: (01865) 407003 Fax: (01865) 407390 E-mail: martingibson@exceldee.co.uk *Glass cutting machinery manufrs*

▶ Excelerated Performance Consulting, 6 Romani Close, Warwick, CV34 4TY Tel: 01926 402667 Fax: 01926 402667 E-mail: info@excelerated-performance.co.uk *EPC help people who are new to management or graduates who already have a lot of potential, but perhaps lack the direction, drive, or strategies to help reach their potential. Workshops on self management, free tips and tools, free e-courses, forum.*

Excell Metal Spinning Ltd, 27 Gunners Buildings, Limberline Road, Portsmouth, PO3 5BJ Tel: +44 (023) 9266 6456 Fax: +44 (023) 9266 5456 E-mail: excellmetal@btconnect.com *Excell Metal Spinning Ltd based in Hampshire UK are specialist metal spinners involved with aluminium, stainless steel and many more spun metal components.*

▶ Excell Precision Europe, Stanton Upon Hine Heath, Shrewsbury, SY4 4LW Tel: (01939) 250699 *Scale manufrs*

Excelsior Packers, Brookside Lane, Oswaldtwistle, Accrington, Lancashire, BB5 3NY Tel: (01254) 356622 Fax: (01254) 356677 E-mail: sales@gemweb.co.uk *Contract packaging & powder mixing services*

▶ Excelsior Professional Search Ltd, 34 South Molton Street, London, W1K 5RG Tel: 020 7495 3088 Fax: 020 7495 3089 E-mail: general@excelsiorsearch.com *London based, niche market, search consultancy specialising in recruitment solutions for information technology vendors, service providers and management consultancies servicing the Global Financial Markets.*

Excelsior Rotational Moulding Ltd, Ferngrove Mills, Rochdale Old Road, Bury, Lancashire, BL9 7LS Tel: 0161-797 0855 Fax: 0161-763 1614 E-mail: sales@excelsior-ltd.co.uk *Manufacturers of plastic vacuum cases*

Excelsyn Ltd, Mostyn Road, Holywell, Flintshire, CH8 9DN Tel: (01352) 717100 Fax: (01352) 717171 E-mail: info@excelsyn.com *Chemical research, development & chemical manufrs*

▶ Exceptional Thinking LLP, 10 Orchard Road, Alderton, Tewkesbury, Gloucestershire, GL20 8NS Tel: (0845) 6449371 Fax: 0870 751 8215 E-mail: info@exceptionalthinking.co.uk *Business support services. Marketing /Business planning /Retaining & motivating staff /On-line training /Will your business idea work in the market?*

▶ Excess Baggage, 4 Hannah Close, Great Central Way, London, NW10 0UX Tel: (020) 8324 2000 Fax: (020) 8324 2089

Exchange Angling, 184 Elfredton Road, Nottingham, NG7 3PE Tel: 0115-942 4941 Fax: 0115-978 4158 *Fishing tackle RETAIL*

Exchange Communications Ltd, Exchange House, Kerr Stree, Glasgow, G66 1LF Tel: (0870) 0855000 Fax: (0870) 0505555 E-mail: info@exchangecommunications.co.uk *Telecommunication systems*

Exchange Engineering Ltd, Ruston Road, Grantham, Lincolnshire, NG31 9SW Tel: (01476) 578505 Fax: (01476) 590908 E-mail: admin@exchange-engineering.co.uk *Distributors of spares for pressure cleaning machines*

Exchem Explosives, PO Box 4, Alfreton, Derbyshire, DE55 7AB Tel: (01773) 832253 Fax: (01773) 520723 *Explosives manufrs*

Exciting Foods Ltd, 127 Cleethorpe Road, Grimsby, South Humberside, DN31 3EW Tel: (01472) 311955 Fax: (01472) 342436 E-mail: sales@excitingfoods.co.uk *Seafood manufrs*

▶ Exclusiv Fitted Interiors, 16a Longfield Road, Eglinton, Londonderry, BT47 3PY Tel: (028) 7181 1114 Fax: (028) 7181 4916 *Manufacturing kitchens & bedrooms*

▶ Exclusive, Unit 20, Butts Pond Industrial Estate, Sturminster Newton, Dorset, DT10 1AZ Tel: (01258) 472001 Fax: (01258) 473884 E-mail: sales@exclusive-furniture.co.uk *Fitted & free standing, modular & bespoke furniture for commercial*

Exclusive Move Solutions, 1 Cooks Road, London, E15 2PW Tel: (020) 8555 5179 Fax: (020) 8555 5172 E-mail: info@move-ems.com *Removal contractors*

Exclusive Salon Products Ltd, 64 High Street, Gravesend, Kent, DA11 0BB Tel: (01474) 320555 Fax: (01474) 320555 *Hair products wholesalers*

Exclusive Screens Ltd, PO Box 183,, Bishop Auckland, County Durham, DL15 8WW Tel: 01388 762377 Fax: 01388 762377 E-mail: info@exclusivescreens.co.uk *Fly screen specialists since 1990, we design , manufacture, supply and fit Domestic and Commercial screens throughout the North East of England. We also supply made to measure screens for self fitting or in diy kit form U.K. wide. See our dedicated website www.exclusivescreens.co.uk for full details..*

▶ Exclusively Skye Ltd, Tigh Shasaig Teangue, Sleat, Isle of Skye, IV44 8RD Tel: (01471) 820225 E-mail: ken@exclusively-skye.co.uk *Exclusively Skye, Scotland, is a world leader in corporate event planning, hospitality, managing corporate events and delivering corporate training and entertainment.*

Exco Fire & Safety Control Ltd, 46 St Gluvias Street, Penryn, Cornwall, TR10 8BJ Tel: (01326) 372878 Fax: (01326) 377135 E-mail: jack@excotec.co.uk *Safety equipment manufrs*

▶ Excubo, Tudor House, Harrogate, North Yorkshire, HG1 8JE Tel: (07710) 470825 *Excubo provides professional services in Surveillance, Intellience and Investigation, including due dilligence. Services also include static security consultancy.*

▶ Exde Software, 2-4 Hoxton Square, London, N1 6NU Tel: (020) 7739 7641 Fax: (020) 7739 7641 *Computer software developers*

▶ Exdel Design, Redwood, Norfolk Road, Turvey, Bedford, MK43 8DU Tel: (01234) 881566 Fax: (01234) 881450 E-mail: exdelservices@aol.com *Dusenbery spares and services*Machine upgrades*Bespoke machine design*

Exe Ltd, Mayfield, Pound Lane, Mannings Heath, Horsham, West Sussex, RH13 6JL Tel: (01403) 243444 E-mail: enquiries@exe.sk *Computer consultants*

Exe Boat Store Marine Ltd, 6 Camperdown Terrace, Exmouth, Devon, EX8 1EJ Tel: (01395) 263095 Fax: (01395) 263095 *Yacht, launch & boat builders & storage suppliers*

Exe Engineering Co. Ltd, 64 Alphington Road, Exeter, EX2 8HX Tel: (01392) 275186 Fax: (01392) 260336 E-mail: sales@exeengineering.co.uk *Grinding machine manufrs*

▶ Exe Print, 12 Flexi Units, Budlake Road, Marsh Barton Trading Estate, Exeter, EX2 8PY Tel: (01392) 204040 Fax: (01392) 494914 E-mail: michelle@exeprint.co.uk *Graphic design, pre-press & litho printers with in-house finishing*

▶ Exe Valley Dataset Ltd, 43 Marsh Green Road West, Marsh Barton Trading Estate, Exeter, EX2 8PN Tel: (01392) 426464 Fax: (01392) 491066 E-mail: sales@evdataset.co.uk *Computer typesetters, direct mail, digital print services*

▶ Exectec Solutions, National Deposit House, 11-13 Goldsmith Street, Nottingham, NG1 5JS Tel: 0115-988 1810 Fax: 0115-950 8900 E-mail: awalker@exectecsolutions.co.uk *Specialist suppliers of technical and executive recruitment either permanent, contract or temporary.*

Executive Autocare Centre, 70 Bury Road, Hemel Hempstead, Hertfordshire, HP1 1HW Tel: (01442) 260796 Fax: (01442) 233294 E-mail: executiveautocare@bt.com *Sunroof & electrical supplies & installation*

Executive Cameras Ltd, 80 York Street, London, W1H 1QW Tel: (020) 7723 4488 Fax: (020) 7723 4488 E-mail: photographers@amserve.co.uk *Camera hire*

Executive Catering Services, 107a High Street, Carrville, Durham, DH1 1BQ Tel: 0191-386 3682 Fax: 0191-383 0280 E-mail: eccs107a@aol.com *We are a catering company in the Northeast of England UK providing catering from business lunches to weddings and funerals no event to large or small*

▶ Executive Coaching & Mentoring Ltd, 67 Hampton Road, Southport, Merseyside, PR8 6QA Tel: (01704) 530821 E-mail: info@ecam.nu *Executive Coaching and Mentoring delivers coaching that helps maximise the return from your greatest asset - your people*

Executive Communications, Hi Tech House, 18 Beresford Avenue, Wembley, Middlesex, HA0 1YP Tel: (020) 8903 3425 Fax: (01784) 431560 E-mail: executivecomm@execs.com *Facsimiles & telephone repairs, sales & service*

Executive Communications Centres, 252-256 Kings Road, Reading, RG1 4HP Tel: 0118-956 6660 Fax: 0118-956 6415 *Business centre agents*

Executive Development, Fairlawns, Normans Green, Plymtree, Cullompton, Devon, EX15 2LA Tel: (01884) 277122 Fax: (01884) 277122 E-mail: info@execdevelop.com *Management development*

Executive Elect Ltd, 17 Brewery Lane, Stansted, Essex, CM24 8LB Tel: (01279) 814971 Fax: (01279) 647259 E-mail: carolineclarke@executive-elect.com *Human resource consultants*

Executive Facilities Ltd, 43 High Street, Marlow, Buckinghamshire, SL7 1BA Tel: (01628) 898556 Fax: (01628) 898139 E-mail: eft@efrecruitment.co.uk *Computer consultants*

Executive Grapevine International Ltd, New Barns Mill, Cottonmill Lane, St. Albans, Hertfordshire, AL1 2HA Tel: (01727) 844335 Fax: (01727) 844779 E-mail: sales@executive-grapevine.co.uk *Executive Grapevine is a publishing company that specialises in the talent management industry. Our products range from annual directories, online data, a monthly magazine and an events division.*

Executive Hotel Services, 165 Victoria Road, Swindon, SN1 3BU Tel: (01793) 615831 Fax: (01793) 513521 E-mail: ehs@btconnect.com *Conference organising services*

Executive Linen & China Hire, Unit 3 Cockshut La Business Centre, Commerce Street, Melbourne, Derby, DE73 8FT Tel: (01332) 694333 Fax: (01332) 694333 *Linen hire*

Executive Optics (Holdings), 205 Trafalgar Road, London, SE10 9EQ Tel: (020) 8858 8585 Fax: (020) 8293 5818 *Manufacturing opticians*

▶ Executive Security Solutions, Unit 6, Kings Ride Park, Ascot, Berkshire, SL5 8BL Tel: (01344) 319403 Fax: (01344) 319404 E-mail: mail@essukltd.co.uk *Private security company offering a number of specialist security services for businesses, government & people of wealth.*

Executive Software, Kings House, Cantelupe Road, East Grinstead, West Sussex, RH19 3BE Tel: (01342) 327477 Fax: (01342) 327390 *Computer software sales*

Executives Online, Dolphin House, St. Peter Street, Winchester, Hampshire, SO23 8BW Tel: (01962) 829705 Fax: (01962) 866116 E-mail: info@executivesonline.co.uk *Interim management agency providing fast track recruitment*

▶ Exedos Computer Services Ltd, 3 Lancaster Mews, South Marston Industrial Estate, Swindon, SN3 4YF Tel: (01793) 822833 Fax: (01793) 822433 *IT support services*

Exeeco Ltd, Regina House, Ring Road, Bramley, Leeds, LS13 4ET Tel: 0113-256 7922 Fax: 0113-236 3310 E-mail: sales@exeeco.co.uk *Gear box manufrs*

Exegesis S D M, 4 New Street, Talgarth, Brecon, Powys, LD3 0AH Tel: (01874) 711145 Fax: (01874) 711156 E-mail: sales@esdm.co.uk *Computer services*

▶ Exel, Brownsburn Industrial Estate, Airdrie, Lanarkshire, ML6 9SE Tel: (01236) 748181 Fax: (01236) 755656

▶ Exel, 33 Thames Road, Barking, Essex, IG11 0HQ Tel: (020) 8532 7201 Fax: (020) 8591 1017

▶ Exel, PO Box 7, Barnsley, South Yorkshire, S71 2QG Tel: (01226) 710025

▶ Exel, Bell Road, Basingstoke, Hampshire, RG24 8PU Tel: (01256) 463392

Exel, Ocean House, The Ring, Bracknell, Berkshire, RG12 1AN Tel: (01344) 302000 Fax: (01344) 710037 *Holding company* Also at: Liverpool

▶ Exel, Smoke Lane, Avonmouth, Bristol, BS11 0YA Tel: 0117-982 4541

▶ Exel, Rowley Road, Coventry, CV3 4LE Tel: (024) 7630 2664

▶ Exel, Berry Hill Industrial Estate, Droitwich, Worcestershire, WR9 9AW Tel: (01905) 794777 Fax: (01905) 796055

▶ Exel, Unit 1 Westfield Industrial Estate, Cumbernauld, Glasgow, G68 9HD Tel: (01236) 730030 Fax: (01236) 738061

Exel P.L.C., 23 Hall Rd, Hebburn, Tyne & Wear, NE31 2UG Tel: 0191-483 2671 Fax: 0191-489 0422 E-mail: jim.edmunds@btinternet.com *MANUFACTURERS OF PULWOUND GLASS FIBRE AND CARBON FIBRE TUBES AND HOLLOW PROFILES COMPOSITE HANDLES AND TELESCOPIC POLES. LATTICE MASTS AND LIGHTWEIGHT STRUCTURES PULTRUDED PROFILES, GLASS AND CARBON FIBRE WITH POLYESTER, VINYLESTER AND EPOXY RESIN SYSTEMS.*

▶ Exel PLC, 2 Hannah Close, London, NW10 0UX Tel: (020) 8903 3533 Fax: (020) 8903 7278

Exel, Harrier Parkway, Magna Park, Lutterworth, Leicestershire, LE17 4XT Tel: (01327) 308400 Fax: (01327) 308404 *Logistics & technology sales*

Exel Ltd, Storage & Interiors Centre, Northbank Industrial Park, Cadishead, Manchester, M44 5AH Tel: 0161-775 1611 Fax: 0161-775 4753 E-mail: sales@brookstore.co.uk *Storage equipment distributors*

Exel Ltd, Solstice House, 251 Midsummer Boulevard, Central Milton Keynes, Milton Keynes, MK9 1EQ Tel: (01908) 244000 Fax: (01908) 244244 E-mail: business.enquiry@exel.com *Suppliers of chain management services*

Exel, McKinney Industrial Estate, Mallusk, Newtownabbey, County Antrim, BT36 8YZ Tel: (028) 9084 3481 Fax: (028) 9083 3153 E-mail: pam.millar@dhl.co.uk *Freight forwarders*

▶ Exel, Sandy La West, Littlemore, Oxford, OX4 6JU Tel: (01865) 774544 Fax: (01865) 775099

Exel Ltd, Fairoak Lane, Whitehouse, Runcorn, Cheshire, WA7 3DU Tel: (01928) 701515 Fax: (01928) 713572 E-mail: sales@exel.net *Manufacturers of glass fibre pultrusions*

▶ Exel Designs Ltd, Danish Buildings, 44-46 High Street, Hull, HU1 1PS Tel: (01604) 517572 E-mail: info@exeldesigns.co.uk *Design and construction of retail and commercial premises, also multi media, product and graphic display systems.*

Exel Engraving Ltd, 19 Brickfields Industrial Estate, Finway Road, Hemel Hempstead, Hertfordshire, HP2 7QA Tel: (01442) 270510 Fax: (01442) 270520 E-mail: exelsales@aol.com *Signs, nameplates & control panels*

Exel Freight Management UK Ltd, Great South West Road, Feltham, Middlesex, TW14 8NE Tel: (020) 8750 7000 Fax: (020) 8890 8444 Principal Export Areas: Worldwide *Freight forwarders*

Exel Freight Management UK Ltd, Great South West Road, Feltham, Middlesex, TW14 8NE Tel: (020) 8750 7000 Fax: (020) 8890 8444 E-mail: derrick.froom@exel.com *Freight forwarders* Also at: Aberdeen, Bracknell & Bradford

▶ Exel Haulage, PO Box 1, Scunthorpe, South Humberside, DN16 1BP Tel: (01724) 865316 Fax: (01724) 847027

Exel Industrial UK Ltd, Unit 4 Lockflight Buildings, Wheatlea Industrial Estate, Wigan, Lancashire, WN3 6XR Tel: (01942) 829111 Fax: (01942) 820491 E-mail: enquiries@exel-uk.com Principal Export Areas: Worldwide *Incorporating Kremlin, Eurotec, Sames and Rexson into Exel Industrial has given us the largest and most diverse coating application equipment and fluid pumping range of all of our competitors. ATEX approved LVLP, HVLP, Conventional Airspray, Airmix, Airless, Electrostatic, Mechanical 2K and Electronic 2/3 or 4K proportioning systems, Total Energy Control powder coating, Flowmax pumps, Powder kitchens, Plastic powder booths, curing or drying systems, Reciprocators, electrostatic Bells are all offered as either independent components or as part of a turn key engineered solution. Using this equipment we have gained a proven track record in the Automotive, Aerospace, Plastic, Furniture, Joinery, Structural steel industries as well as many more. All of this equipment is manufactured by us! If you require any advice on ATEX or how to improve the efficiencies of your coating systems then please contact us. Our advice is free and will be guaranteed to save you money.*

▶ Exel Logisitics Ltd, Haydock Lane Trading Estate, Bahama Close, St. Helens, Merseyside, WA11 9XN Tel: (01942) 271111

▶ Exel Logistics Ltd, Riversdale Road, Carlyon Road Industrial Estate, Atherstone, Warwickshire, CV9 1LP Tel: (01827) 715333

▶ Exel Logistics Plc, Sanders Lodge, Northampton Road, Rushden, Northamptonshire, NN10 6BP Tel: (01933) 413255 Fax: (01933) 412746

Exel Management Ltd, 83-89 Phoenix Street, Sutton-in-Ashfield, Nottinghamshire, NG17 4HL Tel: (01623) 442211 Fax: (01623) 442844 E-mail: enquiries@exelmanagement.com *Fleet software developers*

▶ Exel Morrisons, West Avenue, Coventry, CV6 4QA Tel: (024) 7633 9080 Fax: (024) 7633 7239

▶ Exel For Somerfield, Bishopdyke Road, Sherburn In Elmet, Leeds, LS25 6JH Tel: (01977) 696000

▶ Exel Tankfreight Ltd, Smeaton Road, West Gourdie Industrial Estate, Dundee, DD2 4UT Tel: (01382) 621199

Exel Wheel & Tyre Services, Unit 18-19, Torrington Avenue, Coventry, CV4 9HB Tel: (024) 7646 8131 Fax: (024) 7646 5260 *Contract tyre fitters* Also at: Luton, Marchington & Preston

Ex-Eltronics UK Ltd, Grove House, Headley Road Greyshott, Grayshott, Hindhead, Surrey, GU26 6LE Tel: (01428) 606060 Fax: (01428) 606593 E-mail: sales@exeluk.com *Electronic component procurement agents*

Exergen Corp, Tollgate House, 69-71 High Street, Harpenden, Hertfordshire, AL5 2SL Tel: (01582) 461123 Fax: (01582) 461117 E-mail: sales@qhigroup.com *Temperature monitoring & infrared equipment distributors*

▶ Exescan Ltd, 37 Rolle Street, Exmouth, Devon, EX8 2SN Tel: (01395) 224141 Fax: (01395) 268829 E-mail: info@exescan.co.uk *ExeScan document management, electronic filing, document scanning software & systems*

Exeter Construction Ltd, 1 Pinbrook Industrial Estate, Chancel Lane, Exeter, EX4 8JU Tel: (01392) 464433 Fax: (01392) 464436 *Construction.*

Exeter Express Dispatch, Unit 15 Exeter Business Centre, 39 Marsh Green Road, Marsh Barton Trading Estate, Exeter, EX2 8PN Tel: (01392) 213229 Fax: (01392) 423538 *Immediate courier services dedicated*

Exeter Gearbox Centre, Grace Road Central, Marsh Barton Trading Estate, Exeter, EX2 8QA Tel: (01392) 434049 Fax: (01392) 437131 E-mail: info@gearboxcentre.com *Gear box manufrs*

Exeter Hose & Hydraulics Ltd, Unit 1 Kenton Place, Marsh Green Road, Exeter, EX2 8NY Tel: (01392) 218604 Fax: (01392) 412687 *Hydraulic hose manufrs*

Exeter Scale & Equipment Co., Grace Road Central, Marsh Barton Trading Estate, Exeter, EX2 8QA Tel: (01392) 275324 *Scale & slicer distributors*

▶ Exeye, 20 Denmark Street, London, WC2H 8NA Tel: (0845) 1303291 *Computer systems support & services*

Exfo Photonic Solutions, 2 Bank Place, Falmouth, Cornwall, TR11 4AT Tel: (01326) 311321

Exhall Grinding & Engineering Co. Ltd, Bayton Road, Exhall, Coventry, CV7 9DW Tel: (024) 7636 1111 Fax: (024) 7636 1236 E-mail: bhudson319@aol.com *Precision engineers*

Exhall Timber Products, Bayton Road, Exhall, Coventry, CV7 9EL Tel: (024) 7636 6706 *Joinery manufrs*

Exhausts By Design, West Well Farm, West Well Lane, Tingewick, Buckingham, MK18 4BD Tel: (01280) 847756 Fax: (01280) 847759 E-mail: grahamf@ukonline.co.uk *Exhaust systems manufrs*

▶ Exhibit Design UK, Rudry, Withybed Corner, Walton on the Hill, Tadworth, Surrey, KT20 7UH Tel: (07710) 413896 E-mail: studio@exhibit-design.co.uk *Exhibition Design UK - Provide Stylish 3D Conceptual Visualisations of Exhibition stands. High quality Photo-Realistic effects to compliment any project proposals*

Exhibition Department Ltd, South March, Long March Industrial Estate, Daventry, Northamptonshire, NN11 4PH Tel: (024) 7636 8474 Fax: (01327) 704488 E-mail: sales@theexhibitiondepartment.co.uk *Exhibition & display contractors*

Exhibition House, Exhibition House, 7 Davis Road, Chessington, Surrey, KT9 1TT Tel: (020) 8974 1781 Fax: (020) 8397 1736 E-mail: exhibit@mems.co.uk *Exhibition stand contractors*

The Exhibition & Interiors Co. Ltd, Station Road, Irthlingborough, Wellingborough, Northamptonshire, NN9 5QE Tel: (01933) 650222 Fax: (01933) 655688 E-mail: sales@exhibitionandinteriors.co.uk Principal Export Areas: Central/East Europe & West Europe *Shop fitters, exhibition stand contractors*

Exhibition Services Ltd, 6 271 Merton Road, London, SW18 5JS Tel: (020) 8874 1787 Fax: (020) 8874 1587 E-mail: info@exhibitionservices.com *Exhibition services*

Exhibition Works Ltd, 42 Lanchester Way, Royal Oak Industrial Estate, Daventry, Northamptonshire, NN11 8PH Tel: (01327) 705250 Fax: (01327) 705199 E-mail: sales@exhibitionworks.co.uk *Exhibition contractors & stand contractors services*

Exhibitions International Ltd, Clearwater Indust Estate, Wolverhampton, WV2 2JP Tel: (01902) 450040 Fax: (01902) 450567 E-mail: sales@exhibitionsinternational.co.uk *Promotional services*

Exide Battery Services Ltd, 6 & 7 Parkway Estate, Longbridge Road, Trafford Park, Manchester, M17 1SN Tel: 0161-488 5577 Fax: 0161-786 3334 E-mail: sales@exideuk.co.uk *Automotive battery manufrs*

Exide Technologies Power Network, Unit 14 Gunnels Wood Park, Gunnels Wood Road, Stevenage, Hertfordshire, SG1 2BH Tel: (01438) 359090 Fax: (01438) 727684 E-mail: elainemcleod@eu.exide.com *Industrial battery distribs*

▶ Exigent, Unit F2 Roden House, Roden Street, Nottingham, NG3 1JH Tel: (07974) 818110 E-mail: contact@by-exigent.co.uk *A Nottingham based Portrait Studio specialising in traditional Portraits, LifeStyle Portraits, Weddings and Model Portfolios*

▶ Eximbills Ltd, 31 Bury Street, London, EC3A 5AG Tel: (020) 7648 6060 Fax: (020) 7648 6061 *Computer software developers*

Eximedia UK Ltd, 4 Black Swan Yard, London, SE1 3XW Tel: (020) 7403 1555 Fax: (020) 7403 8524 E-mail: info@eximedia.co.uk *Office & computer supplies*

▶ Exiserv Ltd, 1 Page Heath Lane, Bromley, BR1 2DR Tel: (07931) 970900 Fax: (01474) 873589 E-mail: sales@exiserv.com *Office machinery servicing & maintenance*

Exitech Computers Ltd, Units 2-3, Sovereign Business Centre, Stockingswater Lane, Enfield, Middlesex, EN3 7JX Tel: (020) 8804 9942 Fax: (0845) 3701400 *Computer aided design system suppliers*

Exitflex (UK) Ltd, 5 Airfield Road, Airfield Industrial Estate, Christchurch, Dorset, BH23 3TG Tel: (01202) 478334 Fax: (01202) 488110 E-mail: sales@exitflex.co.uk *High pressure hose manufrs*

Exitile Ltd, 49-61 Jodrell Street, Nuneaton, Warwickshire, CV11 5EG Tel: (024) 7635 2771 Fax: (024) 7635 2761 E-mail: sales@exitile.com *Steel fabricators*

Exito Conveyors Ltd, 1 Woodhill Industries, Nottingham Lane, Old Dalby, Melton Mowbray, Leicestershire, LE14 3LX Tel: (01664) 823351 *Industrial conveyor belt system manufrs*

▶ EXL Coughlin, 4 Renaissance Way, Liverpool, L24 9PY Tel: 0151-448 2100 Fax: 0151-448 2139

▶ Exlen Technology, 172 Chatsworth Road, Chesterfield, Derbyshire, S40 2AR Tel: (01246) 236363 Fax: (01246) 557391 E-mail: mo@exlen.net *Computer & laptop upgrading repairs*

▶ Exmoor Air Conditioning Equipment, Windrush, West Anstey, South Molton, Devon, EX36 3NU Tel: (01398) 341134 *Air conditioning designers*

Exmoor Farm Supplies, Carnarvon Arms Garage, Market Close, Brushford, Dulverton, Somerset, TA22 9AG Tel: (01398) 323933 Fax: (01398) 323327 *Farm suppliers*

▶ Exmoor Manor Hotel, Barbrook, Lynton, Devon, EX35 6LD Tel: (01598) 752404 Fax: (01598) 753636 E-mail: info@exmoormanorhotel.co.uk *Countryside hotel ideal for business conferences*

Exmoor Plastics, Unit 2 4 Trinity Business Centre, South Street, Taunton, Somerset, TA1 3AQ Tel: (01823) 276837 Fax: (01823) 334154 E-mail: sales@exmoorplastics.co.uk *Surgical manufacturers for ent services*

▶ Exmore Metalcraft, Unit 1b Barns Close Industrial Estate, Barns Close, Dulverton, Somerset, TA22 9DZ Tel: (07779) 062850

▶ Exmouth Engineering Ltd, Unit 4, Pound Lane, Exmouth, Devon, EX8 4NP Tel: (01395) 267600 Fax: (01395) 223888 E-mail: sales@exmouthengerneering.co.uk *Engineering steel fabrication*

▶ Exodus Recruitment, Tower Bridge Business Centre, 46-48 East Smiths Field, London, E1W 1AW Tel: (020) 770 92070 Fax: (020) 770 92069 E-mail: nic@exodus-recruitment.com *IT recruitment*

Exol Lubricants Ltd, All Saints Road, Wednesbury, West Midlands, WS10 9LL Tel: 0121-568 2340 Fax: 0121-568 6720 E-mail: sales@exol-lubricants.com *Lubricant distributors & agents*

Exon Mobile House, Ermyn Way, Leatherhead, Surrey, KT22 8UX Tel: (01372) 222000 Fax: (01372) 222556 *Oil exploration & production*

Exoplan International Ltd, Unit 13, Industrial Estate, National Exhibition Centre, Birmingham, B40 1PJ Tel: 0121-780 4513 Fax: 0121-780 4810 E-mail: sales@exoplan.co.uk *Exhibition furniture contractors*

Ex-Or, Haydock Lane, Haydock, St. Helens, Merseyside, WA11 9UJ Tel: (01942) 719229 Fax: (01942) 272767 E-mail: marketing@ex-or.com *Lighting management systems*

Exordia Software Ltd, PO Box 7973, Ayr, KA7 4UQ Tel: (01292) 445599 Fax: (01292) 443343 E-mail: sales@exordia.co.uk *Sage solution centre & software developer*

Exotic Planet Juices Ltd, 17 Westpark, Eaton Rise, London, W5 2HH Tel: (020) 8723 7000 Fax: (020) 8723 7000 E-mail: exoticplanet@breathemail.net *Manufacturer of juice*

Exotic Veneer Co. Ltd, Uplands Trading Estate, Blackhorse Lane, London, E17 5QJ Tel: (020) 8531 3327 Fax: (020) 8531 2820 E-mail: andy@exotic-veneer.co.uk *Veneer merchants*

Expack Packers, 6 King St Industrial Estate, Langtoft, Peterborough, PE6 9NF Tel: (01778) 560381 Fax: (01778) 561118 *Export packaging services*

The Expanded Metal Company, PO Box 14, Hartlepool, Cleveland, TS25 1PR Tel: (01429) 867388 Fax: (01429) 866795 E-mail: sales@expamet.co.uk *Expanded metal products manufrs*

Expanded Piling Co Ltd, Cheapside, Waltham, Grimsby, South Humberside, DN37 0JD Tel: (01472) 822552 Fax: (01472) 220675 E-mail: info@expandedpiling.com *Piling specialists*

Expanded Polystyrene Supplies, Denton Island, Newhaven, East Sussex, BN9 9BA Tel: (01273) 612303 Fax: (01273) 517306 E-mail: sales@pabrico.co.uk *Polystyrene packaging specialists*

▶ Expatboxes, Robyn's Way, Edenbridge, Kent, TN8 5SE Tel: (07840) 891880 E-mail: info@expatboxes.com *Sending british expatriates worldwide their favourite things from home*

Expect Precision Services, 449 Scarborough Avenue, Stevenage, Hertfordshire, SG1 2QB Tel: (07802) 277353 Fax: (01438) 364874 E-mail: sinned72@hotmail.com *Digital readout distributors*

Expectations, 75 Great Eastern Street, London, EC2A 3RY Tel: (020) 7739 0292 Fax: (020) 7256 0910 *Clothing manufrs*

Expedite Precision Tools Ltd, Island Farm Avenue, West Molesey, Surrey, KT8 2UZ Tel: (020) 8979 0474 Fax: (020) 8783 1977 E-mail: expedite@btopenworld.com *Aviation tools & equipment*

Experian, Talbot House, Talbot Street, Nottingham, NG80 1TH Tel: (0870) 0121111 Fax: (01753) 594001 *Information solutions services*

Experience Payment, Eiger Point Swift Park, Old Leicester Road, Rugby, Warwickshire, CV21 1DZ Tel: (01788) 554800 Fax: (01788) 554900 E-mail: enquiries@eiger.co.uk *Computer software developers*

Expert Engineering Ltd, Queen Mary, University of London, Mile End Road, London, E1 4NS Tel: (0845) 6586933 E-mail: jshaikh@expertengineering.co.uk *Expert Engineering provides practical help for SME's who need fast, effective help with manufacturing engineering problems, proof of concept and prototyping. We offer a range of expertise including Fluids & Structural, Medical and Materials Engineering. We also have access to modern engineering test and calibration facilities, which means we can test and measure how your product will perform. This flexible multi-disciplinary approach solves problems quickly and cost effectively. Contact us for a no obligation assessment of your engineering needs. We offer a range of expertise including Fluids & Structural, Medical and Materials Engineering. We also have access to modern engineering test and calibration facilities, which means we can test and measure how your product will perform. This flexible multi-disciplinary approach solves problems quickly and cost effectively. Contact us for a no obligation assessment of your engineering needs.*

Expert Heat Treatments Kent, 12 Tribune Drive, Trinity Trading Estate, Sittingbourne, Kent, ME10 2PT Tel: (01795) 426545 Fax: (01795) 424449 E-mail: southsales@eht.co.uk *Steel heat treatment specialists*

▶ Expert Home and Office Services Ltd, 19 Satanita Close, London, E16 3TJ Tel: 0800 0431143 Fax: 020 4762285 E-mail: info@experthomeandofficeservices.co.uk *Experts in domestic and office cleaning and ironing services for the Greater London area.Quality guaranteed service designed to meet your requirements.*

continued

Expert Lighting Direct Ltd, 15 Cherry Fields, Bradford, West Yorkshire, BD2 1LB Tel: (01274) 722185 Fax: (01274) 722185 *Heat lamp distributors*

▶ Expert Logistics, Bury Road, Radcliffe, Manchester, M26 2XH Tel: 0161-777 1130

▶ Expert Marketing UK Ltd, 3 Simpkin Close Eaton Socon, St. Neots, Cambridgeshire, PE19 8PD Tel: (0778) 8131611 Fax: 01480 471221 E-mail: info@emlbigbags.com *We are the supplier of bigbags (FIBCs) in the UK with manufacturing sites in Turkey.*We can assure you will be very satisfied with our services and the high quality of our bulk bag products. We design quality bags to satisfy your needs...*

Expert Security Systems Ltd, 26 Wellowgate, Grimsby, South Humberside, DN32 0RA Tel: (01472) 241279 *Installers of security systems*

▶ Expertool, Unit 2, Regina Drive, Birmingham, B42 1BZ Tel: 0121-356 2002 Fax: 0121-356 1122 E-mail: expertool@btconnect.com *Tool manufacturers & distributors*

Expertplan Ltd, 471-473 The Arches, Dereham Place, London, EC2A 3HJ Tel: (020) 7739 1080 Fax: (020) 7739 9384 *Stainless steel fabricators*

Expertreat, Unit 3a Top Land Country Business Park, Cragg Road, Hebden Bridge, West Yorkshire, HX7 5HR Tel: (01422) 883535 Fax: (01422) 883535 *Timber treatment services*

Explan Computer Ltd, PO Box 32, Tavistock, Devon, PL19 8YU Tel: (01822) 613868 Fax: (01822) 610868 E-mail: info@explan.co.uk *Computers & software designer & solar powered computer design*

Exploration Electronics Ltd, Suffolk Road, Great Yarmouth, Norfolk, NR31 0ER Tel: (01493) 412040 Fax: (01493) 412044 E-mail: info@exploration-electronics.co.uk *Seismic equipment engineers*

Explorer, Poplar Park, Cliff Lane, Lymm, Cheshire, WA13 0TD Tel: (01925) 757588 Fax: (01925) 755146 E-mail: sales@explorerprocomp.co.uk *4 wheel drive mail-order suspension distributors*

Explosive Developments Ltd, The Airfield, Full Sutton, York, YO41 1HS Tel: (01759) 305568 Fax: (01759) 304873 *Explosives engineers*

Explosive Fibres Direct Ltd, Middlewood House, North Hill, Launceston, Cornwall, PL15 7NN Tel: (01566) 782973 Fax: 01566 782973 *Sportswear distribution*

Expo Display Service Ltd, 84a High Street, Stony Stratford, Milton Keynes, MK11 1AH Tel: (01908) 263656 Fax: (01908) 263616 E-mail: info@expo-display-service.com Principal Export Areas: Worldwide *Portable displays, magnetic pop-up display systems*

Expo Link Alarms Ltd, 35 Knowley Road, Beach Hill, Wigan, Lancashire, WN6 7PZ Tel: (01942) 494004 Fax: (01942) 825991 E-mail: sales@linkalarms.co.uk *Security alarms installers*

Expo Technologies Ltd, Summer Road, Thames Ditton, Surrey, KT7 0RH Tel: (020) 8398 8011 Fax: (020) 8398 8014 E-mail: sales@expoworldwide.com *Purge systems flameproof boxes*

Export Africa, 1 Terminus Industrial Estate, Durham Street, Portsmouth, PO1 1NR Tel: (023) 9282 3590 Fax: (023) 9281 2038 E-mail: sales@rundleholdings.co.uk *Export merchants*

Export Centre, Unit 72 Wimbledon Stadium Business Centre, Rosemary Road, London, SW17 0BA Tel: (020) 8947 6767 Fax: (020) 8944 1414 E-mail: info@london-freight.co.uk *Freight forwarding agents*

Export Courier, The Flarepath, Elsham Wolds Industrial Estate, Brigg, South Humberside, DN20 0SP Tel: (01652) 680093 Fax: (01652) 688459 E-mail: exporters@exportcourier.co.uk *Export marketing & publication*

Export Credits Guarantee Department, PO Box 2200, London, E14 9GS Tel: (020) 7512 7000 Fax: (020) 7512 7649 E-mail: help@ecgd.gsi.gov.uk *Credit insurance & finance packages*

Export & General Packing Co. Ltd, Chapter Street, Manchester, M40 2AY Tel: 0161-205 8948 Fax: 0161-205 4518 *Export packing services*

▶ Export Paperwork Services Ltd, 102 Stansted House, Third Avenue, London Stansted Airport, Stansted, Essex, CM24 1AE Tel: (01279) 680517 Fax: (01279) 680543 E-mail: tim@exportpaperwork.com *Export facilitators & business consultancy*

Exportential, 13 Beccelm Drive, Crowland, Peterborough, PE6 0AG Tel: (01733) 211873 E-mail: info@exportential.co.uk *Export consultancy, export mentoring & export training*

▶ Exporteze Export Business Strategy and Sales, 6 Overthwart Crescent, Worcester, WR4 0JW Tel: 01905 619363 Fax: 01905 619363 E-mail: exporteze@btinternet.com *Business consultancy, to help companies improve exportation market*

Exportmaster Systems Ltd, 33 St Peters Street, South Croydon, Surrey, CR2 7DG Tel: (020) 8681 2321 Fax: (020) 8667 1816 E-mail: info@exportmaster.co.uk *Computerised export systems*

Exposed Design, PO Box 35575, London, NW4 4UH Tel: 020 8202 5964 Fax: 0870 125 9115 E-mail: kellys@exposed.co.uk *Exposed : experts in retail branding.**Exposed create innovative design solutions that express the unique, successfully communicating the strengths of your products and business.**Our designs are focused on projecting your brand with clarity, in a way that your customers will find engaging and compelling.**Our services include:**~ Identity design*~ Interior design*~ Brand merchandising design*~ Retail graphics*~ POS design /in-store promotions*~ Literature design*~ Packaging design*~ Environmental graphics and signage*~ Retail brand strategy**Current clients include:** The Dean & Canons of Windsor* Speciality Retail Group plc* Alpha Retail* Emaar, Dubai* Wi5**We would love the opportunity to show you examples of our work and discuss how we could be of assistance.**Please contact us by email or telephone.*

continued

▶ Expositionists International, 62 Bridge Road East, Welwyn Garden City, Hertfordshire, AL7 1JU Tel: (01707) 390122 Fax: (01707) 390061 E-mail: info@expositionists.co.uk

▶ EXPOSURE, 4, Spinney Cottage, Hardwick Lane, Studley, Warwickshire, B80 7AD Tel: 0845 2304530E-mail: enquiries@exposure-photo.com *Modern wedding, portrait and commercial photography*

Exposure Electronics, 59 North Street, Portslade, Brighton, BN41 1DH Tel: (01273) 423877 Fax: (01273) 430619 E-mail: info@exposurehifi.com *Amplifier manufrs*

▶ Exposure, Marketing and Design Services, 12 FieldFare, Billericay, Essex, CM11 2PA Tel: 01277 621474 E-mail: paula@exposureonline.co.uk *We offer a full range of marketing, design and photography services (for print and the web) specifically for start-ups and firms with smaller budgets and limited resources. Exposure has only one aim and that is to provide you with the professional support you need.*

▶ Exposure Sign and Promotions, Lower Gosford Street, Middlesbrough, Cleveland, TS2 1NU Tel: (01642) 252500 Fax: (01642) 248988 E-mail: contactus@exposuresigns.co.uk *Sign contractors or sign makers or suppliers or installers*

Expotec Ltd, 10 Harles Arces, Hickling, Melton Mowbray, Leicestershire, LE14 3AF Tel: (01664) 822725 Fax: (01664) 822725 E-mail: tony.fox2@ntlworld.com *Consulting engineers, import & export agents*

Expotel Barton Ltd, Kingsgate House, Kingsgate Place, London, NW6 4TA Tel: (020) 7328 9841 Fax: (020) 7328 8021 E-mail: lores@expotel.com *Hotel reservation/ conference organising services*

Expotel Hotel Reservations Ltd, Albert Chambers, 13 Bath Street, Glasgow, G2 1HY Tel: 0141-331 1771 Fax: 0141-331 1117 E-mail: events@expotel.co.uk *Hotel & conference organisers*

Expotel Hotel Reservations Ltd, Leeds Bridge House, Hunslet Road, Leeds, LS10 1JN Tel: 0113-242 3434 Fax: 0113-234 2781 E-mail: info@expotel.co.uk *Hotel reservation, conference organising services & travel*

▶ Expotus Components, The Studio, Warehorne Road, Hamstreet, Ashford, Kent, TN26 2JJ Tel: (01233) 731137 Fax: (01233) 731237 E-mail: sales@expotuscomponents.com *Audio & hi-fi equipment or systems distributors*

Express, Unit 1b Thorn Business Park, Rotherwas, Hereford, HR2 6JT Tel: (01432) 278138 Fax: (01432) 278138 *Plumbers merchants, bath & shower distributors*

Express 2 Automotive Ltd, Tanfield Industrial Estate, Tanfield Lea, Stanley, County Durham, DH9 9NX Tel: (01207) 299859 Fax: (01207) 284896 E-mail: andy.clark@express2automotive.com *Precision engineering of automotive components*

Express 2000 Ltd, Pembley Green, Copthorne Common, Copthorne, Crawley, West Sussex, RH10 3LF Tel: (01342) 713500 Fax: (01342) 713520 E-mail: sales@express2000.co.uk *Freight forwarders & forwarding agents*

Express Bearings & Transmissions, Anglo Trading Estate, Shepton Mallet, Somerset, BA4 5BY Tel: (01749) 330002 Fax: (01749) 330003 E-mail: sales@expressbearings.co.uk *Bearings & transmission suppliers*

Express Bonding Services Ltd, Severn House, Western Road, Oldbury, West Midlands, B69 4LY Tel: 0121-552 0810 Fax: 0121-552 0125 *Laminated plastics fabricators*

Express Cappuccino Servicing, 4 Addison Gardens, Grays, Essex, RM17 5QU Tel: (01375) 385634 Fax: (01375) 396944 *Coffee making equipment suppliers*

Express Circuits Ltd, 22 Roman Way, Coleshill Industrial Estate, Coleshill, Birmingham, B46 1HQ Tel: (01675) 464884 Fax: (01675) 466759 E-mail: cam@express-circuits.co.uk *Printed circuit board manufrs*

Express Cleaning Supplies, Unit 14 190 Malvern Common, Malvern, Worcestershire, WR14 3JZ Tel: (01684) 565552 Fax: (01684) 577707 E-mail: sales@express-cleaning-supplies.co.uk *Commercial cleaning suppliers*

Express Composites Group Ltd, 8 Beccles Road, Loddon, Norwich, NR14 6JQ Tel: (01508) 528000 Fax: (01508) 528764 E-mail: sales@ex-pressplastics.com *Glass fibre mouldings manufrs*

Express Contracts Drying, Unit 8 Rassau Industrial Estate, Rassau, Ebbw Vale, Gwent, NP23 5SD Tel: (01495) 303363 Fax: (01495) 308683 E-mail: info@expresscontractdrying.com *Spray equipment manufrs*

▶ Express Courier Services, Unit 8d Northwood Business Park, Newport Road, Cowes, Isle of Wight, PO31 8PE Tel: (01983) 299944 Fax: (01983) 299944 E-mail: info@ecs-iow.co.uk *National and International Parcel and Document Courier.*Sameday Express Courier.*

Express Cutting & Welding Services Ltd, 245 Dawson Place, Walton Summit Centre, Bamber Bridge, Preston, PR5 8AL Tel: (01772) 334071 Fax: (01772) 628895 E-mail: sales@expressweld.co.uk *Express Cutting and Welding Services Limited based in Preston is a one stop shop for your cutting, welding and tool requirements. We are suppliers of welding equipment, consumables, workwear, safety equipment and hand and power tools. We also offer equipment hire and servicing and repairs of equipment by our highly qualified and approved engineers. We are a small company with a big reputation for being fast, flexible and technically proficient. We are ISO 9001 accredited. We combine excellent service and quality products with a speedy local delivery service at competitive prices to provide our customers with the best possible package.*

▶ Express Dairies Ltd, Smisby Road, Ashby-de-la-Zouch, Leicestershire, LE65 2UF Tel: (01530) 412858 Fax: (01530) 411237

▶ Express Dairies Ltd, Reform Road, Maidenhead, Berkshire, SL6 8BY Tel: (01628) 638892 Fax: (01628) 770650 *Manufacturers of dairy products*

▶ Express Dairies Milk, Hanson Road, Liverpool, L9 7BP Tel: 0151-525 9857

▶ Express Despatch, Unit 10 Horton Road, West Drayton, Middlesex, UB7 8JL Tel: (01895) 437792 Fax: (01895) 437782

Express & Echo Publications Ltd, Heron Road, Sowton Industrial Estate, Exeter, EX2 7NF Tel: (01392) 442211 Fax: (01392) 442294 *Publishing*

Express Electrical, Dunswell Road, Cottingham, North Humberside, HU16 4JG Tel: (01482) 846269 Fax: (01482) 876655 E-mail: sales@express-industrial-exports.co.uk *Industrial equipment distributor*

Express Electrical, Dunswell Road, Cottingham, North Humberside, HU16 4JG Tel: (01482) 846269 Fax: (01482) 876655 E-mail: sales@express-industrial-exports.co.uk *Trace heating systems distributors or agents service*

Express Electrical & Engineering Supplies, 37 Cable Depot Road, Clydebank, Dunbartonshire, G81 1UY Tel: 0141-941 3689 Fax: 0141-952 8155 E-mail: sales@expresselectrical.co.uk *Electrical engineering components distributor/ stockist:-Specialists- CableAccessories/Markers/ Labels/Laser engrav.plastics/st.steel. Produced to drawings/schedules- Sleeves/Heatshrinks/ Braids etc.*

Express Engineering Thompson Ltd, Kingsway North, Team Valley Trading Estate, Gateshead, Tyne & Wear, NE11 0EG Tel: 0191-487 2021 Fax: 0191-487 3172 E-mail: sales@express-group.co.uk *Precision machining & component engineering services*

Express Export Services Ltd, Arlette House, 143 Wardour Street, London, W1F 8WA Tel: (020) 7734 8356 Fax: (020) 7734 3729 E-mail: expressexportservices@ukbusiness.com *Freight forwarders*

Express Fabrications Ltd, 85 Cyncoed Road, Cardiff, CF23 5SD Tel: (029) 2046 4365 Fax: (029) 2073 6898 *Steel fabrication & welding*

Express Fire Equipment Ltd, Unit 4 Mersey Road Industrial Estate, Mersey Road North, Failsworth, Manchester, M35 9LU Tel: 0161-688 5050 Fax: 0161-688 5151 E-mail: john@xpressfire.co.uk *Suppliers of fire protection equipment & spares*

Express Forklift Services, Unit 14 Bell Farm Industrial Park, Nuthampstead, Royston, Hertfordshire, SG8 8ND Tel: (01223) 207964 Fax: (01223) 208664 *Forklift repairers & retailers*

Express Forwarders Ltd, 9 Meadowbrook Industrial Centre, Crawley, West Sussex, RH10 9SA Tel: (01293) 551642 Fax: (01293) 553375 E-mail: sales@expressforwarders.co.uk *International freight forwarders*

▶ Express Freight Services (UK) Ltd, St Andrews House, Tilbury Docks, Tilbury, Essex, RM18 7EB Tel: (01375) 844384

▶ Express Freight Solutions, 15 Leyden Road, Stevenage, Hertfordshire, SG1 2BW Tel: (01707) 333600 Fax: (01438) 725800 E-mail: enfield@xpd.co.uk *Overnight & Economy Parcel Services*Sameday UK*Contract Distribution*Storage & Distribution*

▶ Express Freight Solutions, Marsden Close, Welwyn Garden City, Herts, AL8 6YE Tel: 0870 3505300 Fax: 0870 3505301 E-mail: info@expressfreightsolutions.com *Sameday & Express UK & European Delivery Services*Overnight & Economy Parcel Services*Storage & Distribution*Specialised Delivery Services*International Freight Forwarding*

▶ Express Garden Furniture, 12-13 Lower Cherwell Street, Banbury, Oxfordshire, OX16 5AY Tel: (01295) 220430 Fax: (01295) 220431 *Garden furniture retailers*

▶ Express Heat Treatments, Unisant Trading Estate, Powke Lane, Cradley Heath, West Midlands, B64 5PY Tel: 0121-561 6500 Fax: 0121-561 6509 E-mail: sales@expressheat.co.uk *Shot blasting high volume tumble blast specialists*

▶ Express Heating Co. Ltd, Broughton Market, Edinburgh, EH3 6NU Tel: 0131-556 8242 Fax: 0131-557 2989 E-mail: sales@express-heating.co.uk

Express Hoses, Unit 1 18 West Bank Road, Belfast, BT3 9JL Tel: (028) 9037 0274 Fax: (028) 9037 0256 E-mail: expresshoses@btopenworld.com *Hydraulic hose fittings*

Express Instrument Hire Ltd, Express House, Church Road, Tarleton, Preston, PR4 6UP Tel: (01772) 815600 Fax: (01772) 815937 E-mail: sales@expresshire.net *Industrial electronic equipment & electronic systems hire/ leasing/rental. Also, thermal imaging services, test equipment, predictive maintenance specialists & thermal imaging energy conservation. In addition, thermal imaging equipment, thermal condition monitoring services & temperature infrared sensing equipment hire/ leasing/rental*

▶ Express Maintenance Ltd, 122 Holderness Road, Hull, HU9 1JP Tel: (01482) 325000 Fax: (01482) 325000 E-mail: maintenancecrew@aol.com *We are a Hull based property maintenance company that carry out all property care services through Yorkshire and Lincolnshire.*

Express Metal Finishers, Manchester Road, Mossley, Ashton-under-Lyne, Lancashire, OL5 9QN Tel: (01457) 837718 Fax: (01457) 835801 *Stove enamellers & powder coaters*

Express Moulds Ltd, Jubilee Works, 40 Alma Crescent, Vauxhall, Birmingham, B7 4RH Tel: 0121-359 6378 Fax: 0121-359 3792 E-mail: paul.yeomans@expressmoulds.co.uk *Injection mouldings manufacturers*

▶ Express Moves, 116 Greyhound Lane, London, SW16 5RN Tel: (020) 8677 3436 Fax: (020) 8769 1098 E-mail: sales@expressmoves.co.uk *Removals & storage suppliers*

▶ Express Offset Ltd, Unit 4 Brickfields, Liverpool, L36 6HY Tel: 0151-449 1512 Fax: 0151-449 2817

Company Information

Express Packaging UK Ltd, Express House, 471 Romford Road, Forest Gate, London, E7 8AB Tel: (020) 8519 9786 Fax: (020) 8519 5880 *Polythene bag & refuse sacks manufrs*

▶ Express Parcel Services, Unit 2 Gateside Industrial Estate, Lesmahagow, Lanark, ML11 0JR Tel: (01555) 894300 Fax: (01555) 895117

▶ Express Parcels, Unit 5, Monklands Industrial Estate, Kirkshaws Road, Coatbridge, Lanarkshire, ML5 4RP Tel: (01236) 449922

▶ Express Pipe, 1 Tylers Road, Roydon, Harlow, Essex, CM19 5LJ Tel: (01279) 792233 Fax: (01279) 792334

▶ Express Pipeworks Systems, 33 West Donington Street, Darvel, Ayrshire, KA17 0AW Tel: (01560) 320758 Fax: (01560) 323254

Express Polythene Ltd, Barford Street, Birmingham, B5 6AH Tel: 0121-622 2319 Fax: 0121-622 1179 E-mail: sales@expresspolythene.co.uk *Polythene bag sheeting distributor*

▶ Express Print, 66 Londesborough Road, Scarborough, North Yorkshire, YO12 5AF Tel: (01723) 351464 Fax: (01723) 507955

Express Radiators & Bathrooms Ltd, Abbey Mills, Charfield Road, Kingswood, Wotton-under-Edge, Gloucestershire, GL12 8RL Tel: (01453) 521166 Fax: (01453) 521799 *Heating distributors*

Express Refrigeration, Stoneleigh, 12 High Street, Bugbrooke, Northampton, NN7 3QF Tel: (01604) 832788 Fax: (01604) 832788 *Refrigeration units service*

Express Refrigeration Contractors Ltd, 2 Princess Street, Immingham, South Humberside, DN40 1LN Tel: (01469) 574561 Fax: (01469) 574628 *Refrigeration & air conditioning suppliers*

Express Reinforcements Ltd, Fordwater Trading Estate, Ford Road, Chertsey, Surrey, KT16 8HG Tel: (01932) 579600 Fax: (01932) 579601 E-mail: chertseysales@expressreinforcements.co.uk *Steel reinforcements*

Express Reinforcements Ltd, Eaglebush Works, Milland Road Industrial Estate, Neath, West Glamorgan, SA11 1NJ Tel: (01639) 645555 Fax: (01639) 645558 E-mail: sales@expressreinforcements.co.uk *Reinforcing bar & meshing specialists manufrs*

Express Reinforcements Ltd, High Street, Newburn, Newcastle upon Tyne, NE15 8LN Tel: 0191-264 3311 Fax: 0191-264 7842 *Cutting steel reinforcement*

Express Reinforcements Ltd, Unit 3A Denver Industrial Estate, Ferry Lane, Rainham, Essex, RM13 9BU Tel: (01708) 630767 Fax: (01708) 630787 *Steel reinforcing*

▶ Express Removals, 48 Clyde Street, Clydebank, Dunbartonshire, G81 1NW Tel: 0141-952 6000 Fax: 0141-951 4527

▶ Express Removals, 48 Clyde Street, Clydebank, Dunbartonshire, G81 1NW Tel: 0141-952 6000 Fax: 0141-951 4527

Express Rewinds, 28 Meteor Close, Norwich, NR6 6HR Tel: (01603) 411971 Fax: (01603) 426704 *Electric motor repairs*

▶ Express Security Systems, 88 Vallance Road, London, E1 5BW Tel: (020) 7377 6565 Fax: (020) 7900 1691 E-mail: marketing@etsuk.co.uk *electrical contractors*

Express Services, Henson Way, Telford Way Industrial Estate, Kettering, Northamptonshire, NN16 8PX Tel: (01536) 481778 Fax: (01536) 521412 E-mail: sales@express-services.uk.com *Rubber stamps manufrs*

Express Sewing Machines, 196 Pasley Street, Stoke, Plymouth, PL2 1DT Tel: (01752) 606262 Fax: (01752) 708999 *Sewing machine suppliers*

Express Signs, 66 Soundwell Road, Bristol, BS16 4QP Tel: 0117-957 1793 Fax: 0117-957 1793 E-mail: andy@expresssigns.fsnet.co.uk *Signs manufrs*

Express Signs, 1 Vulcan House, Vulcan Road, Solihull, West Midlands, B91 2JY Tel: 0121-709 0749 Fax: 0121-709 1059 *Sign manufrs*

Express Tanker (UK) Limited, 17 Ensign House, ADMIRALS WAY, CANARY WHARF, LONDON, E14 9XQ Tel: 0207 863 1790 Fax: 0700 597 6260 E-mail: info@expresstanker.com *TANKER CHARTERING SERVICES*Express Tanker is actively involved in filling tanker transportation requirements for the major oil companies, independents, most national oil companies and international *trading firms. We are also closely aligned with European and international tanker owners and work to secure profitable businesses for them. We offer our clients support in spot or period chartering of vessels for the transportation of crude oil and petroleum products and post-contract operations and communications related to tanker *chartering. Concluding several contracts daily, the Chartering Group stays abreast of the rapidly changing global oil and tanker markets through a worldwide contact network *and integrated information management system.***

▶ Express Toughening Ltd, 51-55 Fowler Road, Ilford, Essex, IG6 3XE Tel: (020) 8500 1010 Fax: (020) 8500 1010

Express T-Shirts Ltd, 194 Kingston Road, New Malden, Surrey, KT3 3RJ Tel: (020) 8949 4099 Fax: (020) 8949 3121 *T-shirt printing & embroidery*

Express Typesetters Ltd, 11 Riverside Park, Dogflud Way, Farnham, Surrey, GU9 7UG Tel: (01252) 724112 Fax: (01252) 721874 E-mail: sales@arrowpress.co.uk *Trade typesetters & printers*

Express Welding Suppliers Ltd, Express House, Wilmington Commercial Park, Bedford St, Hull, HU8 8AR Tel: (01482) 223745 Fax: (01482) 210350 E-mail: paul.woodgate@brc.com *Protective clothing suppliers & safety equipment*

Express Welding Supplies Ltd, Unit B3 Empress Park, Empress Road, Southampton, SO14 0JX Tel: (023) 8022 8668 Fax: (023) 8063 9697 *Welding supplies agents*

Express Wills, 1-3 Tonbridge Road, Barming, Maidstone, Kent, ME16 9HB Tel: (01622) 729333 Fax: 01622 729333 *Wheel manufrs*

▶ Express Windows, 7 Tufthorn Industrial Estate, Stepbridge Road, Coleford, Gloucestershire, GL16 8PJ Tel: (01594) 835755 Fax: (01594) 835755 *Window frames*

▶ Express Windows, 1 Bishopgate Business Park, Widdrington Road, Coventry, CV1 4NA Tel: (024) 7663 0430 Fax: (024) 7623 1811

Express Windows, 1 Trovers Way, Holmethorpe Industrial Estate, Redhill, RH1 2LH Tel: (01737) 768833 Fax: (01737) 768832 E-mail: mail@expresswindows.co.uk *Windows doors & conservatories supply & fit*

▶ Expressfire Co. UK, Duck Farm Workshops, Bockhampton, Dorchester, Dorset, DT2 8QL Tel: 01305 848222 Fax: 01305 848222 E-mail: sales@expresfire.co.uk *Sales & service of fire extinguishers & allied safety equipment*

Expro North Sea Ltd, Unit B2, Kirkhill Place, Kirkhill Industrial Estate, Dyce, Aberdeen, AB21 0GU Tel: (01224) 214600 Fax: (01224) 770295 E-mail: marketing.enquiries@exprogroup.com *Oil & gas services providers*

Exsa UK Ltd, 29 Marylebone Road, London, NW1 5JX Tel: (020) 7487 3989 Fax: (020) 7487 5179 *Textile converters*

▶ Exscentrix, 8 Fox Covert, River View Park, Nottingham, NG4 2DD Tel: 0115-847 8146 E-mail: sales@exscentrix.co.uk *Retail suppliers of Incense, Essential Oils, Fragrance oils, Incense burners, oil burners, vapourisers, accessories and related products*

▶ Exsup, Malvern View, Callow Farm, Hillside, Martley, Worcester, WR6 6QW Tel: (01886) 888392 Fax: (01886) 888392 E-mail: sales@exsup.co.uk *Suppliers of Quality Injection and Extrusion machinery for the plastics industry*

▶ Extec Screens & Crushers Ltd, Unit 9 Gortrush Industrial Estate, Omagh, County Tyrone, BT78 5EJ Tel: (028) 8224 3790 Fax: (028) 8224 1940 *Construction plant or equipment services*

Extec Screens & Crushers Ltd, Hearthcote Road, Swadlincote, Derbyshire, DE11 9DU Tel: (01283) 212121 Fax: (01283) 217342 E-mail: sales@extecscreens.co.uk *Screening plant & crusher manufrs*

▶ Extech 2000 Ltd, Albion House, 25 Bridge Street, Macclesfield, Cheshire, SK11 6EG Tel: (01625) 422992 Fax: (01625) 427150 E-mail: sales@extech.co.uk *IT solutions company*

Extech (Environmental Systems & Services) Ltd, Unit 2 Building 6, Stanmore Industrial Estate, Bridgnorth, Shropshire, WV15 5HR Tel: (01746) 767414 Fax: (01746) 767345 *Dust & fume extraction*

Extechnology Ltd, Wolfelands House, High Street, Westerham, Kent, TN16 1RQ Tel: (01959) 568168 Fax: (01959) 569933 E-mail: info@extechnology.com *Odour control services*

▶ Extend A Home, Veitch Place, Lennoxtown, Glasgow, G66 7JL Tel: (01360) 312300

▶ Extensor Ltd, Live & Let Live Cottage, Fore Street Weston, Weston, Hitchin, Hertfordshire, SG4 7AS Tel: (01462) 790444 Fax: 0870 762 5925 E-mail: enquiries@extensor.co.uk *Extensor is a training and development company with a difference. **We specialise in building bespoke leadership, management and business development programmes that combine training, coaching and targeted development workshops that are linked to the specific goals and objectives of the organisation. **Delivering an integrated combination of services in this way has a far greater impact on performance and therefore delivers a much better return on investment.**To assist students in translating classroom theory into practical application, Extensor's unique Knowledge Network provides them with personal access to a network of senior business leaders and experts from a variety of backgrounds. **

▶ Exterior-Coatings, 42 Heol Las, North Cornelly, Bridgend, Mid Glamorgan, CF33 4BD Tel: (01656) 740342 E-mail: support@exterior-coatings.com *Exterior coatings including painting, high pressure cleaning services*

External Bliss, Calder House, Spring Lane, Colne, Lancashire, BB8 9BD Tel: (01282) 857188 E-mail: info@externalbliss.co.uk *lancashire & yorkshire garden designer based in Colne. Scale drawings, planting, plants, sculpture, pots, patios, summerhouses, ponds & water features.*

Extinguisher Rental Service, 29-31 Bayes Street, Kettering, Northamptonshire, NN16 8EH Tel: (01536) 417231 Fax: (01536) 411484 *Fire & safety consultants*

▶ Extinguishers Direct, Suite 304 Great Northern House, 275 Deansgate, Manchester, M3 4EL Tel: 0800 5875835 E-mail: sales@extinguishers-direct.com *Fire extinguisher training*

Extinguishers Direct, 33 Harrington Rd, Worcester, WR2 5HD Tel: 01905 424044 *Fire extinguishers*

Extra Technology Services Ltd, 52-56 Shambles Street, Barnsley, South Yorkshire, S70 2SH Tel: (01226) 771117 Fax: (01226) 771118 E-mail: sales@extracomputers.co.uk *Computer repairers*

Extra Trade UK Ltd, 22 Sherwell Rise, Allerton, Bradford, West Yorkshire, BD15 7AP Tel: 01274 481994 Fax: 01274 547989 E-mail: extratradeuk@btinternet.com *importers and distributors agents for ironmongery,builders hardware,aluminium hardware,black antique hardware,curtain fitments,door and windows and cabinet hardware etc*

Extracair Services, 250 Bournemouth Road, Poole, Dorset, BH14 9HZ Tel: (01202) 736999 Fax: (01202) 736777 E-mail: sales@extracair.co.uk *Air conditioning & ventilation specialists*

Extract Technology Ltd, Bradley Junction Industrial Estate, Leeds Road, Huddersfield, HD2 1UR Tel: (01484) 432659 Fax: (01484) 432659 E-mail: info@extract-technology.com *Powder containment systems manufrs*

Extracta Products Ltd, Third Avenue, Team Valley Trading Estate, Gateshead, Tyne & Wear, NE11 0PR Tel: 0191-482 5005 Fax: 0191-491 0462 E-mail: extracta@extracta.co.uk *Carpet cleaning machine manufrs*

▶ ExtraMoneyTime, Byecroft, Bircher, Leominster, Herefordshire, HR6 0BP Tel: (01568) 780848 *An amazing opportunity to run your own part time (or full time) business from home*

▶ extremelives limited, Extreme House, Campbell Park, Milton Keynes, MK9 3FT Tel: 0870 0428607 *Thanks to the massive development of extreme sports over the last few years, we are pleased to welcome you to extremelives, the first company of its kind to offer a wide range of extreme sports coaching, holidays and expertise across Europe.**

Extronics Ltd, Meridian House, Roe Street, Congleton, Cheshire, CW12 1PG Tel: (01260) 297274 Fax: (01260) 297280 E-mail: sales@extronics.com *Global supplier and manufacturer of intrinsically safe and explosion proof equipment.*

▶ Extrucut 2000 Ltd, Unit 6 Francis Woodcock Trading Estate, Barton Street, Gloucester, GL1 4JD Tel: (01452) 303100 Fax: (01452) 303475 *Aluminium cutting service*

Extrude Hone Ltd, 1 Sovereign Business Park, Joplin Court, Crownhill, Milton Keynes, MK8 0JP Tel: (01908) 263636 Fax: (01908) 262141 E-mail: miltonkeynes.sales@extrudehone.com *Deburring of parts specialists*

▶ Extruded Windows Systems, River Street, Bolton, BL2 1BX Tel: (01204) 454455 Fax: (01204) 454456 E-mail: david.coleman@ewsbolton.co.uk *Aluminium fabricators*

Extrusion Form Tools Ltd, Malvern View Business Park, Stella Way, Bishops Cleeve, Cheltenham, Gloucestershire, GL52 7DQ Tel: (01242) 673377 Fax: (01242) 677711 E-mail: ash@extrusionformtools.com *Designers & manufacturers of extrusion die to the aluminium industry*

Extrusion & Moulding Compounds Ltd, Cwmavon, Pontypool, Gwent, NP4 8UW Tel: (01495) 772534 Fax: (01495) 772251 *Plastics processing & waste recovery*

Exvenda Export & Import Agents, 52 Eastwood Road, Manchester, M40 3TF Tel: 0161-688 0647 Fax: 0161-688 4182 E-mail: enquiries@expenda.com *Export merchants or agents*

Exward Services, Unit 5A, Merebrook Industrial Estate, Hanley Swan, Malvern, Worcestershire, WR13 6NP Tel: (01684) 310989 Fax: (01684) 310989 *Machine tool repair services*

Exwold Technology, Tees Bay Business Park, Brenda Road, Hartlepool, Cleveland, TS25 2BU Tel: (01429) 230340 Fax: (01429) 232996 E-mail: sales@exwold.com *Industrial blending, grinding powder & liquid filling services*

Exxon Mobil Group, Exxon Mobil House, Ermyn Way, Leatherhead, Surrey, KT22 8UX Tel: (01372) 222000 Fax: (01372) 222556 *Oil specialists*

▶ Exxonmobil Chemical Ltd, Unit 1, Harcourt Way, Meridian Business Park, Leicester, LE19 1WP Tel: 0116-289 6122 Fax: 0116-263 1055 *Thermoplastic material manufrs*

▶ Eye 4 Design, Turner Lane, Whiston, Rotherham, South Yorkshire, S60 4HY Tel: (01709) 373911 Fax: (01709) 720811 E-mail: sales@eye4design.co.uk *Web design specialists*

Eye Bolt Testing Services, 41 West Hill Drive, Dartford, DA1 3DU Tel: (01322) 402200 Fax: (01322) 402201 *Testing & installing for eyebolt*

▶ Eye For Design, PO BOX 4657, Shrewsbury, SY1 9AD Tel: 01743 353536 E-mail: sales@eyefor.co.uk *Eye For Design - the Shrewsbury based Graphic design specialists.*Eye For Design is about bringing excellent, affordable, and professional graphic design to you and your company...**

Eye Of The Heart Woodworking, Friday Street, Bridge Farm, Brandeston, Woodbridge, Suffolk, IP13 7BP Tel: (01728) 685890 *Build & fit kitchens, wood furniture design & manufrs*

▶ Eye Killer, 8 Dufferin Court, Bangor, County Down, BT20 3BX Tel: (028) 9146 2888 E-mail: info@eyekiller.com *Corporate identities, high impact web site design & development service*

▶ Eye Level Sunglasses, D2 Europa Trading Estate, Stoneclough Road, Radcliffe, Manchester, M26 1GG Tel: (01204) 864874 Fax: (01204) 864875 E-mail: sales@colvininternational.com *Export sunglasses internationally*

Eyebright Designs Ltd, 107 Leicester Road, Wolvey, Hinckley, Leicestershire, LE10 3HJ Tel: (01455) 220835 Fax: (01455) 220895 E-mail: info@eyebright.demon.co.uk *Electronics design*

▶ Eyecandy Model & Promotions Agency, 11-13 Derby Street, Manchester, M8 8QE Tel: 0161-833 3888 E-mail: info@eyecandy-promo.co.uk *Model & promotions specialists*

Eyecatchers Signs Ltd, Old Mill Victoria Road, Eccleshill, Bradford, West Yorkshire, BD2 2BH Tel: (01274) 630640 Fax: (01274) 630644 *Sign makers*

Eyecote International Ltd, Unit 10-11 Singleton Court Business Centre, Wonastow Road Industrial Estate, Monmouth, Gwent, NP25 5JA Tel: (01600) 772433 Fax: (01600) 715749 E-mail: sales@eyecote.com *Compact disc manufacturing equipmentdistributors*

Eyelevel Displays, 18 Market Square, Bishops Castle, Shropshire, SY9 5BN Tel: (01588) 630200 Fax: (01588) 630559 E-mail: info@eyelevel-displays.co.uk *Exhibition systems & graphic producers*

Eyeline Of England, 1 South Orbital Trading Park, Hedon Road, Hull, HU9 1NJ Tel: (01482) 327512 Fax: (01482) 224279 E-mail: info@eyelineuk.com *Manufacturing opticians*

Eyeline Visual Merchandising Ltd, Amsterdam Road, Hull, HU7 0XF Tel: (01482) 824191 Fax: (01482) 824193 E-mail: enquiries@eyeline.co.uk *Shop-fitters & suppliers of shop fittings*

▶ Eyestorm, Units G & H, The Network Centre, Berkley Way, Hebburn, Tyne & Wear, NE31 1SF Tel: 0191-424 2242 E-mail: michael.davison@eyestorm.com *Contemporary & Modern Art at Eyestorm **Our growing list of contemporary art with Eyestorm and Britart galleries, provides the ideal opportunity for you to see many of the popular works available online. Solo and group online exhibitions will be presented on a regular basis to herald the launch of new bodies of work, generally the more popular works are kept in stock.**Visit our main e-commerce gallery sites to buy and view online. **www.eyestorm.com www.britart.com*

Eyetag Ltd, Albert Works, Melville Street, Bradford, West Yorkshire, BD7 1JD Tel: (01274) 721332 Fax: (01274) 740196 *Tag label manufrs*

Eynesbury Warehousing, Eynesbury Hardwicke, St. Neots, Cambridgeshire, PE19 6XJ Tel: (01480) 215555 Fax: (01480) 470736 E-mail: eynesburyplant@btinternet.com *Plant & Machinery Hire*

Eynsham Park Sawmill, Cuckoo Lane, North Leigh, Witney, Oxfordshire, OX29 6PS Tel: (01993) 881391 Fax: (01993) 881391 E-mail: sales@eynshamparksawmill.co.uk *Sawmill, garden sundries, outdoor timber suppliers*

▶ Eyre & Baxter (Stampcraft) Ltd, 229 Derbyshire Lane, Sheffield, S8 8SD Tel: 0114-250 0153 Fax: 0114-258 0856 E-mail: sales@eyreandbaxter.co.uk *Manufacturers of nameplates, plaques, badges, labels, steel stamps, type dies, branding irons, stencil plates, electrochemical etching equipment, screen printed signs, fire & safety signs, control panels, rubber stamps, daters, markers, inks, machine engravers & general marking specialists*

▶ Eyre Colchester, Crown Business Centre, Old Ipswich Road, Ardleigh, Colchester, CO7 7QR Tel: (01206) 231870 Fax: (01206) 231325

▶ Eyre Electrical, C4 Castle Trading Estate, Snedshill, Telford, Shropshire, TF2 9NP Tel: (01743) 363650 Fax: (01952) 612715

Eyre & Elliston Ltd, Unit 1 Moseley Street, Birmingham, B12 0RT Tel: 0121-766 7273 Fax: 0121-766 7275 *Electrical supplies wholesalers*

Eyre & Elliston Ltd, H Bolton Central Industrial Estate, St Marks Street, Bolton, BL3 6NR Tel: (01204) 366601 Fax: (01204) 366602 E-mail: bolton@eyreandelliston.co.uk *Wholesale electrical distributors*

Eyre & Elliston Ltd, New Henry Street, Leicester, LE3 5AL Tel: 0116-262 9951 Fax: 0116-251 5542 E-mail: leicester@eyreandelliston.co.uk *Wholesale electrical supplies*

Eyre & Elliston Ltd, 49-57 Bridgewater Street, Liverpool, L1 0AU Tel: 0151-709 3154 Fax: 0151-709 6775 E-mail: liverpool@eyreandellitson.co.uk *Electrical wholesale distribs* Also at: Leeds, Warrington & Wrexham

Eyre & Elliston Ltd, 68 Arthur Street, Redditch, Worcestershire, B98 8JY Tel: (01527) 510101 Fax: (01527) 510131 *Wholesale electrical supplies* Also at: Lye & Stratford-on-Avon

Eyre & Elliston Ltd, 40 Brownfields, Welwyn Garden City, Hertfordshire, AL7 1AX Tel: (01707) 326344 Fax: (01707) 372334 *Electrical wholesale suppliers* Also at: Letchworth, Southall & Teston, Chesterfield

Eyre & Elliston Holdings Ltd, 191 Chatsworth Road, Chesterfield, Derbyshire, S40 2BD Tel: (01246) 274358 Fax: (01246) 220512 *Holding company*

Eyres Forgings Ltd, Lord North Street, Miles Platting, Manchester, M40 8HT Tel: 0161-205 1090 Fax: 0161-203 4513 *Drop forging manufrs*

Eyrevac Plastics Ltd, 7-15 Hungerford Road, Bristol, BS4 5HU Tel: 0117-971 5480 Fax: 0117-972 3593 E-mail: mailbox@eyrevac.co.uk Principal Export Areas: Worldwide *Plastic forming processors*

▶ EZ Wrap Ltd, Team House, 27 Nine Mile Ride, Finchampstead, Wokingham, Berkshire, RG40 4QD Tel: 0118-973 5000 Fax: 0118-973 7878 E-mail: enquires@ezwrap.co.uk *Supplier of DVD, CD and VHS stylish, quick and easy gift wraps.*

Ezy-Clean Windows Ltd, Parsonage Oast, East Sutton Hill, East Sutton, Maidstone, Kent, ME17 3DG Tel: (01622) 842727 Fax: (01622) 843827 E-mail: businesscentre@ezy-clean.co.uk *Domestic window cleaning in all areas throughout Kent using modern technology*

▶ ezyShopping4u, 59 Valentine Rd, Kings Heath, Birmingham, B14 7AJ Tel: (07929) 140030 E-mail: sam@ezyshopping4u.com

▶ EzyWebSpace.com, 63 Hitchin Street, Biggleswade, BEDS, SG18 8BE Tel: 01767 641131 Fax: 01767 640352 E-mail: support@ezywebspace.com *Great value web hosting packages can be tailored to suit personal or business packages. Online Web Design services available.*

Ezze Rise Trailer Solutions Ltd, 5 The Brookside Centre, Red Marsh Drive, Thornton-Cleveleys, Lancashire, FY5 4HG Tel: (01253) 875840 E-mail: info@ezrisetrailersolutions.co.uk *At last!!!!Self + Easy Loading Motorcycle Trailer. ... For those of you who have motorcycle trailers, you know the difficulty of loading your motorcycle on to the trailer, specially if you have a heavy bike. Moving the motorcycle up a ramp is never an easy task, and often you need two people to accomplish it right.*No longer! The solution comes from the U.K. and it''s called EZ Rise Trailer Solutions. The new type of motorcycle trailer lowers itself to the ground so you can roll on/off your motorcycle without a bother !***

▶ Ezze UK Ltd, 619 Sewall Highway, Coventry, CV6 7JE Tel: (024) 7666 7755 Fax: (024) 7672 7819 E-mail: wah@ezzeconsevatories.com *DIY conservatories to trade & domestic suppliers*

F 1 Services, 19 Bridge Street, Newark, Nottinghamshire, NG24 1EE Tel: (01636) 701832 Fax: (01636) 707114 E-mail: a.forman@f1services.co.uk *Computer repairers*

F A C E Schamu, The Stables, The Dean Estate, Wickham Road, Fareham, Hampshire, PO17 5BN Tel: (01329) 282049 Fax: (01329) 221707 E-mail: enquiries@schamu.co.uk *Fire alarm installation & manufrs*

continued

F A C T Delta Solutions Ltd, 10Th Floor, Alexandra House, 1 Alexandra Road, Swansea, SA1 5ED Tel: (01792) 465503 Fax: (01792) 465504 E-mail: mailbox@factdelta.com *Business support group IT solutions*

F A Gill Ltd, Parkfield Road, Wolverhampton, WV4 6EH Tel: (01902) 331141 Fax: (01902) 340772 E-mail: fagill@btconnect.com *Abattoir & sausage manufrs*

F & A Hill Ltd, 80 Brewer Street, London, W1F 9TZ Tel: (020) 7734 0652 Fax: (020) 7434 3698 *Cashmere, lambs wool, angora & lambs wool knitwear distributors*

F A I Automotive plc, Chiltern Trading Estate, Grovebury Road, Leighton Buzzard, Bedfordshire, LU7 4TU Tel: (0870) 8391800 Fax: (0870) 8391804E-mail: sales@faiauto.com *Automotive component distributors*

F A North Carlton Ltd, 179 Carlton Hill, Carlton, Nottingham, NG4 1GZ Tel: 0115-987 2339 Fax: 0115-987 7504 *Joinery manufrs*

▶ F A S E, 16 Bridge St, Bailie Gate Industrial Estate, Sturminster Marshall, Wimborne, Dorset, BH21 4DB Tel: (01258) 858101 *Sheet metal engineering*

F A S Products, Unit 140 142 Block 15, Newhouse Industrial Estate, Newhouse, Motherwell, Lanarkshire, ML1 5RX Tel: (01698) 833780 Fax: (01698) 831300 *Wholesale bakers*

F A Saunders & Son, 32 Franklyn Road, Canterbury, Kent, CT2 8PS Tel: (01227) 457241 Fax: (01227) 768136 E-mail: roberttwymp@aol.com *Services & repairers of waste disposal units*

F A Simpson Ltd, 186 Solly Street, Sheffield, S1 4BB Tel: 0114-272 5561 Fax: 0114-276 1500 *Pattern makers*

F A T I International Ltd, 9 Wight Way, Selsey, Chichester, West Sussex, PO20 0UD Tel: (01243) 606007 Fax: (01243) 606007 E-mail: fatiint@btconnect.com *Industrial electric heater manufrs*

F A Would Ltd, Ladysmith Road, Grimsby, South Humberside, DN32 9SH Tel: (01472) 241303 Fax: (01472) 360262 E-mail: enquries@wouldgroup.com *Builders & developers & care home operators*

F Askew Engineers Ltd, Thorpe Road, Howden, Goole, North Humberside, DN14 7AY Tel: (01430) 430035 Fax: (01430) 431869 E-mail: enqury@askewengineers.co.uk *Precision engineers*

F B A Spring Engineers, 4 Howard Road, Park Farm Industrial Estate, Redditch, Worcestershire, B98 7SE Tel: (01527) 523524 Fax: (01527) 523524 *Wire formed & straightening services*

F B Chain Ltd, Jubilee Road, Letchworth Garden City, Hertfordshire, SG6 1NE Tel: (01462) 670844 Fax: (01462) 480745 E-mail: phil.taylor@fbchain.com *Chain & associated parts manufrs*

F B Design Cabinet Makers, The Old Granary Workshop, Herriard Park, Herriard, Basingstoke, Hampshire, RG25 2PL Tel: (01256) 381855 Fax: (01256) 381856 E-mail: david@fbdesign.co.uk *Cabinet makers*

F B G Trident, Unit 1, Humber Road, Cricklewood, London, NW2 6DN Tel: (020) 8830 8000 Fax: (020) 8830 5347 *Tubular glass container manufrs*

F & B Hosiery Manufacturing Co. Ltd, 10 Nether Street, Manchester, M12 6HY Tel: 0161-273 5689 Fax: 0161-273 5691 *Hosiery manufrs*

F B Jennings & Sons, Mount Farm, Milverton, Taunton, Somerset, TA4 1QZ Tel: (01823) 400226 Fax: (01823) 401201 *Joinery manufrs*

F B Jesper & Son Ltd, 14 Oxford St, Harrogate, North Yorkshire, HG1 1PU Tel: (01423) 503998 E-mail: harrogate@jespers.co.uk *Retail & commercial stationery, office furniture & business machines*

F B M Group Services Ltd, 349-357 Ilderton Road, London, SE15 1NW Tel: (020) 7639 6991 Fax: (020) 7252 8017 *Building merchants*

▶ F B Ross & Co. Ltd, Rose Hill, 165 Lutterworth Road, Leicester, LE8 4DX Tel: 0116-277 1861 Fax: 0116-277 9986

F B S Engineering & Sanitary Supplies Ltd, Cockburn Works, Gowan Avenue, Falkirk, FK2 7HJ Tel: (01324) 628431 Fax: (01324) 611175 E-mail: fsb.distribution@btconnect.com *Sanitary ware distributor*

▶ F B Whitworth, 36 Queen Street, Clay Cross, Chesterfield, Derbyshire, S45 9EQ Tel: (01246) 862960 Fax: (01246) 862960

F Ball & Co. Ltd, Churnetside Business Park, Station Road, Cheddleton, Leek, Staffordshire, ST13 7RS Tel: (01538) 361633 Fax: (01538) 361622 E-mail: webmaster@f-ball.co.uk *Adhesive & floor levelling compound manufrs*

F Bamford & Co. Ltd, Ajax Works, Whitehill Industrial Estate, Stockport, Cheshire, SK4 1NT Tel: 0161-480 6507 Fax: 0161-477 7990 E-mail: sales@bamfordajax.com *Marine engineers & holding agents*

▶ F Beardsell & Son Ltd, Spring Gardens, Huddersfield, HD1 3PL Tel: (01484) 420974 Fax: (01484) 431528 E-mail: sales@fbeardsell.com

F Bennett & Son Ltd, 9 Chester Square Mews, London, SW1W 9DS Tel: (020) 7730 6546 Fax: (020) 7823 4864 E-mail: info@fbennettandson.co.uk *French polishing contractors*

F Bode & Sons Ltd, 1 Street Cottages, Stubbins Lane, Claughton-on-Brock, Preston, PR3 0QH Tel: (01995) 643210 Fax: (01995) 643211 E-mail: sales@bode.co.uk *Welding positioner manufrs*

F Brinklow & Co. Ltd, 121 Clare Street, Northampton, NN1 3JA Tel: (01604) 636845 Fax: (01604) 636862 *Sheet metalworkers*

▶ F & B's Pine Shop, 119 Falls Road, Belfast, BT12 6AA Tel: (028) 9023 0124

F Bullett & Co., Island Farm Road, West Molesey, Surrey, KT8 2UU Tel: (020) 8979 1573 Fax: (020) 8941 7352 E-mail: nickbullet@fbullet.com *Non-ferrous metal founders & pattern makers*

F C Ltd, Cromwell Road, Ellesmere Port, CH65 4DP Tel: 0151-355 8234 Fax: 0151-357 1223 *Manufactures & suppliers of perfume*

F & C Automatic Production Ltd, Quarry Road, Newhaven, East Sussex, BN9 9DG Tel: (01273) 515485 Fax: (01273) 517827 *Precision turned parts manufacturers & capstan machinists*

F C Brown Steel Equipment Ltd, 17 Queens Road, Bisley, Woking, Surrey, GU24 9BJ Tel: (01483) 474577 Fax: (01483) 489962 *Office furniture manufrs*

F C Curran Ltd, Duke Street, Nottingham, NG7 7JN Tel: 0115-970 6801 Fax: 0115-942 2221 E-mail: enquiries@fccurran.co.uk *General engineers*

F C E Ltd, Unit 15, St. Davids Square, Fengate, Peterborough, PE1 5QA Tel: (01733) 314387 Fax: (01733) 314487 E-mail: fce.ltd@ukonline.co.uk *Electrical contractors*

▶ F C E Materials Handling Ltd, Taylor Stiles Building, Methilhaven Road, Methil, Leven, Fife, KY8 3LA Tel: (01333) 429434 Fax: (01333) 423582 E-mail: info@fcegroup.com *Manufacture & maintenance of paper mills & bottling plants*

F & C Electric Ltd, 45 Luff Close, Windsor, Berkshire, SL4 4NP Tel: (01753) 866944 Fax: (01753) 866944 *Electrical contractors*

F C F Ltd, Suite 210 Spitfire Studios, 63-71 Collier Street, London, N1 9BE Tel: (020) 7713 6888 Fax: (020) 7713 5749 *Software developers*

F C Frost Ltd, 7 Benfield Way, Braintree, Essex, CM7 3YS Tel: (01376) 329111 Fax: (01376) 347002 E-mail: sales@fcfrost.com *Drainage & architectural product suppliers.*

▶ F C G Designs, 6 Conniston Crescent, Slough, SL1 6EE Tel: (07796) 858491 E-mail: fcgregory@fcgdesigns.co.uk *Sheet metal design*

F C Garlick & Sons, Garway Hill, Hereford, HR2 8RT Tel: (01981) 580365 Fax: (01981) 580365 *Agricultural contracting & mixed farmers*

F C Hammonds, 13-17 Dove Lane, Newfoundland Road, Bristol, BS2 9HS Tel: 0117-955 1377 Fax: 0117-987 2377 E-mail: f.c.hammonds@btclick.com *Sheet metalworkers*

▶ F C I Ltd, Unit 1, Burnhead Road, Port Glasgow Industrial Estate, Port Glasgow, Port Of Glasgow, Renfrewshire, PA14 5XQ Tel: (01475) 742621

F C Paton Southport Ltd, 43a Old Park Lane, Southport, Merseyside, PR9 7PR Tel: (01704) 227717 Fax: (01704) 227717 *Nail care & toiletries manufrs*

F C R Metal Fabrications, Summerfield, Chacley, Gloucester, GL19 4EE Tel: (01684) 274756 Fax: (01684) 274756 *Metal fabricators*

F C Richardson & Son Ltd, 194 Yardley Road, Acocks Green, Birmingham, B27 6LR Tel: 0121-706 6701 Fax: 0121-706 6701 *Demolition contractors*

F C Walker, The Archway, Bracondale, Norwich, NR1 2EE Tel: (01603) 626903 Fax: (01603) 762194 *Sheet metalworkers*

F.C. Whittle(Birmingham) Ltd, Unit 7, Union Road, Oldbury, West Midlands, B69 3EX Tel: 0121-544 7572 Fax: 0121-544 8132 *Sheet metal fabricators*

F Chadwick, Woodview, Willington Road, Willington, Tarporley, Cheshire, CW6 0ND Tel: (01829) 752211 Fax: (01829) 759080 *Joinery manufrs*

▶ F Chapman & Sons Ltd, International House, 19 Kennet Road, Dartford, DA1 4QN Tel: (01892) 833313 Fax: (01322) 556882

F Cuff & Sons, The Joinery Works, Alweston, Sherborne, Dorset, DT9 5HS Tel: (01963) 23219 Fax: (01963) 23053 E-mail: david@cuffandsons.freeserve.co.uk *Joinery services*

The F D A, Boston House, Little Green, Richmond, Surrey, TW9 1QE Tel: (020) 8332 9955 Fax: (020) 8332 2585 E-mail: nicola.breeze@thefda.org.uk *Representing the factoring & invoice discounting industry*

F D Anderson & Son, 19 St. Sepulchre Street, Scarborough, North Yorkshire, YO11 1QG Tel: (01723) 360072 Fax: (01723) 360072 *Joinery manufrs*

F D Copeland & Sons Ltd, 5 Westfield Street, London, SE18 5TL Tel: (020) 8854 8101 Fax: (020) 8854 1077 E-mail: sales@copelandoil.co.uk *Essential oil importers & exporters*

F D Electronics Ltd, Unit U1, Riverside Industrial Estate, Bridge Road, Littlehampton, West Sussex, BN17 5DF Tel: (01903) 734160 Fax: (01903) 734170 E-mail: info@fd-electronics.net *Electrical contractors*

F D H (Lisnaskea) Ltd, Main Street, Lisnaskea, Enniskillen, County Fermanagh, BT92 0JE Tel: (028) 6772 1697 Fax: (028) 6672 2468 *Food products wholesalers & distributors*

▶ F D Hutcheson, Unit 13 Clydebank Business Centre, 31 Clyde Street, Clydebank, Dunbartonshire, G81 1PF Tel: 0141-952 5868 Fax: 0141-952 5868

F D L Packaging Group, Abbeyway South, Vista Road, Haydock, St. Helens, Merseyside, WA11 0RW Tel: (01942) 722299 Fax: (01942) 271325 E-mail: sales@fdlgroup.co.uk *Fibre drum manufrs*

F D O'Dell & Sons Ltd, Cow Close Langford Road, Langford Road, Biggleswade, Bedfordshire, SG18 9JT Tel: (01767) 313113 Fax: (01767) 313113 *Scrap metal merchants*

▶ F & D Print Finishers Ltd, Engine Lane, Horbury, Wakefield, West Yorkshire, WF4 5NH Tel: (01924) 271034 Fax: (01924) 265866

F D Products, 1-5 Olympus Park Business Centre, Quedgeley, Gloucester, GL2 4NF Tel: (01452) 722944 Fax: (01452) 722825 *Stainless steel products*

F D S Ltd, F D S House, 94-104 John Wilson Busn Park, Chestfield, Whitstable, Kent, CT5 3QZ Tel: (01227) 741111 Fax: (0845) 0741112 E-mail: info@fds-uk.com *Field marketing consultants*

F D S International Ltd, The Ground Floor, Hill House, London, N19 5NA Tel: (020) 7272 7766 Fax: (020) 7272 4466 E-mail: enquiries@fdf.co.uk *Market researchers*

F D Statton & Son, Stone Farm, Hatherleigh, Okehampton, Devon, EX20 3LU Tel: (01837) 810237 Fax: (01840) 261216 *Abattoir plant*

▶ F D T Transport Ltd, 1 Crane Street, Manchester, M12 6EF Tel: 0161-274 4017

F D W Packaging, Allerton Mills, Allerton Road, Allerton, Bradford, West Yorkshire, BD15 7QX Tel: (01274) 491013 Fax: (01274) 481752 *Packaging suppliers*

F Dickson Transport Ltd, 51 Imperial Way, Croydon, CR0 4RR Tel: (020) 8686 6707 Fax: (020) 8686 9297 E-mail: higher@dicksons.co.uk *Road transport, haulage & freight services*

F Drury & Sons Ltd, The Abattoir, Tockenham Corner, Tockenham, Swindon, SN4 7PF Tel: (01793) 852467 Fax: (01793) 848470 *Abattoirs*

F Dunn, 84 Newtownards Road, Donaghadee, County Down, BT21 0PT Tel: (028) 9188 3243 Fax: (028) 9188 8483 *Agricultural machinery suppliers*

F E Bailey, Highgate Factory, High Gate, Helpringham, Sleaford, Lincolnshire, NG34 0RD Tel: (01529) 421219 Fax: (01529) 421580 E-mail: rosemary@rbaily22.freeserve.co.uk *Joinery manufrs*

F E Burman Ltd, 4 Rich Industrial Estate, Crimscott Street, London, SE1 5TF Tel: (020) 7206 1000 Fax: (020) 7206 1040 E-mail: info@feburman.co.uk *Direct mail services & printing reprographics*

F E C Services Ltd, National Agricultural Centre, Stoneleigh Park, Kenilworth, Warwickshire, CV8 2LS Tel: (024) 7669 6512 Fax: (024) 7669 6360 E-mail: sales@farmenergy.com *Agricultural consultancy technical & marketing services*

F E Export Ltd, 63-66 Hatton Garden, London, EC1N 8LE Tel: (020) 7242 2606 Fax: (020) 7242 4407 E-mail: john@fexport.demon.co.uk *Paper board exporters*

F E Harris Ltd, Barn Close, Plympton, Plymouth, PL7 5HQ Tel: (01752) 338311 Fax: (01752) 340748 E-mail: feharris@btconnect.com *Coffin makers*

F E I, Philips House Cambridge Business Park, Cowley Road, Cambridge, CB4 0HF Tel: (01223) 468555 Fax: (01223) 468599 *Scientific instrument distributors*

F E & J R Hopkinson Ltd, 124 Scotland Street, Sheffield, S3 7DE Tel: 0114-272 7486 Fax: 0114-275 0290 E-mail: sales@sheffieldknives.co.uk *Knife & tool manufrs*

F & E Joinery Ltd, 288 Croxted Road, London, SE24 9DA Tel: (020) 8671 1771 Fax: (020) 8674 3294 E-mail: fejoineryltd@gmail.com *Joinery manufrs*

F E Jones Builders Ltd, 303 Mount Road, Manchester, M19 3ET Tel: 0161-224 8001 Fax: 0161-224 8001 E-mail: fej.builders@emerson.co.uk *Joinery services*

F E L Valves Ltd, Pickmere Lane, Wincham, Northwich, Cheshire, CW9 6EB Tel: (01565) 733137 Fax: (01565) 733841 E-mail: fel.valves@virgin.net *Valve manufrs*

F E M, Bradware Industrial Park, Leonard Street, Bingley, West Yorkshire, BD16 1DP Tel: (01274) 511911 Fax: (01274) 511913 *Metal spinners & manufrs*

F E Moss Glass Ltd, 678 Green Lane, Ilford, Essex, IG3 9RX Tel: (020) 8590 5180 Fax: (020) 8599 1008 *Glass merchants*

F E Mottram Ltd, Oakes Green, Stevenson Road, Sheffield, S9 3XG Tel: 0114-244 6723 Fax: 0114-242 5344 E-mail: ferrometals@femottram.co.uk *Ferro alloy producers*

F E Mottram Non Ferrous Ltd, Radnor Park Industrial Estate, Congleton, Cheshire, CW12 4XE Tel: (01260) 271122 Fax: (01260) 271324 E-mail: info@femottram.co.uk *Aluminium manufrs*

F E Peacock Construction Ltd, Southdown, South Road, Bourne, Lincolnshire, PE10 0DX Tel: (01778) 391520 Fax: (01778) 391539 E-mail: enquiries@fepeacock.co.uk *Building contractors*

F E Philcox & Sons, 24 Church Road, Catsfield, Battle, East Sussex, TN33 9DP Tel: (01424) 892391 Fax: (01424) 892141 E-mail: mail@fep-gates.co.uk *Steel fabricators, gates & railings manufrs*

F E Robinson Hooton Ltd, Station Works, Hooton Road, Ellesmere Port, CH66 7NF Tel: 0151-327 1315 Fax: 0151-328 1694 E-mail: sales@ferobinson.co.uk *Precision engineers*

F E S C O, 201 Wylds Lane, Worcester, WR5 1EL Tel: (01905) 351058 Fax: (01905) 351058 *Fire safety equipment suppliers*

▶ F E S Recruitment & Personnel, 298 Stanley Road, Bootle, Merseyside, L20 3ET Tel: 0151-922 9392 Fax: 0151-922 9592 E-mail: craig@fes-recruitment.co.uk *We are a recruitment agency that specialize in HGV, Construction and Warehouse Staff*

F E Shaw Ltd, Acton Close, Long Eaton, Nottingham, NG10 1FZ Tel: 0115-973 3816 Fax: 0115-973 0708 *Chair frame makers*

F Eastwood & Sons plc, London Works, Ripple Road, Barking, Essex, IG11 0SY Tel: (020) 8591 7200 Fax: (020) 8591 4193 E-mail: sales@feastwood.co.uk *Shelving & racking importers & distributors*

▶ F Edmondson & Sons, Southgate, White Lund Industrial Estate, Morecambe, Lancashire, LA3 3DA Tel: (01524) 382211 Fax: (01524) 60729

▶ F F A Concepts, Rutherford Drive, Park Farm Industrial Estate, Wellingborough, Northamptonshire, NN8 6AQ Tel: (01933) 671980 *Metal & plastic suppliers*

F F G Hillebrand, Dissigna House, Weston Avenue, West Thurrock, Grays, Essex, RM20 3ZP Tel: (01708) 689000 Fax: (01708) 689001 E-mail: sales@ffg-hil.com *International freight forwarders*

F F G International Manchester Ltd, 24-26 Brook Street, Chadderton, Oldham, OL9 6NN Tel: 0161-626 8686 Fax: 0161-678 8407 E-mail: sales@ffg.co.uk *European freight forwarding agents*

F F P Packaging Solutions Ltd, 1-7 Tenter Road, Moulton Park Industrial Estate, Northampton, NN3 6PZ Tel: (01604) 643535 Fax: (01604) 790042 E-mail: sales@ffpkg.co.uk *Packaging material, goods & products manufrs*

F & F Promotions, Lower Gunstone, Bideford, Devon, EX39 2DE Tel: (01237) 422477 Fax: (01237) 422633 E-mail: sales@rockbymail.co.uk *Badge makers*

F G Adamson & Son, Adamsons, Occupation Lane, Swanland, North Ferriby, North Humberside, HU14 3QZ Tel: (01482) 636200 Fax: (01482) 631672 E-mail: enquiry@buyamower.co.uk *Horticultural engineers*

F G Barnes, Cuxton Road, Parkwood Industrial Estate, Maidstone, Kent, ME15 9YF Tel: (01622) 755531 Fax: (01622) 692216 E-mail: sales@fgbarnes.co.uk *Motor vehicle bodywork repairers*

F & G Cleaners Ltd, 31 Engleheart Road, London, SE6 2HN Tel: (020) 8698 1337 Fax: (020) 8697 0391 E-mail: mainoffice@fandgcleaners.co.uk *Cleaning contractors*

F G Curtis & Co Plc, Crownhall House, Elm Grove, London, SW19 4HE Tel: (020) 8947 8178 Fax: (020) 8944 1530 E-mail: info@fgcurtis.co.uk *Carton & cardboard box manufrs*

F G Davis & Sons Contractors Ltd, Smestow Bridge Industrial Estate, Bridgnorth Road, Wombourne, Wolverhampton, WV5 8AY Tel: (01902) 892364 Fax: (01902) 895283 *Construction Material Solutions.*

F G F Ltd, Fernhurst Road, Bristol, BS5 7XN Tel: 0117-951 7755 Fax: 0117-935 4231 E-mail: sales@fgfltd.co.uk *Fire protection materials distributors* Also at: Birmingham, Leeds, London, Manchester & Southampton

F G F Ltd, West Quay Road, Southampton, SO15 1GZ Tel: (023) 8021 2121 Fax: (023) 8022 3274 E-mail: southampton@fgflimited.co.uk *Fire protection equipment manufrs*

F G F Continental Ltd, Shadwell House, Shadwell Street, Birmingham, B4 6LJ Tel: 0121-233 1144 Fax: 0121-212 2539 E-mail: sales.fgf@ukonline.co.uk *Technical products exporters & importers*

▶ F G Fennell & Co. Ltd, Service House, Wildes Street, Lowestoft, Suffolk, NR32 1XH Tel: (01502) 572065 Fax: (01502) 588933

F G G Plant, Fyfield Hall, Fyfield, Ongar, Essex, CM5 0SA Tel: (01277) 899495 Fax: (01277) 899613 *Plant hire contractors*

F G H Controls Ltd, Openshaw Way, Letchworth Garden City, Hertfordshire, SG6 3ER Tel: (01462) 686677 Fax: (01462) 480633 E-mail: sales@fgh.co.uk *Calibration instruments & process control manufrs*

F G H Instrument Services, 29 Oldmill Street, Stoke-on-Trent, ST4 2RP Tel: (01782) 414445 Fax: (01782) 414486 E-mail: sales@fghinst.fsbusiness.co.uk *Temperature controller distribs*

F & G Lancaster, 16 Hockley Street, Birmingham, B18 6BL Tel: 0121-554 1454 Fax: 0121-554 1454 *Hand & machine engravers*

F G Lang Grays Ltd, 44 Clarence Road, Grays, Essex, RM17 6QL Tel: (01375) 374901 Fax: (01375) 374216 E-mail: info@langs.co.uk *Engineers supplies*

F G Parker & Co. Ltd, The Factory, 20 East Road, Bridport, Dorset, DT6 4AA Tel: (01308) 422987 Fax: (01308) 458257 *Woodworking*

F G Portable Buildings, North Barn Farm, Winterborne Stickland, Blandford Forum, Dorset, DT11 0ED Tel: (01258) 881350 Fax: (01258) 880668 *Portable buildings manufrs*

F G Precision Ltd, 10 Arkwright Gate, Andover, Hampshire, SP10 3SB Tel: (01264) 324231 Fax: (01264) 324231 E-mail: fgprecision@lineone.net *Precision engineers & toolmakers*

F & G Services, Charfield Road, Kingswood, Wotton-Under-Edge, Gloucestershire, GL12 8RL Tel: (01453) 842307 Fax: (01453) 844303 *Industrial cleaning equipment suppliers & manufrs*

F & G Smart (Shop Fittings) Ltd, Tyseley Industrial Estate, Seeleys Road, Birmingham, B11 2LA Tel: 0121 7725634 Fax: 0121 7668995 E-mail: info@smartshopfittings.co.uk *Birmingham'''s shop fitting warehouse*has been established since 1870 supplying quality retail shop fittings to small independent shops, independent groups and shop fitters. ** **We are a Tegometall Servicecenter we supply the no 1 shop fitting and shelving system in Europe and the UK, with continually replenished stocks of Tegometall shopfitting products, Tegometall Shelving and Tegometall units.**Full Range of Tegometall shop fittings From Stock Including: *Tegometall Shop Shelving *Storage Racking *Arneg Refrigerated Cabinets *Slatwall & Fittings *Counters *Gridwall *Slatwall *Display Cases *Card Racks *Dump Bins & Basket Units *Garment Rails *Hangers *Acrylic shop fittings Of All Types *Security Mirrors/Cameras *Shopfittings Leasing *

F G Stacy, Moor Park, Clawton, Holsworthy, Devon, EX22 6PQ Tel: (01409) 211201 Fax: (01409) 211565 *Steel fabricators*

F G Whitley & Sons Co. Ltd, Padeswood Road, Buckley, Clwyd, CH7 2JJ Tel: (01244) 550792 Fax: (01244) 549397 *Civil engineering contractors*

F H Browne & Sons Ltd, The Street, Ash, Canterbury, Kent, CT3 2AA Tel: (01304) 813146 Fax: (01304) 812142 E-mail: brownefh@aol.com *Church organ manufrs*

F & H Engineering Ltd, Victoria Works Industrial Estate, Accrington Road, Burnley, Lancashire, BB11 5EF Tel: (01282) 433178 Fax: (01282) 832247 *Engineering & contracting services*

F H Fashion, 2-6 Shaftesbury Rd, London, E7 8PD Tel: 020 84707215 *Clothing manufrs*

F H Gilman & Co., Bolton Hill Quarry, Tiers Cross, Haverfordwest, Dyfed, SA62 3ER Tel: (01437) 892222 Fax: (01437) 899353 *Ready mixed concrete*

Company Information

F H Lambert Ltd, Rembrandt House, King Georges Avenue, Watford, WD18 7PW Tel: (01923) 229444 Fax: (01923) 255717 E-mail: info@fhlambert.co.uk *Electroplating services*

F & H Pattern Makers, 7 Canal Street, Bootle, Merseyside, L20 8AB Tel: 0151-922 1349 Fax: 0151-922 1349 *Engineers' pattern makers*

F H Warden (Steel) Ltd, Landor Street, Birmingham, B8 1AE Tel: 0121-327 7575 Fax: 0121-327 7212 E-mail: sales@fhwarden.co.uk *Steel stockholders*

▶ F Howe & Sons Engineers Ltd, Robert Street, Eastville, Bristol, BS5 6NJ Tel: 0117-939 4400 Fax: 0117-939 3300 *Machining services*

▶ F Humphrey Heating Sussex Ltd, 62 Bates Road, Brighton, BN1 6PG Tel: (01273) 558571 Fax: (01273) 550160

▶ F I Printing Co Ltd, 41 Sherborne Street, Manchester, M8 8LE Tel: 0161-832 3198 Fax: 0161-832 6123 E-mail: sales@fi-printing.co.uk

F I R E Fire Industry Recources Equipment Ltd, Unit 19 Enterprise House, 44-46 Terrace Road, Walton-On-Thames, Surrey, KT12 2SD Tel: (01932) 222010 Fax: (01932) 226201 E-mail: office@firecontingency.com *Firefighting equipment suppliers*

F I S Chemicals Ltd, Chapel Croft, Bucksburn, Aberdeen, AB21 9TN Tel: (01224) 723796 Fax: (01224) 722807 E-mail: sales@fischem.co.uk *Industrial chemical maintenance contractors*

F I S Loveday Ltd, 16-18 Princip Street, Birmingham, B4 6LE Tel: 0121-359 3176 Fax: 0121-359 1098 E-mail: fisloveday@aol.com *Presswork & prototype producers*

F I Technology Ltd, Leyden Road, Stevenage, Hertfordshire, SG1 2BW Tel: (01438) 727270 Fax: (01438) 727271 *Transformer designers & manufrs*

▶ F I Training Services, 13 Rubislaw Terrace, Aberdeen, AB10 1XE Tel: (01224) 640891 Fax: (01224) 637982 E-mail: sales@fitraining.com

F J B Systems, 11 Claremont Road, Claygate, Esher, Surrey, KT10 0PL Tel: (01372) 468839 Fax: (01372) 471056 E-mail: sales@fjb.co.uk *Food plant design & project management*

F J Bamkin & Son Ltd, Unit 3 Washdyke Lane Workshops, Washdyke Lane, Hucknall, Nottingham, NG15 6NH Tel: 0115-963 2020 Fax: 0115-968 0013 E-mail: info@penninebamkin.co.uk *Hosiery manufrs*

F J Banks & Sons, Oldstead Grange, Oldstead, York, YO61 4BJ Tel: (01347) 868634 E-mail: enquiries@spillsave.co.uk *Agricultural engineers*

F J Beswick, 16 Gate Lodge Close, Round Spinney Industrial Estate, Northampton, NN3 8RJ Tel: (01604) 642227 Fax: (01604) 493998 E-mail: salesn@besnorth.co.uk *Wholesale paper merchants* Also at: Hertford & Leicester

F J Beswick Ltd, 10 Dudley Road, Oldbury, West Midlands, B69 3DN Tel: 0121-552 5391 Fax: 0121-552 2350 E-mail: salesoldbury@beswick.co.uk *Paper merchants*

F J Beswick Cotswolds Ltd, Ashville Trading Estate, The Runnings, Cheltenham, Gloucestershire, GL51 9PT Tel: (01242) 514776 Fax: (01242) 580519 E-mail: saleschelt@beswick.co.uk *Wholesale paper merchants service*

F.J.Blissett & Company Ltd, Palmerston Works, Roslin Road Acton, London, W3 8DH Tel: (020) 8992 7183 Fax: (020) 8993 1815 E-mail: gary.blissett@blissets.com *Book binders*

F J Booth & Partners Ltd, Dockside Road, Middlesbrough, Cleveland, TS3 8AT Tel: (01642) 241581 Fax: (01642) 223398 E-mail: enquiries@boothandpartners.co.uk *Structural steel, design & fabrication engineers*

F J C Excavations, 8 Acorn Way, Bootle, Merseyside, L20 6QA Tel: 0151-922 7788 Fax: 0151-922 7889 *Excavation & groundwork contractors*

F J Cambridge & Co. Ltd, 75 Stroud Road, Gloucester, GL1 5AQ Tel: (01452) 523581 Fax: (01452) 523581 *Monumental masons*

F J Campion Ltd, Thames View, Upper Sunbury Road, Hampton, Middlesex, TW12 2DL Tel: (020) 8979 2351 Fax: (020) 8979 2351 *Chain link & wooden fencing erecting*

F J Church Holdings Ltd, Centenary Works, Manor Way, Rainham, Essex, RM13 8RH Tel: (01708) 522651 Fax: (01708) 522786 E-mail: dave@fjchurch.co.uk *Non-ferrous & precious metal recycling services*

F J Cleveland & Co., 40-43 Chancery Lane, London, WC2A 1JQ Tel: (020) 7405 5875 Fax: (020) 7831 0749 E-mail: sales@fjcleveland.com *Patent & trade mark attorneys*

F J Cooper, Old Rumbelows Warehouse, Bryant Avenue, Romford, RM3 0AP Tel: (01708) 349036 Fax: (020) 7739 5777 *Saws sharpening distributors*

F J Dyke & Sons, Rear of 27 Dogfield Street, Cardiff, CF24 4QL Tel: (029) 2022 7074 *U-bolt manufrs*

F J Engineering Ltd, 4 Keyhaven Road, Milford on Sea, Lymington, Hampshire, SO41 0QY Tel: (01590) 644644 Fax: (01590) 644644 E-mail: fjengineer@aol.com Principal Export Areas: Worldwide *Manufacturers of pistons & piston rings*

F & J Exports Ltd, Unit 14, Thornleigh Trading Estate, Blowers Green, Dudley, West Midlands, DY2 8UB Tel: (01384) 213186 Fax: (01384) 456990 *Commercial vehicle spare parts suppliers*

F J & F J Farrington, 2-4 Ferry Lane, Cambridge, CB4 1NT Tel: (01223) 461361 *Fishing & angling equipment*

F J Glass & Co. Ltd, The Workshop, Mill Road, Okehampton, Devon, EX20 1PR Tel: (01837) 52255 *Motor repairs*

F & J Hauck Ltd, Linney Lane, Shaw, Oldham, OL2 8HB Tel: (01706) 848797 Fax: (01706) 844973 *Metal & steel fabricators*

▶ F J Jones Holdings Ltd, 9-10 Yates Lane, Cakemore, Rowley Regis, West Midlands, B65 0RA Tel: 0121-561 4494 Fax: 0121-561 5402

▶ F J Lane & Sons Ltd, 38 Temple Road, Windsor, Berkshire, SL4 1HW Tel: (01753) 866430 Fax: (01753) 850903 E-mail: sales@fjlane.co.uk

F J Luxton & Son, 21 Tip Hill, Ottery St. Mary, Devon, EX11 1BE Tel: (01404) 812646 *Funeral Directors*

F J Payne & Son Ltd, Oakfield Industrial Estate, Eynsham, Witney, Oxfordshire, OX29 4AW Tel: (01865) 882299 Fax: (01865) 882309 E-mail: sales@fjpayne.com *Specialist motor trade engineers services*

F J Purkis & Sons, 1-4 Lower Green West, Mitcham, Surrey, CR4 3AF Tel: (020) 8646 5914 Fax: (020) 8646 5914 *Joinery, general woodworker services*

F J R Engineering Ltd, 65b Blackpole Trading Estate West, Worcester, WR3 8TJ Tel: (01905) 454143 Fax: (01905) 454143 *Manufacturers of valve rotators & split collets for diesel engines & engineers, general engineering*

F J Ratchford Ltd, Kennedy Way, Green Lane, Stockport, Cheshire, SK4 2JX Tel: 0161-480 8484 Fax: 0161-480 3679 E-mail: sales@fjratchford.co.uk *Bookbinding supplies*

F J Williams & Son Ltd, 56 London Road, Teynham, Sittingbourne, Kent, ME9 9QN Tel: (01795) 521650 Fax: (01795) 522963 *Joinery*

F J Wiseman & Co, Ltd, 262 Walsall Road, Cannock, Staffordshire, WS11 0JL Tel: (01543) 504088 Fax: (01543) 574806 *Sporting gun repairs, retail & manufrs*

▶ F J Wookey & Co. Ltd, Lovell Mill, Sutton Hill Road, Bishop Sutton, Bristol, BS39 5UT Tel: (01275) 332377 Fax: (01275) 332377

F K B Electrical Ltd, Unit 10-12, Quakers Coppice, Crewe, CW1 6EW Tel: (01270) 501244 Fax: (01270) 251399 E-mail: fkb@fkb.co.uk *Electrical contractors*

F & K Electrical & Refrigeration Ltd, High Street Village, St. Austell, Cornwall, PL26 7SR Tel: (01726) 822288 E-mail: info@fk-ltd.co.uk *Electrical contractors, refrigeration, air conditioning sales & service*

F K Electrical Services Ltd, Hyde Park Corner, Leeds, LS6 1AE Tel: 0113-275 9044 Fax: 0113-230 4631 E-mail: fkelectrical@fsmail.net *Painting contractors & electrical services*

F K Ellis & Sons Ltd, Unit 2 Lower Sydenham Industrial Estate, Kangley Bridge Road, London, SE26 5BA Tel: (020) 8676 9428 Fax: (020) 8676 9429 E-mail: sales@fkellis.com *Builders & plumbers merchants*

F K F UK Ltd, Strode Road, Clevedon, Avon, BS21 6QQ Tel: (01275) 876021 Fax: (01275) 878480 E-mail: mail@fkf.co.uk *Spherical & plain bearing manufrs*

F K Fiber Products Ltd, The Croft, Long Lane, Waverton, Chester, CH3 7RB Tel: (01244) 335912 Fax: (01244) 332499 E-mail: mike@fkfiber.freeserve.co.uk *Aluminium fibre paper & felt made from 'SAFFIL' alumina fibres for use up to 1600 degrees centrigrade with high purity, low shrinkage & chemical resistance, available form 0.5 to 3mm thickness*

F K Moore & Son Ltd, 5 Wilton Road, Haine Industrial Park, Ramsgate, Kent, CT12 5HD Tel: (01843) 593440 Fax: (01843) 585883 E-mail: sales@fkmoore.co.uk *Screw manufrs*

F Kitchen Lancaster Ltd, Unit 6 Forestgate, Whiteland Industrial Estate, Morecambe, Lancashire, LA3 3PD Tel: (01524) 63835 Fax: 01524 63835 E-mail: sales@fkitchen.co.uk *gates,railings,balconys,wrought iron work,general welding & fabrication*

▶ F & L Accessories Ltd, 4 5 Chosen View Road, Cheltenham, Gloucestershire, GL51 9LT Tel: (01242) 571409 Fax: (01242) 574240 E-mail: sales@flacc.co.uk *Radio towers & masts supply services & steel fabricators*

F L Plastics Ltd, 6 Whiffler Road, Norwich, NR3 2AW Tel: (01603) 418989 Fax: (01603) 418990 E-mail: sales@flplastics.net *Bottle, plastic manufrs*

▶ F L S Metalwork Ltd, PO Box 54, Ipswich, IP7 6WB Tel: (01473) 827263 Fax: (01473) 829762 E-mail: mark@fls1.fsnet.co.uk *Supply & installation of metal architectural work*

▶ F L S Steel Structures Ltd, Garratt Street, Brierley Hill, West Midlands, DY5 1JU Tel: (01384) 484200 Fax: (01384) 484202

F L Smidth Ltd, 17 Lansdowne Road, Croydon, CR9 2JT Tel: (020) 8603 1500 Fax: (020) 8681 7229 E-mail: fls@flsmidth.co.uk Purchasing Contact: R. Heaney Sales Contact: R. Heaney *Cement production plant manufrs*

F & L Smout & Sons Ltd, Woods Lane, Cradley Heath, West Midlands, B64 7AH Tel: (01384) 569508 Fax: (01384) 412155 E-mail: lgreen@smout.sagehost.co.uk *Presswork manufrs*

▶ F Lloyd Penley Ltd, Bridge Road, Wrexham Industrial Estate, Wrexham, Clwyd, LL13 9SQ Tel: (01978) 661751 Fax: (01978) 664408

F M A Systems, Unit 37 Monument Business Park, Warpsgrove Lane, Chalgrove, Oxford, OX44 7RW Tel: (01865) 891682 Fax: (01865) 891685 E-mail: sales@fma-systems.com *Data consultants for oil industry*

F M C Technologies (UK) Ltd, Queensferry Road, Dunfermline, Fife, KY11 8UD Tel: (01383) 731531 Fax: (01383) 731297 *Manufacturers of drilling equipment*

F M Caine & Sons Ltd, Broad Eaves, Penybont Road, Knighton, Powys, LD7 1HB Tel: (01547) 528654 Fax: (01547) 529006 *Animal carcass transportation*

F M Conway, Conway House, Rochester Way, Dartford, DA1 3QY Tel: (020) 8636 8822 Fax: (020) 8636 8827 E-mail: enquires@fmconway.co.uk

F.M. Design Ltd, 2 Huntsworth Muse, London, N1 6DD Tel: (020) 7723 4188 Fax: (020) 7723 8644 E-mail: design@fmgroup.co.uk *Design consultants*

F & M Displays Ltd, Tower Hamlets Road, Dover, Kent, CT17 0BJ Tel: (01304) 208889 Fax: (01304) 205807 *Screen printers*

F M Electronics Ltd, 12 - 14 Forest Vale Road, Forest Vale Industrial Estate, Cinderford, Gloucestershire, GL14 2PH Tel: (01594) 827070 Fax: (01594) 827066 E-mail: sales@fmelectronics.co.uk *Supply & manufacture wire free alarm systems*

▶ F M G Group, Bridge Wharf, High Street, Hornsey, London, N8 7QB Tel: (020) 8340 3434 Fax: (020) 8340 3240E-mail: J.ryan@fmg.uk.net *Loft conversion & roof scaffolding specialists*

F & M Garden Machinery Ltd, The White House, Bentley Heath, Barnet, Hertfordshire, EN5 4RY Tel: (020) 8440 6165 Fax: (020) 8447 0670 E-mail: sales@fmgardenmachinery.com *Grass machinery merchants*

F M Global (T/U F M Insurance Co. Ltd), 52 Leadenhall St, London, EC3A 2BJ Tel: (020) 7480 4000 Fax: (020) 7265 6738 *Insurance underwriters*

F M Instruments, 66A High Street, Oakington, Cambridge, CB4 5AG Tel: (01223) 234141 Fax: (01223) 234141 *Precision engineers*

F M K Ltd, 3a Crown Buildings, The Green, London, E4 7EX Tel: (020) 8524 3595 Fax: (020) 8524 3566 E-mail: sales@fmk.co.uk *Computer consultants, resale & support*

▶ F M Print Ltd, Unit 5 Lennox Road Industrial Mall, Basingstoke, Hampshire, RG22 4DF Tel: (01256) 471072 Fax: (01256) 814915

F M S Ltd, 82 Queens Rd, Brighton, BN1 3XE Tel: 01273 721063 Fax: 01273 721406 *IT consultancy*

F M T Ltd, 606 Green Lane, Ilford, Essex, IG3 9SQ Tel: (020) 8590 3556 Fax: (020) 8599 1561 *Heating spares outlet services*

F M Taylor, High Whinnow Farm, Whinnow Road, Thursby, Carlisle, CA5 6QL Tel: (01697) 342191 Fax: (01697) 345005 E-mail: ftaylor.machinery@virgin.net *Agricultural implement distributors*

F Mace & Son Ltd, 13a Victoria Avenue, Camberley, Surrey, GU15 3HP Tel: (01276) 65798 Fax: (01276) 686525 E-mail: fmacesons@btconnect.com *Precision engineers & metal fabricators*

F Martin & Son Ltd, Bridgeman Street, Walsall, WS2 9NR Tel: (01922) 624666 Fax: (01922) 724198 E-mail: info@fmartinandsonltd.co.uk *Manufacturers of metal hooks & chains*

F Moxham & Son, 43 Higher Market Street, Farnworth, Bolton, BL4 8HQ Tel: (01204) 573342 Fax: (01204) 573342 *Window cleaning equipment suppliers*

F Murphy Metals Ltd, 29-35 Brougham Street, Leicester, LE1 2BA Tel: 0116-262 1468 Fax: 0116-253 2129 *Scrap metal merchants*

▶ F N R GROUNDCARE, F N R GROUNDCARE, LYNN ROAD, WISBECH, CAMBS, PE14 7AP Tel: 01945 581576 E-mail: enquires@fnrgroundcare.co.uk *FNR Groundcare is home to a wide range of quality used mowers, groundcare equipment, mini diggers and compact tractors.**As specialists, we can provide the right machinery and service to fulfill for your requirements, all at very competitive prices**

▶ F N Rice Pirbright Ltd, Toad Hall, Vapery Lane, Pirbright, Woking, Surrey, GU24 0QD Tel: (01483) 472005 Fax: (01483) 797780

F N W (Engineering Developments) Ltd, New Street, Skelmanthorpe, Huddersfield, HD8 9BL Tel: (01484) 861233 Fax: (01484) 864928 *Ventilation grille manufrs*

F & P Bacon Packers Ltd, 50 Nowell La, Leeds, LS9 6JE Tel: 0113-248 8455 Fax: 0113-248 8455 *Bacon packers*

F P Cartons Ltd, Ironmould Lane, Bristol, BS4 5SA Tel: 0117-972 3233 Fax: 0117-971 0381 E-mail: fpcartonltd@freeuk.com *Carton manufrs*

F P Castings Ltd, 40 Glenburn Road, East Kilbride, Glasgow, G74 5BA Tel: (01355) 900020 Fax: (01355) 900021 E-mail: fpcastings@aol.com *Investment & lost wax process castings*

F P Hurley & Sons Ltd, Queens Road, Bridgend Industrial Estate, Bridgend, Mid Glamorgan, CF31 3UR Tel: (01656) 661151 Fax: (01656) 645477 E-mail: bridgend@fphurley.co.uk *Mechanical services contractors* Also at: Cross Hands

F P Industrial Ltd, 78 Leicester Road, Wigston, Leicestershire, LE18 1DR Tel: 0116-281 2714 Fax: 0116-281 2714 *Woodworking machinery engineers*

▶ F P International (UK) Ltd, Boundary Road, Brackley, Northamptonshire, NN13 7ES Tel: (01280) 703161 Fax: (01280) 701915 E-mail: sales@fpintl.com *Polystyrene product manufacturers, recycle polystyrene*

F P M Henderson Ltd, 35 Halley Street, Glasgow, G13 4DJ Tel: 0141-941 1211 Fax: 0141-941 2011 E-mail: sales@fpmhenderson.co.uk Principal Export Areas: Central/East Europe *Marine equipment supply*

F P McCann Ltd, Whitehill Road, Ellistown, Coalville, Leicestershire, LE67 1ET Tel: (01530) 240024 Fax: (01530) 240025 E-mail: info@fpmccann.co.uk *Concrete drainage pipes manufrs*

F P Mailing Northwest, Waterfold Park, Bury, Lancashire, BL9 7BR Tel: 0161-797 7778 Fax: 0161-799 5777 *Mailroom equipment manufrs*

F P Mailing Systems Northern Ltd, 43 Walkington Drive, Market Weighton, York, YO43 3NR Tel: (01430) 871833 Fax: (01430) 873448 *Franking machine installers*

F P Mailing Systems (Services) Ltd, 2 Manor Farm Close, Windsor, Berkshire, SL4 4DJ Tel: (01753) 621868 Fax: (01753) 862566 *Franking machines sales & peripher*

F P Philpott Joinery Ltd, 7 Beehive Workshops Parkengue, Penryn, Cornwall, TR10 9LX Tel: (01326) 377596 Fax: (01326) 377596 E-mail: info@joinerscornwall.com *Joiners*

F P S Ltd, Lichfield Road, Tamworth, Staffordshire, B79 7TD Tel: (01827) 52525 Fax: (01827) 52238 *Servicing trailers*

▶ F P S Fire Protection Ltd, Friemark House, Pioneer Park, Bristol, BS4 3QB Tel: 0117-971 7050 Fax: 0117-935 1605 E-mail: sales@firemarkext.co.uk *Manufacturer of portable fire extinguishers*

F P S International, Flat 45, Sandringham Court Maida Vale, London, W9 1UA Tel: (020) 7289 5158 Fax: (020) 7286 5137 E-mail: bev.colson@fpsinternational.com *Consumer food goods importers/exporters & manufacturers agents*

F P T Industries Ltd, Airport Service Road, Portsmouth, PO3 5PE Tel: (023) 9266 2391 Fax: (023) 9267 0899 E-mail: info@fptind.co.uk *Rubber manufrs*

F P Tools Ltd, Tyseley Lane, Birmingham, B11 3PX Tel: 0121-707 3838 Fax: 0121-707 3097 E-mail: sales@fptools.co.uk *Tool distributors* Also at: Motherwell

F P W Axles Ltd, D4 Enfield Road, Accrington, Lancashire, BB5 6NN Tel: (01254) 383413 Fax: (01254) 390417 *Axle manufrs*

F & P Wholesale, Chantry Road, Woburn Road Industrial Estate, Kempston, Bedford, MK42 7SU Tel: (01234) 845600 Fax: (01234) 840379 *Plumbers' & heating merchants* Also at: Brierley Hill, Camberley, Chorley, Dartford, Leeds & Nottingham

F & P Wholesale, 30 Engate Street, London, SE13 7HA Tel: (020) 8463 1000 Fax: (020) 8297 2661 *Heating & plumbing merchants*

F Parkinson Ltd, Mowbray Drive, Blackpool, FY3 7UN Tel: (01253) 394411 Fax: (01253) 302088 E-mail: sales@fparkinson.co.uk *Building contractors*

▶ F Peart & Co. Ltd, Baltic Works, Baltic Street, Hartlepool, Cleveland, TS25 1PW Tel: (01429) 860308 Fax: (01302) 770051 E-mail: sales@fpeart.com *Steel fencing manufrs*

▶ F R Ball Insurance Ltd, 56 Frogmore Street, Abergavenny, Gwent, NP7 5AR Tel: (01873) 857533 Fax: (01873) 856915 E-mail: sales@frball.co.uk *Insurance company services*

F & R Belbin Ltd, 165-169 Whitley Road, Whitley Bay, Tyne & Wear, NE26 2DN Tel: 0191-252 4703 Fax: 0191-297 0812 E-mail: sales@frbelbin.co.uk Principal Export Areas: Worldwide *Machine tool manufrs*

F R C Services, Coxby House, Bottom Street, Northend, Southam, Warwickshire, CV47 2TH Tel: (01295) 770027 Fax: (01295) 770048 E-mail: richard.bracewell@ukonline.co.uk *Industrial waste containers repairers*

F & R Cawley Ltd, 1 Covent Garden Close, Luton, LU4 8QB Tel: (01582) 492694 Fax: (01582) 847453 E-mail: sales@frcawley.co.uk *Waste disposal contractors*

F R F Alarms Ltd, 136 Mackintosh Place, Cardiff, CF24 4RS Tel: (029) 2075 5799 Fax: (029) 2075 5799 E-mail: frfcardiff@aol.com *Intruder alarms*

F R Fletcher & Son Ltd, Carterton Industrial Estate, Black Bourton Road, Carterton, Oxfordshire, OX18 3EZ Tel: (01993) 844887 Fax: (01993) 840499 E-mail: frfletcher@tiscali.co.uk *Steel fabricators*

F R Hackworthy & Sons, Depository, Elliott Road, Plymouth, PL4 0SB Tel: (01752) 228815 Fax: (01752) 600615 *Office removal specialists*

▶ F & R Jackson Ltd, Woodside House, Barnard Street, Staindrop, Darlington, County Durham, DL2 3ND Tel: (01833) 660367 Fax: (01833) 660882

F R Mount Ltd, Tempest House, Lyon Road, Walton-on-Thames, Surrey, KT12 3PU Tel: (01932) 230011 Fax: (01932) 230022 *Engineers & turned parts*

F R R Ltd, Brockley Combe Road, Backwell, Bristol, BS48 3DR Tel: (01934) 862861 Fax: (01934) 863666 *Forestry consultants*

▶ F R S, 20 Winchcombe Street, Cheltenham, Gloucestershire, GL52 2LY Tel: (01242) 709501 Fax: (01242) 709502 E-mail: info@frs.uk.com *FRS provide complete office interior solutions including Design, Refurbishment and Fit-Out services,Office Furniture,*Partitioning, Suspended Ceilings,*Carpet and Flooring, Redecoration,*Office Moves, CAD Space Planning, Electrical & Mechanical Services,*Air Conditioning.*

F R Scott Ltd, Canning Street, Hull, HU2 8QS Tel: (01482) 324731 Fax: (01482) 214290 E-mail: sales@frscott.co.uk *Bolt & nut stockists*

F.R. Shadbolt & Sons, Ltd, 7 Springwood Drive, Braintree, Essex, CM7 2YN Tel: (01376) 333376 Fax: (020) 8523 2774 E-mail: sales@shadbolt.co.uk *Veneering services of panels & doors*

F R Smith & Co Newton Heath Ltd, Daisy Bank Mill, Terence Street, Manchester, M40 1GD Tel: 0161-681 1313 Fax: 0161-683 4763 *Industrial engineering supplies*

F R Stainless Ltd, Unit 7, Darrows Industrial Esate, John Branning Way, Bellshill, Lanarkshire, ML4 3HD Tel: (01698) 842779 Fax: (01698) 842770 *Catering equipment manufrs*

F R Street Ltd, Frederick House, Hurricane Way, Wickford, Essex, SS11 8YB Tel: (01268) 766677 Fax: (01268) 764534 E-mail: val@street.co.uk *Textile merchants*

▶ F Robbins (Transport) Ltd, Wholesmouth, St Andrews Road, Bristol, BS11 9BP Tel: 0117-982 7804

F S B Wholesale Ltd, Mirror Works, Cuckoo Hall Lane, London, N9 8DH Tel: (020) 8804 4333 Fax: (020) 8804 8777 *Batteries, electrical accessories, hardware tools & DIY distributors* Also at: London SW1

▶ F S C Ltd, Bronte Works, Chesham Street, Keighley, West Yorkshire, BD21 4LG Tel: (0845) 2305332 Fax: (01535) 683301

F S C Stainless & Alloys, Ledra Works, Reservoir Place, Walsall, WS2 9SN Tel: (01922) 612545 Fax: (01922) 637755 E-mail: sales@fscstainless.co.uk Principal Export Areas: Worldwide *Architectural cladding fabricators & manufrs*

F & S Factory Seconds, Church Bridge House, Church Bridge Park, Bridge Street, Cannock, Staffordshire, WS11 3DQ Tel: (01543) 468797 *Pine furniture & leather sofa retail & distribution*

F S Foot & Son, Fourways Farm, Northbrook, Micheldever, Winchester, Hampshire, SO21 3AH Tel: (01962) 774209 Fax: (01962) 774796 *Agricultural engineers*

▶ F & S Gibbs Transport Services Ltd, 40 Boreham Road, Warminster, Wiltshire, BA12 9JR Tel: (01985) 213084

F S L Electronics Ltd, Sandholes Road, Cookstown, County Tyrone, BT80 9AR Tel: (028) 8676 6131 Fax: (028) 8676 2414 E-mail: info@fslelectronics.com *Manufacturing of scoreboards & remote control units*

F S L Electrostatic Systems Ltd, 5 A K Business Park, Russell Road, Southport, Merseyside, PR9 7SA Tel: (01704) 506439 Fax: (01704) 505043 E-mail: salesfsl@aol.com *Electrostatic paint spraying equipment manufrs*

F S M Enterprises Ltd, 2 Adams Close, London, NW9 8PT Tel: (020) 8200 7736 Fax: (020) 8200 6112 E-mail: fmalik1541@aol.com *Export & import merchants*

F S Moore Ltd, Petersham House, 57a Hatton Garden, London, EC1N 8JG Tel: (020) 7232 4700 Fax: (020) 7232 4750 *Printers*

F S W Group Ltd, Manor Farm Barns, Fox Road, Framingham Pigot, Norwich, NR14 7PZ Tel: (01508) 491400 Fax: (01508) 494088 E-mail: mail@fsw.co.uk *Advertising, direct marketing & public relations*

F S W Tooling, Brewery Road, Hoddesdon, Hertfordshire, EN11 8HF Tel: (01992) 469538 Fax: (01992) 468996 *Woodworking tools manufrs*

F Short Ltd, Green Lane, Felling, Gateshead, Tyne & Wear, NE10 0EZ Tel: 0191-469 4627 Fax: 0191-438 4680 *Haulage contractors*

F Simmonds & Sons, 15 Cambridge Road, Granby Industrial Estate, Weymouth, Dorset, DT4 9TJ Tel: (01305) 786389 Fax: (07092) 871904 E-mail: fsimmonds.sons@btconnect.com *Gaming machine specialists*

F Sinclair, 23 Hatton Garden, London, EC1N 8BQ Tel: (020) 7404 9198 Fax: (020) 7404 3252 *Jewellery polishers*

F Stoker & Son, Bishopdyke Road, Sherburn in Elmet, Leeds, LS25 6HP Tel: (01977) 683788 Fax: (01977) 682318 *Cereal produce services*

F T Construction Equipment, Norwich Road, Swainsthorpe, Norwich, NR14 8PU Tel: (01508) 471777 Fax: (01508) 471585 E-mail: sales@ft-construction.co.uk *Construction machinery service & supplies*

F T Engineering, Lane End Works, Skipton Road, Earby, Barnoldswick, Lancashire, BB18 6PX Tel: (01282) 844220 Fax: (01282) 843480 *Precision engineers & toolmakers*

F T Gearing Landscape Services Ltd, Crompton Road Depot, Stevenage, Hertfordshire, SG1 2EE Tel: (01438) 369321 Fax: (01438) 353039 E-mail: fred@ft-gearing.co.uk *Landscaping & grounds maintenance services*

▶ F & T Goodwin Ltd, Maple Tree Farm, Chawston Lane, Chawston, Bedford, MK44 3BH Tel: (01480) 407500 Fax: (01480) 407870

F T L Co. Ltd, Howley Park Road, Morley, Leeds, LS27 0QS Tel: 0113-253 0331 Fax: 0113-289 7748 *Flexible tubing, hose & conduit manufrs*

F T L Foundry Equipment, 6-11 Riley Street, Willenhall, West Midlands, WV13 1RH Tel: (01902) 630222 Fax: 01902 636593 E-mail: ftl_foundry@compuserve.co.uk *Foundry equipment suppliers & manufrs*

F T L Seals Technology, Leeds Twenty-Seven Business Park, Bruntcliffe Avenue, Morley, Leeds, LS27 0TG Tel: 0113-252 1061 Fax: 0113-252 2627 E-mail: tonys@ftlseals.co.uk Principal Export Areas: Worldwide *Bearing seal (including mechanical) distributors or agents*

F T M Marketing Ltd, P O Box 163C, Esher, Surrey, KT10 0YH Tel: (020) 8286 6661 Fax: (020) 8286 2202 E-mail: info@sonneteer.co.uk *Consumer electronics manufrs*

F T Mail Solutions Ltd, Unit 36, Stephenson Road, South Hampshire Industrial Park, Totton, Southampton, SO40 3YD Tel: (023) 8066 5050 Fax: (023) 8066 5066 E-mail: sales@ftmailsolutions.co.uk *Direct mail services*

F T Nixon & Son Ltd, Northend, Wisbech, Cambridgeshire, PE13 1TH Tel: (01945) 583231 Fax: (01945) 466902 *Timber merchants*

F T Pharmaceuticle Services, 43 Brookland, Tiptree, Colchester, CO5 0BU Tel: (01621) 819317 Fax: (01621) 819418 E-mail: ftpharmser@aol.com *Pharmaceutical consultants*

F T Pressings Ltd, Eagle Works, New Road, Studley, Warwickshire, B80 7LY Tel: (01527) 854925 Fax: (01527) 854925 *Lighting industry clips & pressings*

F & T Refrigeration Ltd, D C Griffiths Way, Neath, West Glamorgan, SA11 1BT Tel: (01639) 634171 Fax: (01639) 644422 E-mail: tony@ftrefrigeration.co.uk *Installation & maintenance refrigeration & air conditioning*

F T Refrigeration Ltd, 166 Old Road, Stockport, Cheshire, SK4 1TD Tel: 0161-480 4825 Fax: 0161-480 4825 *Refrigeration & air-conditioning manufrs*

F T Short Ltd, Fitton Road, St Germans, King's Lynn, Norfolk, PE34 3AX Tel: (01553) 617344 Fax: (01553) 617020 E-mail: info@ftshort.co.uk *Contract packers services*

F T V Proclad (UK) Ltd, Viewfield Industrial Estate, Glenrothes, Fife, KY6 2RD Tel: (01592) 772568 Fax: (01592) 775310 E-mail: sales@forthtool.co.uk *Sub-contract engineers & machining services*

▶ F T W Engineers Ltd, 14A Rowantree Avenue, Newhouse Industrial Estate, Newhouse, Motherwell, Lanarkshire, ML1 5SG Tel: (01698) 349010 Fax: (01698) 733314 E-mail: info@ftwengineers.co.uk *CNC engineering, metal products*

F Tollman & Co. Ltd, 85 Tavistock Street, Bedford, MK40 2RH Tel: (01234) 267009 Fax: (01234) 217826 E-mail: sales@tollman.co.uk *Stationery suppliers*

F Tooms & Co., Kings Road, Market Harborough, Leicestershire, LE16 7JU Tel: (01858) 462697 Fax: (01858) 431701 *Tools makers*

F V C Com, Bridge View House, Ray Mead Road, Maidenhead, Berkshire, SL6 8NJ Tel: (01628) 687700 *Video networking*

▶ F V Conservatories & Windows, Colchester Road, Elmstead, Colchester, CO7 7EA Tel: (01206) 825374 Fax: (01206) 825405 E-mail: sales@fvconservatories.co.uk *Fensa registered family company who manufacture and*

continued

install P.V.C.u. Conservatories,windows and doors, including all necessary building work

F V S 2000, 72 Love Lane, Denbigh, Clwyd, LL16 3LU Tel: (01745) 814210 Fax: (01745) 814210 E-mail: sales@fvsvideo.co.uk *Video services*

F W & A J Beckwith, 69 Clotherholme Road, Ripon, North Yorkshire, HG4 2DN Tel: (01765) 600587 Fax: (01765) 602215 *Agricultural engineering repairers*

F W Aldridge Ltd, Unit 3 St Johns Industrial Estate, Dunmow Road, Takeley, Bishop's Stortford, Hertfordshire, CM22 6SP Tel: (01279) 874000 Fax: (01279) 874002 E-mail: fwaldridge@fwaldridge.abel.co.uk *Glass repairs & glass liner suppliers*

F W B Cymru Co. Ltd, Five Crosses Industrial Estate, Ruthin Road, Minera, Wrexham, Clwyd, LL11 3RD Tel: (01978) 720720 Fax: (01978) 720721 E-mail: sales@fwbcymru.co.uk *Distributor of engineers' tools, pipeline & electrical products*

F W B Southwest, Threemilestone Industrial Estate, Threemilestone, Truro, Cornwall, TR4 9LD Tel: (01872) 243520 Fax: (01872) 222191 E-mail: enquiries@fwbsw.co.uk *Engineers merchants*

F W Bramwell & Co Ltd, Old Empress Mills, King Street, Colne, Lancashire, BB8 9HU Tel: (01282) 860388 Fax: (01282) 860389 E-mail: info@bramwellcrafts.co.uk *Knitting yarn & craft products wholesalers*

▶ F W Burnett, Inchmarlo, Banchory, Kincardineshire, AB31 4BT Tel: (01330) 825660 Fax: (01330) 825339

F & W Collins Waste Materials Ltd, 139 Upper Allen Street, Sheffield, S3 7GW Tel: 0114-272 5808 Fax: 0114-272 5808 E-mail: info@collins-skips.co.uk *Skip hire.*

F W Cupit Printers Ltd, The Rope Walk, 23 Louth Road, Horncastle, Lincolnshire, LN9 5ED Tel: (01507) 522339 Fax: (01507) 525438 E-mail: cupits@btinternet.com *General printers*

F W Darby & Co. Ltd, Cannon Lane, Tonbridge, Kent, TN9 1PL Tel: (01732) 350286 Fax: (01732) 357857 E-mail: john.darby3@virgin.co.uk *Builders' merchants* Also at: Tunbridge Wells

F W Hawker & Sons Ltd, North End Joinery Works, Bath, BA1 7HN Tel: (01225) 858233 Fax: (01225) 852530 E-mail: joinery@hawker-bath.co.uk *Building contractors joinery manufrs*

F & W Hetherington Ltd, Garter Street, Sheffield, S4 7QX Tel: 0114-256 1177 Fax: 0114-256 1177 E-mail: fwhetherington@supernet.com *Steel & alloy scrap processors*

F W Hume & Sons (Contractor), Bridge Farm House, Ling Road, Palgrave, Diss, Norfolk, IP22 1AA Tel: (01379) 642620 Fax: (01379) 652738 *Livestock hauler*

▶ F W Leighton Construction Ltd, Station Yard, Station Lane, York, YO30 1BS Tel: (01904) 470838 Fax: (01904) 470432

F & W Manufacturing Co., 95-97 Wigmore Street, London, W1U 1QW Tel: (020) 7224 4882 Fax: (020) 7224 4032 *Casual clothing manufrs*

F W Marsh Electrical & Mechanical Ltd, Ryde Business Park, Nicholson Road, Ryde, Isle of Wight, PO33 1BF Tel: (01983) 562109 Fax: (01983) 615592 *Electrical & mechanical contractors*

F W Mason & Sons Ltd, Private Road, Number 8, Colwick Industrial Estate, Nottingham, NG4 2EQ Tel: 0115-911 3500 Fax: 0115-911 3555 E-mail: mail@masons-timber.co.uk *Timber product manufrs*

F W Parrett Ltd, 65 Ridefield Road, London, SE9 2RA Tel: (020) 8859 3254 Fax: (020) 7504 3536 E-mail: fparrett@aol.com *Manufacture scientific equipment*

F W Patterson Television Ltd, 21C1 Ben Nevis Estate, Claggan, Fort William, Inverness-Shire, PH33 6RU Tel: (01397) 702612 Fax: (01397) 701054 E-mail: fwpatterson@btconnect.com *Television & audio, sales & servicing*

F W Poole (Marble Mason) Ltd, 12 Larkhall Lane, London, SW4 6SP Tel: (020) 7622 5154 Fax: (020) 7622 4232 E-mail: poole.marble@virgin.net *Marble contractors*

F W Sibley 1980 Ltd, 36 Goldcroft Works, Yeovil, Somerset, BA21 4DH Tel: (01935) 423671 Fax: (01935) 433407 E-mail: dillonharris@tiscali.co.uk *Engineers supplies & general merchants*

F W Singleton Scrap Metal Merchants Ltd, Score Street, Manchester, M11 2SN Tel: 0161-220 8058 Fax: 0161-220 8059 E-mail: scrap@fwsingleton.freeserve.co.uk *Scrap metal merchants*

▶ F & W Sourcing, 200 Westward Road, Ebley, Stroud, Gloucestershire, GL5 4ST Tel: 08707 701230 Fax: 08707 701233 E-mail: info@fwsourcing.co.uk *Product Sourcing*

F W Stennett & Sons, New House, High Road, Swilland, Ipswich, IP6 9LP Tel: (01473) 785815 Fax: (01473) 785403 *Agricultural & hydraulic engineers*

F W Thornton & Son, 57 Wyle Cop, Shrewsbury, SY1 1XJ Tel: (01743) 357081 Fax: (01743) 367549 E-mail: fwt@nbcgroup.co.uk *Piston motor factors & distributors*

F W W Brown & Son, 39 Queen Street, Horbury, Wakefield, West Yorkshire, WF4 6LP Tel: (01924) 271696 *Clock & barometer restoration & sales*

F Waites & Sons, Harper Street, Driffield, North Humberside, YO25 6LY Tel: (01377) 253310 Fax: (01377) 253310 *Farmers agricultural stockists*

F Walther Electrics Ltd, Cromwell Road, Bredbury, Stockport, Cheshire, SK6 2RF Tel: 0161-494 1233 Fax: 0161-494 5055 E-mail: mail@walther.demon.co.uk *Industrial plugs & sockets manufrs*

F Worrall, Purdy Road, Batmans Hill Industrial Estate, Bilston, West Midlands, WV14 8UB Tel: (01902) 491366 Fax: (01902) 491366 E-mail: fworreluk@yahoo.com *Precision machinists*

F X Signs, 2 South Street, Isleworth, Middlesex, TW7 7BG Tel: (020) 8560 2124 Fax: (020) 8569 7320 *Vinyl sign manufrs*

F & Y Products, 7a Thurswood House Cranborne Industrial Estate, Cranborne Road, Potters Bar, Hertfordshire, EN6 3JN Tel: (01707) 654221 Fax: (01707) 654224 *Textile goods distributors*

F1 Computing Systems Ltd, 3 Kelso Place, Upper Bristol Road, Bath, BA1 3AU Tel: (01225) 427285 Fax: (01225) 444728 E-mail: sales@f1comp.co.uk *Computer training services*

F1 Manufacturing, 350 Melton Road, Leicester, LE4 7SL Tel: 0116-268 8484 Fax: 0116-268 8489 E-mail: sales@f1manufacturing.com *Specialist sheet metal products services*

▶ F1 Mobile Valeting, Hollins Lane, Bury, Lancashire, BL9 8BS Tel: (07766) 526153 E-mail: enquiries@f1mobilevaleting.co.uk *Domestic and Commercial Car Valeters in the Manchester Area*

▶ F1Group, Kingsley Road, Lincoln Fields, Lincoln, LN6 3TA Tel: (01522) 508080 Fax: (01522) 508085 E-mail: enquiries@f1g.co.uk *IT services*

F2 Chemicals Ltd, Lea Lane, Lea Town, Preston, PR4 0RZ Tel: (01772) 775802 Fax: (01772) 775808 E-mail: gerry.may@fluoros.co.uk *Fluorocarbons & chemicals manufrs*

F2 Magnetics Ltd, Griffon Road, Quarry Hill Industrial Estate, Ilkeston, Derbyshire, DE7 4RF Tel: 0115-932 9000 Fax: 0115-932 9111 E-mail: sales@f2magnetics.co.uk *Manufacturers & supplier of permanent & electromagnetic systems*

▶ F7 Technology Ltd, 1 Michaelson Square, Kirkton, Livingston, West Lothian, EH54 7DP Tel: (01506) 472009 *Software writers*

Fa Solutions, 9 Beckford Way, Maidenbower, Crawley, West Sussex, RH10 7LT Tel: (01293) 886643 E-mail: sales@faselectrical.co.uk *CCTV & electrical installations & home automation*

Faac Security Equipment, Unit 6 Hamilton Close, Basingstoke, Hampshire, RG21 6YT Tel: (01256) 318100 Fax: (01256) 318101 E-mail: sales@faac.co.uk *Barrier & gate manufacturers gate automation systems*

Fab 24 Ltd, 326 Drumoyne Road, Glasgow, G51 4DX Tel: 0141-810 5656 Fax: 0141-810 5000 E-mail: info@fab24.co.uk *Metal manufrs*

▶ Fab Chrome Ltd, 58-60 Tannoch Drive, Lenzie Mills Industrial Estate, Cumbernauld, Glasgow, G67 2XX Tel: (01236) 458451 Fax: (01236) 458581

▶ Fab Food Patisserie Ltd, 151-157 Gosset Street, London, E2 6NR Tel: (020) 7729 7272 Fax: (020) 7729 3434

▶ Fab Serv, Unit 2, Underbank Way, Cars Industrial Estate, Haslingden, Rossendale, Lancashire, BB4 5HH Tel: (01706) 230817 Fax: (01706) 230033 E-mail: enquiries@fabserv.co.uk *Sheet metal & fabrication services*

Fab Signs & Structures UK Ltd, The Boiler House, Thames Industrial Park, Princess Margaret Road, East Tilbury, Tilbury, Essex, RM18 8RL Tel: (01375) 846815 Fax: (01375) 845250 E-mail: fred@fabsignsandstructures.co.uk *Design, of steel fabricators installation & manufrs*

▶ Fab Tech Automotive Ltd, Unit 5-6 Lichfield Trading Estate, Lagrange, Tamworth, Staffordshire, B79 7XD Tel: (01827) 66602 Fax: (01827) 66168 E-mail: sales@fabtechauto.co.uk *Precision sheet metal fabricators, design, manufacture & delivery, laser cutting, pressbrake bending, CNC machining, MIG/TIG welding & finishing. ISO9001:2000*

Fab Vent Engineering, North Road, Stoke-on-Trent, ST6 2BZ Tel: (01782) 219995 Fax: (01782) 219995 *Sheet metalwork engineers & fabricators*

Fabcast Concrete Fencing Products, Unit 4 Speedwall Street, Stoke-on-Trent, ST3 5EB Tel: (01782) 324542 *Concrete & wood fencing manufrs*

Fabco, 33a Groganstown, Dunmurry, Belfast, BT17 0NR Tel: (028) 9062 6666 Fax: (028) 9062 6666 *Steel fabricators*

Fabcon Engineering, 41 Gortlenaghan Road, Dungannon, County Tyrone, BT70 3AJ Tel: (028) 8776 1116 Fax: (028) 8776 1799 *Fork lift attachment manufrs*

Fabcon Projects Ltd, Delta Close, Norwich, NR6 6BG Tel: (01603) 482338 Fax: (01603) 484064 E-mail: andrew@fabcon.co.uk *Stainless steel fabrication to the food & oil industries*

Faber Blinds UK Ltd, Kilvey Road, Brackmills Industrial Estate, Northampton, NN4 7BQ Tel: (01604) 766251 Fax: (01604) 768802 E-mail: sales@faberblinds.co.uk *Window blind manufrs*

Faber & Faber Ltd, 3 Queen Square, London, WC1N 3AU Tel: (020) 7465 0045 Fax: (020) 7465 0034 E-mail: mailbox@faber.co.uk *Printers & publishers* Also at: Harlow

Faber Maunsell Ltd, Marlborough House, 18 Upper Marlborough Road, St. Albans, Hertfordshire, AL1 3UT Tel: (020) 8784 5784 Fax: (020) 8784 5700 E-mail: enquiries@fabermaunsell.com *Consulting engineers*

▶ Faber Systems Ltd, 2nd Floor Unit 2, Century Place, Lamberts Road, Tunbridge Wells, Kent, TN2 3EH Tel: (01892) 517388 Fax: (01892) 774801 E-mail: chris.smith@fabsys.com *Computer software development*

Faberhouse Online Ltd, Faber House, Ibstone, High Wycombe, Buckinghamshire, HP14 3XT Tel: (01491) 638184 Fax: (01491) 638184 E-mail: marketing@purpleandfinelinen.com *Linen fabric suppliers*

Fabermaunsell Ltd, Enterprise House, 160 Croydon Road, Beckenham, Kent, BR3 4DE Tel: (020) 8639 3515 Fax: (020) 8663 6723 E-mail: enquires@fabermaunsell.com *Consulting engineers* Also at: Branches throughout the U.K.

Fabermaunsell, Beaufort House, 94-96 Newhall Street, Birmingham, B3 1PB Tel: 0121-262 1900 Fax: 0121-262 1999 E-mail: libby.caughtry@fabermaunsell.com *Transport consultants & engineers* Also at: Altrincham, Bristol, Cardiff, Edinburgh, St. Albans & York

Fabfold Ltd, Amington Industrial Estate, 30 Sandy Way, Tamworth, Staffordshire, B77 4DS Tel: (01827) 313396 Fax: (01827) 313289 E-mail: fabfold@fabfold.fsnet.co.uk *Sheet metalwork & metal fabrication specialists*

Fabframe Ltd, 2 Whiting Street, Sheffield, S8 9QR Tel: 0114-258 8808 Fax: 0114-255 4465 *Shop fitters*

▶ FabGifts4U.co.uk, Turmore Dale, Welwyn Garden City, Hertfordshire, AL8 6HT Tel: (01707) 395050 Fax: (01707) 338246 E-mail: sales@fabgifts4u.co.uk *Personalised gifts & wedding accessories suppliers*

Fabine Investments Ltd, Unit 3 Pilot Trading Estate, West Wycombe Road, High Wycombe, Buckinghamshire, HP12 3AH Tel: (01494) 462749 Fax: (01494) 522325 E-mail: pilot@pilotgroup.co.uk *Logistics & freight forwarding*

Fablex 2000 Ltd, Unit 1 Tyseley Industrial Estate, Seeleys Road, Birmingham, B11 2LF Tel: 0121-753 0069 Fax: 0121-753 0071 E-mail: elaine@fablex.co.uk *Plastic moulders*

Fabline Metal Finishing Services, Greenway Road, Bilston, West Midlands, WV14 0TJ Tel: (01902) 353511 Fax: (01902) 353511 *Tank lining services, lead & steal fabricators*

Fablink UK Ltd, Arcwell Works, Stafford Road, Fordhouses, Wolverhampton, WV10 7EJ Tel: (01902) 397766 Fax: (01902) 788912 E-mail: sales@fablink.co.uk Principal Export Areas: Worldwide *Pressings & sheet metalworkers*

Fabory UK Ltd, Block D Bay 9 Bescot Industrial Estate, Woden Road West, Wednesbury, West Midlands, WS10 7SG Tel: 0121-556 3474 Fax: 0121-556 7337 E-mail: sales@fabory.com *Fasteners, nuts, bolts & washer distributors*

Fabprene Ltd, Broadway, Globe Lane Industrial Estate, Dukinfield, Cheshire, SK16 4UU Tel: 0161-342 6902 Fax: 0161-342 6903 E-mail: sales@fabprene.co.uk *Rubber extrusions & sponge rubber products*

▶ Fabre, 54 Ryde Avenue, Hull, HU5 1QA Tel: (07958) 346249 E-mail: hello@fabre.co.uk *Fabre is a small design agency with big talent. Based in Hull, East Yorkshire, we excel in combining our creativity and industry knowledge to deliver strategic solutions for identity, print, packaging and web design.*

Fabreeka International Inc, Units 8-12, Jubilee Way, Shipley, West Yorkshire, BD18 1QG Tel: (01274) 531333 Fax: (01274) 531717 E-mail: info@fabreeka-uk.com Principal Export Areas: Worldwide *Manufacturers of anti vibration & shock mountings*

Fabrenco Ltd, Wilton Road, Humberston, Grimsby, South Humberside, DN36 4AW Tel: (01472) 814845 Fax: (01472) 210412 E-mail: fabrenco@quista.net *Sheet metalwork fabricating services*

Fabrianne Collection Ltd, Danielle House, Southmoor Road, Wythenshawe, Manchester, M23 9GP Tel: 0161-945 8001 Fax: 0161-947 8843 *Clothing importers*

Fabric Display Ltd, 11 - 12 The Parker Centre, Mansfield Road, Derby, DE21 4SZ Tel: (01332) 382420 Fax: (01332) 290676 *Manufacturers: fabric pattern & trimming books, fabric hangers, textiles*

Fabric Express Ltd, 54-76 Bissell Street, Birmingham, B5 7HP Tel: 0121-693 3733 Fax: 0121-693 4636 E-mail: info@fabricexpress.co.uk *For over 30 years people have entrusted the manufacture, supply and installation of all types of window furnishings and soft-furnishings to Fabric Express. *From owners of privately owned hotels and stately homes through to purchasing managers for large chains and health authorities, our customers have all experienced the hallmarks of Fabric Express excellence... attention to detail, flexibility and personal service.*

▶ Fabric Filter Services Ltd, 6 Springfield Commercial Centre, Bagley Lane, Farsley, Pudsey, West Yorkshire, LS28 5LY Tel: 0113-256 6964 Fax: 0113-255 0432 E-mail: sales@fabricfilters.co.uk *Filter bag manufacturers, dust extraction filters, collection.*

Fabric Place, 12 High Road, Chilwell, Beeston, Nottingham, NG9 4AE Tel: 0115-943 6636 Fax: 0115-943 1336 E-mail: info@fabricsinternational.com *The Fabric Place, established in 1969, is one of the leading fabric stores in England.*We cater for shops, designers, dancing schools, theatrical and reenactment groups, garment manufacturers, curtain makers and caravan and boat renovators.*Visit our shop in Nottingham, and view 500,000m of fabrics under one roof.*We stock: Acrylic, Barathea, Blind Fabric, Boucle, Brocade, Burn-Out, Calico, Canvas, Chambray, Cheesecloth, Chenille, Heringbone, Chiffon, Chintz, Christmas Fabrics, Corduroy, Cotton, Crafts, Crepe, Crepe de Chine, Curtain, Damask, Denim, Doubleknit, Dupion, Dress Fabrics, Dress Net, Drill, Duchess Satin, Felt, Flannel, Fleece, Flock, Gabardine, Georgette, Gingham, Imitation Fur, Habutai, Hessian, dogtooth, Jacquard, Jersey, Lace, Lame, Lawn, Leather, Linen, Lycra, Melton, Muslin, Organza, Ottoman, Plisse, Polyester, Quilting, Sateen, Satin, Satin-back Crepe, Seersucker, Sequin, Shantung, Sheer, and much more*Visit our eBay store: http://stores.ebay.co.uk/ THE-FABRIC-PLACE*

Fabric Presentation Ltd, Forman Street, Derby, DE1 1JQ Tel: (01332) 290510 Fax: (01332) 340944 E-mail: fabric.presentations@btinternet.com *Pattern card manufrs*

Fabric Service Oxford Ltd, 55 West End, Witney, Oxfordshire, OX28 1NJ Tel: (01993) 772995 Fax: (0845) 363 7151 E-mail: sales@soundservice.co.uk *Acoustic insulation suppliers*

Fabricair Systems Ltd, 5 Burbidge Road, Birmingham, B9 4US Tel: 0121-766 7707 Fax: 0121-766 8356 E-mail: sales@fabricairsystems.co.uk *Air movement engineers*

Fabricast Multi Metals Ltd, Main Street, Hull, HU2 0LF Tel: (01482) 327944 Fax: (01482) 216670 E-mail: sales@fabricast.co.uk *Non-ferrous metal manufrs*

Fabricate UK Ltd, Kelwood Mill, Farnham Road, Bradford, West Yorkshire, BD7 3JF Tel: (01274) 575126 Fax: (01274) 575127 E-mail: info@fabricateuk.com *Sheet metalworkers*

Fabricated Products, 4 Foundry House, Sheffield Road, Rotherham, South Yorkshire, S60 1BN Tel: (01709) 720842 Fax: (01709) 720846 E-mail: info@fabricatedproducts.co.uk *Fabricate pipework, manufacture chemical dosing pots also air & dist separators*

Fabrication & Design Excellence Ltd, Pegasus Buildings, Olympus Business Park, Quedgeley, Gloucester, GL2 4JA Tel: (01452) 722944 Fax: (01452) 722825 E-mail: sales@fdproducts.co.uk *Prototype design, assembly & manufrs*

Fabrication & Installation Ltd, Units 6-9 Enterprise Way, Ladysmith Road, Grimsby, South Humberside, DN32 9TW Tel: (01472) 240409 Fax: (01472) 240408 *Fabrication, pipe work & welding*

Fabrication & Welding Services, Aldred Close, Norwood Industrial Estate, Killamarsh, Sheffield, S21 2JH Tel: 0114-247 7785 Fax: 0114-247 7785 *Sheet metalworkers*

Fabricolor Ltd, Foley Business Park, Kidderminster, Worcestershire, DY11 7PT Tel: (01562) 744587 Fax: (01562) 865825 E-mail: enquiries@fabricolor.co.uk *Complex architectural fabricators*

Fabricon Ltd, Unit 5 Commerce Way, Leighton Buzzard, Bedfordshire, LU7 4RW Tel: (01525) 850244 Fax: (01525) 850245 E-mail: info@fabricon.ltd.uk *Pipeline, mechanical & civil contractors*

▶ Fabrics By Guardian, 5 Cunningham Road, Stirling, FK7 7SW Tel: (01786) 449912 Fax: (01786) 451014

▶ Fabrics By Guardian, 5 Cunningham Road, Stirling, FK7 7SW Tel: (01786) 449912 Fax: (01786) 451014

Fabrics Motifs & Prints Ltd, 18 Lancaster Road, Hinckley, Leicestershire, LE10 0AW Tel: (01455) 637710 Fax: (01455) 633503 E-mail: enquiries@fabrics.com *Sports motif & badge producers*

Fabrics & Yarns Macclesfield Ltd, Hulley Road, Macclesfield, Cheshire, SK10 2LP Tel: (01625) 427311 Fax: (01625) 424769 *Yarn merchants*

▶ Fabricville Ltd, 83 Mortimer Street, London, W1W 7SL Tel: (020) 7636 2201 Fax: (020) 7631 5399

Fabriform Neken Ltd, Station Road, Liphook, Hampshire, GU30 7DR Tel: (01428) 722252 Fax: (01428) 725053 E-mail: sales@neken.co.uk *Plastic tiles manufrs*

Fabrikat Nottingham Ltd, Hamilton Road, Sutton-in-Ashfield, Nottinghamshire, NG17 5LN Tel: (01623) 442200 Fax: (01623) 442233 *Street columns & guardrail manufrs*

Fabrinos, 22 Station Road, Thurnscoe, Rotherham, South Yorkshire, S63 8AB Tel: (01709) 881432 Fax: (01709) 898116 *Fence manufacturers*

Fabrisign Ltd, 42 Lower Addiscombe Road, Croydon, CR0 6AA Tel: (020) 8688 7764 Fax: (020) 8680 8331 *General sign manufrs*

Fabrite Fixing, 6 Marshall's Lane, High Cross, Ware, Hertfordshire, SG11 1AH Tel: (01920) 485554 Fax: (01920) 486754 *Balustrades installers & fabricators*

▶ Fabriweld Tubular Steel Products Ltd, Gibbons Street, Harrimans Lane, Lenton Lane Industrial Estate, Nottingham, NG7 2SD Tel: 0115-942 2264 Fax: 0115-942 2267 E-mail: jamie@fabriweld.co.uk *Audio visual equipment furniture*

▶ Fabs & Pipeline Services Ltd, Moorfields Industrial Estate, Cotes Heath, Stafford, ST21 6QY Tel: (01782) 791232 Fax: (01782) 791611 E-mail: fpsltd@ukonline.co.uk *Steel & stainless steel fabrications*

▶ Fabtec Upholstery Cleaners, Plevna Place, Alton, Hampshire, GU34 2DS Tel: (01420) 87199 E-mail: michael@fabteccleaning.co.uk *Professional carpet and upholstery cleaning service for domestic and commercial customers*

▶ Fabtech Services, Unit 4b Wilstead Industrial Park, Kenneth Way, Wilstead, Bedford, MK45 3PD Tel: (01234) 741147 Fax: (01234) 741147 E-mail: sales@fabtechservices.co.uk *Suppliers of plastic pipe, valves & fittings*

▶ Fabtek Engineering Ltd, High Street, Lochgelly, Fife, KY5 9JP Tel: (01592) 782616 Fax: (01592) 782675

Fabweld New Mills Ltd, 5 Canal Foundry, Albion Road, New Mills, High Peak, Derbyshire, SK22 3EZ Tel: (01663) 746156 Fax: (01663) 747960 E-mail: fabweld@ntlworld.com *Pipework erection & installation contractors*

Fabwell Ltd, Unti J Balds Lane, Stourbridge, West Midlands, DY9 8TE Tel: (01384) 898288 Fax: (01384) 898289 E-mail: sales@fabwell.co.uk *Fabwell Specialise in building new /reconditioning furnaces to as new condition. Heat Resistant fabrications in all grades of alloys. Site-work including refractory repairs and re-lines, electrical and mechanical repairs and modifications. Most spares are stocked.*

Faccenda Group Ltd, High St, Sutton Benger, Chippenham, Wiltshire, SN15 4RF Tel: (01249) 720733 Fax: (01249) 720958 *Poultry factory*

▶ The Face Agency, Baron Street, London, N1 9LL Tel: (020) 7713 9700 Fax: (020) 7713 9788 E-mail: sales@thefaceagency.co.uk

▶ Face - Fit Limited, 1, Farnham Road, Guildford, Surrey, GU2 4RG Tel: 01483 549052 Fax: 01483 549100 E-mail: jobs@face-fit.com *Welcome to Face-Fit Ltd. We specialise in recruitment for the housebuilding industry. We cater for all disciplines and are instructed by most blue-chip housebuilding clients. Our candidates are Managing Directors, Sales Directors, Construction Directors, Land Directors, Build Directors, Technical Directors, Finance Directors, Sales Managers, Site Managers, Technical Managers, Land Managers, QS, Quantity Surveyors, Sales Negotiators, Commercial Directors, Commercial Managers, Chief Executives, Main Board Directors, Engineers, Architechural Technicians and all house builder related staff.*For career advice or a new job, call today.*

▶ Face Talk, 61 Seamoor Road, Bournemouth, BH4 9AE Tel: (01202) 556000 Fax: (01202) 556000 *Cosmetic services*

Face Time, 15 The Plain, Thornbury, Bristol, BS35 2BD Tel: (01454) 858590 Fax: (01454) 858589 E-mail: info@facetime.ltd.uk *Time according equipment suppliers*

Facelift Access Hire, Kingsbury road, Erdington, Birmingham, B23 6RH Tel: (0800) 521595 Fax: (01444) 881199 E-mail: hiredesk@facelift.co.uk *Powered access equipment hire, machine and safety equipment sales, servicing, and operator training for IPAF and PASMA qualifications*

Facelift Access Hirer, London Road, Hickstead, Haywards Heath, West Sussex, RH17 5LZ Tel: (01444) 881188 Fax: (01444) 882522 E-mail: hiredesk@facelift.co.uk *Access equipment hire, sales, service & operator training*

▶ Facet Industrial UK Ltd, Unit G4, Treforest Industrial Estate, Pontypridd, Mid Glamorgan, CF37 5YL Tel: (01443) 844141 Fax: (01443) 844282 E-mail: uksales@facetinternational.net *Facet is one of the World leaders in the design, manufacture & supply of filters, filter/water separators, oily water separators & associated equipment for the aviation, petrochemical (onshore & offshore), marine, power generation & general industrial markets*

Facet Publishing, 7 Ridgmount Street, London, WC1E 7AE Tel: (020) 7255 0594 Fax: (020) 7255 0591 E-mail: info@facetpublishing.co.uk *Information body for librarians & managers*

Facets Glass Restoration, 107 Boundary Road, London, E17 8NQ Tel: (020) 8520 3392 Fax: (020) 8520 3392 *Glass & antiques repairers & manufrs*

▶ Facilities System Design & Service Ltd, 9 Station Road, Stoke Mandeville, Aylesbury, Buckinghamshire, HP22 5UL Tel: (07000) 373773 Fax: (07000) 373775 E-mail: info@firealarms.gb.com *Install & service fire alarm systems*

Factair Ltd, 49 Boss Hall Road, Ipswich, IP1 5BN Tel: (01473) 746400 Fax: (01473) 747123 E-mail: sales@factair.co.uk *Producers of a comprehensive range of breathing air compressors*

▶ Factoring Partners, The Cottage, Bearley Road, Snitterfield, Stratford-upon-Avon, Warwickshire, CV37 0JH Tel: (01789) 730137 Fax: (01789) 730137 E-mail: julian@factor-broker.co.uk *Factoring. Specialist, independent factoring broker. *Looking for cashflow improvements?, factoring, invoice discounting, trade finance - then Factoring Partners will help.*

Factoring UK Ltd, Gildredge Road, Eastbourne, East Sussex, BN21 4SA Tel: (01323) 411770 Fax: (01323) 430014 E-mail: info@factoringuk.com *Factoring UK provide FREE independent advice on factoring and invoice discounting, and help hundreds of clients each year find the right facilities for their business.*

Factorsafe Ltd, 2341 Coventry Road, Birmingham, B26 3PN Tel: 0121-722 2200 Fax: 0121-722 2200 E-mail: sales@factorsafe.co.uk Purchasing Contact: S. Robbins *Industrial protective clothing*

▶ Factory Building Services Ltd, 76 St.Andrews Road, Birmingham, B9 4LN Tel: 0121-766 8705 Fax: 0121-753 1979

Factory Door Services, 14 Vernon Avenue, Rayleigh, Essex, SS6 9BS Tel: (01268) 786687 Fax: (01268) 780795 E-mail: factorydoors@aol.com *Manufacture, installation & repairs of industrial doors*

Factory Improvements Supplies Ltd, 24-26 Imperial Ave, Shirley, Southampton, SO15 8QH Tel: (023) 8078 6759 Fax: (023) 8070 2989 *Factory Improvement Supplies Ltd we have built their reputation giving good advice, problem solving and selling specialist building materials from major reputable Manufacturers. It is always their aim to ensure that the right product for the job is supplied, saving everybody valuable time and money. We keep a wide range of products on the shelf for immediate collection or delivery but specialist orders can be arranged direct from the Manufacturers. Grouts, Anchors, Joint Sealants, Concrete Repair, Crack Injection, Coating Systems, Protective Systems, Curing Compounds, Surface Treatments, Flooring, Replacement Wall Ties, Waterproofing, Admixtures, Adhesive and Bonding Agents, Restoration.*

Factory Lane Autos Ltd, 9-11 Broton Drive, Halstead, Essex, CO9 1HB Tel: (01787) 474446 Fax: (01787) 475616 *Body repair centre*

Factory & Office Consultants Ltd, Stuart House, 5-7 Wellington Street, Long Eaton, Nottingham, NG10 4LY Tel: 0115-972 5686 Fax: 0115-946 0842 E-mail: sales@fando.co.uk *Design, supply & install commercial office interiors*

Factory Plant Removals UK, European Business Park, Taylors Lane, Oldbury, West Midlands, B69 2BN Tel: 0121-544 4774 Fax: 0121-552 2018 E-mail: barry.jones@factory-plant-removals.co.uk *Removal contractors*

Factory Reconstruction Co. (Manchester) Ltd, Paradise Mill, Bell Street, Oldham, OL1 3PY Tel: 0161-624 5988 Fax: 0161-665 1994 E-mail: ukpallets@aol.com *Wooden pallet & packing case manufrs*

Factorycover Ltd, Eamont Park, Toft Farm West Industrial Estate, Hartlepool, Cleveland, TS25 2BQ Tel: (01429) 863366 Fax: (01429) 263188 *Roofing & sheeting contractors & suppliers*

▶ Factoryprice, Discounthouse, 3/7 Wyndham Street, Aldershot, Hampshire, GU12 4NY Tel: (01252) 312345 Fax: (01252) 680888 E-mail: m.ltd@ntlworld.com *Wholesalers of discounted & graded electrical appliances*

Facts & Figures Scotland Ltd, 4 Polwarth Gardens, Edinburgh, EH11 1LW Tel: 0131-221 0330 Fax: 0131-221 0770 *Chartered accountants*

Facts International Ltd, Facts Centre, 3 Henwood, Ashford, Kent, TN24 8FL Tel: (01233) 637000 Fax: (01233) 626950 E-mail: facts@facts.uk.com *Market research services*

Facultatieve Technologies Ltd, Moor Road, Leeds, LS10 2DD Tel: 0113-276 8888 Fax: 0113-271 8188 E-mail: sales@facultatieve.com *Hospital, industrial incinerators & cremation furnaces*

FaelSafe Fire & Safety, 15 Moorside Vale, Drighlington, Bradford, West Yorkshire, BD11 1DW Tel: 0113-287 9999 Fax: 0113-287 9999 E-mail: andrew@faelsafe.co.uk *Installation & commissioning of any fire alarm*

▶ Fagerult Lighting Ltd, 50 Southwark Street, London, SE1 1UN Tel: (020) 7403 4123 Fax: (020) 7378 0906 *Lighting manufrs*

Fagioli PSC Ltd, The Ridgeway, Iver, Buckinghamshire, SL0 9JE Tel: (01753) 659000 Fax: (01753) 655069 E-mail: info@fagiolipsc.co.uk *Heavy lifting equipment manufacturers & transportation*

Fagor Automation UK Ltd, Unit 2a Brunel Close, Drayton Fields Industrial Estate, Daventry, Northamptonshire, NN11 8RB Tel: (01327) 300067 Fax: (01327) 300880 E-mail: sales@fagorautomation.co.uk *Motor & drive suppliers*

▶ Fahey Concrete Ltd, Penince, Par, Cornwall, PL24 2SX Tel: (01726) 850086 Fax: (01726) 852244 *Ready mix concrete*

Faheys Concrete Ltd, Knowle Quarry, North Road Industrial Estate, Okehampton, Devon, EX20 1RQ Tel: (01837) 52609 Fax: (01837) 54813 *Quarry concrete*

Failsworth Hats Ltd, Crown Street, Crown Street, Failsworth, Manchester, M35 9BD Tel: 0161-681 3131 Fax: 0161-683 4754 E-mail: sales@failsworth-hats.co.uk *Manufacturers of ladies & mens' hats*

▶ Failsworth Haulage, 9-12A Limekilns Road, Cumbernauld, Glasgow, G67 2RN Tel: (01236) 733307

Faint Gobain Abrasives, Doxey Road, Stafford, ST16 1EA Tel: (01785) 222000 Fax: (0845) 6026215 *Abrasive product suppliers*

Fair Business Forms Ltd, 5 Kiln Lane, Horley, Surrey, RH6 8JG Tel: (01293) 432175 Fax: (01293) 432176 E-mail: sales@fbfltd.co.uk *FBF provides a specialist design and print management service combining a personal service with attention to detail.**No matter how insignificant or small the project is, our job is to produce well-designed business documents with the quality you require for the best available price.**FBF's aim is to build close two-way working relationships with all our clients allowing them to focus on their core revenue building activity, whilst benefiting from FBF's objective advice and purchasing skills*

Fair City Precast Ltd, Ladeside, St. Catherines Road, Perth, PH1 5RY Tel: (01738) 629501 Fax: (01738) 629501 *Precast concrete product manufrs*

Fair Deal Fabrications, Hammond Avenue, Stockport, Cheshire, SK4 1PQ Tel: 0161-474 1316 Fax: 0161-480 0635 E-mail: sales@fairdealfab.co.uk *Surface grinding & profile burning services*

Fair Sign Co., Unit E6 Aladdin Workspace, 426 Long Drive, Greenford, Middlesex, UB6 8UH Tel: (020) 8578 3080 Fax: (020) 8578 3082 E-mail: sales@fairsign.co.uk *Signs designers, suppliers & installers*

▶ Fair To Air, Shearwater, Trelawney Road, Ponsanooth, Truro, Cornwall, TR3 7EN Tel: (01872) 870455 Fax: (01872) 870455 *Air conditioning designers*

▶ Fair Trade Wear, 27, Lauriston Street, Edinburgh, EH3 9DQ Tel: 077 08796447 E-mail: info@ftwear.com *Promotional & customised clothing suppliers*

Ernest Fairbairn Ltd, PO Box 1410, Gerrards Cross, Buckinghamshire, SL9 8UB Tel: (01753) 882542 Fax: (01753) 882546 E-mail: ernestfairbairn@aol.com *Hydraulic cylinder & ram manufrs*

▶ J.W. Fairbairn Process Solutions Ltd, 120 Woodneuk Road, Darnley Industrial Estate, Glasgow, G53 7QS Tel: 0141-880 7455 Fax: 0141-880 5290 E-mail: sales@jwfltd.com *Process control instrument suppliers*

Fairbank Brearley International Ltd, Crown Works, Grantham Road, Halifax, West Yorkshire, HX3 6PL Tel: (01422) 360231 Fax: (01422) 355157 E-mail: mail@smarttecgroup.com *Centre/general purpose & CNC lathes. In addition, gs fired rapid heater manufrs*

Fairbank Harding Ltd, 38 Chapeltown, Pudsey, West Yorkshire, LS28 8BL Tel: 0113-257 0020 Fax: 0113-257 0732 E-mail: sales@fairbankharding.co.uk *Sound reproduction equipment*

Fairburn Engineering Ltd, 73-79 Clarence Street, Hull, HU9 1DH Tel: (01482) 323352 Fax: (01482) 229873 E-mail: sales@fairburneng.co.uk Principal Export Areas: Worldwide *Electrical engineers/control panel manufrs*

J. Fairburn Ltd, Waterloo Works, Trafalgar Street, Burnley, Lancashire, BB11 1RF Tel: (01282) 422754 Fax: (01282) 422754 E-mail: pipeprofiling@compuserve.com *Precision engineers*

Fairchild Ltd, Fairchild House, Southampton Street, Southampton, SO15 2ED Tel: (023) 8021 1789 Fax: (023) 8021 1678 E-mail: sales@fairchild.co.uk *Manufacturers & distributors of industrial computers, Rackmount Web Servers & Ruggedised HMI computer products. Please visit our company page to view our online catalogue and website*

Fairchild Fasteners UK Ltd, Unit 6 Bardon 22 Industrial Estate, Bardon Hill, Coalville, Leicestershire, LE67 1TE Tel: (01530) 518900 Fax: (01530) 518910 E-mail: sales@fairchildfasteners.com *Thread inserts*

Harry Fairclough (Construction) Ltd, Howley Lane, Howley, Warrington, WA1 2DN Tel: (01925) 632214 Fax: (01925) 628301 E-mail: post@harryfairclough.co.uk *Building & civil engineering contractors*

Fairclough & Wood Ltd, Unit 10b Carcroft Enterprise Park, Carcroft, Doncaster, South Yorkshire, DN6 8DD Tel: (01302) 726027 Fax: (01302) 330221 E-mail: sales@faircloughwood.co.uk *Cable tray & fastener distribs* Also at: Leeds

▶ Fairfax Communications, 58 Chester Road, Hartlepool, Cleveland, TS24 8QL Tel: (01429) 894089 Fax: (01429) 894089

Fairfax Display Co. Ltd, 137A Cowick Street, St. Thomas, Exeter, EX4 1HS Tel: (01392) 273324 Fax: (01392) 410808 *Catering equipment manufrs*

Fairfield Controlec Ltd, London House, King Edward Street, Grimsby, South Humberside, DN31 3LA Tel: (01472) 268141 Fax: (01472) 243049 E-mail: sales@fairfield-controlec.co.uk *Numatic & electrical control panel manufrs*

Fairfield Displays, Fairfield House Vernon Drive, Battlefield Enterprise Park, Shrewsbury, SY1 3TF Tel: (01743) 462472 Fax: (01743) 462452 *Display manufrs*

Fairfield Graphics Ltd, 34 Station Road, Liphook, Hampshire, GU30 7DS Tel: (01428) 726500 Fax: (01428) 725008 E-mail: fairfield@inkjetsupplies.com *Paper & film converters*

Fairfield Mabey Ltd, Off Station Road, Chepstow, Gwent, NP16 5YL Tel: (01291) 623801 Fax: (01291) 625453 E-mail: mail@fairfieldmabey.com *Steel fabricators*

Fairfield Meat Co., Maelor Abattoir, Bedwell Road, Wrexham, Clwyd, LL13 0TS Tel: (01978) 661794 Fax: (01978) 661774 E-mail: admin@fairfieldmeats.ffs.co.uk *Abattoir manufrs*

Fairfield Security Systems Ltd, 10 Wyndham Cresent, Cardiff, CF11 9EH Tel: (029) 2022 5003 Fax: (029) 2021 5335 *CCTV access control & security systems, fire alarms installation services*

Fairfield Tool & Die Co Maesteg Ltd, Cwmdu Institute, Bridgend Road, Maesteg, Mid Glamorgan, CF34 0NW Tel: (01656) 733455 Fax: (01656) 738710 E-mail: ftdtony@btconnect.com *Precision & CNC engineers*

Fairfields Supplies, Hambleden House, 8 Boulton Road, Reading, RG2 0NH Tel: (0800) 6346410 Fax: (0800) 6346409 *Architectural ironmongers*

▶ Fairford Concrete, Wellford Lane, London Road, Fairford, Gloucestershire, GL7 4DS Tel: (01285) 711460 Fax: (01285) 711461

▶ Fairford Roof Tile Manufacturers, The Rhymes Yard, Rhymes Lane, Fairford, Gloucestershire, GL7 4RD Tel: (01285) 713653 Fax: (01285) 712169 E-mail: fairfordrooftile@aol.com *Roof tile manufrs*

▶ Fairgreen Fish Bar, 37 Denmark Street, Diss, Norfolk, IP22 4BE Tel: (01379) 642412 Fax: (01379) 643857 E-mail: info@fairgreenco.com *Venetian mirrors & mirrored furniture*

Fairgrieve Mouldings Ltd, 15 Sedling Road, Wear Industrial Estate, Washington, Tyne & Wear, NE38 9BZ Tel: 0191-415 9292 Fax: 0191-415 9696 E-mail: lindabiggins@fairgrieve87.freeserve.co.uk *Compression & injection moulders*

Fairgrove Homes Ltd, 1 Heron Court Merlin Way, Quarry Hill Industrial Estate, Ilkeston, Derbyshire, DE7 4RA Tel: 0115-932 6531 Fax: 0115-944 6701 E-mail: sales@fairgrove.co.uk *House builder*

▶ Fairhaven of Anglesey Abbey Ltd, Northfield Farm, Lode Road, Bottisham, Cambridge, CB5 9DN Tel: (01223) 812555

Fairhaven Electronics Ltd, 378 Boulton Lane, Derby, DE24 9DJ Tel: (01332) 670707 Fax: (0870) 0558899 *Electronic design services*

Fairhaven H & V Services, 3 Glenavy Road, Moira, Craigavon, County Armagh, BT67 0LT Tel: (028) 9261 1648 Fax: (028) 9261 1997 E-mail: sales@fairhavenltd.co.uk *Fairhaven supply ventilation equipment to the domestic, commercial and industrial sectors in Northern Ireland. Our range includes fans, air handling units, grilles and diffusers, external louvres, kitchen canopies and air control dampers.*

Fairhead Wones, Beccles Road, Hales, Norwich, NR14 6SR Tel: (01508) 548244 Fax: (01508) 548942 *Agricultural machinery spare parts & repair services*

Fairhurst Ward Abbotts Ltd, 225 London Road, Greenhithe, Kent, DA9 9RR Tel: (01322) 387000 Fax: (01322) 370235 E-mail: works@fwa.dart.co.uk *Painting contractors*

Fairley Brown & Co. Ltd, 77a Wilson Road, Reading, RG30 2RT Tel: 0118-958 1641 Fax: 0118-950 3233 E-mail: office@fairleybrown.fsnet.co.uk *Heating & plumbing engineers*

▶ Fairley Homes Ltd, Fairfields, Moss Road, Dunmore, Falkirk, FK2 8RY Tel: (01324) 831999

Fairleys Paint Stripping, Unit 14 Byron House, Hall Dene Way, Seaham Grange Industrial Estat, Seaham, County Durham, SR7 0PY Tel: 0191-510 0051 Fax: 0191-510 0051 *Wood finishing suppliers*

Fairline Boats plc, Barnwell Road, Oundle, Peterborough, PE8 5PA Tel: (01832) 273661 Fax: (01832) 273432 E-mail: sales@fairline.com *Yacht builders*

Fairline Sales & Marketing, 35 Legacorry Road, Richhill, Armagh, BT61 9LA Tel: (028) 3887 1779 Fax: (028) 3887 0642 *Kitchen furniture manufrs*

Fairmile Cardboard Containers Ltd, Willow Tree Buisness Park, Pattenden Lane, Marden, Tonbridge, Kent, TN12 9QJ Tel: (01622) 832110 Fax: (01622) 833285 E-mail: judylorne@aol.com *Carton manufrs*

Fairmitre Ltd, Village Way, Trafford Park, Manchester, M17 1AD Tel: 0161-872 1841 Fax: 0161-872 2501 E-mail: sales@fairmitre.co.uk *Timber systems company*

▶ Fairnote Ltd, Ivy House, 59 London Road, Bagshot, Surrey, GU19 5DT Tel: (01276) 451272 Fax: (01276) 451690

Fairport Construction Equipment Ltd, Blagden Street, Sheffield, S2 5QS Tel: 0114-276 7921 Fax: 0114-272 0965 E-mail: sales@fairport.uk.com *Manufacturer of light construction equipment*

Fairport Engineering Group Ltd, Market Place, Adlington, Chorley, Lancashire, PR7 4EZ Tel: (01257) 484000 Fax: (01257) 483312 E-mail: info@fairport.co.uk *Complete process technology services*

▶ Fairprint Distribution Ltd, 44 West Henderson Wind, Dundee, DD1 5BT Tel: (01382) 322223

Fairs & Exhibitions (1992) Ltd, Manor House, 1 The Crescent, Leatherhead, Surrey, KT22 8DH Tel: (020) 8391 0999 Fax: (020) 8391 0220 E-mail: info@fairs-exhibs.com *International exhibition organisers*

Fairs & Green (MS) Ltd, 15-17 Vale Road, Tunbridge Wells, Kent, TN1 1BS Tel: (01892) 615678 Fax: (01892) 515788 *Heating & plumbing services*

Fairtrade International Co. Ltd, 12 Cockfosters Parade, Cockfosters Road, Barnet, Hertfordshire, EN4 0BX Tel: (020) 8447 0220 Fax: (020) 8447 0330 E-mail: info@fairtradeint.co.uk *Cosmetic & toiletries manufrs*

Fairview Estates Housing Ltd, 50 Lancaster Road, Enfield, Middlesex, EN2 0BY Tel: (020) 8366 1271 Fax: (020) 8366 0189 E-mail: sales@fairview.co.uk *Residential property developer*

▶ Fairway Decorating Services Limited, Wilson Business Park, Monsall Road, Newton Heath, Manchester, M40 8WN Tel: 0161 205 8000 Fax: 0160 205 8010 E-mail: admin@fairway-decorating.com *Painting & Decorating Contractor*

Fairway Engineering (Bristol) Ltd, Station Road Workshops, Station Road, Kingswood, Bristol, BS15 4PJ Tel: 0117-940 9030 Fax: 0117-940 9030 E-mail: tony@fairwayeng.freeserve.co.uk *Precision engineers*

▶ Fairway Forklifts Ltd, 8 Watt Road, Hillington Industrial Estate, Glasgow, G52 4RY Tel: 0141-882 6242 Fax: 0141-882 7426 E-mail: admin@fairwayforklifts.co.uk *Forklift truck, sales service & rental, warehouse equipment*

Fairway Form Tools, Unit B1-B5 Canklow Meadows Industrial Estate, West Bawtry Road, Rotherham, South Yorkshire, S60 2XL Tel: (01709) 820055 Fax: (01709) 820066 E-mail: sales@fairwayformtools.co.uk *Tungsten carbide cutting tool manufrs*

Fairway Hydraulic & Engineering Co., Unit 96 Blackpole Trading Estate West, Worcester, WR3 8TJ Tel: (01905) 457519 Fax: (01905) 456054 E-mail: fairway.hydraulic@ic24.net *Hydraulic power packs & controls* Also at: Ivybridge

Fairway P S D, Unit 3, Langley Business Centre, Station Road, Langley, Slough, SL3 8DS Tel: (0870) 389 1701 Fax: (0870) 3891751

Fairways Engineering, 3 Chiltern House, Waterside, Chesham, Buckinghamshire, HP5 1PS Tel: (01494) 794600 Fax: (01494) 794600 *Tool makers*

Fairways Fasteners Ltd, Unit 6 Starvale Road Industrial Estate, Lye, Stourbridge, West Midlands, DY9 8PP Tel: (01384) 897535 Fax: (01384) 423611 E-mail: sales@screwsandbolts.co.uk *Bolt & nut distributors*

Ken Fairweather, Seaton Joinery, Seaton Road, Arbroath, Angus, DD11 5SE Tel: (01241) 875265 Fax: (01241) 875265 *Joinery manufrs*

Fairweigh International, 5 Kimpton Enterprise Park, Kimpton, Hitchin, Hertfordshire, SG4 8HP Tel: (01438) 833613 Fax: (01438) 833614 *Weighing equipment suppliers*

Fairwood Engineering Ltd, Dock Road, The Docks, Port Talbot, West Glamorgan, SA13 1RA Tel: (01639) 892117 Fax: (01639) 899238 E-mail: karen@fairwoodengineering.com *Precision engineers*

Fairwood Fabrications Ltd, Docks Road, The Docks, Port Talbot, West Glamorgan, SA13 1RA Tel: (01639) 898002 Fax: (01639) 881908 E-mail: ssharp@fairwoodfabrications.com *Steel fabricators manufrs*

▶ Fairy Management, 38 Mount Pleasant, Bryntirion, Bridgend, CF31 4EF Tel: (08701) 464871 E-mail: sarah@fairymanagement.co.uk

Faisal, C517 New Providence Wharf, 1 Fairmont Avenue, London, UK, E14 9PF Tel: 07976 289139 Fax: 0870 4586531 E-mail: sales@flashdrive-direct.com *Flashdrive-direct online store provides the UK with USB Flash Drives at unbeatable prices, coupled with a fast and efficient service. Custom logo printing available plus pre loaded files.*

Faisal's Enterprises Ltd, 98 Mitcham Road, London, SW17 9NG Tel: (020) 8767 5577 Fax: (020) 8767 8269 E-mail: erick@faisals.co.uk *Exporters of home consumer electronics*

Faisaltex Ltd, Faisal House, 107-109 Fletcher Road, Preston, PR1 5JG Tel: (01772) 704440 Fax: (01772) 794837 *Import clothing suppliers*

▶ Fait UK, 8 Moons Park, Burnt Meadow Road, Moons Moat North Industrial Es, Redditch, Worcestershire, B98 9PA Tel: (01527) 591804 Fax: (0870) 2405957 E-mail: sales@faituk.com *IT consultants*

Faithful Ltd, Northwick Road, Worcester, WR3 7DU Tel: (01905) 450000 Fax: (01905) 457690 E-mail: sales@faithful.co.uk *Industrial protective clothing & workwear manufrs* Also at: Brecon & Telford

Faithfull Floor Coverings, Lady La Industrial Estate, Hadleigh, Ipswich, IP7 6AU Tel: (01473) 822686 Fax: (01473) 829737 E-mail: faithfulls@headlam.co.uk *Distributors to the flooring trade*

Faithlie Ice Co. Ltd, Harbour Road, Fraserburgh, Aberdeenshire, AB43 9TB Tel: (01346) 515010 Fax: (01346) 517025 *Ice merchants*

▶ Fake Bake UK Ltd, Unit C Coalburn Road, Fallside Industrial Estate, Bothwell, Glasgow, G71 8DA Tel: (0844) 8565758 *Toiletries manufrs*

▶ Fakenham Photosetting Ltd, 16 Garrood Drive, Fakenham, Norfolk, NR21 8NN Tel: (01328) 851570 Fax: (01328) 864088 E-mail: info@fakphoto.co.uk *Pre pressed print machine services*

▶ Falburn Engineering, Unit 1 Plean Industrial Estate, Plean, Stirling, FK7 8BJ Tel: (01786) 818549 Fax: (01786) 812350 E-mail: falburneng@aol.com *Engineers & fabricators*

Falcon Ltd, Little Hendra, Treamble, Rose, Truro, Cornwall, TR4 9PS Tel: (01872) 573534

Falcon Automotive Engineering, Unit 8 Victoria Way, Pride Park, Derby, DE24 8AN Tel: (01332) 227280 Fax: (01332) 227289 E-mail: sales@falcon-automotive.co.uk *Exhaust system manufrs*

▶ Falcon Blue, 18 Northumbria Gardens, Abington, Northampton, NN3 2ST Tel: 01604 784915 E-mail: ks@falconblue.co.uk *Falcon Blue is a newly established IT consultancy, with experience in the implementation and configuration of IT solutions for all types of businesses.*

Falcon Computers, 11a Hay Street, Sunderland, SR5 1BG Tel: 0191-567 6669 Fax: 0191-567 6664 E-mail: sales@falconcomputers.co.uk *Computer software & systems manufacturers & distributors*

Falcon Couriers, 21a Brownlow Mews, London, WC1N 2LA Tel: (020) 7831 8734 Fax: (020) 7404 6045 E-mail: mach1ltd@aol.com *Courier services*

Falcon Cycles Ltd, PO Box 3, Brigg, South Humberside, DN20 8PB Tel: (01652) 656000 Fax: (01652) 650040 E-mail: sales@falconcycles.co.uk *Cycle distributors*

Falcon Engineering Ltd, 28 Wash Road, Hutton, Brentwood, Essex, CM13 1TB Tel: (01277) 226861 Fax: (01277) 230091 E-mail: neil@faleng.demon.co.uk *Engineers, CNC machining & fabrication*

Falcon Fabrications, Southlands Farms, Oakhanger, Bordon, Hampshire, GU35 9JD Tel: (01420) 489444 Fax: (01420) 489444 *Steel fabrication*

Falcon Food Equipment Ltd, Unit 3 The Old Station, Wells Road, Hallatrow, Bristol, BS39 6EN Tel: (01761) 453010 Fax: (01761) 452975 E-mail: sales@falconfoodequipment.com *Refurbishment of meat, poultry & processing & packaging equipment*

Falcon Food Service Equipment, Hill Foots Road, Blairlogie, Stirling, FK9 5PY Tel: (01786) 455200

Falcon Food Service Equipment, PO Box 37, Stirling, FK9 5PY Tel: (01786) 455200 Fax: (01786) 469454 E-mail: info@afefalcon.com Purchasing Contact: B. Glen Sales Contact: L. Derick Principal Export Areas: Worldwide *Catering equipment manufacturers & suppliers*

Falcon Forge, 428 Limpsfield Road, Warlingham, Surrey, CR6 9LA Tel: (01883) 623377 Fax: (01883) 624477 E-mail: sales@falconforge.co.uk *Wrought iron light fitting manufrs*

Falcon Grinding, Unit 1 Anne Street, Willenhall, West Midlands, WV13 1EN Tel: (01902) 601478 Fax: (01902) 606055 E-mail: falcongri@aol.com *Grinding services*

▶ Falcon Interiors, Bluesky House, Western Way, Melksham, Wiltshire, SN12 8BZ Tel: (01225) 704084 Fax: (01225) 700843 E-mail: sales@falconinteriors.biz *Interior designers*

Falcon Jeanswear, Argyle Works, Alma Street, Smethwick, Warley, West Midlands, B66 2RL Tel: 0121-565 1533 Fax: 0121-565 1533 E-mail: falcon@euroshops.co.uk *Ladies clothing imports, exports & manufrs*

Falcon Lubricants Ltd, Showfield Lane Industrial Estate, Malton, North Yorkshire, YO17 6BT Tel: (01653) 694019 Fax: (01653) 600283 E-mail: admin@oils.co.uk *Lubricating oil, grease & oil management services*

▶ Falcon (Mapping) Ltd, 35 Couston Drive, Dalgety Bay, Dunfermline, Fife, KY11 9NX Tel: 01383 824886 Fax: 01383 824886 E-mail: webcontact@falmap.com *We are an independent Cartographic company offering a Cartographic Design and Cartographic Drafting service*

Falcon Office Furniture, 1-2 Stillington Road, Easingwold, York, YO61 3JE Tel: (01347) 822911 Fax: (01347) 823503 E-mail: sales@falconfurniture.co.uk *Office furniture manufrs*

Falcon Pest Services, 5 Foxglove Road, Newthorpe, Nottingham, NG16 2BG Tel: (01773) 761254 Fax: (01773) 761254 E-mail: enquiries@falconpestservices.com *Pest control & fly screens*

Falcon Photographic Supplies Ltd, Falcon House, Kerne Bridge, Ross-on-Wye, Herefordshire, HR9 5QT Tel: (01600) 890720 Fax: (01600) 890858 E-mail: sales@falconphotographic.co.uk *Photographic pre-viewing software*

▶ Falcon Photography, 2, Smith Avenue, Irvine, Ayrshire, KA12 9JP Tel: 01294 275912 E-mail: falconphotography@yahoo.co.uk *Wedding Specialist.*

Falcon Plumbing & Heating Engineers, 3 Lingfield Close, Enfield, Middlesex, EN1 2JL Tel: (020) 8360 0115 Fax: (020) 8360 0115 *Plumbing engineers*

Falcon Precision Ltd, Victory Close, Chandler's Ford Industrial Estate, Eastleigh, Hampshire, SO53 4BU Tel: (023) 8027 1666 Fax: (023) 8027 1771 E-mail: sales@falconprecision.co.uk *Falcon Precision is as an established supplier of high quality, fine limit sheet metalwork supplying a diverse range of industries including electronics, medical, security and marine. Operating from our modern premises in Hampshire we are well equipped to handle all aspects of precision sheet metalwork using the latest technology in CNC laser, punching, forming and milling. In order to fully support our customers we offer an assembly and full finishing service including plating, powder coating, wet painting, screen-printing and engraving. We are also able to customise aluminium panels and plastic or die cast enclosures. As part of our flexible approach we operate a fast turn round prototype service and can supply in small batch or large volume with scheduled deliveries or Kanban to suit your requirements exactly. Our staff are focused, accessible and committed to customer service and we are fully accredited to ISO9001:2000.*

Falcon Press, St James Mill Road, St James Business Park, Northampton, NN5 5JW Tel: (01604) 759262 Fax: (01604) 581482 E-mail: sales@falconpress.co.uk *General printers*

Falcon Press (Stockton-on-Tees) Ltd, Task Industrial Estate, Portrack Lane, Stockton-On-Tees, Cleveland, TS18 2ES Tel: (01642) 674298 Fax: (01642) 612382 E-mail: enquiries@falconpress-printing.co.uk *Printers*

Falcon Security Systems South East Ltd, 64 Zealand Road, Canterbury, Kent, CT1 3QB Tel: (01227) 787017 *Burglar alarm installers*

▶ Falcon Shock Absorbers Ltd, 5 Ryan Business Park, Sandford Lane, Wareham, Dorset, BH20 4DY Tel: (01929) 554545 Fax: (01929) 550550 E-mail: falconshockabsorbers@speed-mail.co.uk *Motorcycle shock absorbers manufrs*

Falcon Signs Ltd, 109 Grove Technology Park, Wantage, Oxfordshire, OX12 9FA Tel: (01235) 768872 Fax: (01235) 768822 E-mail: sales@falconsigns.co.uk *Sign consultants, contractors & designer manufrs*

Falcon Sportswear Ltd, Falcon House, Hutson Street, Bradford, West Yorkshire, BD5 7LZ Tel: (01274) 306186 Fax: (01274) 390937 E-mail: email@falconsports.co.uk *Wholesale sports clothing distributors*

▶ Falcon Trunking Systems Ltd, Butterworth Street, Littleborough, Lancashire, OL15 8JS Tel: (01706) 372929 Fax: (01706) 371550 E-mail: sales@falcontrunking.co.uk *Cable manufrs*

Falcon Works, Hanworth Road, Sunbury-on-Thames, Middlesex, TW16 5DE Tel: (01932) 784225 Fax: (01932) 788175 E-mail: enquiries@falconworks.co.uk *Vermin trap manufrs*

▶ Falconer Removals, Foundry Road, Ammanford, Dyfed, SA18 2LS Tel: (01792) 465353 Fax: (01269) 597697

Falcontec Ltd, Falcon House, Mucklow Hill, Halesowen, West Midlands, B62 8DT Tel: 0121-550 1076 Fax: 0121-585 5126 E-mail: info@falcontec.co.uk *Rotary die manufrs*

Falconwood Employment Agency Ltd, 187 High Street, Bromley, BR1 1NN Tel: (020) 8460 1148 Fax: (020) 8313 0984 E-mail: falconwood@ic24.net *Recruitment agency*

Falder Matthews Ltd, 6 Seax Way, Basildon, Essex, SS15 6SW Tel: (01268) 413611 Fax: (01268) 541637 E-mail: enquiries@fmprint.co.uk *General & colour printers suppliers*

Falgard Ltd, 235 Bickenhall Mansions, Bickenhall Street, London, W1U 6BW Tel: (020) 7487 5161 Fax: (020) 7486 0939 E-mail: falgard@falgard.com *Machinery exporters*

Falkingham & Taylor (Vending) Ltd, 40-50 New Cleveland St, Hull, HU8 7EX Tel: (01482) 320600 Fax: (01482) 585766 E-mail: sales@st-vending.com *Complete vending services*

▶ Falkirk Car Carriers, Dalgrain Industrial Estate, Grangemouth, Stirlingshire, FK3 8EB Tel: (01324) 482382 Fax: (01324) 482484

Falkland Islands Trading Co. Ltd, 1ST Floor, Charrington House, The Causeway, Bishop's Stortford, Hertfordshire, CM23 2ER Tel: (01279) 461630 Fax: (01279) 461631 E-mail: admin@fihplc.com *Export buying agents*

Falkus Joinery Ltd, 14 Anning Street, London, EC2A 3LQ Tel: (020) 7729 2424 Fax: (020) 7739 9108 E-mail: enquiries@jerramfalkus.co.uk *Joiners*

▶ Falla R F Ltd, Stony Lane, Christchurch, Dorset, BH23 1HD Tel: (01202) 499399 Fax: (01202) 470660

R.G. Falla Ltd, Bridge House, Rue De La Cache, St. Sampson, Guernsey, GY2 4AF Tel: (01481) 256585 Fax: (01481) 252318 *Building contractors*

Falling Leaf, 1 Lodge Bank, Crown Lane, Horwich, Bolton, BL6 5HY Tel: (01204) 696621 Fax: (01204) 667559 E-mail: sales@bigbuckets.com *Excavator buckets manufrs*

Fallowfield Timber, Ladybarn Road, Fallowfield, Manchester, M14 6WW Tel: 0161-224 3636 Fax: 0161-224 0212 *Timber merchants*

Falmouth Boat Construction Ltd, Little Falmouth, Flushing, Falmouth, Cornwall, TR11 5TJ Tel: (01326) 374309 Fax: (01326) 377689 E-mail: bernie@fal-boat.demon.co.uk *Yacht & boat repair services*

▶ Falmouth Fishselling Co. Ltd, Unit 15, Cardrew Industrial Estate, Redruth, Cornwall, TR15 1SS Tel: (01209) 314111 Fax: (01209) 314888 *Fish merchants*

▶ Falmouth Horsewise, 9 West End Industrial Estate, West End, Penryn, Cornwall, TR10 8RT Tel: (01326) 378828 Fax: (01326) 378828 E-mail: info@falmouthhorsewise.co.uk *Equestrian equipment suppliers*

▶ Falmouth School Of Sailing, The Boat Park, Grove Place, Falmouth, Cornwall, TR11 4AU Tel: (01326) 211311 Fax: (01326) 211311 E-mail: sales@falmouthschoolofsailing.com *A friendly & long-established sailing school, we are a fully RYA accredited school*& offer advanced & beginners powerboat courses as well as advanced &*beginners keelboat & dinghy sailing courses**

Falmouth Towage Co. Ltd, Falmouth Docks, Falmouth, Cornwall, TR11 4NR Tel: (01326) 319451 Fax: (01326) 319451 E-mail: falmouth@ap-group.co.uk *Marine equipment repair services towage division*

▶ Falstream Ahead, West View, Garras, Helston, Cornwall, TR12 6LW Tel: (01326) 221002 E-mail: hazel@falstreamahead.co.uk *A service for small businesses, based in West Cornwall, designing Databases and providing help, advice or training in using Microsoft Access databases.*

Faltec Doors Ltd, Statham Street, Stoke-on-Trent, ST1 4HB Tel: (01782) 205205 *Installation & supply of industrial doors*

Fam Sheet Metal Work Co., Unit 14 Droicon Industrial Estate, Portway Road, Rowley Regis, West Midlands, B65 9BY Tel: 0121-559 6374 *Sheet metal fabricators*

▶ Famac Network Ltd, Unit 5, 200 Swan Lane, Hindley Green, Wigan, Lancashire, WN2 4HD Tel: (01942) 525191

Family Choice Ltd, 440 Bradford Road, Batley, West Yorkshire, WF17 5LS Tel: (01924) 422157 Fax: (01924) 422153 E-mail: sales@fcbeds.co.uk *Bed retailers*

Family Farm Development Ltd, Milestone Centre Termon Business Park Quarry Road, Sixmilecross, Omagh, County Tyrone, BT79 9AL Tel: (028) 8076 1719 Fax: (028) 8076 1779 E-mail: familyfarm@btconnect.com *Agricultural development services*

▶ Family Graves Memorials, Thompson Street, Bilston, West Midlands, WV14 0HQ Tel: (01902) 492772 Fax: (01902) 493721

▶ Famous Grouse, The Hosh, Crieff, Perthshire, PH7 4HA Tel: (01764) 656565 Fax: (01764) 654366 *Whiskey producers*

Fan Engineering (Midlands) Ltd, 19B Sandy Way, Amington Industrial Estate, Tamworth, Staffordshire, B77 4DS Tel: (01827) 57000 Fax: (01827) 64641 E-mail: fanengineering@aol.co.uk *Fan manufrs*

▶ Fan Horn, 12, Clifftown Parade, Southend-on-Sea, SS1 1DP Tel: (01702) 341727 Fax: (01702) 390790

Fan Installation Services Ltd, PO Box 182, Twickenham, TW1 4WR Tel: (020) 8893 3316 Fax: (07946) 689758 E-mail: colin@fanservices.co.uk *Ventilation service to licensed premises*

Fan Maintenance Ltd, Eastern Works 4 Eastern Road, Walthamstow, London, E17 9DU Tel: (020) 8521 1856 Fax: (020) 8521 9421 *Ventilation & ductwork engineers*

Fan Systems Group, Witt House, Brookwoods Industrial Estate, Halifax, West Yorkshire, HX4 9BH Tel: (01422) 378120 Fax: (01422) 378672 E-mail: sales@fansystems.co.uk *Fan manufrs*

The Fancy Fox, Dunroamin, Back Lane, Ilchester, Yeovil, Somerset, BA22 8LZ Tel: (01935) 840481 E-mail: sales@thefancyfox.com *Retailers of Fancy Dress Costumes, Adult and Childrens Costumes, Wigs, Hats, Novelties and a huge range of Accessories. Great Prices, Fast Delivery and unbeatable Customer Service, makes us THE place to shop for Fancy Dress!*

Fancy Metal Goods Ltd, 71 Lifford Lane, Birmingham, B30 3DY Tel: 0121-459 9777 Fax: 0121-459 9595 E-mail: fancymetalgoods@btconnect.com *Cosmetic mirror distributors*

Fands Systems Integrator Ltd, 12 Saxonville, Benfleet, Essex, SS7 5TD Tel: (01268) 795757 Fax: (01268) 795858 E-mail: sales@fands.uk.com *Design specialist PC's*

Fane Acoustics Ltd, Unit 1, Millshaw Park Avenue, Millshaw Park Industrial Estate, Leeds, LS11 0LR Tel: 0113-277 8600 Fax: 0113-277 8700 E-mail: info@fane-acoustics.com *Loudspeaker manufrs*

Fane Valley Co-Operative Society Ltd, Alexander Road, Armagh, BT61 7JJ Tel: (028) 3752 2344 Fax: (028) 3752 7876 E-mail: contact@fanevalley.co.uk *Agricultural & dairy product manufacturers & distributors*

Fane Valley Co-Operative Society Ltd, 61 Clare Road, Tandragee, Craigavon, County Armagh, BT62 2EZ Tel: (028) 3755 1223 Fax: (028) 3755 1223 *Agricultural merchants*

Fanfare Productions Ltd, 2 Wrentham Avenue, London, NW10 3HB Tel: (020) 8969 6994 Fax: (020) 8969 6994 *Fancy goods merchants*

▶ Fanfield Ltd, Oxley House Cottage, Oxley Hill, Tolleshunt D'Arcy, Maldon, Essex, CM9 8EN Tel: (01621) 810095 Fax: (01621) 810095 *Computer systems consultants*

Fan-Master Environmental Products Ltd, Unit 2 Lever Bridge Mills, Radcliffe Road, Bolton, BL3 1RU Tel: (01204) 523556 Fax: (01204) 557951 E-mail: sales@smethurst-security.co.uk *Filter, grille & fan distribs*

Fans & Blowers Ltd, Walrow Industrial Estate, Commerce Way, Highbridge, Somerset, TA9 4AG Tel: (01278) 784004 Fax: (01278) 792848 E-mail: fab-sales@btconnect.com *Designers and manufacturers of an extensive range of proven fan designs suitable for most industrial applications. Standard and customised fans are available including a complete range of options and accessories. Provides a complete application, design, manufacturing, testing and Site Services facility. European distributors compliment an international reputation.*

Fans & Spares Ltd, 72 Cheston Road, Aston, Birmingham, B7 5EE Tel: 0121-322 0200 Fax: 0121-322 0201 E-mail: hq@fansandspares.co.uk *Gas & industrial flexible hoses* Also at: Dudley & Nottingham

Fans & Spares Ltd, 6 Brookmead Industrial Estate, Beddington Lane, Croydon, CR0 4TB Tel: (020) 8683 1241 Fax: (020) 8689 0043 E-mail: croydon@fansandspares.co.uk *Fans, blowers, ventilation & ducting distribution*

Fans & Spares Ltd, 1 Midas Business Centre, Wantz Road, Dagenham, Essex, RM10 8PS Tel: (020) 8595 5226 Fax: (020) 8593 4257 E-mail: info@fansandspares.co.uk *Air conditioner, fan & blower distributors*

Fans & Spares Ltd, 10 Low Mills Road, Leeds, LS12 4UY Tel: 0113-279 0501 Fax: 0113-231 0969 E-mail: sales@fansandspares.co.uk *Distribute ventilation equipment*

Fans & Spares Ltd, Unit 2 Rosevale Road, Parkhouse Industrial Estate We, Newcastle, Staffordshire, ST5 7EF Tel: (01782) 579076 Fax: (01782) 563592 E-mail: stoke@fansandspares.co.uk *Fans & blowers manufacturers & distributors* Also at: Edinburgh & Romsey

Fans & Spares Ltd, Unit 25 Whitemoor Court Industrial Estate, Whitemoor Court, Nottingham, NG8 5BY Tel: 0115-929 4104 Fax: 0115-929 2710 E-mail: nottingham@fansandspares.co.uk *Fan & blower distributors*

Fans & Spares Ltd, Dakota South, 1 Dakota Avenue, Salford, M50 2PU Tel: 0161-873 7212 Fax: 0161-848 7293 E-mail: pattyduncan@fansandspares.co.uk *Distributors of heating & ventilation equipment*

Fantails Garden & Patio Furniture Distributors, 64 Ulwell, Swanage, Dorset, BH19 3DG Tel: (01929) 427676 Fax: (01929) 421509 E-mail: fantails@freenetname.co.uk *Garden furniture manufacturers & distributors*

Fantas Tak Ltd, 2-6 Station Road, Shipley, West Yorkshire, BD18 2JL Tel: (01274) 466666 Fax: (01274) 466664 E-mail: sales@fantastak.com Principal Export Areas: Worldwide *Hot melt adhesive, glue dot & adhesive tape manufrs*

Fantasea Aquatics, Lenton Street, Sandiacre, Nottingham, NG10 5DX Tel: 0115-939 0704 Fax: 0115-939 0704 *Aquatic retailers*

▶ Fantastic Days Out Ltd, The Coach House, 4 Main Street, Humberstone, Leicester, LE5 1AE Tel: 0116-276 6061 Fax: 0116-276 5960 E-mail: enquiries@fantasticdaysout.com *Welcome to FantasticDaysOut.com .Whether it''s a gift for yourself or one for a friend you''ve come to the right site. From very fast days to slow days to wet days to fine days we have got the experience your looking for.*

Fantastic Lighting Ltd, 4 Kennet Road, Dartford, DA1 4QN Tel: (01322) 558649 Fax: (01322) 521117 E-mail: sales@fantastic-lighting.co.uk *Chandelier manufrs*

Fanuc Ltd, Andrew Myhill, Fanuc House, Ruislip, Middlesex, HA4 8LF Tel: (01895) 634182 E-mail: info@fanuc.co.uk

Far East Food Products, Sheffield Road, Conisbrough, Doncaster, South Yorkshire, DN12 2BU Tel: (01709) 860800 Fax: (01709) 860881 *Noodle suppliers*

Far East Mercantile Co., Central House, 7-8 Ritz Parade, London, W5 3RA Tel: (020) 8998 8885 Fax: (020) 8566 8672 E-mail: mail@fareastuk.com *Export merchants*

Far Eastern Freight Conference, Bridge House, 4 Borough High Street, London, SE1 9QZ Tel: (020) 7403 1700 Fax: (020) 7378 6691 E-mail: info@fefclondon.com *Conference services to shipping industries*

Far Landscapes, 2 Cedar Avenue, Methil, Leven, Fife, KY8 2AY Tel: (01333) 421506 E-mail: a.a.ritchie@homecall.co.uk *FAR Landscapes are a landscaping design and installation company based in Leven, Fife. With over 19 years experience in the landscaping business, we are committed to providing a comprehensive and friendly service with quality, value and customer satisfaction our priority. Our range of services include monoblocking, timber decking, new patios and paths, new lawns or gravel, fencing, garden gates, raised flower beds, and made to measure garden furniture. We can provide a service for anyone, from a completely new landscaped garden to a small patio or path. Contact us for a free estimate.*

▶ Faraday Fire & Security Supplies, Unit 26-31 Faraday Mill Business Park, Faraday Road, Plymouth, PL4 0ST Tel: (01752) 660156 Fax: (01752) 660162 E-mail: sales@grelectrical.co.uk

Faraday Technology Ltd, Units 22-26 Croft Road Indust Estate, Newcastle, Staffordshire, ST5 0TW Tel: (01782) 661501 Fax: (01782) 630101 E-mail: sales@faradaytech.co.uk *Video filter manufrs*

Farago Fabrics Ltd, 333 Humberstone Lane, Leicester, LE4 9JR Tel: 0116-276 6556 Fax: 0116-246 1119 *Fabric manufrs*

Farason Ltd, Low Hall Road, Horsforth, Leeds, LS18 4EF Tel: 0113-258 6538 Fax: 0113-258 7149 E-mail: kdmcinnes@aol.com *Bottle filling machine manufrs*

Farcroft Electronic Services Ltd, Tanglewood 88 Jobs Lane, Coventry, CV4 9ED Tel: (024) 7646 0087 Fax: (024) 7647 0369 E-mail: enquires@farcroft-uk.com *Electronics supply to the manufacturing industry*

▶ Fardoors Garage Doors, 85 Mallory Road, Birkenhead, Merseyside, CH42 6QR Tel: 0151-643 9914 Fax: 0151-643 9914 E-mail: leefardoe@aol.com *Supply and fit garage doors, automation of garage doors*

Farebrother Group Ltd, Ridgeway House, Progress Way, Denton, Manchester, M34 2GP Tel: 0161-320 0056 Fax: 0161-320 5010 E-mail: farebrother@farebrother.co.uk *Electrical engineers & contractors*

▶ Farfallina, The Lodge, Gog Magog Hills Estate, Babraham, Cambridge, CB2 4AE Tel: (01223) 413321

Farfeild Clothing, Farfield Mill, Sedbergh, Cumbria, LA10 5LW Tel: (01539) 620169 Fax: (01539) 621716 E-mail: info@farfield.co.uk *Clothing manufrs*

Farge Engineering Stockport Ltd, 4 Greyhound Industrial Estate, Melford Road, Hazel Grove, Stockport, Cheshire, SK7 6DD Tel: 0161-456 8209 Fax: 0161-483 9738 *CNC engineering services*

Fargro Ltd, Toddington Lane, Wick, Littlehampton, West Sussex, BN17 7QR Tel: (01903) 721591 Fax: (01903) 730737 E-mail: sales@fargro.co.uk Principal Export Areas: Worldwide *Distributors & agents of horticultural sundries & chemicals, liquid petroleum gas & natural gas, oil & electricity brokers*

▶ Farillon Ltd, Ashton Road, Romford, RM3 8UE Tel: (01708) 379000

▶ Farish Associates, 94 Sutton Court, Chiswick, London, W4 3JF Tel: (020) 8742 3223 Fax: (020) 8742 3226 E-mail: sales@farish.com *Farish Associates is a design consultancy that specializes in creating and manufacturing bespoke plastic/cardboard products and packaging for the travel industry, coffee shops, direct marketers and retailers. Example products include in-flight plastic meal boxes for children and adults and bespoke products for promotions and mail out campaigns. We manufacture our design solutions through our sister company Smartboxes. Clients include British Airways, Emirates, Saudi Arabian Airlines, BHS, Korean Airways, Coca Cola, Shell International, Blockbuster Video, *Pizza Hut, GSK, Batchelors, Granada, Hitachi, Virgin Megastores, Watermark, Avery, Range Rover, Gordons, De Ster, Virgin Trains and Marks & Spencer. To find out how we can create a relevant and compelling solution for you, please contact*

continued

Andrew Farish who will be happy to discuss your requirements.

Farley Auto Electrics, Salisbury Road, Dartford, DA2 6EJ Tel: (01322) 276998 *Auto electricians*

▶ Farley Electrical, 18 Westway, Caterham, Surrey, CR3 5TP Tel: (01883) 343173 Fax: (01883) 340586

G. Farley & Sons Ltd, Unit 6 Plaza Business Centre, Stockingswater Lane, Enfield, Middlesex, EN3 7PH Tel: (020) 8804 1367 Fax: (020) 8804 8821 E-mail: sales@g-farleyandsons.co.uk *Glass blowers & blown glassware manufrs*

▶ Farley Groundworks, 44 Bath Road, Calcot Row, Reading, RG31 7QJ Tel: 0118-945 4223 Fax: 0118-945 4223 E-mail: contact@farleygroundworks.com *The UK specialists for SEWAGE and GROUNDWORK. All types of sewage treatment and groundwork - supplied, fixed, maintained and installed. *Over 35 years experience.*

Farm 2000 - Teisen Products Ltd, Bradley Green, Redditch, Worcestershire, B96 6RP Tel: (01527) 821621 Fax: (01527) 821665 E-mail: heat@farm2000.co.uk *Solid fuel heating equipment suppliers*

Farm Chemicals Ltd, 82a Charles Street, Portadown, Craigavon, County Armagh, BT62 1DQ Tel: (028) 3833 3509 Fax: (028) 3835 0706 *Chemical merchants*

Farm Direct, 2 Westfield Terrace, Main Road, Flimby, Maryport, Cumbria, CA15 8QW Tel: (01900) 819923 Fax: (01900) 819936 *Agricultural merchants*

Farm Electronics Ltd, Alma Park Industrial Estate, Grantham, Lincolnshire, NG31 9SR Tel: (01476) 591592 Fax: (01476) 591188 E-mail: info@farmelec.co.uk *Refrigeration cooling systems manufrs*

Farm Energy & Control Services Ltd, Wyvols Court Farm, Basingstoke Road, Swallowfield, Reading, RG7 1WY Tel: 0118-988 9093 Fax: 0118-988 9658 E-mail: hugh@farmex.co.uk *Manufacturers of process control equipment*

Farm Fencing Ltd, 105-125 Ashurst Road, Tadworth, Surrey, KT20 5PX Tel: (01737) 812124 Fax: (01737) 812108 E-mail: info@farmfencingltd.co.uk *Wooden or chain link fencing distributors*

Farm & Forest Equipment, 10-12 Spital Terrace, Gainsborough, Lincolnshire, DN21 2HE Tel: (01427) 612504 Fax: (01427) 678578 *Garden machinery, lawnmower distribution & retailers*

Farm & Forestry Equipment, 44 Stuart Street, Ardersier, Inverness, IV2 7RS Tel: (01667) 462608 Fax: (01667) 462902 *Farm & forestry supplies & services*

Farm Harned Ltd, 56 Magdalen Road, Tilney St. Lawrence, King's Lynn, Norfolk, PE34 4RG Tel: (01945) 880582 Fax: (01945) 881511 E-mail: sales@farmharnedsolutions.com *Hospital equipment manufrs*

Farm & Industrial Buildings Ltd, Ryehill Close, Lodge Farm Industrial Estate, Northampton, NN5 7UA Tel: (01604) 753937 Fax: (01604) 758206 E-mail: nigel@farmindustrial.fsnet.co.uk *Erection steel framed buildings & steel fabricators*

▶ Farm Machinery Ltd, The Livestock & Auction Centre, Wenlock Road, Bridgnorth, Shropshire, WV16 4QR Tel: (01746) 769812 Fax: (01746) 769813 E-mail: sales@farm-garden.co.uk *We are main Suzuki ATV dealers & Honda lawn & garden dealers, we offer sales, service & repair of all makes of lawn mowers, quad bikes & other machinery*

Farm Machines & Agricultural, Holwell Barton, Neopardy, Crediton, Devon, EX17 5EP Tel: (01363) 774209 Fax: (01363) 774261 *Agricultural machinery repair & services*

▶ Farm Power, Ivy House Farm, Course Lane, Newburgh, Wigan, Lancashire, WN8 7UG Tel: (01257) 463679

Farm Services Ltd, Old Rifle Range, Common Lane, Fradley, Lichfield, Staffordshire, WS13 8NQ Tel: (01543) 251307 Fax: (01543) 410777 *Supply farmers*

Farm Services Ltd, Chesterton Estate Yard, Banbury Road, Lighthorne, Warwick, CV35 0AF Tel: (01926) 651540 Fax: (01926) 651540 E-mail: info@sportsdrainage.co.uk *Land drainage & water contractors*

Farm & Stable Supplies, Sutton Court Farm, Sutton Lane, Slough, SL3 8AR Tel: (01753) 595022 Fax: (01753) 591395 *Equestrian medication & hardware*

▶ Farm Supplies, Unit F 11, Cumberland Trading Estate, Cumberland Road, Loughborough, Leicestershire, LE11 5DF Tel: (01509) 236677 Fax: 01509 611515 E-mail: sales@farmsl.com *Agricultural equipment & electric fencing suppliers*

Farm Supplies Dorking Ltd, Ansell Road, Dorking, Surrey, RH4 1QW Tel: (01306) 880456 Fax: (01306) 876869 *Garden machinery & horticultural sundries*

Farmade Management Systems Ltd, Clearwater House, Bell Lane, Uckfield, East Sussex, TN22 1QL Tel: (01825) 729000 Fax: (01825) 760932 E-mail: sales@farmade.com Principal Export Areas: Worldwide *Computer software services*

Farmdata Ltd, Westertown, Rothienorman, Inverurie, Aberdeenshire, AB51 8US Tel: (01467) 671457 Fax: (01467) 671448 E-mail: sales@farmdata.co.uk *Software house*

▶ FarmEquip.co.uk, Strichen, Fraserburgh, Aberdeenshire, AB43 6NY Tel: (01771) 637413 *Manufacture, market, tractor cattle handling systems*

▶ FarmEquip.co.uk, 16 Camperdown Road, Boathpark, Nairn, IV12 5AR Tel: (01667) 456842

Farmer Bros, 319 Fulham Road, London, SW10 9QL Tel: (020) 7351 0241 Fax: (020) 7351 4111 *Architectural ironmongery retailers*

Don Farmer & Sons, Rendel Street, Birkenhead, Merseyside, CH41 3NJ Tel: 0151-666 1450 Fax: 0151-666 2540 E-mail: sales@doubleglaze.co.uk *Upvc & timber products installers & manufrs*

Farmers Cottage Lamps, Castle Lane, Coleshill, Birmingham, B46 2RA Tel: (01675) 464705 Fax: (01675) 462857 *Lamp post & water features manufrs*

▶ Farmgear Ltd, The Old Vicarage, Church Close, Boston, Lincolnshire, PE21 6NE Tel: (0845) 6440228 Fax: (0845) 6520124 E-mail: info@farmgear.co.uk *Advertise their new & used agricultural*

▶ Farmhaus Limited, 70 Verwood Drive, Liverpool, L12 0QY Tel: 0151 222 6437 Fax: 0151 222 6437 E-mail: design@thefarmhaus.com *Farmhaus: Creative design for web, e-marketing, interactive media (CD & DVD) and print.*

Farmhill Fitted Furniture, 36 Farmhill Road, Omagh, County Tyrone, BT79 0PY Tel: (028) 8225 2151 Fax: (028) 8225 2151 *Furniture manufrs*

Farmhouse Biscuits Ltd, Brook Street, Nelson, Lancashire, BB9 9PX Tel: (01282) 613520 Fax: (01282) 694796 E-mail: sales@farmhouse-biscuits.co.uk *Biscuits manufrs*

Farmiloe & Farmiloe (WBS) Ltd, 28 Willow Lane, Mitcham, Surrey, CR4 4UH Tel: (020) 8685 6800 Fax: (020) 8685 6850 E-mail: sales@farmilos.com *Sanitary ware distributors*

Farmkey Ltd, Alpha Building, London Road, Nantwich, Cheshire, CW5 7JW Tel: (08708) 707107 Fax: (01270) 616702 E-mail: info@farmkey.co.uk *Horse security marking services*

Farmlea Foods Ltd, 199 Airport Road West, Belfast, BT3 9ED Tel: (028) 9045 4647 Fax: (028) 9073 4834 *Dairy product distributors*

Farmline Agricultural Supplies, 11 Kinallen Road, Dromara, Dromore, County Down, BT25 2NL Tel: (028) 9753 3422 Fax: (028) 9753 3555 *Agricultural health product retailers*

Farmplan Computer Systems, Farmplan House, Rank Xerox Business Park, Mitcheldean, Gloucestershire, GL17 0SN Tel: (01594) 545011 Fax: (01594) 545012 E-mail: sales@farmplan.co.uk *Agricultural business management software producers*

Farmplus Construction Ltd, Shay Lane, Longridge, Preston, PR3 3BT Tel: (01772) 785252 Fax: (01772) 782944 E-mail: enquiries@farmplus.co.uk *Agricultural timber framed buildings*

▶ Farmpro Mail Marketing Ltd, Stephenson Road, Groundwell Industrial Estate, Swindon, SN25 5AN Tel: (01793) 451000 Fax: (01793) 451010 *Direct marketing & mailing services*

Farmview Dairies Ltd, 75a Lisnabreeny Road, Belfast, BT6 9SR Tel: (028) 9044 8553 Fax: (028) 9044 9120 *Milk & dairy product manufrs*

Farmway Ltd, Albion Mill, Albion Street, Driffield, North Humberside, YO25 6QA Tel: (01377) 249700 Fax: (01377) 249709 *Agricultural merchants*

Farmway Ltd, Chirnside, Duns, Berwickshire, TD11 3LJ Tel: (01890) 819400 Fax: (01890) 819409 *Agricultural merchants*

▶ Farmway Ltd, Golden Lion Lane, Market Place, Leyburn, North Yorkshire, DL8 5AS Tel: (01969) 621300 Fax: (01969) 621309 *Agricultural merchants*

Farmway Machinery Ltd, Cock Lane, Piercebridge, Darlington, County Durham, DL2 3TJ Tel: (01325) 374000 Fax: (01325) 374094 E-mail: csd@farmway.co.uk *Agricultural merchants*

Farmway RC Bland, Scarah Mill, Harrogate, North Yorkshire, HG3 3EB Tel: (01423) 774400 Fax: (01423) 324811 E-mail: ripley@farmway.co.uk *Animal health care equipment suppliers*

▶ The Farmyard, 5 Samuel Court, Templecombe, Somerset, BA8 0JN Tel: (01963) 370841 E-mail: info@the-farmyard.com *We specialise in marketing Southwest businesses through the use of exciting, memorable and creative live promotions. *Our expertise cover sampling, roadshows, promotional staffing, PR stunts, exhibitions and consultancy. Our engaging, bespoke promotional campaigns deliver results like no other marketing discipline*

Farnbeck Ltd, 32 Swanfield, Edinburgh, EH6 5RX Tel: 0131-553 5353 Fax: 0131-553 3979 E-mail: dm001@post.almac.co.uk *Printing blanket/rubberised fabric manufrs*

Farndon Marina, North End, Farndon, Newark, Nottinghamshire, NG24 3SX Tel: (01636) 705483 Fax: (01636) 701947 E-mail: sales@farndonmarina.co.uk Principal Export Areas: Africa & Central/East Europe *Marine & hydraulic engineers*

Farnell, Canal Road, Leeds, LS12 2TU Tel: (08447) 111111 Fax: (08447) 111112 E-mail: sales@farnell.com *Farnell, established in 1939, is a world leading high service, low volume distributor of electronic, electrical, industrial and maintenance, repair & operations (MRO) products - with fast, easy access to over 450,000 stocked products, 24 hours a day, 365 days a year. We offer buyers, design and maintenance engineers flexible ordering through a choice of channels and delivery options to suit individual requirements. * Select from over 800 leading manufacturers * The latest technology, available first * Fast, free next day delivery * FREE technical support * Technical data sheets for each and every product * Over 450,000 products stocked * Over 50,000 products reduced in price*

Farnell (Pattern Makers), Abbot St, Arbroath, Angus, DD11 1HH Tel: (01241) 872548 Fax: (01241) 872548 *Engineers' pattern makers*

Farnell Shaw, Haleys Yard, Upper Town Street, Leeds, LS13 3LA Tel: 0113-239 4123 *Manufacturers of joinery products*

▶ Farnham Bros, Meavy Lane, Yelverton, Devon, PL20 6AJ Tel: (01822) 853176

Farnhurst Medical Ltd, Unit 16 Alfold Craft & Business Centre, Loxwood Road, Alfold, Cranleigh, Surrey, GU6 8HP Tel: (01403) 752775 Fax: (01403) 752261 E-mail: sales@farnhurst-medical.co.uk *Medical appliance manufrs*

Farnworth Grinding Co. Ltd, 20 Gladstone Road, Farnworth, Bolton, BL4 7EH Tel: (01204) 571853 Fax: (01204) 574613 *Precision grinders*

Farnworth & Langan Blackburn Ltd, Unit 6 Stancliffe Street Industrial Estate, Blackburn, BB2 2QR Tel: (01254) 676935 Fax: (01254) 680113

continued

E-mail: farnworth-langan@btconnect.com *General engineers*

Faro UK, 9- The Cobalt Centre, Siskin Parkway East, Middlemarch Business Park, Coventry, CV3 4PE Tel: (024) 7621 7690 Fax: (024) 7623 6150 E-mail: uk@faroeurope.com *Portable coordinate measuring machines (CMM)*

Farr Formes, 1-4 Piper Rd, Hardwick Narrows Industrial Estate, King's Lynn, Norfolk, PE30 4NG Tel: (01553) 762705 Fax: (01553) 765245 E-mail: cadroom@farrformes.co.uk *Die cutting services*

Farr & Harris Ltd, 3 Dyffryn Industrial Estate, Pool Road, Newtown, Powys, SY16 3BD Tel: (01686) 626261 Fax: (01686) 622630 E-mail: info@farrharris.co.uk *Plumbers merchants*

Farr & Harris Ltd, Brassey Road, Old Potts Way, Shrewsbury, SY3 7FA Tel: (01743) 236371 Fax: (01743) 271703 E-mail: sales@farrharris.co.uk *Plumbers merchants* Also at: Newtown & Wellington

Farrans Ltd, 99 Kingsway, Dunmurry, Belfast, BT17 9NU Tel: (028) 9061 1122 Fax: (028) 9062 9753 E-mail: construct@farrans.com *Building & civil engineering contractors* Also at: Cambridge, Mid Calder & Wivenhoe

▶ Farrans Construction Ltd, Ely Road, Waterbeach, Cambridge, CB25 9PG Tel: (01223) 440000 Fax: (01223) 440469 E-mail: cambridge@farrans.com

▶ Farrans (Construction) Ltd, Oakbank, Mid Calder, Livingston, West Lothian, EH53 0JS Tel: (01506) 882588 Fax: (01506) 882688

Farrant Electrical Ltd, 1 Homefield Road, Haverhill, Suffolk, CB9 8QP Tel: (01440) 703497 Fax: (01440) 704332 *Electrical contractors*

Farrar Bros, 49 Haugh Shaw Road, Halifax, West Yorkshire, HX1 3AR Tel: (01422) 352198 Fax: (01422) 349539 E-mail: farrarbros@aol.com *Brush & mop manufrs*

George Farrar (Quarries) Ltd, Bradford Street, Keighley, West Yorkshire, BD21 3EB Tel: (01535) 602344 Fax: (01535) 606247 E-mail: sales@farrar.co.uk *Stone merchants & quarriers* Also at: Halifax

Farrar James Brushes Ltd, 103 Northgate, Halifax, West Yorkshire, HX1 1XF Tel: (01422) 361072 Fax: (01422) 361072 E-mail: philip.reid5@btinternet.com *Bottle cleaning & filter & tube brushes manufrs*

Farrel Ltd, PO Box 27, Rochdale, Lancashire, OL11 2PF Tel: (01706) 647434 Fax: (01706) 638982 E-mail: farreluk@farrel.com *Plastic extruding machinery*

Farrell Engineering Ltd, Centre House, St. Leonards Road, London, NW10 6ST Tel: (020) 8965 7578 Fax: (020) 8965 7586 E-mail: farrell497@aol.com *Machine tool merchants & diecasters*

Farrell Fabrications Ltd, Wallis Road, Skippers Lane Industrial Estate, Middlesbrough, Cleveland, TS6 6JB Tel: (01642) 453800 Fax: (01642) 453800 *Security roller shutter services suppliers & installers*

Farrell Furniture, West Harwood Farm, West Calder, West Lothian, EH55 8LF Tel: (01506) 873990 *Furniture maker*

Farrell Products, 1a Aughrim Road, Magherafelt, County Londonderry, BT45 6AY Tel: (028) 7963 2245 Fax: (028) 7963 1702 E-mail: sales@farrellproducts.com *Manufacturing in car washes*

Farrelly Facilities & Engineering Ltd, Facilities House, 386-388 Boldmere Road, Sutton Coldfield, West Midlands, B73 5EZ Tel: 0121-382 9988 Fax: 0121-382 4155 E-mail: sales@farrellyfacilities.com *Building services & environmental engineers*

▶ Farren Training, 25A Fullarton Street, Kilmarnock, Ayrshire, KA1 2QX Tel: (0787) 1551700 E-mail: neil@nfconsultants.com *Hospitality Industry Training Specialist. Please visit our website at www.nfconsultants.com for clarification of our unique training product.*

▶ Farrens Freight, Unit 1a Garrion Business Park, Wishaw, Lanarkshire, ML2 0RY Tel: (01698) 352266 Fax: (01698) 352255

Farriers Equipment Ltd, The Forge, Windsor Road, Chobham, Woking, Surrey, GU24 8QS Tel: (01276) 858416 Fax: (01276) 858416 E-mail: graham@farriersequipment.com *Farriers equipment suppliers*

▶ Farriers Fayre, 23 BARBY ROAD, KILSBY, RUGBY, WARWICKSHIRE, CV23 8XD Tel: 01788 824420 E-mail: andrew@farriersfayre.com *for all your catering needs event trailers ,location catering ,buffet service,vending,interim resturant catering,film set catering,bbq catering ,Roast pork & beef .we cater for events large and small.*

Farringdon Garden Stone, Sandshill, Faringdon, Oxfordshire, SN7 7PQ Tel: (01367) 240774 Fax: (01367) 242980 E-mail: rogers.gardenstone@btinternet.com *Concrete products manufrs* Also at: Farringdon & Wareham

Farringdon Locksmith & Tool Supplies Ltd, 29 Exmouth Market, London, EC1R 4QL Tel: (020) 7837 5179 Fax: (020) 7278 0224 *Locksmiths & ironmongers*

Farringtons Saddle Co., 15 Butts Road, Walsall, WS4 2AR Tel: (01922) 634440 Fax: (01922) 634440 *Saddlery*

Robert Farrow & Associates, 7 Plough Lane, Field Lane, Teddington, Middlesex, TW11 9BN Tel: (020) 8943 4743 Fax: (020) 8943 9383 E-mail: models@rfarrow.fsbusiness.co.uk *Model makers*

Farsight Technologies Ltd, 18 Guildford Road, Brighton, BN1 3LU Tel: (01273) 747487 Fax: (01273) 747333 E-mail: info@farsighttechnologies.com *Software development suppliers*

Farsite Communications Ltd, Tempus Business Centre, 60 Kingsclere Road, Basingstoke, Hampshire, RG21 6XG Tel: (01256) 330461 Fax: (01256) 854931 E-mail: sales@farsite.co.uk *Designs, develops and manufactures high performance WAN Communications Appliances (X.25, SHDSL, V.35, X.21,), ePOS Gateways & Adapters for PCs used in a business environment. The*

continued

continuation
products are supplied throughout the world by our distributors, resellers & local representatives To complement the standard products we also undertakes product customisation, consultancy, & custom development of software &/or hardware for clients

Farsound Engineering Ltd, Unit 3 Highams Park Industrial Estate, Jubilee Avenue, London, E4 9JD Tel: (020) 8498 3888 Fax: (020) 8498 3887 E-mail: sales@farsound.co.uk *Farsound Engineering Ltd is a company with over 25 year's experience in precision engineering services. We offer the best in: **Product Design, Development & Prototyping*CNC Precision Machining & Turning*Sheet Metal Fabrication & Assembly*NDT Inspection (Nadcap & Level 3+ Services)*Ultrasonic Cleaning, Descaling & Harperising*Waterjet & Laser Cutting*Welding (Tig, Mig, Arc, Gas, Brazing, Soldering - NADCAP Approved)*Component Repair, Recovery & Kitting*Comprehensive Supply Chain Management Solutions*Flat and round Braid & Earthing Straps**Our facilities based at strategic locations around the world enable us to cover the following markets:**Aerospace*Marine*Transport* Petrochemical*Medical**Please visit our website at www.farsound.co.uk for further information.**

Farstad Shipping Ltd, Farstad House Badentoy Avenue, Badentoy Industrial Estate, Portlethen, Aberdeen, AB12 4YB Tel: (01224) 784000 Fax: (01224) 783340 E-mail: aberdeen@farstad.co.uk *Ship management agents*

Farthing Saddlery, Southwest View, Punnetts Town, Heathfield, East Sussex, TN21 9DE Tel: (01435) 830440 Fax: (01435) 830440 E-mail: farthings_42@msn.com *Saddlery & harness maker & side saddle specialist*

Farthingale Furniture, 90 High Street, Odiham, Hook, Hampshire, RG29 1LP Tel: (01256) 704080 Fax: (01256) 704080 E-mail: info@farthingalefurniture.co.uk *Reproduction furniture retailers*

W.J. Farvis & Sons Ltd, Temple Works, Morley Road, Southville, Bristol, BS3 1DT Tel: 0117-966 6677 Fax: 0117-966 9893 E-mail: sales@favis.co.uk *Manufacture bitumen heaters*

Fas-Co Engineers Supply Ltd, 1 Caledon Green, Grangemouth, Stirlingshire, FK3 8TR Tel: (01324) 667500 Fax: (01324) 667516 E-mail: sales@fasco.co.uk *Industrial fastener, power & hand tool distributors*

Fashion Craft Ltd, 11 Dolphin Street, Ardwick, Manchester, M12 6BG Tel: 0161-273 3947 Fax: 0161-273 3947 *Ladies' fashion & children's clothing*

Fashion Fair Ltd, Unit 2 Benson Street, Leicester, LE5 4HB Tel: 0116-273 0107 Fax: 0116-273 3837 E-mail: fashionfairltd@yahoo.co.uk *Ethnic clothing manufrs*

Fashion Group Manufacturing Ltd, 21 Turle Road, London, N4 3LZ Tel: (020) 7281 5636 Fax: (020) 7281 8793 *Ladies clothing manufrs*

▶ Fashion Hangers Ltd, 15-19 Garman Road, London, N17 0UR Tel: (020) 8885 3055 Fax: (020) 8885 4426

▶ Fashion Mark Retail Ltd, 88 South Road, Southall, Middlesex, UB1 1RD Tel: (020) 8813 8841 *Clothing manufrs*

Fashion Rate Int Ltd, 1 Salisbury St, Wolverhampton, WV3 0BG Tel: (01902) 313679 Fax: (01902) 713877 *Ladies wear manufacturer*

Fashion Ribbon Ltd, Manners Avenue, Manners Industrial Estate, Ilkeston, Derbyshire, DE7 8EF Tel: 0115-930 8699 Fax: 0115-930 4555 E-mail: chris@fashionribbon.co.uk *Fashion bows, rosebuds & ribbon manufrs*

▶ Fashion Trend Wolverhampton Ltd, Kalair Court, Marston Road, Wolverhampton, WV2 4NJ Tel: (01902) 426900 Fax: (01902) 426900 *Clothing manufrs*

Fashion Warehouse, 64 Whitechapel High Street, London, E1 7PL Tel: (020) 7247 4595 Fax: (020) 7247 4596 *Clothing manufrs*

Fashion Wear Manufacturers Ltd, 135 Gipsy Lane, Leicester, LE4 6RH Tel: 0116-261 1122 Fax: 0116-261 1133 E-mail: enquiries@jeanmaker.co.uk *Jean manufrs*

▶ Fashion-4U, 87 Woolston Avenue, Congleton, Cheshire, CW12 3ED Tel: (07708) 731770 E-mail: sales@fashion-4u.co.uk *Fashion: Trendy Clothes and Accessories For Less.*

Fashionstop Ltd, Unit 1 Redcross Mill, Redcross Street, Rochdale, Lancashire, OL12 0NZ Tel: (01706) 525304 Fax: (01706) 658983 *Fashion clothing manufrs*

Fassi UK Ltd, 26 Blick Road, Heathcote Industrial Estate, Warwick, CV34 6TA Tel: (01926) 889779 Fax: (01926) 885777 E-mail: mail@fassi.co.uk *Truck & crane loading*

Fast 10 Adhesives, Hollytree House, Leeds Road, Tadcaster, North Yorkshire, LS24 9NL Tel: (07949) 274474 Fax: (01937) 832337 E-mail: nrockcliff@fast10.co.uk *Suppliers of cyanoacrylate adhesives (superglue)*

Fast Clean Group Drains R Us, 156 Neachells Lane, Wolverhampton, WV11 3RF Tel: (01902) 736424 Fax: (01902) 865665 *Sale of drain clearance equipment & drain cleaning contractors*

▶ Fast Club, Beacon Lane, Rotherham, South Yorkshire, S66 7SA Tel: 01709 760401

Fast & Easy Computers, Unit 5b Marcliffe Industrial Estate, Macclesfield Road, Hazel Grove, Stockport, Cheshire, SK7 5EG Tel: 0161-483 6656 Fax: 0161-483 6667 E-mail: sales@fasteasy.com *Computer repair services sales*

Fast Engineering Ltd, 5 Windmill Court, Antrim, BT41 2TX Tel: (028) 9442 8686 Fax: (028) 9442 9929 E-mail: info@fastank.com *Tanks & emergency storage containers manufrs*

Fast Engineering Works Ltd, Unit 1, Area C, 241 Wellington Road Industrial Estate, Perry Barr, Birmingham, B20 2QQ Tel: 0121-344 4345 Fax: 0121-344 4535 E-mail: fastengineering@btconnect.com *General machining services & heavy engineering services*

▶ Fast Fences Ltd, 44 Fountain Court, Waterside, Evesham, Worcestershire, WR11 1JX Tel: (0800) 0193019 E-mail: nigelrb@nigelrb.com *First for fuss-free fencing. Front feature fences, panels, overlap, pickets, restorations and repairs. Quality guarantee!*

▶ Fast Fermentation Ltd, Eastbank House, 19 Woodside Road, Northwood, Middlesex, HA6 3QE Tel: (07946) 512551 E-mail: stephen.herman@fastfermentation.co.uk *Fast fermentation is a high performance waste recycling system that turns organic waste into fermented organic fertiliser or feed with 15% water content in around 48 hours.**fast fermentation uses a unique accelerator culture containing 24 different bacteria that positively like to be heated and an exterior heater to get the composting process off to a very fast start. **The whole process takes just 48 hours to produce the same output as competitors achieve in 7-14 days. Although the capital costs are much the same as for other systems, the fast processing time means that costs per tonne are considerably reduced. **The latest DEFRA and EU rules on composting waste streams containing meat recommend heating waste in-vessel to 70C for an hour or 60C for two days.**fast fermentation is the only system currently set up to guarantee processing under the rules as a result of the unique heating and stirring system. **

Fast Food Essentials Direct, PO Box 1, Halesowen, W. Midlands, B63 2RB Tel: (0845) 6014713 Fax: (0845) 6014201 E-mail: sales@fastfoodessentials.com *Catering equipment & catering sundries distribs*

▶ Fast Forward (Scotland) Ltd, Thistle House, Caputhall Road, Deans Industrial Estate, Deans, Livingston, West Lothian, EH54 8AS Tel: (01506) 419977

▶ Fast Key Services Ltd, 5c Russell Court, Russell Gardens, Wickford, Essex, SS11 8QU Tel: (01268) 562562 Fax: (01268) 570121 E-mail: marc@fastkeys.co.uk *Key cutting services*

Fast Lane Auto Ltd, Callywith Gate Industrial Estate, Launceston Road, Bodmin, Cornwall, PL31 2RQ Tel: (01208) 264546 Fax: (01208) 264547 E-mail: sales@fastlaneauto.co.uk *Car ignition leads manufrs*

▶ Fast Lane Consulting & Education Services Ltd, Park House, Park Street, Maidenhead, Berkshire, SL6 1SL Tel: (01628) 673900 Fax: (01628) 673910 *Training & consulting company*

Fast Line Coatings Ltd, 9 Wellfield Business Park, Wellfield Road, Preston, PR1 8SZ Tel: (01772) 563550 Fax: (01772) 563551 E-mail: sales@fastlinecoatings.com *Powder coating services*

Fast Micros, 87 Canterbury Road, Margate, Kent, CT9 5AX Tel: (01843) 227522 Fax: (01843) 225109 *Computer hardware & servicing*

Fast Plant Swindon Ltd, Unit 2267, Dunbeath Road, Elgin Industrial Estate, Swindon, SN2 8EA Tel: (01793) 617854 Fax: (01793) 420809 E-mail: fastplantswindon@btconnect.com *Plant & tool sales & hire*

Fast Signs Scotland Ltd, Unit 1, Millstreet Industrial Estate, Airdrie, Lanarkshire, ML6 6JJ Tel: (01236) 766050 Fax: (01236) 751647 E-mail: fastsigns@btconnect.com *Sign manufrs*

Fast Software, East Street, Olney, Buckinghamshire, MK46 4BT Tel: (01234) 712184 Fax: (01234) 712184 *Computer consultants*

Fast Stik Labels, 41 Norwood Road, London, SE24 9AA Tel: (020) 8671 1818 Fax: (020) 8671 1818 E-mail: fast-sticklables@tiscali.co.uk *Self adhesive labels*

Fast Tools Holdings Ltd, Llanthony Road, Hempsted, Gloucester, GL2 5HL Tel: (01452) 529671 Fax: (01452) 307992 E-mail: sales@fasttoolsltd.co.uk *Tool distributors*

Fast Track Online, Flat 2, 47-49 Victoria Road, Bridlington, East Yorkshire, YO15 2AT Tel: (01262) 602013 E-mail: jennygw@fasttrackonline.co.uk *Web development services*

Fastabs Ltd, Unit 3 Oswin Road, Brailsford Industrial Estate, Leicester, LE3 1HR Tel: 0116-291 6660 Fax: 0116-291 6661 E-mail: fastabs@virgin.net *Labels & business stationery manufrs*

▶ Fastback (UK), 31 Hill Road, Fareham, Hampshire, PO16 8LA Tel: (07931) 568823 E-mail: brnmonks@aol.com *Shot blasting services*

Fastbolt Distributors (UK) Ltd, Sherbourne Drive, Tilbrook, Milton Keynes, MK7 8AW Tel: (01908) 650100 Fax: (01908) 650101 E-mail: fastbolt-uk@compuserve.com *Fastener distributors*

Fastec Engineering Services Ltd, Unit 8 Studlands Park Avenue, Studlands Park Industrial Estate, Newmarket, Suffolk, CB8 7AU Tel: (01638) 660186 Fax: (01638) 667374 E-mail: danny@fastecengineeing.co.uk *A well established sub contract machinery company based in Newmarket, Suffolk we offer Precision CNC Turning & CNC Milling. Precision Engineers in the Turned and machined parts industry, our Sliding head machines keep us competitive within the market. We can also offer most people a one stop shop as we cater for Fabrication, Welding and assembly work. Manufacturers and assemblers of components for a wide spectrum of customers with diverse requirements. These include Pharmaceutical, Optical, Scientific, Instruments, Food & Drink, Laser, Ink - Jet printing, Military, Petro-Chemical, Agricultural, Medical and Robotics. A BSEN ISO 9001:2001 Company and an investor in people, quality is assured from us as we invest as much in personnel and training as we do in machinery and equipment. KANBAN systems enable the company to provide fully manufactured complete finished product to the end user on a just in time basis. Please mention Kellysearch when enquiring*

Fastek Electronics Ltd, Palace House, Edinburgh Road, Linlithgow, West Lothian, EH49 6QS Tel: (01506) 848076 Fax: (01506) 848076 E-mail: fastekelectronice@hotmail.com *Electronics assembly & manufrs*

▶ Fastek Graphic Services Ltd, 3a Sheepscar St South, Leeds, LS7 1AD Tel: 0113-243 9808 Fax: 0113-246 9406 E-mail: sales@fastek.co.uk *Service & hardware supplier ctp & scanners*

Fastener Direct Ltd, Unit 5 The Union Centre, Hillbottom Road, Sands Industrial Estate, High Wycombe, Buckinghamshire, HP12 4HJ Tel: (01494) 442743 Fax: (01494) 474726 E-mail: fastenerdirect@aol.com *Fasteners stockists*

Fastener & Machining Supply Ltd, Unit 12 South Staffs Business Park, Hawkins Drive, Cannock, Staffordshire, WS11 0XU Tel: (01922) 419418 Fax: (01922) 411314 E-mail: enquiries@fmsltd.net *Fasteners & fixing devices*

Fastener Tools Birmingham Ltd, Unit 3-4 St. Andrews Street, Birmingham, B9 4JT Tel: 0121-753 2218 Fax: 0121-753 2240 E-mail: fasttools@btconnect.com *Precision tool makers*

Fastener Warehouse Ltd, 5 Ambassador Industrial Estate, 9 Airfield Road, Christchurch, Dorset, BH23 3TG Tel: (01202) 479621 Fax: (01202) 477222 E-mail: sales@fastenerwarehouse.co.uk Principal Export Areas: Africa *Distributors & manufacturers of bolts & nuts*

Fasteners & Engineering Supplies Ltd, 5 Westgate, Cowbridge, South Glamorgan, CF71 7AQ Tel: (01446) 774888 Fax: (01446) 773778 E-mail: sales@f-e-s.co.uk *Bolt & nut distributors*

Fasteners Midlands Ltd, 16-17 Longford Industrial Estate, Longford Road, Cannock, Staffordshire, WS11 0DG Tel: (01543) 462416 Fax: (01543) 574308 *Fastener distributors*

▶ Fasteq Ltd, 3 Fairbairn Road, Livingston, West Lothian, EH54 6TS Tel: (01506) 460888 Fax: (01506) 461144 E-mail: sales@fasteq.co.uk *Industrial fastener distributor*

Faster By Design, 1 Shildon Business Centre, Dabble Duck Industrial Estate, Shildon, County Durham, DL4 2RF Tel: (01388) 773322 Fax: (01388) 778890 E-mail: mail@fasterbydesign.co.uk *Distributors for Arata exhausts and rearsets, CRG levers, PPTuning, Fren Tubo*

▶ Fastfix, 3 The Maltings, George Street, Newark, Nottinghamshire, NG24 1LU Tel: (0845) 8882001 Fax: (01636) 640029 E-mail: sales@fastfixcomputers.co.uk *Computer maintenance & repair services*

▶ Fastfix Workshop Ltd, 62-64 Victoria Road East, Thornton-Cleveleys, Lancashire, FY5 5HQ Tel: (01253) 850400 Fax: (01253) 850200 E-mail: fastfixworkshop@btconnect.com *Cleaning & maintenance suppliers*

Fastlane Displays Ltd, 19 Arkwright Court, Astmoor Industrial Estate, Runcorn, Cheshire, WA7 1NX Tel: (01928) 569846 Fax: (01928) 569846 *Exhibition display services*

Fastlight.co.uk, Unit 19 Chatsworth Green, Basingstoke, Hampshire, RG22 4QA Tel: (0870) 7601420 Fax: (0870) 7601421 E-mail: rob@fastlight.co.uk *Suppliers of a comprehensive range of high quality energy efficient industrial and commercial lighting products suitable for catering, leisure, hospitality and security applications. Our product range consists of flood, fluorescent, emergency, amenity and corrosion resistant lighting suitable for exposed and hostile environments. Extensive stocks are held to provide next day delivery at cost considerate price levels.*

Fastnets UK Ltd, 20l Hall End Business Park, A5 Watling Street Dordon, Dordon, Tamworth, Staffordshire, B78 1SZ Tel: (01827) 899101 Fax: (0870) 6091707 E-mail: sales@fastnetsuk.com *Safety netting - Industrial Climbing - Edge Protection*

▶ Fastpack 2000, 36 Manor Industrial Estate, Flint, Clwyd, CH6 5UY Tel: (01352) 734366 Fax: (01352) 734399 E-mail: rob@fastpack2000.co.uk *Electronic assembly & distributors*

Fast-Pak Packaging Ltd, Unit 1 Kayley Industrial Estate, Richmond Street, Ashton-under-Lyne, Lancashire, OL7 0AU Tel: 0161-339 0697 Fax: 0161-339 4700 E-mail: fastpak@talk21.com *Corrugated cases & die cuts manufrs*

▶ Fastplas Ltd, Unit 1-2, Block 8, Chapelhall Industrial Estate, Chapelhall, Airdrie, Lanarkshire, ML6 8QH Tel: (01236) 779922 Fax: (01236) 779933 E-mail: sales@fastplas.com *Pvc stock holders*

Fastplas Technical Moulding Ltd, 22 Brunel Road, St. Leonards-on-Sea, East Sussex, TN38 9RT Tel: (01424) 851443 Fax: (01424) 851443 E-mail: info@fastplas.co.uk *Injection moulding plastic services*

Fastrack Services Sun Blinds, 119 High Street, Tranent, East Lothian, EH33 1LW Tel: (0800) 0921021 Fax: (01875) 616677 *Blinds manufrs*

Fastrack Used Racking, Unit 14 Hurricane Way, North Weald Airfield, North Weald, Epping, Essex, CM16 6AA Tel: (01992) 523500 Fax: (01992) 523900 E-mail: janice.cullin@unitedstorage.co.uk *New & used racking suppliers*

Fastrax Conveyors & Components, Shieling Court, Oakley Hay Industrial Estate, Great Oakley, Corby, Northamptonshire, NN18 9QD Tel: (01536) 747770 Fax: (01536) 747990 E-mail: fastraxcc@aol.com *Conveyor rollers manufrs*

Fastsigns, 86 Walcot Street, Bath, BA1 5BD Tel: (01225) 447797 Fax: (01225) 444010 *Sign manufrs*

Fastsigns, Galbraith House 142 Lombard House, Great Charles St Queensway, Birmingham, B3 3LG Tel: 0121-236 2123 Fax: 0121-212 9970 E-mail: martin.drury@fastsigns.com *Sign manufrs*

Fastsigns, 449 Cowbridge Road East, Cardiff, CF5 1JH Tel: (029) 2034 4455 Fax: (029) 2034 4488 E-mail: 868@fastsigns.com *Sign makers*

Fastsigns, 11 Colman Parade, Southbury Road, Enfield, Middlesex, EN1 1YY Tel: (020) 8367 3777 Fax: (020) 8367 3863 *Sign manufrs*

Fastsigns, 55 Western Road, Hove, East Sussex, BN3 1JD Tel: (01273) 726600 Fax: (01273) 722200 E-mail: mike.heath@fastsigns.com *Sign manufrs*

Fastsigns, 12 Boar Lane, Leeds, LS1 6EN Tel: 0113-246 9300 Fax: 0113-246 9393 *Sign manufrs*

Fastsigns Ltd, 36 High St, New Malden, Surrey, KT3 4HE Tel: 020 83360802 Fax: 020 83360914 *Sign manufacturer*

Fastsigns, 630-642 Chesterfield Road, Sheffield, S8 0SA Tel: 0114-255 2553 Fax: 0114-258 8444 *Sign manufrs*

Fastsigns, 222 St Albans Road, Watford, WD24 4AU Tel: (01923) 211777 Fax: (01923) 219191 E-mail: watford@fastsigns.com *Graphic design, sign makers & installation services*

▶ Fastsigns Signs & Graphics, 6 Victoria Court, New Street, Chelmsford, CM1 1GP Tel: (01245) 350450 Fax: (01245) 280022 E-mail: chelmsford.uk@863fastsigns.com *Signage, sign making & sign fitting*

▶ Fastsource Ltd, Pepper Road, Leeds, LS10 2EU Tel: 0113-270 1637 Fax: 0113-270 4366

Faststream Recruitment Ltd, Medina Chambers, Town Quay, Southampton, SO14 2AQ Tel: (023) 8033 4444 Fax: (023) 8033 5555 E-mail: ben@faststream.co.uk *Recruitment consultants*

fast-trak.net, 110 Front Street, Cockfield, Bishop Auckland, County Durham, DL13 5AA Tel: (01388) 710833 Fax: (01388) 710755 *Web Hosting Only £2.08 - 50 MB web space, 3GB bandwidth per month, ASP, Email, aliases, multi-recipient, web mail, spam filtering, anti-virus, Helm control panel ODBC + much more. Business, home & professional accounts available.*

Fasttrak Software Publishing Ltd, 20 Greenhill Crescent, Watford Business Park, Watford, WD18 8JA Tel: (01923) 495496 Fax: (01923) 800190 E-mail: fasttrak.info@polaron.co.uk *Retail software*

▶ Fastway Couriers, A1 Barton Industrial Estate, Faldo Road, Barton-le-Clay, Bedford, MK45 4RP Tel: (0845) 1088000 Fax: (01582) 881767 E-mail: sales@fastwaycouriers.com *Inexpensive next-day couriers*

Fastway Flyers Ltd, 78 Rivington Street, London, EC2A 3AY Tel: (020) 7729 3333 Fax: (020) 7729 3806 E-mail: fastwayflyers@1tel.net.uk *Couriers*

Fastweld '93 Welding Services, Unit 8, Old Farm Buildings, Maiden Lane, Crayford, Dartford, DA1 4LX Tel: (01322) 553145 Fax: (01322) 553145 *Specialist welding & subcontracting services*

▶ Fat Bobs, Rainbow Drive, Leadenhall, Milton Keynes, MK6 5EJ Tel: (01908) 232122

Fata Automation Ltd, Elgar House, Shrub Hill Road, Worcester, WR4 9EE Tel: (01905) 613931 Fax: (01905) 613913 E-mail: info@fatagroup.it *Automated equipment & conveyor systems*

▶ Father Christmas Letters Ltd, Old School Lane, Whittlesford, Cambridge, CB22 4YS Tel: (0870) 7503159 Fax: (0870) 0941215 E-mail: info@fatherchristmasletters.co.uk *Personalised letters from father christmas retailers & wholesalers*

Fathom Technologies Ltd, 8 Windsor Square, Silver Street, Reading, RG1 2TH Tel: 0118-975 0044 Fax: 0118-975 0742 E-mail: info@fathom.co.uk *Software developers & distributors*

Fathomtree Ltd, 5 The Midway, Nottingham, NG7 2TS Tel: 0115-986 0096 Fax: 0115-986 0210 E-mail: sales@fathomtreeltd.com *Nottingham's premier plastic forming specialist, small and large batch work done.*

▶ Fatstrippa Clearflow, Ainsley Grove, Faverdale, Darlington, County Durham, DL3 0GD Tel: (01325) 460040 E-mail: fatstrippa@fsmail.net *Installation of grease removing products*

Faudler Balfour, P O Box 15, Leven, Fife, KY8 4RW Tel: (01333) 423020 Fax: (01333) 427432 E-mail: mailus@pfaudlerbalfour.co.uk *Thermal fluid heating systems & reactor systems glass lined equipment design & manures*

Keith Faulkner Ltd, Park Garage, Macclesfield Street, Stoke-on-Trent, ST6 1EH Tel: (01782) 812990 Fax: (01782) 838991 *Crane hire services*

▶ Faulkner Property, 47 Alston Drive, Bradwell Abbey, Milton Keynes, MK13 9HB Tel: (01908) 321200 Fax: (01908) 321600 E-mail: management@faulknerproperty.co.uk *In 1992 we had a dream of creating the finest Property Letting and Management Company in North Buckinghamshire. Not motivated by the potential for profit but fiercely driven by the excitement of being an integral part of something which is the best. That is still our driving force today.*

Faulks & Co. Ltd, 21 Moat Way, Barwell, Leicester, LE9 8EY Tel: (01455) 848184 Fax: (01455) 844134 E-mail: sales@faulks.co.uk *Recycled containers manufrs*

Faun Municipal Vehicles Ltd, Unit 4 Bryn Cefni Industrial Park, Llangefni, Gwynedd, LL77 7XA Tel: (01248) 722777 Fax: (01248) 750220 E-mail: sales@faun.demon.co.uk *Vehicle manufrs*

Faurecina Midlands Ltd, PO Box 200, Coventry, CV3 1LU Tel: (024) 7663 5533 Fax: (024) 7688 5075 *Vehicle seat trimmings manufrs*

John Fausset Ltd, 56 Rosslyn Avenue, Preesall, Poulton-le-Fylde, Lancashire, FY6 0HE Tel: (01253) 810358 Fax: (01253) 810358 *Precast stone*

Faversham Joinery UK Ltd, Abbey Farm, Abbey Road, Faversham, Kent, ME13 7BL Tel: (01795) 537062 Fax: (01795) 597666 E-mail: enquiries@favershamjoinery.co.uk *Carpenters & joinery manufrs*

Favour Pet Foods, 29 Magherabeg Road, Randalstown, County Antrim, BT41 2PL Tel: (028) 9447 3840 Fax: (028) 9447 2104 E-mail: info@favour.co.uk *Manufacturers of animal feed binders & pet foods*

Company Information

▶ Favouritesweetshop.co.uk, 10 Castle Drive, Kemsing, Sevenoaks, Kent, TN15 6RL Tel: 01732 760480 E-mail: info@favouritesweetshop.co.uk *Online sweetshop offering a wide range of old fashioned sweets including toffees, butterscotch, chocolates, sherbet and much more! All our sweets are competitively priced and ordering is easy using our secure payment system. We also provide wedding favours and party bags, as well as catering for corporate events. Why not take a trip down memory lane and view our range of traditional sweets today at www.favouritesweetshop.co.uk?*

Fawcett Agriculture, Ireby Hall, Cowan Bridge, Carnforth, Lancashire, LA6 2JH Tel: (01524) 242222 Fax: (01524) 42239 E-mail: richard@fawcetts.net *Agricultural contractors*

Fawcett Christie Hydraulics Ltd, Sandycroft Industrial Estate, Chester Road, Sandycroft, Deeside, Clwyd, CH5 2QP Tel: (01244) 535515 Fax: (01244) 533002 E-mail: sales@fch.co.uk *Hydraulic accumulator & cooler manufrs*

David Fawcett Ltd, Tynyronnen, Mynytho, Pwllheli, Gwynedd, LL53 7RT Tel: (01758) 740720 Fax: (01758) 740722 E-mail: fawcett@pipemedia.co.uk *Model boat manufrs*

▶ Fawcett Electrical Ltd, 6 Station Road, Skelmanthorpe, Huddersfield, HD8 9AU Tel: (01484) 863769 Fax: (01484) 864972

Thomas Fawcett & Sons Ltd, 8 Eastfield Lane, Castleford, West Yorkshire, WF10 4LE Tel: (01977) 552490 Fax: (01977) 519076 E-mail: enquiries@fawcett-maltsters.co.uk *Malt, & mail flour processors*

Fawns Recreational Services Ltd, Woodcot Court, 2a Woodcot Gardens, Farnborough, Hampshire, GU14 9RD Tel: (01252) 515199 Fax: (01252) 515858 E-mail: sales@fawns.co.uk *Manufacturing & installing play & recreational equipment*

Fax Typewriter Service, Greenlands, Danes Green, Claines, Worcester, WR3 7RU Tel: (01905) 456705 Fax: (01905) 456705 *Fax & typewriter repairer*

Fax (UK) Ltd, Timber House, Standford Place, Church Stretton, Shropshire, SY6 6DY Tel: (01694) 722333 Fax: (0870) 3665760 E-mail: sales@shopuk.co.uk *Office machinery resellers*

▶ Faxco Maintenance Ltd, Irvine Industrial Estate, Irvine, Ayrshire, KA12 8JJ Tel: (01294) 311796

Faxlink Communications, 7-9 Bellegrove Parade, Welling, Kent, DA16 2RE Tel: (020) 8856 1166 Fax: (020) 8319 4074 E-mail: faxlink@dial.pipex.com *Office equipment suppliers*

Faxtip Ltd, 32 Mason Street, Manchester, M4 5EY Tel: 0161-835 3582 Fax: 0161-835 3582 E-mail: faxtip@yahoo.co.uk *Belts manufrs*

Fay Engineering Ltd, 5 Audley Court, Fison Way, Thetford, Norfolk, IP24 1HT Tel: (01842) 763622 Fax: (01842) 763622 *General engineers, food industry suppliers*

Fayers Bespoke Software, 1A Barton Buisness Park, Barton Road, Bury St. Edmunds, Suffolk, IP32 7BE Tel: (01284) 760276 Fax: (08707) 515984 E-mail: chrisandian@fayresbespoke.com *Computer consultants*

Fayrefield Foods Ireland Ltd, 123 York Street, Belfast, BT15 1AB Tel: (028) 9024 7448 Fax: (028) 9032 6375 E-mail: info@fayrefieldireland.com *Dairy product trading*

Fayrefield Foodtec Ltd, Avoca House, Molivers Lane, Bromham, Bedford, MK43 8JT Tel: (01234) 825704 Fax: (01234) 825705 E-mail: paulc@fayrefield.com Principal Export Areas: Central/East Europe & West Europe *Food products*

▶ Fayrefield FoodTec Ltd, Gateway, Crewe Gates Industrial Estate, Crewe, CW1 6XA Tel: (01270) 211294 Fax: (01270) 580605 *Develop & manufacture food ingredients*

Fays Metals Ltd, 3 37 Colville Road, London, W3 8BL Tel: (020) 8993 8883 Fax: (020) 8993 7200 E-mail: sales@fays-metals.co.uk *Steel stockholders*

Fayton Developments (Precision Sheet Metal), Unit D 3, Dominion Way, Rustington, Littlehampton, West Sussex, BN16 3HQ Tel: (01903) 770192 Fax: (01903) 850498 E-mail: admin@fayton.co.uk *Well established company for over 25 years providing quality products throughout the UK. Friendly efficient and helpful team. Fine limit sheet metals work, prototypes, small to medium batch runs, product development through to completion. CNC plant to take sheet depths of up to 6mm. Polishing, graining and powdercoating provided, out of house. Free delivery within a 100 mile radius. PLANT Wiedeman /Murata C25 Turret CNC punch press. Darley 2500 x 4m guillotine. Safan e-Brake 2m - 50 T - 7 axis CNC press brake. Guilfil 25 /80 - 2500 x 80 ton - 2 axis CNC press brake. Guilfil 25 /30 - 1500 x 30 ton press brake. Boschert 200 x 200 x 4 power notcher. SIP 30Kva spot welder. SIP 180 amp single phase mig welder. SIP 240 amp 3 phase mig welder. Murex Tradestig ac /dc 161i. ESS 230 amp ac / dc square wave tig welder. ESS 220 amp tig welder.*

▶ Faze 3, 23 Abergele Road, Colwyn Bay, Clwyd, LL29 7RS Tel: (01492) 534294 Fax: (01492) 534294 E-mail: alan@faze3.co.uk *Mechanical puzzles including japanese puzzle boxes and traditional, hand-crafted Welsh love spoons.*

Fazeley Signs, Unit 118 Bonehill Mill, Lichfield Street, Fazeley, Tamworth, Staffordshire, B78 3QS Tel: (01827) 261711 Fax: (01827) 261711 E-mail: info@fazeleysigns.co.uk *Sign manufrs*

Fb-Avak, 11 Woolmer Way, Bordon, Hampshire, GU35 9QF Tel: (01420) 477411 Fax: (01420) 488224 E-mail: sales@fb-avak.co.uk *Plastic vacuum formed products manufrs*

FBH Associates Ltd, Hi Point House, Thomas Street, Taunton, Somerset, TA2 6HB Tel: (01823) 335292 Fax: (01823) 332104 E-mail: sales@fbh.co.uk *Computer systems software*

Fbh-Fichet Ltd, 7/8 Amor Way, Letchworth Garden City, Hertfordshire, SG6 1UG Tel: (01462) 472900 Fax: (01462) 472901 E-mail: sales@fbh-fichet.com *Suppliers & manufacturers of cash safes*

Fca Computers, 185 Kingston Road, Epsom, Surrey, KT19 0AA Tel: (020) 8786 7492 Fax: (020) 8786 7493 E-mail: sales@fcacomputers.co.uk *Computer system building*

FCE Engineering Ltd, Methilhaven Road, Methil, Leven, Fife, KY8 3LA Tel: (01333) 423557 Fax: (01333) 423582 *Industrial mechanical handling equipment manufrs*

FCJ, 10a Bushey Hall Road, Bushey, WD23 2EA Tel: (01923) 220137 Fax: (01923) 233027 E-mail: sales@fcjprecisiongrinding.co.uk *Grinding services including precision, cylindrical, internal & surface*

FDE Factdate Engineering (UK) Ltd, Premier Business Centre, 47-49 Park Royal Road, London, NW10 7LQ Tel: 020 8838 4755 Fax: 020 8181 4515 E-mail: info@fdeuk.com *An engineering consultancy we supply industrial machinery and spare parts. Additionally, FDE have two major security products - Security Smoke systems for probably the most secure approach to theft reduction; and our own 3G Biometric Access Systems (fingerprint recognition). *Other major products include seals and gaskets, compressors, diesel generators and spares, ventilation systems, food processing machinery. We supply into the aerospace, automotive, chemical, electronics, pharma and other industries*

▶ FDM Services, 74 Campbell Road, Caterham, Surrey, CR3 5JN Tel: 07879 840286 E-mail: mail@fdmservices.com *Photographic Restoration Alteration and Enhancement*

Fearing International, Creaton Road, Brixworth, Northampton, NN6 9BW Tel: (01604) 881491 Fax: (0800) 581606 E-mail: sales@fearing.co.uk *Manufacturers of animal health care products*

Fearless Ramps, 18 Warren Road, Godalming, Surrey, GU7 3SH Tel: (01483) 420745 Fax: (01483) 416862 E-mail: info@fearlessramps.com *Skate park construction, design satellite & concrete ramps manufrs*

▶ Fearn Web Design, C/O 57 Clough Head, Longwood, Huddersfield, HD3 4UL Tel: 0161-408 0932 E-mail: mail@fearn.org.uk *Web designers*

Fearon Design & Marketing, 3 Brook Lane, Berkhamsted, Hertfordshire, HP4 1SX Tel: (01442) 386135 Fax: (01442) 386529 E-mail: andy@fearon-design.co.uk *Marketing consultants*

Feasibility Ltd, Weston Green, Hampton Court Way, Thames Ditton, Surrey, KT7 0JP Tel: (020) 8398 8088 Fax: (020) 8398 1547 E-mail: feasibility@btconnsct.com *Woodwork, furniture & fitments manufrs*

Feather & Black, Terminus Road, Chichester, West Sussex, PO19 8ZZ Tel: (01243) 380200 Fax: (01243) 790589 E-mail: chichester@featherandblack.com *Bed retailers*

Feather & Black, Regent House, 13-15 Albert Street, Harrogate, North Yorkshire, HG1 1JX Tel: (01423) 536644 Fax: (01423) 529699 *Bedroom items manufrs*

▶ Feather & Financial, Church Street, Shifnal, Shropshire, TF11 9AA Tel: (01952) 462979 *Gunsmiths*

Featherbow Woodcraft, Unit 1 Hillfields Farm, Lighthorne, Warwick, CV35 0BQ Tel: (01926) 651133 Fax: (01926) 651133 *Carpentry services*

▶ Feathers Favours, 16 Burnpark, Catrine, Mauchline, Ayrshire, KA5 6ER Tel: (01290) 553105 E-mail: enquires@feathersfavours.co.uk *Hand crafted product designers*

Featherstone Ltd, Kelleythorpe Industrial Estate, Kellythorpe, Driffield, North Humberside, YO25 9DJ Tel: (01377) 255016 Fax: (01377) 241299 E-mail: office@fetherston.co.uk *Electrical engineers*

▶ Featherstone Computer Centre, 10 Station Lane, Featherstone, Pontefract, West Yorkshire, WF7 5BE Tel: (01977) 700230 *Computer maintenance*

▶ Featherstone Pallets, 2 Smeaton Industrial Park, Went Edge Road, Kirk Smeaton, Pontefract, West Yorkshire, WF8 3LU Tel: (01977) 621111 Fax: (01977) 621122

▶ Feature Fire, 1 2 Warne Park, Warne Road, Weston-super-Mare, Avon, BS23 3TP Tel: (01934) 628142 Fax: (01934) 645625 E-mail: sales@feature-fireplaces.co.uk *Design, sales and installation of fires and fireplaces.*Natural stone fireplace manufacturers, we sell direct to the public. Over 40 displays in large showroom, gas /solid fuel / electric fires on live display.*Established over 20 years; Corgi and HETAS registered.*

featureDECO.co.uk, Unit A5, Link One Industrial Park, George Henry Road, Tipton, West Midlands, DY4 7BU Tel: 0845 200 4956 E-mail: enquiries@featuredeco.co.uk *The featureDECO team manufacture and supply a wide range of quality modern and contemporary products for the home and garden. As many of the products are carefully hand made you can customise them to suit your requirements. We are strictly an online retailer which enables us to keep our overheads low and our prices even lower helping us to pass on greater savings to you! We want you to pay less with no compromise for design, style or quality and hope that you find our selective range of decor a breath of fresh air. Our aim is to supply stylish new and innovative products for your home and garden at a very affordable price.*

Febland Group Ltd, Ashworth Road, Marton, Blackpool, FY4 4UN Tel: (01253) 600600 Fax: (01253) 792211 E-mail: info@febland.co.uk *Furniture distributors*

Federal Communications, PO Box 96, Hengoed, Mid Glamorgan, CF82 7ZR Tel: (0870) 2203995 Fax: (0870) 2203996 E-mail: info@federalcommunications.com *Voice & data communications*

Federal Express Corporation, Federal Express House Bond Gate Chambers, Bond Gate, Nuneaton, Warwickshire, CV11 4AL Tel: (024) 7634 3333 Fax: (024) 7637 5257 *International courier services*

Federal Mogul Friction Products Ltd, Hayfield Road, Chapel-en-le-Frith, High Peak, Derbyshire, SK23 0JP Tel: (01298) 811300 Fax: (01298) 811319 E-mail: info@ferodo.co.uk *Brake & clutch manufrs*

Federal Mogul Systems Protection Group, PO Box 47, Rochdale, Lancashire, OL12 7EZ Tel: (01706) 640100 Fax: (01706) 640110 *Automotive parts suppliers*

Federal-Mogul Camshaft Castings Ltd, Tutnalls, Lydney, Gloucestershire, GL15 5PX Tel: (01594) 842112 Fax: (01594) 841037 *Motor vehicle camshaft manufrs*

Federated Industries Ltd, 30-36 Virginia Street, Aberdeen, AB11 5AU Tel: (01224) 591323 Fax: (01224) 572858 E-mail: federated@btconnect.com *Sheet metalwork engineers*

Federation Of Crafts & Commerce, 4-5 The Briars, Waterberry Drive, Waterlooville, Hampshire, PO7 7YH Tel: (023) 9223 7010 Fax: (023) 9223 2120 E-mail: info@fcc.org.uk *Business association*

Federation Of Piling Specialists, Forum Court, 83 Copers Cope Road, Beckenham, Kent, BR3 1NR Tel: (020) 8663 0947 Fax: (020) 8663 0949 E-mail: fps@fps.org.uk *Trade association*

Fedex, Unit A2 Skyway 14, Calder Way, Poyle, Slough, SL3 0BQ Tel: (01753) 689589 Fax: (01753) 681647 *Air cargo & courier services* Also at: Prestwick

Fedex UK, 41 Rosevale Road, Parkhouse Industrial Estate West, Newcastle, Staffordshire, ST5 7EF Tel: (01782) 564544 Fax: (01782) 561553 E-mail: sales@anc.co.uk *Parts & delivery services.*

Fedwen Bakery, Teifi Mill, Pontwelly, Llandysul, Dyfed, SA44 4AJ Tel: (01559) 362375 Fax: (01559) 363402 *Bakers*

Feedback Data Ltd, Park Road, Crowborough, East Sussex, TN6 2QR Tel: (01892) 601400 Fax: (01892) 601429 E-mail: info@feedback-data.com *Access control system manufrs*

Feedback Instruments Ltd, Park Road, Crowborough, East Sussex, TN6 2QR Tel: (01892) 653322 Fax: (01892) 663719 E-mail: feedback@fdbk.co.uk *Manufacturers of test equipment including educational aid/ laboratory*

Feedwater Ltd, Tarran Road, Tarran Industrial Estate, Wirral, Merseyside, CH46 4TU Tel: 0151-606 0808 Fax: 0151-678 5459 E-mail: enquiries@feedwater.co.uk *Specialists in chemical water treatments*

Feedwell Animal Foods Ltd, Annsborough Park, Castlewellan, County Down, BT31 9NH Tel: (028) 4377 8765 Fax: (028) 4377 1420 E-mail: info@feedwell.com *Dog food manufrs*

▶ Feel Good Clinic, 6 Shaw Road, London, SE22 8DP Tel: 0208 693 1503 E-mail: info@feelgoodclinic.co.uk *Feel Good Clinic is a holistic business providing a range of complementary therapies and information to both individuals and the corporate sector. Specialises in fertility and pregnancy massage, healing and stress management.*

▶ Feel Good Drinks Co., 5 Hardwick Street, London, EC1R 4RG Tel: (020) 7687 7651 Fax: (020) 7687 7654 E-mail: team@feelgooddrinks.co.uk *Soft drinks manufacturer & distributor*

▶ The Feel Good Factory, 3 Boroughgate, Appleby-in-Westmorland, Cumbria, CA16 6XF Tel: (01768) 354129 Fax: (01768) 354129 *Whole food & health retailers*

▶ FeelAmazing, Marvell Rise, Harrogate, North Yorkshire, HG1 3LT Tel: 07976 533827 E-mail: feelamazing@earnyourdream.co.uk *Weight loss, weight gain, sport nutition, skin care, and targeted nutriton (mens health, womens health, healthy heart, Immune health,active body, digestive health, healthy ageing, vitality)*

▶ Feel-Clean, 14 Bow Lane, London, EC4M 9AL Tel: (020) 7613 4954 Fax: (020) 7613 4954 E-mail: info@feelclean.co.uk *Dry cleaning & laundry services*

▶ Feenix E-Learning Ltd, 67 Vancouver Quay, Salford, M50 3TU Tel: 0161-872 5277 Fax: (07092) 115000 E-mail: info2@feenix.co.uk *Supply e-learning tools & services*

▶ Feenix Fabs Ltd, Unit 51 Wellington Industrial Estate, Bilston, West Midlands, WV14 9EE Tel: (01902) 676780 Fax: (01902) 663397

Fegg Hayes Pottery Ltd, 2-4 Beaumont Road, Stoke-on-Trent, ST6 6BE Tel: (01782) 838328 Fax: (01782) 826378 E-mail: info@fegghayespottery.co.uk *Wholesalers of Chinaware*

Feig Electrical, 98 Clarence Road, London, E5 8HB Tel: (020) 8985 7004 Fax: (020) 8985 0107 E-mail: feigelec@aol.com *Electric motor rewinds & repairs*

Fein Industrial Power Tools UK Ltd, 4 Badby Park, Heartlands Business Park, Daventry, Northamptonshire, NN11 8YT Tel: (01327) 308730 Fax: (01327) 308739 E-mail: sales@fein-uk.co.uk *Distribution of professional power tools*

Fel Avionics Ltd, 236 North East Road, Southampton, SO19 8BB Tel: (023) 8044 2970 Fax: (023) 8043 1762 E-mail: info@fel-avionics.co.uk *Aircraft component distributors or agents*

Felber Jucker & Co. Ltd, 48 Minerva Road, Park Royal, London, NW10 6HJ Tel: (020) 8965 9371 Fax: (020) 8961 3732 *Crepe & tissue paper manufrs*

▶ The Felbrigg Design Co, 51 Long Street, Tetbury, Gloucestershire, GL8 8AA Tel: (01666) 505026 Fax: (01666) 505026 E-mail: tetbury@felbriggdesign.com *Our interior design company now proudly presents its first retail outlet. We offer interior design accessories and designer fabrics from Colefax and Fowler, Pierre Frey, Cath Kidston, Nina Campbell, Mulberry and many more.*All the products you*

continued

will see in the shop are now available to buy online.

Felco Electronics Ltd, 2 Rivermead, Pipers Way, Thatcham, Berkshire, RG19 4EP Tel: (01635) 866940 Fax: (01635) 866951 E-mail: sales@felco.co.uk *Switch & keypad suppliers*

Feldaroll Foundry Ltd, Units 14-21A, Bailie Gate Industrial Estate, Sturminster Marshall, Wimborne, Dorset, BH21 4DB Tel: (01258) 857754 Fax: (01258) 857353 *Non-ferrous & iron castings manufrs*

Feldbinder (UK) Ltd, Sutton Bridge, Spalding, Lincolnshire, PE12 9XE Tel: (01406) 353500 Fax: (01406) 353510 E-mail: sales@feldbinder.co.uk Principal Export Areas: Worldwide *Bulk containers, handling equipment & pressure vessels manufrs* Also at: Middlewich & Wokingham

Feldex Ltd, 93 Derwent Avenue, Garforth, Leeds, LS25 1HS Tel: 0113-232 0171 Fax: 0113-232 0171 E-mail: peterfeldex@supanet.com *Construction equipment spare parts distributors*

Feldman Fabrication Co. Ltd, Unit 83, Owen Road Industrial Estate, Owen Road, Willenhall, West Midlands, WV13 2PX Tel: 0121-526 4434 Fax: 0121-526 4201 E-mail: feldmanfabs@btconnect.com *Sheet metalwork fabrications*

Feldroll Foundry Plc, Units 17 & 21, Bailey Gate, Wimborne, Dorset, BH21 4AX Tel: (01258) 857754 Fax: (01258) 857353 E-mail: mark@feldroll.co.uk

Felford Industrial Clothing & Supplies, Riverside, Market Harborough, Leicestershire, LE16 7PT Tel: (01858) 434218 Fax: (01858) 410706 E-mail: felfordsupplies@btconnect.com *Protective safety wear & equipment retailers*

Felgoron Ltd, North Street Industrial Estate, Droitwich, Worcestershire, WR9 8JB Tel: (01905) 771938 Fax: (01905) 774677 *Mechanical installation contractors*

Feline Ltd, 48 Lord Street, Cheetham, Manchester, M3 1HN Tel: 0161-819 2717 Fax: 0161-819 2695 *Ladies clothing*

Felix Campania Ltd, 42 Ditton Hill Road, Surbiton, Surrey, KT6 5JD Tel: (020) 8339 0011 Fax: (020) 8398 5495 E-mail: felix.campania@btinternet.com *Reproduction furniture manufrs*

Felix Communications, 3 Phoenix Industrial Estate, Commissioners Road, Medway City Estate, Rochester, Kent, ME2 4HZ Tel: (01634) 724080 Fax: (01634) 296415 E-mail: pdc@felix.com *Labels manufrs*

▶ Felix Design, Unit 15, Tiverton Way, Tiverton Business Park, Tiverton, Devon, EX16 6SR Tel: (01884) 255420 *Staging*

Felix Engineering, Central Avenue, Lee Mill Industrial Estate, Ivybridge, Devon, PL21 9PE Tel: (01752) 698031 Fax: (01752) 690694 *Boat builders & repairers*

Felixarc Marine, Ground Floor, Wickenden House, The Dock, Felixstowe, Suffolk, IP11 3TZ Tel: (01394) 676497 Fax: (01394) 674039 *Tug operators*

Felixstowe Ferry Boat Yard Ltd, The Ferry, Felixstowe, Suffolk, IP11 9RZ Tel: (01394) 282173 Fax: (01394) 282173 *Boat yard & boat builders*

Felixstowe Freight Ltd, 23 Schneider Close, Felixstowe, Suffolk, IP11 3SS Tel: (01394) 677248 Fax: (01394) 677249 E-mail: graeme@felixstowefreight.co.uk *Customs Brokerage, CFSP, Domestic and International Transport, Freight Agents, Insurance Broker, ERTS warehousing, Long Term Storage, Pick & Pack, Out of Gauge Movements.*

▶ Felixstowe Ironing Services, Elizabeth Way, Felixstowe, Suffolk, IP11 2PQ Tel: (07946) 833767 E-mail: raddas76@yahoo.co.uk *Ironing Service in Felixstowe area with FREE COLLECTION AND DELIVERY*

▶ Felixstowe Ironworks, Lodge Farm, Kirton, Ipswich, IP10 0QE Tel: (01394) 448669 Fax: (01394) 448669 *Gate manufrs*

Roger Fell Ltd, Northside Industrial Park, Whitley Bridge, Goole, North Humberside, DN14 0GH Tel: (01977) 662211 Fax: (01977) 662334 E-mail: fellscarpets@aol.com *Carpet retailers*

Fellcroft Computing, 1 Hill Street, Corbridge, Northumberland, NE45 5AA Tel: (01434) 633300 Fax: (01434) 633440 *Computer manufrs*

Fellowes Ltd, Yorkshire Way, Armthorpe, Doncaster, South Yorkshire, DN3 3FB Tel: (01302) 836800 Fax: (01302) 836899 E-mail: sales@fellowes.com *Office products manufrs*

Fellowes Industrial Technology Ltd, 133 Newhall Street, Cannock, Staffordshire, WS11 1AD Tel: (01543) 503842 Fax: (01543) 503842 *Computer design consultants for industry only*

Fellows, 1 Wattville Road, Smethwick, West Midlands, B66 2NU Tel: 0121-555 8550 Fax: 0121-555 8660 E-mail: trevor@hsfellowsltd.com *Architectural metalwork manufrs*

Fellows & Fullwood Ltd, Prospect Row, Dudley, West Midlands, DY2 8SG Tel: (01384) 213311 Fax: (01384) 214014 *Wholesalers of electrical supplies* Also at: Cradley Heath & Stourbridge

Ian Fellows Ltd, 37 Lower Keyford, Frome, Somerset, BA11 4AR Tel: (01373) 473161 Fax: (01373) 451609 E-mail: sales@ianfellows.co.uk *Precision electronic weighing machines*

▶ Fellows & Jones Builders)Ltd, Pinfold Street, Wednesbury, West Midlands, WS10 8SY Tel: 0121-526 4418

▶ Fellows Stringer Ltd, 83-84 Cinder Bank, Dudley, West Midlands, DY2 9BH Tel: (01384) 459978 Fax: (01384) 458963 E-mail: dan@fellows-stringer.co.uk *From winches, & chain blocks, remote control, maintanance contracts, complete overhauls, cab to pendant conversions, gantry modifications, general lifting equipment, proof load testing & crane modificationsranging to complete crane & factory installations..*

Fellside Plastics Ltd, Wilson Way, Pool, Redruth, Cornwall, TR15 3RX Tel: (01209) 212917 Fax: (01209) 212919 E-mail: fellside@blowit.fsbusiness.co.uk *Plastic blow moulding & injection moulding manufrs*

▶ Felltech Ltd, St Johns House, Garrigill, Alston, Cumbria, CA9 3DS Tel: (01434) 380000 E-mail: info@felltech.com *Telecom equipment manufrs*
Fellwood Products, Cherryfields, Fullers Road, Rowledge, Farnham, Surrey, GU10 4DF Tel: (01252) 793807 *Fencing manufacturers & contractors*
Felspar Finishings Ltd, C Phoenix Works, Windsor Road, Redditch, Worcestershire, B97 6DJ Tel: (01527) 585878 Fax: (01527) 63167 E-mail: felsparfinish@aol.com *Powder coating services*
Feltech Electronics Ltd, 7 Long Spring, Porters Wood, St. Albans, Hertfordshire, AL3 6PE Tel: (01727) 834888 Fax: (01727) 848704 E-mail: sales@feltech.co.uk *Television systems design services*
Feltham Associates Ltd, Carlton House, Carlton Road, Kibworth Harcourt, Leicester, LE8 0PE Tel: 0116-279 3232 Fax: 0116-279 2473 E-mail: fal@btinternet.com *IT consultants*
▶ Feltham Construction Ltd, Mandarin Court, Hambridge Road, Newbury, Berkshire, RG14 5SY Tel: (01635) 523526 E-mail: info@felthamconstruction.co.uk
Feltham Tyres, Green Man Lane, Feltham, Middlesex, TW14 0QD Tel: (020) 8890 7138 Fax: (020) 8751 4428 E-mail: sales@felthamtyre.co.uk *Motor tyre dealers* Also at: Newbury & Slough
Felton Engineering, Unit 7, Hoddesdon Industrial Centre, Pindar Road, Hoddesdon, Hertfordshire, EN11 0DD Tel: (01992) 443723 Fax: (01992) 465257 E-mail: feltonengineer@aol.com *Precision engineering services*
Felton Production Solutions Ltd., 87 High Street, Knaphill, Woking, Surrey, GU21 2QD Tel: (01483) 475500 Fax: (01483) 475226 E-mail: martin.felton@btinternet.com *Design and manufacture of special purpose production machinery. Design and build of special purpose control systems including PLC"s*
Feltonquest Turned Parts Ltd, Unit 16 Britannia Estate, Leagrave Road, Luton, LU3 1RJ Tel: (01582) 738892 Fax: (01582) 721634 E-mail: tony.abbott@feltonquest.co.uk *Precision turned parts manufrs*
Female Health Co. (UK) P.L.C., 1 Sovereign Park, Coronation Road, Park Royal, London, NW10 7QP Tel: (020) 8965 2813 Fax: (020) 8453 0324 E-mail: info@female.condom.org Principal Export Areas: Worldwide *Medical disposables*
Femme Top Dezigne, 117 Asfordby Street, Leicester, LE5 3QF Tel: 0116-253 0130 Fax: 0116-253 0130 *Garments*
Femsys Ltd, 158 Upper New Walk, Leicester, LE1 7QA Tel: 0116-254 1475 Fax: 0116-255 8982 E-mail: info@senses.co.uk *Software house*
▶ Fen Digital, Highfield House, Upend, Newmarket, Suffolk, CB8 9PH Tel: 01638 731547 E-mail: webdesign@fendigital.co.uk *Website design*
Fen Fruits Ltd, Eastfield Farm, Chapel Road, Tilney Fen End, Wisbech, Cambridgeshire, PE14 8JL Tel: (01945) 880380 Fax: (01945) 880308 *Fruit processing specialists*
Fen Manufacturing Engineers Ltd, Blenheim Way, Northfields Industrial Estate, Market Deeping, Peterborough, PE6 8LD Tel: (01778) 344994 Fax: (01778) 344040 *General engineers*
Fen Pest Control, 1 Langley Park Cottages, Sutton Road, Langley, Maidstone, Kent, ME17 3NQ Tel: (01622) 862210 Fax: (01634) 685068 *Pest control*
▶ Fenbank Builders, Welbourne Lane East, Holbeach, Spalding, Lincolnshire, PE12 8AB Tel: (01406) 424071 Fax: (01406) 490871
Fenbelt Ltd, 107 Clay Street, Soham, Ely, Cambridgeshire, CB7 5HL Tel: (01353) 723955 Fax: (01353) 723953 E-mail: sales@fenbelt.co.uk *Conveyor belting distributors or agents*
Fenbrook Kitchen & Antique Pine Furniture, 103 Sidbury, Worcester, WR1 2HU Tel: (01905) 767537 *Antique pine restorers*
Fenceco Ltd, Unit 15-16 Weaver Park Estate, Mill Lane, Frodsham, WA6 7JA Tel: (01928) 735243 Fax: (01928) 735493 *Fencing manufrs*
Fenchurch Environmental Group Ltd, Dennow Farm, Firs Lane, Appleton, Warrington, WA4 5LF Tel: (01925) 269111 Fax: (01925) 269444 E-mail: sales@fengroup.com *Carbon filter manufrs*
Fencing Co., 3 Morgan Street, Llanbradach, Caerphilly, Mid Glamorgan, CF83 3LW Tel: (029) 2088 5976 Fax: (029) 2088 5976 *Industrial gates*
Fencing, 238 Gateford Road, Worksop, Nottinghamshire, S81 7AS Tel: (01909) 501176 *Domestic & garden fencing suppliers*
Fencing Centre, Chapel Lane, Parley, Christchurch, Dorset, BH23 6BG Tel: (01202) 579539 Fax: (01202) 579792 E-mail: sales@fencingcentre.co.uk *Fencing suppliers*
Fencing Centre, Higher Farm Industrial Estate, Preston Road, Yeovil, Somerset, BA20 2ET Tel: (01935) 412241 Fax: (01935) 412741 E-mail: info@fencingcentre.co.uk *General fencing sales & manufrs*
Fencing Products Ltd, 10 King Street Lane, Winnersh, Wokingham, Berkshire, RG41 5AS Tel: 0118-978 5162 Fax: 0118-977 6422 E-mail: j.a.o.@btinternet.com *Fencing contractors & manufrs*
Fencing Supplies Holdings Ltd, Bond 36 Mellors Road, Trafford Park, Manchester, M17 1PB Tel: 0161-872 8813 Fax: 0161-872 3221 *Security fencing manufrs*
Fenclocks Suffolk Ltd, 85 Gregory Road, Mildenhall, Bury St. Edmunds, Suffolk, IP28 7DF Tel: (01638) 712981 Fax: (01638) 712956 E-mail: time@fenclocks.freeserve.co.uk *Grandfather clock manufrs*
Fenco-Aldridge (Barton) Ltd, Lovat Court, Caldecote St, Newport Pagnell, Buckinghamshire, MK16 0YZ Tel: (01908) 614646 Fax: (01908) 214482 E-mail: fab@fenco.co.uk *Die casting lubricant systems manufrs*
Fencol Hydraulic Fittings Ltd, Unit 5 Europa Way, Britannia Enterprise Park, Lichfield, Staffordshire, WS14 9TZ Tel: (01543) 416343 Fax: (01543) 416343 E-mail: nick@fencol.com *Hydraulic fitting manufacturer & build of hydraulic hose assemblies*
Fencrete Products, Church Lane, Marsworth, Tring, Hertfordshire, HP23 4LZ Tel: (01442) 824174 Fax: (01442) 827856 *Concrete product manufrs*
▶ Fendequip, Unit 12, Lawerance Hill Business Centre, Wincanton, Somerset, BA9 9RT Tel: (01963) 33322 Fax: (01963) 33344 E-mail: info@fendequip.com *Manufacturer of Fender Covers & Fender Socks*
Fendius Ltd, 20 Milverton Terrace, Leamington Spa, Warwickshire, CV32 5BA Tel: (01926) 470760 Fax: (01926) 470761 E-mail: fendiusltd@dial.pipex.com *Machine tool agents*
Fengate Fasteners Ltd, Putney Close, Brandon, Suffolk, IP27 0PA Tel: (01842) 810771 Fax: (01842) 814097 E-mail: sales@fengatefasteners.co.uk *Industrial fastener stockholders*
Fengrove Ltd, 4 Mapledale Road, Liverpool, L18 5JE Tel: 0151-733 7628 Fax: 0151-733 0036 E-mail: copiers@fengrove.sagehost.co.uk *Photocopier sales & service*
▶ Fenhams Contracts, 2-6 Ivy Road, Gosforth, Newcastle Upon Tyne, NE3 1DB Tel: 0191-223 0600
Fenland Coolbox, Commercial Corner Barn, Mouth Lane, North Brink, Wisbech, Cambridgeshire, PE13 4UG Tel: 01945 450800 *Cold storage*
Fenland Ironworks Ltd, Unit 18a-18b Highlode Industrial Estate, Stocking Fen Road, Ramsey, Huntingdon, Cambridgeshire, PE26 2RB Tel: (01487) 814049 Fax: (01487) 814049 E-mail: fenlandiron@boltblue.net *Wrought iron arches, gates & railings*
Fenland Laundries Ltd, Roman Bank, Skegness, Lincolnshire, PE25 1SQ Tel: (01754) 767171 Fax: (01754) 610344 *Overall rental, supply services & launderers*
Fenland Shops Ltd, Jubilee Garage, Abbey Road, Bourne, Lincolnshire, PE10 9EF Tel: (01778) 423041 Fax: (01778) 423041 *Agricultural suppliers*
Fenmarc Ltd, Moor Lane, Swinderby, Lincoln, LN6 9LX Tel: (01522) 868484 Fax: (01522) 868835 *Food processing plant*
J.G. Fenn Ltd, Fenn House, Duke Street, Stoke-on-Trent, ST4 3PT Tel: (01782) 315782 Fax: (01782) 344060 E-mail: enquiries@fenns.co.uk *Commercial stationary retail suppliers*
Fenn Tool Ltd, 44 Spring Wood Drive, Springwood Industrial Estate, Braintree, Essex, CM7 2YN Tel: (01376) 347566 Fax: (01376) 550827 E-mail: enquiries@fenntool.co.uk *Drill & cutting tool distribs*
Fenner plc, Hesslewood Office Park, Ferriby Road, Hessle, North Humberside, HU13 0PW Tel: (01482) 626500 Fax: (01482) 626502 E-mail: info@fenner.com *Polymer engineers services*
Fenner Drives Ltd, Hudson Road, Leeds, LS9 7DF Tel: (0870) 7577007 Fax: 0113-248 9656 E-mail: sales@fennerdrives.com *Polyurethane belting manufrs*
Fenner Dunlop Europe, Marfleet, Hull, HU9 5RA Tel: (01482) 781234 Fax: (01482) 785438 E-mail: paul.mackman@fennerdunlop.com Principal Export Areas: Worldwide *Conveyor belting manufrs*
Fenner Paper Co. Ltd, Unit 15 Orchard Business Centre, Vale Rd, Tonbridge, Kent, TN9 1QF Tel: (01732) 771100 Fax: (01732) 771103 E-mail: info@fennerpaper.co.uk *Paper merchants*
Fenns (Farnborough) Ltd, 77 Alexandra Road, Farnborough, Hampshire, GU14 6BN Tel: (01252) 541221 Fax: (01252) 512890 E-mail: info@fennprint.co.uk *Aircraft instrument manufrs*
Fensell Properties Ltd, Oak Lodge, Homedowns, Tewkesbury, Gloucestershire, GL20 7BQ Tel: (01684) 273091 Fax: (01684) 273090 E-mail: simonbillinghurst@yahoo.com *Manufactures & stockists of flexible duct supports*
▶ Fentek Marine Systems UK Ltd, Grange Lane North, Scunthorpe, South Humberside, DN16 1BT Tel: (01724) 278883 Fax: (01724) 278884
Fenton Bed Warehouse, 267 City Road, Stoke-on-Trent, ST4 2QA Tel: (01782) 415649 Fax: (01782) 415649 E-mail: sales@fentonbeds.co.uk *Bed resellers*
Fenton Engineering Ltd, Finedon Sidings, Station Road, Finedon, Wellingborough, Northamptonshire, NN9 5NY Tel: (01536) 723488 Fax: (01536) 726642 E-mail: sales@fentonprecision.co.uk *Injection mould toolmakers*
Fenton Flooring & Ceramics, 157 Queens Road, Buckhurst Hill, Essex, IG9 5AZ Tel: (020) 8504 0529 Fax: (020) 8504 1296 *Flooring contractors*
Fenton Hadley Contracts Ltd, Arrowhead Road, Theale, Reading, RG7 4AE Tel: 0118-988 3266 Fax: 0118-988 4538 E-mail: waste@hadley.co.uk *Excavation & demolition contractors*
Fenton Industrial Ltd, 291 Edge Lane, Droylsden, Manchester, M43 6BS Tel: 0161-370 1568 Fax: 0161-370 9116 E-mail: info@fentonindustrial.co.uk *Electrical engineers*
▶ Fenton Mcintosh, 3 Eastern Terrace Mews, Kemptown, Brighton, BN2 1EP Tel: (01273) 628700 E-mail: iain@fenton-mcintosh.co.uk *Design and manufacture of designer lighting. "Electronic Engineering. Woodturning."Plastics."*
▶ Fenton Packaging Leeds Ltd, Bridge Street, Morley, Leeds, LS27 0LE Tel: 0113-252 8222 Fax: 0113-253 6394 E-mail: info@pspackaging.co.uk *Suppliers of plastic buckets & other plastic & metal containers*
Fenton Pharmaceuticals Ltd, 4J Portman Mansions, Chiltern Street, London, W1U 6NS Tel: (020) 7224 1388 Fax: (020) 7486 7258 *Pharmaceuticals manufrs*
Fenton Plant Hire, A Culverlands Industrial Estate, Winchester Road, Shedfield, Southampton, SO32 2JF Tel: (01329) 830011 Fax: (01329) 833683 E-mail: sales@fentonplant.co.uk *Hoist hire company*
▶ Fenton Transport Ltd, Mains of Duncrub, Dunning, Perth, PH2 0QN Tel: (01764) 684244
Fenweld Engineering Services, Unit 8 Addington Works, Knutsford Way Sealand Indust Estate, Chester, CH1 4LT Tel: (01244) 380880 Fax: (01244) 380294 E-mail: fenweld@compuserve.com *Heating installation & maintenance-industrial*
Fenweld Steel Fabricators, Bramley Road, St. Ives, Cambridgeshire, PE27 3WS Tel: (01480) 300877 Fax: (01480) 492120 *Steel fabricators; staircases, metal & welding services*
▶ Fenwick Haulage Ltd, Church Lane, Adwick-le-Street, Doncaster, South Yorkshire, DN6 7AY Tel: (01302) 728496 Fax: (01302) 726489
Feorge Plant & Fabrications Ltd, Unit 4 Transport Depot, Thorney, Langport, Somerset, TA10 0DW Tel: (01458) 253140 Fax: (01458) 253309 *Metal fabrication & commercial plant repair services*
Feralco (UK) Ltd, Ditton Road, Widnes, Cheshire, WA8 0PH Tel: 0151-802 2940 Fax: 0151-802 2999 E-mail: info@feralco.com Principal Export Areas: Worldwide *water treatment chemicals*
Fercell Engineering Ltd, Unit 1, Old Mill Lane, Aylesford, Kent, ME20 7DT Tel: (01622) 791414 Fax: (01622) 791515 E-mail: info@fercell.com *Pollution control engineers*
Ferdinand Kelly Solicitors, Yew House, Tamworth, Staffordshire, B78 2EY Tel: (01827) 895039 Fax: (01827) 895039 E-mail: info@ferdinandkelly.co.uk *Ferdinand Kelly is a niche commercial firm of solicitors specialising in fast-track, creative solutions to complex business problems. We can offer much more immediate, cost-effective solutions to problems because we have combined, in-house experience and expertise of barrister and solicitor.*
Fereday & Pocock, 7 The Micro Centre, Gillette Way, Reading, RG2 0LR Tel: 0118-975 5222 Fax: 0118-975 3520 *Blind manufrs*
▶ FeRFA the Resin Flooring Association, 99 West Street, Farnham, Surrey, GU9 7EN Tel: (01252) 739149 Fax: (01252) 739140 E-mail: ferfa@associationhouse.org.uk *Trade association*
▶ Fergal Contracting Co., The Downs Road, Stand Lake, Witney, Oxfordshire, OX29 7YP Tel: (01865) 300666 Fax: (01865) 300974
Ferguson Engineering, 6 Middlefield Road, Falkirk, FK2 9AG Tel: (01324) 627352 Fax: (01324) 633672 E-mail: enquiries@smith-electrical.co.uk *Machinery maintenance & repair*
Ferguson Engineering Northern Ltd, 2 Coulton Road, Brierfield, Nelson, Lancashire, BB9 5ST Tel: (01282) 447500 Fax: (01282) 447600 E-mail: sales@f-e-n.com *Bakery engineers*
▶ J. & J. Ferguson, 33 Strathaven Road, Kirkmuirhill, Lanark, ML11 9RN Tel: (01555) 892695
Ferguson & Mcilveen, Beechill House, 40 Beechill Road, Belfast, BT8 7RP Tel: (028) 9070 5111 Fax: (028) 9079 5651 E-mail: belfast@fermac.com *Civil & structural engineers & architects service*
Ferguson Mcilveen LLP, Victoria House, 159 Albert Road, Middlesbrough, Cleveland, TS1 2PX Tel: (01642) 218476 Fax: (01642) 223582 E-mail: postmaster@fermac.com *Consulting civil & structural engineers* Also at: Belfast & Woking
Ferguson Marine plc, Castle Road, Port Glasgow, Renfrewshire, PA14 5NG Tel: (01475) 742300 Fax: (01475) 741269 E-mail: davehe@fergusons6.demon.co.uk *Ship builders & steel fabricators*
Ferguson & Menzies Ltd, 312 Broomloan Road, Glasgow, G51 2JW Tel: 0141-445 3555 Fax: 0141-425 1079 E-mail: sales@fergusonmenzies.co.uk *Specialist resin suppliers natural oils & manufrs of lubricants*
Ferguson Polycom Ltd, Windsor Mill, Hollinwood, Oldham, OL8 3RA Tel: 0161-947 1326 E-mail: info@fergusonpolycom.co.uk *Rubber sheet manufrs*
Ferguson Print Keswick Ltd, 24 St John Street, Keswick, Cumbria, CA12 5AT Tel: (01768) 772486 Fax: (01768) 771121 E-mail: fergusonbrosltd@btconnect.com *Printers*
Ferguson Seacabs Ltd, Denmore Road, Bridge of Don, Aberdeen, AB23 8JW Tel: (01224) 706464 Fax: (01224) 706455 E-mail: info@fergusonseacabs.com *Freight container, accommodation modules leasing & rental services*
Thomas Ferguson & Co. Ltd, 54 Scarva Road, Banbridge, County Down, BT32 3QD Tel: (028) 4062 3491 Fax: (028) 4062 2453 E-mail: info@fergusonsirishlinen.com Principal Export Areas: Worldwide *Luxury household textiles suppliers*
▶ Ferguson Transport (Spean Bridge) Ltd, Tigharan, Spean Bridge, Inverness-Shire, PH34 4EP Tel: (01397) 712396 Fax: (01397) 712462
▶ Ferguson Transport (Spean Bridge) Ltd, Tigharan, Spean Bridge, Inverness-Shire, PH34 4EP Tel: (01397) 712396 Fax: (01397) 712462
Fergusons (Blyth) Ltd, Ennerdale Road, Kitty Brewster Estate, Blyth, Northumberland, NE24 4RD Tel: (01670) 353761 Fax: (01670) 357401 E-mail: sales@fergusonsremovals.co.uk *Removals, warehousing & haulage* Also at: Sunderland
▶ Ferguss Home Leisure, Deneswood House, High Close, Rawdon, Leeds, LS19 6HF Tel: 0113-250 2213 Fax: 0113-250 2746 E-mail: sales@ferguss.com *Suppliers of home entertainment products*
▶ Fergusson Group, Castlecraig Business Park, Players Road, Stirling, FK7 7SH Tel: (01786) 477222 Fax: (01786) 463522 *Sales, process coal*
Fericon Press Ltd, 12 Stadium Way, Tilehurst, Reading, RG30 6BX Tel: 0118-945 6100 Fax: 0118-945 4146 E-mail: fericon@dercon.co.uk *Graphic printers & designers*
Feridax 1957 Ltd, Park Lane, Halesowen, West Midlands, B63 2NT Tel: (01384) 410384 Fax: (01384) 638287 E-mail: info@feridax.com *Motorcycle component wholesalers*
Fermax UK Ltd, Fermax House, Bebington Close, Billericay, Essex, CM12 0DT Tel: (01277) 634777 Fax: (01277) 634666 E-mail: sales@fermaxuk.com *Fermax access control equipment distributors*
Fermex International Ltd, Unit E3 Blackpole Trading Estate East, Blackpole Road, Worcester, WR3 8SG Tel: (01905) 755811 Fax: (01905) 754145 E-mail: info@fermex.co.uk *Bread improvers*
Fern Computer Consultancy Ltd, Fern Court, Derby Road, Denby, Ripley, Derbyshire, DE5 8LG Tel: (01332) 780790 Fax: (01332) 780788 *Computer consultants*
Fern Computer Services Ltd, Kennedy Enterprise Centre, Kennedy Way Industrial Estate, Belfast, BT11 9DT Tel: (028) 9080 8000 Fax: (028) 9080 8001 E-mail: sales@fern.co.uk *Computer services & systems*
▶ Fern Joinery, Cowie Road, Bannockburn, Stirling, FK7 8JW Tel: (01786) 816701
T.W. Fern, Unit 1 Sulivan Enterprises, Sivan Rd, London, SW6 3DJ Tel: (020) 7371 5191 *Church organ repairers & manufrs*
Fernau Avionics Ltd, Unit C Airport Executive Park, President Way, Luton, LU2 9NY Tel: (01582) 483111 Fax: (01582) 484404 E-mail: info@fernau.com *Ground based navigation aids manufrs*
Fernco International Ltd, Newlands Way, Valley Park, Wombwell, Barnsley, South Yorkshire, S73 0UW Tel: (01226) 340209 Fax: (01226) 340400 E-mail: enquiries@fernco.co.uk Principal Export Areas: Worldwide *Drain & tube coupling manufrs*
▶ Ferndale Pharmaceutical Ltd, Unit 605, Thorp Arch Trading Estate, Thorp Arch, Wetherby, West Yorkshire, LS23 7BJ Tel: (01937) 541122 Fax: (01937) 849682 E-mail: info@ferndalepharma.co.uk *Pharmaceutical suppliers*
Fernden Construction Winchester Ltd, Barfield Close, Winchester, Hampshire, SO23 9SQ Tel: (01962) 866400 Fax: (01962) 864139 E-mail: sales@ferndenwin.co.uk *Fencing contractors*
Ferndown Finishing Ltd, 12 Cobham Road, Ferndown Industrial Estate, Wimborne, Dorset, BH21 7PS Tel: (01202) 877755 Fax: (01202) 877744 *Metal finishing, polishing specialists*
Ferndowne, Reform Industrial Estate, Maidenhead, Berkshire, SL6 8BY Tel: (01628) 630211 Fax: (01628) 623459 *Gravity diecasting services*
▶ Fernhall Associates Ltd, 15 Sturdon Road, Bristol, BS3 2BA Tel: 0117-378 9137 Fax: (07092) 229193 E-mail: info@fernhall.co.uk *Database technology & custom software solutions*
Ayles Fernie International Ltd, Unit D5 Chaucer Business Park, Watery Lane, Kemsing, Sevenoaks, Kent, TN15 6YU Tel: (01732) 762962 Fax: (01732) 761961 E-mail: sales@aylesfernie.co.uk *Oil dispersant spraying system manufrs*
Fernite Of Sheffield Ltd, Fernite Works, Coleford Road, Sheffield, S9 5NJ Tel: 0114-244 0527 Fax: 0114-244 5922 E-mail: sales@fernite.co.uk *Machine knives manufrs*
▶ Fernlea Nurseries, Dodgers Wood, Kings Somborne, Winchester, Hampshire, SO20 6NL Tel: 01794 388597 Fax: 01794 388597 E-mail: info@fernleanurseries.co.uk *Supply of Garden Shrubs*
▶ Fernleigh Design Ltd, Unit 5 Parc Ty Glas, Llanishen, Cardiff, CF11 7BF Tel: 02920 763524 Fax: 02920 763525 E-mail: amanda@fernleighdesign.co.uk *Exhibition Stand design, build, installation and storage - primarily throughout the UK and Europe. Design, build and installation of museum exhibitions, visitor/tourise centers and heritage interpretations. Custom build plus modular and portable systems. Graphic design for display panels and corporate literature, websites etc*
Fernley Airport Services Ltd, Concorde House, Colndale Road, Colnbrook, Slough, SL3 0HQ Tel: (0870) 8400611 Fax: (0870) 8400622 *Office cleaners*
Fernlow Fencing, Hall Farm, School Lane, East Stoke, Newark, Nottinghamshire, NG23 5QL Tel: (01636) 525966 Fax: (01636) 525966 *Garden fence manufrs*
Fernox, Sheer Water, Forsyth Road, Woking, Surrey, GU21 5RZ Tel: (0870) 6015000 Fax: (0870) 6015005 E-mail: sales@fernox.com Principal Export Areas: Worldwide *Water treatment chemicals & corrosion inhibitor manufrs*
Fernwood Craft Ltd, Unit 2C, Sewstern Industrial Estate, Sewstern, Grantham, Lincolnshire, NG33 5RD Tel: (01476) 860440 Fax: (01476) 861313 E-mail: info@fernwoodcraft.co.uk *Boat builders*
Fernyhough Restoration, Hall End Farm, Watling Street, Dordon, Tamworth, Staffordshire, B78 1SZ Tel: (01827) 330944 *Antique furniture restoration*
Ferrabyrne Ltd, Fort Road Industrial Estate, Wick, Littlehampton, West Sussex, BN17 7QU Tel: (01903) 721317 Fax: (01903) 730452 E-mail: sales@ferrabyrne.co.uk Principal Export Areas: Worldwide *Manufacturers of anti-vibration mountings, products rubber mouldings*
Ferranti Air Systems Ltd, The Oaks Business Park, Crewe Road, Manchester, M23 9SS Tel: 0161-946 3600 Fax: 0161-946 3601 E-mail: sales@ultra-as.com *Flight information services*
Ferranti Technologies Group Ltd, Cairo Mill, Greenacres Road, Oldham, OL4 3JA Tel: 0161-624 0281 Fax: 0161-624 5244 E-mail: sales@ferranti-technologies.co.uk *Electro mechanical equipment manufrs*

▶ Ferrari Electroplating, C Station Works, Bury Road, Radcliffe, Manchester, M26 2UA Tel: 0161-723 0202 Fax: 0161-724 8699 *Metal finishing services*

Ferrari Packaging Ltd, Eastfield Industrial Estate, Penicuik, Midlothian, EH26 8HJ Tel: (01968) 678100 Fax: (01968) 676060 E-mail: jockcwm@aol.com *Polyethylene bag manufrs*

Ferrari Stainless & Alloys Ltd, Unit 89, Woolsbridge Industrial Park, Three Legged Cross, Wimborne, Dorset, BH21 6SU Tel: (01202) 823346 Fax: (01202) 823903 *Stainless & alloy stockholders*

▶ Ferrari Trackdays, PO Box 169, Wymondham, Norfolk, NR18 0WL Tel: (0870) 9103786 E-mail: info@ferraritrackdays.co.uk *Welcome to FerrariTrackdays.co.uk the UK's specialist in Ferrari Trackdays, Racing & Driving Experiences.*

▶ Ferretteria, Culberry Nursery, Dappers Lane, Angmering, Littlehampton, West Sussex, BN16 4EW Tel: (07733) 142726 E-mail: sales@ferretteria.co.uk *Ferretteria is a Sussex based business where engineering and blacksmithing come together for the creation of bespoke wrought ironwork, architectural iron work and iron sculptures.*

▶ Ferriday & Alder, 4 Acre Road, Reading, RG2 0SX Tel: 0118-986 2510 Fax: 0118-975 1358 E-mail: info@movers.co.uk

Ferrier Pumps Ltd, Burlington Street, Leith, Edinburgh, EH6 5JL Tel: 0131-554 1200 Fax: 0131-553 1272 E-mail: edinburgh@ferrierpumps.co.uk *Pump distributors*

Ferrier Pumps (Aberdeen) Ltd, Unit 4-5 Barclayhill Place, Portlethen, Aberdeen, AB12 4PF Tel: (01224) 782022 Fax: (01224) 780050 E-mail: aberdeen@ferrierpumps.co.uk *Pump maintenance, repair services & manufrs*

Ferring Laboratories Ltd, The Courtyard, Waterside Drive, Slough, SL3 6EZ Tel: (01753) 214800 Fax: (020) 8893 1577 E-mail: contact@ferring.co.uk *Pharmaceutical distribs*

Ferris Stevedores Ltd, 2 Corry Place, Belfast Harbour Estate, Belfast, BT3 9HY Tel: (028) 9074 8371 Fax: (028) 9074 6500 E-mail: robert@ferris-belfast.freeuk.com *Warehousing contractors & stevedoring services*

Ferrisgate Coating Ltd, Ferrisgate House, Burrell Way, Thetford, Norfolk, IP24 3RA Tel: (01842) 766308 Fax: (01842) 754438 E-mail: ferriscoatings@aol.com *Coating & laminating services*

Ferrite Fabrications Ltd, 1 Wrights Yard, Top Road, Wimbish, Saffron Walden, Essex, CB10 2XJ Tel: (01799) 599907 Fax: (01799) 599914 *Steel fabricators*

▶ Ferro Electronic Component Distributors, 1 Lime Grove Estate, Falconer Road, Haverhill, Suffolk, CB9 7XU Tel: (01440) 711980 Fax: (01440) 711981 *Electronic material manufrs*

Ferro (G B) Ltd, Westgate, Aldridge, Walsall, WS9 8YH Tel: (01922) 741300 Fax: (01922) 741327 *Manufacturers of powder coatings*

Ferro Great Britain Ltd, Nile Street, Stoke-on-Trent, ST6 2BQ Tel: (01782) 820400 Fax: (01782) 820402 *Ceramic coating & colour manufrs*

Ferro Great Britain Ltd, Westgate, Aldridge, Walsall, WS9 8YH Tel: (01922) 458300 Fax: (01922) 741399 *Masterbatch (colour & pigment for plastic)*

Ferro Metal & Chemical Corporation Ltd, 179 Kings Road, Reading, RG1 4EX Tel: 0118-960 4700 Fax: 0118-950 9216 E-mail: sales@phibrochem.com *Chemical trading company*

Ferro Monk Systems Ltd, 16 Astley Way, Astley Lane Industrial Estate, Swillington, Leeds, LS26 8XT Tel: 0113-287 7577 Fax: 0113 287 7778 E-mail: info@ferromonk.co.uk *Sewer renovation & drainage contractors*

Ferrob Ltd, Regency House, Kingsclere Park, Kingsclere, Newbury, Berkshire, RG20 4SW Tel: (01635) 299266 Fax: (01635) 299277 E-mail: sales@ferrob.co.uk *Ventilation systems manufrs*

Ferro-Betol (UK), Southgreen Farm, Southgreen, Sittingbourne, Kent, ME9 7RR Tel: (01622) 884454 Fax: (01622) 884433 *Rust removers*

Ferrograph Ltd, New York Way, New York Industrial Park, Newcastle upon Tyne, NE27 0QF Tel: 0191-280 8800 Fax: 0191-280 8810 *Visual communication systems*

Ferromatik Milacron Ltd, Klockner House, Carrwood Road, Chesterfield, Derbyshire, S41 9QB Tel: (01246) 260666 Fax: (01246) 260474 E-mail: admin@ferromatik.co.uk *Injection moulding machine suppliers*

Ferrostatics International Ltd, Kings Court, 5 Waterloo Road, Stalybridge, Cheshire, SK15 2AU Tel: 0161-303 2200 Fax: 0161-303 2211 E-mail: sales@ferrostatics-int.com *High pressure equipment*

Ferrosteel (Structures) Ltd, 60 Lichfield St, Walsall, WS4 2BX Tel: (01922) 637467 Fax: (01922) 720364 *Reinforced concrete contractors & engineers*

Ferrotec UK Ltd, Unit 3 I O Centre, Skeffington Street, London, SE18 6SR Tel: (020) 8317 3100 Fax: (020) 8317 9559 E-mail: info@ferrotec.co.uk *Magnetic fluid seals manufrs*

Ferrous Protection Ltd, Hanson House, Grains Road, Delph, Oldham, OL3 5RN Tel: (01457) 873419 Fax: (01457) 871091 E-mail: ferrous_protection@yahoo.com *Corrosion prevention treatments*

Ferry Boat Yard, Ferry Boatyard, Lower Upnor, Upnor, Rochester, Kent, ME2 4XA Tel: (01634) 723272 *Boat builders & repairers*

Ferry Chem Ltd, Unit 3c Pentre Industrial Estate, Pentre Queensferry, Pentre, Deeside, Clwyd, CH5 2DQ Tel: (01244) 533033 Fax: (01244) 533033 *Janitorial supply services*

▶ Ferryfast Produce Ltd, Ascot Road, Pershore, Worcestershire, WR10 2JJ Tel: (01386) 552131 Fax: (01386) 562407 E-mail: sales@ferryfast.co.uk

▶ Ferryman Ltd, Unit 2, Newbridge Road Industrial Estate, Pontllanfraith, Blackwood, Gwent, NP12 2XF Tel: (01495) 222300 Fax: (01495) 222302 E-mail: sales@ferryman.org.uk *Transport, Distribution +*Warehousing*

Ferschl Hose & Hydraulics Ltd, Dukesway, Team Valley Trading Estate, Gateshead, Tyne & Wear, NE11 0PZ Tel: 0191-482 2511 Fax: 0191-491 0604 E-mail: info@jferschl.co.uk *Hydraulic hose assembly distributors & manufrs*

▶ Ferschl Tube Form, 2 Doxford Drive, South West Industrial Estate, Peterlee, County Durham, SR8 2RL Tel: 0191-518 0878 Fax: 0191-518 0938 *CNC tube benders & tube fabricators*

Fersina Windows, Unit 3 Dysart Road, Grantham, Lincolnshire, NG31 7EJ Tel: (01476) 593830 Fax: (01476) 590687 E-mail: fersinalincs@aol.com *Windows, doors, conservatory distributors & manufrs*

▶ Fertecon, The Pantiles, Tunbridge Wells, Kent, TN2 5TE Tel: (01892) 701710 Fax: (01892) 701711 *Fertilizers info & consultancy*

▶ FETCH, BIRMINGHAM, WEST MIDLANDS, BIRMINGHAM, B20 3RN Tel: 07725 441306 E-mail: eric@fetch.cc *FETCH, Birmingham''s newest bike courier specialising in collecting and delivering small parcels within the hour.*If it''s important to you then trust it with us. FETCH will deliver your parcel anywhere in Birmingham within the hour. V.I.P Very Important Parcels*

Fete & Fiesta, 72/73 Orion House, Riverside 3, Thomas Longley Road, Rochester, Kent, ME2 4DU Tel: (01634) 294600 Fax: (01634) 730415 *Bouncy castle hire*

▶ Fettercairn Distillery, Distillery Road, Fettercairn, Laurencekirk, Kincardineshire, AB30 1YB Tel: (01561) 340205 Fax: (01561) 340447

Fewell Fasteners Ltd, Unit 47, Victoria Industrial Park, Victoria Road, Dartford, DA1 5AJ Tel: (01322) 291595 Fax: (01322) 289524 *Industrial fasteners & fastenings*

Fewkes Ltd, Morley Avenue, Nottingham, NG3 5FW Tel: 0115-960 3561 Fax: 0115-969 2136 *Lace manufrs*

FGH Products, 68 Hunters Vale, Birmingham, B19 2XH Tel: 0121-554 4329 Fax: 0121-554 1857 E-mail: fghsilver@btconnect.com *Silver giftware suppliers*

▶ fhp engineering services solutions, 178-202 Great Portland Street, London, W1W 5JD Tel: (020) 7291 7777 Fax: (020) 7580 4472 E-mail: london@fhpess.com *Engineering consultancy practice, providing mechanical & electrical engineering asset management for the built environment, the company operates across a spectrum of engineering & property management, from the pre-purchase stage through to maintenance & refurbishment*

Fiamma Ltd, Siddon Factory Estate, Howard Street, West Bromwich, West Midlands, B70 0TE Tel: 0121-556 1618 Fax: 0121-556 2132 E-mail: fiamma@talktalk.business.net *Electric heating appliance manufrs*

Fiat Auto UK, Fiat House, 240 Bath Road, Slough, SL1 4DX Tel: (01753) 511431 Fax: (01753) 511471 *Motor car importers*

Fibaform Products Ltd, 22a Caton Road, Lansil Industrial Estate, Lancaster, LA1 3PQ Tel: (01524) 60182 Fax: (01524) 389829 E-mail: info@fibaform.co.uk *GRP glass fibre manufrs*

Fibercill, The Moorings, Hurst Business Park, Brierley Hill, West Midlands, DY5 1UX Tel: (01384) 482221 Fax: (01384) 482212 E-mail: mail@fibercill.com *Mouldings manufrs*

Fibergrate Composite Structures Ltd, Wass Way, Eaglescliffe, Stockton-on-Tees, Cleveland, TS16 0RG Tel: (01642) 784747 Fax: (01642) 784748 E-mail: info@fibergrate.co.uk *Fibreglass manufrs*

Fibermark Red Bridge International Ltd, Ainsworth, Ainsworth, Bolton, BL2 5PD Tel: (01204) 522254 Fax: (01204) 384754 E-mail: sales@redbridge.co.uk *Bookbinding manufrs*

Fibernet Group plc, Rosalind House, Jays Close, Basingstoke, Hampshire, RG22 4BS Tel: (01256) 858685 Fax: (01256) 858601 *Data communication equipment distribution*

Fibrax Ltd, Queensway, Wrexham, Clwyd, LL13 8YR Tel: (01978) 356744 Fax: (01978) 356206 E-mail: info@fibrax.co.uk *Rubber moulding services*

Fibre Box Co. Ltd, Victoria Works, Barton Road, Dukinfield, Cheshire, SK16 4US Tel: 0161-308 4856 Fax: 0161-339 1666 E-mail: dalesmanu@hotmail.co.uk *Cases manufrs*

Fibre Cement Manufacturers Association Ltd, Station Road East, Stowmarket, Suffolk, IP14 1RQ Tel: (01449) 676053 Fax: (01449) 770028 E-mail: fcma@ghyllhouse.co.uk *Fibre & cement building products association*

▶ Fibre Depot, 1 Magellan Terrace, Gatwick Road, Crawley, West Sussex, RH10 9PJ Tel: (01293) 571100 Fax: (01293) 560789 E-mail: sales@fibredepot.com *Fibre optics distributors*

Fibre Drums Ltd, Abbeyway South, Vista Road, Haydock, St. Helens, Merseyside, WA11 0RW Tel: (01942) 722299 Fax: (01942) 271325 E-mail: sales@fdlgroup.co.uk *Fibre drum manufrs*

Fibre Glass Specialists, 31 Ringstead Road, London, SE6 2BU Tel: (020) 8461 0146 Fax: (020) 8698 8639 E-mail: patriciabroug@aol.com *Glass fibre moulders & repairers*

Fibre Glass Technology, Wellington House, Pollard St East, Manchester, M40 7FS Tel: 0161-273 1273 Fax: 0161-273 1273 *Fibre glass manufrs*

▶ Fibre Optic Communications Ltd, Unit 2F, Normandy Way, Marchwood, Southampton, SO40 4PB Tel: (023) 8066 7314

Fibre Optic Systems Ltd, Unit 127 Whitehall Industrial Estate, Whitehall Road, Leeds, LS12 5JB Tel: 0113-263 0633 Fax: 0113-263 8868 E-mail: sales@fibreopticsystems.co.uk *Our team is always available to work with clients to either supply the highest quality systems, or to help create a unique design concept for your individual requirements, through to final installation*

Fibre Technics, Unit 7a Mulberry Road, Canvey Island, Essex, SS8 0PR Tel: (01268) 511171 Fax: (01268) 511170 *Glass fibre fabricators & manufrs*

Fibre Technology Ltd, Brookhill Road, Pinxton, Nottingham, NG16 6NT Tel: (01773) 864205 Fax: (01773) 580287 E-mail: sales@fibretech.com *Rapidly solidified metal products*

▶ Fibre World, 7 West Caplaw, Neilston, Glasgow, G78 3AW Tel: (01505) 812884 Fax: (01505) 814910 E-mail: enquires@fibreworlduk.com *Manufacture of glass reinforced plastics & architectural features*

▶ Fibrecare, 29 Brooks Road, Street, Somerset, BA16 0PN Tel: (01458) 447460 Fax: (01458) 447491 E-mail: sales@fibrecare.co.uk *Carpet cleaning services*

Fibrecomm Solutions, 12 Devonshire Avenue, Long Eaton, Nottingham, NG10 2EP Tel: 0115-946 5777 Fax: 0115-946 5888 E-mail: enquiries@fibrecomm.co.uk *Fibre optic suppliers*

▶ Fibrecount U K Ltd, Thomas Ho, 88-90 Goodmayes Rd, Goodmayes, Ilford, Essex, IG3 9UU Tel: (020) 8597 8785 Fax: (020) 8597 5605 E-mail: info@fibrecount.co.uk Purchasing Contact: C. Thomas Sales Contact: C. Thomas *Fibrecount UK Ltd specialise in the delivery of a complete range of asbestos project management services, which includes the survey report and asbestos register, compilation of tender documents, specification documentation, air testing and bulk identification.*

Fibrecraft Glass Fibre, Main Hall Farm, Conington, Cambridge, CB23 4LR Tel: (01954) 267622 Fax: (01954) 267622 *Fibre glass mouldings manufrs*

▶ Fibrefusion Ltd, Unit 9e, Spencer Carter Works, Tregoniggie Industrial Estate, Falmouth, Cornwall, TR11 4SN Tel: (01326) 378787 Fax: (01326) 377065 E-mail: paul@fibrefusion.com *Fibrefusion specialise in the manufacture of high performance fibre re-enforced flat laminated panels that are accurately cut to shape on their in-house waterjet cutter. They also offer a comprehensive subcontract waterjet profiling service that can cut virtually any material up to 250mm. Please call us or email us to find out how we can help you.*

Fibreglass Mouldings, 36 High Street, Moulton, Northampton, NN3 7SR Tel: (01604) 643913 Fax: (01604) 643913 E-mail: 36manfield@tiscali.co.uk *Industrial & commercial specialists*

Fibreline Yorkshire Ltd, Victoria Park Mills, Hard Ings Road, Keighley, West Yorkshire, BD21 3ND Tel: (01535) 681218 Fax: (01535) 611265 E-mail: sales@fibreline-ltd.co.uk *Cushion manufacturers in fibre feather & foam*

▶ Fibreon, Unit 2 Dadsford Bridge Industrial Estate, Plant Street, Stourbridge, West Midlands, DY8 5SY Tel: (01384) 262211 Fax: (01384) 262211 *Fibreglass manufrs*

Fibrerod Pultrusions, Wemco House 477, Whippendell Road, Watford, WD18 7PS Tel: (01923) 221255 Fax: (01923) 221255 E-mail: sales@fibrerodpultrusions.co.uk *Glass fibre pultrusion, rod manufrs*

Fibresand International Ltd, Ash House Ransom Wood Business Park, Southwell Road, Rainworth, Mansfield, Nottinghamshire, NG21 0HJ Tel: (01623) 675305 Fax: (01623) 675308 E-mail: enquiries@fibresand.com *Fibresand export business*

▶ Fibresec Holdings Ltd, Unit 2, Snaygill Industrial Estate, Keighley, Skipton, North Yorkshire, BD23 2QR Tel: (01756) 799822

Fibresports Glass Fibre, 34 Bowlers Croft, Basildon, Essex, SS14 3ED Tel: (01268) 282723 Fax: (01268) 282273 E-mail: fibresports@aol.com *Manufacturers of glass fibre & acrylic mouldings*

Fibrestar Drums Ltd, Redhouse Lane, Disley, Stockport, Cheshire, SK12 2NW Tel: (01663) 764141 Fax: (01633) 762967 E-mail: sales@harcostar.co.uk *Manufacturers of a wide range of products, including rigid plastic containers, exceptionally tough, reliable & UN rated.*

Fibrestar Drums Ltd, Redhouse Lane, Disley, Stockport, Cheshire, SK12 2NW Tel: (01663) 764141 Fax: (01633) 762967 E-mail: sales@fibrestar.co.uk Purchasing Contact: T. Gould Principal Export Areas: Central/East Europe & West Europe *Fibre/ fibreboard drum & paper tube manufrs*

Fibretek UK Ltd, Brick Kiln Lane, Long Stratton, Norwich, NR15 2LH Tel: (01508) 473077 Fax: (01508) 471377 E-mail: sales@fibretekuk.co.uk *Group based manufrs*

Fibretex Mouldings, Waterloo Road, Pudsey, West Yorkshire, LS28 8DQ Tel: 0113-236 1094 Fax: 0113-255 5345 *Glass fibre products*

Fibrocell Ltd, Willow Street, Oldham, OL1 3QB Tel: 0161-624 1035 Fax: 0161-627 3045 E-mail: john@britanniamill.totalserve.co.uk *UPVC window frame manufrs*

▶ Fibrotec Mouldings Ltd, Earls Colne Business Centre, Airfield, Earls Colne, Colchester, CO6 2NS Tel: (01787) 223912 Fax: (01787) 224444 E-mail: enquiry@fibrotec.co.uk *GRP fibreglass boat builders & industrial tank linings suppliers*

Fibrous Ltd, Unit E2, Newton Business Park, Talbot Road, Newton, Hyde, Cheshire, SK14 4UQ Tel: (0845) 4508935 Fax: (0845) 4508936 E-mail: info@fibrous.com *Exhibition materials distributors*

Fichtner Consulting Engineers Ltd, Frederick House, 8 Acorn Business Park, Heaton Lane, Stockport, Cheshire, SK4 1AS Tel: 0161-476 0032 Fax: 0161-474 0618 E-mail: sales@fichtner.co.uk *Consulting engineers*

Fiction Clothing Co. (UK) Ltd, 112-114 North Acton Road, London, NW10 6QH Tel: (020) 8961 9202 Fax: (020) 8961 9051 *Distributors of clothes & ladies wear*

Fiddes & Son Ltd, Florence Works, Brindley Road, Cardiff, CF11 8TX Tel: (029) 2034 0323 Fax: (029) 2034 3235 E-mail: finishes@fiddes.co.uk *Lacquer & varnish manufrs*

Fiddlers Ferry Boatyard, Ferry Boatyard, Fiddlers Ferry, Penketh, Warrington, WA5 2UJ Tel: (01925) 727519 Fax: (01925) 727519 *Boat builders*

Fidelity International Investment Advisors UK Ltd, Oakhill House, 130 Tonbridge Road, Hildenborough, Tonbridge, Kent, TN11 9DZ Tel: (020) 7283 9911 Fax: (01732) 838886 *Investment management* Also at: UK & Worldwide

Fidgeon Ltd, 11 Enterprise Court, Seaham Grange Industrial Estate, Seaham, County Durham, SR7 0PS Tel: 0191-521 1233 Fax: 0191-521 1252 E-mail: sales@fidgeon.co.uk Principal Export Areas: Africa *X-ray film distributors*

Fiducial Design Ltd, Chroma House, Shire Hill, Saffron Walden, Essex, CB11 3AQ Tel: (01799) 508039 Fax: (01799) 500379 E-mail: contact@fiducial.co.uk *Printed circuit designers*

Field Box More Labels, Roman Bank, Bourne, Lincolnshire, PE10 9LQ Tel: (01778) 426444 Fax: (01778) 421862 *Self-adhesive label manufrs*

Field Boxmore, Millennium Way West, Nottingham, NG8 6AW Tel: 0115-979 6300 Fax: 0115-979 6333 Principal Export Areas: Worldwide *Carton & self-adhesive label manufrs*

Field Boxmore, 9a Delta Drive, Tewkesbury, Gloucestershire, GL20 8HB Tel: (01684) 850020 Fax: (01684) 850141 *Specialised packaging manufrs*

▶ Field Boxmore Healthcare Leaflets, 3-4 Fairway Drive, Greenford, Middlesex, UB6 8PW Tel: (020) 8575 9119 Fax: (020) 8566 6174

▶ Field Boxmore Healthcare Packaging Belfast Ltd, Enterprise Way, Hightown Indusst Estate, Newtownabbey, County Antrim, BT36 4EW Tel: (028) 9080 4000 Fax: (028) 9080 4300 E-mail: sales@boxmore.com

Field Boxmore Healthcare Packaging Belfast Ltd, Enterprise Way, Hightown Indusst Estate, Newtownabbey, County Antrim, BT36 4EW Tel: (028) 9080 4000 Fax: (028) 9080 4300 E-mail: sales@boxmore.com *Packaging agents*

Field Developments Hull Ltd, Staithes Road, Hull, HU12 8TJ Tel: (01482) 896240 Fax: (01482) 896510 E-mail: info@shopfituk.co.uk *Joinery manufacturers & shop fitters*

Field Electronics Ltd, 23 Star Road, Star Trading Estate, Partridge Green, Horsham, West Sussex, RH13 8RA Tel: (01403) 713772 Fax: (0870) 0271033 E-mail: sales@fieldelectronics.com *Electronic control & aquisition systems*

Field Engineering (Poole) Ltd, 10 Factory Road, Upton Industrial Estate, Poole, Dorset, BH16 5HT Tel: (01202) 622166 Fax: (01202) 632439 E-mail: dave@fieldengineering.co.uk *Precision engineers services*

Field Engineering Services Ltd, West Park, Torryleith, Newmachar, Aberdeen, AB21 0QE Tel: (01651) 863321 Fax: (01651) 863411 E-mail: georgefieldeng@aol.com *Agricultural electronics repairers*

Field First Label Access, Label House Kingsland Rading Estate, St. Philips Road, Bristol, BS2 0JZ Tel: 0117-954 3131 Fax: 0117-955 0739 E-mail: sales.labelaccess@fieldgroup.com *Self adhesive label manufrs*

Field Group Ltd, Misbourne House Badminton Court, Church Street, Amersham, Buckinghamshire, HP7 0DD Tel: (01494) 720200 Fax: (01494) 431138 E-mail: marketing@fieldgroup.com *Designers & producers of packaging* Also at: Bradford, East Kilbride, Newcastle upon Tyne, Nottingham, Portsmouth & Thatcham

Field International Ltd, Radfield House, 18-20 Nuffield Road, Nuffield Industrial Estate, Poole, Dorset, BH17 0RB Tel: (01202) 676331 Fax: (01202) 684043 E-mail: sales@fieldinternational.com *Precision engineers & aircraft ground support equipment manufrs*

Field International UK, Unit 5 Gordleton Farm, Silver Street, Sway, Lymington, Hampshire, SO41 6DJ Tel: (01425) 628075 Fax: (01425) 628570 E-mail: peter@fieldsupplies.demon.co.uk *Chemicals & specialist cleaning products manufrs*

▶ Field Measurement Services, 32 High Street, Thatcham, Berkshire, RG19 3JD Tel: (01635) 860046 Fax: (01635) 860008 E-mail: sales@fieldmeasurmentservices.co.uk

▶ Field Packaging, Bellhill North Industrial Estate, Bellshill, Lanarkshire, ML4 3EE Tel: (01698) 748384 Fax: (01698) 843946 *Manufacture shaped drinks tubes*

▶ Field Solutions, 1 Windsor Court, Clarence Drive, Harrogate, North Yorkshire, HG1 2PE Tel: (01423) 532990 *Software developers*

Field Sports, 99 Hartforde Road, Borehamwood, Hertfordshire, WD6 5HY Tel: (020) 8207 1300 *Saddlers & riding clothing*

Field & Stream, 24 Charlemont Street, Moy, Dungannon, County Tyrone, BT71 7SL Tel: (028) 8778 9533 Fax: (028) 8778 9533 E-mail: sales@fieldandstream.ie *Shooting & fishing supplies*

Field Textiles Sewing Machines, Brewery House, Station Road, Bulwell, Nottingham, NG6 9AA Tel: 0115-979 7676 Fax: 0115-913 3244 *Industrial sewing machine repair services*

Field & Trek plc, Market Cross, Ambleside, Cumbria, LA22 9BT Tel: (01539) 434350 Fax: (01539) 431067 E-mail: info@fieldandtrack.com *Outdoor equipment retailer*

Field & Trek plc, 3 Palace Street, Canterbury, Kent, CT1 2DY Tel: (01227) 470023 Fax: (01227) 477072 *Outdoor products suppliers*

Field & Trek UK Ltd, Langdale House, Sable Way, Southfields Business Park, Basildon, Essex, SS15 6SR Tel: (0870) 7771071 Fax: (01268) 494432 E-mail: sales@fieldandtrek.co.uk *Camping equipment suppliers*

▶ Field Vehicle Maintenance, Sundon Road, Harlington, Dunstable, Bedfordshire, LU5 6LN Tel: (01525) 876240 Fax: (01525) 876240 *Vehicle body builders & repairers*

Field Water Services, Church-Farm, Ulcombe Hill, Ulcombe, Maidstone, Kent, ME17 1DN Tel: (01622) 844044 Fax: (01622) 842959 E-mail: irrigation@fieldwater.co.uk *Irrigation contractors*

Fieldcare Ltd, Gamston Airfield, Gamston, Retford, Nottinghamshire, DN22 0QL Tel: (01777) 839000 Fax: (01777) 839111 E-mail: sales@procam.co.uk *Arable farming specialists & pesticide supplier*

Fielde Engineering Ltd, Unit 6-7 The Warren, East Goscote, Leicester, LE7 3XA Tel: 0116-260 8217 Fax: 0116-260 7921 E-mail: field@btconnect.com *Precision engineers & fabrication*

Fieldens plc, Star House, Onehouse, Stowmarket, Suffolk, IP14 3EL Tel: (01449) 675071 Fax: (01449) 678282 E-mail: sales@fieldens.co.uk *Tyre & wheel distributors*

Fieldfare Trailer Centre, Fieldfare House, Old Malthouse Lane, Ford, Salisbury, SP4 6DR Tel: (01980) 611853 Fax: (01980) 611130 E-mail: info@fieldfairtrailers.co.uk *Road trailer suppliers*

Fieldgrove Engineering Services Ltd, Doynton Mill, Mill Lane, Doynton, Bristol, BS30 5TQ Tel: 0117-937 4139 Fax: 0117-937 3560 E-mail: dhyde@fieldgrove.co.uk *Component manufrs*

Fieldguard Ltd, Horsham Road, Cranleigh, Surrey, GU6 8EH Tel: (01483) 275182 Fax: (01483) 275341 *Equestrian safety surfaces & supplies*

Fieldhouse & Husbands, Cemetery Road, Houghton Regis, Dunstable, Bedfordshire, LU5 5BZ Tel: (01582) 867709 Fax: (01582) 861255 E-mail: dnoel@freewire.net *Crash repair specialists*

Fieldhouse Industrial Services Ltd, Unit 1 & 2, Moderna Business Park, Mytholmroyd, Hebden Bridge, West Yorkshire, HX7 5QQ Tel: (01422) 883313 Fax: (01422) 881338 E-mail: sean@fis-ltd.co.uk *Machine tool & Pressbrakes & Guillotine service repairs & maintenance.*Machine Tool Instalation.Machine Guarding & Swarf Conveyors.Machine Tool Overhauls.*

Fieldhouse Riding Equipment Ltd, Green Lane, Birchills, Walsall, WS2 8LE Tel: (01922) 638094 Fax: (01922) 622921 E-mail: sales@fieldhouse.co.uk *Saddle manufacturers & wholesalers*

Fielding Engineering UK Ltd, 2 Lancaster Way, Earls Colne Industrial Park, Earls Colne, Colchester, CO6 2NS Tel: (01787) 224844 Fax: (01787) 224344 E-mail: jfield@fieldingltd.co.uk *Jig, fixture & tool manufrs*

Fielding Group Ltd, 18 Eynecourt Road, Woodside Estate, Dunstable, Bedfordshire, LU5 4TS Tel: (01582) 632300 Fax: (01582) 632500 E-mail: beth@fieldinggroup.co.uk *Clothing importers & manufrs*

▶ Fielding Transport, 21 Askew Farm Lane, Grays, Essex, RM17 5XR Tel: (01375) 399496 Fax: (01375) 399493

Fieldmount Terrazzo Ltd, 7-8 Liddell Road, London, NW6 2EW Tel: (020) 7624 8866 Fax: (020) 7328 1836 E-mail: enquiries@nftmms.co.uk *Terrazzo flooring specialists*

Fields Engine Service Ltd, 2a Leslie Road, London, E11 4HG Tel: (020) 8539 5205 Fax: (020) 8539 7622 *Engine component machinists/ reconditioners*

Fields International C A Ltd, Cavendish Avenue, Sheffield, S17 3NJ Tel: 0114-235 0103 Fax: 0114-236 2815 E-mail: sales@fields-international.com *Construction machinery suppliers*

Fields Reading Ltd, 5 Metro Centre, Toutley Road, Wokingham, Berkshire, RG41 1QW Tel: 0118-977 6066 Fax: 0118-940 1195 *Painting & decorating contractors*

Fieldsports Equipe, 20a Elwy Street, Rhyl, Clwyd, LL18 1BP Tel: (01745) 353476 Fax: (01745) 353476 E-mail: enquiries@fieldsports.co.uk *Guns & field sports suppliers*

Fieldsports Wigglesworth Gunsmiths, 45 Market Place, South Cave, Brough, North Humberside, HU15 2BS Tel: (01430) 424666 Fax: (01430) 471203 E-mail: info@wigglesworthgunsmiths.co.uk *Gunsmiths firearms dealers*

Fieldyork International Ltd, The Manor, 306 -308 Leicester Road, Wigston, Leicestershire, LE18 1JX Tel: 0116-257 1572 Fax: 0116-257 8969 *Export merchants*

Fiennes Restoration Ltd, Clanfield Mill, Little Clanfield, Bampton, Oxfordshire, OX18 2RX Tel: (01367) 810438 Fax: (01367) 810532 E-mail: enquiries@fiennes.co.uk *Vintage car restorers*

Fiesta, Farley Farms Bridge Farm, Reading Road, Arborfield, Reading, RG2 9HT Tel: 0118-976 2310 Fax: 0118-976 2311 E-mail: enquiries@fiestamarqueehire.co.uk *Marquee & catering equipment hire*

Fiesta Blinds & Fabrics Ltd, 36 Waterloo Street, Londonderry, BT48 6HF Tel: (028) 7126 1961 Fax: (028) 7137 4387 *Blind suppliers*

Fiesta Blinds & Fabrics Ltd, 1 Springgrowth Business Park, Springtown Road, Londonderry, BT48 0LY Tel: (028) 7126 2605 Fax: (028) 7137 4387 *Blinds manufrs*

Fiesta Blinds & Fabrics Ltd, 1 Springgrowth Business Park, Springtown Road, Londonderry, BT48 0LY Tel: (028) 7126 2605 Fax: (028) 7137 4387 *Blind manufrs*

Fife Chamber of Commerce & Enterprise, Wemyssfield House, Wemyssfield, Kirkcaldy, Fife, KY1 1XN Tel: (01592) 201932 Fax: (01592) 641187 E-mail: enquiries@fifechamber.co.uk *Chamber of commerce*

Fife Council, Fife House, North Street, Glenrothes, Fife, KY7 5LT Tel: (01592) 414141 Fax: (01592) 414142 E-mail: fifecouncil@fife.gov.uk *Local authority*

Fife Engineering Co. Ltd, Longrigg, Swalwell, Newcastle upon Tyne, NE16 3AW Tel: 0191-496 1133 Fax: 0191-496 5502 E-mail: admin@fife-engineering.com *Rubber roller covering manufrs*

Fife Fabrications Ltd, 29 Rutherford Road, Glenrothes, Fife, KY6 2RT Tel: (01592) 776700 Fax: (01592) 772101 E-mail: sales@fifab.co.uk Principal Export Areas: Worldwide *Precision sheet metal workers*

Fife Joinery Manufacturing Ltd, Telford Road, Glenrothes, Fife, KY7 4NX Tel: (01592) 773181 Fax: (01592) 773253 *Roof window manufrs*

▶ Fife Paving, 179 Affric Road, Glenrothes, Fife, KY7 6XA Tel: (01592) 748882 E-mail: info@fifepaving.co.uk *Full driveway installation service*

Fife Plastics, Fordell, Woodend, Cowdenbeath, Fife, KY4 8EY Tel: (01383) 510256 Fax: (01383) 510256 *Plastics fabricators*

Fife Shutter Services, Unit 11 Coal Wynd, Kirkcaldy, Fife, KY1 2RA Tel: (01592) 266868 Fax: (01592) 642868 E-mail: info@fifeshutterservices.co.uk *Shutters manufrs*

Fife Signs Screen Printers, 3 Waverley Road, Kirkcaldy, Fife, KY1 3NH Tel: (01592) 655646 Fax: (01592) 655330 E-mail: sales@caledoniasigns.co.uk *Signs manufrs*

Fife Tidland Ltd, 70-72 Manchester Road, Denton, Manchester, M34 3PR Tel: 0161-320 2000 Fax: 0161-320 4513 E-mail: sales_uk@maxcess.de *Web management control systems*

▶ Fife Warehousing Co. Ltd, Wemyss Road, Dysart, Kirkcaldy, Fife, KY1 2XZ Tel: (01592) 651065 Fax: (01592) 652360 E-mail: sales@fifegroup.com *Warehousing*

▶ Fifield Decorators Ltd, 14 The Spinney, Plympton, Plymouth, PL7 1AG Tel: (01752) 337722 Fax: (01752) 337722 E-mail: enquiries@fifielddecorators.co.uk *Providing quality painting and decorating for commercial and industrial projects, including new build and referbishment.*

▶ Fifield Fencing Services, 898 Fifield, Enford, Upavon, Pewsey, Wiltshire, SN9 6DQ Tel: (01980) 670680 E-mail: mike@mgermany.freeserve.co.uk

Fifth Column Design & Print, 276 Kentish Town Road, London, NW5 2AA Tel: (020) 7485 8599 Fax: (020) 7267 3718 E-mail: sales@fifthcolumn.co.uk *Screen printers*

Fifth Dimension Computer Solutions Ltd, Park House, Maidenhead Road, Cookham, Maidenhead, Berkshire, SL6 9DS Tel: (01628) 851970 *Software development*

Figen Fashions Ltd, 2-4 Tottenham Road, London, N1 4BZ Tel: (020) 7254 1610 Fax: (020) 7249 9772 *Ladies clothing manufrs*

▶ Michelle Figg Freelance Marketing Communications, 9A Orsett Terrace, London, W2 6AJ Tel: (07973) 221331 E-mail: michelle@michellefigg.com *Freelance business solutions & advice*

Fi-Glass Developments Ltd, Station Road, Edenbridge, Kent, TN8 6EB Tel: (01732) 863465 Fax: (01732) 867287 E-mail: sales@fi-glass.co.uk *Glass fibre mouldings manufacturers & custom moulders*

F.J. Fildes, Stourbridge Road, Lye, Stourbridge, West Midlands, DY9 7BU Tel: (01384) 892939 Fax: (01384) 892903 E-mail: postmaster@rmgroup.co.uk *Motor vehicle body repairers rental & servicing*

▶ File Express Ltd, Walton Lane, Bosham, Chichester, West Sussex, PO18 8ED Tel: (01243) 575858 Fax: (01243) 575123 E-mail: enquiries@file-express.co.uk *Document archive company*

Fileder Filter Systems Ltd, St. Leonards Road, Allington, Maidstone, Kent, ME16 0LS Tel: (01622) 691886 Fax: (01622) 621932 E-mail: office@fileder.co.uk *Filter distributor*

Filenet Ltd, Waterside House 4 Cowley Business Park, High Street, Cowley, Uxbridge, Middlesex, UB8 2FN Tel: (01895) 207300 Fax: (01895) 207365 *Software*

Filigree Ltd, Carter Lane East, South Normanton, Alfreton, Derbyshire, DE55 2EG Tel: (01773) 811619 Fax: (01773) 862777 E-mail: enquiries@filigree.demon.co.uk *Lace & net curtain suppliers*

▶ Fillinghams Transport, Unit B1 Abbey La Industrial Estate, Abbey Lane, Burscough, Ormskirk, Lancashire, L40 7SR Tel: (01704) 897917 Fax: (01704) 897918

▶ Fillink Computer Consumables, 572 London Road, Isleworth, Middlesex, TW7 4EP Tel: (020) 8560 4444 Fax: (020) 8560 0694 E-mail: sales@fillink.co.uk *Producers of environmentally friendly printers*

Fillmore Packaging Ltd, Unit 15, Bowthorpe Industrial Estate, Norwich, NR5 9JE Tel: (01603) 745911 Fax: (01603) 747519 E-mail: sales.norwich@fillmorepackaging.co.uk *Packaging materials & equipment services* Also at: Devizes, Glenrothes, Warrington & Wellingborough

Fillworth (UK) Ltd, Unit 2, Baltic Road, Felling, Gateshead, Tyne & Wear, NE10 0SB Tel: 0191-500 0230 Fax: 0191-500 0231 E-mail: mail@fillworth.com Principal Export Areas: Worldwide *Manufacturers of : Industrial Mixing Machines and Equipment Dispersing and blending machines Mixers - chemical, adhesives, sealants, mastics, resins, paints /surface coatings, inks, food, pharmceutical .. Process(ing) Systems, Equipment and Technology*

Filma Ltd, Clarke Street, Derby, DE1 2BU Tel: (01332) 347571 Fax: (01332) 294960 *Foundation garment manufrs*

▶ Filmscape Media UK, 6 Stammerham Business Centre, Capel Road, Rusper, Horsham, West Sussex, RH12 4PZ Tel: (01306) 710144 E-mail: info@filmscapemedia.com *Broadcast HDV - DVCAM Equipment hire, Sony HVR Z1 - Glidecam V8 stabilisers - camera crane 200 - cobra cranes - steady tracker - based in London and LA*

▶ Filmtape Ltd, PO Box 400, Southampton, SO30 3XN Tel: (023) 8047 1922 E-mail: sales@filmtape.co.uk *Protective floor covering suppliers*

Filofax Time Management, Unit 3 Victoria Gardens, Burgess Hill, West Sussex, RH15 9NB Tel: (01444) 238100 Fax: (01444) 238119 E-mail: enquiries@filofax.co.uk *Filo fax corporate sales - practical products to luxury gifts*

▶ Filon Products, Unit 3 Ring Road Zone 2, Burntwood Business Park, Burntwood, Staffordshire, WS7 3JQ Tel: (01543) 687300 Fax: (01543) 687303 E-mail: admin@filon.co.uk *GRP roofing manufrs (glass reinforced plastic)*

Filsol Solar, Unit 15 Ponthenry Industrial Estate, Ponthenry, Llanelli, Dyfed, SA15 5RA Tel: (01269) 860229 Fax: (01269) 860979 E-mail: info@filsol.co.uk *Manufacturers & suppliers & installation of solar water heating*

Filta Group Ltd, The Locks, Hillmorton, Rugby, Warwickshire, CV21 4PP Tel: (01788) 550100 Fax: (01788) 551839 E-mail: sales@filtagroup.com *FiltaFry Plus based in Rugby, Warwickshire provides a mobile on-site service for the micro-filtration of cooking oil, the vacuum-based cleaning of deep fryers, and full fryer management to restaurants, hotels, airports... in fact, wherever food is fried.*

Filtair Ltd, 9 Brookvale Trading Estate, Moor Lane, Birmingham, B6 7AQ Tel: 0121-356 9595 Fax: 0121-356 9538 *Air filter manufrs*

Filtakleen (Manufacturing) Ltd, Forelle Centre, 30 Black Moor Road, Ebblake Industrial Estate, Verwood, Dorset, BH31 6BB Tel: (01202) 826280 Fax: (01202) 813207 E-mail: sales@filtakleen.co.uk *Engine & hydraulic oil filters*

Filtech 2000 Ltd, East Market Street, Newport, Gwent, NP20 2AY Tel: (01633) 253878 Fax: (01633) 267914 E-mail: bc.hydraulics@btinternet.com *Industrial filtration distributors*

Filter Fabrications, 2 Pound Lane Industrial Estate, Maypole Fields, Halesowen, West Midlands, B63 2QB Tel: (01384) 635630 Fax: (01384) 566884 E-mail: info@filterfabs.co.uk *Filter & strainer manufrs*

Filter & Press Cloth Co. Ltd, 26 Town Road, Hillchurch Street, Stoke-on-Trent, ST1 2EX Tel: (01782) 281819 Fax: (01782) 281819 *Manufacture bakery textiles & dust collecting*

Filter Screen Supply Ltd, 2 Paynes Place Farm, Cuckfield Road, Burgess Hill, West Sussex, RH15 8RG Tel: (01444) 244406 Fax: (01444) 230303 E-mail: sales@filterscreensupply.co.uk *Manufacturers of sieving equipment and spare parts*

Filter Services (UK) Ltd, Units 6/7/8, Broombank Park, Sheepbridge, Chesterfield, Derbyshire, S41 9RT Tel: (01246) 455481 Fax: (01246) 455346 E-mail: sales@filter-services.co.uk *Established in 1982, Filter Services (UK Limited) have grown to be one of the largest suppliers of filters and automotive filtration products in the UK. Filter Service (UK) Ltd have a specialist product range directed primarily at the off-highway and commercial vehicle market. Filter Services (UK) Limited are proud to be the largest independent distributor and stockist for Fleetguard filters in the UK. Filter Services (UK) Ltd are also main distributors for Coopers, Mann & Hummel and Baldwin filters, Donaldson filter components, together with a number of specialist hydraulics. From warehouses in Derbyshire, Leicestershire & Yorkshire, Filter Services offer a delivery service which covers the Derbyshire, Nottinghamshire, Leicestershire, Lincolnshire, Yorkshire and surrounding areas and nationwide UK coverage using national overnight carriers. Our customer base includes most of the major plant hire companies, utilities and truck fleet operators.*

Filter Specialists International Ltd, Unit H1 Taylor Business Park, Warrington, WA3 6BL Tel: (01925) 762576 Fax: (01925) 763875 E-mail: info@fsiltd.demon.co.uk *Filter bag & sleeve manufrs*

Filter Technology, Unit 11 Boundary Business Centre, Boundary Way, Woking, Surrey, GU21 5DH Tel: (01483) 776649 Fax: (01483) 740588 E-mail: dennis@filtertechnology.co.uk *Filter manufacturers including cartridge & compressed air gas filters*

Filterall Ltd, PO Box 29, Daventry, Northamptonshire, NN11 1AQ Tel: (01327) 877624 Fax: (01327) 705749 E-mail: filterall@btconnect.com *Manufacture, Supply & Export of Oil Filtration & Purification Plant: Mobile and Stationary Installations: -Transformer Oil Filtration -Cable,..Hydraulic .Turbine. Lube Oils Manufacture, Supply and Export of Transformer Oil Regeneration Plant: -Mobile and Stationary Installations. -Transformer Oil Reclamation - Online & Tank to Tank Supply and Export of PCB Destruction Plant: -Mobile and Stationary Installations: -Transformer Oil Reclamation -PCB Decontamination Supply and Export of Transformer Oil: -Bulk and Drummed Transformer Oil Purification Service. Transformer Oil Analysis Service. Supply and Export of Replacement Filter Elements: -Pleated Media Liquid and Air..Radial Fin Elements Liquid and Air..Depth Elements for soft contaminant removal..Wound Elements for Food & Pharmaceutical Industry..Absorption Elements for water removal from Oils..Fullers Earth Cartridges for removal of soluble contaminants .Carbon Elements for odour removal. Coalescer & separator Elements for water removal from oils & light fuels Air /Oil Separator Elements for oil mist removal. Spin-on Elements in self contained housing for hydraulic and lub. oils. Metal Elements for removal of hard, coarse particle contaminants. Filtration Bags with large filtration areas Supply and Export Vacuum Generation Units and Pumps: -Transformer Evacuation for Drying prior to Oil Fill. -Industrial Applications Supply and Export of Air Drying Units. Export Procurement Services.*

Filterite Ltd, Unit E Alfred Court Saxon Business Park, Hanbury Road, Stoke Prior, Bromsgrove, Worcestershire, B60 4AD Tel: (01527) 836201 Fax: (01527) 836202

continued

E-mail: sales.filterite@tesco.net *Air filtration equipment manufrs*

Filtermax Filtration Services Ltd, Unit 17, Bradwell Works, Davenport Street, Stoke-on-Trent, ST6 4LL Tel: (01782) 816300 Fax: (01782) 790767 E-mail: sales@filterspares.com *Filter manufrs*

Filtermist International Ltd, Faraday Drive, Bridgnorth, Shropshire, WV15 5BA Tel: (01746) 765361 Fax: (01746) 766882 E-mail: sales@filtermist.com *Air filtration equipment manufrs*

Filters For Industry, 12c Queensway, New Milton, Hampshire, BH25 5NN Tel: (01425) 628533 Fax: (01425) 621767 E-mail: sales@porvairfiltration.com *Filter manufrs*

Filterwell International Ltd, Penton, Carlisle, CA6 5QB Tel: (01228) 577339 Fax: (01228) 577442 *Filtration specialists*

Filterworld, 4a Middlebrook Way, Cromer, Norfolk, NR27 9JR Tel: (01263) 510118 Fax: (01263) 514335 E-mail: enquiry@filterworld.co.uk *Compressed air filtration manufrs*

Filtex Filters, 4 7 Union Park, Navigation Way, West Bromwich, West Midlands, B70 9DF Tel: 0121-553 1283 Fax: 0121-500 5289 E-mail: sales@ioi.co.uk *Dust extraction equipment manufrs*

Filton Ltd, Caswell Rd, Sydenham Industrial Estate, Leamington Spa, Warwickshire, CV31 1QF Tel: (01926) 423191 Fax: (01926) 450610 E-mail: sales@filtonltd.co.uk Purchasing Contact: Murray Sales Contact: B. Haggit *UK leaders in fluid transfer engineering, based in Warwickshire in the heart of the West Midlands with distributors globally manufacturing a range of products including rotary unions, rotating unions, rotary joints swivel joints, air breather filters*

▶ Filton Masonic Hall Ltd, 140 Park Road, Stapleton, Bristol, BS16 1DT Tel: 0117-965 5541 E-mail: secretary@fmhcl.org.uk *Masonic Hall, Stapleton, Bristol in Province of Gloucestershire - 7 Lodges plus 6 other degrees offering information, links and contact*

Filton Process Control Engineering, 5a Boltro Road, Haywards Heath, West Sussex, RH16 1BP Tel: (01444) 417880 Fax: (01444) 417668 E-mail: sales@filton.com Principal Export Areas: Worldwide *Filton Process Control Engineering based in Haywards Heath, West Sussex are industrial Flow Measurement Systems manufacturers*

▶ FILTRAN Trade & Translation Services, 12 Learmonth Gardens, Edinburgh, EH4 1HB Tel: 0131 3326065 Fax: 0131 3431428 E-mail: sales@filtran.co.uk *Specialised business translations from French and Arabic to English. Other language combinations available on request.*

▶ Filtration Medic, 15 Hughes Place, Warrington, WA2 0EJ Tel: 01925 453228 E-mail: info@filtrationmedic.co.uk *Filtration Medic is a small, family run business, based in Warrington, with over 17 years experience in filter plant maintenance.**All Filtration Medic staff work to strict site and company safety procedures and requirements, Risk Assessments and Method statements will be provided for every job.**You will find Filtration Medic very flexible, we can be contacted 7 days a week and for those last minute out of hours inquires your call will be answered by a well trained person ready to listen and proactively handle all your requests.**We are happy to visit any site to provide a price*quotation for all our customers.*

Filtration Service Engineering Ltd, Unit 15 Oldington Trading Estate, Kidderminster, Worcestershire, DY11 7QP Tel: (01562) 60233 Fax: (01562) 748387 E-mail: info@fse.co.uk *Centrifugal filter manufrs*

Filtrex Environmental, Unit 18 Burnt Mill Industrial Estate, Elizabeth Way, Harlow, Essex, CM20 2HS Tel: (01279) 457590 Fax: (01279) 457591 *Manufacturers of filters*

Filtronic, Millennium Way, Heighington Lane Business Park, Newton Aycliffe, County Durham, DL5 6JW Tel: (01325) 301111 Fax: (01325) 306177 *Semi conductor chip manufrs*

Filtronic Comtek Ltd, 11 Standalane, Stewarton, Kilmarnock, Ayrshire, KA3 5BG Tel: (01560) 482207 Fax: (01560) 485027 E-mail: enquiries@filtroniccomtek.co.uk *General engineering services*

▶ Fimex Ltd, 4 Fimex Industrial Park, Victoria Road, Leeds, LS14 2LA Tel: 0113-218 8855 Fax: 0113-218 8866

Fin Engineering Group Ltd, 541 Saintfield Road, Belfast, BT8 8ES Tel: (028) 9081 4074 Fax: (028) 9081 4957 E-mail: info@fin-engineering.com *Industrial design consultants & construction & project management*

▶ Final Events, PO Box 41, Derby, DE1 9ZR Tel: 0870 027 3656 Fax: 0870 027 3656 E-mail: info@finalevents.co.uk *DVD documentary and movie on earths final events and bible prophecy. What is 666, who is teh beast, What is the mark of the beast - all these wil be answered.*

▶ Finance Direct, PO Box 127, Birmingham, B20 2XB Tel: (0800) 1973707 *commercial mortgages & loans*residentials mortgages *spanish mortgages*

▶ FinanceCVs.co.uk, 18 Bedfordshire Down, Warfield, Bracknell, Berkshire, RG42 3UA Tel: (07006) 300980 E-mail: info@financecvs.co.uk *UK online financial recruitment specialists. Free listings of finance & accountancy vacancies and a great low cost per application. Job searching by county with discrete pages for searching at work.*

▶ Financial Consultancy, 244a Broadway, Bexleyheath, Kent, DA6 8AS Tel: (0845) 4668866 Fax: (0845) 4668877 E-mail: sales@thefinancialconsultancy.com *The Financial Consultancy offers bespoke advice on, mortgages, remortgages, bad credit mortgages and all other mortgages.*We are also Independent Financial advisers and can offer advice on a full range of financial services.*

Financial Management Systems (UK) P.L.C., 4 Hillbrow House, Linden Drive, Liss, Hampshire, GU33 7RJ Tel: (01730) 894789 Fax: (01730) 892387 E-mail: info@fmsuk.com *Software developers*

Financial Objects International Ltd, Seven Dials Village, 45 Monmouth Street, London, WC2H 9DG Tel: (020) 7836 3010 Fax: (020) 7240 5790 E-mail: enquiries@finobj.com *Banking software services*

Financial Planning Software Ltd, Mill House, High Street, Kinver, Stourbridge, West Midlands, DY7 6ER Tel: (01384) 873430 *Computer software for financial advisors*

Financial Strategies South Yorks, Unit 27 53 Mowbray Street, Sheffield, S3 8EN Tel: 0114-221 2632 Fax: 0114-276 6013 *Sliding sash window renovation suppliers*

▶ Finavon Fabrics, 128 Murray Street, Montrose, Angus, DD10 8JG Tel: (01674) 676141

Finbarr's Whole Foods & Organic Wines, 57 George St, Hastings, E. Sussex, TN34 3EE Tel: (01424) 443025 Fax: (01424) 443025 *Whole food business*

Finch & Co., Homestead, Eastwick Road, Bookham, Leatherhead, Surrey, KT23 4BA Tel: (01372) 452711 Fax: (01372) 450957 E-mail: info@machinemovers.co.uk Purchasing Contact: R. Finch Sales Contact: A. Finch *Removal & machinery removal contractos. Also machinery engineers, dismantling/erecting/installing*

Fincham Fasteners, 18 Industrial Estate, Sanders Road, Bromsgrove, Worcestershire, B61 7DG Tel: (01527) 875413 Fax: (01527) 875413 E-mail: sales@finchamfasteners.com *Nail & screw distribs*

Finchdata Ltd, Grove Ho, Lutyens Cl, Lychpit, Basingstoke, Hants, RG24 8AG Tel: (0870) 7460895 Fax: (0870) 1317493 E-mail: sales@finchdata.co.uk *Radio products, modems, LANS & CCTV*

▶ Finchpalm Ltd, Albion House, Albion Way, Wembley, Middlesex, HA9 0LP Tel: (020) 8903 2033 Fax: (020) 8903 4604 E-mail: finchpalm@edmund-nuttall.co.uk *Railway Engineering Contractors experienced in Main Line and Light Rail projects whilst specialising in London Underground Project Management*

Ingo Fincke & Son, 24 Battersea Rise, London, SW11 1EE Tel: (020) 7228 7966 Fax: (020) 7652 7966 E-mail: ben@ingofincke.com *Picture frame makers & gallery*

▶ Find A Reflexologist Ltd, 35 Coventry Road Flushing, Flushing, Falmouth, Cornwall, TR11 5TX Tel: (0870) 2432320 E-mail: info@findareflexologist.com *Find your local fully-qualified Reflexologist at a clinic or mobile, from the UK's first register of Reflexologists from all the recognised examining bodies. Find a Refflexologist Ltd also serves as the hub of Reflexology on the web, helping the public make an informed choice about the benefits of Reflexology and to find those best to treat them.*

Findel Education Ltd, Hyde Building, Ashton Road, Hyde, Cheshire, SK14 4SH Tel: 0161-882 5300 Fax: 0161-882 5300 *Educational equipment & supplies*

Findel Education Ltd, Gazelle Road, Weston-super-Mare, Avon, BS24 9BJ Tel: (01934) 413606 Fax: (01934) 626421 *Biological teaching aid manufrs*

Finders-Seekers, Mill Cotts, Lamerton, Tavistock, Devon, PL19 8RJ Tel: (01822) 618717 Fax: (01822) 618717 E-mail: enquire@finders-seekers.co.uk *UK property shop for the licensed trade, selling pubs, restaurants & hotels*

Findhorn Supplies, 106 Findhorn Street, Dundee, DD4 9PN Tel: (01382) 509381 Fax: (01382) 509381 *Clothing manufrs*

▶ Findlay Campbell Blacksmiths Ltd, Waverley Street, Coatbridge, Lanarkshire, ML5 2BE Tel: (01236) 626662 Fax: (01236) 626664

Findlay G W & Sons, 262 Alma Road, Enfield, Middlesex, EN3 7BB Tel: (020) 8805 0575 Fax: (020) 8805 0575 *Steel fabricators*

▶ Findlay H & Sons Ltd, 52a Nutwell Lane, Armthorpe, Doncaster, South Yorkshire, DN3 3JF Tel: (01302) 830072 Fax: (01302) 830074

Findlay Irvine Ltd, 42-44 Bog Road, Penicuik, Midlothian, EH26 9BU Tel: (01968) 671200 Fax: (01968) 671237 E-mail: sales@findlayirvine.com *Electronic equipment manufrs*

Findlay Publications Ltd, Hawley Mill, Hawley Road, Dartford, DA2 7TJ Tel: (01322) 221144 Fax: (01322) 862644 E-mail: pring@findlay.co.uk *Publishers*

Findlay's Ltd, Pitcox, Dunbar, East Lothian, EH42 1RQ Tel: (01368) 850720 Fax: (01368) 850740 E-mail: sales@findlays-spring.com *Producers of bottled mineral water*

▶ Fine Arts Colour Ltd, Unit 11 Boundary Business Court, 92-94 Church Road, Mitcham, Surrey, CR4 3TD Tel: (020) 8646 7007 Fax: (020) 8646 3100

Fine Ceramic Trophies, 26 Chain St, Stoke-on-Trent, ST6 1NA Tel: 01782 577255 Fax: 01782 577255 *Mug painting*

Fine China Restoration, 15 Heathfield Gardens, London, W4 4JU Tel: (020) 8994 8990 *China & glassware repairs & manufrs*

Fine Confectionery Co. Ltd, Unit 20 The Mead Business Centre, Mead Lane, Hertford, SG13 7BJ Tel: (01992) 551075 Fax: (01992) 581780 E-mail: info@fineconfectionery.co.uk *Confectionery importers, packers & distributors*

Fine Controls UK Ltd, Bassendale Road, Bromborough, Wirral, Merseyside, CH62 3QL Tel: 0151-343 9966 Fax: 0151-343 0062 E-mail: sales@finecontrols.com *Precision pneumatic control distributors*

▶ Fine Cut Graphic Imaging Ltd, Marlborough Road, Lancing Business Park, Lancing, West Sussex, BN15 8UF Tel: (01903) 751666 Fax: (01903) 750462 E-mail: info@finecut.co.uk Principal Export Areas: Worldwide *Fine Cut Precision Ltd was formed in 1982 and continued to grow and expand as precision engravers of Labels & Nameplates. Due to the demand for different types of labels, especially screen*

continued

printed, Fine Screen Ltd was formed, as a natural progression. With our many and varied customers dealing with both companies, for different types of labels and marking, it became obvious that to simplify the supply chain, the two companies should merge into one larger all encompassing one. In 1986 Fine Cut Precision merged with Fine Screen to become Fine Cut Graphic Imaging Ltd.

Fine English Bridals, Unit 2 Mayfield Workshops, 19 Wednesbury Rd, Walsall, WS1 3RU Tel: 01922 722033 *Equestrian goods*

Fine English Toiletries Ltd, 15-17 Landsdown Road, Shirley, Southampton, SO15 4HD Tel: (023) 8077 8080 Fax: (023) 8077 5545 *Toiletries & skin care products manufrs*

▶ Fine Finish, 58 Randolph Street, Buckhaven, Leven, Fife, KY8 1AT Tel: (01592) 719039 *Wood polishing services*

Fine Form Architects Design & Model Makers, Searsons F M, Cordys Lane, Trimley, Felixstowe, Suffolk, IP11 0UD Tel: (01394) 672299 Fax: (01394) 672289 E-mail: sales@fineform.co.uk *Architectural model makers*

▶ Fine Furniture Design, Unit 2e Honeybourne Airfield Trading Estate, Honeybourne, Evesham, Worcestershire, WR11 7QF Tel: (01386) 833452 Fax: (01386) 833878

▶ Fine Glass Finishers, 1 Park Farm, Park Road, Great Chesterford, Saffron Walden, Essex, CB10 1RN Tel: (01799) 530655 Fax: (01799) 531752 E-mail: sales@fineglassfinishers.co.uk *Metal lapping services*

Fine Grinding Ltd, Blackhole Mine, Foolow Road, Eyam, Hope Valley, Derbyshire, S32 5QS Tel: (01433) 630827 Fax: (01433) 631554 E-mail: finegrind@btconnect.com *Mineral grinders & processors*

Fine Group Son Ltd, 93 Manor Farm Road, London, Wembley, Middlesex, HA0 1XB Tel: (020) 8214 8600 Fax: (020) 8997 8410 E-mail: sales@hfine.co.uk *Textiles & leather engineering*

Fine Group Son Ltd, 93 Manor Farm Road, London, Wembley, Middlesex, HA0 1XB Tel: (020) 8214 8600 Fax: (020) 8997 8410 E-mail: sales@finegoup.co.uk *Textile & leather engineers*

Fine Homes, Grove House, 227-233 London Road, Hazel Grove, Stockport, Cheshire, SK7 4HS Tel: 0161-483 0202 Fax: 0161-483 0202 E-mail: info@finehomes.co.uk *Furniture (bed & pine) retailer*

▶ Fine Interiors Ltd, 78 Croydon Road, West Wickham, Kent, BR4 9HY Tel: (020) 8462 3994 Fax: (020) 8462 8808

Fine Line Communications E A Ltd, Logic House, Harfreys Road, Great Yarmouth, Norfolk, NR31 0LS Tel: (01493) 441114 Fax: (01493) 441124 E-mail: clairey@finelinecoms.co.uk *Telephone systems distributors*

Fine Line Interiors, Surrex Farm, Colchester Road, Coggeshall, Colchester, CO6 1RR Tel: (01376) 561611 Fax: (01376) 561110 *Furniture*

M. Fine & Co., 4 Hoghill Road, Collier Row, Romford, RM5 2DH Tel: (01708) 741489 Fax: (01708) 741489 *French polishers & upholsterers*

▶ Fine Mesh Metals, Unit 10, Wallows Industrial Estate, Wallows Road, Brierley Hill, West Midlands, DY5 1QA Tel: (01384) 263268 Fax: (01902) 898179 E-mail: sales@finemeshmetals.co.uk *Suppliers & manufactures of security cages, mod & insurance approved*

Fine Mood Ltd, Essentia House, Upper Bond Street, Hinckley, Leicestershire, LE10 1RS Tel: (01455) 615466 Fax: (01455) 615054 E-mail: info@shirleyprice.com *Aromatherapy products manufrs*

Fine Print Stockport Ltd, Unit 6f Lowick Close, Hazel Grove, Stockport, Cheshire, SK7 5ED Tel: 0161-484 2244 Fax: 0161-484 2255 E-mail: info@fineprint-stockport.co.uk *Commercial printers service*

Russell Fine Chemicals Ltd, Unit 68, Third Avenue, Deeside Industrial Park, Deeside, Clwyd, CH5 2LA Tel: (01244) 281333 Fax: (01244) 281878 E-mail: info@russellipm.com *Pest control products*

Fine Sign, Oldcotes Road, Dinnington, Sheffield, S25 2QX Tel: (01909) 518886 Fax: (01909) 518662 *Sign manufrs*

Fine Signs, Lower Road, Cookham, Maidenhead, Berkshire, SL6 9EH Tel: (01628) 522023 Fax: (01628) 528731 E-mail: signs@finesigns.co.uk *Sign makers*

Fine Wine Shipping Agency, Golf Road, Deal, Kent, CT14 6QQ Tel: (01304) 368877 Fax: (01304) 363101 E-mail: info@bmexpressfreight.co.uk *Wine transporters*

Fine Woollen Company Ltd, Savile House, Glendale Mills Sheffield Road, New Mill, Holmfirth, HD9 7EN Tel: (01484) 688848 Fax: (01484) 683469 E-mail: wainshiell@compuserve.com *Woollen & worsted cloth merchants*

▶ Fineandandie, Unit 12, Westbrook Trading Estate, Westbrook Road, Trafford Park, Manchester, M17 1AY Tel: (0870) 1660757 Fax: (0870) 1660759 E-mail: andrea@fineandandie.co.uk *Suppliers of Arts & Craft materials for Cardmaking & Scrapbooking.*

Fineban Ltd, Units 5-6, Curran Road, Cardiff, CF10 5DF Tel: (029) 2039 8211 Fax: (029) 2064 1193 *Non-ferrous metal merchants*

FineCal (Cymru) Ltd, 3 Rhymney River Bridge Road, Rumney, Cardiff, CF23 9AF Tel: (029) 2046 2644 Fax: (029) 2048 4522 E-mail: sales@finecal.co.uk *Industrial wholesalers & distributors of self-adhesive tapes*

Finecal Distributors, 2 Temple Trading Estate, Cole Road, Bristol, BS2 0UG Tel: 0117-971 1111 Fax: 0117-977 2326 E-mail: sales@finecal.co.uk *Industrial tape & adhesive suppliers*

Finecraft Engineering Ltd, Arundel Road, Uxbridge, Middlesex, UB8 2RP Tel: (01895) 233101 Fax: (01895) 231933 *Tube manipulators*

Finecraft Upholstery, 11 Teesdale Yard, London, E2 6QE Tel: (020) 7739 2000 Fax: (020) 7739 2000 *Upholsterers*

▶ Finedining.co.uk, 9a Ty Draw, Little Mill, Pontypool, Gwent, NP4 0HR Tel: (01495) 785449 E-mail: tracey@finedining.co.uk *Mobile and Static Catering providing quality home made food for: Weddings, Corporate events,*Private functions, Daily lunches.*Sunday Lunches. Evening meals coming soon.***

Fine-Focus, 55 Warren Terrace, Hertford, SG14 3JF Tel: (0845) 2261726 E-mail: info@fine-focus.co.uk *Internet web design, cd rom design & development*

▶ Fineline, The Old Quarry, Clevedon Road, Failand, Bristol, BS8 3TU Tel: 01275 395000 Fax: 01275 395001 E-mail: Dave@fineline.uk.com *Bespoke manufacturing services & lighting for entertainment industry*

Fineline Joinery, Littlemoor Road, Mark, Highbridge, Somerset, TA9 4NQ Tel: (01278) 641352 Fax: (01278) 641352 *Joiners*

▶ Fineline Networks Ltd, 37 Southwood Road, London, SE9 3QE Tel: (020) 8294 2499 E-mail: info@fineline-net.co.uk *IT system planners. Risk management and business continuity planners.*

▶ Finesco Financial Services Ltd, 6 Woodside Cresent, Glasgow, G3 7UL Tel: 0141-332 3113 Fax: 0141-331 2039 E-mail: sales@finesco.co.uk

▶ Finesse Ltd, 7 St. Pancras Commercial Centre, Pratt Street, London, NW1 0BY Tel: (020) 7485 7766 Fax: (020) 7485 7799

Finesse Group, Cobbswood Industrial Estate, Brunswick Road, Ashford, Kent, TN23 1EH Tel: (01233) 663399 Fax: (01233) 665599 E-mail: info@finessegroup.com *Finesse Group is a leading designer and builder of exhibition stands. We offer a complete project management service, such as liaising with exhibition organisers, submitting drawings and completing risk assessment on your behalf. We build all exhibition stands in-house, allowing you to check work in progress at any time. We will also personally transport and build your stand anywhere in the world and then store it when not needed*

Finesse North West Partnership, 138 Leigh Road, Leigh, Lancashire, WN7 1SJ Tel: (01942) 682000 Fax: (01942) 670030 *PVC products*

▶ The Finesse Organisation Ltd, The Barn, Green Farm Maidstone Road, Nettlestead, Maidstone, Kent, ME18 5HD Tel: (0870) 1900007 Fax: (0870) 1900008 E-mail: usave@thefinesseorg.com *Profit Enhancers and Licensed Credit Brokers - Fine tuning your costs,enhancing your profits*

▶ Finesse PVC U Ltd, Arburn House Chapel Place, Dentonholme Trading Estate, Carlisle, CA2 5DF Tel: (01228) 522581 Fax: (01228) 810947 E-mail: info@finessegroup.co.uk *Cumbria and South West Scotland. Sliding Sash Windows, bespoke designs...Conservatories, Windows, Doors, Garage Doors, Roofline & Blinds.*

▶ Finewood Joinery Products, Middlefield Industrial Estate, Falkirk, FK2 9HQ Tel: (01324) 673100 Fax: (01324) 673199 E-mail: sales@fine-wood.co.uk *Import & distribution*

Finger Prints, Unit 3 Andrews Court, Andrews Way, Barrow-in-Furness, Cumbria, LA14 2UE Tel: (01229) 432959 Fax: (01229) 431955 E-mail: info@fingerprints.co.uk *Unrivalled design, high speed full colour printing and direct mail from Finger Prints - the printing company that puts ink on paper perfectly*

Fingerpost Co. Ltd, 11 Northington Street, London, WC1N 2JF Tel: (020) 7404 0107 Fax: (020) 7404 0558 E-mail: sales@fingerpost.co.uk *Software developers*

Fingerprint Ltd, 7 Station Field Industrial Est, Kidlington, Oxfordshire, OX5 1JD Tel: (01865) 848080

Fingerprint Embroiderers, 19 Bank Street, Kirriemuir, Angus, DD8 4BE Tel: (01575) 572373 Fax: (01575) 540371 *Leisure wear embroiderers & printers*

▶ Fingertip Designs, 17 Hildenley Close, Scarborough, North Yorkshire, YO12 5DU Tel: (01723) 351668 E-mail: fingertipdesigns@yahoo.co.uk *Website design & illustration services*

Fini (UK) Ltd, Unit A5 & A6, Greenwood Court, Veasey Close, Attleborough Fields Industrial Estate, Nuneaton, Warwickshire, CV11 6RT Tel: (024) 7632 2850 Fax: (024) 7634 9607 E-mail: finicompressors@yahoo.co.uk *Air compressor suppliers*

▶ Finish Architectural, Unit 9 12, Westwood Business Park, Dulverton Road, Birmingham, B6 7EQ Tel: 0121-327 0523

Finish-Adapt Ltd, Unit 8 Hillmead Industrial Estate, Marshall Road, Swindon, SN5 5FZ Tel: (01793) 758720 Fax: (01793) 876059 E-mail: sales@finishadapt.com *Fibre Optic Splice Protector Sleeve components manufacturers and worldwide distributors.*

Finishing Aids & Tools, Unit 25 Woolfold Industrial Estate, Mitchell Street, Bury, Lancashire, BL8 1SF Tel: 0161-705 1300 Fax: 0161-763 1959 *Import, distributors & manufacturers of abrasives*

Finishing Components Co., 1-8 Silverdale, Meadow Road, Worthing, West Sussex, BN11 2RZ Tel: (01903) 205155 Fax: (01903) 205166 E-mail: finishingcomponents@supanet.com *Suppliers of abrasive finishing products*

Finishing Connect Ltd, 865 Plymouth Road, Slough, SL1 4LP Tel: (01753) 676788 Fax: (01753) 676790 E-mail: fincon@technocom.com *Paint spraying distributors or agent*

Finishing Plus Ltd, 34 Lanchester Way, Royal Oak Industrial Estate, Daventry, Northamptonshire, NN11 8PH Tel: (01327) 301155 Fax: (01327) 301070 E-mail: finishingplus@btconnect.com *Direct mail services*

Finishing Techniques Ltd, Halter Inn Works, Holcombe Brook, Ramsbottom, Bury, Lancashire, BL0 9SA Tel: (01706) 825819 Fax: (01706) 825748 E-mail: sales@fintek.co.uk *Finishing Techniques Ltd was set up over 20 years ago by Jonathan Dean, as a UK agent for overseas specialists in surface finishing technology. The business is focused on*

continued

representing three market leaders within their sectors who produce finishing machines, precision laser welding and laser engraving tools and vacuum pressure casting machines.

▶ Finishing Touch, 251 Lower Shelton Road, Marston Moretaine, Bedford, MK43 0LS Tel: (0845) 4724454 Fax: (01234) 764098 E-mail: susan@sodell.freeserve.co.uk *"At Home" service for bespoke curtains and soft furnishings. Curtain poles, blinds, chaise longue, ottomans and footstools. Complete service to include measuring, design, make-up and hanging. Own fabric make-up service also available. Fabrics from Anne & Robert Swaffer, Casamance, Au Maison, Warwick and Academy Clairtex.*

Finishing Touches, 4 North Erskine Park, Bearsden, Glasgow, G61 4LZ Tel: 0141-942 2226 Fax: 0141-943 9103 *Belgian chocolate company manufrs*

Finishright Powder Coatings, Horsham Trading Estate, Foundry Lane, Horsham, West Sussex, RH13 5PX Tel: (01403) 274374 Fax: (01403) 210057 *Stove enamelling & powder coating services*

Finite Element Analysis Consultant, 11 Ullswater Close, Dronfield Woodhouse, Dronfield, Derbyshire, S18 8NW Tel: (01246) 290638 Fax: (01246) 290638 E-mail: samir-mizban@bee.net *Finite element analysis & engineering industry*

Finkl UK Ltd, Langley Green Road, Oldbury, West Midlands, B69 4TR Tel: 0121-544 4506 Fax: 0121-544 1706 E-mail: sales@finkl-uk.co.uk *Steel stockholders & forging manufrs*

▶ Finko Ltd, Unit 20, Stevenage Enterprise Centre, Orchard Road, Stevenage, Hertfordshire, SG1 3HH Tel: (01438) 729356 Fax: (01438) 729367 *Electroplating & Anodising*

Finlay B M E, Aghnagar Road, Ballygawley, Dungannon, County Tyrone, BT70 2HW Tel: (028) 8556 7799 Fax: (028) 8556 7007 E-mail: sales@finlaygroup.co.uk *Block equipment manufrs*

David Finlay Ltd, 9 Main Street, Kingskettle, Cupar, Fife, KY15 7PN Tel: (01337) 830549 Fax: (01337) 831646 *Joinery services*

Finlay Hire Ltd, Lakeside House, Ladford Covert Industrial Park, Seighford, Stafford, ST18 9QL Tel: (01785) 282323 Fax: (01785) 282991 E-mail: sales@finlay-group.demon.co.uk *Quarry plant & equipment stockholders & distributors*

Finlay Hydrascreens, 6 Gillygooly Road, Omagh, County Tyrone, BT78 5PN Tel: (028) 8224 5127 Fax: (028) 8224 4294 E-mail: sales@terexfinlay.com *Mobile crushing, screening, washing & recycling equipment manufrs*

▶ Finlayson Ltd, 76 Northumberland Street, Edinburgh, EH3 6JG Tel: 0131-557 0779 Fax: 0131-557 9195 E-mail: mail@finlayson.org.uk

Finlaysons, Botany Mill, Roxburgh Street, Galashiels, Selkirkshire, TD1 1PB Tel: (01896) 752673 Fax: (01896) 751239 *Building contractors*

Finley Structures, Whinbank Road, Aycliffe Industrial Park, Newton Aycliffe, County Durham, DL5 6AY Tel: (01325) 328120 Fax: (01325) 328121 E-mail: r.mrsj@finleyfinleystructures.co.uk *Steel Fabrication*

Finmatica Ltd, Finmatica House, Ashted Lock, Aston Science Park, Birmingham, B7 4AZ Tel: 0121-359 5096 Fax: 0121-359 0375 E-mail: enquiries@finmatica.com *Software developers & support service*

Finna Fans, Unit 2 Hill Street, Kidderminster, Worcestershire, DY11 6TD Tel: (01562) 60035 Fax: (01562) 753188 *Industrial fan distributors*

Finnforest UK Ltd, 46 Berth Tilbury Docks, Tilbury, Essex, RM18 7HS Tel: (01375) 856855 Fax: (01375) 851555 E-mail: email@finnforest.com *Plywood & panel product distributors* Also at: Salisbury

Finning Mak Ltd, Rennell House, 40-42 Mill Place, Kingston upon Thames, Surrey, KT1 2RL Tel: (020) 8541 4747 Fax: (020) 8541 4371 *Marine diesel engine manufrs*

Finning UK Ltd, Cobbswood Industrial Estate, Brunswick Road, Ashford, Kent, TN23 1EN Tel: (01233) 635466 Fax: (01233) 645046 *Plant machinery servicing*

Finning UK Ltd, Orbital 7, Orbital Way, Cannock, Staffordshire, WS11 8XW Tel: (01543) 465165 Fax: (01543) 437801 *Fork lift trucks manufrs*

Finning UK Ltd, Orbital 7, Orbital Way, Cannock, Staffordshire, WS11 8XW Tel: (01543) 465165 Fax: (01543) 437801 *Sell & hire forklift trucks*

Finning UK Ltd, Nettlehill Road, Houstoun Industrial Estate, Livingston, West Lothian, EH54 5DL Tel: (01506) 449899 Fax: (01506) 448998 E-mail: info@sethire.com

Finning UK Ltd, 688-689 Stirling Road, Slough, SL1 4ST Tel: (01753) 497300 Fax: (01753) 497333 E-mail: mbarnes@finning.co.uk *Manufacturers of combined heat, power (CHP) systems & gas engines* Also at: Branches throughout the U.K.

Finning UK Ltd, Units 1, 3 & 5, Delphwood Drive, Sherdley Park Industrial Estate, Sherdley Road, St. Helens, Merseyside, WA9 5JE Tel: (01744) 451075 Fax: (01744) 451767 E-mail: lisad@birchwood-mechanical.co.uk *Fork lift truck sales & hire* Also at: Crewe

Finnlines UK Ltd, 8 Heron Quay, London, E14 4JB Tel: (020) 7519 7300 Fax: (020) 7536 0255 E-mail: info@finnlines.co.uk *Ferry freight operators*

Finnpave, Thorbury Avenue, March Trading Estate, March, Cambridgeshire, PE15 0AZ Tel: (01354) 658600 Fax: (01354) 661888 E-mail: sales@finnpave.co.uk *Road surfacing machine & equipment dealers & manufrs*

Finns Aquaria, 232 Warwick Road, Sparkhill, Birmingham, B11 2NB Tel: 0121-753 0162 *Tropical fish & aquariums*

Finova Capital P.L.C., 11 Albemarle St, London, W1S 4HH Tel: (020) 7493 5518 Fax: (020) 7493 3521 *Aviation finance*

Finrone Ltd, 52C Strabane Road, Castlederg, County Tyrone, BT81 7HZ Tel: (028) 8167 9918 Fax: (028) 8167 9399 E-mail: info@finrone.com *Sectional buildings*

Fins, Cressing Road, Braintree, Essex, CM77 8DH Tel: (01376) 343686 Fax: (01376) 343687 E-mail: sales@fins.co.uk *Aquatic centre*

▶ Finsbury Instruments Ltd, Unit 13 Mole Business Park, Randalls Road, Leatherhead, Surrey, KT22 7BA Tel: (01372) 360830 Fax: (01372) 360779 E-mail: sales@finsbury.org

The Finsbury Springs Mattress King, 76 Gillespie Road, London, N5 1LN Tel: (020) 7226 2591 Fax: (020) 7503 8439 *Bed & mattress retailers*

▶ Finspa Storage Handling Ltd, 3 Dewing Road, Rackheath Industrial Estate, Rackheath, Norwich, NR13 6PS Tel: (01603) 722002 Fax: (01603) 720322 E-mail: info@finspa.com *Fabricating services*

▶ Fion Construction Ltd, 30a Ben Nevis Industrial Estate, Ben Nevis Industrial Estate, Fort William, Inverness-Shire, PH33 6PR Tel: (01397) 702834 Fax: (01397) 706001

▶ Fior D I Latte, Unit 22, Jubilee Drive, Loughborough, Leicestershire, LE11 5XS Tel: (01509) 211310 *Dairy product suppliers*

▶ Fiora Electronics, The Meridian, 4 Copthall House, Station Square, Coventry, CV1 2FL Tel: (0870) 7669425 Fax: (0870) 7669427 E-mail: enquiries@fioraelectronics.co.uk *We supply leading USA and International brands of Car Audio, Visual, and Accessories, including Alpine, Audiopipe, American Pro, Blaupunkt, JVC, Kenwood, Sony and Veba, at very competitive prices. Free delivery in the UK on orders over £300.*

Fir Tree Design Co., 2 Turpyn Court, Woughton on the Green, Milton Keynes, MK6 3BW Tel: (01908) 661100 Fax: (01908) 670055 E-mail: info@firtreedesign.com *Graphic design consultants*

Firbeck Construction Ltd, 3 Lawn Court, Carlton-in-Lindrick, Worksop, Nottinghamshire, S81 9ED Tel: (01909) 733255 Fax: (01909) 733235 E-mail: info@firb.co.uk *Civil & building contractors consultants*

Firber Engineering Ltd, Sidings Road, Lowmoor Business Park, Kirkby-in-Ashfield, Nottingham, NG17 7JZ Tel: (01623) 757794 Fax: (01623) 688990 E-mail: sales@firber.co.uk *Steel fabricators*

Firco Construction Ltd, 1 Denton Slipways Site, Wharf Road, Gravesend, Kent, DA12 2RU Tel: (01474) 351644 Fax: (01474) 358936 E-mail: firco@gravesend.demon.co.uk *Interior refurbishment & joinery manufrs*

Fircroft Engineering Services Ltd, Trinity House, 114 Northenden Road, Sale, Cheshire, M33 3FZ Tel: 0161-905 2020 Fax: 0161-969 1743 E-mail: recruitment@fircroft.co.uk *Recruitment services*

Fire Ltd, 97A Rochdale Road, Bury, Lancashire, BL9 7BA Tel: 0161-764 8999 Fax: 0161-764 8979 *Fire extinguishers & fire alarms suppliers*

Fire Alarm Services, 71 Burfield Road, Old Windsor, Windsor, Berkshire, SL4 2LN Tel: (01753) 841140 Fax: (01753) 856717 E-mail: sales@firealarmservices.co.uk *Fire alarm maintenance & installers*

Fire Appliance Components Ltd, Penallta Industrial Estate, Hengoed, Mid Glamorgan, CF82 7QZ Tel: (01443) 813959 Fax: (01443) 812545 *Fire appliances manufrs*

Fire Appliance Industries (Dundee) Ltd, 38 Brown Street, Dundee, DD1 5DT Tel: (01382) 322410 Fax: (01382) 322410 E-mail: fireahendo@aol.com *Fire fighting equipment manufrs*

▶ Fire Break Fire Securities, Tweedside Trading Estate, Tweedmouth, Berwick-upon-Tweed, TD15 2XF Tel: (01289) 307691

Fire Check Services, 61 Beechdale Avenue, Great Barr, Birmingham, B44 9DJ Tel: 0121-605 7049 Fax: 0121-605 7049 *Fire protection services*

Fire Check Services, 34 Gibbons Grove, Wolverhampton, WV6 0JF Tel: (01902) 746842 Fax: (01902) 836556 E-mail: sales@firecheckservives.co.uk *Fire extinguisher suppliers*

▶ Fire Defence, 6 Listullycurran Road, Dromore, County Down, BT25 1RB Tel: (028) 9269 8710 Fax: (028) 9269 8710 E-mail: info@firedefenceni.co.uk *Fire house*

▶ Fire Defence plc, Pathfields Indust Estate, South Molton, Devon, EX36 3DW Tel: (01769) 574070 Fax: (01769) 574079 E-mail: fds@fire-defence.com *Fire Sprinkler-Design Instillation Service and Maintance. Dry/Wet Risers. Gas systems. Nationwide coverage.*

Fire Equipment Services Ltd, 269-271 Billinge Road, Wigan, Lancashire, WN5 8DF Tel: (01942) 228170 Fax: (01942) 228170 E-mail: info@fire-equipmentuk.com *Fire protection*

The Fire Escape Specialist, Unit 6 Barton Road Industrial Units, Barton Road, Torquay, TQ2 7NS Tel: (01803) 322299 Fax: (01803) 322299 *Fire escapes & evacuation good services*

Fire Escapes Unlimited, Unit 2 Atlas Trading Estate, Colebrook Road, Birmingham, B11 2NT Tel: 0121-772 4443 Fax: 0121-753 4222 E-mail: feunlimited@aol.com *Fire escape & balustrade manufrs*

Fire Extinguisher Rental, Alfred Works, Woodhill Street, Bury, Lancashire, BL8 1AT Tel: 0161-764 1434 Fax: 0161-764 1434 *Fire protection engineers*

The Fire Extinguisher Supply Company Ltd, 40 Barncroft Road, Chell Heath, Stoke-on-Trent, ST6 6QF Tel: (01782) 814590 Fax: (01782) 814590 *Fire extinguisher manufrs*

▶ Fire Extinguisher Valve Co. Ltd, Unit 10, Ford Lane Business Park, Ford, Arundel, West Sussex, BN18 0UZ Tel: (01243) 555566 Fax: (01243) 555660 E-mail: sales@f-e-v.co.uk *Fire extinguisher manufrs*

▶ Fire Fault Ltd, Bedfont House, Holywell Lane, Upchurch, Sittingbourne, Kent, ME9 7HN Tel: (01634) 262860 Fax: (01634) 262798 E-mail: enquiries@firefault.co.uk *Fire alarm services including design, supply, installation, commissioning and maintenance of fire alarms to BS5839. Supply and installation of fire extinguishers. Training for your staff on fire alarm system use and controlling your fire alarm panels.*

Fire Fighting Enterprises, 9 Hunting Gate, Hitchin, Hertfordshire, SG4 0TJ Tel: (01462) 444740 Fax: (0845) 4024201 E-mail: sales@ffeuk.com *Manufacturer of beam smoke detectors & gaseous fire extinguishing systems*

Fire Fighting Equipment, Unit 20, Tait Road Industrial Estate, Croydon, CR0 2DP Tel: (020) 8665 4120 Fax: (020) 8665 4125 E-mail: tonyc@ffe.co.uk *Fire protection engineers*

Fire Fogging Systems Ltd, 1 Church Lane, Newmains, Wishaw, Lanarkshire, ML2 9BF Tel: (01698) 386444 Fax: (01698) 386869 E-mail: sales@scotkleen.co.uk *Fire fighting systems manufrs*

Fire Imc, Manley House, 10 Dargan Cresent, Belfast, BT3 9JP Tel: (028) 9077 4388 Fax: (028) 9077 6906 E-mail: sales@fireimc.co.uk *Integrated marketing communications services*

Fire Industry Confederation, 55 Eden Street, Kingston Upon Thames, Surrey, KT1 1BW Tel: (020) 8549 8839 Fax: (020) 8547 1564 E-mail: fic@abft.org.uk *Trade association*

Fire Instrumentation & Research Equipment Ltd, Holmesfield Road, Warrington, WA1 2DS Tel: (01925) 646643 Fax: (01925) 646622 E-mail: info@fire-uk.com *Fire testing instruments manufrs*

Fire & Iron Ltd, Rowhurst Forge, Oxshott Road, Leatherhead, Surrey, KT22 0EN Tel: (01372) 386453 Fax: (01372) 386516 E-mail: sales@fireandiron.co.uk *Wrought ironworkers & craft gallery*

Fire Island, Southdowns, Redruth, Cornwall, TR15 2NW Tel: (01209) 314448 Fax: (01209) 313191 E-mail: sales@fireisland.co.uk *Outdoor furniture manufrs*

▶ Fire Logistics, 4 Union Street, Newcastle upon Tyne, NE2 1AH Tel: 0191-230 3647 Fax: 0191-230 3650 E-mail: sales@firelogistics.co.uk *Sprinkler systems designers, suppliers & installers*

▶ Fire Maintenance Services, Unit 26 Swan Road, Swan Industrial Estate, Washington, Tyne & Wear, NE38 8JJ Tel: 0191-497 2929 Fax: 0191-415 0061 E-mail: fms@whfc.net *Fire safety consultants*

▶ Fire Place, Clarence Road, Worksop, Nottinghamshire, S80 1QA Tel: (01909) 530626 E-mail: sales@fireplacegallery.co.uk *Manufactures of Timber and Mdf Fireplace Surrounds and associated furniture products. Trade supplies and Bespoke Products.*CNC Routing and component machining.*

Fire Proof Ltd, Unit 14 Matrix House, Constitution Hill, Leicester, LE1 1PL Tel: 0116-248 9555 Fax: 0116-248 9555 *Fire protection equipment suppliers*

Fire Protection Centre, Atkinsons Way, Foxhills Industrial Estate, Scunthorpe, South Humberside, DN15 8QJ Tel: (01724) 854199 Fax: 01724 854213 E-mail: btholden@fireprotectioncentre.com *Distributors of fire sprinklers, fire extinguishers*

Fire Protection Services, Unit B7, Imperial Business Estate, West Mill, Gravesend, Kent, DA11 0DL Tel: (0800) 317195 Fax: (01474) 535111 E-mail: info@fire-protection-services.co.uk *Fire extinguisher sales & service*

Fire Protection Services, 4 Churchill Avenue, Haverhill, Suffolk, CB9 0AA Tel: (01440) 708833 *Fire protection engineers*

Fire Protection Services Se, 215 London Road, Ewell, Epsom, Surrey, KT17 2BU Tel: (020) 8393 2897 Fax: (020) 8786 8793 *Fire alarms services & sales*

Fire Queen Ltd, 23-37 Broadstone Road, Stockport, Cheshire, SK5 7AR Tel: 0161-442 5500 Fax: 0161-442 2664 *Fire fighting equipment suppliers*

Fire Rite, Unit G1 Caerphilly Business Park, Caerphilly, Mid Glamorgan, CF83 3ED Tel: (029) 2086 7222 Fax: (029) 2086 7333 E-mail: sales@firerite.com *Fire protection specialists, fire alarms, emergency lighting systems & fire extinguishers. Emergency 24hr call out, Fire hose reels, Hydrants, H & S Fire Training, Dry risers safety signs, Nurse call systems, Fire Blankets, Access control.*

Fire Safety Express, Tesla Court, Innovation Way, Lynch Wood, Peterborough, PE2 6FL Tel: (01733) 234504 Fax: 01733 234504 E-mail: enquiries@firesafetyexpress.co.uk *For your fire safety needs in Peterborough and Cambridgeshire. We supply, install and service portable fire extinguishers. Approved contractor to Cambridgeshire Fire and Rescue Service. Fire Safety Training. Fire Risk Assessment. Value driven inclusive pricing structure. No hidden extras. Buy on-line. Service area within 80 miles of Peterborough including London and the home counties.*

Fire Service Appliance Co., Bojea Industrial Estate, Bodmin Road, St. Austell, Cornwall, PL25 5RJ Tel: (0800) 3897930 Fax: (0800) 0195902 *Fire equipment & fire equipment maintenance*

▶ Fire Solutions, Units 1 & 2 The Great Barn, Earls Croome, Worcester, WR8 9DF Tel: (01905) 371321 Fax: E-mail: info@firesolutions.co.uk *Suppliers of fire protection equipment*

▶ The Fire & Stove Shop, Merthyr Road, Tongwynlais, Cardiff, CF15 7LF Tel: (029) 2081 1478 E-mail: sales@decoheat.co.uk *Supply & install stoves, fires, cookers & chimneys*

Fire Systems Ltd, Station House, 5 Ridsdale Road, London, SE20 8AG Tel: (020) 8659 7235 Fax: (020) 8659 7237 E-mail: enquiries@firesystems.co.uk *Fire alarm installers*

Fire Trade, Mayflower House, Bodmin Road, Coventry, CV2 5DB Tel: (024) 7661 6600 Fax: (024) 7662 1990 *Specialist fire protection equipment distributors*

▶ Fire Without Smoke Software Ltd, Queens Road, Bridgend Industrial Estate, Bridgend, Mid Glamorgan, CF31 3UT Tel: (01656) 669119 Fax: (01656) 890723 E-mail: sales@fwoss.com *Ent managed, e-commerce enabled websites.**Our content management system fwossFRESH (developed for the .NET framework & XML-based) is capable of maintaining AAA website accessibility, & has been developed with usability in mind: more* *continued* *information about fwossFRESH is available on our website www.fwoss.com**Based in South Wales, we work with a wide-ranging client base from local SME"s to international corporations, across both private & public sectors. **Please contact Polly Nelson for more information.*

▶ Firebird Metals Ltd, 1 Canal Street, Sheffield, S4 7ZE Tel: (0870) 7622333 Fax: (0870) 7622334 E-mail: neil@firebirdmetals.com *Metal stockholder*

Firecare Ltd, 72 Tartnakilly Road, Limavady, County Londonderry, BT49 9NA Tel: (028) 7776 4002 E-mail: sales@fire-care.co.uk *Suppliers, installers & service of fire equipment*

▶ Firecraft Manufacturing, 1159 Melton Road, Syston, Leicester, LE7 2JS Tel: 0116-269 7030 Fax: 0116-269 7031 *Manufacture fire places*

Fired Earth Ltd, 1-3 Twyford Mill, Oxford Road, Adderbury, Banbury, Oxfordshire, OX17 3SX Tel: (01295) 812088 Fax: (01295) 810832 E-mail: info@firedearth.com *Interior period design & decorative ceramic manufrs*

▶ Firedup Marketing Communications, Unit 2, Lakeside, Festival Way, Stoke-on-Trent, ST1 5RY Tel: (01782) 207336 E-mail: studio@getfiredup.co.uk *Strategic web development, advertising and marketing consultancy.*

Firefill International, Trocell House, Wakening Road, Barking, Essex, IG11 8PD Tel: (020) 8594 9599 Fax: (020) 8594 1933 E-mail: info@firefill.co.uk *Fire protection installers*

Firefly Ltd, 6 Odun Road, Appledore, Bideford, Devon, EX39 1PT Tel: (01237) 478014 Fax: (01237) 425741 E-mail: david@firefly.ltd.uk *Design port equipment*

▶ Firefly Lighting Design, 4th Floor Threshold House, 65-69 Shepherds Bush Green, London, W12 8TX Tel: (020) 8746 2991 E-mail: info@fireflylightingdesign.com *UK-based lighting consultancy*

Firefly Tonics Ltd, 1 Petersham Mews, London, SW7 5NR Tel: (020) 7052 9720 Fax: (020) 7052 9729 E-mail: info@fireflytonics.com *Developing and marketing 'Firefly' - all-natural herbal drinks designed for busy health-conscious people.*

Fireguard Ltd, 24-26 Boulton Road, Stevenage, Hertfordshire, SG1 4QX Tel: (01438) 313276 Fax: (01438) 727681 *Manufacturers of intumescent paint*

Fireguard Services, Unit 1 Milton Business Centre Wick Drive, New Milton, Hampshire, BH25 6RH Tel: (01425) 616139 Fax: (01425) 616139 E-mail: office@fireguardservices.co.uk *Fire extinguisher retailers*

▶ Firehawk Ltd, Unit 6-14, Peele Street, Manchester, M35 0UF Tel: 0161-683 5424 Fax: 0161-682 2233 E-mail: info@firehawk.ltd.uk *Portable appliance testing & electrical testing*

Fireking Ltd, Sefton Lodge, Rough Road, Woking, Surrey, GU22 0RB Tel: (020) 8786 8100 Fax: (01483) 476024 *Fireworks & displays manufrs*

Firelog Ltd, Unit 5C-5D, Caxton Trading Estate, Printing House Lane, Hayes, Middlesex, UB3 1BE Tel: (07932) 644613 Fax: (020) 8569 1165 E-mail: firelogltd@yahoo.co.uk *Leather goods importer*

Firemaster Alarms Ltd, Unit 11 Wedgewood Court, Wedgewood Way, Stevenage, Hertfordshire, SG1 4QR Tel: (01438) 737900

Firenzi Asphalte Drayton Park Ltd, Triumph Trading Estate, Tariff Road, London, N17 0EB Tel: (020) 8801 8016 Fax: (020) 8801 8015 *General roofing contractors & salt merchants*

Fireplan Installations Ltd, Tuesnoad Grange, Bethersden, Ashford, Kent, TN26 3EH Tel: 01233 820292 *Fire alarm suppliers*

Firepoint Scotland Ltd, 13 London Street, Larkhall, Lanarkshire, ML9 1AQ Tel: (01698) 881775 Fax: (01698) 307077 *Fire fighting equipment suppliers & maintenance contractors*

Firepoint Services Ltd, 134 Great Lime Road, Newcastle Upon Tyne, NE12 7NJ Tel: 0191-268 6854 Fax: 0191-268 6854 *Fire extinguishers service & sales*

Firepro Fire Protection Consultants, J7 Business Park, Blackburn Road, Clayton le Moors, Accrington, Lancashire, BB5 5JW Tel: (01254) 600002 Fax: (01254) 392955 E-mail: firepro@ntlworld.com *Fire equipment & alarm suppliers*

Fireprotect Chester Ltd, Factory Road, Sandycroft, Deeside, Clwyd, CH5 2QJ Tel: (01244) 536595 Fax: (01244) 533592 E-mail: sales@fireprotect.co.uk *Fire retardant adhesive tape manufrs*

Fires4U, PO Box 6843, Swadlincote, Derbyshire, DE12 7XX Tel: (0845) 6120001 E-mail: sales@fires4u.co.uk *Online store for gas fires & electric fires*

Firesafe, PO Box 1350, Harlow, Essex, CM20 2BQ Tel: (01279) 626000 Fax: (01279) 730505 *Suppliers of fire extinguishers*

Fireshields Extinguisher Services Ltd, 7 Princes Gardens, Whitley Bay, Tyne & Wear, NE25 8EA Tel: 0191-291 0444 Fax: 0191-252 2340 *Fire fighting equipment sale & services*

Fireside Brews, 22 Commercial Street, Shipley, West Yorkshire, BD18 3SP Tel: (01274) 599592 *Cake Decorations*

Firesoft Computer Consultants, 13 Roe Green Lane, Hatfield, Hertfordshire, AL10 0SH Tel: (01707) 271073 *Computer consultants*

Firesolve Ltd, Unit 2a Skelmanthorpe Technology Park, Station Road, Skelmanthorpe, Huddersfield, HD8 9GA Tel: (01484) 866614 Fax: (01484) 864466 E-mail: sales@fireslove.co.uk *Fire equipment sales & services*

Firestone Industrial Products Inc, Church Street, Staines, Middlesex, TW18 4EP Tel: (01784) 462326 Fax: (01784) 462327 E-mail: sales@firestoneindustrial.com *Motor vehicle suspension systems manufrs*

Firestool, Auckland Street, Stoke-on-Trent, ST6 2AY Tel: (01782) 819164 Fax: (01782) 835642 *Manufactures of pottery equipment*

Firetec Ltd, Wessex House, Great Western Road, Gloucester, GL1 3NG Tel: (01452) 530142 Fax: (01452) 380791 E-mail: paul@firetecltd.btconnect.co.uk *Fire alarm system services*

Firetex, Tower Works, Kestor Street, Bolton, BL2 2AL Tel: (01204) 521771 Fax: (01204) 381826 E-mail: enquiries@leighspaints.co.uk *Fire protection equipment manufrs*

Firetrace, Unit 22 Knightsdale Road, Ipswich, IP1 4JJ Tel: (01473) 744090 Fax: (01473) 744901 *Specialist fire detection equipment manufrs*

▶ Firewire Computer Solutions, 86 Coniston Road, Kings Langley, Hertfordshire, WD4 8DE Tel: (07909) 518101

▶ Firework Events, 5 Hanover Road, Scarborough, North Yorkshire, YO11 1LS Tel: (01723) 507357 E-mail: jmevents4@aol.com *Firework retailers*

Firework Factors Ltd, Pegs Farm, Staplow, Ledbury, Herefordshire, HR8 1NQ Tel: (01531) 640441 Fax: (01531) 640004 E-mail: info@fireworkfactors.com *Fireworks suppliers*

▶ Fireworks Studios Ltd, 68 High Street, Wargrave, Reading, RG10 8BY Tel: 0118-967 3900 E-mail: info@fireworks-studios.com *Interactive design agency, multimedia developers and new media consultants.*

▶ Firing Squad, 20 Sea Front, Hayling Island, Hampshire, PO11 9HL Tel: (023) 9246 6500 *Ceramic suppliers*

Firkser Chemicals Ltd, 24 Willow Court, Abbey Road, Macclesfield, Cheshire, SK10 3PD Tel: (01625) 612900 Fax: (01625) 503763 *Industrial cleaning chemical manufrs*

▶ Firm Solutions Associates, Exploration House, Burton Close, Daventry, Northamptonshire, NN11 0TX Tel: (01327) 311993 Fax: (01327) 312900 E-mail: quality@q9001.co.uk *Quality assurance & control specialists*

Firma Nicand Plastic Products Ltd, Unit D Woodley Airfield, Headley Road East, Woodley, Reading, RG5 4SA Tel: 0118-969 6939 Fax: 0118-944 1625 E-mail: kiran@firmanicand.com *Injection mouldings*

▶ Firmac Signs Ltd, Unit 5 Marrtree Business Park, Thunderhead Ridge, Castleford, West Yorkshire, WF10 4UA Tel: (01977) 667444

Firmafix Fastenings, Unit 3, Pioneer Park Clough Road, Hull, HU8 8BB Tel: (01482) 224334 Fax: (01482) 224341 E-mail: sales@firmafix.com *Fixings & fastening distributors*

Firmco Ltd, 127-129 Stanley Road, Ilford, Essex, IG1 1RQ Tel: (020) 8514 5544 Fax: (020) 8478 3133 E-mail: info@firmco.co.uk *Building contractors*

Firmhelm Ltd, Pwllheli Boatyard, Outer Harbour, Pwllheli, Gwynedd, LL53 5AY Tel: (01758) 612244 Fax: (01758) 614790 E-mail: enqieries@firmhelm.com *Boat builders, repairers & marine retail*

Alan Firmin Ltd, Mid Kent Business Park, Sortmill Road, Snodland, Kent, ME6 5GP Tel: (01634) 241200 Fax: (01622) 820823 E-mail: transport@alanfirmin.co.uk *Storage contractors*

▶ Firmin Coates Ltd, Earls Road, Grangemouth, Stirlingshire, FK3 8XG Tel: (01324) 471356 Fax: (01324) 489260

Firmin Coates Ltd, Wares Farm, Redwall Lane, Linton, Maidstone, Kent, ME17 4BB Tel: (01622) 820273 Fax: (01622) 820823 E-mail: afl@alanfirmin.co.uk *Road transport, haulage & freight services*

Firmin Coates Ltd, The Pines, Fordham Road, Newmarket, Suffolk, CB8 7LG Tel: (01638) 720481 Fax: (01638) 721240 E-mail: i.murfitt@firmincoates.co.uk *Warehousing & distribs*

▶ Firmin & Sons P.L.C., Firmin House, 82-86 New Town Row, Birmingham, B6 4HU Tel: 0121-380 0800 Fax: 0121-359 3321 E-mail: sales@firmin.co.uk *Manufacture & supply of all requirements for state ceremonials*

Firmware Computer Systems, 68 Hendre Road, Pencoed, Bridgend, Mid Glamorgan, CF35 6TN Tel: (01656) 863639 Fax: (01656) 863639 E-mail: plynham@technologist.com *Computer software - specialist in agricultural software*

Firn Overseas Packaging Ltd, Firn House, 61 Church Street, Hungerford, Berkshire, RG17 0JH Tel: (01488) 683193 Fax: (01488) 684701 E-mail: sales@firn.org *Paper & packaging product exports*

▶ Firscall Data Ltd, Unit 4, Carlton Court, Brown Lane West, Leeds, LS12 6LT Tel: 0113-242 7220 Fax: 0113-242 7217 E-mail: sales@firscall.co.uk *Suppliers of computer accessories & consumables*

Firsmere Engineering Ltd, Aston Lane, Sharnford, Hinckley, Leicestershire, LE10 3PA Tel: (01455) 273940 Fax: (01455) 273996 *Contractors of suspended ceiling systems*

First, Corporate Communications Macmillan House, Paddington, London, W2 1FG Tel: (020) 7291 0500 Fax: (020) 7636 1338 *Holding company, corporate & legal services*

First 4 It, Sceptre House, 1 Hornbeam Square North, Harrogate, North Yorkshire, HG2 8PB Tel: (01423) 859370 Fax: (01423) 859371 E-mail: sales@first4it.co.uk *Commercial It support services*

▶ First Aid Focus, Atrium Business Centrenorth Caldeen Road, Coatbridge, Lanarkshire, ML5 4EF Tel: (01236) 702011 Fax: (01236) 702021

▶ First Aid Nursing Enterprises, Unit 6, Consett Business Park, Consett, County Durham, DH8 6BP Tel: (01207) 693828 E-mail: mike.green@fane.org.uk *Provider of Health and Safety, Food Safety and First Aid training. Accredited and Nationally recognised with bespoke courses available to meet your company needs. Also available -HACCP training as part of the "Safer Food Better Business" Initiative*

First Aid Supplies & Training Wales, 305 Gladstone Road, Barry, South Glamorgan, CF63 1NL Tel: (01446) 735680 Fax: (01446) 735680 *First aid training at work*

Company Information

First For Aid Training, 30 Cennon Group, Ingleby Barwick, Stockton-On-Tees, Cleveland, TS17 5DB Tel: (01642) 769014 E-mail: firstforaid@talk21.com *First aid training*

First Assist Group Ltd, 32-42 High Street, Purley, Surrey, CR8 2PP Tel: (020) 8763 3000 Fax: (020) 8668 1262 E-mail: corporate.info@firstassist.co.uk *Assistance company*

First Assist Group Ltd, Marshalls Court, Marshalls Road, Sutton, Surrey, SM1 4DU Tel: (020) 8652 1313 Fax: (020) 8661 7604 E-mail: corporate.info@firstassit.co.uk *Insurance & assistants company service providers*

First Base, Enterprise House, Ocean Way, Southampton, SO14 3XB Tel: (023) 8033 1666 Fax: (023) 8033 2050 E-mail: southampton@fbase.com *Business centre-serviced offices*

▶ First Bed & Pine Centre, 67 London Road, East Grinstead, West Sussex, RH19 1EQ Tel: (01342) 322700 Fax: (01342) 301252 *Bed & pine retailers*

▶ First Call, 134 Stanley Green Road, Poole, Dorset, BH15 3AH Tel: (01202) 666663 Fax: (01202) 666664 E-mail: sales@allvehicleswanted.co.uk *Land communication*

First Call Communications, St. Magnus House, 21 Guild Street, Aberdeen, AB11 6NJ Tel: (0500) 567500 Fax: (01224) 574448 E-mail: stuart.taylor@first/cal/comms.co.uk *Telephone answering services*

▶ First Call Construction, Shrasbury Street, Derby, DE23 8YB Tel: (01332) 203703 Fax: (01332) 203703 E-mail: christinaistcall@aol.com *Sewer cleaning services*

▶ First Call Contract Services Ltd, 30 Church Street, Enfield, Middlesex, EN2 6BA Tel: (020) 8370 9001 Fax: (020) 8367 1516 E-mail: info@firstcall-enfield.co.uk *Specialist location for Special Events & Leisure Industries.*In-house Food Hygiene training; Industrial & Driving contract labour.*

▶ First Call Contract Services, 267 High Street, Waltham Cross, Hertfordshire, EN8 7AT Tel: (01992) 635363 Fax: (01992) 633304 E-mail: info@firstcall-waltham.co.uk *The Branch specialises in LGV Drivers and industrial/contract personnel. Experienced in Food Production contracts and Airfreight. Also offers Level-4 training courses to ensure staff comply with Dft Regulations for sensitive working areas, i.e Bonded Warehouses.*

▶ First Call Plumbing, The Old Farmhouse, 9 North Street, Ipplepen, Newton Abbot, Devon, TQ12 5RT Tel: (01803) 814514 Fax: (01803) 814069 E-mail: fcplumbing@btinternet.com *For all you Plumbing needs no matter how small.*24 hour emergency service. *NO CALL OUT CHARGES**

▶ First Capital Finance Ltd, 360 Charminster Road, Bournemouth, BH8 9RX Tel: 01202 512233 Fax: 01202 510011 E-mail: jon.wedge@firstcapitalfinance.co.uk *Finance brokers for UK businesses. Also very competitive on consumer finance for cars and boats.**We have excellent relationships with the main UK banks and are perfect if you need a number of credit facilities in place for you or your business.**Can provide the best rates around as we arrange to borrow around £3m a year from the banks.**Give us a call, we''ll see if we can help.*

▶ First Choice Ltd, 12 High Street, Aberdour, Burntisland, Fife, KY3 0SW Tel: (01383) 860000

First Choice Business Systems Ltd, Unit 4-6 Murray Business Centre, Murray Road, Orpington, Kent, BR5 3RE Tel: (01689) 828182 Fax: (01689) 899399 E-mail: sales@firstchoiceltd.co.uk *Interior designers*

First Choice Computers West Midlands Ltd, 40 Waterloo Road, Wolverhampton, WV1 4BL Tel: (01902) 712166 Fax: (01902) 427900 E-mail: enquiries@fcc-online.co.uk *Computer consultants*

First Choice Expedition Foods, Heads Road, Stape, Pickering, North Yorkshire, YO18 8HX Tel: (01751) 473330 E-mail: info@expeditionfoods.com *Freeze dried foods*

▶ First Choice Group, Stileway Business Park, Lower Strode Road, Clevedon, Avon, BS21 6UU Tel: (01275) 871111 Fax: (01275) 871115 *Photocopying machine suppliers*

▶ First Choice It Ltd, 13 Renshaw Close, Luton, LU2 8TD Tel: (0845) 0510136 Fax: (0871) 8729611 E-mail: info@firstchoiceit.co.uk *ONSITE COMPUTER HOME & OFFICE REPAIRS UPGRADES ONSITE VIRUS REMOVAL / FIREWALL PROTECTION ON-LOCATION HOME /OFFICE NETWORK INSTALLATIONS (both wired and wireless!) EMERGENCY DATA RECOVERY REMOTE COMPUTING/VIRTUAL PRIVATE NETWORK SOLUTIONS CUSTOM BUILT COMPUTERS & WARRANTY PERSONAL COMPUTERS, SERVERS ONSITE COMPUTER SUPPORT AVAILABLE*

▶ First Choice Joinery, 3 Drayton Road, Tonbridge, Kent, TN9 2BE Tel: (01622) 873348 Fax: (01732) 365696 E-mail: sales@shawleygroup.co.uk

▶ First Choice Recruitment & Training Ltd, 72-73 Bartholomew Street, Newbury, Berkshire, RG14 5DU Tel: (01635) 551111 Fax: (01635) 46000 E-mail: firstchoice@bposs.co.uk *Recruitment Consultancy specialising in Commercial, office and light industrial recruitment*

First Choice Technology Solutions Ltd, Broadhurst House, Bury Old Road, Salford, M7 4QX Tel: 0161-740 4400 Fax: 0161-740 4411 *Telecommunication services*

First Choice Training & Development Ltd, 37 Langdale Crescent Eston, Grange Middlesbrough, Middlesbrough, Cleveland, TS6 7RB Tel: (01642) 511877 E-mail: firstchoicetraining@ntlwolrd.com *First Choice Training Middlesbrough offers course in Health and Safety, First Aid, Manual Handling, Risk Assessment, Forklift Truck. We can tailor course to your needs in any subject.*

▶ First Choice Windows Ltd, 58 Castle Lane, Benfleet, Essex, SS7 2AL Tel: (01702) 555570 Fax: (01702) 555988

First Circuit Group, PO Box 7226, Redditch, Worcestershire, B98 7WR Tel: (01527) 503503 Fax: (01527) 456170E-mail: info@1stcircuit.com *Printed circuit board manufacturers & distributors of electronic cable harness test systems*

First City Insurance Brokers Ltd, 13-15 Folgate Street, London, E1 6BX Tel: (020) 7247 6595 Fax: (020) 7410 4818 *Insurance brokers* Also at: Birmingham, Bristol, Leeds & Poole

First Class Buisness Solutions Ltd, 8 Hanover Street, London, W1S 1YE Tel: (020) 7290 2650 Fax: (020) 7290 2655 *Business equipment sales*

▶ First Class Leisure, 1e Darlaston Lane, Bilston, West Midlands, WV14 7BW Tel: (01902) 635003 Fax: (01902) 609783 E-mail: info@1stclassleisure.co.uk *Leisure hire & sales*

1st Class Linen Services, Unit 9 Chapman Court, Charfleets Road Industrial Estate, Canvey Island, Essex, SS8 0PQ Tel: 01268 691222 Fax: 01268 510947 E-mail: brettbarber@fsmail.net *Laundry,linen hire and linen sales*

▶ First Class Printing Ltd, Unit 3, Mugiemoss Road, Aberdeen, AB21 9US Tel: (01224) 683066

First Components, The Wallows Industrial Estate, Fens Pool Avenue, Brierley Hill, West Midlands, DY5 1QA Tel: (01384) 262068 Fax: (01384) 482383 E-mail: carl@firstcomponents.co.uk *Precision turned parts manufrs*

▶ First Concepts Ltd, Concept House, 7 Holly Grove, Tabley, Knutsford, Cheshire, WA16 0HR Tel: (0845) 4567684 Fax: (0845) 4567694 E-mail: info@firstconcepts.co.uk *We specialise in designing and implementing logistics and supply chain strategies across all industry sectors. With a team that has over one hundred years of combined knowledge within the logistics sector we pride ourselves on our home grown expertise.*

▶ First Contact, Romford Road, London, E12 5JG Tel: (020) 8911 8787 Fax: (020) 8553 4440 E-mail: Faisal@FirstContactUk.net *If you are considering selling, buying, letting or renting, we offer professional property services designed to meet your needs/requirements. **Our team of experienced staff has a detailed knowledge of property management, residential lettings and housing law. We are specialists in residential letting and property management and pride ourselves in providing an expert service carried out by our professional and friendly staff. Our reputation is built upon an extremely professional and efficient service and our highly trained staff can manage all types of property portfolios.*

First Copy Ltd, 187 High Street, Bottisham, Cambridge, CB5 9BB Tel: (0800) 592566 Fax: (01223) 813850 E-mail: info@firstcopy.co.uk *Office equipment retailers*

▶ First Dance UK, 11 Thorn Road, Wrecclesham, Farnham, Surrey, GU10 4TU Tel: (01252) 792078 E-mail: adam@firstdanceuk.co.uk *First Dance UK - Wedding Dance Specialists. We provide dance lessons for couples for their first dance at their wedding. First Dance UK choreograph a unique routine for couples to dance to their song.*

First Degree Software Systems Ltd, 28 Oakwood Close, Warsash, Southampton, SO31 9PW Tel: (01489) 603383 Fax: (01489) 603384 *Computer software agents*

First Degree Systems, 73-74 Branston Road, Burton-On-Trent, Staffordshire, DE14 3BY Tel: (0870) 4422361 Fax: (0870) 4422362 E-mail: alan-bark@first-degree-systems.com *Computer software, windows (glazing) design*

First Diesel Injection (Croydon) Ltd, 240 Thornton Road, Croydon, CR0 3EU Tel: (020) 8689 1806 Fax: (020) 8684 8060 E-mail: service@firstdieselinjection.co.uk *Diesel fuel injection specialists*

First EBusiness Solutions Ltd, Burghmuir Way, Inverurie, Aberdeenshire, AB51 4FT Tel: (01467) 622720 Fax: (01467) 624120 E-mail: info@firstebusiness.co.uk *Business solutions provider*

▶ First Economics Ltd, 48 Westway Gardens, Redhill, RH1 2JB Tel: (020) 7537 3605 E-mail: info@first-economics.com *Economic consultancy, based in London UK, advising companies, regulators and government on regulatory issues in the utility and transport sectors*

First Edition Translations, 22 Newmarket Rd, Cambridge, CB5 8DT Tel: (01223) 356733 Fax: (01223) 321488 E-mail: info@firstedit.co.uk *Translation & editorial services*

First Effluent Ltd, 42a High Street, Sutton Coldfield, West Midlands, B72 1UJ Tel: 0121-355 2907 Fax: 0121-355 6134 *Effluent treatment plant manufrs*

▶ First Engineering Ltd, Station Road, Crianlarich, Perthshire, FK20 8QN Tel: (01838) 300255

First Engineering Ltd, 137 Euston Road, London, NW1 2AA Tel: (020) 7387 0109 Fax: (020) 7387 0010 *Railway engineers*

First Engineering Services, Unit 1, Hare Street, Bilston, West Midlands, WV14 7DX Tel: (01902) 354735 Fax: (01902) 354805 E-mail: first.engineering@virgin.net *General engineers*

First Farm Foods Ltd, South Hams Business Pk, Churchstow, Kingsbridge, Devon, TQ7 3QR Tel: 01548 856565 *Food manufacturers*

▶ First Fencing, 585, Southleigh Road, Emsworth, Hampshire, PO10 7TE Tel: 01243 430502 E-mail: info@firstfencing.co.uk *Fencing Contractors*Please viset website for discription www.firstfencing.co.uk**

First Field, Unit B5 3 Bradbury Street, London, N16 8JN Tel: (020) 7690 4990 Fax: (020) 7690 4494 E-mail: firstfield@clara.co.uk *Video & new media production*

▶ First Flooring, 9 Rosedale Gardens, Sutton-in-Ashfield, Nottinghamshire, NG17 1ND Tel: (01623) 476988 Fax: (01623) 477326 E-mail: firstflooring@ntlworld.com *Contract & domestic floor fitting, supply & services*

First Hose Ltd, 21 Denmore Industrial Estate, Denmore Road, Bridge of Don, Aberdeen, AB23 8JW Tel: (01224) 823413 Fax: (01224) 823113 E-mail: sales@1st-hose.co.uk *Hose assembly & coupling distributors hire of test equipment*

▶ First Image, 54 Swinburne Avenue, Hitchin, Hertfordshire, SG5 2RA Tel: (01462) 457458 E-mail: firstimagesales@aol.com *Suppliers of promotional items for corporate branding including t-shirts, mugs, mouse mats, coasters, etc.*

First Impression (Doncaster), PO Box 812, Doncaster, South Yorkshire, DN1 9AE Tel: 01302 874381 E-mail: contact@firstimpression.co.uk *Specialists in corporate communications, including staff newsletters, magazines and ezines.*

First Impression Training Ltd, Maidstone, Kent, ME16 0GL Tel: (0870) 4294866 Fax: (01622) 761321 E-mail: fit@calltraining.co.uk *Training centre*

▶ First Impressions Castings, 25 High Street, Market Deeping, Peterborough, PE6 8ED Tel: (01778) 344541 Fax: (01778) 344541 E-mail: info@firstimpressionscastings.co.uk *Baby casting services*

First In Safety Ltd, Unit 71 Campbell Street, Brierley Hill, West Midlands, DY5 3YG Tel: (01384) 346858 Fax: (01384) 346861 *First aid equipment suppliers*

First In Service Ltd, Windsor Industrial Estate, Rupert Street, Birmingham, B7 4PR Tel: 0121-333 3301 Fax: 0121-333 3302 E-mail: sellis@firstinservice.co.uk *First in Service Ltd based in Birmingham provide customers all over the UK with design, installation, service and maintenance of air conditioning, ventilation and extract systems, heating, electrical and security systems, catering and refrigeration equipment, coffee equipment, building services and premises management.*

The First & Last, First & Last, Herne Common, Herne Bay, Kent, CT6 7JU Tel: (01227) 364465 *Pub, restaurant & banqueting room services*

▶ First Light Direct, 4 Bentsbrook Road, North Holmwood, Dorking, Surrey, RH5 4HW Tel: (01306) 881314 E-mail: sales@firstlightdirect.com *Fluorescent Tube and Light Bulb suppliers, including Aquatic Lighting, Tanning and Sunbed Fluorescent Tubes.*

▶ First Light Lamps Ltd, Unit 23 Lancaster Way Business Park, Ely, Cambridgeshire, CB6 3NW Tel: (01353) 659922 Fax: (01353) 668883 E-mail: info@firstlightlamps.com *Lighting manufrs*

First Line Ltd, Bessemer Close, Bicester, Oxfordshire, OX26 6QE Tel: (01869) 248484 Fax: (01869) 240472 E-mail: sales@firstline.co.uk *Water pump distributors & agents*

▶ First Line, Unit B7 Evans Easyspace, Deeside Industrial Park, Deeside, Clwyd, CH5 2JZ Tel: (01244) 289714 Fax: (01244) 289713 E-mail: sales@firstlinemaintenance.co.uk *Printer fax machine, computer repairers, sales & hire services*

▶ First Line Contracts Ltd, 5 Delaware Drive, Tongwell, Milton Keynes, MK15 8HG Tel: (01908) 611229

First Link Computing Ltd, York House, High Street, Amblecote, Stourbridge, West Midlands, DY8 4BT Tel: (01384) 377007 Fax: (01384) 377178 E-mail: sales@pcwarranty.co.uk *Maintenance contracts & warranty provisions of PC manufrs*

First Manufacturing Ltd, Bagley Road, Wellington, Somerset, TA21 9PZ Tel: (01823) 667879 Fax: (01823) 661317 E-mail: sales@firstman.co.uk *Shop fitters & manufrs*

First Micronics Ltd, 602-604 Kingsbury Road, Erdington, Birmingham, B24 9PJ Tel: 0121-250 5000 Fax: 0121-250 5019 E-mail: sales@fml.net *Computer services*

First Milk, Cirrus House Glasgow Airport Business Park, Marchburn Drive, Abbotsinch, Paisley, Renfrewshire, PA3 2SJ Tel: 0141-887 6111 Fax: 0141-848 0015 *Farmers co-operative*

▶ The First Milk Cheese Co. Ltd, Merlins Bridge, Haverfordwest, Dyfed, SA61 1JN Tel: (01437) 762852 Fax: (01437) 760624 *Cheese & concentrates manufrs*

First National, First National House, 15 College Road, Harrow, Middlesex, HA1 1BY Tel: (020) 8909 4646 *Mortgage lender & consumer finance company*

First National Security, 58 Castle Boulevard, Nottingham, NG7 1FN Tel: 0115-979 9299 Fax: 0115-979 9799 E-mail: info@firstnationalsecurity.co.uk

First Option Ltd, Signal House, Jacklyns Lane, Alresford, Hampshire, SO24 9JJ Tel: (01962) 738200 Fax: (01962) 738201 E-mail: mail@firstoption.net *Computer software developer & support*

▶ First Plate, Metro House, Darlaston Road, Wednesbury, West Midlands, WS10 7SW Tel: 0121-505 7878 Fax: 0121-505 6550 *Motor vehicle number plate manufrs*

First Projects Ltd, City Business Centre, Station Rise, York, YO1 6GA Tel: (01904) 613361 Fax: (01904) 612936 *Electric cable laying & engineering consultants*

▶ First Refurbishment & Demolition Ltd, 16 Lyon Road, Walton-on-Thames, Surrey, KT12 3PU Tel: (01932) 269301 Fax: (01932) 269303

▶ First Response, Unit 1, 48 Beacon Lane, Exeter, EX4 8LJ Tel: (01392) 499951 Fax: (01392) 499696 *First aid & medical training services*

First Secure Ltd, 157 Adnitt Rd, Northampton, NN1 4NH Tel: 01604 472060 Fax: 01604 472060 *Surveillance*

First Security Ltd, European Business Centre, The Hyde, Belgrave Road, London, NW9 5AE Tel: (020) 8374 4007 Fax: (020) 8952 4535 *Security Systems Installation*

First Signs & Labels Ltd, Unit 1, Raynham Close, Raynham Road Industrial Estate, Raynham Road, Bishop's Stortford, Hertfordshire, CM23 5PJ Tel: (01279) 467999 Fax: (01279) 467888 E-mail: sales@firstsafetysigns.co.uk *Sign manufrs*

▶ First Software Systems Ltd, c/o Giant Strongbox Ltd, 1 New Oxford Street, London, WC1A 1GG Tel: 07721 043866 E-mail: admin@firstsoft-design.co.uk *Industrial Automation *Design Service :**Software Engineering, Computer + Electrical Control System Design, (SCADA, DCS, HMI, plc's, Variable Speed Drives), Electronic and Embedded Systems, Project Engineering.*

▶ First Source Ltd, Elmdon Grange, Elmdon Park, Solihull, West Midlands, B92 9EL Tel: 0121-722 3900 Fax: 0121-743 4794 E-mail: firstsource@orange.net *Specialist garment cover suppliers*

▶ First Source & Supply Ltd, Unit 1 High Hall Farm, Oxley Hill, Heybridge, Maldon, Essex, CM9 8ES Tel: (01621) 810893 Fax: (01621) 840054 E-mail: info@firstsourcesupply.co.uk Principal Export Areas: Central/East Europe & West Europe *Plastic consultancy design*

▶ First Spread Bet Ltd, 87 Boclair Road Milngavie, Glasgow, G62 6EP Tel: 013606 20745 E-mail: list@financial-spread-betting.com *Specialist financial spread betting site giving news, views, articles and information relating to the worlds of spreadbetting, day trading and cfds in all their forms.*

▶ First Stage Machining Co. Ltd, First Stage House, Brimington Road North, Chesterfield, Derbyshire, S41 9BE Tel: (01246) 273167 Fax: (01246) 203225 *Engineering company*

▶ First Stop Marine Services, Galmpton, Brixham, Devon, TQ5 0EH Tel: (01803) 846333 Fax: (01803) 846333

▶ First Stop Sign Shop, Unit 2, The Hyde, Brighton, BN2 4JE Tel: (01273) 270131 Fax: (01273) 270469 E-mail: Kellys@firststopsignshop.co.uk *Sign manufrs*

First Technicare Co. Ltd, Unit 10 Acorn Production Centre, 105 Blundell Street, London, N7 9BN Tel: (020) 7609 8761 Fax: (020) 7607 1062 E-mail: tripos3@aol.com *Pressure-care mattresses manufrs*

First Training, Woodford Road, Wilmslow, Cheshire, SK9 2LT Tel: (01625) 549287 Fax: (01625) 537284 E-mail: sales@firsttraining.net *Computer consultants*

▶ The First Web, 91 Augusta Drive, Macclesfield, Cheshire, SK10 2UR Tel: (01625) 430379 E-mail: admin@thefirstweb.com *Website design & creation services*

First4seals P.L.C., Mount Street, Bradford, West Yorkshire, BD3 9SN Tel: (01274) 720775 Fax: (01274) 729022 E-mail: seals@first4seals.com *Mechanical seal manufrs*

▶ Firstaid4sport.co.uk, 6A Exchange Close, North Hykeham, Lincoln, LN6 3TR Tel: (01522) 883344 Fax: (01522) 875253 E-mail: gemma.newlove@firstaid4sport.co.uk *First aid supplies*

Firstan Ltd, Trafalgar Way, Bar Hill, Cambridge, CB3 8SQ Tel: (01954) 201010 Fax: (01954) 782923 E-mail: sales@firstan.co.uk *Carton manufrs*

Firstek, Harvey Road, Burnt Mills Industrial Estate, Basildon, Essex, SS13 1EP Tel: (01268) 727472 Fax: (01268) 729872 *Manufacturers parts motor industry*

Firstfire Ltd, Howe House, 13 Somers Road, Halesowen, West Midlands, B62 8EN Tel: 0121-585 3870 Fax: 0121-585 3871 E-mail: first.fire@dial.pipex.com *Fire fighting equipment suppliers*

▶ Firstgear Clothing, The Croft, Lower Brand, Griffydam, Coalville, Leicestershire, LE67 8HE Tel: 01530 224474 Fax: 01530 224474 E-mail: info@firstgearclothing.co.uk *Promotional printing & embroidery*

Firstlight Products Ltd, 22 Erica Road, Stacey Bushes, Milton Keynes, MK12 6HS Tel: (01908) 310221 Fax: (01908) 310229 E-mail: flp@firstlight-products.co.uk *Light fitting importers*

Firstneat Ltd, 99 Mabgate, Leeds, LS9 7DR Tel: 0113-245 4039 Fax: 0113-245 4039 *Clothing manufrs*

Firstpress Plastic Moulders Ltd, 10 Haden Street, Balsall Heath, Birmingham, B12 9BH Tel: 0121-446 6266 Fax: 0121-446 6269 E-mail: info@firstpress.co.uk *Manufacturers of injection mouldings*

Firstworld Systems Ltd, 20 Bytham Heights, Castle Bytham, Grantham, Lincolnshire, NG33 4ST Tel: (01780) 410847 *Systems Consultancy*

▶ Firth Buildings Scotland Ltd, 125 Auchterderran Road, Lochgelly, Fife, KY5 9BR Tel: (01592) 780405

▶ Firth Fire Protection Servicing Co. Ltd, Stony Lane, Christchurch, Dorset, BH23 7LQ Tel: (01202) 476902 Fax: (01202) 479493

Joseph Firth, 10 Pepper Road, Leeds, LS10 2EU Tel: 0113-271 1148 Fax: 0113-270 3101 E-mail: sales@josephfirth.co.uk *Engineering & welding suppliers*

Firth Manufacturing Ltd, Hole House Lane, Stocksbridge, Sheffield, S36 1BS Tel: 0114-288 3298 Fax: 0114-288 4176 E-mail: info@firths.co.uk *Joinery manufrs*

Firth Powerfix, 71 Gelderd Road, Leeds, LS12 6HF Tel: 0113-245 1626 Fax: 0113-242 3887 E-mail: sales@powerfixonline.co.uk *Fixing & power tool distribs*

Firth Rixson P.L.C, PO Box 644, Sheffield, S9 1JD Tel: 0114-219 3000 Fax: 0114-219 1111 E-mail: info@firthrixson.com Principal Export Areas: Worldwide *Rings, forging, steels, metals & distribution divisions*

Firth Rixson Forgings Ltd, Dale Road North, Darley Dale, Matlock, Derbyshire, DE4 2JB Tel: 0114-219 3005 E-mail: info@firthrixson.com *General presswork manufrs*

Firth Rixson Forgings Ltd, Meadowhall Road, Wincobank, Sheffield, S9 1HD Tel: 0114-219 3001 Fax: 0114-219 1131 E-mail: fsales@firthrixson.com *Drop stampings & press extrusions*

Firth Rixson Superalloys Ltd, Shepley Street, Glossop, Derbyshire, SK13 7SA Tel: (01457) 854351 Fax: (01457) 855529 E-mail: lbrierley@firthrixson.com *Nickel chrome cobalt alloys*

▶ Firth Ross Martin, 7 Castle Street, Edinburgh, EH2 3AH Tel: 0131-220 6669 Fax: 0131-225 8180

Firth Sheet Metal Ltd, Barrys Lane, Scarborough, North Yorkshire, YO12 4HA Tel: (01723) 376771 Fax: (01723) 351325 E-mail: info@firmac.co.uk *Ventilation & ductwork engineers*

William Firth & Son Ltd, Wombwell Lane, Barnsley, South Yorkshire, S70 3NT Tel: (01226) 287717 Fax: (01226) 730348 *Scrap metal merchants*

Firthglow Ltd, 1 Papyrus Road, Werringtone, Peterborough, PE4 5BH Tel: (01733) 570345 Fax: (01733) 576115 *External wallcoatings manufrs*

▶ Firth's Furnishings, 103 Commercial Street, Batley, West Yorkshire, WF17 5DQ Tel: (01924) 478294 *Furniture shop*

Firth's Jewellers, 4 Gage St, Lancaster, LA1 1UH Tel: (01524) 848442 Fax: (01524) 63819 *Jewellery*

Firthstones Ltd, 22-24 Brindley Road, Bayton Road Industrial Estate, Coventry, CV7 9EP Tel: (024) 7636 1010 Fax: (024) 7636 0970 E-mail: sales@firthstones.co.uk *Precision engineers*

Firwood, Collingwood Avenue, Blackpool, FY3 8QH Tel: (01253) 392211 Fax: (01253) 392216 *Timber & builders' merchants*

Firwood Paints Ltd, Victoria Works, Oakenbottom Road, Bolton, BL2 6DP Tel: (01204) 525231 Fax: (01204) 362522 E-mail: sales@firwood.co.uk *Industrial paint manufacturers*

Firwood Timber & Building Supplies, 8 Greengate Lane, Prestwich, Manchester, M25 3HW Tel: 0161-798 8404 Fax: 0161-773 5386 E-mail: firwood@prestwichm25.wanadoo.co.uk *Builders & plumbers merchants*

Fisadco Eng (1980) Ltd, Raywell Street, Hull, HU2 8EP Tel: (01482) 324564 Fax: (01482) 222564 E-mail: daren@fisadco.co.uk *Precision machining engineers*

▶ Fischbach Fans, 17 Siddeley Way, Royal Oak Industrial Estate, Daventry, Northamptonshire, NN11 8PA Tel: (01327) 315012 Fax: (01327) 315013 E-mail: fischbachacv@aol.com *Distributor of fischbach fans & controls*

Fischbein-Saxon, 274 Alma Road, Enfield, Middlesex, EN3 7RS Tel: (020) 8805 6111 Fax: (020) 8344 6625 E-mail: sales@fischbein-saxon.co.uk *Heat sealing machine manufrs*

Fischer Group Of Companies, Whiteley Road, Hithercroft Industrial Estate, Wallingford, Oxfordshire, OX10 9AT Tel: (01491) 827919 Fax: (01491) 827953 E-mail: sales@fischer.co.uk *Fixings manufrs*

Fischer Instrumentation (GB) Ltd, Department K, Gordleton Industrial Park, Hannah Way, Pennington, Lymington, Hampshire, SO41 8JD Tel: (01590) 684100 Fax: (01590) 684110 E-mail: mail@fischergb.co.uk *Non-destructive testing equipment*

Fisco Ltd, 21 Brook Road, Rayleigh, Essex, SS6 7XD Tel: (01268) 747074 Fax: (01268) 782801 E-mail: sales@fisco.co.uk *Manufacturers of measuring equipment*

Fisco Fasteners Ltd, Sirdar Road, Rayleigh, Essex, SS6 7XF Tel: (01268) 745421 Fax: (01268) 745467 E-mail: sales@fisco-fasteners.co.uk *Cold headed products, rivet & fasteners (special specification) manufrs*

Fiscol Engineering, 85 Greenland CR, Southall, Middlesex, UB2 5ES Tel: (020) 8574 1065 Fax: (020) 8813 9780 *Steel fabricators*

Fish Are Us, Millers Lane, Wellingborough, Northamptonshire, NN8 2NF Tel: (01933) 442384 Fax: (01933) 442418 *Aquatic suppliers*

▶ Fish Contemporary, North Quay Road, Newhaven, East Sussex, BN9 0AB Tel: (01273) 513611 E-mail: info@fishcontemporaryfurniture.com *Furniture manufrs*

Fish & Field, 60 Broad Street, Chipping Sodbury, Bristol, BS37 6AG Tel: (01454) 314034 Fax: (01454) 314034 *Fishing & angling equipment*

Fish Friers Review Ltd, 4 Greenwood Mount, Meanwood, Leeds, LS6 4LQ Tel: 0113-230 7009 Fax: 0113-230 7010 E-mail: mail@federationoffishfriers.co.uk *Magazine publishers*

Fish In Crewe Engineering Ltd, 14 Gateway, Crewe, CW1 6YY Tel: (01270) 251200 Fax: (01270) 251300 E-mail: sales@fishincrewe.co.uk *Machinery manufrs*

M. Fish (Packaging) Ltd, 7 Faraday Close, Oakwood Business Park, Clacton-On-Sea, Essex, CO15 4TR Tel: (01255) 475964 Fax: (01255) 221125 E-mail: sales@m-fish.co.uk *Quality box makers*

▶ Fish Promotions Ltd, PO Box 561, Altrincham, Cheshire, WA15 8NY Tel: 0161-980 2805 E-mail: sales@fish-promotions.com *Suppliers of branded business gifts and promotional merchandise e.g. pens, stationery, clocks and balloons. We provide a complete design and sourcing service and work together with you to maximise your promotional marketing budget.*

▶ Fish Trade Supplies, 8 Riverside Industrial Park, Rapier Street, Ipswich, IP2 8JX Tel: (01473) 601680 Fax: (01473) 687556 E-mail: Sales@fishtradesupplies.co.uk *Suppliers to the Catering Trade: Cooking Oils & Fats, Battermix, Flours, Breadings, Paper & Bags , Sauces & Pickles, Cups & Containers , Drinks, Wire Products & Sundries*

Fisher & Co., Units 2-4 Cary Court, Somerton Business Park, Somerton, Somerset, TA11 6SB Tel: (01458) 274017 Fax: (01458) 274145 E-mail: info@fisherandcompany.co.uk *Street lighting manufrs*

▶ Fisher Brian, 40 Fuller Road, Harleston, Norfolk, IP20 9EA Tel: (01379) 853052 Fax: (01379) 854713 E-mail: furnish@brianfisher.co.uk *Manufacturers of soft furnishings to the trade & residential*

Fisher Clark, Horncastle Road, Boston, Lincolnshire, PE21 9HZ Tel: (01205) 365501 Fax: (01205) 364825 E-mail: fisherclark@fisherclark.co.uk *Self-adhesive label manufrs*

▶ Fisher Construction Ltd, 2 Station Street, Wakefield, West Yorkshire, WF1 5AF Tel: (01924) 255662

Fisher Consultants Derbyshire Ltd, 8 Parkside, Belper, Derbyshire, DE56 1HY Tel: (0845) 3707760 *Fibre Optic Systems plus*Electronic design & production*

Fisher & De Domenici, 10 Church Road, Wimbledon Village, London, SW19 5DL Tel: (020) 8946 9781 Fax: (020) 8946 9781 *Picture framers*

Fisher Engineering Ltd, Main Street, Ballinamallard, Enniskillen, County Fermanagh, BT94 2FY Tel: (028) 6638 8521 Fax: (028) 6638 8706 E-mail: info@fisher-engineering.co.uk *Structural steel engineers*

Harry Fisher & Co., London Works, Bridge St, Sheffield, S3 8NT Tel: 0114-272 1998 Fax: 0114-275 2489 *Manufacturers of carbon steel, steel strip & high speed steel tool bits*

James Fisher & Sons P.L.C., Fisher House, Michaelson Road, Barrow-in-Furness, Cumbria, LA14 1HR Tel: (01229) 615400 Fax: (01229) 836761 E-mail: postmaster@james-fisher.co.uk *Ship owners & stevedores* Also at: Heysham, Leith, Newhaven, Whitehaven & Manchester

James Fisher Tankships Ltd, 4th Floor, 7 Birchen Lane, London, EC3V 9BW Tel: (020) 7338 5800 Fax: (020) 7338 5850 E-mail: info@james-fisher.co.uk *Shipping agents*

Fisher Leak Systems Ltd, 7 Industrial Estate, Tame Road, Birmingham, B6 7HS Tel: 0121-328 2515 Fax: 0121-327 8324 E-mail: sales@fisherleaksystems.co.uk *Leak detectors; leak detectors air/gas; leak detector test systems; special purpose custom built machinery; leak detection services*

Fisher Offshore, North Meadows, Oldmeldrum, Inverurie, Aberdeenshire, AB51 0GQ Tel: (01651) 873932 Fax: (01651) 873939 E-mail: info@fisheroffshore.com Principal Export Areas: Worldwide *Winch distributors/agents/ suppliers, air compressor distributors or agents, lifting gear distributors/agents/stockholders, pneumatic control systems manufacturers; winches, hydraulic; winches, man riding/ winches, wire rope, pneumatic*

Fisher Outdoor Leisure, Unit 8 9 Brick Knoll Park, Ashley Road, St. Albans, Hertfordshire, AL1 5UG Tel: (01727) 798340 Fax: (0800) 9807129 E-mail: sales@fisheroutdoor.co.uk *Cycle accessory manufrs*

Fisher Research Ltd, Royal Works, 78 Bilton Way, Enfield, Middlesex, EN3 7LW Tel: (020) 8804 1891 Fax: (020) 8443 1868 E-mail: mail@fisherresearch.com *Own Label Cleaning and Maintenance Chemicals for worldwide delivery. Research, development, manufacture, and full technical support, for industrila cleaning and maintenance chemicals*

Fisher Scales, 11-11a Unit, Station Road Industrial Estate, Attleborough, Norfolk, NR17 2NP Tel: (01953) 450310 Fax: (01953) 456391 E-mail: fisher.scales@virgin.net *Scale & cash register repairers*

Fisher Scientific Holding UK Ltd, Bishop Meadow Road, Loughborough, Leicestershire, LE11 5RG Tel: (01509) 231166 Fax: (01509) 231893 E-mail: info@fisher.co.uk *Laboratory equipment distributors*

Fisher & Sons Fakenham Ltd, 7 Dereham Road, Hempton, Fakenham, Norfolk, NR21 7LD Tel: (01328) 862781 Fax: (01328) 856229 E-mail: mail@fishers-fakenham.co.uk *Building & heating contractors*

Fisher Tarpaulins, Unit 5-6 The Maltings, Navigation Drive, Hurst Business Park, Brierley Hill, West Midlands, DY5 1UT Tel: (01384) 571313 Fax: (01384) 261666 *Manufacturers of canvas goods*

Fisher Technology Ltd, Acre House, 11-15 William Road, London, NW1 3ER Tel: (020) 7874 7888 Fax: (020) 7380 4900 E-mail: enquiries@fishtech.net *IT solutions*

Fisher W.H Agricultural Contractor, Intack House, Ivegill, Carlisle, CA4 0QF Tel: (01697) 476373 *Agricultural contractors*

▶ Fisher Wrathall, The Old Warehouse, Castle Hill, Lancaster, LA1 1YP Tel: (01524) 68822 Fax: (01524) 642211 E-mail: greg@fisherwrathall.co.uk *Fisher Wrathall provides services similar to a chartered architects. These services include; Architectural Services, Building Design and Surveying Services.*

Fishermans Cove Angling Centre, 60 Milton Road, Ellesmere Port, CH65 5DD Tel: 0151-356 9030 Fax: 0151-356 9030 E-mail: sales@fishermanscove.co.uk *Fishing tackle wholesalers & retailers*

Fishermans Friends, 194-196 Jamaica Road, London, SE16 4RT Tel: (020) 7237 7702 Fax: (020) 7237 7702 *Fishing tackle & animal suppliers*

Fishermans Knockout, 1118 Stratford Road, Hall Green, Birmingham, B28 8AE Tel: 0121-777 0307 *Fishing tackle suppliers*

Fishermans Tacklebox Wirral, 36 Downham Drive, Heswall, Wirral, Merseyside, CH60 5RF Tel: 0151-342 5207 Fax: 0151-342 5207 E-mail: paullynnemeadows@hotmail.com Principal Export Areas: Worldwide *With many years experience behind us, the Fishermans Tackle Box will cater for all your fishing needs; To order or view our products please go onto our E-commerce website, view our online Fladen Catalogue or give us a call. We are a family-owned business with friendly staff always available for help and advice. We cater for sea and course fishermen and are the main stockist of Fladen fishing equipment and clothing. Our range of products include Fishing Tackle, Fishing rods, Fishing Reels, Fishing boxes, Waterproof Clothing, Thermal Clothing, Buoyancy Aids, Lifejackets and Accessories, Children's Clothing, Flotation Suits, Safety Clothing, Waders, Boots etc. We handle inquiries from all over the Wirral, Merseyside, North West, UK and Worldwide, please feel free to call or view our products online*

▶ Fishermate, Belsize Avenue, Peterborough, PE2 9JA Tel: (01733) 314868 *Full range of fishing tackle and bait*

Fisherprint Ltd, Padholme Road, Peterborough, PE1 5UL Tel: (01733) 341444 Fax: (01733) 349416 E-mail: enquiries@fisherprint.co.uk *General printers*

Fishers Cooperage, 357 Shettleston Road, Glasgow, G31 5JL Tel: 0141-556 1850 Fax: 0141-556 4075 *Supplier of barrels to whisky trade*

Fish-house Ltd, Dean Feld Way, Link 59 Business Park, Clitheroe, Lancashire, BB7 1QU Tel: (01200) 427527 Fax: (01200) 427027 E-mail: john@fish-house.co.uk *Specialist fish wholesalers*

Fishing Shop, 293 Ings Road, Hull, HU8 0NB Tel: (01482) 781926 Fax: (01482) 781926 *Fishing tackle retail outlet*

Fishleighs Of Galsworthy, Galsworthy, Buckland Brewer, Bideford, Devon, EX39 5NP Tel: (01409) 261231 Fax: (01409) 261231 *Agricultural engineers*

FISHWICK INDUSTRIAL SUPPLY COMPANY, Caxton Road, Fulwood, Preston, PR2 9ZT Tel: (01772) 705005 *Distributor of disposable paper products*

Fishy Business, Glyndley Garden Centre, Hailsham Road, Stone Cross, Pevensey, East Sussex, BN24 5BS Tel: (01323) 847868 Fax: (01323) 847868 *Pond supplies & aquariums*

Fiskars (U K) Ltd, Newlands Avenue, Brackle Industrial Estate, Bridgend, Mid Glamorgan, CF31 2XA Tel: (01656) 655595 Fax: (01656) 659582 E-mail: sales@fiskars.com *Kitchen knife manufrs*

S.H. Fiske Ltd, The Coachworks, Kingsfield Lane, Longwell Green, Bristol, BS30 6DL Tel: 0117-960 4136 Fax: 0117-960 0187 E-mail: info@sh-fiske.com *Box & carton manufrs* Also at: Bristol

Fiskeby Board Ltd, Lloyd Berkeley Place, Pebble Lane, Aylesbury, Buckinghamshire, HP20 2JH Tel: (01296) 426219 Fax: (01296) 482682 E-mail: pat.bannerman@fiskeby.com *Recycled board sales company*

Fispak Ltd, Marsmount Road, Shawfarm Industrial Estate, Prestwick, Ayrshire, KA9 2TQ Tel: (01292) 474455 Fax: (01292) 474022 E-mail: lehodge@msn.com *Food casings & packaging materials manufrs* Also at: Redditch

Fitcast (Plastic Fabrications) Ltd, Unit 12A, Shaw Road Industrial Estate, Speke, Liverpool, L24 9JT Tel: 0151-448 1299 Fax: 0151-448 0716 E-mail: davidfitcast@aol.com *Plastic fabricators*

Fitchett & Woolacott, Willow Road, Nottingham, NG7 2PR Tel: 0115-993 1111 Fax: 0115-993 1151 E-mail: enquries@fitchett.co.uk *Timber merchants & flooring sales*

▶ Fit-ex.com, 36 Hobhouse Close, Great Barr, Birmingham, B42 1HB Tel: 0121 2411164 E-mail: steve.burns@fit-ex.com *Curtain tracks, wood/metal poles and all types of blinds supplied and fitted. Clean professional curtain and blind fitting service.*

▶ Fit-Ex.Com, 30 Hans Apel Drive, Brackley, Northamptonshire, NN13 6HD Tel: (01280) 701090 Fax: (01280) 701090 E-mail: fitex@btinternet.com *Supplier of Curtain Tracks and Poles, all types of Blinds. Purchase from Fit-ex.com, or we can fit your own if you have already purchased them. Curtains professionally hung, dressed and steamed. Internal shutters can be supplied and also external awnings.*

Fitfield Ltd, Unit 21 Chanters Industrial Estate, Tyldesley Old Road, Atherton, Manchester, M46 9BE Tel: (01942) 886888 Fax: (01942) 891921 *Groundwork contractors*

Fithandel (Scotland) Ltd, 1 Woodside Road, Bridge of Don Industrial Estate, Aberdeen, AB23 8EF Tel: (01224) 704964 Fax: (01224) 825421 E-mail: sales@fithandle.com *Pipe fittings & flange suppliers*

Fitlock, 6 Vaughan St Industrial Estate, Manchester, M12 5BT Tel: 0161-231 3724 Fax: 0161-231 7392 E-mail: sales@fitlocksystems.com *Bolt, nut & fastener stockists*

Fitlock Systems Ltd, Albert Street, Off Hanson Lane, Halifax, West Yorkshire, HX1 5NW Tel: (01422) 354286 Fax: (01422) 383413 E-mail: elaine.Whatley@fitlocksystems.com *Fixing & fastening*

Fit-Lock Systems Ltd, Unit 3/A, Aspect Court, Cannel Row, Silverdale Enterprise Park, Silverdale, Newcastle, Staffordshire, ST5 6SS Tel: (01782) 626450 Fax: (01782) 614197 E-mail: sales@fitlocksystems.com *Rivet distributors*

▶ Fitness Equipment Clearance, Boland House, Nottingham South & Wilford Industrial Estate, Nottingham, NG11 7EP Tel: 0115-982 2844 Fax: 0115-982 6775 E-mail: sales@fitness-equipment-clearance.co.uk *Refurbished fitness equipment*

Fitness Focus, Little Farm, St. Neots Road, Bolnhurst, Bedford, MK44 2EP Tel: (01234) 376246 Fax: (01234) 378936 E-mail: sales@fitnessfocus.co.uk *Fitness equipment suppliers*

▶ Fitness Warehouse, 2b Linton Street, Fulwood, Preston, PR2 3BJ Tel: (01772) 712888 Fax: (01772) 788938 E-mail: sales@gyms4home.com *Retail of a wide range of home & commercial fitness equipment*

▶ Fits Ltd, Quarry Road, Chipping Sodbury, Bristol, BS37 6AX Tel: (01454) 312247 Fax: (01454) 312281

Fitt Signs Ltd, 60-62 Pitt Street, Norwich, NR3 1DF Tel: (01603) 619128 Fax: (01603) 760524 E-mail: info@fitt-signs.co.uk *Complete sign service*

▶ Fitted Bedroom Co., Block 5, Inveresk Industrial Estate, Musselburgh, Midlothian, EH21 7UL Tel: 0131-665 1990 Fax: 0131-665 1770 *Retail & manufacture, bedroom furniture*

▶ Fitted Furniture Supplies, Nash House, Pym Street, Leeds, LS10 1PG Tel: 0113-234 7676 Fax: 0113-234 7979 *Built in furniture manufrs*

▶ The Fitted Wardrobe Site, 3 Salvington Road, Crawley, West Sussex, RH11 8XE Tel: 01293 223398 *Free help and advice with buying fitted wardrobes*

▶ Fitters Mate Ltd, Unit B8f Broadlands, Heywood Distribution Park, Heywood, Lancashire, OL10 2TS Tel: 0161-761 5055 Fax: 0161-761 2050 E-mail: sales@thefittersmate.com

Fitura Kitchens, 14 Newlands Road, Westoning, Bedford, MK45 5LD Tel: (01525) 717586 Fax: (01525) 717586 E-mail: sales@fiturakitchens.co.uk *Kitchen Installer & manufr*

Fitzgerald Contractors Ltd, 125 Cheston Road, Birmingham, B7 5EA Tel: 0121-326 0402 Fax: 0121-328 1963 E-mail: sales@fitzgerald-uk.com *Civil engineering contractors*

Fitzmaurice Carriers Ltd, Avian Way, Salhouse Road, Norwich, NR7 9AJ Tel: (01603) 429277 Fax: (01603) 788562 *Carriers & warehousing services*

Fitzpatrick Contractors Ltd, Hertford Road, Hoddesdon, Hertfordshire, EN11 9BX Tel: (01992) 305000 Fax: (01992) 305001 E-mail: enquiries@fitzpatrick.co.uk *Civil engineering, building, highway & rail contractors*

▶ Fitzpatrick Contractors Ltd, Ryedale Court, London Road, Riverhead, Sevenoaks, Kent, TN13 2DN Tel: (01732) 455222 Fax: (01732) 452224

Fitzpatrick Doors Ltd, Rushey Lane, Birmingham, B11 2BL Tel: 0121-706 6363 Fax: 0121-708 2250 E-mail: fitzuk1@aol.com *Fitzpatrick are a bespoke metal doorset manufacturer specialising in a variety of performances including fire, acoustics and security.*

▶ Fitzpatrick Wilkes & Co. Ltd, The Old Forge Cottages, The Green, Beeston, Sandy, Bedfordshire, SG19 1PF Tel: (01767) 692473 E-mail: info@fitzpatrick-wilkes.co.uk *Business Improvement Services - we help you to make more Net Profit. **See our web site for further details - www.Fitzpatrick-Wilkes.co.uk*

Fitzroy Group, Radford Court Industrial Estate, Nottingham, NG7 3DY Tel: (0870) 4289102 Fax: (0870) 4289186 *Shop fitters*

Fitzroy Joinery, Garden Close, Langage Business Park, Plympton, Plymouth, PL7 5EU Tel: (01752) 334940 Fax: (01752) 334942 E-mail: sales@fitzroy.co.uk *Architectural joiners*

▶ Fitzsimmons G & Son, 25 Thornton Road, Rosewell, Midlothian, EH24 9DP Tel: 0131-448 2186 Fax: 0131-448 2186 *Blacksmiths*

▶ Five Castles Press Ltd, Raeburn Road South, Ipswich, IP3 0ET Tel: (01473) 718719 Fax: (01473) 712122

Five Fish Ltd, 77 Richmond Road, Twickenham, TW1 3AW Tel: (020) 8538 9277 Fax: (020) 8538 9270 E-mail: info@fivefish.co.uk *Complete sign & design service for businesses digital print, banners*

Five Star Edible Products Ltd, Phoenix Works, Avery Hill Road, London, SE9 2BD Tel: (020) 7538 4448 Fax: (020) 7538 4495 E-mail: enquiries@gandhi5star.co.uk *Catering trade food suppliers*

Five Star Fish Ltd, Great Grimsby Business Park, Sargon Way, Great Coates, Grimsby, South Humberside, DN37 9SY Tel: (01472) 344962 Fax: (01472) 250113 E-mail: info@fivestarfish.co.uk *Fish process manufrs*

▶ The Five Star Knitwear (UK) Ltd, Majid House, 49 Devonshire St North, Manchester, M12 6JR Tel: 0161-273 6009

Five Star Saw Service Ltd, 3 All Saints Industrial Estate, All Saints Street, Birmingham, B18 7RJ Tel: 0121-551 5341 *Saw repair services*

Five Star Security Systems, 217 Manchester Road, Oldham, OL8 4QY Tel: 0161-682 9999 Fax: 0161-682 8787 *Alarm installers*

▶ Five Star Units, Leigh Park Depot, Fulflood Road, Havant, Hampshire, PO9 5AX Tel: (023) 9248 6101 Fax: (023) 9248 6666 E-mail: sales@fivestarunits.co.uk *Supply & fitting of gearboxes & reconditioned petrol & diesel engines for cars, vans, & other light commercial vehicles*

▶ Five Star Windows, 385 Tong Street, Bradford, West Yorkshire, BD4 9RU Tel: (01274) 680476 Fax: (01274) 680476 *Joinery & glass manufrs*

Five Valleys Photography, Unit 4 Salmon Springs TDG Estate, Cheltenham Road, Stroud, Gloucestershire, GL6 6NU Tel: (01453) 766660 Fax: (01453) 766388 E-mail: info@fivevalleys.co.uk *Commercial photographers & processers*

▶ Five Valleys Removals, 22 Quedgeley Trading Estate East, Haresfield, Stonehouse, Gloucestershire, GL10 3EX Tel: (01452) 729056 Fax: (01452) 729494

Fivemiletown & Brookeborough Co-Operative Agricultural & Dairy So, 14 Ballylurgan, Fivemiletown, County Tyrone, BT75 0RX Tel: (028) 8952 1209 Fax: (028) 8952 1863 E-mail: billcurry@fivemiletown.com *Dairy*

Fivesix Media Ltd, 77 Church Walk, London, N16 8QR Tel: (020) 7193 7696 E-mail: info@fivesix.co.uk *FiveSix media is a London based Promotion & Design consultancy providing its clients with fresh and innovative solutions. FiveSix specialises in art exhibitions, publishing and the Internet.*

Fix A Door Ltd, 1 Library Road, Ferndown, Dorset, BH22 9JP Tel: (01202) 855999 Fax: (01202) 855888 E-mail: fixadoor@aol.com *Industrial door manufacturers, installation & repair*

▶ Fix It Devon, 24 Jasmine Grove, Paignton, Devon, TQ3 3TH Tel: (01803) 404326 Fax: (01803) 404326 E-mail: sales@fix-it-devon.com *Computer building, services, repairs & networks*

Fix It Engineering, North Back Lane, Terrington, York, YO60 6NS Tel: (01653) 648446 Fax: (01653) 648293 *Agricultural commercial & plant engineers*

Fixfast Fasteners & Fixing Devices Ltd, Forge Works, Horsham Road, Mid Holmwood, Dorking, Surrey, RH5 4EJ Tel: (01306) 880299 Fax: (01306) 880038 E-mail: *Suppliers of roof fittings*

Fixfire, Mayflower House, Bodmin Road, Coventry, CV2 5DB Tel: (024) 7661 6699 Fax: (024) 7662 1990 *Fire protection equipment*

Fixfirm Fasteners & Fixing Devices, Pyke Road, Lincoln, LN6 3QS Tel: (01522) 500002 Fax: (0870) 7773828 *Industrial fastener distribs*

Fixing Point Ltd, Rowan Trade Park, Neville Road, Bradford, West Yorkshire, BD4 8TQ Tel: (01274) 370078 Fax: (01274) 738678 E-mail: enquiries@fixingpoint.com *Fixing manufrs*
Fixing Point Ltd, Runnings Road, Kingsditch Trading Estate, Cheltenham, Gloucestershire, GL51 9NQ Tel: (01242) 265100 Fax: (01242) 236155 E-mail: sales@fixing.point.co.uk *Metal roofing component manufrs*
The Fixings Co. Ltd, Fixings House, 658 Oldham Road, Failsworth, Manchester, M35 9DU Tel: 0161-682 7822 Fax: 0161-682 7099 *General fixings for the industrial trade*
Fixings Delivery, Unit 6 Catford Road, Roundthorn Industrial Estate, Roundthorn Industrial Estate, Manchester, M23 9LR Tel: 0161-945 0444 Fax: 0161-947 2710 *Fixings & fasteners specialists*
▶ Fixings Direct, Castle Court, Bodmin Road, Coventry, CV2 5DB Tel: (024) 7660 4406 Fax: (024) 7661 2545 *Fixings, fasteners & power tools suppliers*
I.C. Fixings Ltd, Unit 4, Church Lane Industrial Estate, West Bromwich, West Midlands, B71 1AR Tel: 0121-525 2252 Fax: 0121-525 2253 E-mail: sales@icfixings.co.uk *Constructional fixing wholesaler*
Fixings & Power Tool Center, Brighton Road, Salfords, Redhill, RH1 5EQ Tel: (01293) 820088 Fax: (01293) 820099 *Power tool fixings suppliers*
Fixings & Power Tools Direct Ltd, Tunbridge Wells Tool Room Stag Trade Park, Longfield Road, Tunbridge Wells, Kent, TN2 3BF Tel: (0800) 365598 Fax: (01892) 520888 E-mail: sales@fixings-direct.co.uk *Power tools & fixings, fastenings manufrs*
▶ Fixings Warehouse, Old Printworks, Medway Street, Maidstone, Kent, ME14 1JS Tel: (01622) 766321 Fax: (01622) 664011 *Fixings sales to building industry*
▶ Fixit Systems Support, The Diary House Roxby Place, Rickett Street, London, SW6 1RU Tel: (0845) 1303595 Fax: (0870) 1374300 E-mail: sales@fixit.co.uk *We provide remote, onsite and telephone based computer support for companies in London. We offer support for Microsoft products, online backups, computer network installation, wireless networking and we are a Microsoft Certified Partner.With stress free solutions and up to the minute technology, fixit guarantee a sound, reliable and trustworthy it service*
Fixmart Services, 80 A The Brent, Dartford, DA1 1YW Tel: (01322) 274226 Fax: (01322) 278178 *Fixing system stockholders*
▶ Fixmeathome Computer Maintenance, 8 Lower Sand Hills, Surbiton, Surrey, KT6 6RP Tel: (020) 8399 5949 *Computer maintenanace & repairers*
▶ Fixture Signs South Ltd, 40 Bennett Close, Welling, Kent, DA16 3HU Tel: (020) 8316 7505
▶ Fizzpotzz, Carr Barn, Tissington, Ashbourne, Derbyshire, DE6 1RA Tel: (01335) 350195 E-mail: info@fizzpotzz.co.uk *Supplier & distributor of specialist make your own cosmetics kits*
▶ FJF Labels, 74 Deer Park Drive, Plymouth, PL3 6SR Tel: (01752) 292807 Fax: (01752) 249065 *Label manufrs*
Fjord Seafoods, Unit 1 Marybank Industrial Estate, Marybank, Isle of Lewis, HS2 0DB Tel: (01851) 707600 Fax: (01851) 704834 *Salmon processors*
FJS Services, Westfield Road, Manea, March, Cambridgeshire, PE15 0LN Tel: (01354) 680752 Fax: (01354) 680176 *Engineering & steel fabricators*
FKI Switchgear Ltd, Newport Road, Pontllanfraith, Blackwood, Gwent, NP12 2XH Tel: (01495) 223001 Fax: (01495) 225674 Principal Export Areas: Worldwide *Manufacturers of Switchgear & Transformers*
▶ Flack & Chapman, 12 Station Road, St. Ives, Cambridgeshire, PE27 5BH Tel: (01480) 494155
▶ Flack Tackle, Veitchii Barn, New Barn Road, Swanley, Kent, BR8 7PW Tel: (01322) 660770 Fax: (01322) 660790 E-mail: sales@flacktackle.co.uk *Fishing tackle retailers*
Flack & Tucker Joinery Services, Hunts Farm, Bardfield Road, Shalford, Braintree, Essex, CM7 5HX Tel: (01371) 850055 Fax: (01371) 850055 *Joinery supplier services*
Flacke Turner & James, Elm Street Lane, Cardiff, CF24 3QQ Tel: (029) 2049 2023 Fax: (029) 2049 2023 *Joinery manufrs*
Flag Services & Supply Co., 302 Westbourne Grove, Westcliff-on-Sea, Essex, SS0 0PT Tel: (01702) 333343 Fax: (01702) 343330 *Banner, bunting, flags & flagpole manufrs*
Flagmaker Ltd, 20 Clarion Court, Clarion Close, The Enterprise Park, Llansamlet, Swansea, SA6 8RF Tel: (01792) 700795 Fax: (0845) 0613915 E-mail: support@mrflag.com *Flag manufrs*
Flags & Banners Ltd, Springfield Industrial Estate, Burnham-on-Crouch, Essex, CM0 8TE Tel: (01621) 783221 Fax: (01621) 783532 E-mail: sales@flags-banners.co.uk *Banner & flag manufacturers or printers*
Flags Flags Poles & Masts, 10 Monton Green, Eccles, Manchester, M30 9LW Tel: 0161-788 0131 Fax: 0161-788 0131 *Flags*
▶ Flags UK Ltd, Clifford House, 7-9 Clifford Street, York, YO1 9RA Tel: (01904) 784444 E-mail: info@euroflags.net *Corporate, Advertising Flags and Banners.Flags Poles.Banner stands*
▶ Flags of the World, 41 Fisher Street, Stranraer, Wigtownshire, DG9 7LH Tel: 01776 700266 Fax: 0845 4664222 E-mail: sales@flagsoftheworld.co.uk *Flags, flagpoles & bunting, banners printed & embroidered clothing suppliers*
Flails Direct Ltd, Marsh Lane, Laughterton, Lincoln, LN1 2JX Tel: (01427) 717449 Fax: (01427) 718016 E-mail: eng-hire@dial.pipex.com *Cutting equipment manufrs*
Flair Blinds Ltd, 123 Chester Road, Sunderland, SR4 7HG Tel: 0191-510 1111 Fax: 0191-510 0666 *Blind manufrs*
Flair Electronic Systems Ltd, Britannia House, Boulton Road, Stevenage, Hertfordshire, SG1 4QX Tel: (01438) 727391 Fax: (01438) 740232 E-mail: sales@flairelectronics.co.uk *Connector distributors*
▶ Flair Plastic Products Ltd, Unit 9d Minworth Industrial Estate, Stockton Close, Minworth, Sutton Coldfield, West Midlands, B76 1DH Tel: 0121-624 5001 Fax: 0121-624 5004 E-mail: sales@flairplasticproducts.co.uk *Double glazing services*
▶ Flairlight Designs Ltd, 12 Hillcrest Close, Epsom, Surrey, KT18 5JY Tel: (01372) 807661 Fax: (01372) 807660 E-mail: mike@flairlight.co.uk *Specialist lighting design & supply company*
▶ Flairmet, Unit 1 2, Ladfordfields Industrial Park, Seighford, Stafford, ST18 9QE Tel: (01785) 282301 Fax: (01785) 282626 E-mail: flairmet@weathervane.uk.com *Wrought iron gates, planters & rose arches distributors*
Flambeau Europlast Ltd, Manston Road, Ramsgate, Kent, CT12 6HW Tel: (01843) 854000 Fax: (01843) 854010 E-mail: sales@flambeaueuro.com *Flambeau EuroPlast Ltd based in Ramsgate, Kent are manufacturers of plastic blow mouldings & plastic injection mouldings.* Also at: Rushden
Flamborough Marine Ltd, Tower Street, Flamborough, Bridlington, North Humberside, YO15 1PD Tel: (01262) 850943 Fax: (01262) 850943 E-mail: gm@flamboroughmarine.co.uk *Traditional sweaters & knitting kits manufrs*
▶ Flamboyance, 483 Green Lanes, London, N13 4BS Tel: (0845) 8382542 Fax: (0871) 2423304 E-mail: sales@FlamboyanceLtd.co.uk *Luxurious Designs for your Home! - Duvet Covers and Pillowcases, Bedspreads, Quilts, Cushions, Faux Fur Throws, Rugs, Curtains, and Lampshades.*
Flamco Ltd, 4 St. Michaels Road, St. Helens, Merseyside, WA9 4WZ Tel: (01744) 818100 Fax: (01744) 830400 E-mail: info@flamco.co.uk *Heating equipment, systems & flue pipes suppliers*
Flame Ltd, 12 Kings Park, Primrose Hill, Kings Langley, Hertfordshire, WD4 8ST Tel: (01923) 272900 Fax: (01923) 270141 E-mail: sales@flame1.com *Prepress equipment & support services & apple service computers*
Flame Hardeners Ltd, Shorter Works, Bailey Lane, Sheffield, S1 3BL Tel: 0114-276 8167 Fax: 0114-273 8657 *Heat treatment specialists*
Flame Kut Profiles, Unit 39 Darlaston Central Trading Estate, Wednesbury, West Midlands, WS10 8XB Tel: 0121-526 6919 Fax: 0121-568 6447 E-mail: sales@flamekut.fsbusiness.co.uk *Precision grinding services & cutting services*
▶ Flame UK Ltd, 1 Mode Wheel Road, Salford, M5 5DQ Tel: 0161-737 2115 Fax: 0161-736 0871 *Ladies wear supplier*
▶ Flameboy Graphix, 9 Halliday Drive, Armley, Leeds, LS12 3PA Tel: 01132 891205 Fax: 0113 891205 E-mail: info@flameboygraphix.co.uk *Professional illustrator*
Flameburst Effects, Grassmere, Dinton, Salisbury, SP3 5EG Tel: (01722) 716434 Fax: (01722) 716515 *Firework display providers*
▶ Flame-Equip Ltd, 8 Mandervelle Road, Oadby, Leicester, LE2 5LQ Tel: 0116-271 3364 Fax: 0116-272 0126 E-mail: sales@flame-equip.demon.co.uk *Engineers*
▶ FlameFix Ltd, Charlton House, 32 High Street, Cullompton, Devon, EX15 1AE Tel: (07883) 037667 E-mail: ksales@flamefix.co.uk *Oil & gas service & maintenance*
Flameproof Electrical Enclosures Ltd, Units 1-1a St Martins Industrial Estate, Tat Bank Road, Oldbury, West Midlands, B69 4NP Tel: 0121-541 1315 Fax: 0121-552 0592 E-mail: flameproof@btinternet.com *Electrical enclosures for hazardous areas*
Flameskill Ltd, Unit 1 R & A Development, Great Yarmouth, Norfolk, NR31 0LT Tel: (01493) 440464 Fax: (01493) 440581 E-mail: admin@flameskill.co.uk *Fire fighting equipment distributors*
Flamex Firefighting Equipment, Sir Frank Whittle Business Centre, Great Central Way, Rugby, Warwickshire, CV21 3XH Tel: (01788) 577977 Fax: (01788) 577977 E-mail: phuddlestone@tiscalli.co.uk *Fire protection equipment suppliers*
Flamgard Engineering Ltd, Unit 2-3 Pontnewynydd Industrial Estate, Pontnewynydd, Pontypool, Gwent, NP4 6YW Tel: (01495) 757347 Fax: (01495) 755443 E-mail: sales@flamgard.co.uk *Manufacturers of dampers*
▶ Flaming Ltd, The Exchange, 26 Haslucks Green Road, Shirley, Solihull, West Midlands, B90 2EL Tel: (0845) 4660182 Fax: (0845) 4660183 E-mail: sales@flamingltd.com *IT services*
▶ Flamingo Blinds & Signs, 12 Chaseville Parade, Chaseville Park Road, London, N21 1PG Tel: (020) 8881 0751 Fax: (020) 8881 0771 E-mail: admin@flamingoblinds.co.uk *Commercial & domestic blinds manufrs*
▶ Flamtek Ltd, Unit 21, Midway Business Centre, Bridge Street, Clay Cross, Derbyshire, S45 9NU Tel: 01246 273925 Fax: 01246 277452 E-mail: kevin@flamtek.com *Manufacture of portable and fixed profile cutting machines; retrofitting and updating existing machines with CNC; Psion-based software enabling CNC programming on small machines.*
Flangecombe Ltd, 147 Stringes Lane, Willenhall, West Midlands, WV13 1LW Tel: (01902) 602030 Fax: (01902) 604050 E-mail: info@flangecombe-ltd.fsbusiness.co.uk Principal Export Areas: Africa *Pneumatic equipment, systems distributors, agents, stockholders*
Flanges Ltd, Portrack Trading Estate, Stockton-on-Tees, Cleveland, TS18 2PL Tel: (01642) 672626 Fax: (01642) 617574 E-mail: sales@flanges-ltd.co.uk *Flange manufrs*
Flangetrade, Houghton Road, North Anston Trading Estate, North Anston, Sheffield, S25 4JJ Tel: (0845) 1300316 Fax: (0845) 1300304 E-mail: sales@flangetrade.co.uk *Stainless steel flange manufrs*
Flaps Envelopes Ltd, 70 Summer Lane, Birmingham, B19 3NG Tel: 0121-693 7377 Fax: 0121-693 0354 *Envelope printers*
Flare Imaging Ltd, 200 Brook Drive, Greenpark, Reading, RG2 6UB Tel: 0118-922 2999 Fax: 0118-986 7999 E-mail: nick@flareimaging.com *Web site design*
Flare Products Ltd, 14 Broadmead Business Park, Broadmead Road, Stewartby, Bedford, MK43 9NX Tel: (01234) 767755 Fax: (01234) 768624 E-mail: stuartalansimpson@btopenworld.com *Combustion engineers*
Flare Software Systems UK Ltd, Kings Court, Parsonage Lane, Bath, BA1 1ER Tel: (01225) 485000 Fax: (01225) 485020 *Local authorities software*
Flaretec Alloys & Equipment Ltd, Hardwick View Road, Holmewood, Chesterfield, Derbyshire, S42 5SA Tel: (01246) 853522 Fax: (01246) 852415 E-mail: contact@flaretec.com Principal Export Areas: Worldwide *Manufacturers of pressure vessels, pipework skid assembly & heating (direct & indirect fired) systems*
Flat Glass Ltd, 186 Wigan Road, Westhoughton, Bolton, BL5 2AG Tel: (01942) 813037 Fax: (01942) 812203 E-mail: info@flatglass.co.uk *Glass merchants* Also at: Westhoughton
▶ Flat Glass Merchants, Unit C, Cronin Road Weldon South Indust Estate, Weldon South Industrial Estate, Corby, Northamptonshire, NN18 8AG Tel: (01536) 268419 Fax: (01536) 268469 E-mail: sales@flatglassmerchants.com *Flat glass merchants*
▶ Flat Pack Amigos Ltd, Alpine House, 28 Church Road, Rainford, St. Helens, Merseyside, WA11 8HE Tel: (01744) 886670 E-mail: info@flatpackamigos.co.uk *Flat pack assembly service for home, garden & office furniture*
▶ Flat Pack Man Ltd, 53 Warwick Road, Cliftonville, Margate, Kent, CT9 2JU Tel: (0800) 0407744 E-mail: whirlyweston1@hotmail.com *Flat pack furniture (flatpack) assembly service, office furniture fitting service, laminate flooring fitting service, hardwood flooring fitting service, hardwood and laminate flooring supplied and fitted, kent and surrounding area"s, thanet, canterbury, hernbay, whitstable, surry*
▶ Flat Roofing Supplies, Tinsley Lane North, Crawley, West Sussex, RH10 9FF Tel: (01293) 590970 Fax: (01293) 543562 *Industrial fixings, fasteners & sealants suppliers*
Flat Vision Products, PO Box 1880, Stoke-On-Trent, ST2 9WA Tel: (01782) 305550 Fax: (01782) 305540 E-mail: sales@flatvision.co.uk *Flat screen display solutions suppliers*
Flatau Dick & Co. Ltd, Bings, High Street, Limpsfield, Oxted, Surrey, RH8 0DR Tel: (01883) 730707 Fax: (01883) 717100 E-mail: sales@flataudick.co.uk *Timber agent*
Flatman Irrigation, Stud Farm, The Street, Bradfield, Manningtree, Essex, CO11 2UU Tel: (01255) 870867 Fax: (01255) 870047 *Irrigation*
Flavell Precision Engineering Ltd, Moore Street, Wolverhampton, WV1 2HE Tel: (01902) 456583 Fax: (01902) 456583 E-mail: sales@precisionengineering.gbr.fm *Blacksmiths & general engineers*
Flavell Printers, Laurieston Road, Grangemouth, Stirlingshire, FK3 8XX Tel: (01324) 489900 Fax: (01324) 489911 E-mail: print@flavell.com *Printers*
Flavells, 4 Peasehill Road, Ripley, Derbyshire, DE5 3JG Tel: (01773) 741502 Fax: (01773) 741502 *Cleaning cloths supplier*
Flavormatic UK Ltd, The Heath Business & Technical Park, Runcorn, Cheshire, WA7 4QX Tel: (0870) 7579300 *Food flavour suppliers*
▶ Flaxstyle Factory Outlet, Tariff Road, London, N17 0DY Tel: (020) 8808 4088 Fax: (020) 8885 3139 E-mail: info@flaxstyle.co.uk *Clothing manufrs*
Flaxton Street Auto Spares, Fifield Indust Estate, Usworth Road, Longhill Industrial Estate, Hartlepool, Cleveland, TS25 1PD Tel: (01429) 260592 Fax: (01429) 273339 *Joinery manufrs*
Flayre Press & Printing Services, Unit 1, Thames Industrial Estate, High St South, Dunstable, Bedfordshire, LU6 3HD Tel: (01582) 605085 Fax: (01582) 472249 *Printers*
▶ FLC Property Services, Granitehill Enterprise Centre, Unit4 Granitehill Road, Aberdeen, AB16 7AX Tel: (01224) 662030 Fax: (01224) 662010 E-mail: flowclean1@aol.com *Ventilation & water chlorination services*
FLD Pumps And Power, 2 Ness Road, Erith, Kent, DA8 2LD Tel: (01322) 350088 Fax: (01322) 350066 E-mail: erith@fldpumpspowerpowerent.co.uk *Generator & generating set hire, lease & rental*
Fleck Bros, 85 Templepatrick Road, Ballyclare, County Antrim, BT39 9RQ Tel: (028) 9332 3866 Fax: (028) 9335 2830 *Motor vehicle body builders*
Fleet Cash Registers, 3 Henage Cottage, Henage Street, Queensbury, Bradford, West Yorkshire, BD13 2EX Tel: (01274) 880804 *Sales & Service Electronic Cash Registers*
Fleet Computer Services Ltd, Station Road, Ruabon, Wrexham, Clwyd, LL14 6DL Tel: (01978) 810746 Fax: (01978) 810603 E-mail: mail@fleet-computers.co.uk *Computer systems consultant services*
▶ Fleet Electrical & Safety Direct Ltd, Unit 10, Commerce Business Centre, Commerce Close, West Wilts Trading Estate, Westbury, Wiltshire, BA13 4LS Tel: (01373) 823242 Fax: (01373) 823206 E-mail: sales@fleetelectrical.co.uk *Nationwide distributors of reversing aids & other vehicle & plant*
Fleet Factors Ltd, 1b Beels Road, Stallingborough, Grimsby, South Humberside, DN41 8DN Tel: (01469) 577888 Fax: (01469) 578003 *Commercial vehicle parts retailer*
Fleet Factors Ltd, Unit G, South Orbital Trading Estate, Folland Way, Hull, HU9 1NB Tel: (01482) 227423 Fax: (01482) 325746 E-mail: hull@fleetfactors.co.uk *Air brake & friction material distributors & paint re-finish services*
Fleet Finish Ltd, Carseview Road, Forfar, Angus, DD8 3BT Tel: (01307) 468616 Fax: (01307) 468618 *Commercial vehicle refinishers*
Fleet Line Markers Ltd, Spring La South, Malvern, Worcestershire, WR14 1AT Tel: (01684) 573535 Fax: (01684) 892784 E-mail: sales@fleetlinemarkers.com *Sports ground marking machines & materials*
▶ Fleet Optimise Ltd, 47 Hundred Acre Road, Streetly, Sutton Coldfield, West Midlands, B74 2LA Tel: (0871) 2106686 Fax: (0871) 2106687 E-mail: enquiries@fleetoptimise.co.uk *Supply vehicle tracking systems*
Fleet Partnership, The Lower Court, Stationers' Hall, Ave Marie La, London, EC4M 7DS Tel: (020) 7246 6500 Fax: (020) 7246 6501 *Financial recruitment consultants*
Fleet Parts Ltd, New Cut Industrial Estate, New Cut Lane, Woolston, Warrington, WA1 4AG Tel: (01925) 824019 Fax: (01925) 838496 E-mail: sales@fleetparts.com *Commercial vehicle air brake repairers*
▶ Fleet Removals, Bolesworth Road, Tattenhall, Chester, CH3 9HL Tel: (01829) 770169
Fleet Removals Of Liverpool, Fleet House, Stretton Way, Liverpool, L36 6JF Tel: 0151-489 7990 Fax: 0151-480 6277 E-mail: malf@fleetremovals.co.uk *Removal contractors*
Fleet Shipping International Ltd, 41-47 Blue Anchor Lane, London, SE16 3UL Tel: (020) 7232 0777 Fax: (020) 7232 2600 E-mail: sales@fwwshipping.com *Export forwarding agents*
Fleet Speed Coachworks Ltd, Unit 7-11 Plot 6 Fairfields, Free Prae Road, Chertsey, Surrey, KT16 8EA Tel: (01932) 568848 Fax: (01932) 568840 *Commercial vehicle repairers*
Fleet Street Flyers, 21a Brownlow Mews, London, WC1N 2LA Tel: (020) 7242 6666 Fax: (020) 7404 6045 *Courier & messenger services*
Fleetbest UK, Northgate, White Lund Trading Estate, Morecambe, Lancs, LA3 3AY Tel: (01524) 61818 Fax: (01524) 67014
Fleetclean Ltd, Common Lane, Knottingley, West Yorkshire, WF11 8BN Tel: (01904) 674674 Fax: (01977) 607004 E-mail: enquiries@fleetclean.co.uk *Industrial cleaning equipment machine sales*
Fleetfield Chemical Co. Ltd, Norfolk Barocks, 76-136 Edmund Road(Clough Road Entrance), Sheffield, S2 4EE Tel: 0114-273 8999 Fax: 0114-243 3739 *Cleaning chemicals*
▶ Fleetlink, Rose Cottage, Churchway, Curry Rivel, Langport, Somerset, TA10 0EF Tel: (01458) 259581 Fax: (01458) 259582 E-mail: jeff@fleetlink.org.uk *claims handling for LCV, HGV is different. organising the process from incident to return to use has been identified by Insurers, Brokers, Transport Managers and Engineers as highly stressful. We work differently with our customers Fleetlink manages Accident repairs to the tune of a 20% reduction to date approaches £00 per claim.We then provide you, over time, with aggregated MI, strategically useful to your organisation.We minimise downtime whilst ensuring appropriate and qualified repairs. Repairers work for us on merit, relieved that we do not place unseen secondary referral charges upon them The processes we use allowing us to make our direct savings against lost time and repair expenditure whilst recording the key information you can use to enhance your company's performance. Our existing customers are feeling the benefits they are increasing their Fleetlink work, to further save money, obtain additional MI, improve their operation and reduce working pain.*
Fleetmoulds Mould Mnfrs, Old Bexley Business Park, Bourne Road, Bexley, Kent, DA5 1LR Tel: (01322) 554228 Fax: (01322) 555679 E-mail: barrie@fleetmould.co.uk *Injection mould manufrs*
Fleetwood Caravans Ltd, Hall Street, Long Melford, Sudbury, Suffolk, CO10 9JP Tel: (0870) 7740008 Fax: (0870) 7740009 E-mail: fleetwoodcaravans@dial.pipex.com *Touring caravan services*
Fleetwood Engineering Co. Ltd, 1 Lechmere Rd, London, NW2 5DA Tel: (020) 8459 3444 Fax: (020) 8459 3444 *Stove enamelling*
▶ Fleetwood Fox, 96 Springfield Road, Wellington, Somerset, TA21 8LH Tel: (01823) 667337 *Carpet manufrs*
Fleetwood Trawlers Supply Company, 1 Denham Way, Fleetwood, Lancashire, FY7 6PR Tel: (01253) 873476 Fax: (01253) 773230 E-mail: info@ftsgroup.co.uk *Ship chandlers*
▶ Flegg Transport, College Road North, Aston Clinton, Aylesbury, Buckinghamshire, HP22 5EZ Tel: (01296) 630234 Fax: (01296) 631826
▶ Fleinns Medicare, Phoenix Park, Chickenhall Lane, Eastleigh, Hampshire, SO50 6RP Tel: (023) 8061 3333 Fax: (023) 8065 0230 *Disability equipment*
▶ Fleinns Medicare Ltd, Unit 5-6 The Boatyard Industrial Estate, Mill Road, Fareham, Hampshire, PO16 0TA Tel: (01329) 823258 Fax: (01329) 822353
Fleming Agri Products, New Buildings Industrial Estate, Victoria Road, Newbuildings, Londonderry, BT47 2SX Tel: (028) 7134 2637 Fax: (028) 7134 4735 E-mail: info@fleming-agri.co.uk *Agricultural machinery manufrs*
Fleming Buildings Ltd, 23 Auchinloch Road, Lenzie, Kirkintilloch, Glasgow, G66 5ET Tel: 0141-776 1267 Fax: 0141-775 1394 E-mail: office@fleming-buildings.co.uk *Building contractors*
Fleming Enterprise Investment Trust P.L.C, 20 Finsbury Street, London, EC2Y 9AQ Tel: (020) 7638 5858 Fax: (020) 7880 3486 *Investment trust company*
Fleming Fabrications Ltd, 2 Derby Road, London, N18 2PA Tel: (020) 8884 1752 Fax: (020) 8884 1756 *Steel fabrication manufrs*
Fleming Howden Ltd, Whitemyres Avenue, Masterick Industrial Estate, Aberdeen, AB16 6HQ Tel: (01224) 692897 Fax: (01224) 683931 *Bakery distributors*

Fleming Howden, Unit 2, Newbridge Industrial Estate, Newbridge, Midlothian, EH28 8PJ Tel: 0131-333 6666 Fax: 0131-333 6633 *Bakers ingredient & prepared material producers*

James Fleming Plastics Ltd, 7 Linden Place, Glasgow, G13 1EF Tel: 0141-959 9765 Fax: 0141-954 6693 *Plastic fabricators & vacuum formed plastic products*

John Fleming & Co. Ltd, Silverburn Place, Bridge Of Don, Aberdeen, AB23 8EG Tel: (01224) 258200 Fax: (01224) 825377 E-mail: aberdeen@buildbase.co.uk *Buildbase is one of the UK's fastest growing builders merchants. All of our branches are long established companies which have been serving local trades people for many years, with knowledge and experience to match. We believe strongly in understanding the needs of trades professional and our business has been developed specifically to meet those demands. Massive stocks, top quality products, competitive pricing, reliable delivery, specialist staff and exceptional customer service.*

Fleming & Co. (Machinery) Ltd, 60 Woodhead Road, Glasgow, G53 7NX Tel: 0141-881 8155 Fax: 0141-881 8268 E-mail: sales@flemingandcompany.co.uk *Traffic managers & tool distributors*

Fleming Technical Ltd, Brunel Road, Croft Business Park, Wirral, Merseyside, CH62 3NY Tel: 0151-343 1800 Fax: 0151-343 1801 E-mail: gil@fleming-tech.co.uk *Cleaning contractors & chemical manufrs*

► Flemings Business Printers, 20 Warwick Road, Worthing, West Sussex, BN11 3ET Tel: (01903) 211700 Fax: (01903) 211900

Fleming's Ropes & Twines Woolston Ltd, Bridge Road, Woolston, Warrington, WA1 4AT Tel: (01925) 499955 Fax: (01925) 492208 *Manufacturers of polypropylene twines, injection moulding & packaging*

Flemings Seals Ltd, Atlas Mills, Atlas Mill Road, Brighouse, West Yorkshire, HD6 1ES Tel: (01484) 718391 Fax: (01484) 711585 E-mail: sales@flemings-seals.co.uk *Hydraulic/ fluid seal manufacturers..Also injection moulding (plastic) manufrs*

Fleming's Textiles Ltd, Belford Mills, Lawson Street, Kilmarnock, Ayrshire, KA1 3HZ Tel: (01563) 525203 Fax: (01563) 522022 *Textile manufrs*

Fletcher, Jubilee Lodge, Jubilee Way, Chessington, Surrey, KT9 1TR Tel: (020) 8391 1876 Fax: (020) 8391 1876 *Heating & air conditioning engineers*

E. Fletcher (Timber) Ltd, Queen Street, Walsall, WS2 9PE Tel: (01922) 631254 Fax: (01922) 724589 *Timber merchants*

Fletcher European Containers Ltd, 49-51 Sanders Road, Finedon Road Industrial Estate, Wellingborough, Northamptonshire, NN8 4NL Tel: (01933) 440446 Fax: (01933) 270377 E-mail: sales@fletchereuropean.co.uk *Plastic rotational mouldings manufrs*

► Fletcher Gallery Services, 1 Newbury Street, London, EC1A 7HU Tel: (020) 7726 4811 Fax: (020) 7606 1826 E-mail: fletcher@fletcherframes.co.uk *Picture framing service*

Herbert Fletcher Transport Ltd, M62 Trading Estate, Rawcliffe Road, Goole, North Humberside, DN14 8JW Tel: (01405) 769968 Fax: (01405) 762513 E-mail: enquiries@herbertfletcher.co.uk *Temperature controlled distribution & storage services*

Fletcher Joinery, Wildmoor Mill Farm, Mill Lane, Wildmoor, Bromsgrove, Worcestershire, B61 0BX Tel: (01527) 835015 Fax: (01527) 835015 *Joinery manufrs*

Fletcher Joinery, 261 Whessoe Road, Darlington, County Durham, DL3 0YL Tel: (01325) 357347 Fax: (01325) 357347 E-mail: enquiries@fletcherjoinery.co.uk *Joinery manufacturers & installers*

► Fletcher Kennedy Ltd, 15 Junction Place, Haslemere, Surrey, GU27 1LE Tel: (01428) 656600 Fax: (01428) 656745 E-mail: cf@fletcherkennedy.com *We are limited company formation specialists providing a comprehensive range of company formation related services.*Using the latest technology and our extensive experience we can form a UK limited company for you within 5 working hours from as little as £68***

Fletcher Moorland Ltd, Elenora Street, Stoke-On-Trent, ST4 1QG Tel: (01782) 411021 Fax: (01782) 744470 E-mail: info@fletchermoorland.co.uk *Electrical Engineering, Electronic Engineering, Electric Motor Rewinds, Servo Motor Repair, Mechanical Repair Services.*

► Fletcher Roofing Ltd, 11 Ash Furlong Close, Balsall Common, Coventry, CV7 7QA Tel: (01676) 530373 E-mail: fletcher_roofing@yahoo.co.uk *Fletcher Roofing Ltd provide a service witch includes all aspects of roofing be it Tiling, Slating, Felt Roofing,corrigated sheeting,Lead Burning, UPVC Fascia, Soffit & Guttering, whether it be a complete renewall or a small repair E.G Ridge Tiles, Broken Tiles, Chimneys, Gas Cowles, Pointing ,Cement work, Felt roof repair and Coating systems weve got all aspects of roofing covered. WE WILL BEAT ANY GUNUINE LIKE FOR LIKE QUOTE!! with a service that tops the rest (01676)530373*

Fletcher Smith, 33 Brunel Parkway, Pride Park, Derby, DE24 8HR Tel: (01332) 636000 Fax: (01332) 636020 E-mail: info@fletchersmith.com *Sugar machinery engineers & suppliers*

► The Fletcher Thompson Practice Limited, Mill House, 21 High Street, Ely, Cambs, CB7 5XR Tel: 0870 2323130 Fax: 0870 2323120 E-mail: info@fletcher-thompson.co.uk *Chartered Accountants providing accountancy, taxation and assurance services to the owner managed business. Preparation of self assessment tax returns and provision of tax advice to individuals*

► Fletcher UK Ltd, PO Box 150, Houghton le Spring, Tyne & Wear, DH5 9DY Tel: 0191-526 9195 Fax: 0191-526 9195 E-mail: info@fletcheruklimited.com *Bar and shop fitting specialists providing maintenance and refurbishment service to licensed premises,shops,offices and call centres.*

Fletchers Bakeries Ltd, Claywheels Lane, Sheffield, S6 1LY Tel: 0114-234 8171 Fax: 0114-232 4987 E-mail: enquiries@fletchers.co.uk *Bakers wholesale manufrs*

Fletchers Packaging, Wilsom Road, Omega Park, Alton, Hampshire, GU34 2QE Tel: (020) 8684 4201 Fax: (020) 8681 5453 E-mail: sales@fletchers-packaging.co.uk *Packaging material distributors*

Fletchers Removals, Racecourse Industrial Park, Mansfield Road, Derby, DE21 4SX Tel: (01332) 371470 Fax: (01332) 294397 E-mail: sales@webbesremovals.net *Removal & storage contractors*

Fletcher-Stewart Ltd, Unit 1, Newby Road Industrial Estate, Hazel Grove, Stockport, Cheshire, SK7 5DA Tel: 0161-456 8450 Fax: 0161-483 5569 E-mail: info@fletcherstewart.co.uk *Horticultural machinery repairs*

R.B. Flett Ltd, Central Garage, Watten, Wick, Caithness, KW1 5XG Tel: (01955) 621255 Fax: (01955) 621260 *Agricultural engineers*

Fleur D E Leys Pies Ltd, Baxenden, Accrington, Lancashire, BB5 2SA Tel: (01706) 221993 Fax: (01706) 228044 *Savoury pie manufrs*

Fleur De Lis Furnishings Ltd, Collingwood House, Coach Lane, North Shields, Tyne & Wear, NE29 6TN Tel: 0191-258 1531 Fax: 0191-259 1318 E-mail: sales@fleur-de-lis.co.uk *Soft furnishings manufrs*

Fleur De Lys, 230 Gloucester Road, Bishopston, Bristol, BS7 8NZ Tel: 0117-957 1229 Fax: 0117-957 1229 *Reproduction furniture*

Fleurtations Workshop, Unit 11, Whin Park Industrial Estate, Cockenzie, Prestonpans, East Lothian, EH32 0JL Tel: 01875 813171 *Interior landscapers*

Flex Ability Ltd, Prospect Way, Park View West Industrial Estate, Hartlepool, Cleveland, TS25 1UD Tel: (01429) 860233 Fax: (01429) 869696 E-mail: sales@flex-ability.co.uk *Flexible & rigid printed circuits manufrs*

Flex Automation Ltd, 28 Scardale Way, Durham, DH1 2TX Tel: 0191-384 1048 *Electrical controls & automation services*

Flex Computer Services, 62 Clifton Road, Shefford, Bedfordshire, SG17 5AN Tel: (01462) 638777 *Computer maintenance*

► Flexadux Plastics Ltd, Middlefield Lane, Gainsborough, Lincolnshire, DN21 1UU Tel: (01427) 617547 Fax: (01427) 810128 E-mail: sales@flexadux.co.uk *Ventilation ducting suppliers*

Flexal Springs UK, 179 Park Avenue, London, NW10 7XH Tel: (020) 8453 0867 Fax: (020) 8961 9181 E-mail: flexalspringsuk@btconnect.com *Spring manufrs*

Flexbore, Pontygwindy Industrial Estate, Caerphilly, Mid Glamorgan, CF83 3HU Tel: (029) 2088 3552 Fax: (029) 2086 6410 *Stainless steel flexible tube assemblies*

Flexcon Glenrothes Ltd, Whitworth Road, Glenrothes, Fife, KY6 2TF Tel: (01592) 663200 Fax: (01592) 663201 E-mail: enquiries@flexcon-europe.nl *Self-adhesive films manufrs*

► FlexEJ, 28 Hadcroft Grange, Stourbridge, West Midlands, DY9 7EP Tel: (0845) 0204323 Fax: (01384) 896875 E-mail: sales@flexej.co.uk *Design & distribution*

Flexel International Ltd, Queensway Industrial Estate, Flemington Road, Glenrothes, Fife, KY7 5QF Tel: (01592) 757313 Fax: (01592) 754535 E-mail: sales@flexel.co.uk *Radiant heating system manufrs*

Flexell, Unit 3, Bypass Park Estate, Sherburn in Elmet, Leeds, LS25 6EP Tel: (01977) 685755 Fax: (01977) 685778 *Flexible packaging material suppliers*

Flexello Ltd, Bagnall Street, Hill Top, Golds Hill, West Bromwich, West Midlands, B70 0TS Tel: 0121-506 1770 Fax: 0121-502 2658 E-mail: sales@flexello.co.uk *Castor manufrs*

Flexfilm, Road One Industrial Estate, Winsford Industrial Estate, Winsford, Cheshire, CW7 3QE Tel: (01606) 550100 Fax: (01606) 551111 E-mail: enquiries@flexfilm.co.uk *Polyethylene/ polythene extrusions, films/sheets & heavy duty sheeting. In addtion, shrink film/wrapping materials manufrs*

Flexform Ltd, 34 Montgomery Road, Belfast, BT6 9HL Tel: (028) 9079 2155 Fax: (028) 9079 9031 E-mail: info@cablespecialists.co.uk *Specialist cable & lead set manufacturer & supplier. Also period lighting accessories*

Flexiable Surface Tecnology Ltd, Nairn Road, Deans, Livingston, West Lothian, EH54 8AY Tel: (01506) 460515 Fax: (01506) 460510 *Electroplaters anodizes & plating manufrs*

Flexible Connections Ltd, King Street Trading Estate, Middlewich, Cheshire, CW10 9LF Tel: (01606) 836024 Fax: (01606) 836241 E-mail: flexibles@talk21.com *Industrial rubber product distributors & manufrs*

Flexible Ducting Ltd, Cloberfield Industrial Estate, Milngavie, Glasgow, G62 7LW Tel: 0141-956 4551 Fax: 0141-956 4847 E-mail: sales@flexibleducting.co.uk *Flexible Ducting Limited is a Glasgow-based manufacturer of quality ducting and hose solutions for many applications, such as vacuum cleaners, domestic appliances, industrial fume and dust extraction, materials handling, air conditioning and ventilation, garage and automotive under-bonnet applications. Our products, which can be found in the Kellysearch library, include: neoprene ducting, silicone ducting, PVC ducting, polyurethane ducting, TPE ducting, stretch hose, vacuum cleaner hose, air-conditioning ducting, and much more. We often supply off-the-shelf products, but where necessary, we work closely with our customers to ensure that the product we supply is tailored to their exact requirements.*

Flexible Heating Hoses Ltd, Unit Z Sapcote Trading Centre, 68 Wyrley Road, Aston, Birmingham, B6 7BN Tel: 0121-250 2525 Fax: 0121-250 2526 E-mail: sales@flexible-heated-hoses.co.uk *Hose (heated), adhesive application/coating equipment & sealant application equipment manufacturers. Als o adhesives, hot melt*

Flexible Hose Supplies Ltd, 12 Osyth Close, Brackmills Industrial Estate, Northampton, NN4 7DY Tel: (01604) 762175 Fax: (01604) 769915 E-mail: sales@fhsn.co.uk *Hose distributors or agents*

Flexible Lamps Ltd, Barrows Road, Pinnacles Estate, Harlow, Essex, CM19 5FA Tel: (01279) 406406 Fax: (01279) 406407 E-mail: admin@flexible-lamps.co.uk *Commercial vehicle lamp manufrs*

► Flexible Lining Products Ltd, Vantage Point Business Village, Mitcheldean, Gloucestershire, GL17 0DD Tel: (0845) 2262478 Fax: (0845) 2269697 E-mail: info@flexibleliningproducts.co.uk *UK distributors & fabricators of pond liner*

Flexible Machining Systems Ltd, 2-3 Blatchford Road, Horsham, West Sussex, RH13 5QR Tel: (01403) 270466 Fax: (01403) 270458 E-mail: sales@fmsltd.co.uk *Precision engineers*

Flexible Management Systems Ltd, Fielden Ho, 28 London Bridge St, London, SE1 9SG Tel: (020) 7378 6788 Fax: (020) 7357 0577 *Banking software solutions*

► Flexible Medical Packaging Ltd, Unit 8, Hightown, White Cross Industrial Estate, Lancaster, LA1 4XS Tel: (01524) 68737 Fax: (01524) 67110 E-mail: sales@flexible-medical.com *Flexible Medical is an established Medical Device and Pharmaceutical packing company with extensive print and substrate converting facilities. In conjunction with our packaging design capabilities, FMP can provide a single supply chain solution for outsourced product packaging. Additional services include full sterilisation and project management, offering both end users, Pharmaceutical and Medical Device companies cost effective packaging solutions.*

Flexible Packagings Ltd, Unit B Kingsbridge Industrial Estate, Kingsbridge Road, Barking, Essex, IG11 0BD Tel: (020) 8507 1200 Fax: (020) 8507 8979 E-mail: flexiblepackagings@talk21.com *Carton packaging distributors*

► Flexible Packing Services Ltd, Unit 4, Cedab Road, Ellesmere Port, CH65 4FE Tel: 0151-355 2333 Fax: 0151-355 3332 E-mail: enquiries@flexpackservices.co.uk *Food quality contract packing & sachet service*

► Flexible Reinforcements Ltd, Bancroft Road, Burnley, Lancashire, BB10 2TP Tel: (01282) 478222 Fax: (01282) 478210 E-mail: sales@flexr.co.uk *PVC sheeting & polypropylene, reinforced & unsupported manufrs*

► Flexible Technology, 23 Wolverstone Drive, Brighton, BN1 7FB Tel: (01273) 566922 Fax: (01273) 566922 E-mail: kb-ftl@netpointproject.net *Flexible printed circuit manufrs*

Flexicare Medical Ltd, CWM Cynon Business Park, Mountain Ash, Mid Glamorgan, CF45 4ER Tel: (01443) 474647 Fax: (01443) 474222 E-mail: sales@flexicare.com *Manufactures of disposable medical devices*

Flexicon Ltd, Roman Way, Coleshill, Birmingham, B46 1HG Tel: (01675) 466900 Fax: (01675) 466901 E-mail: sales@flexicon.uk.com Sales Contact: C Legg *Conduits, electric; conduits, metal; conduit (electric) fittings or accessories manufacturers; flexible tubing/hose/conduit manufacturers. Manufacturers of flexible conduit, fittings and accessories for cable management applications. PVC, Fire Performance, Stainless Steel, Liquid Tight, Cutting Tools, Nylon, Quick Fit, Pliable, Screened, Spiral, Overbraided, Underground, Locknuts*

The Flexicon Company, 1 Larch Lea Trading Estate, Whitefield Road, Liverpool, L6 5BN Tel: 0151-260 6141 Fax: 0151-260 4477 E-mail: info@flexicon.org.uk Sales Contact: N. Carmichael *Based in the North West FLEXICON provides a specialist industrial fabricating service to industry, with an extensive knowledge of the manufacturing of all types of flexible fabric bellows, connections and expansion joints, as well as a variety of other individual industrial components where use dictates application of flexible fabric. With a comprehensive range of materials, both in natural and synthetic fibres, FLEXICON have developed design, cutting and stitching techniques that now achieve an outstanding degree of fine tolerance.*

Flexicovers, The Courtyard, Thrush Road, Poole, Dorset, BH12 4NP Tel: (01202) 721309 Fax: (01202) 733047 E-mail: sales@flexicovers.co.uk *Boat cover manufrs*

Flexiform Business Furniture Ltd, The Office Furniture Centre, 1392 Leeds Road, Bradford, West Yorkshire, BD3 7AE Tel: (01274) 656013 Fax: (01274) 665760 E-mail: sales@flexiform.co.uk *Office furniture & filing system manufrs*

Flexiforms Birmingham Ltd, 7 Lee Bank House, Blucher Street, Birmingham, B1 1HP Tel: 0121-643 7368 Fax: 0121-643 7366 *Cutting & creasing forme manufrs*

Flexigate Ltd, Vicarage Lane, Hoo, Rochester, Kent, ME3 9LB Tel: (01634) 251328 Fax: (01634) 250558 E-mail: sales@flexigate.co.uk *Pvc stationery manufrs*

Flexioffices, 46 Manchester Street, London, W1U 7LS Tel: (020) 7831 2201 Fax: (020) 7831 1753 E-mail: search@flexioffices.com *Free & impartial search for serviced offices & business centres*

Flexi-Plan Partitions Ltd, Unit J1, Halesfield 19, Telford, Shropshire, TF7 4QT Tel: (01952) 586126 Fax: (01952) 581174 E-mail: flexplanpartitions@btopenworld.com *Partitioning & suspended ceiling contractors*

Flexiquip Hydraulics Ltd, Altona Road, Lisburn, County Antrim, BT27 5QB Tel: (028) 9267 7131 Fax: (028) 9260 7231 E-mail: flexequip.sales@flexequip.com *Hydraulic equipment manufrs*

Flexiskills Recruitment, Washington House, 14-16 High Street, Belfast, BT1 2BD Tel: (028) 9032 4436 Fax: (028) 9032 4436 E-mail: info@flexiskills.co.uk *Supplying Temporary and permanent recruitment solutions throughout Northern Ireland. Specialising in Senior appointments, and -Professional/ Technical/Secretarial/Industrial recruitment*

► Flexistore Storage Services, Pomathorn Road, Penicuik, Midlothian, EH26 8PJ Tel: (01968) 670246 Fax: (01968) 676010 E-mail: sales@flexistore.co.uk

Flexistyle Ltd, 446 Gipsy Lane, Leicester, LE4 9DB Tel: 0116-276 8442 Fax: 0116-276 8443 *Knitwear & textiles manufrs*

Flexitallic Ltd, PO Box 3, Cleckheaton, West Yorkshire, BD19 5BT Tel: (01274) 851273 Fax: (01274) 851386 E-mail: ukmarketing@flexitallic.com Principal Export Areas: Worldwide *Manufacturer of gaskets & seals*

Flexitallic Scotland Ltd, Unit 18d Wellheads Crescent, Aberdeen, AB21 7GA Tel: (01224) 725241 Fax: (01224) 722911 *Sealant & gasket manufrs*

► Flexitrans Ltd, Magnum House, 62 Leopold Road, Felixstowe, Suffolk, IP11 7NR Tel: 01394 458800 Fax: 01394 458811 E-mail: andy.brendt@flexitrans.co.uk *At Flexitrans we are a freight forwading company who will help with any transport be it from the smallest of packages to the lagest of abnormal loads and to anywhere in the world.*

Flexiwall Co. Ltd, 15 Iliad Street, Liverpool, L5 3LU Tel: 0151-207 1103 Fax: 0151-207 1588 *Partition contractors*

Flexleigh Audio Tours Ltd, Highview House, Charles Square, Bracknell, Berkshire, RG12 1DF Tel: (01344) 860125 Fax: (01344) 390732 E-mail: office@flexitours.com *Audio guides*

Flexo Springs Ltd, Hill Street, Kingswood, Bristol, BS15 4HB Tel: 0845 4941786 Fax: 0117-935 2597 E-mail: sales@flexosprings.com Purchasing Contact: M. Fawcett Sales Contact: N. Vincent *Based in Bristol, Flexo Springs Ltd is a UK Manufacturer, Stockist and Supplier. Product range includes Compression Springs, Extension Springs, Compression Lengths, Tension Lengths, Torsion Springs and Wireforms. We are one of the most competitively priced supplier's of springs in the UK and have supplied leading companies in a wide range of industries for over 70 years. We also specialise in smaller quantities of bespoke designed springs.*Choose from our extensive range of springs that have been pre designed and can be viewed on www.flexosprings.com.*

Flexon plc, Upper Church Lane, Tipton, West Midlands, DY4 9PA Tel: 0121-521 3600 Fax: 0121-520 0822 E-mail: sales@flexon.co.uk *Chains for power transmission & conveyor system manufacturers. Supplier of agricultural chains, flat top, roler chains, sprockets, leaf chains.*

Flexopack Ltd, Mallard Road, Victoria Business Park, Netherfield, Nottingham, NG4 2PE Tel: 0115-940 3939 Fax: 0115-940 3837 E-mail: sales@flexopack.co.uk *Polypropylene & polythene bag manufrs*

Flexovac Ltd., Unit 9, 12-48 Northumberland Park, London, N17 0TX Tel: (020) 8216 9299 Fax: (020) 8216 9372 E-mail: info@flexovac.com *Converter of films into printed and unprinted vacuum pouches, gold/silver metallised pouches, lidding films, gold/silver salmon boards, gold/silver food boards and interleaving sheets for the food industry. Flexovac also supply a range of vacuum packing, tray sealing and thermoforming machinery*

Flexsys (UK) Ltd, The Courtyard, Green Lane, Heywood, Lancashire, OL10 2EX Tel: (01706) 362130 Fax: (01706) 362133 E-mail: sales@flexsys-group.com *Established in 1991, Flexsys (UK) Limited provides cost-effective, professional and reliable computer related services.**Our products include computer and network support services to companies (SMEs) in the North West of England and application development and support services to international clients of all sizes.**Flexsys has developed a range of hardware products, including devices that allow hotels, internet cafés, marinas etc. to provide controlled Internet access to their customers. These devices are installed in 14 countries around the world.**By providing excellent customer service, Flexsys enjoys an enviable track record of customer retention; our first client remains a client after 15 years and our largest client, for whom we provide 24 hour support, 7 days per week, has been supported by Flexsys since 1996.**Flexsys (UK) Limited is the largest company in the Flexsys Group. We employ over 50 people world-wide with offices in UK, USA, Germany, France and Spain.*

Flextol Ltd, 20 Swannington Road, Cottage Lane Industrial Estate, Broughton Astley, Leicester, LE9 6TU Tel: (01455) 285333 Fax: (01455) 285238 E-mail: sales@flextol.co.uk *Flexible shaft tool manufrs*

Flextraction Ltd, 10 Digby Drive, Leicester Road Industrial Estate, Melton Mowbray, Leicestershire, LE13 0RQ Tel: (01664) 410641 Fax: (01664) 480244 E-mail: sales@flextraction.co.uk Principal Export Areas: Central/East Europe & West Europe *Flextraction Ltd is a UK independent firm specialising in the manufacture and supply of products for dust extraction and fume extraction. In particular, Downflow Booths, spot extractors and associated items that have been specially designed for the capture and extraction of dusts and hazardous fumes.*

Flextronics Ltd, West Avenue, The Phoenix Linwood, Paisley, Renfrewshire, PA1 2FB Tel: 0141-849 5600 Fax: 0141-849 5640 *Warehouse, distribution & logistics*

► Fli Backward Ltd, 557 Wilmslow Road, Manchester, M20 4GJ Tel: 0161-445 0273 *advertising, graphic design, new media, direct marketing, consultancy, illustration, artwork*

► Flight Academy Scotland.com, Building 25, Inverness Airport, Inverness, IV2 7JB Tel: 01667 461181 Fax: 01667 462202 *A fully interactive training programme for both fixed wing and helicopter pilots. The most modern aircraft and commercial instructors give the highest standard of pilot training available in the UK.*

continued

► indicates data change since last edition

▶ Flight Logistics, The Cabair Building, Elstree Aerodrome, Borehamwood, Hertfordshire, WD6 3AW Tel: (0870) 620 8046 Fax: (0870) 620 8047 E-mail: operations@flight-logistics.co.uk *Organisers of aerial filming*

Flight Refueling, Brook Road, Wimborne, Dorset, BH21 2BJ Tel: (01202) 882121 Fax: (01202) 880096 E-mail: sales@cobham.com *Precision engineers & aerospace*

▶ Flightcase Warehouse Ltd, Meltex House, 2 Mariner, Tamworth, Staffordshire, B79 7XE Tel: (01827) 60009 Fax: (01827) 313877 E-mail: sales@flightcasewarehouse.co.uk *Flight case manufacturer*

Flightline Support Ltd, 49 Brize Norton Road, Minster Lovell, Witney, Oxfordshire, OX29 0SG Tel: (01993) 776564 Fax: (01993) 778953 E-mail: ray@flightline-support.co.uk *Aviation ground support equipment manufrs*

Flightplan Ltd, PO Box 1159, Farnborough, Hampshire, GU14 6XA Tel: (01252) 52 62 82 Fax: (01252) 52 62 89 E-mail: info@flightplan.org.uk *Flightplan are one of Europe"s leading Air Charter Brokers, providing a 24 *hour per day, 365 days per year service. Over 20,000 aircraft available *worldwide from small twin propeller to trans-continental airliners. *Passenger or cargo.**

Flights Of Fancy, 15 New Street, Leamington Spa, Warwickshire, CV31 1HP Tel: (01926) 423436 Fax: (01926) 311925 E-mail: mail@flightsoffancy.co.uk *Wood & paper giftware designers & manufrs*

Thomas Flinn & Co., 114 Harvest Lane, Sheffield, S3 8EG Tel: 0114-272 5387 Fax: 0114-272 5389 E-mail: info@flinn-garlick-saws.co.uk *Hand saw manufrs*

Flint Ltd, Walker Road, Bardon Hill, Coalville, Leicestershire, LE67 1TU Tel: (01530) 510333 Fax: (01530) 510275 E-mail: info@flint.co.uk Principal Export Areas: Worldwide *Electronic component distributors or agents*

Flint Casual Wear, Amundsen House, Hinckley, Leicestershire, LE10 0DP Tel: (01455) 633937 Fax: (01455) 890464 *Clothing manufrs*

Flint Group UK Ltd, Slinfold, Horsham, West Sussex, RH13 0SH Tel: (01403) 790332 Fax: (01403) 790617 *Printing ink specialists* Also at: Liverpool & Wolverhampton

▶ Flint & Neill Partnership, Stonehaven, Stone, Berkeley, Gloucestershire, GL13 9LD Tel: (01454) 260910 Fax: (01454) 260784 E-mail: sales@flintneill.co.uk

Flint Schmidt, Vauxhall Industrial Estate, Ruabon, Wrexham, Clwyd, LL14 6HU Tel: (01978) 823456 Fax: (01978) 823331 Principal Export Areas: Worldwide *Inks manufrs*

Flint Scmidt Ltd, Qualcast Road Industrial Estate, Wolverhampton, WV1 2QP Tel: (01902) 871028 Fax: (01902) 457461 E-mail: sales@flint-schmidt.com *Printing ink manufrs*

Flint & Son, 43 Nursery Road, Hockley, Birmingham, B19 2XN Tel: 0121-523 2875 *Engravers & engine turning service*

Flintnine Fasteners Ltd, Highfield Road, Little Hulton, Manchester, M38 9ST Tel: 0161-790 7817 Fax: 0161-703 8314 E-mail: sales@flintnine.co.uk *Fastener distributors*

Flintshire Fabrications Ltd, St. Asaph Road, Lloc, Holywell, Clwyd, CH8 8RD Tel: (01352) 711701 Fax: (01352) 711817 E-mail: info@flintshirefabrications.com *Steel fabricators*

Flip Lock Ltd, 177 Ashby Road, Scunthorpe, South Humberside, DN16 2AQ Tel: (01724) 865692 E-mail: mgdeans@btconnect.com *Strapping distributors*

Flipstick (International) Ltd, 40a Rowland Street, Rugby, Warwickshire, CV21 2BW Tel: (01788) 542109 Fax: (01788) 542116 E-mail: info@flipstick.co.uk *Manufacturers of walking stick seats*

Flite Electronics Ltd, Church House Farm, Clewer Hill, Waltham Chase, Southampton, SO32 2LN Tel: (01489) 892422 Fax: (01489) 897929 E-mail: sales@flite.co.uk *Microprocessor systems & electronic training equipment*

Flitwick Motor Cycles, Station Road, Flitwick, Bedford, MK45 1JR Tel: (01525) 750380 Fax: (01525) 750390 E-mail: sales@flitwickmotorcycles.co.uk *Motorcycle retailers & repairers*

▶ Flix, 16a Chelsea Wharf, Lots Road, London, SW10 0QJ Tel: (020) 7352 5216 Fax: (020) 7376 3509 E-mail: sharan@videotomobile.com *Mobile telecommunication suppliers*

Flixborough Wharf Ltd, Trent Port House, Flixborough, Scunthorpe, North Lincolnshire, DN15 8RS Tel: (01724) 867691 Fax: (01724) 851207 E-mail: info@flixboroughwharf.co.uk *Freight forwarders, warehouse & distributors*

▶ Flixx Recruitment, 25 St. Mary's Street, Whitchurch, Shropshire, SY13 1RZ Tel: 01948 667177 E-mail: fraynor@flixxrecruitment.com *Pro-active Recruitment Agency recruiting for office based staff around Shropshire, Cheshire and North Wales.*

▶ Floaters, 10 Estcourt Road, Great Yarmouth, Norfolk, NR30 4JG Tel: (01493) 853700 Fax: (01493) 721171 *Fishing tackle retailers*

▶ Floaters, 1A Oxford Street, Guiseley, Leeds, LS20 9AX Tel: (01943) 870467

Floating Sensations Ltd, 1 Fox Cottages, Wellhouse, Hermitage, Thatcham, Berkshire, RG18 9UD Tel: (01635) 201007 Fax: (01635) 202774 E-mail: sales@balloonflights.co.uk *Balloon flight services*

▶ Floboth (London) Ltd, Unit 1 C, Middlegreen Trading Estate, Langley, Slough, SL3 6DF Tel: (01753) 521878

▶ Flocap Packaging Materials, 16d Coal Hill Lane, Farsley, Pudsey, West Yorkshire, LS28 5NA Tel: 0113-236 3026 Fax: 0113-236 3148 E-mail: sales@flocap.co.uk *Inline cape tightening machine manufrs*

Flock Development & Research Co. Ltd, Clarence Mill, Clarence Street, Stalybridge, Cheshire, SK15 1QF Tel: 0161-339 4946 Fax: 0161-343 2045 E-mail: flock@flockdev.co.uk *Paint pads & paint rollers manufrs*

Ian Flockton Developments Ltd, Estate Road 1, South Humberside Industrial Estate, Grimsby, South Humberside, DN31 2TB Tel: (01472) 359634 Fax: (01472) 241392 E-mail: info@ianflockton.co.uk *Plastic vessel fabricators & plastic material manufrs*

Flo-Code (UK) Ltd, Gable End, Holmbury St. Mary, Dorking, Surrey, RH5 6LQ Tel: 01306 731863 Fax: 01306 731864 E-mail: info@flo-code.co.uk *Pipeline identification & engraving services*

Flocon Valves & Fittings Ltd, Treforest Industrial Estate, Pontypridd, Mid Glamorgan, CF37 5YB Tel: (01443) 841666 Fax: (01443) 841461 E-mail: sales@flocon.co.uk *Stockists & distributor of industrial valves & associated products*

Floform Ltd, Henfaes Lane, Welshpool, Powys, SY21 7BJ Tel: (01938) 552611 Fax: (01938) 555339 E-mail: sales@floform.co.uk *Precision components*

Flogas UK Ltd, Unit W, Barton Industrial Estate, Faldo Road, Barton-Le-Clay, MK45 4RP Tel: (01582) 600858 Fax: (01582) 882256 *Bottled gas distributors*

Floline, Whitehall Industrial Estate, Whitehall Road, Leeds, LS12 5JB Tel: 0113-235 9349 Fax: 0113-235 9348 *Distribution of plastic pipe*

Flomar Ltd, Marlborough Drive, Fleckney, Leicester, LE8 8UR Tel: 0116-240 3430 Fax: 0116-240 4012 E-mail: admin@flomar.co.uk *Steam system designer*

Flomax Racing, Ruskin Works, Oakridge Road, High Wycombe, Buckinghamshire, HP11 2PE Tel: (01494) 465678 Fax: (01494) 465678 *Plastic project engineers manufrs & suppliers*

Flomotion Rental Ltd, 7 Wilton Close, Partridge Green, Horsham, West Sussex, RH13 8RX Tel: (01403) 711170 Fax: (01403) 711059 *Intermediate bull containers*

Floodlighting & Electrical Services Ltd, Unit 22-23 Woodlands Workshops, Coedcae Lane, Pontyclun, Mid Glamorgan, CF72 9DW Tel: (01443) 226009 Fax: (01443) 225481 E-mail: info@floodlighting-electrical.co.uk *Floodlighting specialists*

▶ Flooks, Crown Industrial Estate, Crown Road, Warmley, Bristol, BS30 8JJ Tel: 0117-960 6069 Fax: 0117-960 6009

Floor Coverings Of Doncaster, 2 Richmond Road, Doncaster, South Yorkshire, DN5 8TB Tel: (01302) 812198 E-mail: sales@fcdoncaster.co.uk *Wood, laminates & vinyl flooring supplies & carpets*

▶ Floor Exposure, Jubilee Park, Hanson Close, Middleton, Manchester, M24 2UH Tel: 0161-655 7019 Fax: 0161-655 7002

Floor Maintenance Services Ltd, 215 Melton Road, Edwalton, Nottingham, NG12 4AF Tel: 0115-945 2186 Fax: 0115-974 7656 E-mail: sonia.mabbott@ntlworld.com *Floor renovation & treatment services*

▶ Floor Prep Services Ltd, 38c Hoylake Road, South Park Industrial Estate, Scunthorpe, North Lincolnshire, DN17 2AZ Tel: (07710) 248677 Fax: (01724) 875353 E-mail: Info@floorprepservices.co.uk *Shot Blasting, Scabbling, Diamond Grinding,HCA Burning, Concrete cleaning,Dust free surface preparation,Concrete Profiling,Industrial Flooring,Floor Preparation**

Floor To Ceiling Fitted Bedrooms, 4 Far Field Road, Edenthorpe, Doncaster, South Yorkshire, DN3 2NS Tel: (01302) 886074 Fax: (01302) 886074 *Manufacturers of home office & bedroom furniture*

▶ Floorboy, 9 Malpas drive, Northampton, NN5 6XL Tel: (01604) 461142 E-mail: floorboy@hotmail.com *Specialists in Supply & Installation of Hardwood & Laminate flooring to Commercial & Domestic clients*

Floorcraft Contractors Ltd, 17a Station Road, London, E17 8AA Tel: (020) 8521 4446 Fax: (020) 8521 9165 E-mail: mailbox@floorcraft.co.uk *Flooring contractors*

FloorFit LLP, 60 Windsor Avenue, London, SW19 2RR Tel: 0800 8818124 Fax: 0870 1217073 E-mail: floorfitsales@floorfit.co.uk *Floor Fitter, Flooring, Floor Installation, Floor Fitting, Floor Polishing, Floor Sanding, and Floor Repair.**Flooring in London and M25 area: Laminate, Hardwood, Stone, Tile, Vinyl, and Custom Flooring.**

Flooring & Blinds, 20 Chester Street, Mold, Clwyd, CH7 1EG Tel: (01352) 750874 Fax: (01352) 750872 *Blinds sales & manufrs*

▶ The Flooring Directory, The Coach House, Lower Denbigh Road, St. Asaph, Clwyd, LL17 0EF Tel: (01745) 584868 E-mail: webmaster@carpetfitters.biz *Find laminate & hardwood flooring, installers, carpet fitters & tools*

▶ The Flooring Firm Ltd, 131 Station Road, Bamber Bridge, Preston, PR5 6QS Tel: (01772) 316688 Fax: (01772) 624111 *Carpet retailers*

Floorings Of Frome, Textile House, Manor Furlong, Frome, Somerset, BA11 4RJ Tel: (01373) 462666 Fax: (01373) 466651 E-mail: fromecarpetsandflooring@btconnect.com *Flooring contractors & carpet retailers*

▶ Floors 2 Go P.L.C., Microtech House, 74 New Town Row, Birmingham, B6 4HA Tel: 0121-359 0234 Fax: 0121-359 4316 E-mail: info@floors2go.co.uk *Home furnishing suppliers*

▶ Floors Galore, Centurion Park, Shrewsbury, SY1 4EH Tel: (01743) 467001 E-mail: info@floors-galore.co.uk *Floor specialists services*

Floplast Ltd, Eurolink Industrial Centre, Castle Road, Sittingbourne, Kent, ME10 3FP Tel: (01795) 431731 Fax: (01795) 431188 E-mail: sales@floplast.co.uk *Plastic mouldings manufrs*

▶ Flora Design, 106 Cromwell Road, St. Andrews, Bristol, BS6 5EZ Tel: 0117-944 1494 Fax: 0117-944 1494 E-mail: sales@floradesign.co.uk *Garden design service, creating imaginative & stylish*

▶ Florabundance.Co.Uk, 73 London Road, East Grinstead, West Sussex, RH19 1EQ Tel: (01342) 311478 Fax: (01342) 311542 E-mail: sales@florabundance.co.uk *Florist shop, same day delivery service*

▶ Florada Garden Buildings Ltd, Unit W2 Continental Approach, Westwood Industrial Estate, Margate, Kent, CT9 4JG Tel: (01843) 223345 Fax: (01843) 298923 E-mail: admin@florada.co.uk *Export of garden buildings*

Florco, Aylesford Way, Thatcham, Berkshire, RG19 4NW Tel: (01635) 863456 Fax: (01635) 871024 E-mail: info@florco-sales.co.uk *Floor covering distributors*

Florentine Shoes, European Cargo Centre, Motherwell Way, Grays, Essex, RM20 3XD Tel: (01708) 867111 Fax: (01708) 862110 E-mail: mikeluff@florentineshoes.freeserve.co.uk *Footwear wholesalers & retailers* Also at: Basildon, Bromley, London & Tunbridge Wells

Florida Blinds, 16 Noran Cresent, Troon, Ayrshire, KA10 7JF Tel: (01292) 318203 Fax: (01292) 318203 *Window blind retailers*

The Florida Group Ltd, Dibden Road, Norwich, NR3 4RR Tel: (01603) 426341 Fax: (01603) 424354 E-mail: mailroom@floridagroup.co.uk *Ladies shoe manufrs*

Florida Marquees, Bradbury Street, Sheffield, S8 9QQ Tel: 0114-258 9626 Fax: 0114-250 7527 E-mail: rmitchell@apex-marquees.u-net.com *Marquee hire & sales*

▶ Florida Villa Finder, 5, 1 Station Lofts, Strathblane, Glasgow, G63 9BD Tel: (01360) 771856 E-mail: enquiries@florida-villa-finder.com *We are dedicated to finding the right Florida villas to match your specific needs whether it be in Orlando, Kissimmee or any other resort.*

▶ Florimont Gaumier, 33 Turnpike Way, Markfield, Leicestershire, LE67 9QT Tel: (01530) 245544

Floringo Ltd, Enterprise House, 133 Blyth Road, Hayes, Middlesex, UB3 1DD Tel: (020) 8587 3400 Fax: (020) 8569 1445 E-mail: floringo@globalnet.co.uk *Textile manufrs*

▶ Floryn Ltd, Mid Kent Business Park, Sortmill Road, Snodland, Kent, ME6 5UA Tel: (01634) 240444 Fax: (01634) 241444 *Packaging, warehousing & distribution services*

▶ Flostream Ltd, Springheath House, Kelpatrick Road, Slough, SL1 6BW Tel: 01628 669548 Fax: 01628 669256 E-mail: sales@flostream.co.uk *Flostream Limited is the specialist Mail, Fulfilment, Storage and Distribution organisation created to provide services to anyone with a priority for efficiency and cost effective distribution solutions.**Our team comprises experts from Mail, Freight, IT and Fulfilment industries enabling us to offer and manage a wide variety of distribution projects. **

Flotec Industrial Ltd, Royal Way, Loughborough, Leicestershire, LE11 5XR Tel: (01509) 230100 Fax: (01509) 264100 *Hose distributors*

Flotech Solutions Ltd, Stuart Road, Bredbury Park Industrial Estate, Bredbury, Stockport, Cheshire, SK6 2SR Tel: 0161-406 2200 Fax: 0161-406 9196 E-mail: enquiries@flotech.co.uk *Instrumentation engineers*

Flotronic Pumps Ltd, Ricebridge Works, Brighton Road, Bolney, Haywards Heath, West Sussex, RH17 5NA Tel: (01444) 881871 Fax: (01444) 881860 E-mail: salesdept@flotronicpumps.co.uk *Double diaphragm pump manufrs*

Flouch Engineering Co. Ltd, Hazlehead, Crow Edge, Sheffield, S36 4HH Tel: (01226) 763239 Fax: (01226) 370205 E-mail: sales@flouch-engineering.co.uk *Manufacturer of refractory fixings and anchors. Heat and corrosion resistant fixings in special alloys. Standard anchors from stock.*

▶ Flourish Gardens Ltd, 47 St. Johns Road, Tunbridge Wells, Kent, TN4 9TP Tel: (01892) 547146 Fax: (01892) 546525 E-mail: diana.segal@flourishgardens.co.uk *Garden shop with garden design and landscaping consultancy. Site includes description of garden design/landscaping/ planting services. Online product catalogue.*

Flow Control Co. Ltd, Cooper Drive, Springwood Industrial Estate, Braintree, Essex, CM7 2RF Tel: (01376) 321211 Fax: (01376) 321222 E-mail: flowcontrolco@lineone.net *Valve ball stockists*

▶ Flow Control Solutions Ltd, Unit D Knowl Street, Stalybridge, Cheshire, SK15 3AL Tel: 0161-303 9777 Fax: 0161-303 9888 E-mail: rob@flowcontrolsolutions.com *Valve distributors*

Flow Science Ltd, Goldstein Laboratory, Liverpool Road, Eccles, Manchester, M30 7RU Tel: 0161-787 8749 Fax: 0161-787 8749 E-mail: flowsci@fs1.ae.man.ac.uk *Aerodynamic researchers*

Flow Serve Flow Control Ltd, Victoria Way, Burgess Hill, West Sussex, RH15 9NF Tel: (01444) 245826 *Pipe line valves water line & gas*

▶ Flow Stop Services, 97 Holmsdale Grove, Bexleyheath, Kent, DA7 6PA Tel: (01322) 525616 Fax: (01322) 522227

Flow Tronix Ltd, Unit Vernon Place, Northern Court, Basford, Nottingham, NG6 0DE Tel: 0115-979 4886 Fax: 0115-979 4889 E-mail: info@flowtronix.co.uk *Manufactures of bespoke Liquid Filling Machines 200g - 1500kg+, Weigh filling, Flow & Mass Flow Meter Filling*

Flowco Mariflo Ltd, 19 Auriol Park Road, Worcester Park, Surrey, KT4 7DP Tel: (020) 8330 2487 Fax: (020) 8330 2487 E-mail: mariflo@flowco.co.uk *Flow limiting valves & water saving energy efficiency specialists*

Flowcool Systems, Wimsey Way, Somercotes, Alfreton, Derbyshire, DE55 4LS Tel: (01773) 608888 Fax: (01773) 609001 E-mail: sales@flowcool.com *Chiller & cooler manufrs*

Flowdata Systems, PO Box 71, Newbury, Berks, RG20 0YN Tel: (01488) 668810 Fax: (01488) 668883 E-mail: sales@flowdatasystems.co.uk *Manufacturers of flow measurement systems, meters, digital totalisers & indicators*

Flower Bowl Of Mayfair, 91 Edgware Road, London, W2 2HX Tel: (020) 7723 0153 Fax: (020) 7723 8559 E-mail: sales@flowerbowl.biz *Florists*

Francis Flower, Gurney Slade Quarry, Gurney Slade, Radstock, BA3 4TE Tel: (01749) 841146 Fax: (01749) 841285 E-mail: sales@francisflower.co.uk *Limestone filler suppliers & mineral processors*

▶ Flower Shop, 29 Foxhall Road, Ipswich, IP3 8JU Tel: (01473) 255970 Fax: (01473) 255970 E-mail: sheila.bloom@intamail.com *Online shop features include over one hundred flower arrangement. These have been carefully selected & placed into an array of special collections. Feel free to browse the shop for your convenience & order flowers online. Delivery arranged throughout the world*

Flowerbox designs, Units 5 & 6,, Twyford Business Park, Station Road, Twyford, RG10 9JU Tel: 0118 9340077 Fax: 0118 9343667 E-mail: info@boxinnovations.co.uk

▶ Flowerworks Florists, 15 Windsor Street, Uxbridge, Middlesex, UB8 1AB Tel: (01895) 810885 Fax: (01895) 810008 E-mail: sales@actionflowers.com *Quality & artistic floral & plant arrangements*

Flowflex Components Ltd, Samuel Blaser Works, Tongue Lane Industrial Estate, Buxton, Derbyshire, SK17 7LR Tel: (01298) 77211 Fax: (01298) 72362 E-mail: flowflex@compuserve.com *Compression fittings manufrs*

Flowfood Ltd, South Street, Ashton-under-Lyne, Lancashire, OL7 0PH Tel: 0161-330 0411 Fax: 0161-343 2193 E-mail: sales@flowfood.co.uk *Frozen food processors & products manufrs*

▶ Flowguard Ltd, Watford Bridge Road, New Mills, High Peak, Derbyshire, SK22 4HJ Tel: (01663) 745976 Fax: (01663) 742788 E-mail: sales@flowguard.com Principal Export Areas: Worldwide *Pressure vessel manufrs*

Flowhire Hire Centres, Riverside, Canal Road, Sowerby Bridge, West Yorkshire, HX6 2AY Tel: (0800) 0356944 Fax: (07000) 356944 E-mail: sales@flowhire.co.uk *Hire, leasing & rental of flow meters*

Flowline Civil Engineering Ltd, Merthyr Tydfil Industrial Park, Pentrebach, Merthyr Tydfil, Mid Glamorgan, CF48 4DR Tel: (01443) 691452 Fax: (01443) 692397

Flowline Engineering (UK) Ltd, Trafford Park Road, Newbridge, Trafford Park, Manchester, M17 1HG Tel: 0161-872 1421 Fax: 0161-872 5247 E-mail: flowline01@aol.com *Pipework & steel fabricators*

▶ Flowline Mailing Systems, The Seedbed Centre, Langston Road, Loughton, Essex, IG10 3TQ Tel: (020) 8787 7122 Fax: 01268 493031 E-mail: info@flowlineservice.co.uk *UK's premier supplier of Mailing products,Folders,Inserters,Scales,Letter Openers,Sealing,Franking Machines and all Mailing Systems.*

Flowline Manufacturing Ltd, 11a Shenley Road, Borehamwood, Hertfordshire, WD6 1AD Tel: (020) 8207 6565 Fax: (020) 8207 3082 E-mail: sales@flowline.co.uk *Distributors or agents of flow meters; electromagnetic*

Flowmaster International, The Maltings, Alderton Road, Towcester, Northamptonshire, NN12 7TB Tel: (01327) 306000 Fax: (01327) 306020 *Software manufrs*

FLOWMECH LTD, 14 Beech Close, Hatfield, Hertfordshire, AL10 8NT Tel: 01707 690311 Fax: 01707 883718 E-mail: JOHNCOLEY@HOTMAIL.CO.UK *SUPPLIER OF SEALANTS ,SILICONE,POLYURETHANES, MS POLYMERS,BUTYLS, FABRICATIONS IN ALL METALS, COMMERCIAL VEHICLE FITTINGS INC WINDOWS , HORSEBOX FITTINGS.*

▶ Flowmetersdirect.co.uk, Unit E1, Hanson Park, Hanson Close, Middleton, Manchester, M24 2QZ Tel: 0161-643 9802 Fax: 0161-643 9835 E-mail: info@flowmetersdirect.co.uk *Manufacturer of Low Cost Liquid Turbine Flowmeters*

▶ Flowprint Ltd, E Boyn Valley Industrial Estate, Boyn Valley Road, Maidenhead, Berkshire, SL6 4EJ Tel: (01628) 778600 Fax: (01628) 773500 E-mail: sales@flowprint.com

▶ Flowquip Ltd, Riverside, Canal Road, Sowerby Bridge, W. Yorkshire, HX6 2AY Tel: (01422) 829920 Fax: (01422) 829921 E-mail: sales@flowquip.co.uk *Manufacturers of flowmeters & flow measurement systems including steam, turbine & food industry*

Flowrite Ltd, 6 Walnut Tree Close, Cheshunt, Waltham Cross, Hertfordshire, EN8 8NH Tel: (01992) 639205 Fax: (01992) 623993 E-mail: pumps@flowrite.co.uk *Pumping equipment*

▶ Flowrite Drainage Services Ltd, The Kilns, Lynwick Street, Rudgwick, Horsham, West Sussex, RH12 3DG Tel: (01403) 822485 E-mail: info@flowrite-drainage.co.uk *Drainage inspection & repair services & treatment plant*

Flowrite Industrial Dampers Ltd, The Glasshouse Kings Lane, Norwich, NR1 3PS Tel: (01603) 633163 Fax: (01603) 633763 E-mail: sales@industrialdampers.com Principal Export Areas: Worldwide *Industrial dampers manufrs*

Flowseal Ltd, 34h Aston Road, Waterlooville, Hampshire, PO7 7XQ Tel: (023) 9226 5031 Fax: (023) 9224 0382 E-mail: sales@flowseal.co.uk *Oil seal & gasket manufrs*

Flowserve, Abex Road, Newbury, Berkshire, RG14 5EY Tel: (01635) 42297 Fax: (01635) 36034 E-mail: jrobinson@flowserve.com *Valve actuator manufrs*

Flowserve Ltd, Dakota Avenue, Salford, M50 2PU Tel: 0161-869 1200 Fax: 0161-869 1235 *Fluid seals*

Flowserve Flow Control UK Ltd, Burrell Road, Haywards Heath, West Sussex, RH16 1TL Tel: (01444) 314400 Fax: (01444) 314401 E-mail: ukfcinfo@flowserve.com Principal Export Areas: Africa *We are leading manufacturers of a wide range of flow control products & equipment, including isolation & control valves, actuation equipment & boiler house equipment. Brands include Worcester Controls, Norbro, Serck Audco, Automax, Valtek, Limitorque, Argus &*

continued

continuation
Gestra. Selling globally through a network of specialist distribution outlets

Flowserve Pumps Ltd, PO Box 17, Newark, Nottinghamshire, NG24 3EN Tel: (01636) 705151 Fax: (01636) 705991 E-mail: newark@flowserve.com *Pump manufrs*

Flowsoft Watercare, Baytrees, Pluckley Road, Charing, Ashford, Kent, TN27 0AQ Tel: (01233) 712610 Fax: (01233) 712610 E-mail: flowsoftwatercare@intamail.com *Water softening & drinking water filters*

Flowsolve Ltd, 130 Arthur Road, London, SW19 8AA Tel: (020) 8944 0940 Fax: (020) 8944 1218 E-mail: cfd@flowsolve.com *Computer consultants*

Flowstop Ltd, 98 Wellington Street, Sheffield, S1 4HX Tel: 0114-275 0509 Fax: 0114-279 8158 *Pipe seals manufrs*

Flowstore Systems plc, 39 Frogmore Industrial Estate, Clayton Road, Hayes, Middlesex, UB3 1AU Tel: (020) 8581 5555 Fax: (020) 8581 5575 E-mail: sales@flowstore.co.uk *Pallet racking & storage equipment system manufrs*

Flowtech Ltd, Pimbo Road, Skelmersdale, Lancashire, WN8 9RB Tel: (01695) 52770 Fax: (0800) 2987230 E-mail: sales@flowtech.co.uk *Distributor of Rectus, Norgren and Festo valves and cylinders.*Other products include quick acting couplers, pvc hoses, tube, hose assemblies and malleable fittings*

FlowTech Design Ltd, 355 Green Lane, Bolton, BL3 2LU Tel: (01204) 362622 Fax: (01204) 362622 E-mail: clive.fenn@flowtechdesign.com *Computer simulation of injection moulding*

▶ Flowtech Precision Mouldings Ltd, Unit 3 Cambrian Industrial Park, Clydach Vale, Tonypandy, Mid Glamorgan, CF40 2XX Tel: (01443) 420130 Fax: (01443) 420140 *Manufacture precision injection moldings*

Floyd Automatic Tooling Ltd, 17 Bondor Business Centre, London Road, Baldock, Hertfordshire, SG7 6HP Tel: (01462) 491919 Fax: (01462) 490835 E-mail: info@floydautomatic.co.uk *Knurling tool distributors*

▶ Floyd Schofield Haulage, Unit 11 Sowarth Industrial Estate, Settle, North Yorkshire, BD24 9AF Tel: (01729) 825396 Fax: (01729) 825396

Flucon Pumps Ltd, 1 High Street, St. Asaph, Clwyd, LL17 0RG Tel: (01745) 584772 Fax: (01745) 582096 E-mail: info@flucon.co.uk *Pump sales, service & design & repairs*

Flude Hosiery, Rugby Road, Hinckley, Leicestershire, LE10 0QQ Tel: (01455) 615543 Fax: (01455) 615543 E-mail: sales@flude.co.uk *Hosiery manufrs*

Flude Machine Tools, 7 Central City Industrial Estate, Red Lane, Coventry, CV6 5RY Tel: (024) 7666 1220 Fax: (024) 7666 1220 *Machine tool servicing, repairs & reconditioning*

▶ Flue Stax, 5 Longford Industrial Estate, New Street, Bridgtown, Cannock, Staffordshire, WS11 0DT Tel: (01543) 571358 Fax: (01543) 571673

Flueclean Installations Services Ltd, Lytham Street Works, Stockport, Cheshire, SK3 8JB Tel: 0161-480 8551 Fax: 0161-477 7769 E-mail: sales@flueclean.com *Boiler cleaners & engineers*

Fluency Voice Technology Ltd, Block 6, 1St Floor Westbrook Centre, Cambridge, CB4 1YG Tel: (01223) 300101 Fax: (01223) 326701 E-mail: enquires@vocalis.com *Speech recognition*

▶ Fluent Contact Marketing, Lok' N' Store Building Unit 2, Etheridge Avenue, Brinklow, Milton Keynes, MK10 0BB Tel: (0870) 1277310 Fax: (0870) 1277329 E-mail: sales@fluent-marketing.co.uk *Marketing services*

Flues & Flashings Ltd, Unit 246 Ikon Industrial Estate, Droitwich Road, Hartlebury, Kidderminster, Worcestershire, DY10 4EU Tel: (01299) 250049 Fax: (01299) 250947 E-mail: info@fluesandflashings.co.uk *Steel chimney & flue pipe manufrs*

Fluid Controls Ltd, 4 Minerva House, Calleva Park, Aldermaston, Reading, RG7 8NA Tel: 0118-981 1004 Fax: 0118-981 0775 E-mail: sales@fluidcontrols.co.uk *Instrument distributors*

▶ Fluid Creativity Ltd, 5 Fifth Avenue, Dukinfield, Cheshire, SK16 4PP Tel: (0845) 6588373 Fax: 0161-343 5577 E-mail: lee@fluidcreativity.co.uk *Designers of web, print design, multimedia, animation consultants*

Fluid Equipment International Ltd, 10 Blandford Heights Industrial Estate, Blandford Forum, Dorset, DT11 7TE Tel: (01258) 459401 Fax: (01258) 459068 E-mail: sales.feil@btconnect.com *Pump manufrs*

Fluid Lift Systems Ltd, 4b Loxley Road, Wellesbourne, Warwick, CV35 9JY Tel: (01789) 470264 Fax: (01789) 470266 E-mail: info@fluidliftsystems.co.uk *Hydraulic equipment systems maintenance*

Fluid Power Centre Ltd, 4th Avenue Zone 2, Deeside Industrial Park, Deeside, Clwyd, CH5 2NR Tel: (01244) 289231 Fax: (01244) 289232 *Hydropneumatic accumulator recertification & servicing*

Fluid Power Components, 14 The Oakwood Centre, Downley Road, Havant, Hampshire, PO9 2NP Tel: (023) 9245 4981 Fax: (023) 9245 4981 E-mail: sales@fluidpowercomponents.com *Hydraulic & pneumatic equipment distribs*

Fluid Power Services Ltd, 1 Aston Court, Kingsland Grange, Woolston, Warrington, WA1 4SG Tel: (01925) 828590 Fax: (01925) 828590 E-mail: sales@fluidpowerservices.co.uk *Manufacturers & distributors of hydraulic hose assemblies in mild steel & stainless steel & pneumatic control systems. Extensive range of off-the-shelf products, includiing stainless steel hose*

Fluid Technologies Environmental Ltd, 50 Old London Road, Kingston upon Thames, Surrey, KT2 6QF Tel: (020) 8549 7722 Fax: (020) 8549 7733 E-mail: info@fluidtechnologies.com *Air emmission control equipment.*

▶ Fluid Technology Generation Ltd, Drum Industrial Estate, Chester le Street, County Durham, DH2 1SR Tel: 0191-411 1777 Fax: 0191-411 1888 E-mail: flutechnolgy@btconnect.com *Chemicals*

Fluid Transfer Ltd, Nailsworth Mills Estate, Avening Road, Nailsworth, Stroud, Gloucestershire, GL6 0BT Tel: (01453) 833381 Fax: (01453) 833529 E-mail: sales@fluid-transfer.co.uk *Automatic & manual hose reels*

▶ Fluid UK Ltd, 4 Falcongate Industrial Estate, Old Gorsey Lane, Wallasey, Merseyside, CH44 4HD Tel: 0151-638 0869 Fax: 0151-638 5800 E-mail: sales@fluideng.co.uk *Mechanical seal retail & manufrs*

▶ Fluidic Ltd, 4-8 Lochend Street, Motherwell, Lanarkshire, ML1 1RX Tel: (01698) 327372 Fax: (01698) 327281 E-mail: sales@fluidic-ltd.co.uk *Instrument engineering services*

▶ Fluiditi, Unit 86 88, Christian Mill Business Park, Tamerton Foliot Road, Plymouth, PL6 5DS Tel: (01752) 242300

▶ Fluidprint, 56-58 Bolton Street, Bury, Lancashire, BL9 0LL Tel: (0161) 7646464 Fax: (0161) 7610408 E-mail: sales@fluidprint.net *Printing products, business stationery, letterheads & graphic design*

▶ Fluke Networks, Egale 1, 80 St. Albans Road, Watford, WD17 1RP Tel: (01923) 281300 Fax: (01923) 281301 E-mail: sales-uk@flukenetworks.com *Cabling & networking solutions services*

▶ Fluke (UK) Ltd, 52 Hurricane Way, Norwich, NR6 6JB Tel: (020) 7942 0700 Fax: (020) 7942 0701 E-mail: industrial@uk.fluke.nl *Established in 1948 the Fluke Corporation is an international business providing professional electronic test tools for a wide range of applications. Test tool users in nearly every country and every industry consider the capabilities of Fluke test equipment to be critical to their livelihood. Fluke products are sold and serviced in more than 100 countries around the world with a portfolio which includes Hand Held DMM's, Electrical testers, Power Quality Tools, ScopeMeterâ, Thermal Imaging cameras and temperature measurement equipment, Indoor Air Quality, Process and Calibration Tools.*

Fluke UK Ltd, 52 Hurricane Way, Norwich, NR6 6JB Tel: (01603) 256600 Fax: (01603) 483670 E-mail: sales@flukeprecision.co.uk Principal Export Areas: Worldwide *Manufacturers of industrial electronic equipment & electronic measuring instruments*

Fluor Ltd, Portland House, Bressenden Place, London, SW1E 5BH Tel: (020) 7932 1700 Fax: (020) 7932 1722 *Engineering construction & management consultants*

Fluorel Ltd, 312 Broadmead Road, Woodford Green, Essex, IG8 8PG Tel: (020) 8504 9691 Fax: (020) 8506 1792 E-mail: djones@fluorel.co.uk *Lighting fittings manufrs*

Fluorescent Lighting Services, Granville House, 181/187 Moseley Street, Birmingham, B12 0RT Tel: 0121-683 1515 Fax: 0121-683 1516 E-mail: sales@fls-lighting.co.uk *Electrical contractors*

Fluoro Precision Coatings, Units 19-20 Hewitts Industrial Estate, Elmbridge Road, Cranleigh, Surrey, GU6 8LW Tel: (01483) 276887 Fax: (01483) 276130 E-mail: gs@fluoroprecision.co.uk *Fluoroplastic coating specialists*

Fluorocarbon Co. Ltd, Excalibur Way, Irlam, Manchester, M44 5DL Tel: 0161-777 6300 Fax: 0161-776 2503 E-mail: seals@fluorocarbon.co.uk *PTFE sheet & tape manufrs*

Fluorocarbon Bakeware Systems Ltd, Unit B, Lilac Grove, Beeston, Nottingham, NG9 1PF Tel: 0115-943 1111 Fax: 0115-943 1177 E-mail: sales@fluorocarbon.co.uk *FBS is the leading designer and producer of industrial bakeware in Europe. A state of the art manufacturing division supported by a dedicated finishing division ensures that FBS industrial bakeware products offer longevity and economy to consistently meet the high demands of the baking industry. Specialising in both the very large run requirements for the commercial bakeries as well as the bespoke products for the smaller companies, FBS offers a comprehensive service. A wide range of stock items are also carried, and can be viewed on the website.*

Fluorocarbon Coatings (Sheffield Division) Ltd, Burlyvale Avenue, Sheffield, S12 2AX Tel: 0114-253 0353 Fax: 0114-253 0355 E-mail: info@fluorocarbon.co.uk *Fluorocarbon & PTFE coating processors*

Fluorocarbon Scotland Ltd, 6 Rutherford Square, Brucefield Industrial Estate, Livingston, West Lothian, EH54 9BU Tel: (01506) 411865 Fax: (01506) 412720 E-mail: engineeringplastics@fluorocarbon.co.uk *Supply & engineering services of plastic*

Fluorochem Ltd, Wesley Street, Glossop, Derbyshire, SK13 7RY Tel: (01457) 865698 Fax: (01457) 869360 E-mail: enquiries@fluorochem.co.uk *Chemical manufacturers & distributors*

Fluorotech Dispersions Ltd, 11 Hampers Common Industrial Estate, Petworth, West Sussex, GU28 9NR Tel: (01798) 343586 Fax: (01798) 343586 *Fluro carbon coating processor manufrs*

▶ Flutterby Designs, 12 Cypress close, Taverham, Norwich, NR8 6QG Tel: (01603) 868643 E-mail: flutterbydesigns1@hotmail.com *We supply a vast range of unusual & high quality card making & scrapbooking items. These are packaged in small quantities at competitive prices.*

▶ Fly By Wireless, 34 Rathmore Road, Prenton, Merseyside, CH43 2HF Tel: 07979 906762 Fax: 0151 5136110 E-mail: enquiries@flybywireless.com *Fly By Wireless(FBW) www.flybywireless.com - I.T. Wireless & Wired Networking; Networks, Windows 2000 servers, consultancy, design, development, maintenance, computer system design, construction & supplies, Web Design, E-commerce, Domain registration and all I.T. related services. Based in Birkenhead, Merseyside, England, UK*

▶ The Fly Factory, Unit 325, Vale Enterprise Centre, Hayes Road, Sully, Penarth, South Glamorgan, CF64 5SY Tel: (01446) 700401 Fax: (01446) 404646 E-mail: sales@theflyfactory.co.uk *Manufacture & distribution of fly's for fishing*

▶ Fly Kill, 50 Bentfield Gardens, Stansted, Essex, CM24 8JE Tel: (01279) 817674 Fax: (0870) 1268038 E-mail: mail@fly-kill.co.uk *Insecticides traps, electric fly killers fly screens & wasp*

Flybe, Jack Walker House, Clyst Honiton, Exeter, EX5 2HL Tel: (01392) 366669 Fax: (01392) 366151 E-mail: caroline.fletcher@flybe.com *Airline maintenance company*

Flydor Ltd, Unit 3 Priory Works, Newton Street, Newton St. Faith, Norwich, NR10 3AD Tel: (01603) 897799 Fax: (01603) 897280 E-mail: sales@flydor.co.uk Principal Export Areas: Worldwide *Insect screening distributors or agents*

▶ Flyers Group P.L.C., 1 Windsor Industrial Estate, 424 Ware Road, Hertford, SG13 7EW Tel: (01992) 538003 Fax: (01992) 507109 E-mail: sales@flyers-clothing.co.uk *Children's clothing suppliers*

Flyght Golf Ltd, 21 Biglands Drive, Huyton, Liverpool, L36 0XS Tel: 0151-480 3645 Fax: 0151-480 1785 E-mail: johnfarrell7200@tiscali.co.uk *Golf ball & equipment suppliers*

Flying Colours, Unit 5-6 Orchard Court, Iles Lane, Knaresborough, North Yorkshire, HG5 8PP Tel: (01423) 860007 Fax: (01423) 861858 E-mail: sales@flag-makers.co.uk *Flag, bunting & banner manufacturers flagpoles & sign suppliers*

▶ Flying Monk Ltd, 4 Twatley Cottages Sherston, Road Malmesbury, Malmesbury, Wiltshire, SN16 0QX Tel: (0845) 056 3989 Fax: (01666) 825773 E-mail: info@flyingmonkgroup.com *Purchasing & supply chain consultants*

Flying Monk Graphics, 9 Malmesbury Business Park, Beuttell Way, Malmesbury, Wiltshire, SN16 9JU Tel: (01666) 829228 Fax: (01666) 829229 E-mail: sales@flyingmonkgraphics.co.uk *Large format printing providers*

Flying Pizza Co., 5 Barnwell Business Park, Barnwell Drive, Cambridge, CB5 8UX Tel: (01223) 244875 *Home pizza delivery service*

Flying Service Engineering (Sales) Ltd, 5 Springfield Road, Chesham, Buckinghamshire, HP5 1PP Tel: (01494) 786666 Fax: (01494) 791813 E-mail: fsee@talk21.com *Aircraft passenger seat manufrs*

Flying Services, Newtown Industrial Estate, Cross Keys, Newport, Gwent, NP11 7PZ Tel: (01495) 272712 Fax: (01495) 270211 *Aircraft seats manufrs*

Flynet Ltd, King William House, The Causeway, Burwell, Cambridge, CB5 0DU Tel: (01638) 611111 Fax: (01638) 611115 E-mail: info@flynet.co.uk *Web Integrators*

▶ Flynn Product Design, 5 Crewkerne, Nailsea, Bristol, BS48 2SN Tel: (07730) 530636 E-mail: chris@flynn-product-design.com *Product design consultants, product design, industrial design & development service*

▶ Flynn Surfacing Ltd, Sandfold Lane, Manchester, M19 3BJ Tel: 0161-248 8842 Fax: 0161-248 8805

Flynn's Bread Supplies, The Warehouse, Paradise Rd, Downham Market, Norfolk, PE38 9JE Tel: 01366 386511 *Bread distributor*

▶ Flyte So Fancy, The Cottage, Pulham, Dorchester, Dorset, DT2 7DX Tel: (01300) 345229 Fax: (01300) 345229 E-mail: anne@flytesofancy.freeserve.co.uk *Flyte so Fancy is a family-run company manufacturing beautiful Poultry Housing, Dovecotes, Kennels & pet houses. Based near Dorchester, Dorset we sell all kinds of Poultry Supplies & Electric Fencing.*

FM Engineering Services Ltd, Burtonhead Road, St. Helens, Merseyside, WA9 5EA Tel: (01744) 746800 Fax: (01744) 746810 E-mail: markowens@fmengineering.co.uk *Trailer repairs services*

FMB UK Ltd, P O Box 5222, Leicester, LE4 8ZE Tel: 0116-260 7744 Fax: 0116-260 7222 E-mail: sales@fmbuk.co.uk *Machine tool hire services*

▶ FMC Measurement Solutions, Unit 6 Baird Way, Thetford, Norfolk, IP24 1JA Tel: (01842) 822900 Fax: (01842) 765402 E-mail: sales@fmcmeasurementsolutions.com *Gas measurement solutions*

Fmi, Queens House, 1 Leicester Place, London, WC2H 7BP Tel: (020) 7758 0700 Fax: (020) 7758 0701 *Computer solutions centre*

Foam 4 U Army & Navy Stores, 21 Chestergate, Macclesfield, Cheshire, SK11 6BX Tel: (01625) 425164 *Foam for army & navy*

Foam Centre, 29 Howard Street, Glasgow, G1 4BA Tel: 0141-221 7578 Fax: 0141-221 7578 E-mail: sales@foamcentre.co.uk *Foam product suppliers*

Foam & Fabric Shop, 23 Broad Street, Seaford, East Sussex, BN25 1LS Tel: (01323) 893716 *Upholsterers & upholstery supplies*

▶ Foam Forge, 6 Rempstone Barns, Rempstone, Corfe Castle, Wareham, Dorset, BH20 5JH Tel: (01929) 480600 Fax: (01929) 480600 E-mail: sales@foamforge.co.uk *Moulding PE,PP,EVA foam*

Foam Place, Market Place South, Leicester, LE1 5HB Tel: 0116-251 9538 Fax: 0116-251 1573 *Foam products retail*

Foam Techniques Ltd, 39 Booth Drive, Park Farm South, Wellingborough, Northamptonshire, NN8 6GR Tel: (01933) 400096 Fax: (01933) 400095 E-mail: sales@foamtechniques.co.uk Sales Contact: V. Relan Principal Export Areas: Worldwide *As a totally customer focused business Foam Techniques Ltd offers the technical, material, production & delivery capabilities demanded to support your market & application. As converters of Polyurethane foam, expanded polyethylene, rubber and allied products, applications & markets include Packaging, Acoustic Insulation, Air Filtration, Water Filtration, Medical, MOD, Construction, Aerospace, Consumer Goods, Automotive, Passenger Vehicles, Air Conditioning, HVAC, Thermal Insulation, Sealing/Gasketing, Specialist Vehicles, Personal Protection to name but a few. *Production Processes include water jet cutting, die cutting, multi layer lamination, thermo-compression forming, splitting, profiling, routing. Our production unit can handle orders of all sizes from small one off batches to large weekly batches, all produced in line with the companies ISO9001 quality systems to ensure consistency & quality. *With over 500 different grades, Foam Techniques is simply 'The Home of Foam'*

▶ Foam Wizards Ltd, 3 Canal Street, Stourbridge, West Midlands, DY8 4LU Tel: (01384) 377018 Fax: (01384) 376757 E-mail: knettleford@aol.com *Foam & upholstery suppliers*

Foamline Ltd, Unit A-B Industrial Estate, Floors Street, Johnstone, Renfrewshire, PA5 8PE Tel: (01505) 327155 Fax: (01505) 503811 E-mail: sales@foamline.co.uk *Cosmetic applications*

Fobbed Off, 3 The Mews, Breadcroft Lane, Harpenden, Hertfordshire, AL5 4TF Tel: (01582) 768295 Fax: (01582) 768295 E-mail: nick@ncooper45.freeserve.co.uk *Carrier bags manufrs*

Focal Design Ltd, The Old Bakery, Albion Road, New Mills, High Peak, Derbyshire, SK22 3EX Tel: (01663) 746100 Fax: (01663) 746920 E-mail: sales@focaldesign.co.uk *Exhibition stand designers & printers*

Focal Plastics Ltd, 34-40 Cutlers Road, South Woodham Ferrers, Chelmsford, CM3 5XJ Tel: (01245) 322788 Fax: (01245) 323194 E-mail: sales@focalplastics.co.uk Principal Export Areas: Africa *Plastic vacuum forming*

Focal Point Audio Visual Ltd, 1-3 Kew Place, Cheltenham, Gloucestershire, GL53 7NQ Tel: (01242) 693118 Fax: (01242) 693118 *Educational video suppliers*

▶ Focal Point Manufacturing Company Ltd, 436 Hillington Road, Hillington Industrial Estate, Glasgow, G52 4BL Tel: 0141-883 9178 Fax: 0141-883 5592

▶ Focal Projects Ltd, 4 Waterside Business Park, Armitage Road, Rugeley, Staffordshire, WS15 1LJ Tel: (01889) 586150 Fax: (01889) 575374 E-mail: sales@focalprojects.co.uk

Focke & Co. UK Ltd, Courtenay Works, Monument Way East, Woking, Surrey, GU21 5LY Tel: (01483) 756094 Fax: (01483) 765099 E-mail: fockeuk@btconnect.com *Packaging equipment merchants*

▶ Focus Air Conditioning, Unit Laker Hosue Canning Street, Maidstone, Kent, ME14 2RX Tel: 01622 690559 Fax: 01622 690559 E-mail: focusac@talktalk.net *we are a small family run business with over thirty years experience. Our expertise in air conditioning and refrigeration means that we are able to offer you excellent services in both new installations and maintaining existing plant.*

FOCUS Eap, 1st Floor The Podium, Metropolitan House Darkes Lane, Potters Bar, Hertfordshire, EN6 1AG Tel: (01707) 661300 Fax: (01707) 661242 E-mail: info@focuseap.co.uk *Eap services*

FOCUS Interior Contracts Ltd, Unit 14 Victoria Way, Pride Park, Derby, DE24 8AN Tel: (01332) 200556 Fax: (01332) 299226 E-mail: sales@focusinteriors.co.uk *Commercial interior installers*

FOCUS Interiors Ltd, Wellsway Works, Wells Road, Radstock, BA3 3RZ Tel: (01761) 420055 Fax: (01761) 420077 E-mail: enquiries@focusinteriorsltd.co.uk *Partitioning & ceiling contractors*

FOCUS Marketing Rubber Band Specialist, 62 Broadoak Avenue, Maidstone, Kent, ME15 6DH Tel: (01622) 755517 E-mail: sales@bandit.co.uk *Rubber bands manufrs*

FOCUS Microsystems, Belmont House, Bayswater Farm Road, Headington, Oxford, OX3 8BX Tel: (0871) 2500021 Fax: (01865) 750937 E-mail: enquiries@focus-property.co.uk *Software publishers*

FOCUS Organic Ltd, 14 Thoroughfare, Halesworth, Suffolk, IP19 8AH Tel: (01986) 872899 Fax: (01986) 872995 *Health food suppliers*

FOCUS Print & Marketing Ltd, Digital House, Stourport Road, Kidderminster, Worcestershire, DY11 7QH Tel: (01562) 862888 Fax: (01562) 820144 *Computer stationery brokers*

▶ FOCUS Promotions, 397 Tamworth Road, Long Eaton, Long Eaton, Nottingham, NG10 3JP Tel: (0800) 3164457 Fax: 0115-946 1245 E-mail: sales@jbpromotions.com

FOCUS Sb Ltd, Napier Road, St. Leonards-on-Sea, East Sussex, TN38 9NY Tel: (01424) 440734 Fax: (01424) 853862 E-mail: sales@focussb.co.uk *Sussex Brassware is an e-commerce company selling decorative wiring accessories and architectural ironmongery direct to the end user. These high quality ranges offer traditional and contemporary designs to suit new build and restoration projects.*

FOCUS Signs Ltd, 136a St. Johns Road, Woking, Surrey, GU21 7PS Tel: (01483) 776716 Fax: (01483) 776716 *Sign manufrs*

FOCUS Washrooms, Unit 9, Fieldings Road, Cheshunt, Waltham Cross, Hertfordshire, EN8 9TL Tel: (01992) 625990 *Washroom cubicles*

FOCUS Windows Ltd, Unit A Technology Centre, White Oak Square, London Road, Swanley, Kent, BR8 7AG Tel: (01322) 614551 Fax: (01322) 613366 *UPVC & aluminium windows doors & conservatories suppliers*

FOCUS Windows Fascias Cladding Soffits, 9-15 Christchurch Lane, Market Drayton, Shropshire, TF9 1DZ Tel: (01630) 655717 Fax: (0871) 2422482 E-mail: info@focuswindows.co.uk *Commercial conservatory*

Focused Nutrition Ltd, 8 Vaughan Road, Stockport, Cheshire, SK4 2PQ Tel: 0161-443 1295 E-mail: sales@focus-nutrition.co.uk *Manufacturer of cereal bars*

Focusrite Audio Engineering Ltd, Windsor House, Turnpike Road, High Wycombe, Buckinghamshire, HP12 3FX Tel: (01494) 462246 Fax: (01494) 459920

continued

▶ indicates data change since last edition

continuation
E-mail: sales@focusrite.com *Audio amplifier equipment supply*

Fodder The Health Store, 26-27 Church Street, Hereford, HR1 2LR Tel: (01432) 358171 Fax: (01432) 277861 *Natural foods retailers*

▶ Fodder Mongers, 3 Barratt Industrial Park, Whittle Avenue, Fareham, Hampshire, PO15 5SL Tel: (01489) 565040 Fax: (01489) 564041 E-mail: enquiries@foddermongers.com *Sandwich, buffet delivery & outside catering services*

Foden Ibex Ltd, Ibex House Ferrofields, Scaldwell Road, Brixworth, Northampton, NN6 9UA Tel: (01604) 880605 Fax: (01604) 880802 E-mail: sales@fodenibex.co.uk *Leather belt manufrs*

Foerster UK Ltd, 2 Bonehill Mews, Fazeley, Tamworth, Staffordshire, B78 3QU Tel: (01827) 831290 Fax: (01827) 284982 E-mail: sales@foersteruk.com Principal Export Areas: Africa *Sales & service of non-destructive test equipment & systems*

Fogarty Ltd, Havenside, Fishtoft Road, Boston, Lincolnshire, PE21 0AH Tel: (01205) 361122 Fax: (01205) 353202 E-mail: info@fogarty.co.uk *Pillows & quilt manufrs*

Foil & Bookcraft, Unit 27 Baldock Industrial Estate, London Road, Baldock, Hertfordshire, SG7 6NG Tel: (01462) 490074 Fax: (01462) 490074 *Hot foil printing & book binding*

Foil Engineering Ltd, 12c Gorst Road, London, NW10 6LE Tel: (020) 8961 3466 Fax: (020) 8961 3466 *Heating element manufrs*

Foil Ribbon & Impact Printing Scotland Ltd, 4 Rutherford Court, 15 North Avenue, Clydebank Business Park, Clydebank, Dunbartonshire, G81 2QP Tel: 0141-952 5525 Fax: 0141-952 5524 E-mail: scotland@foilribbon.com *Print & foil blockers*

Foil & Tool Services Ltd, Tudor Business Centre, Marsden Road, Redditch, Worcestershire, B98 7AY Tel: (01527) 65352 Fax: (01527) 591790 E-mail: foilandtoolservices@onetel.net.com *Hot stamping foils & machines suppliers*

▶ Foila Ltd, Valley House Hornbeam Park, Hookstone Road, Harrogate, North Yorkshire, HG2 8QT Tel: (01423) 810480 Fax: (01423) 810490 E-mail: info@foila.co.uk *Manufacture and supply a fully automatic salon highlighting foil dispenser.*

Foilco Ltd, Enterprise Way, Lowton, Warrington, WA3 2BP Tel: (01942) 262622 Fax: (01942) 267200 E-mail: sales@foilco.co.uk Principal Export Areas: Africa *Hot & stamping foils. In addition, holographic paper or board*

Folbigg Fabrications, Ramsden Road, Rotherwas Industrial Estate, Hereford, HR2 6LR Tel: (01432) 271481 Fax: (01432) 268773 E-mail: folbigg@rotherwas.fsbusiness.co.uk *Steel fabricators*

Fold Hill Foods Ltd, Reg Office, Fold Hill, Stickney, Boston, Lincolnshire, PE22 8HQ Tel: (01205) 270500 Fax: (01205) 270596 E-mail: info@foldhillfoods.fsnet.co.uk *Pet food manufrs*

▶ Folder Workshop, 4 Lyon Road, Walton-on-Thames, Surrey, KT12 3PU Tel: (01932) 246046 Fax: (01932) 246066 E-mail: info@folderworkshop.com *Ring binder manufrs*

Folders Galore Ltd, 3-4 Advance Road, London, SE27 9LT Tel: (020) 8670 7416 Fax: (020) 8670 9605 E-mail: mail@foldersgalore.com *Folder & binder manufrs*

▶ Folding Sliding Doors, FSD Works, Hopbine Avenue West Bowling, Bradford, West Yorkshire, BD5 8ER Tel: (01274) 715880 Fax: (0845) 6446631 E-mail: info@foldingslidingdoors.co.uk *Folding sliding Timber/Upvc/Aluminium door manufacturers.Also available from Summer 2004 sliding door gear at very competitive prices.*

Foleshill Metal Finishing Ltd, 13 Bayton Road, Exhall, Coventry, CV7 9EJ Tel: (024) 7636 2960 Fax: (024) 7636 5876 E-mail: queries@foleshill.co.uk *Powder coating services*

Folex Film Ltd, Unit 19 Monkspath Business Park, Shirley, Solihull, West Midlands, B90 4NY Tel: 0121-733 3833 Fax: 0121-733 3222 E-mail: sales@folex.co.uk *Specialist film & paper manufrs*

▶ Foley & Miles, 732 London Road, Grays, Essex, RM20 3NL Tel: (01708) 869986 Fax: (01708) 869987 *Haulage*

Folgate Risk Solutions Ltd, 2 Cathedral Square, Groat Market, Newcastle Upon Tyne, NE1 1EH Tel: (0870) 9056202 Fax: (0870) 9056203 E-mail: neil.forrest@towergate.co.uk *Insurance brokers*

Folglade Pipe & Fittings Ltd, Penlake Industrial Estate, Reginald Road, Sutton, St. Helens, Merseyside, WA9 4JA Tel: (01744) 820119 Fax: (01744) 811412 E-mail: sales@folglade.co.uk *Flanges & pipeline fittings manufrs*

Folkard Bolding, 27 The Vale, London, W3 7RR Tel: (020) 8749 1021 Fax: (020) 8740 1466 *Sanitary ware merchants*

Folkes Group Ltd, 7orge House, Dudley Road, Stourbridge, West Midlands, DY9 8EL Tel: (01384) 424242 Fax: (01384) 424425 *Industrial development agents*

Folkes Plant & Aggregates Ltd, Welcome Pits, Butt Lane, Burgh Castle, Great Yarmouth, Norfolk, NR31 9PY Tel: (01493) 780274 Fax: (01493) 781118 *Contractors' plant hire*

Folkestone & Dover, The Cherry Garden, Cherry Garden Lane, Folkestone, Kent, CT19 4QB Tel: (01303) 298888 Fax: (01303) 276712 E-mail: enquiries@fdws.co.uk *Water supply*

Folknoll Ltd, 26 Old North Road, Royston, Hertfordshire, SG8 5DT Tel: (01763) 248834 Fax: (01763) 248014 E-mail: general@folknoll.co.uk *Specialist audio communications manufrs*

Folmer Amtoft Ltd, 4 Hounslow Road, Twickenham, TW2 7EX Tel: (020) 8898 6031 Fax: (020) 8893 3502 E-mail: info@folmeramtoft.com *Manufacturing jewellers*

Folsana Pressed Sections Ltd, Sidney Street, Bolton, BL3 6BF Tel: (01204) 393355 Fax: (01204) 393377 E-mail: dm@folsana.co.uk *Manufacturers of steel sections*

Fonad Products, 99a Webster Road, Liverpool, L7 4LG Tel: 0151-733 0000 Fax: 0151-733 0000 *Bed supplier*

Fone Installations, Unit 2 Douglas Buildings, Lodge Road, Staplehurst, Tonbridge, Kent, TN12 0QZ Tel: (01580) 893377 Fax: (01580) 893434 E-mail: mail@foneinstallations.co.uk *Suppliers & fitters of hands free car kits*

▶ Fone Options UK, Kingsbury House 468 Church Lane, Kingsbury, London, NW9 8UA Tel: 0800 1804814 E-mail: sales@foneoptions.co.uk *Foneoptions provides upgrades and new contracts to customers on all the leading networks.*

▶ Fonebittz Ltd, 146 Cricket Road, Oxford, OX4 3DL Tel: (01865) 204422 Fax: (01865) 204100 E-mail: sales@fonebitz.co.uk *Latest contract deals, Sim free phone, Remote unlocking, Pay as you go phones, Logos & Ringtones, International calling cards, Mobile phone accessories, Sim cards....*

▶ Fonefixation, 31-37 Etna Road, Falkirk, FK2 9EG Tel: (0871) 250 2555 *Telecommunications company*

Fontaine International Europe Ltd, Enterprise Way, Newton Road, Lowton, Warrington, WA3 2AG Tel: (01942) 686000 Fax: (01942) 686006 E-mail: info@fifthwheeleurope.com *Fifth wheels & couplings manufrs*

▶ Fontanaprint, 32 Randolph Road, Frome, Somerset, BA11 1LP Tel: (07837) 697415 E-mail: fontanaprint@fontanaprint.co.uk *T shirt printers, t shirts and garments screen printed to the highest quality. Clubs, business or occasions. Stag and hen night. School and playgroup. Short or long run garment printing. Competitive prices, secure payment and ordering. On line t shirt printing.*

Fontley Wrought Iron, Fontley Road, Titchfield, Fareham, Hampshire, PO15 6QZ Tel: (01329) 847700 *Wrought iron manufrs*

Fontware Ltd, 25 Barnes Wallis Road, Fareham, Hampshire, PO15 5TT Tel: (01489) 505075 Fax: (0870) 0515816 E-mail: sales@fontware.com *Computer software designers*

Fontworks UK Ltd, New North House, 202-208 New North Road, London, N1 7BJ Tel: (020) 7226 4411 Fax: (020) 7226 4422 E-mail: sales@type.co.uk *Font software manufrs*

▶ Food Business Ltd, St. Georges House, 50 Adelaide Street, St. Albans, Hertfordshire, AL3 5BG Tel: (01727) 832834 Fax: (01727) 832836 E-mail: sally@thefoodbusiness.co.uk *Food technology consultants*

Food Business Development Consultancy, 68 Park Street, St. Albans, Hertfordshire, AL2 2PW Tel: (01727) 873303 Fax: (01727) 874063 E-mail: susan@fbdc.co.uk *Food technology consultants*

Food Centre Wales, Horeb, Llandysul, Dyfed, SA44 4JG Tel: (01559) 362230 Fax: (01559) 362086 E-mail: jen@foodcentrewales.org.uk *Food technology centre & research developers*

▶ Food Chain, 2 Steppingley Road, Flitwick, Bedford, MK45 1AJ Tel: (01525) 718766 Fax: (01525) 717319

▶ Food Diligence Systems Ltd, Tamerton House, Furzefield Avenue, Speldhurst, Tunbridge Wells, Kent, TN3 0LD Tel: (01892) 861074 Fax: (01892) 861078

▶ Food & Drug Analytical Services Ltd, BioCity Nottingham, Pennyfoot Street, Nottingham, NG1 1GF Tel: 0115-912 4265 Fax: 0115-912 4267 E-mail: office@fdas.org *FDAS offer fast, customer driven analytical testing services. We are an independent contract laboratory performing a wide array of chemical and microbiological services. Our experienced analytical team within our state of the art, GMP facility provide all the technical expertise needed to guarantee accurate results that meet the requirements and rigours of any regulatory body.*

▶ Food Forming Machines Ltd, 15 Gosditch Street, Cirencester, Gloucestershire, GL7 2AG Tel: (01285) 658995 Fax: (01285) 659099 E-mail: mail@foodformingmachines.com *We specialise in the design and manufacture of industrial, food forming machines and process lines for a wide variety of products including hamburgers, chicken-nuggets and fish-sticks to name just a few.*

Food From Britain Fast Track, Manning House, 22 Carlisle Place, London, SW1P 1JA Tel: (020) 7233 5111 Fax: (020) 7233 9515 E-mail: fasttrack@foodforbritain.co.uk *Marketing company*

Food Machinery Co. Ltd, Fenn Corner, Rochester, Kent, ME3 8RS Tel: (01634) 272345 Fax: 01634 272200 E-mail: sales@food-machineryco.com *As a Company we offer a wide range of food processing equipment, including cooking kettles, volumetric depositors, Tray washers, bait rollers vacuum packers, form fill seal equipment, refridgeration, bakery, and so much more.*

▶ Food Network Corporation, 4 Harwood Court, Riverside Park Industrial Estate, Middlesbrough, Cleveland, TS2 1PU Tel: (01642) 891499 Fax: (01642) 891466

▶ Food Pac Ltd, 2 Enderby Road Industrial Estate, Whetstone, Leicester, LE8 6HZ Tel: 0116-275 0836 Fax: 0116-275 0834

▶ The Food & Packaging Company, 84 Tenter Road, Moulton Park, Northampton, NN3 6AX Tel: 01604 493020 Fax: 01604 492228 E-mail: info@thefandp.com *Supplying a wide product range to a broad base of customers including the travel industry, catering, wholesale and pub restaurant sector.**Specialising in the design of packaging, sourcing products from an extensive range of chocolates, savoury snacks, confectionery and drinks, and delivering the finished packed products. BRC Higher Level accredited since 2002 and recognised by Cadbury Trebor Bassett and Thorntons as approved contract packers.**We are an Investor in People company with a dedicated team of trained packers. We do not use agency staff or home workers. Food safety and quality assurance are of paramount importance, and the Company operates HACCP working practices and fully implemented Quality Systems.**

Food Partners Kilmarnock Ltd, Rowallan Business Park, Southcraig Avenue, Kilmarnock, Ayrshire, KA3 6BQ Tel: (01563) 556000 Fax: (01563) 570040 *Sandwich manufrs*

▶ Food Process Engineering Ltd, The Creamery, Sheriffiats Road, Thankerton, Biggar, Lanarkshire, ML12 6PA Tel: (01899) 308591 Fax: (01899) 308776 E-mail: sales@foodprocess.co.uk

Food Safety Services Ltd, West View, Longleat Lane, Holcombe, Radstock, BA3 5DX Tel: (01761) 232146 Fax: (01761) 233697 *Pest control services*

Food Service Engineers Ltd Ltd, Ilkley Road, Wharfedenk Business Centre, Otley, W. Yorkshire, LS21 3JP Tel: (01943) 467467 Fax: (01943) 467565 E-mail: beamhouse@aol.com *Repair commercial catering equipment*

Food Service Packaging Association, 64 High Street, Kirkintilloch, Glasgow, G66 1PR Tel: 0141-777 7272 Fax: 0141-777 7747 E-mail: npc@natpack.org.uk *Trade association*

▶ Food Services, Ruthvenfield Road, Inveralmond Industrial Estate, Perth, PH1 3EE Tel: (01738) 646666 Fax: (01738) 646667 E-mail: enquiries@callumwalker.com

Foodmek Ltd, 17 Shanwell Road, Tayport, Fife, DD6 9EA Tel: (01382) 553577 Fax: (01382) 552173 E-mail: enquiries@foodmek.co.uk *Food machines manufrs*

▶ Foodphotography.me.uk, Leicester, LE8 Tel: (0787) 6560216 *Specialists in food and retail photography (LBIPP & LBPPA qualifications)- based in the North & East Midlands, but will travel anywhere in the UK for location work with our mobile studio. Clients include Sainsburys & Marriott Hotels. Professional level film & digital equipment used in our dedicated studio.*

▶ Foods Of Asia Ltd, 490 London Road, Westcliff-on-Sea, Essex, SS0 9LD Tel: (01702) 348811

▶ Football Equipment UK, 6 Bridge Garth, South Milford, LEEDS, LS25 5BJ Tel: 07949 145674 Fax: 0870 1342495 E-mail: markhalpin@ic24.net *We are the internets lowest priced football equipment supplier. Selling all sorts of soccer equipment, football training equipment, balls, samba goals, training bibs, boundary poles, speed agility ladders, nets, pumps, ball bags. We are the UKs number one for everything football*

Football Kits Direct Ltd, Bridge Trading Estate, Bridge St North, Smethwick, West Midlands, B66 2BZ Tel: 0121-558 5846 Fax: 0121-555 7109 E-mail: salesunderscorefootballkitsdirect@nsn.com *Sports clothing manufrs*

▶ Footlogic Ltd, 571 Southmead Road, Westbury-On-Trym, Bristol, BS10 5NL Tel: 0117-969 7600

▶ Footprint Communications, 24 West Street, Alresford, Hampshire, SO24 9AT Tel: (01962) 738718 E-mail: info@footprint-comms.co.uk *Freelance, interim and part-time PR and marketing communications.*

Footprint Tools Ltd, PO Box 19, Sheffield, S1 3HY Tel: 0114-275 3200 Fax: 0114-275 9613 E-mail: sales@footprint-tools.co.uk *Hand tool manufrs*

▶ Footprints Solutions, Unit 1 Blakes Business Park Radcliffe Road, Huddersfield, HD3 4LX Tel: (01484) 648500 *Commercial Colour Printers producing Corporate Brochures, Leaflets, Folders, Newsletters, Books and General Business Stationery*

Footsure Western Ltd, 1 Alvin Street, Gloucester, GL1 3EJ Tel: (01452) 422002 Fax: (01452) 307220 E-mail: david.bush@footsure.net *Safety & industrial footwear distributors*

▶ Footwear-Safety, 117 South Quay, Great Yarmouth, Norfolk, NR30 3LD Tel: (01493) 842289 Fax: (01493) 853416 E-mail: sales@footwear-safety.co.uk *On line supplier of safety footwear & walking boots*

For-A (UK) Ltd, Unit C71, Barwell Business Park, Leatherhead Road, Chessington, Surrey, KT9 2NY Tel: (020) 8391 7979 Fax: (020) 8391 7978 E-mail: info@for-a.com *Innovation of audio & video technology*

Forac, Unit 8 9 Riverbank Business Centre, Old Shoreham Road, Shoreham-by-Sea, West Sussex, BN43 5FL Tel: (01273) 467100 Fax: (01273) 467101 E-mail: sales@forac.co.uk *Valve & pneumatic actuator manufrs*

Forbes Blinds, 45 West Road, Peterhead, Aberdeenshire, AB42 2AR Tel: (01779) 470350 Fax: (01779) 470350 *Blinds sales & manufrs*

Forbes Campbell Ltd, Forbes House, 9 Artillery Lane, London, E1 7LP Tel: (020) 7377 8484 Fax: (020) 7377 0032 E-mail: rcompton@casley.co.uk *Export merchants*

Forbes Refrigeration Ltd, Ythanview, Station Road, Ellon, Aberdeenshire, AB41 9AY Tel: (01358) 720853 Fax: (01358) 721898 E-mail: nncg@dialstart.net *Refrigeration installers*

Forbes Technologies Ltd, Unit 3, Pinnacle Hill Estate, Kelso, Roxburghshire, TD5 8DW Tel: (01573) 224499

Forbes West Ltd, 128 Tutbury Road, Burton-on-Trent, Staffordshire, DE13 0NU Tel: (01283) 564351 Fax: (01283) 535707 *Builders & civil engineers*

▶ Forbes & Whiteford Ltd, 5 New Mill Road, Kilmarnock, Ayrshire, KA1 3JG Tel: (01563) 522298 Fax: (01563) 524812

▶ Forbidden Fruits, Telford Way, Severalls Industrial Park, Colchester, CO4 9QP Tel: (01206) 514049 Fax: (0870) 1693473 E-mail: enquiry@forbiddenfruits.net *Cigarette vending, fruit machines, juke boxes suppliers*

Forbo Swift Adhesives Ltd, Bridge Street, Chatteris, Cambridgeshire, PE16 6RD Tel: (01354) 692345 Fax: (01354) 696661 *Adhesive manufrs*

▶ Force 8 Upvc Conservatories Ltd, Unit 1c School Street, Hazel Grove, Stockport, Cheshire, SK7 4RA Tel: 0161-483 1997 Fax: 0161-483 5374 E-mail: dennis@force8.co.uk *Window merchants*

Force Components 89 Ltd, Suit 8 Grove Park Industrial Estate, Waltham Road, White Waltham, Maidenhead, Berkshire, SL6 3LW Tel: (01628) 820066 Fax: (01628) 825530 E-mail: sales@force89ltd.co.uk *Semi conductive component distributors*

▶ Force Dredging Systems UK Ltd, 26 Scratchface Lane, Havant, Hampshire, PO9 3NG Tel: (023) 9247 2710 Fax: (023) 9247 2710 E-mail: fdsuk@btopenworld.com *Sewage work services*

Force Engineering Ltd, Old Station Close, Shepshed, Loughborough, Leicestershire, LE12 9NJ Tel: (01509) 506025 Fax: (01509) 505433 E-mail: enquiries@force.co.uk *Bespoke linear induction motors designers & manufrs*

Force Fire Consultants Ltd, 11 Gorse La Industrial Estate, Brunel Road, Clacton-on-Sea, Essex, CO15 4LU Tel: (01255) 221515 Fax: (01255) 222493 E-mail: info@forcefire.com *Fire consultants & engineers*

Force Heating & Cooling Services, 80 Rawmarsh Hill, Parkgate, Rotherham, South Yorkshire, S62 6EX Tel: (01709) 527920 Fax: (01709) 526290 E-mail: force.heating@virgin.net *Heating & ventilation engineers*

Force Hydraulics, 14a Saxon Business Park, Hanbury Road, Stoke Prior, Bromsgrove, Worcestershire, B60 4AD Tel: (01527) 575704 Fax: (01527) 576668 *Hydraulic cylinder, ram & hydraulic equipment suppliers*

Force Measurement Systems Ltd, 3-5 Lister Road, Glasgow, G52 4BH Tel: 0141-882 8858 Fax: 0141-810 3434 E-mail: sales@forcemeasurement.co.uk *Manufacturers of load cells, strain gauge & monitoring systems*

Force Seven Bearings, First Avenue, Team Valley Trading Estate, Gateshead, Tyne & Wear, NE11 0NU Tel: 0191-487 2421 Fax: 0191-491 0842 E-mail: force7@nbcgroup.com *Distributors of bearings & manufacturers of seals & sprockets*

Force Systems International, 81 Edwin Street, Arnold, Nottingham, NG5 6AX Tel: 0115-875 8682 E-mail: info@forcesystemsinternational.com *Force Systems International designs and manufactures quality force testing systems. These range from manual force gauge test stands to advanced computer controlled dynamic systems. At the top end of the range these systems have control and analysis software. Custom made systems are produced to order. The application of these systems is across many industries where force in tension or compression has to be measured precisely. Weighing systems and force gauges are also available.*

Forcecombe Ltd, 23 Havelock Street, Hull, HU3 4JH Tel: (01482) 227722 Fax: (01482) 227722 *Pipework engineers*

Forcefield Software Ltd, 9 Hall Lane, Wiveton, Holt, Norfolk, NR25 7TG Tel: (01263) 741368 *Computer software developers*

Forcewell Ltd, 3A/3B Denaby Lane Industrial Estate, Denaby, Doncaster, South Yorkshire, DN12 4JL Tel: (01709) 860019 Fax: (01709) 869617 *Injection moulders*

Forco Electrical Services Ltd, Alphinbrook Road, Marsh Barton Trading Estate, Exeter, EX2 8RG Tel: (01392) 272639 Fax: (01392) 270498 E-mail: post@forco.co.uk *Electric motor repair, rewind, special services gear box & unit distributors*

Ford, 25 Poyser Street, London, E2 9RE Tel: (020) 7739 7779 Fax: (020) 7739 3307 E-mail: sales@wgford.co.uk *Sheet metalworkers*

▶ Ford, 2 Alexandria Trading Estate, Alexandria Road, Sidmouth, Devon, EX10 9HA Tel: (01395) 571020 Fax: (01395) 571005

Ford, 2 Alexandria Trading Estate, Alexandria Road, Sidmouth, Devon, EX10 9HA Tel: (01395) 571020 Fax: (01395) 571005 *Plumbing, heating & electrical contractors services*

Allen Ford, London Road, Coventry, CV3 4AA Tel: (024) 7650 7000 Fax: (024) 7650 4393 *Ford dealership*

Ford & Barley Exhibitions Ltd, Unit 2 Fulwood Road South, Sutton-in-Ashfield, Nottinghamshire, NG17 2JZ Tel: (01623) 551120 Fax: (01623) 440063 E-mail: ford.barley@btconnect.com *Exhibition stand contractors*

Ford Component Manufacturing Ltd, East Side, Tyne Dock, South Shields, Tyne & Wear, NE33 5ST Tel: 0191-454 0141 Fax: 0191-456 0028 E-mail: sales@fordcomps.co.uk Principal Export Areas: Central/East Europe & West Europe *Manufacturers of aircraft components precision turned parts*

Ford Electro Plating Ltd, Block B4 Ford Airfield Industrial Estate, Ford, Arundel, West Sussex, BN18 0HY Tel: (01903) 717424 Fax: (01903) 717424 *Electroplating services*

Ford Electronics Ltd, Brewood Hall, Sparrows End Lane, Brewood, Stafford, ST19 9DB Tel: (01902) 455555 E-mail: sales@fordelectronics.co.uk *Telecoms equipment & industrial electronics*

Ford Green Engineering Ltd, Clarence Road, Longton, Stoke-On-Trent, ST3 1AZ Tel: (01782) 342530 Fax: (01782) 599692 E-mail: mail@fge.co.uk *Plant conveyor manufrs*

The Ford Group (Nottingham) Ltd, Park Lane Works, Old Basford, Nottingham, NG6 0EU Tel: 0115-977 0724 Fax: 0115-976 1041 E-mail: ford@fordgroup.co.uk *Communication equipment suppliers*

James Ford & Son, 5 Hide Hill, Berwick-upon-Tweed, TD15 1EQ Tel: (01289) 306081 Fax: (01289) 306081 *Bakery*

James Ford & Son, 11 West Street, Norham, Berwick-upon-Tweed, TD15 2LB Tel: (01289) 382248 Fax: (01289) 382248 *Bakers*

John Ford & Sons Ltd, Longships Road, Cardiff, CF10 4RP Tel: (029) 2046 1579 Fax: (029) 2046 1579 E-mail: rwford@supanet.com *Scrap metal merchants & skip hire, general haulage*

▶ Ford Mainwaring Ltd, 2a Eagle Street, Stoke-on-Trent, ST1 3PE Tel: (01782) 271772 Fax: (01782) 204969

Ford Motor Co. Ltd, Trafford House, Station Way, Basildon, Essex, SS16 5XX Tel: (01268) 703000 Fax: (01268) 703000 E-mail: enquiries@ford.co.uk *Car products & production providers*

Ford Motor Co. Ltd, Central Head Office, Eagle Way, Brentwood, Essex, CM13 3BW Tel: (023) 8058 7300 *Motor vehicle manufrs* Also at: Branches throughout the U.K.

Ford Motor Co Ltd, Waterton Industrial Estate, Bridgend, Mid Glamorgan, CF31 3PJ Tel: (01656) 672300 Fax: (01656) 672201 *Motor engine manufrs*

▶ Ford Motor Co. Ltd, Royal Oak Way South, Royal Oak Industrial Estate, Daventry, Northamptonshire, NN11 8NT Tel: (01327) 305300 *Ford dealer part & distribution centre*

▶ Brian Ford Powell Executive Recruitment, Claybrooke House, Claybrooke Parva, Lutterworth, Leicestershire, LE17 5AE Tel: (01455) 209968 Fax: (01455) 202788 E-mail: contact@bfpexecutiverecruitment.co.uk *Specialist recruitment agency*

Ford Signs, 1A Burgess Street, Leicester, LE1 4QJ Tel: 0116-251 8185 Fax: 0116-251 6595 E-mail: sales.fordsigns@virgin.net *Sign manufrs*

Ford & Slater Of Peterborough, America House, Newark Road, Peterborough, PE1 5YD Tel: (01733) 295000 Fax: (01733) 295010 E-mail: enquiries@fordandslater.co.uk *Commercial vehicle engineers* Also at: Leeds

Ford & Son Ltd, Station House, Station Road, Holton-le-Clay, Grimsby, South Humberside, DN36 5HR Tel: (01472) 840452 Fax: (01472) 840177 *Crane hire services*

▶ Ford Steel Services, 33 Dawley Trading Estate, Stallings Lane, Kingswinford, West Midlands, DY6 7AP Tel: (01384) 288966 Fax: (01384) 292114 *Steel stockholding*

Ford Systems Ltd, Park La, Nottingham, NG6 0EU Tel: 0115-927 2821 Fax: 0115-976 1041 E-mail: arthur.ford@fordgroup.co.uk *Data network solutions*

Ford & Wright Ltd, 73 Spencer Bridge Road, Northampton, NN5 7DP Tel: (01604) 587021 *Software house*

Fordahl Sa), 225 Hampton Lane, Blackfield, Southampton, SO45 1XA Tel: (023) 8089 8899 Fax: (023) 8089 8899 E-mail: fordahluk@fordahl.com *Frequency control product manufrs*

▶ Fordbrook Furniture Co., Fordbrook Estate, Marlborough Road, Pewsey, Wiltshire, SN9 5NT Tel: (01672) 562851 Fax: (01672) 562044 *Kitchen manufrs*

Forde Edwards & Partners, Monton House, Monton Green, Eccles, Manchester, M30 9LE Tel: 0161-788 9099 Fax: 0161-788 9155 E-mail: forde@totalise.co.uk *Chartered quantity surveyors*

Forden Concrete Products, Station Yard, Forden, Welshpool, Powys, SY21 8NN Tel: (01938) 580309 *Concrete drinking troughs manufrs*

Fordham Electrical Contracting & Management Services Ltd, 7 Industrial Estate, Old Church Road, East Hanningfield, Chelmsford, CM3 8AB Tel: (01245) 400200 Fax: (01245) 400777 E-mail: info@fordhamelec.co.uk

▶ Fordham Johns, 31 Regent Street, Great Yarmouth, Norfolk, NR30 1RR Tel: (01493) 843012 Fax: (01493) 330084

Fordingbridge plc, Arundel Road, Fontwell, Arundel, West Sussex, BN18 0SD Tel: (01243) 554455 Fax: (01243) 554433 E-mail: sales@nurserybitz.co.uk *Horticultural market canopy & walkways product manufrs*

Fordman Systems Ltd, The Broadway, Woodhall Spa, Lincolnshire, LN10 6ST Tel: (01526) 354000 Fax: (01526) 354511 E-mail: lorraine@fordman.co.uk *Computer software solutions provider*

Fords Of Blythe Bridge Ltd, 203 Groveindley Lane, Blythe Bridge, Stoke-on-Trent, ST11 9JS Tel: (01782) 392125 Fax: (01782) 396622 E-mail: fords@blythebridge30.fsbusiness.co.uk *Sectional building manufrs*

Fordwater Pumping Supplies Ltd, Unit 32 Forest Vale Road, Forest Vale Industrial Estate, Cinderford, Gloucestershire, GL14 2PH Tel: (01594) 826780 Fax: (01594) 826780 E-mail: fordwater@hotmail.com *Pumps & related equipment, sewage systems*

George Fordy & Son Ltd, Construction House, Northallerton, North Yorkshire, DL7 8ED Tel: (01609) 780700 Fax: (01609) 777236 E-mail: fordy@ftcg.co.uk *Builders & property developers*

Forecourt Systems, 1a Downpatrick Street, Saintfield, Ballynahinch, County Down, BT24 7AY Tel: (028) 9751 1644 Fax: (028) 9751 0860 *Petrol stations supplier*

▶ Foredowel Welders, 4 Seaway Drive, Seaway Parade Industrial Estate, Port Talbot, West Glamorgan, SA12 7BR Tel: (01639) 814578 Fax: (01639) 823184 *Sheet metal workers*

Foregale Ltd, Union Road, Liversedge, West Yorkshire, WF15 7JS Tel: (01924) 401020 Fax: (01924) 405872 *Steel reinforcing suppliers*

▶ Forem Universal Products Ltd, Canal Wharf, Wyther Lane, Leeds, LS5 3BT Tel: 0113-224 2000 Fax: 0113-224 2200 E-mail: sales@forceproducts.co.uk

▶ Foreman Electrical Services, B6 Dovers Corner Industrial Estate, New Road, Rainham, Essex, RM13 8QT Tel: (01708) 555381 Fax: (01708) 525897 E-mail: foreman.electric@btconnect.com *Repair electric motors - lift trade*

L.P. Foreman & Sons Ltd, Farrow Road, Wigford Industrial Estate, Chelmsford, CM1 3TH Tel: (01245) 264521 Fax: (01245) 495232 E-mail: sales@lpforeman.co.uk *Packing case makers & packing services*

Foremost Coatings, Unit 40 Hobbs Industrial Estate, Newchapel, Lingfield, Surrey, RH7 6HN Tel: (01342) 833455 Fax: (01342) 832623 E-mail: david@foremostcoatings.co.uk *Brass cleaning & powder coatings services*

Foremost International Ltd, Unit C Mill Mead, Staines, Middlesex, TW18 4UQ Tel: (01784) 464319 Fax: (01784) 466418 E-mail: ops@foremost-worldcargo.co.uk *International freight forwarder*

Foremost Scaffolding (Supplies) Ltd, Green Acres Trading Estate, Aveley Road, Upminster, Essex, RM14 2TN Tel: (01708) 225549 Fax: (01708) 225607E-mail: foremostscaffold@btconnect.com *Scaffolding contractors*

Forensic Access Ltd, The Health Centre, Bath Road, Thatcham, Berkshire, RG18 3HD Tel: (01635) 862123 Fax: (01635) 869020 E-mail: science@forensic-access.co.uk *Forensic science*

Foresite Systems Ltd, Foresite House, Willenhall Lane, Binley, Coventry, CV3 2UA Tel: (024) 7665 2111 Fax: (024) 7665 5219 E-mail: info@foresite.org *Software developers*

Forest Alarms, Fetter Hill, Coleford, Gloucestershire, GL16 7LU Tel: (01594) 832739 Fax: (01594) 836464 *Security & intruder alarm installers*

▶ Forest Catering, 165 Sion Avenue, Kidderminster, Worcestershire, DY10 2YL Tel: (01562) 823502 Fax: (07799) 063021 E-mail: info@forestcatering.co.uk *Providing fast food for all events burgers,hot dogs,fish"n"chips,pork/beef carvery 4 various sized units available all serving hot and cold drinks car boots also welcome*

▶ Forest Companies Ltd, Unit 5, Northfield Farm, Wantage Road, Great Shefford, Hungerford, Berkshire, RG17 7DQ Tel: (01488) 649120 Fax: (01488) 649121 E-mail: sales@forestcompanies.com *Packaging material & kraft paper suppliers*

Forest Countrywear, 3 High Street, Fordingbridge, Hampshire, SP6 1AS Tel: (01425) 655393 Fax: (01425) 655393 E-mail: sue@forestsaddlery.freeserve.co.uk *Clothing repair & retail services*

Forest Craft, 3 West Shore Road, Edinburgh, EH5 1QB Tel: 0131-552 8287 Fax: 0131-552 6367 *Fencing & sheds manufrs*

▶ Forest Craft, Unit 14-15 200 Woodville Park Industrial Estate, Woodville Street, Glasgow, G51 2RL Tel: 0141-445 4856

▶ Forest Edge Water, Mill Cottage, Beaulieu, Hampshire, SO42 7YG Tel: (01590) 611227 Fax: (01590) 611487 *Suppliers of water coolers for chilled water for offices, schools, factories, hospitals & clubs*

Forest Electrical Services Ltd, Forest Farm, Windmill Hill, Ashill, Ilminster, Somerset, TA19 9LP Tel: (01823) 480905 Fax: (01823) 481042

▶ Forest Engineering, Tulliemet, Ballinluig, Pitlochry, Perthshire, PH9 0NY Tel: (01796) 482408 *Testing equipment service*

Forest Engineering Designs, 57 West Street, Pontypridd, Mid Glamorgan, CF37 4PS Tel: (01443) 409536 Fax: (01443) 405936 *Plastics injection mould design*

Forest Enterprise Signs Workshop, Coed Y Brenin Centre, Ganllwyd, Dolgellau, Gwynedd, LL40 2HY Tel: (01341) 440215 Fax: (01341) 440622 E-mail: sales@signworkshop.co.uk *Manufacturers of timber signs*

Forest & Field Engineering, The Workshop, Mains of Arthurstone Farm, Meigle, Blairgowrie, Perthshire, PH12 8QY Tel: (01828) 640606 Fax: (01828) 640899 E-mail: fm@ffengineering.co.uk *Engineers*

Forest Fireworks, 97-99 Shipston Road, Stratford-upon-Avon, Warwickshire, CV37 7LW Tel: (01789) 295563 Fax: (01789) 295563 *Firework display technicians*

Forest Freight Ltd, Fairview Indust Park, Barlow Way, Rainham, Essex, RM13 8BT Tel: (01708) 552222 Fax: (01708) 553330 E-mail: sales@forestfreight.co.uk *Road transport, haulage & freight service providers*

Forest Garden plc, Unit 291 296, Hartlebury Trading Estate, Hartlebury, Kidderminster, Worcestershire, DY10 4JB Tel: (0870) 1919800 Fax: (0870) 1919898 E-mail: info@forestgarden.co.uk *Timber fencing & sheds suppliers & manufrs*

Forest Hall Joinery, The Dovecotts, Ryes Lane, Hatfield Heath, Bishop's Stortford, Hertfordshire, CM22 7BS Tel: (01279) 730021 Fax: (01279) 730021 *Joinery & cabinet work*

Forest Heath Ltd, 195 Bexhill Road, St. Leonards-on-Sea, East Sussex, TN38 8BG Tel: (01424) 714888 Fax: (01424) 714888 E-mail: forestheath@hotmail.co.uk *General engineers*

Forest Hydraulics Ltd, 19-20 Greenshield Industrial Estate, Bradfield Road, London, E16 2AU Tel: (020) 7474 5738 Fax: (020) 7474 5181 E-mail: forest.hydraulics@virgin.net *Manufacturers of hydraulic fittings*

Forest Joinery, 87 Larch Street, Leicester, LE5 0ES Tel: 0116-253 6721 Fax: 0116-253 6721 *Joining manufrs*

Forest Joinery Ltd, 47 Framfield Road, Uckfield, East Sussex, TN22 5AJ Tel: (01825) 766466 Fax: (01825) 766468 E-mail: info@forestjoineryltd.com *Joinery manufrs*

Forest Personnel Ltd, Cross Keys House, 11 Bridge Street, Reading, RG1 2LR Tel: 0118-958 7272 Fax: 0118-939 1404 E-mail: mail@forestpersonnel.co.uk *Employment agents*

Forest Press Hydraulics Ltd, 6 Hollywood Works, Valley Road, Cinderford, Gloucestershire, GL14 2PD Tel: (01594) 826009 Fax: (01594) 822377 E-mail: sales@forestpresshyd.com *Hydraulic equipment reconditioners*

Forest Products, 2 Ridgeway Farm, Evesham Road, Weethley, Alcester, Warwickshire, B49 5LZ Tel: (01789) 400206 Fax: (01789) 400204 E-mail: roderick@globalnet.co.uk *Furniture component designers*

Forest Products Ltd, Workshop Forestry Commission Lightmoor Dept, Speech House Road, Cinderford, Gloucestershire, GL14 3HU Tel: (01594) 822223 Fax: (01594) 826901 E-mail: enquiries@forest-products.com *Timber treatment & preservation* Also at: Huntley

Forest Software Ltd, 9 Pembroke Grove, Glinton, Peterborough, PE6 7LG Tel: (01733) 253332 Fax: (0870) 7474942 E-mail: sales@forestsoftware.co.uk *Software consultants, website hosting & development, search engine positioning*

▶ Forest Systems (FPE), 4 Farriers Field, Upavon, Pewsey, Wiltshire, SN9 6NW Tel: (07973) 921456 *Printing machine suppliers*

Forest Traffic Signals Ltd, Albany Street, Newport, Gwent, NP20 5NJ Tel: (01633) 850222 Fax: (01633) 822000 E-mail: davidwilliams@foresttraffic.co.uk *Traffic management consultants*

Forest (UK) Ltd, 7 Hurstwood Court, Mercer Way, Shadsworth Business Park, Blackburn, BB1 2QU Tel: (0870) 850 0301 Fax: (0870) 850 0302 E-mail: contactus@forest-uk.com *Forest UK provides Commercial Refrigeration Sales and Service throughout the United Kingdom. Please visit our Website for details on our complete range of products and services.*

Forestbrook Linen Services Ltd, Forestbrook Ave, Rostrevor, Newry, Co. Down, BT34 3BX Tel: (028) 4173 8848 *Contract linen services*

Forestdale Business Services Ltd, Unit 3, Wandle Way, Mitcham, Surrey, CR4 4NB Tel: (020) 8640 3340 Fax: (020) 8640 3374 E-mail: sales@forestdalebs.co.uk *Janitorial supply services*

Forestdale Windows Ltd, 4 Lakeside, Neptune Close, Medway City Estate, Rochester, Kent, ME2 4LT Tel: (01634) 717860 Fax: (01634) 719399 E-mail: pjenn59165@aol.com *Pvc conservatory manufrs*

▶ Forestmaze Ltd, Anderstaff Industrial Estate, Hawkins Lane, Burton-on-Trent, Staffordshire, DE14 1QH Tel: (01283) 535497 Fax: (01283) 569593 *Engineering services*

Forestry Products Kent, Sharsted Avenue, Newnham, Sittingbourne, Kent, ME9 0JX Tel: (01795) 890683 Fax: (01795) 890895 *Fencing manufacturer*

Robin Forestry Surveys Ltd, Coulton House, Tannery Road, Harraby Green Business Park, Carlisle, CA1 2SS Tel: (01228) 409469 Fax: (01228) 540439 E-mail: jaqs@robinsurveys.co.uk *Tree management system providers*

▶ The Forever Aloe Store, 1 Argyle Street, Gorse Hill, Swindon, SN2 8BP Tel: (01793) 641732 E-mail: sales@theforeveraloestore.co.uk *Suppliers of aloe vera health & skincare products*

Forever England, 51c Fore Street, Totnes, Devon, TQ9 5NJ Tel: (01803) 868149 Fax: (01803) 868149 *Soft furnishing goods importers*

▶ Forever Foods, Unit 7-8 Leeway House, Leeway Industrial Estate, Newport, Gwent, NP19 4SL Tel: (01633) 281777 Fax: (01633) 280651 *Confectionery*

Forever Jewellery Ltd, Hall Fabrications, Site F, Lamby Way, Rumney, Cardiff, CF3 2EQ Tel: (029) 2077 9210 Fax: (029) 2077 8838 E-mail: sales@foreverjewellery.co.uk *Wholesale jewellery*

▶ Forever Living Products, 35 St. James Road, Hastings, East Sussex, TN34 3LH Tel: (01424) 444851

▶ Forever Living Products, 19 Boyn Hill Avenue, Maidenhead, Berkshire, SL6 4EY Tel: (01628) 776708 *Health food retailers*

Forever Living Products UK Ltd, Longbridge Manor, Longbridge, Warwick, CV34 6RB Tel: (01926) 626600 Fax: (01926) 626636 E-mail: customerservices@flpuk.net *Distribution of aloe vera products*

▶ Forever Warm Homes Ltd, 3a Ballymoyer Road, Newtownhamilton, Newry, County Down, BT35 0AH Tel: (028) 3087 8950 Fax: (028) 3087 8599 E-mail: seals@foreverwarmhomes.com *Timber frame manufrs*

Forewood Timber, Rossway Drive, Bushey, WD23 3RX Tel: (020) 8421 8231 Fax: (01208) 421850 *Timber & joiners*

▶ Forfab Ltd, Station Road, Bucksburn, Aberdeen, AB21 9PB Tel: (01224) 712555 Fax: (01224) 716555 E-mail: aberdeen@forfab.com *Off shore manufrs*

▶ Forfar Galvanisers Ltd, Carseview Road, Forfar, Angus, DD8 3BT Tel: (01307) 460222 Fax: (01307) 460444

▶ The Forfar Roof Truss Company Ltd, Orchardbank Industrial Estate, Forfar, Angus, DD8 1TD Tel: (01307) 468030 Fax: (01307) 468817 E-mail: alan.hampton@forfarrooftruss.co.uk *Roof truss manufrs*

Forg Welding & Engineering Co. Ltd, 4 Block 2 Mariner Way, Felnex Industrial Estate, Newport, Gwent, NP19 4PQ Tel: (01633) 274690 Fax: (01633) 270975 E-mail: sales@forg.co.uk *Aircraft maintenance & repairs*

The Forge, 1 Alverstone Road, East Cowes, Isle of Wight, PO32 6NZ Tel: (01983) 292716 Fax: (01983) 282131 E-mail: forgewhip@rann5979.freeserve.co.uk *Steel fabricators*

The Forge, Hillier Garden Centre, Brighton Road, Horsham, West Sussex, RH13 6QA Tel: (01403) 272894 Fax: (01403) 272894 *Blacksmith services*

The Forge, 2a Watson Road, Worksop, Nottinghamshire, S80 2BB Tel: (01909) 501745 Fax: (01909) 501745 *Wrought iron work manufrs*

Dean Forge, Dean Prior, Lower Dean, Buckfastleigh, Devon, TQ11 0LS Tel: (01364) 643574 Fax: (01364) 643982 E-mail: stoves@dean-forge.co.uk *Stove manufrs*

Forge Engineering, Tarran Way Industrial Estate, Pasture Road, Tarran Industrial Estate, Wirral, Merseyside, CH46 4TP Tel: 0151-678 7777 Fax: 0151-677 0006 *Plant & commercial vehicle repairers*

Forge Europa, 35 Princes Street, Ulverston, Cumbria, LA12 7NQ Tel: (01229) 580000 Fax: (01229) 586890 E-mail: sales@forge-europa.co.uk *High performance visible & infrared optoelectronic component designers*

Forge Fabrications Ltd, The Street, Lyng, Norwich, NR9 5QZ Tel: (01603) 872088 Fax: (01603) 872744 E-mail: enquiries@forgefabrications.co.uk *Architectural & secondary steel metalworkers*

Forge Fabrications, 8 South Street, Crowland, Peterborough, PE6 0AJ Tel: (01733) 211441 Fax: (01733) 211258 E-mail: justin@forgefabrications.co.uk *Wrought iron workers & steel fabricators*

Forge Group, Holbrook Commerce Park, Holbrook Close Holbrook Indust Estate, Holbrook, Sheffield, S20 3FJ Tel: 0114-248 2222 Fax: 0114-248 2222 *Wrought iron gate manufrs*

Forge Leisure Ltd, Forge Industrial Centre, Morpeth Road, Ashington, Northumberland, NE63 8QG Tel: (01670) 522022 Fax: (01670) 522072 E-mail: forgeleisure@btconnect.com *Pool cover manufrs*

▶ Forge Products Ltd, Unit 9-10 Two Gates Trading Estate, Watling Street, Two Gates, Tamworth, Staffordshire, B77 5AE Tel: (01827) 260387 Fax: (01827) 288683

▶ Forge Services Ltd, Forge House & Stables, Whistley Road, Potterne, Devizes, Wiltshire, SN10 5TD Tel: (01380) 722238 Fax: (0870) 479165 E-mail: enquiry@forge-services.co.uk *Agricultural machinery & spare parts, accessories suppliers*

Forge Tech Services Ltd, Gatefield Works, Whitelands Road, Ashton-under-Lyne, Lancashire, OL6 6UG Tel: 0161-339 1120 Fax: 0161-343 2257 E-mail: info@forgetechservices.com *Forging plant & tool manufrs*

Forged Flanges & Fittings Ltd, Castle House, Station Road, New Barnet, Hertfordshire, EN5 1PE Tel: (020) 8440 6541 Fax: (020) 8441 6911 E-mail: franklissauer@iraco.co.uk *Flange stockists & manufrs*

Forged Products, Venture House, Cross Street, Macclesfield, Cheshire, SK11 7PG Tel: (01625) 428399 Fax: (01625) 508200 E-mail: forgedproducts@dial.pipex.com *Open die forgings & seamless rolled rings*

▶ Forget Marketing, 118 Kidmore Road, Caversham, Reading, RG4 7NB Tel: 0118-947 7396 Fax: 0118-954 5132 E-mail: sales@forgetmarketing.com *Forget Marketing provides a marketing outsource solution specialising in direct response copywriting and fulfillment*

Forgetec Engineering, Scatterford Smithy, Newland, Coleford, Gloucestershire, GL16 8NG Tel: (01594) 835363 Fax: (01594) 835363 E-mail: sales@forgetec.co.uk *Stainless steel & aluminium treadplate distributors & manufrs*

Forgetrack Ltd, Thistle House, St Andrews Street, Hertford, SG14 1JA Tel: (01992) 500900 Fax: (01992) 589495 E-mail: info@forgetrack.co.uk *ForgeTrack has been affiliated with Primavera Systems Inc since 1984. ForgeTrack has distinguished itself by providing premier Project Management software and implementation services to a wide range of clients. To this end we employ a staff of Project Management professionals to assure a specific and successful implementation of Project "Management in your organisation.** ***

Forgeville Logiscitcs Ltd, Unit 3, Senate Place, Whitworth Road, Stevenage, Hertfordshire, SG1 4QS Tel: (01438) 369461 Fax: (01438) 743084 E-mail: sales@forgeville.co.uk *Filter distributors & specialists*

Forgeway Engineering Co. Ltd, 2-3 Forgehammer Industrial Estate, Cwmbran, Gwent, NP44 3AA Tel: (01633) 485468 Fax: (01633) 875439 *General engineers*

Forizo Co., Walker Street, Higher Tranmere, Birkenhead, Merseyside, CH42 0LY Tel: 0151-652 2275 *Horticultural & garden requisites*

▶ Fork Lift Mechanical Services Ltd, East Hermiston Farm, Currie, Midlothian, EH14 4AJ Tel: 0131-442 2002 Fax: 0131-442 2662 E-mail: gus@forkliftserviceslimited.co.uk *Sales & repair services for fork lift trucks*

Fork Lift Repairers, Bryn CWR Industrial Estate, Gwalchmai, Holyhead, Gwynedd, LL65 4PU Tel: (01407) 720944 *Crane & fork lift truck repair*

Fork Truck Direct, Unit 5, Redhills Road, South Woodham Ferrers, Chelmsford, CM3 5UL Tel: (01245) 322252 Fax: (01245) 322227 E-mail: forktruck.direct@virgin.net *Fork truck sales, hire & training*

Fork Truck Maintenance, Units 1-2 Ewenny Industrial Estate, Bridgend, Mid Glamorgan, CF31 3EX Tel: (01656) 766200 Fax: (01656) 767976 E-mail: barryr@ftmbridgend.co.uk *Fork lifts hire & sales*

Fork Truck Service Ltd, Derby Road, Wingerworth, Chesterfield, Derbyshire, S42 6NB Tel: (01246) 209632 Fax: (01246) 206633 E-mail: enquiries@forktruckbreakers.com *Hire, sales & service of forklift trucks*

Fork Truck Services Aberdeen Ltd, Silverburn Crescent, Bridge of Don Industrial Estate, Aberdeen, AB23 8EW Tel: (01224) 703366 Fax: (01224) 828533 *Fork lift trucks hire*

The Forklift Co., 4 Bank View, Froghall, Stoke-On-Trent, ST10 2HA Tel: (01538) 755500 Fax: (01538) 752821 *Forklifts machinery services*

Forklift (Midlands), Unit 4, Balds Lane, Jubilee Business Park, Lye, Stourbridge, West Midlands, DY9 8SH Tel: (01384) 898984 Fax: (01384) 897590 E-mail: enquiries@clarkliftmidland.co.uk *Fork lift truck hire, sales & service*

Forklift Services, Site 4 The Old Airfield, Crabtree Lane, High Ercall, Telford, Shropshire, TF6 6AP Tel: (01952) 771166 Fax: (01952) 771177 *Forklift truck distributor*

Forkway Ltd, Shaw Cross Court, Horace Waller V C Parade, Shaw Cross Business Park, Dewsbury, West Yorkshire, WF12 7RF Tel: (01924) 465999 Fax: (01924) 465888 E-mail: dewsbury@forkway.co.uk *Forklift trucks*

Forkway Group Ltd, Unit 7 Corinium Industrial Estate, Raans Road, Amersham, Buckinghamshire, HP6 6JQ Tel: (01494) 723456 Fax: (01494) 723724 E-mail: sales@forkway.co.uk *Fork lift truck hire & sales & service providers*

▶ Form Automation, 42 Harwell Road, Nuffield Industrial Estate, Poole, Dorset, BH17 0GE Tel: (01202) 660400 Fax: (01202) 660470 E-mail: sales@formautomation.co.uk

Form Fab Worcester Ltd, 9-11 Bache Road, Sandy Lane Industrial Estate, Stourport-on-Severn, Worcestershire, DY13 9QB Tel: (01299) 879271 Fax: (01299) 877339 E-mail: sales@form-fab.com *Steel fabrications*

Form Fabrications, 21-25 The Crescent, Hockley, Birmingham, B18 5LU Tel: 0121-551 3561 Fax: 0121-551 6258 E-mail: enquiries@formfabs.com *Architectural metalworkers/fabricators*

Form Weld Ltd, Unit 3C, Cutters Close, Narborough, Leicester, LE19 2FZ Tel: 0116-286 6654 Fax: 0116-275 0877 E-mail: formweld@btconnect.com *Sheet metal fabricators & engineers*

Forman Construction Ltd, 6 Donalds Lane, Dundee, DD2 4PF Tel: (01382) 610612 Fax: (01382) 400464 E-mail: enquiries@formanconstruction.co.uk *Building contractors*

Forman Metal Products Ltd, Portrack Grange Road, Stockton-on-Tees, Cleveland, TS18 2PH Tel: (01642) 674314 Fax: (01642) 672899 E-mail: info@formanmetalproducts.co.uk *Sheet metalwork engineers*

Formana Leathers, 1st Floor, 42A Fieldgate Street, London, E1 1ES Tel: (020) 7375 3113 Fax: (020) 7375 3317 *Suede & leather clothing manufrs*

Formark Engineering Ltd, Unit 319, Fauld Industrial Estate, Tutbury, Burton-On-Trent, Staffordshire, DE13 9HS Tel: (01283) 520520 Fax: (01283) 815582 *Precision engineering*

Format Quality Assurance Services Ltd, 25-27 Brindley Road, Reginald Road Industrial Estate, St. Helens, Merseyside, WA9 4HY Tel: (01744) 816225 Fax: (01744) 820161 E-mail: bjjformat@msn.com *Non-destructive test services*

▶ Format Recruitment, 44 Rutland Road, Hove, East Sussex, BN3 5FF Tel: (01273) 772200 Fax: (01273) 748735 E-mail: nadina@formatrecruitment.com *Engineering recruitment agency*

Format Screen Printers, Prospect Farm, Thirsk Road, Easingwold, York, YO61 3HL Tel: (01347) 824248 Fax: (01423) 860287 E-mail: studio@screenprint.fsbusiness.co.uk *Screen printers*

Formative Fun, 5 Charles Street, Worcester, WR1 2AQ Tel: (01905) 22353 Fax: (01905) 22353 E-mail: worcester@formativefun.com *Educational toys manufrs*

Formatrix, Hayne Barton, Whitestone, Exeter, EX4 2JN Tel: (01392) 811766 *Lithographic printintg & scanning services*

Formbend Ltd, Unit 4-5 Charles St Industrial Estate, Charles Street, West Bromwich, West Midlands, B70 0AZ Tel: 0121-557 0555 Fax: 0121-557 0888 E-mail: sales@formbend.com *Tube manipulation services*

Forme Display 1990 Ltd, 8 Millbrook Road, Birkenhead, Merseyside, CH41 1FL Tel: 0151-691 1592 Fax: 0151-639 0403 *Cutter formes for printing trade*

Formech International Ltd, 4 Thrales End Farm, Thrales End Lane, Harpenden, Hertfordshire, AL5 3NS Tel: (01582) 469797 Fax: (01582) 469646 E-mail: sales@formech.com Sales Contact: J. Costa *Vacuum forming machines*

Formerton Ltd, Forton Works, First Avenue, Millbrook Trading Estate, Southampton, SO15 0LG Tel: (023) 8036 5555 Fax: (023) 8070 1197 E-mail: southampton@formertonroofing.co.uk *Roofing material supplies merchants*

Formes Alutek Ltd, Cromwell Road, Ellesmere Port, CH65 4LF Tel: 0151-357 1998 Fax: 0151-356 1078 E-mail: info@formesalutek.co.uk *Aluminium windows & curtainwall manufrs*

Formet Ltd, Harley Works, Paxton Hill, St. Neots, Cambridgeshire, PE19 6TA Tel: (01480) 475041 Fax: (01480) 472820 E-mail: sales@4met.co.uk *Precision & sheet metalwork engineers*

Formet Division Ltd, Wincomblee Road, Low Walker, Newcastle Upon Tyne, NE6 3QQ Tel: 0191-263 8686 Fax: 0191-262 6428 E-mail: sales@hipg.co.uk *Open die forgings manufrs*

Formet Sheet Metal Ltd, Unit F Hoo Farm Industrial Estate, Worcester Road, Kidderminster, Worcestershire, DY11 7RA Tel: (01562) 744440 Fax: (01562) 829976 *Sheet metalwork & fabrication*

Formica Ltd, Block 2, Kinnoull Road, Dunsinane Industrial Estate, Dundee, DD2 3PZ Tel: (01382) 833733 Fax: (01382) 832208 E-mail: bill.lang@formica-europe.com *Laminated plastics distributors*

Formil Engineering Ltd, Coppice Side Industrial Estate, Brownhills, Walsall, WS8 7EX Tel: (01543) 371604 Fax: (01543) 372208 E-mail: formileng@ukonline.co.uk *CNC machinists & fabricators*

▶ Formleaf Ltd, 37 Larkswood Road, Corringham, Stanford-Le-Hope, Essex, SS17 9DF Tel: (01375) 400099 Fax: (01245) 353007 E-mail: paul.formleaf@btinternet.com *Landscaping services to the construction industry*

Formlo Leisure Products Ltd, Cleadon House, Church Lane, Tibberton, Droitwich, Worcestershire, WR9 7NW Tel: (01905) 345496 Fax: (01905) 345827 E-mail: formlo.leisure@virgin.net *Garden furniture & metal, wood & resin logo parasols manufrs*

Formost Air Conditioning Ltd, Unit 9 Wilford Lane Industrial Estate, Ruddington Lane, Wilford, Nottingham, NG11 7EP Tel: 0115-945 5033 Fax: 0115-974 5527 E-mail: smurphy@formost.co.uk *Air conditioning sales & service*

▶ Formost Machinery Services, Holly Lane Industrial Estate, Atherstone, Warwickshire, CV9 2QX Tel: (01827) 721010 Fax: (01827) 721012 *Machine tool & metalforming equipment, sales & service*

Formost Packaging Ltd, 10 Dawson Road, Bletchley, Milton Keynes, MK1 1LJ Tel: (01908) 376444 Fax: (01908) 373937 E-mail: sales@formost-packaging.com *Plastic vacuum formed products manufrs*

Forms Plus Ltd, The Willows, Church Street, Helston, Cornwall, TR13 8GT Tel: (01326) 564331 Fax: (01326) 564086 E-mail: mail@formsplus.co.uk *Print supply consumables*

Formseal South Ltd, 23 Snowdrop Close, Narborough, Leicester, LE19 3YB Tel: 0116-275 0052 Fax: 0116-286 5808 E-mail: sales@brushstrip.co.uk *Industrial brush strip manufrs*

Formston Evans Ltd, Kent Street, Bolton, BL1 2LN Tel: (01204) 523424 Fax: (01204) 529644 E-mail: pat@formstonevans.co.uk *Chair frame manufrs*

Formtech Sheet Metal Work, Royds Close, Leeds, LS12 6LL Tel: 0113-231 1030 Fax: 0113-279 4125 E-mail: sales@formtech.co.uk *Sheet metal workers sub-contract*

Formula Business Form, 5 Block 5 Shenstone Trading Estate, Bromsgrove Road, Halesowen, West Midlands, B63 3XB Tel: 0121-585 6333 Fax: 0121-585 5620 E-mail: sales@formulabusinessforms.co.uk *Printing services & computer stationery manufrs*

Formula Incentives Ltd, 1 Lockside Office Park, Lockside Road, Preston, PR2 2YS Tel: (01772) 721122 Fax: (01772) 326850 E-mail: sales@incentives.co.uk *Promotional specialists*

Formula One Pipelines Ltd, Unit 20, Delph Road, Delph Road Industrial Estate, Brierley Hill, West Midlands, DY5 2TW Tel: (01384) 482211 Fax: (01384) 482223 *Flange & tube fittings manufrs*

Formula Plastics Ltd, Unit 12 I E S Centre, Horndale Avenue, Aycliffe Industrial Park, Newton Aycliffe, County Durham, DL5 6DS Tel: (01325) 304104 Fax: (01325) 304103 E-mail: john.suggate@formula-plastics.co.uk *Injection mouldings, plastic & tooling*

Formulated Polymer Products Ltd, 8 Garden Street, Ramsbottom, Bury, Lancashire, BL0 9BQ Tel: (01706) 828208 Fax: (01706) 828820 E-mail: neil@polymers.co.uk *Synthetic latex compounding manufrs*

Formulated Resins Ltd, Greg Street, Stockport, Cheshire, SK5 7LY Tel: 0161-480 2121 Fax: 0161-480 4445 E-mail: info@formulatedresins.com *Formulated Resins Limited are manufacturers of tailor-made epoxy and polyurethane resins, based in the North-West.**With over 30 years" experience, Formulated Resins has built a strong reputation for reliable, efficient service and technical expertise.**We have worked with many large businesses such as Dinorwig and Voith-Siemens, solving highly complex problems, as well as with smaller businesses, whom we supply our standard products to on a regular basis.*

Formwise Export Ltd, 15 The Promenade, Swansea, SA1 6EN Tel: (01792) 462113 Fax: (01792) 650850 E-mail: sales@formwise.co.uk *Computer software house*

▶ Forr Mobility, Frith Field, Aldington Frith, Aldington, Ashford, Kent, TN25 7HH Tel: (01233) 721589 Fax: (01233) 721591 E-mail: sales@forrmobility.co.uk *Suppliers of mobility equipment*

The Forrest, 24 The Square, Portsoy, Banff, AB45 2NX Tel: (01261) 842320 Fax: (01261) 843921 E-mail: info@forrestthebaker.co.uk *Bakery suppliers*

Forrest Contracts, Pleckgate Road, Blackburn, BB1 8QW Tel: (01254) 245122 Fax: (01254) 245259 *Joinery manufrs*

▶ Forrest Electrical Ltd, 80-84 Ormskirk Business Park, New Court Way, Ormskirk, Lancashire, L39 2YT Tel: (01695) 573187 Fax: (01695) 577899

Forrest Fabrications, York Street, Accrington, Lancashire, BB5 4BT Tel: (01254) 381386 Fax: (01254) 399571 *General sheet metalworkers*

Forrest Precision Engineering Co. Ltd, 538 Edgefauld Road, Glasgow, G21 4NB Tel: 0141-557 3555 Fax: 0141-558 6216 *Precision engineers & gear cutters*

Forrest Transformers Ltd, 349 Haslucks Green Road, Shirley, Solihull, West Midlands, B90 2NQ Tel: 0121-744 2483 Fax: 0121-733 2178 E-mail: sales@forrest-transformers.co.uk *Electrical transformer manufrs*

Forrester & Boehmert, Forrester House, 52 Bounds Green Road, London, N11 2EY Tel: (020) 8889 6625 Fax: (020) 8801 1088 E-mail: fklondon@forresters.co.uk *Chartered patent agents*

Forrester Ketley & Co., 105 Piccadilly, London, W1J 7NJ Tel: (020) 8889 6622 Fax: (020) 8881 1088 E-mail: fklondon@forresters.co.uk *Patent & trade mark attorneys*

Forrester Wood & Co. Ltd, Heron Street, Hawksley Industrial Estate, Oldham, OL8 4UJ Tel: 0161-620 4124 Fax: 0161-627 1050 E-mail: info@forresterwood.com *Manufacturer of flavourings, colours and essential oils for the food, beverage and pharmaceutical industries.*

Forrestford Engineering Ltd, Polo Grounds, New Inn, Pontypool, Gwent, NP4 0TW Tel: (01495) 756007 Fax: (01495) 750065 E-mail: darren@fford31.freeserve.co.uk *Subcontract engineers*

Forsham Cottage Arks Ltd, Gorseside, Great Chart, Ashford, Kent, TN26 1JU Tel: (01233) 820229 Fax: (01233) 820157 E-mail: office@foreshamcottagearks.com *Wooden goods manufrs*

Forst UK Ltd, 14 Dartford Road, Leicester, LE2 7PR Tel: 0116-245 2000 Fax: 0116-245 2037 E-mail: sales@forst.co.uk Principal Export Areas: Worldwide *Broach & broaching machine manufrs*

Forsteel Ltd, 18 St Johns Road, Slough, SL2 5EY Tel: (01753) 517322 Fax: (01753) 517832 E-mail: lsimm42778@aol.com *Steel stockholders*

Forster & Hales Ltd, 24 Wadsworth Road, Greenford, Middlesex, UB6 7JD Tel: (020) 8998 9057 Fax: (020) 8998 2922 E-mail: sales@forsterandhales.com *Pressure vessel manufacturer ISO 9001*Air Line Coupling Manufacturer BSAU8b:2000 and BSAU8a*Self sealing air safety valves*

▶ Mike Forster Consultancy, Thorpe Nurseries, Littlethorpe, Ripon, North Yorkshire, HG4 3LY Tel: (01765) 608883 E-mail: mike.forster1@btopenworld.com *Food safety & quality control consultancy*

▶ Forsyth Building Ltd, 50 West Harbour Road, Edinburgh, EH5 1PP Tel: 0131-552 9393

Forsyth Glazing Ltd, 30 London Road, Glasgow, G1 5NB Tel: 0141-552 5343 Fax: 0141-552 5133 *Glass merchants*

Forsyth J B & G, 79 West Regent St, Glasgow, G2 2AS Tel: 0141-332 8761 Fax: 0141-332 9294 *Property management agents*

Forsyths, Station Road, Rothes, Aberlour, Banffshire, AB38 7AD Tel: (01340) 831787 Fax: (01340) 831558 E-mail: enquiries@forsyths.com Principal Export Areas: Worldwide *Copper, stainless steel & pressure vessel manufrs*

Forsyths Of Wooler Ltd, Bridge End, South Road, Wooler, Northumberland, NE71 6QE Tel: (01668) 281567 *Agricultural merchants service*

▶ Fort Chapard Ltd, Prospect House, 32 Sovereign Street, Leeds, LS1 4BJ Tel: 0113-389 1085 Fax: 0113-389 1190 E-mail: info@fortchapard.com *Career advice, career management and corporate outplacement specialists.We work on a one-to-one basis with our clients to help them to develop their careers and unlock their potential*

Fort House Systems Ltd, Fort House Factory, East Street, South Molton, Devon, EX36 3DF Tel: (01769) 574603 Fax: (01769) 573035 E-mail: sales@forthouse.com *Computer sellers & repairers*

Fort Jason Ltd, Stourvale Trading Estate, Banners Lane, Halesowen, West Midlands, B63 2AX Tel: (01384) 567165 Fax: (01384) 567626 *Materials handling equipment manufrs*

Fort Knox, 1 Mount Vernon Road, Liverpool, L7 8TY Tel: 0151-708 9333 Fax: 0151-709 8908 *Security car alarms*

Fort Knox Security, Tollhurst Farm, Blackham, Tunbridge Wells, Kent, TN3 9UB Tel: (01892) 740839 Fax: (01892) 740839 E-mail: sales@fortknoxsecurity.ltd.uk *Security*

Fort Precision Engineering, Unit 2 3, Golden Hill Park, Freshwater, Isle of Wight, PO40 9UJ Tel: (01983) 753502 Fax: (01983) 755855 E-mail: toolspring@fsbdial.co.uk *Precision engineers*

Fort Vale Engineering Ltd, Parkfield Works, Brunswick Street, Nelson, Lancashire, BB9 0SG Tel: (01282) 440000 Fax: (01282) 440046 E-mail: sales@fortvale.com *A World Leader in the precision manufacture of the valves and fittings for transportation in the Road Tanker and Tank Container Industries.*

Fortafix Ltd, First Drove, Fengate, Peterborough, PE1 5BJ Tel: (01733) 566136 Fax: (01733) 315393 E-mail: sales@fortafix.com *Heat resistant adhesive manufrs*

Forte Lubricants Ltd, Unit 4 Parbrook Close, Coventry, CV4 9XY Tel: (024) 7647 4069 Fax: (024) 7647 1213 *Automotive lubricant distribs*

Forte Posthouse, 215 Haverstock Hill, Hampstead, London, NW3 4RB Tel: (0870) 4009037 Fax: (020) 7435 5586 *Hotel, restaurant with conference facilities*

Fortec T A Ltd, 5 Upminster Trading Park, Warley Street, Upminster, Essex, RM14 3PJ Tel: (01708) 224713 Fax: (01708) 641029 E-mail: kp@fortectraining.co.uk *Training services including computer, machinery & technical*

Fortent, 56th Floor 18 Manesll, 80-110 New Oxford Street, London, E1 8AA Tel: (020) 7255 1065 Fax: (020) 7436 9443 *Computer software developers*

Forteq UK Ltd, Tandem Industrial Estate, Wakefield Road, Tandem, Huddersfield, HD5 0QR Tel: (01484) 424384 Fax: (01484) 535053 *Plastic injection moulded gear manufrs* Also at: Birmingham

▶ Fortesite Ltd, Flat 3, Weyhill Farm, Weyhill, Andover, Hampshire, SP11 8DE Tel: (01264) 771728

Fortex P C Drills Ltd, 17 Fleetwood Road, Leicester, LE2 1YA Tel: 0116-270 8937 Fax: 0116-270 0532 *P C B equipment manufrs*

▶ Forth Business Systems, 53 Burnside, Auchtermuchty, Cupar, Fife, KY14 7AJ Tel: (01337) 828567 E-mail: sales@forthbusiness.com *We design web sites and applications for all sizes and types of companies or organisations.*

Forth Engineering Services Ltd, 8 West Shore Bus Centre, Long Craig Rigg, Edinburgh, EH5 1QT Tel: 0131-551 5300 Fax: 0131-551 6610 E-mail: sales@forthengineering.co.uk Principal Export Areas: Worldwide *Engineers*

Forth Estuary Engineering Ltd, Edinburgh Dock, Leith Docks, Edinburgh, EH6 7DW Tel: 0131-554 6434 Fax: 0131-555 1890 E-mail: info@forthestuary.co.uk *Ship repair services*

Forth & Foyle Euro Ltd, 3 Carrakeel Industrial Park, Maytown, Londonderry, BT47 6SZ Tel: (028) 7186 0661 Fax: (028) 7186 0699 E-mail: s_hegarty@btinternet.com *General engineers* Also at: Grangemouth

▶ Forth It, Unit 2 Scion House, Stirling University Innovation Park, Stirling, FK9 4NF Tel: (01786) 442022 Fax: (01786) 451523 E-mail: sales@forthit.com *Electronics & software design*

▶ Forth Paving Ltd, Jamieson Mcgregor Yard, Kelliebank, Alloa, Clackmannanshire, FK10 1NU Tel: (01259) 212945 Fax: (01259) 212945

Forth Steel Ltd, 28 South Gyle Cresent, Edinburgh, EH12 9EB Tel: 0131-316 4360 Fax: 0131-316 4343 E-mail: forth_steel@mih.co.uk *Forth Steel is Scotland's leading steel plate profiler and stockholder. We offer multi-head gas profile cutting of plate up to 350mm thick from stock. We support a wide range of sectors including structural fabrication, Oil & Gas, Shipbuilding & Marine, Power Generation and Renewable Energies. We are approved to ISO 9002 and source our plate from EEC mills, to ensure we offer you a quality product. We operate 24/7, to give you a fast turnaround of your order, and deliver using our own transport fleet to provide a fast, reliable service throughout the UK. We have strong export knowledge, supplying critical components worldwide. We offer structural and offshore specifications including: EN10 025 - S275JR, S355K2+N & S690QL1 EN10 225 - 355G3+N, 355G8+N, 460G2+M BS7191 -*

continued

355EMZ & 450EMZ We are part of the Murray Metals Group; a Murray International Holdings company.

Forth Systems, 36-40 Yardley Road, Olney, Buckinghamshire, MK46 5ED Tel: (01234) 717007 Fax: (01234) 717010 E-mail: steven@forthsystems.co.uk *Storage system suppliers*

▶ Forth Valley Packaging, 2a Glasgow Road, Denny, Stirlingshire, FK6 5DW Tel: (01324) 820008 Fax: (01324) 820920 *Paper products*

▶ Forthcare, Unit 7, Hardengreen Industrial Estate, Dalkeith, Midlothian, EH22 3NX Tel: 0131-663 7175 Fax: 0131-663 7175

▶ Forthstream Ltd, Locks Street, Coatbridge, Lanarkshire, ML5 3RT Tel: (01236) 424333

Forti Crete Ltd, Shearstone Factory, Midsomer Norton, Radstock, BA3 4EA Tel: (01761) 413605 Fax: (01761) 413609 E-mail: stone@forticrete.com *Reconstruction of walling & capstone products*

Forticrete Ltd, Bridle Way, Bootle, Merseyside, L30 4UA Tel: 0151-521 3545 Fax: 0151-521 5696 E-mail: sswift@forticrete.com *Architectural masonry manufrs* Also at: Buxton, Dewsbury, Durham, Leicester, Leighton Buzzard, Rippon, Shepton Mallet, Stourport-on-Severn, Stretton, Wath & Wellington

Forticrete Ltd, Thornhill Works, Calder Road, Dewsbury, West Yorkshire, WF12 9HY Tel: (01924) 456416 Fax: (01924) 430697 E-mail: enquiries@forticrete.com *Concrete building block manufrs*

Forticrete Roofing Products Ltd, Boss Avenue, Off Grovebury Road, Leighton Buzzard, Bedfordshire, LU7 4SD Tel: (01525) 244900 Fax: (01525) 850432 E-mail: forticretetechnical@compuserve.com *Concrete products manufrs*

Fortis Bank, 5 Aldermanbury Square, London, EC2V 7HR Tel: (020) 7444 8000 Fax: (020) 7444 8888 *Financial services*

▶ Fortis Technologies Ltd, 34 Coalbrookdale Road, Clayhill Industrial Park, Neston, CH64 3UG Tel: 0151-336 2266 Fax: 0151-336 2669 E-mail: info@fortis-technologies.com *Manufacture & supply of chromatography columns & consumables*

Fortnum & Mason P.L.C., 181 Piccadilly, London, W1A 1ER Tel: (020) 7734 8040 Fax: (020) 7437 3278 *Departmental store*

▶ Fortoak, Ground Floor Block B Moseley Building, Derby Road, Loughborough, Leicestershire, LE11 5AH Tel: (01509) 266529 Fax: (01509) 216218 E-mail: sales@foroak.co.uk *Till & credit card roll manufrs*

Forton Packaging Ltd, 11 Brookgate, Bristol, BS3 2UN Tel: 0117-953 7222 Fax: 0117-953 7456 E-mail: sales@fortonpack.com *Corrugated carton manufrs*

▶ Fortress, Next To Darnley Auto Works, Cuxton Road, Rochester, Kent, ME2 2JA Tel: (01634) 714425 Fax: (01634) 714425

▶ Fortress, Next To Darnley Auto Works, Cuxton Road, Rochester, Kent, ME2 2JA Tel: (01634) 405056 Fax: (01634) 714425 *Fencing & gardening manufrs*

Fortress Electrical & Security, 19 Birch Avenue, Sunderland, SR6 7AR Tel: 0191-529 3844 Fax: 0191-529 3844 E-mail: fortresselec@btinternet.com *We carry out all types of electrical work and specialise in electrical testing.Periodic testing and inspecting to 2391. Has your wiring been tested in the past 10 years? If not it is advisable you get it checked. Most mortgage companies now ask for an electrical test certificate before releasing funds.Installation and service of new and existing burglar alarms. Access control, door entry systems.20 years experience. NICEIC Part 'P' Approved.*

Fortress Industries Ltd, 6 Trench Road, Newtownabbey, County Antrim, BT36 4TY Tel: (028) 9034 2655 Fax: (028) 9034 2651 E-mail: info@fortressindustries.com *Industrial door manufrs*

Fortress Interlocks Ltd, Birmingham New Road, Wolverhampton, WV4 6NT Tel: (01902) 499600 Fax: (01902) 499610 E-mail: sales@fortress-interlocks.co.uk *Industrial interlock safety devices & safety equipment*

Fortress Lock & Safe Co., 107 Brixton Hill, London, SW2 1AA Tel: (020) 8674 6657 Fax: (020) 8674 6439 E-mail: info@fortresslock.co.uk *Locksmiths*

Fortress Packaging Ltd, 21 Lake Road, Tunbridge Wells, Kent, TN4 8XT Tel: (01892) 545769 Fax: (01892) 545769 *Packaging material manufrs*

Fortress Roof Systems Ltd, Grovewood House, Russell Gardens, Wickford, Essex, SS11 8FU Tel: (01268) 571222 Fax: (01268) 570847 E-mail: sales@gts-plastics.com *Plastic fabricators*

▶ Fortron UK Ltd, 307 Ecroyd Suite, Turner Road, Lomeshaye Business Village, Nelson, Lancashire, BB9 7DR Tel: (01282) 607893 Fax: (01282) 607894 E-mail: service@fortron.uk.com *Sole UK agent for HURON Machine Tools.*Sales,installation,service.*

▶ Fortune, North Western Street, Manchester, M12 6DX Tel: 0161-273 5257 *Pallets & packing crates manufrs*

Fortune Die & Tool Co. Ltd, 293 Knella Road, Welwyn Garden City, Hertfordshire, AL7 3NS Tel: (01707) 331430 Fax: (01707) 331430 *Telecommunications systems distribs*

James Fortune Associates, 32 Plough Lane, Purley, Surrey, CR8 3QA Tel: (020) 8763 1995 Fax: (020) 8763 1539 E-mail: sales@jfaworld.com *Computer consultants*

Fortune UK Ltd, Wyvenhoe, Farnham Road, Farnham Royal, Slough, SL2 3AE Tel: (01753) 669471 Fax: (01753) 669472 E-mail: info@fortuneuk.com *Commercial engravers*

Fortunes Fish Smokers, 22 Henrietta Street, Whitby, North Yorkshire, YO22 4DW Tel: (01947) 601659 *Fish smokers*

▶ Fortyeft Ltd, Lumber House, Ashwell Bus Pk, Ashwell, Ilminster, Somerset, TA19 9DX Tel: (01935) 706077 Fax: (01935) 706077 *Designers & suppliers of security software*

Forum Bioscience Holdings Ltd, 41-51 Brighton Road, Redhill, RH1 6YS Tel: (01737) 773711 Fax: (01737) 770053 *Holding company*

Forum Executive Bureau Ltd, Orwell House, Cowley Road, Cambridge, CB4 0PP Tel: (01223) 506850 Fax: (01223) 420251 E-mail: info@forumexecutive.com *Business centre*

Forum Softwear Ltd, Rock House, Sandy Haven, St. Ishmaels, Haverfordwest, Dyfed, SA62 3DN Tel: (01646) 636363 Fax: (01646) 636737 E-mail: sales@forumboats.com *Computer software for yacht brokers*

Forvm Designs, 8 Bucklers Close, Warden, Sheerness, Kent, ME12 4PT Tel: (01795) 511100 Fax: (01795) 511734 E-mail: forvmdesigns@aol.com *Architectural & engineering models manufrs*

Forvus Computer Services, Forvus House, 53 Clapham Common South Side, London, SW4 9BX Tel: (020) 7819 1000 Fax: (020) 7498 1939 E-mail: sales@forvus.co.uk *IT consultants*

Forward Fastners Ltd, 4 Blews Street, Birmingham, B6 4EP Tel: 0121-687 0018 Fax: 0121-687 0024 E-mail: forwardfastenersmfgr@ciscali.co.uk *Fasteners, metal & industrial manufacturers & engineers*

Forward Forklifts & Engineering, Forward House Future Court, George Summers Close, Medway City Estate, Rochester, Kent, ME2 4EL Tel: (01634) 730200 Fax: (01634) 730193 E-mail: enquiries@forwardforklifts.co.uk *Fork lift truck hire*

Forward Group plc, 57 Buckland Road, London, E10 6QS Tel: (020) 8558 7110 Fax: (020) 8558 5974 E-mail: sales@forward-group.co.uk Purchasing Contact: P. Davis Sales Contact: P. Davis Principal Export Areas: Africa *Forward Group was formed in 1976, to give you fast access to over 25,000 office products from all the major suppliers. With Forward Group you get everything, from a paperclip to a complete office re-fit. Original manufacturer's products are backed by a no-quibble guarantee for your peace of mind. Forward Group supply all their products within a Quality Management System based on the requirements of ISO 9001:2000 With an online ordering account for you to place orders 24 hours a day, and Guaranteed next day delivery, we offer unbeatable choice from a single source!*

Forward Industrial Products Group Ltd, Unit 2 Tyseley Park, Wharfedale Road Tyseley, Birmingham, B11 2DF Tel: 0121-707 2555 Fax: 0121-708 3081 E-mail: info@forwardindustrial.com *Precision parts suppliers*

Forward Microsystems Leicester Ltd, 40 Northgate Street, Leicester, LE3 5BY Tel: 0116-262 7974 Fax: 0116-262 4864 E-mail: sales@formicro.co.uk *Microprocessor control systems manufrs*

Forward Pattern Co. Ltd, 4 Long Acre Trading Estate, Long Acre, Birmingham, B7 5JD Tel: 0121-328 8228 Fax: 0121-328 8228 E-mail: roger@forward15.freeserve.co.uk *Engineers patterns & castings*

Forward Protective Coating, Vernon St Industrial Estate, Shirebrook, Mansfield, Nottinghamshire, NG20 8SS Tel: (01623) 741910 Fax: (01623) 748730 E-mail: forwardpc@fornet.com *Blasting & painting*

Forward Signs Ltd, 81-83 Cato Street, Birmingham, B7 4TS Tel: 0121-333 3338 Fax: 0121-333 3341 E-mail: rpg@forwardsigns.co.uk *Sign manufrs*

Forward & Thompson Ltd, Atlas Road, North York Trading Estate, Clifton Moor, York, YO30 4UR Tel: (01904) 690999 Fax: (01904) 690960 *Adhesive tape applicator manufrs*

Forward Vision Solutions, 156 London Road, Ruscombe, Reading, RG10 9HJ Tel: 0118-932 0890 Fax: 0118-932 0891 E-mail: info@avspecialists.co.uk *Audio-visual production & presentation services*

Forwessun Test Systems Ltd, Unit 2 Newton Court, 2 Wavertree Technology Park, Liverpool, L13 1EJ Tel: 0151-220 5558 Fax: 0151-259 6407 E-mail: admin@forwessun.com *Electronics*

Fosco Hayes-Hurdley Ltd, Carlton House, 41 Smith Street, Hockley, Birmingham, B19 3EN Tel: 0121-554 7421 Fax: 0121-523 4452 E-mail: enquiries@foscos.co.uk *Screen & digital printers*

Foseco FS Ltd, Coleshill Road, Tamworth, Staffordshire, B78 3TL Tel: (01827) 289999 Fax: (01827) 250806 E-mail: enquiries@foseco.com *Chemical & metallurgical product manufrs*

▶ Fosker & Lynn, Hawkins Road, Colchester, CO2 8JX Tel: (01206) 790027 Fax: (01206) 791583

Fosse, 12 Enderby Road Industrial Estate, Whetstone, Leicester, LE8 6HZ Tel: 0116-286 7844 Fax: (0870) 2247842 E-mail: sales@fosse.co.uk Principal Export Areas: Middle East, Africa, Central/East Europe & West Europe *Manufacturers of absorbents; oil absorbents; spill kits; spill risk assessments; spill prevention ; oil spillage/pollution absorbent materials; chemical absorbents; oil spillage/ pollution dispersal/clean up contractors/services & absorbent material; accredited spill response training; spill pallets*

Fosse Bearing Units Ltd, Bearing House, 887 Melton Road, Thurmaston, Leicester, LE4 8EF Tel: 0116-260 2548 Fax: 0116-260 2548 E-mail: fosse.bearings@btinternet.com *Ball bearing distributors & stockists*

Fosse Electrical, White Gates, Goldcliff, Newport, Gwent, NP18 2AU Tel: (01633) 271420 Fax: (01633) 271420 *Electrical contractors*

Fosse Precision Ltd, East Street, Coventry, CV1 5LS Tel: (024) 7622 5263 Fax: (024) 7652 0919 E-mail: fosse.precision@zen.co.uk *Precision & repetition engineers*

Fosse Security Systems, South View, Sawbridge Road, Grandborough, Rugby, Warwickshire, CV23 8DN Tel: (01788) 812662 Fax: (01788) 812662 *Security alarm systems services*

Fosseway Homes, Coly House, Swan Hill Road, Colyford, Colyton, Devon, EX24 6HE Tel: (01297) 553562 Fax: (01297) 553563 E-mail: michael.gardener@totalise.co.uk *Building contractors & developers*

Fosseway Technical Tapes, 8 Ladywood Works, Leicester Road, Lutterworth, Leicestershire, LE17 4HD Tel: (01455) 550515 Fax: (01455) 550122 E-mail: sales@fossewaytapes.co.uk *Adhesives, tapes, abrasives & fixings distributors*

Fossey Engineering, A 2 Venture Court, Ackworth Road, Portsmouth, PO3 5RY Tel: (023) 9269 0246 Fax: (023) 9267 8218 *Precision engineers*

Fossitt & Thorne UK Ltd, 46 Fydell Street, Boston, Lincolnshire, PE21 8LF Tel: (01205) 319960 Fax: (01205) 319972 E-mail: fossitt.thorne@virgin.net *Garage tyres & exhausts*

Fossitt & Thorne UK Ltd, Eastgate, Bourne, Lincolnshire, PE10 9LB Tel: (01778) 424331 Fax: (01778) 424421 *Tyre exhaust centre*

Stephen Fossler Co. Inc., 24 The Business Village, Wexham Road, Slough, SL2 5HF Tel: (01753) 553413 Fax: (01753) 518532 E-mail: fossleruk@aol.com *Embossed foil seals*

Fossoft, Newstead House, Lake View Drive, Annesley, NG15 0DT Tel: (01623) 720012 Fax: (01623) 720006 *Software developers*

Fostech Ltd, 10 Carnreagh Road, Hillsborough, County Down, BT26 6LH Tel: (028) 9268 2652 Fax: (028) 9268 9091 E-mail: fostech@nireland.com *Process technology consultants*

Foster Agricultural Services, Wingfield, Diss, Norfolk, IP21 5QT Tel: (01379) 384479 Fax: (01379) 384188 *Agricultural engineers*

▶ Foster Baxter Cooksey Solicitors, 6-10 George St, Snow Hill, Wolverhampton, WV2 4DN Tel: (01902) 311711 Fax: (01902) 311102 E-mail: solicitors@fbcsolicitors.co.uk *Commercial property solicitor, conveyancing and litigation services from a Wolverhampton law firm also specialising in family cases involving divorce, wills and inheritance.*

Foster Crane & Equipment Ltd, Unit 2A, Dunstal Court, Astwood Lane, Feckenham, Redditch, Worcestershire, B96 6QH Tel: (01527) 894400 Fax: (01527) 894940 E-mail: andrewfoster@fostercranes.co.uk *Foster Crane & Equipment Ltd are the UK's largest supplier of used mobile cranes, all our machines are purchased direct from end users enabling us to offer the very best deal available to our customers. We have the largest stock available in the UK. and all our cranes are checked and repaired prior to sale, all machines are supplied in a ready to work condition. Buy with confidence from Foster Crane & Equipment Ltd.*

Foster & Cross (Lifts) Ltd, Black Country House, Rounds Green Road, Oldbury, West Midlands, B69 2DG Tel: (0845) 004 8027 Fax: (0870) 068 1354 E-mail: info@phosters.co.uk *Foster & Cross provide a full lift design, installation and maintenance service.*

▶ Foster D Architect, 11 Isabel House, Victoria Road, Surbiton, Surrey, KT6 4JL Tel: (020) 8390 7555 Fax: (020) 8390 7555 E-mail: duncanfoster.architect@virgin.net *Architects*

▶ Foster & Done Ltd, 6 Priory Street, Birkenhead, Merseyside, CH41 5DX Tel: 0151-647 7336

Foster Environmental Ltd, Scotter Road South, Bottesford, Scunthorpe, South Humberside, DN17 2BW Tel: (01724) 270717 Fax: (01724) 271410 E-mail: darren@forsterac.co.uk *Air conditioning & refrigeration supplier*

Foster Group UK Ltd, Unit 41 Golds Nurseries Business Park, Jenkins Drive, Elsenham, Bishop's Stortford, Hertfordshire, CM22 6JX Tel: (01279) 815596 Fax: (01279) 815526 E-mail: sales@fostergroup.co.uk *Suppliers of work wear, sports wear, school wear*

H. Foster & Co. Ltd, 103 Kirkstall Road, Leeds, LS3 1JL Tel: 0113-243 9016 Fax: 0113-242 2418 E-mail: sales@hfoster.co.uk *Fatty acid stearine & olein distributors*

Foster Industrial, Church Street, Lenton, Lenton, Nottingham, NG7 2FH Tel: 0115-970 0598 Fax: 0115-942 3388 E-mail: richard@fosterindustrial.co.uk *Industrial gas manufrs* Also at: Leicester

John Foster, Thorpe Road, Carlton, Stockton-on-Tees, Cleveland, TS21 3LB Tel: (01740) 631110 Fax: (01740) 631112 E-mail: enquiries@johnfostergunmaker.co.uk Principal Export Areas: Central/East Europe, Central America & Worldwide *Gunsmiths, repair & restoration, export sports guns*

Foster Laws & Co. Ltd, 9 D Park View West Industrial Estate, Hartlepool, Cleveland, TS25 1PE Tel: (01429) 275541 Fax: (01429) 869177 *Metal fabricators*

Foster Needle Ltd, Groz-Beckert House, 139 Gloucester Crescent, Wigston, Leicestershire, LE18 4YL Tel: 0116-258 1570 Fax: 0116-258 1579 E-mail: sales@fosterneedle.co.uk *Felting needle distributors*

David Foster Photography and Video, 4, Southfields, Leek, Staffordshire, ST13 5LR Tel: 01538 386403 E-mail: admin@weddingstorybook.co.uk *Wedding photography and Video throughout Cheshire and the midlands. Black and white clasical and reportage. Own your own negative and copyright*

▶ Foster Plant Hire, 74 Acredales, Haddington, East Lothian, EH41 4NU Tel: (01620) 824823 Fax: (01620) 829457

Foster Tachograph Ltd, 17 Fulwood Hall Lane, Fulwood, Preston, PR2 8DB Tel: (01772) 655155 Fax: (01772) 793739 E-mail: enquiries@fostertachographs.co.uk *Tachograph chart analysis services*

Foster Tachographs, 189 Watling Street Road, Fulwood, Preston, PR2 8AE Tel: (01772) 655155 Fax: (01772) 793739 E-mail: enquiries@fostertachographs.co.uk *Tachograph chart forensic analysis*

Foster Wheeler Energy Ltd, Foley House, 5 Seaward Place, Glasgow, G41 1HH Tel: 0141-420 3414 Fax: 0141-420 3416 *Process plant engineers*

Foster Wheeler Energy Ltd, High Force Road, Riverside Park Industrial Estate, Middlesbrough, Cleveland, TS2 1RH Tel: (01642) 230600 Fax: (01642) 241097 *Process plant engineers services*

Foster Wheeler Energy Ltd, Shinfield Park, Shinfield, Reading, RG2 9FW Tel: 0118-913 1234 Fax: 0118-913 2333 E-mail: fw-sales@fwuk.fwc.com *Offshore oil & gas design specialists*

▶ Fosters Bakery, Towngate, Mapplewell, Barnsley, South Yorkshire, S75 6AS Tel: (01226) 382877 Fax: (01226) 390087 *Bakery product supplies*

▶ Fosters Construction Ltd, Emmanuel, Trusthorpe Road, Sutton-on-Sea, Mablethorpe, Lincolnshire, LN12 2LL Tel: (01507) 443649 Fax: (01507) 443649 E-mail: neale.bloomfields@homecall.co.uk *Specialising in building and groundworks of all types.*

Fosters Mobile Plant Services Ltd, Ferndale, Egmanton Road, Tuxford, Newark, Nottinghamshire, NG22 0NR Tel: (01777) 870068 *Engineering repair & maintenance services*

▶ Fosters Pottery Ltd, Wilson Way, Pool, Redruth, Cornwall, TR15 3RX Tel: (01209) 314410 Fax: (01209) 210246

Fotheringhay Forge & Woodburners, The Old Forge, Fotheringhay, Peterborough, PE8 5HZ Tel: (01832) 226323 Fax: (01832) 226323 E-mail: enquiries@woodburnersat fotheringhay. co.uk *Wood burner, wrought iron & solid fuel heating equipment & manufrs*

▶ Foto Inside, 9 Moore Close, Cambridge, CB4 1ZP Tel: (0870) 0114911 Fax: (0871) 5601675 E-mail: kelly@fotoinside.co.uk *Online digital photo printing service*

Foto Theme Digital, 70 Wells Street, London, W1T 3QD Tel: (020) 7436 7998 Fax: (020) 7255 1213 E-mail: info@fotothemedigital.co.uk *Commercial photographers*

Fotomechanix Ltd, 30 Curzon Street, Birmingham, B4 7XD Tel: 0121-380 0116 Fax: 0121-359 3313 *Pre-sensitised laminate manufrs*

▶ FotoStation, 146 High Street, Ruislip, Middlesex, HA4 8LJ Tel: (01895) 674000 E-mail: info@fotostation.co.uk *Winners Of High Street Digital Lab 04. KODAK Express for Film and Digital Printing of Digital cameras, Colour, B&W, Slide, E6 Films. Transfer Cine VHS DVD. Print canvas posters Personalised Photo gifts Mugs T-Shirts, puzzles. Bespoke framing Tapestry, canvas,football shirts.*

W. Foulsham & Co. Ltd, The Publishing House, Bennetts Close, Slough, SL1 5AP Tel: (01753) 526769 Fax: (01753) 535003 E-mail: belasco@foulsham.com *Publishers*

Foundation Developments Ltd, Foundation House, Clarendon Road, Wallington, Surrey, SM6 8QX Tel: (020) 8669 8600 *Ground work contractors*

▶ Foundry Craft Body Builders, Hick Lane Mills, Bradford Road, Batley, West Yorkshire, WF17 5LY Tel: (01924) 479020 Fax: (01924) 479020

The Foundry Visionmongers Ltd, 1 Wardour Street, London, W1D 6PA Tel: (020) 7434 0449 Fax: (020) 7434 1550 E-mail: info@thefoundry.co.uk *Software developers*

Fountain Foods Ltd, New Road, Upwell, Wisbech, Cambridgeshire, PE14 9AB Tel: (01945) 773333 Fax: (01945) 772174 E-mail: fountainfoods@supernet.com *Frozen products & fresh vegetables preparation*

Fountain Timber Products Ltd, Brockley Combe Road, Backwell, Bristol, BS48 3DF Tel: (01934) 862710 Fax: (01934) 863298 E-mail: sales@fountaintimber.co.uk *Timber sales & manufrs*

Fountains Direct Ltd, 41 Dartnell Park Road, West Byfleet, Surrey, KT14 6PR Tel: (01932) 336338 Fax: (01932) 353223 E-mail: sales@fountains-direct.co.uk *Fountain & water displays consultants & equipment suppliers*

Four Jays Site A Loo, Barling Farm, East Sutton, Maidstone, Kent, ME17 3DX Tel: (01622) 843135 Fax: (01622) 844410 E-mail: sales@fourjays.co.uk *Marquee, tent & portable toilet hire*

▶ Four Letter Word Design Consultants, 49-51 Farringdon Road, London, EC1M 3JP Tel: (020) 7831 8331 Fax: (020) 7831 8339 E-mail: neil@fourletterword.co.uk *Graphic design*

▶ Four Paws, 34 Sedbury Road, Sompting, Lancing, West Sussex, BN15 0LL Tel: (01903) 521499 E-mail: sarahj@fourpaws.wanadoo.co.uk *The ultimate in care and attention for pet dogs. From a simple bath and brush out to coat styling with lots of TLC.*

▶ Four Point Printing & Copying, Unit 3 Fordwater Trading Estate, Ford Road, Chertsey, Surrey, KT16 8HG Tel: (01932) 561163 Fax: (01932) 568010 E-mail: info@fourpoint.co.uk *Four Point Printing specialises in the production of newsletters,NCR sets, case report forms, protocols, Regulatory Copying, On Demand Publishing and Multi-original work.*** Quality * Service * Speed * Value **

Four Seasons Ltd, Unit 14, Papermill End, Aldridge Road, Great Barr, Birmingham, B44 8NH Tel: 0121-356 0909 Fax: 0121-356 0513 *Upvc window manufrs*

Four Seasons, 59 High Street, Barwell, Leicester, LE9 8DS Tel: (01455) 844991 *Garden ornaments manufrs*

Four Seasons, Hamilton Place, Park Lane, London, W1A 1AZ Tel: (020) 7499 0888 Fax: (020) 7493 1895 *Hotel*

Four Seasons Control Ltd, Astley Way, Astley La Industrial Estate, Swillington, Leeds, LS26 8XT Tel: 0113-286 5222 Fax: 0113-287 6759 *Air conditioning suppliers*

Four Seasons Village, Kirkpatrick Hill, Closeburn, Thornhill, Dumfriesshire, DG3 5JY Tel: 01848 330273 Fax: 01848 330848 E-mail: info@fourseasonsvillage.co.uk *Ribbon printing & rosette making*

▶ Four Speed Express Ltd, 6 27-29 Station Road, Kings Norton, Birmingham, B38 8SN Tel: 0121-433 3359 Fax: 0121-433 3449

Four Tees Engineers Ltd, 1 Dewar Close, Segensworth West, Fareham, Hampshire, PO15 5UB Tel: (01489) 885899 Fax: (01489) 885928 E-mail: admin@fourtees.co.uk *Steel fabricators*

Four Ways Engineering Co., Unit 18 Bennerley Court, Blenheim Industrial Estate, Sellars Wood Drive, Bulwell, Nottingham, NG6 8UT Tel: 0115-977 0018 Fax: 0115-977 0018 *Metal finishing & polishing services*

Fourfold Mouldings, New Close Mills, Howden Road, Silsden, Keighley, West Yorkshire, BD20 0HA Tel: (01535) 654604 Fax: (01535) 654829 E-mail: sales@fourfold.co.uk *Fourfold supply injection moulded plastic components to customer specification from their new custom built factory in Keighley, West Yorkshire from many types of thermoplastic materials including Acrylic, Acetal, ABS, Nylon, Polycarbonate, Polypropylene, Polystyrene and others. From our range of modern machines between 40-320 tonnes we supply automotive components and sub-assemblies, medical components, Empot horticultural trays, engineering components, leisure products, moulded shot glasses and drinks glasses, parts for aerospace, electrical components, etc. From concept through design, tool manufacture to production of plastic injection moulded components Fourfold can advice and supply products to your specification.*

Fourjay Ltd Presswork, Royal Works, Coleshill Street, Sutton Coldfield, West Midlands, B72 1SJ Tel: 0121-354 1115 Fax: 0121-354 1205 E-mail: enquiries@fourjay.co.uk *Precision pressings. Also pressings electronic components/non ferrous metal/general presswork*

Fourjays Machinery Services, 16 Kingsway, Nettleham, Lincoln, LN2 2QA Tel: (01522) 754880 Fax: (01522) 595269 *Machine tool suppliers*

Fourposters Ltd, 127 London Rd, Hurst Green, Etchingham, E. Sussex, TN19 7PN Tel: (01580) 860252 Fax: (01580) 860252 *Furniture manufrs*

▶ Fourquarters IS Ltd, Technology House, Lissadel Street, Salford, M6 6AP Tel: 0161-278 2444 Fax: (0870) 199 1225 E-mail: info@fourquarters.biz *Accessible web design, training & consultancy*

Foursome Vehicle Heaters Ltd, Brockhill Works, Windsor Road, Redditch, Worcestershire, B97 6DJ Tel: (01527) 64126 Fax: (01527) 584611 E-mail: info@vehicleheaters.co.uk *Motor vehicle heating equipment manufrs*

▶ FourSquare Innovations LLP, 6 Hawksworth Grove, Leeds, LS5 3NB Tel: (0870) 3930044 Fax: (0870) 1326527 E-mail: info@foursquareinnovations.co.uk *Computing consultants & educators*

Fourstones Paper Mill Co. Ltd, South Tyne Mill, Hexham, Northumberland, NE46 3SD Tel: (01434) 602444 Fax: (01434) 607046 E-mail: team@fourstonespapermill.co.uk *Hospital disposable products manufrs*

Foursys Ltd, 14 Science Park, Milton Road, Cambridge, CB4 0FQ Tel: (01223) 423311 Fax: (01223) 423855 E-mail: info@fourcys.co.uk *Internet security & anti- virus resellers*

Four-Tec Fabrications Ltd, Unit 2 Whieldon Industrial Estate, Whieldon Road, Stoke-on-Trent, ST4 4JP Tel: (01782) 844434 Fax: (01782) 744351 E-mail: fourtecfabs@aol.com *Metal engineers*

Fourth Dimension Integrated Design Solutions, 36-38 Mill Green Road, Mitcham, Surrey, CR4 4HZ Tel: (020) 8240 2244 Fax: (020) 8240 2223 E-mail: 4d@combined.uk.com *Packaging designers*

▶ Fourthstreet, Bertha the Queen, Cumberland Avenue, Canterbury, Kent, CT1 1SL Tel: (01227) 450740 E-mail: enquires@fourthstreet.co.uk *Exclusive Poker Sportswear & Gifts of Distinction.*Clothing, Playing Cards, Jewellery, DvD, Books, Dealer Buttons, Card Protectors, Tables, Chips, etc.*

Fourway Communication Ltd, Delamare Road, Cheshunt, Waltham Cross, Hertfordshire, EN8 9SH Tel: (01992) 629182 Fax: (01992) 639227 E-mail: info@fourway.co.uk *Communications contractor to transport industry*

Fourway Electronics Ltd, 3 Bone Lane, Newbury, Berkshire, RG14 5SH Tel: (01635) 45955 Fax: (01635) 551140 E-mail: 4wayelectronic@btclick.com *Electronic instrument wiring & assembly*

Fourways Bandsaw Service, 5b Cannock Wood Industrial Estate, Cannock Wood Street, Cannock, Staffordshire, WS12 0PL Tel: (01543) 879711 Fax: (01543) 423654 *Bandsaw services*

▶ Fourways Plant Ltd, Second Avenue, London, N18 2PG Tel: (020) 8884 3339 Fax: (020) 8807 8477

Fowey Boat Yard, 10 Passage Street, Fowey, Cornwall, PL23 1DE Tel: (01726) 832194 *Boat builders & repairers*

Fowkes & Danks Ltd, Howard Road, Park Farm Industrial Estate, Redditch, Worcestershire, B98 7SE Tel: (01527) 830800 Fax: (01527) 830801 E-mail: enquiries@fowkes&danks.co.uk *Pressings manufrs*

Fowle & Co. Ltd, Tremlon House, Menzies Road, St. Leonards-on-Sea, East Sussex, TN38 9BQ Tel: (01424) 444666 Fax: (01424) 720442 E-mail: lauren.edwards@btconnect.com *Steel sheet stockholders* Also at: Felpham

▶ Fowler Architects Ltd, The Studio, Jackeaves House, Tinkers Lane, Tring, Herts, HP23 6JB Tel: 01442 871496 Fax: 01442 876555

Fowler Bros, Brook Farm, Mark Road, Burnham-on-Crouch, Essex, CM0 8NA Tel: (01621) 782877 *Abattoirs*

▶ Fowler Fire Alarms, 3 Hermitage Walk, London, E18 2BP Tel: (020) 8530 8005 Fax: (020) 8530 8281 *Fire alums & protection services*

Fowler Sheldon Ltd, Argyle Street, Birmingham, B7 5TJ Tel: 0121-328 5434 Fax: 0121-322 2014 E-mail: fowlersheldon@aol.com *Builders of commercial vehicles bodywork*

▶ Fowler Welch & Coolchain, Deptford Road, Gateshead, Tyne & Wear, NE8 3AZ Tel: 0191-490 0083

Fowler Welch Coolchain P.L.C., West Marsh Road, Spalding, Lincolnshire, PE11 2BB Tel: (01795) 580056 Fax: (01795) 980307 *Haulage & chill storage manufrs*

Fowlers Specialist Treatments Ltd, 126 129 Pritchett Street, Aston, Birmingham, B6 4EH Tel: 0121-359 8571 Fax: 0121-359 4037 E-mail: enquiries@fowlersindustrial.co.uk *Powder coating, shot blasting etc, metal finishers*

Fowlmere Engineering Ltd, Rectory Lane, Fowlmere, Royston, Hertfordshire, SG8 7TJ Tel: (01763) 208265 Fax: (01763) 208515 *Industrial gas & welding supplies*

Fox Aluminium Systems Ltd, Wentworth Way, Tankersley, Barnsley, South Yorkshire, S75 3DH Tel: (01226) 749910 Fax: (01226) 749920 E-mail: sales@foxaluminium.co.uk *Architectural aluminium fabricators*

Fox Architectural Ltd, Providence Street, Stourbridge, West Midlands, DY9 8HS Tel: (01384) 424744 Fax: (01384) 424745 *Architectural metalworkers*

Fox Brothers & Co., Milverton Road, Wellington, Somerset, TA21 0BA Tel: (01823) 662271 Fax: (01823) 666963 E-mail: enquiries@foxflannel.com *Woollen & worsted fabrics manufrs*

▶ Fox Construction Ltd, Block 4, Chapelhall Industrial Estate, Chapelhall, Airdrie, Lanarkshire, ML6 8QH Tel: (01236) 754301 E-mail: mail@foxconstruction.co.uk

Fox & Cooper Ltd, Lancaster Approach, North Killingholme, Immingham, South Humberside, DN40 3JZ Tel: (01469) 540461 Fax: (01469) 541028 E-mail: power4@foxandcooper.co.uk *Generator set hire, leasing & rental services* Also at: Grimsby

Fox Country Furniture, Reapsmoor, Longnor, Buxton, Derbyshire, SK17 0LG Tel: (01298) 84467 Fax: 01298 84467 *Hard wood furniture manufrs*

D.E. Fox (Joinery) Ltd, Chapel Works, Bamforth St, Sheffield, S6 2HE Tel: 0114-234 8036 Fax: 0114-234 8036 *Joinery manufrs*

▶ David Fox Design, Briars Lane, Stainforth, Doncaster, South Yorkshire, DN7 5AZ Tel: (01302) 849299 Fax: (01302) 849299 E-mail: info@davidfoxdesign.com *Industrial design*

Derek Fox & Sons (Timber) Ltd, Shay Lane Industrial Estate, Shay Lane, Longridge, Preston, PR3 3BT Tel: (01772) 784626 Fax: (01772) 785103 E-mail: info@derekfoxtimber.co.uk *Timber merchants*

Fox Electrical, 239 Queens Road, Beeston, Nottingham, NG9 2BP Tel: 0115-922 1005 Fax: 0115-922 1005 *Electrical contractors*

▶ Fox Group Ltd, 10 Somerset Road, Cwmbran, Gwent, NP44 1QX Tel: (0800) 3893863 E-mail: sales@fox-moving.com

Fox Hill Foods, Barton Hall, Hardy Street, Eccles, Manchester, M30 7SB Tel: 0161-789 6315 Fax: 0161-787 8068 *Food wholesale & distributors*

James J. Fox & Robert Lewis, 19 St. Jamess Street, London, SW1A 1ES Tel: (020) 7493 9009 Fax: (020) 7495 0097 E-mail: brady@jjfox.co.uk *Cigar & tobacco merchants* Also at: Dublin

Maurice Fox Ltd, Warehouse Unit, Foel, Welshpool, Powys, SY21 0NS Tel: (01938) 820664 Fax: (01938) 820642 *Cleaning chemicals equipment distribution*

Fox Moving & Storage, Block C, Stourbridge Industrial Estate, Mill Race Lane, Stourbridge, West Midlands, DY8 1YL Tel: (01384) 395072 Fax: (01384) 440520 E-mail: stourbridge@fox-moving.com *Removal & storage specialists*

Fox Moving & Storage Groups Ltd, Pentland Close, Llanishen, Cardiff, CF14 5DJ Tel: (029) 2075 0967 Fax: (029) 2074 7383

Fox Office Machinery, Rumdoodle, Cotehill, Carlisle, CA4 0EG Tel: (01228) 561669 *Office equipment*

Fox Pathe Home Entertainment, 20th Century House, 31-32 Soho Square, London, W1D 3AP Tel: (020) 7753 0015 Fax: (020) 7434 1435 *Feature film video* Also at: London

Fox & Pheasant Ltd, Fox & Pheasant Center, Colchester Road, White Colne, Colchester, CO6 2PS Tel: (01787) 223297 Fax: (01787) 224497 E-mail: sales@foxandpheasant.co.uk *Kitchen furniture manufrs*

▶ Fox Plant (Owmby) Ltd, Caenby Hall, Caenby Corner, Market Rasen, Lincolnshire, LN8 2BU Tel: (01673) 878444 Fax: (01673) 878644 E-mail: office@foxowmby.com *Civil engineering & earthworks contractors*

Fox Pollution Systems (UK) Ltd, Unit 8, Strensham Business Park, Strensham, Worcester, WR8 9JZ Tel: (01684) 299804 Fax: (01684) 299805 *Suppliers of waste handling systems to naval & merchant shipping worldwide*

Fox Pool (UK) Ltd, Mere House, Stow Road, Sturton By Stow, Lincoln, LN1 2BZ Tel: (01427) 788662 Fax: (01427) 788526 E-mail: grayfoxswi@aol.com *Swimming pool distributors*

Fox Precision Machine Ltd, 95 Leigh Street, Sheffield, S9 2PR Tel: 0114-244 3969 Fax: 0114-243 9256 E-mail: sales@foxprecision.co.uk *Precision engineers & machinists*

Fox Refrigeration Services Ltd, 369 London Road, Grays, Essex, RM20 4AA Tel: (01375) 392545 Fax: (01375) 382156 *Industrial refrigeration engineering*

Richard Fox & Associates, 8-28 Luton Avenue, Croydon, CR0 2BP Tel: (020) 8683 3331 Fax: (020) 8683 2223 E-mail: richard@foxsilver.net *Goldsmiths & silversmiths*

Fox Sewing Machine Ltd, 60 Babington Lane, Derby, DE1 1SX Tel: (01332) 347941 Fax: E-mail: fox sawing machine@tiscali.co.uk *Sewing machine retailers*

Thomas Fox & Co. Ltd, 3 Rhodes Way, Watford, WD24 4YA Tel: (01923) 811700 Fax: (01923) 811710 E-mail: enquiries@thomasfox.co.uk *Safe dealers or agents*

Fox VPS Ltd, Minekeep House, Bridge Road, Camberley, Surrey, GU15 2QR Tel: (01276) 683331 Fax: (01276) 683332 E-mail: sales@foxvps.co.uk *FOX-VPS manufacture precision machined components, castings, & finished assemblies for industry and design & manufacture specialist hydraulic cylinders and fire fighting equipment for a global market.*

Foxall Industrial Supplies Ltd, Unit 9 Millards Industrial Estate, Izons Lane, West Bromwich, West Midlands, B71 3PX Tel: 0121-553 7937 Fax: 0121-553 7937 E-mail: foxallindsupplies@btopenworld.com *Personal protective equipment*

William Foxall Ltd, Balds Lane, Stourbridge, West Midlands, DY9 8SG Tel: (01384) 422727 Fax: (01384) 892309 *Foundry supply services*

Foxe Graphics Ltd, Enterprise Road, Golf Road Industrial Estate, Mablethorpe, Lincolnshire, LN12 1NB Tel: (01507) 477748 Fax: (01507) 473128 E-mail: alex@foxe.co.uk *Manuals business forms & datamailers*

Foxell & James, 57 Farringdon Road, London, EC1M 3JB Tel: (020) 7405 0152 Fax: (020) 7405 3631 E-mail: sales@foxellandjames.co.uk *Paint distribs*

▶ Foxer Leisure, Sheppey Way, Bobbing, Sittingbourne, Kent, ME9 8PD Tel: (01795) 841717 Fax: (01795) 841717 *Sports goods equipment accessory manufrs*

Foxglove Kitchens, 56-58 High Street, Swavesey, Cambridge, CB4 5QU Tel: (01954) 230263 Fax: (01954) 230263 *Furniture manufrs*

Foxhall Engineering, Delta House, Delta Way, Thorpe Industrial Estate, Egham, Surrey, TW20 8RX Tel: (01784) 472220 Fax: (01784) 472221 E-mail: foxhalleng@hotmail.co.uk *Steel fabricators*

▶ Foxhill Commercial Printers, 80 Sidney Street, Cleethorpes, South Humberside, DN35 7NQ Tel: (01472) 242777 Fax: (01472) 242255 E-mail: spectrumprint@lineone.net *Commercial printers*

▶ Foxley Tagg Planning Ltd, Corinth House, Bath Road, Cheltenham, Gloucestershire, GL53 7SL Tel: (01242) 222107 Fax: (01242) 222112 E-mail: mail@ftlplanning.co.uk *Established since 2000 Foxley Tagg has become one of the UK'''''''''''''''s most innovative town and transport planning consultancies. **Our reputation for adding value is based on sound professional skills and an ability to work with*complex projects what ever the size with demanding deadlines. With special expertise in environmental assessment, master planning, project management, travel planning and urban design over a wide range of projects**

Foxmoor Nurserys, Haywards Lane, Wellington, Somerset, TA21 9PH Tel: (01823) 662188 Fax: (01823) 665605 E-mail: foxmooruk@aol.com *Floral & garden displays*

Foxon's Ltd, Foxon'S Tackle, Lower Denbigh Road, St. Asaph, Clwyd, LL17 0ED Tel: (01745) 583583 Fax: (01745) 583175 E-mail: info@foxons.co.uk *Fishing tackles shop*

Fox-Pitt Kelton Ltd, 25 Copthall Avenue, London, EC2R 7BP Tel: (020) 7933 4000 *Broker dealers*

▶ Foxprint Printers, 1 Factory Street, Shepshed, Loughborough, Leicestershire, LE12 9AQ Tel: (01509) 505413 Fax: (01509) 650413 E-mail: print@foxprint.co.uk *Printing services*

Fox's Biscuits, Wellington Street, Batley, West Yorkshire, WF17 5JE Tel: (01924) 444333 Fax: (01924) 470200 *Manufacturer of biscuits*

Fox's Biscuits, Dove Valley Bakeries, Cheadle Road, Uttoxeter, Staffordshire, ST14 7BT Tel: (01889) 563131 Fax: (01889) 565379 E-mail: sales@elkes-biscuits.co.uk *Biscuit manufrs*

Fox's Marina Ipswich Ltd, The Strand, Ipswich, IP2 8SA Tel: (01473) 689111 Fax: (01473) 601737 E-mail: foxsmarina@oystermarine.com *Boat yard & mariners*

Foxwell Instruments, Unit 19 Bond Indust Estate, Wickhamford, Evesham, Worcestershire, WR11 7RJ Tel: (01386) 833522 Fax: (01386) 833544 E-mail: info@foxwellinstruments.com *Process Control calibration, service, sales and repair*

Foxwood Boring & Grinding Ltd, 17 Whitting Valley Road, Old Whittington, Chesterfield, Derbyshire, S41 9EY Tel: (01246) 260199 Fax: (01246) 455274 E-mail: ken@foxwooddiesel.com *Cylinder re-boring services & engine reconditioning services*

Foxwood Ceramics, 729 Woodbridge Road, Ipswich, IP4 4NB Tel: (01473) 717717 Fax: (01473) 717639 E-mail: info@foxwoodceramics.co.uk *Ceramic tiling suppliers*

Foxwood Engineering, 8 Park Trading Estate, Park Road, Hockley, Birmingham, B18 5HB Tel: 0121-554 7567 Fax: 0121-554 3834 *Precision engineers*

Foy Steels, Unit 4 Chevin Mill, Leeds Road, Otley, West Yorkshire, LS21 1BT Tel: (01943) 850183 Fax: (01943) 461034 E-mail: sales@foysteel.co.uk *Steel mill agents*

▶ Foyle Blinds Co., Unit 12b Springtown Industrial Estate, Springtown Road, Londonderry, BT48 0LY Tel: (028) 7137 3877 Fax: (028) 7137 3877 E-mail: sales@foyleblinds.com *Blinds retailers*

Foyle Vent Fabrications, Blighs Lane, Londonderry, BT48 9PJ Tel: (028) 7127 9494 Fax: (028) 7127 9495 *Ventilation contractors*

Fozmula Ltd, Berrington Road, Leamington Spa, Warwickshire, CV31 1NB Tel: (01926) 466700 Fax: (01926) 450473 E-mail: e.marketing@fozmula.com Purchasing Contact: R. Smythe Sales Contact: S. Jackson Principal Export Areas: Worldwide *Fozmula designs and manufactures a wide range of liquid level measuring, gauging, switching and sensing equipment to our ISO9001:2000 accreditation. We also distribute Kelch mechanical contents gauges, caps and dipstick and the Rochester Gauges Inc range of level senders, gauges and transmitters.*

Fpe, 21 Blatchford Close, Horsham, West Sussex, RH13 5RG Tel: (01403) 269069 Fax: (01403) 211391 *Engineering sub-contractors*

FPF Packaging & Tubes, 8 Leafield Industrial Estate, Leafield Way, Corsham, Wiltshire, SN13 9SW Tel: (01225) 810103 Fax: (01225) 810663 E-mail: enquires@fpf.com *Stretch wrap film suppliers*

▶ FPZ UK Ltd, Grateley Business Park, Cholderton Road, Grateley, Andover, Hampshire, SP11 8SH Tel: (01264) 889001 Fax: (01264) 889003 E-mail: uk@fpz.com *Manufacture comprehensive range of side channel blowers*

FR Aviation Services Ltd, Bournemouth Airport, Hurn, Christchurch, Dorset, BH23 6NE Tel: (01202) 409100 Fax: (01202) 576709 E-mail: fra-marketing@dial.pipex.com *Aircraft maintenance, repairs & mission flying*

▶ FR Joinery & Construction Services, New Road, Littleborough, Lancashire, OL15 8LX Tel: 01706 379200 Fax: 01706 379200

▶ Frac Roc, Islwyn, Lon Gernant, Menai Bridge, Anglesey, LL59 5SU Tel: (01248) 717999 Fax: (01248) 717999 E-mail: rockbusters@btinternet.com *Silent, Environmentally safe,Rock and Concrete Breaking Products*

Fracino Catering Equipment, Unit 17-19 Birch Road East Industrial Estate, Birch Road East, Birmingham, B6 7DA Tel: 0121-328 5757 Fax: 0121-327 3333 E-mail: sales@fracino.com *An award winning & visionary company. One of the UK's only manufacturer of cappuccino & expresso coffee machines & associated equipment*

John Frackelton & Son Ltd, 25 Imperial Drive, Belfast, BT6 8JH Tel: (028) 9073 2231 Fax: (028) 9073 1764 E-mail: tiles@frackeltons.co.uk *Paint & tile wholesalers*

John Frackelton & Son Ltd, 30c Sydney Street West, Belfast, BT13 1RP Tel: (028) 9035 1049 Fax: (028) 9074 5312 *Glazing contractors*

▶ Fradley Patio & Landscape Centre Ltd, Hungry Horse Craft Centre, Weeford Road, Sutton Coldfield, West Midlands, B75 6NA Tel: 0121-323 4555

Fragrance Oils International Ltd, Eton Hill Road, Radcliffe, Manchester, M26 2FR Tel: 0161-724 9311 Fax: 0161-725 5225 E-mail: uk_sales@fragrance-oils.com *Perfume compound manufrs*

▶ Fragrance Online Ltd, 19 High Street, Buxton, Derbyshire, SK17 6ET Tel: (01298) 73955 E-mail: sales@fragranceonline.co.uk *Retail & wholesale of designer fragrances & skincare products*

Fraikin Ltd, Torwood Place, Westwood Business Park, Coventry, CV4 8HX Tel: (024) 7669 4494 Fax: (024) 7647 0419 *Transport consultancy services*

Fral Products Ltd, 15 Dukes Close, Earls Way Industrial Estate, Thurmaston, Leicester, LE4 8EY Tel: 0116-260 1062 Fax: 0116-293 8013 E-mail: sales@multi-wing.co.uk *Axial fan impeller manufrs*

Fram Concrete Products Ltd, Gilfach Road, Tonyrefail, Porth, Mid Glamorgan, CF39 8YN Tel: (01443) 674624 Fax: (01443) 672433 *Concrete product suppliers*

Frama UK Ltd, Unit 15 Limes Court, Conduit Lane, Hoddesdon, Hertfordshire, EN11 8EP Tel: (01992) 451125 Fax: (01992) 441013 *Franking machines distribution*

Framar Health Foods, 391 Ormeau Road, Belfast, BT7 3GP Tel: (028) 9069 4210 Fax: (028) 9066 3891 *Distributors of health products*

Frame Craft Minitures Ltd, Lichfield Road, Brownhills, Walsall, WS8 6LH Tel: (01543) 373076 Fax: (01543) 453154 E-mail: sales@framecraft.com *Handicraft material manufrs*

▶ Frame Fast UK Ltd, 1 Ascot Drive, Derby, DE24 8ST Tel: (01332) 347544 Fax: (01332) 347544 *Upvc & aluminium windows, doors & conservatories*

Frame Homes South West, Jenson House, Cardrew Industrial Estate, Redruth, Cornwall, TR15 1SS Tel: (01209) 310560 Fax: (01209) 310561 E-mail: enquiries@framehomes.co.uk *Prefabricated houses*

▶ Frame Wise Ltd, Unit 5 Presteigne Industrial Estate, Presteigne, Powys, LD8 2UF Tel: (01544) 260125 Fax: (01544) 260707 E-mail: sales@framewiseltd.co.uk *Sell & supply timber frames*

▶ Frameforce Conservatories, Claymore, Wilnecote, Tamworth, Staffordshire, B77 5DQ Tel: (01827) 268003

▶ Frameline PVC U Products, 16-17 Faraday Road, Knowsley Industrial Park, Liverpool, L33 7UT Tel: 0151-546 5577 Fax: 0151-546 5588 *Supply window frames*

Framepak Ltd, 21 Robjohns Road, Widford Industrial Estate, Chelmsford, CM1 3AG Tel: (01245) 266633 Fax: (01245) 266933 E-mail: info@framepakltd.com *Framepak, a family business, established in 1991 to deliver high quality photo frames/framed mirrors/prints ranges to the retail trade at the most competitive pricing in the UK. We are currently marketing & selling, photo & picture frames, framed art prints, plain & decorative mirrors, digital printing on canvass, oil paintings on canvass, decorative filled boxed frames, recessed empty frames & a modern range of oil painting on board adorned with routed abstract grooves & decorative embossings, enhanced with gold & silver leaf. Framepak prides itself on providing comprehensive low cost but high value, innovative & exclusive designs for all types of wall art decor. By working closely with retailers, our in house product development & design teams both here & in China are able to provide high quality ranges tailored to individual customer needs & requirements*

▶ Frames, 6 Ladbroke Park, Millers Road, Warwick, CV34 5AN Tel: (01926) 419784 Fax: (01926) 419784 E-mail: info@framesuk.co.uk *Manufacturers, framed pictures mirrors & garden mirrors bespoke*

Frames & Fabric Ltd, Unit D1 West End Mills, Leopold Street, Long Eaton, Nottingham, NG10 4QD Tel: 0115-972 6282 Fax: 0115-946 1697 *Chair frame manufrs*

▶ Framework, 5 Station Parade, Ashford, Middlesex, TW15 2RX Tel: (01784) 258800 Fax: (01784) 250503 E-mail: sales@jandmframework.com *Full picture framing service.*Wide selection of ready made frames and mounts.*Lots of limited edition prints. Now stocking military prints. We can make mirrors to size.*Corporate framing welcomed.*

▶ Framework Specialist Works, North Bridge Road, Berkhamsted, Hertfordshire, HP4 1EH Tel: (01442) 877566 Fax: (01442) 874999

▶ Framing Fantastic, 149 Seven Mile Straight, Muckamore, Antrim, BT41 4QT Tel: (028) 9443 9287 Fax: (028) 9443 9287 E-mail: info@framingfantastic.com *Online art gallery & picture framing*

▶ Framing Workshop, 16-18 Clarendon Place, Glasgow, G20 7PZ Tel: 0141-332 3817 Fax: 0141-331 0163 E-mail: moira@framingscotland.co.uk *Personal picture framing service*

Framlington Unit Management Ltd, 8th Floor, 155 Bishopsgate, London, EC2M 3XJ Tel: (020) 7374 4100 Fax: (020) 7330 6644 E-mail: contact@framlington.co.uk *Unit trusts & investment management services*

Framptons Ltd, 76 Charlton Road, Shepton Mallet, Somerset, BA4 5PD Tel: (01749) 341000 Fax: (01749) 341051 E-mail: enquiries@framptons.ltd.uk *Manufacturer of processed egg products*

France Security, 176 East Street, Epsom, Surrey, KT17 1ES Tel: (01372) 726575 Fax: (01372) 726575 *Car security device installations services*

Franchi Hardware Merchants, 144-146 Kentish Town Road, London, NW1 9QB Tel: (020) 7267 3138 Fax: (020) 7485 4637 E-mail: sales@franchi.co.uk *Architectural ironmongers, tool merchants & locksmiths*

Franchi Locks & Tools Ltd, 278 Holloway Road, London, N7 6NE Tel: (020) 7607 2200 Fax: (020) 7700 4050 E-mail: info@franchi.co.uk *Architectural ironmongers, tool merchants & locksmiths*

Franchise Development Services Ltd, Franchise House, Surrey Street, Norwich, NR1 3FD Tel: (01603) 620301 Fax: (01603) 630174 E-mail: sales@franchise-group.com *Franchise consultants & publishers services*

Francis and Francis Ltd (Schmidt, Poggi & KBK), The Stables Works, Station Road, Kenley, Surrey, CR8 5JA Tel: (020) 8668 9792 Fax: (020) 8668 9793 E-mail: sales@powertransmissions.co.uk Sales Contact: Haas *UK & Eire Main Dealers for SCHMIDT Kupplung GmbH 'Offset', 'Semiflex', 'Controlflex', 'Omniflex' & 'GL' flexible, CV shaft Couplings; POGGI Trasmissioni Mecc. Spa., Spiral Bevel Gearboxes, Nylon & Steel Sleeve Gear Couplings, 'Lok-Fit' Rings, etc.; KBK Antriebstechnik GmbH, Metal Bellows, Flexible 'Spider' & Overload- protection/Safety Clutch Couplings; AWEK Trip Dogs & Rails; PROXITRON GmbH Electronic proximity, flow & hot material Sensors & Others.*

Francis Anthony, Blowing House Hill, St. Austell, Cornwall, PL25 5AH Tel: (01726) 61264 Fax: (01726) 69533 E-mail: info@francis-antony.co.uk *Colour printers*

▶ Francis Barker Ltd, Fircroft Way, Edenbridge, Kent, TN8 6HA Tel: (01732) 864111 Fax: (01732) 865945

Francis Bugler Ltd, Rimpton Road, Marston Magna, Yeovil, Somerset, BA22 8DP Tel: (01935) 850426 Fax: (01935) 851376 E-mail: all@mardentractors.co.uk *Agricultural engineers*

Francis Chambers & Co., Taylors Lane, Parkgate, Rotherham, South Yorkshire, S62 6EE Tel: (01709) 522175 Fax: (01709) 522944 E-mail: fcco@freenetname.co.uk *Electric motor rewinders & stockists*

Francis Construction Ltd, Armour House, Colthrop Lane, Thatcham, Berkshire, RG19 4PD Tel: (01635) 862222 Fax: (01635) 876997 E-mail: info@francisconstruction.co.uk *Building contractors*

Francis Hotel, Queen Square, Bath, BA1 2HH Tel: (0870) 4008223 Fax: (01225) 319715 E-mail: h6636-rm@accor.com *Hotel with conference facilities*

Francis & Lewis International, Waterwells Drive, Waterwells Business Park, Quedgeley, Gloucester, GL2 2AA Tel: (01452) 722200 Fax: (01452) 722244 E-mail: sales@fli.co.uk *Communication towers & mast manufrs*

▶ Francis N Lowe Ltd, New Road, Middleton, Matlock, Derbyshire, DE4 4NA Tel: (01629) 822216 Fax: (01629) 824348

Francis Searchlights, Union Road, Bolton, BL2 2HJ Tel: (01204) 527196 Fax: (01204) 558979 E-mail: sales@francis.co.uk *Vehicle lighting & searchlight manufrs*

Francis & Thomson Ltd, Postgate House, Castleton, Whitby, North Yorkshire, YO21 2ET Tel: (01287) 660757 E-mail: moira@franthom.co.uk *Computer consultants*

▶ Francis Transport, 15 Dell Avenue, Grimethorpe, Barnsley, South Yorkshire, S72 7HN Tel: (01226) 710032

Francis W Birkett & Sons Ltd, PO Box 16, Cleckheaton, West Yorkshire, BD19 5JT Tel: (01274) 873366 Fax: (01274) 851615 E-mail: info@swbirkett.com Principal Export Areas: Asia Pacific, Central Asia & Africa *Non-ferrous metal casting manufrs*

Francis Willey British Wools 1935 Ltd, Ravenscliff Mills, Ravenscliffe Road, Calverley, Pudsey, West Yorkshire, LS28 5RY Tel: (01274) 612541 Fax: (01274) 613012 E-mail: fw@francis-willey.freeserve.co.uk *Wool warehousing services*

Francotyp Postalia Ltd, Unit 74 Lakeside Business Park, Hawley Road, Dartford, DA1 1EF Tel: (01322) 405000 Fax: (01322) 405040 *Mailing machine & equipment services*

Francotyp-postalia Ltd, 130 High Street, Barkway, Royston, Hertfordshire, SG8 8EG Tel: (01763) 849360 Fax: (01763) 848900 E-mail: mike@spexecutiveagency.co.uk *Franking machines*

Frandsen Fine Arts Ltd, 7 Lillie Yard, Lillie Road, London, SW6 1UB Tel: (020) 7385 9930 Fax: (020) 7610 1404 *Picture framers*

▶ Franek Computer Systems, Holly Tree Cottage, Sprigs Holly Lane, Chinnor, Oxfordshire, OX39 4BY Tel: (01494) 482345 Fax: (01494) 482244 *Computer software development*

Frank A Mccaughan, 27 Ann Street, Ballycastle, County Antrim, BT54 6AA Tel: (028) 2076 2480 Fax: (028) 2076 3225 *Veterinary pharmacies*

Frank Allart & Co. Ltd, 15-35 Great Tindal Street, Birmingham, B16 8DR Tel: 0121-454 2977 Fax: 0121-456 2234 E-mail: sales@allart.co.uk *Architectural hardware manufrs*

▶ Frank B Dehn & Co Ltd, 179 Queen Victoria Street, London, EC4V 4EL Tel: (020) 7206 0600 Fax: (020) 7206 0700 E-mail: mail@frankbdehn.com *Patent & trade mark attorneys* Also at: Brighton

Frank B Forman & Sons, The Mill, Rotten Row, Theddlethorpe, Mablethorpe, Lincolnshire, LN12 1NX Tel: (01507) 473472 Fax: (01507) 473701 *Agricultural merchants & distributors*

Frank Bailey Machine Tools Ltd, 1 Hadfield Street, Globe Square, Dukinfield, Cheshire, SK16 4RL Tel: 0161-330 4738 Fax: 0161-343 4365 *Machine tool distributor*

Frank Baines Saddlery Ltd, Northcote Street, Walsall, WS2 8BQ Tel: (01922) 640847 Fax: (01922) 616475 E-mail: enquiries@frankbaines-saddlery.com *Saddlery manufrs*

Frank Brewer & Son, Moorgate Farm, Dinckley, Blackburn, BB6 8AN Tel: (01254) 248858 Fax: (01254) 246916 *Agricultural contractors*

Frank Bundy Electrical Engineers, 2 Darwin Crescent, Plymouth, PL3 6DX Tel: (01752) 667212 Fax: (01752) 667212 *Electrical engineers*

▶ Frank Burton Transport Ltd, Gomer Street West, Willenhall, West Midlands, WV13 2NR Tel: (01902) 605311 Fax: (01902) 606719

Frank Corrigan & Co., Regent House, 26 Queens Road, Coventry, CV1 3DQ Tel: (024) 7655 5594 Fax: (024) 7655 1194 E-mail: frank@corrigan-group.demon.co.uk *Insurance brokers*

Frank Dale Foods Ltd, Station Road, Tivetshall St. Margaret, Norwich, NR15 2ED Tel: (01379) 677273 Fax: (01379) 674443 E-mail: sales@frankdalefoods.co.uk *Food manufrs*

Frank Dawson Engineering, Rockfield Road, Barrs Court Works, Hereford, HR1 2UA Tel: (01432) 278190 Fax: (01432) 344760 *Precision engineers*

Frank Guy, Bidston House, Astwith Close, Holmewood, Chesterfield, Derbyshire, S42 5UR Tel: (01246) 851222 Fax: (01246) 851225 E-mail: sales@frank-guy.co.uk *Aircraft interior refurbishers*

Frank H Dale Ltd, Mill Street, Leominster, Herefordshire, HR6 8EF Tel: (01568) 612212 Fax: (01568) 619402 E-mail: sales@fhdale.co.uk *Steel framed building constructors*

Frank Hand Ltd, Private Road No 7, Colwick Industrial Estate, Nottingham, NG4 2AD Tel: 0115-987 0508 Fax: 0115-940 0793 E-mail: info@trentshot.com *Galvanising*

Frank Haslam Milan, F H M House, Church Hill, Coleshill, Birmingham, B46 3AB Tel: (01675) 461661 Fax: (01675) 461662

Frank Howard, Unit 11 Lakes Industrial Park, Lower Chapel Hill, Braintree, Essex, CM7 3RU Tel: (01376) 327454 Fax: (01376) 552025 *Power Tools, Fixings Fasteners & PVC Building plastics inc. underground drainge supplier.*

▶ Frank Hoyle Ltd, 2 Broadway, Hyde, Cheshire, SK14 4QQ Tel: 0161-368 8444 Fax: 0161-368 8555

▶ Frank Hudson Transport Ltd, Etherley Bank, High Etherley, Bishop Auckland, County Durham, DL14 0LG Tel: (01388) 832247 Fax: (01388) 835645

Frank Key Nottingham Ltd, Portland Street, Daybrook, Nottingham, NG5 6BL Tel: 0115-920 8208 Fax: 0115-967 0393 E-mail: sales@frank-key.co.uk, *Builders' merchants*

Frank Layton (Display), 9 Broadway Place, London, SW19 3TP Tel: (020) 8946 5041 Fax: (020) 8944 7324 *Printing services*

Frank P Kirk Ltd, 122 Queens Road East, Beeston, Nottingham, NG9 2FD Tel: 0115-967 7330 Fax: 0115-967 7303 *Lace, net & veiling manufrs*

Frank Peters Ltd, Bretton Street, Dewsbury, West Yorkshire, WF12 9BL Tel: (01924) 451881 Fax: (01924) 456864 E-mail: sales@frank-peters.co.uk *Lithographic printers*

Frank Pike, 14 Hatton Wall, London, EC1N 8JH Tel: (020) 7405 2688 Fax: (020) 7831 9680 *Jewellers' tool merchant*

▶ Frank Rogers (Building Contractors) Ltd, The Stables, Larkhill Lane, Liverpool, L13 9BR Tel: 0151-226 7172 Fax: 0151-270 2854

Frank Tucker Ltd, Victoria Works, Rook Lane, Bradford, West Yorkshire, BD4 9NL Tel: (01274) 681221 Fax: (01274) 688902 E-mail: franktuker@franktuker.co.uk *Civil engineers & road surfacing*

Frank Usher, Unit 1 Staples Corner Retail Park, Geron Way, London, NW2 6LW Tel: (020) 8208 2881 Fax: (020) 8452 0444 E-mail: sales@frankusher.co.uk *Wholesalers*

Frank W Marshall & Co. Ltd, 25 Wolsey Mews, London, NW5 2DX Tel: (020) 7485 1212 *Specialized joinery*

Walter Frank & Sons Ltd, PO Box 16, Hightown Road, Cleckheaton, West Yorkshire, BD19 5JT Tel: (01226) 201771 Fax: (01226) 284218 E-mail: it@walterfrank.co.uk *Experts inFire Fighting Equipment,Fire Hydrant Valves,BS 336 Firehose Fittings,Instantaneous Couplings,Non Ferrous Castings,Gravity Die Casting,Sandcasting,Shell Moulding,Toolmaking,Machining,3D CAD & CNC.**

Frank Whitfield & Co., 126 English Street, Hull, HU3 2BT Tel: (01482) 227376 Fax: (01482) 227376 *General engineers & ironwork manufrs*

▶ Frank Wyatt & Son Builders Ltd, 70 Dorchester Road, Upton, Poole, Dorset, BH16 5NT Tel: (01202) 622207

Frank-a-Label, Ellesmere Rd, Weybridge, Surrey, KT13 0HQ Tel: 01932 855526 Fax: 01932 820801 *Print Labels & Tags*

Frankham Ventilation Ltd, 4 Oak St Trading Estate, Oak Street, Quarry Bank, Brierley Hill, West Midlands, DY5 2JQ Tel: (01384) 262755 Fax: (01384) 70468 *Manufacturers of ductwork*

Frankie Wainman, Foster Cliffe Farm South, Low Lane, Silsden, Keighley, West Yorkshire, BD20 9JH Tel: (01535) 652487 Fax: (01535) 658286 *Mending tractors & wagons*

Franking People, PO Box 1579, Bristol, BS40 5LL Tel: (01934) 863428 Fax: (01934) 863406 E-mail: sales@thefrankingpeople.co.uk *Sale of franking machines*

Frankle Trimmings, 281-285 Bethnal Green Road, London, E2 6AH Tel: (020) 7739 0621 Fax: (020) 7739 0751 E-mail: ftrim@aol.com *Fashion trimming merchants & wholesalers*

Franklin & Andrews, Sea Containers House, 20 Upper Ground, London, SE1 9LZ Tel: (020) 7633 9966 Fax: (020) 7928 2471 E-mail: michelle.swales@franklinandrews.com *International property & construction consultants*

▶ Franklin College, Chelmsford Avenue, Grimsby, North East Lincolnshire, DN34 5BY Tel: (01472) 875000 Fax: (01472) 875019

Franklin Cooper, 7 Derrydown Road, Birmingham, B42 1RZ Tel: 0121-356 8184 *Sign suppliers & manufrs*

Franklin Electric (Henley), Treetops House, Gillotts Lane, Henley-On-Thames, Oxfordshire, RG9 1PT Tel: (01491) 579118 Fax: (01491) 412211 E-mail: fesales@acdcsystems.com *Electric motors including drip & splashproof distributors*

F.F. Franklin & Co. Ltd, Platt Street, Sheffield, S3 8BQ Tel: 0114-272 1429 Fax: 0114-272 7030 E-mail: sales@franklin-tools.co.uk *Manufacturers & distributors of professional automotive tools*

G.W. Franklin & Son Ltd, 4 Drakes Courtyard, 291 Kilburn High Road, London, NW6 7JR Tel: (020) 7328 6611 Fax: (020) 7328 4932 *Electrical & mechanical engineers*

Franklin Hire Ltd, 1 Rawreth Industrial Estate, Rawreth Lane, Rayleigh, Essex, SS6 9RL Tel: (01268) 784888 Fax: (01268) 782329 *Demolition services, self-drive vans, trucks, cars & plant hire*

Franklin M & E Services Ltd, 6 Hoffmanns Way, Chelmsford, CM1 1GU Tel: (01245) 505050 Fax: (01245) 505051 E-mail: me@franklingroup.co.uk *Mechanical & electrical engineering specialists*

Franklin Mechanical Fittings, Unit 40 New Enterprise Workshop, Mount Street, Nechells, Birmingham, B7 5RD Tel: 0121-327 6493 Fax: 0121-327 6493 *Steel fabricators*

Franklin Silencers Ltd, 1 Grafton Place, Grafton Street Industrial Estate, Northampton, NN1 2PS Tel: (01604) 626266 Fax: (01604) 233757 E-mail: sales@franklinsilencers.co.uk *Industrial silencer manufrs*

Franklin Steel Stockholders P.L.C., Franklin Park, Patterson Street, Blaydon-On-Tyne, Tyne & Wear, NE21 5TL Tel: 0191-499 0222 Fax: 0191-499 0223 E-mail: sales@franklinsteel.co.uk *Steel & non ferrous metal stockholders*

▶ Franklin Steel Stockholders plc, Heathhall Industrial Estate, Heathhall, Dumfries, DG1 3PH Tel: (01387) 268877 Fax: (01387) 259101 *Steel stockholders*

Tim Franklin, 379a-379b Gloucester Road, Horfield, Bristol, BS7 8TN Tel: 0117-983 5511 Fax: 0117-983 5512 E-mail: sales@poolandsnooker.com *Pool snooker services*

▶ Franklins International Ltd, Scarva Road, Banbridge, County Down, BT32 3AU Tel: (028) 4062 2230 Fax: (028) 4062 3540 E-mail: info@franklinsgroup.net *Badge weaving*

Franklins Sewing Centre, 48 Fisherton Street, Salisbury, SP2 7RB Tel: (01722) 554466 Fax: (01722) 554466 *Sewing machines & needlecraft retailer*

Franklite Factory Shop, Snowdon Drive, Winterhill, Milton Keynes, MK6 1AP Tel: (01908) 443090 Fax: (01908) 691939 E-mail: info@franklite.ltd.uk *Electric light fittings manufrs*

Frankly Packaging, Unit 25-27 Delph Industrial Estate, Delph Road, Brierley Hill, West Midlands, DY5 2UA Tel: (01384) 263328 Fax: (01384) 79283 E-mail: frankley@brierleyhill55.freeserve.co.uk *Adhesive tape distributors or agents*

Franks & Co. Ltd, 15 Jessops Riverside, Brightside Lane, Sheffield, S9 2RX Tel: 0114-256 2677 Fax: 0114-249 9666 E-mail: franksco@franksco.com *Chartered patent & european trademark attorneys*

David Franks & Co., PO Box 33, Newmarket, Suffolk, CB8 8SH Tel: (01638) 751132 Fax: (01638) 750933 *Export management services*

Franks International Ltd, Unit 1 Bessemer Way, Great Yarmouth, Norfolk, NR31 0LX Tel: (01493) 443044 Fax: (01493) 443055 E-mail: email.barrywoodhouse@franks.co.uk *Casing & tubing manufrs* Also at: Aberdeen

R.H.H. Franks (New Milton) Ltd, Stem Lane, Gore Road, New Milton, Hampshire, BH25 5NE Tel: (01425) 614730 Fax: (01425) 616472 E-mail: johnh@rhhfranks.co.uk *Aerospace engineers*

Frannan International Ltd, 1 Chiswick Square, London, W4 2QG Tel: (020) 8994 7475 Fax: (020) 8994 1393 E-mail: office@frannan.com *Medical, scientific & educational equipment exporters*

Frans Maas (U K) Ltd, 36 North Quay, Great Yarmouth, Norfolk, NR30 1JE Tel: (01493) 336600 Fax: (01493) 858730 E-mail: sales@fmaas.co.uk *International freight forwarders* Also at: Branches throughout the U.K.

Fransen Transport Ltd, 6 Lisle Avenue, Foley Park, Kidderminster, Worcestershire, DY11 7DE Tel: (01562) 820261 Fax: (01562) 754977 E-mail: info@fransentransport.fsnet.co.uk *Temperature controlled transport*

Frasc Construction Ltd, Orchard House, Ellenbrook Road, Manchester, M28 1GB Tel: 0161-702 5500 Fax: 0161-702 5502 *Plumbing & mechanical services*

Fraser Anti Static Techniques Ltd, 1 Station Road, Pinhoe, Exeter, EX1 3SA Tel: (01398) 331114 Fax: (01398) 331411 E-mail: sales@fraser-antistatic.co.uk Principal Export Areas: Worldwide *Manufacturers of static eliminators, anti-static products, ionising bars, ionising blowers, antistatic brushes, static generators, electrostatic meters and other static measuring instruments.*

▶ Fraser Brown Engineering Ltd, Unit 11, Evanton Indust Estate, Evanton, Dingwall, Ross-Shire, IV16 9XJ Tel: (01349) 831144 Fax: (01349) 831012 E-mail: info@eyelevels.co.uk

▶ Fraser Bruce, Millhall, Stirling, FK7 7LT Tel: (01786) 448822 Fax: (01786) 451192 E-mail: info@fraser-bruce.com *Concrete repair specialists*

Fraser C Robb, Arendale, Stirling Road, Drymen, Glasgow, G63 0AA Tel: (01360) 660688 Fax: (01360) 660814 E-mail: admin@frasercrobb.com *Agricultural horticultural engineers*

▶ Fraser Cleaning Technologies, 11-13 Woodside Walk, Hamilton, Lanarkshire, ML3 7HY Tel: (01698) 459003

Colin Fraser, Unit 2 Raik Road, Aberdeen, AB11 5QL Tel: (01224) 593132 Fax: (01224) 591772 *Fish merchants*

Fraser Crane & Lifting Services, 52 Block 3 Coltswood Road, Coatbridge, Lanarkshire, ML5 2AB Tel: (01236) 607063 Fax: (01236) 607063 E-mail: frasercranes@aol.com *Crane repair*

▶ Fraser Electrical Ltd, 37 West Street, Bexleyheath, Kent, DA7 4BE Tel: (020) 8303 6140 Fax: (020) 8301 4999 E-mail: info@fraserelectrical.co.uk

▶ Fraser Electrical, The Old School, Dewar Street, Dunfermline, Fife, KY12 8AB Tel: (01383) 720569 Fax: (01383) 720722

Fraser & Ellis, 80-100 Gwynne Road, London, SW11 3UW Tel: (020) 7228 9999 Fax: (020) 7228 7250 *Plumbers merchants*

▶ Fraser & Evans, Newhouse Industrial Estate, Newhouse, Motherwell, Lanarkshire, ML1 5RX Tel: (01698) 833173 Fax: (01698) 833855 E-mail: sales@fraserandevans.com *Light engineering, high definition plasma, powder & plastic coating*

Fraser Hydraulic Power, Unit BT 96/4 Fisher Industrial Estate, Fisher St, Walker, Newcastle upon Tyne, NE6 4LT Tel: 0191-263 7272 Fax: 0191-263 4016 E-mail: joanner@fhpltd.co.uk *Manufacturers of subsea/underwater cable laying equipment/ systems & power packs. In addition, hydraulic engineers, installation or services, hydraulic equipment systems maintenance/repair services & marine winches*

▶ Fraser Langdon Southern Ltd, The Old Bakery, 17 Hyde Road, Paignton, Devon, TQ4 5BW Tel: (01803) 666619 Fax: (01803) 526622

Fraser & Macdonald Electric Motors Ltd, 176 Woodville Street, Glasgow, G51 2RN Tel: 0141-445 3874 Fax: 0141-425 1135 E-mail: frasmcd@aol.com *Electrical engineers*

Fraser & Renwick, 2 Mansfield Cresent, Hawick, Roxburghshire, TD9 8AQ Tel: (01450) 372148 Fax: (01450) 372148 *Construction & joiners*

Fraser Ross Finance Ltd, 185-187 High Road, Romford, RM6 6NA Tel: (020) 8597 8781 Fax: (020) 8597 8673 E-mail: sales@alex-fraser.co.uk *Import & export merchants*

Stewart Fraser Ltd, Henwood Industrial Estate, Ashford, Kent, TN24 8DR Tel: (01233) 625911 Fax: (01233) 633149 E-mail: sales@stewartfraser.com *Architectural metal workers*

Fraserburgh Commercial Co. Ltd, Harbour Office, Whitehall Buildings, Shore Street, Fraserburgh, Aberdeenshire, AB43 5BR Tel: (01346) 512111 Fax: (01346) 514068 E-mail: steve@euroline-shipping.co.uk *Shipping agents*

Fraserburgh Ice Co. (1988) Ltd, Portacabin, Saltoun Jetty, Fraserburgh, Aberdeenshire, AB43 9RY Tel: (01346) 514048 Fax: (01346) 510511 *Ice merchants*

Fratelli, 5 Coundon Industrial Estate, Coundon, Bishop Auckland, County Durham, DL14 8NR Tel: (01740) 629010 Fax: (01740) 629064 E-mail: grahameparnaby@hotmail.com *Wire woven cloth*

Fray Design Ltd, Ghyll Way Airedale Business Centre, Keighley Road, Skipton, North Yorkshire, BD23 2TZ Tel: (01756) 704040 Fax: (01756) 704041 E-mail: sales@fraydesign.co.uk *Conference & training room furniture including office desking*

Frazer, Mid Craigie Road, Dundee, DD4 7RN Tel: (01382) 458989 Fax: (01382) 458998 E-mail: calum.hynes@frazer.eu.com *Pipeline fittings, flanges & pipeline supplies distributors* Also at: Branches throughout the U.K.

Frazer, Station Road, Hebburn, Tyne & Wear, NE31 1BD Tel: 0191-428 7801 Fax: 0191-483 3628 E-mail: sales.northern@ashworth-frazer.co.uk *Engineers*

Frazer Designers Ltd, 6 Hampstead West, 224 Iverson Road, London, NW6 2HL Tel: (020) 7624 6011 Fax: (020) 7328 6085 E-mail: info@frazerdesigners.com *Product innovation & design consultants*

Frazer Nash Consultancy Ltd, Stonebridge The Dorking Business Park, Station Road, Dorking, Surrey, RH4 1HJ Tel: (01306) 885050 Fax: (01306) 886464 E-mail: info@fnc.co.uk *Design engineering consultants*

Frazer-Nash Consultancy Ltd, Quay Head House, Colston Ave., Bristol, BS1 1EB Tel: 0117-922 6242 Fax: 0117-922 6524 E-mail: sales@fnc.co.uk *Engineering consultant*

Frazer-Nash NDT Ltd, Bradshaw Street, Heywood, Lancashire, OL10 1PL Tel: (01706) 628794 Fax: (01706) 627289 E-mail: enquiries@frazer-nash-btconnect.com *Non-destructive test services*

▶ Fre Flo Plumbing & Heating Services Ltd, Unit 29 800 Brightside Lane, Sheffield, S9 2RX Tel: 0114-242 0004 Fax: 0114-244 5948

Frech (UK) Ltd, The Production Centre, Boundary Industrial Estate, Fordhouses, Wolverhampton, WV10 7EL Tel: (01902) 786616 Fax: (01902) 786626 E-mail: info@frech.co.uk *Die casting machine manufrs*

Fred A Lodge & Sons Ltd, Stonebridge Mills, Stonebridge Lane, Leeds, LS12 4QL Tel: 0113-263 7341 Fax: 0113-263 7341 *Property owners*

Fred Balls, Unit 3 National Avenue Industrial Estate, Bontoft Avenue, Hull, HU5 4HF Tel: (01482) 445447 Fax: (01482) 492162 *Bulk suppliers of multiple screws & nails*

Fred Blake (Tools) Ltd, 143a Balaam Street, London, E13 8AF Tel: (020) 8552 1221 Fax: (020) 8471 8909 *Engineers suppliers*

Fred C Robinson Ltd, 40 Hillhead Road, Ballyclare, County Antrim, BT39 9DS Tel: (028) 9334 0455 Fax: (028) 9335 2393 E-mail: info@fcrobinson.co.uk *Meat (processed & cooked) product manufrs*

Fred G Alden Ltd, Langford Locks, Kidlington, Oxfordshire, OX5 1LJ Tel: (01865) 855000 Fax: (01865) 855008 *Heating & ventilating engineers* Also at: Cambridge

▶ Fred Hall & Son Builders Ltd, Old School, Whittington, Carnforth, Lancashire, LA6 2NY Tel: (01524) 271322 Fax: (01524) 272460

▶ Fred Margarson Ltd, R/O 12 Southfield Road, Grimsby, South Humberside, DN33 2PL Tel: (01472) 822226 Fax: (01472) 827709

Fred Olsen Cruise Lines, 42 Whitehouse Road, Ipswich, IP1 5LL Tel: (01473) 292200 Fax: (01473) 292345 E-mail: reservations@fredolsen.co.uk *Ship owners & tour operators*

Fred Singleton Huddersfield Ltd, Cliffe End Mills, Dale Street, Longwood, Huddersfield, HD3 4TG Tel: (01484) 653153 Fax: (01484) 649009 *Textile fibre reclaimers*

Fred Smith & Sons Motor Bodies Ltd, Sams Lane, West Bromwich, West Midlands, B70 7EG Tel: 0121-525 8359 Fax: 0121-553 0578 E-mail: james@fredsmithandsons.co.uk *Motor car body builders & repairers*

▶ Fred Sweeting & Sons, Orchardlea, Station Road, Sandford, Winscombe, Avon, BS25 5RQ Tel: (01934) 822341 Fax: (01934) 820445

Fred Watson & Co. Ltd, Grove Mills, High Street, Heckmondwike, West Yorkshire, WF16 0AW Tel: (01924) 403386 E-mail: geoff@grovemills.com *Commercial Industrial property**

Fredan Engineering Ltd, London Road, Little Irchester, Wellingborough, Northamptonshire, NN8 2EA Tel: (01933) 440135 Fax: (01933) 273490 *Structural steel fabricators*

Freddy Products Ltd, Units 6-7, Goodwood Rd, Pershore, Worcestershire, WR10 2JL Tel: (01386) 561113 Fax: (01386) 556401 E-mail: sales@freddy-products.co.uk *Fluid management & heavy duty industrial cleaning equipment*

Fredenhagen Ltd, Keynes House, Alfreton Road, Derby, DE21 4AS Tel: (01332) 340077 Fax: (01332) 340614 E-mail: sales@fredenhagen.co.uk *Manufacturers of Material Handling equipment, conveyors, lifts, turntables and all other mechanical handling products.*

▶ Frederick & Co., 19 Sandyford Place, Glasgow, G3 7NQ Tel: 0141-221 5575 Fax: 0141-221 1161 E-mail: sales@frederickandco.co.uk

Frederick Allen Ltd, 24 Winchcombe Street, Cheltenham, Gloucestershire, GL52 2LX Tel: (01242) 514869 Fax: (01242) 514869 *Watch & jewellery wholesalers*

Frederick Bone & Co Ltd, Masterbaker Works, 53 Whytecliffe Road South, Purley, Surrey, CR8 2AZ Tel: (020) 8668 2234 *Food industry oven manufrs*

Frederick Johnson, Lee House, 10 Alpine Street, Nottingham, NG6 0HS Tel: 0115-978 0767 Fax: 0115-978 2658 E-mail: fjlace@aol.com *Lace manufrs*

▶ Frederick R Miller Ltd, Home Farm, By-Pass Road, Hurtmore, Godalming, Surrey, GU8 6AD Tel: (01483) 811297 Fax: (01483) 810073 E-mail: sales@frederickmiller.co.uk

▶ Frederick Smith Electrical Ltd, 54 Nottingham Road, Leicester, LE5 4GH Tel: 0116-276 5755 Fax: 0116-276 8342

Frederick Thomas & Co. Ltd, Linden Court House, 52 Liverpool Street, Salford, M5 4LT Tel: 0161-745 7761 Fax: 0161-737 6061 E-mail: zedfred@aol.com *Textile importers*

▶ Frederick Thomas (Building Services) Ltd, Units 11 & 19, Attenburys Park Estate, Attenburys Lane, Timperley, Altrincham, Cheshire, WA14 5QE Tel: 0161-905 2302

John Fredericks Plastics Ltd, Lindley Moor Road, Huddersfield, HD3 3RW Tel: (01422) 314100 Fax: (01422) 310001 E-mail: sales@johnfredericksplastics.com *Window, door & conservatory manufrs*

Fredrick Smith & Sons Furniture Ltd, 10 Rigg Approach, London, E10 7QN Tel: (020) 8539 0158 Fax: (020) 8556 3030 E-mail: sales@smithandsons.co.uk *Reproduction furniture manufrs*

Fredrose Furniture, 17 Rutland Gardens, Sandy, Bedfordshire, SG19 1JG Tel: (01767) 681923 Fax: (01767) 691931 *Kitchens, bedrooms & bathrooms manufrs*

Free Enterprise (Technical) Ltd, Swale Marina, Conyer, Sittingbourne, Kent, ME9 9HM Tel: (07810) 391393 *Vending machine specialists*

Free Flow Ltd, Free Flow House, Eple Bay Avenue, Birchington, Kent, CT7 9HT Tel: (0800) 7316261 Fax: (01843) 840934 E-mail: Alan@FreeFlowKent.co.uk *Free Flow Drains provides a professional and effective drainage and sewerage investigation service. The company is part of the Free Flow Group and provides national coverage.**The company offers internal inspection using colour CCTV cameras (crawler and pushrod) and offers DVD or VHS recordings as well as full professional reporting with still images, condition grading and recommendations for rehabilitation or repairs where appropriate.**Free Flow Drains also provides a mapping and tracing service to provide accurate location assessments as well*

continued

continuation
*as co-ordinated manhole and structure data. Dye tracing and electronic tracking are used to pinpoint the location and alignment of unknown drains, sewers and culverts.**Please phone 01227 710900 for a free quotation for answers to your questions related to drains and sewers.**Free Flow is an independent company that supplies quality of service, professional approach, response and value for money.*

▶ Free Scale Semi Conductor UK Ltd, Colvilles Road, East Kilbride, Glasgow, G75 0TG Tel: (01355) 355000 Fax: (01355) 234582

▶ Free Scale Semi Conductor UK Ltd, Colvilles Road, East Kilbride, Glasgow, G75 0TG Tel: (01355) 355000 Fax: (01355) 234582

Freebird Guitars, 40 Marrowbrook Lane, Farnborough, Hampshire, GU14 0AE Tel: (01252) 541417 E-mail: enquiries@freebirdguitars.com *Guitar tuition services*

▶ Freebox Computing Ltd, Botley Mills, Botley, Southampton, SO30 2GB Tel: (01489) 795000 Fax: (01489) 795950 E-mail: sales@montanaretail.co.uk *Software & hardware retail solutions services*

▶ Freed Of London Ltd, 35 Rydal Street, Leicester, LE2 7DS Tel: 0116-254 8010

Freedmans Ltd, 7-8 Ashburton Terrace, London, E13 0JB Tel: (020) 8472 1357 Fax: (020) 8472 1303 E-mail: freedmanbalers@talk21.com *Recycling machinery dealers packaging manufrs*

Freedman's At Salters, 17-19 Barking Road, London, E6 1PW Tel: (020) 8472 2892 Fax: (020) 8472 2811 E-mail: enquiries@freedmansatsalters.co.uk *Baby & nursery product retailers*

▶ Freedom Ltd, Woodlands Needham Road, Badley, Ipswich, IP6 8RS Tel: (01449) 675999 Fax: (01449) 745000 E-mail: admin@lanva.co.uk

Freedom, Gate Lane, Sutton Coldfield, West Midlands, B73 5TX Tel: 0121-355 8668 Fax: 0121-355 2113 E-mail: sales@swimcap.com *Sports bags & clothing*

Freedom Communications, Olds Approach, Tolpits Lane, Watford, WD18 9RX Tel: 01923 654321 Fax: 01923 654323 E-mail: enquiries@freedomcomms.com *Telephone & data company*

▶ Freedom Computing, 97 Hargate Way, Hampton Hargate, Peterborough, PE7 8DY Tel: (01733) 893097 Fax: 01733 893097 E-mail: Freedom_Computing@Hotmail.com *Problems with your computer?*Troubleshooting, Repairs and Installation.*Low Cost Call Out for Home and Business.*

▶ Freedom Computing, 23 Caldervale, Orton Longueville, Peterborough, PE2 7HX Tel: (01733) 361117

▶ Freedom Engineering Co. Ltd, 34 Springfield Way, Anlaby, Hull, HU10 6RJ Tel: (01482) 565566 Fax: (01482) 500826 E-mail: mike@freedomgears.fsnet.co.uk Principal Export Areas: Worldwide *Freedom Engineering are the gear specialists. Gear & spline manufacturers including spiral, Bevel, Helical, worm Wheel, Spur, Racks, spiral & angular spiral bevels. A Specialist family run business established in 1947 offering a friendly & personal service.*

Freedom Marine Ltd, 3 Westfield Industrial Estate, Westfield Lane, Etchinghill, Folkestone, Kent, CT18 8BX Tel: (01303) 862215 Fax: (01303) 863066 E-mail: freedom@engines10.freeserve.co.uk *Marine engineers*

▶ Freedom Wireless Ltd, Bedford Heights, Manton Lane, Bedford, MK41 7PH Tel: 08707 480153 E-mail: info@freedom-wireless.co.uk *We are an online shop catering for all of your wireless networking needs.*

Freelance Cash Register Services, 31 Wood Green Road, Oldbury, West Midlands, B68 0DE Tel: 0121-421 3973 Fax: 0121-421 3973 *Cash register sales & services*

Freelance Euro Contracting Ltd, Eaton Place Business Centre, 114 Washway Road, Sale, Cheshire, M33 7RF Tel: 0161-374 4777 Fax: 0161-374 4778 E-mail: enquiries@freelance-euro.com *Freelance Euro Contracting Ltd (FECL) provides contractors and freelance professionals with a complete Managed Limited Company service both UK and world-wide. Our specialist accountancy services ensure not only that one-man limited companies comply with the Revenue Authorities from a taxation perspective and operate in legally compliant manner (IR 35 compliance), but that our contractors maximise their income from each and every invoice (Through expert tax-optimisation), putting more money in their pockets.*

Freelance Software Ltd, East Street, Bingham, Nottingham, NG13 8DS Tel: (01949) 838988 Fax: (01949) 838112 E-mail: info@centralone.co.uk *Bespoke software suppliers*

▶ Freelancealot.co.uk, No 1 Appletree Cottage, Smallwood Manor, Uttoxeter, Staffordshire, ST14 8NR Tel: 0870 432 1566 Fax: 0870 432 1565 E-mail: info@freelancealot.co.uk *Assistant partnership providing professional & confidential web design*

Freeland Freight Services Ltd, Blackness Road, Altens Industrial Estate, Aberdeen, AB12 3LH Tel: (01224) 873601 Fax: (01224) 879863 E-mail: enquiries@freelandfreight.co.uk *Road transport contractors*

▶ Freeman Associates, 92 Church Street, Swinton, Mexborough, South Yorkshire, S64 8DQ Tel: (01709) 578078 Fax: (01709) 578153 E-mail: designs@freemanassociates.co.uk *Freeman Associates - Leading Structural Engineers Architectural Designers and Engineering Services*

▶ Freeman Christie, 1 Spinners Court, 53 West End, Witney, Oxfordshire, OX28 1NH Tel: (01993) 899000 E-mail: hello@freemanchristie.co.uk *Creative communication*

▶ Freeman Elevators, Unit 87, City Business Park, Somerset Place, Stoke, Plymouth, PL3 4BB Tel: 0845 8382833 E-mail: sales@freemanelevators.co.uk *Lift installation, repair and servicing company. Specialists in passenger and freight lifts, stairlifts and disabled access. Indoor or outdoor installations. Guaranteed work, service contracts available, fully qualified engineers, 24Hr service 365 days a year, NO CALL CENTRES USED, all enquires dealt with by our staff whatever the hour of the day for speedy and efficient service.*

Freeman & Co Installations Ltd, 152 High Street, Ongar, Essex, CM5 9JJ Tel: (0845) 6444354 Fax: (0845) 6444353 E-mail: sales@freemanandcompany.co.uk *Electrical engineers*

▶ Philip Freeman Mobile Welders Ltd, Bertram House, 7 Bertram Street, Hamilton, Lanarkshire, ML3 0QS Tel: (01698) 712920 Fax: (01698) 712990 E-mail: sales@philipfreeman.co.uk

Freeman & Proctor, PO Box 22, Nuneaton, Warwickshire, CV11 4XY Tel: (024) 7638 2032 Fax: (024) 7637 4353 E-mail: info@freemanandproctor.co.uk *Stainless steel tube services & fabricators*

Freeman Technology, Boulters Farm Centre, Castlemorton Common, Welland, Malvern, Worcestershire, WR13 6LE Tel: (01684) 310860 Fax: (01684) 310236 *Scientific equipment manufrs*

William Freeman, Wakefield Road, Staincross, Barnsley, South Yorkshire, S75 6DH Tel: (01226) 284081 Fax: (01226) 731832 E-mail: sales@williamfreeman.com *Rubber & plastic moulding manufrs*

Freemans, Salvesen Way, Brighton Street Industrial Estate, Hull, HU3 4UQ Tel: (01482) 221366 Fax: (01482) 221343 E-mail: hull@isotank.co.uk *Road transport, haulage & freight services*

▶ Freemans Maintenance & Building Services Ltd, Unit 62, Mill Lane, Fazeley, Tamworth, Staffordshire, B78 3QD Tel: (01827) 260085

William Freer Ltd, 350-360 Melton Road, Leicester, LE4 7SL Tel: 0116-268 9660 Fax: 0116-268 9650 *Plumbing & heating engineers*

Freerange Design, 521 Royal Exchange, Manchester, M2 7EN Tel: 0161-835 2312 Fax: 0161-835 3121 E-mail: paulb@freerangedesign.com *Design consultancy, graphics & packaging design*

Freerose Ltd, 26 Apex Business Centre, Boscombe Road, Dunstable, Bedfordshire, LU5 4SB Tel: (01582) 472274 Fax: (01582) 475574 E-mail: info@freerose.co.uk *Telecommunications distributors*

Freeston Stockholding Ltd, Unit 11, Eclipse Industrial Estate, Sedgley Road West, Tipton, West Midlands, DY4 8AB Tel: 0121-520 2281 Fax: 0121-522 3853 *General stockholders & pressings*

Freeston Water Treatment Ltd, West Quay Road, Southampton, SO15 1GZ Tel: (023) 8022 0738 Fax: (023) 8063 9853 E-mail: info@freeston.co.uk *Manufacturers of water softening equipment, water treatment chemical products & water treatment plant & equipment. In addition, water tank cleaning/ relining & water treatment (legionella control) services*

▶ Freestyle Case Co. Ltd, Dale House, Brewery Lane, Thornhill, Dewsbury, West Yorkshire, WF12 9HU Tel: (01924) 455414

Freestyle Hair Co. Ltd, Unit 22 Haigh Park, Haigh Avenue, Stockport, Cheshire, SK4 1QR Tel: 0161-476 1115 Fax: 0161-429 0730 E-mail: info@freestylehair.co.uk *Import wholesaler wigs & hairpieces*

▶ Freestyle Of London Ltd, Swan Wharf, 60 Dace Road, London, E3 2NQ Tel: (020) 8985 9985 Fax: (020) 8533 1816 E-mail: creff@freestyleoflondon.co.uk *Furnishings*

Freestyle Marketing Communications Ltd, 3 Pelham Road, Nottingham, NG5 1AP Tel: 0115-985 6954 Fax: 0115-985 6955 E-mail: ed@freestyleuk.com *Advertising agency*

▶ Freestyle Sign & Print, 8 Sheeplands Farm, Twyford Road, Wargrave, Reading, RG10 8DL Tel: 0118-940 4000 Fax: 0118-940 6275 E-mail: freestyle@provider.co.uk *Sign manufrs*

▶ Freestyle Sports & Play Surfaces, 129 Cheshire Street, Market Drayton, Shropshire, TF9 3AH Tel: (01630) 656336 Fax: (01630) 658366 E-mail: lee@freestylesurfaces.com *Playground equipment manufrs*

▶ Freeview Receiver, Returns Department, Sequoia Technical Services, County Estate Nunn Brook Road, Huthwaite, Sutton-in-Ashfield, Nottinghamshire, NG17 2HU Tel: (0870) 4430638 E-mail: sales@freeviewreceivers.co.uk

Freeway Commerce Ltd, Unit 12, Sceptre Court, Sceptre Way, Bamber Bridge, Preston, PR5 6AW Tel: (01772) 646000 Fax: (01772) 646001 E-mail: info@freewaycommece.co.uk *E commerce & electronic data suppliers*

▶ Freeway Lift Services Ltd, Dolphin Wharf, Rockingham Road, Uxbridge, Middlesex, UB8 2UB Tel: (01895) 811025 Fax: (01895) 811026

Freeway Signs Ltd, Chalkwell Road, Sittingbourne, Kent, ME10 2LJ Tel: (01795) 426724 Fax: (01795) 431180 E-mail: freewaysigns@lineone.net *Sign makers & road marking*

Freeway Tools & Fixings, 14 Victoria Way, Burgess Hill, West Sussex, RH15 9NF Tel: (01444) 873000 Fax: (01444) 873001 E-mail: admin@freewayfixings.com *Tools distribution*

▶ Freewing Masts, Clachnaharry Works Lock, Clachnaharry Road, Inverness, IV3 8RA Tel: (01463) 243161 Fax: (01463) 794506 *Yacht masts & components manufrs*

▶ Freewing Masts, 17 Birchwood Road, Westhill, Inverness, IV2 5DW Tel: (01463) 791101 Fax: (01463) 794506 E-mail: richard@freewingmasts.co.uk *Carbon fibre yaght builders*

Freeze Master, Unit A1, Connaught Business, London, NW9 6JL Tel: (020) 8205 7672 Fax: (020) 8205 7674 *The Freeze Master is easy to use. Just connect the purpose-designed freeze heads to the pipework, upstream and downstream of the area you want to work on. In a little under five minutes, two solid ice plugs can be formed allowing you to carry out your repair quickly and efficiently within the isolated area. This has no adverse effect on the pipes. At the end of the work, simply remove the freezer heads thus allowing the ice to thaw in minutes. No more drain downs*

▶ Freezing Systems, 5 Highland Close, St Helen's Way, Thetford, Norfolk, IP24 1HG Tel: (01842) 762511 Fax: (01842) 763322 E-mail: enquiries@jackstonefreezing.co.uk *Industrial freezer manufrs*

Freight Clearance Ltd, New Bridge House, New Bridge, Dover, Kent, CT16 1JS Tel: (01304) 211020 Fax: (01304) 209753 *Customs clearance agents*

▶ Freight Control Services Ltd, Unit 10 Cambrian Industrial Estate East Side, Coedcae Lane, Pontyclun, Mid Glamorgan, CF72 9EW Tel: (01443) 222796 Fax: (01443) 223006

Freight Data 2000 Ltd, Foremost House, Radford Way, Billericay, Essex, CM12 0BT Tel: (01622) 861323 E-mail: uksales@freightdata.com *Suppliers of international freight software including air freight, deep sea & road transport. Also cargo tracking with CargoFind*

▶ Freight Express Ltd, Pomathorn Store, Penicuik, Midlothian, EH26 8PJ Tel: (01968) 670066 Fax: (01968) 676010 E-mail: sales@freightexpress.co.uk

Freight Co. International Ltd, Unit 5 Howe Moss Drive, Dyce, Aberdeen, AB21 0GL Tel: (01224) 771881 Fax: (01224) 770730 E-mail: info@freightco-group.co.uk *Freight forwarders & air charterers*

▶ Freight Solutions, Honywood Road, Basildon, Essex, SS14 3DS Tel: (01268) 287979 Fax: (01268) 287978 E-mail: sales@freightsolutionsuk.com

▶ Freight Speed Commercial, Highland House, The Heath, Tendring, Clacton-on-Sea, Essex, CO16 0DA Tel: (01255) 870622

Freight Transport Ltd, C3-C5 Unit, Railway Triangle, Walton Road, Portsmouth, PO6 1TW Tel: (023) 9232 4213 Fax: (023) 9221 0324 E-mail: sales@freighttransport.co.uk *Freight forwarders, national & international haulage*

Freightlocators, The Sidings, Windmill La, Ringwood, Hants, BH24 2DQ Tel: (01425) 478861 E-mail: freightlocators@aol.com *Freight movement*

▶ Freight-Mate, 463 Stourport Road, Kidderminster, Worcestershire, DY11 7BD Tel: (01562) 638508

▶ Freightroute Ltd, 90 Bristol Road, Gloucester, GL1 5SQ Tel: (01452) 310301 Fax: (01452) 310300

▶ freis fresche ltd, Acklam Road, Middlesbrough, Cleveland, TS5 7HA Tel: 0870 8965715 *Designer clothes /jeans t-shirts shirts , jackets , knitwear*

▶ Fremantle Training & Transport LLP Ltd, 90 Barewell Road, Torquay, TQ1 4PA Tel: (01404) 43433 Fax: 01803 293555 *Fremantle provide ADR driver training, DGSA - Dangerous Goods Safety Advisor, CPC and Health & Safety services to the transport industry.*

Fremantlemedia Tems, 1 Stephen Street, London, W1T 1AL Tel: (020) 7691 6000 Fax: (020) 7691 6100 *Television producers*

Fremar Communications, Unit 3 Loyaltrade, Loyaltrade Business, Stephenson Road, Churchfields Industrial Estate, Salisbury, SP2 7NS Tel: (0845) 0068820 Fax: (0845) 0068830 E-mail: chrispitman@radiocomms.net *Radio communications equipment supplier, maintenance & hire*

Anna French Ltd, 36 Hinton Road, London, SE24 0HJ Tel: (020) 7737 6555 E-mail: info@annafrench.co.uk *Furnishing fabric designers*

▶ French Bros, 60 Main Street, Kibworth Harcourt, Leicester, LE8 0NQ Tel: 0116-279 6767 Fax: 0116-279 6868 E-mail: helen@insulate.co.uk *Installers of all types of industrial insulation, particularly in food and chemical industries. Also supply and fitting of trace heating.*

▶ French Bros Ltd, Clewer Boathouse, Clewer Court Road, Windsor, Berkshire, SL4 5JH Tel: (01753) 851900 Fax: (01753) 832303

French Electrical Services, Chapel House, 25 Chapel Street, Loughborough, Leicestershire, LE12 9AF Tel: (01509) 502533 Fax: (01509) 505773 E-mail: wtfrench@btinternet.com *Public address system installers & induction loops*

French Equipment, Runnymede Boat House, Windsor Road, Old Windsor, Windsor, Berkshire, SL4 2JL Tel: (01784) 439626 Fax: (01784) 433309 *Excavation & groundwork contractors*

▶ French Flavour Ltd, PO Box 2192, Wrexham, Clwyd, LL14 2TB Tel: (01978) 844378 Fax: (01978) 844378 E-mail: info@frenchflavour.co.uk *French Flavour Ltd, offer quality produce from small producers within France who have a good repution for the products that they make. *Most of the Products that we select are normally sold only within France. We import into the UK for sale here via the Internet or to retail outlets. Check out the Website for details of a selection of our products.*If you are looking for a particular Produce not shown on the site, we can usually source and provide a no obligation quote for you. *Our full list of products is available on request.*

▶ French Property, PO Box 46, Wirral, Merseyside, CH60 9LR Tel: (07747) 888181 E-mail: frenchproperty@ic24.net *French Property required in Provence France.*

Samuel French Ltd, 52 Fitzroy Street, London, W1T 5JR Tel: (020) 7387 9373 Fax: (020) 7387 2161 E-mail: theatre@samuelfrench-london.co.uk *Publishers*

Thomas French Ltd, James Street, Bury, Lancashire, BL9 7EG Tel: 0161-764 5356 Fax: 0161-764 6416 E-mail: peter.owen@thomasfrench.com *Cushions manufacturers & distributors*

▶ Frenchy's Kitchen, 1 Cypress Close, Caerleon, Newport, NP18 3RN Tel: (01633) 431428 E-mail: pascal@frenchyskitchen.co.uk *outside catering, buffet, dinner party, barbecue,*

Frenco Ltd, 24 Worcester Street, Kidderminster, Worcestershire, DY10 1ED Tel: (01562) 69442 Fax: (01562) 820410 *Motor vehicle spare parts*

Frenco International, 11 Fortnum Close, Birmingham, B33 0LG Tel: 0121-789 7895 Fax: 0121-789 7050 E-mail: sales@frenco.co.uk *Manufacturers of Spline Gauges,*Master Gears,Indicating Gauges*

▶ Frenni Transport Ltd, Station Road, Crymych, Dyfed, SA41 3RL Tel: (01239) 831557

▶ Frens, 1 Malabar Road, Truro, Cornwall, TR1 3QU Tel: (01872) 260196 E-mail: info@frensclothing.com

Frenstar, Unit 240 Ordinance Business Park, Aerodrome Road, Gosport, Hampshire, PO13 0FG Tel: (01329) 233445 Fax: (01329) 233450 E-mail: info@frenstar.co.uk *Suppliers of butterfly valves in; iron, steel, stainless steel, duplex*

Frequentis UK Ltd, Gainsborough House, 2 Sheen Road, Richmond, Surrey, TW9 1AE Tel: (020) 8973 2616 *Telecom distributors*

▶ Frerrie, Holly Close, Holly Road, Thornton-Cleveleys, Lancashire, FY5 4LR Tel: (01253) 851088 *Glass fibre suppliers*

Fresenius Medical Care (UK) Ltd, Nunn Brook Road, Huthwaite, Sutton-In-Ashfield, Nottinghamshire, NG17 2HU Tel: (01623) 445100 Fax: (01623) 552409 *Dialysis disposable product manufrs*

Fresh Air Ventilation Systems, 35a Salhouse Road, Rackheath, Norwich, NR13 6PD Tel: (01603) 720330 Fax: (01603) 720331 E-mail: sales@thefreshaircompany.co.uk *Air conditioning, ventilation, refrigeration suppliers & installers*

Fresh Bacon Co., Ty Verlon Industrial Estate, Cardiff Road, Barry, South Glamorgan, CF63 2BE Tel: (01446) 700900 *Bacon & ham curers & merchants*

▶ Fresh Biz Marketing, 1 Oban Close, Wakefield, West Yorkshire, WF3 1JU Tel: 0870 284 6180 Fax: 0870 284 6181 E-mail: info@freshbizmarketing.com *Marketing provides web design,*

Fresh Farm Catering, Unit 2 96 White Post Lane, London, E9 5EN Tel: (020) 8525 0809 Fax: (020) 8525 6729 *Fruit & vegetable preparation company*

Fresh Freight Ltd, North East Fruit & Vegetable Market, Team Valley Trading Estate, Gateshead, Tyne & Wear, NE11 0QY Tel: 0191-491 0505 Fax: 0191-491 0090 *Road transport, haulage & freight services*

▶ Fresh Lemon, Unit 17 Wrotham Business Park, Wrotham Park, Barnet, Hertfordshire, EN5 4SZ Tel: (020) 8275 8585 Fax: (020) 8275 8586 E-mail: info@freshlemon.co.uk *CD roms, sales & marketing, advertising, web campaigns, interactive*

▶ Fresh Peeled Produce Ltd, Sutton Road, Walpole Cross Keys, King's Lynn, Norfolk, PE34 4HD Tel: (01553) 829481 Fax: (01553) 827095

Fresh Produce Journal, 430 438 Market Towers, 1 Nine Elms Lane, London, SW8 5NN Tel: (020) 7501 0300 Fax: (020) 7720 8451 E-mail: sales@freshinfo.com *Publishers*

▶ Fresh Start Recruitment UK, Ashfield Avenue, Mansfield, Nottinghamshire, NG18 2AE Tel: (01623) 404525 Fax: 01623 404234 E-mail: mansfield@barecruitment.co.uk *BA RECRUITMENT LTD Specialists for Accountancy Professionals! *Welcome to Ba Recruitment - Recruitment specialists for Accountancy Jobs in the Derbyshire and Nottinghamshire areas.*

▶ Fresh Technical Solutions, Artillery Lane, London, E1 7LP Tel: (0845) 4587500 E-mail: info@fresh-uk.com *Computer software & network support services*

▶ Fresh Water Filter Company, Carlton House, Aylmer Road, London, E11 3AD Tel: (020) 8558 7495 Fax: (0870) 4423639 E-mail: info@freshwaterfilter.com *Manufacturer of drinking water*

▶ Fresh Web Services Ltd, 52 Craighill Road, Leicester, LE2 3FB Tel: 0116-270 4887 E-mail: kellys@freshwebservices.com *Web design, web hosting, domain name registration, e-commerce, online shops, search engine optimisation, Java software for internet & desktop, xml, database design, internet marketing, content managment systems, open source.*

Fresh Wharf Estates Ltd, 1 Fresh Wharf Estate, Highbridge Road, Barking, Essex, IG11 7BP Tel: (020) 8594 2400 Fax: (020) 8594 5105 E-mail: sales@freshwharf.co.uk *Property management*

Fresh & Wild, 208-210 Westbourne Grove, London, W11 2RH Tel: (020) 7229 1063 Fax: (020) 7792 1341 E-mail: guini.short@wholefoods.com *Health food & products*

Freshair Ltd, Unit 5 Horseshoe Close, London, NW2 7JJ Tel: (020) 8452 4266 Fax: (020) 8452 2904 E-mail: sales@freshair.co.uk *Screen printers*

▶ Freshair, Newport Road, Market Drayton, Shropshire, TF9 2AA Tel: (01630) 657606 Fax: (01630) 655545 *Subcontract installers*

Freshbake Wholesale Bakery, 9 Malcolm Place, London, E2 0EU Tel: (020) 8983 4045 Fax: (020) 8880 6696 *Bakery*

▶ Freshbins UK Ltd, 95 Kingsland Road, Hemel Hempstead, Hertfordshire, HP1 1QB Tel: (01442) 265606 Fax: (01442) 263310 E-mail: sales@freshbins-uk.com

▶ fresh-coconut organic virgin coconut oil, 145A Wembley Park Drive, Wembley, Middx, HA9 8HQ Tel: 07950 606390 *Organic Virgin Coconut Oil **We are an online shop for food we believe is good for you. We believe in unprocessed natural foods. Virgin coconut oil is one such food. The health benefits people get from this virgin coconut oil are numeruos. But also other unrefined organic oils like flax oil or hemp seed oil are a long establishd surce for good health.*

▶ Freshflow Water Coolers, 6 Churchlands Farm Industrial Estate, Bascote Road, Ufton, Leamington Spa, Warwickshire, CV33 9PL Tel: (01926) 613906 Fax: (01926) 614215 *Water cooler manufrs*

Fresh-pak Chilled Foods Ltd, 21-22 Kernan Drive, Loughborough, Leicestershire, LE11 5JT Tel: (01509) 233327 Fax: (01509) 269468 E-mail: info@fresh-pak.co.uk *Food manufrs*

Freshtec Ltd, PO Box 18, Dawlish, Devon, EX7 9YL Tel: (01626) 867090 Fax: (01626) 867199 E-mail: sales@freshtec.co.uk *Water & air purification services*

Freshtime UK Ltd, Marsh Lane, Boston, Lincolnshire, PE21 7RJ Tel: (01205) 312010 Fax: (01205) 357838 E-mail: sales@freshtime.co.uk *Vegetable manufrs*

▶ Freshwashed Herbs Ltd, Chestnuts Farm, Langton Green, Eye, Suffolk, IP23 7HL Tel: (01379) 871410 Fax: (01379) 873322 E-mail: info@freshwashedherbs.co.uk *Fresh, fresh, fresh Herbs now available to Caterers/ Hotels/Restaurants. Next day delivery anywhere in mainland Britain, year round supply. Fresh Coriander, Basil, Tarragon, Parsley's, Chives, Rosemary, Mint, Thyme, Sage to name a few!*

Freshwater Cruisers, Riverside Estate, Brundall, Norwich, NR13 5PS Tel: (01603) 717355 Fax: (01603) 717355 *Boat yard, marine chandlers & boat safety*

Freshwater UK, Freshwater House, Cardiff Gate Business Park, Pontprennau, Cardiff, CF23 8RS Tel: (029) 2054 5370 Fax: (029) 2054 5380 E-mail: sales@freshwater-uk.com *PR design, marketing & advertising*

▶ Freshwebdesign Com Ltd, 28 Imperial Park, Rawreth Lane, Rayleigh, Essex, SS6 9RS Tel: (0870) 8302999

Fretfoil Ltd, 13-15 Izons La Industrial Estate, West Bromwich, West Midlands, B70 9BY Tel: 0121-525 6588 Fax: 0121-525 6735 E-mail: fretfoilltd@aol.com *Packaging merchants*

Fretwell-Downing Hospitality, Brincliffe House, 861 Ecclesall Road, Sheffield, S11 7AE Tel: 0114-281 6060 Fax: 0114-281 6061 E-mail: info@fdhospitality.com *Sheffield-based Fretwell-Downing Hospitality are catering management software providers. They also offer training and support services.*

Fretwells Ltd, Oslo Road, Hull, HU7 0YN Tel: (01482) 835511 Fax: (01482) 835368 E-mail: info@fretwells.co.uk *Printers*

Freudenberg Building Systems, Gilmorton Road, Lutterworth, Leicestershire, LE17 4DU Tel: (01455) 261200 Fax: (01455) 556529 E-mail: norauk@freudenberg.com *Floor coverings*

▶ Freudenberg Household Products, 2 Chichester Street, Rochdale, Lancashire, OL16 2AX Tel: (01706) 759597 Fax: (01706) 350143 E-mail: steve.barber@fhp.com Sales Contact: K. Wright *Industrial cleaning equipment/materials manufacturers & distributors. Also janitorial supply services*

▶ James Frew Ltd, 83 New Street, Stevenston, Ayrshire, KA20 3HD Tel: (01294) 468113 Fax: (01294) 469371 E-mail: admin@jamesfrew.co.uk

Frewer Brothers Ltd, 3 Wealdstone Road, Sutton, Surrey, SM3 9QN Tel: (020) 8641 7171 Fax: (020) 8644 4779 E-mail: mail@frewerbrothers.co.uk *Printers, thermographers & watermarkers*

Friargreen Construction, Woodlands, Skeet Hill Lane, Orpington, Kent, BR5 4HB Tel: (01689) 823749 Fax: (01689) 832047 *Building underpinner*

Friars & Co., Unit 2b Shakespeare Industrial Estate, Shakespeare Street, Watford, WD24 5RU Tel: (01923) 249420 Fax: (01923) 818142 E-mail: friars@ukf.net *Printers & packers*

Friary Metal Products Ltd, 106-110 Bishop Street, Birmingham, B5 6JP Tel: 0121-622 2088 Fax: 0121-666 7277 E-mail: info@thefriarygroup.co.uk *Pressworkers*

Friary Mill, Oakfield Place, Plymouth, PL4 0QA Tel: (01752) 255113 Fax: (01752) 662946 *Bakery wholesalers*

Frictec Ltd, Robinson Way, Portsmouth, PO3 5SA Tel: (023) 9266 6816 Fax: (023) 9269 0425 E-mail: sales@frictec.co.uk *Machine knife manufrs*

Friction & Hydraulic Services, Gower Street Industrial Estate, St. Georges, Telford, Shropshire, TF2 9HW Tel: (01952) 615793 Fax: (01952) 620408 E-mail: sales@friction-hydraulics.co.uk *Industrial hose hydraulic component distributors*

Friction Linings Southampton Ltd, Unit 2 Easton La Business Park, Easton Lane, Winchester, Hampshire, SO23 7RQ Tel: (01962) 867666 E-mail: info@frictionlinings.co.uk *Motor vehicle parts distribs* Also at: Branches throughout Southern England

Friction Welding Products, Castle Mill Works, Birmingham New Road, Dudley, West Midlands, DY1 4DA Tel: (01384) 236961 Fax: (01384) 236982 E-mail: adv102@gbfederal.co.uk *Leading manufacturers of direct drive and inertia friction welding machines. Comprehensive sub-contract friction welding division offers a full range of components including dissimilar materials and specialising in tube-tube, bar-bar, end-end.*

Fridays Ltd, Chequertree Farmhouse, Swattenden Lane, Cranbrook, Kent, TN17 3PN Tel: (01580) 710200 Fax: (01580) 713512 E-mail: fridays@fridays.co.uk *Processed egg product manufrs*

▶ Friday's Child, 2 Market Square, Narberth, Dyfed, SA67 7AU Tel: (01834) 869944 Fax: (01834) 869922 *Baby care appliance retailers*

Fridge Controls Ltd, 4-5 Plantagaenet Estate, Kineton, Warwick, CV35 0HU Tel: (01926) 640171 Fax: (01926) 641707 E-mail: sales@fridgecontrols.co.uk *Control panel manufrs*

The Fridge Group, Suite 6 Broomburn Court, 8 Broomburn Drive, Newton Mearns, Glasgow, G77 5JL Tel: 0141-577 7644 Fax: 0141-577 7645 *IT consultancy*

Fried Jerry & Co. Ltd, Saltmeadows Road, Gateshead, Tyne & Wear, NE8 3BQ Tel: 0191-490 1313 Fax: 0191-490 1907 E-mail: lionel@jerryfried.co.uk *Sewing machines distributors*

Friedenthals Ltd, Marine Propeller Works, Croft Street, Preston, PR1 8XD Tel: (01772) 254255 Fax: (01772) 204829 *Ships' propellers & sterngears*

Friedman Corporation Ltd, 1 Chapel Court, Holly Walk, Leamington Spa, Warwickshire, CV32 4YS Tel: (01926) 741600 Fax: (01926) 741601 E-mail: uksales@friedmancorp.co.uk *Computer software suppliers*

▶ Friel Homes Ltd, Cross Keys Farm, 46 Hill Street, Hednesford, Cannock, Staffordshire, WS12 2DN Tel: (01543) 425544 Fax: (01543) 425205

▶ Friend Contracting, Miller Court, Millbay Road, Plymouth, PL1 3LQ Tel: (01752) 670555 Fax: (01752) 212303

P.F. Friend & Son Ltd, 3 Rolle Cottages, Rolle Street, Barnstaple, Devon, EX31 1JL Tel: (01271) 343058 Fax: (01271) 325319 E-mail: pffriend@hotmail.co.uk *Electrical & fire alarm contractors*

Friendly Computers, 274 Harehills Lane, Leeds, LS9 7BD Tel: 0113-216 1999 Fax: 0113-216 1400 *Computer retailers & manufrs*

▶ Friendly People Ltd, The Old Post Office, 2, Church Street, Brigstock, Kettering, Northamptonshire, NN14 3EX Tel: (01536) 373648 E-mail: info@friendly-people.co.uk *friendlypeople recruitment provides permanent, contract & temporary staff wihtin various industries including Media, Oil and Engineering, Sales, Marketing, Services, Manufacturing, IT, HR, Retail, Call Centre, etc*

Friends' Provident P.L.C., Pixham End, Dorking, Surrey, RH4 1QA Tel: (0870) 6083678 Fax: (01306) 651802 *Life assurance agents* Also at: Branches throughout the U.K.

Friends Provident, UK House, Castle Street, Salisbury, SP1 3SH Tel: (0870) 6071352 Fax: (0870) 5314151 *Insurance broker* Also at: Branches throughout the U.K.

Friendship Mill Beds Ltd, Unit 22 Friendship Mill, Whalley Road, Read, Burnley, Lancashire, BB12 7PN Tel: (01282) 772662 Fax: (01282) 772662 *Pine bed manufrs*

Fri-Jado UK, Ashley House, Ashley Road, Uxbridge, Middlesex, UB8 2GA Tel: (01895) 272227 Fax: (01895) 256360 E-mail: sales@frijado.co.uk *Fri-Jado UK based in Uxbridge, Middlesex offers bake off ovens, waste disposal compactors, heated display cabinets and cases, refrigerated display cabinets and cases and rotisseries.*

Frillies Ltd, First Floor Shell Leyland, Wigan Road, Leyland, PR25 5UD Tel: (01772) 621037 Fax: (01772) 621037 *Babywear*

Frimatec UK Ltd, 5 Townsend Centre Blackburn Road, Townsend Industrial Estate, Houghton Regis, Dunstable, Bedfordshire, LU5 5BQ Tel: (01582) 471600 Fax: (01582) 472050 E-mail: frimatec@nildram.co.uk *Cold room manufacturers & installers*

Frimstone Ltd, Norton Hill, Snettisham, King's Lynn, Norfolk, PE31 7LZ Tel: (01485) 570182 Fax: (01485) 543458 *Quarry owners* Also at: Cambridge

Fringe Electronics Ltd, 50 Mansfield Rd, Clipstone Village, Mansfield, Nottinghamshire, NG21 9EQ Tel: (01623) 643802 Fax: (01623) 625407 E-mail: enquiries@fringeelectronics.co.uk *Television aerial amplifier manufrs*

▶ Fringes, Strode Road, Newnham Industrial Estate, Plympton, Plymouth, PL7 4AY Tel: (01752) 345464 Fax: (01752) 345464 *Carpet retailers*

Frio UK Ltd, Whitleys, Wolfscastle, Haverfordwest, Dyfed, SA62 5DY Tel: (01437) 741755 Fax: (01437) 741781 E-mail: frio@btinternet.com *Cooling products manufrs*

Frisby Construction Ltd, 16 Glenfield Avenue, Weddington, Nuneaton, Warwickshire, CV10 0DZ Tel: (024) 7634 0958 Fax: (024) 7638 7173 E-mail: frisbyhomes@enta.net *Builders, contractors & developers*

Frisby Extrusion Services Ltd, Unit F Tyson Courtyard, Weldon South Industrial Estate, Corby, Northamptonshire, NN18 8AZ Tel: (01536) 263545 Fax: (01536) 205184 E-mail: welcome@fes-ltd.com *Precision component engineers suppliers*

Frise M S & Sons Ltd, 7 Trowbridge Road, Westbury, Wiltshire, BA13 3AY Tel: (01373) 826333 Fax: (01373) 826444 E-mail: sales@frise.co.uk *Air conditioning services & plumbing ventilation*

Frith's Flexible Packaging Ltd, 1 The Forum Coopers Way, Temple Farm Industrial Estate, Southend-on-Sea, SS2 5TE Tel: (01702) 462605 Fax: (01702) 616954 E-mail: sales@friths.co.uk *Flexible packaging manufrs*

Friulsider UK Ltd, Unit 16 Court Farm Business Park, Bishops Frome, Worcester, WR6 5AY Tel: (01885) 490445 Fax: (01885) 490452 E-mail: sales@friulsider.co.uk *Industrial fixing systems*

Frixos Metal Works Ltd, Unit 4, 30 Aden Road, Brimsdown, Enfield, Middlesex, EN3 7SY Tel: (020) 8443 1050 Fax: (020) 8440 1233 E-mail: jimmy@frixosmetalworks.co.uk *Sheet metal fabricators*

Frodex, Everitt Close, Denington Industrial Estate, Wellingborough, Northamptonshire, NN8 2QE Tel: (01933) 225564 Fax: (01933) 226093 *Shelving & racking distributors*

Frodsham Sign & Display Ltd, 1 Millfield Lane, Haydock, St. Helens, Merseyside, WA11 9TW Tel: (01942) 272330 Fax: (01942) 272331 E-mail: sales@frodshamsigns.co.uk *Signs manufrs & installation services*

Frog Networking Solutions Ltd, 1 Lion Works, Cambridge, CB2 4NL Tel: (01223) 493500 Fax: (0870) 4446772 E-mail: system@frog.co.uk *Computer consultants*

FROGSBACKPLASTERING, 234 High st, LONDON, UK, NW10 4TD Tel: 020 88634773 E-mail: frogsbackplastering@hotmail.com *we provide a top quality work in polished plaster,plastering and dry lining comercial and residential*

continued

▶ From All Around the World, 25 Warwick Road, Balderton, Newark, Notts, NG24 3QE Tel: 01636 703444E-mail: info@fromallaroundtheworld.com *Language courses and individual language tuition. French & Spanish safari language courses. Weekend TEFL courses. Language bookshop online. Supply of teachers curriculum.*

Frome Sign Co. Ltd, Unit 3 Lakeside Park, Mells, Frome, Somerset, BA11 3RH Tel: (01373) 813666 Fax: (01373) 813777 E-mail: fromesigns@aol.com *Sign makers & screen printers*

Frome Tool & Gauge Ltd, Manor Road, Marston Trading Estate, Frome, Somerset, BA11 4BL Tel: (01373) 462226 Fax: (01373) 452123 E-mail: frometandg@btconnect.com *Precision engineers*

▶ FromFiz, 39 Melford Grove, Ingleby Barwick, Stockton-on-Tees, Cleveland, TS17 0YF Tel: 07854 768673 *Hand Finished Wedding Rings available in 9ct and 18ct Yellow and White Gold. Free Postage on all orders.*

▶ Front Line Construction Ltd, Burnside Road, Bathgate, West Lothian, EH48 4PX Tel: (01506) 632510

▶ Front Runner, 144-146 Chorley Old Road, Bolton, BL1 3AT Tel: (01204) 361837 Fax: (01204) 361837

Front Runner Race Horse Transport, Jennet Tree Lane, Madresfield, Malvern, Worcestershire, WR13 5BE Tel: (01905) 831161 Fax: (01905) 831161 *Race horse transporters*

Frontec (uk) Ltd, Merchants Ho, Wapping Rd, Bristol, BS1 4RW Tel: 0117-929 7309 Fax: 0117-922 1927 *Software maintenance*

Frontier, 51a Hallgate, Holbeach, Spalding, Lincolnshire, PE12 7JA Tel: (01406) 422606 Fax: (01406) 423780 *Agricultural/chemical merchants, crop protection*

Frontier Agriculture Ltd, Red Shute Mill, Hermitage, Thatcham, Berkshire, RG18 9QU Tel: (01635) 204100 Fax: (01635) 201417 Principal Export Areas: Worldwide *Agricultural merchants*

Frontier Design, 1 Capital Place, Lovet Road, Harlow, Essex, CM19 5AS Tel: (01279) 427945 Fax: (01279) 641330 E-mail: enquiries@frontierdesign.co.uk *Product design & development services*

▶ Frontier Print & Design Ltd, Pickwick House, Chosen View Road, Cheltenham, Gloucestershire, GL51 9LT Tel: (01242) 573863 Fax: (01242) 511643 E-mail: sales@frontier-uk.com

Frontline Consultancy Business Services Ltd, Frontline House, Epsom Avenue, Handforth, Wilmslow, Cheshire, SK9 3PW Tel: (0870) 2410715 Fax: (0870) 6067300 E-mail: sales@frontline-consultancy.co.uk *IT consultants*

Frontline Electronics, 25 Laundry Road, Minster, Ramsgate, Kent, CT12 4HY Tel: (01843) 821512 Fax: (01843) 821603 E-mail: sales@frontlineelectronics.co.uk *Electronic design & manufrs*

▶ Frost Computer Services, 2 Church Mount, Guilsborough, Northampton, NN6 8QA Tel: (01604) 743017 Fax: (01604) 743017 E-mail: sales@frostcomputerservices.co.uk *Computer maintenance & repair services*

▶ Frost Conservatories, The Old Forge Tempsford, Great North Road, Sandy, Bedfordshire, SG19 2AG Tel: (01767) 640808 Fax: (01767) 640561 E-mail: sales@frostconservatories.co.uk *Conservatories*

Frost Duval Ltd, Stanley Works, Stanley Road, Sidcup, Kent, DA14 4DQ Tel: (020) 8300 2483 Fax: (020) 8300 5754 *Refrigeration & air conditioning contractors*

F.W. Frost (Engineers) Ltd, Bidewell Close, Drayton High Road, Norwich, NR8 6AP Tel: (01603) 867301 Fax: (01603) 261586 E-mail: sales@fwfrost-engineers.co.uk *Steel fabricators & precision engineers*

▶ John Frost Designer Bridalwear, 44 Smawthorne Lane, Castleford, West Yorkshire, WF10 4EW Tel: (01977) 552913 Fax: (01977) 604646 *Bridal tiaras & veils*

Frost Rochdale Ltd, Eagle Iron Works, Crawford Street, Rochdale, Lancashire, OL16 5NU Tel: (01706) 644929 Fax: (01706) 860338 E-mail: sales@frost.co.uk *Sheet metal, bending & cutting machinery*

Frost & Smith, Tweesden, Cray Road, Sidcup, Kent, DA14 5BZ Tel: (020) 8300 2242 Fax: (020) 8309 6964 *Motor body repairers*

Frost & Sullivan Ltd, Sullivan House, 4 Grosvenor Gardens, London, SW1W 0DH Tel: (020) 7730 3438 Fax: (020) 7730 3343 *Business information advisory service*

▶ Frost Thomas & Sons, 16-18 Ferry Street, Montrose, Angus, DD10 8DA Tel: (01674) 672953 *Bakers*

Frost Woodworking, 3 School Lane, Parkgate, Rotherham, South Yorkshire, S62 6FH Tel: (01709) 522251 Fax: (01709) 719510 *Joinery manufacturing*

▶ Frostbite, 98 Eastbourne Avenue, Gateshead, Tyne & Wear, NE8 4NH Tel: 0191-478 4159 *Meat product suppliers*

Frostechnic, Power Park, Station Approach, Banbury, Oxfordshire, OX16 5AB Tel: (01295) 266500 Fax: (01295) 275434 E-mail: info@frostechnic.com *Control panel manufrs*

Frostree Ltd, 31 Station Street, Middlesbrough, Cleveland, TS1 1SR Tel: (01642) 224151 Fax: (01642) 247973 E-mail: sales@frostree.co.uk *Manufacturers & installers of windows & doors*

Frosts Of Clerkenwell Ltd, 60-62 Clerkenwell Road, London, EC1M 5PX Tel: (020) 7253 0315 Fax: (020) 7253 7454 *Clock & watch repairers*

Frost's Rosettes, 365 Totnes Road, Paignton, Devon, TQ4 7DE Tel: (01803) 664848 Fax: (01803) 664848 *Rosettes manufrs*

Froude Hofmann, Blackpole Road, Worcester, WR3 8YB Tel: (01905) 856800 Fax: (01905) 856811 E-mail: sales@froude.fki-eng.com *Automotive engine & vehicle test equipment services*

Frozen In Time Ltd, The Industrial Estate, York Road, Sheriff Hutton, York, YO60 6RZ Tel: (01347) 878158 Fax: (01347) 878303 E-mail: info@freezedriers.com *Freeze drying machine manufrs*

▶ Frudd Building Services Ltd, Byidon House, Rolleston Drive, Nottingham, NG5 7JP Tel: 0115-955 5888

▶ Fruit of the Loom Distributors Ltd, Cramhurst Lane, Witley, Godalming, Surrey, GU8 5QZ Tel: (01428) 682546 Fax: (01428) 684900 E-mail: sales@ucs-group.co.uk *Stockists & distributors of screen stars & fruit of the loom products*

▶ Fruit Of The Loom T-Shirt Printers, Unit 4C Dover House Industrial Estate, Witley, Godalming, Surrey, GU8 5QZ Tel: (01483) 860270 E-mail: sales@ucs-group.co.uk *Screen printers of screen stars, hanes & other fine t-shirts*

▶ Fruit Promotional Products, 1 Whitehall Road, Leeds, LS1 4AW Tel: (0870) 7702638 Fax: (0870) 7702639 E-mail: sales@fruit-pp.co.uk *Specialist supplier of promotional products and clothing to the childcare service sector.*

▶ Fruit Sallad, 1 Blue Slates Close, Wheldrake, York, YO19 6NB Tel: (01904) 448080 E-mail: fruitsaladcom@btinternet.com *Suppliers of quality fresh fruit, salads & vegetables*

▶ Fruitcake Design Associates Ltd, Flat 8, Aquatico, Walnut Tree Close, Guildford, Surrey, GU1 4UL Tel: (07855) 576565 E-mail: clee@fruitcake.co.uk *Graphic design consultancy*

Fruition Systems Ltd, Unit 3, Claylands Road, Bishops Waltham, Southampton, SO32 1BH Tel: (01489) 890820 Fax: (01489) 897690 E-mail: info@fruitionsystems.co.uk *Computer consultants & services*

Fruits Of The Earth, 2a Victoria Grove, Bridport, Dorset, DT6 3AA Tel: (01308) 425827 *Health food retailers*

▶ Fruity Websites, PO Box 7143, Kettering, Northamptonshire, NN16 6BT Tel: 01536 738198 E-mail: hello@fruitywebsites.co.uk *Fruity Websites is a full-service web design company based in Kettering, Northamptonshire, UK. We provide everything to put a website on the Internet.*

Frujet Beverages Ltd, 4 Manor Road, London, N16 5SA Tel: (020) 8809 4646 Fax: (020) 8809 4747 *Drink distributors & manufrs*

Frutarom UK Ltd, Belasis Avenue, Billingham, Cleveland, TS23 1LQ Tel: (01642) 379900 Fax: (01642) 379901 E-mail: sales@frutarom.com *The development, manufacture & supply of: resinoids, oleoresins, natural & fortified extracts, essential oils, compounded flavour ingredients, aroma chemicals & fragrance & flavour specialities*

Frutarom UK Ltd, 3 Kingsthorne Park, Henson Way, Telford Way Industrial Estate, Kettering, Northamptonshire, NN16 8PX Tel: (01536) 532300 Fax: (01536) 532301 E-mail: sales@frutarom.com *Food flavour manufrs*

William Fry & Co. Ltd, Mitre Works, Neasden Goods Depot, Neasden Lane, London, NW10 2UG Tel: (020) 8459 5141 Fax: (020) 8459 2290 E-mail: md@metalandwaste.com *Steel stock holding and Fabrication. Rebar, Industrial cladding, Engineering, Structural drawings and steel erection.*

David Fryer Studios, Bracken Hill, Welsh Newton Common, Monmouth, Gwent, NP25 5RT Tel: (01989) 770402 Fax: (01989) 770807 E-mail: d.a.fryer@btopenworld.com *Porcelain, bone china designers & manufrs*

Fryer's Ltd, Old Church Hall, Battle Green, Pelton Fell, Chester le Street, County Durham, DH2 2QW Tel: 0191-388 4914 Fax: 0191-388 4974 E-mail: fryersltd@aol.com *Specialist joinery services*

Frymaster Catering Equipment, 9 North Street, Rugby, Warwickshire, CV21 2AB Tel: (01788) 537111 Fax: (01788) 541199 *Catering equipment manufrs*

FSC, Cheddar Business Park, Wedmore Road, Cheddar, Somerset, BS27 3EB Tel: (01934) 745600 Fax: (01934) 745631 E-mail: sales@foodservicecentre.co.uk *Food consultants*

FSC Agronomy, Lancaster Park, Newborough Road, Needwood, Burton-on-Trent, Staffordshire, DE13 9PD Tel: (01283) 575571 Fax: (01283) 575574 E-mail: nigel.francis@masstock.co.uk *Agro-chemicals distributors*

FSC (Halifax) Ltd, Grantham House, Grantham Road, Halifax, West Yorkshire, HX3 6PL Tel: (01422) 347872 Fax: (01422) 321758 E-mail: kw@fscooper.com *Lift engineers supply services*

FSG, Newtown Industrial Estate, Llantwit Fardre, Pontypridd, Mid Glamorgan, CF38 2EE Tel: (01443) 202281 Fax: (01443) 205747 E-mail: admin@fsgtoolanddie.co.uk *Toolmakers & precision engineers*

FT Audio Visual Ltd, Valley House, Hornbeam Park, Hookstone Road, Harrogate, North Yorkshire, HG2 8QT Tel: (01423) 810052 Fax: (01423) 810053 E-mail: info@ftav.co.uk *Audio visual equipment hire sales & installation*

▶ FT Contact Centres, FT House, 35 High Street, Bridlington, North Humberside, YO16 4PR Tel: 0845 00 42 9 42 Fax: 0845 00 42 9 32 E-mail: info@ftcontactcentres.co.uk *Call centre*

FT Print, Centrus Business Park, Mead Lane, Hertford, SG13 7AW Tel: (01992) 501500 Fax: (01992) 501352 E-mail: printed@forms-technology.co.uk *Direct mailing company & printing form services*

FTC Fastrak Ltd, 39 Beaufort Crescent, Stoke Gifford, Bristol, BS34 8QY Tel: 0117-987 7737 *Accounting & payroll services*

FTF Worldwide, 15 Mill Lane, Campton, Shefford, Bedfordshire, SG17 5NX Tel: (0870) 2643010 Fax: (0870) 2643020 E-mail: info@ftfworldwide.net *Fireworks & entertainment suppliers*

Fuchs Lubricants (UK) Plc, P O Box 20, Stoke-on-Trent, ST1 5HU Tel: (0870) 1200400 Fax: (01782) 202072 E-mail: contact-uk@fuchs-oil.com *Greases,*

continued

Company Information

continuation
lubricating, oil cutting oil/fluid products & lubricant (general purpose) manufrs

Fuda International Trading Co. Ltd, Middle Engine Lane, North Shields, Tyne & Wear, NE29 8HG Tel: 0191-258 2233 Fax: 0191-258 2267 *Soft furnishings manufrs*

D. Fudge & Sons Ltd, 564-566 Harrow Road, London, W9 3QH Tel: (020) 8969 5991 Fax: (020) 8964 1215 *Cycle accessories factors* Also at: London W4, W5, W9 & W12

Fudge Jeans Ltd, Queens Mill, Queen Street, Ossett, West Yorkshire, WF5 8AW Tel: (01924) 263391 Fax: (01924) 278419 *Jeans (clothing) manufrs*

Fuel Economy Ltd, 10 Whittle Road, Ferndown Industrial Estate, Wimborne, Dorset, BH21 7RU Tel: (01202) 895544 Fax: (01202) 897798 E-mail: sales@savastat.co.uk *Boiler energy controls*

Fuel Oils London, Swedish Wharf, Townmead Road, London, SW6 2SN Tel: (020) 7731 3456 Fax: (020) 7731 0281 *Oil distributors*

▶ Fuel Recruitment, Clarendon Place, Leamington Spa, Warwickshire, CV32 5QL Tel: (01926) 833000 Fax: (01926) 833001 E-mail: info@bigfishrecruitment.com *Big fish are a leading recruitment consultancy specailsing in advertising, marketing, PR, creative, digital and sales. We represent some of the best talent in the UK so whether you're a talented individual looking for your next career move or a great leader looking for your next star performer, we"re well worth a look.*

Fuel Services, Airport Road West, Belfast, BT3 9ED Tel: (028) 9045 3333 Fax: (028) 9045 0243 E-mail: sales@fuelservicesoil.com *Oil suppliers*

▶ Fuel Tanks Direct, Norman Street, Elland, West Yorkshire, HX5 9BS Tel: (01422) 310111 Fax: (01422) 370786 E-mail: craig@fueltanksdirect.co.uk *Well established Motor Factors providing nationwide delivery service. Website offering fuel tanks, oil sumps and other quality products.**

Fuel Wood Harvesting, Weirburn House, Abbey St Bathans, Duns, Berwickshire, TD11 3TX Tel: (01361) 840251 Fax: (01361) 840248 E-mail: wsj.dobie@btconnect.com *Forestry & saw milling equipment suppliers*

Fuelboss Air Conditioning, The Maltings, Westbury Leigh, Westbury, Wiltshire, BA13 3SF Tel: (01373) 858188 Fax: (01373) 858444 E-mail: sales@fuelboss.co.uk *Air conditioning suppliers & repairers*

▶ Fueltech Gas & Oil Boiler service, The Bungalow, Upper Clwyd street, Ruthin, Denbighshire, LL15 1HY Tel: 0845 0942715 Fax: 01824 709537 E-mail: fueltech@tiscali.co.uk *We provide a 24Hr service,maintenance, repairs and replacments of gas and oil Domestic and light commerical,boilers and burners and replacment of oil tanks, Domestic, commerical and agrcultral fuel bunded filling points Air conditioning service and repairs 24Hrs contacted number Mobile 07876630674*

Fugro Ltd, Hithercroft Road, Wallingford, Oxfordshire, OX10 9RB Tel: (0870) 4021300 Fax: (0870) 4021599 E-mail: uk@geos.com *Oceanographers*

Fugro Ltd, Hithercroft Road, Wallingford, Oxfordshire, OX10 9RB Tel: (0870) 4021300 Fax: (0870) 4021399 E-mail: info@fugro.co.uk *Geotechnical consultants* Also at: Glasgow

Fugro Seismic Imaging, Horizon House, Azalea Drive, Swanley, Kent, BR8 8JR Tel: (01322) 668011 Fax: (01322) 613650 E-mail: info@fugro-fsi.com *Geophysical & geological services*

Fugro Survey Ltd, Morton Peto Road, Great Yarmouth, Norfolk, NR31 0LT Tel: (01493) 440320 Fax: (01493) 440319 E-mail: admin@svitzer.co.uk *Seismic surveys*

Fuhrmann Signs, Old Station Road, Ventnor, Isle of Wight, PO38 1DX Tel: (01983) 854520 Fax: (01983) 852118 *Sign makers*

Fuji Films Sericol UK Ltd, Pysons Road, Broadstairs, Kent, CT10 2LE Tel: (01843) 866668 Fax: (01843) 872184 E-mail: uksales@sericol.com *Man of screen printing inks*

Fuji Seal Europe Ltd, Scimitar Close, Gillingham Business Park, Gillingham, Kent, ME8 0RJ Tel: (01634) 378656 Fax: (01634) 379179 E-mail: sales@uk.fujiseal.com Principal Export Areas: Africa, Central/East Europe & West Europe *Shrink sleeve technology & solutions*

Fujifilm Electronics Imaging Ltd, Bretton Way, Bretton, Peterborough, PE3 8YG Tel: (01733) 260490 Fax: (01733) 462222 *Prepress equipment for the printing industry*

Fujikura Europe Ltd, Unit C51 Barwell Business Park, Leatherhead Road, Chessington, Surrey, KT9 2NY Tel: (020) 8240 2000 Fax: (020) 8240 2010 E-mail: ddk_connectors@fujikura.co.uk *Connector suppliers*

▶ Fujipoly Europe Ltd, Unit 17 Third Avenue, Bletchley, Milton Keynes, MK1 1DR Tel: (01908) 277800 Fax: (01908) 379916 E-mail: rob.humberstone@fujipolyeurope.co.uk *Thermal management products, thermal insulators & elastomer connectors manufrs*

Fujitsu General UK Co Ltd, Unit 150 Centennial Park, Centennial Avenue, Elstree, Borehamwood, Hertfordshire, WD6 3SG Tel: (020) 8731 3450 Fax: (020) 8731 3451 *Air conditioning distributors & agents*

Fujitsu Services Ltd, Wenlock Way, West Gorton, Manchester, M12 5DR Tel: (08702) 345555 *IT solutions*

Fujitsu Services Ltd, Swan House, The Causeway, Staines, Middlesex, TW18 3BF Tel: (0870) 2345555 Fax: (0870) 2424445 *Computer maintenance services* Also at: Solihull

Fujitsu Services, Trafalgar House, Temple Court, Risley, Warrington, WA3 6GD Tel: (01925) 432000 Fax: (01925) 432233 *Personal computer distribution*

Fujitsu Siemens Computers Ltd, The Boulevard, Cain Road, Bracknell, Berkshire, RG12 1HH Tel: (01344) 475000 Fax: (01344) 475666 E-mail: sales@fujitsu-siemens.com *Personal computers & pen computers*

Fujitsu Telecommunications Europe Ltd, Solihull Parkway, Birmingham Business Park, Birmingham, B37 7YU Tel: 0121-717 6000 Fax: 0121-717 6014 E-mail: rcpt@ftel.co.uk *Telecommunication network & systems manufrs*

▶ Fujitsu Telecommunications Europe Ltd, Unit 12 Honiton Business Park, Ottery Moor Lane, Honiton, Devon, EX14 1BG Tel: (01404) 45405 Fax: (01404) 45938

Fujitsu U K Ltd, Hayes Park Central Building, Hayes End Road, Hayes, Middlesex, UB4 8FE Tel: (020) 8573 4444 Fax: (020) 8573 2643 E-mail: sales@uk.fujitsu.com *Computer & electronic product suppliers*

Ful Ton Fork Lifts, Argyle Crescent, Hillhouse Industrial Estate, Hamilton, Lanarkshire, ML3 9BH Tel: (01698) 286490 Fax: (01698) 429531 E-mail: sales@ful-ton-forklifts.com *Fork lift truck repairers*

▶ Fulbourn Medical, 5 Station Yard, Wilbraham Road, Fulbourn, Cambridge, CB21 5ET Tel: (01223) 880909 Fax: (01223) 880078 E-mail: info@fulbournmedical.com *Fulbourn Medical designs,installs, services and repairs, operating theatre lighting for UK health service clients. The company also designs and manufactures operating light battery backup units and theatre control panels with a wide range of functions to fulfill user specified requirements.*

▶ Fulcrum Connections, Ross House Binley Business Park, Harry Weston Road, Coventry, CV3 2TX Tel: (024) 7644 6463 Fax: (024) 7644 6475

Fulcrum Headsets, Unit 19, Apex Business Centre, Boscombe Road, Dunstable, Bedfordshire, LU5 4SB Tel: (0845) 4304070 Fax: (0845) 4304061 E-mail: sales@fulcrum-headsets.co.uk *Telephony headset repair specialist & supplier*

▶ Fulcrum Manufacturing, 19 Challenge Enterprise Centre, Sharps Close, Portsmouth, PO3 5RJ Tel: (023) 9269 9331

Fulcrum Software Ltd, 3 Saxon Gate, Back of The Walls, Southampton, SO14 3HA Tel: (023) 8071 0903 Fax: 023 80360333 *Software writers*

Fulcrum Systems, Hillbottom Road, Sands Industrial Estate, High Wycombe, Buckinghamshire, HP12 4HJ Tel: (0845) 4304060 Fax: (01494) 473324 E-mail: sales@fulcrum-systems.co.uk *Voice telecommunications manufrs*

▶ Fulfilment House, Unit 4, Beaver Industrial Estate, 8 Airfield Road, Christchurch, Dorset, BH23 3TG Tel: 0800 0195139 E-mail: info@fulfilmenthouse.co.uk *Fulfillment services*

Fulham Gas & Heating Services, 54 Chesilton Road, London, SW6 5AB Tel: (020) 7736 3254 Fax: (020) 7385 8685 *Heating & plumbing engineers*

Full Range Finishing Ltd, Unit 14 Jubilee Trade Centre, Jubilee Road, Letchworth Garden City, Hertfordshire, SG6 1SP Tel: (01462) 684294 Fax: (01462) 683312 E-mail: sales@fullrange.fsnet.co.uk *Stove enamellers & powder coating services*

▶ Full Service Centre, La Route De St. Aubin, St. Helier, Jersey, JE2 3SD Tel: (01534) 625911 Fax: (01534) 723904 E-mail: sales@fullservicecentre.co.uk *Vehicle mechanics*

Full Supply Ltd, Unit 29a Dawley Trading Estate, Stallings Lane, Kingswinford, West Midlands, DY6 7AP Tel: (01384) 402101 Fax: (01384) 402501 E-mail: sales@fullsupply.co.uk *Stockholders of flanges & fittings*

Fullbrook Systems Ltd, Unit 4 Bourne End Mills, Hemel Hempstead, Hertfordshire, HP1 2UJ Tel: (01442) 876777 Fax: (01442) 877144 E-mail: sales@fullbrook.com *Chemical & process equipment*

Fulleon, Llantarnam Industrial Park, Cwmbran, Gwent, NP44 3AW Tel: (01633) 628500 Fax: (01633) 866346 E-mail: sales@fulleon.co.uk *Manufacturers of electronic sounders*

Brian Fuller & Co., 106 Brockhurst Rd, Gosport, Hants, PO12 3DG Tel: (023) 9258 3107 Fax: (023) 9258 3107 E-mail: brian.fuller3@btinternet.com *Industrial doors and garage doors*

James Fuller & Son, 51 Huntingdon Road, Chatteris, Cambridgeshire, PE16 6ED Tel: (01354) 692740 Fax: (01354) 692740 *Sack & bag merchants*

Fuller & Sons Warehouse Ltd, Kelvin Way, West Bromwich, West Midlands, B70 7LH Tel: 0121-553 6211 Fax: 0121-525 9085 E-mail: fullerandsonsltd@aol.com *Road transport contractors*

Fuller Water Systems, Cyder Works, High Street, Ixworth, Bury St. Edmunds, Suffolk, IP31 2HT Tel: (01359) 231481 Fax: (01359) 232345 E-mail: enq@fullerwatersys.co.uk *Irrigation, water filter & valves contractors*

▶ Fullers Logistics Group Holdings Ltd, 126 Fairlie Road, Slough, SL1 4PY Tel: (01753) 519000 Fax: (01753) 519001

Fullpoint Probe Services, 170 Heath Road, Ipswich, IP4 5SR Tel: (01473) 717810 Fax: (01473) 717863 E-mail: sales@fullpoint.net *Agricultural irrigation consultants*

▶ Fullpoints Ltd, 40, Nursery Road, London, SW9 8BP Tel: (020) 7924 9971

Fullwell Mill Ltd, Unit 5d Southwick Industrial Estate, Sunderland, SR5 3TX Tel: 0191-548 0050 Fax: 0191-516 9946 E-mail: info@fmfoods.co.uk *Food manufrs*

Fullwith Textiles Ltd, Sunnybank Mills, Town Street, Farsley, Pudsey, West Yorkshire, LS28 5UJ Tel: 0113-257 9811 Fax: 0113-257 7064 *Textile manufrs*

Fullwood Ltd, Grange Road, Ellesmere, Shropshire, SY12 9DF Tel: (01691) 627391 Fax: (01691) 627361 E-mail: sales@fullwood.com *Milking machine manufrs*

Fullwood Ltd, 20 Merchants Quay, Pennygillam Industrial Estate, Launceston, Cornwall, PL15 7QA Tel: (01566) 777794 Fax: (01566) 777761 E-mail: launceston@fullwood.com *Milking equipment supply & installation*

▶ Fullwood Holdings Ltd, 10 Jerviston Street, New Stevenston, Motherwell, Lanarkshire, ML1 4LY Tel: (01698) 733351

Fulmak Rewinding Co., 236a Bennett Street, Long Eaton, Nottingham, NG10 4HH Tel: 0115-973 3216 Fax: 0115-946 9493 E-mail: fulmak@supernet.com *Armature & electric motor repair services*

Fulton Joinery, 144 Fulton Road, Sheffield, S6 3JP Tel: 0114-234 7676 *Joinery manufrs*

▶ Fulton Leasing Ltd, Layton Rd, Brentford, Middlesex, TW8 0QJ Tel: 0208 569 9191 Fax: 0208 569 8487 E-mail: graham@fultonleasing.co.uk *Vehicle and Equipment Leasing broker.Hire Purchase and Operating Lease. Supply of vehicles and all associated financial products.*Fleet management.*

Fulwood Fabrications Ltd, Farndale Road, Staveley, Chesterfield, Derbyshire, S43 3YN Tel: (01246) 477346 Fax: (01246) 280035 E-mail: sales@fulwood.uk.com *Steel fabricators*

Fulworth Engineering 1991 Ltd, Atley Works, Dalton Lane, Keighley, West Yorkshire, BD21 4HT Tel: (01535) 665188 Fax: (01535) 610186 E-mail: sales@fulworth.co.uk *Foundry engineers & merchants of used plant*

▶ Fume Extraction Services, 1 Mowbray Street, Sheffield, S3 8EN Tel: 0114-278 7570 Fax: 0114-278 7600 E-mail: sales@fumeextraction.net *Fume extraction equipment installers*

Fumeo U K, The Old Warehouse, 2 Ashford Road, Brighton, BN1 6LJ Tel: (01273) 508622 Fax: (01273) 564693 *Importers of visual equipment*

Fumex Ltd, 411 Effingham Rd, Sheffield, S9 3QD Tel: 0114-243 0538 Fax: 0114-243 2394 E-mail: enquiries@fumex.co.uk *Fume extraction installation services*

Fumex Coshh & Service Ltd, 23 Hoyland Road, Sheffield, S3 8AB Tel: 0114-234 1114 Fax: 0114-234 1441 E-mail: info@fumex-coshh.co.uk *Cosh services*

▶ Fun Art Design, Suite 205, The Citadel Business Centre, Bath Road, Chippenham, Wiltshire, SN15 2AB Tel: (0794) 0716747 E-mail: info@funartdesign.co.uk *Themed rooms and interior design for childrens rooms and play areas. We specialise in creative interior designs for boys and girls bedrooms (toddlers and children of all ages)*

Fun Busters, PO Box 7148, Redditch, Worcestershire, B98 7WW Tel: (01527) 578200 Fax: (01527) 517473 *Children's entertainment*

▶ Fun & Games, 17 St. Martins Walk, Dorking, Surrey, RH4 1UT Tel: (01306) 877334 Fax: (01306) 877334 E-mail: info@funandgamesshop.com *Fun & Games of Dorking are a traditional, battery free toy shop. Vast range of toys, games, crafts and activities for indoors and out.*

Fun Junction, 29 County Place, Perth, PH2 8EE Tel: (01738) 444222 Fax: (01738) 450481 E-mail: perth@funjunctiononline.com *Educational toys suppliers*

▶ The Fun Squad, Little Firs, Carloggas, St. Mawgan, Newquay, Cornwall, TR8 4EQ Tel: (01637) 860956 E-mail: info@thefunsquad.co.uk *Family party entertainment & bouncy castles hire*

Fun to Learn, 5 Ardfreelin, Newry, County Down, BT34 1JG Tel: (028) 3025 0960 Fax: (028) 3025 0960 *Educational equipment & supplies*

▶ Fun4Kids, 1 Stuart Drive, Warrington, WA4 2BT Tel: (01925) 499688 E-mail: l.hardin@ntlworld.com *Bouncy castle hire, obstacle courses*

Funasset Ltd, Orchards, 14 Townsend, Ilminster, Somerset, TA19 0AU Tel: (01460) 57065 Fax: (01460) 53538 E-mail: enquiries@funasset.com *FunAsset are a design and manufacturing company that specialise in enterprise connectivity, data conversion, data processing, and output management and distribution products.*

▶ Functional Art, 127 Homesdale Road, Bromley, BR2 9LE Tel: (0796) 7077808 E-mail: rosanna@functional-art.co.uk *We specialize in suppling Functional Art. Our motto is use your art! We stock candles, kitchen and homeware from Africa and Europe and manufacture wine glass charms.*

Functional Foam Beacons Products, Efi Industrial Estate, Brecon Road, Merthyr Tydfil, Mid Glamorgan, CF47 8RB Tel: (01685) 350011 Fax: (01685) 388396 E-mail: sales@beaconsproducts.co.uk *Polyurethane, non cross linked, cross linked rubber foam converters, protective packaging for the electronics, automotive, medical, construction, marine, camping, leisure industries, underlay for laminated wood flooring, self inflating mats, bespoke foam products*

Functionpoint Ltd, Newlands Cottage, Weedon Hill, Hyde Heath, Amersham, Buckinghamshire, HP6 5RN Tel: (01494) 791995 Fax: (01494) 792014 E-mail: alan@functionpoint.co.uk *Software designers*

Fund it UK Ltd, The Rectory, Babworth, Retford, Nottinghamshire, DN22 8ET Tel: (0845) 2011787 Fax: (0845) 2011786 E-mail: info@fundit.co.uk *Raise more money fast with the innovative new fundraising program for schools, charities & any sized non-profit group. Free sample, personalisation, prize program & delivery.*

▶ Funki Fresh, 13 Upper Ground, London, SE1 9PP Tel: (020) 7928 1100 *Knitwear retailers*

▶ Funkie World Entertainments Ltd, 7 Trevarrick Court, Horwich, Bolton, BL6 6TF Tel: (07005) 981782 E-mail: aquatane@aquatane.co.uk *Funkie World Entertainments provides artist management services as well as tailor made events entertainments including karaoke, discos, quiz nights, kids parties and weddings.*

▶ Funktees, 51 Edgeworth, Yate, Bristol, BS37 8YN Tel: (0778) 6653999 E-mail: funktees@hotmail.co.uk *Hand made funky t-shirts, all originally designed and made on site. Reasonable prices and completely different styles for men, women and children.*

▶ Funkton Films Ltd, Dixon Street, Old Town, Swindon, SN1 3PL Tel: (01793) 336299 E-mail: mathew@funktonfilms.co.uk *Film & video production*

Funkwerk Information Technologies York Ltd, 39 Blossom Street, York, YO24 1AQ Tel: (01904) 639091 Fax: (01904) 639092 E-mail: info@vit-vossloh.com *Computer software consultants*

Funky Junk, 409 Hornsey Road, London, N19 4EF Tel: (020) 7609 5479 Fax: (020) 7609 5483 E-mail: sales@funky-junk.co.uk *Audio equipment retailers*

▶ Funtastic Entertainment, 55 Friars Lane, Barrow-in-Furness, Cumbria, LA13 9NS Tel: (01229) 820718 E-mail: funadmin@funtastic-entertainment.co.uk *We hire rodeo bulls, sumo wrestling for adults and children, bouncy boxing and other inflatable games, giant games and more. We also arrange disco DJ"s, Karaoke and other forms of entertainment. Nationwide coverage and very competative rates.*

Funtimz, UNIT 14 Masonfield Drive, Newton Stewart, Wigtownshire, DG8 6QA Tel: (01671) 402139 E-mail: sales@funtimz.co.uk Principal Export Areas: Worldwide *Adult online retail store*

Furlong Mills Ltd, Furlong Lane, Stoke-on-Trent, ST6 3LE Tel: (01782) 838428 Fax: (01782) 834199 E-mail: admin@furlongmills.co.uk *Pottery material manufrs*

Furlong Services Ltd, 148 Sculcoates Lane, Hull, HU5 1EE Tel: (01482) 444666 Fax: (01482) 444664 E-mail: enquiries@furlong-services.co.uk *Audio visual equipment services*

Furmanite Engineering Ltd, 7 Colville Court, Winwick Quay, Warrington, WA2 8QT Tel: (01925) 418858 Fax: (01925) 418863 E-mail: enquiries@furmanite.com *Engineering solutions & services*

Furmanite International Ltd, Worldwide Way, Kiln La Trading Estate, Stallingborough, Grimsby, South Humberside, DN41 8DY Tel: (01469) 575143 Fax: (01469) 571074 E-mail: enquiries@furmanite.com *Valve repairers*

Furmanite International Ltd, Furman House, Shap Road, Kendal, Cumbria, LA9 6RU Tel: (01539) 729009 Fax: (01539) 729359 E-mail: enquiry@furmanite.com *Specialised engineering company*

Furmanite International Ltd, Owens Road, Skippers Lane Industrial Estate, Middlesbrough, Cleveland, TS6 6HE Tel: (01642) 455111 Fax: (01642) 465692 *Engineering subcontractors* Also at: Aberdeen

Furmanite Ipsco (UK) Ltd, Sunningdale House, Sunningdale Road, South Park Industrial Estate, Scunthorpe, North Lincolnshire, DN17 2TY Tel: (01724) 849904 Fax: (01724) 861033 E-mail: info.ipsco@furmaniteipsco.com *Pipeline plugging services*

Furnace Construction Co. Ltd, Newton Moor Industrial Estate, Hyde, Cheshire, SK14 4LF Tel: 0161-368 8419 Fax: 0161-368 3813 E-mail: sales@furnace-construction.co.uk *Furnace & cremators manufrs*

Furnace Construction Co. Ltd, Newton Moor Industrial Estate, Hyde, Cheshire, SK14 4LF Tel: 0161-368 8419 Fax: 0161-368 3813 E-mail: sales@furnace-construction.co.uk *Furnace & cremators manufrs*

Furnace End Fires, Ersthaus, Atherstone Road, Coleshill, Birmingham, B46 2LP Tel: (01675) 481653 E-mail: info@fefbadges.com *Enamelled badges & collectables*

Furnace Engineering, Unit 1d Howsgill Industrial Park, Knitsley Lane, Consett, County Durham, DH8 7NU Tel: (01207) 590121 Fax: (01207) 505762 E-mail: sales@furnaceengineering.co.uk *Furnace builders & repairs*

Furnace Maintenance Co., 20 Swanbourne Road, Sheffield, S5 7TL Tel: 0114-245 6842 Fax: 0114-245 6842 *Furnace maintenance*

Furnace & Oven Technologies, PO Box 10114, Redditch, Worcestershire, B97 6WD Tel: (01527) 595971 Fax: (01527) 596043 *Furnaces industrial*

Furnace Services, 42 Ellison Avenue, Scunthorpe, Lincolnshire, DN16 3TD Tel: (01724) 868578 *Steel industry powder retailer*

Furneaux Industrial Supplies Ltd, 5 Sinclair House, Hastings Street, London, WC1H 9PZ Tel: (020) 7387 8450 Fax: (020) 7388 0197 E-mail: furnlocks@fsbdial.co.uk *Locksmith retailers*

Furneaux Riddall & Co. Ltd, Alchorne Place, Portsmouth, PO3 5PA Tel: (023) 9266 8621 Fax: (023) 9269 0521 E-mail: info@furneauxriddall.com *Automotive & marine distributors & manufrs*

Furnell Transport, Enterprise House, Maxted Road, Hemel Hempstead, Hertfordshire, HP2 7BT Tel: (01442) 212744 Fax: (01442) 255244 E-mail: sales@furnell.com *Road transport, haulage & freight services*

Furnells Signs, Unit 5 Crusader Industrial Estate, 167 Hermitage Road, London, N4 1LZ Tel: (020) 8880 2771 Fax: (020) 8880 2333 E-mail: sales@furnells.com *NAMEPLATES, ENGRAVING, BADGES, LABELS, GLASS ENGRAVING, SIGNS, PLAQUES, ETCHING, VINYL GRAPHICS, ACRYLIC ENCAPSULATION, DESIGN, LETTERING, AWARDS & TROPHIES, DESK & DOOR PLATES, GOLD FOIL BLOCKING, COMMEMORATIVE PLAQUES.*

Furness Aquatics, 70a Kent Street, Barrow-in-Furness, Cumbria, LA13 9QR Tel: (01229) 870970 Fax: (01229) 580606 *Tropical fish merchants*

Furness Brick & Tile Co. Ltd, Dalton Road, Askam-in-Furness, Cumbria, LA16 7HF Tel: (01229) 462411 Fax: (01229) 462363 E-mail: furnessbrick@mac.com *Brick manufacturing*

Furness Controls Ltd, Beeching Road, Bexhill-on-Sea, East Sussex, TN39 3LJ Tel: (01424) 730316 Fax: (01424) 730317 E-mail: sales@furness-controls.com Principal Export Areas: Africa & North America *A calibration laboratory, UKAS accredited. Manufacturers of leak detectors including air/gas & leak detector test systems. Also manufacturers of flow meters including gas flow & pitot tube & flow detectors. In addition, calibrator (pressure/ temperature/electrical), transmittor (temperature/*

continued

continuation
pressure), transducers, pressure & gauges, differential manufrs

Furness Engineering & Technology, Ellers Mill, The Ellers, Ulverston, Cumbria, LA12 0AQ Tel: (01229) 584043 Fax: (01229) 586440 E-mail: mail@fetl.co.uk *Engineering design & documentation*

Furness Heating Components Ltd, 19 Abbey Road, Barrow-in-Furness, Cumbria, LA14 5UD Tel: (01229) 430575 Fax: (01229) 433080 *Heating components*

▶ Furness Logistics UK Ltd, 1 Maidstone Road, Kingston, Milton Keynes, MK10 0BD Tel: (01908) 282870 Fax: (01908) 282872

Furness & South Cumberland Supply Association Ltd, Foxfield, Broughton-in-Furness, Cumbria, LA20 6BX Tel: (01229) 716229 Fax: (01229) 716860 *Agricultural merchants* Also at: Cark in Cartmel, Egremont & Ulverston

Furness & South Cumberland Supply Association Ltd, Neville Street, Ulverston, Cumbria, LA12 0BJ Tel: (01229) 582122 *Agricultural suppliers*

▶ Furnico Ltd, Bradford House, Phillips Lane, Colne, Lancashire, BB8 9PQ Tel: (01282) 869888 Fax: (01282) 862972 *Furnishings*

Furniss & White Foundries Ltd, Unit 17 Abbey Way, North Anston Trading Estate, North Anston, Sheffield, S25 4JL Tel: (01909) 568831 Fax: (01909) 569322 E-mail: upgrading@f-w-f.co.uk *Casting repairs, fabricators & welders*

Furnitubes International Ltd, Meridian House, Royal Hill, London, SE10 8RD Tel: (020) 8378 3200 Fax: (020) 8378 3250 E-mail: sales@furnitubes.com *Street Furniture Manufrs.*

▶ Furniture By Jonathan Elwell, Bryn Teg Workshop, Tanrallt Road, Gwespyr, Holywell, Flintshire, CH8 9JT Tel: (01745) 887766 E-mail: jonathanelwell@ukonline.co.uk *Makers & designers of freestanding solid wood furniture*

▶ Furniture Diamond, 198 Newlands Road, Glasgow, G44 4EY Tel: 0141-633 0414 Fax: 0141-633 0414 E-mail: furniturediamond@hotmail.co.uk *French polishing company*

Furniture Direct, Southfield Street, Nelson, Lancashire, BB9 9QA Tel: (01282) 690921 Fax: (01282) 690921 *Furniture retail & manufrs*

Furniture Fusion, Bedford Road, Apsley Guise, Milton Keynes, MK17 8DJ Tel: (01908) 586334 Fax: (01908) 586332 E-mail: info@furniturefusion.co.uk *Furniture Fusion based in Milton Keynes are manufacturers of furniture including chairs, tables and beds, as well as makers of upholstery and rugs.*

Furniture Maker Furniture Maker, Unit 19, Hoobrook Enterprise Centre, Worcester Road, Kidderminster, Worcestershire, DY10 1HB Tel: (01562) 825995 *Cabinet maker*

Furniture Technique Ltd, New Garden Street, Blackburn, BB2 3RE Tel: (01254) 581255 Fax: (01254) 694215 *Fitted furniture manufrs*

The Furniture Warehouse, The Seed House, Bell Walk, Bell Lane, Uckfield, East Sussex, TN22 1AB Tel: (01825) 769202 E-mail: sales@sofasandfurniture.co.uk *Leather sofas, suites, pine, dining & cane furniture*

Furniture Wise, 40 Edderthorpe Street, Bradford, West Yorkshire, BD3 9JX Tel: (01274) 306918 Fax: (01274) 306918 *3 piece suites manufrs*

Furniture Works, Pullens Farm, Lamberhurst Road, Horsmonden, Tonbridge, Kent, TN12 8ED Tel: (01892) 723474 *Cabinet makers*

Furniture World, Queens Road, Halifax, West Yorkshire, HX1 3NS Tel: (01422) 349860 Fax: (01422) 349860 *Furniture retailer, beds & bedroom furniture*

▶ Furniture World, 283 Shirley Road, Southampton, SO15 3HT Tel: (023) 8057 1918 Fax: (023) 8077 9033 E-mail: info@fwtc.co.uk *Office & house furniture manufrs*

▶ Furntech Services, Unit 13 Smestow Bridge Industrial Estate, Bridgnorth Road, Wombourne, Wolverhampton, WV5 8AY Tel: (01902) 326030 Fax: (01902) 326030 *Furnace services*

Furrytails, 26-28 Standard Road, London, NW10 6EU Tel: (020) 8965 6836 Fax: (020) 8965 2172 E-mail: furrytails@compuserve.com *Soft toy designers & manufrs*

Furs of Mayfair Ltd, 47 South Molton Street, London, W1K 5RY Tel: (020) 7437 6276 Fax: (020) 7629 6324 *Fur garment manufrs*

W.J. Furse Ltd, Wilford Road, Nottingham, NG2 1EB Tel: 0115-964 3800 Fax: 0115-986 0538 E-mail: sales@furse.com *Electrical equipment manufrs*

▶ FURSTENBRUNN LIMITED, 11-15 Coventry Road, Market Harborough, Leicestershire, Market Harborough, Leicestershire, LE16 9BX Tel: 0870 4604226 Fax: 0870 4604228 E-mail: info@furstenbrunn.com *Process and Laboraotory Quality Control Instrumentation,Process Plant for food,brewing and soft drinks industries.Tempest Computers Division,Biometric ID Card Systems and Secure Systems for Governments,Diplomatic and Security Services.Telecomms Services.*

Furtex, Hopton Mills, Hopton, Mirfield, West Yorkshire, WF14 8HE Tel: (01924) 490591 Fax: (01924) 495605 E-mail: furtex@eu.interfaceinc.com *Upholstery velvet & moquette manufrs*

Furuno (U K) Ltd, South Breakwater, Fraserburgh, Aberdeenshire, AB11 5QA Tel: (01346) 518300 Fax: (01346) 512545 E-mail: sales@furuno.co.uk *Marine electronic engineers*

Furuno UK Ltd, Ocean House Parklands Business Park, Forest Road, Denmead, Waterlooville, Hampshire, PO7 6XP Tel: (023) 9223 0303 Fax: (023) 9223 0101 E-mail: denmead@furunouk.freeserve.co.uk *Marine electronics suppliers*

Fuselodge Ltd, 267 Acton Lane, Chiswick, London, W4 5DG Tel: (020) 8994 6275 Fax: (020) 8994 6275 E-mail: fuse.lodge@virgin.net *Conductor component distributors*

▶ Fuser Tech, Plaistow Road, Loxwood, Billingshurst, West Sussex, RH14 0TS Tel: (01403) 752520 Fax: (01403) 752520 *Refurbishers*

Fusion, 9 Fishwicks Industrial Estate, Kilbuck Lane, Haydock, St. Helens, Merseyside, WA11 9SZ Tel: (01942) 271517 Fax: (01942) 716187 E-mail: northwest@fusiongroup.co.uk *Suppliers of polyethylene pipes*

Fusion Automation Inc, Barrows Rd, The Pinnacles, Harlow, Essex, CM19 5FD Tel: (01279) 443122 Fax: (01279) 424057 E-mail: salesuk@fai-uk.com *For over 45 years, Fusion has been providing automation solutions for manufacturers engaged in production brazing and soldering. Fusion takes a process approach to automating your application.*This process consists of three key ingredients: Paste Alloys, Applicator Equipment, and Automatic Machines. Your operation will be transformed with the overall goal of reducing metal joining costs through increased productivity.*With the Fusion Process, joint quality is virtually guaranteed, due to the elimination of human error.*Material costs are controlled, since filler metal and flux are applied in a single step?in just the right amount. Labour costs become insignificant, as one operator turns out hundreds of brazed or soldered assemblies per hour.*

Fusion for Business Ltd, 25 The Grove, Coulsdon, Surrey, CR5 2BH Tel: (0870) 4322900 Fax: (0870) 4322951 *Technology providers*

▶ Fusion Business Solutions, 1 Wallbrook Business Centre, Green Lane, Hounslow, TW4 6NW Tel: (020) 8814 4888 Fax: (020) 8570 8240 E-mail: info@fusion.co.uk *Re-sellers & developers of software*

Fusion Electrical Assembly, Unit 4, Station Industrial Estate, Burnham-On-Crouch, Essex, CM0 8RW Tel: (01621) 784107 Fax: (01621) 784327 *Electrical assemblers & assembly services*

▶ Fusion Four Telecoms Ltd, 7 Saffron Court, Southfields Business Park, Laindon, Basildon, Essex, SS15 6SS Tel: (01268) 417500 Fax: (01268) 543355 E-mail: fft@fusiontelecom.co.uk *Suppliers of telecoms*

Fusion ICS, Broadwall House, 21 Broadwall, London, SE1 9PL Tel: (020) 7960 5100 Fax: (020) 7928 5961 E-mail: info@fusion-ics.com *General telecommunition services* Also at: London NW1

Fusion Metal Smiths, Flat 1 Wixenford Farm, Colesdown Hill, Plymouth, PL9 8AA Tel: (01752) 481778 E-mail: steve@fusionmetalsmiths.com *Designers & manufacturers of costume jewellery*

▶ Fusion R2R - Recruitment to Recruitment, Suite 273, 27 Colmore Row, Birmingham, B3 2EW Tel: 01902 631778 Fax: 01902 631778 E-mail: info@fusionr2r.co.uk *Established in 2002, Fusion R2R offers a fresh outlook and a young, innovative and professional approach to recruitment, for the recruitment industry. **Fusion R2R believes in "success through service" and adopts a flexible approach to business. We aim to develop effective working relationships and a strong partnership, with clients and candidates alike. **Our approach to any business, large or small, remains the same, with a strong determination for us to deliver a quality recruitment solution that will add value to your organisation. **Repeat business is important to us. **Fusion R2R - Recruitment to Recruitment in confidence*

Fusion Technologies Ltd, 26 Avonbank Industrial Estate, West Town Road, Bristol, BS11 9DE Tel: 0117-982 6606 Fax: 0117-982 6616 *Manufacturers of laser systems equipment*

▶ Fusion Technology Plastics, 9 Buckland Road, Leicester, LE5 0NT Tel: 0116-274 1308 Fax: 0116-274 2038

▶ Fusionxs, 7 Wisley Close, West Bridgford, Nottingham, NG2 7NY Tel: 0115-878 7003 Fax: (0845) 8688485 E-mail: info@fusionxs.co.uk *Affordable website design & hosting services*

Fussell Wadman Ltd, Hopton Industrial Estlondon Road, Devizes, Wiltshire, SN10 2EU Tel: (01380) 731970 Fax: (01380) 731971 E-mail: fussell_wadman@dealers.peugeot.co.uk *Peugeot dealers*

Fussell's Rubber Co. Ltd, 2 Brimbleworth Lane, St. Georges, Weston-Super-Mare, Avon, BS22 7XS Tel: (01934) 513473 Fax: (01934) 521019 *Rubber moulding distributors*

Fussey Piling Ltd, Lancaster Approach, North Killingholme, Immingham, South Humberside, DN40 3JZ Tel: (01469) 540644 Fax: (01469) 540849 E-mail: info@fusseyengineering.com *Structural steelwork & steel flooring manufrs*

Futaba Tenneco UK Ltd, Liverpool Road, Burnley, Lancashire, BB12 6HJ Tel: (01282) 433171 Fax: (01282) 450778 *Exhaust silencer & catalytic converter manufrs*

Futon Co. Ltd, 147 Finchley Road, London, NW3 6JH Tel: (020) 7586 7444 Fax: (020) 7586 7555 *Futon manufrs*

Futon Co. Ltd, 100 Battersea Rise, London, SW11 1EJ Tel: (020) 7978 4498 Fax: (020) 7978 4029 *Futon retailer*

Futon Co Ltd, 72-74 Upper Parliament Street, Nottingham, NG1 6LF Tel: 0115-959 9616 Fax: 0115-950 7511 *Futon suppliers & manufrs*

Futon UK Com, 28 Far Gosford Street, Coventry, CV1 5DW Tel: (0870) 3500027 Fax: (0870) 3500027 *Retailers & manufacturers of futons*

Futons Direct, The Old Malthouse, Queen Street, Eynsham, Witney, Oxfordshire, OX29 4JD Tel: (01865) 880005 E-mail: sales@futons-direct.co.uk *Futon manufrs*

▶ Futronics Ltd, Nepicar House, London Road, Wrotham Heath, Sevenoaks, Kent, TN15 7RS Tel: (01732) 783130 Fax: (01732) 887227 *Designers & manufacturers of sustain applications*

Futura Consulting UK Ltd, 51 Downside Close, Blandford Forum, Dorset, DT11 7SD Tel: (01258) 451007 Fax: (01258) 451007 E-mail: mick.gordon@futuraconsulting.com *Computer consultants*

Futura Foods UK Ltd, Wynchfield House, Calcot, Tetbury, Gloucestershire, GL8 8YJ Tel: (01666) 890500 Fax: (01666) 890522 E-mail: info@futura-foods.com *Dairy product importers*

Futurama Ltd, Island Farm House, Island Farm Road, West Molesey, Surrey, KT8 2TR Tel: (020) 8941 1999 Fax: (020) 8783 1687 E-mail: postbox@futurama.ltd.uk *Point of sales services, corporate imaging & neon sign manufrs*

Future Access Technologies, 18 Cherry Lane, Pond Park, Lisburn, County Antrim, BT28 3JT Tel: (028) 9262 9689 Fax: (028) 9267 6573 E-mail: info@futureaccess.co.uk *Security installation*

▶ Future Cad Services Ltd, 44 Chandlers, Orton Brimbles, Peterborough, PE2 5YW Tel: (01733) 230008 E-mail: chris@futurecadservices.co.uk *Professional Design & Drafting Service for Industrial Metalwork & Mechanical Engineering*

Future Data International Ltd, 14 High Street, Lyndhurst, Hampshire, SO43 7BD Tel: (023) 8028 4369 Fax: (023) 8028 4369 E-mail: gary@futuredata.com *Creative solutions in computer technology*

▶ Future Designs Ltd, The Lighthouse, Fircroft Way, Edenbridge, Kent, TN8 6EJ Tel: (01732) 867420 Fax: (01732) 863459

Future Electronics Ltd, 123 Renfrew Road, Paisley, Renfrewshire, PA3 4EA Tel: 0141-840 6500 Fax: 0141-849 6971 *Electronic component distributors*

Future Electronics Ltd, Future House, Poyle Road, Colnbrook, Slough, SL3 0AA Tel: (01753) 763000 Fax: (01753) 689100 E-mail: lcdwizard@futureelectronics.com *Electrical connector distributors*

▶ Future Engraving, 98 Appin Road, Birkenhead, Merseyside, CH41 9HH Tel: 0151-647 0715 Fax: 0151-647 0714 E-mail: sales@future-engraving.co.uk

Future Forwarding Co. Ltd, Building 305, World Freight Terminal, Manchester Airport, Manchester, M90 5PY Tel: 0161-436 8181 Fax: 0161-499 0654 E-mail: andreadelves@futureforwarding.com *Freight forwarders*

Future Furnishings Ltd, 41 Hollywood Rd, Bolton, BL1 6HP Tel: 01204 495711 Fax: 01204 495711 *Soft furnishings manufrs*

Future Garments Ltd, Aqua House, Buttress Way, Smethwick, West Midlands, B66 3DL Tel: 0121-555 7167 Fax: 0121-555 7168 E-mail: sales@future-gmts.com *Protective clothing manufrs*

Future Generation Services Ltd, A Future Court, George Summers Close, Medway City Estate, Rochester, Kent, ME2 4EL Tel: (01634) 718662 Fax: (01634) 718646 E-mail: services@bnol.co.uk *Touch screen kiosks manufrs*

Future Image Ltd, 26 Church Road, Holywood, County Down, BT18 9BU Tel: (028) 9042 3314 Fax: (028) 9042 4773 E-mail: newsdesk@futureimage.co.uk *Public relations*

▶ Future Inclusive Access Consultants, 90 Station Road, Kegworth, Derby, DE74 2FR Tel: (01509) 557848 Fax: (01509) 557848 E-mail: info@futureinclusive.co.uk *Future Inclusive Access Consultants carry out access audits, access statements and access appraisals. We advise on meeeting the duties imposed by the Disability Discrimination Act, and on meeting ADM and planning requirements for inclusive design of buildings*

Future Industrial Welding Supplies, 21-23 Cotton Street, Aberdeen, AB11 5EG Tel: (01224) 212288 Fax: (01224) 212164 *Welding supply agents & distributors*

▶ Future It Services, 32 Uphill Way, Hunston, Chichester, West Sussex, PO20 1PH Tel: (01243) 783288 Fax: (01243) 783288 E-mail: info@futureitservices.co.uk *Web design services*

Future Knitting Co. Ltd, 39 Upper Bond Street, Hinckley, Leicestershire, LE10 1RH Tel: (01455) 619053 Fax: (01455) 619053 *Knitted outerwear manufrs*

Future Labs Ltd, Regus House, 400 Thames Valley Park Drive, Reading, RG6 1PT Tel: (01344) 301155 Fax: (01344) 450380 E-mail: sales@computabits.com *IT consultancy & hardware & software supplier*

Future Leisure, Napier Works Spencer Park, Greasbrough Street, Rotherham, South Yorkshire, S60 1RF Tel: (01709) 360359 Fax: (01709) 360359 *Clothing manufrs*

▶ Future Machines Ltd, Unit 20 Fleetway Business Park, Wadsworth Road, Greenford, Middlesex, UB6 7LF Tel: (020) 8997 4488 Fax: (020) 8997 4334 E-mail: info@leisuremachinesdirect.co.uk

Future Machines Ltd, Unit 20 Fleetway Business Park, Wadsworth Road, Greenford, Middlesex, UB6 7LF Tel: (020) 8997 4488 *Amusement machine hire & repair*

Future Perfect, 14 Harebell Close, Minster on Sea, Sheerness, Kent, ME12 3ER Tel: (01795) 877577 Fax: (0870) 0558977 E-mail: info@contactmanager.co.uk *IT consultants*

▶ Future Route Ltd, 2 Hatfields, London, SE1 9PG Tel: (020) 7960 9650 Fax: (020) 7960 9651 E-mail: info@validis.com *Software designers*

Future Scope Computers, 204 Warwick Road, Sparkhill, Birmingham, B11 2NB Tel: 0121-771 2502 Fax: 0121-771 2502 E-mail: sales@futuresc.com *Computer systems & software services*

▶ Future Services Ltd, 26 Forth Street, Edinburgh, EH1 1LH Tel: 0131-550 3835 Fax: 0131-550 3834 E-mail: future_services_ltd@hotmail.co.uk *Providing all trades labouerers. Except plumbers and electricians. Temporary and permament stuff.*

Future Signs, 2a Bedford Court, Bedford Street, Leighton Buzzard, Bedfordshire, LU7 1JE Tel: (01525) 373733 Fax: (01525) 850211 E-mail: futuresign@btinternet.com *Sign distributors & manufrs*

Future Software Systems, Woodville, Hatton, Market Rasen, Lincs, LN8 5QG Tel: 01673 857118 Fax: 01673 857176 *Industrial software manufacturers*

Future Technology Heat Sealers Ltd, Yew Tree Farm, Main Street, Barton In The Beans, Nuneaton, Warwickshire, CV13 0DJ Tel: (01455) 299000 E-mail: sales@futuresealers.co.uk *Heat sealing machine manufrs*

Future Windows Ltd, 74 West End Road, Morecambe, Lancashire, LA4 4DY Tel: (01524) 410077 Fax: (01524) 410099 E-mail: admin@future-windows.com *Manufacturing & installing UPVC*

▶ Future You, Lingfield, Walnut Close, Heathfield, East Sussex, TN21 8YL Tel: 0333 4444001 E-mail: coaching@future-you.co.uk *Discover how to shape your life and career options to match your dreams, aspirations and ambitions. You will be more able to meet challenges and overcome obstacles and empowered to step into your future with purpose and confidence.*At 'Future You' we specialise in Personal Life Coaching and Career Coaching tailored to meet your needs and personal situations. We work with the 'whole you' and because we believe that people are naturally creative, resourceful and whole we know that coupled with the Co-Active coaching process our clients are capable of finding their own answers to whatever challenges they face and by taking ownership you will be given a strong sense of responsibility which will encourage you to succeed.**We bring to our clients; strong values, a wealth of knowledge and experience coupled with professional training and a strength of purpose.*Contact us today and together we will take the journey of your life.*

▶ Futurefind Sales Recruitment, Wira House, Ring Road, West Park, Leeds, LS16 6EB Tel: 0113-275 5656 Fax: 0113-278 2181 E-mail: recruitment@futurefind.co.uk *futurefind is a specialist recruitment consultancy handling sales positions. Our consultants have a combination of field sales and sales management experience and extensive recruitment experience specialising in sales.**We operate throughout the UK with offices in the North, Midlands and South East.***

▶ Futureprint Northampton Ltd, 64-72 Roe Road, Northampton, NN1 4PJ Tel: (01604) 639565 Fax: (01604) 622845 E-mail: sales@futureprint-npton.com

Futurestech, Garden House, Frogmore Park, Watton at Stone, Hertford, SG14 3RU Tel: 0+33 388 236671 Fax: 0+33 369 208047 E-mail: info@futurestech.com *Strategy, sales and marketing consulting for industrial companies. Sales training and development.*

▶ Futureware Ltd, 115 London Road, Braintree, Essex, CM77 8PT Tel: (01376) 320276 Fax: (01376) 320288 E-mail: sales@futureware.co.uk *Computer maintenance services*

Fwa, 28 Tynemouth Road, North Shields, Tyne & Wear, NE30 4AA Tel: 0191-259 1099 Fax: 0191-258 2737 E-mail: sales@fwa.uk.com *Sound systems installers & suppliers*

▶ Fwa Solutions, Springboard Innovation Centre, Llantarnam Park, Cwmbran, Gwent, NP44 3AW Tel: (01633) 488080 Fax: (01633) 647806 E-mail: sales@fwasolutions.com *Wireless equipment distributors*

▶ Fwa West Ltd, 15 Warwick Road, West Drayton, Middlesex, UB7 9BT Tel: (01895) 449344

FWB Keithley, C Gresley Road, Keighley, West Yorkshire, BD21 5JG Tel: (01535) 687300 Fax: (01535) 687301 E-mail: sales@fwbkeighley.co.uk *Distributor to trade & industry of building & plumbing supplies*

▶ FWS Europe, 4 Fleethall Road, Purdeys Industrial Estate, Rochford, Essex, SS4 1NF Tel: 01702 530050 Fax: 01702 530030 E-mail: info@weaponstorage.co.uk *Weapon storage equipment for police and military. Weapons storage racking and cabinets and other equipment for armoury use, mobile tactical units, shipboard etc. Flexible system to accomodate very high density storage of wide variety of weapon types in a single location*

▶ FX Direct Ltd, Unit 6c Manor Way, Woking, Surrey, GU22 9JX Tel: (01483) 776676 Fax: (01483) 740447 E-mail: sales@fxdirect.co.uk *Stationery suppliers*

▶ Fyfe & Allan, 90-96 Dykehead Street, Glasgow, G33 4AQ Tel: 0141-774 5900 Fax: 0141-774 7360 *School wear suppliers*

Hugh G. Fyfe Ltd, 78-84 Bell Street, Dundee, DD1 1HW Tel: (01382) 322892 Fax: (01382) 202052 *Mill & factory furnishers*

Fyfe & Mcgrouther, 218-254 Kennedy Street, Glasgow, G4 0BS Tel: 0141-552 4966 Fax: 0141-552 7917 *Comprehensive industrial suppliers*

Fyfe Welding Services Ltd, Western Harbour, Leith Docks, Edinburgh, EH6 6NT Tel: 0131-553 5536 *Steel fabricators*

Fyfe Wilson & Co. Ltd, Raynham Road, Bishop's Stortford, Hertfordshire, CM23 5PF Tel: (01279) 653333 Fax: (01279) 504941 E-mail: sales@fyfewilson.co.uk *Electrical & mechanical engineers*

Fylde Coast Gate, Amy Johnson Way, Blackpool, FY4 2RP Tel: (01253) 347000 Fax: (01253) 407518 *Gate & railing manufrs*

Fylde Electronic Laboratories Ltd, 49-51 Fylde Road, Preston, PR1 2XQ Tel: (01772) 257560 Fax: (01772) 821530 E-mail: sales@fylde.com *Analogue measurement system makers*

Fylde Guitars, Hartness Road, Gilwilly Industrial Estate, Penrith, Cumbria, CA11 9BD Tel: (01768) 891515 Fax: (01768) 868998 E-mail: sales@fyldeguitars.com *Musical instrument manufrs*

Fylde Ice & Cold Storage Co., Wyre Dock, Fleetwood, Lancashire, FY7 6SU Tel: (01253) 873249 Fax: (01253) 777752 E-mail: kelly@fylde-ice.co.uk *Ice cube making machine manufrs*

Fylde Micro Systems Ltd, 8 Avroe Cresent, Blackpool, FY4 2DP Tel: (01253) 407040 Fax: (01253) 407073 *Fylde Micro pioneers in MPT1327 radio trunking infrastructure. We design, develop, manufacture and supply communication solutions to Original Equipment Manufacturers (OEMS), dealers and end-users. Specialists in our field we have been supplying*

continued

Company Information

continuation
trunking for over 20 years and have systems world wide.

▶ Fylde Plastering & Dry Wall Contractors, 42 Tyrone Avenue, Blackpool, FY2 0RR Tel: (01253) 593310 Fax: 01253 358202 E-mail: fpdclimited@btinternet.com *Plastering Dry-Lining Dry-Wall & Suspended Ceilings*

Fylde Shopfitting, 293 Church Street, Blackpool, FY1 3PF Tel: (01253) 620257 Fax: (01253) 291150 *Shop fittings retailers*

Fylde Signs, The Warehouse, Cross Street, Blackpool, FY1 2EA Tel: (01253) 291414 Fax: (01253) 291415 *Sign installers*

Fyna Lite, Wixford Lodge Farm, Georges Elm Lane, Bidford-on-Avon, Alcester, Warwickshire, B50 4JT Tel: (01789) 773320 Fax: (01789) 490326 E-mail: sales@fynalite.co.uk *Stable forks (metal) manufrs*

Fyne Packaging Ltd, PO Box 443, Leighton Buzzard, Bedfordshire, LU7 4WG Tel: (01525) 370765 Fax: (01525) 376010 E-mail: sales@fynepac.co.uk *Carton, cardboard box & machine manufrs*

▶ Fyse Stone, Kemnay Quarry, Aquithie Road, Kemnay, Inverurie, Aberdeenshire, AB51 5PD Tel: (01467) 651000 Fax: (01467) 642342 *Aggregate*

▶ G 2 S Ford & Fulford, Unit 5 Woodford Centre Old Sarum Park, Lysander Way, Old Sarum, Salisbury, SP4 6BU Tel: (01722) 334488 Fax: (01722) 414515 *Install windows, doors*

G A Assembly Ltd, Alma Works, Coke Hill, Rotherham, South Yorkshire, S60 2HX Tel: (01709) 839911 Fax: (01709) 838373 E-mail: sales@gaa-ltd.co.uk *Contract electronic manufrs*

▶ G & A Barnie, 16 Carsegate Road South, Inverness, IV3 8LL Tel: (01463) 710826

G A Blinds & Curtains, 8 Norland House Business Centre, Hackworth Industrial Park, Shildon, County Durham, DL4 1HE Tel: (01388) 777171 *Domestic window blind manufrs*

G A C Engineering Group Ltd, New Works, Burnley Road, Sowerby Bridge, West Yorkshire, HX6 2TF Tel: (01422) 836091 Fax: (01422) 835396 E-mail: sales@gacgroup.co.uk *Machine tools manufacturers, rebuilders & retrofitters*

G A C Services, 79 The Downs, Nottingham, NG11 7DX Tel: 0115-981 9501 Fax: 0115-981 9501 *Air conditioning instillation services*

G A C (UK) Ltd, 56 Llantarnam Park, Cwmbran, Gwent, NP44 3AW Tel: (01633) 861411 Fax: (01633) 838306 *Aerosol fillers & speciality products*

G A Car Alarms, 9 Hudson Cl, Haverhill, Suffolk, CB9 0LF Tel: 01440 705855 Fax: 01440 705855 *Car alarm installation*

G A Collinson Fencing Co Ltd, Stannetts, Laindon, Basildon, Essex, SS15 6DN Tel: (01268) 411671 Fax: (01268) 541134 E-mail: info@collinsonfencing.co.uk *Fencing contractors*

▶ G A Duncan & Sons Ltd, Gordon Castle Farm, Fochabers, Morayshire, IV32 7PQ Tel: (01343) 821609 Fax: (01343) 821413

G A Engineering, Unit 12, Ash Industrial Estate, Flex Meadow, Harlow, Essex, CM19 5TJ Tel: (01279) 414972 Fax: (01279) 416029 *CNC machine engineering service providers*

G A Fabrications Ltd, 8 1 St. Annes Road, Willenhall, West Midlands, WV13 1DY Tel: (01902) 603892 Fax: 01902 603027 E-mail: gafabs@talk21.com *Steel fabricators & welders*Manufacturers of gates, railings, access ladders, platforms, fire escapes, steelwork, ductwork,*

G A Gas Services 2000 Ltd, 676 Pershore Road, Selly Park, Birmingham, B29 7NX Tel: 0121-472 7293 Fax: 0121-472 7294 *Central heating installers*

▶ G A Harper Ltd, Gwynfa House, 677 Princes Road, Dartford, DA2 6EF Tel: (01322) 294994 Fax: (01322) 626900

G A Helmore, 2 Langlands Street, Dundee, DD4 6SZ Tel: (01382) 462154 Fax: (01382) 454004 *Electrical contractors*

G A I Ltd, 8 Stepney Green, London, E1 3JU Tel: (020) 7790 3431 Fax: (020) 7790 8517 E-mail: info@gai.org.uk *Trade association*

G & A Kirsten Ltd, 11 Amwell End, Ware, Hertfordshire, SG12 9HP Tel: (01920) 487300 Fax: (01920) 487304 E-mail: gakirsten@btclick.com *Nameplates manufrs*

▶ G A Mell Ltd, Manor Farm Cottage, The Green, Finningley, Doncaster, South Yorkshire, DN9 3BP Tel: (01302) 770202

G & A Moulding Technology Ltd, Unit 2, Stonehill, Huntingdon, Cambridgeshire, PE29 6ED Tel: (01480) 414933 Fax: (01480) 414899 E-mail: info@gandamoulding.co.uk *Consultants for the plastic industry*

▶ G A P, 88 Castle Street, Portchester, Fareham, Hampshire, PO16 9QG Tel: (023) 9238 6602 Fax: (023) 9261 7230 E-mail: gerry@mobilarm.co.uk *GSM alarms for monitoring vehicles, boats & plants suppliers*

▶ G A P Group Ltd, 79 Salamander Street, Leith, Edinburgh, EH6 7JZ Tel: 0131-554 0503 Fax: 0131-554 0861 E-mail: leith@gap-group.co.uk *Plant & tool hire*

▶ G A P Group Ltd, Peacock View, Dewsbury Road, Fenton Industrial Estate, Stoke-on-Trent, ST4 2TE Tel: (01782) 264040 Fax: (01782) 265050 E-mail: stoke@gap-group.co.uk *Plant & tool hire*

G A P Precision Sheet Metal Work, Units 18-19, Apex Park, Diplocks Way, Hailsham, East Sussex, BN27 3JU Tel: (01323) 440024 Fax: (01323) 441183 E-mail: info@gap-metal.co.uk *Sheet metalwork*

G & A Pine Products, White House Farm, Valley La, Long Bennington, Newark, Notts, NG23 5EE Tel: (01400) 282788 Fax: (01400) 282788 *Pine furniture manufacturer*

G & A Plastics Ltd, Springhill Works, Exchange St, Accrington, Lancashire, BB5 0LE Tel: (01254) 871919 Fax: (01254) 390967 E-mail: david@gaplastics.co.uk *Plastics grp fabricators*

▶ G & A Plumbing & Heating Ltd, 1 Primrose Lane, Arlesey, Bedfordshire, SG15 6RD Tel: (01462) 731896 Fax: (01462) 835588 E-mail: carole@gaplumbing.co.uk

G A Robson & Son, Carlton Husthwaite, Thirsk, North Yorkshire, YO7 2BP Tel: (01845) 501581 Fax: (01845) 501520 E-mail: tim.robson@fwi.co.uk *Farming & agricultural machinery suppliers*

G A Stratton & Son, 4 Stoke Road, Tottenhill, King's Lynn, Norfolk, PE33 0RW Tel: (01553) 810341 *Agricultural repair services*

G A Swinbank, Thorndale Farm, Melsonby, Richmond, North Yorkshire, DL10 5NJ Tel: (01325) 377318 Fax: (01325) 377796 *Agricultural merchants*

G A Watts & Son, Podington Airfield, Hinwick, Wellingborough, Northamptonshire, NN29 7JQ Tel: (01234) 781003 *Timber merchants*

G A Wedderburn & Co. Ltd, 44a Kinson Road, Bournemouth, BH10 4AN Tel: (01202) 523996 Fax: (01202) 523994 E-mail: team@gawedderburnbmth.fsnet.co.uk *Cash registers & scales, sale & repair*

G A Wisbey & Son Ltd, Tile Hall Farm, Little Sampford, Saffron Walden, Essex, CB10 2SA Tel: (01371) 830313 Fax: (01371) 831478 *Farmers*

G Abbott & Co. Ltd, Brenda Road, Hartlepool, Cleveland, TS25 2BJ Tel: (01429) 234841 Fax: (01429) 234445 *Civil engineers & maintenance services.*

G Alderson, 11a Clarke Road, Bletchley, Milton Keynes, MK1 1UA Tel: (01908) 641680 Fax: (01908) 643517 *Food ingredient suppliers*

G Aldridge & Son, 90 Friar Street, Reading, RG1 1EN Tel: 0118-957 2383 Fax: 0118-957 2383 E-mail: info@aldridges.co.uk *Luggage & leather goods retailers*

▶ G Armstrong, Woodbine Cottage, Myreton, Aberlady, Longniddry, East Lothian, EH32 0PZ Tel: (01875) 870229

G B A Electrical Ltd, 3 Williams Way, West Row, Bury St. Edmunds, Suffolk, IP28 8QB Tel: (01638) 718289 Fax: (01638) 718289 *Air-conditioning & refrigeration manufrs*

▶ G B A Flare Systems, Burnham House, 93 High Street, Burnham, Slough, SL1 7JZ Tel: (01628) 610100 Fax: (01628) 610170 E-mail: mark.swann@gba-flares.com *GBA Flares Systems operating from offices in London, Milan and Houston design, fabricate and supply flare tips, ignition systems and flare stacks for offshore and onshore applications.*

G B Access Ltd, 10 Nene Valley Business Park, Oundle, Peterborough, PE8 4HN Tel: (01832) 272408 Fax: (01832) 272484 E-mail: hire@gbaccess.co.uk *Construction hoist hire*

▶ G B Agencies Ltd, Alexandra Dock North, Grimsby, South Humberside, DN31 3UA Tel: (01472) 240416 Fax: (01472) 348751 E-mail: agencies@gbagroup.com *Shipping company*

G B Alarms Ltd, High St, Donington, Spalding, Lincolnshire, PE11 4TA Tel: (01775) 821100 Fax: (01775) 821395 E-mail: admin@gbalarms.com *Fire & security alarm contractors*

G B B UK Ltd, Manchester Road, Burnley, Lancashire, BB11 1JZ Tel: (01282) 414903 Fax: (01282) 410239 E-mail: info@gbb.com *Vehicle assessors*

▶ G B Belting Ltd, 55c Perry Avenue, Teesside Industrial Estate, Stockton-on-Tees, Cleveland, TS17 9LN Tel: (01642) 762686 Fax: (01642) 762604 E-mail: sales@gbbelting.com *Conveyor & transmission belt manufrs*

G.B. Bracket Hire & Jig Sales, 15 Hasse Road, Soham, Ely, Cambridgeshire, CB7 5UN Tel: (01353) 624406 Fax: 01353 624671 *Car body repairs*

G B Business Supplies, 17 Leek Road, Werrington, Stoke-on-Trent, ST9 0HX Tel: (01782) 550830 Fax: (01782) 550813 E-mail: info@gbbusiness.demon.co.uk *Computer resellers*

G B Caleva Ltd, Butts Pond Industrial Estate, Sturminster Newton, Dorset, DT10 1AZ Tel: (01258) 472742 Fax: (01258) 473569 E-mail: sales@gb-caleva.co.uk *Pharmaceutical testing equipment*

G B Catering Engineers, 6 Alma Industrial Estate, Stafford Road, Wednesbury, West Midlands, WS10 8SX Tel: 0121-568 7669 Fax: 0121-568 7669 *Fish & chip machine services*

G B Circuits, Braithwell Way, Hellaby, Rotherham, South Yorkshire, S66 8QY Tel: (01709) 547000 Fax: (01709) 549000 E-mail: gbcircuits@dial.pipex.com *P C B manufacture*

G B Crane Services Ltd, The Slough, Redditch, Worcestershire, B97 5JR Tel: (01527) 402111 Fax: (01527) 403931 E-mail: gbcraneservices@btinternet.com *Sales, Service, Installations, Repairs to Overhead Travelling Cranes, Free Standing Gantries, Swing Jibs, Monorail Runways. Design and Manufacture to Customers Requirements, Service Contracts. Modification and Conversions. Proof Load Testing and Certification. New/Used Cranes/Hoists and Supporting Steelwork. Suppliers of New Loose Lifting Equipment. WE WILL ENDEAVOR TO BEAT ANY WRITTEN QUOTATION. NATIONWIDE COVERAGE*

G B D Ltd, 9 Geilston Park, Cardross, Dumbarton, G82 5ND Tel: (01389) 842021 Fax: (01389) 841751 *It suppliers*

G B D Signs Services, 17 Lloyd Goring Cl, Angmering, Littlehampton, W. Sussex, BN16 4LG Tel: (01903) 779999 Fax: (01903) 779777 *Safety signs manufrs*

G B Direct, The Design Exchange, 34 Peckover Street, Bradford, West Yorkshire, BD1 5BD Tel: (0870) 2007273 E-mail: info@gbdirect.co.uk *Internet training services*

G B Ductwork Ltd, Station Road, Whitworth, Rochdale, Lancashire, OL12 8LJ Tel: (01706) 854900 Fax: (01706) 854990 *Ductwork engineers*

G B Electrical Engineering Co, Springvale Street, Willenhall, West Midlands, WV13 1EJ Tel: (01902) 605934 Fax: (01902) 632198 E-mail: sales@gbelectrical.co.uk *Electric motor rewind specialists*

G & B Electronic Designs Ltd, 54 Woolmer Way, Bordon, Hampshire, GU35 9QF Tel: (01420) 474188 Fax: (01420) 478101 E-mail: sales@gandbelectronics.co.uk *Design, manufacture & assembly of printed circuit boards*

G B Engineering, 111 Wilsons Lane, Longford, Coventry, CV6 6AB Tel: (024) 7636 3634 Fax: (024) 7636 3634 E-mail: gb.eng@talk21.com *Reconditioned machine tools & rebuilding services*

▶ G & B Engineering Services, 20 Manor Drive, London, N14 5JJ Tel: (020) 8368 7056 Fax: (020) 8368 7056 E-mail: info@gbengineeringservices.com *Mechanical designers of piping, pressure vessels & structural steel*

G B Fabrication & Welding Services, Bunkers Hill, Bunkers Hill, Kidlington, Oxfordshire, OX5 3EL Tel: (07770) 761599 Fax: (01869) 331759 E-mail: julian.gbfabf@virgin.net *Steel fabricators*

G & B Fabrications Services, Unit 20 Newfields Industrial Estate, High Street, Stoke-on-Trent, ST6 5PD Tel: (01782) 824600 Fax: (01782) 824700 *Steel fabricators & railing manufrs*

G B Fork Lifts, Unit K1 Innsworth Technology Park, Innsworth Lane, Gloucester, GL3 1DL Tel: (01452) 731350 Fax: (01452) 731373 E-mail: sales@gbforklifts.co.uk *Forklift hire, sales & services*

G B G Fences Ltd, 25 Barns Lane, Walsall, WS4 1HQ Tel: (01922) 623207 Fax: (01922) 722110 E-mail: enquiries@gbgfences.co.uk *Fencing contractors*

▶ G B Guitars, 41 Prestonville Road, Brighton, BN1 3TJ Tel: (01273) 220055 Fax: (01273) 775780 *Hand built base guitar suppliers*

G B H Services Ltd, 17-18 Mercia Way, Bells Close Industrial Estate, Newcastle Upon Tyne, NE15 6UF Tel: 0191-229 0488 Fax: 0191-264 4095 E-mail: sales@gbhservices.co.uk *Steel fabricators*

▶ G B H Utilities, Church Street, Mexborough, South Yorkshire, S64 0HG Tel: (01709) 578578 Fax: (01709) 581589

G.B. Hard Chrome Ltd, 23-25 Nobel Square, Burnt Mills, Basildon, Essex, SS13 1LP Tel: 0845 8550608 Fax: (01268) 727524 E-mail: dan.griffiths@gbhard-chrome.co.uk Purchasing Contact: D. Griffiths Sales Contact: D. Griffiths *G.B. Hard Chrome Ltd - specialists in depositing functional, engineering coatings of Hard Chrome, Electroless Nickel, Nickel and Copper. Techniques have been perfected that allow controlled deposits of Hard Chrome and Electroless Nickel, including composites, to be applied to complex shapes. Ferrous and non-ferrous materials, including aluminium alloys are regularly processed. In-house grinding facilities permit the refurbishment of hydraulic rams and cylinders, print rollers, inking-rollers etc. Surfaces can be lapped and polished to N1. Internal grinding is also available. The directors have been involved for more than 40 years in processing components from industries as diverse as plastics, rubber, aerospace, marine, defence, medical, paper and automotive, to name a few. The company is registered to BS EN ISO9001:2000 for the provision of functional coatings and precision grinding.*

G B J Cabinet Makers, 40b Worcester Road, Titton, Stourport-on-Severn, Worcestershire, DY13 9PD Tel: (01299) 823740 Fax: (01299) 823740 *Furniture manufrs*

▶ G B J Environmental Systems Ltd, 4 Gatewarth Industrial Estate, Barnard Street, Warrington, WA5 1DD Tel: (01925) 635568 Fax: (01925) 242667

▶ G B K Rental Services Ltd, Green Elms Estate, Grays Road, Uddingston, Glasgow, G71 6ET Tel: (01698) 801000 Fax: (01698) 801144 *Crane hire specialists*

G B Kent & Sons plc, London Road, Hemel Hempstead, Hertfordshire, HP3 9SA Tel: (01442) 251531 Fax: (01442) 231672 E-mail: info@kentbrushes.com *Hairbrush manufrs*

G B Knitwear, Abbey Park Street, Leicester, LE4 5AF Tel: 0116-291 2994 *Knitwear manufrs*

G B Lift Trucks Ltd, C Building The Depot Pinnacle Storage Park, Cat & Fiddle Lane, West Hallam, Ilkeston, Derbyshire, DE7 6HE Tel: 0115-930 7901 Fax: 0115-930 8414 *Fork lift truck services*

▶ G B Lifts Ltd, Suite G12-14, 10 Whittle Road, Ferndown Industrial Estate, Wimborne, Dorset, BH21 7RL Tel: (01202) 871012 Fax: (01202) 894345 E-mail: enquiry@gblifts.co.uk *Lift installers*

G B Liners Ltd, 8 Haslemere Industrial Estate, Third Way, Avonmouth, Bristol, BS11 9TP Tel: 0117-982 8141 E-mail: bristol@gbliners.com

G B Liners Ltd, Blaisdon Way, Cheltenham, Gloucestershire, GL51 0WH Tel: (01242) 523785 Fax: (01242) 221189 E-mail: cheltenham@gbliners.com

▶ G B Liners Ltd, 28 Armstrong Way, Southall, Middlesex, UB2 4SD Tel: (020) 8574 1285 Fax: (020) 8574 5992

G B Logan Fabrications Ltd, Deacon Road, Lincoln, LN2 4JB Tel: (01522) 523622 Fax: (01522) 527408 E-mail: logan@enterprise.net *Sheet metalwork engineers*

G B M Engineering, Unit 4 Inngae Park, Holly Lane Industrial Estate, Atherstone, Warwickshire, CV9 2NA Tel: (01827) 712213 Fax: (01827) 718503 *Precision machinists & engineers*

G B M Products, 4 Octavian Way, Team Valley Trading Estate, Gateshead, Tyne & Wear, NE11 0HZ Tel: 0191-487 8004 Fax: 0191-487 1655 E-mail: info@gbmproducts.sagehost.co.uk *Manufacturers of lubricating systems equipment*

G & B Machining Services, 55 Marlborough Road, Margate, Kent, CT9 5SU Tel: (01843) 230876 *General machinists services*

G B Marketing, 218 Nottingham Road, Burton Joyce, Nottingham, NG14 5BD Tel: 0115-961 9126 Fax: 0115-987 4630 *Corporate marketing uniform suppliers*

G B Metal Spinnings Ltd, 68a Glover Street, Birmingham, B9 4EL Tel: 0121-773 5444 Fax: 0121-773 5666 E-mail: lee@gb-metalspinnings.com *Metal spinners & press work*

G B Models, 119 Church Road, Urmston, Manchester, M41 9ET Tel: 0161-747 2900 Fax: 0161-747 2901 *Matchbox models retailers*

G B N Removal Co. Ltd, Estate Way, London, E10 7JN Tel: (020) 8556 2211 Fax: (020) 8532 8519 E-mail: Gbnremoval@aol.com *Removal contractors (office & domestic)*

G B Nationwide Crate Hire Ltd, Heritage House, 345 Southbury Road, Enfield, Middlesex, EN1 1UP Tel: (020) 8219 8180 Fax: (020) 8219 8181 E-mail: moreinfo@gbnationwide.com *Crate hire*

▶ G & B Office Services Group Limited, G & B Corner, Blackbird Road, Leicester, LE4 0BX Tel: 0116-251 7777 Fax: 0116-251 1854 E-mail: peter@gboffice.com *Complete office furniture supply service, including free office space planning, delivery and installation nationwide. Apporved local authority and police contractor.*

G & B Pine Co., 1 Tanhouse Lane, Widnes, Cheshire, WA8 0RZ Tel: 0151-495 1743 Fax: 0151-495 1743 *Pine wholesaler*

G B Plant Hire & Groundwork, 40 Bramley Shaw, Waltham Abbey, Essex, EN9 3NN Tel: (01992) 761307 Fax: (01992) 761307 E-mail: gbbg20@hotmail.com *Groundwork contractors*

G B Precision Engineering Co., 1 Port Hope Road, Birmingham, B11 1JS Tel: 0121-766 7008 Fax: 0121-773 2824 E-mail: info@gbprecision.co.uk *Precision tool & turned part manufrs*

▶ G B Print, C2 Blaby Industrial Park, Winchester Avenue, Blaby, Leicester, LE8 4GZ Tel: 0116-247 7144 Fax: 0116-278 2723 E-mail: info@gbprint.co.uk

G & B Printers, Unit 4 Mount Road Industrial Estate, Feltham, Middlesex, TW13 6AR Tel: (020) 8755 1822 Fax: (020) 8893 3854 E-mail: info@gbprinters.co.uk *Lithographic printing services*

G B Projects Ltd, The Mill, Pepperoyd Street, Dewsbury, West Yorkshire, WF13 1PA Tel: (01924) 467147 Fax: (01924) 458511 E-mail: sales@gbprojects.co.uk *Shop fittings manufrs*

G & B Projects Co., Barnards Green Road, Malvern, Worcestershire, WR14 3LY Tel: (01684) 574367 Fax: (01684) 560225 E-mail: sales@gandbprojects.co.uk *Plastics industrial fastener manufrs*

G B Promotional Products Ltd, The Old Smoke House Potter Street, Sandwich, Kent, CT13 9DR Tel: (01304) 619390 Fax: (01304) 619391 E-mail: sales@gbpromotionalproducts.co.uk *Advertising gift suppliers*

G B Quality Assurance Ltd, 9 Moor Lane Industrial Estate, Chancel Way, Birmingham, B6 7AU Tel: 0121-356 7430 Fax: 0121-344 3837 E-mail: info@gbquality.com *Inspection certification engineers & calibrating services*

G B R Industries Ltd, Galebreaker House, New Mills Industrial Estate, Ledbury, Herefordshire, HR8 2SS Tel: (01531) 637900 Fax: (01531) 637901 E-mail: jps@galebreaker.co.uk *Industrial doors & partitions manufrs*

G B R Refrigeration, 8 Crossmount Court, Carluke, Lanarkshire, ML8 5ST Tel: (01555) 759371 Fax: (01555) 759371 E-mail: gbr_refrigeration@msn.com *Refrigeration sales & services*

G B Refrigeration, 58-60 Brown Street West, Colne, Lancashire, BB8 9ND Tel: (01282) 862646 Fax: (01282) 867631

▶ G & B Roadmarkings, Cairnhill Trading Estate, Unit 9, Cairnhill Rd, Airdrie, Lanarkshire, ML6 9HA Tel: (01236) 764867 Fax: (01236) 767336

▶ G B Services, Blackberry Lane, Lingfield, Surrey, RH7 6NG Tel: (01342) 837691 Fax: (01342) 835655 *Building*

▶ G B Shipping & Forwarding Ltd, Meridian House, Alexandra Dock North, Grimsby, North East Lincolnshire, DN31 3UA Tel: (01472) 345551 Fax: (01472) 346927 E-mail: shipping@gbagroup.com

G B Signs, 5b-5c Chesterbank Business Park, River Lane, Saltney, Chester, CH4 8SL Tel: (01244) 682868 Fax: (01244) 683030 E-mail: sales@gbsigns.co.uk *Sign manufrs*

G B Signs, 274 High Street, Waltham Cross, Hertfordshire, EN8 7EA Tel: (01992) 623819 Fax: (01992) 623819 *General sign makers*

▶ G B Site Services, 21 Bonnyside Road, Bonnybridge, Stirlingshire, FK4 2AD Tel: (01324) 882503 Fax: (01324) 882504

▶ G & B Steelwork, Hope Farm, Gibbons Brook, Sellindge, Ashford, Kent, TN25 6HJ Tel: (01303) 813906 Fax: (01303) 813906 *Steel fabricators*

G B Supplies, Unit 1 Modern House, Summer Lane, Barnsley, South Yorkshire, S70 2NP Tel: (01226) 288008 Fax: (01226) 285565 *Bakers ingredient & prepared material producers*

G B Supplies, Dixons Farmhouse, Dixons Lane, Grimsargh, Preston, PR2 5LG Tel: (01772) 704364 Fax: (01772) 704030 E-mail: gbsupplies@aol.com *'G B Supplies based in Preston offers antislip products, catering non-slip matting, blanket bags, shower curtains, bath mats, bedding storage bags and pillow protectors.*

G B Telecoms, Galamoor House, Netherdale Industrial Estate, Galashiels, Selkirkshire, TD1 3EY Tel: (01896) 752607 Fax: (01896) 661308 E-mail: sales@gbtscotland.co.uk *Telecommunications agents*

G B Truck Service, Cross Keys Works, Cross Keys Lane, Hoyland, Barnsley, South Yorkshire, S74 0QA Tel: (01226) 744114 Fax: (01226) 749999 E-mail: sales@gbtrucks.co.uk *Commercial accident repairers*

G B Welding Services Rutland Ltd, Unit 8 Pillings Road Industrial Estate, Oakham, Leicestershire, LE15 6QF Tel: (01572) 722764 Fax: (01572) 724347 E-mail: admin@gbwelding.co.uk *Steel fabricators & welding engineers services*

G B Wholesale Ltd, 439 Hackney Road, London, E2 9DY Tel: (020) 7729 7373 *Textile fabric import & export merchants*

G B Windows, New Road Business Park, New Road, Halifax, West Yorkshire, HX1 2LH Tel: (01422) 331141 Fax: (01422) 331145 *Pvc window & doors manufrs*

G Bayne, North Lodge, Wolflee, Hawick, Roxburghshire, TD9 9TE Tel: (01450) 860357 *Agricultural contractors*

▶ G Bopp & Co. Ltd, Grange Close, Clover Nook Industrial Park, Somercotes, Alfreton, Derbyshire, DE55 4QT Tel: (01773) 521266 Fax: (01773) 521163 E-mail: info@gbopp.com *Manufacturers of metal & precision synthetic filter cloths. Also diffused bonded woven wire cloth filter medias, precision synthetic sieving materials & wire gauze/cloths. In addition, screen printing fabric, gauze & mesh manufrs*

▶ G Brocklehurst Ltd, Goods Lane, Off Railway Street, Dewsbury, West Yorkshire, WF12 8DZ Tel: (01924) 468811 Fax: (01924) 451161

G Broughton & Sons, Ferneries Road, Barnetby, South Humberside, DN38 6HN Tel: (01652) 688652 Fax: (01652) 688069 *Vehicle body builders*

G Bryan Jones Ltd, Love La Industrial Estate, Bishops Castle, Shropshire, SY9 5DW Tel: (01588) 638638 Fax: (01588) 638741 E-mail: sales@gbj1.freeserve.co.uk *Agricultural & general engineering*

G Bulman Sealants, 6 Bridge Road, Ashton-on-Ribble, Preston, PR2 2JU Tel: (01772) 734129 Fax: (01772) 733225 *Sealant applicators*

▶ G Burley & Sons Ltd, Burleys, Moorhurst Lane, Holmwood, Dorking, Surrey, RH5 4LJ Tel: (01306) 711799 Fax: (01306) 712423

G C A S Designs Ltd, Russell Court, Lisburn Road, Belfast, BT9 6AA Tel: (028) 9055 7700 Fax: (028) 9024 5741 E-mail: advertising@gcasgroup.com *Holding company*

G C A S Public Relations, Russell Court, 38-52 Lisburn Road, Belfast, BT9 6AA Tel: (028) 9055 7777 Fax: (028) 9023 0142 E-mail: lawrenced@gcasgroup.com *Communication consultants*

G C A Transport Ltd, Romy House, 163-167 Kings Road, Brentwood, Essex, CM14 4EG Tel: (01277) 235230 Fax: (01277) 235240 *Bulk transporters*

G C Alarms, Emmslea, Highfield Road, Biggin Hill, Westerham, Kent, TN16 3UX Tel: (0500) 300984 Fax: (01959) 570374 *burglar alarms & CCTV*

G C B Engineering Bilston Ltd, Ash Street, Bilston, West Midlands, WV14 8UP Tel: (01902) 409486 Fax: (01902) 353739 E-mail: gcb@deecon.co.uk *General machinists*

G C Banks & Son Ltd, 5 Harolds Road, Harlow, Essex, CM19 5BJ Tel: (01279) 424019 Fax: (01279) 452203 *General engineers*

G & C Blinds, Unit 4 Green Street, Lane Business Park Green St Lane, Ayr, KA8 8BE Tel: (01292) 260993 Fax: (01292) 260993 *Blind manufrs*

G C Cones, 39 Ennis Road, Redcar, Cleveland, TS10 5JY Tel: (01642) 471988 Fax: (01642) 471988 *Ice cream cone manufacturer*

G C Designs Ltd, Mansion House Buildings, Market Place, Crich, Matlock, Derbyshire, DE4 5DD Tel: (01773) 857388 Fax: (01773) 857388 E-mail: gwyncarless@gcdesigns.co.uk *Lighting design & manufrs*

G C E Fluid Power Ltd, Unit 17 Atlas Estate, Brookvale Road, Witton, Birmingham, B6 7EX Tel: 0121-356 5727 Fax: 0121-344 3629 E-mail: gcefluidpower@btinternet.com *Pneumatic & hydraulic engineers*

G C Electronics, 6 Deighton Avenue, Sherburn in Elmet, Leeds, LS25 6BR Tel: (01977) 683576 *Security alarm installation*

G & C Engineering plc, Cobham Road, Pershore, Worcestershire, WR10 2DL Tel: (01386) 553934 Fax: (01386) 555725 E-mail: sales@gandc.co.uk *Sheet metal fabrications & sub-contract engineers*

G C Equipment Ltd, Unit 6, St Margarets Business Park, Moor Mead Road, Twickenham, TW1 1JN Tel: (020) 8891 1500 Fax: (020) 8891 6735 E-mail: sales@gcequipment.co.uk *Suppliers of crushing, milling & sample preparation*

G C Fox (SW) Ltd, The Docks, Falmouth, Cornwall, TR11 4NJ Tel: (01326) 311300 Fax: (01326) 211334 *Shipping agents* Also at: Camborne, Helston & Truro

G C H Test & Computer Services Ltd, I S C House 5 Progress Business Centre, Whittle Parkway, Slough, SL1 6DQ Tel: (01628) 559980 Fax: (01628) 559990 E-mail: sales@gch-services.com *Fibre channel test equipment distributors*

G C Hurrell & Co. Ltd, Knight Road, Rochester, Kent, ME2 2AH Tel: (01634) 718330 Fax: (01634) 710601 E-mail: *Homogeniser manufacturers & mixers*

G & C Johnson Claxby Ltd, Crosby Grange, Crosby Grange Road, Scunthorpe, South Humberside, DN15 8UH Tel: (01724) 856262 Fax: (01724) 854626 E-mail: gc.johnson@btconnect.com *Road transport contractors & warehousing*

G C Laboratories Ltd, 6 Fen End, Stotfold, Hitchin, Hertfordshire, SG5 4BA Tel: (01462) 733770 Fax: (01462) 733898 E-mail: g.c.labs@btinternet.com *Analytical & consulting chemists*

G C M Ltd, Ratcliffe Buildings, Tuttel Hill, Nuneaton, Warwickshire, CV10 0GA Tel: (024) 7635 2540 Fax: (024) 7635 3223 E-mail: sales@gcmsales.com *Concrete surface preparation & vibrating equipment*

G C N Plant Ltd, Foryd Bank, Green Avenue, Kinmel Bay, Rhyl, Clwyd, LL18 5ET Tel: (01745) 343089 Fax: (01745) 332115 E-mail: gari_hughes@hotmail.com *Trencher Hire & Top Cutter Hire*

▶ G C N (Scotland) Ltd, Garrion Business Park, Wishaw, Lanarkshire, ML2 0RY Tel: (01698) 351343

G C Newbury & Co. Ltd, Walmar House, 296 Regent Street, London, W1B 3HR Tel: (020) 7255 2303 Fax: (020) 7255 1453 E-mail: general@gcnewbury.co.uk *Cotton grey cloth merchants* Also at: Manchester

G C Ogle & Sons Ltd, Victoria Road, Ripley, Derbyshire, DE5 3FX Tel: (01773) 742381 Fax: (0870) 4601807 *Drain jetting machine manufacturer & hydraulics*

G C Parish & Sons, 92 High Street, Bovingdon, Hemel Hempstead, Hertfordshire, HP3 0HJ Tel: (01442) 832341 Fax: (01442) 409313 E-mail: sales@parishremovals.co.uk *Removal & storage contractors*

G C Plant, 24 Perry Road, Witham, Essex, CM8 3YZ Tel: (01376) 512122 Fax: (01376) 512122 *Plant repairers*

▶ G C R, 63 Risbygate Street, Bury St. Edmunds, Suffolk, IP33 3AZ Tel: (01284) 706620 Fax: (0871) 2427521 E-mail: gcrbury@tiscali.co.uk *Portable appliance testing service*

G C S Ltd, Fingal House, East Street, Mayfield, East Sussex, TN20 6TU Tel: (01435) 872833 Fax: (01435) 873762 *Telecommunications equipment & systems*

G C S Alarms, Essex House, Stephenson Road, Clacton-on-Sea, Essex, CO15 4XA Tel: (01255) 220316 Fax: (01255) 479122 E-mail: sales@gcsalarms.co.uk *Alarm design & cctv installation services*

▶ G C S Bookkeeping, 120 Blackhorse Road, Hawkesbury Village, Longford, Coventry, CV6 6DL Tel: (024) 7636 4282 Fax: (024) 7636 4282 E-mail: gailstevens@totalise.co.uk *Specialising in Payroll, Vat, Invoicing and general bookkeeping for small businesses. Good rates with a personal service*

G C Supplies UK Ltd, 13-15a Reliance Trading Estate, Reliance Street, Manchester, M40 3ET Tel: 0161-681 8114 Fax: 0161-947 0148 E-mail: sales@gcstainless.co.uk *Stainless steel tube manufrs*

▶ G C Tech, Unit G70, Chapel Place, Northampton, NN1 4AQ Tel: (01604) 601873 Fax: (01604) 601893

G C W Fabrications Ltd, Unit 23, James Carter Road, Bury St. Edmunds, Suffolk, IP28 7DE Tel: (01638) 515478 Fax: (01638) 717554 *Mild steel fabricators*

G C Welding, Stonelands Farm House, Withyham, Hartfield, East Sussex, TN7 4BH Tel: (01892) 861106 Fax: (01892) 861422 *Welding & steel fabricators*

G Clements & Sons, Redbourne Mere, Kirton Lindsey, Gainsborough, Lincolnshire, DN21 4LE Tel: (01652) 648787 Fax: (01652) 649494 *Agricultural machinery dealers*

G Cox Oldbury Ltd, 146 Dudley Road East, Oldbury, West Midlands, B69 3EB Tel: 0121-552 4413 Fax: 0121-552 1883 *Mobile crane hire service*

G Creations plc, 2 Homefield Road, London, SW19 4QE Tel: (020) 8947 8652 Fax: (020) 8944 1650 *Cosmetics manufrs*

G D Anderson & Co. Ltd, 68 Lombard Street, London, EC3V 9LJ Tel: (020) 7437 5122 Fax: (020) 7481 9100 E-mail: admin@anderson-insurance.co.uk *Insurance brokers*

▶ G D C Precision Engineering Ltd, Unit 2b Princess Road, New Stevenston, Motherwell, Lanarkshire, ML1 4HP Tel: (01698) 834001 Fax: (01698) 834001 *Engineering services*

G D C Steel Fabrications Ltd, Unit H Adamson Industrial Estate, Croft Street, Hyde, Cheshire, SK14 1EE Tel: 0161-367 8990 Fax: 0161-367 8992 E-mail: gdcsteelfab@btconnect.com *Steel fabricators*

▶ G D Chalmers Ltd, 101 Neilston Road, Paisley, Renfrewshire, PA2 6ES Tel: 0141-889 6233 Fax: 0141-889 7806

G D Crichton, Strathenry Mill, Leslie, Glenrothes, Fife, KY6 3HU Tel: (01592) 743181 *Shotblasters & painters*

▶ G & D Cunningham Ltd, Cemetery Road, Galston, Ayrshire, KA4 8HZ Tel: (01563) 820409 Fax: (01563) 822004

▶ G D Designs, 14 Smallford Lane, Smallford, St. Albans, Hertfordshire, AL4 0SA Tel: (01727) 828183 Fax: (01727) 828183 E-mail: g.donovan@virgin.net *Point designers*

▶ G D Direct, 26 Eldon Way, Paddock Wood, Tonbridge, Kent, TN12 6BE Tel: (01892) 835388 Fax: (01892) 832330

G D E Associates UK, Causeway House, The Causeway, Great Hawksley, Colchester, CO6 4EJ Tel: (01206) 272999 Fax: (01206) 272998 E-mail: consult@gde.co.uk *Agricultural & project management consultants*

G D Engineering, Retford Road, Worksop, Nottinghamshire, S80 2PY Tel: (01909) 482323 Fax: (01909) 477902 *Closure products design & manufacture, maintenance*

G & D Engineering Moulton Ltd, Spalding Gate, High Road, Moulton, Spalding, Lincolnshire, PE12 6NT Tel: (01406) 370570 Fax: (01406) 370456 *Agricultural engineers & fabricators*

G & D Engineering Vickers Ltd, Poplars Industrial Estate, Moor Lane, Birmingham, B6 7AD Tel: 0121-356 3378 *Precision presswork toolmakers*

▶ G D Floors Ltd, 8 Broomhill Court, Kilwinning, Ayrshire, KA13 6UL Tel: (01294) 559745 E-mail: info@gdfloors.co.uk *Hardwood floor specialist, floor laying, sanding, sealing & inlays*

G D Hydraulics & Pneumatics, 13 Broadhurst Street, Stockport, Cheshire, SK3 8JH Tel: 0161-480 5151 *Hydraulics & pneumatics distributors*

G & D Joinery, 1 Chater Street, Belfast, BT4 1BL Tel: (028) 9045 1375 Fax: (028) 9073 8414 *Laminate bonding product*

▶ G D K Agencies, Hawthorne House, Malmesbury Road, Leigh, Swindon, SN6 6RH Tel: (01793) 759333 Fax: (01793) 759444 E-mail: geoffkay@gdkagencies.co.uk *Air conditioning specialists*

▶ G D K Engineering Co. Ltd, Unit 65 Blackpole Trading Estate West, Worcester, WR3 8TJ Tel: (01905) 454261 Fax: (01905) 454231 E-mail: sales@gdk-engineering.co.uk *CNC engineering services & gear box, unit & slewing ring manufrs*

G D L Air Systems Ltd, Air Diffusion Works, Woolley Bridge Road, Hadfield, Glossop, Derbyshire, SK13 1AB Tel: (01457) 861538 Fax: (01457) 866010 E-mail: sales@grille.co.uk

continued

Air conditioning equipment diffusers & louvers manufrs

G D L Air Systems Ltd, Air Diffusion Works, Woolley Bridge Road, Hadfield, Glossop, Derbyshire, SK13 1AB Tel: (01457) 861538 Fax: (01457) 866010 E-mail: sales@grille.co.uk *Air distribution products for the Heating and Ventilation Industry from GDL. Providers of grilles, diffusers, louvers and dampers.*

The G D L Partnership, 90 Mell Road, Tollesbury, Maldon, Essex, CM9 8SR Tel: (01621) 862608 Fax: E-mail: gdl.prtnrs@virgin.net *Visual services repairs*

G D M Heat Transfer Ltd, Boston Industrial Estate, Power Station Road, Rugeley, Staffordshire, WS15 2HS Tel: (01889) 574880 Fax: (01889) 575074 E-mail: sales@gdmcoolers.co.uk *Heat exchanger designers & manufrs*

G D M S UK Ltd, 14 The Meadway, Syston, Leicester, LE7 2BD Tel: 0116-264 0381 Fax: 0116-264 0381 E-mail: sales@gdms.org.uk *Cleaning material suppliers*

▶ G D M Surfacing Contractors Ltd, Bottings Industrial Estate, Curdridge, Southampton, SO30 2DY Tel: (01489) 796373 Fax: (01489) 796374

G & D Matthews, Sycamore House, Leaveslake Drove, West Pinchbeck, Spalding, Lincolnshire, PE11 3QJ Tel: (01775) 640230 Fax: (01775) 640230 *Agricultural contractors*

G D Metal Recycling Ltd, Powke Lane, Cradley Heath, West Midlands, B64 5PT Tel: 0121-559 1156 Fax: 0121-561 5371 *Metal & waste recycling facilities*

G D N Security & Home Maintenance Services, 4 Midgley Street, Colne, Lancashire, BB8 0HF Tel: (01282) 863195 *Burglar & intruder alarm system manufrs*

G D P Plastics, Unit 6, Empress Industrial Estate, Anderton Street, Ince, Wigan, Lancashire, WN2 2BG Tel: (01942) 820333

G D R Fabrication, Unit 5 Trevol Business Park, Trevol Road, Torpoint, Cornwall, PL11 2TB Tel: (01752) 816262 Fax: (01752) 816263 *Steel fabricators*

▶ G D S Computer Systems Ltd, 19 St. Lawrence Way, Hurstpierpoint, Hassocks, West Sussex, BN6 9SH Tel: (01273) 832841 E-mail: info@gdsit.co.uk *Supply it solutions to business' & homes including repairs*

G D S Design, 15 Avon Business Park, Lodge Causeway, Fishponds, Bristol, BS16 3JP Tel: 0117-958 6606 Fax: 0117-958 6605 E-mail: info@gds-design.freeserve.co.uk *Precision engineers*

G D S P C B Design, 5 Garton End, Crayspond, Reading, RG8 7QH Tel: (01491) 681235 Fax: (01491) 681380 E-mail: jogilvie@gds.co.uk *Printed circuit multi-chip designers*

G D S Shirts, 4 Barrock Street, Thurso, Caithness, KW14 7DB Tel: (01847) 893197 Fax: (01847) 893197 *Clothing mail-order & manufrs*

G D S Technologies, Swillington Lane, Swillington, Leeds, LS26 8BZ Tel: 0113-286 0166 Fax: 0113-286 4073 E-mail: sales@gds-technologies.co.uk Principal Export Areas: Worldwide *Environmental monitoring & gas detection equipment manufrs*

▶ G & D Scaffolding Services Ltd, Leadside Depot, Wellwood, Dunfermline, Fife, KY12 0RS Tel: (01383) 738783 Fax: (01383) 732353

▶ G D Sign, 62 West Street, Gorseinon, Swansea, SA4 4AF Tel: (01792) 549172 E-mail: sales@gdsign.co.uk *g.dsign-Graphic design services. From initial concept through to print production - for all your design requirements. Corporate Identity. Stationery-letterheads/bus.cards. Brochures. Leaflets. Exhibition Displays.*Posters/Wallcharts.*

G D Technik, 24 High Street, Twyford, Reading, RG10 9AG Tel: 0118-934 2277 Fax: 0118-934 2896 E-mail: sales@gd-technik.com *Distributors of semi conductors*

G D Textile Manufacturing Co., 3 Stocks Mill, Legh Street, Eccles, Manchester, M30 0UT Tel: 0161-788 2100 Fax: 0161-788 2109 E-mail: gd.textstytle@btinternet.com *Water proof clothes manufrs*

G D W Engineering & Plant Services Ltd, Low Mill, Town Lane, Whittle-le-Woods, Chorley, Lancashire, PR6 7DJ Tel: (01257) 262491 Fax: (01257) 241174 E-mail: graham.watkinson@gdwengineeiring.co.uk *Welding fabricators*

G D White & Partners, Old Post Office, Broomfield, Bridgwater, Somerset, TA5 2EH Tel: (01823) 451348 *Agricultural consultants*

▶ G D X Technologies Ltd, 61-63 Back Sneddon Street, Paisley, Renfrewshire, PA3 2DD Tel: 0141-889 8800

G D Yarns Ltd, 200 Gorton Road, Manchester, M12 5DX Tel: 0161-231 0055 Fax: 0161-231 0066 E-mail: gdyarns@btinternet.com *Yarn merchants*

▶ G Dalton Engineering Co. Ltd, Enterprise House, 260 Chorley New Road, Horwich, Bolton, BL6 5NY Tel: (01204) 699675 Fax: (01204) 668300 *Tube bending service*

▶ G Donald (Warehouseman) Ltd, 7 St Andrew St, Peterhead, Aberdeenshire, AB42 1DS Tel: (01779) 474737

G E Aviation, Kings Avenue, Hamble, Southampton, SO31 4NF Tel: (023) 8045 3371 Fax: (023) 8074 4042 E-mail: sales@smiths-aerospace.com *Aircraft component manufrs*

G E Aviation, Wobaston Road, Wolverhampton, WV9 5EW Tel: (01902) 397700 Fax: (01902) 394394 *Aeronautical designers*

G E Bridge & Co. Ltd, 123-125 Old Christchurch Road, Bournemouth, BH1 1HF Tel: (01202) 204802 Fax: (01202) 204800 *Medical & surgical suppliers*

G E Caledonian Ltd, Shawfarm Industrial Estate, Monument Cresent, Prestwick, Ayrshire, KA9 2RX Tel: (01292) 673000 Fax: (01292) 673001 E-mail: d.crews@ae.ge.com *Aircraft engine maintenance*

▶ G E Capital, Beacon Hill Garage, 19 Beacon Hill Lane, Corfe Mullen, Wimborne, Dorset, BH21 3RU Tel: (01202) 659909 Fax: (01202) 659077

▶ G E Capital Equipment Services, Cotes Park Lane, Cotes Park Industrial Estate, Somercotes, Alfreton, Derbyshire, DE55 4PU Tel: (01773) 520777 Fax: (01773) 521005 E-mail: daren.sharpe@ge.com

G E Capital Equipment Services Lnd, Geddington Road, Corby, Northamptonshire, NN18 8AA Tel: (01536) 265505 Fax: (01536) 201258 *Contractors' plant hire* Also at: Airdrie & Batley

G E Capital Modular Space Ltd, 2a Pioneer Works, Crabtree Manorway, Belvedere, Kent, DA17 6AH Tel: (020) 8312 4000 Fax: (020) 8311 7643 *Site accommodation hire services*

G E Capital Modular Space, Langford Bridge, Cambridge Road, Langford, Biggleswade, Bedfordshire, SG18 9PL Tel: (01462) 701711 Fax: (01462) 701355 *Portable building suppliers*

G E Capital Modular Space Ltd, G E House, Ten Pound Walk, Doncaster, South Yorkshire, DN4 5HW Tel: (01302) 732400 Fax: (01302) 732407 E-mail: mick-cleghorn@gecapital.com *Hire & sell site accommodation services*

G E Capital Modular Space Ltd, Hadnock Rd, Monmouth, Gwent, NP25 3NQ Tel: (01600) 712722 Fax: (01600) 712442 *Refurnish, hire & sell portacabins*

G E Capital Modular Space Ltd, Grappenhall Lane, Appleton, Warrington, WA4 4QT Tel: (01925) 268361 Fax: (01925) 268763 *Distribution company*

G E Collis & Sons Ltd, Queen St Industrial Estate, Queens Drive, Burntwood, Staffordshire, WS7 4QF Tel: (01543) 686370 Fax: (01543) 675221 E-mail: sales@collissheds.co.uk *Timber merchants & diy retailers*

G E Commercial Finance Ltd, 24 Bennetts Hill, Birmingham, B2 5QP Tel: 0121-616 3400 Fax: 0121-616 3418 *Business finance*

G E Commercial Finance, Enterprise House, Bancroft Road, Reigate, Surrey, RH2 7RT Tel: (01737) 841200 Fax: (01737) 841357 *Finance services*

▶ G E Computer Supplies, 3 Church View, Wyverstone, Stowmarket, Suffolk, IP14 4SQ Tel: (01449) 782059 E-mail: info@gecomputersupplies.co.uk

G E Cook & Sons Ltd, Tidings Hill Brewery, Halstead, Essex, CO9 1BL Tel: (01787) 475501 Fax: (01787) 475501 *Licensed bar & property management*

G E D Designs, 400 Aviation Park West, Bournemouth Int Airp, Hurn, Christchurch, Dorset, BH23 6NW Tel: (01202) 578537 Fax: (01202) 578537 *Design engineering services*

G E Digital Energy, Wheatfield Way, Hinckley, Leicestershire, LE10 1YG Tel: 0116-290 5280 Fax: 0116-290 5281 E-mail: sales@imv.co.uk *Manufacturers of power supply systems*

▶ G E Energy Services, Badentoy Crescent, Badentoy Industrial Estate, Aberdeen, AB12 4YD Tel: (01224) 785100

G E Energy UK Ltd, Kvaerner House, Ten Pound Walk, Doncaster, South Yorkshire, DN4 5HW Tel: (01302) 761761 Fax: (01302) 760230 *Hydroelectric power generation & water control*

G E Fanuc Automation (UK) Ltd, 15 Basset Court, Loake Close, Grange Park, Northampton, NN4 5EZ Tel: (01604) 744130 Fax: (01604) 744140 E-mail: gef.uk@gefanuceur.ge.com *Factory automation products & solutions services*

G E Fulton & Son, Bisley Camp, Brookwood, Woking, Surrey, GU24 0NZ Tel: (01483) 473204 Fax: (01483) 475011 *Gunsmiths distributors*

G E Garage Doors, 31 Upper Hibbert Lane, Marple, Stockport, Cheshire, SK6 7JQ Tel: 0161-406 7667 E-mail: gegaragedoors@hotmail.co.uk *Garage door installers*

G E Healthcare, Amersham Place, Amersham, Buckinghamshire, HP7 9NA Tel: (01494) 544000 Fax: (01494) 542266 *Health science group*

G E Inspection Technologies, Inspec Ho, 129-135 Camp Rd, St. Albans, Herts, AL1 5HL Tel: (01727) 795500 Fax: (01727) 795400 *Aircraft/aerospace systems & equipment*

▶ G & E Interiors, 27-29 Liverpool Road, Kidsgrove, Stoke-On-Trent, ST7 1EA Tel: (01782) 785965 *Retail showroom*

G E Lighting Ltd, 129 - 135 Camp Road, St. Albans, Hertfordshire, AL1 5HL Tel: (01727) 795493 Fax: (01727) 795422 *Domestic lighting manufrs*

G E M Concrete Products Ltd, Quarry Works, Moor Lane, Little Eaton, Derby, DE21 5AU Tel: (01332) 831449 Fax: (01332) 830198 *Concrete*

G E M Engineering Services, Unit B9 Tweedale Industrial Estate, Madeley, Telford, Shropshire, TF7 4JR Tel: (01952) 588525 Fax: (01952) 588525 *Toolmakers/toolmaking services*

G E M Operations Ltd, Unit 20 Romsey Industrial Estate, Greatbridge Road, Romsey, Hampshire, SO51 0HR Tel: (01794) 519022 Fax: (01794) 516750 E-mail: sales@gem-ltd.co.uk *Energy from a wide variety of waste streams using a non-combustion thermal process with zero emissions toatmosphere producing a clean combustable gas with characteristics similar to natural gas*

G E M Rewinds Ltd, 4 Welton Road, Wedgnock Industrial Estate, Warwick, CV34 5PZ Tel: (01926) 497778 Fax: (01926) 410128 E-mail: mike@gem-group.co.uk *Electric motor repairs & services*

G E M S, 31 Hatchett Street, Birmingham, B19 3NX Tel: 0121-333 4151 Fax: 0121-359 4934 E-mail: gems2@btconnet.com *Engineering maintenance services*

G E Netwrok Solutions, Elizabeth House, 1 High Street, Chesterton, Cambridge, CB4 1WR Tel: (01223) 301144 Fax: (01223) 311145 *Geographical information systems (gis) software*

G E O Services Int UK Ltd, Holdan House, 26 Bridge Street, Witney, Oxfordshire, OX28 1HY Tel: (01993) 706767 Fax: (01993) 773040 *Geo physical site investigations*

G E Oil & Gas, Badentoy Crescent, Badentoy Park, Aberdeen, AB12 4YD Tel: (01224) 785100 Fax: (01224) 785120 *Mechanical & electrical engineering*

Company Information

▶ indicates data change since last edition

G E Plant Services Ltd, 10a Dawkins Road, Poole, Dorset, BH15 4JD Tel: (01202) 676463 Fax: (01202) 665725 E-mail: geplant@btinternet.com *Hydraulic engineers*

G E Power Controls Ltd, East Lancashire Road, Liverpool, L10 5HB Tel: 0151-524 1122 Fax: 0151-523 7007 E-mail: gepcuk.sales@gepc.ge.com *Circuit breaker & motor control gear manufrs*

▶ G E R, Fair Oak, Rumble Street, Monkswood, Usk, Monmouthshire, NP15 1QG Tel: (07966) 228950 *JCB HIRE,LANDSCAPING, EARTH MOVING*

G E R International Ltd, PO Box 7, Colwyn Bay, Clwyd, LL28 4HP Tel: (01492) 544288 Fax: (01492) 547799 *Tableware & ceramic giftware exporters*

G E Richardson & Sons Ltd, 53 New England Street, Brighton, BN1 4GQ Tel: (01273) 570246 Fax: (01273) 570246 E-mail: metcycle@yahoo.co.uk *Scrap metal processors* Also at: Goddards Green

G E Seafoods, Unit 8 March Road Industrial Estate, Buckie, Banffshire, AB56 4BY Tel: (01542) 834987 Fax: (01542) 834987 *Fish merchants*

G E Security Ltd, Unit 5, Ashton Gate, Ashton Road, Harold Hill, Romford, RM3 8UF Tel: (01708) 381496 Fax: (0870) 7773049 *Security, fire, access & CCTV distributors*

G E Sensing, Fir Tree Lane, Groby, Leicester, LE6 0FH Tel: 0116-231 7100 Fax: 0116-231 7101 *Manufacturers of pressure equipment*

G E Starr Ltd, Dixon Street, Wolverhampton, WV2 2BS Tel: (01902) 576675 Fax: (01902) 350099 E-mail: info@gestarr.co.uk *Press workers & press tool manufrs*

G E T, Key Point, 3-17 High Street, Potters Bar, Hertfordshire, EN6 5AJ Tel: (01707) 601601 Fax: (01707) 601708 E-mail: sales@getplc.com *Cable & flex distributors*

G E Ultrasound Ltd, 2 Napier Road, Bedford, MK41 0JW Tel: (01234) 340881 Fax: (01234) 266261 *Ultrasound equipment distributors*

G E W Ec Ltd, Kings Mill Lane, South Nutfield, Redhill, RH1 5NB Tel: (01737) 824500 Fax: (01737) 823822 E-mail: sales@gewuv.com *Ultra violet drying & curing equipment manufrs*

G E Water, Hydro House, Newcombe Way, Orton Southgate, Peterborough, PE2 6SE Tel: (01733) 394555 Fax: (01733) 390179 *Industrial mobile water treatment services*

G E Water & Process Technologies Ltd, Foundry Lane, Widnes, Cheshire, WA8 8UD Tel: 0151-424 5351 Fax: 0151-423 2722 Principal Export Areas: Worldwide *Water & process treatment chemicals suppliers*

▶ G Easton & Son Ltd, South Street, Alford, Lincolnshire, LN13 9AQ Tel: (01507) 463400

▶ G Easton & Son Ltd, South Street, Alford, Lincolnshire, LN13 9AQ Tel: (01507) 463400

G Empson & Sons Ltd, Station Road, Gunness, Scunthorpe, South Humberside, DN15 8TR Tel: (01724) 782459 Fax: (01724) 783077 *Joinery manufrs*

G Ettinger Ltd, 215 Putney Bridge Road, London, SW15 2NY Tel: (020) 8877 1616 Fax: (020) 8877 1146 E-mail: info@ettinger.co.uk *Fine quality leather goods manufrs*

G F A Premier Fire Ltd, Whistons Lane, Elland, West Yorkshire, HX5 9DS Tel: (01422) 377521 Fax: (01422) 379569 E-mail: customer.service@nuswift.co.uk *Fire extinguishers suppliers*

G F Cross & Sons, Unit 10 Kings Meadow, Ferry Hinksey Road, Oxford, OX2 0DP Tel: (01865) 242358 Fax: (01865) 241648 E-mail: info@gfcrossandsons.co.uk *Heating, plumbing & ventilation specialists*

G F E Electrical Wholesale Ltd, Enterprise House, 370-386 Farnham Road, Slough, SL2 1JD Tel: (01753) 537811 E-mail: ask@gfegroup.com *Wholesale lighting & electrical suppliers* Also at: Bracknell, Edgware, High Wycombe, London SW1, London W8, Oxford & Reading

G F G Plastics Fabrication Ltd, Bridge Works, 101 West Dock Street, Hull, HU3 4HH Tel: (01482) 610110 Fax: (01482) 229044 E-mail: greygfg2003@aol.com *Plastic welded goods manufrs*

▶ G F Hill (Malvern) Ltd, Spring Lane, Malvern, Worcestershire, WR14 1AL Tel: (01684) 568456 Fax: (01684) 572401

▶ G F I Enterprises Ltd, Ellon Business Centre, Broomiesburn Road, Ellon, Aberdeenshire, AB41 9RD Tel: (01358) 722799 Fax: (01358) 725220

G F Joinery (Contract) Ltd, Gooder Lane, Brighouse, West Yorkshire, HD6 1HB Tel: (01484) 715116 Fax: (01484) 400089 E-mail: gfgroupltd@freenetname.co.uk *Shop fitters services*

G F L Industrial Finishing, William Kelvin Building, Claylands Road, Bishops Waltham, Southampton, SO32 1BH Tel: (01489) 897480 Fax: (01489) 897489 E-mail: sales@gfl-uk.com *Industrial finishing services*

G F P Engineering Ltd, Europa Way, Britannia Enterprise Park, Lichfield, Staffordshire, WS14 9TZ Tel: (01543) 263121 Fax: (01543) 418873 E-mail: gfpeng@btconnect.com *We specialise in GRP/Fibreglass hand lay and R.T.M. mouldings and also fabricated items*

G F Price & Co., Littlecroft, Chetton, Bridgnorth, Shropshire, WV16 6UE Tel: (01746) 789330 Fax: (01746) 789330 *Effluent treatment plant manufacturers*

G F Redfurn & Co., Lynn House, Ivy Arch Road, Worthing, West Sussex, BN14 8BX Tel: (01903) 820466 Fax: (01903) 820439 E-mail: sueb@gfredfern.com *Chartered european patent agents & trade marks services*

G F S A Ltd, 4 West Court, Buntsford Park Road, Bromsgrove, Worcestershire, B60 3DX Tel: (01527) 831037 Fax: (01527) 836333 E-mail: enquiries@gfsa.co.uk Principal Export Areas: Worldwide *Manufrs of Filters*

▶ G F Tomlinson, Navigation Complex, Navigation Road, Worcester, WR5 3DE Tel: (01905) 764421 Fax: (01905) 769918

G F Williams & Co., 46 Hatton Garden, London, EC1N 8EX Tel: (020) 7405 5477 Fax: (020) 7831 4063 E-mail: jason@gfwilliams.co.uk *Precious stone merchant*

G F Williams & Sons Risca Garages Ltd, 89 Cromwell Road, Risca, Newport, Gwent, NP11 7AD Tel: (01633) 612412 Fax: (01495) 270408 *Vehicle repairers*

▶ G F Wilson & Son, 12 Bunderg Road, Newtownstewart, Omagh, County Tyrone, BT78 4NQ Tel: (028) 8166 1239 Fax: (028) 8166 2009 E-mail: info@gfwilson.net *Civil engineering*

▶ G Force Express Parcels Ltd, Halesfield 2, Telford, Shropshire, TF7 4QH Tel: (01952) 582888 Fax: (01952) 582801

G Franchi & Sons Ltd, 329-331 Grays Inn Road, London, WC1X 8BZ Tel: (020) 7278 8628 Fax: (020) 7833 9049 E-mail: tony@franchi.fsbusiness.co.uk *Locksmiths*

G G Ceramics, Newport Business Park, Audley Road, Newport, Shropshire, TF10 7DP Tel: (01952) 814071 Fax: (01952) 813025 *Kitchen retailers*

▶ G G Compactors Ltd, Lennox House Works, 10 Beeding Close, Bognor Regis, West Sussex, PO22 9TS Tel: (01243) 866565 Fax: (01243) 868301 E-mail: enquires@ggcompactors.co.uk *Compactor suppliers & refurbishers*

▶ G & G Engineering Mechanical Services Ltd, Unit 5 Rockingham Business, Park Rockingham Row Birdwell, Birdwell, Barnsley, South Yorkshire, S70 5TW Tel: (01226) 747684 Fax: (01226) 740901 E-mail: ggeng@btconnect.com *Engineers*

G G Fabrications, St. James Place, Baildon, Shipley, West Yorkshire, BD17 7LD Tel: (01274) 414657 Fax: (01274) 420422 *Wrought iron manufrs*

▶ G G I Furniture (UK) Ltd, Global Way, Lower Eccleshill Road, Darwen, Lancashire, BB3 0RW Tel: (01254) 778500 Fax: (01254) 778519 E-mail: info@ggieurope.com *Manufacture office furniture*

G G I Office Furniture (UK) Ltd, Global Way, Darwen, Lancashire, BB3 0RW Tel: (01254) 778500 Fax: (01254) 778519 E-mail: info@ggieurope.com *Manufacture & distribution of office furniture*

▶ G & G Ornamental Iron Ltd, Bridgnorth Road, Shipley, Pattingham, Wolverhampton, WV6 7EZ Tel: (01902) 700888 E-mail: annerley73@aol.com *Wrought iron products manufacturer, gates, railings, furniture made to order*

G & G Powder Coatings Ltd, 3 Rippleside Commercial Estate, Ripple Road, Barking, Essex, IG11 0RJ Tel: (020) 8592 4555 Fax: (020) 8592 4777 E-mail: info@gg-powdercoating.com *Powder coating services*

G & G Pump Services Ltd, Dragons Wharf, Dragons Lane, Sandbach, Cheshire, CW11 3PA Tel: (01270) 759270 Fax: (01270) 759280 *Sewage pumps & treatment plant*

▶ G G S Engineering Derby Ltd, Atlas Works, Litchurch Lane, Derby, DE24 8AQ Tel: (01332) 299345 Fax: (01332) 299678 *Metalworking & fabrication*

G G S Fashions Ltd, 50 Lamb Lane, London, E8 3PJ Tel: (020) 7923 1911 Fax: (020) 7254 3052 *Women's clothing manufrs*

G & G Sewing, 402 St Helens Road, Bolton, BL3 3RR Tel: (01204) 650878 *Sewing machine repairs*

G G Stevenson Printers, 2 Lower Pleasance, Dundee, DD1 5QU Tel: (01382) 225768 E-mail: stevensonprinters@lineone.net *General & colour printing services*

G & G Textiles Ltd, Unit 3a, St. Georges Houses, Moat Street, Wigston, Leicestershire, LE18 2NH Tel: 0116-257 1170 Fax: 0116-281 0330 *Textiles manufrs*

▶ G Grigg & Sons, Inveresk Mills Industrial Park, Musselburgh, Midlothian, EH21 7UQ Tel: 0131-665 8052 Fax: 0131-665 4737

G H A Group Ltd, 9 Dean St, London, W1D 3RW Tel: (020) 7439 8705 Fax: (020) 7437 5880 E-mail: sales@ghagroup.co.uk *Multimedia equipment hire & presentations*

G H Display, 4-5 Papyrus Road, Peterborough, PE4 5BH Tel: (01733) 570222 Fax: (01733) 320665 E-mail: mail@ghdisplay.co.uk *Exhibition suppliers & services*

G H East & Sons, Little London House, Little London, North Kelsey, Market Rasen, Lincolnshire, LN7 6JP Tel: (01652) 678116 Fax: (01652) 678116 *Agricultural engineering services*

▶ G & H Engineering Services Ltd, 31 Carlyle Avenue, Hillington Industrial Estate, Glasgow, G52 4XX Tel: 0141-810 1160 Fax: 0141-892 0843 E-mail: sales@gh-eng.co.uk *Gasket manufrs*

▶ G H England, Vincients Road, Bumpers Farm, Chippenham, Wiltshire, SN14 6NQ Tel: (01249) 449300 Fax: (01249) 447799 E-mail: sales@englandrefrigeration.co.uk *Refrigeration wholesalers*

G H Enterprises, 10 Coope Road, Bollington, Kerridge, Macclesfield, Cheshire, SK10 5AE Tel: (01625) 574336 Fax: (01625) 573727 E-mail: ghe@breathemail.net *Promotional gifts, diaries & calendars*

G & H Fencing Contractors, 69 Maple Leaf Drive, Birmingham, B37 7JB Tel: 0121-770 0105 Fax: 0121-770 1751 *Fencing contractors*

G.H. Lucas & Co. Ltd, 249 Ordsall Lane, Salford, M5 3WH Tel: 0161-872 7468 Fax: 0161-926 8180 E-mail: info@ghlucas.co.uk *Manufacturers' agents & distributors to the electrical industry*

The G H M Consultancy Group Ltd, Wheathampstead, St. Albans, Hertfordshire, AL4 8BU Tel: (01582) 834233 Fax: (01582) 832176 E-mail: ghm@ghm-group.co.uk *Building & development consultants*

G H Marshall Ltd, 10 Carey St, Reading, RG1 7JT Tel: 0118-959 5522 Fax: 0118-958 5582 E-mail: info@ghmarshall.co.uk *Mechanical services contractors*

▶ G H Martin & Son, Lindleys, Corsham, Wiltshire, SN13 9PG Tel: (01249) 712200

G H Newbery & Son Ltd, 4 Ashton Road, Marsh Barton Industrial Estate, Exeter, EX2 8LN Tel: (01392) 275377 Fax: (01392) 435249 E-mail: ghnewbery@btconnect.com *Non-ferrous scrap metal merchants*

G H Rainey & Sons Ltd, 81 Spencer Street, Birmingham, B18 6DE Tel: 0121-236 8060 *Sports trophy*

G H S Refractories Ltd, Tingley Bar Industrial Estate, Bridge Street, Morley, Leeds, LS27 0HE Tel: 0113-252 7144 Fax: 0113-253 1527 E-mail: info@ghsrefractories.co.uk *Manufacturers and suppliers of refractory products, including firebricks, castables, cements, moudables and ceramic fire products. Suppliers of pottery clay, glazes, tools and equipment for commercial use, educational departments and hobbyists.*

G H Stafford & Son Ltd, Argyle Works, Navigation Street, Walsall, WS2 9LX Tel: (01922) 623993 Fax: (01922) 723403 E-mail: sales@ghstafford.com *Leather goods importers*

G H Tooling Co., Building 107, Prestwick Int Airport, Glasgow Prestwick Intnl Airport, Prestwick, Ayrshire, KA9 2PL Tel: (01292) 474018 Fax: (01292) 671046 E-mail: ghtooling@btinternet.co.uk *Precision engineers*

G H Towers & Son, 528 Aylestone Road, Leicester, LE2 8JB Tel: 0116-283 2033 Fax: 0116-283 2033 *Scrap metal merchants*

G H Tyler, 195 North Street, Romford, RM1 1DT Tel: (01708) 742767 *Jewellers*

G H UK Distribution Ltd, 13 York House, Langston Road, Loughton, Essex, IG10 3TQ Tel: (020) 8502 0100 Fax: (020) 8508 2114 E-mail: ghukdistribution@btconnect.com *Reprographic needs, printer supplies & cartridges & paper products*

G Harraway & Sons, Wrington Vale House, Wrington Road, Congresbury, Bristol, BS49 5AR Tel: (01934) 833000 Fax: (01934) 877330 *Livestock transporters*

G Helson Patterns Ltd, Riverside Works, South Street, Sherborne, Dorset, DT9 3NH Tel: (01935) 813246 Fax: (01935) 813246 *Glass fibre products manufrs*

G Hewitt, Greenway, Stiffkey, Wells-next-the-Sea, Norfolk, NR23 1QF Tel: (01328) 830078 *Boat repairs & manufrs*

G Heyn & Sons Ltd, 1 Corry Place, Belfast, BT3 9AH Tel: (028) 9035 0000 Fax: (028) 9035 0011 E-mail: info@heyn.co.uk *Shipping agents*

G Hodgson Electrical, 37 Back Bolton Street, Ramsbottom, Bury, Lancashire, BL0 9HU Tel: (01706) 821430 *Power tools repairers & suppliers*

G Hooper, 6 Sunnyside Gardens, Kidderminster, Worcestershire, DY11 5JW Tel: (01562) 752290 E-mail: sales@garryhooper.com *Commercial & social photography*

G I A Office Interiors Ltd, Unit 104 Portmanmoor Road Industrial Estate, Cardiff, CF24 5HB Tel: (029) 2044 3850 Fax: (029) 2044 3860 *Office interiors & refurbishments supplier*

▶ G & I Diamond Drilling, Unit 43 Burnhouse Industrial Estate, Whitburn, Bathgate, West Lothian, EH47 0LQ Tel: (01501) 744116 Fax: (01501) 744744 E-mail: sales@gi-diamond-drilling.co.uk

G I Fasteners Ltd, 8 Windmill Road Industrial Estate, Windmill Road, Loughborough, Leicestershire, LE11 1RA Tel: (01509) 260747 Fax: (01509) 217945 *Fastener distributors*

G I G Systems Ltd, Unit 9, 40 Wilton Road, Reading, RG30 2SS Tel: 0118-958 1115 Fax: 0118-958 1117 E-mail: gigssystems@btconnect.com *Electronic sub-contractors*

▶ G I S T Ltd, 22 Lenziemill Road, West Lenziemill Industrial Estate, Cumbernauld, Glasgow, G67 2XN Tel: (01236) 727981

G I Sykes Ltd, The Hayes, Lye, Stourbridge, West Midlands, DY9 8NX Tel: (01384) 891341 Fax: (01384) 894773 *Painting & decorating contractors*

G J Bess & Sons Electrical Contractors, Hayes, Salcombe Hill Road, Sidmouth, Devon, EX10 8JR Tel: (01395) 514662 Fax: (01395) 514662 E-mail: g.bess@virgin.net *Electrical contractors*

G & J Computing, 81 Etherley Lane, Bishop Auckland, County Durham, DL14 7QZ Tel: (01388) 603009 Fax: (01388) 662332 E-mail: sales@gandjcomputing.co.uk *Computer repairers*

G J D Fabrications Ltd, Units 3-4 Holt Street, Newton Heath, Manchester, M40 5AX Tel: 0161-277 9610 Fax: 0161-203 4322 E-mail: doangraham@aol.com *Aluminium fabricators*

▶ G J ELECTRICAL, 65 FAWNBRAKE AVENUE, HERNE HILL, LONDON, SE24 0BE Tel: 020 73264668 E-mail: GJONAS4@HOTMAIL.COM *ELECTRIACAL CONTRACTORS*ELECTRICAL TESTING*COMMISSIONING OF ELECTRICAL INSTALLATIONS.*

G J F Fabrications Ltd, The Chase Link, Lichfield Road, Brownhills, Walsall, WS8 6LA Tel: (01543) 360777 Fax: (01543) 360977 E-mail: gjf@btconnect.com *Skip manufrs*

▶ G J Finch Ltd, 45 St Gabriels Avenue, Plymouth, PL3 4JQ Tel: (01752) 266093 Fax: (01752) 252015

G J Garner & Son, 6a Hawkes Farm, Dores Lane, Braishfield, Romsey, Hampshire, SO51 0QJ Tel: (01794) 368151 Fax: (01794) 368151 E-mail: gjgwheelwrights@aol.com *Wheelwrights*

G & J Greenall, Loushers Lane, Causeway Distillery, Warrington, WA4 6RY Tel: (01925) 650111 Fax: (01925) 414445 E-mail: sales@gjgreenall.com *Distillers*

G & J Hall Ltd, Burgess Road, Sheffield, S9 3WD Tel: 0114-244 0562 Fax: 0114-244 9256 E-mail: sales@gjhall.co.uk *Cutting tool manufrs*

G J Johnson & Sons Ltd, 7 Trinity Court, Brunel Road, Totton, Southampton, SO40 3WX Tel: (023) 8066 9666 Fax: (023) 8066 9606 E-mail: sales@johnsonvalves.com Sales Contact: P. Johnson *Valve, water meter, thermometer, pneumatic control & pressure gauge distributors.Johnson, johnsonvalves, valve, valves, gate, globe, ball, butterfly, check, cast, iron, bronze, steel, valvestock, kent, elster, bailey, birkett, wade, safety, relief, spring, springs, pressure, reducing, meter, meters, PSM, Helix, marine, oil, air, water, steam, contents.*

G J L Electrical, 43 New North Road, Reigate, Surrey, RH2 8LZ Tel: (01737) 246281 *Electrical consultants*

G J Orford & Partners, Hill Farm, Lopham Road, Fersfield, Diss, Norfolk, IP22 2BJ Tel: (01379) 687326 Fax: (01379) 688077 E-mail: gjorfordpartners@btconnect.com *Agricultural services*

G & J Peck Ltd, Main Street, Mareham-le-Fen, Boston, Lincolnshire, PE22 7QJ Tel: (01507) 568484 Fax: (01507) 568585 *Agricultural engineers*

G & J Ping Ltd, 63 Coates Road, Eastrea, Whittlesey, Peterborough, PE7 2BA Tel: (01733) 203383 Fax: (01733) 351204 *Road transport contractors & storage*

G & J Reeves, Coventry Bridge Yard, Tomlow Road, Stockton, Southam, Warwickshire, CV47 8HX Tel: (01926) 815581 Fax: (01926) 811675 E-mail: julie@reevesboatsfsnet.co.uk *Boat builders*

G & J Sales Ltd, G J Automatics, Hounds Road, Chipping Sodbury, Bristol, BS37 6EE Tel: (01454) 321207 Fax: (01454) 321207 E-mail: gandjsales@btconnect.com *Amusement machines equipment & driving simulator sales & hire*

G Jones, Mayville, Pulford Lane, Dodleston, Chester, CH4 9NN Tel: (01244) 660691 Fax: (01244) 660691 *Agricultural & motor engineers*

▶ G K A, Unit 1 Bell Business Park, Smeaton Close, Aylesbury, Buckinghamshire, HP19 8JR Tel: (01296) 678300 Fax: (01296) 678301 E-mail: enquiries@gka.co.uk *GKA are public affairs and planning consultants to the property development sector and have a 17-year track record of success in delivering difficult development schemes for our clients.*

G K Beaulah & Co. Ltd, 23 Park Street, Hull, HU2 8RU Tel: (01482) 223521 Fax: (01482) 216328 E-mail: info@beaulah.co.uk *Heraldic shield & badge manufrs*

▶ G K D Building Services Ltd, 305 Town St, Bramley, Leeds, LS13 3JT Tel: 0113-255 6550

▶ G K D Litho Ltd, Origination House, 15 Strawberry Street, Hull, HU9 1EN Tel: (01482) 325313

G K E Sampson & Sons, 22 Paddock Road, Newbury, Berkshire, RG14 7DG Tel: (01635) 43204 *Farriers & blacksmiths*

G K Fashions, Bingley Street, Wolverhampton, WV3 0HS Tel: (01902) 426255 Fax: (01902) 426281 *Clothing manufrs*

G & K Groundworks, 30 Manor Trading Estate, Brunel Road, Benfleet, Essex, SS7 4PS Tel: (01268) 752298 Fax: (01268) 795529 *Civil engineers*

G K Littlemore Electrical Ltd, Contact House, Ditton Road, Widnes, Cheshire, WA8 0TH Tel: 0151-420 8022 Fax: 0151-420 4260 E-mail: gklittlemore@btconnect.com *Electrical contractors*

G K M (Aerospace) Ltd, Unit 2 Wollaston Way, Burnt Mills Industrial Estate, Basildon, Essex, SS13 1DJ Tel: (01268) 727278 Fax: (01268) 725772 E-mail: gkm@gkm-aero.demon.co.uk *Aircraft component manufrs*

G K M Technical Services, 14 Whessoe Road, Darlington, County Durham, DL3 0QP Tel: (01325) 361670 Fax: (01325) 361670 E-mail: sales@gkm.co.uk *Computer manufacturers, maintenance & repair*

G K Marketing Services Ltd, Unit 22 Crossfield Industrial Estate, Crossfield Road, Lichfield, Staffordshire, WS13 6RJ Tel: (01543) 414130 Fax: (01543) 250660 E-mail: sales@gkmktg.com Principal Export Areas: Worldwide *Heat applied transfer suppliers*

G K N Ltd, Sheepbridge Works, Sheepbridge Lane, Chesterfield, Derbyshire, S41 9QD Tel: (01246) 260026 Fax: (01246) 260022 *Centrifugal casting & cylinder liner manufrs*

▶ G K N P.L.C., 50 Pall Mall, London, SW1Y 5JH Tel: (020) 7930 2424 Fax: (020) 7463 2404 *Automotive & aerospace*

G K N Aerospace Services, Ferry Road, East Cowes, Isle of Wight, PO32 6RA Tel: (01983) 294101 Fax: (01983) 291006 E-mail: info@gknwae.com *Aerospace structures*

G K N Aerospace Transparancy Systems Ltd, Eckersall Road, Birmingham, B38 8SR Tel: 0121-606 4100 Fax: 0121-458 6880 *Glass manufacturers & aircraft bullet resistant*

G K N AutoStructures Ltd, Hadley, Castleworks, Telford, Shropshire, TF1 6TE Tel: (01952) 244321 *Holding company*

G K N Driveline Ltd, Higher Woodcroft, Leek, Staffordshire, ST13 5QF Tel: (01538) 372444 Fax: (01538) 371265 E-mail: sales@gkndrlveline.co.uk *Hydraulic power transmission equipment manufrs*

G K N Export Services Ltd, PO Box 55, Redditch, Worcestershire, B98 0TL Tel: (01527) 517715 Fax: (01527) 517700 E-mail: information@gkn.com *Automotive component manufrs*

G K N Freight Services Ltd, Equity House, 128-136 High St, Edgware, Middlesex, HA8 7EL Tel: (020) 8905 6688 Fax: (020) 8905 6951 E-mail: info.fsl@gkndriveline.com *Freight forwarders*

G K N Hardy Spicer Ltd, Chester Road, Erdington, Birmingham, B24 0RB Tel: 0121-377 7000 Fax: 0121-377 7012 *Constant velocity joint manufrs*

G K N Hardy Spicer Ltd-Birfield Extrusions, Station Works, Old Walsall Rd, Great Barr, Birmingham, B42 1DZ Tel: 0121-623 8818 Fax: 0121-358 4033 *Cold & warm steel forgings* Also at: Branches throughout the U.K.

G K Pest Control, Stone Cottage, Ridgeway Road, Dorking, Surrey, RH4 3EY Tel: (01306) 882708 Fax: (01306) 500876 *Pest control services*

G K Precision 96, 4 Sidings Road, Lowmoor Industrial Estate, Kirkby-in-Ashfield, Nottingham, NG17 7JZ Tel: (01623) 721919 Fax: (01623) 751616 *Injection moulding, spark & wire erosion machining services*

G K S Computers Ltd, One Oclock Lane, Burgess Hill, West Sussex, RH15 0EX Tel: (01444) 250404 Fax: (01444) 250405 E-mail: sales@gkscomputers.co.uk *Computer consultants*

G K Salter & Associates, Azalea Drive, Swanley, Kent, BR8 8HX Tel: (01322) 668933 Fax: (01322) 666019 E-mail: post@gksa.ltd.uk *Building services & design consultants providing solutions for Mechanical, Electrical & Public Health designs. Sustainable and environmentally aware designs coupled with an on-budget and on-time philosophy mean we are the company to help your project erach its sustainable targets. Based in both London & Bristol* Also at: Cardiff

G K & Sons Ltd, 235-243 Sussex Way, London, N19 4JD Tel: (020) 7281 3282 Fax: (020) 7272 8992 *Dress trimming manufrs*

G K Switchgear Ltd, 4 Colts Holm Road, Old Wolverton, Milton Keynes, MK12 5QD Tel: (01908) 225777 Fax: (01908) 225818 E-mail: rjbgks@aol.com *Specialised switchgear manufrs*

G K Systems, Kilbegs Business Park, Kilbegs Road, Antrim, BT41 4NN Tel: (028) 9446 5360 Fax: (028) 9446 0754 E-mail: sales@gksystems.co.uk *Thermal brake specialists*

▶ G & K Transport, UNIT 27, HEMMING ROAD, WASHFORD IND EST, REDDITCH, WORCESTERSHIRE, B98 0DH Tel: 01527 516686 Fax: 01527 516686 E-mail: stevenkirton@blueyonder.co.uk *light transport service *uk collection and delivery*24 hour call out*35 cwt vans*fully insured*

▶ G K Transport Ltd, Patrick Gregory Road, Wolverhampton, WV11 3DU Tel: (01902) 305047 Fax: (01902) 305048

G K W Ltd, Merton Bank Road, St. Helens, Merseyside, WA9 1HP Tel: (01744) 762330 Fax: (01744) 754309 E-mail: kevin.jones@gordonkitto.co.uk *Fabrication & site maintenance (power station) services*

G.L.A.Refrigeration Services Ltd, No 1 Partridge Court, 61 Price Street, Birmingham, B4 6JZ Tel: 0121-359 6731 Fax: 0121-333 4213 *Refrigeration & air conditioning*

G L Calvert, Phoenix Works, Willows Lane, Accrington, Lancashire, BB5 0RT Tel: (01254) 235184 Fax: (01254) 235184 *Butcher sundries*

▶ G & L Coatings, 8 Wallace Way, Hitchin, Hertfordshire, SG4 0SE Tel: (01462) 436668 Fax: (01462) 438982 E-mail: george.cooney@talk21.com *Powder coating services*

G L Events Alfred Bull, 2c Cathedral Hill Industrial Estate, Guildford, Surrey, GU2 7YB Tel: (01483) 575492 Fax: (01483) 573448 E-mail: info@alfredbullmarquees.co.uk *Marquee hire*

G L Events Snowdens, Second Drove, Eastern Industry, Fengate, Peterborough, PE1 5XA Tel: (01733) 344110 Fax: (01733) 314985 E-mail: info@snowdens.co.uk *Marquee hire & rental*

G L Flow Ltd, Hanson Park, Hanson Close, Middleton, Manchester, M24 2QZ Tel: 0161-643 9833 Fax: 0161-643 9835 E-mail: info@glflow.co.uk *Flow meter manufrs*

▶ G & L Home Improvements, 33 Butterside Road, Kingsnorth, Ashford, Kent, TN23 3PD Tel: (01233) 501815 E-mail: garry.laker@ntlworld.com *bathroom and kitchen specialist installers,plumbing,tiling*

G L J Badges, Unit 10 Park Trading Estate, Park Road, Hockley, Birmingham, B18 5HB Tel: 0121-554 9869 Fax: 0121-523 9395 E-mail: sales@gljbadges.co.uk *Metal badge & presswork manufrs*

G L Jones Playgrounds Ltd, 1 Station Road, Bethesda, Bangor, Gwynedd, LL57 3NE Tel: (01248) 600372 Fax: (01248) 602085 E-mail: info@gljones-playgrounds.co.uk *Playground equipment for all children including special needs (DDA) manufrs*

▶ G L Langton Ltd, Unit 2A, Station Way, Leeds, LS12 3HQ Tel: 0113-231 9808

G L M & I S I International Ltd, 143 Woburn Tower, Broomcroft Avenue, Northolt, Middlesex, UB5 6HU Tel: (07956) 877690 Fax: (020) 8845 1010 E-mail: hawigeorge@hotmail.com *Import & export filter presses, sanitary ware*

▶ G L Quine Ltd, Great North Road, South Milford, Leeds, LS25 5LH Tel: (01977) 681999 Fax: (01977) 681888

G L R Processing Co, 11 Tiber Way, Glebe Farm Industrial Estate, Rugby, Warwickshire, CV21 1ED Tel: (01788) 541390 Fax: (01788) 546103 E-mail: g.l.r@btconnect.com *Printed circuit manufrs*

▶ G L Sports, 47 Rydal Crescent, Manchester, M28 7JD Tel: 0161-790 7444 Fax: 0161-790 7444

▶ G L W Engineering & Construction, Unit 3 Wisbech Business Centre, Oldfield Lane, Friday Bridge, Wisbech, Cambridgeshire, PE14 0NX Tel: (01945) 464637 Fax: (07000) 785497 E-mail: geoff@glwengineering.co.uk *Metal fabricators*

G Leddington Electrical Ltd, 15 Church Parade, Telford, Shropshire, TF2 6EX Tel: (01952) 615958 Fax: (01952) 620473 E-mail: info@leddingtons.co.uk *Electrical engineers & contractors*

G Lloyd Evans & Sons, Bryn Hen, Groesffordd Marli, Abergele, Clwyd, LL22 9ED Tel: (01745) 583534 *Farming & milk production*

▶ G Lund Ltd, The Ashes, Cliburn, Penrith, Cumbria, CA10 3AL Tel: (01931) 714515 Fax: (01931) 714545

▶ G M A Construction, The Chalet Turves Farm, Bilsington Road, Ruckinge, Ashford, Kent, TN26 2PB Tel: (01233) 733345 Fax: (01233) 733345

G M A Garnet UK Ltd, PO Box 9, Middlewich, Cheshire, CW10 9FD Tel: (01606) 836233 Fax: (01606) 836610 E-mail: sales@gmagarnet.co.uk *Sandblasting abrasives*

G & M B Manning Ltd, Hog Lane, Ashley Green, Chesham, Buckinghamshire, HP5 3PS Tel: (01442) 866264 Fax: (01442) 877105 *Fencing suppliers*

G M Business Print & Systems Ltd, Cornhill, Liverpool, L1 8DZ Tel: 0151-709 0676 Fax: 0151-709 0678 E-mail: sales@gmbusinessprint.co.uk *General, commercial & jobbing printers*

G M C (Concrete) Ltd, Kelston Farm, Gronant Road, Gwespyr, Holywell, Flintshire, CH8 9LU Tel: (01745) 853827 *Ready mixed concrete suppliers*

G M C Fire & Security-Protection, Service, 14 Railway St, Malton, North Yorkshire, YO17 7NR Tel: (01653) 697917 Fax: (01653) 697836 *Fire & security installers*

G M C Instrumentation (UK) Ltd, Priest House, Priest Street, Cradley Heath, West Midlands, B64 6JN Tel: (01384) 638822 Fax: (01384) 639168 E-mail: sales@gmciuk.com *Process & control instrumentation*

G M Ceramic Mould Making Services, 108 Trentham Road, Dresden, Stoke-on-Trent, ST3 4ED Tel: (01782) 324359 *Mould making services*

G M Computer Systems, Ferguson House, 5 Queen Street, Coleraine, County Londonderry, BT52 1BG Tel: (028) 7032 1888 Fax: (028) 7032 1999 *Computer resellers*

G M Conversions, 69 Staplands Road, Broadgreen, Liverpool, L14 3LJ Tel: (07740) 426233 E-mail: philma76@hotmail.com *Specialists in loft & garages conversions & joinery*

G M D Mouldings Ltd, Dec House, 143-145 Cardiff Road, Reading, RG1 8JF Tel: 0118-957 2188 Fax: 0118-957 1218 E-mail: martin@mclayton.fsbusiness.co.uk *Manufacturers of injection mouldings (plastic), plastic mouldings & injection mouldings (subassembly). Also plastic mouldings (technical/ industrial) custom moulders*

▶ G M Design, Nightingale House, 8 Taylor Street, Liverpool, L5 5AD Tel: 0151-207 5595 Fax: 0151- 207 5601 E-mail: mattjack@agjengineering.co.uk *Cad design services, mechanical handling & general engineering*

G M Developments, 1-3 Riverside Road, London, SW17 0BA Tel: (020) 8879 7878 Fax: (020) 8879 7997 E-mail: info@gmdevelopments.co.uk *Construction and refurbishment of quality properties. Extensions, basement excavation, loft extensions.*"When only the best is good enough"*

▶ G & M Distribution, 2 Block 9, Chapelhall Industrial Estate, Chapelhall, Airdrie, Lanarkshire, ML6 8QH Tel: (01236) 755447 Fax: (01236) 766306

▶ G & M Distribution, Dalcross Industrial Estate, Inverness, IV2 7XB Tel: (01667) 462466 Fax: (01667) 461161

G M E Motor Engineers (Coventry) Ltd, Boston Place, Foleshill, Coventry, CV6 5NN Tel: (024) 7666 4911 Fax: (024) 7666 3020 E-mail: sales@gmesprings.co.uk *Roadsprings & component wholesalers* Also at: Birmingham, Bradford, Coatbridge, Manchester & Sheffield

G M Electronics, 7 Cyprus Avenue, Belfast, BT5 5NT Tel: (028) 9067 1876 Fax: (07092) 877376 E-mail: gme@gmelectronics.fsnet.co.uk *Electronic services*

G M Engineering Ltd, 12 Greenbank Place, East Tullos Industrial Estate, Aberdeen, AB12 3BT Tel: (01224) 895431 Fax: (01224) 871027 E-mail: info@gm-engineering.com Principal Export Areas: Worldwide *Manufacturers of chemical injection pumps*

G & M Engineering, The Stores, Ffostrasol, Llandysul, Dyfed, SA44 4TE Tel: (01239) 851682 Fax: (01239) 851682 *Metal fabricators*

G M Equipment, 106 Morgans Hill Road, Cookstown, County Tyrone, BT80 8BW Tel: (028) 8676 3810 Fax: (028) 8675 8558 *Welding equipment distributors*

G & M Floorlayers Derby Ltd, Sandown Road, Derby, DE24 8SR Tel: (01332) 344282 Fax: (01332) 298491 *General flooring & tiling contractors*

▶ G & M Hats, 119 Pall Mall, Leigh-on-Sea, Essex, SS9 1RF Tel: (01702) 474665 Fax: (01702) 474665 *Manufacturer of hats*

G M I Construction Group plc, Middleton House, Westland Road, Leeds, LS11 5UH Tel: 0113-276 0505 Fax: 0113-276 0180 E-mail: build@gmicon.co.uk *Design & traditional contractors*

G & M Industrial Services Ltd, Shaw Road, Dudley, West Midlands, DY2 8TP Tel: (01384) 236400 Fax: (01384) 235454 E-mail: enquiries@gmskips.com *Skip contractors scrap metal merchants*

G M Instrumentation, 102 Sale Lane, Tyldesley, Manchester, M29 8PZ Tel: 0161-703 9100 Fax: 0161-703 9133 E-mail: gmimanchester@aol.com *Instrumentation reseller*

G M Instruments Ltd, 6 Ashgrove Workshops, Kilwinning, Ayrshire, KA13 6PU Tel: (01294) 554664 Fax: (01294) 551154 E-mail: gminstruments@aol.com *Medical electronics*

G & M Jewellery, 123 High Street, Ryde, Isle of Wight, PO33 2SU Tel: (01983) 611232 Fax: (01983) 611232 E-mail: sales@gmjewellery.co.uk *Jewellery manufrs*

G M K Graphics, 57 Cromwell Road, Belfast, BT7 1JY Tel: (028) 9032 7905 Fax: (028) 9043 8893 E-mail: gmk.graphics@dnet.co.uk *Printing services*

▶ G M Lawrence Electrical Ltd, 43a Abbey Road, Far Cotton, Northampton, NN4 8EY Tel: (01604) 766511

▶ G M Machinery, 13 Den Hill Drive, Springhead, Oldham, OL4 4NR Tel: 0161-633 8880 Fax: 0161-633 7323 E-mail: info@gmmachinery.com *Machinery dealers & distributors*

▶ G M Mining Ltd, Drumshangie, Greengairs, Airdrie, Lanarkshire, ML6 7TY Tel: (01236) 830990

G M Mouldings, 175A Brigstock Road, Thornton Heath, Surrey, CR7 7JP Tel: (020) 8665 5045 Fax: (020) 8665 5045 *Injection moulders*

G M P (Banbury) Ltd, Unit 2, Power Park, Station Approach, Banbury, Oxfordshire, OX16 5AB Tel: (01295) 275300 Fax: (01295) 275400 E-mail: gmpb@globalnet.co.uk *Stainless steel fabricators*

G M Panels, Units 1 & 2, Milvale Street, Stoke-on-Trent, ST6 3NT Tel: (01782) 834600 Fax: (01782) 834602 E-mail: enquiries@gmpanels.co.uk *Commercial vehicle panel manufrs*

G M Pest Control, 290 Rullion Road, Penicuik, Midlothian, EH26 9JN Tel: (01968) 673904 Fax: (01968) 678769 *Pest control services*

▶ G & M Proctor Ltd, 8 Arran Place, North Muirton Industrial Estate, Perth, PH1 3RN Tel: (01738) 636145 Fax: (01738) 643466 E-mail: enquiries@gandmproctor.com *Manufacturers of culture media*

G & M Radiator, 23 Fordneuk Street, Glasgow, G40 2TA Tel: 0141-550 5800 Fax: 0141-550 5858 E-mail: sales@gm-radiator.com *Motor radiator manufrs*

G M S Marketing Ltd, 44 Albert Street, Newark, Nottinghamshire, NG24 4BQ Tel: (01636) 702961 Fax: (01636) 674876 *Catering license suppliers*

G M S Technologies, Unit 22, Brambles Enterprise Centre, Waterberry Drive, Waterlooville, Hampshire, PO7 7TH Tel: (023) 9223 1880 Fax: (023) 9223 1990 *Computer dealers*

G M T C Tools Equipment Ltd, Berrington Road, Leamington Spa, Warwickshire, CV31 1NB Tel: (01926) 334655 Fax: (01926) 311811 *Tool manufrs*

▶ G M Timber Systems, Haugh of Sluie, Banchory, Kincardineshire, AB31 4BA Tel: (01339) 884411 Fax: (01339) 884422 E-mail: info@gmtimbersystems.fsbusiness.co.uk

G & M Tools, Mill Lane, Ashington, Pulborough, West Sussex, RH20 3BX Tel: (01903) 892510 Fax: (01903) 892221 E-mail: sales@gandmtools.co.uk *Engineering tool sales*

G M Trebble Ltd, Unit 17 Perkins Way, Mansfield Road, Derby, DE21 4AW Tel: (01332) 294366 Fax: (01332) 295957 *Pump distributors*

G M Treble Ltd, New Street, Parkfields, Wolverhampton, WV4 6AN Tel: (01902) 333111 Fax: (01902) 340941 E-mail: sales@gmtreble.co.uk *Pump distributors & stockists*

G & M Venditti Compressors Ltd, Unit 1 Park Road, Bury, Lancashire, BL9 5BQ Tel: 0161-764 5667 Fax: 0161-764 1316 *Air compressor distributors & agents*

▶ G McHardy & Son, 26 High Street, Oban, Argyll, PA34 4BG Tel: (01631) 565307

G Mcveigh & Co. Ltd, Timothys Bridge Road, Stratford-upon-Avon, Warwickshire, CV37 9NQ Tel: (01789) 205803 Fax: (01789) 205828 *Civil engineering contractors*

G Middleton Ltd, Crosscroft Industrial Estate, Appleby-in-Westmorland, Cumbria, CA16 6HX Tel: (01768) 352067 Fax: (01768) 353228

G Modiano, 55 Old Broad Street, London, EC2M 1RX Tel: (020) 7012 0000 Fax: (020) 7374 6468 E-mail: wool@gmodiano.com *Wool merchants* Also at: Bradford

G Mullen Steelwork Ltd, 114 Milton Road, Gravesend, Kent, DA12 2PG Tel: (01474) 325664 Fax: (01474) 328917 E-mail: sales@gmullensteelworks.fsnet.co.uk *Steel fabricators*

G Music & Sons Ltd, 88-90 Hatton Garden, London, EC1N 8PN Tel: (020) 7404 4008 Fax: (020) 7831 8346 E-mail: g.m.s.ltd@btinternet.com *Jewellery manufrs*

G & N, 14 East Street, Southampton, SO14 3HG Tel: (023) 8063 4680 *Health food suppliers*

G N C Livewell, 79 Nicholsons Walk, Maidenhead, Berkshire, SL6 1LJ Tel: (01628) 783594 *Health foods retailers*

▶ G N Clothing Ltd, 27, Eldon Street, Walsall, WS1 2JP Tel: (01922) 644748 Fax: (01922) 720702

G N G Foam Converters Lancs Ltd, Todmorden Road, Littleborough, Lancashire, OL15 9EG Tel: (01706) 372222 Fax: (01706) 377991 E-mail: info@gngfoam.com *Foam converters*

G N J Engineering Ltd, Meeting Lane, Brierley Hill, West Midlands, DY5 3LB Tel: (01384) 480818 Fax: (01384) 78176 E-mail: info@gnjengineering.co.uk *Stainless & mild steel fabricators*

G N N International Ltd, Unit 70, Woolsbridge Industrial Estate, Three Legged Cross, Wimborne, Dorset, BH21 6SU Tel: (01202) 823012 Fax: (01202) 821754 E-mail: info@contractpackers.net *Contract packaging services*

G & N Shotblasting Ltd, Brindley Close, Drayton Fields Industrial Estate, Daventry, Northamptonshire, NN11 8RP Tel: (01327) 872569 Fax: (01327) 300878 E-mail: sales@shotblast.co.uk *Shot blasting & blast cleaning services*

▶ G N Solutions, 28 Elm Row, Edinburgh, EH7 4RR Tel: 0131-663 4684 Fax: 0131-663 4684 E-mail: gnsolution1@hotmail.com *Lubricant suppliers.cleaning chemicals*

G N Systems, Undershore Works, Brookside Road, Bolton, BL2 2SE Tel: (01204) 361533 Fax: (01204) 382879 E-mail: gnsystems@provider.co.uk *Electrical & electronic assembly services*

G N T Ltd, Waterside Estate, Cradley Road, Dudley, West Midlands, DY2 9RG Tel: (01384) 236007 Fax: (01384) 236929 E-mail: info@gnt.co.uk *Communication equipment manufrs*

G N X Enterprises Ltd, 55 Jameson Road, Bexhill-on-Sea, East Sussex, TN40 1EL Tel: (01424) 220986 Fax: (01424) 221343 *Laundry equipment installers*

G O C Engineering Services, Buckingham Cottage, Crow Road, Fintry, Glasgow, G63 0XJ Tel: (01360) 860478 Fax: (01360) 860478 E-mail: jchesney@goceng.co.uk *Mechanical & electrical engineers services*

G & O D Thomas & Sons, Castle Road, Richards Castle, Ludlow, Shropshire, SY8 4EW Tel: (01584) 831244 Fax: (01584) 831382 *Agricultural contractors & farmers*

▶ G O International, 15 The Io Centre Whittle Way, Arlington Business Park, Stevenage, Hertfordshire, SG1 2BD Tel: (01438) 745746 Fax: (01438) 745747

continued

E-mail: info@gointernational.co.uk *Importers & wholesalers of party wear & equipment*

▶ G O S S Consultants Ltd, Square Sail House, Charlestown Road, St. Austell, Cornwall, PL25 3NJ Tel: (01726) 71128 Fax: (01726) 71129 E-mail: info@goss-ltd.co.uk *G.O.S.S. Consultants are specialists in the provision of high quality and experienced personnel to the Offshore and Onshore exploration, telecommunication and marine science industries.**

G & O Springs Ltd, Broad Ground Road, Lakeside, Redditch, Worcestershire, B98 8YP Tel: (01527) 523764 Fax: (01527) 527920 E-mail: steve@g-o-springs.com Purchasing Contact: R.F. Boyd Sales Contact: S. Boyd Principal Export Areas: Worldwide *Working across Europe, G & O Springs manufacture springs, including tension compression, clock, conical, extension, double torsion, torsion, flat, from all steels, including carbon steel, spring steel, stainless steel, beryllium copper, nickel alloy, titanium. Springs, to specification, for, aircraft components, pressings for the aerospace industry, to specification, wire formed components, pressformed, staples, circlips, internal, external, washers, spring design. Approval held AS9100:B.*

G P Aerials (1955) Ltd, 7 Maida Vale Business Centre, Maida Vale Road, Cheltenham, Gloucestershire, GL53 7ER Tel: (01242) 515216 Fax: (01242) 519125 E-mail: gp.aerials@virgin.net *TV aerial & satellite installation & supply services*

G P Batteries UK Ltd, Monument View, Chelston Business Park, Wellington, Somerset, TA21 9ND Tel: (01823) 660044 Fax: (01823) 665595 E-mail: sales@gpbatteries.co.uk *Battery suppliers & manufrs*

G P C Industries Ltd, Market St, Spilsby, Lincolnshire, PE23 5JT Tel: (01790) 753835 Fax: (01790) 752109 E-mail: sales@gpcind.co.uk *Pallet truck & trolley manufrs*

G P C International, 40 Long Acre, London, WC2E 9LG Tel: (020) 7395 7171 Fax: (020) 7395 7181 E-mail: info@gpcinternational.com *Political consultants*

G P Compressed Air Services, Unit 2, Bodmin Road, Wyken, Coventry, CV2 5DB Tel: (024) 7662 2200 Fax: (024) 7662 2300 E-mail: info@gpair.co.uk *Air compressor sales, service & installation*

G P Electronics, Pottery Road, Bovey Tracey, Newton Abbot, Devon, TQ13 9DS Tel: (01626) 832670 Fax: (01626) 832670 *Hydroelectric systems*

G P Fabrications Ltd, 10-13 Ashmount Industrial Park, Ford Street, Kinsley, Pontefract, West Yorkshire, WF9 5EE Tel: (01977) 612226 Fax: (01977) 617220 E-mail: gary.gpfabs@sales.com *Light steel fabricators*

G & P Furniture Ltd, Tofts Farm Industrial Estate East, Brenda Road, Hartlepool, Cleveland, TS25 2BS Tel: (01429) 280200 Fax: (01429) 280010 E-mail: sales@gandpfurniture.com *Furniture manufrs*

▶ G P Hire Ltd, The Pleasance, Lanark, ML11 9TG Tel: (01555) 663234 Fax: (01555) 666969 E-mail: info@gpplantscape.com

G P & J Baker, Lancaster House, Lancaster Road, Cressex Business Park, High Wycombe, Buckinghamshire, HP12 3PY Tel: (01494) 686800 Fax: (01494) 474771

▶ G P (M & E) Services Ltd, 1-3 Market Square, Bishop's Stortford, Hertfordshire, CM23 3UP Tel: (01279) 466738

G P M Engineering Systems Ltd, 1585 Bristol Road South, Rednal, Birmingham, B45 9UA Tel: 0121-457 7132 Fax: 0121-457 9035 E-mail: scrow@gpmengineering.com *Mechanical handling equipment*

G P Plastic Materials Ltd, 3 Bathville Business Centre, Armadale Industrial Estate, Armadale, Bathgate, West Lothian, EH48 2ND Tel: (01501) 734483 Fax: (01501) 734484 *Plastic materials recyclers & distributors*

G P Plastics Ltd, 156 Bordesley Middleway, Camp Hill, Birmingham, B11 1BN Tel: 0121-773 1777 Fax: 0121-772 6856 E-mail: admin@gpplastics.co.uk *Retailers of plastics*

G & P Precision Engineers Nottingham Ltd, 38 Hermitage Way, Mansfield, Nottinghamshire, NG18 5ES Tel: (01623) 653576 Fax: (01623) 420526 E-mail: sales@gprecision.co.uk *Sub-contract precision engineers*

G P Print, G P Print Edgerley Business, Challenger Way, Peterborough, PE1 5EX Tel: (01733) 340622 Fax: (08719) 940780 E-mail: info@gpprint.co.uk *Printing stationary, letterheads, posters, business cards*

▶ G P Quoreenton, 3 Barton Industrial Estate, Faldo Road, Barton-le-Clay, Bedford, MK45 4RP Tel: (01582) 882561 Fax: (01582) 883224 E-mail: grahamq@ukonline.co.uk *Manufacturing ventilations*

▶ G P R Groundworks, 3A Baird Road, Kirkton Campus, Livingston, West Lothian, EH54 7AZ Tel: (01506) 464362

▶ G P S, 7 Cardeston Close, Sutton Weaver, Runcorn, Cheshire, WA7 3LH Tel: (01928) 715055 Fax: (01928) 739490 E-mail: gavin@gps1.co.uk *Photocopiers sales, service*

G P S Colour Graphics Ltd, Alexander Road, Belfast, BT6 9HP Tel: (028) 9070 2020 Fax: (028) 9079 8463 E-mail: sales@gpscolour.co.uk *Colour printers*

G P S Document Management, Park House, 15-19 Greenhill Crescent, Watford, WD18 8PH Tel: (01923) 241272 Fax: (01923) 244475 E-mail: info@gpsdm.co.uk *Print management & business printing suppliers*

▶ G P S Installations, Morgan Business Centre, Mylord CR, Camperdown Industrial Estate, Newcastle upon Tyne, NE12 5UJ Tel: 0191-216 1200 Fax: 0191-216 1200 E-mail: sales@gpsinstallations.co.uk *Suppliers & installers of audio/visual equipment & security systems for industry, retail & commerce. Public Address systems, induction loop, projectors, plasma screens*

Company Information

▶ G P S Window Films, 32 Springside Rise, Golcar, Huddersfield, HD7 4RW Tel: (01484) 657735 Fax: (01484) 657735 E-mail: sales@gpswindowfilms.co.uk *safety films, solar film, manifestation, graphics, Regulation 13, window tints*

▶ G P Services Ltd, Seafire Works, Henstridge Industrial Estate, Henstridge, Templecombe, Somerset, BA8 0TN Tel: (01963) 363866

G & P Trading Co. Ltd, 20 Binns Way, Binns Road Industrial Estate, Liverpool, L13 1EF Tel: 0151-259 6604 Fax: 0151-259 0374 *Dry food distributor*

▶ G P Turner Builders Ltd, 4 Central Place, Haltwhistle, Northumberland, NE49 0DF Tel: (01434) 321000

G P W Consultancy, 3 Redcourt, Woking, Surrey, GU22 8RA Tel: (01932) 355770 Fax: (01932) 336454 E-mail: information@gpw.co.uk *IT consultants*

G P Watson Ltd, Unit 5 Lancaster Port, Corintation Road, High Wycombe, Buckinghamshire, HP12 3TD Tel: (01494) 446515 Fax: (01494) 446615 E-mail: sales@gpwatson.co.uk *Building services engineers*

G Pack Manufacturing Ltd, 1 The Green, Glossop, Derbyshire, SK13 6LT Tel: (01457) 858535 *Injection mouldings*

G Parker Engineering Ltd, Grange Lane, Accrington, Lancashire, BB5 1HX Tel: (01254) 384235 Fax: (01254) 872584 E-mail: info@parkereng.com *Pattern makers & toolmakers*

▶ G Potter Joinery Services, 391 Ashby Road, Coalville, Leicestershire, LE67 3LJ Tel: 01530 832204 Fax: 01530 832204 E-mail: v.thornley@btopenworld.com *Carpenter & Joiner for large and small jobs.*Fitted kitchens,wardrobes,shopfitting,*fitting floors, skirting boards, doors, gates etc etc*

G Q Parachutes Ltd, Isfryn Industrial Estate, Blackmill, Bridgend, Mid Glamorgan, CF35 6EQ Tel: (01656) 840300 Fax: (01656) 840396 Principal Export Areas: Worldwide *Parachute designers & manufrs*

▶ G R Bayley Electrical Contractors Ltd, 24 Brown Street, Macclesfield, Cheshire, SK11 6SA Tel: (01625) 423088 Fax: (01625) 669879

G R Bodycote Ltd, Orchard Works, Holliers Walk, Hinckley, Leicestershire, LE10 1QR Tel: (01455) 636271 Fax: (01455) 890025 *Thermal clothing (underwear) manufrs*

▶ G R Bradshaw & Co., 10a High Street, Neston, CH64 9TY Tel: 0151-336 1121 Fax: 0151-353 8385

G R C Electronics Systems Ltd, 157-159 West Street, Bedminster, Bristol, BS3 3PN Tel: 0117-963 9830 Fax: 0117-963 9567 E-mail: sales@grcelex.demon.co.uk *Electronic systems designers & manufrs*

G R C Engraving Ltd, 14 Darley Road, Ferndown, Dorset, BH22 8QX Tel: (01202) 861297 Fax: (01202) 861297 *Industrial engravers*

G R C Extraction Systems, Unit 13 Forbes Court, Billington Road, Burnley, Lancashire, BB11 5UB Tel: (01282) 421130 Fax: (01282) 425971 E-mail: grceng@aol.com *Installation engineers, machining & general fabrication services*

G R Carr Essex Ltd, Archers Fields, Burnt Mills Industrial Estate, Basildon, Essex, SS13 1DN Tel: (01268) 522226 Fax: (01268) 522126 E-mail: grc@grcarr.com *Pipework fabrications & installation*

▶ G & R Contracts, 15 Guthrie Place, Torrance, Glasgow, G64 4HJ Tel: (01360) 620559

G R Controls, 19 109 Sydenham Road, Birmingham, B11 1DG Tel: 0121-773 8007 Fax: 0121-773 8007 E-mail: grcontrols1@yahoo.co.uk *Valve manufrs*

G R Design Sign, 119 The Glade, Croydon, CR0 7QP Tel: (020) 8239 7025 Fax: (020) 8239 7023 *Sign makers*

G & R Engineering (Nantwich) Ltd, Tricketts Lane, Willaston, Nantwich, Cheshire, CW5 6PY Tel: (01270) 661033 Fax: (01270) 664524 E-mail: brian@gr-eng.fsnet.co.uk *Production engineers*

G R Evans & Co., The Abbatoir, Ty Gwyn, Corwen, Clwyd, LL21 9BU Tel: (01490) 412999 Fax: (01490) 413071 *Abattoir*

G R F Engineering Ltd, 18 Bilton Way, Luton, LU1 1UU Tel: (01582) 411717 Fax: (01582) 728700 E-mail: sales@grfeng.co.uk *General engineers*

▶ G R G Print Com, A Treefield Industrial Estate, Gelderd Road, Morley, Leeds, LS27 7JU Tel: 0113-383 3888 Fax: 0113-383 3889

G R Hathaway Joinery, St Georges Close, Grays Lane, Moreton-in-Marsh, Gloucestershire, GL56 0LP Tel: (01608) 651978 Fax: (01608) 651978 *Joinery parts manufrs*

G R I Ltd, Gene House, Queenborough Lane, Rayne, Braintree, Essex, CM77 6TZ Tel: (01376) 332900 Fax: (01376) 344724 E-mail: gri@gri.co.uk *Molecular biological instruments suppliers*

G R & J Atkinson, 7 Baird Close, Drayton Fields Industrial Estate, Daventry, Northamptonshire, NN11 8RY Tel: (01327) 310464 Fax: (01327) 310451 *Plastic & metal drum reconditioners*

G R Joinery, Abernant Workshops, Pontardawe Rd, Rhydyfro/pontardawe, Swansea, SA8 4SX Tel: 01269 820000 *Furniture manufacturer*

G R Lane Health Products Ltd, Sisson Road, Gloucester, GL2 0GR Tel: (01452) 524012 Fax: (01452) 300105 E-mail: export@laneshealth.com *Health food manufrs*

G & R Leigh, Nunsfield Farm, Fairfield, Buxton, Derbyshire, SK17 7HN Tel: (01298) 22725 Fax: (01298) 25138 *General fencing & agricultural & equestrian services*

G R M Engineering & Contract Services Ltd, Ferry Lane, Snaith, Goole, North Humberside, DN14 9LL Tel: (01405) 861720 Fax: (01405) 861991 E-mail: davegrm@btconnect.com *Steelwork fabricators & contract hire*

G R M International Ltd, 4TH Floor, 57-59 Gloucester Place, London, W1U 8JH Tel: (020) 7486 3800 Fax: (020) 7486 3859 E-mail: info@grminternationa.co.uk *Agricultural consultants*

G & R Metals Skip Hire, 64 London Rd, Bexhill-on-Sea, E. Sussex, TN39 3LE Tel: (01424) 730568 *Skip hire/scrap metal merchants*

G R Owen & Son, Gilfach Yard, Chwilog, Pwllheli, Gwynedd, LL53 6SL Tel: (01766) 810320 Fax: (01766) 810320 *Welding agricultural mechanics*

G R P Ltd, Robin Hood Industrial Estate, Alfred St South, Nottingham, NG3 1GE Tel: 0115-924 3244 Fax: 0115-924 3236 *Distributors of glass fibre*

G R P Consultants, 12 The Park Pale, Tutbury, Burton-on-Trent, Staffordshire, DE13 9LB Tel: (01283) 814733 Fax: (01283) 814733 E-mail: sales@grpconsultants.co.uk *Fibre glass laminators*

▶ G R P (Electronic) Ltd, 2 Wham Cottages, Slackgate Lane, Denshaw, Oldham, OL3 5TZ Tel: (01457) 820864 Fax: (01457) 820864 E-mail: pollardgraham@talk21.com *We are a small company involved in recycling of computers and other electonic equipment. We also purchase scrap printed circuit boards.*

G R P Fabrications, Unit 12 Jubilee Industrial Estate, Ashington, Northumberland, NE63 8UB Tel: (01670) 811800 Fax: (01670) 811800 E-mail: info@grpfabrications.com *Glass fibre fabricators & glass fibre mouldings*

▶ G R P Laminates, Prospect Road, Cowes, Isle of Wight, PO31 7AD Tel: (01983) 200988 Fax: (01983) 200995 E-mail: enquiries@grplaminates.com *Boat builders*

G R P Leeds Ltd, Bagley Lane, Farsley, Pudsey, West Yorkshire, LS28 5LL Tel: 0113-255 4664 Fax: 0113-239 3215 E-mail: sales@grp-leeds.co.uk *Refrigerate panel vans*

G.R.P Mouldings, Oak Tree Farm, Stembridge, Martock, Somerset, TA12 6BP Tel: (01460) 240069 Fax: (01460) 240069 *Fibreglass moulders*

▶ G R P Mouldings, Unit 5 Kingswood Trading Estate, Pembroke Dock, Dyfed, SA72 4RS Tel: (01646) 682264 Fax: (01646) 687732 *Contract moulding & boat repairs*

G R P Mouldings, Oakley Wharf, Porthmadog, Gwynedd, LL49 9AS Tel: (01766) 514353 Fax: (01766) 514353 E-mail: info@grpcanopies.co.uk *Boat repairs & builders*

G R P Mouldings (Brightlingsea), Tower Street, Brightlingsea, Colchester, CO7 0AW Tel: (01206) 302387 *Glass fibre moulders*

G R P Specialist, Unit 17 Enterprise Park, Piddlehinton, Dorchester, Dorset, DT2 7UA Tel: (01305) 848548 Fax: (01305) 848548 *Fibre glass manufrs*

▶ G R P Structures Ltd, Fitzherbert Road, Portsmouth, PO6 1RU Tel: (023) 9238 4921 Fax: (023) 9221 0716 E-mail: sales@grpstructures.com

G & R Pollard Engineering Ltd, Alexandra Way, Ashchurch, Tewkesbury, Gloucestershire, GL20 8NB Tel: (01684) 274847 Fax: (01684) 851960 E-mail: grpoll@globalnet.co.uk *Precision engineers*

G R Pook Engineering Ltd, Howden Industrial Estate, Tiverton, Devon, EX16 5HW Tel: (01884) 254331 Fax: (01884) 258834 *General engineering*

G R & R D Taylor, 15 Market Street, Kirkby Lonsdale, Carnforth, Lancashire, LA6 2AU Tel: (01524) 271170 Fax: (01524) 271170 E-mail: sales@gr-rdtaylor.co.uk *Outdoor equipment retail*

G R S Roadstone Ltd, Leicester Road, Wolvey, Hinckley, Leicestershire, LE10 3HL Tel: (01455) 222700 Fax: (01455) 222737 E-mail: west@grsroadstone.co.uk *Road construction materials supplier* Also at: Harpenden & Northampton

G R S Sign Co. Ltd, Tateshall Way, Fairfield Industrial Estate, Louth, Lincolnshire, LN11 0YZ Tel: (01507) 609485 Fax: (01507) 609489 E-mail: sales@grssigns.co.uk *Engravers including computer & general. Also signs including road & safety; sign contractors/sign makers/suppliers/installers. In addition sign consultants or designers*

▶ G R Valeting, 35 Rutland Close, Catterick Garrison, North Yorkshire, DL9 3HJ Tel: (01748) 833434 E-mail: gordon@grvaleting.com *Professional mobile valeting service*

G R Wallace Computer Systems, 11 Queen Street, Carnoustie, Angus, DD7 7AX Tel: (01241) 856249 Fax: (01241) 856250 E-mail: sales@grwallace.co.uk *Computer programming system*

G R Warehousing Ltd, Old Station Road, Mendlesham, Stowmarket, Suffolk, IP14 5RT Tel: (01449) 768009 Fax: (01449) 766823 E-mail: mike@grwarehousing.fsnet.co.uk *Storage & warehousing contractors*

G Reekie Group Ltd, Ruthvenfield Road, Inveralmond Industrial Estate, Perth, PH1 3EE Tel: (01738) 622471 Fax: (01738) 639613 E-mail: info@reekiegroup.wannadoo.co.uk *Fork lift truck distributors* Also at: Aberdeen, Airdrie, Coldstream, Forres, Glasgow & Perth

▶ G Revill (Haulage) Ltd, Kiln Lane, Stallingborough, Grimsby, South Humberside, DN41 8DW Tel: (01469) 575468

G Reyner Ltd, Dowry Street, Oldham, OL8 2LP Tel: 0161-622 2400 Fax: 0161-622 2444

G Reyner Ltd, Dowry Street, Oldham, OL8 2LP Tel: 0161-622 2400 Fax: 0161-622 2444 *Road haulage & distribution service*

G Riggott, Westminster House, Gibbons Road, Mansfield, Nottinghamshire, NG18 5DZ Tel: (01623) 627454 Fax: (01623) 620335 E-mail: graham.roggott@ntlworld.com *Joiners*

G Ross Contractors, Camps Industrial Estate, Kirknewton, Midlothian, EH27 8DF Tel: (01506) 880569 Fax: (01506) 883728 E-mail: billy@rosscontractors.fsnet.co.uk *Fencing contractors, blacksmith & fabrication work services*

G Ryder & Co. Ltd, Denbigh Road, Bletchley, Milton Keynes, MK1 1DG Tel: (01908) 375524 Fax: (01908) 373658 E-mail: john.discombe@ryderbox.co.uk *Bespoke box manufrs*

G S A Engineering Co., Mushroom Street, Leeds, LS9 7NB Tel: 0113-244 4010 Fax: 0113-244 4010 *General engineers, fabricators, gates & grill services*

G S A Tech Source Ltd, Cathedral House, 5 Beacon Street, Lichfield, Staffordshire, WS13 7AA Tel: (0845) 2267200 Fax: (0845) 2267210 E-mail: gsa@gsatechsource.com *IT recruitment services*

G S Adams Ltd, Station House, 98 Station Road, Studley, Warwickshire, B80 7JS Tel: (01527) 857718 Fax: (01527) 857716 E-mail: admin@gsaelec.co.uk *Electrical contractors & engineers services*

▶ G S Brown Construction Ltd, Glencarse, Perth, PH2 7NF Tel: (01738) 860591 Fax: (01738) 860357 E-mail: office@gsbrown.co.uk

▶ G S Brown Gas & Heating Services, 27 Woodbine Terrace, Edinburgh, EH6 8DA Tel: 0131-467 5907

G S Brown Precision Engineers Ltd, Beeches, Ladybank, Cupar, Fife, KY15 7LR Tel: (01337) 830264 Fax: (01337) 831269 E-mail: enquiries@gsbrown.com *Precision engineers*

G S Catering, 36-38 Castleton Boulevard, Skegness, Lincolnshire, PE25 2TS Tel: (01754) 764933 Fax: (01754) 764933 *Catering equipment supplier*

G S Designs, Hardwick Close, Stevenage, Hertfordshire, SG2 8UF Tel: (01438) 813332 Fax: (01438) 812215 E-mail: gary@gsdesign.co.uk *Printed circuit board designers*

G S E Rentals Ltd, Unit 32, Wellheads Industrial Estate, Aberdeen, AB21 7GA Tel: (01224) 771247 Fax: (01224) 723116 E-mail: info@gserentals.co.uk *Marine survey equipment rentals*

G S F Ltd, Unit 9 Gledrid Industrial Estate, Chirk, Wrexham, LL14 5DG Tel: (01691) 770303 Fax: (01691) 776900 E-mail: enquiries@gsfslides.com *Suppliers of telescopic slides, drawer slides and precision linear rail, with products able to carry up to 2000Kg and extension up to 2 metres. Full partial and over extension.Engineering design services based on linear motion expertise.Founded 1988*

G S Fire Protection, 46 Gotham Road, Birmingham, B26 1LB Tel: 0121-244 4747 Fax: 0121-693 3883 E-mail: info@gsfireprotection.co.uk *Fire protection services & suppliers*

G S G Buildings Ltd, Frank Street, Preston, PR1 1PB Tel: (01772) 824953 Fax: (01772) 882606 *Garden equipment*

▶ G S G Cargo Ltd, Unit 14 Northbrook Business Park, Northbrook Road, Worthing, West Sussex, BN14 8PQ Tel: (01903) 204666 Fax: (01903) 212966 E-mail: sales@gsgcargo.com *International & domestic freight forwarders*

GS Group, Aspen Way, Yalberton Industrial Estate, Paignton, Devon, TQ4 7QR Tel: (01803) 528586 Fax: (01803) 554338 E-mail: info@gsgroup.co.uk *GS Group is based in Paignton, Devon and is recognised as one of the top contracting houses for the provision of commercial foodservice schemes nationwide. They offer cooking equipment and utensils, ventilation systems, stainless steel fabrication, safety systems, dining solutions, coverings and specialist services.*

▶ G S Halligan, 175 Knightlow Road, Birmingham, B17 8PY Tel: 0121-420 2227 Fax: 0121-434 3967

G S Hydro UK Ltd, Unit 47 Howe Moss Avenue, Kirkhill Industrial Estate, Dyce, Aberdeen, AB21 0GP Tel: (01224) 772111 Fax: (01224) 772054 E-mail: info@gshydro.co.uk *Non-welded pipe systems*

G S I Lumonics Ltd, Cosford Lane, Swift Valley Industrial Estate, Rugby, Warwickshire, CV21 1QN Tel: (01788) 570321 Fax: (01788) 579824 E-mail: appsexpert@gsig.com *Laser, cutting, welding & marking machine manufrs*

G S I Pallet Force, Seymour House, Dunhams Lane, Letchworth Garden City, Hertfordshire, SG6 1LL Tel: (01462) 485726 Fax: (01462) 678381 E-mail: sales@palletforce.com *A member of the PalletFORCE distribution network- palletised distribution, timed, next day, economy, tail loft, Ireland and services to mainland Europe. Through its expanding shareholder member depot network, full and part loads, warehouse and logistics services are available.*

G & S Jones, Unit 1e Bersham Enterprise Centre, Colliery Road, Rhostyllen, Wrexham, Clwyd, LL14 4EG Tel: (01978) 263160 Fax: (01978) 263135 E-mail: graham@gsjonesprint.co.uk *Lithographic printers*

G S K Fabrications, 3 Capel Road, Clydach, Swansea, SA6 5PZ Tel: (01792) 849494 Fax: (01792) 849494 E-mail: stephen@gsk-fabrications.co.uk *Catering equipment manufrs*

▶ G S L, Ledcom Industrial Estate, Bank Road, Larne, County Antrim, BT40 3SF Tel: (028) 2827 2827 Fax: (028) 2827 9084 *Computer maintenance & repair services*

G S L Embroidery, 1 Berry Bank Lane, Holmfirth, HD9 7LA Tel: (01484) 683142 Fax: (01484) 685246 E-mail: sepiaemb@aol.com *Embroidery merchants & promotional goods*

G S L Lift Services Ltd, Netherton Indust Estate, Netherhall Road, Netherton Industrial Estate, Wishaw, Lanarkshire, ML2 0JG Tel: (01698) 350099 Fax: (01698) 357332 *Lift engineers*

▶ G S M Aluminium Ltd, 16 Maria Street, Burley in Wharfedale, Ilkley, West Yorkshire, LS29 7JA Tel: (01943) 862307 Fax: (01943) 863168 E-mail: gerald@gsmltd.co.uk *Aluminium extrusions, aluminium curtain walling, architectural aluminium systems, aluminium windows, aluminium doors, aluminium shop front, aluminium profiles.*

G S M Graphic Art, Castlegarth Works, Masonic Lane, Thirsk, North Yorkshire, YO7 1PS Tel: (01845) 522184 Fax: (01845) 522206 E-mail: gsmgrapicarts@gsmgroup.co.uk *Nameplate & label manufrs*

G S M Industrial Graphics, Avenue One, Witney, Oxfordshire, OX28 4BZ Tel: (01993) 776511 Fax: (01993) 778238 E-mail: gsmindustrialgraphics@gsmgroup.co.uk *Etched nameplates labels membranes overlays*

G S M International, Upper Neatham Mill Farm, Upper Neatham Mill Lane, Holybourne, Alton, Hampshire, GU34 4EP Tel: (01420) 80617 Fax: (01420) 80617 E-mail: gsminternational@ukonline.co.uk *Pressure gauges*

G S M Primographic, Unit 2b Ffrwdgrech Industrial Estate, Ffrwdgrech Road, Brecon, Powys, LD3 8LA Tel: (01874) 624433 Fax: (01874) 624575 E-mail: info@gsmprimographic.co.uk *Screen printing metal, plastic & glass*

▶ G S Mahal & Co. Ltd, Gaila House, Duke Street, Nottingham, NG7 7JN Tel: 0115-978 0304 Fax: 0115-942 4248 E-mail: sales@gsmahal.co.uk *Distributor of promotional clothing, work wear & school wear*

▶ G S Mechanical, 11 The Green, Brill, Aylesbury, Buckinghamshire, HP18 9RU Tel: (01844) 238800 Fax: (01844) 238890 E-mail: enquiries@gsmechanical.co.uk

G S P K Circuits Ltd, Manse Lane, Knaresborough, North Yorkshire, HG5 8LF Tel: (01423) 865641 Fax: (01423) 798246 E-mail: sales@gspkcircuits.ltd.uk *Printed circuit manufrs*

G S P K Electronics Ltd, GSPK Technology Park, Manse Lane, Knaresborough, North Yorkshire, HG5 8LF Tel: +44 (0) 1423 869151 Fax: +44 (0) 1423 869239 E-mail: mail@gspk-electronics.ltd.uk *Contract electronics manufacturing*

G S Precision, North Weylands Industrial Estate, Molesey Road, Walton-on-Thames, Surrey, KT12 3PL Tel: (01932) 246477 Fax: (01932) 231345 E-mail: chris.brewall@gsprecision.co.uk *Sheet metalwork engineers*

G & S Precision Engineering Bradford Ltd, 6 Tyersal Works, Tyersal Lane, Bradford, West Yorkshire, BD4 0RB Tel: (01274) 660263 Fax: (01274) 669223 *Precision engineers*

▶ G S Pyrotechnics, Woodlands Ways, Birmingham, B37 6RN Tel: 0121-243 7120 Fax: 0121-779 3622 E-mail: gspyrotechnics@blueyonder.co.uk *Pyrotechnic events & occasions from weddings to corporate displays*

G S Robinson & Co. Ltd, Unit B T 4 30 Exmouth Road, West Chirton Industrial Estate South, North Shields, Tyne & Wear, NE29 7TY Tel: 0191-257 5374 Fax: 0191-296 1341 *Sheet metalworkers*

G & S Sheet Metals Ltd, 4a Lea Road, Waltham Abbey, Essex, EN9 1AE Tel: (01992) 713800 Fax: (01992) 713800 *Sheet metal fabricators*

G S Smith Ltd, Lockwood Street, Hull, HU2 0HL Tel: (01482) 323503 Fax: (01482) 223174 E-mail: sales@gssmith.com *Coloured paper & board specialists* Also at: Birmingham & London

G & S Thomson, Dubford, Turriff, Aberdeenshire, AB53 8AJ Tel: (01888) 562500 Fax: (01888) 568672 *Agricultural engineers*

G & S Valves Ltd, Catteshall Lane, Godalming, Surrey, GU7 1JS Tel: (01483) 415444 Fax: (01483) 426891 E-mail: gsvalves@aol.com *Engine valve manufrs*

G S W Haswell, The Workshop, Winchester Street, Botley, Southampton, SO30 2AA Tel: (01489) 785293 *Precision engineers*

G S W Plastics Ltd, Park Mill Industrial Estate, Manchester Road, Mossley, Ashton-under-Lyne, Lancashire, OL5 9BQ Tel: (01457) 834550 Fax: (01457) 834990 *Injection moulds specialists*

▶ G S Whyte & Co. Ltd, 13 Princes Street, Monifieth, Dundee, DD5 4AW Tel: (01382) 532172

G Sait Ltd, 9 Cobham Road, Ferndown Industrial Estate, Wimborne, Dorset, BH21 7PE Tel: (01202) 875612 Fax: (01202) 874412 *Scrap metal merchants*

▶ G Seal, Peatburn Avenue, Heanor, Derbyshire, DE75 7RL Tel: (01773) 761579 Fax: (01773) 711788 *Adhesives & sealant applicator manufrs*

G Stanley, 5 Wyke Street, Hull, HU9 1PA Tel: (01482) 225590 Fax: (01482) 588764 E-mail: sales@gstanleys.co.uk *Cover, tent, marquees & sunblind manufrs*

G Stewart, 7 Mitchell Court, Kilmarnock, Ayrshire, KA1 3DU Tel: (01563) 533845 Fax: (01563) 533845 *Buy & sell cranes*

G Stow plc, Heathercroft Industrial Estate, Lupton Road, Wallingford, Oxfordshire, OX10 9BS Tel: (01491) 834444 Fax: (01491) 827640 E-mail: gstowplc@btinternet.com *Well drillers & waterworks engineers*

G Systems, PO Box 100, Bury St. Edmunds, Suffolk, IP28 7HD Tel: (01638) 717500 E-mail: john@gsystems.co.uk *Computer manufrs*

▶ G T Architectural Metal Services Ltd, Unit 2, Birds Royd Industrial Estate, Birds Royd Lane, Brighouse, West Yorkshire, HD6 1LQ Tel: (01484) 404150 Fax: (01484) 404156 E-mail: sales@gtmetal.co.uk *Manufacturers & installation of metalwork features*

▶ G & T Associates, William Knox House, Britannic Way, Llandarcy, Neath, West Glamorgan, SA10 6EL Tel: (01792) 321202 Fax: (01792) 321295 E-mail: info@gtassociates.co.uk

G T Building Services Ltd, Unit 2, Bath Bridge Business Park, Bath Road, Bridgwater, Somerset, TA6 4SZ Tel: (01278) 455266 Fax: (01278) 455269 *Heating, air conditioning installation & engineers*

G T C Ltd, Woolpit Business Park, Bury Road, Woolpit, Bury St. Edmunds, Suffolk, IP30 9UP Tel: (01359) 240363 Fax: (01359) 244045 *Gas transporters*

▶ G T C Asbestos Removal Services Ltd, Unit 9 Kirkhill Place, Kirkhill Industrial Estate, Dyce, Aberdeen, AB21 0GU Tel: (01224) 722150

G T C Fixings Ltd, 84 Witt Road, Fair Oak, Eastleigh, Hampshire, SO50 7FQ Tel: 0845 5261414 Fax: (0800) 1975000 E-mail: sales@gtc-direct.com *GTC Fixings Ltd is a comprehensive supplier of Stainless Steel Screws covering Machine Screws, Socket Screws, Woodscrews, Self Tapping Screws, Chipboard Screws and Self Drilling Screws. GTC Fixings Ltd UK website is specifically designed to offer to the public and Industry a*

continued

continuation
representation but, by no means comprehensive, idea of what is available. We offer an incredible range of Stainless Steel screws, Bolts and Hexagon sets and, Stainless Steel Fixings (for masonry, concrete and brickwork). The expertise available after 30 years in the trade is second to none. The Range of Stainless Steel Screws has grown out of all recognition over the past 30 years. In Effect, if it is available in Stainless Steel we can probably supply it.

G T Central Welding & Gasses Supply Co., Hunters Lane, Rugby, Warwickshire, CV21 1EA Tel: (01788) 547212 Fax: (01788) 541589 E-mail: sales@gtcentralwelding.co.uk *Welding & gas equipment suppliers*

G & T Computer Services, Brown Gables, Dyers End, Stambourne, Halstead, Essex, CO9 4NE Tel: (01440) 785596 *Electronic engineers*

G T Coulson Fabrication Ltd, Ponders End Industrial Estate, East Duck Lees Lane, Enfield, Middlesex, EN3 7SR Tel: (020) 8804 5961 Fax: (020) 8804 0014 E-mail: info@gtcoulson.com *Steel fabricators*

G T Drawing Services Ltd, Cradock Road, Luton, LU4 0JF Tel: (01582) 502883 Fax: (01582) 572201 E-mail: mail@gtdrawings.com *Engineering & construction designers*

▶ G & T Electrical Services, 46 Bren Way, Hilton, Derby, DE65 5HP Tel: (01283) 730832 E-mail: imbmbren@aol.com *We specialise in all portable appliance testing, plus we have the facility to ""PAT"" test equipment for Bands and Gigs.*

▶ G T Emergo Ltd, 30 Paxton Road, Northampton, NN3 3RL Tel: (01604) 248042 Fax: (01604) 513365 E-mail: sales@gtemergo.co.uk *Manufacturers of flat screen monitor arms*

G T Engineering, Enkalon Industrial Estate, Randalstown Road, Antrim, BT41 4LD Tel: (028) 9446 3882 Fax: (028) 9442 8819 *Wrought iron gates manufrs*

G & T Evans, Dulas Mill, Mochdre Lane, Newtown, Powys, SY16 4JD Tel: (01686) 622100 Fax: (01686) 622220 E-mail: sales@gtevans.co.uk *Timber, builder & agricultural suppliers*

G T Exhausts, Ledra Works, Northgate, Aldridge, Walsall, WS9 8TH Tel: (01922) 745800 Fax: (01922) 745566 E-mail: sales2@gtexhausts.co.uk *Exhaust system wholesalers & manufrs*

G T Fan Services & Repairs Ltd, Unit D Leona Industrial Estate, Nimmings Road, Halesowen, West Midlands, B62 9JQ Tel: 0121-559 1824 Fax: 0121-561 2153 *Fan repairers & manufrs*

G & T Furniture Fittings, Upper Rainham Road, Hornchurch, Essex, RM12 4ES Tel: (07860) 802481 Fax: (01708) 470211 *Furniture fittings suppliers*

G T & G Ltd, 1 Miltons Yard, Petworth Road, Witley, Godalming, Surrey, GU8 5LT Tel: (01428) 683088 Fax: (01428) 680902 *Distributors, agents & suppliers of gas turbines* Also at: Slough

G T G Engineering Co. Ltd, 1 Albert Street, Loughborough, Leicestershire, LE11 2DW Tel: (01509) 215077 Fax: (01509) 234810 E-mail: martingeorge@gtgeng.co.uk *Precision & mechanical test engineers*

▶ G T Grafix, PO Box 154, Ashton-Under-Lyne, Lancashire, OL6 6WB Tel: (0845) 8385167 E-mail: info@gtgrafix.com *Number plates suppliers*

▶ G T Group Ltd, 8 Faraday Road, Peterlee, County Durham, SR8 5AP Tel: 0191-586 2366 Fax: 0191-587 2111 E-mail: info@gtgroup.co.uk *Engineering solutions*

G T I Computers Portsmouth Ltd, Unit 219, Victory Business Centre, Somers Road North, Portsmouth, PO1 1PJ Tel: (023) 9275 0212 Fax: (0870) 0601868 E-mail: sales@gticomputers.co.uk *Computer solutions provider*

▶ G T I Glazing Systems Ltd, The Pavillion Somerton Park, Newport Road, Cowes, Isle of Wight, PO31 8PB Tel: (01983) 280880 Fax: (01983) 290222 *Windows, double glazed*

▶ G T I Powder Coating, Unit 2, Jenning Street, Hull, HU8 7AN Tel: (01482) 211040 Fax: (01482) 211178 *Powder coating suppliers*

G T Industrial Services Ltd, 16 Enterprise Court, Newton Close, Park Farm Industrial Estate, Wellingborough, Northamptonshire, NN8 6UW Tel: (01933) 405088 Fax: (01933) 405099 E-mail: sales@gtihaxaplas.ukf.net *Plastic engineers services*

G T K (U K) Ltd, Unit 1 Maxdata Centre, Downmill Road, Bracknell, Berkshire, RG12 1QS Tel: (01344) 304123 Fax: (01344) 301414 E-mail: sales@gtk.co.uk *Manufacturers & distributors of specialist interconnection devices*

G T Laminators, Rear of 60 Great Norbury Street, Hyde, Cheshire, SK14 1HY Tel: (07979) 286187 Fax: 0161-366 0856 *Film laminating services*

▶ G T M Engineering Co., Station Road, Newent, Gloucestershire, GL18 1BB Tel: (01531) 820118 Fax: (01531) 820698 E-mail: gtmengineering@logimail.co.uk *Engineering services*

G T Morgan & Co. Ltd, Desford Lane, Kirby Muxloe, Leicester, LE9 2BF Tel: (01455) 828022 Fax: (01455) 828001 E-mail: contract@gtmorgan.demon.co.uk *Shop fitters*

G T P (Engineering) Ltd, 118-130 Bushbury Lane, Wolverhampton, WV10 9TW Tel: (01902) 429849 Fax: (01902) 427406 E-mail: sales@gtp-eng.co.uk *Fasteners & turn parts manufrs*

G T P Group Ltd, White Cross Industrial Estate, South Road, Lancaster, LA1 4XE Tel: (01524) 380380 Fax: (01524) 844514 *Information technology consultants*

G & T Packaging Ltd, Unit 10A, Factory Lane, Warminster, Wiltshire, BA12 8LT Tel: (01985) 216441 Fax: (01985) 216491 E-mail: enquiries@gtpack.btopenworld.com *Packaging materials for food industries wholesalers*

G T Paper & Packaging Ltd, Lingard Street, Stoke-on-Trent, ST6 1ED Tel: (01782) 577328 Fax: (01782) 577068 E-mail: sam@gtpaper.co.uk *Packaging merchants*

G T Picton Ltd, Hartham House, Stonely Road, Easton, Huntingdon, Cambridgeshire, PE28 0TT Tel: (01480) 890244 Fax: (01480) 890961 E-mail: sales@finwood.co.uk *Farming contractors*

G & T Plastics, Unit 37 Lythalls La Industrial Estate, Lythalls Lane, Coventry, CV6 6FL Tel: (024) 7663 7983 Fax: (024) 7663 7983 *Custom moulders & glass fibre mouldings manufrs*

G T Pollution Technology Ltd, 3 Medina Court, Arctic Road, Cowes, Isle Of Wight, PO31 7XD Tel: (01983) 280185 Fax: (01983) 280056 E-mail: info@lamor.com *Manufacturers of oil spill response equipment, skimmers, booms, temporary storage & tanks*

G T Pressing Co. Ltd, 46 Freehold Terrace, Brighton, BN2 4AB Tel: (01273) 601222 Fax: (01273) 682367 E-mail: enquiries@gtpressing.co.uk *Metal fabrication engineers*

G T Products Ltd, 3-4 Loomer Road, Newcastle, Staffordshire, ST5 7LB Tel: (01782) 562056 Fax: (01782) 564757 E-mail: sales@gtproducts.co.uk *Edible oil & fat wholesalers*

G T Products Europe Ltd, Unit 14 Ford La Business Park, Ford, Arundel, West Sussex, BN18 0UZ Tel: (01243) 555303 Fax: (01243) 555304 E-mail: enquiries@gtproductseurope.com *Packaging Solutions. Manufacturers and distributors of a wide range of ties, fasteners, closures, adhesive tapes, tags and seals to the packaging, manufacturing & print industry*

G T S Ltd, 85 Templepatrick Road, Ballyclare, County Antrim, BT39 9RQ Tel: (028) 9334 0510 Fax: (028) 9334 9339 E-mail: gts61242@aol.com *Bulk materials haulage contractors services*

G T S Cadbuild Ltd, Woodbrook House, 30 Bridge Street, Loughborough, Leicestershire, LE11 1NH Tel: (08700) 509101 Fax: (08700) 509102 E-mail: sales@gtscad.com *Software suppliers*

G T S Flexible Materials Ltd, G T S House, 3 Wellington Business Park, Dukes Ride, Crowthorne, Berkshire, RG45 6LS Tel: (01344) 762376 Fax: (01344) 761615 E-mail: mail@gts-flexible.co.uk *Flexible electrical laminates*

G T S Moulds, 15 South Lane, New Malden, Surrey, KT3 5HU Tel: (020) 8336 0335 Fax: (020) 8336 0335 E-mail: gtsmoulds@blueyonder.co.uk *Plastic mouldings manufrs*

G T S S Engineers, Hotchkiss Way, Binley Industrial Estate, Binley Industrial Estate, Coventry, CV3 2RL Tel: (024) 7645 9654 Fax: (024) 7645 7006 E-mail: sales@gtssltd.co.uk *Engineering suppliers*

G T Stone & Son, Dudnance Lane, Pool, Redruth, Cornwall, TR15 3QZ Tel: (01736) 763777 Fax: (01209) 710285 *Freight transport services*

G T Supplies, Old Llynf Power Station, Aberkenfig, Bridgend, Mid Glamorgan, CF32 0EJ Tel: (01656) 724656 Fax: (01656) 729261 *Janitorial suppliers*

G T Systems, Alba House, 218 Union Street, Aberdeen, AB10 1TL Tel: (01224) 620200 Fax: (01224) 620020 *Recruitment computers agency*

G T Thermal Ltd, 36 Lanehead Road, Stoke-on-Trent, ST1 5PT Tel: (01782) 279504 Fax: (01782) 279005 *Wholesalers for heating & air conditioning*

G T Tools Ltd, Coxmoor Road, Sutton-in-Ashfield, Nottinghamshire, NG17 4NE Tel: (01623) 551000 Fax: (01623) 550784 E-mail: sales@gttools.co.uk *Plastics mould tool manufrs*

▶ G & T Trade Windows, Oswin Avenue, Balby, Doncaster, South Yorkshire, DN4 0NR Tel: (01302) 857555 *Double glazing suppliers & manufrs*

▶ G & T Transport, Unit 6 Llwyn Y Graig, Gorseinon, Swansea, SA4 9WG Tel: (01792) 899499 Fax: (01792) 899898 E-mail: info@gandttransport.co.uk *G&T Transport Ltd. specialise in domestic and commercial removals and self storage within the UK. **- A local firm, built on its reputation*- Local & National Removals*- Single Items or Full Load*- Piano Specialists*- Full Insurance Cover*- Free & Prompt Estimates*- Packaging Material Supplied**

▶ G T Trax, 11a Orchard Road, Royston, Hertfordshire, SG8 6HL Tel: (0870) 4055588 Fax: (0870) 607733 E-mail: gttrax@hotmail.co.uk *Hire & sales for ground protection road plates*

G T W Storage Services Ltd, 41-45 James Watt Street, Glasgow, G2 8NF Tel: 0141-221 4727 Fax: 0141-224 4520 *Storage contractors*

▶ G T Wall & Sons Ltd, 2 Hall Street, Stourbridge, West Midlands, DY8 2JE Tel: (01384) 394104 Fax: (01384) 371578

G Taylor Midlands Ltd, 9 Haddow Street, Hamilton, Lanarkshire, ML3 7HX Tel: (01698) 283561 Fax: (01698) 457914 E-mail: enquiries@gtlifting.co.uk *Lifting equipment suppliers*

G Tech UK Ltd, Link House, 19 Colonial Way, Watford, WD24 4JL Tel: (01923) 474800 Fax: (01923) 474830 E-mail: first.surname@gtech.com *Computer consultants*

▶ G Thornton (Contracts) Ltd, Metcalf Drive, Altham Industrial Estate, Accrington, Lancashire, BB5 5TU Tel: (01282) 777345

▶ G Towers & Son Ltd, Union Street, Blyth, Northumberland, NE24 2ED Tel: (01670) 352056

▶ G & V A Engineering, Seddon Place, Skelmersdale, Lancashire, WN8 8EB Tel: (01695) 729994 Fax: (01695) 729940

G V A Grimley, Sutherland House, 149 St. Vincent Street, Glasgow, G2 5NW Tel: (0870) 9008990 Fax: 0141-204 1986 *Surveying international property advisors*

G.V.E. Ltd, Ashburton House, Trafford Park Road, Trafford Park, Manchester, M17 1BN Tel: 0161-872 0777 Fax: 0161-872 9324 E-mail: info@gvepumps.co.uk *Ancillary equipment & vacuum pump manufrs*

G W Air Conditioning, 36 Lodge Avenue, Croydon, CR0 4JZ Tel: (020) 8686 6226 Fax: (020) 8686 2657 E-mail: sales@gwac.co.uk *Air conditioning contractors installation service*

▶ G W Architectural Design & Build Services, 15 St. Ronans View, Gateshead, Tyne & Wear, NE9 7TF Tel: 0191-420 8844 Fax: 0191-420 8844 E-mail: info@drawingplans.co.uk *Architectural design and build, from small domestic extension and alterations to new build projects.*

G W Atkins & Sons Ltd, 28 Wellington St, Syston, Leicester, LE7 2LG Tel: 0116-269 1240 Fax: 0116-269 3270 *Production engineers*

G W B Ltd, 113-115 Codicote Road, Welwyn, Hertfordshire, AL6 9TY Tel: (01438) 821088 Fax: (01438) 821421 E-mail: sales@gwbltd.co.uk *Office furniture retailers*

G W Belton Ltd, Heaton Street, Gainsborough, Lincolnshire, DN21 2ED Tel: (01427) 612291 Fax: (01427) 810520 E-mail: sales@gwbelton.com *Printers*

G W Brooks Flooring Ltd, Unit 19 Waterside Industrial Estate, Ettingshall Road, Wolverhampton, WV2 2RH Tel: (01902) 498213 Fax: (01902) 495707 E-mail: sales@brooksflooring.co.uk *Flooring suppliers & installers*

G W Building Consulting Engineers Ltd, Treasure House, 19-21 Hatton Garden, London, EC1N 8NG Tel: (020) 7831 1717 Fax: (020) 7831 6429 E-mail: info@gwconsultants.co.uk *Engineering consultants & designers*

▶ G W Ceramics, 80 North Street, Leighton Buzzard, Bedfordshire, LU7 1ES Tel: (01525) 381736 Fax: (01525) 377702 E-mail: sales@gwceramics.com

G W Chadwick Ltd, Unit 40 Chorley North Industrial Park, Chorley, Lancashire, PR6 7BX Tel: (01257) 234242 Fax: (01257) 234213 E-mail: email@gwchadwick.co.uk *Educational toys & paper products*

G W Commercials, Balklands, Five Ashes, Mayfield, East Sussex, TN20 6JJ Tel: (01825) 830788 Fax: (01825) 830788 *Vehicle repairers*

▶ G W Consumables Ltd, PO Box 15, Wolverhampton, WV5 9YT Tel: (01902) 326717 Fax: (01902) 326844 E-mail: gwc@btconnect.com *Foundry consumables, ceramic foam filters, special high temperature insulation materials, Vacuum and Plasma furnaces, Dross processing and handling equipment.*Micronising mills for media reduction.*

G W Cowler, 16 Merchant Drive, Mead Lane, Hertford, SG13 7AY Tel: (01992) 501494 Fax: (01992) 501495 E-mail: sales@gwcowler.demon.co.uk *Precision engineers*

G W D Ltd, 12-13 Capital Place, Harlow, Essex, CM19 5AS Tel: (01279) 416093 Fax: (01279) 401104 E-mail: sales@gwd.ltd.uk *Point of sale display designers*

G W Dale Diesel Engineer Ltd, 139 Newcastle Street, Stoke-on-Trent, ST6 3QJ Tel: (01782) 837824 Fax: (01782) 839550 *Diesel fuel injection specialists*

G W Day & Co., East Chiltington Forge, Highbridge Lane, East Chiltington, Lewes, East Sussex, BN7 3QY Tel: (01273) 890398 Fax: (01273) 891410 E-mail: petemiccicronin@cs.com *Wrought ironwork manufrs*

G W Deeley Ltd, George House, Herald Avenue, Coventry, CV5 6UB Tel: (024) 7671 8718 Fax: (024) 7660 6363 E-mail: info@deeley.co.uk *Building contractors*

G W Deeley Ltd, Pond Wood Close, Moulton Park Industrial Estate, Northampton, NN3 6RT Tel: (01604) 642201 Fax: (01604) 492000 E-mail: enquiries@northampton.deeley.co.uk *Building contractors*

G W Elliott & Son, 105 Alexandra Road, Newport, Gwent, NP20 2JG Tel: (01633) 264929 Fax: (01633) 246242 E-mail: sales@elliotshipchandler.com *General ship stores*

▶ G W F Engineering Ltd, Woodhouse Road, Scunthorpe, South Humberside, DN16 1BD Tel: (01724) 868646 Fax: (01724) 867747 E-mail: enquiries@gwf.co.uk *Medium to heavy fabrication & machining*

▶ G W Fleming, Gatehead Road, Crosshouse, Kilmarnock, Ayrshire, KA2 0HP Tel: (01563) 523853 Fax: (01563) 523853

▶ G & W Gardener Building Contractors, 67 Dane Road, Margate, Kent, CT9 2AE Tel: (01843) 229063 Fax: (01843) 293137

G & W Grinding Services Ltd, Unit A Thomas Street, Walsall, WS2 8NE Tel: (01922) 723481 Fax: (01922) 724968 *Grinding services including internal, cylindrical & precision*

G W Hutchinson & Co., 31 Anlaby Road, Hull, HU1 2PG Tel: (01482) 223869 *Guns & tackle*

G W J Engineering Ltd, 7 Ruston Road, Alma Park Industrial Estate, Grantham, Lincolnshire, NG31 9SW Tel: (01476) 568703 Fax: (01476) 578639 E-mail: enquiries@gwjengineering.co.uk *Mechanical & industrial engineers*

G W J Weir & Son, 54 Mullybrannon Road, Dungannon, County Tyrone, BT71 7ER Tel: (028) 8772 3205 Fax: (028) 8772 7555 E-mail: weirtrset@aol.com *Tractor suppliers*

G W Lambert Engineers Ltd, 10 Queens Road, High Wycombe, Buckinghamshire, HP13 6AQ Tel: (01494) 525977 Fax: (01494) 528238 *Precision engineers*

G W Lawson Ltd, Units R-U Burnham Trading Estate, Lawson Road, Dartford, DA1 5BH Tel: (01322) 223363 Fax: (01322) 223234 E-mail: gwlawson@btconnect.com *Precision mould toolmakers*

▶ G W Lomas & Sons, Back Spinnerbottom, Birch Vale, High Peak, Derbyshire, SK22 1BN Tel: (01663) 742536 Fax: (01663) 742890 E-mail: info@gwlomasandsons.co.uk *General engineering services*

▶ G W Mckane & Son, 32-34 Station Street, Keswick, Cumbria, CA12 5HF Tel: (01768) 772140 Fax: (01768) 771203

G W Martin & Co. Ltd, 7 Bishopstoke Road, Eastleigh, Hampshire, SO50 6AD Tel: (023) 8064 2922 Fax: (023) 8061 1653 E-mail: andyclark@gwmartin.co.uk *Precision engineers (sub contract machinists)*

G W Metals & Tools, Unit O & Q Newtown Road Trading Estate, Newtown Road, Worcester, WR5 1HA Tel: (01905) 612342 Fax: (01905) 25544 *Non-ferrous metals & engineering tools stockists*

▶ G W P UK Ltd, 3 Old Port Road, Nurston, Barry, South Glamorgan, CF62 3BH Tel: (01446) 711260 Fax: (01446) 711978 E-mail: gwpukltd@btconnect.com *Screen print*

▶ G & W Plant Hire, Mill Lane, Coxley, Wells, Somerset, BA5 1QU Tel: (01749) 671393 Fax: (01749) 671394

G W & S M Mellors & Sons, 23 Meadow Road, Netherfield, Nottingham, NG4 2FR Tel: 0115-961 6213 *Lace finishers*

G W Smith Fabrications, Unit G1 Elvington Industrial Estate, York Road, Elvington, York, YO41 4AR Tel: (01904) 608722 Fax: (01904) 607171 *Fabrication & welding specialists*

▶ G W Sparrow & Co. Ltd, 5 Cobham Centre, Westmead Industrial Estate, Westlea, Swindon, SN5 7UJ Tel: (01793) 541701 Fax: (01793) 541702

G W Trading Ltd, Cottage Beck Road, Scunthorpe, South Humberside, DN16 1TT Tel: (01724) 281222 Fax: (01724) 292704 *Crisps & snack food manufrs*

▶ G W Twilley & Son Ltd, 71 Coburg Road, London, N22 6UB Tel: (020) 8888 1660 Fax: (020) 8888 1660 E-mail: twilly@aol.com

G W Webb Plastics Ltd, Brookside Works Tyseley Industrial Estate, Seeleys Road, Birmingham, B11 2LA Tel: 0121-772 5968 Fax: 0121-773 7653 E-mail: sales@webbplastics.uk.com *Plastic granulations, plastic scrap*

▶ G Wilkinson Construction Ltd, 65a Balby Road, Doncaster, South Yorkshire, DN4 0RE Tel: (01302) 342373

▶ G Woodland & Sons Ltd, Hatch Beauchamp, Taunton, Somerset, TA3 6TW Tel: (01823) 480248 Fax: (01823) 480239

G X Design Engineers, The Mayfield, Usk, Gwent, NP15 1SY Tel: (01291) 673437 Fax: (01291) 673438 E-mail: info@gxl.co.uk *Product design engineers*

G&T, 9 Orwell Court, Hurricane Way, Wickford, Essex, SS11 8YJ Tel: (01268) 766500 Fax: (01268) 766530 E-mail: info@gtoffice.co.uk *Office equipment suppliers*

▶ G1, 280 Western Road, London, SW19 2QA Tel: (020) 8687 3140 Fax: (020) 8687 3141 E-mail: mail@g1.tv *Closed circuit television equipment installers*

▶ G13:Graphics & Multimedia, 47 Clarence Square, Cheltenham, Gloucestershire, GL50 4JR Tel: (01242) 210519 Fax: E-mail: mail@gavinpalmer.com *Graphic Design and Multimedia solutions*

▶ G3 Creative Solutions, 7 Woodside Crescent, Glasgow, G3 7UL Tel: (01389) 875889 Fax: 0141-332 2233 E-mail: mail@g3creative.co.uk *Graphic design*

▶ G5 Graphics Ltd, St Luke's Place, Unit 6, Glasgow, G5 0TS Tel: 0141-429 4240 Fax: 0141-429 4241 E-mail: info@g5graphics.com *Large format digital printing services*

▶ G7 Business Solutions, 104 High Street, London Colney, St. Albans, Hertfordshire, AL2 1QL Tel: (01727) 829190 Fax: (01727) 829199 *Computer system consultants & software*

▶ G8 Environmental Solutions Ltd, B3 Kingsfisher House Kingsway, Team Valley Trading Estate, Gateshead, Tyne & Wear, NE11 0JQ Tel: 0191-482 8760 Fax: 0191-482 8761 E-mail: enquiries@g8environmental.com *Heating, air conditioning services & refrigeration*

G8 Environmental Solutions, 100e Cumbernauld Road, Muirhead, Glasgow, G69 9AB Tel: (0870) 2416697 Fax: (0870) 2416705 *Air con refrigeration heating*

▶ GA GARDEN SERVICES, 12 CEDAR STREET, DUNBAR, EAST LOTHIAN, EH42 1PX Tel: 01368 865773 Fax: 01368 865773 E-mail: PETER@OBRZUD1.WANADOO.CO.UK *GARDEN LANDSCAPE,DESIGN AND MAINTENANCE.*

▶ Ga Services, 99 Cumberland Road, London, E13 8LH Tel: (020) 7476 2746 Fax: (020) 7476 5200

Gable (UK) Ltd, 17-19 Station Road, Hayling Island, Hampshire, PO11 0EA Tel: (023) 9246 6416 Fax: (023) 9246 7142 E-mail: gable@gable.co.uk *Roofing contractors*

The Gables, On The Bridge, Umberleigh, Devon, EX37 9AB Tel: (07866) 819703 E-mail: gablestearooms@tiscali.co.uk *The famous tea rooms by the River Taw, fine country views from tea garden. 0 year of grape vine in tea lounge.*We also have full lunch meals as well as home made cream teas.*

Gablesea Glassfibre Ltd, Howley Park Industrial Estate, Howley Park Road East, Morley, Leeds, LS27 0BN Tel: 0113-252 6511 Fax: 0113-253 1548 E-mail: sales@truckroofs.co.uk *Commercial vehicle roof builders services*

Gabriel & Co. Ltd, Abro Works, 10 Hay Hall Road, Tyseley, Birmingham, B11 2AU Tel: 0121-248 3333 Fax: 0121-248 3330 E-mail: sales@gabrielco.com *Steel casting & handrail manufrs*

▶ Gabriel Ash Ltd, Monument Farm, Churton Road, Farndon, Chester, CH3 6QP Tel: (01829) 271888 Fax: (01829) 271889 E-mail: sales@gabrielash.com

Gabriel Communications Ltd, 1st Floor, St. James's Buildings, Oxford Street, Manchester, M1 6FP Tel: 0161-236 8856 Fax: 0161-236 8530 E-mail: advertising@the-universe.net *Newspaper, magazine & directory publishers*

Gabriel Contractors Ltd, Jeffreys Road, Enfield, Middlesex, EN3 7UA Tel: (020) 8804 5444 Fax: (020) 8805 0813 E-mail: enquiries@gabrielceng.co.uk *Civil engineers*

Company Information

Gabriel Veterinary Supplies & Services, 452 Shaw Road, Royton, Oldham, OL2 6PG Tel: (01706) 881619 Fax: (01706) 881619 *Veterinary suppliers*

William Gabriel Ltd, Bloomfield Road, Bloomfield, Tipton, West Midlands, DY4 9BS Tel: 0121-520 2502 Fax: 0121-522 2913 *Crushed aggregate suppliers*

Gabriel-Chemie UK Ltd, Transfesa Road, Paddock Wood, Tonbridge, Kent, TN12 6UT Tel: (01892) 836566 Fax: (01892) 836979 E-mail: info@gabriel-chemie.com *Colour & additive masterbatch manufrs*

Gabriels Foods Ltd, Higher Poleo, Praze, Camborne, Cornwall, TR14 9PG Tel: (01209) 831284 Fax: (01209) 831228 E-mail: gabrielsfoods@btinternet.com *Food brokers & agents*

GAC Benair Ltd, Building 301 World Freight Terminal, Manchester Airport, Manchester, M90 5BF Tel: 0161-954 3300 Fax: 0161-436 1670 E-mail: manchester@gacworld.com *Freight forwarders & forwarding agents* Also at: Derby & London

▶ Gac Services, 36 Woodstock Grove, London, W12 8LE Tel: (020) 8749 7142 Fax: (020) 8749 7149

Gaddon Consulants, 18 New Royd, Millhouse Green, Sheffield, S36 9NW Tel: (01226) 766999 E-mail: sales@gaddon.co.uk *RF and Test Solution Consultancy.*RF and Electronics training courses.*Training course design*

Gadget & Gizmos, North Gate Business Centre, North Gate, Newark, Nottinghamshire, NG24 1EZ Tel: 01636 642855 Fax: 01636 862400 E-mail: info@gadget-and-gizmos.co.uk *Supplier and distributor for Navman, Road Angel, Origin, Snooper and Holux.*

GadgetandGift.co.uk, 1 Milhouse Crescent, Glasgow, G20 0UD Tel: 0870 7455030 Fax: 0870 7406812 E-mail: sales@gadgetandgift.co.uk *Gadgets and Gift Ideas *Unique gadgets and gifts for every *occasion and ages. Free UK Delivery *www.GadgetandGift.co.uk **

Gadmon Industries Ltd, 57 Glengall Road, London, SE15 6NF Tel: (020) 7277 8878 Fax: (020) 7277 9476 *Pipe lining manufrs*

Gael Force Ltd, 136 Anderson Street, Longman, Inverness, IV3 8DH Tel: (01463) 229448 Fax: (01463) 229421 E-mail: sales@gaelforce.net *Marine equipment distributors*

Gaeltec Ltd, Glendale Road, Dunvegan, Isle of Skye, IV55 8GU Tel: (01470) 521385 Fax: (01470) 521369 E-mail: info@gaeltec.com *Pressure transducer manufrs*

Gaf Interiors, 448 Queens Drive, West Derby, Liverpool, L13 0AR Tel: 0151-230 0033 Fax: 0151-230 0033 E-mail: jeanette@woolrich.fslife.co.uk *Interior design consultant services*

Gaffar Packaging Ltd, 65 Cobden Street, Leicester, LE1 2LB Tel: 0116-253 7766 Fax: 0116-229 0290 E-mail: gaffarpackaging@aol.com *Specialists in plain & printed paper, polythene, poly-prop bags, carrier bags, refuse sacks & adhesive tapes.*

Gaffney Gas Welding Supplies Ltd, 32-33 Brewsdale Road, Middlesbrough, Cleveland, TS3 6LJ Tel: (01642) 223466 Fax: (01642) 230224 *Industrial gas suppliers & welding equipment*

Gaffney Party Products, 215 Shrub End Road, Colchester, CO3 4PZ Tel: (01206) 766688 Fax: (01206) 766688 E-mail: sales@gaffneypartyproducts.co.uk *Party products distributors*

Gage Engineering Ltd, Unit 6 Poole Hall Industrial Estate, Ellesmere Port, CH66 1ST Tel: 0151-357 2070 Fax: 0151-357 3070 *Pipework erection & installation*

Gage Technique International Ltd, PO Box 30, Trowbridge, Wiltshire, BA14 8YD Tel: (01761) 431777 Fax: (01761) 431888 E-mail: info@gage-technique.demon.co.uk *Structural & geotechnical instrumentation engineers*

GAH Heating Products Ltd, Building 846, Bentwaters Park, Rendlesham, Woodbridge, Suffolk, IP12 2TW Tel: (01394) 421160 Fax: (01394) 421170 E-mail: mail@gah.co.uk *Boiler manufrs*

▶ Gaiety Balloons, 90 Kings Road, Brentwood, Essex, CM14 4DU Tel: (01277) 217997 *Party balloon retailers, party ware*

Gailey Marine Ltd, Gailey Wharf, Watling Street, Gailey, Stafford, ST19 5PR Tel: (01902) 790612 Fax: (01902) 791446 E-mail: jdboats@btinternet.com *Canal boat holiday hire*

▶ Gaining Ground Ltd, 4 Tapton Park Gardens, Tapton Park Road, Ranmoor, Sheffield, S10 3FP Tel: 0114 230 6048 Fax: 0870 0560215 E-mail: info@gainingground.co.uk *Complete advice and technical support in all levels of contaminated land assessment, brownfield regeneration and IPPC compliance. We will resolve your environmental problems effectively and efficiently, leaving you free to concentrate on your business*

Gainland International Ltd, Factory Road, Sandycroft, Deeside, Clwyd, CH5 2QJ Tel: (01244) 536326 Fax: (01244) 531254 E-mail: sandralewis@gccdiagnostics.com *Suppliers of chemicals & diagnostic reagents*

Gainsborough, 34-44 Northwood Street, Birmingham, B3 1TU Tel: 0121-236 2335 Fax: 0121-236 2846 E-mail: sales@gainsboroughsilver.co.uk *B.D.G. manufacture a range of the finest quality stainless steel cutlery, EPNS silver plated hotelware and tableware including Gainsborough silverware and Carpathian hotelware and flatware for the trade and industry.*

Gainsborough Ltd, Canal Road, Trowbridge, Wiltshire, BA14 8RQ Tel: (01225) 766341 Fax: (01225) 779129 E-mail: sales@gainsborough.ltd.uk *Furniture manufrs*

Gainsborough bathrooms Ltd, Seafield House, Claylands Avenue, Worksop, Nottinghamshire, S81 7BQ Tel: (01909) 471520 Fax: (01909) 471593 E-mail: keithtaylor@heatraesadia.com *Shower manufrs*

▶ Gainsborough Business Centres, 100 Pall Mall, St. James's, London, SW1Y 5HP Tel: (0800) 3282668 E-mail: sales@gainsbc.co.uk

▶ Gainsborough Communications, 34-36 High Holborn, London, WC1V 6AE Tel: (020) 7190 1700 Fax: (020) 7190 1701 E-mail: info@gainsboroughcomms.com *High-quality, independent financial and corporate communications advice and implementation.*

Gainsborough Craftsmen Ltd, Jennifer Works, Gainsborough, Lincolnshire, DN21 1HU Tel: (01427) 613994 Fax: (01427) 611949 *Designers & manufacturers of packaging systems*

▶ Gainsborough Electrical Services Ltd, Newholme Farm, Lark Hill Road, Canewdon, Rochford, Essex, SS4 3RX Tel: (01702) 257117 Fax: (01702) 258517

Gainsborough Electronic Controls Ltd, Unit 6 Warnford Industrial Estate, Clayton Road, Hayes, Middlesex, UB3 1BQ Tel: (020) 8573 9611 Fax: (020) 8569 2426 E-mail: info@gainsborough-controls.co.uk *Manufacturers of electric/electronic(industrial) equipment*

Gainsborough Engineering Co., Corringham Road Industrial Estate, Corringham Road, Gainsborough, Lincolnshire, DN21 1QB Tel: (01427) 617677 Fax: (01427) 810443 E-mail: info@gains-eng.co.uk *Filling & sealing machinery manufrs*

Gainsborough Industrial Controls Ltd, Foxby House, Foxby Hill, Gainsborough, Lincolnshire, DN21 1PN Tel: (01427) 611885 Fax: (01427) 611883 E-mail: sales@gic.uk.net *Packaging machinery manufrs*

▶ Gainsborough Reproductions Ltd, 1 Northmoor Industrial Estate, Moor Street, Brierley Hill, West Midlands, DY5 3SU Tel: (01384) 261009 Fax: (01384) 480226 E-mail: sales@gainsboroughloungesuites.co.uk *Manufacture 3 piece suites*

Gainsborough Silk Weaving Co. Ltd, Alexandra Road, Sudbury, Suffolk, CO10 2XH Tel: (01787) 372081 Fax: (01787) 881785 E-mail: sales@gainsborough.co.uk *Cotton, silk, furnishing fabrics & wallpapers suppliers & manufrs*

Gainsborough Software Ltd, 39 Anchorage Road, Sutton Coldfield, West Midlands, B74 2PJ Tel: 0121-321 2555 Fax: 0121-321 3555 E-mail: Accounts@gainsborough.com *Computer software & recruitment*

Gainsthorpe Furniture Ltd, Unit 5 Cromwell Centre, Roebuck Road, Ilford, Essex, IG6 3UG Tel: (020) 8501 3712 Fax: (020) 8501 5448 E-mail: info@gainsthorpe.co.uk *Tubular furniture manufrs*

▶ Gaj Construction Ltd, West Oak House, Westwood Way, Westwood Business Park, Coventry, CV4 8LB Tel: (024) 7642 2808 Fax: (024) 7642 2950

▶ Gala Distribution Ltd, 209 Uxbridge Road, London, W13 9AA Tel: (020) 8840 1222

▶ Gala Lights Ltd, Unit 10 , Britannia Business Park, Quarry Wood Industrial Estate, Aylesford, Kent, ME20 7NT Tel: (01622) 882424 Fax: (01622) 792041 E-mail: mick@galalights.com *Christmas illumination*

Gala Marketing Ltd, Farrier House, 221-223 High Street, Henley-In-Arden, West Midlands, B95 5BG Tel: (01564) 794005 Fax: (01564) 793301 *Overseas printing services*

Gala Occasions Ltd, Hurcott Hall Farm, Hurcott, Kidderminster, Worcestershire, DY10 3PH Tel: (01562) 825882 Fax: (01562) 741000 E-mail: galaltd@lineone.net *Marquee hire services*

▶ Galaxy Casino, Highfield Road, Kettering, Northamptonshire, NN15 6HT Tel: (01536) 000000 E-mail: caleb158@hotmail.co.uk *Win big, Win a massive jackpot and more in our superb online UK based casino.*

Galaxy Labels, 16 Imperial Avenue, Gedling, Nottingham, NG4 3NE Tel: 0115-956 1516 Fax: 0115-956 1516 *Label printing*

Galaxy Manufacturing Co., 59 Mere Lane, Rochdale, Lancashire, OL11 3TD Tel: (01706) 642575 Fax: (01706) 642517 *Garment manufrs*

Galboola Ltd, 23 Blenheim Road, St. Dials, Cwmbran, Gwent, NP44 4NA Tel: (01633) 862853 Fax: (01633) 877524 *Civil Engineering*

Galbraith Aerospace Fasteners Ltd, 54b Lilford Road, Camberwell, London, SE5 9HY Tel: (020) 7733 0118 Fax: (020) 7733 0118 *Aircraft fastener manufrs*

Galbraith's Ltd, Bridge Gate House, 124-126 Borough High Street, London, SE1 1BL Tel: (020) 7378 6363 Fax: (020) 7959 1086 E-mail: admin@galbraiths.co.uk *Ship brokers*

Gale & Co. Ltd, 12 Lee Bank House, Blucher Street, Birmingham, B1 1HP Tel: 0121-643 6639 Fax: 0121-643 6161 *Picture framers & restorers*

Gale Construction Co. Ltd, Ayton Road, Wymondham, Norfolk, NR18 0QQ Tel: (01953) 604537 Fax: (01953) 602680 E-mail: info@gale-construction.co.uk *General roofing & industrial cladding contractors*

Gale Furs Ltd, Unit 7 Plough Yard, London, EC2A 3LP Tel: (020) 7247 2014 Fax: (020) 7377 6792 *Fur garment manufrs*

Gale Furs, 65 Regents Park Road, London, NW1 8XD Tel: (020) 7722 5870 Fax: (020) 7722 8830 *Fashion retailers*

▶ Tim Gale Consulting Ltd, Red Shute Mill Business Centre, Red Shute Hill, Hermitage, Thatcham, Berkshire, RG18 9QL Tel: (01635) 202080 Fax: (08700) 940517 E-mail: tim@t-g-c.net *Consulting offers a complete electronic product design service*

Gale Tower Ltd, 102-106 Harrow Road, London, E11 3QE Tel: (020) 8519 3531 Fax: (020) 8519 3531 *Joinery*

Galea Sunblinds, 2 Station Shops, Westborough, Scarborough, North Yorkshire, YO11 1TR Tel: (01723) 353513 Fax: (01723) 341010 *Sunblind manufrs*

Galemain Engineering Services Ltd, New Street, Holbrook Industrial Estate, Holbrook, Sheffield, S20 3GH Tel: 0114-247 3347 Fax: 0114-248 7301 E-mail: galemain@aol.com *Steel erection fabricators & installers*

Galen Herbal Supplies Ltd, Unit 17 St Davids Industrial, Pengam, Blackwood, Gwent, NP12 3SW Tel: (01443) 820024 Fax: (01443) 820037 E-mail: sales@galenherbalsupplies.com *Pharmaceutical distributors & manufrs*

Galena (Fire Engineering) Ltd, Studland Street, London, W6 0JX Tel: (020) 8748 6154 Fax: (020) 8748 9885 E-mail: sales@galena.sagehost.co.uk *Firefighting equipment manufrs*

Galglass Ltd, 321 Hough Lane, Wombwell, Barnsley, South Yorkshire, S73 0LR Tel: (01226) 340370 Fax: (01226) 344200 E-mail: sscott@galglass.co.uk *Specialist designers*

▶ Galgo (UK) Ltd, Mark House, Mark Road, Hemel Hempstead, Hertfordshire, HP2 7UA Tel: (01442) 283890 Fax: (01442) 283891 E-mail: info@galgo.co.uk *Distributions services*

Galgorm Group, 7 Corbally Road, Galgorm, Ballymena, County Antrim, BT42 1JQ Tel: (028) 2564 8521 Fax: (028) 2564 7614 *Hygiene & catering suppliers*

Galgrom Group, 81-87 Academy Street, Belfast, BT1 2LS Tel: (028) 9032 2042 Fax: (028) 9023 3119 E-mail: sales@galgormgroup.com *Catering equipment suppliers*

Galiform Corporate Services Ltd, Thorpe Road, Howden, Goole, North Humberside, DN14 7PA Tel: (01430) 430905 Fax: (01430) 431540 *Kitchen & bedroom manufrs*

Galino Ltd, 2 South Caldeen Road, Coatbridge, Lanarkshire, ML5 4EG Tel: (01236) 449898 Fax: (01236) 449899 E-mail: galino.ltd@virgin.net *Stapling & nailing equipment suppliers & manufrs*

Galito Ltd, 357 Thorp Arch Trading Estate, Thorp Arch, Wetherby, West Yorkshire, LS23 7BJ Tel: (01937) 844698 Fax: (01937) 844509 E-mail: info@gallito.co.uk *Spray & finishing unit manufrs*

▶ Gallacher Bros Haulage Ltd, Morrison Industrial Estate North, Stanley, County Durham, DH9 7RU Tel: (01207) 233334 Fax: (01207) 283552

O. Gallachor Painting & Decorating, 21 Prince George Rd, London, Greater London, N16 8DL Tel: 07879 484286 E-mail: colm01@blueyonder.co.uk *Painting and Decorating*

Gallafent & Co., 9 Staple Inn, London, WC1V 7QH Tel: (020) 7242 3094 Fax: (020) 7539 4999 E-mail: rg@rkallafent.compulink.co.uk *Chartered patent agents*

Gallagher & Mckinney, Carrakeel Drive, Maydown, Londonderry, BT47 6UQ Tel: (028) 7186 1068 Fax: (028) 7186 1069 E-mail: paula@gmck.com *Mechanical engineers & fabricators*

▶ P.J. Gallagher Suspended Ceilings, 61 Berkeley Heights, Killyclogher, Omagh, County Tyrone, BT79 7PR Tel: (028) 8224 4845 Fax: (028) 8224 1670 E-mail: info@pjgallagher.co.uk *Specialists in Metal suud partitions, Drylining and all types of suspended ceilings*

Gallagher Partitioning, Springfield Works, Salwick, Preston, PR4 0XJ Tel: (01772) 721091 Fax: (01772) 721091 *Industrial partitioning installers*

▶ Gallagher Plant Ltd, Coldharbour Lane, Aylesford, Kent, ME20 7NS Tel: (01622) 716543 Fax: (01622) 882366 E-mail: enquiries@gallagher-group.co.uk *Aggregates, building materials, civil engineering & ground worker services*

Gallagher Power Fence (UK) Ltd, Curriers Close, Coventry, CV4 8AW Tel: (0870) 2010101 Fax: (0870) 0111545 E-mail: info@gallagher.co.uk *Provide agricultural materials*

Gallagher Tom Ltd, 156-158 Derby Street, Bolton, BL3 6JR Tel: (01204) 389792 Fax: (01204) 370929 E-mail: tomgallltd@aol.com *Building services engineers*

Gallaher Group plc, Members Hill, Brooklands Road, Weybridge, Surrey, KT13 0QU Tel: (01932) 859777 Fax: (01932) 832792 E-mail: info@gallaherltd.com *Tobacco & cigarette manufrs* Also at: Belfast, Cardiff, Crewe, Hyde & Perival

Gallant 2000 Ltd, 401f The Big Peg, Vyse Street, Hockley, Birmingham, B18 6NF Tel: 0121-212 3410 Fax: 0121-212 3410 E-mail: gallant@netcomuk.co.uk *Traditional & innovative networking events; workshops (focusing on creating business opportunities); business development events; full time staff providing the network hub; consortia & partnership working; consultancy (using business psychology frameworks); linkages to Government funding opportunities*

Gallant Training Services, Brook Works, Main Street, Frodsham, WA6 7AY Tel: (01928) 734300 Fax: (01928) 734300 E-mail: gallanttrngserv@aol.com *R.T.I.T.B accredited for all Forklift Truck Training, from the very smallest pedestrian operator. To the largest container handlers. Also accredited for MEWPs, (ie) mobile elevating work platforms, and hydraulic lorry mounted loaders,(eg) HIAB.*

Gallaway Aquatics & Water Gardens, Bladnoch, Wigtown, Newton Stewart, Wigtownshire, DG8 9AB Tel: (01988) 403363 Fax: (01671) 401333 *Fishing & angling equipment suppliers*

▶ Gallaway Group Northern, Low Mill Lane, Ravensthorpe Industrial Estate, Dewsbury, West Yorkshire, WF13 3LN Tel: (01924) 490056 Fax: (01924) 490763 E-mail: sales.dewsbury@gallowaygroup.co.uk *Ventilation ductwork contractor*

Gallay Ltd, Paterson Road, Finedon Road Industrial Estate, Wellingborough, Northamptonshire, NN8 4BZ Tel: (01933) 224801 Fax: (01933) 279902 E-mail: sales@gallay.co.uk *Heat exchanger manufrs*

▶ Galldris Construction Ltd, Unit C, Mollison Avenue, Enfield, Middlesex, EN3 7UH Tel: (020) 8804 8569

Galleon International Shipping Co. Ltd, Galleon House Thurrock Commercial Centre, Purfleet Industrial Park, Aveley, South Ockendon, Essex, RM15 4YA Tel: (01708) 868068 Fax: (01708) 864321 E-mail: galleon.international@virgin.net *Overseas removal company*

Galleon Jewellery Manufacturing Co. Ltd, 1 Northampton Street, Birmingham, B18 6DU Tel: 0121-236 4600 Fax: 0121-212 1688 *Earring & jewellery manufrs*

Gallery Partnership Ltd, 53-55 The Hop Exchange, 24 Southwark Street, London, SE1 1TY Tel: (020) 7096 2800 Fax: (020) 7096 2810 E-mail: mkemp@gallerypartnership.co.uk *Computer consultants*

▶ Galley Matrix, 1 Waterside Industrial Park, Waterside Road, Leeds, LS10 1RW Tel: 0113-277 7788 Fax: 0113-277 5151

Galley-Pak, Galley-Pak House, 38 Greenfields, Shillington, Hitchin, Hertfordshire, SG5 3NX Tel: (01462) 711545 Fax: (01462) 712970 E-mail: john@galley-pak.com *Packaging equipment, machine & system merchants*

▶ Galleywood Construction Ltd, Lodge Road, Hazeleigh, Chelmsford, CM3 6QX Tel: (01621) 828700 Fax: (01621) 826997

Galliers Ltd, Oxon Business Park, Bicton Heath, Shrewsbury, SY3 5DD Tel: (01743) 232040 Fax: (01743) 355669 E-mail: info@frankgalliers.co.uk *Building & construction contractors*

Galliford Try, Crab Lane, Fearnhead, Warrington, WA2 0XR Tel: (01925) 822821 Fax: (01925) 827924 E-mail: mail@galliford-northan.co.uk *Construction company services*

Galliford Try Partnership Ltd, 50 Rainsford Road, Chelmsford, CM1 2XB Tel: (01245) 494849 Fax: (01245) 493494 E-mail: sales@gallifordtry.co.uk *Public work contractors*

Galliford Try Services Ltd, Cowley Business Park, Packet Boat Lane, Uxbridge, Middlesex, UB8 2AL Tel: (01895) 855001 Fax: (01895) 855298 E-mail: self@gallifordtry.co.uk *Building contractors*

▶ Gallon's Grab & Tipper Hire, 2505 Stratford Road Hockley Heath, Solihull, Birmingham, B94 6NN Tel: (01564) 793419 Fax: (01564) 783451 E-mail: adgallon@hotmail.com *We run 6/8 wheeler Grab Lorries and 8 Wheeler Tipper Muck away Price per Load and site Clearance Call for Details 07971 600 180/190*

Galloway Acoustics, Low Mill Lane, Ravensthorpe Industrial Estate, Dewsbury, West Yorkshire, WF13 3LN Tel: (01924) 498818 Fax: (01924) 498414 E-mail: sales.dewsbury@gallowaygroup.co.uk *Acoustic consultants*

Galloway Boats & Mouldings Ltd, Culdoach Road, Tongland, Kirkcudbright, DG6 4LU Tel: (01557) 331973 Fax: (01557) 331978 E-mail: ian.carsen@talk21.com *Plastics & mouldings manufrs*

Galloway Computer Services, 41 Barnton Road, Dumfries, DG1 4HN Tel: (01387) 259096 Fax: (01387) 259096 *Computer software suppliers*

▶ Galloway Computer Services, 21 Claddyburn Terrace, Cairnryan, Stranraer, Wigtownshire, DG9 8RD Tel: (01581) 200650 E-mail: claddyburn@hotmail.com *ICT*

Galloway Granite Works, Sorbie, Newton Stewart, Wigtownshire, DG8 8EW Tel: (01988) 850350 Fax: (01988) 850340 E-mail: galloway-granite@btconect.com *Granite & stone masons*

Lauries Galloway Tablet, 3 Station Road, Dalbeattie, Kirkcudbrightshire, DG5 4AN Tel: (01556) 610731 *Confectionery manufrs*

Galloway Lodge Preserves, 24-28 High Street, Gatehouse of Fleet, Castle Douglas, Kirkcudbrightshire, DG7 2HP Tel: (01557) 814357 Fax: (01557) 814046 *Preserves manufrs*

Galloway Pest Control, 38 Bluebell Close, Kingsnorth, Ashford, Kent, TN23 3NG Tel: (01233) 502811 Fax: (01233) 502811 E-mail: mark@galloway123wanadoo.co.uk *Pest control*

Galloway Smokehouse, Carsluith, Newton Stewart, Wigtownshire, DG8 7DN Tel: (01671) 820354 Fax: (01671) 820545 *Smoked salmon manufrs*

▶ Galloway Windows, Creebridge Mill, Creebridge, Newton Stewart, Wigtownshire, DG8 6NP Tel: (01671) 404848 Fax: (01671) 404969 *Contraction materials suppliers*

The Gallup Organisation Ltd, Drapers Court, Kingston Hall Road, Kingston upon Thames, Surrey, KT1 2BG Tel: (020) 8939 7000 Fax: (020) 8939 7039 *Market researchers & opinion pollsters* Also at: Thame

Gallyon & Sons Ltd, 4 Dereham Road, Garvestone, Norwich, NR9 4AD Tel: (01953) 850215 Fax: (01953) 851800 E-mail: rgallyon@freenetname.co.uk *Gun manufrs*

Galm Ltd, 129a London Road, Bexhill-on-Sea, East Sussex, TN39 4AB Tel: (01424) 223290 Fax: (01424) 223290 *General engineers*

▶ Galopeur Equestrian Supplies Ltd, Whitebridge Lane, Stone, Staffordshire, ST15 8LQ Tel: (01785) 816969 *Equestrian equipment distributors*

Galpeg Ltd, 70 Hampden Road, London, N10 2NX Tel: (020) 8444 4455 Fax: (020) 8442 0357 E-mail: sales@galpeg.com *Premiums & promotional product specialists*

James Galt & Co. Ltd, Sovereign House, Stockport Road, Cheadle, Cheshire, SK8 2EA Tel: 0161-428 9111 Fax: 0161-428 6597 E-mail: sales@galt.co.uk *Toy manufrs*

▶ Galt Transport, Bankend Road, Broadmeadow Industrial Estate, Dumbarton, G82 2RB Tel: (01389) 765454 Fax: (01389) 730460

▶ Galtec Ltd, Bentham Lane, Witcombe, Gloucester, GL3 4UD Tel: (01452) 863666

Galtee Meats (U K), 45 St Peters Street, Canterbury, Kent, CT1 2BG Tel: (01227) 787900 *Meat distributor*

Galup Ltd, 48 Elmsdale Road, Wooton, Bedford, MK43 9JU Tel: (01234) 768805 Fax: (01234) 767532 E-mail: sales@galupltd.co.uk *Aluminium & alloy tube manufrs*

Galvanised Bolts & Nuts Ltd, 115 Lodgefield Road, Halesowen, West Midlands, B62 8AX Tel: 0121-602 3333 Fax: 0121-602 4040 E-mail: galvanised.boltsandnuts@btconnect.com *Bolt, nut & fastener distributors*

Galvanised Sheet & Coil Ltd, Doris Road, Bordesley Green, Birmingham, B9 4SJ Tel: 0121-773 8341 Fax: 0121-771 0024 *Steel stock holders & de-coilers*

Galvanizers Association, Wrens Court, 56 Victoria Road, Sutton Coldfield, West Midlands, B72 1SY Tel: 0121-355 8838 Fax: 0121-355 8727 E-mail: ga@hdg.org.uk *Market development organisation*

Gamallt Ready Mix Concrete Ltd, Gamallt, Pantygrwndy, Cardigan, Dyfed, SA43 3NP Tel: (01239) 613257 Fax: (01239) 613257 E-mail: sales@gamalt.co.uk *Concrete & mortar ready mixed*

F.L. Gamble & Sons Ltd, Meadow Road Industrial Estate, Dale Road, Worthing, West Sussex, BN11 2RY Tel: (01903) 230906 Fax: (01903) 210569 E-mail: sales@gamble-jarvis.co.uk *Plant & access hire services*

▶ Game, Unit 19 Gallions Reach Shopping Park, Armada Way, London, E6 7ER Tel: (020) 7511 3600 Fax: (020) 7511 3600 *Computer software services*

▶ Game Box, 85 High Street, Lochee, Dundee, DD2 3AT Tel: (01382) 612159 *Computer software suppliers, computer games*

Game Engineering Ltd, Camp Road, Witham St. Hughs, Lincoln, LN6 9TW Tel: (01522) 868021 Fax: (01522) 868027 E-mail: sales@game-security-engineering.com *Materials handling equipment manufrs*

▶ Game Stores Ltd, Bon Accord Centre, George Street, Aberdeen, AB25 1HZ Tel: (01224) 626785 E-mail: sales@game.net

Game Stores Ltd, 120 High Street, Ayr, KA7 1PR Tel: (01292) 266066 *Computer games retailer*

Game Stores Ltd, 43-44 Western Road, Brighton, BN1 2EB Tel: (01273) 734737 *Computer software suppliers*

▶ Game Stores Ltd, 17 Chapel Street, Exmouth, Devon, EX8 1HS Tel: (01395) 260240 *Computer software services*

Game Stores Ltd, 43 Friargate, Freshney Place, Grimsby, South Humberside, DN31 1EL Tel: (01472) 345466 *Software dealer*

Game Stores Ltd, 13 Harvey Centre, Harlow, Essex, CM20 1XN Tel: (01279) 435486 *Software specialists computer games*

Game Stores Ltd, 19 Tavern Street, Ipswich, IP1 3AA Tel: (01473) 230162 Fax: (01473) 230162 *Computer software retail*

Game Stores Ltd, 142-144 The Luton Arndale Centre, Luton, LU1 2TJ Tel: (01582) 457823 *Software supplier*

▶ Game Stores Ltd, 38 High Street, Rhyl, Clwyd, LL18 1ET Tel: (01745) 355060

Game Stores Ltd, 56-72 Market Place, Romford, RM1 3ET Tel: (01708) 768206 *Computer games retailer*

Game Stores Ltd, F Churchway Potteries Shopping Centre, Market Square, Stoke-on-Trent, ST1 1PS Tel: (01782) 280596 Fax: (01782) 280596 *Computer games retailers*

Game Stores Ltd, 45-46 Fore Street, Taunton, Somerset, TA1 1HR Tel: (01823) 321558 Fax: (01823) 354106 *Computer software retailers*

Game Stores Ltd, 4-6 Pydar Street, Truro, Cornwall, TR1 2AR Tel: (01872) 272861 *Computer systems & software distributors*

▶ Games Play UK, 64 Orchard Street, Weston-super-Mare, Avon, BS23 1RL Tel: (01934) 625123 Fax: (01934) 645193 E-mail: gamesplayukinfo@aol.com *Developer of new toys & games*

▶ Games & Print Services, 10 Kings Road, Canvey Island, Essex, SS8 0QY Tel: (01268) 511522 Fax: (01268) 510337

Games Tec, Unit 4 Motorlink, Righead Industrial Estate, Bellshill, Lanarkshire, ML4 3LA Tel: (01698) 843344 Fax: (01698) 740829 *Cement machine distributors*

Gamesoft Amusement Machines, Unit E1 South Point 2, Foreshore Road, Cardiff, CF10 4SP Tel: (029) 2045 3300 Fax: (029) 2045 3301 *Amusement machines & equipment manufrs*

Thomas Gameson & Sons Ltd, PO Box 1, Cannock, Staffordshire, WS11 0AX Tel: (01543) 504191 Fax: (01543) 462482 *Tin plating & tinning services*

Gamestec, Provincial House, Hedworth Lane, Boldon Colliery, Tyne & Wear, NE35 9HS Tel: 0191-581 3233 *Amusement machine suppliers*

Gamestech Ltd, Low Lane, Horsforth, Leeds, LS18 4ER Tel: 0113-258 9495 Fax: 0113-239 0072 *Hire fruit & gaming machines*

Gamestick Ltd, 68H Wyrley Road, Birmingham, B6 7BN Tel: 0121-327 2500 Fax: 0121-327 2500 *Shooting sticks manufrs*

Gamet Bearings, Hythe Station Road, Colchester, CO2 8LD Tel: (01206) 862121 Fax: (01206) 868690 E-mail: sales@gamet-bearings.co.uk *Roller bearing manufrs*

Gametime Leisure, 8 Fleet Business Park, Itlings Lane, Hessle, North Humberside, HU13 9LX Tel: (01482) 647979 Fax: (01482) 647979 *Jukebox & game services*

Gamma Beta Holdings Ltd, Briggella Mills, Bradford, West Yorkshire, BD5 0QA Tel: (01274) 525508 Fax: (01274) 521157 E-mail: furnishing@hield.co.uk *Fine worsted & mohair manufrs* Also at: Morley

▶ Gamma Dataware, Hillington Park Innovation Centre, 1 Ainslie Road, Glasgow, G52 4RU Tel: 0141-585 6338

Gamma Global, 157 Warwick Road, Solihull, West Midlands, B92 7AR Tel: 0121-706 8080 Fax: 0121-706 1188 *Computer hardware distributors*

Gamma Hose Ltd, Gamma Works, New Street, Earl Shilton, Leicester, LE9 7FS Tel: (01455) 847081 Fax: (01455) 842940 E-mail: sales@gammahose.com *Supply all types of industrial hose*

▶ Gamma Illumination Ltd, Conway House, Tenterfields, Thornhill Road, Dewsbury, West Yorkshire, WF12 9QW Tel: (01924) 482777 Fax: (01924) 438388

continued

E-mail: sales@gamma-uk.com *Design & manufacturer, recessed down lights & luminaries for retail*

Gamma Projects Ltd, Willcrick Magor, Undy, Caldicot, Gwent, NP26 3DA Tel: (01633) 883000 Fax: (01633) 882990 E-mail: enquiries@gammaprojects.com *Telecommunications software & consultants*

Gamma Secure Systems, Diamond House, 149 Frimley Road, Camberley, Surrey, GU15 2PS Tel: (01276) 702500 Fax: (01276) 692903 E-mail: dbrewer@gammassl.co.uk *Information security consultancy*

Gammax Independent Inspection Services Ltd, The Grove, The Green, Depten, Bury St. Edmunds, Suffolk, IP29 4BY Tel: (01284) 850888 Fax: (01284) 850808 *Industrial x-ray inspection services*

▶ Gamrie's Candle World, Main Street, Garmond, Turriff, Aberdeenshire, AB53 5TQ Tel: (01888) 544170 Fax: (01888) 544415 E-mail: sales@gamriescandles.co.uk *Manufacturers of coloured, scented & personalised candles*

▶ Gandalf's Garden, Manchester House, Bridge Street, Cardigan, Dyfed, SA43 1HY Tel: (01239) 621107 Fax: (01239) 621107 *Garden furniture, home ware art works suppliers*

▶ Gane Data Scan, Clayton Wood Rise, Leeds, LS16 6RF Tel: (0870) 2417356 Fax: (0870) 2417357 E-mail: sales@ganedatascan.com *Bar coding products*

Brian Ganman, Fordbrook Industrial Estate, Marlborough Road, Pewsey, Wiltshire, SN9 5NT Tel: (01672) 563759 Fax: (01672) 563759 *Precision engineers*

Gannochy Coins & Medals, 46 Burleigh Street, Cambridge, CB1 1DJ Tel: (01223) 461505 Fax: (01223) 461505 E-mail: gannothycoins@aol.com *Coins & medals retailers*

Gantry Railing Ltd, Sudmeadow Road, Gloucester, GL2 5HG Tel: (01452) 300688 Fax: (01452) 300198 E-mail: info@gantry.co.uk Principal Export Areas: Worldwide *Crane track contractors or suppliers & crane track fastenings manufrs*

Gap Ltd, 12 Ridge Way, Donibristle Industrial Park, Hillend, Dunfermline, Fife, KY11 9JN Tel: (01383) 824181 Fax: (01383) 824722 E-mail: mark.adams@gap.uk *Draught excluder & weather seal distributors*

▶ The Gap, 167-201 Argyle Street, Glasgow, G2 8DJ Tel: 0141-221 0629

▶ GaP Management Ltd, PO Box 292, Barnsley, South Yorkshire, S75 3YB Tel: 01226 290288 E-mail: info@gapmanagement.co.uk *Helping SMES across a wide range of industries to increase sales and increase profits with practical advice on sales marketing and business development.*Help for all types of business from start-ups to established businesses.*

Gapint Ltd, The Old Mill, Wellington Street, Ripley, Derbyshire, DE5 3EH Tel: (01773) 741174 Fax: (01773) 570247 E-mail: enquiries@gapint.co.uk *Computer systems integration services*

Garador Enquiries, Bunford Lane, Yeovil, Somerset, BA20 2EJ Tel: (0800) 706670 Fax: (01935) 443744 E-mail: enquiries@garador.co.uk *Door (steel) manufrs*

Garafit Services Ltd, Willis House, Flowers Hill, Bristol, BS4 5JJ Tel: 0117-971 1451 Fax: 0117-977 8022 E-mail: garafit.info@garafit.com *Garage service equipment distribs*

The Garage Door Co., Unit 7 Russell Road Industrial Estate, Sauchiebank, Edinburgh, EH11 2NN Tel: 0131-337 3332 Fax: 0131-313 2778 E-mail: sales@garage-door.co.uk *Industrial door suppliers*

The Garage Door Centre, 6-8 Meadow Close, Wellingborough, Northamptonshire, NN8 4BH Tel: (01933) 229135 Fax: (01933) 442676 *Sectional doors & roller shutter manufrs*

▶ The Garage Door & Gate Automation Co., Unit 7 Block D, Isle of Man Business Park, Isle of Man, IM2 2QY Tel: (01624) 624122 Fax: (01624) 623877 E-mail: info@manxgaragedoors.com *Garage doors & gates installation service*

▶ Garage Door Solutions, 11 Lotland Street, Inverness, IV1 1ST Tel: (01463) 714123 Fax: (01463) 714123

Garage Doors (London) Ltd, 37 Waterloo Road, London, NW2 7TS Tel: (020) 8452 1233 Fax: (020) 8208 2213 *Garage door engineers* Also at: Branches throughout the U.K.

Garage Equipment Maintenance Co. Ltd, 153-165 Bridge Street, Northampton, NN1 1QG Tel: (01604) 828500 Fax: (01604) 232995 E-mail: sales@gemco.co.uk *Repair & sale garage equipment services*

Garage Equipment Services, Unit 2100, The Crescent, Solihull Parkway, Birmingham Business Park, Birmingham, B37 7YE Tel: 0121-329 1154 Fax: 0121-329 1190 E-mail: ges@unipart.co.uk *Workshop & bodyshop design & fitout*

Garage Re Vamps, 71 Town Street, Stanningley, Pudsey, West Yorkshire, LS28 6ES Tel: 0113-257 3441 Fax: 0113-204 0473 E-mail: info@revamp.co.uk *Concrete garage builders*

The Garage Street Shoes, Unit 13 St. Johns Centre, Leeds, LS2 8LQ Tel: 0113-273 9700 Fax: 0113-232 9221 E-mail: waynesshoes@aol.com *Boots & shoes retail & wholesalers*

▶ Garage Wizards, 4 Cambridge Terrace, St James Road, Brackley, Northamptonshire, NN13 7XY Tel: 01280 700563 Fax: 01280 700444 E-mail: info@garagewizards.com *Garage Wizards has developed a garage storage system range to help you transform your garage using a simple-to-install solution designed for those wishing to invest in home improvement. **Our range of storage cabinets, wall units, shelving and storage hooks are designed to help you conquer the mess. The result - an organized garage **

▶ Garan Instruments Ltd, 26 St Agnes Road, Heath, Cardiff, CF14 4AP Tel: (029) 2079 7959 Fax: (029) 2079 7939 E-mail: sales@garan.co.uk *Load weighing system supplier*

Garban Intercapital, Park House, Finsbury Circus, London, EC2M 7UR Tel: (020) 7638 7592 Fax: (020) 7374 6743 *Money brokers*

▶ Garbetts Ltd, 2 New Road, Brading, Sandown, Isle of Wight, PO36 0DT Tel: (01983) 400350 Fax: (01983) 404016 E-mail: office@garbetts.com *Chartered Certified Accountants on the Isle of Wight, UK, specalising in small businesses and taxation.*

V. Garcia & Son, Malakoff Works, Malakoff Street, Stalybridge, Cheshire, SK15 1TD Tel: 0161-303 7383 Fax: 0161-338 2151 E-mail: bill-garcia@btconnect.com *Light engineering services*

Garcross Engineering, Brandon Building, Pepper Road, Leeds, LS10 2RU Tel: 0113-271 4230 Fax: 0113-271 4240 E-mail: sales@garcross.co.uk *Laser cutting services*

▶ Gard Plasticases Ltd, 2 Arnolds Business Park, Branbridges Road, East Peckham, Tonbridge, Kent, TN12 5LG Tel: (01622) 871887 Fax: (01622) 871895 E-mail: sales@gardplasticases.com *Manufacturers & providers of cases*

Garden Buildings Services, 60 Dalton Street, Hartlepool, Cleveland, TS26 9EL Tel: (01429) 861169 Fax: (01429) 861169 E-mail: sales@gardenbuildingservices.co.uk *Garden furniture*

Garden Centre, 53 High Street, Brecon, Powys, LD3 7AP Tel: (01874) 625913 *Garden & pet material distributors*

Garden City Blinds, 7 Factory Place, Saltcoats, Ayrshire, KA21 5LA Tel: (01294) 604016 Fax: (01294) 604016 *Window blind manufrs*

Garden City Packaging Ltd, 10 Blackhorse Road, Letchworth Garden City, Hertfordshire, SG6 1HB Tel: (01462) 686200 Fax: (01462) 677042 E-mail: gcp@idnet.co.uk *Packaging material, goods & product merchants*

Garden Crafts, Workshop Showroom, Forden, Welshpool, Powys, SY21 8NE Tel: (01938) 580401 *Garden furniture manufrs*

▶ The Garden Design Co., 109 Brewery Road, Pampisford, Cambridge, CB22 3EW Tel: (01223) 835889 Fax: (01223) 835889 E-mail: gardendesignco@btinternet.com *From traditional to minimal we create gardens for the individual.**RHS Hampton Court Silver Medal Winners.**Design & Construction. Project Management. Planting Schemes.**All our gardens are carefully designed and constructed to the very highest standards by experienced landscapers, to suit your style and budget.*

▶ Garden Fencing, Shipyard Estate, Brightlingsea, Colchester, CO7 0AR Tel: (01206) 308900 Fax: (01206) 308623 *Fencing & decking manufrs*

The Garden Furniture Centre Ltd, Yew Tree Farm, Stratford Road, Wootton Wawen, Henley-in-Arden, West Midlands, B95 6BY Tel: (01564) 793652 Fax: (01564) 793652 E-mail: sales@gardenfurniturecentre.co.uk *Flat pack garden furniture import service*

▶ Garden Furniture Online, Thorp Arch, Wetherby, West Yorkshire, LS23 7RR Tel: 0800 931 7777 Fax: 0870 7776665 E-mail: sales@gardenfurnitureonline.com *Gardening retailer offering an exclusive range of luxury hardwood garden furniture, patio heaters, garden benches, gas barbeques & garden parasols for commercial & domestic use.*

▶ The Garden Gate Co UK Ltd, Pepperhill Works, Hungary Hill, Stourbridge, West Midlands, DY9 7NH Tel: (01384) 392300 Fax: (01384) 372948 E-mail: enquiries@thegardengate.biz *Quality wrought iron gates, railing & fencing. Associated garden products including coal bunkers, incinerators, compost bins, lawnmowers etc. All available to order on-line with free UK mainland delivery*

Garden House Press Ltd, G H P House, 23 Aintree Road, Greenford, Middlesex, UB6 7LA Tel: (0870) 7773300 Fax: (0870) 7773301 E-mail: sales@garden-house.co.uk *Printing company*

▶ Garden Iron, Four Oaks, Newent, Gloucestershire, GL18 1LU Tel: (01531) 890123 Fax: (01531) 890136 E-mail: info@gardeniron.co.uk *Garden furniture*

Garden Leisure Furniture Ltd, Unit 12 Hartlebury Trading Estate, Hartlebury, Kidderminster, Worcestershire, DY10 4JB Tel: (01299) 251883 Fax: (01299) 251563 .

▶ Garden Machinery Direct, 4 Newtown Road, Worcester, WR5 1HF Tel: (01905) 619522 Fax: (01905) 726241 E-mail: sales@gardenmachinerydirect.co.uk *Garden machinery retailer*

Garden Machines (Northampton) Ltd, 66-70 Kingsthorpe Road, Northampton, NN2 6HD Tel: (01604) 716222 Fax: (01604) 722082 E-mail: sales@gardenmachinesltd.co.uk *Garden machine distributors, selling STIHL, MOUNTFIELD, HONDA, HUSQVARNA, HAYTER, LAWNFLITE, ATCO, BOSCH. WE ALSO STOCK A WIDE RANGE OF ARBORIST EQUIPMENT AND AQUATIC PRODUCTS.*

▶ Garden Offices Limited, 4 Fareham Road, Gosport, Hampshire, PO13 9AX Tel: 01329 285563 Fax: 01329 237056 E-mail: sales@garden-offices.co.uk *A modular building from GARDEN OFFICES is the ideal environment for people working from home in all weather throughout the whole year, especially for a small business. Far cheaper than a building extension, GARDEN OFFICES insulated buildings need almost no maintenance.**Ideal as garden Studio, Games Room, Pool Changing Room, Music Room, Garden Room, Workroom, Garden Workshop, Summerhouse, Home office, Study.*

▶ Garden Options Ltd, 3 The Wynd, Melrose, Roxburghshire, TD6 9LD Tel: (01896) 820630 E-mail: enquiries@gardenoptions.co.uk *Garden design & build landscaping company*

Garden Products, 1 River Side Industrial Estate, Dodsworth Street, Darlington, County Durham, DL1 2UH Tel: (01325) 488341 Fax: (01325) 488341 *Timber buildings*

Garden Scene, Potter La, Higher Walton, Preston, PR5 4EN Tel: 01772 877441 *Floral displays*

Garden Scenes Ltd, The Fourwinds, Bridge Hill Road, Newborough, Peterborough, PE6 7SA Tel: (01733) 810400 E-mail: sean@gardenscenes.fsnet.co.uk *Garden Scenes Ltd of Preson UK put pride and effort into their garden creations, and that is what they do best "Create Garden Scenes". Whatever feel or look you are after Garden Scenes Ltd will give you advice on what will and will not work From making a stunning entrance to your home with a block paved driveway to a full landscaped garden with plants and water features. Decking is the new creation where you get the natural look of wood along with somewhere really special for fresco dining and superb relaxing.*

Garden Supply Nursery, 1 Hill Cottage, Landermere Road, Thorpe-Le-Soken, Clacton-On-Sea, Essex, CO16 0NF Tel: (01255) 860073 *Concrete manufrs*

Garden Systems, 103 Burrell Road, Ipswich, IP2 8AD Tel: (0845) 1181253 Fax: (0845) 1181380 E-mail: sales@gardensystems.co.uk *Water irrigation contractors*

▶ Garden Wizard, Hoghton Road, Leyland, PR25 1XX Tel: (01772) 454724

Gardener Computer Systems Ltd, 6 De Montfort Mews, Leicester, LE1 7FW Tel: 0116-223 0233 Fax: 0116-223 0664 E-mail: mark.gcs@ntlworld.com *Computer consultancy*

▶ Gardenia West Wales Ltd, Spring Gardens, Narberth, Dyfed, SA67 7BT Tel: (01834) 860849 Fax: (01834) 861527 E-mail: sales@gardenia.co.uk *Windows, doors & conservatories installers & manufrs*

▶ Gardening 4 You Ltd, 2 Bull Street Mews, Bull Street, Southam, Warwickshire, CV47 1PT Tel: (01926) 320210 Fax: (01926) 320210 E-mail: info@gardening4you.co.uk *Garden Maintenance services throughout South Warwickshire, together with garden renovation and landscape services*

Gardenscape, Rye Road, Newenden, Cranbrook, Kent, TN18 5QG Tel: (0800) 854663 Fax: (01797) 253554 E-mail: gerald@bourne.uk.com *Horticultural product suppliers*

Gardi Industrial Services Ltd, 9 Kennel Terrace, Brixworth, Northampton, NN6 9DL Tel: (01604) 882442 Fax: (01604) 882880 E-mail: enquiries@gardi.co.uk *Hydraulic machinery*

▶ Gardiner Bodies, Kingswood Farm, Tandridge Lane, Lingfield, Surrey, RH7 6LP Tel: 01342 893535 E-mail: lee@gardinerbodies.com *Building, conversion & accident repair of commercial vehicles*

Gardiner Bros Belfast Ltd, 44-46 Waring Street, Belfast, BT1 2ED Tel: (028) 9023 4271 Fax: (028) 9024 4122 *Wholesale jewellers*

Gardiner Bros & Co. (Leathers) Ltd, 1 Alvin Street, Gloucester, GL1 3EJ Tel: (01452) 422001 Fax: (01452) 307220 E-mail: sales@gardinerbros.co.uk *Boot, shoe & slipper distribs*

Gardiner & Collis Ltd, 4-5 Crofton Close, Allenby Industrial Estate, Lincoln, LN3 4NT Tel: (01522) 533416 Fax: (01522) 514642 *Carpet wholesalers*

▶ Gardiner Design Associates, 34 Malting Mead, Endymion Road, Hatfield, Hertfordshire, AL10 8AR Tel: 07785 790312 E-mail: info@gardinerdesign.co.uk *Interior design, graphic design & web design*

▶ Gardiner & Faulkner Ltd, 21 Carlton Crescent, Southampton, SO15 2ET Tel: (023) 8023 8429

Gardiner Icm, Lower Oldmill, Hatton, Auchterless, Turriff, Aberdeenshire, AB53 8BN Tel: (01888) 560044 Fax: (01888) 544948 *Agricultural suppliers*

▶ Mike Gardiner, 2 Muirfield Way, Deans, Livingston, West Lothian, EH54 8DL Tel: (01506) 204188 E-mail: mike_gardiner2004@msn.com

Gardiner Security Ltd, Unit 2, Castleton Close, Leeds, LS12 2DS Tel: 0113-244 9031 Fax: 0113-244 9096 *Burglar alarms & security system suppliers*

Gardiner Technology Ltd, Queensway, Rochdale, Lancashire, OL11 1TQ Tel: (0845) 7328328 Fax: (01706) 510100 E-mail: sales@gardiner-technology.com *Electronic security equipment*

Gardiners, The Batts, Frosterley, Bishop Auckland, County Durham, DL13 2SE Tel: (07711) 356444 Fax: (01388) 527295 *General engineers & steel fabrications*

▶ Gardinia Windows Kirklees Ltd, 3 Leeds Road, Huddersfield, HD1 6DD Tel: (01484) 542912 Fax: (01484) 451932 E-mail: info@gardiniawindows.co.uk *Installers of new upvc & timber window doors & conservatories*

Gardit Alarms, 18 Oakwood Mews, Worksop, Nottinghamshire, S80 3PF Tel: (01909) 475341 *Commercial & domestic security alarms & cctv installers*

Gardline Information Solutions Ltd, The Design Centre, Hewet Road, Gapton Hall, Great Yarmouth, Norfolk, NR31 0NN Tel: (01493) 440400 Fax: (01493) 442480 E-mail: steve.brown@gardline.co.uk *Project management & design engineers*

Gardline Shipping Ltd, Admiralty Road, Great Yarmouth, Norfolk, NR30 3NG Tel: (01493) 850723 Fax: (01493) 852106 E-mail: sys@gardline.co.uk *Hydrographic surveyors*

Gardman Ltd, High Street, Moulton, Spalding, Lincolnshire, PE12 6QD Tel: (01406) 372222 Fax: (01406) 372233 E-mail: sales@gardman.co.uk *Domestic wire goods suppliers*

Gardner Aerospace Ltd, Hagher Clough Works, Hargher Street, Burnley, Lancashire, BB11 4EG Tel: (01282) 416466 Fax: (01282) 450363 *Aerospace component sub contractors & manufrs*

Gardner Aerospace Basildon Ltd, 2-4 Rowhedge Close, Basildon, Essex, SS13 1QQ Tel: (01268) 729311 Fax: (01268) 728951 E-mail: info@gardner-aerospace-basildon.com *Sheet metalwork precision fine limit engineers*

Gardner Aerospace Wales Ltd, Forge Industrial Estate, Maesteg, Mid Glamorgan, CF34 0AY Tel: (01656) 812100 Fax: (01656) 812101 E-mail: info@gardner-aerospace.com *Aircraft component manufrs*

▶ Gardner Denver (Alton) Ltd, Unit 1, Waterbrook Estate, Waterbrook Road, Alton, Hampshire, GU34 2UD Tel: (01420) 544184 Fax: (01420) 544183 E-mail: ukinfo@eu.gardnerdenver.com *Vacuum pumps & compressors manufrs* Also at: Leeds

▶ Gardner Denver Alton Ltd, Larkfield Trading Estate, New Hythe Lane, Larkfield, Aylesford, Kent, ME20 6SW Tel: (01622) 716816 Fax: (01622) 715115 E-mail: ukinfo@eu.gardnerdenver.com *Vacuum pumps, compressors, blowers & liquid pump suppliers*

Gardner Denver UK Ltd, PO Box 468, Bradford, West Yorkshire, BD5 7HW Tel: (01274) 715240 Fax: (01274) 715241 *Pump, compressor & blower manufrs*

Gardner Electrical Group, Unit D Albion Road, Sileby, Loughborough, Leicestershire, LE12 7RA Tel: (01509) 813111 Fax: (01509) 814254 *Electric motor repairers*

Gardner Energy Management Ltd, 1 John Street, Bristol, BS1 Tel: 0117-917 7010 Fax: 0117-917 7011 E-mail: enq@gemtrap.co.uk Principal Export Areas: West Europe *Steam trap manufacturers & distributors*

Gardner Engineering Co. Ltd, Vale Rise, Tonbridge, Kent, TN9 1TB Tel: (01732) 350100 Fax: (01732) 362409 E-mail: sales@gardnerfloors.com *Mezzanine floor manufrs*

Gardner Freight International Ltd, Mersey Chambers, Covent Garden, Liverpool, L2 8XT Tel: 0151-236 7366 Fax: 0151-243 3463 E-mail: harrisons@liverpool.co.uk *Storage & transport contractors*

Peter Gardner, Water Lane Farm, 9 Water Lane, Sherington, Newport Pagnell, Buckinghamshire, MK16 9NP Tel: (01908) 610333 E-mail: clayshoting@lineone.net *Gun repairs, sales & shooting*

Gardner Plant Hire, Belvoir Way, Fairfield Industrial Estate, Louth, Lincolnshire, LN11 0LQ Tel: (01507) 604849 Fax: (01507) 604849 *Plant hire*

Richard Gardner Ltd, Hadfield Road, Leckwith Industrial Estate, Cardiff, CF11 8AQ Tel: (029) 2022 9764 Fax: (029) 2034 3664 E-mail: yc78@dial.pipex.com *Screen process printer & digital printers*

Gardner Security Ltd, Vine House, Elmbridge Road, Cranleigh, Surrey, GU6 8EL Tel: (01483) 277474 Fax: (01483) 272739 E-mail: sales@statedigitaluk..co.uk *Burglar alarms cctv & door entry system installation*

Gardner Services Ltd, 7 Camphill Industrial Estate, Camphill Road, West Byfleet, Surrey, KT14 6EW Tel: (01932) 346190 Fax: (01932) 353861 E-mail: sales@gardnerservices.co.uk *Precision engineers*

Gardner Systems plc, 1 Faraday Road, Wavertree, Liverpool, L13 1EH Tel: 0151-220 5552 Fax: 0151-220 5715 E-mail: sales@gardsys.co.uk *Computer systems specialists*

Gardners, 149 Commercial Street, London, E1 6BJ Tel: (020) 7247 5119 *Paper bag merchants*

GARDSEC, Unit 82, 571 Finchley Road, Hampsted, London, NW3 7BN Tel: (020) 7183 3999 Fax: (0871) 4334090 E-mail: gardsec@gmail.com *Home & office security systems, intruder alarms, access control, cctv*

Gardwell Coatings Ltd, Ellough Airfield, Ellough, Beccles, Suffolk, NR34 7TE Tel: (01502) 712793 Fax: (01502) 711636 E-mail: sales@gardwellcoatings.co.uk *Protective coating & power coating spraying services*

Garenberg Garden Buildings, 99 Collingwood Road, Manchester, M19 2AW Tel: (01204) 593054 Fax: 01204 792736 E-mail: info@garenberg.co.uk *manufacturer & Supplier of Garden Offices for consumer, corporate purchase and L.A. rental, construction and installation companies. Sturdy, Secure & Sylish*

Gareth James Pharmacy Ltd, 59 Herbert Street, Pontardawe, Swansea, SA8 4ED Tel: (01792) 863217 Fax: (01792) 863217 *Pharmacists*

Garfield Hydrol Ltd, Fengate, Peterborough, PE1 5XG Tel: (01733) 568444 Fax: (01733) 893516 E-mail: sales@rsg.co.uk Principal Export Areas: Africa *Manufacturers of hydraulic cylinders, rams & hydraulic*

Garfield Micro Electronics Ltd, Norfolk House, Herriad Business Park, Herriard, Basingstoke, Hampshire, RG25 2PN Tel: (01256) 384300 Fax: (01256) 384319 E-mail: enquiries@gfmicro.com *Semiconductor design engineers*

Garforth & Goodman Ltd, 1 Cromwell Street, Coventry, CV6 5EY Tel: (024) 7666 4680 Fax: (024) 7666 4685 E-mail: sales@garforthandgoodman.co.uk *Tool manufrs*

Gargsales (UK) Ltd, 240 Fleetside, West Molesey, Surrey, KT8 2NL Tel: (020) 8783 9007 Fax: (020) 8783 9007 E-mail: gargwireuk@yahoo.co.uk *Stainless Steel wire/bars/wire & Zinc Wire*

Gariff Construction Ltd, Village House, Eleventh Street, Trafford Park, Manchester, M17 1JF Tel: 0161-848 9983 Fax: 0161-848 9984 E-mail: leeunsworth@gariff.co.uk *Shop fitters*

Garioch Blinds, 1 Garioch Centre, Constitution Street, Inverurie, Aberdeenshire, AB51 4UY Tel: (01467) 625494 Fax: (01467) 625494 E-mail: sale@gariochblinds.co.uk *Blind suppliers & manufrs*

▶ Garioch Plant Hire, Blackhall Road, Inverurie, Aberdeenshire, AB51 5QF Tel: (01467) 621926 Fax: (01467) 629098

▶ Charles Garland Productions Ltd, PO Box 639, Bury St. Edmunds, Suffolk, IP33 9FE Tel: (01359) 244453 E-mail: charles.garland@talk21.com *Theatre, Film and Television Production Company*

▶ Garland Contracts Ltd, 105 Sanderstead Road, South Croydon, Surrey, CR2 0PJ Tel: (020) 8667 0820 Fax: (020) 8667 9141

Garland Sails, 246a Soundwell Road, Bristol, BS15 1PN Tel: 0117-935 3233 Fax: 0117-935 3233 E-mail: garlandsails@ukonline.co.uk *Custom hood & sail supplies*

Garlands Crusty Connection, The Market Hall, High Town, Hereford, HR1 2AA Tel: (01432) 275080 *Bakery & confectionary suppliers*

Garlics Ltd, Sandpits Acacia Road, Bourneville, Birmingham, B30 2AH Tel: 0121-472 3848 Fax: 0121-414 0065 *Motor vehicle repairs*

Garlock GB Ltd, Premier Way, Lowfields Business Park, Elland, West Yorkshire, HX5 9HF Tel: (01422) 313600 Fax: (01422) 313601 E-mail: jasonsedgwick@compuserve.com *Manufacturers of packings & gaskets seals*

Garmendale Engineering Ltd, Dale Works, Manners Industrial Estate, Ilkeston, Derbyshire, DE7 8EF Tel: 0115-932 7082 Fax: 0115-930 9391 E-mail: garmendale@enquiries.com *Steel fabricators*

Garment Related Services Ltd, 2a Westbury Road, London, E7 8BU Tel: (020) 8555 6555 Fax: (020) 8221 1355 *Clothing & fabrics manufrs*

Garmet Ltd, St. Helens Way, Thetford, Norfolk, IP24 1HG Tel: (01842) 763808 Fax: (01842) 764548 *Tubular fabricators*

▶ Garndene Communications Systems Ltd, Hi-Pylon Works, Slades Road, Golcar, Huddersfield, HD7 4JS Tel: (01484) 658415 Fax: (01484) 656810

Garnell Corporation, 13a London Road, St. Albans, Hertfordshire, AL1 1LA Tel: (01727) 842222 Fax: (01727) 844446 E-mail: sales@garnell.co.uk *Health food product manufrs*

▶ Garner Associates, 138 Bromham Road, Bedford, MK40 2QW Tel: (01234) 354508 Fax: (01234) 349588 E-mail: email@garnerassociates.co.uk *Chartered accountants*

▶ Paul Garner, 4 Poplar Grove, Ravenfield, Rotherham, South Yorkshire, S65 4LJ Tel: (07737) 036085 E-mail: pj1racing@hotmail.com *WE HAVE BEEN SUPPLYING TEA BAG PAPER BEDDING FOR 8 YEARS AND WE HAVE GOOD CUSTOMER BASED BUSINESS*

▶ Garner Projects Ltd, Havenhurst, Back Lane, East Hanningfield, Chelmsford, CM3 8BL Tel: (0870) 7405587 Fax: (0871) 7502352 E-mail: garners@dsl.pipex.com *Project management services*

Garner & Sons, 15 St Petersgate, Stockport, Cheshire, SK1 1EB Tel: 0161-480 3013 Fax: 0161-477 9125 E-mail: enquiries@garnerandsons.co.uk *Commercial property agents*

Garness & Pearson Decorating Contractors Ltd, Summer Lane, Birmingham,.B19 3NG Tel: 0121-359 3711 Fax: 0121-359 7311 *Painting contractors*

Garnet Roofing Ltd, Airport Industrial Estate, Newcastle upon Tyne, NE3 2EF Tel: 0191-286 3215 Fax: 0191-214 2650 E-mail: garnett@dorin.co.uk *Roofing contractors*

Garnett Wire Ltd, Scholes Lane, Scholes, Checkheaton, Cleckheaton, West Yorkshire, BD19 6NJ Tel: (01274) 875741 Fax: (01274) 851675 E-mail: sales@garnettwire.com *Wire formed & shaped components*

Garnham Switchgear Ltd, Unit 2 Olympus Close Business Park, Ipswich, IP1 5LJ Tel: (01473) 240407 Fax: (01473) 463730 E-mail: sales@garnhamswitchgear.co.uk *Electrical contractors*

S.R. Garrad, Stoke Road, Aylesbury, Buckinghamshire, HP21 7TE Tel: (01296) 331555 Fax: (01296) 428438 E-mail: info@srgarrad.co.uk *Fencing & paving contractors*

Garran Lockers Ltd, Garran House, Nantgarw Road, Caerphilly, Mid Glamorgan, CF83 1AQ Tel: (0845) 6588600 Fax: (0845) 6588601 E-mail: garran@garran-lockers.co.uk *Whether you are looking for a standard or bespoke storage locker system Garran Lockers Limited, have solutions for almost every situation and budget. Our lockers are available in a wide range of sizes, door choices, storage compartment options and colours. In fact anywhere people work or play. *Manufactured from 20/22 SWG mild steel with a spot welded construction for maximum strength with rigidity our lockers are built to last. Our strengthened base system helps to minimise damage to the floor and protects the locker from water when cleaning. *All our lockers with a sloping top are integral in that they form part of the sides, therefore avoiding unsightly sit-on top options. *Suppliers to police, fire and ambulance authorities. Plus NHS education and our sales representative are based throughout the UK offering drawing and site surveys recommendations, layout drawings and a full quotation, at no obligation.*

Garrards Removals & Storage, Unit 9b Mill Lane Trading Estate, Mill Lane, Croydon, CR0 4AA Tel: (020) 8688 4979 Fax: (020) 8686 4140 *Commercial removal & storage contractors*

▶ Garrards Transport, 7 Argonaut Park, Galleymead Road, Colnbrook, Slough, SL3 0EN Tel: (01753) 685006 Fax: (01753) 680109 E-mail: office@garrardstransport.co.uk *Computer deliveries,hi-tech,equipment transportation & installation specialists UK/European/international transport.Warehousing, logistics, management.Secure Storage space available Distribution.Near Heathrow Airport.Express,courier service.specialised computer spec Air ride taillift vehicles.high capacity tail lifts.24/7/365 callout. field service spares storage and shipment.relocation service.*telecoms,medical,x-ray gaming machines,recording equipment delicate IT equipment.direct delivery*

W. & G.W. Garratt Ltd, Upper Allen Street Works, Upper Allen Street, Sheffield, S3 7HA Tel: 0114-272 7094 Fax: 0114-272 0115 E-mail: enquiries@garrattsonline.com *Welded fabrications services*

▶ The Garret (UK) Ltd, 5 Green Dragon Court, London Bridge, London, SE1 9AW Tel: (020) 7159 1485 E-mail: iain@thegarret.co.uk *Complete design, print on-demand and fulfilment solution for a wide range of corporate, professional and educational publications.*

Garrett Air Cleaning, 21 Garrett Close, Dunstable, Bedfordshire, LU6 3EG Tel: (01582) 475900 Fax: (01582) 475900 *Air purifying systems*

Frederick Garrett & Sons, Slittingmill Farm, Staveley Lane, Staveley, Chesterfield, Derbyshire, S43 3YQ Tel: (01246) 432294 *Agricultural contractor & plants hire*

▶ Garrett J P Electrical Ltd, 104b Elm Grove, Brighton, BN2 3DB Tel: (01273) 625660 Fax: (01273) 625669

Garrett Lloyd Ltd, Unit 39-40 Derwent Business Centre, Clarke Street, Derby, DE1 2BU Tel: (01332) 206219 Fax: (01332) 206225 E-mail: recruitment@garrett-lloyd.com *Garrett Lloyd is a recruitment specialist based in Derby covering the UK. We specialise in Sales and Marketing appointment at all levels ranging from Director to entry level. We deal with clients in all sectors including capital equipment, telecoms, industrial doors, construction sales and vending sales. Clients are offered a number of recruitment methodologies including Database Contingency search, Advertising assignments and Executive search, all handled in the strictest confidence. Some of the opportunities we recruit for are: Field Sales Executives, Sales Executives Sales Reps, Business Development Managers Sales Managers Sales Directors, Marking Managers, PR Executive, Data Analysts, Marketing Assistants, Marketing Executives and Account Managers*

Garrett & Mcgann, 9 Warren Road, Cheadle Hulme, Cheadle, Cheshire, SK8 5AA Tel: 0161-485 3309 Fax: 0161-485 6327 E-mail: info@garrettmcgann.u-net.com *Printers & retail stationers*

Garretts Saddlers, South View, The Street, Draycott, Cheddar, Somerset, BS27 3TH Tel: (01934) 742367 *Saddlery manufrs*

Garrick Engineering Co. Ltd, Crowland Street Industrial Estate, Crowland Street, Southport, Merseyside, PR9 7RQ Tel: (01704) 534906 Fax: (01704) 537952 E-mail: info@garrickeng.co.uk *Sheet metal finishers & fabricators* Also at: Bamber Bridge

Garrick Freight International Ltd, 6-8 Furrow La, London, E9 6JS Tel: (020) 8985 2789 Fax: (020) 8985 4961 *Air & sea freight forwarders*

▶ Garrick Outdoor Ltd, Unit 4, Langley Place, Burscough Industrial Estate, Ormskirk, Lancashire, L40 8JS Tel: (01772) 816414 Fax: (01772) 816415 E-mail: enquires@garrickoutdoor.co.uk *Manufacturers & suppliers of shelters & street furniture*

Garrick Ridgway Engineering Ltd, 1-4 Gerard, Tamworth, Staffordshire, B79 7UW Tel: (01827) 62948 Fax: (01827) 52717 E-mail: garrickridgeway@aol.com *Machine tool dealers*

▶ Garrigue Wines, Carnoch, Mid Barrwood Road, Kilsyth, Glasgow, G65 0ER Tel: (0845) 8886677 E-mail: themacaloneys@garriguewines.com *Independent wine merchant specialising in the wines from Languedoc-Roussillon in southern France*

▶ Garriock Ltd, 11 Newbridge Industrial Estate, Newbridge, Midlothian, EH28 8PJ Tel: 0131-333 2009 Fax: 0131-333 1979

Garrison Dales Ltd, Unit 8, North St Industrial Estate, Droitwich, Worcestershire, WR9 8JB Tel: (01905) 794555 Fax: (01905) 794592 E-mail: sales@garrisondales.co.uk *Power tool consumables & fixings distributors*

▶ Garrison Vehicle Locks, 3 Rolleston Close, Market Harborough, Leicestershire, LE16 8BZ Tel: (07891) 340168 E-mail: info@garrisonlocks.co.uk *Vehicle locks & security products security locks for vans & commercial vehicles*

Garrod Bros London Ltd, 50 Aden Road, Enfield, Middlesex, EN3 7SY Tel: (020) 8805 6767 Fax: (020) 8805 9810 E-mail: sales@garrodbros.fsnet.co.uk *Flooring wholesalers*

Garrods of Barking Ltd, Abbey Wharf, Kings Bridge Road, Barking, Essex, IG11 0BD Tel: (020) 8594 0224 Fax: (020) 8594 0225 E-mail: info@garrods.com *Furniture, galvanized hollow-ware & storage bin container manufrs*

R.S. Garrow Ltd, 4 Mosspark Avenue, Milngavie, Glasgow, G62 8NL Tel: 0141-956 2732 Fax: 0141-570 2732 E-mail: bobgarrow@rsgarrow.co.uk *Business development consultancy & hands on help*

Garryson Ltd, Spring Road, Ibstock, Leicestershire, LE67 6LR Tel: (01530) 261145 Fax: (01530) 262801 E-mail: sales@garryson.co.uk *Abrasive products (industrial finishing) manufrs*

Garsdale Knitwear Ltd, 64 Chapeltown Street, Manchester, M1 2WQ Tel: 0161-273 7869 Fax: 0161-273 8810 *Knitwear manufrs*

James Garside & Son Ltd, Grantham Works, Grantham Road, Halifax, West Yorkshire, HX3 6PL Tel: (01422) 340559 Fax: (01422) 349465 *Machinery installation & removals*

▶ Garside & Laycock, 4 Beeston Road, Lane End Place, Leeds, LS11 8JY Tel: 0113-244 0071 Fax: 0113-244 0075

Garstone Garden Ornament Wholesalers, 8 New Quay Street, Teignmouth, Devon, TQ14 8DA Tel: (01626) 775925 Fax: (01626) 891745 *Garden ornament manufrs*

▶ Gartec Ltd, 6 Midshires Business Park, Smeaton Close, Aylesbury, Buckinghamshire, HP19 8HL Tel: (01296) 397100 Fax: (01296) 397600 E-mail: sales@gartec.com *Lift & elevator installers*

▶ Garth Bakery Ltd, Pontcynon Industrial Estate, Abercynon, Mountain Ash, Mid Glamorgan, CF45 4EP Tel: (01443) 742080 Fax: (01443) 743014 *Bakery of fresh produce*

Garth Computer Solutions, Blaenpentre, Rhosygarth, Llanilar, Aberystwyth, Dyfed, SY23 4SE Tel: (01974) 241410 *Poster designers*

Pete Garth Autorefinishing Ltd, Riverview Road, Beverley, North Humberside, HU17 0LD Tel: (01482) 882747 Fax: (01482) 865423 *Car body repairers*

Garth T Wright Fasteners, Colwickwood Works, Colwick Road, Nottingham, NG2 4BG Tel: 0115-958 8360 Fax: 0115-948 4967 E-mail: wright@wright-engineers.co.uk *Bolt, nut & industrial fastener distributors*

Garthwest Ltd, Rotterdam Road, Hull, HU7 0XA Tel: (01482) 825121 Fax: (01482) 825229 E-mail: info@garthwest.freeserve.co.uk *Cardboard box manufrs*

Gartmore Securities Ltd, Gartmore House, 16-18 Monument Street, London, EC3R 8QQ Tel: (020) 7623 1212 Fax: (020) 7782 2689 *Unit trust fund investment managers*

Garton, Unit 2a, Swan Lane, Hindley Green, Wigan, Lancashire, WN2 4HD Tel: (01942) 520250 Fax: 01942 520271 E-mail: sales@gartoninternational.com *Fastener Manufacturer & Stockist*

▶ Gartsherrie Engineering Ltd, Gartsherrie Road, Coatbridge, Lanarkshire, ML5 2EU Tel: (01236) 436464 Fax: (01236) 432044 E-mail: info@patersonsquarries.co.uk *Fabrication & machining*

Garvel Clyde, James Watt Dock, Greenock, Renfrewshire, PA15 2AJ Tel: (01475) 725372 Fax: (01475) 725377 *Marine engineering & ship repair*

Garven Antique Reproductions, Gorphwysfa, Defynnog, Brecon, Powys, LD3 8SB Tel: (01874) 638028 Fax: (01874) 638028 *Furniture reproduction & kitchen manufrs*

Garwards Engineering, 8 Progress Way, Mid Suffolk Business Park, Eye, Suffolk, IP23 7HU Tel: (01379) 871337 Fax: (01379) 873041 E-mail: gareth@garwards.com *Steel fabricators*

Garwood Cleaning Services, West Hyde, Brook Road, Tillingham, Southminster, Essex, CM0 7SB Tel: (01621) 779507 Fax: (01621) 779507 *Cleaning services*

Gary Chabot, Newhaven Marina, West Quay, Newhaven, E. Sussex, BN9 9BY Tel: 01273 611076 Fax: 01273 611076 *Boat builders & repairers*

▶ Gary Crook Ltd, Regus House, Southampton International Business Park, George Curl Way, Southampton, SO18 2RZ Tel: (023) 8030 2005 Fax: (023) 8030 2225 E-mail: gary@wsi-internet4business.com *Internet consulting*

▶ Gary Hall Windows, Dixon Street, Consett, County Durham, DH8 5UF Tel: (01207) 591867 Fax: (01207) 591096 E-mail: garyhall@garyhall.plus.com *Windows & conservatory installation*

▶ Gas 2 K, 10 Victoria Road, Richmond, North Yorkshire, DL10 4AS Tel: (01748) 821982 E-mail: contact@gas2k.co.uk *Gas engineers*

Gas Appliance Distributors Ltd, Junction Two Industrial Estate, Demuth Way, Oldbury, West Midlands, B69 4LT Tel: 0121-544 5566 Fax: 0121-544 7437 *Gas appliance distributors*

Gas Arc Group Ltd, Vinces Road, Diss, Norfolk, IP22 4WW Tel: (01379) 652263 Fax: (01379) 644235 E-mail: mail@gas-arc.co.uk *Gas control & welding equipment*Speciality Gas Control Products*Laboratory Gas Control Products*

▶ Gas Call Services Ltd, 2 Queenslie Court, Summerlee Street, Glasgow, G33 4DB Tel: 0141-766 3333

▶ Gas Care Central Heating Ltd, 3 Gripoly Mills, Sloper Road, Cardiff, CF11 8AA Tel: (029) 2066 6622 Fax: (029) 2066 6633 E-mail: sales@gascare.co.uk

▶ Gas Catering Services, 18 Robert Cort Industrial Estate, Britten Road, Reading, RG2 0AU Tel: 0118-975 6500 Fax: 0118-975 1222 E-mail: info@gascatering.co.uk *Catering equipment engineers*

Gas Compressors Ltd, Star Farm, Golden Green, Tonbridge, Kent, TN11 0BE Tel: (01732) 852048 Fax: (01732) 852376 E-mail: sales@gascompressors.co.uk *Special PIPEWORK FABRICATIONS to the Oil and Gas Industry codes and standards - ½" to 40" butt and socket weld. Fuel Gas Compressors. Wellhead Gas Gathering Compressors. Gas Boosters. Any Gases Any Pressures Any Flows Supplied Worldwide.*

▶ Gas Connect Heating Ltd, Leigh House, Broadway West, Leigh-on-Sea, Essex, SS9 2DD Tel: (01702) 474792 Fax: (01702) 471647

Gas Control Equipment Ltd, Yew Tree Way, Golborne, Warrington, WA3 3JD Tel: (01942) 292950 Fax: (01942) 292951 E-mail: sales@gceuk.com *Industrial, medical & scientific gas equipment manufacturers*

▶ Gas Engineering Services Ltd, Griffin Road, Clevedon, Avon, BS21 6HH Tel: (01275) 873535 Fax: (01275) 873525

Gas & Environmental Services Ltd, Unit 9, Little Ridge, Welwyn Garden City, Hertfordshire, AL7 2BH Tel: (01707) 373751 Fax: (01707) 373752 E-mail: kevin.mileson@btinternet.com *Gas detection equipment, systems maintenance & repair services*

▶ Gas Master, 36 Plover Crescent, Anstey Heights, Leicester, LE4 1EB Tel: 0116-236 7705 E-mail: platform40@hotmail.com

▶ Gas Measurement Instruments Ltd, Brownsfield Avenue, Inchinnan, Renfrew, PA4 9RG Tel: 0141-812 3211 Fax: 0141-812 7820 E-mail: enquiries@gmiuk.com *Gas detection equipment manufrs*

Gas Service Agents Ltd, 39-43 Harrison Road, Southampton, SO17 3TL Tel: (023) 8051 6611 Fax: (023) 8067 1968 E-mail: info@gascare.com *Gas appliance engineers*

▶ Gas Style, 374 Blackpool Road, Ashton-on-Ribble, Preston, PR2 2DS Tel: (01772) 761006 Fax: (01772) 761006 *Gas fires, fireplaces, central heating & corgi installations*

Gas Tec At C R E Ltd, P O Box 279, Cheltenham, Gloucestershire, GL52 7ZJ Tel: (01242) 677877 Fax: (01242) 676506 E-mail: enquiries@gastecuk.com *Training & certification*

Gas Technical Services, Unit 1, Richmond Road, West Llanion Business Centre, Pembroke Dock, Dyfed, SA72 6TZ Tel: (01646) 683845 Fax: (01646) 686542 E-mail: gastechnicalservices@hotmail.co.uk *Plumbing & gas installation work, boiler maintenance, gas fires*

▶ Gas Turbine Engineering Services, Nasmyth Building, Nasmyth Avenue, East Kilbride, Glasgow, G75 0QR Tel: (01355) 272660 Fax: (01355) 272665

Gas Turbine Services Ltd, Avon House, Whitwick Business Park, Stenson Road, Coalville, Leicestershire, LE67 4JP Tel: (01530) 814000 Fax: (01530) 812007 E-mail: enquiries@gasturbines.co.uk *Gas turbine spare part distribs*

Gas & Welding Equipment Ltd, 239 Ilkeston Road, Nottingham, NG7 3FX Tel: 0115-942 0519 Fax: 0115-942 3743 E-mail: info@gwe-ltd.com *Welding equipment distributor*Everything for the Welder*Protective clothing & footwear*

Gasarc Engineering, Triangle Works, Triangle North, Bath, BA2 3JB Tel: (01225) 421234 Fax: (01225) 425287 *Steel fabricators*

▶ Gase Marine & General Engineering Services Ltd, 7 Tower Park Road, Crayford, Dartford, DA1 4LB Tel: (01322) 552980 Fax: (01322) 552986 E-mail: info@gaseaero.com *5 Axis Water Jet, Plastic and Metal Precision CNC Maching, Fine Limit Sheet Metal Fabrication and Nadcap Welding*

Gas-Fire Com, 15-17 High Street, Rishton, Blackburn, BB1 4JZ Tel: (0800) 0281936 Fax: (01254) 887569 E-mail: sales@gas-fire.com *Fires & fireplaces*

Gaskells Logistics, Unit 13, Churchfields Business Park, Clensmore Street, Kidderminster, Worcestershire, DY10 2JY Tel: (01562) 820006 Fax: (01562) 820016 *Carpet distributors*

A.F. Gaskin Ltd, Downley Road, Naphill, High Wycombe, Buckinghamshire, HP14 4QY Tel: (01494) 563831 Fax: (01494) 562933 E-mail: sales@afgaskin.co.uk *Toolmakers to the plastics industry*

▶ Gasplan Ltd, 3 East Lane, Paisley, Renfrewshire, PA1 1QA Tel: 0141-889 2425 Fax: 0141-849 1466

▶ Gaswise Services Ltd, Horsleys Fields, King's Lynn, Norfolk, PE30 5DD Tel: (01553) 769404 Fax: (01553) 774033

▶ The Gasworks Company UK Ltd, 24 Baycliff Drive, Dalton-in-Furness, Cumbria, LA15 8XE Tel: (07841) 342298 Fax: (01229) 768266 E-mail: support@thegasworkscompany.co.uk *Specialist repairs & servicing of all gas appliances*

Gate A Mation Ltd, 8 Boundary Business Centre, Boundary Way, Woking, Surrey, GU21 5DH Tel: (01483) 747373 Fax: (01483) 776688 E-mail: sales@gate-a-mation.com *Automatic gates & barriers, installations service*

Gate Machinery International Ltd, Handsford Court, 1 Garston Park Parade, Watford, WD25 9LQ Tel: (01923) 682874 Fax: (01923) 682875 E-mail: info@gatemachinery.com *Machine tool merchants or agents*

Gate Makers, Petford Lea, Buckland, Aylesbury, Buckinghamshire, HP22 5HU Tel: (01296) 630798 Fax: (01296) 631373 E-mail: admin@thegatemakers.co.uk *Timber gates, garden furniture & all types of purpose made joinery*

▶ The Gate Marketing & Design Ltd, Murlain Business Centre, Union Street, Chester, CH1 1QP Tel: 01244 357 242 Fax: 01244 357 215 E-mail: anna@thegatemarketing.com *We"re a full service marketing and design agency with a clear and simple vision: to provide stunning creative, superb service and a refreshingly clear approach to pricing...*

Gate Place, 16 Boston Road, Leicester, LE4 1AU Tel: 0116-236 6525 Fax: 0116-236 6525 *Gate manufrs*

Gate Place, 140 Poulton Road, Southport, Merseyside, PR9 7DB Tel: (01704) 224365 Fax: (01704) 507500 *Manufacture iron gates*

▶ Gate Supplies, Whittington Works, Thompson Street, Chesterfield, Derbyshire, S41 9AR Tel: (01246) 261795 Fax: 01426 261795 E-mail: sales@gatesupplies.co.uk *wrought iron products from brackets to automatic gates to light engineering*

Gateacre Press Ltd, Bilail House, 260 Picton Road, Wavertree, Liverpool, L15 4LP Tel: 0151-734 3038 Fax: 0151-734 2860 E-mail: gpl@gatepress.demon.co.uk *Diaries magazine & printers*

▶ Gatehill Trading Ltd, 18 Gatehill Road, Northwood, Middlesex, HA6 3QD Tel: (01923) 820206 Fax: (01923) 450999 E-mail: gatehill@gtrad.co.uk *Importers & exporters of steel products*

Gatehouse Pharmacy, Gatehouse 1 & 2, 25 Victoria Promenade, Northampton, NN1 1HB Tel: (01604) 635311 Fax: (01604) 635311 *Dispensing pharmaceuticals*

Gatehouse Scientific Instruments, 94c Hampstead Avenue, Mildenhall, Bury St. Edmunds, Suffolk, IP28 7AS Tel: (01638) 510555 Fax: (01638) 510555 E-mail: sales@gatehouseindustrial.com *Sheet metalwork & powder coating*

Gatehouse Trading Estate Ltd, The Gate House, Lichfield Road, Brownhills, Walsall, WS8 6JZ Tel: (01543) 370892 *Commercial property rental*

▶ Gateline Clothing Mnfrs, 6 2 Overbury Road, London, N15 6RH Tel: (020) 8809 2065 Fax: (020) 8809 7786 E-mail: gateline@hotmail.com *Clothing manufrs*

A.A. Gates Ltd, Culver Garden Centre, Cattlegate Road, Crews Hill, Enfield, Middlesex, EN2 9DS Tel: (020) 8367 3500 Fax: (020) 8342 1115 E-mail: argonarc@aol.com *Steel, cast iron stainless steel welding engineers & gate manufrs*

▶ Gates Architectual Metal Work, Alice Street Works, Alice Street, Morecambe, Lancashire, LA4 5NH Tel: (01524) 413513 *Fabricators & welders*

Gates B 2 B Ltd, Electric Wharf, Coventry, CV1 4JF Tel: (024) 7652 5558 Fax: (0870) 6001092 E-mail: steve.williams@gatesb2b.com *Outsourcing, web design & marketing training services & business consultancy*

▶ Gates D I Y, 6 Vesey Path, London, E14 6BT Tel: (020) 7987 4045 Fax: (020) 7987 4015 E-mail: info@gatesdiy.com *DIY & decorating products suppliers*

▶ Gates Power Transmission Ltd, Tinwald Downs Road, Heath Hall, Dumfries, DG1 1TS Tel: (01387) 242000

▶ The Gates & Railings Co., 4 Lea Farm Crescent, Leeds, LS5 3QQ Tel: 0113-217 8901

▶ Gatestore (UK), 682 Anlaby Road, Hull, HU3 6UZ Tel: (0845) 2263123 Fax: (01482) 505001 E-mail: bruce@gatestore.co.uk *Distributors of gate automation equipment & associated products. V2 Elettronica - Italian electric gate & radio control manufacturer*

Gateway Autos Ltd, Units 2-6 Trafford Distribution Centre, Tenax Road, Trafford Park, Manchester, M17 1JT Tel: 0161-872 9559 Fax: 0161-872 9536 *Accident repair centre*

Gateway Centre, Clarence House, Clarence Place, Newport, Gwent, NP19 7AA Tel: (01633) 235110 Fax: (01633) 235111 *Computer aided design & training services*

Gateway Ceramics Ltd, School Lane, Chandler's Ford, Eastleigh, Hampshire, SO53 4DG Tel: (023) 8026 0290 Fax: (023) 8025 1049 *Ceramic flooring & carpet contractors*

Gateway Computing, Whitehouse, 114 Hendford Hill, Yeovil, Somerset, BA20 2RF Tel: (01935) 424356 Fax: (01935) 420549 *Accounting software & developers manufrs*

Gateway Fabrications Ltd, Broad Lane, Gilberdyke, Brough, North Humberside, HU15 2TS Tel: (01430) 440185 Fax: (01430) 441850 E-mail: sales@bathroompods.com *Steel fabrication specialists*

▶ Gateway Global UK Ltd, Unit 2 Amor Way, Letchworth Garden City, Hertfordshire, SG6 1UG Tel: (01462) 670888 Fax: (01462) 670886

▶ Gateway Homes, Learigg Road, Plains, Airdrie, Lanarkshire, ML6 7JL Tel: (01236) 843303

Gateway Textiles Ltd, Northgate Terrace, Unit 3 Northern Road, Newark, Nottinghamshire, NG24 2EU Tel: (01636) 676194 Fax: (01636) 611367 E-mail: sales@gatewaysystems.co.uk *Bedding machinery manufrs*

Gateways Northwest Ltd, 2 St. James Street, Southport, Merseyside, PR8 5AE Tel: (01704) 500056 Fax: (01704) 546080 *Gates & railing manufrs*

Gateweld Metal, Villiers Drive, Oldham, OL8 1ED Tel: 0161-628 5551 Fax: (01706) 370240 *Metal fabricators*

Gatewrights Fence Suppliers, 45 Hawkwood Road, Sible Hedingham, Halstead, Essex, CO9 3JR Tel: (01787) 461500 Fax: (01787) 460880 *Gate & fence carpentry services*

Alexander Gatey & Co. Ltd, Unit 89 West Avenue, Blantyre, Glasgow, G72 0XE Tel: (01698) 821919 Fax: (01698) 823946 E-mail: info@alexandergatey.co.uk *Suspended ceiling specialists*

▶ Gatfield Systems, Surrey Saw Mills, 70 Wrecclesham Hill, Wrecclesham, Farnham, Surrey, GU10 4JX Tel: (01252) 737357 Fax: (01252) 737358 E-mail: info@gatfield-systems.co.uk *Plastic extrusions machinery*

Gathercrest Ltd, Lynton House, 304 Bensham Lane, Thornton Heath, Surrey, CR7 7EQ Tel: (020) 8683 0494 Fax: (020) 8689 8155 *Import & export merchants*

▶ Gating & Fencing Fabrications Ltd, Unit 2 Sams Lane, West Bromwich, West Midlands, B70 7ED Tel: (0845) 8388000

Gatley Engineering Pneumatics Ltd, Unit 6d Lowick Close, Hazel Grove, Stockport, Cheshire, SK7 5ED Tel: 0161-483 8615 Fax: 0161-456 5285 *Pneumatic fittings manufrs*

Gatts Ltd, 11-13 Balmoral Terrace, Aberdeen, AB10 6HH Tel: (01224) 582288 Fax: (01224) 582299 E-mail: gatts@chessgroup.co.uk *Furniture restorers*

Gattzbee Kitchens, Darley Street, Darley Abbey, Derby, DE22 1DX Tel: (01332) 556699 Fax: (01332) 556699 *Bedroom, bathrooms & kitchen furniture designers*

Gatwick Fire Protection, 44 Prince Albert Square, Redhill, RH1 5AW Tel: (0800) 9562006 Fax: (01737) 773949 E-mail: sales@gatwickfire.co.uk *Fire extinguishers sales & services*

Gatwick Park Mechanical Services Ltd, P.O. Box 371, Caterham, Surrey, CR3 6UE Tel: (01883) 347133 Fax: (01883) 343813 E-mail: info@gatwickpark.com *Building service engineers*

Gatwick Plant Hire, Woodside, The Close, Horley, Surrey, RH6 9EB Tel: (01293) 824777 Fax: (01293) 824077 E-mail: sales@gatwickgroup.com *Heavy industrial transport, lifting & storage*

Gatwick Refuelling Services Ltd, Perimeter Road North, London Gatwick Airport, Gatwick, West Sussex, RH6 0JE Tel: (01293) 527044 Fax: (01293) 514669 *Refueling aircraft services*

Gauge Developments Ltd, Langham Street, Ashton-under-Lyne, Lancashire, OL7 9AX Tel: 0161-343 3020 Fax: 0161-343 2969 E-mail: gdev@btconnect.com *Pressure gauge specialists, maintenance & repair services*

▶ Gauge Factors Ltd, Units 5-6 Towergate Industrial Park, Colebrook Way, Andover, Hampshire, SP10 3BB Tel: (01264) 336396 Fax: (01264) 336826 E-mail: sales@gaugefactors.com *Strain gauge installation services - in house and on site. Training courses modules available in all forms of strain gauge application. Full range of PU-encapsulated and weldable strain gauges. Clip gauges and extensometers. Load cell design and manufacture. Installation tools and materials see our latest catalogue. UK and worldwide service and distribution*

Gauge Service & Supply Co (Leamington) Ltd, 3 Park Street, Leamington Spa, Warwickshire, CV32 4QN Tel: (01926) 336137 Fax: (01926) 450636 E-mail: sales@gss.co.uk *Factors for measuring equipment distributors*

Gauge & Tool Makers Association, 3 Forge House, Summerleys Road, Princes Risborough, Buckinghamshire, HP27 9DT Tel: (01844) 274222 Fax: (01844) 274227

continued

E-mail: gtma@gtma.co.uk *Trade associations, organisations & product developers*

Gauge & Tool Makers Association, 3 Forge House, Summerleys Road, Princes Risborough, Buckinghamshire, HP27 9DT Tel: (01844) 274222 Fax: (01844) 274227 E-mail: gtma@gtma.co.uk *Trade association*

Gauge & Welding Equipment Repairs Ltd, PO Box 48, Dartford, DA1 1YA Tel: (01322) 270036 Fax: (01322) 288625 E-mail: mail@gwer.co.uk *Welding equipment suppliers & repairers*

Gaugemaster Co. Ltd, 93 Leopold Street, Birmingham, B12 0UD Tel: 0121-773 6331 Fax: 0121-772 4046 E-mail: enquiries@gaugemaster.net *Precision engineers*

C. Gaunt Technical Services, 14 Hurst Road, Hebden Bridge, West Yorkshire, HX7 8HR Tel: (01422) 842321 E-mail: c.gaunt@c-gaunt.com *Technical support for computer systems*

John Gaunt Pump Supplies Ltd, Unit 15, Norman Way Industrial Estate, Over, Cambridge, CB24 5QE Tel: (01954) 232323 Fax: (01954) 232322 E-mail: sales@johngauntpumps.co.uk *Pump distributors*

Gautrey Engineering, 43 Telegraph Street, Cottenham, Cambridge, CB24 8QU Tel: (01954) 251112 Fax: (01954) 206256 *Precision turning, milling & assembly*

▶ Gavin Craig Plant Hire, Avonside Farm, Drumclog, Strathaven, Lanarkshire, ML10 6RQ Tel: (01357) 440388

Gavin Robertson Furniture, Easter Altourie, Inverness, IV3 8LB Tel: (01463) 861261 Fax: (01463) 861436 *Cabinet maker*

▶ Gavin Sawyer, 4 Swanland Drive, Tonbridge, Kent, TN9 2RA Tel: (01732) 508629 E-mail: photos@gavinsawyer.com *Professional photographer based in Tonbridge, Kent, with 20 years industry experience. Specialist in PR, corporate, press, wedding and social photography*

Gavin Shanks Ltd, Rochsolloch Road, Airdrie, Lanarkshire, ML6 9BG Tel: (01236) 756407 Fax: (01236) 761919

Gawith Hoggarth & Co., Unit 16 Lake District Business Park, Mint Bridge Road, Kendal, Cumbria, LA9 6NH Tel: (01539) 720047 Fax: (01539) 740556 E-mail: enquiries@gawithhoggarth.co.uk *Tobacco products manufrs*

Gawthorpe Metal Spinning, 4 Drakes Industrial Estate, Shay Lane, Ovenden, Halifax, West Yorkshire, HX3 6RL Tel: (01422) 330519 *Metal spinning manufrs*

Gaylee Ltd, Pope Street, Smethwick, West Midlands, B66 2JP Tel: 0121-558 2027 Fax: 0121-558 2029 *Fork lift sales & service, haulage services*

Gaynor Walker, Docklands Business Centre 16 Tiller Road, Near Canary Wharf, London, E14 8PX Tel: (020) 7345 5056 Fax: (020) 7345 5001 E-mail: enquiries@gaynorwalker.com *Property consultants*

Gaytsmaid Wrought Ironwork, Unit 1 St. Johns Lane, Bewdley, Worcestershire, DY12 2QY Tel: (01299) 405153 Fax: (01299) 405153 E-mail: enquiries@gaytsmaid.co.uk *Wrought iron workers*

▶ Gaz Bikes, Beckfield Arabians, Midville Lane, Stickney, Boston, Lincolnshire, PE22 8DN Tel: 08456 434310 Fax: 08456 434310 E-mail: sales@gazbikes.co.uk *Motorcycle Parts & Accessories for Road & Off-Road Bikes, ATV & Quad Bikes.*

▶ Gazelle Logistics, 42 Robert Cort Industrial Estate, Britten Road, Reading, RG2 0AU Tel: 0118-975 6777 Fax: 0118-975 6778 E-mail: info@getgazelle.com *Immediate, Next day, International and Logistics services. Fully integrated and web accessible booking system. Vehicles ranging from motorcycles to Lorries. Employed drivers all security vetted and uniformed. Operating every moment of every day. Superb response times.*

▶ Gazelle Solutions Ltd, York Place Buildings, 6-8 York Place, Leeds, LS1 2DS Tel: 0113-245 3777 Fax: 0113-244 1968

Gazelle Ventures Ltd, 276B New Road, Croxley Green, Rickmansworth, Hertfordshire, WD3 3HH Tel: (01923) 720466 Fax: (01923) 720411 E-mail: sales@gazelleventures.co.uk *Installation of air conditioning & ventilation systems*

▶ Gazy Barns, M T Works, Gannow Lane, Burnley, Lancashire, BB12 6JJ Tel: (01282) 422442

▶ Gazzard Engineering Co. Ltd, Swinbourne Road, Burnt Mills Industrial Estate, Basildon, Essex, SS13 1EH Tel: (01268) 724585 Fax: (01268) 724536 E-mail: enquiries@gazshocks.com *Engineering*

GB Copier Systems Ltd, Waterloo Road, Stoke-on-Trent, ST6 2EH Tel: (01782) 814444 Fax: (01782) 814455 *Service & sell office equipment (photocopiers)*

GB Engineering Ltd, Croespenmaen Industrial Estate, Crumlin, Newport, Gwent, NP11 3AG Tel: (01495) 248080 Fax: (01495) 246470 E-mail: bordergroup@tiscali.co.uk *General engineers*

GB Engineering Services, 6 Town House Farm, Alsager Road, Audley, Stoke-on-Trent, ST7 8JQ Tel: (01782) 723666 Fax: (01782) 723777 *Flow measurement equipment & systems distributors*

GB Farm Services, D Park Farm, Colchester Road, Elmstead, Colchester, CO7 7BA Tel: (01206) 822734 Fax: (01206) 822734 *Agricultural engineering services*

GB Group plc, GB House, Kingsfield Court, Chester Business Park, Chester, CH4 9GB Tel: (01244) 657333 Fax: (01244) 680808 *Data cleansing solutions*

GB Ingredients Ltd, The Heath Business & Technicial Park, Runcorn, Cheshire, WA7 4QX Tel: (01928) 511111 Fax: (01928) 515115 Principal Export Areas: Worldwide *Bakers ingredient*

GB It Services, PO Box 429, Sheffield, S13 8YZ Tel: 0114-248 6200 Fax: (0870) 0517730 E-mail: admin@gbits.com *Computer consultancy*

▶ GB Locking Systems Ltd, Redburn House, Redburn Road, Newcastle upon Tyne, NE5 1NB Tel: 0191-271 6344 Fax: 0191-271 3644 E-mail: sales@gblockingsystems.co.uk *Security products wholesalers*

▶ GB Nametapes, 53 Honeyborough Industrial Estate, Neyland, Milford Haven, Dyfed, SA73 1SE Tel: (01646) 600664 Fax: (01646) 600664 E-mail: enqiury@gbnametapes.co.uk *Woven name tapes manufrs*

▶ GB Packaging Supplies Ltd, Unit 4 Carrside Park, Hatfield, Doncaster, South Yorkshire, DN7 6AZ Tel: (01302) 351751 Fax: (01302) 845178 *Packaging material wholesaler*

GB Transport Engineering, 22 Algores Way, Wisbech, Cambridgeshire, PE13 2TQ Tel: (01945) 461780 Fax: (01945) 587107 E-mail: sales@gb-truckworld.co.uk *Commercial vehicle bodybuilders*

▶ GBA Pen Co. Ltd, Fyfield Business & Research Park, 7 Fyfield Road, Ongar, Essex, CM5 0GN Tel: (01277) 369620 Fax: (01277) 369629 E-mail: gbapen@btconnect.com *Pens & writing instruments distributors & importers*

GBC UK Holdings Ltd, Rutherford Road, Basingstoke, Hampshire, RG24 8PD Tel: (01256) 842828 Fax: (01256) 842581 E-mail: sales@gbcuk.co.uk *Visual planning system manufrs*

▶ GBH Engineering Ltd, 11a Haven Road, Poole, Dorset, BH13 7LE Tel: (01202) 706206 Fax: (01202) 706104 E-mail: info@gbhramps.com *Playground equipment manufrs*

GBH Technical Ltd, Blackness Avenue, Altens Industrial Estate, Altens Industrial Estate, Aberdeen, AB12 3PG Tel: (01224) 879000 Fax: (01224) 899898 E-mail: sales@gbhtechnical.com *Valve stockholders & distributors*McMaster Carr importer*

▶ GBM Civils, Unit 19 Station Estate, Newbridge Hill, Louth, Lincolnshire, LN11 0JT Tel: (01507) 607944 Fax: (01507) 607900

GBR Technology Ltd, 6 Jupiter House, Calleva Park, Aldermaston, Reading, RG7 8NN Tel: 0118-982 0567 Fax: 0118-982 0590 E-mail: sales@gbrtech.co.uk *Lubricant distributors*

GBS Building Services Ltd, 4 Thornybank, Dalkeith, Midlothian, EH22 2NQ Tel: 0131-663 7899 Fax: 0131-660 4074

GBW Panels Ltd, 2 Berkeley Business Park, Wainwright Road, Worcester, WR4 9FA Tel: (01905) 340095 Fax: (01905) 340188 E-mail: mark_cuthbert@gbwuk.com *Door panels & composite doors, stable & double glazed doors manufrs*

▶ GC Fluid Power, 13 Newbolds Road, Wolverhampton, WV10 0SA Tel: (01902) 655792 Fax: (01902) 655792 E-mail: info@gcfluidpower.co.uk *Fluid power consultants*

▶ GC Sound and Light, Unit 5, Premier Business Park, Huntspill Road, Highbridge, Somerset, TA9 3DE Tel: (01278) 794414 E-mail: gcwebsite@aol.com *Sound, lighting equipment suppliers, installers & maintenance services*

▶ GCH 2000, 3-5 High Street, Evington, Leicester, LE5 6FH Tel: 0116-273 4759 Fax: (0845) 1235856 E-mail: vehicles@gch2000.co.uk *Vehicle fleet management*

▶ GCNC Ltd, Dovedale 145 Whalley Road, Langho, Blackburn, BB6 8AA Tel: (01254) 240427 E-mail: sales@gcnc.ltd.uk *Bespoke plaques and signs for all industries. Home, leisure or commercial - we offer a full design and manufacturing service - see our website signsandplaques.com*

GD Automatic Machinery Ltd, Grove Park Industrial Estate, Waltham Road, White Waltham, Maidenhead, Berkshire, SL6 3LW Tel: (01628) 823123 Fax: (01628) 829123 *Wrapping machine manufrs*

▶ GD Gaskets & Seals, Unit 1 Mapplewell Business Park, Staincross, Barnsley, South Yorkshire, S75 6BP Tel: (01226) 381666 Fax: (01226) 381222 E-mail: garydavis1@btconnect.com *Manufacturers of gaskets & seals*

GD Metal Recycling Ltd, Reclamation House, Albion Row, Byker, Newcastle upon Tyne, NE6 1LQ Tel: 0191-224 3113 Fax: 0191-276 0221 E-mail: gd.metals@virgin.net Principal Export Areas: Worldwide *Scrap metal merchants*

▶ GDA Consultancy Ltd, 2 Roughknowles Road, Coventry, CV4 8GX Tel: (07919) 151795 Fax: (024) 7642 2951 E-mail: info@gdaconsultancy.co.uk *Project management & consultancy (business)*

GDB Manufacturing, Leisurewear House, Barnes Road, Bradford, West Yorkshire, BD8 9TG Tel: (01274) 491110 Fax: (01274) 491112 *Corporate clothing manufrs*

GDC Themed Events Ltd, 38-42 Fife Road, Kingston Upon Thames, Surrey, KT1 1SU Tel: (020) 8547 3682 Fax: (020) 8546 8461 E-mail: tim@gdc-events.co.uk *Theme party designers*

Gde Services Ltd, Mayfield House, Tockholes Road, Darwen, Lancashire, BB3 1LL Tel: (01254) 761246 Fax: (01254) 775202 *Service & sales of dishwashing & catering equipment*

GDK Air Conditioning & Refrigeration, Builders Yard, Barton Road, Bramley, Guildford, Surrey, GU5 0EB Tel: (01483) 894160 Fax: (01483) 894162 E-mail: info@gdkltd.co.uk *Air conditioning suppliers*

Gdynia America Shipping Lines (London) Ltd, 5 St. Johns Lane, London, EC1M 4DH Tel: (020) 7549 1693 Fax: (020) 7549 1694 E-mail: shipping@gdynia-america.co.uk *Ships' agent*

▶ John Geaar & Sons Ltd, 288 Main St, Coatbridge, Lanarkshire, ML5 3RH Tel: (01236) 422651 Fax: (01236) 433186 *Distill spirits & bottle it up*

Gear On Line, Bristol, BS99 3YS Tel: 0117-924 6065 Fax: 0117-924 0400 E-mail: sales@gearonline.co.uk *Audio equipment used, recording studio design services*

Gear Service, Oxford Road, Pen Mill Trading Estate, Yeovil, Somerset, BA21 5HR Tel: (01935) 428473 Fax: (01935) 432765 E-mail: yeovilgears@btconnect.com *Gear cutting services*

Gear Technology Ltd, 228 Lythalls Lane, Coventry, CV6 6GF Tel: (024) 7666 2556 Fax: (024) 7666 6355 E-mail: geartec@skelcher-rowe.co.uk *Gear cutting machine & tool manufrs*

Gearing Scientific Ltd, 1 Ashwell Street Ashwell, Baldock, Hertfordshire, SG7 5QF Tel: (01462) 742007 Fax: (01462) 742565 E-mail: gearingsci@yahoo.com *Thermal conductivity measuring equipment distributors*

Gearing & Watson Electronics Ltd, South Road, Hailsham, East Sussex, BN27 3JJ Tel: (01323) 846464 Fax: (01323) 847550 E-mail: sales@dataphysics.com *Gearing & Watson is now fully integrated into Data Physics (UK) Ltd. To view our complete range of Vibration Test Systems, Shakers, Dynamic Signal Analysers and Vibration Control Systems please visit our main Dataphysics (UK) Ltd site.*

Gears, 13b Cypress Road, Southport, Merseyside, PR8 6HE Tel: (01704) 535760 *Gearbox reconditioning*

Gears in Motion, Unit 66 Rovex Business Park, Hy Hall Road, Tyseley, Birmingham, B11 2AQ Tel: 0121-706 8821 Fax: 0121-708 0512 E-mail: info@gearsinmotion.co.uk *Gear wheels & gearing*

Geartech Gearboxes, Unit 240 Ikon Industrial Estate, Droitwich Road, Hartlebury, Kidderminster, Worcestershire, DY10 4EU Tel: (01299) 251261 *Automotive manual gearbox reconditioners*

Geartrodes South Wales Ltd, DC Griffiths Way, Neath, West Glamorgan, SA11 1BT Tel: (01639) 630081 Fax: (01639) 644394 E-mail: info@geartrodesweldingsupplies.co.uk *Welding equipment suppliers* Also at: Newport

Geberit Ltd, New Hythe Business Park, Aylesford, Kent, ME20 7PJ Tel: (01622) 717811 Fax: (01622) 716920 E-mail: salesgb@geberit.com *Plastics plumbing & drainage manufrs*

▶ Gecko It Services Ltd, 89 Chessel Avenue, Southampton, SO19 4DY Tel: (023) 8023 1030 E-mail: sales@gecko-it.com *Gecko is a friendly IT solutions outfit that provides small to medium sized businesses with cost effective IT support. We are here to help and we cover many areas including networking, internet & email, security, web hosting and design and consultancy. Please feel free to call us if you have any questions.*

Gecko Safety Systems Ltd, Unit M5 Cherrycourt Way, Leighton Buzzard, Bedfordshire, LU7 4UH Tel: (01525) 382040 Fax: (01525) 378956 E-mail: info@geckosafety.co.uk *Installation & agents of fall arrest devices*

▶ GECS Cleaning, 3 Church View, Wyverstone, Stowmarket, Suffolk, IP14 4SQ Tel: 01449 781603 E-mail: glenn@gecomputerservices.co.uk *Window and office cleaning*

Geddes Business Systems Ltd, 18 London Road, Peterborough, PE2 8AR Tel: (01733) 560291 Fax: (01733) 558526 *Computer systems supply & development*

▶ Geddes Group Ltd, Swirlburn, Colliston, Arbroath, Angus, DD11 3SH Tel: (01241) 890266 Fax: (01241) 890445 *Quarry masters*

▶ Geddes Group, Ardownie Quarry, Monifieth, Dundee, DD5 4HW Tel: (01382) 533382 Fax: (01382) 535655

▶ Geddes Group, Beanston, Haddington, East Lothian, EH41 3SB Tel: (01620) 861165 Fax: (01620) 861311 E-mail: enquiries@geddesgroup.co.uk *Quarry*

Geddes Packaging, Dumblederry Lane, Walsall, WS9 0DH Tel: (01922) 455988 Fax: (01922) 454988 E-mail: sales@geddespackaging.co.uk *Packing case manufrs*

Gedye & Partners Ltd, 26 The Dean, Alresford, Hampshire, SO24 9AZ Tel: (01962) 734567 Fax: (01962) 734342 *Electrical contractors*

GEDYS-DISKUS, Spencer House, 91 Dewhurst Road, Birchwood, Warrington, WA3 7PG Tel: (01925) 848484 Fax: (01925) 848485 E-mail: info@gedys.co.uk *Computer consultants*

Gee, 138 Richmond Road, Kingston upon Thames, Surrey, KT2 5EZ Tel: (020) 8546 4453 Fax: (020) 8546 2057 E-mail: drewgoater@hotmail.co.uk *Overall retail, distribution & manufrs*

▶ Gee Bee Fashions, 88 Crabmill Lane, Coventry, CV6 5HA Tel: (024) 7663 7022 Fax: (024) 7663 7022

Gee Bee Grinding, Gellan House, Carlisle Street, Gateshead, Tyne & Wear, NE10 0LD Tel: 0191-469 2489 Fax: 0191-469 3898 E-mail: sales@geebeegrinding.co.uk *Precision grinders*

Gee & Bee Stores & Blinds Ltd, 3 The Parade Manor Road, Cottingley Bingley, Bingley, West Yorkshire, BD16 1RP Tel: (01274) 561299 *Blind retailers*

Gee Construction Ltd, PO Box 14, Bridgend, Mid Glamorgan, CF31 3UD Tel: (01656) 653541 Fax: (01656) 657717 *Building contractors services*

E.J. Gee Ltd, PO Box 66, Lingfield, Surrey, RH7 6UP Tel: (01342) 837655 *Catering equipment distributors*

Gee & Co Effluent Control & Recovery Ltd, Gee House, Holbourn Hill, Birmingham, B7 5JR Tel: 0121-326 1700 Fax: 0121-326 1779 E-mail: info@geeco.co.uk *Effluent plant & chemical metering services*

Gee & Garnham Ltd, 1-6 Crescent Mews, London, N22 7GG Tel: (020) 8888 4982 Fax: (020) 8881 1353 E-mail: gg@geeandgarnham.com *Automotive spare parts exporters*

Jay Gee Clothing, Melbourne Works, Melbourne Street, Hebden Bridge, West Yorkshire, HX7 6AS Tel: (01422) 845292 *Trouser manufrs*

Tony Gee & Partners, T.G.P. House, 45-47 High Street, Cobham, Surrey, KT11 3DP Tel: (01932) 868277 Fax: (01932) 866003 E-mail: gmd@tgp.co.uk *Civil & structural engineers*

Gee Publishing Ltd, Customer Service, 100 Avenue Road, London, NW3 3PG Tel: (0845) 6009355 Fax: (020) 7722 4762 *Publishers*

Sue Gee, 9 Arcade, Accrington, Lancashire, BB5 2EL Tel: (01254) 234086 *Knitwear supplier*

Gee Tee Signs Ltd, Bestwood Road, Nottingham, NG6 8SS Tel: 0115-976 1188 Fax: 0115-976 1213 E-mail: sales@geeteesigns.com *Sign makers*

William Gee Ltd, William Gee House, 520-522 Kingsland Road, London, E8 4AH Tel: (020) 7254 2451 Fax: (020) 7249 8116 E-mail: wmgeetrims@aol.com *Wholesale trimmings merchants*

Gee-Co (Precast) Ltd, Upbrooksmill, Taylor Street, Clitheroe, Lancashire, BB7 1NL Tel: (01200) 427960 Fax: (01200) 426719 E-mail: geeco@supernet.com *Concrete product manufrs*

Geedev Ltd, 21 Barndale Drive, Arne, Wareham, Dorset, BH20 5BX Tel: (01929) 551122 Fax: (01929) 552936 E-mail: design@geedev.co.uk *Computers, industrial control; control systems, electronic & process controller/control systems (computer based) manufrs*

Geega Bags Co., 10 Stewart Street, Wolverhampton, WV2 4JW Tel: (01902) 717733 Fax: (01902) 717733 *Bag manufrs*

GeeJay Chemicals Ltd, 1 Beamish Close, Sandy, Bedfordshire, SG19 1SD Tel: (01767) 682774 Fax: (01767) 699697 E-mail: sales@geejaychemicals.co.uk Sales Contact: R. Covington *UK manufacturers of desiccant silica gel sachets since 1984. Standard silica gel sachet sizes (in grams): ½, 1, 3, 5, 10, 25, 50, 100, 250, 500, 1000 and 2500. Available with non-indicating silica gel (white) or self-indicating silica gel (orange to green, orange to colourless and blue to pink). Sachets made in paper, fabric, tyvek or cotton bags. Custom made packing (non-standard shapes and weights), silica gel sachets in foils, in bandoliers and with velcro. Bulk tins and drums of silica gel also available in pack sizes 500g, 1kg, 3kg, 12.5kg , 25kg and 150kg. Silica gel adsorbs moisture from enclosed spaces to help prevent moisture damage to items in transit or store. Desiccant molecular sieves in stock for drying liquids and gases (grades 3A, 4A and 10A) - buy molecular sieve in bulk or in sachets. Desiccant grade activated alumina. Humidity indicator cards and papers. Fast, flexible and reliable service.*

▶ Geek Pixel Ads, c/o NTB Global Trading, 2nd Floor, 145-157 St. John Street, London, EC1V 4PY Tel: (0845) 3104486 E-mail: sales@geek-pixelads.com

Geemarc Telecomm SA, Unit 5 Swallow Court, Swallowfields, Welwyn Garden City, Hertfordshire, AL7 1SB Tel: (01707) 372372 Fax: (01707) 372529 E-mail: sales@geemarc.com *Telephone importers & manufrs*

Geematics Amusement Machines, 57 Chester Street, Flint, Clwyd, CH6 5DH Tel: (01352) 732404 Fax: (01352) 732404 *Amusement machines*

Geere & Co., 233 Dunstable Road, Luton, LU4 8BN Tel: (01582) 730313 Fax: (01582) 727691 E-mail: info@memorialgroup.co.uk *Monumental memorials services & manufrs* Also at: Hitchin

▶ Gee's Haulage Ltd, Unit 2 Monckton Road Industria, Wakefield, West Yorkshire, WF2 7AL Tel: (01924) 372269

Geesink Norba Ltd, Llantrisant Business Park, Llantrisant, Pontyclun, Mid Glamorgan, CF72 8XZ Tel: (01443) 222301 Fax: (01443) 237192 E-mail: sales@pdegeesink.co.uk *Waste transportation equipment*

Geest Mariner, Athenian Way, Great Coates, Grimsby, South Humberside, DN37 9SY Tel: (01472) 254100 Fax: (01472) 254129 E-mail: geest@co.uk *Food processors*

Geest Normanby Food UK, Park Farm Road, Foxhills Industrial Estate, Scunthorpe, North Lincolnshire, DN15 8QP Tel: (01724) 749291 Fax: (01724) 749291 *Chilled goods manufacturer & distributors*

Geetee Investments Ltd, Plant Street, Wordsley, Stourbridge, West Midlands, DY8 5SY Tel: (01384) 79761 Fax: (01384) 480427 E-mail: monarchroofing@btclick.com *Felt roofing contractors*

Gefco UK Ltd, Fields End Business Park, Thurnscoe, Rotherham, South Yorkshire, S63 0JF Tel: (01709) 886000 Fax: (01709) 886006 E-mail: sales.uk@gefco.co.uk *Road transport, haulage & freight services*

Gega Lotz Ltd, Kiln Way, Woodville, Swadlincote, Derbyshire, DE11 8EA Tel: (01283) 214281 Fax: (01283) 222108 E-mail: sales@gegalotz.co.uk *Oxygen cutting machine manufrs*

Geiger Handling, Raleigh Hall Industrial Estate, Eccleshall, Stafford, ST21 6JL Tel: (01785) 851111 Fax: (01785) 859090 E-mail: s.hulse@geigerhandling.com *Automation & robotics*

Kurt Geiger Ltd, 75 Bermondsey Street, London, SE1 3XF Tel: (020) 7546 1888 Fax: (020) 7546 1880 E-mail: info@kurtgeiger.com *Retail supplier*

Geismar UK Ltd, Salthouse Road, Brackmills Industrial Estate, Northampton, NN4 7EX Tel: (01604) 769191 Fax: (01604) 763154 E-mail: admin@geismar.co.uk *Railway track maintenance equipment & service providers*

Geist Manufacturing Co. Ltd, Askern Industrial Estate, Moss Road, Askern, Doncaster, South Yorkshire, DN6 0DD Tel: (0845) 4941681 Fax: (01302) 709988 E-mail: geistmanltd@aol.com *Bespoke metal work of all types Ducting & heating manufacturers. Also fitting Holdover Conservator manufacturers*

Geistlich Sons Ltd, Long Lane, Chester, CH2 2PF Tel: (01244) 347534 Fax: (01244) 319327 E-mail: sales@geistlich.co.uk *Pharmaceutical & healthcare distributors*

▶ Gekko Digital Solutions Ltd, Windrush, Tormarton Road, Marshfield, Chippenham, Wiltshire, SN14 8NN Tel: (01225) 891727 Fax: (01225) 891890 E-mail: info@gekkodigital.co.uk *Graphic & web design studio specialists*

Gekko Entertainments, 42 Theobalds Road, London, WC1X 8NW Tel: (020) 7404 1252 Fax: (020) 7242 1691 E-mail: info@gekkoentertainments.com *Entertainment provider*

Geko Fashion Marketing Ltd, Geko House, Kimberley Road, London, NW6 7SG Tel: (020) 7624 0164 Fax: (020) 7372 5733 *Male clothing distributors*

GeKu UK Ltd, 35B Pattens Lane, Chatham, Kent, ME4 6JR Tel: (01634) 830122 Fax: (01634) 813523 E-mail: gekujohn@btinternet.com Principal Export Areas: Africa & North America *Injection moulding machine ancillary equipment*

Gel Tron International, Unit 3 Cunninghame Road, Irvine Industrial Estate, Irvine, Ayrshire, KA12 8JJ Tel: (01294) 276330 Fax: (01294) 272991 E-mail: sales@geltron.co.uk *Electronic trade suppliers*

▶ Gellan Ltd, Faraday Road, Nottingham, NG7 2DU Tel: (0870) 4019955 Fax: (0870) 4019954 E-mail: info@cadwiseltd.co.uk *Autocad draughting engineers*primarily for *building services*

Geller Business Equipment, Unit 14-15, Fairway Drive, Greenford, Middlesex, UB6 8PW Tel: (020) 8839 1000 Fax: (020) 8839 1030 E-mail: info@geller.co.uk *Cash registers & EPOS systems*

Gelmic Machine Tools Ltd, 28 Old Bedford Road, Luton, LU2 7NZ Tel: (01582) 731371 Fax: (01582) 453189 *Saw blade regrinding, new blades, lubricants & machines suppliers*

Gelpack Excelsior Ltd, Westfields Trading Estate, Hereford, HR4 9NT Tel: (01432) 267391 Fax: (01432) 264809 E-mail: info@gelpack.co.uk *Polyethylene refuse sack manufrs*

Gem Alarms & Security Services, 24 West Bay, Bridport, Dorset, DT6 4HD Tel: (01308) 423470 Fax: (01308) 423470 *Security Systems*

Gem Creations Ltd, DHG House, 152 Mount Pleasant, Wembley, Middlesex, HA0 1RN Tel: (020) 8903 6781 Fax: (020) 8903 6922 E-mail: gemcreationltd@aol.com *Jewellery import & export merchants*

Gem Engineering, Gemini House, Bolton Road Industrial Estate, Westhoughton, Bolton, BL5 3JQ Tel: (01942) 814464 Fax: (01942) 842414 E-mail: gem.engineering@ic24.net *General engineering services*

Gem Engineering Ltd, Factory Road, Sandycroft, Deeside, Clwyd, CH5 2QJ Tel: (01244) 520859 Fax: (01244) 520328 E-mail: sales@gemengineering.co.uk *Steel fabricators*

Gem Engraving, 33 Hayes Close, Wimborne, Dorset, BH21 2JJ Tel: (01202) 881907 Fax: (01202) 887691 E-mail: sales@gemengraving.co.uk *Engraving services*

The Gem & Jewellery Workshop, Boscaswell Downs, Pendeen, Penzance, Cornwall, TR19 7DW Tel: (01736) 788217 *Jewellery manufrs*

▶ Gem Stone Graphics Ltd, 4 Highdown Court, Forestfield, Crawley, West Sussex, RH10 6PR Tel: (01293) 524546 E-mail: info@gsg-ltd.co.uk *Gem Stone Graphics is a multi media graphic design company that produce both design and print for corporate and private customers.*Large or small we do it all!*

▶ gembasket.co.uk, 39 Belmont Drive, Westwood, East Kilbride, Glasgow, G75 8HB Tel: (01355) 232441 E-mail: orders@gembasket.co.uk *Online catalogue of gemstones - no minimum order - free delivery on orders over £50.*

Gemco 2000 Ltd, 3 Export Drive, Huthwaite, Sutton-in-Ashfield, Nottinghamshire, NG17 6AF Tel: (01623) 551818 Fax: (01623) 551717 *New & second hand garage equipment suppliers*

Gemco Equipment Ltd, Unit B1 Fortwilliam Court, 24 Duncrue CR, Belfast, BT3 9BW Tel: (028) 9077 2666 Fax: (028) 9077 9251 E-mail: sales@allenengineering.co.uk *Garage equipment*

Gemflex Engineering Ltd, Unit 4, Cossall Industrial Estate, Coronation Road, Ilkeston, Derbyshire, DE7 5UA Tel: 0115-944 2414 Fax: 0115-944 2771 E-mail: sales@gemflex.co.uk *Precision sheet metal engineers & laser cutting services*

Gemini Blinds, 2 Greenmeadow Works, Ponthir Road, Caerleon, Newport, NP18 3NY Tel: (01633) 872724 Fax: (01633) 872849 *Blind manufrs*

Gemini Blinds, South Arcade, Chester Street, Wrexham, Clwyd, LL13 8BE Tel: (01978) 359972 Fax: (01978) 359972 *Blind manufrs*

Gemini Blinds & Curtains, 732 Borough Road, Birkenhead, Merseyside, CH42 9JF Tel: 0151-608 7100 Fax: 0151-608 7100 *Blind sales & curtain manufrs*

Gemini Bookkeeping Services, 52 Popham Close, Tiverton, Devon, EX16 4GA Tel: 01884 252254 E-mail: hms40@btinternet.com *Bookkeeping Services for small business and sole traders based in Devon*

▶ Gemini Cleaning, Trewilyn, Ruddlemoor, St. Austell, Cornwall, PL26 8XF Tel: (0845) 2260974 Fax: (0845) 2260974 E-mail: gemini_cleaners@hotmail.com *commercial & domestic cleaning service*

Gemini Connections Ltd, 487 Holden Road, Leigh, Lancashire, WN7 2JJ Tel: (01942) 674929 Fax: (01942) 707516 E-mail: gemini.connections@virgin.net *Cable assemblies & telephone accessory suppliers*

Gemini Consultants Ltd, The Gemini Building, Houghton Hall Park, Houghton Regis, Dunstable, Bedfordshire, LU5 5GB Tel: (01582) 868621 Fax: (01582) 868622 E-mail: mail@geminiconsultants.com *Mortgage consultants*

Gemini Corrosion Services Ltd, Spurryhillock Industrial Estate, Broomhill Road, Stonehaven, Kincardineshire, AB39 2NH Tel: (01569) 765488 Fax: (01569) 766315 E-mail: enquiries@gemini-corrosion.co.uk *Shot blasting contractors*

Gemini Digital Colour, North Road, Bridgend Industrial Estate, Bridgend, Mid Glamorgan, CF31 3TP Tel: (01656) 652447 Fax: (01656) 661266 E-mail: sales@geminidigitalcolour.co.uk *Digital colour printers with personalisation facilities*

continued

Gemini Dispersions Ltd, Holt Mill Road, Rossendale, Lancashire, BB4 7JB Tel: (01706) 214751 Fax: (01706) 218152 E-mail: sales@geminidispersions.com *Pigment dispersion & colour manufrs*

▶ gemini fotografik, 2 Littlewood, Stokenchurch, Buckinghamshire, HP14 3TF Tel: (01494) 483462 E-mail: info@geminifotografik.co.uk *Portrait, Fashion, Corporate and Product Photography in the studio or on location in both digital and conventional media formats.*

Gemini Group, Unit 21 Derryloran Industrial Estate, Sandholes Road, Cookstown, County Tyrone, BT80 9LU Tel: (028) 8676 1292 Fax: (028) 8676 5566 E-mail: sales@thegeminigroup.co.uk *Safety sign manufrs*

Gemini Group, Unit 21 Derryloran Industrial Estate, Sandholes Road, Cookstown, County Tyrone, BT80 9LU Tel: (028) 8676 1292 Fax: (028) 8676 5566 *Screen writing & sign making*

Gemini Industries UK Ltd., 18-20 Canterbury Road,, Whitstable, Kent, CT5 4EY Tel: 01406 350572 E-mail: info@geminiindustries.co.uk *Inflatables of all types*Boats *Liferafts*Medical products*Inflatable Boat Repair Kits*Rigid Inflatable Boat Kits*Inflatable Products Design Service*Large Yacht Fenders**

Gemini Kitchens Ltd, Unit 14-15 Worsley Business Park, Mosley Common Road, Worsley, Manchester, M28 1NL Tel: 0161-703 9903 Fax: 0161-703 9934 E-mail: sales@geminikitchens.com *Kitchen manufrs*

Gemini Press Ltd, Unit A1 Dolphin Way, Shoreham-by-Sea, West Sussex, BN43 6NZ Tel: (01273) 464884 Fax: (01273) 464744 E-mail: info@gemini-group.co.uk *Printers, colour printings & lithographic printers suppliers*

Gemini Products, Unit 3, Cruso Street, Leek, Staffordshire, ST13 8BJ Tel: (01538) 373600 Fax: (01538) 372600 E-mail: ivan@tesco.net *Plastic binders & welded goods manufrs*

Gemini Supplies Scotland Ltd, Unit 3 St. Johns Sawmill, Etna Road, Falkirk, FK2 9EG Tel: (01324) 629425 Fax: (01324) 630323 *Fasteners & fixings distributors*

Gemini Technology Reading Ltd, 1 34 Bennet Road, Reading, RG2 0QX Tel: 0118-931 4206 Fax: 0118-931 4213 E-mail: tonybates@gemini-tech.demon.co.uk *Design, manufacture & install mechanical electronic equipment*

▶ Gemini Telecommunications, 78 Britton Street, Gillingham, Kent, ME7 5ET Tel: (01634) 580510 Fax: (01634) 579628 E-mail: sales@gemini-telecom.com *Suppliers, installers & maintainers of business telephone systems*

Geminique Children & Babywear, 1 Small Business Centre, Penmaen Road, Pontllanfraith, Blackwood, Gwent, NP12 2DZ Tel: (01495) 229969 Fax: (01495) 229969 *Infant clothing suppliers*

Gemlog Controls Ltd, 22 Greenfield Way, Storrington, Pulborough, West Sussex, RH20 4PY Tel: (01903) 743835 Fax: (01903) 740071 E-mail: info@gemlog.co.uk *Industrial control products & instrumentation services*

Gemma Group Ltd, Grove Road, Cosham, Portsmouth, PO6 1LX Tel: (023) 9221 0015 Fax: (023) 9221 0058 E-mail: gemma@dial.pipex.com *Holding company*

▶ Gemmedbellybars, 33 Westbury Close, Bransgore, Christchurch, Dorset, BH23 8AZ Tel: (01425) 672711 E-mail: hantsgirl2@hotmail.com *Gemmed belly bar sales*

The Gemmological Association & Laboratory Of Great Britain, 27 Greville Street, London, EC1N 8TN Tel: (020) 7404 3334 Fax: (020) 7404 8843 E-mail: sales@gem-a.info *Gemmological instruments & books*

Gemplus Ltd, 36 New Lane, Havant, Hampshire, PO9 2NR Tel: (023) 9248 6444 Fax: (023) 9247 0628 E-mail: felicity.best@gemplus.com *Plastic card product suppliers*

▶ Gempro Website Design and Development Services, 249 Beaver Lane, Ashford, Kent, TN23 5PA Tel: 01233 334069 E-mail: info@gempro.co.uk *Website design, website development, shopping carts, forum design*

Gems, 51 Spring Rd, Kempston, Bedford, MK42 8LS Tel: 01234 351186 Fax: 01234 351186 *Clothing & fabrics manufrs*

Gems Sensors Pension Trustees Ltd, Lennox Road, Basingstoke, Hampshire, RG22 4AW Tel: (01256) 320244 Fax: (01256) 473680 E-mail: sales@gems-sensors.co.uk Principal Export Areas: Worldwide *Design, manufacture and supply of Pressure, Level & Flow Sensors to ISO 9001. Full technical support for custom design for OEM to aircraft applications with over 40 years experience in providing solutions to the most demanding problems. Catalogues available giving full technical and dimensional data with many items ex-stock.*

▶ Gemsoft Computers, 13 Naworth Drive, Carlisle, CA3 0DD Tel: (01228) 547444 Fax: (01228) 547444 *Computer software development*

Gemstone Designs Ltd, Bath Street, Bakewell, Derbyshire, DE45 1BX Tel: (01629) 815085 Fax: (01629) 815085 E-mail: enquiries@gemstonedesigns.co.uk *Jewellery manufrs*

Gemweld Fabrications & Engineering Co. Ltd, Lancaster Way, Market Deeping, Peterborough, PE6 8LA Tel: (01778) 344733 Fax: (01778) 343988 E-mail: cam@gemweld.co.uk *General engineers & fabricators*

▶ Gemweld (UK) Ltd, 2 Glenburn Road, Prestwick, Ayrshire, KA9 2NS Tel: (01292) 478008

▶ Gen Tek, 20 Thornton Gate, Thornton-Cleveleys, Lancashire, FY5 1JN Tel: (01253) 855589 *Computer maintenance & repair services*

Genalog Ltd, Gills Green Oast, Gills Green, Cranbrook, Kent, TN18 5ET Tel: (01580) 753754 Fax: (01580) 752979 E-mail: sales@genalog.com *Electronic component distributors*

▶ GenCat Ltd, Unit 16, The Edge Business Centre, Humber Road, London, NW2 6EW Tel: 0208 450 6160 Fax: 0208 452 2822 E-mail: info@gencat.co.uk *Suppliers of Catalytic Converters, Particulate Filters for diesel powered plant, GenSets, HGVs and fork lift trucks. Rain Caps of all sizes supplied for any application.*

Gencoa Ltd, Physics Road, Liverpool, L24 9HP Tel: 0151-486 4466 Fax: 0151-486 4488 E-mail: sales@gencoa.com *Vacuum components manufrs*

▶ Gendata Ltd, 3, Church Street, Cirencester, Glos, GL7 1LE Tel: (01285) 659810 Fax: (01285) 644388

Gene Pearl Buttons Ltd, 2 Bridge Rd, London, NW10 9BX Tel: 020 84594460 *Buttons & buckles*

Geneen's Catering Service, Bridgebrook Shop, The Village, Great Waltham, Chelmsford, CM3 1AT Tel: (01245) 362352 Fax: (01245) 362999 *Catering equipment suppliers*

▶ Geneflow Scientific Apparatus, Wood End Lane, Fradley, Lichfield, Staffordshire, WS13 8NF Tel: (01543) 414704 Fax: (01543) 255666 E-mail: sales@geneflow.co.uk *Suppliers of scientific instruments*

Genel 86 Ltd, Kent House, 9 Beech Street, Leicester, LE5 0DF Tel: 0116-251 5156 Fax: 0116-251 5159 E-mail: genel86sales@aol.com *Labels & thread, trimming & fashion labels*

▶ General Anaesthetic Services, Ingrow Bridge Works, Keighley, West Yorkshire, BD21 5EF Tel: (01535) 609615 *Exchange services*

The General Asphalte Company Ltd, La Brea House, Coventry Street, Birmingham, B5 5NJ Tel: 0121-643 1846 Fax: 0121-643 7134 E-mail: gacltd@talk21.com *Asphalt & roofing contractors*

General Bridge & Engineering Ltd, Fleming Road, Earlstrees Industrial Estate, Corby, Northamptonshire, NN17 4SW Tel: (01536) 205744 Fax: (01536) 402456 E-mail: email@genbridge.fsnet.co.uk *Materials handling equipment manufrs*

General Catering Supplies Ltd, 6-8 Weir Road, London, SW12 0NA Tel: (020) 8673 6013 Fax: (020) 8675 9836 E-mail: info@gcsgroup.co.uk *GCS is a family business that has been serving the catering industry since 1969. Their product range includes tableware, disposables, furniture, kitchenware, groceries, hygiene and bar items plus many more.*

General Dietary Ltd, PO Box 38, Kingston upon Thames, Surrey, KT2 7YP Tel: (020) 8336 2323 Fax: (020) 8942 8274 E-mail: greareal.dietary@vigin.net *Special food importers*

▶ General Domestic Appliances, 120 Prime Street, Northwood, Stoke-on-Trent, ST1 6PS Tel: (01782) 204167 E-mail: generaldomestics@aol.com *Repairs, Servicing, and Supply of spare parts for all types of domestic kitchen appliances. Online spares ordering. Qualified Engineers. Plumbing work undertaken.*

▶ General Dynamics, Unit 3 Bryn Brithdir, Oakdale Business Park, Blackwood, Gwent, NP12 4AA Tel: (01495) 236300 Fax: (01495) 236400 E-mail: sales@generaldynamics.uk.com *System engineers*

General Engineering, 11 Seymour Street, Ballymoney, County Antrim, BT53 6JR Tel: (028) 2766 2454 *Steel fabricators*

General Engineers Supply Co. Ltd, 555-557 High Road Leytonstone, London, E11 4PD Tel: (020) 8556 0201 Fax: (020) 8558 9305 E-mail: gens@engineers555.freeserve.co.uk *Engineers supplies*

General Erections, 103 Woodville Road, Hartshorne, Swadlincote, Derbyshire, DE11 7EX Tel: (01283) 216669 Fax: (01283) 216669 *Steel erectors*

General Express Motor Supplies (Leicester) Ltd, Pullman Road, Wigston, Leicestershire, LE18 2DB Tel: 0116-288 1344 Fax: 0116-257 0290 *Motor body finishes factors*

General Fabrications Ltd, 26 Orphanage Road, Birmingham, B24 9HT Tel: 0121-377 6070 Fax: 0121-377 7175 E-mail: info@genfab.co.uk *Adhesive & adhesive tape distributors or agents. Also adhesive tape converters*

General Facilities Management Ltd, Enterprise House, Terrace Road, Walton-on-T, Walton-on-Thames, Surrey, KT12 2SD Tel: (01932) 221191 Fax: (0870) 0527012 E-mail: sales@doctec.co.uk *Document management services*

General Fixings Ltd, Unit 54 Beeches Industrial Estate, Waverley Road, Yate, Bristol, BS37 5QR Tel: (01454) 310015 Fax: (01454) 273164 E-mail: sales@generalfixings.co.uk *Industrial fixings & power tools suppliers*

General High Voltage, New Road, Highley, Bridgnorth, Shropshire, WV16 6NN Tel: (01746) 862555 Fax: (01746) 862666 E-mail: info@genvolt.co.uk *High voltage design manufrs*

General Hoseclips Ltd, Royston Road, Byfleet, West Byfleet, Surrey, KT14 7NY Tel: (01932) 343224 Fax: (01932) 351285 E-mail: info@generalhoseclips.com *Hose clip & clamp manufrs*

General Hydraulics, Banbury Road, Thrupp, Kidlington, Oxfordshire, OX5 1JF Tel: (01865) 377559 *Hydraulic engineers & equipment repair services*

General Imaging Technology UK Ltd, Unit 18 Hortonwood 33, Telford, Shropshire, TF1 7YS Tel: (01952) 677510 Fax: (01952) 676332 E-mail: sam@generalimaging.co.uk *Printer consumable manufrs*

General & Industrial Window Cleaning Co. Ltd, 203-209 Gateford Road, Worksop, Nottinghamshire, S81 7BB Tel: (01909) 472967 Fax: (01909) 472967 *Industrial cleaning contractors*

General Insurance Brokers UK plc, 90 Bishops Bridge Road, London, W2 5AA Tel: (020) 7792 0123 Fax: (020) 7727 5794 *Insurance brokers*

General Kinematics Ltd, Dawley Brook Works, Kingswinford, West Midlands, DY6 7BB Tel: (01384) 273303 Fax: (01384) 273404 E-mail: mail@generalkinematics.co.uk *Vibratory process equipment manufrs*

General Leather Co., 56 Chiltern Street, London, W1U 7QY Tel: (020) 7935 1041 Fax: (020) 7224 4312 E-mail: enquiries@generalleather.co.uk *Leather & suede clothing manufacturers & designers*

General Monitors UK Ltd, 1 Heather Close, Lyme Green Business Park, Macclesfield, Cheshire, SK11 0LR Tel: (01625) 619583 Fax: (01625) 619098 E-mail: info@generalmonitors.co.uk *Gas & flame detection equipment manufrs*

General Nutrition Centre, 7 Chequers Square, Uxbridge, Middlesex, UB8 1LN Tel: (01895) 254538 *Health product retailers*

General Packaging Co., Unit 3 Cooksland Industrial Estate, Bodmin, Cornwall, PL31 2QB Tel: (01208) 265870 Fax: (01208) 72457 E-mail: enquiries@generalpackaging.co.uk *Packaging material merchants*

General Panel Systems Ltd, 1-2 Leicester Street, Bedminster, Bristol, BS3 4DE Tel: 0117-953 1500 Fax: 0117-947 1700 E-mail: info@gpspanels.co.uk *Control panel manufrs*

General Partitioning Ltd, 632 Eastern Avenue, Ilford, Essex, IG2 6PG Tel: (020) 8554 5010 Fax: (020) 8554 5012 *Office refurbishment contractors*

▶ General Physics UK Ltd, 28 High Street, Paisley, Renfrewshire, PA1 2BZ Tel: 0141-840 5950 Fax: 0141-840 5951 *Training services*

General Services Fabrications Ltd, Sudmeadow Road, Gloucester, GL2 5HS Tel: (01452) 304515 Fax: (01452) 504729 *Steel fabricators*

General Steel Services, 45 Sydenham Road, Belfast, BT3 9DH Tel: (028) 9045 6327 Fax: (028) 9045 8096 E-mail: gss@metsteel.co.uk *Steel bar & mesh manufrs*

▶ General Supplies Ltd, 465A Caledonian Road, Holloway, London, N7 9BA Tel: (020) 7609 6111 Fax: (020) 7609 8111 E-mail: sales@generalsupplies.com *Bathroom & Plumbing Merchants*

General Systems Ltd, Stockport Road, Cheadle, Cheshire, SK8 2AA Tel: 0161-495 6700 Fax: 0161-495 6701 *Financial computer software resellers*

General Technology Ltd, Unit E5 Fairchild Place, London, EC2A 3EN Tel: (020) 7375 0000 Fax: (020) 7377 1429 E-mail: hitech@gentec.co.uk *IT consultants*

General Telecom & Data UK Ltd, 3-5 Berringtons Lane, Rainford, St. Helens, Merseyside, WA11 7PZ Tel: (01744) 885828 Fax: (01744) 889515 E-mail: enquiries@generaltel.co.uk *Telecommunication equipment suppliers & installers*

General Transmissions, Wickham Mews, London, SE4 1PQ Tel: (020) 8692 1417 Fax: (020) 8692 3351 *Gearbox re-conditioners*

General Utilities Stockport Ltd, Clough Works, Middlewood Road, Poynton, Stockport, Cheshire, SK12 1SJ Tel: (01625) 876321 Fax: (01625) 876284 E-mail: sales@generalutilities.co.uk *Flame Cut Profiling*Stress Relieving*Surface Grinding*

▶ Generalsoft Computer Systems, Gibbs House, Kennel Ride, Ascot, Berkshire, SL5 7NT Tel: (01344) 890979 Fax: (01344) 884735 E-mail: info@generalsoft.co.uk *Software development of management systems services*

Generated Power Services Ltd, Argosons Hunsdon Stud, Eastwick Road, Hunsdon, Ware, Hertfordshire, SG12 8PP Tel: (01920) 877171 Fax: (01920) 877128 *Generator & generating set hire, leasing & rental*

Generation Music Ltd, Grays Inn House, Unit 14 Mile Oak Industrial Estate, Oswestry, Shropshire, SY10 8GA Tel: (01691) 653970 Fax: (01691) 679403 E-mail: sales@generationmusic.co.uk *Musical instrument accessories & manufrs*

Generation Software, 59 Victoria Road, Tilehurst, Reading, RG31 5AB Tel: 0118-948 2468 Fax: 0118-948 2470 E-mail: office@generationsoftware.com *Training for health & safety*

▶ Genero Ltd, Unit 4, Ty Verlon Industrial Estate, Cardiff Road, Barry, South Glamorgan, CF63 2BE Tel: (0870) 1630700 Fax: (0870) 1630701 E-mail: genero@btinternet.com *Audio visual equipment, conference & event presentation equipment*

▶ Genersys Ireland Ltd, 44 Victoria Square, Rostrevor, Newry, County Down, BT34 3EU Tel: (028) 4173 7777 Fax: (028) 4173 8456 E-mail: genersys@genersys-ireland.com Purchasing Contact: D. Cooper Sales Contact: D. Cooper *Solar thermal panel system suppliers*

Genes Plastics, Unit 21b Stafford Mill, London Road, Thrupp, Stroud, Gloucestershire, GL5 2AZ Tel: (01453) 751000 Fax: (01453) 755556 *Injection mouldings manufrs*

Genese International Ltd, The Old Yard, Main Street, Keyingham, Hull, HU12 9RE Tel: (01964) 622251 Fax: (01964) 622525 *Cosmetic manufrs*

Genesis Aps International Ltd, Ellerbeck Way, Stokesley Industrial Park, Stokesley, Middlesbrough, Cleveland, TS9 5JZ Tel: (01642) 713000 Fax: (01642) 713777 E-mail: enquiries@genesis-aps.com *Tile trim accessories*

▶ Genesis Coaching Ltd, 12 Palmer Close, Wellingborough, Northants, NN8 5NX Tel: 0845 1283980 Fax: 0845 1260330 E-mail: coach@genesis-coaching.co.uk *Life Success and Business Coaching Services. Experienced UK Trained NLP success coach.*I help my clients to take their lives to the next level and beyond.*

▶ Genesis Contractors Ltd, 32 Hillbrook Grove, Birmingham, B33 8DG Tel: 0121-628 2186 Fax: 0121-786 2367

▶ Genesis Design & Print, 111 Whitby Road, Slough, SL1 3DR Tel: (01753) 696940 Fax: (01753) 696941

Genesis Display Ltd, Unit 14 Lee Bank Business Centre, Holloway Head, Birmingham, B1 1HP Tel: 0121-643 4237 Fax: 0121-633 3977 E-mail: rob@genesisltd.wanadoo.co.uk *Screen printing services*

▶ The Genesis Group (UK), Dooks Cottages, South Moor Road, Walkeringham, Doncaster, South Yorkshire, DN10 4LB Tel: (0800) 0895555 E-mail: sales@genesisgroupuk.com *PC, nationwide support & office move management*

▶ Genesis Lifts Ltd, 55 Whitemill Road, Chatteris, Cambridgeshire, PE16 6PG Tel: (0870) 7602268 Fax: (07005) 850036 E-mail: trevorsherwood@dsl.pipex.com *Lifts*

▶ Genesis Lifts Ltd, Drayton Old Lodge Business Centre, 146 Drayton High Road, Norwich, NR8 6AN Tel: 01603 861631 Fax: 0700 5850036E-mail: trevorsherwood@dsl.pipex.com *Lift servicing, breakdowns, call-outs, repairs, modifications to comply with Disability Discrimination Act (DDA), modernisation, refurbishment, new lifts, new disablity access equipment, and upgrade of all types of lifts within the East Anglia area from offices in Norwich and Cambridge. Free quotations without obligation.*

▶ Genesis Medical Pre Installation Ltd, 3 Kingfisher House Crayfields Business Park, New Mill Road, Orpington, Kent, BR5 3QG Tel: (01689) 898978 Fax: (01689) 822777

Genesis Personnel, 2 Marischal Street, Peterhead, Aberdeenshire, AB42 1HU Tel: (01779) 871980 Fax: (01779) 476312 E-mail: phd@genesis-personnel.co.uk *Recruitment solutions*

▶ Genesis Pvcu Ltd, 29 Britannia Way, Britannia Enterprise Park, Lichfield, Staffordshire, WS14 9UY Tel: (01543) 417575 Fax: (01543) 418180

Genesis Scotland Ltd, The Douglas Centre, Marchmont Crescent, Buckie, Banffshire, AB56 4BT Tel: (01542) 834947 Fax: (0870) 3835549 E-mail: genesisltd@btopenworld.com *Telecommunications*

▶ Genesis Seven Ltd, Unit 4 Scotshaw Brook Industrial Estate, Branch Road Lower Darwen, Lower Darwen, Darwen, Lancashire, BB3 0PR Tel: (01254) 666000 Fax: (01254) 666001 E-mail: info@genesis-seven.co.uk

Genesis Trading (UK) Corp, 32 Woodhall Drive, Pinner, Middlesex, HA5 4TQ Tel: (020) 8420 1177 Fax: (020) 8420 1155 E-mail: gentauk@hotmail.com *Import & export merchants*

▶ Genesis Wines Ltd, 78Tachbrook Street, London, SW1V 2NE Tel: (020) 7963 9060 Fax: (0870) 8502038 E-mail: sales@genesiswines.com *Wine importers*

Genesys Communications, Trenewth House, Michaelstow, St. Tudy, Bodmin, Cornwall, PL30 3PE Tel: (01208) 851158 Fax: (01208) 851199 E-mail: john@genesys.sfnet.co.uk *Telecom equipment manufrs*

Genesys I B S Ltd, Singleton Court Business Centre, Wonastow Road, Monmouth, Gwent, NP25 5JA Tel: (01600) 710300 Fax: (01600) 710301 E-mail: nick@genesysibs.com *Services to the telecommunication industry*

Genevac Ltd, 6 Farthing Road, Ipswich, IP1 5AP Tel: (01473) 240000 Fax: (01473) 461176 E-mail: sales@genevac.co.uk *Laboratory vacuum & evaporation systems manufrs*

Gen-Fab Ltd, 302 Neepsend Lane, Sheffield, S3 8AW Tel: 0114-273 0303 Fax: 0114-275 8683 E-mail: enquiry@genfab.co.uk *Steel fabrication, laser cutting*

Genhart Ltd, 3 Malmesbury Road, Kingsditch Trading Estate, Cheltenham, Gloucestershire, GL51 9PL Tel: (01242) 241734 Fax: (01242) 227500 E-mail: frank@genhart.co.uk *Precision & general engineers*

Genie Computing, Unit 1, Gelligron Industrial Estate, Tonyrefail, Porth, Mid Glamorgan, CF39 8ES Tel: (0800) 0198069 E-mail: sales@geniecomputing.co.uk *Computer maintenance & repairers*

▶ Genie Studios, Henson Road, Bedworth, Warwickshire, CV12 0DL Tel: (08700) 272501

▶ Genie UK Ltd, The Maltings, Wharf Road, Grantham, Lincolnshire, NG31 6BH Tel: (01476) 584333 Fax: (01476) 584334 E-mail: infoeurope@genieind.com *Designing & manufacturing lifting equipment with new & used parts*

Genisys Group Ltd, Crockford Lane, Chineham, Basingstoke, Hampshire, RG24 8NA Tel: (01256) 816611 Fax: (01256) 816552 E-mail: sales@genisys.co.uk *Computer equipment suppliers & solution providers*

Genius Sound & Vision, Unit 8 Anchorage Point, 90 Anchor & Hope Lane, London, SE7 7SQ Tel: (020) 8472 9011 Fax: (020) 8472 9012 E-mail: info@genius.uk.com *Audio visual hire & services*

▶ Genner (Web Site) Construction, PO Box 653, Telford, Shropshire, TF3 1ZN Tel: (01952) 411902 E-mail: kevin@genner.co.uk *IT recovery services*

Genpart UK Ltd, 5 Threxton Road Industrial Estate, Watton, Thetford, Norfolk, IP25 6NG Tel: (01953) 882436 Fax: (01953) 885597 E-mail: sales@genpart.co.uk *Control switchgear manufrs*

Genrad Holdings Ltd, Orion Business Park, Bird Hall Lane, Stockport, Cheshire, SK3 0XG Tel: (01483) 569933 Fax: 0161-491 9501 *Electronic test equipment*

▶ Gens Sensors, Lennox Road, Basingstoke, Hampshire, RG22 4AW Tel: (01256) 301400 Fax: (01256) 473680

▶ Gens4Less, 80 Lockitt Street, Crewe, CW2 7BB Tel: (01270) 509276 Fax: (01270) 509297 E-mail: enquiries@edgetechnology.co.uk *Sales of Honda & SDMO portable generators*

▶ Genstar Trading, Unit 2, Colne Way Court, Watford, WD24 7NE Tel: (01923) 806806 Fax: (01923) 805805 E-mail: sales@genstar.co.uk *Software sales services*

Gensys Technology Ltd, 15 Percy Street, London, W1T 1DS Tel: (020) 7255 2022 Fax: (020) 7255 3033 *Computer software development consultants & apple reseller*

L. Gent Ltd, Unit 9 Hemlock Park, Hyssop Close, Cannock, Staffordshire, WS11 7FB Tel: (01543) 578383 Fax: (01543) 573797 E-mail: info@directron.co.uk *Sewing machine manufrs*

Gent Transport, Unit 5, Badminton Road, Yate, Bristol, BS37 5NS Tel: (01454) 881000 Fax: (01454) 881122 *Express transport & warehousing services*

▶ Gentech Electrical (UK) Ltd, Unit 8, Breightmet Industrial Estate, Bury Road, Bolton, BL2 6PX Tel: 0161-761 0484 Fax: 0161-761 0485 E-mail: sales@gentech-electrical.co.uk *We offer generator repairs (on and off site) for all makes, models and size gensets, Standby /back-up power installations, maintenance & servicing programmes are also available. In addition we offer commercial electrical installations plus a wide range of related services*

Gentech International Ltd, Grangestone Eng Co, Grangestone Indust Estat E Ladywell Avenue, Maidens, Girvan, Ayrshire, KA26 9PL Tel: (01465) 713581 Fax: (01465) 714974 E-mail: enquiries@gentech-international.co.uk *Sensors for Liquid Level, Flow and Position*

Genua Madrigal Ltd, 9 Gillian Park Road, Sutton, Surrey, SM3 9JT Tel: (020) 8286 6589 Fax: (020) 8286 6589 E-mail: info@nineservices.co.uk *We provide translation services to/from Western European Languages & Arabic (other languages on application.) We can also provide tailor-made language courses & tuition as well as activity breaks. we also provide a travel service*

▶ Genus Engineering Ltd, 33A Colomendy Industrial Estate, Rhyl Road, Denbigh, Clwyd, LL16 5TA Tel: (01745) 815684 Fax: (01745) 817084 E-mail: enquiry@genusengineering.co.uk *Precision engineers, special purpose machined components manufrs*

The Genus Group, 15/16 Hammond Close, Nuneaton, Warwickshire, CV11 6RY Tel: (024) 7625 4955 Fax: (024) 7638 2319 E-mail: info@genusit.com Purchasing Contact: P. Symons Sales Contact: H. Perry Principal Export Areas: Worldwide *Genus specialises in Document Management, Record Management and Information Archiving Services. Through its subsidiaries The Microfilm Shop and Genus Large Format, Genus supplies microfilm and micrographics equipment, microfilm scanning equipment, wide format and scanners, large format plotters, document management software, workflow solutions, e-mail archiving and digital preservation.*

▶ GENUS IT Large Format Systems, Hammond Close, Nuneaton, Warwickshire, CV11 6RY Tel: (024) 7625 4919 Fax: (024) 7638 2319 E-mail: philjones@genusit.com *Specialist supplier of large format plotters, scanners & printers*

▶ Genus Systems, Prospect House, Halesfield 22, Telford, Shropshire, TF7 4QX Tel: (01952) 587196 Fax: (0845) 1110275 *Computer software developers*

Gen-Vent Metalworkers Ltd, Manor Works, Manor Road, London, SE25 4TA Tel: (020) 8656 3000 Fax: (020) 8655 4038 *Ductwork engineers*

Genweld Supplies Ltd, 41 Unit 2, Wolverhampton, WV1 2RZ Tel: (01902) 351438 Fax: (01902) 351475 E-mail: sales@genweld.com *Welding supplies distributors*

Genzyme Vehicle Leasing Ltd, Hollands Road, Haverhill, Suffolk, CB9 8PU Tel: (01440) 703522 Fax: (01440) 716269 *Pharmaceuticals & fine chemical manufrs*

Geoacoustics Ltd, Shuttleworth Close, Gapton Hall Industrial Estate, Great Yarmouth, Norfolk, NR31 0NQ Tel: (01493) 600666 Fax: (01493) 651100 E-mail: sales@geoacoustics.co.uk *Ocean research equipment manufrs*

Geocel Ltd, Western Wood Way, Langage Business Park, Plympton, Plymouth, PL7 5BG Tel: (01752) 202060 Fax: (01752) 202065 E-mail: info@geocel.co.uk Principal Export Areas: Asia Pacific, North America, Central America & South America *Adhesive & sealant manufr*

Geodelft Environmental, 18 Victoria Avenue, Newtownards, County Down, BT23 7EB Tel: (028) 9182 0061 Fax: (028) 9181 6634 *Environmental remediation specialists*

Geodis Overseas (U K) Ltd, PO Box 92, High Wycombe, Buckinghamshire, HP12 3TW Tel: (01494) 446541 Fax: (01494) 446329 E-mail: hwcustomerservies@geodisuk.com *Freight services*

Geodis UK Ltd, Linwood Industrial Estate, Lyon Road, Linwood, Paisley, Renfrewshire, PA3 3BQ Tel: (01505) 321111 Fax: (01505) 325555 *Road transport, haulage & freight services*

Geoff Greenfield Ltd, Henfield Road, Upper Beeding, Steyning, West Sussex, BN44 3TF Tel: (01903) 879955 Fax: (01903) 879650 *Road Planning. Anti skid removal. All operators have CSCS Cards.*

Geoff Happs Trophies, 21 High Street, Bentley, Doncaster, South Yorkshire, DN5 0AA Tel: (01302) 872296 *Trophies & medals retailers*

▶ Geoff Todd Electrical Ltd, Innisfree, West End, Queensbury, Bradford, West Yorkshire, BD13 2ES Tel: (01274) 883871 Fax: (01274) 815004

Alan Geoffrey, 1a Jerry Clay Lane, Wrenthorpe, Wakefield, West Yorkshire, WF2 0NS Tel: (01924) 362467 Fax: (01924) 362467 *Joinery manufrs*

Geoffrey Budd Partnership, 5 Rothermead, Petworth, West Sussex, GU28 0EW Tel: (01798) 342574 Fax: (01798) 342574 *Plant hire*

▶ Geoffrey Collins & Co., 2 Milkhouse Gate, Guildford, Surrey, GU1 3EZ Tel: (0845) 3309916 Fax: (0845) 3309917 E-mail: geoff.collins@gccta.co.uk *Chartered Accountants and Chartered Tax Advisers. Registered Auditors.*

▶ Geoffrey Osborne Ltd, 18-22 Disney Place, London, SE1 1HJ Tel: (020) 7234 0287 Fax: (020) 7234 0290

▶ Geoffrey Osborne Civil Engineering Ltd, 4-5 Manor Courtyard, Sherington, Newport Pagnell, Buckinghamshire, MK16 9PR Tel: (01908) 614461 Fax: (01908) 614472

▶ Geoffrey Osborne Civil Engineering Ltd, 4-5 Manor Courtyard, Sherington, Newport Pagnell, Buckinghamshire, MK16 9PR Tel: (01908) 614461 Fax: (01908) 614472
E-mail: kevin.kilmartin@osborne.co.uk *Osborne"s business is about building and maintaining the railways, roads, homes, hospitals, schools and offices that we all depend on in our daily lives.**Everything we do is aimed at enhancing people's lives, be they stakeholders in the company, employees, clients or members of the public.*

Geoffrey Photographers, 58 St. Augustine Avenue, Grimsby, South Humberside, DN32 0LD
Tel: (01472) 750033 Fax: (01472) 593829
E-mail: stephen.almond@ntlworld.com *Commercial & industrial photographers*

Geoffrey Sumpter, Barton End House, Barton End, Horsley, Stroud, Gloucestershire, GL6 0QQ
Tel: (01453) 833883 Fax: (01453) 833883 *Model making illustrator*

Geoghegan & Co, 6 St Colme Street, Edinburgh, EH3 6AD Tel: 0131-225 4681 Fax: 0131-220 1132 E-mail: mail@geoghegans.co.uk *Chartered accountants*

Geographer's A - Z Map Co. Ltd, Fairfield Road, Borough Green, Sevenoaks, Kent, TN15 8PP
Tel: (01732) 781000 Fax: (01732) 780677
E-mail: sales@a-zmaps.co.uk *Map publishers*

▶ Geola Technologies Ltd, Sussex Innovation Centre, 10-13 Science Park Square, Falmer, Brighton, BN1 9SB Tel: (01273) 234644
Fax: (01273) 704477 E-mail: sales@geola.com *Precision engineers*

▶ Geolink UK Ltd, Walton Road, Kirkhill Industrial Estate, Dyce, Aberdeen, AB21 0GZ Tel: (01224) 772222 E-mail: sales@geolink.co.uk

Geologistics Ltd, Royal Court, 81 Tweedy Road, Bromley, BR1 1TW Tel: (020) 8460 5050
Fax: (020) 8461 8884
E-mail: prandall@geo-logistics.com *Air freight forwarders & forwarding agents*

Geologistics Ltd, Unit 12 The Brunel Centre, Newton Road, Crawley, West Sussex, RH10 9TU Tel: (01293) 652900 Fax: (01293) 652901 E-mail: gatwick@geo-logistics.com *Import & export freight merchants*

Geologistics Expo Services Ltd, Unit 18 National Exhibition Centre, Third Exhibition Avenue, Birmingham, B40 1PJ Tel: 0121-780 2627
Fax: 0121-780 2329 Principal Export Areas: Worldwide *Exhibition freight forwarding lifting agents* Also at: Bromley

▶ Geomap Ltd, 8 Fairview Close, Watledge, Nailsworth, Stroud, Gloucestershire, GL6 0AX
Tel: (07968) 428655
E-mail: info@geomapltd.co.uk *Chartered land surveyors*

▶ Geometric Furniture Ltd, Geometric House Lark Hill, Townley Street Middleton, Middleton, Manchester, M24 1AT Tel: 0161-653 2233
Fax: 0161-653 2299
E-mail: sales@geometric-furniture.co.uk *Geometric Furniture Ltd has been established for over 30 years, and has a proven track record of contract furniture design and manufacture. The company is based in Middleton, Greater Manchester, in the United Kingdom. Their products include armchairs, chairs, edge details, fixed seating, healthcare, hotel range, sofas, stools and many more.*

Geometrix Ltd, Chase Road, Brownhills, Walsall, WS8 6JU Tel: (01543) 452424 Fax: (01543) 453012 E-mail: enquiries@geometrix.co.uk *School drawing instruments manufacturers & suppliers*

Geomount Ltd, Unit 8 Cranleigh Gardens Industrial Estate, Southall, Middlesex, UB1 2BZ Tel: (020) 8571 7046 Fax: (020) 8571 6992
E-mail: pphillips@geomont.fsnet.co.uk *Precision engineers*

▶ Geoplex Computer Systems, 66 Cumbrian Way, Shepshed, Loughborough, Leicestershire, LE12 9BP Tel: (01509) 507995 Fax: (01509) 507996 E-mail: sales@geoplex.co.uk *Computer software developers*

George A Mackay, Benachie, Halkirk, Caithness, KW12 6UL Tel: (01847) 831636 *Agricultural repairs*

George Anderson Stationers Ltd, 36 Standish Street, Burnley, Lancashire, BB11 1AP
Tel: (01282) 426858 Fax: (01282) 415728
E-mail: kevin@ga-stationers.freeserve.co.uk *Commercial stationers*

Geo. Ashcroft & Co. Ltd, Sandy Road, Seaforth, Liverpool, L21 3TW Tel: 0151-928 2565
Fax: 0151-928 0342 *Timber merchants*

George Barker & Co Leeds Ltd, Highfield Works, Highfield Road, Idle, Bradford, West Yorkshire, BD10 8RF Tel: (01274) 703200 Fax: (01274) 615916 *Refrigeration display manufrs*

George Barker & Sons Ltd, Backbarrow, Ulverston, Cumbria, LA12 8TA Tel: (01539) 531236
Fax: (01539) 530801
E-mail: sales@gbsltd.sagehost.co.uk *English timber merchants importers*

George Beattie & Sons Ltd, Auchinvole Castle, Kilsyth, Glasgow, G65 0SA Tel: (01236) 823160
Fax: (01236) 823201
E-mail: info@beattie-demolition.com *Demolition service*

George Blackett Skip Hire, Brunswick Industrial Estate, Brunswick Village, Newcastle upon Tyne, NE13 7BA Tel: 0191-236 7509 Fax: 0191-217 0176 *Haulage & waste disposal agents*

George Boyd & Graham Ltd, Bothwell St, Easter Road, Edinburgh, EH7 5SQ Tel: 0131-661 6144
Fax: 0131-661 2887 *Ironmongers*

Geo Brady Flooring Ltd, Brunswick Industrial Estate, Brunswick Village, Newcastle upon Tyne, NE13 7BA Tel: 0191-217 0202 Fax: 0191-217 0202 *Flooring contractors*

▶ George Bros Ltd, Holway Green, Taunton, Somerset, TA1 2YJ Tel: (01823) 331444
Fax: (01823) 335222

George Bros Engineers Ltd, Dyffryn Close, Swansea Enterprise Park, Swansea, SA6 8QG
Tel: (01792) 790550 Fax: (01792) 701608 *Steel fabricators & general engineers*

George Broughtons & Co Ltd, Whitebirk Road, Whitebirk, Blackburn, BB1 3HZ Tel: (01254) 295509 Fax: (01254) 295501
E-mail: sales@geo-broughton.co.uk *Petroleum products distributors*

▶ George Brown & Sons, Millett House, Millett Street, Bury, Lancashire, BL9 0JA Tel: 0161-764 9000 Fax: 0161-705 1082

George Danby & Son Ltd, Bank Terrace, Barwell, Leicester, LE9 8GG Tel: (01455) 845522
Fax: (01455) 846633
E-mail: info@phonefirst.co.uk *Packerging manufrs*

Geo Designs Ltd, 17A Sea Grove Avenue, Hayling Island, Hampshire, PO11 9EU Tel: (023) 9246 6750 Fax: (023) 9263 7390
E-mail: info@gdesigns.co.uk *Computer software distributors*

▶ Geo Environmental Management, 4 Village Court, Village Farm Industrial Estate, Pyle, Bridgend, Mid Glamorgan, CF33 6BX
Tel: (01656) 741932 Fax: (01656) 740814
E-mail: groundwater@naturalsols.demon.co.uk *Environmental consultants & remediation contractors, specialising in site investigation, risk assessments & remediation of contaminated land including groundwater fate & transport modeling.*

George F Knowles Ltd, 50 St Anne Street, Liverpool, L3 3EA Tel: 0151-207 1311
Fax: 0151-298 2008 *Furniture wholesale distributors, agents & warehouses* Also at: Crosby & Maghull

Geo Gem Ltd, Unit 15, Colomendy Business Park, Denbigh, Clwyd, LL16 5TA Tel: (01745) 815315
Fax: (01745) 815495
E-mail: sales@geogem.co.uk *Diamond drilling tool manufrs*

George Girwood & Company Dundee Ltd, 2 Lower Pleasance, Dundee, DD1 5QU Tel: (01382) 322435 *Stationers*

George H Greensmith & Co., Hallcar Street, Sheffield, S4 7JY Tel: 0114-272 2808
Fax: 0114-272 7956
E-mail: sales@ghgreensmith.co.uk

George H Kime & Co. Ltd, Main Road, Wrangle, Boston, Lincolnshire, PE22 9AW Tel: (01205) 870282 Fax: (01205) 871024
E-mail: accounts@kimes.co.uk *Road transport, haulage & freight services*

George H Rigby & Son Ltd, 3 Liverpool Road, Great Sankey, Warrington, WA5 1ED
Tel: (01925) 635267 Fax: (01925) 416744 *Steel fabrications*

George Hamilton Machinery, 100 Barnish Road, Randalstown, Antrim, BT41 2NL Tel: (028) 9447 2269 Fax: (028) 9447 9191
E-mail: georgehamilton.mchy@btinternet.com *Agricultural machinery merchants*

George Hammond plc, Hammond House, Limekiln Street, Dover, Kent, CT17 9EE Tel: (01304) 201201 Fax: (01304) 240374
E-mail: georgehammond@p.plc.uk *Petroleum distributors & shipping import & export*

▶ George Hanson Building Contractors Ltd, 61 High Street, Rothesay, Isle of Bute, PA20 9AU
Tel: (01700) 505005 Fax: (01700) 502795

▶ Geo Hanson & Sons (Hucknall) Ltd, 13 Watnall Road, Hucknall, Nottingham, NG15 7LD
Tel: 0115-963 2013

▶ George Hardie & Son Ltd, 36-38 Potterrow, Edinburgh, EH8 9BT Tel: 0131-667 3911

▶ George & Harding Construction Ltd, Sunburst House, Elliott Road, Bournemouth, BH11 8LT
Tel: (01202) 578585 Fax: (01202) 581139

George Higginson Ltd, PO Box 7, Chipping Campden, Gloucestershire, GL55 6UL
Tel: (01386) 841481 Fax: (01386) 841581 *Property management & development*

George Hill Timber Oldham Ltd, Boundary Industrial Estate, Millfield Road, Bolton, BL2 6QY
Tel: (01204) 384867 Fax: (01204) 526601 *Timber merchants & building supplies* Also at: Sale

Geo Houlton & Sons Holdings Ltd, Hyperion Street, Witham, Hull, HU9 1BD Tel: (01482) 320486
Fax: (01482) 228441
E-mail: sales@houlton.co.uk *Building & civil engineers*

George Ibbotson Steels Ltd, 16 Atlas Way, Sheffield, S4 7QQ Tel: 0114-244 7400
Fax: 0114-244 7412
E-mail: sales@ibbotsonsteels.co.uk *Stockholders of steel. Also stainless steel, spring steel, hardened & tempered steel strips*

John George & Sons Ltd, 2-4 Deacon Way, Reading, RG30 6AZ Tel: 0118-941 1234
Fax: 0118-945 1059
E-mail: sales@johngeorge.co.uk *Bolt, nut & nail distributors*

▶ George Jones & Son Ltd, 9 Sheil Road, Liverpool, L6 3AA Tel: 0151-263 2348
Fax: 0151-264 0100
E-mail: mail@georgejones.org.uk *Painting & Decorating & Pre-Decorative Repairs (Joinery - *Window /Door Replacement)*

George Kingsbury, Quay Lane, Hardway, Gosport, Hampshire, PO12 4LB Tel: (023) 9258 0371
Fax: (023) 9250 1741
E-mail: mtools@gkholdings.com Principal Export Areas: Worldwide *CNC machine manufrs*

Geo Kingsbury Holdings Ltd, 45 Portsmouth Road, Cobham, Surrey, KT11 1JQ Tel: (01932) 863836
Fax: (01932) 865596 *Holding company*

▶ George Laing Fencing Ltd, Railway Place, Cupar, Fife, KY15 5HZ Tel: (01334) 655744
Fax: (01334) 656133
E-mail: sales@forestcraft.co.uk *Fencing & sheds*

George Lindley & Co Export Ltd, 3-5 Bleeding Heart Yard, London, EC1N 8SJ Tel: (020) 7242 5772 Fax: (020) 7242 7779 *Precious stone dealers*

George Lister & Sons Ltd, 505 Coldhams Lane, Cambridge, CB1 3JS Tel: (01223) 518888
Fax: (01223) 504700
E-mail: martin@georgelister.co.uk *General engineers*

▶ George Lowden, Down Business Park, 46 Belfast Road, Downpatrick, County Down, BT30 9UP Tel: (028) 4461 9161 Fax: (028) 4461 7043 E-mail: sales@georgelowden.com

▶ George Lowden, Down Business Park, 46 Belfast Road, Downpatrick, County Down, BT30 9UP Tel: (028) 4461 9161 Fax: (028) 4461 7043 E-mail: sales@georgelowden.com *Guitar manufrs*

▶ George M Bolton, 4 Harrison Lane, Edinburgh, EH11 1HG Tel: 0131-337 0000 Fax: 0131-337 0000

▶ George McAlpine & Sons Ltd, 90 Seaward Street, Glasgow, G41 1HJ Tel: 0141-420 1392
Fax: 0141-420 3906
E-mail: info@georgemcalpine.co.uk *Fireplace retail*

George Mackay, 3 March Road East, Buckie, Banffshire, AB56 4BY Tel: (01542) 833948
Fax: (01542) 833953 *Sole trader haulers*

George Martin (Builders) Ltd, 5/9 Fairfield Road, Dundee, DD3 8HR Tel: (01382) 815415
Fax: (01382) 825199E-mail: sales@vycon.co.uk *Building contractors*

▶ George Morrison, Canal Road, Inverness, IV3 8NF Tel: (01463) 222246 Fax: (01463) 225511 E-mail: builders@george-morrison.co.uk

George Morrison Ltd, 22 High Street, Tain, Ross-Shire, IV19 1AE Tel: (01862) 892346
Fax: (01862) 894475
E-mail: kitchens@george-morrison.co.uk *Builders*

George Moss & Son Ltd, Unit C4, 1 Centre Court, Moss Industrial Estate, Leigh, Lancashire, WN7 3PT Tel: (01942) 671231 Fax: (01942) 683768 E-mail: sales@georgemoss.co.uk *Industrial estate developers*

▶ George N Moir, 24 Seafield Street, Whitehills, Banff, AB45 2NR Tel: (01261) 861208
Fax: (01261) 861208 *Pie manufrs*

George Neville Transport Safety Systems Ltd, Southwell Lane Industrial Estate, Summit Close, Kirkby-in-Ashfield, Nottingham, NG17 8GJ
Tel: (01623) 755300 Fax: (01623) 756563 *Automatic sheeting devices*

George Newberry Coachbuilders, 3 Northburn Road, Coatbridge, Lanarkshire, ML5 2HY
Tel: (01236) 710900 Fax: (01236) 710900
E-mail: andy@gnewberrycoachbuilders.com *Coach building*

▶ George P McLaughlan Ltd, Inchcape Place, North Muirton Industrial Estat, Perth, PH1 3DU
Tel: (01738) 634321

George Pickersgill & Sons Ltd, Unit 11 Hirstwood Works, Hirst Wood Road, Shipley, West Yorkshire, BD18 4BU Tel: (01274) 594333
Fax: (01274) 594888
E-mail: sales@georgepickersgill.co.uk *Removal, storage & document storage specialists*

▶ George S Hall Ltd, Building 75, Valley, Holyhead, Gwynedd, LL65 3NY Tel: (01407) 742408
Fax: (01407) 740308

George Schumacher, Unit 1 R A C Estate, Parks Road, Faringdon, Oxfordshire, SN7 8LA
Tel: (01367) 244697 Fax: (01367) 242819 *Equestrian suppliers*

George Sweeney Junior, 39 Whitehill Road, Glenrothes, Fife, KY6 2RW Tel: (01592) 774325
Fax: (01592) 774325 *Stone restoration contractors*

▶ George Taylor & Co (Hamilton) Ltd, Kemp St, Hamilton, Lanarkshire, ML3 6PQ Tel: (01698) 284949 Fax: (01698) 891285
E-mail: office@gtham.co.uk *Iron foundry*

George Taylor & Co (Hamilton) Ltd, Kemp St, Hamilton, Lanarkshire, ML3 6PQ Tel: (01698) 284949 Fax: (01698) 891285
E-mail: office@gtham.co.uk *SG, Grey and Austempered Iron Casting Manufacturers*

George Taylor & Co Lifting Gear Europe Ltd, Brickyard Road, Aldridge, Walsall, WS9 8SR
Tel: (01922) 457916 Fax: (01922) 743664
E-mail: office@gtlifting.co.uk *Manufacturers of lifting gears & wire rope attachments & fittings*

Geo Testing Services Ltd, 1 Dean Street, Bedminster, Bristol, BS3 1BG Tel: 0117-963 4471 Fax: 0117-963 6807 *Ground investigation*

▶ George Thompson Heating Ltd, Thornton Road, Carlisle, CA3 9HZ Tel: (01228) 527390
Fax: (01228) 512627

▶ George Varney (Bulk Services) Ltd, Varneys Yard, Watford, Northampton, NN6 7UF
Tel: (01327) 872288

George Wilkinson Burnley Ltd, Progress Works, Elm Street, Burnley, Lancashire, BB10 1PB
Tel: (01282) 415511 Fax: (01282) 433112
E-mail: info@progresshousewares.com *Baking equipment manufrs*

George Williamson & Co. Ltd, 5 West Mills, Newbury, Berkshire, RG14 5HG Tel: (01635) 522088 Fax: (01635) 551992
E-mail: plantations@williamsontea.com *Holding company & tea manufrs*

George Wilson Associates Ltd, PO Box 70, Whitstable, Kent, CT5 3RG Tel: (01227) 262707
Fax: (01227) 262707
E-mail: gwholdings@aol.com *Building contractors*

George Wilson & Sons Ltd, Thames Street, Sunbury-on-Thames, Middlesex, TW16 6AQ
Tel: (01932) 782067 Fax: (01932) 782067 *Motor boat hire, repair, mooring & storage services*

▶ George Wimpey, 1 Harbour Exchange Square, London, E14 9GE Tel: (020) 7987 0500
Fax: (020) 7531 8383

▶ George Wimpey East Scotland Ltd, 28 Barnton Grove, Edinburgh, EH4 6BT Tel: 0131-338 4000

▶ George Wimpey North, Wessington Way, Sunderland, SR5 3RL Tel: 0191-516 5400
Fax: 0191-516 5401

George Wimpey NW Ltd, Lichfield House, Gadbrook Park, Rudheath, Northwich, Cheshire, CW9 7RF Tel: (01606) 815300 Fax: (01606) 40276 *House builders*

▶ George Wimpey West Midlands Ltd, Dominion Court, 39 Station Road, Solihull, West Midlands, B91 3RT Tel: 0121-703 3300 Fax: 0121-703 3380 E-mail: enquiries@georgewimpey.co.uk

George Wimpey West Scotland Ltd, Trident House, Renfrew Road, Paisley, Renfrewshire, PA3 4EF
Tel: 0141-849 5500 Fax: 0141-849 5550 *House builders*

Georges, 25 High Street, Kington, Herefordshire, HR5 3AX Tel: (01544) 231400 *Health food & dairy*

George's Fishing Tackle, 15 Frog Lane, Wigan, Lancashire, WN6 7DE Tel: (01942) 241932 *Fishing tackle retailers*

Georges Industrial Services Ltd, 49 Theobald Street, Borehamwood, Hertfordshire, WD6 4RZ
Tel: (020) 8207 2455 Fax: (020) 8207 4877
E-mail: london@airconditioningdirect.com *Air conditioning equipment retailers*

▶ George's Lawns, 225 Surbiton Road, Fairfield, Stockton-on-Tees, Cleveland, TS19 7SF
Tel: (01642) 891599 Fax: (07899) 705 473 *George"s Lawns are dedicated to offering professional reliable lawn mowing & maintenance services at great value for money.*

Georgia Pacific GB Ltd, Mansell Way, Horwich, Bolton, BL6 6JL Tel: (01204) 673300
Fax: (01204) 673301 E-mail: *Manufacturers of consumer hygiene products*

Georgia Pacific GB Ltd, Llandow Trading Estate, Llandow, Cowbridge, South Glamorgan, CF71 7PB Tel: (01446) 794011 Fax: (01446) 795208

Georgia Pacific GB Ltd, Lower Street, Newcastle, Staffordshire, ST5 2RS Tel: (01782) 615376
Fax: (01782) 712236 *Tabletop converters*

Georgian Crystal Tutbury Ltd, 1 Silk Mill Lane, Tutbury, Burton-on-Trent, Staffordshire, DE13 9LE Tel: (01283) 814534 Fax: (01283) 520186 *Crystal glass manufrs*

Georgian Hire Ltd, Unit 6 Farrington Fields Trading Estate, Farrington Gurney, Bristol, BS39 6UU
Tel: (01761) 451495 Fax: (01761) 451458
E-mail: sales@georgianhireltd.co.uk *Portable toilet hire*

Georgian Medal Joinery Ltd, Unit 1, Meadow St, Treforest, Pontypridd, Mid Glamorgan, CF37 1UD Tel: (01443) 493288 Fax: (01443) 493288 E-mail: sales@hitec-cathodic.co.uk *Joinery manufacturers & carpenters*

▶ Georgina Ettridge, 12 St. Johns Glebe, Rownhams, Southampton, SO16 8AX Tel: (023) 8073 6704
E-mail: designer@georginaettridge.co.uk *Contemporary handmade precious metal jewellery inspired by nature. The sterling silver collections include Leaves, Twigs and Berries, featuring unique organic style necklaces, earrings, bangles, lapel pins and rings.*

Geoscience Ltd, Falmouth Business Park, Bickland Water Road, Falmouth, Cornwall, TR11 4SZ
Tel: (01326) 211070 Fax: (01326) 212754
E-mail: batchelor@geoscience.co.uk *Consultants & consulting engineers*

Geosynthetic Technology Ltd, Little Bulmer Farm, Wiston Road, Nayland, Colchester, CO6 4LT
Tel: (01206) 262676 Fax: (01206) 262998
E-mail: sales@geosynthetic.co.uk *Reservoir engineering services*

▶ Geotec, PO Box 99, Godalming, Surrey, GU7 2XT Tel: (01483) 271171 *Ground penetrating radar survey services*

Geotech Systems Ltd, 3000 Cathedral Hill Industrial Estate, Guildford, Surrey, GU2 7YB Tel: (01483) 243530 Fax: (01483) 245330 *Computer consultants*

▶ Geotechnical Developments UK Ltd, The Doles Wharf, Priors Marston, Southam, Warwickshire, CV47 7SS Tel: (01926) 813747 Fax: (01926) 813302 E-mail: sales@geotechnical.co.uk *Specialists in geotechnical and geo-environmental investigation and consultancy. See web site for further details. www.geotechnical.co.uk*

Geotechnical Engineering Ltd, Centurion House, Olympus Park, Quedgeley, Gloucester, GL2 4NF
Tel: (01452) 527743 Fax: (01452) 507435
E-mail: sales@geoeng.co.uk *Drilling & ground investigation* Also at: Normanton

Geotechnical Instruments (UK) Ltd, Sovereign House, Queensway, Leamington Spa, Warwickshire, CV31 3JR Tel: (01926) 338111
Fax: (01926) 338110
E-mail: sales@geotech.co.uk *Geotech are a leading global supplier of gas analyzers, offering environmental monitoring solutions to a variety of market sectors (landfill, water, biogas remediation and CDM).*

Geotechnical Services, 28 Rusper Close, Stanmore, Middlesex, HA7 4QD Tel: (020) 8954 4190 Fax: (020) 8954 4190
E-mail: geotservices@aol.com *Soil sampling for geotechnical & environmental investigations*

Geotechnix Computer Services Ltd, 39 West Hill Road, London, SW18 1LL Tel: (020) 8871 1497
Fax: (020) 8333 6714 *Computer consultants*

Geotex Ground Services Ltd, PO Box 5071, Market Harborough, Leicestershire, LE16 7WJ
Tel: (01858) 545111 Fax: (01858) 545914
E-mail: sales@geotex.co.uk *Net insulation*

▶ Geowise Ltd, Edinburgh Business Centre, 11 Maritime Street, Edinburgh, EH6 6SB
Tel: 0131-624 8935 Fax: 0131-624 8936
E-mail: krystal.badenoch@geowise.co.uk *Software statistics mapping services*

Geppert Conveyors UK, Camberley, Surrey, GU17 0RP Tel: (01252) 875871 Fax: (01252) 878804 E-mail: gwilliams@geppert-band.de *Geppert-band conveyors manufrs*

Ger & Co. (UK) Ltd, 3rd Floor St. Thomas House, 3 Gees Court, London, W1U 1JD Tel: (020) 7491 4636 Fax: (020) 7408 0078
E-mail: geruk@btinternet.com *Purchasing agents*

▶ Gerald D Harris & Sons, Rowlands View, Cold Blow, Narberth, Dyfed, SA67 8RG Tel: (01834) 860464 Fax: (01834) 896156

Gerald Eve & Co Services Ltd, 7 Veer Street, London, W1G 0JB Tel: (020) 7493 3338
Fax: (020) 7491 1825
E-mail: evemail@geraldeve.com *Chartered surveyors*

Gerald Hallet, Long Acre, Closworth Road, Halstock, Yeovil, Somerset, BA22 9SY
Tel: (01935) 891616 Fax: (01935) 891617
E-mail: hallettlandrover@btconnect.com *Agricultural engineers*

Gerald Hamill & Sons, 114 Obin Street, Portadown, Craigavon, County Armagh, BT62 1BP Tel: (028) 3833 2297 Fax: (028) 3839 3377 *Crane & forklift hire*

Gerald Weir, 1 Deben Road, Woodbridge, Suffolk, IP12 1AZ Tel: (01394) 610900 Fax: (01394) 610901
E-mail: geraldweirantiques@btinternet.com *Furniture & antiques*

▶ Gerard E Gallagher (Electricalcontractors) Ltd, Cloonrane House, 21 Chorley Old Road, Bolton, BL1 3AD Tel: (01204) 387039

▶ Gerard Removers Ltd, 32 Burnfield Road, Giffnock, Glasgow, G46 7PZ Tel: 0141-954 3939
Fax: 0141-954 5290
E-mail: sales@gerardremovers.co.uk

Gerber Coburn Optical UK Ltd, 1600 Aztec West, Almondsbury, Bristol, BS32 4UA Tel: (01454) 200780 Fax: (01454) 200787 E-mail: info@gerbercoburn.co.uk *Ophthalmic equipment distributors & manufrs*

Gerber Juice Company Ltd, 78 Wembdon Road, Bridgwater, Somerset, TA6 7QR Tel: (01278) 441600 Fax: (01278) 441777 E-mail: enquiries@gerberfoods.com *Fruit juice manufacturers or producers*

Gerber Technology Ltd, 302 Metroplex Business Park, Broadway, Salford, M50 2UE Tel: 0161-772 2000 Fax: 0161-772 2020 *Software hardware for garment industries*

▶ Gerhardt Ltd, Trent La Industrial Estate, Willow Road, Castle Donington, Derby, DE74 2NP Tel: (01332) 853434 Fax: (01332) 810274 E-mail: info@gerhardt.co.uk *Rotary cutting tools, based upon material to be converted*

Gericke Ltd, Victoria House, Cavendish Street, Ashton-under-Lyne, Lancashire, OL6 7DJ Tel: 0161-344 1140 Fax: 0161-308 3403 E-mail: sales@gericke.co.uk *Powder handling equipment manufrs*

Merlin Gerin, 123 Jack Lane, Leeds, LS10 1BS Tel: 0113-290 3500 Fax: 0113-290 3710 E-mail: *Medium voltage industrial switchgear*

Gerling UK Ltd, 50 Fenchurch Street, London, EC3M 3JY Tel: (020) 7696 8099 Fax: (020) 7696 8119 E-mail: receptiondesk@gerling.co.uk *Insurance company* Also at: Birmingham

German Swedish & French, 8 Boss Hall Road, Ipswich, IP1 5BN Tel: (01473) 748166 Fax: (01473) 463814 E-mail: ipswich@gsfcarparts.com *Motor vehicle accessories retailers*

Germar, Unit 16, Riland Industrial Centre, Norris Way, Sutton Coldfield, West Midlands, B75 7BB Tel: 0121-378 2600 Fax: 0121-378 1300 *Power tool accessories*

Gerrard, Temple Court, 35 Bull Street, Birmingham, B4 6ES Tel: 0121-200 2244 Fax: 0121-683 7300 *Stock brokers*

Gerrard, 29 Windsor Place, Cardiff, CF10 3BZ Tel: (029) 2082 9600 Fax: (029) 2022 1061 E-mail: sales@gerrard.com *Stockbrokers*

Gerrard Associates, Mansard, Neston Rd, Burton, Neston, CH64 5SZ Tel: 0151-353 1056 Fax: 0151 3531082 *Computer software reseller*

P. Gerratt Ltd, Baring Road, Northampton, NN5 7BA Tel: (01604) 758545 Fax: (01604) 588755 E-mail: sales@gerratt.com *Brush & mop manufrs*

Gerratts Carpet Planning, 22 Southolm Street, London, SW11 5EZ Tel: (020) 7498 2622 Fax: (020) 7498 6429 *Carpet planning services*

Gerry's Of Nottingham, Radford Boulevard, Nottingham, NG7 3BN Tel: 0115-978 8723 Fax: 0115-979 1989 *Fishing tackle retailers*

▶ Gesta UK Ltd, 8 Centre Park, Slutchers Lane, Warrington, WA1 1QL Tel: (01925) 241424 Fax: (01925) 241416

▶ Gestalt Technology Ltd, The Sawyers House, 113 London Road, Horndean, Waterlooville, Hampshire, PO8 0BJ Tel: (023) 9259 4270 Fax: (023) 9259 4271 E-mail: info@gtg.uk.com *CCTV, digital video, access control, service & maintenance*

▶ Get To It, 8 Coulson Way, Alconbury, Huntingdon, Cambridgeshire, PE28 4WU Tel: (01480) 896704 E-mail: sales@get-to-it.co.uk *We offer onsite computer repairs around the Cambridgeshire & Bedfordshire area*

▶ Get Valeted, Gainsborough House, 17-23 High Street, Slough, SL1 1DY Tel: 0845 0529771 E-mail: info@getvaleted.co.uk *High performance mobile car valeting.First in the industry to introduce wet and dry valets simultaneously.*

▶ getabuilder.co.uk, Offices 343, 14 Clifton Down Road, Clifton Village, Clifton, Bristol, BS8 4BF Tel: 0117 9390418 E-mail: theteam@getabuilder.co.uk *Construction company & online recruitment*

Getinge UK Ltd, Orchard Way, Sutton-in-Ashfield, Nottinghamshire, NG17 1JU Tel: (01623) 510033 Fax: (01623) 440456 *Pharmaceutical sterilizer manufrs*

▶ Getme-Tools, 52 Hamilton Rd, Taunton, Somerset, TA1 2ES Tel: 01823 272066 Fax: 01823 272066 E-mail: sales@getme-tools.co.uk *Suppliers of quality hand tools, toolboxes and tool storage.*

Getronics UK Ltd, Cygnus House, 1 The Southwood Crescent, Apollo Rise, Farnborough, Hampshire, GU14 0NL Tel: (0870) 9068000 Fax: (020) 8874 3014 E-mail: getronics.helpdesk@getronics.com *IT services* Also at: Branches throughout the U.K.

Geutebruck (UK) Ltd, 8 Central Park, Bellfield Road, High Wycombe, Buckinghamshire, HP13 5HG Tel: (01494) 510999 Fax: (01494) 510888 E-mail: info@geutebruck.co.uk *Electronic surveillance equipment manufrs*

Gewefa UK Ltd, Edinburgh Way, Leafield Industrial Estate, Corsham, Wiltshire, SN13 9XZ Tel: (01453) 872074 Fax: (01225) 811388 E-mail: sales@gewefa.co.uk *Machine tool holder systems manufrs*

GF Compressors, Unit 4 Wainwright Street, Birmingham, B6 5TG Tel: 0121-326 9122 Fax: 0121-327 4492 E-mail: sales@gfcompressors.co.uk *Air compressor agents or distributors*

GFH SOUND AND VISION LTD, 39 SHERRARDS WAY, BARNET, HERTS, EN5 2BW Tel: 07815 735607 Fax: (020) 8449 6531 E-mail: garretthenderson345@hotmail.com

▶ GFilmsUK, 1, Stud Barn, Melton Park, Melton Constable, Norfolk, NR24 2NJ Tel: 01263 860901 E-mail: gfilms@homecall.co.uk *Offering the amazing Kuznetsov Applicator to beat back pain. Over 70 million sold worldwide.*Full money back guarantee if not 0% delighted with results.*

▶ GfK NOP, Ludgate House, 245 Blackfriars Road, London, SE1 9UL Tel: 020 7890 9000 Fax: 020 7890 9001 E-mail: ukinfo@gfk.com *As one of the largest full-service market research and business information groups, GfK NOP is a renowned supplier of syndicated and custom research, producing industry specialists, best-in-field design, methodologies and analytics for qualitative, quantitative, ethnographic and online research. GfK NOP also offers arguably*

continued

*the strongest series of Omnibus surveys available in the marketplace.**GfK NOP covers the key markets of Automotive, Business-to-Business, Consumer (including products and retail, travel and new media), Financial, Healthcare, Media, Technology, Social Research and Mystery Shopping. **

GGD Engineering Ltd, Rashierieve Cottages, Newburgh, Ellon, Aberdeenshire, AB41 6AU Tel: (01358) 789920 Fax: (01358) 789919 E-mail: sales@ggdengineering.co.uk *Steel fabricators*

GGH Marketing Communications, 1 West Street, Titchfield, Fareham, Hampshire, PO14 4DH Tel: (01329) 846166 Fax: (01329) 512063 E-mail: geoff@ggh.co.uk *Public relations consultants*

Ghai's Services, 14 Wood End Green Road, Hayes, Middlesex, UB3 2SH Tel: (020) 8569 3721 Fax: (020) 8569 3723 *Air conditioning equipment*

Ghana International Bank Plc, PO Box 77, London, EC2P 2BB Tel: (020) 7248 2384 Fax: (020) 7489 9058 E-mail: info@ghanabank.co.uk *Banking services*

GHD Manufacture, Park Lane, Wolverhampton, WV10 9QE Tel: (01902) 726442 Fax: (01902) 726442 *Ladies & childerns wear manufrs*

Ghinn Signs, 98 Wickham Street, Welling, Kent, DA16 3LU Tel: (020) 8316 5501 Fax: (020) 8854 7612 E-mail: ghinnsigns@aol.com *Poster & sign manufrs*

▶ GHWM, 1 Sandal Hall Close, Sandal, Wakefield, West Yorkshire, WF2 6ER Tel: (01924) 256565 Fax: (01924) 256565 E-mail: hullgeoff@aol.com *New & used woodworking machinery sales*

Ghyll Print Ltd, Ghyll Indust Estate, Heathfield, East Sussex, TN21 8AW Tel: (01435) 866211 Fax: (01435) 861268 E-mail: info@ghyllprint.co.uk *General printers*

Ghyllside Manufacturing, Unit 11 Ivyhouse Lane, Hastings, East Sussex, TN35 4NN Tel: (01424) 465547 *General presswork manufrs*

GIA Design Ltd, 46a Pevensey Road, Eastbourne, East Sussex, BN21 3HP Tel: (01323) 722131 Fax: (01323) 642940 E-mail: greg@duvacourt.co.uk *Architecture, interior design, graphic design & website design specialists*

Gia International Ltd, PO Box 4274, Poole, Dorset, BH14 0LL Tel: (01202) 730535 Fax: (01202) 730535 E-mail: mail@griffininternational.co.uk *Export agents*

▶ Giaicomm Ltd, 76 North Road Avenue, Brentwood, Essex, CM14 4XN Tel: (01277) 230141 *Giaicomm: the complete solution for IT communications.*Internet; Servers; Stand-alones; Networks; and much more.**A personal service to our customers.*

Giant, 36 Queen Square, Bristol, BS1 4QS Tel: 0117 9086666 Fax: 0117 9085566 E-mail: info@gianteffect.co.uk *Design and brand communications.*

▶ Giant Game Co., 1 Wren Close, Northampton, NN4 5AY Tel: (01604) 661759

Giant Technologies, 91 Western Road, Brighton, BN1 2NW Tel: (01273) 243030 Fax: (01273) 270271 E-mail: sales@giant-technologies.com *Computer software manufrs*

▶ Giantpea Limited, PO Box 232, Romsey, Hampshire, SO51 8GE Tel: (01794) 230035 E-mail: hello@giantpea.com *A design & web development company, offering print design, web design, website hosting & management and online application development.*

Gias Services, Breightmet Industrial Estate, Bury Road, Bolton, BL2 6PU Tel: (0870) 5990011 Fax: (01204) 556149 *Spares distributors & service hoover appliances*

Gibbon & Sons Ltd, Richmond Road, Cardiff, CF24 3XA Tel: (029) 2048 3331 Fax: (029) 2048 3333 *Builders' & timber merchants*

Gibbons Drive Systems Ltd, Woodrolfe Road, Tollesbury, Maldon, Essex, CM9 8RY Tel: (01621) 868138 Fax: (01621) 868188 E-mail: sales@gibbonsdrives.co.uk *Electro & mechanical drive systems, repair & retail*

Gibbons Electrical Services, 18 Helford Close, Worcester, WR5 1NB Tel: (01905) 356061 *Electrical engineers*

William Gibbons & Sons Ltd, PO Box 103, Willenhall, West Midlands, WV13 3XT Tel: (01902) 730011 Fax: (01902) 865835 E-mail: gibbowill@aol.com *Web, sheet & promotional printers*

Gibbs, Sandhills Meadow, Shepperton, Middlesex, TW17 9HY Tel: (01932) 242977 Fax: (01932) 222817 E-mail: sales@gibbsmarine.co.uk *Boat sales & servicing*

Gibbs & Ball Ltd, St Margarets Road, South Darenth, Dartford, DA4 9LB Tel: (01322) 862232 Fax: (01322) 864954 *Warehouse storage & transport*

▶ Gibbs Bros, Kitesbridge Farm, Asthall, Burford, Oxfordshire, OX18 4HL Tel: (01993) 878600 E-mail: info@gibbsbrothers.co.uk *Sawmill & fencing contractors*

▶ Gibbs Business Solutions Ltd, 10 Strathearn Road, North Berwick, East Lothian, EH39 5BZ Tel: (01620) 892736 E-mail: charles.gibbs@gbsl.co.uk *Website design*

▶ Gibbs & Dandy, PO Box 17, Luton, LU1 1YB Tel: (01582) 798798 Fax: (01582) 798799 E-mail: mail@gibbsanddandy.com *Building merchants* Also at: Bedford, Northampton, St. Ives & St. Neots

Gibbs & Dandy plc, 462 Bath Road, Slough, SL1 6BQ Tel: (01628) 604343 Fax: (01628) 600744 E-mail: slough@gibbsanddandy.com *Builders merchants* Also at: Maidenhead

Gibbs Gears Precision Engineers Ltd, 58 B Western Road, Tring, Hertfordshire, HP23 4BB Tel: (01442) 828898 Fax: (01422) 828020 E-mail: sales@gibbsgears.com *Gear cutters & manufrs*

Gibbs (General Engineering) Ltd, 7 High Street, Prestatyn, Clwyd, LL19 9AF Tel: (01745) 853759 Fax: (01745) 854360 E-mail: office@gibbsge.com *Steel & welding fabricators*

Lionel W. Gibbs (Horton) Ltd, Horley Road, Hornton, Banbury, Oxfordshire, OX15 6BW Tel: (01295) 670310 Fax: (01295) 670732 *Blacksmiths & welding engineers*

Gibbs & Rustage Ltd, Albert Works, Victoria Road, Dukinfield, Cheshire, SK16 4UP Tel: 0161-339 3379 Fax: 0161-343 2207 *Press tools & plastics moulds*

▶ Gibbs Transport Ltd, 6 Coln Industrial Estate, Old Bath Road, Colnbrook, Slough, SL3 0NJ Tel: (01753) 685566 Fax: (01753) 681700

Gibbz Dot Biz, 42 Hilley Field Lane, Fetcham, Leatherhead, Surrey, KT22 9UX Tel: (01372) 373825

▶ Gibson and Goold, 1-3 Scotland Street, Glasgow, G5 8LS Tel: (01292) 268478 *Fireplaces manufactures & installers*

Gibson Bros, Magherally, Banbridge, County Down, BT32 4YN Tel: (028) 4066 2771 Fax: (028) 4062 6704 E-mail: liam@gibbros.freeserve.co.uk *Quarry owners, aggregate & stone producers*

Gibson Centri-Tech Ltd, Hilltop Works, Eastern Avenue, Lichfield, Staffordshire, WS13 6UY Tel: (01543) 418701 Fax: (01543) 418703 E-mail: sales@gibsoncentritech.co.uk *Centrifugal casting equipment*

Gibson Computers, 69 Bridge Street, Castleford, West Yorkshire, WF10 1HH Tel: (01977) 512412 Fax: (01977) 558970 E-mail: enquiries@gibsoncomputers.co.uk *Build new computers & sell parts*

Gibson Consulting Ltd, 3 The Quadrant, Coventry, CV1 2DY Tel: (024) 7624 3607 Fax: (024) 7624 3608 E-mail: mark.gibson@gibsonconsulting.co.uk *Litigation & arbitration support for the construction industry*

E.A. Gibson Shipbrokers Ltd, PO Box 278, London, EC1P 1HP Tel: (020) 7667 1000 Fax: (020) 7831 8762 E-mail: tanker@eagibson.co.uk *Ship brokers & bunkering agents services*

▶ Gibson Exports (UK) Ltd, 60 Park View, North Acton, Gypsy Corner, London, W3 0PT Tel: (020) 8354 4147 Fax: (020) 8992 5335 E-mail: info@gibsonexports.ltd.uk *Import & export, product marketing, global finance, company management*

▶ Gibson & Goold Ltd, 165-167 Whitletts Road, Ayr, KA8 0JH Tel: (01292) 268478 Fax: (01292) 611949 *Fireplace & fire specialists*

Gibson Hanson Graphics Ltd, 2nd Floor, Amp House Dingwall Road, Croydon, CR0 2LX Tel: (020) 8260 1200 Fax: (020) 8260 1212 E-mail: clare.stead@gibsonhanson.co.uk *Greeting card publishers*

Gibson Information Systems, Tamarisk, The Lizard, Helston, Cornwall, TR12 7PF Tel: (01326) 290304 E-mail: enquiries@gibsoninformationsystems.co.uk *Computer consultants*

James D. Gibson & Co. Ltd, 399 Petre Street, Sheffield, S4 8LL Tel: 0114-243 0385 Fax: 0114-242 5490 E-mail: admin@jamesgibson.co.uk *Broaches & cutting tool suppliers*

John Gibson Agencies Ltd, Queens Way, Middlesbrough, Cleveland, TS3 8TF Tel: (01642) 221761 Fax: (01642) 242938 E-mail: jga@jgagencies.co.uk *Specialist engineers*

▶ Mike Gibson Stonework Ltd, 5 Scawfell Crescent, Seascale, Cumbria, CA20 1LF Tel: (01946) 727122 E-mail: gibstones@tiscali.co.uk *Stonemasonry & general builders*

Gibson Refrigeration, 88 Sullington Mead, Broadbridge Heath, Horsham, West Sussex, RH12 3NW Tel: (01403) 265328 Fax: (01403) 269642 *Repairs & sales of refrigerators*

Gibson Saddlers Ltd, Queensbury Road, Newmarket, Suffolk, CB8 9AX Tel: (01638) 662330 Fax: (01638) 666467 E-mail: gibsonsaddlers@btconnect.com *Saddlery & harness manufrs*

▶ Gibson Taylor Tranzol Ltd, Bent Ley Farm, Bent Ley Road, Meltham, Holmfirth, HD9 4AP Tel: (01484) 859293 Fax: (01484) 859339 E-mail: zoltan.gibsontaylor@btconnect.com Sales Contact: P.S. Gibson *First class freight forwarding services*

Gibson Wight Ltd, 14-18 East Shaw Street, Kilmarnock, Ayrshire, KA1 4AN Tel: (01563) 523633 Fax: (01563) 536472 E-mail: charles.gibson@gibsonwight.co.uk *Heating engineers, electrical engineers, boiler & plant maintenance*

Gibtool Engineers, 1 Whitehall Mill, Whitehall Street, Darwen, Lancashire, BB3 2LP Tel: (01254) 705909 Fax: (01254) 705909 *Light engineering & tool making*

George Gidden Graphics Ltd, 14 Park Street, Guildford, Surrey, GU1 4XB Tel: (01483) 303040 Fax: (01483) 303222 E-mail: paul@giddenplace.com *Computer & exhibition services*

K.L. Giddings Ltd, Lion Works, Station Road East, Whittlesford, Cambridge, CB22 4WL Tel: (01223) 832638 Fax: (01223) 832189 E-mail: enquires@klgiddings.co.uk *Precision engineers & electrophoretic painting*

Giffen Distribution Systems Ltd., Lyon Way, St. Albans, Hertfordshire, AL4 0LQ Tel: (01727) 734600 Fax: (01727) 833680 E-mail: everyone@giffengroup.co.uk *Electrical control gear distributors*

Giffhorn & Co. Ltd, Unit 14, West Point Trading Park, Liverpool Street, Hull, HU3 4UU Tel: (01482) 323844 Fax: (01482) 213198 E-mail: egon@giffhornengkaroo.co.uk *Sheet metalworkers & fabricators*

▶ Giffords Recycling, Kelvin Way, West Bromwich, West Midlands, B70 7JR Tel: 0121-553 1910 Fax: 0121-500 4919 E-mail: info@giffords.biz

▶ The Gift Box Co., 7, Zille Estate, East Street, Ryde, Isle Of Wight, PO33 1JS Tel: (01983) 568844 Fax: (01983) 568844

The Gift Business, St. Swithins House, Trinity Street, Worcester, WR1 2PW Tel: (01905) 724111 Fax: (01905) 745117 E-mail: sales@giftbusiness.co.uk *General gift producers & designers*

Gift Design Co. Ltd, Old Griffin Field, Windsor Street, Pentre, Mid Glamorgan, CF41 7JJ Tel: (01443) 441616 Fax: (01443) 440419 E-mail: mail@gift-design.co.uk *Ribbon & gift wrapping manufrs*

▶ Gifted Holistic Health & Beauty, 5a King Street, Hereford, HR4 9BW Tel: (01432) 350054 E-mail: tinamareafinley@msn.com *Health & beauty product suppliers*

▶ Giftline Giftboxes, Kelmscott House,, Higher Rads End, Eversholt, Milton Keynes, MK17 9ED Tel: (01525) 288266 Fax: (01525) 288277 E-mail: info@giftlineboxes.com *Gift box wrapping suppliers*

▶ Gifts 2 Have, 7 Hunton Bridge Hill, Hunton Bridge, Kings Langley, Hertfordshire, WD4 8PX Tel: (07901) 671349 E-mail: gifts2have@lycos.co.uk *Gifted wrapped ty beanie bears, handmade cards, gift baskets and other gifts.*

▶ Gifts & Gold, 8 Chipstead Valley Road, Coulsdon, Surrey, CR5 2RA Tel: (020) 8763 2520 Fax: (020) 8763 2520 E-mail: giftsandgold@aol.com *Purveyors of Gold, Silver and Platinum. Repairs to same. Clocks, watches & repairs.*Psychic Readings & relvant products.*Crystals, Rock Hanging & Ornamental*

Gig Shop, 322 Beverley Road, Hull, HU5 1BA Tel: (01482) 440982 Fax: (01482) 440982 *Sound equipment hirers & flight case manufrs*

Giga Computer Systems, 30 Mill Road, Billericay, Essex, CM11 2SF Tel: (01277) 630493 Fax: (01277) 651666 *Computer repairers*

GIGA Systems Ltd, 71 Watercall Avenue, Coventry, CV3 5AX Tel: (0870) 7525515 E-mail: info@gigasystems.co.uk *GIGA System provides cost effective Design solutions in RF/ microwave and Mechanical Engineerig using microstrip, MMIC and waveguide technologies for space, defence and commercial applications. We provide considerable experience of design with modern computer computer aided engineering packages.*

Gigabyte Computers, St. Johns Business Park, Penzance Road, Helston, Cornwall, TR13 8HN Tel: (01326) 565676 Fax: (01326) 565676 *IT services*

Gigahertz Marketing Solutions, Croye Close, Andover, Hampshire, SP10 3AF Tel: (01264) 391539 Fax: (0870) 9124158 E-mail: sales@ghz-marketing.com *Manufactures representative*

Gilbarco Veeder Root Ltd, Crompton Close, Basildon, Essex, SS14 3BA Tel: (01268) 533090 Fax: (01268) 524214 E-mail: sales@gilbarco.com *Petrol pump repair & maintainance services* Also at: Alexandria, Bristol, Chester & Halifax

Gilberdyke Dyke, Unit 2 Main Road, Gilberdyke, Brough, North Humberside, HU15 2SW Tel: (01430) 449997 Fax: (01430) 449997 *Kitchen furniture manufrs*

A.J. Gilbert (Birmingham) Ltd, 66-77 Buckingham Street, Birmingham, B19 3HU Tel: 0121-236 7774 Fax: 0121-236 6024 E-mail: lucysox@aol.com *Key fob manufacturers & press workers*

Gilbert & Creasey, 28 Margaret Drive, Boston, Lincolnshire, PE21 9AL Tel: (01205) 366584 Fax: (01205) 366584 *Electrical contractors*

Gilbert Electronics, 35 Lower Road, Malvern, Worcestershire, WR14 4BX Tel: (01684) 576989 Fax: (01684) 576989 *Electronic contract assemblies*

Geoff Gilbert International Ltd, Station Road, Swineshead, Boston, Lincolnshire, PE20 3PN Tel: (01205) 721000 Fax: (01205) 721004 E-mail: transport@geoffgilbert.co.uk *International haulage contractors*

▶ Gilbert & Goode, The Old Workshops, Charlestown Road, St. Austell, Cornwall, PL25 3NJ Tel: (01726) 64800 Fax: (01726) 65159

Gilbert H Elson, The Bungalow, Stretton Lodge, Stretton, Oakham, Leicestershire, LE15 7QS Tel: (01780) 410430 Fax: (01780) 410430 *Agricultural contracting*

Gilbert & Mellish Ltd, 3 Lightning Way, Birmingham, B31 3PH Tel: 0121-475 1101 Fax: 0121-478 0163 E-mail: sales@gilbert-mellish.co.uk *Surgical appliance & specialist footwear & textile appliance manufrs* Also at: West Heath

Gilbert Norris Removals, Wakefield Road, Netherton, Bootle, Merseyside, L30 6TZ Tel: 0151-530 1196 Fax: 0151-524 1808 *Removal & storage specialist*

Gilbert & Sons, Sharrow Vale Road, Sheffield, S11 8XD Tel: 0114-267 0634 Fax: 0114-267 0634 *Pine furniture dealers*

Gilbert & Stamper, Drayton Road, Tonbridge, Kent, TN9 2BG Tel: (01732) 357372 Fax: (01732) 771058 E-mail: tunbridge@gilbertandstamper.com *Electrical contractors & engineers*

▶ Gilbert Sutton Ltd, Unit 9 10 16, Robin Hood Industrial Estate, Alfred Street South, Nottingham, NG3 1GE Tel: 0115-958 4942

Gilbert Tools & Services, Unit 13 Chancel Industrial Estate, Hickman Avenue, Wolverhampton, WV1 2UH Tel: (01902) 455685 Fax: (01902) 455685 *Press tool manufrs*

Gilbert-Ash NI Ltd, 47 Boucher Road, Belfast, BT12 6HR Tel: (028) 9066 4334 Fax: (028) 4177 3488 *Building contractors* Also at: Belfast

Gilberts Blackpool Ltd, Gilair Works, Clifton Road, Blackpool, FY4 4QT Tel: (01253) 766911 Fax: (01253) 767941 E-mail: sales@gilbertsblackpool.com *Manufacturers of air diffusion equipment*

▶ Gilberts Fabrics & Blinds, Swan Centre, Kidderminster, Worcestershire, DY10 2DN Tel: (01562) 755255 E-mail: chrissarjeant@tiscali.co.uk *Soft furnishing fabrics & manufacturers of blinds*

Gilberts Food Equipment Ltd, Gilbert House, 1 Warwick Place, Borehamwood, Hertfordshire, WD6 1UA Tel: (0845) 2300681 Fax: (0845) 2300682 E-mail: info@topgourmet.co.uk *For nearly 50 years Gilberts have supplied the catering equipment and housewares markets, through a nationwide network of distributors, with the finest food equipment from around the world and, in the process, gained an enviable*

continued

continuation
reputation for quality, reliability and service. Offering tried and tested product ranges from world famous brands such as: Gustav Emil Ern, Peugeot, UWO Wolf, Moha, Acea, Westmark, Kisag, Sieger, Paderno, Nemco, Mussana, Garibaldi, Johny, Porkert, Sveico, Zenker, Tucel, Piazza (and many more!), Gilberts offers the discerning customer a "one-stop" source for all their needs. Their products include chefs' knives, kitchenware, salt/pepper/spice storage mills, kitchenware and bakeware, pizza equipment, heavy duty cookware and food safety ware.

Gilberts Foods, Middleton Business Park, Middleton Road, Middleton, Morecambe, Lancashire, LA3 3PW Tel: (01524) 852378 Fax: (01524) 852378 E-mail: andrew@gibertsfoods.com *Meat manufrs*

Gilbey Electrical Ltd, 55-59 Spear Street, Manchester, M1 1DF Tel: 0161-236 5079 Fax: 0161-228 2155 E-mail: sales@gilbeyelectrical.co.uk *Wholesale electric suppliers*

▶ Gilbey Fashions Ltd, 19-21 Great Portland Street, London, W1W 8QB Tel: (020) 7436 3677 Fax: (020) 7436 7006 *Supplier of ladies fashion*

▶ Gilbey Orthopaedic Footwear Ltd, 29 Shuna Place, Glasgow, G20 9ED Tel: 0141-946 4782

Gilbeyco Ltd, 32 Edison Road, Rabans Lane Industrial Area, Aylesbury, Buckinghamshire, HP19 8TE Tel: (01296) 414966 Fax: (01296) 414969 E-mail: enquiries@gilbeyco.com *Electroplating equipment suppliers*

Gilbraith Tankers Ltd, Atlas Garage, Atlas Street, Clayton Le Moors, Accrington, Lancashire, BB5 5JX Tel: (01254) 231111 Fax: (01254) 390505 E-mail: chris@gilbraithtankers.co.uk *Bulk liquid haulage*

Gilca Manufacturing Ltd, 853 Wolverhampton Road, Oldbury, West Midlands, B69 4RU Tel: 0121-544 1929 Fax: 0121-544 6301 E-mail: info@gilca.biz *Industrial insert, foam & rubber sponge manufrs*

Gilchrist & Co., 90 Donegall Passage, Belfast, BT7 1BX Tel: (028) 9023 2453 Fax: (028) 9032 6700 *Plastic nameplate & sign manufrs*

▶ Gilchrist & Lynn Ltd, Hallcraig House, Hallcraig St, Airdrie, Lanarkshire, ML6 6AW Tel: (01236) 764879

Gilchrist & Soames, 1210 Lincoln Road, Peterborough, PE4 6LA Tel: (01733) 384100 Fax: (01733) 384101 E-mail: sales@gilchristandsoames.co.uk *The Gilchrist & Soames name is recognised in many of the world's most luxurious hotels. Our fine toiletries, property-wide solutions and exacting customer service can be found across Europe, Australia, the Far East and the New World. At Gilchrist & Soames, our mission is to provide luxurious product and service solutions that enhance guest experiences at the finest hotels and resorts. We blend rich English formulations, botanical ingredients and unique aromas from around the world to create truly memorable hair, bath, and body products. Please contact us for further information on 01733 384100, or email: sales@gilchristandsoames.co.uk*

Gilco Optics Ltd, North Farm Road, Tunbridge Wells, Kent, TN2 3DH Tel: (01892) 542844 Fax: (01892) 548847 E-mail: gilco.optics@talk21.com *Optical manufacturing services*

Gildair Ltd, 18 Kings Road, Sale, Cheshire, M33 6GB Tel: 0161-973 2176 Fax: 0161-973 2176 *Suspended ceilings & fittings*

Gilder Grids, Unit 11 Withambrook Park Industrial Estate, Grantham, Lincolnshire, NG31 9ST Tel: (01476) 560052 Fax: (01476) 568165 E-mail: sales@gildergrids.co.uk *Electroformed product manufrs*

Gilders Northampton Ltd, 32 Montagu Street, Kettering, Northamptonshire, NN16 8RU Tel: (01536) 514509 Fax: (01536) 525252 *Fishing & angling equipment suppliers*

Gildersons Ltd, 31-35 Pitfield Street, London, N1 6HB Tel: (020) 7324 0180 Fax: (020) 7490 4333 E-mail: studio@gildersons.co.uk *Design studio & print consultants, direct mail, website design & exhibition stands*

Gildon Components, 5 Trafalgar Court, Widnes, Cheshire, WA8 0SZ Tel: 0151-420 2499 Fax: 0151-420 2499 *Hydraulic engineers & hose distributors*

▶ Gilead Sciences Ltd, Granta Park, Abington, Cambridge, CB21 6GT Tel: (01223) 897300 Fax: (01223) 897282 *Pharmaceutical suppliers*

Giles D & B Ltd Service Engineers, 13 Ludgate Close, Waltham, Grimsby, South Humberside, DN37 0LX Tel: (01472) 822662 E-mail: manager@dbgilesltd.f9.co.uk *Boiler maintenance, repair & commissioning engineers*

Giles Engineering Services, 18 William Street, Dunoon, Argyll, PA23 7JH Tel: (01369) 705043 Fax: (01369) 703478 *Drilling equipment suppliers*

▶ Giles Financial Services, 12 Beresford Terrace, Ayr, KA7 2EG Tel: (01292) 619900 Fax: (01292) 610037

▶ Giles Haulage Ltd, Adderson Way, Ipswich, IP6 0RL Tel: (01473) 830644

▶ Giles Higgitt, 7 Hazelwood Road, Walthamstow, London, E17 7AJ Tel: (020) 8509 1487 Fax: (020) 8509 1487 E-mail: info@blood-ties.com *Blood-Ties Family Tracing Service can help end years of fruitless searching. This kind of work is my speciality. All research is carried out with sensitivity to reunite missing friends and family.*

Laurent Giles Naval Architects Ltd, PO Box 130, Lymington, Hampshire, SO41 0TX Tel: (01590) 641777 Fax: (01590) 641888 E-mail: info@laurentgiles.co.uk *Naval architects, consultants & yacht designers*

▶ Giles Machine Tools Ltd, Unit A2, Brook Street Business Centre, Brook Street, Tipton, W. Midlands, DY4 9DD Tel: 0121-557 4400

▶ Giles & Posner Ltd, Victor Works, Barnet Road, St. Albans, Hertfordshire, AL2 1BQ Tel: (01727) 826262 Fax: (01727) 828285 E-mail: sales@giles-posne.com *Confectionery manufrs*

▶ Giles Smith, Corbin Business Park, Caring Lane, Bearsted, Kent, ME14 4NJ Tel: 0845 055 9040 Fax: 0845 055 9038 E-mail: giles.smith@gforces.co.uk *Web management*

Giles W Pritchard-Gordon (Shipowning) Ltd, Slaughan Park, Slaugham, Haywards Heath, West Sussex, RH17 6AH Tel: (01444) 400000 Fax: (01444) 401150 *Ship owners*

Gilbert Gilkes & Gordon Ltd, Canal Iron Works, Kendal, Cumbria, LA9 7BZ Tel: (01539) 720028 Fax: (01539) 732110 E-mail: sales@gilkes.com *Pump & water turbine manufrs*

Gill & Co., 94 Owen Road, Wolverhampton, WV3 0AL Tel: (01902) 420707 Fax: (01902) 420707 *Clothing manufrs*

▶ Gill Akaster, 25 Lockyer Street, Plymouth, PL1 2QW Tel: (01752) 512000 Fax: (01752) 203503 E-mail: steve.turner@gillakaster.com

Gill Demolitions Ltd, Progress Works, Hall Lane, Bradford, West Yorkshire, BD4 7DT Tel: (01274) 733011 Fax: (01274) 392879 E-mail: info@gilldemolitions.co.uk *Demolition services*

Gill Engineering Ltd, 111 Wickham Road, Fareham, Hampshire, PO16 7HZ Tel: (01329) 221341 Fax: (01329) 221388 E-mail: info@gillengineering.co.uk *Precision engineering services*

Gill Enterprises, 6 Cobb Street, London, E1 7LB Tel: (020) 7247 1191 Fax: (020) 7247 1077 E-mail: gillent@tinyworld.co.uk *Watch importers & distributors & exporters*

Ernest Gill & Son, Holmfield Industrial Estate, Holmfield, Halifax, West Yorkshire, HX2 9TN Tel: (01422) 246286 Fax: (01422) 240716 *Office furniture manufrs*

Gill Instruments Ltd, Saltmarsh Park, 67 Gosport Street, Lymington, Hampshire, SO41 9EG Tel: (01590) 613500 Fax: (01590) 613501 E-mail: gill@gill.co.uk *Electronic consultants & designers*

Gill Insulation Eastern Ltd, 39 Boss Hall Road, Ipswich, IP1 5BN Tel: (01473) 462822 Fax: (01473) 241153 E-mail: jon@gilleastern.co.uk *Thermal insulation services*

Gill Insulations Ltd, 5 33 Ebury Road, Nottingham, NG5 1BB Tel: 0115-962 6043 Fax: 0115-969 1688 E-mail: sales@gillins.com *Thermal industrial insulation contractors & engineers*

Gill Jennings & Every, 7 Eldon Street, London, EC2M 7LS Tel: (020) 7377 1377 Fax: (020) 7377 1310 E-mail: gje@gje.co.uk *Patent attorneys*

Gill & Punter Racing Supplies, The Barn, Shere Road, Albury, Guildford, Surrey, GU5 9BW Tel: (01483) 203044 Fax: (01483) 203338 *Horse racing supplies manufrs*

Gillanders & McLeod Ltd, 25 Brougham Place, Edinburgh, EH3 9JU Tel: 0131-228 5535 Fax: 0131-228 2775 E-mail: mail@gandmbagpipes.co.uk *Musical instruments*

James C. Gillespie (Engineering) Ltd, Block 4 Muirhead, Midfield Road, Mitchelston Industrial Estate, Kirkcaldy, Fife, KY1 3PS Tel: (01592) 650333 Fax: (01592) 650729 E-mail: sales@jcgillespie.co.uk *Sheet metal fabrications & laser cutting*

Gillespie (UK) Ltd, Alma House, 38 Crimea Road, Aldershot, Hampshire, GU11 1UD Tel: (01252) 323311 Fax: (01252) 336836 E-mail: info@gillespieuk.co.uk *Glass reinforced gypsum suppliers*

Gillett Cook Ltd, Wildwinds Barn, London Road, Teynham, Sittingbourne, Kent, ME9 9JY Tel: (01795) 532235 Fax: (01795) 538868 *Agricultural merchants*

Gillett & Johnston Croydon Ltd, Unit 9a Twin Bridges Business Park, 232 Selsdon Road, South Croydon, Surrey, CR2 6PL Tel: (020) 8686 2694 Fax: (020) 8681 4028 E-mail: any@gillettjohnston.co.uk *Clock manufrs*

Gillette Group UK, The Gillette Building, Great West Road, Isleworth, Middlesex, TW7 5NP Tel: (020) 8847 7800 Fax: (020) 8847 6165 *Oral hygiene equipment manufrs*

▶ Gilletts Upholstrey, 15 Cranbrook Terrace, Cranleigh, Surrey, GU6 7ES Tel: (01483) 274897 E-mail: gillettsupholstrey@yahoo.co.uk *A family run buisness ,where no job is to big or small and customers are always put first.*2 genarations of experience and customer care is what we are proud of.*

Gillian & Baines, Common Lane, Knottingley, West Yorkshire, WF11 8BN Tel: (01977) 672322 Fax: (01977) 677088 *General engineers*

Gillie & Blair, 178 New Bridge Street, Newcastle upon Tyne, NE1 2TE Tel: 0191-230 4747 Fax: 0191-230 8255 E-mail: mail@gillieblair.com *Ship brokers, owners & agents* Also at: Blythe, Immingham, Ipswich, Seaham & Sunderland

▶ Gillies Armstrong Ltd, 97 Loanbank Quadrant, Glasgow, G51 3HZ Tel: 0141-440 0101 Fax: 0141-440 0660

▶ Gillies Fine Foods Ltd, Inchrory Drive, Dingwall, Ross-Shire, IV15 9XH Tel: (01349) 861100 Fax: (01349) 864400 E-mail: info@gilliesfinefoods.co.uk *Food processors*

Gillman Group Ltd, Chipstead Road, Erdington, Birmingham, B23 5HD Tel: 0121-244 4141 Fax: 0121-244 4142 E-mail: info@gillman-group.com *Construction electrical & plumbing*

▶ Gillman Jones, Rosemede, St. Marys Road, Bowdon, Altrincham, Cheshire, WA14 2PL Tel: 0161-929 2600 Fax: 0161-261 2600 E-mail: manchester@gillmanjones.com *Consultants specialising in the valuation and sale of licensed and leisure industry property.*

▶ Gillmans, Deen House, Station Road, Rochdale, Lancashire, OL11 1DS Tel: (01706) 645004 Fax: 01706 651964 E-mail: office@gillmans.biz *Specialists in coaching & coach training, performance management solutions and public sector consultancy*

▶ Gillott Transport, Steel Street, Rotherham, South Yorkshire, S61 1DF Tel: (01709) 553325 Fax: (01709) 558586

Gills Cables, 25 Apollo, Lichfield Road Industrial Estate, Tamworth, Staffordshire, B79 7TA Tel: (01827) 304777 Fax: (01827) 314568 E-mail: kevinhatton@gillscables.co.uk *Automotive remote control cable manufrs*

Gills Northern Ltd, North CR, Seaham, County Durham, SR7 8RD Tel: 0191-581 3853 Fax: 0191-513 0266 *Road transport contractors*

▶ Gills Transport Ltd, Ever Ready Site Station Road, Four Ashes Industrial Estate, Four Ashes, Wolverhampton, WV10 7DB Tel: (01902) 791366 Fax: (01902) 791538

Gillson Bros Ltd, 4 Conder Quay, East Quay, Bridgwater, Somerset, TA6 4DB Tel: (01278) 422932 Fax: (01278) 453958 E-mail: gillsoles@hotmail.com *Shoe component manufrs, thermoforming and injection moulding specialists*

▶ Gilly Babies, 9-10 Springfield Centre, Kempston, Bedford, MK42 7PR Tel: (01234) 856677

Gilman Control Systems Ltd, 15 Bridge Gate Business Park, Gatehouse Way, Aylesbury, Buckinghamshire, HP19 8XN Tel: (01296) 434810 Fax: (01296) 434847 E-mail: sales@gilman-controls.co.uk *Heating control panel manufrs*

Gilmark Fire Protection, 2 Lonsdale Avenue, Portsmouth, PO6 2PX Tel: (023) 9220 1504 Fax: (023) 9232 1983 *Fire extinguisher supply & maintenance*

Gilmex International Ltd, 78 Conington Road, London, SE13 7LH Tel: (020) 8318 3921 Fax: (020) 8463 0565 E-mail: sales@gilmex.com *Presentation binding systems manufrs*

Gilmore & Aitken Ltd, Auchincarroch Road, Alexandria, Dunbartonshire, G83 9EY Tel: (01389) 752333 Fax: (01389) 755659 E-mail: enquiries@aitkenhoward.co.uk *Timber merchants*

▶ Gilmores Electrical, Owenmore House Upper Dunmurry Lane, Kilwee Business Park, Dunmurry, Belfast, BT17 0HD Tel: (028) 9030 1164 Fax: (028) 9062 3077 *Communication equipment*

Gilmour Ecometal, 245 Govan Road, Glasgow, G51 2SQ Tel: 0141-427 1264 Fax: 0141-427 2205 E-mail: info@gilmour-ecometal.co.uk *Insulated panel manufrs*

Gilmour Extrusion Ltd, 6 Greenhill Industrial Estate, Coatbridge, Lanarkshire, ML5 2AG Tel: (01236) 426165 Fax: (01236) 423263 E-mail: sales@monklandsextrusion.com *Impact extruded aluminium & copper suppliers*

Gilmour Print, Irvinehill Farm, Stewarton, Kilmarnock, Ayrshire, KA3 3EL Tel: (01294) 850217 Fax: (01294) 850444 E-mail: sales@gilmourprint.co.uk *Colour & commercial printing from your PC or Apple Mac files or from copy & photographs, colour leaflets & brochures; delivered on time.*

Gilmour Tools Ltd, Baird Avenue, Strutherhill Industrial Estate, Larkhall, Lanarkshire, ML9 2PJ Tel: (01698) 884856 Fax: (01698) 886634 E-mail: info@gilmourtools.co.uk *Cutting tool manufrs*

▶ Gilmour Ventilation Services Ltd, 44 Main Street, Kilbirnie, Ayrshire, KA25 7BY Tel: (01505) 683505

Gilroy Filtration Ltd, 44 Stranmillis Embankment, Belfast, BT9 5FL Tel: (028) 9080 3888 Fax: (028) 9080 3889 E-mail: custserv@gilroys.com *Industrial filters sales*

Gilson Engineering Newbury Ltd, 3 Sandleford Farm, Sandleford, Newtown, Newbury, Berkshire, RG20 9BB Tel: (01635) 41924 Fax: (01635) 42286 E-mail: info@gilsoneng.co.uk *Hydraulic equipment supply services*

Gilsons The Bakers Ltd, 5 Kingsthorne Park, Henson Way, Telford Way Industrial Estate, Kettering, Northamptonshire, NN16 8PX Tel: (01536) 316400 Fax: (01536) 316428 E-mail: info@delicedefrance.co.uk *Bakery products*

Gilt Edge Plastics, The Elms, Church Road, Harold Wood, Romford, RM3 0JU Tel: (01708) 379005 Fax: (01708) 379045 E-mail: sales@giltedgeplastics.co.uk *Hot foil blocking & plastic injection moulding*

▶ Gilt Edged Promotions Ltd, 1 Regal Close, Kings Park Road, Moulton Park Industrial Estate, Northampton, NN3 6LL Tel: (01604) 671671 Fax: (01604) 671518

Giltech Ltd, 12 North Harbour Industrial Estate, Ayr, KA8 8BN Tel: (01292) 264406 Fax: (01292) 611900 E-mail: innovation@giltech.demon.co.uk Principal Export Areas: Worldwide *Research & development (medical)*

Giltsharp Europe Ltd, PO Box 121, Shipley, West Yorkshire, BD17 5YQ Tel: (01274) 533345 Fax: (0870) 7061721 E-mail: sales@giltsharp.com *Professional hair salon, catering, sporting & outdoor products suppliers*

▶ Giltsharp Wezblade (UK), 1 Collingwood Road, Witham, Essex, CM8 2DY Tel: 07979 307831

▶ Gilvar Lining Ltd, Old Station Yard, Walton Lane, Barton under Needwood, Burton-on-Trent, Staffordshire, DE13 8EJ Tel: (01283) 712450 Fax: (01283) 716525

Gilwood (Fabricators) Co. Ltd, Bradshaw Street, Heywood, Lancashire, OL10 1PL Tel: (01706) 360131 Fax: (01706) 625666 E-mail: sales@gilwood.co.uk *Stainless steel pressure vessel & fabricators*

Gimson Ltd, 30 Boston Road, Leicester, LE4 1AU Tel: 0116-236 8688 Fax: 0116-236 3663 E-mail: a_sims@gimsoneng.co.uk *Design & build of washing & filling equipment*

Gina Shoes Ltd, Fitzroy House, Abbot Street, London, E8 3DP Tel: (020) 7254 9811 Fax: (020) 7249 1984 E-mail: ginashoes@aol.com *Shoe manufacturers & retailers*

T. Ginder (Packaging) Ltd, Upper Brook Street, Walsall, WS2 9PE Tel: (01922) 622251 Fax: (01922) 643265 *Packing case & pallet manufrs*

▶ Ginetta Cars, Old Station Drive, Sheffield, S7 2PY Tel: 0114-236 5900 Fax: 0114-236 5977 *Manufacture specialist sports & race cars*

Ginetta G4 & G12 UK Ltd, 2 The Retreat, West Bergholt, Colchester, CO6 3HN Tel: (01206) 241864 Fax: (01206) 241875 *Car manufrs*

▶ Gingaman, Wyndburgh House, Lincoln Crescent, Wrockwardine Wood, Telford, Shropshire, TF2 6LU Tel: 01952 412312 Fax: 01952 412312 E-mail: smold@gingaman.com *IT Management & Consultancy Services*

Ginsbury Electronics Ltd, 1 Exeter House, Boufort Court, Rochester, Kent, ME2 4FE Tel: (01634) 298900 Fax: (01634) 290904 E-mail: sales@ginsbury.co.uk *Liquid crystal manufacturers & distributors*

Ginsters Ltd, Unit 8 New Street, Bridgend Industrial Estate, Bridgend, Mid Glamorgan, CF31 3UD Tel: (01656) 661658 Fax: (01656) 659466 *Food products manufrs*

Ginsters Ltd, 81 Tavistock Road, Callington, Cornwall, PL17 7XG Tel: (01579) 386200 Fax: (01579) 386387E-mail: info@ginsters.co.uk *Food manufrs*

Ginsters Ltd, 6 Castings Court, Falkirk, FK2 7BA Tel: (01324) 621157 Fax: (01324) 621150 *Savoury & sandwich manufrs*

Giordano Ltd, 38-40 Windmill Street, London, W1T 2BE Tel: (020) 7636 7274 Fax: (020) 7636 5845 *Property management agents*

Gipping Occupational Health Ltd, Mill Lodge, Mendlesham Green, Stowmarket, Suffolk, IP14 5RB Tel: (01449) 766913 Fax: (01449) 766891 E-mail: advice@gipping.co.uk *Health & safety, occupational health, training*

Giraffe Print, PO Box 453, Epsom, Surrey, KT18 7WJ Tel: 0800 328 4712 E-mail: info@giraffeprint.com *A complete design and print service*

▶ Giraffic, Manor Barn, Wilsthorpe, Stamford, Lincolnshire, PE9 4PE Tel: (01778) 560670 Fax: (01778) 560670 E-mail: giraffic@ndirect.co.uk *Ariel photographers*

Girard Industries Europe Ltd, Unit C5, Olympic Business Park, Dundonald, Kilmarnock, Ayrshire, KA2 9BE Tel: (01563) 851062 Fax: (01563) 851411 E-mail: girardindeurope@hotmail.com *Pipeline pigs*

Girdwood Display, 44 St. Marys Street, Edinburgh, EH1 1SZ Tel: 0131-556 7024 Fax: 0131-557 8288 E-mail: girdwooddisplay@aol.com *Screen printing & poster lettering service*

▶ Girl Friday Solutions, 13 Lower Icknield Way, Marsworth, Tring, Hertfordshire, HP23 4LW Tel: (07921) 770516 E-mail: girlfridaysolutions@hotmail.co.uk

Girls Of Elegance Ltd, Office B12, Arena Business Park, Holyrood Close, Poole, Dorset, BH17 7FL Tel: 0845 8385143 Fax: 0845 8385143 E-mail: sales@girlsofelegance.co.uk *Girls Of Elegance Offer a wide range of women"s fashion, and shoes. Including high heel shoes, corsets, dresses, lingerie, wedding wear and boots.*

Girovac Ltd, Units 1 & 2, Douglas Bader Close, North Walsham, Norfolk, NR28 0TZ Tel: (01692) 403008 Fax: (01692) 404611 E-mail: enquiries@girovac.com Sales Contact: R. Lee Principal Export Areas: Worldwide *Girovac Ltd is a leading small UK High Vacuum Company supplying all things for Medium and High Vacuum applications. OUR PRODUCTS AND SERVICES INCLUDE: ROTARY VANE PUMPS + OILS & GREASES, TRAPS & GAUGES, MEDIUM VACUUM PUMPS AND SYSTEMS, CRYOGENIC VESSELS, LEAK DETECTORS /LEAK DETECTION SERVICE, FREEZE DRYERS, MEDICAL VACUUM & AIR PLANT, COATING SYSTEMS, VACUUM TROLLEYS & CENTRAL SYSTEMS, DEGAS SYSTEMS, SPARES, SPARES KITS & SERVICE, PUMP HIRE, FITTINGS - KF, ISO & CF, RECONDITIONED EQUIPMENT. We are especially competitive in REPAIRS, SPARES KITS and HIGH VACUUM OILS*

Girsberger London, 140 Old Street, London, EC1V 9BJ Tel: (020) 7490 3223 Fax: (020) 7490 5665 E-mail: sales@girsberger.com *Office chair manufrs*

John Girvan & Sons Ltd, 26 Wellington Square, Ayr, KA7 1HH Tel: (01292) 267243 Fax: (01292) 611085 E-mail: enquiries@jgirvan.co.uk *Industrial electrical engineers*

Gisco Radio Communication Equipment, 199a Wolverhampton Road West, Walsall, WS2 0DU Tel: (01922) 611384 Fax: (01922) 611384 E-mail: sales@giscouk.com *Radio communications equipment/systems manufrs*

Gissing & Lonsdale Ltd, Wellhouse Road, Barnoldswick, Lancashire, BB18 6DD Tel: (01282) 812821 Fax: (01282) 816135 E-mail: enquiries@gissingandlonsdale.co.uk *Mechanical engineers services*

Gissing Software Ltd, 21-23 Elmfield Road, Bromley, BR1 1LT Tel: (020) 8315 6550 Fax: (020) 8315 6530 E-mail: sales@mighter-gissing.com *Write & develop computer software*

▶ Gist, Three Cherry Trees Lane, Hemel Hempstead Industrial Estate, Hemel Hempstead, Hertfordshire, HP2 7PZ Tel: (01442) 241442 Fax: (01442) 235717

Gist, Wardentree Lane, Pinchbeck, Spalding, Lincolnshire, PE11 3UG Tel: (01775) 764000 Fax: (01775) 764101 *Temperature controlled distribution*

▶ Gist Ltd, Lichfield Road Industrial Estate, Apollo, Tamworth, Staffordshire, B79 7TA Tel: (01827) 310044 Fax: (01827) 310055

▶ Gist, Pickerings Road, Halebank, Widnes, Cheshire, WA8 8XW Tel: 0151-420 8240 Fax: 0151-424 6556

Givaudan UK Ltd, Chippenham Drive, Kingston, Milton Keynes, MK10 0AE Tel: (01908) 242424 Fax: (01908) 282232 *Food flavourings manufrs*

▶ Give Me Graphics, 93 Burnside, Cambridge, CB1 3PA Tel: (07949) 548772 E-mail: sales@givemegraphics.net *Web & graphic design solutions*

GK Group, Wakefield Road, Carlisle, CA3 0HE Tel: (01228) 517200 Fax: (01228) 517349 E-mail: info@gk-ford.co.uk *Ford dealer*

GK Maintenance, Leamore Industrial Estate, 8 Wall End Close, Walsall, WS2 7PH Tel: (01922) 479462 Fax: (01922) 404842 E-mail: staff@gkmaintenance.co.uk *Heating & air condition engineers*

GKN Driveline, 5 Kingsbury Business Park, Kingsbury Road, Minworth, Sutton Coldfield, West Midlands, B76 9DL Tel: 0121-313 1661 Fax: 0121-313 2074 E-mail: ids.Minworth@gkndriveline.com *Driveline build and refurbishment, Universal joints, Cardan Shafts, prop Shafts and Couplings*

GKN Driveshafts Ltd, Middlemoor La West, Aldridge, Walsall, WS9 8DT Tel: (01922) 453371 Fax: (01922) 451716 E-mail: martyn.habgood@gkndriveline.com *Propeller shaft & universal joint manufrs*

GKN Sinter Metals Ltd, PO Box 3, Lichfield, Staffordshire, WS13 6HB Tel: (01543) 403000 Fax: (01543) 403001 E-mail: info@gknsintermetals.co.uk *Sintered metal component manufrs*

▶ GKR Maintenance & Building Co. Ltd, Bedwas House Industrial Estate, Bedwas, Caerphilly, Mid Glamorgan, CF83 8DW Tel: (029) 2086 8585 Fax: (029) 2088 9040 E-mail: enquiries@gkrmaintenance.co.uk *Building & maintenance contractors*

GL Trade Ltd, 47-53 Cannon Street, London, EC4M 5SH Tel: (020) 7665 6200 Fax: (020) 7665 6299 E-mail: enquiries@gltrade.co.uk *Computor software house*

▶ Gladstone, Dalhousie Business Park, 2 Carrington Road, Bonnyrigg, Midlothian, EH19 3HY Tel: 0131-660 6050 Fax: 0131-660 6650

Gladstone Press, 701 Gladstone Court Business Centre, London, SW8 4AT Tel: (020) 7498 0071 Fax: (020) 7498 0067 E-mail: nigelmason@spuk.co.uk *Printers*

▶ Gladwin & Co. Ltd, 204 Cheltenham Road, Bristol, BS6 5QZ Tel: 0117-924 1430

Gladwins Ltd, Church Road, Warboys, Huntingdon, Cambridgeshire, PE28 2RJ Tel: (01487) 822427 Fax: (01487) 823142 E-mail: gladwinsbodyshop@aol.com *Body repair centre*

▶ Gladwish Excavation Contractors, F Mckay Way, Lynch Lane, Weymouth, Dorset, DT4 9DN Tel: (01305) 787200 Fax: (01305) 787200 *Building ground workers*

Glamal Engineering Ltd, Pegasus House, Wynyard Avenue, Wynyard, Billingham, Cleveland, TS22 5TB Tel: (01740) 645040 Fax: (01642) 565831 E-mail: sales@glamal.co.uk *Flange, fitting, pipe stockholders* Also at: Ettingshal & Leiston

Glamalco Ltd, Ipswich Road, Cardiff, CF23 9UR Tel: (029) 2049 7808 Fax: (029) 2047 1796 E-mail: info@glamalco.co.uk *Aluminium designers & fabricators*

▶ Glamorgan Electrical Ltd, Unit 3, Isaacs Place, Port Talbot, West Glamorgan, SA12 6NP Tel: (01639) 895217 E-mail: sales@glamorgan-electrical.com

▶ Glamorgan Engineering Consultancy, The Old Bakery, Moy Road Industrial Estate, Taffs Well, Cardiff, CF15 7GE Tel: (029) 2082 0600 Fax: (029) 2082 0601 E-mail: enquiries@glamorgan-engineering-consultancy.gov.uk

▶ Glamourbox, Unit 6, 9 St. Johns street, Colchester, CO2 7NN Tel: 01206 570976 E-mail: sales@glamourbox.co.uk

Glanbia Cheese Ltd, Glanhwfa Road, Llangefni, Gwynedd, LL77 7TT Tel: (01248) 750351 Fax: (01248) 750566 Principal Export Areas: Worldwide *Food suppliers*

Glandel Ltd, Wareham Road, Corfe Mullen, Wimborne, Dorset, BH21 3RX Tel: (01202) 697282 Fax: (01202) 692364 E-mail: info@glandel.co.uk *Pre-cast concrete products manufrs*

Glas Seal Ni Ltd, 80 Belfast Road, Ballynahinch, County Down, BT24 8EB Tel: (028) 9756 2932 Fax: (028) 9756 1096 E-mail: post@glas-seal.co.uk *Double glazed unit manufrs*

Glasdon Manufacturing Ltd, Industrial Estate, Poulton Industrial Estate, Poulton-le-Fylde, Lancashire, FY6 8JW Tel: (01253) 891131 Fax: (01253) 891923 E-mail: sales@glasdon-manufacturing.co.uk *Kiosk manufrs*

Glasfryn Fencing and Sawmill, Llanaelhaearn Road, Y Ffor, Pwllheli, Gwynedd, LL53 6RN Tel: (01758) 750623 Fax: (01758) 750624 *Timber growers & fencing manufrs*

Glasfryn Hire, Glasfryn Uchaf, Pencaenewydd, Pwllheli, Gwynedd, LL53 6RD Tel: (01766) 810204 Fax: (01766) 810707 E-mail: ema@glasflyn.co.uk *Container hire*

Glasgow Airport Ltd, St. Andrews Drive, Glasgow Airport, Abbotsinch, Paisley, Renfrewshire, PA3 2ST Tel: 0141-887 1111 Fax: (0870) 7511004 E-mail: info@first-travel.co.uk *Chauffeur services*

▶ Glasgow Building Preservation Trust, Wellpark Enterprise Centre, 120 Sydney Street, Glasgow, G31 1JF Tel: 0141-550 7500 Fax: 0141-550 4443

Glasgow City Council, Development & Regeneration Services Business Services Unit, 229 George Street, Glasgow, G2 1DU Tel: 0141-287 0901 Fax: 0141-287 7237 E-mail: ian.nicholson@drs.glasgow.gov.uk *Holding/investment industrial development authority*

▶ Glasgow College Of Nautical Studies, 21 Thistle Street, Glasgow, G5 9XB Tel: 0141-565 2500 Fax: 0141-565 2599 *College navy training (metal work)*

▶ Glasgow Disabled Aid Specialists, 300 Blantyre Ferme Road, Uddingston, Glasgow, G71 7RN Tel: 0141-641 3656 Fax: 0141-641 3656 *Ramp & disabled appliances*

▶ Glasgow Power Steering, 70 Camelon Street, Glasgow, G32 6AF Tel: 0141-764 1919 Fax: 0141-764 1818

Glasgow Precision Ltd, 13 Colquhoun Avenue, Hillington Industrial Estate, Glasgow, G52 4BN Tel: 0141-882 5793 Fax: 0141-810 3061 E-mail: glasp1@netcomuk.co.uk *Precision engineers*

▶ Glasgow Print Studio, 22 King Street, Glasgow, G1 5QP Tel: 0141-552 0704

▶ Glasgow Projector Hire, Unit 25, New Albion Industrial Estate, Halley Street, Glasgow, G13 4DJ Tel: 0141-435 7110 Fax: 0141-435 7109 E-mail: info@glasgow-projector-hire.co.uk *LCD data & video projector hire*

▶ Glasgow Removals, 192 Swanston Street, Glasgow, G40 4HH Tel: 0141-550 8333

▶ Kevin Glashier, 93 Sussex Way*, London, N7 6RU Tel: (020) 7281 7821 E-mail: kevin@kevinglashier.co.uk *Hand painted, gold leaf & vinyl lettering, Heraldic decoration, General sign work, Calligraphy*

Glasmaster Ltd, 20 Enterprise Park, Piddlehinton, Dorchester, Dorset, DT2 7UA Tel: (01305) 848758 Fax: (01305) 848942 E-mail: dickgain@aol.com *Glass fibre fabrications*

Glasplies Ltd, 2 Crowland Street, Southport, Merseyside, PR9 7RZ Tel: (01704) 540626 Fax: (01704) 537322 E-mail: office@glasplies.co.uk *Glass fibre distributors*

Glass Bending & Decorating Ltd, 47 Sutherland Road, London, E17 6BH Tel: (020) 8531 7626 Fax: (020) 8531 4875 E-mail: collintucker4.@btopenworld.com *Glass processing manufrs*

Glass Block Outlet, PO Box 272, Liverpool, L13 7DA Tel: (07940) 895369 Fax: (0845) 2262683 E-mail: info@glassblockoutlet.co.uk *Buy glass blocks (glass bricks)online, ideal for home DIY. Low prices, home delivery*

▶ Glass Block Shop The Ltd, 146 Stamford Street Central, Ashton-under-Lyne, Lancashire, OL6 6AD Tel: (0870) 7601112 Fax: 0161- 343 8834 E-mail: sales@glassblocksuk.com *Glass block supplier*

Glass Blowing Scientific, 5 Union Belvedere Works, Roker Lane, Pudsey, West Yorkshire, LS28 9LE Tel: 0113-236 3322 Fax: 0113-236 3616 E-mail: glassblowingscientific@fsmail.net *Scientific glass blowing manufrs*

Glass Bond N W Ltd, Westside Industrial Estate, Jackson Street, St. Helens, Merseyside, WA9 3AT Tel: (01744) 730334 Fax: (01744) 451661 E-mail: sales@glassbond.co.uk *Plastic moulding materials & lamp adhesive*

Glass Design Ltd, 51-63 Sangley Road, London, SE6 2DT Tel: (020) 8698 8811 Fax: (020) 8695 5181 *Glass merchants*

Glass Design & Decorating, 7a Queens Road, Sunninghill, Ascot, Berkshire, SL5 9AF Tel: (01344) 623017 Fax: (01344) 623017 E-mail: info@gdd-glassdesign.co.uk *Decoration of flat glass*

▶ Glass Doctor, 56 Little Glen Road, Glen Parva, Leicester, LE2 9TS Tel: (0800) 6346494 Fax: 0116-299 1898 E-mail: info@glassandlock.co.uk *Glazing company & locksmiths*

Glass Engraving Services, 60 Northampton Street, Birmingham, B18 6DX Tel: 0121-236 9936 Fax: 0121-236 5624 E-mail: lespol@arteng.fsnet.co.uk *Laser, diamond, rotary & glass engraving*

Glass Express Ltd, Unit 1-2 Cobbswood Industrial Estate, Brunswick Road, Ashford, Kent, TN23 1EL Tel: (01233) 642220 Fax: (01233) 641475 E-mail: info@glassexpress.co.uk *Glazing contractors & merchants*

▶ Glass Fibre Products, 3 Belvedere Road, Lowestoft, Suffolk, NR33 0PR Tel: (01502) 515106

Glass Fibre Workshop Ltd, Unit 2 Drury Square, Beeston, King's Lynn, Norfolk, PE32 2NA Tel: (01328) 701901 Fax: (01328) 701196 *Glass fibre products manufrs*

Glass & Glazing Federation, 44-48 Borough High Street, London, SE1 1XB Tel: (020) 7403 7177 Fax: (020) 7357 7458 E-mail: info@ggf.org.uk Sales Contact: C. Hogan *Glass installation services/trade association & glass (plate/sheet/float) producers*

Glass House Technologies UK, Ocean House, Bourne Business Park, Addlestone, Surrey, KT15 2QW Tel: (0870) 7770017 Fax: (0870) 7770018 *IT consultants*

Glass Northampton Ltd, 25-29 Bailiff Street, Northampton, NN1 3DX Tel: (01604) 233343 Fax: (01604) 233298 E-mail: admin@glassnorthampton.co.uk *UPVC & aluminium windows manufrs*

▶ Glass Products Ltd, 1 Manor Works, Station Road South, Totton, Southampton, SO40 9HP Tel: (023) 8066 8888 Fax: (023) 8066 8899

▶ Glass Scratch Repair, 19 Harwood Lane, Great Harwood, Blackburn, BB6 7SN Tel: (01254) 888557 E-mail: peter_cornwell@lineone.net *Glass scratch repairs*

▶ Glass Scribe International Ltd, Spencer House, Caberfeidh Avenue, Dingwall, Ross-Shire, IV15 9TD Tel: (01349) 867088 Fax: (01349) 867089 E-mail: admin@glassscribe.com *Glass, crystal, glass engraving & printing importers services & manufrs*

▶ Glass Studio, 180 John Wilson Business Park, Chestfield, Whitstable, Kent, CT5 3RB Tel: (01227) 770613 Fax: (01227) 770613 E-mail: sales@theglassstudio.co.uk *Real lead & stained glass windows manufrs*

Glass Style, 9a Stone Cross La North, Lowton, Warrington, WA3 2SA Tel: (01942) 717226 Fax: (01942) 717249 *Picture frame manufrs*

▶ Glass Technics, Church Lane, Hartley Wespall, Basingstoke, Hampshire, RG27 0BB Tel: (01256) 882339 E-mail: tony@glasstechnics.co.uk *Glass repair equipment suppliers & manufrs*

Glassart, Cross Bank Farm, Burnt Fen, Freckenham, Bury St. Edmunds, Suffolk, IP28 8EA Tel: (01353) 675285 Fax: (01353) 675285 E-mail: sales@glassartuk.com *At Glassart we have over 30 years experience in modern SGO production. From bevelled/ decorative fanlight & door pane sealed units to one off unique special leaded designs, our design shop produce decorative panels*

Glassblock Warehouse Ltd, Suite 111, 79 Friar Street, Worcester, WR1 2NT Tel: (01886) 833891 Fax: (01886) 832534 E-mail: 1glassblocks@tiscali.co.uk *Glass blocks distribution services*

▶ Glasscalc Ltd, 5 Valmont Road, Nottingham, NG5 1GA Tel: (0845) 1662624 E-mail: sales@glasscalc.co.uk *Computer software for the glass & glazing industry*

Glassex Holdings Ltd, Ailsa Street, London, E14 0LE Tel: (020) 7987 4191 Fax: (020) 7987 4194 E-mail: glassexltd@virgin.net *Glass merchants*

▶ Glasseye Ltd, 20A Iliffe Yard, London, SE17 3QA Tel: (020) 7701 4300 Fax: (020) 7701 4300 E-mail: info@glasseyeltd.com *Creative team specialising in ideas and content creation for digital media, film, DVD, CD/DVD ROM, & web design/marketing. Glasseye can give you fresh creative ideas for marketing your products or your brand, by delivering and producing projects. Our technical expertese allows us to quickly identify ideas and methods that will work for you. Give us a call.*

▶ Glassline Ltd, Unit 16 Chaucer Industrial Estate, Dittons Road, Polegate, East Sussex, BN26 6JF Tel: (01323) 482000 Fax: (01323) 482111

▶ Glasson Fertillisers, Greens Farm Depot, Park Lane, Winmarleigh, Preston, PR3 0JU Tel: (01524) 752200 Fax: (01524) 753601 E-mail: info@glassongrain.co.uk

Glasson Grain Ltd, Greens Farm Depot, Park Lane, Winmarleigh, Preston, PR3 0JU Tel: (01524) 791483 Fax: (01524) 792335 E-mail: mark.greeves@glassongrain.co.uk *Fertilizer manufrs*

Glasspool & Thaiss, Coughtrey House, 112-116 Broad Street, Chesham, Buckinghamshire, HP5 3ED Tel: (01494) 771314 Fax: (01494) 791455 E-mail: mail@glasspoolandthaiss.com *Consulting Structural Engineers* Also at: Berkhamstead & Isle of Man

Glass's Information Services Ltd, 1 Princes Road, Weybridge, Surrey, KT13 9TU Tel: (01932) 823823 Fax: (01932) 846564 E-mail: enquiries@glass.co.uk *Information provider*

Glasstech Ltd, PO Box 62, Worcester, WR4 9RQ Tel: (01905) 723663 Fax: (01905) 20400 E-mail: sales@glasstech.com *Glass tempering systems*

Glasswell & Last Ltd, 28 Eastern Way, Bury St. Edmunds, Suffolk, IP32 7AB Tel: (01284) 761528 Fax: (01284) 723528 E-mail: sales@glasswell-last.com *Electrical contractors*

▶ Glassworks Ltd, Runcorn Road, Birmingham, B12 8QP Tel: 0121-442 2073 Fax: 0121-442 2079

GlasTechnik, Sagana Lodge, Scotton Rd, Scotter, Gainsborough, Lincs, DN21 3SB Tel: (01724) 761172 Fax: (01724) 764352 E-mail: sightglasses@aol.com Principal Export Areas: Worldwide *Flow indicator, level gauge & sight & gauge glass manufacturers. In addition, liquid level gauges*

Glatselter UK Ltd, Church Road, Lydney, Gloucestershire, GL15 5EJ Tel: (01594) 842235 Fax: (01594) 844213 E-mail: info@crompton.co.uk *Specialist paper manufrs*

Glaxo Smith Klein Leisure Club, Oldfield Lane North, Greenford, Middlesex, UB6 8QD Tel: (020) 8966 2280 Fax: (020) 8966 4499 *Pharmaceutical researchers & developers*

Glaxo Smith Kline (UK) Ltd, Stockley Park West, Uxbridge, Middlesex, UB11 1BT Tel: (020) 8990 9000 Fax: (020) 8990 4321 *Pharmaceutical manufrs*

Glaxosmithkline, Harmire Road, Barnard Castle, County Durham, DL12 8DT Tel: (01833) 690600 Fax: (01833) 692300 Principal Export Areas: Worldwide *Pharmaceutical chemicals suppliers*

▶ Glaxosmithkline, Cobden Street, Montrose, Angus, DD10 8EA Tel: (01674) 672606 Fax: (01674) 666688 *Pharmaceutical distributor & manufrs*

Glaxosmithkline, 11 Stoke Poges Lane, Slough, SL1 3NW Tel: (01753) 533433 Fax: (01753) 502000 *Pharmaceutical & soft drink manufrs*

Glaxosmithkline, Park Road, Ware, Hertfordshire, SG12 0DP Tel: (01920) 469469 Fax: (01920) 463172 *Pharmaceutical manufrs*

Glaze For Trade Ltd, 20 Broom Road, Poole, Dorset, BH12 4NL Tel: (01202) 722220 Fax: (01202) 722002 E-mail: sales@glazefortrade.co.uk *PVCu window fabricators & installers*

▶ Glazpart Ltd, Wildmere Road, Daventry Road Industrial Estate, Banbury, Oxfordshire, OX16 3JU Tel: (01295) 264533 Fax: (01295) 266699 E-mail: sales@glazpart.co.uk *Plastic injection moulders, glazing accessory manufacture*

▶ Glazy Daisy, 45 St Johns Road, Tunbridge Wells, Kent, TN4 9TP Tel: (01892) 519719 *Pottery painters*

Glazzard (Dudley) Ltd, The Washington Centre, Netherton, Dudley, West Midlands, DY2 9RE Tel: (01384) 233151 Fax: (01384) 250224 E-mail: acg@glazzard.co.uk *Architectural metalworks*

▶ GLC Alloys, 119 Drake Road, Harrow, Middlesex, HA2 9DZ Tel: (020) 8868 1738 Fax: (020) 8537 7042 E-mail: ross@glcalloys.co.uk *Suppliers of special, precious & refractory metals*

Gleadell Agriculture Ltd, Lindsey House, Hemswell Cliff, Gainsborough, Lincolnshire, DN21 5TH Tel: (01427) 421200 Fax: (01427) 421230 *Corn & agricultural merchants*

Gleaner Oil & Gas, Milnfield, Elgin, Morayshire, IV30 1UZ Tel: (01343) 557477 Fax: (01343) 548534 E-mail: oilgas@gleaner.co.uk *Oil distributors* Also at: Argyle & Dingwall

Gleave & Co., 111-113 St. John Street, London, EC1V 4JA Tel: (020) 7253 1345 Fax: (020) 7253 0447 E-mail: gleaveandco@aol.com *Watch spare part importer*

Glebe Engineering Ltd, Edensor Works, Greendock Street, Stoke-on-Trent, ST3 2NA Tel: (01782) 599161 Fax: (01782) 324410 E-mail: nick.cresswell@glebe.co.uk *Precision engineers*

Glebe Joinery Ltd, Barrington Road, Orwell, Royston, Hertfordshire, SG8 5QP Tel: (01223) 207800 Fax: (01223) 208888 *Joinery manufrs*

▶ Glebe Radio & Television Ltd, 33 Glebe Farm Road, Birmingham, B33 9LY Tel: 0121-783 3352 Fax: 0121-783 1498 E-mail: glebetv@freedomnames.co.uk *Television repair,Electrical and Gas appliance Retailer Birmingham UK*

Gledco Engineered Materials, Bankfield Terrace, Leeds, LS4 2JR Tel: 0113-275 1144 Fax: 0113-230 4724 E-mail: sales@usggledco.co.uk *Carbon brush, component & carbon seals*

Gledhill Water Storage Ltd, Sycamore Trading Estate, Squires Gate Lane, Blackpool, FY4 3RL Tel: (01253) 474401 Fax: (01253) 474445 E-mail: info@gledhill-cyls.co.uk *Copper water heater manufrs* Also at: Bristol, Dudley, Liverpool, Maidstone, Pinxton, Redbourn & Washington

Gledhill Water Storage Ltd, Unit 22, Corngreves Trading Estate, Charlton Dive, Cradley Heath, West Midlands, B64 7BJ Tel: (01384) 636245 Fax: (01384) 413700 *Domestic copper cylinder manufrs*

▶ Gleeson Framers, 587c Kingston Road, London, SW20 8SA Tel: (020) 8542 5005 Fax: (020) 8542 5005 E-mail: sales@gleesonframers.co.uk *Picture framers*

M.J. Gleeson Group P.L.C., Haredon House, London Road, North Cheam, Sutton, Surrey, SM3 9BS Tel: (020) 8644 4321 Fax: (020) 8641 6110 E-mail: marketing@mjgleeson.com *Building & civil engineers developers*

▶ Glem Gas Spares Ltd, 150 Tarbock Road, Hyton, Huyton, Liverpool, L36 5TJ Tel: (07729) 729129 E-mail: glemgasspares@btinternet.com *Supplier of genuine factory spare parts for Glem Gas cookers.*

Glemsford Silk Mills Ltd, Chequers Lane, Glemsford, Sudbury, Suffolk, CO10 7PW Tel: (01787) 280244 Fax: (01787) 281730 *Silk thrusters & dyers*

Glen Cairn Crystal Studio, 12 Tartraven Place, East Mains Industrial Estate, Broxburn, West Lothian, EH52 5LT Tel: (01506) 856775 *China glassware manufrs*

Glen Castings Ltd, Meadows Mill, Burnley Road, Bacup, Lancashire, OL13 8BZ Tel: (01706) 873967 Fax: (01706) 879234 E-mail: glencas@lancs.co.uk *Specialist Aluminium Pressure and Gravity Diecasters. Suppliers of Ductile, Cast Irons, Drainage Castings, Gully Gratings, Hinge Gratings, Drain Rodding Points, Black Cast Iron Manhole Covers and Block Pavior Trays. We have the ability to produce samples and rapid prototypes using a combination of traditional skills in our sand foundry and the very latest technology of CAD/ CAM and rapid prototyping. Concentrating on small, medium size runs, 2,000 to 100,000 pieces at economical prices*

▶ Glen Catrine Bonded Warehouse Ltd, 7 Laigh Road, Catrine, Mauchline, Ayrshire, KA5 6SR Tel: (01290) 551211 Fax: (01290) 551423 *Warehouse*

Glen Dimplex Cooking Ltd, Stoney Lane, Whiston, Prescot, Merseyside, L35 2XW Tel: 0151-426 6551 Fax: 0151-426 3261 *Domestic appliance manufrs*

Glen Dimplex UK Ltd, Millbrook House, Grange Drive, Hedge End, Southampton, SO30 2DF Tel: (0845) 6005111 Fax: (0870) 7270109 E-mail: enquiries@dimplex.co.uk *Based in Southampton, Dimplex is the UK market leader in electric space and water heating. Our product portfolio covers ground source heat pumps, air to water heat pumps and water source heat pumps which provide sustainable, environmentally friendly heating; domestic heating from economical storage heaters and the revolutionary DuoHeat radiator through to stylish and controllable panel heaters; towel rails and bathroom radiators; commercial heating including air curtains, quartz heaters, ceramic heaters and commercial fan heaters; electric fires including Optiflame flame effect fires and focal point fires; and portable heating including oil filled radiators, portable convectors and portable fan heaters. We also have a free heating design service and offer guidance on how to comply with Part L of the Building Regulations, in addition to a wide range of information on sustainability; government policy initiatives and national standards such as PPS22 and EcoHomes; all of which can be found at www.dimplex-resource.co.uk*

▶ Glen Farrow UK Ltd, Spalding Road, Pinchbeck, Spalding, Lincolnshire, PE11 3UE Tel: (01775) 725444

Glen Fresh Foods, 6 Berryhill Road, Donemana Enterprise Park, Dunamanagh, Strabane, County Tyrone, BT82 0NR Tel: (028) 7139 7969 Fax: (028) 7139 7969 *Food distribution*

Glen Leisure Services Ltd, Unit 1 Strathkelvin Retail Park, Bishopbriggs, Glasgow, G64 2TS Tel: 0141-762 1121 Fax: 0141-762 5126 *Amusement goods suppliers*

Glen Moray Distillery, 1 Glenmoray Distillery Cottages, Elgin, Morayshire, IV30 1YE Tel: (01343) 542577 Fax: (01343) 546195 E-mail: edodson@glenmorangieplc.co.uk *Distillers*

Glen Pac Southern Ltd, 11 The Forty, Cricklade, Swindon, SN6 6HW Tel: (01793) 751527 Fax: (01793) 750551 E-mail: sales@glenpac.com *Packaging & packing material manufrs*

▶ Glen Pitt-Pladdy, Photographer, The Penthouse, 11 Alexandra Road, Reading, RG1 5PE Tel: 0789 9915864 *I provide a wide variety of photography and digital imaging services for businesses in the UK. These include Executive Portraits, Closeup Photography (eg. tech products), Public Relations /Publicity Photos, Digital Manipulation and General Commercial / Industrial Photography.**Based in Reading (Berkshire UK), I am normally available to travel if needed. See website for further details.*

▶ Glen Prince Of Great Britain, Unit 8-8a North Street Workshops, North Street, Stoke-sub-Hamdon, Somerset, TA14 6QR Tel: (01935) 825082 Fax: (01935) 826283 E-mail: sales@glenprince.com *Scarf manufrs*

Company Information

▶ indicates data change since last edition

Glen Surveys Ltd, Hatherley House, 13 Hatherley Road, Sidcup, Kent, DA14 4DS Tel: (020) 8309 5757 Fax: (020) 8309 6362 E-mail: glen@glensurveys.co.uk *Chartered land surveyors*

▶ Glen Turner Distillery Ltd, Starlaw Road, Bathgate, West Lothian, EH47 7BW Tel: (01506) 468550 Fax: (01506) 468570

Glen Tyre Services Ltd, 1286 London Road, Leigh-on-Sea, Essex, SS9 2UD Tel: (01702) 479907 Fax: (01702) 479907 *Puncture sealants*

Glen-Aaron Services, 31 Gravelhill Road, Lisburn, County Antrim, BT27 5RW Tel: (028) 9262 1732 Fax: (028) 9262 1968 *Poultry equipment & suppliers*

Glenaber Engineers Ltd, Denfield House, 5 Smeaton Road, Kirkcaldy, Fife, KY1 2EY Tel: (01592) 651940 Fax: (01592) 651963 E-mail: admin-glenaberengineers@ecosse.net *Paper plant maintenance contractors*

▶ Glenace Electrical Ltd, 60a Station Road, Kiveton Park, Sheffield, S26 6QQ Tel: (01909) 773344 Fax: (01909) 773322

Glenair Ltd, 171-177 Hessle Road, Hull, HU3 4AA Tel: (01482) 223313 Fax: (01482) 229962 E-mail: info@glenair.ltd.uk *Dust & fume extraction & ventilation engineers*

▶ Glenair Contracts Ltd, 17 Hutchinson Street, Leicester, LE2 0BD Tel: 0116-253 2888 Fax: 0116-251 5616

Glenair UK Ltd, 40 Lower Oakham Way, Mansfield, Nottinghamshire, NG18 5BY Tel: (01623) 638100 Fax: (01623) 638111 E-mail: enquiries@glenair.co.uk *Connector accessories*

Glenalmond Tweed Co. Ltd, Culnacloich Farm, Glenalmond, Perth, PH1 3SN Tel: (01738) 880322 Fax: (01738) 880431 E-mail: info@glenalmond.com *Harris tweed goods manufrs*

Glenammer Engineering, 2 Mccalls Avenue, Ayr, KA8 9AE Tel: (01292) 261444 Fax: (01292) 267222 E-mail: sales@glenammer.com *Laboratory sieve manufrs*

Glenbar Electrical, 2-4 North Croft Street, Paisley, Renfrewshire, PA3 4AD Tel: 0141-887 4040 Fax: 0141-889 6789 *Autoelectrics engineers*

▶ Glenbery Upholstery Ltd, Walton Street, Long Eaton, Nottingham, NG10 1PB Tel: 0115-946 0625 Fax: 0115-946 0683

Glenborough Engineering Co. Ltd, Station Road, Glenfield, Leicester, LE3 8BT Tel: 0116-231 4444 Fax: 0116-287 5441 E-mail: sales@glenborough.co.uk *Precision engineers*

▶ Glencadam Distillery Co. Ltd, 16 Park Road, Brechin, Angus, DD9 7AP Tel: (01356) 622217 Fax: (01356) 624905

GlenCall International, 4 Balgedie Court, Glenlomond, Kinross, KY13 9HF Tel: 01592 840 853 E-mail: enquiries@glencall.co.uk *Letter boxes for residential and business use, individual and multiple banks of mail boxes; Personalisation can be applied to any letter box*

▶ Glencarra Textile Printers, Belford Mills, 16 Brewery Road, Kilmarnock, Ayrshire, KA1 3HZ Tel: (01563) 550978

Glenco Food Trade Supplies, 30 Pancake Lane, Hemel Hempstead, Hertfordshire, HP2 4NQ Tel: (01442) 267172 Fax: (01442) 267172 E-mail: graeme.north@ntlworld.com *Speciality seasoning & ingredients*

Glenco Quarry Services, 19 Meadow Bank Avenue, Sheffield, S7 1PB Tel: 0114-258 3734 Fax: 0114-255 0583 *Quarry supplies, conveyor belts & roller distributors*

Glencoe Ltd, Glenco House, Drake Avenue, Staines, Middlesex, TW18 2AW Tel: (01784) 493555 Fax: (01784) 493222 E-mail: sales@fuelsystem.co.uk *Fuel injection pump suppliers & manufrs*

Glencraft, 132 Wellington Road, Aberdeen, AB12 3LQ Tel: (01224) 873366 Fax: (01224) 894659 E-mail: sales@glencraft.co.uk *Bedding manufrs*

Glencrest Seatex Ltd, Heron Avenue, Wickford, Essex, SS11 8DL Tel: (01268) 769641 Fax: (01268) 562950 E-mail: sales@glencrestseatex.com *Garden furniture, cushions & parasol manufrs*

Glendale Developments Ltd, Unit 2a Union Road Trading Estate, Oldbury, West Midlands, B69 3EU Tel: 0121-541 1752 Fax: 0121-544 8774 E-mail: glendaledevelpoments@hotmail.com *Steel & stainless steel handrails manufrs*

▶ Glendale Electrical Ltd, 1014 Cumbernauld Road, Glasgow, G33 2QR Tel: 0141-770 7191 Fax: 0141-770 9337 E-mail: info@glendale-electrical.co.uk

Glendale Filtration Products, 37 Parkhill Drive, Rutherglen, Glasgow, G73 2PW Tel: 0141-613 1550 Fax: 0141-613 1550 *Filtration products distributors*

Glendale Forge, Monk Street, Thaxted, Dunmow, Essex, CM6 2NR Tel: (01371) 830466 Fax: (01371) 831419 E-mail: sales@glendaleforge.co.uk *Blacksmiths" tool manufrs*Forges*

▶ Glendale Grounds Management Ltd, 401 Walsall Road, Perry Barr, Birmingham, B42 1BT Tel: 0121-356 4226 Fax: 0121-331 1871

▶ Glendale Managed Services Ltd, 8 Stonewall Industrial Estate, Stonewall Place, Newcastle, Staffordshire, ST5 6NR Tel: (01782) 712910 Fax: (01782) 712456 *Grounds Maintenance*

Glendale Plastics Ltd, 16 Faraday Road, Glenrothes, Fife, KY6 2RU Tel: (01592) 774888 Fax: (01592) 771680 E-mail: sales@glendaleplastics.co.uk *Plastic vacuum formed products*

Glendale Print & Finishing Ltd, 8 Orchard Business Centre, North Farm Road, Tunbridge Wells, Kent, TN2 3XF Tel: (01892) 544988 Fax: (01892) 548181 E-mail: info@glendaleprintandfinishing.co.uk *Commercial printers*

▶ Glendale Security Systems, Unit 3 62 Muirs, Kinross, KY13 8AU Tel: (01577) 863525 Fax: (01577) 863524

Glendale Security Systems, Unit 3 62 Muirs, Kinross, KY13 8AU Tel: (01577) 863525 Fax: (01577) 863524 *Fire alarm installers*

Glendale Textiles Ltd, 86 Main Street, Queniborough, Leicester, LE7 3DA Tel: 0116-269 5548 Fax: 0116-269 5564 *Textile agents*

Glendenning Plastics Ltd, First Avenue, The Pensnett Estate, Kingswinford, West Midlands, DY6 7TZ Tel: (01384) 278256 Fax: (01384) 400091 E-mail: sales@garlandproducts.com Principal Export Areas: Africa & North America *Manufacturers of plastic injection mouldings*

Glendining Road Marks Ltd, 4 Marsh Lane, Tottenham, London, N17 0XE Tel: (020) 8808 2929 Fax: (020) 8880 9161 E-mail: roadmarks@glendining.com *Road marking contractors*

Glendining Signs, 7 The Markham Centre, Station Road, Theale, Reading, RG7 4PE Tel: 0118-932 3788 Fax: 0118-932 3804 E-mail: sales@glendining.co.uk *Sign manufacturers and suppliers to the UK.*

▶ E. & J.W. Glendinning Ltd, Glentor, Ashburton, Newton Abbot, Devon, TQ13 7LF Tel: (01364) 652601 Fax: (01364) 651118 E-mail: sales@ejwglendinning.co.uk *Quarry & concrete products, ready mixed, bitmac, surfacing & haulage services*

Glendinning Management Consultants Ltd, Glendinning House, 1 Station Road, Addlestone, Surrey, KT15 2AG Tel: (01932) 833600 Fax: (01932) 833601 *Management consultants*

Glendon Products Ltd, 5 St. James Road, St. James Industrial Estate, Corby, Northamptonshire, NN18 8AL Tel: (01536) 403010 Fax: (01536) 266629 E-mail: info@glendonproducts.com *Manufacture of refrigerated and heated food service and display equipment*

Glendower Cutting Tools Ltd, 21 Pinfold Road, Thurmaston, Leicester, LE4 8AS Tel: 0116-269 5999 Fax: 0116-269 3442 E-mail: sales@glendower.co.uk *Tungsten carbide tool manufrs*

▶ Glendronach Distillery Co. Ltd, Glendronach Distillery, Forgue, Huntly, Aberdeenshire, AB54 6DB Tel: (01466) 730202 Fax: (01466) 730313

▶ Gleneagles Of Edinburgh Ltd, 9 Simpson Road, East Mains Industrial Estate, Broxburn, West Lothian, EH52 5NP Tel: (01506) 852566 Fax: (01506) 855735 E-mail: enquiries@gleneaglescrystal.com *Crystal glass giftware retailers*

▶ Glenelg Product Design, Low Barn, Church View, Menston, Ilkley, West Yorkshire, LS29 6EX Tel: (01943) 871117 Fax: (01943) 871002 E-mail: john@glenelgdesign.com *Product design*

▶ Glenfarclas Distillery, Glenfarclas Distillery, Ballindalloch, Banffshire, AB37 9BD Tel: (01807) 500257 *Whisky manufrs*

▶ Glenfield Air Conditioning Ltd, 139a Dominion Road, Glenfield, Leicester, LE3 8JB Tel: 0116-231 4117 Fax: 0116-231 4117 E-mail: darren.web@glenfield96.fsnet.co.uk *Air conditioning installers*

Glenfield Associates, 2b Mossop Drive, Langtoft, Peterborough, PE6 9LY Tel: (01778) 343567 Fax: (01778) 347382 E-mail: sales@glenfieldbs.co.uk *Computer consultancy*

Glenfield Plumbers Ltd, Southfield Industrial Estate, 62 Nasmyth Road, Glenrothes, Fife, KY6 2SD Tel: (01592) 774818 Fax: (01592) 630552 *Plumbing & heating contractors*

▶ Glengall Scotland Ltd, 59 Carcluie Crescent, Alloway, Ayr, KA7 4ST Tel: (01292) 442100 Fax: (01292) 442100 E-mail: glengallscotlandltd@tiscali.co.uk *Kilts & kilt accessories, tartan, pewter ware & engravable giftware suppliers*

Glengarnock Garments Ltd, Unit 1-4 Block 3, River Place, Kilbirnie, Ayrshire, KA25 7EN Tel: (01505) 682759 Fax: (01505) 683105 E-mail: sales@glengarnock.com *Boys & men's trousers manufrs*

▶ Glengarth Construction Ltd, Piercy Mill, Piercy Road, Rossendale, Lancashire, BB4 9JP Tel: (01706) 211999 Fax: (01706) 211888

▶ GlenGolf (Clubmaker), 16 Witchford Road, Lincoln, LN6 0ST Tel: 01522 879830 E-mail: muirfield60@ntlworld.com *Custom built golf clubs using snake eyes clubheads & shafts & grips from major manufacturers like ping, callaway, taylormade, golf pride, graffaloy, UST, true temper, also custom fitting & golf club repairs, retailer of snake eyes golf clubs & golf bags*

▶ Glengowan Engineering Ltd, Block 5, Chapelhall Industrial Estate, Chapelhall, Airdrie, Lanarkshire, ML6 8QH Tel: (01236) 753355 Fax: (01236) 767610 E-mail: sales@glengowan.co.uk *Engineering*

Glenhead Engineering Ltd, 60 Beardmore Way, Clydebank, Dunbartonshire, G81 4HT Tel: 0141-952 9945 Fax: 0141-951 1731 E-mail: info@glenheadengineering.co.uk *Precision engineers*

Glenhowe Of Scotland Ltd, Buccleuch Mills, Green Lane, Hawick, Roxburghshire, TD9 0HR Tel: (01450) 373839 Fax: (01450) 370423 *Knitwear manufrs*

Gleniffer Blinds, 2 Quarry St, Johnstone, Renfrewshire, PA5 8DZ Tel: (01505) 324448 Fax: 01505 342013 *Blind suppliers*

Glenisla Kilts Ltd, Braidhurst Industrial Estate, Motherwell, Lanarkshire, ML1 3ST Tel: (01698) 254579 Fax: (01698) 275372 *Kilt & skirt manufrs*

▶ Glenlake International Ltd, Unit F7 Lockside, Anchor Brook Industrial Park, Aldridge, Walsall, WS9 8BZ Tel: (01922) 458111 Fax: (01922) 458444

▶ Glenlossie Distillery, Birnie, Birnie, Elgin, Morayshire, IV30 8SS Tel: (01343) 862000 Fax: (01343) 862007 *Spirits retailer*

Glenmarco Ltd, 189 Headstone Lane, Harrow, Middlesex, HA2 6ND Tel: (020) 8421 4025 Fax: (020) 8421 3643 *Architectural ironmongers*

Glenmere Timber Co. Ltd, Hoptons Sawmill, Gores Lane, Market Harborough, Leicestershire, LE16 8AJ Tel: (01858) 466390 Fax: (01858) 462733 *Timber import merchants & agents*

Glenmore Foundry Ltd, 7 Pinfold Road, Thurmaston, Leicester, LE4 8AS Tel: 0116-269 7094 Fax: 0116-269 7411 *Non-ferrous metal casting manufrs*

Glenmore Shop, Glenmore, Aviemore, Inverness-Shire, PH22 1QU Tel: (01479) 861253 Fax: (01479) 861253 *Suppliers of sledges*

Glenmuir Ltd, Linnville Factory, 25-29 Delves Road, Lanark, ML11 9DX Tel: (01555) 662244 Fax: (01555) 665734 E-mail: admin@glenmuir.co.uk *Knitwear, embroidery & golf sportswear suppliers*

▶ Glenn Davidson Plant Ltd, Glendal, Corstorphine Road, Thornhill, Dumfriesshire, DG3 5NB Tel: (01848) 330839

Glennans Ltd, Dovefields, Dovefields Industrial Estate, Uttoxeter, Staffordshire, ST14 8HU Tel: (01889) 567338 Fax: (01889) 562701 E-mail: richard.thompson@glennans.co.uk Principal Export Areas: Worldwide *Glennans are producers of high quality snack foods, premium snacks, vegetable crisps, hand cook crisps, pan fried crisps, root vegetable crisps, gourmet snack foods for use in catering garnish.*

Glennfreight Services Ltd, 9 Enterprise Court, Metcalf Way, Crawley, West Sussex, RH11 7RW Tel: (01293) 437770 Fax: (01293) 437775 E-mail: info@glennfreight.co.uk *Air freight forwarders & same day couriers*

▶ Glennleigh Associates, 14 Bateman Street, London, W1D 3AG Tel: (020) 7434 2551 Fax: (020) 7437 2222

James Glennon Packaging Ltd, Upper Dunmurry Lane, 14 Kilwee Business Park, Dunmurry, Belfast, BT17 0HD Tel: (028) 9061 6677 Fax: (028) 9062 6477 *Sack & bag manufrs*

Gleno Industries Ltd, Mansfield Road, Bramley Vale, Chesterfield, Derbyshire, S44 5GA Tel: 01246 858224 Fax: 01246 858223 E-mail: scott.wall@coverworld.co.uk *Roofing & Cladding manufacturers.*

Allen Glenold Ltd, Glenold House, Crosby Road, Market Harborough, Leicestershire, LE16 9EE Tel: (01858) 467789 Fax: (01858) 432932 E-mail: sales@glenold.co.uk *Paper merchants & agents*

▶ Glenrothes Distillery, Burnside Street, Rothes, Aberlour, Banffshire, AB38 7AA Tel: (01340) 872300 Fax: (01340) 872172 *Distillery*

▶ Glenrothes Fabrications Ltd, Glen-Fab, Viewfield, Glenrothes, Fife, KY6 2RD Tel: (01592) 630128 Fax: (01592) 630128 *Metalworking & fabrication services*

Glenrothes Industrial Packing Ltd, 75-76 Whitecraigs Road, Glenrothes, Fife, KY6 2RX Tel: (01592) 771052 Fax: (01592) 620158 *Packing services & pallets manufrs & suppliers*

Glenroy Engineering Services Ltd, Albion Dockside Estate, Hanover Place, Bristol, BS1 6UT Tel: 0117-929 1450 Fax: 0117-925 1938 E-mail: glenroy@nascr.net *Subcontract precision engineers*

Glenroyd Mills Ltd, Occupation Lane, Pudsey, West Yorkshire, LS28 8HW Tel: 0113-256 5667 Fax: 0113-257 6859 E-mail: sales@glenroyd.com *Textile merchants & manufrs*

Glenshane Fashions, 6 Victoria Road, Londonderry, BT47 2AB Tel: (028) 7131 2343 Fax: (028) 7131 2307 E-mail: info@glenshanefashions.com *Clothing manufrs*

Glenshiel Manufacturing Co., 3 Seaview, Kyle, Ross-Shire, IV40 8AS Tel: (01599) 534857 Fax: (01599) 534757 E-mail: stan@glenshiel.co.uk *Motorcycle products manufrs*

▶ Glenside, Block 2 Unit 4 Bandeath Industrial Estate, Throsk, Stirling, FK7 7NP Tel: (01786) 816655 Fax: (01786) 816100 *Organic farming*

Glenside Commercial Interiors, Glenside House, Kitchener Road, High Wycombe, Buckinghamshire, HP11 2SW Tel: (01494) 529803 Fax: (01494) 452212 *Office designers fitters & partition contractors*

▶ Glenside Engineering, Unit 4, Springtown Industrial Estate, Springtown Road, Londonderry, BT48 0LY Tel: (028) 7137 1599 Fax: 028 71371599

▶ Glenside Recycling Ltd, Colliery, Coalpit Lane, Rugeley, Smethwick, West Midlands, B66 2JN Tel: (01889) 574045 Fax: 0121-565 0646 E-mail: mikekillett@glensiderecycling.com

Glenside Tractors Ltd, Millknowe, Campbeltown, Argyll, PA28 6NJ Tel: (01586) 553624 Fax: (01586) 554923 E-mail: glensidetractors@btinternet.com *Agricultural engineers & sales*

▶ Glenthorpe Contracts Ltd, Flat 2, 49 West Cliff Road, Bournemouth, BH4 8BA Tel: (01202) 767926 Fax: (01202) 767948 E-mail: glenthorpecontracts@f2s.com *Supply short & long term refrigerated vehicles*

Glenthorpe Engineering Co. Ltd, 95 Railway Road, Teddington, Middlesex, TW11 8TE Tel: (020) 8977 5433 Fax: (020) 8943 4993 *Swivel coupling manufrs*

Glentworth Precision Engineering Ltd, Molly Millars Bridge, Wokingham, Berkshire, RG41 2WY Tel: 0118-977 1955 Fax: 0118-977 2907 E-mail: john.darcy@glentworth.co.uk *Precision engineers*

Glenvarigill Honda, The Triangle, Perth, PH1 3GA Tel: (01738) 440066 Fax: (01738) 442666 *Vehicle retailers services*

Glenway Products Ltd, Newton Works, Harcourt Road, Wigston, Leicestershire, LE18 3SB Tel: 0116-281 1455 Fax: 0116-281 3389 *Wholesalers of sports trophy components*

Glenwood Bolts, 2 Lintech Court, The Grip, Linton, Cambridge, CB21 4XN Tel: (01223) 893931 Fax: (01223) 894122 E-mail: glenwoodbolts@talk21.com *Bolt & nut distributors*

Glenwood Printing, 4 Peter Baines Industrial Estate, Woods Lane, Derby, DE22 3UD Tel: (01332) 368674 Fax: (01332) 381444 E-mail: sales@glenwood-printing.co.uk *General printers*

Glevum Conservatories, Riverside Lane, Broadoak, Newnham, Gloucestershire, GL14 1JF Tel: (01452) 760000 Fax: (01452) 760001 E-mail: mail@glevum.co.uk *Double glazing installations services*

Glew & Whittaker, Eagle House, Cleveland Street, Hull, HU8 7AU Tel: (01482) 224202 Fax: (01482) 219644 *French polishing contractors & spray finishers*

▶ Glh Haulage, 220 Lynn Road, Broomhill, Downham Market, Norfolk, PE38 9QY Tel: 01366 383500 Fax: 01366 381267 E-mail: glhhaulage@hotmail.co.uk *Collections and deliveries throughout East Anglia, London, Cambs, Beds, Lincs and Northants. We have 3 VW LT35 vans that can carry 4 standard or 5 euro pallets up to 1250kg.*

▶ Glide Rite Products Ltd, Mill Lane, Passfield, Liphook, Hampshire, GU30 7RP Tel: (01428) 751711 Fax: (01428) 751677

Global, PO Box 101, Northampton, NN1 4BS Tel: (01604) 636531 Fax: (01604) 760656 E-mail: info@globalintelligence.ltd.uk *Corporate investigations services*

Global Access Technology Ltd, Unit 3a Beechwood, Lime Tree Way, Chineham, Basingstoke, Hampshire, RG24 8WA Tel: (01256) 374930 Fax: (01256) 374939 E-mail: info@aprimatic.co.uk *Automation warehouse for gates, garages & windows*

▶ Global Address Ltd, Venturers House, Prince St Roundabout, Bristol, BS1 4PB Tel: 0117-915 4018 Fax: 0117-915 4348 E-mail: sales@globaladdress.net *Address cleansing & verification software for data quality*

▶ Global Allianz UK Ltd, Trocall House, Wakering Road, Barking, Essex, IG11 8PD Tel: (020) 8507 3222 Fax: 0208 5073444 E-mail: ram@globalallianz.com *Ferrous and Non ferrous scrap trader worldwide,*Shredded metal Isri 211,HMS-OA grade,Brass honey,Copper,Aluminium scrap.**

Global Analysis, Tappers Building, Huddersfield Road, Mirfield, West Yorkshire, WF14 9DQ Tel: (01924) 499776 Fax: (01924) 499325 E-mail: user@globalanalysis.co.uk *Milk testing & food testing service providers*

▶ Global Automotive Recruitment, 28 Springbourne Court, Beckenham, Kent, BR3 5ED Tel: (0845) 330 9317 Fax: (0845) 330 9318 E-mail: info@garecruitment.com *Specialist automotive recruitment agency placing motor trade personnel in the UK, USA, Canada, Middle East, & Australia, full staffing solutions from trainees to general managers*

Global Blinds, 636 Mansfield Road, Nottingham, NG5 2GA Tel: 0115-985 8181 Fax: 0115-985 8181 *Blind manufrs*

Global Ceramic Materials Ltd, Milton Works, Leek New Road, Stoke-on-Trent, ST2 7EF Tel: (01782) 537297 Fax: (01782) 537867 E-mail: sales@gsb.net *Ceramic raw materials suppliers*

▶ Global Choices, Barkat House, 116-118 Finchley Road, London, NW3 5HT Tel: 0207 433 2501 Fax: 0207 435 1397 E-mail: info@globalchoices.co.uk *Work Experience, Volunteering, Internships, Tax Refunds, Travel Insurance, Discount Cards are among programmes and services we offer. Do it with Global Choices.*

Global Cleaning Supplies, Unit 86-87, John Wilson Business Park, Chestfield, Whitstable, Kent, CT5 3QT Tel: (01227) 266426 Fax: (01227) 770545 E-mail: gcs@global-cleaning-supplies.co.uk *Janitorial & cleaning supply services*

Global Communications, 9 Belfast Road, Bangor, County Down, BT20 3PN Tel: (028) 9145 7900 Fax: (028) 9145 7900 E-mail: info@global-mob.com *Communication*

Global Communications (UK) Ltd, Winterdale Manor, Southminster Road, Athorne, Chelmsford, CM3 6BX Tel: (01621) 743440 Fax: (01621) 743676 E-mail: info@globalcom.co.uk *Satellite communication equipment manufrs*

Global Cooling, Elimdene, Up Brooks, Clitheroe, Lancashire, BB7 1PL Tel: (01200) 428888 Fax: (01200) 444252 E-mail: submit@web-squad.com *Global Cooling Air Conditioning UK - Suppliers and installers of split type heat pumps and cooling only air conditioning systems in the uk. Self Install Kits and Training also offered, benefit from our experience.*

Global Direct, 2 Cartsdyke, Greenock, Renfrewshire, PA15 1DT Tel: (01475) 500011 Fax: (01475) 500022 E-mail: scotland@micsco.co.uk *Industrial suppliers*

Global Display Solutions Ltd, Fairfax House, Cottingley Business Park, Bingley, West Yorkshire, BD16 1PE Tel: (01274) 230150 Fax: (01274) 230144 E-mail: sales@gds.com *Sunlight readable display screen manufrs*

Global Displays Ltd, Global House, Berry Hill, Berry Hill Industrial Estate, Droitwich, Worcestershire, WR9 9RB Tel: (01905) 797978 Fax: (01905) 797919 E-mail: sales@globaldisplays.co.uk *International exhibition contractors*

▶ Global Distribution, Unit 4 Penketh Business Park, Cleveleys Road, Great Sankey, Warrington, WA5 2TJ Tel: (01925) 411441 Fax: 0151-210 2606

▶ Global Drying Systems Ltd, Parkhall Road, Longton, Stoke-on-Trent, ST3 5AT Tel: (01782) 370200 Fax: (01782) 370222 E-mail: neilbeckett@cobwebworld.co.uk *Dryers, Ovens, Refurbishment, Breakdown Service*

Global Engineering, Eagle Iron Works, Crawford Street, Rochdale, Lancashire, OL16 5NU Tel: (01706) 715757 Fax: (01706) 649969 E-mail: sales@golbaleng.co.uk *Precision, general engineers & toolmakers*

Global Engineering Services, Yew Tree Cott, Sampford Moor, Wellington, Somerset, TA21 9QL Tel: (0870) 7651508 Fax: (0870) 7652508 E-mail: mauricepinner@compuserve.com

Global Enterprises, The Old Stores, Penny Royal Road, Danbury, Chelmsford, CM3 4ED Tel: (01245) 226004 Fax: (01245) 225995 E-mail: enquiries@globalheatseal.com Sales Contact: S. Houlden *Heat sealing stainless steel band distributors*

Global Entertainments, PO Box 6945, ILKESTON, Derbyshire, DE7 5TG Tel: 0115-917 2767 Fax: 0115-917 4458 E-mail: global.ents@ntlworld.com *Booking the best in Entertainment Worldwide.**Tribute Bands, Party Bands, Big Bands, After Dinner Speakers, Cabaret Acts, Chart Acts etc etc.*

Global Equipment, 40 George Close, Canvey Island, Essex, SS8 9PU Tel: (01268) 699949 Fax: (01268) 699556 E-mail: info@plasticmachinery.net *Plastic industry & used equipment suppliers*

Global Exchange Services, 1-3 Station Road, Sunbury-On-Thames, Middlesex, TW16 6SU Tel: (01932) 776000 Fax: (01932) 776020 *Computer services* Also at: Kingston upon Thames

Global Executives Ltd, 18 Stoneleigh Court, Frimley, Camberley, Surrey, GU16 8XH Tel: (01276) 671535 Fax: (01276) 671536 E-mail: sales@globalexecutives.com *National & international interim management supplier*

Global Fire Equipment Ltd, Unit A4, Spectrum Business Estate, Anthonys Way, Medway City Estate, Rochester, Kent, ME2 4NP Tel: (01634) 716882 Fax: (01634) 711557 E-mail: martin@global-fire.co.uk *Fire alarm system distributors*

▶ Global Fire Supplies, 2, Old Town Station Business Park, Bridgnorth Road, Cleobury Mortimer, Kidderminster, Worcs, DY14 8SY Tel: (01299) 271548 Fax: (01299) 405542

Global Fire Systems Ltd, Global House, 15 The Triangle, NG2 Business Park, Queen's Drive, Nottingham, NG2 1AE Tel: (0870) 2208211 Fax: (0115) 9438999 E-mail: sales@globalfire.co.uk *Global Fire Systems Ltd are a market leader in providing quality products, solutions & services throughout the fire market place. *We design, supply, install, commission & maintain all forms of Fire & Security Systems throughout the UK, providing service to a diverse client range. It was established in 1999 by the current directors who are actively involved in the daily running. *Global's aim is to provide high levels of service, on time & every time thus achieving total customer satisfaction. Personal service is given, offering tailored packages to suit all areas of business. Constant review, & the performance ownership policy, ensures positive results for all clients. *We specialise in computer based graphics systems, intelligent automatic fire detection, radio detection systems, high sensitivity laser detection, gas extinguishing products, security solutions, emergency lighting products.*

▶ Global Fireworks Ltd, The Cross, Kirkgate, Sherburn in Elmet, Leeds, LS25 6BH Tel: (0870) 7668253 Fax: (0870) 7668293 E-mail: info@globalfireworks.co.uk *Fireworks Importer/Wholesaler*

Global Foodservice Equipment Ltd, Global House, 104-108 School Road, Tilehurst, Reading, RG31 5AX Tel: (0870) 6004333 Fax: (0870) 2434334 E-mail: sales@global-fse.co.uk *Global Foodservice Equipment is one of the largest independent national suppliers of Catering Equipment. With a range of over 15,000 products including Cutlery, Crockery, Glassware, Bar Equipment, Tableservice Equipment, Chafing Dishes & Fuel, Storage & Gastronorm Containers, Kitchen Utensils, Heavy Equipment & Furniture. With Offices in the South & North of England and a network of experienced field sales personnel we can offer a local & national service. All products are available online at www.globalfse.co.uk or simply call our sales office on 0870 600 4333 for advise or our free catalogue .*

Global Group plc, Park Lane, Wolverhampton, WV10 9QD Tel: (01902) 865714 Fax: (01902) 866316 *Meat wholesalers*

▶ Global Heating Services, 15 Wheeler Gate, Nottingham, NG1 2NA Tel: (0800) 2980692 Fax: (0871) 6616082 E-mail: globalheating@bulldoghome.com *Industrial & commercial heating engineers*

Global Hygiene Ltd, Unit 18, Ladford Fields Industrial Park, Seigford, Stafford, ST18 9QE Tel: (01785) 282900 Fax: (01785) 282222 *Hygiene & industrial suppliers*

Global Industries North West Ltd, 36 Arkwright Road, Astmoor Industrial Estate, Runcorn, Cheshire, WA7 1NU Tel: (01928) 577846 Fax: (01928) 560480 E-mail: info@globalindustries.co.uk *Locker suppliers manufacturers & refurbishing*

▶ Global Instrumentation Ltd, Unit 1080 Galley Drive, Sittingbourne Research Centre, Sittingbourne, Kent, ME9 8GA Tel: (0870) 3820001 Fax: (0870) 3820002 *Control engineers*

Global Instrumentation Ltd, Unit 1080 Galley Drive, Sittingbourne Research Centre, Sittingbourne, Kent, ME9 8GA Tel: (0870) 3820001 Fax: (0870) 3820002 E-mail: global@global-associates.co.uk *Instrument technicians & engineers*

▶ Global Insulation Ltd, Unit 12 Monksbridge Trading Estate, Outgang Lane, Dinnington, Sheffield, S25 3QZ Tel: (01909) 550850 Fax: (01909) 550974 E-mail: martyn@globalinsulate.co.uk *Cavity wall & loft insulation services*

Global Interiors Ltd, Broadway, Ilminster, Somerset, TA19 7ER Tel: (01460) 57700 Fax: 01460 52736 *Partitioning manufrs*

▶ Global Jointing Systems, Unit 7, Park Lane Industrial Estate, Corsham, Wiltshire, SN13 9LG Tel: (01249) 715566 Fax: (01249) 715533 E-mail: office@globalresins.co.uk *Manufacturer of cable joint kits tested & approved*

▶ Global Laser Ltd, Medallion Technology Centre, Cwmtillery Industrial Estate, Cwmtillery, Abertillery, Gwent, NP13 1LZ Tel: (01495) 212213 Fax: (01495) 214004 E-mail: davidb@globallasertech.com *Design & manufacture of laser modules*

Global Lifting Services, Silverburn Cresent, Bridge of Don Industrial Estate, Aberdeen, AB23 8EW Tel: (01224) 707585 Fax: (01224) 707646 *Lifting equipment sale & manufrs*

Global Link, Yew Tree House, Maerway Lane, Maer, Newcastle, Staffordshire, ST5 5EN Tel: (0870) 2201626 Fax: (01630) 647524 E-mail: sales@printingconsumables.com *Printing consumables service*

Global Logistics Systems Ltd, 448 Oakshot Place, Bamber Bridge, Preston, PR5 8AT Tel: (01772) 626400 Fax: (01772) 627251 Principal Export Areas: Worldwide *Freight forwarders*

Global M S I plc, Cannon Lane, Tonbridge, Kent, TN9 1PP Tel: (01732) 351358 Fax: (01732) 770563 E-mail: sales@global-msi.com *Garage forecourt canopy manufrs*

Global Machine Tools, Sudmeadow Road, Gloucester, GL2 5HG Tel: (01452) 526089 Fax: (01452) 307157 E-mail: mail@globalmachinetools.com *We supply high quality, branded machine tools to UK engineering and manufacturing companies as well as to the wider international industrial marketplace. *All in all, we prefer to stock the better built machines with names such as Chiron, Citizen, Daewoo, Hardinge, Hitachi Seiki, Makino, Matsuura Mori Seiki, Nakamura Okuma & Howa, Star and Tomos-Bechler.*

▶ Global Maintenance Ltd, Hinderton Court, Quarry Road, Neston, CH64 7UD Tel: 0151-353 8187

▶ Global Manufacturing Supplies Ltd, 9 Keel Row The Watermark, Gateshead, Tyne & Wear, NE11 9SX Tel: (01661) 836900 Fax: (01661) 836905 E-mail: info@gms-uk.com *Engineering Component supplier from China*

Global Maritime, Friars Bridge Court 41-45 Blackfriars Road, London, SE1 8NZ Tel: (020) 7922 8900 Fax: (020) 7922 8901 E-mail: gm@globalmaritime.com *Marine consultants & surveyors* Also at: Aberdeen

▶ Global Measurements & Control Ltd, Unit 17, Ford Lane, Ford, Arundel, West Sussex, BN18 0UZ Tel: (01243) 555277 Fax: (01243) 555177 E-mail: sales@globalltd.co.uk *Temperature monitoring system manufrs*

Global Military Supplies, Unit 2, Deben Way off Wilford Bridge Road, Woodbridge, Suffolk, IP12 1RS Tel: (01394) 611051 Fax: (01394) 388551 E-mail: info@globalmilitarysupplies.co.uk *Suppliers of personal military equipment & military supplies*

▶ Global Moving Solutions, Unit O2 Clyde Workshops, Fullarton Road, Glasgow East Investment Park, Glasgow, G32 8YL Tel: 0141-646 2700 Fax: 0141-646 2704

▶ Global Nutrition, 1 Furness Close, South Wootton, King's Lynn, Norfolk, PE30 3TR Tel: (01553) 671467 E-mail: kath@wellness4all.org.uk *Providing Weight Management, Sports Nutrition and Personal Care products from the Herbalife range. Personal consultation carried out to design individually tailored programmes.*

▶ Global Oilfield Supplies, Buntings Lane, Methwold, Thetford, Norfolk, IP26 4PR Tel: (01366) 727441 Fax: (01366) 727200 E-mail: paul@globaloilfieldsupplies.co.uk *Valves & gasket sales*

Global Orthopaedics UK Ltd, Units 5&6 Dragon Industrial Estate, Fitzherbert Road, Farlington, Portsmouth, PO6 1SQ Tel: (023) 9238 3366 Fax: (023) 9238 3355 E-mail: sales@globalorthopaedics.co.uk *Manufacturers & designers of orthopedic plate wires & screws*

Global Overstock Ltd, 27 Atwood Road, London, W6 0HX Tel: (0800) 0920363 Fax: (020) 8741 9935 E-mail: info@globaloverstock.com *Surplus or slow moving engineering stock*

▶ Global PA Services Ltd, Mayfair House, Heddon Street, London, W1B 4DA Tel: 0207 477 2543 Fax: 0207 477 2543 E-mail: globalpaservices@hotmail.com *International Personal Assistance and Concierge Services, including household and property management, personal shopper, luxury VIP assistance.*

Global Packaging Ltd, 9 Lockwood Way, Black Horse Lane, London, E17 5RB Tel: (020) 8531 3130 Fax: (020) 8503 2319 *Polythene bag & sack manufrs* Also at: London E17

▶ Global Packaging Sources Irm Ltd, 6 West Street, Ramsey, Isle of Man, IM8 1DB Tel: (01624) 812444 Fax: (01624) 812555 E-mail: sales@gpsiom.com *Distributors of all types of flexible packaging*

Global Power & Control Systems Ltd, Unit 3 Hill Farm Barns, School Road, Henley, Ipswich, IP6 0SA Tel: (01473) 785057 Fax: (01473) 785059 E-mail: sales@global-panels.co.uk *Electrical control panels manufrs*

▶ Global Rail Construction Ltd (GRCL), Unit 20, The I O Centre, Hearle Way, Hatfield, Hertfordshire, AL10 9EW Tel: (0870) 9904074 Fax: (0870) 9904075 E-mail: enquiries@grcl.co.uk *Providing signalling solutions to the railway industry.*

Global Recycling Solutions Ltd, Unit 2, Cook House, Brunel Drive, Newark, Nottinghamshire, NG24 2FB Tel: (0870) 7708540 Fax: (0870) 7708541 E-mail: sales@globalrecycling.eu *Agricultural machinery manufrs*

Global Refrigeration & Air Conditioning Co. Ltd, Unit 41, 3 Halifax Road, Metropolitan Centre, Greenford, Middlesex, UB6 8XU Tel: (020) 8575 7557 Fax: (020) 8566 6342 E-mail: enquiries@globalrefrigeration.co.uk *Air conditioning distributors or agents*

▶ Global Registrations Ltd, PO Box 911, Exeter, EX2 5NZ Tel: (01392) 207008 Fax: (01392) 250321 E-mail: info@globalreg.co.uk *Personalised & private number plates suppliers*

Global Robots, Unit 5 Beancroft Farm, Beancroft Road, Marston Moretaine, Bedford, MK43 0QE Tel: (01234) 766450 Fax: (01234) 766623 E-mail: tom@robotsltd.co.uk *We buy and sell used industrial robots and robotic equipment. We stock 6-axis machines by ABB, Kuka, Fanuc and Motoman. We have agents and prefered intergrators worldwide. We stock robot spares and can advise with programming, training and automation applications.*

Global Screw Co. Ltd, Business & Technology Centre, Eccles, Manchester, M30 0RJ Tel: 0161-787 3034 Fax: 0161-787 3112 *Screw distributors*

Global Security Shutters Ltd, 114 Liverpool Road, Kidsgrove, Stoke-On-Trent, ST7 4EH Tel: (07985) 307343 Fax: (01782) 783104 *Roller shutter doors sales repairs & manufrs*

▶ Global Show Management, St. Georges Lane, Ascot, Berkshire, SL5 7ET Tel: (01344) 636421 Fax: (01344) 624041

Global Signs & Engraving Ltd, Admiralty Road, Great Yarmouth, Norfolk, NR30 3PU Tel: (01493) 843300 Fax: (01493) 843340 E-mail: globalsigns@ukonline.co.uk *Sign engravers*

Global Software Publishing, Meadow Lane, St. Ives, Cambridgeshire, PE27 4LG Tel: (01480) 496666 Fax: (01480) 460206 E-mail: sales@gsp.cc *Computer software publishing & distribution*

▶ Global Source & Marketing Ltd, 4 Rookery Lane, Wymondham, Melton Mowbray, Leicestershire, LE14 2AU Tel: (01572) 787888 Fax: (01572) 787222 E-mail: richardchristie@onetel.com *Office supplies*

▶ Global Sporting Event, 29a Stamford New Road, Altrincham, Cheshire, WA14 1EB Tel: 0161-924 0069 Fax: 0161-929 5642 E-mail: anthony@seesportlive.co.uk *Welcome to Global Sporting Events Ltd, specialists in ticket only and Corporate Hospitality*to all sporting events worldwide. We specialise mostly in Football tickets to the English Premiership, *Spain''s La Liga and Italy''s Seria A. Tickets and full Hospitality packages are available to all FA Cup, *Champions League, Uefa Cup games and Finals, World Cup 2006 Qualifiers and Finals in Germany 2006, *6 Nations Rugby, F1 Grand Prix, Wimbledon, Winter Olympics 2006 and all major UK Concerts.*Global sporting Events Ltd is a privately owned ticket brokers who are not connected*with any Official Box Office, Club, Association, Arena or Stadium. We are an alternative to *ticket master uk, which means we don''t charge a fixed booking fee. On most occasions*we have to pay very high premiums to obtain "sold out" and "hard to get" tickets which*is reflected in the price we have to charge.**

▶ Global Storage Agency Ltd, Europarc Innovation Centre, Innovation Way, Grimsby, North East Lincolnshire, DN37 9TT Tel: (01472) 504439 Fax: (01472) 504438 E-mail: ajury@globalstorage.info *Bulk oil & chemical storage services*

Global System Computers North East, 24 John Street, Cullercoats, North Shields, Tyne & Wear, NE30 4PL Tel: 0191-252 4440 Fax: 0191-257 9057 E-mail: bkenyon@fsl.co.uk *Computer system manufrs*

▶ Global TCS Ltd, 29 Cargin Road, Toomebridge, Antrim, BT41 3NU Tel: (028) 7965 9990 Fax: 028796 50192 E-mail: info@globaltcs.com *Steel tube & hollow section*

▶ Global Tech Associates Limited, 2nd Floor, 145 - 157 St. John Street, London, EC1V 4PY Tel: 0207 7887717 Fax: 0870 7628453 *IT and Communications Equipment Reseller*

Global Technology Resource, 741 Oldham Road, Rochdale, Lancashire, OL16 4RH Tel: (01706) 651222 *Computer retailer*

Global Telecommunications Laboratories Ltd, Gladstone House, Gladstone Drive, Bristol, BS16 4RU Tel: 0117-987 0044 Fax: 0117-987 0055 E-mail: gtl@gtlabs.co.uk *Telephone development*

▶ Global Tiles, 115 High Street, Twerton, Bath, BA2 1DB Tel: (01225) 789261 Fax: (01225) 789261 *Ceramic tiles wholesalers & installers*

▶ Global Timber Frames, Global House, Crompton Close, Basildon, Essex, SS14 3AY Tel: (01268) 272550 Fax: (01268) 272554

Global Trace Heating Ltd, Unit 4, Penkridge Industrial Estate, Penkridge, Stafford, ST19 5NZ Tel: (01785) 712211 Fax: (01785) 711168 E-mail: sales@globaltrace.co.uk *Manufacturers of trace heating equipment*

▶ Global Training Ltd, 15 Ripley Crescent, Urmston, Manchester, M41 8PH Tel: (0800) 0730818 E-mail: infoman@globaltrainingltd.com *We are an accredited training organisation offering our services at very competive rates nationwide!! **Please see our website for more details***

▶ Global Training Ltd, 6 Hillside Avenue, Queenborough, Kent, ME11 5LE Tel: (0800) 0730818 E-mail: info@globaltrainingltd.com *We are an accredited training organisation offering our services at very competive rates nationwide!! **Please see our website for more details***

▶ Global Transport Services Ltd, 2 Horton Industrial Park, Horton Road, West Drayton, Middlesex, UB7 8JD Tel: (01895) 447888 Fax: (01895) 420258

Global Tube Fabrications, Navigation Road, Diglis Trading Estate, Worcester, WR5 3DE Tel: (01905) 764302 Fax: (01905) 764305 E-mail: info@globaltube.biz *Tube Bending services*

Global Vacuum Forming Ltd, Vedonis Works, Leicester Road, Lutterworth, Leicestershire, LE17 4HD Tel: (01455) 556891 Fax: (01455) 556099 E-mail: sales@gvf.co.uk *Plastics, vacuum formed products & packing*

▶ Global8, 29 Harley Street, London, W1G 9QR Tel: 0+32 70 704962 E-mail: info@global8.co.uk *Satellite positioning systems manufrs*

▶ Globalbagtag.Com, Everon Centre, 58 John Street, Filey, North Yorkshire, YO14 9NT Tel: (0870) 7657280 Fax: (0870) 7657281 E-mail: sales@globalbagtag.com *Luggage, baggage tags, lost luggage tracking & internet luggage protection*

▶ GlobalExpense Ltd, South Wing, 157 Edgware Road, London, W2 2HR Tel: 0207 2985757 E-mail: andy.bottrill@globalexpense.com *GlobalExpense provides an individually tailored expense management service for businesses across the UK. This enables your organisation to outsource your entire Expense process to an expert third party and benefit both from increased accuracy and reduced administration costs.**Founded in 1999, the GlobalExpense service was designed by a specialist team with expert knowledge of accounting and tax. Our services relieve clients of the high volume, low value time-consuming duty of processing employee expense claims and complying with the law. At the same time, our economies of scale allow us to pass on direct savings, improved management information and an excellent service to you and your employees.**

Globalsantafe Holding Company North Sea Ltd, Greenbank Crescent, East Tullos Industrial Estate, Aberdeen, AB12 3BG Tel: (01224) 404200 Fax: (01224) 404300 *Drilling contractor* Also at: Great Yarmouth

Globe Alarms Ltd, 10 Orient Road, Salford, M6 8LD Tel: 0161-787 7470 *Fitting security alarms*

Globe Apartments, 36 James Street, London, W1U 1AP Tel: (020) 7935 7531 Fax: (020) 7935 7531 E-mail: lettings@globeapt.com *Estate agents, property management & residential lettings*

Globe Electrical Co., 25 Crown Street, Ayr, KA8 8AG Tel: (01292) 269529 Fax: (01292) 611918 *Electrical supplies & wholesalers*

Globe Electronics (UK) Ltd, 19 Westmorland Drive, Warfield, Bracknell, Berkshire, RG42 3QJ Tel: (01344) 420775 Fax: (01344) 421194 E-mail: globeuk@btinternet.com *Active & emech component distributors, UK cosmo ferrite agent*

Globe Engineering, Everite Works, Derby Road, Widnes, Cheshire, WA8 9ND Tel: 0151-495 3759 *Fabrication & pipework engineers*

Globe Freight Ltd, 119 Turnpike Lane, London, N8 0DU Tel: (020) 8340 4395 Fax: (020) 8348 8036 *Freight forwarders*

Globe Heat Treatment Services Ltd, Unit 4 & 5 Venture Works, Charleywood Road, Knowsley Industrial Park, Liverpool, L33 7SG Tel: 0151-548 5281 Fax: 0151-548 3530 E-mail: sales@globeheat.com *Sales & manufacturers of heat treatment equipment*

Globe Ladders, Vincent Street, Birmingham, B12 9SG Tel: 0121-440 6636 Fax: 0121-440 5475 E-mail: info@globeladders.co.uk Principal Export Areas: Middle East & Africa *Wooden, aluminium & fibreglass ladders & steps distributors & manufrs*

Globe Organic Services, Unit S2 Olton Wharf, Richmond Road, Solihull, West Midlands, B92 7RN Tel: 0121-707 4120 Fax: 0121-707 4934 E-mail: globeorganic@btinternet.com *Garden machinery*

Globe Weatherwear, 59 Waterloo Road, Smethwick, West Midlands, B66 4JS Tel: 0121-558 7483 Fax: 0121-558 7483 *Clothing manufrs*

Globebyte Computer Consultants, Kingsgate Business Centre, 12-50 Kingsgate Road, Kingston upon Thames, Surrey, KT2 5AA Tel: (020) 8541 3426 Fax: (020) 8546 7248 E-mail: info@globebyte.com *E computer consultants*

▶ Globebyte Computer Consultants, Kingsgate Business Centre, 12-50 Kingsgate Road, Kingston upon Thames, Surrey, KT2 5AA Tel: (020) 8541 3426 Fax: (020) 8546 7248 E-mail: info@trigon-consultancy.com *Security recruitment services*

Globec UK, Unit 15 Shrivenham Hundred Business Park, Majors Road, Watchfield, Swindon, SN6 8TZ Tel: (01793) 780790 Fax: (01793) 780776 E-mail: info@globec.co.uk *Electronic components to major OEM's*

Globel Technologies Racing, Denmans Lane, Fontwell, Arundel, West Sussex, BN18 0SU Tel: (01243) 545000 Fax: (01243) 545050 *Precision engineers*

Globestock Engineering Ltd, Mile Oak Industrial Estate, Maesbury Road, Oswestry, Shropshire, SY10 8GA Tel: (01691) 654966 Fax: (01691) 661726 E-mail: info@globestock.co.uk *Fall & load arrestors manufrs*

▶ Globetech Cellar Services Ltd, 20a Wilson Street, Bristol, BS2 9HH Tel: 0117-924 8444 Fax: 0117-924 8555

Globetrekker, 25 High Street, Heritage Close, St. Albans, Hertfordshire, AL3 4EH Tel: (01727) 835999 Fax: (01727) 835777 E-mail: m.tearle@fsmail.net *Camping equipment distributors*

Globewatch Securities Ltd, 74 Bewsey Street, Warrington, WA2 7JE Tel: (01925) 232022 Fax: (01925) 232024 *CCTV suppliers to trade*

Globeweigh UK Ltd, Market Street, Tandragee, Craigavon, County Armagh, BT62 2BP Tel: (028) 3884 0714 Fax: (028) 3884 0420 E-mail: sales@globeweigh.com *Industrial weighing & services*

Globright Ltd, 530 Woodbridge Road, Ipswich, IP4 4PN Tel: (01473) 721561 Fax: (01473) 714069 E-mail: sales@globritephotoluminescent.com Principal Export Areas: Worldwide *Photo luminescent material manufrs*

Globus Ltd, 8 Lower Blackhill Industrial Estate, Lerwick, Shetland, ZE1 0DG Tel: (01595) 696222 Fax: (01595) 693771 *Protective clothing distributors*

Glomac Engineering Ltd, Little End Road, Eaton Socon, St. Neots, Cambridgeshire, PE19 8JH Tel: (01480) 215533 Fax: (01480) 405952 E-mail: sales@glomac.co.uk *Lifting equipment manufrs*

Glonav UK Ltd, March House, London Road, Daventry, Northamptonshire, NN11 4NR Tel: (01327) 701270 Fax: (01327) 701299 *Satellite positioning systems manufrs*

Glopac, Eddison Road, Hams Hall Distribution Park, Coleshill, Birmingham, B46 1AB Tel: (01675) 431000 Fax: (01675) 431066 E-mail: sales@glopac.co.uk *Polythene bag importers*

Gloria UK, Parkfield House, Manchester Old Road, Middleton, Manchester, M24 4DY Tel: 0161-654 2216 Fax: 0161-654 2253 E-mail: sales@gloria.co.uk *Fire extinguisher manufrs*

▶ Glorious Flowers & Balloons, Minters Lepe, Purbrook, Waterlooville, Portsmouth, PO7 5QS Tel: (023) 9243 3213 E-mail: info@gloriousfab.com *Balloon decoration & flowers and party supplies for weddings, parties and corporate events. Chair cover hire, balloon printing, customised banners, funeral tributes and florist delivery. We cover Hampshire, London and West Sussex, UK*

Glorywood Ltd, 401 Footscray Road, New Eltham, London, SE9 2DP Tel: (020) 8317 0429 Fax: (020) 8331 6509 E-mail: info@glorywood.com *Windows manufacturers, suppliers & installers*

▶ Glosrose Engineering Ltd, 33 Westcott Venture Park, Westcott, Aylesbury, Buckinghamshire, HP18 0XB Tel: (01296) 655969 Fax: (01296) 655859 *Forklift trucks suppliers*

Glossop Thermoplastics Ltd, Brookfield Industrial Estate, Glossop, Derbyshire, SK13 6JF Tel: (01457) 866111 Fax: (01457) 861802 E-mail: sales@gt-uk.com *Plastic mould toolmakers & injection moulding manufrs*

Glossop Whole Food, 8 Henry Street, Glossop, Derbyshire, SK13 8BW Tel: (01457) 865678 *Health foods retail services*

Gloster Photographic Services Ltd, 6 Francis Woodcock Trading Estate, Barton Street, Gloucester, GL1 4JD Tel: (01452) 413444 Fax: (01452) 413444 E-mail: glosterphoto@fsmail.net *Sign makers*

Gloucester Conpressed Air Specialists Ltd, Staunton Court Business Park, Ledbury Road, Staunton, Gloucester, GL19 3QS Tel: (01452) 840042 Fax: (01452) 840260 *Air compressor maintenance contractors*

Gloucester Heat Treatment Specialists Ltd, Unit 7 Venture Business Centre, Madleaze Road, Gloucester, GL1 5SJ Tel: (01452) 526434 Fax: (01452) 303680 E-mail: heat-treat@ghtl.co.uk *GLOUCESTER HEAT TREATMENT LIMITED, IS A MAJOR PROVIDER OF HEAT TREATMENT SERVICES FOR FERROUS AND NON FERROUS MATERIALS ,TO BOTH THE AEROSPACE AND COMMERCIAL INDUSTRIES WORLDWIDE. HAVING THE HIGHEST APPROVALS IN THE AEROSPACE WORLD, WHICH IS THE NADCAP AS7102 APPROVAL, FOR HEAT TREATING IN ACCORDANCE WITH SAE AEROSPACE STANDARD AS7003. WE RUN A FULLY APPROVED QUALITY SYSTEM, AND MANY INDIVIDUAL APPROVALS WITHIN THE AEROSPACE WORLD. SALT BATH HEAT TREATMENT IS A SPECIALITY, FROM CASE HARDENING TO THROUGH HARDENING. WE HAVE A STRESS RELEIVING TOP HAT FURNACE, QUALIFIED TO AEROSPACE STANDARDS WHICH IS CAPABLE OF TREATING LARGE LOADS OF PRECIPITATION STAINLESS STEELS IN BAR FORM, IN LENGTHS OF UPTO 11 FEET LONG. MOST IMPORTANT IS IF YOU REQUIRE QUALITY, QUICK TURN AROUND, AND A VERY COMPETITIVE PRICE, DO NOT HESITATE TO CONTACT US.*

▶ Gloucester Road Gear Boxes, Barton Manor, Midland Road, Bristol, BS2 0RL Tel: 0117-954 1424 Fax: 0117-941 1596 *Transmissions*

▶ Gloucestershire Hydroponics, Unit 4 Hope Mill Busines Centre, Hope Mill Lane, Brimscombe, Stroud, Gloucestershire, GL5 2SE Tel: (01453) 887481 Fax: (01453) 887481 E-mail: sales@gloucestershirehydroponics.com *Horticultural equipment & machinery suppliers*

▶ Gloucestershire Industrial Services, Unit 26 Severnside Trading Estate, Gloucester, GL2 5HS Tel: (01452) 520438 Fax: (01452) 300850

Gloucestershire Microwave Services, 2-4 Kingsholm Road, Gloucester, GL1 3AT Tel: (01452) 525070 Fax: (01452) 384095 E-mail: gloucestershiremicrowave@svcsfsnet.co.uk *Microwave oven repair services*

▶ Glover, Unit 13, Chivenor, Barnstaple, Devon, EX31 4AY Tel: (01271) 815321 Fax: (01271) 815321 *Furniture manufrs*

▶ J.A. Glover, Unit 701B, Tudor Estate, Abbey Road, London, NW10 7UY Tel: (020) 8961 1666 Fax: (020) 8961 7666 *Ventilation equipment manufrs*

Glover J Agricultural Contractor, Hollies Farm, Ashbourne, Derbyshire, DE6 2FF Tel: (01889) 590351 Fax: (01889) 590351 *Agricultural engineering services*

Alwyn Gloves, Crown East, Rushwick, Worcester, WR2 5TU Tel: (01905) 425624 Fax: (01905) 425624 *Leather dress glove manufrs*

▶ The Glow Company UK Ltd, The Light House 17 Wroot Road, Finningley, Doncaster, South Yorkshire, DN9 3DN Tel: (01302) 771340 Fax: (01302) 771969 *Glow sticks light up novelties & glow in the dark party supplies*

Glowbar Supplies & Power Tools Ltd, 56 Baxters Lane, St. Helens, Merseyside, WA9 3ND Tel: (01744) 816142 Fax: (01744) 816794 E-mail: sales@glowbar.co.uk *Power tool suppliers*

Glowbird Computing Ltd, 157 Alma St, Abertillery, Gwent, NP13 1QD Tel: (01495) 212223 *Pc sales & contract programming*

GLP Glass Fibre Mnfrs, 66 Arundel Road, Worthing, West Sussex, BN13 3EL Tel: (01903) 267249 Fax: (01903) 267249 *Glass fibre manufrs*

▶ Glue Ltd, Windsor House, Spittal Street, Marlow, Buckinghamshire, SL7 3HJ Tel: (01628) 481553 Fax: (01628) 481579 E-mail: sales@glueltd.com *IT consultants*

▶ Glue2 Ltd, Greystones, Front Street, Chedzoy, Bridgwater, Somerset, TA7 8RE Tel: (01278) 439152 Fax: (01278) 439152 *Commercial &industrial software*

Gluegunsdirect.Com Ltd, Regent House, Regent Street, Oldham, OL1 3TZ Tel: 0161-627 1001 Fax: 0161-627 5072 E-mail: sales@gluegunsdirect.com *Glue guns & applicators & adhesives distributors*

▶ Gluemart Ltd, Robins Farm, Matson Lane, Matson, Gloucester, GL4 6DZ Tel: (01452) 423883 Fax: (01452) 308229 E-mail: sales@gluemart.co.uk *Glue & sealant manufacturers & distributors*

Gluten Free Foods Ltd, Unit 270 Centennial Park, Centennial Avenue, Elstree, Borehamwood, Hertfordshire, WD6 3SS Tel: (020) 8953 4444 Fax: (020) 8953 8285 E-mail: info@glutenfree-foods.co.uk *Gluten free food distributors*

▶ Gluten Free Foods Direct, PO Box 156, Selby, North Yorkshire, YO8 6WA Tel: (01757) 630725 Fax: (01757) 630725 E-mail: admin@glutenfreefoodsdirect.co.uk *We specialise in the supply and mail order of Gluten and Wheat free foods. We currently have over a 140 products listed ranging from breakfast cereals to pastas and cakes and biscuits. We*

continued

offer a secure online payment facility and we can deliver directly to any address within the UK

Glycar Computing, 3 Rushton Road, Cheadle Hulme, Cheadle, Cheshire, SK8 6NS Tel: 0161-355 3052 Fax: 0161-355 3052 E-mail: glycar@aol.com *Computer programmers*

Glyn Thomas, Hendy Uchaf Farm, The Werm, Gowerton, Swansea, SA4 3NA Tel: (01792) 873241 Fax: (01792) 873989 *Engineers*

Glyn V Thomas, Church View, Mathry, Haverfordwest, Dyfed, SA62 5HA Tel: (01348) 831391 Fax: (01348) 831389 *Agricultural engineers*

Glyn Webb Group Ltd, Old Darby House, Derker Street, Oldham, OL1 3XF Tel: 0161-6214500 Fax: 0161-621 4501 E-mail: contactus@glynwebb.co.uk *DIY wholesalers*

Glynderi Pottery, Sennybridge, Brecon, Powys, LD3 8TS Tel: (01874) 636564 *Pottery manufacturers*

Glyngary Joinery Ltd, Unit H2, Risley, Warrington, WA3 6BL Tel: (01925) 763836 Fax: (01925) 762388 E-mail: sales@glyngary.co.uk *Window & door manufrs*

Glynn Valley, Station Road, Liskeard, Cornwall, PL14 4DA Tel: (01579) 345677 Fax: (01579) 345677 E-mail: sales@glynnvalley.com *Chef's clothing manufrs*

Glynnway Engineering & Welding Ltd, Salop Street, Bilston, West Midlands, WV14 0TQ Tel: (01902) 495701 Fax: (01902) 497702 E-mail: sales@glynnway.co.uk *Precision & production machinists service*

Glyns Collections, 26 Blackfriars Street, Salford, M3 5BQ Tel: 0161-834 7581 Fax: 0161-834 7581 E-mail: martcgg@aol.com *Fur & leather garment manufrs* Also at: Swansea

▶ Glynwed Pipe Systems Ltd, St. Peters Road, Huntingdon, Cambridgeshire, PE29 7DA Tel: (01480 52121 Fax: (01480) 450430 E-mail: enquiries@gpsuk.com *Polyethylene pipe manufrs*

▶ GM Commercial Ltd, PO Box 14, Worcester, WR8 0YD Tel: (01684) 592836 Fax: (07050) 500152 E-mail: gmai@gmcommercial.co.uk *Sales and marketing agency for FMCG and industrial food products. Sales consulting, key account management and export planning*

Gmac Commercial Finance Plc, Sovereign House, Church St, Brighton, BN1 3WX Tel: (01273) 864069 Fax: (01273) 771501 E-mail: info@gmaccf.co.uk *Factoring services*

▶ Gmap Consulting, 1 Park Lane, Leeds, LS3 1EP Tel: 0113-242 4334 Fax: 0113-242 4554 E-mail: info@gmap.com *GMAP Consulting specialise in advanced GIS software, business modelling and strategic network planning solutions and consultancy services for some of the world's largest global organisations.*

▶ GMB Photography, 127a High Street, Barkingside, Ilford, Essex, IG6 2AR Tel: (020) 8551 6885 E-mail: info@gmbphotography.co.uk *Specialising in Wedding and Portrait photography*

▶ GMC Transport Ltd, 12 Lansdowne Road, Tilbury, Essex, RM18 7QB Tel: (01375) 851607 Fax: (01375) 851607

▶ GMF Bradford, Bowling Ironworks, Bowling Back Lane, Bradford, West Yorkshire, BD4 8YY Tel: (01274) 306830 Fax: (01274) 728679

GMF Equipment Ltd, 9A High Street, Kegworth, Derby, DE74 2DA Tel: (01509) 673656 Fax: (01509) 674729 E-mail: sales@gmfequipment.co.uk *Industrial heating element distributors*

▶ GMK Ltd, Concorde Way, Fareham, Hampshire, PO15 5RL Tel: (01489) 579999 Fax: (01489) 579950 *Guns distributors*

▶ GML Design Engineering Ltd., Cutting House, Pampisford Road, Abington, Cambridge, CB1 6AH Tel: 01223 897905

GML International Ltd, Knighton House, 56 Mortimer Street, London, W1W 7RT Tel: (020) 7580 8588 Fax: (020) 7580 8688 E-mail: info@gml.net *Financial advisors*

GMS, 175 Booth Street, Birmingham, B21 0NU Tel: 0121-551 5440 Fax: 0121-554 5344 E-mail: enquiries@gmspolymer.co.uk *Manufacturers of precision rubber mouldings, gaskets & washer cutting*

GMS Joinery, 6a Denmark Terrace, Fortis Green, London, N2 9HG Tel: (020) 8883 7462 E-mail: graham.gms@virgin.net *Windows, doors & stairs manufrs*

▶ GMS Photography, 24 Hannington Road, Bournemouth, BH7 6JT Tel: (01202) 565500 E-mail: info@gmsfoto.com *GMS Photography offers a personal wedding photography service creating a distinctive and unique memory of your day.*I will photograph your wedding in a creative reportage style of photography.*

▶ GMS Thermal Products, Glover Centre, Egmont Street, Mossley, Ashton-under-Lyne, Lancashire, OL5 9PY Tel: (01457) 835700 Fax: (01457) 832700 E-mail: sales@gmsthermol.co.uk *Heat exchanger services*

GN Great Nordic UK Ltd, Runnymede House, 96-97 High Street, Egham, Surrey, TW20 9HQ Tel: (01784) 220140 Fax: (01784) 220144 *Telecommunication headsets*

▶ GnD Creations, 6 Peterborough Rd, Whittlesey, Peterborough, PE7 1NJ Tel: 01733 206520 E-mail: design@gndcreations.com *We can offer a broad range of design skills, marketing skills, promotional ideas and can create a lasting identity for you. Please take a moment to browse through our various sections to see other companies that have already benefited.*

▶ GNG Group, Units 60/70 BMK Industrial Estate, Wakefield Road, Liversedge, West Yorkshire, WF15 6BS Tel: (01924) 400501 Fax: (01924) 408541 E-mail: sara@gng-group.co.uk *Foam converters*

GNT Engineering, Golden Triangle Industrial Estate, Harrison Street, Widnes, Cheshire, WA8 8TN Tel: 0151-420 3420 Fax: 0151-423 1579 E-mail: geoff@gntfab.fsnet.co.uk *Specialist welding & aluminium casting repairs*

The Go Betweens Couriers Ltd, Panther House, 38 Mount Pleasant, London, WC1X 0AN Tel: (020) 7278 1000 Fax: (020) 7278 1100 *Courier services*

Go Beyond, Oxford Street, Castleford, West Yorkshire, WF10 5RQ Tel: (01977) 710222 Fax: (01977) 710255 E-mail: sales@gobeyond.co.uk *Clothing manufrs*

Go Data, Unity Ct, 431 Meanwood Rd, Leeds, LS7 2LL Tel: 0113-217 9990 Fax: 0113 2179991 *Computer software developer*

Go Go Cobblers, 474 Bromley Road, Bromley, BR1 4PB Tel: (020) 8697 1509 Fax: (020) 8697 1509 *Trophy engravers services*

▶ GO HAVEN LTD, 72A WESTBOURNE RD, HUDDERSFIELD, HD1 4LE Tel: 01484 544300 E-mail: enquire@gohaven.com *"Make Moving Simple"*"Go Haven provide a specialist service from lettings and management of Residential & Commercial properties to advice on buy-to-let investments. The choice of accommodation ranges from contemporary apartments to suburban homes throughout Huddersfield and the surrounding area.**With competitive fees, flexible choice of services and experience of the rental sector; we offer professional services at a more friendly level. Our focus is to ensure that the experience of letting or renting a property is as straightforward as possible.***At Go Haven we understand that tenants lead busy lives so we're flexible, we work around you and can arrange viewings and valuations upto 8pm, 7 days a week.*

Go Hire Access Ltd, 6 Droicon Industrial Estate, Portway Road, Rowley Regis, West Midlands, B65 9BY Tel: 0121-559 0660 Fax: 0121-559 0770 E-mail: dudley@gohireaccess.co.uk *Access equipment hire*

Go Industry P.L.C., New London Bridge House, 25 London Bridge Street, London, SE1 9BQ Tel: (020) 7098 3700 Fax: (020) 7098 3795 E-mail: lucy.moran@goindustry.com *Industrial consultants, auctioneers & valuers*

▶ Go Interiors, 3 Elizabeth Trading Estate, Juno Way, London, SE14 5RW Tel: (020) 8469 3716 Fax: (020) 8469 0037 E-mail: sales@gointeriors.co.uk *Suspended ceilings & dry lining manufrs*

Go Internet Ltd, 36 Gloucester Avenue, London, NW1 7BB Tel: (020) 7419 0001 E-mail: jerry@go.co.uk *Web site design services*

Go Jo Industries Europe Ltd, 15 Avant Business Centre, Bletchley, Milton Keynes, MK1 1DL Tel: (01908) 370757 Fax: (01908) 370797 *Hand cleansing product manufrs*

▶ Go Labels International Co. Ltd, Albion Park, Warrington Road, Glazebury, Warrington, WA3 5PG Tel: (01925) 763091 Fax: (01925) 765741 E-mail: email@golabels.co.uk *Quality self adhesive label manufrs*

▶ Go Plant, Unit 14 Parham Drive, Eastleigh, Hampshire, SO50 4NU Tel: (023) 8061 2727 Fax: (023) 8061 1212 E-mail: sales@gpl-hire.co.uk

▶ Go (UK) Ltd, 28a The Market Place, Melbourne, Derby, DE73 1DS Tel: 0870 7562542 Fax: 0870 7562544 E-mail: freightspeed2@hotmail.com *High pressure washing facilties, delivered by fully self contained units and operated by professionally trained staff. Each van, none more than 18 months old, comes fully equipped with 600-00 litre water tanks, diesel powered hot/cold wash pressure unit. And detergents, (bio-degrable), for all applications.*

▶ Go2Devon, 21 Meadow Court, Ballasalla, Isle of Man, IM9 2DP Tel: (01624) 823768 E-mail: info-fountain@manx.net *New internet Pixel advertising site for businesses and services of Devon*

▶ GoAfrica, 34 St. Barnabas Street, Wellingborough, Northamptonshire, NN8 3HB Tel: (0845) 6447984 E-mail: gwen@goafrica.co.uk *The largest online shopping centre for furniture and furnishings from Africa. Including stunning accessories and prints.*

▶ Goaters Ltd, 86A North Sherwood Street, Nottingham, NG1 4EE Tel: 0115-941 9746

Gobur Caravans Ltd, Peacock Way, Melton Constable, Norfolk, NR24 2BY Tel: (01263) 860031 Fax: (01263) 861494 E-mail: sales@goburcaravans.co.uk *Folding caravans*

▶ John Gocher Computing, St Clair, Rouge Huis Avenue, St. Peter Port, Guernsey, GY1 1RX Tel: (01481) 724778 E-mail: john@gocher.co.uk *Bespoke computer software & application training*

Gochers Laundry Ltd, Alma Street, Lancing, West Sussex, BN15 8AX Tel: (01903) 753615 Fax: (01903) 763725 *Commercial laundry*

▶ GoCruise South, 46 The Crescent, Eastleigh, Hampshire, SO50 9BR Tel: 02380 392 515 E-mail: karen@gocruisedirect.co.uk *Are you thinking of booking a cruise and don""t know where to start? Are you looking advice that goes beyond what""s in the brochure? Are you looking to book with people who treat you like a valued customer, and offer a personal service, not a call centre? Are you part of a group that would love a themed cruise based on your interests? Are you planning a honeymoon or a Hen and Stag night, or would you like to get married on a cruise ship? If you answer yes to any of these, call GoCruise South for a friendly professional service for all of your travel needs. Thinking about how to reward your sales team performance? Cruise presentation evening's available, home visits on request, clubs and groups or association presentations. **Would you buy a home without getting a survey? No! Why book your cruise this way, call GoCruise South today?**Our aim is to make happy customers, who want to book with us again, and who more importantly trust us! **

Goddard & Co 1992 Ltd, Copley Mill, Demesne Drive, St. Pauls Trading Estate, Stalybridge, Cheshire, SK15 2QF Tel: 0161-304 9690 Fax: 0161-304 9694 E-mail: goddardco1992@btinternet.com *Structural & general engineers*

▶ Goddard C H & Co Cartons Ltd, Unit 1-2 Church Trading Estate, Slade Green Road, Erith, Kent, DA8 2JA Tel: (01322) 358940 Fax: (01322) 358949 E-mail: info@chgoddard.com *Packaging equipment manufrs*

Goddard Engineering Ltd, The Workshop, Rumbolds Farm, Plaistow, Billingshurst, West Sussex, RH14 0PZ Tel: (01403) 871144 Fax: (01403) 871134 *Metalwork welding, engineers & fabricators*

Nigel Goddard Ltd, The Barn, Little Blounce, South Warnborough, Hook, Hampshire, RG29 1RX Tel: (01256) 861900 Fax: (01256) 861900 E-mail: nigelgoddardltd@yahoo.co.uk *Playground equipment install & manufrs*

Goddard Warehousing Ltd, Compton House, Furnace Lane, Finedon, Wellingborough, Northamptonshire, NN9 5NY Tel: (01536) 726060 Fax: (01536) 726006 E-mail: admin@goddardwarehousing.com *Warehousing & haulage contractors*

John Godden, Forge Lane, Stoke-on-Trent, ST1 5NP Tel: (01782) 204224 Fax: (01782) 283502 E-mail: stoke@rexelsenate.co.uk *Electrical engineers & wholesalers* Also at: Salford

▶ Godfrey Davis Contract Hire Ltd, Tryford House, High Street, Bushey, WD23 3XX Tel: (020) 8950 0950 Fax: (020) 8950 6145

▶ Godfrey & Hicks Builders Ltd, 109 Fordham Road, Snailwell, Newmarket, Suffolk, CB8 7NB Tel: (01638) 721900 Fax: (01638) 720010

Godfrey Insulations Ltd, Siddons Factory Estate, Howard Street, West Bromwich, West Midlands, B70 0SZ Tel: 0121-556 0011 Fax: 0121-556 9553 *Washer & gaskets manufrs*

M.G. Godfrey & Co. Ltd, 174a Perry Vale, London, Greater London, SE23 2LR Tel: 020 82914168 *Ventilating ducting manufrs*

Godfrey Sports, Abbeyfield Road, Nottingham, NG7 2SZ Tel: 0115-986 4600 Fax: 0115-986 2018 E-mail: sales@godfrey.co.uk *Sportswear manufrs*

Godfrey Syrett Ltd, Littleburn Industrial Estate, Langley Moor, Durham, DH7 8HE Tel: 0191-268 1010 Fax: 0191-378 1660 E-mail: sales@godfreysyrett.co.uk *Design & manufactures office & leisure furniture*

Godfreys Technical Textiles, Arrol Road, Wester Gourdie Industrial Estate, Dundee, DD2 4TH Tel: (01382) 618499 Fax: (01382) 618484 E-mail: sales@godfreysofdundee.co.uk *Polypropylene & jute goods manufrs*

▶ go-displays.co.uk, Welbeck Way, Peterborough, PE2 7WH Tel: (01733) 232000 Fax: (01733) 391825 E-mail: enquiries@go-displays.co.uk *Display boards & signs manufrs*

▶ Godiva Confectionery Mnfrs, 141 Regent Street, London, W1B 4JA Tel: (020) 7734 8113 Fax: (020) 7287 2518 *Chocolate manufrs*

Godiva Guns (Coventry), 191 Canley Road, Coventry, CV5 6AS Tel: (024) 7667 6077 Fax: (024) 7667 6077 E-mail: edward.braso@btopenworld.com *Guns, bows, cross bows retailer*

Godiva Imaging Ltd, Little Heath Industrial Estate, Old Church Road, Coventry, CV6 7ND Tel: (024) 7663 7192 Fax: (024) 7663 7192 *Digital imaging suppliers, to specification*

Godlingston Manor Springs Ltd, Godlingston Manor, Washpond Lane, Swanage, Dorset, BH19 3DJ Tel: (01929) 422910 Fax: (01929) 427974 *Manufrs & distributors of bottled water*

John Godrich, Pellow House, Old Street, Ludlow, Shropshire, SY8 1NU Tel: (01584) 873153 Fax: (01584) 872424 E-mail: johngodrich@johngodrich.co.uk *Corrosion test equipment & mixer manufrs*

Godshaer Herbalist, The Old Stables, Ducking Stool Lane, Christchurch, Dorset, BH23 1DS Tel: (01202) 488122 Fax: (01202) 488122 E-mail: alanhopking@goshaer.co.uk *Herbalist - Western & Chinese*

Godwin, Wick Farm, Luckington, Chippenham, Wiltshire, SN14 6PW Tel: (07754) 726553 Fax: (01454) 238019 *Farming contractors*

Godwin Pumps Ltd, Quenington, Cirencester, Gloucestershire, GL7 5BX Tel: (01285) 750271 Fax: (01285) 750352 E-mail: sales@godwinpumps.co.uk *Engines, pumps & related equipment*

▶ Godwin Transport, Central Way, Feltham, Middlesex, TW14 0UQ Tel: (020) 8844 2121

▶ Going Organic, Ware, Hertfordshire, SG12 Tel: (01920) 484856 E-mail: info@goingorganic.co.uk *A wide variety of organic produce can now be part of your shopping list without the hassle of choosing from the small selection available in the shops.*

▶ Going Pottie, Cathedral Street, Dunkeld, Perthshire, PH8 0AW Tel: (01350) 728044 *Pottery*

▶ Going Potty, 56b North Parade, Matlock Bath, Matlock, Derbyshire, DE4 3NS Tel: (01629) 581816 *Ceramic studio*

Golborne Joinery, Queen Street Saw Mill, Golborne, Warrington, WA3 3AF Tel: (01942) 719170 Fax: (01942) 717982 *Joinery manufrs*

Golco Automation Systems, Unit 323-325, Hartlebury Trading Estate, Hartlebury, Kidderminster, Worcestershire, DY10 4JB Tel: (01299) 253009 Fax: (01299) 253013 E-mail: sales@golco.co.uk *Control systems & system integration*

Golconda, Links House, Southglade Business Park, Hucknall Road, Nottingham, NG5 9RA Tel: 0115-977 1101 Fax: 0115-977 0047 E-mail: golconda@golconda.co.uk *Process control systems designers*

Gold Alice Ltd, 467 Dudley Road, Wolverhampton, WV2 3AF Tel: (01902) 456152 Fax: (01902) 456522 *Jewellery repairers & manufrs*

Gold Bros Ltd, Arches Abc, 408 Ellingfort Road, London, E8 3PA Tel: (020) 8985 7926 Fax: (020) 9898 5729 E-mail: info@goldbros.co.uk *Display wire equipment, fittings, accessories & stand manufrs*

Gold Chip Computer Systems Ltd, 45 Newcastle Road, Sunderland, SR5 1JB Tel: 0191-549 4477 Fax: 0191-549 5577 E-mail: sales@goldchip-uk.com *Computer sales*

Gold Connections Ltd, 15 Key Hill, Hockley, Birmingham, B18 5PB Tel: 0121-554 7222 Fax: 0121-554 8533 *Jewellery manufrs*

Gold Directors, 8 School Street, Wolverhampton, WV1 4LR Tel: (01902) 425777 *Jewellery manufrs*

Gold Investments Ltd, 88 Gracechurch Street, London, EC3V 0DN Tel: (020) 7283 7752 Fax: (020) 7283 7754 E-mail: info@goldinvestments.co.uk *Bullion dealers.*

Gold Key Media, 53-54 Brook's Mews, London, W1K 4EF Tel: (020) 7491 4065 Fax: (08708) 890318 E-mail: duncan@gkml.co.uk *Gold Key Media market and distribute over 30 million newspapers and magazines a year. We supply the finest magazines to the leisure and travel industry. We can develop targeted circulation solutions for your marketing and advertising departments, helping develop brand awareness in core markets. We also offer a comprehensive and competitive distribution service across the UK.****

▶ Gold Medal (Romsey) Ltd, Unit 25, Romsey Industrial Estate, Greatbridge Road, Romsey, Hampshire, SO51 0HR Tel: (01794) 519933 Fax: (01794) 519991 E-mail: information@goldmedalco.com *Hand tool distribution*

▶ Gold Octopus Software, Liberty Barn, Illand, Launceston, Cornwall, PL15 7LS Tel: (01566) 782221 Fax: (01566) 782090

Gold Star Construction Co. Ltd, Smithfield, Melton Road, Melton, Woodbridge, Suffolk, IP12 1NG Tel: (01394) 383056 Fax: (01394) 385898 *Building contractors*

Gold Star Soft Drinks, 4 Abbots Close, Lee Mill Industrial Estate, Ivybridge, Devon, PL21 9GA Tel: (01752) 690051 Fax: (01752) 691147 E-mail: goldstardrinks@btinternet.com *Soft drink manufrs*

▶ Gold Star Transport Ltd, Fenn Corner, St. Mary Hoo, Rochester, Kent, ME3 8RF Tel: (01634) 270061 Fax: (01634) 270075

Gold (UK) Scanning Systems Ltd, 12a Pimlico Road, Runcorn, Cheshire, WA7 4US Tel: (01928) 500505 Fax: (01928) 500242 E-mail: golduk@btconnect.com *Cash register epos distributors*

Gold & Wassall (Hinges) Ltd, Castle Works, Lichfield Road Industrial Estate, Tamworth, Staffordshire, B79 7TH Tel: (01827) 63391 Fax: (01827) 310819 E-mail: enquiries@goldwassallhinges.co.uk *Gold & Wassall are leading manufacturers and developers of Hinges, including special Purpose Hinges, continuous (piano) hinges, butt hinges, hinges, continuous, brass, hinges butt, stainless steel, hinges, door, hinges, lift off, stainless steel, hinges lift off, stainless steel, hinges, backflap, steel, sherardised, hinges backflap, hinges, heavy duty backflap*

Gold Workshop, Printing Office Street, Doncaster, South Yorkshire, DN1 1TR Tel: (01302) 325929 *Jewellery manufrs*

Goldace Industries, Unit 17 Harmill Industrial Estate, Grovebury Road, Leighton Buzzard, Bedfordshire, LU7 4FF Tel: (01525) 851815 Fax: (01525) 852484 E-mail: info@goldaceindustries.com *Mechanical building service pipe work contractors*

Goldburn Engineering Co. Ltd, Unit 12, Uddens Trading Estate, Wimborne, Dorset, BH21 7LL Tel: (01202) 893100 Fax: (01202) 861666 *Precision engineers*

Goldcraft Products, 117 Vyse Street, Hockley, Birmingham, B18 6LP Tel: 0121-236 8270 Fax: 0121-693 8353 *Jewellers*

Goldcrest Adhesive Products Ltd, Unit A, Telford Road, Bicester, Oxfordshire, OX26 4LD Tel: (01869) 243201 Fax: (01869) 244734 E-mail: sales@adhesivelabels.co.uk *Label printers*

Goldcrest Computer Services Ltd, 12 Vermont Place, Tongwell, Milton Keynes, MK15 8JQ Tel: (01908) 211330 Fax: (01908) 211326 E-mail: sales@goldcrest-uk.com *Computer software publishers*

Goldcrest Engineering Ltd, 1 Glebe Close, Swinton, Mexborough, South Yorkshire, S64 8LN Tel: (01709) 577144 Fax: (01709) 577144 *Production engineering services*

Goldcrest Films International Ltd, 65-66 Dean Street, London, W1D 4PL Tel: (020) 7437 8696 Fax: (020) 7437 4448 E-mail: mail@goldcrestfilms.com *Film producers*

▶ Golden Arrow Electronics, 40 Salterns Way, Poole, Dorset, BH14 8JR Tel: (01202) 707007 Fax: (01202) 701155 E-mail: sales@mesltd.co.uk

Golden Castle Caravans Ltd, Cheltenham Road East, Gloucester, GL2 9QL Tel: (01452) 713311 Fax: (01452) 856538 E-mail: info@goldencastle.co.uk *Caravan distributors*

Golden Cow, 25-29 Artabrackagh Road, Portadown, Craigavon, County Armagh, BT62 4HB Tel: (028) 3833 8411 Fax: (028) 3835 0292 *Dairy produce manufrs*

Golden Eye, 150 Huish, Yeovil, Somerset, BA20 1BN Tel: (01935) 478290 *Jewellery manufrs*

Golden Finishes Ltd, 4 Malvern Drive, Llanishen, Cardiff, CF14 5DR Tel: (029) 2075 5733 Fax: (029) 2076 3993 E-mail: gfinishes@aol.com *Sewing services to the trade*

▶ Golden Glen, Unit 1 Lissue Industrial Estate, Lisburn, County Antrim, BT28 2GG Tel: (028) 9262 2336

Golden Hamper Ltd, 19 Queen Street, Seaton, Devon, EX12 2NY Tel: (01297) 21076 Fax: (01297) 21076 E-mail: seatonhealthshop@aol.com *Buyers of retail health food & vitamin supplements*

Golden Larch Fencing, Ringwood Road, Bartley, Southampton, SO40 7LT Tel: (023) 8081 3157 Fax: (023) 8081 2774 E-mail: sales@rfgiddings.com *Fencing manufrs*

Golden Night Beds Co. Ltd, Albion Mills, Bradford Road, Dewsbury, West Yorkshire, WF13 2HD Tel: (01924) 469000 Fax: (01924) 468899 *Beds supply & buyers*

Golden Promotions Ltd, Chartwell, Hundred End Lane, Hundred End, Preston, PR4 6XL Tel: (01772) 815931 Fax: (01772) 815097 E-mail: george@goldenpromotions.co.uk *Sun bed services*

Golden River Traffic Ltd, Talisman Road, Bicester, Oxfordshire, OX26 6HR Tel: (01869) 362800 Fax: (01869) 246858 E-mail: sales@goldenriver.com *Traffic information systems & weighbridge manufrs*

▶ Golden Solutions Ltd, 245 Markfield, Courtwood Llane, Forestdale, Croydon, CR0 9HW Tel: 020 84059337

Golden Soney Agri Fencing, The Gables, Golden Soney, Tockholes, Darwen, Lancashire, BB3 0NL Tel: (01254) 773648 *Agricultural fencing suppliers*

Golden Triangle Power Generation, Units 1-2 Weaver Park Industrial Estate, Mill Lane, Frodsham, WA6 7JB Tel: (01928) 722137 Fax: (01928) 722240 E-mail: hire@gtgen.co.uk *Generator, generating set & emergency lighting hire*

Golden Valley Supplies Ltd, N2b Unit Inchbrook Trading Estate, Bath Road, Woodchester, Stroud, Gloucestershire, GL5 5EY Tel: (01453) 832976 Fax: (01453) 836976 E-mail: sales@gvend.f9.co.uk *Vending machine services*

▶ Golden Valley Tarmacadam Ltd, 62 Quarry Road, Tupsley, Hereford, HR1 1SL Tel: 01432 267670 E-mail: enquiries@goldenvalleytarmacadam.com *Groundwork and Tarmac Specialists*No project too large or too small*ALL Major Credit Cards accepted*Free same day survey and Quotation*Based in Hereford*

Golden West Foods Ltd, Hareshill Road, Heywood, Lancashire, OL10 2TN Tel: (01706) 620580 Fax: (01706) 620572 E-mail: sales@goldenwest.co.uk *Food suppliers to McDonalds*

Golden Wonder Ltd, Edinburgh House, Abbey Street, Market Harborough, Leicestershire, LE16 9AA Tel: (01858) 410410 Fax: (01858) 414110 E-mail: talktous@golden-wonder.co.uk *Potato crisp & snack manufrs* Also at: Corby & Widnes

Golden Wonder Snack Services, Unit 4 Nelson Industrial Park, Herald Road, Hedge End, Southampton, SO30 2JH Tel: (01489) 789077 Fax: (01489) 789272 E-mail: mathewblake@walkers.co.uk *Snack distributors of crisps & nuts*

▶ Goldeneye Executive Resourcing Ltd, Flat 6 Kings Court, 40 Hersham Road, Walton-on-Thames, Surrey, KT12 1JE Tel: (07779) 134007 *Goldeneye Executive Careers specialises in Executive Resourcing and Coaching services. We combine a good eye for the right people with a steady hand of coaching and developing leadership skills for technology businesses.*

Goldenfry Foods Ltd, Sandbeck Way, Wetherby, West Yorkshire, LS22 7DW Tel: (01937) 583631 Fax: (01937) 580024 *Food product manufrs*

Goldenline Ltd, 7 Providence Industrial Estate, Providence Street, Stourbridge, West Midlands, DY9 8HQ Tel: (01384) 892578 Fax: (01384) 423855 E-mail: sales@goldenline.ltd.uk *Shop fitting suppliers*

Golder Associates (UK) Ltd, Clyde House, Reform Road, Maidenhead, Berkshire, SL6 8BY Tel: (01628) 771731 Fax: (01628) 770699 E-mail: golder_uk@golder.com *Consulting engineers*

Goldgem Belvoir Ltd, Belvoir House, Paddock Street, Wigston, Leicestershire, LE18 2AN Tel: 0116-288 1909 Fax: 0116-257 0184 *Knitwear, thermal goods, leisure & work wear manufrs*

Golding Audio, 8 Peartree Business Centre, Peartree Road, Stanway, Colchester, CO3 0JN Tel: (01206) 762462 Fax: (01206) 762633 E-mail: enquiries@goldingaudio.co.uk Principal Export Areas: Worldwide *Public address system contractors*

G.D. Golding Ltd, 220 Hatfield Road, St. Albans, Hertfordshire, AL1 4LW Tel: (01727) 841321 Fax: (01727) 831462 E-mail: tailors@goldings.co.uk *Clothing manufrs*

Golding, Hoptroff & Co. Ltd, Unit 8 Aintree Buildings, Aintree Way, Retail & Business Park, Liverpool, L9 5AQ Tel: 0151-525 2381 Fax: 0151-530 1351 E-mail: sales@goldinghop.demon.co.uk *Shipping & forwarding transport agents*

Golding Joinery Ltd, 4 Fern Close, Pen-Y-Fan Industrial Estate, Crumlin, Newport, Gwent, NP11 3EH Tel: (01495) 248778 Fax: (01495) 245296 E-mail: wgoldingjoinery@tiscali.co.uk *Joinery specialists*

Peter Golding Ltd, Barton Stacey, Winchester, Hampshire, SO21 3QL Tel: (01962) 760792 Fax: (01962) 760692 E-mail: sales@petergoulding.co.uk *Aquatic goods wholesalers*

Golding Products Ltd, Unit 24 Hortonwood 33, Telford, Shropshire, TF1 7YQ Tel: (01952) 606667 Fax: (01952) 670267 E-mail: sales@goldingproducts.com *Suppliers of CD-R, CD-Rom, 8cm CD and DVD. We have full in-house services for design, print and multimedia packaging so you can have your CD-R's designed and printed to your exact specifications.*Other services we provide include a small run print service (from 50 pieces), CD ROM service, Pad, Thermal and Inkjet print service.*

Goldingham Contracts, Crawley Barns, Uley, Dursley, Gloucestershire, GL11 5BH Tel: (01453) 860860 Fax: (01453) 860864 E-mail: admin@goldingham-contracts.co.uk *Mobile seed processing & pest control contractors. Grain store cleaning and treatment, crop cooling and conditioning. Liquid N for millwheat farming.*

Goldline F1 Ltd, Stafford Park 17, Telford, Shropshire, TF3 3DG Tel: (01952) 292401 Fax: (01952) 292403 E-mail: info@goldlinebearings.co.uk *Ball bearing distributors*

▶ Goldlogic Control Systems Ltd, Smithfold Lane, Worsley, Manchester, M28 0GP Tel: 0161-799 4222 Fax: 0161-799 4262 E-mail: admin@gcs-house.co.uk *Industrial computer programming & control systems specialists*

Goldman Sachs International Ltd, Peterborough Court, 133 Fleet Street, London, EC4A 2BB Tel: (020) 7774 1000 *Investment bankers*

▶ Goldnet Ltd, 3 Shire Close, Whiteley, Fareham, Hampshire, PO15 7BQ Tel: (01489) 886843 Fax: (01489) 886828 E-mail: info@goldnetltd.co.uk *Site design & build services*

Goldney Electronics UK, 6 Queen Anne's Gardens, Leatherhead, Surrey, KT22 7JE Tel: (01372) 378194 Fax: (01372) 375759 E-mail: purchasing@goldney.net *Electronic components & distributors*

Goldpress, 1 Lower Green Avenue, Scholes, Cleckheaton, West Yorkshire, BD19 6PB Tel: (01274) 878488 Fax: (01274) 878488 E-mail: davidkelly@goldpress.co.uk *Offering a next day express delivery service we specialise in SMALL QUANTITY, low cost, fundraising & promotional pens All our products offer exceptional value for money , whether you are fundraising, giving as a memento for a special event, stocking your camp, centre or museum shop or bookstall.We supply Guides, Scouts, Schools, Churches, and Museums*

Goldrite Ltd, 322 Coleford Road, Darnall, Sheffield, S9 5PH Tel: 0114-243 3011 Fax: 0114-242 1902 *Finishes for kitchens & bathrooms & lighting*

▶ Goldschmidt & Howland, 47 Maida Vale, London, W9 1SH Tel: (020) 7289 6633 Fax: (020) 7289 6646 E-mail: lvs@g-h.co.uk *sales,lettings,new homes,land,investments*

Goldschmidt UK Ltd, Flimby Works, Main Road, Flimby, Maryport, Cumbria, CA15 8RP Tel: (01900) 813333 Fax: (01900) 815622 *Chemical manufrs*

Goldschmidt UK Ltd, Tego House, Chippenham Drive, Kingston, Milton Keynes, MK10 0AF Tel: (01908) 582250 Fax: (01908) 582254 E-mail: angus.smith@degussa.com *Chemical & antifoaming agent manufrs*

Goldsmith & Co. Ltd, 221 High Street, Henley-in-Arden, West Midlands, B95 5BG Tel: (01564) 794616 Fax: (01564) 794451 E-mail: diagold@fgoldsmith.fsnet.co.uk *Jewellery manufrs*

Anthony Goldsmith, 17 Wentworth Hill, Wembley, Middlesex, HA9 9SF Tel: (020) 8908 6296 Fax: (020) 8908 9296 E-mail: agolex.went@virgin.net *Exporters*

Oliver Goldsmith Eyewear Ltd, The Studio, St Nicholas Close, Elstree, Borehamwood, Hertfordshire, WD6 3EW Tel: (020) 8207 5153 Fax: (020) 8207 2747 E-mail: oliver@ogspecs.force9.net *Optical design consultants*

▶ Goldstar Double Glazing Ltd, 3a Harpings Road, Hull, HU5 4JF Tel: (01482) 471399 Fax: (01482) 471501 E-mail: goldstar@goldstar.karoo.co.uk *Aluminium fabricators & installers*

Goldstar Fabrication & Ventilation, Haven Road, Colchester, CO2 8HT Tel: (01206) 867770 Fax: (01206) 867771 E-mail: enquiries@goldstatfabs.demom.co.uk *Industrial kitchen manufrs*

Goldstar Services Ltd, Unit 1 Spiral Tube Works, Osmaston Park Road, Derby, DE24 8BT Tel: (01332) 363313 Fax: (01332) 361355 E-mail: sales@doningtongroup.co.uk *Polythene bag & tubing manufrs*

L. Goldstein, 32 Alderney Rd, London, E1 4EG Tel: 020 77904144 Fax: 02077028166 *Smoked salmon*

▶ Goldstock Epos Systems, Unit 13, Rea Industrial Estate, Inkerman Street, Birmingham, B7 4SH Tel: 0121-359 0191 Fax: 0121-359 5387 *Computer components distributors*

▶ Goldstyle Limousines, 84 Sidney Avenue, Stafford, ST17 4EN Tel: (07915) 282346 E-mail: goldstyle.limousines@ntlworld.com *Uniformed chauffeur driven American limousine services*

Goldtec Astell Ltd, 16 London Road, Peterborough, PE2 8AR Tel: (01733) 558267 Fax: (01733) 558287 E-mail: info@goldtec.co.uk *Computer consultants & network design*

Goldwell Services Ltd, Cherry Tree Road, Milford, Godalming, Surrey, GU8 5AX Tel: (01483) 422083 Fax: (01483) 421198 *Electrical & mechanical engineers*

▶ Golf Finance Ltd, 4 Church Road, North Berwick, East Lothian, EH39 4AD Tel: (01620) 890200 Fax: (01620) 895895 E-mail: sales@golffinance.co.uk *Dedicated finance for the golf and groundscare industry. We can assist in financing tractors, mowers, vehicles, golf cars, sheds, lockers, clubhouse & course redevelopments, irrigation & drainage, computers & entry systems, GPS, yardage books*

▶ Golf & Leisure Breaks, 20 Greys Road, Henley-on-Thames, Oxfordshire, RG9 1RY Tel: (01491) 572580 Fax: (01491) 573763 E-mail: sales@golf-leisurebreaks.co.uk *golf holidays, golf hotel accommodation, golf breaks and golfing holidays packages in the UK and worldwide*

▶ Golfsim, 30 Elvington, King'S Lynn, King's Lynn, Norfolk, PE30 4TA Tel: (07956) 090436 E-mail: info@golfsimulation.co.uk *Golf simulator hire*

▶ Goliath Computing, Unit 4e Munday Works, Morley Road, Tonbridge, Kent, TN9 1RP Tel: (01732) 365355 Fax: (01732) 365345 E-mail: steve@goliathcomputing.co.uk *Distributors in computer parts*

Goliath Footwear Ltd, Goliath House, Chain Bar Road, Cleckheaton, West Yorkshire, BD19 3QF Tel: (0845) 3306430 Fax: (0845) 3306431 E-mail: enquiries@goliath.co.uk *Goliath Footwear are a maker of Safety, Fire, Police and Military footwear. Based in West Yorkshire, we hold a full range of stock items for immediate delivery.*

Golz UK Ltd, Springhead Enterprise Park, Springhead Road, Gravesend, Kent, DA11 8HB Tel: (01474) 321679 Fax: (01474) 321477 E-mail: sales@goelz.com Principal Export Areas: Worldwide *Manufacturers of diamond core drilling machines*

Gomaco International Ltd, 769 Buckingham Avenue, Slough, SL1 4NL Tel: (01753) 821926 Fax: (01753) 693093 E-mail: pavinguk@gomaco.com *Construction equipment manufrs*

Goman Couriers Ltd, 58c Arthur Street, Redditch, Worcestershire, B98 8JY Tel: (01527) 515055 Fax: (01527) 510779 *Courier services haulage*

Gomer Electrical Ltd, Alfred Cook Building, Canal Parade, Cardiff, CF10 5RD Tel: (029) 2022 8384 Fax: (029) 2082 1000 E-mail: khill@gomer-electrical.co.uk *Electrical engineers & contractors*

Gomex Tools Ltd, Orchard Road, Finedon, Wellingborough, Northamptonshire, NN9 5JF Tel: (01933) 680492 Fax: (01933) 680693 E-mail: sales@gomex.co.uk *TCT circular saw blade & other TCT tool manufrs*

Gondrand U.K., Gondrand House, 2 Oriental Road, London, E16 2BZ Tel: (020) 7540 2000 Fax: (020) 7540 2001 E-mail: info@gondrand.co.uk *Forwarding & air freight transporters*

Gooch & Housego plc, Cornhill, Ilminster, Somerset, TA19 0AB Tel: (01460) 52271 Fax: (01460) 54972 E-mail: info@goochandhousego.com *Optical component manufrs*

▶ Gooch Ict Ltd, 56 Coulson Road, Lincoln, LN6 7BG Tel: (01522) 546624 Fax: (01522) 546624 E-mail: hayley@goochict.co.uk *Telecommunication equipment*

Good Acre Engraving, 120 Main Street, Sutton Bonington, Loughborough, Leicestershire, LE12 5PF Tel: (01509) 673082 Fax: (01509) 673082 E-mail: goodacre@ndirect.co.uk *Engravers antiques trade*

Good Buddy's C B Radio & Communications Centre, Norland House, Hackworth Industrial Park, Shildon, County Durham, DL4 1HE Tel: (01388) 778368 Fax: (01388) 775832 E-mail: gbcomms102@aol.com *Radio communication services*

Good Design, 7 Frenchs Wells, Woking, Surrey, GU21 3AS Tel: (01483) 889533 Fax: (01483) 833983 *Silver jewellery & giftware retailers*

Good Directions Ltd, 1D Ravenstor Road, Wirksworth, Derby, DE4 4FY Tel: (01629) 824282 Fax: (01629) 824333 E-mail: info@good-directions.co.uk *Manufacturers of clock towers, internal & external clocks*

Good Directions Ltd, 8 Bottings Industrial Estate, Hillsons Road, Botley, Southampton, SO30 2DY Tel: 01489 797773 Fax: 01489 796700 E-mail: sales@good-directions.co.uk *Clock towers and roof turret manufacturers. Designers of cupolas, clocks and weathervanes.*

▶ Good Health, Shop F Church Road, Port Erin, Isle of Man, IM9 6AH Tel: (01624) 832865 E-mail: thegoodhealthstore@manx.net *Health foods suppliers*

John Good Shipping Ltd, Craven Gate, Lorne Road, Warley, Brentwood, Essex, CM14 5HH Tel: (0845) 2582050 Fax: (01277) 202758 E-mail: london@johngood.co.uk *Freight forwarding agents*

▶ Good Knights Bed & Mattress Centre, 398 Chester Road, Little Sutton, Ellesmere Port, CH66 3RB Tel: 0151-339 1600 Fax: 0151-339 1660 E-mail: sales@goodknights.co.uk *Mattress beds & furniture retailers*

Good Life Foods Ltd, 34 Tatton Court, Kingsland Grange, Woolston, Warrington, WA1 4FF Tel: (01925) 837810 Fax: (01925) 838648 E-mail: enquiry@goodlife.co.uk *Vegetarian frozen food manufrs*

Norman Good & Sons Ltd, Station Road, West Bay, Bridport, Dorset, DT6 4EW Tel: (01308) 422007 Fax: (01308) 421171 *Gravel merchants*

Good Openings, Hockley Business Centre, Hooley Lane, Redhill, RH1 6ET Tel: (01737) 772277 Fax: (01737) 772288 *PVC windows installers & manufrs*

Good Packing Co. Ltd, Mariner, Lichfield Road Industrial Estate, Tamworth, Staffordshire, B79 7TJ Tel: (01827) 65911 Fax: (01827) 59310 E-mail: info@goodpackaging.co.uk *Packing case manufacturers & export packers*

Good Relations Ltd, Hobern Gate, 26 South Hampton Buildings, London, WC2A 1PQ Tel: (020) 7861 3030 Fax: (020) 7861 3200 E-mail: info@good-relations.co.uk *Public relations*

▶ Good Riddance Pest Control, 34 Bryant Gardens, Clevedon, Avon, BS21 5HE Tel: (01275) 879589 E-mail: info@grpc.co.uk

Good Wood Cellars, 16-17 The Quay, Exeter, EX2 4AP Tel: (01392) 498030 Fax: (01392) 202252 *Carpenters*

Goodacre Carpets Of Kendal Ltd, Castle Mill, Aynam Road, Kendal, Cumbria, LA9 7DF Tel: (01539) 792916 Fax: (01539) 732442 E-mail: admin@goodacrecarpets.com Principal Export Areas: Worldwide *Carpet suppliers* Also at: Kendal

Goodall Barnard, Kestrel Court Vyne Road, Sherborne St. John, Basingstoke, Hampshire, RG24 9HJ Tel: (01256) 851155 Fax: (01256) 851234 E-mail: buildit@goodall-barnard.co.uk *Building contractors & developers*

Goodall Bates & Todd Ltd, Albany Road, Gateshead, Tyne & Wear, NE8 3BP Tel: 0191-477 4221 Fax: 0191-477 9544 E-mail: cbaker@gb-lubricants-fuels.co.uk *Holding company to the group*

Goodall Services Ltd, 7 Davenport Centre, Renwick Road, Barking, Essex, IG11 0SH Tel: (020) 8592 2707 Fax: (020) 8592 5716 *Steel fabricators*

▶ Goodbitz Ltd, 52-54 Pillard House Lane, Gainsborough, Lincolnshire, DN21 1HX Tel: (01427) 677399 Fax: (01427) 677433

Goodbrand Knitwear, New Building Easter Corriehoul, Corgarff, Strathdon, Aberdeenshire, AB36 8YL Tel: (01975) 651433 Fax: (01975) 651442 E-mail: sales@highlandtradingpost.com *Knitwear manufrs*

Goodbrand Plastics Ltd, Millbuck Way, Sandbach, Cheshire, CW11 3GQ Tel: (01270) 753006 Fax: (01270) 750329 E-mail: sales@ultrastorage.co.uk *Plastic manufacturing*

Goodchild Marine Services, Burgh Castle Yacht Station, Butt Lane, Burgh Castle, Great Yarmouth, Norfolk, NR31 9PZ Tel: (01493) 782301 Fax: (01493) 782306 E-mail: info@goodchildmarine.co.uk *Boat builders & marine engineers services*

Goodchild Precision Engineering Co Ltd, Unit 5 Chiltern Trading Estate, Earl Howe Road, Holmer Green, High Wycombe, Buckinghamshire, HP15 6QT Tel: (01494) 714728 Fax: (01494) 714728 *Precision engineers*

Thomas Goode & Co. Ltd, 19 South Audley Street, London, W1K 2BN Tel: (020) 7499 2823 Fax: (020) 7629 4230 E-mail: info@thomasgoode.com *Antique retailers*

Angie Gooderham Ltd, 2A Metropolitan Wharf, Wapping Wall, London, E1W 3SW Tel: (020) 7480 6938 Fax: (020) 7702 1968 *Fashion jewellery manufrs*

Peter Goodhind Associates Ltd, Brunel House, George Street, Gloucester, GL1 1BZ Tel: (01452) 503501 Fax: (01452) 308794 E-mail: mail@goodhindassociates.co.uk *Consulting & structural engineers*

Goodies Enterprise Ltd, Mile Road, Bedford, MK42 9TN Tel: (01234) 364104 Fax: (09069) 480201 E-mail: enquiries@goodiesenterprises.com *Electronic repair services*

Goodland Engineering Ltd, Cannon Lane, Tonbridge, Kent, TN9 1PP Tel: (01732) 771010 Fax: (01732) 356472 E-mail: goodlandengineering@yahoo.co.uk *General engineers*

Goodlands Displays, Unit 16 College Fields Business Centre, Prince Georges Road, London, SW19 2PT Tel: (020) 8687 8254 Fax: (020) 8687 8257 E-mail: printing@goodlands.co.uk *Screen & lithographic printers*

Goodman Baylis Ltd, The Trinity Press, London Road, Worcester, WR5 2JH Tel: (01905) 357979 Fax: (01905) 354919 E-mail: theworks@goodmanbaylis.co.uk *Printers & binders*

Goodman Business Parks UK Ltd, Arlington House, Arlington Business Park, Reading, RG7 4SA Tel: 0118-930 4141 Fax: 0118-930 4383 E-mail: rececption@arlington.com *Property developers*

Goodman (Direct Marketing) Ltd, 37 Blenheim Terrace, London, NW8 0EJ Tel: (020) 7328 3961 Fax: (020) 7328 3962 E-mail: peter_gdm@btinternet.com *Management consultants*

Goodman Glass Fibre Ltd, Ryehill Farm, Long Buckby Wharf, Long Buckby, Northampton, NN6 7PW Tel: (01327) 843585 Fax: (01327) 842639 *Glass fibre product manufrs*

Goodman Steel Services Ltd, 98 Cardiff Road, Reading, RG1 8LL Tel: 0118-956 1212 Fax: 0118-956 1218 E-mail: sales@goodsteel.co.uk *Steel stockholders*

Goodmarriott & Hursthouse Ltd, Hooton Street, Nottingham, NG3 5GL Tel: 0115-950 5100 Fax: 0115-958 1200 E-mail: mail@gandh.co.uk *Electrical engineers*

For Goodness Sake, 28 Westgate, Guisborough, Cleveland, TS14 6BA Tel: (01287) 637074 Fax: (01287) 637074 *Health food retailers*

For Goodness Sake, 13 Newport Road, Middlesbrough, Cleveland, TS1 1LE Tel: (01642) 219249 Fax: (01642) 231080 *Health foods*

▶ Goodprint UK Ltd, Stephenson Way, Thetford, Norfolk, IP24 3RU Tel: (01842) 761546 Fax: (01842) 754001

Goodrange Ltd, 296 Wightman Rd, London, N8 0LT Tel: 020 83477670 Fax: 020 83477670 *Ladies clothing manufrs*

Goodrem Nicholson, Export House, Rowley Road, Coventry, CV3 4FR Tel: (024) 7630 5601 Fax: (024) 7630 4663 E-mail: colin@goodrem.co.uk *Freight forwarding agents* Also at: Cheltenham

Goodrich Corporation Rohr Aero Services, Bae Systems, Building 38, Glasgow Prestwick Intnl Airpor, Prestwick, Ayrshire, KA9 2GW Tel: (01292) 670200 Fax: (01292) 672854 E-mail: info@bfgoodrich.com *Aircraft component manufacture & repair*

Goodridge (UK) Ltd, Exeter Airport Business Park, Exeter, EX5 2UP Tel: (01392) 369090 Fax: (01392) 441780 Principal Export Areas: Worldwide *Hose manufrs*

Goodrow Engineering Ltd, Unit 5, Ebbsfleet Industrial Estate, Northfleet, Gravesend, Kent, DA11 9DZ Tel: (01474) 359990 Fax: (01474) 359994 *Light engineering*

Goodrowes Of Chichester Ltd, 6 The Hornet, Chichester, West Sussex, PO19 7JQ Tel: (01243) 784411 Fax: (01243) 784339 E-mail: goodrowesltd@aol.com *Agricultural & dairy engineers*

Goods Protection Ltd, 11/12 Shuttleworth Road, Elm Farm Industrial Estate, Bedford, MK41 0EP Tel: (01234) 327522 Fax: (01234) 270885 E-mail: info@goods-protection.co.uk *Tarpaulin hire*

Goodsell & Co., PO Box 3, Teignmouth, Devon, TQ14 8XS Tel: (01626) 778820 Fax: (01626) 772556 E-mail: sales@goodco.demon.co.uk *Computer resellers*

▶ GoodSource Global Trading Ltd, Unit 26, Cavans Way, Binley Industrial Estate, Coventry, CV3 2SF Tel: (08456) 448148 Fax: (08706) 622166 E-mail: contact@goodsource.co.uk *We are an importer of handcrafted ceramic tiles, contemporary homeware and traditional artwork from the Orient. Our products are unique and inspirational for both home and business environment.*

Goodturn Engineering Ltd, Unit 2 Brook Street, Redditch, Worcestershire, B98 8NG Tel: (01527) 596325 Fax: (01527) 597325 E-mail: mail@goodturn-engineering.co.uk *Turned parts manufrs*

Goodwater Ltd, 23-24 Ivanhoe Road, Hogwood Industrial Estate, Finchampstead, Wokingham, Berkshire, RG40 4QQ Tel: 0118-973 5003 Fax: 0118-973 5004 E-mail: info@goodwater.co.uk *Industrial water treatment*

Goodway Service & Safety Ltd, 8 Foundry Court, Daventry, Northamptonshire, NN11 4RH Tel: (01327) 312468 Fax: (01327) 301404 E-mail: goodwaydist@msn.com *Tube cleaning equipment manufrs*

▶ Goodways, 42 Skylines Village, Limeharbour, London, E14 9TS Tel: (020) 7987 2288

Goodwear Holdings Ltd, Samros House, 1A Finsbury Park Road, London, N4 2LA Tel: (020) 7359 6341 Fax: (020) 7359 5678 E-mail: sales@goodwear.co.uk *Importers & exporters of fabric furnishing trimmings*

Goodwear Shoes 2001 Ltd, 5 Dudlow Drive, Liverpool, L18 2HB Tel: 0151-280 3049 Fax: 0151-280 3049 E-mail: trevordh@blueyonder.co.uk *Footwear importers & distributors*

Goodwill Art Service Ltd, The Old School, Church Street, Upton, Didcot, Oxfordshire, OX11 9JB Tel: (01235) 831990 Fax: (01235) 831990 E-mail: goodwiilart@uptonoxon.demon.co.uk *History & art suppliers*

▶ Goodwill Trade Co. Ltd, 34 Finchley Lane, Hendon, London, NW4 1DL Tel: (020) 8203 8914 E-mail: goodwill-trade@hotmail.com *we specialize in importing and exporting all kinds of textile, leather products, other home appliances and gifts either by OEM or in our own brand, most of which are locally manufactured or processed. Now we are having business with more than 100 companies mainly from the West Europe, North American and Middle East, meanwhile our suppliers spread all over Mainland China, Taiwan and India, and most of them are highly-qualified manufacturers either certified by ISO9000 series or reaching OEKO-TEX100, moreover we have a large quality control department which works together with governmental quality supervision institutions to inspect and monitor our production, which ensures the best quality and satisfaction for any of our customers. In addition, we also have two experienced teams for price and consignment control to offer our customers the unbeatable price and the best delivery time. Based on our own efforts and the co-operations from our suppliers and buyers.*

J.F. Goodwillie Ltd, Saw Mills, 154 London Road, Waterlooville, Hampshire, PO7 5SR Tel: (08707) 705433 Fax: (08707) 705435 *Timber importers & sawmillers*

Goodwills Leisure Hire, 39-41 High Street, Dunmow, Essex, CM6 1AE Tel: (01371) 876666 Fax: (01371) 875544 E-mail: roger@gogb.net *Inflatable products hire service*

Goodwin Air Plasma Ltd, Unit 18 Kernan Drive, Loughborough, Leicestershire, LE11 5JF Tel: (01509) 237369 Fax: (01509) 234942 E-mail: goodwinplasma@aol.com Principal Export Areas: Worldwide *Pipe cutting, beveling & profile cutting equipment manufrs*

Goodwin Alloy Products, Goodwin House, Leek Road, Hanley, Stoke-On-Trent, ST1 3NR Tel: (01782) 220260 Fax: (01782) 228060 E-mail: goodwinplc@goodwin.co.uk *Nickel alloy ingots manufrs*

Harry Goodwin & Sons Ltd, Canal Saw Mills, Barnfield Road Industrial Estate, Leek, Staffordshire, ST13 5QG Tel: (01538) 399027 Fax: (01538) 399472 E-mail: richard@goodwin4timber.co.uk *Timber merchants*

Goodwin International Ltd, Newstead Industrial Trading Estate, Stoke-on-Trent, ST4 8HU Tel: (01782) 654000 Fax: (01782) 208060 E-mail: goodwinplc@goodwin.co.uk *Engineering pumps & valves manufrs*

Goodwin International Ltd, Ivy House Foundry, Hanley, Stoke-on-Trent, ST1 3NR Tel: (01782) 220000 Fax: (01782) 208060 E-mail: goodwinplc@goodwin.co.uk *Valve manufrs*

Goodwin International Ltd, Ivy House Foundry, Hanley, Stoke-on-Trent, ST1 3NR Tel: (01782) 220000 Fax: (01782) 208060 E-mail: goodwinplc@goodwin.co.uk *Steel ingot manufrs*

Goodwin L F P, Wallis House, 24 High Street, Ewell, Epsom, Surrey, KT17 1SJ Tel: (020) 8394 1555 Fax: (020) 8393 7002 *Structural engineers*

Goodwin Tanks Ltd, Pontefract Street, Derby, DE24 8JD Tel: (01332) 363112 Fax: (01332) 294683 E-mail: sales@goodwintanks.co.uk *Civil engineers*

Goodwin Technology Ltd, B2 Prenton Way, North Cheshire Trading Estate, Prenton, Merseyside, CH43 3DU Tel: 0151-608 8666 Fax: 0151-638 2456 E-mail: sales@gtprecision.co.uk *Production machinists*

▶ Goodwinch Lifting Equipment, Eastfoldhay, Zeal Monachorum, Crediton, Devon, EX17 6DH Tel: (01363) 82666 Fax: (01363) 82782 E-mail: sales@davidbowyer.com *Winch distributors, agents, suppliers & manufrs*

Goodwins Power Tools, 93 Canterbury Road, Margate, Kent, CT9 5AX Tel: (01843) 220966 Fax: (01843) 220836 E-mail: info@goodwins-tools.demon.co.uk *Tool & mower & gas suppliers & hot tub installation services*

▶ Goodwood Bathrooms, 1 North Farm, Church Road, North Mundham, Chichester, West Sussex, PO20 1JU Tel: (01243) 532121 Fax: (01243) 533423

Goodwood Communications Ltd, 5 The Square, Petersfield, Hampshire, GU32 3HL Tel: (01730) 235500 Fax: (01730) 235501 *Telecommunications developers*

Goodwood Engineering, Enterprise Way, King's Lynn, Norfolk, PE30 4LJ Tel: (01553) 766574 Fax: (01553) 766574 E-mail: andy@goodwoodeng.co.uk *Precision engineers*

Goodwood Fencing & Co., Spencer Courtyard, Rear of 266 Regents Park Road, London, N3 3HN Tel: (020) 8346 0827 Fax: (020) 8346 6430 E-mail: sales@jwc-gwf.com *Supply, install timber fencing*

Goodwood Furniture Design Ltd, 74 Farndon Road, Newark, Nottinghamshire, NG24 4SE Tel: (01636) 706593 *Furniture manufrs*

Goodwood Timber Products, Plough Business Centre, Plough Road, Great Bentley, Colchester, CO7 7US Tel: (01206) 251711 *Timber merchants*

▶ Goodyear Dunlop, Tyrefort, 88-98 Wingfoot Way, Erdington, Birmingham, B24 9HY Tel: 0121-306 6166 *Tyre manufrs*

Goodyear Great Britain Ltd, Bushbury Lane, Bushbury, Wolverhampton, WV10 6DH Tel: (01902) 327000 Fax: (01902) 327060 *Tyres manufrs* Also at: Branches throughout the U.K.

Goodyer Packaging Ltd, Bunbury Lane, Bunbury, Tarporley, Cheshire, CW6 9QU Tel: (01829) 261052 Fax: (01829) 261129 *Polyethylene film & sheet manufrs*

Goonvean Ltd, St. Stephen, St. Austell, Cornwall, PL26 7QF Tel: (01726) 822381 Fax: (01726) 822341 E-mail: g@goonvean.co.uk *China clay & stone producers*

Goonvean Fibres Ltd, Ottery Moor Lane, Honiton, Devon, EX14 1BW Tel: (01404) 44194 Fax: (01404) 45102 E-mail: office@goonveanfibres.co.uk *Grinding & cutting of textile fibres*

▶ Goose Recruit, Walnut Tree Cottage, Main Road, Theberton, Leiston, Suffolk, IP16 4RU Tel: (01728) 833502 Fax: (01728) 833502 E-mail: rlapage@gooserecruit.co.uk *Recruitment Company - specialising in all types of industry:- construction, drivers, security, industrial - large or small numbers - skilled and semi-skilled staff.*

▶ Goosh Services, 15 Andrews Close, Hereford, HR1 2JX Tel: (07973) 197890 E-mail: derekrmumford@hotmail.com

Gopak Ltd, Range Road, Hythe, Kent, CT21 6HG Tel: (01303) 265751 Fax: (01303) 268282 E-mail: sales@gopak.co.uk *Lightweight aluminium folding tables manufacturers. First for folding tables, and many other items of quality furniture, supplied to education, local authorities, businesses and community organisations.*

Goplant, 88 Hawkcliffe Road, Mount Sorrel, Mount Sorrel, Loughborough, Leicestershire, LE12 7AH Tel: (01509) 414677 Fax: (01509) 416853 *Plant hire contractors* Also at: Branches throughout the U.K.

Goran Plastics Ltd, 5 Caxton Way, Watford Business Park, Watford, WD18 8UA Tel: (01923) 255700 Fax: (01923) 255698 E-mail: sales@goran.co.uk *Sheet extruders and convertors of Polyflute Corrugated Plastic Sheet. Accreditation to ISO9001:2000. Fire Retardant Product Accredited to LPS1207 Corrugated plastic trays, containers, layer pads, slip sheets. Bespoke project management.*

Goratec UK Ltd, 47 Cavendish Road, Eccles, Manchester, M30 9EE Tel: 0161-788 9929 Fax: 0161-788 9930 *Thermal imaging cameras distributors*

Gordano Packaging Ltd, 2a Lansdown Industrial Estate, Gloucester Road, Cheltenham, Gloucestershire, GL51 8PL Tel: (01242) 263765 Fax: (01242) 263768 E-mail: jeb@gordano-packaging.co.uk *Design, manufacture &supply packaging & acking solutions to protect products of all shape, size and fragility in any environment*

Gordon Associates, Suite G1 Monpellier House, Monpellier Drive, Cheltenham, Gloucestershire, GL50 1TY Tel: (01242) 529820 Fax: (01242) 226021 E-mail: sales@gordonassociates.co.uk *Software house*

▶ Gordon Bow Plant Hire, 82-86 East Main St, Broxburn, West Lothian, EH52 5EG Tel: (01506) 855913 Fax: (01506) 856393 E-mail: info@gordonbow.co.uk *Building & site work equipment hire plant*

Campbell Gordon, 50 Queens Road, Reading, RG1 4HU Tel: 0118-959 7555 Fax: 0118-959 7550 E-mail: info@campbellgordon.co.uk *Chartered surveyors*

Gordon Dental Laboratories, Pendrill House, Beverley Road, Hull, HU3 1UP Tel: (01482) 224944 *Dental technicians*

▶ Gordon Derry & Son, Derry Court, Polmorla Road, Wadebridge, Cornwall, PL27 7NE Tel: (01208) 812975 Fax: (01208) 815552

Gordon Durham & Co. Ltd, Moor Lane, East Boldon, Tyne & Wear, NE36 0AG Tel: 0191-536 7207 Fax: 0191-519 0097 E-mail: contracts@gordondurham.com *Building contractors*

F.T. Gordon Building Services Ltd, Meridian Centre, Kings Street, Oldham, OL8 1EZ Tel: 0161-626 7667 Fax: 0161-627 5133 E-mail: info@ftguk.com *Electrical contractors*

▶ Gordon Fozard, 3 Knowsley Terrace, Woodside Road, Chiddingfold, Godalming, Surrey, GU8 4QU Tel: 01428 682911 E-mail: studio@southphotography.co.uk *We specialise in digital packshot and product photography, with set prices from £24, a free email approval service and guaranteed fast turnarounds*

▶ Gordon Giles & Co. Ltd, Rennie House, 57-60 Aldgate High Street, London, EC3N 1AL Tel: (020) 7709 0011 Fax: (020) 7709 0022 E-mail: info@newmangiles.com *Marine consultants & ship surveyors*

▶ Gordon Graham, The Garage, Gilsland, Brampton, Cumbria, CA8 7BT Tel: (01697) 747501 Fax: (01697) 747690

▶ Gordon Greaves Slate Ltd, The Mill, Troutbeck Bridge, Windermere, Cumbria, LA23 1HS Tel: (01539) 446737 Fax: (01539) 442049 E-mail: sales@gordongreaves.co.uk *Stone manufrs*

▶ Gordon Guthrie Contracts, 2 27 Beaverhall Road, Edinburgh, EH7 4JE Tel: 0131-556 9686 Fax: 0131-556 5774

Gordon James Engineers Ltd, Old Station Yard, Newton Stewart, Wigtownshire, DG8 9AL Tel: (01988) 840201 Fax: (01988) 840670 E-mail: nsparts@jgordon.co.uk *Agricultural engineers*

John Gordon Motors Ltd, Rear of, 117a London Road, St. Albans, Hertfordshire, AL1 1LR Tel: (01727) 855096 Fax: (01727) 841966 E-mail: jgordonmotors@aol.com *Car servicing , repairs & mot's*

John Gordon & Son Ltd, Balblair Road, Nairn, IV12 5LY Tel: (01667) 453223 Fax: (01667) 452168 E-mail: enquiries@gordontimber.co.uk *Timber merchants & saw millers services*

Gordon Love Trailers, 192 Bridge St West, Birmingham, B19 2YT Tel: 0121-359 6387 Fax: 0121-359 0317 E-mail: sales@wessex-trailers.co.uk *Trailer, tow bars, roof racks sales & hire*

Gordon Parkes, 1a Johnson Road, Birmingham, B23 6PU Tel: 0121-377 7524 Fax: 0121-377 7524 E-mail: gordon306@tiscali.co.uk *Control panel manufrs*

Gordon Plant, Inglewhite Road, Goosnargh, Preston, PR3 2ED Tel: (01772) 782255 Fax: (01772) 782255 E-mail: gordonplant@hotmail.com *Plant & machinery repairs*

Gordon Press Ltd, Caxton House, 2 Bath House Road, Croydon, CR0 4TT Tel: (020) 8684 0313 Fax: (020) 8689 6715 E-mail: sales@thegordonpress.com *Legal cheques printers & stationers*

S. Gordon, 100 Blakenhale Road, Sheldon, Birmingham, B33 0XA Tel: 0121-786 2482 Fax: 0121-604 4662 *Suspended ceiling contractors & partitioning*

Gordon S Davidson, The Smiddy, Tyrie, Fraserburgh, Aberdeenshire, AB43 7BX Tel: (01346) 541270 Fax: (01346) 541270 *Fabrication engineers*

▶ Gordon S Harding, Bousley End, Bousley Rise, Ottershaw, Chertsey, Surrey, KT16 0LB Tel: (01932) 873096 Fax: (01932) 873096

Gordon Signs & Interior Displays Ltd, St. Faiths Road, Norwich, NR6 7BW Tel: (01603) 486142 Fax: (01603) 486172 E-mail: simon@gordonsigns.co.uk *Sign contractors & display designers*

▶ Gordon Singleton, 4 Poplar Bank, Barrow-in-Furness, Cumbria, LA13 0RB Tel: (01229) 834068 E-mail: gordon@micro-wave.co.uk *Commercial & domestic microwave servicing, portable appliance testing*

Gordon Stones Industrial Services, 177 Tettenhall Road, Wolverhampton, WV6 0BZ Tel: (01902) 713972 Fax: (01902) 714134 *Plant installation, erection & dismantling services*

▶ Gordon Technical Services, 1 Gortgommon Park, Main Street, Newtownbutler, Enniskillen, County Fermanagh, BT92 8GT Tel: (028) 6773 7169 E-mail: info@gtsconstruction.wanadoo.co.uk

Thomas Gordon & Sons, 19 Queen Street, Glasgow, G1 3ED Tel: 0141-221 2234 Fax: 0141-221 2230 *Highland dress & supplier*

Gordons Environmental Ltd, 66-68 Back Sneddon Street, Paisley, Renfrewshire, PA3 2BY Tel: 0141-842 1189 Fax: 0141-842 1139 E-mail: gordonsltd@aol.com *Tankcleaning & waste disposal contractors*

Gormac Coachworks, 5 Thomson Street, Renfrew, PA4 8HQ Tel: 0141-886 4072 Fax: 0141-885 2821 E-mail: gormac@btconnect.com *Motor vehicle bodybuilders*

Gorman Shorrock & Davies Ltd, 52 Heyrod Street, Manchester, M1 2WW Tel: 0161-273 3909 Fax: 0161-273 6690 *Offset colour printing services*

Gormans Metals Ltd, Harlington Works, Kingsteignton Road, Newton Abbot, Devon, TQ12 2QA Tel: (01626) 352266 Fax: (01626) 352266 *Scrap metal merchants*

Gormley (Marble Specialists) Ltd, Gormley House, Waxlow Road, Park Royal, London, NW10 7NU Tel: (020) 8961 5651 Fax: (020) 8961 5658 E-mail: info@gormley.co.uk *Contractors & workers of granite & marble*

Gorno's Speciality Foods Ltd, 3 Fairfield Industrial Estate, Pentyrch Road, Gwaelod-y-Garth, Cardiff, CF15 8LA Tel: (029) 2081 1225 Fax: (029) 2081 1299 E-mail: gornos.foods@virgin.net *Speciality food manufrs*

Gorsis Indian Frozen Foods, Hamer Street, Radcliffe, Manchester, M26 2RS Tel: 0161-723 4536 Fax: 0161-723 1395 *Frozen food processors & products manufrs*

Gortavoy Feeds & Farm Supplies, 73 Shanmaghry Road, Pomeroy, Dungannon, County Tyrone, BT70 2TT Tel: (028) 8775 9283 Fax: (028) 8775 9570 E-mail: info@gortavoyfeeds.co.uk *Animal feed manufrs*

▶ GOSIM, Concorde House, 10 Great North Way, York Business Park, York, YO26 6RB Tel: (0870) 1023400 Fax: (0870) 1023401 E-mail: sales@gosim.com *Telephone equipment suppliers*

Gosling Of Kidderminster, Unit 208 Foley Industrial Estate, Kidderminster, Worcestershire, DY11 7DH Tel: (01562) 68427 Fax: (01562) 68427 E-mail: sales@goslings.co.uk *Motor vehicle repair & breakdown recovery*

William Gosling & Son Ltd, Northwodd Works, 155 Tame Road, Birmingham, B6 7DG Tel: 0121-327 4081 Fax: 0121-326 6032 *Corrugated case makers*

Gosnay's Engineering Co. Ltd, Eastern Avenue West, Romford, RM7 7NS Tel: (01708) 740668 Fax: (01708) 733266 E-mail: sales@gosnays.co.uk *Engine manufrs*

▶ Gospel Frontiers Ltd, 8 Balgowan Road, Beckenham, Kent, BR3 4HJ Tel: (020) 8650 9607 E-mail: ian@gospelfrontiers.co.uk *Gospel Frontiers Ltd provides management services to the gospel music industry and offers gospel music CD"s at lower prices. Also promotes and advertises gospel music event in the UK.*

Gosport Boatyard Ltd, Harbour Road, Gosport, Hampshire, PO12 1BJ Tel: (023) 9252 6534 Fax: (023) 9258 6216 *Boatyard & mooring operators*

Gosport Engineering Co. Ltd, Lordship Lane, London, N17 8NS Tel: (020) 8808 2326 Fax: (020) 8885 2867 E-mail: gosporteng@btconnect.com *Security doors/general engineers*

▶ The Gosport PC Clinic, 69 Brockhurst Road, Gosport, Hampshire, PO12 3AR Tel: (023) 9252 2777 Fax: (023) 9252 2777 E-mail: support@coppcomm.com *IT retail support*

Goss Components Ltd, 43 Fulbourne Road, London, E17 4AF Tel: (020) 8527 5599 Fax: (020) 8527 1142 E-mail: enquiries@gosscomponent.com *Spring & press tool manufrs*

▶ Goss & Co Insurance Brokers Ltd, Clarendon House, 59-75 Queen Road, Reading, RG1 4BN Tel: 0118-955 1800 Fax: 0118 955 1848 E-mail: insure@goss.co.uk *Insurance and Risk Management solutions*
Gostelow Advertising Ltd, 21-22 Francis Street, Hull, HU2 8DT Tel: (01482) 323459 Fax: (01482) 586325 E-mail: alec@gostelow.karoo.co.uk *Travel & leather good manufrs*
▶ GotchaSomething, 44 Penrhyn Road, Far Cotton, Northampton, NN4 8ED Tel: 0845 1565470 E-mail: general@gotchasomething.co.uk *Gifts from GotchaSomething.co.uk UK online shop. We sell Laser Glass, Teddy Bears, Necklaces, Bangles, Bracelets, Soap, Gift Sets etc. Our range is always expanding so come and visit us now.*
Gotec Trading Ltd, Boulton Road, Stevenage, Hertfordshire, SG1 4QL Tel: (01438) 740400 Fax: (01438) 740005 *Importers & exporters of leak detection spray*
Gothard Flight Cases, 322 Beverley Road, Hull, HU5 1BA Tel: (07831) 421751 Fax: (01977) 680271 E-mail: info@gothardflightcases.co.uk *Flight case manufrs*
H. Gothard & Sons Hiab Services, 19 Fairfield Mount, Ossett, West Yorkshire, WF5 0TE Tel: (01924) 260116 E-mail: hiabservices@msn.com *Lorry mounted hiab cranes suppliers*
▶ Gothard Landscape & Land Reclamation Ltd, Gate House, Sandhurst Road, West Tilbury, Tilbury, Essex, RM18 8DH Tel: (01375) 842904 Fax: (01375) 859203
Gothard Neon Ltd, 11 Chorley Road, Blackpool, FY3 7XQ Tel: (01253) 390049 Fax: (01253) 390049 E-mail: dgothard@neon.signs.net *Sign manufrs*
Gothers Moor Fabrications, Gothers Road, Gothers Moor Cottage, St Dennis, St. Austell, Cornwall, PL26 8DF Tel: (01726) 822185 Fax: (01726) 823825 *China clay research & development*
▶ Go-to-Spain, Amberley, Cotswold Close, Tredington, Shipston-on-Stour, Warwickshire, CV36 4NR Tel: (01608) 661801 E-mail: sales@go-to-spain.com *Go-to-Spain: Ebro Valley property and River Ebro Properties: cheap country property with land for sale. Land from 20,000 euros.*
E & S Gott, Priestley Butts, Whitby Road, Pickering, North Yorkshire, YO18 7HL Tel: (01751) 472009 *Cabinet makers*
Gottlieb Packaging Materials Ltd, Unit 1-3 Harp Trading Estate, Guinness Road, Trafford Park, Manchester, M17 1SR Tel: 0161-872 0983 Fax: 0161-872 0984 E-mail: phil_doherty@btconnect.com *Gottlieb Packaging Products in Manchester supply all Packaging Products and Materials. From Cartons to Bubblewrap.*
Henry Gough & Son Ltd, 530 Dudley Road, Wolverhampton, WV2 4DZ Tel: (01902) 351200 Fax: (01902) 454887 *Builders' contractors & shopfitters*
Gough & Kelly Ltd, 6 Hales Road, Leeds, LS12 4PL Tel: 0113-279 4801 Fax: 0113-279 8644 E-mail: sales@gough-kelly.co.uk *Integrated system installers*
Gough Packaging Ltd, 49 Whiffler Road, Norwich, NR3 2AW Tel: (01603) 423860 Fax: (01603) 485000 E-mail: leshgough@aol.com *Solid board & plastic packaging manufrs*
Gould Alloys Ltd, Carrwood Road, Chesterfield, Derbyshire, S41 9QB Tel: (01246) 263300 Fax: (01246) 260999 E-mail: sales@gouldalloys.co.uk *Metal stockist & distributors*
Gould Autoplates & Signs Ltd, 2 Blackfriars Trading Estate, Blackfriars Road, Nailsea, Bristol, BS48 4DJ Tel: (01275) 853853 Fax: (01275) 859426 *Sign writers*
Gould Design & Manufacture Ltd, Sefton Street, Heywood, Lancashire, OL10 2JF Tel: (01706) 898000 Fax: (01706) 364426 E-mail: sales@goulds-ltd.com *Paper converters*
▶ Gould Electronics, 7 Scorrier House Workshops, Scorrier, Redruth, Cornwall, TR16 5AU Tel: (01209) 821804 Fax: (020) 7691 9587 E-mail: dave@gouldelectronics.co.uk *Mobile communications*
Leonard Gould & Co. Ltd, Union Park, Bircholt Road, Maidstone, Kent, ME15 9XT Tel: (01622) 623400 Fax: (01622) 686695 E-mail: sales@leonardgould.co.uk *Industrial Packaging solutions Packaging manufacturers*wood, corrugated board, foam blisters, flight cases*
M. Gould (Scunthorpe) Ltd, Midland Road, Scunthorpe, South Humberside, DN16 1DQ Tel: (01724) 866772 Fax: (01724) 855708 E-mail: m.gouldscunthorpeltd@btconnect.com *Civil engineers*
Gould Pulleys & Drives Ltd, Unit 19, Worcester Road Industrial Estate, Chipping Norton, Oxfordshire, OX7 5XW Tel: (01608) 643311 Fax: (01608) 643050 E-mail: sales@gouldpulleys.com *Belt suppliers, gear, power transmission & timing pulley manufrs. Also gears, spur & pulleys, timing.*
▶ Sally Gould, Paper Mill Cottages, Harcourt, Stanton upon Hine Heath, Shrewsbury, SY4 4LS Tel: (01939) 200444 Fax: (01939) 200555 *Audio visual equipment hire*
Gould & Williams Engineers, 8-10 The Kerridge Industrial Estate, Station Road, Alton, Hampshire, GU34 2PT Tel: (01420) 87318 Fax: (01420) 84065 E-mail: gouldandwilliams@btinternet.com *Precision engineers & toolmakers*
Goulding & Bird Ltd, 31 Hatton Wall, London, EC1N 8JJ Tel: (020) 7242 7525 *Bullion dealer & jewellery retailer*
Goulds Jewellers, 145 Highland Road, Southsea, Hampshire, PO4 9EY Tel: (023) 9273 1436 Fax: (023) 9278 8878 E-mail: sales@gouldjewllers.co.uk *Jewellery tools importers* Also at: Portsmouth
Goundrey Horticultural Equipment, Unit 18 Enstone Airfield, Enstone, Chipping Norton, Oxfordshire, OX7 4NP Tel: (01608) 678724 Fax: (0870) 2421091 E-mail: sales@goundreys.co.uk *Compost & turf suppliers*
Gourdomichalis & Co. (Chartering) Ltd, Mitre House, 12-14 Mitre Street, London, EC3A 5BU Tel: (020) 7283 9621 Fax: (020) 7283 3108 E-mail: mail@gourdochart.co.uk *Ship brokers*
Gourmet Food Co. Ltd, Taylor Street, Bury, Lancashire, BL9 6DW Tel: 0161-797 8600 Fax: 0161-763 1116 *Food manufrs*
▶ The Gourmet Garden Co., 23 Belle Vue Road, Salisbury, SP1 3YD Tel: (01722) 328906 E-mail: sarah@thegourmetgarden.co.uk *Sophisticated Gourmet Gift Boxes and Hampers with a difference. Corporate Gifts. Topiaries, Gourmet Plants. Original Gift Boxes and a Bespoke Service for creating Original and Memorable Gifts. Original gifts for birthdays, anniversaries, celebrations, housewarmings or simply to say thank you.*
▶ The Gourmet House, Market Place, Durham, DH1 3NJ Tel: 0191-375 7511 E-mail: info@thegourmethouse.co.uk *Delicatessan & Hamper company*
Government Office For London, Riverwalk House, 157-161 Millbank, London, SW1P 4RR Tel: (020) 7217 3222 Fax: (020) 7217 3473 *Housing & planning government office*
▶ Govin & Clarke Ltd, 11 Greendale Crescent, Leigh, Lancashire, WN7 2LQ Tel: (01942) 604018
Gowen Ocean Sailmakers Ltd, 130 Coast Road, West Mersea, Colchester, CO5 8PG Tel: (01206) 384412 Fax: (01206) 382834 E-mail: sales@gosails.com *Sail & cover manufrs*
Gower Business Systems Ltd, 2 Newmill Court, Enterprise Park, Swansea, SA7 9FG Tel: (01792) 762646 Fax: (01792) 796292 E-mail: gbs@gowerbiz.co.uk *Computer software developers*
Gower Chemicals Ltd, Crymlyn Burrows, Swansea, SA1 8PT Tel: (01792) 473344 Fax: (01792) 456578 E-mail: stewarth@gowerchemicals.ltd.uk *Chemical distributors & waste disposal*
Gower Consultants Ltd, 20 Davigdor Road, Hove, East Sussex, BN3 1TT Tel: (01273) 204646 Fax: (01273) 733043 E-mail: gowerconsultants@compuserve.com *Software house*
Gower Timber Ltd, Crofty Indust Estate, Crofty, Swansea, SA4 3SW Tel: (01792) 851140 Fax: (01792) 850128 E-mail: classact@gowertimberltd.fsnet.co.uk *Timber importers & merchants*
Gowing Technical Services, 21 Norris Way, Rushden, Northamptonshire, NN10 6BP Tel: (01933) 350350 Fax: (01933) 350222 *Portable appliance testing*
▶ Gowise Print, 4 Belmore Road, Norwich, NR7 0PT Tel: (01603) 431304
▶ Gowllands Ltd, 3 Gladstone Road, Croydon, CR0 2BQ Tel: (020) 8689 4125 Fax: (020) 8684 2525 E-mail: sales@gowlands.co.uk *Surgical instrument retailers*
▶ Gowrie Growers, Longforgan, Dundee, DD2 5HJ Tel: (01382) 360620 *Processing vegetable suppliers*
Goyen Controls Co. UK Ltd, Unit 3B, Beechwood, Chineham Business Park, Basingstoke, Hampshire, RG24 8WA Tel: (01256) 817800 Fax: (01256) 843164 E-mail: *Manufacture/sale valves/dust control*
A.K. Goymer & Co. Ltd, Units 2-4, Hazlegreen Works, 62 Edward Road, New Barnet, Barnet, Hertfordshire, EN4 8AZ Tel: (020) 8440 2241 Fax: (020) 8441 8558 E-mail: admin@akgoymer.co.uk *Architectural metalworkers*
▶ GP Cleaners, Unit F3, Innsworth Technology Park, Innsworth Lane, Gloucester, GL3 1DL Tel: (01452) 731630 Fax: (01452) 739212 E-mail: sales@gpcleaners.com *Suppliers of cleaning equipment & products*
GP Precision Engineering Ltd, Unit 19 Nineteen Morses Lane, Industrial Estate, Brightlingsea, Colchester, CO7 0SF Tel: (01206) 303668 Fax: (01206) 303668 E-mail: Enquiries@GPPrecisionEngineering.co.uk *Sub-contract Machining, CNC milling, CNC turning, assembly*
Gpa Signs & Graphics, 51 Rowms Lane, Swinton, Mexborough, South Yorkshire, S64 8AA Tel: (01709) 588856 Fax: (01405) 815503 E-mail: gpa.signs@virgin.net *Manufacture of all types of signs*
GPG Sales Ltd, Unit 6, Luton Street, Liverpool, L5 9XR Tel: 0151-298 1509 Fax: 0151-298 2276 E-mail: sales@gpg-sales.com *Supply toilet cubicles*
Gpi UK Ltd, Unit 6 Merlin Way, North Weald, Epping, Essex, CM16 6HR Tel: (01992) 524439 Fax: (01992) 524522 *Food packaging*
GPS Developments Ltd, 14 Dardion Close, Sandy, Bedfordshire, SG19 1RW Tel: (01767) 681560 Fax: (01767) 691685 E-mail: sales@gpsdevelopments.co.uk *Manufacturers of plastic nameplates & facia panels. Also switches, membrane/keyboard/touch panels & labels plastic, self-adhesive*
▶ GPS Document Management, Forum Suite, Beacon Buildings, Leighswood Road, Aldridge, WS9 8AA Tel: (01922) 456308 Fax: (01922) 459818 E-mail: walsall@gpsdm.co.uk *Printed business cards, letterheads, computer stationery & cheques suppliers*
▶ GPS4Less, The Chimneys, Dauntsey Lock, Chippenham, Wiltshire, SN15 4HD Tel: (0845) 4309207 Fax: (0845) 4309208 E-mail: sales@gps4less.co.uk *Discount GPS sales*
GPT Communications Systems Ltd, 11 Brunswick Road, Plymouth, PL4 0NP Tel: (01752) 660226 Fax: (01752) 601419 *Telecommunications installation & maintenance*
GR Scientific Ltd, Hiam Business Centre, New Road, Maulden, Bedford, MK45 2BG Tel: (01525) 404747 Fax: (01525) 404848 *Scientific equipment manufrs*
▶ GR8-conservatories.co.uk, PO BOX 697, Telford, Shropshire, TF7 9AL Tel: 01952 282069 Fax: 0845 2802071 E-mail: info@gr8-services.co.uk *DIY & Self build conservatories. Design & Planning. Plus building maintenance & carpentry services.*
Gra Bern Electrical, Unit 26, Tweedale Court, Tweedale North Industrial Estate, Telford, Shropshire, TF7 4JZ Tel: (01952) 586038 Fax: (01952) 583365 *Electrical contractors*
▶ Grabby Hire Ltd, Tewkesbury Road, Upton-upon-Severn, Worcester, WR8 0PW Tel: (01684) 592654
Grabern Engraving, Oyster Place, 28 Montrose Rd, Chelmsford, CM2 6TX Tel: (01245) 468223 Fax: (01245) 469121 E-mail: sales@grabernengraving.com Purchasing Contact: K. Troubridge Sales Contact: K. Troubridge Principal Export Areas: Central/East Europe *Manufacturers of spark erosion electrodes. Also general engravers & hot foil stamping. silicon rubber foiling dies.*
A.W. Grace & Son, Unit 124, Culham Site 1, Culham, Abingdon, Oxfordshire, OX14 3DA Tel: (01235) 531462 Fax: (01235) 534021 E-mail: info@awgrace.co.uk *AW Grace & Son are specialists in bespoke metal fabrication, working with mild steel, stainless or aluminium, undertaking major projects or one off commissions. **As metal stockholders we supply all types of metal fabric to the commercial and domestic market, from stainless steel sheets to basic nuts and bolts. If we do not have your requirement in stock, our service extends to sourcing it for you at no additional cost. **Based in Culham, Oxfordshire, we operate throughout the Thames Valley area and beyond, fabricating on site when needed or in our extensive workshops at Culham.*
Grace Construction Products Ltd, 851-852 Birchwood Boulevard, Birchwood, Warrington, WA3 7QZ Tel: (01925) 824824 Fax: (01925) 824033 E-mail: enquiries@gcp-grace.com *Manufrs of admixtures for construction industry*
▶ Grace Consulting Care Advisory Service, The Street, Orchard House, Albury, Guildford, Surrey, GU5 9AG Tel: (01483) 203066 Fax: (01483) 202535 E-mail: info@graceconsulting.co.uk *Care & nursing home*
▶ Gracechurch Container Line Ltd, 1stFloor, Port Of Liverpool, Building Pier Head, Liverpool, L3 1BY Tel: 0151-231 1144
▶ Graceful Reproductions, The Pantile Building, Rendlesham, Woodbridge, Suffolk, IP12 2RJ Tel: (01394) 460014 Fax: (01394) 460014 *Cabinet manufrs*
Gracelands Ltd, Unit 3 Queensway, New Milton, Hampshire, BH25 5NN Tel: (01425) 621200 Fax: (01425) 638637 E-mail: theoffice@gracelandsltd.freeserve.co.uk *Civil engineers*
▶ Gracelands Landscapes Ltd, The Yard, Bramshill Close, Arborfield Cross, Reading, RG2 9PT Tel: 0118-976 0660 Fax: 0118-976 0990 E-mail: info@gracelands-landscapes.co.uk *Landscaping & grounds maintenance services*
Gracey & Associates Ltd, Threeways, High Street, Chelveston, Wellingborough, Northamptonshire, NN9 6AS Tel: 01933 624212 Fax: 01933 624608 E-mail: hire@gracey.com *Sound & vibration instrumentation hire services*
▶ Grade 1 Computers, Hamlin Lodge, Station Road, Ollerton, Newark, Nottinghamshire, NG22 9BN Tel: (01623) 825885 Fax: (01623) 824524 E-mail: sales@grade1computers.co.uk *Computer consultants*
▶ Grade One, Orchansy, Wells Road, Radstock, BA3 3UW Tel: (01761) 420072 Fax: (01761) 420323 E-mail: gdgrade1@aol.com *Polyurethane moulders of elastomer manufrs*
Grade Packaging Ltd, 8 Vulcan Court, Vulcan Way, Coalville, Leicestershire, LE67 3FW Tel: (01530) 275755 Fax: (01530) 275766 E-mail: sales@gradepackaging.com *Polythene converters & distributors*
Gradel Line, 39 Bavaria Road, London, N19 4EU Tel: (020) 7281 7674 E-mail: gradeline@btclick.com *Clothing manufrs*
Gradko International Ltd, St Martins House, 77 Wales Street, Winchester, Hampshire, SO23 0RH Tel: (01962) 860331 Fax: (01962) 841339 E-mail: sales@gradko.co.uk *Laboratory accessories & air monitoring systems manufrs*
Gradus Carpets Ltd, Chapel Mill, Park Green, Macclesfield, Cheshire, SK11 7LZ Tel: (01625) 859000 Fax: (01625) 850352 E-mail: sales@gradusworld.com *Slip resistant stair edgings, tread manufrs*
Gradwood Ltd, Lansdown House, 85 Buxton Road, Stockport, Cheshire, SK2 6LR Tel: 0161-480 9629 Fax: 0161-474 7433 E-mail: sales@gradwood.co.uk *Heating, ventilation, air conditioning engineers*
▶ Peter Graeme Ltd, Unit 14 Flemington Industrial Park, Craigneuk Street, Motherwell, Lanarkshire, ML1 2NT Tel: (01698) 269111 Fax: (01698) 269666
Graeme Scott Furniture, 11 Westcombe, Bideford, Devon, EX39 3JQ Tel: (01237) 424227 Fax: (01237) 470432 *Furniture manufrs*
▶ Graepel Perforators Ltd, Unit 5 Burtonwood Industrial Centre, Phipps La, Burtonwood, Warrington, WA5 4HX Tel: (01925) 229809 Fax: (01925) 228069 E-mail: sales@graepeluk.com Principal Export Areas: Worldwide *Slip resistant flooring & perforated metal products manufrs*
▶ Graepel Perforators Ltd, Unit 5 Burtonwood Industrial Centre, Phipps Lane, Burtonwood, Warrington, WA5 4HX Tel: 0845 4941749 Fax: (01925) 228069 E-mail: sales@graepeluk.com Principal Export Areas: Worldwide *Graepel Perforators and Weavers, Jones & Thomas, Ireland, UK, perforated metal, woven wire, mesh, staircases, spiral staircases, screens, trommels, profile edging, steel flooring, Safedeck flooring, handrails, balustrades, expanded metal, fabrication, duct covers, fly screens, filters, fine woven mesh, woven mesh, wheelchair ramps, portable pedestrian bridge, balustrade infill, square perforations, round perforations, slotted perforations, picture perforations, architectural uses, ceiling panels, balcony panels.*
Graff Diamonds (Japan) Ltd, 29 Albemarle Street, London, W1S 4JA Tel: (020) 7290 6760 Fax: (020) 7581 3415 E-mail: graff@graffdiamonds.com *Jewellery manufrs*
Graff of Newark Ltd, Woodhill Road, Collingham, Newark, Nottinghamshire, NG23 7NR Tel: (01636) 893036 Fax: (01636) 893317 E-mail: sales@graffofnewark.co.uk *High speed audio cassette duplicators*
Graffiti Design International, Design House, Bell Lane Industrial Estate, Uckfield, East Sussex, TN22 1QL Tel: (01825) 763690 Fax: (01825) 763815 E-mail: sales@graffitidesign.co.uk *Sign makers, graphic design suppliers & manufrs*
Graffiti Signs, Parrs Corner Shopping Centre, Stanley Road, Bootle, Merseyside, L20 3EX Tel: 0151-933 2906 Fax: 0151-933 2506 E-mail: sales@graffitisignworks.co.uk *Sign manufrs*
▶ Grafico, Unit 9, Holmbush Farm, Crawley Road, Faygate, Horsham, West Sussex, RH12 4SE Tel: (01293) 852002 Fax: (01293) 852004 *Sign manufrs*
Grafityp (UK) Ltd, 103 Mariner, Tamworth, Staffordshire, B79 7UL Tel: (01827) 300500 Fax: (01827) 51333E-mail: sales@grafityp.co.uk *Sign making systems & print media*
Grafix Signmakers Ltd, Parkhill Road, Kingstown Industrial Estate, Carlisle, CA3 0EX Tel: (01228) 541456 Fax: (01228) 511000 E-mail: info@grafixsigns.co.uk *Sign manufrs*
▶ GrafNic, 12 Kerry Hill Way, Ringlestone, Maidstone, Kent, ME14 2GZ Tel: (01622) 671601 E-mail: nic@grafnic.com
Grafoplast, PO Box 159, Stevenage, Hertfordshire, SG2 7QA Tel: (01438) 861166 Fax: (01438) 861123 E-mail: sales@grafoplasteurope.com *Cable & wire marker manufrs*
Grafton Optical Co. Ltd, 2a Cherry Tree Walk, London, EC1Y 8NX Tel: (020) 7628 7358 Fax: (020) 7628 7359 E-mail: frames@graftonop.fsnet.co.uk *Optical goods importers* Also at: Watford
Grafx Digital Technologies, 73 Market Street, Cheltenham, Gloucestershire, GL50 3NJ Tel: (01242) 704330 Fax: (01242) 704338 E-mail: sales@grafx.co.uk *Apple Macintosh support*
Graggo Ltd, Littlebrook Industrial Park, Dartford, DA1 5PZ Tel: (0845) 6013350 Fax: (01322) 293138 E-mail: geer.sales@ge.com *Generator hire & temporary event power*
Graham Ash Plumbing & Heating Installations, Highways, Station Hill, Lynton, Devon, EX35 6LB Tel: (01598) 753592 *Plumbers*
▶ Graham Barber Electrical Services Ltd, Unit 12 The Dock, Ely, Cambridgeshire, CB7 4GS Tel: (01353) 666831 Fax: (01353) 668132
Graham Bell Design Ltd, 43, Halnaker, Chichester, West Sussex, PO18 0NQ Tel: (01243) 755910 Fax: (01243) 755911 E-mail: john@gbd.co.uk *Internet site design & creation services*
Graham & Brown Ltd, Harwood Street, Blackburn, BB1 3BD Tel: (01254) 691321 Fax: (01254) 582208 E-mail: customer.services@grahambrown.com *Wallpaper manufrs*
Graham Builders Merchants Ltd, Bridgeman Street, Bolton, BL3 6BS Tel: (01204) 389500 Fax: (01204) 363205 *Plumbers merchants* Also at: Branches throughout UK
Graham Builders Merchants Ltd, Block 4 Cadzow Industrial Estate, Hamilton, Lanarkshire, ML3 7QU Tel: (01698) 422522 Fax: (01698) 423284 E-mail: sales@grahamgroup.com *Builders merchants*
▶ Graham Construction Division, Peppercorn House, 8 Huntingdon Street, St. Neots, Cambridgeshire, PE19 1BH Tel: (01480) 404404 Fax: (01480) 403377
Graham D Davies, Cwmgeifr, Llandilo Graban, Builth Wells, Powys, LD2 3SJ Tel: (01982) 560246 Fax: (01982) 560246 *Agricultural contractors*
Graham Engineering Ltd, Edward Street, Whitewalls Industrial Estate, Nelson, Lancashire, BB9 8SY Tel: (01282) 695121 Fax: (01282) 698498 E-mail: sales@graham-eng.co.uk *Prototype development engineering*
Graham Environmental Services Ltd, 34 Bellfield Street, Dundee, DD1 5HZ Tel: (01382) 206552 Fax: (01250) 870055 *Pest control*
▶ Graham Firth Communications Ltd, 9-10 Armley Link, Armley Road, Leeds, LS12 2QN Tel: 0113-279 1601 Fax: 0113-231 0619 *CCTV maintenance & manufrs*
▶ Graham Fox Garden Design and Landscaping, Clover Cottage, 75 Compton Bassett, Calne, Wiltshire, SN11 8SN Tel: 07796 654775 Fax: 01249 760460 E-mail: gbl.fox@btinternet.com *Graham Fox Garden Design and Landscaping is a small company *that provides a comprehensive range of garden design and construction services in Wiltshire and surrounding areas. We will conduct a free visit and provide free estimates for any proposed project. *Designs are produced, by hand, in colour and with planting and hard landscaping plans. *Landscaping includes: clearance, terracing/patios and other paving (e.g. paths), pergolas, ponds, lighting, water features, walls, irrigation, drainage, bed edging, etc, etc. *Garden maintenance tasks can also be undertaken (tree pruning, lawn laying and improvement, hedge and grass cutting, planting, clearing, etc. etc).*
James Graham, 85 Derryloughan Road, Loughgall, Armagh, BT61 8PH Tel: (028) 3889 1312 Fax: (028) 3889 1843 *Garage services*
Graham Jones & Co 77 Beaconsfield R D, Beaconsfield Road, London, SE3 7LG Tel: (020) 8858 4039 Fax: (020) 8293 5920 *Patent attorney agent*
Graham Jones Crane Hire Ltd, Rhosddu Industrial Estate, Rhosrobin, Wrexham, Clwyd, LL11 4YL Tel: (01978) 366458 Fax: (01978) 310573 E-mail: jonescranehire@aol.com *Graham Jones Crane Hire ; a rapidly expanding based in North Wales, bordering Cheshire and with further depots in Telford, Shropshire and Warrington Lancashire.*Our name has become synonymous with a swift, efficient and professional service which in turn has led to the continued and rapid expansion of the Company.*Every lift is attended by our team of specialists working hand in hand with our clients to ensure that a Safe and cost effective lifting solution is applied, resulting in each and every customers satisfaction.*Our*

continued

Company Information

continuation
range of Cranes is varied but include Limited access Machines such as 20 ton city Cranes and Iron Fairys right up to all terrain Cranes of 120 Ton Capacity whilst awaiting delivery of a Fourth Spierings Five Axle Mobile Tower Crane later this year. "We would be pleased to arrange a free survey, and promise to deliver the most cost effective lifting solution with no obligation whatsoever.

Graham Leonard Ltd, Alexander House, Ringtail Place, Burscough Industrial Estate, Ormskirk, Lancashire, L40 8LA Tel: (01704) 895421 Fax: (01704) 895471 *Crane service & repair*

Graham Lloyd Bedford Ltd, Ampthill Road, Bedford, MK42 9JN Tel: (01234) 267810 Fax: (01234) 212942 E-mail: graham@grahamlloyd.co.uk *We have traditionally packed confectionery and gift products for Christmas & Easter. At the same time we have been developing partnerships with a range of companies locally and nationally and have packed many different types of products; most recently a line of consumer products for Fuji. We also offer a picking and packing service which includes dispatch throughout the UK and worldwide. Early in 2002 we attained British Retail Consortium (BRC) accreditation - although through our connections with larger manufacturers we have previously been approved directly by Sainsbury and Tesco as well as Debenhams, Safeway, Boots, Terry's, Thornton's and Kraft foods.*

Mick Graham Plastics Ltd, Unit 17 19, Argall Avenue, London, E10 7QP Tel: (020) 8539 7388 Fax: (020) 8539 2355 *Rotational moulders*

▶ Graham Packaging, Irton House, Warpsgrove Lane, Chalgrove, Oxford, OX44 7TH Tel: (01865) 400315 Fax: (01865) 893100

▶ Graham Paul, 372-374 Cyncoed Road, Cardiff, CF23 6SA Tel: (029) 2068 1980 Fax: (029) 2068 1981 *Accountants*

Graham Plumbing & Heating Merchants, Hillam Road, Bradford, West Yorkshire, BD2 1QN Tel: (01274) 735831 Fax: (01274) 720395 *Building & plumbers merchants*

▶ Graham Robertson Electrical Ltd, 5 Fountain Road, Bridge of Allan, Stirling, FK9 4ET Tel: (01786) 832246 Fax: (01786) 834335

Graham Systems, Lagan Mills, Dromore, County Down, BT25 1AS Tel: (028) 9269 0291 Fax: (028) 9269 3854 E-mail: info@grahamsystems.co.uk *Stationery & computer sales*

Graham Taylor Sales Ltd, Camps Farm, Hoe Lane, Nazeing, Waltham Abbey, Essex, EN9 2RG Tel: (01279) 635651 Fax: (01992) 892907 *Ventilation suppliers*

Thomas Graham & Sons Ltd, The Maltings, Shaddongate, Carlisle, CA2 5TU Tel: (01228) 525364 Fax: (01228) 547313 E-mail: sales@thomas-graham.co.uk *Steel stockholders*

Thomas Graham & Sons Ltd, Maple Works, Northgate, White Lund Estate, Morecambe, Lancashire, LA3 3AZ Tel: (01524) 69112 Fax: (01524) 841076 E-mail: morecambe@thomas-graham.co.uk *Fasteners, bolt & nut distributors* Also at: Carlisle & Egremont

▶ Graham Tiso, 41 Commercial St, Edinburgh, EH6 6JD Tel: 0131-554 0804 Fax: 0131-554 9682 E-mail: mail@tiso.co.uk *Suppliers of camping & outdoor equipment*

Graham Toms Displays, 13 Lindsay Street, Kettering, Northamptonshire, NN16 8RG Tel: (01536) 510858 Fax: (01536) 510858 E-mail: info@grahamtoms.co.uk *Exhibition system graphics*

W.F. Graham (Northampton) Ltd, Pond Wood Close, Moulton Park Industrial Estate, Northampton, NN3 6RT Tel: (01604) 642212 Fax: (01604) 648414 E-mail: books@wfgraham.co.uk *Children's book publishers*

Graham Wood, Chartwell Road, Lancing, West Sussex, BN15 8TY Tel: (01903) 755991 Fax: (01903) 755384 E-mail: mail@grahamwoodstructural.co.uk *Structural steelwork engineers*

Graham & Woolnough, Suite 9, SMM Business Park, Dock Road, Birkenhead, Merseyside, CH41 1DT Tel: 0151-653 7948 Fax: 0151-653 7990 E-mail: information@grahamwoolnough.com *Marine surveyors & naval architects*

Philip Grahame International Ltd, Dukes Park Industrial Estate, Montrose Road, Chelmsford, CM2 6TE Tel: (01245) 451717 Fax: (01245) 451870 E-mail: sales@pgrahame.com *Cable support systems manufrs*

Graham's Cartons, Garston Quays, Blackburn Street, Liverpool, L19 8EL Tel: 0151-427 6565 Fax: 0151-427 5123 E-mail: colin.graham@grahams-cartons.co.uk *Carton merchants & manufrs*

▶ Grahams Dairies, Changue Farm, Cumnock, Ayrshire, KA18 2QU Tel: (01290) 421155 Fax: (01290) 425988 *Dairy services*

Grahams Garden Machinery Ltd, Brighton Cross Grampound Road, Grampound Road, Truro, Cornwall, TR2 4HD Tel: (01726) 884001 Fax: (01726) 883991 E-mail: parkinsgm@bt.connect.com *Grass cutting machine distributors*

Grahams Group plc, 96 Temple Park Cresent, Edinburgh, EH11 1JR Tel: 0131-228 2345 Fax: 0131-228 5405 E-mail: mikedick@graham-group.co.uk *Plumbing, electrical, heating dealers merchants*

Grahams Machinery Sales Ltd, Deva House, Knutsford Way, Sealand Industrial Estate, Chester, CH1 4NX Tel: (01244) 376764 Fax: (01244) 377177 E-mail: sales@grahams-machinery.co.uk *Welding equipment distributors-engineers distribs*

Graig Consultants Ltd, 25 Heol Cefn Onn, Lisvane, Cardiff, CF14 0TP Tel: (029) 2044 0200 Fax: (029) 2044 0207 E-mail: mail@graig.com *Ship owners*

J.M. Grail (General Engineers) Ltd, Newtown Road, Steam Mills, Cinderford, Gloucestershire, GL14 3JE Tel: (01594) 822054 Fax: (01594) 826654 E-mail: info@grail.eu.com *Precision*

continued

machining, factory maintenance & fabrication specialists

Grail & Preece Ltd, 44 Hamstead Road, Hockley, Birmingham, B19 1DB Tel: 0121-554 6667 Fax: 0121-554 6992 E-mail: info@grailandpreece.co.uk *Plumbing & central heating services*

Grain Farmers U A P, Honey Pot Lane, Colsterworth, Grantham, Lincolnshire, NG33 5LY Tel: (01476) 862790 Fax: (01476) 862795 E-mail: info@grainfarmers.co.uk *Agricultural grain storage services*

Grain & Feed Trade Association Ltd, Chapel Court, 6 Chapel Place, London, EC2A 3SH Tel: (020) 7814 9666 Fax: (020) 7814 8383 E-mail: post@gafta.com *International trade association*

Grain Plant Sales Ltd, Barton Road, Haslingfield, Cambridge, CB23 1LW Tel: (01223) 872595 Fax: (01223) 872600 *Construction equipment suppliers*

▶ Grainfarmers Agricultural Services, Northfield, Portington Road, Eastrington, Goole, North Humberside, DN14 7QE Tel: (01430) 410149 Fax: (01430) 410150 *Agricultural services*

Grainfarmers Uap Ltd, Lark Whistle Farm Road, Michelldever Station, Micheldever, Winchester, Hampshire, SO21 3BG Tel: (01962) 794000 Fax: (01962) 794001 *Agricultural merchants*

Graingate, 2 Lockwood Close, Nottingham, NG5 9JN Tel: 0115-967 1888 Fax: 0115-967 1777 E-mail: info@graingate.co.uk *Plastic vacuum formers, plastic mouldings, laser cutting, thermoformed products, vacuum formed products, point of sale products, laser cutting*

Grainge & Hodder Ltd, 26-27 Marshall Street, Birmingham, B1 1LE Tel: 0121-632 6079 Fax: 0121-632 6079 E-mail: grainge@globalnet.co.uk *Photo etching services for model railway & clock components*

Grainger Building Services Ltd, 163 Church Road, Holywood, County Down, BT18 9BZ Tel: (028) 9042 2555 Fax: (028) 9042 5428 E-mail: info@grainger-uk.com *Roofing & cladding contractors*

Grainger Fire Protection, Unit 1a Newton Court, Wavertree Technology Park, Liverpool, L13 1EJ Tel: 0151-220 4068 Fax: 0151-259 4365 E-mail: enquiries@graingersystems.co.uk *Fire extinguishers, alarms & lighting*

Grainger Plastics Ltd, Unit 3 Joseph Wilson Industrial Estate, Millstrood Road, Whitstable, Kent, CT5 3PS Tel: (01227) 276806 Fax: (01227) 770731 *Plastic & injection mouldings manufrs*

Grainger Tubolt Ltd, Unit A, Meyrick Owen Way, Pembroke Dock, Dyfed, SA72 6WS Tel: (01646) 683584 Fax: (01646) 621392 E-mail: sales@grainger-tubolt.co.uk *Tubular jointing systems manufrs*

Grainger & Worrall Ltd, Unit 1-4 Stanmore Industrial Estate, Bridgnorth, Shropshire, WV15 5HP Tel: (01746) 768250 Fax: (01746) 768251 E-mail: sales@gwcast.co.uk *Prototype development pattern makers*

Grainword Ltd, 3 Warnford Industrial Estate, Clayton Road, Hayes, Middlesex, UB3 1BQ Tel: (020) 8561 2401 Fax: (020) 8756 0501 E-mail: sales@supapress.com *Nameplate & label manufrs*

Gram (UK) Ltd, 2 The Technology Centre, London Road, Swanley, Kent, BR8 7AG Tel: (01322) 616900 Fax: (01322) 616901 E-mail: info@gramuk.co.uk *Gram Commercial A/S manufacturers refrigerators and freezers for professional use. Their product range is designed to meet the needs of commercial kitchens, canteens, restaurants, fast food outlets etc. They aim to be the market leader in terms of quality, functional design and consideration for the environment. Gram has strong market positions in Denmark, Great Britain, Norway, Sweden, Germany and the Netherlands, where they offer all their customers expert local service.*

Grampian A T VS, Inverythan Garage, Fyvie, Turriff, Aberdeenshire, AB53 8JU Tel: (01888) 511511 Fax: (01888) 511511 E-mail: rena.findlay@btinternet.com *We are the largest secondhand utility and race quadbike dealer in the North East of Scotland. All major makes and models - Honda, Yamaha, Bombardier, Suzuki. On-site sales, hire, lease, repairs and servicing of all ATV""s available. Also a large selection of Quad trailers and attachments for spraying/brushing/snowploughs and other Logic agricultural equipment available on request.*

Grampian Business Bureau, 23 Carden Place, Aberdeen, AB10 1UQ Tel: (01224) 625836 Fax: (0845) 4508346 E-mail: info@gbb.co.uk *Accountants*

Grampian Catering Equipment Ltd, Unit 2, New Inn Buildings, Market Street, Ellon, Aberdeenshire, AB41 9JD Tel: (01358) 729500 Fax: (01358) 729501 E-mail: sales@grampiancateringequipment.co.uk *Suppliers of catering, bar & fast food equipment, specialists in sales & service of rancilio espresso coffee machines*

Grampian Country Pork Ashton, Mackeson Road, Ashton-under-Lyne, Lancashire, OL6 8HZ Tel: 0161-344 5601 Fax: 0161-339 2644 *Food packers*

Grampian Country Pork Case, Sandy's Moor, Wiveliscombe, Taunton, Somerset, TA4 2TU Tel: (01984) 624642 Fax: (01984) 624353 *Abattoir*

Grampian Country Pork Suffolk Ltd, Little Wratting, Haverhill, Suffolk, CB9 7TD Tel: (01440) 704444 Fax: (01440) 762120 E-mail: grampian@gcfg.com *Processed & cooked meat products manufrs*

Grampian Country Porks Ltd, Mile Bank, Whitchurch, Shropshire, SY13 4JX Tel: (01948) 662367 Fax: (01948) 662369 *Food products manufrs*

Grampian Electronic Components Ltd, 19-25 Don Street, Woodside, Aberdeen, AB24 2RR Tel: (01224) 481000 Fax: (01224) 480111 E-mail: info@grampian-electronics.com *Bespoke computer systems manufrs*

▶ Grampian Fastners, Grampian House, Pitmedden Road, Dyce, Aberdeen, AB21 0DP Tel: (01224) 772777 Fax: (01224) 772778 E-mail: sales@grampianfasteners.com *Distributor & stockist of industrial fasteners & fixings*

Grampian International Freight Ltd, Grampian House, Hewett Road, Gaptus Hall Industrial Estate, Great Yarmouth, Norfolk, NR31 0NN Tel: (01493) 441212 Fax: (01493) 440391 E-mail: gtyarmouth@gif.co.uk *International transportation agents* Also at: Liverpool

Grampian Leisure, 5-13 Duff Street, Aberdeen, AB24 5LF Tel: (01224) 646422 Fax: (01224) 646630 *Amusement machine maintenance services*

▶ Grampian Maclennan Distribution Services, Industrial Estate, Cornhill Road, Aberchirder, Huntly, Aberdeenshire, AB54 7ST Tel: (01466) 780345 Fax: (01466) 780644

▶ Grampian Maclennan's Distribution Services Ltd, Station Road, Fordoun, Laurencekirk, Kincardineshire, AB30 1NN Tel: (01561) 320641 Fax: (01561) 320643

Grampian Oat Products, Boyndie, Boyndie, Banff, AB45 2LR Tel: (01261) 843330 Fax: (01261) 843394 *Oat processing plant services*

▶ Grampian Packaging Supplies Ltd, 9 Kirkton Avenue, Pitmedden Industrial Estate, Dyce, Aberdeen, AB21 0BF Tel: (01224) 770056 Fax: (01224) 770067 E-mail: info@grampian-packaging.co.uk *Packaging supply services*

Grampian Plant & Machinery, Moss-Side of Arthrath, Ellon, Aberdeenshire, AB41 8EF Tel: (01358) 711393 Fax: (01358) 711398 *Hydraulic spares suppliers*

Grampian Steel Services Ltd, Greenford, Oldmeldrum, Inverurie, Aberdeenshire, AB51 0BH Tel: (01651) 872040 Fax: (01651) 872069 E-mail: grampiansteel@compuserve.com *Steel stockholders*

▶ Grampiansteel Buildings, The Show Site, 2 Ugie Road, Peterhead, Aberdeenshire, AB42 1NR Tel: (01779) 480700 Fax: (01779) 480701 E-mail: sean@grampiansteelbuildings.co.uk *Designers & erectors of steel buildings*

Gramton Engineering Ltd, Unit 5 Moilliett Court, Soho Way, Smethwick, West Midlands, B66 2SU Tel: 0121-565 0563 Fax: 0121-565 0563 *Press tools, jigs & fixture manufrs*

Granada Typewriters & Copiers, 38 Cardinal Ave, Kingston upon Thames, Surrey, KT2 5SB Tel: (020) 8549 9785 Fax: (020) 8549 9785 *Office equipment sales & services*

Tom Granby Liverpool, Caddick Road, Knowsley Business Park, Prescot, Merseyside, L34 9HP Tel: 0151-548 8768 Fax: 0151-549 1979 E-mail: a.smith@dbcfoodservice.co.uk *Cold storage distributors*

Grand Age Engineering Ltd, Elm Tree Farm, Kirby Misperton, Malton, North Yorkshire, YO17 6XT Tel: (01653) 668288 Fax: (01653) 668289 E-mail: sales@grandsweep.com *Manufacturers & designers of specialist equipment*

Grand Atlantic Hotel, The Grand Atlantic, Beach Road, Weston-super-Mare, Avon, BS23 1BA Tel: (01934) 626543 Fax: (01934) 415048 *Hotel & conference facility*

Grand Chain Ltd, Maple House, Laughton Road, Ringmer, Lewes, East Sussex, BN8 5SY Tel: (01273) 813345 Fax: (01273) 814 153 E-mail: sales@grandchain.co.uk *Transformer manufrs*

Grand Engineering, Premier Works, Providence Street, Cradley Heath, West Midlands, B64 5DR Tel: (01384) 562551 Fax: (01384) 410144 *Industrial distribution*

Grand Junction Boat Co., Canal Maintenance Yard, Blisworth Arm, Blisworth, Northampton, NN7 3EF Tel: (01604) 858043 Fax: (01604) 858043 *Boat testing & repairs*

Grand Prix Express, Swan Road, Mochdre Business Park, Mochdre, Colwyn Bay, Clwyd, LL28 5HB Tel: (01492) 545293 Fax: (01492) 546241 E-mail: john@grandprixexpress.com *Parcel couriers*

Grandisson, Unit 27, Finnimore Industrial Estate, Ottery St. Mary, Devon, EX11 1NR Tel: (01404) 814425 Fax: (01404) 813332 *Decorative plaster to retail & trade*

Grandrew Securities, 7 Linden Avenue, Wembley, Middlesex, HA9 8BB Tel: (020) 8902 5674 Fax: (020) 8900 9218 *Install & maintain burglar alarms & intercom systems*

▶ Grandscapes, 36 Kendal Avenue, London, N18 1NG Tel: 07908 772505 E-mail: info@grandscapes.co.uk *Gardening, landscaping & garden design services based in north london, provides professional landscape design, construction services & free estimates*

▶ Grandstand Hire & Services, 6 Maltings Way, Grimsby, South Humberside, DN31 1QS Tel: (01472) 813271 Fax: (01472) 813271

▶ Granelli McDermott Ltd, Demmings Road, Cheadle, Cheshire, SK8 2PE Tel: 0161-428 7595

Granflex (Roofing) Ltd, Brick Kiln Lane, Basford, Stoke-On-Trent, ST4 7BT Tel: (01782) 202208 Fax: (01782) 273601 E-mail: sales@granflexroofing.co.uk *Roofing contractors, felt*

Grange Aggregates, Waterloo Road, Stoke-on-Trent, ST6 3HX Tel: (01782) 212765 Fax: (01782) 537900 *Refractories manufrs*

Grange Arable Consultancy, Peplow Grange, Peplow, Market Drayton, Shropshire, TF9 3JT Tel: (01952) 541633 Fax: (01952) 541633 *Arable consultants*

▶ Grange Buildig Services, Granary Cottage, Vogrie, Gorebridge, Midlothian, EH23 4NT Tel: 0131-665 0101

▶ Grange Building Services, Vogrie Grange, Gorebridge, Midlothian, EH23 4NT Tel: (01875) 823366 Fax: (01875) 823399 E-mail: gbs@vogrie.co.uk

Grange Controls Ltd, Unit 3 Midland Way, Thornbury, Bristol, BS35 2BS Tel: (01454) 418256 Fax: (01454) 415214 E-mail: sales@grangecontrols.co.uk *Valve distributors & agents*

Grange Engineering, Trenholme Bar, Northallerton, North Yorkshire, DL6 3LE Tel: (01642) 706074 Fax: (01642) 701641 *Engineers*

Grange Flooring (S.G. Lersch) Ltd, Unit H6, Park Avenue Estate, Sundon Park, Luton, LU3 3BP Tel: (01582) 596999 Fax: (01582) 599638 *Flooring contractors*

Grange Gaskets (Bradford) Ltd, Carnarvon Works, Bolton Lane, Bradford, West Yorkshire, BD2 1AE Tel: (01274) 734238 Fax: (01274) 306594 *Manufacturers of gaskets, washer seals & other metal products*

Grange Hill Products Ltd, 124 Countesthorpe Road, Wigston, Leicestershire, LE18 4PG Tel: 0116-277 6255 Fax: 0116-277 6255 *Pattern & mould vacuum manufrs*

Grange Industries, Unit 2 Bessemer Close, Cardiff, CF11 8DL Tel: (02920) 345366 Fax: (02920) 399111 E-mail: ryan@grangeindustries.co.uk *Grange Industries was established in 1980. It has grown & diversified, & is now an E & I design house, as well as a fabrication & panel building workshop. . Grange Industry also manufactures vent caps (to SR25 spec) as well the Grippia & Tornado. Project management & installation is another aspect of Grange Industries. We can provide turn-key projects, with full on sight documentation. Instrumentation, Electrical & telemetry software: Design, appraisals, approvals, Project installation, project management; Training; Consultancy; metering; telemetry programming (isagraph & Ulysses) Panels: - (Electrical; Electronic; Pneumatic) Design, build, testing, Installation Kiosk builds - (grp telemetry rooms, electrical, c.p, various) Design, build, testing, installation Mechanical: Fabrication, Steel services, Pneumatic panels Innovations: Grippia; Tornado; Production: Tornado; Weather Caps; Grippia Projects: Feasibility studies, scope of works, Designs, Installation, management.*

Grange Joinery, Trent Business Centre, Canal Street, Long Eaton, Nottingham, NG10 4HN Tel: 0115-946 3433 *Joinery manufrs*

Grange Products Ltd, Unit 4 Station Road, Reddish, Stockport, Cheshire, SK5 6ND Tel: 0161-480 3318 *Electronic assembly manufrs*

▶ Grange Roller Shutter, 12 32 Dryden Road, Loanhead, Midlothian, EH20 9LZ Tel: 0131-440 7000 Fax: 0131-440 7003 E-mail: sales@grangedoor.com

Grange Square Ltd, Halloughton Grange Whitacre Heath, Nether Whitacre, Coleshill, Birmingham, B46 2HP Tel: (01675) 481661 Fax: (01675) 481615 *Precision CNC machining manufrs*

Grange Steels, P O Box 2, Stoke-on-Trent, ST8 6JZ Tel: (01782) 510210 Fax: (01782) 510211 E-mail: grangesteels@asdplc.co.uk *Steel stockholders*

▶ Grange Storage & Distribution, Grange Road, Batley, West Yorkshire, WF17 6LW Tel: (01924) 420777

Grange Technology Ltd, Rosebank, Stream Road, Upton, Didcot, Oxfordshire, OX11 9JG Tel: (01235) 851818 Fax: (01235) 851818 E-mail: gkt@gtech.demon.co.uk *Produces computer software*

Grange Total Solutions Ltd, The Grange, Grange Lane, Downham, Billericay, Essex, CM11 1LE Tel: (01268) 710209 Fax: (01268) 710095 E-mail: info@grangetotalsolutionsfsnet.co.uk *Vending machine manufrs*

Grange Vehicle Security, 36 The Crescent, Bricket Wood, St. Albans, Hertfordshire, AL2 3NF Tel: (01923) 673456 *Vehicle security domestic & industrial security suppliers*

Grange Welding Services, Earl Street, Sheffield, S1 4PY Tel: 0114-272 7606 Fax: 0114-272 7606 *Wrought ironworkers & security grille manufrs*

▶ Grangefix Leeds Ltd, 107 Whitehall Road East, Birkenshaw, Bradford, West Yorkshire, BD11 2LQ Tel: (01274) 684684 Fax: (01274) 684684

Grangemouth Ship Repairs Ltd, Carron Dock, Grangemouth, Stirlingshire, FK3 8UH Tel: (01324) 665745 Fax: (01324) 665742 E-mail: emple@gsrship.co.uk *Ship & marine engineers*

Grangers International Ltd, Grange Close, Clover Nook Industrial Park, Somercotes, Alfreton, Derbyshire, DE55 4QT Tel: (01773) 521521 Fax: (01773) 521262 E-mail: grangers@grangers.co.uk *Waterproofing solution manufrs*

Grangestone Engineering Co., Grangestone Industrial Estate, Ladywell Avenue, Girvan, Ayrshire, KA26 9PL Tel: (01465) 712505 Fax: (01465) 712505 *Precision & general engineering services*

Grangestone Grain Co., Girvan Distillery, Grangestone Industrial Estate, Girvan, Ayrshire, KA26 9PT Tel: (01465) 713531 Fax: (01465) 713533 *Wheat processing*

Grangewards Agricultural Engineers, 454 Hern Road Ramsey St Marys, Ramsey St. Marys, Ramsey, Huntingdon, Cambridgeshire, PE26 2TJ Tel: (01733) 844590 *Agricultural engineers*

Grangewood Fencing Supplies, Grangewood, Netherseal, Swadlincote, Derbyshire, DE12 8BG Tel: (01283) 762662 Fax: (01283) 762642 *Fencing equipment suppliers*

▶ Grangewood Fencing Supplies, Midland House, Brent, Wilnecote, Tamworth, Staffordshire, B77 5DF Tel: (01827) 288713 Fax: (01827) 288713 *Gate & fencing suppliers*

Granit Ops Ltd, West Dean Road, West Tytherley, Salisbury, SP5 1QG Tel: (01980) 862253 Fax: (01980) 863073 E-mail: stone@granit-ops.co.uk *Kitchen worktops & marble manufrs*

▶ Granite City Events, 27 Justice Street, Aberdeen, AB11 5HS Tel: (01224) 633733 Fax: (01224) 633733 E-mail: info@granitecityevents.com *Event Managment, Fun Days, Lighting, Pa, Star cloths, effects, Table decorations, dinner dances*

Granite City Ice Ltd, Unit 3A, Albert Quay, Aberdeen, AB11 5PX Tel: (01224) 581888 Fax: (01224) 582666 *Ice manufrs*

Granite Financial Management, Quayside House, King Edward Quu, Colchester, CO2 8JB Tel: (01206) 505035 Fax: (01206) 505034 E-mail: info@granitecomputers.co.uk *Computer services*

Granite Granite Ltd, Russell Gardens, Wickford, Essex, SS11 8QG Tel: (01268) 761214 Fax: (01268) 560088 *Granite & marble importers*

Granning Engineering Ltd, 37 Melford Court, Hardwick Grange, Woolston, Warrington, WA1 4RZ Tel: (01925) 810400 Fax: (01925) 817153 E-mail: sales@grannings.com *Suspension & axles retailers*

▶ Granny Kearneys, 10 Down Business Centre Down Business Park, 46 Belfast Road, Downpatrick, County Down, BT30 9UP Tel: (028) 4483 8883 Fax: (028) 4483 8883 *Food manufrs*

Granny S Kitchen Ltd, St Catherines Mill, Broad Lane, Leeds, LS13 2TD Tel: 0113-255 3884 Fax: 0113-239 3694 *Preserve manufrs*

▶ Grant Ameristone Ltd, Cawdor House, London Road, Woolmer Green, Knebworth, Hertfordshire, SG3 6JE Tel: (01438) 811009

▶ Grant Contractors Ltd, The Mill Works, Station Lane, Bristol, BS7 9NB Tel: 0117-951 5959 Fax: 0117-951 5155 E-mail: grantcontractors@aol.com *Groundwork's civil engineering, tarmac & paving services*

D. Grant Crawley Ltd, Henrys Farm Cottage, Carr Lane, Lathom, Ormskirk, Lancashire, L40 4BT Tel: (0845) 1473626 Fax: (0870) 4602061 E-mail: grant@dgc.co.uk *Computer systems & software suppliers*

▶ Grant Dufftown Ltd, 33 Balvenie Street, Dufftown, Keith, Banffshire, AB55 4AS Tel: (01340) 820241 Fax: (01340) 820997

The Grant Group Ltd, 47A Linfield Industrial Estate, Belfast, BT12 5LA Tel: (028) 9032 3329 Fax: (028) 9032 3218 E-mail: info@thegrantgroup.com Principal Export Areas: Africa *Heating control manufrs*

Grant Handling Ltd, Unit 8 Alma Place, Rochester, Kent, ME2 2AE Tel: (01634) 714142 Fax: (01634) 290512 E-mail: sales@forktrucks.co.uk *Fork lift truck suppliers*

▶ Grant Handling Ltd, 1 Rosse Close, Washington, Tyne & Wear, NE37 1ET Tel: 0191-417 6660 Fax: 0191-417 6661 E-mail: newcastle@forktrucks.co.uk *Fork lift repairers & suppliers*

J. & G. Grant, Glenfarclas Distillery, Ballindalloch, Banffshire, AB37 9BD Tel: (01807) 500209 Fax: (01807) 500234 E-mail: enquiries@glenfarclas.co.uk *Distillers*

▶ Jo Grant Photographer, St. Davids Road, Southsea, Hampshire, PO5 1QJ Tel: (023) 9283 9139 *Portrait and Event Photographer including Weddings, Family, Maternity, Babies and Makeovers*

Grant & Livingston Ltd, Kings Road, Canvey Island, Essex, SS8 0RA Tel: (01268) 696855 Fax: (01268) 697018 E-mail: gandl.canvey@btconnect.com *Tanks, vessels, steelwork & pipework manufrs*

Peter Grant Papers Ltd, Caton Road, Lansil Industrial Estate, Lancaster, LA1 3PQ Tel: (01524) 843678 Fax: (01524) 843644 *Manufacturers of speciality tissue*

Peter Grant Papers Ltd, Stafford Park 12, Telford, Shropshire, TF3 3BJ Tel: (01952) 292200 Fax: (01952) 291108 E-mail: sales@pgpapers.com *Paper merchants*

▶ Grant Pneumatic Services, Malvern Road, Maidenhead, Berkshire, SL6 7RD Tel: (01628) 621161 Fax: (01628) 784419 E-mail: info@grantpneumatics.co.uk *Compressed air systems for the industry.*

Grant Print Ltd, North Esplanades West, Aberdeen, AB11 5RJ Tel: (01224) 574329

Samuel Grant Ltd, 146-148 Garnet Road, Leeds, LS11 5LA Tel: 0113-270 7221 Fax: 0113-277 9867 E-mail: sales@samuelgrant.co.uk Principal Export Areas: Worldwide *Adhesive tapes, paper & packaging distributors*

Samuel Grant (North East) Ltd, Unit 13-16, Tanfield Lea South Industrial Estate, Tanfield Lea, Stanley, County Durham, DH9 9QX Tel: (01207) 283510 Fax: (01207) 290063 E-mail: nesales@samuelgrant.com *Packaging distributors*

▶ Grant Saw, Norman House, 110-114 Norman Road, London, SE10 9EH Tel: (020) 8858 6971 Fax: (020) 8858 5796 E-mail: enquiries@grantsaw.co.uk *Solicitors*

▶ Grant Smith Electrical, 16 Hutcheson Drive, Largs, Ayrshire, KA30 8EE Tel: (07717) 734880 E-mail: enquiry@gselectrical.com *Electrical contractor. Domestic and commercial installations, fully qualified and insured. Shop fitting, lighting, alarms, 415 Volt, inspection and testing.*

Grant, Spencer, Caisley & Porteous, 16 High Holborn, London, WC1V 6BY Tel: (020) 7216 5888 Fax: (020) 7831 6925 E-mail: grant@gscp.co.uk *Registered trade mark agents*

Grant & Stone Ltd, 54 Montem Lane, Slough, SL1 2QJ Tel: (01753) 520462 Fax: (01753) 511582 E-mail: sales@grant-stone.co.uk *Builders merchants*

Grant Systems Ltd, Crown House, 72 Hammersmith Road, London, W14 8TH Tel: (020) 7559 9778 Fax: (020) 7559 3401 *IT solutions service provider*

W. Grant, 122 Main Street, Aberchirder, Huntly, Aberdeenshire, AB54 7TD Tel: (01466) 780227 Fax: (01466) 780227 *Agricultural engineers*

▶ William Grant & Sons Ltd, Glenfiddich Distillery, Dufftown, Keith, Banffshire, AB55 4DH Tel: (01340) 820000 Fax: (01340) 820805 *Distillery*

▶ Granta Design Ltd, Rustat House, 62 Clifton Road, Cambridge, CB1 7EG Tel: (01223) 518895 Fax: (01223) 506432 E-mail: info@grantadesign.com *Software providers*

▶ Grantchester Construction Ltd, 54 Broad Street, Ely, Cambridgeshire, CB7 4AH Tel: (01353) 667800 Fax: (01353) 667900

▶ Grantham Clothing Co., Unit 1a Partnership House, Withambrook Park Industrial Estate, Grantham, Lincolnshire, NG31 9ST Tel: (01476) 594330 Fax: (01476) 593863 E-mail: granthamclothing@btclick.com

Grantham Fabrications & Profile Services Ltd, Venture Way, Grantham, Lincolnshire, NG31 7XS Tel: (01476) 577037 Fax: (01476) 576967 E-mail: reception@g-fabs.demon.co.uk *General engineers*

Grantham Roofing Services, Withambrook Park Industrial Estate, Grantham, Lincolnshire, NG31 9ST Tel: (01476) 570771 Fax: (01476) 570746 E-mail: granroof@btinternet.com *Roofing contractors*

Grantham Welding Ltd, Unit3 & 4 North Bank, Berry Hill Industrial Estate, Droitwich, Worcestershire, WR9 9AU Tel: (01905) 773335 Fax: (01905) 773335 *Welded fabrication manufrs*

Grantham Woodmill Ltd, Ruston Road, Grantham, Lincolnshire, NG31 9SW Tel: (01476) 568175 Fax: (01476) 591427 *General woodworkers*

Granthams, Corporation Street, Preston, PR1 2UQ Tel: (01772) 250207 Fax: (01772) 555108 E-mail: sales@granthams.co.uk *Graphic technology consultants*

Granton Engineering & Manufacturing Ltd, 1 Davis Way, Fareham, Hampshire, PO14 1JF Tel: (01329) 231144 Fax: (01329) 822759 E-mail: sales@granton-eng.co.uk *Precision engineers*

▶ Grantrial, New City Court, 20 St Thomas Street, London, SE1 9RS Tel: (020) 7939 3100

▶ Grants Coachworks, Stable Road, Shotts, Lanarkshire, ML7 5BH Tel: (01501) 826888

Grants Of Dalvey Ltd, Unit 6 Dailnanrocas, Teaninich Industrial Estate, Alness, Ross-Shire, IV17 0XT Tel: (01349) 884111 Fax: (01349) 884100 E-mail: sales@dalvey.com *Stainless steel gifts & accessories*

Grants Electrical Services (NI) Ltd, Queens Road, Queens Island, Belfast, BT3 9DU Tel: (028) 9045 7061 Fax: (028) 9045 0708 E-mail: sales@grantselectrical.co.uk *Electric motor rewinders*

Grants Of Shoreditch Ltd, 25 Hackney Road, London, E2 7NX Tel: (020) 7729 3380 Fax: (020) 7613 3610 E-mail: sales@grantsint.com *Natural stone contractors*

Grant's Sign Shop, 76 Croydon Road, Elmers End, Beckenham, Kent, BR3 4DF Tel: (020) 8658 7578 Fax: (020) 8663 3780 *Engravers of nameplates & signs*

Grantura Plastics Ltd, Unit 10 Hoo Hill Industrial Estate, Bispham Road, Blackpool, FY3 7HJ Tel: (01253) 392058 Fax: (01253) 302207 *GRP manufrs*

Granville Cold Storage Co., Granville Road, Dungannon, County Tyrone, BT70 1NJ Tel: (028) 8772 6336 Fax: (028) 8772 7187 *Cold storage services*

Granville Oil & Chemicals Ltd, Unit 29 Goldthorpe Industrial Estate, Commercial Road, Goldthorpe, Rotherham, South Yorkshire, S63 9BL Tel: (01709) 890099 Fax: (01709) 891121 E-mail: info@granvilleoilchem.co.uk *Car care chemicals & lubricant suppliers*

▶ Granville Paul (Lamps) International, Unit 3 E, Larpool Lane Industrial Estate, Whitby, N. Yorkshire, YO22 4LX Tel: (01947) 825956 Fax: (01947) 825996

Granville Reprographics Ltd, Demmings House, Brookfield Road, Demmings Industrial Estate, Cheadle, Cheshire, SK8 2PE Tel: 0161-428 1236 Fax: 0161-428 0418 E-mail: sales@directimaging.co.uk *Photo-litho reproducers & digital printing services*

Granville Steel Contracting plc, Steel Close, Eaton Socon, St. Neots, Cambridgeshire, PE19 8TT Tel: (01480) 213513 Fax: (01480) 405994 E-mail: jane.taylor@aggregate.co.uk *Asphalt road surfacing contractors*

Granville Supplies Peterborough Ltd, Fengate, Peterborough, PE1 5XB Tel: (01733) 340100 Fax: (01733) 898370 E-mail: sales@granvillesupplies.co.uk *Motor body re-finisher services*

Granwood Flooring Ltd, Greenhill Lane, Riddings, Alfreton, Derbyshire, DE55 4AT Tel: (01773) 602341 Fax: (01773) 540043 *Sports hall flooring manufrs* Also at: Harrow

Granwood Flooring Group Ltd, Stubben Edge Hall, Ashover, Chesterfield, Derbyshire, S45 0EU Tel: (01246) 590543 Fax: (01246) 590449 *Property holding company*

Grapevine, 83 Broadway, Southbourne, Bournemouth, BH6 4EJ Tel: (01202) 429232 Fax: (01202) 424559 E-mail: sales1@grapevine-comms.co.uk *Communications & data cable installation services*

Grapevine Communications London, 488 St. Albans Road, Watford, WD24 6QU Tel: (01923) 219992 Fax: (01923) 219993 E-mail: info@grapevinecomms.co.uk *Telecommunications & cable distributors*

▶ Grapevine Computers Ltd, 20 Greenwood Street, Altrincham, Cheshire, WA14 1RZ Tel: 0161-941 6978 Fax: 0161-941 6979 E-mail: sales@grapevinecomputers.co.uk *Specialists in computer repairs & bespoke computer system builders*

Grapevine Instruments, PO Box 598, Canterbury, Kent, CT4 7GW Tel: (07010) 707940 Fax: (01227) 730892 E-mail: sfigures@netcomuk.co.uk *Measurement & control systems*

Grapevine Productions Ltd, 2 St. Marys Avenue, Teddington, Middlesex, TW11 0HZ Tel: (020) 8943 9899 Fax: (020) 8943 1626 *Video production company*

▶ Grapevine Trading Ltd, 5 Cloughside, Marple Bridge, Stockport, Cheshire, SK6 5BS Tel: (0870) 1620693 Fax: (0870) 1620694 *Design company*

Graphic plc, Down End, Lords Meadow Industrial Estate, Crediton, Devon, EX17 1HN Tel: (01363) 774874 Fax: (01363) 775753 E-mail: sales@graphic.plc.uk *Printed circuit manufrs*

Graphic Co, 35 Oldacres, Maidenhead, Berkshire, SL6 1XH Tel: (01628) 638541 Fax: (01628) 776564 *Signs & nameplates*

Graphic Art Cambridge Ltd, Trinity Hall Farm Industrial Estate, Nuffield Road, Cambridge, CB4 1TG Tel: (01223) 424421 Fax: (01223) 426040 E-mail: mail@graphic-art.co.uk *Screen printers*

Graphic Art Services, 81-82 Mackley Industrial Estate, Henfield Road, Small Dole, Henfield, West Sussex, BN5 9XR Tel: (01273) 495793 Fax: (01273) 494887 E-mail: design@graphicart.co.uk *Studio print & finishers*

Graphic Arts Coventry, 69-71 Hearsall Lane, Coventry, CV5 6HF Tel: (024) 7667 3415 *Label manufrs*

▶ Graphic Biz, 6 Cherry Walk, Chanterhill, Enniskillen, County Fermanagh, BT74 4BJ Tel: (0870) 7669061 Fax: (0870) 7669062 E-mail: sales@customer-stamps.co.uk *An independent stamp manufacturer selling to UK and Ireland. Manufacturer of self inking, traditional stamps. Specialist supplier to the trade and public. Incredible prices you won't find anywhere else.*"

Graphic Controls, Southcombe House, Southcombe, Chipping Norton, Oxfordshire, OX7 5QH Tel: (01608) 646303 Fax: (01608) 646304 E-mail: rickfordham@btconnect.com *Engineers*

Graphic Core, 117 Gorseinon Road, Penllergaer, Swansea, SA4 9AA Tel: (01792) 895 100 Fax: (01792) 895 114 E-mail: studio@graphic-core.com *Graphic Core deliver effective design which will exceed any expectations and best of all its jargon free and at a competitive price! A professional service whatever your business size. If you need a design solution, what are you waiting for...*

Graphic Data UK Ltd, 550 Broadway, Salford, M50 2UE Tel: 0161-877 1099 Fax: 0161-877 1151 E-mail: gary_newbury@graphicdata.co.uk *Document imaging bureau*

Graphic Displays Ltd, Selhurst 13 Coates Hill Road, Bickley, Bromley, BR1 2BJ Tel: (020) 8467 5700 Fax: (020) 8467 5277 E-mail: steve@graphicdisplays.co.uk *Screen printers & display designers*

Graphic Engineering Northern Ltd, Sheaf Bank Business Park, Prospect Road, Heeley, Sheffield, S2 3EN Tel: 0114-250 0151 Fax: 0114-255 5161 E-mail: sales@graphicengineering.co.uk *Nameplate engravers & screen printers*

Graphic Engravers, 354 Halliwell Road, Bolton, BL1 8AP Tel: (01204) 844159 Fax: (01204) 849445 E-mail: graphicengravers@btconnect.com *Control panel manufrs*

▶ Graphic Evidence Ltd, Wood Farm, Moreton Road, Ongar, Essex, CM5 0EY Tel: (01277) 890900 Fax: (01277) 890473 E-mail: info@graphic-evidence.co.uk *Design communication services*

Graphic Forming Ltd, 31a Clerkenwell Green, London, EC1R 0DU Tel: (020) 7251 4041 Fax: (020) 7253 8338 E-mail: sleggatt@btconnect.com *Point of sale manufrs* Also at: London E14

▶ Graphic House Ltd, 83 London Road, Preston, PR1 4AS Tel: (01772) 257657 Fax: (01772) 821562 E-mail: design@graphichouse.co.uk

Graphic Impression, C3 Enterprise Point, Melbourne Street, Brighton, BN2 3LH Tel: (01273) 571645 Fax: (01273) 571645 E-mail: amprints@hotmail.com *Screen process printing services*

Graphic Innovation Ltd, 35 Chequers Hill, Amersham, Buckinghamshire, HP7 9DQ Tel: (01494) 431500 Fax: (01494) 431500 E-mail: info@graphicinnovation.com *Self adhesive graphic manufrs*

Graphic International Display Ltd, 31-33 Fowler Road, Hainault Industrial Estate, Ilford, Essex, IG6 3UT Tel: (020) 8500 5544 Fax: (020) 8500 7197 *Plastic vacuum formed products manufrs*

▶ Graphic Line Machinery Ltd, 45 Prestongate, Hessle, North Humberside, HU13 0RD Tel: (01482) 645645 Fax: (020) 7691 7913 E-mail: info@glm.co.uk *Buy & sell printing machinery*

Graphic Metal Co., 3 Lyon Road, Walton-on-Thames, Surrey, KT12 3PU Tel: (01932) 254669 Fax: (01932) 252628 *Sign manufrs*

▶ Graphic Office Supplies Ltd, 244 Poplar High Street, London, E14 0BB Tel: (020) 7515 7162 Fax: (020) 7515 4410 E-mail: graphic@btconnect.com

Graphic Office Systems, 64 Pen Y Bryn, Wrexham, Clwyd, LL13 7HY Tel: (01978) 261168 Fax: (01978) 263224 E-mail: sales@graphicofficesystems.com *Office equipment supplier*

Graphic Output Technology Ltd, South Bank Technopark, 90 London Road, London, SE1 6LN Tel: (020) 7928 8889 Fax: (020) 7928 9929 *Digital pre-press & printing services*

▶ Graphic Pavement Signs Ltd, Letchworth Garden City, Hertfordshire, SG6 3XH Tel: (01462) 673831 Fax: (01462) 481703 E-mail: mail@posterholders.fsnet.co.uk *Display stands & display boards suppliers & manufrs*

▶ Graphic Press (Grimsby) Ltd, Upper Spring Street, Grimsby, South Humberside, DN31 1QP Tel: (01472) 359036

Graphic Resources Group Ltd, Cedan House, 102 Kirkstall Road, Leeds, LS3 1JA Tel: 0113-228 8400 Fax: 0113 2284426 *Graphic & printing services*

Graphic Results, 99 Bridge Street, Belper, Derbyshire, DE56 1BA Tel: (01773) 599159 Fax: (01773) 599259 E-mail: sales@graphic-results.co.uk *Graphic design, marketing & communication consultancy*

Graphic Services UK Ltd, 26 Eastcott Hill, Swindon, SN1 3JG Tel: (01793) 542678 Fax: (01793) 430788 *Signmakers & exhibition contractors*

Graphic Signs, 157 Fulford Road, York, YO10 4HH Tel: (01904) 621499 Fax: (01904) 621499 *Sign writers & makers*

Graphic Solutions, 9 Simmonds Buildings, Bristol Road, Hambrook, Bristol, BS16 1RY Tel: 0117-956 3222 Fax: 0117-956 2332 E-mail: nigel@grahicsol.co.uk *Exhibition graphics*

▶ Graphica Plus Ltd, Bentworth, Alton, Hampshire, GU34 5RP Tel: (01420) 563646 Fax: (01420) 561897 E-mail: sales@andersons.uk.net *Distribute sign making & digital printing systems*

Graphical Impact, 61 Hoe Street, London, E17 4SA Tel: (020) 8925 2333 Fax: (020) 8925 2332 E-mail: info@graphicalimpact.com *Sign designers*

Graphico Printing Ltd, 69-71 London Road, Croydon, CR0 2RF Tel: (020) 8681 1101 Fax: (020) 8688 8588 E-mail: sales@graphico.com *Security & general printers*

Graphicomm Ltd, 17 Willow Court, St. Modwen Road, Plymouth, PL6 8LQ Tel: (01752) 670099 Fax: (01752) 265700 E-mail: sales@graphicomm.co.uk *Printers*

Graphicraft Ltd, 6-8 Singer Way, Woburn Road Industrial Estate, Kempston, Bedford, MK42 7AN Tel: (01234) 846000 Fax: (01234) 843601 E-mail: sales@cgi-visual.com *Self adhesive transfers, vinyl graphics, badges & chrome weld manufrs*

Graphics Arts Equipment Ltd, 11 Aintree Road, Greenford, Middlesex, UB6 7LE Tel: (020) 8997 8053 Fax: (020) 8997 7706 E-mail: info@gae.co.uk *Printing machinery importers*

Graphics By Jeff & Chris, 85 Market Street, Hollingworth, Hyde, Cheshire, SK14 8JA Tel: (01457) 765995 Fax: (01457) 765995 E-mail: grafixgrafix@aol.com *Signs & graphic designers*

Graphics Factory, 339 Church Road, St. George, Bristol, BS5 8AA Tel: 0117-902 6318 Fax: 0117-902 6318 E-mail: sales@thegraphicsfactory.co.uk *Signs & digital printing*

The Graphics Network Ltd, 27 Moor Lane, Fairford, Gloucestershire, GL7 4AL Tel: (01285) 713297 E-mail: enquiries@tgn.co.uk Principal Export Areas: Worldwide *Software developers*

▶ Graphics Store, Clough Mill, Bradford Road, Gomersal, West Yorkshire, BD19 4AZ Tel: (01274) 862051 Fax: (01274) 851173 E-mail: info@graphics-store.co.uk *Graphic & exhibition designers*

▶ Graphisign Sign Makers, B Castle Park Industrial Estate, Bower Street, Oldham, OL1 3LN Tel: 0161-628 9997 Fax: 0161-628 9992 E-mail: mail@graphisign.co.uk *Design and manufacture digital print signs. With vinyl and silkscreen printing for building wraps and banners, vehicle livery, exhibition graphics and signage for corporate and retail clients.*

Graphite Electrodes Ltd, Coke Lane, Rotherham, South Yorkshire, S60 2JS Tel: (01709) 838522 Fax: (01709) 835340 *Machine manufrs*

Graphite Services Co., 19-20 Station Lane Industrial Estate, Old Whittington, Chesterfield, Derbyshire, S41 9PX Tel: (01246) 260360 Fax: (01246) 260367 E-mail: selwyn@graphiteservices.co.uk *Industrial & colloidal graphite product manufrs*

Graphoidal Developments Ltd, Broombank Road, Chesterfield, Derbyshire, S41 9QJ Tel: (01246) 266000 Fax: (01246) 269269 E-mail: sales@graphoidal.com *Graphoidal Developments Ltd is a specialist lubrication and engineering company, supplying systems to the glass container and tableware industries. Our expertise is in precise pumping, control of mixing, dosing and spraying of lubricants & coatings which are a vital part of the glass production process, both in hot end and cold end areas. Other products include cold end formed twin axis systems and single axis systems, cold end dosing units, modular shear spray systems provides a cost saving and reliable gob shearing operation, shear spray nozzles and shear spray bars. The Graphoidal Single Feeder Shear Spray Unit provides a cost effective alternative to centralized systems. The Hot-End Row Monitor is mounted across the entrance to the Annealing Lehr. Trade names include the Speedy Gob, Handy IV (temperature measurement probe), AUTOSWABBING, CWM-2000 (cold end coating system), FRICTION GLIDE GRAD and GRADMATIC (spraying equipment).*

Graphoprint Ltd, 1 North House, Bond Avenue, Mount Farm, Milton Keynes, MK1 1AY Tel: (01908) 371110 Fax: (01908) 371130 *Web printers* Also at: Clywd

Grasam Samson Ltd, Doulton Trading Estate, Doulton Road, Rowley Regis, West Midlands, B65 8JQ Tel: (01384) 634162 Fax: (01384) 568051 E-mail: grasamsamson@aol.com *Engineers tool merchants*

Grasmere (Digital) Imaging Ltd, Bramley Business Centre, Stanningley Road, Leeds, LS13 4EN Tel: 0113-224 8600 Fax: 0113-239 3166 E-mail: admin@grasmeredigital.co.uk *Digital imaging printers & services*

The Grass Roots Group UK Ltd, Pennyroyal, Station Road, Tring, Hertfordshire, HP23 5QY Tel: (01442) 829400 Fax: (01442) 829405 E-mail: contactus@grg.com *Business incentive systems*

▶ Grassby & Sons Ltd, Dorchester Road, Grimstone, Dorchester, Dorset, DT2 9NA Tel: (01305) 269678 Fax: (01305) 250309 E-mail: info@glassby-stone.co.uk *Memorials, stone products*

Grasshopper Babywear (Wolverhampton) Ltd, Hunter Street, Wolverhampton, WV6 0QZ Tel: (01902) 426506 Fax: (01902) 426649 *Baby wear*

▶ Grasshopper Films Ltd, 3rd Floor 14 Bacon Street, London, E1 6LF Tel: (020) 7739 7154 Fax: (020) 7739 6359 E-mail: info@grasshopperfilms.com *Grasshopper Films covers all areas of production, from commercials to features and pop videos to documentaries. Recent clients include: Puma, Sony New York, MTV Europe and Guerlain perfume. We also act as a service company, clients include: NFL Films, Premiere Heure, Lieberman Productions and Emotional Pictures.*

Grasslin UK Ltd, Tower House, Vale Rise, Tonbridge, Kent, TN9 1TB Tel: (01732) 359888 Fax: (01732) 354445 *Quartz & digital time switch manufrs*

Company Information

Grate Glow Fires, Mill Lane, Old Swan, Liverpool, L13 4AJ Tel: 0151-252 6600 Fax: 0151-220 5277 E-mail: info@robinson-willey.com *Decorative gas fire manufrs*

Gratel Signs & Nameplates, 4 Blatchford Close, Horsham, West Sussex, RH13 5RG Tel: (01403) 210385 Fax: (01403) 218282 *Sign contractors, sign makers, suppliers & installers*

The Grating Co. Ltd, 1 Warner Way, Chilton Business Park, Sudbury, Suffolk, CO10 2GG Tel: (01787) 319922 Fax: (01787) 319963 E-mail: info@gratingco.co.uk *Fibreglass gratings, ladders, walkways, platforms & stairs manufrs*

Gratte Brothers Ltd, 2 Regents Wharf, All Saints Street, London, N1 9RL Tel: (020) 7837 6433 Fax: (020) 7837 6779 E-mail: info@gratte.com *Building services engineers*

Gravatom Engineering Systems Ltd, William Kelvin Building, Claylands Road, Bishops Waltham, Southampton, SO32 1BH Tel: (01489) 896010 Fax: (01489) 894382 E-mail: sales@gravatom.com *Supply equipment for nuclear industry*

▶ Gravaton Engineering Systems, H-J Fort Wallington Industrial Estate, Military Road, Fareham, Hampshire, PO16 8TT Tel: (01329) 237010 Fax: (01329) 287492 *Sheet metalwork engineers or fabricators*

▶ Gravell Holdings Ltd, 6 Banc Pendre, Kidwelly, Dyfed, SA17 4TA Tel: (01554) 890436 Fax: (01554) 891338 *Renault main dealers*

Gravell & Jones Ltd, 12 Heron Court, Cranes Farm Road, Basildon, Essex, SS14 3DF Tel: (01268) 522611 Fax: (01268) 281188 *Chair frame manufrs*

▶ Gravelle Plant Hire, Riverside Works, Penybanc Road, Ammanford, Dyfed, SA18 3RB Tel: (01269) 591049 Fax: (01269) 591040

Graves Aircraft Components Ltd, 2 Lightning Way, Birmingham, B31 3PJ Tel: 0121-475 5181 Fax: 0121-411 1071 *Aerospace component manufrs*

Julian Graves Ltd, 1 The Podium, Northgate Street, Bath, BA1 5AL Tel: (01225) 448404 Fax: (01225) 448404 *Health food retailers*

▶ Julian Graves Ltd, 21 Toll Gavel, Beverley, North Humberside, HU17 9AR Tel: (01482) 880866 Fax: (01482) 880866 *Retail shop, fruit vegetables vitamins*

Julian Graves Ltd, Tudor Arcade, South Street, Dorchester, Dorset, DT1 1BN Tel: (01305) 257934 Fax: (01384) 297707 *Sell dried fruits*

Julian Graves Ltd, 9 The Sovereign Centre, High Street, Weston-super-Mare, Avon, BS23 1HL Tel: (01934) 643144 Fax: (01934) 643144 *Health food manufacturers & retailers*

▶ Julien Graves, Isaac Newton Centre, Grantham, Lincolnshire, NG31 6EE Tel: (01476) 594529 Fax: (01476) 594529 *Sweets, dry fruits, nuts, & spice suppliers*

Gravesend Engineering Co. Ltd, East Crescent Road, Gravesend, Kent, DA12 2AR Tel: (01474) 365475 Fax: (01474) 365475 *General engineers & fabricators*

Gravesend Metal Recycling Denton Wharf Ltd, 7 Wharf Road, Gravesend, Kent, DA12 2RU Tel: (01474) 361244 Fax: (01474) 568172 *Scrap metal merchants*

Gravitech Ltd, 136 Kentish Road, Middlemore Industrial Estate, Birmingham, B21 0AY Tel: 0121-558 0847 Fax: 0121-555 8171 *Aluminium gravity die castings*

Gravutex Eschmann International Ltd, Unit 10 Peakdale Road, Brookfield Industrial Estate, Glossop, Derbyshire, SK13 6LQ Tel: (01457) 867627 Fax: (01457) 855536 E-mail: aharrison@gravutexeshman.co.uk *Plastic mould tool surface engravers*

Gray & Adams Ltd, Lyneburn Industrial Estate, Halbeath Place, Dunfermline, Fife, KY11 4JT Tel: (01383) 731707 Fax: (01383) 730519 *Build refrigerated vehicle bodies*

Gray & Adams Doncaster Ltd, Pipering Lane, Doncaster, South Yorkshire, DN5 9EL Tel: (01302) 787755 Fax: (01302) 783675 E-mail: sales@gray-adams-donc.co.uk *Vehicle refrigeration manufrs*

Gray & Adams (Ireland) Ltd, Houstons Corner, Ballyearl, Newtownabbey, County Antrim, BT36 4TP Tel: (028) 9034 2160 Fax: (028) 9084 8933 E-mail: b.dougan@grayadamsireland.com *Refridgerated trailer & coach builders*

Gray Audio Visual, 34-36 Bickerton Road, London, N19 5JS Tel: (020) 7263 9561 Fax: (020) 7272 0146 E-mail: office@gray-av.co.uk *Audio visual equipment hire*

Gray & Co. (Brassfounders) Ltd, Block 4, Cowlairs Industrial Estate, Glasgow, G22 5DQ Tel: 0141-558 7003 Fax: 0141-633 0950 E-mail: nismith@compuserve.com *Brass founders & fabricators*

Gray Campling Ltd, 91a Southcote Road, Bournemouth, BH1 3SN Tel: (01202) 291828 Fax: (01202) 297304 E-mail: sales@graycampling.co.uk *Spray equipment services*

Gray Electrics Stafford Ltd, Unit 1c Hollins Business Centre, 62 Rowley Street, Stafford, ST16 2RH Tel: (01785) 223010 Fax: (01785) 211360 E-mail: grayelectrics@aol.com *Electrical contractors*

Gray Engineering, Hirfron, Mountain, Holyhead, Gwynedd, LL65 1YW Tel: (01407) 760525 Fax: (01407) 760525 E-mail: contact@graysengineering.co.uk *Steel fabricators*

Gray Fabrications UK Ltd, 57 Clement Way, Upminster, Essex, RM14 2NX Tel: (01708) 703505 Fax: (01708) 703505 E-mail: gray.fabrications@ntlworld.com *Sheet metalworking or fabricators*

Gray & Mcdonnell, Unit 3 4 City Cross Business Park, Salutation Road, London, SE10 0AT Tel: (020) 8858 8050 Fax: (020) 8269 1513 E-mail: mirrors@graymcdonnell.co.uk *Mirror manufrs*

▶ Gray Matter Ltd, 18 Davy Avenue, Knowlhill, Milton Keynes, MK5 8PL Tel: (01908) 675444 E-mail: marketing@graymatter.co.uk *Web based marketing specialists. Advertising, corporate identity and advertising.*

Gray PCB Designs, 62 Warren Road, St. Ives, Cambridgeshire, PE27 5NW Tel: (01480) 496235 Fax: (01480) 496235 E-mail: graham@gray-pcb-designs.demon.co.uk *Printed circuit board services*

Gray Precision Engineering, Units 1-3, Castle Court, Bankside Industrial Estate, Falkirk, FK2 7UU Tel: (01324) 612679 Fax: (01324) 612209 E-mail: stuart.gray@btconnect.com *Toolmakers & precision engineers*

Gray Purdue Solicitors, Wellesley House, 202 London Road, Waterlooville, Hampshire, PO7 7AN Tel: (023) 9226 5251 Fax: (023) 9224 1597 E-mail: contact@graypurdue.co.uk *Gray Purdue Solicitors are a UK based legal firm offering legal advice to private and commercial clients. We specialize in divorce and family law, conveyancing, wills and testaments, personal injury, disputes and employment law.*

▶ Graybar Electrical Contractors, 10 Fleming Close, Park Farm Industrial Estate, Wellingborough, Northamptonshire, NN8 6UF Tel: (01933) 676700 Fax: (01933) 676800 E-mail: sales@graybar.co.uk

Graydon Castings Ltd, Canal Side Indust Estate, Brettell Lane, Brockmoor, Brierley Hill, West Midlands, DY5 3JU Tel: (01384) 571559 Fax: (01384) 571559 *Grey iron casting manufacturers*

Graydon UK Ltd, 66 College Road, 2nd Floor Hygeia Building, Harrow, Middlesex, HA1 1BE Tel: (020) 8515 1400 Fax: (020) 8515 1499 E-mail: mail@graydon.co.uk *Credit information services*

Graylands Trading Co., 38 Sherwood Road, Winnersh, Wokingham, Berkshire, RG41 5NJ Tel: 0118-989 0002 Fax: 0118-989 0003 E-mail: graylands@supernet.com *Commercial, outdoor & amenity lighting*

▶ Graylaw Freight Group, Graylaw Freight Terminal, Gillibrands Road, Skelmersdale, Lancashire, WN8 9TA Tel: (01695) 729101 Fax: (01695) 729125 *Innovators in freight*

Grayling, 1 Bedford Avenue, London, WC1B 3AU Tel: (020) 7255 5400 Fax: (020) 7255 5454 E-mail: info@uk.grayling.com *Public relations consultants* Also at: Branches throughout the U.K.

Graypen Ltd, Prince Henry Drive, Queens Road, Immingham, South Humberside, DN40 1QY Tel: (01482) 794323 Fax: (01469) 552900 E-mail: info@graypen.co.uk *Ship brokers & tanker agents*

Grays Blinds, 44 Bridge Road, Grays, Essex, RM17 6BU Tel: (01375) 379022 Fax: (01375) 390109 *Blinds & curtains manufrs*

Grays Of Cambridge (International) Ltd, Whitwell Way, Coton, Cambridge, CB23 7PW Tel: (01954) 210446 Fax: (01954) 212225 *Sport equipment distribution*

Gray's Electronic Services, 10a Union Street, Troon, Ayrshire, KA10 6BS Tel: (01292) 313430 Fax: (01292) 318888 *Computer maintenance & repairers*

Grays Engineering Contracts Ltd, Globe Industrial Estate, Rectory Road, Grays, Essex, RM17 6ST Tel: (01375) 372367 Fax: (01375) 375079 E-mail: grayseng@btopenworld.com *Steel fabricators*

Grays Foil Blockers, Unit 10 White Post Lane, London, E9 5EN Tel: (020) 8985 6518 Fax: (020) 8986 0396 *Foil blocking & blind embossing, embossing cement manufrs*

Grays International Ltd, Station Road, Robertsbridge, East Sussex, TN32 5DH Tel: (0845) 0661823 Fax: (01580) 881156 E-mail: sales@grays-hockey.co.uk *Netball, soccer & rugby ball manufrs*

Grays Picture Framers, 19 West Tower Street, Carlisle, CA3 8QT Tel: (01228) 531837 Fax: (01228) 531837 *Picture frame manufr & supplier*

Grays Traditional Marquees, Southbank, Blackwater, Newport, Isle Of Wight, PO30 3BG Tel: (01983) 525221 Fax: (01983) 529296 E-mail: info@islandmarquees.co.uk *Tent & marquee hirers*

Grays Transport, The Rearing Site, Oldbury Lane, Oldbury-On-Severn, Bristol, BS35 1RF Tel: (01454) 411773 Fax: (01454) 281373 *Electric vehicles manufrs*

Grayshott Stoneware Ltd, School Road, Grayshott, Hindhead, Surrey, GU26 6LR Tel: (01428) 604404 Fax: (01428) 604944 E-mail: sales@grayshottpottery.com *Stoneware & pottery manufrs*

Grayson Millward Ltd, Wharf Road Industrial Estate, Pinxton, Nottingham, NG16 6LE Tel: (01773) 810144 Fax: (01773) 860321 E-mail: *Thread rolling die manufrs*

Graysons Freight Services Ltd, Border Freight Terminal, 4 Hollands Road, Haverhill, Suffolk, CB9 8PP Tel: (01440) 762558 Fax: (01440) 707119 E-mail: sales@graysons.net *Freight forwarders & warehousing* Also at: Manchester

▶ Grayston Automotive Ltd, Station Yard, Station Lane, Nateby, Preston, PR3 0LT Tel: (01995) 602116 Fax: (01995) 600188 E-mail: sales@grayston.co.uk

Graythorpe Forge & Engineering Ltd, 99 Graythorp Industrial Estate, Hartlepool, Cleveland, TS25 2DP Tel: (01429) 273268 Fax: (01429) 236553 *Fabrication engineers*

J.A.V. Grazebrook & Co., Stourport-On-Severn, Worcestershire, DY13 0YB Tel: (01299) 827440 Fax: (01299) 827048 *Materials handling equipment manufrs*

▶ Grazedean Ltd, Unit 27, 865 Ringwood Road, Bournemouth, BH11 8LL Tel: (01202) 581645 Fax: (01202) 593824 E-mail: info@grazedean.com *Supply electrosurgical cables, fibre optic cables*

Grease Guardian, Greenbank Industrial Estate, Newry, County Down, BT34 2PB Tel: (028) 3026 6616 Fax: (028) 3026 3233 E-mail: gg@fmenvironmental.com *International commercial grease management specialists, automatic grease removal devices, internal & external traps, selling in Ireland, the UK, throughout Europe, the middle east, South East Asia, China & Australia*

▶ Grease Guardian Products, Unit 1 Wareley Road, Woodston, Peterborough, PE2 9PF Tel: 01733 755500 Fax: 01733 704795 E-mail: sales@greaseguardian.info *Grease Separation System for Waste Water Treatment for Commercial Kitchens. EN 1825 Certified, products include Grease Guardian Units, In Sink Strainers and In Floor Strainers.*

▶ Grease Lightning, 22 Windrush Road, Berinsfield, Wallingford, Oxfordshire, OX10 7PF Tel: (01865) 341166 Fax: (01865) 341176 E-mail: greaselightningcouriers@yahoo.co.uk *24hr 7days sameday courier service from envelope to pallet collection & delivery secure service fully insured reliable fast friendly service*

▶ Great Art, Normandy House, 1 Nether Street, Alton, Hampshire, GU34 1EA Tel: (01420) 593332 Fax: (01420) 593333 E-mail: welcome@greatart.co.uk *Art materials suppliers*

Great Bear Distribution Ltd, 6 Glendale Park Glendale Avenue, Sandycroft Industrial Estate, Sandycroft, Deeside, Clwyd, CH5 2QP Tel: (01244) 520020 Fax: (01244) 537716

▶ Great Bear Distribution Ltd, N Industrial Estate, Sinfin Lane, Derby, DE24 9GL Tel: (01332) 770099 Fax: (01332) 770061

▶ Great Bear Distribution Ltd, Moulton Park Business Centre, Redhouse Road, Moulton Park Industrial Estate, Northampton, NN3 6AQ Tel: (01604) 643648 Fax: (01604) 643649

Great Bridge Welding Co., Bagnall Street, Golds Hill, West Bromwich, West Midlands, B70 0TS Tel: 0121-557 2325 *Welders, fabricators & builders*

▶ The Great British Courier Co., 33 Harris Crescent, Needingworth, St. Ives, Cambridgeshire, PE27 4TE Tel: (01480) 465450 E-mail: gbcc@btinternet.com *Sameday express courier. Local, National and European. *We can deliver to all parts of the UK and Europe.* We have vehicles capable of carrying anything from documents up to 3 pallets.*We are experienced in high value shipments and have goods in transit insurance to cover £250,000 per consignment. This is much more than most standard courier companies.*We have drivers trained in hazardous goods transport and drivers who have attended a level 4 aviation security course.*We have vans leaving Heathrow, Stansted and Gatwick airports several times throughout the day and night returning to Cambridgeshire.**Our drivers are smart, helpful and contactable at all times.***

Great Fleet P.L.C., 85 Gracechurch Street, London, EC3V 0AA Tel: (0845) 8810700 Fax: (0845) 8810723 E-mail: info@greatfleet.co.uk *Search & selection consultants for the financial industry*

Great Guns, 43-45 Camden Road, London, NW1 9LR Tel: (020) 7692 4444 Fax: (020) 7692 4422 E-mail: greatguns@greatguns.com *Production company*

▶ Great Hookley Farm, Hookley Lane, Elstead, Godalming, Surrey, GU8 6JD Tel: (01252) 702121 Fax: (01252) 703716

Great Northern Windows, 4 Great Northern Road, Eastwood, Nottingham, NG16 3PD Tel: (01773) 533633 Fax: (01773) 533432 *Upvc windows & doors installers*

Great Portland Estates P L C, 33 Cavendish Square, London, W1G 0PW Tel: (020) 7647 3000 Fax: (020) 7016 5500 E-mail: firstname.lastname@gpe.co.uk *Property investment services*

▶ Great Repairs, Torwood Place, Ormiston CR, Dundee, DD4 0UD Tel: (01382) 801659 E-mail: greatrepairs@blueyonder.co.uk *leather repairs for car interiors and upholstery*

▶ Great Taste, 5 Garfield Road, Netley Abbey, Southampton, SO31 5DN Tel: (023) 8045 3181 E-mail: enquiries@great-taste.co.uk *Great Taste provide high quality catering services including buffets, BBQs, dinner parties, office functions... All using the finest seasonal and local ingredients.*

Great Warley Forge, The Forge, Great Warley Street, Great Warley, Brentwood, Essex, CM13 3JF Tel: (01277) 226547 *Ironwork*

Great Western Balloons, 6 Redwood Close, Honiton, Devon, EX14 2XS Tel: (01404) 45968 Fax: (01404) 45968 *Balloon decorators*

Great Yarmouth Coach Works, 15 Queens Road, Great Yarmouth, Norfolk, NR30 3HT Tel: (01493) 843835 Fax: (01493) 330800 E-mail: ian@greatyarmouthcoachworks.co.uk *Car sales & mot centre*

Great Yarmouth Glass, 113 Nelson Road Central, Great Yarmouth, Norfolk, NR30 2NJ Tel: (01493) 842323 Fax: (01493) 850913 E-mail: info@gyglass.co.uk *Glazing contractors & home improvement specialists services*

▶ Great Yarmouth Port Co., 20-21 South Quay, Great Yarmouth, Norfolk, NR30 2RE Tel: (01493) 335500 Fax: (01493) 852480 E-mail: gypa@gypa.co.uk *Port & dock authorities, supply base/warehouse operators for the oil industry, warehousing (storage) contractors/facilities/services & freight container terminal operators*

Great Yarmouth Pottery, 18-19 Trinity Place, Great Yarmouth, Norfolk, NR30 3HA Tel: (01493) 850585 *Ceramic manufrs*

▶ Great Yarmouth Printing Services Ltd, Gapton Hall Road, Great Yarmouth, Norfolk, NR31 0NL Tel: (01493) 603061 Fax: (01493) 442648 E-mail: sales@midcontinentgy.com

Greatdale Ltd, The Lakes Glass Centre Oubas Hill, Ulverston, Cumbria, LA12 7LB Tel: (01229) 584400 Fax: (01229) 581132 E-mail: sales@cumbriacrystal.freeserve.co.uk *Lead crystal tablewear & giftware manufrs*

Greater (Altrincham) Chamber of Commerce, Trade & Industry, 6B Old Market Place, Altrincham, Cheshire, WA14 4NP Tel: 0161-941 3250 Fax: 0161-941 1909 *Business support services*

Greater London Hire, GLH House, 12-18 High Road, London, N2 9PJ Tel: (020) 8883 5000 Fax: (020) 8444 2026 *Mini cabs & courier services*

Greater Merseyside Enterprise Ltd, Egerton Housetower Road, Birkenhead, Merseyside, CH41 1FN Tel: (0845) 3300151 Fax: (08453) 300150 E-mail: information@gme.org.uk *Business information advisory services*

▶ Greatwell Designs, 68 Pullman Road, Wigston, Leicestershire, LE18 2DB Tel: 0116-257 1444

Greaves Amusement Supplies, Ashfield House, 8 Enderby Road, Blaby, Leicester, LE8 4GD Tel: 0116-277 6297 Fax: 0116-278 9184 *Amusement machine sales & hires*

Greaves Art Metalwork Ltd, Ireland Close, Staveley, Chesterfield, Derbyshire, S43 3PE Tel: (01246) 280672 Fax: (01246) 280673 *Architectural metalworkers*

Frank Greaves (Moulding) Co. Ltd, Unit 68, Roman Way Industrial Estate, Longridge Road, Grinsargh, Preston, PR2 5BD Tel: (01772) 652902 Fax: (01772) 797748 E-mail: info@eurotransman.co.uk *Plastic moulding manufrs*

James Greaves & Co., Brazennose House, Manchester, M60 2JA Tel: 0161-834 0991 Fax: 0161-832 0753 E-mail: jamesgreavesco@btinternet.com *Export buying houses*

Greaves Sports Ltd, 82 Sauchiehall Street, Glasgow, G2 3DF Tel: 0141-333 0030 Fax: 0141-333 9443 *Sports goods & clothing merchants*

Greaves Welsh Slate Co. Ltd, Llechwedd Slate Mines, Blaenau Ffestiniog, Gwynedd, LL41 3NB Tel: (01766) 830522 Fax: (01766) 830711 E-mail: llechwedd@aol.com *Natural slate producers-roofing & architectural manufrs*

▶ The Greek Delicatessen Ltd, 152 Pixmore Way, Letchworth Garden City, Herts, SG6 1QS Tel: (0845) 4507557 E-mail: panos@thegreekdeli.com *Importers & Distributors of Greek Gourmet Food including Organic & Infused EVOO, the Pelekan Canned Ready to Eat Food, Olives, Feta Cheese, Fresh Baklava, Thyme Honey & the whole Mylelia range.*

▶ Green, Welsh Road, Deeside, Clwyd, CH5 2LR Tel: (01244) 289751

A. & J. Green Engineering Ltd, Units 12-13, Enfield Industrial Estate, Redditch, Worcestershire, B97 6BG Tel: (01527) 62666 Fax: (01527) 584298 E-mail: ddptools@aol.com *Press workers*

▶ Green Acres Homes (Exmouth) Ltd, Unit 2 Swifts Unit, Pound Lane, Exmouth, Devon, EX8 4NP Tel: (01395) 275304

Green Arc Fabrications Ltd, Market Farm, Honey Pot Lane, Kemsing, Sevenoaks, Kent, TN15 6NT Tel: (01732) 761243 Fax: (01732) 763705 *Fabricators*

Green Baby, 345 Upper Street, London, N1 0PD Tel: (0870) 2406894 Fax: (020) 7226 9244 *Natural baby products & goods*

▶ Green Batteries, 71 Barn Park, Buckfastleigh, Devon, TQ11 0AT Tel: (01364) 642126 E-mail: battery@ukf.net *Supplier of rechargeable batteries & chargers*

Bob Green Sewing Machines, Moor Lane Business Centre, Moor Lane, Widnes, Cheshire, WA8 7AQ Tel: 0151-420 5565 Fax: 0151-420 5565 *Sewing machine repairers*

Green Bros Ltd, 44 High Street, Corby, Northamptonshire, NN17 1UU Tel: (01536) 265754 Fax: (01536) 206460 E-mail: enquiries@greenbros.co.uk *Quality cleaning contractors*

▶ Green Bros (U K) Ltd, 11 Middleton Avenue, Strutherhill Industrial Estate, Larkhall, Lanarkshire, ML9 2TL Tel: (01698) 885911

▶ Green & Cameron Ltd, Canisbay, Wick, Caithness, KW1 4YB Tel: (01955) 611316 Fax: (01955) 611451

Green & Carter, Vulcan Works, Rectory Road, Ashbrittle, Wellington, Somerset, TA21 0LQ Tel: (01823) 672365 Fax: (01823) 672950 E-mail: general@greenandcarter.com *Water treatment equipment hire & service*

Charles Green & Son Ltd, 37-42 Tenby Street, Birmingham, B1 3EF Tel: 0121-236 1874 Fax: 0121-236 6617 E-mail: info@charles-green.co.uk *Jewellery manufrs*

▶ Green Connections Ltd, 36 Shannon Drive, Walsall, WS8 7LA Tel: (01543) 361076 Fax: (01543) 361075 E-mail: greenconnections@btinternet.com *Electrical Contractors based in the Midlands specialising in Domestic, comercial and industrial wiring. Part P registered. ECA registered company.*

Green Cuisine Food Products Ltd, Unit 3 Threxton Industrial Estate, Watton, Thetford, Norfolk, IP25 6NG Tel: (01953) 882991 Fax: (01953) 885401 E-mail: greencuisine@btinternet.com *Herb & spice packers*

D.B. Green Ltd, Brook House, Southdown Business Park, Brooks Road, Lewes, East Sussex, BN7 2BY Tel: (01273) 480251 Fax: (01273) 480252 E-mail: sales@dbgreen.co.uk *Air conditioning, ventilation & heating specialists services*

David A. Green, 5 Ruskin Grove, Stockport, Cheshire, SK6 1DP Tel: 0161-430 7099 Fax: 0161-430 7099 *Sign writing*

▶ Green Electronics, 1 Kennet Enterprise Centre, Charnham Lane, Hungerford, Berkshire, RG17 0EY Tel: (01488) 686244 *Electronic subcontract manufrs*

▶ Green Energy Centre, Ambassador House, Brigstock Road, Thornton Heath, Surrey, CR7 7JG Tel: (020) 8683 6683 Fax: (020) 8683 6601

Green Engineering, Cheethams Mill, Park Street, Stalybridge, Cheshire, SK15 2BT Tel: 0161-303 7129 Fax: 0161-303 7129 *Turning, milling & drilling*

Green Farm Health, Romanby Road, West Garth, Northallerton, North Yorkshire, DL7 8NB Tel: (01609) 779548 Fax: (01609) 779548 *Animal Health & Feed*

Green Field Signs, 23 Oak Road, Newcastle, Staffordshire, ST5 6DE Tel: (01782) 768031 Fax: (01782) 768031 E-mail: greenfieldsigns@ntlworld.com *Sign writing*

▶ Green Fig Catering Ltd, 47 Station Road, Alresford, Colchester, CO7 8BU Tel: 01206 826682 E-mail: enquiries@greenfigcatering.com *High experienced, quality outside catering throughout East Anglia. Catering for weddings,*

continued

continuation
private parties, society events, and corporate. Contracts also considered. Please call or email.
George Green (Keighley) Ltd, Parkwood Works, Parkwood Street, Keighley, West Yorkshire, BD21 4PN Tel: (01535) 603728 Fax: (01535) 610340 E-mail: enquiries@georgegreen-uk.com *Steel fabrication (medium to heavy) & complete installation services*
Green Goose Tooling Co., Unit 1-2 Falcons Gate, Dean Road, Yate, Bristol, BS37 5NH Tel: (01454) 312948 Fax: (01454) 313704 *Plastics & metal engineers*
The Green House, Unit 60-61 Markethall, High Rd, Wood Green Shopping City, London, N22 6YE Tel: 020 88811471 *Health food*
Green Island Ltd, The Lighthouse, Eastwood Road, Penryn, Cornwall, TR10 8LA Tel: (01326) 377775 Fax: (01326) 377773 E-mail: ianbibby@greenisland.co.uk *Lighting manufrs*
Green It Solutions Ltd, Unit 1 King George Court, High Street, Billericay, Essex, CM12 9BY Tel: (01277) 844940 Fax: (01277) 844941 E-mail: info@greenit.co.uk *IT solution providers*
Green of Lincoln, Pyke Road, Lincoln, LN6 3QS Tel: (01522) 500006 *Disposables & cleaning products wholesalers*
Green Marine Ltd, Waterloo Road, Lymington, Hampshire, SO41 9DB Tel: (01590) 672356 Fax: (01590) 679124 E-mail: high@greenmarine.co.uk *Boat builders*
Green Mech Ltd, The Mill Industrial Park, Kings Coughton, Alcester, Warwickshire, B49 5QG Tel: (01789) 400044 Fax: (01789) 400167 E-mail: sales@greenmech.co.uk *Leading manufacturers of wood chippers, green waste shredders and stump grinders.*
Green Oak Equipment Ltd, 11 Boleyn Court, Manor Park, Runcorn, Cheshire, WA7 1SR Tel: (01928) 579971 Fax: (01928) 579269 E-mail: greenoak.runcorn@fsbdial.co.uk *Dairy plant & equipment distribution*
Green Piling Ltd, Smithy Brook Road, Renishaw, Sheffield, S21 3JS Tel: 08450 511800 Fax: 08450 511811 E-mail: info@greenpiling.co.uk *Specialist steel tubular & pre cast concrete piling contractors*
Green & Preece Grinding Ltd, Rufford Road, Stourbridge, West Midlands, DY9 7NE Tel: (01384) 397040 Fax: (01384) 440267 E-mail: green-preece-grinding.co.uk@zetnet.co.uk *Centreless grinding specialists*
▶ Green Slate Trophies, 1 Derby Street, Burnley, Lancashire, BB11 1RL Tel: (01282) 411400 Fax: (01282) 432308 *Trophies, annual shields, silverware & engraving, service & suppliers*
Green Speed Power Coating, Slack Street, Macclesfield, Cheshire, SK11 7JP Tel: (01625) 439993 Fax: (01625) 439993 *Metal powder coating*
Green Standards Ltd, Green Standards House, Lower Ledge Farm, Dyrham, Chippenham, Wiltshire, SN14 8EY Tel: (0870) 2401445 E-mail: admin@greenstandards.org *Corporate social responsibility solutions provider*
Green Stone Arts, Watcarrick, Eskdalemuir, Langholm, Dumfriesshire, DG13 0PL Tel: (01387) 373230 Fax: 013873 73230 *Fridge magnet manufrs*
▶ Green Therapeutics, Pintail Close, Quedgeley, Gloucester, GL2 4LN Tel: (01452) 560429 E-mail: sales@green-t.info *Aromatherapy & massage service*
Tom Green Construction Ltd, Old Station Yard, The Limes, Ingatestone, Essex, CM4 0AZ Tel: (01277) 354141 Fax: (01277) 355505 *Building contractors*
Green Top Snack Foods Ltd, Gagarin, Litchfield Road, Tamworth, Staffordshire, B79 7TA Tel: (01827) 60008 Fax: (01827) 60007 E-mail: enquiries@gts-ltd.com *Snack food manufrs*
▶ Green Tree, Tudworth Road, Hatfield, Doncaster, South Yorkshire, DN7 6NL Tel: (01302) 840305 Fax: (01302) 840592
Green Tree Press Ltd, Unit 1 Parham Drive, Eastleigh, Hampshire, SO50 4NU Tel: (023) 8061 1234 Fax: (023) 8064 4432 E-mail: sales@greentreepress.co.uk
Green Tyre Co. P.L.C., Riverside Park Road, Middlesbrough, Cleveland, TS2 1UU Tel: (01642) 223322 Fax: (01642) 223313 E-mail: sales@greentyre.co.uk *Tyre manufacturers & distributors*
▶ Green Valet, 59 Valentine Crescent, Sheffield, S5 0NX Tel: 0114-245 9909 Fax: 0114-245 9909 *Stock controllers*
Green Ways, Upper Norton Farm, Norton, Sutton Scotney, Winchester, Hampshire, SO21 3QF Tel: (01962) 761600 Fax: (01962) 761696 *Algae controlling materials or products manufrs*
Green & Weatherly Ltd, 16 Bushey Hall Road, Bushey, WD23 2EA Tel: (01923) 228992 Fax: (01923) 241254 *Crankshaft grinders & engine reconditioners*
Green & White Ltd, 112 Fortune Green Road, London, NW6 1DH Tel: (020) 7794 7783 Fax: (020) 7433 1143 E-mail: green.white.ltd@lineone.net *Cleaning equipment distrbs*
Greenacres Vermin Control, Foulby Lodge, Doncaster Road, Foulby, Wakefield, West Yorkshire, WF4 1PY Tel: (01924) 863562 Fax: (01924) 860418 *Pest control service*
Greenapple Systems Ltd, 6 Curo Park, Park Street Frogmore, St. Albans, Hertfordshire, AL2 2DD Tel: (01727) 872525 Fax: (01727) 872525 *Furniture distributors*
Greenaway & Co. Ltd, Penybont Bryncrug, Tywyn, Gwynedd, LL36 9PT Tel: (01654) 710073 Fax: (01654) 711846 E-mail: mail@greenawayuk.fsnet.co.uk *Manufacturer of centre & special purpose bolts*
▶ Greenbank Group Inc, Hartshorne Road, Woodville, Swadlincote, Derbyshire, DE11 7GT Tel: (0870) 6078880 Fax: (0870) 6078889 E-mail: info@greenbank.tv Principal Export Areas: Worldwide *Abrasion & low friction prevention systems, pipework supply & installation, general engineering services, heavy industrial fabrication, specialist PF valves & PF diffusers*
Greenbank Patterns, Southwell Lane, Kirkby-in-Ashfield, Nottingham, NG17 8FN Tel: (01623) 759919 Fax: (01623) 755834 E-mail: sales@greenbankpatterns.com *Pattern & mould makers*
Greenbank Technology Ltd, Unit 420 Glenfield Park Two, Blakewater Road, Blackburn, BB1 5QH Tel: (01254) 690555 Fax: (01254) 690666 E-mail: info@greenbanktechnology.co.uk *Manufacturers of industrial & radio frequency plant or equipment*
Greenberg Glass Ltd, 10 Bard St, Birmingham, B11 4SA Tel: 0121-753 1900 Fax: 0121-772 3683 E-mail: website@greenbergglass.co.uk *Glazing contractors and glass processors*
Greenberg Glass Ltd, Beddington Lane, Croydon, CR0 4TD Tel: (020) 8684 9207 Fax: (020) 8689 8189 E-mail: croydon@greenbergglass.co.uk *Glass merchants & glaziers*
Greenberg Glass Contract Ltd, unit 33 Dunes Way, Liverpool, L5 9RJ Tel: 0151-207 2574 Fax: 0151-298 1050 *Aluminium & glazing contractors* Also at: Branches throughout the U.K.
Greenberry Bros Engineers Ltd, Brunel Drive, Newark, Nottinghamshire, NG24 2EG Tel: (01636) 676694 Fax: (01636) 675830 E-mail: sales@greenberrybros.co.uk *General engineers*
Greenbirches Joiners Ltd, Unit 1, Greenbirches Industrial Estate, Stoke-on-Trent, ST6 5US Tel: (01782) 834888 *Joiners*
Greenbooth Construction Co. Ltd, Hunt Lane, Chadderton, Oldham, OL9 0LR Tel: 0161-633 4815 *Civil engineers & plant hire*
Greenbow Services, 17 Murhall Street, Stoke-on-Trent, ST6 4BL Tel: (01782) 867038 E-mail: esme.w@ntlworld.com *24 hour callout, lock work and safe work undertaken*
▶ Greenbox Heat Exchangers, 11 Wassage Way, Hampton Lovett, Droitwich, Worcestershire, WR9 0NX Tel: (01905) 777050 Fax: (01905) 777051 E-mail: sales@greenbox.uk.com Principal Export Areas: Central/East Europe & West Europe *Heat recovery plant & systems*
Greenbrook, 62 West Road, Harlow, Essex, CM20 2BG Tel: (01803) 527524 Fax: (01803) 526789 E-mail: meters@rdluk.com *Meter repairs*
▶ GreenCards, 71 Knockdarragh, Fullerton Road, Newry, County Down, BT34 2GA Tel: (028) 3025 6013 *Wedding stationery*
Greencore Malt, 24-25 Eastern Way, Bury St. Edmunds, Suffolk, IP32 7AD Tel: (01284) 772000 Fax: (01284) 753349 E-mail: greencoremalt@greencoremalt.com *Malt manufrs*
▶ Greenduck, Confectionery Works, Western Way, Bury St. Edmunds, Suffolk, IP33 3SP Tel: (01284) 700015 Fax: (01284) 700016 E-mail: info@greenduck.co.uk *I.T recruitment agents*
Greene King Brewing & Retailing Ltd, Westgate Brewery, Bury St. Edmunds, Suffolk, IP33 1QT Tel: (01284) 763222 Fax: (01284) 706502 E-mail: gregwilliams@greeneking.co.uk *Brewers*
Greene Tweed & Co. Ltd, Mere Way, Ruddington, Nottingham, NG11 6JS Tel: 0115-931 5777 Fax: 0115-931 5888 E-mail: mktng@gtweed.com *Greene, Tweed design & manufacture, thermoplastic, elastomer & composite seal solutions, custom engineered components & electrical & fibre optic connectors to high performance industries including Aerospace & Defence, Fluid Handling, Oilfield, Industrial, Semiconductor & Medical & Biotechnology*
Greener Interior Landscaping, Three Acres, The Avenue, Medburn, Newcastle upon Tyne, NE20 0JD Tel: (01661) 825238 Fax: (01661) 825522 E-mail: sales@greenerinteriors.com *Floral & plant displays*
Greenery Bristol, 5 Wholesale Fruit Centre, Albert Crescent, Bristol, BS2 0YJ Tel: 0117-977 3366 Fax: 0117-977 8984 E-mail: brenda@greenery-bristol.co.uk *Wholesale fruit, vegetables, flowers, plants suppliers*
▶ Greenfarm Engineering, The Bungalow, Station Road, Wath-upon-Dearne, Rotherham, South Yorkshire, S63 7DG Tel: (01709) 876711 Fax: (01709) 875899 *Fabricators*
▶ Greenfern Bakery Ltd, 13 Greenfern Road, Aberdeen, AB16 5PY Tel: (01224) 691335 Fax: (01224) 691881 *Bakery manufrs*
▶ Greenfield Engineering, Unit 2a Dobles Lane Industrial Estate, Holsworthy, Devon, EX22 6HL Tel: (01409) 254400 Fax: (01409) 254898 E-mail: sales@greenfieldengineering.co.uk *Sheet metal fabricators sub contractors*
Greenfield Engineering Titanium Ltd, 44 Hockley Street, Hockley, Birmingham, B18 6BH Tel: 0121-507 0994 E-mail: getiuk@aol.com *Titanium jewellery manufrs*
Greenfield Stationery, Unit 7 Northside Business Centre, Wellington Street, Birmingham, B18 4NR Tel: 0121-515 5100 Fax: 0121-515 5101 E-mail: mail@greenfieldstationery.com *Printing & promotional items*
Greenford Timber & Builders Merchants, 328 Uxbridge Road, London, W12 7LJ Tel: (020) 8743 6517 Fax: (020) 8743 6517 *Building merchants*
Greengage Computer Products, Hilary House, Main Road, Woolverstone, Ipswich, IP9 1BA Tel: (01473) 780080 Fax: (01473) 780077 E-mail: sales@greengage.com *Computer resellers*
Greengate Engraving Ltd, 292 High Street, Stoke-on-Trent, ST6 5TY Tel: (01782) 822884 Fax: (01782) 815345 *General engravers*
Greengate Metal Components Ltd, Greengate, Middleton, Manchester, M24 1RU Tel: 0161-653 3443 Fax: 0161-643 4991 E-mail: sales@greengatemetal.co.uk *Precision sheet metalworkers*
Greengauge (Sports) Ltd, 5 Gateside, Commercial Park, Haddington, East Lothian, EH41 3SE Tel: (0845) 5400012 Fax: (0845) 1308029 *Sports equipment distributors*
Greengrace Floral & Plant Displays, 129 Elmbridge Avenue, Surbiton, Surrey, KT5 9HE Tel: (020) 8399 8174 Fax: (020) 8390 1871 *Floral & plant displays for hire for offices & businesses*
Greenhalgh's Craft Bakery Ltd, Bee Hive Industrial Estate, Crescent Road, Lostock, Bolton, BL6 4BU Tel: (01204) 696204 Fax: (01204) 669061 E-mail: info@greenhalghs.com *Bakers wholesale manufrs*
Greenham Ltd, Tinsley Lane North, Crawley, West Sussex, RH10 9TP Tel: (01293) 525955 Fax: (01293) 522971 E-mail: crawley.sales@greenham.co.uk *Janitorial supplies & industrial clothing distributors*
Greenham Regis Ltd, Kings Saltern Road, Lymington, Hampshire, SO41 3QD Tel: (01590) 671144 Fax: (01590) 679517 E-mail: lymington@greenham-regis.com *Marine radio equipment suppliers* Also at: Emsworth, Hamble & Poole
Greenham Trading Ltd, Kilmaine Close, Cambridge, CB4 2PH Tel: (01223) 423422 Fax: (01223) 424882 E-mail: cambridge.sale@greenham.co.uk *Protective equipment distributors*
Greenhaven Ltd, 11 Club Row, London, E1 6JX Tel: (020) 7613 2345 Fax: (020) 7613 5977 *Leather garments (clothes) import & export*
Greenhaven Letting Agents, 10 Bradford Road, Stanningley, Pudsey, West Yorkshire, LS28 6DD Tel: 0113-255 8333 Fax: 0113-204 0200 E-mail: greenhaven@btinternet.com *Property management*
Greenheart Design Ltd, The Tall House, Harberton, Totnes, Devon, TQ9 7SQ Tel: (01803) 868685 Fax: (01803) 866694 *Kitchens and fitted furniture.*
▶ Greenhill Construction Derby Ltd, 611 Burton Road, Derby, DE23 6EJ Tel: (01332) 604055 Fax: (01332) 604058
Greenhill Leisure Products, Harmby Road, Leyburn, North Yorkshire, DL8 5QA Tel: (01969) 624324 Fax: (01969) 624324 E-mail: mail@green2hill.co.uk *Manufacture quality golf trolleys & carts*
▶ Greenhills Electric Ltd, 1a Puller Road, Hemel Hempstead, Hertfordshire, HP1 1QL Tel: (01442) 264126 Fax: (01442) 232193
Greenhous, March Way, Battlefield Enterprise Park, Shrewsbury, SY1 3JE Tel: (01743) 467904 Fax: (01743) 457500 E-mail: enquiries@greenhous.co.uk *Daf truck & ldv van dealers* Also at: Hanley, Telford & Wolverhampton
▶ Greenhouse Water Gardens, 87 Chase Cross Road, Romford, RM5 3RP Tel: (01708) 726726 Fax: (01708) 780557 E-mail: goosegreenn114@aol.com *Suppliers and installers of everything to do with Ponds, Fountains and Waterfeatures*
Greenhunter Ltd, Unit 583B, Perimeter Road South, London Gatwick Airport, Gatwick, West Sussex, RH6 0PQ Tel: (01403) 871440 Fax: (01293) 568768 E-mail: info@greenhunter.co.uk *Pest control services*
Greenlight Locksmith, 42 Preston Parade, Whitstable, Kent, CT5 4AJ Tel: (01227) 274738 E-mail: greenlightlocks@btinternet.com *Locksmiths*
▶ Greenlight Sytems, 8a Heene Terrace, Worthing, West Sussex, BN11 3NP Tel: (01903) 205307 E-mail: leroysalih@greenlightsystems.co.uk *Greenlight Systems is a web design and applications software house.*We specialise in assisting companies to generate revenue ro reduce costs utilising Internet Technologies.*
Greenline Ni Ltd, Mallusk Park, Mallusk Road, Newtownabbey, County Antrim, BT36 4FS Tel: (028) 9083 6000 Fax: (028) 9034 2593 E-mail: info@greenlinebuildings.com *Portable building hire, sale, manufr*
Greenline Tanks Ltd, Townwell, Cromhall, Wotton-under-Edge, Gloucestershire, GL12 8AG Tel: (01454) 294801 Fax: (01454) 294799 E-mail: chris@greenlinetanks.co.uk *Fuel tank manufrs*
▶ Greenmount Fans, 8 Saville Street, Bolton, BL2 1BY Tel: (01204) 364362 Fax: (01204) 364368 E-mail: sales@greenmountfans.co.uk *Manufacturer of industrial fans*
Greenoaks Ltd, Greenoaks House, Siemens Road, Irlam, Manchester, M44 5AH Tel: 0161-775 0956 Fax: 0161-776 1951 E-mail: info@greenoaks.ltd.uk *New & secondhand shelving & pallet racking*
Greenock Telegraph, 2 Crawfurd Street, Greenock, Renfrewshire, PA15 1LH Tel: (01475) 726511 Fax: (01475) 783734 E-mail: advertising@greenocktelegraph.co.uk *Newspaper publishers*
▶ Greenplant Ltd, London Road, Wheatley, Oxford, OX33 1JH Tel: (01865) 876000 Fax: (01865) 876222
Greens Accident Repair Centre, 1 Mercer Road, Warnham, Horsham, West Sussex, RH12 3RL Tel: (01403) 254506 Fax: (01403) 254695 *Accident repair & recovery services*
Greens Of Mepal, 1 Brangehill Lane, Mepal, Ely, Cambridgeshire, CB6 2AL Tel: (01353) 778450 *Garden buildings manufr*
Greens The Signmakers Ltd, Brighton Street, Kingston-upon-Hull, East Riding of Yorkshire, HU3 4UW Tel: (01482) 327371 Fax: (01482) 228050 E-mail: davidragan@greens-signmakers.co.uk *Screen printers & sign contractors*
Greens Water Systems, Longacre Business Park, Westminster Road, North Hykeham, Lincoln, LN6 3QH Tel: (01522) 697785 Fax: (01522) 823899 E-mail: info@water-systems.co.uk *Closed circuit television contractors*
▶ Greenserve Cleaning Services, 63 Tenter Road, Moulton Park Industrial Estate, Moulton Park Industrial Estate, Northampton, NN3 6AX Tel: (01604) 494605 Fax: (01604) 645786 E-mail: enquiries@greenservecleaning.co.uk *Cleaning services*
Greenshields, Cowie & Co. Ltd, Greenshields House, Perimeter Road, Knowsley Industrial Park North, Liverpool, L33 3BA Tel: 0151-546 2044 Fax: 0151-546 1967 *Freight forwarding agents* Also at: Sutton
Greenshields JCB Ltd, Clipper Close, Medway City Estate, Rochester, Kent, ME2 4QP Tel: (01634) 296660 Fax: (01634) 296670 *Contractors plant distributors*
Greensmith Upholstery Ltd, New Tythe Street, Long Eaton, Nottingham, NG10 2DL Tel: 0115-973 3446 Fax: 0115-946 0743 *Upholstery manufrs*
▶ Greensplash Ltd, 308 Chester Road, Hartford, Northwich, Cheshire, CW8 2AB Tel: (01606) 884123 Fax: (01606) 884212 E-mail: enquiries@greensplash.com *Design & communications agency, specialising in web design,*
Greentec Industries Ltd, Unit 8 Omni Business Centre, Omega Park, Wilsom Road, Alton, Hampshire, GU34 2QE Tel: (01420) 88088 Fax: (01420) 88099 E-mail: flynn@btconnect.com *Road cone retrieval machine manufrs*
▶ Greentimber Forest Products, 3 Victoria Road, Harpenden, Hertfordshire, AL5 4EA Tel: (01582) 799050 Fax: (01582) 799040 E-mail: green@greentimber.com *Timber importers*
▶ Greenwald & Gregory, 116 A Hallowell Road, Northwood, Middlesex, HA6 1DU Tel: (01923) 820974
Greenway & Partners Ltd, 1 Bedford Street, Leamington Spa, Warwickshire, CV32 5DY Tel: (01926) 337430 Fax: (01926) 428964 E-mail: sales@gapl.co.uk *Building design consultants*
Greenway Pepper Precision Engineering Ltd, Parkhouse Road East, Parkhouse Industrial Estate East, Newcastle, Staffordshire, ST5 7RB Tel: (01782) 563020 Fax: (01782) 565540 E-mail: office@greenwaypepper.co.uk *Precision engineers*
▶ GreenwayDirect, The Barn, Oaklands Home Farm, Church Street, Barrowford, Nelson, Lancashire, BB9 6EB Tel: (01282) 693661 E-mail: peter.maltby@greenwaydirect.com *Sale of high quality forestry, horticultural, landscaping products*
▶ Greenways Construction (Midlands) Ltd, Weatherby Road, Osmaston Park Industrial Estate, Derby, DE24 8HL Tel: (01332) 370702
Greenweld, C/O Permex Ltd, Riverside House, Plumpton Road, Hoddesdon, Hertfordshire, EN11 0PA Tel: (01992) 452980 Fax: (01992) 452981 E-mail: bargains@greenweld.co.uk *Electronic components & mail order*
Greenwich Design Associates, 11a Greenwich South Street, London, SE10 8NJ Tel: (020) 8853 3028 Fax: (020) 8858 2128 E-mail: simon@greenwich-design.co.uk *Innovative concepts. Creative strategies. Thoughtful design solutions for modern business.*
Greenwich Instruments, Meridian House, Park Road, Swanley, Kent, BR8 8AH Tel: (0870) 0505404 Fax: (0870) 0505405 E-mail: sales@greenwichinst.co.uk *We are a manufacturer of add-ons and peripherals for personal and palm type computers. We also manufacture memory products, data transfer equipment and stepper motor controllers. We are recognised as leading product developers within the electronics industry.*
▶ Greenwich Windows & Conservatories, Unit 5 Woodhouse Business Centre, Wakefield Road, Normanton, West Yorkshire, WF6 1BB Tel: (01924) 220770 E-mail: sales@greenwitchwindows.com *Installers of double glazing*
Greenwich Wood Works, 1-5 Lewisham Road, London, SE13 7QS Tel: (020) 8694 8449 Fax: (020) 8694 8616 E-mail: sales@greenwichwoodworks.co.uk *Hand-built kitchen & furniture manufrs*
Greenwood Air Management Ltd, Brookside Industrial Estate, Rustington, Littlehampton, West Sussex, BN16 3LF Tel: (01903) 771021 Fax: (01903) 782398 E-mail: info@greenwood.co.uk *Ventilation system manufrs*
Greenwood Audio Visual, 1 Wolverhampton Road, Kingswinford, West Midlands, DY6 7HX Tel: (01384) 287337 Fax: (01384) 287347 *Presentation equipment sales*
Greenwood & Coope Ltd, Holme Mill, Railway Street, Ramsbottom, Bury, Lancashire, BL0 9AU Tel: (01706) 825211 Fax: (01706) 827633 E-mail: info@cormarcarpets.co.uk *Carpet manufrs*
Greenwood & Coope Ltd, Brookhouse Mill, Holcombe Road, Greenmount, Bury, Lancashire, BL8 4HR Tel: (01204) 881234 Fax: (01204) 887722 E-mail: info@cormarcarpets.co.uk *Carpet manufrs* Also at: Orpington
Greenwood Gears Ltd, Digital House, Royd Way, Keighley, West Yorkshire, BD21 3LG Tel: (01535) 604393 Fax: (01535) 680587 E-mail: sales@hewitt-topham.co.uk *Gear manufacturers including helical & cnc vertical machining*
Greenwood J.F, Barton Lane, Eccles, Manchester, M30 0HN Tel: 0161-786 1075 Fax: 0161-787 7613 E-mail: sjb@behrens.co.uk *Fabric converters*
▶ Greenwood Overseas, 25 Regent Street, Rugby, Warwickshire, CV21 2PE Tel: (01788) 552050 Fax: (01788) 579164 E-mail: zlf@greenwoodoverseas.com *Spain, Portugal, Cyprus, Turkey.*Villas, townhouses, apartments, traditional dwellings for your retirement, holiday or pure investment.*
Greenwood Structures, 67 Trafalgar Road, Moseley, Birmingham, B13 8BL Tel: 0121-449 0278 Fax: 0121-249 2499 *Building & structural engineers*
Greenwood & Walsh Ltd, Melbourne Street, Morley, Leeds, LS27 8BG Tel: 0113-253 8611 Fax: 0113-252 6849 *Woollen cloth manufrs*
Greenwoods (Coleshill) Ltd, Unit 28, Roman Way, Coleshill, Birmingham, B46 1HQ Tel: (01675) 464280 Fax: (01675) 467160 E-mail: sales@greenwoodtools.demon.co.uk *Hand tool distributors*
▶ Greenwoods Stock Boxes Ltd, Abbeyfield Road, Lenton, Nottingham, NG7 2SP Tel: 0115-985 1851 Fax: 0115-985 1852 E-mail: sales@boxesdirect.co.uk *Boxes, cardboard boxes, packaging & storage*
Greer Publications, 5B Edgewater Business Park, Belfast Harbour Estate, Belfast, BT3 9JQ Tel: (028) 9078 3200 Fax: (028) 9078 3210 E-mail: mail@greerpublications.com *Grocers &*
continued

continuation
catering & food technology & packaging specialists

Greet Steel Properties Ltd, 1 Salters Lane, West Bromwich, West Midlands, B71 4BG Tel: 0121-553 1700 Fax: 0121-553 1700 *Property owners & managers*

Greeting Card Association, United House, North Road, London, N7 9DP Tel: (020) 7619 0396 Fax: (020) 7607 6411 *Trade association*

Greetings UK, South Orbital Trading Park, Hedon Road, Hull, HU9 1NN Tel: (01482) 328383 Fax: (01482) 621298 *Greeting card manufrs*

▶ greetings2u.co.uk, 7 Coldstream Terrace, Riverside, Cardiff, CF11 6LJ Tel: 07855 282576 E-mail: anthony.thomas120@ntlworld.com *Supply a selection of original greetings cards*

▶ Greg & Co Ltd, Tent Street, London, E1 5DZ Tel: (020) 7481 0222 Fax: (020) 7481 3233 E-mail: info@gregandco.com

Gregg & Patterson Engineers Ltd, Ballyskeagh Road, Lisburn, County Antrim, BT27 5TD Tel: (028) 9061 8131 Fax: (028) 9062 2813 *Structural engineers*

Greggs plc, 36 Dryden Road, Loanhead, Midlothian, EH20 9LZ Tel: 0131-440 4852 Fax: 0131-440 9918 E-mail: info@greggs.co.uk *Bakery retail*

Gregoire Besson UK Ltd, Bourne Road Carlby, Stamford, Lincolnshire, PE9 4NP Tel: (01778) 590223 Fax: (01778) 590645 E-mail: bill@gregoire-besson.co.uk *Import farm machinery*

Gregory Audio Visual Ltd, 190 St. Aidans Avenue, Blackburn, BB2 4EA Tel: (01254) 674444 Fax: (01254) 674444 E-mail: sales@gregoryav.co.uk *Audio visual equipment hire*

Gregory, Bottley & Lloyd, 13 Seagrave Road, London, SW6 1RP Tel: (020) 7381 5522 Fax: (020) 7381 5512 *Dealers in geological supplies*

Gregory Bros, The Timber Yard, Lucas Green Road, West End, Woking, Surrey, GU24 9YB Tel: (01483) 472264 Fax: (01483) 799548 *Timber merchants*

▶ Gregory Distribution, St Erth Industrial Estate, Rose-An-Grouse, Canonstown, Hayle, Cornwall, TR27 6LP Tel: (01736) 754291

Gregory Distribution Ltd, 118-124 London Road, Amesbury, Salisbury, SP4 7ZS Tel: (01980) 590100 Fax: (01980) 624355 E-mail: amesburytransport@compuserve.com *Road transport contractors*

Gregory Pank, 86-87 Digbeth, Birmingham, B5 6DY Tel: 0121-643 3008 Fax: 0121-643 3360 *Tool merchants*

▶ Gregory Pennington Ltd, Pennington House, Carolina Way, Salford, M50 2ZY Tel: (0800) 0839630 Fax: 0161-972 7100 *Gregory Pennington one of the UK's leading financial and debt management companies offering helpful and friendly advice on debt management, financial management and other debt solutions.*

Gregson Studio, 42 Bury Close, Gosport, Hampshire, PO12 3TU Tel: (023) 9252 0808 E-mail: m.sowdon@fsbdial.co.uk *Photographic studio services*

Gregsons, Brookside, Drointon Road, Rugeley, Staffordshire, WS15 3NX Tel: (01889) 500572 Fax: (01889) 500415 *Agricultural machinery dealers*

Gregton Confectionery Ltd, Wantz Road, Dagenham, Essex, RM10 8PR Tel: (020) 8984 8811 E-mail: sales@gregtons.freeserve.co.uk *Confectionery*

▶ Grehan Contractors Ltd, Grehan House, Molewood Road, Hertford, SG14 3AQ Tel: (01992) 500051 Fax: (01992) 500262

Greif UK Ltd, Merseyside Works, Oil Sites Road, Ellesmere Port, CH65 4EZ Tel: 0151-373 2000 Fax: 0151-373 2072 E-mail: kathy.turton@tri-sure.com *Closure systems distributors*

Greiner Extrusion Technology UK Ltd, Unit 5 Queens Avenue, Hurdsfield Industrial Estate, Macclesfield, Cheshire, SK10 2BN Tel: (01625) 616061 Fax: (01625) 613689 E-mail: s.wood@greiner-extrusion.co.uk *Extrusion tool refurbishing services*

▶ Grelson Industries Ltd, Marlowe House, Stewkins, Stourbridge, West Midlands, DY8 4YW Tel: (01384) 444333

Gremida Screen Print Ltd, Sunnybank Works, Sunnybank Street, Ossett, West Yorkshire, WF5 8PE Tel: (01924) 265957 Fax: (01924) 265957 E-mail: gremida.screenprint@virgin.net *Screen, digital printing service providers & manufrs*

Grenadier Guards Security Services, Grenadier House, Condover, Shrewsbury, SY5 7BG Tel: 08450 539198 E-mail: info@grenadiersecurity.co.uk *Grenadier Guards Security was established in 2002 and has since established a enviable reputation as a prestige quality supplier of Security Services based across the Uk.*

Grenadier Security Nationwide, Quarry House, Telford, Shropshire, TF6 6NP Tel: (0845) 0539198 E-mail: info@grenadiersecurity.co.uk *Offices Located in london, Midlands, Shropshire and North Wales , NATIONWIDE COVERAGE,**Grenadier Security is an established market leader in the provision of Manpower Security Services. We are Fully insured and all employees are SIA Licensed. We are ISO 9001 Compliant and comply with BS 7858 Vetting . We have offices Nationwide offering full UK Coverage. We offer a Commitment to provide the highest quality service.**· Static Guarding*· Mobile Patrols*· Event Security*· Keyholding Services*· Retail Officers*· Fully Insured*· ISO 9001*· BS 7858*· SIA Licensed Staff*· 24 Hour Control Room*· Parking Management*· Cleaning Services*· No Obligation Site survey and Quote.*· References Available upon Request*· Onsite Training Facilities·*

Grenadine Trading Ltd, Bay 36-38 Circular Road, Storforth Lane Trading Estate, Hasland, Chesterfield, Derbyshire, S41 0QL Tel: (01246) 209391 Fax: (01246) 550718 E-mail: ben.bramley@ntworld.com *Bed retailer*

Grenco Reefer Services Ltd, Hauliers Road, Felixstowe, Suffolk, IP11 3SF Tel: (01394) 613116 Fax: (01394) 613133 *Marine refrigeration service*

The Greno Garage & Engineering, Penistone Road, Grenoside, Sheffield, S35 8QG Tel: 0114-246 7409 Fax: 0114-246 7409 *Propeller shaft manufrs*

▶ Grenrose Scaffolding, Crompton Road, Stevenage, Hertfordshire, SG1 2EE Tel: (01438) 813948 Fax: (01438) 742917

Grenson Shoes Ltd, Queen Street, Rushden, Northamptonshire, NN10 0AB Tel: (01933) 358734 Fax: (01933) 410106 E-mail: enquiries@grenson.com *Premium quality mens shoe manufrs*

Grenville Engineering Stoke On Trent Ltd, 3 Newfields Industrial Estate, High Street, Stoke-on-Trent, ST6 5PD Tel: (01782) 577929 Fax: (01782) 575672 E-mail: greneng@greneng.co.uk *Sheet metal & light fabrications*

Gresco Brush Ltd, 16 Liberty Close, Woolsbridge Industrial Estate, Three Legged Cross, Wimborne, Dorset, BH21 6SY Tel: (01202) 826600 Fax: (01202) 826600 E-mail: paul@gresco.freeserve.co.uk *Cosmetic brush manufrs*

Gresham Computer Services Ltd, Mitchell House, Brook Avenue, Southampton, SO31 9ZA Tel: (01489) 555500 Fax: (01489) 555560 E-mail: info@gresham-computing.com *Bespoke software writers*

Gresham Consultants, 7 Veryan, Fareham, Hampshire, PO14 1NN Tel: (01329) 236881 Fax: (0845) 8330873 *Business consultancy services*

Gresham Engineering, 104 Maybury Road, Woking, Surrey, GU21 5JL Tel: (01483) 765538 Fax: (01483) 765320 E-mail: sales@hacltd.co.uk *Gas & air sampling equipment manufrs*

Gresham Forms Ltd, The Potting Shed Arkwright Road, Willowbrook East Industrial Estate, Willowbrook North Industrial Estate, Corby, Northamptonshire, NN17 5AE Tel: (01536) 408408 Fax: (01536) 408381 E-mail: sales@greshamticket.co.uk *Printers, tickets & labels for clothes*

Frank Gresham & Co. Ltd, Kingston Chambers, 17 Princes Dock Street, Hull, HU1 2LT Tel: (01482) 324675 Fax: (01482) 226863 E-mail: mail@greshams.karoo.co.uk *Timber importers & merchants* Also at: Brough & Sheffield

Gresham House plc, 36 Elder Street, London, E1 6BT Tel: (020) 7588 7352 Fax: (020) 7377 2946 *Investment trust company*

▶ Gresham Office Furniture, Lynstock Way, Lostock, Bolton, BL6 4SA Tel: (01204) 664400 Fax: (01204) 664433 E-mail: info@gof.co.uk *Office furniture designers & manufrs*

Gresham Power Electronics, Gresham House, Telford Road, Salisbury, SP2 7PH Tel: (01722) 413060 Fax: (01722) 413034 E-mail: info@greshampower.com *Commercial & defence applications*

▶ Gresham Scientific Instruments, Sirius House, Watery Lane, Wooburn Green, High Wycombe, Buckinghamshire, HP10 0AP Tel: (01628) 533060 Fax: (01628) 533034 E-mail: e2vsi.admin@e2v.com *Scientific instrument manufrs*

Brian Greslow, 6-8 lime grove, Seaforth, liverpool, L21 3TT Tel: (0800) 458 1920 Fax: 0151-474 5353

▶ Grest Finance, 9A Flowergate, Halls Place, Whitby, North Yorkshire, YO21 3BD Tel: 07917 207287 E-mail: Daniella.m@btinternet.com *Buy a holiday home or property abroad! We offer FULL instant cash for up to £250'000 for a property abroad! Thats up to 100% cash for the home in the sun! We move fast and get you the money you need quickly. contact me for more details..*

Gretton Ward Electrical Ltd, 112 Peckham Rye, London, SE15 4HA Tel: (020) 7639 3275 Fax: (020) 7358 1389 E-mail: grettonward@lineone.net *Electronic cinema equipment manufrs*

Greville Hardfacing & Engineering Co. Ltd, 4 Palmers Road, Redditch, Worcestershire, B98 0RF Tel: (01527) 525395 Fax: (01527) 510949 E-mail: ghf@btconnect.com *Hardfacing & machining services*

Grewcock Fabrics Ltd, 15-29 Dartford Rd, Leicester, LE2 7PQ Tel: 0116-283 8551 Fax: 0116-244 0715 *Fabric manufrs*

▶ Charles Grey, 27 Alton Road, Richmond, Surrey, TW9 1UJ Tel: (07703) 533703 E-mail: charles@greyuk.net *Heating engineer*

Grey Matter Ltd, 2 Prigg Meadow, Ashburton, Newton Abbot, Devon, TQ13 7DF Tel: (01364) 654100 Fax: (0870) 3665577 E-mail: info@greymatter.com *Software sales*

▶ Grey Tone Services, Yew Tree Cottage, Deepdean, Ross-on-Wye, Herefordshire, HR9 5SQ Tel: (01989) 768403 Fax: (01989) 768115 *Computer consultants & suppliers*

Greycon Ltd, 7 Calico House, Clove Hitch Quay, London, SW11 3TN Tel: (020) 7978 0700 Fax: (020) 7978 6222 E-mail: jm@greycon.com *Computer development software services*

Greyfriars Filters, 6 Douglas Road Industrial Park, Douglas Road, Kingswood, Bristol, BS15 8PD Tel: 0117-960 4249 Fax: 0117-947 5729 *Filter distributors*

Greyhound Ltd, Duckfield Barn, Bakers Road, Belchamp St. Paul, Sudbury, Suffolk, CO10 7DG Tel: (01787) 277372 Fax: (01787) 278787 *Backgammon sets & antique restoration*

▶ Greyhound Business Systems Ltd, PO Box 5306, Leicester, LE2 4SS Tel: 0116-271 8808 Fax: 0116-271 8808 E-mail: sales@greyhound-business.co.uk *Payroll & accounting services*

Greyhound Leisure Ltd, 10 Gores Lane, Market Harborough, Leicestershire, LE16 8AJ Tel: (01858) 432328 Fax: (01858) 469555 E-mail: greyhound.leisure@virgin.net *Playground equipment manufrs*

Greyland Ltd, Greg Street, Stockport, Cheshire, SK5 7BX Tel: 0161-476 3607 Fax: 0161-477 1870 E-mail: greyland@cwcom.net *Cleaning chemical products manufrs*

Greyland Plastics Ltd, Greylands, Laurels Road, Offenham, Evesham, Worcestershire, WR11 8RE Tel: (01386) 421422 Fax: (01386) 421423E-mail: greylandplastics@btconnect.com *Suppliers of plastic materials*

Greys Of Alnwick, Station Yard, Alnwick, Northumberland, NE66 2NP Tel: (01665) 510020 Fax: (01665) 604530 E-mail: info@hardycomposites.co.uk *Fishing rod manufrs*

▶ Greystone Plumbing Ltd, 23 Townhead Street, Strathaven, Lanarkshire, ML10 6AB Tel: (01357) 522037 Fax: (01357) 520214

Gribben Motors, 159 Keady Road, Armagh, BT60 3AE Tel: (028) 3752 4614 Fax: (028) 3752 4614 *Motor vehicle body service*

Gribbin Construction Co. Ltd, 140 Creagh Road, Castledawson, Magherafelt, County Londonderry, BT45 8EY Tel: (028) 7946 8636 Fax: (028) 7946 8949 *Building contractors*

Gridfeed Thornber Ltd, Brearley Mill, Halifax Road, Todmorden, Lancashire, OL14 6EF Tel: (01706) 815131 Fax: (01706) 815455 E-mail: gridthorn@aol.com *Poultry equipment suppliers*

Gridmaster Ltd, Weekley, Kettering, Northamptonshire, NN16 9UP Tel: (01536) 484948 Fax: (01536) 484948 E-mail: sales@gridmaster.co.uk *Engineering software suppliers*

Griff Chains Ltd, Quarry Road, Dudley Wood, Dudley, West Midlands, DY2 0ED Tel: (01384) 569415 Fax: (01384) 410580 E-mail: sales@griffchains.co.uk Principal Export Areas: Worldwide *Manufacturers of agricultural machinery spare parts/wearing parts; chains, marine & chains, industrial. Also CNC engineering services/machinists*

Griff Woodwork Co. Ltd, Unit 4A, The Ridgeway Trading Estate, Iver, Buckinghamshire, SL0 9HW Tel: (01753) 652616 Fax: (01753) 652616 *Joiners*

Griffen Dental Laboratory, 9 High Road, Byfleet, West Byfleet, Surrey, KT14 7QH Tel: (01932) 340580 Fax: (01932) 340941 E-mail: griffindental@lineone.net *Dental technicians*

Griffin Cardwell Ltd, 87 Fleet Road, Fleet, Hampshire, GU51 3PJ Tel: (01252) 365500 Fax: (01252) 612875 E-mail: sales@griffincardwell.com *Materials handling equipment.*

Griffin Design & Print Services Ltd, 713 High Road, Leyton, London, E10 5AB Tel: (020) 8558 4721 Fax: (020) 8558 4415 E-mail: mail@griffindp.freeserve.co.uk *Screen & lithographic printing*

Griffin Education, Bishop Meadow Road, Loughborough, Leicestershire, LE11 5RG Tel: (01509) 233344 Fax: (01509) 231893 E-mail: info@fisher.co.uk *Educational laboratory supplies*

▶ Griffin Electronics Ltd, Griffin House 5 Laura Avenue, Paignton, Devon, TQ3 2LS Tel: (01803) 523537 E-mail: info@griffinelectronics.co.uk *Electronic hardware contract test engineering*

Griffin Enamellers Ltd, Navigation Road, Worcester, WR5 3DF Tel: (01905) 350511 Fax: (01905) 354500 E-mail: griffin@intrac.co.uk *Powder coating & wet paint services*

Griffin Europe Marketing, 1 Peterborough Business Pk, Lynch Wood, Peterborough, PE2 6FZ Tel: 01733 361144 Fax: 01733 361189 *Agrochemical merchants*

Griffin Fastener Supplies Ltd, PO Box 7098, Solihull, West Midlands, B93 9LD Tel: (01564) 772161 Fax: (01564) 772162 *General & standard bolt & nut manufrs*

Griffin & Fudge Ltd, Whiteheads Lane, Bradford-on-Avon, Wiltshire, BA15 1JU Tel: (01225) 863391 Fax: (01225) 864060 E-mail: jon@griffin-fudgeltd.demon.co.uk *Rubber mould toolmakers*

Griffin & General Fire Services Ltd, 7 Willow Street, London, EC2A 4BH Tel: (020) 7251 9379 Fax: (020) 7729 5652 E-mail: headoffice@griffinfire.co.uk *Fire protection services*

Griffin Grilles & Shutters, Maryfields, Bangors Road North, Iver, Buckinghamshire, SL0 0BH Tel: (01753) 652129 Fax: (01753) 717686 *Roller shutters manufrs*

Griffin Grilles & Shutters, Maryfields, Bangors Road North, Iver, Buckinghamshire, SL0 0BH Tel: (01753) 652129 Fax: (01753) 717686 E-mail: griffingp@tiscali.co.uk *Manufacturers & installers of security products*

Griffin Mill Garages Ltd, Upper Boat, Pontypridd, Mid Glamorgan, CF37 5YE Tel: (01443) 842216 Fax: (01443) 842584 E-mail: info@griffinmill.co.uk *Motor vehicle company*

Griffin Nuu Med, Pipers Farm, Berhill, Ashcott, Bridgwater, Somerset, TA7 9QN Tel: (01458) 210324 Fax: (01458) 210396 E-mail: info@numnah.co.uk *Manufacturers equestrian accessories*

Griffin Print Ltd, 2-4 Belgic Square, Peterborough, PE1 5XF Tel: (01733) 553530 Fax: (01733) 555668 E-mail: info@griffinprint.co.uk *Commercial printers*

Griffin & Son, 106 Pavenhill, Purton, Swindon, SN5 4DB Tel: (01793) 770807 Fax: (01793) 771807 E-mail: pete@griffinandson.uk.com *Bead & grit blasting*

Griffin & Stenning, 2 Workshop, Milton Ave, Bath, BA2 4QZ Tel: (01225) 331069 *Joinery manufacturer*

Griffin Stone Ltd, Brookmede, Halstead Road, Fordham, Colchester, CO6 3LW Tel: (01206) 240318 *Manufacturers & retailers of garden ornaments*

▶ Griffin Stringer Ltd, Allenway, Sunningdale Road, Leicester, LE3 1UX Tel: 0116-231 2840 Fax: 0116-231 2840 *Ferrous & non-ferrous scrap metal merchants*

Griffin Windows Ltd, Unit 37 Abergorki Industrial Estate, Treorchy, Mid Glamorgan, CF42 6DL Tel: (01443) 777333 Fax: (01443) 776773 E-mail: suzm@griffinwindows.co.uk *Manufacturers of windows & doors*

Griffin Woodhouse, Greenfields, Romsley Lane, Shatterford, Bewdley, Worcestershire, DY12 1RS Tel: (01299) 861829 Fax: (01299) 861830 E-mail: sales@griffin-woodhouse.co.uk *Integral stud link chain manufrs*

Ernest Griffith & Sons Ltd, Praed Rd, Trafford Park, Manchester, M17 1PQ Tel: 0161-877 1655 Fax: 0161-877 6577 E-mail: pdbrearley@aol.com *Established since 1941, Ernest Griffith & Sons specialise in the wholesale supply of fabric dust sheets to many outlets such as DIY Superstores, Builder Merchants, Plumbing suppliers, as well as the smaller independent painting and decorating centres. Our latest product SLIPROTEX is an antislip dust sheet and has been specially designed to prevent those sorts of accidents occurring with its anti-slip backing that prevents it from moving when placed on any surface from highly polished laminate or tiled floor to carpeted areas such as stairs. SLIPROTEX is also fully absorbent, light and manageable. We also provide grey cloth, synthetic dust covers, cotton dust sheets, polythene dust covers - all in a variety of sizes and qualities. In addition to our dust sheet range we supply numerous sundry products e.g. Tarpaulins, Stockinette, Polypropylene Sacks and various fabric Hand Wipes. Please visit our website for more details*

John Griffith, Pant Hwfa, Llanllechid, Bangor, Gwynedd, LL57 3LA Tel: (01248) 600344 Fax: (01248) 602909 *Agricultural contractors*

Griffith Laboratories Ltd, Cotes Park Estate, Somercotes, Alfreton, Derbyshire, DE55 4NN Tel: (01773) 837000 Fax: (01773) 837001 *Bread crumb & food seasoning manufrs*

William Griffith & Sons (Birmingham) Ltd, 55-57 Vittoria St, Birmingham, B1 3NY Tel: 0121-236 1772 *Jewellery*

Griffiths & Co., Gwar Y Rhos, Y Ffor, Pwllheli, Gwynedd, LL53 6NF Tel: (01766) 810334 Fax: (01766) 810248 *Tractor Machinery sales*

▶ A.J. Griffiths Transport, 193 Birmingham Road, Walsall, WS1 2NX Tel: (07976) 372316 Fax: (07789) 909005 *Courier specialising in carriage of dangerous goods*

▶ Griffiths Air Conditioning & Electrical Contractors, 115 Station Road, Burton Latimer, Kettering, Northamptonshire, NN15 5PA Tel: (01536) 420666 Fax: (01536) 721133 E-mail: griffiths.aircon@ntlworld.com *Air conditioning installers & services*

Griffiths & Armour Ltd, 110 Fenchurch Street, London, EC3M 5JT Tel: (020) 7204 0014 Fax: (020) 7204 0019 E-mail: info@gallimited.com *Insurance brokers*

Arthur S. Griffiths, 2B Wonastow Road, Monmouth, Gwent, NP25 5AH Tel: (01600) 712626 *Agricultural merchants*

Griffiths Associates Ltd, Penylan House, Penprysg Road, Pencoed, Bridgend, Mid Glamorgan, CF35 6LT Tel: (01656) 862653 Fax: (01656) 864243 E-mail: john.griffiths@galtd.co.uk *Computer consultants*

Griffiths Devereaux, 334 Bristol Road, Gloucester, GL2 5DN Tel: (01452) 520418 Fax: (01452) 307877 *General engineers*

Griffiths Fabrications, Unit A10 Dovers Corner Industrial Estate, New Road, Rainham, Essex, RM13 8QT Tel: (01708) 523797 Fax: (01708) 522698 *Steel fabricators*

▶ Griffiths & James Ltd, Brecon House, William Brown Close, Llantarnam Industrial Park, Cwmbran, Gwent, NP44 3AB Tel: (01633) 877900 Fax: (01633) 877733 E-mail: office@4growth.biz *We work closely with our clients and offer a wider range of services than traditional accountants.**Once we have systems to accurately measure your numbers, we then identify those that are most important to you, and work to change them. These can be financial indicators such as turnover or profit, or non-financial such as hours worked, and even abstract numbers such as enjoyment or team happiness.**All of our work can be carried out on fixed price agreements, and we include unlimited telephone calls, so you need never worry about unexpected bills.**We try to remove some of the perceived barriers between accountants and clients. We are easy to contact - try it!*

Griffiths Mcalister Insurance, The Old School House, 14 Mill Road, Burgess Hill, West Sussex, RH15 8DR Tel: (01444) 242666 Fax: (01444) 245777 E-mail: general@griffiths-mcalister.com *Insurance brokers*

Griffiths - McGee Demolition Co. Ltd, Alperton Lane, Wembley, Middlesex, HA0 1EB Tel: (020) 8998 1101 Fax: (020) 8997 7689 E-mail: mail@mcgee.co.uk *Demolition contractors*

Griffiths & Nielsen Ltd, Wyvern House, 49 Station Road, Billingshurst, West Sussex, RH14 9SE Tel: (01403) 784881 Fax: (01403) 784988 E-mail: sales@g-and-n.com *Distributors of laboratory disposables*

Griffiths Precision Engineering, 5 Hicks Road, Markyate, St. Albans, Hertfordshire, AL3 8LG Tel: (01582) 841192 Fax: (01582) 841395 E-mail: griff@griffithseng.co.uk *Precision engineers services*

Griffiths & Son, 34 Clwyd Close Manor Lane, Hawarden Industrial Park, Hawarden, Deeside, Clwyd, CH5 3PZ Tel: (01244) 537800 Fax: (01244) 537757 E-mail: griffiths-son@btinternet.com *Mechanical service engineers*

Thomas Griffiths & Son Ltd, 84 Chorlton Road, Manchester, M15 4AL Tel: 0161-226 1834 Fax: 0161-226 3773 *Builders' & plumbers' merchants*

Griffon Hoverwork Ltd, Quay Road, Ryde, Isle Of Wight, PO33 2HB Tel: (01983) 565181 Fax: (01983) 812859 E-mail: info@hoverwork.co.uk *Company specialising in the design, manufacture and servicing of large commercial, diesel powered hovercraft.*

Griffon Studios, PO Box 5047, Alexandria, Dunbartonshire, G83 8YR Tel: (01389) 830600 Fax: (01389) 830600 *Signs Manufrs*

Griffvale Ltd, Alexandra Indust Estate, Alexandra Road, Denton, Manchester, M34 3DX Tel: 0161-335 0175 Fax: 0161-336 0513 E-mail: griffvaleltd@btconnect.com *Production engineers*

▶ Grillford Ltd, 26 Peverel Drive, Bletchley, Milton Keynes, MK1 1QZ Tel: (01908) 626700

Grimaldi Agencies Ltd, 28-29 St. James's Square, London, SW1Y 4JH Tel: (020) 7930 5683 Fax: (020) 7839 1961 E-mail: switchboard@grimaldi.co.uk *Shipping lines & agency*

Grimes Industrial Machinery & Equipment Solutions Ltd, 199 Hyde End Rd, Spencers Wood, Reading, RG7 1BU Tel: 0118-988 4825 Fax: 0118-988 4825 E-mail: grimesindmach@aol.com *Turbine steam manufacturers & fans, air driven. Also air compressor distributors/agents & generator/ generating set distributors/agents/stockholders*

▶ Grimley Smith Associates, Bramble Island, Great Oakley, Harwich, Essex, CO12 5JW Tel: (01255) 886613 Fax: (01255) 886612 *Chemical refiners*

Rachel Grimmer Ltd, 1 Cambridge Terr, Harrogate, N. Yorkshire, HG1 1PN Tel: (01423) 524236 Fax: (01423) 524236 *Knitwear manufrs*

Grimmitt Holdings Ltd, Woodgate Business Park, Kettleswood Drive, Birmingham, B32 3GH Tel: 0121-421 7000 Fax: 0121-421 9081 *Holding companies*

Grimshaw Kinnear Ltd, St. Peters Works, Tewkesbury Road, Cheltenham, Gloucestershire, GL51 9AL Tel: (01242) 513251 Fax: (01242) 226396 E-mail: sales@grimshawgroup.co.uk *Civil engineering contractors. Sports surface contractors & sports equipment suppliers. Sports & external works maintenance*

▶ Alan Grinding, Unit 2H, Alverdiscott Road Industrial Estate, Bideford, Devon, EX39 4LQ Tel: (01237) 477458 Fax: (01237) 477458 E-mail: alan@alangrinding.co.uk *Precision engineering, press tool & mould tool spares*

Grinding Centre, 62 Berkeley Street, Glasgow, G3 7DS Tel: 0141-564 8888 Fax: 0141-564 1084 E-mail: sales@thegrindingcentre.co.uk *Abrasive wheel merchants*

Grindrite Grinding Equipment Es, 14 Hertburn Estate, Hertburn, Washington, Tyne & Wear, NE37 2SF Tel: 0191-416 3654 Fax: 0191-416 3729 *Precision grinding & cutting tool manufrs*

Grinnall Specialist Cars, Westridge House, Jennings Wood Lane, Heightington, Bewdley, Worcestershire, DY12 2YJ Tel: (01299) 822862 Fax: (01299) 822889 E-mail: mark@grinnallcars.com *Car manufrs*

▶ GrinsBritishBikeSpares, Templehall, Kirkcaldy, Fife, KY2 6LT Tel: (01592) 262803 E-mail: grintriumph@blueyonder.co.uk *Triumph classic motorcycles dealer*

Grip Steel Reinforcements, Atlas Works, Robinson Street, Stalybridge, Cheshire, SK15 1TH Tel: 0161-338 2607 Fax: 0161-303 0871 E-mail: gripsteel@boltblue.com *Reinforced concrete specialists*

▶ Gripp Belgique Ltd, 11-12 Godric Square, Peterborough, PE2 7JJ Tel: (01733) 394393 Fax: (01733) 361151 E-mail: info@grippbelgique.com *Oil field drilling spare suppliers*

Griptone Ltd, A Link 580, 188 Moorside Road, Swinton, Manchester, M27 9LB Tel: 0161-727 9011 Fax: 0161-727 9021 E-mail: sales@griptone.co.uk *Commercial vehicle component manufrs*

Gripworks, Units 11-13 Spectrum West, 20-20 Maidstone Business Estate, St. Laurence Avenue, Allington, Maidstone, Kent, ME16 0LL Tel: (0800) 7311150 Fax: (01622) 693201 E-mail: sales@sinclair-rush.co.uk *Plastic grip & handle manufrs*

▶ Griselda Hill Pottery, Kirkbrae, Ceres, Cupar, Fife, KY15 5ND Tel: (01334) 828273 Fax: (01334) 828008 E-mail: info@wemyss-ware.co.uk

Griturn Engineering Ltd, Unit 21d, Icknield Way Farm, Tring Road, Dunstable, Bedfordshire, LU6 2JX Tel: (01582) 661878 Fax: (01582) 472980 E-mail: enquiries@srb-griturn.com *Precision engineers & optical component manufrs*

GRM Rigging Services, 7 Tarbet Street, Gourock, Renfrewshire, PA19 1UF Tel: (01475) 638811 Fax: (01475) 638811 *Architectural marine industrial rigging services*

Grob Machine Tools UK Ltd, Wellesbourne House, Walton Road, Wellesbourne, Warwick, CV35 9JB Tel: (01789) 470047 Fax: (01789) 470176 E-mail: grobuk@btconnect.com *Manufacturers of machine tools & centres*

Groeneveld UK Ltd, Unit 29a Loughborough Motorway Trading Estate, Gelders Hall Road, Shepshed, Loughborough, Leicestershire, LE12 9NH Tel: (01509) 600033 Fax: (01509) 602000 E-mail: groenevel.uk@talk21.com *Lubricating system manufrs*

Groestar Ltd, 1 Morley Business Centre, Tonbridge, Kent, TN9 1RA Tel: (01732) 771121 Fax: (01732) 771124 E-mail: sales@groestar.co.uk *Electrical engineers*

Grohe Ltd, Blays House, Wick Road, Englefield Green, Egham, Surrey, TW20 0HJ Tel: (0871) 2003414 Fax: (020) 8594 8898 E-mail: info@grohe.co.uk *Tap & shower manufrs*

Grok Developments Ltd, 103 Acre Road, Kingston upon Thames, Surrey, KT2 6ES Tel: (020) 8547 2304 Fax: (020) 8547 2305 E-mail: support@grok.co.uk *Software development*

Grommets Ltd, Unit 2 Hollands La Industrial Estate, Henfield, West Sussex, BN5 9QY Tel: (01273) 493355 Fax: (01273) 493388 E-mail: sales@grommets.co.uk Principal Export Areas: Central/East Europe & West Europe *Manufacturers of grommet & rubber mouldings*

David Groom Joinery, 5-8 Eastfield Road, Wollaston, Wellingborough, Northamptonshire, NN29 7RU Tel: (01933) 664494 Fax: (01933) 663085 *Joinery manufrs*

Groom & Hornsby Ltd, 496 Cowley Road, Oxford, OX4 2DP Tel: (01865) 455400 Fax: (01865) 776236 E-mail: info@groom-hornsby.co.uk *Motor body repairers*

Grooms House Turnery, Grooms House, Stanshawes Court, Yate, Bristol, BS37 4DZ Tel: (01454) 325525 Fax: (01454) 325525 E-mail: info@grooms-house-turnery.co.uk *Wooden product manufrs*

Groove Associates Ltd, Unit 2, Alton Business Centre, Omega Park, Alton, Hampshire, GU34 2YU Tel: (01420) 88776 Fax: (01420) 88777 E-mail: sales@groove-ltd.com *Underwater electrical equipment suppliers & high voltage*

▶ Groove Yard, 79 Larkswood Road, London, E4 9DU Tel: (020) 8523 8083 E-mail: info@groove-yard-productions.com *Recording studio*

GrooveDancewear, High Street, Chatteris, Cambridgeshire, PE16 6BE Tel: (01354) 693595 E-mail: sales@groovedancewear.co.uk *Cheaper Dancewear and Free Delivery, Leotards to Sneakers.*

Grorud Engineering Ltd, Castleside Industrial Estate, Spruce Way, Consett, County Durham, DH8 8JA Tel: (01207) 590471 Fax: (01207) 599810 E-mail: mail@grorud.com *General presswork manufrs*

▶ John Grose Group Ltd, Park Road, Diss, Norfolk, IP22 4WT Tel: (01379) 642311 Fax: (01379) 644378 E-mail: enquiries@johngrose.co.uk *Ford car suppliers*

▶ John Grose Group Ltd, Beveridge Way, Hardwick Narrows, King's Lynn, Norfolk, PE30 4NB Tel: (01553) 770060 Fax: (01553) 778226 *Ford dealership*

▶ John Grose Group Ltd, Ipswich Road, Woodbridge, Suffolk, IP12 4BX Tel: (01394) 383333 Fax: (01394) 384501 *Motor vehicles*

Henry Gross Ltd, Willcox House, London, SE1 1LB Tel: (020) 7407 0942 Fax: (020) 7407 5942 E-mail: sales@henrygross.co.uk *Basketware importers*

Grosvenor Blinds, 23 Rhos Road, Rhos on Sea, Colwyn Bay, Clwyd, LL28 4RS Tel: (01492) 548866 Fax: (01492) 548866 *Blind retailers & manufrs*

Charles Grosvenor Ltd, 300 Birchfield Road, Redditch, Worcestershire, B97 4LZ Tel: (01527) 543668 Fax: (01527) 550125 E-mail: cgltg@btconnect.com *Loft conversion contractors*

Grosvenor Electronic Supplies, Priory Tec Park Saxon Way, Priory Park, Hessle, North Humberside, HU13 9PB Tel: (01482) 627327 Fax: (01482) 627328 E-mail: sales@grosvenor-group.com Principal Export Areas: Worldwide *Solder, flux, kapton tape, dots & adhesive distributors*

▶ Grosvenor Executive Travel, 7 Pencoed Lane, Llanmartin, Newport, Gwent, NP18 2ED Tel: (0800) 4583874 E-mail: sales@grosvenorexecutivetravel.co.uk *Grosvenor Executive Travel is a private hire, chauffeur company based in Newport but ideally placed to operate throughout South East Wales, Cardiff and the South West.**We specialise in corporate and executive travel requirements; weddings; airport transfer; all port and cruise liner terminals covered; sporting events and theatre trips, individually tailoring its service to our valued clients" needs**Our range vehicles, include Mercedes E & V class, Chrysler Grand Voyager luxury people carriers, and coach travel from mini bus to luxury 54 seater. **Complimentary newspapers magazines and soft drinks are offered on all journeys, with picnic hampers available upon request for special occasions such as Ascot, Wimledon, Twickenham, the Henley regatta, birthday celebrations, or any occasion our customers desire.**

Grosvenor Fabrications, Limes House, Silver Street, Stansted, Essex, CM24 8HE Tel: (01279) 814146 Fax: (01279) 814179 E-mail: sales@grosvenorfabrications.co.uk *Grosvenor Fabrications based in Stansted, Essex, are a leading supplier of conference and banqueting chairs and restaurant furniture. They offer a wide range of tables and chairs, many of which are in stock or can be finished to the client's specification. Their ranges also include aluminium outdoor furniture specially designed for the restaurant, café, hotel and leisure industries.*

▶ Grosvenor Health, Grosvenor House, Prospect Hill, Redditch, Worcestershire, B97 4DL Tel: (01527) 532100 Fax: (01527) 592732 E-mail: info@grosvenorhealth.com *Occupational health consultants*

Grosvenor House Papers, Westmorland Business Park, Gilthwaiterigg Lane, Kendal, Cumbria, LA9 6NP Tel: (01539) 726161 Fax: (01539) 733678 E-mail: info@ghpkendal.co.uk *Paper merchants*

Grosvenor Of London plc, International House, 66 Chiltern Street, London, W1U 4JT Tel: (020) 7470 1900 Fax: (020) 7470 1903 E-mail: info@golplc.com *Toiletries retailer & manufrs*

Grosvenor Northampton Ltd, Unit D Stonecircle Road, Round Spinney, Northampton, NN3 8RF Tel: (01604) 670673 Fax: (01604) 648438 *Designers, photographers & printers services*

Grosvenor Press, Station Yard, Station Approach, Shanklin, Isle of Wight, PO37 7AS Tel: (01983) 867030 Fax: (01983) 867030 *General commercial printers*

Grosvenor Printing Co., 112-114 Grosvenor Road, Bristol, BS2 8YA Tel: 0117-955 6544 Fax: 0117-955 6544 *Commercial printers*

Grosvenor Scaffolding Co. Ltd, Station Road, Bagillt, Clwyd, CH6 6AF Tel: (01352) 732148 Fax: (01352) 763628 *Scaffolding contractors*

Grosvenor Securities Ltd, 28 Bolton Street, Mayfair, London, W1J 8BP Tel: (020) 7629 9933 Fax: (020) 7493 5561 E-mail: rogermoss@grosvenorsecurities.com *Property investment consultants*

▶ Grosvenor Telecom, Unit 30 Whitegate Industrial Estate, Whitegate Road, Wrexham, Clwyd, LL13 8UG Tel: (01978) 291950 Fax: (01978) 312252 E-mail: mail@grosvenortelecom.co.uk *Maintenance & installation of control systems services*

Grosvenor Tooling Services, Unit 12, Ash Road, Wrexham Industrial Estate, Wrexham, Clwyd, LL13 9UF Tel: (01978) 664359 Fax: (01978) 664359 *Precision engineers*

Grosvenor Workspace Solutions, Compass House, Chivers Way, Histon, Cambridge, CB24 9AD Tel: (01223) 475555 Fax: (01223) 475566 E-mail: info@grosvenor.uk.com *Office designers & refurbishers*

▶ Grote International, Wrexham Technology Park, Wrexham, Clwyd, LL13 7YP Tel: (01978) 362243 Fax: (01978) 362255 E-mail: sales@intl.grotecompany.com *Suppliers of processing machine*

Ground Engineering, Newark Road, Peterborough, PE1 5UA Tel: (01733) 568153 Fax: (01733) 315280E-mail: admin@groundengineering.co.uk *Site investigation*

Ground Form Gears Ltd, Unit 4-5 Abeles Way, Holly Lane Industrial Estate, Atherstone, Warwickshire, CV9 2QZ Tel: (01827) 718555 Fax: (01827) 718789 E-mail: gearsground@yahoo.co.uk *Gear grinding services to the trade, spur profile ground, helical*

Ground Restoration Ltd, Unit 15 Ingoldmells Court, Edinburgh Way, Corsham, Wiltshire, SN13 9XN Tel: (01225) 810818 Fax: (01225) 811030 E-mail: grla1cad@aol.com *Environmental services*

Ground Solutions Group Ltd, Cobbs Wood Industrial Estate, Hanover Close, Ashford, Kent, TN23 1EJ Tel: (01233) 658270 Fax: (01233) 658299 E-mail: gsg@groundsolutions.co.uk *Site Investigation Consultants.*

▶ Ground Works And Plant Hire, 19, Bentinck Street, Kilmarnock, Ayrshire, KA1 4AW Tel: (01563) 570285 Fax: (01563) 541052

▶ Groundforce, Beckwith Knowle, Otley Road, Beckwithshaw, Harrogate, North Yorkshire, HG3 1UD Tel: (01423) 852295 Fax: (01423) 536731 E-mail: groundforce.northern@vibroplant.co.uk *Trench shoring equipment - hire & sale*

▶ Groundforce Gardening, 94 Church Road, Emneth, Wisbech, Cambridgeshire, PE14 8AF Tel: (01945) 466555 Fax: (01945) 466192 E-mail: graham.brindley@groundforcegardening.net *Suppliers of ground stabilisation grids for gravel & grass, weedcontrol fabrics, protection fleece & woven ground cover*

Groundhog UK, Ynysygerwn Avenue, Aberdulais, Neath, West Glamorgan, SA10 8HH Tel: (01639) 641166 Fax: (01639) 641188 E-mail: info@groundhog.co.uk *Portable storage unit manufrs*

▶ Groundplant Ltd, Nuttaberry Works, Nuttaberry, Bideford, Devon, EX39 4DT Tel: (01237) 475048 Fax: (01237) 475049

▶ Groundshire Ltd, 41a Spout Lane, Washington, Tyne & Wear, NE38 7HP Tel: 0191-416 1108 Fax: 0191-415 1347

Groundwater Lifttrucks Ltd, Spurryhillock Industrial Estate, Broomhill Road, Stonehaven, Kincardineshire, AB39 2NH Tel: (01569) 763247 Fax: (01569) 766288 E-mail: sales@groundwater.uk.com *Forklift truck hire services*

Group 100 Electronics, 145 Avon Road, Worcester, WR4 9AH Tel: (01905) 22875 Fax: (01905) 22875 *Electronic design & ionizer manufrs*

Group 2, Chilton, Ferryhill, County Durham, DL17 0SZ Tel: (01388) 720741 Fax: (01388) 721741 *Fire protection equipment suppliers*

Group 4 Engineering, Pontardawe Industrial Estate, Pontardawe, Swansea, SA8 4EN Tel: (01792) 865000 Fax: (01792) 865099 E-mail: mail@group4engineering.co.uk *Precision engineers*

Group 4 Security Systems Ltd, Challenge House, Northway LaneInternational Drive, Tewkesbury, Gloucestershire, GL20 8UQ Tel: (01684) 274874 Fax: (01684) 294845 *Access control card manufrs*

Group 4 Security Systems Ltd, New Challenge House, International Drive, Tewkesbury Business Park, Tewkesbury, Gloucestershire, GL20 8UQ Tel: (01684) 850977 Fax: (01684) 294845 E-mail: sales@g4tec.co.uk *Plantime, the flexible time recording systems designed and manufactured by Group 4 Technology, facilitates flexible working practices. The systems employ the latest Windows-based technology, alongside 'active' LAN terminals, to ensure that both managers and staff alike have the latest personnel data available to them at the touch of a button.*

Group 4 Technology Ltd, Challenge House, International Drive, Tewkesbury, Gloucestershire, GL20 8UQ Tel: (01684) 277175 Fax: (01684) 294845 E-mail: sales@group4technology.com *Group 4 Technology Ltd are market leaders in the design, manufacture, installation and service of integrated security solutions throughout the UK. With more than 30 years experience of developing, installing and servicing leading edge access control and time management systems, in addition to installing advanced digital video (CCTV) technology, we offer a range of affordable security solutions designed to protect your staff, premises and equipment.*

Group Business Services Ltd, Wincheap Indust Estate, Simmonds Road, Canterbury, Kent, CT1 3RA Tel: (01227) 478377 E-mail: sandra@groupbusiness.co.uk *Office stationary & equipment suppliers*

Group Canopies Ltd, Ramsay Street, Coalsnaughton, Tillicoultry, Clackmannanshire, FK13 6LH Tel: (01259) 753800 Fax: (01259) 753801 *Designers, manufacturers & installers of canopies & carports*

Group Components Ltd, The Potteries, Woodgreen Road, Waltham Abbey, Essex, EN9 3TN Tel: (01992) 715900 Fax: (01992) 711993 E-mail: sales@groupcomponents.co.uk *Bolt & nut distributors*

Group Four Glass Fibre Co. Ltd, Unit 42 Church Road Business Centre, Church Road, Sittingbourne, Kent, ME10 3RS Tel: (01795) 429424 Fax: (01795) 476248 E-mail: info@groupfourglassfibre.co.uk *Glass fibre mouldings*

Group Interiors, Shingle Hall, Epping Upland, Epping, Essex, CM16 6PD Tel: (01992) 572373 Fax: (01992) 575543 *Office ceilings & partitioning manufrs*

Group Lotus P.L.C., Potash Lane, Hethel, Norwich, NR14 8EZ Tel: (01953) 608000 Fax: (01953) 608127 E-mail: group@lotuscars.co.uk *Engineering consultancy & car manufrs*

▶ Group Sales Limited, GSL House, 21 Kitchener Close, Daventry, Northamptonshire, NN11 9AJ Tel: 0870 6094591 Fax: 0870 1709874 E-mail: enquiries@groupsales.co.uk *GROUP SALES LIMITED (GSL) forms Purchasing Groups for small to medium sized companies. These Groups make the members stronger; effectively turning the individual from a small fish in an ocean of suppliers to a larger one.**As a wholesale products and services supplier products/services are available direct to the public at wholesale prices. Paintball represents one business and is available via http:// www.paintballsuppliesdirect.co.uk or http:// stores.ebay.co.uk/gsl-trading.**

Groupage Shipping Services Ltd, Ten Acres, Station Road, Rushall, Walsall, WS4 1ET Tel: (01922) 638711 Fax: (01922) 722883 *Freight forwarders & forwarding agents*

Groupco Ltd, 18 Tresham Road, Orton Southgate, Peterborough, PE2 6SG Tel: (01733) 234750 Fax: (01733) 235246 E-mail: sales@groupcoltd.co.uk *Door & window fittings distribs*

Groutage & Ingram Ltd, Jack O Watton Industrial Estate, Lichfield Road, Water Orton, Birmingham, B46 1NU Tel: 0121-749 1414 Fax: 0121-749 5333 E-mail: sales@grangewoodfencing.com *Pre-cast concrete fencing suppliers*

Grove Advertising Services Ltd, 104 Kennerley Road, Stockport, Cheshire, SK2 6EY Tel: 0161-483 9000 Fax: 0161-483 9669 *Advertising & marketing agents*

Grove Consultants Software Engineering, 40 Ryles Park Road, Macclesfield, Cheshire, SK11 8AH Tel: (01625) 616279 *Consultancy & training*

▶ Grove Contractors, 16 Brookside Way, Kingswinford, West Midlands, DY6 9AW Tel: (01384) 277969 Fax: (01384) 277969 E-mail: mail@grovecontractors.co.uk *Building contractors, complete building service*

▶ Grove Creative Ltd, 15 Wentworth Grove, Winsford, Cheshire, CW7 2LJ Tel: (01606) 553793 E-mail: info@grovecreative.co.uk *Graphic design & advertising service providers*

Grove Electronic Sales, 1 Grange Road Business Centre, Grange Road, Christchurch, Dorset, BH23 4JD Tel: (01425) 275060 Fax: (01425) 275070 E-mail: sales@grovesales.co.uk *Suppliers of electronics consumables*

▶ Grove Electronics Ltd, 26 Grove Court, Rampley Lane, Little Paxton, St. Neots, Cambridgeshire, PE19 6PQ Tel: (01480) 382909 Fax: (01480) 382909 E-mail: info@groveelectronics.co.uk *Electronic consultancy and design services.*Hardware and software design. **Embedded systems and product development solutions.**Expertise in advanced analogue/ digital/microcontroller/dsp based systems including firmware.**Expertise in windows based software design.*

Grove Engineering (Bristol) Ltd, Units M1 & M2, Lawrence Drive, Stover Trading Estate, Yate, Bristol, BS37 5PG Tel: (01454) 317766 Fax: (01454) 317334 E-mail: sales@grove-engineering.co.uk *Precision engineers & toolmakers*

Grove Engineering Services Ltd, Unit C, The Grove, Corby, Northamptonshire, NN18 8EW Tel: (01536) 402732 Fax: (01536) 401133 E-mail: grove_engineering@ic24.net *Precision engineers*

Grove Galleries Ltd, Phoenix House, Ellesmere Street, Manchester, M15 4JY Tel: 0161-834 8051 Fax: 0161-834 8051 *Picture framing services*

James Grove & Sons Ltd, PO Box 5, Halesowen, West Midlands, B63 3UW Tel: 0121-550 4015 Fax: 0121-501 3905 E-mail: sales@jamesgroveandsons.co.uk *Button manufrs & giftware manufrs*

Grove Packaging, Unit 2c Old Park Industrial Estate, Old Park Road, Wednesbury, West Midlands, WS10 9LR Tel: 0121-556 4735 Fax: 0121-556 4579 *Corrugated box & case manufrs*

Grove Plumbing & Heating Supplies Ltd, Unit 11a National Trading Estate, Bramhall Moor Lane, Hazel Grove, Stockport, Cheshire, SK7 5AA Tel: 0161-456 4495 Fax: 0161-456 2678 E-mail: sales@groveplg.co.uk *Plumbing & heating supplies services*

Grove Systems Ltd, 3 Ashlyn Grove, Manchester, M14 6YG Tel: 0161-224 4465 E-mail: donald@grove.demon.co.uk *Computer services*

▶ Grove Training, 16 The Precinct, Romiley, Stockport, Cheshire, SK6 4EA Tel: 0161-406 0201 Fax: 0161-291 9176 *Training center*

▶ Grovelands Investments, Business Centre, 120 West Heath Road, London, NW3 7TU Tel: (020) 8731 9777 Fax: (020) 8731 9773 E-mail: info@grovelands.net *Residential and Commercial Lettings & Property Management*London & South East*

Groveley Engineering Ltd, Anchor Works, Groveley Road, Christchurch, Dorset, BH23 3HB Tel: (01202) 483497 Fax: (01202) 486658 E-mail: sales@groveley.co.uk *Precision components manufrs*

Grover Clarke Ltd, The Street, Thorndon, Eye, Suffolk, IP23 7JN Tel: (01379) 678149 Fax: (01379) 678691 E-mail: info@groverclarke.com *Engravers of rubber cover rollers*

Company Information

Groves & Banks, Drakes Drive Industrial Estate, Long Crendon, Aylesbury, Buckinghamshire, HP18 9BA Tel: (01844) 258100 Fax: (01844) 258058 E-mail: sales@groves-banks.com *Haberdashery & needlecraft distributors*

Stuart Groves Furniture, Folly Works, 8 Dashwood Avenue, High Wycombe, Buckinghamshire, HP12 3DN Tel: (01494) 446460 Fax: (01494) 446461 *Furniture makers*

Grow & Show Ltd, The Weld Arms Barn, East Lulworth, Wareham, Dorset, BH20 5QQ Tel: (01929) 400293 Fax: (01372) 469445 *Wrought Ironmongers*

Growing Success Ltd, Unit 8 Oakwell Brewery, Barnsley, South Yorkshire, S71 1HJ Tel: (01226) 289966 Fax: (01226) 733711 *Contract packaging services*

▶ Growlighting.co.uk, Unit 19 Chatsworth Green, Basingstoke, Hampshire, RG22 4QA Tel: (01256) 320350 Fax: (01256) 320350 E-mail: rob@growlighting.co.uk *Quality 250w, 400w and 600w hydroponic plant lighting systems, growlighting starter kits, indoor lights and growing equipment. Economy growlights, 125w envirolights and envirolites, spare HPS sodium, grolux and metal halide replacement lamps, timers, fans and contactors. Confidential credit card, cheque, cash or postal order payments. Discreet packaging. UK next day delivery.*

Growmoor Horticulture Ltd, 207 Derrylee Road, Dungannon, County Tyrone, BT71 6NY Tel: (028) 3885 2346 Fax: (028) 3885 1050 E-mail: info@growmoor.co.uk *Compost manufrs*

Groz-Beckert UK Ltd, Groz-Beckert House, Gloucester Crescent, Wigston, Leicestershire, LE18 4YL Tel: 0116-264 3500 Fax: 0116-264 3505 *Knitting machine manufrs*

Grumac Ltd, Gonerby Road, Gonerby Hill Foot, Grantham, Lincolnshire, NG31 8HE Tel: (01476) 561873 Fax: (01476) 561873 E-mail: grumac@btclick.com *Tyre retreading equipment & consumables distribs*

Grundfos Manufacturing Ltd, Ferryboat Lane, Castletown, Sunderland, SR5 3JL Tel: 0191-549 5555 Fax: 0191-516 0067 *Multi stage & domestic circulator manufrs*

Grundfos Pumps Ltd, Orford Court, Green Fold Way, Leigh, Lancashire, WN7 3XJ Tel: (0870) 7503888 Fax: (01942) 605970 *Water pump manufrs*

Grundfos Pumps Ltd, Grovebury Road, Leighton Buzzard, Bedfordshire, LU7 4TL Tel: (01525) 850000 Fax: (01525) 850011 E-mail: ukindustry@grundfos.com *Pump manufrs*

Grundon Waste Ltd, Lakeside Industrial Estate, Colnbrook By Passage, Colnbrook, Slough, SL3 0EG Tel: (01753) 686777 Fax: (01753) 686002 *Waste management*

Grundon Waste Management Ltd, Goulds Grove, Ewelme, Wallingford, Oxfordshire, OX10 6PJ Tel: (01491) 834311 Fax: (01491) 832272 E-mail: enquiries@grundin.com *Aggregates*

Grundy & Co. Excavations Ltd, The Liver Yard, Ditton Road, Widnes, Cheshire, WA8 0TH Tel: 0151-257 8816 Fax: 0151-424 4153 *Bulk excavation*

Gerald Grundy Computer Services Ltd, 78 Vicarage Lane, Coventry, CV7 9AE Tel: (024) 7664 5990 Fax: (024) 7636 5445 E-mail: gerald.grundy@btinternet.com *Computer maintenance & repair services*

Grupo Antonin, 795 London Road, Grays, Essex, RM20 3LH Tel: (01708) 683500 Fax: (01708) 683555 *Car interior manufrs*

Gryphon Computer Support Ltd, 7 Nightingale Gardens, Nailsea, Bristol, BS48 2BH Tel: (01275) 857990 Fax: (01275) 851558 E-mail: sales@gryphon-group.co.uk *Computer support*

Gryphonn Concrete Products, Old Mill Works, Lower Gelligroes, Pontllanfraith, Blackwood, Gwent, NP12 2HY Tel: (01495) 232050 Fax: (01495) 222553 *Pre-cast concrete products manufrs*

Gryson Air Conditioning Equipment Ltd, Unit 37 Penmaen Small Business Centre, Penmaen Road, Pontllanfraith, Blackwood, Gwent, NP12 2DZ Tel: (01495) 221200 Fax: (01495) 228432 E-mail: enquiries@gryson-aircon.com *Air conditioning installers*

G's Fresh Beetroot, Hostmoor Avenue, March Industrial Estate, March, Cambridgeshire, PE15 0AX Tel: (01354) 652659 Fax: (01354) 658292 *Beetroot packers*

▶ GS Gardening Services, 36 Japonica Way, Havant, Hampshire, PO9 2FN Tel: (023) 9261 0279 E-mail: george.stew@ntlworld.com *GENERAL MAINTENANCE OF GARDENS IN THE AREA LAWNMOWING, WEEDING, CUTTING BACK, TIDY-UP ETC. ALL RUBBISH TAKEN.*

GS Hydro Ltd, Unit C Endeavour Court, Hall Dene Way, Seaham Grange Industrial Estat, Seaham, County Durham, SR7 0HB Tel: 0191-523 9643 Fax: 0191-521 8001 E-mail: sales@gshydro.com *Hydraulic pipework & fittings*

▶ GS Productivity Solutions, 37 Baileys Mead Road, Stapleton, Bristol, BS16 1AE Tel: 0117-965 0300 E-mail: info@gspsltd.co.uk *Reseller of the GibbsCAM and Renishaw Productivity Plus suite of software products, we specialise in Software based machining and inspection (probing) solutions; training, support and customisation.*

▶ gsa Ltd, Unit 3, Devonshire Business Park, Borehamwood, Herts, WD6 1NA Tel: 0208 236 2531 *gsa is a business growth and marketing consultancy that delivers practical and results-led marketing, strategic planning, telemarketing, communications, B2B business development, brand and product management and data protection services to enhance the efficiency and productivity of your organisation.*

GSB Fabrication Ltd, Unit 3, Castle Trading Estate, Fareham, Hampshire, PO16 9SF Tel: (023) 9221 0787 Fax: (023) 9220 1252 *Steel fabricators & erectors*

GSD Associates Ltd, 48 High Street, Stourport-on-Severn, Worcestershire, DY13 8BX Tel: (01299) 827592 Fax: (01299) 827593 E-mail: support@gsdassociates.co.uk *Computer software suppliers*

GSF, 21-23 Fort Industrial Park, Chester Road, Castle Vale, Birmingham, B35 7AR Tel: 0121-749 8800 Fax: 0121-749 8801 E-mail: enquiries@uro.co.uk *Continental automotive spares*

GSH Ltd, GSH House, Forge Lane, Stoke-on-Trent, ST1 5PZ Tel: (01782) 200400 Fax: (01782) 285552 E-mail: vacancies@gshgroup.com *Building maintenance services* Also at: Airdrie, Bristol, Birmingham, Edinburgh, Leeds London SE11, Manchester, Newcastle & Winchester

▶ GSL Consulting, 40 Avebury, Slough, SL1 5SY Tel: (07764) 751762 Fax: (01753) 533226 E-mail: giles@gslconsulting.co.uk *Offering tailored customer service training courses. Specialising in retail and phone training. Also offering a mystery shopper service.*

▶ GSL Heat Exchangers Ltd, Unit 7 Swann Street, Hull, HU2 0PH Tel: (01482) 606988 Fax: (01482) 606633 E-mail: sales@gslheat.karoo.co.uk *Heat Exchanger Repairs & Servicing*Calorifier Tube Nests*Plate Heat Exchangers*Finned Coils*Angelery Coils*Nationwide Service*

▶ GSR Services, 1 Gristmill Close, Cheltenham, Gloucestershire, GL51 0PZ Tel: (01242) 708407 Fax: 01242 708407 E-mail: sales@gsrservices.co.uk *Licensed trade stocktaking*

GSS Projects Ltd, 12 Ambassador Place, Stockport Road, Altrincham, Cheshire, WA15 8EQ Tel: 0161-926 9510 Fax: 0161-926 9536 *Project support services*

▶ Gt ElectroPlating, 28 aurodrome road, Unit 3 A, Hendon, London, NW4 4SS Tel: 07985 444891 Fax: 07985 444891 E-mail: terret007@hotmail.com *We specialise in brush plating and Polishing of all metals. We plate in gold, silver, chrome and black chrome. We do silver and gold leaf on request.*We have a mobile unit to do fittings in bathrooms and kitchens which are difficult and expensive to remove and which can be done in situ.*Car emblems can be done at our workshop or at the customers home or office address.*We offer a mail service with a turn around time of approximately one week.*A free collection and delivery service is offered within a 5 mile radius from Hendon, London.*We look forward to hearing from you.*

GT Exhaust Ni Ltd, Carran Business Park, Enniskillen, County Fermanagh, BT74 4RZ Tel: (028) 6632 2282 Fax: (028) 6632 3391 E-mail: sales@gtexhausts.co.uk *Exhaust manufacturers & distributors*

▶ GT Express Logistics, 283 Henwick Road, Worcester, WR2 5PG Tel: 07976 835328 E-mail: gillypep79@hotmail.com *Professional and reliable courier delivery services. Vehicles available for envelopes to pallet loads. Express, sameday, nextday consignments undertaken.*

GT Printers London Ltd, 5 Maverton Road, London, E3 2JE Tel: (020) 8981 7638 Fax: (020) 8980 1941 E-mail: sales@gtprinters.co.uk *Lithographic printers*

▶ GT Vision Ltd, Hazelsub Depo Unit Camps Road, Haverhill, Suffolk, CB9 9AS Tel: (01440) 714737 Fax: (01440) 714737 E-mail: sales@gt-vision.com *Scientific instrument suppliers & manufrs*

▶ GT4 Drivers Club, 21 Glenesha Gardens, Fareham, Hampshire, PO15 6QH Tel: 01202 772695 E-mail: contactus@gt4dc.co.uk *Maintain, modify and drive your GT4...*

Gta UK Ltd, 34 Nottingham South Estate, Ruddington Lane Wilford, Nottingham, NG11 7EP Tel: 0115-981 5703 Fax: 0115-945 5106 E-mail: mail@gtauk.demon.co.uk *Medical suppliers for radiology*

▶ GTL Partnership, The Studio, 1 Irwin Drive, Horsham, West Sussex, RH12 1NL Tel: (01403) 259220 E-mail: info@gtl-partnership.com *GTL Partnership are a foundations solutions company that design & build piling and foundation solutions. *A Screwpile foundation is an innovative solution for all your foundation requirements.*

▶ GTM Consulting Ltd, 44 Thorpe Downs Road, Church Gresley, Swadlincote, Derbyshire, DE11 9FB Tel: 0771 254 1175 E-mail: gtmconsulting@btinternet.com *Management & business consultancy*

GTOS Ltd, Bordesley Hall, The Holloway, Alvechurch, Birmingham, B48 7QA Tel: (0845) 0589686 Fax: (0845) 0589687 E-mail: documentmanagement@gtos.co.uk *We provide Document management solution for you! Wether you use Window or iSeries we can help you keep track of your documents and ensure you never lose a document again.*

▶ GTS Scaffolding, 90 Albert Drive, Deganwy, Conwy, Gwynedd, LL31 9RL Tel: (01492) 585343

▶ GTS Transport Ltd, Thornton Yard, Strathore Road, Thornton, Kirkcaldy, Fife, KY1 4DF Tel: (01592) 631880 Fax: (01592) 770101

Guala Closures UK Ltd, 6 Whitburn Road, Bathgate, West Lothian, EH48 1HH Tel: (01506) 637501 Fax: (01506) 637502 E-mail: guala@guala.demon.co.uk *Plastic closure & container manufrs*

Guaranteed Exhaust Systems Ltd, Unit 4-5 Willand Industrial Estate, Willand, Cullompton, Devon, EX15 2QW Tel: (01884) 821237 Fax: (01884) 820631 E-mail: enquiries@stainlesssteelexhausts.net Principal Export Areas: Worldwide *Stainless steel exhaust manufrs*

Guaranteed Website Promotion, 30 Duke Street, Windsor, Berkshire, SL4 1SA Tel: (01753) 852888 Fax: (01753) 855599 E-mail: george@guaranteed-website-promotion.co.uk *Website promotion*

Guardall Ltd, Lochend Industrial Estate, Queen Anne Drive, Newbridge, Midlothian, EH28 8PL Tel: 0131-333 2900 Fax: 0131-333 4919 E-mail: sales@guardall.co.uk *Security devices*

Guardbase Ltd, Far Cockcroft, Rishworth, Sowerby Bridge, West Yorkshire, HX6 4RE Tel: (01422) 822990 Fax: (01422) 824885 *Computer software*

▶ Guardian, 9-10 Capricorn Centre, Cranes Farm Road, Basildon, Essex, SS14 3JJ Tel: (01268) 287477 Fax: (01268) 287156 E-mail: info@gwtltd.com *Water treatment*

Guardian Alarms Ltd, 20-22 Sydenham Road, Croydon, CR0 2EF Tel: (020) 8686 8777 Fax: (020) 8686 9777 E-mail: sales@guardianalarms.co.uk *Commercial & residential alarm systems installers*

Guardian Electronic Security UK Ltd, Willow House, Mersey View, Liverpool, L22 6QA Tel: 0151-931 5511 Fax: 0151-284 5005 *Security alarms installers*

▶ Guardian Environmental, 117 Clophill Road, Maulden, Bedford, MK45 2AE Tel: (01525) 862528 Fax: (01525) 862163 E-mail: val.barnes@guardian.uk.com *Air conditioning design/installation/commissioning; heating & ventilation engineers & building services engineers*

Guardian Finance Ltd, 207 Barkby Road, Leicester, LE4 9HZ Tel: 0116-276 6631 Fax: 0116-246 0447 E-mail: sales@guardian-finance.co.uk *Leasing & hire purchase financiers*

Guardian Fire Ltd, Hurricane Way, Norwich, NR6 6EY Tel: (01603) 787679 Fax: (01603) 787996 E-mail: guardfire@aol.com *Fire extinguisher manufrs*

Guardian Industrial Doors Ltd, 45 Progress Road, Leigh-On-Sea, Essex, SS9 5PR Tel: (0800) 7836602 Fax: (01702) 510015 E-mail: ross@guardiandoors.com Principal Export Areas: Worldwide *Guardian Doors has been established for 30 years. We manufacture, install, maintain and repair, all manner of commercial and industrial door systems. Including Rolling shutters and grilles Steel personnel doors Sectional overhead doors High speed PVC doors Folding doors Our ranges can be broken down into the following categories General purpose Thermally Insulated Acoustically Insulated Fire resistant Security Fast operation Please contact us or see our website for CAD drawings and PDF brochures Accreditations include ISO 9001 - Quality assurance Firas - Accredited fire product installer DHF repair and maintenance standard TS004 CHAS SAFE CONTRACTOR Please view our website for more details and latest projects.*

Guardian Knitwear Ltd, Majid House, 37-49 Devonshire Street North, Manchester, M12 6JR Tel: 0161-272 8130 Fax: 0161-272 6078 *Knitwear manufrs*

Guardian Lock & Engineering Co. Ltd, Imperial Works, Wednesfield Road, Willenhall, West Midlands, WV13 1AL Tel: (01902) 633396 Fax: (01902) 630675 *General & security lock manufrs*

Guardian Media Group P.L.C., Number 1, Scott Place, Manchester, M3 3GG Tel: 0161-832 7200 Fax: 0161-832 5351 *Newspaper editorial*

▶ Guardian Moving & Storage, Clifton View, East Mains Industrial Estate, Broxburn, West Lothian, EH52 5NE Tel: 0131-551 6780 Fax: 0131-552 1269 E-mail: sales@guardianremovals.co.uk

Guardian Newspapers Ltd, 119 Farringdon Road, London, EC1R 3ER Tel: (020) 7278 2332 Fax: (020) 7837 2114 *Publishers of newspapers, magazines, books & websites*

Guardian Press Boston Ltd, Nelson Way, Boston, Lincolnshire, PE21 8TS Tel: (01205) 363497 Fax: (01205) 310575 *Designers & printers*

Guardian Security, Byre House, Cow Lane, Wincheap Industrial Estate, Canterbury, Kent, CT1 3RW Tel: (01227) 762128 Fax: (01227) 764638 *Alarm installers*

Guardian Security, 1 North Lane, Sandgate, Folkestone, Kent, CT20 3AS Tel: (01303) 226452 Fax: (01303) 248399 E-mail: *Alarms installation & fire extinguishers*

Guardian Security Group (UK) Ltd, 5 Axis, Hawkfield Business Park, Hawkfield Way, Bristol, BS14 0BY Tel: 0117-946 5505 Fax: 0117-946 5506 E-mail: sales@guardiansecurity.co.uk *Locking & security doors manufrs*

Guardian Self Storage Centre, Sherriff Street, Worcester, WR4 9AB Tel: (01905) 24700 Fax: (01905) 24764 *Self storage rooms for business & home*

Guardian Shutter Co. Ltd, 23 Sefton Street, Toxteth, Liverpool, L8 5SL Tel: 0151-708 0819 Fax: 0151-709 1279 E-mail: sales@guardian-shutter.co.uk *Roller shutter installers & manufrs*

Guardian Water Engineering Ltd, Woodland Croft, Orchard Road, Matlock Bath, Matlock, Derbyshire, DE4 3PF Tel: (01629) 55655 Fax: (01629) 55655 *Water treatment consultants*

Guardline Technology Ltd, 5 Brunel Way, Thetford, Norfolk, IP24 1HP Tel: (01842) 822150 Fax: (01842) 820300 E-mail: sales@guardline.co.uk *Gloves, face masks, nitrogen & hydrogen generation manufrs*

Guardpack Ltd, 12 & 14 Grafton Place, Dukes Park Industrial Estate, Chelmsford, CM2 6TG Tel: (01245) 451770 Fax: (01245) 451710 E-mail: jeremy@guardpack.co.uk *Guardpack is a well established privately owned sachet and wipe manufacturer specialising in private label manufacturing of sachets. Our products cover the requirements of a variety of industries including Personal Care, Office Cleaning, Catering, Healthcare, Industrial Cleaning and Hospitality. Our clients range from small local business to multi nationals. We pride ourselves on a friendly professional service, where we take time to understand our client's individual requirements. All products are manufactured using vigorous quality control systems, with the maximum amount of effort to ensure the product is received on time and to the agreed client specification. We carry a wide range of materials and liquids allowing our clients to receive quick turnarounds at competitive pricing.*

Guardsman Ltd, 24 Pasture Lane, Leicester, LE1 4EY Tel: 0116-253 8688 Fax: 0116-251 4202 E-mail: sales@guardsmanltd.co.uk *Industrial protective clothing*

Guardwise & Co., 18 Jamaica St, Liverpool, L1 0AF Tel: 0151-708 0241 Fax: 0151-708 0241 *Steel work fence manufrs*

▶ Guava Ltd, Hurst Grove, Sandford Lane, Hurst, Reading, RG10 0SQ Tel: 0118-932 1100 Fax: 0118-932 1222 E-mail: info@guava.co.uk *Creates & implements innovative online*

continued

*communications solutions.*Search engine marketing. Pay Per Click.*

Gudel Lineartec (U.K.) Ltd, Unit 5 Wickmans Drive, Banner Lane, Coventry, CV4 9XA Tel: (024) 7669 5444 Fax: (024) 7669 5666 E-mail: info@uk.gudel.com *Gantry robots suppliers*

Guernsey Electricity, PO Box 4, Guernsey, GY1 3AD Tel: (01481) 200700 Fax: (01481) 246942 E-mail: admin@electricity.gg *Electricity supplier & retailer*

Guernsey Freight Services, Airport Complex, Forest, Guernsey, GY8 0DJ Tel: (01481) 238180 Fax: (01481) 235479 *Freight forwarders & couriers*

Guernsey Glass & Window, Industrial Estate, Braye Road, St. Sampson, Guernsey, GY2 4WX Tel: (01481) 243535 Fax: (01481) 243390 E-mail: gsyglass@guernsey.net *Conservatory & window frame manufrs*

Guernsey Press, PO Box 57, Guernsey, GY1 3BW Tel: (01481) 240240 Fax: (01481) 240235 E-mail: newsroom@guernsey-press.com *Local newspaper manufrs*

Guest Foundry Machines Ltd, Unit 14 Berry Hill, Droitwich, Worcestershire, WR9 9AB Tel: (01905) 776242 Fax: (01905) 776318 E-mail: gfmfoundrymach@btconect.com *Foundry machines manufrs*

Francis Guest, Park Street, Teddington, Middlesex, TW11 0LT Tel: (020) 8255 1004 Fax: (020) 8977 9907 E-mail: fguest@globalnet.co.uk *Joinery & cabinet making*

Guest Gear Services, Higham Mead, Higham Road, Chesham, Buckinghamshire, HP5 2AF Tel: (01494) 794667 Fax: (01494) 794668 E-mail: guestgears@yahoo.com *Bevel gear specialists manufrs*

Guest & Sons Ltd, Cherry Trees, Delmonden Road, Hawkhurst, Cranbrook, Kent, TN18 4XB Tel: (01580) 753357 Fax: (01580) 753357 *Pest control*

Guhring Ltd, Castle Bromwich Business Park, Tameside Drive, Castle Vale, Birmingham, B35 7AG Tel: 0121-749 5544 Fax: 0121-776 7224 E-mail: info@guhring.co.uk *Engineers' cutting tool manufacturers & distributors*

▶ Guide to International Travel, 3rd Floor Dukeminster House, Church Street, Dunstable, Bedfordshire, LU5 4HU Tel: 01582 676878 Fax: 01582 676893 E-mail: dggtravel@rbi.co.uk *Guide to International Travel gives you instant access to vital destination information for all countries worldwide.**From passport and visa requirements to vaccinations, currencies to customs, airport information to weather trends, the site ensures you can fully brief your customers before they travel.*

▶ Guild Anderson Furniture Ltd, 'Waterways', Watery Lane, Bishopstrow, Warminster, Wiltshire, BA12 9HT Tel: (01985) 216044 Fax: (0870) 0914517 E-mail: info@guildandersonfurniture.co.uk *We make handmade kitchen furniture*

▶ Guild Homes Tayside Ltd, Chapelpark House, 17 Academy Street, Forfar, Angus, DD8 2HA Tel: (01307) 460011 Fax: (01307) 460022

▶ J.M. Guild, Market Street, Forfar, Angus, DD8 3EW Tel: (01307) 464794

▶ Guildford Computers, 5 High Street, Guildford, Surrey, GU2 4AB Tel: (01483) 458468 Fax: (01483) 458468

Guildford Fitted Furniture, 5 Elm Close, Ripley, Woking, Surrey, GU23 6LE Tel: (01483) 211722 Fax: (01483) 211722 *Fitted kitchens & bedrooms designers*

Guildford Partitions, Tylers Croft, Abbotswood Close, Guildford, Surrey, GU1 1XA Tel: (01483) 539068 Fax: (01483) 539068 *Office practitioners*

Guildford Timber Frame Ltd, Brewhurst Sawmill, Roundstreet Common, Wisborough Green, Billingshurst, West Sussex, RH14 0AL Tel: (01403) 752888 Fax: (01403) 752471 E-mail: info@gtf.uk.com *Timber frame builders*

Guildford Tool Supplies Ltd, A Victoria Farm, Brunswick Road, Brookwood, Woking, Surrey, GU24 0AQ Tel: (01483) 480000 Fax: (01483) 486886 E-mail: sales@guildfordtools.co.uk *Engineers supplies*

Guildsrealm Recruitment Agency, 39 Ensign Way, Hamble, Southampton, SO31 4RF Tel: (023) 8074 4440 Fax: (023) 8045 8135 E-mail: office@guildsrealm.com *Executive search & selection recruitment consultants*

Guildway Ltd, 194 London Road, Boston, Lincolnshire, PE21 7HJ Tel: (01205) 350555 Fax: (01205) 359261 E-mail: mail@guildway.ltd.uk *Prefabricated building & timber frame manufrs*

Guilford (Europe) Ltd, Cotes Park Lane, Somercotes, Alfreton, Derbyshire, DE55 4NJ Tel: (01773) 841200 Fax: (01773) 547315 *Knitters, dyers & weavers for the automotive industry*

Guilform Ltd, 5 Alban Park Industrial Estate, Hatfield Road, St. Albans, Hertfordshire, AL4 0JJ Tel: (01727) 841111 Fax: (01727) 832710 *Architectural metalworkers services*

▶ Guilfram Heating Co. Ltd, 1 Wonersh Common, Wonersh, Guildford, Surrey, GU5 0PJ Tel: (01483) 894248 Fax: (01483) 894219 E-mail: ianwarner@guilfram.co.uk *Heating contractors*

Guillot-Ygnis Heating Ltd, 2 Fitzhamon Court, Featherstone Road, Wolverton Mill, Milton Keynes, MK12 6LB Tel: (01908) 227720 Fax: (01908) 227716 E-mail: smalcolm@groupe-atlantic.com *Industrial boiler distributors*

▶ Guiness U D V, Talisker Distillery, Carbost, Isle of Skye, IV47 8SR Tel: (01478) 640203

▶ Guiness Udv P.L.C., Glen Ord Distillery, Muir Of Ord, Ross-Shire, IV6 7UJ Tel: (01463) 870421

▶ Guiness United Distillers & Vintners, Moray House, 1 Trinity Road, Elgin, Morayshire, IV30 1UF Tel: (01343) 547891 Fax: (01343) 548398

▶ Guinness, Teaninich, Alness, Ross-Shire, IV17 0XB Tel: (01349) 885001 *Spirits retailers*

▶ Guisborough Dental Laboratory, 4 Redcar Road, Guisborough, Cleveland, TS14 6DB Tel: (01287) 635555 Fax: (01287) 634902

Guiseley Engineering Co. Ltd, Hallam Street, Guiseley, Leeds, LS20 8AG Tel: (01943) 874512 Fax: (01943) 879361 E-mail: sales@guiseley-eng.co.uk *Confectionery production equipment spares manufrs*

▶ Guitar Spares & Repairs, 89 Old Snow Hill, Next to Sound Control, Birmingham, B4 6HW Tel: 0121 2455867 E-mail: info@guitarsparesandrepairs.com *Professional Guitar and String instrument repair & customising service. On site repair workshops. Pickup fitting and custom wiring including Sustainiac. Wax Potting & Rewinds. We fit Customer supplied parts. Spare Parts Counter. Open Mon to Sat am to 5pm closed Wednesdays.*

Guitel Ltd, Unit E, Flaxley Park Way, Stechford Retail Park, Birmingham, B33 9AN Tel: 0121-783 4747 Fax: 0121-783 5959 E-mail: sales@guitel-castors.com *Wheel distributors & assemblers*

Guitel Ltd, Unit 1, Lisle Road, High Wycombe, Buckinghamshire, HP13 5SH Tel: (01494) 473030 Fax: (01494) 473031 E-mail: guiteluk@msn.com *Castor & wheel distributors*

GUL International Ltd, Callywith Gate Industrial Estate, Bodmin, Cornwall, PL31 2RQ Tel: (01208) 262400 Fax: (01208) 262474 E-mail: gul@gul.com *Gul is the leading UK wetsuit and surf lifestyle brand offering a complete range of mens and ladies clothing, wetsuits, sailing apparel and accessories for water sports enthusiasts.*

Gulf Coast Seal (UK) Ltd, 2 Seaforth Road South, Hillington, Glasgow, G52 4PB Tel: 0141-302 5000 Fax: 0141-302 5100 *Distributors rubber for oil, gas & seals*

Gulf Helicopters Co., 1 Stockwell Works, Stephenson Way, Crawley, West Sussex, RH10 1TN Tel: (01293) 401333 Fax: (01293) 611566 E-mail: mgr_uk@gulfhelicopters.com *Procurement services*

▶ Gulf Lubricants U K Ltd, Bowcliffe Hall, Bowcliffe Grange, Bramham, Wetherby, West Yorkshire, LS23 6UL Tel: (01937) 541111 Fax: (0845) 1214536 E-mail: enquiries@gulfoil.co.uk *Supplier of high quality metalworking fluids & lubricants*

Gulfex Medical Supplies Ltd, 7 Burgess Wood Road South, Beaconsfield, Buckinghamshire, HP9 1EU Tel: (01494) 675353 Fax: (01494) 675399 *Hospital & laboratory supply services*

Gullane Leisure Furniture Ltd, 22 Bowlers Croft, Basildon, Essex, SS14 3EE Tel: (01268) 274140 Fax: (01268) 274180 *Furniture manufrs*

Gullco International (UK) Ltd, 5 Stonecrop, North Quarry Business Park, Appley Bridge, Wigan, Lancashire, WN6 9DB Tel: (01257) 253579 Fax: (01257) 254629 E-mail: sales@gullco.co.uk *Welding & cutting automation*

▶ Gullett & Sons Ltd, Unit 15 Saxway Business Centre, Chartridge Lane, Chartridge, Chesham, Buckinghamshire, HP5 2SH Tel: (01494) 778080 Fax: (01494) 776566

Gulliver Timber Treatments Ltd, Bank Buildings, Station Road, Sevenoaks, Kent, TN14 5QX Tel: (01959) 524966 Fax: (01959) 525176 E-mail: enquiries@gullivertt.co.uk *Timber treatment & damp proofing services*

Gultronics, 45 New Oxford Street, London, WC1A 1BH Tel: (020) 7240 6030 Fax: (020) 7240 6030 *Computer software*

▶ Gum Away Co., Unit E 1, Kestrel Road, Trafford Park, Manchester, M17 1SF Tel: (0845) 6440901 Fax: (0845) 6440902 E-mail: info@gum-away.co.uk

Gun Drill & Reamers Ltd, 37 Southfields Industrial Park, Hornsby Square, Basildon, Essex, SS15 6SD Tel: (01268) 415197 Fax: (01268) 410692 *Precision engineers*

Gunform Equipment Supplies Ltd, 33 Carsthorne Road, Hoylake, Wirral, Merseyside, CH47 4FB Tel: 0151-632 6333 Fax: 0151-632 6444 E-mail: gunform@gunform.u-net.com *Concrete products, spraying machines & accessories manufrs*

Gunn J C B Ltd, Atlantic Street, Broadheath, Altrincham, Cheshire, WA14 5DN Tel: 0161-941 2631 Fax: 0161-942 3399 E-mail: enguireies@gunn-jcb.co.uk *Machine sales*

Gunn JCB Ltd, Victoria Road, Stoke-on-Trent, ST4 2HY Tel: (01782) 744943 Fax: (01782) 744713 E-mail: sales@gunnjcb.co.uk *Construction & plant machinery distributors*

▶ John Gunn & Sons Ltd, Swiney Lybster, Lybster, Caithness, KW3 6BT Tel: (01593) 721236 E-mail: info@jgunn.co.uk

Thomas Gunn Navigation Services Ltd, Anchor House, 62 Regent Quay, Aberdeen, AB11 5AR Tel: (01224) 595045 Fax: (01224) 584702 E-mail: info@thomasgunn.com *International admiralty chart distributors*

Gunnebo Ltd, Woolaston Road, Park Farm North, Redditch, Worcestershire, B98 7SG Tel: (01527) 522560 Fax: (01527) 510185 E-mail: sales@gunnebo.co.uk Principal Export Areas: Worldwide *Lifting gear distributors or agents*

Gunnebo Entrance Control Ltd, Optimus, Bell Lane, Bellbrook Industrial Estate, Uckfield, East Sussex, TN22 1QL Tel: (01825) 761022 Fax: (01825) 763835 E-mail: info@gunneboe.co.uk *Turnstile door & barrier manufrs*

Gunnebo Perimiter Protection (UK) Ltd, Bishops Hull, Taunton, Somerset, TA1 5EA Tel: (01823) 271911 Fax: (01823) 335763 E-mail: info@gunnebo.co.uk *Perimeter security suppliers & installers*

Gunnebo UK Ltd, Wolverhampton, WV10 0BY Tel: 01902 455111 E-mail: marketing@gunnebo.com *Safe manufrs*

Gunness Wharf Ltd, Gunness Wharf, Gunness, Scunthorpe, South Humberside, DN15 8SY Tel: (01724) 867691 Fax: (01724) 851207 E-mail: info@flixboroughwharf.co.uk *Stevedoring services*

▶ Gunning Electrical & Mechanical, 3 Nisbet Way, Ravenstruther, Lanark, ML11 7LT Tel: (01555) 871010 Fax: (01555) 871012

▶ Gunns Bakery, 8 Market Square, Sandy, Bedfordshire, SG19 1HU Tel: (01767) 680434 Fax: (01767) 691666 *Baker*

▶ Gunns International Transport & Shipping Ltd, Bronze Age Way, Erith, Kent, DA8 1AX Tel: (01322) 441188 Fax: (01322) 441199

▶ Gunns Upholstery Cleaners, 65 Mitchell Gardens, South Shields, Tyne & Wear, NE34 6EF Tel: 0191-454 2819 E-mail: stevegunn@gunnscleaning.co.uk *Carpet & upholstery cleaning services*

Gunson Ltd, Bristol Road, Bridgwater, Somerset, TA6 4BX Tel: (01278) 436240 Fax: (01278) 450567 E-mail: gunson@globalnet.co.uk *Motor vehicle test tune & maintenance devices manufrs*

▶ Gunstones, Gunstones Bakery, Stubley Lane, Dronfield, Derbyshire, S18 1PF Tel: (01246) 414651 Fax: (01246) 410866 E-mail: sales@gunstonesbakery.com *Bakery*

Gunter Haas Export Marketing Ltd, 20 Goonwartha Road, Looe, Cornwall, PL13 2PJ Tel: (01503) 265601 Fax: (01503) 265607 E-mail: sales@gunta-sport.com *Sports goods exporters*

Gunther UK Ltd, 52 Lambardes, New Ash Green, Longfield, Kent, DA3 8HU Tel: (01474) 879774 Fax: (01474) 873063 E-mail: info@gunther.co.uk *Hot runner systems distributors*

▶ Gur Sewing Machine Co., 162 Halesowen Street, Rowley Regis, West Midlands, B65 0ES Tel: 0121-561 5169 Fax: 0121-559 3449 E-mail: sales@gur.co.uk *Suppliers of sewing machines & accessories to schools, colleges and public. main agents for Brother, Janome, Babylock, Pfaff and Stitchmaster.*

Guralp Systems Ltd, 3 Midas House, Calleva Park, Reading, RG7 8QZ Tel: 0118-981 9056 Fax: 0118-981 9943 E-mail: guralp@guralp.com *Instrumentation manufrs*

Gurit, St. Cross Business Park, Newport, Isle of Wight, PO30 5WU Tel: (01983) 828000 Fax: (01983) 828100 E-mail: info@gurit.com Purchasing Contact: P. Lyon Sales Contact: Tyler Principal Export Areas: Worldwide *Leading supplier of high performance cost effective composite technology solutions. Products include: Adhesives, Laminating Systems, Coatings, Reinforcements, Prepregs, SPRINT*

Gurney Reeve & Co. Ltd, Station Road, Spooner Row, Wymondham, Norfolk, NR18 9SR Tel: (01953) 603303 Fax: (01953) 601331 E-mail: sales@sweepersuton.co.uk *Agricultural & industrial manufacturing engineers*

Walter Gurney & Son Ltd, 64 Bute Street, Luton, LU1 2EY Tel: (01582) 729471 Fax: (01582) 721060 *Ladies' hats & millinery material merchant*

Gurso Plant & Lining Ltd, Landywood Lane, Cheslyn Hay, Walsall, WS6 7AL Tel: (01922) 418005 Fax: (01922) 412641 E-mail: sales@gurso.demon.co.uk *Plastic, steel fabricators & tank lining*

Gustav Kaser Training International Ltd, Essex House, 118 High Street, Ongar, Essex, CM5 9EB Tel: (01277) 365335 Fax: (01277) 365277 E-mail: sales@gustavkaeser.com *Management training specialists*

▶ Gustharts Chainsaw Centre, Unit 22-23 Milkhope Centre, Berwick Hill Road, Seaton Burn, Newcastle upon Tyne, NE13 6DA Tel: (01670) 789701 Fax: (01670) 789002 E-mail: enquiries@gustharts.com *Suppliers of arboricultural equipment, horticultural machinery*

Gutermann Ltd, Bullsbrook Road, Hayes, Middlesex, UB4 0JR Tel: (020) 8589 1600 Fax: (020) 8589 1636 E-mail: christine.williams@gutermann.com *Sewing thread manufrs*

Tom Gutherless Ltd, 34 & 34a St James Street, Hull, HU3 2DH Tel: (01482) 214184 Fax: (01482) 215211 E-mail: print@tom-guther.co.uk *Printers rubber stamp manufrs*

▶ Guthrie & Craig, Prospect Business Park, Crookhall Lane, Leadgate, Consett, County Durham, DH8 7PW Tel: (01207) 580033 Fax: (01207) 581903 E-mail: guthriecraigrjc@msn.com *Inspection engineers*

Guthrie Douglas Ltd, Collins Rd, Heathcote Industrial Estate, Warwick, CV34 6TF Tel: (01926) 452452 Fax: (01926) 336417 E-mail: sales@guthrie-douglas.uk.com *Automatic & electronic door systems*

▶ Guthrie & Robertson (Builders) Ltd, Pittenzie Road, Crieff, Perthshire, PH7 3JN Tel: (01764) 653676 Fax: (01764) 655305 E-mail: info@guthrie-and-robertson.co.uk

F. Gutkind & Co. Ltd, Suite F8, Oxford Centre For Innovation, Mill Street, Oxford, OX2 0JU Tel: (01865) 812031 Fax: (01865) 249261 E-mail: info@fgutkind.com *Food ingredient distributors*

W.N. Gutteridge Ltd, 11-13 Wellington Street, Leicester, LE1 6HH Tel: 0116-254 3825 Fax: 0116-247 0276 E-mail: buttons@gutteridge.co.uk *Button & trimmings merchants*

Guttermaster Ltd, Healey Works, Shawclough Road, Rochdale, Lancashire, OL12 6ND Tel: (01706) 869550 Fax: (01706) 869551 E-mail: sales@guttermaster.co.uk *Aluminium gutters, fascias, soffits & rainwater pipes manufrs*

Paul Guy & Co. Ltd, Unit 10, The Busiiness Centre, Corinium Industrial Estate, Raans Road, Amersham, Buckinghamshire, HP6 6FB Tel: (01494) 432121 Fax: (01494) 432727 E-mail: guypauluk@aol.com *Cake decorating materials & bakery equipment distributors*

Guy Property Developments Ltd, Pacioli House 9 Brookfield, Duncan Close, Moulton Park Industrial Estate, Northampton, NN3 6WL Tel: (01604) 496666 Fax: (01604) 499676 *Building design & construction contractors*

Guy Raymond Engineering Company Ltd, Rollesby Road, King's Lynn, Norfolk, PE30 4LX Tel: (01553) 761401 Fax: (01553) 767459 E-mail: info@guy-raymond.co.uk *Office furniture fittings manufrs*

▶ Guys Magnets, 12 Barbel Close, Calne, Wiltshire, SN11 9QP Tel: (01249) 811372 Fax: (01249) 812778 E-mail: guy@guysmagnets.com *Retail magnets, magnetic jewellery, magnetic toys*

Guyson International Ltd, Southview Business Park, Ghyll Royd, Guiseley, Leeds, LS20 9PR Tel: (01943) 870044 Fax: (01943) 870066 E-mail: enquiries@guyson.co.uk *Hansen quick-release couplings, dry-break couplings, self-sealing couplings, cam lock couplings, breakaway couplings. Kaptech flexible hose assemblies, stainless steel hose, PTFE hose, hygienic hose, rubber hose, wash-down equipment, hose reels.*

▶ GVA Grimley Ltd, 211-213 West George Street, Glasgow, G2 2LW Tel: 0141-225 5729 *Charted surveyors*

▶ GW Severn Software, The White House, Hockliffe Street, Leighton Buzzard, Bedfordshire, LU7 1HD Tel: (01525) 243570 Fax: (01525) 243571 *Software consultants*

▶ Gwasg Dinefwr Press, Rawlings Road, Llandybie, Ammanford, Dyfed, SA18 3YD Tel: (01269) 850935 Fax: (01269) 851024

Gwasg Helygain Ltd, 70 Kinmel Street, Rhyl, Clwyd, LL18 1AW Tel: (01745) 331411 Fax: (01745) 331310 *General printers*

Gweek Quay Boatyard, Gweek, Helston, Cornwall, TR12 6UF Tel: (01326) 221657 Fax: (01326) 221685 E-mail: info@gweek-quay.com *Boatyard & boat repair services*

Gwent Hydraulics, 8 Skillion Business Centre, Corporation Road, Newport, Gwent, NP19 4RF Tel: (01633) 280005 Fax: (01633) 273140 *Hydraulic hose distributors*

Gwent Powder Coatings Ltd, Unit 37 Springvale Industrial Estate, Cwmbran, Gwent, NP44 5BD Tel: (01633) 860901 Fax: (01633) 872030 E-mail: gpowdercoatings@btconnect.com *Powder coating services*

Gwent Repetition Engineers Ltd, Factory Road, Newport, Gwent, NP20 5FA Tel: (01633) 251112 Fax: (01633) 246940 *Precision turned parts manufrs*

▶ GWG Legal Services Ltd, 12 Ainley Close Birchencliffe, Huddersfield, HD3 3RJ Tel: (01422) 440058 E-mail: info@gwgls.co.uk *Will writing services, Power of Attorney, Property Protection Trusts. Home visits. Member of the Institute of Professional Will writers*

▶ GWIBS24-7, 39 Moorbridge Road, Bingham, Nottingham, NG13 8GG Tel: (01949) 831821 *I t & data cabling*

▶ Gwili Pottery, Alltwalis Road, Carmarthen, Dyfed, SA32 7DU Tel: (01267) 253449 Fax: (01267) 253449 *Potters, hand thrown, individually decorated ceramics*

D.C. Gwillim Enterprises Ltd, Charnwood House, 251 Loughborough Road, Mountsorrel, Loughborough, Leicestershire, LE12 7AS Tel: (01509) 621272 Fax: (01509) 620911 *Agents for textile manufrs*

GWK Engineering, 8 Ham Bridge Trading Estate, Willowbrook Road, Worthing, West Sussex, BN14 8NA Tel: (01903) 232773 Fax: (01903) 211062 *Engineering*

GWL Security Ltd, 10 Row 48, Great Yarmouth, Norfolk, NR30 1HU Tel: (01493) 857434 Fax: (01493) 857434 *Locksmiths*

GWR Engineering Ltd, 36 Derby Road, Liverpool, L20 1AB Tel: 0151-933 3150 Fax: 0151-944 2410 E-mail: gwrengineering@aol.com *Container parts manufrs*

GWR Systems, 258 Upper Shoreham Road, Shoreham-by-Sea, West Sussex, BN43 6BF Tel: (01273) 889333 Fax: (01273) 889556 E-mail: gwrsys@aol.com *Thermal transfer ribbon distributors*

GWS Engineers Ltd, First Avenue, Flixborough Industrial Estate, Flixborough, Scunthorpe, South Humberside, DN15 8SE Tel: (01724) 856665 Fax: (01724) 280805 E-mail: mail@gws-engineers.co.uk Principal Export Areas: Central/East Europe & West Europe *GWS are the UK's leading manufacturer and hirer of industrial vacuum cleaning equipment.**Our industrial vacuum cleaning systems are ideal for collecting large amounts of dust, aggregates and liquids - anything that will flow up a hose! Material can be collected into convenient Hoppers, Skips and Hook-Lift containers.**Our entire range of new and ex-hire vacuum equipment is available for sale worldwide. And we also operate one of the UK's largest hire fleets of industrial vacuum cleaning equipment.*

▶ Gwyn Davies Transport, Unit 3, Llandow Industrial Estate, Cowbridge, South Glamorgan, CF71 7PB Tel: (01446) 774862

Gwynedd Disposables, 14 Glanydon Industrial Estate, Pwllheli, Gwynedd, LL53 5YT Tel: (01758) 614747 Fax: (01758) 701009 *Janitorial suppliers*

Gwynedd Environmental Services, 10 St. Georges Drive, Deganwy, Conwy, Gwynedd, LL31 9PP Tel: (01492) 582018 Fax: (01492) 580007 *Pest controllers*

Gwynedd Farm Machinery Ltd, Dinas, Caernarfon, Gwynedd, LL54 5UG Tel: (01286) 830009 Fax: (01286) 831498 E-mail: sales@gwyneddfarmmachinery.co.uk *Agricultural machinery services*

Gwynedd Shipping Ltd, Chapel Yard, London Road, Holyhead, Gwynedd, LL65 2PB Tel: (01407) 760232 Fax: (01407) 765344 E-mail: info@gwyneddshipping.com *Freight forwarders & transport operators*

▶ Gwynne TV & Electrical Services, 18-20 Benfield Way, Braintree, Essex, CM7 3YS Tel: (01376) 322567 Fax: (01376) 329666 E-mail: info@gwynne-tv.co.uk *TV, plasma, lcd, video & domestic appliances repairs*

GX Microscopes, Hazelstub Depot, Camps Road, Haverhill, Suffolk, CB9 9AF Tel: (01440) 714737 Fax: (01440) 709421 E-mail: eurosales@gxmicroscopes.com *Scientific equipment suppliers*

▶ GX Optical, Cherry Gardens Industrial Estate, Helions Bumpstead Road, Haverhill, Suffolk, CB9 7AA Tel: 01440 714737 Fax: 01440 709421 E-mail: eurosales@gxoptical.com *Imaging, automation and monitoring products for science, industry and education. Including microscopy*

continued

equipment, cameras, telescopes, binoculars, image analysis, motorised stages, sample preparation equipment for microbiology, laboratory monitoring systems, environmental air samplers and industrial stepper motors and controllers

Gy Roll Ltd, Sand Road Industrial Estate, Sand Road, Great Gransden, Sandy, Bedfordshire, SG19 3AH Tel: (01767) 677377 Fax: (01767) 677900 E-mail: sales@gyroll.com *Multi-spindle drilling equipment*

▶ Gymking, 67 Belvedere Avenue, Ilford, Essex, IG5 0UH Tel: 0208 5512285 E-mail: gymking1@hotmail.co.uk *We stock supplenments from over 150 cpompanies including Maximuscle - EAS - Dymatize - Twinlab - Met Rx - Garnell - Labrada - Isatori and many many more. We supply Protein - Creatine -Weight Gain - Muscle Gain - Slimming Aids - Home Gym Equipment - DVD"s.... The list is endless.... Please visit our website for a complete listing of all or our fantastic products...*

Gymphlex Ltd, Boston Road, Horncastle, Lincolnshire, LN9 6HU Tel: (01507) 523243 Fax: (01507) 524421 E-mail: sales@gymphlex.co.uk *Sports clothing manufrs* Also at: Leicester

▶ Gymphlex Ltd, Stamford Buildings, Stamford Street, Leicester, LE1 6NJ Tel: 0116-255 6326 Fax: 0116-247 1215 E-mail: enquiries@gymphlex.co.uk *Uniforms sports clothing or footwear*

Gyrographic Communications, 603 The Chambers, Chelsea Harbour, London, SW10 0XF Tel: (020) 7351 1550 Fax: (020) 7351 3318 *Market researchers*

Gyrus International Ltd, 410 Wharfedale Road, Wokingham, Berkshire, RG41 5RA Tel: 0118-921 9700 Fax: 0118-921 9800 *Medical sales*

H.A.C. Catherwood Ltd, 1a Langlands Drive, Kelvin South Business Park, East Kilbride, Glasgow, G75 0YH Tel: (01355) 570011 Fax: (01355) 570022 E-mail: sales@catherwood.co.uk *Supply construction materials to building & construction Industry*

H A D Metal Ltd, 7 Grosvenor Drive, Loughton, Essex, IG10 2JX Tel: (020) 8508 8842 Fax: (020) 8508 8842 *Metal fabrication & finishers*

H A Davie Ltd, Market Place Industrial Estate, Houghton le Spring, Tyne & Wear, DH5 8AN Tel: 0191-584 2652 Fax: 0191-584 2752 E-mail: mail@hadavie.co.uk *Refrigeration contractors*

H A England, Comtech Business Park, Manchester Road, Westhoughton, Bolton, BL5 3QY Tel: (01942) 814435 Fax: (01942) 814943 E-mail: sales@haengland.co.uk *Precision engineers*

▶ H & A Hight Services Ltd, 8 Snowdon Road, Middlesbrough, Cleveland, TS2 1LP Tel: (01642) 218607 Fax: (01642) 217149

H A Jordon & Co. Ltd, 139A New Bond St, London, W1S 2TN Tel: (020) 7495 4874 Fax: (020) 7495 4804 E-mail: hajordan@tiscele.co.uk *Jewellery manufrs*

H A Light Ltd, Tram Way, Oldbury Road, Smethwick, West Midlands, B66 1NY Tel: 0121-327 2009 Fax: 0121-558 7513 E-mail: angelajones@btconnect.com *Jewellery findings*

H A Light Multiforms, Woods Lane, Cradley Heath, West Midlands, B64 7AL Tel: (01384) 569283 Fax: (01384) 633712 *Wire formed & shaped components*

H A Mcewen Boiler Repairs Ltd, Farling Top Boilerworks, Farling Top, Cowling, Keighley, West Yorkshire, BD22 0NW Tel: (01535) 634674 Fax: (01535) 636802 E-mail: maria@mcewen82.fsnet.co.uk *Specialists in Industrial Boiler Repairs, Supply & Installations of boilers, pipework fabrications. Hotwell Tanks built & installed. Valves overhauled and supplied. Boiler Removal & dismantling. Manufacture and Repair of Locomotive boilers. McEwen Boilermakers have over 35 years experience in the Boiler industry both Industrial & Heritage.*

H A N Jewellery Ltd, 14 Hylton Court, 27 Hylton Street, Birmingham, B18 6HJ Tel: 0121-551 1134 Fax: 0121-554 5155 E-mail: hanjewellery@hotmail.com *Jewellery manufrs*

▶ H A Newall & Co Merseyside Ltd, 24 Dublin Street, Liverpool, L3 7DT Tel: 0151-298 1438 Fax: 0151-298 1469 E-mail: sales@hanewall.co.uk

H A Office Supplies, 25 Pittfield Street, London, N1 6HB Tel: (020) 7608 3670 Fax: (020) 7608 3670 *Office equipment suppliers*

H A R Banfield & Son Ltd, 103-105 Barry Road, London, SE22 0HW Tel: (020) 8693 5022 Fax: (020) 8299 3197 *Timber merchants*

H A Rayson Ltd, Jill House Cornishway North, Galmington Trading Estate, Taunton, Somerset, TA1 5LY Tel: (01823) 275044 Fax: (01823) 338135 *Motor radiator repair specialists* Also at: Yeovil

H A Ross Structural Engineers, Workshop, Stephen Road Industrial Estate, Huntly, Aberdeenshire, AB54 8SX Tel: (01466) 793153 Fax: (01466) 794395 *Structural engineers*

H.A.S. Supplies Ltd, Unit 2, Chamberlayne Road, Moreton Hall Industrial Estate, Bury St. Edmunds, Suffolk, IP32 7EY Tel: (01284) 767547 Fax: (01284) 769057 E-mail: info@has-supplies.co.uk *Hydraulic hose assemblers*

▶ H A V Solutions, 103 Maiden Place, Lower Earley, Reading, RG6 3HE Tel: (07910) 303555 Fax: 0118-947 3107 *Audio Visual Consultants, specialising in multiroom system design. Additional services include Computer Network Design and installation and Aerial installations.*

H A Window Cleaning, 48 Aberley Avenue, Stourport-On-Severn, Worcestershire, DY13 0LZ Tel: (07801) 369265 E-mail: a.muir1@btinternet.com *Window maintenance service*

H A Z Environmental, Bullock Street, West Bromwich, West Midlands, B70 7HE Tel: 0121-580 3055 Fax: 0121-580 3056 E-mail: mail@haz-enviro.co.uk *Waste management services*

H Attrill & Sons Isle Of Wright Ltd, The Duver, St. Helens, Ryde, Isle of Wight, PO33 1YB Tel: (01983) 872319 Fax: (01983) 874313 E-mail: attrillboats@aol.com *Boat repairers*

H B A Creative Ltd, Mortimer Hall, 1 Birmingham Road, Kidderminster, Worcestershire, DY10 2BU Tel: (01562) 822208 Fax: (01562) 754639 *Marketing consultants; creative promotional services*

H B A Distribution, 3A Upper Darkley Road, Keady, Armagh, BT60 3RE Tel: (028) 3753 1155 Fax: (028) 3753 8231 E-mail: info@hba.ie *Power tools & garage suppliers*

H B Aluminium Fabrications Ltd, California House, Leathley Road, Leeds, LS10 1BG Tel: 0113-243 8195 Fax: 0113-242 2561 E-mail: admin@hb-aluminium.co.uk *Windows & shop front manufrs*

H B Bearings Ltd, Riverside Works, Honley, Huddersfield, HD9 6PQ Tel: (01484) 665116 Fax: (01484) 662619 E-mail: sales@hb-bearings.com *Bearing modification & manufrs*

H & B Computer Services, 46 Coombe Drive, Sittingbourne, Kent, ME10 3DA Tel: (01795) 422560 Fax: (08701) 375225 E-mail: enquiries@handbcomputers.co.uk *Computer engineers*

H B D Engineering 2000, Unit F4 The Seedbed Centre, Harlow, Essex, CM19 5AF Tel: (01279) 436894 Fax: (01279) 436894 E-mail: sales@hbd2000.co.uk *General & precision engineers*

H B D Floors Ltd, 6 Falcon Units, Bradley Lane, Newton Abbot, Devon, TQ12 1NB Tel: (01626) 366333 Fax: (01626) 366444 *Flooring & carpet contractors*

H & B Fabrication Ltd, John Street, Walkley Lane, Heckmondwike, West Yorkshire, WF16 0NA Tel: (01924) 412609 Fax: (01924) 412609 *Steel fabricators*

H B Fuller UK Ltd, Outram Road, Globe Lane Industrial Estate, Dukinfield, Cheshire, SK16 4XE Tel: (01773) 601315 Fax: (0161) 666 0667 *Adhesive manufrs*

▶ H B G Construction, 32 Hailes Avenue, Edinburgh, EH13 0LZ Tel: 0131-441 7348

▶ H B G Construction Western Ltd, Millennium Gate, Gifford Court, Fox Den Road, Bristol, BS34 8TT Tel: 0117-944 8800

▶ H B H Fixings Ltd, Unit 4, Mardle Way Business Park, Mardle Way, Buckfastleigh, Devon, TQ11 0JL Tel: (01364) 644766 Fax: (01364) 644768

H B Halstead & Sons Ltd, 247 Eldon Street, Ashton-on-Ribble, Preston, PR2 2BB Tel: (01772) 252820 Fax: (01772) 202609 E-mail: sales@hbhalstead.com *Precision engineers*

H B Humphries & Co. Ltd, Telford Way, Telford Way Industrial Estate, Kettering, Northamptonshire, NN16 8UN Tel: (01536) 512588 Fax: (01536) 410140 E-mail: enquiries@hbhumphries.co.uk *Sheet metalwork engineers*

H B Industrial Services Ltd, 15 Kingdom Close, Fareham, Hampshire, PO15 5TJ Tel: (01489) 575222 Fax: (01489) 575666 E-mail: sales@hbindustrialservices.co.uk *Bearings agents & distributors*

▶ H B Lewis & Sons Ltd, Langford Mill, Charfield Road, Kingswood, Wotton-under-Edge, Gloucestershire, GL12 8RL Tel: (01453) 845405 Fax: (01453) 521757 E-mail: admin@hblewis.co.uk

▶ H & B Logistics, Unit 3, Elizabeths Park, Denton, Manchester, M34 3RU Tel: 0161-335 9009 Fax: 0161-335 9747

H B M UK Ltd, 1 Churchill Court, 58 Station Road, North Harrow, Harrow, Middlesex, HA2 7SA Tel: (020) 8515 6100 Fax: (020) 8515 6149 E-mail: info@uk.hbm.com *Data acquisition systems, strain gauge, torque meters manufrs*

H B Pearce Contractors Ltd, Grey Gables, Pytchley Road, Kettering, Northamptonshire, NN15 6NE Tel: (01536) 310234 Fax: (01536) 310638 *Property development*

H B Pine Products, Herrington Burn, Houghton Le Spring, Tyne & Wear, DH4 4JW Tel: 0191-385 2822 Fax: 0191-385 2267 *Pine furniture manufrs*

H B Printing, 175 Bramhall Lane, Stockport, Cheshire, SK2 6JA Tel: 0161-480 5818 Fax: 0161-480 5819 *Commercial printers*

▶ H B Projects, 56 Commerce Court, Challenge Way, Bradford, West Yorkshire, BD4 8NW Tel: (01274) 269010 Fax: (01274) 669983

H B Rentals Ltd, Howe Moss Drive, Kirkhill Industrial Estate, Dyce, Aberdeen, AB21 0GL Tel: (01224) 772304 Fax: (01224) 772641 E-mail: sales@dm-accommodation.com *Cabin manufrs*

H B S Ltd, 3 Sycamore Close, Maidenhead, Berkshire, SL6 3HU Tel: (01628) 636849 Fax: (01628) 777218 E-mail: hbs.ltd@lineone.net *Air conditioning contractors*

▶ H B S Bar Stock Ltd, 125 Lodgefield Road, Halesowen, West Midlands, B62 8AX Tel: 0121-559 4251 Fax: 0121-561 4565 *Manufacture pipe fittings*

H B S Consultants Ltd, 6 Brooks Road, Raunds, Wellingborough, Northamptonshire, NN9 6NS Tel: (0800) 0199850 Fax: (01933) 461663 *Technology consultants*

▶ H B S Engineering Co., Unit 11 2 Palatine Industrial Estate, Causeway Avenue, Warrington, WA4 6QQ Tel: (01925) 632388 Fax: (01925) 445904 *Metalworking & fabrication services*

H B S Facilities Management Ltd, Ireland House, 150 New Bond Street, London, W1S 2TU Tel: (020) 7317 4800 Fax: (020) 7317 4801 E-mail: enquiries@hbsf.com *Facilities Management*

H B Tools Ltd, 2 Langley Court, Langley Road, Burscough Industrial Estate, Ormskirk, Lancashire, L40 8JR Tel: (01704) 897722 Fax: (01704) 897303 E-mail: sales@hbtools.co.uk *Engineering cutting tool distributors*

H Beesley Ltd, Commercial Square, Freemans Common, Leicester, LE2 7SR Tel: 0116-255 4233 Fax: 0116-255 4366 E-mail: enquiries@hbeesley.co.uk Principal Export Areas: Central/East Europe *Precision engineers & general engineering*

▶ H Bentley & Co., 4 Pool Street, Birkenhead, Merseyside, CH41 3NL Tel: 0151-647 8494 Fax: 0151-647 5497

H. Breakell & Co. (Blackburn) Ltd, P1/15 Parklands, Heywood Distribution Park, Heywood, Lancashire, OL10 2TT Tel: (01706) 369272 Fax: (01706) 629448 E-mail: enquirires@breakell-lifts.co.uk *Lift installers & manufrs*

H Bronnley & Co. Ltd, Bronnley Works, Radstone Road, Brackley, Northamptonshire, NN13 5AU Tel: (01280) 702291 Fax: (01280) 703912 E-mail: uksales@bronnley.co.uk *High quality toiletries manufrs*

H Brown, 172-180 St Andrews Road, Northampton, NN2 6DB Tel: (01604) 714121 *Skip contractors*

H Butterfield Ltd, Selbourne Road, Luton, LU4 8QF Tel: (01582) 491100 Fax: (01582) 490969 E-mail: enquiries@butterfieldnatstone.co.uk *Natural stone manufrs*

H & C Building Services, Group House, 52 Sutton Court Road, Sutton, Surrey, SM1 4SL Tel: (020) 8915 0909 Fax: (020) 8915 0734 E-mail: info@handcgroup.com *Building mechanical/electrical*

H C C M Systems Ltd, 3 Church Street, Leamington Spa, Warwickshire, CV31 1EG Tel: (01926) 451551 Fax: (01926) 451556 E-mail: sales@hccm.co.uk *Computer software developers*

H C Controls Ltd, Wetherby Close, Portrack Interchange Business Park, Stockton-on-Tees, Cleveland, TS18 2SL Tel: (01642) 671681 Fax: (01642) 676100 E-mail: admin@hccontrol.co.uk *Control panels manufrs*

H & C Fabrications Ltd, Corporation Road, Birkenhead, Merseyside, CH41 8FA Tel: 0151-653 7677 Fax: 0151-652 0626 *Roller shutter & industrial door manufrs*

▶ H C Herbert & Son Maesteg Ltd, 3 Brynmawr Place, Maesteg, Mid Glamorgan, CF34 9PB Tel: (01656) 733264 Fax: (01656) 736800

H C Holifield Oxford Ltd, Nuffield Way, Abingdon, Oxfordshire, OX14 1RX Tel: (01235) 520284 Fax: (01235) 559001 E-mail: sales@holifields.co.uk *Subcontract engineering*

H C L Safety Ltd, Unit 1 Ball Street, Walsall, WS1 2HG Tel: (01922) 619470 Fax: (01922) 619471 E-mail: birmingham@hclgroup.co.uk *Fall arrest, fall restraint & fall protection system specialists*

H C Lewis & Co. Ltd, 47 Hogshill Street, Beaminster, Dorset, DT8 3AG Tel: (01308) 862421 Fax: (01308) 863782 E-mail: hclewisandson@hotmail.com *Asphalt tarmac surfacing contractors*

▶ H C M Electrical Ltd, Market Place, Codnor, Ripley, Derbyshire, DE5 9QA Tel: (01773) 570596 Fax: (01773) 570933

H C M Engineering Ltd, Pedmore Road, Stourbridge, West Midlands, DY9 7DZ Tel: (01384) 422643 Fax: (01384) 899210 E-mail: simonh@hcmeng.co.uk *CNC engineering services*

H C S Automation, 3 Alvechurch Highway, Lydiate Ash, Bromsgrove, Worcestershire, B60 1NZ Tel: 0121-453 8053 Fax: 0121-453 8053 E-mail: hcsautomation@aol.com *Automatic gates*

H C S Tools Ltd, Unit T, Millmeade Industrial Estate, Staines, Middlesex, TW18 4UK Tel: (01895) 257265 Fax: (01895) 235630 E-mail: alan@hcstools.fsnet.co.uk *Toolmakers*

H C Slingsby plc, 1303 Argyle Street, Glasgow, G3 8TL Tel: 0141-339 2256 Fax: 0141-339 4775 *Commercial & industrial equipment distributors*

H C Slingsby plc, Otley Road, Shipley, West Yorkshire, BD17 7LW Tel: (01274) 535030 Fax: (01274) 535033 E-mail: sales@slingsby.com *Materials handling & equipment manufrs.* Also at: Belfast, Birmingham, Bristol, Gateshead, Glasgow, Liverpool, London SW18 & Manchester

H.C Turk Engineering Services Ltd, 4a The Mews, Bentley Street, Gravesend, Kent, DA12 2DH Tel: (01474) 325331 Fax: (01474) 353140 *Precision engineers*

H C White & Son, Pegswood Village, Pegswood, Morpeth, Northumberland, NE61 6UD Tel: (01670) 513660 Fax: (01670) 513660 *Joiners & undertakings*

H & C Whitehead Ltd, Prospect Works, Bailiffe Bridge, Brighouse, West Yorkshire, HD6 4DJ Tel: (01484) 712151 Fax: (01484) 716187 E-mail: info@hcwhitehead.co.uk *Fabric finishers*

H C Wilson Transport Ltd, Grove Lane, Elmswell, Bury St. Edmunds, Suffolk, IP30 9HN Tel: (01359) 240558 Fax: (01359) 240437 E-mail: traffic@hcwilsontransport.com *Abnormal load haulers*

H Careers.Company Co .Uk, Iverson Road, London, NW6 2QT Tel: (0800) 0851335 Fax: (020) 7372 4466 E-mail: mike@hcareers.co.uk *On-line recruitment for hotel, restaurant, pub/bar & catering jobs*

H Case & Son Cradley Heath Ltd, Mount Works, Foxoak Street, Cradley Heath, West Midlands, B64 5DQ Tel: (01384) 566358 Fax: (01384) 634601 E-mail: sales@h-caseandson.co.uk *Overhead transmission steelwork*

▶ H Clarke & Sons Ltd, Linton, Skipton, North Yorkshire, BD23 5HH Tel: (01756) 752319 Fax: (01756) 752319

H Cocker & Sons Ltd, Reed Heald Works, Jubilee Street, Halifax, West Yorkshire, HX3 9HY Tel: (01422) 353358 Fax: (01422) 353358 *Reed & heald manufrs*

H Colvin & Sons, 82 Ballybollen Road, Ahoghill, Ballymena, County Antrim, BT42 2RF Tel: (028) 7965 0222 Fax: (028) 7965 0217 E-mail: hcolvinandson@aol.com *Agricultural merchants*

H Conduit, 4 King William Enterprise Park, King William Street, Salford, M50 3ZP Tel: 0161-877 0877 Fax: 0161-877 3434 E-mail: hconduit@btconnect.com *Business promotion service*

H Cooper & Sons Bristol, Westerleigh Road, Yate, Bristol, BS37 8QA Tel: (01454) 312081 Fax: (01454) 318880 E-mail: info@hcooper.net *Agricultural equipment manufrs*

H Curtis & Sons, Stanton Wick Farm, Stanton Wick, Pensford, Bristol, BS39 4DB Tel: (01761) 490372 Fax: (01761) 490004 E-mail: andrew@hcurtis.co.uk *Farming & haulage*

H D A International, 4 Park Place, 12 Lawn Lane, Vauxhall, London, SW8 1UD Tel: (020) 7820 9199 Fax: (020) 7735 8175 E-mail: admin@hda.co.uk *Career management & counselling services*

H & D Air Conditioning Ltd, 133 Royal George Road, Burgess Hill, West Sussex, RH15 9TD Tel: (01444) 232552 Fax: (01444) 246568 E-mail: brighton@mail.aireserv.com *Air conditioning specialists*

▶ H D Chadwick & Sons, Gorton Road, Manchester, M11 2DZ Tel: 0161-223 1701 Fax: 0161-231 6752 E-mail: roger.chadwick@tesco.net *Curtain net & voile importers & wholesalers*

H D Ebbutt & Son, 63 Jarvis Road, South Croydon, Surrey, CR2 6HW Tel: (020) 8688 1157 *Building & plumbing services*

▶ H & D Electrical, 1 Poulton Business Park, Poulton Close, Dover, Kent, CT17 0HL Tel: (01304) 226999 Fax: (01304) 226888

▶ H D Fraser & Sons, Balblair Cottage, Balblair, Dingwall, Ross-Shire, IV7 8LG Tel: (01381) 610268 Fax: (01381) 610292

H D Howden Ltd, 10 Belgowan Street, Bellshill Industrial Estate, Bellshill, Lanarkshire, ML4 3NS Tel: (01698) 573100 Fax: (01698) 573121 E-mail: sales@howden-electroheating.com *For full details see: Howden Electro Heating,*

H D K Industries Ltd, 13 Whalley Avenue, Sale, Cheshire, M33 2BP Tel: 0161-905 1869 Fax: 0161-905 1879 *Industrial textile manufrs*

▶ H D L Audio Visual Services Ltd, 4 Hop Gardens, Henley-on-Thames, Oxfordshire, RG9 2EH Tel: (01491) 579020 Fax: (01491) 579037 E-mail: hires@hdlaudiovisualservices.com *Supply & build conference systems*

H D M Plastics, Waldeck Road, Maidenhead, Berkshire, SL6 8BR Tel: (01628) 673832 Fax: (01628) 673832 E-mail: hdmplastics68@yahoo.co.uk *Plastic mould tool makers*

▶ H D Management, 18 Claremont Crescent, Edinburgh, EH7 4HX Tel: 0131-556 9001 Fax: 0131-558 9704

▶ H D Ricketts Ltd, 110 Summer Road, Erdington, Birmingham, B23 6DY Tel: 0121-382 5151 Fax: 0121-377 7282 E-mail: ricketts.hd@btconnect.com *JCB & tipper hire & suppliers of sand & gravel*

H D S Design Consultants Ltd, 22 South Street, Rochford, Essex, SS4 1BQ Tel: (01702) 530043 Fax: (01702) 530051 E-mail: projects@hdsdesign.com Principal Export Areas: Worldwide *Consulting engineers*

H D Shopfitters Ltd, May Avenue, Northfleet, Gravesend, Kent, DA11 8RH Tel: (01474) 567788 Fax: (01474) 536403 E-mail: hdshopfit@aol.com *Joinery manufrs*

H D Simpson & Co Polishers Ltd, Downing Street Industrial Estate, Smethwick, West Midlands, B66 2JH Tel: 0121-558 3469 Fax: 0121-558 3469 *Metal polishing & finishing services*

H & D Worm Drive Clips, 197-199 Mare Street, London, E8 3QF Tel: (020) 8985 0752 Fax: (020) 8985 3123 E-mail: nautilus@talk21.com *Hose clip distributors & agents*

H Dawson Sons & Co (Wool) Ltd, Mercury House, Essex St, Bradford, West Yorkshire, BD4 7PG Tel: (01274) 727464 Fax: (01274) 723326 E-mail: info@h-dawson-wool.com *Raw wool suppliers, brokers & merchants*

H Dobson Ltd, 26-28 West Row, Stockton-on-Tees, Cleveland, TS18 1BN Tel: (01642) 676480 Fax: (01642) 670698 E-mail: sales@dobsonglass.co.uk *UPVC installers & glazing contractors service*

H Docherty Ltd, Red Shute Hill Industrial Estate, Red Shute Hill, Hermitage, Thatcham, Berkshire, RG18 9QL Tel: (01635) 200145 Fax: (01635) 201737 E-mail: info@docherty.co.uk *Sheet metal workers*

H Downs & Sons Huddersfield Ltd, Peacock Works, Leeds Road, Huddersfield, HD2 1XR Tel: (01484) 428203 Fax: (01484) 546993 E-mail: sales@hdowns.co.uk *Iron founders*

H Dunstan & Sons, Carnsew Farm, Treliever Road, Penryn, Cornwall, TR10 9EY Tel: (01326) 372240 Fax: (01326) 372240 E-mail: dunstan@mabe25.go-plus.net *Plant hire & ground workers*

▶ H E C, Electric House, BIlndustrial Lane, Todmorden, Lancashire, OL14 5HZ Tel: (01706) 814389

▶ H E Computing Ltd, Grosvenor Road, Bircotes, Doncaster, South Yorkshire, DN11 8EY Tel: (01302) 746053 Fax: (01302) 752643 E-mail: hec@harworth.biz *Computer maintenance, repair*

H E Humphries Ltd, Monway House, Portway Road, Wednesbury, West Midlands, WS10 7DZ Tel: 0121-556 0097 Fax: 0121-556 9427 *Demolition contractors*

▶ H & E Installations, Telford Way, Severalls Industrial Park, Colchester, CO4 9QP Tel: (01206) 844334 Fax: (01206) 844992

▶ H E Jones Ltd, Tyseley Industrial Estate, Seeleys Road, Birmingham, B11 2LA Tel: 0121-772 0114 Fax: 0121-773 9364

H & E Knowles (Lye) Ltd, Britannia Works, Talbots Lane, Brierley Hill, West Midlands, DY5 2YX Tel: (01384) 78877 Fax: (01384) 79012 E-mail: sales@heknowles.freeserves.co.uk *Pressings, general presswork & shearing (steel plate) facilities*

H E Lupton & Sons 1952 Ltd, Quebec Works, Elland Lane, Elland, West Yorkshire, HX5 9DU Tel: (01422) 370349 Fax: (01422) 370349 E-mail: sales@lupton1952.wanado.co.uk *Marine & offshore bronze valve manufrs*

H E M Group Ltd, H E M House, Kirkstall Road, Leeds, LS4 2BT Tel: 0113-263 2222 Fax: 0113-231 0237 E-mail: info@heminteriors.com *Partitions & office furnishings*

H E Marshalls of Slough, Petersfield Avenue, Slough, SL2 5EF Tel: (01753) 522421 Fax: (01753) 531233 *Car body repairers & sprayers*

H E Olby & Co. Ltd, 299-313 Lewisham High Street, London, SE13 6NW Tel: (020) 8690 3401 Fax: (020) 8690 1408 E-mail: mail.heolby@virgin.net *Builders merchants* Also at: Frant

H E P Rolled Sections, Bayton Road, Exhall, Coventry, CV7 9EJ Tel: (024) 7658 5600 Fax: (024) 7658 5649 E-mail: info@metsec.com Principal Export Areas: Worldwide *Manufacturers of galvanized sections*

H E Payne, 66 The Lane, Wyboston, Bedford, MK44 3AP Tel: (01480) 212798 Fax: (01480) 212070 E-mail: admin@hepayne.co.uk *Road transport, haulage & freight services*

H.E.R.S., 15 Bills St, Darlaston, W. Midlands, WS10 8BB Tel: 0121 526 3608 Fax: 0121 568 6487 *Hairdressing equipment & shower installations*

H E Randall & Son, Longworth Street, Chorley, Lancashire, PR7 2HT Tel: (01257) 263854 Fax: (01257) 263854 *Electrical heating*

H.E.S. Maintenance Co. Ltd, 141-143 Worcester Road, Bromsgrove, Worcestershire, B61 7HN Tel: (01527) 878707 Fax: (01527) 575264 *Heating equipment maintenance*

H E S Sales UK Ltd, 14 Bentley Way, Royal Oak Industrial Estate, Daventry, Northamptonshire, NN11 8QH Tel: (01327) 300322 Fax: (01327) 311411 E-mail: daventry@hes-sales.com *Power tool distributors & repairers*

H & E Scaffolding, Unit 16 Trench Lock 2, Telford, Shropshire, TF1 5SW Tel: (01952) 254248 Fax: (01952) 222084 E-mail: john@hescaffolding.co.uk *Contract scaffolding specialists*

▶ H E Services (Plant Hire) Ltd, Riverside Industrial Estate, Langley Park, Durham, DH7 9TT Tel: 0191-373 7114

H E Services (Plant Hire) Ltd, Membury Business Park, Lambourn Woodlands, Hungerford, Berkshire, RG17 7TJ Tel: (01488) 73444 *Plant hire, specialist excavator hire*

H & E Smith Ltd, Brittanic Works, Broom Street, Stoke-on-Trent, ST1 2ER Tel: (01782) 281617 Fax: (01782) 269882 E-mail: sales@hesmith.co.uk *Ceramic & glazed tiles manufrs*

H E Textiles, 20b The Nook, Cosby, Leicester, LE9 1RQ Tel: 0116-275 3353 Fax: 0116-275 3389 E-mail: nicola.pollock@pgen.net *Yarn agents*

H E Woolley Ltd, Newport Works, Forty Foot Road, Middlesbrough, Cleveland, TS2 1HG Tel: (01642) 247337 Fax: (01642) 250188 E-mail: info@he-woolley.co.uk *Fire protection engineers services*

H Eggleston Junior & Son Ltd, Lanchester, Durham, DH7 0TP Tel: (01207) 520869 Fax: (01207) 521941 E-mail: h.eggleston@onyxnet.co.uk *Wood shavings & pet bedding*

H Erben Ltd, Lady Lane, Hadleigh, Ipswich, IP7 6AS Tel: (01473) 823011 Fax: (01473) 828252 E-mail: enquiries@urban.co.uk *Bottling & packaging services*

H F B Trailers (Leek), Horton Head Farm, Horton, Leek, Staffordshire, ST13 8PQ Tel: (01538) 306212 Fax: (01538) 306396 E-mail: nathan@hfbtrailers.com *Trailers*

H F Bates & Sons, 94 Fairfield Road, London, E3 2QP Tel: (020) 8980 1133 Fax: (020) 8980 1797 *Metal recycling*

▶ H F Brown & Son Ltd, Portland Works, Main Street, Hemingbrough, Selby, North Yorkshire, YO8 6QF Tel: (01757) 638262

▶ H F Comms Ltd, 100 Albert Drive, Glasgow, G41 2SJ Tel: 0141-429 9377 Fax: 0141-570 3181 E-mail: hf@hfplec.co.uk *Electrical contractor services*

H F Creation International Ltd, B6 Bordesley Green Road, Birmingham, B9 4TA Tel: 0121-766 8288 Fax: 0121-773 2944 E-mail: info@paul-andrew.com *Clothing manufrs*

H & F Drilling Supplies Ltd, 16a Cunningham Road, Stirling, FK7 7SW Tel: (01786) 479575 Fax: (01786) 465803 *Rock drilling distributors*

H F H Fumecupboards, 9a Aire Place Mills, 103 Kirkstall Road, Leeds, LS3 1JL Tel: 0113-245 4111 Fax: 0113-246 9964 E-mail: hfhmail@yahoo.co.uk *Fume cupboard manufrs*

H F Northan Ltd, High Street, Haxey, Doncaster, South Yorkshire, DN9 2HH Tel: (01427) 752708 Fax: (01427) 752173 *Machinery for fusion piping hire*

▶ H F Owen Transport Ltd, Ddol Farm Bethel, Bethel, Caernarfon, Gwynedd, LL55 1UN Tel: (01248) 670487 Fax: (01248) 671201 E-mail: enquiries@hfowentransport.co.uk

H F Systems, 97 Hill Top, West Bromwich, West Midlands, B70 0RU Tel: 0121-556 5821 Fax: (0845) 8689918 E-mail: info@hfsystems.co.uk *Software developers*

H F T Forklift Ltd, Unit A, Ramsden Road, Rotherwas Industrial Estate, Hereford, HR2 6NP Tel: (01432) 277180 Fax: (01432) 352249 E-mail: info@hftforklifts.com *Fork lift truck, sales, hire, services, driver training, parts*

H F W Plastics Ltd, Albany Road, Gateshead, Tyne & Wear, NE8 3AT Tel: 0191-477 6519 Fax: 0191-490 1345 E-mail: sales@hfwplastics.co.uk *Plastic packaging, PVC ring binders & office stationery products*

H F X Ltd, The Clock House, Green Street, Elsenham, Bishop's Stortford, Hertfordshire, CM22 6DS Tel: (01279) 647474 Fax: (01279) 647700 E-mail: info@hfx.co.uk *Flexible working hour time recorders & access control systems suppliers*

H Fisher Distributors & Factors Fareham Ltd, 9-10 Highbury Buildings, Portsmouth Road, Portsmouth, PO6 2SN Tel: (023) 9237 2111 Fax: (023) 9238 0243 E-mail: sales@hfishertools.co.uk *Engineering distributors*

▶ indicates data change since last edition

▶ H Frost & Sons Transport Ltd, Lower Chare Farm, Barningham Road, Stanton, Bury St. Edmunds, Suffolk, IP31 2DT Tel: (01359) 250226 Fax: (01359) 251770

H G A Creative Communications, The Old Exchange, 514 Liverpool Road, Irlam, Manchester, M44 6AJ Tel: 0161-775 7890 Fax: 0161-775 7916 E-mail: info@hgacreative.com *Marketing communications*

H G Aerospace Engineering Ltd, 30-31 Castleham Road, St. Leonards-on-Sea, East Sussex, TN38 9NS Tel: (01424) 853444 Fax: (01424) 851690 E-mail: sales@hgaerospace.com *Aeronautical design & engineering services*

H G Blatcher Memorial Masons Ltd, 409 Sutton Road, Southend-on-Sea, SS2 5PQ Tel: (01702) 468950 Fax: (01702) 600274 E-mail: info@memorialmasons.co.uk *Manufacturers of high quality hand carved memorials*

▶ H G Bruce & Partners Ltd, Nelson Road, Winchester, Hampshire, SO23 0QG Tel: (01962) 853968 Fax: (01962) 862141

H G Brunner, Bradbourne House, East Malling, West Malling, Kent, ME19 6DZ Tel: (01732) 873715 Fax: (01732) 875610 E-mail: sales@hgbrunner.com *Precision turned parts & spirit level distributors*

H G Compressors, Unit 3, 3 Tyersal Lane, Bradford, West Yorkshire, BD4 0RB Tel: (01274) 669733 Fax: (01274) 669797 E-mail: ahmad@hgcompressors.co.uk *Refrigeration engineers*

H. G. Construction (Holdings) Ltd, 4 Hunting Gate, Hitchin, Hertfordshire, SG4 0TJ Tel: (01462) 454444 Fax: (01462) 455924 E-mail: mail@hunting-gate.co.uk *Building contractors, Property developers**

H G Froud & Son, 24 Newtown Road, Verwood, Dorset, BH31 6EJ Tel: (01202) 822444 *Wood fencing manufrs*

H G H Components Ltd, 77 River Road, Barking, Essex, IG11 0DS Tel: (020) 8594 7500 Fax: (020) 8594 7533 *Commercial vehicle motor factor suppliers*

H G Hughes & Son, 10 Back Greenfield Road, Colwyn Bay, Clwyd, LL29 8EP Tel: (01492) 533409 *Joinery manufrs*

▶ H G Hussey & Sons Ltd, 38 West Street, Bridport, Dorset, DT6 3QP Tel: (01308) 423384 Fax: (01308) 427398 E-mail: husseythebakers@hotmail.co.uk *Bakery*

H G Jones, Pantyrafallen Bach, Y Felinheli, Gwynedd, LL56 4QN Tel: (01248) 670194 Fax: (01248) 670194 *Dairy engineering*

H G S Cleaning Supplies, Unit F, 61 Albert Road North, Reigate, Surrey, RH2 9EL Tel: (01737) 240162 Fax: (01737) 223384 E-mail: sales@hgscleaningsupplies.co.uk *Janitorial supply services*

▶ H G S Marketing, Elmgrove Lodge, 47A Elmgrove Road, Weybridge, Surrey, KT13 8PB Tel: (01932) 829419 E-mail: info@hgsmarketing.com *HGS specialises in Marketing Communications solutions in Advertising, Direct Marketing, Design, CRM, Events and publishing, primarily in the Financial Services, Aerospace and Defence sectors.*

H G Systems Ltd, Dunston House Sheepbridge Works, Dunston Road, Chesterfield, Derbyshire, S41 9QD Tel: (01246) 260270 Fax: (01246) 450323 E-mail: sales@hgsystems.co.uk *Consultants & designers of automation equipment & systems*

H G Timber Ltd, Three Ways Wharf, Rigby Lane, Hayes, Middlesex, UB3 1ET Tel: (020) 8561 3311 Fax: (020) 8569 2122 E-mail: sales@hgtimber.co.uk *Pallet & stillage manufrs*

H G Trading Northern Ltd, Unit 3a Rainford Industrial Estate, Mill Lane, Rainford, St. Helens, Merseyside, WA11 8LS Tel: (01744) 886444 Fax: (01744) 886355 *Scrap metal distributors*

H G V Truck & Trailer Parts, Marsh Lane, Boston, Lincolnshire, PE21 7SJ Tel: (01205) 365258 Fax: (01205) 355225 E-mail: info@hgvtruckparts.com *Commercial vehicle spares distributors*

H Gilbert, Whiteridden Farm, Kilbirnie, Ayrshire, KA25 7JY Tel: (01505) 684162 Fax: (01505) 684162 *Agricultural contractors*

▶ H Gittins, 27 Aston Road, Bromsgrove, Worcestershire, B60 3EX Tel: (01527) 870400 Fax: (01527) 870403 E-mail: haulage@gittinstransport.co.uk *Road haulage services, flat bed work, cranes, vehicle repairs*

▶ H Gittins, 27 Aston Road, Bromsgrove, Worcestershire, B60 3EX Tel: (01527) 870400 Fax: (01527) 870403 E-mail: haulage@gittinstransport.co.uk

▶ H Goodman (Midway) Ltd, Unit 6, Ringway Business Park, Swadlincote, Derbyshire, DE11 8JL Tel: (01283) 217275

H & H Alloy Sales Ltd, J A S House, Titford Lane, Rowley Regis, West Midlands, B65 0PY Tel: 0121-559 6466 Fax: 0121-559 8723 E-mail: signs@warleyholdings.co.uk *Aluminium stockholders & fabricators*

▶ H H Aluminium & Building Products Ltd, Unit 1/3, Park Gate Business Centre, Chandlers Way, Park Gate, Southampton, SO31 1FQ Tel: (01489) 589655 Fax: (01489) 589322 E-mail: peter@hhali.co.uk *Manufacturers, supplies & installs aluminium windows, doors & screens*

▶ H H Associates Ltd, City House, Sutton Park Road, Sutton, Surrey, SM1 2AE Tel: (020) 8770 7300 Fax: (020) 8770 9970

H H B Management Consultants Ltd, Estate Office, Highbrook, Mertyn La, Carmel, Holywell, Clwyd, CH8 8QN Tel: (01352) 713213 Fax: (01352) 710945 *Consultancy*

H & H Celcon Ltd, Heck Lane, Pollington, Goole, North Humberside, DN14 0BA Tel: (01405) 861212 Fax: (01405) 862168 *Building blocks manufrs*

H & H Ceramics, 85 South Street, Pennington, Lymington, Hampshire, SO41 8DY Tel: (01590) 679026 Fax: (01590) 679026 *Ceramic contractors*

H & H Commercial Refinishers, 8 Marsh Lane, Henstridge, Templecombe, Somerset, BA8 0TG Tel: (01963) 363651 Fax: (01963) 363651 *Commercial refinishers services*

▶ H & H Construction, 29 Tangley Lane, Guildford, Surrey, GU3 3JU Tel: (01483) 233885 Fax: (01483) 233885

H & H Construction Co., 4 Brookhollow Way, Wollescote, Stourbridge, West Midlands, DY9 8XJ Tel: (01384) 422587 Fax: (01384) 865780 *Steel erectors*

H & H Electrical Contractors, Suite 14 Stubbings House, Henley Road, Maidenhead, Berkshire, SL6 6QL Tel: (01628) 824131 Fax: (01628) 824131

H & H Fish, Poynernook Road, Aberdeen, AB11 5QX Tel: (01224) 212094 Fax: (01224) 212429 *Fish merchants*

H & H Industrial Fasteners Midlands Ltd, The Paddocks, Somersal Herbert, Ashbourne, Derbyshire, DE6 5PD Tel: (01283) 585473 Fax: (01283) 585625 E-mail: john@h-hfasteners.com *Fastener distributors*

H & H Iron Foundries Ltd, St. Annes Road, Willenhall, West Midlands, WV13 1DY Tel: (01902) 607988 Fax: (01902) 609987 E-mail: chris@hhironfoundries.com *Iron & steel engineers*

H & H Metals Fabrications Ltd, Unit 1, New Railway St, Willenhall, West Midlands, WV13 1LJ Tel: (01902) 635418 Fax: (01902) 635418 *Sheetmetal fabricators*

H & H Patterns, 18 Monument Way West, Woking, Surrey, GU21 5EN Tel: (01483) 769101 Fax: (01483) 740848 E-mail: sales@hhpaytterns.co.uk *Engineers' pattern makers*

H H Pegg Ltd, Elsinore House, 77 Fulham Palace Road, London, W6 8JA Tel: (020) 8237 6000 Fax: (020) 8237 6049 *Paper manufrs*

▶ H & H Property Services, 3 Whittle Road, Ferndown Industrial Estate, Wimborne, Dorset, BH21 7RJ Tel: (07915) 086899 Fax: 01202 877064 E-mail: hhpropertyservices@tiscali.co.uk *Building Company based in Bournemouth covering all aspects of the Building Industry, Domestic and Commercial work undertaken including Insurance Work*

H H S Gluing Systems, Peterborough Business Park, Lynch Wood, Peterborough, PE2 6FZ Tel: (01733) 391333 Fax: (01733) 391555 E-mail: sales@hhsuk.co.uk *Adhesive application systems for hot melt & aqueous dispersions*

▶ H & H Scaffolding Ltd, 33 London Road, Marks Tey, Colchester, CO6 1DZ Tel: (01206) 212860

H & H Services, 25 Albert Road, Eccles, Manchester, M30 9QJ Tel: 0161-707 6250 *Lifting equipment suppliers*

H & H Services, Unit 1 Straw House Farm, Kirkby Road, Ripon, North Yorkshire, HG4 3JU Tel: (01765) 600144 Fax: (01765) 600144 *Water engineering company*

H & H Tool & Engineering Ltd, Unit 4, Harvey Industrial Estate, Shelah Road, Halesowen, West Midlands, B63 3PG Tel: 0121-550 2231 Fax: 0121-585 5789 E-mail: office@hhtools.com *Press tool manufrs*

H Hammond & Sons Ltd, D Little Moor Lane, Loughborough, Leicestershire, LE11 1SF Tel: (01509) 212095 Fax: (01509) 238849 *Builders & contractors*

H Hipkiss & Co. Ltd, Park House, Clapgate Lane, Birmingham, B32 3BL Tel: 0121-421 5777 Fax: 0121-421 5333 E-mail: info@hipkiss.co.uk *Metal pressworkers*

▶ H Hirst & Sons, 350 Lewisham High Street, London, SE13 6LE Tel: (020) 8690 2297

H Humphrey & Co Ltd, Church Road, Romford, RM3 0JA Tel: (01708) 377000 Fax: (01708) 377343 E-mail: services@h-humphrey.com *Mechanical services*

H & I Engineering Ltd, Solway Works, Annan Road, Eastriggs, Annan, Dumfriesshire, DG12 6NJ Tel: (01461) 40500 Fax: (01461) 40801 E-mail: admin@hi-engineering.co.uk *Boiler maintenance & repair services*

▶ H I Quality Steel Castings Ltd, Foundry Street, Wittington Moor, Chesterfield, Derbyshire, S41 9AX Tel: (01246) 260303 Fax: (01246) 260245 E-mail: steven@hiqsc.com *Steel foundry services*

▶ H I Services Ltd, Unit 2a Woodfalls Business Centre, Gravelly Ways, Laddingford, Maidstone, Kent, ME18 6DA Tel: (01622) 873004 Fax: (01622) 873005

H I T Training Ltd, Minerva Mill Innovation Centre, Station Road, Alcester, Warwickshire, B49 5ET Tel: (0800) 0935892 E-mail: info@hittraining.co.uk

H Ireland & Son, 201 Hillhead Rd, Ballyclare, County Antrim, BT39 9LP Tel: (028) 9335 2844 Fax: (028) 9334 2382 E-mail: sales@h-ireland.co.uk *Conveyor belting distributors*

▶ H J Ceramics Ltd, Armytage Road, Brighouse, West Yorkshire, HD6 1PT Tel: (01484) 380000

H J Chard & Sons, Albert Rd, St Philips, Bristol, BS2 0XS Tel: 0117-977 7681 Fax: 0117-971 9802 *Builders merchants & engineers*

H J Contracts General Woodworkers Ltd, 43b Hardingham Road, Hingham, Norwich, NR9 4LX Tel: (01953) 851448 Fax: (01953) 851443 *Furniture manufrs*

H J Cooper Timber Ltd, Thornleigh Trading Estate, Dudley, West Midlands, DY2 8UB Tel: (01384) 254591 Fax: (01384) 237119 E-mail: info@coopersttimber.co.uk *Timber merchants*

H J Enthoven & Sons Ltd, Darley Dale Smelter, South Darley, Matlock, Derbyshire, DE4 2LP Tel: (01629) 733291 Fax: (01629) 733092 Principal Export Areas: Worldwide *Lawyers*

H J Fletcher & Newman Ltd, 5 Bourne Enterprise Centre, Wrotham Road, Borough Green, Sevenoaks, Kent, TN15 8DG Tel: (01732) 886555 Fax: (01732) 884789 E-mail: enquiries@fletcher-newman.co.uk *Musical hardware wholesalers & manufrs*

H & J Forbes Middlesbrough Ltd, 147 Stockton Street, Middlesbrough, Cleveland, TS2 1BU Tel: (01642) 222611 Fax: (01642) 232419 E-mail: frances@forbes-group.demon.co.uk *Licensed bar, bank & shop fitters*

H J Heinz Co. Ltd, South Building, Hayes Park, Hayes, Middlesex, UB4 8AL Tel: (020) 8573 7757 Fax: (020) 8848 2325 E-mail: enquiries@heinz.co.uk *Canned food product manufrs*

H & J Howells, Ardenmore, Marros, Pendine, Carmarthen, Dyfed, SA33 4PN Tel: (01994) 453609 Fax: (01994) 453786 *Welding pressing & rolling services*

H J Jennings & Co., St Francis, Silver Street, Shepton Beauchamp, Ilminster, Somerset, TA19 0JZ Tel: (01460) 240499 Fax: (01460) 242179 *Toolmaking services*

H J M Services, 12 Regent Sqsure, Northampton, NN1 2NQ Tel: (01604) 639792 Fax: (01604) 630919 E-mail: hjm@dial.pipex.com *Electrical & electronic engineers*

H J Mears & Son Boat Builders, The Harbour, Axmouth, Seaton, Devon, EX12 4AA Tel: (01297) 20964 Fax: (01297) 20964 *Boat builders & repairers*

H & J Moore, 3 Nelson Road, Fakenham, Norfolk, NR21 9EN Tel: (01328) 862088 *Bakery suppliers*

H J S J Ltd, Unit 5 Gorslas Road Industrial Estate, Gorslas, Llanelli, Dyfed, SA14 7NN Tel: (01269) 831181 Fax: (01269) 845648 E-mail: sales@hjsjltd.co.uk *Supply, Deliver & Install Sliding Folding Partitions acoustic & glass*

▶ H J S Services, 75 Lifford Lane, Birmingham, B30 3JH Tel: 0121-486 1929 Fax: 0121-486 1930

H & J Speake Ltd, Strawberry Lane Industrial Estate, Strawberry Lane, Willenhall, West Midlands, WV13 3RS Tel: (01902) 607188 Fax: (01902) 635802 E-mail: hjspeake@freenetname.co.uk *Die casting consultants*

H & J Transport Ltd, Blakeley Hall Road, Oldbury, West Midlands, B69 4ET Tel: 0121-552 1078 Fax: 0121-544 8872 *Fuel & oil distributors*

H J Weir Engineering Co. Ltd, Bulwark Industrial Estate, Bulwark, Chepstow, Gwent, NP16 5QZ Tel: (01291) 622036 Fax: (01291) 627350 E-mail: sales@hjweir.co.uk *Textile fabric folding machine manufrs*

H Jenkinsons & Co. Ltd, Kitling Road, Knowsley Business Park, Prescot, Merseyside, L34 9JR Tel: (0870) 7517744 Fax: (0870) 7525374 E-mail: sales@jenkinsons.co.uk *Office supplies distribution services*

▶ H K B Joinery Ltd, Mountney Bridge Industrial Estate, Eastbourne Road, Westham, Pevensey, East Sussex, BN24 5NH Tel: (01323) 762704 Fax: (01323) 740200

H K B Steels Services Ltd, Autobase Industrial Estate, Tipton Road, Tividale, Oldbury, West Midlands, B69 3HU Tel: 0121-557 8361 Fax: 0121-520 8810 E-mail: sales@hkb-steel.co.uk *Steel stockholders*

H & K Joinery Ltd, Moravian Road, Bristol, BS15 8ND Tel: 0117-960 2849 Fax: 0117-961 8250 *Joinery manufrs*

H K L Gaspower Ltd, 260 Windsor Street, Nechells, Birmingham, B7 4DX Tel: 0121-359 6131 Fax: 0121-359 8580 E-mail: shirley@hkl-gaspower.co.uk *Lpg production equipment manufrs*

H K Process Measurement Ltd, Princess Works, Birds Royd Lane, Brighouse, West Yorkshire, HD6 1LQ Tel: (01484) 400334 Fax: (01484) 400779 E-mail: martin.hindle@hkprocess.co.uk *Designers, manufacturers & repairers of all types of scales, weighing equipment & process control equipment*

H & K (Rugby) Ltd, 1 Crosford Lane, Swift Valley, Rugby, Warwickshire, CV21 1QN Tel: (01788) 554000

H K Technologies Ltd, Unit 7 Hadrians Way, Glebe Farm Industrial Estate, Rugby, Warwickshire, CV21 1ST Tel: (01788) 577288 Fax: (01788) 562808 E-mail: admin@hktechnologies.com *Laser marking*

▶ H K Thorburn & Sons, Marjoriebanks, Lochmaben, Lockerbie, Dumfriesshire, DG11 1QH Tel: (01387) 810263 Fax: (01387) 810700 *Builders*

▶ H & K Tools/Fasteners, Office Nos. 7-8 A to Z, Lyon Way, off Greg Street, Reddish, Stockport, Cheshire, SK5 7DH Tel: 0161-474 7100 Fax: 0161-474 7100 E-mail: Enquiries@handktools.co.uk *HandKtools Manchester, UK*Pre-Packed Nails /Fixings / Fasteners /Bolts /Nuts /Staples /Blades /Masonry Anchors /Most Types of Nail Supplied /Packed in Tubs or Bags/fixings/diy/plumbing/copper fittings/ tools/boilers/sanitary/bath suitefor £180. Nationwide Supplier, Based in Northwest, Manchester, UK.**

▶ H K V Engineering, 16 Crawford House, West Avenue, Wigston, Leicestershire, LE18 2FB Tel: 0116-288 7751 Fax: 0116-288 7751 E-mail: carolrobinson@aol.com *Engineering components manufrs*

H Kane & Son, 31 Legavara Road, Ballintoy, Ballycastle, County Antrim, BT54 6NG Tel: (028) 2076 2613 Fax: (028) 2076 2027 E-mail: sales@hunterkaneandson.com *Agricultural machinery sales & services*

H Kilburn Ltd, 18 The Arcade, New Market Hall, Huddersfield, HD1 2UJ Tel: (01484) 423565 Fax: (01484) 423565 *Retail food & restaurant wholesalers*

H Kimber Friction Ltd, Printing Trades House, Bond Street, Southampton, SO14 5QA Tel: (023) 8022 6577 Fax: (023) 8063 1154 E-mail: pscott.hkimber@auto-net.co.uk *Brake lining wholesalers*

H Kuhnke, 21 Abbey Enterprise Centre, Premier Way, Romsey, Hampshire, SO51 9AQ Tel: (01794) 514445 Fax: (01794) 513514 E-mail: sales@kuhnke.co.uk *Pneumatic control systems manufrs*

H L, H L House, Riverside Business Park, Dockfield Road, Shipley, West Yorkshire, BD17 7AD Tel: (01274) 531709 Fax: (01274) 594578 E-mail: jackie.perry@hl-rim.co.uk *Point of purchase display manufrs*

H L Brown & Son Ltd, Leopold Street, Sheffield, S1 1LZ Tel: 0114-272 5440 Fax: 0114-272 4580 E-mail: info@hl-brown.co.uk *Diamond merchants & retail jewellers*

H L C Engineering Ltd, 4 Harvey Road, Burnt Mills Industrial Estate, Basildon, Essex, SS13 1QJ Tel: (01268) 590080 Fax: (01268) 590141 E-mail: steelwork@hlcengineering.com *Steel fabricators & installers*

H L C (Wood Products) Ltd, High Road, Needham, Harleston, Norfolk, IP20 9LB Tel: (01379) 852873 Fax: (01379) 852761 E-mail: sales@hlcwood.demon.co.uk *Timber pallet & case manufrs*

H & L Ceilings Ltd, The Old Workhouse, Hudds Vale Road, Bristol, BS5 7HY Tel: 0117-941 4222 Fax: 0117-941 2678 E-mail: johnhawke_hl@hotmail.com *Suspended ceilings*

H L D Ltd, Old Shipyard, Gainsborough, Lincolnshire, DN21 1NG Tel: (01427) 611800 Fax: (01427) 612867 E-mail: technical@hld.co.uk *Design & manufacturer of external timber structures*

▶ H L Friel & Son Ltd, 47-49 Mearns Street, Greenock, Renfrewshire, PA15 4BN Tel: (01475) 722056

H & L Garages Ltd, Grange Lane North, Scunthorpe, South Humberside, DN16 1BT Tel: (01724) 856655 Fax: (01724) 868493 E-mail: info@handlgarages.co.uk *HGV garage*

H L Hazeltine Aveley Ltd, Arcany Road, South Ockendon, Essex, RM15 5TB Tel: (01708) 852030 Fax: (01708) 856464 E-mail: hazelstinest@aol.com *Manufacturer of stainless steel products*

H L N Supplies, 67 Upper Accommodation Road, Leeds, LS9 8JP Tel: 0113-240 2000 Fax: 0113-240 4000 E-mail: sales@hlnsupplies.co.uk *Plastics fabricators*

H L Plastics Ltd, Duffield Road Industrial Estate, Little Eaton, Derby, DE21 5EH Tel: (01332) 832389 Fax: (01332) 830867 E-mail: sales@hlplasticsltd.co.uk *Plastic extrusion manufacturers & plastic engineering services*

H & L Sims, Unit 1-2 Business Park, Oldfield Lane, Wisbech, Cambridgeshire, PE13 2RJ Tel: (01945) 583682 Fax: (01945) 463754 E-mail: les4154s@aol.com *Control panel manufacturers & electrical engineer*

H L Tool Co Ltd, Gardenvale Mill, Greenfield Road, Colne, Lancashire, BB8 9PD Tel: (01282) 864850 Fax: (01282) 870244 E-mail: sales@hltool.co.uk *Press tool jig & fixtures manufrs*

H Langdon & Son Chatham Ltd, 51-53 Second Avenue, Chatham, Kent, ME4 5BA Tel: (01634) 842485 Fax: (01634) 831037 *Steel fabrications*

H Lee & Son, The Woodyard, Belle Vue Road, Ashbourne, Derbyshire, DE6 1AT Tel: (01335) 342530 *Timber merchants & joiners*

H Lesser & Sons London Ltd, 43-53 Markfield Road, London, N15 4QA Tel: (020) 8275 6400 Fax: (020) 8275 6401 E-mail: info@hlesser.co.uk *Woollen merchants*

H M B, 24 Springfield Cresent, Harpenden, Hertfordshire, AL5 4LF Tel: (01582) 712889 Fax: (01582) 760680 E-mail: hb@hmbolg.demon.co.uk *Computer software house*

H M B Machinists & Engineers Ltd, 7 Meadow Lane, Alfreton, Derbyshire, DE55 7EZ Tel: (01773) 835868 Fax: (01773) 520359 *General engineers*

H M Brand, 28 Trades Lane, Dundee, DD1 3ET Tel: (01382) 226576 Fax: (01382) 225971 E-mail: harrymbrand@aol.com *Engineering supplies distributors*

▶ H M C Property Maintenance, 17 Perry Road, Tiptree, Colchester, CO5 0UA Tel: (0870) 9009960 Fax: (0870) 9009970 E-mail: andrea@hmcproperty.com *Industrial, retail & residential maintenance services*

H M Clothing Co., Sycamore House, Crawford Street, Rochdale, Lancashire, OL16 5RS Tel: (01706) 715512 Fax: (01706) 715512 *Clothing manufrs*

H & M Compressors & Pumps Ltd, B Enterprise Centre, Paycocke Road, Basildon, Essex, SS14 3DY Tel: (01268) 531288 Fax: (01268) 532013 E-mail: hmcompressos@tiscali.co.uk *Compressors & pump distributors*

H M Computing Ltd, Harmac House, Enigma Park, Malvern, Worcestershire, WR14 1GP Tel: (01684) 581850 Fax: (01684) 581851 E-mail: sales@hmcomputing.net *Design computers*

▶ H & M Consulting Ltd, 61 George Street, Perth, PH1 5LB Tel: (0870) 7606897

▶ H M D Group plc, Olympia House, 4 Garnet Close, Watford, WD24 7JY Tel: (01923) 237012 Fax: (01923) 817421 E-mail: sales@hmdgroup.com *Screen, digital & litho process computer aided design system & pick & pack services*

H M Doors, 620 Bradford Road, Batley, West Yorkshire, WF17 8HF Tel: (01924) 440114 Fax: (01924) 477761 *Door manufrs*

H M Dunlop, 35 Barnish Road, Kells, Ballymena, County Antrim, BT42 3PA Tel: (028) 2589 2194 Fax: (028) 2589 2194 *Butchers suppliers*

H M E Technology, Priory House, Saxon Park, Hanbury Road, Stoke Prior, Bromsgrove, Worcestershire, B60 4AD Tel: (01527) 839000 Fax: (01527) 839001 E-mail: contactus@hme-tech.com *Educational equipment for schools Technology Departments offering turnkey solutions with full installation and servicing. HME Technology have been in existence since 1984 and we are the market leaders in our product range. We supply a full range of equipment including metal, woodworking and plastics facilities. *HME's range of products include gas fired Heat Treatment equipment including Forges, Brazing Hearths, Furnaces and support producers of Welding Benches, Fume Extraction Systems, Kilns and associated extraction, Moulding/Acid Pickle Benches, Woodworking Equipment, Wood Dust Extraction Systems, Jewellery Benches/ Torches, PCB Equipment, Gas Safety Systems, Metal Finishing and CNC machines. We also*

continued

Company Information

continuation
*supply Fume Cupboards and Ventilation Systems for Science Departments, and offer a LEV testing service for both Science and Design Technology Departments. In our range we also supply bulk materials handling equipment to industry including Belt Cleaners and Air Blasters.**

H M Electric Motor Repair & Sales, 65 Nile Street, London, N1 7RD Tel: (020) 7253 9496 Fax: (020) 7490 2743 *Industrial motor repairers*

H M Electrics, 95 Glen Road, Maghera, County Londonderry, BT46 5JG Tel: (028) 7964 2112 Fax: (028) 7964 3945 E-mail: enquiries@hmelectrics.com *Electrical contractors*

H M Fashions, 10 Sycamore Road, Handsworth, Birmingham, B21 0QL Tel: 0121-554 1068 Fax: 0121-523 4891 E-mail: mandeepranu84@hotmail.com *H M Fashion Ltd is a School garment manufacturer who specialise in boys trousers.*

H M Foam Distributors Ltd, Shelburne Road, Calne, Wiltshire, SN11 8ER Tel: (01249) 816686 Fax: (01249) 817199 E-mail: h_m_foam@lineone.net *Foam converters, upholstery supplies, upholsterers & coach trimmers*

▶ H & M Freight Services Ltd, Pier Road, Feltham, Middlesex, TW14 0TW Tel: (020) 8844 0088 Fax: (020) 8844 0099 E-mail: info@hmfreight.co.uk *Freight forwarding*

H & M Graphics, 1 Kinneil Road, Bo'ness, West Lothian, EH51 0AY Tel: (01506) 829388 Fax: (01506) 829393 E-mail: hm.graphics@btconnect.com *Sign manufrs*

H M Hampson Ltd, 29-31 Shaw Street, St. Helens, Merseyside, WA10 1DG Tel: (01744) 23881 Fax: (01744) 453485 *Tool merchants*

H M Howard & Sons, Manor Farm, Close Lane, Marston, Devizes, Wiltshire, SN10 5SN Tel: (01380) 723986 Fax: (01380) 730600 E-mail: howardagri@btconnect.com *Tractor suppliers*

H M James & Sons Ltd, 736 Romford Road, London, E12 6BT Tel: (020) 8477 1000 Fax: (020) 8478 4091 E-mail: mail@hmjames.co.uk *Sanitary ware specialists*

▶ H M L Group Ltd, Unit 76 Riverside Estate, Sir Thomas Longley Road, Medway City Estate, Rochester, Kent, ME2 4BH Tel: (01634) 715120 Fax: (01634) 715001

H M Lowe & Son Ltd, 476 Garrison Lane, Birmingham, B9 4NT Tel: 0121-772 0330 Fax: 0121-771 3759 E-mail: enquiries@hmlowe.co.uk *Timber merchants & allied products*

H M Machinery UK Ltd, 41 Scholey Close, Halling, Rochester, Kent, ME2 1JZ Tel: (01634) 244600 Fax: (01634) 244599 *Wholesales & resellers of engineering machinery*

H M Plant Ltd, Monkton Business Park North, Hebburn, Tyne & Wear, NE31 2JZ Tel: 0191-430 8400 Fax: 0191-430 8500 E-mail: info@hmplant.ltd.uk *Industrial plant services* Also at: Branches throughout the U.K.

H M Plant Ltd, 964 Weston Road, Slough Trading Estate, Slough, SL1 4HR Tel: (01753) 213900 Fax: (01753) 213901 E-mail: info@hmplant.ltd.uk *Excavator manufrs*

H & M Plating Ltd, 37 Little Green Lane, Birmingham, B9 5AY Tel: 0121-773 6931 Fax: 0121-773 6931 *Electroplating services*

▶ H M Price Ltd, Gelli Wern Ganol Farm, Felindre, Swansea, SA5 7PJ Tel: (01792) 885396 Fax: (01792) 885801

H M Printers Ltd, The Cromwell Centre, 24-30 Minerva Road, London, NW10 6HH Tel: (020) 8965 4621 Fax: (020) 8965 4181 E-mail: print@hmprinters.com *Printers*

H M S Designs, Wenlock Way, Leicester, LE4 9HU Tel: 0116-274 1244 Fax: 0116-276 4086 E-mail: hmsdesigns@freeuk.com *Shop fitters*

▶ H M S Highway Maintenance Specialists Ltd, Bruntingthorpe Industrial Estate, Lutterworth, Leicestershire, LE17 5QZ Tel: 0116-279 9099 E-mail: sales@hmslimited.co.uk

H M S L Group Ltd, Mayflower House, 11 Caxton Hill, Hertford, SG13 7NE Tel: (01992) 500555 Fax: (01992) 554241 E-mail: sales@hmsl.co.uk *Document scanning & data management services*

H M Sales, Templewood Estate, Stock Road, West Hanningfield, Chelmsford, CM2 8LA Tel: (01277) 840172 Fax: (01702) 333492 E-mail: info@hmsales.co.uk *Aircraft dismantlers*

H M Sitec Ltd, St. Georges Lodge, 33 Oldfield Road, Bath, BA2 3NE Tel: (01225) 428221 Fax: (01225) 444697 E-mail: info@hmbath.com *Design engineering consultants* Also at: Branches throughout the U.K.

H M Skenfield Ltd, Laneside Mills, Laneside, Morley, Leeds, LS27 7NR Tel: 0113-253 4120 Fax: 0113-253 4120 *Precision engineers & mechanical design engineers*

H M Stainless Fabrications Ltd, 227 Bradford Road, Batley, West Yorkshire, WF17 6JL Tel: (01924) 266422 Fax: (01924) 266423 E-mail: david.keylorson@btconnect.com *Manufacturers of catering equipment & lab furniture*

H M T Ltd, Unit 7, Bessemer Park, Bessemer Road, Basingstoke, Hampshire, RG21 3NB Tel: (01256) 819977 Fax: (01256) 819988 E-mail: hampshire@hmtplastics.com *Injection tool manufrs*

H M T Plastics Ltd, 31a Framfield Road, Uckfield, East Sussex, TN22 5AH Tel: (01825) 769393 Fax: (01825) 769494 E-mail: hmtp@aol.com *Manufacturers of key fobs & tags (plastic bag)*

H M Temple & Co. Ltd, 111 Broughton Street, Edinburgh, EH1 3RZ Tel: 0131-556 4791 Fax: 0131-556 3609 *Wholesale*

▶ H Mcclelland & Sons, Unit 7, Cadzow Industrial Estate, Hamilton, Lanarkshire, ML3 7QU Tel: (01698) 283314 Fax: (01698) 286677 E-mail: info@mcclellandremovals.co.uk *Removal Contractor*

▶ H Mcmurray & Son Ltd, Kilmacolm Road, Bridge of Weir, Renfrewshire, PA11 3PU Tel: (01505) 613289

H Mell & Son, Old Trent Road, Beckingham, Doncaster, South Yorkshire, DN10 4PY Tel: (01427) 848210 Fax: (01427) 848869 *Agricultural & on-shore oil field*

▶ H Mills & Sons Ltd, Bleak Hill Sidings, Mansfield, Nottinghamshire, NG18 5EP Tel: (01623) 624015

H Mitton Ltd, 451 Cleckheaton Road, Low Moor, Bradford, West Yorkshire, BD12 0HS Tel: (01274) 691177 Fax: (01274) 691188 E-mail: projects@mittonmechanical.com *Heating & plumbing ventilating contractors*

H Morrell & Sons Ltd, 173-175 Kensington Lane, London, SE11 4HG Tel: (020) 7735 1681 Fax: (020) 7587 0533 *Builders*

H Mullins Earby Ltd, Western Road, Jarrow, Tyne & Wear, NE32 3DB Tel: 0191-489 1617 Fax: 0191-428 0375 E-mail: h.mullins@mullins.co.uk *Tube manipulation & bending services*

H N Cooper, 353-355 High Street, West Bromwich, West Midlands, B70 9QG Tel: 0121-553 0836 Fax: 0121-553 0836 *Commercial stationers & printers*

H N D UK Ltd, Unit 15 Shrub Hill Industrial Estate, Worcester, WR4 9EL Tel: (01905) 29294 E-mail: info@hnd-uk.com *Import merchants & marble table manufrs*

H N L Engineering Ltd, Dukesway, Teesside Industrial Estate, Stockton-On-Tees, Cleveland, TS17 9LT Tel: (01642) 765553 Fax: (01642) 762899 E-mail: sales@hnl-uk.com Principal Export Areas: Asia Pacific, Central Asia, Middle East, Central/East Europe, West Europe & North America *Manufacturers of transmitters, switches & manifold valves*

H N T Creative, 70-74 Stewarts Road, London, SW8 4DE Tel: (020) 7720 0223 Fax: (020) 7622 3666 *Designers of furniture*

H O Bowley, Hudson Street, Loughborough, Leicestershire, LE11 1EJ Tel: (01509) 212161 Fax: (01509) 212167 *Knitted fabric manufrs*

▶ H O H Internet Consultancy, Linden House, Springfield Road, Quenington, Cirencester, Gloucestershire, GL7 5BU Tel: (08707) 606737 E-mail: info@hoh.co.uk *Web site development service*

▶ H O S Plant Ltd, School Farm Buildings, School Road, Langham, Colchester, CO4 5PB Tel: (01206) 273131 Fax: (01206) 271919 E-mail: sales@hosplant.co.uk *Plant & equipment retailers*

H P C Engineering Plc, Victoria Gardens, Victoria Gardens Industrial Estate, Burgess Hill, West Sussex, RH15 9RQ Tel: (01444) 241671 Fax: (01444) 247587 E-mail: peterhowell@hpcplc.co.uk *Precision engineering compressor supply*

H P C Engineering Plc, Victoria Gardens, Victoria Gardens Industrial Estate, Burgess Hill, West Sussex, RH15 9RQ Tel: (01444) 241671 Fax: (01444) 247304 E-mail: info@hpcplc.co.uk *Manufacturers of air compressors*

H P C Services Ltd, Unit 14 Solomon Road, Ilkeston, Derbyshire, DE7 5UA Tel: 0115-932 3773 Fax: 0115-932 2857 E-mail: sales@slidinghead.com *Sliding-head precision turning specialists*

H P Chemie Pelzer UK Ltd, Speke Hall Avenue, Liverpool, L24 1UU Tel: 0151-448 2300 Fax: (08702) 429393 *Acoustics for the car industry*

H P D Software Ltd, Aspley House, 176 Upper Richmond Road, London, SW15 2SH Tel: (020) 8780 6800 Fax: (020) 8780 6801 E-mail: sales@hpdsoftware.com *Computer software house*

H P Design Jet Repair, Park Farm, Station Road, Basingstoke, Hants, RG23 7EH Tel: (0870) 7524808 Fax: (0870) 7524809 E-mail: info@re-solution.gb.com *HP laser jet printer & design services*

▶ H & P Double Glazing Ltd, Kelsall Street, Oldham, OL9 6HR Tel: 0161-678 9144 E-mail: enquires@hpdoubleglazing.co.uk *Ground floor framing, Curtain walling, Ground floor treatment, Casement windows, Turn and tilt, Top swing fully reversible, Domestic, Commercial, Sliding, ISO 9002, guarantee, Shop fronts, doors, insulation, Ventilation, Draught proof, Security features, Secondary Double glazing, Structural aluminium, Speed installation, FENSA, Registered, Maintenance, Architectural aluminium systems, Reversible, Disabled access, Glazing systems, Patio doors, Patios, Conservatories, installers, Hardwood frames, Upvc, Polyester, Pilkington K glass, AIMS scheme, Government quality mark scheme, Supply, trade, Bungalow, Porch, Porches, Residential, French, Decorative, Safety, Burglar, anti-intruder, alarm, features, replacement, Cold, External, noise, Manchester, North, East, West, South, Rochdale, Bury, Prestwich, Oldham Athletic FC, sponsors*

H P F Energy Services, 1 Links Place, Aberdeen, AB11 5DY Tel: (01224) 584588 Fax: (01224) 211938 E-mail: sales@hpf-energy.com *Pipeline fittings & flange stockholders*

H P F Energy Services, 3 Kinwarton Farm Road, Arden Forest Industrial Estate, Alcester, Warwickshire, B49 6EH Tel: (01789) 761212 Fax: (01789) 761222 E-mail: alcester@hpf-energy.com *Pipeline, tube fittings & flange stockholders*

H P F Energy Services Ltd, 2-4 Queen Elizabeth Avenue, Hillington Industrial Estate, Glasgow, G52 4NQ Tel: 0141-882 4611 Fax: 0141-883 0826 E-mail: glasgow@hpf-energy.com *Stockists & distributors of pipe fittings*

H P F Energy Services, 99 Sadler Foster Way, Teeside Industrial Estate, Stockton-on-Tees, Cleveland, TS17 9JY Tel: (01642) 750009 Fax: (01642) 750044 E-mail: thornaby@hpf-energy.com *Pipeline fittings stockholders*

▶ H P Foils Ltd, 6B Coopers Way, Temple Farm Industrial Estate, Southend-On-Sea, SS2 5TE Tel: (01702) 602444

H P Foods Ltd, 253 Tower Rd, Birmingham, B6 5AB Tel: 0121-359 4911 Fax: 0121 3595452 *Sauce manufr*

▶ H & P Freightways Ltd, 1203 Hedon Road, Hull, HU9 5LY Tel: (01482) 702185 Fax: (01482) 701722 E-mail: enquiries@hpfreightways.com

▶ H & P Hire, 5 Black Stick Road, Killyhevlin Industrial Estate, Enniskillen, County Fermanagh, BT74 4EB Tel: (028) 6632 2250 Fax: (028) 6632 3326 E-mail: ronnie@handphire.co.uk *Plant & tool hire*

H P M Ltd, Unit 9, Ascot Industrial Estate, Lenton St, Nottingham, NG10 5DL Tel: 0115-939 0716 Fax: 0115-949 1106 E-mail: info@hpmltd.com *Plastic moulding manufrs*

▶ H P Mouldings Ltd, Units 7-8 Clarkes Meadow, Bromyard Road, Tenbury Wells Business Park, Tenbury Wells, Worcestershire, WR15 8FA Tel: (01584) 819739 Fax: (01584) 811396 E-mail: colin@hpmouldings.com *Rotational moulding manufrs*

H Pickles Ltd, Lincoln Road, Cressex Business Park, High Wycombe, Buckinghamshire, HP12 3RQ Tel: (01494) 520613 Fax: (01494) 465373 E-mail: sales@scsaws.co.uk *Saw manufrs*

▶ H Plus H Celcon Ltd, 3 Quartermaster Road, West Wilts Trading Estate, Westbury, Wiltshire, BA13 4JT Tel: (01732) 886333 Fax: (01373) 827631 *Manufacturers air crete building blocks*

H Pollock Ltd, 13 Shudehill, Manchester, M4 2AF Tel: 0161-834 3103 Fax: 0161-839 6397 E-mail: stephen@pollock79.freeserve.co.uk *Diamond & wholesale jewellers*

H Pontifex & Sons Ltd, Pepper Road, Leeds, LS10 2NJ Tel: 0113-271 3411 Fax: 0113-277 7985 E-mail: info@pontifex.co.uk Principal Export Areas: Worldwide *Stainless steel vessel fabricators*

H Postill, The Old Chapel, Fangfoss, York, YO41 5QP Tel: (01759) 368209 *Furniture manufrs*

H Powell Ltd, Booth Street, Smethwick, West Midlands, B66 2PF Tel: 0121-555 5527 Fax: 0121-555 6208 *Steel stockholders & shearers*

H Preston, 103 Worcester Road, Malvern, Worcestershire, WR14 1EP Tel: (01684) 575486 Fax: (01684) 575594 E-mail: jpreston@hpreston.co.uk *Video services sales & hire*

H Q C Ltd, North Florida Road, Haydock, St. Helens, Merseyside, WA11 9UB Tel: (01942) 722770 Fax: (01942) 270235 E-mail: hqcsales@hqc.co.uk *Precision sheet metal work assemblies manufrs*

H Q Fibre Products Ltd, Blofield Road, Lingwood, Norwich, NR13 4AJ Tel: (01603) 713972 Fax: (01603) 713972 *Carbon composite mouldings manufrs*

H Q Industrial Supplies Ltd, 44a Masters Lane, Halesowen, West Midlands, B62 9HL Tel: 0121-559 3776 Fax: 0121-559 3777 *Work wear retailer*

H Quibell & Sons, 20 Hockley Street, Birmingham, B18 6BL Tel: 0121-554 1250 E-mail: enquiries@hquibell-silversmiths.co.uk *Manufacturing silversmiths*

H R Adcock Ltd, 17 Gelders Hall Road, Loughborough, Leicestershire, LE12 9NH Tel: (01509) 502493 Fax: (01509) 650442 *Precision engineers*

H & R Boilercare, 58a Amwell Street, Hoddesdon, Hertfordshire, EN11 8UA Tel: (01992) 463919 Fax: (01992) 451326 E-mail: shaun.raynor@ntlworld.com

H & R Chempharm, Tipton Works, Dudley Road, Tipton, West Midlands, DY4 8EH Tel: 0121-522 0100 Fax: 0121-522 0115 E-mail: info@hur-chempharm.com *Lubricating oil & wax manufrs*

▶ H R Dashboards, 22A Clarence Road, Southend-On-Sea, SS1 1AN Tel: (01702) 342266 Fax: (01702) 342266 *Software developers*

H R Denne Ltd, 40 Bedford Street, Belfast, BT2 7FF Tel: (028) 9024 2866 Fax: (028) 9033 3117 E-mail: dennesbel@btconnect.com *Shirt manufrs*

H & R ESP, Witan Gate House, 500-600 Witan Gate, Milton Keynes, MK9 1ES Tel: (01908) 853596 Fax: (01908) 853896 E-mail: wethers@bp.com *Wax suppliers*

H R Filtration & Co., The Green Barn Complex, The Scarr, Newent, Gloucestershire, GL18 1DQ Tel: (01531) 820320 Fax: (01531) 822253 E-mail: sales@hrfiltration.com *Filter bag manufrs*

H R Fire & Safety Ltd, Forge House, Whitehall Industrial Estate, Whitehall Road, Leeds, LS12 5JB Tel: 0113-279 4078 Fax: 0113-279 4768 E-mail: darren@hrfireandsafety.co.uk *Fire fighting equipment engineers*

▶ H & R Gray Haulage Ltd, 1a Bandeath Industrial Estate, Throsk, Stirling, FK7 7NP Tel: (01786) 489111 Fax: (01786) 489222

H R Holfeld Belfast Ltd, Altona Road, Lisburn, County Antrim, BT27 5RU Tel: (028) 9267 7523 Fax: (028) 9266 0263 *Water & sewage engineers*

H & R Interiors, 155 High Street, Rhyl, Clwyd, LL18 1UF Tel: (01745) 344443 Fax: (01745) 343303 *Suspending ceiling contractors*

H R International Crushing & Screening Ltd, Huntingdon Court, Huntingdon Way, Measham, Swadlincote, Derbyshire, DE12 7NQ Tel: (01530) 272799 Fax: (01530) 272787 E-mail: hril@lineone.net Principal Export Areas: Central/East Europe & West Europe *Quarry plant*

H R Mann Ltd, Cape Road Industrial Estate, Cattell Road, Cape Industrial Estate, Warwick, CV34 4JN Tel: (01926) 492132 Fax: (01604) 750152

H R N Tractors Ltd, South Road, Insch, Aberdeenshire, AB52 6XF Tel: (01464) 820661 Fax: (01464) 820082 E-mail: sales@hrntractors.com *Agricultural machinery distributors*

H R N Tractors Ltd, Denside, Turriff, Aberdeenshire, AB53 8BJ Tel: (01888) 562101 Fax: (01888) 568940 E-mail: mail@hrntractors.com *Repair services*

H R Nicholson, 19 Ballyardle Road, Kilkeel, Newry, County Down, BT34 4JX Tel: (028) 4176 3104 Fax: (028) 4176 9216 E-mail: harold@hillsideinteriors.freeserve.co.uk *Kitchen furniture manufrs*

H R P Ltd, Rougham Industrial Estate, Rougham, Bury St. Edmunds, Suffolk, IP30 9XA Tel: (01359) 271131 Fax: (01359) 272225 E-mail: sales@hrpltd.co.uk *Refrigerator component & spare parts distributors*

H R P Ltd, 140 St. Andrews Road, Glasgow, G41 1PP Tel: 0141-420 1606 Fax: 0141-420 1755 E-mail: glasgow@hrpltd.co.uk *Refrigeration & air conditioning wholesale*

H R P Ltd, National Road, Hunslet Business Park, Leeds, LS10 1TD Tel: 0113-277 5000 Fax: 0113-270 6800 *Refrigeration equipment distributors*

H R Refridgeration Ltd, 43 Morpeth Road, London, E9 7LD Tel: (020) 8525 1151 Fax: (020) 8525 1420 *Refrigeration*

H R S Heat Exchangers Ltd, 10-12 Caxton Way, Watford Business Park, Watford, WD18 8TX Tel: (01923) 232335 Fax: (01923) 230266 E-mail: mail@hrs.co.uk *Heat exchanger & transfer equipment manufrs*

H R & W E Burnell & Son, Bathealton, Taunton, Somerset, TA4 2BG Tel: (01398) 361266 *Agricultural contractors*

H R Wallingford Ltd, Howbery Park, Wallingford, Oxfordshire, OX10 8BA Tel: (01491) 835381 Fax: (01491) 832233 E-mail: info@hrwallingford.co.uk *Environmental research consultants & testing services*

H R West, 19 Melton Road, Burton Lazars, Melton Mowbray, Leicestershire, LE14 2UR Tel: (01664) 562182 Fax: (01664) 567862 *Sports equipment distributors & manufrs*

H Raley & Sons, Hill Farm, Escrick Road, Stillingfleet, York, YO19 6HT Tel: (01904) 728665 Fax: (01904) 728665 *Agricultural contractors*

H Reis Ltd, Powke Lane, Cradley Heath, West Midlands, B64 5QF Tel: (01384) 567727 Fax: (01384) 410317 E-mail: terry.reis@chromebar.co.uk *Hard Chrome Plating*Centreless Grinding*Stainless Chrome Bar*Hard Chrome Tubes* Also at: Brierley Hill

H Ripley & Co., Apex Way, Hailsham, East Sussex, BN27 3WA Tel: (01323) 440672 Fax: (01323) 841282 E-mail: jason@hripleys.co.uk *Scrap merchants*

H Rothwell & Co. Ltd, Duke Street, Rochdale, Lancashire, OL12 0LS Tel: (01706) 649231 Fax: (01706) 647906 E-mail: sales@rothwells.co.uk *Engineers' supplies & distributors*

▶ H S Ltd, Fair View, Drayton, Swineshead, Boston, Lincolnshire, PE20 3JU Tel: (01205) 820044

H S B Engineering, Marycutler Rd, Portlethen, Aberdeen, AB12 4RB Tel: (01224) 784785 Fax: (01224) 784785 *General engineers*

H S B Inspection Quality Ltd, Cairo Mill, Greenacres Road, Oldham, OL4 3JA Tel: (01928) 579595 Fax: 0161-621 5680 E-mail: sales@hsbiq.com *Engineering inspection consultants*

H S Bassett & Son Ltd, Unit 13 Coronet Way, Swansea Enterprise Park, Swansea, SA6 8RH Tel: (01792) 790022 Fax: (01792) 790033 E-mail: sonia@hsbassett.co.uk *Laminated plastics fabricators*

H S C Ltd, Welsh Harp, Trelystan, Leighton, Welshpool, Powys, SY21 8JB Tel: (01938) 570428 Fax: (01938) 570653 E-mail: enquiries@hyteq.com *Computer software developer*

H & S Computer Solutions Ltd, 9-10 Gilchrist Close, Norwich, NR4 3AT Tel: (01603) 617677 Fax: (01603) 617144 *Computer maintenance*

▶ H & S Contractors Ltd, Kingsnorth Industrial Estate, Hoo, Rochester, Kent, ME3 9ND Tel: (01634) 253545 Fax: (01634) 251145 E-mail: mail@hscontractors.co.uk

H & S Enamelling (U K) Ltd, Unit 10, Highbridge Industrial Estate, Oxford Rd, Uxbridge, Middlesex, UB8 1LX Tel: (01895) 233251 Fax: (01895) 810800 E-mail: sales@hsenamelling.co.uk *Powder coating & stove enamellers*

H S Fishing 2000 Ltd, Sutton Road, Great Yarmouth, Norfolk, NR30 3NA Tel: (01493) 858118 Fax: (01493) 859517 E-mail: hsfishing@gy2000.fsnet.co.uk *Fish curing & smoking*

H S G Packing Cases Ltd, Long Row, New Works Road, Low Moor, Bradford, West Yorkshire, BD12 0QN Tel: (01274) 601137 Fax: (01274) 678597 E-mail: sales@hsg-packing-cases.co.uk *Heavy duty & conventional carton suppliers*

H S G Pump Services, Unit 13 Riverbank Enterprise Centre, Scout Hill Road, Dewsbury, West Yorkshire, WF13 3RQ Tel: (01924) 453547 Fax: (01924) 452009 E-mail: haj@hsgpumpservices.com *Pump maintenance & repairers*

▶ H S H Coldstores, Birchin Way, Grimsby, South Humberside, DN31 2SG Tel: (01472) 264900 Fax: (01472) 347984 *Cold storage & transport services*

H S H Leisure, Llwyn Coed, Rhydyfelin, Aberystwyth, Dyfed, SY23 4QD Tel: (07767) 632913 Fax: (01970) 624080 *Bouncy castle suppliers*

H S Harbon & Sons Ltd, Gordon Street, Doncaster, South Yorkshire, DN1 1RS Tel: (01302) 361140 Fax: (01302) 325745 E-mail: peter@harbon.co.uk *Electrical engineers & contractors*

H S Harper & Sons, 11 Kinallen Road, Dromara, Dromore, County Down, BT25 2NL Tel: (028) 9753 2677 Fax: (028) 9753 3555 *Agricultural merchants*

H S Lifting Services Ltd, 12 Canyon Road, Netherton Industrial Estate, Wishaw, Lanarkshire, ML2 0EG Tel: (01698) 327811 Fax: (01698) 327838 *Lifting gear manufrs*

▶ H S M Computers, 1 Afan Valley Close, Neath, West Glamorgan, SA11 3AJ Tel: (01639) 761503 Fax: (0871) 2771665 E-mail: sales@hsmcomputers.co.uk

H & S Partners Ltd, Forstal Road, Aylesford, Kent, ME20 7AD Tel: (01622) 717387 Fax: (01622) 710211 E-mail: hspartners@btconnect.com *Carton manufrs*

H S Pipequipment Ltd, Red Shute Hill Industrial Estate, Hermitage, Thatcham, Berkshire, RG18 9QL Tel: (01635) 201329 Fax: (01635) 201941 E-mail: info@hso.co.uk *Oil & gas valve distributors* Also at: Aberdeen, Middlesbrough & Newport Gwent

H S Pipequipment (Aberdeen) Ltd, Unit 2 Hillview Road, East Tullos Industrial Estate, Aberdeen, AB12 3HB Tel: (01224) 249900 Fax: (01224) 249222 *Valve agents, stockholders & distributors*

H & S Polythene Ltd, 36 Redburn Industrial Estate, Woodall Road, Enfield, Middlesex, EN3 4LE Tel: (020) 8050217 Fax: (020) 8050227 E-mail: sales@hspolythene.com *Polythene bag manufrs*

▶ H S Realisations Ltd, Unit 10 Locomotion Industrial Estate, Chorley New Road, Horwich, Bolton, BL6 5UE Tel: (01204) 695989 Fax: (01204) 669343

▶ H S Retail Design Ltd, Tadman Street, Wakefield, West Yorkshire, WF1 5QU Tel: (01924) 371333 Fax: (01924) 372191 E-mail: enquiries@tjhowley.co.uk *Shop fitting manufrs*

▶ H & S Roe & Sons Ltd, Roe House, Boundry Lane, South Hykeham, Lincoln, LN6 9NQ Tel: (01522) 681542 Fax: (01522) 680199 *Plant hire services*

H S Rowe & Partners, Building 80, First Avenue, Pensnett Trading Estate, Kingswinford, West Midlands, DY6 7FQ Tel: (01384) 293862 Fax: (01384) 271805 E-mail: sales@buxtonhayes.co.uk *Precision turned parts manufrs*

H S S Ltd, 344 King Street, Hammersmith, Hammersmith, London, W6 0RX Tel: (020) 8748 6740 Fax: (020) 8563 2483 *Tool equipment hire*

H S S Lift & Shift, Eastern Avenue Industrial Estate, Eastern Avenue, Dunstable, Bedfordshire, LU5 4JY Tel: (01582) 673256 Fax: (01582) 411320 *Construction plant equipment & lifting equipment hire*

H S S Lift & Shift, Unit 12 Industrial Estate, Thomas Road, London, E14 7BN Tel: (020) 7987 4787 Fax: (020) 7987 4887 *Lift hiring equipment*

H S S Lift & Shift P.L.C., Unit 4, Aquarius Business Park, Priestley Way, London, NW2 7AN Tel: (020) 8830 8080 Fax: (020) 8452 1050 *Equipment hire*

H S S Lift & Shift, Pryme Works, Silvercroft Street, Manchester, M15 4WG Tel: 0161-839 6122 *Tool hire*

H S S Lift & Shift, 169-177 Lincoln Road, Peterborough, PE1 2PN Tel: (01733) 313123 Fax: (01733) 313377 *Lifting Gear Hire*

H S S Lift & Shift, 6 Colville Court, Winwick Quay, Warrington, WA2 8QT Tel: (01925) 231262 Fax: (01925) 231219 *Hire lifting equipment*

▶ H S S Service Hire Group Ltd, 816 Oxford Road, Reading, RG30 1EL Tel: 0118-950 8882 Fax: 0118-975 0841

▶ H & S Scaffolding Ltd, 1-3 Comet Street, London, SE8 4AN Tel: (020) 8692 4818

H & S Sheetmetal Fabrication Co., Unit 1, All Saints Industrial Estate, Shildon, County Durham, DL4 2RD Tel: (01388) 777172 Fax: (01388) 775034 *Sheet metalwork engineers*

H S Sports Ltd, Unit 5 Radnor Park Industrial Estate, Congleton, Cheshire, CW12 4XN Tel: (01260) 275708 Fax: (01260) 278352 E-mail: info@hssports.co.uk *Electronic sports timing retailers*

H S Wood Textiles, Park View Mills, Raymond Street, Bradford, West Yorkshire, BD5 8DT Tel: (01274) 734322 Fax: (01274) 744592 E-mail: wgroup@globalnet.co.uk *Textile waste export merchants*

H Schreiber, Stadium Industrial Estate, 8 Cradock Road, Luton, LU4 0JF Tel: (01582) 575727 Fax: (01582) 575733 E-mail: laraine@techscrew.com *Chemical & fastener importers*

H Seal & Co. Ltd, Church Lane, Whitwick, Coalville, Leicestershire, LE67 5DJ Tel: (01530) 832351 Fax: (01530) 813382 E-mail: sales@hseal.co.uk Principal Export Areas: Worldwide *Manufacturers of woven & knitted elastic & rigid webbing*

H Shawyer & Sons Ltd, 1-3 Redburn Industrial Estate, Woodall Road, Enfield, Middlesex, EN3 4LF Tel: (020) 8805 7080 Fax: (020) 8804 3883 E-mail: sales@hshawyer.demon.co.uk *H Shawyer & Sons Ltd, based in Enfield London, are manufacturers of high quality architectural wood veneered panels and doors servicing shopfitters, joinery manufacturers, interior designers and bespoke furniture manufacturers all across the UK.*

H Skeels Leigh On Sea, 5 London Road, Leigh-on-Sea, Essex, SS9 3JJ Tel: (01702) 476295 Fax: (01702) 471324 *Builders merchants*

▶ H Sladen & Son Ltd, Daniels Way, Hucknall, Nottingham, NG15 7LL Tel: 0115-840 2203 Fax: 0115-840 2204

▶ H Smith (Electrical) Ltd, 1 Thompsons Yard, Westgate, Wakefield, West Yorkshire, WF1 2TP Tel: (01924) 372425

▶ H Smith & Sons Ltd, Quarry Works, Honingham, Norwich, NR9 5AP Tel: (01603) 880258

H Snelson Engineers Ltd, Nat Lane, Winsford, Cheshire, CW7 3BS Tel: (01606) 553580 Fax: (01606) 861084 E-mail: sales@snelsons.co.uk *Aluminium fabricators, anodisers & powder coaters*

H Systems Ltd, 4 St Helens Cres, Hove, E. Sussex, BN3 8EP Tel: 01273 414011 Fax: 01273 414311 *Supplier of tracking system*

H T Brigham & Co. Ltd, Station Road, Coleshill, Birmingham, B46 1JQ Tel: (01675) 463882 Fax: (01675) 467441 E-mail: admin@htbrigham.co.uk Principal Export Areas: Middle East, Central/East Europe, West Europe & North America *Pressings, deep drawn; pressings, general presswork, non-ferrous metal*

H T C Fastenings Ltd, Lyon Way, Hatfield Road, St. Albans, Hertfordshire, AL4 0LR Tel: (01727) 832131 Fax: (01727) 843234 E-mail: info@hertstools.co.uk *Industrial fastener distributors*

H T Cables, 40 Lancaster Gardens, Penn, Wolverhampton, WV4 4DN Tel: (01902) 339926 Fax: (01902) 659426 E-mail: seona_macrae@lineone.net *High temperature electric cables*

▶ H T Electrical Services, 17 Peasley Cross Lane, St. Helens, Merseyside, WA9 3BG Tel: (01744) 730099 Fax: (01744) 26610

H T Fabrications Ltd, 420 Thurmaston Boulevard, Leicester, LE4 9LE Tel: 0116-276 1814 Fax: 0116-246 0576 E-mail: ht@fabs.freeserve.co.uk *Sheet metal works services*

H T G Trading Ltd, Hillview, Church Road, Otley, Ipswich, IP6 9NP Tel: (01473) 890522 Fax: (01473) 890758 E-mail: info@hubbard.co.uk *Refrigeration equipment manufrs*

▶ H T Gaddum & Co. Ltd, 3 Jordangate, Macclesfield, Cheshire, SK10 1EF Tel: (01625) 427666 Fax: (01625) 511331 E-mail: sales@gaddum.co.uk *Niche products suppliers*

H T Industrial Supplies, Chapel Street, Goole, North Humberside, DN14 5RJ Tel: (01405) 766428 Fax: (01405) 768053 E-mail: htsupplies@ic24.net *Protective equipment distributors*

H & T Mirage Ltd, 471 Kirkstall Road, Leeds, LS4 2QD Tel: 0113-263 0116 Fax: 0113-263 3770 E-mail: info@htmirage.co.uk *PAT testing, electrical contractors & control gears manufrs*

H T S Optical Group Ltd, Industrial House, Conway Street, Hove, East Sussex, BN3 3LU Tel: (01273) 773918 Fax: (01273) 737246 *Optical manufacturing services*

H T S Precision Engineering Co. Ltd, Unit 3, Shamrock Quay, William Street, Northam, Southampton, SO14 5QL Tel: (023) 8033 3668 Fax: (023) 8063 7216 *CNC machining specialists*

H T Security Systems, 36 Loxwood Road, Waterlooville, Hampshire, PO8 9TU Tel: (023) 9259 9479 Fax: (023) 9259 9479 *CCTV & alarm systems distributors*

H T Servo Ltd, 5 Westmarch Business Centre, River Way, Andover, Hants, SP10 1NS Tel: (01264) 355079 Fax: (01264) 337450 E-mail: info@htservo.com Sales Contact: G.B. Tucker *HT Servo provide servo solutions for the more demanding application within the aerospace/defence and associated customised markets. Our product range includes direct drive, geared motors and high precision feedback devices with matching controllers.*

H T W Thanet Refrigeration, Stanley Place, Ramsgate, Kent, CT11 7NT Tel: (01843) 592905 Fax: (01843) 850256 *Commercial refrigeration sales, service & installation*

H Tempest Ltd, The Colour Laboratory, Lelant, St. Ives, Cornwall, TR26 3HU Tel: (01736) 752411 Fax: (01736) 751463 *School photographers*

▶ H Tideswell & Sons Ltd, The Glebe Garage, Hazles Cross Road, Kingsley, Stoke-on-Trent, ST10 2AX Tel: (01538) 753887 Fax: (01538) 750385

H Tipton Jones Ltd, 5 Worrall Street, Salford, M5 4TH Tel: 0161-877 1122 Fax: 0161-877 1145 E-mail: sales@tiptonjones.com *Pipeline fittings & flanges stockholders* Also at: Warrington

▶ H Tomlinson & Son Ltd, Birchills Street, Walsall, WS2 8NG Tel: (01922) 623035 Fax: (01922) 623204 E-mail: sales@htomlinsonandson.co.uk

▶ H Tonge & Sons, 32 Parliament Street, Upholland, Skelmersdale, Lancashire, WN8 0LN Tel: (01695) 623063 Fax: (01695) 623341

H Turnbull & Co. Ltd, 226 Mulgrave Road, Sutton, Surrey, SM2 6JT Tel: (020) 8642 0513 Fax: (020) 8642 5246 E-mail: enquiries@turnbullgroup.co.uk *Building contractors*

H Tyson & Co. Ltd, Gibson House, Walpole St, Blackburn, BB1 1DB Tel: (01254) 266000 Fax: (01254) 266001 E-mail: info@tyson-lighting.co.uk *Lighting fittings*

H V Bowen & Sons Transport Ltd, Dwyrhiew Mill, New Mills, Newtown, Powys, SY16 3BS Tel: (01686) 650242 Fax: (01686) 650727 *Agricultural merchants*

▶ H & V Commissioning Services Ltd, 16 Barrmill Road, Galston, Ayrshire, KA4 8HH Tel: (01563) 821991 Fax: (01563) 822220 E-mail: karen@handv.co.uk *Heat & ventilation services*

H & V Fabrications, Church Road, Stockton-on-Tees, Cleveland, TS18 2LZ Tel: (01642) 670813 Fax: (01642) 670813 E-mail: h.andv@hotmail.co.uk *Metal Fabricators*

H V P Security Shutters Ltd, 4 Grace Road West, Marsh Barton, Exeter, EX2 8PU Tel: (01392) 270218 Fax: (01392) 278548 E-mail: info@hvpshutters.co.uk *Security grille manufrs*

H V S Animal Health, 27 Inch Abbey Road, Downpatrick, County Down, BT30 9AT Tel: (028) 4461 2678 Fax: (028) 4461 4801 E-mail: info@hvsanimalhealth.com *Animal health care product suppliers*

H V S Cartridge Services, 9-13 Hart Lane, Hartlepool, Cleveland, TS26 8RJ Tel: (01429) 262568 Fax: (01429) 860257 E-mail: t-teef@hvs.uk.com *Computer systems & software*

H V Skan Ltd, 425-433 Stratford Road, Shirley, Solihull, West Midlands, B90 4AE Tel: 0121-733 3003 Fax: 0121-733 1030 E-mail: info@skan.co.uk *Optical & industrial glasses distributor*

H.V. Wooding Ltd, Range Road Industrial Estate, Hythe, Kent, CT21 6HG Tel: (01303) 264471 Fax: (01303) 262408 E-mail: sales@hvwooding.co.uk *Producers of precision engineered components & assemblies to many diverse industries across Europe & the World, established since 1968. The multi-site operation is approved to ISO 9001/2000 & is geared to provide design & prototype assistance as well as volume production. Capabilities include toolmaking, metal pressings, sub-assemblies, electro-plating, CNC wire erosion & copper busbar manufacture*

H Varley Ltd, Unit 5, Century Park, Unit 5, Pacific Road, Altrincham, Cheshire, WA14 5BJ Tel: 0161-928 9617 Fax: 0161-928 7824 E-mail: sales@varley.co.uk Principal Export Areas: Worldwide *Industrial wheel & castor distributors*

H Vaughan Ltd, 26 Naval Row, London, E14 9PS Tel: (020) 7515 4551 Fax: (020) 7515 4551 *Chair frame manufrs*

H W Audio Ltd, 180-198 St. Georges Road, Bolton, BL1 2PH Tel: (01204) 385199 Fax: (01204) 364057 E-mail: sales@hwaudio.co.uk *Stage & mobile sound systems*

H W Coates Ltd, Main Street, Cosby, Leicester, LE9 1UW Tel: 0116-284 8403 Fax: 0116-275 0417 *Warehousing & distribution contractors* Also at: Lutterworth & Whetstone

H W D Shopfitters Ltd, 65 Marlborough Road, Newport, Gwent, NP19 0BY Tel: (01633) 211761 Fax: (01633) 843014 E-mail: enquire@hwdshopfitters.co.uk *Shopfitters, aluminium curtain walling, entrances, windows etc.*

H W Dansies, 409 Chatsworth Road, Chesterfield, Derbyshire, S40 2DH Tel: (01246) 235455 Fax: (01246) 220862 E-mail: sales@dansies.co.uk *Office equipment suppliers*

H W Designs, 3 Hod Drive, Stourpaine, Blandford Forum, Dorset, DT11 8TJ Tel: (01258) 452114 *Furniture restoration & manufrs*

H W Engineering Ltd, Cemetery Road, Ince, Wigan, Lancashire, WN3 4NN Tel: (01942) 866091 Fax: (01942) 863158 *Light steel & steel fabrications*

H W Feeds, Pantygarn, Eglwyswrw, Crymych, Pembrokeshire, SA41 3SY Tel: (01239) 891516 Fax: (01239) 891516 *Agricultural merchants*

H W Fisher & Son Ltd, 22-24 Elms Road, Aldershot, Hampshire, GU11 1LJ Tel: (01252) 324008 Fax: (01252) 324498 E-mail: admin@hwfisherandson.co.uk *Building contractors*

▶ H W Gaymer, 9 Old Water Yard, Curtis Road, Dorking, Surrey, RH4 1DY Tel: (01306) 875777 Fax: (01306) 876700

H W J Fencing, 85 Belmont St, Swadlincote, Derbyshire, DE11 8JZ Tel: (01283) 550262 *Domestic panel manufrs*

H W L Engineering Ltd, 99-105 Canterbury Road, Croydon, CR0 3HH Tel: (020) 8689 8300 Fax: (020) 8689 8920 *Printers engineers & equipment supplies*

H W Mclean, 1-5 George Place, Paisley, Renfrewshire, PA1 2HZ Tel: 0141-889 9268 Fax: 0141-889 9268 *Engraving services*

H W Morgan & Sons, 12 Sufton Rise, Mordiford, Hereford, HR1 4EN Tel: (01432) 850436 Fax: (01432) 850792 E-mail: julie5557@hotmail.co.uk *Wooden tent pegs manufrs*

▶ H W Plastics, Britannia House Stanley Matthews Way, Trentham Lakes South, Stoke-on-Trent, ST4 8GR Tel: (01782) 645700 Fax: (01782) 645727

H W Richmond & Sons, Swanston Road, Great Yarmouth, Norfolk, NR30 3NQ Tel: (01493) 842066 *Marine engineers*

H W Taroni Metals Ltd, Aston Church Road, Saltley, Birmingham, B8 1QF Tel: 0121-327 2959 Fax: 0121-327 4140 E-mail: paul@h-taroni.fsnet.co.uk *Car & lorry dismantlers*

H W Ward Service Spares Ltd, Ajax Works, Whitehill Industrial Estate, Stockport, Cheshire, SK4 1NT Tel: 0161-429 6962 Fax: 0161-480 7693 E-mail: ward@bamfordajax.com *Turret lathes spares services*

H W Whiteley Engineering, Holmfield Industrial Estate, Holmfield, Halifax, West Yorkshire, HX2 9TN Tel: (01422) 244870 Fax: (01422) 248666 E-mail: gordonwhitaker@hwwhiteley.co.uk *General light engineers*

H Walton, Old Goole Mill, South Park Road, Goole, North Humberside, DN14 8BD Tel: (01405) 762928 Fax: (01405) 763542 *Agricultural merchants*

▶ H Watson & Son York, 9 Hawthorne Grove, York, YO31 7YA Tel: (01904) 424306

H Webber & Sons Ltd, Bridge House, Station Road Gomshall, Guildford, Surrey, GU5 9NP Tel: (01483) 202963 Fax: (01306) 740811 E-mail: info@hwebber.co.uk *Upholstery & leather tools distributors*

H West Prees Ltd, Lower Heath, Prees, Whitchurch, Shropshire, SY13 2BT Tel: (01948) 840465 Fax: (01948) 841055 E-mail: sales@harrywest.co.uk *Agricultural builders*

H Whittaker & Son Ltd, Heapy Street, Macclesfield, Cheshire, SK11 7JD Tel: (01625) 424637 Fax: (01625) 613470 *Road transport contractors*

H Wicks Lindel, Park Road, Sowerby Woods Industrial Estat, Barrow-in-Furness, Cumbria, LA14 4QR Tel: (01229) 432114 Fax: (01229) 432056 E-mail: sales@wicksgroup.co.uk *Recycling services*

▶ H Williams Haulage, 115 Hampstead Hill, Birmingham, B20 1BX Tel: 0121-358 5755 Fax: 0121-358 4020

H Williams & Sons Ltd, Wallace Way, Stevenage, Hertfordshire, SG1 1XX Tel: (01462) 454872 Fax: (01462) 421805 *Scrap iron & steel merchants*

▶ H Wilson Alfriston Ltd, Yard & Office, 8 West Street, Alfriston, Polegate, East Sussex, BN26 5UX Tel: (01323) 870236 Fax: (01323) 870916

H X Marquees, 77 Cliffe End Road, Oakes, Huddersfield, HD3 4FG Tel: (01422) 200960 E-mail: mailbox@halifax-marquees.co.uk *Halifax Marquees Hires Out Tents To Lacla Businesses Individuals & Organisations for a wide variety of uses. The most common being local events and fesitvals aswell as garden parties.*

H Y M A (UK) Ltd, Units 2-3, Westpoint Industrial Estate, Hargreaves Street, Oldham, OL9 9ND Tel: 0161-620 4137 Fax: 0161-627 0713 *Foam production machine manufrs*

▶ H Young Ltd, Main Street, Glengarnock, Beith, Ayrshire, KA14 3BD Tel: (01505) 682101 Fax: (01505) 682333

▶ H Zone Clothing, Unit 15 Ladford Covert Industrial Park, Seighford, Stafford, ST18 9QL Tel: (01785) 282821 Fax: (01785) 282822 E-mail: info@hzoneuk.com *Equestrian clothing suppliers*

H+H Celcon Ltd, Celcon House, Ightham, Sevenoaks, Kent, TN15 9HZ Tel: (01732) 886333 Fax: (01732) 886810 E-mail: marketing@celcon.co.uk *Heavyside building materials*

H2 Organisation, Hop Farm Country Park, Maidstone Road, Paddock Wood, Tonbridge, Kent, TN12 6PY Tel: (01622) 872123 E-mail: sales@h2organisation.co.uk *Event management consultants*

▶ H2 Plumbing Ltd, Unit L24 The Old Laboratories, 2 Michael Road, London, SW6 2AD Tel: (020) 7751 3344 E-mail: info@h2plumbing.co.uk *Recommended firm of plumbers, electricians, heating and gas engineers and bathroom and kitchen installers. For peace of mind that you are dealing with true professionals, call our friendly office staff on 020 7751 3344**Plumbing - leaks, washing machines, showers, tanks, pumps*Gas/Heating - Landlord Certificates, gas cookers, boiler repairs, boiler servicing, new heating installations, power flushing radiators*Electricians - Electrical Certificates and Landlord Certificates, small electrical repairs and maintenance, full electrical rewires, new fuse boards*Kitchen and Bathroom Installations - Plumbing, tiling, carpentry and plastering all carried out by our experienced all-round tradesmen**We are fully insured. NICEIC Approved electricians. Corgi Registered.**

▶ H2 Specialist Coating Solutions Ltd, The Old Cooperage High Street, Rothes, Aberlour, Banffshire, AB38 7AU Tel: (01340) 831104 Fax: (01340) 831104 E-mail: chris@henderson-decorators.co.uk *Coating application & sales suppliers*

▶ H20 Bathroom Studio, 61-65 Bell Lane, Bury, Lancashire, BL9 6BB Tel: 0161-762 9119 Fax: 0161-762 9339 E-mail: mark@h2obathroomstudio.co.uk *Bathroom retailers*

▶ H20 Products Ltd, Brestwers Corner, Pendicke Street, Southam, Warwickshire, CV47 1PN Tel: (01926) 810111 Fax: (01926) 811040 E-mail: mail@h-2-o.co.uk *Customised shower enclosures, screens and doors. Frameless options*

H2O Group, 1 Gammons Lane, Watford, WD24 6GB Tel: (01923) 225454 Fax: (01923) 225450 *Water treatment machine manufrs*

▶ H2o Plumbing Services Ltd, 158 Beeches Road, Birmingham, B42 2HN Tel: 0121-357 9400 Fax: 0121-357 9400

▶ H2o Sports, 5 Harbour Masters Building, Pwllheli, Gwynedd, LL53 5AY Tel: (01758) 612867 Fax: (01758) 612685

H2o Window Cleaning, 47 Muirfield, Blunsdon, Swindon, SN25 2DD Tel: (07833) 681329 E-mail: info@h2owindowcleaning.co.uk *Premier commercial & domestic window cleaning, Swindon, *reach & wash system specialists, allows us to work upto 60"""""" from the safety of the ground & in total compliance with health & safety legislation, environmentally friendly, fully insured - £5 million public liability, all staff fully trained & certified by the British Window Cleaning Academy, *members of the National Federation of Master Window & General Cleaners,*Highly recommended & customer focused,*Covering Wiltshire & bordering counties,*Free no-obligation quotation & survey, *All work carries our 0% satisfaction guarantee,*uniformed, professional, reliable service**

▶ H4 Marine Ltd, 7 Richmond Terrace, Buckland Monachorum, Yelverton, Devon, PL20 7LU Tel: (01822) 852466 Fax: 01822 853179 E-mail: sales@H4Marine.com *Oil recovery socks, materials.*Adsorbents not absorbents.*Marine rope cutters and bearing protection systems. QuicKutter/SandStopper *A new design as supplied to VT Halmatic/RNLI and commercial fishing boats.*

▶ H4 Sports, 2 Cudsdens Court, Chesham Road, Great Missenden, Buckinghamshire, HP16 0QX Tel: (01494) 862370 Fax: (01494) 862730 E-mail: info@h4sports.com *Providing a comprehensive range of sports balls and accessories*

▶ HA Solutions Limited, The Chimes, 260 London Road, Wokingham, Berkshire, RG40 1QY Tel: 0845 0943092 E-mail: info@hasolutions.co.uk *IT Services including:*IT Architectural Advice*IT Support*Security*Networks including wireless*Backup and Recovery including remote*Disaster Recovery*

▶ Haa Design, 109 Hope Street, Glasgow, G2 6LL Tel: 0141-221 6234 Fax: 0141-221 6543

Haagensen Wardrobes, F A Would, Ladysmith Road, Grimsby, South Humberside, DN32 9SH Tel: (01472) 343030 Fax: (01472) 341333 E-mail: adrian@haaggensonwardrobes.com *Wardrobe manufrs*

Haani Cables Ltd, Tofts Farm Industrial Estate East, Brenda Road, Hartlepool, Cleveland, TS25 2BS Tel: (01429) 221184 Fax: (01429) 272714 E-mail: info@haanicables.co.uk *Electric cable manufrs*

Haas Associates, 20 Baldock Road, Buntingford, Hertfordshire, SG9 9DA Tel: (01763) 272865 Fax: (01763) 273869 E-mail: sales@haas-uk.com *Bespoke software developers*

Haas Automation Ltd, Bradgate House, 13 Unthank Road, Norwich, NR2 2PA Tel: (01603) 760539 Fax: (01603) 760542 *Machine tool distributors*

▶ Haas Tek, Broomhouse Industrial Park, Kirkburn, Dryfe Road, Lockerbie, Dumfriesshire, DG11 2RF Tel: (01576) 203074 Fax: (01576) 204594 E-mail: info@haas-tek.co.uk *Plant relocation, machinery removal & installation*

Habasco International Ltd, Stafford Mills, George Street, Milnsbridge, Huddersfield, HD3 4JD Tel: (01484) 642115 Fax: (01484) 640058 E-mail: sales@habasco.net *Cane furniture, basket & gift ware importers*

Company Information

Habasit Rossi Ltd, Habegger House, Keighley Road, Silsden, Keighley, West Yorkshire, BD20 0EA Tel: (0870) 8359555 Fax: (0870) 8359777 E-mail: info@habasitrossi.com *Manufacturers of belting*

W. Habberley Meadows Ltd, 5 Saxon Way, Chelmsley Wood, Birmingham, B37 5AY Tel: 0121-770 0103 Fax: 0121-770 6512 E-mail: gold@habberleymeadows.co.uk *Gold leaf artists/manufrs*

Habgood & Co., Gas Lane, Bristol, BS2 0QL Tel: 0117-955 6423 Fax: 0117-955 6423 *Scrap metal merchants*

▶ Habitat U.K. Ltd, 196 Tottenham Court Road, London, W1T 7LG Tel: (020) 7631 3880 Fax: (020) 7614 5209 E-mail: store.tcr@habitat.co.uk *Contemporary home furnishings distributors* Also at: Branches throughout the U.K.

Habko Tools & Fastenings Ltd, Unit 1, Joseph Wilson Industrial Estate, South St, Whitstable, Kent, CT5 3PS Tel: (01227) 265444 Fax: (01227) 263517 *Bolt, nut & fastener distributors*

Hac Tac Ltd, The S M D Group Ltd, Faringdon, Oxfordshire, SN7 8LA Tel: (01367) 242818 Fax: (01367) 242819 E-mail: info@hac-tac.co.uk *Saddlery & riding gear manufrs*

HACCP Solutions Ltd, 18 Knoll Drive, Woodloes Park, Warwick, CV34 5YQ Tel: 01926 408 375 Fax: 01926 409 635 E-mail: info@haccpsolutionsltd.com *HACCP Solutions Ltd is a provider of quality training courses and consultancy services for Food & Safety & HACCP. Our objective is to maintain consistency and to provide recognised qualifications, the Chartered Institute of Environmental Health certificates all of our open training courses. We guarantee that we will consistently provide a professional and high quality service to our customers.*

Hacel Lighting Ltd, Harcel House, Silverlink, Wallsend, Tyne & Wear, NE28 9ND Tel: 0191-280 9911 Fax: 0191-263 1144 E-mail: purchasing@hacel.co.uk *Lighting systems & equipment manufrs*

Hach Langer Ltd, 5 Pacific Way, Salford, M50 1DL Tel: 0161-872 1487 Fax: 0161-848 7324 E-mail: info@hach-lange.co.uk *Flow measuring distributors*

Hach Ultra Analytics, Unit 4 Chesterfield Road, Holmewood, Chesterfield, Derbyshire, S42 5US Tel: (01246) 599760 Fax: (01246) 599778 E-mail: uksales@hachultra.com *Scientific instrument suppliers*

Hachette Livre, 338 Euston Road, London, NW1 3BH Tel: (020) 7873 6000 Fax: (020) 7873 6024 *Book publishers*

Charles Martin Hacker, 2 Lansdown Place Lane, Cheltenham, Gloucestershire, GL50 2JZ Tel: (01242) 522308 *Engine & machinery reconditioning services*

▶ Hackers Tack, Shute Barn, Lerryn, Lostwithiel, Cornwall, PL22 0QE Tel: (01208) 871220 *QUALITY SECOND HAND RIDING CLOTHES AND EQUIPMENT. Hackers has perhaps the largest selection of good quality second hand show, hacking, tweed and hunt jackets in the west country. Sizes from tiny tots to adults. Jodhpurs, boots Lindisfarne Browbands part xchange and mail order.*

Hacketts Connect Ltd, Bell Street, West Bromwich, West Midlands, B70 7BX Tel: 0121-553 0134 Fax: 0121-553 2320 E-mail: info@hackcon.demon.co.uk *Suppliers of tubes & fittings*

▶ Hackfield Leasing Ltd, 121 High Street, Cranfield, Bedford, MK43 0BS Tel: (01234) 756152 Fax: (01234) 750850 E-mail: rex.holton@hacfield.com *Leasing services*

Simon Hacking & Associates, Cile Cotes House, Oxford Road, Marlow, Buckinghamshire, SL7 2NT Tel: (01628) 488475 Fax: (0870) 8918762 *Textile agents*

Hackney Angling Centre, 28 Broadway Market, London, E8 4QJ Tel: 020 72750059 *Fishing & angling equipment*

Hackney Press Ltd, Unit 1 Phoenix Business Centre, 2-4 Bow Common Lane, London, E3 4AX Tel: (020) 7537 7579 Fax: (020) 7538 5691 E-mail: sales@hackneypress.co.uk *Printing & publishing services*

Had Fab Ltd, Macmerry Industrial Estate, Tranent, East Lothian, EH33 1RD Tel: (01875) 611711 Fax: (01875) 612711 E-mail: sales@hadfabltd.co.uk *Steel fabricators*

▶ Hadden Construction Ltd, 1 Maidenplain Place, Aberuthven, Auchterarder, Perthshire, PH3 1EL Tel: (01764) 660011 Fax: (01764) 660022 E-mail: sales@hadden.co.uk

Haddenham Healthcare Ltd, Crendon House, Drakes Drive, Long Crendon, Aylesbury, Buckinghamshire, HP18 9BB Tel: (01844) 208842 Fax: (01844) 208843 E-mail: sales@hadhealth.com *Medical devices manufrs*

▶ Haddon Costello Ltd, 34 Percy Road, Leicester, LE2 8FP Tel: 0116-233 8858 Fax: 0116-233 8857

Haddoncraft Forge, Forge House, Church Lane, East Haddon, Northampton, NN6 8DB Tel: (01604) 772027 Fax: (01604) 772027 E-mail: info@haddoncraft.co.uk *Traditional handcrafted wrought iron work*

Haddonstone Ltd, The Forge House, East Haddon, Northampton, NN6 8DB Tel: (01604) 770711 Fax: (01604) 770027 E-mail: info@haddonstone.co.uk *Haddonstone Ltd based in Northampton are manufacturers of architectural and ornamental cast stone. They offer the world's most comprehensive collection of fine garden and landscape ornaments, fireplaces and architectural cast stone.*

Hadee Engineering Co. Ltd, New Street, Holbrook Industrial Estate, Holbrook, Sheffield, S20 3GH Tel: 0114-248 3711 Fax: 0114-247 7858 E-mail: peterlowe@hadee.co.uk *Welded fabrications machinists*

Haden Browne, 278 Barton Street, Gloucester, GL1 4JJ Tel: (01452) 525314 Fax: (01452) 300671 *Plastics tube & sheet distributors*

Haden Building Management Ltd, 10a Fore Street, St. Marychurch, Torquay, TQ1 4NE Tel: (01803) 329435 Fax: (01803) 324982 *Maintenance & service engineers*

Haden Building Management Ltd, Summit House, Glebe Way, West Wickham, Kent, BR4 0RJ Tel: (020) 8918 4200 Fax: (020) 8918 4391 *Property maintenance & facilities services* Also at: Branches throughout the U.K.

Haden Building Services Ltd, 44 Clarendon Road, Watford, WD17 1DR Tel: (01923) 232959 Fax: (01923) 295000 E-mail: headoffice@hadenyoung.co.uk *Mechanical & electrical contractors*

Haden Young Ltd, 11 Britannia Road, Patchway, Bristol, BS34 5TD Tel: 0117-969 3911 Fax: 0117-979 8711 E-mail: bristol@hadenyoung.co.uk *Electrical & mechanical contractors services*

▶ Haden Young Ltd, 93-105 Blenheim Street, Newcastle upon Tyne, NE1 4BW Tel: 0191-222 9200 Fax: 0191-232 3334

Hadfield Cawkwell Davidson, 17 Broomgrove Road, Sheffield, S10 2LZ Tel: 0114-266 8181 Fax: 0114-266 6246 E-mail: sales@hcd.co.uk *Architects, structural engineers*

Hadfield CNC & Electronics Co. Ltd, 15 Retford Road, Worksop, Nottinghamshire, S80 2PT Tel: (01909) 500760 Fax: (01909) 542800 E-mail: service@hcnc.co.uk *CNC machinery & systems*

▶ Philip Hadfield, 10 Queens Drive, Stockport, Cheshire, SK4 3JW Tel: 0161-442 0907 *New Roof /Repairs*Slating Specialist*Ridge Tiles / Pointing Chimneys Dropped & Capped*

▶ Hadfields Bakery Ltd, Factory Lane, Huddersfield, HD3 4LY Tel: (01484) 657059 Fax: (01484) 644740 *Bakery*

▶ Hadham Engineers, 20-21 Twyford Business Centre, London Road, Bishop's Stortford, Hertfordshire, CM23 3YT Tel: (01279) 757834 Fax: (01279) 501108 *Structural steelwork*

Hadham Water Ltd, Church End, Little Hadham, Ware, Hertfordshire, SG11 2DY Tel: (01279) 771248 Fax: (01279) 771057 E-mail: sales@hadham.co.uk *Spring bottling manufrs*

Hadleigh Burglar Alarm Co., Essex House, Josselin Road, Burnt Mills Industrial Estate, Basildon, Essex, SS13 1EL Tel: (01268) 727173 Fax: (01268) 728553 E-mail: sales@hadleigh-security.co.uk *Alarm system fitting*

Hadleigh Castings Ltd, Pond Hall Road, Hadleigh, Ipswich, IP7 5PW Tel: (01473) 827281 Fax: (01473) 827879 E-mail: info@hadleighcastings.com *Aluminum foundry manufrs*

Hadleigh Enterprises Ltd, Unit 11, Buckingham Square, Wickford, Essex, SS11 8YQ Tel: (01268) 572255 Fax: (01268) 572121 E-mail: info@hadleigh.u-net.com *Adhesive tape distributors or agents*

Hadleigh Maid Ltd, 35-37 George Street, Hadleigh, Ipswich, IP7 5BD Tel: (01473) 822305 Fax: (01473) 824654 E-mail: sales@hadleighmaid.co.uk *Chocolate manufrs*

Alan Hadley Ltd, Colthrop Lacolthrop Business Park, Thatcham, Berkshire, RG19 4NB Tel: 0118-988 3266 Fax: 0118-988 4538 E-mail: waste@hadleys.co.uk *Waste, sludge & slurry disposal services*

Hadley Bathrooms, 683 London Road, Hadleigh, Benfleet, Essex, SS7 2EE Tel: (01702) 552233 Fax: (01702) 554292 *Bathroom installation & designers*

Hadley Healthcare Solutions Ltd, 96 Worcester Road, Malvern, Worcestershire, WR14 1NY Tel: (01684) 578678 Fax: (01684) 578510 E-mail: enquiries@hadleyhealthcare.co.uk *Computer suppliers*

Hadley & Ottaway Ltd, The Depository, Muspole Street, Norwich, NR3 1DJ Tel: (01603) 622538 E-mail: info@hadleyandottaway.co.uk

Hadley Park Training, 163 Hadley Park Road, Leegomery, Telford, Shropshire, TF1 6QF Tel: (01952) 257343 Fax: (01952) 257343 E-mail: maggiepoole1@aol.com *Management training consultancy services*

▶ Hadley Southern Ltd, Rollins St Scaffold Yard, London, SE15 1EP Tel: (020) 7635 5141 Fax: (020) 7635 7297

▶ Hadleys Ltd, 13 Winstanley Way, Basildon, Essex, SS14 3BP Tel: (01268) 533121 Fax: (01268) 286879

Hadley's Fencing Contractors Ltd, Kiln House Saw Mill, Pottery Road, Bovey Tracey, Newton Abbot, Devon, TQ13 9DS Tel: (01626) 835726 Fax: (01626) 834860 E-mail: sales@hadleysfencing.co.uk *All types of fencing: wood block a new concept, decking-trellis-chain link, close board & panels, security-steel paliside, playgrounds, security-post & rail*

Hado Polythene, Spring Lane, Malvern, Worcestershire, WR14 1AJ Tel: (01684) 574800 Fax: (01684) 892450 E-mail: sales@hadopolythene.co.uk *Polyethylene, polythene bag, carrier bag & sack manufrs*

Hadrian Air Conditioning & Refrigeration Co. Ltd, 3 Rosse Close, Parsons Industrial Estate, Washington, Tyne & Wear, NE37 1ET Tel: 0191-415 0055 Fax: 0191-415 0888 E-mail: sales@hadrian-air.co.uk *Repair & install air conditioning equipment*

Hadrian Farm Services Ltd, 6 Mcmullen Road, Darlington, County Durham, DL1 1ZY Tel: (01325) 350038 Fax: (01325) 354527 *Agricultural engineers*

▶ Hadrian Security Shopfitters Ltd, 39 Bede Close, Newcastle Upon Tyne, NE12 9SP Tel: 0191-215 1444 Fax: 0191-215 1555 E-mail: sales@hadriansecurity.co.uk *Design, manufacture & installation of security screens*

Hadron Engineering Ltd, Building 8/4 Carlson Suite, Vantage Point Business Village, Mitcheldean, Gloucestershire, GL17 0DD Tel: (01594) 546440 Fax: (01594) 546441 E-mail: info@hadronengineering.co.uk *Supplier of roots type blowers & exhauster packages*

Haelan Centre, 41 The Broadway, London, N8 8DT Tel: (020) 8340 4258 Fax: (020) 8292 2232 *Organic foods*

Haes Systems Ltd, Columbia House Tomo Industrial Estate, Packet Boat Lane, Uxbridge, Middlesex, UB8 2JP Tel: (01895) 422066 Fax: (01895) 420603 E-mail: enquiries@haes-systems.co.uk *Fire alarm systems manufrs*

Haesler Machine Tools, 14 Leyden Road, Stevenage, Hertfordshire, SG1 2BW Tel: (01438) 350835 Fax: (01438) 229482 E-mail: ben.haesler@ntlworld.com *Machine tool merchants, rotary transfer, swab handling, cleaning*

Kurt Hafner Associates, 24 Robin Hill Drive, Camberley, Surrey, GU15 1EG Tel: (01276) 682247 Fax: (01276) 683381 *Food consultants*

▶ Hagan Homes Ltd, 183 Templepatrick Road, Doagh, Ballyclare, County Antrim, BT39 0RA Tel: (028) 9334 2234 Fax: (028) 9334 0674

Hagemeyer Group, Unit 34 Minworth Industrial Park, Forge Lane, Sutton Coldfield, West Midlands, B76 1AH Tel: 0121-351 5222 Fax: 0121-351 4851 E-mail: sales@hageneyer.com *Data cable distributors*

Hagemeyer Service Centre, Blaydon Banks Works, Blaydon-On-Tyne, Tyne & Wear, NE21 4AU Tel: 0191-414 5657 Fax: 0191-499 0153 *Control instrumentation distributors*

Hager Engineering Ltd, 50 Horton Wood, Telford, Shropshire, TF1 7FT Tel: (0870) 2402400 Fax: (0870) 2400400 E-mail: info@hager.co.uk Principal Export Areas: Worldwide *Circuit breakers, miniature, moulded case, residual current (RCD), also manufacturers of distribution boards (electrical), trunking systems (cable), wiring accessories, cable management systems & switches (electric)*

▶ Sue Hagerty Illustration, Unit 16, 100 Trostre Road Workshops, Llanelli, Dyfed, SA15 2EA Tel: (01554) 746504 E-mail: sue@suehagertyillustration.co.uk *Freelance illustrator*

Haggart Commercial Marine, 98-100 Vauxhall Street, Plymouth, PL4 0DD Tel: (01752) 660117 Fax: (01752) 660117 *Marine & general engineers*

Hagger Electronics, Unit 7 Business Centre West, Avenue One, Letchworth Garden City, Hertfordshire, SG6 2HB Tel: (01462) 677331 Fax: (01462) 675016 E-mail: sales@hagger.co.uk *Blind, deaf & disabled aids & equipment suppliers*

▶ Haggetts Original Pies, 4-5 Alansway, Finnimore Industrial Estate, Ottery St. Mary, Devon, EX11 1NR Tel: (01404) 814401 Fax: (01404) 814401

Haggie Financial Ltd, Roman House, Wood Street, London, EC2Y 5BA Tel: (020) 7417 8989 Fax: (020) 7417 8247 E-mail: reception@haggie.co.uk *Financial & corporate communications*

▶ Haggle4me, Omnia Offices, Sheffield, S1 2DU *A bargain hunting and saving sharing community where shoppers can list a pending purchase and other users search and haggle to find the lowest price.*

Hagglund Drives, Foxbridge Way, Normanton Industrial Estate, Normanton, West Yorkshire, WF6 1TN Tel: (01924) 220100 Fax: (01924) 890111 E-mail: sales@hagglund.com *Variable speed drive manufrs*

Hagley Engineering Ltd, Blackbrook Road, Holly Hall, Dudley, West Midlands, DY2 0QP Tel: (01384) 261858 Fax: (01384) 77394 E-mail: hagleye@btconnect.com *Steel fabricators & machining, press brake manufrs*

Hagner Photometric Instruments Ltd, 6-7 Broadbridge Business Centre, Delling Lane, Bosham, Chichester, West Sussex, PO18 8NF Tel: (01243) 575723 Fax: (01243) 573238 E-mail: sales@hagnerlightmeters.com *Photometric instruments agents*

Hagsplay Ltd, Holwell Road, King Stag, Sturminster Newton, Dorset, DT10 2BA Tel: (01258) 817981 Fax: (01258) 817523 E-mail: info@hags.co.uk *Playground equipment*

▶ Hagston Carpets, Skiff Lane, Holme-On-Spalding-Moor, York, YO43 4AZ Tel: (01430) 427820 Fax: (01430) 427820 *Carpet retailers*

▶ Hahl Extrusions Ltd, St Helens Industrial Estate, Bishop Auckland, County Durham, DL14 9AD Tel: (01388) 661818 Fax: (01388) 450733 E-mail: sales@hahl-extrusions.co.uk *Synthetic mono filaments*

Haig Engineering, Unit 7 Bottings Industrial Estate, Curdridge, Southampton, SO30 2DY Tel: (01489) 790910 Fax: (01489) 790911 E-mail: office@ers1996.freeserve.co.uk *Precision engineers*

Haigh & Ellis, St Andrews Road, Huddersfield, HD1 6SB Tel: (01484) 421647 Fax: (01484) 428324 E-mail: mark@haighandellis.fsbusiness.co.uk *Steel fabricators & welding engineers*

The Haigh Group Ltd, Alton Road, Ross-on-Wye, Herefordshire, HR9 5NG Tel: (01989) 763131 Fax: (01989) 766360 E-mail: sales@haigh.co.uk *Sewage macerator manufrs.*

Hailey Wood Sawmill Ltd, Stroud Road, Coates, Cirencester, Gloucestershire, GL7 6LA Tel: (01285) 652191 Fax: (01285) 654649 *Fencing materials & garden furniture manufacturers & suppliers*

Hailsham Structures Ltd, 2 Wentworth House, George Street, Hailsham, East Sussex, BN27 1AD Tel: (01323) 847545 Fax: (01323) 442223 *Steel fabricators*

▶ Alexander Haines Ltd, Hatherley Lane, Cheltenham, Gloucestershire, GL51 6PN Tel: (01242) 225500 *Software developers*

▶ Haines Brothers, No1 Dawsons Lane, Barwell, Leicester, LE9 8BE Tel: (01455) 845855 Fax: (01455) 840168 *Cleaning cloth manufrs*

▶ Haines Clark, Wellington House, 11 Merse Road, Redditch, Worcestershire, B98 9HL Tel: (01527) 61111

Haines Marine Construction, Old Mill Works, The Street, Catfield, Great Yarmouth, Norfolk, NR29 5DH Tel: (01692) 582180 Fax: (01692) 582441 E-mail: bob@hainesmarine.co.uk *Boat builders & maintenance manufrs*

Hainsworths Boatyard Ltd, Fairfax Road, Bingley, West Yorkshire, BD16 4DR Tel: (01274) 565925 Fax: 01274 773803 E-mail: post@boattransporter.co.uk *Hainsworths Boat Transport can safely move your boat to any destination in Europe or beyond, We are capable of handling all vessels up to 55ft long and 32 tons. visit our web site for more info.*

Hair & Beauty Direct Trading Co., Unit D.5 Seedbed Centre, Davidson Way, Romford, RM7 0AZ Tel: (01708) 714251 Fax: (01708) 714222 *Hairdressing suppliers*

▶ Hair Braid, 3 Mossley Hall, Congleton, Cheshire, CW1 2LZ Tel: 07092 847194 Fax: (07092) 306109E-mail: sandrawalkden@googlemail.com *Afro & European Human Hair Extensions On-Line Shop.**Hair Extensions supplier and distributor.**Afro & European Mobile Hair Extensions Specialist.*

Hair Cosmetics Ltd, 11 Queens Court Business Centre, Carrmere Road, Leechmere Industrial Estate, Sunderland, SR2 9TW Tel: 0191-521 4000 Fax: 0191-521 4040 *Hair cosmetics supplier*

▶ Hair Extensions By Beautiful Manes, 20 Oakpits Way, Rushden, Northants, NN10 0PP Tel: 07901 948830 *Call Jenny at Beautiful Manes now for a FREE consultation *Tel - 07901 948830*Jenny is able to come to you at your own home, therefore avoiding higher salon costs - but you will still receive a personal and professional service.*Email - hairextensions@beautiful-manes.co.uk**

The Hair Factory, 4 North Square, London, N9 0HW Tel: (020) 8660 5520 *Hair & cosmetics*

Hairdressers Electrical Equipment, 38-42 Sussex St, Leeds, LS9 8SE Tel: 0113-235 0502 Fax: 0113-235 0502 *Hairdressers equipment & supplies*

Hairdressing & Beauty Suppliers Association Ltd, Greenleaf House, 128 Darkes Lane, Potters Bar, Hertfordshire, EN6 1AE Tel: (01707) 649499 Fax: (01707) 649497 E-mail: davidmacklin@aol.com *Trade association*

Haironville T A C Ltd, Abbotsfield Road, Abbotsfield Road, Abbotsfield Industrial Park, St. Helens, Merseyside, WA9 4HU Tel: (01744) 818181 Fax: (01744) 851555 E-mail: technical@haironvilletac.co.uk *Metal roofing & walls manufrs*

Haith Industrial, Cowhouse Lane, Armthorpe, Doncaster, South Yorkshire, DN3 3EE Tel: (01302) 831911 Fax: (01302) 300173 E-mail: sales@haith.co.uk *Mechanical handling engineers*

Haith-Tickhill Group, Cowhouse Lane, Armthorpe, Doncaster, South Yorkshire, DN3 3EE Tel: (01302) 831911 Fax: (01302) 300173 E-mail: sales@haith.co.uk *Food processing machinery manufrs*

Haji Cash & Carry Wholesalers, Haji House, Lower Tweedale Street, Rochdale, Lancashire, OL11 1HG Tel: (01706) 715959 Fax: (01706) 715960 *Catering suppliers*

Hakens Meat Wholesale, 2 Third Avenue, Greasley Street, Nottingham, NG6 8ND Tel: 0115-976 2995 Fax: 0115-979 5733 *Food production*

Haki Ltd, Magnus, Tame Valley Industrial Estate, Wilnecote, Tamworth, Staffordshire, B77 5BY Tel: (01827) 282525 Fax: (01827) 250329 E-mail: info@haki.co.uk *Suppliers & hirers of scaffolding*

Hako Machines Ltd, Eldon Close, Crick, Northampton, NN6 7SL Tel: (01788) 823535 Fax: (01788) 823969 E-mail: sales@hako.co.uk *Floor care machine manufrs* Also at: Bathgate, Hayes, Livingston & Warrington

Hal Computer Solutions, Priority Business Park, Barry, South Glamorgan, CF63 2AW Tel: (01446) 731204 E-mail: info@capitalnetworks.co.uk *CNS is a Cisco Systems Premier with Wireless LAN specialist accreditation. CNS provides the complete range of network consultancy services including network design, installation and support with a particular interest in wireless networking, security and remote access solutions. We also provide an extensive range of PC and Server Support Solutions for SME"s and multi national clients.*

▶ halalsweeties.com, Unit 1, London, NW9 Tel: 020 82389877 Fax: 020 82389877 E-mail: customerservices@halalsweeties.com *Supplier of halal sweets, chocolates, mithai. We cater for weddings and parties.*

Halan Machine Tools & Engineering, Unit D1 Sketchley Meadows, Hinckley, Leicestershire, LE10 3EN Tel: (01455) 617226 Fax: (01455) 617226 *Engineering & drilling*

Halbro Sportswear Ltd, Chorley New Road, Horwich, Bolton, BL6 7JG Tel: (01204) 696476 Fax: (01204) 699479 E-mail: sales@halbro.com *Rugby clothing manufrs*

Halcion Logistics Ltd, Unit 1 Parkhouse Road East, Parkhouse Industrial Estate East, Parkhouse Industrial Estate Ea, Newcastle, Staffordshire, ST5 7RB Tel: (01782) 566665 Fax: (01782) 565667 E-mail: info@halcion.co.uk *Delivery services*

▶ Halcon Printing Ltd, Unit 5-7 Spurryhillock Industrial Estate, Broomhill Road, Stonehaven, Kincardineshire, AB39 2NH Tel: (01569) 762250 Fax: (01569) 766054

Halcrow Asia Partnership Ltd, Vineyard House, 44 Brook Green, London, W6 7BY Tel: (020) 7602 7282 Fax: (020) 7603 0095 E-mail: info@halcrow.com *Transportation consultants*

Halcrow Crouch Ltd, City Park, 368 Alexandra Parade, Glasgow, G31 3AU Tel: 0141-552 2000 Fax: 0141-552 2525 E-mail: hcglasgow@halcrow.com *Consulting engineers* Also at: Branches throughout the U.K.

▶ Halcrow Group Ltd, Falcon Road, Sowton Industrial Estate, Exeter, EX2 7LB Tel: (01392) 444252 Fax: (01392) 444301

Halcrow Group Ltd, Arndale House, Otley Road, Leeds, LS6 2UL Tel: 0113-220 8220 Fax: 0113-274 2924 *Consulting engineers* Also at: Liverpool & Wakefield

► Halcrow Group Ltd, Deanway Technology Centre, Wilmslow Road, Handforth, Wilmslow, Cheshire, SK9 3FB Tel: (01625) 540456 Fax: (01625) 549325

► Halcyon Card, Grimshaw Hill, Ullenhall, Henley-in-Arden, West Midlands, B95 5NJ Tel: (01564) 793337 Fax: (01564) 793274 E-mail: mailbox@thehalcyoncard.co.uk *We run a national loyalty card scheme supplying co-branded privilege cards & bespoke packages of privileges to companies and organisations of all sizes across the UK.*

► Halcyon Design & Manufacture, Watton Road, Ware, Hertfordshire, SG12 0AE Tel: (0845) 2579696 Fax: (01920) 486035 *Manufacturing metal parts*

Halcyon Drives Ltd, 7 Butler Way, Stanningley, Pudsey, West Yorkshire, LS28 6EA Tel: 0113-236 1509 Fax: 0113-239 3776 E-mail: sales@halcyon-drives.co.uk *Control panel manufrs*

Halcyon Paper Co. Ltd, Unit E, Menin Works, Bond Road, Mitcham, Surrey, CR4 3HG Tel: (020) 8646 4060 Fax: (020) 8648 6197 E-mail: halcyon.paper@cwcom.net *Paper merchants*

Halcyon Plastics Ltd, Halcyon House, The Court Yard, Waterloo Farm, Stotfold Road, Arlesey, Bedfordshire, SG15 6XP Tel: (01462) 833000 Fax: (01462) 734414 E-mail: sales@halcyonplastics.co.uk *Suppliers of plain & printed flexible packaging*

► Halcyon Recruitment UK Ltd, Direct House, 38-39 Centurion Way, Farington, Leyland, PR25 4GU Tel: (01772) 641268 E-mail: admin@halcyonrecruitment.co.uk *Hotel and Catering Recruitment specialists with consultants in Bournemouth, Manchester, Newcastle and Preston. Job opportunities available in bars, restaurants, general management, chefs, housekeeping, reception, leisure clubs, Reservations, Sales, Revenue, Accounts and Financial Control*

Halcyon (Shipping) Ltd, 40 South Quay, Great Yarmouth, Norfolk, NR30 2RL Tel: (01493) 856831

Halcyon Software Ltd, 5 The Forum, Minerva BSNS Park, Orton Wistow, Peterborough, PE2 6FT Tel: (01733) 234995 Fax: (01733) 234994 E-mail: sales@halcyonsoftware.com *Software development specialists*

Halda Ltd, Quay Business Centre, 12 Harvard Court, Winwick Quay, Warrington, WA2 8LT Tel: (01925) 629926 Fax: (01925) 629929 E-mail: haldauk@aol.com *Taxi meter manufacturers & data systems* Also at: Glasgow

Haldane Fisher, Castle Street, Portadown, Craigavon, County Armagh, BT62 1BD Tel: (028) 3833 7321 Fax: (028) 3833 0896 E-mail: sales.portadown@haldane-fisher.com *Builders merchants*

Haldane & Fisher Ltd, Isle Of Man Business Park, Douglas, Isle Of Man, IM2 2QY Tel: (01624) 624466 Fax: (01624) 661335 E-mail: wigan@enterprize.net *Builders' merchants* Also at: Ramsey

Haldane Fisher, Carnbane Industrial Estate, Newry, County Down, BT35 6QQ Tel: (028) 3026 3201 Fax: (028) 3026 8101 E-mail: dgrayhaldanefisher@btinternet.com *Timber merchants*

Haldane Foods Ltd, Howard Way, Newport Pagnell, Buckinghamshire, MK16 9PY Tel: (01908) 211311 Fax: (01908) 210514 *Health food product manufrs*

Haldane (U K) Ltd, 7 Blackwood Way, Bankhead Industrial Estate, Glenrothes, Fife, KY7 6JF Tel: (01592) 775656 Fax: (01592) 775757 E-mail: sales@haldaneuk.com *Purpose made timber handrail manufrs*

Haldex Brake Products Ltd, Moons Moat Drive, Redditch, Worcestershire, B98 9HA Tel: (01527) 499499 Fax: (01527) 499500 E-mail: info@hbpuk.haldex.com *Brake manufrs*

Hale & Co., Nailbridge, Drybrook, Gloucestershire, GL17 9JW Tel: (01594) 545300 Fax: (01594) 545301 E-mail: hale_companie@hotmail.com *Builders' merchants*

Hale Hamilton Ltd, Cowley Road, Uxbridge, Middlesex, UB8 2AF Tel: (01895) 236525 Fax: (01895) 231407 E-mail: enquiries@halehamilton.com *High pressure valve manufrs*

Hale & Murray Ltd, 3 Abingdon Road, Nuffield Industrial Estate, Poole, Dorset, BH17 0UG Tel: (01202) 678431 Fax: (01202) 687843 E-mail: admin@haleandmurray.co.uk *Manufacturers for fitted kitchens, bedrooms & office furniture*

Hale Paper, Premier House, Faringdon Avenue, Romford, RM3 8SP Tel: (01708) 330380 Fax: (01708) 330390 E-mail: information@paper.co.uk *Paper merchants*

► Hale Products Europe Ltd, Charles Street, Warwick, CV34 5LR Tel: (01926) 623614 Fax: (01926) 623689 E-mail: sales@haleeurope.com *Fire fighting equipment manufrs*

Hale Refrigeration, Unit 8 Paper Mill End Industrial Estate, Birmingham, B44 8NH Tel: 0121-344 3345 Fax: 0121-344 3346 E-mail: halerefrigeration@compuserve.com *Refrigeration engineers*

Hales, Hammond Road, Knowsley Industrial Park, Liverpool, L33 7UL Tel: 0151-546 5249 Fax: 0151-545 1010 E-mail: deb@halestrans.u-net.com *Freight forwarders, forwarding agents & haulage* Also at: Birmingham, Dublin & London

Hales Freight Ltd, Horseshoe Farm, London Road, Harlow, Essex, CM17 9LH Tel: (01279) 421122 Fax: (01279) 439144 E-mail: philipveltom@halesfreight.com *Express freight*

Hales Waste Control Ltd, Coronation Road, Cressex Business Park, High Wycombe, Buckinghamshire, HP12 3TZ Tel: (01494) 521221 Fax: (01992) 640212 E-mail: marketing@biffa.co.uk *Waste, refuse disposal & skip contractors*

Halesowen Components Ltd, 126 Coombs Road, Halesowen, West Midlands, B62 8AF Tel: 0121-559 3771 Fax: 0121-561 5323 E-mail: sales@halesowencnc.co.uk *Cnc engineering services or machinists*

Halesowen Engines Ltd, Bromsgrove Road, Halesowen, West Midlands, B63 3JG Tel: 0121-550 3211 Fax: 0121-550 4671 E-mail: sales.halesowen-engines@ssmail.net *Industrial engine spare part distributors*

Halesowen Fabricators Ltd, Unit 8 Granada Industrial Estate, Oldbury, West Midlands, B69 4LH Tel: 0121-552 4360 Fax: 0121-511 1247 *Steel fabricators*

Halewood Business Forms, Fountain House South Horizon West, Canal View Road, Newbury, Berkshire, RG14 5XF Tel: (01635) 231641 Fax: (01635) 231664 E-mail: halewood@tape27.freeserve.co.uk *Tape & packaging material distributors*

Halewood Chemicals Group Ltd, Horton Road, Stanwell Moor, Staines, Middlesex, TW19 6BJ Tel: (01753) 682402 Fax: (01753) 685440 E-mail: halewood@lineone.net *Pharmaceutical exporters & manufrs*

► Haley Bros Builders Ltd, Burlees House, Hangingroyd Lane, Hebden Bridge, West Yorkshire, HX7 7DD Tel: (01422) 842858 Fax: (01422) 845896

Haley Engineering Ltd, Bellcombe, Brent Road, East Brent, Highbridge, Somerset, TA9 4DB Tel: (01278) 760591 Fax: (01278) 760587 E-mail: sales@haleyengineering.co.uk *Steel frame building manufrs*

Halfen Ltd, 31 Humphrys Road, Woodside Estate, Dunstable, Bedfordshire, LU5 4TP Tel: (01582) 470300 Fax: (0870) 5316304 E-mail: sales@halfen.co.uk *Cast-in channel manufacturers, concrete reinforcement, lifting and fixings systems, brickwork support & restraint. Stone support & restraint.*

Halfords Ltd, Icknield St Drive, Redditch, Worcestershire, B98 0DE Tel: (01527) 517601 Fax: (01527) 513201 *Car, bike parts & accessories suppliers*

Halgrove Ltd, Unit A2 Stafford Park 11, Telford, Shropshire, TF3 3AY Tel: (01952) 290548 Fax: (01952) 290549 *Wood manufrs*

Halicombe Trimmings Ltd, 15-16 Margaret Street, London, W1W 8RW Tel: (020) 7580 5423 Fax: (020) 7323 0245 E-mail: halicombe@aol.com *Button merchants*

► Halifax Castings Ltd, Grantham Works, Grantham Road, Halifax, West Yorkshire, HX3 6PL Tel: (01422) 364111 Fax: (01422) 321758

Halifax Castings Brass Founders, Clarence House, Akeds Road, Halifax, West Yorkshire, HX1 2TR Tel: (01422) 365760 *Engineering foundry services*

Halifax Computers, 55 Pellon Lane, Halifax, West Yorkshire, HX1 5SP Tel: (01422) 347868 Fax: (01422) 256666 *Computers repair services*

Halifax Fabrications & Engineering Ltd, Grantham Works, Grantham Road, Halifax, West Yorkshire, HX3 6PL Tel: (01422) 364163 Fax: (01422) 254135 E-mail: hfe-ltd@dsl.pipex.com *Steel Fabricators & General Engineering.*

Halifax Ironworks Ltd, Walker Lane, Sowerby Bridge, West Yorkshire, HX6 2AR Tel: (01422) 836470 Fax: (01422) 834490 *Wrought iron manufrs*

Halifax Optical 1992 Ltd, 3 Clover Hill Road, Halifax, West Yorkshire, HX1 2YG Tel: (01422) 365969 Fax: (01422) 381225 *Manufacturing & wholesale opticians*

Halifax Process Engineering Ltd, 4 Shay Lane Works, Shay Lane, Ovenden, Halifax, West Yorkshire, HX3 6SF Tel: (01422) 367931 Fax: (01422) 349023 E-mail: sales@halifaxprocess.co.uk *Mechanical handling equipment manufrs*

Halifax Scale Co., Brighouse Road, Hipperholme, Halifax, West Yorkshire, HX3 8EF Tel: (01422) 201016 Fax: (01422) 203775 E-mail: info@halifaxscale.co.uk *Weighing machine sales & service*

Halifax Sheet Metal & Ventilation, Pellon Industrial Estate, Queens Road, Halifax, West Yorkshire, HX1 4PR Tel: (01422) 362361 Fax: (01422) 340591 E-mail: info@hsmv.co.uk *Fabrication engineers*

► Halkon Hunt Designer, Unit 1 14-20 Gunhills Lane, Armthorpe, Doncaster, South Yorkshire, DN3 3EB Tel: (01302) 834145 Fax: (01302) 833274 *Manufacture promotional clothing (fishing)*

Hall, 11 Back Avondale Road East, Heysham, Morecambe, Lancashire, LA3 1SW Tel: (01524) 414638 Fax: (01229) 466462 *Blind manufrs*

A.D. Hall Ltd, Chemical Lane, Longbridge Hayes Indrustrial Estate, Stoke-on-Trent, ST6 4PB Tel: (01782) 577605 *Steel stockholders*

Adam Hall Ltd, 3 The Cordwainers, Temple Farm Industrial Estate, Southend-on-Sea, SS2 5RU Tel: (01702) 613922 Fax: (01702) 617168 E-mail: sales@adamhall.co.uk *Audio visual equipment & flight case fittings*

Hall B W Of Oxford, 13 Elmthorpe Road, Wolvercote, Oxford, OX2 8PA Tel: (01865) 310857 Fax: (01865) 310857 *Shed & summerhouse etc manufrs*

Hall & Blenkinsop Ltd, Hetton Lyons Industrial Estate, Hetton-Le-Hole, Houghton Le Spring, Tyne & Wear, DH5 0RF Tel: 0191-526 2114 Fax: 0191-517 0112 *Rail & steel fabricators*

Hall Bros Of Colchester Ltd, Haye Lane, Fingringhoe, Colchester, CO5 7AE Tel: (01206) 735287 Fax: (01206) 735889 E-mail: craftsman@hall-brothers.co.uk *Joiners, bespoke conservatories*

Hall Bros Lifting Gear Ltd, Unit 15 Olds Close, Watford, WD18 9RU Tel: (01923) 770292 Fax: (01923) 896696 E-mail: sales@halls-lifting-gear.co.uk *Lifting equipment manufrs*

Hall & Campey Enviromental Services Ltd, Cavendish Works, Cavendish St, Nottingham, NG7 2TJ Tel: 0115-978 0321 Fax: 0115-942 3973 E-mail: sales@hallandcampey.co.uk *Oil waste recycling/disposal/recovery contractors*

► Claudette Hall Writer & Editor, 40 Devon Close, Perivale, Greenford, Middlesex, UB6 7DP Tel: (020) 8997 2617 E-mail: claudettehall@supanet.com *Copywriting, editing and proofreading for all business-to-business communications - print and online.*

Hall Construction Group, Clay Street, Hull, HU8 8HE Tel: (01482) 329204 Fax: (01482) 587722 E-mail: addressee@hallgroup.co.uk *Building & civil engineering contractors*

► David Hall Communications, 19 Taylor Avenue, Cringleford, Norwich, NR4 6XY Tel: (01603) 506602 E-mail: david@davidhallcomms.co.uk *Supply, installation & service of commercial pa, walkie talkies*

Hall Farm Nursery, Hall Farm, Harpswell, Gainsborough, Lincolnshire, DN21 5UU Tel: (01427) 668412 Fax: (01427) 667478 E-mail: products@hall-farm.co.uk *Light steel fabrication & architectural work services*

Hall Fire Protection, Unit 2 Holloway Drive, Wardley Business Park, Worsley, Manchester, M28 2LA Tel: 0161-793 4822 Fax: 0161-794 4950 E-mail: info@hallfire.co.uk *Sprinkler manufrs*

Hall Green Hire Ltd, 282-284 Fox Hollies Road, Acocks Green, Birmingham, B27 7PT Tel: 0121-706 8940 Fax: 0121-604 6633 *Small tool hire plant & air conditioning services*

► J. & E. Hall, Questor House, 191 Hawley Road, Dartford, DA1 1PU Tel: (01322) 394420 Fax: (01322) 394421 E-mail: helpline@jehall.co.uk *Refrigeration engineers*

► Hall Management Consultants Ltd, Unit 3, Brookend Business Park, Brookend Lane, Kempsey, Worcester, WR5 3LF Tel: 01905 769086 E-mail: enquiry@hmc-online.co.uk *Sales Acceleration for Technology Based Companies*

Hall Partitions Ltd, 113 Church Hill, Loughton, Essex, IG10 1QR Tel: (0845) 6780737 Fax: (0845) 6780747 *Partition manufrs*

Peter Hall Export Services, Flaunden Lane, Bovingdon, Hemel Hempstead, Hertfordshire, HP3 0QA Tel: (01442) 833241 Fax: (01442) 834142 E-mail: peter@exportservices.co.uk *Export marketing & turnkey export contracts*

Peter Hall & Son, Danes Road, Staveley, Kendal, Cumbria, LA8 9PR Tel: (01539) 821633 Fax: (01539) 821905 E-mail: info@peter-hall.co.uk *Furniture restoration & upholsterers*

Hall & Pickles, Blackvein Industrial Estate, Cross Keys, Newport, Gwent, NP11 7PX Tel: (023) 8065 1815 Fax: (01495) 271563 E-mail: cksales@hallandpickles.co.uk *Steel products distribs*

Hall & Pickles, Poynton Industrial Estate, Poynton, Stockport, Cheshire, SK12 1NB Tel: (01625) 878787 Fax: (01625) 855573 E-mail: sales@hallandpickles.co.uk *Steel & steel tube stockholders*

Hall Pine, 45 Westdale Lane, Carlton, Nottingham, NG4 3JN Tel: 0115-961 2926 Fax: 0115-961 2926 *Pine furniture manufrs*

► Hall Plant Hire Ltd, The Birches, Hollins, Old Brampton, Chesterfield, Derbyshire, S42 7JH Tel: (01246) 567233 Fax: (01246) 567248

Hall Refrigeration Ltd, Unit 17 Palace Industrial Estate, Bircholt Road, Maidstone, Kent, ME15 9XU Tel: (01622) 663379 Fax: (01622) 663282 E-mail: hallrefrigeration@mistral.co.uk *Refrigeration servicing*

Hall & Rhodes Security Ltd, 138-140 Blackmoorfoot Road, Huddersfield, HD4 5RL Tel: (0800) 521271 Fax: (01484) 658897 *Engineers*

Hall & Rogers Ltd, Hillkirk Street, Manchester, M11 3EZ Tel: 0161-273 8800 Fax: 0161-273 7279 E-mail: prigby@hallandrogers.co.uk *Builders merchants & dry wall insulation specialists*

Hall Seals & Components, Oak Avenue, Hindley, Wigan, Lancashire, WN2 4LZ Tel: (01942) 522140 Fax: (01942) 522141 *Hydraulic engineers*

Hall Shaw Farm Supplies Ltd, 46 East Green, West Auckland, Bishop Auckland, County Durham, DL14 9HJ Tel: (01388) 833678 Fax: (01388) 834883 *Animal health care product suppliers*

► Simon Hall Ltd, 1 Willersey Business Park Willersey Industrial Estate, Badsey Road, Willersey, Broadway, Worcestershire, WR12 7RR Tel: (01386) 858555 Fax: (01386) 858501 E-mail: enquires@simonhallltd.com *Removals & shipping*

Hallam Consultants, 30 Main Rd, Twycross, Atherstone, Warwickshire, CV9 3PL Tel: (01827) 880158 *IT consultancy*

Jack Hallam & Sons, 33 Buxton Road, Whaley Bridge, High Peak, Derbyshire, SK23 7HT Tel: (01663) 733900 Fax: (01663) 733900 *Gunsmiths*

Hallam Materials Handling Ltd, 232-234 Woodbourn Road, Sheffield, S9 3LQ Tel: 0114-275 3000 Fax: 0114-275 3222 E-mail: hallam-mh@btconnect.com *Fork lift truck attachments & materials handling services*

Hallam Polymer Engineering Ltd, Trasco House, Callywhite Lane, Dronfield, Derbyshire, S18 2XR Tel: (01246) 415511 Fax: (01246) 414818 E-mail: sales@hallampolymer.com *Hallam Polymer Engineering Ltd (HPE) is the most experienced custom moulder of hot cast polyurethane and solid polyurethane elastomer in the UK. We have over 50 years manufacturing experience with approved supplier status. HPE process MDI-Ether & Ester, TDI-Ether & Ester Urethanes in Shore hardness 40A through to 90D, using raw materials from top suppliers. Components include centrifuged sheet, rod, block, roller coating, wheel tyring, scraper blades & segments, pulleys, sheaves, guide strips, screen mats, pump lining, hydrocyclones, concrete moulds, towing sleeves, diablo rollers, seals, gaskets, buffers, springs, wear parts, bonding to metals, impact bars, tension pads, mud flaps, suspension buffers, press tool material, abrasion resistant parts, custom moulding, spraycoating, noise reduction, impact absorption. Injection moulding, machining, cut sheet, rod in acrylic, polycarbonate, PET, polyethylene, polypropylene, nylon, PVC, acetal, PTFE. Rubber roller covering.*

Hallam Signs, Cherry Tree, Union Road, Sheffield, S11 9EF Tel: 0114-249 3141 Fax: 0114-249 3145 E-mail: hallamsigns@talk21.com *Sign manufrs*

Hallams, Wolsey Drive, Kirkby-in-Ashfield, Nottingham, NG17 7JR Tel: (01623) 723777 Fax: (01623) 723888 *Joinery*

Hallamshire Brewery Services Ltd, Liverpool Street, Sheffield, S9 2PU Tel: 0114-243 1721 Fax: 0114-256 0130 E-mail: sam@hallamshire.u-net.co.ukj *Beer dispenser suppliers & refurbishers*

Hallamshire Hardmetal Products Ltd, 315 Coleford Road, Sheffield, S9 5NF Tel: 0114-244 1483 Fax: 0114-244 2712 E-mail: sales@halhard.co.uk *Components (Tungstent) manufrs*

► Hallamshire Manufacturing, Unit 2 Dannemora Drive, Sheffield, S9 5DF Tel: 0114-256 1330 Fax: 0114-256 1332 E-mail: sales@hm-limited.co.uk *Mezzanine flooring manufrs*

Hallanshire Engineering Holdings Ltd, Unit 14, North Anston Trading Estate, Dinnington, Sheffield, S25 4JJ Tel: (01909) 562091 Fax: (01909) 550206 E-mail: sales@heh.co.uk *Mechanical handling plant*

Hallcalm UK, Redworth Street, Hartlepool, Cleveland, TS24 7LG Tel: (01429) 891011 Fax: (01429) 236746 E-mail: engineering@hallcalm.co.uk *Specialist welding & engineering*

Hallcrest Temperature Monitoring Systems Mnfrs, 20 Downing Road, West Meadows Industrial Estate, Derby, DE21 6HA Tel: (01332) 382421 Fax: (01332) 291208 E-mail: sales@hallcrest.com *Micro encapsulation services (fluid etc)*

Hallcrest Temperature Monitoring Systems Mnfrs, 20 Downing Road, West Meadows Industrial Estate, Derby, DE21 6HA Tel: (01332) 382421 Fax: (01332) 291208 E-mail: sales@hallcrest.com *Temperature indicating label & strip manufrs*

Halle Models Leek Ltd, Belle Vue Road, Leek, Staffordshire, ST13 8EP Tel: (01538) 399731 Fax: (01538) 399354 *Ladies lingerie & childware designer & importers*

Hallen Engineering Ltd, PO Box 27, Wednesbury, West Midlands, WS10 7SZ Tel: 0121-556 3324 Fax: 0121-502 0194 E-mail: sales@hallen.co.uk Principal Export Areas: Central Asia & North America *Manufacturers of pipeline fittings & tubular products to specification*

Hallen Motor Bodies, Collins Street, Bristol, BS11 9JJ Tel: 0117-982 3314 Fax: 0117-982 3314 *Commercial vehicle repairs*

Hallford Refurbishments, A Silver End Business Park, Brettell Lane, Brierley Hill, West Midlands, DY5 3LG Tel: (01384) 573845 Fax: (01384) 573848 *Industrial cladding & sheeting*

Halliburton, Howe Moss Place, Dyce, Aberdeen, AB21 0GS Tel: (01224) 776600 Fax: (01224) 793193 Principal Export Areas: Central/East Europe, West Europe & North America *Designers of down hole drilling & completion tools*

► Halliburton Manufacturing & Services Ltd, Kirkhill Industrial Estate, Howemoss Cresent, Aberdeen, AB21 0GN Tel: (01224) 795000

Halliburton Manufacturing & Services Ltd, Kirkhill Industrial Estate, Howemoss Cresent, Aberdeen, AB21 0GN Tel: (01224) 795000 Fax: (01224) 728495 *Fixed cutter, rollercone & downhole specialists*

Halliburton Manufacturing & Services Ltd, Kirkhill Industrial Estate, Howemoss Cresent, Aberdeen, AB21 0GN Tel: (01224) 795000 Fax: (01224) 771438 *Engineering services*

► Halliburton Manufacturing & Services Ltd, Forties Road, Montrose, Angus, DD10 9ET Tel: (01674) 675959

Halliday Electrical, Unit 31 Lynedoch Industrial Estate, Greenock, Renfrewshire, PA15 4AX Tel: (01475) 888440 Fax: (01475) 888220 E-mail: info@hallidayelectrical.co.uk *Electrical contractors*

► Halliday Fraser Munro, 8 Victoria Street, Aberdeen, AB10 1XB Tel: (01224) 388700 Fax: (01224) 388777 E-mail: info@hfm.co.uk

► John Halliday, 348 Lanark Road West, Currie, Midlothian, EH14 5RR Tel: 0131-538 8858 Fax: 0131-451 5072 E-mail: enquiries@jhalliday.co.uk

John Halliday & Sons, Chapelton Smithy, Borgue, Kirkcudbright, DG6 4SN Tel: (01557) 870200 Fax: (01557) 870200 *Agricultural engineers*

Halliday Leisure Ltd, 90-94 Green Street, Ayr, KA8 8BG Tel: (01292) 267575 Fax: (01292) 267575 E-mail: halliday.leisure@virgin.net *Amusement machine supply*

HallidayBooks, Hawthorn Cottage, 32 Rowsham Road, Hulcott, Aylesbury, Buckinghamshire, HP22 5DZ Tel: 01296 426671 E-mail: info@hallidaybooks.com *HallidayBooks - Original Children's Books - Unique Gift Books. The Lonely Tree is the sublime children's debut from HallidayBooks. Beautifully written and stunningly illustrated, The Lonely Tree tells the story of an evergreen growing within the heart of an oak wood. From the snow bound winter to the bright hope of spring, the lonely tree struggles with life and loss before he is finally rewarded by the renewal of the seasons.*Using natural textures within the very latest 3D computer software, each character has been painstakingly developed to awaken this charming story. Join the old oak, the snowy owl, a cloud dragon and the squirrels to find out why the lonely tree is so lonely, and how love and friendship can heal the wounds of a young life.*

Halligan Direct Mail Ltd, 66 Addison Road, Bromley, BR2 9HQ Tel: (020) 8290 9000 Fax: (020) 8290 9002 E-mail: info@halligans.co.uk *Direct mail company & litho printers*

Halligan & Raby, 55 The Avenue, Rubery, Rednal, Birmingham, B45 9AL Tel: 0121-453 1741 Fax: 0121-453 7657 E-mail: sales@halliganraby.co.uk *Screen printers & graphic designers*

Hallis Hudson Group Ltd, Unit B1, Redscar Business Park, Longridge Road, Preston, PR2 5NJ Tel: (01772) 909500 Fax: (01772) 909599 E-mail: info@hallishudson.com *Suppliers*

continued

Company Information

continuation of soft furnishings for windows Also at: Bury & Glasgow

Hallite France Ltd, 130 Oldfield Road, Hampton, Middlesex, TW12 2HT Tel: (020) 8941 2244 Fax: (020) 8783 1669 E-mail: seals@hallite.com *Hydraulic seal manufrs*

Halliwell Electrical Contractors, 16 Hartington Road, Bramhall, Stockport, Cheshire, SK7 2DZ Tel: 0161-439 7694 Fax: (01625) 850117 *Electrical contractors*

▶ Hallmark Blinds Ltd, 173 Caledonian Road, London, N1 0SL Tel: (020) 7837 8181 Fax: (020) 7833 1693 E-mail: info@hallmarkblindsltd.co.uk *Commercial blind manufrs* Also at: Grimsby

Hallmark Cards, Dawson Lane, Dudley Hill, Bradford, West Yorkshire, BD4 6HW Tel: (01274) 784200 Fax: (01274) 784002 E-mail: name@hallmark.com *Cards, wrapping paper & crackers manufrs*

Hallmark Concrete Crushing & Plant Hire, Units 1 & 2, 28 Hayes Road, Deanshanger, Milton Keynes, MK19 6HW Tel: (07970) 059927 Fax: (01908) 566527 E-mail: sales@hallmarkconstruction.co.uk *Hallmark Concrete Crushing and Plant Hire (Milton Keynes) offer Concrete Crusher Hire and Plant Hire, including Concrete Crushing Machines, Digger Hire, Mini Digger Hire, Mini Excavator Hire, Excavator Hire, and general Plant Hire. Based in Milton Keynes, we Hire Concrete Crushing Machines and Plant Hire, as well as Bags of Concrete Aggregates throughout the UK, but are local to Luton, Bedford, Buckinghamshire (Bucks), Bedfordshire, Hertfordshire (Herts) and Northamptonshire (Northants). If you need a Concrete Crushing Machine or any Plant Hire Equipment, just call today and we'll sort you out! Other areas in which we offer Concrete Crushing Equipment and Plant Hire include London, the South East, East Midlands, West Midlands, Home Counties, St. Albans, Watford, Milton Keynes, Bedford, Luton, Buckingham, Oxford, etc. For Concrete Crusher Hire Milton Keynes, Oxford, Luton, Bedford, St. Albans, Watford, Stevenage, Flitwick, or any areas in the UK, just call us today on 07970-059927.*

Hallmark Electronics Ltd, Hallmark House Loomer Road Industrial Estate, Loomer Road, Newcastle, Staffordshire, ST5 7LA Tel: (01782) 562255 Fax: (01782) 565684 E-mail: info@hallmarkelectronics.com Purchasing Contact: M. McHenry Sales Contact: J. Rowe *Contract electronic manufacturer, providing the complete EMS solution/partnership for all industries*

Hallmark Engraving, 116-118 Selsdon Road, South Croydon, Surrey, CR2 6PG Tel: (020) 8686 6649 Fax: (020) 8760 0899 E-mail: sales@hallmarksigns.co.uk *Engraving etchings & signs*

Hallmark Fire Ltd, Systems House, Stoke Road, Hoo, Rochester, Kent, ME3 9NT Tel: (08700) 111150 Fax: (08700) 111160 E-mail: sales@hallmarkfire.co.uk *Fire alarm systems*

Hallmark Fraulo Ltd, Units 55-56, Hillgrove Business Park, Nazeing Road, Nazeing, Waltham Abbey, Essex, EN9 2HB Tel: (01992) 899025 Fax: (01992) 899026 E-mail: info@hallmarkfraulo.co.uk *With over 30 year's experience, Hallmark Fraulo Limited provide specialist surface finishing and bonding solutions to industry providing a high level of customer service and techncial support. The diverse nature of today's manufacturing industries requires careful selection of abrasive and adhesive products. Our partnership with the leading brands such as SIA, Mirka, Hermes, Norton, Acmos, Hexion, Beardow Adams, Apollo and Kleiberit ensures you will always receive the right product for the job. Abrasive range includes coated paper & cloth belts, rolls, sheets, discs, foam pads, foam blocks, Dynabrade and non woven products. Adhesive range includes PVA's, urea formaldehyde and phenolic resorcinol resins, EVA hotmelts, polyurethane, Permagrip & Evostick contact adhesives, animal glues and epoxy resin systems. We also supply many consumables such as Pizzi, Pfohl & Klebo applicators, glue brushes, bottles, wood veneer edging, veneer tapes, Timbafil & Brummer wood fillers and much more.*

Hallmark Labels, 10 Oakwood Hill Industrial Estate, Oakwood Hill, Loughton, Essex, IG10 3TZ Tel: (020) 8532 0620 Fax: (020) 8532 0621 E-mail: hallmark@hallmarklabels.demon.co.uk *Fabric label manufrs*

Hallmark Tractors Ltd, Smisby Road, Ashby-de-la-Zouch, Leicestershire, LE65 2UE Tel: (01530) 412811 Fax: (01530) 412512 E-mail: sales@tractors.co.uk *Agricultural tractor & 4x4 sales, spares, accessories & repair*

Hallons Display Fixtures, Riverside Works, Forde Road, Newton Abbot, Devon, TQ12 4AD Tel: (01626) 358700 Fax: (01626) 358701 E-mail: sales@hallons.co.uk *Mail order*

Halls Beeline Ltd, Northgate, White Lund Trading Estate, Morecambe, Lancashire, LA3 3PA Tel: (01524) 63233 Fax: (01524) 65792 E-mail: sales@hallsbeeline.net Principal Export Areas: Africa, Central/East Europe & West Europe *Decorating supplies specialists*

Hall's Carpets Ltd, 80-82 Pretoria Road, Edmonton, London, N18 1SP Tel: (020) 8803 1400 Fax: (020) 8803 8904 E-mail: sales@hallsfloorings.co.uk *Flooring distributors*

Frank Halls & Son, Mill Lane, Walton on the Naze, Essex, CO14 8PF Tel: (01255) 675596 Fax: (01255) 677772 *Boat & yacht builders & repairers*

Halls Garden Products, PO Box 947, Maidstone, Kent, ME20 6SQ Tel: (01622) 791234 Fax: (01622) 791060 E-mail: enquiries@halls.uk.com *Greenhouse manufrs*

Halls Group Ltd, Riverside Road, Gorleston, Great Yarmouth, Norfolk, NR31 6PX Tel: (01493) 663144 Fax: (01493) 440225 E-mail: info@hallsgroup.uk.com *Builders merchants*

Halls Mica Hardware, 116 Market Street, Chapel-en-le-Frith, High Peak, Derbyshire, SK23 0HZ Tel: (01298) 812260 Fax: (01298) 816143 *Installation kitchen, bedroom & double glazing windows*

Halls Northern Ltd, Unit 9 Stadium Industrial Estate, Gateshead, Tyne & Wear, NE10 0XF Tel: 0191-378 4500 Fax: 0191-378 9796 E-mail: enquiries@hallsnorthern.co.uk *Bar sundries & detergent suppliers*

▶ Halls Removals, Phoenix Works, Tram Street, Platt Bridge, Wigan, Lancashire, WN2 5JE Tel: (01942) 867448 Fax: (01942) 864814

Halls Specialised Services, Brooklyn Farm, North Hill, Horndon-on-the-Hill, Stanford-le-Hope, Essex, SS17 8QA Tel: (01375) 361408 Fax: (01375) 361448 E-mail: enquiries@hallsspecialisedservices.co.uk *Blast cleaning & industrial coating contractors*

John Hally, Moray Street, Blackford, Auchterarder, Perthshire, PH4 1PY Tel: (01764) 682277 Fax: (01764) 663817 *Blacksmiths & structural engineers*

Halma P.L.C., Misbourne Court, Rectory Way, Amersham, Buckinghamshire, HP7 0DE Tel: (01494) 721111 Fax: (01494) 728032 E-mail: halma@halma.com *Safety & environmental technology*

Halmatex Converting Ltd, Queens Avenue, Hurdsfield Industrial Estate, Macclesfield, Cheshire, SK10 2BN Tel: (01625) 429315 Fax: (01625) 508288 E-mail: sales@halmatex.com *Slitting & rewinding of advanced flexible materials upto 2400mm*

▶ Halmond Engineering Products Ltd, 3 Mosshall Industrial Estate, Blackburn, Bathgate, West Lothian, EH47 7LY Tel: (01506) 633476 Fax: (01506) 656022 *Engineering*

Halo, Kings Cross Freight Depot, York Way, London, N1 0UZ Tel: (020) 7837 3300 Fax: (020) 7837 3310 E-mail: info@halo.co.uk *Technical lighting*

▶ Halo Data Recovery, 9 June Crescent, Amington, Tamworth, Staffordshire, B77 3BH Tel: (0870) 3501012 Fax: (08703) 501013

▶ Halo Financial, Suite 5 Port House, Square Rigger Row, London, SW11 3TY Tel: (020) 7350 5474 Fax: (020) 7350 5475 E-mail: help@halofinancial.com *Foreign exchange dealers*

Halo Foods Ltd, Pendre Industrial Estate, Tywyn, Gwynedd, LL36 9LW Tel: (01654) 711171 Fax: (01654) 711744 E-mail: sales@halofoods.co.uk *Manufacturers of confectionery*

Halo Reflective Wear Ltd, Pump Station House, Daleside Road, Nottingham, NG2 4DH Tel: 0115-911 8183 Fax: 0115-911 8074 E-mail: sales@haloreflectivewear.co.uk *We offer a general Cut/Make/Trim service & specialise in the manufacture of general workwear and high visibility clothing, with in-house embroidery & 24 hour digitising service.*

Halolux Electric Motors, 606 Romford Road, London, E12 5AF Tel: (020) 8478 8262 Fax: (020) 8478 1686 *Stockists of horse power motors*

Halpen Marketing Management Ltd, 44 Fulham Road, London, SW3 6HH Tel: (020) 7581 9911 Fax: (020) 7581 8151 E-mail: mail@halpen.com *Graphic production & design*

Halson Refrigeration, 9 Tonacliffe Way, Whitworth, Rochdale, Lancashire, OL12 8SN Tel: (01706) 344557 Fax: (01706) 344557 *Refrigeration & air conditioning suppliers*

Halstan & Co. Ltd, 2-10 Plantation Road, Amersham, Buckinghamshire, HP6 6HJ Tel: (01494) 725525 Fax: (01494) 432305 E-mail: sales@halstan.co.uk *General printing services*

Halstead Associates, 27 Windsor Pl, Cardiff, CF10 3BZ Tel: (029) 2066 6505 Fax: (029) 2066 5584 *Design offices*

Halstead Auto Electrical, 3 Halstead Business Centre, Factory Lane West, Halstead, Essex, CO9 1EX Tel: (01787) 477474 Fax: (01787) 477474 E-mail: robbo@halautoelec.freeserve.co.uk *Electronics engineers*

Halstead Boilers Ltd, 16-22 First Avenue, Halstead, Essex, CO9 2EX Tel: (01787) 475557 Fax: (01787) 475588 E-mail: sales@halsteadboilers.co.uk *Domestic heating equipment manufrs*

Halstead & Fowler, 4 Park Road, Holbeach, Spalding, Lincolnshire, PE12 7EE Tel: (01406) 425173 Fax: (01406) 425173 E-mail: sales@halsteadandfowler.co.uk *Cabinet makers*

Henry Halstead Ltd, 492 Holly Place, Walton Summit, Bamber Bridge, Preston, PR5 8AX Tel: (01772) 339521 Fax: (01772) 332233 E-mail: sales@henry-halstead.co.uk *Industrial fasteners & consumables*

Halstock Cabinets Makers Ltd, Higher Halstock Leigh, Yeovil, Somerset, BA22 9QZ Tel: (01935) 891762 Fax: (01935) 891967 E-mail: andy@halstock-designs.co.uk *Furniture manufrs*

Halton Chamber Of Commerce & Enterprise, Halton Business Forum, Victoria Square, Widnes, Cheshire, WA8 7QZ Tel: 0151-420 9400 Fax: 0151-420 9424 E-mail: sales@exporters-alliance.org.uk *Chamber of commerce*

Halton Communications Ltd, Unit 12 King Edward Industrial Estate, Gibraltar Row, Liverpool, L3 7HJ Tel: 0151-236 9323 Fax: 0151-236 2875 E-mail: admin@haltoncommunications.co.uk *Radio communication systems provider*

Halton Concrete, Macdermott Road, Widnes, Cheshire, WA8 0PF Tel: (01925) 444397 *Ready mix concrete suppliers*

▶ Halton Container Services, 6 Waterloo Centre, Waterloo Road, Widnes, Cheshire, WA8 0PR Tel: 0151-420 0092 Fax: 0151-420 0092 E-mail: hcsl@merseymail.com *Refurbishes of waste containers for local councils*

Halton Panelcraft Ltd, 2 Gavin Road, Widnes, Cheshire, WA8 8RE Tel: 0151-424 0022 Fax: 0151-424 2058 E-mail: panelcraft@lineone.net *Enclosures manufrs*

Halton Print & Promotional, High Street, Knutton, Newcastle, Staffordshire, ST5 6BX Tel: (01782) 712909 Fax: (01782) 713626 E-mail: info@haltonpromotional.co.uk *Flag & banner printers & manufrs*

Halton Products Ltd, 5 Waterside Business Park, Eastways, Witham, Essex, CM8 3YQ Tel: (01376) 503040 Fax: (01376) 503060 E-mail: enquiries@haltongroup.com *Air distribution equipment*

Halton Refrigeration, 83 Lynton Crescent, Widnes, Cheshire, WA8 7NT Tel: 0151-424 5293 Fax: 0151-424 5293 *Refrigeration & air conditioning*

Halver Ltd, Pearith Farm, Appleford Road, Abingdon, Oxfordshire, OX14 4TG Tel: (01235) 511666 Fax: (01235) 811566 E-mail: halver@halver.com Principal Export Areas: Worldwide *Manufacturers of castors (general purpose), wheels*

Halyard Fabrications Ltd, 4 Whittle Road, Ferndown Industrial Estate, Wimborne, Dorset, BH21 7RW Tel: (01722) 710922 Fax: (01202) 894705 *Marine equipment manufrs*

▶ Ham Baker Hartley, Garner Street, Etruria, Stoke-on-Trent, ST4 7BH Tel: (01782) 202300 Fax: (01782) 203639 E-mail: sale@hambaker.co.uk *Manufacturer of penstocks, flap valves stop logs*

Ham Baker Hartley, Garner Street, Etruria, Stoke-on-Trent, ST4 7BH Tel: (01782) 202300 Fax: (01782) 203639 E-mail: enquiries@hambaker.co.uk *Ductile iron, pipe work & pipeline fitters*

Ham Packers Ltd, Saltash Industrial Estate, Saltash, Cornwall, PL12 6LF Tel: (01752) 845235 Fax: (01752) 842333 *Solid meat canners*

HAM Technology UK Ltd, 8 Brookfield, Duncan Close, Moulton Park, Northampton, NN3 6WL Tel: (01604) 494106 Fax: (01604) 499008 E-mail: janet@ham-tech.co.uk *Printed circuit materials & precision tools suppliers*

Hama Ltd, Unit 4 Cherrywood, Chineham Business Park, Basingstoke, Hampshire, RG24 8WF Tel: (01256) 374700 Fax: (01256) 374749 E-mail: sales@hama.co.uk *Photo, audio, video & mobilcom accessories*

Hamamatsu Photonics UK Ltd, 10 Tewin Road, Welwyn Garden City, Hertfordshire, AL7 1BW Tel: (01707) 294888 Fax: (01707) 325777 E-mail: info@hamamatsu.co.uk *Opto-electronic component manufrs*

Hamar Acrylic Fabrications Ltd, 238-240 Bethnal Green Road, London, E2 0AA Tel: (020) 7739 2907 Fax: (020) 7739 7807 *Acrylic sheet stockholders & sign manufrs*

Hamber Safes, Radford Way, Billericay, Essex, CM12 0EG Tel: (01277) 624450 Fax: (01277) 657533 *Safe manufrs*

Hamble Ropes & Rigging Ltd, 65-69 Bernard Street, Southampton, SO14 3BA Tel: (023) 8033 8286 Fax: (023) 8033 8288 E-mail: info@hrrlcovercraft.fsnet.co.uk *Industrial rigging manufrs*

Hambleden Group Ltd, PO Box 16980, London, NW8 9WP Tel: (020) 7289 4443 Fax: (020) 7289 1943 E-mail: information@hambleden.co.uk *Managing change/investors in people*

▶ Hamblemill Ltd, 13 A Harbey Crescent, Southampton, SO31 9TA Tel: (01489) 575161 Fax: (01489) 575161 E-mail: admin@hamblemill.com

Hambleside Business Gift Solutions Ltd, 23 Robjohns Road, Widford Industrial Estate, Chelmsford, CM1 3AG Tel: (01245) 293610 Fax: (01245) 293615 E-mail: gillian@hambleside.co.uk *Promotional gift items*

Hambleside Danelaw Ltd, 2-8 Bentley Way, Royal Oak Industrial Estate, Daventry, Northamptonshire, NN11 8QH Tel: (01327) 701900 Fax: (01327) 701909 E-mail: marketing@hambleside-danelaw.co.uk *Glass fibre profiled sheet manufrs* Also at: Inverness

▶ Hamblin Water Mains Ltd, The Old Barn, Poplar Lane, Winnersh, Wokingham, Berkshire, RG41 5JR Tel: 0118-989 1500 Fax: 0118-989 1555 E-mail: sales@hamblinwatermains.co.uk

Craig Hambling Ltd, Hindle Street, Accrington, Lancashire, BB5 1QT Tel: (01254) 301211 Fax: (01254) 393508 E-mail: construction@hambling.co.uk *Building contractors*

Hambridge Investments Newbury, 4 Vulcan Close, Sandhurst, Berkshire, GU47 9DD Tel: (01252) 860043 Fax: (01252) 890154 *Industrial estate development commercial refurbishments services*

Hambrook Pallets Ltd, Ironchurch Road, Avonmouth, Bristol, BS11 9AF Tel: 0117-982 1236 Fax: 0117-982 2252 *Wooden pallet manufrs*

▶ Hambrook Pallets Ltd, Fairfax Road, Heathfield Industrial Estate, Newton Abbot, Devon, TQ12 6UD Tel: (01626) 834148 Fax: (01626) 834677

Hambry's Angling Equipment, 8 Tamworth Road, Polesworth, Tamworth, Staffordshire, B78 1JH Tel: (01827) 895011 *Fishing tackle & pet suppliers (retail outlet)*

▶ Hambury Construction, Royal Mail House, Terminus Terrace, Southampton, SO14 3FD Tel: (023) 8033 7901 Fax: (023) 8033 8901 E-mail: info@hambury.co.uk *Construction and office refurbishments in the South - Hambury Construction Ltd*

Hambury Machine Tools, Unit 17, Malmesbury Road, Kingsditch Trading Estate, Cheltenham, Gloucestershire, GL51 9PL Tel: (01242) 690390 Fax: (01242) 690391 *Machine tool merchants*

Hamden System Sales Ltd, Granville Way, Bicester, Oxfordshire, OX26 4JT Tel: (01869) 324944 Fax: (01869) 242979 E-mail: enquiries@hamden.co.uk *Food Processing Equipment*

Hameg UK Ltd, 18 Glebe Lane, Buckden, St. Neots, Cambridgeshire, PE19 5TG Tel: (01480) 812100 Fax: (01480) 819187 E-mail: hameguk@btopenworld.com *Oscilloscope importers & distributors*

Hamelin Stationery Ltd, River Street, Brighouse, West Yorkshire, HD6 1LU Tel: (01484) 385600 Fax: 01484 385602 E-mail: sales@oxfordstationery.com *Stationery suppliers & manufrs*

Hamer Jack & Son Tottington Ltd, 200a Bury Road, Tottington, Bury, Lancashire, BL8 3DX Tel: (01204) 883867 Fax: (01204) 888592 E-mail: info@jackhamer-son.co.uk *Building contractors*

Hamerville Magazines Ltd, Regal House, Regal Way, Watford, WD24 4YF Tel: (01923) 237799 Fax: (01923) 246901 E-mail: office@hamerville.co.uk *Publishing professional electrician & builders*

Hames Electronics Ltd, 106A Fair Road, Wibsey, Bradford, West Yorkshire, BD6 1QL Tel: (01274) 606007 Fax: (01274) 607793 *Radio communication services*

Hamilton Acorn Ltd, Halford Road, Attleborough, Norfolk, NR17 2HZ Tel: (01953) 453201 Fax: (01953) 454943 E-mail: sales@hamilton-acorn.co.uk *Paint brush & roller manufrs*

Hamilton Acorn Ltd, Callywhite Lane, Dronfield, Derbyshire, S18 2XP Tel: (01246) 418306 Fax: (01246) 410334 E-mail: info@hamilton-acorn.co.uk *Decorating tool manufrs*

Hamilton Adhesive Labels Ltd, 3 Highmeres Road, Troon Industrial Area, Leicester, LE4 9LZ Tel: 0116-246 0064 Fax: 0116-246 1645 E-mail: gcook@hamilton-labels.co.uk *Adhesive label manufrs*

Hamilton Bros Engineering Ltd, Barmore Road, Tarbert, Argyll, PA29 6TT Tel: (01880) 820249 Fax: (01880) 820249 *Agricultural engineers suppliers*

Hamilton Engineering, 65-67 Corporation Road, Birkenhead, Merseyside, CH41 3NG Tel: 0151-647 6444 Fax: 0151-666 1065 *Sheet metalwork engineers*

Hamilton Fabrications Ltd, Crab Tree Lane, Atherton, Manchester, M46 0AG Tel: (01942) 883745 Fax: (01942) 897481 E-mail: sales@hamiltonfab.co.uk *Precision sheet metal engineers & fabricators*

▶ Hamilton Forms, 37 Westley Grange, Chartwell Drive, Wigston, Leicestershire, LE18 2FL Tel: 0116-257 1600 Fax: 0116-257 1880

Hamilton Frazer Seatstore Ltd, 7 Ravenstone Road, Camberley, Surrey, GU15 1SN Tel: (01276) 23903 Fax: (01276) 683799 E-mail: info@hamiltonfrazer.co.uk *Office furniture retailers*

Hamilton Grant Software Ltd, Seymour House, Lower South Street, Godalming, Surrey, GU7 1BZ Tel: (01483) 422404 Fax: (01483) 422401 E-mail: sales@hamilton-grant.com *Special purpose computer software*

Hamilton Hall Consultants Ltd, 3-4 The Windmills, St Marys Close, Alton, Hampshire, GU34 1EF Tel: (01420) 548548 Fax: (01420) 548549 E-mail: admin@hamiltonhall.co.uk *Solutions providers*

Hamilton House Mailings Ltd, Earls Trees Court, Earls Trees Road, Corby, Northamptonshire, NN17 4HH Tel: (01536) 399000 Fax: (01536) 399012 E-mail: sales@hamilton-house.com *Direct mail services*

▶ Hamilton Hydraulics Ltd, 3 Richmondhill Road, Aberdeen, AB15 5EQ Tel: (01224) 315285 Fax: (01224) 315285 E-mail: info@hamiltonhydraulics.co.uk *Specialists in mechanical & hydraulic systems manufrs*

Hamilton & Inches Ltd, 87 George Street, Edinburgh, EH2 3EY Tel: 0131-225 4898 Fax: 0131-220 6994 *Silverware manufrs*

Hamilton Jet UK Ltd, Unit 4a Birches Industrial Estate, East Grinstead, West Sussex, RH19 1XZ Tel: (01342) 313437 Fax: (01342) 313438 E-mail: info@hamjetuk.com *Marine engineers, water jets steering & controls*

Hamilton & Kinneil Ltd, Riccarton Sawmill, Hamilton, Lanarkshire, ML3 7UE Tel: (01698) 282452 Fax: (01698) 283884 *Gate suppliers*

▶ Hamilton & Kinneil (1987) Ltd, Lennoxlove Estate Office, Haddington, East Lothian, EH41 4NZ Tel: (01620) 823720

▶ Hamilton Knight Development, 16 17 Canalside Industrial Park, Kinoulton Road, Cropwell Bishop, Nottingham, NG12 3BE Tel: 0115-989 4333 Fax: 0115-989 4333 E-mail: hkdevelopments@btconnect.com

Hamilton Laboratory Glass Ltd, Unit A1 Continental Approach, Westwood Industrial Estate, Margate, Kent, CT9 4JG Tel: (01843) 232633 Fax: (01843) 232644 E-mail: sales@hamiltonlabglass.com *Manufacturer of Laboratory Glassware*

Hamilton Mcbride, Churchill Way, Nelson, Lancashire, BB9 6RT Tel: (01282) 878282 Fax: (01282) 614464 E-mail: enquiries@hamiltonmcbride.co.uk *Household textiles importers & distributors*

Hamilton Machinery Sales Ltd, Hamilton House, Broadfields, Bicester Road, Aylesbury, Bucks, HP19 8BU Tel: (01296) 318222 Fax: (01296) 397005 E-mail: john.hat@hamac.co.uk *Distributors of filtration by-pass (hydraulic equipment) systems, plastic raw/basic materials purgin*

Hamilton Plastic Packaging, 18 Galowhill Road, Brackmills Industrial Estate, Northampton, NN4 7EE Tel: (01604) 766329 Fax: (01604) 701790 E-mail: sales@hamiltonpp.com *Vacuum forming manufrs*

Hamilton & Pollock, Kenton Lane Farm, Kenton Lane, Harrow, Middlesex, HA3 8RT Tel: (020) 8909 0601 Fax: (020) 8909 0602 E-mail: info@hampol.co.uk *Suppliers commercial caterers & food manufrs*

Hamilton Precision Engineering, 7 Hamilton Way, Gore Road Industrial Estate, New Milton, Hampshire, BH25 6TQ Tel: (01425) 613181 *Precision engineers*

Hamilton Rand, Paper Mill End Industrial Estate, Birmingham, B44 8NH Tel: 0121-344 3202 Fax: 0121-344 3202 *Marking punch & die manufrs*

Hamilton Rentals P.L.C., Hamilton House, North Circular Road, London, NW10 7UB Tel: (020) 8963 8080 Fax: (020) 8961 8385 E-mail: info@hamilton.co.uk *Computer & audio visual hire services*

Hamilton Shipping Ltd, 14 Clarendon Road, Belfast, BT1 3BG Tel: (028) 9053 3200 Fax: (028) 9053 3222 E-mail: containers@hamiltonshipping.com *Shipping agents*

Hamilton Sundstrand International Corporation, Kingfisher House, 160-162 High Street, Egham, Surrey, TW20 9HP Tel: (01784) 414600 Fax: (01784) 438092 E-mail: alison.doran@hs.utc.com *Aircraft generators & parts manufrs*

Tom Hamilton Transport, Burnside, Kinglassie, Lochgelly, Fife, KY5 0UP Tel: (01592) 882307 E-mail: tom@tht.co.uk *Road transport, haulage & freight services & storage*

Hamiltons Accountants & Business Advisors, Meriden House, 6 Great Cornbow, Halesowen, West Midlands, B63 3AB Tel: 0121-585 6655 Fax: 0121-585 6228 E-mail: enquiries@hamiltons-group.co.uk *Accountants & business advisors*

Hamites Ltd, Unit 3 The Pound, Coate, Devizes, Wiltshire, SN10 3LG Tel: (01380) 860833 Fax: (01380) 860926 *Toner cartridge recyclers suppliers*

Hamlet Computer Group Ltd, 5 Oriel Court, Omega Park, Alton, Hampshire, GU34 2YT Tel: (01420) 83550 Fax: (01420) 541364 E-mail: sales@hamletcg.co.uk *Business systems manufrs*

Hamlin Electronics Europe Ltd, Saw Mills Road, Diss, Norfolk, IP22 4NX Tel: (01379) 649700 Fax: (01379) 649702 E-mail: simon.pitkin@hamlin.com *Switches, proximity; relays, reed manufrs*

Hamlin Model Making Ltd, Old Tractor Shed, Welsh Road, Offchurch, Leamington Spa, Warwickshire, CV33 9BE Tel: (01926) 614147 Fax: (01926) 612899 E-mail: sales@hamlinrpd.co.uk *Model making & prototype development*

Hammer Film Productionltd, 131-151 Great Titchfield Street, London, W1W 5BB Tel: (020) 7637 2322 Fax: (020) 7665 6465 E-mail: pete@skylineaudiopost.com *Audio post production providers*

Hammerite Products Ltd, Eltringham Works, Prudhoe, Northumberland, NE42 6LP Tel: (01661) 830000 Fax: (01661) 835760 E-mail: sales@hammerite.com *Specialised paint manufrs* Also at: Newcastle

▶ Hammersmith Engineering Ltd, 4 Berkeley Court Earl Russell Way, Lawrence Hill, Bristol, BS5 0BX Tel: 0117-955 1800 E-mail: sales@hammersmith-engineering.co.uk *Install garage equipment*

Hammerstones Ltd, Dewsbury Road, Elland, West Yorkshire, HX5 9BG Tel: (01422) 310842 Fax: (01422) 376713 *Joinery manufacturing.*

Hammertex Ltd, Nationwide House, 7 Victoria Way, Burgess Hill, West Sussex, RH15 9NF Tel: (01444) 257733 Fax: (01444) 257744 E-mail: sales@hammertex.co.uk *Textile merchants, converters & fabric stockists*

Hammerwood Film Producers & Distributors, 110 Trafalgar Road, Portslade, Brighton, BN41 1GS Tel: (01273) 277333 Fax: (01273) 705451 E-mail: filmangels@freenetname.co.uk *Film producers & tv programmes & documentary makers*

Hammond & Co. Ltd, Finway Road, Hemel Hempstead Industrial Estate, Hemel Hempstead, Hertfordshire, HP2 7PT Tel: (01442) 212211 Fax: (01442) 252003 E-mail: sales@hammco.com *Gun drilling & gage manufrs*

▶ Hammond, Clive Villas, Cemetery Road, Shelton, Stoke-on-Trent, ST4 2DL Tel: (01782) 202255 Fax: (01782) 202266 E-mail: max@hammondcosschalk.co.uk *Creative Design & Artwork.*

▶ A. Hammond & Sons Ltd, Worton House, Church Street, Sturminster Newton, Dorset, DT10 1DB Tel: (01258) 472394 Fax: (01258) 473716 E-mail: info@a-hammond.co.uk *Building contractors*

▶ Hammond Builders, 9 Tyler Hill Road, Blean, Canterbury, Kent, CT2 9HP Tel: (01227) 470710 Fax: (01227) 470716

Hammond Chemicals Ltd, Canal Street, Brierley Hill, West Midlands, DY5 1JR Tel: (01384) 480600 Fax: (01384) 480680 *Industrial solvent distributors*

Hammond of Hendon Ltd, 189c Brent Crescent, London, NW10 7XR Tel: (020) 8965 5339 Fax: (020) 8965 5338 E-mail: hammondofhendon@btconnect.com *Car body repairers*

▶ The Hammond Recruitment Group, 217 West Street, Fareham, Hampshire, PO16 0ET Tel: (01329) 825925 Fax: (01329) 826926 E-mail: enquiries@hrguk.com *Recruitment services*

Hammond Suddards Edge Solicitors, 148 Edmund Street, Birmingham, B3 2JR Tel: 0121-222 3000 Fax: 0121-222 3001 E-mail: sales@hammondsuddardsedge.com *Solicitors* Also at: Leicester & London

Hammond Vivian Ltd, Power House, 27 Market Road, Richmond, Surrey, TW9 4LZ Tel: (020) 8876 6600 Fax: (020) 8392 1946 E-mail: info@hammondvivian.co.uk *Printers & lithographers*

Hammonds A V S Ltd, 34 -36 Oak End Way, Gerrards Cross, Buckinghamshire, SL9 8BR Tel: (01923) 239733 Fax: (01753) 887163 *Audio visual data equipment services*

Hammonds Furniture Ltd, Great Bridge Road, Bilston, West Midlands, WV14 8LB Tel: (01902) 490133 Fax: (01902) 494936 *Fitted bedrooms showroom & installators*

▶ Hamnavoe Engineering, Cairston Road, Stromness, Orkney, KW16 3JS Tel: (01856) 850576 Fax: (01856) 851200 *Engineering welding & fabricators*

Hamnett Machinery Removals, Gibbet Street, Halifax, West Yorkshire, HX2 0AR Tel: (01422) 345571 Fax: (01422) 346766 E-mail: hamnett@btinternet.com *Machinery, factory & office removals*

Hamon UK Ltd, Units1-2 Ropery Park, Alferd Street, Hull, HU3 2DF Tel: (01482) 787767 Fax: (01482) 706151 E-mail: info.huk@hamon.com Sales Contact: S. Howells *Cooling tower, condenser (air cooled) & dust collecting equipment manufrs*

▶ Hamp Products Ltd, 2F, Everite Road Industrial Estate, Westgate, Widnes, Cheshire, WA8 8RA Tel: 0151-422 0123

Hampco Ltd, Blairs College, South Deeside Road, Blairs, Aberdeen, AB12 5LF Tel: (01224) 860300 Fax: (01224) 860301 E-mail: admin@hampco.com *Consulting & design engineers*

Hampden Test Equipment Ltd, Satra House, Rockingham Road, Kettering, Northamptonshire, NN16 9JH Tel: (01536) 518563 Fax: (01536) 519256 E-mail: hampden-test@satra.co.uk *Testing machine manufrs*

Hampshire Bolt & Tool Supplies Ltd, Armstrong Road, Daneshill East, Basingstoke, Hampshire, RG24 8NU Tel: (01256) 329781 Fax: (01256) 817150 E-mail: jillcorreale@aol.com *Bolt & tool merchants*

Hampshire Canopies, 12 Delme Court, Maytree Road, Fareham, Hampshire, PO16 0HX Tel: (023) 9265 0001 Fax: (01329) 239689 *Window blinds & shop awnings manufrs*

▶ Hampshire Computer Clinics Ltd, 203E West Street, Fareham, Hampshire, PO16 0EN Tel: (023) 9243 5675 E-mail: mail@gosportpccentre.com *IT maintenance, sales & repairs services*

Hampshire Cosmetics Ltd, Brambles House, Waterberry Drive, Waterlooville, Hampshire, PO7 7UW Tel: (023) 9225 7341 Fax: (023) 9226 2003 E-mail: sales@hants-cosmetics.co.uk *Contract manufacturer to the cosmetic & toiletry industries*

Hampshire Electrical, 15 Park Lane, Old Basing, Basingstoke, Hampshire, RG24 7HF Tel: (01256) 359838 Fax: (01256) 364684 *Electrical contract workers*

Hampshire Electroplating Co Ltd, 69-75 Empress Road, Southampton, SO14 0JW Tel: (023) 8022 5639 Fax: (023) 8063 9874 E-mail: enquiries@hepcoltd.co.uk *Heated towel rail manufrs*

Hampshire Grain Ltd, Overton Road, Micheldever Station, Winchester, Hampshire, SO21 3AN Tel: (01962) 774531 Fax: (01962) 774531 E-mail: info@hampshire-grain.co.uk *Agricultural merchants*

Hampshire Insulations Products, Hotel & Conference Centre, Owslebury, Winchester, Hampshire, SO21 1JY Tel: (01962) 777730 Fax: (01962) 777740 E-mail: hampshireinsulations@tiscali.co.uk *Polystyrene manufacturers, insulation supply & conversion*

Hampshire Mezzanine Floors Ltd, Hawkeswood Road, Southampton, SO18 1AB Tel: (023) 8063 1888 Fax: (023) 8023 0033 E-mail: sales@hmf-uk.com *Mezzanine floor/ platform constructors/contractors/manufacturers/ suppliers. Offering full office and mezzanine refurbishment, racking/shelving/partitioning/ ceilings/conveyor systems/office furniture, workstations, etc . Experts at offereing a total solution, covering the South of England.*

Hampshire Mouldings Ltd, Jetpac Works, Gravel Lane, Chichester, West Sussex, PO19 8PG Tel: (01243) 782296 Fax: (01243) 781933 E-mail: sales@oringslimited.co.uk *Industrial rubber product manufrs*

Hampshire Packaging Services Ltd, Unit 3, International House, Spring Hall Road, Burnley, Lancashire, BB11 2LQ Tel: (01282) 434446 Fax: (01282) 484452 *Shrink wrapping machinery manufrs*

Hampshire Polythene Manufacturing Ltd, 2 Queensway, Walworth Industrial Estate, Andover, Hampshire, SP10 5LG Tel: (01264) 332466 Fax: (01264) 356641 *A Family Business since 1987 Better service starts here. We can design and manufacture polythene products to your bespoke specification and in our work we consider all orders - large and small. Bags - plain, coloured & printed. Carrier Bags - plain & coloured (printed not available) Resealable Bags. Refuse Sacks & Bin Liners. Centre-fold polythene Sheeting. Single wound sheeting. Sheets. Pallet Wrap. Layflat Tubing Packaging Tape Providing the best service at the best prices, we supply and deliver nationwide. PROMPT DELIVERY NATIONWIDE Call for a quote Small quantities considered*

The Hampshire Pond Centre, 414 London Road, Portsmouth, PO2 9LB Tel: (023) 9265 0839 *Pond centre*

▶ Hampshire Sewing Machines, 122-124 West Street, Fareham, Hampshire, PO16 0EP Tel: (01329) 280499 Fax: (01329) 280499 E-mail: machines@sewingmachines.uk.com *Retail sewing machine parts & accessories*

Hampshire Sound Services, 39 Fairoak Road, Eastleigh, Hampshire, SO50 6LF Tel: (023) 8061 3339 Fax: (023) 8061 3339 E-mail: hantsound@aol.com *Sound & communications specialists*

Hampshire Tile Warehouse Ltd, Hollybush Industrial Park, Hollybush Lane, Aldershot, Hampshire, GU11 2PX Tel: (01252) 333333 Fax: (0800) 3284481 E-mail: admin@htw.co.uk *Wall & floor tile distributors* Also at: Brighton & Southampton

Hampshire Tile Warehouse Ltd, 5 Grange Industrial Estate, Albion Street, Southwick, Brighton, BN42 4EN Tel: (01273) 597070 Fax: (0800) 3284483 E-mail: admin@htw.co.uk *Ceramic tile distributors*

Hampson Aerospace, 129 Scudamore Road, Leicester, LE3 1UQ Tel: 0116-232 2233 Fax: 0116-232 2311 E-mail: sales@mibert.com *Aircraft engine components manufrs*

Hampson Aerospace Machining Ltd, Pegasus House, Bromford Lane, Birmingham, B24 8DW Tel: 0121-683 6200 Fax: 0121-683 6201 E-mail: info@hampsongroup.com *Precision engineers*

Hampson Composites Ltd, Vale Mill, Vale Street, Bolton, BL2 6QF Tel: (01204) 381626 Fax: (01204) 529457 E-mail: liz@hampson-composites.co.uk *Composite compression moulders*

▶ Hampson Haulage Ltd, 49 Grove Lane, Smethwick, West Midlands, B66 2SZ Tel: 0121-558 3235 Fax: 0121-555 5774

Hampton Cast Stone, Unit 7, Merretts Mill, Woodchester, Stroud, Gloucestershire, GL5 5EU Tel: (01453) 836677 Fax: (01453) 835005 E-mail: sales@hamptoncaststone.co.uk *Cast stone manufrs*

Hampton Colours Ltd, Toadsmoor Mills, Brimscombe, Stroud, Gloucestershire, GL5 2UH Tel: (01453) 731555 Fax: (01453) 731234 E-mail: sales@hamptoncolours.co.uk *Master batch compound manufactures & suppliers of dry colourant blends*

Hampton Leasing Ltd, 7 Mount Mews, High Street, Hampton, Middlesex, TW12 2SH Tel: (020) 8979 2262 Fax: (020) 8941 2645 E-mail: info@messagebase.com *Office business centre & communications services*

Hampton Steel & Wire, London Road, Wellingborough, Northamptonshire, NN8 2DJ Tel: (01933) 233333 Fax: (01933) 442701 E-mail: sales@hamptonsteel.co.uk Principal Export Areas: Africa *Agricultural, domestic & industrial wire products & fencing services*

Hampton Utilities, Meeting House Lane, Balsall Common, Coventry, CV7 7GD Tel: (01676) 534438 E-mail: colin.harrison1@tinyworld.co.uk *Silversmiths manufrs*

▶ Hampton Ventilation, 2 Alexandria Road, Sutton Scotney, Winchester, Hampshire, SO21 3LF Tel: (01962) 760734 Fax: (01962) 760104

Hampton Works Ltd, Twyning Road, Stirchley, Birmingham, B30 2XZ Tel: 0121-458 2901 Fax: 0121-433 3819 E-mail: sales@hampton-works.co.uk *Precision presswork manufrs* Also at: London NW4

▶ Hamson Engineering, 18 Braefoot Avenue, Milngavie, Glasgow, G62 6JZ Tel: 0141-956 4144 Fax: 0141-956 6946 *Packaging manufrs*

Hamster Baskets, Aylhill, Aylton, Ledbury, Herefordshire, HR8 2QJ Tel: (01531) 670209 Fax: (01531) 670630 E-mail: richard@hamsterbaskets.co.uk Principal Export Areas: Worldwide *Plastic coated domestic & industrial wire products & dog cages manufrs*

Hamworthy P.L.C., Fleets Corner, Poole, Dorset, BH17 0JT Tel: (01202) 662600 Fax: (01202) 662636 E-mail: info@hamworthy.com *Marine equipment manufrs*

Hamworthy Combustion Engineering Ltd, Fleets Corner, Poole, Dorset, BH17 0LA Tel: (01202) 662700 Fax: (01202) 669875 E-mail: info@hamworthy-combustion.com Sales Contact: M. Wignall *Manufacturers of combustion systems, flame detection equipment, flare stack (petroleum refinery) ignition systems, gas burners & oil burners (industrial)*

Hamworthy Heating Ltd, Shady Lane, Birmingham, B44 9ER Tel: 0121-360 7000 Fax: 0121-325 2309 E-mail: hayley.miller@hamworthy-heating.com *Manufacturers of fans & flues*

Hamworthy Heating Ltd, Fleets Corner, Poole, Dorset, BH17 0HH Tel: (01202) 662500 Fax: (01202) 662550 E-mail: sales@hamworthy-heating.com *Manufacturers of commercial boilers, water heating & flue systems*

Hamwyn Joinery, Bodenham, Hereford, HR1 3HT Tel: (01568) 797650 Fax: (01568) 797650 *Joinery manufrs*

Hanatek Services Ltd, 10 Sunny Close, Goring-By-Sea, Worthing, West Sussex, BN12 4BD Tel: (01903) 246418 Fax: (01903) 506815 E-mail: info@hanatek.co.uk *Electronic test equipment manufrs*

▶ Hanbury Davies Containers Ltd, 1 Walton Avenue, Felixstowe, Suffolk, IP11 3AG Tel: (01394) 675356 Fax: (01394) 673538

Hanbury Electronics Ltd, Blatchford Close, Blatchford Road Industrial Estate, Horsham, West Sussex, RH13 5RG Tel: (01403) 251300 *Electronic assemblies*

▶ Hanbury FP Ltd, 12 Wharfedale Road, Ipswich, IP1 4JP Tel: (01473) 241516 Fax: (01473) 241517 E-mail: enquiries@hanburyfp.co.uk

Bernard Hancock, Rolle Quay, Barnstaple, Devon, EX31 1JE Tel: (01271) 345545 Fax: (01271) 378777 E-mail: rolle.quay@tiscali.co.uk *Agricultural engineers services*

Hancock Corfield & Waller Ltd, 33 High Street, Ewell, Epsom, Surrey, KT17 1SA Tel: (020) 8394 2785 Fax: (020) 8393 7058 E-mail: hcwltd@compuserve.com *Point of sale advertising*

Hancock & Lant, 164-170 Queens Road, Sheffield, S2 4DH Tel: 0114-272 2176 Fax: 0114-270 0289 *Furniture & carpet wholesalers*

M . Hancock & Son Ltd, Hanover Mills, Mersham, Ashford, Kent, TN25 6NU Tel: (01233) 720871 Fax: (01233) 721200 E-mail: mhancockson@btinternet.com *Agricultural merchants*

R. Hancocks Watch And Clocks Ltd, 17 Warstone Mews, Warstone Lane, Birmingham, B18 6JB Tel: 0121-236 9368 Fax: 0121-233 1358 *Watch, clockmakers & jewellers*

Hand Held Products, 109 Dallam Court, Dallam Lane, Warrington, WA2 7LT Tel: (01925) 240055 Fax: (01925) 631280 E-mail: euro-sales@handheld.com *Bar code scanning equipment manufrs*

▶ Hand & Lock, 86 Margaret Street, London, W1W 8TE Tel: (020) 7580 7488 Fax: (020) 7580 7499 E-mail: enquiries@handembroidery.com *Hand Embroiderers -Military accoutrements,Bespoke embroidery for TV, Film, Theatre, Fashion, Interiors and Private Individuals.*

▶ Hand Made Chocolate Co. Ltd, Unit 10 Pitt Street, Denton, Manchester, M34 6PT Tel: 0161-320 0660 Fax: 0161-320 0770 E-mail: sales@handmadechocolate.co.uk *Chocolate*

Hand Tools Ltd, Stubley Works, Wreakes Lane, Dronfield, Derbyshire, S18 1PN Tel: (01246) 413139 Fax: (01246) 415208 E-mail: handtools@tiscali.co.uk *Garden tool manufrs*

Handcraft Artistic Furniture, Sterling Industrial Estate, Rainham Road South, Dagenham, Essex, RM10 8TX Tel: (020) 8593 0184 Fax: (020) 8984 8384 *High quality reproduction furniture manufrs*

Handcross Aquatics Centre Country Gdn(S), Wyevale Country Gardens, London Road A23, Handcross, Haywards Heath, West Sussex, RH17 6BA Tel: (01444) 401004 Fax: (01444) 401004 *Aquatics centre & water features*

▶ Handell Outdoor, Ware, Hertfordshire, SG12 9WX Tel: (01920) 871228 E-mail: info@handy.uk.com *Camping equipment wholesalers*

Handfield Accessories Ltd, 2 Industrial Centre, Gower Street, Ipswich, IP2 8EX Tel: (01473) 686846 Fax: (01473) 686846 *Gloves & slippers manufrs*

J. Handford & Son Ltd, Milford House, 431 Buxton Road, Stockport, Cheshire, SK2 7HE Tel: 0161-487 3888 Fax: 0161-487 4555 *Limestone, grit stone sand & gravel suppliers*

Handicars, 56 Lee High Road, London, SE13 5PT Tel: (020) 8852 1122 Fax: (020) 8244 2901 E-mail: handicars@freenet.uk.com *Cab & courier services*

Handley Plant & Vehicle Repairs, Ashmead, 62 Petersfield Road, Midhurst, West Sussex, GU29 9JR Tel: (01730) 816785 Fax: (01730) 816785 *Commercial vehicle repairers*

Handley Printers Ltd, 125 Stockport Road West, Bredbury, Stockport, Cheshire, SK6 2AN Tel: 0161-430 8188 Fax: 0161-406 6032 E-mail: puzzhand@aol.com *Colour printers*

Handley Steel Ltd, 4 Burkitt Drive, Tipton, West Midlands, DY4 0QE Tel: 0121-556 7037 Fax: 0121-568 6387 *Steel stockholders & manufrs*

Handley Steel Ltd, Phoenix Works Industrial Estate, Richards Street, Wednesbury, West Midlands, WS10 8BZ Tel: 0121-568 6387 Fax: 0121-568 6387 *Profile cutting services, steel stockholders & steel fabricators*

Handling Aids Ltd, Crowe Arch Lane, Ringwood, Hampshire, BH24 1PB Tel: (01425) 472263 Fax: (01425) 471248 *Trailer manufrs*

The Handling Conceps, Unit E, Swallow Court, Bromsgrove, Worcestershire, B60 4FE Tel: (01527) 570900 Fax: (01527) 570947 E-mail: sales@handlingconcepts.co.uk *Materials handling equipment manufrs*

Handling Logistics Ltd, Unit 45, Oakhill Trading Estate, Devonshire Road, Worsley, Manchester, M28 3PT Tel: (07818) 000968 Fax: (01204) 570350 E-mail: sales@handlinglogistics.co.uk *Suppliers of forklift handling parts & forklift truck accessories*

Handling Techniques Ltd, Units 30-31, Upper Mills Estate, Stonehouse, Gloucestershire, GL10 2BJ Tel: (01453) 826016 Fax: (01453) 823994 E-mail: david@handlingtechniques.co.uk *Materials handling systems manufrs*

Handling Technology, 11 Cavendish Road, Halesowen, West Midlands, B62 0DB Tel: 0121-421 6153 Fax: 0121-423 1709 *Conveyor systems*

Handling Truck Services Ltd, 28-34 Latimer Road, Luton, LU1 3UZ Tel: (01582) 458405 Fax: (01582) 722655 E-mail: sales@handlingtruck.com *Forklift spare parts for all makes, new & used forklift sales and servicing, hydraulic hoses & fittings*

The Handmade Cake Co., 55 St Marks Road, Maidenhead, Berkshire, SL6 6DP Tel: (01628) 770908 Fax: (01628) 639248 E-mail: sales@handmadecake.co.uk *Cake manufrs*

Handmade Curtain Co., 49 Turner Rise, Oadby, Leicester, LE2 5SH Tel: 0116-271 6954 E-mail: info@handmade-curtains.co.uk *Handmade curtains producer*

Handmade Direct, 152-154 Merton Road, London, SW19 1EH Tel: (020) 8542 0321 Fax: (020) 8543 6521 *Handmade furniture manufrs*

Handmade Places, 14 Old Station Way, Bordon, Hampshire, GU35 9HH Tel: (01420) 474111 Fax: (01420) 474222 *Playground equipment manufrs*

Handmade Shoes UK Ltd, Lever Hall, Steelworks Road, Ebbw Vale, Gwent, NP23 6AA Tel: (01495) 309040 Fax: (01495) 301404 *Horse shoe manufr*

Handmade Soap Co. Ltd, Ty'r Waun Bach, Gwernogle, Carmarthen, Dyfed, SA32 7RY Tel: (0870) 0789721 Fax: (01570) 421415 *Manufacture toiletries*

▶ Handmade Wedding Invitations & Stationery By Datz Creationz, 5 Alwin Road, Rowley Regis, West Midlands, B65 8BN Tel: (07759) 820406 E-mail: datzcreationz@blueyonder.co.uk *Handcrafted cards & stationary*

Handmark Engineering, Unit 3c Park Road Industrial Estate, Park Road, Barrow-in-Furness, Cumbria, LA14 4EQ Tel: (01229) 835922 Fax: (01229) 877461 E-mail: enquiries@handmark-engineering.co.uk *Precision machinists & light to heavy fabricators*

Handrail Design Ltd, Sail & Colour Loft, The Historic Dockyard, Chatham, Kent, ME4 4TE Tel: (01634) 817800 Fax: (01634) 817711 E-mail: enquiries@handraildesign.co.uk *Handrail & balustrade manufrs*

▶ handryers.net, Ladybird House, 26 The Avenue, Rubery, Rednal, Birmingham, B45 9AL Tel: (0870) 7542640 Fax: (0870) 7542650 E-mail: info@handryers.net *Leading suppliers of hand dryers*

▶ Hands 3 Communications UK Ltd, The Lodge, Darenth Hill, Dartford, DA2 7QR Tel: (07900) 511526 E-mail: mick@hands3communications.com *tracker and hands free car kit installers*

▶ Hands On, 23 Seldon Road, Worthing, West Sussex, BN11 2LN Tel: 07731 522290 E-mail: info@five-minute-massage-company.com *Corporate and Private Massage*Massage Therapy Services*Corporate Entertainment*Event Services*

Hands On Design & Print Ltd, The Rookery, Flansham Lane, Bognor Regis, West Sussex, PO22 6EP Tel: (01243) 583271 *Hemp & fabric production services*

Company Information

Hands Woodcraft, Northgate, Aldridge, Walsall, WS9 8TH Tel: (01922) 455331 *Pine furniture manufrs*

Hands Of Wycombe, 36 Dashwood Avenue, High Wycombe, Buckinghamshire, HP12 3DX Tel: (01494) 524222 Fax: (01494) 526508 *High quality office furniture manufrs*

▶ Phil Handsaker, 2 St. Johns Road, Tipton, West Midlands, DY4 9PB Tel: (07834) 689399 Fax: 0121-530 2049 E-mail: info@fourfootsnake.com *FourFootSnake this is your chance to win an Ipod... Feeling lucky then come on in!*

▶ Handscombe Financial Planning Ltd, Telford House, 102 Collingdon Street, Luton, LU1 1RX Tel: (01582) 400202 Fax: (01582) 400951 E-mail: advice@handscombes.com *We are Independent Financial Advisers specialising in Life Assurance, Pensions, Retirement Planning, Inheritance Tax & sound Financial Planning. Our Mission at Handscombes is to offer you help & financial advice, to maximize the returns on your money, to minimize the taxes you pay, and to help you construct a permanent income to ensure you can live as you wish for the rest of your life. We also place great emphasis on ensuring that family assets pass to children, grandchildren and other family members, as you direct, and with a minimum of additional tax.*

Handsfree Computing Ltd, Enterprise House, Old London Road, Hickstead, Haywards Heath, West Sussex, RH17 5LZ Tel: (01444) 880880 Fax: (01444) 880888 E-mail: info@hands-free.co.uk *Computer sales development services*

▶ Handsfree Warehouse, 25 Portland Road, Kilmarnock, Ayrshire, KA1 2BT Tel: (01563) 521000 E-mail: david@telecom3.co.uk *Mobile Phone Contracts & Accessories*

Handsome Horses, 195a High Street, Cottenham, Cambridge, CB24 8RX Tel: (01954) 206061 Fax: 01954 206061 E-mail: enquiries@handsomehorses.8k.com *Saddlery seller*

Handsworth Crown Memorial Co., 283 Oxhill Road, Birmingham, B21 8EY Tel: 0121-554 3234 Fax: 0121-554 3234 *Monumental masons*

▶ Handsworth Refractories Ltd, Liverpool Street, Sheffield, S9 2PU Tel: 0114-244 2315 Fax: 0114-256 0559 E-mail: enquiries@hrluk.com *Specialist in new, redundant & spent refractory products*

Handsworth Welding Co., 110 Handsworth New Road, Birmingham, B18 4QE Tel: 0121-554 0137 *Welding specialists*

Handtmann Ltd, 23-24 North Luton Industrial Estate, Sedgewick Road, Luton, LU4 9DT Tel: (01582) 576116 Fax: (01582) 597164 E-mail: enquiries@handtmann.co.uk *Food processing machinery distributors*

▶ Handy Lift, 121a Bitterne Road West, Southampton, SO18 1AR Tel: (023) 8034 7750 Fax: (023) 8034 7752 E-mail: info@handylift.co.uk *Supplier of new & used fork lift trucks also plant hire*

▶ Handy Vans, 23 West Street, Enderby, Leicester, LE19 4LT Tel: 0116-286 9249 E-mail: sales@handyvans.co.uk *Sameday Delivery Service offering a fast, efficent service at great prices.*Full POD Supplied, account facilities available, contracts welcome.*When you next need a Delivery making why not give us a call? We will not be beaten on price for a like for like service.*

▶ HandyFix.It, Clemens Street, Leamington Spa, Warwickshire, CV31 2DL Tel: (01926) 458131 E-mail: info@handyfix.it *Handyfix.it is part of Age Concern Warwickshire and is managed to provide access to vetted and trusted trades people for the residents of Warwickshire*

▶ Handyhire Ltd, Trinity Road, Chelmsford, CM2 6HS Tel: (01245) 353555 Fax: (01245) 493380 E-mail: handyhire@btconnect.com

Handyman, Unit 4 Lower Rectory Farm, Great Brickhill, Milton Keynes, MK17 9AF Tel: (01908) 366228 Fax: (01908) 366661 *Food machinery service & repair*

▶ Handyman Express, 19a Archel Road, London, W14 9QJ Tel: (020) 7385 7751 E-mail: info@handymanexpress.co.uk *A reliable London Handyman Services company that doesn''t charge a call out fee. For all your carpentry, decorating, electrical and plumbing requirements.*

▶ HandyMan Services, Lyell Street, Scarborough, North Yorkshire, YO12 7LW Tel: 01723 378848 E-mail: round@trip82.fsnet.co.uk *HandyMan Services - Residential property care and repair - Specialising in small jobs and emergencies - Assured Friendly Service assisting homeowners and Landlords............ 'Just One Call' © Give Me A Call! The Small Job Solution Crew.....01723 378848 or 07947 771493......Don't delay call today! Plumbing - Electrical - Joinery - Decorating - Locks - Shelves - Curtain Rails - Flat Pack furniture - Glazing - Sockets - Taps - Doors - Sheds - Security Lights - Tap Washers - Toilet Seats - Door Closers - Patio Pressure Washing - Turfing - Hard boarding Floors - Tiling - Change Locks - Wallpapering - Painting - Sash Cords - Fencing - Pictures Hung - Light Fittings - Outside Taps - Doors Eased - Work Tops - Consumer Boards - Kitchens Installed - Sliding Door Wardrobes - Dado Rails - Saniflo replacement - and more!*

▶ Handymann Ltd, 8 Belgowan Street, Bellshill North Industrial Estate, Bellshill, Lanarkshire, ML4 3NS Tel: (01698) 749595 Fax: (01698) 740503 *Vacuum's sales*

▶ Handysoft, 288 Bishopsgate, London, EC2M 4QP Tel: (020) 7959 3042 Fax: (020) 7959 3041

Hane Instruments Ltd, 691 Stirling Road, Slough, SL1 4ST Tel: (01753) 530313 Fax: (01753) 823301 E-mail: info@haneinstruments.co.uk *Hane instruments are precision sheet metal fabrication engineers based in slough with a paint finishing plant in bognor regis.*

Hanes International UK, Unit 11 Trans Pennine Trading Estate, Gorrells Way, Rochdale, Lancashire, OL11 2PX Tel: (01706) 514250 Fax: (01706) 712848 E-mail: sales@hanesindustries.com *Manufacturers of furniture component*

Hanford Trailer Spares, 152 Stone Road, Stoke-on-Trent, ST4 8NS Tel: (01782) 658594 *Trailer & spares manufrs*

▶ Hangersnest Ltd, PO Box 2403, Woodford Green, Essex, IG8 1AL Tel: (07921) 245058 *Hangersnest Ltd is a UK based company that manufactures innovative foldable coat hangers. EasyHanger is a revolutionary product that makes it easy to hang and remove items with a small neck area as well as regular clothes. It can be folded by pressing a button. It is compact and great for travel also.*

Hanging Gardens, The Laurels, Wildmoor Lane, Sherfield-on-Loddon, Hook, Hampshire, RG27 0JD Tel: (01256) 880647 Fax: (01256) 880651 E-mail: sales@hanginggarden.co.uk *Landscape gardening & floral display designers*

▶ Hanjin Shipping, Trinity Terminal, Oysterbed Road, Felixstowe, Suffolk, IP11 4SH Tel: (01394) 606800 Fax: (01394) 673742

▶ Hankinsons Cheshire Ltd, Middlewich Road, Northwich, Cheshire, CW9 7DW Tel: (01606) 338770 Fax: (01606) 48597 E-mail: mail@hankinsons.co.uk

▶ Hankison Ltd, Hazleton Interchange, Lakesmere Road, Horndean, Waterlooville, Hampshire, PO8 9JU Tel: (023) 9257 2828 Fax: (08707) 367377 E-mail: stuart.rielly@airtreatment.spx.com *Manufacturers and suppliers of compressed air treatment equipment, including Refrigerant, Desiccant and Membrane drying technology. Nitrogen generation, compressed air filtration, oil water seperation and condensate management.*

Hankison Ltd, Hazleton Interchange, Lakesmere Road, Horndean, Waterlooville, Hampshire, PO8 9JU Tel: (023) 9257 2828 Fax: (0870) 7367377 E-mail: hankisonuk@aol.com *Compressed air & gas dryer & filter manufrs*

Hankoe Advanced Surface Treatments Ltd, 823 Yeovil Road, Slough Trading Estate, Slough, SL1 4JA Tel: (01753) 522779 Fax: (01753) 539320 E-mail: hankoe@btconnect.com *Powder coating services*

Hanley Precision Tools, 21b Wildmere Road, Banbury, Oxfordshire, OX16 3JU Tel: (01295) 253534 Fax: (01295) 268927 E-mail: sales@glazpart.co.uk *Precision toolmakers*

Hanley Smith Ltd, 7 South Road, Harlow, Essex, CM20 2AP Tel: (01279) 414446 Fax: (01279) 635101 E-mail: info@hanleysmith.co.uk *Aircraft components repair & overhaul services*

Hanlin Export & Import Agents, 167a Wood Lane, Earlswood, Solihull, West Midlands, B94 5JL Tel: (01564) 702116 Fax: (01564) 703978 E-mail: hanlin.uk@btinternet.com *Sheepskin products & chamois products*

Hanlon Computer Systems, Unit 4 Victoria Court, Kent Street, Nottingham, NG1 3LZ Tel: 0115-959 0077 Fax: 0115-941 7432 E-mail: info@hcs-ltd.co.uk *Computer software designers*

Hanlon & Wright Ltd, Tudor House, Park Road, Dukinfield, Cheshire, SK16 5LX Tel: 0161-330 7631 Fax: 0161-330 0436 E-mail: sales@hanlonandwright.co.uk *Specialist machinery handling services*

▶ Hanly Accounting Services, 59 Surbiton Hill Park, Surbiton, Surrey, KT5 8EH Tel: 020 83992074 E-mail: accounting@hanly.co.uk *Hanly Accounting Services provide personalised yet simple bookkeeping solutions tailored to meet the requirements of small businesses as they grow and develop*

▶ P.R. Hanman (Tools), The Market, Burwash Road, Heathfield, East Sussex, TN21 8RA Tel: (01435) 860760 E-mail: tools@hanman.fsnet.co.uk *Restoration & sales of Hand tools*

Hanman Surface Technology, Unit 1-2 Springmill Industrial Estate, Avening Road, Nailsworth, Stroud, Gloucestershire, GL6 0BS Tel: (01453) 833416 Fax: (01453) 834775 *Stove enamelling services*

Hanmere Polythene Ltd, Blackhorse Road, Letchworth Garden City, Hertfordshire, SG6 1HD Tel: (01462) 482222 Fax: (01462) 481096 E-mail: sales@hanmere.co.uk *Polyethylene packaging designers*

Hann Tucker Associates Ltd, Duke House, Duke Street, Woking, Surrey, GU21 5BA Tel: (01483) 770595 Fax: (01483) 729565 E-mail: enquiries@hanntucker.co.uk *Acoustic, vibration & noise control*

Hanna Bros, 80 Moyad Road, Kilkeel, Newry, County Down, BT34 4HH Tel: (028) 4176 2358 Fax: (028) 4176 4909 *Fitted furniture manufrs*

▶ Hannaford, Unit 6, Handley Page Way, Colney Street, St. Albans, Hertfordshire, AL2 2DQ Tel: (01923) 851070 Fax: (01923) 839873 E-mail: email@krhannaford.co.uk *Fine joinery & refurbishment*

Hannaford & Marshall Ltd, Hanmar House, 42 Bethnal Green Road, London, E1 6HZ Tel: (020) 7739 2834 Fax: (020) 7613 0011 E-mail: mail@hanmar.co.uk *Wholesale stationers*

Hannaford Upright Building Services Consulting Engineers, Stuart House, 80-82 Maybury Road, Woking, Surrey, GU21 5JH Tel: (01483) 730221 Fax: (01483) 773970 *Building services consulting engineers*

▶ Hannah & Howie Services Ltd, 26 Tollpark Road, Cumbernauld, Glasgow, G68 0LW Tel: (01236) 737414 Fax: (01236) 457607

Hannahs Pies Of Ormskirk, Bridge Street, Ormskirk, Lancashire, L39 4RJ Tel: (01695) 578385 Fax: (01695) 578385 *Bakery*

▶ Hannaman Engineering, 38 Drome Road, Deeside Industrial Park, Deeside, Clwyd, CH5 2NY Tel: (01244) 288652 Fax: (01244) 280038 E-mail: d.hannamanengltd@btinternet.com *Forklift sales, hire, repair & service*

Hannan Blinds & Window Fashions, 72-74 Plungington Road, Preston, PR1 7RA Tel: (01772) 254140 Fax: (01772) 202198 *Blind retailers*

John W. Hannay & Co. Ltd, Linwood Avenue, East Kilbride, Glasgow, G74 5NE Tel: (01355) 225455 Fax: (01355) 231463 E-mail: sales@hannay.co.uk *Waste paper processors* Also at: Aberdeen, Belfast, Dublin, Dundee, Edinburgh

Hannover Associates, 4 Hurst View Road, South Croydon, Surrey, CR2 7AG Tel: (020) 8688 9541 Fax: (020) 8681 0069 E-mail: sales@hannoverfairs.co.uk *Trade fairs*

Hanover Displays Ltd, Unit 24, Cliffe Industrial Estate, South St, Lewes, East Sussex, BN8 6JL Tel: (01273) 477528 Fax: (01273) 407766 E-mail: sales@hanoverdisplays.com *Passenger information systems manufrs*

Hanover Maloney (U K) Ltd, Westgate, Aldridge, Walsall, WS9 8EX Tel: (01922) 450200 Fax: (01922) 450210 E-mail: info@hanover-maloney.co.uk *Dehydration equipment manufrs*

Hanovia Uv Ltd, 145 Farnham Road, Slough, SL1 4XB Tel: (01753) 515300 Fax: (01753) 534277 E-mail: sales@hanovia.com *UV water treatment manufrs*

Peter Hanratty, Albion Street, Whitehaven, Cumbria, CA28 9AA Tel: (01946) 693954 Fax: (01946) 693954 E-mail: phanratty2003@yahoo.co.uk *Scrap metal merchant & skip hire*

Hans H Meyer Ltd, Unit 15 Haigh Park, Haigh Avenue, Stockport, Cheshire, SK4 1QR Tel: 0161-480 6464 Fax: 0161-480 4082 E-mail: sales@meyer-uk.com *Fork lift truck attachment suppliers*

Hansett Electronics, 38 Kimpton Road, Sutton, Surrey, SM3 9QP Tel: (020) 8644 1777 E-mail: hansett@aol.com *Security systems*

Hanslope Land Link Ltd, White House, Bruisyard, Saxmundham, Suffolk, IP17 2EE Tel: (01728) 638082 Fax: (01728) 638741 *Agricultural products*

Hanslope Pine & Craft, 16 High Street, Hanslope, Milton Keynes, MK19 7LQ Tel: (01908) 510226 Fax: (01908) 510226 *Antique pine furniture retailers*

Hanson Ltd, Cotes Park Industrial Estate, Birchwood Way, Somercotes, Alfreton, Derbyshire, DE55 4NH Tel: (01773) 602432 Fax: (01773) 603134 *Pre-cast floor & stair manufrs*

Hanson Aggregates Ltd, Hall Lane, Bradford, West Yorkshire, BD4 7DN Tel: (0845) 1206293 Fax: (01274) 607855 *Concrete suppliers*

▶ Hanson Aggregates Ltd, Hingston Down Quarry, Gunnislake, Cornwall, PL18 9AU Tel: (01822) 832271 Fax: (01822) 833342

▶ Hanson Aggregates Ltd, Caer Glaw Quarry, Gwalchmai, Holyhead, Gwynedd, LL65 4PW Tel: (01407) 720292 Fax: (01407) 720106 *Quarry*

Hanson Aggregates Ltd, Ashby Road East, Shepshed, Loughborough, Leicestershire, LE12 9BU Tel: (01509) 507050 Fax: (01509) 504120 *Suppliers of aggregates & ready mix concrete & ashfelt*

▶ Hanson Aggregates Ltd, Clee Hill Quarry, Clee Hill, Ludlow, Shropshire, SY8 3QA Tel: (01584) 890516

Hanson Aggregates Ltd, Broad Quay Road, Felnex Industrial Estate, Newport, Gwent, NP19 4PN Tel: (01633) 271728 Fax: (01685) 882005 *Ready mixed concrete delivery*

Hanson Aggregates Ltd, Premix Concrete Plant, Horspath Road, Oxford, OX4 2RP Tel: (01865) 772956 *Concrete products manufrs*

Hanson Aggregates Ltd, Chywoon Quarry, Chywoon, St. Gluvias, Penryn, Cornwall, TR10 9AF Tel: (01209) 860555 Fax: (01209) 860555 *Concrete production*

Hanson Aggregates, Charnley Fold Lane, Bamber Bridge, Preston, PR5 6QJ Tel: (0845) 1205722 *Concrete suppliers*

▶ Hanson Aggregates, Brindister Quarry, Gulberwick, Shetland, ZE2 9EX Tel: (01595) 692401

Hanson Aggregates Ltd, Station Road, South Molton, Devon, EX36 3LL Tel: (01769) 572817 Fax: (01769) 574733 *Manufacturers of building blocks & concrete products*

Hanson Aggregates Ltd, Marine Parade, Southampton, SO14 5JF Tel: (023) 8023 7210 Fax: (023) 8082 8248 *Dredging contractors & ship owners*

▶ Hanson Aggregates Ltd, Ermin Street, Swindon, SN3 4LW Tel: (01793) 822000 *Concrete, ready mixed suppliers*

Hanson Aggregates Ltd, Clifford House, York Road, Wetherby, West Yorkshire, LS22 7NS Tel: (01937) 581977 Fax: (01937) 545889 E-mail: sales.orderswest@hanson-aggregates.com *Aggregate producers, processors, merchants & suppliers*

Hanson Aggregates Ltd, 23 Queen St, Wigan, Lancashire, WN3 4DZ Tel: (01942) 239617 *Ready mixed concrete manufrs*

Hanson Aggregates Ltd, Grovesend, Tytherington, Wotton-under-Edge, Gloucestershire, GL12 8UW Tel: (01454) 416161 Fax: (01454) 411821 *Manufacturers of pre mix cement*

Hanson Aggregates N W Area Office P.L.C., Edge Green Road, Ashton-In-Makerfield, Wigan, Lancashire, WN4 8YA Tel: (01942) 721776 Fax: (0870) 1207422 *Building material manufrs*

Hanson Aggrigates Ltd, Edge Green Road, Ashton-In-Makerfield, Wigan, Lancashire, WN4 8YA Tel: (0845) 1205725 Fax: (01942) 724650 *Supplier of concrete*

▶ Hanson Auto Supplies, 9 Furze Road, Woodbury, Exeter, EX5 1PF Tel: (01395) 233747 Fax: (01395) 233434 *Wholesaler*

▶ Hanson Bath & Portland Stone, Avon Mill Lane, Keynsham, Bristol, BS31 2UG Tel: 0117-986 9631 Fax: 0117-986 7115

Hanson & Beards Ltd, Garden Field, Wyke, Bradford, West Yorkshire, BD12 9NH Tel: (01274) 601010 Fax: (01274) 601666 E-mail: sales@hansonandbeards.co.uk *Shop & office fitters, general joinery & fire door manufrs*

Hanson Brick Ltd, Heather Brick Works, Mill Lane, Heather, Coalville, Leicestershire, LE67 2QE Tel: (01530) 260209 Fax: (01530) 263258 *Brick manufrs*

▶ Hanson Brick Ltd, Station Road, Kirton, Newark, Nottinghamshire, NG22 9LG Tel: (01623) 860481 Fax: (01623) 862064 *Bricks, General Purpose/Building*

Hanson Building Products, Sutton Courtenay Lane, Milton, Sutton Courtenay, Abingdon, Oxfordshire, OX14 4DD Tel: (01235) 811811 Fax: (01235) 510342 E-mail: ron.leese@hamsonplc.com *Concrete block manufrs*

Hanson Building Products, Stewartby, Bedford, MK43 9LZ Tel: (0870) 5258258 Fax: (01234) 762040 E-mail: info@hanson.biz *Building & construction supplies & manufrs* Also at: Branches throughout the U.K.

Hanson Building Products, Unicorn House, Wellington Street, Ripley, Derbyshire, DE5 3DZ Tel: (0870) 5258258 Fax: (01773) 514040 E-mail: info@hanson.biz *Manufacturers of building products*

Hanson Cement Ltd, 3160 Solihull Parkway, Birmingham Business Park, Birmingham, B37 7YN Tel: (0845) 6001616 Fax: 0121-606 1436 E-mail: customer.services@castlecement.co.uk *Cement manufrs* Also at: Bradford, Middlesbrough & Shap

Hanson Cement Ltd, Ribblesdale Works, West Bradford Road, Clitheroe, Lancashire, BB7 4QF Tel: (01200) 422401 Fax: (01200) 414139 *Cement manufrs*

Hanson Cement Ltd, Cefn Mawr Quarry, Pantybuarth, Mold, Flintshire, CH7 5EA Tel: (01244) 550330 Fax: (01352) 742009 *Stone & cement manufr*

Hanson Concrete Products plc, Shepherds Spring Lane, Andover, Hampshire, SP10 1DL Tel: (0845) 6000671 *Ready mixed concrete manufrs*

▶ Hanson Concrete Products plc, Sproughton Road, Ipswich, IP1 5AN Tel: (01473) 461771 Fax: (01473) 464717 E-mail: alanharding@hanson.biz *Manufacturers of concrete beams & concrete blocks*

Hanson Concrete Products plc, 21 Wilden Road, Pattinson Industrial Estate, Washington, Tyne & Wear, NE38 8QB Tel: 0191-417 0066 Fax: 0191-417 0131 E-mail: sales@omnideck.co.uk *Precast concrete permanent formwork suppliers*

Hanson Concrete Products Hoveringham Ltd, Hoveringham Lane, Hoveringham, Nottingham, NG14 7JX Tel: (01636) 832000 Fax: (01636) 832020 E-mail: enquiries@jetfloor.co.uk *Concrete floor manufrs*

Hanson Green, 110 Park Street, London, W1K 6NX Tel: (020) 7493 0837 Fax: (020) 7355 1436 E-mail: info@hansongreen.co.uk *Recruitment agents*

▶ Hanson Logistics Ltd, 303 Brownsburn Industrial Esta, Airdrie, Lanarkshire, ML6 9SE Tel: (01236) 768822

▶ Hanson Myrefield Ltd, North Baileygate, Pontefract, West Yorkshire, WF8 1ES Tel: (01977) 600131 Fax: (01977) 602131 E-mail: sales@hansongarages.co.uk *Manufacturer of concrete sectional garages, workshops & light industrial buildings*

Hanson Plywood Ltd, Unit 15 Drakes Industrial Estate, Shay Lane, Ovenden, Halifax, West Yorkshire, HX3 6RL Tel: (01422) 330444 Fax: (01422) 330706 E-mail: panels@hanson-plywood.co.uk *Importers & distributors of a complete range of panel products. The company offers a bespoke service supplying a complete range of panel products to a wide cross section of customers from some of the most comprehensive stocks held in the UK. The company has built its reputation on supplying customers with almost every type of material available on the market today.*

Hanson Premix plc, Pinfold Lane, Bridlington, North Humberside, YO16 6XP Tel: (01262) 674431 *Ready mixed concrete suppliers*

Hanson Premix plc, Coldstores Road, Cardiff, CF10 4LR Tel: (029) 2046 5383 *Ready mixed concrete manufrs*

Hanson Premix plc, Allerton Park Pit, Allerton Park, Knaresborough, North Yorkshire, HG5 0SD Tel: (0845) 1206297 Fax: (01423) 324967 *Pre mix cement manufrs*

▶ Hanson Premix plc, Endeavour Way, London, SW19 8UH Tel: (020) 8946 7694 Fax: (020) 8947 9182 E-mail: sam.whittington@hansonplc.com *Concrete furniture & stadiums services*

Hanson Premix plc, Stacey Avenue, London, N18 3PL Tel: (020) 8807 4966 Fax: (020) 8803 8714 *Ready mixed concrete to trade & retail*

Hanson Premix, 231 Tunnel Avenue, London, SE10 0QE Tel: (020) 8423 5333 Fax: (020) 8858 1142 *Ready mixed concrete merchants* Also at: Denham, Kings Cross, Twickenham & Wimbledon

Hanson Premix plc, Castle An Dinas, Ludgvan, Penzance, Cornwall, TR20 8AG Tel: (01736) 364455 *Concrete ready mix suppliers*

Hanson Premix plc, Harvil Road, Ickenham, Uxbridge, Middlesex, UB10 8AJ Tel: (01895) 270011 Fax: (01895) 270458 *Concrete & mortar ready mixed suppliers*

▶ Hanson Premix (UK) Ltd, Bulls Lodge Quarry, Generals Lane, Boreham, Chelmsford, CM3 3HR Tel: (01245) 451644 *Concrete production, general aggregates*

Hanson Projects, The Ridge, Chipping Sodbury, Bristol, BS37 6AY Tel: (01454) 338650 Fax: (01454) 338660 E-mail: info@hanson.co.uk *Road surfacing company*

Hanson Q P E, Mill Pond St, Ross-on-Wye, Herefordshire, HR9 7AP Tel: (01989) 563363 *General aggregate suppliers*

▶ Hanson Quarry Products Europe Ltd, The Ridge, Chipping Sodbury, Bristol, BS37 6AY Tel: (01454) 316000 Fax: (01454) 325161

Hanson Quarry Products Europe Ltd, The Ridge, Chipping Sodbury, Bristol, BS37 6AY Tel: (01454) 316000 Fax: (01454) 325161 *Building material suppliers*

▶ Hanson Quickfall Ltd, Enterprise Way, Ladysmith Road, Grimsby, South Humberside, DN32 9TW Tel: (01472) 341117 Fax: (01472) 250212 E-mail: info@hanserve.com

Hanson Recycling & Demolition, Sheffield Bottom, Off Station Road, Theale, Reading, RG7 4AJ Tel: 0118-957 6243 *Removal specialists*

Hanson Springs Ltd, Lincoln Street, Rochdale, Lancashire, OL11 1NP Tel: (01706) 522124 Fax: (01706) 640571 E-mail: sales@hanson-springs.co.uk *Spring manufrs*

Hanson Support Services, Scotter Road South, Bottesford, Scunthorpe, South Humberside, DN17 2BU Tel: (01724) 842637 Fax: (01724) 282411 E-mail: enquiries@hanserve.com *Supplies labour to steel works*

Hanson Textiles Ltd, Surcon House, 11a Copson Street, Manchester, M20 3HE Tel: 0161-718 3888 Fax: 0161-718 3323 E-mail: sales@hansontextiles.co.uk *Tea towels, aprons & tablecloths manufrs*

Hanson Tower Ltd, Hanson House, Knight Road, Rochester, Kent, ME2 2JH Tel: (01634) 713363 Fax: (01634) 721099 E-mail: sales@hanson-tower.com *Leather finishers & manufrs*

Hanson (UK) Ltd, 81A Marlowes, Hemel Hempstead, Hertfordshire, HP1 1LF Tel: (01442) 270444 Fax: (01442) 270666 E-mail: sales@hansonuk.com *Scale manufrs*

Hansson Of Guildford, 108 Woodbridge Road, Guildford, Surrey, GU1 4PY Tel: (01483) 451625 Fax: (01483) 451602 E-mail: sales@hansson-silks.co.uk *For all occasions & needs, exclusive & extensive selection of wedding silks & soft furnishing silks. Silk Dupion, Crepes, Satins, Chiffons, Organza, Georgetts, Duchesse, Zibeline, Velvets, Raw silks, Supreme silk, Jacquard, Brocades, Tartans, Checks, Stripes, I Kat, Prints etc. Also exquisite silk embroideries & french laces*

▶ Hantall Developments Ltd, Kingston Mill, Manchester Road, Hyde, Cheshire, SK14 2BZ Tel: 0161-368 5885 Fax: 0161-351 9082

Hanteck Ltd, 887 Plymouth Road, Slough Trading Estate, Slough, SL1 4LP Tel: (01753) 811550 Fax: (01753) 811551 E-mail: sales@hanteck.com *Power handling equipment manufrs*

Hanwell Glass Co. Ltd, 183 Uxbridge Road, London, W7 3TH Tel: (020) 8567 2186 Fax: (020) 8840 0042 *Double glazing installers*

Hanworth Laboratories Ltd, The Grip, Hadstock Road, Linton, Cambridge, CB21 4XN Tel: (01223) 892217 Fax: (01223) 893623 E-mail: sales@hanworthlabs.co.uk *Manufacturers of toiletries*

Hanworth Timber Co. Ltd, White Post Road, Hanworth, Norwich, NR11 7HN Tel: (01263) 761766 Fax: (01263) 768903 *Timber merchants*

Hapag-Lloyd UK Ltd, Hapag-Lloyd House, 50 Cambridge Road, Barking, Essex, IG11 8HH Tel: (020) 8507 4000 Fax: (020) 8507 4193 E-mail: info.de@hlcl.com *Importers & exporters of clothing* Also at: Birmingham, Glasgow, Liverpool & London EC3

▶ Ha'penny Press, Unit 4 Appletree Barns, Folly Lane, Copdock, Ipswich, IP8 3JQ Tel: (01473) 730055 Fax: (01473) 730169 E-mail: tickets@raffle.co.uk

▶ Happich Profiles Ltd, Unit 31 Fort Industrial Park, Chester Road, Castle Vale, Birmingham, B35 7AR Tel: 0121-748 1005 Fax: 0121-748 1006 E-mail: sales@happich.com *Rubber extrusions manufrs*

▶ Happy Hands Domestic Cleaning Agency, PO Box 30418, London, NW6 7FX Tel: (020) 8451 7070 Fax: (020) 8830 0443 E-mail: paul@happy-hands.biz *Domestic Cleaning Agency and Facilities & Maintenance Agency.*Covers all Areas of London*

Happy Hedgehog Wrought Ironsmiths Ltd, Pascall House, 51 Gatwick Road, Crawley, West Sussex, RH10 9RD Tel: (01293) 611611 Fax: (01293) 510333 E-mail: happyhedgehog@tiscali.co.uk *Ironwork gates, railings, beds, fire furniture, table & chairs manufrs*

Happy Mats Ltd, 23 Mill Road, Glasson, Wigton, Cumbria, CA7 5EE Tel: (01697) 351152 Fax: (01697) 351000 *Stencil mats manufrs*

▶ Happy Paws, Wilfrids Cottage, Primrose Hill, East Coker, Yeovil, Somerset, BA22 9NH Tel: (07971) 256582 *Doggy Day Care in our Home, Dog Walking, Pet to Vet Taxi and Home Pet Visits in Yeovil,Crewkerne, Chard, Ilminster and surrounding areas (Somerset, UK). Police Checked, Fully Insured and References Available. Friendly, experienced and reliable service.*

Happy Talk, 17 Gateside Street, Hamilton, Lanarkshire, ML3 7HT Tel: (01698) 282813 Fax: (01698) 282813 *Novelty balloon suppliers*

▶ Happy Tuesdays Ltd, 11 Woodstock Avenue, West Ealing, London, W13 9UQ Tel: (0796) 6207504 Fax: (020) 8537 0849 E-mail: ianm@happytuesdays.co.uk *Automated graphics systems for television, using vizRT, ventuz; Editing, and special effects, compositing using After Effects/Fusion; Programming using Flex, Flash, C#; Web site production using ASP, PHP and video streaming.*

Haqson Corporation, 12 Neville Road, Wirral, Merseyside, CH62 7JE Tel: 0151-334 9796 *Protective clothing manufrs*

Harada Industries Europe Ltd, Bell Heath Way, Birmingham, B32 3BZ Tel: 0121-423 2222 Fax: 0121-423 2121 E-mail: hie@harada.co.uk *Aerial & antenna manufrs*

▶ Harbeam Systems, Merlin House, 122-126 Kilburn High Road, London, NW6 4HY Tel: (020) 7692 0879 Fax: (020) 8529 1793

Harbec Services, 1A Leaphill Road, Pokesdown, Bournemouth, BH7 6LS Tel: (01202) 417725 Fax: (01202) 417732 E-mail: sales@harbec.co.uk *Ventilation & air duct cleaning*

Harber Display Ltd, 10 Park Road, Irthlingborough, Wellingborough, Northamptonshire, NN9 5PW Tel: (01933) 624079 Fax: (01933) 460253 E-mail: harbersales@btconnect.com *Display equipment suppliers*

Harbeth Audio Ltd, 3 Lindfield Enterprise Park, Lewes Road, Lindfield, Haywards Heath, West Sussex, RH16 2LH Tel: (01444) 484371 Fax: (01444) 487629 E-mail: sound@harbeth.co.uk *Loudspeaker manufacturers & designers*

Harbex Profiling & Grinding Ltd, Blackberry Farm, High Oak Hill, Bobbing, Sittingbourne, Kent, ME9 8QD Tel: (01795) 842925 Fax: (01795) 843868 E-mail: sales@harbex.co.uk *Profile cutting services*

Harbison-Walker Refractories Ltd, Dock Road South, Bromborough, Wirral, Merseyside, CH62 4SP Tel: 0151-641 5900 Fax: 0151-641 5910 E-mail: sales@hwr.co.uk *Refractory materials*

Harborlite (UK) Ltd, The Westwood, Beverley, North Humberside, HU17 8RQ Tel: (01482) 645265 Fax: (01482) 641176 *Perlite filter media manufrs*

Harborne Garage Ltd, 2 Ewhurst Avenue, Birmingham, B29 6EY Tel: 0121-472 4300 Fax: 0121-472 4400 E-mail: admin@harbornegarage.co.uk *Motor vehicle body repair & servicing*

The Harborough Rubber Co. Ltd, Riverside, Market Harborough, Leicestershire, LE16 7PT Tel: (01858) 410610 Fax: (01858) 410006 E-mail: admin@harboro.co.uk *Qualified provider of custom moulded solutions within automotive, electronics, aerospace, defence and other markets. UK based production facilities combined with global manufacturing partners, supplying moulded rubber parts and associated assembly services, extrusions and seals, keypads, foam parts and rubber to metal bondings throughout the world.*

Harbour, Unit 4 Premier Industrial Units, Castle Street, Castlepark Industrial Estate, Ellon, Aberdeenshire, AB41 9RF Tel: (01358) 722422 Fax: (01358) 722880 E-mail: harboureng@btinternet.com *Steel & aluminium stockholders*

▶ Harbour Haulage Ltd, Damhead Way, Peterhead, Aberdeenshire, AB42 3GY Tel: (01779) 481410 Fax: (01779) 490727

Harbour Jig & Tool Ltd, 1a Harwoods Road, Watford, WD18 7RB Tel: (01923) 231112 Fax: (01923) 232330 E-mail: harbourjigtools1@btconnect.com *Welders, fabricators & machinists*

Harbour Marine Services Ltd, Blackshore, Southwold, Suffolk, IP18 6TA Tel: (01502) 724721 Fax: (01502) 722060 E-mail: johnbuckley@harbourmarine.uk.com *Boat builders & chandlery*

Harbour Welding Services Ltd, 91-93 Sterte Avenue West, Poole, Dorset, BH15 2AL Tel: (01202) 668692 Fax: (01202) 666158 E-mail: harbourwelding@btopenworld.com *Welding fabrication*

Harbridge (Sheet Metal) Ltd, Philip Street, St. Philips Marsh, Bristol, BS2 0TA Tel: 0117-977 8850 Fax: 0117-977 5145 E-mail: harbridge@totalise.co.uk *Ductwork, ducting fabricators*

Harbro Ltd, Unit 6 Admiralty Site, Corpach, Fort William, Inverness-Shire, PH33 7NA Tel: (01397) 772434 Fax: (01397) 773159 *Feed & agricultural supplies manufrs*

Harbro Ltd, Steven Road, Huntly, Aberdeenshire, AB54 8SX Tel: (01466) 793405 Fax: (01466) 794575 *Agricultural merchants*

Harbro Ltd, Unit 2 Station Road Industrial Estate, Mintlaw, Peterhead, Aberdeenshire, AB42 5EE Tel: (01771) 622627 Fax: (01771) 622903 E-mail: sales@harbro.co.uk *Animal food suppliers*

Harbro Country Stores, Agricultural Centre, Staney Hill Industrial Estate, Lerwick, Shetland, ZE1 0QY Tel: (01595) 693744 Fax: (01595) 696741 *Agricultural food producers*

Harbro Supplies Ltd, Morland Street, Bishop Auckland, County Durham, DL14 6JG Tel: (01388) 605363 Fax: (01388) 603263 E-mail: harbrosupplies@hotmail.com *Stone & monumental masons requisites & quarries*

Harbrook Engineering, Limefield House, Wrexham Road, Burland, Nantwich, Cheshire, CW5 8ND Tel: (01270) 524263 Fax: (01270) 524343 E-mail: sales@steelfabrication.co.uk *Steel fabricators*

Harbruc Engineering Co., Charlwoods Road, East Grinstead, West Sussex, RH19 2HU Tel: (01342) 315775 Fax: (01342) 327298 E-mail: sales@harbruc.com *Handling equipment distributors*

Harco Engineering Ltd, Canal Street, Harts Hill, Brierley Hill, West Midlands, DY5 1JJ Tel: (01384) 480280 Fax: (01384) 480399 E-mail: info@harcoeng.co.uk *Precision machining services*

Harcol Ltd, 5 Croxstalls Road, Walsall, WS3 2XU Tel: (01922) 494951 Fax: (01922) 710370 E-mail: harcol@engs.fslife.co.uk Principal Export Areas: Central/East Europe & West Europe *CNC engineers*

▶ Harcourt Ltd, 465 Hornsey Road, London, N19 4DR Tel: (020) 7281 4555 Fax: (020) 7281 4888 E-mail: info@harcourt.uk.com *Leatherwork, upholstery & furniture manufrs*

Harcourt Education, Linacre House, Jordan Hill, Oxford, OX2 8DP Tel: (01865) 888000 Fax: (01865) 314222 *Book publishers*

▶ Harcourts Civil Engineering, Cross Green Approach, Leeds, LS9 0SG Tel: 0113-391 8210 Fax: 0113-391 8219

Harcross Engineering Co. Ltd, Unit 1 The Ember Centre, Hersham, Walton-On-Thames, Surrey, KT12 3PU Tel: (01932) 222201 Fax: (01932) 224722 E-mail: sales@harcross-eng.co.uk *Packaging equipment/machine/systems & machine knife manufrs*

Harcross Engineering Barnstaple Ltd, Pilland Way, Pottington Business Park, Barnstaple, Devon, EX31 1LP Tel: (01271) 372235 Fax: (01271) 344642 *Tapping machine & pneumatic clamps & pinion lifters manufrs*

Hard Anodising Ltd, Firs Industrial Estate, Kidderminster, Worcestershire, DY11 7QN Tel: (01562) 865158 Fax: (01562) 66118 E-mail: sales@hard-anodising.co.uk *Hard anodising processors or services*

▶ Hard Rock UK, 2a Lowercroft Business Park, Lowercroft Road, Bury, Lancashire, BL8 3PA Tel: 0161-762 4106 Fax: (01706) 220795 E-mail: sales@hardrockuk.co.uk *Polished stone products suppliers*

J. Hardacre Ltd, Gannow Lane, Burnley, Lancashire, BB12 6JX Tel: (01282) 415155 Fax: (01282) 457904 *Cook meads & baking suppliers*

Hardacre & Maltpress Ltd, Fernhill Road, Bootle, Merseyside, L20 9EA Tel: 0151-933 9592 Fax: 0151-922 1501 E-mail: hardmalt@liverpool1985.freeserve.co.uk *Electrical engineers & contractors*

Hardakers Removal & Storage Ltd, 87-89 Gillett Street, Hull, HU3 4JF Tel: (01482) 323069 Fax: (01482) 580652 E-mail: enquries@hardakers.co.uk *Removal & storage contractors*

▶ Hardall International Ltd, Fairway Works, Southfields Road, Dunstable, Bedfordshire, LU6 3EP Tel: (01582) 500860 Fax: (01582) 690975 E-mail: sales@hardall.co.uk *Manufacture refuge chutes*

James Harden, 85 Falls Road, Belfast, BT12 4PE Tel: (028) 9029 0700 *Furniture reproducers*

Harden Pumps & Tanks Ltd, Unit 1 Vantage Point, Howley Park Road East, Morley, Leeds, LS27 0SU Tel: 0113-253 3152 Fax: 0113-252 7394 E-mail: sales@hardenpumps.co.uk *The supply, installation and service of Commercial Fuelling Equipment including storage tanks, dispensing pumps, key and card electronic control units and all ancilliary equipment.*

Harder Bros, Valley Road, Morley, Leeds, LS27 8EX Tel: 0113-253 5325 Fax: 0113-252 4522 E-mail: harderbros@aol.com *Sausage casing manufrs*

Hardex Fittings, Shilton Industrial Estate, Bulkington Road, Coventry, CV7 9JY Tel: (024) 7658 7600 Fax: (024) 7658 7606 E-mail: enquiries@hardex.co.uk *Furniture fittings distributors*

Joseph Hardgrave Ltd, 42-44 Church Lane, Bishopthorpe, York, YO23 2QG Tel: (01904) 704161 Fax: (01904) 703711 *Roofing contractors*

Hardie Polymers Ltd, 53 Stockiemuir Avenue, Bearsden, Glasgow, G61 3JJ Tel: 0141-942 3330 Fax: 0141-942 4001 *Plastics sales agency & distributor*

Hardie Secure Products Ltd, 17 Station Road, Flitwick, Bedford, MK45 1JT Tel: (01525) 716736 Fax: (01525) 716736 E-mail: hsfabrications@msn.com *Steel, stainless steel & aluminium fabricators*

William Hardill Sons & Co. Ltd, Westbury Works, Sticker Lane, Bradford, West Yorkshire, BD4 8RU Tel: (01274) 664422 Fax: (01274) 664433 E-mail: info@hardill.demon.co.uk *Pulley & conveyor belt drum manufrs*

Harding Bros Shipping Contractors Ltd, Avonmouth Way, Bristol, BS11 8DD Tel: 0117-982 5961 Fax: 0117-982 7276 E-mail: sc@hardingbros.co.uk *Shipping suppliers & contractors* Also at: Tilbury

E. Harding & Sons Ltd, Units 10 & 11, Walker Industrial Estate, Walker Road, Guide, Blackburn, BB1 2QE Tel: (01254) 581276 Fax: (01254) 677012 E-mail: sales@ehardings.co.uk Purchasing Contact: J. Fitzgerald Sales Contact: R. Hutchinson *Profile cutting services & stainless steel plate sawing & profiling cutting services, also stainless*

Harding Electricals Distributors, 475-499 Lichfield Road, Birmingham, B6 7SP Tel: 0121-326 9229 Fax: 0121-328 0589 E-mail: aston.268@eel.co.uk *Electrical components distributors* Also at: Bristol

F. Harding (Macclesfield) Ltd, Kershaw Mill, Newton Street, Macclesfield, Cheshire, SK11 6QJ Tel: (01625) 429625 Fax: (01625) 612836 E-mail: sales@f-harding.com Principal Export Areas: Worldwide *Doubled, polypropylene & hose yarns manufrs*

▶ Harding Internet, 11 Whitehouse Wynd, West Rounton, Northallerton, North Yorkshire, DL6 2LY Tel: (01609) 882080 Fax: (01609) 882085 E-mail: enquiries@harding.co.uk *Web site design & e-commerce specialists*

Harding McDermott & Partners, 12 Exmouth Market, London, EC1R 4QE Tel: (020) 7833 9533 Fax: (020) 7833 3633 *Consultant engineers*

Samuel Harding & Sons Ltd, 57 Bath Lane, Leicester, LE3 5BA Tel: 0116-262 3000 Fax: 0116-262 9000 *Industrial development company*

Harding-Crosweller, Unit G Imber Court Trading Estate, Orchard La, East Molesey, Surrey, KT8 0BY Tel: (020) 8398 9625 Fax: (020) 8398 7486 *Consulting engineers & designers*

Hardings, Old Express Yard, Corwen Road, Pontybodkin, Mold, Clwyd, CH7 4TG Tel: (01352) 771575 *Vehicle repair services*

Hardings Bakery, Oldlands, Alphington Street, Exeter, EX2 8AU Tel: (01392) 255062 *Bread manufrs*

Harding's International Coaches, Oxleasow Road, Redditch, Worcestershire, B98 0RE Tel: (01527) 525200 *Coach hire*

Harding's Oriental Food Supplies, Parlas, 3-5 Stanhope, South Shields, Tyne & Wear, NE33 4BA Tel: 0191-454 2000 Fax: 0191-454 2005 E-mail: hofs@perlas.co.uk *Oriental food suppliers*

Hardman & Cain Fencing Ltd, Stotts Pit Yard, Church Street, Westhoughton, Bolton, BL5 3QW Tel: (01942) 815312 Fax: (01942) 815312 E-mail: enquiries@hardmancainfencing.co.uk *Fencing & concrete post manufrs*

▶ Hardman Construction Ltd, Brow Top, Quernmore, Lancaster, LA2 0QW Tel: (01524) 845456

John Hardman Trading Co. Ltd, Lightwoods House, Lightwoods Park, Hagley Road West, Birmingham, B67 5DP Tel: 0121-429 7609 Fax: 0121-420 2316 E-mail: info@hardmantrading.com *Artists in stained glass*

Hardmet Grinding Co., 18 The Meadows, Houston, Johnstone, Renfrewshire, PA6 7DJ Tel: (01505) 615066 Fax: (01505) 615066 *Engineers merchants*

▶ Hardmetal Engineering Cornwall Ltd, Treleigh Industrial Estate, Jon Davey Drive, Redruth, Cornwall, TR16 4AX Tel: (01209) 202809 Fax: (01209) 202819

continued

E-mail: sales@tungsten-carbide.com Sales Contact: A. Hosking Principal Export Areas: Worldwide *High precision machining of hard & difficult metals especially Tungsten Carbide. We provide a subcontract and support service to a wide range of industries using CNC wire & spark erosion, CNC milling, CNC turning, grinding (internal, surface, profile,) fine drilling, polishing, honing.*

Hardre Knitwear Ltd, 12 Briton Street, Leicester, LE3 0AA Tel: 0116-254 9784 Fax: 0116-285 4624 E-mail: s.harbot@hardreknitwear.co.uk *Knitwear manufrs*

Hardware Associates Ltd, Colhook Indust Park, Petworth, West Sussex, GU28 9NB Tel: (01428) 707900 Fax: (01428) 707866 E-mail: sales@hardwarespairs.com *Dell computers spare parts suppliers*

▶ Hardware.com Ltd, Inda House, The Mallards, Broadway Lane, South Cerney, Cirencester, Glos, GL7 5TQ Tel: (01285) 869483 Fax: (01285) 776325 E-mail: enquiries@hardware.com *Hardware.com supply new & refurbished 3Com, Alcatel, Cisco, Dell, Emulex, Epicenter, Extreme, Foundry, HP, IBM, MGE, Nortel, Polycom, PowerDsine, Prolabs, Sun, Usystems plus approved & compatible GBICs, memory, cables and accessories.*

▶ Hardwareability Computer Systems, Endeavour House, 8a Cambridge Road, Kingston upon Thames, Surrey, KT1 3JU Tel: (020) 8547 3600 Fax: (020) 8547 3698

The Hardwicke Collection, Castee Works, 21 Sandy Lane, Aston, Birmingham, B62 1TP Tel: 0121-326 7013 Fax: 0121-327 9964 *Gift manufrs*

Hardwicks, 32 Greenfield Road, Newport Pagnell, Buckinghamshire, MK16 8DA Tel: (01908) 217315 Fax: (01908) 617617 *Office equipment repair*

Hardwood Dimensions Ltd, Trafford Park Road, Trafford Park, Manchester, M17 1WH Tel: 0161-872 5111 Fax: 0161-873 7004 E-mail: sales@hardwooddimensions.ltd.uk *Timber import & export merchants. FSC Beech, Beech, FSC Ash, Ash, Maple, Rosewood, Edge Laminated Panels.*

Hardwood Interiors Ltd, 1 Whitethorn Gardens, Croydon, CR0 7LL Tel: (020) 8656 9520 Fax: (020) 8656 9520 *Partition & office interior services*

▶ Hardwood Timber Products Ltd, 3 West Coppice Road, Coppice Industrial Estate, Walsall, WS8 7HB Tel: (01543) 370370 Fax: (01543) 375280

Hardy Antiques, Wisteria Cottage, The Street, Hacheston, Woodbridge, Suffolk, IP13 0DS Tel: (01728) 746568 Fax: (01728) 746568 *Antique pine furniture retailers*

Hardy Engineering, Unit D Foundry Lane, Burnham-on-Crouch, Essex, CM0 8SH Tel: (01621) 782726 Fax: (01621) 785645 E-mail: email@hardyengineering.com Principal Export Areas: Worldwide *Marine & hydraulic engineering services*

Hardy Fabrics Ltd, 565 Blandford Road, Poole, Dorset, BH16 5BW Tel: (01202) 631637 Fax: (01202) 632918 E-mail: sales@hardyfabrics.com *Furnishing fabric*

Hardy & Hanson Ltd, Summit Works, Longlands Road, Staincliffe, Dewsbury, West Yorkshire, WF13 4AB Tel: (01924) 462353 Fax: (01924) 457883 E-mail: enquiries@hardy-hanson.co.uk Principal Export Areas: Worldwide *Manufacturers of felt components including display*

Hardy J, 64a Ballinderry Bridge Road, Coagh, Cookstown, County Tyrone, BT80 0BT Tel: (028) 8673 7134 Fax: (028) 8673 7134 *Agricultural machinery repairers*

Hardy Marine Ltd, Gaymers Way, North Walsham, Norfolk, NR28 0AN Tel: (01692) 408700 Fax: (01692) 406483 E-mail: sales@hardymarine.co.uk *Boat builders*

Hardy Sheet Metal, 156 Sandridge Road, St. Albans, Hertfordshire, AL1 4AP Tel: (01727) 837833 Fax: (01727) 837833 *Sheet metalworkers & welding fabricators*

Hardy Sherwood Special Projects Ltd, 32 Hemmells, Basildon, Essex, SS15 6ED Tel: (01268) 417733 Fax: (01268) 541135 E-mail: specialproducts@hardysherwood.fsnet.co.uk *Industrial roofing & cladding*

Hardy Signs, Unit 10 Falcon Close, Burton-on-Trent, Staffordshire, DE14 1SG Tel: (01283) 569102 Fax: (01283) 540001 E-mail: sales@hardysigns.co.uk *Sign manufrs*

▶ Hardy Technical Services Ltd, 69 Lake Drive, Hainworthy, Poole, Poole, Dorset, BH15 4LR Tel: (01202) 674916 Fax: (0871) 2420922 E-mail: info@hardytechnicalservices.co.uk *Provide computing solutions to both business & private users*

Hardy UK Ltd, 175 Fernhill Road, Bootle, Merseyside, L20 9DU Tel: 0151-922 2291 Fax: 0151-933 4164 E-mail: hardyuk@aol.com *Machine knife manufrs*

Hardy's D.I.Y. Ltd, 652 Warwick Rd, Tyseley, Birmingham, B11 2HJ Tel: 0121-706 2646 Fax: 0121-624 2662 *Do-it-yourself materials distribs*

James Hare Ltd, PO Box 72, Leeds, LS1 1LX Tel: 0113-243 1204 Fax: 0113-234 7648 E-mail: sales@jameshareilks.co.uk *Silk merchants*

▶ Hare & Ransome, Unit 9a Ebor Industrial Estate, Hallfield Road, York, YO31 7XQ Tel: (01904) 438833 Fax: (01904) 438825 E-mail: mail@hareandransome.com *Specialist in architectural joinery*

William Hare Ltd, Brandlesholme House, Brandlesholme Road, Bury, Lancashire, BL8 1JJ Tel: 0161-609 0000 Fax: 0161-609 0491 E-mail: hq@hare.co.uk Principal Export Areas: Worldwide *Structural engineers services* Also at: Astley & Bury

▶ William Hare Ltd, Orchard Court, Dunslow Road, Eastfield, Scarborough, North Yorkshire, YO11 3UT Tel: (01723) 584121 Fax: (01723) 582310 E-mail: hq@hare.co.uk *Structural engineers*

Company Information

▶ Haredata Electronics Ltd, 14 Crown House, Hornbeam Square North, Hornbeam Park, Harrogate, North Yorkshire, HG2 8PB Tel: (01423) 853180 Fax: (01423) 853199 E-mail: sales@haredata.co.uk *Haredata Electronics, now in our 24th year, offer a true one stop shop for Power Supplies, Chargers and Battery Packs. As the sole UK Agent for FRIWO Geratebau GmbH, we have the knowledge and experience to support your business growth." Friwo, one of the worlds leading manufacturers of low voltage Power Supplies, combine the flexibility and responsiveness of European Manufacture with the competitive cost of Far East Manufacture." With links to volume battery manufacturers from Europe and the Far East, we are confident that we can supply the right pack for your Charger from one source.*

Harefield Doors Ltd, 7 Chiltern Trading Estate, Earl Howe Road, Holmer Green, High Wycombe, Buckinghamshire, HP15 6QT Tel: (01494) 716316 Fax: (01494) 718198 E-mail: sales@harefielddoors.co.uk *PVC & grp door suppliers*

Hares Of Snape Holdings Ltd, Manor House, Snape, Bedale, North Yorkshire, DL8 2TA Tel: (01677) 470269 Fax: (01677) 470681 *Steel erectors & fabricators*

▶ Hareslade Webs, 32 Hareslade, Bishopston, Swansea, SA3 3DX Tel: (01792) 234782 E-mail: p.hailey@virgin.net *Ecommerce services for S.M.E"s, web design, South/Mid Wales UK preferred area*

Harewood Products Ltd, Unit 1, Union Road, The Valley, Bolton, BL2 2DT Tel: (01204) 395730 Fax: (01204) 388018 E-mail: info@adboards.com *Harewood Products Ltd - Adboards was established in 1984 and is a British manufacturer of educational High quality presentation and display products. The product range includes - pinable noticeboards, fire rated Blazemaster noticeboards, dry wipe whiteboards, lockable tamperproof noticeboards, fire rated Blazemaster lockable tamperproof noticeboards, internal and external showcases, folding panel display boards, large foyer display boards, glass showcases, column boards for use with interactive whiteboards, quick change snap frames, and rail mounted board systems. Their 32,000 sq. ft. factory is based in Bolton, Lancashire and has a showroom open daily. Adboards supplies retail businesses, schools, colleges, universities and local education authorities with an extensive range of presentation equipment to a high quality standard. Harewood Products Ltd prides itself in high manufacturing standards, quick delivery time due to a large stock holding, and friendly and efficient service.*

▶ Harfield Bros Contracting Ltd, Unit C4, Premiere Bus Centre, Speedfield Industrial Estate, Fareham, Hampshire, PO14 1TY Tel: (01329) 827567 Fax: (01329) 828639 E-mail: office@harfieldbros.com

Harford Ceramics, Susan Clough Designs, 13 The Paddocks, Burke Road, Totnes, Devon, TQ9 5XT Tel: (01803) 864780 Fax: (01803) 862036 *Ceramic product manufrs*

Harford Cost Control, 35 Harford Street, Flat 2, Trowbridge, Wiltshire, BA14 7HL Tel: (01225) 764461 Fax: (01225) 769733 E-mail: admin@harfordcontrol.com *Weight control & quality system*

Hargood Engineers Ltd, 134a Virginia Street, Southport, Merseyside, PR8 6SP Tel: (01704) 534668 Fax: (01704) 501862 E-mail: john@hargood-eng.freeserve.co.uk *Precision engineering*

▶ Hargreaves Bulk Liquid Transport, Fryers Road, Walsall, WS3 2XJ Tel: (01922) 470799 Fax: (01922) 470790 *Haulage services*

Hargreaves Construction Co. Ltd, Rustington House, Worthing Road, Rustington, Littlehampton, West Sussex, BN16 3PS Tel: (01903) 777777 Fax: (01903) 777700 *Property developers*

Hargreaves Foundry Drainage Ltd, Carr House, Water Lane, Halifax, West Yorkshire, HX3 9HG Tel: (01422) 330607 Fax: (01422) 320349 E-mail: sales@hargreavesfoundry.co.uk *Iron founders*

Hargreaves Hamilton Gears Ltd, Nelson Mill Gaskell Street, Bolton, BL1 2QE Tel: (01204) 456190 Fax: (01204) 371355 *Gears engineering & manufrs*

Hargreaves Hamilton Gears Ltd, PO Box 33, Bolton, BL1 2QE Tel: (01204) 456190 Fax: (01204) 364002 E-mail: info@hargreaveshamilton.co.uk *Textile machinery merchants & industrial systems manufrs*

James Hargreaves (Bacup) Ltd, Irwell Mill, Lee Street, Bacup, Lancashire, OL13 0AG Tel: (01706) 874701 Fax: (01706) 877005 E-mail: info@jameshargreaves.co.uk *Stockinet, industrial wipers & cleaning products suppliers & manufrs*

John Hargreaves (Collyhurst & Stalybridge) Ltd, Knowl Street, Stalybridge, Cheshire, SK15 3AJ Tel: 0161-338 6011 Fax: 0161-338 4194 E-mail: jack@john-hargreaves.co.uk *Corrugated paper & board manufrs*

Hargreaves & Son Ltd, 16-18 Spring Gardens, Buxton, Derbyshire, SK17 6DE Tel: (01298) 23083 Fax: (01298) 25323 E-mail: hargreaves.son@freeuk.com *Cookware, gifts & crystal retailers*

Hargreaves Sports Ltd, 2-3 Solent Twentyseven, Walton Road, Portsmouth, PO6 1SX Tel: (023) 9232 1200 Fax: (023) 9237 1212 E-mail: sales@hargreaves-sports.co.uk *Sports equipment & retailers*

Harkess Ord Ltd, Bellerive House, 3 Muirfield Crescent, Docklands, London, E14 9SZ Tel: (020) 7459 3300 Fax: (020) 7459 3333 *Corporate image consultants*

Harkison Petermill Crafts, 2 Block 3 Lochshore South Industrial Estate, Caledonia Place, Glengarnock, Beith, Ayrshire, KA14 3AZ Tel: (01505) 683353 Fax: (01505) 683353 *Pewter giftware manufrs*

Harkness Hall Ltd, Norton Road, Stevenage, Hertfordshire, SG1 2BB Tel: (01438) 725200 Fax: (01438) 344400 E-mail: sales@harkness-screens.com *Projection surfaces & systems for cinema*

Harland Machine Systems, 2 Michigan Ave, Salford, Manchester, M50 2GY Tel: 0161-848 4800 Fax: 0161-848 4830 E-mail: enquiries@harland-hms.com *Design & manufacture of a comprehensive range of high quality, reliable, efficient & cost effective pressure sensitive (PS) label handling & application systems* Also at: Baldock, France, USA and China

Harland & Wolff Ltd, Queens Island, Belfast, BT3 9DU Tel: (028) 9045 8456 Fax: (028) 9045 8515 E-mail: webmaster@harland-wolff.com *Ship builders*

Harlands of Hull Ltd, Burma Drive, Hull, HU9 5SD Tel: (01482) 785300 Fax: (01482) 785329 E-mail: enquiries@harlands.co.uk *Self-adhesive labels manufrs*

Harlech Tool & Engineering Co., 5 Ynyscedwyn Industrial Estate, Trawsffordd Road, Ystradgynlais, Swansea, SA9 1DT Tel: (01639) 849044 Fax: (01639) 849045 E-mail: info@harlech-tools.co.uk *Precision engineers*

Harlequin Colour Laboratories, 6 Newlands End, Basildon, Essex, SS15 6DU Tel: (01268) 540932 Fax: (01268) 541633 E-mail: harlequincolour@aol.com *Exhibition stand builders*

▶ Harlequin Colour Press, Coedcae Lane, Pontyclun, Mid Glamorgan, CF72 9EW Tel: (01443) 222219 Fax: (01443) 226544

▶ Harlequin Electrical, Kings Close Cottage, South Walsham Road, North Burlingham, Norwich, NR13 4EJ Tel: (0800) 5118978 Fax: (01603) 270415 E-mail: info@harlequinelectrical.co.uk *Engineering services to manufacturing & industry*

Harlequin Fabric & Wallcoverings Ltd, Ladybird House, Beeches Road, Loughborough, Leicestershire, LE11 2HA Tel: (0870) 8300355 Fax: (0870) 8300359 E-mail: sales@harlequin.uk.com *Fabric, wallpaper & vinyl distributors*

Harlequin Fixings & Sealants Ltd, 23 East Main Street, Darvel, Ayrshire, KA17 0HR Tel: (01560) 323832 Fax: (01560) 320361 *Fastener suppliers*

Harlequin Foods Ltd, Harlequin Avenue, Great West Road, Brentford, Middlesex, TW8 9EQ Tel: (020) 8560 3211 Fax: (020) 8326 1530 *Frozen food processors & products distributors*

▶ Harlequin Kitchens, 3 Chain Bar Mill, 809 Moston Lane, Manchester, M40 5RT Tel: 0161-684 9585 Fax: 0161-684 9585 *Kitchen & bedroom furniture manufrs*

▶ Harlequin Knitwear, Maranatha, Nelson Road, Forres, Morayshire, IV36 1DR Tel: (01309) 676455

Harlequin Software Consultants Ltd, The Old Vicarage Coach House, Finches Lane, Baydon, Marlborough, Wiltshire, SN8 2JJ Tel: (01672) 541541 Fax: (01672) 542111 E-mail: enquiries@hquin.co.uk *Software consultants, specialising in NHS software*

Harlequin Sports Trophies, 1 Bloomfield Place, Bathgate, West Lothian, EH48 1PB Tel: (01506) 634069 Fax: (01506) 634069 *Trophy manufrs*

▶ Harlequin Swimming Pools Ltd, Innersdown Farm, Micheldever, Winchester, Hampshire, SO21 3BW Tel: (01962) 774004 Fax: (01962) 774008

Harlequin Woodcraft, 7 Industrial Road, Cambridge Road Industrial Estate, Milton, Cambridge, CB4 6AZ Tel: (01223) 420885 Fax: (01223) 420885 *Joinery manufrs*

Harleston Firs Saw Mill, Harlestone Road, Northampton, NN5 6UJ Tel: (01604) 581444 Fax: (01604) 759611 E-mail: sales@hfstimber.co.uk *Wooden gate manufrs*

Alexander Harley Seeds Ltd, Thomanean, Milnathort, Kinross, KY13 0RF Tel: (01577) 862586 Fax: (01577) 862823 E-mail: petermclellan@harleys.co.uk *Seed Merchants Wholesale Distributors*

Harley Blinds Ltd, 13 Ryton Street, Worksop, Nottinghamshire, S80 2AY Tel: (01909) 482320 Fax: (01909) 482639 *Blinds manufrs*

Harley Haddow Partnership, 8 Coates Crescent, Edinburgh, EH3 7BY Tel: 0131-226 3331 Fax: 0131-226 2563 E-mail: edin@harleyhaddow.com *Consulting civil engineers*

Harley & Co. (Peterhead)Ltd, 44-46 Queen Street, Peterhead, Aberdeenshire, AB42 1TR Tel: (01779) 472109 Fax: (01779) 475924 E-mail: info@harleyofscotland.com *Knitwear manufrs*

Harley Street Supplies Ltd, 29 Westfields Aveue, Barnes, London, SW13 0AT Tel: (020) 8876 2113 E-mail: sales@harveystreetsupplies.com *Pharmaceutical manufrs*

Harleyford Aggregates, Harleyford, Henley Road, Marlow, Buckinghamshire, SL7 2DY Tel: (01628) 475976 Fax: (01628) 481640 E-mail: info@harleyford.co.uk *Sand & gravel*

Harleys Corrugated Cases Ltd, Lonsdale Road, Thurmaston, Leicester, LE4 8JF Tel: 0116-269 3303 Fax: 0116-269 2828 *Corrugated box & container manufrs*

Harline Ltd, 1 Kelmore Villas, East Dulwich, London, SE22 9BJ Tel: (020) 8693 0990 Fax: (020) 8693 0991 E-mail: admin@harline.co.uk *Network cabling, computer service & repair*

▶ Harling Collection, The Old Greyhound Barn, Bury Road, Hopton, Diss, Norfolk, IP22 2NU Tel: (01953) 688352 Fax: (01953) 688352

Harling Fabrications Ltd, Bunns Bank, Attleborough, Norfolk, NR17 1QD Tel: (01953) 453682 Fax: (01953) 453758 E-mail: harlingfabs@btconnect.com *Metal office furniture component manufrs*

Harling Security Products, 237 Church Road, Hayes, Middlesex, UB3 2LG Tel: (020) 8561 3787 Fax: (020) 8848 0999 E-mail: harlingsec@aol.com *Industrial door & rolling shutter fitting manufrs*

Harling & Watson Ltd, 416 Ashton Old Road, Manchester, M11 2DT Tel: 0161-231 4978 Fax: 0161-220 9193 E-mail: sales@harlingandwatson.sagehost.co.uk *Glass merchants & glazing contractors*

▶ Harliquin.co.uk, Dover Street, Totton, Southampton, SO14 6GL Tel: (07050) 196660 E-mail: ian@harliquin.co.uk *Broadcast & corporate video production*

Harlock Joinery Ltd, Brook Street, Redditch, Worcestershire, B98 8NG Tel: (01527) 68541 Fax: (01527) 68541 E-mail: harlockjoinery@btconnect.com *Cabinet shop fitters joinery manufrs*

Harlow & Milner Ltd, Milner Way, Ossett, West Yorkshire, WF5 9JN Tel: (01924) 277771 Fax: (01924) 280102 E-mail: info@harlow-milner.co.uk *Building contractors*

Harlow Moat House Hotel, Southern Way, Harlow, Essex, CM18 7BA Tel: (01279) 829988 Fax: (01279) 635094 E-mail: revhar@queensmoat.co.uk *Hotel & conference facilities*

Harlow Pressings Ltd, 57-60 Llantarnam Industrial Park, Cwmbran, Gwent, NP44 3AW Tel: (01633) 487400 Fax: (01633) 863010 *Precision presswork & pressings* Also at: Harlow

Harlow Spraytech, St. James Centre, 7 East Road, Harlow, Essex, CM20 2BJ Tel: (01279) 414665 Fax: (01279) 416828 *Powder coating services*

Harlow Springs Ltd, Unit B Cartel Business Estate, Edinburgh Way, Harlow, Essex, CM20 2TT Tel: (01279) 429004 Fax: (01279) 635953 E-mail: sales@harlowsprings.co.uk *Spring manufrs*

Harlow Transmissions, Shenfield Court, Perry Road, Harlow, Essex, CM18 7LR Tel: (01279) 426943 E-mail: dom.daily@tesco.net *Car repairers*

Harltex Ltd, 12 Norman-D-Gate Industrial Estate, Norman-D-Gate, Northampton, NN1 5NT Tel: (01604) 632343 Fax: (01604) 632344 E-mail: harltex@btconnect.com *Rubber products manufrs*

Bob Harman Performance Ltd, 101-107 Sutton Road, Watford, WD17 2QG Tel: (01923) 224303 Fax: (01923) 226596 *Engine reconditioners*

Harman Electronic Services, 1 Perth Street, Stoke-on-Trent, ST4 3PJ Tel: (01782) 598662 Fax: (01782) 598662 *Specialist/bespoke electronic solutions*

Harman Plant Hire Ltd, The Hyde, Brighton, BN2 4JE Tel: (01273) 603021 Fax: (01273) 690647 E-mail: info@harmanhire.co.uk *Plant & tool hire services* Also at: Hove, Portslade & Worthing

Harman Warehousing Ltd, Old Aerodrome, Crabtree Lane, High Ercall, Telford, Shropshire, TF6 6AP Tel: (01952) 770266 Fax: (01952) 770116 *Storages & sell warehouse space*

Harmbridge Ltd, 27 Brimble Hill, Wroughton, Swindon, SN4 0RQ Tel: (01793) 814745 Fax: (01793) 814178 E-mail: sales@harmbridge.co.uk *Semi conductor production machines manufrs*

Harmen Motive Ltd, Bennett Street, Bridgend Industrial Estate, Bridgend, Mid Glamorgan, CF31 3SH Tel: (01656) 645441 Fax: (01656) 650327 E-mail: pselby@harmenbecker.com *Loudspeaker manufrs*

Harmen Technology Ltd, Ilford Way, Mobberley, Knutsford, Cheshire, WA16 7JL Tel: (01565) 650000 Fax: (01565) 872734 *Photographic material manufrs* Also at: Mobberley

▶ Harmer Personal Care Ltd, Unit 5, City Link Industrial Park, Phoenix Way, Bradford, West Yorkshire, BD4 8JP Tel: (01274) 660110

Harmon Precision Grinding, 55 Haviland Road, Ferndown Industrial Estate, Ferndown Industrial Estate, Wimborne, Dorset, BH21 7PY Tel: (01202) 654198 Fax: (01202) 654199 E-mail: info@harmon.co.uk *Machine component manufrs*

Harmoni Its Ltd, Parklands Business Park, Forest Road, Denmead, Waterlooville, Hampshire, PO7 6XP Tel: (023) 9226 8133 Fax: (023) 9226 8160 E-mail: wci@wcigroup.com *IT consultants*

▶ Harmonic Solutions Ltd, Unit 5C, Millwey Rise Industrial Estate, Axminster, Devon, EX13 5HU Tel: (01297) 34344 Fax: (01297) 34344 E-mail: richard@harmsol.co.uk *Harmonica manufrs*

Harmony Blinds, Harmony House, 11 Slater Street, Oldham, OL9 6ES Tel: 0161-626 9688 Fax: 0161-626 9688 *Blinds suppliers*

Harmony Blinds Rayleigh Ltd, 128 B High Street, Rayleigh, Essex, SS6 7BU Tel: (01268) 778377 Fax: (01268) 741705 *Blind manufrs*

Harmony Centre, 26 Lower Hillgate, Stockport, Cheshire, SK1 1JE Tel: 0161-480 8030 Fax: 0161-480 8030 *Medical aid retailers*

▶ Harmony Construction Ltd, Old Rayne, Insch, Aberdeenshire, AB52 6TB Tel: (01464) 851581 Fax: (01464) 851581

Harmony Fitted Furniture, Main Street, Rear of 51, Willerby, Hull, HU10 6BY Tel: (01482) 650685 Fax: (01482) 650685 E-mail: info@harmony.co.uk *Furniture manufrs*

▶ Harmony Internet Ltd, 3 The Granary Buildings, Millow, Biggleswade, Bedfordshire, SG18 8RH Tel: (01767) 317614 Fax: (01767) 317647 E-mail: info@harmony.co.uk *Website design & development services*

Harmony Kitchens, 32 Torrington Rd, Wallasey, Merseyside, CH44 3BU Tel: 0151-638 8370 *Kitchens manufrs*

Harmony Signs & Design Services Ltd, 18 Fisher St, Paignton, Devon, TQ4 5EL Tel: (01803) 559317 Fax: (01803) 522357 E-mail: admin@harmonysigns.co.uk *Sign manufrs*

Harnam Engineering Works, 7 Adler Industrial Estate, Betam Road, Hayes, Middlesex, UB3 1ST Tel: (020) 8561 4828 Fax: (020) 8573 2960 E-mail: harinder@harnameng.co.uk *Precision engineers*

Harnden Plastics, Manchester Road, Hyde, Cheshire, SK14 2BP Tel: 0161-368 1817 Fax: 0161-368 1140 E-mail: harnden@a-m.co.uk *Polyethylene converting machines*

▶ Harnesscom, Unit 3 King Street Buildings, King Street, Enderby, Leicester, LE19 4NT Tel: 0116-284 1050 Fax: 0116-284 1048 E-mail: sales@harnesscom.co.uk *Manufacturer of small volume (-00) harness assemblies, wire sets, panel wiring, PCB assemblies and automotive audio harness assy.*

Harnessflex Ltd, PO Box 7690, Birmingham, B46 1HT Tel: (01675) 468200 Fax: (01675) 464930 E-mail: sales@harnessflex.co.uk *Vehicle electric conduit systems manufrs*

Haroby Ltd, Unit 139 Bradley Hall Trading Estate, Bradley Lane, Standish, Wigan, Lancashire, WN6 0XQ Tel: (01257) 478100 Fax: (01257) 478109 E-mail: fasteners@haroby.co.uk Purchasing Contact: A. Byrne Sales Contact: A. Byrne *Furniture & industrial fastener distributors/ agents/stockholders. Also bolt & nut (including stainless steel), screw & stainless steel bolt & nut distributors/agents. In addition, blind rivets*

Harold Hayles Yarmouth Ltd, The Quay, Bridge Road, Yarmouth, Isle of Wight, PO41 0RS Tel: (01983) 760373 Fax: (01983) 760666 E-mail: info@spurscutters.co.uk *Boat builders*

Harold Jones Removals & Storage, 15 Westfield Road, Rhyl, Clwyd, LL18 4PN Tel: (01745) 855145 Fax: (01745) 855145 *Removal contractors*

▶ Harold & Wylie Enviroflo Engineering, 10A Newton Court, Westrand, Pendeford Business Park, Wolverhampton, WV9 5HB Tel: (01902) 784848 Fax: (01902) 784242 E-mail: wylie@enviroflo.co.uk *Dust extraction services*

Harp International Ltd, Gelli-Hirion Industrial Estate, Pontypridd, Mid Glamorgan, CF37 5SX Tel: (01443) 842255 Fax: (01443) 841805 E-mail: sales@harpintl.com *Refrigerant gas - reclaim & store*

Harp Software, PO Box 1101, Stourbridge, West Midlands, DY9 8YL Tel: (0845) 2261671 Fax: (01384) 892169 E-mail: harp@harpsoftware.co.uk *Computer software distributors*

Harper Collins Publisher Ltd, Westerhill Rd, Glasgow, G64 2QT Tel: 0141-772 3200 Fax: 0141-306 3104 E-mail: vivion.mccormack@harpercollins.co.uk *Map & atlas publishers*

Harper & Eede Ltd, Broyle House, The Broyle, Ringmer, Lewes, East Sussex, BN8 5NN Tel: (01273) 812707 Fax: (01273) 814040 E-mail: sales@harperandeede.co.uk *Agricultural engineers* Also at: Hurst Green (Sussex) & Hurstpierpoint

▶ Harper Electrical Contractors Ltd, 281 Vicarage Road, Kings Heath, Birmingham, B14 7NE Tel: 0121-441 2561 Fax: 0121-441 2993

J. Harper Ltd, 32A Temple Street, Wolverhampton, WV2 4AN Tel: (01902) 422865 Fax: (01902) 422865 *Rope & twine merchant*

Harper- Little Ltd, 50 Brunswick Square, Hove, East Sussex, BN3 1EF Tel: (020) 7993 4087 Fax: (0870) 6220607 *Supplier of Cashmere Fashion & Home Accessories. **Harper-Little, is for pure and healthy living, each of our products is made from natural material. We have the finest Mongolian cashmere and exclusive organic Tibaten brown cashmere. **Corporate Gifts: Giving your customers or staff a luxury cashmere product with the logo of your company on is a great way to improve relations.*

Harper Reg Engineering, 19 Tallon Road, Hutton, Brentwood, Essex, CM13 1TE Tel: (01277) 223130 Fax: (01277) 212179 *Precision engineers*

Harper Signs Ltd, 12-20 Diana Street, Newcastle upon Tyne, NE4 6DA Tel: 0191-232 4926 Fax: 0191-261 0676 E-mail: sales@harpersigns.co.uk *Sign manufrs*

Harper & Simmons Ltd, 19 Howard Road, Park Farm, Redditch, Worcestershire, B98 7SE Tel: (01527) 518121 Fax: (01527) 518123 E-mail: robertsimmons@harperandsimmons.co.uk *Precision toolmakers*

▶ Harper Tether Associates, 3 Sansome Road, Shirley, Solihull, West Midlands, B90 2BJ Tel: 0121 745 2456 Fax: 0121 745 2456 E-mail: kdharper@h-t-a.co.uk *Production of health & safety files related to industry*

▶ Harper Window Systems Ltd, The Gables, Ash Lane, Alvechurch, Birmingham, B48 7TT Tel: 0121-445 0104 Fax: 0121-445 3138 E-mail: enquiries@harperwindows.co.uk *PVC, window & door commercial manufacture & installers*

Harpercollins Pubrs Ophelia House, Fulham Palace Road, London, W6 8JA Tel: (020) 8741 7070 Fax: (020) 8307 4440 E-mail: vibecke.olsen@harpercollins.co.uk *Map drawers, cartographers & publishers*

Harpercollins Pubrs Ophelia House, Fulham Palace Road, London, W6 8JA Tel: (020) 8741 7070 Fax: (020) 8307 4813 E-mail: human.resources@harpercollins.co.uk *Publishers*

Harpers Ltd, Media House, Azalea Drive, Swanley, Kent, BR8 8HU Tel: (01322) 611217 Fax: (01322) 616305 E-mail: info@harpers-wine.com *Publishers*

Harpers A V Ltd, 16 Woking Business Park, Albert Drive, Woking, Surrey, GU21 5JY Tel: (01483) 757577 Fax: (01483) 729449 E-mail: sales@harpersav.com *Audio visual suppliers*

Harpers Weybridge, 135 Stubbington Lane, Fareham, Hampshire, PO14 2NF Tel: (01329) 662293 Fax: (01329) 665518 *Heating & boiler maintenance services*

Harpham Precision Engineering, Unit 5, Eastwood End, Wimblington, March, Cambridgeshire, PE15 0QQ Tel: (01354) 741336 Fax: (01354) 741517 *CNC precision engineering services*

Edward Harpley Ltd, Crownings, Brettenham, Ipswich, IP7 7PA Tel: (01449) 737999 Fax: (01449) 736111 E-mail: edwardharpley@btconnect.com *Curtain poles, rails, fittings & accessories suppliers*

▶ Harpspring Designs Ltd, Bridge House, 3 Fleet Road, Farnborough, Hampshire, GU14 9RU Tel: 0118-375 7661 Fax: (07973) 856954 E-mail: harpsspring.designs@ntlworld.com *Design engineering*

Harquejas Publications Ltd, 2 Shenley Close, Leighton Buzzard, Bedfordshire, LU7 3DG Tel: (01525) 852370 E-mail: sales@harquejas.co.uk *Technical publications*

Harradines Removals, 25-27 Gordon Road, London, SE15 2AF Tel: (020) 7639 1791 Fax: (020) 7639 9408 E-mail: enquiries@harradines.co.uk

Harri Roberts Computer Training, 99 Mansel Street, Mansel House, Swansea, SA1 5UE Tel: (01792) 411991 Fax: 01792 411991 *Computer consultancy*

▶ Harridge Stoves, Anglo Trading Estate, Commercial Road, Shepton Mallet, Somerset, BA4 5BY Tel: (01749) 347272 *Woodburners, Woodburning stoves, Multifuel stoves, Gas stoves, Electric stoves, Oil Stoves and Range Cookers at fair prices direct to the trade and public.*

▶ Harridge Stoves Ltd, 5A Rumbridge Street, Totton, Southampton, SO40 9DQ Tel: (023) 8067 5757 E-mail: harridgestoves@btconnect.com *Stove sales*

▶ Harridge Woodburning Stoves, 7 Oakendene Industrial Estate, Bolney Road, Cowfold, Horsham, West Sussex, RH13 8AZ Tel: (01403) 865853 E-mail: harridgestoves@btconnect.com *Wood burning stoves retailer*

Harrier Engineering Ltd, 20a Kendale Road, Scunthorpe, South Humberside, DN16 1DT Tel: (01724) 872935 Fax: (01724) 271218 *Welders & fabricators*

▶ Harrier Fluid Power Ltd, Parys Road, Ludlow Business Park, Ludlow, Shropshire, SY8 1XY Tel: (01584) 876033 Fax: (01584) 876044 E-mail: sales@harrieronline.co.uk Principal Export Areas: Asia Pacific, Middle East, Africa, Central/East Europe, West Europe, North America, Central America & South America *Hydraulic equipment system manufacturers and global distributors, agents and stockholders, hydraulic pumps, hydraulic valves, solenoid valves, cetop valves, bell housings, oil coolers, hydraulic powerunits, hydraulic motors, hydraulic handpumps, hydraulic flow control valves, hydraulic manifolds, hydraulic tanks, flow meters, hydraulic adaptors, hose clips, hydraulic filters, pressure gauges, filtration products.*

Harrier Pneumatics Ltd, 5 Belgrave Industrial Estate, Belgrave Road, Southampton, SO17 3EA Tel: (023) 8055 8857 Fax: (023) 8055 6200 *Pneumatics equipment distributors* Also at: Bristol, Launceston & Reading

▶ Harrier Shoes Ltd, Kenmuir Road, Finedon, Wellingborough, Northamptonshire, NN9 5LS Tel: (01933) 681401

Harries Bakery, 37 Heol Cae Gurwen, Gwaun Cae Gurwen, Ammanford, Dyfed, SA18 1HG Tel: (01269) 823268 Fax: (01269) 823268 *Wholesale bakery products*

Harrington Associates Ltd, Unit 1 Bright St., Coventry, CV6 5EB Tel: (024) 7666 2731 Fax: (024) 7663 8058 E-mail: sales@harringtonassociates.co.uk *Office refurbishers*

E.& H. Harrington, Cowdray Centre House, Cowdray Avenue, Colchester, CO1 1QB Tel: (01206) 543680 *Jewellery manufrs*

Harrington Generators International Ltd, Ravenstor Road, Wirksworth, Matlock, Derbyshire, DE4 4FY Tel: (01629) 824284 Fax: (01629) 824613 E-mail: sales@harringtongen.co.uk *Portable & static generator manufrs*

▶ Harrington & Jessop Ltd, Priest Lane, West End, Woking, Surrey, GU24 9NA Tel: (01483) 472423 *Compos manufrs*

Harringtons Caravans Ltd, Chester Road, Oakmere, Northwich, Cheshire, CW8 2HB Tel: (01606) 882032 Fax: (01606) 889213 E-mail: sales@harringtonscaravans.co.uk *Caravan retailers* Also at: Blackburn

▶ Harringtons Fabrications Ltd, 5 Gentlemens Field, Westmill Road, Ware, Hertfordshire, SG12 0EF Tel: (01920) 463913 Fax: (01920) 463944 E-mail: sales@harringtonfabrications.com *Architecural Metalworkers/Fabricators*

Harris, Charlotte Road, Stirchley, Birmingham, B30 2BT Tel: 0121-451 1664 Fax: 0121-433 3864 E-mail: sales@harrisofstirchley.co.uk *Builders, plumbers & timber merchants*

Harris & Co., Farrs Lane, Bristol, BS1 4PZ Tel: 0117-927 7434 Fax: 0117-925 2354 *Recovery processors manufrs*

▶ Harris, 30 Cecil Street, Rothwell, Kettering, Northamptonshire, NN14 6EZ Tel: (01536) 418899 Fax: (01536) 418877

Harris Active Sports, PO Box 1292, Basildon, Essex, SS15 6PY Tel: (01268) 491036 Fax: (01268) 544008 E-mail: sales@harris-active.co.uk *Sport nutrition products distributor*

Harris & Bailey Ltd, 50 Hastings Road, Croydon, CR9 6BR Tel: (020) 8654 3181 Fax: (020) 8656 9369 E-mail: mail@harris-bailey.co.uk *Extensive stock of both Lightside and Heavyside materials*

Harris Custom Woodworking, 3 New Firms Centre, Fairground Way, Walsall, WS1 4NU Tel: (01922) 611122 Fax: (01922) 611122 *Cabinet makers*

▶ Harris Design Ltd, 19 Glenorrin Close Lambton, Washington, Tyne & Wear, NE38 0DZ Tel: 0191-417 6752

Harris Engineering, 400 Catesby Park, Kings Norton, Birmingham, B38 8SE Tel: 0121-433 3302 Fax: 0121-433 3047 E-mail: Sales@harrisengineering.co.uk *Window blind components*

▶ Harris Engineering, 400 Catesby Park, Kings Norton, Birmingham, B38 8SE Tel: 0121-433 3302 Fax: 0121-433 3047

Harris Fine Furniture Ltd, 1 Bulmer Road Industrial Estate, Sudbury, Suffolk, CO10 7HJ Tel: (01787) 375527 Fax: (01787) 377036 E-mail: hsf.co@easynet.co.uk *Reproduction furniture*

Harris & Garrod Ltd, Humber Bank South, Grimsby, South Humberside, DN31 3SD Tel: (01472) 343965 Fax: (01472) 240878 E-mail: hggrimsby@aol.com *General engineers*

George Harris, The Towing Path, Oxford, OX4 4EL Tel: (01865) 243870 Fax: (01865) 243870 E-mail: info@harrisracing.co.uk *Racing boat building & repairers*

Harris Glass Ltd, St Albans Works, Commercial Road, Wolverhampton, WV1 3RD Tel: (01902) 452709 Fax: (01902) 455722 E-mail: anthony@harrisglass.fsnet.co.uk *Glass merchants*

Harris Group, 170 Cardigan Road, Leeds, LS6 1LL Tel: 0113-203 3129 Fax: 0113-203 3128 E-mail: pwcharrisaggs@aol.com *Quarry owners & builders merchants*

▶ Harris & Harris, 5 New Street, Barnsley, South Yorkshire, S70 1RX Tel: (01226) 280280 Fax: (01226) 280280

▶ Harris & Harris Construction Ltd, Unit 1a, The Polden Business Centre, Bristol Road, Bridgwater, Somerset, TA6 4AW Tel: (01278) 431565

Harris Hart & Co. Ltd, Gregge Street Works, Gregge Street, Heywood, Lancashire, OL10 2EJ Tel: (01706) 625355 Fax: (01706) 360570 E-mail: sales@epsom-salts.com *Magnesium sulphate manufrs*

Harris Interactive, International House, Pepper Road, Hazel Grove, Stockport, Cheshire, SK7 5BW Tel: 0161-615 2300 Fax: 0161-615 2394 *Market researchers*

J. Harris, 31 Trinity Avenue, Llandudno, Gwynedd, LL30 2SJ Tel: (01492) 873157 Fax: (01492) 871997 E-mail: y2000pc@aol.com *Computer consultants*

J.A. Harris Ltd, Malinslee, Telford, Shropshire, TF4 2BN Tel: (01952) 505537 Fax: (01952) 504456 E-mail: accounts.harris@virgin.net *Precision machinists*

▶ Harris & Johnston, 162 Brunton Gardens, Montgomery Street, Edinburgh, EH7 5ER Tel: 0131-661 3121 Fax: 0131-661 3122 E-mail: sales@harrisjohnson.co.uk

Harris Kafton, 54-58 High Street, Edgware, Middlesex, HA8 7EJ Tel: (020) 8381 3770 Fax: (020) 8381 3470 *Chartered accountants*

Harris Looms, Kingsnorth Industrial Estate, Wotton Road, Ashford, Kent, TN23 6JY Tel: (01233) 622686 Fax: (01233) 645801 E-mail: sales@emir.co.uk *Hand loom manufrs*

▶ The Harris Lord Group Ltd, 45a Carfax, Horsham, West Sussex, RH12 1EQ Tel: (01403) 273370 Fax: (01403) 273364

▶ Harris Management Training, Teviotbank Gardens, Denholm, Hawick, Roxburghshire, TD9 8PB Tel: (01450) 870688 Fax: (01450) 870688

▶ Harris Moore, Unit 311 Jubilee Trade Centre, Pershore Street, Birmingham, B5 6ND Tel: 0121-248 0030 Fax: 0121-248 0030 E-mail: sales@stretchershop.co.uk *Bespoke artists stretched canvases, linens & boards*

▶ Neil Harris, 3 Wethersfield Road, Oxton, Prenton, Merseyside, CH43 9UN Tel: (0800) 0838818 E-mail: neil@ricsonline.org *Chartered building surveyors and construction specialists. Extension of the NHA group which offers Project consulting, Home Surveys, and real estate services.*

▶ Harris Office Furniture Ltd, 41 Grove Street, Edinburgh, EH3 8AF Tel: 0131-229 3180 Fax: 0131-228 3767 *Office furniture wholesalers*

Harris Performance Products Ltd, 6 Marshgate Drive, Hertford, SG13 7AQ Tel: (01992) 532500 Fax: (01992) 587052 E-mail: sales@harris-performance.com *Motor cycle manufrs*

Philip Harris International, Hyde Building, Ashton Road, Hyde, Cheshire, SK14 4SH Tel: (01530) 418550 E-mail: exportsales@philipharris.co.uk *Educational & scientific equipment distributors*

Harris & Porter, 49 Whitehall, London, SW1A 2BX Tel: (020) 7839 6064 Fax: (020) 7839 3876 E-mail: handp@nnpland.demon.co.uk *Property management*

▶ Harris Printers, 16-18 Mary Street, Porthcawl, Mid Glamorgan, CF36 3YA Tel: (01656) 788038 Fax: (01656) 785017

Harris Repair Consultancy Service Ltd, Unit 3, Crondal Road, Exhall, Coventry, CV7 9NH Tel: (024) 7636 4848 Fax: (024) 7664 4411 E-mail: g.harris@harrisrcs.com *CNC turned parts machinists*

Harris & Russell Ltd, Eagle Way, Sowton Industrial Estate, Exeter, EX2 7HY Tel: (01392) 257666 Fax: (01392) 256880 *Electric supplies distributors*

Harris & Russell, 124 East Road, London, N1 6AF Tel: (0870) 7277551 Fax: (020) 7608 2970 E-mail: harrisrussell@msn.com *Electrical wholesalers* Also at: Exeter, London NW1 & Salisbury

Harris & Sheldon Group Ltd, North Court, Packington Park, Meriden, Coventry, CV7 7HF Tel: (01676) 522990 Fax: (01676) 523609 E-mail: group@harris-sheldon.co.uk *Holding company*

The Harris Sign Group Ltd, Springfield Road, Coventry, CV1 4GN Tel: (024) 7622 9950 Fax: (024) 7638 1320 *Sign manufrs*

▶ Harris & Spilsbury Ltd, 131 St Margarets Road, Ward End, Birmingham, B8 2BD Tel: 0121-327 1095 Fax: 0121-326 0818 E-mail: sales@harris-and-spilsbury.co.uk *Manufacturers of polyethylene/polythene bags/ carriers/sacks & polyethylene/polythene film/ sheet. Also crrier bags, polythene & packaging flexible products*

Harris Springs Ltd, Ruscombe Works Tavistock Industrial Estate, Ruscombe Lane, Ruscombe, Reading, RG10 9LR Tel: 0118-934 0024 Fax: 0118-934 1365 E-mail: sales@harris-springs.com *Springs*

▶ Harris Stratex Networks UK. Ltd, 4 Bell Drive, Hamilton International Technology Park, Blantyre, Glasgow, G72 0FB Tel: (01698) 717200 Fax: (01698) 717204 *Products, solutions & services for wireless networks*

Harris Systems Ltd, Ferry Works, Summer Road, Thames Ditton, Surrey, KT7 0QJ Tel: (020) 8339 1800 Fax: (020) 8390 5087 *Computer software development services*

Harris Systems Ltd, Eskdale Road, Winnersh, Wokingham, Berkshire, RG41 5TS Tel: 0118-969 8787 Fax: 0118-964 8001 *Digital telecommunication systems* Also at: Cheadle

Harris Tobias Ltd, 3 Station Road, Stansted, Essex, CM24 8BE Tel: (01279) 647164 Fax: (01279) 647038 E-mail: info@harristobias.com *Animal & vegetable oil traders. Waste food recylers & suppliers to the bird food industry*

▶ Harris Truck & Van, 5 Wheaton Road, Witham, Essex, CM8 3UJ Tel: (01376) 533680 *Commercial vehicle body builders*

Harris Tweed Trading Co. Ltd, Sandwick Road, Stornoway, Isle of Lewis, HS1 2SJ Tel: (01851) 702772 Fax: (01851) 705271 *Textiles Manufrs*

Harris Walton Lifting Gear Ltd, Two Woods Lane, Brierley Hill, West Midlands, DY5 1TR Tel: (01384) 74071 Fax: (01384) 74070 E-mail: sales@harriswaltonliftinggear.co.uk *Lifting gear manufrs*

Harris Windows & Joinery Ltd, Brighton Road, Tadworth, Surrey, KT20 6UP Tel: (01737) 832328 Fax: (01737) 833964 *Domestic pvc windows, doors & joinery*

Harrison Adams Ltd, Victoria Mills, Knowler Hill, Liversedge, West Yorkshire, WF15 6DP Tel: (01924) 402435 Fax: (01924) 404814 E-mail: travor@harrisonadamsmouldings.wannado.co.uk *Plastics mouldings manufrs*

Harrison Blinds, 136 Long Street, Easingwold, York, YO61 3JA Tel: (01347) 822496 Fax: (01347) 823329 *Blind manufrs*

Harrison Castings Ltd, Gough Road, Leicester, LE5 4AP Tel: 0116-276 9351 Fax: 0116-246 0199 E-mail: contacts@harrisoncastings.com *Aluminum castings manufrs*

Harrison & Clough Ltd, PO Box 9, Keighley, West Yorkshire, BD21 4EG Tel: (0870) 8892222 Fax: (0870) 8892233 *Bolt & nut stockists*

Harrison Cowley, Regus House, George Curl Way, Southampton, SO18 2RZ Tel: (023) 8033 7237 Fax: (023) 8023 1665 E-mail: enquiries@harrisoncowley.com *Public relations consultants*

Harrison & Cross Ltd, Unit 6 The Sidings Industrial Estate, Settle, North Yorkshire, BD24 9RP Tel: (01729) 823423 Fax: (01729) 823423 *Refrigeration engineers*

Harrison Direct Ltd, 152 Castleford Road, Normanton, West Yorkshire, WF6 2EP Tel: (01924) 895598 Fax: (01924) 895077 *Clothing retailers*

▶ Harrison Electrical Ltd, 1 Wyther Lane, Leeds, LS5 3BT Tel: 0113-278 2247

Harrison Europac Ltd, Stayton House, 93 Stayton Road, Sutton, Surrey, SM1 2PS Tel: (020) 8254 2300 Fax: (020) 8254 2301 E-mail: hep@harrison-europac.co.uk *Plastic packaging for food*

Harrison Fisher & Co. Ltd, 78 Milton Street, Sheffield, S3 7WJ Tel: 0114-272 4221 Fax: 0114-275 4187 E-mail: sales@harrison-fisher.co.uk *Cutlery manufrs*

Harrison Flagpoles, Borough Road, Darlington, County Durham, DL1 1SW Tel: (01325) 355433 Fax: (01325) 461726 E-mail: sales@flagpoles.co.uk *Flagpole & flag manufrs*

▶ Fred Harrison Ltd, 5 Brakynbery, Northchurch, Berkhamsted, Hertfordshire, HP4 3XN Tel: (01442) 874720 Fax: (01442) 870934 E-mail: sales@fredharrison.co.uk *UK Distributor of the Disclean & Renew cleaning products.**Also Karcher agent supplying the Puzzi 0 Carpet/upholstery cleaner.**Supplier of Hagerty Silver & Jewellery care products.*

George Harrison Ltd, Selsdon House, 212-220 Addington Road, South Croydon, Surrey, CR2 8LD Tel: (020) 8768 3200 Fax: (020) 8768 3201 E-mail: sales@ghuk.co.uk *Timber & paper mill agents*

Harrison Goddard Foote, Lincolns Inn Chambers, 40-43 Chancery Lane, London, WC2A 1JA Tel: (020) 7440 8900 Fax: (020) 7440 8901 E-mail: hgf-london@hgfit.com *Patent agents & attorneys*

Harrison & Greenwood Transformers Ltd, Mill Lane, Halifax, West Yorkshire, HX3 6TR Tel: (01422) 329003 Fax: (01422) 329009 *Transformer manufrs*

Harrison & Hutchinson Ltd, Field Road, Heysham, Morecambe, Lancashire, LA3 2XU Tel: (01524) 850200 Fax: (01524) 850605 E-mail: harrison.hutchin@btconnect.com *Precision engineers*

Harrison Industrial Ltd, Rodney Road, Southsea, Hampshire, PO4 8SY Tel: (023) 9275 1687 Fax: (023) 9281 8564 E-mail: harrison.indl@btclick.com *Ductwork systems designed manufacturer & installed*

Harrison, J.A. & Co. Ltd, Britain Works, Sherborne Street, Manchester, M8 8HP Tel: 0161-832 2282 Fax: 0161-832 3263 E-mail: enquiries@jaharrison.co.uk *Jointing & gasket manufrs*

J.L. Harrison & Son (Air Conditioning) Ltd, Unit 17, Olympic Business Centre, Paycocke Road, Basildon, Essex, SS14 3EX Tel: (01268) 532414 Fax: (01268) 532415 E-mail: info@chillerservices.co.uk *Air conditioning maintenance*

Harrison Jewitt Ltd, Flat, The Brickyard, Scotter Road South, Scunthorpe, South Humberside, DN17 2BT Tel: (01724) 281453 Fax: (01724) 281453 E-mail: sales@jewittonline.co.uk *Builders of sand timber supplies & landscaping services*

John Harrison Sports Ltd, 79 Hough Lane, Leyland, PR25 2YD Tel: (01772) 423054 Fax: (01772) 456294 E-mail: sales@jhsports.co.uk *Medal, trophy manufrs*

Harrison Locks, Pump Street, Worcester, WR1 2QX Tel: (01905) 20999 Fax: (01527) 892612 E-mail: harrison.lock@btinternet.com *Locksmiths*

Harrison Matthews & Co. Ltd, 28 College Road, Sutton Coldfield, West Midlands, B73 5DJ Tel: 0121-355 4760 Fax: 0121-243 1104 *Industrial fastener distribs*

Harrison Packaging, Easter Park, Teesside Industrial Estate, Stockton-on-Tees, Cleveland, TS17 9NT Tel: (01642) 754600 Fax: (01642) 769900 E-mail: sales@harrisonpack.com *Printed carton manufrs*

▶ Peter Harrison, Bonds Mill, Bristol Road, Stonehouse, Gloucestershire, GL10 3RG Tel: (01453) 826406 Fax: (01453) 826406 *Computer training agents*

Harrison Products, East Gate House, Moreton Road, Longborough, Moreton-in-Marsh, Gloucestershire, GL56 0QJ Tel: (01451) 830083 Fax: (01451) 830830 *Printing trade finishing equipment manufrs*

Harrison Saw & Tool Ltd, Underbank Way, Carrs Industrial Estate, Haslingden, Rossendale, Lancashire, BB4 5HR Tel: (01706) 225221 Fax: (01706) 831409 E-mail: sales@harrisonsaw.co.uk *Saw doctors*

Harrison Sheetmetal, Smyrna Street, Radcliffe, Manchester, M26 4BN Tel: 0161-723 4122 Fax: 0161-723 4122 *Sheet metalwork*

Harrison Sportswear, 95-97 Market Street, Little Lever, Bolton, BL3 1HH Tel: (01204) 791356 Fax: (01204) 791356 E-mail: johnachild5@hotmail.com *Sportswear manufrs*

Harrison Suspended Ceilings, Shirley House, Oldham Street, Hyde, Cheshire, SK14 1LJ Tel: 0161-368 1315 Fax: 0161-367 8005 *Suspended ceiling fitting contractor*

▶ Harrison Technical Publications Ltd, Glen Garth, Ireleth Road, Askam-in-Furness, Cumbria, LA16 7DP Tel: (07813) 890408 E-mail: info@htpl.co.uk *A professional supplier of technical documentation and associated services.*

Harrison Thompson & Co. Ltd, Yeoman House Whitehall Industrial Estate, Whitehall Road, Leeds, LS12 5JB Tel: 0113-279 5854 Fax: 0113-231 0406 E-mail: info@yeomanshield.com *Grp mouldings & plastic extrusions*

▶ Harrison Traditional Builders, 3 Windyridge, Mount, Bodmin, Cornwall, PL30 4EX Tel: (01208) 821300 Fax: (01208) 821392 E-mail: HTBcornwall@aol.com *Building contractors*

Harrison Verity Products Ltd, Veritas House, Sett End Road, Shadsworth Business Park, Blackburn, BB1 2PT Tel: (01254) 662979 Fax: (01254) 698580 E-mail: sales@hvp.co.uk *Polythene bag manufrs*

W.W. & B.T. Harrison, Moorthorpe Farm, Drumacre Lane East, Longton, Preston, PR4 4SD Tel: (01772) 613373 *Agricultural contractors*

Harrison-field Ltd, Martyn Street, Airdrie, Lanarkshire, ML6 9AU Tel: (01236) 747771 Fax: (01236) 766880 *Clothing manufrs*

Harrison-Page Refrigeration Ltd, 63 Lion Road, Bexleyheath, Kent, DA6 8NN Tel: (020) 8303 7484 *Refrigeration & air conditioning*

Harrisons Burley Ltd, Sandylands, Anderton Street, Cross Hills, Keighley, West Yorkshire, BD20 7ED Tel: (01535) 637410 Fax: (01535) 637498 E-mail: sales@harrisonsburley.co.uk *Worsted & woollen cloth manufrs*

▶ Harrisons Electrical Mechanical & Property Services Ltd, Harrison House, Sheep Walk, Langford Road, Biggleswade, Bedfordshire, SG18 9RB Tel: (01767) 600259 Fax: (01767) 600269 E-mail: info@harrisonselec.co.uk *Electrical contractors*

Harrisons Pipeline Engineering Ltd, Curtis Road, Norwich, NR6 6RB Tel: (01603) 426928 Fax: (01603) 414225 E-mail: darren@harrisons-eng.com *Pipe fittings manufrs*

▶ Harris's Sports, 22a Griffin Road, Clevedon, Avon, BS21 6HH Tel: (01275) 874351 Fax: (01275) 349806 E-mail: ddavies@harrissports.co.uk *Sports equipment sports work wear suppliers*

Harrocell Ltd, 15e Wintersells Road, Byfleet, West Byfleet, Surrey, KT14 7LF Tel: (01932) 356347 Fax: (01932) 356347 E-mail: harrocell@btconnect.com *Variable transformers, power supplies & sheet metal work manufrs*

Harrod Business Promotions Ltd, 3 Goodwood Rise, Marlow BTM, Marlow, Buckinghamshire, SL7 3QE Tel: (01628) 891133 Fax: (01628) 891134 E-mail: sales@harrodpromotions.com *Promotional gifts suppliers*

Harrod UK Ltd, 1 Pinbush Road, Lowestoft, Suffolk, NR33 7NL Tel: (01502) 583515 Fax: (01502) 582456 E-mail: sales@harrod.uk.com *Sports ground/netting equipment manufrs*

▶ Harrogate Communications, 6 Nydd Vale Terrace, Harrogate, North Yorkshire, HG1 5HA Tel: (01423) 532977 Fax: (01423) 532979 E-mail: info@1stcoms.co.uk *Business Telecommunications and Data Cabling.*

▶ Harrogate Printing Ltd, Ripon Way, Harrogate, North Yorkshire, HG1 2AU Tel: (01423) 523449 Fax: (01423) 506160

Harrogate Trailer & Towbar Centre, 6 Provincial Works, The Avenue, Harrogate, North Yorkshire, HG1 4QE Tel: (01423) 884962 Fax: (01423) 888953 *Tow bar & leisure manufrs*

Harrold Manufacturing Co. Ltd, Hinstock House, 30 Station Road, Firsby, Spilsby, Lincolnshire, PE23 5PX Tel: (01754) 830679 Fax: (01754) 830477 *Protective & safety eye shields & visors manufrs*

▶ Harron Homes, Chadwick House, Warrington Road, Birchwood Park, Warrington, WA3 6AE Tel: (01925) 823555

▶ Harrow Green, 5 Centrus, Arenson Way, Houghton Regis, Dunstable, Bedfordshire, LU5 5BN Tel: (01582) 500890 Fax: (01582) 665777

Harrow Green Ltd, Cooks Road, London, E15 2PW Tel: (020) 8522 0101 Fax: (020) 8522 0252 E-mail: info@harrowgreen.com *Removal & storage contractors*

Harrow Green Removals Ltd, Unit Q1, Queen Elizabeth Distribution Park, Purfleet, Essex, RM19 1TT Tel: (020) 8551 3555 Fax: (020) 8551 9199 E-mail: sales@harrowgreen.com *Specialist & export packers & shippers*

Harrow Watch & Jewellery Clinic, Unit 4 St. Anns Shopping Centre, St. Anns Road, Harrow, Middlesex, HA1 1AS Tel: (020) 8424 2601 Fax: (020) 8424 2601 *Jewellers repair services*

▶ Harrowden It, Carradale, Campbeltown, Argyll, PA28 6QG Tel: (01583) 431428 Fax: (01583) 431428 E-mail: info@HarrowdenIT.co.uk *Developers of bespoke software and databases for the Pegasus Opera and Opera II range of accounting packages.**Custom database solutions.**Specialist web design and*

continued

continuation
*component developers.**Website hosting and domain registration***

Harry Adcock & Son, Saw Mills, Corby Glen, Grantham, Lincolnshire, NG33 4LB Tel: (01476) 550231 Fax: (01476) 550363 E-mail: richard@harryadcock.a-i-s.co.uk *Home grown timber merchants*

▶ Harry Armistead Ltd, Unit 2 Woodgate Park, Middlegate, White Lund Industrial Estate, Morecambe, Lancashire, LA3 3PS Tel: (01524) 848500 Fax: (01524) 848600

▶ Harry Burrows Fabrications Ltd, 8 Bayton Way, Exhall, Coventry, CV7 9ER Tel: (024) 7636 1313 Fax: (024) 7636 8279 E-mail: admin@harryburrows.co.uk *Steel fabrication services*

Harry Fry Spray Equipment Training Specialist, The Linhay, Manor Road, Stourpaine, Blandford Forum, Dorset, DT11 8TQ Tel: 01258 452364 Fax: 01258 452364 E-mail: spraytrain@btinternet.com *The training of paint sprayers in all aspects of use of equipment and Health & safety relating to this*

Harry G Smith Ltd, PO Box 89, Aberdeen, AB12 3DA Tel: (01224) 897044 Fax: (01224) 894648 E-mail: office@harrygsmith.co.uk *Wholesale clothing & textile specialists*

Harry Hancock Bar & Caterering Equipment, 12c Scott Lidgett Industrial Estate, Scott Lidgett Road, Stoke-on-Trent, ST6 4NQ Tel: (01782) 837303 Fax: (01782) 838612 E-mail: sales@hancocks-catering.co.uk *Wholesale bar & catering equipment services distribute*

Harry Irving & Co. Ltd, Hi Craft House, Sandy Road, Seaforth, Liverpool, L21 1AG Tel: 0151-928 2487 Fax: 0151-920 0617 E-mail: sales@hi-pet.com *Pet accessory manufrs*

▶ Harry J Palmer (Broadstone) Ltd, Manor Works, 4 Dunyeats Road, Broadstone, Dorset, BH18 8AG Tel: (01202) 690701

Harry Peers & Co. Ltd, Elton Street, Mill Hill, Bolton, BL2 2BS Tel: (01204) 528393 Fax: (01204) 362363 E-mail: sales@peers.co.uk *Structural engineers*

▶ Harry Sim & Sons Ltd, 115 Loch Street, Aberdeen, AB25 1DH Tel: (01224) 637904 Fax: (01224) 637904

Harry Taylor Ltd, Kitsons Works, Aylesbury Road, Bromley, BR2 0QZ Tel: (020) 8464 0915 Fax: (020) 8464 0916 E-mail: heaters@harrytaylor.co.uk *Warm air heating industrial distributors*

Harsco Track Technologies Ltd, Unit 1 Chewton Street, Eastwood, Nottingham, NG16 3HB Tel: (01773) 539480 Fax: (01773) 539481 E-mail: enquiries@harscotrack.com *Railway track maintenance equipment manufrs*

Harsh Ltd, The Industrial Estate, Full Sutton, York, YO41 1HS Tel: (01759) 372100 Fax: (01759) 371414 E-mail: sales@harshuk.com *Vehicle tipping gear manufrs*

Hart & Co. Ltd, 18-19 Greenhey Place, Skelmersdale, Lancashire, WN8 9SA Tel: (01695) 732525 Fax: (01695) 50951 E-mail: reception@hartandco.gb.com *Window & door manufrs*

Hart Automation Ltd, Icknield Road, Luton, LU3 2NY Tel: (01582) 599545 Fax: (01582) 579818 *Engineering services*

Hart Boulton & Co. Ltd, Hampton Street, Joiners Square Industrial Estate, Stoke-on-Trent, ST1 3EX Tel: (01782) 260723 Fax: (01782) 263466 *Specialist printing services*

Hart Bros & Co., Office Suite 14, Tower Building 22 Water Street, Liverpool, L3 1BA Tel: 0151-236 1786 Fax: 0151-236 3969 *Shipping agents & freight forwarders*

Hart Brothers Engineering Ltd, Sothall Works, Sothall, Oldham, OL4 2AD Tel: 0161-737 6791 Fax: 0161-633 5316 E-mail: xk220@aol.com *Casting repair & welding services*

Hart & Clough Ltd, Ezra House, Littlewood Drive, West 26 Industrial Estate, Cleckheaton, West Yorkshire, BD19 4TQ Tel: (01274) 863200 Fax: (01274) 863201 E-mail: info@hartandclough.co.uk *Established in 1885, Hart & Clough is a family firm, providing a quality print service from design to delivery. We print a huge range of items, including books, header cards, brochures & large sheet format*

Hart Coating Technology, PO Box 10, Brierley Hill, West Midlands, DY5 2RQ Tel: (01902) 895446 Fax: (01902) 897469 E-mail: tony@hartcoating.demon.co.uk Principal Export Areas: Central/East Europe & West Europe *Suppliers of metallic & metal-coated pigments*

Hart Fenton & Co. Ltd, First Floor Norman House, Kettering Terrace, Portsmouth, PO2 7AE Tel: (023) 9287 5277 Fax: (023) 9287 5280 E-mail: hf@hart-fenton.co.uk *Consulting naval architects marine engineers*

▶ Hart Interiors Midlands Ltd, Unit 10 The Mushroom Farm, Bottesford Lane, Orston, Nottingham, NG13 9NX Tel: (01949) 851800 Fax: (01949) 851800 *Cabinet manufrs*

Hart Lifts, 2 Block 2, Huntershill Way, Bishopbriggs, Glasgow, G64 1XP Tel: 0141-772 9797 Fax: 0141-772 4447 *Service & repair*

▶ Hart of the Matter, St. Marys Cottage, Winterbourne Abbas, Dorchester, Dorset, DT2 9LU Tel: (01305) 889374 E-mail: joe.hartcpl@tiscali.co.uk *Technical & business development consultancy*

Hart Metal Craft, Wivenhoe Business Centre, 23-24 Brook Street, Wivenhoe, Colchester, CO7 9DP Tel: (01206) 822017 Fax: (01206) 822017 *Steel fabricators*

Hart Models Ltd, The Cricket Grn, Hartley Wintney, Hook, Hants, RG27 8QB Tel: 01252 842637 Fax: 01252 842637 *Scale model vehicle*

Hart & Co Windsor, 151 St Leonards Road, Windsor, Berkshire, SL4 3DW Tel: (01753) 864075 Fax: (01753) 830251 E-mail: sales@hartstents.co.uk *Suppliers of tents & marquees for hire*

Hartburn Security Alarms, 8 Spalding Rd, Hartlepool, Cleveland, TS25 2LD Tel: (01429) 871111 *CCTV & security*

Hartcrown Ltd, 3 Mantle Road, London, SE4 2DU Tel: (020) 7252 9380 Fax: (020) 7277 9606 *Construction & ground workers services*

▶ Harte Electrical Ltd, Springfield Mill, Spa Street, Ossett, West Yorkshire, WF5 0HW Tel: (01924) 280000 Fax: (01924) 263836

Hartek Engineers Ltd, Hadrian Works, Wellington Road, Dunston, Gateshead, Tyne & Wear, NE11 9JL Tel: 0191-460 0672 Fax: 0191-460 1555 E-mail: techservices.ne@btinternet.com *Heat treatment specialists*

▶ Hartest Precision Instruments Ltd, 4 St Georges Industrial Estate, Richmond Road, Kingston upon Thames, Surrey, KT2 5BQ Tel: (020) 8541 4333 Fax: (020) 8549 3374 E-mail: sales@sheeninstruments.com Principal Export Areas: Worldwide *Rubber & plastics testing machinery designers & manufrs*

▶ Hartfield Homes Ltd, Pentland House, Damhead, Edinburgh, EH10 7DP Tel: 0131-445 5855 Fax: 0131-445 2235 E-mail: sales@hartfieldhomes.com

Hartford Engineering Ltd, Bradford Road, Winsford, Cheshire, CW7 2PE Tel: (01606) 860888 Fax: (01606) 860889 E-mail: he@hartford-eng.co.uk *Manufacturers of industrial robot attachments & accessories to injection moulding machines. Also manufacturers of automation special purpose equipment, industrial robot systems & special purpose/ custom built machinery*

Hartford Russel Supply Co. Ltd, 5 Trafalgar Trading Estate, Jeffreys Road, Enfield, Middlesex, EN3 7TY Tel: (020) 8804 2425 Fax: (020) 8804 8283 E-mail: hrsupplycode@aol.com *Cleaning products suppliers*

▶ Hartford Security, 16,Nelson Street, Dewsbury, West Yorkshire, WF13 1NA Tel: (01924) 467269 Fax: (01924) 430800 E-mail: info@harfordssecurity.co.uk *Locksmiths security & alarms*

▶ HartfordPharma, 4 Kingsley Close, Hartford, Northwich, Cheshire, CW8 1SD Tel: (01606) 79230 Fax: (07092) 150518 E-mail: admin@hartfordpharma.com *HartfordPharma is a provider of specialised pharmaceutical training and other services. We cover Good Manufacturing Practice (GMP) including Basic, Refresher, Validation, Auditing, Laboratories, Warehousing and Distribution, Packaging as well as Cleanrooms, Pharmaceutical Microbiology and Personal Hygiene. Other services include Technical Authoring of Training Manuals, SOPs and GMP compliance audits.*

Hartgrove Bros, Station Road, Redcar, Cleveland, TS10 1RD Tel: (01642) 489937 Fax: (01642) 489937 *Removal & storage contractors*

Hartham Press Ltd, 5a Marshgate Trading Estate, Hertford, SG13 7AB Tel: (01992) 589334 Fax: (01992) 554826 E-mail: sales@harthampress.com *Lithographic printers distributors*

Harthill Developments Ltd, Mansfield Road, Aston, Sheffield, S26 5PQ Tel: 0114-287 4522 Fax: 0114-287 6397 E-mail: sales@harthill.com Principal Export Areas: Worldwide *Manufacturers of new special cutting tools to customer drawings, made of tungsten hard metal or high speed steel*

Harthill House Group Ltd, Harthill House, Woodhall Lane, Harthill, Sheffield, S26 7YQ Tel: (0870) 3501309 Fax: (01909) 772785 E-mail: sales@hhg.uk.com *Computer systems & software developers*

Harthills Motor Cycles, 10 Caledonia Street, Bilston, West Midlands, WV14 6AE Tel: (01902) 492481 *Motorcycle engineering & mot testing*

Hartigan Readymix Ltd, Chesney Wold, Bleak Hall, Milton Keynes, MK6 1NE Tel: (01908) 668766 Fax: (01908) 676323 *Ready mix concrete suppliers*

Hartigan Readymix Ltd, 98 High Street, Newport Pagnell, Buckinghamshire, MK16 8EJ Tel: (01908) 611126 Fax: (01908) 210534 E-mail: info@gfxhartiganltd.co.uk *Ready mix concrete producers*

Hartington Litho Ltd, Marlborough Road, Lancing Business Park, Lancing, West Sussex, BN15 8UF Tel: (01903) 761401 Fax: (01903) 767301 E-mail: micheal@hartingtonlitho.co.uk *Printers & die cutters*

Hartland Crane Hire, Sneyd Hill, Stoke-on-Trent, ST6 2DY Tel: (01782) 575554 Fax: (01952) 587848 *Crane hire*

Hartle I G E Ltd, Unit 5, Ilford Trading Estate, Paycocke Road, Basildon, Essex, SS14 3DR Tel: (01268) 520496 Fax: (01268) 285477 E-mail: sales@hartleige.com *Industrial garage equipment manufrs*

Hartle Lane Sawmill, Hartle Lane, Belbroughton, Stourbridge, West Midlands, DY9 9TJ Tel: (01562) 730583 *Timber merchants*

▶ Hartlebury Plant & Motor Services, Unit 7 Oldington Trading Estate, Kidderminster, Worcestershire, DY11 7QP Tel: (01562) 824300 Fax: (01562) 827500 *Commercial vehicle workshop*

Hartley Bancks, 15 Britannia Road, Sale, Cheshire, M33 2XX Tel: 0161-905 1314 Fax: 0161-905 1381 E-mail: info@hbcc.co.uk *Computer consultants*

Hartley Botanic Ltd, Wellington Road, Greenfield, Oldham, OL3 7AG Tel: (0870) 7770320 Fax: (0870) 7770323 E-mail: info@hartleybotanic.co.uk *Aluminium structure fabricators horticultural*

▶ Hartley Haulage, 150 Stevenson Road, Sheffield, S9 3XG Tel: 0114-243 4569 Fax: 0114-243 4621

Hartley Precision Engineering Co. Ltd, Caddick Road, Knowsley Business Park, Prescot, Merseyside, L34 9HP Tel: 0151-548 0777 Fax: 0151-549 1191 E-mail: hartleyprecision@btconnect.com *Precision engineers*

Hartley & Sugden, Atlas Works, Gibbet Street, Halifax, West Yorkshire, HX1 4DB Tel: (01422) 355651 Fax: (01422) 359636 *Boiler manufrs*

Hartman Marine Services, Unit C2 The Boatyard, Stonar Industrial Estate, Sandwich, Kent, CT13 9LY Tel: (01304) 614121 Fax: (01304) 615070 E-mail: hartman.marine@virgin.net *Commercial diesel engine repairers*

Hart-Marler Leisure, The Flaxmill, Flaxmill Lane, Pinchbeck, Spalding, Lincolnshire, PE11 3YP Tel: (01775) 725670 Fax: (01775) 714670 E-mail: benhart@btinternet.com *Game & amusement machine hire services*

Hartnell Taylor Cook, 18 Canynge Road, Bristol, BS8 3JX Tel: 0117-923 9234 Fax: 0117-923 9237 E-mail: sales@hartnelltaylorcook.co.uk *Chartered surveyors*

Hartoms Engineers, 26-30 Theobald Street, Borehamwood, Hertfordshire, WD6 4SG Tel: (020) 8953 5062 Fax: (020) 8207 1176 *Prototype engineering, production engineers & machinists*

Harton Services Ltd, Unit 6 Thistlebrook Industrial Estate, Eynsham Drive, London, SE2 9RB Tel: (020) 8310 0421 Fax: (020) 8310 6785 E-mail: hartons@globalnet.co.uk *Manufacturers of pre-fabricated plumbing & booster sets*

Hartridge, Tingewick Road, Buckingham, MK18 1EF Tel: (01280) 825600 Fax: (01280) 825601 E-mail: sales@hartridge.co.uk *World Leaders in Diesel Fuel Injection Test Equipment.*

Hartridges Ltd, West Street, Hambledon, Waterlooville, Hampshire, PO7 4SN Tel: (023) 9263 2882 Fax: (023) 9263 2540 E-mail: sales@hartridges.co.uk *Soft drink manufrs*

Harts Farm Enterprises, Highgrove Farm House, Main Road, Bosham, Chichester, West Sussex, PO18 8EH Tel: (01243) 573232 *Agricultural contractors*

Harts Timber Buildings, 181 Broad Oak Road, St. Helens, Merseyside, WA9 2AQ Tel: (01744) 730004 *Sectional garden builders*

C.M. Hartshorne & Co. Ltd, Hawke Street, Sheffield, S9 2SU Tel: 0114-249 5408 Fax: 0114-249 5407 E-mail: cmhartshorne@aol.com *Used induction melting furnaces supply*

K. Hartwall Ltd, Green Lane Industrial Estate, Spennymoor, County Durham, DL16 6BP Tel: (01388) 824700 Fax: (01388) 824724 *Wire formed component manufrs*

Hartwell Truck, London Road, Dunstable, Bedfordshire, LU6 3DT Tel: (01582) 597575 Fax: (01582) 582650 *Ford commercial vehicle main dealer*

Harval Fitted Furniture, 4 Horbury Junction Industrial Estate, Calder Vale Road, Horbury, Wakefield, West Yorkshire, WF4 5ER Tel: (01924) 270121 Fax: (01924) 262115 E-mail: sales@harval.co.uk *Fitted furniture manufrs*

Harvard Industries Ltd, Wood Lane, Erdington, Birmingham, B24 9QR Tel: 0121-386 6621 Fax: 0121-386 6721 E-mail: johncauser@aol.com *Steel tube & fitting distributors*

Harver Packaging Co. Ltd, 479 Chester Road, Manchester, M16 9HF Tel: 0161-786 3900 Fax: 0161-848 8656 E-mail: sales@harverpac.co.uk *Paper importers & converters* Also at: Chelmsford & Glasgow

▶ Harvest Homemaker, Unit 1, Elgin Works, Elgin Street, Dunfermline, Fife, KY12 7SD Tel: (01383) 736291

Harvest Installations, Unit H1 North Yard, The Brents, Faversham, Kent, ME13 7DZ Tel: (01795) 533903 Fax: (01795) 538524 E-mail: mike@harvestinstallations.co.uk *Grain drying equipment*

Harvest Marketing Communications, 35 Havant Business Centre, Harts Farm Way, Havant, Hampshire, PO9 1HU Tel: (023) 9244 9655 Fax: (023) 9248 1760 E-mail: info@harvestpr.co.uk *Public relations consultants & marketing communications*

Harvest Natural Foods Ltd, 37 Walcot Street, Bath, BA1 5BN Tel: (01225) 465519 Fax: (01225) 401143 *Health food retailers*

Harvest Pine, 6 Pepper Street, Nantwich, Cheshire, CW5 5AB Tel: (01270) 627776 Fax: (01270) 627776 *Pine furniture*

▶ Alan Harvey, 76 Curbar Road, Great Barr, Birmingham, B42 2AU Tel: (0786) 3555365 Fax: E-mail: aharvey76@hotmail.com *Courier services*

▶ Harvey & Clark, 9-11 Swadlincote Road, Woodville, Swadlincote, Derbyshire, DE11 8DE Tel: (01283) 221451 Fax: (01283) 550992

Harvey Fabrication Ltd, Hancock Road, Bow, London, E3 3DA Tel: (020) 8981 7811 Fax: (020) 8981 7815 *Fabrications in steel*

▶ Harvey Hays Ltd, PO BOX 4544, Walsall, WS9 1AJ Tel: 01922 44 21 58 E-mail: admin@harveyhays.com *For Your Number One Recruitment Solutions*

J.A. Harvey (Bassingham) Ltd, The Old Dairy, Navenby Lane, Bassingham, Lincoln, LN5 9JF Tel: (01522) 788111 Fax: (01522) 788195 E-mail: ja.harvey@btconnect.com *Steel, light & non-ferrous metal fabricators*

J.R.H. Harvey & Co., 45 Clogher Rd, Hillsborough, Co. Down, BT26 6PJ Tel: (028) 9268 2668 Fax: (028) 9268 2668 *Pre-cast concrete manufrs*

Harvey Manchester Ltd, Oldham Street, Denton, Manchester, M34 3SW Tel: 0161-336 3951 Fax: 0161-336 3936 E-mail: sales@harveymanchester.com *Aerospace engineers, total engineering solutions services*

▶ Harvey Miller Wine & Spirit, Unit 27 Dunfermline Business Centre, Izatt Avenue, Dunfermline, Fife, KY11 3BZ Tel: (0870) 2418459 Fax: (01383) 844991 E-mail: info@hmwsa.com *Wine merchants*

N.S. Harvey, Station Farm, Sleaford Road, Tattershall, Lincoln, LN4 4JG Tel: (01526) 343719 Fax: (01526) 343729 *General & livestock haulers*

Harvey Quilting, 11 Robin Hood Industrial Estate, Alfred St South, Nottingham, NG3 1GE Tel: 0115-958 5777 Fax: 0115-950 3339 E-mail: tonyatharveys@hotmail.com *Commission quilters*

Harvey Reed Top Table Ltd, Sterling Way, Borehamwood, Hertfordshire, WD6 2BT Tel: (020) 8207 2666 Fax: (020) 8207 6173 *Glassware distribs*

Harvey Scruton, North Lane, Huntington, York, YO32 9SU Tel: (01904) 400878 Fax: (01904) 400120 *Manufacturing chemists & export agents*

Harvey Spack Field, 33 Bruton Street, London, W1J 6QU Tel: (020) 7629 9663 Fax: (020) 7491 1964 *Property consultants*

Harvey Steel Lintels Ltd, Commerce Way, Colchester, CO2 8HH Tel: (01206) 792001 Fax: (01206) 792022 E-mail: harvey@lintels.co.uk *Builders equipment manufrs*

Harvey Strong Ltd, Unit 1 Oakway Place, Radlett, Hertfordshire, WD7 7NR Tel: (01923) 670088 Fax: (01923) 858004 *Label manufrs*

Harvey Williams Associates, Unit 3-4 Hurstfold Workshop, Fernhurst, Haslemere, Surrey, GU27 3JG Tel: (01483) 831619 Fax: (01428) 658237 E-mail: simon@harvey-williams.com *Manufacturer bespoke furniture*

Harveys Ltd, Edgefield Road Industrial Estate, Loanhead, Midlothian, EH20 9SX Tel: 0131-440 0074 Fax: 0131-440 3478 E-mail: sales@harveys.ltd.uk *Silkscreen printers*

Harveys Catering, Unit 4 King James Court, London, SE1 0DH Tel: (0800) 214719 Fax: (020) 7401 7794 E-mail: enquiries@harveys-catering.co.uk *Caterers & catering equipment hire*

Harveys & Co. Clothing Ltd, Glodwick Road, Oldham, OL4 1YU Tel: 0161-624 9535 Fax: 0161-627 2028 E-mail: info@harveys.co.uk *Protective clothing & overall manufrs*

Harveys Furnishing Ltd, Amberley House, New Road, Rainham, Essex, RM13 8QN Tel: (01708) 521177 Fax: (01708) 521514 *Furniture & household textiles retailers*

Harveys Garden Buildings, Woodside Garden Centre, Arterial Road, Rayleigh, Essex, SS6 7TZ Tel: (01268) 775770 Fax: (01268) 769155 E-mail: harveysgarden@btconnect.com *Portable & prefabricated building manufrs*

Harveys Garden & Leisure Buildings Ltd, Sectional Building Centre, Unit 5, Maltings Road, Battlesbridge, Wickford, Essex, SS11 7RH Tel: (01268) 768616 Fax: (01268) 769155 *Timber & portable building manufrs*

Harveys Pickled Products, 2 Court Barton, Crewkerne, Somerset, TA18 7HW Tel: (01460) 72384 *Pickling onions & eggs*

Harvey's Sandwich & Espresso Bar, 73-75 Nantwich Road, Crewe, CW2 6AW Tel: (01270) 255255 Fax: (01270) 255602 E-mail: harveyssandwiches@btconnet.co.uk *Bakery*

Harvington Lesiure, Kimberley Cottage, Worcester Road, Harvington, Kidderminster, Worcestershire, DY10 4LJ Tel: (01562) 777255 *Garden furniture retailers & manufrs*

Harwell Enterprises Ltd, 43 Platts Eyot, Hampton, Middlesex, TW12 2HF Tel: (020) 8783 0666 Fax: (020) 8941 6977 E-mail: sales@harwell.co.uk *Promotional gift advertisers*

Harwell Scientifics, 551 South Becquerel Avenue, Didcot, Oxfordshire, OX11 0TB Tel: (01235) 841970 Fax: (01235) 832287 E-mail: sales@scientifics.com *Independent analytical testing laboratory*

Harwin Shipping Agency Ltd, 40 Bowling Green Lane, London, EC1R 0NE Tel: (020) 7837 3759 Fax: (020) 7278 0745 E-mail: harwinship@aol.com *Ship brokers*

Harwood Bros Ltd, 45 Walker Street, Wirral, Merseyside, CH47 2DY Tel: 0151-632 4327 Fax: 0151-632 4327 *Pipes lighters & smokers sundries*

Mark Harwood Photographic Studio, 12 Waterside, 44-48 Wharf Rd, London, N1 7SF Tel: (020) 7490 8787 Fax: (020) 7490 1009 E-mail: mark.harwood@appleonline.net *Commercial photography*

Harwoods Cleaning Contractors Ltd, Unit 3 Block 13 Whiteside Industrial Estate, Bathgate, West Lothian, EH48 2RX Tel: (01506) 633584 Fax: (01506) 636868 E-mail: harcc@aol.com *Office & industrial cleaning & janitorial service & providers*

Harwoods For Steel Ltd, Whitegate Farm, Waterlooville, Hampshire, PO8 0TG Tel: (023) 9259 3442 Fax: (023) 9259 6010 *Steel fabricators & sheet metalwork engineers*

Harzer Cosmetik Pinsel UK Ltd, Taylor Lane, Loscoe, Heanor, Derbyshire, DE75 7TA Tel: (01773) 534314 Fax: (01773) 534314 *Cosmetic & artistic brush manufrs*

▶ Hasan Hangers Ltd, 3 Mousell Street, Manchester, M8 8HY Tel: 0161-819 1001 Fax: 0161-819 1002 *Injection moulding manufrs*

Hasco-Thermic Ltd, 134 Birchfield Lane, Oldbury, West Midlands, B69 2AY Tel: 0121-552 4911 Fax: 0121-544 8143 E-mail: mail@hasco.co.uk *Galvanizing furnaces & associated equipment*

Haselbech Oak & Country Furniture, Haselbech Hill, Haselbech, Northampton, NN6 9LL Tel: (01604) 686360 Fax: (01604) 686360 E-mail: enquiries@haselbechoak.co.uk *Hand made oak furniture retailers*

Haselden Manufacturing Co., PO Box 349A, Surbiton, Surrey, KT5 9YG Tel: (020) 8337 7284 Fax: (020) 8337 7284 *Manual re-wind hose reel manufrs*

Haseltine Lake & Co., West Riding House, 67 Albion Street, Leeds, LS1 5AA Tel: 0113-233 9400 Fax: 0113-233 9401 E-mail: sales@haseltinelake.co.uk *Patent & trade mark agents*

Hasfield Systems, Yartleton Oak, Yartleton Lane, May Hill, Longhope, Gloucestershire, GL17 0RF Tel: (01452) 831881 Fax: (01452) 831881 E-mail: systems@hasfield.demon.co.uk *Prototype automation special equipment engineers*

Hashimoto Forming Industry Co. Ltd, 5 Didcot Way, Boldon Business Park, Boldon Colliery, Tyne & Wear, NE35 9PD Tel: 0191-519 0088 Fax: 0191-519 0460 E-mail: admin@hashimoto.ltd.uk *Manufacturing of car components*

▶ Haskayne Country Pets & Equine, Moor Farm, School Lane, Downholland, Ormskirk, Lancashire, L39 7JG Tel: (01704) 840234

Haskel Energy Systems Ltd, North Hylton Road, Sunderland, SR5 3JD Tel: 0191-549 1212 Fax: 0191-549 0911 E-mail: sales@haskel.co.uk Principal Export Areas: Middle East, Africa, Central/East Europe & West Europe *Haskel are the international leader and suppliers of high*

continued

continuation pressure products that include their own manufacture of air driven liquid pumps, gas boosters, air amplifiers. Butech who are a Haskel subsidiary manufacturers a range of of high pressure valves and fittings that are complementary with the pump ranges. Also Haskel manufacture a wide range of standard and customised packaged systems including pressure and hydrostatic test rigs, power packs, hose and valve test benches, chemical injection skids and gas transfer and pressurisation units

Haskel Energy Systems Ltd, North Hylton Road, Sunderland, SR5 3JD Tel: 0191-549 1212 Fax: 0191-549 0911 E-mail: sales@haskel.co.uk *Centralised cleaning & hygiene systems service*

Haskel Energy Systems Ltd, North Hylton Road, Sunderland, SR5 3JD Tel: 0191-549 1212 Fax: 0191-549 0911 E-mail: sales@haskel.co.uk *Butech specializes in equipment custom designed to meet the requirements of new processes, harsh environments & severe applications, as well as extreme pressures & temperatures.*

Haskoning (UK) Ltd, 4 Deans Yard, London, SW1P 3NL Tel: (020) 7222 2115 Fax: (020) 7222 2659 E-mail: info@london.royalhaskoning.com *Engineering consultants* Also at: Peterborough

▶ Haslam Preservation Ltd, 49 Norbreck Road, Thornton-Cleveleys, Lancashire, FY5 1RR Tel: (01253) 503111 Fax: (01253) 503110

▶ Haslam Printers Ltd, Standish Street, Chorley, Lancashire, PR7 3AJ Tel: (01257) 263777 Fax: (01257) 261404 E-mail: sales@haslamprinters.co.uk

Haslimann Taylor Ltd, 1 Wrens Court, 53 Lower Queen Street, Sutton Coldfield, West Midlands, B72 1RT Tel: 0121-355 3446 Fax: 0121-355 3393 E-mail: info@haslimanntaylor.com *Public relations & design consultants*

Hass Interiors, 14 Union Road, Sheffield, S11 9EF Tel: 0114-249 3142 Fax: 0114-250 0006 *Shop fittings manufrs*

▶ Hassall & Lucking Ltd, 36 Cross Street, Long Eaton, Nottingham, NG10 1HD Tel: 0115-973 3292 Fax: 0115-946 2120

Hasselblad UK Ltd, 385 Centennial Park, Centennial Avenue, Elstree, Borehamwood, Hertfordshire, WD6 3TJ Tel: (020) 8731 3250 Fax: (020) 8731 3251 E-mail: hasselblad.uk@hasselblad.com *Camera importers*

Hassett Fencing Ltd, Old Quarry Field, Harborough Road, Pitsford, Northampton, NN6 9RU Tel: (01604) 820902 Fax: (01604) 820899 *Fencing suppliers*

Hassett Industries plc, Larkhill Road, Durrington, Salisbury, SP4 8DS Tel: (01980) 654333 Fax: (01980) 654326 E-mail: hassett@globalnet.co.uk *Infrared heating element manufrs*

Hastie & Co, Morfa Road, Swansea, SA1 2EP Tel: (01792) 651541 Fax: (01792) 468119 E-mail: steven.miller@hastiegroup.co.uk *Grit blasting, metal spraying & powder coating*

Hastings Angling Centre, 33 The Bourne, Hastings, East Sussex, TN34 3AY Tel: (01424) 432178 *Angling equipment distributors*

Hastings & Henshaw, Bridgecroft Mills, Tanyard Road, Millsbridge, Huddersfield, HD3 4NF Tel: (01484) 647111 Fax: (01484) 647111 *Tarpaulin & canvas goods manufrs*

Jim Hastings Ltd, Seghill Industrial Estate, Seghill, Cramlington, Northumberland, NE23 7DR Tel: 0191-237 0633 Fax: 0191-237 2656 *Building & civil engineers*

Hastings Metal Finishers, Unit 7-8 Prince Consort Industrial Estate, Hebburn, Tyne & Wear, NE31 1EH Tel: 0191-483 9213 Fax: 0191-483 9213 E-mail: hmf.sales@tiscali.co.uk *Metal platers service*

▶ Hastings Pine Furniture Warehouse, A 409 Battle Road, St. Leonards-on-Sea, East Sussex, TN37 7BE Tel: (01424) 855120 Fax: (01424) 855120 *Cabinet manufrs*

▶ Hastingwood Basket Works, 99B Main Street, West Kilbride, Ayrshire, KA23 9AP Tel: (01294) 829012 Fax: (01294) 829012 E-mail: sales@hastingwoodbasketworks.com *Basket maker*

Charles Haswell & Partners Ltd, 3900 Parkside, Birmingham Business Park, Birmingham, B37 7YG Tel: 0121-717 7744 Fax: 0121-717 0902 E-mail: enquiries@severntrent.com Principal Export Areas: Asia Pacific, Central Asia, Middle East, Central/East Europe & West Europe *Civil engineering & gas systems design consultants*

Hat Box, 1 The Courtyard, George Street, Pontypool, Gwent, NP4 6LR Tel: (01495) 761901 E-mail: david@davidhead.wanadoo.co.uk *WE ARE A HAT HIRE AND HAT SALES BUSINESS SPECIALISING IN DESIGNER HATS AND FASCINATORS FOR SPECIAL OCCASSIONS.STOCKISTS OF NIGEL RAYMENT,WHITELEY,FAILSWORTH AND BALFOUR.COMPLETE THE LOOK WITH OUR RANGE OF HANDBAGS,SHOES AND JEWELLERY.*NEW FOR THIS SEASON,TAKE ADVATAGE OF OUR FREE DESIGN SERVICE FOR TIARAS,FASCINATORS AND BRIDAL JEWELLERY.*

Hatcham Motor Services, 1 Hatcham Park Road, London, SE14 5QE Tel: (020) 7732 7942 Fax: (020) 7732 7942 *Clutch fitting services*

Thomas Hatchard & Sons Ltd, Wellington Road, Brighton, BN41 1DN Tel: (01273) 430740 Fax: (01273) 410734 E-mail: sales@ths-eng.com *Precision Engineering - Thomas Hatchard & Sons Ltd, precision engineers. Manufacturers of high value single components and complete working assemblies for a wide range of industries.*

The Hatchwell Co. Ltd, Unit G1 Riverside Industrial Estate, Hermitage Street, Rishton, Blackburn, BB1 4NF Tel: (01254) 888479 Fax: (01254) 883822 E-mail: sales@hatchwell.co.uk *Pet treats & accessories manufrs*

Hatfield Catering Equipment, Foundry Street, Chesterfield, Derbyshire, S41 9AU Tel: (01246) 454533 Fax: (01246) 455316 E-mail: sales@hatfieldcatering.co.uk *Supply catering equipment fabricate steel*

Hatfield Machine Tool Co. Ltd, 2 Sandiford Road, Sutton, Surrey, SM3 9RD Tel: (020) 8644 6661 Fax: (020) 8644 4233 E-mail: sales@hatmac.co.uk *Machine tool merchants sheet metalworking machinery*

Rob Hatfield Ltd, Tower House Lane, Hedon, Hull, HU12 8EE Tel: (01482) 898286 Fax: (01482) 896862 *Road haulage & storage services*

▶ Hatfield Rob Haulage, Beechcroft, Main Street, Kilnwick, Driffield, North Humberside, YO25 9JD Tel: (01377) 270005 Fax: (01377) 270006

Hathaway & Muddiman Ltd, 35 Frederick Street, Birmingham, B1 3HH Tel: 0121-233 3069 Fax: 0121-233 3029 *Gem set ring manufrs*

Hathaway Roofing Ltd, Tindale Cresent, Tindale Crescent, Bishop Auckland, County Durham, DL14 9TL Tel: (01388) 605636 Fax: (01388) 608841 *Roofing & cladding contractors*

Hather Plant Hire, Aldwarke Road, Parkgate, Rotherham, South Yorkshire, S62 6BZ Tel: (01709) 528585 Fax: (01709) 710822 E-mail: gary@hatherplant.freeserve.co.uk *Plant hire*

Hathern Forge, Hathern Nurseries, Derby Road, Hathern, Loughborough, Leicestershire, LE12 5LD Tel: (01509) 646990 Fax: (01509) 646990 E-mail: sales@hathernforge.co.uk *Ornamental ironworkers*

Hatherway Office Furniture Ltd, The Farmhouse On The Green, Upper Quinton, Stratford-Upon-Avon, Warwickshire, CV37 8SX Tel: (01789) 721113 Fax: (01789) 721220 E-mail: fbs@freeola.com *Office furniture suppliers*

Hatmet Ltd, Interiors House, Lynton Road, London, N8 8SL Tel: (020) 8341 0200 Fax: (020) 8341 9878 E-mail: info@hatmet.co.uk *Suspended ceilings & partitions manufrs* Also at: Farnham & Nottingham

▶ Hatrick-Bruce Properties Ltd, Market House, Milnathort, Kinross, KY13 9XB Tel: (01577) 863967 E-mail: sales@hatrickbruce.co.uk

▶ Hats 4 Tots Ltd, 25 Longacre, Woodthorpe, Nottingham, NG5 4JS Tel: 0115-967 1371 *Children's clothing manufrs*

▶ Hatters Catering Co., 6 Southgate Parade, Crawley, West Sussex, RH10 6ER Tel: (01293) 550333 Fax: (01293) 552254 E-mail: admin@hatterscatering.co.uk *Professional catering (Sussex) company with over 30 years experience in all aspect of catering from private parties to weddings, funerals, canapés, bbq''s spit roasts, corporate events, contract catering, etc. We are also fully licenced with our own mobile bars.**

Hattersley Aladdin UK, Greengate, Keighley, West Yorkshire, BD21 5JL Tel: (01639) 730997 Fax: (01535) 610195 E-mail: info@hattersley.co.uk Principal Export Areas: Worldwide *Manufacturers of industrial, military & upholstery webbing, narrow fabric, braid, fabric tape & glass fibre tape & webbing. In addition oil heater/lamp wick manufrs*

Hattersley Newman Hender Ltd, 2 Burscough Road, Ormskirk, Lancashire, L39 2XG Tel: (01695) 577199 Fax: (01695) 578775 E-mail: uksales@hattersley.com *Valve manufrs*

Hatton Fans, Unit 20 Brymau Four Trading Estate, River Lane, Saltney, Chester, CH4 8RF Tel: (01244) 677633 Fax: (01244) 681034 E-mail: hattonfansc@aol.com *Ventilating fan stockists* Also at: Manchester

Hatton Garden Safe Deposit Ltd, 88-90 Hatton Garden, London, EC1N 8PN Tel: (020) 7405 9600 Fax: (020) 7242 5682 *Safe deposit facilities & services*

Hatton Logistics Ltd, Station Road, Blaxton, Doncaster, South Yorkshire, DN9 3AG Tel: (01302) 770284 Fax: (01302) 771663 E-mail: msmith@hattonlogistics.fsbusiness.co.uk *Road transport, haulage & freight services*

▶ Hatton Traffic Management Ltd, Brunswick Industrial Estate, Brunswick Village, Newcastle upon Tyne, NE13 7BA Tel: 0191-236 8060 Fax: 0191-236 2035

Hattons Office Furniture, 2-8 Borough Road, St. Helens, Merseyside, WA10 3SY Tel: (01744) 753337 Fax: (01744) 611976 *Office furniture distributors*

Hatwell's Leisure, 68 High Street, Witney, Oxfordshire, OX28 6HJ Tel: (01865) 884334 Fax: (01865) 884334 *Funfair equipment hire*

Haughton Design Ltd, Business Innovation Centre, Gates Court, Staffordshire Technology Park, Stafford, ST18 0AR Tel: (01785) 243767 Fax: (01785) 243768 E-mail: adm@haughtondesign.co.uk *Engineering design consultants, design service & can supply drawings, images or animations that can really set your design, product or equipment apart from the rest, our services:*cad, project management, *finite element analysis, *design knowledge, *product design, *general mechanical, *special purpose machine, *test rigs, *tooling, *process equipment, *cad software, *solidworks pro, *catia v5, *cosmos, *autocad ***

▶ Haughtons Business Sales, Gladstone Street, Kibworth, Leicester, LE8 0HL Tel: 0116-279 2509 Fax: 0116-279 2509 E-mail: alan@hbsales.co.uk *Business transfer agents*

Hauhinco Water Hydraulics Ltd, PO Box 51, Heckmondwike, West Yorkshire, WF16 9DP Tel: (01924) 510600 Fax: (01924) 511539 E-mail: info@hauhinco.co.uk *Hydraulic water pump & valve manufrs*

Haul Small Ltd, Unit 2 Knightwood Court, Edison Way, Gapton Hall Industrial Estate, Great Yarmouth, Norfolk, NR31 0NG Tel: (01493) 604691 Fax: (01493) 604692 *Road transport services*

▶ Hauler Europe Ltd, Moll Springs, Netherton, Huddersfield, HD4 7DN Tel: (01484) 660291 Fax: (01484) 660295

▶ Haulmark Equipment Ltd, Barleycastle Lane, Appleton, Warrington, WA4 4RB Tel: (01925) 269900 Fax: (01925) 269901 E-mail: sales@haulmarkltd.co.uk *Supply equipment for the demolition, recycling & re-handling industries*

▶ Haulways Road Haulage Services, Pleasant Street, Lyng, West Bromwich, West Midlands, B70 7DP Tel: 0121-553 1975 Fax: 0121-500 5845

Hauni London Ltd, Hope House, 45 Great Peter Street, London, SW1P 3LT Tel: (020) 7222 3956 Fax: (020) 7222 8648 *Cigarette machinery manufrs*

Hauppauge Computer Works Ltd, Bank Chambers, 6 Borough High Street, London, SE1 9QQ Tel: (020) 7378 1997 Fax: (020) 7357 9771 E-mail: support@hauppauge.co.uk *Multimedia computer cards manufrs*

Hauser Ltd, Unit 2 Westpoint Enterprise Park, Clarence Ave, Trafford Park, Manchester, M17 1QS Tel: 0161-877 3317 Fax: 0161-872 0293 E-mail: enquiries@hauser.co.uk *International freight forwarders*

▶ Hauser Ltd, Heighington Lane, Aycliffe Industrial Park, Newton Aycliffe, County Durham, DL5 6UE Tel: (01325) 300855 Fax: (01325) 300844 E-mail: northeast@hauser.co.uk *Freight forwarders*

▶ Hauser Sheffield Ltd, Alliance House, Roman Ridge Road, Sheffield, S9 1GB Tel: 0114-244 9977 Fax: 0114-242 3481 E-mail: sheffield@hauser.co.uk *Freight forwarders*

Hausherr (U K) Ltd, High St, Clay Cross, Chesterfield, Derbyshire, S45 9PF Tel: (01246) 252000 Fax: (01246) 865077 E-mail: hausherr@btconnect.com *Mining & quarrying machinery manufrs*

▶ Havana Coffee Co., Unit 11 Gratton Court, Gratton Way, Roundswell Business Park, Barnstaple, Devon, EX31 3NL Tel: (01271) 374376 Fax: (01271) 374376 *Commercial coffee equipment manufrs*

▶ Havana Technologies Ltd, Cumberland House,, 35 Park Row,, Nottingham, NG1 6EE Tel: 0115 9886085 Fax: 0115 9886086 E-mail: enquires@havtech.co.uk *We are a technology consulting and systems integration firm dedicated to raising business value through the innovative application of industrial automation using RFID, wireless technologies and information technologies.*

Havant Sheet Metal Co. Ltd, Downley Road, Havant, Hampshire, PO9 2NN Tel: 0845 5314135 Fax: (023) 9247 0563 E-mail: sales@havantsheetmetal.co.uk Sales Contact: N.C. Jurd *Havant Sheet Metal Co. Ltd based in Havant, Hampshire are sheet metalwork engineers including precision fine limit, engraving, fabrication, cutting & fabricating. **Havant Sheet Metal Co. Ltd has been producing quality sheet metal components & fabrications for over 60 years. Operating from our 24,000 sq ft manufacturing facility located on the South Coast in Havant near Portsmouth, we offer the complete sheet metal fabrication service including powder coating & stove enamelling. **Our experienced and versatile workforce combined with the latest CNC machinery and stringent quality controls have gained us a reputation for producing quality products efficiently and on time.*

Havas Packing & Shipping Ltd, Little Parrock Farm, Shepherds Hill, Colemans Hatch, Hartfield, East Sussex, TN7 4HP Tel: (01342) 824388 Fax: (01342) 825541 E-mail: enquiries@havas.co.uk *Freight forwarders & export packers*

Havelock Alarms, 6 Duncombe Avenue, Clydebank, Dunbartonshire, G81 6PP Tel: (01389) 873794 Fax: (01389) 876666 *Burglar alarm systems installation*

▶ Havelock (Europa) Plc, Moss Way, Hill End Industrial Estate, Dalgety Bay, Dunfermline, Fife, KY11 9JH Tel: (01383) 820044 Fax: (01383) 820064 *Havelock Europa PLC is a leading provider of - retail, healthcare, hotel, corporate office and financial services interiors; *educational furniture and supplies; Point of sale merchandising display*

▶ Havelock Secretarial Services, Havelock Secretarial Services, Enterprise 5, Five Lane Ends, Idle, Bradford, West Yorkshire, BD10 8EW Tel: 01274 618821 Fax: 01274 612604 E-mail: ltaylor@tayloredwebs.co.uk *Secretarial and administrative services including word processing, mailshots, telephone answering service, printing and design, photocopying, laminating, binding, scanning and email.*

Haven Automation Ltd, Kingsway, Fforestfach, Swansea, SA5 4EX Tel: (01792) 588722 Fax: (01792) 582624 E-mail: sales@haven.co.uk *Manufacturers and suppliers of a range of calibration equipment covering temperature, pressure and electrical requirements from hand-held instruments to complete instrument workbenches and laboratory furniture. Full UKAS-accredited laboratory facilities for calibration and repair of a range of instruments.*

Haven Colourprint UK Ltd, The Print Works, London Road Industrial Estate, Pembroke Dock, Dyfed, SA72 4RZ Tel: (01646) 623700 Fax: (01646) 621121 E-mail: enquiries@havencolourprintuk.com *Lithographers, designers & scanners*

Haven Equipment Co., Duncote Mill, Walcot, Telford, Shropshire, TF6 5ER Tel: (01952) 740484 Fax: (01952) 740464 E-mail: sales@havenequipment.co.uk *Manufacturers/refurbishers of conveyor systems*

▶ Haven Industries Ltd, 5 Allington Lane, Fair Oak, Eastleigh, Hampshire, SO50 7DA Tel: (023) 8069 5544 Fax: 01489 89090 E-mail: ralphybruce.@hotmail.com *Fibre glass mouldings manufrs*

▶ Haven Mouldings, 17 White Road, Off Charfleets Road, Canvey Island, Essex, SS8 0PQ Tel: (01268) 698823 Fax: (01268) 697125 E-mail: haven@btconnect.com *Make glass fibre molding*

Haven Warehousing & Distribution Ltd, Sixth Avenue, Flixborough, Scunthorpe, South Humberside, DN15 8SH Tel: (01724) 854735 Fax: (01724) 281687 E-mail: havendst@aol.com *Storage*

continued

▶ Havenscroft Ltd, 3 Barn Close, Stone Cross, Pevensey, East Sussex, BN24 5EN Tel: (01323) 769260 Fax: (01323) 766351

Haverfordwest Coin Operator, 3 Cromwell House, City Road, Haverfordwest, Dyfed, SA61 2EH Tel: (01437) 763094 Fax: (01437) 769177 *Distributors of coin machines*

▶ Haverill PC Bureau, Homefield Road, Haverhill, Suffolk, CB9 8QP Tel: (0871) 8712100 Fax: (0871) 8712101 E-mail: sales@hpcb.co.uk *Computer maintenance & repair services*

Havering Building Specialists Ltd, 48 Brentwood Road, Romford, RM1 2EP Tel: (01708) 744574 Fax: (01708) 732722 E-mail: sales@hbsltd.uk.com *Building contractors.*

Havering College, 81-85 High Street, Brentwood, Essex, CM14 4RR Tel: (01708) 769235 Fax: (01277) 202752 E-mail: bw.iltlc@topenworld.com *Computer training*

Havering Fencing Co, 237 Chase Cross Road, Romford, RM5 3XS Tel: (01708) 747855 Fax: (01708) 721010 E-mail: enquiries@haveringfencing.com *Fencing contractors & repairers*

Hawaiian Airlines Reservations, The Office at Pond View, Downyard, Compton Pauncefoot, Yeovil, Somerset, BA22 7EL Tel: (0844) 4844336 Fax: (01933) 315702 E-mail: reservations@hawaiianair.co.uk *Hawaiian Airlines Reservations Europe*

Hawco Direct, 8 Cranfield Road, Lostock Industrial Estate, Lostock, Bolton, BL6 4SB Tel: (01204) 675000 Fax: (01204) 675010 E-mail: catalogue@hawcodirect.co.uk *Thermometer & temperature control distributors*

Hawco Refridgeration, The Wharf, Abbey Mill Business Park, Lower Eashing, Godalming, Surrey, GU7 2QN Tel: (01483) 869070 Fax: (01483) 869001 E-mail: sales@hawco.co.uk *Thermometer & temperature control distributors*

Haweka UK Ltd, Unit No 5 Beta, Orchard Industrial Estate, Toddington, Cheltenham, Gloucestershire, GL54 5EB Tel: (01242) 621001 Fax: (01242) 620558 E-mail: John.Pullin@haweka.co.uk *Wheel balancing adaptor distributors*

Hawes Group Ltd, Sandfield Close, Moulton Park, Northampton, NN3 6EU Tel: (01604) 790000 Fax: (01604) 790190 E-mail: info@hawes.co.uk *Sign installers & manufrs*

▶ Hawes Plant Hire, Navigation Way, Loughborough, Leicestershire, LE11 1QD Tel: (01509) 212024 Fax: (01509) 611655

Hawick Cashmere, 20 Montpellier Parade, Harrogate, North Yorkshire, HG1 2TG Tel: (01423) 502519 Fax: (01423) 502519 *Cashmere suppliers*

Hawk Ltd, Suite 2, Concourse House, 432 Dewsbury Road, Leeds, LS11 7DF Tel: 0113-270 4415 Fax: (01274) 305551 E-mail: leeds@ies.com *Security systems cctv*

Hawk Cars Ltd, Oakdene, Wadhurst Road, Frant, Tunbridge Wells, Kent, TN3 9EP Tel: (01892) 750341 Fax: (01892) 750071 E-mail: gerry@hawkcars.co.uk *Car manufrs*

▶ Hawk Cricket & Leisure, The Forge, Drayton, Belbroughton, Stourbridge, West Midlands, DY9 0BN Tel: (01562) 731115 *Sports goods manufrs*

▶ Hawk Development Ltd, Charleston House, The Grange, Loppington, Shrewsbury, SY4 5SY Tel: (01939) 233153 Fax: (01939) 233510

Hawk Electronics Ltd, Malt Street, Accrington, Lancashire, BB5 1DR Tel: (01254) 389515 Fax: (01254) 389505 E-mail: sales@hawkelectronics.co.uk

Hawk Engineering, Bessemer Road, Sheffield, S9 3XN Tel: 0114-281 7111 Fax: 0114-281 7222 E-mail: sales@hawkengineering.co.uk *Precision engineers & CNC machinists*

Hawk Fabrications & Engineering Ltd, Unit 10 Wanstead Industrial Park, Wanstead Road, Leicester, LE3 1TR Tel: 0116-287 3749 Fax: 0116-287 4692 *General engineering*

Hawk Fasteners Ltd, Brunel Road, Middlesbrough, Cleveland, TS6 6JA Tel: (01642) 468581 Fax: (01642) 440880 E-mail: sales@hawkfast.com *Precision & general machinists*

Hawk Furniture Ltd, Holme Industrial Estate, Skiff Lane, Holme-on-Spalding-Moor, York, YO43 4BB Tel: (01430) 861229 Fax: (01430) 861225 E-mail: enquiries@hawkfurniture.co.uk *Furniture manufrs*

▶ Hawk Industrial Services, 12 The Paddock, East Keswick, Leeds, LS17 9EN Tel: 01937 574338 Fax: 01937 572896 E-mail: hawkindustrial@btconnect.com *Products & services to keep your business moving*

Hawk Information, Glebe Farm House, Milton, Banbury, Oxfordshire, OX15 4HH Tel: (01295) 720251 Fax: (01295) 722207 E-mail: cjr@hawk-eye.demon.co.uk *Information suppliers*

▶ Hawk Lana Ltd, 26 Tarragon Way, Burghfield Common, Reading, RG7 3YU Tel: 0118-983 4630 Fax: E-mail: sales@hawklana.f2s.com

Hawk Mouldings, Mill Rythe Lane, Hayling Island, Hampshire, PO11 0QG Tel: (023) 9246 3864 Fax: (023) 9246 7204 E-mail: sales@hawkmouldings.co.uk *Marine products manufrs*

▶ Hawk P O S Ltd, 7 Church Road, Flamstead, St. Albans, Hertfordshire, AL3 8BN Tel: (01582) 849313 Fax: (01582) 840144 E-mail: sales@hawkpos.co.uk *Specialists in Point of Sale, supplying promotional items into the drinks industry.*

Hawk Plant Hire Ltd, Charleston House, The Grange, Loppington, Shrewsbury, SY4 5SY Tel: (01939) 233730 Fax: (01939) 235206 E-mail: hire@hawk-group.co.uk *Plant & tractor hire*

Hawk Property Services Ltd, Unit 3A, Britland Estate, Northbourne Road, Eastbourne, East Sussex, BN22 8PW Tel: (01323) 641110 Fax: (01323) 641112 E-mail: mail@hawkps.co.uk *We are a small, privately run, building and contracting company based in East Sussex. We operate within Sussex, Kent, Surrey and South London but*

continued

continuation
have the capability to operate further afield for individual clients or on particular projects. Contact us for all your building, maintenance, refurbishment, design or planning needs.

▶ Hawk Systems London Ltd, Uplands Business Park, Blackhorse Lane, London, E17 5QJ Tel: (020) 8531 4473 Fax: (020) 8523 1403

Hawk & Trowel Plastering Centre, Office Address:, 3 Overhill Gardens, Brighton, BN1 8ND Tel: (01273) 557932 E-mail: poddie@ntlworld.com *Professonal, value for money plastering training. We offer day, 5 day, weekend and evening plastering courses. For full details please visit our website.*

▶ Hawke Cable Glands Ltd, Oxford St West, Ashton-under-Lyne, Lancashire, OL7 0NA Tel: 0161-308 3611 Fax: 0161-830 6648 E-mail: sales@ehawke.com *One of the leading manufacturers of hazardous area Cable Glands as well as electrical equipment for hazardous locations, with an innovative range of cable connection, termination & barrier products*

Hawke Systems, Unit 1 14 Newlands Drive, Colnbrook, Slough, SL3 0DX Tel: (01753) 686686 Fax: (01753) 686747 E-mail: sales@hawke.co.uk *Systems solution providers*

Hawker Ltd, Rake Lane, Clifton Junction, Swinton, Manchester, M27 8LR Tel: 0161-794 4611 *Industrial battery manufrs*

Hawker Electronics Ltd, 57 The Avenue, Rubery, Rednal, Birmingham, B45 9AL Tel: 0121-453 8911 Fax: 0121-453 3777 E-mail: info@hawker-electronics.co.uk *OEM level control of liquids & powders manufrs*

Hawker Siddeley Switchgear Ltd, Newport Road, Pontllanfraith, Blackwood, Gwent, NP12 2XH Tel: (01495) 223001 Fax: (01495) 225674 E-mail: sales@hss-ltd.com *Electrical industrial switchgear makers*

Hawkes Metalmex, Holbrook Trading Estate, Old Lane, Halfway, Sheffield, S20 3GZ Tel: 0114-251 0251 Fax: 0114-251 0151 E-mail: sales@pct-automotive.co.uk *Press toolmakers*

Hawkes Refrigeration Engineers, 2 Gibcracks, Basildon, Essex, SS14 1PE Tel: (01268) 556663 Fax: (01268) 584525 E-mail: sales@refrigeration-uk.com *Refrigeration, air conditioning & ventilation*

Hawkes Technical Ltd, Spencer Parade, Stanwick, Wellingborough, Northamptonshire, NN9 6QJ Tel: (01933) 622492 Fax: (01933) 624092 E-mail: info@hawkestechnical.com *Since 1975 Hawkes have supplied innovative die cutting solutions, die cutting presses and die cutting systems. Including: Swing beam cutting presses, Travelling head cutting presses, Beam cutting presses, Receding head cutting presses, Foam cutting presses, High speed cutting presses, Kiss cutting presses and systems, Automatic travelling head cutting presses, Plastic card cutting systems, Knife cutting tables and more. Both new and reconditioned cutting presses available in manual, automatic or fully tailored systems offering you total cutting solutions for a wide range of materials. Hawkes team aims to exceed your expectations and in addition offer consultancy for cutting solutions, cutting press service, cutting press machine moving, cutting press spare parts, cutting belts and cutting boards. Servicing a wide range of brands including: Atom, Cox & Wright, Pedersen, Samco-Strong, Sandt, Schoen, Suteau and Sysco. You are always welcome to visit Hawkes large cutting press showroom to see the equipment quality and performance.*

William Hawkes Ltd, 183 & 184 High St, Deritend, Birmingham, B12 0LH Tel: 0121-772 2694 Fax: 0121-772 2694 *Architectural & artistic ironworks*

Hawkesford Buildbase, Adderley Road, Market Drayton, Shropshire, TF9 3SW Tel: (01630) 652481 Fax: (01630) 655489 E-mail: marketdrayton@buildbase.co.uk *Buildbase is one of the UK's fastest growing builders merchants. All of our branches are long established companies which have been serving local trades people for many years, with knowledge and experience to match. We believe strongly in understanding the needs of trades professional and our business has been developed specifically to meet those demands. Massive stocks, top quality products, competitive pricing, reliable delivery, specialist staff and exceptional customer service.*

Hawkesley Engineering Ltd, Unit 3, Avery Dell Industrial Estate, Birmingham, B30 3DZ Tel: 0121-433 4277 Fax: 0121-433 4280 E-mail: enquiries@hawkesley.co.uk *Steel fabricators*

Hawkeye Aerial Photography, Mansewood, Bellfield Road, Kirkintilloch, Glasgow, G66 1DS Tel: 0141-775 0673 Fax: 0141-775 0673 *Aerial photography*

Hawkins Clock Co. Ltd, PO Box 39, Peterborough, PE6 8XQ Tel: (01733) 330222 Fax: (01733) 333700 E-mail: sales@hawkinsclocks.co.uk *Clock retailers & manufrs*

Dennis Hawkins Welding, Westside Farm, High Street, Stoke Goldington, Newport Pagnell, Buckinghamshire, MK16 8NP Tel: (01908) 551400 *Welding services*

Peter Hawkins Ltd, Castle Lane, Castle Street, Melbourne, Derby, DE73 8DY Tel: (01332) 864747 Fax: (01332) 864748 E-mail: sales@phawkins.co.uk *Glass working machine distribs*

Hawkins Roofing Ltd, Unit 9 Thorpe Way, Banbury, Oxfordshire, OX16 4SP Tel: (01295) 252363 Fax: (01295) 251008 E-mail: hawkins-roofing@telinco.co.uk *Industrial roofing & steelwork specialists*

Hawkins Russell Jones, 7-8 Portmill Lane, Hitchin, Hertfordshire, SG5 1AS Tel: (01462) 628888 Fax: (01462) 631233 E-mail: hitchin@hrjlaw.co.uk *Solicitors*

Hawkridge Dairy, Hawkridge Farm, Coldridge, Crediton, Devon, EX17 6AR Tel: (01363) 884222 Fax: (01363) 83939 *Dairy products & cooked meat wholesalers*

▶ Hawkriver Software Designs, 8 St. Pauls Terrace, Easton, Wells, Somerset, BA5 1DX Tel: (0870) 1993812 Fax: (07092) 807649

Hawks Chemical Co. Ltd, 2 Tower Street, Hyde, Cheshire, SK14 1JW Tel: 0161-367 9441 Fax: 0161-367 9443 E-mail: sales@hawks-chem.com *Chemical & corrosion inhibitive packaging distributors*

Hawksley Engineering Ltd, Burringham Road, Gunness, Scunthorpe, South Humberside, DN17 3LT Tel: (01724) 782511 Fax: (01724) 783577 E-mail: hawkeng@ic24.net *Structural & mechanical engineering services*

Hawksley & Sons Ltd, Marlborough Road, Lancing, West Sussex, BN15 8TN Tel: (01903) 752815 Fax: (01903) 766050 E-mail: enquiries@hawksley.co.uk *Laboratory & hospital equipment manufacturer.*

▶ Hawkspare Ltd Commercial Vehicle Exptrs, Green St Groveeen Road, Dartford, DA2 8DP Tel: (01474) 706971 Fax: (01474) 703402 E-mail: info@hawkspare.co.uk

Haworth Castings Ltd, Budds Lane, Romsey, Hampshire, SO51 0HA Tel: (01794) 512685 Fax: (01794) 830086 E-mail: sales@haworthcastings.com *Non-ferrous metal casting manufrs*

Richard Haworth Ltd, Kearsley Mill, Stoneclough, Radcliffe, Manchester, M26 1RH Tel: (01204) 702300 Fax: (01204) 705772 E-mail: info@richardhaworth.co.uk *Richard Haworth is a leading supplier to the hospitality marketplace. With a broad range of bed linens from crisp cotton sheets to practical prints, and an extensive range of towels, bath robes and slippers. In addition the reputed table linen collection from Richard Haworth includes the revolutionary Signature Plus fabric and is truly unique with the table linen market, along with traditional cotton satin band. The Company also offer a design, manufacture and installation service on soft furnishings to include curtains, cushions and bed throws, and can complete single room refurbishments to full project managed new build installations. Duvets, pillows along with all the bed essentials complete the product range all backed by an exacting quality standard synonymous with the Richard Haworth name.*

Haworth Scouring Co., Cashmere Works, Birksland Street, Bradford, West Yorkshire, BD3 9SX Tel: (01274) 846500 Fax: (01274) 846501 *Commission wool scourers*

Haws Watering Cans, 120 Beakes Road, Smethwick, West Midlands, B67 5AB Tel: 0121-420 2494 Fax: 0121-429 1668 E-mail: sales@haws.demon.co.uk *Watering can manufrs*

▶ Hawthorn Gardening Services, The Hawthorns, Ewell, Epsom, Surrey, KT17 2QA Tel: 07929 196344 E-mail: jon@hawthorn-gardening.com *A friendly and professional company offering landscaping, lawncare, design, treecare, and all other aspects of gardencare including regular maintenance.*

▶ Hawthorn Window Services Ltd, Unit 5-6 Vernon Trading Estate, New John Street, Halesowen, West Midlands, B62 8HT Tel: 0121-559 6320 Fax: 0121-559 6106

Hawthorne Engineering Ltd, Unit 5 Hexthorpe Trading Park, Littlewood Street, Hexthorpe, Doncaster, South Yorkshire, DN4 0EJ Tel: (01302) 321990 Fax: (01302) 349939 E-mail: sales@hawthorneengineeringltd.co.uk *Steel fabricators & fire escape installations*

▶ Hawthorne Timber Fabrications Ltd, 31 Markethill Road, Newtownhamilton, Newry, County Down, BT35 0BE Tel: (028) 3087 8283 Fax: (028) 3087 8926 *Timber manufrs*

Haxton Safety Ltd, Unit 17 Langlands Avenue, East Kilbride, Glasgow, G75 0YG Tel: (01355) 221818 Fax: (01355) 220333 E-mail: info@haxton.co.uk *Protective clothing distributors service*

Hay & Brecon Farmers Ltd, The Old Station, Newport Street, Hay-On-Wye, Hereford, HR3 5BH Tel: (01497) 820516 Fax: (01497) 821007 E-mail: farmershay@aol.com *Agricultural & fertiliser merchants* Also at: Brecon, Builth Wells, Penybont & Sennybridge

Hay & Brecon Farmers Ltd, Station Yard, Llandrindod Wells, Powys, LD1 5BE Tel: (01597) 824851 Fax: (01597) 823914 *Agricultural merchants*

Hay & Co. Buildbase, Freefield Road, Lerwick, Shetland, ZE1 0NH Tel: (01595) 693057 Fax: (01595) 696037 E-mail: lerwick@buildbase.co.uk *Buildbase is one of the UK's fastest growing builders merchants. All of our branches are long established companies which have been serving local trades people for many years, with knowledge and experience to match. We believe strongly in understanding the needs of trades professional and our business has been developed specifically to meet those demands. Massive stocks, top quality products, competitive pricing, reliable delivery, specialist staff and exceptional customer service.*

Hay Engineering, 22-25 Moreland Road, Forton Industrial Estate, Gosport, Hampshire, PO12 4UU Tel: (023) 9258 7453 Fax: (023) 9258 7453 E-mail: robert@hayengineering.com *Precision engineering*

▶ Hay Forres Ltd, Plasmon Yard, Fleurs Place, Forres, Morayshire, IV36 1LX Tel: (01309) 672400 Fax: (01309) 676403

Hay Group, Unit 2635 Kings Court, The Crescent, Birmingham Business Park, Birmingham, B37 7YE Tel: 0121-717 4600 Fax: 0121-717 4601 *Management consultancy*

▶ Ian Hay Engineering Ltd, Unit 1-2, Badentoy Place, Badentoy Industrial Estate, Portlethen, Aberdeen, AB12 4YF Tel: (01224) 782280 Fax: (01224) 781277 *Engineering machine shop*

Hay Joinery, Chapel Road, Lingwood, Norwich, NR13 4NY Tel: (01603) 712392 Fax: (01603) 714248 E-mail: build@jshay.co.uk *Joinery contractors*

Hay Machine Tools Ltd, Lythalls Lane, Coventry, CV6 6FX Tel: (024) 7668 8641 Fax: (024) 7663 7162 E-mail: office@heymachinetools.co.uk *Machine tool manufrs*

Hay Metal Craft, Elemore House, Easington Lane, Houghton Le Spring, Tyne & Wear, DH5 0QT Tel: 0191-517 1284 Fax: 0191-517 1284 *Metal workers*

Hay Nisbet Press Ltd, 11 Dilwara Avenue, Glasgow, G14 0SQ Tel: 0141-959 3325 Fax: 0141-958 1161 E-mail: Studio@haynisbet.com *Lithographic printers & direct mailers*

Hayburn Wood Products, 299 Galgorm Road, Ahoghill, Ballymena, County Antrim, BT42 1JU Tel: (028) 2587 1442 Fax: (028) 2587 1177 E-mail: info@hayburn.co.uk *Kitchen & joinery product manufrs*

Haycock & Hague, The Vivars Indust Centre, Vivars Way Canal Road, Selby, North Yorkshire, YO8 8BE Tel: (01757) 290011 Fax: (01757) 212112 E-mail: sales@haycockandhague.co.uk *Our organisation has a reputation synonymous with Safety, Quality and Flexibility. We offer pipework fabrication services enhanced by our ability to provide total turn-key engineering solutions. Please visit our website for further details.*

Haycock Hotel, London Road, Wansford, Peterborough, PE8 6JA Tel: (01780) 782223 Fax: (01780) 783031 E-mail: sales@arcadianhotel.co.uk *Hotel & conference centre*

Haydens Saw & Cutter Service, 1 The Mazes, East Street, Braintree, Essex, CM7 3JJ Tel: (01376) 325380 Fax: (01376) 552286 *Saw sharpening sales, services & repairs*

▶ Haydock Finance Ltd, 2 The Cottage, Main Street, Kinnesswood, Kinross, KY13 9HN Tel: (01592) 840480 Fax: (01592) 840480

Haydock Park Race Course Co. Ltd, Lodge Lane, Newton-le-Willows, Merseyside, WA12 0HQ Tel: (01942) 725963 Fax: (01942) 270879 E-mail: info@haydock-park.com *Racecourses*

Roger Haydock & Co. Ltd, Mersey View Road, Widnes, Cheshire, WA8 8LN Tel: 0151-425 2525 Fax: 0151-425 4141 E-mail: rdh@haydockwidnes.demon.co.uk *Timber importers & pole ladder manufrs* Also at: Colwyn Bay, Liverpool & Whitchurch

▶ Haydon Mechanical & Electrical, The Isis Building Thames Quay, 193 Marsh Wall, London, E14 9SG Tel: (020) 7987 3555

Haydon Switch (HSI) (Henley), Treetops House, Gillotts Lane, Henley-on-Thames, Oxfordshire, RG9 1PT Tel: (01491) 579118 Fax: (01491) 412211 E-mail: sales@acdcsystems.com *Electric motors*

Allan Hayes Engineering Ltd, Charlwoods Road, East Grinstead, West Sussex, RH19 2HR Tel: (01342) 324536 Fax: (01342) 312556 *Precision engineers*

▶ Austin Hayes Ltd, Cemetery Road, Yeadon, Leeds, LS19 7BD Tel: 0113-250 2255 Fax: 0113-250 2200 E-mail: info@austinhayes.co.uk *Shot blasting & painting contractors*

▶ Hayes Computing Solutions, 2 Central Close, Hethersett, Norwich, NR9 3ER Tel: (01603) 811367 E-mail: info@hcoms.co.uk *HCOMS offers website design , web hosting, website promotion and software /hardware solutions. We are experts in providing website design,e-commerce,website hosting using a wide range of technology. We are a Norfolk Website Design and IT Company.**We are experts in providing be-spoke and off the shelf , software to businesses either as web-based applications, stand-alone windows-based software or native to Microsoft Office. We are offical Sage Line 50 Developers.***

Hayes Control Systems, The Boathouse, Station Road, Henley-on-Thames, Oxfordshire, RG9 1AZ Tel: (01491) 410539 Fax: (01491) 577267 E-mail: sales@hayescontrol.co.uk *Control systems suppliers*

Hayes Engineering & Garage Services, Unit 2a Europa Trading Estate, Fraser Road, Erith, Kent, DA8 1QL Tel: (01322) 440332 Fax: (01322) 439930 E-mail: sales@hayescharters.com *Engine reconditioning*

Hayes & Finch Ltd, Hanson Road, Liverpool, L9 7BP Tel: 0151-523 6303 Fax: 0151-523 4537 E-mail: sales@hfltd.com *Church furnisher & candle manufrs*

Hayes Hygiene, Paddock Barn Farm, Woldingham, Caterham, Surrey, CR3 7JD Tel: (01883) 330173 Fax: (01883) 330174 *Hygiene chemicals*

Hayes Industries Ltd, 2 Marchington Industrial Estate, Stubby Lane, Marchington, Uttoxeter, Staffordshire, ST14 8LP Tel: (01283) 820402 Fax: (01283) 820648 E-mail: enquiries@able-engineering.co.uk *Steel fabricators*

Hayes Inter-Selection, Roman Wall House, 1-2 Crutched Friars, London, EC3N 2HT Tel: (020) 7680 0077 Fax: (020) 7680 1052 *Employment agency & financial services*

▶ Nick Hayes Sales & Marketing Consultancy, 22 Southcote Way, Penn, High Wycombe, Buckinghamshire, HP10 8JG Tel: (01494) 815916 Fax: (01494) 815916 E-mail: info@nickhayessales.com *Supplier of new business generation services to SME companies*

Hayes Parsons Services Ltd, St Lawrence House, Broad Street, Bristol, BS1 2HF Tel: 0117-929 9381 Fax: 0117-926 5644 E-mail: marine@hayesparsons.co.uk *Insurance intermediaries*

Hayes (Plastic) Engineering, Unit 59, Station Road Industrial Estate, Hailsham, East Sussex, BN27 2ES Tel: (01323) 844455 Fax: (01323) 844488 E-mail: info@hayesplastics.com *Plastics injection mouldings manufrs*

▶ Hayes Translations, 45 Northfield Road, Doncaster, South Yorkshire, DN5 8AY Tel: (01302) 781142 E-mail: monica@hayestranslations.co.uk *Hayes Translations offers professional translation and interpreting services in the fallowing languages: German, English, French, Spanish and Romanian. Other services include: website design, creating multilingual websites, private tuition. Using native speakers, Hayes Translations provides reliable, fast and professional translation/interpreting services.*

Hayes Tubes Ltd, Balds Lane, Lye, Stourbridge, West Midlands, DY9 8NN Tel: (01384) 422373 Fax: (01384) 422877 E-mail: hayestubes@enterprise.net *Welded tube manufrs*

Hayes UK Ltd, 7 Eagle Estate, Brookers Road, Billingshurst, West Sussex, RH14 9RZ Tel: (0870) 0711700 Fax: (0870) 0711701 E-mail: sales@hayes-uk.com *Manufacturers of consumables for plumbers & gas engineers*

Hayfield Engineering Ltd, Sutherland Avenue, Wolverhampton, WV2 2JH Tel: (01902) 352930 Fax: (01902) 351620 E-mail: sales@hayfield.co.uk *Precision machining*

Hayford Systems Ltd, 147 Commercial St, London, E1 6BJ Tel: (020) 7247 3005 *Computer consultants*

▶ Hayley Roof Line, Unit 4, Old Forge Trading Estate, Dudley Road, Stourbridge, West Midlands, DY9 8EL Tel: (01384) 896989 Fax: (01384) 898303 E-mail: mike@hayleywindows.co.uk *Supply & installation of windows & doors*

Hayling Industrial Ltd, Units 8-9 Hayling Billy Business Centre, Furniss Way, Hayling Island, Hampshire, PO11 0ED Tel: (023) 9246 3868 Fax: (023) 9246 3873 E-mail: sales@haylingindustrial.com *Distributors/agents/stockholders of bearings, ball bearings & motor vehicle accessories wholesale (including components/spare parts)*

Hayling Pontoons Ltd, Mill Rithe, Hayling Island, Hampshire, PO11 0QQ Tel: (023) 9246 3592 Fax: (023) 9246 4432 E-mail: haylingyacht@mcmail.com *Boat repairers moorings & storage service*

Hayling Rubber Stamps, 17 Sea Front Estate, Hayling Island, Hampshire, PO11 9JJ Tel: (023) 9246 1962 Fax: (023) 9246 1962 E-mail: sales@haylingrubberstamps.com *Rubber stamp manufacturers and General Printers*

Haylock & Rolph, Unit 9 Hall Barn Road Industrial Estate, Hall Barn Road, Isleham, Ely, Cambridgeshire, CB7 5RJ Tel: (01638) 781715 Fax: (01638) 781716 E-mail: enquiries@haylockandrolph.co.uk *Asbestos removal services*

Hayloft Woodwork Ltd, 3 Bond Street, Chiswick, London, W4 1QZ Tel: (020) 8747 3510 Fax: (020) 8742 1860 *Furniture designers & manufrs*

Haymarket Publishing, Teddington Studios, Broom Road, Teddington, Middlesex, TW11 9BE Tel: (020) 8943 5000 Fax: (020) 8267 5872 E-mail: name@haymarketgroup.com *Publishers*

▶ Haymills Contractors Ltd, 32 St. Peters Road, Huntingdon, Cambridgeshire, PE29 7DA Tel: (01480) 414191 Fax: (01480) 414186

▶ Haymills Contractors Ltd, Wigmore Street, London, W1U 3RS Tel: (020) 7009 0900 Fax: (020) 700 90901 E-mail: london@haymills.com *Building contractors, new build & refurbishment works*

Hayne Ingleby Ltd, 895 High Road, Chadwell Heath, Romford, RM6 4HL Tel: (020) 8590 6232 Fax: (020) 8590 6568 *Gasket manufrs*

Hayne West, Unit 2 Stoney Hill Industrial Estate, Whitchurch, Ross-on-Wye, Herefordshire, HR9 6BX Tel: (01600) 890119 Fax: (01600) 890133 E-mail: sales@hayne--west.co.uk *Cast aluminium post box retailers & manufrs*

Haynes Agricultural Ltd, Parkwood Industrial Estate, Sutton Road, Maidstone, Kent, ME15 9NH Tel: (01622) 755726 Fax: (01622) 672634 E-mail: agrienquiries@haynesgrp.co.uk *Agricultural engineers*

▶ Haynes Agricultural Ltd, Squires Farm Industrial Estate, Easons Green, Uckfield, East Sussex, TN22 5RB Tel: (01825) 841100 Fax: (01825) 841122 E-mail: sales@haynesgrp.co.uk *Agricultural tractor distributors.*

Haynes Agricultural Kent Ltd, 1 The Street, Appledore, Ashford, Kent, TN26 2BU Tel: (01233) 758395 Fax: (01233) 758242 E-mail: j.burt@haynesgrp.co.uk *Agricultural parts & machinery suppliers*

Haynes Agricultural Kent Ltd, Mill Lane, Eastry, Sandwich, Kent, CT13 0JS Tel: (01304) 611112 Fax: (01304) 619006 E-mail: sales@rpv.org.uk *Agricultural machinery services*

Haynes & Cann Ltd, 1-9 Overstone Road, Northampton, NN1 3JL Tel: (01604) 626143 Fax: (01604) 604721 *Military footwear & flying helmets*

Haynes Graphic Arts Ltd, Policrom House, Station Road, Motspur Park, New Malden, Surrey, KT3 6JJ Tel: (020) 8949 5411 Fax: (020) 8949 4907 E-mail: info@haynes-graphic-art.co.uk *Print & graphic consumable suppliers & distributors*

Haynes International Ltd, Parkhouse St, Openshaw, Manchester, M11 2ER Tel: 0161-230 7777 Fax: 0161-223 2412 E-mail: memarycz@haynesint.co.uk *Developers, manufacturers & distributors of high performance nickel & cobalt based alloys. Distributors of Stainless & Titanium material. Laser & water jetting facilities available on site.*

Haynes Manufacturing UK, Marlowe House, Stewkins, Stourbridge, West Midlands, DY8 4YW Tel: (01384) 371416 Fax: (01384) 371416 E-mail: info@haynes-uk.co.uk *Condensation control services & ventilation consultants*

Norman Haynes Ltd, 900 Thornton Road, Bradford, West Yorkshire, BD8 0JG Tel: (01274) 545115 Fax: (01274) 545113 *Printers engineers & suppliers*

Haynes Publishing, Sparkford, Yeovil, Somerset, BA22 7JJ Tel: (01963) 440635 Fax: (01963) 440001 E-mail: sales@haynes.co.uk *Publishers, printers & distributors of books*

Haynes & Sons Daventry Ltd, 3 Badby Park, Heartlands Business Park, Daventry, Northamptonshire, NN11 8YT Tel: (01327) 703824 *Building contractors*

Hayneswood Engineering UK, Acorn Street, Lees, Oldham, OL4 3DE Tel: 0161-620 5337 Fax: 0161-621 5974 E-mail: engineering@hayneswood.co.uk *Precision engineers*

▶ Hay's Distribution, Penilee Road, Hillington Industrial Estate, Glasgow, G52 4UW Tel: 0141-883 4555

Hays Legal, 37 Sun Street, London, EC2M 2PL Tel: (020) 7523 3700 Fax: (020) 7523 3839 E-mail: info@hayslegal.com *Legal recruitment consultants*

▶ Hays Logistics, Unit 7 Clydesmill Place, Clydesmill Industrial Estate, Glasgow, G32 8RF Tel: 0141-643 3800 Fax: 0141-643 3801

Hays Macintyre & Co., Fairfax House, 15 Fullwood Place, London, WC1V 6AY Tel: (020) 7969 5500 Fax: (020) 7969 5600 E-mail: sales@haysmcintyre.com *Chartered accountants* Also at: Cambridge & Exeter

Hays Technology, Appletree Road, Chipping Warden, Banbury, Oxfordshire, OX17 1LL Tel: (01295) 663000 Fax: (01295) 660361 E-mail: logistics@haystechnology.com *Logistics services*

Hay-Tech Engineering, 12 Market Street, Bracknell, Berkshire, RG12 1JG Tel: (01344) 868011 Fax: (01344) 867979 E-mail: wood.c@btconnect.com *Precision machining & mechanical engineering*

Hayter Ltd, Spellbrook La West, Spellbrook, Bishop's Stortford, Hertfordshire, CM23 4BU Tel: (01279) 723444 Fax: (01279) 723821 E-mail: sales@hayter.co.uk *Lawn mower manufrs*

A.J. Hayton Ltd, Bainsbeck Garage, Arkholme, Carnforth, Lancashire, LA6 1BA Tel: (01524) 222242 Fax: (01524) 222242 *Steel fabricators*

Hayton Automatics Ltd, 36 Brookfield Way, Heanor, Derby, DE75 7NX Tel: 01773 711738 E-mail: spayne111@hotmail.co.uk *Suplliers and operators of fruit machines, pool tables, touchscreen video games and juke boxes.Fully licenced by the gaming authorities.*All machines available for rental or sale.*Rental /H*

▶ Hayton Coulthard Ltd, The Garage, Kirk Brae, Twynholm, Kirkcudbright, DG6 4NX Tel: (01557) 860661 Fax: (01557) 860293

Hayward, Portland Street, Walsall, WS2 8AD Tel: (01922) 621417 Fax: (01922) 642943 E-mail: supertruckin@haytrans.co.uk *Nationwide depots, specialising in general haulage for the steel, concrete and construction industries, as well as container haulage.*

Hayward, Portland Street, Walsall, WS2 8AD Tel: (01922) 621417 Fax: (01922) 642943 E-mail: supertruckin@haytrans.co.uk *Road transport, haulage & freight services*

Hayward & Cook Ltd, 125 Cheston Road, Birmingham, B7 5EA Tel: 0121-327 5699 Fax: 0121-327 5899 *Metal recyclers*

▶ David Hayward Design UK, 29 Suffolk Parade, Cheltenham, Gloucestershire, GL50 2AE Tel: (01242) 570314 Fax: (01242) 263674 E-mail: sales@davidhayward.com *Writing instrument & giftware manufacturers & design*

Hayward Engineering, Unit 6 11-15 Francis Avenue, Bournemouth, BH11 8NX Tel: (01202) 573235 Fax: (01202) 581903 E-mail: sales@haywardeng.co.uk *Precision engineers*

Hayward & Green Aviation Ltd, Unit 1 & 2 Terrys Cross Farm, Horn Lane Woodmancote, Woodmancote, Henfield, West Sussex, BN5 9SA Tel: (01273) 492237 Fax: (01273) 493898 *Aircraft spares*

Hayward Holdings Ltd, 5 Howard Industrial Estate, Chilton Road, Chesham, Buckinghamshire, HP5 2AS Tel: (01494) 775075 Fax: (01494) 784861 E-mail: enquiries@hayward-holdings.demon.co.uk *Coil winders sub contractors*

M. Hayward & Daughter (South Wales) Ltd, Cwmau Bach, St. Peters, Carmarthen, Dyfed, SA31 3RR Tel: (01267) 235467 Fax: (01267) 220641 *Repairs coaches & lorries*

Marshall Hayward Ltd, Sharston Industrial Estate, Shentonfield Road, Sharston, Manchester, M22 4RW Tel: 0161-428 8062 Fax: 0161-491 4298 *Commercial printers*

Hayward Signs, Unit 1-2 Bay Works, Marine Road, Pevensey Bay, Pevensey, East Sussex, BN24 6EG Tel: (01323) 740266 Fax: (01323) 460245 E-mail: superscreen@btconnect.com *Sign manufrs*

▶ Hayward Tyler Sumo Ltd, Nerston Industrial Estate, East Kilbride, Glasgow, G74 4QZ Tel: (01355) 221301

Hayward United Farmers Ltd, Benacre Road, Ellough, Beccles, Suffolk, NR34 7XD Tel: (01502) 475111 Fax: (01502) 476533 E-mail: steve@hufl.co.uk *Machinery distributors*

▶ Haywards Building Services, East Court Road, Worthing, West Sussex, BN14 7DB Tel: (01903) 600499 E-mail: darronhayward@hotmail.co.uk *High quality building services - *Competitive prices - *Completed on time -**At HBS our number one priority is to put the needs of our customers first. Our attention to detail ensures that our work exceeds all national standards and regulations. HBS has strengths in the many different building disciplines.***

Haywards Tewksbury Ltd, 126 High Street, Tewksbury, Tewkesbury, Gloucestershire, GL20 5JX Tel: (01684) 292282 Fax: (01684) 850634 *Plumbing & building merchants* Also at: Upton-on-Severn

Hayway Tool & Hardware Co. Ltd, Cunliffe Drive, Kettering, Northamptonshire, NN16 8LD Tel: (01536) 481114 Fax: (01536) 483514 E-mail: sales@haywaytools.com *Hand & power tool distributors*

Haywood Office Services, Trafalgar Close, Chandlers Ford Industrial Estate, Chandler's Ford, Eastleigh, Hampshire, SO53 4BW Tel: (023) 8025 4454 Fax: (023) 8026 7986 E-mail: sales@haywoodofficeservices.co.uk *Located at Southampton servicing the Hampshire and Dorset areas. We offer a bespoke office and home furniture designing service taylored to your own requirements and budget. New and quality used furniture also readily available to view in our spacious showroom, the largest in the south. We also supply office chairs, office desks, conference furniture, plus orthopaedic chairs with free delivery within a 30 mile radius.*

Haywood Transport Services, Chelmsford Road, Rawreth, Wickford, Essex, SS11 8SY Tel: (01268) 561305 Fax: (01268) 561304 *Hauliers*

Haywood Upholstery, Kinver Street, Stourbridge, West Midlands, DY8 5AB Tel: (01384) 839454 *Upholstery & re-upholstery services*

▶ HAZ Afro Cosmetics, Unit 2, Alpine House, Honeypot Lane, London, NW9 9RX Tel: (020) 8732 2929 Fax: (020) 8204 9955 E-mail: hussain@hazafro.co.uk *Hair & skin cosmetics specialists*

Hazard Safety Products, 55-57 Bristol Road, Birmingham, B5 7TU Tel: 0121-446 4433 Fax: 0121-446 4230E-mail: sales@hazard.co.uk *Industrial safety equipment*

Hazchem Signs, The Old Rectory, Main Street, Shalstone, Buckingham, MK18 5LT Tel: (01280) 841400 Fax: (01280) 840599 *Supplies equipment to haulers*

Hazell Engineering Ltd, 42 Union Terrace, Aberdeen, AB10 1NP Tel: (01224) 630123 Fax: (01224) 620622 E-mail: recruitment@hazelleng.com *Personnel recruitment*

Hazelwood Cardiff, Unit 46 Splott Indust Estate, Portmanmoor Road, Cardiff, CF24 5FF Tel: (029) 2049 5950 Fax: (029) 2049 5607 *Bespoke joinery manufrs*

▶ Hazelwood Development Ltd, 14 Wortley Road, High Green, Sheffield, S35 4LU Tel: 0114-286 9990 Fax: 0114-286 9991 E-mail: cupton@hazelwood-dev.co.uk

Hazelwood Foods, Mansfield Road, Wales Bar, Sheffield, S26 5PF Tel: (01909) 770861 Fax: (01909) 772797 E-mail: info@hwpm.com *Food manufrs*

Hazelwood Products Wattle Hurdles, Golden Dell, Golden Dell, Herriard, Basingstoke, Hants, RG25 2PE Tel: (01256) 381266 *Wattle hurdles manufrs*

Hazid Technologies, 21a S G C S Business Park, Technology Drive, Beeston, Nottingham, NG9 2ND Tel: 0115-922 4115 Fax: 0115-922 4115 E-mail: sales@hazid.com *Hardware & software design services*

Hazlewood Trailers, Bishampton Road, Rous Lench, Evesham, Worcestershire, WR11 4UN Tel: (01386) 792916 Fax: (01386) 793320 E-mail: admin@hazelwoodtrailers.co.uk *Manufacture, repair, hire, modify, buy/sell trailers up to 3500 kgs*

HazMat Logistics Ltd, Unit 3, Links Industrial Estate, Popham Close, Hanworth, Feltham, Middlesex, TW13 6JE Tel: (020) 8898 1654 Fax: (020) 8898 1643 E-mail: info@hazmatlogistics.co.uk *Hazardous and dangerous goods importers & exporters*

▶ Hazrem Environmental Ltd, Chambers House, Blackwood Road, Pontllanfraith, Blackwood, Gwent, NP12 2XB Tel: (01495) 233400 E-mail: sales@hazrem.co.uk *Hazardous Waste Disposal, Waste Analysis, Environmental Managment Sytems, Environmental Impact Assesments, Asbestos Surveying, Contaminated Land Remediation*

▶ Hazwaste Environmental Ltd, 30 Minster Drive, Urmston, Manchester, M41 5HA Tel: 0161-748 4750 Fax: 0161-748 4750 E-mail: sales@hazwaste.co.uk *Waste disposal*

▶ HB Carbon (UK), Room C2 College Business Centre, The College, Uttoxeter New Road, Derby, DE22 3WZ Tel: (01332) 869310 E-mail: enquiry@hbcarbon.co.uk *Activated carbon supplies*

▶ HB Computers, 264 Hesketh Lane, Tarleton, Preston, PR4 6RJ Tel: (01772) 811409 Fax: (01772) 811409 *Computer hardware retailers*

▶ HB Crane Hire UK, Carnaby Industrial Estate, Carnaby, Bridlington, East Riding of Yorkshire, YO15 3QY Tel: (01262) 673346 E-mail: hire@crane-hire-uk.com *National mobile crane hire & contract lift specialist - mainland UK*

HBG Construction Ltd, Merit House, Edgware Road, London, NW9 5AF Tel: (020) 8200 7070 Fax: (020) 8200 3997 *Construction consultants services*

HBG Construction Scotland Ltd, Kelvin House, Buchanan Gate Business Park, Stepps, Glasgow, G33 6FB Tel: 0141-779 8888 *Building construction & property development* Also at: Edinburgh

HBM Ltd, H B House, 31 Chalfont Road, Beaconsfield, Buckinghamshire, HP9 2QP Tel: (01494) 671246 Fax: (01494) 678112 E-mail: sales@hbm.co.uk *Communications for exhibition industry*

▶ Hca, Unit 6 Kingsway, Andover, Hampshire, SP10 5LQ Tel: (01264) 351640 Fax: (01264) 350302 E-mail: adam@hcacoating.co.uk *Specialists in powder coating*

HCC Protective Coatings Ltd, Bates Business Centre, Church Road, Harold Wood, Romford, RM3 0JF Tel: (01708) 378666 Fax: (01708) 378868 E-mail: hcc.pc@btconnect.com Purchasing Contact: P. Collier Sales Contact: S. Holland *Protective coating manufacturers*

HCH Engineering Ltd, Unit 4 Charlton Drive, Corngreaves Trading Estate, Cradley Heath, West Midlands, B64 7BJ Tel: (01384) 413233 Fax: (01384) 633637 E-mail: hch@ntlbusiness.com *Rebuild, sell new & used fastener machinery*

▶ HCL Developments Limited, 26, Cornwall Road, Ruislip, Middlesex, HA4 6AN Tel: (07961) 111245 E-mail: sc@hcld.co.uk *Building Surveying, Architectural Design, Land Development & Property Refurbishment*

HCL Technologies Europe Ltd, Network House, Norreys Drive, Maidenhead, Berkshire, SL6 4FJ Tel: (01628) 778555 Fax: (01628) 777566 E-mail: semipractice@hcltech.com *IT software solutions*

HCS Control Systems Ltd, Unit V2, Viewfield Industrial Estate, Glenrothes, Fife, KY6 2RG Tel: (01592) 770786 Fax: (01592) 775737 E-mail: sales@hcscsl.com *Hydraulic engineers & equipment distributors*

▶ HCT International Industry Limited, Unit 14,, Agecroft Network Centre, Lamplight Way, Swinton, Manchester, M27 8UJ Tel: 0161-351 6758 Fax: 0161-351 6759 *Ball Bearing Importers, Nationwide distributors, stockists, metric ball bearings, imperial, miniature, instrument, stainless, linear ball bearings, thin, needle, taper, roller, RHP, self lube, SKF, keysteel, FK, MBA, TR, Locknuts, plummer block, housing, inserts, spherical, thrust precision, rod end. Northwest Based Company in Stockport. UK*

HCVF Video Production Companies, 67-69 Kenneth Street, Inverness, IV3 5QF Tel: (01463) 224788 Fax: (01463) 711460 E-mail: info@hcvf.co.uk *Television & video production services*

▶ HDA Marketing Services Ltd, 58 Summerhouse Drive, Bexley, Kent, DA5 2HP Tel: (01322) 525224 Fax: (01322) 523209 E-mail: richardjones30@btinternet.com *Direct marketing production, direct mail, response handling, printing services*

▶ HDias Construction, 83 Riffel Road, London, NW2 4PG Tel: (020) 8438 8806 Fax: (020) 8438 8806 E-mail: HDiasConstruction@yahoo.co.uk *With dedication and pride in our work we have gained a solid reputation for reliable, fast and excellent quality job. Supply tape-jointers, plasterers and dryliners. All CIS registered, with own tools and transport. Health and Safety Policy, Health and Safety Officer for risk assesment. References available on demand.*

HDS Freight Services Ltd, 12 Saxon Way, West Drayton, Middlesex, UB7 0LW Tel: (020) 8564 9955 Fax: (020) 8564 7060 E-mail: operations@hdsfreight.co.uk *Freight forwarders*

▶ hdvcameraman, 4 Salt Lane, Hydestile, Godalming, Surrey, GU8 4DG Tel: (01483) 202206 E-mail: paul@hdvcameraman.co.uk *NTSC & PAL shooting, editing, high definition video crew & facilities*

Head Braiding Ltd, Armstrong Works, Raynham Rd, Bishop's Stortford, Herts, CM23 5PB Tel: (01279) 658271 Fax: (01279) 503566 Purchasing Contact: D.J. Haworth Sales Contact: J. Raven Principal Export Areas: Worldwide *Connector (electrical) & wire braiding) manufacturers. Flexible tubing/hose/conduit overbraiding services. Also connectors, flexible (electrical)*

Charles Head Ltd, 78 Tavistock Street, Bletchley, Milton Keynes, MK2 2PN Tel: (01908) 372250 Fax: (01908) 371023 E-mail: sales@charles-head.co.uk *Steel fabricators*

Head Fine Foods, 135 Kingston Road, New Malden, Surrey, KT3 3NX Tel: (020) 8942 0582 Fax: (020) 8288 1040 *Butchers*

▶ Head & Robins, 29 North Street, Pewsey, Wiltshire, SN9 5ES Tel: (01672) 562320 Fax: (01672) 562676

Headland Agrochemicals Ltd, Rectors Lane, Pentre, Deeside, Clwyd, CH5 2DH Tel: (01244) 537370 Fax: (01244) 532097 E-mail: john.hughes@headlandmanufacturing.com *Agricultural chemical manufrs*

Headley Brothers Ltd, The Invicta Press, Queens Road, Ashford, Kent, TN24 8HH Tel: (01233) 623131 Fax: (01233) 612345 E-mail: printing@headley.co.uk *Magazine & journal printers*

Headline Filters Ltd, Mill Hall Business Estate, Mill Hall, Aylesford, Kent, ME20 7JZ Tel: (01622) 718927 Fax: (01622) 882448 E-mail: sales@headlinefilters.com *Gas & liquid filter manufrs*

▶ Headline Promotions, Press and Public Relations, 25 Basingfield Close, Old Basingstoke, Basingstoke, Hampshire, RG24 7BG Tel: 01256 329742 E-mail: info@headlinepromotions.co.uk *Headline Promotions, Press & PR provide PR, promotions, event management, marketing and web design support for small business in the UK **Our speciality is in the manufacturing, retail, internet radio, security, professional services, hospitality, leisure & entertainment sectors but we are well-versed across many sectors.**

Headliners European Ltd, Unit 10 Abbey Court, Wallingford Road, Leicester, LE4 5RD Tel: 0116-266 6629 Fax: 0116-266 6679 E-mail: info@pc-headliners.freeserve.co.uk *Computer consumable suppliers*

Headstock Distribution Ltd, Deal Park Road, Coombswood Industrial Estate West, Halesowen, West Midlands, B62 8HD Tel: 0121-508 6666 Fax: 0121-508 6677 E-mail: sales@laney.co.uk *Musical amplifier services*

Headway Consultancy Ltd, Unit 19 Church Farm Business Park, Corston, Bath, BA2 9AP Tel: (01225) 872333 Fax: (01225) 872266 E-mail: contact@headway-ltd.com *IT consultants*

Headway Storage Systems Ltd, 142 Bath Road, Totterdown, Bristol, BS4 3EF Tel: 0117-971 2222 Fax: 0117-972 4912 *Mezzanine floor manufrs*

J.M. Heaford Ltd, Unit 9 Century Park, Pacific Road, Altrincham, Cheshire, WA14 5BJ Tel: 0161-928 5679 Fax: 0161-927 7517 E-mail: sales@jmheaford.co.uk *Mounting & proofing equipment*

Heal & Son Ltd, The Heals Buildings, 196 Tottenham Court Road, London, W1T 7LQ Tel: (020) 7896 7555 Fax: (020) 7637 5582 *Furniture retailer*

Healey Duct Installations Ltd, 11 Clayton Road, Brighton, BN2 9ZP Tel: (01273) 691955 Fax: (01273) 691955 E-mail: bjhealey@aol.com *Air conditioning*

Healey & Sprowson Ltd, Stuart Road, Bredbury Park Industrial Estate, Bredbury, Stockport, Cheshire, SK6 2SR Tel: 0161-494 1126 Fax: 0161-406 6162 E-mail: hs@absonline.net *Grinding & hard chrome plating services*

▶ Healey Transport Ltd, Herring Lane, Pinchbeck, Spalding, Lincolnshire, PE11 3ST Tel: (01775) 722946 Fax: (01775) 722549

▶ Healing Within (Herbalife), 5 Bentham Hill House, Stockland Green Road, Tunbridge Wells, Kent, TN3 0TJ Tel: 01892 541621 E-mail: rachel.scriven@btopenworld.com *Healing Within offers nutritional and health advice to individuals or business owners interested in the health and wellbeing of their staff.*Free Consultation and office presentations are offered in order to explain the benefits of having healthy working staff. Working with a range of products available in 61 countries so can offer advice by email or phone worldwide.*

Health & Beauty Salon, Quadrant House, The Quadrant, Sutton, Surrey, SM2 5AS Tel: (020) 8652 3500 Fax: (020) 8652 3793 *Occupational health specialists*

▶ Health Care Centre, Alexandra Buildings, The Roe, St. Asaph, Clwyd, LL17 0NA Tel: (01745) 584818 Fax: (01754) 584775 *Health care services*

The Health Corner, 41b High St, Grantown-on-Spey, Morayshire, PH26 3EG Tel: (01479) 870400 Fax: (01479) 851293 *Health food & products*

Health & Diet Centres Ltd, 65 Princess Square, Bracknell, Berkshire, RG12 1LA Tel: (01344) 411870 *Health food & supplements retailers*

Health & Diet Centres Ltd, 201 Centre Court Shopping Centre, 4 Queens Road, London, SW19 8YE Tel: (020) 8947 3583 *Health foods & products*

Health Food Centre, 91 High Street, Gorleston, Great Yarmouth, Norfolk, NR31 6RQ Tel: (01493) 662162 *Health food centre*

The Health Haven, 63 Murray Street, Montrose, Angus, DD10 8JZ Tel: (01674) 676854 *Health foods & product suppliers*

▶ Health Haven, 173 Findon Road, Worthing, West Sussex, BN14 0BQ Tel: (01903) 877717 E-mail: info@health-haven.com *Specialist Natural Health Shop, All products Vegetarian (except fish oils). Web, Mailorder or direct sales.*Homeopathy, Aromatherapy oils, vitamins, minerals, health foods, homeovitics.*

Health Intelligence Ltd, Bradwall Road, Sandbach, Cheshire, CW11 1GE Tel: (01270) 765124 Fax: (01270) 765078 E-mail: info@health-intelligence.com *Computer systems & software consultants*

Health Leads UK Ltd, 2 St. Clears Business Park, Tenby Road, St. Clears, Carmarthen, SA33 4JW Tel: (01994) 231940 Fax: (01994) 231941 E-mail: mail@healthleadsuk.com *Manufacturer & supplier of health products*

▶ Health Management, Scottish Health Service Centre, Crewe Road South, Edinburgh, EH4 2LF Tel: 0131-623 2535 Fax: 0131-315 2369

Health Matters, 8 Widmore Road, Bromley, BR1 1RY Tel: (020) 8460 3894 Fax: (020) 8313 3443 *Health food suppliers*

Health Matters, 34 Chatsworth Parade, Orpington, Kent, BR5 1DE Tel: (01689) 824953 Fax: (01689) 823253 *Specialist health food retail outfit*

Health Of The Nation, P O Box 4833, Reading, RG10 8XY Tel: 0118-940 1794 Fax: 0118 9404143 *Natural weight loss company*

Health Options Ltd, 27-28 The Water Front, Soverign Harbour, Eastbourne, East Sussex, BN23 5UZ Tel: (01323) 470090 Fax: (01323) 470851 *Medical analysis*

Health Perception (U K) Ltd, Unit 12 Lakeside Business Park, Swan Lane, Sandhurst, Berkshire, GU47 9DN Tel: (01252) 861454 Fax: (01252) 861455 *Health supplement suppliers*

▶ Health & Safety Signs, Unit 6, The Old School Studios, 40 Lynchford Road, Farnborough, Hampshire, GU14 6EF Tel: (01252) 512817 E-mail: phil@health-safety-signs.uk.com *Health & safety signs for business*

Health & Safety Specifier, 32 Portland St, Cheltenham, Glos, GL52 2PE Tel: (01242) 583222 Fax: (01242) 222331 *Magazine publishers*

Health & Safety Technology & Management Ltd, The Old Bakehouse, Fullbridge, Maldon, Essex, CM9 4LE Tel: (01621) 854111 Fax: (01621) 851756 E-mail: hastam@hastam.co.uk *Health safety & environmental health consultants*

Health Screening UK Ltd, 1 Church Square, Taunton, Somerset, TA1 1SA Tel: (01823) 325022 Fax: (01823) 325024 E-mail: info@screen4health.com *Health screening*

Health Warehouse, 15 Post House Wynd, Darlington, County Durham, DL3 7LU Tel: (01325) 468570 *Health food retailers*

▶ Health & Well-Being, 4 Crathorne Avenue, Wolverhampton, WV10 6BT Tel: (01902) 786785 E-mail: battlingtheweight@btinternet.com *Health, nutrition & well being manufrs*

Health-Air UK, Norwich House, Water Street, Liverpool, L2 9XW Tel: 0151-236 8388 Fax: 0151-236 2369 *Air purifier services*

▶ Healthcare Logistics, Kilbuck Lane, Haydock, St. Helens, Merseyside, WA11 9UX Tel: (01942) 402690 Fax: (01942) 402697

Healthcheck Services Ltd, Unit 49 Riverside Estate, Sir Thomas Longley Road, Medway City Estate, Rochester, Kent, ME2 4DP Tel: (01634) 296234 Fax: (01634) 712607 E-mail: info@healthcheckservices.co.uk *Weighing machines manufrs*

▶ Healthfarm, 23 Cumpsty Road, Liverpool, L21 9HX Tel: 0151 9206654 E-mail: stephmc.uk@hotmail.co.uk *Our mission is to guide you to improve your nutritional well-being through the use of quality herbal nutrition products. These products provide a great way to lose weight and to enjoy a healthier lifestyle for all the family.*

Healthmatic Ltd, Redman Road, Porte Marsh Industrial Estate, Calne, Wiltshire, SN11 9PR Tel: (01249) 822063 Fax: (01249) 823140 E-mail: ops@healthmatic.com *Sanitary engineers & public convenience distributors*

Healthquest Ltd, Unit 7 Waverley Industrial Business Park, Hailsham Drive, Harrow, Middlesex, HA1 4TR Tel: (020) 8424 8844 *International natural toiletries*

Healthright Health Foods, 48c Friars Square, Aylesbury, Buckinghamshire, HP20 2SP Tel: (01296) 397022 *Health food & supplements retailers*

Healthsites, Annexe House, 6 Shinfield Road, Reading, RG2 7BW Tel: 0118-942 0993 E-mail: t.underwood@healthsites.co.uk *Portal to medical & health information services*

▶ Healthspan Health Foods, 47 King Street, St. Helier, Jersey, JE2 4WE Tel: (01534) 758391 E-mail: sales@healthspan.com

continued

continued

Healthy Life, 4 Little Brittox, Devizes, Wiltshire, SN10 1AR Tel: (01380) 725558 Fax: (01380) 727772 *Natural food producers*

▶ Healthy Living, 31 Newland Street, Witham, Essex, CM8 2AF Tel: (01376) 520374 Fax: (01376) 520374 *Healthcare product retailers*

▶ Healthy Living Shop, 282-284 St. Pauls Road, London, N1 2LH Tel: (020) 7704 8123 Fax: (020) 7704 6050 *Health care products retailers*

Healthy Products, 3 Gordon Cres, Broadmeadows, South Normanton, Alfreton, Derbyshire, DE55 3AJ Tel: 01773 863034 Fax: 01773 863034 *Aromatherapy & air purification*

▶ Healthy Spirit, 37 Barlow Moor Road, Manchester, M20 6TW Tel: 0161-434 6784 Fax: 0161-434 6784 *Health food shop*

Healthy Way, 30 High Street, Ilfracombe, Devon, EX34 9DA Tel: (01271) 865883 *Health food retailers*

Healy Bearings International Ltd, 4 Earls Close Industrial Estate, Earls Close, Thurmaston, Leicester, LE4 8FZ Tel: 0116-260 0849 Fax: 0116-260 0867 E-mail: healybearings@aol.com *Bearing manufrs*

Hean Studio, Kingsland, Leominster, Herefordshire, HR6 9QU Tel: (01568) 708966 Fax: (01568) 708901 E-mail: heanstudio@dial.pipex.com *Steel casting manufrs*

▶ John Heaney (Electrical) Ltd, Fairbairn Road, Howdenwest, Livingston, West Lothian, EH54 6TS Tel: (01506) 464000

▶ Heaning Brook Wholesale, Dean Field Court, Link 59 Business Park, Clitheroe, Lancashire, BB7 1QS Tel: (01200) 427527 Fax: (01200) 427027 E-mail: sales@fish-house.co.uk *Fresh fish suppliers*

▶ Heanor Haulage Ltd, Wesley Street, Langley Mill, Nottingham, NG16 4AL Tel: (01773) 715265 Fax: (01773) 530829 E-mail: sales@heanorhaulage.co.uk

Heap Dawson Ltd, Oldham Road, Rochdale, Lancashire, OL11 1BU Tel: (01706) 656222 Fax: (01706) 641852 E-mail: enquiries@heapdawson.co.uk *Design & manufacture of industrial heat exchangers*

Heap & Digby Ltd, 6a Park Road, Oxted, Surrey, RH8 0AL Tel: (01883) 717102 Fax: (01883) 381405 E-mail: sales@heapdigby.co.uk *Electrical & mechanical consulting engineers*

Heap & Partners Ltd, Britannia House, Newton Road, Hoylake, Wirral, Merseyside, CH47 3DG Tel: 0151-632 3393 Fax: 0151-632 4453 E-mail: info@heaps.co.uk *Engineers & engineers' agents* Also at: London, Manchester & Middlesbrough

Heaps, Arnold & Heaps Ltd, Unit D1, Quintec Court, Barbot Hall Industrial Estate, Rotherham, South Yorkshire, S61 4RN Tel: (01709) 837669 Fax: (01709) 837671 E-mail: heaps@heapsarnold.com *Established in 1770, we are the market leading manufacturer and supplier of Lead Products, including Lead Sash Bar, Lead Wire, Lead Tape, Lead Weights, Lead Came, Lead Tubes and Chrome Plating Anodes. We also manufacture High Quality Pure Tin Anodes, including Pure Tin Ovals, Pure Tin Plate, Pure Tin Balls and Pure Tin Slugs. In addition, we manufacture a range of Solders including Lead Free Solder Wire, Leaded Solder Wire, Solder Bars and Resin Cored Solder Wire.*

H.F. Heard Ltd, Lloyd Maunder Road, Willand, Cullompton, Devon, EX15 2PJ Tel: (01884) 821768 Fax: (01884) 821866 *Road transport, haulage & freight services*

Heard Oke & Letheren, Market Place, Hatherleigh, Okehampton, Devon, EX20 3JN Tel: (01837) 810576 Fax: (01837) 810605 *Agricultural merchants*

W.J. Heard, Ford Farm, Seven Crosses, Tiverton, Devon, EX16 5NW Tel: 01884 254250 *Agricultural contractors*

Hearing & Healthcare, 376 Buxton Road, Macclesfield, Cheshire, SK11 7ES Tel: (01625) 433108 Fax: (01625) 502323 E-mail: hearinghc@aol.com *Noise assessment & health screening consultancy services*

Hearl Heaton Ltd, Halifax Road, Liversedge, West Yorkshire, WF15 6JJ Tel: (01924) 406721 Fax: (01924) 400803 E-mail: info@hearlheaton.co.uk *Industrial reel & plastic reel manufrs*

Hearngrange Trading Ltd, Suite 202 Banderway House, 156-162 Kilburn High Road, London, NW6 4JQ Tel: (020) 7372 2010 Fax: (020) 7328 4996 Principal Export Areas: Worldwide *Carrier bag*

Heart Electronics Ltd, 2 King Edward Road, Nuneaton, Warwickshire, CV11 4BB Tel: (024) 7635 3615 Fax: (024) 7635 3616 E-mail: info@heartelectronics.com *Cable harness design & manufrs*

Heart Of England Balloons, Cross Lanes Farm, Walcote, Alcester, Warwickshire, B49 6NA Tel: (01789) 488219 Fax: (01789) 488366 E-mail: hoebinfo@ukballoons.com *Leisure hot air balloon flights*

Heart Of England Promotions, Old Hall, Wallhill Road, Fillongley, Coventry, CV7 8DX Tel: (01676) 540333 Fax: (01676) 540365 E-mail: sales@heartofengland.co.uk *Corporate promotion & entertainment service*

▶ Heart Of England Training, 30 William Street, Rugby, Warwickshire, CV21 3HA Tel: (01788) 553501 Fax: (01788) 552957 E-mail: info@hoet.co.uk

Heart of Oak Co. Ltd, English Farm, Nuffield, Henley-On-Thames, Oxfordshire, RG9 5TH Tel: (01491) 641250 Fax: (01491) 641250 E-mail: info@oak-frame.com *Sectional & portable buildings installers & manufrs*

Heartfield Technologies Ltd, Bromley, BR2 0WL Tel: (020) 8313 3088 Fax: (020) 8313 3002 E-mail: info@heartfield.co.uk *Computer software consultants*

Hearthstead Homes Ltd, 14 Station Rd., Crossgates, Leeds, LS15 7JX Tel: 0113-232 6634 Fax: 0113-232 6564 E-mail: sales@hearthstead.com *Building contractors*

Heartland Contractors Ltd, 3A Belwell Lane, Sutton Coldfield, West Midlands, B74 4AA Tel: 0121-323 2533

Heartland Extrusion Forge Ltd, Rocky Lane, Nechells, Birmingham, B7 5EU Tel: 0121-359 6861 Fax: 0121-359 2972 E-mail: enquiries@hef.co.uk *Axle shaft manufrs*

▶ Heartlands Joint Managed Projects, 54-76 Bissell Street, Birmingham, B5 7HP Tel: 0121-666 6600 Fax: 0121-666 7700

Heasell Electromechanical Services Ltd, 9-11 Baldock Street, Royston, Hertfordshire, SG8 5AY Tel: (0871) 2227896 Fax: (01763) 248108 E-mail: gary@abrams-netlineuk.net *Electrical & mechanical engineers*

Heasman & Sadler Ltd, 29 Park Road, Faringdon, Oxfordshire, SN7 7BP Tel: (01367) 240286 Fax: (01367) 242056 *Ductwork installers & manufrs*

Heasons Heat Treatment Co, Commerce Way, Lancing, West Sussex, BN15 8TQ Tel: (01903) 755038 Fax: (01903) 767046 E-mail: heasons@btopenworld.com Purchasing Contact: B. Griffiths Sales Contact: B. Griffiths *Metal heat treatment services*

▶ Heat & Cool, Sands Business Centre, Sands Road, Farnham, Surrey, GU10 1PX Tel: (0870) 0427484 E-mail: sales@heatandcool.co.uk *Suppliers of Electric radiators, Electric Panel Heaters, Electric Water filled radiators, Electric Storage Heaters, Electric Conservatory Heating, Energy Efficient Electric radiators, Electric Boilers*

Heat Exchange Industries Ltd, Willow Road, Trent Lane, Castle Donnington, Castle Donington, Derby, DE74 2NP Tel: (01332) 853862 Fax: (01332) 3850590 *Heat exchanger manufrs*

▶ Heat Exchanger Testing Services, Oaktree Business Park, Spitfire Way, South Marston Park, Swindon, SN3 4TX Tel: 01793 836150 Fax: 01793 836151 E-mail: info@heat-exchanger-testing.co.uk *Professional testing and inspection services of equipment and machinery used in the food, dairy, drink and brewing industries. Specialists in testing of plate and tubular heat exchangers and pasteurisers and Holding time testing.*

▶ Heat Force, 135 Maindy Road, Cardiff, CF24 4HN Tel: (029) 2037 8887 Fax: (029) 2037 8889 E-mail: enquiries@heatforce.co.uk *Heating & plumbing specialists*

Heat Hire Ltd, 109-111 Beverley Road, Hull, HU3 1TS Tel: (01482) 218288 Fax: (01482) 227897 *Portable gas heater hire*

▶ Heat Plant Services, 4 Lauradale, Bracknell, Berkshire, RG12 7DT Tel: (01344) 427861 Fax: (01344) 427861 E-mail: heatplant5@aol.com *Heating & maitenance & repair*

Heat Pump Technology, Woodlands, Brackendene Drive, Gateshead, Tyne & Wear, NE9 6DP Tel: 0191-482 3922 Fax: 0191-482 3922 E-mail: john@jweddle.freeserve.co.uk *Energy conservation consultants*

▶ Heat Radiation Ltd, Belvedere Trading Estate, Taunton, Somerset, TA1 1BH Tel: (01823) 253177 Fax: (01823) 336076 *Heating & plumbing*

Heat Treatment 2000 Ltd, Brandon Way, West Bromwich, West Midlands, B70 9PQ Tel: 0121-526 2000 Fax: 0121-500 0809 E-mail: heattreat2000@aol.com *Heat treatment services*

Heat Treatments Northampton Ltd, Sheaf Close, Lodge Farm Industrial Estate, Northampton, NN5 7UL Tel: (01604) 586920 Fax: (01604) 759286 E-mail: sales@heat-treatment.co.uk *Heat treatment specialists*

Heat Works Ltd, Unit 2 Moorend Indust Estate, Bradford Road, Cleckheaton, West Yorkshire, BD19 3TT Tel: (01274) 852900 Fax: (01274) 852911 E-mail: info@heatworks.co.uk *Air conditioning, heating, ventilation & process cooling engineers*

Heatcall Group Services, Nottingham Road, Belper, Derbyshire, DE56 1JT Tel: (01773) 828100 Fax: (01773) 828123 *Domestic boilers manufrs*

▶ Heatcare, 112 Maxwell Avenue, Bearsden, Glasgow, G61 1HU Tel: 0141-943 2200

▶ Heatcare Services Scotland Ltd, 1 16 Wellington Road, Bishopbriggs, Glasgow, G64 2SA Tel: 0141-772 1515 Fax: 0141-772 1616

Heatcon Composite Systems (Europe) Ltd, Blackstone Road, Stukeley Meadows Industrial Estate, Huntingdon, Cambridgeshire, PE29 6EF Tel: (01480) 410740 Fax: (01480) 433195 E-mail: ukinfo@heatcon.com *Aircraft & aerospace component manufs*

Heater Bands Ltd, Bott Lane, Walsall, WS1 2JQ Tel: (01922) 636888 Fax: (01922) 722360 E-mail: brian@heaterbands.freeserve.co.uk *Heating element manufrs*

Heatfast Mechanical Services Ltd, 55 Halesowen Road, Netherton, Dudley, West Midlands, DY2 9PY Tel: (01384) 235054 Fax: (01384) 455343 *Heating & pipework contractors*

▶ Heath & Arnold Ltd, St Day Road, Redruth, Cornwall, TR15 2EH Tel: (01209) 213886 Fax: (01209) 313047

Arthur Heath & Co. Ltd, Hall Road, Aylesford, Kent, ME20 7QZ Tel: (01622) 717507 Fax: (01622) 710551 E-mail: admin@arthurheath.com *Manufacturers of dowel (wooden), furniture component (wood), toy materials/components (wood), wood turnery manufacturer/wood turners. Also woodwork (repetition) machinists, handles wood & handicraft/hobby materials*

Heath Filtration Ltd, PO Box 1, Stoke-on-Trent, ST6 4SH Tel: (01782) 838591 Fax: (01782) 835508 E-mail: info@heathfiltration.com *Dust collecting bags & filter bags manufrs*

Heath Lambert, Cloister House, New Bailey Street, Salford, M3 5AG Tel: 0161-935 2935 Fax: 0161-839 2839 *Insurance brokers* Also at: London E18

Heath Lambert Overseas Ltd, 133 Houndsditch, London, EC3A 7AH Tel: (020) 7560 3000 Fax: (020) 7560 3000 E-mail: info@heathgroup.com *Insurance brokers or agencies*

Heath Pest Control, Woodhouse Farm, Woodhouses, Melbourne, Derby, DE73 1DN Tel: (01530) 415577 E-mail: enquiries@heathpest.co.uk *Pest control*

▶ Heath Press, Harrem House, Ogilvie Road, High Wycombe, Buckinghamshire, HP12 3DS Tel: (01494) 536117 Fax: (01494) 531298 *Printing services*

Samuel Heath & Sons P.L.C., Cobden Works, Leopold Street, Birmingham, B12 0UJ Tel: 0121-772 2303 Fax: 0121-772 3334 E-mail: info@samuel-heath.com *Brassware manufacturers & exporters*

Heath Saws, Leeside Works, Lawrence Avenue, Stanstead Abbotts, Ware, Hertfordshire, SG12 8DL Tel: (01920) 870230 Fax: (01920) 871996 *Tool manufacture & service providers*

Heath Scientific Co Ltd, 1 North House, Bond Avenue, Bletchley, Milton Keynes, MK1 1SW Tel: (01908) 646700 Fax: (01908) 645209 E-mail: info@heathsien.com *Scientific instrument distributors*

Heath & Smith Ltd, Cherry Tree Road, Hexthorpe, Doncaster, South Yorkshire, DN4 0BJ Tel: (01302) 342097 Fax: (01302) 739513 E-mail: heathandsmith@aol.com *Drinks wholesalers*

Sydney Heath & Son Ltd, P O Box 1 Bycars Road, Stoke-on-Trent, ST6 4SH Tel: (01782) 839121 Fax: (01782) 839124 E-mail: sales@sydney-heath.co.uk Principal Export Areas: Worldwide *Plastic foam suppliers, millers & manufrs*

Heath Technical Services, 83 Corsletts Avenue, Broadbridge Heath, Horsham, West Sussex, RH12 3NY Tel: (01403) 249152 Fax: (01403) 265093 *Heating installation & maintenance*

Heathcast Ltd, 66 Sydney Road, Watford, WD18 7QX Tel: (01923) 212628 Fax: (01923) 223427 E-mail: sales@heathcast.com *Brass fabricators*

Heathcol Welding Supplies Ltd, 257a Dukesway, Team Valley Trading Estate, Gateshead, Tyne & Wear, NE11 0PZ Tel: 0191-487 2922 Fax: 0191-487 2924 *Welding suppliers*

Heathcote Press, Harriott Drive, Heathcote Industrial Estate, Warwick, CV34 6TJ Tel: (01926) 883306 Fax: (01926) 314017 E-mail: heathcotepress@freeuk.com *General printers & lithographers*

▶ Heather Developments Woking Ltd, Mayford Green, Woking, Surrey, GU22 0PN Tel: (01483) 765848 Fax: (01483) 762414

Heatherbank Drawing Office Supplies, 4 Milethorn Lane, Doncaster, South Yorkshire, DN1 2SU Tel: (01302) 325146 *Drawing office suppliers*

Heatherside Engineering Ltd, Old Oak Close Industrial Estate, Old Oak Close, Arlesey, Bedfordshire, SG15 6XD Tel: (01462) 731575 Fax: (01462) 731575 E-mail: heatherside@btconnect.com *Light non-ferrous metal & welding fabricators*

Heatherslaw Bakery, Heatherslaw Mill, Cornhill-on-Tweed, Northumberland, TD12 4TJ Tel: (01890) 820208 Fax: (01890) 820208 *Cake & biscuit manufrs*

▶ Heathfield & Co., 2 Priory Road, Tonbridge, Kent, TN9 2AF Tel: (01732) 350450 Fax: (01732) 353525 E-mail: sales@heathfield.co.uk *Lighting manufrs*

Heathfield Hire, Browning Road, Heathfield, East Sussex, TN21 8DB Tel: (01435) 864144 Fax: (01435) 866622 E-mail: sds-navron@line1.net *Tool & plant hire*

Heathfield Pine, Heathfield Farm Cottage, 30 Manor Road, Hatfield, Doncaster, South Yorkshire, DN7 6SD Tel: (01302) 846781 *Furniture manufrs*

▶ Heathfield Studios, Heathfield, Heathlands Road, Wokingham, Berkshire, RG40 3AR Tel: (01344) 751125 E-mail: info@heathfield-studios.co.uk *Photographic restoration, manipulation & enhancement graphic design*

▶ Heathmans Mastering Ltd, Unit 7 & 19, Heathmans Road, London, SW6 4TJ Tel: (020) 7371 0978 *Music mastering*

Heathrow Buildbase, Longford House, Long Lane, Staines, Middlesex, TW19 7AT Tel: (01784) 253221 Fax: (01784) 241728 E-mail: heathrow@buildbase.co.uk *Buildbase is one of the UK's fastest growing builders merchants. All of our branches are long established companies which have been serving local trades people for many years, with knowledge and experience to match. We believe strongly in understanding the needs of trades professional and our business has been developed specifically to meet those demands. Massive stocks, top quality products, competitive pricing, reliable delivery, specialist staff and exceptional customer service*

▶ Heathrow Chauffeurs Ltd, 13 Victoria Road, Slough, SL2 5ND Tel: (01753) 511430 Fax: (01753) 511530 E-mail: steve@heathrowchauffeurs.com *Heathrow Chauffeurs offers luxury airport and venue transportation for London. We provide the ultimate in comfort and convenience, offering courteous door-to-door transfers for any occasion."*

▶ Heathrow Packing, Unit 4, Poyle Tech Center, Willow Road, Colnbrook, Slough, SL3 0DP Tel: (01753) 730081 Fax: (01753) 730082 E-mail: chris@atlaspacking.co.uk *Export packing service*

▶ Heathrow Truck Centre, Lakeside Industrial Estate, Bath Road, Colnbrook, Slough, SL3 0ED Tel: (01753) 681818 Fax: (01753) 680270 *Commercial vehicle repair*

▶ Heathy Options, 83 Argyll Street, Dunoon, Argyll, PA23 7DH Tel: (01369) 703892

Heathyards Engineering Co. Ltd, Unit 10 Maybrook Industrial Estate, Maybrook Road, Walsall, WS8 7DG Tel: (01543) 376754 Fax: (01543) 452645 E-mail: sales@heathyards.com *Tube manipulation/bending for boiler pressure parts*

▶ Heating & Boiler Services Ltd, Sayce Street, Widnes, Cheshire, WA8 6EE Tel: 0151-420 4030 Fax: 0151-420 4071 E-mail: sales@heatingandboilerservices.co.uk

▶ Heating & Building Maintenance, 24 Kansas Avenue, Salford, M50 2GL Tel: 0161-877 5060 Fax: 0161-877 5040

▶ Heating Controls, 72 Ackhurst Park Industrial Estate, Foxhole Road, Chorley, Lancashire, PR7 1NW Tel: (01257) 220100 Fax: (01257) 220200 E-mail: sales@heatingcontrols.net *Distributors pf burner, combustion & boiler spares*

Heating & Industrial Pipework Ltd, 19-35 Warwick Street, Coventry, CV5 6ET Tel: (024) 7667 2224 Fax: (024) 7671 3391 E-mail: hipcov@aol.com *Pipework installation services*

The Heating People Ltd, 1 Brooklands, Filey, North Yorkshire, YO14 9BA Tel: (0845) 8382732 Fax: (01723) 513981 E-mail: enquiries@theheatingpeople.co.uk *Domestic heating installation, service & repair*

Heating & Pipework Installations Leeds Ltd, 353 Tong Road, Leeds, LS12 4QG Tel: 0113-263 0318 Fax: 0113-231 0687 E-mail: drawings@hpileeds.co.uk *Heating & ventilation engineers*

▶ Heating & Plumbing Discounts Co UK Ltd, 14 Willowdown, Worle, Weston-super-Mare, Avon, BS22 9LX Tel: (01934) 514411 Fax: (01934) 514411 E-mail: plumbersunited@aol.com *Total property care plumbing heating building maintenance*

Heating & Process Engineering Services Ltd, Crompton Road Industrial Estate, Ilkeston, Derbyshire, DE7 4BG Tel: 0115-930 5838 Fax: 0115-930 8899 E-mail: sales@heatpro.co.uk *Heating equipment manufacturers & hire services*

Heating & Ventilating Services Ltd, 50 Park Lane, Basford, Nottingham, NG6 0DT Tel: 0115-978 1445 Fax: 0115-978 1596 *Heating & ventilation engineers*

Heating World, 53 Whitchurch Road, Shrewsbury, SY1 4DT Tel: (01743) 446775 Fax: (01743) 460385 E-mail: info@heatingworld.com *Kitchen & bathroom fittings suppliers & stoves*

▶ Heatmiser UK Ltd, Primrose House, Primrose Street, Darwen, Lancashire, BB3 2DE Tel: (01254) 776343 Fax: (01254) 704143 E-mail: info@heatmiser.co.uk *Industrial heat controls & thermostats manufrs*

Arthur Heaton & Co. Ltd, Valley Works, Station Lane, Heckmondwike, West Yorkshire, WF16 0NF Tel: (01924) 403731 Fax: (01924) 410069 *Textile machinery accessory manufrs*

Heaton Catering Equipment Ltd, 160 Heaton Park Road, Newcastle Upon Tyne, NE6 5NR Tel: 0191-265 6709 Fax: 0191-265 6506 E-mail: sales@heatoncateringequipment.co.uk *Catering equipment distributors*

Heaton Green (Dust Control) Ltd, Atlas Quarry Works, Upper Howard Street, Batley, West Yorkshire, WF17 6AA Tel: (01924) 430430 Fax: (01924) 430898 E-mail: user@heatongreen.co.uk *Dust & fume extraction equipment manufrs*

J.S. Heaton Ltd, 11 Provident Way, Timperley, Altrincham, Cheshire, WA15 6PR Tel: 0161-980 0531 Fax: 0161-980 0531 *Sign makers*

▶ Heaton & Jeremiah Ltd, Unit 13, Collins Road, Warwick, CV34 6TF Tel: (01926) 885858 Fax: (01926) 885959 *Furniture manufrs*

Heaton Paper Co. Ltd, Eldon Street, Gateshead, Tyne & Wear, NE8 3ND Tel: 0191-477 3783 Fax: 0191-490 0247 E-mail: sales@heatonpaper.co.uk *Carnival & party goods manufacturers & importers*

Heaton Shopfitters Ltd, 88 Tatton Road South, Stockport, Cheshire, SK4 4LX Tel: 0161-442 5786 Fax: 0161-718 3519 *Shop fitters*

Heatrae Industrial, Duncombe Road, Bradford, West Yorkshire, BD8 9TB Tel: (01274) 362798 Fax: (01274) 493580 E-mail: sales@heatrae-industrial.com Sales Contact: M. Carter Principal Export Areas: Worldwide *Manufacturers of oil heating systems (electric), oil preheaters, process heating plant, steam boilers/generators/raisers & water heaters, electric heaters- flameproof/gas/air/ industrial/heating elements, industrial & heating elements, special purpose*

Heatrae Sadia, 1 Hurricane Way, Norwich, NR6 6EA Tel: (01603) 420100 Fax: (01603) 420218 E-mail: sales@heatraesadia.com *Electric hand dryer, shower, & heater manufrs*

Heatrae Sadia Ltd, Brooks House, Coventry Road, Warwick, CV34 4LL Tel: (0870) 0603262 Fax: (0870) 0600403 E-mail: sales@heatraesadia.com *Water heaters manufrs*

Heatric, 46 Holton Road, Holton Heath Trading Park, Poole, Dorset, BH16 6LT Tel: (01202) 632299 Fax: (01202) 632299 E-mail: sales@heatric.com *Printed circuit heat exchanger design & manufrs*

Heatrite Stockport Ltd, 24 Carnforth Road, Heaton Chapel, Stockport, Cheshire, SK4 5LE Tel: 0161-432 8825 Fax: 0161-432 5057 *Pipework erection contractors & heat engine gas installers*

Heatsense Cables Ltd, 3 Astra Centre, Royle Barn Road, Rochdale, Lancashire, OL11 3DT Tel: (01706) 355330 Fax: (01706) 657691 E-mail: sales@heatsensecables.co.uk *Cable & wire manufrs*

▶ Heatshop, Unit 44, Westley Grange, West Avenue, Wigston, Leicestershire, LE18 2FB Tel: 0116-288 4333 Fax: 0116-288 1444 *Providers of industrial heating in gas & electrical, air conditioning*

Heatstar Ltd, 22 Daish Way, Newport, Isle of Wight, PO30 5XB Tel: (01983) 521465 Fax: (01983) 822016 E-mail: info@heatstar.co.uk *Heat pump & dehumidifier manufrs*

Heattend Ltd, 9 Concorde Road, Norwich, NR6 6BH Tel: (01603) 787505 Fax: (01603) 429500 E-mail: sales@heattend.co.uk *Suppliers of electric radiant panel conservatory heaters.*

Heaven Dowsett & Co. Ltd, 197 Shady Lane, Birmingham, B44 9ES Tel: 0121-360 0345 Fax: 0121-360 7328 E-mail: richarddowsett@heavendowsett.com *Plastic machinists & fabricators*

▶ Heaven Made Foods, 1-3 Hempstead Road, Holt, Norfolk, NR25 6DL Tel: (01263) 711222 Fax: (01263) 712814

▶ Heaven Sent, St Pauls Church, Darwall Street, Walsall, WS1 1DA Tel: (01922) 633073 E-mail: post@heaventsentgifts.uk.com *Cards & gifts retailers*

▶ Heavenly Halos (UK), Churston, Paignton, Devon, TQ4 Tel: 0845 833 0938 E-mail: sales@heavenlyhalos.co.uk *Quality unique designs of Fascinators, Fascinator Hats,*

continued

continuation
Feather Fascinators, Bridal Headwear, Ladies Headwear, Tiaras, Combs and Headbands

Heavey & Co Engineers Ltd, Fielding Street, Eccles, Manchester, M30 0GJ Tel: 0161-789 1469 Fax: 0161-787 8226 E-mail: gedheavey@supanet.com *Aluminium & stainless steel fabricators*

Heavy Machining Services Ltd, 19 Ashville Way, Cambridge Road, Whetstone, Leicester, LE8 6NU Tel: 0116-275 2225 Fax: 0116-275 2005 *Quarry plant & equipment manufrs*

Heavy Parts Hydraulics, 89 Baillie Street East, Rochdale, Lancashire, OL16 2BY Tel: (01706) 356676 Fax: (01706) 646185 E-mail: sales@heavyparts.co.uk *Hydraulic equipment repair & re-conditioning*

Heavy Vehicle Brakes Ltd, 3 Sampson Business Park, Berwick Lane, Hallen, Bristol, BS10 7RS Tel: 0117-959 3582 Fax: 0117-959 3588 *Heavy duty brake suppliers*

Hebbard, 18 Park Lane, Little Downham, Ely, Cambridgeshire, CB6 2TF Tel: (01353) 698338 Fax: (01353) 698995 E-mail: workshop@hebbard3d.com *Suppliers of cad cam solutions*

Hebble Hydraulic Services Ltd, Spring Grove Mills, Linthwaite, Huddersfield, HD7 5QG Tel: (01484) 846688 Fax: (01484) 847701 E-mail: hebble@btconnect.com *Hydraulic pneumatic cylinders repairers & manufrs*

Hebden Cord Co Ltd, 17 Old Gate, Hebden Bridge, West Yorkshire, HX7 6EW Tel: (01422) 843152 Fax: (01422) 846354 E-mail: hebcord@aol.com *Retail tailoring & country clothing*

Hebden Dyeing & Finishing Co. Ltd, Crimsworth Dye Works, Midgehole, Hebden Bridge, West Yorkshire, HX7 7AN Tel: (01422) 842888 Fax: (01422) 845689 E-mail: hebdyefin@dial.pipex.com *Commission dyers & finishers*

Hebden Metal Spinners, Melbourne Works, Melbourne Street, Hebden Bridge, West Yorkshire, HX7 6AS Tel: (01422) 843804 Fax: (01422) 843804 *Metal spinners*

▶ Hebei Light (UK) Ltd, 38 Appledore Avenue, South Ruislip, Ruislip, Middlesex, HA4 0UU Tel: (020) 8841 8291 Fax: (020) 8831 4615 E-mail: heli.uk@btinternet.com *clothing, cast iron products, promotional items etc.*

Heber Ltd, Belvedere Mill, Chalford Industrial Estate, Chalford, Stroud, Gloucestershire, GL6 8NT Tel: (01453) 732300 Fax: (01453) 885013 E-mail: sales@heber.co.uk *Electronic product & system designers & manufrs*

▶ Hebrides Haulage Ltd, Rigs Road, Stornoway, Isle of Lewis, HS1 2RF Tel: (01851) 703255 Fax: (01851) 706001

▶ Hebron (UK) Ltd, Oxford Road, Yeovil, Somerset, BA21 5HR Tel: (01935) 403000 Fax: (01935) 403025 E-mail: info@hebron.co.uk *Creators of specialised MIS software for schools*

▶ Hecas Ltd, Units 2 & 3 Middlegate House, Middlegate, White Lund Industrial Estate, Morecambe, Lancashire, LA3 3BN Tel: (01524) 63444 Fax: (01524) 63440 E-mail: mike@hecas.co.uk *Suppliers of heating spares*

Hech Engineering Ltd, Barrington Industrial Estate, Bedlington, Northumberland, NE22 7DQ Tel: (01670) 823588 Fax: (01670) 826744 E-mail: hecheng@aol.com *Control panel manufrs*

▶ Hecket Multiserve Steelphalt Ltd, Sheffield Road, Rotherham, South Yorkshire, S60 1DR Tel: (01709) 300500 Fax: (01709) 300599

Heckett, Harsco House, Regent Park, Leatherhead, Surrey, KT22 7SG Tel: (01372) 381400 Fax: (01372) 381499 *Provider of specialised outsourced services to the steel & metals industry*

Heckmondwike F B Ltd, PO Box 7, Liversedge, West Yorkshire, WF15 7XA Tel: (01924) 406161 Fax: (01924) 413613 E-mail: sales@heckmondwike-fb.co.uk Principal Export Areas: Worldwide *Carpet, including tile & fibre bonded manufrs*

R.R. Hector, 18 Windmill Hill, North Curry, Taunton, Somerset, TA3 6NA Tel: (01823) 490236 *Willow growers & merchants*

Heda, Unit D5, Chaucer Business Park, Kemsing, Sevenoaks, Kent, TN15 6YU Tel: (01732) 765474 Fax: (01732) 765478 *Manufacturers of gates, barriers, turnstiles*

▶ Heddle Civil Engineers, Grainshore Road, Hatston, Kirkwall, Orkney, KW15 1FL Tel: (01856) 888666 Fax: (01856) 877666

Heddleworth Amusements Ltd, 1 Clearway House Industrial Estate, Overthorpe Road, Banbury, Oxfordshire, OX16 4US Tel: (01295) 259863 Fax: (01295) 270559 *Gaming & amusement hire & services*

The Hedgehog Press, Unit B5, Imperial Bus Estate, West Mill, Gravesend, Kent, DA11 0DL Tel: (01474) 322153 Fax: (01474) 535570 E-mail: info@thehedgehogpress.co.uk *General printers*

Hedgerow Publishing Ltd, 325 Abbeydale Road, Sheffield, S7 1FS Tel: 0114-255 4873 Fax: 0114-250 9400 E-mail: sales@hedgerow.co.uk *Manufacturers of picture postcards*

Hedgers Racehorse Transport, Nigel Hardy Transport, Melcroft, Eastergate Lane, Eastergate, Chichester, West Sussex, PO20 3SJ Tel: (01243) 543863 Fax: (01243) 543913 *Horse transport*

Hedinair Ovens Ltd, 3 Pilot Close, Fulmar Way, Wickford, Essex, SS11 8YW Tel: (01268) 761777 Fax: (01268) 760210 E-mail: sales@hedinair.co.uk Purchasing Contact: D Banstead Sales Contact: D Banstead Principal Export Areas: Worldwide *Manufacturers of industrial ovens incorporating standard ranges and custom design of batch and convectorized ovens to meet evey need*

Hedley (Engineering Services) Ltd, West Havelock Street, South Shields, Tyne & Wear, NE33 5DZ Tel: 0191-456 0250 Fax: 0191-455 6040 E-mail: info@hedley.co.uk Principal Export Areas: Worldwide *Heat exchanger & transfer equipment manufrs*

▶ Hedley Griffin Films, The Old Bank House, High Street, Laxfield, Woodbridge, Suffolk, IP13 8DX Tel: (01986) 798613 Fax: (01986) 798172 E-mail: hedley@hedleygriffinfilms.com *2D computer animation for film, video*

Hedley Hydraulics Ltd, High Street, Crigglestone, Wakefield, West Yorkshire, WF4 3HT Tel: (01924) 259999 Fax: (01924) 252211 E-mail: hedley@hedley-hyd.com *System build & distribution*

▶ Hedley Material Handling, 16 Baronald Street, Rutherglen, Glasgow, G73 1AH Tel: 0141-647 4422 Fax: 0141-647 5413 *Forklifts truck specialists*

Hedleys Gold Embossers, Unit 8-9 Poland Industrial Estate, Manchester, M4 6AZ Tel: 0161-205 4496 Fax: 0161-205 4496 E-mail: sales@goldblocking.co.uk *Gold block & hot foil stampings*

Hednesford Brick Cutting Ltd, B Uxbridge Court, Littleworth Road, Cannock, Staffordshire, WS12 1NN Tel: (01543) 871244 Fax: (01543) 425946 *Brick cutting*

Hedon Salads Ltd, Main Road, Newport, Brough, North Humberside, HU15 2PR Tel: (01430) 441552 Fax: (01430) 441720 *Salad manufrs*

▶ Heel2toe.co.uk Ltd, Unit 9 Meadow Heights, Fir Street, Ramsbottom, Bury, Lancashire, BL0 0BN Tel: (07779) 151881 *We provide high street ladies fashion shoes at wholesale prices. '000s of bargain shoes.*Ladies shoes, ladies boots, womens shoes, court shoes, sandals, stiletto's, evening shoes, dimante shoes - we cater for all your needs*

Heeley Installations Ltd, 202 Whitehall Road, Drighlington, Bradford, West Yorkshire, BD11 1AU Tel: 0113-285 2679 Fax: 0113-285 2762 *Electrical engineers & contractors*

Heelman Ltd, Unit 17-18 Sheet Road Indust Estate, Ludlow, Shropshire, SY8 1LR Tel: (01584) 875030 Fax: (01584) 875030 *Precision turned parts manufrs*

Heenan Multiform Machines, Unit 34 Springvale Industrial Estate, Millfield Road, Bilston, West Midlands, WV14 0ST Tel: (01902) 401781 Fax: (01902) 401781 *Spare machinery part manufrs*

Heer Platers Ltd, 9 Auster Industrial Estate, Silverdale Drive, Thurmaston, Leicester, LE4 8NG Tel: 0116-264 0931 Fax: 0116-264 0931 *Electro plating manufrs*

Heerema Hartlepool Ltd, Greenland Road, Hartlepool, Cleveland, TS24 0RQ Tel: (01642) 340200 Fax: (01642) 340208 E-mail: info@heerema.co.uk *Oil & gas industry merchants*

Hegan & Co., 56 Distillery Street, Belfast, BT12 5BJ Tel: (028) 9032 5143 Fax: (028) 9023 8349 *Cycle accessories & spare parts distributors*

▶ Hegarty Demolition, 188-194 Barford Street, Highgate, Birmingham, B5 7EP Tel: 0121-622 2722

Hegartys (Fitted Furniture) Ltd, 79 Scraghy Road, Killen, Castlederg, County Tyrone, BT81 7SL Tel: (028) 8167 0979 Fax: (028) 8167 9979 *School furniture manufrs*

Hegner, 8 North Cresent, Diplocks Way, Hailsham, East Sussex, BN27 3JF Tel: (01323) 442440 Fax: (01323) 840696 E-mail: sales@hegner.co.uk *Universal saws & woodturning lathes*

Heidelberg Graphic Equipment Ltd, Intercity Way, Leeds, LS13 4LX Tel: 0113-224 8300 Fax: 0113-239 3118 *Printing machine manufrs*

Heidenhain (GB) Ltd, 200 London Road, Burgess Hill, West Sussex, RH15 9RD Tel: (01444) 247711 Fax: (01444) 870024 E-mail: sales@heidenhain.co.uk *Position feedback device specialists*

Heidrick & Struggles Ltd, 3 Burlington Gardens, London, W1S 3EP Tel: (020) 7075 4000 Fax: (020) 7075 4100 E-mail: lo@h-s.com *Executive search*

▶ Height & Light, 2 Green Lane Bungalows, Woodredon Road, Waltham Abbey, Essex, EN9 3SY Tel: (01992) 653977 Fax: 01992 653977 E-mail: sales@heightandlight.co.uk *Specialists in tree surgery & tree reports*

Heil Europe Ltd, Taxi Way, Hillend Industrial Park, Hillend, Dunfermline, Fife, KY11 9ES Tel: (01383) 823625 Fax: (01383) 824062 E-mail: sales@heileuro.com *Refuse collection vehicle manufrs*

Heimbach, Bradnor Road, Sharston Industrial Area, Manchester, M22 4TS Tel: 0161-998 6911 Fax: 0161-998 8095 *Paper machine wire manufrs*

F. Heinemann Ltd, PO Box 76, Northwood, Middlesex, HA6 3AJ Tel: (01923) 829993 Fax: (01923) 825519 E-mail: heinecas@btinternet.com *Sausage casing & knife dealers*

Heinrich Georg Manufacturing Ltd, Unit 8 Dunstall Hill Estate, Gorsebrook Road, Wolverhampton, WV6 0PJ Tel: (01902) 715110 Fax: (01902) 715221 E-mail: enquiries@georguk.com *Manufacturers special purpose machinery*

Heinz Foodservice, South Building, Hayes Park, Hayes, Middlesex, UB4 8AL Tel: (0800) 575755 E-mail: foodservice.enquiry@uk.hjheinz.com *Heinz foodservice develops and supplies catering solutions to foodservice operators across the UK, from independent caterers through to multi-national restaurant groups.**In 2005 Heinz Foodservice added the HP Foods portfolio of products including HP sauce, Daddies Sauce, Lea & Perrins and Amoy to it's range.**On top of these great brands, the Heinz Foodservice portfolio ranges fro consumer favourites such as Heinz baked Beans, Ketchup, condiments, sauces and soups, through to branded and bespoke back of house condiment sauces and food solutions.**with such a breadth of food offerings to compliment any dish, Heinz Foodservice products are enjoyed by consumers at different meal occasions, from morning to night*

▶ Heinzmann UK Ltd, Durham Tees Valley Airport, Darlington, County Durham, DL2 1PD Tel: (01325) 332805 Fax: (01325) 333631 E-mail: info@heinzmannuk.com *Analogue & digital speed governors for industrial genset, marine & off-highway applications. **Generator*

continued

*management systems for island, parallel & group installations, standard interfaces to Heinzmann & other products. **Service & repair of Heinzmann products.**Sole UK importer of Heinzmann Speed Governor and Generator Management equipment.100% owned by Heinzmann GmbH & Co KG*

heirlooms.uk.com, 11 Fontaine Road, London, SW16 3PB Tel: 02086 792196 Fax: 020 7738 9787 E-mail: info@heirlooms.uk.com *Personalised embroidered wedding ring cushions, full size, picture, christening & anniversary cushions, christening shawls & embroidered silk pictures created by leading textile and graphic designers Lin Gomm and Geoff Perkin.*

Heitz GmbH, 8 Priory Close, Deeping St. James, Peterborough, PE6 8PR Tel: (01778) 347164 Fax: (01778) 349240 E-mail: heitzbellows@yahoo.co.uk *Metal bellows manufrs*

Heitz Engineering Ltd, 24 Charles Wood Road, Dereham, Norfolk, NR19 1SX Tel: (01362) 692114 Fax: (01362) 695360 E-mail: sales@heitzeng.com *Precision engineers*

Helanbeck Provisions, 6A High Street, Hythe, Southampton, SO45 6AH Tel: (023) 8084 7987 *Health food suppliers*

Helbar Automation Ltd, 478 Rayleigh Rd, Eastwood, Leigh-on-Sea, Essex, SS9 5HZ Tel: (01702) 522425 Fax: (01702) 522425 E-mail: info@helbar.com *Precision & prototype engineers*

▶ Helen Agutter, 1 Bedford Place, Brighton, BN1 2PT Tel: (01273) 231310 Fax: (01273) 231310 E-mail: helen.agutter@ntlworld.com *I am a chartered accountant based in Brighton specialising in all aspects of starting a business from business plans to registering for VAT*** **

Helen Bull Ceramics Ltd, 4 Alexandria Industrial Estate, Moor Lane, Widnes, Cheshire, WA8 7AE Tel: 0151-420 7963 Fax: 0151-420 7963 *Ceramics manufrs*

▶ Helen Lowrie, 40 Roxborough Road, Harrow, Middlesex, HA1 1PA Tel: (020) 8427 2674 E-mail: info@helenlowrie.co.uk *Complete Garden Design Service.*

▶ Helen Redfern, 21 Vincent Road, Croydon, CR0 6ED Tel: (020) 8405 3392 E-mail: helen@helenredfern.co.uk *What's Your Next Step?*Helen Redfern Life Coaching will help you to determine what it is that you really want to achieve in your life - both on a personal and professional level.*Together with the coach you will assess what is good, and not so good, in your life at the moment and construct an action plan for you to achieve your objectives.*Helen Redfern Life Coaching works with individuals and corporations in achieving individual and firm-wide objectives.**

Helena Laboratories UK Ltd, Colima Avenue, Sunderland Enterprise Park, Sunderland, SR5 3XB Tel: 0191-549 6064 Fax: 0191-549 6271 E-mail: info@helena.co.uk *Clinical re-agent manufrs*

▶ Helena's Nursery Equipment, Sligo Road, Enniskillen, County Fermanagh, BT74 7JY Tel: (028) 6632 0505 *Baby care equipment suppliers*

Helexco Co. Ltd, 31 High Street Colliers Wood, London, SW19 2JE Tel: (020) 8542 4916 Fax: (020) 8540 8047 E-mail: kookies@btconnect.com *Commercial & ocean going shipping*

▶ Heli Beds, Newbridge Road Industrial Estate, Pontllanfraith, Blackwood, Gwent, NP12 2AN Tel: (01495) 223658 Fax: (01495) 223401 *Beds & bedding retailers*

▶ Helibeds, 69 Roundponds, Melksham, Wiltshire, SN12 8EB Tel: (01793) 688999 Fax: (01225) 790990 *Bed suppliers*

Helica Instruments Ltd, 1 Heriot-Watt Research Park, Riccarton, Currie, Midlothian, EH14 4AP Tel: 0131-449 4933 Fax: 0131-449 2204 *Medical instruments*

Helical Bar Chiswell Street Ltd, 11-15 Farm Street, London, W1J 5RS Tel: (020) 7629 0113 Fax: (020) 7408 1666 E-mail: tjm@helical.co.uk *Property investment developers*

Helical Components Coventry Ltd, Telford Road, Exhall, Coventry, CV7 9ES Tel: (024) 7636 1058 Fax: (024) 7636 7270 *Thread grinding specialists*

Helical Technology Ltd, Dock Road, Lytham, Lancashire, FY8 5AQ Tel: (01253) 733122 Fax: (01253) 794880 E-mail: sales@helical-technology.co.uk Principal Export Areas: Worldwide *Pressure actuators and vacuum actuators for turbochargers. Pneumatic actuators for exhaust gas coolers in exhaust gas recirculation systems. Piston sealing rings for turbochargers. Valve rotators, rotocoils for diesel and gas engines.*

Helifix Ltd, 21 Warple Way, London, W3 0RX Tel: (020) 8735 5200 Fax: (020) 8735 5201 E-mail: info@helifix.co.uk *Manufacturers of fixing systems*

Helifix Ltd, Unit B2 First Avenue, Tyne Tunnel Trading Estate, North Shields, Tyne & Wear, NE29 7SU Tel: 0191-257 4577 Fax: 0191-257 0426 E-mail: brian.breeze@helifix.co.uk *Wall tie replacement manufacturers & distributors*

Helikon Shipping Enterprises Ltd, St Clare House, 30-33 Minories, London, EC3N 1DH Tel: (020) 7481 8601 Fax: (020) 7488 2226 *Ship managers*

Helios Fabrications Ltd, Lakeside Business Park, Broadway Lane, South Ferney, Cirencester, Gloucestershire, GL7 5XL Tel: (01285) 869988 Fax: (01285) 869999 *Steel fabricators*

Helipad Construction Ltd, 15 Friern Park, London, N12 9DE Tel: (020) 8343 9556 Fax: (020) 7831 9489 E-mail: helipad@helicopter99.fsnet.co.uk *Hospital helipads, free surveys*

Helipebs Controls Ltd, Premier Works, Sisson Road, Gloucester, GL2 0RE Tel: (01452) 423201 Fax: (01452) 307665 E-mail: sales@helipebs.co.uk *Engineers*

▶ Helitune Ltd, Hatchmoor Industrial Estate, Torrington, Devon, EX38 7HP Tel: (01805) 624650 Fax: (01805) 624689

Helium3, 3A Great Minster Street, Winchester, Hampshire, SO23 9HA Tel: (01962) 626318 Fax: (01962) 626319 E-mail: james.turner@helium3.co.uk *Product design consultancy*

Helix Group plc, Lye, Engine Lane, Stourbridge, West Midlands, DY9 7AJ Tel: (01384) 424441 Fax: (01384) 892617 E-mail: info@helixhq.com *Drawing instrument manufrs*

▶ Helix Precision Machining, Unit 18, Unitfactory Estate, Hull, HU8 7QF Tel: (01482) 323131 Fax: (01482) 226639 E-mail: office@helixprecision.co.uk *Standard machining services*

Helix Recruitment Limited, George Street, Hailsham, East Sussex, BN27 1AD Tel: (01323) 445464 Fax: (01323) 440814 E-mail: kelly@helixrecruitment.co.uk *Helix Associates and Helix Recruitment have merged to create HELIX RECRUITMENT LIMITED which continues to offer highly specialised recruitment services in two market sectors: Operations and Technical staff for Food Manufacturing companies, and sales, marketing and technical support staff for the healthcare and laboratory supply industry.*

Helix Services Consultancy, 5 Saturn House, Calleva Park, Aldermaston, RG7 3PW Tel: 0118-981 9000 Fax: 0118-981 9001 E-mail: mail@helixconsultancy.com *Mechanical & electrical engineering consultants*

Hella Manufacturing, Wildmere Road, Banbury, Oxfordshire, OX16 3EY Tel: (01295) 272211 Fax: (01295) 278025 *Automotive lighting*

▶ Hellabys Ltd, 8 Hallsford Bridge Industrial Estate, Stondon Road, Ongar, Essex, CM5 9RB Tel: (01277) 363993 Fax: (01277) 366997

▶ Hellenic Systems Ltd, 73-75 Haltwhistle Road, South Woodham Ferrers, Chelmsford, CM3 5ZA Tel: (01245) 325753 Fax: (01245) 328002 *Industrial computers*

Heller Machine Tools, Acanthus Road, Ravensbank Business Park, Redditch, Worcestershire, B98 9EX Tel: 0121-275 3300 Fax: 0121-275 3340 E-mail: sales@heller.co.uk *CNC machine tools assemblers*

Esmond Hellerman Ltd, Hellerman House, Harris Way, Sunbury-on-Thames, Middlesex, TW16 7EW Tel: (01932) 781888 Fax: (01932) 789573 E-mail: sales@hellermans.com *Education suppliers*

Hellermann Tyton, 1 Robeson Way, Manchester, M22 4TY Tel: 0161-945 4181 Fax: 0161-947 2233 E-mail: enquiries@hellermantyton.co.uk *Cable ties, clips & accessories manufrs*

Hellermann Tyton, Ratcliff House, 43-45 Salthouse Road, Brackmills Industrial Estate, Northampton, NN4 7EX Tel: (01604) 706633 Fax: (01604) 705454 *Structured cabling systems manufrs*

Hellermanntyton, Wharf Approach, Aldridge, Walsall, WS9 8BX Tel: (01922) 458151 Fax: (01922) 743237 E-mail: sales@hellermantyton.co.uk *Cable product sales*

▶ Hellesdon Park Electrical Co. Ltd, 98 Hellesdon Park Road, Drayton High Road, Norwich, NR6 5DR Tel: (01603) 407033 Fax: (01603) 409458

Robert Hellin Ltd, 5 Mill Street, London, W1S 2AY Tel: (020) 7499 5777 Fax: (020) 7409 2727 *Clothing manufrs' agents*

Hellmann Worldwide Logistics Ltd, Hellmann House Lakeside Industrial Estate, Colnbrook By Passage, Colnbrook, Slough, SL3 0EL Tel: (01753) 688500 Fax: (01753) 684771 *Freight forwarders* Also at: Birmingham, Bradford, Cardiff, Gatwick, Luton & Manchester

Claude Hellowell Ltd, Thorpe Garage, Triangle, Sowerby Bridge, West Yorkshire, HX6 3DL Tel: (01422) 823248 Fax: (01422) 824234 *Road transport, haulage & storage services*

Helly Hansen, 26a Pingle Drive, Bicester, Oxfordshire, OX26 6WD Tel: (01869) 325944 Fax: (01869) 325973 *Outdoor wear*

Helm Exhibitions Ltd, 27-29 Speedwell Road, Haymills, Birmingham, B25 8HU Tel: 0121-766 6755 Fax: 0121-766 6752 E-mail: enquiries@helmx.co.uk *Steel fabricators*

Helm Fertilizer Great Britain, The Exchange, Station Parade, Harrogate, North Yorkshire, HG1 1PL Tel: (01423) 527799 Fax: (01423) 527799 E-mail: info@helmag.com *Chemical traders*

Helm Godfrey Ltd, Warnford Court, 29 Throgmorton Street, London, EC2N 2AT Tel: (020) 7614 1000 Fax: (020) 7614 1001 E-mail: info@helmgodfrey.com *Insurance consultants*

Helm Great Britain Ltd, Wimbledon Bridge House, 1 Hartfield Road, London, SW19 3RU Tel: (020) 8544 9000 Fax: (020) 8544 1011 E-mail: chemicals@helmgreatbritain.co.uk *Chemical distributors*

▶ Helm Office Interiors Ltd, 42 Erleigh Road, Reading, RG1 5NA Tel: 0118-926 6611 Fax: 0118-926 6700 E-mail: sales@helmoffice.com *Office design, planning & installation, office equipment suppliers*

▶ Helmbalm Ltd, 12 Leeds Road, Mirfield, West Yorkshire, WF14 0ET Tel: (01924) 490803

Helmdart Ltd, 10a Robin Hood Road, Woking, Surrey, GU21 8SP Tel: (01483) 760338 Fax: (01483) 729158 E-mail: helmdart@btconnect.com *Computer consultants*

Helme & Hallett Ltd, 42b High Street, Cuckfield, Haywards Heath, West Sussex, RH17 5EL Tel: (01444) 454776 Fax: (01444) 417716 E-mail: office@helme.co.uk *Building contractors*

▶ Helmer & Dyer Ltd, High Wych, Sawbridgeworth, Hertfordshire, CM21 0JS Tel: (01279) 723441

Helmet Integrated Systems, 3 Focus 4, Fourth Avenue, Letchworth Garden City, Hertfordshire, SG6 2TU Tel: (01462) 478000 Fax: (01462) 478010 E-mail: sales@helmets.co.uk *Safety helmets manufrs*

Helmrick Engineers Ltd, Ossett Lane, Dewsbury, West Yorkshire, WF12 8LS Tel: (01924) 462743 Fax: (01924) 430229 E-mail: helmrickuk@aol.com *Precision engineers*

Helmsman, Northern Way, Bury St. Edmunds, Suffolk, IP32 6NH Tel: (01284) 727600 Fax: (01284) 727601 E-mail: sales@helmsman.co.uk *Coin operated locker manufrs*

Helmsman Electronics Ltd, 31 Faringdon Avenue, Blackpool, FY4 3QQ Tel: (01253) 343056 Fax: (01253) 408004 E-mail: mail@helmsmanuk.co.uk *Electronic designers*

Helmstone Communications Ltd, 18 Guildford Road, Brighton, BN1 3LU Tel: (01273) 747447 Fax: (01273) 747333 E-mail: nisbett@helmstone.com *Software developers*

▶ Help 4 You Ltd, 6 Deal Castle Road, Deal, Kent, CT14 7BB Tel: (07773) 380133 E-mail: enquiries@help4you.ltd.uk *We offer business or personal coaching - often to sharpen your Marketing, increase your Sales, streamline your Inventory, tighten your Cashflow and help YOU to achieve your goals.*

Help4IT Ltd, 61 Queen Street, London, EC4R 1AE Tel: (0845) 2574448 Fax: (0845) 2574449 E-mail: sanjay.patel@help4it.co.uk *IT consultancy, suppliers of hardware & software*

Helpdesk Institute, 21 High Street, Green Street Greens, Orpington, Kent, BR6 6BG Tel: (01689) 862999 Fax: (01689) 889227 E-mail: info@hdi-europe.com *Membership helpdesk services*

▶ Helpit Systems Ltd, 9 North Street, Leatherhead, Surrey, KT22 7AX Tel: (01372) 360070 Fax: (01372) 360081 E-mail: sales@helpit.com *Data cleansing software tools*

▶ Help-ME-Park.com, 7th Floor, Norfolk House, South Terminal, Gatwick Airport, Crawley, West Sussex, RH6 0NN Tel: 0870 3006009 E-mail: info@help-me-park.com *Meet and greet valet parking for Gatwick north and south terminals. I deal for business and pleasure Travel. Help-me-Park is the future of airport parking.*

Helptoday Ltd, 8 Farrier Road, Lincoln Industrial Park, Lincoln, LN6 3RU Tel: (01522) 501001 Fax: (01522) 500099 E-mail: gary.cheshire@helptoday.co.uk *Diesel engine component merchants*

Helston Engineering Ltd, Unit 10 Bentley La Industrial Estate, Bentley Lane, Walsall, WS2 8TL Tel: (01922) 641556 Fax: (01922) 746161 *Precision engineers*

Heltor Warehouses, Heltor Business Park, Old Newton Road, Heathfield, Newton Abbot, Devon, TQ12 6RW Tel: (01626) 832516 Fax: (01626) 834373 E-mail: admin@heltor.co.uk *Fuel oil*

Hemax Ceilings Ltd, 167 The Grove, Biggin Hill, Kent, TN16 3UJ Tel: (01959) 701554 Fax: (01959) 573006 *Ceilings & partitions contractors*

▶ Hember Plant Hire Ltd, Eagle House 8 Heol Mostyn, Village Farm Industrial Estate, Pyle, Bridgend, Mid Glamorgan, CF33 6NU Tel: (01656) 744240 Fax: (01656) 744460

Hember Plant Hire Ltd, Lilford Street, Warrington, WA5 0LA Tel: (01925) 656023 Fax: (01925) 653104 E-mail: hire@hemberplant.co.uk *Welding plant hire* Also at: Barton on Humber & Bridgend

▶ David Hembrow Basketmaker, 70 St. Albans Road, Cambridge, CB4 2HG Tel: (01223) 528563 *Maker of traditional English Willow baskets*

Hemington Rustics, Cheneys Farm, Romsey Road, Ower, Romsey, Hampshire, SO51 6AF Tel: (023) 8073 9217 *Rustic garden furniture producers*

A. Hemingway & Sons Ltd, Whitley Lane, Grenoside, Sheffield, S35 8RP Tel: 0114-246 7676 Fax: 0114-257 0264 *Motor vehicle engineering services*

▶ Hemini P.L.C., Hemini Complex, Stirling Way, Elstree, Borehamwood, Hertfordshire, WD6 2BT Tel: (020) 8207 2000 Fax: (020) 8207 2222 E-mail: sales@hemini.com *IT Products and Services*

▶ Hemisphere Outdoors, 73 Widnes Road, Widnes, Cheshire, WA8 6AZ Tel: 0151-423 3958 Fax: 0151-423 3958 E-mail: info@hemoutdoors.fsnet.co.uk *Outdoor specialists in the sale of camping and hiking gear, workwear and army combat gear*

▶ Hemisphere Outdoors, 73 Widnes Road, Widnes, Cheshire, WA8 6AZ Tel: 0151-423 3958 Fax: 0151-423 3958 E-mail: info@hemoutdoors.fsnet.co.uk *Outdoor specialists in the sale of camping and hiking gear, workwear and army combat gear*

Hemming Group, 32 Vauxhall Bridge Road, London, SW1V 2SS Tel: (020) 7973 6404 Fax: (020) 7233 5052 E-mail: customer@hgluk.com *Directory & magazine publishers*

Hemming & Morris (Shopfitters) Ltd, 60 Lincoln Road, Olton, Birmingham, B27 6NZ Tel: 0121-706 5740 Fax: 0121-706 6192 E-mail: sales@hemmingmorris.co.uk *Shopfitters*

Hemmings Waste Management Ltd, St. Gabriels Road, Easton, Bristol, BS5 0RU Tel: (0117) 951 2000 Fax: (0117) 935 4524 *Refuse collections & skip hire*

Hempel Metals UK Ltd, Primrose Park, Greasbrough Road, Rotherham, South Yorkshire, S60 1RH Tel: (01709) 376966 Fax: (01709) 361589 E-mail: info@hempel-wire.com *Non-ferrous metal merchants* Also at: Rotherham

Hempel UK Ltd, Ty Coch Way, Llantarnam Industrial Park, Cwmbran, Gwent, NP44 3XF Tel: (01633) 874024 Fax: (01633) 489089 E-mail: sales@hempel.com *Industrial marine & metal protection paints manufrs*

Hemphill Castings Ltd, 273 Bromford Lane, Washwood Heath, Birmingham, B8 2SG Tel: 0121-327 5459 Fax: 0121-322 2040 *Non-ferrous metal castings services*

Hempstead & Johnson Ltd, Oakridge Road, High Wycombe, Buckinghamshire, HP11 2PF Tel: (01494) 444971 Fax: (01494) 462636 *Precision engineering*

Hempstead & Johnson Ltd, Oakridge Road, High Wycombe, Buckinghamshire, HP11 2PF Tel: (01494) 444971 Fax: (01494) 462636 E-mail: hemstead.johnson@btinternet.com *Cutting tool manufrs*

Hemsec Developments Ltd, Stoney Lane, Rainhill, Prescot, Merseyside, L35 9LL Tel: 0151-426 7171 Fax: 0151-493 1331 E-mail: sales@hemsec.com *Insulated panel manufrs*

Hemsley Orrell Partnership, 41 Church Road, Hove, East Sussex, BN3 2BE Tel: (01273) 223900 Fax: (01273) 326767

R. Hemsworth & Son (Gosport) Ltd, 8 Westfield Industrial Estate, Gosport, Hampshire, PO12 3RX Tel: (023) 9258 2731 Fax: (023) 9251 0436 *Joinery manufrs*

John Hemy (Systems) Ltd, Dukesway, Teesside Industrial Estate, Stockton-On-Tees, Cleveland, TS17 9LT Tel: (01642) 769440 Fax: (01642) 763440 E-mail: info@johnhemysystems.co.uk *Instrumentation engineers & contractors*

▶ Henderson Alan & Sons, Unit 6 Morgan Drive, Guisborough, Cleveland, TS14 7DH Tel: (01287) 619191 Fax: (01287) 619191 E-mail: upholstery@ntlworld.com *Upholstery specialists*

Henderson Bearings, Crow Arch Lane, Ringwood, Hampshire, BH24 1NZ Tel: (01425) 477787 Fax: (01425) 478883 E-mail: sales@hendersonbearings.com *Ball & roller bearing stockists*

Henderson Biomedical Ltd, 97 Avenue Road, Beckenham, Kent, BR3 4RX Tel: (020) 8402 4426 Fax: (020) 8778 4571 E-mail: info@henderson-biomedical.co.uk *Hospital repair & maintain of equipment servicing*

Henderson Engineering (N E) Ltd, Vickers Close, Preston Farm Industrial Estate, Stockton-on-Tees, Cleveland, TS18 3TD Tel: (01642) 608008 Fax: (01642) 612636 E-mail: enquiries@hendersonengineering.com *Steel & pipework fabricators*

Henderson Fuels Domestic Industrial Agricultural, 36 Cranagh Road, Coleraine, County Londonderry, BT51 3NN Tel: (028) 7035 5980 Fax: (028) 7035 5980 *Oil distributors*

▶ Henderson Global Imports Ltd, Limpet House, Itchenor Road Itchenor, Chichester, West Sussex, PO20 7DH Tel: (01243) 513511 Fax: (01243) 512359 E-mail: sales@hgimports.com *Henderson Global Imports Ltd. Queue Management, Cafe Barriers, Giant Umbrellas, Infra Red Heaters. Wet Umbrella Wrappers & Wet Umbrella Bags.*

Henderson Global Investors, 4 Broadgate, London, EC2M 2DA Tel: (020) 7818 1818 Fax: (020) 7818 1819 E-mail: sales@henderson.co.uk *Investment company*

▶ Henderson Grass Machinery Ltd, Tweedbank Industrial Estate, Tweedbank, Galashiels, Selkirkshire, TD1 3RS Tel: (01896) 753870 Fax: (01896) 752598

Henderson Grass Machinery Ltd, Bye-Pass Road, Haddington, East Lothian, EH41 3PQ Tel: (01620) 823171 Fax: (01620) 826696 E-mail: info@hendersongm.co.uk *Agricultural & Horticultural Engineers*

▶ Henderson Homes Ltd, 5 Sherdley Road, St. Helens, Merseyside, WA9 5BW Tel: (01744) 832777 Fax: 0151-487 7606 E-mail: info@hendersonhomes.co.uk

Henderson Kerr Ltd, Kirklee Road, Bellshill, Lanarkshire, ML4 2QW Tel: (01563) 541325 Fax: (01563) 541325 E-mail: info@hendersonkerr.com *Processing all grades ferrous/non ferrous metals, eg steel scrap, copper, brass, aluminium, stainless steels/ alloys, cable stripping, reusable steels. Factory clearances/contracts, collection service 8-50 cubic yard skips. Authorised Treatment Facility for de-pollution of scrap cars, Scrap exports'.*

Henderson Management Services, 208 Henley Road, Caversham, Reading, RG4 6LR Tel: 0118-947 9159 Fax: 0118-946 4779 E-mail: hms@dial.pipex.com *Management & business consultants*

Henderson Plastics, Lyng Hall Lane, Wood Norton, Dereham, Norfolk, NR20 5BJ Tel: (01362) 683364 Fax: (01362) 683529 E-mail: sales@hendersons.co.uk Principal Export Areas: Worldwide *Plastic fabricators*

▶ Henderson Warnock, 38 New City Road, Glasgow, G4 9JT Tel: 0141-353 2444 Fax: 0141-353 2585

▶ Hendersons, Eachwick Lodge, Eachwick, Newcastle upon Tyne, NE18 0BL Tel: (07779) 107713 Fax: (01661) 854155 E-mail: windows2clean@yahoo.co.uk *Specialists in Commercial Window Cleaning, Professional & Reliable ~ Quality Guaranteed. Platform Access & Water-fed Pole Systems.*Covering North East England*and London Areas.**

Hendersons Insurance Brokers, 5 Acorn Business Park, Woodseats Close, Sheffield, S8 0TB Tel: 0114-262 9911 Fax: 0114-280 2831 E-mail: enquiries@ecsbrokers.com *Insurance & financial advisors*

Hendon Sign Co., 25-27 The Burroughs, London, NW4 4AR Tel: (020) 8202 8900 Fax: (020) 8202 4071 *Signs manufrs*

Hendra Health Store, 8 Lemon Street, Truro, Cornwall, TR1 2LQ Tel: (01872) 223799 Fax: (01872) 273031 *Health food distributors*

Hendrick Industrial Equipment Ltd, Unit 32d The Washford Industrial Estate, Heming Road, Redditch, Worcestershire, B98 0DH Tel: (01527) 523712 Fax: (01527) 514545 E-mail: heat@hendrick.co.uk *Industrial furnace & oven manufrs*

Hendry, Glenlatterach Cottage, Birnie, Elgin, Morayshire, IV30 8RR Tel: (01343) 860217 Fax: (01343) 860217 *Water authority*

Hendry Electrical Contractors, 2 Holton Business Park, Holton Court, Holton-le-Clay, Grimsby, South Humberside, DN36 5EE Tel: (01472) 825825 Fax: (01472) 825461

Hendry Ferguson Company, 6 Blackwood Road, Milngavie, Glasgow, G62 7LA Tel: 0141-955 0041 Fax: 0141-955 1541 E-mail: sales@hfco.sol.co.uk *Fax broadcasting*

▶ Hendry Fleetwood & Sons Ltd, Baker Street, Lossiemouth, Morayshire, IV31 6NZ Tel: (01343) 813015 Fax: (01343) 812054

Hendry Hydraulics Ltd, Pinefield Industrial Estate, 2 Perimeter Road, Elgin, Morayshire, IV30 6DF Tel: (01343) 545207 Fax: (01343) 545200 E-mail: enquiries@hendry-hydraulic-cylinders.co.uk *Hydraulics manufrs*

Hendry Ramsay & Waters, 55-57 North Methven Street, Perth, PH1 5PX Tel: (01738) 623679 Fax: (01738) 443327 E-mail: sales@scothunt.co.uk *Sporting agents & gunsmith*

Hendry & Sons Ltd, Station Road, Foulsham, Dereham, Norfolk, NR20 5RG Tel: (01362) 683249

Hendy Group Ltd, Southampton Road, Cosham, Portsmouth, PO6 4RW Tel: (023) 9232 2900 Fax: (023) 9232 2960 E-mail: accounts@hendy-group.com *Reconditioning engines & new engine sales services*

M.R. Hendy, Middle Hill Farm, Langford Budville, Wellington, Somerset, TA21 0RS Tel: 01823 400476 *Agricultural engineers*

Hengelmolen Engineering Ltd, Great Bridge Industrial Estate, Tipton, West Midlands, DY4 0HR Tel: 0121-520 1181 Fax: 0121-557 5201 E-mail: hengelmolen@btconnect.com *Furnace manufrs*

Henkel Ltd, Apollo Court, Bishops Square Business Park, Hatfield, Hertfordshire, AL10 9EY Tel: (01707) 635000 Fax: (01707) 635099 E-mail: ukcorp.communications@henkel.co.uk *Adhesive products manufrs*

Henkel, Technologies House, Wood La End, Hemel Hempstead, Hertfordshire, HP2 4RQ Tel: (01442) 278000 Fax: (01442) 278071 *Chemical manufrs*

Henkel, Technologies House, Wood La End, Hemel Hempstead, Hertfordshire, HP2 4RQ Tel: (01442) 278000 Fax: (01442) 278071 E-mail: customer.enquiry@henkel.com *Solder paste, powder & adhesives manufrs*

Henley Brothers UK Ltd, 27 Sunters Wood Close, Booker, High Wycombe, Buckinghamshire, HP12 4DZ Tel: (01494) 536872 Fax: (01494) 446910 *Electronic component distributors*

Henley & Burton Business Machines Ltd, 130 South Street, Lancing, West Sussex, BN15 8AU Tel: (01903) 762719 Fax: (0870) 7058679 *Office machines retailers*

The Henley Centre, 9 Bridewell Place, Bridewell Gate, London, EC4V 6AW Tel: (020) 7955 1800 Fax: (020) 7353 2899 E-mail: future@henleycentre.com *Consumer consultancy*

▶ Henley Hill, Nimlett House, Nimlet, Cold Ashton, Chippenham, Wiltshire, SN14 8JX Tel: (01225) 891992 Fax: (01225) 891010 *Fencing contractors & fabricators*

▶ Henley Metal Products, Whitley, Edge Lane, Henley-in-Arden, West Midlands, B95 5DT Tel: (01564) 795389 Fax: (01564) 795171 *Fabrication & metal work*

Henley Sign People, Unit 1b Vines Farm, Reading Road, Cane End, Reading, RG4 9HE Tel: 0118-972 4567 Fax: 0118-972 3205 E-mail: sales@signpeople.com *Sign makers*

Henleys Medical Supplies Ltd, Brownfields, Welwyn Garden City, Hertfordshire, AL7 1AN Tel: (01707) 333164 Fax: (01707) 334795 E-mail: sales@henleysmed.com *Medical supplies & surgical instrument distributors* Also at: Harlow & Westbury

▶ Henllan Bread, Colomendy Industrial Estate, Rhyl Road, Denbigh, Clwyd, LL16 5TA Tel: (01745) 817321 Fax: (01745) 814774 *Wholesale bakery*

▶ Henlow Building Supplies, 3/Pegasus Mews, Stratton Business Park, Biggleswade, Bedfordshire, SG18 8QA Tel: (01767) 312800 Fax: (01767) 318371 E-mail: sales@henlowbuildingsupplies.co.uk *Builders merchant*

John Henman Ltd, 81 High Street, West Wickham, Kent, BR4 0LS Tel: (020) 8777 4853 *Beds & carpets retailers*

Henri Lloyd International Ltd, Smithfold Lane, Worsley, Manchester, M28 0GP Tel: 0161-799 1212 Fax: 0161-975 2500 E-mail: information@henrilloyd.co.uk *Waterproof & sailing clothing manufrs*

Henri Picard & Frere, 8 Pixham Court, Pixham Lane, Dorking, Surrey, RH4 1PG Tel: (020) 8949 3142 Fax: (020) 8949 3142 E-mail: sales@picard.co.uk *Distributors of optical instruments & tools*

M.T. Henrick Ltd, 22 Tenby Street, Birmingham, B1 3EE Tel: 0121-236 1627 Fax: 0121-212 1742 *Jewellers*

Henrion, Ludlow & Schmidt Ltd, 12 Hobart Place, London, SW1W 0HH Tel: (020) 7245 4600 Fax: (020) 7245 4601 E-mail: info@henrion.com *Corporate identity consultants*

Henrob, Second Avenue, Deeside Industrial Park, Deeside, Clwyd, CH5 2NX Tel: (01244) 837220 Fax: (01244) 837222 E-mail: sales@henrob.co.uk Principal Export Areas: Worldwide *Automotive industry & industrial fasteners & rivet manufrs*

A. Henry & Co., Langford Arch, London Road, Sawston, CB2 4EE Tel: (01223) 833132 Fax: (01223) 833400 *Hide & skin brokers*

Henry Boot Construction, 71 Ardwick Green North, Manchester, M12 6FX Tel: 0161-272 6162 Fax: 0161-272 7334

Henry Boot Estates Ltd, Banner Cross Hall, Sheffield, S11 9PD Tel: 0114-255 5444 Fax: 0114-258 5548 E-mail: pr@henryboot.co.uk *Building contractors*

Henry Boot Training Ltd, Callywhite Lane, Dronfield, Derbyshire, S18 2XN Tel: (01246) 410111 Fax: (01246) 410595 *Building & civil engineers* Also at: Birmingham

▶ Henry Bros Scotland Ltd, Claddoch House, Cardross, Dumbarton, G82 5HG Tel: (01389) 842210 Fax: (01389) 842220

Henry Cowan & Son Ltd, 40 Bethnal Green Road, London, E1 6HZ Tel: (020) 7739 8627 Fax: (020) 7739 0729 E-mail: sales@cowansdirect.co.uk *Retailers of stationery*

Henry Curtis Ltd, 20 Verney Road, London, SE16 3DY Tel: (020) 7237 4500 Fax: (020) 7232 1568 *Tin box distributors*

▶ Henry Gillies, Roman Camp Blaes Bing, Drumshoreland Road, Pumpherston, Livingston, West Lothian, EH53 0LH Tel: (01506) 431622 Fax: (01506) 439954

▶ Henry Gillies Haulage Contractors, 62 Pumpherston Road, Uphall Station, Livingston, West Lothian, EH54 5PT Tel: (01506) 431321 Fax: (01506) 439954

Henry Good, 37 Bowlers Croft, Basildon, Essex, SS14 3DZ Tel: (01268) 272880 Fax: (01268) 272887 *General printers*

▶ Henry Gray, 4 Randolph Place, Randolph Industrial Estate, Kirkcaldy, Fife, KY1 2YX Tel: (01592) 652684

Henry Hall Displays Fittings Ltd, Cherrytree, Union Road, Sheffield, S11 9EF Tel: 0114-255 1351 Fax: 0114-250 0006 E-mail: sales@retaildisplay.com *Shop fitting suppliers & fitters & display item sales*

Henry Isaac Fireplaces, The Foundry, St. Ippolyts, Hitchin, Hertfordshire, SG4 7NX Tel: (01462) 442588 Fax: (01462) 421618 *Metal products manufrs*

▶ Henry Jones Criccieth Ltd, Maes Workshop, Criccieth, Gwynedd, LL52 0AB Tel: (01766) 522854 Fax: (01766) 523463

▶ Henry Kemp (Road Maintenance) Ltd, Century House, Century Road, Retford, Nottinghamshire, DN22 7TD Tel: (01777) 703643

Henry Krank & Co. Ltd, 100-104 Lowtown, Pudsey, West Yorkshire, LS28 9AY Tel: 0113-256 9163 Fax: 0113-257 4962 *Sporting goods manufrs*

Henry Lewis & Son Ltd, 7 Bolling Road, Bradford, West Yorkshire, BD4 7HN Tel: (01274) 307359 Fax: (01274) 370784 *Rolling shutters & wire goods*

Henry Mills Ltd, 30 Chester Street, Aston, Birmingham, B6 4BE Tel: 0121-359 4671 Fax: 0121-333 3153 E-mail: binding@henrymills.co.uk *Bookbinders & print finishers*

Henry Monk Gunmaker Ltd, 8 Queen Street, Chester, CH1 3LG Tel: (01244) 320988 Fax: (01244) 320988 *Gunmakers & fishing tackle dealers*

Henry Moore & Co., 5 The Broadway, London, SW13 0NY Tel: (020) 8878 0656 Fax: (020) 8878 0656 *Re-upholstery & furniture manufrs*

Henry Morris 1958 Ltd, Old Town Dock, Newport, Gwent, NP20 2BW Tel: (01633) 265603 Fax: (01633) 253186 *Industrial lubricant manufrs*

▶ Henry Pels, 34 Montague Close, Walton-on-Thames, Surrey, KT12 2NQ Tel: (01932) 240707 Fax: (01932) 247638 E-mail: henrypels@btconnect.com *Machine tool manufrs*

Henry R Ayton Ltd, 40 The Cutts, Dunmurry, Belfast, BT17 9HS Tel: (028) 9061 8511 Fax: (028) 9060 2436 E-mail: sales@hrayton.com *General engineers*

Henry R Taylor, 21 Church Lane, Rasharkin, Ballymena, County Antrim, BT44 8QZ Tel: (028) 2957 1316 *Agricultural Engineers*

Henry Schein Equipment, Commondale Court, Unit 14 Commondale Way, Euroway Industrial Estate, Bradford, West Yorkshire, BD4 6SF Tel: (01274) 474400 Fax: (01274) 474405 *Dental retailers*

Henry Smith Constructional Engineer Ltd, Wharton Steel Works, Deakins Road, Winsford, Cheshire, CW7 3BW Tel: (01606) 592121 Fax: (01606) 559134 E-mail: admin@hs-steel.co.uk *Design & manufacture of steel frame buildings*

Henry Squire & Sons Ltd, Unit 2 Hilton Cross Business Park, Cannock Road, Wolverhampton, WV10 7QZ Tel: (01902) 308050 E-mail: info@henry-squire.co.uk *Can openers (mechanical) manufacturers, general & industrial locks*

Henry Technologies Ltd, Mossland Road, Hillington Industrial Estate, Glasgow, G52 4XZ Tel: 0141-882 4621 Fax: 0141-882 4624 E-mail: sales@henrytech.co.uk *Industrial, commercial refrigeration components & equipment hire*

▶ Henry W Pollard & Sons Ltd, Monmouth Street, Bridgwater, Somerset, TA6 5EJ Tel: (01278) 422211 Fax: (01278) 445775 E-mail: info@pollard-ltd.com

▶ Henry Wadsworth, 42 28 Old Brompton Road, London, SW7 3SS Tel: (0870) 6091773 Fax: (0870) 6091774 E-mail: info@henrywadsworth.com *Henry Wadsworth Luxury Shirtmakers are specialist makers and distributors of tailored shirts bringing you Jermyn Street quality without the Jermyn Street price tag. Our shirts are cut from the finest two fold cotton and offered through our classic, casual and women ranges in the latest weaves, patterns and colours. At Henry Wadsworth, we remain committed to excellent standards in workmanship and quality so that we always provide you with the very best shirt money can buy.*

Henry Watson Potteries Ltd, Pottery House, Pottery Hill, Wattisfield, Diss, Norfolk, IP22 1NH Tel: (01359) 251239 Fax: (01359) 250984 E-mail: sales@henrywatson.com *Earthenware distributors*

Henry Winning & Co. Ltd, 16-18 Caroline Street, Glasgow, G31 5DD Tel: 0141-554 2767 Fax: 0141-554 8496 E-mail: sales@twines.co.uk *Twines suppliers*

Henry's Blind & Carpet Centre, 77-79b Mid Street, Fraserburgh, Aberdeenshire, AB43 9JD Tel: (01346) 514357 Fax: (01346) 514357 *Blinds & carpet suppliers*

Hensall Mechanical Services (Holdings) Ltd, Roall, Goole, North Humberside, DN14 0NA Tel: (01977) 661318 Fax: (01977) 662127 E-mail: enquiries@hensall.com *Heating, ventilation & air conditioning pipe work installers services*

Charles Henshaw & Sons Ltd, Russell Road, Edinburgh, EH11 2LS Tel: 0131-337 4204 Fax: 0131-346 2441 E-mail: admin@charles-henshaw.co.uk *Glazing fire screens*

Henshaw Manufacturing Co. Ltd, Stratford St North, Birmingham, B11 1BP Tel: 0121-772 2232 Fax: 0121-771 1788 E-mail: weekshenshaw@aol.com *Metal smallware manufrs*

Henson Refrigeration Service, 6 Olympus Square, London, E5 8PL Tel: (020) 8533 5322 Fax: (020) 7686 0851 *Refrigeration engineers*

▶ Henton & Co., St. Andrews House, St. Andrews Street, Leeds, LS3 1LF Tel: 0113-246 7900 Fax: 0113-246 9200 *Computer software manufrs*

A.O. Henton Engineering Co. Ltd, Cotes Road, Burbage, Hinckley, Leicestershire, LE10 2HJ Tel: (01455) 238331 Fax: (01455) 251023 E-mail: david.english@aohenton.co.uk *Sub-contract machinists*

Henton & Chattell Ltd, London Road, Nottingham, NG2 3HW Tel: 0115-986 6646 Fax: 0115-986 6169 E-mail: info@hentonandchattell.co.uk *Grass cutting machinery distributors*

Henton Guarding Ltd, Unit 14 Eversley Way, Thorpe Industrial Estate, Egham, Surrey, TW20 8RG Tel: (01784) 439255 Fax: (01784) 477860 *Industrial machine guard manufrs*

Henwood & Dean, Greenlands Farm, Dairy Lane, Hambleden, Henley-on-Thames, Oxfordshire, RG9 3AS Tel: (01491) 571692 Fax: (01491) 411514 *Boat building services*

▶ Hepburn Loveday International, The Gate House, Mansion Gate, Chapel Allerton, Leeds, LS7 4RF Tel: 0113-262 3336 Fax: 0113-262 3345 E-mail: info@hepburnloveday.com *Specialist 'Off Market' land and property brokers, sourcing residential and commercial projects for developers, fund managers and other buying organisations. We source 'Off Market' land, with or without planning permission, and existing commercial property, in the UK and abroad, and have exclusive access to 'Off Plan' sales for multiple residential purchasers and commercial portfolio acquisitions.*

Heppenstall Metal Co. Ltd, Heppenstall Lane, Sheffield, S9 3XB Tel: 0114-244 1839 Fax: 0114-244 3861 *Non-ferrous metal merchants*

Hepworth Acoustics Ltd, 5 Bankside, Crosfield Street, Warrington, WA1 1UP Tel: (01925) 579100 Fax: (01925) 579150 E-mail: enquiries@hepworth-acoustics.co.uk *Noise & vibration consultants*

Hepworth Building Products, 90 Blackisland Road, Portadown, Craigavon, County Armagh, BT62 1NQ Tel: (028) 3885 1207 Fax: (028) 3885 2219 E-mail: enq@hepworthconcrete.co.uk Principal Export Areas: Worldwide *Concrete Products Manufacturer*

Hepworth Building Products Ltd, 47 Coppice Side, Swadlincote, Derbyshire, DE11 9AA Tel: (01283) 552467 Fax: (01283) 221034 *Drainage & tile manufrs*

Hepworth Building Products Holdings Ltd, Hazlehead, Crow Edge, Sheffield, S36 4HG Tel: (01226) 763561 Fax: (01226) 764827 E-mail: info@hepworth.co.uk *Water supply pipe manufacturers & building products* Also at: Burnley, Doncaster, Edlington & Newton Abbot

Hepworth Composites, Pollard Moor, Padiham, Burnley, Lancashire, BB12 7JR Tel: (01282) 683444 Fax: (01282) 683445 E-mail: ann.booth@hepworth.co.uk *Manufacturers of molded glass fibre reinforced materials*

Hepworth Marine, Hepworth House, Brook Street, Redditch, Worcestershire, B98 8NF Tel: (01527) 61243 Fax: (01527) 66836 E-mail: bhepworth@b-hepworth.com *Windscreen wiper system manufrs*

Hepworths Building Products Ltd, Woodville Works, Woodville, Swadlincote, Derbyshire, DE11 8BQ Tel: (01283) 216111 Fax: (01283) 522009 *Clay drainage*

Hepworths Shipyard Ltd, Main Street, Paull, Hull, HU12 8AN Tel: (01482) 338817 Fax: (01482) 338820 E-mail: hepworths@rix.co.uk *Ship builders & repairers*

Heraeous Noble Light Analytics Ltd, Unit 2-4, Nuffield Close, Cambridge, CB4 1SS Tel: (01223) 424100 Fax: (01223) 426338 E-mail: *Light sources services*

▶ Heraeus Electro Nite UK Ltd, 655 Sheffield Road, Chesterfield, Derbyshire, S41 9ED Tel: (01246) 454849 Fax: (01246) 453898

Heraeus Noblelight Ltd, Unit 1 Millenium Court, Clayhill Industrial Estate, Buildwas Lane, Neston, CH64 3UZ Tel: 0151-353 2710 Fax: 0151-353 2719 E-mail: ian.bartley@heraeus.com Sales Contact: I. Bartley *Manufacturer of infrared emitters & purpose built heating & drying systems. Fully equipped test & development facility to evaluate most suitable infrared wavelength for any given application. Portable test units available for online appraisals*

▶ Heraeus Quartz Ltd, 5 Langlands Place, Kelvin South Business Park, East Kilbride, Glasgow, G75 0YF Tel: (01355) 244456

▶ Heraeus Quartz Ltd, 5 Langlands Place, Kelvin South Business Park, East Kilbride, Glasgow, G75 0YF Tel: (01355) 244456

Heraeus Silica & Metals Ltd, Cinderhill Industrial Estate, Stoke-on-Trent, ST3 5LB Tel: (01782) 599423 Fax: (01782) 599802 E-mail: enquiries@4cmd.com *Precious metals, ceramic media & cover coats supplier*

▶ Herald Graphics Ltd, Elgar Road South, Reading, RG2 0BZ Tel: 0118-931 1488

Herald Marketing Ltd, 174 Billet Road, London, E17 5DX Tel: (020) 8507 7900 Fax: (020) 8507 2914 *Plastic disposables manufrs*

The Herald Press Ltd, Burnside Drive, Arbroath, Angus, DD11 1NS Tel: (01241) 872000 Fax: (01241) 870707 E-mail: printing@theheraldpress.fsnet.co.uk *Printers & stationers*

▶ Heraldlink Ltd, 25 East Hill, Dartford, DA1 1RX Tel: (01322) 294488

Heras Readyfence Service, Unit B1, Castle Road, Eurolink, Sittingbourne, Kent, ME10 3RL Tel: (01795) 423261 Fax: (01795) 426351 E-mail: readyfence.sales@readyfence.co.uk *Supplier of temporary fencing, barriers & hoarding systems*

Heras UK Fencing Systems, Herons Way, Balby, Doncaster, South Yorkshire, DN4 8WA Tel: (01302) 364551 Fax: (01302) 322401 E-mail: heras.sales@heras.co.uk *Fencing, gateposts & railings manufrs* Also at: Airdrie, Birmingham, Doncaster, Liverpool, Norwich & Stockton-on-Tees

▶ Heraues Quartz Tech Ltd, 4 Tannery House, Tannery Lane, Send, Woking, Surrey, GU23 7EF Tel: (01483) 213324 Fax: (01483) 213329 E-mail: byfleet.sales@heraeus.com *Lamps & lights manufrs*

▶ Herbal Wellbeing, 37 Marlowe Road, Herringthorpe, Rotherham, South Yorkshire, S65 2JQ Tel: (01709) 305627 Fax: (0709) 2865304 E-mail: herbalwellbeing@yahoo.co.uk

▶ Herbalbrew, 7 Greenhill Road, Coleraine, County Londonderry, BT51 3JE Tel: (028) 7035 7225 E-mail: kat@herbalbrew.co.uk *Purveyor of organic herbs, spices, essential oils*

Herbalife, 5b Third Avenue, Hove, East Sussex, BN3 2PB Tel: (01273) 723884 Fax: (01273) 723884 *Health nutrition & beauty services, consultancy*

Herbalife Independent Distributor, 9 Willenhall Close, Luton, LU3 3XX Tel: (01582) 591906 *Nutritional supplements distributors*

▶ Herbalife - Top Nutrition 99, 3 Talbot Avenue, Edgerton, Huddersfield, HD3 3BQ Tel: 01484 531426 E-mail: mikestephenson50@hotmail.com *Top nutrition99 is an independent distributor of Herbalife products, one of the world market leaders in nutritional technology. We provide high quality naturally derived nutrients which support healthy lifestyles, weight loss programmes and sports nutrition, and personal on-going advice is available FOC if desired. Business is by phone or internet and an advisor is available throughout the normal working day and until 9pm every evening and weekends. Free presentations given on sports nutrition to any sports, athletics or club. Discounts are available for referrals, and commissions are paid on orders received from members of any club joining our internet affiliate scheme - ask for details of this great fund-raising idea.*

Herbalife UK Ltd, Units 6-7 Perth Trading Estate, Perth Avenue, Slough, SL1 4XX Tel: (01895) 819000 Fax: (01753) 898627 *Herbal product supplier*

Herbert & Criddan, 11 Alliance Close, Attleborough Fields Industrial Estate, Nuneaton, Warwickshire, CV11 6SD Tel: (024) 7638 3400 Fax: (024) 7638 5999 E-mail: ken@herbertandcridan.com *Machine tools & spare parts*

Herbert G Winfield, Winfields Yard, Hartspring Lane, Watford, WD25 8AQ Tel: (01923) 256133 Fax: (01923) 256133 *Sand & builders merchants* Also at: Aldenham

Herbert Marx Ltd, New House, 67-68 Hatton Garden, London, EC1N 8JY Tel: (020) 7242 4135 Fax: (020) 7831 9327 E-mail: herbertmarx@dial.pipex.com *Jewellery manufrs*

▶ Herbert Pool Engineering Ltd, 28 Waterfront Business Park, Fleet, Hampshire, GU51 3QT Tel: (01252) 614824 Fax: (01252) 625585

Herbert Tooling Ltd, Roseme, Sandy Lane, Fillongley, Coventry, CV7 8DD Tel: (01676) 540040 Fax: (01676) 540040 E-mail: info@herbert-tooling.com *Machine tool spares & ancillary production tooling suppliers*

Herbert Tooling Ltd, Rosne, Sandy Lane, Fillongley, Coventry, CV7 8DD Tel: (01676) 540040 Fax: (01676) 542093 E-mail: info@herbert-tooling.com *Machine tools spares & equipment*

Herberts Foam & Textiles, 108 Victoria Road, Aldershot, Hampshire, GU11 1JX Tel: (01252) 332838 Fax: (01252) 345002 Purchasing Contact: D. Walters Sales Contact: D. Herbert *Cushion (filled) & (foam filled) manufacturers & foam distributors or agents*

Herbie Frogg Group Ltd, 2nd Floor, 125 New Bond Street, London, W1S 1DY Tel: (020) 7629 0446 Fax: (020) 7629 0423 E-mail: admin@herbie-frogg.co.uk *Menswear wholesalers*

Herbies Health Food, 72 High Street, Biddulph, Stoke-on-Trent, ST8 6AS Tel: (01782) 522133 *Health food distributors*

▶ Herbmoon Hollow, 25 Valentine Row, Callington, Cornwall, PL17 7DH Tel: (01579) 389251 E-mail: herbmoon@herbmoonhollow.com *Suppliers of herbs, resins, barks, flowers, seeds & powders*

▶ Herbs Gardens & Health, 27 Northdown Road, Broadstairs, Kent, CT10 2UW Tel: (01843) 600201 Fax: (01843) 863134 E-mail: juliet@herbsgardenshealth.com *Health food products*

Hercules C S M D, Unit 14-16 Nelson Road, Townstal Industrial Estate, Dartmouth, Devon, TQ6 9LA Tel: (01803) 833736 Fax: (01803) 834846 E-mail: herculescsmd@aol.com *Fabrication engineers*

Hercules Security Fabrications Ltd, 1 Agl Business Park, Coundon Industrial Estate, Coundon, Bishop Auckland, County Durham, DL14 8NR Tel: (01388) 458794 Fax: (01388) 458806 E-mail: info@hercules-security.co.uk *Security fencing fabricators*

Herd Mundy Richardson Ltd, Oak House Bredbury Parkway, Ashton Road, Bredbury Park Industrial Estate, Stockport, Cheshire, SK6 2QN Tel: 0161-406 6767 Fax: 0161-494 8400 E-mail: sue.richardson@hmrlabs.com *Chemistry*

Hereford Abrasives Co. Ltd, Unit 702, Fordshill Road, Rotherwas Industrial Estate, Hereford, HR2 6NS Tel: (01432) 270289 Fax: (01432) 274278 E-mail: sales@blasting.freeserve.co.uk *Shot blasting services*

Hereford Catering Supplies, 9 Gruneisen Street, Hereford, HR4 0DX Tel: (01432) 357028 *Food wholesalers*

Hereford Galvanisers Ltd, Grandstand Road, Hereford, HR4 9NS Tel: (01432) 267664 Fax: (01432) 352735 E-mail: zink@hereford.galvanizers.co.uk *Galvanizing services*

Hereford Industrial Supply Co. Ltd, Units 18-20, Three Elms Trading Estate, Hereford, HR4 9PU Tel: (01432) 353232 Fax: (01432) 352505 E-mail: sales@herefordindustrial.co.uk *Engineering suppliers*

Hereford Metal Finishers, 10 Ramsden Road, Rotherwas Industrial Estate, Hereford, HR2 6LR Tel: (01432) 357630 Fax: (01432) 357630 *Electroplaters*

Hereford Metal Recycling, Units 109-110 Holmer Trading Estate, College Road, Hereford, HR1 1JS Tel: (01432) 269154 *Scrap metal merchants*

Hereford Rewinds Ltd, Unit 12a Thorn Business Park, Rotherwas, Hereford, HR2 6JT Tel: (01432) 275002 Fax: (01432) 353484 E-mail: admin@herefordrewinds.co.uk *Motor rewinds & pump repairers*

Hereford Scale Co., 1 Vaga Street, Hereford, HR2 7AT Tel: (01432) 356472 Fax: (01432) 352646 *Weighting equipment distributors*

Hereford Security Services Ltd, Unit 5 50 Catherine Street, Hereford, HR1 2DU Tel: (01432) 264544 Fax: (01432) 264544 E-mail: mail@herefordsecurityservices.co.uk *Security systems installers*

Hereford Tool Hire, Sandark House, Netherwood Road, Rotherwas Industrial Estate, Hereford, HR2 6JU Tel: (01432) 353476 Fax: (01432) 352372 *Industrial fastener sales & industrial tool hire*

Hereford Utilities Ltd, Unit 1a, Techway, Wonastow Road Industrial Estate (West), Monmouth, Gwent, NP25 5JA Tel: (01600) 713330 Fax: (01600) 714440 E-mail: herefordutilities@hotmail.com *Agricultural manufacturing*

Herefordshire Environmental Services Ltd, Jondori, Moreton-on-Lugg, Hereford, HR4 8DE Tel: (01432) 769232 Fax: (01432) 769232 *Pest control services*

Herefordshire Fire Protection Services, Unit A2, Holmer Trading Estate, College Rd, Hereford, HR1 1JS Tel: (01432) 269094 Fax: (01432) 344095 *Fire protection services*

Hereward Engineering Services Ltd, 6 The Sq, Vicarage Farm Rd, Peterborough, PE1 5TS Tel: (01733) 311448 Fax: (01733) 343927 *Pump valve maintenance, repair & sales*

V.J. Herington, 11 South Park Rd, Harrogate, N. Yorkshire, HG1 5QU Tel: 01423 531721 Fax: 01423 531721 *Soft furnishings manufrs*

Heriot Video, 8-10 Shandon Place, Edinburgh, EH11 1QL Tel: 0131-337 7513 Fax: 0131-327 9886 *Professional video suppliers*

Heritage Boatbuilders, Kings Road, Evesham, Worcestershire, WR11 3BU Tel: (01386) 48882 Fax: (01386) 48882 E-mail: enquiries@heritageboatbuilders.co.uk *Marine vessels & boats*

▶ Heritage Building Co. Ltd, 1 Kinneil Road, Bo'ness, West Lothian, EH51 0AY Tel: (01506) 828202

Heritage Buttons, 8 Armadale Road, Chichester, West Sussex, PO19 7NR Tel: (01243) 775462 Fax: (01243) 531032 E-mail: info@buttonscompany.co.uk *Manufacturer of polyester buttons*

Heritage Cabinet Makers, 1 Mushroom Farm, Bottesford Lane, Orston, Nottingham, NG13 9NX Tel: (01949) 851505 *Bespoke manufacturers of kitchen, bathroom & bedroom furniture*

▶ Heritage Carpets, 47 Formans Road, Sparkhill, Birmingham, B11 3AR Tel: 0121-778 6444 Fax: 0121-778 6444 E-mail: sales@heritagecarpets.co.uk *Carpet retailers*

Heritage Chocolates, Unit 17, 1-21 Carew Street, London, SE5 9DF Tel: (020) 7733 7268 Fax: (020) 7274 0151 *Chocolate coin manufrs*

▶ Heritage Conservatories, 68 Tudor Road, Godmanchester, Huntingdon, Cambridgeshire, PE29 2DW Tel: (01480) 437774 Fax: (01480) 456184 *Design & building*

Heritage Construction, Unit 9 Hollywell Farm, Stoke Prior, Leominster, Herefordshire, HR6 0NF Tel: (01568) 760540 Fax: (01568) 760532

Heritage Dove Plastics, 3 Watnall Road, Hucknall, Nottingham, NG15 7LD Tel: (01623) 796847 Fax: (01623) 797555 E-mail: kdove@heritagedoveplastics.co.uk *Plastic garment hanger manufrs*

Heritage Furniture, Springbank Farm, Monument Farm Lane, Foxhall, Ipswich, IP10 0AQ Tel: (01473) 611522 Fax: (01473) 635803 *Cabinet makers*

▶ The Heritage Garden Specialist, 51 Glencoe Road, Ipswich, IP4 3PP Tel: (01473) 694451 E-mail: selina.marie@ntlworld.com *garden design, restoration, plant sales, historic houses*

Heritage Group, 62 Green Lane, Small Heath, Birmingham, B9 5DB Tel: 0121-773 0724 Fax: 0121-766 6073 E-mail: sales@heritage-silverware.com *The Heritage Group, based in Birmingham, are manufacturers of holloware, flatware, stemware and blueprint china to major hotels, restaurants and bars around the world. From tea stands to wine trolleys, they can innovate and manufacture products to suit your tastes whether they be traditional or contemporary.*

▶ Heritage Hardwood, Star Crossroads, Star, Gaerwen, Gwynedd, LL60 6AL Tel: (01248) 715280 Fax: (01248) 713383 E-mail: sales@heritage-hardwood.co.uk *Suppliers of pvc & wooden windows, doors & conservatories*

▶ Heritage Inlay Designs, 1a Hollingbury Road, Brighton, BN1 7JB Tel: (01273) 506080 Fax: (01273) 506080 E-mail: joe@heritageinlay.com *Established in 1984, Heritage Inlay supply highest quality hand sawn and laser cut marquetry, marquetry inlays, motifs, panels, table tops and more, to either stock designs or bespoke.Also provides a laser cutting and engraving service for other materials such as leather, fabric and perspex.*

Heritage Joinery London Ltd, Alphabess Works, Selinas Lane, Dagenham, Essex, RM8 1QH Tel: (020) 8517 5171 Fax: (020) 8517 5172 *Joinery*

▶ Heritage Law, Wellfield House, Springfield Road, Woolacombe, Devon, EX34 7BX Tel: (01271) 870506 E-mail: kevinderham@btopenworld.com *Professional Will Writing, Inheritance Tax Planning, Enduring Powers of Attorney, Property Severence, Bespoke Trusts, Lifetime Will Changes, Lifetime Document Storage, Probate Assistance*

Heritage Leathergoods Co. Ltd, 24-32 Princip Street, Birmingham, B4 6LE Tel: 0121-333 3339 Fax: 0121-359 3487 E-mail: inquiries@heritageleathergoods.co.uk *Leather goods manufrs*

Heritage Linen Hire Service Ltd, Market Place, Tetney, Grimsby, South Humberside, DN36 5NN Tel: (01472) 812161 Fax: (01472) 812161 E-mail: heritage.linen@hotmail.com *Catering equipment hire*

Heritage Packaging, 3 Whitebridge Industrial Estate, Whitebridge Lane, Stone, Staffordshire, ST15 8LQ Tel: (01785) 819189 Fax: (01785) 819089 E-mail: heripak@hotmail.com *Packaging materials supplier & rigid box manufrs*

▶ Heritage Refurbishment, Cherry Holt Road, Bourne, Lincolnshire, PE10 9LA Tel: (01778) 425543 Fax: (01778) 423998

Heritage Restoration Services Ltd, 18 Derby Road, Burton-on-Trent, Staffordshire, DE14 1RU Tel: (01283) 546266 Fax: (01283) 546266 E-mail: davekeytes@btopenworld.co.uk *Architectural cleaning service on listed buildings*

▶ Heritage Of Scotland.Com, 459-461 Lawnmarket, Edinburgh, EH1 2NT Tel: 0131-225 1140 Fax: 0131-225 8448 E-mail: info@heritageofscotland.com *Kilts*

▶ Heritage Window Co. Ltd, Unit 23 Bellingham Trading Estate, Franthorne Way, London, SE6 3BX Tel: (020) 8695 0055 Fax: (020) 8695 6500 E-mail: oliver.dolan@thwc.co.uk *Building renovation, housing windows & doors*

Herman Ltd, Herman Miller Estate, Bath Road, Chippenham, Wiltshire, SN14 0AT Tel: (01249) 657011 Fax: (01249) 654942 *Office furniture manufrs*

▶ Hermann & Associates, 18 St Werburghs Road, Manchester, M21 0TN Tel: 0161-881 3034 Fax: 0161-862 9585 E-mail: sales@nhatranslations.com *We are a UK-based business providing professional language services for commerce and industry. Our clients - many of whom come to us by recommendations - include global players, international organisations, SMEs and private individuals. Norbert Hermann is a long-standing Member of the Institute of Translation and Interpreting (ITI) and a Founder Member of the Northwest Translators' Network (NWTN). He is also a qualified engineer and has previously worked in industry, bringing together the linguistic adeptness and technical understanding of the services we offer. As most of your work is of a highly technical nature we engage the services of experienced and qualified suppliers, engineers and other professionals, who have the necessary know-how to carry out your assignments to the required standards. We can support all European and major non-European languages.*

▶ Hermes Abrasives Ltd, Wyncolls Road, Severalls Industrial Park, Colchester, CO4 9LW Tel: (01206) 754400 Fax: (01206) 754401 E-mail: jason.banner@btinternet.com *Manufacturers of all bonded and coated abrasives, next day delivery on ext stock items and 1 week on manufactured products.*

Hermes Abrasives Ltd, Wyncolls Road, Severalls Industrial Park, Colchester, CO4 9LW Tel: (01206) 754400 Fax: (01206) 754401 E-mail: huk@hermes-abrasives.com *Abrasive coated products*

Hermes Datacommunications International Ltd, Hermes House, Oxon Business Park, Bicton Heath, Shrewsbury, SY3 5DD Tel: (01743) 235555 Fax: (01743) 271717 E-mail: info@hermes.com *Communication systems distributors*

Hermes Medical, Kilburn Park Road, London, NW6 5XD Tel: (020) 7625 8014 Fax: (020) 7487 2986 E-mail: marketing@hermesmed.co.uk *Exporters of medical supplies & pharmaceutical*

Hermitage S M Ltd, 25 Knowl Piece, Wilbury Way, Hitchin, Hertfordshire, SG4 0TY Tel: (01462) 422421 Fax: (01462) 422026 E-mail: sales@hermitagesm.co.uk *Sheet metalwork engineers & fabricators*

Herne Hill Timber Co, 301 Railton Road, London, SE24 0JN Tel: (020) 7274 2548 *DIY suppliers*

Hero Electronics Ltd, 10 Doolittle Mill Business Park, Froghall Road, Ampthill, Bedford, MK45 2ND Tel: (01525) 405015 Fax: (01525) 402383 E-mail: kelly@heroelec.co.uk *Hero Electronics is a specialist distributor of Optoelectronic Components and ICs. The company has four operating divisions dedicated to providing both commercial and technical support to the UK Electronics Manufacturing sector. From a wide range of leading-edge and established components, Hero is able to propose the optimum choice for the user.*

Hero UK LLP, Bishop Dyke Road, Sherburn In Elmet, Leeds, LS25 6JA Tel: (01977) 684937 Fax: (01977) 683654 E-mail: info@supercook.co.uk *Bakers ingredients & cake decorations suppliers*

Heron Broadwick Ltd, Heron House, 19 Marylebone Road, London, NW1 5JL Tel: (020) 7486 4477 Fax: (020) 7486 3349 *Property developers*

Heron Conversions, 45 Herons Way, Pembury, Tunbridge Wells, Kent, TN2 4DW Tel: (01892) 823891 Fax: (01892) 825287 E-mail: bdwhero@aol.com *Design consultants*

Heron Fabrications, Unit 4, Berry court farm, Little london, Basingstoke, Hampshire, RG26 5AT Tel: 01256 850963 Fax: 01256 850963 E-mail: info@heronfabrications.co.uk *Engineering*

Heron Frozen Foods Ltd, Station Road, Worstead, North Walsham, Norfolk, NR28 9RY Tel: (01692) 403211 Fax: (01692) 405911 *Frozen food processors*

Heron Labels Ltd, Unit 24 Pier Road Industrial Estate, Pier Road, Gillingham, Kent, ME7 1RZ Tel: (01634) 581979 Fax: (01634) 582120 E-mail: heron@heron-labels.co.uk *Self adhesive labels*

Heron Marketing Services Ltd, First Floor, 61-65 High Street, Standish, Wigan, Lancashire, WN6 0HD Tel: (01257) 472148 Fax: (01257) 472148 E-mail: info@heronmarketing.co.uk *Professional marketing services*

Company Information

Heron Press, 19-24 White Hays North, Quartermaster Road, West Wilts Trading Estate, Westbury, Wiltshire, BA13 4JT Tel: (01373) 825602 Fax: (01373) 825603
E-mail: sales@heron-press.co.uk *General & printers design services*

Heronridge Services (Nottingham) Ltd, Units 2, Palm Court, Palm Street, New Basford, Nottingham, NG7 7HU Tel: 0115-979 0644 Fax: 0115-979 0438
E-mail: sales@heronridge.co.uk *Ventilation & air conditioning installations services*

Heronsgate Ltd, Unit 18-20 Herons Gate Trading Estate, Paycocke Road, Basildon, Essex, SS14 3EU Tel: (01268) 288637 Fax: (01268) 272585 E-mail: sales@heronsgateprint.com *High quality colour printers & digital printing*

▶ Heronsgate Printers, 1 Bay Tree Avenue, Kingston Road, Leatherhead, Surrey, KT22 7UE Tel: (01372) 376635 Fax: (01372) 386521

▶ HeronSoft Ltd, 29 Chatteris Park, Sandymoor, Runcorn, Cheshire, WA7 1XE Tel: (01928) 571620 Fax: (01928) 571620
E-mail: heronsoft@aol.com *INDUSTRIAL AUTOMATION SOFTWARE SPECILIST using SIEMENS PCS7, S5, S7, SCADA WinCC, Wizcon, Bespoke packages - Large and small projects. Many satisfied customers in manufacturing. Company established 20 yrs.*

Herrington Industrial Services Ltd, Crown Works, Crown Road, Sunderland, SR5 2BS
Tel: 0191-516 0634 Fax: 0191-548 1553 *Shot blasting contractor services*

Herschel Systems, PO Box 598, Beaconsfield, Buckinghamshire, HP9 1HB Tel: (01494) 675104 Fax: (01494) 677831
E-mail: sales@herschel.co.uk *Computer software consultants*

Hertel Services, Sotherby Road, Skippers Lane Idustrial Estate, Middlesbrough, Cleveland, TS6 6LP Tel: (01642) 469532 Fax: (01642) 445614 E-mail: info@hertel.co.uk *Industrial contracting, access & thermal insulating*

▶ Hertel Services, Sellafield, Seascale, Cumbria, CA20 1PG Tel: (01946) 727417 Fax: (01946) 729126

Hertel Services UK Ltd, Bromfield Road, Ludlow, Shropshire, SY8 1DN Tel: (01584) 875658 Fax: (01584) 879921 *Scaffolding contractors*

▶ Hertford Joinery Ltd, Great Northern Works, Hartham Lane, Hertford, SG14 1QN Tel: (01992) 550587 Fax: (01992) 558992

Hertford Sign Services, Unit 4 Dicker Mill, Hertford, SG13 7AA Tel: 01920 877655 Fax: 01920 877654 *Sign advertising*

Hertfordshire (Diamond) Products Ltd, Unit F, Gunnels Wood Park, Gunnels Wood Road, Stevenage, Hertfordshire, SG1 2BH Tel: (01438) 748758 Fax: (01438) 362060 *Diamond tools manufrs*

▶ Hertfordshire Diamonds Products, Unit 3 Heathfield Caravan Park, Hurn, Christchurch, Dorset, BH23 6AS Tel: (01202) 481282 Fax: (01202) 481282 *Industrial diamond product manufrs*

▶ Hertfordshire Fireplace Gallery, 9 Barnet Road, Potters Bar, Hertfordshire, EN6 2QX Tel: (01707) 657070 Fax: (01707) 657064
E-mail: sales@hertsfireplacegallery.co.uk *Supply fireplaces, fires & stoves in marble & cast iron*

▶ Hertfordshire Graphics Ltd, 6 St Andrew Street, Hertford, SG14 1JE Tel: (01992) 503636 Fax: (01992) 503244
E-mail: sales@hertfordshiregraphics.co.uk *Art Shop and Gallery; suppliers of graphic art materials to commercial design studios and advertising agencies.*

Hertfordshire Storage Systems Ltd, 6 Winton Road, Ware, Hertfordshire, SG12 7AX Tel: (01920) 467027 Fax: (01920) 462563
E-mail: info@hertfordshirestorage.co.uk *Shelving & racking suppliers*

Herting & Son plc, Frederick House, 25 Armstrong Way, Southall, Middlesex, UB2 4SD Tel: (020) 8606 7000 Fax: (020) 8606 7010
E-mail: sales@fpherting.co.uk *Suppliers to the building trade*

▶ Hert's Cooling Ltd, Bridgeman House, Pindar Road, Hoddesdon, Hertfordshire, EN11 0DA Tel: (01992) 470740 Fax: (01992) 470220

▶ Herts Demolition Contractors, 14 Waltham Gardens, Enfield, Middlesex, EN3 6PG Tel: (01992) 763669 Fax: (01992) 763669

▶ Herts & Essex Business Supplies, Unit 1 Lea Road, Waltham Abbey, Essex, EN9 1AE Tel: (01920) 413685 Fax: (01992) 651651
E-mail: sales@heb-supplies.co.uk *Stationery & office products suppliers*

Herts & Essex Precision Engineers, Unit 10 Zone B Chelmsford Road Industrial Estate, Chelmsford Road, Dunmow, Essex, CM6 1HD Tel: (01371) 875459 Fax: (01371) 872270
E-mail: hertsessex@aol.com *Precision engineers & cnc machines*

▶ Herts & Essex Printers Ltd, Unit 14 Mead Business Centre, Mead Lane, Hertford, SG13 7BQ Tel: (01992) 554768

The Herts Meter Co. Ltd, Unit 10 Bury Road, Hatfield, Hertfordshire, AL10 8BJ Tel: (01707) 270404 Fax: (01707) 270152
E-mail: info@hertsmeter.com *Alarm systems*

Herts Precision Engineering, Unit 1, Riverside Estate, Coldharbour Lane, Harpenden, Hertfordshire, AL5 4UN Tel: (01582) 462728 Fax: (01582) 462805 *Precision engineers*

Hertsmere Group Services, 2 Chartmoor Road, Leighton Buzzard, Bedfordshire, LU7 4WG Tel: (01525) 219227 Fax: (01525) 219220
E-mail: sales@hgs-uk.com *Office equipment suppliers*

K. Hertwall Ltd, Flemington Road, Glenrothes, Fife, KY7 5QJ Tel: (01592) 753745 Fax: (01592) 753747 Principal Export Areas: Worldwide *Industrial truck & trolley manufrs*

▶ Hertz Car Sales, Unit 2 Aire Place Mills, Kirkstall Road, Chipping Warden, Banbury, Oxfordshire, OX17 1LL Tel: (01295) 667000 Fax: (01295) 667017 *Car sales*

▶ Hertz Rent A Car Ltd, 34-62 Staines Road, Hounslow, TW3 3LZ Tel: (020) 8570 5000 Fax: (020) 8750 3978 *The UK division of the Hertz Corporation (the largest vehicle rental company in the World), Hertz provides car and*

continued

van rental for business or leisure use. Ex-fleet are sold through Hertz Car Sales.

Herve Engineering Ltd, 9 Towerfield Road, Shoeburyness, Southend-on-Sea, SS3 9QE Tel: (01702) 293617 Fax: (01702) 297410
E-mail: sales@herveengineering.co.uk *Turned parts manufrs*

J. & N. Herz Ltd, Broadstone House, Broadstone Road, Reddish, Stockport, Cheshire, SK5 7DL Tel: 0161-443 3030 Fax: 0161-443 0345
E-mail: jherz@herz.co.uk *If you are looking to purchase famous UK ex-chain store ladies, mens and childrens wear, this is the Company for you! J & N Herz Ltd is probably the largest and most successful importing wholesaler, specialising in the sale of well known ex-high street chainstore garments, famous brands and sportswear. Established for over 25 years, supplying all sectors of the trade with over 500 lines. Exemplary service is backed up by personal service from a team of dedicated, friendly sales assistants.. Visit the new "state of the art" on line clothing store to view and purchase some of the best lines, with new styles being made available daily by the Internet staff. Free delivery over £500 and a next day delivery service. Starter pack available.*

Herz Valves (UK) Ltd, Progress House, Moorfield Point, Moorfield Road, Guildford, Surrey, GU1 1RU Tel: 01483 502211 Fax: 01483 502025 E-mail: sales@herzvalves.com *Control valve manufacturers and distributors.*

Herzbi Ltd, Grosvenor Works, Mount Pleasant Hill, London, E5 9NE Tel: (020) 8806 3232 Fax: (020) 8806 3236 *Abrasive products importers.*

Hes Ltd, 43a Old Barn Road, Bournville, Birmingham, B30 1PX Tel: 0121-459 9646 Fax: 0121-628 1997

Hes Engineering Services Ltd, Bingswood Trading Estate, Whaley Bridge, High Peak, Derbyshire, SK23 7LY Tel: (01663) 735333 Fax: (01663) 735377 *Pipework fabricators*

Hesco Bastion Ltd, Unit 41 Knowsthorpe Way, Leeds, LS9 0SW Tel: 0113-248 6633 Fax: 0113-248 3501
E-mail: info@hescobastion.com Principal Export Areas: Worldwide *Corrosion control & prevention, protective coating & services*

Heselwood Audio Visual, 361 Sutton Road, Maidstone, Kent, ME15 9BU Tel: (01622) 751578 Fax: (01622) 755706 *Audio-visual equipment hire & sales services*

Walter Heselwood Ltd, Stevenson Road, Sheffield, S9 2SG Tel: 0114-244 2042 Fax: 0114-243 2806
E-mail: aiden@heselwood.com *Scrap metal merchants*

Hesflo Installations Ltd, 6 Dial Lane, Bristol, BS16 5UH Tel: 0117-970 1930 Fax: 0117-970 1931 E-mail: design@hesflo.co.uk *Air conditioning services*

Hesketh Gallery & Potters Supplies, 4 Lansdown Place, Lewes, East Sussex, BN7 2JT Tel: (01273) 487150
E-mail: enquiries@heskethps.co.uk *Potters suppliers*

James Hesketh & Co. Ltd, New Works, Sion Street, Radcliffe, Manchester, M26 3SB Tel: 0161-723 2789 Fax: 0161-725 9072 *Chain sprocket manufrs*

John Hesketh & Son Ltd, Castlecroft Ironworks, Bury Grounds, Bury, Lancashire, BL9 0HU Tel: 0161-764 1109 Fax: 0161-763 1285 *Forge masters*

Hesketh Refrigeration, 190 Preston Road, Standish, Wigan, Lancashire, WN6 0NP Tel: (01257) 423571 Fax: (01257) 423571 *Refrigeration manufrs*

Heskin Fabrications Ltd, Whalley Works, Whalley Road, Heskin, Chorley, Lancashire, PR7 5NY Tel: (01257) 451483 Fax: (01257) 453242
E-mail: heskinfabs@btconnect.co.uk *Steel fabricators & steel formwork manufrs*

Heskins Tapes, Churchill Road, Brinscall, Chorley, Lancashire, PR6 8RQ Tel: (01254) 832266 Fax: (01254) 832476 E-mail: mail@heskins.com *Adhesive (non slip) tape manufrs*

Hesley Trading London Ltd, 37 Emperors Gate, London, SW7 4HJ Tel: (020) 7370 5933 Fax: (020) 7244 8214
E-mail: kenhes@tiscali.co.uk *Export agents*

▶ The Hessian Co., 5 Weston Avenue, Leighton Buzzard, Bedfordshire, LU7 4QY Tel: (01525) 853950 Fax: (01525) 372877
E-mail: andrew.strang@thehessiancompany.co.uk *Blind retailers*

Hessian Co., 27 Palace Avenue, Paignton, Devon, TQ3 3EQ Tel: (01803) 556782 Fax: (01803) 664656 *Curtain & blind manufrs*

▶ Hestia Fireside Design, Unit 6, Newhailes Industrial Estate, Newhailes Road, Musselburgh, Midlothian, EH21 6SY Tel: 0131-653 1900

Heswall Army & Navy Stores, 7 The Mount, Heswall, Wirral, Merseyside, CH60 4RE Tel: 0151-342 4538 Fax: 0151-342 8626 *Retailers*

Heta UK, The Stove Shop, The Street, Hatfield Peverel, Chelmsford, CM3 2DY Tel: (01245) 381247 Fax: (01245) 381606 *Sellers of wood burners*

Hetheringtons Shoe Services Ltd, 80 Front Street West, Bedlington, Northumberland, NE22 5UA Tel: (01670) 821505 Fax: (01670) 821505 *Shoe repairers*

Heuft, Unit 24 26 Innage Park, Abeles Way, Holly Lane Industrial Estate, Atherstone, Warwickshire, CV9 2QX Tel: (01827) 717002 Fax: (01827) 716146 E-mail: dominic.metcalfe@heuft.com *Container inspection equipment manufrs*

Heuston Technologies, 39 Princetown Road, Bangor, County Down, BT20 3TA Tel: (028) 9147 8054 Fax: (028) 9147 8054
E-mail: richardheuston@utvinternet.co.uk *CCTV & satellite communications installation*

Hevantac Control Services Ltd, Unit 3 125 Park Road, Beckenham, Kent, BR3 1QJ Tel: (020) 8658 7218 Fax: (020) 8650 1243
E-mail: barry@aimteq.co.uk *Environmental control systems*

Heventech Mechanical Service Ltd, 3 Redbridge Enterprise Centre, Thompson Close, Ilford, Essex, IG1 1TY Tel: (0845) 1298565
E-mail: sales@heventech.co.uk *Heating, ventilation & airconditioning engineers*

Hevertech, Unit 2 Treefield Industrial Estate, Gelderd Road, Morley, Leeds, LS27 7JU Tel: 0113-238 3355 Fax: 0113-253 5443
E-mail: enquiries@hevertech.co.uk *Heating, ventilation & air conditioning suppliers*

Heward & Dean Ltd, Spurling Works, Pindar Road, Hoddesdon, Hertfordshire, EN11 0DB Tel: (01992) 467557 Fax: (01992) 467477
E-mail: sales@hewardanddean.com *Engineers' merchants & tool dealers* Also at: Ware

▶ Heward Microjets Ltd, 8 Beagle Court, Cottenham, Cambridge, CB24 8RS Tel: (01526) 322266 E-mail: pheward@yahoo.com *We design and produce small turbojet and turbofan engines of 20 - 400lb thrust for unmanned (UAV) model aircraft and experimental aviation craft*

Hewart Electronics Ltd, 2 Blakelow Bank, Macclesfield, Cheshire, SK11 7GD Tel: (01625) 422030 Fax: (01625) 422030 *Microprocessor control systems*

Hewaswater Ltd, Hewas Water Ltd, Hewas Water, St. Austell, Cornwall, PL26 7JF Tel: (01726) 885200 Fax: (01726) 885212
E-mail: info@heltd.demon.co.uk *General engineers*

Hewats Of Edinburgh, 11-12 Teviot Place, Edinburgh, EH1 2RA Tel: 0131-225 5705 Fax: 0131-226 6885 E-mail: sales@hewats.com *Workwear distributors*

Hewden, Trafford House, Chester Road, Stretford, Manchester, M32 0RL Tel: 0161-848 8621 Fax: 0161-848 2298
E-mail: brian.sherlock@hewden.co.uk *Contractors of plant hire* Also at: Branches throughout the U.K.

▶ Hewden Crane Hire Ltd, Billingham Reach Industrial Estate, Haverton Hill Road, Billingham, Cleveland, TS23 1PX Tel: (01642) 853737 Fax: (01642) 853738

Hewden Crane Hire Ltd, St Andrews Road, Holesmouth, Avonmouth, Bristol, BS11 9BN Tel: 0117-938 4777 Fax: 0117-938 4555 *Crane hire*

Hewden Crane Hire Ltd, Willowbridge Lane, Castleford, West Yorkshire, WF10 5NJ Tel: (01977) 664300 Fax: (01977) 664306 *Access platform hire & leasing*

Hewden Crane Hire Ltd, Hawley Road, Dartford, DA1 1PD Tel: (01322) 351155 Fax: (01322) 351144 *Crane hire*

Hewden Crane Hire Ltd, Hawley Road, Dartford, DA1 1PD Tel: (01322) 351155 Fax: (01322) 351144 *Contractors' plant hire*

▶ Hewden Crane Hire Ltd, 8 Kings Road, Immingham, South Humberside, DN40 1AL Tel: (01469) 575158 Fax: (01469) 578303

Hewden Crane Hire, Brigg Road, Scunthorpe, North Lincolnshire, DN16 1XA Tel: (01724) 277741 Fax: (01724) 843222 *Crane hire*

Hewden Hire Centres, Unit 2, 4-14 Commerce Street, Aberdeen, AB11 5EB Tel: (01224) 595102 Fax: (01224) 584611 *Plant hire* Also at: Branches throughout the U.K.

▶ Hewden Hire Centres Ltd, Brunswick Road, Ashford, Kent, TN23 1EL Tel: (01233) 634885 Fax: (01233) 665636

▶ Hewden Hire Centres, Unit 5 Brett Drive, Bexhill-on-Sea, East Sussex, TN40 2JP Tel: (01424) 210601 Fax: (01424) 427722

Hewden Hire Centres Ltd, 39-40 New Summer Street, Birmingham, B19 3QN Tel: 0121-359 4282 Fax: 0121-333 6866 *Tool hire merchants*

▶ Hewden Hire Centres Ltd, 107 Slateford Road, Edinburgh, EH11 1QY Tel: 0131-337 9494 Fax: 0131-337 9595

▶ Hewden Hire Centres Ltd, 88-92 Kilbirnie Street, Glasgow, G5 8JD Tel: 0141-429 7431 Fax: 0141-429 5139

Hewden Hire Centres Ltd, 1640 London Road, Glasgow, G31 4QG Tel: 0141-550 0300 Fax: 0141-556 2239 *Power tool distributors* Also at: Arbroath, Dumfries, Dundee, Edinburgh, Kilmarnoch & Paisley

▶ Hewden Hire Centres Ltd, Coal Wynd, Kirkcaldy, Fife, KY1 2RA Tel: (01592) 265656 Fax: (01592) 646061

Hewden Hire Centres Ltd, 110 Commercial Road, Leeds, LS5 3AB Tel: 0113-230 4200 Fax: 0113-275 8830 *Tool hire services*

Hewden Hire Centres Ltd, Pinfold Road, Thurmaston, Leicester, LE4 8AZ Tel: 0116-269 4881 Fax: 0116-264 0039 *Contractors' plant hire & leasing* Also at: Branches throughout the U.K.

Hewden Hire Centres Ltd, 2 Brandon Road, York Way, London, N7 9AA Tel: (020) 7607 8344 Fax: (020) 7607 9632 *Plant hire leasing contractors*

▶ Hewden Hire Centres, 1 Ringway Trading Estate, Shadow Moss Road, Manchester, M22 6LX Tel: 0161-499 9413 Fax: 0161-437 0114

▶ Hewden Hire Centres Ltd, Penn Street, Newcastle upon Tyne, NE4 7BG Tel: 0191-273 4491 Fax: 0191-226 1393

▶ Hewden Hire Centres Ltd, 471 Attercliffe Road, Sheffield, S9 3RA Tel: 0114-244 1887 Fax: 0114-261 8298

Hewden Hire Centres Ltd, Main Road, Long Hanborough, Witney, Oxfordshire, OX29 8SY Tel: (01993) 883939 Fax: (01993) 882877 *Contract plant hire*

Hewden Hire Plant Ltd, Howard Road, Park Farm, Redditch, Worcestershire, B98 7SE Tel: (01527) 524020 Fax: (01527) 527320 *Plant hire* Also at: Bedford, Corsham, Huntingdon, Leicester, Redruth & Swindon

Hewden Instant Access Ltd, Hawley Road, Dartford, DA1 1PD Tel: (01322) 425800 Fax: (01322) 350920 *Building contractors plant hire*

Hewden Instant Access Ltd, Unit C1 Fort Wallington Industrial Estate, Military Road, Fareham, Hampshire, PO16 8TT Tel: (01329) 231123 Fax: (01329) 827533 *Aerial platforms rental*

▶ Hewden Instant Access Ltd, 20 Carmaben Road, Glasgow, G33 4UN Tel: 0141-781 0555 Fax: 0141-781 0318

▶ Hewden Instant Access Ltd, 20 Carmaben Road, Glasgow, G33 4UN Tel: 0141-781 0555 Fax: 0141-781 0318

Hewden Instant Access Ltd, Staceys Yard, Station Road, Langley, Slough, SL3 6DB Tel: (01753) 548849 Fax: (01753) 540655 *Plant hire & access*

▶ Hewden Instant Access Ltd, Ashmore Lake Way, Willenhall, West Midlands, WV12 4LF Tel: (01902) 608666 Fax: (01902) 603322

Hewden Plant Hire Ltd, Bryn Works, Llandygai, Bangor, Gwynedd, LL57 4LE Tel: (01248) 364944 Fax: (01248) 370462 *Earth moving & plant hire contractors*

Hewden Plant Hire Ltd, Cambridge Road, Bedford, MK42 0LH Tel: (01234) 340801 Fax: (01234) 343423 *Plant & crane hire*

▶ Hewden Plant Hire Ltd, 251 Bordesley Green Road, Birmingham, B8 1BY Tel: 0121-772 5900 Fax: 0121-772 4821

▶ Hewden Plant Hire Ltd, Sloper Road, Cardiff, CF11 8AB Tel: (029) 2023 3491 Fax: (029) 2038 3134

Hewden Plant Hire Ltd, Shieldgate House, Shadon Way, Birtley, Chester le Street, County Durham, DH3 2SW Tel: 0191-492 9900 Fax: 0191-492 3086 *Contractors* Also at: Aberdeen, Castleford, Dundee, Edinburgh, Newarthill & Stockton-on-Tees

▶ Hewden Plant Hire Ltd, Pound Mead, Corsham, Wiltshire, SN13 9NZ Tel: (01249) 712362 Fax: (01249) 701080

Hewden Plant Hire Ltd, Quarry Lane, Dewsbury, West Yorkshire, WF12 7JQ Tel: 0113-253 1121 Fax: 0113-252 7756 *Sales & hire of accommodation & hoists*

▶ Hewden Plant Hire Ltd, 40 Old Glamis Road, Dundee, DD3 8JQ Tel: (01382) 889922 Fax: (01382) 884222

▶ Hewden Plant Hire Ltd, Unit 13 Parham Drive, Eastleigh, Hampshire, SO50 4NU Tel: (023) 8061 8733 Fax: (023) 8061 1758

▶ Hewden Plant Hire Ltd, New Elgin Road, Elgin, Morayshire, IV30 6BE Tel: (01343) 550400 Fax: (01343) 549965

▶ Hewden Plant Hire Ltd, 20 Carmaben Road, Glasgow, G33 4UN Tel: 0141-771 1777 Fax: 0141-771 2777

Hewden Plant Hire, 119 Hamilton Road, Mount Vernon, Glasgow, G32 9QW Tel: (0141) 762 4076 Fax: (0141) 764 0578 *Plant hire* Also at: Edinburgh & Leeds

▶ Hewden Plant Hire Ltd, Cattle Market, St. Oswalds Road, Gloucester, GL1 2SR Tel: (01452) 500959 Fax: (01452) 307988

Hewden Plant Hire Ltd, Wallwork Road, Astley, Tyldesley, Manchester, M29 7JX Tel: (01772) 459460 Fax: (01772) 459295 *Portable building hire, leasing & rental*

Hewden Plant Hire Ltd, Ellis Road, Mitcham, Surrey, CR4 4HX Tel: (020) 8648 7070 Fax: (020) 8687 0482 *Plant maintenance & repair* Also at: Birmingham & Portsmouth

▶ Hewden Plant Hire Ltd, 158 Park Street, Motherwell, Lanarkshire, ML1 1PF Tel: (01698) 252424 Fax: (01698) 275188

Hewden Plant Hire Ltd, Tank Farm Road, Llandarcy, Neath, West Glamorgan, SA10 6EN Tel: (01792) 321111 Fax: (01792) 321346 *Plant hire* Also at: Ashford, Cardiff, Eastleigh, Lewes, London SE8, Newbury & Peterborough

Hewden Plant Hire Ltd, Vicarage Farm Road, Peterborough, PE1 5TN Tel: (01733) 564378 Fax: (01733) 566480 *Plant hire contractors*

Hewden Plant Hire Ltd, 21-23 Willis Way, Poole, Dorset, BH15 3SR Tel: (01202) 674371 Fax: (01202) 665560 *Contractors, plant hire & leasing services*

▶ Hewden Plant Hire Ltd, Mount Carbis Road, Redruth, Cornwall, TR15 2QQ Tel: (01209) 218730 Fax: (01209) 315262

▶ Hewden Plant Hire Ltd, Kinmel Park, Abergele Road, Bodelwyddan, Rhyl, Clwyd, LL18 5TY Tel: (01745) 583121 Fax: (01745) 582528

▶ Hewden Plant Hire Ltd, 99 Station Road, Thatcham, Berkshire, RG19 4QH Tel: (01635) 864418 Fax: (01635) 866897

▶ Hewden Plant Hire Ltd, Meadow Road, Whitehaven, Cumbria, CA28 9HY Tel: (01946) 694311 Fax: (01946) 691431

▶ Hewden Plant Hire Ltd, Vauxhall Industrial Estate, Ruabon, Wrexham, Clwyd, LL14 6HA Tel: (01978) 821717

▶ Hewden Self-Drive, 119 Hamilton Road, Glasgow, G32 9QW Tel: 0141-764 0590

▶ Hewden Stewart Plc, 1 Ellis Muir Way, Tannochside Park, Uddingston, Glasgow, G71 5PX Tel: (01698) 805500

▶ Hewden Stuart Plc, 2300 London Road, Glasgow, G32 8YU Tel: 0141-778 8571

Hewden Tool Hire, Unit 1 Kingstanding Business Park, Tunbridge Wells, Kent, TN2 3UP Tel: (01892) 616318 Fax: (01892) 616353
E-mail: steve.davies@hewden.co.uk *Plant hire & tool contractors* Also at: Ashford, Bexhill & Hailsham

Hewdon Portable Buildings, Norman Road, Belvedere, Kent, DA17 6JY Tel: (020) 8311 9796 Fax: (020) 8310 7265 *Port cabin hire & distributors*

▶ Hewer Text Ltd, 109 Ferry Road, Edinburgh, EH6 4ET Tel: 0131-445 4440

Hewes Products, Wren Park, Cinques Road, Gamlingay, Sandy, Bedfordshire, SG19 3NJ Tel: (01767) 651333 Fax: (01767) 651311
E-mail: info@hewes.co.uk *Photographic processing equipment*

Hewitson North East, Unit 24E North Tyne Industrial Estate, Whitley Road, Longbenton, Newcastle Upon Tyne, NE12 9SZ Tel: 0191-266 6194 Fax: 0191-266 6194 *Roofing*

Hewitt & Booth Ltd, St Andrews Road, Huddersfield, HD1 6RZ Tel: (01484) 546621 Fax: (01484) 450580
E-mail: sales@hewittandbooth.com *Pipe cleaners & chenille manufrs*

Hewitt Ladders Ltd, 37 Melrose Street, Leicester, LE4 6FD Tel: 0116-266 3304 Fax: 0116-261 3033 E-mail: hewittladdersltd@btconnect.com *Hewitt Ladders are a family run business, based in central Leicester and established in 1938, celebrating 70 years worth of experience in the field, supplying Council, Building Trade, Local Businesses, and the Public with high quality products. We offer friendly advice and provide a maintenance service to all ladders purchased from us. Just some of our ranges consists of Aluminium Ladders, Aluminium Steps, Combination Ladders, Multi Ladders, Podium Steps, Window Cleaners, Roof & Surveyors, Orange Steel, Pole Ladders, Loft Ladders,*

continued

continuation
Trestles & Stagings, Telescopic Ladder, Fibreglass Steps, Warehouse Steps, Timber Steps, Kitchen Steps, Staircases, Towers, Staging Systems, Hop-Ups, and Ladder Accessories.

Hewitt & Maughan Ltd, 11 Albion Close, Worksop, Nottinghamshire, S80 1RA Tel: (01909) 473581 Fax: (01909) 477960 E-mail: office@hewittandmaughan.sagehost.co.uk *General building contractors & joinery manufrs*

▶ Hewitts Fine Foods Ltd, 38 Manor Industrial Estate, Flint, Clwyd, CH6 5UY Tel: (01352) 730488 Fax: (01352) 730489 *Manufacturers & distributors of pies*

▶ Hewlett Civil Engineering Ltd, Prestige Court, Beza Road, Leeds, LS10 2BD Tel: 0113-277 6677 Fax: 0113-270 9537 *Civil engineers*

Hewlett Packard, 29 Valepits Road, Garretts Green, Birmingham, B33 0TD Tel: 0121-784 7445 Fax: 0121-783 4015 E-mail: enquiries@synstar.com *Disaster recovery services*

Hewlett Packard Ltd, Erskine Ferry Road, Bishopton, Renfrewshire, PA7 5PP Tel: 0141-814 8000 Fax: 0141-812 7745 *Computer manufrs*

Hewlett Packard Ltd, Cain Road, Bracknell, Berkshire, RG12 1HN Tel: (01344) 360000 Fax: (01344) 363344 E-mail: info@jobshp.com *Computer software manufrs*

Hewlett Packard Ltd, 3 Dunlop Square, Deans, Livingston, West Lothian, EH54 8SB Tel: (01506) 419111 Fax: (01506) 460135 *Computer network services & maintenance*

Hewlett Packard Office Centre, 57 Holborn Viaduct, London, EC1A 2FD Tel: (020) 7651 6651 Fax: (020) 7236 4385 E-mail: service@ebm.co.uk *Computer consultants*

Hewmor Products Ltd, Unit D4 Hilton Trading Estate, Hilton Road, Lanesfield, Wolverhampton, WV4 6DW Tel: (01902) 491144 Fax: (01902) 401952 E-mail: hewmor.products@btconnect.com *CNC engineering services or machinists*

Hewpack Industries Ltd, 35 Stapledon Road, Orton Southgate, Peterborough, PE2 6TD Tel: (01733) 239639 Fax: (01733) 370967 *Product printing & packaging*

Hewson Smith & Sons, Old Main Road, Scamblesby, Louth, Lincolnshire, LN11 9XG Tel: (01507) 343249 Fax: (01507) 343779 *Crane Hire*

Hewson & Turrell Ltd, Robinson Lane, Grimsby, South Humberside, DN31 3SF Tel: (01472) 351475 Fax: (01472) 242611 E-mail: sales@hewsonandturrell.co.uk *Marine, general & motor engineering services*

▶ Hewston Engineering (Midlands) Ltd, Unit 7 Modulrate Court, Enterprise Drive, Four Ashes, Wolverhampton, WV10 7DF Tel: (01902) 791492

▶ Hew-Vac Ltd, 2a Inchmuir Road, Whitehill Industrial Estate, Bathgate, West Lothian, EH48 2EP Tel: (01506) 654512 Fax: (01506) 654512 E-mail: sales@hewvac.co.uk *Vacuum pumps & leak detection*

Hex A Tec Systems Ltd, The Courtyard, Ochrelands, Fellside, Hexham, Northumberland, NE46 1SB Tel: (01434) 605575 Fax: (01434) 607800 E-mail: sales@hexatec.com *SCADA software for supervisory control*

Hex Solutions Ltd, 6 Queen Street, Burntwood, Staffordshire, WS7 4QH Tel: (01543) 677792

▶ Hexagon International Transport Ltd, Cheetwood Road, Manchester, M8 8AQ Tel: 0161-792 1912

Hexagon Metrology, Halesfield 13, Telford, Shropshire, TF7 4PL Tel: (01952) 681300 Fax: (01952) 681311 E-mail: enquiry@hexmet.co.uk *Manufacturers of co-ordinate measuring machines, portable measuring devices and large scale measurement with laser trackers*

Hexagon Safety Products Sales Ltd, Unit 4A Elstree Film Studios, Shenley Road, Borehamwood, Hertfordshire, WD6 1JG Tel: (020) 8207 0003 Fax: (020) 8905 1036 E-mail: borehamwood.hiredesk@hireorbuy.co.uk *Protective clothing & equipment*

Hexagon Software Ltd, Unit 8 Highnam Business Centre, Highnam, Gloucester, GL2 8DN Tel: (01608) 811801 Fax: (01608) 811852 E-mail: sales@hexagon.co.uk *Computer software suppliers*

▶ Hexaware Technology UK Ltd, Cornwall House, High Street, Slough, SL1 1BZ Tel: (01753) 217160 Fax: (01753) 217161 E-mail: sales@euhexaware.com *IT consultants*

Hexel Developments Ltd, Wash Lane, Warrington, WA4 1HS Tel: (01925) 444439 Fax: (01925) 655899 E-mail: admin@hexel.net *Pc building services*

Hexham Sealants & Coatings, Station Yard, Station Road, Corbridge, Northumberland, NE45 5AZ Tel: (01434) 633344 Fax: (01434) 633346 E-mail: sales@hexhamsealant.co.uk *Waterproofing suppliers & manufrs*

▶ Hexis (UK) Ltd, 70 Britannia Way, Britannia Enterprise Park, Lichfield, Staffordshire, WS14 9UY Tel: (01543) 411221

▶ HeyAnita Europe, 46a Northbrook Street, Newbury, Berkshire, RG14 1DT Tel: (01635) 521200 Fax: (01635) 521150

Heybeck Garage Ltd, Leeds Road, Dewsbury, West Yorkshire, WF12 7RB Tel: (01924) 472660 *Motor vehicle recovery services*

John Heyer Paper Ltd, Langwood House, 63-81 High Street, Rickmansworth, Hertfordshire, WD3 1EQ Tel: (0870) 2423355 Fax: (0870) 2421114 E-mail: sales@johnheyerpaper.co.uk *Paper agents*

▶ Heyes Validator Ltd, Hafan Corwen Road Pontybodkin, Flintshire, Pontybodkin, Mold, Clwyd, CH7 4TG Tel: (01352) 770900 *Heyes Validator Ltd are fully insured TREE SURGEONS operating throughout Wales and the North West.*

▶ Heygates Ltd, Eagle Roller Mills, Downham Market, Norfolk, PE38 9EP Tel: (01366) 383361 Fax: (01366) 384687 *Flour millers*

▶ Heygates Ltd, Tringford Road, Tring, Hertfordshire, HP23 4JN Tel: (01442) 823311 Fax: (01442) 890283

Heylin Engineering, Cartref, Four Crosses, Llanymynech, Powys, SY22 6RG Tel: (01691) 830440 Fax: (01691) 830410 *Agricultural engineers*

Heymark Metals Ltd, Becklands Close, Bar Lane, Roecliffe, York, YO51 9NR Tel: (01423) 323388 Fax: (01423) 326888 E-mail: enquiries@heymark.co.uk *Stainless steel & nuclear specialist alloy producers*

Heynau, Unit 43, Britannia Way, Enterprise Industrial Park, Lichfield, Staffordshire, WS14 9UY Tel: (01543) 255995 Fax: (01543) 250316 E-mail: acdcpowerdrives@aol.com *Mechanical speed power & transmission equipment*

Heynes Estate Management, 7 Gildredge Road, Eastbourne, East Sussex, BN21 4RB Tel: (01323) 410975 Fax: (01323) 726163 *Chartered surveyors & property management* Also at: Bexhill

Heys-Shawl Ltd, Waterloo House, Langham Street Industral Estate, Ashton-Under-Lyne, Lancashire, OL7 9AX Tel: 0161-343 2060 Fax: 0161-343 1542 *Roofing material manufrs*

Heywood Ltd, 2 Victoria Street, Altrincham, Cheshire, WA14 1ET Tel: 0161-613 4200 Fax: 0161-927 7132 E-mail: sales@heywood.co.uk *Software systems consultants*

Heywood & Palmer Engineering Ltd, The Coach House, William Street, Ashton-under-Lyne, Lancashire, OL7 0BH Tel: 0161-339 0601 Fax: 0161-285 2295 E-mail: sales@heywoodandpalmer.co.uk *Grinding, precision & production services*

▶ Heywood Scaffolding Services, Unit 4 Green Lane, Heywood, Lancashire, OL10 2EU Tel: (01706) 365742 Fax: (01706) 627377 E-mail: enquiries@heywoodscaffolding.co.uk

Heywood Williams Group plc, Field Mills, Red Doles Lane, Huddersfield, HD2 1YG Tel: (01484) 533142 Fax: (01484) 435175 E-mail: sales@hmfltd.co.uk *Anodising aluminium manufrs*

▶ HFBC Events, 33 St. Michaels Road, Kirkham, Preston, PR4 2TQ Tel: (01772) 687455 E-mail: info@hfbc-events.co.uk *Event entertainment specialist*

HFC Bank Ltd, North Street, Winkfield, Windsor, Berkshire, SL4 4TD Tel: (01344) 890000 Fax: (01344) 890014 *Finance & banking services* Also at: Branches throughout the U.K.

HFS Engineering Ltd, 20 Dorsey Road, Cullyhanna, Newry, County Down, BT35 0QA Tel: (028) 3086 8228 *Farm machinery hire & repairs*

▶ HGM Landscapes Ltd, 90 Harrowby Road, Grantham, Lincolnshire, NG31 9DS Tel: (01476) 573345 Fax: (01476) 573345 E-mail: enquiries@hgmlandscapes.co.uk *Design & build gardens*

HHT Midlands Ltd, Heath Road, Darlaston, West Midlands, WS10 8LU Tel: 0121-526 4771 Fax: 0121-526 4153 E-mail: sales@hht.co.uk *Contract heat treatment specialists*

Hi Bond Chemicals Ltd, 32 Bryn Street, Ince, Wigan, Lancashire, WN3 4RX Tel: (01942) 615800 Fax: (01942) 615801 E-mail: info@hibond.fsnet.co.uk *Epoxy resins material manufrs*

Hi Bond Tapes Ltd, 1 Crucible Road, Corby, Northamptonshire, NN17 5TS Tel: (01536) 260022 Fax: (01536) 260044 E-mail: sales@hi-bondtapes.co.uk *Adhesive tape manufrs*

▶ Hi Chrome (Europe) Ltd, Heathenford Industrial Estate, Widowhill Road, Burnley, Lancashire, BB10 2TT Tel: (01282) 418300 Fax: (01282) 418310 E-mail: sales@hycrome.com *Electroplaters & power pack pumps manufrs*

▶ Hi Class Blinds, Aberaman Industrial Estate, Aberaman, Aberdare, Mid Glamorgan, CF44 6DA Tel: (01685) 872431 Fax: (01685) 872431

▶ HI Digital Solutions, 26 Caledonia House, Evanton Way, Glasgow, G46 8JE Tel: 0141-270 9735 Fax: 0141-270 9738 E-mail: admin@hids.co.uk *Hi digital solutions lease buy or rental of photocopiers*

Hi Europe, Hattori House, Vanwall Road, Maidenhead, Berkshire, SL6 4UB Tel: (01628) 770077 Fax: (01628) 785433 E-mail: sales@hieurope.com *Market research services*

Hi Flex Fluids, 2 Cowan Road, Blaydon-on-Tyne, Tyne & Wear, NE21 5TW Tel: 0191-414 7771 Fax: 0191-414 0625 E-mail: sales@hiflex-fluidpower.com *Hydraulic equipment systems distributors* Also at: Carlisle, Crawlington, Teesside, Sunderalnd & Wallsend

Hi Line Services Lichfield Ltd, 56 Britannia Way, Britannia Enterprise Park, Lichfield, Staffordshire, WS14 9UY Tel: (01543) 258741 Fax: (01543) 250925 E-mail: info@hilineservices.co.uk *Processors of pipe work & stainless steel vessels*

▶ Hi Lo Flare Systems & Services UK Ltd, Fairewell House, Yarmouth Road, Ormesby, Great Yarmouth, Norfolk, NR29 3QB Tel: (01493) 730095 Fax: (01493) 731043 E-mail: hi-lo@hi-loflare.co.uk *Enclosed flare systems, services, hire & sales*

Hi Mark Ltd, Unit A Spectrum Business Park, Wrexham Industrial Estate, Wrexham, Clwyd, LL13 9QA Tel: (01978) 660444 Fax: (01978) 660200 E-mail: sales@hi-mark.co.uk *Plastic moulding manufrs*

Hi Profile Precision Ltd, Units 1 & 2, Dyson Street, Bradford, West Yorkshire, BD9 4DE Tel: (01274) 482218 Fax: (01274) 482219 E-mail: hpprecisionltd@aol.com *Sub Contract Toolmakers, specialise in Wire Erosion, and also provide a full range of precision engineering services which include Press Tool design& manufacture & repair, CNC Milling, Turning & Grinding.*

Hi Q Ltd, Southdownview Way, Worthing, West Sussex, BN14 8NL Tel: (01903) 236734 *Garage tyre services*

Hi Seal Ltd, Bellbanks Corner, Mill Road, Hailsham, East Sussex, BN27 2AH Tel: (01323) 841392 Fax: (01323) 442719 *Windows fabricators*

▶ Hi Search Technology Hist Ltd, Unit 47 Mount St Business Centre, Mount Street, Nechells, Birmingham, B7 5RD Tel: 0121-326 6689 Fax: 0121-326 6689 E-mail: sales@hist.co.uk *Testing & chemical analysis & metallurgical expert testimony services*

▶ Hi Security Ticket Printing, 4th Floor, 7 Collingwood Road, Witham, Essex, CM8 2DY Tel: 0870 4901491 Fax: 0870 4901481 E-mail: office@hisecuritytickets.com *We offer high security ticket printing for concerts, events and parties, uk and worldwide service.*

Hi Spec Precision Toolmakers Ltd, 36 Rumer Hill Bus Estate, Rumer Hill Road, Cannock, Staffordshire, WS11 0ET Tel: (01543) 505323 Fax: (01543) 505230 E-mail: neil@hispec.uk.com *Plastic injection & zinc die cast tooling & tool trials manufrs*

Hi Spec UK Ltd, 189-191 Willow Lane, Lancaster, LA1 5SG Tel: (01524) 844124 Fax: (01524) 844124 *Electrical testing services*

▶ Hi Spek Roofing Ltd, Hi-Spek House, Pitsford Road, Moulton, Northampton, NN3 7RS Tel: (01604) 492999 Fax: (01604) 492666 E-mail: info@hispekroofing.co.uk *Industrial, commercial & domestic roofing contractors service*

Hi Tec Bradford Ltd, Cliffe House Prospect Road, Otley Road, Bradford, West Yorkshire, BD3 0HT Tel: (01274) 626379 Fax: (01274) 626381 E-mail: sales@hi-tecbradford.co.uk *Computer dealers repairs, sales & networking*

Hi Tec Interface Ltd, Unit 15 The Wenta Business Centre, Colne Way, Watford, WD24 7ND Tel: (020) 8958 4735 Fax: (020) 8958 9770 E-mail: hitec@himet.com *Membrane switch panel & keypad manufacturers*

▶ Hi Tec Lift Systems, 3 Rosevale Road, Parkhouse Industrial Estate We, Newcastle, Staffordshire, ST5 7EF Tel: (01782) 562000 Fax: (01782) 562121 E-mail: hiteclifts@btconnect.com *Lift designers & manufrs*

Hi Tec Plastics, 1 Sett End Road, Shadsworth Business Park, Blackburn, BB1 2PT Tel: (01254) 581405 Fax: (01254) 680285 E-mail: dennishi-tech@quista.net *Plastic injection mouldings*

Hi Tec Print, 9-10 Houghton Road, North Anston Trading Estate, North Anston, Sheffield, S25 4JJ Tel: (01909) 568533 Fax: (01909) 568206 E-mail: sales@hitecprint.co.uk *Printing services*

Hi Tech E D M Services Ltd, 18 Bayton Road, Bayton Road Industrial Estate, Exhall, Coventry, CV7 9EJ Tel: (024) 7664 4404 Fax: (024) 7636 3777 E-mail: sales@hitechaerospace.com *Spark, wire erosion machining & milling services*

Hi Tech Graphics Machinery Ltd, 252 Old Brompton Rd, London, SW5 9HW Tel: 020 72440334 Fax: 020 72440366 *Printing machinery import & export*

Hi Tech Hardware, 219 Station Road, Harrow, Middlesex, HA1 2TH Tel: (020) 8863 9462 Fax: (020) 8863 9462 *Engravers*

Hi Tech Recruitment Services Ltd, 144 Evesham Street, Redditch, Worcestershire, B97 4HP Tel: (01527) 65999 Fax: (01527) 62500 *Recruitment agencies*

Hi Tech Solutions, 6 Fairwater Drive, Woodley, Reading, RG5 3HH Tel: 0118-926 7252 *Computer programming & website building*

Hi Tech Steel Services Ltd, Neills Road, Bold Industrial Park, Bold, St. Helens, Merseyside, WA9 4TU Tel: (01744) 818767 Fax: (01744) 818706 E-mail: sales@hitechsteels.co.uk *Steel stockholders & steel coil cutting*

Hi Tek Products Ltd, 2a Dawkins Road, Poole, Dorset, BH15 4JP Tel: (01202) 661300 Fax: (01202) 661230 E-mail: gjb@hitekproducts.com *Masking products*

Hi Trim Ltd, Meadow Mill, Water Street, Stockport, Cheshire, SK1 2BY Tel: 0161-480 4366 Fax: 0161-480 4366 E-mail: sales@hi-trim.co.uk *Metal spinners & spinning manufrs*

Hiatco Ltd, West Road, Annfield Plain, Stanley, County Durham, DH9 8NJ Tel: (01207) 282314 Fax: (01207) 283599 E-mail: hiatco@btinternet.com *Aluminium & stainless steel fabricators*

Hiatt Hardware Ltd, Hiatt Industrial Estate, Baltimore Road, Great Barr, Birmingham, B42 1HZ Tel: 0121-358 4970 Fax: 0121-357 6033 E-mail: sales@hiatt-hardware.com *Hardware & furniture fitting wholesalers*

Hibbs W G & Co. Ltd, Solent Industrial Estate Caird Avenue, Lymington Road, New Milton, Hampshire, BH25 5QA Tel: (01425) 611660 Fax: (01425) 619927 *Concrete manufrs*

Hibiscus plc, Hudswell Road, Leeds, LS10 1AG Tel: 0113-242 4272 Fax: 0113-242 4230 E-mail: info@hibiscus-plc.com *Suppliers of labels for the chemical industry*

Hi-Brite Polishing, 160 Clayton Road, Hayes, Middlesex, UB3 1AN Tel: (020) 8561 5102 Fax: (020) 8561 6949 *Metal finishing services*

Hibrow Computing Consultancy, 40 North Street, Hornchurch, Essex, RM11 1EW Tel: (01708) 449999 Fax: (01708) 447555 E-mail: admin@hibrow.co.uk *Computer consultants*

Hichrom Ltd, 1 The Markham Centre, Station Road, Theale, Reading, RG7 4PE Tel: 0118-930 3660 Fax: 0118-932 3484 E-mail: sales@hichrom.co.uk *Laboratory equipment manufrs*

▶ Hick Logisticks, Unit 57 Symondscliffe Way, Severn Bridge Industrial Estate, Portskewett, Caldicot, Gwent, NP26 5PW Tel: (01291) 421954 Fax: (01291) 430504

Hickey & Co. Ltd, Slade Green Road, Erith, Kent, DA8 2HX Tel: (01322) 347004 Fax: (01322) 335733 E-mail: sales@hickey.co.uk *Pharmaceutical production plant*

Colin Hickey Fork Trucks Ltd, Unit 4 Ribble Industrial Estate, Newport Lane, Stoke-on-Trent, ST6 3BB Tel: (01782) 838888 Fax: (01782) 819000 *Hire & sell forklift trucks*

Hicking Pentecost & Co. (N.I) Ltd, 64-66 Leighinmohr Avenue, Ballymena, County Antrim, BT42 2AN Tel: (028) 2565 6551 Fax: (028) 2565 9868 *Dyers/finishers of knitted fabrics*

▶ Hickling & Squires Ltd, 1 Moorgreen Industrial Park, Engine Lane, Newthorpe, Nottingham, NG16 3QU Tel: (01773) 536400 Fax: (01773) 536444 E-mail: sales@hickling-squires.co.uk

▶ Hickman Brothers Ltd, Unit 5, Eagle Industrial Estate, Church Green, Witney, Oxfordshire, OX28 4YR Tel: (01993) 772774 Fax: (01993) 703057

Hickman Shearer, 7 Buttermarket, Thame, Oxfordshire, OX9 3EW Tel: (01844) 215755 Fax: (01844) 214549 E-mail: officehs@hickman-shearer.co.uk *Industrial plant & machinery valuers*

Hickman Steels International Ltd, PO Box 6, Bridgnorth, Shropshire, WV16 5JJ Tel: (01746) 761733 Fax: (01746) 767299 E-mail: mikemansfield@hickmansteels.com *Euro & American steel section stockholders*

Hicks Casings, 11 Inswell Court, Tavistock, Devon, PL19 8LS Tel: (01822) 613512 *Sausage case manufrs*

Hicks Metals & Alloys, 170-176 Fazeley Street, Birmingham, B5 5SE Tel: 0121-772 1896 Fax: 0121-771 2085 *Scrap metal merchants*

Hicks & Weatherburn Ltd, Lawnswood Works, Otley Road, Leeds, LS16 8AA Tel: 0113-267 1057 Fax: 0113-267 1057 *Paint manufrs*

▶ Hidden Hearing Ltd, 51 New Row, Coleraine, County Londonderry, BT52 1EJ Tel: (028) 7032 0301 Fax: (028) 7035 8210 *Hearing aid suppliers*

Hidden Technology, Unit C5 Star Business Centre, Marsh Way, Rainham, Essex, RM13 8UP Tel: (01708) 631333 Fax: (01708) 631444 E-mail: info@hiddentec.com *Suppliers of covert equipment*

Hiddleston Joiners, The Old School, Terregles, Dumfries, DG2 9RY Tel: (01387) 720100 Fax: (01387) 720555 *Joinery manufrs*

Hide & Hides Ltd, Portishead Road, Leicester, LE5 0JN Tel: 0116-276 6514 *Shoe components*

Hidebound, Unit R1a Rocket Trading Centre, Bowring Park Rd, Liverpool, L14 3NZ Tel: 0151-252 2272 Fax: 0151 252 2273 *Leather goods manufrs*

Hideinstyle Ltd, Dutch Barn, Church Farm, Ulcombe Hill, Ulcombe, Maidstone, Kent, ME17 1DN Tel: (01622) 892235 E-mail: info@hideinstyle.co.uk *LEATHER INTERIOR SPECIALISTS, FURNITURE DESIGNERS AND LEATHER INTERIOR ACCESSORIES, HAND STITCHED LEATHER TABLES, RECYCLED LEATHER FLOOR TILES.*

Hiden Analytical Ltd, 420 Europa Boulevard, Westbrook, Warrington, WA5 7UN Tel: (01925) 445225 Fax: (01925) 416518 E-mail: info@hiden.co.uk *State of the art solutions in mass spectrometry and surface science worldwide. Hiden Analytical was founded in 1981 and is presently situated in a 2,130m² manufacturing plant in Warrington, England with a staff of 60. As a privately owned company our reputation is built on creating close and positive relationships with our clients. Many of these customers are working at the forefront of new technology - in the fields of plasma research, surface science, vacuum processing and gas analysis. To maintain this reputation we have, over the years, established exceptional levels of technical expertise in these areas within our company. Providing instruments for exact science: Residual gas analysers, RGA; Triple filter quadropole mass spectrometers; Process control systems; Laboratory & Research Gas Analysers; Gas Sampling Valves, Catalyst Characterisation; Surface Science; Plasma Characterisation.*

▶ Christopher Hiett & Associates Ltd, 15 Oaklea Avenue, Chelmsford, CM2 6BY Tel: (01245) 283729 Fax: (01245) 600126 E-mail: chiett@christopherhiett.co.uk *Providing Consultancy Services in the Aerospace and Automotive sectors:*Design and Engineering,*Manufacturing Engineering,*Cost reduction,*Strategy Development,*Strategic Sourcing/Partnerships,*Tender/Bid/RFQ Preparation,*Business Case Development and *Project Management*

Hiflex Doors, Unit 16 Such Close, Letchworth Garden City, Hertfordshire, SG6 1JF Tel: (01462) 620250 Fax: (01462) 620330 E-mail: hiflex@ukonline.co.uk *Industrial door manufrs*

Hiflex Fluid Power, Units 8-9 Sun Valley Business Park, Winnall Close, Winchester, Hampshire, SO23 0LB Tel: (01962) 860311 Fax: (01962) 860673 E-mail: winchester@dunlophiflex.com *Hydraulic industrial hose manufacturers & service*

Hiflex Fluidpower Ltd, Unit 6, Monklands Industrial Estate, Kirkshaws Road, Coatbridge, Lanarkshire, ML5 4RP Tel: 01236 702680 Fax: 01236 702685 E-mail: sales@hiflex-fluidpower.com *Hydraulic hose fittings distributors* Also at: Chapelhall, Edinburgh, Macduff & Tollcross

Hiflex Hose, P O Box 87, Preston, PR5 2DL Tel: (01772) 421704 Fax: (01772) 422928 E-mail: sales@dunlop-hiflex.com *Hydraulic hoses distributors*

Hiflex Powerbend Ltd, Pennywell Industrial Estate, Sunderland, SR4 9EN Tel: 0191-534 0000 Fax: 0191-534 0012 E-mail: tim.dearnley@hiflex-europe.com *Tube manipulation*

Hi-Flux Magnets, 9 North St Industrial Estate, Droitwich, Worcestershire, WR9 8JB Tel: (01905) 778853 Fax: (01905) 779867 E-mail: hi-fluxmagnets@aol.com *Magnetic separator manufrs*

Hi-Force Ltd, Royal Oak Industrial Estate, Bentley Way, Daventry, Northamptonshire, NN11 8QH Tel: (01327) 301000 Fax: (01327) 706555 E-mail: sales@hi-force.com *Hydraulic & pneumatic equipment distributors* Also at: Cardiff, London, Newcastle upon Tyne & Rotherham

Higar Engineering Ltd, Gore Road Industrial Estate, New Milton, Hampshire, BH25 6TH Tel: (01425) 617511 Fax: (01425) 629463 E-mail: sales@higar.com *Precision engineering*

Company Information

Higgins Electronics, 116-120 High Street, Aberlour, Banffshire, AB38 9PA Tel: (01340) 871275 Fax: (01340) 871275 *Security systems & CCTV contractors*

Higgins Engineering Ltd, 816A Oxford Road, Reading, RG30 1EL Tel: 0118-957 1058 Fax: 0118-957 1058 E-mail: higginsengineering@ntlworld.com *Precision & general engineers*

P.S. Higgins Electrical Services, Clarence House, 30 Queen Street, Market Drayton, Shropshire, TF9 1PS Tel: (01630) 655416 Fax: (01630) 658415 E-mail: info@pshiggins.co.uk *Industrial & domestic electricans*

Higgs Designs, 5 Woodgates Farm, Woodgates End, Dunmow, Essex, CM6 2BN Tel: (01279) 851115 *Cabinet makers*

Higgs International, Unit 7, Thameside Industrial Estate, London, E16 2HB Tel: (020) 7867 9944 Fax: (020) 7511 1976E-mail: sales@higgs.co.uk *Air freight forwarders*

Higgs Removals Great Barr Ltd, 31 Rippingille Road, Birmingham, B43 7DJ Tel: 0121-360 9366 Fax: 0121-325 0921 *Removal contractors*

▶ High Access Cleaning Co., Unit E1, The Courts, Kestrel Road, Trafford Park, Manchester, M17 1SF Tel: (0845) 6440901 Fax: (0845) 6440902 E-mail: info@highaccesscleaning.co.uk *Industrial & commercial cleaning services*

▶ High Access Cleaning & Maintenance Ltd, Unit 3 Ansa House, 7 Monsall Road, Manchester, M40 8FY Tel: 0161-202 5080

High Class Metal Polishing, Unit 1-2 Lower Mills, Bridgend, Stonehouse, Gloucestershire, GL10 2BB Tel: (01453) 825464 Fax: (01453) 825464 *Metal polishing services*

High Cross Electrical Ltd, 4A West Market Street, Newport, Gwent, NP20 2AU Tel: (01633) 216897 Fax: (01633) 214840 E-mail: enquires@highcrosselectrical.co.uk *Electrical contractors*

▶ High Cross Forecourt Canopies Ltd, Pretoria House, Norwich Road, Besthorpe, Attleborough, Norfolk, NR17 2LB Tel: (01953) 456565 Fax: (01953) 456058 E-mail: sales@high-cross.com *Manufacturers & installation canopies for use on loading bays*

▶ High Demand Clothing, PO BOX 58, Longfield, Kent, DA3 7YQ Tel: (020) 8123 4985 E-mail: info@hdclothing.co.uk *Style Fashion Sense is our philosophy. Bringing you the latest high fashion designer labels straight from the catwalks of the world to your door in style. An astonishing collection of men's and ladies clothing and accessories and well as some great gift ideas. Brands on offer include Diesel, 55DSL, Miss Sixty, Armani and many more. With fast and free UK delivery and customer service second to none, we are certain that you will be shopping with us again soon!*

▶ High Edge Consulting Ltd, 115 Musters Road, Ruddington, Nottingham, NG11 6JA Tel: 0115-921 6200 E-mail: info@highedge.co.uk *Consultancy on quality systems - specialist in iso 9001 & iso 13485*

High Edge (UK) Ltd, 70 Maes Hyfryd, Beaumaris, Anglesey, LL58 8HN Tel: (01248) 810112 E-mail: info@highedge-uk.com *Roof Cladding Contractors or Fixing Services - UK (England ...We cover all aspects of roofing & have demonstrated that we work to high standards with ... Industrial, commercial roofing & cladding contractors **

High Energy Financial Management Ltd, Windmill House, Windmill Hill, Pudsey, West Yorkshire, LS28 8JQ Tel: 0113-303 0404 E-mail: info@hefm.co.uk *Business accounting and finance, commercial management, start-up assistance, business plans. VAT Sage Line 50, business models and on going support*

▶ High Force Research Ltd, Bowburn North Industrial Estate, Bowburn, Durham, DH6 5PF Tel: 0191-377 9098 Fax: 0191-377 9099

▶ High Hill Electronics, 127 High Hill Road, New Mills, High Peak, Derbyshire, SK22 4HQ Tel: 0161 654 9842 E-mail: sales@highhill.co.uk *PCB specialists design*

▶ High Kite, Fordham, Linden Avenue, Odiham, Hook, Hampshire, RG29 1AW Tel: (01256) 704876 E-mail: info@highkite.co.uk *Graphic design services including corporate identity design, point of sale, direct mail, web design, company literature & much more*

High Lee Engineering Co. Ltd, Unti 1 Princess Street, Rochdale, Lancashire, OL12 0HA Tel: (01706) 644269 Fax: (01706) 524810 *General machining*

High Line Yachting Ltd, Mansion Lane, Iver, Buckinghamshire, SL0 9RG Tel: (01753) 651496 Fax: (01753) 630095 E-mail: sales@high-line.co.uk *Marine engineering services*

High Oak Auto Salvage, High Oak Works, High Oak Road, Wicklewood, Wymondham, Norfolk, NR18 9QP Tel: (01953) 601156 Fax: (01953) 601156 *New & secondary roller shutter doors*

▶ High Peak Remedial Services, New Mill, Park Road, Dukinfield, Cheshire, SK16 5LX Tel: 0161-339 4655 Fax: 0161-339 8216 *Builders & joiners*

High Peak Steels Ltd, Thornfield House Brookfield Industrial Estate, Peakdale Road, Glossop, Derbyshire, SK13 6LQ Tel: (01457) 866911 Fax: (01457) 869178 E-mail: mark@highpeaksteels.com *Steels from stock*

High Point Rendel, Suite 3 Bowling Hill Business Park, Quarry Road, Chipping Sodbury, Bristol, BS37 6JL Tel: (01454) 312266 Fax: (01454) 312666 E-mail: bris-hpr@netcomuk.co.uk *Consultants in management, development & engineering*

High Point Rendel Ltd, 61 Southwark Street, London, SE1 1SA Tel: (020) 7654 0400 Fax: (020) 7654 0401 E-mail: london@highpointrendel.com *Consultancy providing management business & engineering services*

High Precision Machining Ltd, Unit 10 Washington Centre, Washington Street, Dudley, West Midlands, DY2 9RE Tel: (01384) 233133 Fax: (01384) 212755

continued

E-mail: enquiries@eurac-group.com *Disc brake manufrs*

High Pressure Welding Ltd, Sundon Business Park, Dencora Way, Luton, LU3 3HP Tel: (01582) 565400 Fax: (01582) 565500 E-mail: hpweldingltd@aol.com *Welding & pipework fabricators*

High Profile, 9 Haslemere Way, Banbury, Oxfordshire, OX16 5RW Tel: (01295) 267966 Fax: (01295) 272477 E-mail: sales@high-profile.co.uk *Manufacturers of promotional premium products*

▶ High Quality Joinery & Aluminium Services, Lynchford Lane, Farnborough, Hampshire, GU14 6JD Tel: (01252) 548702 Fax: (01252) 548898 E-mail: sales@highqualityjoinery.co.uk

High Speed & Carbide Ltd, Freedom Works, John St, Sheffield, S2 4QT Tel: 0114-279 6197 Fax: 0114-279 7550 E-mail: sales@hscknives.co.uk *Machine knife manufrs*

▶ High Speed Communications Ltd, 5 Nevin House, Bourne Avenue, Hayes, Middlesex, UB3 1QU Tel: (0845) 6868021 Fax: (0845) 6868024 E-mail: glen.freeman@hscgroup.co.uk *Network service provider*

High Speed Engineering (West Bromwich) Ltd, Unit 22 Spartan Industrial Centre, Brickhouse Lane, West Bromwich, West Midlands, B70 0DH Tel: 0121-520 9655 Fax: 0121-520 9588 E-mail: sales@highspeedeng.co.uk *Precision engineers*

High Speed Hardening Sheffield Ltd, Naseby Street, Sheffield, S9 1BR Tel: 0114-244 1516 Fax: 0114-244 1516 *General hardening & steel tool manufrs*

High Speed Hire, 47 High Street, Nailsea, Bristol, BS48 1AW Tel: (01275) 810364 Fax: (01275) 859464 *Tool hire leasing & rental*

High Speed Piercing Ltd, Pindar Road, Hoddesdon, Hertfordshire, EN11 0DE Tel: (01992) 445123 Fax: (01992) 466541 E-mail: admin@highspeedpiercing.co.uk *Sheet metalwork engineers*

High Street Signs, 5b Denham Road, Sheffield, S11 8NE Tel: 0114-268 4224 Fax: 0114-268 4224 E-mail: info@high-street-signs.co.uk *Sign manufrs*

High Style Furnishings, Saxon Way, Melbourn, Royston, Hertfordshire, SG8 6DN Tel: (01763) 261837 Fax: (01763) 262489 E-mail: enq@highstyle.co.uk *Ready-made curtain & fabric wholesalers*

High Tech Engineering Ltd, 3 Mayer Way, Houghton Regis, Dunstable, Bedfordshire, LU5 5BF Tel: (01582) 662277 Fax: (01582) 472235 E-mail: hightech2@compuserve.com *Precision engineers*

High Tech Environmental Engineering Ltd, Environmental House, Cross Street, Standish, Wigan, Lancashire, WN6 0HQ Tel: (01257) 426969 Fax: (01257) 426812 *Air filtration services*

▶ High Tech Living, 112 Prospect Lane, Solihull, West Midlands, B91 1HT Tel: (0845) 0090237 Fax: (0871) 2364804 E-mail: sales@high-tech-living.com *Intelligent Innovations, Gadgets & Modern Furniture for the 21st Century Home & Business * Italian & Designer Furniture, Kitchens, Bathrooms, Steam showers with tv, Chemical free Hot tubs, Infrared saunas, Granite & marble tiles and worktops, Bathroom tvs, Touchscreen Internet tv"s, Mirror tvs, Gadgets, Home automation, Biometric Fingerprint door locks.*

High Technology Solvents UK Ltd, Millfield, Ashwells Road, Brentwood, Essex, CM15 9SF Tel: (01277) 375222 Fax: (01277) 373115 E-mail: htsukltd@aol.com *Solvent manufrs*

High Tensile Bolts Ltd, Imperial Works, 93 Lockfield Avenue, Enfield, Middlesex, EN3 7PY Tel: (020) 8805 8510 Fax: (020) 8805 1553 E-mail: kebrell@montal-internet.co.uk *Nut, bolt & industrial fastener distributors, agents & stockholders* Also at: Caldicot, Darlaston & Worksop

High Voltage Maintenance Services, Littlebrook Business Centre, Littlebrook Manorway, Dartford, DA1 5PZ Tel: (01322) 273100 Fax: (01322) 294413 E-mail: enquiries@hvms.co.uk Principal Export Areas: Worldwide *High voltage engineers*

High Voltage Technology Ltd, Flitch Industrial Estate, Chelmsford Road, Dunmow, Essex, CM6 1XJ Tel: (01371) 875668 Fax: (01371) 875665 E-mail: sales@essex-x-ray.com *Diode manufrs*

High Wood Security, 2-4 Slaters Road, Stanningley, Pudsey, West Yorkshire, LS28 6EY Tel: 0113-257 7707 Fax: 0113-257 4051 *Shutter & grille suppliers*

▶ Higham Furniture, Flint Barn, New Barns Farm, Drove Road, Southwick, Fareham, Hampshire, PO17 6EW Tel: (0845) 8684477 Fax: (0870) 0681067 E-mail: tim@higham.co.uk *Handmade kitchen furniture manufacture to customer specification*

Highams Group Ltd, Grape Mill, New Coin Street, Royton, Oldham, OL2 5JB Tel: 0161-633 2241 Fax: 0161-627 3275 E-mail: mailbox@highamsgroup.co.uk *Yarn spinners & merchants*

Highbank Tools Ltd, Unit 7 Reliance Trading Estate, Manchester, M40 3AG Tel: 0161-681 2506 Fax: 0161-683 4937 *Toolmakers, toolmaking services*

▶ Highbell Ltd, Unit 20, Ivanhoe Road, Hogwood Lane Industrial Estate, Wokingham, Berkshire, RG40 4QQ Tel: 0118-973 0357 Fax: 0118-973 1991 E-mail: barriehighbell@btconnect.com *Self contract engineers*

▶ Highbridge Scaffolding Ltd, 1 Roscow Road, Fishbrook Industrial Estate, Kearsley, Bolton, BL4 8NX Tel: (01204) 794073 Fax: (01204) 794073

Highbridge Turned Parts Ltd, 23a Highbridge Street, Waltham Abbey, Essex, EN9 1BZ Tel: (01992) 713333 Fax: (01992) 713333 E-mail: highbridgetp@supanet.com *Precision turned parts manufrs*

Highbury Design, 3 Catton Road, Arnold, Nottingham, NG5 7JD Tel: 0115-967 1188 E-mail: info@highburyblinds.co.uk *Manufacturer & installer of all types of window blinds & curtains*

Highcliffe Engineering Ltd, Unit C Old Housecraft Yard, Church Street, Mexborough, South Yorkshire, S64 0HH Tel: (01709) 581656 Fax: (01709) 581656 *Crane hire*

Highcrest Accident Repair Centre Ltd, James Street, Markham, Blackwood, Gwent, NP12 0QN Tel: (01495) 221767 Fax: (01495) 220486 *Commercial vehicle bodybuilders & repairers*

▶ Higher Elevation, 35 Union Street, Maidstone, Kent, ME14 1ED Tel: (01622) 682973 E-mail: info@higherelevation.co.uk *Supply, install & maintain all types of lifts*

Higher Platforms South Ltd, Archers Fields, Burnt Mills Industrial Estate, Basildon, Essex, SS13 1DH Tel: (01268) 525566 Fax: (01268) 525544 *Access (platform) hire*

Hilary Highet, Archway Studio, Market Square, Axminster, Devon, EX13 5NJ Tel: (01297) 34538 Fax: (01297) 35627 *Knitwear designers*

Highfield CNC Engineering Ltd, 39 Knowl Piece, Wilbury Way, Hitchin, Hertfordshire, SG4 0TY Tel: (01462) 442252 Fax: (01462) 442257 E-mail: highfieldcnc@aol.com *CNC precision turned parts manufrs*

Highfield Computing Services Ltd, Highfields, Haselor, Alcester, Warwickshire, B49 6LX Tel: (01789) 488088 Fax: (01789) 488770 E-mail: hcsl@compuserve.com *Computer training & consultants*

▶ Highfield Haulage Bilston Ltd, 27 Highfields Road, Bilston, West Midlands, WV14 0SD Tel: (01902) 492181 Fax: (01902) 497798

Highfield Human Solutions Ltd, 1 London Road, Newbury, Berkshire, RG14 1JL Tel: (01635) 33923 Fax: (01635) 38837 E-mail: admin@highfielduk.co.uk *Executive search & selection consultants*

Highfield International Exhibition Services Ltd, Unit 1A, Worcester Trading Estate, Blackpole Rd, Worcester, WR3 8HR Tel: (01905) 754158 Fax: (01905) 456218 *Exhibition stand designers*

High-Fire Ltd, 37a Cyprus Rd, Leicester, LE2 8QP Tel: 0116-232 7980 *Boiler & industrial burner engineers*

▶ Highgate Beds Ltd, Bradford Street, Dewsbury, West Yorkshire, WF13 1EN Tel: (01924) 454678 Fax: (01924) 459266 E-mail: sales@sleepincomfort.com *Bedding company*

Highgate Felt Roofing, 18a Moat Road, Walsall, WS2 9PJ Tel: (01922) 648791 Fax: (01922) 625183 E-mail: enquiries@highgateroofing.fsbusiness.co.uk *Roofing contractors*

Highgate Joinery, 18 Wightman Road, London, N4 1SQ Tel: (020) 8341 4823 Fax: (020) 8341 5656 *Joinery workshop*

Highgrove Computer Services, Melbourne Road, Staunton Harold, Ashby-de-la-Zouch, Leicestershire, LE65 1RT Tel: (01332) 695050 Fax: (01332) 695001 E-mail: postmaster@highgrove.co.uk *Computer software consultants*

Highland Blindcraft, 38 Ardconnel Street, Inverness, IV2 3EX Tel: (01463) 233662 Fax: (01463) 710809 E-mail: sales@highlandblindcraft.co.uk *Bedding manufacturers & upholstery services*

Highland Catering Resources, Suite 4 Upper Mall, Grampian Road, Aviemore, Inverness-Shire, PH22 1RH Tel: (01479) 810270 Fax: (01479) 810270 *Catering equipment & management*

▶ Highland Celtic Leather Scotland, 1 Benmore House, Portnellan, Crianlarich, Perthshire, FK20 8QS Tel: (07092) 240355 Fax: (07092) 240355

▶ Highland Distillers Ltd, Tamdhu Distillery, Knockando, Aberlour, Banffshire, AB38 7RP Tel: (01340) 872200 Fax: (01340) 872144 *Distillery*

▶ Highland Dress Hire, 246 Brown Royd Avenue, Dalton, Huddersfield, HD5 9NW Tel: (01484) 546915 Fax: (01484) 432589 E-mail: laurie@highlandhire.co.uk *Highland kilts manufrs*

▶ Highland Dress Hire, 39, Scotland Way,, Horsforth, Leeds, LS18 5SQ Tel: 0113 2280146 Fax: 0113 3682650 E-mail: john@highlandhire.co.uk *Suppliers & hire of highland wear*

Highland Electroplaters Ltd, Howemoss Drive, Kirkhill Industrial Estate, Aberdeen, AB21 0GL Tel: (01224) 725581 Fax: (01224) 725591 E-mail: enquires@hiplaters.co.uk *Electroplating services & metal finishers*

Highland Fine Cheese Ltd, Blarliath Farm, Tain, Ross-Shire, IV19 1EB Tel: (01862) 892034 Fax: (01862) 894289 *Cheese manufrs*

Highland Fish Products, 31 Sinclair Road, Aberdeen, AB11 9PL Tel: (01224) 875401 *Fish merchants*

Highland Grain Group Ltd, Glackmore, North Kessock, Inverness, IV1 3UD Tel: (01463) 811435 Fax: (01463) 811618 *Grain distributors*

▶ Highland Haulage Ltd, 11 Walker Place, Inverness, IV1 1TY Tel: (01463) 714444 Fax: (01463) 714445

Highland Health Store, 7 St John Street, Perth, PH1 5SP Tel: (01738) 628102 Fax: (01738) 447541 *Health foods & products*

Highland Industrial Supplies Ltd, 36 Seafield Road, Inverness, IV1 1SG Tel: (01463) 239160 Fax: (01463) 233424 E-mail: sales@hisltd.co.uk *Power & hand tools distributors*

▶ Highland Metal Developments Ltd, 3 Pinefield Parade, Elgin, Morayshire, IV30 6FG Tel: (01343) 548855 Fax: (01343) 545551 E-mail: enquiries@higalv.co.uk *Corrosion protection services*

Highland Motor Parts Ltd, 21 Henderson Road, Inverness, IV1 1SN Tel: (01463) 223700 Fax: (01463) 711351 E-mail: sales@highlandmotorparts.co.uk *Motor factors*

▶ Highland Park Distillery, Holm Road, St. Ola, Kirkwall, Orkney, KW15 1SU Tel: (01856) 874619 Fax: (01856) 876091 E-mail: webmaster@highlandpark.co.uk *Distillery*

▶ Highland Printing & Publishing Group, 13 Henderson Road, Inverness, IV1 1SP Tel: (01463) 224444

Highland Roller Shutters, Unit 3 Evanton Industrial Estate, Evanton, Dingwall, Ross-Shire, IV16 9XJ Tel: (01349) 830555 Fax: (01349) 830530 E-mail: highlandrollerdoors@hotmail.com *Roller shutters manufrs*

Highland Saddlery Repairs, Easter Brightmony Farmhouse, Auldearn, Nairn, IV12 5JZ Tel: (01309) 641491 *I am a working saddler with 30 years experience of making and repairing saddlery. I now make other items like dog leads and dog collars, leather belts and handbags not forgetting saddlery items - bridles, head collars, etc. All these items are hand-made and to the customers requirements, all are made out of the finest English or Italian bridle leather with the best quality fittings. **I also supply some top quality belt buckles of all types so if you are looking for something special we may be able to find it for you...***

Highland Scientific, Unit 16 Bedford Business Centre, Mile Road, Bedford, MK42 9TW Tel: (01234) 216636 Fax: (01234) 271991 E-mail: sales@highland-scientific.com *Component and spares suppliers to Vacuum Deposition System Users in the Semiconductor, Optical and Ophthalmic Industries Highland Scientific stocks thousands of new and pre-owned spare parts sourced globally from leading companies.*

Highland Smiddy Ltd, 54 Thornbush Road, Inverness, IV3 8AF Tel: (01463) 232905 Fax: (01463) 711529 *Steel fabricators*

Highland Smoked Salmon (Scotland) Ltd, Blar Mhor Industrial Estate, Lochyside, Fort William, Inverness-Shire, PH33 7PT Tel: (01397) 703649 Fax: (01397) 705632 E-mail: sales@highlandsmokedsalmon.com *Salmon smokers*

Highland Stoneware Scotland Ltd, Baddidarroch, Lochinver, Lairg, Sutherland, IV27 4LP Tel: (01571) 844376 Fax: (01571) 844626 E-mail: potters@highlandstoneware.co.uk *Ceramic manufrs*

Highland Truffle Co., 16 Pinefield Parade, Elgin, Morayshire, IV30 6AG Tel: (01343) 552200 Fax: (01343) 552200 E-mail: sales@highlandtruffles.co.uk *Chocolate manufrs*

Highland Wood Windows Ltd, 46 Station Road, Worthing, West Sussex, BN11 1JP Tel: (01903) 237613 Fax: (01903) 820253 E-mail: sales@parker-joinery.com *Joinery & staircase manufrs*

Highlander Ltd, Islington Business Design Centre, 52 Upper Street, London, N1 0QH Tel: (0800) 1560777 Fax: (0870) 3309911 E-mail: info@highlander.co.uk *IT solutions*

▶ Highlander Computing Solutions Ltd, Systems House, Unit 7 Shepcote Office Village, Shepcote Lane, Sheffield, S9 1TG Tel: 0114-292 3800 Fax: 0114-292 3838 E-mail: sales@highlanderuk.com *Computer systems consultants*

Highlands & Islands Enterprise, Cowan House, Highlander Way, Inverness Business & Retail Pa, Inverness, IV2 7GF Tel: (01463) 234171 Fax: (01463) 244469 E-mail: hie.general@hient.co.uk *Government development agents*

▶ Highlandwear Direct, 4-9 Huntly Street, Inverness, IV3 5PR Tel: (01463) 229200 Fax: (01463) 229201 E-mail: sales@highlandweardirect.com *Manufacturers of highland dress for gents, ladies & children; kilts, kilted skirts, trews, trousers, waistcoats, handsewn & machine sewn garments available, made in the city of Inverness in the highlands of Scotland*

Highline Access Ltd, PO Box 2089, Bristol, BS99 7SZ Tel: (0870) 0435531 Fax: (0870) 0435532 E-mail: enquiries@highlineaccess.com Sales Contact: K Young *Highline is a Bristol based rope access company servicing the whole of the UK. Our abseiling experience includes all aspects of working at height. Our main areas of expertise are building cleaning, building maintenance, building surveys, banner installation, pest control, church restoration, and the installation of safety and fall arrest systems. The number one benefit of rope access is that it offers a cost effective alternative to scaffolding and cherry pickers. Highline combines the worker and the means of access - this combined service saves the customer time and money, every time. All of our technicians are IRATA certified and have worked extensively in the field of rope access both in the UK and abroad. CALL - 0870-043-5531 OR E-MAIL - enquiries@highlineaccess.com.*

Highline Precision Engineering, Old Mill La Industrial Estate, Mansfield Woodhouse, Mansfield, Nottinghamshire, NG19 9BG Tel: (01623) 654251 Fax: (01623) 621384 *Injection mould toolmakers*

Highline Precision Engineering, Old Mill La Industrial Estate, Mansfield Woodhouse, Mansfield, Nottinghamshire, NG19 9BG Tel: (01623) 654251 Fax: (01623) 621384 *Precision engineers*

▶ Highpoint, 165 Glenfield Road, Leicester, LE3 6DJ Tel: 0116-258 0000 Fax: 0116-258 0033 E-mail: eventsales@highpoint.org.uk *Conference centre*

Highridge Computers Ltd, 275 Tutbury Road, Burton-on-Trent, Staffordshire, DE13 0NZ Tel: (01283) 500530 Fax: (01283) 500540 E-mail: karl@highridge.net *Computer upgrades & repairs*

Highspeed Lubricants Ltd, 1 Newbridge Industrial Estate, Pitt Street, Keighley, West Yorkshire, BD21 4PQ Tel: (01535) 611103 Fax: (01535) 611546 E-mail: info@highspeed.co.uk *Fuel oil additive distributor or agent*

▶ Highspeed Office Ltd, Epworth House, 25 City Road, London, EC1Y 1AA Tel: (020) 7847 4500 Fax: (020) 7847 4599 E-mail: sales@highspeedoffice.net *IT solutions & management*

Highstone Insulation Co. Ltd, 6 Hasluck Gardens, New Barnet, Barnet, Hertfordshire, EN5 1HT Tel: (020) 8449 4273 Fax: (020) 8449 4273 *Thermal insulation engineers*

High-Tech Business Machines, 18 Kirkgate, Birstall, Batley, West Yorkshire, WF17 9PB Tel: (01924) 420803 Fax: (01924) 420804 E-mail: info@hi-techbm.co.uk *Office equipment sales & services*

▶ Hightech Engineering Services Ltd, Green Lane, Romiley, Stockport, Cheshire, SK6 3JG Tel: 0161-406 0793 Fax: 0161-292 5908 *Crane engineers services*

▶ Hightex Coatings, Unit 14 Chapel Farm, Hanslope Road, Hartwell, Northampton, NN7 2EU Tel: (01604) 861250 Fax: (01604) 871116 E-mail: sales@hightexcoatings.co.uk *UK textured property coatings specialists offering wall protector, damp treatment, brickwork repairs, prevention of penetrating damp, weather proofing house using trowel applied coatings (rather than spray on) and now Protectguard and cellar conversions! Water proofing basements for dry storage and more.*

▶ HighVeld Select, P O Box 196, Morpeth, Northumberland, NE61 6WQ Tel: (01670) 789965 *HIGHVELD SELECT is a North East based recruitment consultancy specialising in filling industrial, sales and financial vacancies throughout the UK. In addition to the North East, we have consultants located in Scotland, Yorkshire, the Midlands and Thames Valley. **At HIGHVELD SELECT we provide our clients with a variety of options for the recruitment of personnel. However, our core belief is that Search & Select (headhunting) is the most efficient and effective method of finding the best talent regardless of the level of seniority; headhunting is not confined to senior executive positions. ***

▶ Highway Care Ltd, Wharton Court, Hereford Road, Wharton, Leominster, Herefordshire, HR6 0NX Tel: (01568) 610909 Fax: (01568) 620007 E-mail: nigel@highwaycare.co.uk *Suppliers of temporary steel barrier, plastic barriers, road safety products, speed reduction vms signs & road maintenance contractors*

▶ Highway Care Ltd, Wharton Court, Hereford Road, Wharton, Leominster, Herefordshire, HR6 0NX Tel: (01568) 610909 E-mail: info@tcshighway.co.uk *Traffic contractors*

Highway Commercial Engineers, Tywardreath Highway, St Blazey, Par, Cornwall, PL24 2RN Tel: (01726) 814580 Fax: (01726) 817845 *Vechicle bodybuilders*

▶ Highway Electronics Ltd, Unit 2, Metherell Avenue, Brixham, Devon, TQ5 9QB Tel: (01803) 850460 Fax: (01803) 850470 E-mail: enquiries@highwaysoftware.co.uk *Software developers for the glass & glazing industries*

Highway & Industrial Equipment Ltd, East Moors Road, Cardiff, CF24 5EE Tel: (029) 2049 4623 Fax: (029) 2048 3611 *Road sign makers & tool suppliers*

▶ Highway Pilots - Escort Services, 34 Norton Crescent, Towcester, Northamptonshire, NN12 6DN Tel: 01327 354502 Fax: 01327 354502 E-mail: potentsolutions@yahoo.co.uk *Wide and Abnormal Load Escort services throughout the UK and Europe. Fully accredited Highways Agency spec vehicle. Daily or hourly rates, located centrally in Towcester for onward or continuation journeys. Contact us for a friendly response.*

Highway Safety Systems Ltd, Units 4A-B, Manor Lane Business Park, Manor Lane, Holmes Chapel, Crewe, CW4 8AF Tel: (01477) 536000 Fax: (01477) 536006 *Reflective & protective coatings for crash barriers*

Highwayman Couriers, 31 Firs St, Dudley, West Midlands, DY2 7DW Tel: (01384) 456976 Fax: (01384) 457146 E-mail: enquiries@hiwaymancouriers.co.uk *Couriers & light haulage contractors*

▶ Highwire Ltd, 4 Fairfield Avenue, Fairfield Wells, Droylsden, Manchester, M43 6ED Tel: 0161-612 7633 Fax: 0161-612 2105 E-mail: sales@highwire.info *Fall arrest & safety harness restraint systems*

Highwood, Millers Close, Dorchester, Dorset, DT1 1HW Tel: (01305) 266058 Fax: (01305) 263155 E-mail: enquiry@highwood-farming.co.uk *Agricultural supplies & repairs*

▶ Highwood Consultants Ltd, Park Road, Ryde, Isle of Wight, PO33 1HH Tel: (01983) 568154 Fax: (01983) 568146

Highwood Engineering Ltd, Parkfield Road, Birmingham, B8 3AZ Tel: 0121-327 9212 Fax: 0121-327 4329 *Manufacturers of industrial, interlock machine guards*

Highworth Computer Centre, 27 Newburgh Place, Highworth, Swindon, SN6 7DN Tel: (01793) 766866 Fax: (01793) 766162 *Computer systems service & repair*

▶ Higman Windows, Unit 8, Treloggan Industrial Estate, Newquay, Cornwall, TR7 2SX Tel: (01637) 879343 E-mail: sales@higman-windows.co.uk *Insulation of windows & doors*

Hi-Grade Computers plc, Hi-Grade House, 43 Thames Road, Barking, Essex, IG11 0HQ Tel: (020) 8532 6111 Fax: (020) 8532 6101 E-mail: sales@higrade.com Principal Export Areas: Worldwide *Computer software*

Hike & Bike, 1 North Street, Alfriston, Polegate, East Sussex, BN26 5UG Tel: (01323) 871861 Fax: (01323) 871861 E-mail: mike@hikeandbike.co.uk *Outdoor clothing retailers*

Hilbar Plastics, Windley Works, Wolsey Street, Radcliffe, Manchester, M26 3BB Tel: 0161-724 4325 Fax: 0161-725 9158 *Plastics injection mouldings manufrs*

Hilbre Engineering Design Services, 71 Park Rd, Meols, Wirral, Merseyside, CH47 7BD Tel: 0151-632 2995 Fax: 0151-632 2850 E-mail: heds@tinyonline.co.uk *Engineer designs, finite element consultants*

Hilclare Ltd, Unit 1 Bond Street Industrial Estate, Mancunian Way, Manchester, M12 6HW Tel: 0161-274 3626 Fax: 0161-274 3731 E-mail: sales@hilclare.com *Commercial & industrial lighting manufrs*

Hilcrest Design Ltd, Lea Road, Waltham Abbey, Essex, EN9 1AJ Tel: (01992) 713005 Fax: (01992) 710268 E-mail: sales@hilcrest.co.uk *Plastic injection designers*

Hilden Manufacturing Co. Ltd, Clifton Mill, Pickup Street, Accrington, Lancashire, BB5 0EY Tel: (01254) 391131 Fax: (01254) 770770 E-mail: sales@hilden.co.uk *Hilden Manufacturing Co. Ltd based in Accrington, Lancashire are fabric manufacturers, producing tablelinen, bedlinen, bath mats and shower curtains.*

Hildon Ltd, Broughton, Hampshire, SO20 8DQ Tel: (01794) 302056 Fax: (01794) 301033 E-mail: hildon@hildon.com *Natural mineral water.*

Hildred Engineering Co. Ltd, Units 2 4 & 6, Parkway Court, Nottingham, NG8 4GN Tel: 0115-928 2217 Fax: 0115-985 4998 E-mail: hildredengco@aol.com *Precision engineers & press tool manufrs*

Hiley Engineering (Halifax) Co. Ltd, Station Road, Shay Lane, Holmfield, Halifax, West Yorkshire, HX2 9AY Tel: (01422) 248327 Fax: (01422) 240610 E-mail: hileyeng@hileyeng.co.uk *Capital plant equipment fabricators*

Hi-lite Signs Ltd, 100 Sinclair Road, Aberdeen, AB11 9PP Tel: (01224) 248532 Fax: (01224) 248479 *Sign makers*

Hilka Tools (UK) Ltd, 1 Roebuck Place, Roebuck Road, Chessington, Surrey, KT9 1EU Tel: (020) 8391 7570 Fax: (020) 8391 7575 E-mail: hilka@bix.co.uk *Hand tool import merchants*

Adam Hill Ltd, Union St, Lurgan, Craigavon, Co. Armagh, BT66 8EG Tel: (028) 3831 6158 Fax: (028) 3832 1354 *Dressing gown manufrs*

Hill Biscuits Ltd, Smith Street, Ashton-Under-Lyne, Lancashire, OL7 0DB Tel: 0161-330 3617 Fax: 0161-343 2108 *Biscuits manufrs*

Hill Brook Printing Inks Ltd, New Hey Rd, Outlane, Huddersfield, HD3 3YJ Tel: 01484 841061 Fax: 01484 377324 *Ink manufrs*

Hill Bros Ltd, 14 Stone Street, Brighton, BN1 2HB Tel: (01273) 326200 Fax: (01273) 326200 E-mail: info@hill-bros.co.uk *Roofing contractors & general builders*

Hill Bros Building Supplies Ltd, Well Lane, Wolverhampton, WV11 1XS Tel: (01902) 731253 Fax: (01902) 306424 *Building material & timber merchants*

Claude Hill Dental Supplies, Unit 2 Premier Industrial Estate, The Leys, Brierley Hill, West Midlands, DY5 3UT Tel: (01384) 262121 Fax: (01384) 77781 *Dental supplies distributors*

▶ The Hill Education & Conference Centre, Pen Y Pound Road, Abergavenny, Gwent, NP7 7RP Tel: (01495) 333770 Fax: (01495) 333778 E-mail: hill@coleggwent.ac.uk *Adult education & conference services*

Edwin Hill, 18 Saville Row, London, W1S 3PW Tel: (020) 7287 2020 Fax: (020) 7734 1255 E-mail: ehlondon@edwinhill.co.uk *Chartered surveyors*

▶ Hill Electrical Services, Unit 32 Blue Chalet Industrial Park, West Kingsdown, Sevenoaks, Kent, TN15 6BQ Tel: (01474) 855300 Fax: (01474) 855301

▶ Hill Engineering Ltd, 1 Sandy Road, Newry, County Down, BT34 2LB Tel: (028) 3025 2555 Fax: (028) 3026 4020 E-mail: sales@hillengineeringltd.com *Automatic excavator equipment designers & manufrs*

▶ Hill Engineering (Catford) Ltd, 1-5 Mercy Terrace, London, SE13 7UX Tel: (020) 8690 2163

George Hill Ltd, Biddings Lane, Bilston, West Midlands, WV14 9NW Tel: (01902) 403631 Fax: (01902) 492308 E-mail: sales@g-hill2000.co.uk *Heavy duty cases manufrs* Also at: Newport (Salop)

H.C. Hill Ltd, PO Box 137, Beckenham, Kent, BR3 4WY Tel: (020) 8650 7890 Fax: (020) 8650 0535 E-mail: enquiries@hchill.co.uk *Scaffolding hire & sales*

▶ Hill & Hay Ltd, 58 Rogart Street, Glasgow, G40 2AA Tel: 0141-554 2205 Fax: 0141-556 6023 E-mail: sales@hillhay.co.uk

Hill Hire plc, Wharfedale Road, Euroway Industrial Estate, Bradford, West Yorkshire, BD4 6SG Tel: (0870) 5133423 Fax: (01274) 651347 E-mail: sales@hillhire.co.uk *Truck & trailer rental services*

Ivor Hill Ltd, 413 Durnsford Road, London, SW19 8EE Tel: (020) 8946 8650 Fax: (020) 8946 8650 *Property investors*

J Hill, 1 Culm View, Honiton Road, Cullompton, Devon, EX15 1NX Tel: (01884) 841557 Fax: (01884) 841134 *Farm buildings*

Jesse Hill, 1a Ash Tree Road, Birmingham, B30 2BJ Tel: 0121-458 3625 *Gunsmith repair & manufrs*

Hill & Knowlton (UK) Ltd, 20 Soho Square, London, W1A 1PR Tel: (020) 7413 3000 Fax: (020) 7413 3111 E-mail: info@hillandknowlton.com *Public relations consultants*

Peter Hill Machine Sales, PO Box 3402, Birmingham, B44 8DG Tel: 0121-249 7272 Fax: 0121-244 2378 E-mail: info@peterhillmachinesales.com *New & used machine tool distributors*

Hill & Priest Ltd, 187 Halesowen Rd, Cradley Heath, W. Midlands, B64 6HE Tel: (01384) 569747 Fax: (01384) 569747 *Electrical contractor*

▶ R.S. Hill, The Row, Douglastown, Forfar, Angus, DD8 1TL Tel: (01307) 466176 Fax: (01307) 468643 *Joiners & building contractors*

Hill Shorter Group, 54 Roebuck Lane, West Bromwich, West Midlands, B70 6QP Tel: 0121-553 7011 Fax: 0121-500 5162 E-mail: sales@hillshorter.com *Colour printers specialists*

Hill & Smith Holdings plc, Unit 2 Highlands Court, Cranmore Avenue, Shirley, Solihull, West Midlands, B90 4LE Tel: 0121-704 7430 Fax: 0121-704 7439 E-mail: enquiries@hsholdings.co.uk *Holding company*

▶ Hill & Son, Bottings Industrial Estate, Curdridge, Southampton, SO30 2GE Tel: (01489) 782343 Fax: (01489) 789213 E-mail: chriscook@hillsltd.com *Haulage, Abnormal Loads (Site and Road Haulage),* *continued* *Abnormal Load Escorts, Experienced in Heavy and Abnormal Haulage.*

Hill & Sons, Ringstones, Bridgemont, Whaley Bridge, High Peak, Derbyshire, SK23 7PD Tel: (01663) 732607 Fax: (01663) 734913 E-mail: hillsriddles@btinternet.com Sales Contact: M. Turnock Principal Export Areas: Africa & North America *Wire products manufrs*

▶ Hill Steels Ltd, Peartree Lane, Dudley, West Midlands, DY2 0XB Tel: (01384) 255455 Fax: (01384) 258333 E-mail: markpickering@hillsteels.co.uk *Steel stockholder*

Hill Taylor Dickinson, Dukes Place, London, EC3A 7LQ Tel: (020) 7283 9033 Fax: (020) 7283 1144 E-mail: sales@htd.co.uk *Solicitors*

Hill Taylor Partnership, Alexandra House, Pound Lane, Exmouth, Devon, EX8 4NP Tel: (01395) 222242 Fax: (01395) 225858 E-mail: enquiries@hilltaylor.co.uk *Marketing & Social Research*

Hill Top, 36-38 Breeze Hill, Bootle, Merseyside, L20 9NZ Tel: 0151-922 5487 Fax: 0151-933 6818 *Pub & restaurant*

Hill Top, Ridgacre Road, West Bromwich, West Midlands, B71 1BB Tel: 0121-555 1470 Fax: 0121-555 1471 E-mail: sales.hts@hadleygroup.co.uk *Cold rolled steel sections*

Hill Top Fabrications Co 1998 Ltd, Unit 22 Siddons Factory Estate, Howard Street, West Bromwich, West Midlands, B70 0SU Tel: 0121-556 9666 Fax: 0121-556 3777 E-mail: hilltopfab@supanet.com *Tubular fabrications manufrs*

Hill & Tyler, Glaisedale Drive, Bilbrough, Nottingham, NG8 4LX Tel: 0115-929 9422 Fax: 0115-929 6026 E-mail: sales@hillandtyler.co.uk *Printing letterpresses*

Hill & Webster Ltd, Ashbourne Indust Estate, Ashbourne, Derbyshire, DE6 1HD Tel: (01335) 343119 Fax: (01335) 346400 E-mail: hillwebster@compuserve.com *General engineers & fabricators*

Hilladam Coburn Ltd, 6 Wyvern Estate, Beverley Way, New Malden, Surrey, KT3 4PH Tel: (020) 8336 1515 Fax: (020) 8336 1414 E-mail: sales@hilladam.co.uk *Sliding door gear manufrs* Also at: Bolton, Clevedon & Glasgow

Hillam Farm Machinery, Brookside Works, Brick Street, Cleckheaton, West Yorkshire, BD19 5LD Tel: (01274) 870632 Fax: (01274) 862815 E-mail: geanne@hilams.freeserve.co.uk *Agricultural machinery manufrs*

Joseph Hillary Ltd, Station Road, Aspatria, Wigton, Cumbria, CA7 3JW Tel: (01697) 320251 Fax: (01697) 321180 E-mail: duncan@josephhilary.co.uk *Agricultural machinery distributors*

Hillary's Blinds Ltd, 38 Queens Arcade, Queen Street, Cardiff, CF10 4BY Tel: (029) 2022 8911 Fax: (029) 2023 3190 E-mail: sales@hillary.co.uk *Blinds manufrs*

Hillary's Blinds Ltd, 105 Holt Farm Close, Leeds, LS16 7SE Tel: 0113-230 1669 Fax: 0113-228 6894 *Blind sales & installers*

Hillarys Blinds Ltd, Private Road 2, Colwick Industrial Estate, Nottingham, NG4 2JR Tel: 0115-961 7420 Fax: 0115-852 2525 E-mail: enquiries@hillarys.co.uk *Blinds retailers & manufrs*

Hillary's Blinds Ltd, Spire Road, Glover, Washington, Tyne & Wear, NE37 3ES Tel: 0191-461 1800 Fax: (0870) 2430451 E-mail: enquiries@hillarys.co.uk *Blinds supplier*

Hillbrook Printing Inks Ltd, New Street, Slaithwaite, Huddersfield, HD7 5BB Tel: (01484) 843535 Fax: (01484) 840031 *Printing ink manufrs*

Hillbury Press Ltd, Cranborne Industrial Estate, Cranborne Road, Potters Bar, Hertfordshire, EN6 3JN Tel: (01707) 658948 Fax: (01707) 655254 E-mail: printers@hillbury.co.uk *Printers*

Hillcliff Tools Ltd, 11 Catley Road, Sheffield, S9 5JF Tel: 0114-244 3665 Fax: 0114-242 3319 E-mail: jj@hillcliff-tools.com *Tool distributors*

Hillco Engineering Ltd, Beehive Works Beehive Lane, Chelmsford, CM2 9JY Tel: (01245) 354507 Fax: (01245) 354507 E-mail: hillco@acedial.co.uk *Precision engineers*

▶ Hillcote Partnership, 32 London Road, Guildford, Surrey, GU1 2AB Tel: (01483) 230310 *Perseus Partnership-an Executive Search consultancy covering UK and international appointments at Board, Director and Senior Executive level.*

Hillcrest Engineering Instrumentation Ltd, Upper Hulme, Leek, Staffordshire, ST13 8TY Tel: (01538) 300259 Fax: (01538) 300421 E-mail: sales@hei-engine.co.uk *Instrument engineering services*

Hillcrest Furnishings Ltd, Unit 18, Miners Road, Llay Industrial Estate, Llay, Wrexham, Clwyd, LL12 0PJ Tel: (01978) 854966 Fax: (01978) 854966 *Commercial furniture manufrs*

Hillcrest Homes Ltd, Hillcrest, Knutsford Road, Grappenhall, Warrington, WA4 3LA Tel: (01925) 267314 Fax: (01925) 212171

Hillcrest Machinery Engineering Portchester Ltd, 1 Pennant Park, Standard Way, Fareham, Hampshire, PO16 8XU Tel: (01329) 231245 Fax: (01329) 822753 E-mail: office@hillcresteng.co.uk *Precision engineers & engravers*

Hillday Leasing & Supplies Ltd, 1a Haverscroft Industrial Estate, New Road, Attleborough, Norfolk, NR17 1YE Tel: (01953) 454014 Fax: (01953) 454014 E-mail: hillday@btinternet.com *Stamp & ticket machine manufrs*

Hillend, Ridge Way, Hillend Industrial Park, Hillend, Dunfermline, Fife, KY11 9JH Tel: (01383) 823621 Fax: (01383) 823090 E-mail: nat.hillend@btconnect.com *Stainless steel fabricators*

Hillfax Ltd, Park Road, Willenhall, West Midlands, WV13 1AQ Tel: (01902) 606442 Fax: (01902) 634982 E-mail: sprint@btclick.com *Precision engineers*

▶ Hillfoot Homes Ltd, Hillfoots Farm, Dollar, Clackmannanshire, FK14 7PL Tel: (01259) 740000 Fax: (01259) 742090

Hillfoot Special Steels Ltd, 16 Hertburn Estate, Hertburn, Washington, Tyne & Wear, NE37 2SF Tel: 0191-417 0185 Fax: 0191-415 4740 E-mail: washington@hillfoot.com *Steel stockholders*

▶ Hillgate Electrical Services, 480 Hale Road, Hale Barns, Altrincham, Cheshire, WA15 8XT Tel: 0161-904 0700 Fax: 0161-904 7878

Hillhampton Salads, Hillhampton, Great Witley, Worcester, WR6 6JU Tel: (01299) 896717 Fax: (01299) 896717 E-mail: laura@hillhamptonsalads.co.uk *Suppliers of leafy salad products.*

Hillhouse Precast Concrete, Mains Road, Beith, Ayrshire, KA15 2HR Tel: (01505) 502711 Fax: (01505) 502569 E-mail: info@hillhousegroup.co.uk *Concrete product manufrs*

Hillhouse Quarry Group, Hillhouse Quarry, Troon, Ayrshire, KA10 7HX Tel: (01292) 310482 Fax: (01292) 314640 *Quarry operators*

Hilliard & Winn, 2 Sovereign House, Butterley Street, Leeds, LS10 1AW Tel: 0113-242 2542 Fax: 0113-244 4405 E-mail: hilliard@btconnect.com *Neon sign manufrs*

▶ Hillington Innovation Centre, 1 Ainslie Road, Hillington Park, Glasgow, G52 4RU Tel: 0141-585 6300

▶ Gideon Hillman Consulting, 47A Lansdowne Crescent, Willes Road, Leamington Spa, Warwickshire, CV32 4PR Tel: (01926) 430883 E-mail: info@hillman-consulting.co.uk *Material handling & supply chain consultants*

Hillmar Products, New Victoria Mills, Wellington Street, Bury, Lancashire, BL8 2AL Tel: 0161-763 5598 Fax: 0161-764 1368 E-mail: hilmarproducts@btopenworld.com *We specialise in manufacturing for fashion houses and mail order companies. We also specialise in promotional items from leather to PVC, handbags, purses, vanity cases, menu covers etc. We can also design & manufacture bespoke items to specification for industry to customer specification. Minimum order value £500 excluding tooling charges.*

Hillmeglynn Ltd, Ground Floor Marshall Mill, Marshall Street, Leeds, LS11 9YJ Tel: 0113-246 5577 Fax: 0113-244 2926 E-mail: info@hillmeglynn.co.uk *Construction, engineering, industrial & manufacturing recruitment*

Hill-Rom UK Ltd, Clinitron House, Ashby Park, Ashby-de-la-Zouch, Leicestershire, LE65 1JG Tel: (01530) 411000 Fax: (01530) 411555 E-mail: name@hill-rom.co.uk *Furniture*

▶ Hills, Eddystone House, Aberderfyn Road, Johnstown, Wrexham, Clwyd, LL14 1PB Tel: (01978) 846609 Fax: (01978) 843954 E-mail: sales@hillsaccountants.supanet.com

Hills Components Ltd, Valley Park, Olds Approach, Watford, WD18 9TL Tel: (01923) 772773 Fax: (01923) 421421 E-mail: sales@hillscomponents.co.uk *Computer component distributors*

Hills Construction, Wood Road, Kingswood, Bristol, BS15 8RA Tel: 0117-967 0014 Fax: 0117-961 8939 E-mail: sales@hillsconstruction.co.uk *Building contractors refurbishment service providers*

▶ Hills Contractors Ltd, Unit 12 Holland Industrial Park, Bentley Road South, Wednesbury, West Midlands, WS10 8LN Tel: 0121-568 7432 Fax: 0121-568 6394 E-mail: sales@hillscontractors.co.uk

▶ Hills Delivery Ltd, Feeder Road, Bristol, BS2 0TW Tel: 0117-971 1717

▶ Hills Electrical & Mechanical plc, Unit 42 Vale Business Park, Llandow, Cowbridge, South Glamorgan, CF71 7PF Tel: (01446) 774002 Fax: (01446) 773002

▶ Hills Electrical & Mechanical plc, 106-114 Salkeld Street, Glasgow, G5 8HE Tel: 0141-429 6008 Fax: 0141-429 6009

▶ Hills Electrical & Mechanical plc, Tootal Grove, Salford, M6 8DN Tel: 0161-743 0400 Fax: 0161-743 0228

Hills Electrical & Mechanical plc, Green Lane, Walsall, WS2 8HB Tel: (01922) 721105 Fax: (01922) 721151 E-mail: admin@hillelec.plc.uk *Electrical & mechanical installers* Also at: Manchester & Worcester

The Hills Group Ltd, Ailesbury Court, High Street, Marlborough, Wiltshire, SN8 1AA Tel: (01672) 516111 Fax: (01672) 516198 E-mail: mhayes@hills-group.co.uk *Recycling & waste disposal specialists*

Hills Industries Ltd, Pontygwindy Industrial Estate, Caerphilly, Mid Glamorgan, CF83 3HU Tel: (029) 2088 3951 Fax: (029) 2088 6102 E-mail: info@hills-industries.co.uk *Clothes drying equipment manufrs*

Hills Labels, 2 Chiswell Green Lane, St. Albans, Hertfordshire, AL2 3AH Tel: (01727) 830429 Fax: (01727) 830429 E-mail: hillslabels@talk21.com *Label design & manufrs*

Margaret Hills, 7 Millar Court, 43 Station Road, Kenilworth, Warwickshire, CV8 1JD Tel: (01926) 850019 *Health food, vitamins & herbs retailers*

Hills Numberplate Holdings plc, Unit 6 Electric Avenue, Birmingham, B6 7JJ Tel: 0121-623 8050 Fax: 0121-623 8011 E-mail: orders@hillsnumberplates.com *Motor number plate*

Hills Packaging, Lincoln Street, Rochdale, Lancashire, OL11 1LB Tel: (01706) 352398 Fax: (01706) 657808 E-mail: sales@hillspackaging.co.uk *Packaging merchants*

Hills Panels Products Ltd, Crown Works, Rotherham Road, Beighton, Sheffield, S20 1AH Tel: 0114-269 3009 Fax: 0114-269 8202 *Furniture components distributors*

Hills Poly Print Ltd, Alma Park Road, Grantham, Lincolnshire, NG31 9SE Tel: (01476) 577132 Fax: (01476) 590368 E-mail: sales@hillspoly-print.com *Polyethene bags & carriers manufrs*

Hill's Rubber Co. Ltd, 85 Bedford Road, Reading, RG1 7EZ Tel: 0845 4940717 Fax: 0118-950 3083 E-mail: hillsrubber@hotmail.com *Industrial rubber products*

Company Information

Hills Of Shoeburyness Ltd, 17 Towerfield Road, Shoeburyness, Southend-on-Sea, SS3 9QL Tel: (01702) 296321 Fax: (01702) 297072 E-mail: sales@hillsofshoeburyness.com *Architectural metalworkers & joinery manufrs*

Hills Waste Sollutions Ltd, Ailesbury Court, High Street, Marlborough, Wiltshire, SN8 1AA Tel: (01672) 516999 Fax: (01672) 516699 *Disposal of minerals, waste & recycling services*

Hills Westmidlands Ltd, Lickhill Quarry, Bewdley Road North, Stourport-On-Severn, Worcestershire, DY13 8RN Tel: (01299) 827782 Fax: (01299) 827421 *Ready mixed concrete aggregates & skip hire* Also at: Cirencester

Hillsborough Steelstock Ltd, Penistone Road North, Sheffield, S6 1LE Tel: 0114-285 5525 Fax: 0114-232 0972 *Steel stockholders*

Hillside Adr Ltd, 9 Quarry Park Close, Moulton Park Industrial Estate, Northampton, NN3 6QB Tel: (01604) 671251 Fax: (01604) 670868 E-mail: sales@hillsideadr.co.uk *Hillside ADR have 20 years experience in the manufacture of extruder sleeves, feed screws and dies for the snack food industry. We also offer CNC machining services to all industries, including rail track maintenance gauges.*

▶ Hillside Electrical (Southern) Ltd, Unit 7 Kingdom Close, Fareham, Hampshire, PO15 5TJ Tel: (01489) 577465 Fax: (01489) 481816 E-mail: info@hillside-electrical.co.uk *Deal with all your electrical needs*

▶ Hillside Garage, Laundry Lane, Ingleton, Carnforth, Lancashire, LA6 3DA Tel: (01524) 241595 Fax: (01524) 241595 E-mail: sales@hillsidegarage.f9.co.uk *Garage*

Hillside Kitchens Bedrooms & Bathrooms, 302 Liverpool Road, Southport, Merseyside, PR8 4PW Tel: (01704) 560758 Fax: (01704) 560716 E-mail: sales@hillsidekitchens.com *Kitchens, bedrooms & bathrooms retailers*

Hillside Metals Ltd, Cranborne Industrial Estate, Cranborne Road, Potters Bar, Hertfordshire, EN6 3JU Tel: (01707) 658131 Fax: (01707) 650777 E-mail: sales@hillsidemetals.com *Ventilation engineers*

Hillside Plastics Ltd, St. Johns Road, Meadowfield, Durham, DH7 8XQ Tel: 0191-378 0598 Fax: 0191-378 9346 E-mail: enquiries@hillside-plastics.co.uk *Injection moulders*

Hillsmen Engineering Ltd, 2 Bergen Way, Hull, HU7 0YQ Tel: (01482) 877111 Fax: (01482) 877112 E-mail: sales@hillsmen2000.freeserve.co.uk *General engineers*

Hillstone Products Ltd, Unit 2, Portland Industrial Estate, Portland Street, Bury, Lancashire, BL9 6EY Tel: 0161-763 3100 Fax: 0161-763 3158 E-mail: sales@hillstone.co.uk *Load banks for testing batteries, specialist*

Hillsyde Foundry (Staffordshire) Ltd, Apedale Works, Rowhurst Industrial Estate, Chesterton, Newcastle, Staffordshire, ST5 6BD Tel: (01782) 564411 Fax: (01782) 562546 E-mail: sales@hillsyde.com *Grey, sg & austentic iron casting manufrs*

Hilltop Seeds, Clayhanger, Tiverton, Devon, EX16 7NT Tel: (01398) 361387 *Agricultural seeds merchants*

David Hillyard Ltd, Rope Walk, Littlehampton, West Sussex, BN17 5DG Tel: (01903) 713327 Fax: (01903) 722787 E-mail: info@hillyards.co.uk *Yacht builder & repairer*

Hilmar Tubes Ltd, Hardy Street, Eccles, Manchester, M30 7NB Tel: 0161-787 7747 Fax: 0161-787 7748 E-mail: graham@hilmar.co.uk *Steel tube stockholders suppliers & distributors*

▶ Hilmax Precision Engineering Ltd, Unit 31, Sedgewick Road, Luton, LU4 9DT Tel: (01582) 573384 Fax: (01582) 508868 E-mail: info@hilmax.co.uk *Aerospace parts subcontractors & manufrs*

Hilsea Engineering Ltd, 3 St Georges Indust Estate, Rodney Road, Southsea, Hampshire, PO4 8SS Tel: (023) 9273 1676 Fax: (023) 9282 7801 E-mail: hilseaeng@fsbdial.co.uk *General engineers*

Hilson, Acre House, Shentonfield Road, Sharston Industrial Area, Manchester, M22 4RW Tel: 0161-491 7800 Fax: 0161-428 1179 E-mail: sales@hilson.co.uk *Wire workers*

Hilta TW, Flowplant House, Unit 8A-B Summit Crescent, Summit Estate, Smethwick, West Midlands, B66 1BT Tel: 0121-525 9955 Fax: 0121-525 0748 E-mail: hilta@hiltapumps.com *Pump manufrs*

▶ Hiltek Microwave Ltd, Newton House, Winch Road, Sittingbourne Research Centre, Sittingbourne, Kent, ME9 8EF Tel: (01795) 420998 Fax: (01795) 421998

Hilti Centre (Belfast), Unit 7 Loughside Industrial Park, Dargan Cresent, Belfast, BT3 9JP Tel: (0870) 4281024 Fax: (0800) 886200 *Hilti is one of the world's leading companies specialising in the field of fastening and demolition systems in the construction industry and allied trades.*

▶ Hiltingbury Motors Ltd, 72 Hiltingbury Road, Chandlers Ford, Eastleigh, Hampshire, SO53 5SS Tel: (023) 8026 6688 Fax: (023) 8026 6680 E-mail: sales@hiltingburymazda.com *We offer everthying for the motorist, whether personal or business. New Cars from the Mazda range, Used cars, Servicing, Parts as well as a finance package designed to fit your needs and the acquisition oif your next car simpler.*

Hilton Building Services Ltd, Waterway St West, Nottingham, NG2 3AD Tel: 0115-986 1221 Fax: 0115-986 6870 E-mail: sales@hiltons.co.uk *Design, installation & maintenance of heating, ventilation services*

Hilton Charles Ltd, Airey House, 57 Shepherd Road, Lytham St. Annes, Lancashire, FY8 3ST Tel: (01253) 789444 Fax: (01253) 722989 *Systems & software leasing*

▶ Hilton Creative Ltd, 37 Rosewood Way, Farnham Common, Slough, SL2 3QD Tel: (01753) 648149 E-mail: design@hiltoncreative.co.uk *UK Based design and creative consultancy specialising in design for print & web, brand & logo development, corporate id, SEO, e-commerce, marketing and training.*

Hilton Docker Mouldings Ltd, Freedo Mill, Foxcroft Street, Littleborough, Lancashire, OL15 8LB Tel: (01706) 379358 Fax: (01706) 378546 E-mail: sales@hiltondoc.co.uk *Glass fibre mouldings manufrs*

Hilton Heath Agencies, 67 High Street, Great Missenden, Buckinghamshire, HP16 0AL Tel: (01494) 865120 Fax: (01494) 866152 E-mail: j.hilton@tiscali.co.uk *Packaging products distributors*

Hilton Hotel, Maple Court, Reeds Cresent, Watford, WD24 4QQ Tel: (020) 7850 4000 Fax: (020) 7856 8001 *Hotel industry & betting company*

Hilton Industrial Services Ltd, The Old Cheese Factory, Stone Road, Hill Chorlton, Newcastle, Staffordshire, ST5 5DR Tel: (01782) 680680 Fax: (01782) 680546 *Manufacturers of wooden pallets & packing cases*

Hilton Instruments Ltd, 32 Holland Street, Aberdeen, AB25 3UL Tel: (01224) 620121 Fax: (01224) 620125 E-mail: info@hilton-instruments.co.uk *Supply scientific components*

▶ Hilton International Properties (UK) Ltd., 1 Bury Old Road, Manchester, M25 0FQ Tel: 0161 7735916 Fax: 0161 7735916 E-mail: info@propertyforsaleinspain.com *Long established specialists in the sale of Villas, Apartments and Country Properties in Spain. Each of our Directors has over 36 years experience in Spanish property sales. Their advice is absolutely invaluable to you.*

Hilton of London, Flat 11, Leamington House, 11 Stonegrove, Edgware, Middlesex, HA8 7TN Tel: (020) 8958 9372 Fax: (020) 8905 4954 E-mail: brian@hiltonoflondon.co.uk *Importers of alcohol & textiles*

▶ Hilton Security Systems, Rose Cottage, Pailton Fields, Pailton, Rugby, Warwickshire, CV23 0QJ Tel: 01788 551966 Fax: 01788 338989 E-mail: info@hiltonsecurity.co.uk *Installation and service of CCTV, Intruder and Door Access Control. (Contractor to the trade)*

Hilton Studios, Elsing Street, Stoke-on-Trent, ST4 2PR Tel: (01782) 411321 E-mail: sales@hiltonstudios.co.uk *Exhibition & conference designers*

Hilton's Brush Mnfrs, 84 Uxbridge Street, Ashton-under-Lyne, Lancashire, OL6 7EH Tel: 0161-339 2390 Fax: 0161-343 2627 *Manufacture brushes*

Himanet, 125 Moor Street, Mansfield, Nottinghamshire, NG18 5SG Tel: (01623) 420646 Fax: (01623) 420646 *Steel engineers*

Himfen Alarms, 25 Station Road, Hockley, Essex, SS5 4BZ Tel: (01268) 750070 *Alarm system installers*

Ernest Hinchliffe (Peak Mix Concrete) Ltd, Peak Works, Peak Forest, Buxton, Derbyshire, SK17 8EW Tel: (01298) 23671 Fax: (0870) 0638909 *Concrete suppliers*

▶ Hinckley Computer Peripherals Ltd, Telford Way, Stephenson Industrial Estate, Coalville, Leicestershire, LE67 3HE Tel: (01530) 838555 Fax: (01530) 814250 E-mail: hcpuk@btclick.com *Computer & office suppliers*

▶ Hind Garden Design, 2 St Clair Road, Otley, West Yorkshire, LS21 1DE Tel: 01943 464986 *Garden design and construction for all sizes of garden or project, from a complete redesign to sympathetic additions and improvements to existing gardens.*

▶ Leonard Hind, 4 Abbots Road, Grangemouth, Stirlingshire, FK3 8HX Tel: (01324) 483652

▶ Leonard Hind & Son, Mandal House, South Shore Road, Grangemouth, Stirlingshire, FK3 8AE Tel: (01324) 474719 Fax: (01324) 473211 E-mail: sales@lenhind.com

Hinderwell Joinery, 6 Rose Hill, Hinderwell, Saltburn-by-the-Sea, Cleveland, TS13 5EU Tel: (01947) 840685 Fax: (01947) 840685 *Joinery manufrs*

Hindhay Agricultural Services, Green Lane Farm, Coningsby Lane, Fifield, Maidenhead, Berkshire, SL6 2PF Tel: (01628) 621160 Fax: (01628) 635861 E-mail: office@hindhay.co.uk *Lime supplier & general agricultural supplies*

▶ Hindle (Bradford), Nelson Street, Bradford, West Yorkshire, BD5 0EL Tel: (01274) 732284 Fax: (01274) 740237 E-mail: autos@hindle.co.uk *Engine component maintenance repair & manufrs*

Hindle Gears, Caledonia Street, Bradford, West Yorkshire, BD5 0EL Tel: (01274) 727234 Fax: (01274) 737343 E-mail: gears@hindle.co.uk *Gears & cutters manufrs*

▶ Hindle Lowther, 28 Rutland Square, Edinburgh, EH1 2BW Tel: 0131 2216560 E-mail: mail@hindlelowther.com *UK and European Patent and Trade Mark Attorneys based in Edinburgh, Scotland.*

Hindle Valves, Hindle Cockburns Ltd, Victoria Road, Leeds, LS11 5UG Tel: 0113-244 3741 Fax: 0113-244 1872 E-mail: sales_hindle@tyco-valves.com Principal Export Areas: Worldwide *Industrial ball valve manufrs*

Hindles Ltd, 22 Moorland Way, Lincoln, LN6 7JP Tel: (01522) 683000 Fax: (01522) 500127 E-mail: sales@psm-sportswear.co.uk *Ductwork specialists & fabrications*

▶ Hindley Engineering, Cemetery Road, Ince, Wigan, Lancashire, WN3 4NN Tel: (01942) 862894 Fax: (01942) 862894 *Plant repairs & engineers*

Hindleys Bakeries, Wharf Road, Rugeley, Staffordshire, WS15 1BL Tel: (01889) 583161 Fax: (01889) 583846 *Bakery wholesalers*

David Hinds Ltd, Unit B Chiltern Industrial Estate, Grovebury Road, Leighton Buzzard, Bedfordshire, LU7 4TU Tel: (01525) 852696 Fax: (0844) 170588 E-mail: astro@dhinds.co.uk *Distributor of astronomical telescopes & binoculars*

Hine Engineering Ltd, 149 Bolton Hall Road, Bolton Woods, Bradford, West Yorkshire, BD2 1BQ Tel: (01274) 401850 Fax: (01274) 401850 E-mail: rod@akili.demon.co.uk *Control systems manufrs*

▶ Hine Labels Ltd, Hope Street, Rotherham, South Yorkshire, S60 1LH Tel: (01709) 369222 Fax: (01709) 363660 E-mail: enquiries@hinelabels.com *Labels*

▶ Hine Systems, 85 Richmond Park Road, Kingston upon Thames, Surrey, KT2 6AF Tel: (0845) 0954463 E-mail: kellysearch@hinesystems.com *Web Design: "Unlimited" Pages £250****** Contact us for a FREE Customised Online Demonstration****** Business automating - disability discrimination act compliant -*edit yourself - search engine friendly - web design at an amazing price****** Book your FREE no-obligation consultation today*

Bruce Hines, 50 Churchdale Road, Sheffield, S12 4XU Tel: 0114-239 5423 *Boiler maintenance engineers*

Hines Milling & Processing Ltd, Scott Lidgett Industrial Estate, Scott Lidgett Road, Longport, Stoke-On-Trent, ST6 4NQ Tel: (01782) 819616 Fax: (01782) 837174 E-mail: hines@iclwebkite.co.uk *Zircon manufrs*

Hingerose Ltd, 5 Ryder Court, Corby, Northamptonshire, NN18 9NX Tel: (01536) 461441 Fax: (01536) 461600 E-mail: info@hingerose.co.uk *Dosatron water powered injectors distributor*

Austin Hinkley Furniture Ltd, Wilson Way, Redruth, Cornwall, TR15 3RS Tel: (01209) 310910 Fax: (01209) 212045 *Flat pack furniture manufacturers & distributors*

Hinton Electrical Services, 4 Trem Cinmel, Towyn, Abergele, Clwyd, LL22 9NJ Tel: (01745) 338019 Fax: (01745) 338088 E-mail: mail@hintons.co.uk *Electrical engineers & contractors*

Hinton, Perry & Davenhill Ltd, Pensnett, Brierley Hill, West Midlands, DY5 4TH Tel: (01384) 77405 Fax: (01384) 74553 E-mail: office@drednort.tiles.co.uk *Brick & tile manufrs*

Hio Tec Services Scotland Ltd, 62 Queen Street, Alva, Clackmannanshire, FK12 5EJ Tel: (01259) 760977 Fax: (01259) 769819 E-mail: hiotec@hiotec.plus.com *Domestic appliance repairs*

▶ Hi-Point Scaffolding Ltd, Valley Works, Grange Lane, Sheffield, S5 0DQ Tel: 0114-257 7600 E-mail: info@hi-pointscaffolding.co.uk

Hippo Composites Ltd, Maserati House, Gelderd Road, Leeds, LS12 1AS Tel: 0113-279 4144 Fax: 0113-279 7935 E-mail: sales@widdsigns.co.uk *Glass fibre moldings manufrs*

Hippo Engineering Ltd, 1 Dunelm, Kelverton, Nottingham, NG14 6NN Tel: 0115-965 5138 Fax: 0115-965 5148 *Pump distributors*

Hippo Marine Ltd, 1 Gilston Road, Saltash, Cornwall, PL12 6TW Tel: (01752) 843333 Fax: (01752) 843333 *Marine products, offshore & onshore*

Hippo Sports Ltd, 1 Woodcroft Farm, Water End Road, Potten End, Berkhamsted, Hertfordshire, HP4 2SH Tel: (01442) 876010 Fax: (01442) 876020 E-mail: sales@zoppohippo.com *Hockey stick distributors*

▶ Hippowash, Poplar Grove, Crewe, CW1 4AZ Tel: 01270 252669 Fax: 01270 252670 E-mail: info@hippowash.com *Wheel wash system manufrs*

Hi-Press Hydraulics Ltd, Riverside Works, Forge Road, Whaley Bridge, High Peak, Derbyshire, SK23 7HY Tel: (01663) 735089 Fax: (01663) 735090 E-mail: sales@hi-press.co.uk *Hydraulic equipment distributors & service centre*

Hi-Pro Pressure Products Ltd, Unit 9, Beffemer Crescent, Rabans Lane Industrial Area, Aylesbury, Buckinghamshire, HP19 8TF Tel: (01296) 431804 Fax: (01296) 431845 E-mail: sales@hi-pro.co.uk *Pressure test equipment distributors*

Hira Company Ltd The, Elizabeth House, Elizabeth Street, Manchester, M8 8JJ Tel: 0161-834 2868 Fax: 0161-832 4566 E-mail: info@texet.com *General import & export merchants*

▶ Hirata Corporation Of Europe, Grafton Road, Burbage, West Grafton, Marlborough, Wiltshire, SN8 3BA Tel: (01672) 811728 Fax: (01672) 811666 E-mail: sales@hirata.co.uk *Materials handling equipment manufrs*

Hircocks Engineers Ltd, College Lodge Works, Wisbech St. Mary, Wisbech, Cambridgeshire, PE13 4SW Tel: (01945) 450404 Fax: (01945) 450595 E-mail: sales@hircocks.com *Agricultural engineering*

Hird Fan Systems, Town Hall, Westfield Road, Horbury, Wakefield, West Yorkshire, WF4 6HR Tel: (01924) 273731 Fax: (01924) 263096 *Dust extraction systems manufrs*

▶ Hire 4 Lower Tool Hire & Sales Ltd, 171, 172 Sail Street, London, SE11 6NQ Tel: (0845) 4667777 Fax: 0845 466 6666 E-mail: info@hire4lower.org *Tool & Equipment Rental & Sales*

Hire Intelligence, The Old Farm, Mill Lane, Alhampton, Shepton Mallet, Somerset, BA4 6PX Tel: (01749) 860301 Fax: (01749) 860089 E-mail: sales@hiresouthwest.co.uk *Computer hardware hire*

▶ Hire Intelligence (Leicester) Ltd, 3 Hawthorn Grove, Oadby, Leicester, LE2 4ED Tel: 0116-271 0091 Fax: 0116-271 0095 E-mail: leicester@hire-intelligence.co.uk *Audio visual & computer rentals*

▶ Hire Intelligence Southwest England - Exeter, 40 Southernhay East, Exeter, EX1 1PE Tel: (0800) 0857667 Fax: (0870) 2202752 E-mail: sales@hiresouthwest.co.uk *IT & rental services*

Hire It, Magnum House, Cookham Road, Bracknell, Berkshire, RG12 1RB Tel: (01344) 477744 Fax: (01344) 477789 E-mail: sales@hireit.co.uk *Computer equipment suppliers*

Hire Service Shops Ltd, 865 Fulham Road, London, SW6 5HP Tel: (020) 7736 1769 Fax: (020) 7736 3127 *Plant hire*

▶ Hire Services Southern Ltd, Manor Way, Woking, Surrey, GU22 9JX Tel: (01483) 740960 Fax: (01483) 740135 *Toll hire services*

▶ H.S.S. Hire Shops P.L.C., Unit 5 Rippleside Commercial Estate, Ripple Road, Barking, Essex, IG11 0RJ Tel: (020) 8595 3666 Fax: (020) 8595 4666 *Power tool hire services*

▶ The Hire Station, Unit 8, Warren Road, Trafford Park, Manchester, M17 1QR Tel: 0161-877 1234 Fax: 0161-888 5205 E-mail: sales@vp.com *Tool hire machinery hire*

Hire Station, Manor House Road, Long Eaton, Nottingham, NG10 3GA Tel: 0115-946 1151 Fax: 0115-946 1151 *Portable toilet hire & traffic management*

Hire Technicians Group, Chalk Hill House, 8 Chalk Hill, Watford, WD19 4BH Tel: (0845) 2303340 Fax: (0845) 2303345 E-mail: sales@hiretech.biz *Floor sanding machines manufrs* Also at: Branches throughout the U.K.

Hi-Reach Wales, Moy Road Industrial Estate, Taffs Well, Cardiff, CF15 7QR Tel: (029) 2081 3413 Fax: (029) 2081 3848 *Access equipment hire*

▶ Hireman (London) Ltd, Unit 4, Apex Industrial Estate, 22 Hythe Road, London, NW10 6RT Tel: (020) 8964 2464 Fax: (020) 8964 1343 *Supply tools to the building trade*

Hiremech Ltd, 1 Triumph Trading Estate, Tariff Road, London, N17 0EB Tel: (020) 8880 3322 Fax: (020) 8880 3355 E-mail: paul@hiremech.co.uk *Folk lift hire*

Hirepro Ltd, Unit 6 Atlas Business Centre, Oxgate La, Staples Corner, London, NW2 7HJ Tel: (020) 8438 0200 Fax: (020) 8438 0300 *Heating & lighting equipment*

Hirose Electric UK Ltd, Crownhill Business Centre, 22 Vincent Avenue, Crownhill, Milton Keynes, MK8 0AB Tel: (01908) 305400 Fax: (01908) 563309 E-mail: sales@hirose.co.uk *Electronic connectors & components*

Hiross, Thame Valley Industrial Estate, 1 Claymore, Wilnecote, Tamworth, Staffordshire, B77 5DQ Tel: (01827) 260056 Fax: (01827) 261196 E-mail: sales@zanderuk.com *Manufacturers of compressed air & gas*

Hirschfelds Ltd, Suite 26, 88-90 Hatton Garden, London, EC1N 8PN Tel: (020) 7405 1536 Fax: (020) 7831 4762 E-mail: info@hirschfelds.co.uk *Jewellery distributors*

▶ Hirst & Danson Ltd, Butts Close, Thornton-Cleveleys, Lancashire, FY5 4HT Tel: (01253) 859262 Fax: (01253) 864953 E-mail: enquiries@hirstanddanson.co.uk

Hirst Magnetic Instruments Ltd, Pesla House, Tregoniggie Industrial Estate, Falmouth, Cornwall, TR11 4SN Tel: (01326) 372734 Fax: (01326) 378069 E-mail: dudding@hirst-magnetics.com *Flux meter gas meter magnetic measuring instruments manufrs*

Hirt Combustion Engineers Ltd, Woodford Green Works, Leslie Road, Woodford Park Industrial Estate, Winsford, Cheshire, CW7 2RB Tel: (01606) 861366 Fax: (01606) 861408 E-mail: sales@hirt.co.uk *Manufacturers of combustion systems & thermal oxidisers (incinerators)*

His Contracts, 24-28 Pritchards Road, London, E2 9AP Tel: (020) 7739 1455 Fax: (020) 7729 9438 E-mail: info@hiscontracts.co.uk *Carpeting contractors*

Hiscock Engineers Trowbridge Ltd, 28 Union Street, Trowbridge, Wiltshire, BA14 8RY Tel: (01225) 752106 Fax: (01225) 751326 *Steel, stainless steel & aluminium fabricators*

Hiserve Computing Ltd, 11 Chiltern Close, Warminster, Wiltshire, BA12 8QU Tel: (01985) 846266 *Computer software consultants*

Hi-Span Ltd, Ayton Road, Wymondham, Norfolk, NR18 0RD Tel: (01953) 603081 Fax: (01953) 607842 E-mail: sales@hi-span.com *Cold rolled steel sections & purlins manufrs*

HiSpark Batteries Golf International Ltd, 450 Chester Road North, Sutton Coldfield, W. Midlands, B73 6RG Tel: 0121-568 8887 Fax: 0121-355 7807 *Battery charger manufrs*

▶ Hi-Spec Engineering, Unit 9 Windmill Industrial Estate, Windmill, Fowey, Cornwall, PL23 1HB Tel: (01726) 833844 Fax: (01726) 833811 E-mail: sales@hi-spec-eng.com *2d & 3d design & draughting services*

▶ Hi-Spec Precision Engineering, 1 Thistleton Road, Market Overton, Rutland, Oakham, Leicestershire, LE15 7PP Tel: (01572) 768036 Fax: (01780) 481696 E-mail: hi-spec_eng@lycos.co.uk *General & precision machined components & sub assemblies manufrs*

Histogram Ltd, Belmont Industrial Estate, Durham, DH1 1ST Tel: 0191-386 7111 Fax: 0191-383 3481 *Soft drinks packaging suppliers*

Histon Overalls Ltd, Unit 7, Cambrian Court, Ferryboat Close, Swansea Enterprise Park, Swansea, SA6 8PZ Tel: (01792) 772870 Fax: (01792) 772870 *Industrial overall clothing manufrs*

Hi-Store Ltd, Station Approach, Four Marks, Alton, Hampshire, GU34 5HN Tel: (01420) 562522 Fax: (01420) 564420 E-mail: sales@hi-store.com *Mezzanine floors, racking & storage equipment*

Hitachi Automotive Systems (Europe) Ltd, Aspinall Way, Middlebrook Business Park, Bolton, BL6 6JH Tel: (01204) 469879 Fax: (01204) 469748 *Automotive components manufrs*

▶ Hitachi Cable UK Ltd, Unit 39-40, Rassau Industrial Estate, Rassau, Ebbw Vale, Gwent, NP23 5SD Tel: (01495) 308304 Fax: (01495) 356809

Hitachi Denshi UK, Windsor House, Britannia Road, Waltham Cross, Hertfordshire, EN8 7NX Tel: (01992) 704595 Fax: (0845) 1212180 E-mail: sales@hitachi-ke-eu.com *Closed circuit television distributors*

Hitachi Hi-Technology Corporation, 7 Ivanhoe Road, Hogwood Industrial Estate, Finchampstead, Wokingham, Berkshire, RG40 4QQ Tel: 0118-932 8632 Fax: 0118-932 8779 E-mail: sales@hitachi-hitec-uk.com *Scientific instruments sales service*

Hitachi Home Electronics (Europe) Ltd, Whitebrook Park, Lower Cookham Road, Maidenhead, Berkshire, SL6 8YA Tel: (01628) 643000 Fax: (01628) 778322 *Electric appliance manufrs*

Hitachi Power Tools (UK) Ltd, Precedent Drive, Rooksley, Milton Keynes, MK13 8PJ Tel: (01908) 354700 Fax: (01908) 606642 E-mail: info@hitachi-powertools.co.uk *Power tool & accessories distribs*

Lionel Hitchen (Essential Oils) Ltd, Gravel Lane, Barton Stacey, Winchester, Hampshire, SO21 3RQ Tel: (01962) 760815 Fax: (01962) 760072 E-mail: info@lhn.co.uk *Citrus oil spice & herb oleoresins*

John Hitchin Cars, Unit 3 Dean Street, Bedford, MK40 3EQ Tel: (01234) 348527 Fax: (01234) 348753 *Car body repairers*

Hi-Tec Beds Ltd, Unit 2 Albion Mills, Bradford Rd, Dewsbury, West Yorkshire, WF13 2HD Tel: 01924 459393 Fax: 01924 488900 *Beds & mattress manufrs*

Hi-Tec Controls (Bolton) Ltd, Unit 4 Riverside, Waters Meeting Road, The Valley, Bolton, BL1 8TU Tel: (01204) 392172 Fax: (01204) 391660 E-mail: info@hiteccontrols.co.uk *Hi-Tec Controls (Bolton) Ltd, based in Bolton near Manchester specialise in the design, manufacture and installation of a wide range of sliding and hinged power operated Gates, barriers, bollards for domestic, commercial and industrial application. With having over 20 years experience we can carefully select the best system to suit the individual site requirements. We also have Safe contractor accreditation and are accredited installers and distributors of BFT Automation and Magnetic Traffic control barriers. We have fully qualified engineers who are experienced in all different types of automation and can service/repair all types of gates and barriers. Many leading regional and national companies have elected to use the products and services offered by Hi-Tec Controls (Bolton) Ltd. For further information please telephone our sales team or visit our website detailed below.*

Hitec Lift Trucks Ltd, 12 Bradfield Road, Finedon Road Industrial Estate, Wellingborough, Northamptonshire, NN8 4HB Tel: (01234) 350404 Fax: (01933) 440296 E-mail: sales@askhitec.co.uk *Fork lift truck sales & hire & training services*

▶ Hi-Tec Roofing, 4 Gallowhill Road, Paisley, Renfrewshire, PA3 4TF Tel: 0141-887 5775 Fax: 0141-887 5775 E-mail: sales@hi-tecroofing.co.uk *non slip safety products for stairs,floors,ramps,work stations,jetties ect.*

Hitec Suspended Ceilings, 44 Inisclan Road, Mountfield, Omagh, County Tyrone, BT79 7QB Tel: (028) 8077 1422 Fax: (028) 8077 1122 E-mail: hitecceilings@hotmail.com *Suspended ceilings & partitions suppliers*

Hi-Tech Aerials, 5 Golden Noble Hill, Colchester, CO1 2AG Tel: (0800) 3897091 Fax: (0800) 3897091 E-mail: info@hitechaerials.co.uk *Aerial & satellite installations & repairs*

Hi-Tech Alarms, 5 Tingley Crescent, Tingley, Wakefield, West Yorkshire, WF3 1JF Tel: 0113-252 9917 *Security alarm installers*

Hi-Tech Audio Ltd, 68 Turnberry Drive, Wilmslow, Cheshire, SK9 2QN Tel: (01625) 521302 Fax: (01625) 526345 E-mail: info@hitechaudio.com *Professional audio equipment specialists*

Hi-Tech Distribution Ltd, Unit 5 Phoenix Trading Estate, Bilton Road, Perivale, Greenford, Middlesex, UB6 7DZ Tel: (020) 8991 8700 Fax: (020) 8991 8776 *Computer distribution*

Hitech Equipment Ltd, 36 Clark Street, Paisley, Renfrewshire, PA3 1RB Tel: 0141-887 5689 Fax: 0141-887 7846 E-mail: gaynor@hitech-env.co.uk *Industrial cleaners & waste disposal consultants*

▶ Hi-Tech Horticulture, Setters Farm, Mount Pleasant Lane, Lymington, Hants, SO41 8LS Tel: (01590) 672835 Fax: (01590) 688932

Hi-Tech Logistics Ltd, Greenford Green Business Park, Rockware Avenue, Greenford, Middlesex, UB6 0RZ Tel: (020) 8566 6060

Hi-Tech Moulding Ltd, Unit 34, Kettlestring Lane, York, YO30 4XF Tel: (01904) 479888 Fax: (01904) 479966 E-mail: enquiries@hi-techmoulding.com *Thermo plastic injection moulders*

Hi-Tech Mouldings Ltd, Tyak House, Silverthorne Way, Waterlooville, Hampshire, PO7 7XY Tel: (023) 9225 9259 Fax: (023) 9236 6663 E-mail: sales@hitechltd.com *Able to offer total manufacturing solutions from design to manufacture. Hi-Tech Design provide design solutions, Hi-Tech Tooling provide injection mould tools & Hi-Tech Mouldings technical injection moulding & assembly.*

Hi-Tech Seals & Polymers Ltd, Unit 3, Castellian Road, Wessington North Industrial Estate, Sunderland, SR5 3BE Tel: 0191-549 1100 Fax: 0191-549 1557 E-mail: billy@hitechseals.co.uk *Blastomeric seal manufacturer & puttee materials supplier*

Hi-Tech Security Services Ltd, Fortune Business Park, Brook Lane, Worthing, West Sussex, BN12 5JD Tel: (01903) 709000 Fax: (01903) 709002 E-mail: cust.serv@guardianhitech.com *Electronic security services*

Hi-Tech Sheet Metal Ltd, Molyneux House, Unit B, Fort Road Ind Est, Fort Road, Littlehampton, West Sussex, BN17 7QU Tel: 01903 711222 Fax: 01903 711227 E-mail: sales@htsm-ltd.co.uk *Sub-contract Sheetmetal Company and Precision Laser Profiling*

Hitech Signmakers Ltd, 65-81 Townsend St, Glasgow, G4 0LA Tel: 0141-332 4111 Fax: 0141-331 1906 E-mail: sales@hitechsigns.co.uk *Sign contractors*

Hi-Tech Tubebending, Saunders House, Moor Lane, Witton, Birmingham, B6 7HH Tel: 0121-356 2224 Fax: 0121-356 2220 E-mail: info@scottandbarnett.co.uk *Tube manipulation*

Hitek Ltd, Unit 2, Foundry Court, Foundry Lane, Horsham, West Sussex, RH13 5PY Tel: (01403) 243535 Fax: (01403) 243536 E-mail: sales@hitek.co.uk *Calibration services*

Hitek Electronic Materials Ltd, 15 Wentworth Road, Scunthorpe, South Humberside, DN17 2AX Tel: (01724) 851678 Fax: (01724) 280586 E-mail: sales@hitek-ltd.co.uk *Emc, microwave & polymer systems*

Hitel Communication Systems, 97 Stanley Road, Bootle, Merseyside, L20 7DA Tel: 0151-944 1276 Fax: 0151-933 1313 E-mail: info@hitelcommunications.com *Telecommunication services*

Hitex (UK) Ltd, University of Warwick Science Park, Sir William Lyons Road, Coventry, CV4 7EZ Tel: (024) 7669 2066 Fax: (024) 7669 2131 E-mail: sales@hitex.co.uk *Microprocesser development systems manufrs*

Hitherbest Ltd, Heath Hill Court, Heath Hill Industrial Estate, Dawley, Telford, Shropshire, TF4 2RH Tel: (01952) 632100 Fax: (01952) 632109 E-mail: sales@hitherbest.co.uk *Sheet metal fabrication company*

▶ The Hitman, Cheltenham Street, Bath, BA2 3EX Tel: (0808) 1000881 *Vehicle accident repair*

▶ Hi-Ton (International) Ltd, Montgomery Street, Sparkbrook, Birmingham, B11 1DY Tel: 0121-772 2711

▶ Hitss Safety Training Ltd, Foxgloves, Millers Lane, Hornton, Banbury, Oxfordshire, OX15 6BS Tel: (01295) 678200 Fax: (01295) 670252 E-mail: sales@hitss.co.uk *Health & safety training & consultancy*

Hiva Products, Disraeli Street, Leicester, LE2 8LX Tel: 0116-283 6977 Fax: 0116-283 5265 E-mail: info@hiva.co.uk Principal Export Areas: Worldwide *Flock coating services*

▶ Hivac Engineering Ltd, 14 Ivyhouse Lane, Hastings, East Sussex, TN35 4NN Tel: (01424) 461007 Fax: (01424) 461009

The Hive, 37 Dean Street, London, W1D 4PT Tel: (020) 7565 1000 Fax: (020) 7494 0059 *Audio-visual equipment manufrs*

Hive Industries, 28 High Street, Arlesey, Bedfordshire, SG15 6RA Tel: (01462) 735151 Fax: (08707) 708089 *Audio visual hire*

Hivolt Capacitors Ltd, Maydown, Londonderry, BT47 6UQ Tel: (028) 7186 0265 Fax: (028) 7186 0479 E-mail: hivoltcapacitors@easynet.co.uk *Electrical rectifiers & capacitors manufrs*

Hi-Way Hi-Fi Ltd, 318-324 Edgware Road, London, W2 1DY Tel: (020) 7723 5251 Fax: (020) 7535 3280 *TV & video distributors*

Hixons, 45 Denton Road, Audenshaw, Manchester, M34 5BL Tel: 0161-336 3725 Fax: 0161-336 4184 E-mail: sales@hixons.com *Electric screwdrivers & pneumatic tool importers*

HK Food Products, 2-3 Helmsley Place, London, E8 3SB Tel: (020) 7249 4130 Fax: (020) 7249 4137 E-mail: hkfood@btinternet.com *Noodles suppliers & manufrs*

HK Wentworth Ltd, Kingsbury Park, Midlington Road, Swadlincote, Derbyshire, DE11 0AN Tel: (01283) 222111 Fax: (01283) 550177 E-mail: afsales@hkw.co.uk *Office equipment cleaning products manufrs*

HKS, Head Office, Ghyll Industrial Estate, Heathfield, East Sussex, TN21 8AW Tel: (01435) 866166 Fax: (01435) 866667 *Furnishing manufrs*

▶ HLB International, 21 Ebury Street, London, SW1W 0LD Tel: (020) 7881 1100 Fax: (020) 7881 1109 E-mail: mailbox@hlbi.com *Accountants*

▶ HLBB Shaw, 303 Science Park, Milton Road, Cambridge, CB4 0WG Tel: (01223) 425891 Fax: 01223 423701 E-mail: mail@hlbb.com *Patent & Trade Mark Attorneys with expertise in the following technologies - chemistry & materials science; pharma & nutrition; life sciences; electronics, telecoms & computer science; engineering.*

▶ Hlbbshaw, 10th Floor Metropolitan House, 1 Hagley Road, Birmingham, B16 8TG Tel: 0121-454 4962 Fax: 0121-454 4523 E-mail: enquiries@laurenceshaw.co.uk *Patent & Trade Mark Attorneys with expertise in the following technologies - chemistry & materials science; pharma & nutrition; life sciences; electronics, telecoms & computer science; engineering.*

Hlbbshaw, Shaw House, Pegler Way, Crawley, West Sussex, RH11 7AF Tel: (01293) 528000 Fax: (01293) 528900 E-mail: mail@hlbbshaw.com *European Patent & Trade Mark Attorneys with expertise in the following technologies - chemistry & materials science; pharma & nutrition; life sciences; electronics, telecoms & computer science; environmental technology and engineering.*

Hlbbshaw, Bloxam Court, Corporation Street, Rugby, Warwickshire, CV21 2DU Tel: (01788) 577000 Fax: (01788) 540783 E-mail: mail@hlbbshaw.com *Patent & Trade Mark Attorneys with expertise in the following technologies - chemistry & materials science; pharma & nutrition; life sciences; electronics, telecoms & computer science; engineering.*

▶ HMC Electrical Services Ltd, Maidstone Road, Nettlestead, Maidstone, Kent, ME18 5HP Tel: (01622) 870088 Fax: (01622) 870077 E-mail: hmcelectrical@btconnect.com *Fixed wire, portable appliance (PAT) services*

HMG Coatings South Ltd, Faraday Park, Andover, Hampshire, SP10 3SA Tel: (01264) 337824 Fax: (01264) 338123 E-mail: mail@hmgcoatings.co.uk Principal Export Areas: Africa *Paint & powder coating manufacturers & distributors*

▶ HMK Ltd, 416 Westcott Venture Park, Aylesbury, Buckinghamshire, HP18 0NP Tel: (01296) 655285 Fax: (01296) 655795 E-mail: kevin@hmknives.demon.co.uk *Specialists in the development & manufacture of tungsten carbide*

HNC Electronics, 70 Oxford Street, London, W1D 1BP Tel: (020) 7436 0844 *Electronic resellers*

Hne Huntleigh Ltd, Unit 11b Brooklands Way, Boldon Business Park, Boldon Colliery, Tyne & Wear, NE35 9LZ Tel: 0191-536 1291 Fax: 0191-536 1307 *Pressure releasing mattresses*

Hoad & Taylor Ltd, 5 Manfield Park, Cranleigh, Surrey, GU6 8PT Tel: (01483) 204800 Fax: (01483) 204801 *AGA services*

L.F. Hoare Ltd, Unit 18, Shrivenham Hundred Business Park, Majors Road, Watchfield, Swindon, SN6 8TZ Tel: (01793) 783880 Fax: (01793) 782977 E-mail: info@welding.fsnet.co.uk *Holding company*

Hoare, Lea, Glen House, 200-208 Tottenham Court Road, London, W1T 7PL Tel: (020) 7890 2500 Fax: (020) 7436 8466 E-mail: joebrookes@londonhoarelea.com Principal Export Areas: Worldwide *Consulting engineers & designers* Also at: Branches throughout the U.K.

Hobart UK, 51 The Bourne, Southgate, London, N14 6RT Tel: (0844) 8887777 Fax: (020) 8886 0450 E-mail: info@hobartuk.com *For over 100 years Hobart has set the industry benchmark in Warewashing, Food Preparation, Cooking and Beverage Equipment. A customer driven and customer focused organisation, Hobart's range is the most comprehensive and technologically advanced in the market place Whether it's a mixer or a pass through warewasher, all of our equipment includes advanced features that deliver real operational benefits. Hobart stands for quality, reliability and innovation - to help us keep this promise our fully trained, dedicated technicians will look after your investment throughout its life. That's why Hobart is the World's No.1 Choice. Sales enquiries: 020 8920 2900 www.hobartuk.com*

Hobbs Electrical Services, 121 High Street, Stony Stratford, Milton Keynes, MK11 1AT Tel: (01908) 565577 Fax: (01908) 261211 E-mail: hobbs.electrical@btinternet.com *Electrical engineers & contractors*

▶ Steve Hobbs Logistics, 8 Harrowden Road, Luton, LU2 0SP Tel: (01582) 457040 Fax: *24 Hour Sameday Express Couriers *We Get Parcels To Places In Style*

▶ Hobby Casuals, The Sanderson Centre, Lees Lane, Gosport, Hampshire, PO12 3UL Tel: (023) 9258 3826 Fax: (023) 9251 0287 *Clothing manufrs*

Hobby Homes, 3 Industrial Estate, Thomas Road, London, E14 7BN Tel: (020) 7987 0550 Fax: (020) 7537 6501 E-mail: sales@hobbyhomes.com *Electrical fixing & fastening distributors*

▶ Hobbycraft Superstores Ltd, Unit 2 Harlech Retail Park, Cardiff Road, Newport, Gwent, NP20 3BA Tel: (01633) 652070 *Art material retailers*

Hobday Ltd, Aston Brook St East, Aston, Birmingham, B6 4RR Tel: 0121-359 4431 Fax: 0121-608 2008 *Shop fittings manufrs*

▶ Hobdens Removals, 6 The Courtyard, Barns Ground, Kenn Business Park, Clevedon, Somerset, BS21 6TB Tel: (01275) 877122 Fax: (01275) 875000 E-mail: enquiries@hobdensremovals.co.uk *General removals packing & removal of antiques pianos*

Hoblongs Engineering, Hoblongs Industrial Estate, Chelmsford Road, Dunmow, Essex, CM6 1JA Tel: (01371) 874550 Fax: (01371) 872698 *Sheet metal fabricators*

Hobs Reprographic, 244-256 Deansgate, Manchester, M3 4BQ Tel: 0161-832 6670 Fax: 0161-833 2228 *Printers*

Hobs Reprographics, 56d Milton Park, Milton, Abingdon, Oxfordshire, OX14 4RX Tel: (01235) 833044 Fax: (01235) 831666 E-mail: abington@hobsrepro.com *Drawing office & graphic products* Also at: Reading

Hobs Reprographics, 178 Old Christchurch Road, Bournemouth, BH1 1NU Tel: (01202) 553233 Fax: (01202) 557616 E-mail: bournemouth@hobsrepro.com *Reprographic printing services*

Hobs Reprographics, 52-60 Woodlands Road, Glasgow, G3 6HA Tel: 0141-333 9535 Fax: 0141-332 6395 E-mail: glasgow@hobsrepro.com *Drawing office equipment distributors*

Hobs Reprographics, 18a Slater Street, Liverpool, L1 4BS Tel: 0151-709 0261 Fax: 0151-709 4769 E-mail: liverpool@hobsrepro.com *Reprographics*

Hobs Reprographics, 9-11 Grosvenor Gardens, London, SW1W 0BD Tel: (020) 7834 1187 Fax: (020) 7834 0045 E-mail: grosvenor@hobsrepro.ndirect.com *Dyeline printers*

▶ Hobs (UK) Ltd, 29 Lilley Drive, Kingswood, Tadworth, Surrey, KT20 6JA Tel: (01737) 831426

J. Reuben Hobson & Co. Ltd, Albany House, 6 Wicker Lane, Sheffield, S3 8HQ Tel: 0114-272 1604 Fax: 0114-275 5567 *Drinking glassware, crockery & cutlery wholesalers*

Hobson Paragon UK Ltd, Commercial Way, Oakengates, Telford, Shropshire, TF2 6SG Tel: (01952) 619111 Fax: (01952) 616921 *Packaging material manufrs*

▶ Hobson & Porter Ltd, Malmo Road, Hull, HU7 0YF Tel: (01482) 823999 Fax: (01482) 823733

Hobsons Publishing plc, 42 Adler Street, London, E1 1EE Tel: (020) 7958 5000 Fax: (020) 7958 5001 E-mail: london.recception@hobsons.co.uk *Publishers* Also at: London SW1

Hobstar Ltd, Palace Chemicals Ltd, Speke Hall Industrial Estate, Liverpool, L24 4AB Tel: 0151-486 6101 Fax: 0151-448 1982 E-mail: sales@palacechemicals.co.uk *DIY products supplier*

Hoburne Business Systems Ltd, 9a Saulfland Place, Christchurch, Dorset, BH23 4QP Tel: (01425) 280009 Fax: (01425) 280905 E-mail: sales@hoburnesystems.co.uk *In this constantly changing computer industry, systems are becoming smaller and more powerful. With costs generally falling it is vital that businesses buy into the latest technologies to remain competitive. Hoburne Business Systems is committed to finding high quality solutions to suit the emerging needs of our business, corporate and educational customers alike.*

Hocken Audio Visual Ltd, 5 Waterhouse Lane, Kingswood, Tadworth, Surrey, KT20 6EB Tel: (01737) 370371 Fax: (01737) 370372 E-mail: sales@hockenav.co.uk *Audio visual equipment & services*

Hocken Sound Contracts Ltd, 50 Sovereign Road, Kings Norton Business Centre, Birmingham, B30 3HN Tel: 0121-459 4242 Fax: 0121-433 5362 E-mail: sales@hockensound.co.uk *Sound, lighting & visual equipment suppliers & installers*

Hockerill Engraving, 2d Willis Vean Industrial Estate, Mullion, Helston, Cornwall, TR12 7DF Tel: (01326) 240400 Fax: (01326) 240620 E-mail: hockerill@dial.pipex.com *Nameplate & commemorative plaque manufrs*

▶ Hocking Marketing Partnership, 22 Armstrong Close, Crownhill, Milton Keynes, MK8 0AU Tel: (01908) 563883 E-mail: info@hmpltd.co.uk *Telesales services*

Hockley Enterprises Ltd, Grainger Road, Southend-on-Sea, SS2 5BZ Tel: (01702) 614067 Fax: (01702) 462163 *Electroplaters*

Hockley Pattern & Tool Company Ltd, Lodgefield Road, Halesowen, West Midlands, B62 8AR Tel: 0121-561 4665 Fax: 0121-525 0595 E-mail: sales@hockleypattern.co.uk *Hockley Pattern & Tool Co. Ltd based in Halesowen, West Midlands are engineer's pattern manufacturers. They manufacturer jigs, fixtures, moulds, tool and patterns for automotive and aerospace industries.*

Hocklynn Ltd, Netham Road, Bristol, BS5 9PQ Tel: 0117-955 6294 Fax: 0117-935 1062 E-mail: hocklynnlimited@aol.com *Metal fabricators & engineers*

▶ Hockman, 4 Church Street, Amersham, Buckinghamshire, HP7 0DB Tel: (01494) 726963 Fax: (01494) 431248 E-mail: johnwootton@btconnect.com *Service station equipment suppliers*

▶ Hocus Pocus, 38 Gardner Street, Brighton, BN1 1UN Tel: (01273) 572212 Fax: (01273) 572207 E-mail: info@hocuspocus.co.uk *Candles, tarot cards & occult paraphernalia suppliers*

Hoddam Contracting Co. Ltd, Hoddom Road, Ecclefechan, Lockerbie, Dumfriesshire, DG11 3BY Tel: (01576) 300634 Fax: (01576) 300798 *Quarrymasters ready mix concrete concrete blocks*

Hoddesden Plant Hire Ltd, Unit 21, Pindar Road, Hoddesdon, Hertfordshire, EN11 0DE Tel: (01992) 443161 Fax: (01992) 451679 *Contractors' plant hire & sales*

▶ Hodge Ltd, 4 North Howard Street, Belfast, BT13 2AS Tel: (028) 9024 1812 Fax: (028) 9024 6866 *Sales & installation of office furniture*

L. Hodge Engineering Ltd, Unit 12, Chiltern Business Village, Arundel Road, Uxbridge, Middlesex, UB8 2SN Tel: (01895) 813758 Fax: (01895) 812468 E-mail: john@lhodge-engineers.co.uk *Machine knife manufrs*

▶ Hodge Plant, Craighead Farm, Abington, Biggar, Lanarkshire, ML12 6SQ Tel: (01864) 502577 E-mail: hire@hodgeplant.com

Hodge Recruitment Ltd, 22 Henrietta Street, London, WC2E 8ND Tel: (020) 7420 3950 *Employment agency*

Samuel Hodge Ltd, 2 Bluecoats Avenue, Hertford, SG14 1PB Tel: (01992) 558675 Fax: (01992) 581881 *Engineering services*

Hodge Separators Ltd, 1 Jennings Road, Kernick Road Industrial Estate, Penryn, Cornwall, TR10 9LY Tel: (01326) 375388 Fax: (01326) 377235 E-mail: sales@hodge-separators.com *Marine oily water specialists*

Geo Hodges & Son Ltd, 82 Horninglow Street, Burton-on-Trent, Staffordshire, DE14 1PN Tel: (01283) 565461 Fax: (01283) 510338 E-mail: contract@hodges.co.uk *Building & civil engineers*

▶ Hodges & Lawrence Ltd, Baccabox Lane, Hollywood, Birmingham, B47 5DD Tel: (01564) 823049 Fax: (01564) 826599 E-mail: enquiries@hnl-fencing.co.uk *Making & erecting of fencing*

▶ Hodges & Marten, Unit 6-7 Ringmer Business Centre, Chamberlaines Lane, Lewes, East Sussex, BN8 5NF Tel: (01273) 812771 Fax: (01273) 812746

Hodges Print & Design, 12 Hazeldell, Watton At Stone, Hertford, SG14 3SN Tel: (01920) 411288 Fax: (01920) 411288 *Print design & advertising services*

J.F. Hodgett & Co. Ltd, 66 Bedford Street South, Leicester, LE1 3JR Tel: 0116-251 0705 Fax: 0116-251 2877 E-mail: jfhodgett@hotmail.com *Knitted fabric manufrs, to stock & to order. Stock colour ranges in cotton & nylon*

James Hodgins & Sons Ltd, 77 Coustonholm Road, Glasgow, G43 1UF Tel: 0141-632 6241 Fax: 0141-636 1184 *Painting & decorating contractors*

Hodgkinson Bennis Ltd, Highfield Road, Little Hulton, Manchester, M38 9SS Tel: 0161-790 4411 Fax: 0161-703 8505 E-mail: enquiries@hbcombustion.com *Mechanical stoker manufacturers & heating engineer services*

Hodgson Engineering Ltd, Unit 8 Metcalfe Road, Skippers Lane Industrial Estate, Middlesbrough, Cleveland, TS6 6PT Tel: (01642) 440888 Fax: (01642) 440888 E-mail: dene@hodgson-engineering.com *Valve refurbishers*

Hodgson & Hodgson Group, Audio House, Progress Road, Sands Industrial Estate, High Wycombe, Buckinghamshire, HP12 4JD Tel: (01494) 519000 Fax: (01494) 465274 E-mail: ecomax@easynet.co.uk *Industrial noise control equipment, systems engineers & fabricators* Also at: Corby

Hodgson Lighting, 41 High Street, Hampton Hill, Hampton, Middlesex, TW12 1NB Tel: (020) 8941 3375 Fax: (020) 8979 5178 E-mail: johnatjhlight@tiscali.co.uk *Domestic lighting fittings distributors & manufrs*

Hodgson Sealants Ltd, Belprin Road, Beverley, North Humberside, HU17 0LN Tel: (01482) 868321 Fax: (01482) 870729 E-mail: sales@hodgson-sealants.co.uk *Sealant manufacturer, Hodgson Sealants provides foam tapes, preformed butyl sealants, mastics, silicone sealants & putty for glazing, roofing , cladding industrial automotive & caravan markets. Fire resistant intumescent sealants, adhesive tapes, polyurethane retardant foam for doors & screens, complete the range.*

William Hodgson & Co., 73A London Road, Alderley Edge, Cheshire, SK9 7DY Tel: (01625) 599111 Fax: (01625) 599222 *Edible oil & fat producers*

Company Information

▶ Hodkin & Co., 42-44 Copthorne Road, Felbridge, East Grinstead, West Sussex, RH19 2NS Tel: (01342) 325765 Fax: (01342) 325479 *Solicitors: Wills; Conveyancing; Probate; Civil Litigation; Immigration*

Hodkin & Jones (Sheffield) Ltd, Callywhite Lane, Dronfield, Derbyshire, S18 2XP Tel: (01246) 290890 Fax: (01246) 290292 *Fibre manufrs*

Hodkin & Jones (Sheffield) Ltd, Callywhite Lane, Dronfield, Derbyshire, S18 2XP Tel: (01246) 290890 Fax: (01246) 290292 E-mail: info@hodkin-jones.co.uk *Glass fibre mouldings manufrs*

Hodson Engineering, 16 Second Drove Industrial Estate, Peterborough, PE1 5XA Tel: (01733) 562323 Fax: (01733) 562323 *Aluminium fabrications*

Hodsons Bloxwich Ltd, Bloxwich Road, Walsall, WS2 7BD Tel: (01922) 649649 Fax: (01922) 631823 *Scrap metal merchants or processors*

▶ Hoe Grange Holidays, Brassington, Matlock, Derbyshire, DE4 4HP Tel: 01629 540261

▶ Hoecker Structures UK Ltd, Robinson Way, Telford Way Industrial Estate, Kettering, Northamptonshire, NN16 8PT Tel: (01536) 316970 Fax: (01536) 316979 E-mail: sales@hoecker.plus.com *Marquees, party pavilions, temp stores, warehouses supply & manufrs*

Hoerbiger, Edderthorpe Street, Bradford, West Yorkshire, BD3 9RB Tel: (01274) 733801 Fax: (01274) 736887 E-mail: sales@hrpu.co.uk *Compressor parts manufrs*

Hoerbiger UK Ltd, 1649 Pershore Road, Stirchley, Birmingham, B30 3DR Tel: 0121-433 3636 Fax: 0121-433 3854 E-mail: info.huk@hoerbiger.com *Valve repairers*

Hofmann Ceramic Ltd, 291 Thompson Hill, High Green, Sheffield, S35 4JT Tel: 0114-284 8161 Fax: 0114-284 6975 E-mail: hofmann.ceramic@btinternet.com *Industrial ceramic product suppliers*

Hoganas GB Ltd, Munday Works, Morley Road, Tonbridge, Kent, TN9 1RP Tel: (01732) 362243 Fax: (01732) 770262 E-mail: sales@powdrex.com *High speed steel powder manufrs*

Hogarth Estates, 16b Hogarth Place, London, SW5 0QT Tel: (020) 7373 5222 Fax: (020) 7370 7960 E-mail: hogarthestates@btinternet.com *Estate agents*

G.W. Hogarth, Town End Farm, Glassonby, Penrith, Cumbria, CA10 1DU Tel: (01768) 898317 *Agricultural merchants*

John Hogarth Ltd, PO Box 6, Kelso, Roxburghshire, TD5 7HR Tel: (01573) 224224 Fax: (01573) 225461 E-mail: johnhogarth@kelsomills.freeserve.co.uk *Oatmeal manufacturers & millers*

Hoge 100 Business Systems Ltd, I M S House, Prescott Drive, Worcester, WR4 9NE Tel: (01905) 455227 Fax: (01905) 455035 E-mail: sales@hoge100.co.uk *Computer software developers*

Hogg Engineering Ltd, Lawson Street, North Shields, Tyne & Wear, NE29 6TF Tel: 0191-259 5181 Fax: 0191-296 0641 E-mail: hogg-engineering@talk21.com Principal Export Areas: Central/East Europe & West Europe *Case making packing services*

Hogg Pneumatics Ltd, Collingwood House, Lawson Street, North Shields, Tyne & Wear, NE29 6TG Tel: 0191-258 2623 Fax: 0191-296 1445 E-mail: sales@james-hogg.demon.co.uk *Pneumatic blasting & finishing services*

▶ Hogg Robert Joiner, 36 Mount Stewart Street, Carluke, Lanarkshire, ML8 5EB Tel: (01555) 772627

Hohner Automation Ltd, Unit 15 Whitegate Industrial Estate, Whitegate Road, Wrexham, Clwyd, LL13 8UG Tel: (01978) 363888 Fax: (01978) 364586 E-mail: uksales@hohner.com *Encoder manufrs*

Hoist & Co., Bonnyacre Farm, Wrotham Road, Meopham, Gravesend, Kent, DA13 0RF Tel: (01732) 823826 Fax: (01732) 823826 *Fencing manufrs*

▶ Hoist & Access Services Ltd, 2-2a Dalsholm Avenue, Glasgow, G20 0TS Tel: 0141-945 0101 Fax: 0141-946 5200 E-mail: sales@hoistandaccess.com

Hoist Mec Ltd, Brook Farm, Drayton Road, Newton Longville, Milton Keynes, MK17 0BH Tel: (01908) 641949 Fax: (01908) 641988 *Forklift truck & side loader specialist sales, service, repair*

Holbar Engineering, Unit 31B, Parsonage Farm Industrial Estate, Forest Hall Road, Stansted, Essex, CM24 8TY Tel: (01279) 814344 Fax: (01279) 814995 E-mail: holbar@btconnect.com *Precision sub-contract machining*

▶ Holbeach Computing Solutions, 17 Spalding Road, Holbeach, Spalding, Lincolnshire, PE12 7HG Tel: (01406) 426342 E-mail: don.scott@holbeachcomputing.co.uk *IT Solutions*Microsoft Appications and Operating Systems including WIN9x, Windows XP Windows 2000 Server and Windows 2003*Linux and Unix*TCP/IP Networking*

Holbeach Wholefoods, 32 High Street, Holbeach, Spalding, Lincolnshire, PE12 7DY Tel: (01406) 422149 Fax: (01406) 362939 *Health food retailers*

Holbein, 142A Canbury Park Road, Kingston upon Thames, Surrey, KT2 6LE Tel: (020) 8974 5695 Fax: (020) 8974 5635 *Decorative curtain pole manufrs*

Holborn Direct Mail, Capacity House, 2-6 Rothsay Street, London, SE1 4UD Tel: (020) 7407 6444 Fax: (020) 7357 6065 E-mail: peter@holborndirectmail.co.uk *Direct mail, database management*

Holborn Enterprises Ltd, 8 & 9 Scott Skinner Square, Banchory, Kincardineshire, AB31 5SE Tel: (01330) 824545 Fax: (01330) 824545 *Computer systems & software*

Holborn Waste Ltd, Massie Works, 305 A -335 Lichfield Road, Aston, Birmingham, B6 7ST Tel: 0121-327 1046 Fax: 0121-327 3968 E-mail: hwsales@btconnect.com *Waste paper merchants & skip hire*

Holbourne Engineering, Wem Engineering Centre, Church Lane, Wem, Shrewsbury, SY4 5HS Tel: (01939) 235124 Fax: (01939) 235126 E-mail: info@holborne-engineering.co.uk *Building fabrication*

C.A. Holbrook Ltd, St. Georges Works, Faire Street, Derby, DE22 3WB Tel: (01332) 347021 Fax: (01332) 380750 E-mail: info@presteagebinders.com *Cardboard box & carton manufrs*

Holbrook Removals, 24 Abingdon Road, Ryde, Isle of Wight, PO33 2RR Tel: (01983) 566616 Fax: (01983) 566616 *Removal contractors*

Holbrooks Printers Ltd, Norway Road, Portsmouth, PO3 5HX Tel: (023) 9266 1485 Fax: (023) 9267 1119 E-mail: sales@holbrooks.com *Magazine, brochure & catalogue printers*

Holbros Ltd, Morvil House Maypole CR, Darent Industrial Park, Erith, Kent, DA8 2JZ Tel: (01322) 335424 Fax: (01322) 333703 E-mail: info@holbros.co.uk *Sponge & foam manufrs*

Holbrow Brookes & Partners, Pinewood, Bell Heath Way, Birmingham, B32 3BZ Tel: 0121-423 4000 Fax: 0121-423 4230 E-mail: info@holbrowbrookes.co.uk *Chartered quantity surveyors & project managers*

Holcrofts Catering Suppliers, Coldwell Burn Farm, Haswell, Durham, DH6 2XS Tel: 0191-517 0414 Fax: 0191-517 0162 *Fruit & vegetable wholesalers*

Holdcroft Aviation Services Ltd, Hinton In The Hedges Airfield, Steane, Brackley, Northamptonshire, NN13 5NS Tel: (01295) 810287 Fax: (01295) 812247 *Aviation services*

Holden Aluminium Technologies Ltd, Linton Trading Estate, Bromyard, Herefordshire, HR7 4QT Tel: (01885) 482222 Fax: (01885) 482000 E-mail: info@alloy.uk.com *Aluminium manipulators & fabricators*

Brian Holden Ltd, 14 Racca Green, Knottingley, West Yorkshire, WF11 8AT Tel: (01977) 672791 Fax: (01977) 672791 *Country wear manufrs*

Holden & Brooke Ltd, Wenlock Way, Manchester, M12 5JL Tel: 0161-223 2223 Fax: 0161-220 9660 E-mail: marketing@holdenbrooke.com *Pump distributors & manufrs*

Holden Engineering (U K) Ltd, 35a Oxford Road, Penmill Trading Estate, Yeovil, Somerset, BA21 5HR Tel: (01935) 410615 Fax: (01935) 410617 E-mail: holden.uk@talk21.com *Stainless steel fabricators*

Holden Environmental Ltd, Shore Road, Perth, PH2 8BH Tel: (01738) 634747 Fax: (01738) 637150 E-mail: sales@holden-enviro.com *Scrap metal merchants, skip hire & waste management*

Holden Manufacturing Ltd, 4 Clarendon Drive, Wymbush, Milton Keynes, MK8 8DA Tel: (01908) 563636 Fax: (01908) 569778 E-mail: general@holdenmanufacturing.com *Electronic contract manufacturing services*

Phil Holden Fasteners Ltd, 23 Swannington Road, Cottage Lane Industrial Estate, Broughton Astley, Leicester, LE9 6TU Tel: (01455) 285888 Fax: (01455) 285105 E-mail: enquiries@phs-ltd.com *Bolt & nut distributors*

Holdens Pattern & Tooling Ltd, Unit 3 Hargreaves Street, Haslingden, Rossendale, Lancashire, BB4 5RQ Tel: (01706) 213711 Fax: (01706) 213007 E-mail: holdenspatterns@aol.com *Engineering*

Holdens Supaseal Ltd, 505 Garretts Green Lane, Birmingham, B33 0SG Tel: 0121-789 7766 Fax: 0121-789 7237 E-mail: info@holdens-supaseal.co.uk *Double glazing manufrs*

Holderness Aggregates Ltd, Mill Hill Quarry, Hull Road, Keyingham, Hull, HU12 9ST Tel: (01964) 622347 *Sand & gravel producers & merchants*

Holderness Energy Group Ltd, 9-11 Godmans Lane, Kirk Ella, Hull, HU10 7NX Tel: (01482) 652632 Fax: (01482) 651295 E-mail: bernet@ukgateway.net *Shipping company*

Holderness Ship Repairers Ltd, Wassand Street, Hull, HU3 4AL Tel: (01482) 216055 Fax: (01482) 216056 E-mail: holdernessshiprepairers@compuserve.com Principal Export Areas: Worldwide *Ultrasonic cleaning services & engineers*

Holders Ltd, 55-59 Bensham Grove, Thornton Heath, Surrey, CR7 8DD Tel: (07802) 377122 Fax: (020) 8653 3011 E-mail: sales@holders.ltd.uk *Plastics vacuum products engineering & manufrs*

Holders Fine Furniture, 169-173 Malden Road, London, NW5 4HT Tel: (020) 7485 2741 Fax: (020) 7916 9259 E-mail: sales@holders-pine.co.uk *Furniture retail & finishing services*

Holder's Sheet Metal, Back Clare Street, Blackpool, FY1 6HS Tel: (01253) 341147 Fax: (01253) 341404 *Sheet metalwork engineers or fabricators*

Holdfast Manufacturing Ltd, Platts Road, Amblecote, Stourbridge, West Midlands, DY8 4YR Tel: (01384) 397575 Fax: (01384) 390458 *General presswork manufrs*

Holdfast Radiator Valves Ltd, Bagnall Road, Bagnall, Stoke-on-Trent, ST9 9JY Tel: (01782) 544982 Fax: (01782) 544983 *Valves & pipe manufrs*

Holdsworth Chocolate Ltd, Station Road, Bakewell, Derbyshire, DE45 1GE Tel: (01629) 813573 Fax: (01629) 813850 E-mail: info@holdsworthchocolates.co.uk *Manufacturer of confectionery*

▶ Holdsworth Contruction Ltd, 1210 Coventry Road, Yardley, Birmingham, B25 8DA Tel: 0121-772 1675 Fax: 0121-766 5262

D.B. Holdsworth Ltd, 66-69 Pegholme, Ilkley Road, Otley, West Yorkshire, LS21 3JP Tel: (01943) 858358 Fax: (01943) 858359 E-mail: wool@dbholdsworth.demon.co.uk *Wool speciality fibre merchants*

James Holdsworth & Bros Ltd, Unit 18, West Slaithwaite Road, Huddersfield, HD7 6LS Tel: (01924) 494471 Fax: (01484) 847153 E-mail: info@jamesholdsworth.com *Card clothing manufrs*

Holdsworth Ventilations Ltd, Greenside Works, Stoke-on-Trent, ST6 4HU Tel: (01782) 811900 Fax: (01782) 811902 E-mail: mark@holdsworthventilations.co.uk *Air ventilation, dust & fume extraction engineers*

Holdsworths, 91-93 St. James Mill Road, St. James Business Park, Northampton, NN5 5JP Tel: (01604) 581411 Fax: (01604) 581864 *Frozen food processors & product distributors*

Holdtite Ltd, 1 Oughton Road, Birmingham, B12 0DF Tel: 0121-440 2617 Fax: 0121-440 2716 E-mail: holdtite@globalnet.co.uk *Hose clips & related products manufrs*

Holemasters Demtech, Unit 2-4 Dixon Street, Westhoughton, Bolton, BL5 3PX Tel: (01942) 840600 Fax: (01942) 840700 E-mail: enquiries@holemasters.co.uk *Holemasters provides the construction industry with a wide range of diamond drilling, and specialist demolition services using Brokk remote machines. Diamond cutting methods are an accepted method of controlling HAVS, and our operative are trained to CSCS standards.* Also at: Blackpool & London

Holemasters (N I) Ltd, The Ferguson Centre, 57-59 Manse Road, Newtownabbey, County Antrim, BT36 6RW Tel: (028) 9034 2235 Fax: (028) 9034 2053 E-mail: holemastersni@btinternet.com *Concrete core drilling contractors*

Holemoor Engineering Ltd, Shaw Road, Dudley, West Midlands, DY2 8TP Tel: (01384) 237574 Fax: (01384) 230013 *Honing specialists*

Holford Engineering Ltd, Olivers Lane, Stotfold, Hitchin, Hertfordshire, SG5 4DH Tel: (01462) 730288 Fax: (01462) 733508 *Subcontract precision engineering*

Holford Engineering Ltd, 13 Cromwell Road, St. Neots, Cambridgeshire, PE19 2EU Tel: (01480) 217271 Fax: (01480) 219687 *Precision engineers & toolmakers*

▶ Holgate & French Shelford Ltd, 71a Newnham Street, Ely, Cambridgeshire, CB7 4PQ Tel: (01353) 668811 Fax: (01353) 668822

Holgate Roller Shutters, 3 Wicket Grove, Clifton, Swinton, Manchester, M27 6ST Tel: 0161-728 4767 Fax: 0161-728 4767 *Roller shutter manufrs*

Holger Christiansen UK Ltd, Unit 7-8 Glaisdale Business Centre, Glaisdale Parkway, Nottingham, NG8 4GP Tel: 0115-928 0086 Fax: 0115-928 0033 *Auto-electrical component manufrs*

▶ Holhomes, The Pavilion, Torpenhow, Montgomery Hill, Wirral, Merseyside, CH48 1NF Tel: 0151-625 1104 *Self catering holiday cottage near eswick, Lake District, Cumbria.*

Holiday Inn Ltd, Brook Street, Brentwood, Essex, CM14 5NF Tel: (0870) 4009012 Fax: (01277) 264264 E-mail: brentwoodm25@6c.com *Conference facilities & health club & hotel*

The Holiday Inn, Pentwyn Road, Cardiff, CF23 7XA Tel: (08704) 008141 Fax: (029) 2054 9147 *Hotel with conference facilities*

Holiday Inn Ltd, Leigh Road, Eastleigh, Hampshire, SO50 9PG Tel: (0870) 4009075 Fax: (023) 8064 3945 E-mail: reservations-eastleigh@6c.com *Hotel & conference facilities*

Holiday Inn Ltd, 132 Corstorphine Road, Edinburgh, EH12 6UA Tel: (0870) 4009026 Fax: 0131-334 9237 *Hotel & conference facility services*

The Holiday Inn, Junction 18 M1, Crick, Northampton, NN6 7XR Tel: (0870) 4009059 Fax: (01788) 823955 E-mail: reservations-rugby@6c.com *Hotel, conference & leisure facilities*

Holiday Inn Ltd, Herbert Walker Avenue, Southampton, SO15 1HJ Tel: (0870) 4009073 Fax: (023) 8033 2510 *Hotel with conference facilities*

Holiday Inn Ltd, Tadcaster Road, Dringhouses, York, YO24 1QF Tel: (0870) 4009085 Fax: (01904) 702804 *Hotel*

▶ Holistic Approach to Training Ltd, The Steam Mill, Steam Mill Street, Chester, CH3 5AN Tel: 01244 346444 Fax: 01244 329444 E-mail: ha2t@fsmail.net *Provider of bespoke key awareness training such as Deaf Awareness, Sign Language, Disability and Diversity.*

Holland & Barrett Ltd, 54-55 The Pallasades, Birmingham, B2 4XH Tel: 0121-633 0104 *Health food suppliers*

Holland & Barrett Ltd, 12a South Street, Bishop's Stortford, Hertfordshire, CM23 3AT Tel: (01279) 651637 *Health food vitamins manufrs*

Holland & Barrett Ltd, 14 St Marys Way, Thornbury, Bristol, BS35 2BH Tel: (01454) 417201 *Health food shop*

Holland & Barrett Ltd, 14 Carlton Lanes Shopping Centre, Castleford, West Yorkshire, WF10 1AD Tel: (01977) 603858 *Health food manufrs*

Holland & Barrett Ltd, 25 London Road, East Grinstead, West Sussex, RH19 1AL Tel: (01342) 325089 *Health food shop*

Holland & Barrett Ltd, 64 Towngate, Keighley, West Yorkshire, BD21 3QE Tel: (01535) 663338 *Health food producers*

Holland & Barrett Ltd, 55 St Johns Wood High Street, London, NW8 7NL Tel: (020) 7586 5494 *Health food & products*

Holland & Barrett Ltd, 42 Kilburn High Road, London, NW6 4HJ Tel: (020) 7624 9297 *Health food shop*

Holland & Barrett Ltd, 31 Tranquil Vale, London, SE3 0BU Tel: (020) 8318 0448 *Health food products manufrs*

Holland & Barrett Ltd, 81 Golders Green Road, London, NW11 8EN Tel: (020) 8455 5811 *Health foods*

Holland & Barrett Ltd, 3 Selborne Walk, London, E17 7JR Tel: (020) 8520 5459 *Health food retail & manufrs*

Holland & Barrett Ltd, 39 High Street, Nantwich, Cheshire, CW5 5DB Tel: (01270) 610041 *Health food store*

Holland & Barrett Ltd, 105a Northbrook Street, Newbury, Berkshire, RG14 1AA Tel: (01635) 552218 *Health food retail & supplies*

Holland & Barrett Ltd, 13 The Broadwalk, The Broad Marsh Centre, Nottingham, NG1 7LE Tel: 0115-979 9409 *Health food merchants*

Holland & Barrett Ltd, 55a High Street, Rayleigh, Essex, SS6 7EW Tel: (01268) 779249 *Health food & vitamin supplement retailers & manufrs*

Holland & Barrett Ltd, 77 Town Square, Halton Lea, Runcorn, Cheshire, WA7 2EU Tel: (01928) 791188 *Health food & vitamin supplements manufrs*

Holland & Barrett Ltd, 59 Silver Street, Salisbury, SP1 2NG Tel: (01722) 324064 *Health foods & products retailers*

Holland & Barrett Ltd, 1 Gaolgate Street, Stafford, ST16 2BG Tel: (01785) 252758 *Health food suppliers & manufrs*

Holland & Barrett Ltd, 28 Union Street, Torquay, TQ2 5PW Tel: (01803) 212215 *Health food suppliers*

Holland & Barrett Ltd, 52 The Mall, Warrington, WA1 1QE Tel: (01925) 418424 *Health food company*

Holland Brothers Ltd, Tawney Street, Boston, Lincolnshire, PE21 6RS Tel: (01205) 355566 Fax: (01205) 358172 E-mail: enquiries@hollandbrothers.co.uk *Jaguar dealership & repairs*

Holland Colours UK Ltd, Unit 16 Sabre Court, Gillingham Business Park, Gillingham, Kent, ME8 0RW Tel: (01634) 388727 Fax: (01634) 388910 E-mail: hcuk@hollandcolours.com *Colour manufactures for plastics industry*

Holland Engineering, Victoria House, Paxton Street, Stoke-on-Trent, ST1 3SD Tel: (01782) 283364 Fax: (01782) 284241 E-mail: info@hollandengineering.co.uk *Boiler engineers*

Holland & Harrison Ltd, 46 Vale Road, Bushey, WD23 2HQ Tel: (01923) 220752 Fax: (01923) 234011 E-mail: cnc@hollandandharrison.co.uk *Precision engineers*

▶ Holland Heating UK Ltd, United Technologies House, Guildford Road, Fetcham, Leatherhead, Surrey, KT22 9UT Tel: (01372) 220230 Fax: (01372) 220221

Holland & Holland, 906 Harrow Road, London, NW10 5JT Tel: (020) 8960 4358 Fax: (020) 8969 3523 *General engineers*

Holland & Holland Holdings Ltd, 31-33 Bruton Street, London, W1J 6HH Tel: (020) 7499 4411 Fax: (020) 7499 4544 *Gun dealers* Also at: London NW10

Owen Holland Engineering Ltd, Holland Way, Blandford Forum, Dorset, DT11 7TA Tel: (01258) 452461 Fax: (01258) 480169 E-mail: sales@owenholland.com *Airport & industrial trailers manufrs*

Holland Of Rye, 145 South Undercliff, Rye, East Sussex, TN31 7HW Tel: (01797) 222648 Fax: (01797) 224909 *Furniture production*

Holland & Sherry (Furnishing) Ltd, 5th Floor, C/O Holland & Sherry Limited, London, W1S 3PF Tel: (020) 7437 0404 Fax: (020) 7734 6110 E-mail: enquiries@hollandandsherry.com *Woollen merchants* Also at: Peebles

Holland UK Ltd, 12 Conway Units, Stephenson Road, Clacton-on-Sea, Essex, CO15 4XA Tel: (01255) 431773 Fax: (01255) 221393 E-mail: sales@hollanduk.co.uk *Edible oil merchants*

Walter Holland & Sons, Blackburn Road, Accrington, Lancashire, BB5 2SA Tel: (01706) 213591 Fax: (01706) 228044 E-mail: enquiries@hollands-pies.co.uk *Pie manufrs*

Holland & Watts, 1 Paragon Court, Tongham Road, Aldershot, Hampshire, GU12 4AA Tel: (01252) 344200 Fax: (01252) 343466 E-mail: sales@hollandandwatts.com *Printing trade finishing services*

Holland & Welsh Ltd, Unit 13 Riverside Industrial Park, Treforest, Pontypridd, Mid Glamorgan, CF37 5TG Tel: (01443) 660255 Fax: (01443) 660651 E-mail: sales@hollandandwelsh.com *Solid wood flooring and accesories*

Hollander Hyams Ltd, 9 Berners Place, London, W1T 3HH Tel: (020) 7636 1562 Fax: (020) 7636 1564 E-mail: sales@hollanderhyams.com *Hide & skin merchants*

▶ Hollands & Long, Unit 6 Gilly Gabben Industrial Estate, Mawgan, Helston, Cornwall, TR12 6BL Tel: (01326) 221468 Fax: (01326) 221774

Hollands Recycling Ltd, 1 Holland Park, Bentley Road South, Wednesbury, West Midlands, WS10 8LN Tel: 0121-526 2454 Fax: 0121-568 6148 E-mail: enquiries@hollands-recycling.co.uk *Waste paper merchants* Also at: Dalaston

▶ Hollex (UK) Ltd, Unit 8C, 1 Sir Francis Ley Industrial E, Shaftsbury Street, Derby, DE23 8XA Tel: (01332) 340501

Trevor Holley Associates, Little London, Combs, Stowmarket, Suffolk, IP14 2ES Tel: (01449) 612084 Fax: (01449) 771027 E-mail: t.holley@btinternet.com *Industrial chemical distributors*

Charles Holliday & Co., Railway Station, Green Road, Newmarket, Suffolk, CB8 9WT Tel: (01638) 661603 Fax: (01638) 665124 E-mail: brookefairbairn@btconnect.com *Furnishing fabric wholesalers*

Holliday Pigments Ltd, Morley Street, Hull, HU8 8DN Tel: (01482) 329875 Fax: (01484) 329791 E-mail: sales@holliday-pigments.com *Pigment & colour manufrs*

Holliday Precision Engineers, Unit 11 Pedmore Industrial Estate, Pedmore Road, Brierley Hill, West Midlands, DY5 1TJ Tel: (01384) 261467 *Prototype engineering production*

▶ Hollingbourne Property Services Ltd, Eyhorne Green, Musket Lane, Hollingbourne, Maidstone, Kent, ME17 1UU Tel: (01622) 880000 Fax: (01622) 880668

▶ Hollinger Print Ltd, 12 Burnet Road, Sweet Briar Industrial Estate, Sweet Briar Road Industrial Es, Norwich, NR3 2BS Tel: (01603) 309000 E-mail: info@hollinger.co.uk

Hollinger Trenching, Hollinger, Wheatsheaf Road, Henfield, West Sussex, BN5 9AX Tel: (01273) 492220 Fax: (01273) 492220 *Trenching contractors & water engineers*

▶ Hollingsworth Bros, St. Ives Way, Factory Road, Sandycroft, Deeside, Clwyd, CH5 2QS Tel: (01244) 539922 Fax: (01244) 538504

Hollingsworth Service Co. Ltd, Units 6-7 Norden Court, Hayes Lane Industrial Estate, Great Harwood, Blackburn, BB6 7UR Tel: (01254) 881100 Fax: (01254) 881101 E-mail: pat.turner@btconnect.com *Textile machinery & metallic card clothing suppliers*

▶ indicates data change since last edition

Hollingsworth & Vose Air Filtration Ltd, Waterford Bridge, Kentmere, Kendal, Cumbria, LA8 9JJ Tel: (01539) 825200 Fax: (01539) 825201 E-mail: sales@hvaf.co.uk *Air filtration fabric manufrs*

Hollinwood Sheet Metal Co., Under Lane, Chadderton, Oldham, OL9 7PP Tel: 0161-683 5277 Fax: 0161-684 8608 *Sheet metal & light engineering services*

Hollinwood Wood Precision Engineering Ltd, 8 Victoria Trading Estate, Drury Lane, Chadderton, Oldham, OL9 7PJ Tel: 0161-682 7900 Fax: 0161-681 4900 E-mail: sales@hollinwood.com *Special purpose fasteners, sub contracting*

Hollis Design LLP, 30 St Catherines Road, Winchester, Hampshire, SO23 0PS Tel: (0845) 8382034 E-mail: architect@hollisdesign.co.uk *Building consultancy*

Hollis Horse & Hollis Farriers, Kentisbeare, Cullompton, Devon, EX15 2BT Tel: (01884) 266398 *Horse transport services*

Hollis Publishing Ltd, Harlequin House, 7 High Street, Teddington, Middlesex, TW11 8EL Tel: (020) 8973 3400 Fax: (020) 8977 1133 E-mail: hollis@hollis-pr.co.uk *Directory publishers*

Hollisters Electrical Contractors Ltd, 54-56 Dover Road East, Gravesend, Kent, DA11 0RG Tel: (01474) 564088 Fax: (01474) 560455 E-mail: terry@hollisterselectrical.co.uk *Electrical contractors*

▶ Hollographics Ltd, 2 Wynford, The Pastures, Kings Worthy, Winchester, Hampshire, SO23 7LX Tel: (01962) 882422 Fax: (01962) 882422 E-mail: info@hollographics.com *Custom vinyl graphics*

Holloid Plastics Ltd, Stephenson Road, Basingstoke, Hampshire, RG21 6XR Tel: (01256) 334700 Fax: (01256) 473735 E-mail: mail@holloid-plastics.co.uk *Injection moulders*

Joseph Holloway Ltd, Valencia Wharf, Churchbridge, Oldbury, West Midlands, B69 2AP Tel: 0121-552 2146 Fax: 0121-552 2991 *Road transport, haulage & freight services*

Holloway Plastics Ltd, Willenhall La Industrial Estate, Willenhall Lane, Bloxwich, Walsall, WS3 2XN Tel: (01922) 492777 Fax: (01922) 495820 E-mail: sales@holloway-plastics.co.uk *Plastic fabricators*

Holloway Tool Co. Ltd, 71-75 New Summer Street, Newtown, Birmingham, B19 3TE Tel: 0121-359 3777 Fax: 0121-359 6065 E-mail: cad@hollowaytool.co.uk *Manufacturers of press tools & machinery*

Holloways Furniture, 1 Lower Court, Church Lane, Suckley, Worcester, WR6 5DE Tel: (01886) 884665 Fax: (01886) 884796 E-mail: enquires@holloways.co.uk *Garden & conservatory furniture sales*

Holly Construction Ltd, Wellington Road, Dunston, Gateshead, Tyne & Wear, NE11 9JL Tel: 0191-460 0400

▶ Holly Park Electrical Services, Governor House, 47 Kent Road, Pudsey, West Yorkshire, LS28 9BB Tel: 0113-255 9899 Fax: 0113-236 1758

Hollycroft Engineering Ltd, 7 Teal Business Park, Dodwells Road, Hinckley, Leicestershire, LE10 3BZ Tel: (01455) 635845 Fax: (01455) 250273 E-mail: sales@hollycrofteng.freeserve.co.uk *Aircraft component manufacturers & tool making*

▶ Hollygate Fabrications, Delta Road, Audenshaw, Manchester, M34 5HR Tel: 0161-371 2630 Fax: 0161-371 9694 E-mail: sales@hollygate.co.uk *Welding & fabricators*

Hollygate Fabrications Ltd, The Hollygate, Chestergate, Stockport, Cheshire, SK3 0BD Tel: 0161-371 2630 Fax: 0161-371 9694 E-mail: tony@hollygate.co.uk *Steel fabricators*

▶ Hollyoak Clothing Ltd, Abbey Park Street, Leicester, LE4 5AF Tel: 0116-251 2410 Fax: 0116-233 2225

▶ Hollywell Foods, 90 Nimrod Road, London, SW16 6TG Tel: (020) 8769 8324 Fax: (020 8696 7593 E-mail: info@minarwines.com *Wine exporters, importers & mango wine specialist*

Hollywood Marine Ltd, 176 Highfield Road, Hall Green, Birmingham, B28 0HS Tel: 0121-777 7573 Fax: 0121 7778386 *Boat equipment & accessories*

Hollywood Plasterers, Woodhouse, Packhorse Lane, Kings Norton, Birmingham, B38 0DN Tel: (01564) 824100 Fax: (01564) 823447 *Plastering contractors*

Hollywood Signs Ltd, Coal Valley Business Park, Westwood Avenue, Birmingham, B11 3RF Tel: 0121-773 3123 Fax: 0121-773 3324 E-mail: sales@hollywoodsigns.co.uk *Sign contractors, sign makers, suppliers & installers*

Holman Engineering Co. Ltd, 6 Kings Road Works, Kings Road, New Haw, Addlestone, Surrey, KT15 3BG Tel: (01932) 353555 Fax: (01932) 353666 E-mail: enquiries@holman-engineering.co.uk *Precision machining services*

Holman Kelly Paper Co. Ltd, Wandle House, Riverside Drive, Mitcham, Surrey, CR4 4BU Tel: (020) 8687 7300 Fax: (020) 8687 7333 E-mail: holmankellypaper@btinternet.com *Paper & board merchants & specialist publishers*

Holman Security Systems, 1 Mill View, Hinckley, Leicestershire, LE10 0HE Tel: (01455) 251025 Fax: (01455) 890059 *Security systems*

Holman & Williams Packaging Ltd, Riverside Road, London, SW17 0BA Tel: (020) 8879 1010 Fax: (020) 8944 5162 E-mail: sales@hwpackaging.co.uk *Packaging merchants*

Holman-Wilfley Ltd, Wheal Jane Mine, Baldhu, Truro, Cornwall, TR3 6EE Tel: (01872) 561163 Fax: (01872) 561162 E-mail: mail@holmanwilfley.co.uk *Mining equipment & processing technology manufrs*

▶ Holmbush Paintball, C/O Holmbush Farm, Crawley Road, Faygate, Horsham, West Sussex, RH12 4SE Tel: (01293) 852261 E-mail: euenquiries@holmbushpaintballshop.com *Distributors of paint ball guns & equipment*

Holme, Dodsworth (Rock Salt) Ltd, 59-69 Heaton Park Road, Newcastle upon Tyne, NE6 1SQ Tel: 0191-265 9077 Fax: 0191-276 5125 *Salts suppliers*

▶ Holmefjord Regulatory Affairs, A 10 Dane Hill Road, Kennett, Newmarket, Suffolk, CB8 7QX Tel: (01638) 604355 Fax: (01638) 604355 E-mail: elizabeth@holmefjord.co.uk *Regulatory Affairs*

Holmes, 15 Ffordd Derwyn, Penyffordd, Chester, CH4 0JT Tel: (01244) 545532 Fax: (01244) 545532 E-mail: nigel.holmes1@virgin.net *Special purpose equipment & machinery manufrs*

Holmes, 1 Kilnhurst Business Park, Glasshouse Road, Kilnhurst, Mexborough, South Yorkshire, S64 5TH Tel: (01709) 583338 Fax: (01709) 583338 *Glass fibre or fibreglass manufrs*

Bernard Holmes Precision Ltd, The Old Pony Field, Grosvenor Road, Billingborough, Sleaford, Lincolnshire, NG34 0QN Tel: (01529) 240241 Fax: (01529) 240802 *Sub contract general engineering*

Colin Holmes Refrigeration Ltd, 79 Crossways, Romford, RM2 6AS Tel: (01708) 741143 Fax: (01708) 741143 *Refrigeration sales & service*

Holmes Corporation Ltd, 38-42 Whitfield Street, London, W1T 4HJ Tel: (020) 7813 4333 Fax: (0870) 1245242 E-mail: holmesassociate@blueyonder.co.uk *Film & TV development & production services*

Holmes Engineering, Unit 2 Furtho Court, Towcester Road, Old Stratford, Milton Keynes, MK19 6AN Tel: (01908) 563169 Fax: (01908) 563169 *General & precision engineers*

Gary Holmes Engineering, Unit B, Smiths Yard, Stone Lane, Axford, Marlborough, Wiltshire, SN8 2EY Tel: (01672) 516041 Fax: (01672) 515893 *Agricultural engineering services*

▶ Holmes & Jones, 3 St. Johns Road, Saxmundham, Suffolk, IP17 1BE Tel: (01728) 603504 Fax: (01728) 604825 *Car services & repairs*

Holmes Mann & Co. Ltd, 17 Harris Street, Bradford, West Yorkshire, BD1 5HZ Tel: (01274) 735881 Fax: (01274) 306324 E-mail: oscar@holman.co.uk *Packaging machinery & products manufrs*

Holmes & Mann Associates Ltd, 465 Tachbrook Road, Leamington Spa, Warwickshire, CV31 3DQ Tel: (01926) 426854 Fax: (01926) 426854 E-mail: holmes@holmes-mann.com *Quality consultants*

▶ Holmes Partnership, 80 Commercial Street, Edinburgh, EH6 6LX Tel: 0131-553 2111 Fax: 0131-553 1300 E-mail: edinburgh@holmespartnership.com

Holmes & Pearcey, Breach Farm, St Johns Road, Oakley, Basingstoke, Hampshire, RG23 7DU Tel: (01256) 782575 Fax: (01256) 782575 *Purpose made joinery manufrs*

Holmes Products, 1 Francis Grove, London, SW19 4DT Tel: (020) 8879 4850 Fax: (020) 8947 8272 *Air purification services*

Holmes Refrigeration, 443 Banbury Road, Oxford, OX2 8ED Tel: (01865) 552073 Fax: (01865) 310848 *Air conditioning & commercial refrigeration distributors*

Holmes T Skip Hire Ltd, 14 Pleasant Street, West Bromwich, West Midlands, B70 0RF Tel: 0121-553 2495 Fax: 0121-500 5845 *Skip contractors*

Holmes UK Ltd, 5 Monarch Industrial Park, Kings Road, Tyseley, Birmingham, B11 2AP Tel: 0121-706 6936 Fax: 0121-707 9913 E-mail: sales@holmesmachines.co.uk *Tool manufrs*

Holmfirth Dyers Ltd, Ribbleden Dye Works, Dunford Road, Holmfirth, HD9 2DP Tel: (01484) 682271 Fax: (01484) 681084 E-mail: holmefirthdyers@aol.com *Wool & piece dyers & finishers services*

▶ Holmsley Mill Ltd, Holmsley, Burley, Ringwood, Hampshire, BH24 4HY Tel: (01425) 402507 Fax: (01425) 403516 E-mail: sales@holmsleymill.co.uk

Holmwood Tractors, Norfolk Garage, Horsham Road, Holmwood, Dorking, Surrey, RH5 4ER Tel: (01306) 888627 *Agricultural & industrial parts & supplies*

Holophane (Europe) Ltd, Bond Avenue, Bletchley, Milton Keynes, MK1 1JG Tel: (01908) 649292 Fax: (01908) 367618 E-mail: info@holophane.co.uk *Industrial & commercial lighting fittings & equipment*

▶ HoloVis, The Brick Barn Bittesby Farm, Mere Lane, Lutterworth, Leicestershire, LE17 4JH Tel: (01455) 553924 Fax: (01455) 557746 E-mail: info@holovis.com *Developers & manufacturers of turn-key digital display solutions*

Holrow Building Refurbishment, Jubilee Court, Copgrove, Harrogate, North Yorkshire, HG3 3TB Tel: (01423) 340888 Fax: (01423) 340999 E-mail: sales@holrow.co.uk *Oak frame suppliers*

Holroyd Components Ltd, Shire Hill Industrial Estate, Saffron Walden, Essex, CB11 3AQ Tel: (01799) 523177 Fax: (01799) 513714 E-mail: sales@holroydcomponents.com *Holroyd Components are manufacturers of industrial electric heating elements for over 25 years. Specialists in the manufacture of silicone rubber surface heaters in both wire wound and etch foil element. The etch foil technology has expanded to also include polyester and Kapton insulation materials. We also manufacture a range of drum heating equipment, specifically designed for melting or reducing the viscosity of many different materials or for protection against freezing conditions. All products are designed using state of the art CAD systems and are manufactured in modern air-conditioned workshops. Holroyd Components are a UL registered firm for ISO9001:2000. In order to maintain the high standard of quality and service we have an ongoing programme of investment in plant and resources which enables us to offer quality products with fast delivery for both small quantity and large batch orders.*

Holroyd Construction Ltd, Park Hill, Walton Road, Wetherby, West Yorkshire, LS22 5DZ Tel: (01937) 583131 Fax: (01937) 580034 *Building contractors*

Holroyds, 499 Bath Road, Saltford, Bristol, BS31 3HQ Tel: (01225) 873000 Fax: (01225) 873834 E-mail: info@holroyds.org *Auctioneer Valuers & Suppliers of Used Food Machinery*

Holscot Plastic Products, 9 Burnmill Industrial Estate, Burnmill Road, Leven, Fife, KY8 4RA Tel: (01333) 427555 Fax: (01333) 422929 E-mail: hnd@holscot.com Principal Export Areas: Central/East Europe & West Europe *Teflon plastic manufrs*

A. Holt & Sons Ltd, 115 Whitecross Street, London, EC1Y 8JQ Tel: (020) 7256 2222 Fax: (020) 7638 3578 E-mail: sales@aholt.co.uk Sales Contact: S. Holt Principal Export Areas: Worldwide *Manufacturers of calico, muslin & cheesecloth. Also filter cloth (fabric) & bookbinding cloth (woven) manufacturers.*

Holt Broadcast Services Ltd, Unit 13 Nimrod Industrial Estate, Nimrod Way, Reading, RG2 0EB Tel: 0118-931 0770 Fax: 0118-931 0696 E-mail: sales@holtbs.co.uk *Sheet metalwork fabrication specialising in custom solutions from design to fabrication to full finishing services. We also produce a range of standard products available to order including cases, panles, MDU units.*

Holt Bros Horwich, Brunel Works, Brunel Street, Horwich, Bolton, BL6 5NX Tel: (01204) 697393 Fax: (01204) 697393 *Wrought iron gates & railings manufrs*

Curtis Holt Ltd, Longreach, Gallion Boulevard, Crossways Business Park, Dartford, DA2 6QE Tel: (01322) 321300 Fax: (01322) 383641 E-mail: sales@toolbank.com *Hand tool & power tool manufrs*

Curtis Holt (North West), Toolbank House, Appleton Thorn Trading Estate, Lyncastle Way, Appleton, Warrington, WA4 4ST Tel: (01925) 261333 Fax: (01925) 604478 *Hand & power tool distributors*

▶ Holt Heat, 23 Dukehaugh, Peebles, EH45 9DN Tel: (01721) 720366

Holt Hosiery Co. Ltd, Deane Road Mill, Bolton, BL3 5AR Tel: (01204) 525611 Fax: (01204) 394620 *Thermal wear manufrs*

Holt JCB Ltd, Unit 11, Cooksland Industrial Estate, Bodmin, Cornwall, PL31 2QB Tel: (01208) 78078 Fax: (01208) 78019 *Plant maintenance services*

▶ Holt JCB Ltd, Third Way, Avonmouth, Bristol, BS11 9ZG Tel: 0117-982 7921 Fax: 0117-982 1028 E-mail: becky.selby@holtjcb.co.uk *Heavy plant machinery repair*

Holt Lloyd (International) Ltd, Oakhurst Drive, Lawnhurst Industrial Estate, Cheadle Heath, Stockport, Cheshire, SK3 0RZ Tel: 0161-491 7391 Fax: 0161-491 7393 E-mail: info@holtsauto.com *Car care products distributors & manufrs*

M. Holt (M/C) Ltd, 159 Cheetham Hill Road, Manchester, M8 8LG Tel: 0161-832 2210 Fax: 0161-839 5217 *Underwear & nightwear wholesalers*

Holt & Martin Electrical Ltd, 100 & 102 Gigg Lane, Bury, Lancashire, BL9 9EW Tel: 0161-797 7782 Fax: 0161-761 5127 E-mail: holt.martin@btinternet.com *Electric motor rewind services*

Holt Security Systems, 24a Royal George Road, Burgess Hill, West Sussex, RH15 9SE Tel: (01444) 241666 Fax: (01444) 243666 E-mail: holtsecurity@hotmail.com *Security intruder alarm installers*

Holtbolt Ltd, Victoria Road, Halesowen, West Midlands, B62 8HZ Tel: 0121-561 3114 Fax: 0121-561 4566 E-mail: sales@holtbolt.co.uk *Bolt & nut stockists*

▶ Holten Heath Glass Ltd, The Hailey Centre Units 16 19, 46 Holton Road, Holton Heath Trading Park, Poole, Dorset, BH16 6LT Tel: (01202) 621566 Fax: (01202) 621577 E-mail: office@holtonheathglass.co.uk

▶ Holthurst Ltd, 2 The Crescent, Station Road, Woldingham, Caterham, Surrey, CR3 7DB Tel: (01883) 653366

Holtite Ltd, Jubilee Works, Woods Lane, Cradley Heath, West Midlands, B64 7AW Tel: (01384) 560611 Fax: (01384) 410214 E-mail: holtite@aol.com *Anchors chains & mooring equipment*

Holton Conform Ltd, Albany House, Elliott Road, Bournemouth, BH11 8JH Tel: (01202) 581881 Fax: (01202) 581789 E-mail: enquiries@holton-conform.com *Extruder & extrusion machine (aluminium & coppers) manufrs*

Holtractors Ltd, 1 St.Andrews Close, Golden Cross, Hailsham, East Sussex, BN27 3UB Tel: (01323) 841024 Fax: (01323) 441196 E-mail: holtractors@hotmail.com *Agricultural dealers*

Holts, Embankment, London, SW15 1LB Tel: (020) 8789 5557 Fax: (020) 8789 8365 E-mail: sales@holtallen.com *Boat fittings wholesalers* Also at: London SW18

Holt's Fishing Tackle, 122 Marston Road, Stafford, ST16 3BX Tel: (01785) 251073 *Fishing tackle retailers*

Holtwood Marketing Ltd, 11 Brassey Drive, Aylesford, Kent, ME20 7QL Tel: (01622) 710921 Fax: (01622) 717945 E-mail: ward@holtwood.co.uk *Surveying equipment distributors*

Holywell Engineering Ltd, Station Road, Backworth, Newcastle Upon Tyne, NE27 0AE Tel: 0191-268 4365 Fax: 0191-268 9506 E-mail: eng@holywell.com *Mining & tunnelling equipment manufrs*

▶ Holywell Joinery Ltd, Unit 13, Delaval Trading Estate, Seaton Delaval, Whitley Bay, Tyne & Wear, NE25 0QT Tel: 0191-237 0190

Holzer Ltd, Neachells Lane, Wednesfield, Wolverhampton, WV11 3QG Tel: (01902) 866355 Fax: (01902) 734073 E-mail: admin2@holzerltd-metalldyne.fsnet.co.uk *Cold extruders & cold forgers*

Homag UK Ltd, 10c Sills Road, Castle Donington, Derby, DE74 2US Tel: (0870) 2433244 Fax: (01332) 856400 E-mail: sales@homag-uk.co.uk *Woodworking & plastic cutting machine manufrs* Also at: Pontefract

▶ Home Bakeries Ltd, 6 Sandown Industrial Estate, Sandown Road, Watford, WD24 7UB Tel: (01923) 219119 Fax: (01923) 237506

▶ Home Bakery Ltd, Well Road, Buckie, Banffshire, AB56 1LJ Tel: (01542) 832024 Fax: (01542) 839034

Home Bargains, 22 Moor Street, Ormskirk, Lancashire, L39 2AQ Tel: (01695) 581245 *General household & toiletries retailers*

▶ Home & Business Computer Service, 12 David Close, Braunton, Devon, EX33 2AT Tel: (01271) 815262 E-mail: info@handbcs.co.uk *We offer onsite repairs and small upgrades carried out at your convenience onsite during the day, evenings or weekends in the North Devon area.*

Home Care Products UK Ltd, Consort House, Princes Road, Ferndown, Dorset, BH22 9JG Tel: (01202) 871717 Fax: (01202) 876161 E-mail: homecare@btconnect.com *Home hardware distributors*

▶ Home & Commercial Protection (Supersafes), Firs Farm, Church Lane, Stockerston, Oakham, Leicestershire, LE15 9JD Tel: (01572) 722234 E-mail: keith@supersafes.co.uk *Supplier & installer of all types of safes, business & home*

▶ Home Computer Services, 6 Lower Road, Breachwood Green, Hitchin, Hertfordshire, SG4 8NS Tel: (0845) 3105645 E-mail: peter@home-computer-services.co.uk *Computer repairs, computer upgrades, computer problems, computer systems. Specialists in virus, spyware and adware removal. We offer an 'at home' service.*

▶ Home Computing, 12 Camps Close, Waterbeach, Cambridge, CB25 9NT Tel: (01223) 860242 E-mail: l.l@virgin.net *Provides friendly advice & support to users of computers at home*

Home Counties Toilet Hire, Fairfield Farm, Newton Road, Stoke Hammond, Milton Keynes, MK17 9DE Tel: (01525) 270181 Fax: (01525) 270464 E-mail: sales@hccc.co.uk *Toilet hire*

Home County Fire Protection, 31 Fern Towers, Harestone Hill, Caterham, Surrey, CR3 6SL Tel: (01883) 341634 Fax: (01883) 342540 *Fire extinguisher contractors*

▶ Home Delivery Network, Arkwright Way, North Newmoor Industrial Estate, Irvine, Ayrshire, KA11 4JU Tel: (01294) 213458 Fax: (01294) 217244

▶ Home Delivery Network Ltd, Abbott House, Abbey Road, London, NW10 7UA Tel: (020) 8961 8774 Fax: (020) 8961 3763

▶ Home Delivery Network Ltd, Heathcote Way, Heathcote Industrial Estate, Warwick, CV34 6QP Tel: (01926) 311430 Fax: (01926) 450605

▶ Home Entertainment & Management Systems, 124 Harborough Road, Rushden, Northamptonshire, NN10 0LP Tel: (09065) 840201 Fax: (08701) 638572 E-mail: info@heams.co.uk *Design technology consultancy*

Home Fair Blinds UK Ltd, Unit 9 Wrightson House, Thornaby, Stockton-on-Tees, Cleveland, TS17 9EP Tel: (01642) 645511 Fax: (01642) 645511 *Blind suppliers*

Home Form Group, Unit 1, Renley Road Retail Park, Ipswich, IP2 0AQ Tel: (01473) 226009 *Kitchen, bathroom & bedroom furniture suppliers*

▶ Home & Hearth, 451 Hillington Road, Hillington Industrial Estate, Glasgow, G52 4BL Tel: 0141-891 4891 Fax: 0141-882 7807 *Fire place retailers*

Home Heating & Plumbing Supplies Ltd, 17 Middle Hillgate, Stockport, Cheshire, SK1 3AY Tel: 0161-477 2897 Fax: 0161-476 5034 *Plumbers merchants*

Home Improvement Bureau, 21-23 Station Road, New Barnet, Barnet, Hertfordshire, EN5 1PH Tel: (020) 8441 0352 Fax: (020) 8441 0219 *Bathroom product distributors*

Home Improvement Centre, 229-231 Dunstable Road, Luton, LU4 8BN Tel: (01582) 722189 Fax: (01582) 402789 E-mail: hic10@hotmail.com *Wholesale hardware merchants* Also at: Luton, Stevenage & Welwyn Garden City

Home & Leisure Products, 13 Derby Road, Hinckley, Leicestershire, LE10 1QD Tel: (01455) 234448 Fax: (01455) 250277 *Retail furniture distributors*

▶ Home & Office Ltd, 9 Mead Lane, Farnham, Surrey, GU9 7DY Tel: (01252) 820455 Fax: (01252) 820455 *Timber frame builders*

Home & Office Fire Extinguishers Ltd, Unit 6, Saffron Business Centre, Elizabeth Close, Saffron Walden, Essex, CB10 2NL Tel: (01799) 513360 Fax: (01799) 513713 E-mail: fire@pslink.co.uk *Sales & service of all types of fire extinguishers*

Home Protection Security Grilles Ltd, 11a Bedford Road, London, SW4 7SH Tel: (020) 7737 2228 Fax: (020) 7737 2228 *Manufacturers of security grilles*

▶ Home Recycling Ltd, Bulton Brow, Sowerbry, Ingleby Barwick, Sowerby Bridge, West Yorkshire, HX6 2AG Tel: (0845) 6123191 Fax: (0845) 6123292 E-mail: sales@homerecycling.co.uk *Making recycling easier with a range of recycling bins & accessories*

Home Securities, 55 Piccadilly, Stoke-on-Trent, ST1 1EA Tel: (01782) 204646 Fax: (01782) 204646 E-mail: homesecurities@btconnect.com *Security alarms retailer*

▶ Home Security Services UK Ltd, 3 Campbell Street, Roe Lee, Blackburn, BB1 9AF Tel: (0800) 6520642 Fax: (01254) 698064 E-mail: sales@homesecurityservicesuk.co.uk *Installation & repairs of intruder alarms, CCTV, fire alarms & access control*

▶ Home Security Services UK Ltd, 51 Highbank, Blackburn, BB1 9SX Tel: (0800) 6520642 Fax: (01254) 698064 E-mail: Info@hssukltd.co.uk *Installation, Service, and repair of Intruder alarms, CCTV, Access Control, and fire alarms. Contracting also undertaken*

▶ Home Zone, 19 Dalrymple Street, Girvan, Ayrshire, KA26 9EU Tel: (01465) 715961 *Household item retailers*

▶ Homeandleather, W9, The Innovation Centre, Festival Drive, Ebbw Vale, Gwent, NP23 8XA Tel: (01495) 356789 *Homeandleather manufactures and sells leather products of quality and distinction from the POPPA designer range.*

Homeblown, Gilbert Coombe, Redruth, Cornwall, TR16 4HG Tel: (01209) 314446 Fax: (01209) 314446 E-mail: info@homeblown.co.uk *Surfboard blanks suppliers & manufrs*

▶ HomeCAD Architectural Services, 2 Cumbernauld Business Park, Wardpark Road, Cumbernauld, Glasgow, G67 3JZ Tel: (0800) 0838288 Fax: (01236) 795579 E-mail: info@homecad.org *A dedicated Architectural Design Service preparing plans for residential extensions, conservatories, alterations, loft conversions, garage conversions and new build projects.*

▶ HomeCall+, Pendle Innovation Centre, Brook Street, Nelson, Lancashire, BB9 9PS Tel: 01282 877160 Fax: 01282 877139 E-mail: info@homecallplus.co.uk

▶ Homecare Contracts Ltd, 18 Dryden Vale, Bilston Glen Estate, Loanhead, Midlothian, EH20 9HN Tel: 0131-440 5550 Fax: 0131-440 3539

▶ Homecare Technology, Unit 9a Marshfield Bank, Crewe, CW2 8UY Tel: (01270) 508989 Fax: (01270) 215753 E-mail: sales@homecareproducts.co.uk *Cleaning products manufrs*

▶ Homechoice Blinds Ltd, 21a Manor Road, Southport, Merseyside, PR9 7LE Tel: (01704) 505656 Fax: (01704) 505992 *Blind manufacturers & suppliers*

Homedics Group Ltd, 211 Vale Road, Tonbridge, Kent, TN9 1SU Tel: (01732) 354828 Fax: (01732) 358631 E-mail: uksales@homedics.co.uk *Domestic weighing scale & well being product manufrs*

Homefair Blinds, Viking Precinct, Jarrow, Tyne & Wear, NE32 3LF Tel: 0191-428 6587 Fax: 0191-521 4446 *Blinds, awnings & canopies manufrs*

Homefair Blinds Ltd, 59 Fawcett Street, Sunderland, SR1 1SE Tel: 0191-567 8200 Fax: 0191-564 0424 *Blinds retailer*

Homefair Blinds North West, 3 Gorton Retail Market, Gortoncross Street, Manchester, M18 8LD Tel: 0161-231 8855 Fax: 0161-231 2828 *Blinds manufrs*

Homefair Blinds (U K), Dundas Street, Middlesbrough, Cleveland, TS1 1HT Tel: (01642) 217181 Fax: 0191-521 4446 *Blinds retailers*

Homefair Blinds (UK) Ltd, 73-77 Newgate Street, Bishop Auckland, County Durham, DL14 7EQ Tel: (01388) 458890 Fax: (01388) 458890 *Blinds & accessory manufrs*

▶ Homefield Leisure Ltd, Poolclean, Winterdown Road, Esher, Surrey, KT10 8LS Tel: (01372) 465531 Fax: (01372) 469117 E-mail: sales@homefieldleisure.co.uk *Swimming pools & heat pumps manufrs*

Homeguard Security Systems Ltd, 3 Grimsdells Corner, Sycamore Road, Amersham, Buckinghamshire, HP6 5EL Tel: (01494) 728989 Fax: (01494) 728189 E-mail: sales@homeguardsecurity.co.uk *Security alarm manufrs*

Homeguard Security Systems, 4 Courtney Cl, Tewkesbury, Glos, GL20 5FB Tel: (01242) 676070 Fax: (01242) 676070 *Alarm systems*

Homeguard (South East) Ltd, 19 Broadmead Road, Folkestone, Kent, CT19 5AN Tel: (01702) 471666 Fax: (0845) 3703883 E-mail: linda@dwcuk.com *Damp proof contractors*

Home-Key Ltd, Units 1-3 Admiral Park Estate, Airport Service Road, Portsmouth, PO3 5RQ Tel: (023) 9267 3535 Fax: (023) 9269 5543 E-mail: home.key@virgin.net *Paint brushes, rollers & dust sheets*

▶ HomeLANs Ltd, 71 Windsor Road, Bray, Maidenhead, Berkshire, SL6 2DN Tel: 0845 1665106 Fax: 0777 9014223 E-mail: mail@homelans.co.uk *IT Services, Home Networks, Wireless Networks, Broadband installations, PC Troubleshooting, Upgrades, Repaires, Helpdesk Services, Small Businesses, Home Services, Anti-virus solutions and anything else IT related*

Homelec, Kings Way House, Laporte Way, Luton, LU4 8RJ Tel: (01582) 544510 Fax: (01582) 544511 *Low voltage light fittings distribs*

▶ Homemove, 2 Clifton Grove, Mansfield, Nottinghamshire, NG18 4HZ Tel: (01623) 453937 E-mail: sales@homemove.tv *Mansfield Based Estate Agents with fixed fee rates featuring Full Screen Virtual Tours*

Homepride Builders Merchants Ltd, Blackfen Road, Sidcup, Kent, DA15 8PW Tel: (020) 8850 1589 Fax: (020) 8850 4044 *Builders merchants*

James Homer Ltd, 78 Mill Lane, Walsall, WS4 2BH Tel: (01922) 623683 Fax: (01922) 723747 E-mail: info.jameshomar@virgin.net *Leather goods manufrs*

Homers Of Quarry Bank, 46-47 High Street, Quarry Bank, Brierley Hill, West Midlands, DY5 2AA Tel: (01384) 564180 Fax: (01384) 636719 E-mail: homers@homersquarrybank.co.uk *Electrical goods retail, repair & services*

▶ Homes Go Fast, Floor 6, 456-458 Strand, London, WC2R 0DZ Tel: (0845) 4581413 E-mail: sales@homesgofast.com *We are an internet publishers, advertising properties on the internet on behalf of private sellers and real estate agents in the UK, Dubai Florida, Spain and the Caribbean.Our marketing of real esate extends past the internet.We offer clients a free property finding service and information about buying abroad. We put sellers of real estate in touch with buyers.We are a division of MARR INTERNATIONAL LTD a company registed in England Wales no 5159185*We are unique in the fact that we work both with real estate agents and private sellers alike.We have also combined the UK property market with that of the worlds most popular destinations for a second or retirement homes.*MARR INTERNATIONAL LTD websites *www.Carribeanhomes4sale.com *www.Spanishhomes4sale.co.uk *www.Floridahomes4sale.co.uk *www.Dubaihomes4sale.co.uk ***

▶ Homes In Focus, 5 South Knowe, Crossgates, Cowdenbeath, Fife, KY4 8AW Tel: (01383) 514114 Fax: (01383) 514114 E-mail: enquiries@homesinfocus.co.uk *Properties - Flats, Houses, Rooms or*

continued

Apartments - to rent throughout scotland - fife, dunfermline. edinburgh, glasgow, dundee, aberdeen, aberdeenshire, borders.

Homeseeker Homes Ltd, Shipton Way Express Business Park, Rushden, Northamptonshire, NN10 6GL Tel: (01933) 651644 Fax: (01933) 652601 E-mail: sales@homeseekerhomes.com *Mobile homes & park homes manufrs*

Homeserve Servowarm, 3 Clarke Industrial Estate, Wetmore Road, Burton-on-Trent, Staffordshire, DE14 1QT Tel: (01283) 511244 Fax: (01283) 569162 E-mail: admin@servowarm.co.uk *Central/gas heating installers/services*

Homeshield, 21townley Street, Middleton, Manchester, M24 1AT Tel: 0161-643 4433 Fax: 0161-643 4466 E-mail: sales@homesheildshutters.co.uk *Domestic shutter manufrs*

Homestart Carrickfergus, 8 Meadowbank Road, Carrickfergus, County Antrim, BT38 8YF Tel: (028) 9332 8875 Fax: (028) 9336 9979 E-mail: info@ceal.co.uk *Business advice consultants*

Homestead, Wyndham House, Lupton Road, Wallingford, Oxfordshire, OX10 9BT Tel: (01491) 839421 Fax: (01491) 825973 E-mail: enquiries@homesteadtimberbuildings.co.uk *Timber buildings manufrs*

Homestead Court Hotel, Homestead Lane, Welwyn Garden City, Hertfordshire, AL7 4LX Tel: (01707) 324336 Fax: (01707) 326447 E-mail: enquiries@homesteadcourt.co.uk *Hotel & conference facilities*

Homestead Foods Ltd, 108 High Street, Godalming, Surrey, GU7 1DW Tel: (01483) 860006 Fax: (01483) 429837 E-mail: enquiries@homestead-foods.co.uk *Frozen vegetable manufrs*

▶ Homestyle Artprints, 9 A West Church Street, Newmilns, Ayrshire, KA16 9EG Tel: (01560) 329356

▶ Homestyle Blinds Stirling, 45 Barnton Street, Stirling, FK8 1HF Tel: (01786) 450659 Fax: (01786) 451751

▶ Homestyle Direct Ltd, Unit 21 Hainault Works, Hainault Road, Little Heath, Romford, RM6 5SS Tel: (020) 8599 8080 Fax: (020) 8599 7070 E-mail: sales@homestyle-bathrooms.co.uk *Bathrooms distributors*

▶ HomeSupply.co.uk, County House, 12-13 Sussex Street, Plymouth, PL1 2HR Tel: (01752) 260607 E-mail: kellys@homesupply.co.uk *HomeSupply.co.uk is a great online source of central heating appliances, bathroom products inc. whirlpool baths and top of the range showers, designer taps, designer radiators, towel rails, brassware, fires and fireplaces. Our inventory will continue to grow over the coming months to enable us to offer an outstanding range for our growing customer base.*

▶ Hometec UK, 401 Rayleigh Road, Leigh-On-Sea, Essex, SS9 5JG Tel: (01702) 421421 Fax: (01702) 521521 E-mail: sales@hometec.co.uk *Doors & windows, pvc products manufrs*

▶ Hometrader Ltd, 71-73 Long Street, Middleton, Manchester, M24 6UN Tel: 0161-643 9090

Honda Connectors Ltd, Unit B1, Marston Gates, South Marston Park, Swindon, SN3 4DE Tel: (01793) 836250 Fax: (01793) 836255 E-mail: sales@hondaconnectors.co.uk *Harness electrical manufrs*

Honda UK Ltd, 470 London Road, Slough, SL3 8QY Tel: (01753) 590500 Fax: (01753) 590000 *Motor car manufrs*

Honey Bros, New Pond Road, Peasmarsh, Guildford, Surrey, GU3 1JR Tel: (01483) 575098 Fax: (01483) 535608 E-mail: sales@honeybros.co.uk *Forestry equipment suppliers*

Honey Well Comsumer Products Group, Oakhurst Drive, Cheadle Heath, Stockport, Cheshire, SK3 0RZ Tel: 0161-491 7391 Fax: 0161-491 7399 E-mail: info@holtsauto.com *Automotive chemical producers*

Honeycomb Information Services Ltd, 23 Cedarland Crescent, Nuthall, Nottingham, NG16 1AG Tel: 0115-927 4521 *Computer software developers*

Honeycrown Ltd, Miners Road, Llay Industrial Estate, Llay, Wrexham, Clwyd, LL12 0PJ Tel: (01978) 853730 Fax: (01978) 856320 E-mail: sales@honeycrown.co.uk *Manufacture industrial rubber seals & square cut washer seals*

Honeyfield Trailers, 279 Bristol Road, Gloucester, GL2 5DD Tel: (01452) 423871 Fax: (01452) 505604 E-mail: darren@honeyfieldtrailers.co.uk *Supply & repair trailers, electric bikes & fit towbars*

Honeyglen Anodising Limited, 62, Sampson Road North, Sparkbrook, Birmingham, B11 1BG Tel: 0121 7736179 Fax: 0121 7667021 E-mail: john@honeyglen.co.uk *Aluminium Finishers to the trade*Anodisers*

Honeypass Ltd, 16 Ardsheal Close, Worthing, West Sussex, BN14 7RP Tel: (01903) 212774 Fax: (01903) 238226 E-mail: info@honeypass.com *Computer suppliers*

Honeypot Health Foods, 96 Lumley Road, Skegness, Lincolnshire, PE25 3ND Tel: (01754) 767387 Fax: (01754) 767387 *Health food suppliers*

Honeysuckle Health Foods, 4 Hawthorn Lane, Wilmslow, Cheshire, SK9 1AA Tel: (01625) 526144 Fax: (01625) 526144 *Health food suppliers*

▶ Honeywell Ltd, Unit 14 Wellheads Terrace, Wellheads Industrial Estate, Aberdeen, AB21 7GF Tel: (01224) 805000 Fax: (01224) 805480

▶ Honeywell, 2 President Buildings, Savile St East, Sheffield, S4 7UQ Tel: 0114-286 0910 Fax: 0114-286 0911 *Control solutions*

Honeywell Aerospace Ltd, Edison Road, Basingstoke, Hampshire, RG21 6QD Tel: (01256) 722200 Fax: (01256) 722201 E-mail: richard.davies@honeywell.com *Aircraft instrument repair services*

Honeywell Aerospace Ltd, Enterprise Way, Aviation Park, Hurn, Christchurch, Dorset, BH23 6EW Tel: (01202) 581818 Fax: (01202) 581919 E-mail: sales@honeywell.com *Aircraft component repair & overhaul services*

Honeywell Analytics Ltd, Hatch Pond House, 4 Stinsford Road, Nuffield Estate, Poole, Dorset, BH17 0RZ Tel: (01202) 676161 Fax: (01202) 678011 E-mail: tracy.dawe@honeywell.com *Flammable & toxic gas detection systems manufrs* Also at: Aberdeen, Lowestoft & Sutton-in-Ashfield

Honeywell Control Systems Ltd, Honeywell House Arlington Business Park, Downshire Way, Bracknell, Berkshire, RG12 1EB Tel: (01344) 656000 Fax: (01344) 656240 E-mail: uk.infocentre@honeywell.com *Control system manufrs*

Honeywell Control Systems Ltd, 150 Aztec West, Almondsbury, Bristol, BS32 4UB Tel: (01454) 848048 Fax: (01454) 848049 *Controls & instrumentation consultants*

Honeywell Control Systems Ltd, 8 Hill Street Industrial Estate, Cwmbran, Gwent, NP44 7PG Tel: (01633) 872628 Fax: (01633) 860886 E-mail: mandy.wills@honeywell.com *Industrial controllers*

▶ Honeywell Control Systems Ltd, Newhouse Industrial Estate, Motherwell, Lanarkshire, ML1 5SB Tel: (01698) 481000 Fax: (01698) 481011

Honeywell Hymatic Engineering Co. Ltd, Burnt Meadow Road, North Moons Moat, Redditch, Worcestershire, B98 9HJ Tel: (01527) 64931 Fax: (01527) 591117 E-mail: redwich.sales@honeywell.com *Defence & aerospace engineers*

Honeywell The Oval, Bunford Lane, Yeovil, Somerset, BA20 2YD Tel: (01935) 475181 Fax: (01935) 427600 E-mail: angus.maclean@honeywell.com *Manufacturers of air conditioning equipment & systems* Also at: Bournemouth, Chard, & Crewkerne

Honeywell Process Solutions, Unit 1 Headlands Business Park, Salisbury Road, Blashford, Ringwood, Hampshire, BH24 3PB Tel: (01425) 463950 Fax: (01425) 463953 E-mail: uksales@trendview.com *Process controller & control instrumentation manufrs*

▶ Honeywell Refrigeration Control, Newhouse Industrial Estate, Motherwell, Lanarkshire, ML1 5SB Tel: (01698) 481698 Fax: (01698) 481699 E-mail: refrigerationcontrol@honeywell.com *Honeywell Refrigeration Control designs, manufactures and globally supplies networkable temperature control systems and products for industrial and commercial refrigeration applications.*

▶ Honeywell Spark Plugs, Unit D6, Treforest Industrial Estate, Pontypridd, Mid Glamorgan, CF37 5YP Tel: (01443) 844992 Fax: (01443) 842275 E-mail: sparkplugs@honeywell.com *Spark plug distributors*

Honeywill & Stein Ltd, Times House, Throwley Way, Sutton, Surrey, SM1 4AF Tel: (020) 8770 3455 Fax: (020) 8770 3464 E-mail: schuelerm@honeywill.co.uk *Honeywill & Stein Ltd based in Sutton, Surrey are chemical merchants & distributors. Including lubricants, detergents & food chemicals*

▶ Hong Wans, Unit 39 Enterprise Industrial Estate, Bolina Road, London, SE16 3LF Tel: (020) 7231 1628

Honnor Marine Ltd, Caxton Street, Heywood, Lancashire, OL10 1AL Tel: (01706) 368068 Fax: (01706) 623189 E-mail: info@honnormarine.co.uk *Boat builders*

John Hood & Co., 55 Cheapside Street, Glasgow, G3 8BH Tel: 0141-221 2433 Fax: 0141-221 0508 *Non-ferrous metal merchants*

Hood Sailmakers Ltd, Bath Road, Lymington, Hampshire, SO41 3RW Tel: (01590) 675011 Fax: (01590) 673797 E-mail: sales@hoodsails.com *Sail makers*

Hood Yacht Spars Ltd, Wick Road, Burnham-on-Crouch, Essex, CM0 8LT Tel: (01621) 782821 Fax: (01621) 785162 E-mail: hoodsparuk@aol.com *Spar manufrs*

Hoof Aloof, 29 Oakwood Drive, Ravenshead, Nottingham, NG15 9DP Tel: (01623) 795628 Fax: (01623) 795628 E-mail: sales@hoofaloof.co.uk *Riding wear & equestrian products suppliers*

Hook Data Services, The Old Village Stores, Slinfold, Horsham, West Sussex, RH13 0RP Tel: (01403) 790739 Fax: (01403) 790160 E-mail: malcolmb@hookdata.co.uk *Computer programmer*

Hook & Tucker Zenyx Ltd, Vulcan Way, New Addington, Croydon, CR0 9UG Tel: (01689) 843345 Fax: (01689) 841792 E-mail: sales@htz.biz *Scientific instrument manufrs*

▶ Hooked In Scotland, 1028 Shettleston Road, Glasgow, G32 7PP Tel: 0141-778 6600 Fax: 0141-778 6600 *Fishing tackle manufrs*

Hooker Group Ltd, Waterside, Brightlingsea, Colchester, CO7 0AU Tel: (01206) 302611 Fax: (01206) 305014 E-mail: sales@hooker.co.uk *Precision castings services in all metals*

Hookings Mastics Ltd, Unit B11 Suttons Business Park, New Road, Rainham, Essex, RM13 8DE Tel: (01708) 522090 Fax: (01708) 526147 E-mail: ken@hookingsmastics.com *Sealant application services*

Bernard Hooper Engineering Ltd, PO Box 4155, Bridgnorth, Shropshire, WV15 5WY Tel: (01746) 761425 Fax: (01746) 761425 E-mail: bhe1@breathemail.net *Design & development consultancy, specialising in the design of IC engines for automotive, defence, industrial & marine applications*

Hooper Engineering Ltd, Nelson St, Oldbury, West Midlands, B69 4NY Tel: 0121-552 2835 Fax: 0121-552 3821 E-mail: hooper.sheetmetal@virgin.net *Sheet metalworkers*

Hooper Knight & Co., St Albans Road, Gloucester, GL2 5FW Tel: (01452) 502888 Fax: (01452) 502960 E-mail: intray@hooperknight.com *Workbench & Storage Systems*

▶ Hooper Safety, 25 Honey Lane, Buntingford, Hertfordshire, SG9 9BQ Tel: (01763) 271051 Fax: (01763) 271051 E-mail: ian@hoopersafety.net *Hooper Safety is an independant provider of specialist safety advice and training. We believe that compliance is not about strangling commercial success, its about putting you in a position of control. So lets us help you with your food safety and health and safety issues. We are able to assist you with policy development, supplier management, training and many other issues. We aim to work with you to ensure compliance while you get on with your business.*

Hoopers Surplus, 20 Pottergate, Norwich, NR2 1DX Tel: (01603) 764375 Fax: (01603) 665585 *Government surplus equipment dealers*

▶ Hoori Falsafi, Upper Ground, London, SE1 Tel: (0795) 6658343 E-mail: hoorif@yahoo.com

▶ Hoots Lift Trucks, Atlas House, 15 Bell Street, West Bromwich, West Midlands, B70 7BT Tel: 0121-500 5885 Fax: (07980) 701827 E-mail: info@hoots4forklifts.co.uk *Fork lifts sales & rental services*

Hooty's Supplies (Wholesale) Ltd, Longacre, Willenhall, West Midlands, WV13 2JX Tel: (01902) 369900 Fax: (01902) 636713 E-mail: hootyssuperstore@aol.com *Fancy goods wholesalers*

Hoover Candy Group, New Chester Road, Bromborough, Wirral, Merseyside, CH62 3PE Tel: 0151-334 2781 Fax: 0151-334 0185 *Kitchen appliance manufrs*

Hop Farm Country Park, Hop Farm, Maidstone Road, Paddock Wood, Tonbridge, Kent, TN12 6PY Tel: (01622) 872068 Fax: (01622) 872630 E-mail: info@thehopfarm.co.uk *Conference centre*

Hope Allan Joinery, Orphans Yard, Brixton Station Road, London, SW9 8QB Tel: (020) 7274 6418 Fax: (020) 7274 6418 *Joinery manufrs*

Hope & Brown Ltd, Blackburn Road, West End, Oswaldtwistle, Lancashire, BB5 4LL Tel: (01254) 390050 Fax: (01254) 223609 *Cleaners*

Hope Education, Hyde Building, Ashton Road, Hyde, Cheshire, SK14 4SH Tel: (0870) 2433400 Fax: 0161-367 2009 E-mail: enquiries@hope-educational.co.uk *Educational mail order suppliers*

Eric Hope Knitwear, 58 High Street, Hawick, Roxburghshire, TD9 7EE Tel: (01450) 370549 Fax: (01450) 370549 *Knitwear*

Ken Hope Material Handling Specialists, Unit 38 C WB House, Bingswood Industrial Estate, Whaley Bridge, High Peak, Derbyshire, SK23 7LY Tel: (01663) 734641 Fax: (01663) 734767 E-mail: kenhope@wbhouse.co.uk *Recycling services*

▶ Kerry Hope, 3 Amhurst Terrace, London, E8 2BT Tel: (020) 7254 3322 Fax: (020) 7254 3354 E-mail: sales@kerryhope.co.uk *Manufactures of clothing*

Hope Technical Developments Ltd, High Street, Ascot, Berkshire, SL5 7HP Tel: (01344) 624855 Fax: (01344) 626237 E-mail: info@hope-tecdev.com *Tow bar manufrs*

Hopefield Fabrications Ltd, Windacre Works, Mather Road, Bury, Lancashire, BL9 6RA Tel: 0161-797 1991 Fax: 0161-764 1461 E-mail: gary@hopefieldfab.fsnet.co.uk *Stainless steel fabricators*

▶ Hoperole Ltd, 4 Norman Way Indust Estate, Over, Cambridge, CB24 5LY Tel: (01954) 230900 Fax: (01954) 230990 *Fork lift truck specialists suppliers*

Hopespare Ltd, 3 Plaza Business Centre, Stockingswater Lane, Enfield, Middlesex, EN3 7XT Tel: (020) 8804 9001 Fax: (020) 8805 3359 E-mail: sales@hopespare.com *Hydraulic equipment manufrs* Also at: Biggleswade

Hopespare Ltd, Units 2, East Burrowfields, Welwyn Garden City, Hertfordshire, AL7 4TB Tel: (01707) 321212 Fax: (01707) 371717 E-mail: darrene@hopespare.com *Hydraulic hose assembly manufrs*

Hopkins, Prospect House, Jameson Road, Birmingham, B6 7SJ Tel: (0845) 4563018 Fax: (0845) 4563019 E-mail: enquires@hopkinsfittings.co.uk Principal Export Areas: Middle East & Africa *Manufacturers of rolling shutter fittings*

▶ Hopkins Bros, The Tythings Commercial Centre, Wincanton, Somerset, BA9 9RZ Tel: (01963) 32993 Fax: (01963) 34455 E-mail: les@hopkins.uk *Concrete products & aggregates suppliers*

Bruce Hopkins Ltd, Shenington Airfield, Shenington, Banbury, Oxfordshire, OX15 6NZ Tel: (01295) 680711 Fax: (01295) 680780 E-mail: bruce@brucehopkins.co.uk *Agricultural engineers*

Hopkins & Bryant Small Tools Ltd, Phillips Street Industrial Estate, 103 Phillips Street, Birmingham, B6 4PT Tel: 0121-359 2195 Fax: 0121-359 1843 *Engineers' suppliers. Stockists and suppliers of socket screws and all types of fasteners. Main agents for Taylor and Jones Reamers. Main agents for Brooke Cutting Tools. Main agents for Sandfield Clamps. Machine and cutting oils and compounds. Cutting tools HSS cobalt and carbide. Silver steel and gauge plate. Free fast delivery service. Trade counter service. No minimum order charge.*

▶ Hopkins Plumbers Ltd, Unit 10 Oaks Industrial Estate, Festival Drive, Loughborough, Leicestershire, LE11 5XN Tel: (01509) 212332 Fax: (01509) 233704 E-mail: sales@hopkins-plumbers.co.uk

Robert Hopkins & Son Ltd, Bullock Street, West Bromwich, West Midlands, B70 7HE Tel: 0121-553 0403 Fax: 0121-525 6448 *Waste transfer & disposal services*

T. Hopkins, 112 Main Street, Woodhouse Eaves, Loughborough, Leicestershire, LE12 8RZ Tel: (01509) 891133 Fax: (01509) 891133 *Steam equipment*

William Hopkins & Sons Ltd, Gardine House, 147-149 Dollman Street, Nechells, Birmingham, B7 4RS Tel: 0121-333 3577 Fax: 0121-333 3480 E-mail: info@william-hopkins.co.uk *Decorative tube stockholders*

Hopkins X L Ltd, 151 Kent Road, Pudsey, West Yorkshire, LS28 9NF Tel: 0113-257 7934 Fax: 0113-257 6759 E-mail: sales@hopkins.biz Principal Export Areas: Worldwide *Manufacturers of catering equipment*

Hopkinson Construction & Plant Hire, Valley Farm, Middle Bridge Road, Gringley-on-the-Hill, Doncaster, South Yorkshire, DN10 4SD Tel: (01777) 816791 Fax: (01909) 731937

▶ Hopkinson Memorials Ltd, 395 City Road, Sheffield, S2 1GB Tel: 0114-275 9926 Fax: 0114-257 9926 E-mail: sales@hopkinsonmemorials.co.uk

Thomas Hopkinson & Son Ltd, Victor Works, Bolton Hall Road, Bradford, West Yorkshire, BD2 1BQ Tel: (01274) 582056 Fax: (01274) 531328 E-mail: ian@triple-king.co.uk *Display equipment & fittings distributor & manufrs*

Hopkinson White, 46 Brook Street, Aston Clinton, Aylesbury, Buckinghamshire, HP22 5ES Tel: (01296) 631898 Fax: (01296) 630321 E-mail: info@hopkinson-white.co.uk *Corporate event organisers & public relations*

▶ Hopkinsons Fairdeals Ltd, Mayfield Farm, Doncaster Road, East Hardwick, Pontefract, West Yorkshire, WF8 3EQ Tel: (01977) 620418 Fax: (01977) 620419 E-mail: sales@hopdeals.com *Britains Leading Municipal Vehicle Specialist*

▶ Hopol Central Heating, 4a Rhiw Road, Colwyn Bay, Clwyd, LL29 7TE Tel: (01492) 536676 Fax: (01492) 535193 E-mail: sales@hopol.com

Hoppe UK Ltd, Gailey Park, Gravelly Way, Standeford, Wolverhampton, WV10 7GW Tel: (01902) 484400 Fax: (01902) 484406 *Established in 1952, the HOPPE group, Europe's door and window hardware market leader, operates with a refreshing approach to business, placing a higher value on long-term productive relationships with its employees and customers than short term success. This forward looking approach, combined with HOPPE's environmental policy has earned it respect for its social responsibility. **HOPPE (UK) was formed in 1988 to meet the demand for high quality door and window hardware in the UK. Operating from its modern 50,000 sq ft base in the Midlands HOPPE(UK) offer a broad product range, the highest standards and continuous innovation. This has enabled HOPPE to become the UK's door handle market leader. Further refinements to the popular Tōkyō suite, the Designer range and a new stainless steel range as well as PAS 24 solutions will enable HOPPE to consolidate this position in 2006.**

Hoppings Softwood Products, Bones Lane, Newchapel, Lingfield, Surrey, RH7 6HR Tel: (01342) 844449 Fax: (01342) 844449 E-mail: sales@hoppings.co.uk *Timber importers* Also at: Epping

Hopson Packaging Ltd, 135 High Street, Newton-le-Willows, Merseyside, WA12 9SQ Tel: (01925) 222533 Fax: (01925) 222711 *Nationwide adhesive tape distributors*

Hopsuns Blinds, Hunthay Farm, Axminster, Devon, EX13 5RJ Tel: (01297) 33488 Fax: (01297) 35855 *Blind manufrs*

▶ Hopton Fire Prevention Services, Camp Road, Lowestoft, Suffolk, NR32 2LL Tel: (01502) 572564 Fax: (07802) 573023 *Manufacture fire fighting equipment*

Hopton Fire Prevention Services, Camp Road, Lowestoft, Suffolk, NR32 2LL Tel: (01502) 572564 Fax: (07802) 573023 *Fire Equipment*

Roy Hopwood Ltd, Hibbert Street, Whitehill Industrial Estate, Stockport, Cheshire, SK4 1NS Tel: 0161-429 6066 Fax: 0161-429 6166 E-mail: info@rhf.co.uk *Suppliers of rivet nuts, blind rivets & industrial fasteners*

Horace Battin & Co., 119 Warkton Lane, Barton Seagrave, Kettering, Northamptonshire, NN15 5AD Tel: (01536) 511464 Fax: (01536) 523455 *Leather brokers*

Horace Fuller Ltd, 72 Park Street, Horsham, West Sussex, RH12 1BY Tel: (01403) 265030 Fax: (01403) 217500 E-mail: sales@horacefuller.com *Lawn mowers & model cars retailers*

Horan Fencing Ltd, 220 Easter Road, Edinburgh, EH6 8LE Tel: 0131-555 3155 Fax: 0131-555 4610 *Security services*

▶ Horbury Building Systems Ltd, South Grove House, South Grove, Rotherham, South Yorkshire, S60 2AF Tel: (01709) 515044 Fax: 01709 515066 E-mail: dpriestley@horburygroup.com *Electrical Contractors available from Horbury Building Systems Ltd based in Rotherham, South Yorkshire. Click the links below to visit our website or contact us via our profile page.*

Hore Station P.L.C., D1 Armthorpe Enterprise Centre, Rands Lane, Armthorpe, Doncaster, South Yorkshire, DN3 3DY Tel: (01302) 835191 Fax: (01302) 830741 *Lifting equipment hire*

Horiba Instruments Ltd, Kyoto Close, Summerhouse Road, Moulton Park, Northampton, NN3 6FL Tel: (01604) 542500 Fax: (01604) 542699 Principal Export Areas: Worldwide *Manufacturers of environmental monitoring equipment*

▶ Horizon Conservatories Ltd, Strikes Garden Centre, Red Hall Lane, Wellington Hill, Leeds, LS17 8NA Tel: 0845 2301560 Fax: 0845 2301570 E-mail: info@horizonconservatories.co.uk *Horizon Conservatories providing the total concept of design, manufacture, installation and service ensure that our conservatories become a beautiful addition of comfortable living space to your home.*

Horizon Instruments Ltd, Unit 12 Ghyll Industrial Estate, Heathfield, East Sussex, TN21 8AW Tel: (01435) 864239 Fax: (01435) 865222 E-mail: mail@horizoninstruments.co.uk *Machinery manufrs*

Horizon Knitwear Manufacturers Ltd, Harkness Street, Manchester, M12 6BT Tel: 0161-273 6410 Fax: 0161-273 2133 *Knitwear manufrs*

Horizon Mechanical Services International Ltd, Unit 1 Willment Way, Bristol, BS11 8DJ Tel: 0117-982 1415 Fax: 0117-982 0630 E-mail: sales@horizon-int.com *Air pollution control equipment manufrs*

▶ Horizon Print & Design, Unit 4, Falkirk Enterprise Park, Falkirk, FK2 9HQ Tel: (01324) 670237

Horizon Recruitment Ltd, 6 Piccadilly, Bradford, West Yorkshire, BD1 3LW Tel: (01274) 744991 Fax: (01274) 744992 *Employment & recruitment agency*

Horizon Specialist Contracting Ltd, Horizon House, Criffin Enterprise Centre, Oxton Road, Epperstone, Nottingham, NG14 6AT Tel: (0870) 0104915 Fax: (0870) 0104916 E-mail: sales@horizonsc.co.uk *Steeplejack & lightning conductor engineers*

Horizon Technology, Units 1-2, Dacre Castle, Dacre, Penrith, Cumbria, CA11 0HL Tel: (01768) 486711 Fax: (01768) 486770 *Ceramic engineering*

Horizon Windows (Wales) Ltd, CWM Cynon Business Park, Mountain Ash, Mid Glamorgan, CF45 4ER Tel: (01443) 479993 Fax: (01443) 475738 E-mail: info@venturewales.com *Plastic injection moulding*

Horizont UK Ltd, Gloucester, GL2 8YS Tel: (01452) 300450 Fax: (01452) 308776 E-mail: bramley@horizont.com *Electric fencing equipment*

▶ Horizontal Boring Services, 1 Lamberhead Industrial Estate, Leopold Street, Wigan, Lancashire, WN5 8EG Tel: (01942) 224805 Fax: (01942) 224848 *Engineering*

Horley Garden Centre, Station Approach, Horley, Surrey, RH6 9HQ Tel: (07866) 433473 *Garden buildings & furniture manufrs*

Horley Metal Productions Ltd, 30 Balcombe Road, Horley, Surrey, RH6 9AA Tel: (01293) 820234 Fax: (01293) 820235 *General engineers & steel stockists*

Horley Services Ltd, Salfords Industrial Estate, Salfords, Redhill, RH1 5ES Tel: (01293) 771481 Fax: (01293) 786701 E-mail: sales@horleysg.demon.co.uk *Warehouse & logistics services* Also at: Chichester

Horn UK Ltd, Townfoot Industrial Estate, Brampton, Cumbria, CA8 1SW Tel: (01697) 741080 Fax: (01697) 741022 E-mail: eng@cumbrian.co.uk *Polyethylene producT manufacturer*

Hornby Hobbies Ltd, H1-H2 Unit Enterprise Road, Westwood Industrial Estate, Margate, Kent, CT9 4JX Tel: (01843) 233500 Fax: (01843) 233513 E-mail: hornby@btinternet.com *Toy manufacturers & distributors*

John Hornby & Sons Ltd, Old Crown Dyeworks, Birkshall Lane, Bradford, West Yorkshire, BD4 8TB Tel: (01274) 390856 Fax: (01274) 728825 *Steel recycling & steel stockholders services*

Horncastle Pine, 13 Bull Ring, Horncastle, Lincolnshire, LN9 5HU Tel: (01507) 526666 Fax: (01507) 526666 *Pine furniture retailer*

Hornchurch Electronics, 251 Goodwood Avenue, Hornchurch, Essex, RM12 6DD Tel: (01708) 441224 Fax: (01708) 620060 *Fire alarm installation & services*

Horne & Banks Group Ltd, 3 Merchant Drive, Mead Lane Industrial Estate, Hertford, SG13 7BH Tel: (01992) 501289 Fax: (01992) 501318 E-mail: david@horneandbanks.co.uk *Zip fastener distributors or agents & precision engineers, injection mouldings & plastic*

▶ Horne Engineering Ltd, PO Box 7, Johnstone, Renfrewshire, PA5 8BD Tel: (01505) 321455 Fax: (01505) 336287 E-mail: info@horne.co.uk Purchasing Contact: V. McInnes Sales Contact: J. Horne Principal Export Areas: Worldwide *Manufacturers of thermostatic mixing & shower valves. Temperature control valves & steam valves*

Robert Horne Ltd, 4A Kingfisher Court, Brambleside, Bellbrook Industrial Estate, Uckfield, East Sussex, TN22 1QQ Tel: (01825) 748494 Fax: (01273) 478546 E-mail: rh.uckkfield@roberthorne.co.uk *Paper merchants* Also at: Bognor Regis, Reading, Tonbridge & Swindon

Robert Horne Group Ltd, 1 Brooklands Way, Boldon Business Park, Boldon Colliery, Tyne & Wear, NE35 9LZ Tel: 0191-537 7177 Fax: 0191-537 7178 E-mail: rh.newcastle@roberthorne.co.uk *Paper merchants or agents*

Robert Horne Group P.L.C., Huntsman House, Pontefract Road, Leeds, LS10 1DD Tel: 0113-387 2424 Fax: 0113-271 9408 E-mail: rh.leeds@roberthorne.co.uk *Paper merchants & agents services*

Robert Horne Industrial Plant Ltd, Quantam House, Gee Business Centre, Holborn Hill, Birmingham, B7 5JR Tel: 0121-327 5050 Fax: 0121-327 2818 *Plastic materials, products & components stockists*

Horne Robert Paper Company Ltd, Huntsman House, 40 Tameside Drive, Birmingham, B35 7BD Tel: 0121-776 7777 Fax: 0121-749 2670 E-mail: rh.birmingham@roberthorne.co.uk *Paper board & plastic merchants or agents*

Stanley Horne & Sons Ltd, Bentley Mill Close, Walsall, WS2 0BN Tel: (01922) 611451 Fax: (01922) 726070 E-mail: sales@stanleyhorne.co.uk *CNC precision machinists*

Horner Bros, Southgate Avenue, Mildenhall, Bury St. Edmunds, Suffolk, IP28 7AT Tel: (01638) 712587 Fax: (01638) 715121 E-mail: hornerbros@fast24.co.uk *Auto-electrical services*

Hornett Bros & Co. Ltd, Ferry Lane, Rainham, Essex, RM13 9YH Tel: (01708) 556041 Fax: (01708) 557546 E-mail: sales@hornett.net *Oil additive manufrs*

▶ Horns Garden Sheds, 1 Winchester Drive, South West Industrial Estate, Peterlee, County Durham, SR8 2RJ Tel: 0191-518 1098 Fax: 0191-518 1098

P.R. Hornsby & Co. Business Sales Ltd, 72 East Hill, Colchester, CO1 2QW Tel: (01206) 793790 Fax: (01206) 793791 E-mail: hornsbysales@btconnect.com *Chartered accountants*

▶ Horny Toys, 60 Acacia Road, London, W3 6HF Tel: 02088 961103 E-mail: info@hornytoys.co.uk *LIGERIE&ADULT ACCESSORIES*WE GIVE YOU A DISCREET, SAFE& SECURE ONLINE SERVICE WITHUNLIMITED PRODUCTS.All orders posted with unmarked packaging,**

Horobin Ltd, Willenhall Trading Estate, Midacre, Willenhall, West Midlands, WV13 2JW Tel: (01902) 604060 Fax: (01902) 603366 E-mail: sales@horobin.co.uk *Drain testing & cleaning equipment suppliers*

▶ Horological Repair Service, 37 Green End, Denton, Manchester, M34 7PT Tel: 0161-336 5215 Fax: 0161-336 5215 E-mail: info@hrs-clocks.co.uk *Clock repairs & antique clock parts & restoration*

▶ Horrex Davis Design Associates Ltd, 6 Dorset Street, London, W1U 6QL Tel: (020) 7486 8132 Fax: (020) 7487 2936 E-mail: design@hdda.co.uk *Graphic design*

Horse Bits Dorset Ltd, 1a Froud Way, Corfe Mullen, Wimborne, Dorset, BH21 3UU Tel: (01202) 600550 Fax: (01202) 386841 E-mail: trish@horsebitsdorset.co.uk *Saddlery & riding wear suppliers*

▶ Horse Box, 3 Shifnal Shopping Centre, Bradford Street, Shifnal, Shropshire, TF11 8AU Tel: (01952) 460976 E-mail: beckyhorsebox@yahoo.co.uk *Equestrian equipment retailers*

Horse Power Self Drive Equine Transport, 7 Riverside, Storrington, Pulborough, West Sussex, RH20 4NN Tel: (01903) 746800 Fax: (0845) 1275210 E-mail: sales@horsebox-selfdrive.com *Renault Master 2.5D two horse carriers for hire from £80.00 per day inc. VAT, comprehensive insurance and roadside rescue.*Based West Sussex, ideal for Kent, Hampshire and East Sussex*

Horse Requisites Newmarket Ltd, Black Bear Lane, Newmarket, Suffolk, CB8 0WB Tel: (01638) 664619 Fax: (01638) 661562 *All ironmongery & equestrian products*

Horse & Rider, 7 Exeter Street, Launceston, Cornwall, PL15 9EQ Tel: (01566) 774253 Fax: (01566) 774253 *Saddlers & riding clothes*

▶ Horse World Suppliers, Unit 5-7 Brook Farm, Stoneleigh Road, Coventry, CV4 7AB Tel: (024) 7669 6997 Fax: (024) 7669 7145 *Equestrian goods suppliers*

▶ Horse-Aholics, Bankside Industrial Estate, Falkirk, FK2 7UY Tel: (01324) 637722 Fax: (01324) 637722

Horsehay Ltd, Horsehay Estate, Telford, Shropshire, TF4 3PY Tel: (01952) 503344 Fax: (01952) 503356 E-mail: richard@horsehay.uk.com *Data storage specialists*

Horsell Electrics Ltd, 30 Hollingdean Road, Brighton, BN2 4AA Tel: (01273) 694124 Fax: (01273) 603361 E-mail: horsell@globalnet.co.uk *Lighting fittings manufrs*

▶ horsemat.co.uk, 4 & 5 Goldingham Hall, Bulmer, Sudbury, Suffolk, CO10 7ER Tel: (01787) 880433 Fax: (0871) 4338858 E-mail: sales@horsemat.co.uk *Suppliers of equestrian matting products*

Horseproud Containers, Main Road, Ryton, Tyne & Wear, NE40 3AG Tel: 0191-413 4936 Fax: 0191-413 1700 *Used horse box supplier*

▶ horse-showing.com, Aubers Farm, Manor Road, Lower Sundon, Luton, LU3 3PA Tel: (07835) 141418 *Bespoke Show Ring Accesories.*

▶ Horseswap.co.uk, East Lodge, Potterhanworth, Longhills, Branston, Lincoln, LN4 1HR Tel: (01522) 797131 Fax: (01522) 797131 E-mail: gaynor@horseswap.co.uk *Have your own private deals, advertise your horses & equestrian items for sale or swap also what you would swap for whether it be another horse or whatever, swap anything for anything********

Joseph Horsfall & Sons Ltd, Pellon Lane, Halifax, West Yorkshire, HX1 4AA Tel: (01422) 360213 Fax: (01422) 321579 E-mail: info@jhorsfall.com *Worsted & speciality yarn spinners*

Horsham & District Laundry Ltd, Unit D, Foundry Close, Horsham, West Sussex, RH13 5TX Tel: (01403) 243340 Fax: (01403) 254539 *Industrial laundry services*

Horsham Engraving Ltd, Foundry Lane, Horsham, West Sussex, RH13 5PX Tel: (01403) 260729 Fax: (01403) 210057 E-mail: horshamengraving@aol.com *Engraving silk screen printing labels*

Horsham Sheet Metal, Foundry Lane, Horsham, West Sussex, RH13 5PX Tel: (01403) 264137 Fax: (01403) 272386 E-mail: sales@horshamsheetmetal.co.uk *Sheet metalwork engineers & fabricators*

Horsley Joinery, Manston Green Industrial Estate, Preston Road, Manston, Ramsgate, Kent, CT12 5BA Tel: (01843) 824002 Fax: (01843) 848354 *Joinery*

▶ Horsleys Of Stafford, Unit 2, Tollgate Drive, Tollgate Industrial Estate, Stafford, ST16 3HS Tel: (01785) 253723 Fax: (01785) 257662 E-mail: sales@horsleysofstafford.co.uk

▶ Horsnell Ltd, 190 Galleywood Road, Great Baddow, Chelmsford, CM2 8NB Tel: (01245) 471108 Fax: (01245) 471108 E-mail: chris@horsnellltd.fsnnet.co.uk *Building contractor*

Horstmann Group Ltd, Roman Farm Road, Bristol, BS4 1UP Tel: 0117-978 8700 Fax: 0117-987 8701 E-mail: reception@horstmann.co.uk *Time control manufrs*

▶ Horta Soils Ltd, 4 Carn Court Road, Portadown, Craigavon, County Armagh, BT63 5YX Tel: (028) 3833 7160

▶ Hortec Solutions, Bromyard Road, Ledbury, Herefordshire, HR8 1LG Tel: (01531) 636511 Fax: (01531) 632172 *Agricultural farmers*

Hortech Landscape, The Nurseries, Moddershall, Stone, Staffordshire, ST15 8TQ Tel: (01785) 818080 Fax: (01785) 285452 E-mail: enquiries@hortech.co.uk *Landscape management services*

Hortech Systems Ltd, Hallgate, Holbeach, Spalding, Lincolnshire, PE12 7LG Tel: (01406) 426513 Fax: (01406) 426515 E-mail: wayne@hortech.irrigation.co.uk *Pump repairers*

Horticultural Ltd, Newferry Road, Bellaghy, Magherafelt, County Londonderry, BT45 8ND Tel: (028) 7938 6555 Fax: (028) 7938 6741 E-mail: info@bulrush.co.uk Principal Export Areas: Worldwide *Horticultural peat extractors*

▶ Horticulture, 2 Laburnam Cottages, Shortfield Common, Frensham, Farnham, Surrey, GU10 3BJ Tel: (01252) 790688 E-mail: info@revolverevents.co.uk *Landscaping & garden maintenance*

Horton Automatics Ltd, Hortonwood 31, Telford, Shropshire, TF1 7YZ Tel: (01952) 670169 Fax: (01952) 670181 E-mail: sales@horton-automatics.ltd.uk *Automatic doors*

Horton Commercial Ltd, 63 Haviland Road, Ferndown Industrial Estate, Wimborne, Dorset, BH21 7PY Tel: (01202) 877704 Fax: (01202) 870261 E-mail: info@abacuscarhire.co.uk *Commercial bodybuilders & repairers*

Horton International UK Ltd, Audley House, 13 Palace Street, London, SW1E 5HX Tel: (020) 7630 0200 Fax: (020) 7630 0322 E-mail: london@horton-intl.com *Executive management search consultants*

Horton & Newberry (Sales & Marketing) Ltd, 53a High Street Wanstead, London, E11 2AA Tel: (020) 8989 5903 Fax: (020) 8530 4118 E-mail: sales@hortonandnewberry.co.uk *Advertising & business gifts specialists*

▶ Horton Print Group, Rosse Street, Bradford, West Yorkshire, BD8 9AS Tel: (01274) 777801 Fax: (01274) 777802 E-mail: sales@hortonprint.com

Horwich Signs Ltd, 4 Stirling Industrial Estate, Chorley New Road, Horwich, Bolton, BL6 6DU Tel: (01204) 669500 Fax: (01204) 669500 *Sign manufrs*

Horwood Homewares Ltd, Avonmouth Way, Bristol, BS11 9HX Tel: 0117-940 0000 Fax: 0117-940 1100 E-mail: sales@horwood.co.uk *Distributors of housewares*

Hosch (GB) Ltd, 97 Sadler Forster Way, Teesside Industrial Estate, Stockton-On-Tees, Cleveland, TS17 9JY Tel: (01642) 751100 Fax: (01642) 751448 E-mail: mail@hosch.co.uk *Conveyor belt scraper manufrs*

Hose Components, Enterprise Works, 2 Hunsley Street, Sheffield, S4 8DY Tel: 0114-261 9766 Fax: 0114-261 7464 E-mail: richard.garlick@hosecomponents.co.uk *Rubber sheeting & matting products, hose clips & fittings distributors*

Hose Depot Direct Ltd, Units 8 Brunel Park, Blyth Road, Harworth, Doncaster, South Yorkshire, DN11 8NE Tel: (01302) 746969 Fax: (01302) 746974 *Hose distributors & agents*

Hose & General Supplies Ltd, Daux Road, Billingshurst, West Sussex, RH14 9SJ Tel: (01403) 783221 Fax: (01403) 783221 *Hose distributors & agents*

▶ Hose Inspection Testing & Supply Ltd, 2 White Horse Lane London, Colney St Albans, London Colney, St. Albans, Hertfordshire, AL2 1JX Tel: (01727) 825307 Fax: (01727) 821810 E-mail: jeff.blakeley@btinternet.com *hoses for all industrial,marine&transport applications.specialist on site hose testing and certification for the road tanker,chemical&petroleum inds*

Hose Tech Ltd, 3 Wheatlea Industrial Estate, Wheatlea Road, Wigan, Lancashire, WN3 6XP Tel: (01942) 233036 Fax: (01942) 322915 E-mail: sales@hose-tech.co.uk *AEROQUIP HYDRAULIC HOSE ASSEMBLIES UP TO 3" ID - AQP : Scientifically Superior */MATCHMATE PLUS - High performance colour-coded hydraulic hose assembly system /*LARGE BORE SWAGING - Fittings & flanges in all materials - Testing & certification /*HYGIENIC HOSE ASSEMBLIES - FDA approved rubber, PTFE & silicone hose /*STAINLESS STEEL HYGIENIC FITTINGS & FABRICATIONS - Quick release couplings /*SYNFLEX THERMOPLASTIC HOSE & TUBING - High & low pressure specialist applications / *INDUSTRIAL RUBBER HOSE UP TO 20" ID - Air, oil, water, steam & petrochemical / *MATERIAL HANDLING & CUSTOM BUILT HOSE - Design & build service available*

Hoselines Ltd, 25 Longfields Road, Carlton, Barnsley, South Yorkshire, S71 3HT Tel: (01226) 240838 Fax: (01226) 204315 *Hydraulic hose assembly services*

Hoselines & Industrial Supplies (North West) Ltd, Units 8 & 9 Knoll Street Industrial Estate, Bury New Rd, Salford, M7 2BL Tel: 0161-792 0481 Fax: 0161-792 5328 E-mail: sales@hoselines.com *Industrial Hoses, Hose Couplings, Distributors and agents, Hose Nozzles, Hose Reels, Fittings, Chemical Hoses, Composite Hoses, Automotive and Aircraft Refuelling Hoses, Exhaust and Furnace Door Hoses, Hydraulic Hose, Jetting Hose, Sewer Jetting Hose, Pump Hoses, Water Hoses.*

Hoses Direct, Brighton, BN2 5AW Tel: (0800) 6526038 Fax: (0800) 6526039 E-mail: sales@hoses.co.uk *Hydraulic hose, valve & tube fittings distributors/agents*

Hoshizaki UK, Unit 2 Marquis Business Centre, Royston Road, Baldock, Hertfordshire, SG7 6XL Tel: (0845) 4560585 Fax: (01462) 499080 E-mail: sales@hoshizakiuk.co.uk *Hoshizaki UK based in Baldock, Hertfordshire are manufactures of ice machines, including ice and water dispensers, sushi cases, refrigerators and freezers.*

▶ Hosie Electrical Ltd, 70 Market Place, Inverurie, Aberdeenshire, AB51 3XN Tel: (01467) 620831 Fax: (01467) 621255

Jade Hosiery Ltd, 598 Atlas Road, Wembley, Middlesex, HA9 0JH Tel: (020) 8902 1292 Fax: (020) 8902 7942 E-mail: sales@jade.co.uk *Hosiery manufrs*

Thomas Hosking & Sons Ltd, Dumballs Road, Cardiff, CF10 5FE Tel: (029) 2048 0324 Fax: (029) 2049 2075 E-mail: thomashosking@btconnect.com *Commercial motor body builders*

Hoskins Joinery, Honey Hill Lane, Wimbotsham, King's Lynn, Norfolk, PE34 3QD Tel: (01366) 383103 Fax: (01366) 385957 *Joinery manufrs*

Hoskins Medical Equipment, Woodsbank Trading Estate, Woden Road West, Wednesbury, West Midlands, WS10 7BL Tel: 0121-707 6600 Fax: 0121-502 2092 E-mail: sales@hoskinsme.co.uk *Hospital & patient handling equipment*

Company Information

▶ Karina Hoskyns Photography, Hareshaw, The Platt, Dormansland, Lingfield, Surrey, RH7 6QX Tel: (07778) 599146 Fax: (01342) 836987 E-mail: enquiries@karinahoskynsphotos.co.uk *Top award-winning photographer.*Personal, friendly & professional service at affordable prices.*Quality portraits in your own home.*Colour or black and white.*Families: individual and group portraits.*Elegant, stylish, glamorous portraits for women.*Model portfolios.*Pets.*Schools, sports, social.*Corporate photography.*

Hospital Engineering Ltd, 6 Mercury Park, Mercury Way, Urmston, Manchester, M41 7HS Tel: 0161-866 9066 Fax: 0161-865 3378 E-mail: simonmcde@heis.co.uk *X-ray film distribs*

Hospital Metalcraft Ltd, Blandford Heights, Blandford Forum, Dorset, DT11 7TG Tel: (01258) 451338 Fax: (01258) 455056 E-mail: sales@bristolmaid.com *Steel hospital furniture & equipment manufrs*

Hospital Plan Insurance Services, 44 Baker Street, London, W1A 4WJ Tel: (020) 7487 4411 Fax: (020) 7487 5747 E-mail: info@hpis.co.uk *Hospital indemnity insurance*

Hospitality Equipment Supplies Ltd, Calderwood House, 7 Montpellier Parade, Cheltenham, Gloucestershire, GL50 1UA Tel: (01242) 573227 Fax: (01242) 226121 E-mail: sales@h-e-s.co.uk *Hospitality Equipment Supplies are international suppliers to the hospitality and foodservice industries. They are a specialist export company and for the last 11 years have been supplying clients around the world offering a truly global service. Their products range from cutlery to fryers, dishwashers and pizza ovens plus many more.*

Hospitality Tills, 92 Corporation Road, Cardiff, CF11 7AW Tel: (0870) 0420320 Fax: (0870) 0420230 E-mail: sales@hospitalitytills.com *We supply and install touch screen EPOS Till systems to customers in the pub, restaurant and hotel trades. We offer training and off site support for all kinds of PC based EPOS system.*

Hossacks Clothing Mnfrs, 106 Park Street Lane, Park Street, St. Albans, Hertfordshire, AL2 2JQ Tel: (01727) 875586 Fax: (01727) 875581 E-mail: info@hossacks.com *Leisurewear manufrs*

▶ Host Broker Services, 16 Chilwell Avenue, Little Haywood, Stafford, ST18 0QZ Tel: 01889 883081 E-mail: info@hostbroker.co.uk *IT equipment broker*

Host Von Schrader, Unit 6 Capenhurst Technology Park, Capenhurst, Chester, CH1 6EH Tel: 0151-347 1900 Fax: 0151-347 1901 E-mail: host@hostvs.co.uk *Carpet & upholstery cleaning equipment*

▶ HostofCOLOURS LTD, Ivybridge, Devon, PL21 0JW Tel: (07814) 434075 E-mail: info@hostofcolours.co.uk *Web Hosting starts from as little as £1.49 a month which is packed with more than enough features to get you up and running in no time.*UK Domain Names start from an amazing £1.50 a year.**

▶ Hostpipe Ltd, 18 Sherwood Road Sherwood Road, Tetbury, Gloucestershire, GL8 8BU Tel: (01666) 505570 Fax: (01666) 505570 E-mail: rob@hostpipe.co.uk *IT consultancy specialising in website design & hosting, data harvesting & network hardware installation, database design*

▶ hostukdomain.com, Flat 1, 23 Acock Grove, Northolt, Middlesex, UB5 4RT Tel: (0800) 0409695 E-mail: sales@hostukdomain.com *We design affordable websites which you can update and manage in seconds. No programming skills required to use. Please call us free on 0800 040 9695 or visit our web site.**

▶ Hot Air Balloons, 1 Home Farm Cottage, Lenham Heath Road, Sandway, Maidstone, Kent, ME17 2HX Tel: (01622) 858956 Fax: (01622) 853817 E-mail: lizmeek@ballooning.fsnet.co.uk *Balloons, hot air & publicity supplier*

▶ Hot Chocolates - Chocolate Fountain Hire, 83 Findon Road, Elson, Gosport, Hampshire, PO12 4ER Tel: (023) 9250 1416 E-mail: enquiries@hotchocolates.co.uk *Chocolate fountain hire services*

▶ Hot Dog Screenprint, Liddicoat Road, Lostwithiel, Cornwall, PL22 0YY Tel: (01208) 873839 Fax: (01208) 873839 E-mail: enquiries@hotdog-decals.com *Screenprinters, Signmakers & Designers.*Specialist areas - vinyl stickers, fibre-glass tissue decals for the surfing industry, contract T.shirt/textile printing, motorsport rally plates, signs & display & vinyl vehicle graphics.*

▶ Hot Fires & Heating, 33 West Auckland Road, Darlington, County Durham, DL3 9EL Tel: (01325) 351351 Fax: (01325) 351351 E-mail: hotfires@btconnect.com *Fire & fireplace retail & installation, gas central heating & boilers*

Hot Metal Press, Museum Works Elscar Workshops, Wath Road, Elsecar, Barnsley, South Yorkshire, S74 8HJ Tel: (01226) 740498 Fax: (01226) 350201 E-mail: info@hotmetalpress.co.uk *Hot foil, envelope & litho printers, letterpresses & overprinting*

▶ Hot Tool, 7 The Frenches, Redhill, RH1 2HF Tel: (01737) 778589 Fax: (01737) 778549 E-mail: martin@hottool.co.uk *Computer consultants*

Hotbray Ltd, 16 Jubilee Way, London, SW19 3GZ Tel: (020) 8545 0011 Fax: (020) 8545 0020 E-mail: sales@hotbray.co.uk *Exporters of motor vehicle spare parts*

Hotchkiss Air Supply, 6 Sovereign Park, Coronation Road, London, NW10 7QP Tel: (020) 8965 2066 Fax: (020) 8965 2088 E-mail: has.london@virgin.net *Circular ductwork & accessories distributors*

Hotchkiss Air Supply (HAS), Heath Mill Road, Wombourne, Wolverhampton, WV5 8AP Tel: (01902) 895161 Fax: (01902) 892045 E-mail: info@hotchkissairsupply.co.uk *Hotchkiss Air Supply is one of the leading 'supply only' manufacturers and distributors of circular and flat oval ductwork and accessories in the UK.* Based in the Midlands we stock a comprehensive range of air distribution products*

continued

for the heating and ventilation industry including a full range of Flexible Ducting, Access Doors, Dampers, Accessories, Acoustics products and our Colourduct system. Also at: Eastbourne

Hotel Elizabeth Grimsby, Little Coates Road, Grimsby, South Humberside, DN34 4LX Tel: (01472) 240024 Fax: (01472) 241354 E-mail: elizabeth.grimsby@elizabethhotels.co.uk *Conference facilities & hotel*

Hotelscene, 17 Portland Square, Bristol, BS2 8SJ Tel: 0117-916 6300 Fax: (0844) 8264423 E-mail: tom.whitney@hotelscene.co.uk *Established in 1981, Hotelscene is one of the foremost hotel and conference booking agents in the UK, and the acknowledged industry leader in corporate online hotel bookings. Hotelscene is a specialist in managing large corporate hotel and conference accounts. *Hotelscene has developed capabilities that are innovate and leading edge, including the market-leading online booking tool, Corporate Xtranet. Hotelscene clients can book online or over the telephone with experienced reservation agents based in Bristol, UK.*

Hotelware Ltd, 14 Dobson Place, Leeds, LS11 5PG Tel: 0113-271 7885 Fax: 0113-270 8576 E-mail: sales@hotelwareltd.co.uk *Catering equipment suppliers*

Hotfrost, 72-76 Brighton Road, Surbiton, Surrey, KT6 5PP Tel: (020) 8399 7151 Fax: (020) 8399 9549 *Heating equipment & refrigerator component distributors* Also at: Edinburgh

▶ Hothouse Integrated Marketing Ltd, 8 Tenby Street, Birmingham, B1 3AJ Tel: 0121-233 0533 Fax: 0121-200 2567

Hothouse Product Development Partners, Unit 1 College Fields Business Centre, Prince Georges Road, Merton, London, SW19 2PT Tel: (020) 8687 2093 Fax: (020) 8646 1822 E-mail: studio@hothouse-design.com *Industrial designers*

Hotline Electric Fencing Ltd, Wharf Road, NEWTON ABBOT, Devon, TQ12 2DA Tel: (01626) 331188 Fax: (01626) 331810 E-mail: sales@hotline-fencing.co.uk *Electric fencing manufrs*

Hotline Signs, 18a Bridge Street, Buxton, Derbyshire, SK17 6BS Tel: (01298) 25491 Fax: (01298) 78452 *Signs manufrs*

▶ Ho'Ton Heating Ltd, Chilton Moor School, Chilton Moor, Houghton le Spring, Tyne & Wear, DH4 6LU Tel: 0191-385 4556 Fax: 0191-385 5472

Hotset UK Ltd, Unit M, Bowen Industrial Estate, Aberbargoed, Bargoed, Mid Glamorgan, CF81 9EP Tel: (01443) 875581 Fax: (01443) 831422 E-mail: sales@hotset.u-net.com *Band, cartridge & coil heaters manufrs*

Hotstorm Jewellery, Sheepy Parva, Atherstone, Warwickshire, CV9 3RL Tel: 07929 726821 E-mail: info@hotstorm-jewellery.co.uk *Online jewellery retailer. Womens, mens, childrens & pets jewellery. Bridal, fashion, gold & silver collections.*

Hottot Transport, Blue Waters Industrial Estate, Bovey Tracey, Newton Abbot, Devon, TQ13 9YF Tel: (01626) 833147 Fax: (01626) 834200 *Road transport/haulage/freight services*

▶ Hotwire Orthodontics, Highgate Works, Tomtits Lane, Forest Row, East Sussex, RH18 5AT Tel: (01342) 827750

▶ Hotwork Combustion Technology Ltd, Bretton Street, Savile Town, Dewsbury, West Yorkshire, WF12 9DB Tel: (01924) 506506 Fax: (01924) 506311 E-mail: engineering@hotworkct.com *Furnace & combustion systems engineers*

Houchin Aerospace Ltd, Hilton Road, Ashford, Kent, TN23 1DZ Tel: (01233) 623211 Fax: (01223) 638403 E-mail: sales@houchinaero.com *Aircraft ground power equipment manufrs*

▶ Houdini Marine Windows Ltd, 1 Hallmark Industrial Estate, Hall Road, Southminster, Essex, CM0 7EH Tel: (01621) 773293 Fax: (01621) 773852 E-mail: sales@houdini-marine.co.uk *Manufacturer of custom built aluminium framed marine windows, hatches, windscreens and doors*

Hough Engineering, 138A High Street, Silverdale, Newcastle, Staffordshire, ST5 6LX Tel: (01782) 633984 Fax: (01782) 715987 E-mail: houghengineering@supnet.com *Fire escape staircase manufrs*

Houghton plc, Beacon Road, Trafford Park, Manchester, M17 1AF Tel: 0161-874 5000 Fax: 0161-877 9764 E-mail: info@houghtonintl.com *Industrial oil & chemicals manufrs*

Houghton Concrete Ltd, 8 Firsdale Industrial Estate, Nangreaves Street, Leigh, Lancashire, WN7 4TN Tel: (01942) 676446 Fax: (01942) 608018 *Concrete products manufrs*

Houghton Grear, 7 Harley Street, London, W1G 9QD Tel: (020) 7580 9357 Fax: (020) 7580 4716 *Chartered surveyors*

Houghton Oils & Chemicals, 19 Tandragee Road, Newry, County Down, BT35 6QE Tel: (028) 3026 7119 Fax: (028) 3026 6610 *Machine oils & lubricant producers*

Houghton Refrigeration, 24 Birkhall Avenue, Inchinnan, Renfrew, PA4 9QA Tel: 0141-812 1434 Fax: 0141-812 1434 *Air conditioning & refrigeration engineers*

Houghton Trailers, Colliery Lane, Hetton-le-Hole, Houghton le Spring, Tyne & Wear, DH5 0BG Tel: 0191-517 0154 Fax: 0191-517 0154 *Industrial trailer manufrs*

Houghton-Parkhouse Ltd, Grisleymire Lane, Milnthorpe, Cumbria, LA7 7RF Tel: (01539) 563347 Fax: (01539) 562472 E-mail: sales@houghtons.co.uk *Commercial motor body builders*

Houghtons Waste Paper Ltd, York Street Mill, York Street, Audenshaw, Manchester, M34 5TN Tel: 0161-330 4971 Fax: 0161-343 4055 E-mail: info@houghtons-wp.co.uk *Confidential shredding & secure destruction services*

Houlder Ltd, 59 Lafone Street, London, SE1 2LX Tel: (020) 7357 7317 Fax: (020) 7403 8201 E-mail: mail@houlder-offshore.co.uk *Consulting engineers & designers* Also at: Bridge of Don

Houlihan & Co Excavations Ltd, Ashford House, 46-48 Littleton Road, Ashford, Middlesex, TW15 1UQ Tel: (01784) 250650 Fax: (01784) 248296 *Groundwork civil engineers*

Hoults Removals Ltd, Crown House, Earlsway, Team Valley Trading Estate, Gateshead, Tyne & Wear, NE11 0RQ Tel: 0191-265 3696 Fax: 0191-482 4259 E-mail: houltsremovals@hoults.co.uk *Removal & storage specialists* Also at: Branches throughout the U.K.

Hounslow Angling Centre, 265-267 Bath Road, Hounslow, TW3 3DA Tel: (020) 8570 6156 Fax: (020) 8570 8885 *Fishing tackle & accessories*

▶ Hour Glass, Abernant Enterprise Workshop, Pontardawe Road, Rhydyfro, Pontardawe, Swansea, SA8 4SX Tel: (01269) 825999 Fax: (01269) 825999 *Double glazing installation & manufrs*

Hourcover Ltd, 2 Thorgate Road, Wick, Littlehampton, West Sussex, BN17 7LU Tel: (01903) 714234 Fax: (01903) 722877 E-mail: hourcover@aol.com *Industrial powder coating services*

Hourglass Productions Ltd, 27 Princes Road, Wimbledon, London, SW19 8RA Tel: (020) 8543 8396 Fax: (020) 8544 0787 E-mail: productions@hourglass.co.uk *Film & television production company*

▶ Hourglass Seal Ltd, Queen Ann's Gate, Stonehouse, Gloucestershire, GL10 3RH Tel: (01453) 828956 Fax: (01453) 821795 E-mail: sales@shop4glass.co.uk

House & Co., 6 Gordleton Industrial Estate, Hannah Way, Pennington, Lymington, Hampshire, SO41 8JD Tel: (01590) 682285 Fax: (01590) 683553 E-mail: saleshouseandco@aol.com *Shopping baskets & aquarium pond net manufrs*

▶ House Beauticians, Trefechan, Aberystwyth, Ceredigion, SY23 1BY Tel: (01970) 610042 E-mail: buffydog@hotmail.com *A very cheap way of keeping your house professionally clean.....*Why not enjoy your free time?*By letting us handle the grime.*Prices start from £. *Carpet Cleaning also available*

House Of Blinds, 6 Galloway Court, Falkirk, FK1 1HQ Tel: (01324) 613066 Fax: (01324) 814717 E-mail: sales@houseofblinds.co.uk *Blind retailers*

House Of Bollywood, 117 Ladypool Road, Birmingham, B12 8LH Tel: 0121-440 7454 Fax: 0121-440 7454 *Audio visual retail & hire*

House Builder XL Ltd, Citypoint, Temple Gate, Bristol, BS1 6PL Tel: (0870) 8502444 Fax: (0870) 8502555 E-mail: sales@hbxl.co.uk *Software building & suppliers*

▶ House Builders Montrose Ltd, 20 Castle Place, Montrose, Angus, DD10 8AL Tel: (01674) 673429 Fax: (01674) 673002

House Of Caduceus Ltd, 5 Richards Ave, Lincoln, LN6 8SJ Tel: 01522 688142 Fax: 01522 688142 *Audio cassette retailers & manufrs*

▶ House Couturier Ltd, 285 New Kings Road, London, SW6 4RD Tel: (020) 7371 9255 E-mail: info@housecouturier.eu *Interior design service*

▶ House Of Creation, 97 Hildyard Road, Leicester, LE4 5GG Tel: 0116-261 2805 *Clothing manufrs*

House Of Dorchester, Unit 10 Alton Business Centre, Omega Park, Alton, Hampshire, GU34 2YU Tel: (01420) 84181 Fax: (01420) 543047 E-mail: sales@hotchoc.com *Chocalate manufrs*

House Of Dreams, 3 Hayes Road, Paignton, Devon, TQ4 5PD Tel: (01803) 664076 Fax: (01803) 664096 *Bed manufrs*

House of Fraser (Stores) Ltd, Head Office, 1 Howick Place, London, SW1P 1BH Tel: (0870) 1607270 Fax: (020) 7821 5348 *Departmental store* Also at: Branches throughout the South-East

▶ House of Hamilton Publishing, 0 Hamilton Road, Felixstowe, Suffolk, IP11 7BA Tel: 01394 274440 E-mail: enquiries@houseofhamiltonpublishing.co.uk *Online publishing*

House Of Hastings Ltd, 181-182 Queens Road, Hastings, East Sussex, TN34 1RQ Tel: (01424) 423072 Fax: (01424) 431501 E-mail: enquiries@houseofhastings.com *Portable power tool distributors*

House of Hill Data & Records Management, 45 Thames Road, Barking, Essex, IG11 0HQ Tel: (0870) 9088000 Fax: (020) 8591 4422 *Data & records management, secure offsite storage & retrieval of files, documents & magnetic media, full barcode tracking, multiple sites throughout UK.*

House Hold Furniture Stores Ltd, Unit 11, Lake Business Centre, Tariff Road, London, N17 0YX Tel: (020) 8374 9691 Fax: (020) 8374 8106 E-mail: kelly@furnituredomesticdirect.com *Furniture distributors*

House Of Marbles Ltd, Pottery Road, Bovey Tracey, Newton Abbot, Devon, TQ13 9DS Tel: (01626) 835358 Fax: (01626) 835315 E-mail: sales@houseofmarbles.com *Industrial glass ball, decorative glassware retailers & manufrs*

House & Patten, 1 Kennard Road, Kingswood, Bristol, BS15 8AA Tel: 0117-967 3347 Fax: 0117-967 3347 *Timber merchants*

House Of Pine, 25 St. Martins Precinct, Church Street, Caversham, Reading, RG4 8BA Tel: 0118-947 2333 Fax: 0118-947 2333 *Pine furniture*

House Of Play Ltd, Play House, 91 Abbey Road, Dunscroft, Doncaster, South Yorkshire, DN7 4LE Tel: (01302) 846876 Fax: (01302) 842947 *Playground equipment manufrs*

▶ House Proud Installations, Courtyard 3, Wentworth Road, Mapplewell, Barnsley, South Yorkshire, S75 6DT Tel: (01226) 388220

House Removals, Fosse Way, Thrussington, Leicester, LE7 4TF Tel: (0800) 9805866 Fax: (01664) 424919 E-mail: sales@houseremovals.com *House removals & storage*

House Of Scotland, 467 Oxford Street, London, W1C 2PX Tel: (020) 7499 2404 Fax: (020) 7499 2404 *Knitwear distributors*

House of Welding Ltd, 18 Wildwood Drive, Wildwood, Stafford, ST17 4PY Tel: (01785) 661890 Fax: (01785) 661890 *Welding equipment distributors*

House Of York, Norham Road, North Shields, Tyne & Wear, NE29 7UN Tel: 0191-257 0101 Fax: 0191-258 6649 *Manufacturer of confectionery*

Houseguard Security Systems Ltd, 35 Peabody Road, Farnborough, Hampshire, GU14 6HA Tel: (01252) 377688 Fax: (01252) 375387 *Distributors & agents of burglar alarms*

Household Automation Ltd, Fox Way, Pinkhurst Lane, Slinfold, Horsham, West Sussex, RH13 0QR Tel: (0870) 3300071 E-mail: afe@globalnet.co.uk *Home automation sales & services*

▶ Household Electrics, The Workshop, Terregletown Farm, Terregles, Dumfries, DG2 9RW Tel: (01387) 268672

▶ Household Essentials, 25 Amberley Close, Littlehampton, West Sussex, BN17 6HW Tel: 01903 714355 E-mail: enq@household-essentials.co.uk *Home shopping by catalogue and online shop supplying home,cleaning,garden and personal care products to your door*

Household Services, Unit 2 Cartlich Street, Stoke-on-Trent, ST6 5PG Tel: (01782) 838058 Fax: (01782) 838058 *Upholstery repairers*

▶ House-Hunters, Floor 1 (BST), 3 Marloes Road, Kensington, London, W8 6LQ Tel: (0845) 108 0187 Fax: (0870) 116 1813 E-mail: info@house-hunters.co.uk *House-Hunters is one of London's fastest growing property investment company. We provide a professional and personalised service to suit our client's property investments requirements. Our dynamic and innovative practice makes it easy for our clients be it as an investor, seller, buyer, landlord or as a tenant. We are experienced in all aspects of the property sector and our clients choose us because of the excellent service we provide. We will be glad to hear of your requirements.*

Housepoints Pine Furniture, 13 The Borough, Canterbury, Kent, CT1 2DR Tel: (01227) 451350 *Furniture suppliers*

▶ Housesmiths Ltd., 60 Hampstead House, 176 Finchley Road, London, NW3 6BT Tel: 020 7558 8693 E-mail: kellysearch@housesmiths.co.uk *London based residential building and refurbishment company delivering a high quality service in and around London.*

Housing Direct, Sandwell Road, West Bromwich, West Midlands, B70 8TB Tel: 0121-569 6038 Fax: 0121-569 6041 *Arms length management offices services*

Housing Software Services Ltd, 89 Gleneagle Road, London, SW16 6AZ Tel: (020) 8677 2253 Fax: (020) 8677 2101 *Software for housing associations production*

Housley & Birks, 7 Weston Street, Heanor, Derbyshire, DE75 7NG Tel: (01773) 716892 *Joinery manufrs*

▶ Houston Associates, 183-185 Kirkdale, London, SE26 4QH Tel: (020) 8778 1900 Fax: (020) 8659 9191 E-mail: richard@houston-associates.com *Houston Associates offers results driven, large agency methodologies with the dynamics and originality of a growing agency. - Marketing - Top 150 agency - PR Week - Top 50-technology agency - PR Week - Top 150 agency -*

Leslie Houston, 25 Ballylig Road, Broughshane, Ballymena, County Antrim, BT43 7HH Tel: (028) 2586 1068 *Farm contractor*

Houston & Sons Ltd, Victoria Avenue, Crewe, CW2 7SR Tel: (01270) 500312 Fax: (01270) 587428 E-mail: info@houston-and-sons.co.uk *Scrap metal merchants* Also at: Congleton

▶ Houston Warehousing Ltd, Wright Street, Renfrew, PA4 8AN Tel: 0141-848 5511

Houston's Of Cupar Ltd, Station House, Station Road, Cupar, Fife, KY15 5HX Tel: (01334) 655331 Fax: (01334) 656437 E-mail: sales@houstons.co.uk *Steel fabricators & blower manufrs*

Hout Tek, Lodge Farm Mill Lane, Colne Engaine, Colchester, CO6 2HX Tel: (01787) 223136 Fax: (01787) 224535 E-mail: info@hout-tek.co.uk *Joinery manufrs*

Hov & Dokka UK Ltd, 9 Green Hill Road, Camberley, Surrey, GU15 1PF Tel: (01276) 22599 Fax: (01276) 25333 *Office furniture distributors & manufrs*

Hoval Ltd, North Gate, Newark, Nottinghamshire, NG24 1JN Tel: (01636) 672711 Fax: (01636) 673532 E-mail: boilersales@hoval.co.uk *Air receiver & boiler manufrs*

Hovat, Westmead, New Hythe Lane, Larkfield, Aylesford, Kent, ME20 6XJ Tel: (01622) 791193 Fax: (01622) 791192 E-mail: executive.hovat@btinternet.com *Flexographic printing services*

Hove Park Reproductions, 93 Old Shoreham Road, Hove, East Sussex, BN3 7AQ Tel: (01273) 737305 Fax: (01273) 737305 *Reproduction furniture*

▶ Hoveair Building Services Ltd, 24-26 Hermitage Lane, London, SE25 5HH Tel: (020) 8656 7744

Hover Marine Services Ltd, 135 Powers Hall End, Witham, Essex, CM8 1LS Tel: (07903) 193140 E-mail: andy@hoverhire.co.uk *hovercraft and crews available for Environmental monitering,surveys,safety boat, film /tv camera platform, corporate training days.Four craft available ranging from fully enclosed twenty foot craft to fourteen foot inflatable open craft.*

Hovercam Ltd, White House Drakes View, Staddon Heights, Plymouth, PL9 9SP Tel: (01752) 482711 Fax: (01752) 482744 E-mail: info@hovercam.com *Aerial photographers*

Hovercraft Consultants, Unit 43 South Hampshire Industrial Park, Totton, Southampton, SO40 3SA Tel: (023) 8087 1188 Fax: (023) 8087 1799 E-mail: enquiries@duratank.com *Manufacturers of hover craft parts & tanks for the marine industry*

▶ Hovertravel Ltd, Quay Road, Ryde, Isle of Wight, PO33 2HB Tel: (01983) 811000 Fax: (01983) 562216

Hoverwood Ltd, Alresford Business Centre, Colchester Main Road, Alresford, Colchester, CO7 8DJ Tel: (01206) 826868 Fax: (01206) 826868 *Pine furniture manufrs*

▶ How About Now, 10 Waynflete Lane, Farnham, Surrey, GU9 7BH Tel: (01252) 891790 Fax: E-mail: adam@howaboutnow.co.uk *Party organisers*

▶ How Furniture, J Coronation Road, Ilkeston, Derbyshire, DE7 5UA Tel: 0115-932 0215 Fax: 0115-932 0216 *Built in & fitted furniture manufrs*

Howard 2000 Ltd, Howard Centre, Paper Mill End, Great Barr, Unit 4, Birmingham, B44 8NH Tel: 0121-356 9833 Fax: 0121-356 0280 *Injection mould tools*

Alan Howard, Unit6 Park Road, Timperley, Altrincham, Cheshire, WA14 5AB Tel: 0161-973 5457 Fax: 0161-973 5424 *Hairdressing & beauty product suppliers*

▶ Alan Howard, 2 41 Clifford Road, Blackpool, FY1 2PU Tel: (01253) 628008 Fax: (01253) 628008 *Wholesale hairdressing*

Alan Howard (Stockport) Ltd, Hulley Road, Macclesfield, Cheshire, SK10 2LX Tel: (01625) 422424 Fax: (01625) 425147 *Hairdressing product distribution*

Howard Basford Ltd, Portside North, Ellesmere Port, CH65 2HQ Tel: 0151-357 6000 Fax: 0151-357 1026 *Accident repair agents*

▶ Howard Berkin, Victoria Road, Ripley, Derbyshire, DE5 3FX Tel: (01773) 513800 Fax: (01773) 513600 E-mail: howardberkin@tiscalli.co.uk *Welding & steel fabricators*

Howard & Buckner Ltd, Unit E1, The Seedbed Centre, Harlow, Essex, CM19 5AF Tel: (01279) 422955 Fax: (01279) 422955 *Plumbing & heating engineers*

Christopher Howard Cars, Forge Engineering Works, Pye Corner, Ulcombe, Maidstone, Kent, ME17 1EH Tel: (01622) 851140 *Vehicle repair services*

Howard Cole Developments Ltd, 4 Peterborough Road, Crowland, Peterborough, PE6 0BA Tel: (01733) 211351 Fax: (01733) 211441 *Steel fabricators*

Howard Construction, Boot Street, Great Bealings, Woodbridge, Suffolk, IP13 6PB Tel: (01473) 735315 Fax: (01473) 738383 E-mail: glenn@howardconstruction.co.uk *Groundwork contractors*

▶ Howard Consultancy, 26 The Loont, Winsford, Cheshire, CW7 1EU Tel: (01606) 552189 Fax: (01606) 552189 E-mail: roberthoward@onetel.net *Plastics consulting*

Howard De Walden Estates Ltd, 23 Queen Anne Street, London, W1G 9DL Tel: (020) 7580 3163 Fax: (020) 7436 8152 E-mail: olwen-seear@howard-de-walden.co.uk *Property investors*

Howard Electrical Services, Unit 19 Such Close, Letchworth Garden City, Hertfordshire, SG6 1JF Tel: (01462) 678915 Fax: (01462) 679815 E-mail: sales@howardelectricalservices.co.uk *Electrical contractors*

Howard Environmental Services, Unit 5 Faygate Business Centre, Faygate, Horsham, West Sussex, RH12 4DN Tel: (01293) 852211 Fax: (01293) 852244 *Air conditioning engineers*

Howard Fabrications, Swainshill, Hereford, HR4 7QA Tel: (01432) 353100 Fax: (01432) 353100 *Welders & blacksmiths*

Howard Filter Systems, East Skirdle, Waterrow, Taunton, Somerset, TA4 2AY Tel: (01984) 623112 Fax: (01984) 624770 E-mail: hfsl@btconnect.co.uk *Candle & pressure filters*

Francis Howard Ltd, Aberdeen Works, Trafalgar Street, Sheffield, S1 3RL Tel: 0114-249 3314 Fax: 0114-249 3316 *Silverware & cutlery manufrs*

George Howard Ltd, 94 Folly Lane, Warrington, WA5 0NG Tel: (01925) 444455 Fax: (01925) 444466 E-mail: georgehowardltd@btconnect.com *Metal merchants*

George Howard Packaging Ltd, Unit 5-6, Power Industrial Estate, Slade Green Road, Erith, Kent, DA8 2HU Tel: (01322) 338855 Fax: (01322) 349022 *Cardboard box manufrs*

Howard Grove Ltd, 93 Regent Street, Cambridge, CB2 1AW Tel: (01223) 312910 Fax: 01233 312911 E-mail: webmaster@howard-holdings.com *Property developers, commercial finance & entrepreneurs*

Howard Houlder & Partners Ltd, Osborn House, 74-80 Middlesex Street, London, E1 7EZ Tel: (020) 7247 9090 Fax: (020) 7360 4201 *Ship brokers*

Howard J Bangert, 1 Pointer Grove, Halton, Lancaster, LA2 6QR Tel: (01524) 811455 *Joinery manufrs*

▶ James Howard, Carrs Industrial Estate, Commerce Street, Haslingden, Rossendale, Lancashire, BB4 5JT Tel: (01706) 833511 Fax: (01706) 833550 E-mail: sales@james-howard.co.uk *Equestrian equipment suppliers*

▶ Howard Lambert, Suite 15 Concorde House, Grenville Place, London, NW7 3SA Tel: (020) 8959 8813 Fax: (020) 8906 7821 *Exporters of secondary aluminium ingos*

Howard Marketing, Westfield House, Broad Lane, Bramley, Leeds, LS13 3HA Tel: 0845 4941649 Fax: 0113-255 8540 E-mail: enquiries@howardmarketing.co.uk *UK MANUFACTURERS OF BAGS, CASES AND COVERS TO YOUR OWN DESIGN. WE WORK WITH ALL TYPES OF FABRIC TO PRODUCE SAMPLE BAGS - MEDICAL BAGS - PROTECTIVE BAGS - PADDED BAGS - PANEL BAGS - CANVAS BAGS - PROMOTIONAL BAGS - STAND BAGS - DISPLAY BAGS - SCIENTIFIC BAGS - INDUSTRIAL BAGS - IN FACT ALMOST ANY TYPE OF BAG, CASE OR COVER THAT YOU REQUIRE. WE CAN ALSO MANUFACTURE OTHER PRODUCTS OF BESPOKE OR CUSTOM DESIGN FROM CANVAS, NYLON AND POLYESTER TYPE FABRICS. WE OFFER A FULL SCREEN PRINTING AND EMBROIDERY SERVICE TO*

continued

DECORATE YOUR PRODUCTS. WE WELCOME ALL TYPES OF WORK OUTSIDE THE GARMENT INDUSTRY. ALL ITEMS ARE MADE IN OUR FACTORY AT LEEDS. WE OFFER REALISTIC MINIMUM MAKING QUANTITIES AND PROMPT DELIVERY TIMES.

Howard Motors, 2 Aqueduct St Industrial Estate, Aqueduct Street, Preston, PR1 7JJ Tel: (01772) 727552 Fax: (01772) 727552 *Mechanical repairers*

Howard Pallet Truck Services, 4 Bridgwater Court, Oldmixon CR, Weston-super-Mare, Avon, BS24 9AY Tel: (01934) 621777 Fax: (01934) 621888 E-mail: sales@howardhandling.co.uk *Pallet truck sales, rental, service & repairs*

Howard Plastics Ltd, Unit 16 Alexandra Way, Ashchurch, Tewkesbury, Gloucestershire, GL20 8NB Tel: (01684) 298206 Fax: (01684) 850425 E-mail: sales@howardplastics.com *Blow moulders & bottle manufrs*

Howard S Cooke & Co Holdings Ltd, Arrow Road, Redditch, Worcestershire, B98 8PA Tel: (01527) 63231 Fax: (01527) 66770 E-mail: sales@protex.com *Precision cold forging manufrs*

Howard Scale Co. Ltd, 14 Oughton Road, Birmingham, B12 0DF Tel: 0121-446 5190 Fax: 0121-446 5191 E-mail: sale@howardscale.com *Electronic count machine manufrs*

Howard Shipping Services Ltd, Showell Road, Wolverhampton, WV10 9JY Tel: (01902) 738838 Fax: (01902) 862962 E-mail: peterhoward@hoship.com *European haulage contractors*

Howard & Sons, Forge Workshop, Moor Road, North Owersby, Market Rasen, Lincolnshire, LN8 3PR Tel: (01673) 828888 Fax: (01673) 828888 *Agricultural engineers*

Howard Tenens Andover Ltd, Unit 2c Macadam Way, West Portway, Andover, Hampshire, SP10 3LF Tel: (01264) 324449 Fax: (01264) 332253 E-mail: boston@tenens.com *Road transport, warehousing & freight* Also at: Boston, Coventry, Normanton, Stroud & Swindon

Howard Tenens Associates Ltd, Kingfisher Business Park, London Road, Thrupp, Stroud, Gloucestershire, GL5 2BY Tel: (01453) 885087 Fax: (01453) 886145 E-mail: enquiries@tenens.com *Property, management services & equipment, warehousing* Also at: Andover, Boston, Swindon & Warwick

Howard Tenens Boston Ltd, Riverside Industrial Estate, Marsh Lane, Boston, Lincolnshire, PE21 7SZ Tel: (01205) 311808 Fax: (01205) 354086 E-mail: sales@tenens.com *Road transport & warehousing*

Howard Wipers Ltd, Unit 13 Winchester Avenue, Denny, Stirlingshire, FK6 6QE Tel: (01324) 822599 Fax: (01324) 826555 *Cleaning cloth manufs*

Howarine, Calvert Ltd, Howarine House, 5-6 Empire Way, Wembley, Middlesex, HA9 0XA Tel: (0870) 4420077 Fax: (0870) 4420078 E-mail: graham@howarine.co.uk *Printing trade suppliers & industrial adhesive manufrs*

Howarth 1985 Ltd, Alma St Work Meadow Croft, Alma Street, Radcliffe, Manchester, M26 4FU Tel: 0161-723 2024 Fax: 0161-723 2024 *Sheet metalwork & fabrication engineers*

Howarth Bros Haulage Ltd, Unit 3 Moss Lane, Royton, Oldham, OL2 6HR Tel: (01706) 847514 Fax: (01706) 882607 E-mail: howarth.bros@btinternet.com *Road transport contractors & hirers*

Howarth Packaging Ltd, Units 7-11, Hugh Business Park, Waterfoot, Rossendale, Lancashire, BB4 7BT Tel: (01706) 214531 Fax: (01706) 224060 E-mail: server@howarthpackaging.demon.co.uk *Printed folding carton manufrs*

Howarth Switchgear Ltd, Finlas Street, Cowlairs Industrial Estate, Glasgow, G22 5DT Tel: 0141-557 3553 Fax: 0141-558 0614 E-mail: sales@howarthswitchgear.co.uk *Electrical manufacturers & control*

Howarth Timber and Building Merchants Ltd, Medlock Sawmills, Shaw Road, Oldham, OL1 3LJ Tel: 0161-620 2128 Fax: 0161-620 9527 E-mail: htoldh@plp.howarth-timber.co.uk *Timber merchants* Also at: Blackburn, Bolton, Burnley, Bury, Manchester, Rochdale & Sale

Howarth Timber Ashton, Katherine Street, Ashton-under-Lyne, Lancashire, OL7 0AG Tel: 0161-330 1634 Fax: 0161-339 7618 E-mail: htasht@pop.howarth.timber.co.uk *Timber importers & truss manufrs*

Howarth Timber Engineering Ltd, Howarth House, Hollow Road, Bury St. Edmunds, Suffolk, IP32 7QW Tel: (01284) 772700 Fax: (01284) 755567 E-mail: sales@howarthengineering.co.uk *Roof trusses manufrs*

Howarth (Timber Importers) Ltd, Lincoln Castle, Lincoln Castle Way, New Holland, Barrow-upon-Humber, South Humberside, DN19 7RR Tel: (01469) 532300 Fax: (01469) 531867 E-mail: info@howarth-timber.co.uk *Timber importers*

Howarth Windows & Doors Ltd, The Dock, New Holland, Barrow-upon-Humber, North Lincolnshire, DN19 7RT Tel: (01469) 530577 Fax: (01469) 531559 E-mail: windows&doors@howarth-timber.co.uk *Door & window manufrs*

Howat John Agricultural Contractors, Rosemount, Closeburn, Thornhill, Dumfriesshire, DG3 5JH Tel: (01387) 740338 *Agricultural contractors*

▶ Howatson, Cae Bricks Brickfield Lane, Denbigh Road, Ruthin, Clwyd, LL15 1PE Tel: (01824) 703638 Fax: (01824) 707210 E-mail: dave.burke@tarmac.co.uk

▶ Howatson, Cae Bricks Brickfield Lane, Denbigh Road, Ruthin, Clwyd, LL15 1PE Tel: (01824) 703638 Fax: (01824) 707210

Howbeck Engineering, White House, London Road, Stapeley, Nantwich, Cheshire, CW5 7JU Tel: (01270) 841446 Fax: (01270) 841446 E-mail: roger.howbeck@virgin.net *Subcontract machining. Turning, milling, Jigs & Fixtures.*

Howco Quality Alloys Ltd, Carbrook Street, Sheffield, S9 2JN Tel: 0114-244 6711 Fax: 0114-244 7469 E-mail: sales@howcogroup.com *Steel & steel bar stockholders*

Howco UK Ltd, 3 Blairlinn Road, Cumbernauld, Glasgow, G67 2TF Tel: (01236) 454111 Fax: (01236) 454222 Principal Export Areas: Worldwide *Stainless steel stockholders*

▶ Howden Blacksmiths Ltd, 15 Castle Road, Bankside Industrial Estate, Falkirk, FK2 7UY Tel: (01324) 630930 Fax: (01324) 670888 E-mail: scotthowden@aol.com *Steelworks fabricators*

Howden Compressors Ltd, 133 Barfillan Drive, Glasgow, G52 1BE Tel: 0141-882 3346 Fax: 0141-882 8648 E-mail: sales@howdencompressors.co.uk *Screw compressor manufrs* Also at: Feltham

Howden Electro Heating (Howden Electroheating), 10-12 Belgowan Street, Bellshill Industrial Estate, Bellshill, Lanarkshire, ML4 3NS Tel: (01698) 573111 Fax: (01698) 573121 E-mail: sales@howden-electroheating.com Sales Contact: I. Seikman *Howden Electro Heating design & manufacture elements & electric heating equipment suitable for Domestic, Building Services, Industrial, Process, Catering & Marine applications. ISO 9001:2000 approved & over 50 years established*

Howden Industrial, Braehead Industrial Estate, Old Govan Road, Renfrew, PA4 8XJ Tel: 0141-885 7500 Fax: 0141-886 1963 E-mail: hpc.sales@howden.com *Process compressors & blowers suppliers*

Howden Industrial, Braehead Industrial Estate, Old Govan Road, Renfrew, PA4 8XJ Tel: 0141-885 7500 Fax: 0141-886 1963 E-mail: huk.sales@howden.com *Mechanical & engineering services*

▶ Howden Industrial, Braehead Industrial Estate, Old Govan Road, Renfrew, PA4 8XJ Tel: 0141-885 7500 Fax: 0141-886 1963 E-mail: marketing@howden.com *Industrial fan and rotary air heater manufacturers for utilities and process industry. Equipment supplied to meet customer specifications. Revamping & upgrading.*

▶ Howden Joinery Ltd, 5 Shenstone Trading Estate, Bromsgrove Road, Halesowen, West Midlands, B63 3XB Tel: 0121-501 1621 Fax: 0121-585 7580 *Joiners*

▶ Howden Process Compressors Donkin Division, Holmewood Industrial Park, Park Road, Holmewood, Chesterfield, Derbyshire, S42 5UY Tel: (01246) 859053 Fax: (01246) 859054 E-mail: hdb.sales@howden.com *Manufacture, supply & repair of blowers*

▶ Howden's Joinery Ltd, Unit 8a Tweedside Trading Estate, Tweedmouth, Berwick-upon-Tweed, TD15 2XF Tel: (01289) 307830 Fax: (01289) 331619 *Joiners*

▶ Howden's Joinery Ltd, 4 Grange Road, Houstoun Industrial Estate, Livingston, West Lothian, EH54 5DE Tel: (01506) 444358

▶ Howdens Joinery Ltd, Blackhouse Way, Blackhouse Industrial Estate, Peterhead, Aberdeenshire, AB42 1BQ Tel: (01779) 480579 Fax: (01779) 480641 *Suppliers to the joinery trade*

▶ Howden's Joinery Ltd, Unit 428 Camp Hill Close, Ripon, North Yorkshire, HG4 1QY Tel: (01765) 698407 Fax: (01765) 698289 *Kitchen joinery suppliers*

Howdens Signs Ltd, 94 Burley Road, Leeds, LS3 1JP Tel: 0113-245 7752 Fax: 0113-242 6993 E-mail: sales@howdenssigns.com Principal Export Areas: Worldwide *Sign contractors*

Howdon Power Transmission Ltd, Paganhill Lane, Stroud, Gloucestershire, GL5 4JT Tel: (01453) 750814 Fax: (01453) 765320 E-mail: sales@howdon.co.uk *Overload release clutches & torque limiting couplings manufrs*

John Howe, Gardeners Cottage, Leek Old Road, Sutton, Macclesfield, Cheshire, SK11 0HZ Tel: (01625) 610943 Fax: (01625) 610943 *Civil engineers, septic tanks suppliers*

▶ Howe Suspended Ceilings, 12 Heatherbrae, Bishopbriggs, Glasgow, G64 2TA Tel: 0141-762 3915 Fax: 0141-762 3915 E-mail: enquiries@howesuspendedceilings.co.uk *Suspended ceilings*

Howe Suspended Ceilings, 78 Eastburn Road, Glasgow, G21 3NS Tel: 0141-557 5299 *Suspended ceiling contractors*

Howe Suspended Ceilings, Kirklands, Skegness Road, Ingoldmells, Skegness, Lincolnshire, PE25 1NL Tel: (01754) 763124 Fax: (01754) 763124 E-mail: info@howesuspendedceilings.co.uk *Suspended ceilings fitting*

Howe UK Ltd, 22 Jaggard Way, London, SW12 8SG Tel: (020) 8673 9777 Fax: (020) 8675 9111 E-mail: sales@howeuk.co.uk *Office furniture distributors* Also at: Barnsley

Edward Howell Galvanizers Ltd, Watery Lane, Willenhall, West Midlands, WV13 3SU Tel: (01902) 637463 Fax: (01902) 630923 E-mail: edward.howell@wedge-galv.co.uk *Hot dip galvanizing organisation*

Peter Howell Office Interiors, 105 Dockfield Road, Shipley, West Yorkshire, BD17 7BE Tel: (01274) 592337 Fax: (01274) 531595 E-mail: info@peter-howell.com *Demountable office partition systems suppliers & installation services* Also at: London

▶ Howell Wade, 55 Church Road, London, SW19 5DQ Tel: (020) 8947 6912 Fax: (020) 8947 4936 E-mail: mail@howellwade.com *Howell Wade have been established for over 70 years during which time they have continued to develop expertise in all aspects of accountancy, auditing and taxation services.*

Howell-Blys Engineering Co. Ltd, Unit 23 Parkfield Mills, Queens Road, Morley, Leeds, LS27 0PF Tel: 0113-238 1444 Fax: 0113-238 1356 E-mail: howellblys@aol.com *Security fencing contractors*

Howells Associates Ltd, 32 Freemans Way, Harrogate, North Yorkshire, HG3 1DH Tel: (01423) 812800 *Computer software designers*

D.V. Howells Ltd, The MPSC, Milford Haven, Dyfed, SA73 3AQ Tel: (01646) 697041 Fax: (01646) 696345 E-mail: info@dvhowells.com *Incident response - oil manufrs*

Howells Glazing, Clock House, Forge Lane, Cradley Heath, West Midlands, B64 5AL Tel: (01384) 820060 Fax: (01384) 820061 E-mail: enquiries@howellsglazing.co.uk *Patent glazing contractors*

Howells Group plc, Longley Lane, Sharston Industrial Area, Manchester, M22 4SS Tel: 0161-945 5567 Fax: 0161-945 5597 E-mail: j.dolan@howells-railway.co.uk *Transformer manufacturers & equipment for railways*

▶ Howes Garden Services, 4 Charleston Court, Basildon, Essex, SS13 1TA Tel: (01268) 724213

▶ Howford Hydraulics, Old Howford Road, Catrine, Ayrshire, KA5 5JX Tel: (01290) 551428 Fax: (01290) 550549 E-mail: sales@howford.demon.co.uk

Howgate & Lane Ltd, Stukeley Road, Huntingdon, Cambridgeshire, PE29 6HF Tel: (01480) 413566 Fax: (01480) 433726 E-mail: howgate2000@aol.com *Rubber & plastic components manufrs*

▶ Howie Forest Products Ltd, Kenmuir Sawmill, Dalbeattie, Kirkcudbrightshire, DG5 4PL Tel: (01556) 610876 Fax: (01556) 611488 *Sawn & planed wood services*

Howie Minerals Ltd, Dornie Quarry, Torlundy, Fort William, Inverness-Shire, PH33 6SW Tel: (01397) 702227 Fax: (01397) 702308 E-mail: blaurie@howie-forest.co.uk *Lime & aggregate producers*

Howies Ltd, 10 Kings Haugh, Peffermill Industrial Estate, Edinburgh, EH16 5UY Tel: 0131-661 7302 Fax: 0131-661 7479 *Printing services*

Howkel Carpets, 1 Taylor Mills, Fair Lea Road, Huddersfield, HD4 6HA Tel: (01484) 424919 *Carpet suppliers*

Howkell Rugs Ltd, Lower Viaduct Street, Huddersfield, HD1 6BN Tel: (01484) 425422 Fax: (01484) 425422 *Carpet retailers, wholesalers & manufrs*

▶ Howland Haulage Co., Fernside, London Road, Dunkirk, Faversham, Kent, ME13 9LL Tel: (01227) 751465 Fax: (01227) 752586

Howle Carbides Ltd, Picts Lane, Princes Risborough, Buckinghamshire, HP27 9EA Tel: (01844) 275171 Fax: (01844) 342514 E-mail: info@howlecarbides.com *Tungsten carbide manufrs*

Howley Engineering Ltd, 33 Melford Court, Hardwick Grange, Woolston, Warrington, WA1 4RZ Tel: (01925) 810810 Fax: (01925) 813477 E-mail: sales@howley-engineering.co.uk *Power transmission engineers*

Howmet Ltd, Kestrel Way, Sowton Industrial Estate, Exeter, EX2 7LG Tel: (01392) 429700 Fax: (01392) 429701 E-mail: info@howmet.com *Manufacturers of investment castings & turbine blades & components*

A.N. Howorth, 11 Cleveleys Road, Accrington, Lancashire, BB5 5ET Tel: (01254) 233482 Fax: (01254) 233482 *Suspended ceilings installation*

Howorth Airtech Ltd, Victoria Works, Lorne Street, Farnworth, Bolton, BL4 7LZ Tel: (01204) 700900 Fax: (01204) 862378 E-mail: info@howorthairtech.co.uk *Medical clean air systems*

Howorths Nelson, Manor Mill, Hallam Road, Nelson, Lancashire, BB9 8DN Tel: (01282) 612382 Fax: (01282) 695130 E-mail: howorthsnelson@btconnect.com *Yarn suppliers*

Hows Racesafe, 9 Carlton Road, Wilbarston, Market Harborough, Leicestershire, LE16 8QD Tel: (01536) 771051 Fax: (01536) 779144 *Equestrian clothing manufrs*

▶ Howses Paint & Powder Ltd, Cakemore Road, Rowley Regis, West Midlands, B65 0RD Tel: 0121-559 1451 Fax: 0121-559 2722 E-mail: sales@howsepaints.co.uk *Industrial paint/powder coatings manufrs*

Howson Signs & Screenprint, 52-54 Thompson Close, Chesterfield, Derbyshire, S41 9AZ Tel: (01246) 454676 Fax: (01246) 260302 E-mail: howsons@aol.com *Sign contractors*

Howth Chains & Chain Assemblies, Unit 6 Brierley Trading Estate, North St, Brierley Hill, W. Midlands, DY5 3SL Tel: (01384) 79458 Fax: (01384) 79458 *Playground manufacturers, distributors & suppliers as well as industrial chains & chain assemblies*

Howton Contractors Ltd, Howton Farm, Pillaton, Saltash, Cornwall, PL12 6QY Tel: (01579) 350781 Fax: (01579) 351420 *Agricultural & plant hire contractors*

Howvale Ltd, 53 Bridgford Road, West Bridgford, Nottingham, NG2 6AU Tel: 0115-945 5050 Fax: 0115-945 5511 *Air conditioning installers*

Hoxton Bibliotech, 239 Old Street, London, EC1V 9EY Tel: (020) 7553 4470 Fax: (020) 7251 3130 *Computer training centre*

Hoya Lens UK Ltd, Wrexham Industrial Estate, Wrexham, Clwyd, LL13 9UA Tel: (01978) 663400 Fax: (01978) 663135 E-mail: enquiries@hoya.co.uk *Optical lens manufrs*

Hoyer UK Ltd, 517 Leeds Road, Huddersfield, HD2 1YJ Tel: (01484) 548221 Fax: (01484) 518933 E-mail: enquires@hoyer-group.com *Road transport & freight services*

Hoyes & Son Ltd, 22 Oakland Road, Leicester, LE2 6AN Tel: 0116-270 1760 Fax: 0116-244 8727 E-mail: hoyes@fsbdial.co.uk *Drinks wholesalers*

Hoyland Fox Ltd, Manchester Road, Millhouse Green, Sheffield, S36 9NR Tel: (01226) 762244 Fax: (01226) 370022 E-mail: hfsales@hoylandfox.com *Umbrella frame makers*

▶ Hoyle & Dean Ltd, Hillcrest Garage, Argyle Street, Accrington, Lancashire, BB5 1DJ Tel: (01254) 232467 Fax: (01254) 872821

Hoyles Fire & Safety Ltd, Sandwash Close, Rainford Industrial Estate, Rainford, St. Helens, Merseyside, WA11 8LY Tel: (01744) 885161 Fax: (01744) 882410 E-mail: customer.service@hoyles.co.uk *Fire fighting equipment distributors*

▶ indicates data change since last edition

Hozelock Ltd, Midpoint Park, Kingsbury Road, Minworth, Sutton Coldfield, West Midlands, B76 1AB Tel: 0121-313 4242 Fax: 0121-313 4243 *Hose fittings manufrs*

▶ HP Manufacturing Ltd, Erskine Ferry Road, Bishopton, Renfrewshire, PA7 5PP Tel: (0870) 0130790 Fax: 0141-812 7745 *Manufacture of servers*

▶ HP Plotter Servicing, 12b Walworth Enterprise Centre, West Way, Andover, Hampshire, SP10 5AP Tel: (0870) 7667512 Fax: (0870) 7061224 E-mail: sales@hp-plotter-servicing.co.uk *On-site servicing & repairs*

▶ Hpa Services, 267 Wickham Street, Welling, Kent, DA16 3LS Tel: (020) 8855 5666

HPC Gears Ltd, Unit 14, Foxwood Industrial Park, Foxwood Road, Chesterfield, Derbyshire, S41 9RN Tel: (01246) 268080 Fax: (01246) 260003 E-mail: sales@hpcgears.com *Gear manufacturers & stockists*

HPF Energy Services, 5 Hoyer Industrial Estate, Bridges Road, Ellesmere Port, CH65 4LB Tel: 0151-357 3322 Fax: 0151-357 1334 E-mail: ellesmere@hpf-energy.com *Pipeline fittings & flanges stockholders*

▶ HPL Prototypes, Windmill Industrial Estate, Birmingham Road, Allesley, Coventry, CV5 9QE Tel: (024) 7640 7718 E-mail: sales@hplp.co.uk *Engineering*

▶ HPR Limited, 55 Park Lane, London, W1K 1NA Tel: 020 7409 9039 E-mail: services@hprlimited.co.uk *Specialists in the maintenance, repair, cleaning, staffing and refurbishment of luxury homes throughout London.*

HPS Group, 7 Spitfire Quay, Hazel Road, Southampton, SO19 7GB Tel: (023) 8044 4428 Fax: (023) 8042 0005 *Plastic injection, insert & moulding services*

HPSC Moxons Ltd, Courtney Street, Hull, HU8 7QF Tel: (01482) 229016 Fax: (01482) 589562 E-mail: info@hpcsltd.co.uk *High pressure cleaning equipment distributors*

▶ HPSS Pa Hire, 5 Dairycoates Industrial Estate, Wiltshire Road, Hull, HU4 6PA Tel: (01482) 221810 Fax: (01482) 221735 E-mail: hire@hpss.co.uk *Stage sound & lighting hire*

HPW Electrical Installations, Zair Works, 111-119 Bishop Street, Birmingham, B5 6JL Tel: 0121-622 7111 Fax: 0121-622 7111 E-mail: sales@hpwelectrical.co.uk *Electrical contractors*

HR Insight Ltd, Reeves Way, South Woodham Ferrers, Chelmsford, CM3 5XF Tel: (01245) 324824 Fax: (01245) 324103 E-mail: support@hrinsight.co.uk *Human resources & business development consultants*

▶ HR Personnel Ltd, Unit 5a Hogarth Court, Hogarth Crescent, Croydon, CR0 2JE Tel: 020 8683 7110 Fax: 0870 8903884 E-mail: rt_hrpersonnel@btconnect.com *Recruitment company dealing with Construction and industrial sectors. We provide staffing requirements to the clients specification, requirements, standards expected by there own personnel function.*

▶ HR2HR Solutions Ltd, Ravensbourne, Westerham Road, Keston, Kent, BR2 6HE Tel: (01689) 868068 Fax: (01689) 868069 E-mail: info@hr2hrsolutions.co.uk *Human Resource Consultancy for SME's for employment law compliance solutions.*

▶ HRP Ltd, Unit 18 Britannia Industrial Estate, Poyle Road, Colnbrook, Slough, SL3 0BH Tel: (01753) 688100 Fax: (01753) 688101 *Selling air conditioning spares & units*

HRP Sales Ltd, The Teardrop, London Road, Swanley, Kent, BR8 8TJ Tel: (01322) 614811 Fax: (01322) 614733 *Air conditioning & refrigeration wholesale*

▶ HRvacancies, Carlton Place, Greenwood Street, Altrincham, Cheshire, WA14 1RZ Tel: 0161 282 3252 Fax: 0161 282 3252 E-mail: info@hrvacancies.com *HRvacancies is an innovative vacancy search portal which operates throughout the UK in 18 company sectors. The search engine enables a jobseeker to search for suitable vacancies that are advertised on corporate websites empowering direct recruitment. *For companies, minimal integration is required and corporate branding easily maintained as applicants apply through their existing website. The main benefits are an increased number and improved quality of direct applicants.*

HSBC P.L.C., 12 Calthorpe Road, Edgbaston, Birmingham, B15 1QZ Tel: 0121-455 3255 Fax: 0121-455 3244 *Finance company*

HSBC Bank plc, 21 Farncombe Road, Worthing, West Sussex, BN11 2BW Tel: (0800) 343435 Fax: (01903) 214101 E-mail: info@invoicefinance.hsbc.co.uk *Factoring & invoice discounting*

HSBC Equipment Finance (UK) Ltd, 12 Calthorpe Road, Edge Baston, Birmingham, B15 1HT Tel: 0121-450 1515 Fax: (0845) 6076067 *Sales & leasing services* Also at: Birmingham

HSBC Insurance Brokers Ltd, Bishops Court, 27-33 Artillery Lane, London, E1 7LP Tel: (020) 7247 5433 Fax: (020) 7377 2139 *Financial services*

HSBC Invoice Finance, 12 Calthorpe Road, Edgbaston, Birmingham, B15 1RA Tel: 0121-455 2611 Fax: 0121-455 2190 E-mail: sales@invoicefinance.hsbc.co.uk *Factoring invoices*

HSE Group, PO Box 9, Ripon, North Yorkshire, HG4 1WT Tel: (01765) 698107 E-mail: phild@pdenvironmental.co.uk *Health, safety and environmental management including audit and training services*

▶ Hshtc Ltd, Radford Way, Billericay, Essex, CM12 0DX Tel: (01277) 633444 E-mail: training@hshtc.com *Health & safety consultancy*

HSP Milners, Ironworks Road, Barrow-in-Furness, Cumbria, LA14 2PG Tel: (01229) 823392 Fax: (01229) 870274 E-mail: headoffice@hsp-milners.demon.co.uk *General & lithographic printers*

▶ HSS Hire, Unit 1 Swan Industrial Estate, Gatteridge Street, Banbury, Oxfordshire, OX16 5DH Tel: (01295) 261660 Fax: (01295) 261770 *Tool hire services*

▶ HSS Hire, Unit 20 Basingstoke Business Centre, Winchester Road, Basingstoke, Hampshire, RG21 8UE Tel: (01256) 461959 Fax: (01256) 331449 *Hire company*

▶ HSS Hire, 2 Market Street, Bracknell, Berkshire, RG12 1JG Tel: (01344) 486060 Fax: (01344) 459418 *Plant hirers*

▶ HSS Hire, Wakefield Road, Bradford, West Yorkshire, BD4 7LX Tel: (01274) 308055 Fax: (01274) 724773

▶ HSS Hire, 35-38 Lewes Road, Brighton, BN2 3HQ Tel: (01273) 620588 Fax: (01273) 600656 *Tool hire services*

▶ HSS Hire, Farwig Lane, Bromley, BR1 3RB Tel: (020) 8290 4800 Fax: (020) 8290 1880 E-mail: hire@hss.com *Tool hire services*

▶ HSS Hire, 5 Admiralty Way, Camberley, Surrey, GU15 3DT Tel: (01276) 32988 Fax: (01276) 35344 *Tool hire services*

▶ HSS Hire, 3-5 Coldhams Lane, Cambridge, CB1 3EP Tel: (01223) 313140 Fax: (01223) 313141 *Tool & Equipment Hire*

▶ HSS Hire, 1a 65-68 Bognor Road, Chichester, West Sussex, PO19 8NS Tel: (01243) 789070 Fax: (01243) 789085 *Tool hire services*

▶ HSS Hire, Manor Royal, Crawley, West Sussex, RH10 9PY Tel: (01293) 551115 Fax: (01293) 527315 *Tool hire services*

▶ HSS Hire, Eastern Avenue Industrial Estate, Eastern Avenue, Dunstable, Bedfordshire, LU5 4JY Tel: (01582) 673256 Fax: (01582) 696294 *Tool hire services*

▶ HSS Hire, Felbridge Forge, London Road, Felbridge, East Grinstead, West Sussex, RH19 2RQ Tel: (01342) 316006 Fax: (01342) 316016 *Tool hire services*

▶ HSS Hire, 403 Seaside, Eastbourne, East Sussex, BN22 7RT Tel: (01323) 410057 Fax: (01323) 431119 *Tool hire services*

▶ HSS Hire, Unit 3 9 High Street, Edgware, Middlesex, HA8 7EE Tel: (020) 8952 8032 Fax: (020) 8952 8042 *Tool hire services*

▶ HSS Hire, 30 Great Cambridge Road, Enfield, Middlesex, EN1 1UT Tel: (020) 8342 1888 Fax: (020) 8342 1777 *Tool hire services*

▶ HSS Hire, 137 Gosport Road, Fareham, Hampshire, PO16 0PZ Tel: (01329) 822488 Fax: (01329) 822988 *Tool hire services*

▶ HSS Hire, Oakland House, Solartron Road, Farnborough, Hampshire, GU14 7QL Tel: (01252) 510241 Fax: (01252) 510273 *Tool hire services*

▶ HSS Hire, 12-14 Cheriton High Street, Folkestone, Kent, CT19 4ER Tel: (01303) 270809 Fax: (01303) 272104 *Tool hire services*

▶ HSS Hire, 119 West Street, Glasgow, G5 8BA Tel: 0141-429 6141 Fax: 0141-429 1342

▶ HSS Hire, Harmony Works, Edinburgh Way, Harlow, Essex, CM20 2DA Tel: (01279) 444997 Fax: (01279) 721422 *Tool hire services*

▶ HSS Hire, 312 Kenton Road, Harrow, Middlesex, HA3 8DF Tel: (020) 8907 3614 Fax: (020) 8907 9776 *Tool hire*

▶ HSS Hire, 406 Uxbridge Road, Hayes, Middlesex, UB4 0SE Tel: (020) 8561 3846 Fax: (020) 8561 8626 *Tool hire*

▶ HSS Hire, 7 The Broadway, Haywards Heath, West Sussex, RH16 3AQ Tel: (01444) 451613 Fax: (01444) 458296 *Tool hire services*

▶ HSS Hire, 45 Oxford Road, High Wycombe, Buckinghamshire, HP11 2EB Tel: (01494) 464959 Fax: (01494) 461125 *Tool hire services*

▶ HSS Hire, Unit 1 Haslemere Heathrow Estate, Silver Jubilee Way, Hounslow, TW4 6NF Tel: (020) 8759 9225 Fax: (020) 8759 9226 *Tool hire services*

▶ HSS Hire, 686 London Road, Hounslow, TW3 1PG Tel: (020) 8577 5836 Fax: (020) 8577 7884 *Tool hire services*

▶ HSS Hire, 20 Blatchington Road, Hove, East Sussex, BN3 3YN Tel: (01273) 329838 Fax: (01273) 733472 *Tool hire services*

▶ HSS Hire, 364 High Road, Ilford, Essex, IG1 1QP Tel: (020) 8478 9911 Fax: (020) 8478 9922 *Tool hire services*

▶ HSS Hire, 151 Abbey Lane, Leicester, LE4 5NZ Tel: 0116-268 1441 Fax: 0116-268 1257

HSS Hire, 166-178 Great Howard Street, Liverpool, L3 7DW Tel: 0151-207 4747 Fax: 0151-207 3386 *Tool hire services*

▶ HSS Hire, 336 Battersea Park Road, London, SW11 3BY Tel: (020) 7223 0025 Fax: (020) 7223 0035 *Tool hire services*

▶ HSS Hire, 307-311 Camberwell New Road, London, SE5 0TF Tel: (020) 7701 3838 Fax: (020) 7701 2998 *Power tool hire services*

▶ HSS Hire, 45-49 Barking Road, London, E16 4HB Tel: (020) 7474 7040 Fax: (020) 7474 7080 *Power tool hire services*

▶ HSS Hire, 11-15 Lillie Road, Earls Court, London, SW6 1TX Tel: (020) 7381 4433 Fax: (020) 7385 5552 *Power tool hire services*

▶ HSS Hire, 208-210 High Road, London, N2 9AY Tel: (020) 8883 3818 Fax: (020) 8444 1297 *Plant hirers*

▶ HSS Hire, 70 Blackstock Road, London, N4 2DR Tel: (020) 7704 8787 Fax: (020) 7704 8717 *Plant hire services*

▶ HSS Hire, 865 Fulham Road, London, SW6 5HP Tel: (020) 7736 1769 Fax: (020) 7736 3127 *Power tool hire services*

▶ HSS Hire, 143 Caledonian Road, London, N1 0SL Tel: (020) 7837 9999 Fax: (020) 7278 1717 *Tool hire services*

▶ HSS Hire, 293 Lewisham High Street, London, SE13 6NL Tel: (020) 8314 5900 Fax: (020) 8314 5714 *Tool hire services*

▶ HSS Hire, 135 Leytonstone Road, London, E15 1LH Tel: (020) 8555 0293 Fax: (020) 8221 0415 *Tool hire services*

▶ HSS Hire, Homebase, 3 Station Road, London, N11 1QJ Tel: (020) 8368 8158 Fax: (020) 8361 6907 *Tool Hire services*

▶ HSS Hire, 192 Campden Hill Road, London, W8 7TH Tel: (020) 7727 0897 Fax: (020) 7221 3248 *Tool hire services*

▶ HSS Hire, 14 The Vale, Shepherds Bush, London, W3 7SB Tel: (020) 8743 6300 Fax: (020) 8743 7555 *Tool hire services*

▶ HSS Hire, 340 Clapham Road, London, SW9 9AJ Tel: (020) 7498 8866 Fax: (020) 7720 7421 *Tool hire services*

▶ HSS Hire, 620 Streatham High Road, London, SW16 3QJ Tel: (020) 8679 4948 Fax: (020) 8679 7119 *Tool hire services*

▶ HSS Hire, 451-453 High Road, London, N17 6QH Tel: (020) 8801 3261 Fax: (020) 8493 0145 *Tool Hire*

▶ HSS Hire, 95 Tower Bridge Road, London, SE1 4TW Tel: (020) 7357 9207 Fax: (020) 7357 9208 *Tool hire services*

▶ HSS Hire, Railway Arches, 76-77 Goding Street, London, SE11 5AW Tel: (020) 7735 6500 Fax: (020) 7735 6215 *Tool hire services*

▶ HSS Hire, Point Pleasant Works, 92 Putney Bridge Road, London, SW18 1TU Tel: (020) 8877 3503 Fax: (020) 8877 3532 *Tool hire services*

▶ HSS Hire, Wimbledon Builders Merchants, Gap Road, London, SW19 8JA Tel: (020) 8879 6100 Fax: (020) 8879 6200 *Hire services*

▶ HSS Hire, Circle House, Lostock Road, Urmston, Manchester, M41 0HS Tel: 0161-749 4090 Fax: 0161-749 4094

▶ HSS Hire, 34 Upper Green East, Mitcham, Surrey, CR4 2PB Tel: (020) 8685 9500 Fax: (020) 8685 9600 *Tool hire services*

▶ HSS Hire, 25 Willow Lane, Mitcham, Surrey, CR4 4TS Tel: (020) 8260 3100 Fax: (020) 8687 5005 E-mail: hire@hss.co.uk *Contractors plant hirers*

▶ HSS Hire, 1 Roundtree Way, Norwich, NR7 8SH Tel: (01603) 788556 Fax: (01603) 788539

▶ HSS Hire, 17 Carlton Parade, Orpington, Kent, BR6 0JB Tel: (01689) 834646 Fax: (01689) 830609 *Tool hire services*

HSS Hire, Unit 1 Bardell Terrace, Rochester, Kent, ME1 1NG Tel: (01634) 880227 Fax: (01634) 880259 E-mail: hire@hss.com *Tool & equipment hire services*

▶ HSS Hire, 238 London Road, Romford, RM7 9EL Tel: (01708) 725029 Fax: (01708) 754242 *Power tools & lifting equipment hire services*

▶ HSS Hire, 85 Brighton Road, South Croydon, Surrey, CR2 6EE Tel: (020) 8686 5646 Fax: (020) 8688 8346 *Tool hire services*

▶ HSS Hire, 52 Oxford Road, Denham, Uxbridge, Middlesex, UB9 4DH Tel: (01895) 252727 Fax: (01895) 238638 E-mail: enquiries@touch-stone.co.uk *Tool hire services*

▶ HSS Hire, Units 1-2, Lythgoes Lane, Warrington, WA2 7XE Tel: (01925) 658389 Fax: (01925) 244062 E-mail: hire@hss.com *Hire company*

▶ HSS Hire, 317-319 Lower High Street, Watford, WD17 2JD Tel: (01923) 224253 Fax: (01923) 223347 *Tool hire services*

▶ HSS Hire, 5a Wembley Hill Road, Wembley, Middlesex, HA9 8AF Tel: (020) 8903 9919 Fax: (020) 8902 4646 *Power tools & lifting equipment hire services*

HSS Hire, 74-82 Smithfield Road, Wrexham, Clwyd, LL13 8EP Tel: (01978) 311346 Fax: (01978) 311476 *Lifting equipment hire*

▶ HSS Hire Shops Ltd, Mace Lane, Ashford, Kent, TN24 8PE Tel: (01233) 610348 Fax: (01233) 622834 *Tool hire services*

▶ HSS Hire Shops Ltd, Chandlers Building Supplies, Timber Yard Lane, Lewes, East Sussex, BN7 2AU Tel: (01273) 471188 Fax: (01273) 478574 *Tool hire services*

▶ HSS Hire Shops Ltd, 128 High Street, Staines, Middlesex, TW18 4BY Tel: (01784) 456349 Fax: (01784) 454413 *Tool hire services*

HSS Lift & Shift, 3 Triangle Business Park, Oakwell Way, Birstall, Batley, West Yorkshire, WF17 9LU Tel: (01924) 444299 Fax: (01924) 422755 *Lifting gear hire*

HSS Lift & Shift, 176-178 Shore Road, Belfast, BT15 3QA Tel: (028) 9078 1818 Fax: (028) 9078 1122 *Plant hire*

HSS Lift & Shift, Hartland House, Pritchett Street, Birmingham, B6 4EX Tel: 0121-333 5704 Fax: 0121-333 5705 *Lifting equipment hire*

HSS Lift & Shift, 265-271 Penarth Road, Cardiff, CF11 8TT Tel: (029) 2045 4544 Fax: (029) 2064 1661 *Hiring out lifting equipment*

HSS Lift & Shift, 240 Whifflet Street, Coatbridge, Lanarkshire, ML5 4RX Tel: (01236) 436986 Fax: (01236) 440280 *Lifting gear hire services*

HSS Lift & Shift, 8 Oakwood Industrial Park, Gatwick Road, Crawley, West Sussex, RH10 9AZ Tel: (01293) 611010 Fax: (01293) 618041 *DIY hire equipment*

HSS Lift & Shift, 772 London Road, Alvaston, Derby, DE24 8UT Tel: (01332) 755699 Fax: (01332) 756715 *Lifting equipment hire*

HSS Lift & Shift, 4 Seafield Road, Edinburgh, EH6 7LD Tel: 0131-554 0298 Fax: 0131-554 9542 *Plant hire*

HSS Lift & Shift, 760 South Street, Glasgow, G14 0SY Tel: 0141-959 0217 Fax: 0141-959 4280 *Hire company*

HSS Lift & Shift, Adam Smith Street, Grimsby, South Humberside, DN31 1SJ Tel: (01472) 250005 Fax: (01472) 250270 *Hire services*

HSS Lift & Shift, 2 Bilton Way, Hayes, Middlesex, UB3 3NF Tel: (020) 8561 1655 Fax: (020) 8561 0994 *Lifting gear hire*

HSS Lift & Shift, 399 York Road, Leeds, LS9 6TA Tel: 0113-240 7707 Fax: 0113-240 9944 *Plant machinery hire suppliers*

HSS Lift & Shift, Crafton St East, Leicester, LE1 2DG Tel: 0116-262 7179 Fax: 0116-262 7179 *Hire equipment*

HSS Lift & Shift, 765 Old Kent Road, London, SE15 1NZ Tel: (020) 7732 4558 Fax: (020) 7000 8684 *Lifting gear hire suppliers*

HSS Lift & Shift, Sotherby Road, Middlesbrough, Cleveland, TS3 8BS Tel: (01642) 246015 Fax: (01642) 251411 *Materials handling equipment hire*

HSS Lift & Shift, Unit G12 Narvik Way, Tyne Tunnel Trading Estate, North Shields, Tyne & Wear, NE29 7XJ Tel: 0191-296 1126 Fax: 0191-258 2128 *Lifting equipment hirers*

HSS Lift & Shift, 148 Exeter Street, Plymouth, PL4 0AR Tel: (01752) 601225 Fax: (01752) 601225 *Lifting gear hire & sale*

HSS Lift & Shift, 3 Orwell Close, Rainham, Essex, RM13 8UB Tel: (01708) 526946 Fax: (01708) 525984 *Hire of lifting equipment*

HSS Lift & Shift, Unit 37, City Industrial Park Southern Road, Southampton, SO15 1HA Tel: (023) 8033 8844 Fax: (023) 8063 0730 *Lifting gear hire*

HSS Lift & Shift, 288 Hartshill Road, Stoke-on-Trent, ST4 7NA Tel: (01782) 412266 Fax: (01782) 846643 *Lifting gear hire services*

HSS Lift & Shift, 3 Barnfield Road, Swindon, SN2 2DJ Tel: (01793) 480044 Fax: (01793) 480257 *Lifting equipment manufrs*

HSS Premiere Centre, Stoneferry Road, Hull, HU8 8BZ Tel: (01482) 618007 Fax: (01482) 493189 *Hire shop service*

HT Cooling services, 65 Park View, Moulton, Northampton, NN3 7UZ Tel: (01604) 645135 Fax: (01604) 645135 E-mail: colin.htcooling@btopenworld.com *Refrigeration & air conditioning services*

HTDL, 6 Ardent Court, William James Way, Henley-in-Arden, West Midlands, B95 5GF Tel: 01564 797420 Fax: 01564 795247 E-mail: post@htdl.co.uk *Multi-disciplinary design services*

Hte Controls, 4 Cala Trading Estate, Ashton Vale Road, Bristol, BS3 2HA Tel: 0117-966 5925 Fax: 0117-966 1940 E-mail: sales@htecontrols.co.uk *Electric control gear distribs* Also at: Gloucester, Swindon & Yeovil

Htec Ltd, Unit H George Curl Way, Southampton, SO18 2RX Tel: (023) 8068 9200 Fax: (023) 8068 9201 E-mail: sstocks@htec.co.uk *Plastic card systems manufrs*

▶ HTS, 68 Whirlow Road, Baillieston, Glasgow, G69 6QE Tel: 0141-573 1700 Fax: 0141-573 2860 *Contract labors for shelving & racking*

HTS Design Services Ltd, 379 Anlaby Road, Hull, HU3 6AB Tel: (01482) 351236 Fax: (01482) 566052 E-mail: office@ahgsltd.co.uk *Consulting engineers*

Hub Electronics Ltd, Unit 1 Foundry Court, Foundry Lane, Horsham, West Sussex, RH13 5PY Tel: (01403) 255225 Fax: (01403) 263154 E-mail: tina@hubelectronics.co.uk *Distributors of connectors*

Hub Le Bas, Rose Street, Bilston, West Midlands, WV14 8TS Tel: (01902) 493506 Fax: (01902) 353687 E-mail: westsales@hublebas.co.uk *Steel tube stockholders*

Hubbard Architectural Metalwork Ltd, 3 Hurricane Way, Norwich, NR6 6HS Tel: (01603) 424817 Fax: (01603) 487158 E-mail: tony.hubbard@hubbardsmetalwork.co.uk Sales Contact: A. Hubbard *Whilst based in Norwich, our range of operation typically covers London, East Anglia, the South and South East of England with other areas of the UK always being fully considered. We design, manufacture and install all types of architectural metalwork, general metalwork, steel stairs, escape stairs, steel balconies, steel walkways, steel balustrade and wall rail. We also produce our own stainless steel elliptical and oval tube for use in many different ways including handrails, wall rails, lift call pedestals, special applications or bespoke projects. Both slotted and un-slotted elliptical tubes are available from our range for delivery both within the UK and abroad.. We are also able to produce non-standard elliptical sections that are outside our normal product range and enquiries are always welcome for any special requirements. Hubbard Architectural Metalwork can provide technical advice and assistance with material specification to meet individual customer needs.*

Hubbell Ltd, Brunel Drive, Stretton, Burton-On-Trent, Staffordshire, DE13 0BZ Tel: (01283) 500500 Fax: (01283) 500400 *Electric wiring accessories & control gear manufrs*

Hubert Davies & Sons, The Green, Neath, West Glamorgan, SA11 1SE Tel: (01639) 643022 *Steel fabricators*

▶ Hubert's Clocks, 9-10 Beatrice Street, Swindon, SN2 1BB Tel: 01793 335752 *Watch & clock repairers*

Hubner, Tree Tops House, Gillotts Lane, Henley-on-Thames, Oxfordshire, RG9 1PT Tel: (01491) 412055 Fax: (01491) 413006 E-mail: sales@sensortronic.co.uk *Rotary transducer manufrs*

Hubner Elektromaschinen A.G., PO Box 4022, Reading, RG8 8UD Tel: 0118-984 5351 Fax: 0118-984 3979 E-mail: sales@powertronic.co.uk *Rotary encoder manufrs*

Hubron Sales, Albion Street, Failsworth, Manchester, M35 0WW Tel: 0161-681 2691 Fax: 0161-683 4045 E-mail: sales@hubron.com *Rubber & plastic compounder manufrs*

▶ Hucke Ltd, Berners House, 47-48 Berners Street, London, W1T 3NF Tel: (020) 7580 7890 Fax: (020) 7580 7442 E-mail: sales@hucke.com *Fashion company*

Hucklesby's Tack Shop, Pear Tree Farm Long Road, Saham Waite, Shipdham, Thetford, Norfolk, IP25 7RH Tel: (01362) 820235 Fax: (01362) 821033 *Equestrian suppliers*

Hucknall Joinery, Lowmoor Road, Kirkby-in-Ashfield, Nottingham, NG17 7JE Tel: (01623) 721277 Fax: (01623) 722210 E-mail: info@hucknalljoinery.co.uk *Joinery*

Hucknall Manufacturing Co Ltd, Titchfield Street, Hucknall, Nottingham, NG15 7BH Tel: 0115-963 3034 Fax: 0115-963 5947 *Scarf manufrs*

Huco Lightronic Ni Ltd, 3 Aghanloo Industrial Estate, Aghanloo Road, Limavady, County Londonderry, BT49 0HE Tel: (028) 7776 8567 Fax: (028) 7776 8515 E-mail: sales@huco.co.uk *Lighting controls manufrs*

Huddersfield & District Textile Training Co. Ltd, Textile House, Red Doles Lane, Huddersfield, HD2 1YF Tel: (01484) 346500 Fax: (01484) 346501 E-mail: hdtt@textile-training.com *The Textile Centre of Excellence provides information on textiles, training, development and conferencing services in Huddersfield.**

Huddersfield Fine Worsteds, Kirkheaton Mills, Huddersfield, HD5 0NS Tel: (01484) 420377 Fax: (01484) 429156 *Fine worsted manufrs*

Huddersfield Plate Glass Co. Ltd, 43 Spring Street, Huddersfield, HD1 4BA Tel: (01484) 535106 Fax: (01484) 535106 E-mail: sales@hpglass.com *Glass merchants*

Huddersfield Saw & Tool Co., Vine Street, Huddersfield, HD1 6NT Tel: (01484) 424055 Fax: (01484) 421244 *Woodworking machines & chain saws suppliers*

Hudevad Britain, Bridge House, Bridge Street, Walton-on-Thames, Surrey, KT12 1AL Tel: (01932) 247835 Fax: (01932) 247694 E-mail: sales@hudevad.co.uk *Radiators manufrs*

Hudson, Doncaster Road, Bawtry, Doncaster, South Yorkshire, DN10 6NX Tel: (01302) 710711 Fax: (01302) 710782 E-mail: info@johnhudson.co.uk *Commercial vehicle contractors & hirers*

▶ Hudson, 14 Jupiter Heights, Uxbridge, Middlesex, UB10 0TA Tel: (01895) 271457 Fax: (01895) 271460

▶ Hudson Engineering Ltd, 134 High Road, Benfleet, Essex, SS7 5LD Tel: (01268) 759575

Hudson Global Resources Ltd, Grosvenor House, 14 Bennetts Hill, Birmingham, B2 5RS Tel: 0121-633 0010 Fax: 0121-633 0862 *Search & selection executive recruitment services*

▶ Hudson Haulage, Unit 8 Grove Lane, Elmswell, Bury St. Edmunds, Suffolk, IP30 9HN Tel: (01359) 242777 Fax: (01359) 242567 E-mail: info@hudsonhaulage.com

Hudson House, 8 Albany Street, Edinburgh, EH1 3QB Tel: 0131-473 2300 Fax: 0131-473 2309 E-mail: info@jupsys.co.uk *Veterinary applications software services*

J. Hudson & Co. (Whistles) Ltd, 244 Barr Street, Hockley, Birmingham, B19 3AH Tel: 0121-554 2124 Fax: 0121-551 9293 E-mail: sale@acmewhistles.co.uk *Whistle manufrs*

Leonard Hudson, 2 Queen Anne Drive, Edinburgh, EH28 8LH Tel: 0800 0181412 Fax: 0808 1806030 E-mail: sales@leonardhudson.co.uk *School uniform suppliers*

Hudson & Middleton, Sutherland Works, Normacot Road, Stoke-on-Trent, ST3 1PP Tel: (01782) 319256 Fax: (01782) 343300 E-mail: enquiries@hudsonandmiddleton.co.uk *Fine bone china manufrs*

Hudson & Pearson Ltd, Bradwood Works, Manchester Road, Dunnockshaw, Burnley, Lancashire, BB11 5PW Tel: (01706) 210582 Fax: (01706) 215692 *Commercial printers*

Percy A. Hudson Ltd, Northumberland Street, North Shields, Tyne & Wear, NE30 1DW Tel: 0191-257 5099 Fax: 0191-257 9461 *Timber merchants & importers services*

Hudson's, Unit 33-35 Nailsea Trading Estate, Southfield Road, Nailsea, Bristol, BS48 1JE Tel: (01275) 857335 Fax: (01275) 810587 E-mail: hudsoneng@btconnect.com *Precision engineers*

Hudsons Of Dudley Ltd, Canal St/Brickkiln Street, Brierley Hill, West Midlands, DY5 3LQ Tel: (01384) 262126 Fax: (01384) 481170 E-mail: hudsonsofdudley@aol.com *Ferrous scrap metal merchants & haulage contractors*

Hudsons Instruments & Lasers, 123 Foundry Lane, Southampton, SO15 3GB Tel: (023) 8070 4704 Fax: (023) 8070 2828 E-mail: sales@hudsons-uk.com *Surveying equipment manufrs*

▶ Hudsons Pantry, Hudsons Pantry, Towcester, Northamptonshire, NN12 7HT Tel: (01327) 352443 E-mail: Info@hudsonspantry.co.uk

Huf UK Ltd, Neptune Industrial Estate, Owen Road, Willenhall, West Midlands, WV13 2PZ Tel: (01902) 366023 Fax: (01902) 366424 *Lock & handles sales & manufrs*

Huggett Electrical Ltd, Twerton Mill, Lower Bristol Road, Bath, BA2 1EW Tel: (01225) 426271 Fax: (01225) 448154 E-mail: mail@huggettelectrical.co.uk *MCC switchboard manufrs*

▶ Hugh Bourn Ltd, Louth Road, Wragby, Market Rasen, Lincolnshire, LN8 5PH Tel: (01673) 858831 Fax: (01673) 857006 E-mail: info@hughbourn.co.uk

Hugh Crawshaw, 94 Matilda Street, Sheffield, S1 4QF Tel: 0114-273 9799 Fax: 0114-270 0229 *General silverware*

Hugh Evans HDR Window Cleaning Services, 25 Trent Valley Rd, Lichfield, Staffs, WS13 6EZ Tel: 01543 258339 E-mail: Randa@tadelevenone.fsnet.co.uk *Reach & Wash Pure Water Window Cleaning - Commercial and Domestic - Birminghmam and W.Midlands area - Family Business - Free Demo and quote*

Hugh J O'Boyle Ltd, 1 The Green, Irish Street, Downpatrick, County Down, BT30 6BE Tel: (028) 4461 2278 Fax: (028) 4461 3132 E-mail: info@hjob.co.uk *Building contractors*

▶ Hugh K Clarkson & Sons Ltd, Lochiel Works, Young Street, West Calder, West Lothian, EH55 8EQ Tel: (01506) 872241 Fax: (01506) 871827

▶ Hugh K Gillies Ltd, 23 Kyle Road, Irvine Industrial Estate, Irvine, Ayrshire, KA12 8LE Tel: (01294) 274296 Fax: (01294) 277284 E-mail: hkgillies@btconnect.com *Engineering services*

Hugh Page Sussex Ltd, Station Road, Heathfield, East Sussex, TN21 8DH Tel: (01435) 862235 Fax: (01435) 865653 *Garden machinery services & distributors*

▶ Hugh Stirling Ltd, 87 Middlesex Street, Glasgow, G41 1EE Tel: 0141-420 1666 Fax: 0141-429 2615

A.C. Hughes Ltd, 1 High Street, Hampton Hill, Hampton, Middlesex, TW12 1NA Tel: (020) 8979 1366 *Bird ring manufrs*

A. & D. Hughes Ltd, Pope's Lane, Nelson Street, Oldbury, West Midlands, B69 4PA Tel: 0121-552 4500 Fax: 0121-511 1072 *Repetition sub-contract machinists*

Alexander Hughes Ltd, 14-16 Regent Street, London, SW1Y 4PH Tel: (020) 7331 1800 Fax: (020) 7331 1888 E-mail: info@alexanderhughes.co.uk *Management consultants*

Hughes & Allen Ltd, Canalside Industrial Estate, Oil Sites Road, Ellesmere Port, CH65 4EN Tel: 0151-355 3170 Fax: 0151-355 5074 *Wood machinists & joinery manufrs*

Ben Hughes Engineering Ltd, Gwydr Place, Loughor, Swansea, SA4 6TW Tel: (01792) 892794 Fax: (01792) 898299 E-mail: bheng@btconnect.com *General engineers*

C. Hughes, 89 Station Rd, Flitwick, Bedford, MK45 1LA Tel: (01525) 717270 Fax: (01525) 717270 E-mail: clive.hughes1@ntlworld.com *All building & associated trades*

Hughes & Coleman Ltd, Delta Close, Norwich, NR6 6BG Tel: (01603) 426159 Fax: (01603) 486853E-mail: sales@hughesandcoleman.co.uk *Greeting cards & stationery gift distributors*

▶ Hughes Design Ltd, Tai Tywyn Business Centre, Sandy Lane, Prestatyn, Clwyd, LL19 7SF Tel: (01745) 888828 Fax: (01745) 859020 E-mail: sion@hughesdesign.ltd.uk *Graphic Design & printing*

▶ Hughes Drylining Ltd, 90 Bradley Avenue, Winterbourne, Bristol, BS36 1HR Tel: (07779) 622502 Fax: (01454) 776638 *Specialise in Drywall Systems and all types of Suspended Ceilings. *Including;*Gyp Wall Framing,*Metal Stud Partitions,*Taping and jointing,*Plastering and rendering,*Fire-proofing and insulating,*Metsec Steel Framing.*

David Hughes Enterprises Ltd, New Cottage, Oulton, Norbury, Stafford, ST20 0PG Tel: (01785) 284410 Fax: (01785) 284410 *Fire Saftey Engineers*

Hughes Environmental Services Ltd, 8 High Street, West Molesey, Surrey, KT8 2NA Tel: (020) 8979 7352 Fax: (020) 8979 9400 *Water treatment*

Hughes Forrest Ltd, Bolt Street, Newport, Gwent, NP20 2UP Tel: (01633) 250515 Fax: (01633) 843289 *Builders' merchants*

Frank Hughes & Son Ltd, Lunts Heath Road, Widnes, Cheshire, WA8 5SG Tel: 0151-424 5731 Fax: 0151-495 2063 E-mail: sales@frankhughes.co.uk *Steel stockholders*

Hughes & Holmes, Unit F, Key Industrial Park, Fernside Road, Willenhall, West Midlands, WV13 3YA Tel: (01902) 728888 Fax: (01902) 727111 E-mail: willenhall@lister.co.uk *Engineers merchants & ironmongers* Also at: Great Bridge, Telford & Walsall

Joseph Hughes & Sons Ltd, Black Flag Works, Pottery Street, Castleford, West Yorkshire, WF10 1NJ Tel: (01977) 552424 Fax: (01977) 551105 E-mail: juilebresnan@josephughes.co.uk *Road transport, haulage & freight services*

Kelvin Hughes Ltd, New North Road, Hainault, Ilford, Essex, IG6 2UR Tel: (020) 8502 6887 Fax: (020) 8500 0837 E-mail: sales@kelvinhughes.co.uk Principal Export Areas: Worldwide *Navigational instrument manufacturers & radar navigational equipment*

Kelvin Hughes Ltd, Kilgraston House, 11-13 Southampton Street, Southampton, SO15 2ED Tel: (023) 8063 4911 Fax: (023) 8033 0014 E-mail: southampton@kelvinhughes.co.uk *Charts & book suppliers* Also at: Folkestone, London EC3 & Poole

Hughes Light, Unit 11, Shell Corner Trading Estate, Long Lane, Halesowen, West Midlands, B62 9LD Tel: (0793) 9087548 E-mail: tim@hugheslight.co.uk *Specialised Light fitting manufacturers*Emergency Lighting Conversions*Lighting Assembly & Refurbishment*Bespoke Luminaires*

Hughes Light, 1 Mill Cottages, Hurcott, Kidderminster, Worcestershire, DY10 3PH Tel: (01562) 742082 Fax: 0121-440 7477 *Lighting accessories manufrs*

Hughes & Mcleod, 5 Black Causeway Road, Strangford, Downpatrick, County Down, BT30 7LX Tel: (028) 4488 1880 Fax: (028) 4488 1880 E-mail: info@bagpipers.co.uk *Manufacturers of synthetic reeds for bagpipes*

Ron Hughes, Glanfaes, Llanybydder, Dyfed, SA40 9TZ Tel: (01570) 480376 Fax: (01570) 480376 *Agricultural contractors & plant hire*

Hughes Safety Showers Ltd, Whitefield Road, Bredbury, Stockport, Cheshire, SK6 2SS Tel: 0161-430 6618 Fax: 0161-430 7928 E-mail: sales@hughes-safety-showers.co.uk *Industrial safety shower, eye & face wash unit & fountain manufrs*

Hughes Safety Showers Ltd, Whitefield Road, Bredbury, Stockport, Cheshire, SK6 2SS Tel: 0161-430 6618 Fax: 0161-430 7928 E-mail: sales@hughes-safety-showers.co.uk *Industrial safety showers emergency & portable shower manufrs*

Hughes & Salvidge, 11 Flathouse Road, Portsmouth, PO1 4QS Tel: (023) 9275 3733 Fax: (023) 9275 5189 E-mail: info@hughes-salvidge.co.uk *Demolition & dismantling engineers*

▶ Hughes Walker Solicitors Ltd, 82, Bolton Street, Bury, Lancs, BL9 0LL Tel: 0161 7633388 Fax: 0161 7637558 E-mail: enquiry@hughes-walker.co.uk *Lawyers for personal injury, RTA & debt collection*

▶ Hughescrafts, Hughescrafts, 33 Thorntondale Drive, Marton Lodge, Bridlington, East Riding of Yorkshire, YO16 6GW Tel: (01262) 602180 E-mail: john@hughescrafts.com *We sell photographs of military aircraft and Yorkshire Landscapes, we also provide a photography service (not weddings)*

Huhtamaki (UK) Ltd, Rowner Road, Gosport, Hants, PO13 0PR Tel: (023) 9251 2434 Fax: (023) 9251 2330 E-mail: sales@gb.huhtamaki.com *Huhtamaki manufacture innovative foodservice disposables including paper, plastic and moulded fibre packaging, as well as biodegradable products. The company's BioWare range of environmentally-friendly packaging is manufactured by Huhtamaki in Europe. The comprehensive range of products is certified in accordance with EN13432, the European norm for compostability of packaging. The range fully composts to soil within 60 days (under the correct conditions). Products are supplied in stylish designs, and Huhtamaki is also able to custom-print products in up to eight colours. Simply provide Huhtamaki with a company name, logo, message or promotional concept, and they do the rest! Huhtamaki is committed to working with its customers to provide products*

continued

that meet their needs, so for cups, tumblers, lids, food containers, plates and carry trays, or to find out more about BioWare - an ideal choice if you are looking for a simple way to contribute towards a sustainable environment - call Huhtamaki

Huhtamaki Van Leer, 180 Gilford Road, Portadown, Craigavon, County Armagh, BT63 5LE Tel: (028) 3836 7200 Fax: (028) 3836 7280 E-mail: portadown@gb.huhtamaki.com *Plastic manufrs*

Huish Horseboxes, East Huish Farm, Tedburn St. Mary, Exeter, EX6 6AF Tel: (01647) 61716 Fax: (01647) 61716 E-mail: sales@huishengineering.co.uk *Horse box manufrs*

Huktra Road Haulage Services, Westpoint Enterprise Park, Clarence Avenue, Trafford Park, Manchester, M17 1QS Tel: 0161-877 8488 Fax: 0161-877 8522 E-mail: info@huktra.com *Inter model logistics operators service*

Huktra UK Ltd, Pickerings Road, Halebank, Widnes, Cheshire, WA8 8XW Tel: 0151-420 3443 Fax: 0151-423 5427 E-mail: sales@huktratanks.com *Tank container operators*

Hulbert Developments Ltd, 6 Grazebrook Industrial Park, Peartree Lane, Dudley, West Midlands, DY2 0XW Tel: (01384) 239019 Fax: (01384) 457280 E-mail: enq@hulbert-group.co.uk *Engineering specialists & property developers*

Hulco UK Ltd, 21 Meadow Close, Ise Valley Industrial Estate, Wellingborough, Northamptonshire, NN8 4BH Tel: (01933) 223743 Fax: (01933) 441534 *Conveyor manufrs*

Hulett Aluminium International, Securehold Business Centre, Studley Road, Redditch, Worcestershire, B98 7LG Tel: (01527) 516222 Fax: (01527) 517199 E-mail: sales@hulett-hydro.co.za *Metal tube extrusion manufrs*

Hull Aero, Unit 14 The Street, Catfield, Great Yarmouth, Norfolk, NR29 5AA Tel: (01692) 582888 Fax: (01692) 580850 *Aircraft restoration*

Hull Blyth & Co. Ltd, 2 Coldbath Square, London, EC1R 5HL Tel: (020) 7696 9688 Fax: (020) 7696 9686 E-mail: enquiries@hull-blyth.com *Freight forwarders & shipping agencies*

Hull Cartridge Co. Ltd, Bontoft Avenue, Hull, HU5 4HZ Tel: (01482) 342756 Fax: (01482) 346103 E-mail: sales@hullcartridge.co.uk *Ammunitions manufacturers shot cartridges*

Hull & Humber Chamber Of Commerce, 34-38 Beverley Road, Hull, HU3 1YE Tel: (01482) 324976 Fax: (01482) 213962 E-mail: b.massie@hull-humber-chamber.co.uk *Business support & membership organisation*

▶ Hull Local Labour Initiative, 12-13 Bishop Lane, Hull, HU1 1PA Tel: (01482) 229986

Hull Vac, Unit 8 South Orbital Trading Park, Hedon Road, Hull, HU9 1NJ Tel: (01482) 320633 Fax: (01482) 213671 E-mail: hullvac@aoil.com *Cleaning product distributors*

▶ Hullachan Pro, 6 Milrig Road, Rutherglen, Glasgow, G73 2NH Tel: 0141-647 0257 E-mail: craig.coussins@btinternet.com *Irish Dancing shoes, Scottish and Highland DANCING SHOES, Irish Dance Shoes*

Hulland Saddlery, Hulland Ward, Ashbourne, Derbyshire, DE6 3EA Tel: (01335) 370858 Fax: (01335) 370858 *Saddlery Retail*

Hullmatic Engineering Ltd, 1 Lancaster Way Earls Colne Business Park, Airfield, Earls Colne, Colchester, CO6 2NS Tel: (01787) 222099 Fax: (01787) 224317 E-mail: hullmatic@aol.com *Repetition turned parts manufrs*

Hullternative Pest Control Service, 1260 Kingsbury Road, Castle Vale, Birmingham, B35 6AG Tel: 0121-351 5598 Fax: 0121-351 2733 *Pest control services*

E. Hulme & Son Ltd, 13-15 Cecil Street, Walsall, WS4 2BD Tel: (01922) 622082 Fax: (01922) 722442 *Leather goods & gifts supplier*

Hulme & Gibson Ltd, Mount Pleasant, Stoke-on-Trent, ST1 4AY Tel: (01782) 262525 Fax: (01782) 274057 E-mail: hgrewinds@btinternet.com *Electrical mechanical engineers*

John Hulme Ltd, 2 Burnside Road, Bolton, BL1 6EP Tel: (01204) 846077 *Kitchen towels & toilet roll wholesalers*

Hulse Engineering, Duke Street, Stoke-on-Trent, ST4 3NR Tel: (01782) 316589 Fax: (01782) 598504 E-mail: hulsefabricationsltd@hotmail.com *Mechanical & electrical engineers*

Human Computer Interaction York Ltd, 3 Innovation Close, Heslington, York, YO10 5ZF Tel: (01904) 428600 Fax: (01904) 428628 *Software consultants*

▶ Human Concepts, Suite 10 The White House, 42 The Terrace, Torquay, TQ1 1DE Tel: (01803) 390490 Fax: (01803) 203304 E-mail: sales@orgplus.co.uk *HumanConcepts provides industry-leading software solutions for managing organisational change and supporting critical business decisions. OrgPlus integrates with HR databases to automatically create and publish organisational charts and with Microsoft Office software for budgeting and presentation purposes. Managers and Human Resources professionals use OrgPlus to collaborate on and support organisational change decisions.*

Human Factors International, 8 Staple Inn, London, WC1V 7QH Tel: (020) 7831 3123 Fax: (020) 7831 8643 E-mail: mail@humanfactors.co.uk *Business consultants & psychologists*

Human Nature, 13 Malvern Road, London, NW6 5PS Tel: (020) 7328 5452 *Health food wholesaler & retailer, massage*

▶ Human Recognition Systems Ltd, First Floor Vortex Court, Enterprise Way, Liverpool, L13 1FB Tel: 0151-254 2888 Fax: 0151-254 2999 E-mail: identify@hrsltd.com *Biometric & single sign-on specialists*

▶ Human Resources Consultancy, 50 Keedwell Hill, Long Ashton, Bristol, BS41 9DR Tel: (01275) 540510 Fax: (01275) 540510 E-mail: melaniehall@hrc-bristol.co.uk *Selection & assessment, graduate recruitment services*

▶ Humanware Europe Ltd, Russell Smith House Unit 2, Bullmatt Business Centre, Northampton Road, Rushden, Northamptonshire, NN10 6AR Tel: (01933) 415800 Fax: (01933) 411029

continued

E-mail: eu.info@humanware.com *Medical or surgical supplies*

Humark Engineering, Cavendish Bridge, Shardlow, Derby, DE72 2HL Tel: (01332) 799999 Fax: (01332) 799999 *Cnc & manual machinists*

Humax Horticulture Ltd, Richardson House, Mill Hill, Gretna, Dumfriesshire, DG16 5HU Tel: (01461) 339260 Fax: (01461) 339269 E-mail: sales@humax.co.uk *Horticultural suppliers*

Humber Cooperage Co. Ltd, Stone Ferry Industrial Estate, Rix Road, Hull, HU7 0BT Tel: (01482) 838965 Fax: (01482) 838965 *Drum reconditioners & merchants*

Humber Electrical Engineering Co. Ltd, 45-46 Portland Place, Hull, HU2 8QP Tel: (01482) 323042 Fax: (01482) 326811 E-mail: info@humberelectrical.com *Switchboard & enclosure manufrs*

Humber Europe Ltd, Shorten Brook Drive, Altham Business Park, Altham, Accrington, Lancashire, BB5 5YH Tel: (01282) 770333 Fax: (01282) 776888 E-mail: info@humberbigbag.com *Flexible intermediate bulk containers manufrs*

Humber Fabrications (Hull) Ltd, 99 Wincolmlee, Hull, HU2 8AH Tel: (01482) 226100 Fax: (01482) 215884 E-mail: sales@rigid-inflatables.com *Inflatable boat repairers & manufrs*

Humber Joiners Ltd, Stepney Lane, Hull, HU5 1HX Tel: (01482) 341954 Fax: (01482) 449516 *Joinery manufrs*

Humber Quality Foods Ltd, Brigg Road, Scunthorpe, South Humberside, DN15 6TZ Tel: (01724) 270306 Fax: (01724) 270345 E-mail: john@hqf.co.uk *Food processors*

Humber Sand & Gravel Ltd, West Quay, Alexandra Dock, Hedon Road, Hull, HU9 1TA Tel: (01482) 328144 Fax: (01482) 585163 *Sand & gravel suppliers*

Humber Workboats Ltd, North Killingholme, Immingham, South Humberside, DN40 3LX Tel: (01469) 540156 Fax: (01469) 540303 E-mail: elliotmorton@humberworkboats.co.uk *Crane, safety boat hire & dredging service*

Humberclyde Farm Finance, Northern Cross, Basing View, Basingstoke, Hampshire, RG21 4HL Tel: (0845) 2267378 Fax: (0845) 2267379 E-mail: enquiries@humberclyde.co.uk *Leasing & finance company* Also at: Birmingham, Manchester & York

Humberside Aggregates & Excavations Ltd, The Quarry, Newport Road, North Cave, Brough, North Humberside, HU15 2NU Tel: (01430) 421503 Fax: (01430) 421116 E-mail: enquiries@hag.com *Excavation & demolition contractors & aggregate suppliers*

Humberside Blocks Ltd, The Industrial Estate, Ellifoot Lane, Burstwick, Hull, HU12 9EF Tel: (01964) 670682 Fax: (01964) 671947 E-mail: enquiries@humberside-blocks.com *Concrete block manufrs*

Humberside Food Machinery Ltd, Spyvee Street, Hull, HU8 7JJ Tel: (01482) 211956 Fax: (01482) 211957 E-mail: user@humbfood.co.uk *Refrigeration equipment suppliers*

Humberside Gear Co. Ltd, Thrunscoe House, Thrunscoe Road, Cleethorpes, South Humberside, DN35 8TA Tel: (01472) 601111 Fax: (01472) 602143 E-mail: humberside.gears@virgin.net *Precision engineers & gear manufrs*

Humberside Instruments Ltd, 13-15 Barkhouse Lane, Cleethorpes, South Humberside, DN35 8RA Tel: (01472) 691157 Fax: (01472) 692585 E-mail: sales@humbrsideinstruments.co.uk *Instrument engineering & pressure instrumentation hire services*

Humberside International Airport Ltd, Humberside Int Airport, Kirmington, Ulceby, South Humberside, DN39 6YH Tel: (01652) 688456 Fax: (01652) 680524 E-mail: m.mumby@humbairport.co.uk *Airport facilities*

Humberside Marquees, 400 Wincolmlee, Hull, HU2 0QL Tel: (01482) 610102 Fax: (01482) 609955 E-mail: info@humbersidemarquees.com *Contract marquee & catering hire*

Humberside Offshore Training Association Ltd, Malmo Road, Hull, HU7 0YF Tel: (01482) 820567 Fax: (01482) 823202 E-mail: bookings@hota.org Principal Export Areas: Worldwide *Training services*

▶ Humberside Optical Services, 11 Antelope Road, Humber Bridge Industrial Estate, Barton-upon-Humber, South Humberside, DN18 5RS Tel: (01652) 660070 Fax: (01652) 660084 E-mail: sales@lensnet.co.uk

Humberside Sun Blinds Ltd, Marlin House, Kings Road, Immingham, South Humberside, DN40 1AW Tel: (01469) 574490 Fax: (01469) 578164 E-mail: humbersideblinds@aol.com *Blinds manufrs*

▶ Humberstone & Pulford Ltd, 113 Brackenborough Road, Louth, Lincolnshire, LN11 0AG Tel: (01507) 603001 Fax: (01507) 609646 E-mail: info@h-pbuilders.co.uk *General builders & contractors*

Humberts, Mansfield House, Silver Street, Taunton, Somerset, TA1 3DN Tel: (01823) 331234 Fax: (01823) 332034 E-mail: taunton.ag@humberts.co.uk *Agricultural valuers & agents*

Hume Sweet Hume, Pierowall, Westray, Orkney, KW17 2BZ Tel: (01857) 677259 Fax: (01857) 677259 E-mail: info@humesweethume.com *Textiles design & manufrs*

▶ Humidity Control Systems Ltd, 8 The Green, Nettleham, Lincoln, LN2 2NR Tel: (01522) 753722 Fax: (01522) 753822 E-mail: sales@humiditycontrol.co.uk *Suppliers of industrial dehumidifiers*

J. & H. Humphrey, Unit 1, Fareham Enterprise Centre, Newgate Lane, Fareham, Hampshire, PO14 1TH Tel: (01329) 318463 Fax: (01329) 317342 E-mail: info@preforming.co.uk *Component performing specialists suppliers*

Humphrey & Stretton (Properties) Ltd, Stretton House, 20 Pindar Road, Hoddesdon, Hertfordshire, EN11 0EU Tel: (01992) 462965 Fax: (01992) 463996 E-mail: sales@humphreystretton.com *Joinery & flush door*

▶ Humphrey-Evans Intellectual Property Services Ltd, 1 Hawkes Close, Wokingham, Berkshire, RG41 2SZ Tel: 0118-979 7788 Fax: 0118- 979 7789 E-mail: edward@heips.com *We can provide value-based help and guidance relating to a number of intellectual property issues regarding generation, ownership and protection in the fields of patents, designs, copyright and trade marks.**

▶ Humphreys Electrical Ltd, Unit 21 Shrivenham Hundred Business Park, Majors Road, Watchfield, Swindon, SN6 8TZ Tel: (01793) 783964 Fax: (01793) 783995

Humphreys Garage Bearwood Ltd, Anderson Road, Smethwick, West Midlands, B67 5DR Tel: 0121-429 1741 Fax: 0121-429 1741 *Motor vehicle repair & servicing*

John G. Humphreys (Electrical) Ltd, 15 Burbeck Road, Caldicot, Gwent, NP26 4DX Tel: (01291) 421978 Fax: (01291) 420576 E-mail: ijhumphreys@aol.com *Electrical contractors*

▶ Humphreys Signs, 6 Spencer Trading Estate, Rhyl Road, Denbigh, Clwyd, LL16 5TQ Tel: (01745) 813113 Fax: (01745) 815374 E-mail: will@humphreys-signs.co.uk *Sign manufrs*

Humphreys & Sons Ltd, Newton Lane, Wigston, Leicestershire, LE18 3SG Tel: 0116-288 1105 Fax: 0116-288 0661 E-mail: ian@europasports.co.uk *Sportswear distributors & manufrs*

▶ Humphries Engineering, 14 Murrell Green Business Park, London Road, Hook, Hampshire, RG27 9GR Tel: (01256) 760144 Fax: (01256) 760056 E-mail: steve@humphriesengineering.co.uk *CNC & manual milling & precision engineering services*

Humphries Video Services Ltd, Unit 2 Willow Business Centre, 17 Willow Lane, Mitcham, Surrey, CR4 4NX Tel: (020) 8648 6111 Fax: (020) 8648 5261 E-mail: sales@hvs.co.uk *Video tape duplicating & digital encoding service providers*

Hungate Health Store, 4 Hungate, Beccles, Suffolk, NR34 9TL Tel: (01502) 715009 *Health food retailers*

Hunprenco Group of Companies Ltd., Hunmanby Industrial Estate, Bridlington Road, Hunmanby, Filey, North Yorkshire, YO14 0PH Tel: (01723) 890105 Fax: (01723) 890018 E-mail: hunprenco@btinternet.com *Precision engineering*

Hunprenco Precision Engineering Ltd, Bridlington Road, Hunmanby Industrial Estate, Filey, North Yorkshire, YO14 0PH Tel: (01723) 890105 Fax: (01723) 890018 *Precision & general engineering & gear manufacturers & cutters*

▶ Hunsbury School of Motoring, 32 Barn Owl Close, East Hunsbury, Northampton, NN4 0UA Tel: (01604) 702808 E-mail: hsmdrive@aol.com *Driving school based in Northampton offering lessons to pupils of all ages and experiences including training for re tests.*

▶ Hunslet Engine Co., 2 Maple Park, Lowfields Avenue, Leeds, LS12 6HH Tel: 0113-277 4007 Fax: 0113-277 3005 E-mail: info@hunsletenginw.com *Locomotive selling & engineering metals*

Hunslet-Barclay Ltd, Caledonia Works, West Langlands Street, Kilmarnock, Ayrshire, KA1 2QD Tel: (01563) 523573 Fax: (01563) 541076 E-mail: mail@hunsletbarclay.co.uk *Diesel locomotive refurbishment services*

Hunt & Co. (Bournemouth) Ltd, PO Box 3470, Sherborne, Dorset, DT9 4YZ Tel: (01935) 814848 Fax: (01935) 814333 *Holding company*

Hunt Bros & Co. Ltd, Argyle Buildings, 69-71 Argyle Street, Birkenhead, Merseyside, CH41 6LQ Tel: 0151-647 4541 Fax: 0151-666 1045 E-mail: hardwoods@huntbros.co.uk *Timber material & panel products agents*

▶ Hunt Bros Ltd, Sankey Valley Industrial Estate, Junction Lane, Newton-le-Willows, Merseyside, WA12 8DN Tel: (01925) 222068 Fax: (01925) 220407

D.R. Hunt, 29 Alexandra Road, Margate, Kent, CT9 5SP Tel: (01843) 209800 *Protective clothing manufrs*

▶ Hunt Engineering Ltd, Swanston Road, Great Yarmouth, Norfolk, NR30 3NQ Tel: (01493) 332847 Fax: (01493) 330520 *Precision engineering services*

Hunt Engineering, Chestnut Court, Burton Row, Brent Knoll, Highbridge, Somerset, TA9 4BP Tel: (01278) 760188 Fax: (01278) 760199 E-mail: sales@hunteng.co.uk *Signal processing hardware suppliers*

G. Hunt Filtration Ltd, Portland Mill, Portland Street South, Ashton-Under-Lyne, Lancashire, OL6 7SX Tel: 0161-330 7337 Fax: 0161-343 2365 E-mail: sales@hunt-filtration.co.uk *Filter & dust collecting bag manufrs*

▶ Hunt Grange Landrover, Vale Rise, Tonbridge, Kent, TN9 1TB Tel: (01732) 353637 Fax: (01732) 376000 E-mail: enquiries@huntgrange.co.uk *Approved new & used land rovers dealership*

Hunt & Co Hinckley Ltd, 4 Turville Close, Burbage, Hinckley, Leicestershire, LE10 2GZ Tel: (01455) 637263 Fax: (01455) 637263 *Industrial property lettings & audio visual agents*

Hunt & Holditch Ltd, Unit 12, 236-242 Lockwood Road, Huddersfield, HD1 3TG Tel: 01484 542148 Fax: 01484 549147 E-mail: hholditch@aol.com *Belt & braces manufrs*

Hunt Hotel, 19 Church Road, Leighton Buzzard, Bedfordshire, LU7 2LR Tel: (01525) 374692 Fax: (01525) 382782 *Hotel with function room*

J. & D. Hunt, Whitegate House, 77 Scott Street, Burnley, Lancashire, BB12 6NJ Tel: (01282) 772745 Fax: (01282) 772745 E-mail: huntcast@btconnect.com *Iron & aluminium casting consultant*

Jason Hunt, 57 Shelton Street, Wilnecote, Tamworth, Staffordshire, B77 5DB Tel: (01827) 282892 *domestic & commercial window cleaning*

Hunt & Keal, 53-57 Minerva Road, London, NW10 6HJ Tel: (020) 8838 2332 Fax: (020) 8838 2800 *Coach builders*

Hunt & Merriman Ltd, Gas Works Site, Liverpool Street, Salford, M5 4DG Tel: 0161-745 7272 Fax: 0161-743 9920 *Ground works & landscaping contractors*

Elizabeth Hunt Recruitment Consultants Ltd, Coin House, 2 Gees Court, St. Christophers Place, London, W1U 1JA Tel: (020) 7535 5050 Fax: (020) 7535 5053 E-mail: ehwesthunt@elizabethhunt.co.uk *Employment agency*

Hunt S Removals Ltd, 11-13 Market Close, Crewe, CW1 2NA Tel: (01606) 44655 Fax: (01270) 255884 E-mail: enquiries@huntsremovals.co.uk *Removal & storage services for uk*

▶ Huntcard Litho Ltd, Unit 4 Platt Industrial Estate, Maidstone Road, Platt, Sevenoaks, Kent, TN15 8JL Tel: (01732) 882088 Fax: (01732) 882148

▶ Huntdene Ltd, Thames Europort Clipper Boulevard, Crossways, Dartford, DA2 6QB Tel: (01322) 278855 Fax: (01322) 278866

▶ Hunted Cow Studios Ltd, 100 High Street, Elgin, Morayshire, IV30 1BW Tel: (01343) 550855 Fax: (01343) 550855 *Pc games retailers*

Hunter & Associates, 161 Henrietta St, Ashton-under-Lyne, Lancs, OL6 8PH Tel: 0161-330 8460 Fax: 0161-339 7858 E-mail: hunters@moggs.demon.co.uk *Chemical engineering consultants*

Bernard Hunter Ltd, 600 Gilmerton Road, Edinburgh, EH17 8RY Tel: 0131-663 7268 Fax: 0131-654 2592 E-mail: info@bernardhunter.com *Crane hire*

▶ Hunter Biltong Ltd, 2 Lyon Business Park, River Road, Barking, Essex, IG11 0JS Tel: (020) 8591 8221 Fax: (020) 8591 8224 *South African food manufrs*

Chas Hunter Ltd, Upper Villiers Street, Wolverhampton, WV2 4NR Tel: (01902) 424411 Fax: (01902) 424733 E-mail: chas.hunterltd@virgin.net *Protective clothing wholesalers*

▶ Hunter & Clark Ltd, Quay Road, Rutherglen, Glasgow, G73 1LD Tel: 0141-613 3500 Fax: 0141-613 3522

Hunter & Clark Ltd, 1173 Gallowgate, Glasgow, G31 4EG Tel: 0141-554 2327 Fax: 0141-554 4974 E-mail: enquires@hunterandclark.co.uk *Masonary contractors*

Hunter Douglas Ltd, Battersea Road, Stockport, Cheshire, SK4 3EQ Tel: 0161-432 5303 Fax: 0161-431 5087 E-mail: info.general@luxaflex-sunway.co.uk *Manufacturers of window blinds*

Hunter Douglas Ltd, Unit 8a Swanscombe Business Centre, London Road, Swanscombe, Kent, DA10 0LH Tel: (01322) 624580 Fax: (01322) 624558 E-mail: info.contract@luxaflex-sunway.co.uk *Manufacturers of blinds including roller type*

Hunter Electronic Components Ltd, Unit 9 Ely Road, Theale Estate, Reading, RG7 4BQ Tel: (01628) 675911 Fax: 01189 325136 E-mail: sales@hcal.co.uk *Hunter Cable Assembly is a specialist supplier and manufacturer of*cable assemblies, cable wiring, cable harnesses, cable looms, box builds and sub-assemblies.*

Hunter Gears Ltd, Addison Works, Haugh Lane, Blaydon-on-Tyne, Tyne & Wear, NE21 4SB Tel: 0191-414 4545 Fax: 0191-414 0135 *Gear manufrs*

Graham Hunter (Shirts) Ltd, Springtown Road, Springtown Industrial Estate, Londonderry, BT48 0LY Tel: (028) 7126 2542 Fax: (028) 7126 3556 E-mail: info@hunterapparelsolutions.com *Ladies & gentleman's clothing manufrs*

Hunter & Hyland Ltd, 201-205 Kingston Road, Leatherhead, Surrey, KT22 7PB Tel: (01372) 378511 Fax: (01372) 370038 E-mail: enquiries@hunterandhyland.co.uk *Curtain rail manufrs*

▶ Hunter Mabon, 10 Barrow Court, Barrow Gurney, Bristol, BS48 3RP Tel: (0870) 2012495 Fax: (01285) 770003 E-mail: cv@huntermabon.co.uk *We are a recruitment company specialising in bespoke recruitment solutions for high - Tech Uk companies.*

Michael Hunter & Sons Ltd, Moorgate, Ormskirk, Lancashire, L39 4RX Tel: (01695) 576911 Fax: (01695) 570489 *Builders, plumbers & timber merchants*

▶ Hunter & Morrison, Precast Shed, Kirkhouse, Whiteness, Shetland, ZE2 9LL Tel: (01595) 840240

Hunter Neil Packaging Ltd, Unit 5, Hilltop Meadows, Old London Road, Knockholt, Sevenoaks, Kent, TN14 7JW Tel: (01959) 532200 Fax: (01959) 534400 E-mail: info@hunterneil.co.uk *Bottling equipment supplies & sheet metalworkers*

Hunter Nicholas Ltd, Unit 17 Chiltern Business Centre, Garsington Road, Oxford, OX4 6NG Tel: (01865) 777365 Fax: (01865) 773856 E-mail: office@nicholashunter.com *Name badges, identity badges & lanyards manufrs*

Hunter & Partners Group Ltd, 26 28 Hammersmith Grove, Hammersmith, London, W6 7HU Tel: (020) 8237 8200 Fax: (020) 8741 2814 E-mail: mail@hunters.co.uk *Project managers services*

Hunter Penrose Supplies Ltd, 32 Southwark Street, London, SE1 1TU Tel: (020) 7407 5051 Fax: (020) 7378 1800 E-mail: info@hunterpenrose.co.uk *Suppliers to the lpre-press trade*

Hunter Plastics Ltd, Nathan Way, London, SE28 0AE Tel: (020) 8317 1551 Fax: (020) 8317 7764 E-mail: info@hunterplastics.co.uk *Hunter Plastics has earned its place as a UK leader in the above and below ground gravity drainage market. They offer a wide range of rainwater, plumbing and underground services including pipes and gutters.*

Hunter Saddlery, Redhills Business Park, Redhills Lane, Redhills, Penrith, Cumbria, CA11 0DT Tel: (01768) 899919 Fax: (01768) 899919 *Saddlery repairs*

▶ Hunter Scientific Ltd, Unit 1 Priors Hall, Widdington, Saffron Walden, Essex, CB11 3SB Tel: (01799) 541688 Fax: (01799) 541703 E-mail: sales@hunterscientific.com *Manufacturers & suppliers of medical devices*

Hunter Security Ltd, Walnut Tree Farm, Cockmannings Lane, Orpington, Kent, BR5 4HF Tel: (01689) 870951 Fax: (01689) 822363 E-mail: enquiries@huntersecurity.com *Security systems*

Hunter Signs Ltd, 5 Pill Farm Industrial Estate, Caldicot, Gwent, NP26 5JG Tel: (01291) 430617 Fax: (01291) 430070 E-mail: alison@westbase.uk.com *Sign manufrs*

Hunter Steel Coatings Ltd, Pinfold Lane, Alltami, Mold, Flintshire, CH7 6NZ Tel: (01244) 541177 Fax: (01244) 549310 E-mail: huntersteel@btconnect.com *Abrasive blast cleaning & protective coating services*

Hunter Systems Ltd, 46-48 Alfreton Road, Nottingham, NG7 3NN Tel: 0115-847 5210 Fax: 0115-847 5212 E-mail: info@hunter-systems.co.uk *IT consultants*

Hunters Employment Services, 65 Commercial Road, Swindon, SN1 5NX Tel: (01793) 433383 Fax: (01793) 422259 E-mail: hunterses@btclick.com *Employment services*

▶ HuntHouses.co.uk, 2 Wessex Close, Devizes, Wiltshire, SN10 3BB Tel: (0870) 8034939 E-mail: info@hunthouses.co.uk *Online Property Agent. There"s a new way to buy & sell property. For all your buying or selling property needs. Sell your property from only £49, don't pay £0000"s in high estate agents commissions, get a better service at a modern price! Call us today.*

Hunting plc, 3 Cockspur Street, London, SW1Y 5BQ Tel: (020) 7321 0123 Fax: (020) 7839 2072 E-mail: pr@hunting.plc.uk *Oil & gas services*

Hunting Energy Services, Silverburn Place, Bridge of Don Industrial Estate, Aberdeen, AB23 8EG Tel: (01224) 820909 Fax: (01224) 823123 E-mail: dave@cromar.com *Well service equipment manufrs*

Hunting Energy Services, Silverburn Place, Bridge of Don Industrial Estate, Aberdeen, AB23 8EG Tel: (01224) 820909 Fax: (01224) 823123 E-mail: cromar@cromar.com *Wire-line equipment manufrs*

Hunting Gate Wilshere Ltd, 2 Hunting Gate, Hitchin, Hertfordshire, SG4 0TJ Tel: (01462) 434444 Fax: (01462) 435905 E-mail: build@hunting-gate.co.uk *Property developers & investors*

▶ Hunting Oilfield Services International Ltd, Badentoy Avenue, Badentoy Industrial Estate Portlethen, Aberdeen, AB12 4SQ Tel: (01224) 787000 *Chemicals & metals suppliers*

Huntingdon Life Sciences, Occold, Eye, Suffolk, IP23 7PX Tel: (01480) 892000 Fax: (01379) 651165 E-mail: sales@ukorg.huntingdon.com *One of the World's foremost product development companies with 50 years of history and heritage. We work with a wide variety of products, including pharmaceuticals, agrochemicals, industrial chemicals, veterinary products, foods and flavourings, to help their manufacturers develop safer products for the market*

P. Huntington & Co. Engineering Ltd, 1 Millbrook Road, West Float Industrial Estate, Birkenhead, Merseyside, CH41 1FL Tel: 0151-637 0028 Fax: 0151-639 9919 *Precision & mechanical engineers*

Huntleigh Healthcare Ltd, 35 Portmanmoor Road Industrial Estate, East Moors, Cardiff, CF24 5HN Tel: (029) 2048 5885 Fax: (029) 2049 2520 E-mail: info@huntleigh-diagnostics.co.uk *Medical electronic equipment manufrs*

Huntleigh Healthcare Ltd, 310-312 Dallow Road, Luton, LU1 1TD Tel: (01582) 413104 Fax: (01582) 459100 E-mail: sales.admin@huntleigh-healthcare.com Principal Export Areas: Worldwide *Pressure area management equipment manufrs*

Huntleigh Nesbit Evans Ltd, Woodsbank Trading Estate, Woden Road West, Wednesbury, West Midlands, WS10 7BL Tel: 0121-556 1511 Fax: 0121-502 2092 E-mail: sales@huntcare.co.uk *Hospital beds & patient trolleys manufrs*

Huntleigh Renray, Huntleigh Renray Ltd, Road Five, Winsford Industrial Estate, Winsford, Cheshire, CW7 3RB Tel: (01606) 593456 Fax: (01606) 861354 E-mail: sales@renraydavidbaker.co.uk *Contract furniture & furnishing services*

Huntley Refrigeration & Air-Conditioning, 80 Broad Street, Coventry, CV6 5AZ Tel: (024) 7666 5252 Fax: (024) 7627 7102 E-mail: sales@huntleyrefrigeration.co.uk *Refrigeration & air conditioning services*

Hunton Ltd, Hilton Rd, Cobbs Wood Industrial Estate, Ashford, Kent, TN23 1EW Tel: (01233) 628976 Fax: (01233) 664909 E-mail: sales@mjallen.co.uk *Manufacturers of press tool punches,presses, hand actuated, die-set tools & grinding machines, punch & die*

Hunton Legg (Running Gear) Ltd, Bridge Works, Bruisyard, Saxmundham, Suffolk, IP17 2DT Tel: (01728) 663010 Fax: (01728) 664057 E-mail: sales@huntonlegg.co.uk *Agricultural trailer manufrs*

▶ Hunton - R M T - Gabro Machines, Cobbs Wood Industrial Estate, Hilton Road, Ashford, Kent, TN23 1EW Tel: (01233) 628976 Fax: (01233) 664909 E-mail: sales@mjallen.co.uk *Sheet metal machinery manufacture & sales.*

Huntrose UK Ltd, Jarman Way, Chard Business Park, Chard, Somerset, TA20 1FB Tel: (01460) 61895 Fax: (01460) 67088 E-mail: huntrose@lineone.net *Printed circuit board manufrs*

▶ Hunts, 62 Alston Drive, Bradwell Abbey, Milton Keynes, MK13 9HB Tel: (01908) 322080 Fax: (01908) 322070 E-mail: sales@huntselectrical.com *Industrial electrical distributors to industry*

Hunts Frozen Foods Bristol Ltd, Unit 3 Pucklechurch Trading Estate, Pucklechurch, Bristol, BS16 9QH Tel: 0117-937 2341 Fax: 0117-937 4160 E-mail: sales@hunts-food-service.co.uk *Frozen food products distributers*

Huntsman, Hitchen Lane, Shepton Mallet, Somerset, BA4 5TZ Tel: (01749) 335200 Fax: (01749) 344221 *Chemical manufrs*

Huntsman Tioxide, Haverton Hill Road, Billingham, Cleveland, TS23 1PS Tel: (01642) 370300 Fax: (01642) 370290 *Titanium tioxide producers*

Huntsman Tioxide, Greatham Works, Hartlepool, Cleveland, TS25 2DD Tel: (01642) 545200 Fax: (01642) 546016 E-mail: info@huntsmen.com *Titanium dioxide producers*

Huntsmans Quarries Ltd, The Old School, Naunton, Cheltenham, Gloucestershire, GL54 3AE Tel: (01451) 850555 Fax: (01451) 850670 E-mail: john.milner@huntsmanquarries.co.uk *Quarry operators*

Huntsworth, 15-17 Huntsworth Mews, London, NW1 6DD Tel: (020) 7402 2272 Fax: (020) 7706 4732 E-mail: info@huntsworth.com *Public relation services*

Huntsworth, 15-17 Huntsworth Mews, London, NW1 6DD Tel: (020) 7402 2272 Fax: (020) 7706 4732 *Public relations*

▶ Huramic Developments Ltd, Manor Mead, Manor Farm Lane, Oldbury, Bridgnorth, Shropshire, WV16 5HG Tel: (01746) 766948

Hurco Europe Ltd, Halifax Road, Cressex Business Park, High Wycombe, Buckinghamshire, HP12 3SN Tel: (01494) 442222 Fax: (01494) 443350 E-mail: sales@hurco.co.uk *Cnc machine tools suppliers*

Hurcombs Lace, Unit 38, Unity Road, Lowmoor Industrial Estate, Kirkby-In-Ashfield, Nottingham, NG17 7LE Tel: (01623) 722774 Fax: (01623) 723332 *Lace wholesalers & manufrs*

Hurley Engine Services Ltd, 7 The Maltings Industrial Estate, Brassmill Lane, Bath, BA1 3JL Tel: (01225) 336812 Fax: (01225) 442477 E-mail: sales@hurleyengines.co.uk *Automotive engine rebuilders industrial & reconditioned*

▶ Hurlston 4 Design, 31 Howard Drive, Tarleton, Preston, PR4 6DA Tel: (01772) 813547 Fax: (01772) 813539 E-mail: tim@h4d.co.uk *Graphic Design, Photography, Art Work, P.R. Marketing, Print Services.*

▶ Hurlstone & Champ Ltd, 95 High Street, Silverdale, Newcastle, Staffordshire, ST5 6LY Tel: (01782) 626575 Fax: (01782) 710950

Hurn Bridge Saddlery, Hurn Bridge Equestrian Centre, Hurn, Christchurch, Dorset, BH23 6AD Tel: (01202) 483931 *Saddlery distributors*

Hurn Waste Oil Ltd, 20 Winkham Business Park, Shaftesbury, Dorset, SP7 9QJ Tel: (01747) 858561 Fax: (01747) 858562 E-mail: oilwaterltd@hotmail.com Principal Export Areas: Worldwide *Industrial waste disposal & recovery contractors*

Hurricane Protective Clothing, Tame Valley Industrial Estate, Wilnecote, Tamworth, Staffordshire, B77 5DQ Tel: (01827) 250808 Fax: (01827) 250808 E-mail: hurricane@mgrubber.com *Protective clothing manufrs*

Hursley Emc Services Ltd, Unit 16 Brickfield Lane, Chandler's Ford, Eastleigh, Hampshire, SO53 4DP Tel: (023) 8027 1111 Fax: (023) 8027 1144 E-mail: sales@hursley-emc.co.uk *Emc testing services*

Hurst Blinds, Units 6 & 7, 49 Nuffield Industrial Estate, Poole, Dorset, BH17 0RR Tel: (01202) 683300 Fax: (01202) 683300 E-mail: sales@hurstblinds.co.uk *Blind manufrs*

Charles Hurst Group, 62 Boucher Road, Belfast, BT12 6LR Tel: (028) 9038 1721 Fax: (028) 9066 4688 *Motor vehicle repairers & dealers* Also at: Branches throughout Northern Ireland

▶ Hurst Environmental Solutions, 4 Heol Gwendoline, The Waterfront, Barry, South Glamorgan, CF62 5AN Tel: (0845) 0569687 Fax: (01446) 744862 E-mail: info@hurstsolutions.co.uk *Asbestos surveying & management*

G. Hurst & Sons Contractors Ltd, Hallcroft Industrial Estate, Aurillac Way, Retford, Nottinghamshire, DN22 7PX Tel: (01777) 702208 Fax: (01777) 709889 E-mail: mail@ghurstcontractors.co.uk *Building contractors*

Hurst Green Plastics Ltd, 1st Floor, Bowland House, The Sidings Business Park, Whalley, Clitheroe, Lancashire, BB7 9SE Tel: 01254 825588 Fax: 01254 824521 E-mail: info@hurstgreenplastics.com *Cereal dispensers, Juice and Milk dispensers, Catering equipment, fastener management systems, TwinBin.*

H. Hurst & Sons Contractors Ltd, Bolton's Mill, Bridge End, Waterfoot, Rossendale, Lancashire, BB4 7BY Tel: (01706) 214136 Fax: (01706) 214136 *Jute waste puller*

Hurst Interior Contracts Ltd, Hurst House, Fordcombe Road, Fordcombe, Tunbridge Wells, Kent, TN3 0RT Tel: (01892) 740586 Fax: (01892) 740660 *Office refurbishers*

Hurst Packaging Ltd, Unit 6, Cromwell Centre, Stepfield, Witham, Essex, CM8 3BZ Tel: (01376) 520642 Fax: (01376) 501757 E-mail: sales@hurstpackaging.co.uk *Contract packers & vacuum forming services*

Hurst Pierce & Malcolm, Celtic House, 33 Johns Mews, London, WC1N 2QL Tel: (020) 7242 3593 Fax: (020) 7405 5274 E-mail: hurstpm@globalnet.co.uk *Civil & structural engineers*

Hurst Plant Sales Ltd, Station Yard Station Road, Haxey Junction, Doncaster, South Yorkshire, DN9 2NL Tel: (01427) 753030 Fax: (01427) 752030 E-mail: sales@hurstplantsales.co.uk *Construction machinery merchants & sales*

▶ Hurst Plastics Ltd, 1 Kingston Int Business Park, Somerden Road, Hull, HU9 5PE Tel: (01482) 790790 Fax: (01482) 790690 E-mail: sales@hurst-plastics.co.uk *Door panel manufrs*

▶ Hurst Point Yacht Charters Ltd, Little Howdens, Rhinefield Close, Brockenhurst, Hampshire, SO42 7SU Tel: (01590) 623765 E-mail: info@hurstpointyachts.co.uk *Yacht charter, skippered and self hire (bareboat), corporate events and hospitality, team building, tuition, stag and hen parties, red letter days, mile building, sailing holidays, river cruises. *Modern well equipped yachts at various Solent bases. Good service and keen pricing.*

▶ Hurst (Transport) Ltd, Osborne Road, Stallingborough, Grimsby, South Humberside, DN41 8DG Tel: (01469) 577077

Hurst Warne Ltd, 323 Kingston Road, Leatherhead, Surrey, KT22 7TU Tel: (01372) 360190 Fax: (01372) 360211 E-mail: enquiries@hurstwarne.co.uk *Commercial property consultants & chartered surveyors*

Hurstmoor Ltd, 4 Castle Meadow, Sible Hedingham, Halstead, Essex, CO9 3PZ Tel: (01787) 463113 Fax: (01787) 462052 E-mail: sales@hurstmoor.co.ok *Laboratory & scientific goods exporters*

Hurstway Insulation Co. Ltd, Lawrence House, Transfesa Road, Paddock Wood, Tonbridge, Kent, TN12 6UT Tel: (01892) 838444 Fax: (01892) 833111 E-mail: hurstway@totalise.co.uk *Cold Room Manufacturer*

G.H. Hurt & Son Ltd, 65 High Road, Chilwell, Nottingham, NG9 4AJ Tel: 0115-925 4080 Fax: 0115-925 5904 *Lace knitwear manufrs*

Husbands Group Ltd, Shelah Road, Halesowen, West Midlands, B63 3PP Tel: 0121-550 1560 Fax: 0121-585 5285 E-mail: sales@servicelifts.co.uk *Service lift manufrs*

Husbands Lift Solutions, Shelah Road, Halesowen, West Midlands, B63 3PP Tel: 0121-550 1560 Fax: 0121-585 5285 E-mail: enquiries@husbands.co.uk

Husco International Ltd, 6 Rivington Road, Whitehouse Industrial Estate, Runcorn, Cheshire, WA7 3DT Tel: (01928) 701888 Fax: (01928) 710813 E-mail: uksales@huscointl.com *Valves & hydraulic equipment*

Hushon UK Ltd, A6 Railway Triangle, Walton Road, Drayton, Portsmouth, PO6 1TN Tel: (023) 9232 4335 Fax: (023) 9232 4348 E-mail: sales@hushonuk.co.uk *Air conditioning distributors*

Husqvarna Outdoor Products Ltd, Oldends Lane Industrial Estate, Stonedale Road, Stonehouse, Gloucestershire, GL10 3SY Tel: (01453) 820300 Fax: (01453) 826936 E-mail: info.husqvarna@husqvarna.co.uk *Forestry & garden machinery distribution*

Husqvarna Studio, 27 Charles Street, Bath, BA1 1HU Tel: (01225) 482413 Fax: (01225) 482420 E-mail: enquiries@husqvarnastudio.co.uk *Fabric retailers & sewing machine repair services*

Hussains Accountants, 38 Devonshire Street, Keighley, West Yorkshire, BD21 2AU Tel: (01535) 661700 Fax: (01535) 662664 E-mail: info@hussains.biz *Accountancy, Auditing, Taxation & Company Formations*

Hussey & Greaves Ltd, 94 Hutton Road, Shenfield, Brentwood, Essex, CM15 8ND Tel: (01277) 226262 Fax: (01277) 261287 E-mail: sales@husseyandgreaves.co.uk *Drawing & graphic equipment & suppliers* Also at: Chelmsford & Ipswich

Hussey & Greaves Ltd, 52 Moulsham Street, Chelmsford, CM2 0JA Tel: (01245) 268601 Fax: (01245) 491230 E-mail: chel@husseyandgreaves.co.uk *Computer system, stationery & fine art & reprographics*

Hussey & Greenhow Ltd, Unit 4 Hercules Way, Bowerhill, Melksham, Wiltshire, SN12 6TS Tel: (01225) 707888 Fax: (01225) 790523 E-mail: judy@husseygreenhow.co.uk *Contractors' plant, welding & machine hire services*

Hussey & Knights Ltd, 60 Bethel Street, Norwich, NR2 1NR Tel: (01603) 428110 Fax: (01603) 761032 E-mail: sales@hussey-knights.co.uk *Reprographic bureau*

L. Hussey & Sons Ltd, 29 Brissenden Close, Upnor, Rochester, Kent, ME2 4XW Tel: (01634) 295358 *Lightning conductors manufrs*

Hussey & Saunders Builders Merchants, Potkiln Lane, Jordans, Beaconsfield, Buckinghamshire, HP9 2XB Tel: (01494) 874116 Fax: (01494) 874685 E-mail: husseysaunders@aol.com *Builders' merchants*

▶ Husseys Bakeries Ltd, Ashford Hill, Thatcham, Berkshire, RG19 8BJ Tel: 0118-981 3663 Fax: 0118-981 0076 *Bakery*

Hussmann (Europe) Ltd, 4-5 Bonville Road, Brislington, Bristol, BS4 5NF Tel: 0117-971 2121 Fax: 0117-971 9098 *Air conditioning & refrigeration distributors & manufrs*

Hussmann Refrigeration Ltd, Clydeway Skypark, 8 Elliot Place, Glasgow, G3 8EP Tel: 0141-285 8500 Fax: 0141-227 2734 *Refrigeration distributors*

William Hustler & Sons Ltd, Henshaw Works, Henshaw Lane, Yeadon, Leeds, LS19 7RW Tel: 0113-250 3166 Fax: 0113-250 1272 *Steel fabricators*

▶ Hutch Hire Bouncy Castles, 11 Sunny Bank, Widmer End, High Wycombe, Buckinghamshire, HP15 6PA Tel: (01494) 716453 Fax: (0709) 2002053 E-mail: info@hutch-hire.co.uk *Bouncy Castle Hire*Various sizes*Indoor and Outdoor Use*Free Collection and Delivery*All Complete with rain Covers*Public Liability cover*

Hutchcoat Powder Coatings, Manor Farm, Ganthorpe, York, YO60 6QD Tel: (01653) 648436 Fax: (01653) 648436 *Powder coating services*

Hutcheon Services Ltd, Bowtree House, Minto Drive, Altens Industrial Estate, Aberdeen, AB12 3LW Tel: (01224) 874875 Fax: (01224) 895975 E-mail: info@hutcheon-services.ltd.uk *Electrical plumbing & heating engineers*

▶ Hutchesons Of Portsoy, 27 Seafield Terrace, Portsoy, Banff, AB45 2FB Tel: (01261) 842396 Fax: (01261) 843981

Hutchhouse Ltd, 20 Donnington Place, Childrey, Wantage, Oxfordshire, OX12 9YE Tel: (01235) 771917 E-mail: enquiries@hutchhouse.com *Web design & development, audio & video production*

Hutchings & Carter Ltd, The Avenue, Lasham, Alton, Hampshire, GU34 5SU Tel: (01256) 381338 Fax: (01256) 381876 E-mail: robert.white@hncltd.com *Civil engineer & plant hire*

Hutchings & Harding Group Ltd, 163 High Street, Sawston, Cambridge, CB22 3HN Tel: (01223) 832281 Fax: (01223) 836401 E-mail: sales@chamois.com *Leather manufrs*

▶ Hutchinson Demolition (Yorkshire) Ltd, Day St, Ravensthorpe, Dewsbury, West Yorkshire, WF13 3LJ Tel: (01924) 491616

Hutchinson Engineering Ltd, Hutchinson Street, Widnes, Cheshire, WA8 0PZ Tel: 0151-423 5850 Fax: 0151-495 1688 E-mail: enquiries@hutchinsonengineering.co.uk *Engineering contractors services*

J. Hutchinson (Fuels) Ltd, 74 Church Street, Leatherhead, Surrey, KT22 8EN Tel: (01372) 372084 Fax: (01372) 360188 *Fireplace & wood burning stoves suppliers*

J.T. Hutchinson, Baileywood Farm, Baileywood Lane, Holme-On-Spalding-Moor, York, YO43 4HH Tel: (01430) 860161 *Commercial vehicle repairers*

Mark Hutchinson Ltd, 105 Elliot Rise, Hedge End, Southampton, SO30 2RW Tel: (01489) 798723 E-mail: m.r.hutchinson@talk21.com *Electrical & instrumentation system design*

Hutchinson & Mudd, Tower Hill, Grewelthorpe, Ripon, North Yorkshire, HG4 3DS Tel: (01765) 658580 Fax: (01765) 658580 *Agricultural engineers*

George Hutchison Associates Ltd, 51 Brookfield Road, Cheadle, Cheshire, SK8 1ES Tel: 0161-491 4600 Fax: 0161-491 4700 E-mail: enquiries@stressstrain.com *Civil & structural engineers*

Huthwaite International, Hoober House, Hoober, Rotherham, South Yorkshire, S62 7SA Tel: (01709) 710081 Fax: (01709) 710065 E-mail: sales@huthwaite.co.uk *Sales training specialists*

The Hutson Motor Company Ltd, Pawson Street, Bradford, West Yorkshire, BD4 8DF Tel: (01274) 669052 Fax: (01274) 669685 E-mail: hutsonmc@talk21.com *Classic car components manufrs*

Hutsons Ltd, 65 Wide Bargate, Boston, Lincolnshire, PE21 6SG Tel: (01205) 362107 Fax: (01205) 358030 E-mail: signs@hutsons.ltd.co.uk *Sign making & cook shop*

A.J. Hutt & Co., Unit 18, Peerglow Industrial Estate, Olf Approach, Tolpits Lane, Watford, WD18 9SR Tel: (01923) 718777 Fax: (01923) 718933 *Wrought ironworkers*

Hutt Refrigeration, 11-13 Station Parade, Station Hill, Cookham, Maidenhead, Berkshire, SL6 9BR Tel: (01628) 530605 Fax: (01628) 530505 *Refrigeration & air conditioning services*

Huttenes Albertus UK Ltd, Blackbrook Road, Dudley, West Midlands, DY2 0QR Tel: (01384) 77377 Fax: (01384) 261519 E-mail: info@huttenes-albertus.co.uk *Foundry suppliers*

Hutton Construction Ltd, Birch Business Centre, Maldon Road, Birch, Colchester, CO2 0LT Tel: (01206) 330386 Fax: (01206) 331177 E-mail: colchester@hutton-group.co.uk *Building contractors services*

Hutton Construction Ltd, Alsa Business Park, Alsa Street, Stansted, Essex, CM24 8SQ Tel: (01279) 647333 Fax: (01279) 647380

Hutton Debt Recovery, 7 Atholl Crescent, Perth, PH1 5NG Tel: (01738) 639864 Fax: (01738) 630043 E-mail: dept@aahutton.co.uk *Debt recovery services* Also at: Dundee

Hutton Engineering (Precision) Ltd, 31 Wedgwood Road, Bicester, Oxfordshire, OX26 4UL Tel: (01869) 243933 Fax: (01869) 249869 E-mail: sales@hepltd.co.uk *CNC engineering services, machinists, precision machining servcies, high pessure water jet cutting services, turning services including centre lathe, & CNC, milling, engineering (CNC & 3D), drilling (CNC),machining (CNC), machinists (engineers) general machinery, machining/turning(metal) & engineers subcontract services. Also manufacturer of precision & CNC precision turned parts, machinists turned parts, machinists subcontract & engineers, general engine*

▶ Hutton Leisure Buildings Ltd, Hutton Garden Centre, Banwell Road, Hutton, Weston-super-Mare, Avon, BS24 9UB Tel: (01934) 822392 Fax: (01934) 822021 E-mail: mike@huttonconservetories.co.uk *New conservatories built*

▶ Hutton Mechanical & Electrical, 18 West Bank Road, Belfast, BT3 9JL Tel: (028) 9077 2888 Fax: (028) 9037 0322

▶ Hutton Premises Solutions, Station Road, Bagshot, Surrey, GU19 5AS Tel: (01276) 472400 Fax: (01276) 470996 E-mail: ben.hutton@virgin.net *Interiors, offices, electrics, plumbing, carpeting, etc*

Hutton & Co. (Ships Chandlers) Ltd, Connaught Road, Kingswood, Hull, HU7 3AP Tel: (01482) 329925 Fax: (01482) 580588 E-mail: sales@huttons-chandlers.com *Marine food suppliers*

Hutton & Co. (Ships Chandlers) Ltd, Connaught Road, Kingswood, Hull, HU7 3AP Tel: (01482) 329925 Fax: (01482) 580588 E-mail: sales@huttons-chandelers.com *Holding company* Also at: Middlesbrough

Hutton Textiles Supplies, Julian House, 32 Warkworth Drive, Chester le Street, County Durham, DH2 3JR Tel: 0191-388 7657 Fax: 0191-387 1450 *Suppliers of accessories for textiles*

Hutton Timber Products Ltd, Birch Business Centre, Maldon Road, Birch, Colchester, CO2 0LT Tel: (01206) 331450 Fax: (01206) 331581 E-mail: htp@globalnet.co.uk *Joinery manufrs*

▶ Huttons, 16 St. Andrews Crescent, Cardiff, CF10 3DD Tel: (029) 2037 8621 Fax: (029) 2038 8450 E-mail: nigel.hutton@huttons-solicitors.co.uk *Solicitors*

Huw R Thomas, 35 Commercial Street, Kenfig Hill, Bridgend, Mid Glamorgan, CF33 6DH Tel: (01656) 740391 Fax: (01656) 740391 *Saddlery & riding wear suppliers*

Huws Light & Sound, 2 Pisgah Street, Kenfig Hill, Bridgend, Mid Glamorgan, CF33 6BY Tel: (01656) 741414 Fax: (01656) 741414 *Discotheque equipment suppliers*

Huxley Bertram Engineering, Brookfield Business Centre, Twentypence Road, Cottenham, Cambridge, CB24 8PS Tel: (01954) 250809 Fax: (01954) 251991 E-mail: info@huxleybertram.com *Design, development & prototype engineers*

Huxley Print Ltd, Unit 1 12 John Street, Walsall, WS2 8AF Tel: (01922) 623691 Fax: (01922) 623206 E-mail: info@huxleyprint.co.uk *Commercial printing services*

Huyton Asphalt Ltd, Merton Bank Road, St. Helens, Merseyside, WA9 1HZ Tel: (01744) 755291 Fax: (01744) 451696 *Road surfacing contractors*

Huyton Heat Treatments Ltd, Unit 6 Brickfields, Liverpool, L36 6HY Tel: 0151-480 4135 Fax: 0151-480 7336 E-mail: sales@huyton-heat-treat.co.uk *Heat treatment services*

HVDS, Site B Hixon Industrial Estate, Church Lane, Hixon, Stafford, ST18 0PY Tel: (01889) 270079 Fax: (01889) 271616 *Manufacturers of air filtration equipment & filters including air, carton & gas turbine*

HVR International Ltd, Bede Trading Estate, Jarrow, Tyne & Wear, NE32 3EN Tel: 0191-489 7771 Fax: 0191-483 9501 E-mail: info@hvrint.com *High voltage, non-Inductive, linear ceramic carbon resistors suppliers*

HW Architectural Ltd, Birds Royd Lane, Birds Royd Lane, Brighouse, West Yorkshire, HD6 1NG Tel: (01484) 717677 Fax: (01484) 400148 E-mail: info@hwa.co.uk *Shop front manufrs*

HXF Fine Foods Ltd, Pidney, Hazelbury Bryan, Sturminster Newton, Dorset, DT10 2EB Tel: (01258) 817529 Fax: (01258) 817561 *Dairy produce & other food suppliers*

Hy Clad, Avonbridge, Falkirk, FK1 2LF Tel: (01324) 861307 Fax: (01324) 861307 *Vinyl decking & fencing products*

Hy Pro International, Arenson Centre, Arenson Way, Houghton Regis, Dunstable, Bedfordshire, LU5 5BN Tel: (01582) 670100 *Sporting equipment manufrs*

Hy Protec Health & Safety Ltd, Withambrook Park Industrial Estate, Grantham, Lincolnshire, NG31 9ST Tel: (01476) 573460 Fax: (01476) 563635 E-mail: paul@hy-protec.com *Safety clothing & equipment suppliers*

Hy Tec East London, 303 Higham Hill Road, London, E17 5RG Tel: (020) 8925 0400 Fax: (020) 8925 0411 E-mail: sales@hy-tec.co.uk *Cleaning contractors*

Hy Ten Welded Mesh Co., Dunstall Hill Industrial Estate, Gorsebrook Road, Wolverhampton, WV6 0PJ Tel: (01902) 712200 Fax: (01902) 714096 E-mail: sales@hy-tengabions.com *Gabion, suppliers, designers & manufrs*

Hyacinth, The Rickyard, Eashing Lane, Godalming, Surrey, GU7 2QA Tel: (01483) 417851 Fax: (01483) 417906 E-mail: sales@hyacinth.uk.com *Conservatory & garden furniture importers*

Hyatol Windows Ltd, 24 West Station Industrial Estate, Spital Road, Maldon, Essex, CM9 6EB Tel: (01621) 857685 Fax: (01621) 850971 *Aluminium windows manufrs*

▶ Hybrid Computers, 15 Rembrandt End, Aylesbury, Buckinghamshire, HP19 8SL Tel: (01296) 484888 E-mail: info@hybrid-computers.biz *The Home Visiting PC Repair Specialists.*

▶ Hybro Ltd, 50 Altys Lane, Ormskirk, Lancashire, L39 4RQ Tel: (01695) 581489 Fax: (01695) 572715 E-mail: Hybroltd@aol.com *We specialise in adaptations for disabled people*

Hyclone UK Ltd, 9 Atley Way, North Nelson Industrial Estate, Cramlington, Northumberland, NE23 1WA Tel: (01670) 734093 Fax: (01670) 732537 *Liquid cell culture media*

▶ Hyco Manufacturing Ltd, Units 1 & 2, Calder Works, Methley Road, Castleford, West Yorkshire, WF10 1NX Tel: (01977) 517555 Fax: (01977) 517666 E-mail: sales@hycomanufacturing.co.uk *Water heaters, hand dryers, water coolers, quartz heaters, convector heaters, electric flykillers*

Hycon Ltd, F Bridge Farm, Reading Road, Arborfield, Reading, RG2 9HT Tel: 0118-976 1616 Fax: 0118-976 1626 E-mail: hydroliccontrol@aol.com *Supplies & distributors hydraulic components*

Hydac Technology Ltd, Woodstock Road, Charlbury, Charlbury, Chipping Norton, Oxfordshire, OX7 3ES Tel: (01608) 811211 Fax: (01608) 811259 E-mail: info@hydac.co.uk *Fluid technology & hydraulic component manufrs*

▶ Hydair, Unit 5, Morley Business Centre, Morley Road, Tonbridge, Kent, TN9 1RA Tel: (01732) 773844

Hydar Fluid Power Ltd, Unit 20-21, Midsomer Enterprise Park, Radstock Road, Midsomer Norton, Radstock, BA3 2BB Tel: (01249) 651666 Fax: (01761) 414050 E-mail: carol@hydar.co.uk *Power packs & special system suppliers & manufrs*

Hyde Aero Products Ltd, Ashton Street, Dukinfield, Cheshire, SK16 4RR Tel: 0161-343 5844 Fax: 0161-343 5833 E-mail: enquiries@hydeaero.co.uk *Precision engineers*

Brian Hyde Ltd, Stirling Road, Shirley, Solihull, West Midlands, B90 4LZ Tel: 0121-705 7987 Fax: 0121-711 2465 E-mail: sales@brianhyde.co.uk *Hand tool importers & distribs*

Hyde Die Casting & Manufactring Ltd, 1 Providence Mill, Alexandra Street, Hyde, Cheshire, SK14 1DX Tel: 0161-368 0996 Fax: 0161-368 6022 E-mail: hydediecasting@aol.com *Pressure & pressure zinc die castings suppliers & manufrs*

▶ Hyde Electrical Services, 5-7 Outram Road, Dukinfield, Cheshire, SK16 4XE Tel: 0161-214 8160 Fax: 0161-214 8161

Hyde Group Ltd, Hadfield Street, Dukinfield, Cheshire, SK16 4QX Tel: 0161-308 2111 Fax: 0161-330 2680 E-mail: sales@hydetool.co.uk Principal Export Areas: Asia Pacific, Central Asia, Africa & North America *Precision engineers*

Hyde Group Ltd, Hadfield Street, Dukinfield, Cheshire, SK16 4QX Tel: 0161-308 2111 Fax: 0161-330 2680 E-mail: sales@hydetool.co.uk *Computer aided engineering services & recruitment agency*

K.W. Hyde Ltd, 16 Blackthorne Road, Canvey Island, Essex, SS8 7BJ Tel: (07970) 461172 Fax: (07970) 110690E-mail: kevin@kwhyde.com *Road safety & traffic engineering services*

Norman Hyde Ltd, Rigby Close, Heathcote Industrial Estate, Warwick, CV34 6TL Tel: (01926) 497375 Fax: (01926) 832352 E-mail: sales@normanhyde.co.uk *Motor cycle components suppliers & manufrs*

Hyde Park Riding Ltd, 63 Bathurst Mews, London, W2 2SB Tel: (020) 7706 8968 Fax: (020) 7823 4512 E-mail: info@hydeparkstables.com *Saddler & riding wear supplier*

▶ Hyde Park West Hotel, 25-26 Pembridge Square, Hyde Park, Bayswater, London, W2 4DR Tel: (020) 7229 3400 Fax: (020) 7229 5933 E-mail: info@majestic-london.co.uk *The Hyde Park West Hotel situated in a Historic London Square, within minutes of Royal Kensington Palace & Gardens, offers quality hotel rooms at very reasonable prices.*

Hyde Precision Components Ltd, Oldham Street, Denton, Manchester, M34 3SA Tel: 0161-337 9242 Fax: 0161-335 0787 E-mail: sales@hyde-precision.co.uk *Aircraft component manufrs*

Roger Hyde Ltd, 4 St. James Street, Castle Hedingham, Halstead, Essex, CO9 3EJ Tel: (01787) 463348 Fax: (01787) 461868 E-mail: info@rogerhyde.co.uk *Refurbish, install, maintenance services, floors, sports surfaces*

Hyde Transport, Pretoria Road, Chertsey, Surrey, KT16 9LW Tel: (01932) 567964 Fax: (01932) 567964 *General haulage & road transport services*

Hyde Windings Ltd, Westbury Street, Hyde, Cheshire, SK14 4QP Tel: 0161-368 1468 Fax: 0161-367 9454 *Electric motor maintenance*

Hyder Consulting Ltd, Wellington House, Market Street, Douglas, Isle of Man, IM1 2PQ Tel: (01624) 624694 Fax: (01624) 661760 *Engineering management consultants*

Hyder Consulting UK Ltd, 10 Medawar Road, Surrey Research Park, Guildford, Surrey, GU2 7AR Tel: (01483) 535000 Fax: (01483) 535051 *Engineering management consultants*

Hyder Consulting UK Ltd, 29 Pressenden Place, London, SW1E 5DZ Tel: (0870) 0003006 Fax: (0870) 0003906 E-mail: info@hyderconsulting.com *Consulting Design Engineers*

▶ Hyder Infrastructure Services, Wellhall Road, Hamilton, Lanarkshire, ML3 9BZ Tel: (01698) 422588

Hyders 1994 Ltd, Landway House, Basted Lane, Borough Green, Sevenoaks, Kent, TN15 8PY Tel: (01732) 886988 Fax: (01732) 886988 *Wrought iron*

Hydestile Joinery, Hambledon Road, Hydestile, Godalming, Surrey, GU8 4DE Tel: (01483) 420006 Fax: (01483) 416869 *Purpose made joiners*

▶ Hydewood Ltd, 149 Lea Industrial Estate, Lower Luton Road, Harpenden, Hertfordshire, AL5 5EQ Tel: (01582) 460546 Fax: (01582) 766527 *Wooden furniture component manufrs*

Hydo Aluminium U K, Unit 4 Newton Court Westrand, Pendeford Business Park, Wolverhampton, WV9 5HB Tel: (01902) 396630 Fax: (01902) 396640 E-mail: sales@hydro-aluminium.com *Aluminium rolled products manufrs*

Hydor Ltd, Unit 8, Parkers Close, Downton Industrial Estate, Salisbury, SP5 3RB Tel: (01725) 511422 Fax: (01725) 512637 E-mail: info@hydor.co.uk *Manufacturers of horticultural, agricultural & industrial equipment*

Hydra P.L.C., 145 Cannon Street, London, EC4N 5BQ Tel: (020) 7337 2777 Fax: (020) 7337 2772 E-mail: sales@hydranet.co.uk *Network systems integrator*

Hydra Myst Services, 166 Clifton Road, Aberdeen, AB24 4HA Tel: (01224) 491825 Fax: (01224) 488616 *Supplying & servicing industrial floor care equipment, we can now offer an extensive supply of pigeon products i.e. Bucktons food & Harker & Gem products.*

▶ Hydra Technologies Ltd, Unit 3 Queensway Business Centre, 4 The Queensway, Fforestfach, Swansea, SA5 4DT Tel: (01792) 586800 Fax: (01792) 561606 *Chemical manufrs*

Hydraclamp, Unit 2, Burnsall Road Industrial Estate, Burnsall Road, Coventry, CV5 6BU Tel: (024) 7667 4646 Fax: (024) 7671 2742 E-mail: steadkm@aol.com Principal Export Areas: Worldwide *We develop and manufacture systems and products in the field of Hydraulic Bolt Tensioners, Hydraulic Nuts and accessories thereof and various Hydraulic High Pressure Tools, Hydraulic High Pressure Generators and Control Units. Please quote "kellysearch" when making your enquiry*

Hydrafeed Ltd, Talgarth House, Bond Avenue, Bletchley, Milton Keynes, MK1 1JD Tel: (01908) 376630 Fax: (01908) 647843 E-mail: info@hydrafeed.co.uk *Bar feed manufacturers & machine tool accessories manufacturers*

Hydrafit Ltd, 40 Brighton Street, Coventry, CV2 4JH Tel: (024) 7645 6621 Fax: (024) 7644 5256 *Hydraulic components fittings manufacturers & distributors*

Hydrafit Ltd, Walsall Street, Wolverhampton, WV1 3LN Tel: (01902) 451172 Fax: (01902) 450804 E-mail: hydrafit@btinternet.com *Hose couplings, hydraulic components & fittings manufrs*

Hydrafit Hydraulic Equipment, 4 Sanderson Street, Sheffield, S9 2TW Tel: 0114-244 6721 Fax: 0114-243 5969 *Hydraulic components & fittings distributors manufrs*

Hydraflow Hydraulics (UK) Ltd, Unit 1, Price Street, Bristol Road, Gloucester, GL1 5SZ Tel: (01452) 387061 Fax: (01452) 381332 *Hydraulic ram engineers & manufrs*

Hydraflow Systems, Strathfield House, Smithymoor, Stretton, Alfreton, Derbyshire, DE55 6FE Tel: 01246 250958 Fax: 05600 492268 E-mail: sales@hydraflowsystems.co.uk *Hydraulic power pack, equipment & systems manufrs*

Hydrainer Pumps Ltd, Bedgrave Close, Norwood Industrial Estate, Killamarsh, Sheffield, S21 2HB Tel: 0114-248 4868 Fax: 0114-251 0136 E-mail: info@hydrainer-pumps-ltd.co.uk

continued

Company Information

continuation
Hydraulic, electrical submersible pump distributors & manufrs

Hydrair Ltd, Berry Hill, Berry Hill Industrial Estate, Droitwich, Worcestershire, WR9 9AB Tel: (01905) 772302 Fax: (01905) 770309 E-mail: name@hydrair.demom.co.uk *Pump & container manufrs*

Hydralube Ltd, 72A Parker Road, Hastings, East Sussex, TN34 3TT Tel: (01424) 465527 Fax: (01424) 201363 E-mail: sales@hydralube.co.uk *Advanced lubricants*

Hydram Engineering Ltd, Avenue Two, Chilton Industrial Estate, Chilton, Ferryhill, County Durham, DL17 0SG Tel: (01388) 720222 Fax: (01388) 721025 E-mail: hydram@hydram.co.uk *Sheet metalworkers & light engineers*

Hydramaster, The Chapel, Treskillard, Redruth, Cornwall, TR16 6JY Tel: 01209 710335 Fax: 01209 714050 *Import & distribution of carpet cleaners*

▶ Hydramatic Source & Supply Ltd, Unit 4 Oakes Green Court, Oakes Green, Sheffield, S9 3WR Tel: 0114-261 0667 Fax: 0114-261 9671 E-mail: chris@hsslimited.co.uk *Suppliers of hydraulic & pneumatic equipment*

Hydramatic Source & Supply Ltd, Unit 4 Oakes Green Court, Oakes Green, Sheffield, S9 3WR Tel: 0114-261 0667 Fax: 0114-261 9671 E-mail: sales@hsslimited.co.uk *Industrial retail*

Hydramatics Ltd, Unit 2b The Quantum, Marshfield Bank Industrial Estate, Crewe, CW2 8UY Tel: (01270) 584348 Fax: (01270) 584348 E-mail: hydramatics@aol.com *Hydraulic equipment distributors*

Hydramec Ltd, Haverscroft Industrial Estate, New Road, Attleborough, Norfolk, NR17 1YE Tel: (01953) 458500 Fax: (01953) 458509 E-mail: mail@hydramec.co.uk *Test systems designers*

Hydramotion Ltd, Unit 1a, York Road Business Park, Malton, North Yorkshire, YO17 6YA Tel: (01653) 600294 Fax: (01653) 693446 E-mail: sales@hydramotion.com *Designers & manufacturers of portable & process viscometers*

Hydrapower Ltd, Middlemore Lane, Aldridge, Walsall, WS9 8SP Tel: (01922) 458760 Fax: (01922) 743186 *Stainless steel fabricators*

HYDRAQUIP, Unit 7, Oakhurst Business Park, Wilberforce Way, Southwater, Horsham, West Sussex, RH13 9RT Tel: (01403) 731322 Fax: (01403) 730276 E-mail: salmons@hydraquip.co.uk *Valve, tube & fitting distributors*

Hydraquip Hose, Head Office, 2 Raleigh Court, Crawley, West Sussex, RH10 9PD Tel: (01293) 615166 Fax: (01293) 614965 E-mail: sales@hydraquip.co.uk *Manufacturers of hoses*

Hydrassist Ltd, Unit 15 Fordhouse Road Industrial Estate, Steel Drive, Wolverhampton, WV10 9XB Tel: (01902) 787000 Fax: (01902) 397963 *Actuators-hydraulic & hydraulic equipment manufrs*

Hydrastore Ltd, Sandtoft Industrial Estate, Belton, Doncaster, South Yorkshire, DN9 1PN Tel: (01427) 874445 Fax: (01427) 874436 E-mail: sales@hydrastore.co.uk *Hydrastore Ltd based in Doncaster, South Yorkshire offer hydraulic components & systems. They design, supply, install and commission complete solutions for mobile and industrial applications.*

Hydrasun Ltd, Hydrasun House, 392 King Street, Aberdeen, AB24 3BU Tel: (01224) 618618 Fax: (01224) 618701 E-mail: info@hydrasun.com Sales Contact: C. Sangster *Hydraulic hose & hose fitting distributors or agents. Also distributors of the following:- air filtration equipment, bellows, compression fittings, copper tube fittings, filters, fire hoses, flanges, flexible tubing/hose/conduit, gauges, hose assembly hose/clip/clamps, hydraulic hoses (flexible), hydraulic tubing, hydraulic components/fittings, instrumentation equipment (pneumatic/hydraulic), oilfield equipment, pipe clamps, plastic hoses, pneumatic tube/tubing couplings/fittings, rig equipment, rubber hoses, semi-conductor components & stainless steel tube fittings. In addition, manufacturers of couplings (quick release & tube), filters (hydraulic & stainless steel), flexible metallic hose/tubing, blow out preventer hoses, hose assembly, hose couplings (high pressure/quick release), hose fittings (stainless steel), hydraulic hose flexible assemblies, umbilicals, hydraulic components/ fittings, hydraulic tube/tubing couplings/fittings (fire safe & rigid), plastic extrusion, polyurethane extrusion & steel tubes (cold drawn seamless). Stockholders of alloy steel, nickel alloy tube, tube fittings & valves. Hose assembly & hose fitting assembly services.* Also at: Edinburgh, Elgin, Glasgow & Inverness

Hydrasun Ltd, 61h Lord Avenue, Thornaby, Stockton-on-Tees, Cleveland, TS17 9JX Tel: (01642) 750405 Fax: (01642) 750704 *Instrumentation suppliers & distributors*

▶ Hydrasun (Dundee) Ltd, Unit 1, Slessor Court, Claverhouse Industrial Park, Dundee, DD4 9UA Tel: (01382) 505400 Fax: (01382) 503503 *Hydraulic Hose Fitters*

▶ Hydratec Lift Services Ltd, 1b Business Village, Blackbushe Business Park, Yateley, Hampshire, GU46 6GA Tel: (01252) 871664 Fax: (01252) 873601 E-mail: sales@hydratec-lifts.co.uk *Lift engineers*

Hydratech CoolFlow Specialist Antifreeze, Units 3 & 4 Queensway Business Centre, The Queensway, Fforestfach, Swansea, SA5 4DT Tel: (01792) 586800 Fax: (01792) 561606 E-mail: sales@hydratech.co.uk *Specialist glycol antifreeze for chilled water and HVAC systems. CoolFlow FG is USP propylene glycol with food-grade corrosion and scale inhibitors. CoolFlow IG is ethylene glycol with corrosion, scale and biological inhibitors.*

Hydratorc Pneumatic Systems, Unit 11 Bedwas House Industrial Estate, Bedwas, Caerphilly, Mid Glamorgan, CF83 8DW Tel: (029) 2088 8883 Fax: (029) 2086 0004 E-mail: appliedtorque@aol.com *Hydraulic & pneumatic talk equipment*

▶ Hydraulic Actuators & Controls, Minekeep House, Bridge Road, Camberley, Surrey, GU15 2QZ Tel: (01276) 24914 Fax: (01276) 683332 E-mail: sales@hacltd.co.uk *Hydraulic Actuators & Controls, based in Surrey, design and manufacture ancillary hydraulic valves and electronic controls for hydraulic actuators and systems.*

▶ Hydraulic Alliance Ltd, 80 Allaston Road, Lydney, Gloucestershire, GL15 4EZ Tel: (01594) 843322 Fax: (01594) 843322 E-mail: sales@hydraulicalliance.com *Suppliers of bosch racine*

Hydraulic Analysis Ltd, Mill House, Hawksworth Road, Horsforth, Leeds, LS18 4JP Tel: 0113-258 1622 Fax: 0113-259 0863 E-mail: sales@hydraulic-analysis.com *Fluid flow consultants*

Hydraulic Components & Systems Ltd, Unit 14 Sovereign Park, Cleveland Way, Hemel Hempstead, Hertfordshire, HP2 7DA Tel: (01442) 240202 Fax: (01442) 243133 E-mail: hydcompdrf@hotmail.com *Hydraulics distributor*

Hydraulic Crane Services, Uplands Farm, Highstreet Road, Hernhill, Faversham, Kent, ME13 9EJ Tel: (01227) 751588 Fax: (01227) 751458 E-mail: hydecraneserv@aol.com *Maintenance & repair of hydraulic equipment*

▶ Hydraulic & Engineering Services Ltd, Unit 5-6 Victory Park, Trident Close, Medway City Estate, Rochester, Kent, ME2 4ER Tel: (01634) 295650 Fax: (01634) 295670 E-mail: info@hydraulicengineering.co.uk Purchasing Contact: S. Matthews *The company's aim is to supply a quality service to meet the customers needs. We operate a quality system manual based on ISO 9002 requirements. Our quality assurance manual is available for your inspection. We are happy to submit quotations for specific customer drawings or to provide a complete design, manufacture, supply, install and commission service to customer requirements.*

Hydraulic Engineering Services, 5 Station Yard, Swaffham, Norfolk, PE37 7JE Tel: (01760) 722296 Fax: (01760) 722296 *Repair & supply of hydraulic components*

Hydraulic Equipment Supermarkets Ltd, 424 Bromford Lane, Washwood Heath, Birmingham, B8 2RX Tel: 0121-327 2664 Fax: 0121-322 2488 E-mail: birmingham@dowco.co.uk *Suppliers of hydraulic equipment*

Hydraulic Equipment Supermarkets Ltd, 7a Drum Industrial Estate, Drum Industrial Estate, Chester le Street, County Durham, DH2 1AG Tel: 0191-410 6619 Fax: 0191-411 1055 E-mail: durham@dowco.co.uk *Hydraulic equipment suppliers*

Hydraulic Equipment Supermarkets Ltd, J Innsworth Technology Park, Innsworth Lane, Gloucester, GL3 1DL Tel: (01452) 730774 Fax: (01452) 731637 E-mail: sales@dowco.co.uk *Hydraulic equipment distributors*

Hydraulic Equipment Supermarkets Ltd, 7 Glover Way, Leeds, LS11 5JP Tel: 0113-270 3213 Fax: 0113-270 3213 E-mail: leeds@grouphes.com *Suppliers of hydraulic equipment*

Hydraulic Equipment Supply Co. Ltd, 419 New Kings Road, London, SW6 4RN Tel: (020) 7736 7391 Fax: (020) 7736 7019 *Hose assemblies, hydraulic*

Hydraulic Equipment Supply Co. Ltd, 67 Victoria Road, Worthing, West Sussex, BN11 1UN Tel: (01903) 203154 Fax: (01903) 236147 *Hydraulic hose & equipment suppliers*

Hydraulic & Gas Services Ltd, Unit 4a Ford Street, Stockport, Cheshire, SK3 0BT Tel: 0161-480 9966 Fax: 0161-480 9922 E-mail: sales@hgservicesltd.co.uk *Supply & distribute pipes & tubing*

Hydraulic Pipework Services, 4 Smallbridge Industrial Park, Riverside Drive, Rochdale, Lancashire, OL16 2SH Tel: (01706) 345670 Fax: (01706) 641112 *Hydraulic components distributors*

Hydraulic & Pneumatic Cylinders Ltd, 4 Birmingham New Enterprise Workshops, All Saints Road, Birmingham, B18 7RL Tel: 0121-523 8400 Fax: 0121-523 8400 E-mail: sales@hydraulic-pneumatic-cylinders.co.uk *Hydraulic & pneumatic cylinder manufacturers & repairers*

Hydraulic & Pneumatic Power Services, Methilhaven Road, Methil, Leven, Fife, KY8 3LA Tel: (01333) 429690 Fax: (01333) 422952 E-mail: info@fcegroup.com *Hydraulic cylinder ram manufrs*

Hydraulic Pneumatic Services, Unit 3b King Street Trading Estate, Middlewich, Cheshire, CW10 9LF Tel: (01606) 835725 Fax: (01606) 737358 E-mail: kinfo@madan.uk.com *Pump manufrs*

Hydraulic Pneumatic Services, Unit 23-24 The Old Mill, School Lane, Bamber Bridge, Preston, PR5 6SY Tel: (01772) 629993 Fax: (01772) 629995 E-mail: info@hps-group.co.uk *Hose manufrs*

Hydraulic & Pneumatic Supplies Ltd, Unit 39, Second Drove Industrial Estate, Fengate, Peterborough, PE1 5XA Tel: (01733) 894500 Fax: (01733) 894892 E-mail: sales@hps-ltd.co.uk *Hydraulic & pneumatic distributors or agents*

▶ Hydraulic Power Services Ltd, 84 Bridgeman Street, Bolton, BL3 6AT Tel: (01204) 363660 Fax: (01204) 363670 E-mail: info@hydraulicpower.co.uk *Since 1988, we have been providing specialist hydraulic engineering services to OEM and after-market customers. Hydraulic Power Services have established an excellent reputation with our customers for unrivalled technical support and service backup. Our repair and test facility is the hub of our technical service operation. We have accumulated a wealth of experience in a wide range of industrial hydraulic systems, from simple presses to multi-axis servo controlled stretch forming machines. Our experienced engineers are capable of troubleshooting the most complex of system and are on standby for emergency situations whenever they arise. Our* *continued* *service vehicles are fully equipped and carry the latest diagnostic and off-line filtration equipment enabling us to monitor and evaluate system and pump performance on site.*

Hydraulic Pressure Services Ltd, 289 Elland Road, Leeds, LS11 8AX Tel: 0113-271 1310 Fax: 0113-270 0254 E-mail: hps.leedsonline@absonline.net *Hydraulics*

Hydraulic Project Ltd, Shutterton Industrial Estate, Dawlish, Devon, EX7 0NH Tel: (01626) 863634 Fax: (01626) 866283E-mail: sales@hypro.co.uk *Hydraulic valve manufrs*

▶ Hydraulic Ram, Mayday House, 2 Mossland Road, Hillington Industrial Estate, Glasgow, G52 4XZ Tel: 0141-882 4724 Fax: 0141-883 3350 *Hydraulic cylinder or ram maintenance or repair*

Hydraulic Spares Centre Ltd, Unit 18 Pilot Industrial Estate, Manchester Road, Bolton, BL3 2ND Tel: (01204) 388233 Fax: (01204) 383037 E-mail: hydsc.ltd@tiscali.co.uk *Hydraulic equipment sales & service*

Hydraulic Supplies Ltd, Unit 5-6 Block 2, Wednesbury Trading Estate, Wednesbury, West Midlands, WS10 7JN Tel: 0121-505 3663 Fax: 0121-505 3375 E-mail: sales@hydraulicsupplies.co.uk *Chrome bar stockholders*

Hydraulic System Products Ltd, Monckton Road, Wakefield, West Yorkshire, WF2 7AL Tel: (01924) 364748 Fax: (01924) 290450 E-mail: sales@h-s-p.co.uk Principal Export Areas: Africa *Hydraulic components, fittings, valves & test equipment manufrs*

Hydraulic Technical Services Ltd, 10-12 Galleymead Road, Colnbrook, Slough, SL3 0EN Tel: (01753) 689689 Fax: (01753) 689700 E-mail: info@hydraulictechnical.co.uk *Hydraulic engineers*

Hydraulic Transmission Services Ltd, Whitehall Road, Leeds, LS12 5JB Tel: 0113-279 3017 Fax: 0113-279 5505 E-mail: hts@btinternet.com *Hydraulic equipment & hoses manufrs*

Hydrax Ltd, Wylds Road, Bridgwater, Somerset, TA6 4BH Tel: (01278) 727600 Fax: (01278) 727601 E-mail: info@hydrax.co.uk *Hydraulic lift components & turnkey hydraulic systems manufrs*

Hydrema Plant & Machinery Dealer, Barker Business Park, Melmerby Green Lane, Melmerby, Ripon, North Yorkshire, HG4 5NB Tel: (01765) 641940 Fax: (01765) 641942 E-mail: twa@hydrema.com *Articulated dumprtuck sales and service*

Hydrex Equipment UK Ltd, Peartree Lane, Dudley, West Midlands, DY2 0UX Tel: (01384) 256600 Fax: (01384) 256200 *HYDREX Limited is a UK market leader in the provision of tailored solutions to customers operating in the UK rail and materials handling industries. Services typically include specifying and supplying mobile plant, providing trained operators with the necessary licenses, maintaining the equipment through a national depot network, and ensuring compliance with all health and safety matters.*

Hydrex Equipment UK Ltd, Duntilland Road, Salsburgh, Shotts, Lanarkshire, ML7 4NZ Tel: (0870) 3501350 Fax: (01698) 871350 E-mail: vincentscott-halton@hydrex.co.uk *HYDREX Limited is a UK market leader in the provision of tailored solutions to customers operating in the UK rail and materials handling industries. Services typically include specifying and supplying mobile plant, providing trained operators with the necessary licenses, maintaining the equipment through a national depot network, and ensuring compliance with all health and safety matters.*

Hydro 2000 Whirlpools, Avondale Way, Wakefield, West Yorkshire, WF2 7QU Tel: (01924) 387444 Fax: (01924) 387444 *Bathroom accessory distributors*

Hydro Aluminium Deeside Ltd, Bridge Road, Wrexham Industrial Estate, Wrexham, Clwyd, LL13 9PS Tel: (01978) 660231 Fax: (01978) 661125 E-mail: hydro.deeside@hydro.com *Aluminium billet manufrs*

Hydro Aluminium Extrusion Ltd, Pantglas Industrial Estate, Bedwas, Caerphilly, Mid Glamorgan, CF83 8DR Tel: (029) 2085 4600 Fax: (029) 2086 3728 E-mail: haeuk@hydro.com *One of the world's leading suppliers of light metals, Hydro Aluminium sells almost 3 million metric tonnes of aluminium a year. The company has the experience & expertise to meet a whole host of aluminium extrusion requirements. From extensive design facilities through to manufacturing, finishing & fabricating, Hydro Aluminium has the complete capability.*

Hydro Aluminium Extrusion, Durham Road, Birtley, Chester le Street, County Durham, DH3 2AH Tel: 0191-301 1200 Fax: 0191-301 1234 E-mail: sales@hydro.com *One of the world's leading suppliers of light metals, Hydro Aluminium sells almost 3 million metric tonnes of aluminium a year. The company has the experience & expertise to meet a whole host of aluminium extrusion requirements. From extensive design facilities through to manufacturing, finishing & fabricating, Hydro Aluminium has the complete capability.*

Hydro Automotive Structures, Williamson Road, Worcester, WR5 1SG Tel: (01905) 363700 Fax: (01905) 363715 E-mail: Alan.Blizzard@Hydro.com *Automotive aluminium components*

▶ Hydro Bond Engineering Ltd, 2b Woodside Road, Bridge of Don Industrial Estate, Aberdeen, AB23 8EF Tel: (01224) 822996 Fax: (01224) 825142 E-mail: sales@hydrohouse.co.uk *Underwater connectors manufrs*

Hydro Chem UK, 112 Broad Street, Coventry, CV6 5AZ Tel: (024) 7666 6482 Fax: (024) 7663 8472 E-mail: sales@hydro-chem.co.uk *Water treatment service*

Hydro Dynamic Products Ltd, Unit 2-3, Harbour Way, Shoreham-by-Sea, West Sussex, BN43 5HZ Tel: (01273) 464881 Fax: (01273) 464626 E-mail: sales@hdp.co.uk *Press room chemical manufrs*

▶ Hydro Dynamix, 46 Langham Road, Standish, Wigan, Lancashire, WN6 0TF Tel: (01257) 424555 E-mail: info@hydro-dynamix.com *Advanced carpet & upholstery cleaning - carpets dry in 1 hour. Specialists in cream/white carpets, spot removal,rugs, hard floors and leather suites. Flood experts recommended by Insurance Companies and fully insured for your peace of mind.*

Hydro Mechanical Services Ltd, Unit 1-2 17 Reddicap Trading Estate, Sutton Coldfield, West Midlands, B75 7BU Tel: 0121-378 4000 Fax: 0121-311 1523 E-mail: mailbox@hydrogroup.co.uk *Heating & ventilation control installation services*

Hydro Pneumatic Services, Bastion House, Harlequin Avenue, Brentford, Middlesex, TW8 9EW Tel: (020) 8560 4968 Fax: (020) 8560 4958 *Filter distributors & agents*

Hydro Polymers Ltd, Aycliffe Industrial Park, Newton Aycliffe, County Durham, DL5 6EA Tel: (01325) 300555 Fax: (01325) 300215 *PVC resins & compounds manufrs*

Hydro Project Engineering, Sutton Lane, Etwall, Derby, DE65 6LQ Tel: (01283) 730073 *Suppliers & installers of high pressured pumps*

Hydro Pumps Ltd, 19 High Mead, Fareham, Hampshire, PO15 6BL Tel: (01329) 823420 Fax: (01329) 823425 E-mail: sales@hydro-pumps.co.uk *Hydro demolition work*

Hydro Static Extrusions Ltd, Arran Road, North Muirton Industrial Estate, Perth, PH1 3DX Tel: (01738) 629381 Fax: (01738) 633933 E-mail: sales@hydrostatic.co.uk *Aluminium extrusion services*

Hydroclean, 54 Fendale Park, Cullybackey, Ballymena, County Antrim, BT43 5PU Tel: (028) 25881348 Fax: (028) 25881348 E-mail: h_ydroclean@msn.com *External cleaning contractors*

Hydrocut Ltd, PO Box 2926, Colchester, CO6 2QP Tel: (01787) 222266 Fax: (01787) 222210 E-mail: sales@hydrocut.co.uk *Forestry machine manufrs*

Hydroelectic (UK) Ltd, 3 High Road, Byfleet, West Byfleet, Surrey, KT14 7QE Tel: (01932) 334210 Fax: (01932) 334211 E-mail: sales@qualflex.demon.co.uk *Hose assembly manufrs*

Hydroflow Europe Ltd, Gillmans Industrial Estate, Billingshurst, West Sussex, RH14 9EZ Tel: (01403) 783741 Fax: (01403) 784442 E-mail: hydroflowe@aol.com *Filtration equipment*

Hydrokem Aerosols Ltd, Hickmans Road, Birkenhead, Merseyside, CH41 1JH Tel: 0151-630 4414 Fax: 0151-638 2353 E-mail: sales@hydrokem.co.uk *Aerosol filling & contract packaging*

Hydroklear Services Ltd, 50 Linister Crescent, Howwood, Johnstone, Renfrewshire, PA9 1DS Tel: (01505) 704111 Fax: (01505) 706500 E-mail: sales@hydroklear.co.uk *Water & effluent treatment*

Hydromarque Ltd, 21 Stapledon Road, Orton Southgate, Peterborough, PE2 6TD Tel: (01733) 370545 Fax: (01733) 361249 E-mail: mail@hydromarque.com *Pump distributors*

Hydropac Ltd, Unit 76, Lincoln Road, Cressex Business Park, High Wycombe, Bucks, HP12 3RH Tel: (01494) 530182 Fax: (01494) 538539 E-mail: sales@hydropac.co.uk *Cooling products*

Hydropath UK Ltd, Acorn Park, Lenton Lane Industrial Estate, Nottingham, NG7 2TR Tel: 0115-986 9966 Fax: 0115-986 9944 E-mail: sales@hydroflow.com *Water treatment plant & equipment designers & manufrs*

Hydroplan Interior Landscapes Ltd, Cassidy Court, Kansas Avenue, Salford, M50 2QW Tel: 0161-873 7349 Fax: 0161-872 0254 E-mail: hdryoplanltd@aol.com *Floral, plant displays & interior landscape services*

Hydropure Water Suppliers, 5h Lynwell Road, Lyntown Trading Estate, Eccles, Manchester, M30 9QG Tel: 0161-786 7600 Fax: 0161-786 7608 *Steel fabricators*

▶ Hydrorod Drainage Services, 48 Birchy Barton Hill, Exeter, EX1 3EX Tel: (01392) 498899 Fax: (01392) 498877 E-mail: mail@hydrorod.com *Drainage & pumping services large stock of spares, skilled engineers & fully equipped vehicles to solve any problem on or off site*

▶ Hydrosave Water Engineers, Swallow Court, Kettering Parkway, Kettering, Northamptonshire, NN15 6XX Tel: (01536) 515110 Fax: (01536) 515119 E-mail: sales@hydrosave.co.uk *Water management consultants & water leakage contractors*

▶ Hydrosense Scientific Apparatus, Unit 1-2 Braehead Business Units, Braehead Road, Linlithgow, West Lothian, EH49 6EP Tel: (01506) 840888 Fax: (01506) 840777

Hydroserve Sewage Disposal, Kingsley House, Ganders Park, Kingsley, Bordon, Hampshire, GU35 9LU Tel: (01420) 470800 Fax: (01420) 470820 E-mail: enquiries@conderproducts.com *Sewage tank servicing*

Hydrosphere UK Ltd, Units C & D, Westend Centre, Colt House Lane, Upper Froyle, Alton, Hampshire, GU34 4JR Tel: (01420) 520374 Fax: (01420) 520373 E-mail: sales@hydrosphere.co.uk *Suppliers of navigational aides*

Hydrostal Ltd, 4-5 The Galloway Centre, Newbury, Berkshire, RG14 5TL Tel: (01635) 550440 Fax: (01635) 550140 E-mail: sales@hidrostal.co.uk *Municipal & industrial solids handling pumps*

Hydrotec UK Ltd, 5 Manor Courtyard, Hughenden Avenue, High Wycombe, Buckinghamshire, HP13 5RE Tel: (01494) 796040 Fax: (01494) 796049 E-mail: sales@hydrotec.co.uk *Water treatment equipment & services*

Hydrotechnik UK Ltd, Unit 10, Easter Park, Lenton Lane, Nottingham, NG7 2PX Tel: 0115-900 3550 Fax: 0115-970 5597 E-mail: sales@hydrotechnik.co.uk *Engineering distribution*

Hydrovern Ltd, Unit 21, Wilden Industrial Estate, Wilden Lane, Stourport-On-Severn, Worcestershire, DY13 9JY Tel: (0870) 7706222 Fax: (0870) 7706223 E-mail: info@hydrovern.co.uk *Injection moulding & plastic manufrs*

Hydroweld Divers, 46 Bedford Drive, Sutton Coldfield, West Midlands, B75 6AX Tel: 0121-378 1230 Fax: 0121-378 1281 E-mail: info@hydroweld.com *Underwater welding equipment & services*

Hydro-X Water Treatment Ltd, Unit 3a Eden Place, Outgang Lane Dinnington, Dinnington, Sheffield, S25 3QT Tel: (01909) 565133 Fax: (01909) 564301 E-mail: office@hydro-x.co.uk *Treatment plant manufrs*

Hyflex Roofing, Halfords Lane, Smethwick, West Midlands, B66 1BJ Tel: 0121-555 6464 Fax: 0121-555 5862 E-mail: smethwick@hyflex.co.uk *Roofing contractors*

Hygenitec Disposables Ltd, Units G7 & 9, Blackpole Trading Estate East, Worcester, WR3 8SG Tel: (01905) 755535 Fax: (01905) 755705 *Cleaning & janitorial suppliers*

Hygenitec Disposables, Unit G7/9, Blackpole Trading Estate East, Worcester, WR3 8SG Tel: (01905) 755535 Fax: (01905) 755705 *Industrial cleaning materials suppliers*

▶ Hygieco Ltd, Clockhouse Estate, Cavendish Lane, Glemsford, Sudbury, Suffolk, CO10 7PZ Tel: (01787) 281188 Fax: (01787) 282222 E-mail: sales@hygieco.co.uk *Wash room service providers*

▶ Hygieia Healthcare Ltd, PO Box 117, Bideford, Devon, EX39 1AA Tel: (01237) 473128 Fax: (01237) 425742 E-mail: sales@hygieia.co.uk *Antibacterial skin moisturising barrier cream*

Hygiene Express Ltd, Brookfield House, Heald Lane, Bacup, Lancashire, OL13 8QZ Tel: (01706) 879442 Fax: (01706) 879251 *Janitorial suppliers*

▶ Hygiene Express Delivery Ltd, Unit 20 Portland Industrial Estate, Bury, Lancs, BL9 6EY Tel: 0871 288 4221 E-mail: Sales@h-e-d.co.uk *Hygiene, Janitorial and Bar supplies.*

Hygiene First Ltd, Melton Road, Queniborough, Leicester, LE7 3FP Tel: 0116-269 4393 Fax: 0116-269 4395 E-mail: sales@hygienefirst.co.uk *Protective clothing*

Hygiene Group Ltd, 409-412 Montrose Avenue, Slough, SL1 4TJ Tel: (01753) 820991 Fax: (01753) 578189 E-mail: sales@hygiene.co.uk *Industrial & pharmaceutical cleaning contractors*

▶ Hygiene Logistics UK Ltd, Unit 1 Wellington Street, Castleford, West Yorkshire, WF10 1NW Tel: (01977) 667666 Fax: (01977) 667999

Hygiene Pest Control, 116 Montagu Street, Kettering, Northamptonshire, NN16 8RZ Tel: (01536) 523430 E-mail: info@hygienepestcontrol.co.uk *Pest control services*

Hygiene Pest Control, 300 City Road, Sheffield, S2 5HQ Tel: 0114-272 2926 Fax: 0114-275 3776 *Pest control services*

Hygiene Warehouse, Unit 6, Ashmead Park, Ashmead Road, Keynsham, Bristol, BS31 1SU Tel: 0117-946 1978 Fax: 0117-946 1959 E-mail: sales@hygienewarehouse.co.uk *Paper converters & general cleaning suppliers*

▶ Hygienedepot, Unit 6, Ashmead Park, Ashmead Road, Keynsham, Bristol, BS31 1SU Tel: (020) 7339 7979 Fax: 0117-946 1959 E-mail: sales@liptonspapermills.co.uk *Suppliers of disposable hygiene products, janitorial supplies*

Hygienic Valves & Fittings Ltd, Huffwood Trading Estate, Partridge Green, Horsham, West Sussex, RH13 8AU Tel: (01403) 710255 Fax: (01403) 710338 *Stainless steel suppliers*

Hygienique Cleaning Materials, Unit C1 Broadway Industrial Estate, King William Street, Salford, M50 3UQ Tel: 0161-872 3666 Fax: 0161-873 7474 E-mail: hygienique@btopenworld.com *Hygiene & chemical products distributors*

▶ Hygrade Foods Ltd, Banda Trading Estate, Nursteed Road, Devizes, Wiltshire, SN10 3DY Tel: (01380) 730822 Fax: (01380) 730823 *Cold meats services*

▶ Hygrade Industrial Plastics Ltd, Hunters Lane, Rugby, Warwickshire, CV21 1EA Tel: (01788) 571316 Fax: (01788) 541184 E-mail: techsales@hygradeplastics.com *Gas scrubbing equipment manufrs*

▶ Hygromatik UK, PO Box 99, Southampton, SO18 9AA Tel: (023) 8044 3127 Fax: (0870) 1670346 E-mail: ac@hygromatik.co.uk *Worldwide Manufactures of high quality humidification systems. Electrode, Resistance heater, steam injection, adiabatic, nozzle and de-humidification systems. Fully serviceable and maintainable.Humidifier*

Hylec Components Ltd, 6 Stanton Close, Finedon Road Industrial Estate, Wellingborough, Northamptonshire, NN8 4HN Tel: (01933) 234400 Fax: (01933) 234411 E-mail: sales@hylec.co.uk *Distributors & agents of cable glands*

Hyloc Ltd, Unit 5, Jensen Court, Astmoor, Runcorn, Cheshire, WA7 1SQ Tel: (01928) 590110 Fax: (01928) 590905 E-mail: info@hyloc.com *Industrial adhesives*

▶ Hylton Nomis Computer Services, Unit D, Greenforde Farm, Stoner Hill Road, Froxfield, Petersfield, Hants, GU32 1DY Tel: (01730) 266123 Fax: (01730) 263645

▶ Hylton Stormaster Ltd, 7 Harvey Close, Crowther, Washington, Tyne & Wear, NE38 0AB Tel: 0191-417 0055

HY-MAC Construction Equipment, No 1 Berkeley Street, Mayfair, London, WC1 1UH Tel: (0870) 7602671 Fax: (0870) 7602672 E-mail: info@hy-mac.com *Construction equipment. excavators.track + wheel.*dump trucks.fork lifts multi fuel.*dumpers.rollers. loading shovels.*

Hymans Robertson, Finsbury Tower, 103-105 Bunhill Row, London, EC1Y 8LZ Tel: (020) 7847 6000 Fax: (020) 7847 6060 *Actuaries*

Hymas Refrigeration & Catering Ltd, 178 Grove Green Road, London, E11 4EL Tel: (020) 8539 4222 E-mail: hymas_ref@fsmail.net *Refrigeration, air conditioning & catering equipment sales services*

Hymec Backspin Ltd, Omega, Gipsy Lane, Wokingham, Berkshire, RG40 2HP Tel: 0118-978 0557 Fax: 0118-978 0558 E-mail: tt@hymec.co.uk Purchasing Contact: T. Tizzard Sales Contact: T. Tizzard *Hydraulic equipment distribs*

▶ Hymec Precision Engineering Ltd, Darklake View, Estover, Plymouth, PL6 7TL Tel: (01752) 511002 Fax: (01752) 511003 *Engineering*

Hymid Hydraulics Ltd, 9 Glenbarr Avenue, Leicester, LE4 0AE Tel: 0116-251 8888 Fax: 0116-251 8800 E-mail: sales@hymid.com *Hydraulic power pack manufrs*

Hymix Fabricators, C10-C11 Unit, Stafford Park 11, Telford, Shropshire, TF3 3AY Tel: (01952) 200900 Fax: (01952) 200901 E-mail: mail@hymix.com *Concrete mixer & pump manufrs*

▶ Hyndford Plant Ltd, Anstruther Place, Douglas Water, Lanark, ML11 9LR Tel: (01555) 880350 Fax: (01555) 880350

▶ Hyndman Consultants, Kyrle Grange, Peterstow, Ross-on-Wye, Herefordshire, HR9 6JZ Tel: (01989) 768767 Fax: (01989) 768766 E-mail: john@hyndman.co.uk *Hyndman Consultants founded in 1987 is one of the leading UK healthcare business and technical recruitment consultancies for sales, marketing, clinical, technical and management opportunities.*

▶ Hype Studios, 72 Princes Street, Dunstable, Bedfordshire, LU6 3AX Tel: (01582) 663925 Fax: (01582) 663925 E-mail: info@hypestudios.co.uk *Specialists in design for print & interactive flash design*

Hypec, Royal Works, Atlas Street, Clayton-Le-Moors, Accrington, Lancashire, BB5 5LP Tel: (01254) 615100 Fax: (01254) 615199 E-mail: sales@allspeeds.co.uk *Hydraulic jacks & equipment manufrs*

▶ Hyperdrug Veterinary Supplies, Station Bank, Middleton-in-Teesdale, Barnard Castle, County Durham, DL12 0NG Tel: (01833) 641112 Fax: (01833) 641032 E-mail: sales@hyperdrug.co.uk *horse wormers, eqvalan, strongid, equest and furexel, dog wormers such as Drontal and Panacur, home of the equine pharmacy, canine chemists, and pigeon pharmacy. Veterinary prescriptions dispensed.*

Hyperion Systems Ltd, 12 The Mount, Guildford, Surrey, GU2 4HN Tel: (01483) 301793 Fax: (01483) 561657 E-mail: glor.benson@chyp.com *IT consultants*

▶ Hyperion Wall Furniture Ltd, Unit 7, Brook Way, Kingston Road, Leatherhead, Surrey, KT22 7NA Tel: (01372) 378279 Fax: (01372) 362004 E-mail: enquiries@hyperion-furniture.co.uk *Furniture manufacturers & retailers*

▶ Hypermania Design, Woodmancote, Clay Lane, Fishbourne, Chichester, West Sussex, PO18 8DW Tel: (01243) 780385 E-mail: sean@hypermania.com *Graphic Design, advertising, print,printing,illustration,direct mail, marketing,web design,design for print*

Hypertac Ltd, 36-38 Waterloo Road, London, NW2 7UH Tel: (020) 8450 8033 Fax: (020) 8208 4114 E-mail: info@hypertac.co.uk *Electrical connector manufrs*

Hypertec Ltd, Unit 2 Swangate, Hungerford, Berkshire, RG17 0YX Tel: (01488) 686844 Fax: (01488) 686845 E-mail: info@hypertec.co.uk *Printed circuit board assemblies*

Hypertherm UK Ltd, 9 Berkeley Court, Manor Park, Runcorn, Cheshire, WA7 1TQ Tel: (01928) 579074 Fax: (01928) 579604 E-mail: info@hypertherm.co.uk *Plasma cutting equipment*

Hyphose Ltd, 2 Witney Road, Nuffield Industrial Estate, Poole, Dorset, BH17 0GH Tel: (01202) 673333 Fax: (01202) 687788 E-mail: sales@hyphose.com *Hose & couplings distributors/agents* Also At: Portsmouth

Hypoguard Ltd, Dock Lane, Melton, Woodbridge, Suffolk, IP12 1PE Tel: (01394) 387333 Fax: (01394) 380152 E-mail: enquiries@hypoguard.co.uk *Medical equipment for diabetics*

▶ Hypostyle Architects, 49 St. Vincent Cresent, Glasgow, G3 8NG Tel: 0141-204 4441 Fax: 0141-204 4897

Hyprosteps Ltd, Unit 6-7 Brandon Business Centre, Putney Close, Brandon, Suffolk, IP27 0PA Tel: (01842) 815972 Fax: (01842) 815347 E-mail: hyprosteps@aol.com *Access equipment & steps (safety) manufrs*

▶ Hyrdrovane Air Compressor Services, 1d North Crescent, London, E16 4TG Tel: (020) 7473 3424 Fax: (020) 7511 0194 E-mail: sales@awphillips.co.uk *Air compressor sales*

Hyspec Screen Process Printers, Brunel Road, Bedford, MK41 9TG Tel: (01234) 217972 Fax: (01234) 328182 E-mail: info@hyspec.co.uk *Screen printing, printing & embroidery services*

Hyspeed CNC Ltd, Clovelly Road, Southbourne, Emsworth, Hampshire, PO10 8PE Tel: (01243) 377751 Fax: (01243) 377754 E-mail: sales@hyspeed.co.uk *Precision engineering services*

Hyster Europe, Flagship House, Reading Road North, Fleet, Hampshire, GU51 4WD Tel: (01252) 810261 Fax: (01252) 770702 E-mail: sales@hyster.co.uk Principal Export Areas: Worldwide *Manufacturers of fork lift trucks*

Hytec Electronics Ltd, 5 Craddock Road, Reading, RG2 0JT Tel: 0118-975 7770 Fax: 0118-975 7566 E-mail: sales@hytec-electronics.co.uk *Control & data acquisition systems*

Hytec Industrie, PO Box 642, Guildford, Surrey, GU2 7WE Tel: (01483) 827065 Fax: (01483) 827075 E-mail: uk@hytec-industrie.com *Effluent water treatment specialists*

Hytec Information Security Ltd, Units 9-10, Oasis Park, Stanton Harcourt Road, Eynsham, Witney, Oxfordshire, OX29 4TP Tel: (01865) 887423 Fax: (01865) 887444 E-mail: info@hytec.co.uk *IT security services*

Hytec Plastic Mouldings Ltd, Unit 2e & 2g Chase Park Industrial Estate Ring Road, Chasetown Industrial Estate, Burntwood Business Park, Burntwood, Staffordshire, WS7 3JQ Tel: (01543) 687200 Fax: (01543) 673392 E-mail: peterlucas@hytecplastics.com *Plastics mouldings manufrs*

Hytech Water Ltd, Unit 36 Southfield Road Trading Estate, Southfield Road, Nailsea, Bristol, BS48 1JG Tel: (01275) 858386 Fax: (01275) 858387 E-mail: sales@hytech-water.co.uk *Project engineers*

Hytek Alarms Ltd, 115 Fossdale Moss, Leyland, Leyland, PR26 7AS Tel: (01772) 436317 Fax: (01772) 467402 *Alarms & mobile phones retail*

Hytek Europe, 11 Elliott Road, Love Lane Industrial Estate, Cirencester, Gloucestershire, GL7 1YS Tel: (01285) 659349 Fax: (01285) 657915 E-mail: enquiries@hytekeurope.co.uk *Ultra thin diamond & CBN cutting wheels manufrs*

Hytemp Ltd, Lowther Rd, Sheffield, S6 2DQ Tel: 0114-233 8163 Fax: 0114-233 8211 E-mail: sales@hytemp.com *Stockholders of nickel alloy & nickel alloy flanges/fittings*

Hythe Marine Services, Prospect Place, Hythe, Southampton, SO45 6AU Tel: (023) 8084 8782 Fax: (023) 8084 6760 E-mail: raymithchener@btconnect.com *Boat builders & commercial slipping*

Hythe Offset, Telford Way, Severalls Park, Colchester, CO4 9QP Tel: (01206) 848904 Fax: (01206) 852054 E-mail: cards@hythe-uk.com *Plastic cards printers & manufrs*

Hytner Exhibitions Ltd, Bullock Road, Washingley, Peterborough, PE7 3SJ Tel: (01733) 246950 Fax: (01733) 246951 E-mail: exhibits@hytner.co.uk *Exhibition stand contractors*

Hy-Tops Ltd, Budden Road, Coseley, Bilston, West Midlands, WV14 8JZ Tel: 0121-557 2191 Fax: 0121-520 3020 E-mail: sales@hickmanandlove.co.uk *Scaffold guards manufrs*

Hytrac Lifts, Telford Way, Stephenson Indust Estat, Coalville, Leicestershire, LE67 3HP Tel: (01530) 832155 Fax: (01530) 832154 E-mail: info@hytraclifts.co.uk *Lifts installation & upgrade services*

Hyundai Heavy Industries Co. Ltd, Second Floor The Triangle, 5-17 Hammersmith Grove, London, W6 9LT Tel: (020) 8741 0501 Fax: (020) 8741 5620 *Ship manufrs*

▶ Hyundai Merchant Marine Europe Ltd, 204-207 Berth, Western Docks, Southampton, SO15 1DA Tel: (023) 8078 7700 Fax: (023) 8078 7233

Hyundai Motors UK Ltd, St. Johns Court, Easton Street, High Wycombe, Buckinghamshire, HP11 1JX Tel: (01494) 428600 Fax: (01494) 428699 *Motor car concessionaires*

▶ Hyway Logistics, Lincoln Court, Washington Street, Bolton, BL3 5EZ Tel: (01204) 365403 Fax: (01204) 365418 E-mail: delivery@hywaylogistics.co.uk

Hyzed Engineering Ltd, Old Colliery Road, Graddfa Industrial Estate, Llanbradach, Caerphilly, Mid Glamorgan, CF83 3QS Tel: (029) 2088 4874 Fax: (029) 2085 1557 *Engineers*

Company I Ltd, 42 New Broad Street, London, EC2M 1SB Tel: (020) 7382 0750 Fax: (08701) 667001 *Computer consultants*

I A C (Industrial Acoustics Company) Ltd, I A C House, Moorside Road, Winchester, Hampshire, SO23 7US Tel: (01962) 873000 Fax: (01962) 873123 E-mail: info@iacl.co.uk *IAC is the world""s leading supplier of noise and acoustic control products, structures and test facilities. With European HQ based at Winchester in the UK, the company also has subsidiaries in USA, France, Germany, Italy, Spain and Denmark, and licensed agents in many other countries worldwide. IAC""s high performance, laboratory tested acoustic products are the preferred choice of specifiers in a wide range of application areas: construction; building services; media and entertainment; medical and lifestyle; industry and power generation; and aeroengine testing.*IAC""s products meet or exceed all relevant international technical standards. **

▶ I A & C Maciver Ltd, Unit 4 & 5, Parkend Industrial Estate, Sandwick, Isle Of Lewis, HS2 0AN Tel: (01851) 705050

I A C Plastics, Oak Mill, Manchester Road, Dunnockshaw, Burnley, Lancashire, BB11 5PW Tel: (01706) 212225 Fax: (01706) 229926 E-mail: sales@iacplastics.com *IAC Plastics based in Burnley Lancashire are manufacturers and machinists of engineering thermoplastic materials inclusing UHM polyethelene, nylons & acetals. We specialise in engineering plastic components and materials all stock items for resale. We also supply wear strips, cast nylon products and materials, thermoplastic materials and polyethene products and materials. Trade names include Corromide, Corroplas and Corrothene.*

▶ I & A Crowhurst Ltd, Anker Bridge House, Bridge St, Polesworth, Tamworth, Staffordshire, B78 1DR Tel: (01827) 898527

I A E Ltd, 2 Hanger, Cranfield Airfield, Cranfield, Bedford, MK43 0JR Tel: (01234) 750661 Fax: (01234) 751731 E-mail: sales@iae.org.uk *Aircraft maintenance & repair services*

I A L Consultants, 109 Uxbridge Road, London, W5 5TL Tel: (020) 8832 7780 Fax: (020) 8566 4931 E-mail: ial@brg.co.uk *Market research services*

I A M Engineering Services, Fornighty Schoolhouse, Nairn, IV12 5JB Tel: (01667) 453509 Fax: (01667) 453066 E-mail: iameng@btinternet.com *Testing cranes & all types of lifting equipment suppliers*

I A S Smarts, Clarence Mill, Clarence Road, Bollington, Macclesfield, Cheshire, SK10 5JZ Tel: (01625) 578578 Fax: (01625) 578579 E-mail: sue@iasbranding.co.uk *Marketing & communication*

I A S Storage Systems, Newtonsyde, Charleston, Nigg, Aberdeen, AB12 3LL Tel: (01224) 897300 Fax: (01224) 897305 E-mail: ias@totalise.co.uk *Storage systems suppliers, pallet racking, shelving, mezzanine floors*

I A W F, Rushenden Road, Queenborough, Kent, ME11 5HH Tel: (01795) 580365 Fax: (01795) 580649 E-mail: sales@sheppyfertilisers.co.uk *Fertiliser manufrs*

I A W S Ltd, North Side North Dock, Alexandra Dock, Newport, Gwent, NP20 2NP Tel: (01633) 255999 Fax: (01633) 250999 *Import fertilisers & blend together to suit farmers requirements*

I A W S Fertilisers UK Ltd, Maxwell Road, Plymouth, PL4 0SN Tel: (01752) 601124 Fax: (01752) 223758 *Chemical fertiliser manufrs*

I.B.C. Recovery Services Ltd, 28 Brewsdale Road, Middlesbrough, Middlesbrough, Cleveland, TS3 6JZ Tel: 01642 249844 Fax: 01642 220245 E-mail: bagman@ibc-recovery.com *Polypropylene bag cleaning services*

▶ I B Industries, 7 Browning Close, Bolton, BL1 3XF Tel: (01204) 410585 Fax: (01204) 441212 E-mail: sales@ibindustries.co.uk *Cleaning & degreasing machine suppliers*

I B L Bulk Liquids, Lime Street, Hull, HU8 7AS Tel: (01482) 320736 Fax: (01482) 226162 E-mail: phil@intbl.co.uk *Providers of logistics services throughout the UK for products which require specialised storage & distribution*

I B M (UK) Ltd, 1 New Square, Feltham, Middlesex, TW14 8HB Tel: (020) 8818 6060 Fax: (020) 8818 5499 *Manufacturers & distributors of IT software*

I B M (UK) Ltd, Palace Street, Plymouth, PL1 2DE Tel: (01752) 660042 Fax: (01752) 224230 *Computer servicing*

I B M (UK) Ltd, Po Box 41, Portsmouth, PO6 3AU Tel: (023) 9256 1000 Fax: (023) 9238 8914 E-mail: uk_crc@uk.ibm.com *Market sell & manufacture business machines*

I B M (UK) Ltd, Rosanne House, Bridge Road, Welwyn Garden City, Hertfordshire, AL8 6UB Tel: (01707) 363000 Fax: (01707) 338732 E-mail: info@ibm.com *Computer manufrs*

I B N, 138-140 Wapping High Street, London, E1 9NQ Tel: (020) 7369 1200 Fax: (020) 7369 1217 *Disaster recovery specialists*

I B P Conex Ltd, Alexander Street, Dundee, DD3 7DT Tel: (01382) 221301 Fax: (01382) 201292 E-mail: salesuk@ibpgroup.com Principal Export Areas: Central/East Europe & West Europe *Plumbing tube fitting manufrs*

I B S Ltd, 30 Glenburn Road, East Kilbride, Glasgow, G74 5BA Tel: (01355) 244555 Fax: (01355) 241974 E-mail: sales@tapes.co.uk *Adhesive tape distributors*

I B S Bearings Ltd, A1 Trading Estate, Lewisham Road, Smethwick, West Midlands, B66 2BN Tel: 0121-558 4141 Fax: 0121-555 5564 *Bearing & transmission product distributors*

I B S Consulting Services Ltd, 5 Parkshot House, Kew Road, Richmond, Surrey, TW9 2PR Tel: (020) 8334 8018 Fax: (020) 8334 8558 E-mail: press@ibs-uk.co.uk *IT consultants*

I B S Specialist Joinery Ltd, Wyfield Manor, Boxford, Newbury, Berkshire, RG20 8DY Tel: (01488) 608895 Fax: (01488) 608895 E-mail: enquiries@ibs4doors.com *Joinery manufrs*

I B W Ltd, 64 Seven Kings Road, Ilford, Essex, IG3 8DG Tel: (020) 8220 1177 Fax: (020) 8220 1166 *Bag designer & manufrs*

I C A Motor Products, 146 University Street, Belfast, BT7 1HH Tel: (028) 9024 2191 Fax: (028) 9033 3866 *Brake & clutch components*

I C Blinds Ltd, 26 Fulton Gardens, Houston, Johnstone, Renfrewshire, PA6 7NU Tel: (01505) 327802 Fax: (01698) 326633 *Blind manufrs*

I C C Communications Ltd, 14A Boxer Place, Mosside Industrial Estate, Leyland, PR26 7QL Tel: (01772) 622621 Fax: (01772) 622300 E-mail: networks@icc-comms.co.uk *Design of total networking solutions*

I C C Information Ltd, First Floor, Rooms 8-10, Scottish Mutual Building, 16 Donegall Square South, Belfast, BT1 5JG Tel: (028) 9055 9559 Fax: (028) 9055 0072 E-mail: reports@iccinformationni.com *Business information services*

I C C S Ltd, 4 Market Street, Edenfield, Ramsbottom, Bury, Lancashire, BL0 0JN Tel: (01706) 822233 Fax: (01706) 822277 E-mail: info@iccs-ltd.co.uk *Computer software*

I C Ceramics UK Ltd, 21 Dovedale Road, Liverpool, L18 5EP Tel: 0151-280 6732 Fax: 0151-280 6742 *Ceramic tiles*

▶ I C D Ltd, 1 Paxton Place, Skelmersdale, Lancashire, WN8 9QH Tel: (01695) 722031 Fax: (01695) 51803

▶ I C E Installations, 246 Cannock Road, Heath Hayes, Cannock, Staffordshire, WS12 3HA Tel: (01543) 271630 Fax: (01543) 271630 E-mail: iceinstalations@tiscalli.co.uk *In car entertainment, stereo retailers*

I C E Sportswear, 145 Ryhope Road, Sunderland, SR2 7UG Tel: 0191-565 8387 Fax: 0191-565 8387 *Sportswear clothing manufrs*

▶ I C Electrical Ltd, Wetmore Road, Burton-on-Trent, Staffordshire, DE14 1SN Tel: (01283) 530666 Fax: (01283) 538666

▶ I.C.F. (Industrial Concrete Flooring)., 51 Manor Road, Wakefield, West Yorkshire, WF2 8QN Tel: 01924 290292 Fax: 01924 377897 E-mail: industrialconcreteflooring@hotmail.co.uk *We are nationwide industrial concrete floor layers, specialising in the laying of re-inforced concrete internal and external floors, to easyfloat, brush and powerfloat finish.*

I C G Electronics, Unit 35 Second Drove Industrial Estate, Peterborough, PE1 5XA Tel: (01733) 557447 Fax: (01733) 314711 *Electronic contract services*

I C Gears, 50 Bracken Road, Ferndown, Dorset, BH22 9PF Tel: (01202) 891324 E-mail: sales@icgears.co.uk *Ice cream equipment suppliers*

I C L Environmental Services Ltd, Firs Industrial Estate, Stourport Road, Kidderminster, Worcestershire, DY11 7QN Tel: (01562) 744655 Fax: (01562) 829207 E-mail: sales@iclenvironmental.co.uk *Asbestos removal contractors*

I C L Plastics Ltd, Grovepark Mills, Hopehill Road, Glasgow, G20 7NF Tel: 0141-332 1331 Fax: 0141-332 9186 *Plastics coaters & fabricators*

I C L Sorbus (UK) Ltd, Unit 9 Amelia St, London, SE17 3PY Tel: 020 77082481 *Computer services*

I C M (Plastic Moulding) Ltd, Enterprise Close, Medway City Estate, Rochester, Kent, ME2 4LY Tel: (01634) 298500 Fax: (01634) 714338 E-mail: info@icm-plasticmoulding.co.uk *Manufacturers of injection mouldings*

I C M Team Computer Group, 27 Wells Street, Inverness, IV3 5JU Tel: (01463) 711302 Fax: (01463) 713825 E-mail: icm@computergroup.co.uk *Computer maintenance & repairers*

I C Market, PO Box 20379, Henley-on-Thames, Oxfordshire, RG9 2BH Tel: (01491) 410719 Fax: (01491) 412912 E-mail: emma@icemktg.co.uk *Commercial vehicle specialists*

I C O UK Ltd, 24 Norris Way, Wellingborough Road, Rushden, Northamptonshire, NN10 6BP Tel: (01933) 315500 Fax: (01933) 313300 *Pigment for plastics*

I C Optical Systems Ltd, 190-192 Ravenscroft Road, Beckenham, Kent, BR3 4TW Tel: (020) 8778 5094 Fax: (020) 8676 9816 E-mail: sales@icopticalsystems.com *Prisms & lens manufrs*

I C P Projects Ltd, Cwm Cynon Business Park, Mountain Ash, Mid Glamorgan, CF45 4ER Tel: (01443) 477970 Fax: (01443) 476707 E-mail: sales@icpprojects.co.uk *Manufacturers control panels & systems*

I C Publications Ltd, 7 Coldbath Square, London, EC1R 4LQ Tel: (020) 7713 7711 Fax: (020) 7713 7898 E-mail: icpubs@africasia.com *Publishers*

I C Refrigeration & Air Conditioning, 12 Broad Meadow, Ipswich, IP8 3SP Tel: (01473) 680629 Fax: (01473) 680629 *Air conditioning & refrigeration*

I C Resources Ltd, Capital House, 67 - 69 St Johns Road, Isleworth, Middlesex, TW7 6NL Tel: (020) 8400 2444 Fax: (020) 8560 2445 E-mail: enquiry@ic-resources.co.uk *Recruitment consultants*

▶ I C Rushton, 16 Rostherne Avenue, High Lane, Stockport, Cheshire, SK6 8AR Tel: (01663) 762540 E-mail: IanCRushton@aol.com *Gas Installions*Gas Central Heating Installations*Servicing and repairs*Plumbing Installations*Bathroom design and installations*Tiling wall and floor*Corgi registered*

▶ I C S, 1 Barnfield Wood Rd, Beckenham, Kent, BR3 6SR Tel: 020 86505993 *Pest & vermin control*

I C S, Royal Mail House, 37 Terminus Terrace, Southampton, SO14 3FD Tel: (023) 80227878 Fax: (023) 80227878

I C S, 178 Reddicap Heath Road, Sutton Coldfield, West Midlands, B75 7ET Tel: 0121-241 2299 Fax: 0121-241 4623 E-mail: wayne@ics-mail.com *Quality management certification body*

▶ I C S Europe, Multi Media Exchange, 72-80 Corporation Road, Middlesbrough, Cleveland, TS1 2RF Tel: (01642) 230676 Fax: (01642) 219636 *Cosmetic packaging suppliers*

I C S Group, Gore Road Industrial Estate, New Milton, Hampshire, BH25 6SA Tel: (01425) 625900 Fax: (01425) 639041 E-mail: info@industrialcooling.co.uk *Air conditioning distributors*

I C S (Industrial & Consumer Supplies), Tor-Y-Mynydd Farm, Devauden, Chepstow, Gwent, NP16 6NU Tel: (01600) 860869 Fax: (01600) 860869 *Fibrin asbestos free sealing compound manufrs*

I C S London Ltd, 26 Thackeray Mall, Fareham, Hampshire, PO16 0PQ Tel: (01329) 228200 Fax: (01329) 233191

I C S Software Ltd, The Square, Ramsbury, Marlborough, Wiltshire, SN8 2PE Tel: (01672) 521212 Fax: (01672) 521002 E-mail: mike@folio2000.co.uk *Software distributors service*

I C S Triplex, 10-14 Hall Road, Heybridge, Maldon, Essex, CM9 4LA Tel: (01621) 854444 Fax: (01621) 859221 E-mail: sales@icsplc.co.uk *Safety & control systems*

▶ I C Surveys, 9 Pendle Street East, Sabden, Clitheroe, Lancashire, BB7 9EQ Tel: 01282 680152 Fax: 01282 680679 E-mail: surveys@stonybank.plus.com *Asbestos surveys, management, health & safety consultants*

I C T S Ltd, Solent Road, Havant, Hampshire, PO9 1JH Tel: (023) 9249 9123 Fax: (023) 9249 9108 E-mail: sales@ictsltd.co.uk *Structural steelwork engineers*

▶ I C T Solutions & Services Ltd, 78 Cavalry Drive, March, Cambridgeshire, PE15 9DP Tel: (01354) 659587 Fax: (01354) 659601 E-mail: enquiries@ictss.com *IT support & consultants*

▶ I C U (Global) Ltd, Building 3, Chiswick Park, 566 Chiswick High Road, London, W4 5YA Tel: (0870) 3516580 Fax: (0870) 3516591 E-mail: info@icuglobal.co.uk *Audio & video conferencing services*

I C W Power Ltd, Joule House, 108-110 Primrose Hill, Kings Langley, Hertfordshire, WD4 8HR Tel: (01923) 266869 Fax: (01923) 264472 E-mail: sales@icwpower.com *Power distribution systems, distributors & manufrs*

▶ I & C Watts Ltd, 59 Electric Avenue, Harrogate, North Yorkshire, HG1 2BB Tel: (01423) 508773 Fax: (01423) 508773

I Caudwell, Church Street, Billinghay, Lincoln, LN4 4HN Tel: (01526) 861179 Fax: (01526) 861762 E-mail: emailcaudwell@globalnet.co.uk *Blacksmiths*

▶ I Change Ltd, Birchwood, South Munstead Lane, Godalming, Surrey, GU8 4AG Tel: (01483) 208505 Fax: (01483) 208505 E-mail: info@i-change.biz *We facilitate Change & Communication in your business, and support you in making that happen*

▶ I Craig (Haulage) Ltd, Eilanda, Drove Loan, Head of Muir, Denny, Stirlingshire, FK6 5LE Tel: (01324) 812250

▶ I Cy Group, Hurst House, Crown Heights, Guildford, Surrey, GU1 3TX Tel: (01483) 539090

▶ I D Aromatics Ltd, 12 New Station Street, Leeds, LS1 5DL Tel: 0113-242 4983 Fax: 0113-243 3613 E-mail: info@idaromatics.co.uk *Great range of products for the aromatics user (wholesaler)*

I D Business Solutions Ltd, 2 Occam Court, Occam Road, Surrey Research Park, Guildford, Surrey, GU2 7QB Tel: (01483) 595000 Fax: (01483) 595001 E-mail: info@idbs.com *Data management software suppliers*

I D & C Ltd, 15 Colebrook Industrial Estate, Longfield Road, Tunbridge Wells, Kent, TN2 3DG Tel: (01892) 548364 Fax: (01892) 519048 E-mail: sales@idcband.co.uk *Admission controllers*

I D C Holdings Ltd, 86 Hatton Garden, London, EC1N 8QQ Tel: (020) 7242 5303 Fax: (020) 7242 9406 E-mail: idc@idcholdings.com *Industrial diamonds*

I D C Signs & Engraving, 26 Harwood Street, Blackburn, BB1 3BS Tel: (01254) 263679 Fax: (01254) 263699 E-mail: sales@idcsigns.co.uk *General engravers, screen printers & sign makers*

I D Computer Services, 9 Bolton Road West, Ramsbottom, Bury, Lancashire, BL0 9NA Tel: (01706) 824080 Fax: (01706) 829930 E-mail: mail@idcomputerservices.co.uk *Computer supplies & services*

I D Computer Services (Scotland) Ltd, Barncluith Bus Centre, Townhead St, Hamilton, Lanarkshire, ML3 7DP Tel: (01698) 458200 Fax: (01698) 421188 E-mail: info@idcsl.com *IT consultants*

I D Data Ltd, The New Mint House, Bedford Road, Petersfield, Hampshire, GU32 3AL Tel: (01730) 235700 Fax: (01730) 235711 E-mail: enquiry@iddata.com *Data capture systems manufrs*

I D Design, 48 Broadway Avenue, Harlow, Essex, CM17 0AG Tel: (01279) 415548 Fax: (01279) 415548 E-mail: iddesign@dial.pipex.com *Creative design & print*

▶ I D E- Architecture, Unit 205, Spitfire Studios, 63-71 Collier Street, London, N1 9BE Tel: (020) 7837 4000 Fax: (020) 7837 4222 *Architecture consultants*

I D E SS Ltd, 3 West Road, Harlow, Essex, CM20 2BQ Tel: (01279) 400140 Fax: (01279) 400150 *Shop fitters*

▶ I D E Systems, Unit 6, Swaffield Park Hyssop Close, Cannock, Staffordshire, WS11 7FU Tel: (01543) 574111 Fax: (01543) 571444 E-mail: sales@idesystems.co.uk *Sales and rental of power distribution equipment, specialists in temporary power applications*

I D G (U K) Plc, Topley House, 52 Wash Lane, Bury, Lancashire, BL9 6AU Tel: 0161-797 5729 Fax: 0161-762 9322 E-mail: labm@idgplc.com *Supplier of microbiology test products*

I D H Alarms Co. Ltd, 17 Edwin Street, Gravesend, Kent, DA12 1EH Tel: (01474) 363535 Fax: (01474) 535418 *Security alarm installers services*

I D Howitt Ltd, Spring Hill Farm, 584 Doncaster Road, Crofton, Wakefield, West Yorkshire, WF4 1PR Tel: (01924) 862820 Fax: (01924) 865129 *Electrical & Machanical Engineering*

I D Installations, 202 Nuthurst Road, Manchester, M40 3PP Tel: 0161-682 4595 Fax: 0161-682 4595 E-mail: david@idinstallations.freeserve.co.uk *Telecommunication system installers*

I D J Ltd, 81 Piccadilly, London, W1J 8HY Tel: (020) 7355 1200 Fax: (020) 7495 1149 E-mail: sales@idj.co.uk *Corporate finance services*

I D Labels Ltd, 1 Eagle Estate, Brookers Road, Billingshurst, West Sussex, RH14 9RZ Tel: (01403) 786800 Fax: (01403) 786700 *Suppliers of self adhesive labels*

▶ I D M, 48 Clarence Square, Cheltenham, Gloucestershire, GL50 4JR Tel: (01242) 581800 E-mail: enquiries@idm.org *Web design and e-commerce*

I D M Environmental Services Ltd, Bourn House, Biddisham Lane, Biddisham, Axbridge, Somerset, BS26 2RG Tel: (01934) 751287 Fax: (01934) 751289 E-mail: idmpestcontrol@totalise.co.uk *Pest control services*

I D M Southern Ltd, Unit 1, Lavernham Road, Brent Eleigh, Sudbury, Suffolk, CO10 9PB Tel: (01449) 740040 Fax: (01449) 744950 E-mail: mail@idmsouthern.co.uk *Internal partitions & office refurbishers services*

I D Machinery Ltd, 78 Alston Drive, Bradwell Abbey, Milton Keynes, MK13 9HG Tel: (01908) 321778 Fax: (01908) 322707 E-mail: sales@idmachinery.com *New & used corrugated paper machinery manufrs*

I D Mailing Ltd, 1-4 Fleming Close, Parkfarm Industrial Estate, Wellingborough, Northamptonshire, NN8 6UF Tel: (01933) 678650 Fax: (01933) 678651 E-mail: enq@id-mailing.co.uk *Direct mail services & mailing house*

I D Management Systems, Temple Court, Cathedral Road, Cardiff, CF11 9HA Tel: (0870) 7413000 Fax: (0870) 7413001 E-mail: info@idmanagement.com *Identification card manufrs*

I D O M Consulting Ltd, Royal London House, 22-25 Finsbury Square, London, EC2A 1DX Tel: (020) 7588 1118 Fax: (020) 7588 1117 E-mail: info@idom.co.uk *Computer consultants*

I D P (Europe) Ltd, Phoenix Works, Davis Road, Chessington, Surrey, KT9 1TH Tel: (020) 8391 3888 Fax: (020) 8974 2895 E-mail: info@holbine.co.uk *Curtain & blinds manufrs*

I D Rawlinson Contractors, Marton, Ulverston, Cumbria, LA12 0NR Tel: (01229) 465665 Fax: (01229) 465665 *Agricultural contractors*

I D S Plastics, Unit 42 The Acorn Centre, Barry Street, Oldham, OL1 3NE Tel: 0161-627 1054 Fax: 0161-624 4500 E-mail: info@showcasesonline.com *Plastic fabricators & display equipment distributors*

▶ I D S Transport, Unit 1, Honeybourne Airfield Trading Estate, Honeybourne, Evesham, Worcestershire, WR11 7QF Tel: (01386) 841363 Fax: (01386) 835574

I D U Science Museum, 23 Blythe Road, London, W14 0QX Tel: (020) 7610 4074 Fax: (020) 7371 4885 *Model making agents*

I E A Ltd, South Road, Bridgend Industrial Estate, Bridgend, Mid Glamorgan, CF31 3PU Tel: (01656) 673300 Fax: (01656) 673329 E-mail: sales@iealtd.co.uk *Computer aided design services*

I E Bolt & Nut Ltd, Unit 14 Alma Works, Alma Street, Cutler Heights, Bradford, West Yorkshire, BD4 9JE Tel: (01274) 686805 Fax: (01274) 680361 E-mail: sales@iebolt.co.uk *Bolt & nut distributors*

I E C, The Street, Somerleyton, Lowestoft, Suffolk, NR32 5QB Tel: (01502) 732733 Fax: (01502) 730255 E-mail: info@i-e-c.co.uk *Noise, vibration & air quality consultancy services*

I E C Ltd, 41 Harwell Road, Nuffield Industrial Estate, Poole, Dorset, BH17 0BD Tel: (01202) 680333 Fax: (01202) 680101 E-mail: info@iecltd.co.uk Sales Contact: R. Blackaller *Distributors of technically advanced mechanical components,miniature,thin section bearings, ball screws, bearing lock nuts, laminar sealing rings, disc springs and safety washers, development components as well as High Security Electric Strikes, High Security Solenoid Bolts, Waterproof Keypads and Switches, together with Door closures & Locks, and special Door Handles.*

I E C Engineering Ltd, Brookside Avenue, Rustington, Littlehampton, West Sussex, BN16 3LF Tel: (01903) 773337 Fax: (01903) 786619 E-mail: info@ieceng.co.uk *Precision engineers*

I E C Precision Ltd, 3 Daux Road, Billingshurst, West Sussex, RH14 9SJ Tel: (01403) 783629 Fax: (01403) 784792 E-mail: sales@iecprecision.co.uk *Precision engineers*

I E C Services, Spinney Lodge, Birch Lane, Ascot, Berkshire, SL5 8RF Tel: (01344) 883440 Fax: (01344) 890856 *Air-conditioning control system*

I E I Ltd, Southern Cross, Basing View, Basingstoke, Hampshire, RG21 4HG Tel: (01256) 352361 Fax: (01256) 470259 E-mail: gen@iei-engineers.com *Building services engineers* Also at: Leeds

I E L Identequip Ltd, Tenmat Buildings, Ashburton Road West, Trafford Park, Manchester, M17 1RU Tel: 0161-876 4679 Fax: 0161-876 0009 E-mail: iel@identequip.com *Hot steel marking machines for slabs, blooms, billets & sections*

I E P, 21 Mapleton Rd, Risley, Derby, DE72 3QQ Tel: 01332 874290 Fax: 01332 874040 *Computer suppliers*

I E P Gardening Products, Unit 3 Budds Lane, Romsey, Hampshire, SO51 0HA Tel: (01794) 830899 Fax: (01794) 830923 E-mail: iepgp@btinternet.com *Stainless steel & aluminium welders metal garden products manufrs*

I E S A Ltd, Dallon Lane, Warrington, WA2 7PZ Tel: (01925) 634301 Fax: (01925) 417762 E-mail: info@iesa.co.uk *Engineers' merchants & ironmongers* Also at: Newcastle upon Tyne

▶ I E S Robust Tanks, Fountain House, Brindley Close, Holly Lane Industrial Estate, Atherstone, Warwickshire, CV9 2GA Tel: 0121-351 7219 Fax: (01827) 714534 *Water treatment plant & equipment manufacturers. Also tanks general & tanks water storage GRP*

I E T G plc, Oxford House, 2 Sixth Avenue, Doncaster Finningley Airport, Doncaster, South Yorkshire, DN9 3GG Tel: (01302) 802000 Fax: (01302) 802001 E-mail: sales@ietg.co.uk *Land, air & water surveyors*

▶ I F A Systems Ltd, 27 New Street, Charfield, Wotton-under-Edge, Gloucestershire, GL12 8ES Tel: (01453) 521855 Fax: (0870) 4208391 E-mail: sales@ifa-systems.co.uk *IFA Systems offers a complete website design & maintenance service exclusively for professional financial advisers & financial planners, including bespoke or templated website solutions, & a comprehensive range of website addons*

I F C C O Systems Ltd, Unit 3, Basingstoke Business Centre, Winchester Road, Basingstoke, Hampshire, RG22 4AU Tel: (01256) 357351 Fax: (01256) 357354 *Computer retailers & manufrs*

▶ I F Cardboard Creation Ltd, 40B, Burgate, Pickering, North Yorkshire, YO18 7AU Tel: (01751) 475757 E-mail: info@thatcompanycalled.com

▶ I F Controls Ltd, 102A Pedmore Road, Lye, Stourbridge, West Midlands, DY9 8DG Tel: (01384) 896577

I.F.E Ltd, 8 Well Street, London, E9 7PX Tel: (020) 8985 6501 Fax: (020) 8985 6501 E-mail: sales@ife-co.com *Hair piece suppliers*

I F M Services Ltd, Unit 14 Lodge Hill Industrial Estate, Station Road, Wells, Somerset, BA5 1EY Tel: (01749) 870942 Fax: (01749) 870087 *Wholesalers of industrial food machinery*

▶ I F P Systems Ltd, 10 Cameron Drive, Falkland, Cupar, Fife, KY15 7DL Tel: (01337) 857198 Fax: (01337) 857175

I F S Chemicals Ltd, Station Road, Roydon, King's Lynn, Norfolk, PE32 1AW Tel: (01485) 601155 Fax: (01485) 601144 E-mail: sales@ifs-group.com Principal Export Areas: Worldwide *Polyurethane chemicals suppliers*

▶ I F S Electronic Security Division, 20 St. Johns Road, Bootle, Merseyside, L20 8NJ Tel: 0151-955 4200 Fax: 0151-955 4240 E-mail: phill.ashton@ifscontractors.com *Building company*

▶ I F S UK Ltd, Oakdale House, Penny Pot Lane, Killinghall, Harrogate, North Yorkshire, HG3 2SD Tel: (01423) 509189 Fax: (01423) 562842

I Fay, 93 Ridgeway, Sherborne, Dorset, DT9 6DB Tel: (01935) 814018 Fax: (01935) 816950 *Joinery manufrs*

▶ I Fix PC'S, 29 Fuchsia Lane, Ipswich, IP4 1QB Tel: (01473) 422373 E-mail: andy@ifixpc.co.uk *ALL PC AND LAPTOP REPAIRS IN IPSWICH AND SUFFOLK.*Virus Removal,Crashes,hardware problems computer upgrades,hard drive problems,ipswich,suffolk,uk,east anglia,troubleshooting*

▶ I Fraser & Sons, 42 High Street, Rothes, Aberlour, Banffshire, AB38 7AY Tel: (01340) 831302 Fax: (01340) 831351

I G Ltd, Avondale Road, Cwmbran, Gwent, NP44 1XY Tel: (01633) 486486 Fax: (01633) 486492 E-mail: info@igltd.co.uk *Steel lintels manufrs*

I & G Cohen Ltd, Castle Works, Bazaar Street, Salford, M6 6GS Tel: 0161-736 8899 Fax: 0161-745 8697E-mail: sales@igcohen.com *Textile recyclers & secondhand clothing experts*

I G Index plc, Friars House, 157-168 Blackfriars Road, London, SE1 8EZ Tel: (020) 7896 0011 Fax: (020) 7896 0010 E-mail: igindex@igindex.co.uk *Financial book manufrs*

I G Industries plc, The Flarepath, Elsham Wolds Industrial Estate, Brigg, South Humberside, DN20 0SP Tel: (01652) 688888 Fax: (01652) 688808 E-mail: sales@igindustries.co.uk *Polythene film sheet & printed film manufrs*

I G P (UK) Ltd, Saltcoates Industrial Estate, 1-5 Cutlers Road, South Woodham Ferrers, Chelmsford, CM3 5WD Tel: (01245) 323555 Fax: (01245) 323762 E-mail: sales@igp-ukltd.co.uk *Suppliers to the printing & graphics industry*

▶ I G S Technical Services, 2239 London Road, Glasgow, G32 8XL Tel: 0141-764 0362

I G T C Ltd, 7 Huston Close, Barrow Upon Soar, Loughborough, Leicestershire, LE12 8NB Tel: (0845) 2020235 Fax: (0870) 7202265 E-mail: sales@safetyshopdirect.com *Suppliers of personal protective equipment*

I. & H. I & H Brown Ltd, PO Box 51, Perth, PH1 3YD Tel: (01738) 637171 Fax: (01738) 637175 E-mail: enquiries@ihbrown.com *Civil engineering contractors*

I H C Ltd, The Innovation Centre, Vienna Court, Kirkleatham Business Park, Redcar, Cleveland, TS10 5SH Tel: (01642) 777733 Fax: (01642) 777744 E-mail: enquiries@qai.co.uk *Food hygiene certification*

I H C Plating (Nelson) Ltd, Unit 2 Valley Trading Estate, Southfield Street, Nelson, Lancashire, BB9 0LD Tel: (01282) 693195 Fax: (01282) 696117 *Tool repair*

I H I Europe Ltd, America House, 2 America Square, London, EC3N 2LU Tel: (020) 7481 8180 Fax: (020) 7481 4955 E-mail: vicki@ihieuro.co.uk Principal Export Areas: Worldwide *Ship building & heavy industry*

I H Laboratories Ltd, Station Approach, Meopham, Gravesend, Kent, DA13 0LT Tel: (01474) 814917 Fax: (01474) 813117 *Research laboratories*

▶ I H R Ltd, 17 Eleanor Grove, Ickenham, Uxbridge, Middlesex, UB10 8BH Tel: (07005) 964088 Fax: (07005) 964099 E-mail: lynn.claydon@tiscali.co.uk *HR Consultancy, training & development services*

I H S Energy Group, 28 Church Street, Epsom, Surrey, KT17 4QP Tel: (01372) 745959 Fax: (01372) 727091 *Consultant engineers - oil & gas*

I H S Global Insight, Wimbledon Bridge House, 1 Hartfield Road, London, SW19 3RU Tel: (020) 8544 7800 Fax: (020) 8544 7801 E-mail: receptionist.london@globalinsight.com *Economics, information & marketing analysts services*

I H S Technical Indexes Ltd, Viewpoint One, Willoughby Road, Bracknell, Berkshire, RG12 8FB Tel: (01344) 426311 Fax: (01344) 328004 E-mail: info@ihs.com *Technical trade information service*

I I C O N Ltd, Regent House, Hubert Road, Brentwood, Essex, CM14 4JE Tel: (01277) 264404 Fax: (01277) 264405 *Computer consultants*

I J C (International) Ltd, 9 Lisburne Square, Torquay, TQ1 2PT Tel: (01803) 211350 Fax: (01803) 211351 E-mail: sales@ijcinternational.com *Grab distributors*

I J G Machines, 59 The Promenade, Portstewart, County Londonderry, BT55 7AF Tel: (028) 7083 3154 *Vending machines maintenance & suppliers*

I J Parkash Ltd, 30 Brunswick Street, Manchester, M13 9TQ Tel: 0161-273 5883 Fax: 0161-273 7262 E-mail: rajiv@absonline.net *Import merchants for textiles*

I J Quality Services, 28 Beresford Drive, Sutton Coldfield, West Midlands, B73 5QZ Tel: 0121-355 5159 Fax: 0121-355 5159 E-mail: ivorjones@ijqs.co.uk *Management system consultancy & auditing services*

I J Textiles (Clothing Manufacturers), 229 Westminster Road, Handsworth, Birmingham, B20 3NB Tel: 0121-356 3860 Fax: 0121-356 4864 *Textile & clothing manufrs*

I Johns & Sons, Leafield Pig Farm, Purrants Lane, Leafield, Witney, Oxfordshire, OX29 9PN Tel: (01993) 878526 *Agricultural contractors*

I K A Retail Solutions Ltd, 2 Hazelwood Lane, London, N13 5EX Tel: (020) 8447 9164 Fax: (020) 8292 9009 E-mail: sales@ikaepos.com *Supplier of epos with stock control systems for hospitality & general retail*

▶ I K M Tiles Marble & Granite, 55 Bangor Road, Edinburgh, EH6 5JX Tel: 0131-467 8900 Fax: 0131-467 8901 *Marble & granite manufrs*

I K O (Nippon Thompson), 2 Vincent Ave, Crownhill, Milton Keynes, MK8 0AB Tel: (01908) 566144 Fax: (01908) 565458 E-mail: sales@iko.co.uk *IKO NipponThompson manufacture a comprehensive range of linear slide units for almost every application need. Superbly engineered to exacting tolerances, the range includes miniature rails and slides plus high capacity structural units.*

I K Portable Solutions Ltd, I K House, Plough Road, Wellington, Telford, Shropshire, TF1 1ET Tel: (01952) 242000 Fax: (01952) 223789 E-mail: iki@netcomuk.co.uk *Hand held & automated data capture*

I & K Supplies, 8 Barrasgate Road, Fraserburgh, Aberdeenshire, AB43 9HH Tel: (01346) 510424 Fax: (01346) 510424 *Chemicals & cleaning product suppliers*

I L P Protective Packaging, 75 Woodburn Road, Carrickfergus, County Antrim, BT38 8PS Tel: (028) 9336 8448 Fax: (028) 9335 1447 E-mail: sales@ilp-plaswood.co.uk *Packaging manufrs*

I L S Ltd, Third Avenue, Pensnett Trading Estate, Kingswinford, West Midlands, DY6 7XX Tel: (01384) 402200 Fax: (01384) 402201 E-mail: marketing@ilsonline.com *Industrial fastener specialists*

▶ I L S Irrigation Systems & Equipment, 1 High Street, Brington, Huntingdon, Cambridgeshire, PE28 5AD Tel: (01832) 710029 Fax: (01832) 710136 *Irrigation systems & equipment designers*

▶ I M A Cooling Systems, Hamburg Way, North Lynn Industrial Estate, King's Lynn, Norfolk, PE30 2ND Tel: (01553) 767446 Fax: (01553) 767457 *Air conditioning*

▶ I M A Cooling Systems Ltd, Unit A3-A4, 156 St. Albans Road, Sandridge, St. Albans, Hertfordshire, AL4 9LP Tel: (01727) 840090 Fax: (01727) 830679 E-mail: reception@imacooling.co.uk *Refrigeration equipment suppliers & manufrs*

▶ I M A G E Nation.Com, 23 Vine Place, Sunderland, SR1 3NA Tel: (0870) 8502286 Fax: 0191-568 9555 E-mail: sales@imag-e-nation.com *Retail arts & crafts suppliers & picture framing*

I M A (UK) Ltd, 3 Arden Road, Alcester, Warwickshire, B49 6HN Tel: (01789) 400880 Fax: (01789) 400810 E-mail: hotdesk@imauk.co.uk *Packaging machinery sales, service & spares*

▶ I M B Cleaning & Maintenance, 29 Milton Road, Caterham, Surrey, CR3 5JG Tel: (01883) 334521 E-mail: imbcleaning@tiscali.co.uk *Cleaning services*

I M B Systems, 298 Nantwich Road, Crewe, CW2 6NY Tel: (01270) 663306 Fax: (01270) 650010 E-mail: imbsystems@btconnect.com *Hardware, software & consumables*

I M C Ltd, Unit 1, Abbey Road, Wrexham Industrial Estate, Wrexham, LL13 9RF Tel: (01978) 661155 Fax: (01978) 729990 E-mail: mail@imco.co.uk *IMC, based in Wrexham, is a leading company in the United Kingdom, manufacturing commercial bar and catering equipment.*

I M C C O Ltd, 1 Ashleigh Close, Barby, Rugby, Warwickshire, CV23 8UG Tel: (01788) 891866 Fax: (01788) 891953 E-mail: imcco_2000@yahoo.com *Cleaning chemical products*

I M C D UK Ltd, Times House, Throwley Way, Sutton, Surrey, SM1 4AF Tel: (020) 8770 7090 Fax: (020) 8770 7295 E-mail: *Chemical merchants*

I & M Controls Ltd, 75 Villa Street, Birmingham, B19 2XL Tel: 0121-551 7877 Fax: 0121-554 3846 E-mail: sales@iandmcontrols.co.uk *Control panel manufrs*

I M Dempster Ltd, 15 Caesar Avenue, Carnoustie, Angus, DD7 6DR Tel: (01241) 852822 E-mail: imdempsterltd@aol.com *Oil related electrical & instrumentation designers*

I M Design & Repair, 4 Hockley Lane, Ettington, Stratford-Upon-Avon, Warwickshire, CV37 7SS Tel: (01789) 740870 Fax: (01789) 740870 E-mail: ian@windowcontrols.com *Electronics designers & consultants*

I M Dunn, Quay Cottage, Salter Mill, Landulph, Saltash, Cornwall, PL12 6QG Tel: (01752) 845673 Fax: (01752) 845673 *Suspended ceilings installation*

▶ I M E L, Unit 6, Pages Industrial Park, Eden Way, Leighton Buzzard, Bedfordshire, LU7 4TZ Tel: (01525) 383555 Fax: (01525) 383700 E-mail: info@imel.biz *Underfloor heating specialist contractors*

I M E S Ltd, Tern Place, Denmore Road, Bridge of Don, Aberdeen, AB23 8JX Tel: (01224) 705777 Fax: (01224) 824808 E-mail: marketing@imes-group.com *Engineering services*

▶ I M E S, Unit 4 Castle Building, Gilston Road, Saltash, Cornwall, PL12 6TW Tel: (01752) 841433 Fax: (01752) 841433 *Testing & installation of lifting equipment*

I M F Technical Services Ltd, Unit 5 50 Cotton Street, Aberdeen, AB11 5EE Tel: (01224) 210147 Fax: (01224) 572752 E-mail: ian@imftech.freeserve.co.uk *Non-destructive test services*

I & M Findlay, Broadgate, Mouswald, Dumfries, DG1 4LY Tel: (01387) 830241 Fax: (01387) 830241 *Agricultural contractors*

I M H Birmingham Ltd, Unit 2 Clyde Street, Birmingham, B12 0NY Tel: 0121-773 2240 Fax: 0121-773 2275 E-mail: sales@imhltd.com *Tubular handrail manufrs*

I M I Cornelius, 39-41 Nuffield Way, Abingdon, Oxfordshire, OX14 1AE Tel: (01235) 555123 Fax: (01235) 555456 *Beer & soft drinks dispenser manufrs*

I M I Cornelius UK Ltd, 1-3 Tything Road East, Kinwarton, Alcester, Warwickshire, B49 6EU Tel: (01789) 763101 Fax: (01789) 763644 E-mail: sales@cornelius.com *Drinks dispense/ refrigeration equipment* Also at: Brighouse, Leicester & Sheffield

▶ I M I Cornelius (UK) Ltd, Rawson Spring Way, Sheffield, S6 1PG Tel: 0114-285 2345 Fax: 0114-285 3087 E-mail: gaskellsales@corneliusuk.com *Spirit measure dispenser manufrs*

I M I Watson Smith Ltd, Cross Chancellor Street, Leeds, LS6 2RT Tel: 0113-245 7587 Fax: 0113-246 5735 E-mail: enquiries@watsonsmith.com *Precision engineers*

▶ I M L Ltd, 8 London Road, Liphook, Hampshire, GU30 7AN Tel: (01428) 727476 *Computerised response system manufrs*

I M O Electronics Ltd, Unit 15, 1000 North Circular Road, London, NW2 7JP Tel: (020) 8452 6444 Fax: (020) 8450 2274 E-mail: imo@imopc.com *Electronic & electrical suppliers*

I M O (Marketing) Ltd, Whynscar House, The Ring, Bracknell, Berkshire, RG12 1BP Tel: (01344) 319770 Fax: (01344) 460112 *Food ingredient importers*

I M Plastech Ltd, 7 Levellers Lane, Eynesbury, St. Neots, Cambridgeshire, PE19 2JL Tel: (01480) 407214 Fax: (01480) 406737 *Specialist design & stainless steel fabricators*

I M Products Ltd, 2 London Hill Farm, London Road, Stockbridge, Hampshire, SO20 6EN Tel: (01264) 810261 Fax: (01264) 810642 *Welding fabricators*

I M Refinishers, 2 Northampton Road, Brixworth, Northampton, NN6 9DY Tel: (01604) 880880 Fax: (01604) 881222 E-mail: ideal.motors@virgin.net *Motor vehicle crash repairers*

▶ I M S Inovation Ltd, Fairykirk Road, Rosyth, Dunfermline, Fife, KY11 2QQ Tel: (01383) 410121

I M S International Marketing Services Ltd, Boulton Works, 54 College Road, Perry Barr, Birmingham, B44 8BS Tel: 0121-344 5500 Fax: 0121-344 5504 E-mail: sales@ims-ltd.co.uk *Universal joints, prop shafts & driveline product manufrs*

I M S Supplies Ltd, 3 Clifton Road, Huntingdon, Cambridgeshire, PE29 7EJ Tel: (01480) 411763 Fax: (01480) 417170 E-mail: imssupplies@cs.com *Producers of Press Tools, Fixtures. Jigs, Dies, Cutting Blades. Machine Parts, Sheet Metal Work, Special Purpose Machines, Machined Components. Wire Eroding, CNC Machining, Spark Eroding, Manual/Machines.*

I M Services, 2 Premier Way, Ampfield, Romsey, Hampshire, SO51 9DQ Tel: (01794) 518866 Fax: (01794) 518877 *Commercial vehicle body repairers*

I & M Steiner Ltd, 5 Reynard Business Park, Windmill Road, Brentford, Middlesex, TW8 9LY Tel: (020) 8847 4422 Fax: (020) 8847 3322 *Leisure equipment*

I Macpherson, Conisby, Bruichladdich, Isle of Islay, PA49 7UN Tel: (01496) 850295 Fax: (01496) 850295 *Agricultural contract services*

I Marvin, Unit 10a Clintons Yard, Rigs Road, Stornoway, Isle of Lewis, HS1 2RF Tel: (01851) 702178 Fax: (01851) 704233

I Mediation Ltd, Sussex Ho, 6 The Forbury, Reading, RG1 3EJ Tel: 0118-925 3338 Fax: 0118 9253200 *Software sales*

I N E C Engineering Co. Ltd, 73 Mornington Street, London, NW1 7QE Tel: (020) 7383 2385 Fax: (020) 7383 3471 *Construction plant, equipment export*

I N I Environmental Services Ltd, 77 Westwood Glen, Tilehurst, Reading, RG31 5NW Tel: 0118-942 7314 Fax: 0118-942 7313 E-mail: inienviro@aol.com *Water hygiene treatment services*

▶ I Need That Mortgage.com, 129 High St, Watton at Stone, Hertford, SG14 3SB Tel: 0870 991 7255 Fax: 07005 931146 E-mail: salesinformation@ineedthatmortgage.com *Independent Financial Consultants, from mortgages and related protection insurances to private medical insurance and pensions. Mortgages, Re-mortgages, Buy-to-Let, First Time Buyers, Mortgage Protection, Private Medical Insurance, Office in Caddington and Hertford*

I Nemetnejad Ltd, 403-405 Edgware Road, London, NW2 6LN Tel: (020) 8830 5511 Fax: (020) 8530 5522 E-mail: info@inemetnejad.com *Oriental carpet importer*

I Net Synergy Ltd, Martini House, 55 Newbury Street, Wantage, Oxfordshire, OX12 8DJ Tel: (01235) 766788 Fax: (01235) 766788 E-mail: phil-smith@inet-synergy.co.uk *Computer consultants*

I O E S Ltd, 6 Princeton Court, Felsham Road, London, SW15 1AZ Tel: (020) 8780 1222 Fax: (020) 8780 1812 E-mail: sales@ioes.net *Oilfield equipment suppliers*

I O Systech Ltd, 8 Willow Walk, Englefield Green, Egham, Surrey, TW20 0DQ Tel: (01784) 432058 E-mail: enquiries@iosystech.co.uk *Computer consultants*

I O T P.L.C., Crompton Close, Basildon, Essex, SS14 3AZ Tel: (01268) 523366 Fax: (01268) 527135 E-mail: eoe@eurocopy.co.uk *Copy equipment services & distributors*

I P 21 Ltd, 1 Cornhill, London, EC3V 3ND Tel: (020) 7645 8250 Fax: (020) 7645 8251 E-mail: info@ip21.co.uk *Patent & trade mark agents*

▶ I P 21 Ltd, Norwich Research Park, Colney, Norwich, NR4 7UT Tel: (01603) 457008 Fax: (01603) 251125 E-mail: info@ip21.co.uk *Patent agents & specialists*

I P 3, 83 Guildford Street, Chertsey, Surrey, KT16 9AS Tel: (0870) 3308625 Fax: (0870) 3308615 E-mail: admin@ip3.org.uk *Publishers, printers & promoters*

I P A Controls, 30 Craftmans Way, East Goscote, Leicester, LE7 3SL Tel: 0116-269 7100 Fax: 0116-269 6880 *Electrical control manufrs*

▶ I P A Print Associates Ltd, F Chiltern Commerce Centre, 45 Asheridge Road, Chesham, Buckinghamshire, HP5 2PY Tel: (01494) 791532 Fax: (01494) 783690 E-mail: sales@ipaprint.com

I P A Systems Ltd, 3 Aberford Road, Garforth, Leeds, LS25 1PZ Tel: 0113-287 5337 Fax: 0113-287 5338 E-mail: sales@ipasystems.co.uk *Computer software developer & publisher*

I P A Systems Ltd, 4 Liberty Court, 101-103 Bell Street, Reigate, Surrey, RH2 7JB Tel: (01737) 225010 Fax: (01737) 771827 E-mail: sales@ipasystems.co.uk *Electronic pre-press suppliers*

I P C Media, Focus House, 9 Dingwall Avenue, Croydon, CR9 2TA Tel: (020) 8726 8000 Fax: (020) 8726 8199 *Publishers-consumer specialist magazines & annuals*

I P C Media Ltd, Blue Fin Building, 110 Southwark Street, London, SE1 0SU Tel: (020) 3148 5000 Fax: E-mail: press_office@ipc.media.com *Publishers of books, magazines & electronic media*

I P C Systems Computer & Telecommunications Systems, Fairview House, Rigg Road, Cumnock, Ayrshire, KA18 3JB Tel: (01290) 421613 Fax: (01290) 425586 *Computer software house*

I & P Clark, Granville Street, Willenhall, West Midlands, WV13 1DN Tel: (01902) 636957 *French polishers*

▶ I P Creative Ltd, Northgate Business Centre, 38 North Gate, Newark, Nottinghamshire, NG24 1EZ Tel: (01636) 642819 Fax: (01636) 642801 E-mail: john.morrissey@ipcreative.co.uk *Marketing & graphic design services, including marketing strategy, planning, message development, advertising, corporate/brand identity, print, packaging, digital & exhibitions*

I P D Signs, 162 Walsall Road, Norton Canes, Cannock, Staffordshire, WS11 9RB Tel: (01543) 270033 Fax: (01543) 279911 E-mail: info@ipdsigns.co.uk *Sign makers*

▶ I P E C Furniture Ltd, Lodge Mill, Victoria Street, Accrington, Lancashire, BB5 0PG Tel: (01254) 235487 Fax: (01254) 871035 E-mail: info@ipecfurniture.co.uk *Office furniture*

I P L, Unit 16, Llys y Fedwen, Parc Menai, Poundbury, Bangor, Gwynedd, LL57 4BN Tel: (01248) 672122 E-mail: sales@ipl-int.com Principal Export Areas: Worldwide *Manufacturers of infrared detectors & infrared sensing equipment*

I P L Information Processing Ltd, Eveleigh House, Grove Street, Bath, BA1 5LR Tel: (01225) 475000 Fax: (01225) 444400 E-mail: sales@iplbath.com *Computer software developer & consultants*

I & P Lifting Gear Ltd, 237 Scotia Road, Stoke-on-Trent, ST6 4PS Tel: (01782) 814411 Fax: (01782) 575510 E-mail: info@iandplifting.co.uk *Lifting gear specialists*

I P S, 41 Central Avenue, West Molesey, Surrey, KT8 2QZ Tel: (020) 8481 9720 Fax: (020) 8481 9729 *Pharmaceutical manufrs*

I P S Fencing Supplies, 65 Toms Lane, Kings Langley, Hertfordshire, WD4 8NJ Tel: (01923) 268431 Fax: (01923) 261459 E-mail: info@ipsfencing.com *Garden Fencing, Sheds, Summer Houses and Decking supplied and installed.*

I P S Group Ltd, Lloyds Avenue House, 6 Lloyds Avenue, London, EC3N 3ES Tel: (020) 7481 8111 Fax: (020) 7481 0994 E-mail: enquiries@ipsgroup.co.uk *Insurance recruitment consultants*

I P S Hospital Services, Unit 5 Featherstall Road South, Oldham, OL9 6HS Tel: 0161-626 1844 Fax: 0161-627 5202 E-mail: ips@ipshospitalservices.co.uk *Disposable paper products manufrs*

I Palmer & Son Ltd, 106 Lower Parliament Street, Nottingham, NG1 1EH Tel: 0115-950 3458 Fax: 0115-941 3458 *Cardboard box manufrs*

I Q C International Ltd, PO Box 1024, Arundel, West Sussex, BN18 0LT Tel: (0870) 0130999 Fax: (0870) 0130888 E-mail: sales@iqc.co.uk *Industrial connector distributors*

I Q E Europe Ltd, Cypress Drive, St. Mellons, Cardiff, CF3 0EG Tel: (029) 2083 9400 Fax: (029) 2083 9401 E-mail: info@iqep.com Principal Export Areas: Worldwide *Semi-conductor material manufrs*

I Q L Ltd, Stirling Road, Cressex Business Park, High Wycombe, Buckinghamshire, HP12 3ST Tel: (01494) 463636 Fax: (01494) 439639 E-mail: sales@iqllimited.co.uk *Rubber lining applicators suppliers & manufrs*

I Q Software Systems, Old Brewery House, Redbrook, Monmouth, Gwent, NP25 4LU Tel: (01600) 719229 Fax: (01600) 719049 E-mail: enquiries@iqss.co.uk *Software developers*

I Q T Ltd, 42-44 The Street, Appledore, Ashford, Kent, TN26 2BX Tel: (01233) 758772 Fax: (01233) 758773 E-mail: iqtltd@aol.com *Engineers tools & equipment*

I Q Textiles, Mid Road, Prestonpans, East Lothian, EH32 9ER Tel: (01875) 811200 Fax: (01875) 811452 *PVC, polyurethane coated fabric processors & manufrs*

▶ I R A T A, 99 West Street, Farnham, Surrey, GU9 7EN Tel: (01252) 739150 Fax: (01252) 739140 E-mail: info@irata.org *Trade association for the rope access industry*

I R B Ltd, Harlin House, 4th Floor, 47-51 Great Suffolk Street, London, SE3 9RQ Tel: (020) 8265 5000 Fax: (020) 6333 0315 E-mail: info@irb.co.uk *Market research services*

▶ I R D Ltd, Block 3 Brymau One Trading Estate, River Lane, Saltney, Chester, CH4 8RQ Tel: (01244) 682222 Fax: (01244) 675439 E-mail: sales@irdbalancing.com *Balancing machines suppliers*

I R Group, Forbes House, Whitefriars Estate, Tudor Road, Harrow, Middlesex, HA3 5SS Tel: (020) 8420 0211 *Electronic measuring instruments* Also at: Aberdeen & Manchester

I R L Group Ltd, C1 Swingbridge Road, Loughborough, Leicestershire, LE11 5JD Tel: (01509) 217101 Fax: (01509) 611004 E-mail: info@irlgroup.com *Floor wall resin coating specialists*

I R Laidlaw, The Building Centre, 26 Store Street, London, WC1E 7BT Tel: (020) 7436 0779 Fax: (020) 7436 0740 E-mail: infolondon@laidlaw.net *Architectural ironmongers*

I R Laidlaw, Strawberry Lane Industrial Estate, Strawberry Lane, Willenhall, West Midlands, WV13 3RS Tel: (01902) 600400 Fax: (01902) 600490 *Architectural ironmongers* Also at: Cheadle

I R S Ltd, Lion Works, Castle Acre Road, Swaffham, Norfolk, PE37 7HS Tel: (01760) 721399 Fax: (01760) 723726 E-mail: sales@irs-ltd.co.uk *Road sign manufrs*

I R S Structural Solutions Ltd, Unit 6, Beta Terrace, Masterlord Business Park, West Road, Ransomes Europark, Ipswich, IP3 9SX Tel: (0870) 7607607 Fax: (0870) 7607607 E-mail: info@irs-group.com *Undertake situational repairs*

I R Security & Safety, 1 Berrington Road, Leamington Spa, Warwickshire, CV31 1NB Tel: (01926) 437000 Fax: (01926) 437005 E-mail: ir_customerservice@eu.irco.com *Access maintenance door & shutter repairs*

I R T S Ltd, Hillside, Sewell, Dunstable, Bedfordshire, LU6 1RP Tel: (01582) 600080 Fax: (01582) 666447 *Steam cleaning service*

I R T Surveys Ltd, Unit D, Software Media Centre, Prospect House, Technology Park, Dundee, DD2 1TY Tel: (01382) 598510 Fax: (01382) 598533 E-mail: info@irtsurveys.co.uk *Infrared thermographic surveyors*

▶ I R W (Enclosures) Ltd, Unit 7, Liskeard Enterprise Centre, Station Road, Liskeard, Cornwall, PL14 4DA Tel: (01579) 344334

I S C Ltd, Deiniolen, Caernarfon, Gwynedd, LL55 3DE Tel: (01286) 871999 Fax: (01286) 870127 E-mail: sales@iscwales.com *Strength related metal component manufrs*

I S C Computers Plc, 2 Pioneer Way, Lincoln, LN6 3DH Tel: (01522) 686464 *Computer dealership*

I S C Networks, Solar House, Blackstone Road, Stukeley Meadows Industrial Es, Huntingdon, Cambridgeshire, PE29 6EF Tel: (01480) 420000 Fax: (01480) 420080 E-mail: enquiries@iscnet.co.uk *Computer reseller*

I S C Textile Machinery Ltd, 1 Town St, Farsley, Pudsey, W. Yorkshire, LS28 5EN Tel: 0113-257 7015 *Textile importers*

▶ I S E Fire Products & Services Ltd, 4 Duke Street, Burton Latimer, Kettering, Northamptonshire, NN15 5SG Tel: (01536) 420333 Fax: (01536) 420444 E-mail: sales@isefireproducts.co.uk *Fire extinguisher manufrs*

I S Enterprises International, Clement House, Commerce Way, Colchester, CO2 8HY Tel: (01206) 798131 Fax: (01206) 791186 E-mail: sales@isenterprisesintl.co.uk *Promotional clothing manufrs* Also at: Luton

I S F Paints Ltd, Thurmaston BLVD, Leicester, LE4 9HS Tel: 0116-274 2222 Fax: 0116-274 3333 *Industrial paint manufrs*

I & S Fashions Ltd, 5 Vine Court, London, E1 1JH Tel: (020) 7247 9526 Fax: (020) 7377 8853 *Ladies & children's clothes manufrs*

I S G Direct Ltd, 31 Courthouse Road, London, N12 7PH Tel: (020) 8445 1631 Fax: (020) 8343 8326 *Computer systems & software*

I S & G Steel Stockholders Ltd, Cooting Road Industrial Estate, Aylesham, Canterbury, Kent, CT3 3ER Tel: (01304) 840300 Fax: (01304) 840600 E-mail: aylesham@isg-steel.co.uk *Steel stockholders*

I S & G Steel Stockholders Ltd, Temple Wood, Stock Road, West Hanningfield, Chelmsford, CM2 8LL Tel: (01277) 840471 Fax: (01277) 840234 E-mail: chelmsford@isg-steel.co.uk *Steel stockholders* Also at: Ashford, Beckenham, Chelmsford, Ipswich & London SE17

I S Group, Unit 1 Enterprise House Aber Park, Aber Road, Flint, Clwyd, CH6 5EX Tel: (01352) 792000 Fax: (01352) 792001 E-mail: sales@impactsigns.co.uk *Manufacturers of signs*

I S Integration Ltd, Westpoint, 4 Redheughs Rigg, Edinburgh, EH12 9DQ Tel: (0131) 338 6106 Fax: (0131) 338 6700 *Consultants*

▶ I S L (Computers) Ltd, 67 Bradford Road, Brighouse, West Yorkshire, HD6 1ST Tel: (0845) 6002526 Fax: (0845) 721339 E-mail: geremi@isl-computers.co.uk *Computer services*

I S O Covers Ltd, Trent Valley Industrial Estate, Station Road, Rugeley, Staffordshire, WS15 2HQ Tel: (01889) 574333 Fax: (01889) 574111 E-mail: info@isocovers.com *Insulation for plastic industry & insulation jackets manufrs*

I S P C Surface Preperation Ltd, Wakefield Road, Ossett, West Yorkshire, WF5 9AW Tel: (01924) 276303 Fax: (01924) 277829 E-mail: uk-info@surfacepreperation.com Principal Export Areas: Worldwide *Shot blasting & blast cleaning equipment manufrs*

I S P Industrial Support Products Ltd, Unit H2 Lambs Farm Business Park, Basingstoke Road, Swallowfield, Reading, RG7 1PQ Tel: 0118-988 6873 Fax: 0118-988 6576 E-mail: info@isp-cablejointing.co.uk *Cable jointing kits & accessories*

I S S Group Ltd, Pellowe House, Francis Road, Withington, Manchester, M20 4XP Tel: 0161-445 5446 Fax: 0161-445 4914 E-mail: sales@iss-group.co.uk *Scientific instrument distributors &sub-contract services*

▶ I S S Machinery Services Ltd, 37 Eastcheap, London, EC3M 1DT Tel: (020) 7626 3505 Fax: (020) 7626 3606 *Spare parts for ships*

I S S Support Services, Strathdon Drive, London, SW17 0PS Tel: (020) 8947 9045 Fax: (020) 8947 9732 *Contract cleaning & support services*

I S S UK Ltd, Wells House, 65 Boundary Road, Woking, Surrey, GU21 5BS Tel: (01483) 754960 Fax: (01483) 745999 E-mail: iss@uk.issworld.com *Business support services* Also at: Branches throughout the U.K.

I S T (UK) Ltd, St. Andrew House, Otley Road, Skipton, North Yorkshire, BD23 1EX Tel: (01756) 700741 Fax: (01756) 700734 E-mail: info@uk.ist-uv.com *Industrial drying systems ultra violet suppliers & manufrs*

I Soft P.L.C., Lomond Court, The Castle Business Park, Stirling, FK9 4TU Tel: (01786) 450532 Fax: (01786) 449504 *Information technology consultants*

I Spi Ltd, 47 Mansionhouse Road, Mount Vernon, Glasgow, G32 0RP Tel: 0141-764 1600 Fax: 0141-764 1600 *Signs & promotions*

▶ I Support Ltd, 8-9 Rodney Road, Southsea, Hampshire, PO4 8SY Tel: (023) 9286 3504 Fax: (023) 9273 4510 E-mail: martin@isupport-uk.com *IT support*

▶ I T @ Spectrum Ltd, 1 Trinity Street, Hull, HU3 1JR Tel: (01482) 586732 Fax: (01482) 211428 E-mail: smonkman@itatspectrum.co.uk *Canon office equipment suppliers*

continued

I T A Ceilings Ltd, Unit 4 107 Summerway, Exeter, EX4 8DP Tel: (01392) 468781 Fax: (01392) 465476 E-mail: itacielings@aol.com *Suspended ceiling manufrs*

▶ I T A Distribution, Suite 7, Alperton House, Bridgewater Road, Wembley, Middlesex, HA0 1EH Tel: (020) 8903 4442

I T At Bicester, 15 Manorsfield Road, Bicester, Oxfordshire, OX26 6EH Tel: (01869) 353939 E-mail: apine@occ.ac.uk *Computer trainers*

I T Business Solutions Ltd, 17 Park Mans, London, W6 0YD Tel: 0208 563 2188 Fax: 0208 5638634 *IT solutions providers*

I T C, 114 East Street, Southampton, SO14 3HD Tel: (01747) 842230 Fax: (0870) 7443381 E-mail: itc@itcinternet.com *Computer hardware retailers*

I T C, 68 High Street, Witney, Oxfordshire, OX28 6HJ Tel: (01993) 709999 Fax: (01993) 778367 *Telecommunications contractors*

▶ I T C (Epos) Ltd, Barnsley Business & Innovation Centre, Innovation Way, Barnsley, South Yorkshire, S75 1JL Tel: (01226) 731785 Fax: (01226) 731867 E-mail: sales@itcepos.co.uk Sales Contact: O. Gleadall *We are Designers, Developers and Suppliers of a range of specialist software modules for use in the management and control of retail businesses. The software is scalable for any size of business and meets the needs of nearly every type of retail outlet! Our Merlin range of software modules cover the whole retail sector and controls all aspects of the business from procurement to sales, both 'Customer Present' and 'Customer Not Present' transactions, including facilities for e-Commerce.*

▶ I T C Group, 1 Wearington Business Centre, Piparates Road, Peterborough, PE4 5BH Tel: (01733) 292810 Fax: (01733) 327112 E-mail: sales@itcgroup.co.uk *Computer sales & maintenance*

I T C Infotech Ltd, 118 Saxon Gate West, Milton Keynes, MK9 2DN Tel: (01908) 230055 Fax: (01908) 695573 E-mail: sales@itcinfotech.co.uk *Software consultants*

I T I C Ltd, International House, 26-28 Creechurch Lane, London, EC3A 5BA Tel: (020) 7338 0150 Fax: (020) 7338 0151 *Insurance company*

▶ I T I Techmedia, 191 West George Street, Glasgow, G2 2LB Tel: 0141-240 1180 Fax: 0141-240 1190 E-mail: email@ititechmedia.com *Research& development technology, media*

▶ I T Installations Ltd, Aizlewoods Mill, Nursery Street, Sheffield, S3 8GG Tel: 0114-282 3301 Fax: 0114-282 3302 E-mail: sales@it-installations.co.uk *Voice, data & network cabling solutions*

▶ I T Logic, Unit G10 Malthouse Business Centre, 48 Southport Road, Ormskirk, Lancashire, L39 1QR Tel: (01695) 580102 Fax: (01695) 580100 E-mail: info@it-logic.biz *Computer systems consultants*

I T M A B Ltd, Unit 2 Rushtons Farm Estate, Warren House Road, Wokingham, Berkshire, RG40 5RE Tel: 0118-977 5977 Fax: 0118-977 5624 *Audio visual conferencing*

▶ I T M S, Unit 1, Great Bridge Industrial Estate, Tipton, West Midlands, DY4 0HR Tel: 0121-522 3622 Fax: 0121-522 3822 *Fork lifts & engineering services*

I T P S A, North York Trading Estate, Kettlestring Lane, York, YO30 4XF Tel: (01904) 690644 Fax: (01904) 690653 E-mail: sales@itp.es *Aircraft engine repairers*

I T Professionals International, 306 Grantham Park, Fulham, London, SW6 1SE Tel: (020) 7381 4620 E-mail: mahmoodint@aol.com *Global outsourcing & internet recruitment agency*

▶ I & T Projects & Installations Ltd, Unit 2, James W. Properties Business Park, Wood Street, Burton-On-Trent, Staffordshire, DE14 3AB Tel: (01283) 541702 Fax: (01283) 548954 E-mail: sales@iandtprojects.co.uk *Ovens, industrial powder coating plant spray booth manufrs*

I T Protocol Ltd, 3 Weston Farm, The Street, Albury, Guildford, Surrey, GU5 9BZ Tel: (01483) 203000 Fax: (01483) 203030 E-mail: sales@itprotocol.com *Computer systems & software suppliers*

▶ I T R M Ltd, Thames House, St. Johns Road, Sidcup, Kent, DA14 4HD Tel: (07000) 284876 Fax: (020) 8308 3301 E-mail: info@itrm.co.uk *IT service & support & recruitment solutions*

I T S Ltd, PO Box 331, Slough, SL2 3DQ Tel: (01753) 642144 Fax: (01753) 646461 E-mail: dir@its.ltd.uk *Industrial consultants*

I T S L Net Ltd, 2 Marsh Lane, Birmingham, B23 6NX Tel: (0870) 7437780 Fax: (0870) 7437781 E-mail: sales@itslnet.com *Computer systems & software development*

I T S Projects Ltd, 42-44 Portman Road, Reading, RG30 1EA Tel: 0118-950 0225 Fax: 0118-950 3267 E-mail: info@itsprojects.co.uk *Suspended ceilings & partitioning supply & fit service*

I T S Tools Ltd, Daish Way, Dodnor Lane Industrial Estate, Newport, Isle of Wight, PO30 5XB Tel: (01983) 526344 Fax: (01983) 821547 E-mail: itstools@tiscali.co.uk *Power tools, garden machinery, small plant items etc. Distributors for Dewalt Bosch Fein Metabo Skil Elektra Makita*

▶ I T S Trac, Unit 6a Tractor Spares Industrial Estate, Strawberry Lane, Willenhall, West Midlands, WV13 3RN Tel: (01902) 633614 Fax: (01902) 633625 E-mail: pford@itstrac.co.uk *Contractors of plant hire*

I T S (UK) Ltd, PO Box 335, Cardiff, CF23 7YQ Tel: (029) 2073 6080 Fax: (029) 2073 6080 E-mail: training@itsukltd.com *Fork lift truck operator & instructor training services*

▶ I T S Western, 1 Apex Court, Woodlands, Bradley Stoke, Bristol, BS32 4JT Tel: (01454) 619928 Fax: (01454) 619391 E-mail: spencertownsley@itswestern.co.uk *ITS Western operates exclusively in the construction marketplace for both permanent and temporary vacancies. From our bases in Bristol and Cardiff we are ideally placed to assist you in your staffing requirements through the South West, South Wales, and the Midlands.*We are part of*

continued

*the ITS Group - an independently owned group of recruitment companies, specialising in the supply of personnel to construction companies across Central and South West England and South Wales since 1973.*Our hands-on management team have unrivalled experience in the industry and an equally impressive client list; we can proudly claim to have supplied every major contractor within the UK, besides many overseas.*We have succeeded for so long by ensuring that we meet all of our client''s requirements, whether they are temporary or permanent, unskilled or management. Our workforce encompasses all the skill classifications a 21st century construction project requires from operatives through to senior management*

▶ I T Shaw Ltd, Low Mill Business Park, Ulverston, Cumbria, LA12 9EE Tel: (01229) 581928 Fax: (01229) 587624

I T Solution Ltd, Concord House, Providence Drive, Stourbridge, West Midlands, DY9 8HQ Tel: (0871) 7000081 Fax: (01384) 892777 *It Solution*

▶ I T Solutions, 2 Lea Court, Orchard End Avenue, Amersham, Buckinghamshire, HP7 9LS Tel: 01494 765494 E-mail: jeremy@it-solutions.me.uk *computer repair and small networks wireless etc.*

▶ I T Solutions, 31a The Broadway, St. Ives, Cambridgeshire, PE27 5BX Tel: (01480) 494908 Fax: (01480) 494913 *Computer suppliers & repairers*

I T Solutions UK Ltd, Alpine House, Honeypot Lane, London, NW9 9RX Tel: (020) 8206 2874 Fax: (020) 8204 8487 E-mail: enquiries@swiftpro.com *Computer maintenance & repairers*

I T Source International, Sheldon House, 29 Morley Street, Bradford, West Yorkshire, BD7 1AG Tel: (01274) 725572 Fax: (01274) 725572 *Computer software distributors*

▶ I T Supplies, 7 Grange Road, Houstoun Industrial Estate, Livingston, West Lothian, EH54 5DE Tel: (01506) 430400 Fax: (01506) 430500 E-mail: sales@itsuppliesuk.com *Computer software consultants*

I T T Water & Waste Water, Colwick Indust Estate, Colwick Industrial Estate, Nottingham, NG4 2AN Tel: 0115-940 0111 Fax: (01202) 631008 E-mail: admin@allweiler-pumps.demon.co.uk Purchasing Contact: R. Randall Sales Contact: B. Allen *Manufacturers of pumps, including chemical, glandless, hydraulic, hygienic, magnetic drive, marine, screw & thermal oil*

▶ I T Telecoms Ltd, 34 Avenue Parade, Accrington, Lancashire, BB5 6PP Tel: (01254) 394608 Fax: (01254) 395649 E-mail: sales@it-telecoms.org *Telecommunications*

I T Telecoms Ltd, 34 Avenue Parade, Accrington, Lancashire, BB5 6PP Tel: (01254) 394608 Fax: (01254) 395649 E-mail: sales@it-telecoms.org *Electronic manufrs*

I T Trading UK Ltd, Unit 4a Scotts Close, Batten Road, Downton Industrial Estate, Salisbury, SP5 3RA Tel: (01725) 513403 Fax: (01725) 513714 E-mail: info@ittrading.co.uk *Recycling of corporate IT equipment*

I T W Ltd, PO Box 87, Swansea, SA5 4ED Tel: (01792) 563400 Fax: (01792) 580525 *Industrial fastener manufrs*

I T W Angleboard, Crackley Way, Peartree Lane, Dudley, West Midlands, DY2 0UW Tel: (01384) 253290 Fax: (01384) 253321 E-mail: uksales@itwangleboard.net *Edge guard manufrs*

I T W betaprint, Unit 5, Shepperton Business Park, Govett Avenue, Shepperton, Middlesex, TW17 8BA Tel: (01932) 230030 Fax: (01932) 247404 E-mail: doverhill@itwinfo.com *Suppliers of thermal transfer printers & thermal ribbon*

▶ I T W Contstructions Products, Unit R8, Blair Coart, 110 Borain Street, Portdundas Business Park, Glasgow, G4 9XG Tel: 0141-342 1660 Fax: 0141-332 7489 E-mail: sales@itwcp.co.uk *Building construction*

I T W Devcon, Unit 3 Shipton Way, Express Business Park, Rushden, Northamptonshire, NN10 6GL Tel: (0870) 4587388 Fax: (0870) 4589077 E-mail: sales@itw-devcon.co.uk *Manufacturers of epoxy resin*

I T W Foils, Kays & Kears Industrial Estate, Blaenavon, Pontypool, Gwent, NP4 9AZ Tel: (01495) 796500 Fax: (01495) 790797 E-mail: info@itwfoils.co.uk *Hot stamping foil*

I T W McMurdo Connectors, Norway Road, Hilsea, Portsmouth, PO3 5HT Tel: (023) 9269 4971 Fax: (023) 9265 3356 E-mail: itwswitch1@aol.com *Connector & switch manufrs*

I T W Plexus, Unit 3, Shipton Way, Express Business Park, Rushden, Northamptonshire, NN10 6GL Tel: (0870) 4587588 Fax: (0870) 4589077 E-mail: sales@itwplexus.co.uk Principal Export Areas: Africa *Manufacturer of methacrylate structural adhesives*

I.T.W Welding Products Group, Horwich Business Park Chorley New Road Unit 102, Rivington House, Horwich, Bolton, BL6 5UE Tel: (01204) 469058 Fax: (01204) 473039 E-mail: sales@itw-welding.co.uk *Welding equipment manufrs*

▶ I T West, 5 Dowren House, Foundry Lane, Hayle, Cornwall, TR27 4HD Tel: (01736) 758370 Fax: (01736) 758348 E-mail: info@itwest.co.uk *Computer software manufrs*

I T Works Alba Ltd, Building 1020 Rosyth Dockyard, Rosyth, Dunfermline, Fife, KY11 2YD Tel: (01383) 411442 Fax: (01383) 411488 E-mail: enquiries@itworks-alba.co.uk *IT consultants*

I V A X Pharmaceutical UK Ltd, Whitehouse Vale, Aston La North, Runcorn, Cheshire, WA7 3FA Tel: (01928) 707800 Fax: (01928) 707790 *Healthcare*

I V M Ltd, Unit 3-4, Willington, Crook, County Durham, DL15 0UT Tel: (01388) 746538 Fax: (01388) 746538 E-mail: contact.ivm@btconnect.com *Plastic injection moulders with a full range of related services including new tool validation, material selections, production runs and assembly.*

continued

Accredited with ISO 9001:2000 we supply various market sectors and have an appreciation of the quality, deadlines and expectations of every project undertaken.

I V S International Ltd, 715 New Hey Road, Huddersfield, HD3 3YL Tel: (01422) 310333 Fax: (01422) 310332 E-mail: sales@ivsinternational.co.uk *Recycled machinery suppliers*

▶ I View Multimedia, 30-40, Elcho Street, London, SW11 4AU Tel: (020) 7223 8691 Fax: (020) 7504 3619 E-mail: info@iview-multimedia.com *Computer maintenance & repair services*

I W F Ltd, Ilderton Station, West Lilburn, Alnwick, Northumberland, NE66 4PH Tel: (01668) 217900 Fax: (01668) 217909 E-mail: neil@iwf.co.uk *Gymnastic equipment & stain glass windows manufrs*

I W I S Chain Ltd, Bridge House, Seven Bridge, Bewdley, Worcestershire, DY12 1AB Tel: (01299) 400080 Fax: (01299) 404588 E-mail: sales@iwischain.co.uk *Chain importers & distributors*

▶ I Want To Be Face Painters, 15 Westwood Close, Great Holm, Milton Keynes, MK8 9EE Tel: (01908) 561262 E-mail: iwanttobe@f2s.com *FACEPAINTER. creatives designs for any occassion, such as fetes, birthday parties, open days, weddings, or even just for that one off special face for a fancy dress party.... What ever the event! .. Whatever the age! PL insured and police checked. Good prices!*

I Y E England Co Ltd, 1 Towerfield Road, Shoeburyness, Southend-on-Sea, SS3 9QE Tel: (01702) 291291 Fax: (01702) 291391 E-mail: info@iye-england.co.uk *Sailboat hardware & deck safety equipment*

I Y S Control Systems, 15e West Station Yard, Spital Road, Maldon, Essex, CM9 6TW Tel: (01621) 858185 Fax: (01621) 893769 E-mail: design_john@europe.com *Marine control system manufrs*

▶ i2i Technology Ltd, The Forum, 277 London Road, Burgess Hill, West Sussex, RH15 9QU Tel: (0870) 4445201 Fax: (0870) 4445204 E-mail: philip@i2ic.com *IT & media services*

▶ i2i Television Ltd, The Studio, Bankhead Farm Road, Strathaven, Lanarkshire, ML10 6TR Tel: (01698) 794100 E-mail: crews@i2itv.com *Video production services , equipped broadcast television camera crews*

I3s, Higher Barn, Wildboarclough, Macclesfield, Cheshire, SK11 0BD Tel: (01260) 227377 Fax: (01260) 227399 *Simulation products & services*

▶ I4 Product Design, Technopole Centre, Bush Estate, Edinburgh, EH26 0PJ Tel: 0131-448 2266 Fax: (0871) 6619674 E-mail: gmiller@i4productdesign.co.uk *Product design service*

I4c Publicity, 3 Broad Street, Coventry, CV6 5AX Tel: (024) 7666 7440 Fax: (024) 7666 3736 E-mail: sales@i4cpublicity.co.uk *Supplier promotional gifts, pin badges, tie & headscarf*

▶ i4insurance, Ipswich, IP1 Tel: (01473) 268210 E-mail: advertising@i4insurance.co.uk *Introducing i4insurance.co.uk*I4insurance is the exciting new website dedicated to helping customers find insurance quickly and cheaply. By matching customer's details and car to a panel of top UK insurance companies, i4insurance for FREE can return a list of suitable companies for them to call.**This is a really useful service for customers as not all insurance companies are compatible with certain people, therefore i4insurance puts them in touch with the most suitable companies first time. No longer will customers have to trawl the internet or Yellow Pages, they log on to i4insurance and all the information needed is provided in just a few minutes**

Iab Laboratory Specialists, Park Studios, Parkwood St, Keighley, West Yorkshire, BD21 4PJ Tel: 01535 611299 Fax: 01535 680836 *Laboratory furnishing suppliers*

Iain Glass, Wrangham, Philips Lane, Darrington, Pontefract, West Yorkshire, WF8 3BH Tel: (01977) 795497 Fax: (01977) 790777 E-mail: iainglass@btclick.com *Bottle inspection machinery distributors*

▶ Iain M Crosbie, Beechfield Road, Willowyard Industrial Estate, Beith, Ayrshire, KA15 1LN Tel: (01505) 504848 Fax: (01505) 504674

Ian Bannings Car Audio & Security Ltd, 3 The Riverside Business Centre, Walnut Tree Close, Guildford, Surrey, GU1 4UG Tel: (01483) 301500 Fax: (01483) 300813 *Audio communication distributors*

▶ Ian Craig (Haulage) Ltd, 44-46 Broomhill Road, Bonnybridge, Stirlingshire, FK4 2AN Tel: (01324) 812250

Ian Crawford, Whitelees Road, Lanark, ML11 7LD Tel: (01555) 664432 Fax: (01555) 661262 E-mail: sales@signsandsafety.com *Agricultural contractor & country stores*

▶ Ian Howard Caravans, 1 Didcot Drive, Nottingham, NG8 5EQ Tel: 0845 838 7570 Fax: 08719 895259 E-mail: ian@howardcaravans.co.uk *For All Your Caravan Holiday Rental''''s Come To Ian Howard caravans**I have hundreds Of Static Caravans available At Locations all over the UK**Tel 0845 8387570 (Local Rate)*Email ian@howardcaravans.co.uk*

Ian & Janet Downer Ltd, 2 Orient Road, Paignton, Devon, TQ3 2PB Tel: (01803) 527068 Fax: (01803) 527068 *Catering equipment hire*

Ian Keat Jewellers Ltd, 28 The Straight, Lincoln, LN2 1JD Tel: (01522) 539800 Fax: (01522) 520213 E-mail: enquiries@keat.com *Jewellery repairers & manufrs*

▶ Ian McBain Garden Design, Tythorne Lodge, Oasby, Grantham, Lincolnshire, NG32 3NA Tel: 01529 455755 E-mail: mail@ianmcbain.co.uk *The complete garden design and planting service for private and trade clients. Pubs, hotels, offices, property developers.*

▶ Ian Milne Electrical Ltd, Newlands, Alyth, Blairgowrie, Perthshire, PH11 8HE Tel: (01828) 632893

Ian Mitchell, Stones Top, Hebden Bridge Road, Oxenhope, Keighley, West Yorkshire, BD22 9QH Tel: (07973) 692225 Fax: (01535) 643893 *Plant machinery hire*

▶ Ian Reid Removals, Hagdale Industrial Estate, Baltasound, Unst, Shetland, ZE2 9DS Tel: (01957) 711410

▶ Ian Ryall, 157a, Wood Street, London, E17 3LX Tel: (07775) 933371

▶ Ian T Cobb, 8 Poplar Avenue, Birstall, Leicester, LE4 3DU Tel: 0116-267 6063 Fax: 0116-267 6063 E-mail: ian@iantcobb.co.uk *Clock making materials, brass, sheet, bar, angle, wheel blanks manufrs*

▶ Ian W Harrison, 16 Wainman Road, Peterborough, PE2 7BU Tel: (01733) 390815 Fax: (01733) 390817 *Lifting equipment manufrs*

Ian Waddington (live Stock) Ltd, Kimberly House, Mounsey Road, Preston, PR5 6LS Tel: (01772) 629988 Fax: (01772) 629988 *Livestock agents*

▶ Ian White General Moulders, 27/28 Stirling Close, Washington, Tyne & Wear, NE38 8QD Tel: 0191-417 1040 Fax: 0191-417 1040 E-mail: iangrp@hotmail.co.uk *Moulders*

▶ Ian Williams Ltd, Stratford St North, Birmingham, B11 1BP Tel: 0121-766 5700 Fax: 0121-766 8715

Ian Williams, Station Road, Warmley, Bristol, BS30 8XG Tel: 0117-960 9510 Fax: 0117-935 3772 E-mail: lynne.westcott@ianwilliams.co.uk *Painting & property repairs* Also at: Birmingham, Cambridge, Cardiff, Farnham, Plymouth, Portsmouth & Teddington

Ian Wilson Gunmakers, 53 Wide Bargate, Boston, Lincolnshire, PE21 6SH Tel: (01205) 365668 *Gunsmiths repair & country wear retailers*

▶ ianart.co.uk, Egremont, Arterial Road, Basildon, Essex, SS14 3JN Tel: (01268) 520899 Fax: (01268) 520899 E-mail: ian@ianart.co.uk *Artist - specialising in Caricatures (including 'Live Caricature Entertainment' and Logo designs*

Ias Smarts Ni Ltd, 157 /159 High Street Citigate, Holywood, County Down, BT18 9HU Tel: (028) 9039 5500 Fax: (028) 9039 5600 *Public relations consultants*

Arthur Ibbett Ltd, River Lane, Great Paxton, St. Neots, Cambridgeshire, PE19 6RD Tel: (01480) 473452 Fax: (01480) 405026 E-mail: aibbet@lineone.net *Agricultural engineers*

Ibcc, 9 Ferndown Close, Bristol, BS11 0UP Tel: 0117-968 2691 Fax: 0117-962 6500 E-mail: ibcc@btinternet.com Principal Export Areas: North America, Central America & South America *Management marketing finance computer consultants*

Ibd Ltd, 3 City Park Industrial Estate, Gelderd Road, Leeds, LS12 6DR Tel: 0113-279 6988 Fax: 0113-231 0336 E-mail: douglas@barclays.net Principal Export Areas: Worldwide *Bearing & power transmission equipment suppliers*

IBESS Ltd, Birley Hill, Bush Bank, Hereford, HR4 8EN Tel: (01432) 830044 Fax: (01432) 830055 E-mail: sales@ibess.com *Industrial dough mixing equipment suppliers*

Ibex, 92-94 Manchester Road, Mossley, Ashton-under-Lyne, Lancashire, OL5 9AY Tel: (01457) 831600 Fax: (01457) 831669 E-mail: sales@ibexropes.com *Manufacturers of elastic shock cord & assembly products*

Ibex Business Systems Ltd, 63a Brighton Road, Shoreham-By-Sea, West Sussex, BN43 6RE Tel: (01273) 565699 Fax: (01273) 728275 *Reseller of sage accounting software*

Ibex Geo-tech Ltd, Ibex House, Malt Mill Lane, Halesowen, W. Midlands, B62 8JJ Tel: 0121-559 3862 Fax: 0121-559 9404 E-mail: jane.palmer@ibexgeotech.com *Standard and Intelligent pigging systems; oil, water and gas industries; Data collection, monitoring and results analysis; well head operations from down hole cleaning through to reservoir and tank inspection; cathodic production of underground pipelines.*

Ibex Systems Maidstone Ltd, Mill House Quarry Wood Industrial Estate, Mills Road, Aylesford, Kent, ME20 7NA Tel: (01622) 791991 Fax: (01622) 882900 E-mail: sales@ibexsystems.co.uk *Computer consultants*

Ibl, Acornfield Road, Knowsley Industrial Park, Liverpool, L33 7YX Tel: 0151-549 1082 Fax: 0151-549 1246 *Cold storage services & distributors*

Ibm UK Ltd, Weybridge Business Park, Addlestone Road, Addlestone, Surrey, KT15 2UF Tel: (01932) 814000 Fax: (01932) 850011 E-mail: enquiries@uk.ibm.com *Computer peripheral manufrs*

Ibrahim & Sons Ltd, 313-319 Katherine Road, London, E7 8PJ Tel: (020) 8471 4051 Fax: (020) 8552 4375 Principal Export Areas: Central/East Europe & West Europe *Garments manufrs*

▶ Ibrahim & Zainab UK Ltd, 9 New Croft, Newtown, Birmingham, B19 2JP Tel: 0121-240 4559 Fax: 0121 241 3434 E-mail: dan@izuk.co.uk *Ibrahim & Zainab (UK) Limited is a young company involved in all sorts of textiles, bed linen, household textiles, clothing manufacturing and importing. We supply to distributors, wholesalers and retailers in the UK and Europe. Whatever your needs are please do not hesitate to contact us.*

Ibs Open Systems, Carrs Road, Cheadle, Cheshire, SK8 2EE Tel: 0161-491 5111 Fax: 0161-491 5892 E-mail: sales@ibs-public-services.co.uk *Computer software consultants*

▶ Ibs Publishing Ltd, 8 Stade Street, Hythe, Kent, CT21 6BD Tel: (01303) 262636 Fax: (01303) 262646 E-mail: enquiries@ibspublishing.com *Publishing*

Ibstock Brick Ltd, Over Lane, Almondsbury, Bristol, BS32 4BX Tel: (01454) 456800 Fax: (0870) 9040696 *General purpose brick manufrs*

Ibstock Brick Ltd, Lodge Lane Factory, Lodge Lane, Cannock, Staffordshire, WS11 0LT Tel: (01922) 708000 Fax: (01922) 417808 *Brick manufrs*

Ibstock Brick Ltd, Hamsey Road, Sharpthorne, East Grinstead, West Sussex, RH19 4PB Tel: (01342) 810678 Fax: (01342) 810453 *Brick manufrs*

Ibstock Brick Ltd, Leicester Road, Ibstock, Leicestershire, LE67 6HF Tel: (01530) 261999 Fax: (01530) 257457 E-mail: marketing@ibstock.co.uk *Brick manufrs*

Ibstock Brick Ltd, Stourbridge Factory, Tansey Green Road, Kingswinford, West Midlands, DY6 7LS Tel: (01384) 294124 Fax: (01384) 274547 *Brick manufrs*

Ibstock Brick Ltd, Dorket Head Factory, Lime Lane, Arnold, Nottingham, NG5 8PZ Tel: 0115-926 0441 Fax: 0115-967 0121 *Facing bricks manufrs*

Ibstock Brick Ltd, Chester Lane, St. Helens, Merseyside, WA9 4EN Tel: (01744) 831500 E-mail: parkhousesales@ibstock.co.uk *Brick manufrs*

Ibstock Brick Ltd, Swanage Factory, Godlingston, Swanage, Dorset, BH19 3DH Tel: (01929) 422257 Fax: (01929) 425786 E-mail: info@ibstock.co.uk *Brick manufacturer*

Ibstock Brick Ltd, Atlas Factory, Stubbers Green Road, Walsall, WS9 8BL Tel: (01922) 459194 Fax: (01922) 741761 *Bricks manufrs*

Ibstock Bricks Ltd, Turkey Road, Bexhill-on-Sea, East Sussex, TN39 5HY Tel: (01424) 846273 Fax: (01424) 846415 *Brick manufrs*

Ibstock Building Products Ltd, Union Brickworks, Station Lane, Birtley, Chester le Street, County Durham, DH2 1AJ Tel: 0191-410 2555 Fax: 0191-492 0601 *Brick manufrs*

Ibstock Building Products Ltd, South Holmwood Factory, Newdigate Road, Beare Green, Dorking, Surrey, RH5 4QE Tel: (01306) 711223 Fax: (01306) 711466 *Brick manufrs*

Ibstock Building Products Ltd, Pinhoe Factory, Harrington Lane, Exeter, EX4 8DT Tel: (01392) 466561 Fax: (01392) 466423 *Brick manufacturer*

Ibstock Building Products Ltd, Throckley Works, Throckley, Newcastle upon Tyne, NE15 9EQ Tel: (0870) 9034004 Fax: 0191-229 0502 *Brick manufrs*

Ibstock Building Products Ltd, Funton Factory, Sheerness Road, Lower Halstow, Sittingbourne, Kent, ME9 7EG Tel: (01795) 842551 Fax: (01795) 845387 *Building bricks manufr*

Ibstock Building Products Ltd, Ravenhead Factory, Chequer Lane, Upholland, Skelmersdale, Lancashire, WN8 0DD Tel: (01695) 625511 Fax: (01695) 624287 E-mail: w.lord@ibstock.co.uk *Brick manufrs*

Ibstock Building Products Ltd, Brickyard Road, Aldridge, Walsall, WS9 8TB Tel: (01922) 741400 Fax: (01922) 743086 *Facing bricks manufrs* Also at: Branches throughout the U.K.

Ibstock Gun & Tackle Ltd, 61 Chapel Street, Ibstock, Leicestershire, LE67 6HF Tel: (01530) 260901 Fax: (01530) 260901 *Fishing tackle & gun retailers*

Ibstock Scottish Brick Ltd, Tannochside Factory, Old Edinburgh Road, Uddingston, Glasgow, G71 6HL Tel: (01698) 810686 Fax: (01698) 812364 *Brick manufrs*

Ic International Ltd, Gower Street Trading Estate, St. Georges, Telford, Shropshire, TF2 9HW Tel: (01952) 620206 Fax: (01952) 620456 E-mail: sales@ic-international.com *Manufacturers of fire blankets, welding drapes & curtains*

▶ IC Wedding Video Services, 1 Ringwood Road, Oldfield Park, Bath, BA2 3JJ Tel: (01225) 336112 E-mail: icves@blueyonder.co.uk

Ica Solutions Ltd, 1 115 Loverock Road, Reading, RG30 1DZ Tel: 0118-939 3663 Fax: 0118-939 3653 E-mail: info@icasolutions.co.uk *Control systems & control panels manufrs*

Icam Ltd, Unit 2, Spring Gardens, Washington, Pulborough, West Sussex, RH20 3BS Tel: (01903) 892222 Fax: (01903) 892277 E-mail: icam@icam.ltd.uk *Gas & smoke analysis & detection equipment manufrs*

▶ Icam Engineering Ltd, Dock Road Industrial Estate, Connah's Quay, Deeside, Clwyd, CH5 4DS Tel: (01244) 831143 Fax: (01244) 831338 E-mail: icam@daisyconnect.com *Precision engineers*

ican DESIGN LTD, ST PETER'S GATE, CHARLES ST, SUNDERLAND, SR6 0AN Tel: 0191 5561074 Fax: 0191 5561001 E-mail: STUDIO@ICANDESIGN.CO.UK *ICAN DESIGN is a graphic design firm specialising in design for print and new media communications. We distinguish ourselves by providing sharp analysis, a proven approach and a high level of expertise in disciplines such as identity management, design, communication, publishing, and interaction.**We provide design solutions for both large and small businesses worldwide. The majority of our clientele are national companies in various trade disciplines such as service providers, trade and industry, government, non-profit, property and culture.* **

Icarus Housewares, Unit 1 & 2 Newman Lane, Alton, Hampshire, GU34 2PJ Tel: (01420) 593479 Fax: (01420) 87389 E-mail: lunchboxes@icarus-housewares.com *Promotional lunch box manufrs*

ICB COMPUTERS, 4 Downlands Road, Purley, Surrey, CR8 4JE Tel: (020) 8668 8828 Fax: (020) 8668 8828 *Computer consultants*

▶ Icc Information Ltd, Field House, 72 Old Field Road, Hampton, Middlesex, TW12 2HQ Tel: (020) 7426 8510 Fax: (020) 7426 8551 E-mail: sales@icc-credit.co.uk *Company search & tracing services*

i-cD Publishing (UK) Ltd, 50 Sulivan Road, London, SW6 3DX Tel: (020) 7909 2200 Fax: (020) 7610 9024 *Direct enquiries software designer*

▶ Ice Age Media, The Cottage, Old Mold Road, Gwersyllt, Wrexham, LL11 4SB Tel: (01978) 758071 E-mail: andy@theiceage.co.uk *Ice Age Media is a modern design studio based in Wrexham, North Wales, providing cutting edge Web Design and Graphic Design solutions.*

Ice Boys Ltd, Unit 8, IO Centre, Fingle Drive, Stonebridge, Milton Keynes, MK13 0AT Tel: (01908) 211099 Fax: (01908) 320700 E-mail: sales@iceboys.co.uk *Air conditioners*

Ice Channel Ltd, International Building, Middleton Business Park, Cleckheaton, West Yorkshire, BD19 5LY Tel: (01274) 870600 Fax: (01274) 870222 E-mail: info@alicecollins.com *Ladies knitwear & co-ordinates*

▶ Ice Clothing Co. Ltd, 13 Hessel Street, London, E1 2LR Tel: (020) 7488 3234 Fax: (020) 7488 2808 E-mail: info@ice-clothing.co.uk *Manufacturer & wholesaler of fine ladies wear*

Ice Cold Refrigeration, The Laurels, Main Road, East Boldre, Brockenhurst, Hampshire, SO42 7WU Tel: (01590) 626253 Fax: (01590) 626225 *Refrigerator service providers*

Ice Cool Environments Ltd, Elms Farm, 90 Frog End, Shepreth, Royston, Hertfordshire, SG8 6RF Tel: (01763) 264152 Fax: (01763) 264153 E-mail: info@icecool.uk.com *Refrigeration & Catering equipment, Repair, Servivce, maintenance and Installations*

Ice Cream Container Co. Ltd, 6 Beresford Avenue, Wembley, Middlesex, HA0 1SA Tel: (020) 8903 9021 Fax: (020) 8900 2472 E-mail: sales@icecream-cont.co.uk *Food & ice cream container distributors*

▶ Ice Cryogenic Engineering Ltd, Unit 3, Ferrymills, Osney Mead, Oxford, OX2 0ES Tel: (01865) 202300 Fax: (01865) 727759 E-mail: sales@iceoxford.com *Scientific instrument manufrs*

▶ Ice Fashions Ltd, 32-34 Great Titchfield Street, London, W1W 8BG Tel: (020) 7436 1022 Fax: (020) 7436 1077 *Clothing manufrs*

Ice Guard Group, Mold Road, Cefn-y-Bedd, Wrexham, Clwyd, LL12 9UL Tel: (01978) 761881 Fax: (01978) 761789 *Installation & design engineers*

Ice House Hire & Kool Trailers Hire Limited, PO Box 7366, Hook, Hampshire, RG27 7EZ Tel: (01256) 703687 Fax: (07718) 161141 E-mail: info@icehousehire.co.uk *Whether it's a one-off hire for a party at home, a number of coldrooms for a large corporate event or the provision of a coldroom in an emergency, Ice House Hire provides the complete service solution. Based in Hook, Hampshire, they offer high performance walk-in coldrooms in a range of sizes for long- and short-term hire, multi-functional cooling in ice cold perfection and refrigeration to suit all needs - from gastronomy and outside catering to pharmaceutical.*

Ice Lite Ltd, Pendle House, Mead Way, Shuttleworth Mead, Padiham, Lancashire, BB12 7NG Tel: (0870) 770 7458 Fax: (0870) 770 7459 E-mail: sales@icelite.co.uk *Commercial vehicle builders services*

Ice 'N' Easy, 25 High Street, Chipping Sodbury, Bristol, BS37 6BA Tel: (01454) 312205 *Cake decorating services*

▶ The Ice Co (Polarcube) Ltd, Jessop Way, Northern Road Industrial Estate, Newark, Nottinghamshire, NG24 2ER Tel: (01636) 704232 Fax: (01636) 611943 E-mail: ice@iceco.co.uk *Supply packaged ice for retail*

Ice Refrigeration Ltd, Spring Court House, High Street, Stapleford, Nottingham, NG9 8AG Tel: 0114-230 6555 Fax: 0115-949 9275 E-mail: john@agrice.co.uk *Refrigeration & air conditioning*

Ice Sculptures Ltd, 33 St. James Road, Little Paxton, St. Neots, Cambridgeshire, PE19 6QW Tel: (01480) 213245 Fax: (01480) 476928 *Ice sculptures*

▶ Iceberg Building Services Ltd, 1 Station Court, Station Approach, Wickford, Essex, SS11 7AT Tel: (01268) 739450 Fax: (01268) 739459 E-mail: iceberg@btconnect.com *Air conditioning designers*

▶ Iceberg Trading (UK) Limited, 61 Strattondale Street, Poplar, London, E14 3HG Tel: 078 30311941 E-mail: info@iceberdesign.co.uk *Carved or engraved dying ostrich eggs are processed at our own studio as the only ostrich egg designer.They are formed as table or bedside lamps. You can choose throughout our website catolog alternatively you may offer your own logo or design.*We have wide range of product kinds in stock and we ship all over the world.*Our vision is to provide you with special designs as special as you are.*

Icel Group, Ashmill Bus Park, Ashford Road, Lenham, Maidstone, Kent, ME17 2GQ Tel: (01622) 858200 Fax: (01622) 850065 E-mail: sales@icel-group.co.uk *Power generation services*

▶ Iceni Amber, 53 Waveney Road, Bungay, Suffolk, NR35 1LJ Tel: (01986) 895542 Fax: (01986) 895542 E-mail: sales@iceni-amber.co.uk *Beautiful amber, celtic & baltic jewellery specialists*

▶ Iceni Music, The Surridge, 2 Stepfield, Witham, Essex, CM8 3TH Tel: (01376) 500820 Fax: (01376) 585636 E-mail: sales@zootbass.co.uk

Iceni Pest Control Ltd, 65 Brecklands, Mundford, Thetford, Norfolk, IP26 5EG Tel: (01842) 878784 Fax: (01842) 879598 *Pest control*

▶ Iceni Printed Tiles, 8 Transopel House, Queens Square, Attleborough, Norfolk, NR17 2AE Tel: 01953 451313 E-mail: info@icenitiles.co.uk *Printing tiles manufrs*

Iceni Productions Ltd, The Studio, Long Lane, Fradley, Lichfield, Staffordshire, WS13 8NX Tel: (01283) 792990 Fax: (01283) 792993 E-mail: sales@iceni.tv Sales Contact: A. Jepson *iceni is listed in the top 50 UK corporate communication companies, and number 1 in our region. We are an established, creative and professional business video, corporate television and screen media production company producing business television, video, web content, CD-ROM and DVD projects for clients across the UK. Our midlands production studio is within easy reach of the M6 toll road and Birmingham International Airport.*

Ichthus Blinds, 2 Hebburn Dr, Bury, Lancashire, BL8 1ED Tel: 0161-762 9599 *Blind manufrs*

Ici Packaging Coatings Ltd, Bordesley Green Road, Bordesley Green, Birmingham, B9 4TQ Tel: 0121-766 6600 Fax: 0121-766 6601 E-mail: enquiries@ici.com *Paint, varnish & lacquer manufrs*

Ici Paints plc T/As Dulux, Wexham Road, Slough, SL2 5DS Tel: (01753) 550000 Fax: (01753) 578218 E-mail: sales@dulux.com *Paint manufrs*

Icing On The Cake, 19 South Walk, Basildon, Essex, SS14 1BZ Tel: (01268) 286970 Fax: (01268) 530839 *Cake decorators*

Icis Lor Group Ltd, Quadrant House, The Quadrant, Sutton, Surrey, SM2 5AS Tel: (020) 8652 3535 Fax: (020) 8652 3929 E-mail: sales.uk@icislor.com *Chemical market*

John Icke Ltd, Margate Road, Broadstairs, Kent, CT10 2PR Tel: (01843) 603399 Fax: (01843) 603201 *Gaming machines suppliers*

Icklesham Joinery Ltd, Main Road, Icklesham, Winchelsea, East Sussex, TN36 4BA Tel: (01424) 814303 Fax: (01424) 814744 E-mail: enquiries@ickleshamjoineryltd.com *Joinery manufs*

Icm Computer Group plc, 3 Phoenix Place, Nottingham, NG8 6BA Tel: 0115-870 1000 Fax: (0870) 1218354 E-mail: sales@icm-computer.co.uk *Computer resellers & total service providers*

Icn Pharmaceuticals Ltd, Cedarwood Crockford Lane, Chineham Business Park, Chineham, Basingstoke, Hampshire, RG24 8WD Tel: (01256) 707744 Fax: (01256) 707334 E-mail: sales@valeant.com *Pharmaceutical distribution* Also at: High Wycombe

Icode Systems Ltd, Icode System Ltd Grange Business Park, Sandy Lane, Shedfield, Southampton, SO32 2HQ Tel: (01329) 835335 Fax: (01329) 835338 E-mail: sales@icode.co.uk *Computer consultants*

▶ ICOM International Ltd, Norwood House, 53 Brighton Grove, Manchester, M14 5JT Tel: 0161-259 0100 E-mail: info@internetcommunication.co.uk *Web development & Web design at Manchester : Internet Communication, I-COM offers 'Total Internet Solutions',- more than a mere website. Our Web service benefits include : consultation, design, development, hosting, optimisation, training and marketing support.*

▶ Icom Spray Paint Systems, Penn Road, Hazlemere, High Wycombe, Buckinghamshire, HP15 7PB Tel: (01494) 812733 E-mail: mail@icomsps.freeserve.co.uk *On-site paint spraying service*

▶ Icom Web Ltd, 140A Longden Coleham, Shrewsbury, SY3 7DN Tel: (01743) 340034 Fax: (01743) 368214 E-mail: team@icomweb.net *IT services*

Icomm Structured Wiring Systems, 5 Wychwood Close, New Duston, Northampton, NN5 6QL Tel: (01604) 584655 Fax: (01604) 584652 *Structured cabling solutions manufrs*

Icon, Unit 2-3 Beldray Park, Beldray Road, Bilston, West Midlands, WV14 7NH Tel: (01902) 491122 Fax: (01902) 404044 E-mail: icon@icon-fasteners.co.uk *Standard & non-standard fastener distributors*

Icon, Allbright House, 156 St. Albans Road, Sandridge, St. Albans, Hertfordshire, AL4 9LP Tel: (08707) 587600 Fax: (08707) 587636 E-mail: ray.pitchforth@icon-plc.co.uk *Distributor*

▶ Icon College Of Technology & Management Ltd, Unit 21 St. Boniface Church, 1-13 Adler Street, London, E1 1EE Tel: (020) 7377 2800 Fax: (020) 7377 0822 *Computer training services*

▶ Icon Colour Ltd, Westerham House, Fircroft Way, Edenbridge, Kent, TN8 6EL Tel: (01732) 866833 Fax: (01732) 866882

Icon Corporation Sales Ltd, Unit 11 Pilgrims Close, Flitwick, Bedford, MK45 1UL Tel: (01525) 715715 Fax: (01525) 715717 E-mail: paulbelger@iconcsl.co.uk *Importer of Americas Leading Anti Ageing Serum, Be the First to Stock this amazing product, with more exciting anti ageing products being developed now, for lauch next year.*

Icon Display, 130-136 Maidstone Road, Sidcup, Kent, DA14 5HS Tel: (020) 8302 4921 Fax: (020) 8302 3971 E-mail: icondisplay@cix.co.uk *Sign, exhibition backdrop, flag & banner manufrs*

▶ Icon Emergency Lighting Ltd, 9 Craven Way, Newmarket, Suffolk, CB8 0BW Tel: (01638) 561138 Fax: (01638) 561687 E-mail: sales@icon-emergencylighting.com *Icon Emergency Lighting specialises in the manufacture and supply of emergency lighting equipment including the conversion of mains luminaires, central supply systems and our own range of architecurally biased mains/emergency luminaires.*

Icon Engineering, Europa Way, Wisbech, Wisbech, Cambridgeshire, PE13 2TZ Tel: (01945) 474411 Fax: (01945) 474144 E-mail: paul@icon-eng.co.uk *Steel fabrications*

Icon Health & Fitness, 4 Revie Road, Leeds, LS11 8JG Tel: 0113-387 7122 Fax: 0113-387 7124 E-mail: sales@iconeurope.com *Health & fitness machine*

▶ Icon Health & Safety, 34 Aylward Drive, Stevenage, Hertfordshire, SG2 8UR Tel: (01438) 748208 Fax: (01438) 759299 E-mail: info@iconhealthandsafety.co.uk *First aid & safety training courses, seminars, fire warden training services*

Icon Labels Ltd, 1 Lower Oakham Way, Oakham Business Park, Mansfield, Nottinghamshire, NG18 5BU Tel: (01623) 421241 Fax: (01623) 421251 E-mail: sales@iconlabels.co.uk *Numbered & bar coded labels*

Icon Polymer Group Ltd, Thrumpton Lane, Retford, Nottinghamshire, DN22 6HH Tel: (01777) 714300 Fax: (01777) 709739 E-mail: info@iconpolymer.com *Rubber product manufrs*

Icon Polymer Group Ltd, Thrumpton Lane, Retford, Nottinghamshire, DN22 6HH Tel: (01777) 714300 Fax: (01777) 709739 E-mail: info@iconpolymer.com *Rubber bands & rubber products (industrial) components manufrs*

▶ Icon Republic, 14 Orchard Street, Bristol, BS1 5EH Tel: 0117-905 5338

Icon Research Ltd, Raw Holdings, East Calder, Livingston, West Lothian, EH53 0HY Tel: (01506) 885000 Fax: (01506) 885501 *Industrial measuring equipment designers*

Icon Sign Manufacturing, 16 East Parade, Ilkley, West Yorkshire, LS29 8EZ Tel: (01535) 211456 Fax: (01943) 433400 *Sign manufrs*

Icon Technologies Ltd, Broadgate Court, 199 Bishopsgate, London, EC2M 3TY Tel: (020) 7814 6669 Fax: (020) 7814 7934 E-mail: sales@icontech.co.uk *Computer services*

▶ Icon Welding Co. Ltd, Station Lane Industrial Estate, Station Lane, Old Whittington, Chesterfield, Derbyshire, S41 9QX Tel: (01246) 454618 Fax: (01246) 455618 *Steel fabricators*

▶ Iconic Imaging Ltd, 18 Squirrel Lane, Ashford, Kent, TN25 4GG Tel: (01233) 663866 E-mail: sales@iconicimaging.co.uk *Canvas prints for all your interior design needs. Iconic Imaging is committed to producing the highest possible quality canvas prints for your home and workplace by combining beautiful, original images with the best materials available.*

▶ Iconium Computer Systems, Exchange House, Worthing Road, Horsham, West Sussex, RH12 1UU Tel: (01403) 754300 *Computer consultants*

Iconology Computer Consultants, Park Farm, Brabourne Lees, Ashford, Kent, TN25 6RG Tel: (01303) 813700 Fax: (01303) 813900 E-mail: info@iconology.co.uk *Computer consultants*

Icopal, Barton Dock Road, Stretford, Manchester, M32 0YL Tel: 0161-865 4444 Fax: 0161-864 1178 E-mail: marketing.uk@icopal.com *Manufacturer of waterproofing & insulation systems*

Icore Ltd, 10-12 King Henry Terrace, Sovereign Close, London, E1W 3HE Tel: (020) 7464 8414 Fax: (020) 7481 9230 *Software consultants*

Icp Claning Supplies, Unit 1, Fernie Road, Market Harborough, Leicestershire, LE16 7PH Tel: (01858) 462338 Fax: (01858) 433367 E-mail: icpcleaning@btconnect.com *Hygiene materials distributors*

Icp Hygiene, 14 Ronald Close, Woburn Road Industrial Estate, Kempston, Bedford, MK42 7SH Tel: (01234) 843666 Fax: (01234) 843636 E-mail: icpsales@jangro.net *Disposable paper products & cleaning equipment distributors*

▶ Ics Ltd, Land Park Lane, Woodview, Kensworth, Dunstable, Bedfordshire, LU6 2PZ Tel: (01582) 871850 Fax: (0870) 4436469 E-mail: info@icstele.com *Installation & maintenance of structured cabling & telephones systems*

Ics Computing Ltd, Wessex House, Oxford Road, Newbury, Berkshire, RG14 1PA Tel: (01635) 580802 Fax: (01635) 580803 E-mail: enquiries@icscomputing.co.uk *Payroll services & integrated HR software*

Ics Installations Ltd, 5 Bates Close, Larkfield, Aylesford, Kent, ME20 6TG Tel: (01732) 848550 Fax: (01732) 848550 E-mail: lloyd.porter@ics-installations.com *Subsea power, fibre optic & range cable installers, client consultancy services, client installation services,client engineering services, WAN & LAN technology*

▶ Ict Express, Coleshill Freight Terminal, Station Road, Coleshill, Birmingham, B46 1JJ Tel: (01675) 463000 Fax: (01675) 465999

Ict Networks Ltd, Unit 8 Palmerston Street, Joiners Square Industrial Estate, Stoke-on-Trent, ST1 3EU Tel: (01782) 406406 Fax: (01782) 406444 E-mail: sales@ict-networks.co.uk *Network installation*

▶ Id Fencing, 24 Hayle Avenue, Warwick, CV34 5TW Tel: (01926) 496753 Fax: (01926) 496753 E-mail: info@idfencing.co.uk *Fencing services*

▶ ID Pages Ltd, 9 Cornfield Lane, Eastbourne, East Sussex, BN21 4NE Tel: 01323 479728 Fax: 01323 439485 E-mail: sales@idpages.co.uk *Designers,Providers & Hosters of Web-Based Business Cards*

▶ Id Properties, 4-6 University Way, London, E16 2RD Tel: (020) 7060 1089 Fax: (08452) 264692 E-mail: marketing@idproperties.co.uk *idpropeties.co.uk is a marketing advertising website which basically advertise properties privately starting from £75, the price of a kitchen sink for a 2 mths add, £150 for a 6 mths add and £450 for a permanent add.*

Id Signs Scotland Ltd, 200 Swinton Road, Baillieston, Glasgow, G69 6DB Tel: 0141-773 3666 Fax: 0141-773 1690 *Sign & flag makers*

Id Wall, The Mill, 150 Penistone Road, Shelley, Huddersfield, HD8 8JQ Tel: (01484) 603020 E-mail: info@id-wall.com *Trying to create that unique look ? Transform and enhance the look of your interior with bespoke fit photo wallpaper or fine-art Giclée large format canvas prints. All photo wallpaper is printed to order via the myfotowall® system to your exact size specification and delivered ready to hang with fitting guidelines. Our Canvas Club print collections range from the contemporary to the quirky and all orders are hand crafted in UK to the highest quality standards. **

▶ Id76 Creative, 4 Whitley Park Lane, Reading, RG2 7BE Tel: (07946) 881875 Fax: (07092) 864176 E-mail: info@id76.com *Graphic design specialists*

▶ Idacom Steel Buildings Ltd, Idacom Steel Building, Hull, HU11 5SP Tel: (01964) 544617 Fax: (01964) 544422 E-mail: idacom@jmcglynn.f9.co.uk *Manufacturers of steel anti vandal security units**

Idea Computers, 26 Stuart Road, Warlingham, Surrey, CR6 9JH Tel: (01883) 623327 Fax: (01883) 626102 *IT systems corporate suppliers*

Idea Systems UK Ltd, 2 Whiting Street, Sheffield, S8 9QR Tel: 0114-258 3155 Fax: 0114-255 4465 E-mail: info@idea-systems.co.uk *Display location & shop fitting services*

Ideal Boilers Ltd, PO Box 103, Hull, HU5 4JN Tel: (01482) 492251 Fax: (01482) 448858 E-mail: enquires@idealboilers.com *Domestic & industrial boiler manufrs*

Ideal Building Systems Ltd, Carnaby Industrial Estate, Lancaster Road, Carnaby, Bridlington, North Humberside, YO15 3QY Tel: (01262) 606750 Fax: (01262) 671960 E-mail: sales@idealbuildingsystems.co.uk *Prefabricated building manufrs*

Ideal Business Supplies Ltd, Marsh Lanelords Meadow Industrial Estate, Lords Meadow Industrial Estate, Crediton, Devon, EX17 1ES Tel: (01363) 775999 Fax: (01363) 775996 E-mail: info@idealbusinesssupplies.co.uk *Ideal Business Supplies Ltd is a major supplier of new and good quality used office furniture offering a*

continued

▶ indicates data change since last edition

continuation
free delivery and installation service throughout the mainland UK

Ideal Chemical Products, Unit D5 Taylor Business Park, Risley, Warrington, WA3 6BL Tel: (01925) 765934 Fax: (01925) 766220 *Construction chemicals*

Ideal Chemicals Ltd, Atlas House, Burton Road, Wellingborough, Northamptonshire, NN9 5HX Tel: (01933) 681616 Fax: (01933) 681042 E-mail: enquiries@idealmanufacturing.com *Chemical manufrs*

Ideal Cleaning Services Ltd, 2581 Coventry Road, Sheldon, Birmingham, B26 3PX Tel: 0121-743 5802 Fax: 0121-742 5040 *Contract cleaning services*

Ideal Computing Ltd, 78 Bruntsfield Place, Edinburgh, EH10 4HG Tel: 0131-466 5557 Fax: (07021) 117216 E-mail: enquiries@idealcomputing.co.uk

▶ Ideal Furniture Ltd, Hancock Road, London, E3 3DA Tel: (020) 8980 6838 Fax: (020) 8981 2240 E-mail: sales@idealfurn.co.uk

Ideal Handling Bath, 19 Highfield Gardens, Bitton, Bristol, BS30 6RN Tel: (07717) 294840 Fax: 0117-932 8130 E-mail: les@ideal-handling-bath.co.uk *Ideal Handling (Bath) provide a total Health and Safety service to local businesses and organisations, including: *Health and Safety Reports to help you with your H & S Policy and Risk Assessment compliance. *FREE walkthrough Audit to assess needs *Portable appliance testing *Home Office/Workstation H&S Reviews from £99.00! Now qualified to undertake P402 Asbestos Surveys from £150.00!!(depending on size of survey) Office equipment solutions - do away with all those cables that cause trouble and look messy - we can tidy them up and hide them away! TRAINING - I can offer most of your training needs, either in-house or externally. Interested? then call me and I will tell you how!.If you have any H & S issues - lets talk -IT COULD SAVE YOU A LOT OF MONEY!Contact me on 07717 294840 or fax 0117 932 8130*

▶ Ideal Handling (Stoke-on-Trent) Ltd, 73 Fern Crescent, Congleton, Cheshire, CW12 3HQ Tel: (01260) 295417 Fax: (01260) 295417 E-mail: simon@ideal-stoke-on-trent.co.uk *Health and Safety Solutions provider to industry specialising in portable appliance testing, compliance with Legionella and Asbestos legislation and a wide range of Manual Hanling and workplace products.*

▶ Ideal Handling (West Wales), Westerleigh, Brackla Way, Bridgend, Mid Glamorgan, CF31 2JS Tel: (01656) 656660 Fax: (01656) 646316 E-mail: sales@ideal-west-wales.co.uk *Portable appliance testing safety equipment & materials*

Ideal Hose & Safety Ltd, Spring Lane, Northampton, NN1 2JW Tel: (01604) 621964 Fax: (01604) 232936 E-mail: sales@idealhose.co.uk *Hose & tube distributors & manufrs* Also at: Rugby

Ideal Packaging Co, Unit 49, Queens Court Trading Estate Greets Green Road, West Bromwich, West Midlands, B70 9EL Tel: 0121-557 3624 Fax: 0121-520 5316 E-mail: sales@idealpackaging.co.uk *Printed cartons board & PVC manufrs*

▶ Ideal Pat Testing, 200 Gorse Cover Road, Severn Beach, Bristol, BS35 4NT Tel: (01454) 631331 Fax: (01454) 631331 E-mail: idealhandling@tiscali.co.uk *Electrical safety testing services*

▶ Ideal Pat Testing (West Midlands), 4 Brooklyn Grove, Coseley, Bilston, West Midlands, WV14 8YH Tel: 0121-557 5254 Fax: 0121-557 5254 E-mail: k-share_13@tiscali.co.uk **Professional Portable Appliance Testing service which allows all companies to meet their safety at work obligations. We offer a friendly, professional service and there are no hidden extras or nasty surprises. Prices start from as little as £1 PER ITEM and are fully inclusive with quality detailed reports which you also get on CD at no extra cost. Call now for your free PAT brochure.*

▶ Ideal PC's, The Maltings, Roydon Road, Stanstead Abbotts, Ware, Hertfordshire, SG12 8UU Tel: (01920) 871687 E-mail: sales@ideal-pcs.co.uk *Computer repair services*

Ideal Plastic Products Ltd, 37a Irlam Road, Bootle, Merseyside, L20 4AE Tel: 0151-922 7221 Fax: 0151-922 3326 *Plastic manufrs*

Ideal Saddle Co., The Old School, Hollyhedge Lane, Walsall, WS2 8PZ Tel: (01922) 620233 Fax: (01922) 623853 *Saddle distributors*

Ideal Sand & Die Casting Co., Unit 5, New Field Industrial Estate, High St, Stoke-on-Trent, ST6 5PB Tel: (01782) 818866 Fax: (01782) 836750 E-mail: sales@idealcasting.co.uk *Aluminium & alloy castings manufrs*

Ideal Signs, Lerburn Place, The Lerburne, Wedmore, Somerset, BS28 4ED Tel: (01934) 712888 Fax: (01934) 713777 *Signs & screen printers*

Ideal Software & Systems, 49 High St, Sandy, Beds, SG19 1AG Tel: 01767 682851 Fax: 01767 683884 *Computer software installation service & sales*

Ideal Standard Social Club, County Road North, Hull, HU5 4HS Tel: (01482) 343852 Fax: (01482) 445886 E-mail: ideal-standard@asvr.com *Bathroom equipment manufrs* Also at: Middlewich

Ideal Upholstery Ltd, 319 Railway Street, Nelson, Lancashire, BB9 0JD Tel: (01282) 697769 Fax: (01282) 698869 E-mail: enquiries@ideal-upholstery.co.uk *Furniture manufrs*

▶ Ideal Web Solutions, PO Box 487, Wigan, Lancashire, WN2 4WP Tel: (0789) 1989138 *Website builders/designers.*We specialise in fast, easy to navigate websites for businesses, home users and sole traders.*Highly qualified designers.*Competitive rates.*

Ideal Window Blinds, Denmark Street, Glasgow, G22 6DB Tel: 0141-336 4400 Fax: 0141-336 4400

▶ Ideal Window Blinds, 596 Alexandra Parade, Glasgow, G31 3BS Tel: 0141-550 4400 Fax: 0141-550 4400 *Blind supplier*

▶ Idealogic, Focal Point, 88 Coronation Avenue, Bath, BA2 2JP Tel: 01225 483322 Fax: 01225 483322 E-mail: kirstie@idealogicuk.com *Full service graphic design agency. Services include; corporate identity and branding, company literature, press advertising, exhibitions, direct mail and advertising.*

▶ Ideal-Pat, 6 Bishop Street, Alfreton, Derbyshire, DE55 7EF Tel: (07904) 763289 Fax: (01773) 834508 E-mail: david@ideal-handling-derby.co.uk *PAT tests with written and disc (microsoft readable)report, which also aids asset management and tracking.Need it today? No problem!Prices start @ £1.09*

▶ Ideals Lighting Mnfrs, Unit 3 Brookside, Sumpters Way, Temple Farm Industrial Estate, Southend-on-Sea, SS2 5RR Tel: (01702) 460855 Fax: (01702) 460655 E-mail: sales@idealsgb.co.uk *Lighting manufrs*

IDEAS, 21 Falkland Square, Crewkerne, Somerset, TA18 7JS Tel: 01460 271190 Fax: 01460 271191 E-mail: enquiries@ideasfordesign.co.uk *IDEAS is a dynamic company that offers a comprehensive range of project management and design services to the shop fitting, retail and allied industries. Whether you require project design management, design development or equipment cost analysis and reductions, then IDEAS have a team of experienced industry proven, project managers and designers that will deliver the results your business demands.**In addition to these areas of expertise, IDEAS also provides comprehensive engineering drawing, store planning and graphic design services.**So if you have design projects that require experienced project managers, if you have development, planning or drawing work that needs undertaking, then IDEAS may be just the company that you are looking for.**

▶ Ideas In Automation, Unit 4 Silver House, Adelphi Way, Ireland Idustrial Estate, Staysly, Chesterfield, Derbyshire, S43 3LJ Tel: (0870) 2000499 Fax: (0870) 2000599 E-mail: sales@ideas-in-automation.ltd.uk *Automation special purpose equipment systems constructors & manufrs*

Idec Ltd, Concorde House, Concorde Way, Preston Farm Industrial Estate, Stockton-on-Tees, Cleveland, TS18 3RB Tel: (01642) 677333 Fax: (01642) 603641 E-mail: sales@idec.ltd.uk *High voltage protection equipment designers*

▶ Ideka Ltd, 57 Barleyfields Road, Wetherby, West Yorkshire, LS22 7PT Tel: (01937) 582942 Fax: (01937) 582942 E-mail: sales@ideka.co.uk *Offer design & build service for web sites & online applications*

▶ Ident Design Ltd, Ground Floor Suite, 7 Woodlands Grove, Isleworth, Middlesex, TW7 6NS Tel: (07941) 007175 E-mail: info@identdesign.co.uk *Creative and professional web and print design services*

Ident Machines Ltd, Stapleton Lane, Barwell, Leicester, LE9 8HE Tel: (01455) 840056 Fax: (01455) 848070 E-mail: ident.machines@talk21.com *Rotary cutters manufrs*

Identalink Ltd, Bedrup Moor, Forthbridge, Cheltenham, Gloucestershire, GL54 3JR Tel: (01285) 721030 *Biometric security software design*

Identec Ltd, Mercantile Road, Rainton Bridge Industrial Estate, Houghton le Spring, Tyne & Wear, DH4 5PH Tel: 0191-584 4084 Fax: 0191-584 9077 E-mail: info@identic.co.uk *Surveillance equipment manufrs*

Identicar, Rushland Farm, Knowle Lane, Wookey, Wells, Somerset, BA5 1LD Tel: (01749) 677381 *Vehicle identification services*

Identifile Systems Ltd, Unit 2 Bridge Gate Centre, Martinfield, Welwyn Garden City, Hertfordshire, AL7 1JG Tel: (01707) 395396 Fax: (01707) 394083 E-mail: sales@identifile.co.uk *Photo identification & identity card systems suppliers*

Identify Ltd, Smugglers End, The Street, Hythe, Kent, CT21 4LQ Tel: (01303) 239939 Fax: (01303) 267671 E-mail: mjager@identify_ltd.co.uk *CCTV suppliers*

Identify UK Ltd, Prestongate, Hessle, North Humberside, HU13 0RD Tel: (01482) 222070 Fax: (01482) 327214 E-mail: info@rfidsystems.co.uk *Security consultants*

Identilabel Ltd, Unit 2a The Gattinetts, Hadleigh Road, East Bergholt, Colchester, CO7 6QT Tel: (01206) 299777 Fax: (01206) 299007 E-mail: sales@identilabel.co.uk *Manufacturers of; signs, labels, control panels, plaques, nameplates, serial plates, lapel badges, keytags, vinyl lettering, shop fascias, free-standing signs, labels on rolls, domed labels, warning/safety signs. East Anglia, Essex, Suffolk, Colchester, Ipswich, Chelmsford, Witham, Harwich and Clacton areas.*

Identilam plc, Faygate Business Centre, Faygate Lane, Faygate, Horsham, West Sussex, RH12 4DN Tel: (01293) 851711 Fax: (01293) 851742 E-mail: sales@indentilam.co.uk *Identification systems manufrs*

Identisys Ltd, Unit S5, The Nene Centre, Freehold Street, Northampton, NN2 6EW Tel: 01604 710462 E-mail: sales@identisys.co.uk *Identisys can supply a range of machines to suit your plastic card application/metal plate embosser. Whether it be Thermal printing, embossing and tipping, magnetic strip encoding or chip programming we can provide a competitive solution to fit your company"s individual requirements. From low volume requirements for membership schemes to multiple machines to produce ,000 cards per hour for loyalty card applications, Identisys can provide both the equipment and service support to suit your needs.***

▶ Identity Signs (London) Ltd, Identity House, Chase Farm, Southgate Road, Potters Bar, Hertfordshire, EN6 5ER Tel: (01707) 644715

IDEO London, White Bear Yard, 144A Clerkenwell Road, London, EC1R 5DF Tel: (020) 7713 2600 Fax: (020) 7713 2601 E-mail: mhoenle@ideo.com *Product designers*

iDeveloperNetwork, Suite 7, Grove House, Kensal Road, London, W10 5BZ Tel: (020) 7900 2071 Fax: (020) 7900 2071 E-mail: uk_contact@idevelopernetwork.com *Software & website development*

▶ IDM Doors Ltd, Rock Wharf, Mill Parade, Newport, Gwent, NP20 2UL Tel: (01633) 843098 Fax: (01633) 259079 E-mail: info@idmdoorsltd.co.uk *High performance composite fiberglass doors manufrs*

I-DocumentSystems Ltd, Tontine House, 8 Gordon Street, Glasgow, G1 3PL Tel: 0141-574 1900 Fax: 0141-574 1901 E-mail: ruth.rintoul@idoxplc.com *Information service, publishers & consultants*

▶ IDP Safety Services Ltd, 289 Kings Drive, Eastbourne, East Sussex, BN21 2YA Tel: (01323) 507017 Fax: (01323) 507017 E-mail: info@idpsafety.co.uk *Health & safety consultancy & golf & leisure wear retailers*

▶ IDR Services Ltd, 32 St Peters Close, Crabbs Cross, Redditch, Worcestershire, B97 5LE Tel: 01527 542501 Fax: 01527 542501 E-mail: idrservices@blueyonder.co.uk *Servicing Industry X Ray & Computed radiography equipment*

Ids Indata, Hanley Swan, Worcester, WR8 0DN Tel: (01684) 311350 Fax: (01684) 311330 *Computer system integration & services*

Ids Security Systems Ltd, Unit 11 Field Way, Cardiff, CF14 4HY Tel: (029) 2052 2885 Fax: (029) 2052 2747 *CCTV access systems installators*

IDT Europe, Prime House, Barnet Wood Lane, Leatherhead, Surrey, KT22 7DE Tel: (01372) 363339 Fax: (01372) 363052 *Integrated circuit manufrs*

▶ IDVE Design, 2 Hillside Road, HASTINGS, East Sussex, TN34 2QT Tel: 0845 2571965 E-mail: contact@idve.co.uk *Creative Graphic Design.*

IES Ltd, 1 Portview Road, Bristol, BS11 9LS Tel: 0117-938 0600 Fax: 0117-938 0900 E-mail: info@ies.co.uk *Import & export services, storage & distributors*

Ies Pca Ltd, The Millcourt Centre, Pleasley Vale, Mansfield, Nottinghamshire, NG19 8RL Tel: (01623) 819319 Fax: (01623) 819329 E-mail: info@iespca.com *Manufacturers of control systems & panels for process, industrial, environmental & combustion control*

▶ If Cardboard Creation (UK) Ltd, If House, Thornton Road, Pickering, North Yorkshire, YO18 7JB Tel: (01751) 475757 Fax: (01751) 472555 E-mail: info@thatcompanycalledif.com *Book related giftware suppliers*

IFI Scotland Ltd, Rennie Place, East Kilbride, Glasgow, G74 5HD Tel: (01355) 598440 Fax: (0800) 6520780 E-mail: sales@ifiltd.net *Fastener distributors & window products*

Ifp Engineering Ltd, 23 Cuttlers Road, South Woodham Ferrers, Chelmsford, CM3 5WA Tel: (01245) 328391 Fax: (01245) 329330 E-mail: ted@hazledine.com *Fork lift truck distributors*

Ifs Global Logistics Ltd, I F S Logistics Park, Seven Mile Straight, Muckamore, Antrim, BT41 4QE Tel: (028) 9446 4211 Fax: (028) 9446 7723 E-mail: sales@antrim.ifsgroup.com *International freight forwaders express parcels groupage operators*

▶ Ifull Productions Ltd, 11 Ralph Road, Coventry, CV6 1DH Tel: (024) 7626 9163 Fax: (07075) 020955 E-mail: enquiries@ifullproductions.com *Marketing, telemarketing & creative consultants*

IG Block, 49 Nags Head Lane, Brentwood, Essex, CM14 5NL Tel: (01277) 848884 Fax: (01277) 848885 E-mail: sales@coinscope.co.uk *Pool & snooker tables*

IGE Energy Services (UK) Ltd, 2 Kelvin Close, Science Park North, Birchwood, Warrington, WA3 7BL Tel: (01925) 818504 Fax: (01925) 817819 *Proximity transducers, vibration & meter systems manufrs*

Igg Component Technology Ltd, Waterside House, Waterside Gardens, Fareham, Hampshire, PO16 8RR Tel: (01329) 829311 Fax: (01329) 829312 E-mail: enquiries@igg.co.uk *Procurement & testing of electronic components*

Iggesund Paperboard Ltd, Siddick, Workington, Cumbria, CA14 1JX Tel: (01900) 601000 Fax: (01900) 605000 Principal Export Areas: Worldwide *Printing board*

▶ Igl Oil & Gas Consultants Ltd, Exchange House, Union Street, Aberdeen, AB11 5BJ Tel: (01224) 212300 Fax: (01224) 212301

▶ Igneous Products Ltd, Aquaduct Works, Marple Bridge, Stockport, Cheshire, SK6 5LD Tel: 0161-449 7666 Fax: 0161-449 7666 *Packaging material manufrs*

Igniters Combustion Engineering Ltd, Unit 6 Prospect Drive, Britannia Enterprise Park, Lichfield, Staffordshire, WS14 9UX Tel: (01543) 251478 Fax: (01543) 257850 E-mail: renglish@igniters.co.uk *Combustion control systems manufrs*

Igoe Ltd, 100 Brooker Road, Waltham Abbey, Essex, EN9 1JL Tel: (01992) 655600 Fax: (01992) 655631 E-mail: enquiries@igoe.co.uk *Furniture manufrs*

▶ IGroup Ltd, 16-17 Yorke Street, Wrexham, Clwyd, LL13 8LW Tel: (0845) 8382184 E-mail: info@igroupltd.co.uk *Igroup is a leading supplier of mobile data capture solutions & digital signage.*

Igrox, A1 Ferrybridge Business Park, Fishergate, Knottingley, West Yorkshire, WF11 8NA Tel: (01977) 678008 Fax: (01977) 607203 E-mail: enquires@idroxomd.co.uk *Pest controllers*

Ihkos Digital Ltd, Coventry, CV2 3WB Tel: (024) 7626 7622 Fax: (024) 7672 9855 E-mail: info@ihkos.co.uk *Laser engraved gifts services*

▶ Iicorr Ltd, Greenbank Place, East Tullos, Aberdeen, AB12 3BT Tel: (01224) 898282 Fax: (01224) 898202 E-mail: dennis.parr@iicorr.co.uk Principal Export Areas: Worldwide *Corrosion control, monitoring & sound measuring instruments manufrs*

▶ IID Solutions Ltd, Units 9 & 10 Wesley House, Huddersfield Road, Birstall, Batley, West Yorkshire, WF17 9EJ Tel: (01924) 424600 Fax: (01924) 424601 E-mail: sales@iidsolutions.co.uk *Resellers of thermal printing systems*

II-VI UK Ltd, 21 Burley road, Oakham, Leicestershire, LE15 6DH Tel: (01572) 771778 Fax: (01572) 771779 E-mail: ii-vi@oakham.uk *Industrial laser optic suppliers*

Ikas Ltd, Kingsview House Kingsview Court, Hodgson Way, Wickford, Essex, SS11 8YF Tel: (01268) 562689 Fax: (01268) 575545 E-mail: sales@ikas.co.uk *Kitchen & appliance distributors*

Ikegami Electronics, Unit E1 Cologne Court, Brooklands Close, Sunbury-on-Thames, Middlesex, TW16 7EB Tel: (01932) 769700 Fax: (01932) 769710E-mail: info@ikegami.co.uk *Broadcasting equipment manufrs*

Iken Business Ltd, Froomsgate House, Rupert Street, Bristol, BS1 2QJ Tel: (0845) 4509201 Fax: (0845) 4509209 E-mail: info@iken.com *Computer systems*

Ikm Network Communications Ltd, Intec House, St.Nicholas Close, Fleet, Hampshire, GU51 4JA Tel: (01252) 365700 Fax: (01252) 622131 E-mail: sales@ikm.co.uk *Network & communications services*

IKO Ltd, Appley Lane North, Appley Bridge, Wigan, Lancashire, WN6 9AB Tel: (01257) 255771 Fax: (01257) 252514 *Roofing felt & damp course manufrs*

▶ Ikographics, 47 Beechy Avenue, Eastbourne, East Sussex, BN20 8NU Tel: (01323) 724461 Fax: (01323) 511418 E-mail: info@ikographics.co.uk *Graphic design specialists*

Ikon AVS Ltd, Unit 238 Ikon Estate, Droitwich Road, Hartlebury, Kidderminster, Worcestershire, DY10 4EU Tel: (01299) 250991 Fax: (01299) 250983 E-mail: sales@Ikonavs.com *Manufacturers of audio visual equipment*

▶ Ikon Designs, Ridge House, Clay Street, Penkridge, Stafford, ST19 5AF Tel: (01785) 716116 Fax: (01785) 716702

Ikon Office Solutions Ltd, Ikon House, 15 Ullswater Crescent, Coulsdon, Surrey, CR5 2HR Tel: (020) 8763 1010 Fax: (020) 8763 1110 *Photocopying machine distributors*

Ikon Office Solutions plc, Ikon Court, 150 Great Cambridge Road, Enfield, Middlesex, EN1 1PW Tel: (020) 8366 9666 Fax: (020) 8367 6729 *Office equipment suppliers*

Ikon Office Solutions plc, Ikon House Angels Wing, Hunslet Road, Leeds, LS10 1AF Tel: 0113-244 5050 Fax: 0113-244 9191 *Office equipment suppliers*

Ikon Office Solutions plc, James House, 55 Welford Road, Leicester, LE2 7AP Tel: 0116-254 0999 Fax: 0116-285 4812 E-mail: sales@ikon.com *Sales & service of office equipment*

Ikon Office Solutions plc, 160 Edinburgh Avenue, Slough, SL1 4UE Tel: (01753) 771000 Fax: (01753) 696045 *Office equipment suppliers*

Ikon Office Solutions Dublin Ltd, Ikon House, 30 Cowcross Street, London, EC1M 6DQ Tel: (020) 7253 4545 Fax: (020) 7250 3690 *Office equipment suppliers*

▶ I-Konic Ltd, 60 Grayshill Road, Cumbernauld, Glasgow, G68 9HQ Tel: (01236) 729435 Fax: (01236) 729515 *Computer systems consultants & services*

▶ Ikonik Ltd, Unit 19, Victoria Way, Pride Park, Derby, DE24 8AN Tel: (01332) 224176 *Computer Systems, components, blank media, ink and paper, sales and repairs.*

Ilapak Ltd, Chalfont House, Silverdale Road, Hayes, Middlesex, UB3 3BN Tel: (020) 8797 2000 Fax: (020) 8797 2050 E-mail: sales@ilapak.co.uk *Packaging machinery sales & service*

Ilasco Ltd, 52-53 Nasmyth Road, Southfield Industrial Estate, Glenrothes, Fife, KY6 2SD Tel: (01592) 771241 Fax: (01592) 771071 E-mail: sales@ardmel-group.co.uk *Outdoor protective clothing manufrs*

▶ iLearn2Learn, 2-2 Grandfield, Edinburgh, EH6 4TJ Tel: 0131-551 4654

Iles Bros, Blackwood Rd, Blackwood, Gwent, NP12 2BW Tel: 01495 223400 *Bakery & confectionery supplies*

Iles Colour Print Ltd, Chase House, 1-2 Russell Town Avenue, Bristol, BS5 9LT Tel: 0117-954 7460 Fax: 0117-935 1243

Iles Colour Print Ltd, Chase House, 1-2 Russell Town Avenue, Bristol, BS5 9LT Tel: 0117-954 7460 Fax: 0117-935 1243 E-mail: ilescp@btconnect.com *Printers*

Ilfield Computer Consultancy Ltd, 7 Halsford Park Road, East Grinstead, West Sussex, RH19 1PW Tel: (01342) 321873 Fax: (01342) 316182 E-mail: enquiries@icc-ltd.co.uk *Computer consultants*

Ilford Engineering Co. Ltd, Bentalls, Basildon, Essex, SS14 3BY Tel: (01268) 526756 Fax: (01268) 531485 *Aluminium & steel sheet fabricators*

Ilford Engineering Co. Ltd, Bentalls, Basildon, Essex, SS14 3BY Tel: (01268) 526756 Fax: (01268) 531485 E-mail: mike@ilfordengineering.co.uk *Precision engineers & toolmakers*

Ilga U K Ltd, 175 Cocklaw Street, Kelty, Fife, KY4 0DH Tel: (01383) 831626 Fax: (01383) 831499 E-mail: info@taybuildscotia.co.uk *Rubber product manufrs*

▶ Ilkam, 17 Brynsmoor Road, Brinsley, Nottingham, NG16 5DD Tel: (01773) 764209 Fax: (01773) 764209 E-mail: enquire@ilkam.co.uk *Trailer & machine protective covers, tool bags ,extra pouches & webbing straps . PVC ,Nylon ,high frequency welding ,making up of industrial textiles*

Ilkeston Sewing & Janone Centre, Market Place, Ilkeston, Derbyshire, DE7 5QG Tel: 0115-930 7664 Fax: 0115-930 7664 E-mail: sales@ilkestonsewingcentre.co.uk *Sewing machines & accessories*

Ilkley It Services Ltd, Nat West Bank Chambers The, Grove Ilkley, Ilkley, West Yorkshire, LS29 9LS Tel: (01943) 601601 E-mail: info@ilkleyitservices.co.uk *Computer support service & maintenance*

Illingworth Bros, Unit 7 Greendykes Industrial Estate, Broxburn, West Lothian, EH52 6PG Tel: (01506) 854248 Fax: (01506) 856641 *Timber & upvc windows & doors*

▶ Illson Builders & Contractors Ltd, North Parade, Burley in Wharfedale, Ilkley, West Yorkshire, LS29 7JR Tel: (01943) 862022 Fax: (01943) 864191

Illston & Robson Ltd, Herbert Road, Small Heath, Birmingham, B10 0QQ Tel: 0121-772 5674 Fax: 0121-766 6452 E-mail: illstonandrobson@tiscali.co.uk *Air brake couplings manufacturers & ball joint & linkage manufrs*

Illuma Lighting Ltd, 11a Sills Road, Castle Donington, Derby, DE74 2US Tel: (01332) 818200 Fax: (01332) 818222 E-mail: info@illuma.co.uk *Lighting fitting manufrs*

Illuma Research Ltd, Richmond Bridge House, 419 Richmond Road, Twickenham, TW1 2EX Tel: (020) 8296 6600 Fax: (01935) 841693 E-mail: info@illumaresearch.co.uk *Market researchers*

Illuminaries Ltd, Sheffield Science Park Cooper Buildings, Arundel Street, Sheffield, S1 2NS Tel: 0114-270 0800 Fax: 0114-221 1801 E-mail: enquiries@illuminaries.co.uk *Computer software*

Illumination, Unit 7, North Medburn Farm, Watling Street, Elstree, Borehamwood, Hertfordshire, WD6 3AA Tel: (020) 8953 1414 Fax: (020) 8207 3040 E-mail: info@illumelec.co.uk *Electrical contractors*

Illuminations Of Camberley, 66-68 High Street, Camberley, Surrey, GU15 3RS Tel: (01276) 24941 Fax: (01276) 61718 E-mail: sales@illuminationsofcamberley.co.uk *Lighting distributors*

▶ Illy Computer Systems Ltd, 11 Hoxton Square, London, N1 6NU Tel: (020) 7749 2222 Fax: (020) 7749 2233 E-mail: info@illycorp.com *Computer software*

▶ Ilott Engineering Ltd, 25 Cowley Road, Nuffield Industrial Estate, Poole, Dorset, BH17 0UJ Tel: (01202) 661038 Fax: (01202) 661150 E-mail: info@acurate-controls.co.uk *Metalworking & fabrication service*

▶ Ils, 25-29 Brearton Street, Bradford, West Yorkshire, BD1 3ED Tel: (01274) 740494 Fax: (01274) 740504 E-mail: marketing@ilsonline.com *Engraving services*

Ilsley & Challis Ltd, Unit 1 ESME House, Coronation Road, Basingstoke, Hampshire, RG21 4ET Tel: 0845 5314149 Fax: (01256) 840204 E-mail: info@ilsley-challis.co.uk *Ilsley & Challis are a precision engineering and CNC turning company with over 50 years experience in all areas of precision engineering. We can take on any size job and offer a fast and efficient turn around time to suit your business needs. We are fully equipped to produce for the aerospace industry and automotive industry and all other industries that require precision engineered parts. Call us for a competitive quotation now.*

ILX Group P.L.C., George House, Princes Court, Beam Heath Way, Nantwich, Cheshire, CW5 6GD Tel: (01270) 611600 Fax: (01270) 628513 E-mail: sales@ilxgroup.com *Multi-media training software suppliers & manufrs*

Im Technical Services Ltd, Eagle House, Craigshaw Road, West Tullos Industrial Estate, Aberdeen, AB12 3AR Tel: (01224) 870004 Fax: (01224) 870004 E-mail: sales@imtechnical.com *Information technology consultants & training providers*

▶ IM3D Ltd, Axis 3, High Carr Business Park, Newcastle, Staffordshire, ST5 7UF Tel: (01782) 564888 Fax: (01782) 564344 E-mail: info@im3duk.com *Plastic Printing and In Mould Decorating. We offer reel to reel screen printing, laminating and die-cutting in clean room conditions for the manufacture of flexible conductive ink products, 2D/3D in mould labels and decorative plastic printing. Our moulding capability includes a full design, development and manufacturing in mould decorating service.*

IMA Ltd, Parkwell House, Otley Rd, Guiseley, Leeds, LS20 8BH Tel: 0845 4941692 Fax: (01943) 879988 E-mail: sales@ima.co.uk Purchasing Contact: D. Parker Sales Contact: P. Tetley Principal Export Areas: Worldwide *IMA have the widest possible range of moisture & humidity measurement products. From dewpoint meters, relative humidity sensors or water in oil measurements have been key to its success-helping with trace moisture, rh measurement or water in liquids & moisture in solids applications, providing complete moisture measurement solutions.*Moisture analysis, dewpoint measurement, or relative humidity measurement, can be just a spot check or a permanent, fixed installation. Tracking or logging measurements with clear indications on our range of digital panel meters or computer based HMI systems can make significant savings for operators. *The introduction of tunable diode laser systems now include other parameters such as hydrogen sulphide (H2S), carbon dioxide (CO2) & other trace level gases. IMA measure dewpoint & moisture concentration for the oil & gas industries, monitor nuclear reactors, optimise compressed air dryers, help process companies control the humidity & moisture level in food & chemical processing & liquids production.*

▶ Image, 378 Union Road, Oswaldtwistle, Accrington, Lancashire, BB5 3NW Tel: (01254) 393045 *Beauty salon uniform supplies & manufrs*

Company Image, 334 Selbourne Road, Luton, LU4 8NU Tel: (01582) 503010 Fax: (01582) 572069 E-mail: companyimage@btconnect.com *General printers*

▶ Image Ltd, Murhall Street, Stoke-on-Trent, ST6 4BL Tel: (01782) 825006 Fax: (01782) 825474

▶ Image + (Imageplus + plus), Unit 1 The Depot, Electric Wharf, Coventry, CV1 4JP Tel: (024) 7683 4780 Fax: (024) 7683 4781 E-mail: info@image-plus.co.uk *Image+ offers graphic design for web site design, new media (multimedia, corporate presentations and interactive CD ROMs) and print solutions. Based*

continued

in Coventry, we cover the Midlands including Birmingham, Leamington Spa and Stratford.

▶ Image 2 Ltd, 68 Nightingale Road, Rickmansworth, Hertfordshire, WD3 7BT Tel: (01923) 775098 Fax: (01923) 896679 E-mail: prrk@image2photo.co.uk *Commercial & corporate photography*

Image 90, Unit 12 Far Green Industrial Estate, Chell Street, Stoke-on-Trent, ST1 6AZ Tel: (01782) 215531 Fax: (01782) 215533 *Ceramic & printing specialists*

Image Advertising & Promotions Ltd, 7 The Circle, Tredegar, Gwent, NP22 3PS Tel: (01495) 712900 Fax: (01495) 712905 E-mail: info@imagead.net *Advertising agency & marketing consultant*

Image Aviation, 12A Court Park, Thurlestone, Kingsbridge, Devon, TQ7 3LX Tel: (01548) 562324 E-mail: fotos967@hotmail.com *Aerial photographers*

Image Blinds, 1 Century Park, Garrison Lane, Birmingham, B9 4NZ Tel: 0121-771 3000 Fax: 0121-773 9690 E-mail: sales@imageblinds.co.uk *Window blind manufrs*

Image Business Machines, 24 Long Croft, Yate, Bristol, BS37 7YW Tel: (01454) 325350 Fax: (01454) 325142 *Photocopier servicing*

Image Business Systems UK Ltd, 455 Maxwell Avenue, Harwell Intnl Business Centre, Didcot, Oxfordshire, OX11 0PY Tel: (01235) 865500 Fax: (01235) 865511 E-mail: sales@imagebusinesssystems.co.uk *Presentation training room equipment suppliers*

Image Ceilings Ltd, 82 Lind Road, Sutton, Surrey, SM1 4PL Tel: (020) 8770 3300 Fax: (0870) 8901146 E-mail: info@imageceilings.co.uk *Ceilings, partitioning & dry-lining contractors*

Image Colourprint Ltd, Grange Park Lane, Willerby, Hull, HU10 6EB Tel: (01482) 652323 Fax: (01482) 651899 E-mail: admin@imagedata.co.uk *Printers & barcode systems services*

Image Composites Ltd, Govan Road, Fenton Industrial Estate, Fenton, Stoke-on-Trent, ST4 2RS Tel: (01782) 411611 Fax: (01782) 411888 E-mail: info@imageplastics.co.uk *Image Plastics are GRP & Composite Engineering specialist producing; GRP Industrial Housings, Kiosks, Cabinets and covers.*

Image Computer Systems Ltd, 27 Cobham Road, Ferndown Industrial Estate, Wimborne, Dorset, BH21 7PE Tel: (01202) 876064 Fax: (01202) 897682 E-mail: sales@image-cs.co.uk *Bar coding & labelling systems & software suppliers*

▶ Image Data Ltd, Burley Hill Trading Estate, Leeds, LS4 2PU Tel: 0113-389 4050 Fax: 0113-278 4826 *Printers*

The Image Depot Ltd, The Old Exchange, Wellington Court, Belper, Derbyshire, DE56 1UP Tel: (01773) 827610 Fax: (01773) 826630 E-mail: adrianheapy@adrianheapy.co.uk *Commercial photographers*

Image Design, Hangar SE38, Gloucestershire Airport, Staverton, Cheltenham, Gloucestershire, GL51 6SP Tel: (01452) 712000 Fax: (01452) 857785 E-mail: info@imagedesignuk.com *Modular exhibition systems*

▶ Image Directors, Power House, Powerscroft Road, Sidcup, Kent, DA14 5EA Tel: (0870) 4584475 Fax: (0870) 4584476 E-mail: steve@imagedirectors.co.uk *Graphic design, web design & advertising*

Image Grafix, 6 Manse Parade, London Road, Swanley, Kent, BR8 8DA Tel: (01322) 614669 Fax: (01322) 614878 E-mail: imagegrafix@btconnect.com *Label manufrs*

Image House Ltd, 67-73 Constitution Hill, Birmingham, B19 3JX Tel: 0121-233 3569 Fax: 0121-233 0139 E-mail: vchobera@compuserve.com *Textile merchants*

Image HQ Ltd, 15a Balgownie Road, Bridge of Don, Aberdeen, AB23 8JN Tel: (01224) 825900 Fax: (01224) 709440 *Computer consultancy*

Image Management Technology, 16 The Oakwood Centre, Downley Road, Havant, Hampshire, PO9 2NP Tel: (023) 9245 6564 Fax: (023) 9236 7050 E-mail: wcteurope@worldcircuit.com *Flexible PCB design & manufacture*

Image Matters, Unit B12, Laser Quay, Rochester, Kent, ME2 4HU Tel: (01634) 296400 Fax: (01634) 296444 E-mail: sales@imagematters.co.uk *Promotion & incentive items & cloth*

Image Optics Components, Harvey Road, Basildon, Essex, SS13 1ES Tel: (01268) 728477 Fax: (01268) 590445 E-mail: sales@image-optics.fsnet.co.uk *Sapphire & silica optics suppliers*

Image Optics Components, Harvey Road, Basildon, Essex, SS13 1ES Tel: (01268) 728477 Fax: (01268) 590445 E-mail: sales@image-optics.fsnet.co.uk *Optical filters*

Image Playgrounds, 4-6 Allen Farmerby Way, York, YO60 6PG Tel: (01347) 868149 Fax: (01347) 667502 *Playground equipment suppliers*

The Image Projections Co. Ltd, Wickhurst Studios, Wickhurst Lane, Broadbridge Heath, Horsham, West Sussex, RH12 3LA Tel: (01403) 211110 E-mail: support@imageprojections.co.uk *Exhibition display designers*

Image Ry, 110 Harper Lane, Shenley, Radlett, Hertfordshire, WD7 9HG Tel: (01727) 828000 Fax: (01727) 828222 E-mail: sales@image-ry.co.uk *Digital, litho & large format printers*

▶ Image Scotland Ltd, Fisherrow Industrial Estate, Newhailes Road, Musselburgh, Midlothian, EH21 6RU Tel: 0131-665 1414 Fax: 0131-665 1919 E-mail: sales@imagescotland.com *Sports clothing, t-shirt & sweatshirts manufrs*

Image Sign Co, Stretham Station Road, Wilburton, Ely, Cambridgeshire, CB6 3QD Tel: (01353) 648208 Fax: (01353) 648208 *Sign manufrs*

▶ Image Tint, 31 Snowdon Avenue, Maidstone, Kent, ME14 5NW Tel: (01622) 672272 E-mail: info@imagetint.co.uk *Vehicle & building window tints*

Image Video, 33 Walters Road, Llanelli, Dyfed, SA15 1LS Tel: (01554) 777416 *Video producers*

▶ Image Visual Communications, Samson Close, Stephenson Industrial Estate, Newcastle upon Tyne, NE12 6DX Tel: 0191-268 8000 Fax: 0191-268 6573 E-mail: sales@image-viscom.co.uk

▶ Image Website Design, 10 Hereford Close, Exmouth, Devon, EX8 5QT Tel: (01395) 223255 Fax: (01395) 223255 E-mail: sales@imagewebsitedesign.co.uk *Innovative website design and hosting for todays budget conscious small business.*Personal and professional service.*Quick turnaround from original concept to working website.*Clear costings with no hidden charges. Inexpensive e-commerce solutions.*

▶ The Image Works Ltd, 1 Carside, Lome Shay Industrial Estate, Nelson, Lancashire, BB9 6RX Tel: (01282) 447385

Image X P S Ltd, 11 North Street, Portslade, Brighton, BN41 1DH Tel: (01273) 421242 Fax: (01273) 421210 *Digital printing services*

Imageon Ltd, White Cross Industrial Estate, South Road, Lancaster, LA1 4XQ Tel: (01524) 382777 Fax: (01524) 382777 E-mail: info@imageonltd.fsbusiness.co.uk *Textile & ceramic printers*

▶ Imagery Ltd, 3 Prince Road, Kings Norton Business Centre, Birmingham, B30 3HB Tel: 0121-486 1616 Fax: 0121-486 1282

Images Labels Ltd, 12 Aintree Avenue, Eckington, Sheffield, S21 4JA Tel: (01246) 436876 Fax: (01246) 435987 E-mail: info@imageslabels.com *Label & nameplate manufrs*

Images Storage & Partitioning Ltd, 68 Iron Mill Lane, Dartford, DA1 4RR Tel: (01322) 525975 Fax: (01322) 558032 E-mail: mrimages@globalnet.co.uk *Partitioning & storage equipment*

Imagestore Ltd, Ecchinswell Road, Kingsclere, Newbury, Berkshire, RG20 4QG Tel: (01635) 297297 Fax: (01635) 298603 E-mail: sales@imagestore.co.uk *IT data storage providers*

▶ Imagey - photo print and display products, 16 Bull Lane, London, N18 1SX Tel: 0845 833 0783 Fax: 0845 833 0793 E-mail: info@imagey.co.uk *UK company offering a range of printing and display products, print signs and graphics. **Imagey create wall art and photographic interior products from your images - canvas prints, block mount panels, direct digital acrylic prints, perspex box frames, acrylic sandwich and desktop blocks,framed prints, light boxes and more. **Imagey also supply roller banners, printed vinyl and portable display systems and printed graphics for trade and exhibition. **We can offer trade and quantity discounts, and manufacture most of our products at our London base. Commercial digital photography services for product, packshot and creative photography also undertaken for clients.*

Imagic UK P.L.C., Potterne, Devizes, Wiltshire, SN10 5XG Tel: (01380) 729099 Fax: (01380) 729092 E-mail: info@imageaccess.co.uk *Digital imaging systems*

Imagination Signs, 43 Birdham Road, Chichester, West Sussex, PO19 8TB Tel: (01243) 783569 Fax: (01243) 785011 E-mail: sales@imaginationsigns.co.uk *Sign manufrs*

Imagination Technologies, Turing House, Station Road, Chepstow, Gwent, NP16 5PB Tel: (01291) 625422 Fax: (01291) 620301 E-mail: info@ensigma.com *Communications technologies*

▶ Imaginative Interiors, 11 Burnside Close, Harrogate, North Yorkshire, HG1 2BQ Tel: (01423) 565959 *A specialist decorative paint effects company creating unique and inspiring murals, trompe l''oeils, and paint effects such as marbling, antiquing and coulourwashes for both private and commercial interiors.*

▶ Imagine, 28 Buckingham Grove, Scartho Top, Grimsby, North East Lincolnshire, DN33 3RR Tel: (01472) 314266 E-mail: monkey5000@ntlworld.com *block paving, concrete, patio''s, fencing and landscape design.* *

▶ Imagine 20 20 Ltd, 23 Eastgate, Worksop, Nottinghamshire, S80 1RH Tel: (01909) 473329 Fax: (01909) 477216 E-mail: info@imagine2020.co.uk *Art & craft material suppliers*

▶ imaginecolour.com, PO Box 814, Doncaster, South Yorkshire, DN1 9AG Tel: (0800) 1071860 Fax: (01302) 365850 E-mail: info@imaginecolour.com *Cheap colour printers suppliers*

Imagineering, Sittingbourne Research Centre Room 30 Building 940, Security, Sittingbourne, Kent, ME9 8AG Tel: (01795) 479120 Fax: (01795) 479120 E-mail: tom@imagineering1.co.uk *Product engineers*

Imagineering Plastic Fabrication, 21 Cater Road, Bristol, BS13 7TW Tel: 0117-978 4114 Fax: 0117-978 4114 E-mail: plasticfabrication@hotmail.com *Plastic materials fabricators & industrial machine guards manufrs*

Imagineers Ltd, Abercromby Avenue, High Wycombe, Buckinghamshire, HP12 3BW Tel: (01494) 473861 Fax: (01494) 473863 E-mail: enquiries@imagineersltd.co.uk *Foam products & plastic mouldings manufrs*

▶ ImagineHowe, Rennadal House, Firth, Orkney, KW17 2NY Tel: (07786) 578000

Imaging Associates Ltd, 6 Avonbury Business Park, Howes Lane, Bicester, Oxfordshire, OX26 2UA Tel: (01869) 356240 Fax: (01869) 356241 E-mail: sales@imas.co.uk *Distributors of scientific digital imaging, analysis & microscopes*

▶ Imaginit, Shaw House, Pegler Way, Crawley, West Sussex, RH11 7AF Tel: 0845 6027397 E-mail: solutions@imaginit.net *Web design, website development, website maintenance, promotion & hosting. Website content management. Website application development & consultancy*

Imago, Lyme Tree House, Alexandra Street, Hyde, Cheshire, SK14 1EY Tel: 0161-367 9922 Fax: 0161-367 9933 E-mail: mail@imago-direct.com *Album manufrs*

Imaj Computer Systems Group, Mill Street, Newton Moor Industrial Estate, Hyde, Cheshire, SK14 4LG Tel: 0161-368 1476 Fax: 0161-367 8145 E-mail: sales@imajsystems.co.uk *Computer systems*

Imani Clothing Ltd, 15 Chatley Street, Manchester, M3 1HU Tel: 0161-834 3367 Fax: 0161-833 0490 *Clothing wholesalers & manufrs*

Imarco, Beech House, The Covert, Ascot, Berkshire, SL5 9JS Tel: (01344) 845858 Fax: (01344) 626088 *Food ingredients sales & development*

Imarco Ltd, Herkomer House, 156 High Street, Bushey, WD23 3HF Tel: (020) 8420 4599 Fax: (020) 8420 4273 E-mail: vision@imarco.co.uk *Public relations & commercial marketing*

Imass Ltd, Northumbria House, Regent Centre, Gosforth, Newcastle upon Tyne, NE3 3PX Tel: 0191-213 0526 Fax: 0191-213 0526 E-mail: servicedesk@imass.co.uk *Software development*

IMC Group Consulting Ltd, PO Box 18, Nottingham, NG15 0DT Tel: (01623) 726166 Fax: (01623) 729359 E-mail: mining@imcgcl.com *Mining & consulting engineers.*

Imer Reman, 2 Whitewater Place Maun Way, Boughton Industrial Estate, Boughton, Newark, Nottinghamshire, NG22 9LD Tel: (01623) 863600 Fax: (01623) 863606 E-mail: sales@remanufacturers.co.uk *Auto electrical, electronic equipment & component, cable assembly & harness*

Imerys Minerals Ltd, Par Moor Centre, Par Moor Road, Par, Cornwall, PL24 2SQ Tel: (01726) 818000 Fax: (01726) 811200 E-mail: perfmins@imerys.com Principal Export Areas: Worldwide *Producers & suppliers of calcium carbonate & china clay*

Imerys Minerals Ltd, Furzebrook Road, Wareham, Dorset, BH20 5AR Tel: (01626) 333797 Fax: (01929) 552845 *Clay mining*

Imes, Clyde Submarine Base, Faslane, Helensburgh, Dunbartonshire, G84 8HL Tel: (01436) 811000 Fax: (01436) 811477 *Engineering*

▶ Imes, Clyde Submarine Base, Faslane, Helensburgh, Dunbartonshire, G84 8HL Tel: (01436) 811000 Fax: (01436) 811477

▶ Imes Engineers, 32 South Court The Courtyard, Woodlands, Bradley Stoke, Bristol, BS32 4NH Tel: (01454) 202288 Fax: (01454) 202123 *Engineering*

▶ IMEX Sameday Express Couriers, 54, Melton Road, Barrow on Soar, Loughborough, Leicestershire, LE12 8NX Tel: 01509 620178 Fax: 01509 620178 E-mail: ianmargetts@btinternet.com *Sameday delivery from Leicestershire, large vans to small, competitive rate, personal service.*

Imex Systems Ltd, 34 Old Kilmore Road, Moira, Craigavon, County Armagh, BT67 0LZ Tel: (028) 9261 9233 Fax: (028) 9261 9234 E-mail: sales@ulster.imex.co.uk *Electronic test & measurement equipment distributors*

IMG Industrial Maintenance Group Ltd, Unit M Riverside Industrial Estate, Fazeley, Tamworth, Staffordshire, B78 3RW Tel: (01827) 283322 Fax: (01827) 250143 *Storage contractors*

Imgas Ltd, Sansom House, Portland Street, Daybrook, Nottingham, NG5 6BL Tel: 0115-966 7030 Fax: 0115-966 7031 E-mail: sales@imgas.co.uk *Design, install & maintenance of piped medical*

Imgen Manufrs, New Image Works, 240 Church Road, Layton, London, E10 7JQ Tel: (020) 8887 0709 Fax: (020) 8887 0744 *Plastic binder manufrs*

Imi, Lakeside, Birmingham Business Park, Birmingham, B37 7UX Tel: 0121-717 3700 Fax: 0121-717 3701 *Fluid & indoor climate control suppliers*

Imi Components, Nobel Way, Witton, Birmingham, B6 7ES Tel: 0121-344 5800 Fax: 0121-344 3056 *Components for civil nuclear industry*

Imirp Rapid Prototyping Ltd, Aston Cross Industrial Estate, 51 Lichfield Road, Birmingham, B6 5RW Tel: 0121-327 3525 Fax: 0121-328 5982 E-mail: sales@imirp.co.uk *Rapid prototyping engineers*

▶ Imitza Systems, 26 High Street, Spennymoor, County Durham, DL16 6DB Tel: (01388) 818844 E-mail: info@imitza.co.uk *Imitza Systems support and develop IT systems primarily for small and medium sized businesses in the North East of England.**At Imitza we can use both proprietary and open source technologies to develop solutions best suited to your requirements.*

Iml Labels & Systems Ltd, 6 Brookdale Road, Thorncliffe Park Estate, Chapeltown, Sheffield, S35 2PW Tel: 0114-246 5771 Fax: 0114-240 3410 E-mail: sales@iml-labels.co.uk *A leading UK supplier of high performance labels, entry tickets and branding badges*

Hugh Imlay & Co. Ltd, 3 Duff St, Aberdeen, AB24 5LF Tel: (01224) 640151 Fax: (01224) 647399 E-mail: info@hughimlay.co.uk *Envelopes to specification & business stationery manufrs*

▶ Immaculate UK Ltd, Centre 500, 500 Chiswick High Road, London, W4 8RG Tel: (020) 8987 8900 Fax: (020) 8956 2402 E-mail: info@immaculateuk.com *Immaculate UK are a West London based award winning design and marketing agency that deliver highly effective marketing communications based on strategic thinking and creative execution. We are young, dynamic and passionate about what we do. In an ever more crowded and competitive marketplace clever communication can make the difference. We deliver creative solutions in the following areas: Identity, Branding, Literature, Advertising, Web, Direct Marketing, display, exhibition and events. We will analyse your communications objectives and employ the most effective medium to enable you to connect with your target audience. Our approach is based on three key areas: Strategy, Creativity, Results. Phil Staff*

Immage Studios Ltd, Margaret Street, Immingham, South Humberside, DN40 1LE Tel: (01469) 515151 Fax: (01469) 515152 *Local multimedia & television company*

▶ Immedia Print, 215 North Street, Romford, RM1 4QA Tel: (01708) 733237 Fax: (01708) 733739 E-mail: Immediaprint@AOL.com We supply all types of printing to any industry. In addition, we specialise in large format colour posters up to Ao On Glossy paper or canvas Any enquiry welcomed.

Immediate Transportation Co. Ltd, First Floor, St Nicholas House, Chappel St, Liverpool, L2 8TX Tel: 0151-227 4521 Fax: 0151-236 8036 E-mail: itcolhr@itcolhr.co.uk Freight forwarders Also at: Colnbrook, Dover, Felixstowe, London & Manchester

Immediate Transportation Co. Ltd, Mckay Trading Estate, Blackthorne Road, Colnbrook, Slough, SL3 0AH Tel: (01753) 684644 Fax: (01753) 683338 E-mail: itcolhr@itcolhr.co.uk Freight forwarders import & export

Immingham Railfreight Terminals Ltd, Netherlands Way, Stallingborough, Grimsby, North East Lincolnshire, DN41 8DF Tel: (01469) 576363 Fax: (01469) 571934 E-mail: peterdibdin@tpdibdin.com Warehousing, open storage, steel handling

▶ Immingham Storage Co. Ltd, East Riverside, Immingham Dock, Immingham, South Humberside, DN40 2LZ Tel: (01469) 578889 Fax: (01469) 572001

Immobiliser UK, PO Box 223, Borehamwood, Hertfordshire, WD6 1AH Tel: (020) 8953 9803 Fax: (020) 8905 1541 Electronic component manufrs

Imofa UK Ltd, New Coach House, 21 Grange Way, Colchester, CO2 8HF Tel: (01206) 505909 Fax: (01206) 794095 E-mail: sales@imofa.co.uk Industrial fans & air handling units manufrs

Imorex, Dooley Road, Felixstowe, Suffolk, IP11 3HG Tel: (01394) 607743 Fax: (01394) 607767 E-mail: info@imorex.co.uk Shipping & forwarding agents Also at: Felixstowe

▶ I-MOTUS, 11 West Mills Yard, Kennet Road, Newbury, Berkshire, RG14 5LP Tel: 0845 430 4448 Fax: 01635 524 449 E-mail: info@i-motus.com Training videos, health & safety, sales, customer service & management

Imp Electronics Ltd, Rocol Building, 3 Glebe Road, Huntingdon, Cambridgeshire, PE29 7DL Tel: (01480) 411822 Fax: (01480) 411833 Electronic product design

▶ Imp Freight Services Ltd, The Chapel House, Kings Road, Immingham, South Humberside, DN40 1QS Tel: (01469) 577566 Fax: (01469) 572998

▶ Imp Security Systems Ltd, 14 Raynton Close Washingborough, Lincoln, LN4 1HD Tel: (01522) 793666 Fax: (01522) 797300 E-mail: info@impsecurity.co.uk Security system distributors

▶ Imp Transport, Unit 4, George Street, Lincoln, LN5 8LG Tel: (01522) 560414 Fax: (01522) 535510

▶ Impact, Balcony, 60 Merrion Centre, Leeds, LS2 8NG Tel: 0113-234 9186

▶ Impact, Tuscany Wharf, 4b Orsman Road, London, N1 5QJ Tel: (020) 7729 5978 Fax: (020) 7229 5994

▶ Impact Arts Glasgow Ltd, The Factory, 319-321 Craigpark Drive, Glasgow, G31 2TB Tel: 0141-575 3001

▶ Impact Automotive Services Ltd, Unit 24 Parkside Industrial Estate, Edge La Street, Royton, Oldham, OL2 6DS Tel: 0161-620 2948 Fax: 0161-628 9572 Automotive electronic equipment manufrs

Impact Boston Ltd, Victoria Road, Skegness, Lincolnshire, PE25 3SN Tel: (01754) 767275 Fax: (01754) 613100 E-mail: sales@impactboston.ltd.uk Self-adhesive label manufrs

Impact Calendars, 1 Redwood Park, Capel, Tonbridge, Kent, TN12 6WB Tel: (01892) 838811 Fax: (01892) 836699 E-mail: impactcal@dial.pipex.com Calendar distributors

Impact Carbides Ltd, 36 East Bank Road, Sheffield, S2 3PS Tel: 0114-272 7216 Fax: 0114-272 4854 E-mail: sales@impactcarbides.co.uk Special cutting tool manufrs

Impact Computer Consultants Ltd, 210 Church Road, Hove, East Sussex, BN3 2DJ Tel: (01273) 821820 Fax: (01273) 821010 E-mail: sales@impactcc.co.uk Software developers

▶ Impact Computing & Consulting, Oak Mount, Blackpool Road, Newton, Preston, PR4 3RE Tel: (01772) 684282 Fax: (01772) 681597 E-mail: sales@impactcomputing.co.uk Specialists in reliable support for microsoft based computer networks

▶ Impact Control Systems Ltd, 9 Tapton Way, Liverpool, L13 1DA Tel: 0151-254 2658 Fax: 0151-254 2659 E-mail: admin@impactcontrols.co.uk Heating controls

Impact Design & Advertising, 113 Bradbury Road, Solihull, West Midlands, B92 8AL Tel: 0121-707 4774 Fax: 0121-706 1663 E-mail: steve@impactida.com Advertising and design agency, promoting your business in a creative way to increace your client share and turnover is our goal.

Impact Ducting Sales Ltd, 45 Oakland Road, Leicester, LE2 6AN Tel: 0116-244 8151 Fax: 0116-244 8343 E-mail: impactducting@impactholdings.com Sheet metal ductwork fabricators

▶ Impact Environmental, 401 Ash Bank Road, Werrington, Stoke-on-Trent, ST9 0JP Tel: (01782) 251324 E-mail: impactenvironmental@hotmail.co.uk Pest control services

Impact Europe, Europe House, 170 Windmill Road West, Sunbury-On-Thames, Middlesex, TW16 7HB Tel: (01932) 733700 Fax: (01932) 733710 E-mail: info@impact-europe.com Audio-visual retailers & installers

▶ Impact Factory, Unit 119 Business Design Centre, 52 Upper Street, London, N1 0QH Tel: (020) 7226 1877 Fax: (020) 7354 3505 E-mail: enquiries@impactfactory.com Provides tailor-made professional personal development programmes from presentation skills, communication skills and team building, to

continued

leadership and executive coaching for individuals.

Impact Graphics, 2 Smitham Bridge Road, Hungerford, Berkshire, RG17 0QP Tel: (01488) 685001 Fax: (01488) 685395 E-mail: info@impact-graphics.co.uk Graphic signs manufrs

Impact Kitchens & Bedrooms, Perseverance Mill, Bolton Road, Westhoughton, Bolton, BL5 3JQ Tel: (01942) 812331 Bedroom & kitchen furniture manufrs

▶ Impact Media, The Mm2 Building, 84 Pickford Street, Manchester, M4 5BT Tel: 0161-236 0008 Fax: 0161-236 0204 E-mail: info@impactmediapr.com Impact Media PR is a young and dynamic public relations consultancy based in Manchester City Centre.**We offer a highly personal, bespoke service to our clients. We directly target decision makers and influencers to give you maximum cost effectiveness. Our clients appreciate the impact that promotion through active public relations has on their bottom line. **Whether our clients require a long term PR strategy, PR at key points in their business calendar or simply want to be sure that they are prepared for any unexpected press attention, Impact Media PR will guide them on the right course. We will make it as easy as possible and aim to get clients effective results. * *

Impact Metal Services Ltd, 3 Phoenix Park, Station Road, Rowley Regis, West Midlands, B65 0LJ Tel: 0121-561 2030 Fax: 0121-561 1158 E-mail: sales@impactmetal.co.uk Aluminium stockholders

▶ Impact Plating Technologies, 2, Collingwood Rd, Lower Bebington, Wirral, Merseyside, CH63 7RL Tel: (07725) 050645 E-mail: info@impactplating.com Plating & restoration of gold, silver & zinc.

▶ Impact Precision, 10 New Road, Stapleford, Nottingham, NG9 8GS Tel: 0115-949 0494

Impact Printing Of Coleraine Ltd, Unit 8, The Diamond Arcade, Coleraine, County Londonderry, BT52 1DE Tel: (028) 2076 2469 Fax: (028) 7034 4119 E-mail: info@impactpublishers.co.uk General commercial printers

Impact Refinishers Ltd, Main Street, Hull, HU2 0LF Tel: (01482) 327690 Fax: (01482) 328036 E-mail: enquiries@impactrefinishers.co.uk Motor body refinishers

Impact Security, 304 Linthorpe Road, Middlesbrough, Cleveland, TS1 3QX Tel: (01642) 654000 Fax: (01642) 654500 E-mail: info@impact-security-uk.com Security alarm manufrs

Impact Signs, 2 Mugiemoss Road, Bucksburn, Aberdeen, AB21 9HH Tel: (01224) 684488 Fax: (01224) 684400 Sign makers

▶ Impact Signs, Unit 32 Rabans Close, Rabans Lane Industrial Area, Aylesbury, Buckinghamshire, HP19 8RS Tel: (01296) 485902 Fax: (01296) 488869 E-mail: sales@impactsignssolutions.co.uk Specialists in industrial engraving

Impact Signs, 13-14 Hutton Street, Boldon Colliery, Tyne & Wear, NE35 9LW Tel: 0191-536 0536 Fax: 0191-536 5536 E-mail: info@inpact3dsigns.co.uk Sign makers

Impact Signs & Design Ltd, Unit 59 Atlantic Business Centre, Atlantic Street, Broadheath, Altrincham, Cheshire, WA14 5NQ Tel: 0161-929 9594 Fax: 0161-929 9597 E-mail: sales@impact-signs.co.uk Sign manufrs

Impact Socket Supplies Ltd, Park Mills, Deighton Road, Chorley, Lancashire, PR7 2BL Tel: (01257) 277205 Fax: (01257) 270540 E-mail: sales@impactsockets.co.uk Impact sockets & accessories manufrs

Impact Test Equipment Ltd, Building 21, Stevenston Industrial Estate, Stevenston, Ayrshire, KA20 3LR Tel: (01294) 602626 Fax: (01294) 461168 E-mail: sales@impact-test.co.uk Manufacturers of sieves (test)

Impact Visuals, 1327 Stratford Road, Hall Green, Birmingham, B28 9HH Tel: 0121-702 0888 Fax: 0121-702 0889 E-mail: sales@impactvisuals.co.uk Audio visual equipment hire & installation

Impakt Stationers, Unit 12 Endeavour Way, Croydon, CR0 4TR Tel: (020) 8684 5777 Fax: (020) 8684 5999 E-mail: sales@impakt.co.uk Promotional stationery & advertising gift manufrs

▶ Impala Business Solutions Ltd, Unit 18, Ynyscedwyn Enterprise Park, Ystradgynlais, Swansea, SA9 1DT Tel: 01689 878299 Fax: 01639 841252 E-mail: hgvsolutions@btinternet.com Manufacturer of petrochemical products to clean fuel systems & engines & to reduce emissions for Cars,HGV,Buses,Motorbikes & Marine Engines. Also vehicles sanitising & deordourising fluids tailored to kill bacteria, viruses & insects - meets EU standards.

▶ Impala Business Solutions, Unit 7, Gurnos Industrial Estate, Bethel Road, Ystalyfera, Swansea, SA9 2HW Tel: (01639) 841256 Chemical manufacturer. We mainly operate within the automotive trade but are capable of looking at any potential product and turning it into a reality.

Impalloy Ltd, Alloys House, Willenhall Lane, Bloxwich, Walsall, WS3 2XN Tel: (01922) 714400 Fax: (01922) 714411 E-mail: sales@impalloy.com We are the largest manufacturers in Europe of Aluminium and Zinc sacrificial anodes for Cathodic Protection. We supply the Offshore, Industrial and Marine Industries . We can also supply Magnesium Anodes for fresh water applications.

IMPAMARK, 1Dammerwick Farm, Marsh Road, Burnham-On-Crouch, Essex, CM0 8AG Tel: (01621) 783550 Fax: (01621) 784548 E-mail: info@impamark.co.uk Promotional & advertising gifts

Impaq UK Ltd, Lantern House, Walnut Tree Close, Guildford, Surrey, GU1 4TX Tel: (01483) 466900 Fax: (01483) 466901 E-mail: enquiries@impaq.co.uk Software house consultants & services

Imperial, 65 North Acton Road, London, NW10 6PJ Tel: (020) 8965 8596 Fax: (020) 8961 9352 E-mail: info@iwsm.co.uk Welders & sheet metal workers

Imperial Business Systems, 7 Hill Street, Bristol, BS1 5PU Tel: 0117-925 1700 Fax: 0117-925 2515 E-mail: ibs@imperial.co.uk Information technology consultants

Imperial Cleaning, Unit 7 Springwood, Cheshunt, Waltham Cross, Hertfordshire, EN7 6AZ Tel: (01992) 628342 Fax: (01992) 628342 E-mail: imperialenquiries@btinternet.com Window cleaning contractors

▶ Imperial Colours & Chemicals, Admiral House, Blakeridge Lane, Batley, West Yorkshire, WF17 8PD Tel: (01924) 477433 Textile manufrs

Imperial Components, 7 Sutherland Court, Brownfields, Welwyn Garden City, Hertfordshire, AL7 1BJ Tel: (01707) 321122 Fax: (01707) 321121 Electronic connector & cable distributors

▶ Imperial Design UK Ltd, Hanson Close, Middleton, Manchester, M24 2HD Tel: 0161-643 2266 E-mail: sales@displaydesgins.net Manufacture wedding supplies

▶ Imperial Ductwork Manufacturing, 140 Burnham Road, Dartford, DA1 5AZ Tel: (01322) 285328 Fax: (01322) 285428 Sheet metalworkers

Imperial Finishers Ltd, 8 Windmill Close, Stansted, Essex, CM24 8GH Tel: (01279) 817500 Fax: (01279) 817517 Contracts furniture suppliers

Imperial Garments, 22 Victoria Road, Aston, Birmingham, B6 5HA Tel: 0121-554 0416 Fax: 0121-554 3691 E-mail: sschowlia@aol.com Clothing manufrs

Imperial Innovations Ltd, Imperial College, London, SW7 2AZ Tel: (020) 7581 4949 Fax: (020) 7589 3553 E-mail: sales@imperial.ac.uk Research & development services

Imperial Innovations Ltd, Imperial College, London, SW7 2AZ Tel: (020) 7581 4949 Fax: (020) 7589 3553 E-mail: sales@imperial.ac.uk Science technology & medicine

Imperial Merchants Ltd, 199a Munster Rd, London, SW6 6BX Tel: 0207 385 0333 Alcohol importers

Imperial Pearl, 24 Hatton Garden, London, EC1N 8BQ Tel: (020) 7242 0575 Fax: (020) 7405 7373 E-mail: valdorltd@waitrose.com Pearl importers & jewellery manufrs, wedding rings, clasp mfrs

Imperial Polythene Products Ltd, Unit 3 Lakeside Industrial Estate, Colnbrook, Slough, SL3 0ED Tel: (01753) 686336 Fax: (01753) 682793 Polythene bag & film also biodegradable materials manufrs

▶ Imperial Stone, New Barn Farm, Rake Road, Milland, Liphook, Hampshire, GU30 7JU Tel: (01428) 741175 Fax: (01428) 741175 E-mail: sales@imperialstone.co.uk Manufacturers of architectural & decorative cast stone & glassfibre reinforced concrete (GRC). Specialists in bespoke casting to you specifications

Imperial Swimming Pool Supplies, Magerae, Marriotts Avenue, South Heath, Great Missenden, Buckinghamshire, HP16 9QN Tel: (01494) 863030 Fax: (01494) 891030 E-mail: imperialswimmingpools@btopenworld.com Pool & pool servicing equipment

Imperial Tobacco Ltd, PO Box 244, Bristol, BS99 7UJ Tel: 0117-966 7957 Fax: 0117-966 7405 E-mail: keith.tatham@uk.imptob.com Principal Export Areas: Worldwide Cigar, cigarette & tobacco products manufrs

Imperial Wire Products Ltd, 78 Wharfdale Road, Tyseley, Birmingham, B11 2DE Tel: 0121-706 3802 Fax: 0121-706 8202 Wire rope assembly manufrs

▶ Imperial World Ltd, 40 Station Road, London, SW19 2LP Tel: (020) 8542 0883 Fax: (020) 8542 0992 E-mail: mail@imperial-world.com Furniture retailers

▶ Impermia, 1 shaftesbury Gdns, London, NW10 6LP Tel: (020) 8961 5259 Fax: (020) 8961 5359 E-mail: info@impermia.co.uk Specialise in balconies & terraces, flat roofs, wet room tanking, wall & floor tiling **

Impetus Technologies Ltd, Castle Farm, Cholmondeley, Malpas, Cheshire, SY14 8AQ Tel: (01829) 773200 Fax: (01829) 773208 E-mail: sales@impetusuk.net On site service providers of electronic (pos) & (epos)

Impex (Glassware) Ltd, Impex House, 8 Scrubs Lane, London, NW10 6QR Tel: (020) 8969 6496 Fax: (020) 8960 5337 E-mail: moreinfo@impex.glassware.co.uk Decorative lighting manufrs

Impex Trading Co., 23 Oxford Place, 7 Oxford Road, Manchester, M1 6EY Tel: 0161-273 1908 Fax: 0161-273 7072 Yarn spinners

▶ Imphouse Ltd, Merston Manor Farm, Chapel Lane, Merstone, Newport, Isle of Wight, PO30 3BZ Tel: (01983) 527855 Fax: (01983) 527877

Imphy Ugine Precision UK Ltd, Wessex Road, Bourne End, Buckinghamshire, SL8 5DT Tel: (01628) 850234 Fax: (01628) 850119 Nickel alloy manufrs

▶ Implants International Simco 708 Ltd, 71 Jay Avenue, Teesside Industrial Estate, Stockton-on-Tees, Cleveland, TS17 9LZ Tel: (01642) 769080 Fax: (01642) 765848 E-mail: enquiries@implantsinternational.com Orthopedic implants

Import My Vehicle Ltd, Currie House, Herbert Walker Avenue, Western Docks, Southampton, SO15 1HJ Tel: (023) 8033 6635 Fax: (023) 8033 8833 E-mail: info@importmyvehicle.co.uk Import My Vehicle Ltd specialise in providing a variety of vehicle shipping solutions to both commercial shippers and private individuals. Import My vehicle Ltd is a shipping & sourcing specialist who provides a bespoke service for clients who wish to import vehicles into the UK from either Japan or USA. Our dedicated team have a wealth of shipping and freight forwarding experience, including an extensive knowledge of Customs procedures and completing Customs clearance declarations.

▶ Import Services, Tollbar Way, Hedge End, Southampton, SO30 2UH Tel: (01489) 799500

▶ Impress Bath Ltd, 6 Cork Place, Bath, BA1 3BB Tel: (01225) 315467 Fax: (01225) 470274 E-mail: info@impressbath.co.uk Photocopying services

Impress Cards, Slough Farm, Westhall, Halesworth, Suffolk, IP19 8RN Tel: (01986) 781422 Fax: (01986) 781677 E-mail: sales@impresscards.com Blank cards & handicraft materials

Impress Event Management Ltd, The Annex, 8 Kelsey Way, Beckenham, Kent, BR3 3LL Tel: (020) 8663 6647 Fax: (020) 8663 3195 E-mail: matthew@impressevents.co.uk All types of events covered including weddings, private parties, corporate away days, charity balls and conferences. Small dedicated staff to ensure the personal touch and a high level of service

Impress Express, Unit 10 Merlin Park, Fred Dannatt Road, Mildenhall, Bury St. Edmunds, Suffolk, IP28 7RD Tel: (01638) 718878 Fax: (01638) 711887 E-mail: info@impressexpress.co.uk Sign designers & manufrs

▶ Impress Graphic Equipment Ltd, 14 Howard Court, Nerston Industrial Estate, East Kilbride, Glasgow, G74 4QZ Tel: (01355) 266115 E-mail: alan@lithoegineering.com Print engineers

▶ Impress Leicester Ltd, 8 Morris Road, Leicester, LE2 6BR Tel: 0116-270 0999 Fax: 0116-270 2172

Impress Metal Packaging, Salhouse Road, Norwich, NR7 9AT Tel: (01603) 427313 Fax: (01603) 408571 Can manufrs

Impress North East Limited, Ryton Industrial Estate, Newburn Bridge Road, Blaydon-on-Tyne, Tyne & Wear, NE21 4SQ Tel: 0191-414 8901 Fax: 0191-414 2400 E-mail: sales@impressltd.co.uk Impress North East Limited manufactures a wide range pressings and fully engineered components to customer specification in a variety of exotic materials, including Inconel 718 & 625 and Super Duplex F55 ect, from small to medium quantities. *We provide a solution to your subcontracting problems. Using our extensive engineering background we offer you the best possible service at the right price. **Individual Specification *Experience and Reputation *ISO 9001:2000 Certification *Rapid delivery and unparalleled service *In House Rapid Tooling *Fabrication *General Machining *Lock, Tab Washer to SP Series; SP41,SP42,SP43,SP44,SP45,SP46, SP107, SP108, SP109, SP110, SP111, SP112, AGS194, AGS195, AGS518, DIN93, DIN432, DIN463, DIN462, BS5814 * Flat Washers *Shim Washers *Discs *Flat Springs *Rings *Clips *Brackets *Shim Packs *Gaskets *Circlips *And Many More!

Impress Printers Ltd, 54 Burners Lane, Kiln Farm, Milton Keynes, MK11 3HD Tel: (01908) 262111 Fax: (01908) 262555 E-mail: carol@impress-envelopes.co.uk Impress supply and manufacture printed envelopes to the trade and direct mail industry. We overprint in 1-5 colours and convert printed sheets in houses. Our staff are experienced and dedicated to providing the service you need.

▶ Impress Printers, Unit 72 Lower Bethesda Street, Stoke-on-Trent, ST1 3DE Tel: (01782) 287677 Fax: (01782) 287517 E-mail: sales@impressprinters.co.uk

▶ IM-Press Promotions Ayr Ltd, 3 Barclaugh Drive, Coylton, Ayr, KA6 6HS Tel: (01292) 570495 Fax: (01292) 570495 E-mail: im-pressayr@btconnect.com Specialist Supplier of Promotional Products & Personalised Clothing

▶ Im-Press Promotions Derby, 2 Marston Brook, Hilton, Derby, DE65 5HS Tel: (01283) 732994 Fax: 01283 732994 E-mail: im-pressderby@btconnect.com Corporate Gifte and Clothing to suit all tastes and budgets. Full personalisation and sourcing service.

▶ Impress Repro By Design, 2 A1 Parkway, Southgate Way, Orton Southgate, Peterborough, PE2 6YN Tel: (01733) 397350 Fax: (01733) 397351 Reprographics digital print work

Impress Solutions Ltd, 268-272 North Street, Romford, RM1 4QN Tel: (01708) 759760 Fax: (01708) 759761 E-mail: accounts@impress-solutions.com Accounting software manufrs

Impressions, 31 Shannon Way, Canvey Island, Essex, SS8 0PD Tel: (01268) 694175 Fax: (01268) 682000 Foil blockers

Impressions, J1 Dunkerswell Business Park, Dunkerswell Airfield, Honiton, Devon, EX14 4LE Tel: (01404) 891850 Fax: (01404) 891850 E-mail: rob@impressions1990.co.uk Quality table mat & coaster manufrs

Impressions Design Ltd, Sutherland Works, Beaufort Road, Stoke-on-Trent, ST3 1RH Tel: (01782) 329535 Fax: (01782) 329535 E-mail: info@impressionsdesignltd.co.uk China souvenirs & ceramic transfers & t-shirt printers

Impreza Computer Services Ltd, Lingley House, Commissioners Road, Rochester, Kent, ME2 4EE Tel: (01634) 299801 Fax: (01634) 297161 Computer company

Imprint, Victory House, Dalton Lane, Keighley, West Yorkshire, BD21 4JH Tel: (01535) 667954 Fax: (01535) 600072 E-mail: info@inprintkeighley.co.uk Printers & stationers

Imprint (Bournemouth) Ltd, 2-4 Acland Road, Bournemouth, BH9 1JJ Tel: (01202) 520552 Fax: (01202) 521949 Lithographic printers

Imprint Business Systems Ltd, Poplars, High Easter, Chelmsford, CM1 4RB Tel: (01245) 231670 Fax: (01245) 231789 E-mail: sales@imprint-mis.co.uk Management information software & print services

Imprint Colour Printers Ltd, Wrightsway, Lincoln, LN2 4JY Tel: (01522) 539570 Fax: (01522) 534794 E-mail: guy@imprintcolourprinters.com Lithographic printers

Imprint Offset, Unit 12A, Warrington Central Trading Estate, Bewsey Road, Warrington, WA2 7LP Tel: (01925) 651141 Fax: (01925) 651335 E-mail: sales@imprintoffset.co.uk Lithographic printers

Improcom Ltd, Management House, Cottingham Road, Corby, Northamptonshire, NN17 1TD Tel: (01536) 207107 Fax: (01536) 265699 E-mail: admin@improcom.co.uk *Independent communications consultancy & advisory services*

▶ Imr Transport, Unit 10 Ballon Wood Industrial Estate, Coventry Lane, Bramcote, Nottingham, NG9 3GJ Tel: 0115-928 8683 Fax: 0115-928 1197

Imray Laurie Norie & Wilson Ltd, Wych House, 20 Broadway, St. Ives, Cambridgeshire, PE27 5BT Tel: (01480) 462114 Fax: (01480) 496109 E-mail: enquiries@imray.com *Chart & nautical works publishers*

Ims, Ten Pound Walk, Doncaster, South Yorkshire, DN4 5HX Tel: (01302) 554996 Fax: (01302) 554996 E-mail: sales@ukims.co.uk *Specialists in Field Marketing, Mystery Shopping ,POS, Auditing and Merchandising in the UK and Ireland*

▶ IMS (Cheshire) Ltd, Ion Path, Road Three, Winsford Industrial Estate, Winsford, Cheshire, CW7 3GE Tel: (01606) 550099 Fax: (01606) 556418 E-mail: enquiries@imscheshire.com *Industrial cleaning & industrial maintenance services*

IMS Hot Runners, Unit 58B, Lincoln Road, Cressex Business Park, High Wycombe, Buckinghamshire, HP12 3RH Tel: (01494) 536900 Fax: (01494) 536999 E-mail: ims-hotrunners@btconnect.com *Hot runner systems distributors & manufrs*

▶ Ims International Ltd, Little Braxted Hall, Little Braxted, Witham, Essex, CM8 3EU Tel: (01376) 500068 Fax: (01376) 500160 E-mail: info@imsworld.org *UKAS Accredited Certification Body offering ISO 9001:2000, ISO 14001:1996, OHSAS 18001, Training, Quality Scheme, BRC Services. See website for more information www.imsworld.org*

Ims UK, International House, Saltley Trading Estate, Saltley, Birmingham, B8 1BB Tel: 0121-326 3100 Fax: 0121-326 3105 *Steel stockholders*

Imscan Systems Ltd, Yew Tree House Yew Tree Court, Warrington Road, Risley, Warrington, WA3 6WP Tel: (01925) 761000 Fax: (01925) 766334 E-mail: sales@imscan.co.uk *Document imaging services* Also at: London W1

Imstra Ltd, 63 Church Lane Oldton, Oulton, Stone, Staffordshire, ST15 8UB Tel: (01785) 816110 E-mail: gayle@imstra.co.uk *Do you want someone to take on your marketing for you? A professional who will do the work for you and notice opportunites as they arise, all on your behalf?"If so, then speak to Gayle at Imstra or visit our website at www.imstra.co.uk*

▶ Imsys Ltd, 15 Dawlish Close, Blackburn, BB2 4NS Tel: (01254) 692077 Fax: (01254) 671539 E-mail: abw@imsys.biz *Quality, environmental and health and safety advisory and training services.*

▶ Imtech Marine & Industry UK Ltd, 3 Belasis Court, Greenwood Road, Billingham, Cleveland, TS23 4AZ Tel: (01642) 567100 Fax: (01642) 567105

Imtech Services, 33 The Warren, Worcester Park, Surrey, KT4 7DH Tel: (020) 8337 6254 Fax: (020) 8337 6254 E-mail: ian.male@btopenworld.com *Hand tools & metal roofing machines suppliers*

Imtex Computer Consultants, Stratford Arcade, 75 High Street, Stony Stratford, Milton Keynes, MK11 1AY Tel: (01908) 261216 Fax: (01908) 261216 *IT consultants*

▶ In 2 Faces, 6 The Ball, Bratton, Westbury, Wiltshire, BA13 4SB Tel: 01380 830772 E-mail: becky@in2faces.co.uk *Face Painting and Tempory Tattoos for children and adults, Parties and functions, private and corporate.*

In A Nutshell, 31 Chesterfield Road, Sheffield, S8 0RL Tel: 0114-250 8555 *Health foods*

▶ In Camera Photography, 11 Hambleton Terrace, Knaresborough, North Yorkshire, HG5 0DD Tel: (01423) 546322 E-mail: enquiries@incameraphotography.com *Corporate, PR & editorial photography*

▶ In Car Centre Ltd, Unit 2 Magnet Road, Wembley, Middlesex, HA9 7RG Tel: (020) 8908 0777 Fax: (020) 8904 8465 E-mail: sales@incarcentre.com *Car alarm system installers*

In Car Connection Ltd, 3 Stirling Road, Dunblane, Perthshire, FK15 9EP Tel: (01786) 825581 Fax: (01786) 825581 *Car security installation & supply*

▶ In Car Discount, Festival House, Jessop Avenue, Cheltenham, Gloucestershire, GL50 3SH Tel: (0870) 7606110 Fax: (01684) 292200 E-mail: sales@incardiscount.co.uk *In-car audio systems, sat-nav, multimedia, hands free kits, security*

In Car Music, 605 High Road Leyton, London, E10 6RF Tel: (020) 8558 6221 Fax: (020) 8556 3948 E-mail: sales@incarmusic.co.uk *Car security & audio*

In Comm Business Services Ltd, Unit 12 Hayward Industrial Park, Vigo Place, Walsall, WS9 8UG Tel: (01922) 457686 Fax: (01922) 453211 E-mail: info@in-comm.co.uk *Training services*

In Doors Manufacturing Ltd, 49 Creagh Road, Toomebridge, Antrim, BT41 3SE Tel: (028) 7965 9555 Fax: (028) 7965 9559 *Door manufrs*

In Focus Ltd, Wild Fowl Trust Newgrounds, Slimbridge, Gloucester, GL2 7BT Tel: (01453) 890978 Fax: (01453) 890267 E-mail: infocus@netcomuk.co.uk *Optical supplier*

▶ In Focus Interiors, Oxenwood, Westhill Road South, South Wonston, Winchester, Hampshire, SO21 3HP Tel: (01962) 883092 Fax: (01962) 885144 *Retailers of furniture store*

In Form Consultants Ltd, Weathervane House, Old Shire Lane, Chorleywood, Rickmansworth, Hertfordshire, WD3 5PW Tel: (01923) 283694 E-mail: info@inform-consult.com *In-Form Consult provides independent consultancy services for planning, cost justifying & selecting electronic document management, records management & amp*

▶ In Futuro, 23 Badger Walk, Broxburn, West Lothian, EH52 5TW Tel: (01506) 853353

▶ IN GEAR EVENT SUPPORT, Unit 7 Coppen Road, Dagenham, Essex, RM8 1HJ Tel: 020 8593 0550 Fax: 020 8593 0552 E-mail: Glenn@ingearevents.fsbusiness.co.uk *A fully logistical company for all your exhibition/ event requirements. Stand building to your specific requirements. Furniture ans signage rental also available.*

In House, The Old Church, 31 Rochester Road, Aylesford, Kent, ME20 7PR Tel: (0845) 8732390 Fax: (0800) 6190212 E-mail: info@inhouse-hygiene.co.uk *In House, based in Beaconsfield, Bucks, offer food hygiene and health and safety services. In House are trusted, professional advisors in food hygiene and safety.*

▶ In House Catering, 1 Garrards Way, Swindon, SN3 3HY Tel: (01793) 693636 Fax: (01793) 693636 E-mail: contact@inhousecatering.co.uk *Hospitality & Corporate catering Foodservice company located in swindon wiltshire*

In N Out Trading, 946 North Circular Rd, Staples Corner, London, NW2 7JR Tel: (020) 8452 0300 Fax: (020) 8452 0077 E-mail: ash@innout.co.uk *Furniture Manufacturer*

In Parallel Computer Staff Ltd, 3 Church Street, Tewkesbury, Gloucestershire, GL20 5PA Tel: (01684) 291143 Fax: (01684) 291144 E-mail: inparallell@peachs.demon.co.uk *Computer consultants services*

In Print, Seven Street, York Road Business Park, Malton, North Yorkshire, YO17 6YA Tel: (01653) 697261 Fax: (01653) 695456

▶ In Signs, The Old Council Yard, Dane Valley Road, St. Peters, Broadstairs, Kent, CT10 3JJ Tel: (01843) 871321 Fax: (01843) 871321 E-mail: insigns@tiscali.co.uk *Trade manufacturer of built up & flat cut metal letters*

▶ In Stainless, Unit 5, Hookstone Chase, Harrogate, North Yorkshire, HG2 7HW Tel: (01423) 885885 Fax: (01423) 819819 E-mail: sales@instainless.co.uk *Sheet Metal work.*

In Stitches, 2 Rawstorn Road, Colchester, CO3 3JE Tel: (01206) 573356 Fax: (01206) 573356 *Designer garments manufrs*

In Synergy Ltd, 2 Carver Hill Rd, High Wycombe, Bucks, HP11 2TY Tel: (01494) 444104 Fax: (01494) 637163 *Computer Consultants*

In Touch Cellular Ltd, Newbury, Gillingham, Dorset, SP8 4HZ Tel: (01747) 822525 Fax: (01747) 825364 *Telecommunication system services*

▶ In Touch International, 43 Brace Street, Walsall, WS1 3PS Tel: (0870) 7507090 Fax: (0870) 7550033

In Tuition, 210 Borough High Street, London, SE1 1JX Tel: (020) 7403 7259 Fax: (020) 7403 2861 E-mail: mktmgn@intuition.co.uk *Computer trainers & room hire*

In2connect Design & Marketing Ltd, Acton Grove, Long Eaton, Nottingham, NG10 1FY Tel: 0115-901 1100 Fax: 0115-901 1111 E-mail: info@in2connect.net *Electronic component parts manufrs*

▶ In2interiors, 34 Aspen Gardens, Ashford, Middlesex, TW15 1ED Tel: (01784) 252900 Fax: (01784) 252900 E-mail: enquiries@in2interiors.co.uk *Specialising in making curtains, blinds and soft furnishings. Including roman, wood, venetian, roller and conservatory blinds and all styles of curtains. Free home consultations with fabrics and samples brought to you, all the measuring is done for you and curtains or blinds are expertly made and fitted. Call 01784-252900 for details.*

▶ In2Scuba Dive School, 27 Poyntell Road, Staplehurst, Tonbridge, Kent, TN12 0SA Tel: (01580) 891711 E-mail: steve@in2scuba.co.uk *Professional scuba diving school*

▶ in2style Ltd, 143 Richmond Road, London, E8 3NJ Tel: (020) 7249 4286 E-mail: info@in2style.org

In4tek Ltd, Unisys House, 20 Barrington Road, Altrincham, Cheshire, WA14 1HB Tel: 0161-941 5833 Fax: 0161-927 7629 E-mail: in4mation@in4tek.com *Software developers*

Inabata UK, Oaktree Place Road 35, Hortonwood Industrial Estate, Telford, Shropshire, TF1 7FR Tel: (01952) 670192 Fax: (01952) 608548 E-mail: enq@ikp.co.uk Principal Export Areas: Africa *Plastic injection moulders*

Inbev Ireland Ltd, Ulster Brewery, Glen Road, Belfast, BT11 8BY Tel: (028) 9030 1301 Fax: (028) 9062 4884 *Home-made beer ingredient manufacturers.*

INBIS Ltd, Club Street, Bamber Bridge, Preston, PR5 6FN Tel: (01772) 645000 Fax: (01772) 645001 E-mail: mailbox@assystems.com *Consulting engineers or designers*

INBIS Group Ltd, St. Johns House, Church Street, Wolverhampton, WV2 4LS Tel: (01902) 427463 Fax: (01902) 714239 *Consulting engineers & recruitment agency*

Inbis Technology Ltd, 1 The Brooms, Emersons Green, Bristol, BS16 7FD Tel: 0117-987 4000 Fax: 0117-987 4040 E-mail: careers@inbis.com *Recruitment agency for consulting engineers*

▶ Inbound Solutions Ltd, Unit 8, Greenham Park, Common Road, Witchford, Ely, Cambridgeshire, CB6 2HF Tel: (0800) 0776907 Fax: (01353) 661147 E-mail: contact@inboundsolutions.co.uk *Telephone systems suppliers & manufrs*

▶ Inbound Solutions, Unit 8 Greenham Park, Common Road, Witchford, Ely, Cambridgeshire, CB6 2HY Tel: (0800) 0776902 E-mail: pgrant@inboundsoloutions.co.uk *Telecommunications*

▶ Inbowles & Leisure, Sportsman Farm, Hollywood Road, Mellor, Stockport, Cheshire, SK6 5LR Tel: 0161-484 5488 Fax: 0161-484 5486

Inca, 12-13 Oaklands Business Park, Ferndale, Mid Glamorgan, CF43 4UG Tel: (01443) 733355 Fax: (01443) 733366 *Shop display items manufrs*

Inca Co-Packing Services Ltd, Unit 2g Nelson Way, Nelson Park West, Cramlington, Northumberland, NE23 1WG Tel: (01670) 590428 *Packing services & contract packing*

▶ Inca Developments Ltd, 1 Totterdown Lane, Weston-super-Mare, Avon, BS24 9LU Tel: (0845) 2304622 Fax: (0845) 2304622

▶ Inca Infotech Ltd, Unit 6 Radford Crescent, Billericay, Essex, CM12 0DU Tel: (01277) 631773 Fax: (01277) 623800

▶ Inca Jewellery Ltd, Unit 2, Gelders Hall Ind Est, Shepshed, Loughborough, Leics, LE12 9NH Tel: 01509 501000 Fax: 01509 501010 E-mail: sales@IncaUK.com *Importers of fashion jewellery, hair accessories and other fashion accessories. We supply the trade at all levels across Europe.*

Inca Tooling Ltd, Unit 9 Northbrook Close, Worcester, WR3 8BP Tel: (01905) 26937 Fax: (01905) 23593 E-mail: sales@incatooling.co.uk *Toolmakers*

▶ Incaforce Civil, The Coach House, Rectory Road, Cliffe, Rochester, Kent, ME3 7RP Tel: (01634) 222061

Incamesh Filtration Ltd, Dingle Lane, Appleton, Warrington, WA4 3HR Tel: (01925) 261900 Fax: (01925) 860568 E-mail: sales@incamesh.co.uk Principal Export Areas: Worldwide *Vibratory screens, reconditioned & new including spare parts for all vibratory sieves. Also woven wire mesh in roll & fabricated form including filter elements. Liquid filtration housing & cartridges of all types*

Incamet Ltd, Springhill Industrial Estate, Douglas, Lanark, ML11 0RE Tel: (01555) 851280 Fax: (01555) 851127 E-mail: info@incametltd.co.uk *Investment casting manufrs*

Incanite Foundries Ltd, Solar Works, Cornwall Road, Smethwick, West Midlands, B66 2JR Tel: 0121-565 2882 Fax: 0121-555 5190 E-mail: sales@incanite.co.uk *High duty iron castings manufrs*

Incare International Ltd, Headlands Business Park, Salisbury Road, Blashford, Ringwood, Hampshire, BH24 3PB Tel: (01425) 479932 Fax: (01425) 471146 E-mail: freight@incare.co.uk *Freight forwarders*

▶ Incendo Ltd, Unit H Sheen Lane, London, SW14 8AE Tel: (020) 8876 5333 Fax: (020) 8876 5322 E-mail: info@incendo.co.uk *Audio visual equipment hire & live events company*

▶ Incense Magic (UK) Ltd, 23 Baugh Gardens, Downend, Bristol, BS16 6PN Tel: 0117-970 2100 Fax: 0117-970 2100 E-mail: Enquiries@IncenseMagic.co.uk *Retailers and wholesalers of medicinal and culinary herbs and tinctures since 1994, now also supplying Chinese herbal tinctures, glycerites and more.*

▶ inCharge.co.uk, 49 Kingston Street, Cambridge, CB1 2NU Tel: (01223) 579600 *Take full control of your website with our low cost, easy to use web based content management system for website owners and designers. Perfect for small businesses. inCharge.co.uk also provide technical servces to independent web designers.*

Inchcape P.L.C, 22a St James Square, London, SW1Y 5LP Tel: (020) 7546 0022 Fax: (020) 7546 0010 *Distributors of motor vehicles*

▶ Inchcape Automotive (Scotland) Ltd, Arrol Square, Deans Industrial Estate, Deans, Livingston, West Lothian, EH54 8QZ Tel: (01506) 465000 Fax: (01506) 463322

Inchcape Fleet Solutions, Haven House, Compass Road, Portsmouth, PO6 4RP Tel: (0870) 1914444 Fax: (0870) 1914455 E-mail: rental@ifs.inchcape.co.uk *Motor retailers & distributors*

Inchcape Ford, 245 Finchampstead Road, Wokingham, Berkshire, RG40 3JS Tel: 0118-936 1100 Fax: 0118-979 7135 *Car dealership*

Inchcape Motors International P.L.C., 22A St. James Square, London, SW1Y 5LP Tel: (020) 7546 0011 Fax: (020) 7546 0010 E-mail: contact@inchcape.com *Holding company*

Inchcape Shipping Services UK Ltd, Berth 2 Forest Products Terminal Gordano Quay, Royal Portbury, Portbury, Bristol, BS20 7XF Tel: (01275) 375868 Fax: (01275) 375380 *Shipping services*

Inchcape Shipping Services UK Ltd, North Side Albert Dock, Leith Docks, Edinburgh, EH6 7DN Tel: 0131-553 5969 Fax: (01324) 478803 *Shipping services*

Inchcape Shipping Services UK Ltd, Unit 53 Evans Business Centre, Earls Road, Grangemouth, Stirlingshire, FK3 8XE Tel: (01324) 492777 Fax: (01324) 492776 E-mail: gbgrg@iss-shipping.com *Shipping services*

Inchcape Shipping Services UK Ltd, East Side Locks, Immingham Dock, Immingham, South Humberside, DN40 2LZ Tel: (01469) 571400 Fax: (01469) 571309 *Shipping services*

Inchcape Shipping Services UK Ltd, Portland Port, Castletown, Portland, Dorset, DT5 1PP Tel: (01305) 822775 Fax: (01305) 822623 E-mail: gbptl@iss-shipping.com *Shipping services*

Inchcape Shipping Services UK Ltd, Main Gate, 1 Sheerness Docks, Sheerness, Kent, ME12 1RT Tel: (01795) 660556 Fax: (01795) 580121 *Shipping services*

Inchlines Ltd, 11 Hilltop Road, Hamilton Industrial Park, Leicester, LE5 1TT Tel: 0116-276 5111 Fax: 0116-276 6596 E-mail: info@inchlines.com *Cams*

Inch's Saddlery, Unit 5 Hannington Farm, Hannington, Tadley, Hampshire, RG26 5TZ Tel: (01635) 297090 Fax: (01635) 297993 E-mail: inches@btinternet.com *Riding accessories & dressage services*

▶ Inciner8, Shakespeare House, 37-39 Shakespeare Street, Southport, Merseyside, PR8 5AB Tel: (01704) 548508 Fax: (01704) 542461 E-mail: info@inciner8.com

▶ incisive edge-industrial machine knives, 12 carson mount, Sheffield, S12 3GA Tel: 07901 835190 Fax: 01142 654946 E-mail: dniks@tiscali.co.uk *replacing/regrinding industrial machine knives,packaging machine knives,paper knives, graphic knives,food processing knives, specialising in regrinding tray seal knives saving up to 80% of new price.*

Incisive Media, 32 & 34 Broadwick Street, London, W1A 2HG Tel: (020) 7316 9000 Fax: (020) 7316 9003 *Publishers*

▶ Incisus Ltd, Geddes House, Kirkton North, Livingston, West Lothian, EH54 6GU Tel: (01506) 407680 Fax: (01506) 407689

▶ Incline, Kestrel View, Willow House, Strathclyde Business Park, Bellshill, Lanarkshire, ML4 3PB Tel: (01698) 464180

▶ Incline, Kestrel View, Willow House, Strathclyde Business Park, Bellshill, Lanarkshire, ML4 3PB Tel: (01698) 464180

Inco Europe Ltd, 5th Floor Windsor Ho, 50 Victoria St, London, SW1H 0XB Tel: (020) 7931 7733 Fax: (020) 7931 0083 *Nickel mining & refiners*

▶ INCO Software Solutions, 11 Pendeford Place, Pendeford Business Park, Wobaston Road, Wolverhampton, WV9 5HD Tel: (0870) 0460060 Fax: (0870) 0460061 *Web , e-commerce & application development*

▶ Incognito Visual Communications, 2 Sheraton Street, London, W1F 8BH Tel: (020) 7851 4470 Fax: (01832) 733875 E-mail: lance@ivcltd.co.uk *Advertising agency*

Incom Telecommunications, Water Side, Trafford Park, Manchester, M17 1WD Tel: 0161-935 1000 Fax: 0161-935 1001 E-mail: sales@incomtelecoms.co.uk *Distributors of telecommunication products*

Incomes Data Services Ltd, 77 Bastwick Street, London, EC1V 3TT Tel: (020) 7250 3434 Fax: (020) 7608 0949 E-mail: sales@incomesdata.co.uk *Industrial relations & publishers*

Incomestyle Ltd, 1 Wayfarers, Newton-le-Willows, Merseyside, WA12 8DF Tel: (01925) 221931 Fax: (01925) 221931 E-mail: james@incomestyleltd.wanadoo.co.uk *Bulk excavation & site clearance service*

▶ Incontrol Gas Services, 130 Queens Road, Nuneaton, Warwickshire, CV11 5LG Tel: (024) 7635 0066 Fax: (024) 7635 0056

▶ Incorporatewear Ltd, Eddison Road, Hams Hall Distribution Park, Coleshill, Birmingham, B46 1DA Tel: (0870) 2647227 Fax: (0870) 8709653 E-mail: icw@icwuk.com *Corporate wear manufrs*

Incotest, Holmer Road, Hereford, HR4 9SL Tel: (01432) 352230 Fax: (01432) 353545 E-mail: info@incotest.co.uk *Analytical chemists & contract testing services*

Incup Soft Drinks, Unit 2d Drum Industrial Estate, Chester le Street, County Durham, DH2 1SS Tel: (07966) 733394 Fax: 0191-492 0394 E-mail: sales@incupdrinks.com *Pre-packed drink manufrs*

▶ Indaba UK Ltd, Grove House, Chineham, Basingstoke, Hampshire, RG24 8AG Tel: (01256) 316530 Fax: (01256) 316559 E-mail: indaba@indaba.uk.com *HR strategy and management training focused on corporate transformational change. Leadership, facilitation, vision implementation, communication programmes, executive coaching and personal development*

Indachem Process Valves Ltd, The Valve Centre Calder Road, Ravensthorpe, Dewsbury, West Yorkshire, WF13 3JS Tel: (01924) 438353 Fax: (01924) 438373 *Valve & actuator distributors*

Indacom Group Ltd, 131 Hollywood Lane Wainscott, Rochester, Kent, ME3 8AS Tel: (01634) 716286 Fax: (01634) 724821 E-mail: adavis.indacom@btopenworld.com *Management & business consultants*

Indala Ltd, 8-10 Clos Menter, Excelsior Business Park, Cardiff, CF14 3AY Tel: (029) 2052 0022 Fax: (029) 2052 8519 E-mail: sales@mraccess.com *Magnetic resistive sensors & systems*

Indaux UK Ltd, Mga House, Ray Mill Road East, Maidenhead, Berkshire, SL6 8ST Tel: (01628) 780250 Fax: (01628) 780251 E-mail: sales@indaux.com *Furniture fittings suppliers*

Indeco UK Ltd, 11 Oasis Business Park Road One, Winsford, Cheshire, CW7 3RY Tel: (01606) 553918 Fax: (01606) 597561 E-mail: enquiries@indeco.uk.com *Hydraulic breakers*

Indenco Co., Unit 35, St. Richards Road, Four Pools Industrial Estate, Evesham, Worcestershire, WR11 1XJ Tel: (01386) 443946 Fax: (01386) 45279 E-mail: enquiries@indenco.co.uk *Metal pressing services*

Indentec Hardness Testing Machines Ltd, Lye Valley Industrial Estate, Bromley Street, Lye, Stourbridge, West Midlands, DY9 8HX Tel: (01384) 896949 Fax: (01384) 424470 E-mail: mail@indentec.demon.co.uk *Hardness testing machines manufrs*

Indepen Consulting Ltd, Diespeker Wharf, 38 Graham Street, London, N1 8JX Tel: (020) 7226 6336 Fax: (020) 7704 0872 E-mail: info@indepen.co.uk *Management consultants*

▶ Independant Document Systems Ltd, Brickyard Road, Roecliffe, York, YO51 9NS Tel: (01423) 326632 Fax: (01423) 326523 E-mail: sales@idslimited.com *Photocopier suppliers & services*

▶ Independant Herbalife Distributor Network International, 258, Kingsland Road, London, E8 4DG Tel: (020) 7923 7827 Fax: (020) 7923 7827

▶ Independence Homes Ltd, Airport House, Purley Way, Croydon, CR0 0DZ Tel: (020) 8668 4947 Fax: 0208 288 3614 *Residential care homes and supported workshop, employment and education programmes. Individual care programmes, activities, outings and supported holidays for people with epilepsy and learning difficulties.*

▶ Independent Access Supplies Ltd, 115B, Burcott Road, Bristol, BS11 8AD Tel: 0117-982 6800 Fax: 0117-982 1555 *Access equipment distributors*

Independent Agronomy Ltd, 60 Stowupland Road, Stowmarket, Suffolk, IP14 5AL Tel: (01449) 677294 Fax: (01449) 771245 E-mail: tanya@indagronomy.co.uk *Agricultural consultants*

▶ Independent Buyers Ltd, Station Road, Hatton, Derby, DE65 5YX Tel: (01283) 516517 Fax: (01283) 512481 E-mail: info@independentbuyers.com *Purchasing consultancy*

▶ Independent Cars Ltd, Hydra Business Park, Nether Lane, Ecclesfield, Sheffield, S35 9ZX Tel: (0845) 4303020 Fax: 0114-232 9130 E-mail: info@independentcars.co.uk *All makes & models of new & used cars, hp & leasing*

Independent Catering Engineers Ltd, Crossley New Road, Todmorden, Lancashire, OL14 8RP Tel: (01706) 819901 Fax: (01706) 819902 *Catering engineers*

▶ Independent Circuit Design, 52 North Street, Biddenden, Ashford, Kent, TN27 8AS Tel: (01580) 292239 Fax: (0870) 7059061 E-mail: ian@icdnet.co.uk *Printed circuit board design*

▶ Independent Crane Services Ltd, Worcester Road, Upton Warren, Bromsgrove, Worcs, B61 7ER Tel: (01527) 869028 Fax: (01527) 869147

Independent Design & Display, Independent, 275 Meanwood Road, Leeds, LS7 2JD Tel: 0113-242 9944 Fax: 0113-242 9669 E-mail: info@independentdesign.co.uk *Exhibition display designers & suppliers*

▶ Independent Fire Services Ltd, 2 West Colinton House, 40 Woodhall Rd, Colinton, Edinburgh, EH13 0DU Tel: 0131-441 7246 Fax: 0131-441 7246 E-mail: info@independentfireservices.co.uk *Fire Protection Engineers.*Fire training specialists.*Fire protection equipment suppliers*

Independent Footwear Retailers Association, Bank House, 81 St. Judes Road, Englefield Green, Egham, Surrey, TW20 0DF Tel: (0870) 3308623 Fax: (0870) 3308621 E-mail: info@shoeshop.org.uk *Retail association services*

▶ Independent Forgings & Alloys Ltd, Victoria Forge, Livesey Street, Sheffield, S6 2BL Tel: 0114-234 3000 Fax: 0114-234 0261 *Metalworking, fabrication*

▶ Independent Freight Solutions Ltd, 91 Chaytor Drive, Chapel End, Nuneaton, Warwickshire, CV10 9SU Tel: (024) 7639 8663 Fax: (024) 7639 2757 E-mail: ifsltd@btconnect.com *Company offer a one stop shop for all freigth forwarding activities to anywhere in the World. Services include air & sea freight, express delivery, packing and warehousing.*

▶ Independent Glass Co. Ltd, 540-550 Lawmoor Street, Glasgow, G5 0UA Tel: 0141-429 8700 Fax: 0141-429 8524

▶ Independent Handling & Driver Training Ltd, Wilsher Barn, Haldon Hill, Kennford, Exeter, EX6 7XU Tel: (07787) 795508 Fax: E-mail: fwilliams@independenthandling.co.uk *Provider of driving training*

Independent Integrity Inspection, Unit 13 Oak Tree Business Park, Spitfire Way, South Marston, Swindon, SN3 4TX Tel: (01793) 836150 Fax: (01793) 836151 E-mail: problem.solved@indei.co.uk *Inspection & testing of machinery & equipment specialists*

Independent Lifting Services Ltd, James Court, Faraday Road, Great Yarmouth, Norfolk, NR31 0NF Tel: (01493) 650952 Fax: (01493) 657737 E-mail: mail@ilsltd.ffnet.co.uk *Lifting equipment manufrs*

Independent Lifts Ltd, Devonshire House, 10 Devonshire Terrace, Holmewood, Chesterfield, Derbyshire, S42 5RF Tel: (01246) 850785 Fax: (01246) 854171 *Lift installation & maintenance*

Independent Magazines U K Ltd, 191 Marsh Wall, London, E14 9RS Tel: (020) 7005 5000 Fax: (020) 7005 2999 E-mail: krolfe@img-uk.demon.co.uk *Magazine publishers*

▶ Independent Optics Ltd, 20 Norman Way Indust Estate, Norman Way, Cambridge, CB2 1NS Tel: (01954) 231545 Fax: (01954) 231340

Independent Property Preservation Group, Woodlawn, Sydenham Avenue, Belfast, BT4 2DT Tel: (028) 9065 1750 Fax: (028) 9065 0090 *Timber care & remedial treatments*

Independent Roofing Systems Ltd, 118 Eastbourne Road, Darlington, County Durham, DL1 4ER Tel: (01325) 466423 Fax: (01325) 466493 E-mail: irsltd@globalnet.co.uk *For twenty years roofing refurbishment specialists to industry, specialising in sheeting and cladding both metal and cement fibre, waterproofing systems and sure-weld and allitra single ply systems including green roofs.*

Independent Safes, 5 Hatton Garden, London, EC1N 8AA Tel: (020) 7405 1540 Fax: (020) 7405 1640 E-mail: independentsafes@aol.com *Safe dealers*

▶ Independent Sewing Machines, 87 Barnoldswick Road, Barrowford, Nelson, Lancashire, BB9 6BQ Tel: (01282) 601012 Fax: (01282) 601012 *Sewing machine sales, service & rental*

Independent Storage Installation Services Ltd, 1 Calder Vale Mills, Healey Road, Ossett, West Yorkshire, WF5 8NF Tel: (01924) 281219 Fax: (01924) 281219 E-mail: info@independentstorage.co.uk *New & used racking systems suppliers*

Independent Tool Consultants Ltd, Unit 7, Bamfurlong Industrial Park, Staverton, Cheltenham, Gloucestershire, GL51 6SX Tel: (01452) 712519 Fax: (01452) 714786 E-mail: intoco.extrusion@virgin.net *Extrusion press tooling manufrs*

Independent Twine Manufacturing Co. Ltd, Westbank Road, Llay Industrial Estate, Llay, Wrexham, Clwyd, LL12 0PZ Tel: (01978) 854812 Fax: (01978) 854229 E-mail: keithmacguire@indtwineco.com *Rope & twine manufrs*

Indespension Ltd, 38a Nimmings Road, Halesowen, West Midlands, B62 9JE Tel: 0121-561 5467 Fax: 0121-561 2180 E-mail: westmids@indespention.com *Trailer sales, repair & manufrs*

▶ Indestep International Ltd, 20 Chantry Close, Sunbury-on-Thames, Middlesex, TW16 7TH Tel: (01932) 780377 Fax: (08700) 510781 E-mail: indestep@e-opus.com *Indestep Injection Moulding Machines for Plastics and associated Mould Tooling. Rotary multi-station special purpose machines. Highly innovative. Hot Runner System can be part of the injection unit rather than part of the mould tools. Insert moulding and twin injection capabilities, and* *continued* *suited to automation. Aimed at producing high throughputs of small /medium sized 'value added' Mouldings.*

Indestructible Paint Ltd, 23-25 Pentos Drive, Sparkhill, Birmingham, B11 3TA Tel: 0121-702 2485 Fax: 0121-778 4338 E-mail: sales@indestructible.co.uk *Specialist coating manufrs*

Index Business Supplies Ltd, 127-129 Becontree Avenue, Dagenham, Essex, RM8 2UL Tel: (020) 8598 9912 Fax: (020) 8598 8658 E-mail: info@indexbs.com *Commercial stationery suppliers*

Index Communications Meeting Services Ltd, Crown House, 28 Winchester Road, Romsey, Hampshire, SO51 8AA Tel: (01794) 511332 Fax: (01794) 511455 E-mail: icms@indexcommunications.com *Meetings & incentive consultants*

Index Fabrications Southampton Ltd, Rochester Street, Southampton, SO14 5QW Tel: (023) 8063 1484 Fax: (023) 8063 1484 E-mail: indexfabs@aol.com *Steel fabricators*

Index Instruments Ltd, Bury Road Industrial Estate, Ramsey, Huntingdon, Cambridgeshire, PE26 1NF Tel: (01487) 814313 Fax: (01487) 812789 E-mail: sales@indexinstruments.com *Polarimeter & refractometer manufrs*

Index Machining, James Scott Road, Halesowen, West Midlands, B63 2QT Tel: (01384) 410925 Fax: (01384) 410925 *General engineers & special products*

Index Plastic Tooling, 31a Newtown Street, Cradley Heath, West Midlands, B64 5LD Tel: (01384) 569165 Fax: (01384) 569165 *Plastic mould toolmakers*

Index Precision Co., 8a Power Court, Luton, LU1 3JJ Tel: (01582) 728528 Fax: (01582) 728528 *Small batch milling prototype manufrs*

Index Software Ltd, 4 Highfield Road, Weston-super-Mare, Avon, BS24 9LZ Tel: (01934) 811190 Fax: (01934) 811191 E-mail: indexsoftwarelimited@btinternet.com *Software development*

Indexing Specialists UK Ltd, Indexing House, 306a Portland Road, Hove, East Sussex, BN3 5LP Tel: (01273) 424411 E-mail: indexers@indexing.co.uk *Write indexes to books & manuals*

Indialinks Fashion Shops, 317 Regent Street, London, W1B 2HT Tel: (020) 7637 1070 *Clothing retailers*

Indian Ocean Trading Co., Castle Grounds, Hawarden, Deeside, Clwyd, CH5 3NY Tel: (01244) 537906 Fax: (01244) 537737 *Teak garden furniture manufrs*

▶ Indigo Computing, First Floor St. Marys House, St. Marys Road, Market Harborough, Leicestershire, LE16 7DS Tel: (0800) 5428814 *Computer maintenance & repair services*

▶ Indigo Concept Packaging, Knowll House Union Wharf, Leicester Road, Market Harborough, Leicestershire, LE16 7UW Tel: (01858) 410710 Fax: (01858) 410810 E-mail: sales@indigocp.com *Retail packers*

▶ Indigo HR Consulting Ltd, Oxford Cottage, 22 Conisboro Avenue Caversham, Reading, RG4 7JB Tel: (07949) 552403 E-mail: louise@indigohr.com *Indigo HR Consulting Ltd provides practical human resources and training support to companies. We provide help and advice to large and small organisations specialising in:**Employee Relations including a "health check" to ensure companies are up to date in HR issues, Recruitment & psychometric assessments and Training.*

Indigo Industrial Supplies Ltd, Unit 3B, Sopwith Crescent, Wickford Business Park, Wickford, Essex, SS11 8YU Tel: (01268) 768768 Fax: (01268) 768764 E-mail: sales@indigoshop.co.uk *Fastener distributors*

▶ Indigo Northern Ltd, 61 Saville Street, North Shields, Tyne & Wear, NE30 1AY Tel: 0191-258 2220

▶ Indigo Products Ltd, Barn Piece Swag, Brickyard Road, Aldridge, Walsall, WS9 8SR Tel: (01922) 743202 Fax: (01922) 743277 E-mail: sales@indigoproducts.com *Windows manufrs*

Indigo Shadings Solutions, Unit 4 New Way Business Centre, Oakdale Road, Wallasey, Merseyside, CH44 7HT Tel: 0151-630 3582 Fax: 0151-630 6914 E-mail: sales@indigoawnings.com *Indigo's parasols are well known within the industry as being the best parasols in the world. With 3 shapes, our parasol sizes range from 3.5m to a massive 9m in diameter, and we have the ability to customise if required. *Our complete range means that we now have the largest offering of commercial retractable awnings available in the UK. They can be free-standing or fixed to the host structure and are available in sizes ranging from 2m wide by 1.5m projection, up to a huge 18m wide with 5m projection. *We supply a variety of accessories that will allow you to personalise your chosen awning or parasol. *All awnings and some parasols can be powder coated to any RAL colour to match or contrast with an existing colour scheme or chosen fabric. Side curtains, linking gutters and electric heaters are all available to enhance the comfort of your customers and provide all year round use.*

▶ Indigo Software Ltd, Indigo House, Belmont Business Park, Durham, DH1 1TW Tel: 0191-375 6700 Fax: 0191-375 6702 *Computer software manufrs*

▶ Indigoideas.Co.Uk, 3 Farm Road, Edgware, Middlesex, HA8 9LS Tel: (020) 8959 8337 E-mail: info@indigoideas.co.uk *Indigo offers a high quality and professional website design and development service, printing, graphic design, photography and packaging design. Call us on 020 8959 8337 for a no obligation quotation NOW!*

▶ Indigovision Ltd, Darwin House, The Edinburgh Technopole, Penicuik, Midlothian, EH26 0PJ Tel: 0131-475 7200 Fax: 0131-475 7201 *Security cameras manufrs*

Individual Fires & Stoves, Chimneys, Brookgate Farm, London Road, Hurstgreen, Etchingham, East Sussex, TN19 7QY Tel: (01580) 860976 Fax: (01580) 860988 *Stove distributors*

Indmar Sheet Metal, Swan Lane, Hindley Green, Wigan, Lancashire, WN2 4HD Tel: (01942) 520200 Fax: (01942) 520201 *Sheet metalwork engineers*

Indo African Exports Ltd, Failsworth Mill, Ashton Road West, Failsworth, Manchester, M35 0FR Tel: 0161-934 4004 Fax: 0161-683 4280 E-mail: indo@fabric.co.uk *Textile merchants & textile converters*

Indoor Controlled Ltd, 250-252 Tiverton Road, Birmingham, B29 6BU Tel: 0121-472 2480 Fax: 0121-414 1107 *Air conditioning installation, maintenance & service*

Indoor Garden Design Ltd, Woodside Works, Summersby Road, London, N6 5UH Tel: (020) 8444 1414 Fax: (020) 8444 3414 E-mail: office@igd.uk.com *Plant & flower display agents*

▶ Indrum Website & Graphic Design, 2c Bennett Road, Brighton, BN2 5JL Tel: (01273) 530275 E-mail: indrum@indrum.com *Web design consultants & graphic artists*

Indtherm Ltd, 120 Wellington Road, Dudley, West Midlands, DY1 1UB Tel: (01384) 456666 Fax: (01384) 456666 E-mail: action@indtherm.co.uk *Mechanical engineering*

Induchem, Unit 1 Greenfield Farm Industrial Estate, Congleton, Cheshire, CW12 4TR Tel: (01260) 277234 Fax: (01260) 277649 E-mail: sales@induchem.ie *Valves, including ball, butterfly chemical & plug manufrs*

Inductelec Ltd, 137 Carlisle Street, Sheffield, S4 7LJ Tel: 0114-272 3369 Fax: 0114-276 1499 E-mail: sales@inductelec.co.uk *Induction heating, handling systems, servicing & spares.*

Induction Heat Treatment Ltd, Station Works, Station Road, New Mills, High Peak, Derbyshire, SK22 3JB Tel: (01663) 742483 Fax: (01663) 746223 E-mail: sales@inductionheat.co.uk *Heat treatment services, manufacture & repair of coils, transformers*

Induction Heating Service Ltd, Unit 28, Watery Lane Industrial Estate, Willenhall, West Midlands, WV13 3SU Tel: (01902) 605578 Fax: (01902) 605652 E-mail: sales@david-finch.fsnet.co.uk *Induction heat treatment of metals*

Induction Services Ltd, 16 Wharfedale Cresent, Droitwich, Worcestershire, WR9 8TU Tel: (01905) 771669 Fax: (01905) 797609 E-mail: sales@inductionservices.co.uk *Foundry services*

Induction Technology Group Ltd, Unit B Quinn Close, Coventry, CV3 4LH Tel: (024) 7630 5386 Fax: (024) 7630 7999 E-mail: sales@itgairfilters.com *Air filter manufrs*

Inductotherm Europe Ltd, The Furlong, Berry Hill Industrial Estate, Droitwich, Worcestershire, WR9 9AH Tel: (01905) 795100 Fax: (01905) 795138 E-mail: sales@inductotherm.co.uk *Manufacturers of furnaces including electric, induction & melting*

Inductotherm Heating & Welding Technologies Ltd, Thermatool House, Crockford Lane, Chineham, Basingstoke, Hampshire, RG24 8NA Tel: (01256) 337722 Fax: (01256) 467224 E-mail: sales@inductoheat.co.uk *Induction heating equipment manufrs*

Indumat Systems Ltd, 25 Campbell Court Business Park, Bramley, Tadley, Hampshire, RG26 5EG Tel: (01256) 880228 Fax: (01256) 880338 E-mail: info.uk@ek-automation.com *Automated guided vehicles*

▶ Induna IT Ltd, Unit 9, Station Yard Workshops, Alston, Cumbria, CA9 3HN Tel: (01434) 382825 Fax: (01434) 382825 E-mail: enquires@indunait.com *Computer maintenance consultants*

Indus (International) Ltd, Britannia Wharf, Monument Road, Woking, Surrey, GU21 5LW Tel: (01483) 722777 Fax: (01483) 721166 E-mail: sales@indusinternational.com *Software developers*

▶ Indus Object Technologies, Jolyon House, Amberley Way, Hounslow, TW4 6BH Tel: (0870) 8700140 Fax: (020) 85729461

Indusfoto Ltd, 39-41 Margravine Road, London, W6 8LL Tel: (020) 7385 7618 Fax: (020) 7381 0047 E-mail: mark@indusfoto.co.uk *Commercial photographers*

Industrial Abrasives & Tool Co. Ltd, Amberwood, Wantage Road, Harwell, Didcot, Oxfordshire, OX11 0LL Tel: (01235) 834850 Fax: (01235) 832857 E-mail: trudy@industrialabrasives.net *Abrasive distributors*

Industrial & Agricultural Engineers, Riverside Works, Macclesfield Road, Leek, Staffordshire, ST13 8LB Tel: (01538) 399200 Fax: (01538) 373005 E-mail: sales@iae.co.uk *Gate & livestock equipment manufrs*

Industrial Air Control Ltd, Bath Lodge, Park Street, Royton, Oldham, OL2 6QN Tel: 0161-626 0242 Fax: 0161-627 0231 E-mail: sales@iacontrol.co.uk *Heating ventilation & air conditioning contractors dust collection services*

Industrial Apparatus Consultants Ltd, 116 Baker Street, London, W1U 6TS Tel: (020) 7486 6474 Fax: (020) 7487 2757 *Environmental protection products including Imbiber Beads® a unique superabsorbent polymer product specially engineered to absorb oils, hydrocarbons and a wide range of organic chemicals. GE Ionics Oil On Water Leak Detection Equipment. Ecoceane Pollution Control Boats.*

Industrial Applied Elements, 10 Bronte Drive, Kidderminster, Worcestershire, DY10 3YU Tel: (01562) 755490 Fax: (01562) 755490 *Electrical equipment hire & agents*

Industrial Automation Ltd, 8 The Midway, Nottingham, NG7 2TS Tel: 0115-840 0500 Fax: 0115-840 5959 E-mail: sales@ind-auto.com *At Industrial Automation we have over twenty years experience of supplying automation solutions to the automotive, food logistics and pharmaceutical industries. Our systems are designed and built in house, and we are proud* *continued* *to be system integrators for both Denso and Kawasaki robots.*

Industrial Automation Systems Ltd, Unit 1, Springwater Park, Crews Hole Road, St. George, Bristol, BS5 8AN Tel: 0117-954 1212 Fax: 0117-954 1321 E-mail: sales@accupac.co.uk *Automation control services*

Industrial Automation & Technology Ltd, 18 Malhamdale Rd, Congleton, Cheshire, CW12 2DA Tel: 01260 277993 Fax: 01260 277993 *Automation consultants*

Industrial Battery & Charger Services Ltd, 46 Catley Road, Sheffield, S9 5JF Tel: 0114-243 3993 Fax: 0114-242 4845 E-mail: peterpgarrat@ibcsltd.demon.co.uk *Industrial & general purpose battery suppliers*

Industrial Belting International Ltd, Unit A1 The Sidings, Station Road, Ampthill, Bedford, MK45 2QY Tel: (01525) 840800 Fax: (01525) 840900 E-mail: sales@ibiuk.com *Conveyor belting distributors*

Industrial Blowers Services Ltd, Trumpers Way, London, W7 2QA Tel: (020) 8571 3988 Fax: (020) 8571 3955 E-mail: sales@ibsblowers.com *Blower maintenance, repair services*

Industrial Bulk Containers Ltd, Newton Business Park, Talbot Road, Hyde, Cheshire, SK14 4UQ Tel: 0161-367 8695 Fax: 0161-367 8685 E-mail: ibc@industrialbulk.freeserve.co.uk *Bulk container manufrs*

Industrial Calibration Ltd, Sunbeam Road, Kempston, Bedford, MK42 7BZ Tel: (01234) 857171 Fax: (01234) 840371 E-mail: clive@industrialcalibration.com *Electronic test equipment repairers*

Industrial Capacitors Wrexham Ltd, Miners Road, Llay Industrial Estate, Llay, Wrexham, Clwyd, LL12 0PJ Tel: (01978) 853805 Fax: (01978) 853785 E-mail: sales@icwltd.co.uk *ICW are manufacturers of metallised film capacitors for the electronics industry. *Specialising in the medium voltage (63V - 2000Vdc) range; utilising polyester and different types of metallised polypropylene films the company excels at offering customers a wide range of standard and bespoke capacitors for applications such as dc link, filtering, induction, railway signalling, aerospace, solar inverters etc. The company also has an audio capacitor division which produces the highly respected Claritycap line of capacitors.*

Industrial Catering Industries Ltd, Sterling Works, Clarence Road, Cardiff, CF10 5FA Tel: (029) 2049 8498 Fax: (029) 2048 8838 E-mail: sales@phoenix-saxton.com *Janitorial supply services*

Industrial Chains & Gears, 45 Copeland Avenue, Tittensor, Stoke-on-Trent, ST12 9JA Tel: (01782) 374300 Fax: (01782) 373804 E-mail: peter@i-c-g.fsnet.co.uk *Supplier of power transmission chain, gears & bearings*

Industrial Chemicals Ltd, Titan Works, Hogg Lane, Grays, Essex, RM17 5DU Tel: (01375) 389000 Fax: (01375) 389110 *Chemical processing services*

Industrial Chemicals & Equipment Ltd, 59 Cranes Park, Surbiton, Surrey, KT5 8AS Tel: (020) 8399 9333 Fax: (020) 8399 9555 E-mail: ice.ltd@virgin.net *Industrial cleaning chemical suppliers*

Industrial Cleaning Machine Manufacturers Association, Westminster Tower, 3 Albert Embankment, London, SE1 7SL Tel: (020) 7793 3042 Fax: (020) 7793 3003 E-mail: icmma@beama.org.uk *Trade association*

Industrial Cleaning Machines, Icm House, Showell Road, Wolverhampton, WV10 9LN Tel: (01902) 306039 Fax: (01902) 304774 E-mail: sales@industrialcleaningmachines.co.uk *Industrial cleaning machine manufrs*

Industrial Cleaning Supplies Liverpool Ltd, 7-29 Brasenose Road, Liverpool, L20 8HL Tel: 0151-922 2000 Fax: 0151-922 3733 E-mail: sales@theicsgroup.co.uk *Cleaning & hygiene services*

Industrial Clutch Parts Ltd, Unit 11 Bingswood Trading Estate, Whaley Bridge, High Peak, Derbyshire, SK23 7LY Tel: (01663) 734627 Fax: (01663) 733023 E-mail: sales@icpltd.co.uk *Manufacturers & distributors of industrial brakes*

▶ Industrial Coating Services Ltd, 370 Farm Street, Birmingham, B19 2UA Tel: 0121-551 1984 Fax: 0121-523 4157 E-mail: info@industrial-coating-services.ltd.uk *Industrial coating services ltd is a midland based company specialising in on site abrasive blast cleaning,protective coatings and maintenance painting, with a reputation for quality and reliability.We have a fully trained work force that has over 20 years of experience in all aspects of protective coatings.*

▶ Industrial & Commercial Environment Ltd, Bowdens, Broad Oak, Sturminster Newton, Dorset, DT10 2HG Tel: (01258) 471954 Fax: (01258) 471904 E-mail: office@ice-uk.eu.com *Heating, ventilation, air conditioning, maintenance & installation*

▶ Industrial & Commercial Heating Ltd, Unit 42 Stirling Enterprise Park, Stirling, FK7 7RP Tel: (01786) 445525 Fax: (01786) 445525

Industrial & Commercial Services Ltd, 38 Dunster Street, Northampton, NN1 3JY Tel: (01604) 636661 Fax: (01604) 629818 E-mail: mail@tinston.co.uk *Electrical contractors*

Industrial Composites Ltd, Churchill Way, Nelson, Lancashire, BB9 6RT Tel: (01282) 619336 Fax: (01282) 619337 E-mail: info@indcomps.co.uk *Manufacturers of vulcanised fibre coil & sheets*

Industrial & Construction Plant Ltd, Clarence Road, Stoke-on-Trent, ST3 1AZ Tel: (01782) 316791 Fax: (01782) 599411 E-mail: enquiries@longtoncranehire.co.uk *Plant distributors*

Industrial Contract Supplies, Unit 10, Swan Lane Industrial Estate, Swan Lane, West Bromwich, West Midlands, B70 0NU Tel: 0121-553 4505 Fax: 0121-553 4505

Industrial Control & Communication Ltd, Unit 1 Manor Park, West End, Nailsea, Bristol, BS48 4DE Tel: (01275) 856552 Fax: (01275) 856593 E-mail: info@icc.win-uk.net *Consultants electronic design & electronic engineering services*

Industrial Control Distributors, 8-9 Bridle Close, Finedon Road Industrial Estate, Wellingborough, Northamptonshire, NN8 4RN Tel: (01933) 446464 Fax: (01933) 442244 E-mail: sales@i-c-d.com *Cables distribution agent*

Industrial Controls Ltd, Unit 1 Audley Court, Lodge Way, Thetford, Norfolk, IP24 1HT Tel: (01842) 750800 Fax: (01842) 765900 E-mail: sales@industrialcontrols.co.uk *Distributors of proximity sensors & switches, machine guards & bar code readers*

Industrial Cooling Equipment Ltd, 101 Chadwick Road, Astmore Industrial Estate, Runcorn, Cheshire, WA7 1PW Tel: (01928) 568800 Fax: (01928) 568822E-mail: sales@ice-ltd.co.uk *Refrigeration contractors*

Industrial Copolymers Ltd, Iotech House, Miller Street, Preston, PR1 1EA Tel: (01772) 201964 Fax: (01772) 255194 E-mail: info@incorez.com *Synthetic resin manufrs*

▶ Industrial Development Bangor (U W B) Ltd, Dean Street, Bangor, Gwynedd, LL57 1UT Tel: (01248) 382749 Fax: (01248) 372105 E-mail: info@idb-tech.com *Specialist electronic instruments & control systems design & manufrs*

Industrial Development & Farm Services, Newcastle, Monmouth, Gwent, NP25 5NF Tel: (01600) 772126 Fax: (01600) 750396 *Constructional engineers*

▶ Industrial Devices (GB) Ltd, Glebe House, Ratlinghope, Shrewsbury, SY5 0SN Tel: (01588) 650551 Fax: (01588) 650130 E-mail: sales@actuators-electric.co.uk *Industrial electric linear actuators & telescopic columns manufrs*

Industrial Door Co. Ltd, 23 Lord Byron Square, Salford, M50 2XH Tel: 0161-736 6484 Fax: 0161-736 6364 E-mail: enquires@industrialdoorco.net *Roller shutters & security*

Industrial Door Parts Master, PO Box 291, Bolton, BL5 3XE Tel: (0870) 6084040 Fax: (0870) 6081271 *Industrial door parts*

Industrial Door Repair, Unit 4 Windmill La Industrial Estate, Denton, Manchester, M34 3RB Tel: 0161-336 2228 Fax: 0161-336 8742 *Industrial door repairs, maintenance & service*

Industrial Doors Ltd, 8 Alexandra Industrial Estate, Locarno Road, Tipton, West Midlands, DY4 9SJ Tel: 0121-557 8757 Fax: 0121-520 9011 E-mail: mac@mandsshutterservicesltd.co.uk *Industrial doors & rolling shutter maintenance & repair services*

Industrial Doors Scotland Ltd, 199 Broughton Road, Edinburgh, EH7 4LN Tel: 0131-553 6685 Fax: 0131-555 0482 E-mail: industrialdoors@talk21.com *Emergency door repairs & door distributors*

Industrial Doors Systems Ltd, Unit 51, Waverley Road, Beeches Industrial Estate, Bristol, BS37 5QR Tel: (01454) 324410 Fax: (01454) 324412 E-mail: idsbristol1@aol.com *Industrial door manufrs*

Industrial Electrical Repairs, Mount Ambrose, Redruth, Cornwall, TR15 1NR Tel: (01209) 214764 Fax: (01209) 213631 *Electric motor rewind services*

▶ Industrial Electrical Services I E S Ltd, Teybrook Farm, 2 Brook Road, Great Tey, Colchester, CO6 1JE Tel: (01206) 211222 Fax: (01206) 211251 E-mail: sales@iesworks.co.uk *Control Panels*PLC's*SCADA*MCC's*Design*Install* Service**

▶ Industrial Electrical Services UK Ltd, 4b5 Unit, Blar Mhor Industrial Estate, Lochyside, Fort William, Inverness-Shire, PH33 7PT Tel: (01397) 703732 Fax: (01397) 703732

Industrial Electronic Control By Design, Unit F5 Bersham Enterprise Centre, Colliery Road, Rhostyllen, Wrexham, Clwyd, LL14 4EG Tel: (01978) 368099 Fax: (01978) 354333 E-mail: sales@iecd.co.uk *Electronic equipment & circuit board repairers*

▶ Industrial Electronic Repairs, Unit 11 Business Centre West, Letchworth Business Centre, Avenue, Letchworth Garden City, Hertfordshire, SG6 2HB Tel: (01462) 671001

Industrial Electronic Wiring, 10 Birch, Kembrey Park, Swindon, SN2 8UU Tel: (01793) 694033 Fax: (01793) 496295 E-mail: info@iew.co.uk *I.E.W Ltd is a highly successful company which has been providing a quality sub-contracting service to the electronics industry for over 25 years. Our services include the assembly of cables, looms, PCBs, chassis and panels to customer's specifications.* Our internal processes are approved to BS EN ISO9001: 2000 and our quality standards are critical both to our continued success and to maintaining our customers' satisfaction levels. We have an extensive electrical test capability including two sets of "Cirris" Automatic Test Equipment and all assemblies are fully inspected to ensure that they are fault free before leaving our premises. I.E.W also works closely with its customers to ensure that our ordering and scheduling systems mesh seamlessly with their own thus enabling us to provide a trouble free service whether it be MRP, Kanban, Faxban or J.I.T.*

▶ Industrial Electronics Ltd, 153 City Road, Stoke-on-Trent, ST4 4ND Tel: (01782) 415533 Fax: (01782) 747315 E-mail: info@industrialelectronicsltd.co.uk *Electronic repair services*

Industrial Electronics Consultants, 855 Holderness Road, Hull, HU8 9BA Tel: (01482) 374437 Fax: (01482) 796853 E-mail: ray@rayeldred.carouy.co.uk *Industrial electronics*

Industrial Encoders Direct Ltd, D1 Dutton Road, Redwither Business Park, Wrexham, Clwyd, LL13 9UL Tel: (01978) 664722 Fax: (01978) 664733 E-mail: sales@industrialencodersdirect.co.uk *Electrical component manufrs*

Industrial Engineering Services Southern Ltd, 44 New Borough, Wimborne, Dorset, BH21 1RB Tel: (01202) 888865 Fax: (01202) 841801 E-mail: klia@lineone.net *Recruitment agency*

Industrial Fasteners Ltd, Chilcott Avenue, Brynmenyn Industrial Estate, Brynmenyn, Bridgend, CF32 9RQ Tel: (01656) 724775 Fax: (01656) 729612 *Engineers supplies & distributors*

▶ Industrial Fasteners Ltd, Unit 10 Sundon Business Park, Dencora Way, Luton, LU3 3HP Tel: (01582) 563100 Fax: (01582) 563040 E-mail: sales@anixterfasteners.com *Engineers supplies & distributors of fasteners*

▶ Industrial Fasteners Ltd, 7 Bell Park Bell Close, Newnham Industrial Estate, Plympton, Plymouth, PL7 4TA Tel: (01752) 341100 Fax: (01752) 346012 *Engineers supplies & distributors*

▶ Industrial Fasteners Ltd, 6 Station Road, Thatcham, Berkshire, RG19 4RB Tel: (01635) 865885 Fax: (01635) 871511 *Engineers supplies & distributors*

▶ Industrial Filter Services Ltd, PO Box 286, Leeds, LS26 1AU Tel: 0113-287 2951 Fax: 0113-287 2951 E-mail: sales@ifsltd.co.uk *IFS design, supply & install dust & fume extraction equipment*

Industrial Fixing Systems Ltd, 16 & 17 North Leith Sands, Industrial Estate, Edinburgh, EH6 4ER Tel: 0131-553 6323 Fax: 0131-555 0161 *Engineer suppliers*

▶ Industrial Floor Treatments Ltd, 10 Lithgow Place, College Milton, East Kilbride, Glasgow, G74 1PW Tel: (01355) 233600 Fax: (01355) 225777 E-mail: contoact@ift.co.uk *Flooring materials*

Industrial Flooring Services Ltd, Sankey Valley Industrial Estate, Newton-le-Willows, Merseyside, WA12 8DN Tel: (01925) 220000 Fax: (01925) 220011 E-mail: info@industrial-flooring.co.uk *Industrial Flooring Service Ltd was established in 1970 & has developed into a leading producer of specialist building maintenance chemicals. The company has extensive technical & manufacturing resources & a customer base comprising Works Engineers, Architects & Builders. Whilst the emphasis to date has been assisting factory & warehouse staff with advice regarding solving of problems relating toworn concrete flooring with the well known 'Floorsaver' range, the Company has lately turned it's attention to the Construction industry & is utilising the latest resin technology in the introduction of new, quickly applied, fast setting & low cost flooring & sealing products*

Industrial Flow Control Ltd, Unit 1, Askews Farm Lane, Grays, Essex, RM17 5XR Tel: (01375) 387155 Fax: (01375) 387420 E-mail: sales@inflow.co.uk *Petroleum equipment manufrs*

▶ Industrial Hydraulic Services Ltd, Unit 19-20, Seymour Street, Millers Bridge Industrial Estate, Bootle, Merseyside, L20 1EE Tel: 0151-922 6927 Fax: 0151-944 2076 E-mail: ihs@i12.com *Hydraulic systems engineers*

Industrial Instrumentation Services, 124 Hinton Way, Great Shelford, Cambridge, CB22 5AL Tel: (01223) 842127 E-mail: iis.cooper@ntlworld.com *Industrial instrument engineers*

Industrial Insulation Services, Unit 2 Osborne Mill, Osborne Street, Oldham, OL9 6QQ Tel: 0161-626 0973 Fax: 0161-627 4846 *Thermal insulation contractors & asbestos removal services*

Industrial Latex Compounds Ltd, Burns Mill, Manchester Street, Heywood, Lancashire, OL10 1DN Tel: (01706) 366161 Fax: (01706) 625664 E-mail: enquiries@indlatex.co.uk *Rubber adhesive manufrs*

Industrial Links Ltd, Unit 19 Ventura Place, Poole, Dorset, BH16 5SW Tel: (01202) 632996 Fax: (01202) 632997 E-mail: sales@industrial-links.com *Bearing & power transmission distributors*

Industrial Machine Guards, 2 Dormston Trading Estate, Burton Road, Dudley, West Midlands, DY1 2UF Tel: (01902) 676485 Fax: (01902) 880987 *Machine guard designers & manufrs*

Industrial Maintenance Suppliers, 23-29 Pasture Lane, Leicester, LE1 4EY Tel: 0116-262 0729 E-mail: sales@imsleicester.co.uk *Cleaning materials suppliers*

Industrial & Marine Hydraulics Ltd, 2 Snowdon Rd, Middlesbrough, Cleveland, TS2 1LP Tel: (01642) 802700 Fax: (01642) 802701 E-mail: info@imh-uk.com Purchasing Contact: P. Griffiths Sales Contact: D. Laver Principal Export Areas: Worldwide *IMH provide Service and Repair for a wide range of hydraulic equipment. We have provided this service to customers locally, throughout the UK, Europe, and World-wide. Our team of hydraulic service engineers, technicians, fitters and pipefitters are available 24Hrs a day throughout the year to provide unrivalled service and customer support for all our customers in areas such as Offshore, Marine, Industrial, Nuclear, and Mobile, from repairing the smallest leak on a machine to complete plant shutdown maintenance and service routines. From our 1500m2 premises we operate a fully equipped fabrication and assembly area with overhead crane provision, 'clean workshop' and test facility, bonded storage area with trade counter. An extensive secure area is also available external of the main workshops. Internally the design, procurement, projects and senior management offices are configured around a central boardroom from which an 'open forum' regime is operated.*

▶ Industrial & Marine Lift Services, The Courtyard, Green Lane, Heywood, Lancashire, OL10 2EX Tel: (01706) 369794 Fax: (01706) 628542 *Servicing lifts*

Industrial & Marine Power Services Ltd, Whisby Way, North Hykeham, Lincoln, LN6 3LQ Tel: (01522) 881000 Fax: (01522) 883555 E-mail: chris@ind-marpower.co.uk Principal Export Areas: Worldwide *Diesel engine components & spare parts*

Industrial Marine Rubber, 3 Spurryhillock Industrial Estate, Broomhill Road, Stonehaven, Kincardineshire, AB39 2NH Tel: (01569) 766344 Fax: (01569) 766419 *Rubber mouldings fabricators*

Industrial & Marine Switchgear Ltd, Amsterdam Road, Sutton Fields Industrial Estate, Hull, HU7 0XF Tel: (01482) 831222 Fax: (01482) 826696 E-mail: information@ims-swgr.karoo.co.uk *Electrical control engineers*

Industrial Measurements, Willow Industrial Park, Willow Road, Castle Donington, Derby, DE74 2NP Tel: (01332) 810240 Fax: (01332) 812440 E-mail: mail@indmeas.co.uk Principal Export Areas: Worldwide *Torque meter manufrs*

Industrial & Medical Electronics Ltd, 140 Rocky Lane, Perry Barr, Birmingham, B42 1QF Tel: 0121-356 0061 Fax: 0121-356 0061 *Medical electronics*

Industrial Metal Forms Ltd, Units 15 Wynford Industrial Trading Estate, Wynford Road, Birmingham, B27 6JP Tel: 0121-765 4800 Fax: 0121-765 4810 *General sheet metalwork*

Industrial Metal Services Ltd, Metalstock House, Metal Stock House, Vanguard Way, Southend-on-Sea, SS3 9RE Tel: (01702) 296922 Fax: (01702) 296444 E-mail: sales@industrialmetal.co.uk *Steel stockholders supplies of mild steel, stainless steel, aluminium,brass,copper,plastic, bright steel and structural sections.*

Industrial Microwave Services Ltd, Swannington Road, Cottage Lane Industrial Estate, Broughton Astley, Leicester, LE9 6TU Tel: (01455) 285666 Fax: (01455) 285599 E-mail: sales@industrialmicrowaveservices.com *Industrial microwave maintenance & repair services*

Industrial (Motor) Rewinds Ltd, Haut De L'Orme, Rue De Haut De L'Orme, Trinity, Jersey, JE3 5FP Tel: (01534) 865782 Fax: (01534) 865786 E-mail: rayimp@hotmail.com *Contract engineers* Also at: St. Peter Port

Industrial Moulded Products Ltd, Unit 7 Reaymer Close, Walsall, WS2 7QZ Tel: (01922) 497376 Fax: (01922) 491117 E-mail: general@inmodprod.demon.co.uk *Plastic injection & rubber moulders*

Industrial & Municipal Project Ltd, 1 Wester Burn St, Glasgow, G32 6AT Tel: 0141-763 1234 Fax: 0141-763 0333 E-mail: info@impo.co.uk *Industrial cleaning contractors*

Industrial Paint & Powder Ltd, 45 Lanark Road, Edinburgh, EH14 1TL Tel: 0131-443 8793 Fax: 0131-455 7806 E-mail: sales@indpaintandpowder.co.uk *Industrial paint supplier*

Industrial Paint Services S W Ltd, 1 Lyte Building, Wern Trading Estate, Rogerstone, Newport, Gwent, NP10 9FQ Tel: (01633) 897766 Fax: (01633) 897716 *Paints, metal protection & paint distributors*

▶ Industrial Painters, 13C Beveland Road, Canvey Island, Essex, SS8 7QU Tel: (01268) 511433 Fax: (01268) 691362 E-mail: louis@industrialpainters.com *Industrial painting contractors, storage tanks & height work*

▶ Industrial Pallet Services, Charles Street, Kilnhurst, Mexborough, South Yorkshire, S64 5TG Tel: (01709) 583519 Fax: (01709) 581177

Industrial Pallet & Transport Services, Kirkhaw Lane, Knottingley, West Yorkshire, WF11 8RD Tel: (01977) 671886 Fax: (01977) 671995 *Pallet reconditioner & manufrs*

▶ Industrial Pipe Services, North Road, Widmer End, High Wycombe, Buckinghamshire, HP15 6NE Tel: (01494) 711150 Fax: (01494) 711180

Industrial Pipe Work Ltd, Unit 5 Heol Ty Gwyn Industrial Estate, Maesteg, Mid Glamorgan, CF34 0BQ Tel: (01656) 738855 Fax: (01656) 738917 *Pipework contractors*

Industrial Pipework Supplies Ltd, Unit 6 Carr Mills Business Centre, Bradford Road, Birstall, West Yorkshire, WF17 9JY Tel: (01924) 470227 Fax: (01924) 470846 E-mail: peteropazs@hotmail.com Principal Export Areas: Worldwide *Industrial tube, valve & fittings suppliers. Lloyds approved repair clamps. Dry riser units. Same day service nationwide if required. Free technical advice. Lincoln Office: Grimsby, Head Office: Birstall*

Industrial Plant Development Ltd, 4 Gloucester Road, Luton, LU1 3HX Tel: (01582) 731925 Fax: (01582) 480448 E-mail: ipdltd@btinternet.com *Precision engineers*

Industrial Plastic Coatings Ltd, St Helens Way, Thetford, Norfolk, IP24 1HG Tel: (01842) 753529 Fax: (01842) 754060 E-mail: sales@industrialplasticcoatings.co.uk *Powder & plastic coating processors or services*

Industrial Plastic Supplies Ltd, 3 Milestone Court, Stanningley, Pudsey, West Yorkshire, LS28 6HE Tel: 0113-257 2222 Fax: 0113-257 2222 E-mail: sales@industrialplastics.co.uk Principal Export Areas: Worldwide *a range of services from raw materials to finished components, using machining, fabrication, vacuum forming, injection moulding & thermoforming. Advice & design assistance,& full technical backing*

Industrial Plastics Ltd, Unit 13 Canterbury Industrial Park, 297 Ilderton Road, London, SE15 1NP Tel: (020) 7252 9600 Fax: (020) 7252 9601 E-mail: sales@ipl-london.co.uk Principal Export Areas: Worldwide *Screen changers & diverter valves manufacturer*

Industrial Pneumatic Services Liverpool Ltd, 13 Dunnings Bridge Road, Bootle, Merseyside, L30 6TE Tel: 0151-525 9381 Fax: 0151-525 1982 *Filter stockists & distributors*

Industrial Powder & Paint Services, 9a Boss Hall Road, Ipswich, IP1 5BN Tel: (01473) 463333 Fax: (01473) 747153 E-mail: sales@ippsltd.co.uk *Suppliers of powder & paint products*

Industrial Power Units Ltd, Churchbridge, Oldbury, West Midlands, B69 2AS Tel: 0121-511 0400 Fax: 0121-511 0401 E-mail: ipu@ipu.co.uk *Diesel engine product importers*

Industrial Press, Oldbury Road, West Bromwich, West Midlands, B70 9DQ Tel: (024) 7663 2000 Fax: 0121-500 4994 *Lithographic printers*

Industrial Product Solutions Ltd, Unit 3 Healey Lane Business Centre, Healey Lane, Batley, West Yorkshire, WF17 8EZ Tel: (01924) 444059 Fax: (01924) 444058 E-mail: ipsl@btinternet.com *Maintenance product suppliers*

Industrial Protective & Safetywear, Unit 4-8, Reginald Street, Stoke-on-Trent, ST6 1DU Tel: (01782) 821923 Fax: (01782) 575011 E-mail: ipstoke@hotmail.com *Protective & safety wear manufrs*

Industrial Proteins Ltd, 97 Burbage Road, London, SE24 9HD Tel: (020) 7501 9145 Fax: (020) 7737 1739 *Food ingredient flavouring manufrs*

Industrial Purification Systems Ltd, Unit 10 Lea Green Business Park, St. Helens, Merseyside, WA9 4TR Tel: (01744) 811652 Fax: (01744) 833687 E-mail: info@industrial-purification.co.uk *Industrial filtration suppliers*

Industrial Refrigeration Services Ltd, 2 West Court, Buntsford Park Road, Bromsgrove, Worcestershire, B60 3DX Tel: (01527) 577999 Fax: (01527) 578300 E-mail: refrigeration@irs.co.uk *Refrigeration systems maintenance & distribution*

Industrial & Rubber Supplies Ltd, 184 Smithdown Road, Liverpool, L15 3JR Tel: 0151-733 7859 Fax: 0151-733 4980 E-mail: indrub@talk21.com *Industrial rubber product manufrs*

Industrial Safety Inspections Ltd, Lea Lodge, Ansley, Nuneaton, Warwickshire, CV10 0QU Tel: (01675) 481779 Fax: (01675) 481780 E-mail: sales@isi-uk.net *Engineering inspection & marine surveyors*

Industrial Scales UK Ltd, B2-B3 Hilton Trading Estate, Hilton Road, Lanesfield, Wolverhampton, WV4 6DW Tel: (01902) 354141 Fax: (01902) 402252 *Weighing machines & cash registers*

Industrial Science & Technology Ltd, The Watch Oak, Chain La, Battle, E. Sussex, TN33 0YD Tel: (01424) 775001 Fax: (01424) 775002 *Railway systems engineering consultants*

▶ Industrial Seating, 18 Pennythorne Drive, Yeadon, Leeds, LS19 7DS Tel: (0870) 6094017 Fax: 0113-255 6580 E-mail: info@industrialseating.co.uk *Manufacturers of all types of industrial chairs & stools*

Industrial Self Adhesives Ltd, Robey Close, Linby, Nottingham, NG15 8AA Tel: 0115-968 1895 Fax: 0115-963 2821 E-mail: sales@isatape.co.uk *Adhesive label & tape stockists*

Industrial Services York Ltd, Station Estate, Station Road, Tadcaster, North Yorkshire, LS24 9SG Tel: (01937) 832761 Fax: (01937) 833012 E-mail: info@suremark.ltd.uk *Felt marking pen manufrs*

Industrial Sewing Services Birmingham Ltd, 225 Lozells Road, Birmingham, B19 1RJ Tel: 0121-554 5073 Fax: 0121-554 5073 *Industrial sewing machine repairers & sales*

Industrial Signs Ltd, 8 Astor Park, Padholme Road, Peterborough, PE1 5XL Tel: (01733) 555153 Fax: (01733) 555157 E-mail: isignsltd@compuserve.com *Sign makers & engraving services*

▶ Industrial Solutions, Gemini House, Maritime Close, Medway City Estate, Rochester, Kent, ME2 4DJ Tel: (01634) 719666

Industrial Springs Ltd, 2 Whitefield Road, Glasgow, G51 2YB Tel: 0141-427 6717 Fax: 0141-427 1680 E-mail: ind.spring@which.net *Spring manufrs*

Industrial Suppliers (Wimborne) Ltd, Higher Merley Lane, Corfe Mullen, Wimborne, Dorset, BH21 3EG Tel: (01202) 882331 Fax: (01202) 841282 E-mail: enquiries@iswgroup.co.uk *Suppliers of chemicals & chemical services, packing & waste management*

Industrial Supplies, Unit 4 Martin Court, Bleneim Industrial Estate, Nottingham, NG6 8US Tel: 0115-927 2681 Fax: 0115-975 1135 E-mail: industialsuppliesnottm@yahoo.co.uk *Janitorial supplies services* Also at: Ipswich & Peterborough

Industrial Supplies (Peterborough) Ltd, Unit B, Great Blakenham Trading Estate, Gipping Road, Ipswich, IP6 0NX Tel: (01473) 831360 Fax: (01473) 830243 E-mail: isipswich@aol.com *Janitorial supply services*

Industrial Supplies Peterborough Ltd, Waterworks Lane, Glinton, Peterborough, PE6 7LP Tel: (01733) 252771 Fax: (01733) 252362 E-mail: ispeterborough@aol.com *Cleaning material distributors* Also at: Ipswich & Nottingham

Industrial Supplies Wrayson Ltd, 3-4 Brookfield Road, Cheadle, Cheshire, SK8 2PN Tel: 0161-428 0707 Fax: 0161-428 1304 E-mail: sales@wrayson.com *Protective clothing & disposable paper products distributors*

Industrial Supply Specialists Ltd, Unit 2, Nelson Way, Nelson Park West, Cramlington, Northumberland, NE23 1WG Tel: (01670) 734422 Fax: (01670) 738877 E-mail: iss@ukf.net *Industrial hose & fittings manufrs*

Industrial Switchgear Ltd, 8 Howard Road, Park Farm Industrial Estate, Redditch, Worcestershire, B98 7SE Tel: (01527) 527346 Fax: (01527) 510186 E-mail: industrialswitch@btconnect.com *Control panel manufrs*

▶ Industrial Switchgear Services, Unit 5A Corn Mill, Ravensfield Industrial Estate, Charles Street, Dukinfield, Cheshire, SK16 4SD Tel: 0161-344 1117

Industrial System Solutions Ltd, 21 Summerhill, East Herrington, Sunderland, SR3 3NJ Tel: (07949) 566186 Fax: 0191-511 0732 E-mail: enquiries@industrialsystemsolutions.co.uk *PLC control systems, PAT testing & instrumentation*

Industrial Systems & Controls Ltd, 50 George Street, Glasgow, G1 1QE Tel: 0141-553 1111 Fax: 0141-553 1232 E-mail: iscmail@isc-ltd.com *Engineering*

Company Information

▶ Industrial Tape Solutions Ltd, 2-6 Station Road, Shipley, West Yorkshire, BD18 2JL Tel: (01274) 592244 Fax: (01274) 591144 E-mail: sales@tapesolutions.co.uk *Glazing tape distributors*

Industrial & Technical Services Co., Victoria House, 28 Borneo Street, Walsall, WS4 2HY Tel: (01922) 644239 Fax: (01922) 644239 *Engineering consultants*

▶ Industrial Textiles & Plastics Ltd, Easingwold Business Park, Oaklands Way, Easingwold, York, YO61 3FA Tel: (01347) 825200 Fax: (01347) 825222E-mail: sales@indtex.co.uk *Manufacturers & suppliers of technical textiles*

Industrial Tools Supplies (London) Ltd, 607-617 High Road, Leyton, London, E10 6RF Tel: (020) 8539 2231 Fax: (020) 8558 0247 E-mail: sales@itslondon.co.uk *Industrial power tool distributor*

Industrial & Tractor Ltd, Navigation Road, Worcester, WR5 3DF Tel: (01905) 763777 Fax: (01905) 763008 E-mail: sales@intrac.co.uk *Tube bending services*

Industrial Trading Co. Ltd, PO Box 51, Worcester, WR1 1QE Tel: (01905) 20373 Fax: (01905) 27158 *Manufacturers of industrial fasteners & disc springs. Also distributors/agents/ stockholders of bolts & nuts, dowel pins, nuts, shims, taper pins & washers including metallic*

Industrial Vacuum Co., Poynton Water, Mill Lane, Totley Rise, Sheffield, S17 4HQ Tel: 0114-262 0111 Fax: 0114-262 0111 *Industrial vacuum cleaner manufrs*

Industrial Washing Machines Ltd, Unit 2, Facet Road, Kings Norton, Birmingham, B38 9PT Tel: 0121-459 9511 Fax: 0121-451 3241 E-mail: sales@indwash.co.uk *Industrial washing machine designers & manufrs*

Industrial Water Engineering Ltd, North Road, Bristol, BS6 5AQ Tel: 0117-940 1230 Fax: (01454) 778624 E-mail: iwe.ltd@cwcom.net *Control systems & water treatment*

Industrial Wear Parts Sheffield Ltd, Speedlock Works, Petre Street, Sheffield, S4 8LN Tel: 0114-261 0651 Fax: 0114-242 3030 E-mail: sales@iwp-ltd.co.uk *Shot blasting engineers manufrs*

Industrial & Welding Systems Ltd, Fallons Road, Wardley Industrial Estate, Worsley, Manchester, M28 2NY Tel: 0161-728 3366 Fax: 0161-728 5878 E-mail: paul.rushton@boc.com *Industrial & welding supplies* Also at: Wrexham

Industeel UK, Hallow Park, Hallow, Worcester, WR2 6PG Tel: (01905) 641444 Fax: (01905) 641555 *Steel plate manufrs*

Industria Engineering Products Ltd, 45 Kelvin Way, West Bromwich, West Midlands, B70 7TP Tel: 0121-525 2988 Fax: 0121-525 3607 E-mail: sales@industria.co.uk *Bearing distributors*

IndustrialMachines.Net Ltd, Ipsley Street, Redditch, Worcestershire, B98 7AA Tel: (0870) 8890270 Fax: (0870) 8890271 E-mail: sales@industrialmachines.net *Industrial plant, machinery bought & sold worldwide*

Industrious Ltd, 5th Floor, Radcliffe House, Blenheim Court, Solihull, West Midlands, B91 2AA Tel: 0121-712 6660 Fax: 0121-712 6661 E-mail: info@industrious.co.uk *Property investment & development consultants*

Industry Direct Ltd, 5 Kinsbourne Court, 96-100 Luton Road, Harpenden, Hertfordshire, AL5 3BL Tel: (01582) 462266 Fax: (01582) 461874 E-mail: sales@idlworldwide.com *Marketing consultants*

▶ Industry Specific Interactive Training Ltd, 125 Wortley Rd, High Green, Sheffield, S35 4LS Tel: 07910 313705 E-mail: manage@isit-training.co.uk *We design custom-built training courses to suit your needs. At present we are focusing on interactive training software, but we will be conducting online and face-to-face training in the near future.*If you have staff that need training on costly electronic devices or machinery, we can provide the necessary interactive training and testing before those staff actually handle these devices. We utilise demonstrations, student practice and testing in our training. The emphasis is on getting the learner to use the machinery/devices in a simulation(without injuring themselves, others or damaging your property). The interactive software can be used on a single computer or over a network.*

▶ Indusvent Engineering Northern Ltd, Smallbridge Industrial Park, Riverside Drive, Rochdale, Lancashire, OL16 2SH Tel: (0870) 7583280 Fax: (0870) 7583299 E-mail: mail@indusvent.com *Ventilation engineers*

Inelco Ltd, Unit 3 Theale Technology Centre, Station Raod, Theale, RG7 4XX Tel: (0870) 4203561 Fax: (0870) 4203563 E-mail: sales@inelco.co.uk *Electronic component distributors*

Inenco Group Ltd, Petros House, St. Andrews Road North, Lytham St. Annes, Lancashire, FY8 2NF Tel: (01253) 785000 Fax: (01253) 785001 E-mail: enquiries@inenco.com *Energy cost control & conservation*

INEOS Enterprises Ltd, Salt Business, Mersey View Road, Weston Point, Runcorn, Cheshire, WA7 4HB Tel: (0800) 590810 Fax: (01928) 572261 E-mail: salt-enquiries@ineosenterprises.com *Rock salt products suppliers*

Inex Inspection System, Unit 14 First Avenue, Trafford Park, Manchester, M17 1JZ Tel: 0161-876 1700 Fax: 0161-876 1701 *Bottle inspection machinery service retailers*

▶ Infatrans Ltd, 4 New Road, Great Kingshill, High Wycombe, Buckinghamshire, HP15 6DR Tel: (01494) 712212 Fax: (01494) 712212 E-mail: sales@infatrans.co.uk *IT consultancy*

Infield Systems Ltd, 15 London Fruit Exchange, Brushfield Street, London, E1 6HB Tel: (020) 7426 9660 Fax: (020) 7247 5035 E-mail: data@infield.com *Research databases & analytical services*

Infineon Technologies UK Ltd, Infineon House, Fleet Mill, Minley Road, Fleet, Hampshire, GU51 2RD Tel: (01252) 772200 Fax: (01252) 772201 E-mail: wendy.walker@infineon.com *Semiconductor manufrs*

▶ Infinite Distance Secretarial Services, 35 Nursery Road, Edgbaston, Birmingham, B15 3JX Tel: 0121-244 3633 E-mail: infinitedistance@blueyonder.co.uk *Offer full secretarial solution to individuals and small to medium-sized businesses. We can undertake any copy-typing,audio-typing, and word-processing tasks ranging from typing CVs and letters to transcribing medical notes or other secretarial tasks. We also*produce or revise electronic or printed presentations of any size*required.**Also provide services including proof-reading,website design and creation, spreadsheet design and creation and data entry.**

▶ Infinite Field Marketing Solutions, Infinite House 7 Woodside, South Marston Park, South Marston Industrial Estat, Swindon, SN3 4WA Tel: (01793) 829196 E-mail: business.services@infinitefms.com *Provision of field marketing services including: Sales promotions, demonstration days, merchandising, stock checking, sales drives, leaflet distribution ro mention a few....*Please see www.infinitefms.com or our sister company www.fmandcg.co.uk for more information*

Infinitely Presentation Services, Washbrook Meadow, Great Horwood Road, Winslow, Buckingham, MK18 3LX Tel: (01296) 712532 Fax: (01296) 712532 E-mail: sales@infinately.co.uk *Audio visual duplicators*

▶ Infinity Business Solutions, Shinfield Grange, Cutbush Lane, Shinfield, Reading, RG2 9AF Tel: 0118-988 2777 E-mail: sales@infinity-bf.com *It consultancy*

▶ Infinity I O Ltd, The Old Waterhouse, The Elvetham, Hook, Hampshire, RG27 8AS Tel: (01252) 847400 Fax: (01252) 848608 E-mail: info@infinityio.co.uk *Computer training services*

▶ Infinity Technologies Ltd, Hamlet House, 366-368 London, Westcliff-on-Sea, Essex, SS0 7HZ Tel: (01268) 777039 Fax: (08700) 548697 E-mail: bpb@inftech.co.uk *Voice & data networking services*

Infix Holdings Ltd, 85 87 Stapleton Road, Bristol, BS5 0QF Tel: 0117-955 3987 Fax: 0117-955 9833 E-mail: enquiries@infix.co.uk *Power tool distributors & specialist construction fixings*

▶ Infl8 Bouncy Castle Hire, 4 Provender Walk, Belvedere Road, Faversham, Kent, ME13 7NF Tel: (01795) 537227 *Bouncy Casle Hire for any occassion. Birthdays, Parties, Fetes, BBQs, Weddings etc.Covering Kent and the South East.*Indoor and Outdoor events. All equipment safety tested and less than 1 year old. Fully insured. We can also supply Balloons and Party packs for any occassion.*

▶ Inflated Ideas By Claire, 76 Clifton Road, Rochford, Essex, SS4 3HJ Tel: (01702) 543757 *Balloons suppliers*

Inflight Cleaning Services, Room 295 Ground Floor, International Pier Terminal Buiding, Glasgow Airport, Abbotsinch, Paisley, Renfrewshire, PA3 2TD Tel: 0141-848 7118 Fax: 0141-848 7112 *Air craft cleaners*

Inflight (Southend) Ltd, North Hangar, Aviation Way, Southend-On-Sea, SS2 6UN Tel: (01702) 348601 Fax: (01702) 541534 *Aircraft maintenance services*

Inflite Engineering Services Ltd, Unit A, Broadlink, Manchester, M24 1UB Tel: 0161-653 4222 Fax: 0161-655 3375 E-mail: enquiries@ultratools.co.uk *Multi-impression hot runner moulds manufrs*

Inflite The Jet Centre, Hanger 173, First Avenue, London Stansted Airport, Stansted, Essex, CM24 1RY Tel: (01279) 831000 Fax: (01279) 837900 E-mail: swan@stanstead.demon.co.uk *Aircraft agents*

Inflow UK Ltd, Unit 5a+6 Mount Industrial Estate, Mount Road, Stone, Staffordshire, ST15 8LL Tel: (01785) 812150 Fax: (01785) 812031 E-mail: sales@inflowuk.co.uk *Water treatment plant & equipment suppliers*

▶ Influence International, Cedar Crt, London, SE1 3GA Tel: (07802) 944593 E-mail: csykes@influenceinternational.com *Influence International works with some of the most successful companies in a wide range of industries. We deliver innovative and effective real-world solutions based on our unique research into organisational decision making and the behavior and strategies of the most effective salespeople in the world. Our interventions are effective and designed to create the maximum impact and benefit for both our clients and participants.**We have been developing and delivering sales performance improvements for our clients internationally. We have continually re-invested in research and development, helping our clients achieve sustainable competitive advantage through their people and business models.***

▶ Info Basis, 9 Napier Court, Barton Lane, Abingdon, Oxfordshire, OX14 3YT Tel: (0870) 2000350 Fax: (0870) 2000351 *Skills management software services*

▶ Info Logic It, Unit 2 Hertfordshire Business Centre, Alexander Road, London Colney, St. Albans, Hertfordshire, AL2 1JG Tel: (01727) 823000 Fax: (01727) 822332 *Computer systems consultancy or services, software*

Info Sign Systems Ltd, 17 East Cromwell Street, Edinburgh, EH6 6HD Tel: 0131-553 6433 Fax: 0131-554 5259 E-mail: admin@ellinfo.co.uk *Sign manufrs*

▶ Info Tech Distribution Ltd, 11b Dawkins Road, Poole, Dorset, BH15 4JP Tel: (01202) 845989 Fax: (01202) 845985

Infocomp Ltd, 48 Front Street, Framwellgate Moor, Durham, DH1 5BL Tel: 0191-384 7734 Fax: 0191-384 7734 E-mail: sales@infocomp.co.uk *Computer consultancy*

Infogain Ltd, 18 Forlease Road, Maidenhead, Berkshire, SL6 1RU Tel: (01628) 580600 Fax: (01628) 580610 E-mail: info@infogain.com *Computer software developers*

Infogrames UK Ltd, 21 Castle Street, Manchester, M3 4SW Tel: 0161-827 8000 Fax: 0161-827 8001 *Computer software design*

Infographics UK Ltd, 12 Hanover Court, North Street, Glenrothes, Fife, KY7 5SB Tel: (01592) 750677 Fax: (01592) 610534 E-mail: sales@infographics.co.uk *Computer software systems developers*

▶ Infographics UK Ltd, Leslie House, Allen Road, Livingston, West Lothian, EH54 6TQ Tel: (01592) 750677 Fax: (01592) 610534 *Software developer*

Infolink Communications Ltd, 2 Camden Road, London, NW1 9DL Tel: (020) 7482 1888 Fax: (020) 7482 2255 *Telecommunications agents*

Infolist Ltd, Valley Business Centre Church Road, Newtownabbey, County Antrim, BT36 7LP Tel: (028) 9085 1133 Fax: (028) 9085 4708 E-mail: info@infolistltd.com *Stationary printers*

Infologistix Ltd, 4 Wesleyan Chapel Walk, Stapleford, Nottingham, NG9 8BQ Tel: 0115-939 9907 Fax: 0115-939 9117 E-mail: info@infologistix.co.uk *Computer consultants*

▶ Infolonx5 Computer Consultants, 5 Lenton Boulevard, Nottingham, NG7 2BY Tel: 0115-970 8111 Fax: 0115-970 5111 E-mail: sales@infolonxf.com *Computer systems consultants*

Infomatrix Ltd, The Old School, High Street, Fen Drayton, Cambridge, CB24 4SJ Tel: (01954) 232010 Fax: (01954) 230031 E-mail: chris.jones@infomatrix.com *Software solutions for wireless communications*

▶ Info-mercial Marketing Services Ltd, 57 Heathwood Road, Bournemouth, BH9 2JZ Tel: (0845) 4592103 E-mail: mike.e@info-mercial.biz *A "One Stop" Internet Media Specialist. Web Design and Optimisation feature alongside Video Communications products. E-Commerce, Corporate Branding and Software Solutions available. Flash and 3D designs, our business cards and commercials and many more facilities are previewed on our Web.*

Infometal, Moseley Street, Birmingham, B12 0RT Tel: 0121-693 3800 Fax: 0121-693 3803 E-mail: info@barnies.co.uk *Scaffolding equipment manufrs*

▶ Infomill Ltd, Pentagon House, Sir Frank Whittle Road, Derby, DE21 4XA Tel: (01332) 253170 Fax: (01332) 295360 E-mail: info@infomill.com *Specialists in software development*

Infonet Services Europe Ltd, Prospect House, Fishing Line Road, Redditch, Worcestershire, B97 6EW Tel: (01527) 593000 Fax: (01527) 593100 *Global communications*

▶ Infonic Document Management Ltd, 8 Copperhouse Court, Caldecotte Business Park, Milton Keynes, MK7 8NL Tel: (01908) 366388 Fax: (0844) 2252251 *Infonic Document Management Ltd is a document management and workflow system provider who have developed a range of document management solutions based upon Document Manager, a scalable workflow suite of products.*

Infoquest Systems Ltd, Lawday Place Lane, Farnham, Surrey, GU9 0BT Tel: (01252) 723721 Fax: (01252) 723721 E-mail: sales@infoquest-systems.co.uk *Computer systems & software provider*

Infor, Needles House, Birmingham Road, Studley, Warwickshire, B80 7AS Tel: (01527) 496200 Fax: (01527) 496300 *Computer software house manufrs*

Infor Global Solutions Frimley Ltd, 1 Lakeside Road, Farnborough, Hampshire, GU14 6XP Tel: (01276) 417200 Fax: (01276) 417201 *Computer software developers*

Inforalgo Information Technology Ltd, 131 Lincoln Road North, Birmingham, B27 6RT Tel: 0121-708 1155 Fax: 0121-707 7331 *Computer software developers*

Inform Atika, 25 Parkholme Rd, London, E8 3AG Tel: (020) 7241 2269 Fax: (020) 7241 2269 E-mail: cameron.martin@btinternet.com *Computer & software consultants*

▶ Inform Design & Development, 84a Watling St East, Towcester, Northamptonshire, NN12 6BS Tel: (0845) 1662466 Fax: (01327) 359689 E-mail: info@informdevelopment.com *Industrial design, mechanical engineering & interaction design*

▶ Inform I T, 55 Beauchamp Place, London, SW3 1NY Tel: (020) 7350 0191 Fax: (07050) 616471 E-mail: info@inform-it.com *Small home office computer services*

Informatica Computer Solutions Ltd, 40 St. Peters Street, Bedford, MK40 2NN Tel: (01234) 273700 Fax: (01234) 365163 E-mail: sales@informatica200.co.uk *Computer hardware & software support*

▶ Information Data Systems Ltd, Exchange House, Exchange Street, Attleborough, Norfolk, NR17 2AB Tel: (01953) 452249 *Computer software development*

Information Flow Ltd, 280 Yorktown Road, Sandhurst, Berkshire, GU47 0PZ Tel: (01276) 35323 E-mail: ray.ursell@informationflow.co.uk *Website developers*

Information Press Ltd, Southfield Road, Eynsham, Witney, Oxfordshire, OX29 4JB Tel: (01865) 882588

Information Search & Analysis Consultants, 89 Chandos Avenue, London, N20 9EG Tel: (020) 8446 2776 Fax: (020) 8343 9471 E-mail: dr.g.munday@issaconsult.co.uk *Chemical & safety engineering consultants*

Information Systems For Business Ltd, 80 Buttermarket Street, Warrington, WA1 2NN Tel: (01925) 240240 Fax: (01925) 240250 E-mail: sales@isbl.co.uk *Computer software suppliers*

Information Technology Services, 4 Ashley Road, Epsom, Surrey, KT18 5AX Tel: (01372) 800466 Fax: (01372) 740544 E-mail: sales@it-services.co.uk *IT consultants*

▶ Information Technology Systems, Commodore House, 51 Conway Road, Colwyn Bay, Clwyd, LL29 7AW Tel: (01492) 534483 *Web design & marketing*

Information Technology Systems, 16 Gremista Industrial Estate, Gremista/Lerwick, Lerwick, Shetland, ZE1 0PX Tel: (01595) 741400 Fax: (01595) 741401 E-mail: mail@its-online.co.uk *Computer supplies & services*

Information Technology Systems, Cygnet Lodge, Worcester Road, Worcester, WR8 0EA Tel: (01684) 311463 Fax: (01684) 311402 E-mail: sales@itsystems.co.uk *Computer consultants*

Information Transfer, Burleigh House, 15 Newmarket Road, Cambridge, CB5 8EG Tel: (01223) 312227 Fax: (01223) 310200 *Training & communications consultants & publishing*

Informatiq Consulting Ltd, Gresham House, 53 Clarendon Road, Watford, WD17 1FT Tel: (01923) 224481 Fax: (01923) 224493 E-mail: permanant@informatiq.co.uk *IT recruitment agents*

▶ Informed It Solutions, Carlson House, Bradfield Road, Wix, Manningtree, Essex, CO11 2SP Tel: (01255) 870999 E-mail: enquiries@informedit.com *Computer services and Consultancy*Technology service provider, email, internet client server networking Cat5 structured cabling voice and data*

Informed Solutions Ltd, The Old Bank, Old Market Place, Altrincham, Cheshire, WA14 4PA Tel: 0161-942 2000 Fax: 0161-942 2015 *Computer consultants*

▶ InforSolving.com, 19 Coatbank Street, Coatbridge, Lanarkshire, ML5 3SP Tel: (01236) 707927 Fax: (01236) 429445 E-mail: info@infosolving.com *IT consultancy that can answer and solve your problems. From the smallest desktop solution to Enterprise projects. Services Include: Networking, Software Supply & Design, Web Design, CRM, Business Consulting, Project Management and many more..*

Infosculpt Ltd, 36 Dorien Road, London, SW20 8EJ Tel: (020) 8544 0592 Fax: (020) 8544 1043 E-mail: cdrequest@infosculpt.org *Financial software manufrs*

Infosigns Signs & Nameplates, Unit 1 Howsell Road Industrial Estate, Malvern, Worcestershire, WR14 1UJ Tel: (01684) 577744 Fax: (01684) 566862 E-mail: info@infosigns.uk.com *Sign manufrs*

▶ Infosoft Solutions, Kenton Park Parade, Kenton Road, Harrow, Middlesex, HA3 8DQ Tel: (020) 8909 1313 Fax: (020) 8909 1414 E-mail: info@infosoftsolutions.co.uk *Computer maintenance & repair services*

Infostaff Ltd, 16 North Silver Street, Aberdeen, AB10 1RL Tel: (01224) 336200 Fax: (01224) 428500 E-mail: info@infostaff.co.uk *Technical employment agency*

Infosystems, Bridge Farm, Holt Lane, Ashby Magna, Lutterworth, Leicestershire, LE17 5NJ Tel: (01455) 201000 Fax: (01455) 201001 E-mail: sales@infosystems.co.uk *IT & communications*

Infotec Ltd, The Maltings, Tamworth Road, Ashby-de-la-Zouch, Leicestershire, LE65 2PS Tel: (01530) 560600 Fax: (01530) 560111 E-mail: sales@infotech.co.uk *Electronic display system manufrs*

▶ Infotec Computer Training, 29 College Road, Moseley, Birmingham, B13 9LS Tel: 0121-248 1416

Infotec UK Ltd, 1230 Arlington Business Park, Theale, Reading, RG7 4TX Tel: 0118-928 4900 Fax: 0118-928 4901 *Office equipment suppliers* Also at: Chelmsford, Croydon & Shoreham-by-Sea

▶ Infotech Enterprises Europe Ltd, Holborn Hall, 100 Gray's Inn Road, London, WC1X 8AL Tel: (020) 7404 0640 Fax: (020) 7404 0664 E-mail: info@insotech-europe.com *IT software*

▶ Infoterra Ltd, Atlas House, 41 Wembley Road, Leicester, LE3 1UT Tel: 0116-273 2391 Fax: 0116-273 2400 E-mail: info@infoterra-global.com *Survey services*

▶ Infotrack Ltd, Trackcom House 2 Newmarket Court, Chippenham Drive, Kingston, Milton Keynes, MK10 0AQ Tel: (01908) 288285 Fax: (01908) 288280 E-mail: info@infotrack.com *Alarm systems manufacturer & distributor*

Infotrends Ltd, Sceptre House, 7-9 Castle Street, Luton, LU1 3AJ Tel: (01582) 400120 Fax: (01582) 411001 E-mail: info@capv.com *Computer consultants*

▶ Infra Red Optics (UK) Ltd, 7 Meadowbank Road, Kirknewton, Midlothian, EH27 8BH Tel: (01506) 884881 Fax: (01506) 884881

▶ Infra Safety Services Ltd, 6 Cotton Brook Road, Shaftesbury Street, Sir Francis Ley Industrial Park South, Derby, DE23 8YJ Tel: (01332) 542800 Fax: (01332) 542829 E-mail: enquiries@infrasafetyservices.co.uk *Specialist in automatic track warning systems atws, training*

▶ Infrastructure Associates Ltd, Weir Bank, Monkey Island Lane, Bray, Maidenhead, Berkshire, SL6 2ED Tel: (01628) 762730 Fax: (01628) 762730 E-mail: scherry@infrastructureassociates.com *Physical infrastructure consulting engineers & project managers*

Infro Heat Ltd, 2 Landport Road, Wolverhampton, WV2 2QJ Tel: (01902) 351025 Fax: (01902) 352552 E-mail: sales@infroheat.co.uk *Electric trace heating equipment manufrs*

▶ Infront Communications, The Heath Business & Technical Park, Runcorn, Cheshire, WA7 4QX Tel: 08707 662301 Fax: (01928) 589113 E-mail: info@infrontcommunications.co.uk *Supplier and Installers of Voice & Data Solutions.*

▶ Ingenia Solutions Ltd, 71 Victoria Road, Burgess Hill, West Sussex, RH15 9TR Tel: (01444) 876920 Fax: (01444) 876929 E-mail: sales@ingeniasolutions.co.uk *Special purpose machines & production line automation*

Ingenion Design Ltd, 10 Kym Road, Kimbolton, Huntingdon, Cambridgeshire, PE28 0LW Tel: (01480) 860606 Fax: (01480) 861122 E-mail: sales@ingenion.co.uk *Instrumentation designers*

▶ Ingenious, 16 Jackdaw Close, Stevenage, Hertfordshire, SG2 9DA Tel: (0845) 345 2576 Fax: (01438) 860359 E-mail: chris@ingeniousdisplays.co.uk *Vehicle livery, sign boards, exhibition graphics*

▶ Ingenius One, Express Courtyard, Luke Lane, Brailsford, Ashbourne, DE6 3BY Tel: (01335) 361199 Fax: (01335) 361188 E-mail: enquiries@ingeniusone.com *Marketing web design*

Ingersoll International UK Ltd, 7 Sopwith Way, Drayton Fields, Daventry, Northamptonshire, NN11 5PB Tel: (01327) 313500 Fax: (01327) 313509 E-mail: inggmbh@ingersoll-uk.co.uk *Machine tools sales & maintenance*

Ingersoll Rand Co. Ltd, Swan Lane, Hindley Green, Wigan, Lancashire, WN2 4EZ Tel: (01942) 257171 Fax: (01942) 522747 *Air compressors maintenance or repair services*

Ingersoll-Rand Dor-O-Matic Ltd, Berrington Road, Sydenham Industrial Estate, Leamington Spa, Warwickshire, CV31 1NB Tel: (01926) 437000 Fax: (01926) 437005 E-mail: doromatic_sales@irco.com *Automatic door systems manufrs*

Ingham (Toolmakers) Ltd, Willow Hall Works, Willowfield Road, Halifax, West Yorkshire, HX2 7NF Tel: (01422) 342189 Fax: (01422) 342497 E-mail: info@inghamtools.co.uk *CNC sub-contractors & manufacturers of printing machine parts*

Ingimex Ltd, Halesfield 19, Telford, Shropshire, TF7 4QT Tel: (01952) 585833 Fax: (01952) 580940 E-mail: sales@ingimex.com *Ingimex Ltd specialise in the design and volume manufacture of light commercial vehicle bodies and body components. We manufacture dropside, tippers and box van bodies in a variety of sizes to suit all commercial vehicle 3.5 tonne chassis.**Ingimex provides a specialist service to many of Europe's leading manufacturers, as well as end customers, and more.*

Inglecliff Ltd, Unit 2 Barsbank Lane, Lymm, Cheshire, WA13 0ER Tel: (01925) 752471 Fax: (01925) 755784 E-mail: sales@inglecliff.co.uk *Industrial rubber product manufrs*

Ingleson David Carbide Sales Services, Canada Crescent, Cleveleys, Rawdon, Leeds, LS19 6LT Tel: 0113-250 6013 *Engineering & cutting tools*

E.E. Ingleton Engineering Ltd, Adelaide Works, 55 Mowbray St, Sheffield, S3 8EZ Tel: 0114-275 7834 Fax: 0114-272 9672 E-mail: sales@eeingleton.co.uk *E E Ingleton are the UK's leading manufacturer of custom perforated panels & screens for the architectural & engineering industries. Specialised CAD-CAM technology enables production of highly cost-effective solutions for individual project & product requirements. Architects & designers need not be constrained by standard sizes & specifications; unique & creative designs can be tailored for each project to produce a superior visual quality or function. Typical applications include balustrades, stairways, infills, plant screening, cladding, ventilation, bespoke furniture & architectural features. We also offer a range of granulator screens for most machine types used for tyre processing & plastic recycling, green waste & wood waste, as well as hardened screens & hammers for various hammer-mills, granulators, pulverisors, shredders & crushers. We are the UK's market leader in the supply of beaters, screens & parts for the feedmilling & by-products processing industries.*

Inglis Allen Ltd, 40 Townsend Place, Kirkcaldy, Fife, KY1 1HF Tel: (01592) 267201 Fax: (01592) 206049 E-mail: info@scottishcalendars.com *Office printing equipment suppliers*

J.T. Inglis & Sons Ltd, Riverside Works, Carolina Port, Dundee, DD1 3LU Tel: (01382) 462131 Fax: (01382) 462846 *Textile processor*

▶ Inglis James Shoemaker, Cavalry Park, Peebles, EH45 9BU Tel: (01721) 722422 Fax: (0845) 8951051 E-mail: sales@jamesinglis.com *Ladies narrow fitting shoe retailers*

▶ Ingram Consultancy Ltd, Manor Farm House, Chicklade Hindon, Hindon, Salisbury, SP3 5SU Tel: (01747) 820170 Fax: (01747) 820175 E-mail: enquiries@ingram-consultancy.co.uk *Consultants for conservation service & repairs*

Ingram Foods Ltd, 4 Blackbrook Valley Industrial Estate, Narrowboat Way, Dudley, West Midlands, DY2 0XQ Tel: (01384) 237551 Fax: (01384) 240017 E-mail: ingramfoodslimited@btinternet.com *Meat (processed & cooked) products manufrs*

Ingram Foundry Industries Ltd, Unit E1 Dudley Central Trading Estate, Shaw Road, Dudley, West Midlands, DY2 8QX Tel: (01384) 253022 Fax: (01384) 213339 E-mail: sales@ingram-industries.com *Foundry supply services*

Ingram & Glass Ltd, Catteshall Lane, Godalming, Surrey, GU7 1LB Tel: (01483) 415262 Fax: (01483) 426951 E-mail: patrick@ingram-glass.co.uk *Electroplating services & surface treatment*

Ingram Installations Ltd, Unit 13, Newby Road Industrial Estate, Hazel Grove, Stockport, Cheshire, SK7 5DA Tel: 0161-456 8288 Fax: 0161-456 8089 E-mail: sales@ingraminstallations.co.uk *Supply, installation & maintenance of diesel generators*

Ingram Insurance Services Ltd, 55-57 Southbourne Grove, Bournemouth, BH6 3QU Tel: (01202) 431041 Fax: (01202) 431043 E-mail: admin@ingraminsurance.demon.co.uk *Insurance intermediaries*

Ingram Salisbury Ltd, 44 Catherine Street, Salisbury, SP1 2DD Tel: (01722) 333802 Fax: (01722) 333802 *Saddler & riding wear manufrs*

Ingrid West Machinery Ltd, Unit 5L, Delta Drive, Tewkesbury Business Park, Tewkesbury, Gloucestershire, GL20 8HB Tel: (01684) 273164 Fax: (01684) 273171 E-mail: enquiries@ingridwest.co.uk *Machinery agency coil winding machines*

Inhouse Interiors, 84 Front Street, East Boldon, Tyne & Wear, NE36 0SG Tel: 0191-537 2406 Fax: 0191-537 2406 *Interior design & soft furnishings agents*

Inidam Ltd, Budds Lane Industrial Estate, Romsey, Hampshire, SO51 0HA Tel: (01794) 830388 Fax: (01794) 830066 E-mail: ndt@inidam.com *Non destructive testing services*

Inigo Jones & Co. Ltd, Tudor Slate Works, Caernarfon, Gwynedd, LL54 7ST Tel: (01286) 830242 Fax: (01286) 831247 E-mail: slate@inigojones.co.uk *Slate craftsmen*

Inios, PO Box 21, Grangemouth, Stirlingshire, FK3 9XH Tel: (01324) 483422 *Oil refiners & chemicals industry manufrs*

▶ In-I-T.Co.Uk, 5, The Courtyard, 51 St. Marys Road, Weybridge, Surrey, KT13 9PX Tel: (01932) 821127 Fax: (01932) 821137

Initial, Botany Brow, Chorley, Lancashire, PR6 0HX Tel: (01257) 272311 Fax: (01257) 233575 *Textiles*

Initial A To Z Couriers, 21a Brownlow Mews, London, WC1N 2LA Tel: (020) 7841 1741 Fax: (020) 7404 6045 E-mail: danbrown@initial-atoz.co.uk *International courier services*

Initial Attendo Ltd, Shadsworth Business Park, Blackburn, BB1 2PR Tel: (01254) 688688 Fax: (01254) 696460 E-mail: info@attendo.co.uk *Care communication systems & solutions*

Initial Building Services, Unit 5 Kings Castle Business Park, The Drove, Bridgwater, Somerset, TA6 4AG Tel: (01278) 444487 *Air conditioning & refrigeration contractors*

▶ Initial City Link, 8 Logman Centre, Greenbank CR, East Tullos Industrial Estate, Aberdeen, AB12 3BG Tel: (01224) 249966 Fax: (01224) 249624

▶ Initial City Link, Unit 15 Belton La Industrial Estate, Grantham, Lincolnshire, NG31 9HN Tel: (01476) 577428 Fax: (01476) 577173

▶ Initial City Link, 12-13 Blenheim Road, Cressex Business Park, High Wycombe, Buckinghamshire, HP12 3RS Tel: (01494) 769030 Fax: (01494) 512635

Initial City Link Ltd, Wellington House, 61-73 Staines Road West, Sunbury-On-Thames, Middlesex, TW16 7AH Tel: (01932) 822622 Fax: (01932) 785560 E-mail: enquiries@city-link.co.uk *Express parcel delivery services*

Initial Cleaning Services, Unit 2, Rhymney River Bridge Road, Cardiff, CF3 7AF Tel: (029) 2046 4243 Fax: (029) 2048 7248 E-mail: initialcleaning@rentokilinitial.com *Cleaning services*

Initial Electronic Security, Maxwelltown Industrial Estate, Glasgow Road, Dumfries, DG2 0NW Tel: (01387) 261060 Fax: (01387) 250708 E-mail: dumfries@ies.uk.com *Alarm systems installation & maintenance*

▶ Initial Electronic Security, 44 Colquhoun Avenue, Hillington Industrial Estate, Glasgow, G52 4BN Tel: 0141-882 1179 Fax: 0141-810 4957

▶ Initial Electronic Security Systems Ltd, 19 Castle Park Road, Whiddon Valley Industrial Estate, Barnstaple, Devon, EX32 8PA Tel: (01271) 371309 Fax: (01271) 321115

▶ Initial Electronic Security Systems Ltd, Unit A Sett End Road North, Shadsworth Business Park, Blackburn, BB1 2PT Tel: (01254) 844600 Fax: (01254) 696218 *Electronic fire security*

Initial Electronic Security Systems Ltd, Unit 22 Sea Vixen Industrial Estate, 3 Wilverley Road, Christchurch, Dorset, BH23 3RU Tel: (01202) 484172 Fax: (01202) 475828 E-mail: christchurch@ies.uk.com *Intruder alarm installers*

Initial Electronic Security Systems Ltd, 1 Orbit Centre, Ashworth Road, Bridgemead, Swindon, SN5 7YG Tel: (01793) 531955 Fax: (01793) 488850 E-mail: swindon@ies.uk.com *Security systems installers* Also at: Branches throughout the U.K.

Initial Electronic Security Systems Ltd, Wilson House, Waterberry Drive, Waterlooville, Hampshire, PO7 7XX Tel: (023) 9223 0566 Fax: (023) 9223 0567 *Fire alarm systems*

▶ Initial Electronic Security Systems Ltd, Sunley House, Olds Approach, Watford, WD18 9TB Tel: (01923) 775099 Fax: (01923) 770616 E-mail: watfordfire@ifs.com *Fire Alarm Systems*

▶ Initial Fire & Security Ltd, Unit 13, Barnwell Business Park, Barnwell Drive, Cambridge, CB5 8UY Tel: (01223) 214677 Fax: (01223) 412374 *Security systems*

Initial Fire & Security Ltd, Enterprise House, Waldeck Road, Maidenhead, Berkshire, SL6 8BR Tel: (01628) 783561 Fax: (01628) 776953 E-mail: j.sharam@ies.uk *Physical & electronic securities*

Initial Garment Services, PO Box 392, Bradford, West Yorkshire, BD7 2YY Tel: (01274) 575656 Fax: (01274) 504960 *Workwear supply services*

Initial Images, Unit 218, Tedco Business Works, Henry Robson Way, South Shields, Tyne & Wear, NE33 1RL Tel: 0191-455 8128 *Personalised uniform designs*

Initial Incentives, Unit 4, Parr Road, Stanmore, Middlesex, HA7 1NP Tel: (020) 8381 3300 Fax: (020) 8381 3700 E-mail: sales@initialonline.com *Promotional & advertising gift products*

Initial Monogram Co. Ltd, 18 Capel Road, Watford, WD19 4AE Tel: (01923) 255540 Fax: (01923) 819003 E-mail: initialmonogram@ntlworld.com *Ornamental name & number plaques*

Initial Packaging Solutions Ltd, Unit 16 Westgate, Everite Industrial Estate, Widnes, Cheshire, WA8 8RA Tel: 0151-420 4333 Fax: 0151-423 4451 E-mail: sales@initialpackaging.co.uk *Polythene printers & manufrs*

Initial Security Ltd, Unit 14 Sovereign Enterprise Park, King William Street, Salford, M50 3UP Tel: 0161-848 0141 Fax: 0161-848 0520 *Security services* Also at: Birmingham, Leeds & Liverpool

Initial Textile Services, Unit 10, Eldon Way, Bristol, BS4 3QQ Tel: 0117-971 2387 Fax: 0117-971 6612 E-mail: briscsu@initialtextileservices.co.uk *Towel, linen & workwear services*

Initial Window Cleaning, Solecast House, 13-27 Brunswick Place, London, N1 6DX Tel: (020) 7466 7776 Fax: (020) 7466 7775 *Window cleaners*

Initiative.Net, 7 Gewans Meadow, South Orne Road, St. Austell, Cornwall, PL25 4RS Tel: (01872) 223100 Fax: (01872) 223134 *Computer sales & software developers*

▶ Initiative2 Web Site Design, Rosewood, Hareburn Road, Bridge of Don, Aberdeen, AB23 8AR Tel: (01224) 820960 E-mail: sales@initiative2.com *Search engine optimisation, online catalogues & directories*

▶ Inviveo Ltd, PO Box 2493, Leek, Staffordshire, ST13 5WZ Tel: (05511) 400146 E-mail: enquiries@inviveo.co.uk *Electronics Design Consultancy*

Inject Plastics (Devon) Ltd, 1-6 The Stables, Ford Road, Totnes, Devon, TQ9 5LE Tel: (01803) 863704 Fax: (01803) 865991 E-mail: sales@injectplastics.co.uk *Plastic mouldings manufrs*

Injection Moulding Co., Unit 1b Betton Way, Moretonhampstead, Newton Abbot, Devon, TQ13 8NA Tel: (01647) 440055 Fax: (01647) 441055 E-mail: timco@tiscali.co.uk *Plastic injection moulders*

Injection Mouldings Ltd, Cotswold Court Park, Gloucester Road, Staverton, Cheltenham, Gloucestershire, GL51 0TF Tel: (01452) 854077 Fax: (01452) 855077 E-mail: info@injectionmouldingsltd.co.uk *Plastic & injection mouldings*

Injection Plastics Ltd, Winston Avenue, Croft, Leicester, LE9 3GQ Tel: (01455) 283898 Fax: (01455) 285330 E-mail: injectplasleics@aol.com *Injection moulders & toolmakers*

Ink 4 U Ltd, Unit 11, Sharp St, Dewsbury, West Yorkshire, WF13 1QZ Tel: (01924) 455556 Fax: (01924) 458060 E-mail: nancybell@ink4u.co.uk *Computer systems, software & cartridge sales*

The Ink Cycle, 24 Savile Rd, Huddersfield, HD3 3DQ Tel: (01484) 450987 Fax: (01484) 450987 *Ink cartridges recycling & suppliers*

Ink Cycle Ltd, Drinsey Nook, Gainsborough Road, Saxilby, Lincoln, LN1 2JJ Tel: (01522) 704555 Fax: (01522) 704128 E-mail: sales@inkcycle.co.uk *Ink jet cartridges suppliers*

▶ Ink Design & Print Ltd, 1 Wessex Road, Bourne End, Buckinghamshire, SL8 5DT Tel: (01628) 524415 Fax: (01628) 529856 E-mail: info@inkltd.co.uk

Ink & Media Ltd, 104 Bridgwater Drive, Westcliff-on-Sea, Essex, SS0 0DH Tel: (01702) 434505 E-mail: sales@inkandmedialtd.co.uk *Specialises in selling compatible and manufacturer's original inkjet cartridges and laser toners. Also offers rewritable CD and DVD discs.*

▶ Ink Promotions Ltd, 225 High Road, Woodford, London, E18 2PB Tel: (020) 8505 2510 Fax: (020) 8181 7537 E-mail: sales@inkpromotions.co.uk *Sourcing and supply of promotional merchandise, cover mounts, promotional and corporate clothing and printed literature /stationery. We have in-house litho-printing facilities*

Ink Slinger Ltd, Red Lion Business Centre, Red Lion Road, Surbiton, Surrey, KT6 7QD Tel: (020) 8974 2425 Fax: (020) 8974 2423 *Lithographic plate manufrs & printers*

▶ Ink Xpress, 6 The Wharf Centre, Wharf Street, Warwick, CV34 5LB Tel: (01926) 411060 Fax: (01926) 498258 *Stationary suppliers*

▶ Inka Security Solutions, 4 Sycamore Road, Farnborough, Hampshire, GU14 6PF Tel: 0131-208 0392 Fax: (01252) 651983 E-mail: Webcams@inka.co.uk *We supply ZTV wireless multi channel camera & receiver equipment on a world wide basis. Please contact us if you would be interested in becoming an agent/reseller or if you are a retailer looking for ZTV wireless equipment for your retail outlet. Our LCD Palmboy receiver with 1 x indoor and 1 x outdoor wireless cameras sold out on QVC UK on 21/08/2005! Please visit our wireless camera web page for more information.*

▶ Inkinkink Net, The Gospel Hall, Amanwy, Llanelli, Dyfed, SA14 9AH Tel: (0845) 2261941 Fax: (07092) 031765 E-mail: admin@inkinkink.net *Ink cartridge retail*

▶ Inkjec, Inkjec House, Deepdale Mill Street, Preston, PR1 5BY Tel: (01772) 794300 Fax: (01772) 252215 E-mail: info@inkjec.com *Manufacturer & distributor of bulk ink & inkjet refill product*

▶ Inkjet Cartridges, 101 New Town Row, Birmingham, B6 4HG Tel: 0121-333 5554 Fax: 0121-333 5554 E-mail: tradecartridges@btconnect.com *UK reseller of printer Inkjet Cartridges and refills for Epson ink jet printers Inkjet,bubblejet,colour refillable Inkjet cartridges for canon printers.*

Inkjet Direct, Stow Mill, Stow, Galashiels, Selkirkshire, TD1 2RB Tel: (01578) 730477 Fax: (01578) 730387 E-mail: sales@proprint.co.uk *Computer & printer consumables*

▶ The Inkjet Market, Rockwell Crescent, Thurso, Caithness, KW14 7PL Tel: (01847) 895581 E-mail: enquiries@theinkjetmarket.co.uk *Supplier of Professional Inkjet Photopapers for the professional and the keen enthusiast. Also a large range of other inkjet papers, art papers and films. We have large inkjet refill kits for most common printers together with a range of remanufactured cartridges.*

▶ Inkjet-Pruducts4u, 78 Southbridge Road, Croydon, CR0 1AE Tel: 0208 649 7900 Fax: 0208 681 4007 E-mail: sales@injet-products4u.com *Welcome to inkjet-products4u.com Save over 100% on your printing when you buy direct Remanufactured ink cartridges-Original and compatible cartridges Printer supplies including laser toner cartridges-inkjet refill kits & inkjet paper BUY TODAY AND SAVE OVER 100%Our Prices are for 5 Cartridges!!!!Yes 5 NEW PRODUCTS BEING ADDED DAILY Designated trademarks and brands are the property of their respective owners*

▶ Inkley Ink, 65 Stockwell Head, Hinckley, Leicestershire, LE10 1RD Tel: (01455) 619222 *Computer accessories suppliers*

▶ Inkon Printers, 63-79 Oldham Street, Hyde, Cheshire, SK14 1LL Tel: 0161-368 3444 Fax: 0161-367 8257

Inkost Ltd, Signal Buildings, Brunel Road, Newton Abbot, Devon, TQ12 4FD Tel: (01626) 333485 Fax: (01626) 335441 *Laser jet cartridge manufrs*

Inkreadible Label Co., 11 Chatto Way, Torquay, TQ1 4UE Tel: (01803) 326818 Fax: (01803) 313102 E-mail: sales@inkreadible.com *Label manufrs*

Inktec Midlands, PO Box 567, Wolverhampton, WV8 2JW Tel: (01902) 846060 Fax: (01902) 846360 *Printer consumables distributors*

▶ Inktecshop - Printer Ink Cartridge, Unit E6, Rudford Industrial Estate, Ford Road, Ford, Arundel, West Sussex, BN18 0BD Tel: (01903) 730647 Fax: (01903) 731242 E-mail: mrogers@colurfill.co.uk *Retail supply of printer ink cartridges & ink refill kits*

▶ The Inkwell, 64 West Gate, Mansfield, Nottinghamshire, NG18 1RR Tel: (01623) 636222 Fax: (01623) 636222 *Refill ink cartridges for printers*

▶ Inkxpress, 202 Nutgrove Road, St. Helens, Merseyside, WA9 5JP Tel: 0151-493 1005 Fax: 0151-493 1005 *Computer accessories & consumables*

Inkxpress, 106 Rhosddu Road, Wrexham, Clwyd, LL11 2NG Tel: (01978) 261368 Fax: (01978) 262735 E-mail: sales@inkxperts.co.uk *Printer Cartridge & Office Supplies*

▶ Inky.Co.Uk, PO Box 7961, Nottingham, NG9 6WY Tel: 0115-877 0342 Fax: 0115-877 0343 E-mail: sales@inky.co.uk *Supply original & compatible laser toners, ink cartridges & ribbons*

▶ Inland UK Ltd, Unit 4, 73 Canning Road, Wealdstone, Harrow, Middlesex, HA3 7SP Tel: (020) 8863 9248 Fax: (020) 8424 0996 E-mail: sales@inland.co.uk *Inland UK distribute prescription sports eyeware plus optical supplies*

Inlex Locking Ltd, Wood Lane, Wolverhampton, WV10 8HN Tel: (01902) 397300 Fax: (01902) 785372 E-mail: enquiries@anochrome-group.co.uk *Metal finishing & thread locking specialists*

▶ Inlico, Q1 Hawthorne Industrial Estate, Middlemore Road, Handsworth, Birmingham, B21 0BH Tel: 0121-515 3020 Fax: 0121-515 4629 E-mail: info@inlico.com *Electrical components retailers*

▶ Inline Cosmetics Ltd, 1-3 Elland Terrace, Leeds, LS11 9NW Tel: 0113-242 9190 Fax: 0113-242 9005 E-mail: sales@inlinecosmetics.com

Inline Logistics Ltd, The Grange, Brixworth, Northampton, NN6 9DL Tel: (01604) 882200 Fax: (01604) 882323 *Warehouse & office design agents*

▶ Inline Track Welding Ltd, Ashmill Business Park, Ashford Road, Lenham, Maidstone, Kent, ME17 2GQ Tel: (01622) 854730 Fax: (01622) 854731

Inlines Furniture Ltd, PO Box 160, Amersham, Buckinghamshire, HP6 6UH Tel: (01494) 434030 *Importers of furniture*

▶ Inmac Engineering, 13-15 Parc Erissey Industrial Estate, New Portreath Road, Redruth, Cornwall, TR16 4HZ Tel: (01209) 313088 Fax: (01209) 313099 E-mail: admin@inmac-pl3.co.uk *Engineering and Environmental Services Ltd*

Inman & Co Electrical Ltd, 2-4 Orgreave Place, Sheffield, S13 9LU Tel: 0114-254 2400 Fax: 0114-254 2410 E-mail: sales@inmanselectrical.co.uk *Wholesale electrical supplies* Also at: Worksop

Inmar Automation Ltd, Test House, 118 Ringwood Road, Totton, Southampton, SO40 8DS Tel: (023) 8086 4179 Fax: (023) 8086 1613 E-mail: sales@inmar.co.uk *Calibrating services, industrial & marine instrumentation systems*

Inmart Steel Ltd, 2 Bolton Road Workshops, Bolton Road, Wath-upon-Dearne, Rotherham, South Yorkshire, S63 7JY Tel: (01709) 760389 Fax: (01709) 760389 E-mail: info@iron-components.co.uk *Wrought iron components manufrs*

Inmet Aluminium & Stainless Ltd, D Boomes Industrial Estate, New Road, Rainham, Essex, RM13 8BS Tel: (01708) 522673 Fax: (01708) 555743 E-mail: inmet@netcomuk.co.uk *Aluminium & stainless steel strip stockholders*

▶ Inmoshop Limited, 14 Bryony Road, Bicester, Oxfordshire, OX26 3WY Tel: 01869 329932 E-mail: enquiries@inmoshop.co.uk *International property agents specialising in the Costa Blanca Spain. UK and Spanish offices.*

Inmould Ltd, Unit 10 Harmill Industrial Estate, Grovebury Road, Leighton Buzzard, Bedfordshire, LU7 4FF Tel: (01525) 376261 Fax: (01525) 376261 E-mail: sales.inmouldltd@btconnect.com *Plastic injection moulders manufrs*

▶ Inn Vision Multimedia Ltd, Unit 10 Viewpoint, Boxley, Penenden Heath, Maidstone, Kent, ME14 2DZ Tel: (01622) 765345 Fax: (01622) 765345 E-mail: sales@innvision.co.uk *Sound system manufrs*

▶ Inner Space Furniture Ltd, The Old Dairy Church Farm, South Harting, Petersfield, Hampshire, GU31 5QG Tel: (01730) 826633 Fax: (01730) 826644 E-mail: info@innerspacefurniture.co.uk *Furniture manufrs*

Innervisions, Po Box 9, Retford, Nottinghamshire, DN22 7GZ Tel: (01777) 702913 *Business presentation agents*

Paul Innes Construction Ltd, 47 Tennyson Avenue, Hartlepool, Cleveland, TS25 5NX Tel: (01429) 294276 Fax: (01429) 294276 *Steel fabricators*

Innisfail Laundry Ltd, 814 Hollands Road, Haverhill, Suffolk, CB9 8HB Tel: (01440) 702061 Fax: (01440) 712331 *Linen hire & laundry agents*

Innocence Clothing Ltd, 103 Wantz Road, Dagenham, Essex, RM10 8PS Tel: (020) 8593 0593 Fax: (020) 8593 0587 E-mail: info@innocenceclothing.com *Mail order clothing retailers*

Innospec Ltd, Innospec Manufacturing Park, Oil Sites Road, Ellesmere Port, CH65 4EY Tel: 0151 3553611 Fax: 0151 3562349 E-mail: corporatecommunications@innospecinc.com Principal Export Areas: Worldwide *Specialty*

continued

Company Information

continuation
*Chemicals covering:-*Refinery Specialties*Performance Specialties *Heating Specialties *Fuel Borne Catalysts *Renewable Fuels Specialties *Power Specialties *Marine Specialties *Pulp and Paper *Plastics and Polymers *Fragrance Ingredients *Household, Industrial and Institutional *Personal Care*

▶ Innov-8 Ltd, Clayfield Industrial Estate, Tickhill Road, Doncaster, South Yorkshire, DN4 8QG Tel: (01302) 310888 Fax: (01302) 855060 *Joinery manufacturing exhibitions, shop fittings & design*

▶ Innova IT Solutions, 1C Lyon Way, Greenford, Middlesex, UB6 0BN Tel: (020) 8833 7187

▶ Innovar Engineering Services Ltd, Unit 53 131 Lower Bathville, Armadale, Bathgate, West Lothian, EH48 2JS Tel: (01501) 732265 Fax: (01501) 733111 E-mail: ian.pope@btconnect.com *Engineering fabrication*

Innovare Systems Ltd, Wray Coppice, Oaks Road, Reigate, Surrey, RH2 0LE Tel: (0845) 6740020 Fax: (0845) 0730800 E-mail: sales@innovaresystems.co.uk *SIPS panels design supply & erect situational construction systems*

Innovate Logistics, 1 Willow Drive, Annesley, Nottingham, NG15 0DP Tel: (01623) 727300 *Cold & chill stores manufrs*

▶ Innovation 2 Market Ltd, Kings Rd, The Docks, Swansea, SA1 8PH Tel: (01792) 295520 Fax: (01792) 295588 E-mail: sales@i2m-uk.com *I2M was established in August 200 to deliver a number of key objectives. The company has a worldwide patent for the covert laser marking of reflective materials & a US patent based on RFID technology. Both technologies have applications in global brand protection & retail security, a multi-billion dollar market. These technologies are subject to licensing activities in Europe and the USA.*

Innovation Centre Europe Ltd, Winton House, Winton Street, Alfriston, Polegate, East Sussex, BN26 5UH Tel: (01323) 871117 Fax: (01323) 871118 E-mail: sales@iceurope.com *Management consultants-innovation & creativity*

▶ Innovation Glass Co. Ltd, Unit 27-28, Brue Avenue, Bridgwater, Somerset, TA6 5LT Tel: (01278) 426226

▶ Innovation Mouldings, Unit 2 Axis Park, Fort Fareham Industrial Site, Fareham, Hampshire, PO14 1FD Tel: (01329) 234848 Fax: (01329) 234848 E-mail: innovationmouldings@tiscali.co.uk *Fibreglass moulders*

Innovations To Industry, Bowden Rooms The Firs, Bowdon, Altrincham, Cheshire, WA14 2TQ Tel: 0161-929 1062 Fax: 0161-928 7800 E-mail: debbie@i2iuk.com *Computer hardware*

Innovative Clothing Co. Ltd, 51 Victoria Road North, Leicester, LE4 5EX Tel: 0116-261 2803 Fax: 0116-266 5472 *Clothing manufrs*

▶ Innovative Computer Engineering Ltd, 20 Butley Street, Hazel Grove, Stockport, Cheshire, SK7 4BL Tel: 0161-456 6337 E-mail: info@icesolutions.co.uk *IT solutions for businesses*

Innovative Marketing International Ltd, 21 Dorset Square, London, NW1 6QE Tel: (020) 7723 7228 Fax: (020) 7723 1192 E-mail: enquiries@innovativemarketing.co.uk *Sales promotion consultants*

Innovative Measurement Technology, 49 Christchurch Crescent, Bognor Regis, West Sussex, PO21 5SL Tel: (01243) 824506 Fax: (01243) 826340 E-mail: sales@imeasure.co.uk Principal Export Areas: Worldwide *IMT based in Bognor Regis, Sussex manufacture high accuracy gauging transducers. IMT are known as reliable suppliers of precision engineered measurement products, their gauging products cover a wide range from transducers to very sophisticated conditioning electronics. They also supply high quality British made Inductive Displacement Transducers and Optical Encoders for both rotary and linear applications, in absolute and incremental modes. IMT also represents the encoder manufacturer Brown and Sharp for sales of their high resolution optical encoders in the UK.*

▶ Innovative Programming Solutions Ltd, Unit 10, Folgate Road, Lyngate Industrial Estate, North Walsham, Norfolk, NR28 0AJ Tel: 01692 406636 E-mail: info@e-ips.co.uk *Distributors of prepackaged software from various publishers, Education and corporate volume licensing of populuar operating systems, Office suites and much more. see website for more information.*

Innovative Software Solutions Ltd, 5 The Willows, Strensall, York, YO32 5YG Tel: (01904) 492425 Fax: (01904) 492772 *Computer consultants*

Innovative Springs & Wireforms, Unit 17 Millard Industrial Estate, Cornwallis Road, Lyng, West Bromwich, West Midlands, B70 7JF Tel: 0121-553 3373 Fax: 0121-553 3375 *Manufacturers of springs & wireforms*

Innovative Systems Incorporated Ltd, 14 Westminster Court, Hipley St, Woking, Surrey, GU22 9LG Tel: (01483) 730118 Fax: (01483) 730536 E-mail: sales@innovativesystems.net *IT software systems provider*

Innovative Technology Ltd, Derker, Oldham, OL1 4EQ Tel: 0161-620 1990 Fax: 0161 6202090 E-mail: sales@innovative-technology.co.uk *manufacturers of bank note validators and bill acceptors.*

▶ Innovia Films Ltd, Station Rd, Wigton, Cumbria, CA7 9BG Tel: (01697) 342281 Fax: (01697) 341452 E-mail: filmsinfo@innoviafilms.com *Innovia Films is a major producer of speciality Biaxially Oriented Polypropylene (BOPP) & Cellulose films with production sites in the UK, USA, Belgium & Australia. With 17 sales offices & a strong network of distributors & agents we sell into over 110 countries worldwide. We hold a leading global position in the markets where we chose to compete: labels & security films, high performance coated packaging, tobacco overwrap & biodegradable/compostable & sustainable films. Speciality coated films include those for high barrier, high speed, anti-mist, peel*

continued

& re-seal, shrink-tightening, printable & low temperature sealing. We also produce coloured cellulose films, white, clear & metallised film. The range also includes fully biodegradable/ compostable cellulose films which are manufactured from renewable/sustainable resources. Brands include Propafilm, PropaFresh, Propaream, Cellophane, Rayoface, Rayoart, Rayoweb, Rayophane & NatureFlex.

Innovise Software Ltd, Hellier House, Wychbury Court, Brierley Hill, West Midlands, DY5 1TA Tel: (01384) 484032 Fax: (01277) 822566 E-mail: info@innovise.com *Computer software producers*

Innovision Research & Technology P.L.C., Ash Court, 23 Rose Street, Wokingham, Berkshire, RG40 1XS Tel: 0118-979 2000 Fax: 0118-979 1500 E-mail: enquiries@innovision-group.com *Research & technology engineers*

Innovision Surgical Ltd, 25 West Midlands Freeport, Birmingham International Airport, Birmingham, B26 3QD Tel: 0121-782 0105 Fax: 0121-782 2249 E-mail: ray@innovision.fsnet.co.uk *Surgical instrument manufrs*

Innovo Chemicals Ltd, The Common, Cranleigh, Surrey, GU6 8RY Tel: (01483) 277219 Fax: (01483) 268030 E-mail: sales@innovochem.co.uk *Chemical blending & distribution*

▶ Inntact Electronic Systems Ltd, Inntact House, Rawson Green, Kilburn, Belper, Derbyshire, DE56 0LL Tel: (01332) 781199 Fax: (01332) 781188 E-mail: inntact@aol.com *Electronic equipment for security & electro-luminescent lighting designers & manufrs*

Inoplas Technology Ltd, Uddens Trading Estate, Wimborne, Dorset, BH21 7LD Tel: (01202) 866000 Fax: (01202) 866016 E-mail: sales@inoplas.co.uk Principal Export Areas: Worldwide *Cable assembly services*

▶ Ino-Plaz Ltd, Unit B2 Chamberlain Business Centre, Chamberlain Road, Hull, HU8 8HL Tel: (01482) 225996 Fax: (01482) 225920 E-mail: sales@ino-plaz.co.uk *Manufacture of POS /POP in plastic*

Inotec UK, Unit 1, Viking Close, Hull, HU10 6DZ Tel: (01482) 654466 Fax: (01482) 655004 Principal Export Areas: Worldwide *Label & RFID specialists*

Inovis Ltd, 1 Bracken Close, Lichfield, Staffordshire, WS14 9RU Tel: (0870) 3504707 Fax: (0870) 3504717 E-mail: info@inovis.uk.com *Distributors of pneumatic valves cylinders & compressed air equipment*

▶ Inoxia Ltd, PO Box 904, Guildford, Surrey, GU2 8WX Tel: 07952 480296 E-mail: sales@inoxia.co.uk *Inoxia Ltd supply chemicals such as Potassium Nitrate, Copper Oxide, Strontium carbonate, Lithium carbonate, Soluble rice starch, Dextrin, Aluminium powder and Iron filings along with other products such as woven wire mesh, bottles, ball mill jars and scales.*

Inoxta-Realm Ltd, 29-35 Gladstone Road, Croydon, CR0 2BQ Tel: (020) 8689 5521 Fax: (020) 8689 0245 E-mail: inoxta@realm.co.uk *Stainless steel hygienic valves & valve systems*

Inpace Ltd, 100 Brize Norton Road, Minster Lovell, Witney, Oxfordshire, OX29 0SG Tel: (01993) 706303 Fax: (01993) 706305 E-mail: info@inpace.com *Computer accessories*

Inphase Software Ltd, Salamander Quay, Harefield, Uxbridge, Middlesex, UB9 6NY Tel: (01895) 829111 Fax: (01895) 829112 E-mail: info@inphase.com *Software developers*

Inphase Transformers Ltd, Kenyon Business Centre, 21 Kenyon Road, Brierfield, Nelson, Lancashire, BB9 5SP Tel: (01282) 614684 Fax: (01282) 695588 E-mail: inphase-tf-ltd@tiscali.co.uk *Coil winders & transformer manufrs*

Inpine Ltd, Anglia Way Industrial Estate, Anglia Way, Mansfield, Nottinghamshire, NG18 4LP Tel: (01623) 625468 *Pine furniture & beds manufrs*

Inpress Plastics Ltd, 1 Harwood Road, Littlehampton, West Sussex, BN17 7AU Tel: (01903) 724128 Fax: (01903) 730357 E-mail: sales@impressplastics.co.uk *Blow moulding and injection mould manufacturer. Tool maker*

Inprints (Screenprinters) Ltd, 32-36 Garden St, Sheffield, S1 4BJ Tel: 0114-272 7733 Fax: 0114-272 1976 E-mail: sales@inprints.co.uk *Screen printers & business gifts suppliers*

Inprojex International UK Ltd, 58 Uxbridge Road, London, W5 2ST Tel: (020) 8567 9680 Fax: (020) 8579 5241 E-mail: inprojex@inprojex.co.uk *Export agents & managers*

▶ Input Joinery Ltd, The Fairground, Weyhill, Andover, Hampshire, SP11 0QN Tel: (01264) 771900 Fax: (01264) 771901 E-mail: info@inputjoinery.co.uk *Joiners*

Inputideal Ltd, Tame House, Wellington CR, Fradley Park, Lichfield, Staffordshire, WS13 8RZ Tel: (01543) 444708 Fax: (01543) 444709 E-mail: webmaster@patech-solutions.com *Data input services*

▶ Ins Sudlows (Electrical) Ltd, Ducie Works, Hulme Hall Lane, Manchester, M40 8HH Tel: 0161-205 4900 E-mail: sales@inssudlows.com *Voice & data solutions services*

Insafe International Ltd, Westcombe House 4th Floor, 2-4 Mount Ephraim, Tunbridge Wells, Kent, TN4 8AS Tel: (01892) 533000 Fax: (01892) 525100 E-mail: sales@insafe.co.uk *Safe dealers & locksmiths*

Inscape Ltd, 23 Elizabeth Avenue, Tattershall Bridge, Lincoln, LN4 4JJ Tel: (01526) 344627 Fax: (01526) 344627 E-mail: sales@inscapeuk.com *Stretch ceiling specialists*

Insect Lore, PO Box 1420, Milton Keynes, MK19 6ZH Tel: (01908) 563338 Fax: (01908) 262654 *Mail order services*

Inserv Ltd, Willow House, Buckley Hill Lane, Milnrow, Rochdale, Lancashire, OL16 4BU Tel: (0870) 0112030 Fax: (0870) 0112040 E-mail: service@inserv.co.uk *Scienctific instrumentation repair and service*

Insewer Surveys, Unit 22 Lordswood Industrial Estate, Revenge Road, Chatham, Kent, ME5 8UD Tel: (01634) 861768 Fax: (01634) 201376 E-mail: enquiries@hydrogroup.demon.co.uk *Cctv surveying specialists*

Inshore Fish & Frozen Foods, Unit 3 Princes Way, The Old Filling Station, Leasgill, Milnthorpe, Cumbria, LA7 7ET Tel: 015395 64748 Fax: 015395 64110 *Fresh fish & frozen foods*

Inside Communications Ltd, Bank House, 23 Warwick Road, Coventry, CV1 2EW Tel: (024) 7657 1000 Fax: (024) 7625 2241 *Conference organising services & publishers*

▶ Inside Out Property Maintenance & Landscaping, 25 Roundhill Way, Guildford, Surrey, GU2 8HJ Tel: 01483 459344 E-mail: insideoutpml@btinternet.com

▶ Inside Track Marketing, Beech House, Padgate Business Park, Green Lane, Padgate, Warrington, WA1 4JN Tel: 01925 820600 Fax: 01925 822488 E-mail: info@inside-track.co.uk *Advertising, direct marketing, public relations and communications agency*

▶ Inside View Ltd, Suite 3 Hamlet House, 80a High Street, Alton, Hampshire, GU34 1EN Tel: (01420) 542518 Fax: (01420) 542518 E-mail: contact@insideview.co.uk *We are located in Alton, Hampshire and dedicated to supporting small and medium sized companies in the southern counties of England. Our aim is to provide a quality service that our customers are happy to recommend to others, we believe that the money other companies spend on bulk advertising is better spent on our existing customers who, in turn, are willing to recommend our company. We won't deny that even with our help your computer may have problems from time to time, it's almost inevitable in today's fast changing world with complex software and a multitude of connected Printers, Scanners, Backup Systems and other peripherals. What matters is the way the problem is dealt with and how well any disruption is minimised. Our business has grown steadily since we started in 1994 and includes companies from within a wide range of sectors including Medical, Accountancy, Publishing and many smaller local companies who we value just as much (after all, we want them to expand as much as they do!)*

Insider Technologies Ltd, Spinnaker Court Chandlers Point, 37 Broadway, Salford, M50 2YR Tel: 0161-876 6606 Fax: 0161-868 6666 E-mail: sales@insidertech.co.uk *Software manufrs*

Insight Ltd, Sandys Road, Malvern, Worcestershire, WR14 1JJ Tel: (01684) 577444 Fax: (01684) 577555 E-mail: sales@insightprecision.co.uk *Precision engineers*

▶ Insight Access & Handling Ltd, Unit 6 Thornleigh Trading Estate, Dudley, West Midlands, DY2 8UB Tel: (01384) 252524 Fax: (01384) 255444 E-mail: info@insightahl.com *Lifting equipment manufrs*

▶ Insight Architectural Glazing Ltd, Insight House, Wesley Street, Langley Mill, Nottingham, NG16 4AL Tel: (01773) 767772 Fax: (01773) 767987 E-mail: enquireies@aluminium-shopfronts.co.uk *Manufacturing & installation of windows, doors & curtain walling*

▶ Insight Associates, Meadowview House, 191 Queens Road, Norwich, NR1 3PP Tel: (01603) 767669 Fax: (01603) 776585

▶ Insight Automation, 6 Pegasus Mews, Stratton Business Park, Biggleswade, Bedfordshire, SG18 8QA Tel: (01767) 315402 Fax: (01767) 601619 E-mail: ditec@hotmail.co.uk *Industrial door contractors, installation & service*

Insight Consulting, Churchfield House, 3 & 5 The Quintet, Churchfield Road, Walton-On-Thames, Surrey, KT12 2TZ Tel: (01932) 241000 Fax: (01932) 244590 E-mail: insight@insight.co.uk *Independent risk management consultancy*

▶ Insight NDT Ltd, 3 Kilnhurst Business Park, Glasshouse Road, Kilnhurst, Mexborough, South Yorkshire, S64 5TH Tel: (01709) 571710 Fax: (01709) 571712 E-mail: info@insightndt.co.uk *We provide Non Destructive testing by means of X-Ray. *Our site has 2 bays with fork lift access enabling us to carry out X-ray examination on larger items. Please see our website for further details or e-mail us at info@insightndt.co.uk*

▶ Insight NDT Equipment Ltd, The Old Cider Mill, Wrigglebrook, Kingsthorne, Hereford, HR2 8AW Tel: (01981) 541122 Fax: (01981) 541133 E-mail: sales@insightndt.com *None destruction test equipment*

Insight Services Southern Ltd, Rosebank, Hailsham Road, Polegate, East Sussex, BN26 6RE Tel: (01323) 489005 Fax: (01323) 489006 E-mail: enquiries@insightservices.co.uk *CCTV installation services*

▶ Insight Systems, Insight House, Unit 5 Invicta Business Park, Wrotham, Sevenoaks, Kent, TN15 7RJ Tel: (01732) 2404434 Fax: 0870 240 4426 E-mail: pbaker@insight4systems.com *Sell & service photocopiers*

▶ Insight Systems Group, 150 Minories, London, EC3N 1LS Tel: (020) 7264 2001 Fax: (0870) 240443 E-mail: info@insight4london.com *Consultants & suppliers of document & print management systems*

Insight Training, 67 Main Road, Cumbernauld, Glasgow, G67 4ED Tel: (01236) 733898 Fax: (01236) 733898 *IT training consultants*

▶ Insight Visual Systems Ltd, 1a Foxholes Avenue, Hertford, SG13 7JG Tel: (01992) 505177 Fax: (01992) 505178 E-mail: sales@insight-visual.co.uk *Providing solutions from general audiovisual supply to integrated visualization systems*

Insignia, 20 Common Road, Bristol, BS15 3LL Tel: (01249) 460006 Fax: 0117-935 3916 E-mail: richard@insignia-signs.co.uk *Signs & displays*

Insignia Ltd, 1-6 Chalice Close, Wallington, Surrey, SM6 9RU Tel: (020) 8669 3122 Fax: (020) 8669 7192 E-mail: sales@insigniauk.com *Promotional merchandise*

Insignia Blind Company, 171 New Road, West Parley, Ferndown, Dorset, BH22 8ED Tel: (01202) 650011 Fax: (01202) 604412 E-mail: insigniablinds@btinternet.com *Blind, awning distributors & manufrs*

▶ Insignia Consulting, Knights View, 104 The Street, Little Waltham, Chelmsford, CM3 3NT Tel: (01245) 360121 Fax: (01245) 360614 E-mail: cad@insignia-consulting.com *Building drawing services*

Insignia Signs & Services, Unit 7 Albion Park, Albion Way, Armley Road, Leeds, LS12 2EJ Tel: 0113-243 8533 Fax: 0113-243 8733 E-mail: sales@insigniasigns.biz *Sign manufrs*

Insit Moulded Packaging Ltd, Aintree Avenue, White Horse Business Park, Trowbridge, Wiltshire, BA14 0XB Tel: (01225) 767985 Fax: (01225) 777405 E-mail: sales@insit.co.uk *Packaging materials*

Insite Ltd, PO Box 77, Tunbridge Wells, Kent, TN2 5ZL Tel: (01892) 686000 Fax: (01892) 676002 E-mail: sales@insite-europe.co.uk *Computer consultants*

▶ Insite Systems, Unit 2, Invicta Business Park, London Road, Wrotham, Sevenoaks, Kent, TN15 7RJ Tel: (01732) 887457 Fax: (01732) 886492 *Digital photocopiers, laser printing (colour & mono), fax machines, sales, service, supplies*

▶ Insitu Training Services, 12 Carlton Moor Mews, Leeds, LS10 4ST Tel: 07932467546 Fax: 0113 2705824 E-mail: insitutraining@tiscali.co.uk *On-site lift truck training service. Covering Yorkshire, North Humberside and the Greater Manchester areas. 7 days a week service. Course timetables structured to meet the needs of the customer within legislative guidelines*

Insituform Technologies Ltd, Roundwood Industrial Estate, Ossett, West Yorkshire, WF5 9SQ Tel: (01924) 277076 Fax: (01924) 265107 E-mail: affholder@insituform.com *Pipeline & sewer re-lining & repairs*

Insoll Components Ltd, 39 Wilbury Way, Hitchin, Hertfordshire, SG4 0TW Tel: (01462) 450741 Fax: (01462) 421162 E-mail: sales@insoll.com *PTFE & plastic machinists*

▶ Insolvency Network, 79 Manor Rise, Burntwood, Staffordshire, WS7 4TR Tel: (01543) 686362 *Insolvency Services & free advice on debt problems - R3 certified insolvency practitioners - get debt free in 5 years or less - no fee payable upfront*

▶ Insourcing Business Support Ltd, 16 Saddlers Close, Glenfield, Leicester, LE3 8QU Tel: (07968) 865285 E-mail: info@ibs-ltd.co.uk *Provision of part-time Finance Director Services to SME"s.*

▶ Inspark. Intelligent Business Solutions, Grenville Place, 3 Woodfield Lane, Ashtead, Surrey, KT21 2BQ Tel: (07005) 946896 Fax: (07005) 946899 E-mail: stephen.b.symes@newerasolutions.co.uk *Financial System Management. Software to provide Management with the desktop solutions for information control.*Solution provider, Change Control, Systems Analysis.*

Inspection Ecosse Ltd, Unit 1d, Old Redding Road, Laurieston, Falkirk, FK2 9JU Tel: (01324) 627772 Fax: (01324) 627945

Inspection Software Ltd, 3 Brynau Drive, Mayals, Swansea, SA3 5EE Tel: (01792) 404235 E-mail: isl@inspection.co.uk *Computer software developers*

▶ Inspiration, 37 Nelson Road, Caterham, Surrey, CR3 5PP Tel: (01883) 371444 Fax: (01883) 373737 *Label brokers & manufrs*

Inspirations Design & Communications Ltd, 26 Windermere Drive, Alderley Edge, Cheshire, SK9 7UP Tel: (01625) 599618 E-mail: inspirations@gen.net.uk *Advertising & public relations*

Inspire2Design Limited, 17C Mill Road, Stourport-on-Severn, Worcestershire, DY13 9BG Tel: (01299) 827646 E-mail: info@inspire2design.co.uk *We undertake design and development projects covering; product design, furniture design, office furniture design, seating design, retail furniture design, domestic furniture design, street furniture design, furniture design & make, solid modelling, using Solidworks, detail drawings and project management.*

▶ Inspired Business Marketing Ltd, Bodorgan Road, Bournemouth, BH2 6NL Tel: 07956 852469 E-mail: info@inspiredbusinessmarketing.com *Inspired Business Marketing helps SMEs to realise their potential with marketing & PR focus.*Inspired Business Marketing is about getting to the heart of business problems, defining objectives, and solving them with marketing. **

▶ Inspired By Light, Unit 8C, Beechcroft Farm Industrial Estate, Chapel Wood Road, Ash, Sevenoaks, Kent, TN15 7HX Tel: (0870) 2426232 E-mail: customerservice@inspiredbylight.co.uk *The Quality UK Lighting Shop*

▶ Inspired Photography Ltd, 27 Kirkdale Mount, Leeds, LS12 6AZ Tel: 0113 2109653 E-mail: timlawton1981@yahoo.co.uk

▶ Inspirit Interiors, Repton Road, Nottingham, NG6 9GE Tel: 0115-877 6959 Fax: 0115-877 6959 E-mail: enquiries@inspirit-interiors.co.uk *Interior design company who offer stylish & practical solutions to your design problems. We also offer on-line shopping for handcrafted, original or limited edition pieces for the home or as a gift.*

Instafab Sheet Metal Work, 5 Sunshine Mills, Wortley Road, Leeds, LS12 3HT Tel: 0113-263 4810 Fax: 0113-263 0444 E-mail: instafab@hotmail.com *Sheet metalwork engineers*

Instafoam & Fibre Ltd, Insta House, Ivanhoe Road, Hogwood Business Park, Wokingham, Berkshire, RG40 4PZ Tel: 0118-932 8811 Fax: 0118-932 8314 E-mail: info@instagroup.co.uk *Insulation services*

Instagas Boston Ltd, Industrial Estate, Hamilton Way, Boston, Lincolnshire, PE21 8TT Tel: (01205) 368622 Fax: (01205) 351807 E-mail: enquiries@instagas.co.uk *Cylinder gas & gas appliance retailers*

Instalec Networking Ltd, Arnhall Business Park, Westhill, Aberdeenshire, AB32 6UF Tel: (01224) 746400 Fax: (01224) 746401 E-mail: instalec@instalec.co.uk *Computer networkers*

Installation & Manufacturing Contractors Ltd, Thrifts House, London Road, Ware, Hertfordshire, SG12 9QT Tel: (01920) 468011 Fax: (01920) 460869 E-mail: info@monaflex.com *Tyres & vulcanising equipment manufrs*

▶ Instant Access Garage Doors, Caenant House, Mill Road, Caerphilly, Mid Glamorgan, CF83 3FE Tel: (029) 2088 4622 E-mail: info@autogateswales.co.uk *Garage supply, repair and installation, door automation, electric gates, gate automation, elctric barriers and bollards.W e cover all south wales Cardiff, Caerphilly, Pontypridd, Cwmbran and Newport.We supply doors from Cardale, Hormann, Garador, Henderson, Apex, Gliderol and Wayne Dalton and automation from Chamberlain Liftmaster, ""came"" and Urbaco. We are wales and the wests largest chamberlain liftmaster supplier.*

Instant Business, 8-10 Colston Avenue, Bristol, BS1 4ST Tel: 0117-915 5175 Fax: 0117-915 5185 E-mail: info@ibltd.com *E-business specialists & website design*

Instant Gift International, 1 Leigh Green Industrial Estate, Appledore Road, Tenterden, Kent, TN30 7DF Tel: (01580) 765040 Fax: (01580) 765056 *Gift suppliers*

Instant Home Ltd, Beaulieu House, 78 Ermine Street, Huntingdon, Cambridgeshire, PE29 3EZ Tel: 01480 432230 Fax: 01480 432868 E-mail: hollie@instanthome.co.uk *Hire or buy home furniture. Choose individual items or select a complete "furniture pack". Quality, contemporary furniture choices with swift delivery and full installation. An invaluable service for property developers, Landlords and anyone with a home furniture need.*

Instant Image, Park Farm, Colchester Road, Elmstead, Colchester, CO7 7BA Tel: (01206) 822121 Fax: (01206) 822121 E-mail: instant.7b@virgin.net *Sign makers*

Instant Installations, Station Lane, New Whittington, Chesterfield, Derbyshire, S43 2AF Tel: (01246) 260056 Fax: (01246) 260056 E-mail: sales@instantinstallationsltd.co.uk *Steel fabrications manufrs*

▶ Instant Security Systems Ltd, 19 The Broadway, East Lane, Wembley, Middlesex, HA9 8JU Tel: (020) 8908 3032 Fax: (020) 8904 2893 E-mail: sales@instantsecurity.co.uk *Supply, fit alarms*

Instant Training Ltd, Audley Avenue Enterprise Park, Newport, Shropshire, TF10 7DW Tel: (01952) 585555 Fax: (01952) 815758 E-mail: sales@instant-training.com *We provide Access, Plant and Health & Safety training either at one of our training centres or on the customers own site.*

Instanta Ltd, Canning Road, Southport, Merseyside, PR9 7SN Tel: (01704) 501114 Fax: (01704) 501115 E-mail: info@instanta.com *Catering equipment manufrs*

Instarmac Group plc, Kingsbury Link, Trinity Road, Piccadilly, Tamworth, Staffordshire, B78 2EX Tel: (01827) 872244 Fax: (01827) 874466 E-mail: enquiries@instarmac.co.uk *Bitumen macadam & highway repairers*

Instaspect Ltd, 18 Miller Road, Ayr, KA7 2AY Tel: (01292) 289146 Fax: (01292) 610554 E-mail: eng@instaspect.co.uk *Inspection & testing services*

▶ Instelec Services, Project House, Well Street, Bolton, BL1 1TZ Tel: (01204) 364643 Fax: (01204) 363525

Institute Of, Fanshaws, Brickendon, Hertford, SG13 8PQ Tel: 0131-331 4678 Fax: (01992) 511548 E-mail: imi@motor.org.uk *Trade association organization providers*

Institute for Animal Health, Pirbright Laboratory, Ash Road, Pirbright, Woking, Surrey, GU24 0NF Tel: (01483) 232441 Fax: (01483) 232448 *Research laboratories*

▶ Institute Of Applied Technology, Mitchelston Industrial Estate, Kirkcaldy, Fife, KY1 3LT Tel: (01592) 568500 Fax: (01592) 223601 *Further education services*

The Institute Of Brewing & Distilling, 33 Clarges Street, London, W1J 7EE Tel: (020) 7499 8144 Fax: (020) 7499 1156 E-mail: enquiries@iob.org.uk *Registered charity*

Institute of Carpenters, 35 Hayworth Road, Sandiacre, Nottingham, NG10 5LL Tel: 0115-949 0641 Fax: 0115-949 1664 E-mail: mail@carpenters-institute.org *Craft association carpentry & joinery organisation*

Institute of Chartered Accountants of Scotland, CA House, 21 Haymarket Yards, Edinburgh, EH12 5BH Tel: 0131-347 0100 Fax: 0131-347 0105 E-mail: enquiries@icas.org.uk *Chartered accountants institutions services*

Institute of Chartered Accountants-England & Wales, PO Box 433, London, EC2P 2BJ Tel: (020) 7920 8100 Fax: (020) 7920 0547 E-mail: feedback@icaew.co.uk *Professional & industrial trade associations*

Institute Of Chartered Secretaries & Administrators, 16 Park Crescent, London, W1B 1AH Tel: (020) 7580 4741 Fax: (020) 7323 1132 E-mail: info@icsa.co.uk *Trade association agents*

Institute Of Corrosion, Eden Way, Leighton Buzzard, Bedfordshire, LU7 4FY Tel: (01525) 851771 Fax: (01525) 376690 E-mail: admin@icorr.demon.co.uk *Professional institute*

The Institute Of Economic Affairs, 2 Lord North Street, London, SW1P 3LB Tel: (020) 7799 3745 Fax: (020) 7799 2137 E-mail: iea@iea.org.uk *Research & educational trusties services*

Institute Of Export Ltd, Export House, Minerva Business Park, Lynch Wood, Peterborough, PE2 6FT Tel: (01733) 404400 Fax: (01733) 404444 E-mail: institute@export.org.uk *Export training & educational services*

Institute of Food Research, Norwich Research Park, Colney, Norwich, NR4 7UA Tel: (01603) 255000 Fax: (01603) 507723 E-mail: ifr.communications@bbsrc.ac.uk *Research institute*

Institute of Inventors, 19-23 Fosse Way, Ealing, London, W13 0BZ Tel: (020) 8998 3540 *Invention consultants & patent services*

Institute Of Marine Engineering Science & Technology, 80 Coleman Street, London, EC2R 5BJ Tel: (020) 7382 2600 Fax: (020) 7382 2670 E-mail: info@imarest.org *Professional body & registered charity*

Institute of Materials, Minerals & Mining, 1 Carlton House Terrace, London, SW1Y 5DB Tel: (020) 7451 7300 Fax: (020) 7451 7406 *Publishers*

Institute Of Measurement & Control, 87 Gower Street, London, WC1E 6AF Tel: (020) 7387 4949 Fax: (020) 7388 8431 E-mail: instmc@instmc.org.uk *Professional association*

▶ Institute For Outdoor Learning, Plumpton, Penrith, Cumbria, CA11 9NP Tel: (01768) 885800 Fax: (01768) 885801 E-mail: institute@outdoor-learning.org *Educational aids equipment suppliers*

Institute of Packaging, IOP Packaging Society, Springfield House, Springfield Road, Grantham, Lincolnshire, NG31 7BG Tel: (01476) 514 590 Fax: (01476) 514591 E-mail: iop@pi2.org.uk *Education & training body.* Also at: Branches throughout the U.K.

Institute of Public Care, 8 Palace Yard Mews, Bath, BA1 2NH Tel: (01225) 484088 Fax: (01225) 330313 E-mail: ipc@brookes.ac.uk *Research & development consultants*

Institute Of Public Relations, 32 St James's Square, London, SW1Y 4JR Tel: (020) 7766 3333 Fax: (020) 7766 3344 E-mail: info@cipr.co.uk *Professional body for public relations practitioners*

Institute of Quality Assurance, 12 Grosvenor Crescent, London, SW1X 7EE Tel: (020) 7245 6722 Fax: (020) 7245 6788 E-mail: enquiry@iqa.org *Quality assurance training services*

Institute Of Sales Promotion, Arena House, 66-68 Pentonville Road, London, N1 9HS Tel: (020) 7837 5340 Fax: (020) 7837 5326 E-mail: enquiries@isp.org.uk *Sales promotion trade association*

Institute Of Sheet Metal Engineering, 48 Holloway Head, Birmingham, B1 1NG Tel: 0121-622 2860 Fax: 0121-666 6316 E-mail: admin@instituteofmetalfinishing.org *Professional body representing surface engineers*

Institute of Transport Administration, Iota House, 7 St. Leonards Road, Horsham, West Sussex, RH13 6EH Tel: (01403) 242412 Fax: (01403) 242413 E-mail: director.iota@btclick.com *Professional transport institute*

Institute Of Vehicle Engineers, 31 Redstone Farm Road, Birmingham, B28 9NU Tel: 0121-778 4354 Fax: 0121-702 2615 E-mail: sales@sae-uk.org *Institute vehicle industries*

Institution of Agricultural Engineers, Barton Road, Silsoe, MK45 4FH Tel: (01525) 861096 Fax: (01525) 861660 E-mail: crw@iagre.org *Professional association*

Institution Of Civil Engineers, Great George Street, London, SW1P 3AA Tel: (020) 7222 7722 Fax: (020) 7222 7500 *Trade association* Also at: London EC1

Institution Of Diesel & Gas Turbine Engineers, Bedford Heights, Brickhill Drive, Bedford, MK41 7PH Tel: (01234) 214340 Fax: (01234) 355493 E-mail: sales@idgte.org *Professional institute*

The Institution Of Engineering & Technology Benevolent Fund, Michael Faraday House, Stevenage, Hertfordshire, SG1 2AY Tel: (01438) 313311 Fax: (01438) 313465 E-mail: postmaster@theiat.org *Publications division & professional engineers*

Institution of Incorporated Engineers, Savoy Hill House, Savoy Hill, London, WC2R 0BS Tel: (020) 7836 3357 E-mail: postmaster@theiet.org.uk *Trade association agents*

Institution of Fire Engineers, 148 Upper New Walk, Leicester, LE1 7QB Tel: 0116-255 3654 Fax: 0116-247 1231 E-mail: info@ife.org.uk *Professional body & fire engineers*

Institution Of Occupational Safety & Health, The Grange, Highfield Drive, Wigston, Leicestershire, LE18 1NN Tel: 0116-257 3100 Fax: 0116-257 3101 *Professional association*

Institution of Structural Engineers, 11 Upper Belgrave Street, London, SW1X 8BH Tel: (020) 7235 4535 Fax: (020) 7235 4294 E-mail: mail@istructe.org.uk *Professional institution*

Instock Disposables Ltd, Howe Moss Drive, Kirkhill Industrial Estate, Dyce, Aberdeen, AB21 0GL Tel: (01224) 723823 Fax: (01224) 725586 *Offshore supply & catering services* Also at: Inverness

Instone Air Services Ltd, Charity Farm, Pulborough Road, Cootham, Pulborough, West Sussex, RH20 4HP Tel: (01903) 740101 Fax: (01903) 740102 E-mail: sales@instoneair.com *Livestock export & air freight*

▶ Instone Labels Ltd, 5 Weighbridge Row, Cardiff Road, Reading, RG1 8LX Tel: 0118-956 8661 Fax: 0118-956 8662 E-mail: sales@instonelabels.com *Self adhesive tape manufrs*

▶ Instore Field Marketing, Blockhouse Close, Worcester, WR1 2BT Tel: (01905) 726079 Fax: (01905) 611063 *Field marketing agency*

Instore Merchandising & Demonstrating, 1 Wallace Avenue, Lisburn, County Antrim, BT27 4AA Tel: (028) 9267 4215 Fax: (028) 9267 2015 *Recruitment agency*

Instra Textiles, 37 Equity Road, Leicester, LE3 0AS Tel: 0116-255 1588 Fax: 0116-255 1589 E-mail: instra@amserve.net *Hosiery distributors & manufrs*

Instro Precision Ltd, Hornet Close, Pysons Road Industrial Estate, Broadstairs, Kent, CT10 2YD Tel: (01843) 604455 Fax: (01843) 861032 E-mail: marketing@instro.com *Optical instrument manufrs*

Instromet, Charlotte Street, Melton Mowbray, Leicestershire, LE13 1NA Tel: (01664) 567797 Fax: (01664) 410254 E-mail: sales@instrometuk.co.uk *Flow control manufrs*

Instron, Coronation Road, High Wycombe, Buckinghamshire, HP12 3SY Tel: (01494) 464646 Fax: (01494) 456123 E-mail: info_news@instron.com *Manufacturers of test equipment*

Instrotech Ltd, Unit A Penfold Trading Estate, Imperial Way, Watford, WD24 4YY Tel: (01923) 442244 Fax: (01923) 252959 E-mail: sales@instrotech.com *Test equipment distributors*

Instrucomm Ltd, 2a Crosier Court, Upchurch, Sittingbourne, Kent, ME9 7AR Tel: (01634) 376147 Fax: (01634) 376147 *Industrial services contractors*

Instrumatics I & E Ltd, Unit 7 Ash Holt Industrial Estat, Bank End Road Finningley, Finningley, Doncaster, South Yorkshire, DN9 3NT Tel: (01302) 772999 Fax: (01302) 770000 E-mail: instrufabb@btconnect.com *Process control systems engineers*

Instrument Component Labels Ltd, Unit L1, Beversbrook Centre, Redman Road, Calne, Wiltshire, SN11 9PR Tel: (01249) 822010 Fax: (01249) 821330 E-mail: robertbromley@ic-labels.com *Screen printed labels services*

Instrument & Control Services Ltd, Unit 2, Westlake Trading Estate, Canal Lane, Stoke-on-Trent, ST6 4NZ Tel: (01782) 819900 Fax: (01782) 575190 E-mail: admin@icsluk.com *Electrical engineering*

Instrument & Gauges Electronics Ltd, Gravel Lane, Banks, Southport, Merseyside, PR9 8DE Tel: (01704) 505333 Fax: (01704) 505334 E-mail: sales@instruments-gauges.co.uk *Thermometer & gauge manufrs*

Instrument Plastics Ltd, 33-37 Kings Grove Industrial Estate, Kings Grove, Maidenhead, Berkshire, SL6 4DP Tel: (01628) 770018 Fax: (01628) 773299 E-mail: sales@instrumentplastics.co.uk *One of the world's leading designers & manufacturers of high quality Optical Filters & Shielded Windows for electronic displays. ISO 9001. IPL specialise in custom-made EMI /RFI Shielded, Contrast Enhancement & Infra Red broadband filters. Optolite clear HSR (High Scratch Resistance) & Optolite Acrylic material is cast in-house & filters are fabricated to any specification. Offering includes cutting, machining, shaping, silk-screening & technical advice at the design stage. Our Optolite material is recommended for LCD's, as it has up to 20 times the scratch resistance of acrylic, combined with optical properties similar to Crown Glass. It is also virtually immune to most common chemicals, some nerve agents & can operate at temperatures up to 100°C. Our filters are provided in a range of standard colours, bespoke thicknesses & a variety of standard or non glare surface finishes. Quality Assurance is paramount through 100% visual inspection.*

Instrument Repair Service, 35 Radcliffe Road, West Bridgford, Nottingham, NG2 5FF Tel: 0115-981 9988 Fax: 0115-945 5358 E-mail: info@irs-gb.com *Vehicle instruments repairs*

▶ Instrument Repairs & Calibration, 7 Howard Court, Nerston Industrial Estate, East Kilbride, Glasgow, G74 4QZ Tel: (01355) 264120 Fax: (01355) 264150

Instrument Solutions, Old Bracknell Lane West, Bracknell, Berkshire, RG12 7AH Tel: (01344) 459314 Fax: (01344) 714868 E-mail: sales@bis.fm *Calibrating services*

Instrument Solutions, The Laurels, The Square, Angmering, Littlehampton, West Sussex, BN16 4EA Tel: (01903) 856846 Fax: (01903) 856516 E-mail: info@instrumentsolutions.com *Electronic design & manufacture*

Instrument Technology Ltd, Menzies Road, Ponswood Industrial Estate, St. Leonards-On-Sea, East Sussex, TN38 9BB Tel: (01424) 442121 Fax: (01424) 719696 E-mail: sales@itl-vacuum.com *Manufacturers of high vacuum equipment*

Instrument Transformers Ltd, 8 Lithgow Place, East Kilbride, Glasgow, G74 1PW Tel: (01355) 236057 Fax: (01355) 239259 E-mail: sales@itl-uk.com Principal Export Areas: Worldwide *Transformers manufrs & crimping tool distributors*

Instrumentation & Control Services, Unit 3 The Old Forge, Peterchurch, Hereford, HR2 0SD Tel: (01981) 550011 Fax: (01981) 550955 E-mail: ics@ics-hereford.co.uk *Manufacturers of prepared cable & wire assemblies*

Instrumentation Laboratory UK Ltd, Kelvin Close, Birchwood, Warrington, WA3 7PB Tel: (01925) 810141 Fax: (01925) 826708 E-mail: sales@il.com *Medical analytical equipment distributors*

Instrumentation Safety Services Ltd, 173 Hall Road, Lowestoft, Suffolk, NR32 3NR Tel: (01502) 500108 Fax: 01502 500108 *Petrochemical Engineers*

Instruments & Controls Hull, Faraday Works, Crowle Street, Hull, HU9 1RH Tel: (01482) 225607 Fax: (01482) 217122 E-mail: sales@instco.co.uk Principal Export Areas: Worldwide *Distributors of sensors & recording instrument charts*

Instruments Direct (Services) Ltd, Unit 8 The Courtyard, Stenson Road, Coalville, Leicestershire, LE67 4jp Tel: (01530) 832500 Fax: (01530) 817087 E-mail: sales@inds.co.uk *Suppliers of Industrial Instrumentaton. Specialise in Flow Meters and environmental measuring equipment*

Instruments To Industry Ltd, Woodward Road, Knowsley Industrial Park North, Knowsley Industrial Park, Liverpool, L33 7UZ Tel: 0151-546 4943 Fax: 0151-548 6262 E-mail: sales@ituk.com *Manufacturers of industrial thermometers & maintenance*

Instyle Leather Goods Ltd, Publicity House, Tweedy Lane, Newport, Gwent, NP19 8DZ Tel: (01633) 282412 Fax: (01633) 282413 E-mail: m-freeman@btinternet.com *Specialists in*

continued

the manufacture of 3D polyurethane domed labels. Wide format digital colour printers of vinyls and banner materials. Quick deliveries, low prices. Specialist CNC engravers. Please contact us for a quote.

Instyle Leather Goods Ltd, Publicity House, Tweedy Lane, Newport, Gwent, NP19 8DZ Tel: (01633) 282412 Fax: (01633) 282413 E-mail: sales@watchstraps-uk.com *Manufacturers of leather watchstraps & keyrings*

Insu, Unit 305, 183A Harrow Road, London, E11 3PX Tel: (020) 8534 4073 Fax: (020) 8555 3870 E-mail: sales@insu.co.uk *Blinds manufacturers & shading products*

▶ Insubuild Direct, 2 Cross Lane, Bradford, West Yorkshire, BD4 0SG Tel: (01274) 653333 Fax: (01274) 653444 E-mail: sales@insubuild.co.uk *Insulation installers to the new build market*

▶ Insu-Build Direct Ltd, Unit 17, Symondscliffe Way, Portskewett, Caldicot, Gwent, NP26 5PW Tel: (01291) 420007 Fax: (01291) 430548 E-mail: wales@insubuild.co.uk *Insulation installers to the new build market*

▶ Insuheat Ltd, Bay 2 Tractor Spares Industrial Estate, Strawberry Lane, Willenhall, West Midlands, WV13 3RN Tel: (01902) 603334 Fax: (01902) 604442 E-mail: admin@insuheat.co.uk *Cavity wall insulation, loft insulation services*

Insulated Tools Ltd, Charlwoods Road, East Grinstead, West Sussex, RH19 2HR Tel: (01342) 324255 Fax: (01342) 327115 E-mail: enquiries@insulatedtools.co.uk *Insulated hand tools for live line working, tested at 10,000 volts ac, recommended for use up to 1,000 volts.*

Insulation Ltd, 6 Kerse Road, Stirling, FK7 7RW Tel: (01786) 451170 Fax: (01786) 451245 *Glass fibre products for industry*

Insulation Machine Services, Coalbrookdale Road, Clayhill Light Industrial Park, Neston, CH64 3UG Tel: 0151-336 7242 Fax: 0151-336 2840 E-mail: timco@imsservices.freeserve.co.uk *Insulating material & thermal production machinery*

Insulation & Machining Services Ltd, Russell Road, Southport, Merseyside, PR9 7SB Tel: (01704) 226878 Fax: (01704) 225857 E-mail: sales@ims-insulation.com *Stockists & machinists of thermal & electrical insulation materials*

▶ Insurance for Car Hire, Trans-World House, 0 City Road, London, EC1Y 2BP Tel: (020) 7012 6300 Fax: (020) 7012 6315 E-mail: iskra@webfactory.bg *Car rental insurances in Europe, USA, Canada, Australia & New Zealand, South Africa: CDW (Collision Damage Waiver), SLI (Supplemental Liability Insurance), LDW (Loss Damage Waiver).*

▶ Insurance Now, 413 Chingford Road, London, E17 5AF Tel: (020) 8531 5336 E-mail: enquiries@insurancenow.com *Online quotes for car insurance, home insurance, business insurance, travel insurance and pet insurance.*

▶ Insurance Repair Solutions Ltd, Unit 6 Beta Terrace, Masterlord Business Park, West Road, Ransomes Europark, Ipswich, IP3 9SX Tel: (0870) 7607607 Fax: (0870) 7607607 E-mail: info@insurancerepairsolutions.co.uk *Fire, flood, escape of water, impact, storm & oil contamination. Most of our work is carried out on domestic properties. Our client list includes national insurance companies, loss adjusters, policyholders, building surveyors, architects & structural engineers. For policyholders, we are pleased to submit a quotation for repairs to your insurance company and, if required, manage the claim on your behalf. Please do not hesitate to contact us for more information. We look forward to being of assistance.*

Insurance Technology Solutions Ltd, International House, 1 St. Katharines Way, London, E1W 1UN Tel: (020) 7553 2500 Fax: (020) 7702 3074 E-mail: sales@intechsolutions.co.uk *Software & networking solutions*

Insure Shop, 2 Brook Square, Rugeley, Staffordshire, WS15 2DR Tel: (01889) 583339 Fax: (01889) 575817 *General insurance brokers*

▶ Insurepair Glasgow Ltd, 24 Lochleven Road, Glasgow, G42 9JU Tel: 0141-649 6969 Fax: 0141-636 6748

▶ Insutech Scotland Ltd, 21 Ainslie Road, Hillington Industrial Estate, Glasgow, G52 4RU Tel: 0141-892 2000 Fax: 0141-892 2200 *Fabricate aluminium framing*

▶ InSync Retail Business Solutions, The Dairy,, Old Brookend Farm, Hurley, Atherstone, Warwickshire, CV9 2JP Tel: 01827 873899 Fax: 01827 872647 E-mail: sales@insync-rbs.com *EPoS solution providers for Microsoft Retail Management System*

Insys Services Ltd, Reddings Wood, Ampthill, Bedford, MK45 2HD Tel: (01525) 843661 Fax: (01525) 843766 *Defence engineering services, manufacturing capability (machining, assembly & filament wound composites)*

▶ Inta Computer Trading Ltd, 22 Alfreton Road, Derby, DE21 4AS Tel: (01332) 616091 Fax: (01332) 200997 *Computer maintenance & repairer engineers*

Inta-Act Ltd, Littleleys, Gosden Common, Bramley, Guildford, Surrey, GU5 0AQ Tel: (01483) 891040 E-mail: cpeatroy@inta-act.co.uk *CRM specialists*

▶ Intaconnet, Unit 40, New Greenham Park, Greenham, Thatcham, Berkshire, RG19 6HW Tel: (01635) 529803 Fax: (01635) 523678 E-mail: info@intaconnet.co.uk *Computer system consultants*

▶ Intact Electronics Ltd, 455 Chorley Old Road, Bolton, BL1 6AH Tel: (01204) 491000 Fax: (01204) 455575 *Security services*

▶ Intak Ltd, Unit 41, Criftin Park, Oxton Road, Epperstone, Nottingham, NG14 6AT Tel: 0115-965 6598 Fax: 0115-956 6546 E-mail: info@intak.co.uk *Manufacture public address systems*

Intake Engineering Ltd, Wingham Industrial Estate, Goodnestone Road, Wingham, Canterbury, Kent, CT3 1AR Tel: (01227) 720282 Fax: (01227) 728398 E-mail: contact@intakeengineering.co.uk *Wire race bearings*

Intalect Ltd, Office 7, Grange Farm Business Park, Newtown Unthank, Leicester, LE9 9FL Tel: (0845) 6448860 Fax: (0845) 6448861 E-mail: info@intalect.co.uk *IT support*

Intama Ltd, The Courtyard, High Street, Chobham, Surrey, GU25 8AF Tel: (01252) 815666 Fax: (01252) 815666 *Computer consultants, e-commerce & security*

Intamet Ltd, Unit 11 The iO Centre, Stephenson Rd, Segensworth, Fareham, Hampshire, PO15 5RU Tel: (01329) 843355 Fax: (01329) 847799 E-mail: sales@intamet.co.uk Principal Export Areas: Central/East Europe *Specialist independent stockholders and worldwide distributors of seamless and welded stainless steel tubes, pipes and long products. Including:- hollow bars, channels, T section, beams, square and rectangular tubes. Extensive range of "H" grade material. Full range of polished tubes including oval tubes and fittings for balustrade markets. In-house cutting services.*

▶ Intamission, Thames Court, 1 Victoria Street, Windsor, Berkshire, SL4 1YB Tel: (01753) 626860 Fax: (01753) 626861 E-mail: info@intamission.com *Middleware software developers*

Intandem Systems Ltd, Watton Farm, Watton Lane, Droxford, Southampton, SO32 3QU Tel: (01489) 877630 Fax: (01489) 877632 E-mail: inbox@intandem.org.uk *Air conditioning control manufrs*

▶ Intangible Business Ltd, Tower Bridge Road, London, SE1 3LJ Tel: (0870) 2407386 E-mail: info@intangiblebusiness.com *Intangible Business was set up in 2001 to fill the need for an independent approach to brand valuation, brand strategy and brand development. As well as experts in brand valuation, Intangible Business is now an internationally recognised market leader in all intangible asset valuation.**

Inta-Trac UK Ltd, Little London, Halifax, West Yorkshire, HX3 7ST Tel: (01422) 206333 Fax: (01422) 204486 E-mail: sales@intatrac.co.uk *Tractor spare parts distributors*

Intavent Orthofix Ltd, Burney Court, Cordwallis Park, Maidenhead, Berkshire, SL6 7BZ Tel: (01628) 594500 Fax: (01628) 789400 E-mail: enquiries@intaventorthofix.com *Medical products distributors*

Intavia Ltd, 1 The Brunel Centre, Newton Road, Crawley, West Sussex, RH10 9TU Tel: (01293) 544706 Fax: (01293) 615800 E-mail: aia@intavia.co.uk *Administration for cargo airline*

Intec, 35 Trelowarren Street, Camborne, Cornwall, TR14 8AD Tel: (01209) 716717 Fax: (01209) 610580 *Electrical retail agents*

Intec Business Colleges, 16 Warwick Street, Rugby, Warwickshire, CV21 3DH Tel: (01788) 575090 Fax: (01788) 575411 E-mail: intec@ibc-rugby.demon.co.uk *Training providers*

Intec Laser Services, Woolaston Road, Park Farm North, Redditch, Worcestershire, B98 7SG Tel: (01527) 518550 Fax: (01527) 518551 E-mail: sales@intec.uk.net *Services include cutting and fabrication of a wide variety of materials including Brass, Aluminium and Stainless Steel, including - Flat Bed, 5-Axis & Tubular laser cutting; Water Jet cutting; CNC Punching; CNC Forming; Mig & Tig Welding.*

▶ Intec Microsystems Ltd, Unit 32, The Business Centre, 20 James Road,, Tyseley, Birmingham, B11 2BA Tel: 0121-707 2121 Fax: 0121-707 4242 E-mail: sales@intecmicros.co.uk *Computer software & hardware retailers*

Intec Storage & Partitioning, 21 Green Lane, Stapleton, Leicester, LE9 8JP Tel: (01455) 841698 Fax: (01455) 841769 *Partitions & ceilings distributors*

Intec Systems Ltd, Intec House, St. Nicholas Close, Fleet, Hampshire, GU51 4JA Tel: (01252) 775400 Fax: (01252) 775444 E-mail: info@intec.co.uk *IT consultants*

Intec Systems Blackburn Ltd, 12 Strawberry Bank, Blackburn, BB2 6AA Tel: (01254) 667106 Fax: (01254) 675925 E-mail: sales@intec-systems.co.uk *Software developers*

Intec Telecom Systems plc, 2 Wells Court, Albert Drive, Woking, Surrey, GU21 5UB Tel: (01483) 745800 Fax: (01483) 745860 E-mail: sales@intec-telecom-systems.com *Software telecommunications*

▶ INTECH, Nant Yr Ynys, Llanpumsaint, Carmarthen, SA33 6LJ Tel: (07092) 872570 Fax: (07092) 872733 E-mail: admin@insteptechnology.net *INTECH is an innovative company offering dynamic powerful web technology suitable for small and medium sized businesses and organisations. Affordable professional e-commerce website created in less than 5 minutes. Do-it-yourself online business websites. Professional design studio with online managers console. Easy to use no programming. It's a snap to create an almost instant internet website. Free 15 day trial. Free domain name. Free technical support.* *

Intech Automation Ltd, Willow Hall Works Cote Hill, Halifax, West Yorkshire, HX2 7LZ Tel: (01422) 355885 Fax: (01422) 355885 *Control panel manufrs*

Inteck Automation Ltd, 9 Cotswold Avenue, Ipswich, IP1 4LL Tel: (07971) 885823 Fax: (01473) 286714 E-mail: inteck@aol.com *System automation & control*

Inteck Products Ltd, 42 Sheephouse Road, Maidenhead, Berkshire, SL6 8EX Tel: (01628) 771101 Fax: (01628) 637426 E-mail: sales@inteck.co.uk *Plastic products*

▶ Integer Consulting, Sussex House, 6 The Forbury, Reading, RG1 3EJ Tel: 0118-925 3336 Fax: 0118-925 3326

▶ Integer Research, 55 Farringdon Road, London, EC1M 3JB Tel: (020) 7092 8100 Fax: (020) 7503 1266 E-mail: sales@integer-research.com *London based Publishing and Consultancy company. Provide a range of strategy and financial benckmark reports on world's leading metals, mining and chemical companies.*

▶ Integra Ltd, 16 Bloomsbury Street, Brighton, BN2 1HQ Tel: (01273) 606565 Fax: (01273) 608721

Integra Buildings Ltd, Main Street, Burstwick, Hull, HU12 9EA Tel: (01964) 626761 Fax: (01964) 626762 E-mail: sales@integrabuildings.co.uk *Building engineering services*

▶ Integra Composites, Unit 8 The Sidings, Wilford Bridge Road, Melton, Woodbridge, Suffolk, IP12 1RB Tel: (01394) 385838 Fax: (01394) 380919 E-mail: sg@integracomposites.co.uk *Manufacturer of carbon*

Integra Contracts Ltd, 119-123 Hackford Road, London, SW9 0QT Tel: (020) 7820 1800 Fax: (020) 7820 1182 E-mail: icl@integracontracts.co.uk *Partitions, office fitters & suspended ceilings suppliers & installers*

Integra Neurosciences, Newbury Road, Andover, Hampshire, SP10 4DR Tel: (01264) 345700 Fax: (01264) 332113 E-mail: sales@integra-is.com *Medical equipment manufrs*

▶ Integral, 1290 Aztec West, Almondsbury, Bristol, BS32 4SG Tel: (01454) 278900 Fax: (01454) 201169

Integral, Broadoak Business Park, Ashburton Road West, Trafford Park, Manchester, M17 1RW Tel: 0161-872 7925 Fax: 0161-872 9508 *Building maintenance services*

Integral, Norris House, Crawhall Road, Newcastle upon Tyne, NE1 2BB Tel: 0191-261 1071 Fax: 0191-232 8069 E-mail: mnew@integral.co.uk *Building service, maintenance & facility management company*

Integral Geotechnique Ltd, West End House, Blackfriars Road, Nailsea, Bristol, BS48 4DJ Tel: (01275) 810580 Fax: (01275) 810581 *Geotechnical & environmental consultants*

Integral Geotechnique (Wales) Ltd, 50 Cathedral Road, Cardiff, CF11 9LL Tel: (029) 2022 0462 Fax: (029) 2034 0789 E-mail: mail@intregralgeotec.com *Geotechnical consultancy*

▶ Integral Mobile Data, Pembroke House, Ty Coch Lane, Llantarnam Park Way, Cwmbran, Gwent, NP44 3AU Tel: (0870) 0801808 Fax: (0870) 0801809 *Software*

▶ Integral Solutions, Rhumhor, Carrick Castle, Lochgoilhead, Cairndow, Argyll, PA24 8AF Tel: (0845) 6444990 Fax: (07092) 117060 E-mail: info@integral-solutions.net *Integral Solutions - Internet Consultancy, Web Design, Virtual Tours*

▶ Integralis, Chadwick House, Warrington Road, Warrington, WA3 6AE Tel: (01925) 854444 Fax: (01925) 854455 *Computer security system suppliers*

Integranet Networking Services Ltd, 71 High Street, Harrold, Bedford, MK43 7BJ Tel: (01234) 721755 E-mail: info@integranet.co.uk *Software distributor & computer consultants*

▶ Integrapak Ltd, Weybourne House, Lenten Street, Alton, Hampshire, GU34 1HH Tel: (01420) 593680 Fax: (01420) 593694 E-mail: info@integrapak.co.uk *Headquartered in Hampshire, the IGM Group has rapidly grown to become a leading provider of printing and packaging machinery to a broad portfolio of industry sectors within the United Kingdom and Ireland.*

▶ Integrate Software, 18 Knightsbridge, Northwich, Cheshire, CW9 8GE Tel: (0845) 1249800 *Support for hardware & software*

Integratech Ltd, 1 Wainwright Road, Worcester, WR4 9FA Tel: (0870) 3661366 Fax: (0870) 3661333 E-mail: info@integratech.co.uk *Computer consultants*

Integrated Broadcast Information Systems Ltd, The Maltings, Charlton Road, Shepton Mallet, Somerset, BA4 5QE Tel: (07002) 255424 Fax: (07002) 329424 E-mail: sales@ibistv.co.uk *Software for broadcasting industry*

▶ Integrated Building Management Ltd, West Atrium, Mercury Court, Tithebarn Street, Liverpool, L2 2QP Tel: 0151-236 8555

Integrated Building Management Systems Ltd, Brunel Drive, Newark, Nottinghamshire, NG24 1SF Tel: (01636) 674875 Fax: (01636) 612228 E-mail: controls@integratedbms.co.uk *Integrated building management system manufrs*

Integrated Building Services Design Partnership plc, Newton House Cambridge Business Park, Cowley Road, Cambridge, CB4 0WZ Tel: (01223) 436600 Fax: (01223) 436601 E-mail: mail@ibs-plc.co.uk *Design engineers of mechanical & electrical installations services*

▶ Integrated Business Systems Ltd, 24 Cottesbrook Park, Heartlands Business Park, Daventry, Northamptonshire, NN11 8YL Tel: (01327) 302999 Fax: (01327) 302990 E-mail: info@integratedbsl.com *Telecommunications*

▶ Integrated Cinema Experience, 11 Chatteris Close, Stoke-on-Trent, ST3 7TX Tel: 01782 399317 Fax: 01782 399317 E-mail: icexperience@yahoo.com *Unique handcrafted home cinema and audio furniture for the home, office, or retail outlet including bespoke and freestanding designs. High quality plasma lift furniture.*

Integrated Circles Ltd, 8 Lebanon Road, London, SW18 1RE Tel: (020) 8874 6666 Fax: (020) 8870 4387 E-mail: info@integrated-circles.com *Audio visual equipment manufrs*

Integrated Communications (Scotland) Ltd, Meikle Road, Kirkton Campus, Livingston, West Lothian, EH54 7DE Tel: (01506) 410780 Fax: (01506) 425400 E-mail: sales@icsscotland.com *Telecommunication equipment sales & maintenance services*

Integrated Computer Services (Scotland) Ltd, 105a Shore Rd, Innellan, Dunoon, Argyll, PA23 7SR Tel: (01369) 830647 Fax: (01369) 830783 E-mail: ics_ltd@netcomuk.co.uk *Analysis of data to determine the durability & efficiency of process plants, vehicle & marine structures*

Integrated Control Systems Ltd, Millars Business Centre, Fishponds Close, Wokingham, Berkshire, RG41 2TZ Tel: 0118-977 2226 Fax: 0118-977 4999 E-mail: sales@icsbms.co.uk *Control panel installation & manufrs*

Integrated Display Systems Ltd, Unit 15, Muarice Road, Wallsend, Tyne & Wear, NE28 6BY Tel: 0191-262 0091 Fax: 0191-262 0091 E-mail: sales@clavis.co.uk *Electronic equipment manufrs*

Integrated Electronic Services, 31 Church Street, Warrington, WA1 2SX Tel: (01925) 652065 Fax: (01925) 650565 E-mail: bjs@ies.ndirect.co.uk *Electronic design & development*

Integrated Energy Systems Ltd, 11a Lune Street, Preston, PR1 2NL Tel: (01772) 250707 Fax: (01772) 258322 E-mail: admin@intergratedenergy.co.uk *Energy consulting engineers*

Integrated Engineering Solutions Ltd, Millbrook Road West, Southampton, SO15 0HW Tel: (023) 8090 5020 Fax: (023) 8070 4073 E-mail: mail@iesl.co.uk *Electronic design consultants*

▶ Integrated Fabrications Ltd, Tavr Drill Hall, Baron Street, Rochdale, Lancashire, OL16 1SJ Tel: (01706) 716670 Fax: (01706) 716601 E-mail: sales@intercompanies.co.uk *Metal fabrication engineer services*

Integrated Geochemical Interpretation, Hallsannery, Bideford, Devon, EX39 5HE Tel: (01237) 471749 Fax: (01237) 421700 E-mail: info@hallsannery.co.uk *Software manufrs*

Integrated Manufacturing Systems, Nelson Street, Rotherham, South Yorkshire, S65 1ET Tel: (01709) 839933 Fax: (01709) 838848 E-mail: info@ims-uniplan.co.uk *Computer development services*

Integrated Media Installations Ltd, Unit K, Manaway Business Park, Holder Road, Aldershot, Hampshire, GU12 4RH Tel: (01252) 350280 Fax: (01252) 350682 E-mail: intermediainstalls@imi-ltd.co.uk *Electronic installation engineer's*

Integrated Micro Systems Ltd, 49 Riverside, Medway City Estate, Rochester, Kent, ME2 4DP Tel: (01634) 714285 Fax: (01634) 715298 *Integrated circuit designers & suppliers*

▶ Integrated Monitoring & Maintenance Services Ltd, 46 Alnwickhill Drive, Edinburgh, EH16 6XX Tel: 0131-664 5052

Integrated Office Systems Ltd, Unit 89 Willows Court, Thornaby, Stockton-on-Tees, Cleveland, TS17 9PP Tel: (01642) 751444 Fax: (01642) 761444 E-mail: enquiries@iosltd.co.uk *Office suppliers*

Integrated Piggery Systems Ltd, Showfield Lane, Malton, North Yorkshire, YO17 6BT Tel: (01653) 694994 Fax: (01653) 696685 E-mail: ipsltd@fsmail.net *Specialist agricultural builders*

Integrated Power Technology UK Ltd, 37 Jubilee Drive, Loughborough, Leicestershire, LE11 5XS Tel: (01509) 556655 Fax: (01509) 557755 E-mail: info@ipt.co.uk *Computer batteries, ups generators, maintenance bypass switches*

Integrated Recycling Systems Ltd, Burnt Meadow Road, North Moons Moat, Redditch, Worcestershire, B98 9PA Tel: (01527) 65432 Fax: (01527) 65868 E-mail: info@mastermagnets.co.uk *Magnetic equipment & recycling equipment manufrs*

Integrated Solutions, New Enterprise House, 149-151 High Road, Chadwell Heath, Romford, RM6 6PL Tel: (020) 8599 8866 Fax: (020) 8597 5971 *Retail computer software & equipment*

Integrated Technologies UK, 30 Coppice Road, Poynton, Stockport, Cheshire, SK12 1SL Tel: (01625) 877249 Fax: (01625) 858825 E-mail: cj.intech@btinternet.com *Electronic contract manufrs*

▶ Integrated Vision Systems Ltd, 38 Mill Road, Ely, Cardiff, CF5 4AG Tel: (0808)) 2026666 Fax: (0871) 2771909 E-mail: info@insightwalesandwest.com *Machine Vision*Automated Inspection*Factory automation*DVT certified integrator*0% inspection*

Integration Services Ltd, 119 Kingston Road, Leatherhead, Surrey, KT22 7SU Tel: (01372) 227400 Fax: (01372) 225120 E-mail: sales@isluk.com *Computer consultants*

Integrator Software Services Ltd, 15 Stafford Street, Edinburgh, EH3 7BR Tel: 0131-718 2400 Fax: 0131-718 2434 *Recruitment consultants*

Integrex Ltd, Portwood Industrial Estate, Church Gresley, Swadlincote, Derbyshire, DE11 9PT Tel: (01283) 550880 Fax: (01283) 552028 E-mail: sales@integrex.co.uk *Reseller of computers*

Integrity Services Ltd, 23 Sandy Lane, Aston, Birmingham, B6 5TP Tel: 0121-327 2872 Fax: 0121-327 0454 E-mail: sales@integrityservices.co.uk *Business machine wholesalers*

Integrity Software Systems Ltd, Crockham Park, Main Road, Edenbridge, Kent, TN8 6SR Tel: (01732) 867555 Fax: (01732) 867115 *Salon management computer software*

Integrity Software Systems Ltd, Centenary House, Whisby Way, Lincoln, LN6 3LQ Tel: (01522) 887200 E-mail: lincolncall@integrity-software.net *Write software*

Intek Electronics, 248 Ashley Road, Poole, Dorset, BH14 9BZ Tel: (01202) 716091 Fax: (01202) 716092 E-mail: info@intek-electronics.co.uk *Sound lighting visual & cctv specialists*

Intek Europe, 24 Thomas Drive, Newport Pagnell, Buckinghamshire, MK16 8TH Tel: (01908) 610093 E-mail: sales@intek.co.uk *Technical training services*

Intek Services Ltd, Smalls Hill Road, Norwood Hill, Horley, Surrey, RH6 0HR Tel: (01293) 863434 Fax: (01293) 863252 E-mail: trevor@intekservices.co.uk *Scientific instrumentation*

Intel Investments UK Ltd, Pipers Way, Swindon, SN3 1RJ Tel: (01793) 403000 Fax: (01793) 641440 *Microprocessor systems manufrs*

Intelek Properties Ltd, South Marston Park, South Marston Park, Swindon, SN3 4TR Tel: (01793) 827000 Fax: (01793) 827578 E-mail: sales@intelek.plc.uk *Holding company*

Intellect, Russell Square House, 10-12 Russell Square, London, WC1B 5EE Tel: (020) 7331 2000 Fax: (020) 7331 2040 E-mail: info@intellectuk.org *Consumer electronics & telecom sectors manufrs*

Intellect Computers, 12 Scarsdale Place, Buxton, Derbyshire, SK17 6EF Tel: (01298) 70055 Fax: (01298) 70066 E-mail: enquiries@oxin.net *Computer sales*

Intellect Security Ltd, 10 The Hub Station Road, Henley-on-Thames, Oxfordshire, RG9 1AY Tel: (01491) 411698 Fax: (01491) 411415 E-mail: sales@intellect.co.uk *Software resellers*

Intellectual Property Office, Patent Office, Concept House, Cardiff Road, Newport, Gwent, NP10 8QQ Tel: (0645) 500505 Fax: (01633) 817777 E-mail: enquiries@ipo.gov.uk *Administration of intellectual property system*

Intellident, Southgate Centre Two, Wilmslow Road, Heald Green, Cheadle, Cheshire, SK8 3PW Tel: 0161-436 9950 Fax: 0161-436 8787 E-mail: sales@intellident.co.uk Sales Contact: R. Moorman *Intellident has over 20 years experience in the design and integration of automatic data capture and asset-tracking solutions RFID, barcoding & mobile solutions.*

▶ Intelligent Access Systems Ltd, 16 Gladstone Terrace, Boldon Colliery, Tyne & Wear, NE35 9HL Tel: 0191-536 9255 Fax: 0191-536 9255 E-mail: laurance.laidlaw@homecall.co.uk *Access control units suppliers*

Intelligent Business Strategies Ltd, Springfield House, Water Lane, Wilmslow, Cheshire, SK9 5BG Tel: (01625) 520700 Fax: (01625) 520700 *Computer consultants*

Intelligent Communications, Market Hall, Market Street, Colne, Lancashire, BB8 0HS Tel: (01282) 864677 Fax: (01282) 860092 E-mail: sales@intelligent-marketing.co.uk *IT suppliers*

Intelligent Control Systems Ltd, 29-31 Gabriels Hill, Maidstone, Kent, ME15 6HZ Tel: (01622) 683830 Fax: (01622) 683025 *Electronic monitoring equipment*

Intelligent Corporate Machines Ltd, North Block, Westminster BSNS Square Durham Street, London, SE11 5JH Tel: (020) 7820 9777 Fax: (020) 7820 9860 E-mail: icmachines@aol.com *Computer suppliers & manufrs*

▶ Intelligent Fleet Ltd, Eden House, 101A Marsland Road, Sale, Cheshire, M33 3HS Tel: (0870) 2856125 Fax: (0870) 2856126 E-mail: mail@intelligentfleet.co.uk *Company vehicle fleet consultancy*

▶ Intelligent Health & Nutrition Consultancy, 4 Woodleys Yard, West Street, Aldbourne, Marlborough, Wiltshire, SN8 2BL Tel: (0800) 6526608

Intelligent Interfaces Ltd, PO Box 80, Eastleigh, Hampshire, SO53 2YX Tel: (023) 8026 1514 Fax: (0870) 0521281 E-mail: sales@intint.demon.co.uk *Scientific & engineering software & hardware designer & retailers*

▶ Intelligent Interiors, Focus House, 6 Tonbridge Road, Maidstone, Kent, ME16 8RP Tel: (01622) 351070 Fax: (01622) 686894

Intelligent Motion Control Ltd, 4 Brunel Close, Drayton Fields Industrial Estate, Daventry, Northamptonshire, NN11 8RB Tel: (01327) 307600 Fax: (01327) 300319 E-mail: info@inmoco.co.uk *Distributors & agents of motors, controllers & actuators*

▶ Intelligent Risk Management Ltd, PO Box 148, Kendal, Cumbria, LA9 7WY Tel: (01539) 736126 Fax: (01539) 736286 E-mail: david.arnold@i-rm.com *Risk management & project management*

▶ Intelligent Service, Unit 13, Marino Way, Finchampstead, Wokingham, Berkshire, RG40 4RF Tel: 0118-973 5050 Fax: 0118-973 5544 E-mail: nigel@4repair.co.uk *Disco lights*Disco equipment*lighting repairs**

Intelligroup Europe Ltd, 1 2 Challenge House, Sherwood Drive, Bletchley, Milton Keynes, MK3 6DP Tel: (01908) 443100 Fax: (01908) 443166 *Computer consultants*

▶ Intense Photoniques, 4 Stanley Boulevard, Hamilton Int Technology Park, Blantyre, Glasgow, G72 0BN Tel: (01698) 827000 Fax: (01698) 827262

Intension Canvas Goods, 6 Anchor Industrial Estate, Dumballs Road, Cardiff, CF10 5FF Tel: (029) 2023 2031 Fax: (029) 2038 3583 E-mail: sales@intension.co.uk *Industrial sewing & tensile structures manufrs*

Intensiv Filter (UK) Ltd, Bath House, Bath Street, Walsall, WS1 3DB Tel: (01922) 628893 Fax: (01922) 613875 E-mail: intensiv@intensiv-filter.co.uk *Manufacturers of dust collecting equipment*

Inter Active Software Services Ltd, Westwood House, Littleton Drive, Huntington, Cannock, Staffordshire, WS12 4TS Tel: (01543) 503611 Fax: (01543) 574566 E-mail: ifs@winteracter.com Principal Export Areas: Worldwide *Software developers*

Inter City Machine Tools (High Wycombe) Ltd, High Wycombe, Buckinghamshire, HP14 3WZ Tel: (01494) 485701 Fax: (01494) 485716 E-mail: sales@intercmt.co.uk *Machine tool merchants*

▶ Inter County Office Furniture, 20-21 Woodside Industrial Park, Works Road, Letchworth Garden City, Hertfordshire, SG6 1LA Tel: (01462) 675609 Fax: (01462) 687025 E-mail: sales@intercounty.com *Office furniture suppliers*

▶ Inter Dynamics, Friarton Bridge Park, 4 Friarton Road, Perth, PH2 8DD Tel: (01738) 626626

Inter Euro Polymers, 7/9 The Quadrangle, 57 Ruchill Street, Glasgow, G20 9PX Tel: 0141-946 1221 Fax: 0141-945 4546 E-mail: intereuro@btinternet.com *Polymer elastomer import' agents*

Inter Lec Ltd, Holland Hill, Low Road, North Wheatley, Retford, Nottinghamshire, DN22 9DS Tel: (01427) 880021 Fax: (01427) 880011 *Motor control panel manufrs*

▶ Inter Pack, 9 Cradock Road, Luton, LU4 0JF Tel: (01582) 570050 Fax: (01582) 570060 E-mail: sales@interpackltd.co.uk *Packaging material distributors*

Inter Print, Unit 3 Rivergate, Westlea, Swindon, SN5 7ET Tel: (01793) 613020 Fax: (01793) 436300 E-mail: sales@interprintswindon.co.uk *Commercial printing services*

Inter Regional Public Relations Ltd, Hill House, 20 Hill House Road, Norwich, NR1 4BE Tel: (01603) 627294 Fax: (01603) 633638 E-mail: pr@interregional.co.uk *Advertising agency*

Inter Steels Ltd, Darent Indust Park, Wallhouse Road, Erith, Kent, DA8 2JT Tel: (01322) 337766 Fax: (01322) 335662 E-mail: sales@intergroupofcompanies.net *Steel fabricators*

Inter Weave Textiles, Whitwell Green Lane, Elland, West Yorkshire, HX5 9BJ Tel: (0870) 2242468 Fax: (0870) 2242469 E-mail: enquiries@interweavetextiles.com *Textiles distributor*

Inter World Marketing, 17 Windermere Road, West End, Southampton, SO18 3PE Tel: (023) 8047 4243 Fax: (023) 8047 6821 E-mail: sales@interworldmarketing.net *Marketing & advertising agents*

Interactive, 84 Marsh Road, Rhyl, Clwyd, LL18 2AF Tel: (01745) 339331 Fax: (01745) 354494 E-mail: admin@womensevillage.co.uk *Computer training services*

Interactive Components, 2A Patrick Way, Aylesbury, Buckinghamshire, HP21 9XH Tel: (01296) 425656 Fax: (01296) 395332 E-mail: interactive@bucksnet.co.uk *Electronic component distributors or agents*

Interactive Data, Fitzroy House, 13/17 Epworth Street, London, EC2A 4DL Tel: (020) 7825 8000 Fax: (020) 7251 2725 E-mail: investorrelations@interactivedatercorp.com *Company information services*

Interactive Ideas Ltd, Centenary Estate, Jeffreys Road, Enfield, Middlesex, EN3 7HB Tel: (020) 8805 1000 Fax: (020) 8805 8962 E-mail: sales@interactiveideas.com *Computer software distributors*

Interactive Media Publications Ltd, 26 Rosebery Avenue, London, EC1R 4SX Tel: (020) 7837 3345 Fax: (020) 7837 8901 *Newsletter publishers*

Interactive Packaging Solutions Ltd, Unit 3 Ash Road North, Wrexham Industrial Estate, Wrexham, Clwyd, LL13 9JT Tel: (01978) 661671 Fax: (01978) 661681 E-mail: sales@ips-uk.co.uk *Packers & packing services*

Interactive Sound & Vision, 11 Ladywood Ave, Cove, Farnborough, Hants, GU14 9SS Tel: 01252 668976 *Web design*

▶ Interactive Technologies Ltd, Unit 14, Moorbrook Park, Didcot, Oxfordshire, OX11 7HP Tel: (01235) 516900 Fax: (01235) 516910 E-mail: mdew@itdisplays.com *Interactive white board suppliers*

Interactive Training Management, Church House, 90 Deansgate, Manchester, M3 2GP Tel: 0161-834 3334 Fax: 0161-834 8696 E-mail: debbiesmithitm@btconnect.com *Private & government sector trainers*

▶ Interactive View, 15 Bowling Green Lane, London, EC1R 0BD Tel: (020) 7566 0430 Fax: (020) 7490 8404 E-mail: info@interactiveview.co.uk *Audio visual services*

Interalia Communications Ltd, Endahna House, Bridge End Road, Grantham, Lincolnshire, NG31 7TS Tel: (01476) 594207 Fax: (01476) 594208 *Telecommunication systems & equipment distributors*

▶ Interbags, PO Box 2083, Hockley, Essex, SS5 4QW Tel: (01702) 205750 Fax: (01702) 204596

Interbar Ltd, Unit 2 Kings Park, Primrose Hill, Kings Langley, Hertfordshire, WD4 8ST Tel: (0845) 2713216 Fax: (0845) 2713217 E-mail: sales@interbar.co.uk *Interbar Ltd based in Kings Langley, Hertfordshire are licensed bar and refrigeration fitters.*

Interbelt Ltd, Unit 5, Glensyn Way, Burton-on-Trent, Staffordshire, DE14 1LX Tel: (01283) 562598 Fax: (01283) 515316 *Conveyor belt manufrs*

Interbrand, 85 Strand, London, WC2R 0DW Tel: (020) 7554 1000 Fax: (020) 7554 1001 E-mail: ukinfo@interbrand.com *Branding consultants*

Interbuild Components Ltd, Milton Mill, Ferry Road, Monifieth, Dundee, DD5 4NZ Tel: (01382) 534341 Fax: (01382) 534444 *Timber builders*

Intercad Workstation Graphics Ltd, 43 Manse Road, Bearsden, Glasgow, G61 3PN Tel: 0141-942 2232 Fax: 0141-942 6555 *Computer graphic services*

Intercal, 99 Windmill Street, Gravesend, Kent, DA12 1LE Tel: (01474) 357479 *Electro medical equipment manufrs*

Intercaps Filling Systems Ltd, 20 Lochend Road, Newbridge, Newbridge, Midlothian, EH28 8SY Tel: 0131-335 3335 Fax: 0131-335 0415 E-mail: sales@intercaps.com *Intercaps Filling Systems, based in Edinburgh, is expanding internationally where we have a growing number of satisfied customers in the soft drinks, whisky, food, cosmetics & detergents industry for both consumables & machinery. Intercaps Filling Systems has joined forces with established & well reputed suppliers of filling & packaging equipment in Italy to promote a full range of packaging machines aimed at small/medium sized users in the UK, Ireland & rest of Europe. Our machinery boasts bottling speeds of up to 20,000 containers per hour, including complete bottling lines, filling machines, capping machines, labelling machines, shrink wrapping equipment, bottle inverters, canning lines & food processing machines. We offer complete ranges of high quality equipment with reliable back up of parts & technical assistance both from Italy & from the UK. Our emphasis is on customer satisfaction, whether you are looking to purchase a complete production line or simply supplement an existing line.*

Intercasa Ltd, P O Box 92, Manchester, M17 1JQ Tel: 0161-877 3637 Fax: 0161 8773637 *Furniture importer*

Intercast UK Ltd, 73 Ringstead Crescent, Crosspool, Sheffield, S10 5SH Tel: 0114-266 6873 Fax: (08704)287885 E-mail: sales@intercastuk.com *Precision, sand & shell mould castings services*

Intercede Ltd, Lutterworth Hall, St. Marys Road, Lutterworth, Leicestershire, LE17 4PS Tel: (01455) 558111 Fax: (01455) 558222 *Computer security*

Interceil Ltd, Fairholme, Ridley Terrace, Cambois, Blyth, Northumberland, NE24 1QS Tel: (01670) 828008 Fax: (01670) 827749 *Suspended ceilings & partitions*

Intercept Telecom Ltd, 4 Angerstein Business Park, Horn Lane, London, SE10 0RT Tel: (020) 8305 4900 Fax: (020) 8305 4901 E-mail: info@intercept-telecom.com *Telecommunication contractors*

Interchain UK Ltd, 44 Shenley Pavilions, Chalkdell Drive, Shenley Wood, Milton Keynes, MK5 6LB Tel: (01908) 521000 Fax: (01908) 522000 E-mail: pbz@interchain.co.uk *Software house supplying chain management service*

Interchange, 2 The Western Centre, Western Road, Bracknell, Berkshire, RG12 1RW Tel: (01344) 861861 Fax: (01344) 487299 E-mail: sales@i-change.co.uk *Computers & accessories*

Interchange Group, Garden Court, Lockington, Derby, DE74 2SJ Tel: (08700) 716716 Fax: (08700) 716789 E-mail: info@interchangegroup.com *Computer software support*

Interchange Group Ltd, 2 Plover Close, Interchange Park, Newport Pagnell, Buckinghamshire, MK16 9PS Tel: (01908) 618161 Fax: (0870) 0716789 E-mail: info@interchangegroup.com *Hardware & software maintenance services*

Interchange Technical Consultancy Ltd, 53 Northop Road, Flint, Clwyd, CH6 5LG Tel: (01352) 733319 E-mail: sales@compumedic.co.uk *Computer consultants*

Interchem (Chemist Wholesale) Ltd, 2-26 Anthony Road, Saltley, Birmingham, B8 3AA Tel: 0121-328 3479 Fax: 0121-328 3479 E-mail: dispharma@aol.com *Pharmaceutical distributors*

Interclass Holdings Ltd, Heathmill Road, Wombourne, Wolverhampton, WV5 8AP Tel: (01902) 324422 Fax: (01902) 324044 E-mail: wombourne@interclass.co.uk *Building & civil engineering contractors*

Interclean Support Services Ltd, Unit 4C Sterling Industrial Estate, Kings Road, Newbury, Berkshire, RG14 5RQ Tel: (01635) 550199 Fax: (01635) 550037 E-mail: sales@icss.co.uk *Contract cleaners*

Intercon Lubrication Services, 28 Harwood Court, Riverside Park Industrial Estate, Middlesbrough, Cleveland, TS2 1PU Tel: (01642) 247157 Fax: (01642) 247157 E-mail: chas_ophield@lineone.net *Fluid handling & lubrication manufrs*

▶ Interco Products Ltd, 11 Clare Park, Amersham, Buckinghamshire, HP7 9HW Tel: (01494) 726961 Fax: (01494) 433411 E-mail: michael.armstrong7@ntlworld.com *Import agents of plastic bottles & glass jars*

Intercoat Industrial Paints & Lacquers Ltd, Bridgeman Street, Walsall, WS2 9NW Tel: (01922) 638821 Fax: (01922) 722952 *Industrial paint services*

Intercole Sub-Contract Services Ltd, 3 Avenger Close, Chandlers Ford, Eastleigh, Hampshire, SO53 4YU Tel: (023) 8025 4727 Fax: (023) 8025 1090 E-mail: subcon@intercole.co.uk *Electronic sub-contract services*

Intercolor Ltd, 795 London Road, Grays, Essex, RM20 3LH Tel: (01708) 899091 Fax: (01708) 899092 E-mail: sales@intercolor-ink.com *Printing inks*

Intercon Scaffolding, Rattle Road, Westham, Pevensey, East Sussex, BN24 5DS Tel: (01323) 767777 E-mail: sales@interconscaffolding.co.uk *Scaffolding throughout Sussex & Kent - Domestic /Commercial /Industrial /Insurance - all types of access - temp roofs , stages and seating stands , Painting , Roofing , chimney stack scaffolds , visit our website for more info and pictures - Thanks*

Interconnect Communications Ltd, Merlin House, Station Road, Chepstow, Gwent, NP16 5PB Tel: (01291) 638400 Fax: (01291) 638401 E-mail: enquiries@icc-uk.com *Telecommunication consultants*

Interconnect Direct Ltd, 22 Edward Road, Arnos Vale, Bristol, BS4 3ES Tel: 0117-907 1880 E-mail: enquiries@interconnect-direct.com *IT solutions provider*

Interconnect Products Ltd, Marlborough Road, Wootton Bassett, Swindon, SN4 7SA Tel: (01793) 849811 Fax: (01793) 849809 E-mail: sales@interconnect.demon.co.uk *Electronic cable & connector manufrs*

▶ Intercontinental Chemical Products Ltd, 56-62 Lincoln Road, Tuxford, Newark, Nottinghamshire, NG22 0HP Tel: (01777) 870756 Fax: (01777) 871766 E-mail: sales@intchems.com *Manufacturers of plastic & wax coatings, ancillary equipment*

Intercontinental Mercantile Ltd, 23 Dollis Hill Estate, 105 Brook Road, London, NW2 7BZ Tel: (020) 8830 7388 Fax: (020) 8830 7388 *Nylon fabric &Webbing merchants*

Intercos UK Ltd, 26 The Strand, Bideford, Devon, EX39 2ND Tel: (01237) 476339 Fax: (01237) 471040 *Cosmetics manufrs*

Inter-Credit International Ltd, 1ST Floor Newby House, 309 Chase Road, Southgate, London, N14 6JS Tel: (020) 8482 4444 Fax: (020) 8482 4455 E-mail: brendanglover@intercred.com *Debt collecting service*

Interdean Interconex Ltd, Interdean House, 15 Central Way, London, NW10 7XW Tel: (020) 8961 4141 Fax: (020) 8965 4484 E-mail: interdean@interconex.co.uk *Relocation company* Also at: Aberdeen, Felixstowe, Glasgow & Manchester

▶ Interdean Relocation, Blackburn Industrial Estate, Kinellar, Aberdeen, AB21 0RX Tel: (01224) 790000 Fax: (01224) 791900

Interdive Services Ltd, Unit 3a Stoke Damerel Business Centre, 5 Church Street, Plymouth, PL3 4DT Tel: (01752) 558080 Fax: (01752) 569090 E-mail: admin@interdive.co.uk *Medical training services*

Interect Construction Services, St. Tewdric, Oakhanger, Bordon, Hampshire, GU35 9JW Tel: (01420) 472610 Fax: (01420) 475225 E-mail: instacliveowen@msn.com *Tank erection & installation replacement services*

Intereel Group Ltd, Unit 11, Mountbatten Road, Tiverton, Devon, EX16 6SW Tel: (01884) 256364 Fax: (01884) 257898 E-mail: sales@intereel.co.uk *Label printing manufrs*

Intereel Group Ltd, Unit 11, Mountbatten Road, Tiverton, Devon, EX16 6SW Tel: (01884) 256364 Fax: (01884) 257898 E-mail: sales@intereel.co.uk *Label manufrs*

Intereurope Ltd, 21-23 East Street, Fareham, Hampshire, PO16 0BZ Tel: (01329) 823047 Fax: (01329) 822058 *Holding company*

▶ Inter-Expo, 15 Stonebridge, Peterborough, PE2 5NF Tel: 01733 237988 Fax: 01733 237988 E-mail: info@ExpoA1.com *Full exhibition & events services company (uk & europe)*

▶ Interface Contracts Ltd, Pennine House, Denton Lane, Chadderton, Oldham, OL9 8PU Tel: 0161-620 0698

Interface D C B Technolgy Ltd, Tyler Close, Normanton Industrial Estate, Normanton, West Yorkshire, WF6 1RL Tel: (01924) 224929 Fax: (01924) 224939 E-mail: general@interf.co.uk *Computer network specialists*

▶ Interface Europe Ltd, Shelf Mills, Halifax, West Yorkshire, HX3 7PA Tel: (01274) 690690 Fax: (01274) 694095 E-mail: info@interface.com *Carpet tile manufrs*

Interface Force Measurements Ltd, Ground Floor, Unit 19 Wellington Business Park, Duke Ride, Crowthorne, Berkshire, RG45 6LS Tel: 0845 4941748 Fax: (01344) 774765 E-mail: info@interface.uk.com *Interface Inc. was founded in 1968, with the goal of making the best load cells in the world, by concentrating exclusively on the design and the manufacture of force transducers and systems. Interface Force Measurements Ltd are the sole UK suppliers of Interface Inc. load cells. *The Interface Inc. mission statement is to be the recognised leader in strain gauge based force transducers and related instrumentation systems which satisfy force measurement needs world-wide. To concentrate on applications that benefit from innovative design and exceptional reliability, performance and service. **Interface Force Measurements Ltd mirrors this approach in producing solutions for force measurement applications nation-wide.*

Interface Solutions International Ltd, International Park, Starley Way, Birmingham, B37 7GN Tel: 0121-780 6000 Fax: 0121-780 6111 E-mail: sales@iface.co.uk *Computer peripheral equipment distributors*

Interfaces UK Ltd, 128 Radcliffe New Road, Whitefield, Manchester, M45 7RW Tel: 0161-796 2783 Fax: 0161-796 2783 *Computer consultants*

Interfax Acuflow Ltd, 2b Reddicap Heath Road, Sutton Coldfield, West Midlands, B75 7DU Tel: 0121-378 2626 Fax: 0121-378 2223 E-mail: sales@acuflow.co.uk *Fluid dispensing systems manufrs*

▶ Interfire Ltd, The Gatehouse, Naworth, Brampton, Cumbria, CA8 2HF Tel: (01697) 742336 Fax: (0870) 1634677 *Computer services*

Interfish Ltd, Wallsend Industrial Estate, Cattedown Wharves, Plymouth, PL4 0RW Tel: (01752) 267261 Fax: (01752) 224252 *Fish processors*

▶ Interfit, 14 Station Road, Reddish, Stockport, Cheshire, SK5 6ND Tel: 0161-431 4626 Fax: 0161-431 4626 E-mail: info@inter-fit.co.uk *Suppliers to the Vehicle Bodybuilding Industry. Agents for Thiriet of France. Stockists of Stainless Steel Hinges, S/S Door Gear, Rubber Buffers,Door Seals and Lights. Also supply sealants and adhesives to both the vehicle industry and the building industry. Established 20 years.*

Interflex Group, Peggys Mill, Mayfield Industrial Estate, Dalkeith, Midlothian, EH22 4AE Tel: 0131-654 2626 Fax: 0131-654 2606 *Waxed paper/flexible film packaging* Also at: Northampton

Interflon Scotland, Woodend Industrial Estate, Cowdenbeath, Fife, KY4 8HW Tel: (01383) 515501 Fax: (01383) 515502 E-mail: scotland@interflon.fsbusiness.co.uk *Teflon lubricants & greasers distributors*

▶ Interfloor Ltd, Edinburgh Road, Heathhall, Dumfries, DG1 1QA Tel: (01387) 253111 Fax: (01387) 268937

Interfoam Ltd, 16 Ronald Close, Woburn Road Industrial Estate, Bedford, MK42 7SH Tel: (01234) 855355 Fax: (01234) 855665 E-mail: sales@interfoam.co.uk *Manufacturers of polyurethane foam*

Interfocus Design Ltd, Unit 4 Molesworth Business Estate, Molesworth, Huntingdon, Cambridgeshire, PE28 0QG Tel: (01832) 710647 Fax: (01832) 710142 *Laboratory furniture manufrs*

Interform Contract Furniture, 8 West Hampstead Mews, London, NW6 3BB Tel: (020) 7328 2340 Fax: (020) 7624 1777 E-mail: enquiries@interform-furniture.co.uk *Furniture manufrs*

Interfreight Ltd, 8 The Felbridge Centre, The Birches Industrial Estate, Imberhorne Lane, East Grinstead, West Sussex, RH19 1XP Tel: (01342) 410454 Fax: (01342) 327237 E-mail: interfreight@lineone.net *Courier & delivery services*

Interfuture Systems Ltd, Kemps Farm, London Road, Balcombe, Haywards Heath, West Sussex, RH17 6JH Tel: (0845) 4522411 Fax: (0845) 4522412 E-mail: david.williams@interfuture.co.uk *Computer network installation & suppliers*

Interglossa Computer Consultants, 31a Chain Street, Reading, RG1 2HX Tel: 0118-956 1919 E-mail: info@glossa.co.uk *Technical software suppliers & consultants*

▶ Intergraphics, 2, Nightingale Court, Weston-super-Mare, Avon, BS22 8SX Tel: (01934) 511001 Fax: (01934) 511006 *Sign makers*

Intergrated Casting Technology, 5 Portersfield Road, Cradley Heath, West Midlands, B64 7BN Tel: (01384) 413678 Fax: (01384) 413660 E-mail: sales@wood-loines.com *Aluminium casting manufacturers*

Intergrated Electrical & Electronic Services, 11 Hutton Street, Boldon Colliery, Tyne & Wear, NE35 9LW Tel: 0191-519 0980 Fax: 0191-519 0705 *Electrical contractors & audio visual & communications installers*

▶ Intergrated Mechanical Service Supplies Ltd, 47 Cobblers Close, Farnham Royal, Slough, SL2 3DT Tel: (01753) 647449 Fax: (01753) 647449 E-mail: info@imss.uk.com

▶ Intergrated Mechanical Service Supplies Ltd, 47 Cobblers Close, Farnham Royal, Slough, SL2 3DT Tel: (01753) 647449 Fax: (01753) 647449 E-mail: sales@imss.uk.com *We are an intergrater to the Comercial, Bus Industries.*

Intergrated Scientific Ltd, 3 Centurion Business Park, Aspen Way, Rotherham, South Yorkshire, S60 1FB Tel: (01709) 830493 Fax: (01709) 830464 E-mail: sales@integsci.com *Suppliers of automated petroleum test equipment*

Intergrated Water Services Ltd, Vincients Road, Bumpers Farm Industrial Estate, Chippenham, Wiltshire, SN14 6NQ Tel: (01249) 461744 Fax: (01249) 461766 *Water tank cleaning services*

Interhatch, Whittington Way, Old Whittington, Chesterfield, Derbyshire, S41 9AG Tel: (01246) 264646 Fax: (01246) 269634 E-mail: sales@interhatch.com *Incubators*

Interhire Power Tool Services Ltd, Park Road, Ilkeston, Derbyshire, DE7 5DA Tel: 0115-930 6382 Fax: 0115-944 0407 *Power tool hire, sales & distribution*

Interiair Aircraft Services, Elstree Aerodrome, Elstree, Borehamwood, Hertfordshire, WD6 3AW Tel: (020) 8953 1995 Fax: (020) 8953 3029 E-mail: interiair@aol.com *Aircraft upholsterers*

▶ Interim Energy Mangagement, 5 Waterside Way, Peterhead, Aberdeenshire, AB42 1GB Tel: (01779) 477287 Fax: (01779) 481074

Interim Resolutions Ltd, 4 Crowtrees Park, Rastrick, Brighouse, West Yorkshire, HD6 3XQ Tel: (01484) 710354 E-mail: b.hemingway@ukonline.co.uk *Consultancy, purchasing, procurement, stores & logistics*

Interior Bedding Centre, 9-10 Station Road, Sunderland, SR6 9AA Tel: 0191-549 9998 Fax: 0191-297 0999 *Pine furniture interiors*

Interior Concepts Ltd, Unit 1, 1 Russett Place, Kirdford, Billingshurst, West Sussex, RH14 0QQ Tel: (01403) 820000 Fax: (05603) 132034 E-mail: enquiry@interiorconcepts.uk.com *We specialise in full commercial refurbishment and maintenance. Our services include:*Partitioning - Alterations, Design & Installation, Restorations & Cleaning. Suspended Ceilings - Repair, New Installations In-situ Cleaning & Acoustic Coatings. Decorating & Furnishings - Vinyl Wallcoverings, Painting, Artificial Plants, Office Furniture, Safety Signage.*Floor Coverings - Carpet Tiles, Vinyl/Ceramic, Carpets, Laminated Timber Flooring.*Glass, Filming & Blinds - Solar/ Opaque/Colour Films. Vertical, Venetian & Roller Blinds.*Electrics & Plumbing - Power Points, Modular Lighting, Heating & Air Conditioning Systems.*CAD - Space Planning, LPA - Approvals.*Building works - Brickwork, Blockwork, Plastering, Artexing" I.T - Design and Installation of Cat5e Networks, telephone switches.*Fire Alarm Systems - Design, Installation and Maintenance.*Mezzanine Floors - Design, Installation and Maintenance"*

Interior Contracts Group, Ethos House, 52 Tanners Drive, Blakelands, Milton Keynes, MK14 5BW Tel: (01908) 216766 Fax: (01908) 216744 *interior refurbishment of commercial premises*

Interior Design Ceiling Co. Ltd, Sundorne House, Astley, Shrewsbury, SY4 4ED Tel: (01939) 250407 Fax: (01939) 250704 *Suspended ceiling contractors*

Interior Designers Guild, 19 Bridge Street, Winchester, Hampshire, SO23 9BH Tel: (01962) 861777 Fax: (01962) 854333 E-mail: enquiries@interiordesignersguild.co.uk *Kitchen furniture design & manufrs*

▶ Interior Door Systems Ltd, Hopton House 3 & 4 Rivington Court, Hardwick Grange, Woolston, Warrington, WA1 4RT Tel: (01925) 813100 E-mail: sales@interiordoorsystems.co.uk

Interior & Facility Contracts Ltd, Excelsior House, Buntsford Park Road, Bromsgrove, Worcestershire, B60 3DX Tel: (01527) 573000 Fax: (01527) 573001 E-mail: enquiries@interior-facility.com *Commercial property fitting-out & refurbishment contractors*

Interior Fitting Services Ltd, Manor House Farm, 10 Addington Road, Woodford, Kettering, Northamptonshire, NN14 4ES Tel: (01832) 733999 Fax: (01832) 737978 *Shop fittings*

Interior Landscaping Products, The Sussex Barn, New Lodge Farm, Hooe, Battle, East Sussex, TN33 9HJ Tel: (01424) 844444 Fax: (01424) 843666 E-mail: sales@interiorlandscaping.co.uk *Interior landscaping suppliers*

▶ Interior Love, 15 Bridle Lane, Streetly, Sutton Coldfield, Birmingham, B74 3PT Tel: (0797) 1425195 E-mail: design@interiorlove.co.uk *Interior design service for domestic and commercial properties. Member or the Guild of Mastercraftsmen. Specialists services including gold leafing and marbling. Full portfolio available. Web design also now available.*

▶ Interior Matters UK Ltd, 18 Cecil Avenue, Bournemouth, BH8 9EH Tel: (01202) 528152 E-mail: sue@interiormatters.co.uk *Interior Matters - Designing and Overseeing quality interiors for both Residential (Private) and Commercial clients.*

Interior One, 4 Alton Holdings, Milton Of Campsie, Glasgow, G66 8AD Tel: 0141-776 3024 Fax: 0141-776 2471 E-mail: ted@mcbrides.fsbusiness.co.uk *Floral & plant displays*

Interior Planting Features, Upshire House, Greenways, Lambourn, Hungerford, Berkshire, RG17 7LE Tel: (01488) 71614 Fax: (01488) 72058 *Floral display contractors*

Interior Projects Southern Ltd, 2 Burstow Park Business Centre, Antlands Lane, Shipley Bridge, Horley, Surrey, RH6 9TF Tel: (01293) 823737 Fax: (01293) 823738 E-mail: ip.s@virgin.net *Interior refurbishment manufrs*

Interior Property Specialists Ltd, Interplan House, Chelmsford Road Industrial Estate, Dunmow, Essex, CM6 1HE Tel: (01371) 874241 Fax: (01371) 873848 E-mail: contact@ips-interiors.co.uk *Office Interiors*

▶ Interior Solutions, 57 Comiston View, Edinburgh, EH10 6LT Tel: 0131-445 2200 Fax: 0131-466 1516 E-mail: mail@interiorsolutionsedinburgh.com *Full Interior Design and Decoration Service*Project Management Service*Soft Furnishings made to order*Bespoke Furniture Designed and Manufactured *Re-upholstery & Restoration Service*Lighting, Accessories & Flooring Sourced and Supplied**

Interiors By Design, 37 The Spinney, Pulborough, West Sussex, RH20 2AP Tel: (01798) 874969 E-mail: interiorsbydesign@ukonline.co.uk *Whole house packages.*Full renovations.*Cosmectic restyling.*Single rooms.*Perspective plans.*Floor plans*

Interkey Engineers, The Workshop, Leigh Sinton, Malvern, Worcestershire, WR13 5EQ Tel: (01886) 830222 Fax: (01886) 830222 *Internal slotting & splines*

Interklima Ltd, Darby House, 62 Bletchingley Road, Merstham, Redhill, RH1 3DN Tel: (01737) 644270 Fax: (01737) 644250 E-mail: info@interklima.co.uk *Suppliers of air conditioning*

▶ Interknickers Ltd, 21 Claremont Drive, Coalville, Coalville, Leicestershire, LE67 2ND Tel: (01530) 460316 E-mail: interknickers@btinternet.com *Novelty lingerie to send as a gift. Send knickers not flowers. Black thong underwear with choice of motif delivered in luxury packaging.*

▶ Interlabel Labels & Tags, 106 The Street, Felthorpe, Norwich, NR10 4DH Tel: (01603) 754944 Fax: (01603) 754955 E-mail: sales@interlabel.co.uk *Labelling systems*

Interlan Computer Maintenance, The Mill, Glasshouses, Harrogate, North Yorkshire, HG3 5QH Tel: (01423) 712222 Fax: (01423) 712958 *Computer maintenance & repairers*

Interline Southwest Ltd, 18-19 Northfields Industrial Estate, Northfields Lane, Brixham, Devon, TQ5 8UA Tel: (01803) 853401 Fax: (01803) 856630 *Builders merchants*

Interline UK, Greenacre Farm, Smallgains La, Stock, Ingatestone, Essex, CM4 9PR Tel: (01245) 477922 Fax: (01245) 475539 E-mail: sales@interlineuk.com *Office furniture sales to the trade*

▶ Interlink Building Systems Ltd, 175 Glasgow Road, Edinburgh, EH12 9BH Tel: 0131-270 3534 Fax: 0131-270 3592

Interlink Computer Communications, 154 Fore Street, London, N18 2XA Tel: (020) 8482 5211 Fax: (020) 8482 5224 E-mail: enquiries@interlink-computers.com *Computer resellers*

Interlink Design & Display Ltd, Unit 2-4 Station Road Industrial Estate, Station Road, Coleshill, Birmingham, B46 1HT Tel: (01675) 467870 Fax: (01675) 467871 E-mail: enquiries@interlinkdesign.co.uk *Exhibition contractors*

▶ Interlink Express, Unit 3 17 Deerpark Road, Bellaghy, Magherafelt, County Londonderry, BT45 8LB Tel: (028) 7938 6575 Fax: (028) 7938 6546

▶ Interlink Express Parcels Ltd, 10 Blackburn Road, Bathgate, West Lothian, EH48 2EY Tel: (01506) 630459 Fax: (01506) 634013

▶ Interlink Express Parcels Ltd, Borderline Garage, Biggar, Lanarkshire, ML12 6JJ Tel: (01899) 221226 Fax: (01899) 221279

Interlink Express Parcels Ltd, Earlesfield Lane, Grantham, Lincolnshire, NG31 7NT Tel: (01476) 570263 Fax: (01476) 570268 E-mail: depot634@interlinkexpress.com *UK overnight & worldwide parcel services*

▶ Interlink Express Parcels Ltd, Unit 2a Meadowbrook Park, Halfway, Sheffield, S20 3PJ Tel: 0114-251 1110 Fax: 0114-251 0888 E-mail: depot444@interlinkexpress.com *Overnight & same day service, motorbike to transit*

▶ Interlink Express Parcels Ltd, 1 Junction Industrial Estate, Dartmouth Road, Smethwick, West Midlands, B66 1AX Tel: 0121-525 2020 Fax: 0121-525 2090

▶ Interlink Express Parcels Ltd, 10 Queens Way, Southampton, SO14 3AZ Tel: (023) 8039 3666

▶ Interlink Express Parcels Ltd, 49d Sadler Forster Way, Teesside Industrial Estate, Stockton-on-Tees, Cleveland, TS17 9JY Tel: (01642) 751122 Fax: (01642) 750055

▶ Interlink Express Parcels Ltd, Units 4-5, Coppice Lane, Walsall Wood, Walsall, WS9 9AA Tel: (01922) 745422 Fax: (01922) 745433

▶ Interlink Express Parcels Ltd, 12 & 13 Shipston Close, Worcester, WR4 9XN Tel: (01905) 754055 Fax: (01905) 754234

Interlink Fabrications Ltd, Interlink House, Commerce Way, Lancing, West Sussex, BN15 8TA Tel: (01903) 763663 Fax: (01903) 762621 E-mail: interlink@interlink-fabs.co.uk *Sheet metal work manufrs*

Interlink Food, Shadsworth Bakery, Sett End Road, Shadsworth Business Park, Blackburn, BB1 2PT Tel: (01254) 55495 Fax: (01254) 663602 E-mail: sales@interlinkfoods.co.uk *Frozen food processors & products manufrs*

Interlink Import Export Ltd, The Rodings, Lancaster Lane, Parbold, Wigan, Lancashire, WN8 7HQ Tel: (01257) 463211 Fax: (01257) 464220 E-mail: peter@interlink.uk.com *Marketing services for copper wire extrusion*

Interlink Systems, 15 Greenacres Avenue, Winnersh, Wokingham, Berkshire, RG41 5SX Tel: 0118-962 9900 Fax: 0118-962 9955 E-mail: interlinksystems@btinternet.com *Fire protection assembly services*

Interlink Systems Engineering Ltd, Po Box 3, Leighton Buzzard, Bedfordshire, LU7 3AG Tel: (01525) 372613 Fax: (01525) 372613 E-mail: interlink.consulting@dial.pipex.com *Industrial technology & management consulting*

Interlinks Fashions Ltd, Park Royal House, Park Royal Road, London, NW10 7JH Tel: (020) 8961 8169 Fax: (020) 8963 0683 *Fashion dress wholesalers*

Interlock Flexible Products Ltd, 1 Burbidge Road, Birmingham, B9 4US Tel: 0121-766 7766 Fax: 0121-766 7799 E-mail: sales@interlockflex.com *Specialist metal fabrication services in all metals*

Interlogic Ltd, Bestway House, Handen Road, Gerrards Cross, Buckinghamshire, SL9 9RY Tel: (01753) 889749 Fax: (01753) 540990 E-mail: sales@wrkgrp.com *Software manufrs*

▶ Interlogistics Ltd, Waldeck House, Waldeck Road, Maidenhead, Berkshire, SL6 8BR Tel: (01628) 621300 Fax: (01628) 621309 E-mail: info@justsurplus.co.uk *Bueyrs and Sellers of Surplus Computers and computer equipment. Desktops, Laptops, Printers, Scanners, GPS and more. Distributor. Based in UK.*

Interlogo London Ltd, High Street, Newport, Isle of Wight, PO30 1BQ Tel: (01983) 522470 Fax: (01983) 532891 E-mail: sales@interlogo.co.uk *Promotional merchandise & clothing supplier*

Interlube Systems Ltd, 85 St. Modwen Road, Plymouth, PL6 8LH Tel: (01752) 676000 Fax: (01752) 676001 E-mail: info@interlubesystems.co.uk Principal Export Areas: Worldwide *Hose & lubricating systems manufrs*

Intermail plc, Canal View Road, Newbury, Berkshire, RG14 5XF Tel: (01635) 565000 Fax: (01635) 41678 E-mail: sales@intermail.co.uk *E-commerce & database agents*

Intermark Leisure Ltd, Winnington Avenue, Winnington, Northwich, Cheshire, CW8 4EE Tel: (01606) 871831 Fax: (01606) 782241 E-mail: sales@intermarkleisure.ltd.uk *Swimming pool enclosure manufrs*

Intermart International Ltd, 29 Victoria Road, Horwich, Bolton, BL6 5NA Tel: (01204) 460600 Fax: (01204) 460666 *Envelope distributors*

▶ Intermec International Inc, Sovereign House, Vastern Road, Reading, RG1 8BT Tel: 0118-987 9400 Fax: 0118-987 9401

Intermec Technologies UK Ltd, Reading International Business Park, Reading, RG2 6DD Tel: 0118-923 0800 Fax: 0118-923 0801 E-mail: infoeurope@intermec.com *Hand held computer manufrs*

Inter-Media, 196 Causeway Green Road, Oldbury, West Midlands, B68 8LS Tel: 0121-552 6622 Fax: 0121-544 5404 E-mail: sales@trackzone.demon.co.uk *Office consumable suppliers*

Intermediate Ltd, 3RD Floor, 21 Great Chapel Street, London, W1F 8FP Tel: (020) 7432 7040 Fax: (020) 7437 1843 E-mail: info@intermediate.co.uk *Advertising agents*

Intermediate Capital Group plc, 20 Old Broad Street, London, EC2N 1DP Tel: (020) 7628 9898 Fax: (020) 7628 2268 *Mezzanine finance services*

Intermediate Technology Development Group, Bourton Hall, Bourton On Dunsmoore, Rugby, Warwickshire, CV23 9QZ Tel: (01926) 634400 Fax: (01926) 634401 E-mail: info@practicalaction.org.uk *Technology information & advice charity*

Intern Transport Systems (U K) Ltd, 421 Nottingham Road, Ilkeston, Derbyshire, DE7 5BP Tel: 0115-930 7724 Fax: 0115-930 1742 E-mail: sales@itsuk.org.uk *An accurate inventory is essential in any modern warehouse. ITS provides equipment for checking incoming, outgoing or stored products in Distribution Warehouses. High Speed Garment Counter for checking hanging garment deliveries. Box Scanner for checking box labels on outgoing orders. Size Gauge for checking the volume and weight of warehouse products. These labour saving devices both reduce manpower costs and drastically reduce errors improving the efficiency of the warehouse. In addition to these products ITS provides Overhead Conveyor Systems for products from 5 to 500Kg*

▶ Internal Communications Installations Ltd, 24 A Progress Business Park, Orders Lane, Kirkham, Preston, PR4 2TZ Tel: (0845) 6340085 Fax: (01772) 687529 E-mail: info@4pm.uk.com *Vehicle tracking & navigation systems*

Internal Communications Network Ltd, 268 Hackney Road, London, E2 7SJ Tel: (020) 7613 0000 Fax: (020) 7723 7300 E-mail: icm@talk21.com *Install systems & cabling*

▶ Internal Freight Auditing Ltd, 5 Keepers Close, Coleshill, Birmingham, B46 3HB Tel: (01675) 437534 E-mail: Info@IF-Audit.com *International and Domestic Freight Auditing company - covering all areas of EMEA.*Specialising in the verification and accuracy of all types of transportation and logistics costs**

Internal T V Contracts, Brooklands Approach, Romford, RM1 1DX Tel: (01708) 725511 Fax: (01708) 730507 E-mail: itcuksales@aol.com *Closed circuit TV security systems*

▶ Internal Transport Garage, Unit 1d, West Byrehill Ind Estate, Kilwinning, Ayrshire, KA13 6HR Tel: (01294) 552129

International Agencies, 670 Pollokshaws Road, Glasgow, G41 2QE Tel: 0141-424 3995 Fax: 0141-424 1357 E-mail: sales@snookpool.co.uk *Retailers of pool tables & accessories & hire*

International Aluminium Institute Ltd, New Zealand House, 80 Haymarket, London, SW1Y 4TE Tel: (020) 7930 0528 Fax: (020) 7321 0183 E-mail: iai@world-aluminium.org *Trade association*

▶ International Aqua-Tech Ltd, Unit 38, Gaerwen Industrial Estate, Gaerwen, Gwynedd, LL60 6HR Tel: (01248) 422253 Fax: (01248) 422317 E-mail: justin.whitford@iat.uk.com *Aquariums & aquaculture manufacturing*

International (British) Marketing Ltd, Birdcage House, Church Hill, Midhurst, West Sussex, GU29 9NX Tel: (01730) 812225 E-mail: info@british-marketing.com *British Marketing Expertise for developing European Markets * *We show businesses in Romania how to develop sophisticated western marketing strategies. *Being part of the EU brings huge opportunities but also great challenges - a business that doesn"t embrace a modern integrated marketing operation will be overwhelmed by its competitor. * **

International Bullion & Metal Brokers Ltd, Kovics House, 57D Hatton Garden, London, EC1N 8JD Tel: (020) 7242 2074 Fax: (020) 7831 3005 E-mail: ibb@ibblondon.com *Jewellery wholesalers*

International Business Networks, Brigade House, Brigade Close, Harrow, Middlesex, HA2 0LQ Tel: (020) 8515 9000 Fax: (020) 8515 9001 E-mail: info@ibnetworks.com *Telecommunications systems & services*

International Business Systems Ltd, IBS House, Elstree Way, Borehamwood, Hertfordshire, WD6 1FE Tel: (020) 8207 5655 Fax: (020) 8207 6770 E-mail: marketing@ibsuk.com *Industrial computer software suppliers*

▶ International Cement Review, 15 High Street, Old Kings Head Court, Dorking, Surrey, RH4 1AR Tel: 01306 740363 E-mail: info@CemNet.co.uk *International Cement Review is the cement industry"s premiere monthly publication.*

International Cheese Centre, Unit 3 The Concourse Liverpool Street Station, Liverpool Street, London, EC2M 7PY Tel: (020) 7628 6637 Fax: (020) 7628 2343 *Cheese suppliers*

International Coffee Organisation, 22 Berners Street, London, W1T 3DD Tel: (020) 7612 0600 Fax: (020) 7580 6129 E-mail: info@ico.org *Inter-governmental organisation for coffee trading*

▶ International Commerce Alliance, 155a Cove Road, Farnborough, Hampshire, GU14 0HQ Tel: (07766) 558748 E-mail: infouk@intnlcommerce.com *We offer Outsourcing solutions in Data Entry, Forms Processing, Accounting, Insurance, Market Research and Analytics areas.**Guaranteed cost savings of atleast 40%.**Free trial period with absolutely no-obligation guarantees your peace of mind.****

International Components Corporation (Europe) Ltd, Pitreavie Drive, Pitreavie Business Park, Dunfermline, Fife, KY11 8UH Tel: (01383) 625030 Fax: (01383) 625040 E-mail: dhunter@iccuk.co.uk *Battery charger suppliers*

▶ International Consultants on Targeted Security, South Block, Tavistock House, Tavistock Square, London, WC1H 9LG Tel: 0207 8747576 Fax: 0207 8747599 E-mail: mark.salter_uk@icts.co.uk *Security services*

International Copiers Ltd, Westfield Farm House, Henley Road, Medmenham, Marlow, Buckinghamshire, SL7 2HE Tel: (01491) 414345 Fax: (01491) 414346 *Internet for business*

▶ International Corporate Response Ltd, 96 High Road, Beeston, Nottingham, NG9 2LF Tel: 0115-925 3060 Fax: 0115-925 0989 E-mail: sales@ic-response.com

▶ International Decision Systems, 1 Stewart Road, Basingstoke, Hampshire, RG24 8NF Tel: (01256) 302000 Fax: (01256) 302005 *Software suppliers*

International Decorative Services, Dukesway, Team Valley Trading Estate, Gateshead, Tyne & Wear, NE11 0PZ Tel: 0191-491 7000 Fax: 0191-491 7007 *Panel product distributors*

International Decorative Surfaces plc, West End Approach, Morley, Leeds, LS27 0NB Tel: 0113-220 3900 Fax: 0113-220 3901 *Melamine laminate distributors*

International Drilling Services Ltd, Carrwood Road, Chesterfield, Derbyshire, S41 9QB Tel: (01246) 269911 Fax: (01246) 269922 E-mail: sales@idsuk.com *Drilling equipment suppliers & manufrs*

International Engine Services, 6 Moss Road, Witham, Essex, CM8 3UQ Tel: (01376) 503115 Fax: (01376) 503118 E-mail: graham@iesracing.co.uk *Precision sub-contract CNC machining*

International Exhibition Design Services Ltd, 62A High Street, Hampton Hill, Hampton, Middlesex, TW12 1PD Tel: (020) 8977 5129 Fax: (020) 8977 0036 E-mail: design@ieds-ltd.com *Exhibition stand designers*

▶ International Exports, 2 Southleigh Road, Taunton, Somerset, TA1 2XZ Tel: (07976) 084155 Fax: (01823) 254487 E-mail: postmaster@internationalexports.co.uk *Global Sourcing & Supplying of Engineering Technology & Components for*Automotive Manufacture.**We offer a professional service to the global automotive production industry, with particular emphasis on the automotive manufacturing industry of Iran.*

International Flavours & Fragrances (I F F) (GB) Ltd, Duddery Hill, Haverhill, Suffolk, CB9 8LG Tel: (01440) 715000 Fax: (01440) 762199 E-mail: iff.uk@iff.com *Aroma chemical manufrs*

▶ International Foreign Exchange, 84 Brook Street, Mayfair, London, UK, W1K 5EH Tel: (020) 7495 8888 Fax: (020) 7495 8890 E-mail: info@internationalfx.com *International Foreign Exchange (IFX) is a specialist consultancy providing tailored foreign exchange services for our clients. Our aim is to make your foreign exchange transactions as simple as possible, while minimizing your costs. IFX consultants who know your business can keep you abreast of developments in currency markets, and help you to make the right decisions consistently. ***

▶ International Furniture Exporters, Old Cement Works, South Heighton, Newhaven, East Sussex, BN9 0HS Tel: (01273) 611251 Fax: (01273) 611574

▶ International Heavy Haulage (GB) Limited, Wesley Street, Langley Mill, NG16 4AL Tel: 01773 768833 Fax: 01773 768844 E-mail: tim.ihhgb@btconnect.com *UK and European Haulage 1 to 200 tons at excellent rates.*Full UK and Europe Permit, Notification and Pilot Car service.*

International Hospitals Group Ltd, Manor House, Park Road, Stoke Poges, Slough, SL2 4PG Tel: (01753) 784777 Fax: (01753) 784784 E-mail: info@ihg.co.uk *Health care consultants*

International House, 106 Piccadilly, London, W1J 7NL Tel: (020) 7518 6999 Fax: (020) 7495 0284 E-mail: info@ihlondon.co.uk *Language schools*

International Insignia, Unit 3 Dunstall Hill Industrial Estate, Gorsebrook Road, Wolverhampton, WV6 0PJ Tel: (01902) 714265 Fax: (01902) 714853 E-mail: sales@internationalinsignia.net *Promotional clothing printers*

▶ International Kitchens & Bedrooms, 753 Holderness Road, Hull, HU8 9AR Tel: (01482) 375251 Fax: (01482) 711364 E-mail: enquiries@internationalkitchens.co.uk *International Kitchens & Bedrooms is Hull's premier studio displaying exclusive German, French & English kitchens together with designer bedrooms. From design, manufacture & installation - kitchen worktops/units/solid surface's/cupboards/preparation space/bedroom units/wardrobes & overhead units*

International Labmate Ltd, Oak Court Business Centre, Sandridge Park Porters Wood, Porters Wood, St. Albans, Hertfordshire, AL3 6PH Tel: (01727) 855574 Fax: (01727) 841694 E-mail: sales@product-search.co.uk *Book publishers*

▶ International Link Services Ltd, 68 Pretoria Road, Birmingham, B9 5LH Tel: 0121-242 1865 Fax: 0121-773 6435 E-mail: chengfen@onetel.net.uk *Engineers wholesale supplies*

International Marketers (London) Ltd, Unit 7, Woolmer Way, Bordon, Hampshire, GU35 9QE Tel: (01420) 482100 Fax: (01420) 482111 E-mail: info@inmalo.co.uk *Contractors plant & tractor spares distributors* Also at: Northampton

▶ International Marketing & Logistics, 11c Stephenson Road, Clacton-on-Sea, Essex, CO15 4XA Tel: (01255) 479864 Fax: (01255) 474705 E-mail: paul.quenet@iml.uk.com *Logistics services*

International Marketing Partners, 6 Lower Grosvenor Place, London, SW1W 0EN Tel: (020) 7828 9400 Fax: (020) 7828 9466 E-mail: info@intermarketingonline.com *Marketing strategy consultants*

International Meehanite Metal Co. Ltd, 38 Albert Road North, Reigate, Surrey, RH2 9EH Tel: (01737) 244786 Fax: (01737) 226644 E-mail: meehaniteltd@btconnect.com *Metallurgists*

International Motion Control, Patrick Gregory Road, Wolverhampton, WV11 3DZ Tel: (01902) 304000 Fax: (01902) 305676 E-mail: sales@imc-uk.com *Pneumatic valve manufrs*

The International Moving Co., Unit B1, Stewart Road, Altrincham, Cheshire, WA14 5GR Tel: 0161-876 8844 Fax: 0161-929 8765 E-mail: sthelens@int-moving.com *Shipping & removal specialists* Also at: Cirencester & Leicester

International Paper Ltd, Inverurie Mills, Inverurie, Aberdeenshire, AB51 5NR Tel: (01467) 627000 Fax: (01467) 627102 E-mail: bill.conn@ipaper.com *Paper manufrs*

International Paper Containers UK Ltd, Haldens Parkway, Thrapston, Kettering, Northamptonshire, NN14 4QS Tel: (01832) 736100 Fax: (01832) 736109 *Cardboard box producers*

▶ International Parcel Express, 1 Quayside Lodge, William Morris Way, London, SW6 2UZ Tel: (020) 7731 6888 Fax: (020) 7384 2384

International Pipeline Supplies Ltd, 3 Cookson House, River Drive, South Shields, Tyne & Wear, NE33 1TL Tel: 0191-455 9648 Fax: 0191-454 0505 E-mail: office@internationalgroup.fsbusiness.co.uk *Specialists in onshore & offshore fittings*

International Plastic Systems Ltd, Seaham Grange Industrial Estate, Seaham, County Durham, SR7 0PT Tel: 0191-521 3111 Fax: 0191-521 3222 E-mail: info@ips-plastics.com Principal Export Areas: Central Asia, Africa, Central/East Europe, West Europe & North America *Manufacturers of plastic pipe fittings & plastic pipe. In addition, fire protection equipment & plastic valves*

International Power Generation, Unit 7c Carcroft Enterprise Park, Carcroft, Doncaster, South Yorkshire, DN6 8DD Tel: (01302) 722888 Fax: (01302) 721202 E-mail: sales@generator.co.uk *Generating set services*

International Precision Products, Station Yard, Thame, Oxfordshire, OX9 3UH Tel: (01844) 217678 Fax: (01844) 215495 E-mail: ask@ippbv.com *Rotary switch, connectors & motors distributors*

International Co Profile, Paulton House, 8 Shepherdess Walk, London, N1 7LB Tel: (020) 7490 0049 Fax: (020) 7566 8319 E-mail: customerservice@icpcredit.com *Business information services*

International Purchasing Services Ltd, Unit 17 Golborne Enterprise Park, Golborne, Warrington, WA3 3DR Tel: (01942) 713777 Fax: (01942) 713888 E-mail: intl.purch.serv@virgin.net *Instrumentation consultants*

▶ International Recruitment Bureau Ltd., Address 274 Hither green lane, London, SE13 6T Tel: 07776 472126 Fax: 02086 959200 *International Recruitment Bureau Ltd. is recruitment agency jointly with Joint stock company "International Recruitment Solutions" recruitment agency based in lithuania. Our main activities is to provide personnel from Eastern Europe for UK employers. **

International Safety Products Ltd, 159 Hawthorne Road, Bootle, Merseyside, L20 6JU Tel: 0151-922 2202 Fax: 0151-922 5874 E-mail: sales@ispl.co.uk *Safety & survival equipment*

International Skycharter Ltd, Diamond House, 36-38 Hatton Garden, London, EC1N 8EB Tel: (020) 7242 9501 Fax: (020) 7405 4255 E-mail: sales@skycharter.co.uk *Air charter brokers*

International Technical Support Ltd, 42 Hackwood Road, Basingstoke, Hampshire, RG21 3AF Tel: (01256) 333226 Fax: (01256) 333860 E-mail: info@itsupports.co.uk *Computer technical support services*

International Timber, Haven Road, Colchester, CO2 8HT Tel: (01206) 866822 Fax: (01206) 878000 E-mail: info@internationaltimber.com *Timber importers & distributors*

International Timber, Timber Division, Earls Road, Grangemouth, Stirlingshire, FK3 8UU Tel: (01324) 666000 Fax: (01324) 666111 *Timber importers & sawmilling services*

International Timber, West Yard, Trafford Wharf Road, Trafford Park, Manchester, M17 1DJ Tel: 0161-848 2900 Fax: 0161-848 2901 *Timber merchants & importers*

International Training Service, Wellington Park, Belfast, BT9 6DJ Tel: (028) 9092 3388 Fax: (028) 9092 3386 E-mail: info@itsconsult.com *Management consultants*

International Transformers, Longley Lane, Sharston Industrial Area, Manchester, M22 4RU Tel: 0161-428 9507 Fax: 0161-428 0052 E-mail: info@int-transformers.co.uk *Designers & manufacturers of non standard transformers*

International Valves Ltd, Willie Snaith Road, Newmarket, Suffolk, CB8 7GG Tel: (01638) 665000 Fax: (01638) 664000 E-mail: info@international-valves.com *Valve manufacturers & distributors*

▶ Internet Brain Ltd, 76 Iford Lane, Bournemouth, BH6 5QZ Tel: (0845) 3452567 E-mail: gregblack@internetbrain.co.uk *Internet & marketing suppliers*

▶ Internet For Business Ltd, 387 Union Street, Aberdeen, AB11 6BX Tel: (01224) 333300 Fax: (01224) 333321 E-mail: sales@ifb.net *Internet services business*

Internet Central Ltd, The Innovation Centre, University of Keele, Keele, Newcastle, Staffordshire, ST5 5NB Tel: (01782) 667788 Fax: (01782) 667799 E-mail: enquiries@netcentral.co.uk *Internet service providers*

Internet Consultancy & Management Ltd, 12 Sycamore Avenue, Glapwell, Chesterfield, Derbyshire, S44 5LH Tel: (0800) 0431057 Fax: (0870) 1270965 E-mail: support@icamltd.co.uk *Internet consultancy*

Internet Marketing Kent, 70c High Street, Whitstable, Kent, CT5 1BB Tel: (01227) 281611 Fax: (01227) 264727 E-mail: mark.smith@i-m-k.co.uk *Internet web designers*

▶ Internet Signs Direct, Ballens Road, Chatham, Kent, ME5 8PG Tel: (01634) 309295 *Sign makers*

Internet Video Communication, Alexander House Mere Park, Dedmere Road, Marlow, Buckinghamshire, SL7 1FX Tel: (01628) 484446 Fax: (01628) 475708 *Video conferencing*

▶ Internetfiresdirect, Bent Ley Industrial Estate, Meltham, Holmfirth, HD9 4EP Tel: (0870) 2242847 Fax: (01484) 854867 E-mail: richard.kaye@adamsurrounds.co.uk *Internet retail of fires & fireplaces*

▶ Internormen Technology, Unit G14, Westthorpe Fields Road, Killamarsh, Sheffield, S21 1TZ Tel: 0114-218 0614 Fax: 0114-218 0615 E-mail: northsales@reacttechnologies.com *Systems integrator for secure wireless & laser services*

Interoute Transport Services Ltd, Rycote Lane, Thame, Oxfordshire, OX9 2JB Tel: (01844) 214141 Fax: (01844) 261297 E-mail: craig.fowler@interoute-transport.com *Road tanker operator services*

▶ Interpane Glass (UK) Ltd, Warmco Industrial Estate, Manchester Road, Mossley, Ashton-Under-Lyne, Lancashire, OL5 9XA Tel: (01457) 837779

▶ Interparcel, Norman House, 15 Stephenson Way, Crawley, West Sussex, RH10 1TN Tel: 08700 273733 Fax: 01293 785990 E-mail: sales@interparcel.com *Discounted UK & International courier services. Instant quote & online booking at www.interparcel.com. Pay by Credit Card or Paypal.*

Interpart (U K) Ltd, 2 Warsall Road, Wythenshawe, Manchester, M22 4RH Tel: 0161-998 9911 Fax: 0161-946 0131 E-mail: info@interpart.co.uk *Wholesale distributors of spare parts*

Interphase Electrical Services, 67b High Street, Halstead, Essex, CO9 2JD Tel: (01787) 472222 Fax: (01787) 472222 *Electrical designers & contractors*

▶ Interphone CCTV Ltd, PO Box 1, Harrow, Middlesex, HA3 5UH Tel: (020) 8621 6000 Fax: (020) 8621 6100

Interphone CCTV Ltd, Interphone House, P O Box 1, Harrow, Middlesex, HA3 5UH Tel: (020) 8621 6000 Fax: (020) 8621 6100 E-mail: security@interphone.co.uk *Door entry systems contractors*

Interplan Panel Systems Ltd, 7-11 Glentanar Road, Glasgow, G22 7XS Tel: 0141-336 4040 Fax: 0141-336 4433 *Laminate fabricators*

Interplan Sign Systems Ltd, Abbey Road Industrial Estate, Durham, DH1 5HB Tel: 0191-384 0645 Fax: 0191-384 2423 E-mail: sales@interplan-signs.co.uk *Sign manufrs*

Interplas Coatings Ltd, Lygon Buildings, Peartree Lane, Dudley, West Midlands, DY2 0QU Tel: (01384) 236327 Fax: (01384) 255428 E-mail: sales@interplascoatings.com *Paint spraying services*

Interplex PMP Ltd, Elliot Industrial Estate, Arbroath, Angus, DD11 2NN Tel: (01241) 873867 Fax: (01241) 879597 E-mail: pmp@pmp-interplex.co.uk *Stampings for electronic industry*

Interpro Computers, 40 Blackburn Road, Darwen, Lancashire, BB3 1QJ Tel: (01254) 760917 Fax: (01254) 606797 *Computer accessories & repairs*

▶ InterProfile, Wellington Street, Long Eaton, Nottingham, NG10 4NF Tel: (07854) 435262 E-mail: info@interprofile.co.uk

Interquad Distribution Ltd, Rath House, 55-65 Uxbridge Road, Slough, SL1 1SG Tel: (01753) 536464 Fax: (01753) 898306 E-mail: info@interquad.com *Computer distributors*

▶ Interquartz, Pennine House, Salford Street, Bury, Lancashire, BL9 6YA Tel: 0161-763 3122 Fax: 0161-763 4029 E-mail: roy.stephenson@interquartz.co.uk *We manufacture premium quality analogue business telephones. As well as our standard ranges, we also have the capability to modify and customise our products in a variety of ways, to better fit your requirements. See our website for more details.*

▶ Interquest UK Ltd, 20-23 Grevibbe Street, London, EC1N 8SS Tel: (020) 7025 0100 Fax: (020) 7025 0101 E-mail: info@interquest.co.uk *I.T recruitment agents*

Interroll Ltd, Brunel Road, Earlstrees Industrial Estate, Corby, Northamptonshire, NN17 4UX Tel: (01536) 200322 Fax: (01536) 748505 E-mail: gb-sales@interroll.com *Interroll is one of the world's leading suppliers of components as well as subsystems and modules for materials handling, conveyor technology, and automation.*

Intersack Systems Ltd, 10 Foster La, Bolton, BL2 5HW Tel: 01204 532663 Fax: 01204 532663 *Sack handling & closing machines*

Interseals Engineers' Merchants, Lowlands Industrial Estate, Braye Road, Vale, Guernsey, GY3 5XG Tel: (01481) 246364 Fax: (01481) 248235 E-mail: sales@interseals.co.uk Principal Export Areas: Worldwide *Manufacturers of gaskets & oil seals, hydraulic packing & jointing*

Intersell Agencies Toys Nursery Agents, 8 Nelson Trade Centre, Nelson Street, Belfast, BT15 1BH Tel: (028) 9024 3730 Fax: (028) 9023 8327 *Toys importers*

Interserve, Consort House, Princes Road, Ferndown, Dorset, BH22 9JG Tel: (01202) 861702 Fax: (01202) 894325 E-mail: ferndown.office@interserveprojects.com *Building contractors & services*

Interserve Engineering Services Ltd, Intersection House, 110-120 Birmingham Road, West Bromwich, West Midlands, B70 6RP Tel: 0121-500 5000 Fax: 0121-525 5574 E-mail: info@interserve-eng.com *Building services engineers* Also at: Glasgow, Liverpool & Southampton

Interserve Holdings plc, Tilbury House, Ruscombe Park, Reading, RG10 9JU Tel: 0118-932 0123 Fax: 0118-932 0206 E-mail: info@interserveplc.co.uk *Infrastructure & facilities management*

▶ Interserve Industrial Services Ltd, Burcott Road, Bristol, BS11 8AD Tel: (01446) 753674 Fax: 0117-923 5299

▶ Interserve Industrial Services Ltd, Rough Hey Road, Grimsargh, Preston, PR2 5AR Tel: (01772) 792268 Fax: (01772) 703122 E-mail: info@interservices.co.uk

Interserve Industrial Services Ltd, PO Box 3, Redditch, Worcestershire, B98 0FH Tel: (01527) 507500 Fax: (01527) 507501 *Asbestos Solutions, Access solutions, Electrical Control and Instrumentation, Power Transmission and Distribution, Industrial Cleanaing and Industrial Painting, Protective Coatings, Training Division and Thermal Insulation.*

Interserve Project Service Ltd, Crabtree Manorway South, Belvedere, Kent, DA17 6BH Tel: (020) 8311 5500 Fax: (020) 8311 1701 E-mail: belvedere.office@interserveprojects.com *Building contractors & civil engineers*

Interserve Project Services Ltd, 395 George Road, Erdington, Birmingham, B23 7RZ Tel: 0121-344 4888 Fax: 0121-344 4801 E-mail: information@interserveprojects.com *Building & civing engineering contractors*

Interserve Project Services Ltd, Cambrian Buildings, Mount Stuart Square, Cardiff, CF10 5FL Tel: (029) 2048 1560 Fax: (029) 2048 3825 E-mail: cardiff.office@interserveprojects.com *Constructors building & civil engineers*

Interserve Project Services Ltd, 1 Thunderhead Ridge, Glass Houghton, Castleford, West Yorkshire, WF10 4UA Tel: (01977) 522300 Fax: (01977) 522301 E-mail: leeds.office@interserveprojects.com *Building contractors*

Interserve Project Services Ltd, Interserve House, Oberon Road, Exeter Business Park, Exeter, EX1 3QD Tel: (01392) 203350 Fax: (01392) 203347 E-mail: exeter.office@tilbury.co.uk *Building contractors*

Interserve Project Services Ltd, Balmoral Suite Windsor House, Troon Way Business Centre, Humberstone Lane, Leicester, LE4 9HA Tel: 0116-276 3773 Fax: 0116-276 2992 E-mail: leicester.office@interserveprojects.com *Building & civil engineering contractors*

Interserve Project Services Ltd, Clerk Street, Loanhead, Midlothian, EH20 9DP Tel: 0131-448 2800 Fax: 0131-448 2600 E-mail: edinburgh.office@interserveprojects.com *Building contractors*

Interserve Project Services Ltd, Tilbury House, Hermitage Lane, Mansfield, Nottinghamshire, NG18 5HE Tel: (01623) 633216 Fax: (01623) 659438 E-mail: mansfield.office@interserveprojects.com *Civil engineering contractors services*

Interserve Project Services Ltd, Ross Road, Stockton-On-Tees, Cleveland, TS18 2NN Tel: (01642) 675125 Fax: (01642) 601970 E-mail: stockton.office@interserveprojects.com *Building contractors*

Interserve Project Services Ltd, 138 Heol-Y-Gors, Cwmbwrla, Swansea, SA5 8LT Tel: (01792) 464001 Fax: (01792) 467499 E-mail: swansea.office@interserveprojects.com *Construction contractors services*

Interserve Projects Ltd, Edwinstowe House, High Street, Edwinstowe, Mansfield, Nottinghamshire, NG21 9PR Tel: (01623) 827840 Fax: (01623) 827841 E-mail: edwinstowe.office@interserveprojects.com *Civil engineering & water industry*

Interserve Property Services, 35 Station Road North, Newcastle upon Tyne, NE12 7AR Tel: 0191-215 1434 Fax: 0191-215 1435 E-mail: newcastle.office@interserveprojects.com *Building & construction company*

Interserve Site Services, Brickyard Road, Aldridge, Walsall, WS9 8YP Tel: (01922) 749000 Fax: (01922) 745973 E-mail: siteservices@interserveprojects.com *Site services*

Interserve Site Services, Woodhouse Drive, Wigan, Lancashire, WN6 7NT Tel: (01942) 236434 Fax: (01942) 824159 E-mail: wigan.office@interserveprojects.com *Building contractors*

Intersign Signs & Nameplates, 92 Bowesfield Lane, Stockton-on-Tees, Cleveland, TS18 3EU Tel: (01642) 674242 Fax: (01642) 617203 E-mail: intersign@lineone.net *Sign manufrs*

Intersoft Entertainment, Unit 1 Matheran Ho, 24 Newlands, Daventry, Northants, NN11 4DU Tel: 01327 703030 Fax: 01327 703397 *Computer software distributor*

Intersoft Systems & Programming Ltd, The Mill, Horton Road, Staines, Middlesex, TW19 6BJ Tel: (01753) 687979 Fax: (01753) 687655 E-mail: sales@intersoft.co.uk *Software developers*

▶ Interspace Ltd, Gate House, 1-3 St. John's Square, London, EC1M 4DH Tel: (020) 7251 6868 Fax: (020) 7253 6868 E-mail: info@interspace.ltd.uk *Interspace is a contractor specialising in fitting out and refurbishment of interior space, together with other construction related activities, working with clients and professionals in the financial, commercial and development sectors*

Interspace Communications Ltd, Fourth Floor Trafalgar House, 11 Waterloo Place, London, SW1Y 4AU Tel: (020) 7930 8001 Fax: (020) 7930 0465 E-mail: isclon@msn.com *Buying & manufacturers agents*

Intersped Logistics UK Ltd, Unit 9 Gatesway Business Centre, Tom Cribb Road, London, SE28 0EZ Tel: (020) 8316 4300 Fax: (020) 8316 1210 E-mail: logistics@intersped.co.uk *Haulage & freight transport agents*

Interspiro Ltd, 7 Hawksworth Road, Central Park, Telford, Shropshire, TF2 9TU Tel: (01952) 200190 Fax: (01952) 299805 E-mail: enquiries@interspiro.com *Breathing apparatus manufrs*

Intersplash Ltd, 14 London House, Canons Corner, Edgware, Middlesex, HA8 8AX Tel: (020) 8958 2002 Fax: (020) 8958 1810 *Washroom products, soap dispensers & air fresheners*

Interstart Ltd, Unit 8a Shirebrook Business Park, Acreage Lane, Shirebrook, Mansfield, Nottinghamshire, NG20 8RN Tel: (01623) 748987 Fax: (01623) 748987 *Auto eectrical suppliers*

Intersteel, European Business Pk, Taylors Lane, Oldbury, West Midlands, B69 2BN Tel: 0121-627 9279 Fax: 0121-627 9270 E-mail: sales@intersteel.co.uk *Tool steel stockholder*

Interstrip, 127 Downham Road, Tranmere, Birkenhead, Merseyside, CH42 6PA Tel: 01766 830141 E-mail: popsaw19@talktalk.com *Wirral,North Wales dust free parquet floor sanding , service*

▶ interstrip.co.uk, 127 Downham road, Tranmere, Birkenhead, Merseyside, CH42 6PA Tel: 0151-641 9925 E-mail: interstrip@talktalk.net *Dust free, Floor sanding,sealing ,repairs on the Wirral and North Wales,*

▶ InterSys Solutions Limited, 22 Pump Hill, loughton, Essex, IG10 1RU Tel: 07970 610002 E-mail: mg@intsl.com *InterSys is a small consultancy with over 10 years experience of*providing highly skilled and dedicated IT support.**With implementation and support expertise in a wide variety of technologies,*we can provide one of our consultants to assist you.**Our client list includes organisations as diverse as city financial institutions*and small family run manufacturing businesses.**InterSys takes prides in the absolute satisfaction of our clients*and believe in the importance of maintaining your business functionality at all times.**

Intersystem Ltd, 10 Edenham Close, Lower Earley, Reading, RG6 3TH Tel: 0118-926 1187 Fax: 0118-926 2224 E-mail: sales@intersystem.co.uk *Computer dealers*

Intertec, Unit 5, Verwood Industrial Estate, Black Hill, Verwood, Dorset, BH31 6HA Tel: (01202) 822277 Fax: (01202) 821188 E-mail: sales@intertec-inst.co.uk *Manufacturers of cabinets (glass fibre/GRP), enclosures (glass fibre) (instrumentation) & glass fibre kiosks*

▶ Intertek Caleb Brett Ltd, Rossmore Industrial Estate, Rosscliffe Road, Ellesmere Port, CH65 3BS Tel: 0151-355 2005 Fax: 0151-355 2006 E-mail: uklaboratory@intertek.com *Petroleum technology*

▶ Intertek Caleb Brett, Caleb Brett House, 734 London Road, West Thurrock, Grays, Essex, RM20 3NL Tel: (01708) 680200 Fax: (01708) 680264 E-mail: uklaboratory@intertek.com *Laboratory testing experts & services*

▶ Intertek Caleb Brett Ltd, Seal Sands, Middlesbrough, Cleveland, TS2 1UB Tel: (01642) 546669 E-mail: cbopperation.teeside@intertek.com *Tests fuels manufrs*

▶ Intertek Testing Services U K Ltd, Avonmouth Dock, Bristol, BS11 9DH Tel: 0117-982 4807 Fax: 0117-982 2290 E-mail: cb.avonmouth@intertek.com *Test imports & exports*

▶ Intertek Testing Services (U K) Ltd, Western Jetty, Immingham Dock, Immingham, South Humberside, DN40 2NT Tel: (01469) 572353 Fax: (01469) 571197

continued

E-mail: uklaboratory@intertek.com *Chemical testing services*

Intertex Data Systems Ltd, 29 Abington Road, Kensington, London, W8 6AH Tel: (020) 8870 6924 Fax: 020 88706924 *Computer software development & sales*

▶ Intertex UK Ltd, 6 St Gildas Close, Langport, Somerset, TA10 9QH Tel: (01458) 252060 Fax: 01458 252977 E-mail: itexuk@aol.com *Supplier of Spunbonded Polypropylene Fabric, Cushion Ticks (Inner Bag for filling with polyester fibre))*

Intertrain Executrain, Witan Court, 294 Witan Gate West, Milton Keynes, MK9 1EJ Tel: (01908) 206700 Fax: (01908) 206701 *Computer training services*

Intertronics Electronic Equipment Component, 17a Station Field Industrial Estate, Kidlington, Oxfordshire, OX5 1JD Tel: (01865) 842842 Fax: (01865) 842172 E-mail: enquiries@intertronics.co.uk *Adhesives specialists manufrs*

▶ Intervend, 31 Abbey Road, West Bridgford, Nottingham, NG2 5NG Tel: 0115-981 0100 *Water suppliers*

Intervet UK Ltd, Walton Manor, Walton, Milton Keynes, MK7 7AJ Tel: (01908) 665050 Fax: (01908) 664778 E-mail: info@intervet.com *Veterinary preparations manufrs*

Intervideo Video Filming Equipment, 87 Boundary Road, London, NW8 0RG Tel: (020) 7624 1711 Fax: (020) 7624 2683 E-mail: admin@intervideo.co.uk *Video tape duplicators*

Intervoice, Brite Court, Park Road, Gatley, Cheadle, Cheshire, SK8 4HZ Tel: 0161-495 1000 Fax: 0161-495 1001 E-mail: sales@intervoice-brite.com *Voice response & enhanced telecommunications*

▶ Interweave Consulting Ltd, 21 The Drove Horton Heath, Horton Heath, Eastleigh, Hampshire, SO50 7NX Tel: (023) 8060 1752 Fax: (0870) 1343404 E-mail: sales@iwcon.net *Business web consulting agency*

Interworld, Avenue Road, Lasham, Alton, Hampshire, GU34 5SU Tel: (01256) 381641 Fax: (01256) 381378 *Plant & marine equipment suppliers*

Interwoven Europe, Novell House, 1 Arlington Square Downshire Way, Bracknell, Berkshire, RG12 1WA Tel: (01344) 418600 Fax: (01344) 418602 E-mail: info@interwoven.com *Software developer, distributor*

Intex Controls Ltd, Tonbridge Road, Hadlow, Tonbridge, Kent, TN11 0AH Tel: (01732) 850360 Fax: (01732) 852133 E-mail: sales@stonel.impex.com *Manufacturer of valve/damper actuation, communication, monitoring & control systems as used in the oil & gas, power generation, marine & process industries.*

Intex Management Services Ltd, 6 Regent Park, Booth Drive, Wellingborough, Northamptonshire, NN8 6GR Tel: (01933) 402255 Fax: (01933) 402266 E-mail: enquiries@imsresearch.com *Market research services for electronics*

Intex Precision Grinders & Engineers, Bumble Bee Gardens, Sharnford, Hinckley, Leicestershire, LE10 3PD Tel: (01455) 274165 *Precision grinding services*

Intex Software Ltd, Diamond Court, Douglas Close, Preston Farm Industrial Estate, Stockton-on-Tees, Cleveland, TS18 3TP Tel: (01642) 672200 Fax: (01642) 671199 E-mail: sales@intex.co.uk *Computer payroll software specialists*

▶ Intext Bespoke, Tameside Works, Dukinfield, Cheshire, SK16 5PT Tel: 0161-339 1285 Fax: 0161-344 2744 E-mail: sales@intextjoinery.co.uk *Manufacturers of bespoke furniture*

Intier Automotive Ltd, Golden Valley Mill, Mill Lane, Bitton, Bristol, BS30 6HL Tel: 0117-932 5656 Fax: 0117-932 7525 *Motor door panels manufrs*

Intier Automotive Seating Ltd, Newmanleys Road, New Eastwood, Nottingham, NG16 3JG Tel: (01773) 716131 Fax: (01773) 712587 *Car seating designers*

Intier Automotives, Tachbrook Park Industrial Estate, Apollo Way, Warwick, CV34 6RW Tel: (01926) 468800 Fax: (01926) 468801 *Automotive interiors*

Intime Engineering Ledbury Ltd, 7c Lower Road, Ledbury, Herefordshire, HR8 2DH Tel: (01531) 633450 Fax: (01531) 635197 E-mail: colin@intime-eng.com *Precision engineers*

▶ Into Africa, The Market, Carmarthen, Dyfed, SA31 1QY Tel: (01267) 232333

Into Design, 8 Dyke Road Avenue, Brighton, BN1 5LB Tel: (01273) 330070 E-mail: intodesi@btconnect.com *Giftware manufrs*

▶ Intoco, Unit 7 Bamfurlong Industrial Park, Staverton, Cheltenham, Gloucestershire, GL51 6SX Tel: (01452) 712519 Fax: (01452) 714786 E-mail: sales@intoco.co.uk *Stockholders of hot work toolsteels*

Intona Imaging, Middlebrook Way, Holt Road, Cromer, Norfolk, NR27 9JR Tel: (01263) 517007 Fax: (01263) 517002 E-mail: info@intona.com *Computer consumables, laser & inkjet cartridges for all major printer manufacturers*

▶ In-Toon Ltd, 17b Beacon Hill, London, N7 9LY Tel: (020) 7609 2071 E-mail: enquiries@intoononline.com *Established in 2001, InToon Productions has foraged forward to be one of the most dynamic creative houses world wide. We are continuously striving to bring a collective of the most talent professionals together under one roof, with a wide variety of skills providing a significant benefit to our clients. Skills including: Flash Animation, 3-D and 2-D animation, Web Design, Soft Game Production, E-Card and Banner Production, Caricatures, Presentations and Advertising, Promotional Video Production. All our clients' projects big or small are produced to the highest standard by our team of highly experienced professionals.*

Intoto Furniture, 46-48 Barbourne Road, Worcester, WR1 1HU Tel: (01905) 24760 Fax: (01905) 726003 E-mail: worcester@intoto.co.uk *Kitchen manufrs*

Intoximeters UK Ltd, The Alpha Centre, Babbage Road, Totnes, Devon, TQ9 5JA Tel: (01803) 868602 Fax: (01803) 868701 *Breathalyser equipment distributors*

Intra Ltd, 27 Wilbury Way, Hitchin, Hertfordshire, SG4 0TS Tel: (01462) 422111 Fax: (01462) 453667 E-mail: info@intra-corp.co.uk *Measuring instrument manufrs*

Intra Systems Ltd, 202 Northwood Lane, Newcastle, Staffordshire, ST5 4DD Tel: (01270) 753509 *Computer systems consultants*

Intracel Ltd, 4 Station Road, Shepreth, Royston, Hertfordshire, SG8 6PZ Tel: (01763) 262680 Fax: (01763) 262676 E-mail: intracel@intracel.co.uk *Research equipment*

Intrada Shipping & Trading Associates Ltd, 75 Main Road, Gidea Park, Romford, RM2 5EL Tel: (01708) 739353 Fax: (01708) 739252 *Chartering & shipping agents*

Intralox Ltd, Building 90, Third Avenue, Pensnett Trading Estate, Kingswinford, West Midlands, DY6 7FW Tel: (0800) 894392 Fax: (01384) 355655 *Manufacturers of plastic conveyor belting*

Intram Barwell Ltd, Barwell Business Park, Leatherhead Road, Chessington, Surrey, KT9 2NY Tel: (020) 8391 7500 Fax: (020) 8974 1629 E-mail: enquiries@ibl.co.uk *Lighting equipment & transformer manufrs*

▶ Intranetmanagers, Swan House, White Hart Street, High Wycombe, Buckinghamshire, HP11 2HL Tel: (01494) 463311 E-mail: sales@intranetmanagers.co.uk

Intras Ltd, Perseus House, Chapel Court Holly Walk, Leamington Spa, Warwickshire, CV32 4YS Tel: (01926) 334137 Fax: (01926) 314755 E-mail: intras@intras.co.uk *Publishers of bi-monthly technical journals*

Intrim Fabrications, The Workshop, Tyte Farm, Sandford, St. Martin, Oxford, OX7 7AH Tel: (01608) 683338 Fax: (01608) 683338 *Steel fabricators*

▶ Intrinsic Surveillance & Investigations, P.O. Box 170, St. Austell, Cornwall, PL25 5DS Tel: 01726 66419 Fax: 0871 2421051 E-mail: intrinsic@tiscali.co.uk *Covert Surveillance in Rural & Urban Environs,Video & Photo Evidence,Process Serving, Tracing,Statement Taking ,Locus Reports also Installation of Electronic Surveillance Systems.*

Intrinsyc Europe, Fountain House, Great Cornbow, Halesowen, West Midlands, B63 3BL Tel: 0121-501 6000 Fax: 0121-501 6035 *Electronic design & consultancy*

Intro 2020 Ltd, Unit 1, Priors Way, Maidenhead, Berkshire, SL6 2HP Tel: (01628) 674411 Fax: (01628) 771055 E-mail: jane@intro2020.co.uk *Photographic wholesale distributors*

Intro Marketing Ltd, Old Freight Depot, Roberts Road, Doncaster, South Yorkshire, DN4 0JW Tel: (01302) 320269 Fax: (01302) 340678 E-mail: sales@intro.co.uk *Automotive chemicals manufrs*

Introland Ltd, Access House, 2 Bilton Road, Erith, Kent, DA8 2AN Tel: (01322) 339595 Fax: (01322) 339994 E-mail: enquiries@introland-testing.com *Fall arrest & safety restraint specialists supplying a fast efficient service via ecommerce. Supply of eyebolts, wire systems, handrails, deadweight, pushlok, signage, ladder restraints. Supply to whole of UK*

Intronics Fire Protection Consultants, 122 Broadmead, Tunbridge Wells, Kent, TN2 5RW Tel: (01892) 516366 Fax: (01892) 512212 E-mail: sales@intronics.co.uk *Flame detectors & explosion detection & supression systems for civilian & military applications*

IntroVision, Units 6-7, The Glover Centre, 23-25 Bury Mead Road, Hitchin, Hertfordshire, SG4 1RP Tel: (01462) 459400 Fax: (01462) 459500 E-mail: introvision@ukonline.co.uk Principal Export Areas: Worldwide *Endoscopes & industrial periscope manufrs*

Intruder 2000 Group Ltd, 47a Newbold Rd, Newbold, Chesterfield, Derbyshire, S41 7PG Tel: 01246 272023 Fax: 01246 239997 *Security alarm distribution*

▶ Intruder Protection Services Ltd, 2 Wenban Road, Worthing, West Sussex, BN11 1HY Tel: (01903) 204845 *Security Systems and Services. Installation and Maintenance of Intruder Alarms,Fire Alarms, CCTV, Access Control and Nurse call systems covering Sussex, Hampshire, Surrey and London areas. 24 Hour*

Intruder Security Services, Security House 6-7 The Downs, Great Dunmow, Dunmow, Essex, CM6 1DS Tel: (01279) 758870 Fax: (01371) 879201 E-mail: info@intruder.co.uk *Security systems installers*

Intrum Justitia Group, Warwick House, Birmingham Road, Stratford-Upon-Avon, Warwickshire, CV37 0BP Tel: (01789) 415181 Fax: (01789) 412072 *Debt collection services & credit management consultants*

Intrusion Security Services, 1 Ancells Court, Rye Close, Fleet, Hampshire, GU51 2UY Tel: (01252) 812030 Fax: (01252) 812040 E-mail: sales@intrusion.com *Security networking*

IntTechCo, 88 Maplewell Road, Woodhouse Eaves, Loughborough, Leicestershire, LE12 8RA Tel: (01509) 891172 *Pc components retailers*

Intuitive Business Solutions Ltd, 8 The Spinney, Haywards Heath, W. Sussex, RH16 1PL Tel: 01444 443175 *Computer consultants*

▶ Intuitive Solution, 4 Suffolk Road, Lowestoft, Suffolk, NR32 1DZ Tel: (01502) 587613 Fax: (01502) 514875 E-mail: sales@intuitivesolutions.net *IT, networks & internet solutions specialists*

Intumescent Protective Coatings Ltd, 1 Jupiter Court Orion Business Park, Tyne Tunnel Trading Estate, North Shields, Tyne & Wear, NE29 7SE Tel: 0191-272 8225 Fax: 0191-272 8226 *Fire protection services*

▶ Intutive IT, Ladypool Road, Birmingham, B12 8LF Tel: 0121-446 6951

▶ Inty Ltd, 1700 Aztec West, Almondsbury, Bristol, BS32 4UA Tel: (01454) 640500 Fax: (0870) 0104689 E-mail: neil.watson@inty.com *Internet service provider*

▶ Inurface Solutions Ltd, Unit H Anton Studios, 2-8 Anton Street, London, E8 2AD Tel: 0207 241 1200 Fax: 0207 241 2800 E-mail: eion@inurface.co.uk *As an Information & Technology provide we provide consultancy and support on most Microsoft compatible systems, we are also an accredited Sage Business Partner. We are currently launching our new product, SageLink-CMS at an Introductory offer (50% refund on all purchases before the 31 March 2005).*SageLink-CMS, is designed for any company with commission paid sales staff. It o actively monitors commission due and paid against all generated sales. With links to Sage Line 50/100 and Sage Payroll, the system will generate Sales orders and invoices in Sage, calculates commission due and update Sage Payroll with the appropriate payment for the respect sales staff.****

Inva Care Ltd, M S S House, Taffs Fall Road, Treforest Industrial Estate, Pontypridd, Mid Glamorgan, CF37 5TT Tel: (01443) 849222 Fax: (01656) 649016 E-mail: uk@inva-care.com *Medical products mattresses & cushion suppliers*

Invacare Ltd, South Road, Bridgend Industrial Estate, Bridgend, Mid Glamorgan, CF31 3PY Tel: (01656) 664321 Fax: (01656) 667532 E-mail: sales@invacare.com *Wheelchair & rehabilitation equipment manufrs*

Invarmex (UK) Ltd, Unit 5, Hollygate Lane Industrial Park, Cotgrave, Nottingham, NG12 3JW Tel: 0115-989 4420 Fax: 0115-989 4463 E-mail: uk@invarmex.com *Swimming pool product manufrs*

Invedia Ltd, 32 Hatton Garden, London, EC1N 8DL Tel: (020) 7242 8965 Fax: (020) 7242 5036 E-mail: koppelman@clara.net *Industrial diamond merchants*

Invek Foods, 18 Birmingham Road, Walsall, WS1 2LT Tel: (01922) 725820 Fax: (01922) 616548 *Poultry processors*

Invensys P.L.C., Portland House, Bressend Place, London, SW1E 5BF Tel: (020) 7834 3848 Fax: (020) 7834 3879 E-mail: sales@invensys.com *Electronic engineering* Also at: Birmingham, Newcastle, Windsor & Wokingham

Invensys Building Systems, Unit 3 Earls Court, Fifth Avenue, Team Valley Trading Estate, Gateshead, Tyne & Wear, NE11 0HF Tel: 0191-499 4500 Fax: 0191-499 4501 E-mail: andrew.kingston@invensys.com *Controlling heating & ventilation systems*

Invensys Metering Systems Ltd, Unit 11 The Quadrangle, Premier Way, Romsey, Hampshire, SO51 9DL Tel: (01794) 526100 Fax: (01794) 526101 E-mail: romseysales@invensys.com *Gas meter manufrs*

Invensys Systems (UK) Ltd, Highbank House, Exchange Street, Stockport, Cheshire, SK3 0ET Tel: 0161-429 6744 Fax: 0161-480 9063 *Computer systems consultants*

Invensys Systems (UK) TLtd, 2 City Place, Beehive Ring Road, London Gatwick Airport, Gatwick, West Sussex, RH6 0PA Tel: (01293) 527777 Fax: (01293) 552640 *Safety shutdown systems manufrs*

▶ Invent Calibration Services, 85 Southdown Road, Harpenden, Hertfordshire, AL5 1PR Tel: (01582) 461666 Fax: (01582) 460077 E-mail: sales@invent-uk.com *Airflow containment manufrs*

Invent Water Treatment Ltd, 2 Hurst Street, Rochdale, Lancashire, OL11 1BH Tel: (01706) 359155 Fax: (01706) 653598 E-mail: sales@inventwater.com *Water treatment plant equipment & water feature designers*

Inventair Fabrications, Carnaby Industrial Estate, Lancaster Road, Carnaby, Bridlington, North Humberside, YO15 3QY Tel: (01262) 400919 Fax: (01262) 401358 E-mail: david@inventair.co.uk *Quality fabricators-dust extraction engineers*

▶ Invention Machine Ltd, 26 Granta Park, Great Abington, Cambridge, CB21 6AL Tel: (01223) 890873 E-mail: sales@invention-machine.com *Computer software suppliers*

Inventor-Net.Com Ltd, 27 President Buildings, President Way, Sheffield, S4 7UR Tel: 0114-275 7494 Fax: 0114-263 4325 E-mail: district5775@rgis.com *Inventory specialists*

▶ Inver House Distillers Ltd, Balmenach Distillery, Cromdale, Grantown-on-Spey, Morayshire, PH26 3PF Tel: (01479) 872569 Fax: (01479) 873829 *Spirits*

Inverawe Smokehouses, Inverawe, Inverawe, Taynuilt, Argyll, PA35 1HU Tel: (01866) 822777 Fax: (01866) 822274 E-mail: info@inverawe.co.uk *Fish smokers & curers*

Inverclean Services Ltd, Port Glasgow Road, Greenock, Renfrewshire, PA15 2UD Tel: (01475) 744223 Fax: (01475) 744224 E-mail: sales@inverclean.co.uk *Office cleaning services*

▶ Inverhouse Distilleries, Speyburn Distillery House, Rothes, Aberlour, Banffshire, AB38 7AG Tel: (01340) 831213 Fax: (01340) 831678 *Distillers*

Inverkeithing Trophy & Engraving Centre, 29 Church Street, Inverkeithing, Fife, KY11 1LG Tel: (01383) 411348 Fax: (01383) 411348 *Engraving services*

Inverlane Marine Services Ltd, 15 Lintlaw Drive, Glasgow, G52 2NS Tel: 0141-883 4834 Fax: 0141-882 8874 E-mail: sales@inverlane-marine.co.uk *Marine equipment distributors*

Inverloch Cheese Co., 22 Kirk Street, Campbeltown, Argyll, PA28 6BL Tel: (01586) 552692 Fax: (01586) 554729 *Cheese manufrs*

Inverness Bearings & Transmission, 5 Harbour Road, Inverness, IV1 1SY Tel: (01463) 243528 Fax: (01463) 225039 *Bearing distribtrs*

▶ Inverness Caledonian Thistle Football Club, Caledonian Stadium, Stadium Road, Inverness, IV1 1FF Tel: (01463) 222880

Inverness Computer Centre, 21-23 Greig Street, Inverness, IV3 5PX Tel: (01463) 239999 Fax: (01463) 710003 E-mail: info@invcomps.co.uk *Computer services & network sales*

Inverness Courier, Stadium Drive, Inverness, IV1 1FF Tel: (01463) 233059 Fax: (01463) 238223 E-mail: sales@inverness-courier.co.uk *Printers & publishing services*

Invertec Ltd, Whelford Road, Fairford, Gloucestershire, GL7 4DT Tel: (01285) 713550 Fax: (01285) 713548 E-mail: sales@invertec.co.uk *Low voltage fluorescent lighting & inverters*

Invertrophy.com, Suit 90, 24 Station Square, Academy Street, Inverness, IV1 1LD Tel: (01463) 238495 Fax: (01463) 729719 E-mail: sales@invertorphy.com *Trophy retailers & engravers*

Inverurie Pre-Cast Ltd, 14 Keith Hall Road, Inverurie, Aberdeenshire, AB51 3UA Tel: (01467) 624367 Fax: (01467) 672145 *Precast concrete manufacturer*

Invesco Asset Management Ltd, 30 Finsbury Square, London, EC2A 1AG Tel: (020) 7065 4000 Fax: (020) 7638 0752 E-mail: enquiry@invescoperpetual.co.uk *Finance agent*

▶ Invest Northern Ireland, 44-58 May Street, Belfast, BT1 4NN Tel: (028) 9023 9090 Fax: (028) 9049 0490 E-mail: info@investni.com *Government agents* Also at: Ballymena, Londonderry, Newry & Omagh

Investec 1 Ltd, 2 Gresham Street, London, EC2V 7QP Tel: (020) 7597 4000 Fax: (020) 7597 4070 E-mail: info@investec.com *Bankers & financial services*

Investec Trust (Jersey) Ltd, PO Box 344, Jersey, JE4 8UW Tel: (01534) 512512 Fax: (01534) 512513 E-mail: enquiries@investectrust.com *Trust, company & management services*

▶ Investigator Direct (Operations) Limited, Floor Six, 456 - 458 Strand, London, WC2R 0DZ Tel: 0870 9903211 Fax: 0870 9903212 E-mail: admin@id-net.co.uk *Discreet and Confidential Established Private Investigators and Enquiry Agents working for Corporate, Legal and Private Client Sectors focused on providing low cost solutions without compromise to high standards.*

▶ Investment Castings Ltd, 130 Great North Road, Birchwood Industrial Estate, Hatfield, Hertfordshire, AL9 5JN Tel: (01707) 262871 Fax: (01707) 271565 E-mail: investmentcastings130@yahoo.co.uk *Lost wax castings manufactured in any metal for all industries, - top quality components delivered on time & at competitive prices. Contact us for a fast response*

Investment Castings Congleton Ltd, Greenfield Farm Industrial Estate, Congleton, Cheshire, CW12 4TR Tel: (01260) 280181 Fax: (01260) 298208 E-mail: info@investment-castings.co.uk *Engineering foundry lost wax castings manufrs*

Investment Management Association, 65 Kingsway, London, WC2B 6TD Tel: (020) 7831 0898 Fax: (020) 7831 9975 *Trade associations & organisations*

Investment Tooling International Ltd, 4a Moston Road, Middleton, Manchester, M24 1SL Tel: 0161-653 8066 Fax: 0161-655 3095 *Plastic mould tool manufrs*

Investment Tooling International Ltd, Sidings Road, Lowmoor Business Park, Kirkby-in-Ashfield, Nottingham, NG17 7JZ Tel: (01623) 754814 Fax: (01623) 754914 E-mail: sales@iti-kirkby.co.uk *Toolmakers & precision engineers*

Investors In People UK, 7-10 Chandos Street, London, W1G 9DQ Tel: (020) 7467 1900 Fax: (020) 7636 2386 E-mail: information@iipuk.co.uk *Service responsible for peoples national standards*

Investors Planning Associates Ltd, Mimosa House, 12 Princes Street, Hanover Square, London, W1B 2LL Tel: (020) 7499 0325 Fax: (020) 7408 0640 *Financial advisors*

Invicta, Westland Square, Leeds, LS11 5SS Tel: 0113-277 1222 Fax: 0113-271 6860 E-mail: sale@invictafork.co.uk *Steel fabricators*

Invicta Analytical Services, Alexandra House, 5 Blyth Road, Bromley, BR1 3RS Tel: (020) 8290 5629 Fax: (020) 8290 4443 E-mail: admin@invictaas.co.uk *Asbestos test analysts*

Invicta Bakeware Ltd, Westgate Business Park, Westgate Carr Road, Pickering, North Yorkshire, YO18 8LX Tel: (01751) 473483 Fax: (01751) 476522 E-mail: sales@invictabakeware.co.uk *Bakery equipment manufacturers*

Invicta (Borough Green Sawmills) Ltd, Invicta Business Centre, Beach Hill Way, Gillingham, Kent, ME8 6PT Tel: (01732) 882012 Fax: (01732) 883062 E-mail: enquiries@invictabgs.co.uk *Pallet & case manufrs*

Invicta Borough Saw Mills, Unit 14, Invicta Buisiness Park, Gillingham, Kent, ME8 6TT Tel: (01732) 882012 E-mail: enquiries@invictabgs.co.uk *Export packers & case manufrs*

Invicta Cleaning Supplies Ltd, 46 Dale Wood Road, Orpington, Kent, BR6 0BZ Tel: (01689) 898785 Fax: (01689) 898785 *Cleaning suppliers*

Invicta Forks & Attachments, Westland Square, Dewsbury Road, Leeds, LS11 5SS Tel: 0113-277 1222 Fax: 0113-271 6860 E-mail: sales@invictaforks.co.uk Principal Export Areas: Worldwide *Fork lift truck attachment manufrs*

Invicta Retail Systems Ltd, 18-20 Newington Road, Ramsgate, Kent, CT12 6EE Tel: (01843) 586955 Fax: (01843) 850543 E-mail: sales@eposgroup.co.uk *Invicta Retail Systems Ltd based in Kent offers hospitality EPoS computer systems, cashless systems and cash registers.*

Invicta Telephone Sales Ltd, Unit 30 Branbridges Industrial Estate, Branbridges Road, East Peckham, Tonbridge, Kent, TN12 5HF Tel: (01622) 870550 Fax: (01622) 870569 E-mail: enquires@itslimited.com *Telecommunications consultants*

Invicta Toys & Games Ltd, PO Box 9, Leicester, LE2 4LB Tel: 0116-272 0555 Fax: 0116-272 0626 E-mail: sales@invictagroup.co.uk Principal Export Areas: Worldwide *Educational material & equipment manufrs*

▶ Invicta Vac Ltd, Two Pines, Sandwich Industrial Estate, Sandwich, Kent, CT13 9LY Tel: (01304) 612514 Fax: (01304) 613120 E-mail: info@invictavac.com

Invicta Valves Ltd, Units 10-11, Boxmend, Bircholt Road, Parkwood Industrial Estate, Maidstone, Kent, ME15 9XT Tel: (01622) 754613 Fax: (01622) 750436 E-mail: sales@invictavalves.co.uk *Valve distribs*

Invictor Neon Signs Ltd, Unit 3, Vernon Works, Nottingham Road, Nottingham, NG6 0FU Tel: 0115-911 3113 Fax: 0115-978 0880 *Neon sign & tubing manufrs*

▶ Invictus Locks & Security, 10c Carnock Road, Dunfermline, Fife, KY12 9AX Tel: (07726) 012000 E-mail: invictuslocks@tiscali.co.uk *A mobile Locksmith and intruder alarm installer covering east central Scotland.Specialist in UPVc locking systems.No call out charges and response within 1 hr*

▶ Invigorative Ltd, 3 26-28 Finchley Road, London, NW8 6ES Tel: (020) 7722 7673 E-mail: office@invigorative.com *As leaders in cross industry consultancy, Invigorative"s business service arm delivers results to the government, education and health care sectors. **The four distinct services we provide include management development, organisational troubleshooting, cultural change and organisational healthcare.**Our sound expertise in aligning both the hard end of business operations and the drives of all stakeholders is what we are recognised for. **The benefit is that we provide expert business analysis and innovative solution finding so that your organisation can build its systems, structure and strategy upon the strong foundation of motivated and engaged people.**

The Invincible Electrical Engineering Company Ltd, Bay 2 Building 1, Dandy Bank Road, Pensnett Trading Estate, Kingswinford, West Midlands, DY6 7PP Tel: (01384) 270114 Fax: (01384) 400155 *Electric motor repairers & rewind specialists*

Inviron Ltd, 17 Portman Road, Ipswich, IP1 2BP Tel: (01473) 219921 Fax: (01473) 231317 *Heating element manufrs* Also at: London NW10 & Norwich

Inviron Ltd, Deben House, 1 Selsdon Way, City Harbour, London, E14 9GL Tel: (020) 7515 5511 Fax: (020) 7515 5551 E-mail: admin@inviron.co.uk Principal Export Areas: Worldwide *Mechanical & electrical engineering services*

▶ Invisible Heating Systems Ltd, Morefield Industrial Estate, Ullapool, Ross-Shire, IV26 2SR Tel: (01854) 613161 Fax: (01854) 613160 E-mail: design@invisibleheating.co.uk

▶ Invision, 5 Eastern Way, Bury St. Edmunds, Suffolk, IP32 7AB Tel: (01284) 749731 Fax: (01284) 747336 E-mail: info@invisionuk.com

▶ Invision Supplies Ltd, 6 Minister Court, Frogmore, St. Albans, Hertfordshire, AL2 2NF Tel: (01727) 766150 Fax: (01727) 758746 E-mail: office@invisionssupplies.com *From Binders Manufacturing, Design to Print, Cd/DVD Duplicating Services*

▶ Invista (UK) Ltd, 60 Clooney Road, Londonderry, BT47 6TH Tel: (028) 7186 0860 *Textiles*

▶ Invoice Finance Ltd, Highfield Close, Kenilworth, Warwickshire, CV8 1QR Tel: (01926) 512876 Fax: (01926) 512876 E-mail: brianbwood@aol.com *Invoice Finance Limited is a specialist Factor broking business to over 70 UK Factors and Discounters.*From new starts to large PLCs we can help you fund your business*

Involvement Packaging Ltd, Park Road, Stalybridge, Cheshire, SK15 1TA Tel: 0161-338 2807 Fax: 0161-338 2807 E-mail: salesstalybridge@involvementpkg.co.uk *Metal & plastic container distributors*

Involvement Packaging Ltd, Chesterton Estate Yard, Banbury Road, Lighthorne, Warwick, CV35 0AJ Tel: (01926) 651800 Fax: (01926) 651177 E-mail: robert@involvementpkg.co.uk *Rigid plastic packaging*

Involvement Packing Ltd, Overthorpe Road, Banbury, Oxfordshire, OX16 4SY Tel: (01295) 258059 Fax: (01295) 265817 E-mail: ipl@ipl-involvement.co.uk *Case makers & export packers*

Involvement & Participation Association Ltd, 42 Colebrooke Row, London, N1 8AF Tel: (020) 7354 8040 Fax: (020) 7354 8041 E-mail: involve@ipa-involve.com *Personnel management consultants*

Invotec Circuits, Unit A1 Halesfield 11, Telford, Shropshire, TF7 4PH Tel: (01952) 683000 Fax: (01952) 683456 E-mail: sales@invotecgroup.com *Printed circuit board manufrs*

▶ Invotec Circuits Tamworth Ltd, 2-28 Hedging Lane, Wilnecote, Tamworth, Staffordshire, B77 5EP Tel: (01827) 263000

Invotec Circuits Tamworth Ltd, 2-28 Hedging Lane, Wilnecote, Tamworth, Staffordshire, B77 5EP Tel: (01827) 263000 Fax: (01827) 263230 E-mail: firstname.surname@invertechgroup.com *Printed circuit board manufrs*

▶ Invotec Solutions, 18 High Greeve, Wootton, Northampton, NN4 6BA Tel: (01604) 876831 Fax: (0845) 8381520 E-mail: info@invotecsolutions.co.uk *Invotec Solutions philosophy is to bring innovative products that add real value to our customer's process within the polymer sector. UK and Eire distributors of Athena Inc. Hot Runner Systems and Process Control, IPS Mould Shields, Curtains, Drum Covers and Drop Chutes along with the industries leading ejector couplings from CTL.*

Inwido UK Ltd, Po Box 10, Droitwich, Worcestershire, WR9 8ES Tel: (01527) 881060 Fax: (01527) 881061 E-mail: mail@inwido.co.uk *A range of high performance windows includes double & triple glazed wndows manufactured to the highest standards in either Swedish redwood or in a complete timber/aluminium construction*

▶ Inwood (Cymru) Ltd, Units 65-65, Greenfield Business Centre, Greenfield, Holywell, Flintshire, CH8 7GR Tel: (01352) 718007 Fax: (01352) 719614

continued

continuation
E-mail: enquiries@woodworkersuk.co.uk *Manufacturer wooden gates & garage doors in hardwood or softwood*

IODS Ltd, 3 Langlands Court, Kelvin South Business Park, East Kilbride, Glasgow, G75 0YG Tel: (01355) 249224 Fax: (01355) 248836 E-mail: ff@iodsltd.com Principal Export Areas: Worldwide *Weld overlay cladding services*

Ioko 365 UK Ltd, Innovation Close, York Centre Science Park, Heslington, York, YO1 5ZD Tel: (01904) 438000 *Computer consultants*

Iolair Signs, Hardengreen Coach Works, Dalkeith, Midlothian, EH22 3LD Tel: 0131-663 2483 Fax: 0131-663 2497E-mail: iolairsigns@aol.com *Sign makers*

Ion Science Ltd, The Way, Fowlmere, Royston, Herts, SG8 7UJ Tel: (01763) 208503 Fax: (01763) 208814 E-mail: info@ionscience.com Principal Export Areas: Worldwide *A designer and manufacturer of highly sensitive gas and leak detectors, for worldwide sale. Specialising in photo ionisation detectors (PID's), SF6 detectors and the measurement of hydrogen permeation through steel.*

▶ Iona Flooring Services Ltd, 109 Langside Drive, Glasgow, G43 2SX Tel: 0141-637 7444 Fax: 0141 6375026 E-mail: ionaflooring@aol.com *Supply, installation and repair of commercial and industrial floorcoverings and vinyl wall claddings. Over 25 years experience.*

Iona Ventilation Co. Ltd, 320 Pinkston Road, Glasgow, G4 0LP Tel: 0141-331 2606 Fax: 0141-333 1055 *Ventilation engineers*

Ionbond Ltd, Factory 36 Number One Industrial Estate, Medomsley Road, Consett, County Durham, DH8 6TS Tel: (01207) 500823 Fax: (01207) 590254 E-mail: info@ionbond.com *Chemical & vapour deposition services*

▶ Ionga, 145-157 St. John Street, London, EC1V 4PY Tel: (0870) 1999852 Fax: (0870) 1330704 E-mail: info@ionga.co.uk *Online PC Systems, Servers, Parts & Accessories*

Ionic Instruments Ltd, Henfield Road, Small Dole, Henfield, West Sussex, BN5 9XE Tel: (01273) 493522 Fax: (01273) 493630 E-mail: *Thermocouple & compression fittings manufrs*

▶ Ionic Solutions, Manningham Mills, Heaton Road, Bradford, West Yorkshire, BD9 4SH Tel: (01274) 549399 Fax: (0845) 6585599 E-mail: information@ionicsolutions.co.uk *Chemical manufrs*

Ionics UK Ltd, 3 Mercury Park, Mercury Way, Urmston, Manchester, M41 7LY Tel: 0161-866 9337 Fax: 0161-866 9630 *Water analysing equipment manufrs*

Iota Device Programming Ltd, Unit A1, Sandy Business Park, Gosforth Close, Sandy, Bedfordshire, SG19 1RB Tel: (01767) 692228 Fax: (01767) 699927 E-mail: sales@iotadpl.co.uk *Device programming services*

▶ IP Centrex Ltd, Unit 5, South Lodge Court, Ironsbottom, Sidlow, Reigate, Surrey, RH2 8QG Tel: (0870) 0487777 E-mail: admin@ipcentrex.ltd.uk *IT based communications*

Ip Test Ltd, 15 The Pines Trading Estate, Broad Street, Guildford, Surrey, GU3 3BH Tel: (01483) 567218 Fax: (01483) 506054 E-mail: sales@iptest.com *Test equipment, automatic & electronics industry*

ipa Purchasing Ltd, Oak House, 39-41 The Parade, Claygate, Surrey, KT10 0PD Tel: (01372) 466966 Fax: (01372) 466062 E-mail: enquiries@ipapurchasing.co.uk *Founded in 1993, we are a leading UK purchasing group dedicated to saving members £1,000's every year on the cost of essential goods and services. *Improve your purchasing power *By grouping together thousands of independent businesses and negotiating prices collectively, it is possible to give each individual business the purchasing power and discounts available to much larger organisations *Membership of ipa is available free of charge to all pubs, bars, clubs, cafes, restaurants, hotels, b&bs, care homes, nursing homes, schools, colleges, independent caterers - indeed any UK business that wishes to increase their buying power. *The benefits of ipa membership: *1) Increased purchasing power *2) Due Diligence Assurance *3) Dedicated Support Staff *4) Supplier Guide *5) Product Sourcing Service*

Ipc Fixings, 1 National Road, Hunslet Business Park, Leeds, LS10 1TD Tel: 0113-277 9444 Fax: 0113-277 9555 *Supplier of power tools*

Ipc Industrial Power Cooling Ltd, 14 Hillmorton Road, Knowle, Solihull, West Midlands, B93 9JL Tel: (01564) 776456 Fax: (01564) 777625 E-mail: nh@ipcltd.freeserve.co.uk *Heat exchangers, air coolers for the power, petrochemical & process industries*

Ipc Publishing, Kings Reach Tower, Stamford Street, London, SE1 9LS Tel: (020) 7261 5711 Fax: (020) 7261 6772 *Magazine publishers*

IPC Services (UK) Ltd, Unit A3, Springhead Enterprise Park, Springhead Road, Northfleet, Gravesend, Kent, DA11 8HB Tel: (01474) 356551 Fax: (01474) 369283 E-mail: sales@ipcservices.co.uk *Instrumentation & Process Control Solution provider for new equipment sales from leading manufacturers including; Bourdon Haenni, Dresser Masoneilan, Druck, Endress + Hauser, Honeywell, mobrey, Moore Industries, PR electronics, Rosemount, Vega, and more...... Extensive instrument service/repair capability - including chemical seals and gas filled systems.*On site services including installation, commissioning and calibration of process instrumentation, including flow.*

▶ Ipc Services UK Ltd, Unit A3 Springhead Enterprise Park, Springhead Road, Northfleet, Gravesend, Kent, DA11 8HB Tel: (01474) 356551 Fax: (01474) 369283 E-mail: sales@ipcservices.co.uk *Instrumentation & Process Control Solution provider for new equipment sales from leading manufacturers including; Bourdon Haenni, Dresser Masoneilan, Druck, Endress + Hauser, Honeywell, mobrey, Moore Industries, PR electronics, Rosemount,*
continued
*Vega, and more...... Extensive instrument service/repair capability - including chemical seals and gas filled systems.*On site services including installation, commissioning and calibration of process instrumentation, including flow.*

Ipeco Engineering Ltd, Aviation Way, Southend-on-Sea, SS2 6UN Tel: (01702) 544939 Fax: (01702) 546480 *Precision machining, Turning, fabrication, Assembly, Painting, Brazing*

Ipeco Europe, Aviation Way, Southend-on-Sea, SS2 6UN Tel: (01702) 549371 Fax: (01702) 540782 E-mail: sales@ipeco.co.uk *Aircrew seat manufrs*

Ipeco Holdings Ltd, Aviation Way, Southend-on-Sea, SS2 6UN Tel: (01702) 209258 Fax: (01702) 542279 *Aerospace manufrs*

▶ IPEVA Ltd, Wilderness Copse, Fernham Road, Shellingford, Faringdon, Oxfordshire, SN7 7PU Tel: (0870) 0802340 Fax: (0870) 0802341 E-mail: mike.vogwell@ipeva.com *Electronic design consultancy services*

Ipf, 37 Whitehill Road, Glenrothes, Fife, KY6 2RW Tel: (01592) 771805 Fax: (01592) 771805 *Industrial painters*

▶ Ipg Imports, Whiteley House, 84 Miller Street, Glasgow, G1 1DT Tel: 0141-204 5288

▶ Ipm, Unit 31 Seymour Street, Millers Bridge Industrial Esta, Bootle, Merseyside, L20 1EE Tel: 0151-922 2252 Fax: 0151-922 2252 E-mail: enquiries@ipmgroup.co.uk

▶ IPNV Limited, PO Box 6882, Kettering, Northants, NN15 6WR Tel: 0845 070 1765 E-mail: info@ipnv.co.uk

▶ iPod Power, Spring Road, Ettingshall, Wolverhampton, WV4 6JX Tel: (0845) 1259520 Fax: (0845) 1259520 E-mail: webmaster@ipodpower.co.uk

▶ iPort (Europe) Ltd, Tudor House, Higham Common Road, Higham, Barnsley, South Yorkshire, S75 1PF Tel: 08701 999 150 Fax: 08701 99 15 15 E-mail: sales@iport.co.uk *iMailit - Online comparative quotes & booking for all UK courier services, same day, next day, express delivery, overnight, pallets, parcels or documents*

▶ Ips, Executive House, Mill Lane, Blaby, Leicester, LE8 4FG Tel: 0116-277 2666 Fax: 0116-276 1199 E-mail: susan@direct-ips.co.uk *Print management services*

▶ Ips Recruitment, 39 westgate, Grantham, Lincolnshire, NG31 6LY Tel: 01476 568225 Fax: 01476 565548 E-mail: dan.nash@ips-recruitment.co.uk *Arecruitment agency supplying workers and search and selection services across Lincolnshire, providing your business with staffing solutions from Directors to labourers.*

Ipsos UK Ltd, Kings House, Kymberley Road, Harrow, Middlesex, HA1 1PT Tel: (020) 8861 8000 Fax: (020) 8861 5515 E-mail: ian.catchpole@ipsos.com *Marketing & general researching services*

Ipswich Hydraulics Ltd, 37 Boss Hall Road, Ipswich, IP1 5BN Tel: (01473) 241271 Fax: (01473) 241293 E-mail: sales@ipswich-hydraulics.co.uk *Hydraulic engineers equipment manufrs*

Ipswich Insulation Ltd, Station House, Station Road, Bentley, Ipswich, IP9 2DB Tel: (01473) 327288 Fax: (01473) 327288 *Thermal insulation services & asbestos removal*

Ipswich Microwave Centre, 420 Spring Road, Ipswich, IP4 5NE Tel: (01473) 725699 Fax: (01473) 727952 E-mail: ipswich@microwavecentre.fsnet.co.uk *Microwaves repair & suppliers*

▶ Ipswich & Norwich Co-Operative Society, Ormond Road, Great Yarmouth, Norfolk, NR30 1QB Tel: (01493) 856750 Fax: (01493) 331810

Ipswich Plastics Ltd, Foxtail Road, Ransomes Industrial Estate, Ipswich, IP3 9RX Tel: (01473) 270101 Fax: (01473) 721446 *Decorative laminates & board distributors*

▶ IQ Software Services, Exchange House, 494 Midsummer Boulevard, Milton Keynes, MK9 2EA Tel: (01908) 237123 Fax: (01908) 604649 E-mail: contact@infoqss.com *Software development services*

Iqbal Bros & Co., IBCO Ltd, Lord North Street, Hulme Hall Lane, Miles Platting, Manchester, M4 8AD Tel: 0161-230 7280 Fax: 0161-202 8201 *Seafood marketing*

Iqual Ltd, Crown House, Home Gardens, Dartford, DA1 1DZ Tel: (0870) 1633320 Fax: (0870) 1633316 *IT consultants*

Ir Martin Roberts, Millen Road, Sittingbourne, Kent, ME10 2AA Tel: (01795) 476161 Fax: (01795) 422463 *Steel door manufrs*

Iran Air, 73 Piccadilly, London, W1J 8QX Tel: (020) 7493 8618 Fax: (020) 7408 1360 *Airline company*

Ireflo Products Ltd, 120 Broughton Road, London, SW6 2LB Tel: (020) 7736 2048 Fax: (020) 7384 2391 E-mail: sales@london-music.co.uk *Stainless steel & steel fabricators*

Ireland Alloys Ltd, PO Box 18, Glasgow, G72 0TQ Tel: (01698) 822461 Fax: (01698) 825166 E-mail: a.addison@ireland-alloys.co.uk *Metal processors & traders*

▶ Ireland-Jones & Williams, 13a Victoria Mount, Oxton, Prenton, Merseyside, CH43 5TH Tel: 0151-670 9988 E-mail: mark1@i-jw.com *i-jw are a partnership delivering Company ID, branding and marketing for the 'Service Sector'.**Service sector businesses such as solicitors, accountants, charities and insurance are fighting in competitive markets where company ID and branding can make a real difference to the bottom line.**i-jw deliver practical solutions with specific documented deliverables.**

Ireland's Farm Machinery Ltd, Bramley House, Old Bolingbroke, Spilsby, Lincolnshire, PE23 4EX Tel: (01790) 763424 Fax: (01790) 763540 E-mail: jonathan.ireland@btinternet.com *Agricultural machinery sales*

▶ Iretex NI Ltd, 75 Woodburn Road, Carrickfergus, County Antrim, BT38 8PS Tel: (028) 9336 8448 Fax: (028) 9335 1447 *Packaging manufrs*

IRevoltion Ltd, Station House, 4-8 High Street, West Drayton, Middlesex, UB7 7DJ Tel: (01895) 444420 Fax: (01895) 444460 *Computer consultants*

Iridium Consulting, 34 Camelot Way, Northampton, NN5 4BG Tel: 07881 636538 *Human Resources Development Consultancy, based in Northampton, specialising in enabling organisations, teams and individuals 'discover their talent'. Our areas of expertise include all areas of talent management. Emotional intelligence, Management and Leadership Development programmes, Neuro linguistic programming, NLP for business, executive coaching, OPQ - occupational personality questionnaire for recruitment and development, Insights Discovery Personal Profiles for Team Building, Myers Briggs Type Indicator (MBTI) personality profiles for personal and team development, Teram coaching, team building, team days, Management skills training, leadership skills training and development, Assessment centres and on site coaching and assessment.*

▶ IRIS Engineering & Technology Ltd, 2 Gill Burn, Sherburn Towers, Rowlands Gill, Tyne & Wear, NE39 2PT Tel: 01207 543914 E-mail: bob.preston@iriset.co.uk *IRIS Engineering & Technology Ltd provides a high level of expertise in the provision Project Management, Consultancy and Engineering Services. IRIS provides a cost effective solution by supplying a number of converging services that will offer our clients a 'single source solution' to any number of project scenarios. These Include*Safety Management -*IPPC -*CDM compliance -*Crisis Recovery -*Work Place Inspections -*Commercial Cost Control -*M&E Design -*Clean Room Systems -*Facilities Management -**

Iris Co Systems, Integra House, 138-140 Alexandra Road, London, SW19 7JY Tel: (020) 8879 3939 Fax: (020) 8879 7880 E-mail: info@computersoftware.com *Software developers*

▶ Irisbus UK Ltd, Iveco House, Station Road, Watford, WD17 1SR Tel: (01923) 259660 Fax: (01923) 259623 E-mail: sales@irisbus.co.uk *Bus manufrs*

▶ Iriscraft, 2 St. Pauls Road, Sarisbury Green, Southampton, SO31 7BB Tel: 01489 605537 E-mail: irisscraft@yahoo.co.uk *Fabrics & wedding supplies*

Irish Ferries, Salt Island, Holyhead, Gwynedd, LL65 1DR Tel: (0870) 5329129 Fax: (01407) 760340 *Ferry shipment services*

Irish Ferries, Custom House, The Dockyard, Pembroke Dock, Dyfed, SA72 6TW Tel: (0870) 5329543 Fax: (01646) 621125 E-mail: ifpembroke@btinternet.com *Ferry operator*

Irish Ferries General Enquiries Passenger Reservations, Fenwick Street, Liverpool, L2 7RB Tel: (0870) 5171717 Fax: 0151-236 0562 *Ship owners*

Irish Waste Services Ltd, 94-96 Hillsborough Road, Carryduff, Belfast, BT8 8HT Tel: (028) 9081 0000 Fax: (028) 9081 0001 E-mail: info@irishwaste.net *Waste disposal services*

Irm Bristol Ltd, Unit 1 2 Armstrong Court, Armstrong Way, Yate, Bristol, BS37 5NG Tel: (01454) 321311 Fax: (01454) 273411 E-mail: sales@irm-bristol.co.uk *Architectural ironmongery distributors*

Iron Art, Unit 1, Birch Industrial Estate, Eastbourne, East Sussex, BN23 6PH Tel: (01323) 722784 Fax: (01323) 722784 E-mail: info@iron-art.co.uk *Blacksmith services*

Iron Awe, Unit 24 Lansil Walk, Lansil Industrial Estate, Lancaster, LA1 3PQ Tel: (01524) 845511 Fax: (01524) 845511 E-mail: petersmalley@ironawe.com *Ornamental ironworkers*

Iron By Design, Unit 31 Steeton Grove, Steeton, Keighley, West Yorkshire, BD20 6TT Tel: (01535) 654146 Fax: (01535) 654146 E-mail: enquiries@iron-by-design.co.uk *General engineering*

Iron Designs Ltd, 117-119 Victoria Road, Portslade, Brighton, BN41 1XD Tel: (01273) 423685 Fax: (01273) 418927 *Metal workers*

▶ Iron Designs, Unit 51 Bowers Mill, Branch Road, Barkisland, Halifax, West Yorkshire, HX4 0AD Tel: (01422) 377555 Fax: (01422) 377555 *Wrought ironworkers*

▶ Iron Mountain Ltd, Unit 25 Wellheads Terrace, Wellheads Industrial Estate, Aberdeen, AB21 7GF Tel: (01224) 796600 Fax: (01224) 729095

▶ Iron Mountain Ltd, 320 Western Road, London, SW19 2QA Tel: (020) 8685 5370 Fax: (020) 8685 5380

Iron Mountain Ltd, Cottons Centre, Tooley Street, London, SE1 2TT Tel: (0800) 270270 Fax: (020) 7939 1501 *Records management services* Also at: Branches throughout the U.K.

Iron Mountain Ltd, 3 The Borough Industrial Estate, Leagrave Road, Luton, LU3 1RJ Tel: (0800) 270270 Fax: (01582) 391602 E-mail: tpowell@ironmountain.co.uk *Document & data storage*

Iron Mountain Ltd, Mill Way, Sittingbourne, Kent, ME10 2PT Tel: (01795) 479241 Fax: (01795) 427224 E-mail: info@ronmountain.co.uk *Secure business record management* Also at: Aberdeen, London SW19 & Sittingbourne

Iron & Steel Fabrications Ltd, PO Box 666, Dunmow, Essex, CM6 1WA Tel: (01371) 876054 Fax: (0870) 7626996 E-mail: sales@ironandsteel.co.uk *Metal works & fabricators*

Iron & Steel Trades Confederation, Swinton House, 324 Grays Inn Road, London, WC1X 8DD Tel: (020) 7239 1200 Fax: (020) 7278 8378 E-mail: istc@istc.te.org *Trade union* Also at: Cardiff, Hamilton, Middlesbrough, Rotherham & Sutton Coldfield

Iron Stores Jersey Ltd, 10-12 Commercial Buildings, St. Helier, Jersey, JE1 3UD Tel: (01534) 877755 Fax: (01534) 727449 *Building merchants*

▶ Iron Works, Old Stone Cottage, Brighton Road, Pease Pottage, Crawley, West Sussex, RH11 9BE Tel: (01293) 553005 E-mail: blacksmith@ironworks-crawley.co.uk *Black smith*

The Iron Works, 138 Stamford Brook Arches, Ravenscourt Park, London, W6 0TQ Tel: (020) 8748 6535 Fax: (020) 8748 5735 *Metal work*

Ironage Wrought Ironwork, Standalone Farm, Wilbury Road, Letchworth Garden City, Hertfordshire, SG6 4JN Tel: (01462) 485395 Fax: (01462) 484542 *Blacksmiths*

Ironbridge Construction Ltd, Unit B6 Hortonwood 10, Telford, Shropshire, TF1 7ES Tel: (01952) 676555 Fax: (01952) 675667 E-mail: sales@ironbridgeconstruction.co.uk *Roofing, cladding, flooring, staircase & structural steelworkers*

Ironcraft, 92 High Street, Earl Shilton, Leicester, LE9 7DG Tel: (01455) 847548 Fax: (01455) 842422 E-mail: office@ironcraft.co.uk *Ironwork manufrs*

▶ Ironcrafts Stroud Ltd, Inchbrook Trading Estate, Bath Road, Woodchester, Stroud, Gloucestershire, GL5 5EY Tel: (01453) 836581 Fax: (01453) 836581 E-mail: martinphill@onetel.com *Wrought Iron makers*

▶ Ironing Bored, Lloyds Bank House, 2 Station Approach, Tadworth, Surrey, KT20 5AD Tel: 07973 984279 E-mail: rosielally@fsmail.net *Fast and professional ironing service. Pick up and delivery. One-offs & regulars welcome.*

▶ The Ironing Lady, 24 Birdwood Grove, Fareham, Hants, PO16 8AF Tel: 01329 516899 E-mail: carol.durrant@ntlworld.com *We provide a high quality and professional ironing service in Fareham and the surrounding areas. We belive in providing excellent service and good value for money.*

▶ The Ironing Maiden Service, 34 The Mews, Trafalgar Street, Brighton, BN34 2DD Tel: 01273 50 70 41 E-mail: e.mokeeva@e3internet.com *Ironing service for busy people in Brighton and the surrounding area. Items picked up and droped off to suit you. Not a chain. Covers Brighton and Sussex area.*

Ironmongery Direct Ltd, 2-4 Eldon Way Trading Estate, Eldon Way, Hockley, Essex, SS5 4AD Tel: (01702) 562770 Fax: (01702) 562799 E-mail: sales@ironmongerydirect.com *DIY products online store suppliers*

Irons Bros Ltd, Factory, St. Breock, Wadebridge, Cornwall, PL27 7JP Tel: (01208) 812635 Fax: (01208) 814884 E-mail: sales@ironsbrothers.com *Castings & yacht keels manufrs*

Ironside Trophies & Engraving, 1b Harmony Shopping Centre, Skyline Drive, Lisburn, County Antrim, BT27 4HP Tel: (028) 9267 8427 Fax: (028) 9267 8427 E-mail: info@ironsidetrophies.con *Trophy engraving services*

▶ Iron-Sides, 67d Dukesway, Teesside Industrial Estate, Stockton-on-Tees, Cleveland, TS17 9LT Tel: (07976) 265331 E-mail: colin@iron-sides.com *wrought iron light fabrication & site services*

Ironsides Lubricants Ltd, Shield Street, Stockport, Cheshire, SK3 0DS Tel: 0161-477 5858 Fax: 0161-480 6203 E-mail: sales@ironsideslubricants.co.uk *Lubricant & grease manufrs*

Ironsun Ltd, Lindon Road, Brownhills, Walsall, WS8 7BG Tel: (01543) 454453 Fax: (01543) 454450 E-mail: admin@ironsun-ltd.com *Die-casting mould & die toolmakers & contract machining*

▶ Ironteam Ltd, 20 Knightsbridge Drive, Nuthall, Nottingham, NG16 1RD Tel: 0115-975 1378 Fax: 0115-975 1378 E-mail: enquiries@ironteam.co.uk *Integrated energy saving solutions for industrial, commercial, public*

Ironworx, Springfield Farm, Springfield Avenue, Morley, Leeds, LS27 9PW Tel: 0113-252 0040 Fax: 0113 252 0040 *Blacksmiths*

Irony Creative Metalwork, Units 20-28 Avenue B, Sneinton, Nottingham, NG1 1DV Tel: 0115-911 7008 Fax: 0115-911 7008 E-mail: enquiries@ironycreative.co.uk *Creative metalwork services*

Irpco Ltd, 9 Glan Llwyd, Tyn Y Bonau Road, Pontarddulais, Swansea, SA4 8SF Tel: (01792) 881212 Fax: (01792) 881119 *Instrumentation engineers*

Irpen UK Ltd, Block A Bescot Industrial Estate, Woden Road West, Wednesbury, West Midlands, WS10 7SG Tel: 0121-556 5534 Fax: 0121-556 1744 E-mail: sales@irpenuk.demon.co.uk *Acrylic sheet distributors, agents & stockholders*

▶ Irphoto, Burn Cottage, Southwick, Dumfries, DG2 8AN Tel: (01387) 780635 E-mail: mackay@irphoto.co.uk *Industrial, commercial & advertising photography; photographic & design services for private and commercial clients*

Irregular Miniatures, 41 Lesley Avenue, York, YO10 4JR Tel: (01904) 671101 Fax: (01904) 671101 E-mail: email@irregularmin.fsnet.co.uk *War game figure suppliers & manufrs*

▶ Irresistible Headdresses Ltd, Plaistow, West Sussex, RH14 Tel: (01403) 871449 Fax: (01403) 871114 E-mail: irresistible1@btopenworld.com *Hairdressing accessories suppliers*

Irrigation Control Ltd, Smithy Paddock, Darnhall Lane, Darnhall, Winsford, Cheshire, CW7 4DE Tel: (01606) 558927 Fax: (01606) 862882 E-mail: mail@irrigationcontrol.co.uk *Irrigation system*

Irrigation Systems & Service, 18 Downton Industrial Estate, Batten Road, Downton Industrial Estate, Salisbury, SP5 3HU Tel: (01725) 513880 Fax: (01725) 513003 E-mail: gholdenparker@aol.com *Irrigation systems & services*

Irvin & Sellers, 24-28 Duncrue Street, Belfast, BT3 9AR Tel: (028) 9035 1224 Fax: (028) 9035 1527 E-mail: info@ijktimber.co.uk *Timber merchants & importers*

Irvine Ltd, Green Street, Enfield, Middlesex, EN3 7FJ Tel: (020) 8361 1123 Fax: (020) 8361 8684 E-mail: sales@irvineltd.com *Engineering model distributors & manufrs*

▶ Irvine Contractors, Unit 14B, Gremista Industrial Estate, Lerwick, Shetland, ZE1 0PX Tel: (01595) 692645

Irvine Spring Co. Ltd, 6 Kyle Road, Irvine Industrial Estate, Irvine, Ayrshire, KA12 8JS Tel: (01294) 279396 Fax: (01294) 277073 E-mail: info@irvinesprings.com *Spring manufrs*

Andrew Irving Associates, Lloyds Bank Building, Muswell Hill Broadway, London, N10 3RZ Tel: (020) 8444 5678 Fax: (020) 8444 9221 E-mail: aia@aiaresearch.co.uk *Market research agency*

Irving Little & Co. Ltd, 213 Cleveland Street, Birkenhead, Merseyside, CH41 3QE Tel: 0151-666 1004 Fax: 0151-666 1013 *Paint & wall covering distributors*

P. Irving & Sons Ltd, Hutton Roof Sawmills, Kirkby Lonsdale, Carnforth, Lancashire, LA6 2PE Tel: (01524) 271510 Fax: (01524) 272410 *Saw mill services*

Robert Irving & Burns, 23-24 Margaret St, London, W1W 8LF Tel: (020) 7637 0821 Fax: (020) 7637 8827 E-mail: props@rib.co.uk *Estate agents*

Irvings Engineering, Denton I, Newhaven, East Sussex, BN9 9BA Tel: (01273) 513032 Fax: (01273) 513032 E-mail: info@plmarine.com *Marine engineers*

Irwin & Campbell (Glasgow) Ltd, 22-24 Polmadie Street, Glasgow, G42 0PQ Tel: 0141-423 8377 Fax: 0141-423 8292 *Sheet metalworkers*

Irwin Industial Tool Co. Ltd, Parkway Works, Kettlebridge Road, Sheffield, S9 3BL Tel: 0114-244 9066 Fax: 0114-256 1788 E-mail: sales@record.co.uk *Drill bit, power tool accessories*

Irwin Industial Tool Co. Ltd, Parkway Works, Kettlebridge Road, Sheffield, S9 3BL Tel: 0114-244 9066 Fax: 0114-256 1788 E-mail: nroshier@recordtools.co.uk *Hand tool distributors*

▶ Irwin Video Productions, 14 Franklyn Court, 65 Promenade, Southport, Merseyside, PR9 0JB Tel: (01704) 547692 E-mail: ronnie@irwin-video.co.uk *Conference filming & events coverage nationwide. Promotional video production.*

Irwins Ltd, Low Hall Road, Horsforth, Leeds, LS18 4EW Tel: 0113-250 6811 Fax: 0113-250 6933 E-mail: sales@irwins.co.uk *Building contractors, refurbishment & specialist joiners* Also at: Birmingham, Reading & Selby

Irwin's Bakery, 5 Diviny Drive, Portadown, Craigavon, County Armagh, BT63 5WE Tel: (028) 3833 2421 Fax: (028) 3833 3918 E-mail: sales@irwinsbakery.com *Bakers wholesale manufacturing*

Isaac Grainger, Century Works, Cradley Heath, West Midlands, B64 5QY Tel: (01384) 637777 Fax: (01384) 637111 E-mail: sales@isaacgrainger.co.uk Principal Export Areas: Worldwide *Manufacturers of tube fitting*

Isatech Ltd, Watermeadow House, Watermeadow, Chesham, Buckinghamshire, HP5 1LF Tel: (01494) 794633 Fax: (01494) 794644 E-mail: info@accumen-technology.co.uk *Information systems & control systems*

▶ Isbir Bulk Bag, G The Granary Business Centre, Coal Road, Cupar, Fife, KY15 5YQ Tel: (01334) 650088 Fax: (01334) 650072 *Packaging manufrs*

▶ Isbister Bros, Quoyloo, Stromness, Orkney, KW16 3LT Tel: (01856) 841525 Fax: (01856) 841525

Tony Isbitt Photography, 107 Burnt Ash Lane, Bromley, BR1 5AB Tel: (020) 8460 5710 Fax: (020) 8460 5710 E-mail: info@tonyisbittphotography.co.uk *Photography services*

▶ Isc Computer Consultants, 16 Holford Way, Luton, LU3 4EB Tel: (01582) 585807 E-mail: gian@gianmahil.com *IT, Support, Services, Outsourcing, Database, Software, Hardware, Network, ORACLE, MS, Microsoft, SQL, RDBMS, Exchange, Server, Desktop, PC, Disaster, Recovery, Operating, System, Remote, Reliable, Performance, Consultancy, Certified, Professional, Security, Secure, Cluster, Windows, Computer, Administration, Data, Prince 2, ITIL*"

Isca, Unit 29 Nine Mile Point Industrial Estate, Ynysddu, Newport, Gwent, NP11 7HZ Tel: (01495) 200747 Fax: (01495) 200757 E-mail: kharris@iscauk.com *ISCA UK is a manufacturer and Chemical supplier for speciality chemicals and raw materials, based near Newport in South Wales. We have extensive warehouse facilities throughout the UK and Europe, enabling us to offer prompt deliveries from stock and a full export service to overseas customers. To complement our comprehensive portfolio of products, ISCA has invested in a modern, custom-built technical centre. From these facilities ISCA's technical staff carry out full product evaluation and development. In addition, we offer our customers a complete formulating service, plus technical and manufacturing problem-solving advice. ISCA Products Additives Aerospace Chemicals JAR-3N ANFO additives Anti-Static Agents Antifoams Biocides Driers & Catalysts Explosive Emulsifiers Flame Retardants Industrial Biocides CMIT & MIT Iron Oxides & Ochres Matting Agents ISCASIL Pigments - Inorganic Organic Specialist Plasticisers Polymers (Solvent Based)*

Isca Agriculture, Venn Ottery, Ottery St. Mary, Devon, EX11 1RY Tel: (01404) 811200 Fax: (01404) 811222 E-mail: enquireies@isca-kinver.co.uk *Agricultural merchants*

▶ Isca Vision Ltd, Isca House 3 Bay Tree Close, Caerleon, Newport, NP18 3RT Tel: (01633) 431551 E-mail: sales@iscavision.com *Computer training services*

Isca-Bags, 47 Marsh Green Road, Marsh Barton, Exeter, EX2 8PN Tel: (01392) 275906 Fax: (01392) 435028 E-mail: info@isca-bags.com *Packaging material agents*

I-Scan Security Systems, 3 Hazel Rd, Berkhamsted, Hertfordshire, HP4 2JN Tel: 01442 866907 *CCTV installers*

Iscar Tools Ltd, Clapgate Lane, Birmingham, B32 3DE Tel: 0121-422 8585 Fax: 0121-421 8255 E-mail: sales@iscaruk.co.uk *Manufacturers & engineers cutting tools*

Isceon Distribution Services, P O Box 46, Bristol, BS11 9YF Tel: 0117-948 4170 Fax: 0117-948 4254 E-mail: andy.cook@eu.rhodia.com *Uk supplier of ISCEON refrigerants & associated services. Range includes both HCFC & HFC non-ozone depleting refrigerants. Also available - refrigeration oils, heat transfer fluids, external cleaning products. Network of dedicated stockpoints & distributors throughout the UK. Technical support & full recovery/reclaim facilities offered as well.*

Ischus Ltd, 37 Water Meadows, Worksop, Nottinghamshire, S80 3DF Tel: (01909) 532288 E-mail: info@ischus.co.uk *Acquisition & data analysis*

Isd Cold Stores Ltd, 125 Business Park, Llanthony Road, Gloucester, GL2 5JQ Tel: (01452) 520649 Fax: (01452) 301910 E-mail: sales@isdcoldstores.co.uk *Manufacturers & installers of coldstores*

ISDN Communications Ltd, The Stable Block, Ronans, Winkfield Row, Bracknell, Berkshire, RG42 6LY Tel: (01344) 899006 Fax: (01344) 899001 *Telecommunications*

▶ ISEC Solutions, Meadowcroft, Nottingham Road, Ravenshead, Nottingham, NG15 9HP Tel: 01623 792200 Fax: 01623 792293 E-mail: mark@isec-solutions.co.uk *ISEC Solutions are one of the UK's leading home automation system specialists. We offer a broad range of products and services through dedicated professionals fully trained in the design and installation of automation systems. These automation systems can range from the custom install of a home cinema system or the design and implementation of lighting control, multi room audio and network surveillance in commercial or residential situation.*

▶ Isg UK Ltd, 830 Romford Road, London, E12 5JG Tel: (020) 8514 8886 Fax: (020) 8553 4440 *Computer maintenance & repair services*

Isgus International Ltd, Unit 10 Springfield Business Centre, Brunel Way, Stroudwater Business Park, Stonehouse, Gloucestershire, GL10 3SX Tel: (01453) 827373 Fax: (01453) 827360 E-mail: admin@isgus.co.uk *Time recorder & attendance distributors*

Isherwood & Ellis, 15 Malone Road, Belfast, BT9 6RT Tel: (028) 9066 3291 Fax: (028) 9068 2727 E-mail: architects@isherwood-ellis.com *Architects, project managers & planning supervisors*

▶ Isherwood Engineering, 17 Hearts of Oak Cottages, Caerau, Maesteg, Mid Glamorgan, CF34 0TU Tel: (01656) 731459 E-mail: stephenisherwood@yahoo.co.uk *Sharpening Service,Scissors,Knives,Woodworking Roter Cutter"s&Circular Saw"s,Metal Cutter"s,H.S.S. & Carbide.*

▶ Isherwoods, 12 Imperial Square, Cheltenham, Gloucestershire, GL50 1QB Tel: (01242) 226999 Fax: (01242) 227444

Ishida Qualitech Ltd, Unit 1 19 Willis Way, Poole, Dorset, BH15 3SS Tel: (01202) 466300 Fax: (01202) 466302 E-mail: sales@ishidaeurope.com *Special purpose machinery*

▶ Isis Centre, 3 Dorset Street, Brighton, BN2 1WA Tel: (01273) 626644 E-mail: info@isiscentre.co.uk *NLP & hypnosis training*

Isis Computer & Electronics (UK) Ltd, 8 Ranmore Road, Dorking, Surrey, RH4 1HA Tel: (01306) 740525 Fax: (01306) 740515 E-mail: peter@isiscomputer.co.uk *Building of computer systems*

▶ Isis Diamond Drilling, 31 Bradley Road, Patchway, Bristol, BS34 5LF Tel: 0117-907 7265 Fax: 0117-907 7265 E-mail: info@isisdiamonddrilling.co.uk *diamond drilling contractors - core drilling chasing floor sawing wall sawing scabbling small controlled demolition core sampling and associated works*

▶ Isis Electronics Cheltenham Ltd, Building 66, Aston Down, Frampton Mansell, Stroud, Gloucestershire, GL6 8GA Tel: (01285) 760777 Fax: (01285) 760163 E-mail: sales@astondown.co.uk *Suppliers of used Electronic Test Equipment*

Isis Fluid Control Ltd, Station Yard The Leys, Chipping Norton, Oxfordshire, OX7 5HZ Tel: (01608) 645755 Fax: (01608) 645532 E-mail: sales@isis-fluid.com *Distributors, agents & stockholders of valves*

Isis Media, PO Box 8209, Solihull, West Midlands, B93 0EN Tel: 0121-685 8225 Fax: 0121-685 8226 E-mail: sales@isismedia.co.uk *Television production*

▶ Isis New Media, 14 Devereaux Road, Ebley, Stroud, Gloucestershire, GL5 4PT Tel: (01453) 828471 E-mail: enq@isisnewmedia.co.uk *Website design, software development & corporate design*

▶ Isis Surveyors Ltd, 7 Ashurst Close, Tadley, Hampshire, RG26 4AH Tel: 0118-981 4614 Fax: 0118-981 4614 E-mail: isissurveyors@ukonline.co.uk *Chartered land surveyors, topographical survey & gps survey*

▶ ISKIV Information Strategies Key Intangible Value Ltd, Middle Spoad Barn, Newcastle, Craven Arms, Shropshire, SY7 8PB Tel: 0207 7887762 E-mail: i-info@iskiv.com *We provide information consultancy, creative eBusiness and eMarketing, accessible Web design and multilingual websites. We manage information and intangible assets. We focus on business development, content and usability and share our enthusiasm with our clients to create their value.*"*ISKIV Limited is a women partnership. We bring a sound experience in the area of information, with a touch of art, marketing and design. Creating value from your intangibles is a part of our expertise.*

Iskra UK Ltd, Redlands, Coulsdon, Surrey, CR5 2HT Tel: (020) 8668 7141 Fax: (020) 8668 3108 *Electronic component manufrs*

Iskraemeco (UK) Ltd, Unit 15 Lenton Business Centre, Lenton Boulevard, Nottingham, NG7 2BY Tel: 0115-924 4511 Fax: 0115-924 4104 E-mail: sales@iskraemeco.co.uk *Electricity meters, energy measurement & management & energy metering systems*

Isl Dardan Security Ltd, Aston House, 18a Bidwell Road, Rackheath, Norwich, NR13 6PT Tel: (01603) 263000 Fax: (01603) 263070 E-mail: sales@isldarden.co.uk *Security and telecoms service suppliers*

Island Blinds, 45 High Street, West Mersea, Colchester, CO5 8QA Tel: (01206) 384555 Fax: (01206) 384555 *Blind retailers*

▶ Island Cement, South Quay, Ramsey, Isle of Man, IM8 1BG Tel: (01624) 814808 Fax: (01624) 620912 *Storage & transport*

Island Clothing, 41-43 Western Boulevard, Leicester, LE2 7HN Tel: 0116-275 6444 Fax: 0116-275 6333 *Clothing importers*

Island Computer Systems Ltd, 41 Horsebridge Hill, Newport, Isle of Wight, PO30 5TJ Tel: (01983) 821717 Fax: (01983) 521608 E-mail: sales@islanddcomputers.co.uk *Computer system sales*

▶ Island Cosmetics, 60-62 Halkett Place, St. Helier, Jersey, JE2 4WG Tel: (01534) 725252 Fax: (01534) 769969 E-mail: info@islandcosmetics.com *Cosmetics suppliers*

▶ Island Leisure Products Ltd, Unit 1a Eurolink Industrial Centre, Castle Road, Sittingbourne, Kent, ME10 3RN Tel: (01795) 436500 Fax: (01795) 436700 E-mail: info@islandleisureproducts.co.uk *Island Leisure Products supplies & makes Rubber Safety Surfacing, Playground Equipment,and can make bespoke products from rubber & metal.*

Island Pine, 64 Union Place, Dungannon, County Tyrone, BT70 1DL Tel: (028) 8775 3545 Fax: (028) 8775 2747 E-mail: sales@islandpine.co.uk *Pine furniture manufrs*

Island Removals, Manners View, Newport, Isle of Wight, PO30 5FA Tel: (01983) 526374 Fax: (01983) 526374 E-mail: info@islandremovals.co.uk *Removal contractors*

Island Scientific Ltd, Old Station Road, Ventnor, Isle of Wight, PO38 1DX Tel: (01983) 855822 Fax: (01983) 852146 E-mail: enquiries@island-scientific.co.uk Purchasing Contact: A. Lloyd Sales Contact: A. Lloyd Principal Export Areas: Worldwide *Island Scientific is the UK's largest supplier of refurbished vacuum pumps and high vacuum equipment, situated on the Isle of Wight we are ideally positioned for both UK and World Wide Export. We deal in Oil sealed Rotary vacuum pumps and Oil sealed Piston vacuum pumps, Dry vacuum pumps and Roots Boosters / Blowers made by all major vacuum pump manufactures including BOC Edwards, Alcatel, Busch, Ebara, Leybold, Balzers, Pfeiffer. Other services offered include; Vacuum Sensor /Gauge Calibration, a large variety of vacuum products and components, vacuum consumables such as oil filters and vacuum oils, large Rotary Vacuum pumps are also available for hire. We design, build and stock a wide range of Vacuum Degassing units for removing air from casting materials; we also offer the building of custom chamber to the customer specifications. ISO9001 Certified.*

Island Structural, Bowcombe Works, Bowcombe Road, Newport, Isle of Wight, PO30 3HZ Tel: (01983) 525070 Fax: (01983) 521632 *Structural steel manufrs*

Island Systems Ltd, 83 Knightwood Crescent, New Malden, Surrey, KT3 5JP Tel: (020) 8949 4422 E-mail: enquirey@islandsys.com *Software consultants*

▶ Island Technology, Highbury, La Route Du Marais, St. Ouen, Jersey, JE3 2GG Tel: (01534) 484151 Fax: (01534) 481202

Islander International Ltd, The Old Vicarage, Somerset Square, Nailsea, Bristol, BS48 1RN Tel: (01275) 810194 Fax: (01275) 851752 E-mail: sales@islander.co.uk *Food ingredient distributors*

Islay Woollen Mill Co. Ltd, Islay Woollen Mill, Bridgend, Isle Of Islay, PA44 7PG Tel: (01496) 810563 Fax: (01496) 810677 *Tweed manufrs & distributors*

▶ Isle Of Arran Distillery Ltd, Enterprise House, Springkerse Business Park, Stirling, FK7 7UF Tel: (01786) 431900 Fax: (01786) 431909 E-mail: info@arranwhisky.com *Manufacturers of whisky*

▶ Isle Of Jura Distillery Co, Craighouse, Isle of Jura, PA60 7XT Tel: (01496) 820240 Fax: (01496) 820344

Isle Of Mull Cheese Ltd, Sgriob-Ruadh Farm, Tobermory, Isle of Mull, PA75 6QD Tel: (01688) 302235 Fax: (01688) 302546 E-mail: mull.cheese@btinternet.com *Farmhouse cheese manufrs*

▶ Isle of Mull Computer Services, Ardshona, Tobermory, Isle of Mull, PA75 6PN Tel: (01688) 302513

Isle Of Wight Grain Storage Ltd, Medina Wharf, Arctic Road, Cowes, Isle of Wight, PO31 7PG Tel: (01983) 282022 *Grain storage & haulage*

▶ Isle of Wight Hardwoods, 45 Central way, Sandown, Isle of Wight, PO36 9DW Tel: (01983) 408322 Fax: (01983) 408322 E-mail: info@isleofwighthardwoods.co.uk *Supply, fit, finish and restoration of solid hardwood flooring*

Isle of Wight Land Drainage, Newnham Farm, Newnham Lane, Ryde, Isle Of Wight, PO33 4ED Tel: (01983) 882423 Fax: (01983) 882423 E-mail: newnhamfarm@talk21.com *Land drainage agricultural services*

Isle Of Wight Studio Glass Ltd, Old Park Road, Ventnor, Isle of Wight, PO38 1XR Tel: (01983) 853526 Fax: (01983) 854054 E-mail: sales@isleofwightstudioglass.co.uk *Hand made glass ware manufrs*

▶ Isleburn Ltd, Industrial Estate, Evanton, Dingwall, Ross-Shire, IV16 9XJ Tel: (01349) 832000 Fax: (01349) 832001 E-mail: enquiries@isleburn.com *Engineering company manufrs*

Isleburn Structural Services, Delny Industrial Estate, Invergordon, Ross-Shire, IV18 0QW Tel: (01862) 843910 Fax: (01862) 843919 E-mail: enquiries@isleburnss.demon.co.uk *Steel fabricators*

▶ Islepac, 1a Macaulay Road, Stornoway, Isle of Lewis, HS1 2HD Tel: (01851) 706911 Fax: (01851) 706911 E-mail: info@islepac.co.uk *Gift packaging company including organza & jute bags*

Isles Of Scilly Steamship Co. Ltd, Hugh Street, St. Mary's, Isles of Scilly, TR21 0LJ Tel: (01720) 422357 Fax: (01720) 422192 *Travel company* Also at: Penzance

Isleward Ltd, Neptune Industrial Estate, Owen Road, Willenhall, West Midlands, WV13 2PZ Tel: 0121-526 5903 Fax: 0121-568 7421 E-mail: sales@isleward.co.uk *Tube manipulation services*

Isleworth Polishing & Plating Ltd, 273 High Street, Brentford, Middlesex, TW8 0JL Tel: (020) 8560 7440 Fax: (020) 8560 7440 *Metal polishers & electro platers*

Islington Chamber of Commerce & Trade Ltd, 64 Essex Road, London, N1 8LR Tel: (020) 7226 1593 Fax: (020) 7226 5437 E-mail: admin@islchamber.org.uk *Chamber of commerce*

▶ Ismag Ltd, 483 Green Lanes, London, N13 4BS Tel: (0870) 7773174 Fax: (0870) 7773176 E-mail: sales@ismag.co.uk *Import & export beauty products*

Ismeca (UK) Ltd, 6 Azalea Drive, Up Hatherley, Cheltenham, Gloucestershire, GL51 3EA Tel: (01242) 863555 Fax: (0870) 7620696 E-mail: mchatfield@ismeca.uk.com *Medical parma automation producers*

IsoCom Components Ltd, Unit 25B, Park View Road West, Park View Industrial Estate, Brenda Road, Hartlepool, Cleveland, TS25 1UD Tel: (01429) 863609 Fax: (01429) 863581 E-mail: sales@isocom.co.uk Principal Export Areas: Worldwide *Optoisolators & interrupter switches*

Isocon Engineering Ltd, 322 Broomloan Road, Glasgow, G51 2JQ Tel: 0141-440 5454 Fax: 0141-425 1344 E-mail: isoconengltd@ibrox4.demon.co.uk *Road tanker repairers & ISO bulk repairers*

Isoform Ltd, Maer Lane Industrial Estate, Llewellyn Roberts Way, Market Drayton, Shropshire, TF9 1QS Tel: (01630) 652772 Fax: (01630) 652518 E-mail: isoform@btinternet.com *Dry bag isostatic presses, tooling & associated equipment. laboratory scale wet bag isostatic presses.*

Isoheat, Unit 5, Aurillac Court, Hallcroft Industrial Estate, Aurilac Way, Retford, Nottinghamshire, DN22 7PX Tel: (01777) 708811 Fax: (01777) 708866 E-mail: isoheat@fsbdial.co.uk *Electric furnace manufrs*

Isola Manufacturing Co (Wythenshaw) Ltd, Harper Road, Wythenshawe, Manchester, M22 4RG Tel: 0161-998 2294 Fax: 0161-946 0390 E-mail: isola.sales@nu-pax.com *Rubber band & adhesive tape distribs*

Isola Werke UK Ltd, 2 Dunlop Square, Deans, Livingston, West Lothian, EH54 8SB Tel: (01506) 412812 Fax: (01506) 410571 *Flexible laminated plastic manufrs*

Isolated Systems Ltd, Adams Close, Heanor, Derbyshire, DE75 7SW Tel: (01773) 761226 Fax: (01773) 760408 E-mail: fshopkins@vitraseal.co.uk *Window manufrs*

▶ iSolve IT Ltd, Haldo House, Western Way, Bury St. Edmunds, Suffolk, IP33 3SP Tel: (0808) 2000911 Fax: (020) 7681 2933 E-mail: info@isolveit.co.uk *Computer support for business*

Isomatic UK Ltd, 9 Pimms Close, Guildford, Surrey, GU4 7YG Tel: (01483) 534634 Fax: (01483) 573624 E-mail: peter.burton@isomatics.biz *Toroidal & ferrite transformers*

Ison Ltd, Victoria St, High Wycombe, Buckinghamshire, HP11 2LT Tel: (01494) 437020 Fax: (01494) 526615 E-mail: fred@isonuk.net *Security & coin lock manufrs*

▶ Isopharm Systems, Unit 2, Umborne Bridge, Dolphin Street, Colyton, Devon, EX24 6LU Tel: (01297) 553775 Fax: (01297) 553775

Isoquest Environmental Consultants, 10 Fontmell Park, Ashford, Middlesex, TW15 2NW Tel: (01784) 252275 E-mail: info@isoquest.co.uk *Isoquest specialise in the development, application and auditing of environmental and quality management systems that meet the requirements of ISO 14001, ISO 9001 or ISO 17025. Contact Isoquest for an informed and pragmatic approach to managing your ISO certification and ensuring compliance with UK environmental regulations.*

Isoscan UK Ltd, Unit 1 Portelant Barns, Cowdown Farm, Micheldever, Winchester, Hampshire, SO21 3DN Tel: (01962) 774411 Fax: (01962) 774477 E-mail: sales@isoscan.co.uk *IT corporate monitoring & security systems services*

▶ Isosceles Finance, PO Box 2898, Ascot, Berkshire, SL5 0UW Tel: (01344) 622169 Fax: (0871) 661 6557 E-mail: info@isoscelesfinance.co.uk *Business accounting*

IsoSpray Foam Roof Systems, Woodside, Within, Within Lane, Stafford, ST18 0AY Tel: (0870) 420 2553 Fax: (0870) 421 5766 E-mail: info@foam-insulation.co.uk *Roofing and Insulation Services are a UK based company and as a national company work all over the UK. IsoSpray spray foam insulation offers excellent thermal roof insulation which is a polyurethane spray foam insulation product.*

▶ Isosure Ltd, 18 Spring Terrace, Goodshawfold, Rossendale, Lancashire, BB4 8QR Tel: (01706) 225419 Fax: (01706) 230784 E-mail: info@isosure.com *Business providing consultancy & training in Occupational Health & Safety, Quality Assurance & Environmental Management Systems*

▶ Isotek, Unit 3, Bode Business Park, Ball Haye Green, Leek, Staffordshire, ST13 6BW Tel: (01538) 384008 Fax: (01538) 384016 E-mail: info@cooltrailers.co.uk *Refrigerated towing trailers & walk-in cold room manufrs*

Isotemp Heating & Ventilating Ltd, Station Road, Loudwater, High Wycombe, Buckinghamshire, HP10 9UD Tel: (01494) 534364 Fax: (01494) 461716 *Based in Loudwater, Buckinghamshire, Isotemp manufacture and install high quality ductwork systems serving mechanical services contractors involved with new builds and refurbishments for hospitals, schools, offices and industrial premises across the UK.*

Isothane Ltd, Newhouse Road, Huncoat Industrial Estate, Accrington, Lancashire, BB5 6NT Tel: (01254) 872555 Fax: (01254) 871522 E-mail: enquiries@isothane.com *Polyurethane systems manufrs*

Isothermal Technology Ltd, 42a Pine Grove, Southport, Merseyside, PR9 9AG Tel: (01704) 544611 Fax: (01704) 544799 E-mail: info@isotech.co.uk *Temperature calibrating equipment manufacturers & services*

Isotron Plc, Moray Road, Elgin Industrial Estate, Swindon, SN2 8XS Tel: (01793) 601000 Fax: (01793) 601010 E-mail: sales@isotron.co.uk *Radiation test & sterilisation services*

Isotron, Thornhill Industrial Estate, South Marston, Swindon, SN3 4TA Tel: (01793) 823451 Fax: (01793) 827320 E-mail: smarston@isotron.co.uk *Sterilization services*

Ispc Surface Preparation Ltd, Craven Road, Craven Road, Altrincham, Cheshire, WA14 5EP Tel: 0161-928 6388 Fax: 0161-929 8017 E-mail: uk-info@wheelabrator.co.uk Principal Export Areas: Worldwide *Manufacturers of shot blasting & blast cleaning equipment*

Isringhausen GB Ltd, Second Avenue, Redwither Industrial Complex, Redwither Business Park, Wrexham, Clwyd, LL13 9XQ Tel: (01978) 666300 Fax: (01978) 660192 E-mail: isrigb@isrigb.co.uk *Commercial vehicle seat manufrs*

ISS Facility Services Ltd, 15A Huntingdon Street, St. Neots, Cambridgeshire, PE19 1BL Tel: (01480) 403404 Fax: (01480) 408579 *Office & factory cleaning services*

iStationers Ltd, Suite 1, 18a Ropergate, Pontefract, West Yorkshire, WF8 1LP Tel: 01226 715194 E-mail: Sales@iStationers.com *iStationers Ltd offers a range of over 8000 higly competativly priced office and stationery supplies to the Home, Home Office, Small and Large business users.*

Istead Business Presentations, 14 Herald Business Park, Golden Acres Lane, Coventry, CV3 2SY Tel: (024) 7645 9702 Fax: (024) 7663 5624 E-mail: admin@istead.co.uk *Conference, event & multi-media production services*

Istil UK plc, Rushenden Road, Queenborough, Kent, ME11 5HS Tel: (01795) 580880 Fax: (01795) 580165 E-mail: *Steel black bar manufrs*

▶ Isu Ltd, PO Box 4370, Wolverhampton, WV1 9AE Tel: (01902) 636588 Fax: (01902) 636588 E-mail: studio@isu-design.co.uk *Contemporary furniture and related product design for domestic and contract leisure market. Furniture design development, 3D product visualisation and web design services to manufacturers, architects and creative individuals.*

Isuzu (UK) Ltd, Ryder Street, Great Bridge, West Bromwich, West Midlands, B70 0EJ Tel: 0121-522 2000 Fax: 0121-520 5025 *Car importers & distributors*

▶ Isvr Consulting, University Road, Southampton, SO17 1BJ Tel: (023) 8059 2162 Fax: (023) 8059 2728 E-mail: consultancy@isvr.co.uk *Consultancy in acoustics, noise & vibration*

▶ Isys Computer Services Ltd, 4 Charlotte Street, Dumbarton, G82 4JB Tel: (0845) 1434040 Fax: (0845) 1434039 E-mail: info@isys-computers.co.uk *Technical support & IT consultancy services*

Isys Computers Ltd, 8 Upper Glenburn Road, Bearsden, Glasgow, G61 4BW Tel: 0141-943 1533 E-mail: enquiries@isysdirect.com *Computer service & support* Also at: Watford

▶ ISYS Integrated Systems, Isys House, 23 Innotec Drive, Bangor, County Down, BT19 7PD Tel: (0845) 0945925 E-mail: info@isysni.com *Security automations & audio visual supplier & installer*

It Architechture Ltd, Chancery House, Tolworth Close, Surbiton, Surrey, KT6 7EW Tel: (020) 8399 6070 Fax: (020) 8399 6696 E-mail: info@it-arc.co.uk *Software suppliers*

It C M L Ltd, Unit 26 Cam Centre, Wilbury Way, Hitchin, Hertfordshire, SG4 0TW Tel: (01462) 635455 Fax: (01462) 635454 E-mail: salesitcml@btconnect.com *General sheet metal fabricators & laser profiling*

▶ It Centre Plus, 2 Stafford Street, Eccleshall, Stafford, ST21 6BH Tel: (01785) 850710 Fax: (01785) 859386

▶ IT.com Solutions (UK), 1-2 North End, Boston, Lincolnshire, PE20 3LR Tel: (01205) 820199 Fax: (01205) 821662 E-mail: enq@itcom-online.co.uk *Computer systems consultants*

▶ It Dept 4 U, 10 Charlesfield Road, Rugby, Warwickshire, CV22 5PQ Tel: (07977) 451208 E-mail: enquiries@itdept4u.co.uk *We specialise in supplying and supporting solutions built around Microsoft technologies. Our services include PC repair/upgrade, computer networking, email setup, web design, bespoke software and much more.**We are honest and straight-forward technicians who aim to relieve your frustrations and ensure your satisfaction. We pride ourselves on doing any work right the first time and ensure the work is carried out quickly and correctly. Our many and diverse clients have come to rely on us and appreciate our personal service. To our business clients we have become the IT department that they needed but thought they couldn''t afford, and to our residential clients we have become the IT equivalent of calling the plumber, electrician or locksmith.*

IT Disposal, 1 Brook Farm, Stapleford Road, Stapleford Abbotts, Romford, RM4 1EJ Tel: (0845) 6445303 Fax: (01708) 688019 E-mail: info@itdisposal.co.uk *Disposal and Destruction of IT Equipment Data Removal and Recycling. Licensed by the Environment Agency for Disposal of all types of IT Equipment, including Monitors, Base Units, Servers, Towers, Scanners, Printers, Plotters, Laptops, Photocopiers, Racks & Cabinets, Keyboards, Mice and Cables in any quantity from 1 to 1000's. Free disposal subject to conditions, for more information visit our website www.itdisposal.co.uk*

It Engineering, Kingsnorth Works, Hoo, Rochester, Kent, ME3 9NZ Tel: (01634) 253920 *Mechanical repairs*

IT First Ltd, St. Nicholas Way, Sutton, Surrey, SM1 1AT Tel: (020) 8643 3344 Fax: (020) 8643 3356 *Computer training centre & consultants*

It Innovation Centre Ltd, 2 Venture Road, Chilworth Science Park, Chilworth, Southampton, SO16 7NP Tel: (023) 8076 0834 Fax: (023) 8076 0833 E-mail: info@it-innovation.soton.ac.uk *IT researchers*

▶ It Is It, 8 Beechwood Drive, Cobham, Surrey, KT11 2DX Tel: (01372) 841439 E-mail: info@it-is-it.co.uk *IT is IT is an Internet Solutions company based in Cobham, Surrey. Providing web site design, hosting, internet marketing, search engine optimisation, consultancy and IT solutions*

▶ It Masters, Polhearne Lane, Brixham, Devon, TQ5 9LE Tel: (01803) 855803 Fax: 08716 611198 E-mail: sales@itmasters.co.uk *Computer consultants*

IT Networks Ltd, 19-21 High Street, Coleshill, Birmingham, B46 1AY Tel: 0870 1616611 Fax: 0870 1616622 E-mail: info@acutec.co.uk *ACUTEC are a network solutions provider, partnering with Microsoft, Novell, Cisco, 3Com and many other manufacturers. We also supply support and advice to SME's, corporates, NHS and local government.*

IT Partnership, 123 Radford Road, Leamington Spa, Warwickshire, CV31 1LG Tel: (01926) 314011 E-mail: help@itpartnership.com *Computer software developers & website designers*

The It Partnership, 4 Upper Mulgrave Road, Sutton, Surrey, SM2 7AZ Tel: (0870) 7270089 Fax: (0870) 7270090 *Builders & suppliers of computers*

▶ IT Performs Ltd, Gainsborough House, Burnett Road, Sutton Coldfield, West Midlands, B74 3EJ Tel: (0845) 1249495 Fax: (0845) 1249496 E-mail: solutions@it-performs.com *Specialist business intelligence service*

▶ It Print, 3 Cockridden Farm Indust Estate, Herongate, Brentwood, Essex, CM13 3LH Tel: (01277) 812501

▶ It Pros Ltd, 15 Strathyre Gardens, Bearsden, Glasgow, G61 2BD Tel: 0141-563 7215 E-mail: dj@it-pros.co.uk *Affordable ecommerce with our easy to use online shops. Based in Glasgow Scotland we will set up your internet shop in 4/5 days with full hosting and payment provision, at a cost of £695.00.*

IT Service Link Ltd, The Black Barn, The Folley, Layer De La Haye, Colchester, CO2 0HZ Tel: (01206) 235000 Fax: (01206) 235001 E-mail: danielle@hi-tech-sales.co.uk *Information technology consultants*

▶ It Services 4 You Ltd, 18 Wright Avenue, Stanground, Peterborough, PE2 8TR Tel: (01733) 563080 E-mail: info@itservices4you.co.uk

▶ It Software Solutions, Dunstable Road, Toddington, Dunstable, Bedfordshire, LU5 6DT Tel: (07811) 741568 E-mail: zoltan@it-software-solutions.com *IT Software Consultancy providing custom software solutions, software purchase advice and hard ware maintenance for your business.*

▶ IT Support Partners, St Johns Innovation Centre, Cowley Road, Cambridge, CB4 0WS Tel: (0870) 2403564 E-mail: info@itsp.co.uk *Provider of it services to small & medium size enterprises*

IT Support Tech, 2 Wells Road, Upper Knowle, Bristol, BS4 2AX Tel: 07787 569913 E-mail: simonlovell_99@yahoo.com *I provide computer hardware and software support for businesses or public. Teaching of Microsoft Office, Internet Explorer and Windows XP. Able to install and set-up networks.*

It World Consultants, 47 Catherine Place, London, SW1E 6DY Tel: (020) 7828 7300 Fax: (020) 7828 7990 E-mail: info@itworld.co.uk *Management consultants*

IT Zone (UK) Ltd, 12B Walworth Enterprise Centre, West Way, Andover, Hampshire, SP10 5AP Tel: (0870) 7667511 E-mail: ralph.griggs@the-it-zone.co.uk *Servicing & repairs to hp laser jet printers & design jet plotters*

Itab G.W.S Group Ltd, Unit E2 Imperial Business Estate, West Mill, Gravesend, Kent, DA11 0DL Tel: (01474) 537744 Fax: (01474) 537860 E-mail: info@gwsgroup.com *Shop fitters & shop equipment manufrs*

Ital Catering Equipment Ltd, 91 Old Oak Common Lane, London, W3 7DD Tel: (020) 8749 4832 Fax: (020) 8743 7885 E-mail: ray@frozen.co.uk *Catering equipment distributors*

▶ Italcomma UK Llp, 1 Bell Lane, Byfield, Daventry, Northamptonshire, NN11 6US Tel: (01327) 260070 Fax: (01327) 260065 E-mail: info@italcomma.co.uk *Italian chairs & glass furniture, both contemporary & traditional styles.*

Italian Chamber Of Commerce For U K, 1 Princes Street, London, W1B 2AY Tel: (020) 7495 8191 Fax: (020) 7495 8194 E-mail: info@italchamind.org.uk *Chamber of commerce*

Italian General Shipping Ltd, Berth 21 Powell Duffryn Ho, Tilbury Docks, Tilbury, Essex, RM18 7JT Tel: (020) 7488 9821 Fax: (020) 7480 5472 *Shipping agents*

▶ Italik, 2B Rudgate Court, Walton, Wetherby, West Yorkshire, LS23 7BF Tel: (01937) 848380 Fax: (01937) 848381 E-mail: info@italik.co.uk *Specialising in it consultancy*

▶ Itarus Ltd, Unit 6-8 Kingsthorpe Business Centre, Studland Road, Northampton, NN2 6NE Tel: (01604) 468100 Fax: (01604) 711736 E-mail: northaampton@itarus.com

Itas Computers, 27a Quay Street, Ammanford, Dyfed, SA18 3DB Tel: (01269) 591810 Fax: (01269) 591810 E-mail: andrew@aingerfield.freeserve.co.uk *Computer repairs & maintenance*

▶ Itasco Precision Ltd, 18 Faraday Road, Glenrothes, Fife, KY6 2RU Tel: (01592) 771285 Fax: (01592) 775164E-mail: sales@itasco.co.uk *Metalworking & fabrication services*

Itasco Precision Ltd, 18 Faraday Road, Glenrothes, Fife, KY6 2RU Tel: (01592) 771285 Fax: (01592) 775164 E-mail: sales@itasco.co.uk *Precision engineers*

Itc Ltd, 2-8 Park Road, Lytham St. Annes, Lancashire, FY8 1QX Tel: (01253) 783990 Fax: (01253) 783993 E-mail: info@itcoms.co.uk *Telecommunications*

▶ ITC Service Ltd, 45 Wedderlaw, Cramlington, Northumberland, NE23 6PA Tel: (07919) 154375 Fax: 0191-416 3003 E-mail: info@itcservive.co.uk *It supply & maintenance services*

▶ ITC Solutions, 2 Riverside Industrial Park, Rapier Street, Ipswich, IP2 8JX Tel: (01473) 604391 *Computer maintenance services*

Itdynamics Ltd, Lion Court, Staunton Harold, Ashby-de-la-Zouch, Leicestershire, LE65 1RT Tel: (01332) 695090 Fax: (01332) 695009 E-mail: info@itdynamics.co.uk *IT business & management consultancy*

▶ i-teamworks, PO Box 556, Peterborough, PE4 6WL Tel: (0845) 4900126 Fax: (0845) 4900127 E-mail: info@iteamworks.com *Software developers*

Itec Associates, 735 Washwood Heath Road, Birmingham, B8 2JY Tel: 0121-322 2444 Fax: 0121-322 2700 *Computer suppliers*

Itec Power Services Ltd, Itec House, 2 Berkeley Street, Ashton-under-Lyne, Lancashire, OL6 7DT Tel: 0161-343 1595 Fax: 0161-343 2341 E-mail: sales@itecpower.co.uk *Power transmission product distributors*

Itec Projects, 30 Severn Road, Aveley, South Ockendon, Essex, RM15 4NR Tel: (01708) 206181 Fax: (0870) 762 8843 E-mail: andrew@i-t-p.com *Mechanical & electrical consultants for building services*

Itech Quality Business Solutions Ltd, Lion Court Storten Harolrd, Whitick Business Park, Stenson Road, Coalville, Leicestershire, LE65 1RT Tel: (0870) 2249295 Fax: (0870) 8519295 E-mail: info@itechqbs.co.uk *Computer consultants*

Item Ltd, 65 Bury Mead Road, Hitchin, Hertfordshire, SG5 1RT Tel: (01462) 453838 Fax: (01462) 453619 E-mail: item@co.com *Industrial electronic engineers*

Item Ltd, Kingsway House, 103 Kingsway, London, WC2B 6QX Tel: (020) 7405 4767 Fax: (020) 7405 4768 E-mail: coms@item.co.uk *Public relations*

Item Systems, Albany House, 26 Nunholm Road, Dumfries, DG1 1JW Tel: (01387) 261969 Fax: (01387) 261969 E-mail: sales@itemsystems.co.uk *Computer systems & software sales*

Itesoft Ltd, Headway House, Crosby Way, Farnham, Surrey, GU9 7XG Tel: (01252) 741500 Fax: (01252) 741515 E-mail: marketing@itesoft-uk.co.uk *Image processing systems & cold workflow*

▶ Itesoft UK Ltd, 19-21 The Woolneed, Farnham, Surrey, GU9 7TT Tel: (01252) 741500 Fax: (01252) 741515 E-mail: marketing@itesoft.com *Data capture software*

Itf Oil & Gas Exploration, Exploration House, Exploration Drive, Bridge of Don, Aberdeen, AB23 8GX Tel: (01224) 853400 Fax: (01224) 853480 E-mail: itf@oil-itf.com *Technology brokers to oil & gas industry* Also at: Edinburgh

▶ Itflex, 1 Victory Close, Grays, Essex, RM16 6RT Tel: (01708) 209924 E-mail: info@itflex.co.uk *IT installations, health-checks, anti virus & security*

▶ It-Freedom Ltd, Minster Court, Tuscam Way, Camberley, Surrey, GU15 3YY Tel: (01276) 686686 Fax: (01276) 671648 E-mail: sales@it-freedom.com *Claims management solutions*

▶ ITH Ltd, Unit 12, Prince Consort Road Industrial Estate, Hebburn, Tyne & Wear, NE31 1EH Tel: 0191-483 2020 Fax: 0191-483 2121 E-mail: sales@ithltd.co.uk *Manufacture and supply of temperature sensors e.g. thermocouples, resistance thermometers (RTD'S), fabricated or mineral insulated and associated components including heads, plugs and mechanical fittings together with electric heating elements including cartridge, band, rod and infrared heaters*

Itheon Ltd, 1 The Boulevard, Welwyn Garden City, Hertfordshire, AL7 1EL Tel: (01707) 336600 Fax: (01707) 336622 E-mail: sales@itheon.com *Software developers*

Iti Security, Aylesford Business Centre, High Street, Aylesford, Kent, ME20 7AX Tel: (01732) 522090 E-mail: sales@itisecurity.co.uk *Burglar & intruder alarm systems cctv & access control*

Itl Impex Ltd, Commercial House, 19 Station Road, Bognor Regis, West Sussex, PO21 1QD Tel: (01243) 841734 Fax: (01243) 841734 E-mail: itl@hopcbroadband.com *Export & import merchants*

▶ ITMAX Ltd, Abbey Drive, Abbots Langley, Hertfordshire, WD5 0TL Tel: (01923) 461405 Fax: (01923) 464106 E-mail: bash@itmax.co.uk *Hardware & software wholesalers & retailers*

▶ ITO, Anson House, Northwick Road, Oxhey, Watford, WD19 6RS Tel: (020) 8428 0288 Fax: (020) 8420 1073 E-mail: info@itowatford.org.uk *High quality, short run, digital printing. Calendars, greeting cards, leaflets, flyers, booklets etc.**All proceeds go to help our work with people with disabilities*

Itochu Europe plc, 2 Ashbys Yard, Medway Wharf Road, Tonbridge, Kent, TN9 1RE Tel: (01732) 363003 Fax: (01732) 367775 *Retail of test systems*

▶ Its A Bouncy Thing, 9 Knowle Avenue, Bexleyheath, Kent, DA7 5LP Tel: (020) 8312 0545 E-mail: info@itsabouncything.com *Adults/ kids Bouncy Castles including Disney princess, Dora, Dalmation, Noah''s Ark multiplay garden games and bubble machines*

It's A Gas, 100 Coventry Road, Market Harborough, Leicestershire, LE16 9DA Tel: (01858) 446216 E-mail: starr@its-a-gas-balloons.co.uk *Party shop balloon decorators*

It's A Wrap Northeast Ltd, Unit 24 Grasmere Way, Kitty Brewster Industrial Estate, Blyth, Northumberland, NE24 4RR Tel: (01670) 543663 Fax: (01670) 543663 E-mail: sales@itsawrap.org.uk *The core of our business is the supply and servicing of Horizontal Form-Fill-Seal machines, more commonly known as "Flowrappers". It''s a Wrap supply a wide range of new and used Flowrappers from the small 450 model Flowrapper to the high performance 750E Flowrapper. These machines can pack a huge range of products using almost any heat sealable or cold-seal wrapping material. Available in basic mechanical or full multi-axis electronic - painted finish or stainless steel - manual feed or automatic feed. All are modern high quality machines designed with the latest features and built to exacting standards in the UK and Italy.*Other Packaging machinery, packaging automation Technical support, maintenance and spares*

Its Computers Ltd, 377 Ladbroke Grove, London, W10 5AA Tel: (020) 8960 1494 Fax: (020) 8960 1484 E-mail: itscomputers@atlas.co.uk *Computer manufrs*

ITS Environmental Services Ltd, Woodside, Sauchen, Inverurie, Aberdeenshire, AB51 7LP Tel: 01330 830240 Fax: 01330 830249 E-mail: lbarron@its-uk.co.uk *A Rental, Sales & Service Company providing Fluid Recovery Equipment, Pressure Washers and Trash Compactors*

▶ It's Here, 3 Holgate Court, Western Road, Romford, RM1 3JS Tel: (01708) 737500 Fax: (01708) 737500 E-mail: info@itshere.uk.com *IT consulting software development & microsoft certified training & education*

Its Testing Services UK Ltd, Wellheads Crescent, Wellheads Industrial Estate, Aberdeen, AB21 7GA Tel: (01224) 723242 Fax: (01224) 722894 *Oil & petroleum laboratories* Also at: Branches throughout the U.K.

ITS WSI Ltd, 9 Augustine Grove, Sutton Coldfield, West Midlands, B74 4XX Tel: 0121-308 4011 E-mail: mal@itswsi.co.uk *Internet consultancy & web development services*

Itsc Ltd, 9 Northfields Prospect, Northfields, London, SW18 1PE Tel: (020) 8874 7282 Fax: (020) 8874 7539 E-mail: itscuk@aol.com *Hydroelectric power supply consultants*

Itstick Labels Ltd, 8-9 Bath Road Trading Estate, Lightpill, Stroud, Gloucestershire, GL5 3QF Tel: (01453) 758010 Fax: (01453) 764089 E-mail: enquiries@itsticklabels.co.uk *Self adhesive label distribs*

▶ Itt Ltd, 2b Bath Court, Bath Row, Birmingham, B15 1NE Tel: 0121-248 1632 Fax: 0121-248 1633 E-mail: richard.ashton@i-t-t.com *Technical translations services*

Itt Cannon Ltd, Viables Industrial Estate, Jays Close, Basingstoke, Hampshire, RG22 4BA Tel: (01256) 311200 Fax: (01256) 322356 E-mail: sales.uk@cannon.de.ittind.com *Electric switch manufrs*

Itt Industries Ltd, Viables Industrial Estate, Jays Close, Basingstoke, Hampshire, RG22 4BA Tel: (01256) 311800 Fax: (01256) 811814 *Electrical connector manufrs*

▶ Ittalent Computer Consultants, 5 Aykley Vale, Aykley Heads, Durham, DH1 5WA Tel: 0191-383 0440 *IT consultants*

ITW Automotive Finishing UK, Lockside, Anchor Brook Industrial Estate, Aldridge, Walsall, WS9 8EG Tel: (01922) 423700 Fax: (01922) 423705 E-mail: info@itwautofin.co.uk *Spray equipment suppliers*

▶ Iubeo Europe Ltd, 82 Tenter Road, Moulton Park, Northampton, NN3 6AX Tel: +44 (01604) 646433 Fax: +44 (01604) 643737 E-mail: david@iubeo-europe.com *Consultancy & sourcing services*

Ivacroft Ltd, Old Guard House, Trimms Green, Sawbridgeworth, Hertfordshire, CM21 0LX Tel: (01279) 724946 Fax: (01279) 722673 *Electrical engineers*

Ivan J Cooper Moorside Ltd, Moorside Works, Ellastone Road, Cauldon Low, Stoke-on-Trent, ST10 3ET Tel: (01538) 702738 Fax: (01538) 702662 E-mail: brenda-prince@btconnect.com *Steel frame building constructors & fabricators*

Ivanhoe Feeds Ltd, Ashby Road, Boundary, Swadlincote, Derbyshire, DE11 7BA Tel: (01283) 212300 Fax: (01283) 221836 *Agricultural merchants*

Ivanhoe Forge Ltd, Station Road, Seaton Delaval, Whitley Bay, Tyne & Wear, NE25 0QB Tel: 0191-237 0676 Fax: 0191-237 6887 *Site welding & fabrication work*

Ivanhoe Printing Co. Ltd, Station Road, Musselburgh, Midlothian, EH21 7PE Tel: 0131-665 8444 Fax: 0131-653 2691 *Colour printing services*

Iveco Ltd, Iveco House, Road One, Winsford Industrial Estate, Winsford, Cheshire, CW7 3QP Tel: (01606) 541000 Fax: (01606) 541126 *Logistics consultants*

▶ Ivett & Reed Ltd, 615 Newmarket Road, Cambridge, CB5 8PA Tel: (01223) 213500 Fax: (01223) 249150 E-mail: sales@ivettandreed.co.uk

IViewCameras.co.uk Ltd, Unit 7 Hurlingham Business Park, Sulivan Road, Fulham, London, SW6 3DU Tel: (0800) 1804260 Fax: (020) 7751 3450 E-mail: sales@iviewcameras.co.uk *View cameras supplies cctv camera systems*

Ivojo Multimedia Ltd, Newton Cross, Hayscastle, Haverfordwest, Dyfed, SA62 5HS Tel: (01348) 840080 Fax: (01348) 841081 E-mail: sales@ivojo.co.uk *Audio visual distributors*

▶ I-volv Recruitment Solutions, 8 Cilfton Road, High Brooms, Tunbridge Wells, Kent, TN2 3AR Tel: 01892 689301 E-mail: recruitment@i-volv.co.uk *I-volv Recruitment Solutions Ltd is an Independent Recruitment Consultancy providing high quality personnel, to companies and organisations throughout the Environmental, Renewable Energy and Water sectors within the UK and Worldwide*

Ivor Hopkins Suspended Ceilings & Partitions, 10 Kingsmead, Station Road, Kings Cliffe, Peterborough, PE8 6YH Tel: (01780) 470048 Fax: (01780) 470039 E-mail: sales@ivorhopkins.co.uk *Ceiling & partition installers*

Ivor Newton & Son Fuel & Car Sales, Aston Road, Haddenham, Aylesbury, Buckinghamshire, HP17 8AF Tel: (01844) 291461 *Joiners & cabinet manufrs*

Ivory Graphics Ltd, 2 Halcyon Court, St. Margarets Way, Stukeley Meadows Industrial Estate, Huntingdon, Cambridgeshire, PE29 6DG Tel: (01480) 417511 Fax: (0870) 3001101 E-mail: info@ivorygraphics.plus.com *Printing manufacturers of playing cards & beer mats*

Ivthing Vale Quality Foods Ltd, Berlin Street, Carlisle, CA1 2NL Tel: (01228) 595373 Fax: (01228) 533288 *Food distributors*

▶ Ivy House Conservatories, Taylors Farm, Stoneygate, Houghton le Spring, Tyne & Wear, DH4 4NL Tel: 0191-511 0262 Fax: 0191-528 1928 *Joinery*

Ivy Learning Software, Ivy House, 235 Roehampton Lane, London, SW15 4LB Tel: (020) 8780 1494 Fax: (020) 8780 1420 E-mail: sales@ivysoft.co.uk *Computer software suppliers*

▶ Ivybridge Tile & Slate Centre, Unit 17 Erme Court, Leonards Road, Ivybridge, Devon, PL21 0SZ Tel: (01752) 690856 Fax: (01752) 690856 *Floor & wall tiles specialist suppliers*

Ivyline, Unit 5, Seven Stars Industrial Estate Wheler Road, Coventry, CV3 4LB Tel: (024) 7621 7600 Fax: (024) 7630 6372 *Ceramic importers*

Ivyplus Fasteners & Fixing Devices, 41 Colmore Flats, Henrietta Street, Birmingham, B19 3PT Tel: 0121-212 2485 Fax: 0121-212 2485 *Special fasteners & modifications manufrs*

Iwaki Pumps UK Ltd, Monkmoor Road, Shrewsbury, SY2 5SX Tel: (01743) 231363 Fax: (01743) 366507 E-mail: info@iwakipumpsltd.co.uk *Pump manufrs*

Iwax Marketing Ltd, 8 Queen Street, Ballymoney, Co. Antrim, BT53 6JA Tel: (028) 2766 6455 Fax: (028) 2766 6549 *Disposable gas cylinders distributor*

▶ Iweave Ltd, 4 Brentham Crescent, Stirling, FK8 2AZ Tel: (01786) 450606 Fax: (01786) 462876

Ixapack UK Ltd, Unit A, King Street, Walsall, WS1 4AF Tel: (01922) 721102 Fax: (01922) 721921 E-mail: enquiries@ixapack.com *Manufacturers of labelling machines & systems*

▶ Ixia UK, Unit 14 Ridgewood Industrial Estate, New Road, Uckfield, East Sussex, TN22 5SX Tel: (01825) 766800 Fax: (01825) 766500 E-mail: ixiauk@cs.com *Automatic pick & place machinery specialists*

▶ Izax Offshore Marine Services, 2 Littlemoor Lane, Newton, Alfreton, Derbyshire, DE55 5TY Tel: (01773) 875986 Fax: (01773) 875986 E-mail: matt_izax@hotmail.com *Sea vessel suppliers*

▶ J 4 Deliveries Ltd, Cromer House, Caxton Way, Stevenage, Hertfordshire, SG1 2DF Tel: (01438) 236022 Fax: (01438) 236023 E-mail: j4deliveries@aol.com *Same Day Deliveries Direct To Any Destination In The UK. With Over Night Collections And A Genuine 24 HR Flexible Service.*

J A B Hire Services Ltd, J A B House, Delamare Road, Cheshunt, Waltham Cross, Hertfordshire, EN8 9SS Tel: (01992) 634666 Fax: (01992) 634777 *Contractors plant hire, towers, contractors plant equipment*

J A B Short Ltd, 214 Sheffield Road, Chesterfield, Derbyshire, S41 7JP Tel: (01246) 232109 Fax: (01246) 220304 E-mail: homes@jabshort.co.uk *Building contractors services*

▶ J A Block Paving Ltd, Railstone Terminal, Marlborough Road, Wootton Bassett, Swindon, SN4 7EH Tel: (01793) 852129 Fax: (01793) 850162

J A Burke, 325 Highfield Road, Hall Green, Birmingham, B28 0BX Tel: 0121-777 7887 Fax: (0709) 287 5995 E-mail: admin@jaburke.co.uk

▶ J. A. Campbell London Sterling Silver, 18 Perseverance Works, 38 Kingsland Road, London, E2 8DD Tel: 020 72534560 Fax: 020 76132729 E-mail: info@jacampbell.co.uk *We create sterling silver products such as drinks related and tabletop items including gifts. Our firm is proud to be doing this for over 32 years.*

J A Chapman, The Forge, 45 Bonehurst Road, Horley, Surrey, RH6 8PJ Tel: (01293) 785060 Fax: (01293) 785060 *Plant & crane hire* Also at: Smallfield

J A Clark & Co Engineers Ltd, Charrold Works, Stephenson Way, Thetford, Norfolk, IP24 3RJ Tel: (01842) 752348 Fax: (01842) 755194 E-mail: sales@jaclark.co.uk *Steel fabricators*

J A E Europe Ltd, Coliseum Business Centre, Riverside Way, Camberley, Surrey, GU15 3YL Tel: (01276) 404000 Fax: (01276) 404010 E-mail: sales@jae.co.uk *Connector & component designers & suppliers*

J A & F Bullock Saddlery, North Moor, Easingwold, York, YO61 3NB Tel: (01347) 823430 Fax: (01347) 823430 *Farming*

▶ J A F Carriers Ltd, 14 Fairfield Street, Dundee, DD3 8HX Tel: (01382) 833366

J & A Ferrie, The Smithy, High Street, Newmilns, Ayrshire, KA16 9EE Tel: (01560) 323002 Fax: (01560) 322382 E-mail: enquiries@j-aferrie.co.uk *Farrier suppliers*

J A Friend & Son, 35 Parkwood Road, Tavistock, Devon, PL19 0HH Tel: (01822) 613726 *Agricultural engineers*

J A G Glazing Ltd, High Street, Cleobury Mortimer, Kidderminster, Worcestershire, DY14 8DP Tel: (01299) 271007 Fax: (01299) 271078 E-mail: sales@jag-glazing.co.uk *UPVC windows & door manufrs*

J A G Services Ltd, 13 Reform Road, Maidenhead, Berkshire, SL6 8BY Tel: (01628) 670909 Fax: (01628) 672016 E-mail: gstuart@jagservices.fsnet.co.uk *Specialist metal workers/welding/fabrication*

J & A Gardner & Company Ltd, The Office Craigmaddie, Milngavie, Glasgow, G62 8LB Tel: 0141-956 6453 Fax: 0141-956 6685 E-mail: admin@jandagardner.co.uk *Shipping lines, ship owners & agents* Also at: Oban

J A Glover Ltd, 23 Lordswood Industrial Estate, Revenge Road, Chatham, Kent, ME5 8UD Tel: (01634) 684419 Fax: (01634) 200423 E-mail: chatham@jagglover.demon.co.uk *Ventilation products distributors & manufrs*

J A Glover Ltd, A Pioneers Industrial Park, Beddington Farm Road, Croydon, CR0 4XY Tel: (020) 8665 7055 Fax: (020) 8665 5108 *Ventilation sales services*

J A Godbold, The Forge, The Garage, Egton, Whitby, North Yorkshire, YO21 1TZ Tel: (01947) 895562 Fax: (01947) 895562 *Blacksmiths*

J.A. Harrison & Co (Manchester) Limited, Britain Works, Sherborne St, Manchester, M8 8HP Tel: 0161 832 2282 Fax: 0161 832 3263 E-mail: ben@alliancegaskets.co.uk *J A Harrison (Manchester) Limited was founded in 1900 and for the past century has provided a service to a wide range of industries for manufactured Seals and Gaskets, Gland Packing, Industrial Textiles, Bellows, Compensators, Flexible Connections, Mechanical Seals, Boiler Spares and allied products. Local, national and international customers receive a service with proven quality, competitive pricing, technical expertise, full on-site and after-sales support. Non-Asbestos Fibres; Synthetic and Natural Rubber; Ceramics; PTFE and PEEK; Glass Fibre; Graphite; Cork; Felt: Millboard; Industrial Papers; Plastics and Leather. Our quality system BS EN ISO 9001:2000 ensures effective customer satisfaction and a planned programme of continual investment in people and manufacturing technology, provides us with the confidence and expertise to further enhance the company's production, supply and service capability. You can reach us by phone, fax, post or e-mail. We will welcome your call.*

▶ J A Hutchinson & Sons Haulage Ltd, Station Road, Ailsworth, Peterborough, PE5 7AH Tel: (01733) 380955

J & A International Ltd, Vale Road, Spilsby, Lincolnshire, PE23 5HE Tel: (01790) 752757 Fax: (01790) 754132 E-mail: ja-int@ja-int.co.uk *Badge, emblem & transfer manufrs*

J A Kent Services East Midlands Ltd, Chestnut Farmhouse, Chestnut Lane, Barton-in-Fabis, Nottingham, NG11 0AE Tel: 0115-983 0691 Fax: 0115-983 1229 E-mail: info@kentservices.fsnet.co.uk *Ground maintenance, pest control & building & tree surgery services*

J A Kinnersley & Co. Ltd, Copenhagen Road, Hull, HU7 0XQ Tel: (01482) 826020 Fax: (01482) 878447 E-mail: sales@j-kinnersley.co.uk Principal Export Areas: Africa *Tube manipulation & powder coating services*

▶ J A Kneen Developments Ltd, 3 Golden Hill, Leyland, PR25 3NN Tel: (01772) 621428 Fax: (01772) 621429

J A Lorrimar & Co., Lorrimar House Hatfield Hi-Tech Park, Goulton Street, Hull, HU3 4DD Tel: (01482) 228173 Fax: (01482) 214106 E-mail: info@lorrimar.co.uk *Scale & slicing machine distribs*

J A M Ltd, 24 Farriers Way, Temple Farm Industrial Estate, Southend-on-Sea, SS2 5RY Tel: (01702) 602333 Fax: (01702) 602330 E-mail: sales@jam.uk.com *Electronic equipment assemblers & manufrs*

J A M Design Screen Print, 143a Croydon Road, Caterham, Surrey, CR3 6PF Tel: (01883) 343444 Fax: (01883) 343444 E-mail: jim.rimmington@btinternet.com *Screen printers*

J A M Y Ltd, Unit 17 Roman Way Small Business Park, London Road, Godmanchester, Huntingdon, Cambridgeshire, PE29 2LN Tel: (01480) 456391 Fax: (01480) 414959 E-mail: sales@jamy.co.uk *Acrylic Awards, Corporate Awards, Acrylic, Encapsulations, Tombstones, Deal Toys, Acrylic Paperweights, Coasters, Point of Purchase Displays, Edge Lit Displays, Plaques in Acrylic & Wood, Partner Plaques, 0Special Projects - using Acrylic & Resin, Vacuum Forming & Hot Wire Bending, Framed Displays, Small Signs, Sand Carving, CNC Routing, Laser, Engraving, Ice Effects, Special Projects*

▶ J & A Mcdougall Ltd, 32 Combie Street, Oban, Argyll, PA34 4HT Tel: (01631) 562304 Fax: (01631) 564408 E-mail: enquiries@apartmentsoban.co.uk

J A Magson Ltd, Magson House, Kettlestring Lane, York, YO30 4XF Tel: (01904) 690097 Fax: (01904) 691018 E-mail: sales@magson.co.uk *Stationery greeting card & toy distributors*

J A Marchant & Son Ltd, Chaddock Lane, Tyldesley, Manchester, M29 7JT Tel: (01942) 882858 Fax: (01942) 897014 E-mail: marchants2003@yahoo.co.uk *Leather gift manufrs*

J A Martin, 2 Beechvale Road, Killinchy, Newtownards, County Down, BT23 6PH Tel: (028) 9754 1062 *Engineers*

J & A Metals, 12 Skidmore Road, Bilston, West Midlands, WV14 8SE Tel: (01902) 497382 Fax: (01902) 497382 *Scrap metal merchants*

J & A Mitchell Co. Ltd, Springbank Distillery, Well Close, Campbeltown, Argyll, PA28 6ET Tel: (01586) 552085 Fax: (01586) 553215 E-mail: info@jandamitchell.com *Whisky distillers*

J A P Contracts, Unit K4 Bentalls Complex, Colchester Road, Heybridge, Maldon, Essex, CM9 4GE Tel: (01621) 855177 Fax: (01621) 855080 E-mail: info@japcontracts.com *JAP Contracts based in Maldon, Essex is a specialist kitchen/bar design and equipment supply*

continued

company, dedicated to providing a quality service to the catering industry. They are able to offer their clients a competitive, tailored, turnkey package, incorporating CAD design, equipment specification, procurement, project management, installation and after sales service.

J & A Precision Engineering, 10 Second Avenue, Chatham, Kent, ME4 5AU Tel: (01634) 406727 Fax: (01634) 832115 E-mail: mail@jandaprecisioneng.co.uk *Precision engineers*

▶ J & A Removals & Car Transport of West Sussex, Lodore, Copthorne Common, Crawley, West Sussex, RH10 3JT Tel: (01342) 714851 E-mail: europeanremovals@aol.com *Family run firm, based in Copthorne, West Sussex. Offering Storage, House removals, car transport & light transport. Local, UK & Europe .Large or small moves. Part loads to France & Spain. Freight upto 4500kg /50 cubic metres. Discounts on return loads to UK. We are in France most weeks 042 714851 or 07958 741224 europeanremovals@aol.com* www.uk-houseremovals.com**

J A Renton & Sons, Ashby Road, Thringstone, Coalville, Leicestershire, LE67 8UH Tel: (01530) 222224 Fax: (01530) 224069 E-mail: renton.lorries@btinternet.com *Machine tool removal contractors*

J A Roskelly & Son, The Forge, 19 Penmare Terrace, Hayle, Cornwall, TR27 4PH Tel: (01736) 753160 *Wrought ironworkers manufrs*

J A S Engineering, Glover Centre, Egmont Street, Mossley, Ashton-under-Lyne, Lancashire, OL5 9PY Tel: (01457) 833181 Fax: (01457) 837981 E-mail: sales@jasengineering.co.uk *Steel work bench manufrs*

▶ J A Salisbury, The Smithy, Whitton, Ludlow, Shropshire, SY8 3DB Tel: (01584) 891715 Fax: (01584) 891714 *Specialists in the supply & service of poultry equipment*

J A Smallshaw, 22a Castle Street, Shrewsbury, SY1 2BJ Tel: (01743) 362482 Fax: (01743) 367668 *Coal suppliers* Also at: Gobowen

J A Smith, Harrowgate Road, London, E9 5ED Tel: (020) 8525 9842 Fax: (020) 8525 9842 *Wrought iron gates & railings manufrs*

J A V Controls, 26 Reson Way, Hemel Hempstead, Hertfordshire, HP1 1NU Tel: (01442) 256617 Fax: (01442) 233099 E-mail: jgurney@javgroup.co.uk *Industrial control suppliers*

J A Williams & Sons Ltd, 30 Birmingham Road, West Bromwich, West Midlands, B71 4JZ Tel: 0121-553 7305 Fax: 0121-553 0503 *Scrap iron & steel merchants*

J A Winward & Sons, Rear of, 120 High St South, London, E6 3RW Tel: (020) 8472 5986 Fax: (020) 8503 4743 E-mail: winward@btconnect.com *Scientific & laboratory glassware manufacturers. Also glass blowers/blown glassware manufrs*

J A Young & Sons, 19-21 Alpine Way, London, E6 6LA Tel: (020) 7473 9300 Fax: (020) 7473 9301 *Insulation material suppliers*

J Alex Swift Ltd, Cross Street, Hathern, Loughborough, Leicestershire, LE12 5LB Tel: (01509) 842284 Fax: (01509) 646106 E-mail: socks@jalexswift.co.uk *Men's & childrens hosiery*

▶ J Allan Osborne Preservations Ltd, 14 John Street, Helensburgh, Dunbartonshire, G84 8BA Tel: (01436) 676095 Fax: (01436) 679329

J Anderson, Bridge End Cottage, Ebchester, Consett, County Durham, DH8 9JA Tel: (01207) 560208 *Agricultural engineers*

J Angus & Partners, 44 Portaferry Road, Kircubbin, Newtownards, County Down, BT22 2RY Tel: (028) 4278 8272 *Agricultural contractors*

J Arthurton, Stonycroft, Heath Road, Hockering, Dereham, Norfolk, NR20 3JB Tel: (01603) 880690 *Timber merchants*

▶ J Ayre J, 114 Westmount Road, London, SE9 1UT Tel: (020) 8850 1786 Fax: (020) 8850 2786 *Bakery & confectionary*

J B A Engineering Ltd, Unit 56b Bradley Hall Trading Estate, Bradley Lane, Standish, Wigan, Lancashire, WN6 0XQ Tel: (01257) 424549 Fax: (01257) 424549 *Vehicle manufrs*

J B A Public Relations, 57 Church Street, Epsom, Surrey, KT17 4PX Tel: (01372) 734200 Fax: (01372) 734201 E-mail: jba@jbapr.com *Public relations consultants*

J B Amusements, 25 High Street, Draperstown, Magherafelt, County Londonderry, BT45 7AB Tel: (028) 7962 7011 Fax: (028) 7962 7411 *Amusement arcades*

J B Angling Centre, 37 Eastside, Kirkintilloch, Glasgow, G66 1QA Tel: 0141-775 0083 Fax: 0141-775 0083 *Fishing tackle & bate retailer*

J B Architectural Ironmongery Ltd, Avis Way, Newhaven, East Sussex, BN9 0DU Tel: (01273) 514961 Fax: (01273) 516764 E-mail: info@jbai.co.uk *Door closers & lock wholesalers*

J B Armstrong & Co. Ltd, Middleton Street, Ilkeston, Derbyshire, DE7 5TT Tel: 0115-932 4913 Fax: 0115-930 0083 E-mail: info@armstrongsmill.co.uk *Men's outwear manufrs*

J B B Textile Agencies Ltd, 19 Bark Street East, Bolton, BL1 2BQ Tel: (01204) 528400 Fax: (01204) 528090 E-mail: info@jbbmachinery.co.uk *Textile machinery merchants*

▶ J B Backhouse, 107 High Street, Airmyn, Goole, North Humberside, DN14 8LD Tel: (01405) 762876 Fax: (01405) 766412 E-mail: sales@honda-uk.com *Sales, parts & service of all garden machinery*

J B Bennett Contracts Ltd, Banton Mill Mill Road, Banton, Kilsyth, Glasgow, G65 0QG Tel: (01236) 823011 Fax: (01236) 821883 *Building contractors*

▶ J B Black, Bairdsmill, Crosshill, Maybole, Ayrshire, KA19 7PU Tel: (01655) 740331 Fax: (01655) 740322

J B Broadley, Reeds Holme Works, Burnley Road, Rossendale, Lancashire, BB4 8LN Tel: (01706) 213661 Fax: (01706) 227786 E-mail: info@jbbroadley.co.uk *Technical coated fabric manufrs*

J B Browning & Son, 32 Boultons Lane, Redditch, Worcestershire, B97 5NY Tel: (01527) 543116 *Agricultural plant hire contractors*

J B C Industrial Services Ltd, Howley Park Road East, Morley, Leeds, LS27 0SW Tel: 0113-220 3830 Fax: 0113-252 1407 E-mail: info@jbcindserv.co.uk *Industrial boiler engineers*

J B Cater Hire, Unit 10 Nursteed Road Trading Estate, William Road, Devizes, Wiltshire, SN10 3EW Tel: (01380) 729192 Fax: (01380) 729192 E-mail: info@wallismarquees.co.uk *Marquee hire & catering equipment suppliers*

J B Christie, Flowerhill Industrial Estate, Airdrie, Lanarkshire, ML6 6BH Tel: (01236) 761437 Fax: (01236) 770249 *Bakery & confectionery suppliers*

J B Communications Group Ltd, 15 Brackenbury Road, London, W6 0BE Tel: (020) 8749 6036 Fax: (020) 8749 9676 E-mail: interest@jbcommunications.co.uk *Conference organizing services*

J B Computer Management, 39 Luckley Road, Wokingham, Berkshire, RG41 2ES Tel: 0118-978 5161 Fax: 0118-977 4108 E-mail: sales@cdc-jbcm.com *Computer consultants*

▶ J & B Construction Co. Ltd, Unit 41-43 Cumberland Business Park, Cumberland Avenue, London, NW10 7RT Tel: (020) 8961 3847 Fax: (020) 8961 3816

J B Contracting Ltd, Orchard House, Green End, Stretham, Ely, Cambridgeshire, CB6 3LF Tel: (01353) 648509 Fax: (01353) 648509 *Agricultural contractors*

J B D Tritec Ltd, 430 Helen Street, Glasgow, G51 3HR Tel: 0141-440 1292 Fax: 0141-440 1240 *Engineering sub-contract services*

J B Developments, Rose Cottage, New Gilston, Leven, Fife, KY8 5TF Tel: (01334) 840512 Fax: (01334) 840640 *Steel structures*

J B Edlington & Co Ltd, Carr Lane, Gainsborough, Lincolnshire, DN21 1LF Tel: (01427) 616869 Fax: (01427) 616869 E-mail: paul@edlington.com *Agricultural machinery manufrs*

J & B Electric Power Tool Co. Ltd, Dorset House, 65a Manchester Road, Bolton, BL2 1ES Tel: (01204) 531891 Fax: (01204) 364735 *Electrical power tools retailers*

J B Electrical Ltd, 5-6 Lion Industrial Park, Northgate Way, Walsall, WS9 8RL Tel: (01922) 459351 Fax: (01922) 743506 E-mail: jeff.bird@fsmail.net *Switchgear (low voltage) manufrs*

▶ J B Electrical Scotland Ltd, Grange Loan, Edinburgh, EH9 2NP Tel: (0870) 0469357

J B Engineering, Unit 16b, 16 Balloo Avenue, Bangor, County Down, BT19 7QT Tel: (028) 9127 4742 *General engineers*

J B Engineering, Scropton Road, Hatton, Derby, DE65 5DS Tel: (01283) 812348 Fax: (01283) 812230 E-mail: info@jbeng-hatton.co.uk *Steel fabrication*

▶ J B Entertainments, 125 Boxley Drive, West Bridgford, Nottingham, NG2 7GN Tel: 0115-923 5747 Fax: 0115-923 5747 E-mail: info@jbentertainments.com *Entertainment Agency for all type of artistes and venues*

▶ J B Fabrication, 71 London Street, Leicester, LE5 3RW Tel: 0116-246 1204 Fax: 0116-246 1204 *Steel fabricators*

▶ J B Fabrication Wrexham Ltd, Bryn Lane, Wrexham Industrial Estate, Wrexham, Clwyd, LL13 9UT Tel: (01978) 664446 Fax: (01978) 664447

▶ J B Fire Systems, 54 Glebe Way, West Wickham, Kent, BR4 0RL Tel: (020) 8402 1847 Fax: (020) 8402 1848 E-mail: sales@jbfiresystems.co.uk *Fire alarm system suppliers*

J.B.G. (Marketing) Ltd, Jay Bee House, 226a Whitehorse Road, Croydon, CR0 2LB Tel: (020) 8683 2610 Fax: (020) 8684 2523 E-mail: enquiries@jbgroves.freeserve.co.uk *Tool importers & distributors*

J B Garage Doors London South East Ltd, 74 Swaisland Drive, Crayford, Dartford, DA1 4HY Tel: (01322) 528059 Fax: (01322) 550560 E-mail: enquiries@jbgaragedoors.co.uk *Garage door installation & suppliers*

J B Hats & Things, 18 Ellesmere Road, Sheffield, S4 7JB Tel: 0114-278 6660 E-mail: jbahatsnthing@aol.com *Hat manufrs*

▶ J & B Hopkins Ltd, 96 Botley Road, Richmond Court, Park Gate, Southampton, SO31 1BA Tel: (01489) 584706

J B I Ltd, Riverside, Bacup, Lancashire, OL13 0DT Tel: (01706) 873355 Fax: (01706) 874047 E-mail: enquires@j-b-i.co.uk *Boot, shoe & slipper wholesalers*

J B Industrial Doors Ltd, Straw Mill Hill, Maidstone, Kent, ME15 6FL Tel: (01622) 679501 Fax: (01622) 685456 *Industrial doors manufrs*

J B Industrial Tooling, 2 Mount Caburn CR, Peacehaven, East Sussex, BN10 8DW Tel: (0870) 1660041 Fax: (0870) 1660042 *Easy raker diamond repointing system & diamond tool manufrs*

J & B Insulations Ltd, Unit 1, Stanley St, Burton-on-Trent, Staffordshire, DE14 1DY Tel: (01283) 531287 Fax: (01283) 511953 *Industrial thermal insulation*

J B Ironworks, Heys Lane, Great Harwood, Blackburn, BB6 7UA Tel: (01254) 889920 Fax: (01254) 889920 *Wrought ironworkers*

J B J Pallets Ltd, Hedingham Road, Wethersfield, Braintree, Essex, CM7 4EQ Tel: (01371) 850035 Fax: (01371) 850420 *Wooden pallet repairers & manufrs*

▶ J B Joinery, Unit 7 Skelmanthorpe Business Park, Elm Street, Skelmanthorpe, Huddersfield, HD8 9DZ Tel: (01484) 860601 Fax: (01484) 860601 *Joiners*

J B Joinery, Aitken Street, Stoke-on-Trent, ST6 3RG Tel: (01782) 825455 Fax: (01782) 825951 *Purpose made joiners*

J B L Printers Ltd, Rabone Lane, Smethwick, West Midlands, B66 3JX Tel: 0121-558 2935 Fax: 0121-558 6591 E-mail: jblprinters@compuserve.com *Printing services*

▶ J & B Landscape Services Ltd, Serenity House 12 Waters Edge, Handsacre, Rugeley, Staffordshire, WS15 4HP Tel: (08000) 112) 114 Fax: 08700 802 329 E-mail: info@jblandscapes.co.uk *All aspects of garden landscaping and design, free home or site visits, we supply fixed price quotations, not estimates along with a full job specification detailing the methods and materials to be used.*

J & B Leathers, 37 Orford Road, London, E17 9NL Tel: (020) 8923 7720 Fax: (020) 8923 7720 E-mail: sales@jbleathers.co.uk *Leather goods*

J & B Limmax, 22 Horsecroft Place, Harlow, Essex, CM19 5BX Tel: (01279) 444243 Fax: (01279) 450571 E-mail: sales@marksmanpaintball.com *Engineering, CNC & toolmaking*

▶ J B Lubes & Tools, Hillborough Business Park, Sweechbridge Road, Herne Bay, Kent, CT6 6TE Tel: (0787) 6025560 Fax: (01227) 740475 E-mail: jblubes@yahoo.co.uk *Engineering cutting oils & industrial lubricant distributors*

J B M International Ltd, Unit 5b Hixon Industrial Estate, Church Lane, Hixon, Stafford, ST18 0PY Tel: (01889) 271491 Fax: (01889) 271191 E-mail: sales@jessebroughmetals.co.uk *Secondary aluminium ingots*

J B N Plastics, White Cottage Farm, Lucas Green Road, West End, Woking, Surrey, GU24 9LZ Tel: (01483) 474979 Fax: (01483) 472487 *Plastic rack informing manufrs*

J & B Novak Metalcraft Ltd, White Cottage Farm, Lucas Green Road, West End, Woking, Surrey, GU24 9LZ Tel: (01483) 474979 Fax: (01483) 472487 *Metal fabricators*

J B Place & Son Welders Ltd, Unit 25 Sapcote Industrial Estate, 20 James Road, Tyseley, Birmingham, B11 2BA Tel: 0121-707 8021 Fax: 0121-707 8021 *Welding engineers*

▶ J B Products, Redhill Works, 200 Prospect Row, Dudley, West Midlands, DY2 8SG Tel: (01384) 240234 Fax: (01384) 240235 *Aluminium fabricator services*

▶ J B Rawcliffe & Sons Ltd, Stanley Way, Stanley Industrial Estate, Skelmersdale, Lancashire, WN8 8EA Tel: (01695) 737880 Fax: (01695) 737881

▶ J B Roberts & Son, Abercwm Eiddaw Works, Upper Corris, Machynlleth, Powys, SY20 9BP Tel: (01654) 761208 Fax: (01654) 761718

J B & S Lees, Trident Steel Works, Albion Road, West Bromwich, West Midlands, B70 8BH Tel: 0121-553 3031 Fax: 0121-553 7680 E-mail: sales@jbslees.co.uk *Steel strip processors*

▶ J B S Master Baker Ltd, Stirling Way, Northfields Industrial Estate, Peterborough, PE6 8LG Tel: (01778) 346168 Fax: (01778) 341918 E-mail: jbs@jbs-engineering.co.uk *Process engineering*

J B S Poyser Mansfield Ltd, Pleasley Vale Works, Pleasley Vale, Mansfield, Nottinghamshire, NG19 8SD Tel: (01623) 810066 Fax: (01623) 812266 *Precision engineers*

J B S Springs & Pressings Ltd, 7 Fordhouse Road Industrial Estate, Steel Drive, Wolverhampton, WV10 9XB Tel: (01902) 784396 Fax: (01902) 784396 E-mail: sales@jbsspringsltd.co.uk *Spring manufrs*

J B S Tooling Co. Ltd, Aizelewood Business Centre, Nursery Street, Sheffield, S3 8GG Tel: 0114-282 3160 Fax: 0114-282 3150 *Precision cutting tools manufrs*

J B Sales Ltd, Fircroft Way, Edenbridge, Kent, TN8 6EL Tel: (01732) 867835 Fax: (01732) 867836 E-mail: colin@jbsales.co.uk *Surveying equipment suppliers*

J B Schofield & Sons Ltd, Greenhead, Linthwaite, Huddersfield, HD7 5TS Tel: (01484) 842766 Fax: (01484) 843638 *Metal merchants*

J B Services Ltd, Mill Street, Stowupland, Stowmarket, Suffolk, IP14 5BJ Tel: (01449) 673232 Fax: (01449) 770981 E-mail: jb@jbsltd.freeserve.co.uk *Agricultural cleaners*

J B Stainless Ltd, 61 Washford Road, Sheffield, S9 3XW Tel: 0114-242 0042 Fax: 0114-243 0043 E-mail: michael@jbstainless.co.uk *Stainless steel including billets stockholders*

J B Systems Ltd, 8 Bridgegate Business Park, Gatehouse Way, Gatehouse Industrial Area, Aylesbury, Buckinghamshire, HP19 8XN Tel: (01296) 489967 Fax: (01296) 393515 E-mail: info@jbsystems.co.uk Sales Contact: P. Jackson Principal Export Areas: Worldwide *Manufacturers of explosion proof (electrical) (hazardous area) equipment & flame detection equipment*

J B Taylor Construction Ltd, Sycamore Farm, Holmefield Lane, Orby, Skegness, Lincolnshire, PE24 5JB Tel: (01754) 811406 Fax: (01754) 811300 *Structure steelwork*

J B Television Services, 633 Abbeydale Road, Sheffield, S7 1TB Tel: 0114-255 2178 Fax: 0114-255 2178 *Technical aerial manufacturers & wholesaler*

▶ J B Textiles, Bluepits Mill, Queensway, Rochdale, Lancashire, OL11 2PG Tel: (01706) 527273

J & B Theatrical UK Ltd, Unit 26, Kansas Ave, Salford, M50 2GL Tel: (07765) 108857 E-mail: jamesjandb@aol.com *Textured latex clothing & accessories retailers, wholesalers & manufrs*

▶ J B Training Services, The Knoll, 175 Lytham Road, Warton, Preston, PR4 1AE Tel: (01772) 632040 E-mail: jill@jbtrainingservices.fsbusiness.co.uk *Training supplier for first aid, health & safety & pool lifeguards*

▶ J B Transport, Leyland House, Old Stone Bridge, Ironville, Nottingham, NG16 5NE Tel: (01773) 602762 Fax: (01773) 540635

J B Wheaton & Sons Ltd, Chard Junction, Chard, Somerset, TA20 4QN Tel: (01460) 220531 Fax: (01460) 221456 E-mail: mark.wheaton@jbwheaton.co.uk *Road transport contractors & warehouse services*

▶ J B Window Fabrication, Unit 8D International House, Battle Road, Heathfield Industrial Estate, Newton Abbot, Devon, TQ12 6RY Tel: (01626) 830030

▶ J Bairner & Sons, 69 Main Street, Douglas, Lanark, ML11 0QG Tel: (01555) 851409 Fax: (01555) 851520

J Barnsley Cranes Ltd, Unit 16 Pedmore Road Industrial Estate, Pedmore Road, Brierley Hill, West Midlands, DY5 1TJ Tel: (01384) 484811 Fax: (01384) 484333 E-mail: jsatch@jbarnsleycranes.com Principal Export Areas: Worldwide *"Design and manufacture overhead cranes, hoists and material handling equipment for the global market. Explosion proof units for hazardous areas.ISO 9001 approved, Explosion proof equipment ATEX certified. 24 hour servicing, maintenance and spares. BRAND NEW OFFICE IN ABU DHAB, UAE TO MEET THE MIDDLE EAST MARKET"*

▶ J Barrett Haulage Ltd, Wellyhole Street, Oldham, OL4 3BB Tel: 0161-633 0224 Fax: 0161-628 7472

J.Barton & Co.(Food Distributors)Limited, J B House, Gower Street, Farnworth, Bolton, BL4 7EY Tel: (01204) 862773 Fax: (01204) 701734 *Bakers ingredient & prepared material producers*

J Beattie & Son Ltd, Marlborough Place, Liverpool, L3 2BZ Tel: 0151-236 8721 Fax: 0151-236 2639 E-mail: sales@beattieslocksmith.co.uk *Locksmiths*

J Bown & Co Dukinfield Ltd, Wharf Street, Dukinfield, Cheshire, SK16 4PQ Tel: 0161-339 9888 Fax: 0161-343 1052 E-mail: sale@jbown.com *Dished & flanged end manufrs*

▶ J Boyd & Sons Carnmoney, 38 The Square, Ballyclare, County Antrim, BT39 9BB Tel: (028) 9334 0866 Fax: (028) 9332 4850

J Bradnam & Sons, Melbourne Bridge, Withersfield, Haverhill, Suffolk, CB9 7RR Tel: (01440) 702110 Fax: (01440) 704463 *Timber merchants*

J Bradshaw & Sons Ltd, High Street, Sturton-By-Stow, Lincoln, LN1 2BX Tel: (01427) 788223 Fax: (01427) 788498 *Road transport, haulage & freight services*

J Brand Ltd, 2 Margaret Street, London, W1W 8RD Tel: (020) 7636 8214 Fax: (020) 7436 0841 E-mail: enquiries@jbrand.co.uk *Electrical contractors*

J Bridgeman, 129a Blackburn Road, Accrington, Lancashire, BB5 0AA Tel: (01254) 384757 *Coins & medal & jewellery suppliers*

J Brierley Macclesfield Ltd, Bakestonedale Road, Pott Shrigley, Macclesfield, Cheshire, SK10 5RX Tel: (01625) 573837 *Coal merchants*

J Brooke Fairbairn & Co., Railway Station, Green Road, Newmarket, Suffolk, CB8 9WT Tel: (01638) 666476 Fax: (01638) 665124 E-mail: brookefairbairn@btconnect.com *Furnishing fabric converters & exclusive furnishing wholesalers*

J Browne Construction Co. Ltd, Beacon House, North Circular Road, London, NW10 0HF Tel: (020) 8451 4111 Fax: (020) 8459 6879 E-mail: info@jbconstruction.co.uk *Civil engineering & public works contractors* Also at: London N18

J Buchan & Sons Ltd, 2 Baltic Place, Peterhead, Aberdeenshire, AB42 1TF Tel: (01779) 475395 Fax: (01779) 479763 *GRP laminators & fabricators, lifeboat repairers, engineers, joiners services*

J Burhouse, Inver Sawmill, Inver, Dunkeld, Perthshire, PH8 0JR Tel: (01350) 727723 Fax: (01350) 727261 *Craft supplies timber & tools*

J Burroughs, Bird Lime Farm, Porton, Salisbury, SP4 0NB Tel: (01980) 611389 Fax: (01980) 611826 *Agricultural*

J Burrows, 18 Telford Way, Thetford, Norfolk, IP24 1HU Tel: (01842) 752211 Fax: (01842) 753868 E-mail: john@burrowseng.ssnet.co.uk *Precision engineering services*

J Burton, Bings Heath, Astley, Shrewsbury, SY4 4BZ Tel: (01939) 250266 *Industrial furnishings*

J C Aldridge & Son Ltd, 10 Market Place, Berkeley, Gloucestershire, GL13 9BB Tel: (01453) 810223 Fax: (01453) 511205 E-mail: sales@jcaldridge.co.uk *Building contractors*

J C B Cab Systems Ltd, Riverside, Rugeley, Staffordshire, WS15 2WA Tel: (01889) 572700 Fax: (01889) 585999 E-mail: enquiries@jcb.com *Cab manufrs*

J C B Compact Products Ltd, Harewood Estate, Leek Road, Cheadle, Stoke-on-Trent, ST10 2JU Tel: (01538) 755641 Fax: (01538) 757590

J C B Landpower Ltd, Lakeside Works, Denstone Road, Rocester, Uttoxeter, Staffordshire, ST14 5JP Tel: (01889) 590312 Fax: (01889) 590588 E-mail: enq@jcbinfo.co.uk *Earth moving machinery manufrs*

▶ J & C Bolton, West Green Cottage, Burgh-by-Sands, Carlisle, CA5 6AQ Tel: (01228) 576682

J C Buck Ltd, 8 The Stafford Estate, Hillman Close, Hornchurch, Essex, RM11 2SJ Tel: (01708) 437099 Fax: (01708) 456761 E-mail: sales@jcbuck.co.uk *Essential oils & aromatic raw materials importers exporters*

J C C Lighting Products, Southern Cross Trading Estate, Lamplighter House, Bognor Regis, West Sussex, PO22 9TS Tel: (01243) 829040 Fax: (01243) 829051 E-mail: sales@jcc-lighting.co.uk *Lighting manufrs*

J C Campbell Ni Ltd, Shore Road, Rostrevor, Newry, County Down, BT34 3AA Tel: (028) 4173 8691 Fax: (028) 4173 8949 E-mail: sales@jccampbell.co.uk *Car dealership*

J C Components Ltd, Unit 7 Paper Mill End Industrial Estate, Birmingham, B44 8NH Tel: 0121-356 3663 Fax: 0121-356 3663 E-mail: jccomponents@mail2worlds.com *Engineering*

J C D Contracts Ltd, 49 Kenilworth Drive, Oadby, Leicester, LE2 5LT Tel: 0116-271 6671 Fax: 0116-271 6672 *Carpentry*

▶ J C Decaux (UK) Ltd, Nottingham South & Wilford Industrial Estate, Nottingham, NG11 7EP Tel: 0115-982 2776 Fax: 0115-982 1467 *Street furniture*

▶ J.C Design, 35 Gainsborough Avenue, Maghull, Liverpool, L31 7AT Tel: 0151-526 5127 E-mail: john@jcdesign.me.com *Website designer*

J C E (Europe) Ltd, East Way, Lee Mill Industrial Estate, Ivybridge, Devon, PL21 9LL Tel: (01752) 690530 Fax: (01752) 690531 E-mail: info.euro@jcegroup.com *Manufacturer & supplier of hazardous area electrical equipment*

▶ J C E George, Lamdin Road, Bury St. Edmunds, Suffolk, IP32 6NU Tel: (01284) 753631 Fax: (01284) 706151

J C Edwardson Ltd, Unit 13 Wigan Enterprise Park, Seaman Way, Ince, Wigan, Lancashire, WN2 2LE Tel: (01942) 820943 Fax: (01942) 829185 *Civil engineering & groundwork contractors*

▶ J C Electrics, 1-3 Verlands Court, Verlands Way, Pencoed, Bridgend, Mid Glamorgan, CF35 6JA Tel: (01656) 863536 Fax: (01656) 863536 E-mail: sales@jcelectrics.com *Electrical accessories manufrs*

▶ J C Electronics, Unit C3, Flightway Business Park, Dunkeswell Aerodrome, Honiton, Devon, EX14 4RD Tel: (01404) 891541 *Hardware, software, analog, electrical design, manufrs*

J C Engineering Ltd, St. Ivel Way, Bristol, BS30 8TY Tel: 0117-961 6535 Fax: 0117-960 5657 E-mail: enquiries@jc-engineering.co.uk *Precision engineers*

J C Engineering, 136 High Street, Cottenham, Cambridge, CB24 8RX Tel: (01954) 206357 Fax: (01954) 206358 *Sheet metal engineers & fabricators*

▶ J C Engineering Co., 6 Market Overton Industrial Estate, Thistleton Road, Market Overton, Oakham, Leicestershire, LE15 7PP Tel: (01572) 767888 Fax: (01572) 767999 *Sheet metalwork engineers or fabricators*

J C Engineering Products, 17-19 Loverock Road, Battle Farm Trading Estate, Reading, RG30 1DZ Tel: 0118-958 1926 Fax: 0118-950 4018 E-mail: sales@jceng.co.uk *JC engineering products provide precision sheet metal fabrication & powder coating services to industry across the south of england, specialising in electronic enclosures, electrical casings, aircraft components & shop fitting fabrications*

J C Fabrics Ltd, 10 Storey Street, Leicester, LE3 5GR Tel: 0116-262 6100 Fax: 0116-262 9610 *Ladies knitwear manufrs*

J C Griffiths & Son, The Green, Bronllys Road, Talgarth, Brecon, Powys, LD3 0HH Tel: (01874) 711317 Fax: (01497) 847144 *Agricultural engineers service*

J C Hammond Ltd, The Windmill, Ringstead Road, Heacham, King's Lynn, Norfolk, PE31 7JA Tel: (01485) 570274 Fax: (01485) 572973 *Agricultural suppliers*

J C Jetting, 84 Bonnington Walk, Bristol, BS7 9XD Tel: 0117-904 1638 Fax: 0117-904 1638 E-mail: rachod@ukonline.co.uk *Hydro demolition*

J C K Joinery, 8 Heanor Street, Leicester, LE1 4DD Tel: 0116-291 2288 Fax: 0116-291 2300 E-mail: enquiries@jckjoinery.co.uk *Joinery security door sets suppliers*

J C Kitchens, Unit A2 Lintown Trading Estate, Old Wellington Road, Eccles, Manchester, M30 9QG Tel: 0161-788 8371 Fax: 0161-707 4217 *Kitchen manufrs*

J C M Scotload Ltd, Greenbank Cresent, East Tullos Industrial Estate, Aberdeen, AB12 3BG Tel: (01224) 877007 Fax: (01224) 895200 E-mail: sales@jcmscotload.co.uk *Instrumentation engineers*

▶ J C M Services Ltd, 44 Burslem Road, Tunbridge Wells, Kent, TN2 3TT Tel: (01892) 526419 E-mail: info@jcmservices.org.uk *Property Management, Lease Extensions, Right To Manage, Block Management, London, Kent, Furnished let Management, Repairs, Commercial Management, Service Charge, Property Portfolio, Major Works, JCM Services Ltd are a property management company based in Tunbridge Wells managing properties in London, Kent, Surrey and Sussex, we undertake right to manage blocks and larger portfolios*

J C Microsystems, 66 Hampstead Way, London, NW11 7XX Tel: (020) 8455 4271 E-mail: jclynes@aol.com *Computer system manufrs*

J C Morris & Sons, Unit 2e Netherton Industrial Estate, St. Monans, Anstruther, Fife, KY10 2DW Tel: (01333) 730658 Fax: (01333) 730658 E-mail: sales@ru-an-fhodar.co.uk *Fish processors & salmon smokers*

▶ J C Morton, 4 Templehill, Troon, Ayrshire, KA10 6BE Tel: (01292) 315789 Fax: (01292) 318480 E-mail: info@jcmortonhomes.co.uk

▶ J & C O'Meara Ltd, Ringtail Industrial Estate, Tollgate Road, Burscough, Ormskirk, Lancashire, L40 8LD Tel: (01704) 893109 Fax: (01704) 232445 E-mail: sale@jcomeara.fs.nt.co.uk *Woodworking machines suppliers*

J C Phillips & Son Ltd, 162a South Street, Bridport, Dorset, DT6 3NP Tel: (01308) 422179 Fax: (01308) 421956 *Sand merchants*

J C Quirk, 55 Waverley Road, Sale, Cheshire, M33 7AY Tel: 0161-973 6238 Fax: 0161-973 7066 *Plumber's merchants*

J & C R Wood, 66 Clough Road, Hull, HU5 1SR Tel: (01482) 345067 Fax: (01482) 441141 E-mail: info@jandcrwood.co.uk *Manufacturers of metalworking tools*

J C Rennie, 62 Stair Street, Drummore, Stranraer, Wigtownshire, DG9 9PT Tel: (01776) 840332 Fax: (01776) 840 332 *Bacon wholesale*

J C S Computing Solutions Ltd, 31 Church Street, Oldbury, West Midlands, B69 3AG Tel: 0121-543 6996 Fax: 0121-543 6997 E-mail: sales@jcs.co.uk *Computer maintenance services*

▶ J C S Express, Bellshill Road, Uddingston, Glasgow, G71 7NT Tel: (01698) 818555 Fax: (01698) 811728

▶ J C Technology, Suite 6,, Lyon House, 10 West Park, Harrogate, North Yorkshire, HG1 1BL Tel: (01423) 530040 E-mail: info@jctechnology.org *Computer building and maintaining.*

J C Tool Hire, Valley St North, Darlington, County Durham, DL1 1QE Tel: (01325) 382038 Fax: (01325) 468539 E-mail: sales@joegreeners.co.uk *Power tool specialists*

J C Trophies, 14 Beech Lane, St. Leonards, Ringwood, Hampshire, BH24 2QD Tel: (01202) 868896 Fax: (01202) 868895 E-mail: sales@jctrophies.co.uk *Sports trophy manufrs*

J C Vents Ltd, J.C. House, Hurricane Way, Wickford Business Park, Wickford, Essex, SS11 8YB Tel: (01268) 561122 Fax: (01268) 560606 E-mail: sales@jcvents.co.uk *Manufactures of air diffusion equipment & grilles*

▶ J C W Computers, 398 Dumbarton Road, Glasgow, G11 6SB Tel: 0141-357 3732 *Computer hardware suppliers*

J C Y Steel Supplies Ltd, 35 Hovefield Avenue, Burnt Mills Industrial Area, Basildon, Essex, SS13 1EB Tel: (01268) 729886 Fax: (01268) 725262 E-mail: sales@jcysteel.com *Steel stockholders & shearers*

J Callander & Son Ltd, Abbotshaugh Sawmill, Abbots Road, Falkirk, FK2 7XU Tel: (01324) 621563 Fax: (01324) 634386 E-mail: info@jcallander.co.uk *Timber merchants*

▶ J Chaplow & Sons Ltd, Helsington Mills, Helsington, Kendal, Cumbria, LA9 5RL Tel: (01539) 720358 Fax: (01539) 735593 E-mail: enquiries@jchaplow.co.uk

J Charles & Son Ltd, Whitbygate, Thornton Dale, Pickering, North Yorkshire, YO18 7RY Tel: (01751) 474303 *Precast concrete product manufrs*

J Clark & Co. Ltd, Hazel Croft, Shipley, West Yorkshire, BD18 2DY Tel: (01274) 590078 Fax: (01274) 598660 E-mail: jclarkco@btinternet.com *Plastic insert moulding, head lice combs, pet combs, perforating segments*

J Clark & Son Kingsbury Ltd, 843-849 Honeypot Lane, Stanmore, Middlesex, HA7 1AR Tel: (020) 8951 1888 Fax: (020) 8951 4882 E-mail: richard.gom1@orange.net *Plumbers' merchants*

J Clarke, Upper Southwick Farm, Southwick, Mark, Highbridge, Somerset, TA9 4LQ Tel: (01278) 783708 Fax: (01278) 783708 *Agricultural supplies distributor*

J Clarke & Sons Enterprises, 213 Muswell Hill Broadway, London, N10 3RS Tel: (020) 8883 9946 Fax: (020) 8883 9947 E-mail: sales@clarkepropertygroup.co.uk *Property letting agents*

J Clegg & Bros Rakewood Ltd, Rakewood Mill, Rakewood Road, Littleborough, Lancashire, OL15 0AP Tel: (01706) 378342 E-mail: peter@jclegg.co.uk *Transfer printers & film laminators*

J Clemishaw & Company Ltd, Barnbrook Building, Barnbrook Street, Bury, Lancashire, BL9 7DT Tel: 0161-764 4614 Fax: 0161-764 4615 *Tarpaulin manufrs*

J Clubb Ltd, Church Hill, Wilmington, Dartford, DA2 7DZ Tel: (01322) 225431 Fax: (01322) 289932 E-mail: sales@jclubb.co.uk *Sand & gravel producers*

J Colburn, Aldrington Basin South, Basin Road South, Portslade, Brighton, BN41 1WF Tel: (01273) 413190 Fax: (01273) 423684 *General engineers*

J Collins & Co. Ltd, 25-26 Warstone Lane, Birmingham, B18 6JQ Tel: 0121-236 2958 Fax: 0121-212 0325 E-mail: evans@j-collins.com *Chain assembly securities & keyrings distributors*

J Computer Logic Ltd, Golden Valley Software Factory, New Mills, Clehonger, Hereford, HR2 9QS Tel: (01981) 251359 E-mail: sales@jclsoftware.com *Software for hire & rental suppliers*

J Cooke Engineering Ltd, Ashwell Street, Baldock, Hertfordshire, SG7 5QT Tel: (01462) 742236 Fax: (01462) 742188 E-mail: sales@jcooke.co.uk *Bolt & nut manufrs*

▶ J Craig Dykes Property Developments Ltd, 3 Brackenholme Cottages, Brackenholme, Selby, North Yorkshire, YO8 6EJ Tel: (01757) 630224 Fax: (01757) 630244

J Crowther Royton Ltd, Eden Works Belgrave Mill, Honeywell Lane, Oldham, OL8 2JP Tel: 0161-652 4234 Fax: 0161-627 4265 E-mail: crowther.marine@tiscali.co.uk *Propeller & sterngear manufrs*

J Cullen Thermals Ltd, 202 Deykin Avenue, Birmingham, B6 7BH Tel: 0121-327 5260 Fax: 0121-327 1124 E-mail: info@jcullenthermals.com *Insulation & asbestos removal*

J Curtis & Sons Ltd, Thrupp Lane, Radley, Abingdon, Oxfordshire, OX14 3NG Tel: (01235) 524545 Fax: (01235) 524545 *Sand & gravel distributors*

▶ J D A Ltd, Unit S2, Second Avenue, Tyne Tunnel Trading Estate, North Shields, Tyne & Wear, NE29 7SY Tel: 0191-270 8406 Fax: 0191-272 8222 E-mail: david.atkin@webfreight.co.uk

J D A Fixings, Unit 7 & 8 Indus Acre, Avro Way, Bowerhill, Melksham, Wiltshire, SN12 6TP Tel: (01225) 709970 Fax: (01225) 709995 E-mail: chris@jdafixings.com *Nut & bolt distributors*

▶ J D C Builders (Devon) Ltd, Filham Park, Filham, Ivybridge, Devon, PL21 0LR Tel: (01752) 698699

▶ J D C Group Ltd, 95 Wright Street, Renfrew, PA4 8AN Tel: 0141-848 1212 Fax: 0141-848 7666 *Electrical installation*

J D C Supplies, 38 Pellew Close, Padstow, Cornwall, PL28 8EY Tel: (01841) 532160 Fax: (01841) 532160 *Suppliers of cleaning materials to hotel & restaurants*

J D Cables Ltd, Park House, Greenhill Cresent, Watford, WD18 8PH Tel: (01923) 222600 Fax: (01923) 222608 E-mail: sales@jdcables.com *Cable suppliers*

▶ J & D Developments, 65 Well Street, Torrington, Devon, EX38 7BW Tel: (01805) 624701 E-mail: info@jandddevelopments.co.uk *J and D developments are local builders based in Great Torrington, North Devon, we carry out all aspects of construction and building renovation to your specific personal requirements*

▶ J D Electrics, 115b Deepcut Bridge Road, Deepcut, Camberley, Surrey, GU16 6SD Tel: (01252) 838087 Fax: (01252) 834511

Company Information

J D Engineering, Unit 5a, Ramsden Road, Rotherwas Industrial Estate, Hereford, HR2 6LR Tel: (01432) 344030 Fax: (01432) 352905 *Precision engineers*

J D Engineering, York House, Sleaford Road, Wellingore, Lincoln, LN5 0HR Tel: (01522) 810215 Fax: (01522) 810525 E-mail: jim.dixon@eliteuk.net *Lifting gear distributors*

J D Fabrications Leicester Ltd, 38 Boston Road, Gorse Hill Industrial Estate, Beaumont Leys, Leicester, LE4 1AU Tel: 0116-236 8622 Fax: 0116-235 6220 E-mail: jdfabsleicesltd@aol.com *Sheet metalwork engineers*

J D Fire Ltd, Wren Metals, Russell Street, Chadderton, Oldham, OL9 9LD Tel: 0161-652 2655 Fax: 0161-624 8303 E-mail: sales@jdfire.co.uk *Manufacturers of fire fighting equipment*

▶ J D Freight Ltd, Unit 3, Hurricane Way, Slough, SL3 8AG Tel: (01753) 545556 Fax: 01753 545557 E-mail: lee.tuppen@jdfreight.co.uk *Heathrow based forwarding agent. Offering a personal service by air, sea or road.*

▶ J D G Contractors, Unit, Cockridden Farm Industrial Estate, Brentwood Road, Herongate, Brentwood, Essex, CM13 3LH Tel: (07809) 071220 Fax: (01277) 811641 E-mail: JDGLtd@aol.com *Essex county council & local authority approved contractor, driveways, patios, paving & landscaping, flexible & rigid road construction, footings, ringbeams & drainage*

J D Groves Ltd, 7 Lenham Road East, Rottingdean, Brighton, BN2 7GP Tel: (01273) 306394 Fax: (01273) 300658 *CCTV & entry phone installation distributors*

J D H T Ltd, Jaguar House, 104 Firle Road, Eastbourne, East Sussex, BN22 8EU Tel: (01323) 410403 Fax: (01323) 411481 E-mail: lys@jdhtsales.co.uk *Motor sport merchandising services*

▶ J & D Hall Ltd, Questor House, 191 Hawley Road, Dartford, DA1 1PU Tel: (01322) 223456 Fax: (01322) 394421

▶ J D Haulage, 1 Wayside Crescent, Eccleshill, Bradford, West Yorkshire, BD2 2JY Tel: (01274) 626999 Fax: (01274) 402381 E-mail: denise@jd-haulage.co.uk *Delivery collection & installation for banks & building societies*

▶ J D Hire, Starlings Bridge, Nightingale Road, Hitchin, Hertfordshire, SG5 1RJ Tel: (01462) 442044 Fax: (01462) 442043

J D Jackson (Electronics), Eastfield Labs, Danethorpe Hill, Newark, Nottinghamshire, NG24 2PD Tel: (01636) 705718 Fax: (01636) 610120 E-mail: sales@jacksonelectronics.co.uk *X-ray disfraction systems*

J & D Joinery Ltd, 6 Brockhill Works, Windsor Road, Redditch, Worcestershire, B97 6DJ Tel: (01527) 69469 Fax: (01527) 69172 *Joinery manufrs*

▶ J D Joinery, Harold Mews, 10 Mews Road, St. Leonards-on-Sea, East Sussex, TN38 0EA Tel: (01424) 425600

J D Joinery Bonnybridge Ltd, Lyndeen Cottage, 61 Broomhill Road, Bonnybridge, Stirlingshire, FK4 2AT Tel: (01324) 813760 *Joinery manufrs*

▶ J D Lewis & Sons Ltd, Gwasg Gomer, Llandysul, Dyfed, SA44 4JL Tel: (01559) 362371 Fax: (01559) 363758 E-mail: gwasg@gomar.co.uk

J D M Diamond Masters Ltd, Unit 1-2a Holmes Chapel Business Park, Manor Lane, Holmes Chapel, Crewe, CW4 8AB Tel: (0845) 3301319 Fax: (0845) 3301369 E-mail: sales@diamondmasters.co.uk *Sellers diamond tools to construction industry*

J D M Office Equipment Services, 66 Harborne Road, Oldbury, West Midlands, B68 9JB Tel: 0121-429 3805 Fax: 0121-554 4627 *Typewriter retailers & service providers*

J & D Mcadam Ltd, Lawmuir Farm, Sheardale, Dollar, Clackmannanshire, FK14 7LY Tel: (01259) 750014 Fax: (01259) 750014 *Agricultural contractors*

J D Mcdougall Ltd, 4 Mcgrath Road, London, E15 4JP Tel: (020) 8534 2921 Fax: (020) 8519 8423 E-mail: sales@mcdougall.co.uk *Flame resistant fabric suppliers & manufrs*

▶ J D Metalfabs Ltd, 30 Wenlock Way, Leicester, LE4 9HU Tel: 0116-299 8885 Fax: 0116-299 9040 E-mail: sales@jd-m.co.uk *Retail & point of sale designers & manufrs*

▶ J D Minto Ltd, Old Dronley Road, Backmuir of Liff, Dundee, DD2 5QT Tel: (01382) 580365 Fax: (01382) 580371 E-mail: sales@minto.webscot.net

▶ J D Narrow Boats, Unit 20, Mount Industrial Estate, Mount Road, Stone, Staffordshire, ST15 8LL Tel: (01785) 815559 Fax: (01785) 815559 *Boat builders & repairers*

J D P Ltd, Collett Way, Yate, Bristol, BS37 5NL Tel: (01454) 323000 Fax: (01454) 310037 E-mail: yate@jdpipes.co.uk *Drainage pipe systems distributors*

J D Painting Contractors Ltd, High Street, Newburn, Newcastle upon Tyne, NE15 8LN Tel: 0191-264 5131 Fax: 0191-264 0485 E-mail: jd.painting@virgin.net *Painting & decorating contractors*

▶ J D Personal Computers, 126, High Street, Canvey Island, Essex, SS8 7SH Tel: (01268) 510101

▶ J D Property Maintenance, 81 Kingsland Road, Worthing, West Sussex, BN14 9EE Tel: (01903) 527449 E-mail: jd_property_maintenance@hotmail.co.uk *Proprietor John Dowling **Offers high quality Property Maintenance at very competitive rates. Fully insured with free advice and quotations, 20 years experience Will respect your home, or business, leaving it secure, clean and tidy.*All property maintenance and repairs undertaken.*Painting and Decorating *Carpentry *Ceramic tiling *Plumbing *Guttering *Roofing Repairs *Glazing*

J D R Cable Systems Ltd, 175 Wisbech Road, Littleport, Ely, Cambridgeshire, CB6 1RA Tel: (01353) 865800 Fax: (01353) 861388 E-mail: uk@jdrcables.com *Sub sea equipment manufrs*

J D Robertson & Co. Ltd, 26 Magdalen St, Colchester, CO1 2LD Tel: (01206) 572368 Fax: (01206) 549167 E-mail: carhire@jdrobertson.co.uk *Engine reconditioners & self drive hire*

J D S Group Ltd, 19 Park Road, Faringdon, Oxfordshire, SN7 7BP Tel: (01367) 241507 Fax: (01367) 241705 E-mail: jdsgroup@btinternet.com *Interior specialists offering fully integrated retail, education and library solutions incorporating project management, design, joinery, metalwork, plastics and signage and site installation management*

J & D Services, Highhouse Indust Estate, Barony Road, Auchinleck, Cumnock, Ayrshire, KA18 2LL Tel: (01290) 423752 Fax: 01290 421587 *Engineers welding fabrications*

▶ J D Services (Hvac) Ltd, Suite 7, Matrix Business Centre, Victoria Road, Dartford, DA1 5AJ Tel: (01322) 271809

▶ J & D Shepherd, 7c Old Queens Head Yard, Morpeth, Northumberland, NE61 1PY Tel: (01670) 517459 Fax: (01670) 511763

J D Sign & Display Ltd, Unit 34 Adams Industrial Estate, Dickerage Lane, New Malden, Surrey, KT3 3SF Tel: (020) 8949 4468 Fax: (020) 8949 7758 E-mail: john@jdsignanddisplay.com *Plastic & acrylic sheet fabricators. Plastic integrated design & manufacturing services & point of sale/ purchase/marketing display designers/producers/ services*

J D Signs, PO Box 317, Camberley, Surrey, GU17 0QG Tel: (01276) 600562 Fax: (01273) 600562 *Sign manufrs*

▶ J & D Software, 161 Ashley Road, Hale, Cheshire, WA15 9SD Tel: (0845) 4504588 *Computer software developers*

J D Stoward Salford Ltd, Dymun Works, Missouri Avenue, Salford, M50 2NP Tel: 0161-736 1238 Fax: 0161-736 8700 *Lead manipulators & fabricators*

▶ J D & T Johnson & Co. Ltd, Unit 6 Pilsworth Way, Bury, Lancashire, BL9 8RE Tel: 0161-796 3040 Fax: 0161-796 3040

J D W Engineering Ltd, Tameside Mill, Park Road, Dukinfield, Cheshire, SK16 5LP Tel: 0161-330 1989 Fax: 0161-343 1905 E-mail: sales@jdwengineering.com *Ventilation ducting contractors*

J & D Wilkie Ltd, Gairie Works, Bellies Brae, Kirriemuir, Angus, DD8 4BL Tel: (01575) 572502 Fax: (01575) 574564 E-mail: sales@jdwilkie.co.uk Principal Export Areas: Asia Pacific & Africa *Industrial & polyester fabric manufacturers & textile merchants*

J D Woodward, 7 Higham Way, Burbage, Hinckley, Leicestershire, LE10 2PU Tel: (01455) 613432 Fax: (01455) 613432 E-mail: sales@jdwoodward.co.uk *Land engineering & diamond fretsaws manufrs*

J D Wyatt, Telford Way, Thetford, Norfolk, IP24 1HU Tel: (01842) 766770 Fax: (01842) 766770 *Metal finishing*

▶ J D'A B Consultancy Ltd, 17 Naseby Road, Congleton, Cheshire, CW12 4QX Tel: (01260) 297974 Fax: (01260) 291674 E-mail: mail@ex-pc.co.uk *Tacograph analysis & LGV driver hire - transport & legal services*

J Davies & Son, Gwastod Abbot, New Inn, Pencader, Dyfed, SA39 9AZ Tel: (01559) 384886 Fax: (01559) 384814 E-mail: jdavies.pencader@btconnect.com *Agricultural engineers*

J Day Stoneworks, Church Lane, Colney Heath, St. Albans, Hertfordshire, AL4 0NH Tel: (01727) 823326 Fax: (01727) 827710 E-mail: jdaystoneworks@btinternet.com *Granite worktop, stove, fireplace, range cooker & architectural salvage retailers*

J De Bruyn Ltd, Units 4 & 6-7, Simonds Road, London, E10 7BN Tel: (020) 8558 4726 Fax: (020) 8539 7050 E-mail: enquiries@de-bruyne.co.uk *Linoleum wholesalers*

J Dewalleg Ltd, 361 Amersham Road, Hazlemere, High Wycombe, Buckinghamshire, HP15 7HR Tel: (01494) 711431 Fax: (01494) 711388 E-mail: sales@jdwltd.com *Upholstery*

J Diver, A 5 School Lane, Impington, Cambridge, CB24 9NS Tel: (01223) 232256 *Joinery manufrs*

J Dodd & Co. Ltd, 6 Byram Street, Huddersfield, HD1 1BX Tel: (01484) 420028 *Health food retailers*

J Doyle Ltd, PO Box 33, Bolton, BL1 2QS Tel: (01204) 527008 Fax: (01204) 364002 E-mail: j.doyle@hargreaveshamilton.co.uk *Scrap metal merchants*

J E A Engineering Components, 18-19 Whitehill Road, Glenrothes, Fife, KY6 2RW Tel: (01592) 771911 Fax: (01592) 771911 *Precision engineers & machinists*

J E B Engineering Design Ltd, Chiswick Avenue, Mildenhall, Bury St. Edmunds, Suffolk, IP28 7AY Tel: (01638) 718435 Fax: (01638) 717962 E-mail: info@jebeng.com *Toolmaking & component production* Also at: Newmarket & Oldham

J E B Supplies Ltd, Wheal Rose, Scorrier, Redruth, Cornwall, TR16 5DE Tel: (01209) 890636 Fax: (01209) 891260 *Iron monger reseller*

▶ J E B Tooling Ltd, Unit 12 Gateway Crescent, Oldham Broadway Business Park, Chadderton, Oldham, OL9 9XB Tel: 0161-684 3983 Fax: 0161-682 2892

J E Bernard & Co. Ltd, Unit 4-5 Lakeside Industrial Estate, Colnbrook By Passage, Colnbrook, Slough, SL3 0EE Tel: (01753) 683161 Fax: (01753) 681624 E-mail: corporate@bernardgroup.plc.uk *Air transport*

J E Cockayne Ltd, The Exchange, Scottish Enterprise Technology Park, East Kilbride, Glasgow, G75 0QU Tel: (01355) 272305 Fax: (01355) 272306 E-mail: ian.cockayne@cockayne.co.uk *Control & instrumentation distributors*

J E D Insulations Ltd, 529 Kingston Road, Ewell, Epsom, Surrey, KT19 0DL Tel: (020) 8661 1050 Fax: (020) 8661 1052 E-mail: jedinsulations@bt.com *Asbestos removal contractors & thermal insulation*

▶ J E Dean Hazel Grove Ltd, 15 Napier Street, Hazel Grove, Stockport, Cheshire, SK7 4EW Tel: 0161-483 5110 Fax: 0161-456 5118

J E Evans, Velindre Park, Pencader, Dyfed, SA39 9HP Tel: (01559) 384242 *Agricultural contractors*

J E Evans Jackson & Co., 13 Northburgh Street, London, EC1V 0JP Tel: (020) 7608 3098 Fax: (020) 7608 2934 E-mail: jeej@markgraaf.co.uk *Trade mark attorneys*

J & E Fabrications Ltd, Unit 25A, Blythe Park, Cresswell Lane, Cresswell, Stoke-on-Trent, ST11 9RD Tel: (01782) 388011 Fax: (01782) 388004 E-mail: jandefabs@aol.com *Steel fabricators*

J E G Design, PO Box 28, Stowmarket, Suffolk, IP14 3AZ Tel: (01449) 770459 Fax: (01449) 678444 E-mail: sales@babypoint.co.uk *Industrial design services*

J E Gordon Ltd, 60 Whitworth St West, Manchester, M1 5WW Tel: 0161-236 1892 Fax: 0161-228 7803 *Sheet metalworkers*

▶ J E Hacking Printer Ltd, Market Street Works, Church, Accrington, Lancashire, BB5 0DP Tel: (01254) 391222 Fax: (01254) 399827

J E Haith Ltd, Park Street, Cleethorpes, South Humberside, DN35 7LX Tel: (01472) 357515 Fax: (01472) 242883 E-mail: sales@haith.com *Bird seed suppliers*

J & E Hall Ltd, 22 Lorn Street, Birkenhead, Merseyside, CH41 6AR Tel: 0151-647 6974 Fax: 0151-666 1873 *Refrigeration & air conditioning contractors services*

▶ J & E Hall Ltd, Unit 94 Christian Mill Business Park, Tamerton Foliot Road, Plymouth, PL6 5DS Tel: (01752) 776840 Fax: (01752) 776840 *Air conditioning designers*

J & E Hall Ltd, 2 Fairbrother Street, Salford, M5 3EN Tel: 0161-872 7022 Fax: 0161-371 0555 *Refrigeration & air conditioning services*

J & E Hall Ltd, 3 28 Botley Road, Hedge End, Southampton, SO30 2HE Tel: (01489) 890200 Fax: (01489) 788292 E-mail: g.warn@jehall.co.uk *Refrigeration contractors & air conditioning*

▶ J E Hall & Co., Unit 2, Gower Street Trading Estate, St George, Telford, Shropshire, TF2 9HW Tel: (01952) 617637

J E Hamer Manufacturing & Joinery, Upper Cockroft Farm, Rishworth, Sowerby Bridge, West Yorkshire, HX6 4RE Tel: (01422) 822873 Fax: (01422) 822873 E-mail: edwin@jehamer.co.uk *Joiners*

▶ J E Harrison Ltd, 103 Knighton Fields Road West, Leicester, LE2 6LH Tel: 0116-283 3611 Fax: 0116-283 3612 E-mail: david@harrisontrim.co.uk *Suppliers to the garment indusry of sewing threads, tapes,buttons, marking chalk etc*

J E Homewood & Son, 20 Weyhill, Haslemere, Surrey, GU27 1BX Tel: (01428) 643819 Fax: (01428) 645419 E-mail: steve@homewoodfencing.co.uk *Chestnut fencing manufrs*

J E Jenkins, 7 Eye Green Industries, Crowland Road, Eye, Peterborough, PE6 7SZ Tel: (01733) 223650 Fax: (01733) 223650 *Steel fabricators & subcontract services*

J E Jones S & D Ltd, Moor Lane, Birmingham, B6 7HH Tel: 0121-356 9169 Fax: 0121-356 0595 E-mail: jejdrums@aol.com *Drum dealers/ reconditioners/suppliers. Also drums, plastic & steel*

J E M (Environmental) Ltd, Furlong Lane, Burslem, Stoke-On-Trent, ST6 3LE Tel: (01782) 834823 Fax: (01782) 575656 E-mail: sales@jemenvironmental.co.uk *Designers & installations of dust & fume extraction equipment*

J E Marchant, Theobalds Bungalow, Theobalds Green, Heathfield, East Sussex, TN21 8BU Tel: (07973) 430836 Fax: (01435) 865321 *Welding supplies distributors*

J E Matthews & Sons Ltd, Southbridge, Cotton End, Northampton, NN4 8BS Tel: (01604) 762188 Fax: (01604) 705218 E-mail: matthews@cottonendfsbusiness.co.uk *Steel fabricators & blacksmiths*

J E Morrison & Sons Ltd, Burton Weir Works, Warren Street, Sheffield, S4 7WT Tel: 0114-270 1525 Fax: 0114-243 4158 *Wood boring tools manufrs*

▶ J E Nixon & Son, Northern Works, Bellingham, Hexham, Northumberland, NE48 2BS Tel: (01434) 220268 Fax: (01434) 220372

▶ J E Nozedar Ltd, 10-12 Lorne Street, Middlesbrough, Cleveland, TS1 5QY Tel: (01642) 224193 Fax: (01642) 217457

▶ J & E Regan Builders & Contractors Ltd, Unit 4 Barncoose Industrial Estate, Barncoose, Redruth, Cornwall, TR15 3RQ Tel: (01209) 211616 Fax: (01209) 210175

▶ J & E Regan Builders & Contractors Ltd, Long Acre, Saltash, Cornwall, PL12 6LZ Tel: (01752) 841660 Fax: (01752) 841653

J E S Manufacturing Co. Ltd, 53 Wharf Road, Tyseley, Birmingham, B11 2DX Tel: 0121-706 1425 Fax: 0121-707 3988 E-mail: sales@jesmanufacturing.co.uk *Wire displays for pottery*

J & E Sedgwick & Co. Ltd, Reservoir Place, Walsall, WS2 9RX Tel: (01922) 622797 Fax: (01922) 724344 E-mail: sales@je-sedgwick.co.uk *Leather manufrs*

J E Sheeran Amusement Arcades Ltd, 18 Argyle Street, Stonehouse, Larkhall, Lanarkshire, ML9 3LL Tel: (01698) 792711 Fax: (01698) 792786 E-mail: sales@jesheeranaa.co.uk *Amusement machines distributors*

J E Simpson & Son, Fir Tree Farm, Bramley Grange, Grewelthorpe, Ripon, North Yorkshire, HG4 3DL Tel: (01765) 658383 Fax: (01765) 658600 *Hay & straw merchants*

J E Smith & Son Upholsterers Ltd, 110-110a Langney Road, Eastbourne, East Sussex, BN22 8AQ Tel: (01323) 734206 E-mail: smith-andson@ic24.net *Upholsterer manufrs*

J E Stacey & Co. Ltd, Inceworth Building Works, Bodmin Street, Holsworthy, Devon, EX22 6BD Tel: (01409) 253555 Fax: (01409) 254496 *Public works & building contractors* Also at: Torrington

J E T Engineering, Ditton Road, Widnes, Cheshire, WA8 0TH Tel: 0151-423 5273 Fax: 0151-495 1390 E-mail: sales@jet-engineering.co.uk *Mechanical & civil engineers*

J E T Industrial Services, 13 Rosemary Lane, Liverpool, L37 3HA Tel: (01704) 872972 Fax: (01704) 833986 E-mail: jetind@fsbdial.co.uk *Plastics injection moulding machine suppliers*

J E Unwin, Pultheley Bank, Hyssington, Montgomery, Powys, SY15 6AX Tel: (01588) 650645 Fax: (01588) 650645 *Agricultural contractors*

J E Wildbore Ltd, Waddington Street, Oldham, OL9 6QU Tel: 0161-624 4475 Fax: 0161-627 0930 E-mail: sales@jwildbore.co.uk *Electrical wholesalers*

J E Wilson & Sons Kendal Ltd, The Mint Cake Works, Cross Lane, Kendal, Cumbria, LA9 5LB Tel: (01539) 720279 Fax: (01539) 730109 E-mail: sales@creativeconfectionery.co.uk *Manufacturer of confectionery*

J & E Woodworks, Barley Mow, Lampeter, Dyfed, SA48 7BY Tel: (01570) 422141 Fax: (01570) 422144 E-mail: sales@je-woodworks.co.uk *Joinery manufrs*

▶ J Eastwood & Son, Holme Iron Works, Sowerby Bridge, West Yorkshire, HX6 3LE Tel: (01422) 835550 Fax: (01422) 836067 *Packaging materials retailers*

J Everitt & Sons, 10 Primrose Hill, Doddington, March, Cambridgeshire, PE15 0SU Tel: (01354) 740524 Fax: (01354) 741721 *Hay & straw merchants*

J Exley Ltd, Park Works, 644 Bradford Road, Batley, West Yorkshire, WF17 8HG Tel: (01924) 472353 Fax: (01924) 440007 E-mail: greg@jexley.co.uk Principal Export Areas: Central/East Europe & West Europe *Machinery removal & mobile crane hire services*

▶ J F A Digital, 9 Dickensons Lane, London, SE25 5HJ Tel: (020) 8655 4355 Fax: (020) 8654 2774 E-mail: sales@jfadigital.com *LARGE FORMAT DIGITAL PRINTING ON PAPER, VINYL, CANVAS ETC. MOUNTING AND LAMINATING.*

J F A Printing plc, Wellington CR, New Malden, Surrey, KT3 3NE Tel: (020) 8640 7777 Fax: (020) 8942 7228 E-mail: sales@jfaprint.co.uk *Lithographic printers & continuous stationery manufrs*

▶ J F Associates, Aberdeen House, 1-3 Cromwell Road, Maidenhead, Berkshire, SL6 6BJ Tel: (01628) 625709 Fax: (01628) 633269 E-mail: info@jfa.org.uk *service & repair to Plasma LCD & all Audio equipment*

J F B Cores Ltd, 7 Boleyn Court, Manor Park, Runcorn, Cheshire, WA7 1SR Tel: (01928) 571812 Fax: (01928) 571813 E-mail: sales@cores.co.uk *Cardboard tube manufrs*

J F C, Daleham House, Hillbottom Road, Sands Industrial Estate, High Wycombe, Buckinghamshire, HP12 4HJ Tel: (01494) 447881 Fax: (01494) 436356 *Precision engineers*

J & F Controls, 2 South Bank, Westerham, Kent, TN16 1EN Tel: (01959) 562490 Fax: (01959) 561110 E-mail: jandfcontrolsltd@ukgateway.net *Electrical & electronic control panels*

J F Donne, 865 Wolseley Road, Plymouth, PL5 1JX Tel: (01752) 362517 *Boat building & repairs*

J F E Steel Corporation, London Int Press Centre, 76 Shoe Lane, London, EC4A 3JB Tel: (020) 7583 1133 Fax: (020) 7583 1144 E-mail: london@jfe-steel.co.uk *Steel works*

J F Engines, Unit 2, The Old Gymnasium, 45 Green Lane, Ewelme, Wallingford, Oxfordshire, OX10 6DA Tel: (01491) 839336 Fax: (01491) 680719 *Racing car engine builders*

J F Germain & Son Ltd, 25 Commercial Buildings, St. Helier, Jersey, JE2 3NB Tel: (01534) 724581 Fax: (01534) 767373 E-mail: sales@jfgermain.co.je *Tobacco product manufrs* Also at: St. Peter Port

J F Heppelthwaite Ltd, Sherwood House 6 Marlborough Parade, Uxbridge Road, Uxbridge, Middlesex, UB10 0LR Tel: (01895) 460002 Fax: (01895) 460004 *Plumbing & heating services*

J & F J Baker & Co. Ltd, Hamlyns Mills, Colyton, Devon, EX24 6PD Tel: (01297) 552282 Fax: (01297) 553274 *Tanners & curriers*

J F K Installations, PO Box 1587, Stafford, ST16 3HR Tel: (01785) 212280 *Dish washer suppliers & maintenance services*

▶ J F K Signs & Stamp Maker, 67 Tylecroft Road, Norbury, London, SW16 4BL Tel: (020) 8679 5428 Fax: (020) 8679 1928 *Signs, engraving & stamp manufrs*

J F L Harvey Ltd, The Bungalow, Polwhele, Truro, Cornwall, TR4 9AE Tel: (01872) 274757 Fax: (01872) 260226 *Plant hire contractors*

J F L Mecelec, Llanthony Road, Gloucester, GL2 5QT Tel: (01452) 413531 Fax: (01452) 307580 E-mail: mtl@mecelec.co.uk Sales Contact: D Peacock *Manufacture, design & service of bespoke automation & specialised testing equipment.*

J F Lloyd & Son, Nottingham Road, Ashby-de-la-Zouch, Leicestershire, LE65 1DR Tel: (01530) 413347 Fax: (01530) 560264 *Scrap metal merchants & waste management*

▶ J.& F.May Ltd, Trinity Works, 1a Hermit Road, London, E16 4HP Tel: (020) 7476 3786 E-mail: sales@jfmay.demon.co.uk

J F Payne, Enterprise House, Herbert Road, Newport, Gwent, NP19 7BH Tel: (01633) 223959 Fax: (01633) 266927 E-mail: jfp@ukonline.co.uk *Welding & fabrication manufrs*

▶ J F Peden (Edinburgh) Ltd, 71 Polton Street, Bonnyrigg, Midlothian, EH19 3DQ Tel: 0131-663 7009

▶ J F Sewing WorldWide, 28 Bickershaw Lane, Abram, Wigan, Lancashire, WN2 5PL Tel: (07968) 507074 Fax: (08708) 319502 E-mail: info@jfsewing.co.uk *Durkopp Adler Specialist*Installation, service, repair, sales and troubleshooting to most of the Durkopp Adler automatic range, Cover for engineers, off sick or on holiday, On site training for factory engineers, on your own machines, we can also supply, a*

continued

▶ indicates data change since last edition

*continuation full range of bagging machines, industrial embroidery machines etc.***

J F Stevens & Co, The Retreat, South Road, South Somercotes, Louth, Lincolnshire, LN11 7QD Tel: (01507) 358714 Fax: (01507) 358758 *Computer systems & software developers*

J & F Tools (Precision Engineers) Ltd, Thornfield, Spring Bank, New Mills, High Peak, Derbyshire, SK22 4AU Tel: (01663) 743129 Fax: (01663) 747572 E-mail: info@jandftools.com *Pipe lining equipment*

J F Windows Ltd, Blackshaw Mills, Farfield Avenue, Bradford, West Yorkshire, BD6 2DN Tel: (01274) 605894 Fax: (01274) 690520 *PVC windows & door manufrs*

J Floris Holdings Ltd, 89 Jermyn Street, London, SW1Y 6JH Tel: (020) 7930 2885 Fax: (020) 7930 1402E-mail: fragrance@florestlondon.com *Perfume & toiletries retailers*

J Forrest, Knowepark, Meikle Wartle, Inverurie, Aberdeenshire, AB51 5BA Tel: (01467) 671415 Fax: (01467) 671415 E-mail: jfengineering@btinternet.com *Steel fabricators*

▶ J Frood & Sons, 47 Wellgate, Lanark, ML11 9DS Tel: (01555) 663927 Fax: (01555) 666158

J Fulton & Co., 19a Rainey Street, Magherafelt, County Londonderry, BT45 5DA Tel: (028) 7963 2329 Fax: (028) 7963 4264 E-mail: meal@fultonandco.com *Food processors*

J & G Archibald, Jagal House, Damson Way, Durham, DH1 2YD Tel: 0191-384 8484 Fax: 0191-386 2432 E-mail: sales@archibald.co.uk *Builders merchants* Also at: Chester-le-Street

J G B Formwork Ltd, 182 Hyde End Road, Spencers Wood, Reading, RG7 1DG Tel: 0118-988 3424 Fax: 0118-988 6259 *JGB Formwork Ltd, based in Reading, provide groundwork and formwork services, specialising in reinforced concrete, to the construction industry across the South of England.*

▶ J G B Logistics Ltd, Altens Lorry Park, Hareness Road, Aberdeen, AB12 3LE Tel: (01224) 876455

J G B Steelcraft (U K) Ltd, Victoria Works, Mary St, Johnstone, Renfrewshire, PA5 8BT Tel: (01505) 326589 Fax: (01505) 382506 E-mail: brendan@jgb-steelcraft.co.uk *Steel fabricators manufrs*

J G B Transport Ltd, Units 1-2 Altens Lorry Park, Hareness Road, Aberdeen, AB12 3LE Tel: (01224) 876674 Fax: (01224) 874222 E-mail: alan.simpson@jgbtransport.com *Transport services*

▶ J G B Transport, Building 789, Murray Road, Europark, Dunfermline, Fife, KY11 2EB Tel: (01383) 416009 Fax: (01383) 414176

▶ J G B Transport, Building 789, Murray Road, Europark, Dunfermline, Fife, KY11 2EB Tel: (01383) 416009 Fax: (01383) 414176

▶ J G Business Machines, Barn Close, Langage Business Park, Plympton, Plymouth, PL7 5HQ Tel: (01752) 330044 Fax: (01752) 331444 *Office machine distributor*

J G Coates Burnley Ltd, Trafalgar Street, Burnley, Lancashire, BB11 1TH Tel: (01282) 424376 Fax: (01282) 456166 E-mail: sales@cotel.co.uk *Industrial plastics moulders*

J & G Coughtrie Ltd, Montrose Avenue, Hillington, Glasgow, G52 4LZ Tel: 0141-810 4516 Fax: 0141-882 0191 E-mail: sales@coughtree.com *Fluorescent light fittings manufrs*

J G Electronics, Wash Lane, Allostock, Knutsford, Cheshire, WA16 9JS Tel: (01565) 723334 Fax: (01565) 723334 *Electronic equipment designers & manufrs*

J G Electronics, Unit 8 Showfield Lane, Malton, North Yorkshire, YO17 6BT Tel: (01653) 695611 Fax: (01653) 695611 *Electronic repairers*

J G Engineering Ltd, Alanbrooke Industrial Park, Station Road, Topcliffe, Thirsk, North Yorkshire, YO7 3SE Tel: (01845) 578097 Fax: (01845) 578097 *Hydraulic ram repairers & manufrs*

J G F Machinery, Windamoore Farm, Doras Green Lane, Ewshot, Farnham, Surrey, GU10 5DZ Tel: (01252) 851266 Fax: (01252) 850968 E-mail: sales@jgfmachinery.co.uk *Agricultural machinery distributor*

J & G Forbes Ltd, Balaclava Quay, Fraserburgh, Aberdeenshire, AB43 9EB Tel: (01346) 518641 Fax: (01346) 571152 *Boat builders & repairers*

J & G Forbes Ltd, Balaclava Quay, Fraserburgh, Aberdeenshire, AB43 9EB Tel: (01346) 518641 Fax: (01346) 571152 E-mail: jforbesco@aol.com *Boat builders & repairers*

J G Markland & Sons, Park Works, Borron Road, Newton-le-Willows, Merseyside, WA12 0EJ Tel: (01925) 220718 Fax: (01925) 220718 *Commercial sign writers*

▶ J & G Mossman Ltd, 42 Parkhead Road, Sauchie, Alloa, Clackmannanshire, FK10 3BH Tel: (01259) 722319 Fax: (01259) 219793

J & G Mossman Ltd, 284 High Street, Glasgow, G4 0QT Tel: 0141-552 2161 Fax: 0141-552 2161 *Monumental memorial manufrs*

J G Neon Signs, 639 Walsall Road, Great Barr, Birmingham, B42 1EH Tel: 0121-357 4033 Fax: 0121-357 4033 *Specialists in neon & perspex*

J G Oldfield & Co., Prince of Wales Dock, Workington, Cumbria, CA14 1BN Tel: (01900) 603701 Fax: (01900) 604823 *Shipping agents*

J G Paxton & Sons Ltd, Front Street, Pity Me, Durham, DH1 5DE Tel: 0191-384 7111 Fax: 0191-386 7806 E-mail: peter@jgpaxtonandsons.ibcos.net *Agricultural engineers*

J G Paxton & Sons Ltd, Roman Road, Brandon, Durham, DH7 8UF Tel: (01609) 783331 Fax: (01609) 783332 E-mail: northallerton@paxtons.co.uk *Agricultural machinery*

J G Plant, Brackla Industrial Estate, Bridgend, Mid Glamorgan, CF31 2AQ Tel: (01656) 652299 *Agricultural machinery repairs & distributors*

J G Ross Bakers Ltd, Costcutter, Elphinstone Road, Port Elphinstone, Inverurie, Aberdeenshire, AB51 3UR Tel: (01467) 620764 Fax: (01467) 623416 E-mail: info@jg-ross-bakers.co.uk *Bakery suppliers*

J G Ross & Co Components Ltd, 19b Pershore Trading Estate, Station Road, Pershore, Worcestershire, WR10 2DD Tel: (01386) 552140 Fax: (01386) 555628 E-mail: info@jgross.co.uk Purchasing Contact: M. Ingleby Sales Contact: J.F. Symons *Formed in 1961 we are Manufacturers all types of washers, wireforms, presswork and springs. We specialise in the pressing and forming of Beryllium Copper, Aluminium, Copper, Phosphor Bronze, Mild Steel, Spring Steel, Stainless Steel. No batch size too small. We manufacture all type of washers, wireforms, presswork, springs. We will work together with you to design and manufacture new components. We are committed to Quality - BSI ISO 9002 Certified.*

▶ J G S Couriers, 13 Crown Meadow, Lower Broadheath, Worcester, WR2 6QJ Tel: (01905) 640518 Fax: (01905) 640518 E-mail: info@jgscouriers.co.uk *sameday 24 hour courier,uk/europe,from an envelope to 1500kgs*

J G S Metalwork, Unit 6 Broomstick Estate, High Street, Edlesborough, Dunstable, Bedfordshire, LU6 2HS Tel: (01525) 220360 Fax: (01525) 222786 E-mail: enquiries@weathervanes.org.uk *Decorative ironworkers*

J G Shelton & Co. Ltd, The Warren, Ashtead, Surrey, KT21 2SH Tel: (01372) 278422 Fax: (01372) 279338 E-mail: mail@jg-shelton.co.uk *Gas furnace manufrs*

J G Smith, Beatrice Road, Kettering, Northamptonshire, NN16 9QR Tel: (01536) 514743 Fax: (01536) 416068 *Joinery*

J G Stamper, The Cottage Brooklands, Carleton Road, Penrith, Cumbria, CA11 8LT Tel: (01768) 863032 Fax: (01768) 863976 *Road transport, haulage & freight services*

▶ J G Tiling, 4 Chapel Barton, High Littleton, Bristol, BS39 6HS Tel: (01761) 472934 E-mail: john.griffin23@btinternet.com *Floor & wall tiling services*

J G Tinkler Ltd, Bowesfield Lane, Stockton-on-Tees, Cleveland, TS18 3HJ Tel: (01642) 675797 Fax: (01642) 673193 E-mail: jgtinklerltd@aol.com *Offshore oil steel fabricators*

▶ J G Turnbull Ltd, Station Approach, East Boldon, Tyne & Wear, NE36 0AD Tel: 0191-536 2090 Fax: 0191-519 0218 E-mail: info@jgturnbullltd.demon.co.uk *Metalwork*

J G Turnbull Ltd, Station Approach, East Boldon, Tyne & Wear, NE36 0AD Tel: 0191-536 2090 Fax: 0191-519 0218 E-mail: office@jgturnballltd.co.uk *Metal & steel fabricators*

▶ J G Winterbottom Charlsworth Ltd, Raglan Street, Hyde, Cheshire, SK14 2DX Tel: 0161-368 9090 Fax: 0161-368 0005

J Gadd, 20 Rancliffe Avenue, Keyworth, Nottingham, NG12 5HY Tel: 0115-937 3155 Fax: 0115-937 3155 *Agricultural contractors*

J Gorstige Ltd, Unit 10 Carlton Mill, Pickering Street, Leeds, LS12 2QG Tel: 0113-279 5200 Fax: 0113-279 5200 *Ladder manufrs*

J Graham & Co., 37-39 Castle Street, Inverness, IV2 3DU Tel: (01463) 233178 Fax: (01463) 710287 E-mail: william@johngrahamandco.co.uk *Gun makers & fishing tackle retailers & manufrs*

J Graham & Sons (Kilkeel)Ltd., 40 Greencastle Street, Kilkeel, Newry, County Down, BT34 4BH Tel: (028) 4176 2777 Fax: (028) 4176 4783 E-mail: j.grahamsons@yahoo.co.uk *Building contractors*

J Greenwood & Sons, 13 North Terrace, Seaham, County Durham, SR7 7EU Tel: 0191-581 2372 Fax: 0191-581 1619 *Commercial stationers & printers*

▶ J Guest Ltd, Knarsboro House, Bradley Road, Stourbridge, West Midlands, DY8 1XB Tel: (01384) 392444 Fax: (01384) 441875

▶ J H B Ltd, Greenhead, Lerwick, Shetland, ZE1 0PY Tel: (01595) 695577 Fax: (01595) 694709 E-mail: sales@jhbltd.co.uk

J H B Ltd, Greenhead, Lerwick, Shetland, ZE1 0PY Tel: (01595) 695577 Fax: (01595) 694709 E-mail: sales@jhbltd.co.uk

J H Brookes Printers Ltd, Sneyd Green Business Park, Sneyd Street Hanley, Stoke-on-Trent, ST6 2NP Tel: (01782) 219475 Fax: (01782) 202603 E-mail: info@brookesdesignprint.com *Print & design services*

J & H Busby Ltd, Leicester Road, Lutterworth, Leicestershire, LE17 4NJ Tel: (01455) 552309 Fax: (01455) 552309 *Engineers pattern makers*

J H Business Forms Ltd, Adams Street, Birmingham, B7 4LT Tel: 0121-359 6693 Fax: 0121-333 3118 E-mail: jhbf@cyberphile.co.uk *Computer stationery manufrs*

J H C Interiors Ltd, 10 Lady Lane, Paisley, Renfrewshire, PA1 2LJ Tel: 0141-849 6349 Fax: 0141-849 7493 E-mail: sales@jhcinteriors.co.uk *Install suspended ceilings & partitions*

▶ J H Civil Engineering Ltd, Carlisle Road, Airdrie, Lanarkshire, ML6 8RH Tel: (01236) 768174 Fax: (01236) 607155

J H Commercials, West Park, Arlington, Barnstaple, Devon, EX31 4SN Tel: (01271) 850860 *Horsebox manufacturers & commercial repairs*

J H Components, Unit 6 Europa Way, Britannia Enterprise Park, Lichfield, Staffordshire, WS14 9TZ Tel: (01543) 417471 Fax: (01543) 419001 E-mail: jhcdis@aol.com *Electronic component distribution Worldwide. Importing and exporting all manner of electronic components to a customer base including distributors, OEM's, automotive industry, MOD, international manufacturers etc. *Kindly e-mail or call for quotations.*

▶ J H Connon Ltd, Harlaw Road, Inverurie, Aberdeenshire, AB51 4FH Tel: (01467) 621406 Fax: (01467) 620806 E-mail: sales@jhconnon.co.uk

J H Cunliffe & Company Ltd, Duke Street Mill, Whitehall Street, Rochdale, Lancashire, OL12 0LW Tel: (01706) 631133 Fax: (01706) 527950 E-mail: brian@jhcunliffe.co.uk *Textile merchants*

▶ J H Cunningham, 13 Glasgow Road, Kilmarnock, Ayrshire, KA3 1TJ Tel: (01563) 522640

▶ J H Davenport & Sons Ltd, Harehills Lane, Leeds, LS9 6JF Tel: 0113-249 5561 Fax: 0113-249 1381 E-mail: info@jhdavenport.co.uk *High level of printing service*

▶ J H Davenport & Sons Ltd, Harehills Lane, Leeds, LS9 6JF Tel: 0113-249 5561 Fax: 0113-249 1381

J H Davies Haulage Ltd, Foundry Lane, Ditton, Widnes, Cheshire, WA8 8TZ Tel: 0151-420 8877 Fax: 0151-495 1994 E-mail: admin@jhdavies.com *Road haulage & warehousing*

J H Garlick Ltd, 180 Park View Road, Welling, Kent, DA16 1ST Tel: (020) 8303 2941 Fax: (020) 8303 0951 E-mail: surveyors@jhgarlickltd.fsnet.co.uk *Damp proofing & woodworm control services*

J H Greene, Netherton Business Centre, West Netherton Street, Kilmarnock, Ayrshire, KA1 4BT Tel: (01563) 539006 Fax: (01563) 571941 *Commercial printers services*

J H Hardy & Son, Dunkirk Street, Halifax, West Yorkshire, HX1 3TD Tel: (01422) 361437 Fax: (01422) 349066 *Precision engineers*

▶ J H Horn, 522 Crow Road, Glasgow, G13 1NU Tel: 0141-954 5911 Fax: 0141-959 9821 E-mail: enquiries@hunterbs.co.uk

▶ J H Horn Plumbers Ltd, 101-103 Holmlea Road, Glasgow, G44 4AQ Tel: 0141-632 0085 Fax: 0141-649 8374

J H Ingle Ltd, 74 Barkston House, Croydon Street, Leeds, LS11 9RS Tel: 0113-243 0239 Fax: 0113-242 6901 E-mail: jhingle@aol.com *Haberdashery goods wholesalers & distributors*

J H Joinery, 33 South Street, Pennington, Lymington, Hampshire, SO41 8EA Tel: (01590) 671870 Fax: (01590) 671966 *Joinery manufrs*

▶ J H Kemp Ltd, 409 Tyburn Road, Birmingham, B24 8HJ Tel: 0121-327 3154 Fax: 0121-326 7542 E-mail: info@jhkemp.co.uk *Transport & logistic services*

J H Lidstone Ltd, Crozier Road, Plymouth, PL4 7LN Tel: (01752) 664253 Fax: (01752) 600680 *Plastering contractors*

J H Lightbody & Son Ltd, 437 Townmill Road, Glasgow, G31 3AN Tel: 0141-550 0666 Fax: 0141-550 0330 E-mail: lightbody@iris-web.co.uk *Automotive & industrial coatings specialists* Also at: Hamilton

J & H M Dickson Ltd, Seath Road, Rutherglen, Glasgow, G73 1RW Tel: 0141-643 0244 Fax: 0141-643 0219 E-mail: sales@dicksonforsacks.co.uk *Sack merchants & bulk bag manufrs*

J H Mason & Sons, The Old Barn, Chester Road, Penyffordd, Chester, CH4 0JZ Tel: (01244) 548944 Fax: (01244) 548944 *Drainage contractors*

J H Mayor Sons Ltd, Saw Mill, Ulnes Walton, Leyland, PR26 8LR Tel: (01257) 451303 Fax: (01257) 453736 *Timber merchants*

J H Morse Ltd, Morfa Lane, Carmarthen, Dyfed, SA31 3AX Tel: (01267) 234704 Fax: (01267) 221376 *Agricultural repairs*

▶ J H P Business Centre, Mason Street, Motherwell, Lanarkshire, ML1 1YE Tel: (01698) 327824 Fax: (01698) 327825 E-mail: motherwell.business.centre@jhp-group.com *National training provider, modern apprenticeships*

J H P Training, Broadacre House, 16-20 Lowther Street, Carlisle, CA3 8DA Tel: (01228) 536373 Fax: (01228) 591236 E-mail: carlisle.business.centre@jhp-group.com *National training providers*

▶ J H P Training, Sutherland House, Matlock Road, Coventry, CV1 4JQ Tel: (024) 7666 2096 Fax: (024) 7663 8214 E-mail: enquiries@jhp-group.com *NVQ business skills training provider & apprenticeships*

J H P Training, Sutherland House, Matlock Road, Coventry, CV1 4JQ Tel: (024) 7666 2096 Fax: (024) 7663 8214 E-mail: coventry.sales@jhp-group.com *National training providers including training for fork lift drivers*

▶ J H P Training, 9-13 Castle Street, Dumfries, DG1 1DJ Tel: (01387) 279828 Fax: (01387) 266050 E-mail: dumfries.business.centre@jhp-group.com *Vocational training & recruitment services*

J H P Training, 9-13 Castle Street, Dumfries, DG1 1DJ Tel: (01387) 279828 Fax: (01387) 266050 E-mail: dumfries.business.centre@jhp-group.com *Business education & training*

J H P Training, 25 Frederick Street, Edinburgh, EH2 2ND Tel: 0131-226 1647 Fax: 0131-226 1648 E-mail: edinburgh.business.centre@jhp-group.com *National training provider. businesses skills training & recruitment solutions*

J H P Training, Crown Buildings, Raby Road, Hartlepool, Cleveland, TS24 8AS Tel: (01429) 860211 Fax: (01429) 866598 E-mail: hartlepool.business.centre@jhp-group.com *Training providers*

▶ J H P Training, 48-50 Lowgate, Hull, HU1 1YZ Tel: (01482) 224340 Fax: (01482) 587992 E-mail: hull.business.centre@jhp-group.com *Specialists in NVQ's & apprenticeships & business training*

▶ J H P Training, Dalziel Centremason Street, Motherwell, Lanarkshire, ML1 1YE Tel: 0141-889 8227 Fax: 0141-889 5402 E-mail: paisley.business.centre@jhp-group.com *Private training service*

J H P Training, Abbey House 26 The Parade, High Street, Watford, WD17 1AA Tel: (01923) 238100 Fax: (01923) 238500 E-mail: watford.business.centre@jhp-group.com *NVQs & apprenticeships bespoke training services*

▶ J H P Training Manchester, 2nd Floor, Flint Glassworks, 64 Jersey Street, Ancoats Urban Village, Manchester, M4 6JW Tel: 0161-605 0829 Fax: 0161-605 0822 E-mail: manchester.business.centre@jhp-group.com *NVQs & apprenticeships national training providers*

▶ J H P Training Stevenage, Southgate House 3Rd Floor, St. Georges Way, Stevenage, Hertfordshire, SG1 1WX Tel: (01438) 368181 Fax: (01438) 365897 E-mail: stevenage@jhptraining.com *NVQ level national training provider, apprenticeship*

▶ J H P Training Stranraer, 82-84 Ashwood Drive, Stranraer, Wigtownshire, DG9 7PD Tel: (01776) 707010 Fax: (01776) 906906 E-mail: stranraer.business.centre@jhp-group.com *National training provider delivering a wide range of courses and programmes, including Modern Apprenticeships, SVQs and Skillseekers. JHP offers businesses skills training and recruitment solutions, and individuals the chance of career success.*

J & H Rosenheim & Co. Ltd, Lancaster Fields, Crewe, CW1 6FF Tel: (01270) 585959 Fax: (01270) 586611 E-mail: enquiries@rosenheim.co.uk *Fastening products & fencing manufrs*

▶ J H S Plumbing & Heating Ltd, Tamsui, Sevenoaks Road, Ightham, Sevenoaks, Kent, TN15 9DS Tel: (01732) 884949 Fax: (01322) 860922 E-mail: korina@draindoctors.biz *Plumbing & drainage services*

J H Shouksmith & Sons Ltd, Murton Way, Osbaldwick, York, YO19 5GS Tel: (01904) 411261 Fax: (01904) 412038 E-mail: rps@shouksmiths.co.uk *Building service engineers*

▶ J H Starbuck Ltd, 9 Union Street, Market Rasen, Lincolnshire, LN8 3AA Tel: (01673) 843483 Fax: (01673) 843483 *Manufacture bakery products*

J H Tool & Pattern Projects Ltd, Unit A, Site 5, Cold Hesledon, Seaham, County Durham, SR7 8ST Tel: 0191-581 5420 Fax: 0191-581 0621 E-mail: johnstand@jh2.co.uk *Vacuum forming tools & pattern making*

J H Walker, Ravensthorpe Mills, Calder Road, Dewsbury, West Yorkshire, WF13 3JS Tel: (01924) 466544 Fax: (01924) 455977 *Jersey fleece/pile fabric manufrs*

J H Young, West Moor, Felton, Morpeth, Northumberland, NE65 9QE Tel: (01670) 787255 *Agricultural engineer*

J Hall & Son Fasteners Ltd, Bentley Mill Industrial Estate, Longmore Avenue, Walsall, WS2 0BW Tel: (01922) 626652 Fax: (01922) 649942 E-mail: jhallsales@btconnect.com *Industrial fastener distributors*

J Hambleton Stove Enamellers, Egerton Street, Droylsden, Manchester, M43 7EL Tel: 0161-301 4444 Fax: 0161-371 0944 *Stove enamelling & spray painting*

▶ J Hanley Builders Ltd, Jute Lane, Enfield, Middlesex, EN3 7PJ Tel: (020) 8804 0908 Fax: (020) 8805 0570

▶ J Harley Building Services Ltd, 24 Fenella Street, Glasgow, G32 7JT Tel: 0141-778 6194 Fax: 0141-778 6194

J Harper & Sons Ltd, Southern Avenue, Leominster, Herefordshire, HR6 0QF Tel: (01568) 612925 Fax: (01568) 613615 E-mail: sales@harpergroup.com *Building contractors* Also at: Blackheath

J Harper & Sons Welding Fabrications Ltd, Willenhall La Industrial Estate, Willenhall Lane, Bloxwich, Walsall, WS3 2XN Tel: (01922) 478419 Fax: (01922) 409553 *Welded fabrication manufrs*

J Harrison, 2 Gorsey Brow, Billinge, Wigan, Lancashire, WN5 7NX Tel: (01744) 892349 Fax: (01744) 892349 *Venetian blind manufrs*

J Harrison & Sons Coal Merchants Ltd, The Coal Yard, Milton Road, Stoke-on-Trent, ST1 6LE Tel: (01782) 534110 Fax: (01782) 535039 E-mail: sales@jharrison-fuel.co.uk *Coal merchants*

▶ J Hawkins Ltd, Q Rocket Trading Centre, Bowring Park Road, Liverpool, L14 3NZ Tel: 0151-220 3767 Fax: 0151-220 7500

J Headridge & Co., 1 Shearer Street, Glasgow, G5 8TA Tel: 0141-429 8911 Fax: 0141-420 1602 *Ironmongery & general hardware wholesalers*

J Hebson, 8 South Parade, Weston-super-Mare, Avon, BS23 1JN Tel: (01934) 624734 *Jewellery repairs & alteration services*

▶ J Hempstock & Co. Ltd, 116-118 South Street, Openshaw, Manchester, M11 2FY Tel: 0161-223 2123 Fax: 0161-220 9259

▶ J Hendry Ashphalt Contractors, Clippens Yard, Loanhead, Midlothian, EH20 9NS Tel: 0131-440 1109 Fax: 0131-440 4231

▶ J Henry & Son, Shinny Road, Macosquin, Coleraine, County Londonderry, BT51 4PS Tel: (028) 7086 8505 Fax: (028) 7086 8811 E-mail: slles@agriplant.co.uk *sales and hire of used agricultural machinery*

J Henty, 21a Lower Road, Eastbourne, East Sussex, BN21 1QE Tel: (01323) 721938 *Blacksmiths & steel fabricators*

J Hesketh Engineering Ltd, Wilcock Street, Wigan, Lancashire, WN3 4AR Tel: (01942) 245114 Fax: (01942) 820240 *Steel fabricators & fire escape manufrs*

J Hewit & Sons Ltd, Kinauld Leather Works, 371 Lanark Road West, Currie, Midlothian, EH14 5RS Tel: 0131-449 2206 Fax: 0131-451 5081 E-mail: sales@hewit.com *Leather dressers*

▶ J Higgs Lowdham Ltd, 10 Kirk Hill, East Bridgford, Nottingham, NG13 8PE Tel: (01949) 20671 Fax: (01949) 21150

J Hill & Co. Ltd, Charlotte St, Melton Mowbray, Leicestershire, LE13 1NA Tel: (01664) 562219 Fax: (01664) 410258 E-mail: sales@hilltrident.co.uk *Steel fencing & gate manufrs*

J Hipwell & Son Ltd, 427 Warwick Road, Greet, Birmingham, B11 2JU Tel: 0121-706 5471 Fax: 0121-706 0502 *Metal spinnings manufrs*

J Hirst, New Bank Street, Morley, Leeds, LS27 8NT Tel: 0113-253 4679 Fax: 0113-201 2977 E-mail: sales@jhirst.co.uk *Motor repairers & distribution*

▶ J Holdsworth Associates, Alexander House, Robinson Terrace, Washington, Tyne & Wear, NE38 7BD Tel: 0191-417 2543 Fax: 0191-417 1486 E-mail: jhassociates1@aol.com *Ceilings & partitions*

Company Information

J Hudson Metals, Hudson Industrial Estate, Dixon Street, Wolverhampton, WV2 2DB Tel: (01902) 457177 Fax: (01902) 457177 *Scrap iron & steel merchants*

J Humphrey & Son, Bleak House Farm, Allens Drove, Gorefield, Wisbech, Cambridgeshire, PE13 4PB Tel: (01945) 410644 Fax: (01945) 410644 *Agricultural contractors*

J I Blackburn Foundry Ltd, Grove Works, West Road, Bridport, Dorset, DT6 5JT Tel: (01308) 459040 Fax: (01308) 459040 *Iron & aluminium machine castings*

▶ J I N Transport Service, Drum Industrial Estate, Drum Industrial Estate, Chester le Street, County Durham, DH2 1AG Tel: 0191-492 0525 Fax: 0191-411 1552

▶ J & I Property Services, 1 Russell Centre, Coniston Road, Flitwick, Bedford, MK45 1QY Tel: (01525) 723800 Fax: (01525) 713137

▶ J & I Smith, 49 Gordon Street, Huntly, Aberdeenshire, AB54 8EQ Tel: (01466) 793588 Fax: (01466) 794014

J I T Industrial Products Ltd, 16 Melford Road, Righead Industrial Estate, Bellshill, Lanarkshire, ML4 3LR Tel: (01698) 748290 Fax: (01698) 749141 E-mail: sales@jitwebsite.com Principal Export Areas: Worldwide *Adhesive tape distributors*

▶ J Innes & Son, Banff, Banff, AB45 2YX Tel: (07896) 999900 Fax: (01261) 843033

J J & A R Jackson Ltd, Bonemill Lane, Worksop, Nottinghamshire, S81 7BA Tel: (01909) 474233 Fax: (01909) 472688 *Building contractors*

J & J Alarms, 171 Arbury Road, Nuneaton, Warwickshire, CV10 7NH Tel: (024) 7634 1508 *Burglar alarm installers*

J & J Associates, 112 Ridgeway, Plymouth, PL7 2HN Tel: (01752) 336465 Fax: (01752) 336466 E-mail: sales@jj-associates.com *Computer consumables distribution*

J & J B Traders Ltd, Hamilton House, 1 Temple Avenue, London, EC4Y 0HA Tel: (020) 7353 2123 Fax: (020) 7583 8823 E-mail: jjbtl@btinternet.com *International traders & exporters, commodity traders* Also at: Manchester

▶ J J Bartlett Haulage Ltd, Hotchkiss Way, Binley Industrial Estate, Coventry, CV3 2RL Tel: (024) 7644 5111 Fax: (024) 7644 5303

▶ J J Blinds, 32 Samson Crescent, Carluke, Lanarkshire, ML8 4RP Tel: (01555) 750436 Fax: (01555) 750436 *Blind suppliers*

J & J Carter Ltd, 8 Lion Court, Basingstoke, Hampshire, RG24 8QU Tel: (01256) 811455 Fax: (01256) 811458 E-mail: sales@jjcarter.com *J & J Carter Ltd are designers, manufacturers and installers of Tensile Structures. Our solutions include Fabric/Textile Architectural Structures, modular tensile canopies, awnings, fabric/frame structures, industrial/leisure buildings, tension structures, sails, and structural steelwork. *Our textile structures can be manufactured with woven fabrics offering life spans up to 30 years with full Class O compliancy for fire retardency, and up to 50% light transmission. *Our structural frames are manufactured in-house, using coded steel and aluminium welders. We offer a variety of frame finishes and colours. *As a standard we always provide a 10 Year Warranty on all textile structures. *J & J Carter are also certified to BS EN ISO 9001:2000 for design, manufacture and installation of Tensile Fabric Structures.*

J J Cavanagh Construction Ltd, Rowhurst Industrial Estate, Apedale Road, Newcastle, Staffordshire, ST5 6BH Tel: (01782) 565789 Fax: (01782) 564740 E-mail: sales@jjcav.co.uk *Building, civil engineering & public works contractors*

J J Churchill Ltd, Station Road, Market Bosworth, Nuneaton, Warwickshire, CV13 0PF Tel: (01455) 299600 Fax: (01455) 292330 E-mail: sales@jjchurchill.com *Precision engineers*

J J Clarke & Son, Lake View, Walesby, Market Rasen, Lincolnshire, LN8 3UW Tel: (01673) 838497 Fax: (01673) 838721 *Forklift truck suppliers*

▶ J J Clothing Ltd, 219 Western Road, Leicester, LE3 0EA Tel: 0116-275 6252 *Clothing manufrs*

▶ J J Computing Ltd, 9 Stamford Close, Potters Bar, Hertfordshire, EN6 5NW Tel: (01707) 642767 E-mail: johnjohnson64@hotmail.com *Web design, computer service & support*

▶ J J Coughlan Ltd, 12 Walmgate Road, Greenford, Middlesex, UB6 7LH Tel: (020) 8991 5909 Fax: (020) 8991 2753

J J Crowhurst Ltd, 4 Vincent Street, Birmingham, B12 9SG Tel: 0121-446 4386 Fax: 0121-446 5188 E-mail: jjcrowhurst.ltd@virgin.net *Iron steel & metal merchants*

J & J Cutting Formes Ltd, Unit 20 Whitworth Drive, Aycliffe Industrial Park, Newton Aycliffe, County Durham, DL5 6SZ Tel: (01325) 319744 Fax: (01325) 304003 E-mail: mail@jandjcuttingformes.co.uk *Cutting formes manufrs*

▶ J & J Denholm Ltd, 18 Woodside Crescent, Glasgow, G3 7UL Tel: 0117-980 2711 Fax: 0141-353 2190

▶ J & J E Contractors Ltd, Borthwick View, Pentland Industrial Estate, Loanhead, Midlothian, EH20 9QH Tel: 0131-448 2220 Fax: 0131-448 2195

▶ J & J Electricals Cumbria, 29 Oxford Street, Workington, Cumbria, CA14 2AL Tel: (01900) 871478 Fax: (01900) 63886

J J Electronics Ltd, 3a Telmere Industrial Estate, Albert Road, Luton, LU1 3QF Tel: (01582) 391156 Fax: (01582) 391896 E-mail: sales@jjelectronics.net *Printed circuit assembly service*

J J Engineering, Rowleys Green Lane, Longford, Coventry, CV6 6AL Tel: (024) 7668 2492 Fax: (024) 7668 2492 *General & precision fabricators*

J & J Engineering, 10 Misson Mill, Bawtry Road, Misson, Doncaster, South Yorkshire, DN10 6DP Tel: (01302) 719531 Fax: (01302) 719531 *Stainless steel fabricators*

J & J Engineering, 2a Tanners Brook Way, Southampton, SO15 0JY Tel: (023) 8051 0638 Fax: (023) 8077 2242 *Fabricating & welding*

J & J Engineering (Walsall) Ltd, Fryers Road, Leamore Enterprise Park, Bloxwich, Walsall, WS2 7LZ Tel: (01922) 710204 Fax: (01922) 710191 E-mail: jwoodall@btconnect.com Principal Export Areas: Worldwide *J & J Engineering (Walsall) Ltd have been manufacturing quality metal pressings welded assemblies over 30 years here in the west midlands and was established in 1978. Let J&J design and help make your metal components for your clients we are specialists in Presswork, Welding Fabrication and toolmaking.*

J J Engineers Supplies Ltd, 35 Valley Road, Banbury, Oxfordshire, OX16 9BH Tel: (01295) 253168 Fax: (01295) 252843 E-mail: sales@jjengineerssupplies.co.uk *Engineers merchants*

J & J Fabrics (Coventry) Ltd, 113-113A Eagle Street, Foleshill, Coventry, CV1 4GP Tel: (024) 7625 1261 Fax: (024) 7622 3589 E-mail: jagdishpopat@aol.com *Knitted fabric manufrs*

J & J Floorings (Watford) Ltd, 18 Caxton Way, Watford Business Park, Watford, WD18 8UA Tel: (01923) 231644 Fax: (01923) 818946 *Contract flooring specialist*

J & J Forktrucks, Farholme Mill, Farholme Lane, Bacup, Lancashire, OL13 0EZ Tel: (01706) 879769 Fax: (01706) 875286 *Forklifts repair & distributors*

J J Hardy & Sons Ltd, Brenda Road, Hartlepool, Cleveland, TS25 2BL Tel: (01429) 279837 Fax: (01429) 860182 E-mail: sales@jjhardy.co.uk *CNC engineering services*

J J Haslam Ltd, Park Works, Clegg Street, Bolton, BL2 6DU Tel: (01204) 527342 Fax: (01204) 388259 E-mail: malcolm.green@jjhaslam.com *Metal plate rolling manufrs*

J J Herbert, High Normanby, Whitby, North Yorkshire, YO22 4PR Tel: (01947) 880459 *Dairy producer*

J J Higgins Ltd, 42 Garden St, Magherafelt, County Londonderry, BT45 5DD Tel: (028) 7963 2369 Fax: (028) 7963 1790 E-mail: info@jjhiggins.com *Joiners*

J J Huber Investments Ltd, Bellbrook, Uckfield, East Sussex, TN22 1QL Tel: (01825) 761533 Fax: (01825) 768274 E-mail: huberuk@aol.com *Suppliers to the printing industry*

J & J Industrial, Barnbrook Boiler Works, Brook Street, Bury, Lancashire, BL9 6AF Tel: 0161-763 6520 Fax: 0161-763 6519 *Industrial gear manufrs*

J & J Insulations Ltd, 27a New Road, Croxley Green, Rickmansworth, Hertfordshire, WD3 3EJ Tel: (01923) 897161 Fax: (01923) 897161 E-mail: jj.insulations@virgin.net *Asbestos removal services & reinsulation*

▶ J J L Artison, Nethermill, Netherton Road, Langbank, Port Glasgow, Port Of Glasgow, Renfrewshire, PA14 6YG Tel: (01475) 540060

▶ J J Long Electrical Contractors Ltd, Killinghall Stone Quarry, Ripon Road, Killinghall, Harrogate, North Yorkshire, HG3 2BA Tel: (01423) 520720 Fax: (01423) 520720

J J M Joinery, Forstal Farm Business Park, Goudhurst Road, Lamberhurst, Tunbridge Wells, Kent, TN3 8AG Tel: (01892) 891040 Fax: (01892) 891040 *Joiners*

J J McCormack Fitted Furniture, 185 Main St, Uddingston, Glasgow, G71 7BP Tel: (01698) 818766 Fax: (01698) 818883 *Fitted & built-in furniture installers*

J J Machines, 38 Hinksley Road, Flitwick, Bedford, MK45 1HH Tel: (01525) 717600 Fax: (01525) 716816 *Straw cutting machines importers*

J J Mckinney & Sons, 120 Railway Street, Armagh, BT61 7ND Tel: (028) 3752 2844 *Timber merchants*

J J Macmahon Ltd, 4 Loy Street, Cookstown, County Tyrone, BT80 8PE Tel: (028) 8676 3899 Fax: (028) 8676 7417 E-mail: jjmacmahon@hotmail.com *Building contractors*

▶ J J Marketing, 60 Rochester Way, Twyford, Banbury, Oxon, OX17 3JX Tel: 01295 814989 E-mail: jjmarketing@fsmail.net *Full Telemarketing service.*Appointment Making*Mail Fulfilment*Database creation and cleansing*Tailored Solutions for Small to Medium size companies.*

J J Melley & Sons (Welsh Feeds), Penybanc Stores, Maes Y Bont Road, Gorslas, Llanelli, Dyfed, SA14 7NA Tel: (01269) 842224 Fax: (01269) 842224 *Building & agricultural suppliers*

J & J Metalspin, 10 Hack Street, Birmingham, B9 4AH Tel: 0121-772 8968 Fax: 0121-772 8968 *General metal spinners*

J & J Motor Engineers Ltd, 405 New Kings Road, London, SW6 4RL Tel: (020) 7736 8161 *Vehicle repairers*

▶ J & J Murdoch, Station Garage Station Yard Industrial Estate, Oakwell Road, Castle Douglas, Kirkcudbrightshire, DG7 1LA Tel: (01556) 502062 Fax: (01556) 503282

J J Network Services Ltd, Meridian House, 62 Station Road, London, E4 7BA Tel: (020) 8559 3211 Fax: (020) 8559 3223 E-mail: info@jjnet.co.uk *Computer consultants*

J J Newland Ltd, 10 Brown Avenue, Leeds, LS11 0DX Tel: 0113-271 7340 Fax: 0113-277 9877 *Stationers & printers*

J & J Pneumatics Ltd, Hillbottom Road, Sands Industrial Estate, High Wycombe, Buckinghamshire, HP12 4HJ Tel: (01494) 530291 Fax: (01494) 463062 E-mail: sales@jjp.co.uk *Air compressors & pneumatic control systems*

J J Prior (Transport) Ltd, Ballat Quay, Fingringhoe, Colchester, CO5 7DB Tel: (01206) 729412 Fax: (01206) 729551 E-mail: sales@jjprior.co.uk *Motor barge owners*

J & J Products Ashford Ltd, 3 River Gardens Business Centre, Spur Road, Feltham, Middlesex, TW14 0SN Tel: (020) 8890 5085 Fax: (020) 8751 1896 E-mail: jj.products@cwcom.net *Steel & sheet metal fabricators & engineers*

▶ J J Quartz, 4 Normans Hall Farm, Shrigley Road, Pott Shrigley, Macclesfield, Cheshire, SK10 5SE Tel: (01625) 571077 Fax: (01625) 571077 E-mail: jjquartz@ntlworld.com *Scientific glassware manufrs*

J & J Ransley, Golden Wood Farm, Brisley Lane, Ruckinge, Ashford, Kent, TN26 2PW Tel: (01233) 733189 Fax: (01233) 731002 *Hay merchants*

▶ J & J Robertson, 3 Poplar Road, Dumbarton, G82 2RD Tel: (01389) 763765

▶ J & J Rothwell & Son, 156 Parrin Lane, Eccles, Manchester, M30 8BH Tel: (07789) 937405 Fax: 0161-281 0238 E-mail: info@rothwellandson.co.uk *Established Corgi registered gas, plumbing and bathroom installers for over 30 years*

J & J Screen Printing, 16 High Street, Stanstead Abbotts, Ware, Hertfordshire, SG12 8AE Tel: (01920) 872284 *Screen printing services*

J J Service, Star Trading Estate, Ponthir, Newport, Gwent, NP18 1PQ Tel: (01633) 420552 Fax: (01633) 430224 *Paper making plant & machinery & repairs*

J & J Services, 29 Dunville Road, Bedford, MK40 4DY Tel: (01234) 378289 Fax: (01234) 325479 E-mail: lindopjj@aol.com' *Industrial cleaning machines*

J & J Services, Gowan Avenue, Falkirk, FK2 7HL Tel: (01324) 620204 Fax: (01324) 885914 E-mail: jr@jjfirepro.co.uk *Fire protection equipment installation providers*

J & J Slitting Services Ltd, 217 Sams Lane, West Bromwich, West Midlands, B70 7EX Tel: 0121-553 1131 Fax: 0121-525 2411 *Metal coil slitters suppliers*

J J Smith Technical Services Ltd, Moorgate Point, Moorgate Road, Knowsley Industrial Park, Liverpool, L33 7DR Tel: 0151-546 1308 Fax: 0151-549 1771 E-mail: sales@jjsmith.co.uk *Woodworking machinery manufrs* Also at: Farnborough

J J Stainless Steel Products Ltd, 35 Bridgewater Street, Liverpool, L1 0AR Tel: 0151-709 2512 Fax: 0151-709 2512 E-mail: support@jjstainless.biz *Stainless steel fabricators*

J & J Systems UK Ltd, Systems House, Downs Park, Herne Bay, Kent, CT6 6BY Tel: (01227) 371375 Fax: (01227) 371377 E-mail: mail@jjsystems.co.uk *Computer consultants*

J J Thompson Ltd, 95 Hill Street, Sheffield, S2 4SP Tel: 0114-275 3090 Fax: 0114-275 8385 E-mail: jjt@eurodontic.co.uk *Manufacturers of orthodontic appliances*

J & J Tooling Services, Bridge House, Railway Street, Radcliffe, Manchester, M26 3AA Tel: 0161-724 7799 Fax: 0161-724 0722 E-mail: sales@jjtooling.co.uk *Machine diamond tipped tool distributors*

▶ J J Tyres, 1 Churchill Building, Churchill Road, Doncaster, South Yorkshire, DN1 2TF Tel: (01302) 341200 *Tyre manufrs*

▶ J J Vaillant Ltd, Number 1 Devon Street, Nechells, Birmingham, B7 4SL Tel: 0121-380 0720 Fax: 0121-380 0726

J J Welding Fabrication Ltd, Greenbank Road, East Tullos Industrial Estate, Aberdeen, AB12 3BQ Tel: (01224) 898889 Fax: (01224) 873139 E-mail: njohnston@twma.co.uk *Welding fabricators*

J J Westaby & Partners, Cape Farm, Sheriff Hutton, York, YO60 6RT Tel: (01347) 878703 Fax: (01347) 878771 E-mail: hydrapower@mcmail.com *Agricultural engineers*

J J Williams Painting Services Ltd, 75 Village Farm Road, Pyle, Bridgend, Mid Glamorgan, CF33 6BN Tel: (01656) 744311 Fax: (01656) 744617 E-mail: enquiries@jjwilliamsltd.com *Painting contractors & decorative grit blasting*

▶ J Jays Ltd, Unit 4, Baron Court, Chandlers Way, Southend-On-Sea, SS2 5SE Tel: (01702) 461777 Fax: (01702) 465176 E-mail: adverts@jjays.com *Per-press type settings service*

J Johnson & Sons, The Basket Centre, Station Road, Bangor-on-Dee, Wrexham, Clwyd, LL13 0AB Tel: (01978) 780417 Fax: (01978) 780781 E-mail: sales@johnsoncanefurniture.co.uk *Basket making & cane furniture distributors*

J Johnstone Engineering Ltd, 86 Skinburness Road, Silloth, Wigton, Cumbria, CA7 4QH Tel: (01697) 332399 Fax: (01697) 332579 *Engineering fabricators*

▶ J Joslin (Contractors) Ltd, Lower Road, Long Hanborough, Witney, Oxfordshire, OX29 8LR Tel: (01993) 882153 E-mail: enquires@j-jocklin.co.uk *Stone machinery company*

J Judge & Sons, 37 Melbourne Road, Ilford, Essex, IG1 4LF Tel: (020) 8554 3347 Fax: (020) 8554 3347 *Automatic transmission repairs*

J K Alarms, 9 Alexandria Street, Rossendale, Lancashire, BB4 8HP Tel: (01706) 218504 Fax: (01706) 218504 *Burglar alarms & CCTV services*

▶ J K Audio Visual Ltd, Unit 7 Newport Business Park, Audley Avenue, Newport, Shropshire, TF10 7DP Tel: (01952) 825088 *Audio visual equipment & accessory suppliers*

J K Cleaning Supplies, 1012 Chester Road, Erdington, Birmingham, B24 0LL Tel: 0121-373 6069 Fax: 0121-382 3462 *Cleaning suppliers*

J K Commercials, Stopes Road, Little Lever, Bolton, BL3 1NP Tel: 0161-724 5579 Fax: 0161-724 5579 *Commercial vehicle painters*

▶ J K Communications, 4 The Courtyard, 188 Galgorm Road, Ballymena, County Antrim, BT42 1HL Tel: (028) 2563 1767 Fax: (0870) 7623785 E-mail: info@jkcomm.co.uk *Computer maintenance services*

▶ J K Computer Solutions, The Dairy, Lynn Road, Hillington, King's Lynn, Norfolk, PE31 6BJ Tel: (07775) 941121 E-mail: john@jkcomputersolutions.com *IT consultancy*

J K Control Systems Ltd, Unit 14 Kernick Industrial Estate, Penryn, Cornwall, TR10 9EP Tel: (01326) 378432 Fax: (01326) 378423 E-mail: info@jkcontrolsystems.co.uk

continued

Manufacture of wiring looms & control systems for the automotive industry

J K Controls Ltd, 12a Rochester Airport Industrial Estate, Laker Road, Rochester, Kent, ME1 3QX Tel: (01634) 685858 Fax: (01634) 685850 E-mail: info@jkcontrols.co.uk *Control system design consultants*

▶ J K Doors Ltd, Unit 4/6, Hanworth Road, Off Common Road, Low Moor, Bradford, West Yorkshire, BD12 0SG Tel: (0845) 0589420 Fax: (0845) 0589421 E-mail: kevin@jkdoors.co.uk *Steel door fabrication*

J K Electric, East Mews, Station Fields, Church Lane, Garforth, Leeds, LS25 1PL Tel: 0113-286 5857 Fax: 0113-286 0659 *Motor repair services*

J K (England) Ltd, Third Floor Walmar House, 296 Regent St, London, W1B 3AW Tel: (020) 7255 1900 Fax: (020) 7255 1991 E-mail: jke@jkengland.u-net.com *Menswear*

J K Enterprises Ltd, Unit 2 Hewell Lane, Barnt Green, Birmingham, B45 8NZ Tel: 0121-447 7678 Fax: 0121-447 8333 *Pipework erection, installation & building services*

▶ J K F Ltd, Scoonie Road, Leven, Fife, KY8 4SE Tel: (01333) 424457 Fax: (01333) 424340 *Fencing & civil engineering*

J.K. Filters Ltd, Unit 4 Heath Road, Industrial Park, Merrylees Road, Leicester, LE9 9FE Tel: (01455) 828697 Fax: (01455) 828680 E-mail: sales@jkfilters.com *Dust extraction filters*

J K Francis & Son Ltd, 16 Fortnum Close, Birmingham, B33 0JY Tel: 0121-783 7568 Fax: 0121-789 7140 *Export packers & case manufrs*

J & K Glass & Glazing Ltd, Units 4-5, Station Road, Terrington St. Clement, King's Lynn, Norfolk, PE34 4PL Tel: (01553) 828555 Fax: (01553) 827035 E-mail: info@jkwindowsanddoors.com *Windows, doors & conservatories installers, suppliers & manufrs*

J K J Manufacturing Ltd, Amsterdam Road, Hull, HU7 0XF Tel: (01482) 825868 Fax: (01482) 878659 E-mail: mail@e-pac.co.uk *Collapsible tube & toiletries manufrs*

J K Marine, Dell Quay Yard, Dell Quay Road, Chichester, West Sussex, PO20 7EB Tel: (01243) 785954 Fax: (01243) 781567 E-mail: info@dellquay.com *Boat repairers*

▶ J K Office Supplies, 21 Rufford Rise, Sothall, Sheffield, S20 2DW Tel: 0114-247 1515 Fax: 0114-247 1515 *Office equipment manufacturers & suppliers*

▶ J K Pipelines Ltd, K121 -123 Pembroke House, Manchester Road, Carrington Business Park, Carrington, Manchester, M31 4DD Tel: 0161-776 4403 Fax: 0161-776 4404 E-mail: jkpipelines@tiscali.co.uk *Ductile iron & steel pipe work products manufrs*

J K Printers, The Old Bakery, Tanyards Lane, Bexley, Kent, DA5 1AH Tel: (01322) 555966 Fax: (01322) 555977 *General printers*

▶ J K R Services Ltd, Orchard Building, Hewitts Road, Chelsfield, Orpington, Kent, BR6 7QL Tel: (01959) 533778 Fax: (01959) 532544 E-mail: admin@soundcraft-doors.co.uk *Door manufrs*

J K S - Boyles UK Ltd, Unit 9 Salcombe Road, Meadow Lane Industrial Estate, Alfreton, Derbyshire, DE55 7RG Tel: (01773) 835323 Fax: (01773) 835075 E-mail: sales@jks-boyles-ltd.co.uk *Supply equipment to drilling industry*

J & K Sheet Metal, Unit 33 Joseph Wilson Industrial Estate, Whitstable, Kent, CT5 3PS Tel: (01227) 274763 Fax: (01227) 773021 *Sheet metal fabricators*

J & K Tackle, 62-64 Sheep Street, Bicester, Oxfordshire, OX26 6LG Tel: (01869) 242589 Fax: (01869) 320821 *Fishing tackle*

J Keeling & Sons, Church Road, Ramsden Bellhouse, Billericay, Essex, CM11 1RH Tel: (01268) 733037 Fax: (01268) 572835 *Wheat farmers*

J King Electronics Ltd, The Stables, Handsworth Road, Handsworth, Sheffield, S13 9BH Tel: 0114-242 4902 Fax: 0114-244 5100 *Alarm installation*

J Knight, 15 Sycamore Avenue, Oldham, OL4 2EL Tel: 0161-633 1222 E-mail: jeff.knightsigns@btinternet.com *Sign manufrs*

J Kool, Acre Holdings, Little Weighton Road, Skidby, Cottingham, North Humberside, HU16 5TP Tel: (01482) 875747 Fax: (01482) 845024 E-mail: sales@jkoo1-engineers.co.uk *Machinery removal contractors*

J Kruczko, 28 High Street, Benson, Wallingford, Oxfordshire, OX10 6RP Tel: (01865) 340040 Fax: (01865) 340040 *Pine furniture manufrs*

J L A Ltd, Meadowcroft Lane, Ripponden, Sowerby Bridge, West Yorkshire, HX6 4AJ Tel: (01422) 822282 Fax: (01422) 824390 E-mail: info@jla.com *JLA, the UK's leading distributor of commercial laundry equipment, provides total laundry solutions for all markets, installation of the finest equipment, full laundry planning and design, service on time - guaranteed. Their product range includes commercial washers, dryers, finishing equipment and sanitisers.*

J L A Computer Services Ltd, 1 Enterprise Court, Lakes Road, Braintree, Essex, CM7 3QS Tel: (01376) 343456 Fax: (01376) 321277 E-mail: sales@jla-computers.co.uk *Manufacturers of computer systems*

J L Aircon Ltd, 15-21 Risborough Street, London, SE1 0HG Tel: (020) 7657 7976 Fax: (020) 7657 7769 *Air conditioning contractors & installers*

J L Allwork Ltd, 177 High Street, Tonbridge, Kent, TN9 1BX Tel: (01732) 352160 Fax: (01732) 352160 E-mail: allwork@lineone.net *Commercial photographers*

J L Bragg Ipswich Ltd, 34 Boss Hall Road, Ipswich, IP1 5BN Tel: (01473) 748345 Fax: (01473) 749889 E-mail: bragg@charcoal.uk.com *Charcoal preparations pharmaceutical manufrs*

J L C Pumps & Engineering Co. Ltd, PO Box 225, Bedford, MK45 4PN Tel: (01582) 881946 Fax: (01582) 881951 E-mail: jlcpumps@btconnect.com *Pump manufrs*

J L Clark & Co., 16 Alliance Close, Ptarmigan Place, Attleborough Fields Industrial Estate, Nuneaton, Warwickshire, CV11 6RX Tel: (024) 7635 2140 Fax: (024) 7635 3347 E-mail: jlandclarksonltd@aol.com *NIC ERC electrical contractors & steam cleaner equipment distributors*

J L Communications Ltd, Ferry Lane, Pembroke, Dyfed, SA71 4RE Tel: (01646) 683123 Fax: (01646) 621111 *Telecommunication systems*

J L Engineering Rixton Ltd, Chapel Lane, Warrington, WA3 6HG Tel: 0161-775 0588 Fax: 0161-775 6613 E-mail: info@jleng.co.uk *General engineering & welders*

J L Fabrications, Unit 7 Winstanley Industrial Estate, Long Lane, Warrington, WA2 8PR Tel: (01925) 633887 Fax: (01925) 630087 *Sheet metalworkers*

J L Fearnley, Manor Farm, Manor Farm Road, Denton, Harleston, Norfolk, IP20 0AX Tel: (01986) 788630 Fax: (01986) 788637 E-mail: sales@fcs.uk.com *Web sites manufrs*

▶ J L Findlow & Sons Ltd, Ball Haye Road, Leek, Staffordshire, ST13 6AF Tel: (01538) 383174 Fax: (01538) 399997

J L Float Ltd, West Gate, Aldridge, Walsall, WS9 8UF Tel: (01922) 455677 Fax: (01922) 743193 E-mail: info@jlfloat.com *Manufacturers of metal spinnings, floats & pressings*

J L G Investments Ltd, 3 Claridge Court, Lower Kings Road, Berkhamsted, Hertfordshire, HP4 2AF Tel: (01442) 877866 Fax: (01442) 877806 E-mail: david@jlginvest.demon.co.uk *Property investment & development company*

▶ J L G Security Services, Westmead House, 123 Westmead Road, Sutton, Surrey, SM1 4JH Tel: (020) 8642 8996 Fax: (020) 8643 6367 E-mail: sales@jlg.co.uk *Installations of security services, cctv systems & alarms*

▶ J L H Print & Promotions, Garth Works, Taffs Well, Cardiff, CF15 7YF Tel: (029) 2081 4195 Fax: (029) 2081 4195 E-mail: sales@jlhprintpromotions.co.uk *Clothing & work wear retailer*

J L Holmes & Sons, 86a Leyland Road, Penwortham, Preston, PR1 9XS Tel: (01772) 743640 Fax: (01772) 743640 *Joinery manufrs*

J & L Industrial Paint Services Ltd, Unit 21, Knightcott Industrial Estate, Banwell, Avon, BS29 6JN Tel: (01934) 820780 Fax: (01934) 820323 E-mail: jl.paints@virgin.net *Industrial paint manufacturers.*

J L Leach & Co. Ltd, Etruscan Street, Stoke-on-Trent, ST1 5SE Tel: (01782) 202001 Fax: (01782) 286868 E-mail: sales@jlleech.com *Engineers supplies distributors* Also at: Shrewsbury

▶ J & L Leonard, Hatston Industrial Estate, Kirkwall, Orkney, KW15 1RE Tel: (01856) 873482

J L M Security, 43 Rosebank Terrace, Aberdeen, AB11 6LQ Tel: (01224) 594200 Fax: (01224) 584571 E-mail: jlmlocks@aol.com *Lock distributors, lock fitting specialists & safe maintenance/installation/repair service*

▶ J L Ornamental Castings, Unit 7, Old Ballynahinch Road, Lisburn, County Antrim, BT27 6TH Tel: (07710) 458636 Fax: (028) 9263 9808 E-mail: johnlavelle@btopenworld.com *Conversation & restoration of medals*

J L Owen Ltd, 13 Blossom Street, Manchester, M4 5AF Tel: 0161-236 0507 Fax: 0161-236 7831 *Edible oil & fat distributors*

J & L Precision, 17-18 Ivanhoe Road, Finchampstead, Wokingham, Berkshire, RG40 4QQ Tel: 0118-932 8274 Fax: 0118-932 8084 *Precision engineers*

J L & S A Edwards, Wood Cottage, Lacon Street, Prees, Whitchurch, Shropshire, SY13 2EP Tel: (01948) 840264 *Agricultural contractors*

J L S Redditch, Holberrow Green, Holberrow Green, Redditch, Worcestershire, B96 6JY Tel: (01386) 791513 Fax: 01386 791518 E-mail: sales@jlsovens.com Principal Export Areas: Worldwide *Worcestershire, UK based manufacturers of industrial ovens and furnaces. Examples include horizontal conveyors and batch ovens, suitable for the automotive, aerospace and plastic industries.*

▶ J L Steel Services, Unit 101, Bandeath Industrial Estate, Stirling, FK7 7NP Tel: (01786) 817081 Fax: (01786) 810981 *Steel fabrication*

▶ J L Wilson Auto Eletrical Parts, 51a Annareagh Road, Richhill, Armagh, BT61 9JT Tel: (028) 3887 1412 Fax: (028) 3887 0669 E-mail: sales@jlwilsonautoelectric.co.uk *Importer, exporter & distributor of auto electrical components*

J L Woodworking Machinery, 40 Sketchley Road, Burbage, Hinckley, Leicestershire, LE10 2DZ Tel: (01455) 251557 Fax: (01455) 251557 E-mail: j.l.wood40@gmail.com *An established family run firm supplying both new & used woodworking machinery, tooling & dust extraction units. * We can supply most makes of new machines at competetive prices. We also go to great lengths to try & locate your particular machinery requirements. A delivery service is available including craned & taillift vehicles*

▶ J L Young, 4 Skye Road, Shawfarm Industrial Estate, Prestwick, Ayrshire, KA9 2TA Tel: (01292) 671716 Fax: (01292) 671716

J Lawrence, Scotland Street, Stoke by Nayland, Colchester, CO6 4QG Tel: (01206) 263459 Fax: (01206) 262166 E-mail: sales@jim-lawrence.co.uk *Wrought ironwork manufrs*

J Lawrence, 1 Alma Street, Walsall, WS2 8JQ Tel: (01922) 628759 Fax: (01922) 639969 *Scrap metal merchant*

J Lawrie, Balchalum Farm, Errol, Perth, PH2 7RR Tel: (01821) 670311 Fax: (01821) 670311 *Agricultural contractors*

J Lawrie & Sons, The Pier, Mallaig, Inverness-Shire, PH41 4QD Tel: (01687) 462224 Fax: (01687) 462871 *Fish processing & curing services*

J Linham & Sons Ltd, Westhay, Meare, Glastonbury, Somerset, BA6 9TL Tel: (01458) 860216 *Concrete & mortar ready mixed*

▶ J Little, Norfolk Street, Nelson, Lancashire, BB9 7SY Tel: (01282) 698777 E-mail: johnlittle@yahoo.co.uk *building & repairing van bodies, curtain siders & drop sides*

J Little, Norfolk Street, Nelson, Lancashire, BB9 7SY Tel: (01282) 698777 *Commercial vehicle body builders*

▶ J Long & Sons (Haulage) Ltd, Sandleas Way, Leeds, LS15 8AW Tel: 0113-264 0106

J Looker & Sons Ltd, Bessell Lane, Stapleford, Nottingham, NG9 7BX Tel: 0115-939 5054 Fax: 0115-939 5978 *Carton manufrs*

J Luke, 101B High Rd, Beeston, Nottingham, NG9 2LH Tel: 0115-925 5616 Fax: 0115-925 5616 E-mail: jdluke@btconect.com *Manufacturers of a superior safety device for warehouses to prevent a trailer from being moved while being loaded or unloaded*

J M, Chandos House, 12-14 Berry Street, London, EC1V 0AQ Tel: (020) 7253 7172 Fax: (020) 7253 0420 *IT recruitment agents*

J M Air Conditioning Ltd, 23 Tollgate Avenue, Redhill, RH1 5HR Tel: 01737 772200 Fax: 01737 772300 E-mail: jmacltd@aol.com *Air conditioning design*

▶ J M B Plant Hire Ltd, 3 Trevithick Road, Willowbrook South Industrial Estate, Willowbrook East Industrial Estate, Corby, Northamptonshire, NN17 5XY Tel: (01536) 200262 Fax: (01536) 275929 E-mail: sales@jmbhire.co.uk

▶ J M Bearings, 22 Meadowsweet, Eaton Ford, St. Neots, Cambridgeshire, PE19 7GR Tel: (01480) 216145 Fax: (01480) 383023 E-mail: andrew.hill137@ntlworld.com *Bearing&Transmissions Stockest&Allied Products*

J M Bell & Son, Archard Garth, Bagby, Thirsk, North Yorkshire, YO7 2PH Tel: (01845) 597205 Fax: (01845) 597971 *Livestock transportation*

J & M Belts Veebelts Bearings Oilseals, 72 Bridge Road, Grays, Essex, RM17 6BZ Tel: (01375) 373975 Fax: (01375) 391541 E-mail: sales@jmbelts.com *Bearing stockists*

J & M Bodman, Cuckoo Corner, Urchfont, Devizes, Wiltshire, SN10 4RA Tel: (01380) 840273 Fax: (01380) 840126 *Farming & contracting*

J M Builders, Hallidays Mill, London Road, Chalford, Stroud, Gloucestershire, GL6 8NR Tel: (01453) 882207 Fax: (01453) 731076

J M Building Systems, 5 Anglesey Place, Great Barton, Bury St. Edmunds, Suffolk, IP31 2TW Tel: (01284) 787408 Fax: (01284) 787408 *Relocatable buildings suppliers*

J M C Aquatic Ltd, Unit 4, Commerce Way Industrial Estate, Stanbridge, Leighton Buzzard, Beds, LU7 8HJ Tel: (01525) 377307 Fax: (01525) 374266 *Aquatics distributor*

J M C Aquatics Ltd, 59 Stubley Lane, Dronfield, Derbyshire, S18 1PG Tel: (01246) 415275 Fax: (01246) 290486 E-mail: janet@jmc-aquatics.co.uk *Tropical fish wholesalers*

▶ J M C Building Services Ltd, 1a Mount Street, Southport, Merseyside, PR9 0RG Tel: (01704) 543914 Fax: (01704) 353561

▶ J M C Logistics UK Ltd, St Francis House, Old Bath Road, Colnbrook, Slough, SL3 0NP Tel: (01753) 689745 Fax: (01753) 684479

J M C Washers & Gaskets, Unit 3 Hartlebury Trading Estate, Hartlebury, Kidderminster, Worcestershire, DY10 4JB Tel: (01299) 251339 Fax: (01299) 251008 *Gasket manufacturers, rubber product merchants & wire forming services*

J M Circuits Ltd, Unit 4 Kingsley, Bordon, Hampshire, GU35 9LY Tel: (01420) 487339 Fax: (01420) 487339 E-mail: info@jmcircuits.freeserve.co.uk *Circuit boards*

▶ J & M Computers, 46c Green Arbour Road, Thurcroft, Rotherham, South Yorkshire, S66 9DB Tel: (01709) 547900 *Computer suppliers*

J M Copiers Ltd, 5 Mansfield Road, Musselburgh, Midlothian, EH21 7DS Tel: 0131-665 3783 Fax: 0131-665 4746 E-mail: jmcopiers@btconnect.com *Photocopier & fax services & sales*

▶ J M D Ltd, Faraday Drive, Bridgnorth, Shropshire, WV15 5BQ Tel: (01746) 768227 Fax: (01746) 767565 E-mail: sales@jmdautomaticdoors.com

J M D Systems Ltd, 7 St. Pauls Yard, Silver Street, Newport Pagnell, Buckinghamshire, MK16 0EG Tel: (01908) 217033 Fax: (01982) 217044 *Network computer manufrs*

▶ J M Dewar Plant Contractors, Broich Road, Crieff, Perthshire, PH7 3RT Tel: (01764) 653951 Fax: (01764) 655358

J M E Ltd, Electron House, Old Nelson St, Lowestoft, Suffolk, NR32 1EQ Tel: (01502) 500969 Fax: (01502) 511932 E-mail: sales@jme.co.uk *Non-destructive test system manufrs*

J M E Rubber Co., Unit 4, Hattersley Industrial Estate, Stockport Road, Hattersley, Hyde, Cheshire, SK14 3QT Tel: 0161-368 9755 Fax: 0161-368 9767 *Rubber mouldings manufrs*

J & M Elston, Washfield, Tiverton, Devon, EX16 9RF Tel: (01398) 351248 Fax: (01398) 351248 *Farmers & timber merchants*

J M F Vision Systems Ltd, The Lindens, Friern Park, London, N12 9DJ Tel: (020) 8445 0452 *CCTV consultants*

J M Fabrications, 11 Rochdale Walk, Birmingham, B10 0DF Tel: 0121-685 1310 Fax: 0121-685 1310 E-mail: jmfabs@aol.com *Plastic fabrications*

▶ J & M Fabrications, 1c Saxby Road Industrial Estate, Hudson Road, Melton Mowbray, Leicestershire, LE13 1BS Tel: (01664) 560118 Fax: (01664) 560119 *Engineering*

J M Fabweld Ltd, Llewellyns Quay, Port Talbot, West Glamorgan, SA13 1RF Tel: (01639) 884550 Fax: (01639) 891015 E-mail: jmfabwellltd@btconnect.com *General engineers services mechanical*

J M Feerick & Partners, 3-5 Church Street, Brierley Hill, West Midlands, DY5 3PT Tel: (01384) 77885 Fax: (01384) 76181 E-mail: johnfeerick@jmfeerickandpatns.co.uk *Consulting civil & structural engineers*

J M Finn Nominees Ltd, Salisbury House, London Wall, London, EC2M 5TA Tel: (020) 7628 9688 Fax: (020) 7628 7314 *Stock broking services*

J & M G Smith, Manor Farm, York Lane, Morthen, Rotherham, South Yorkshire, S66 9JH Tel: (01709) 544632 Fax: (01709) 544632 *Farming contractors*

▶ J M G Systems Ltd, 68a Derry Road, Omagh, County Tyrone, BT78 5ED Tel: (028) 8224 4131 E-mail: info@jmgsystems.co.uk

J M Geggus & Sons, 50 Ferniefields, High Wycombe, Buckinghamshire, HP12 4SL Tel: (01494) 439926 Fax: (01494) 439926 *Haulage contractors*

▶ J M Gorry & Son Ltd, Middlegate, White Lund Industrial Estate, Morecambe, Lancashire, LA3 3BN Tel: (01524) 67530 Fax: (01524) 33446 E-mail: info@jmgorry.co.uk

J M Grant, 73 New Road, Rednal, Birmingham, B45 9JT Tel: 0121-453 8783 Fax: 0121-453 8783 *Coach & car trimming services*

▶ J M H Technology LLP, Unit 3, Highlands Farm, Berden, Bishop's Stortford, Hertfordshire, CM23 1AB Tel: (0845) 0537457 Fax: (07092) 002578 E-mail: sales@jmhtechnology.co.uk *Security system installers cctv, intruder & intercom systems*

J & M Hardware, 75 Scotland Road, Nelson, Lancashire, BB9 7UY Tel: (01282) 613460 Fax: (01282) 617928 *Architectural ironmongers*

J M Heat Exchangers Ltd, 3 Albion Place, Doncaster, South Yorkshire, DN1 2EG Tel: (01302) 325179 Fax: (01302) 760353 E-mail: bryan@jmheatexchanges.com *Heat exchanger manufrs*

J M Hunt & Co. Ltd, 389-391 Castleford Road, Normanton, West Yorkshire, WF6 1RQ Tel: (01924) 890693 Fax: (01924) 893634 E-mail: sales@hunts-pipeline.co.uk *Pipeline suppliers merchants*

J & M Hygiene Supplies, Unit 11 Stanley Green Industrial Estate, Stanley Green CR, Poole, Dorset, BH15 3TH Tel: (01202) 676090 Fax: (01202) 676090 *Janitorial suppliers*

J M J Ltd, Main Street, Skidby, Cottingham, North Humberside, HU16 5TX Tel: (01482) 840103 Fax: (01482) 875052 E-mail: info@jmjwood.co.uk *New and used woodworking machinery suppliers, tooling, dust extraction & accessories. SCM, Minimax, Sedgwick, Wadkin, Volpato sanders, Felder Wallsaws, Casadei Edgebanders,Morso & Scheppach*

J M J Bulk Packaging Ltd, Earlstrees Road, Earlstrees Industrial Estate, Corby, Northamptonshire, NN17 4AZ Tel: (01536) 274400 Fax: (01536) 261180 E-mail: sales@packaging.uk.com Principal Export Areas: Worldwide *Manufacturers of bulk containers*

▶ J M & J M Ratcliffe, Manor Farm Stud, High Street, Chippenham, Ely, Cambridgeshire, CB7 5PR Tel: (01638) 720888 Fax: (01638) 721310 *Race horse transport*

J M J Precision Sheet Metal Ltd, 11 Boulton Road, Stevenage, Hertfordshire, SG1 4QX Tel: (01438) 360711 Fax: (01438) 360721 *Precision sheet metalworkers manufrs*

J M K Ltd, Unit 9 Block 2, Vale of Leven Industrial Estate, Dumbarton, G82 3PW Tel: (01389) 751841 Fax: (01389) 751775 E-mail: jmkfilters@sol.co.uk *Custom design & manufacture of EMI/RFI mains filters*

▶ J M K Business Supplies, Mill Road Industrial Estate, Linlithgow Bridge, Linlithgow, West Lothian, EH49 7SF Tel: (01506) 847840 Fax: (01506) 847762

J M L Packaging Services Ltd, Parnall Road Trading Estate, Parnall Road, Bristol, BS16 3JQ Tel: 0117-965 5259 Fax: 0117-958 5494 E-mail: user@jmlpackaging.co.uk *Corrugated case manufrs*

J M Lane, 121 Harecroft Road, Wisbech, Cambridgeshire, PE13 1RS Tel: (01945) 583292 Fax: (01945) 461435 *Precision engineers*

J M Marriott & Co, Storey House White Cross, South Road, Lancaster, LA1 4XF Tel: (01524) 845611 Fax: (01524) 845612 E-mail: jmt@jmmarriott.co.uk *Business support services*

▶ J M P Consulting, City House, City Wharf, Davidson Road, Lichfield, Staffordshire, WS14 9DZ Tel: (01543) 440700 Fax: (0800) 066 4636

J & M Parker Ltd, 9 New Summer Street, Birmingham, B19 3QN Tel: 0121-359 8897 Fax: 0121-359 4497 E-mail: enquiries@parker.co.uk *Brassware importers & manufrs*

J & M Profile Services Ltd, Vauxhall Iron Works, Beauford Road, Birkenhead, Merseyside, CH41 1HE Tel: 0151-653 6006 Fax: 0151-652 1425 E-mail: jmprofiles@jmprofiles.co.uk *Steel fabricators for gas rigs*

▶ J & M Publishing, 13-15 West Church St, Buckie, Banffshire, AB56 1BN Tel: (01542) 832265

J M & R M Heathman, Lewthorn Cottages, Ilsington, Newton Abbot, Devon, TQ13 9RR Tel: (01364) 661303 Fax: (01364) 661257 *Pottery mould makers*

J M Rennie, Depot, Hen Lon Parcwr, Ruthin, Clwyd, LL15 1NA Tel: (01824) 704842 Fax: (01824) 705400 *Concrete manufrs*

J & M Rule, Sparnon Gate, Redruth, Cornwall, TR16 4JB Tel: (01209) 216460 *Agricultural contractors*

▶ J M S Construction, 28 Lawmoor Road, Dixon Blazes Industrial Estate, Glasgow, G5 0UG Tel: 0141-418 0902

J M S Flagpoles, Ireland Industrial Estate, Adelphi Way, Staveley, Chesterfield, Derbyshire, S43 3LS Tel: (01246) 472949 Fax: (01246) 280476 E-mail: sales@bannerbox.co.uk *Flagstaff, flagpole & banner frame manufrs*

▶ J M S Specialist Joinery Ltd, Unit B Bourne End, Kineton Road Industrial Estate, Southam, Warwickshire, CV47 0NA Tel: (01926) 813813 Fax: (01926) 812777 E-mail: jmsjoineryltd@aol.com *Joinery manufrs*

J & M Sewing Services, 1 Charlotte Square, Newcastle upon Tyne, NE1 4XF Tel: 0191-232 9589 Fax: 0191-230 1215 E-mail: jandmsewing@btconnect.com *A highly recommended company established 1980, making quality church robes, vestments & furnishings. High standards of work but competitive prices with personal service, and items individually made. Customers worldwide*

J M Shutt Pattern Makers Ltd, The Old Engine House Duke, Street Fenton, Stoke-on-Trent, ST4 3BJ Tel: (01782) 316214 Fax: (01782) 599410 *Engineers pattern makers services*

▶ J M T Installations Ltd, 6 Waltham Court, Milley Lane, Hare Hatch, Reading, RG10 9AA Tel: 0118-940 1177 Fax: 0118-940 2344

J M Tatler & Son Ltd, Abbey Street Works, Derby, DE22 3SW Tel: (01332) 342120 Fax: (01332) 293699 E-mail: willtat@fsbdial.co.uk *General printer & diary publishers*

▶ J & M Taylor Haulage Ltd, 9 Wallace Street, Paisley, Renfrewshire, PA3 2BU Tel: 0141-889 3513

J M Tool & Cutter Ltd, 425 Garstang Road, Broughton, Preston, PR3 5JA Tel: (01772) 866211 Fax: (01772) 865010 E-mail: j.m.tools@breathemail.net *Tool & cutter grinding*

J Mccartney Ltd, 168 Park View Road, London, N17 9BL Tel: (020) 8808 0582 Fax: (020) 8365 1884 E-mail: jmccartneylimited@parkviewroad.fsnet.co.uk *Gearbox reconditioners*

J Mccready & Co. Ltd, 123 Corporation Street, Belfast, BT1 3EJ Tel: (028) 9023 2842 Fax: (028) 9023 6187 *Ship chandler & sail manufrs*

▶ J Mchugh, 20 Carmoney Road, Eglinton, Londonderry, BT47 3JJ Tel: (028) 7186 0162

▶ J Mcintyre & Son Ltd, 7 Ratcliffe Fold, Haslingden, Rossendale, Lancashire, BB4 5PZ Tel: (01706) 226180 Fax: (01706) 226180

J Mckee & Partners Ltd, 34 South Quay, Great Yarmouth, Norfolk, NR30 2RG Tel: (01493) 850131 Fax: (01493) 330149 E-mail: mckeeships@aol.com *Survey ship owners & managers*

▶ J Mclaren & Son Ltd, 22-26 Market St, Forfar, Angus, DD8 3EW Tel: (01307) 463315 *Bakery*

▶ J Mcvicar, 97 Dykehead Street, Glasgow, G33 4AQ Tel: 0141-774 5132 Fax: 0141-774 4440

J Marklew Engineering Ltd, Chapel Street, Dudley, West Midlands, DY2 9PN Tel: (01384) 252118 Fax: (01384) 456078 *Precision, general engineering & maintenance*

The J Marshall Partnership Ltd, Brunel Drive, Northern Road Ind Estate, Newark, Nottinghamshire, NG24 2EG Tel: (01636) 705702 Fax: (01636) 677939 *Shop fitting display units installers & manufrs*

J Miller (Patternmakers) Ltd, 22 Beardmore Way, Clydebank Industrial Estate, Dalmuir, Clydebank, Dunbartonshire, G81 4HT Tel: 0141-952 5930 Fax: 0141-952 5930 *Pattern engineers*

J Milner & Sons Ltd, Ingram Road, Leeds, LS11 9RD Tel: 0113-245 3845 Fax: 0113-245 3845 *Steel & plastic container merchants*

J Milom Ltd, Springfield Mills, Sherborne Street, Manchester, M3 1ND Tel: 0161-832 6155 Fax: 0161-833 0663 E-mail: sales@milom.co.uk *Marshall arts equipment manufrs*

▶ J Mitchell & Son (Laurencekirk) Ltd, Aberdeen Road, Laurencekirk, Kincardineshire, AB30 1AJ Tel: (01561) 377357

J Mortimer Fabrications Ltd, Old Station Yard, Kirkby Lonsdale, Carnforth, Lancashire, LA6 2HP Tel: (01524) 271700 Fax: (01524) 272290 E-mail: john@mortimerfabrications.co.uk *Steel fabricators*

J Motor Components Ltd, 1-5 Crimea Road Winton, Bournemouth, BH9 1AR Tel: (01202) 711177 Fax: (01202) 535777 *Brake & clutch distributors* Also at: Oakdale

▶ J Murphy Shaldon Ltd, 3 Bridge Road, Shaldon, Teignmouth, Devon, TQ14 0DD Tel: (01626) 873231 Fax: (01626) 873811

▶ J Murphy & Sons Ltd, 5 Finedon Sidings Industrial E, Furnace Lane, Finedon, Wellingborough, Northamptonshire, NN9 5NY Tel: (01536) 420638

▶ J N B Boliers, Boiler House, Calderhead Road, Shotts, Lanarkshire, ML7 4EQ Tel: (01501) 822177

J N Bentley Ltd, Keighley Road, Skipton, North Yorkshire, BD23 2QT Tel: (01756) 799425 Fax: (01756) 798068 E-mail: info@jnbentley.co.uk *Building & civil engineers*

J N Building Services Ltd, Cooper Yard, Old Cider Works, Abbotskerswell, Newton Abbot, Devon, TQ12 5NF Tel: (01626) 352056 Fax: (01626) 363599 E-mail: enquiries@jnbuildingservices.com *Electrical engineers*

▶ J N E Construction Ltd, Estover Close, Plymouth, PL6 7PL Tel: (01752) 696269 Fax: (01752) 696660

▶ J & N Electrics, 1373 Dumbarton Road, Glasgow, G14 9XT Tel: 0141-434 0434

▶ J N F Employment, 2c The Parade, Edinburgh Drive, Didcot, Oxfordshire, OX11 7LT Tel: (01235) 811600 Fax: (01235) 811601 E-mail: oxfordshire@jnf-employment.co.uk *A leading employment agency for office,technical, scientific and laboratory staff both temporary and permanent throughout Oxfordshire. We also cover other vacancies-just enquire.*

▶ J N Finance, Congress House, 14 Lyon Road, Harrow, Middlesex, HA1 2EN Tel: (020) 8861 4445 Fax: (020) 8861 4450 E-mail: info@jnfinance.com *Residential and commercial mortgages, Large development funding, asset finance, leasing,contract hire, overseas property and general insurance.*

J N G Construction & Engineering Ltd, 23 Hornsby Square, Southfields Industrial Park, Basildon, Essex, SS15 6SD Tel: (01268) 240888

▶ J & N Haulage & Packaging Ltd, 37 Stow Road, Willingham, Gainsborough, Lincolnshire, DN21 5LE Tel: (01427) 787355 Fax: 01427 787355 E-mail: jnhaulage@hotmail.com *Contract Packers, hand assembly, mailing and stuffing envelopes, labelling, boxing and bagging & Packaging Suppliers*Hauliers*

J.N.J. Fabrications Ltd, Ambrose Street, Gorton, Manchester, M12 5DD Tel: 0161-223 7277 Fax: 0161-223 7277 E-mail: sales@jnjfabs.co.uk *General steel fabricators*

continued

Company Information

▶ J N M Electrical Services, 23 Claro Court Business Centre, Claro Road, Harrogate, North Yorkshire, HG1 4BA Tel: (01423) 817187 Fax: (01423) 552512 E-mail: info@jnmonline.co.uk *Providers of shell scheme, electrics, av to exhibition & event industry*

J N R Electronics Assemblies, 158 Wheatfield Road, Luton, LU4 0TD Tel: (01582) 471278 Fax: (01582) 600703 E-mail: admin@jnr.org.uk *Electronics & cable assembly*

J N Supplies Ltd, Unit 27, 27 Beler Way, Melton Mowbray, Leicestershire, LE13 0DG Tel: (01664) 564050 Fax: 01664 564050 E-mail: sales@jnsupplies.co.uk *Internal and external doors **sliding sash and casement windows**stairs *free standing and built-in furniture**specialist mouldings ***

▶ J N Weatherby Ltd, 133 Frankwell, Shrewsbury, SY3 8JX Tel: (01743) 235392 Fax: (01743) 368619 *Heating &ventilation*

J Newbold Joinery & Shopfitters, Sherwood Street, Kirkby-in-Ashfield, Nottingham, NG17 9HU Tel: (01623) 721002 Fax: (01623) 721002 *Joinery manufrs*

J Newby & Sons, Mintsfeet Road South, Kendal, Cumbria, LA9 6ND Tel: (01539) 720819 Fax: (01539) 734607 E-mail: pickfords.preston@pickfords.com *Removal & storage specialists*

J Nicklin & Sons Ltd, 36 Erskine Street, Birmingham, B7 4LL Tel: 0121-359 8101 Fax: 0121-359 6673 E-mail: sales@nicklin.co.uk *Transit packaging manufrs*

▶ J Noble, Unit 3, Sherwood Industrial Estate, Bonnyrigg, Midlothian, EH19 3LW Tel: 0131-660 2275

J O B Export/Import Ltd, 15 Iberian Way, Camberley, Surrey, GU15 1LZ Tel: (01276) 21119 Fax: (01276) 62190 *Distribution of note & coin equipment*

J O & R H Baird Ltd, Industry Road, Newcastle upon Tyne, NE6 5XF Tel: 0191-265 5538 Fax: 0191-265 5833 *Welded & engineers fabrications*

▶ J O'Donnell, 17 Barmouth Grove, Biddulph, Stoke-on-Trent, ST8 7QE Tel: (01782) 511042 E-mail: jodonnell.plastering@hotmail.co.uk

J Oldham & Co. Ltd, Tearne House, Hollington, Stoke-on-Trent, ST10 4HR Tel: (01889) 507353 Fax: (01889) 507212 E-mail: enquiries@joldham.co.uk *Masonry works, architectural stone specialists*

J O'Neill & Co. Ltd, 7 Bromley Street, Hull, HU2 0PY Tel: (01482) 320146 Fax: (01482) 589968 *Welding engineers & locksmiths*

▶ J P & A Coates, Castle Houses Farm, Berry Brow, Huddersfield, HD4 6TS Tel: (01484) 663808 Fax: (01484) 661464 E-mail: sales@castlehousefarm.co.uk *Luxury holiday cottages*

J P Aero-Com Engineering Company Ltd, Station Approach, Cherry Tree Rise, Buckhurst Hill, Essex, IG9 6EY Tel: (020) 8504 8833 Fax: (020) 8505 0697 E-mail: sales@jpaero-com-eng.co.uk *Engineering fastenings distribution*

▶ J P Alarms & Locksmiths Ltd, 9B Vulcans Lane, Workington, Cumbria, CA14 2NX Tel: (01900) 870941 Fax: (01900) 872807 E-mail: office@jpalarms.co.uk *Security alarms & locksmiths*

J P (Automatic Transmissions) Ltd, Units 4A-4B, Pear Tree Industrial Estate, Bath Road, Upper Langford, Bristol, BS40 5DJ Tel: (01934) 852772 Fax: (01934) 852211 E-mail: info@jpat.co.uk *Auto transmission parts distributors*

J P Burners Ltd, 14 Monks Crescent, Leicester, LE4 2WA Tel: 0116-246 0400 Fax: 0116-235 8411 E-mail: sales@jpburners.co.uk Principal Export Areas: Asia Pacific, Middle East, Central/ East Europe, West Europe, North America & South America *Gas burners including wok & catering ring burners*

J P C Commercial Services Ltd, Elm Tree Farm, Cedar Street, Chesterfield, Derbyshire, S43 2LF Tel: (01246) 280123 Fax: (01246) 477421 E-mail: acom1jpc@aol.com *Property management & letting agents*

J P C Engineering, Greenhey Place, Skelmersdale, Lancashire, WN8 9SA Tel: (01695) 729552 Fax: (01695) 725552 *Precision engineers & steel fabricators*

J P C (GB) Ltd, Capitol Ho, Sea St, Herne Bay, Kent, CT6 6PB Tel: 01227 371721 Fax: 01227 371 722 *Computer services repair, upgrade, sales & distribs*

J P C Interiors Ltd, 144 Whitworth Road, Swindon, SN25 3BJ Tel: (01793) 524311 Fax: (01793) 524808 *Suspended ceiling & dry lining installation contractors*

▶ J P C S Ltd, The Sidings, Hampton Heath Industrial Estate, Hampton, Malpas, Cheshire, SY14 8LU Tel: (01948) 820696 Fax: (01948) 820252

▶ J P Callanan & Son Ltd, Unit 16 Harmill Industrial Estate, Grovebury Road, Leighton Buzzard, Bedfordshire, LU7 4FF Tel: (01525) 850061 Fax: (01525) 371810

J P Casuals, 1 Singers Yard, Torquay Road, Paignton, Devon, TQ3 2AH Tel: (01803) 666662 Fax: (01803) 666662 *Lose covers & upholstery manufrs*

▶ J P Construction, Mill Lane, Normanton, West Yorkshire, WF6 1RE Tel: (01924) 220092 Fax: (01924) 223173

J & P Contracts Angus Ltd, 73 Dundee Street, Carnoustie, Angus, DD7 7PN Tel: (01241) 854911 Fax: (01241) 855860 E-mail: sales@jp-coatech.com *General engineers, sheet metal work, powder coaters*

J P Corry, Ballydugan Indust Estate, Downpatrick, County Down, BT30 6HG Tel: (028) 4461 2011 Fax: (028) 4461 5635 E-mail: downpatrick@jpcorry.co.uk *Builders & timber merchants*

J P Corry, 15 Moyola Road, Castledawson, Magherafelt, County Londonderry, BT45 8BH Tel: (028) 7946 8622 Fax: (028) 7946 8948 E-mail: info@ardstimber.com *Builders merchants & timber importers*

J P Corry Lisburn Branch, Lisburn Business Park, 46 Hillsborough Old Road, Lisburn, County Antrim, BT27 5EW Tel: (028) 9266 2047 Fax: (028) 9266 6000 E-mail: lisburn@jpcory.co.uk *Timber building suppliers*

J P Corry N I Ltd, Unit 12a Pennybridge Industrial Estate, Ballymena, County Antrim, BT42 3HB Tel: (028) 2564 2261 Fax: (028) 2564 9175 E-mail: ballymena@jbcorry.co.uk *Timber merchants & builders suppliers*

J P Corry Ni Ltd, 136-210 Tennent Street, Belfast, BT13 3GF Tel: (028) 9075 1756 Fax: (028) 9035 2807 *Building materials merchant & timber merchants*

J & P Engineering, The Old Fire Station, Lows Lane, Stanton-by-Dale, Ilkeston, Derbyshire, DE7 4QU Tel: 0115-944 0388 Fax: 0115-944 0388 E-mail: enquiries@jandpengineering.co.uk *J&P Engineering was established in March 1996. We have ten years' experience providing quality standard and bespoke steelwork and structural fabrications. In addition to our ability to meet a wide range of individual customer requirements, we specialize in manufacturing and providing steelwork accessories, and internal and external refurbishment and repair services, for portable and modular buildings. Please visit our website for a price list of our standard items.**In addition to our steel fabrications, we operate our own fleet of vehicles. All vehicles can be hired independently, and also enable us to provide an integrated solution for transporting, locating, linking and refurbishing portable units, as well as manufacturing and fitting staircases, landings, access ramps, window guards, security doors, effluent tanks, etc.*

▶ J P Engraving Services, Pandy Industrial Estate, Plas Acton Road, Wrexham, Clwyd, LL11 2UB Tel: (01978) 291451 Fax: (01978) 262722 E-mail: sales@jpengraving.co.uk *Engraved signs & labels, Vehicle Graphics Health & Safety signs etc*

J & P Enterprises, West Lodge, West Haddon Road, Crick, Northampton, NN6 7SQ Tel: (01788) 823512 Fax: (01788) 822847 *Heavy earthmoving plant engineers service*

J P Fabrications, C 4 Belcon Industrial Estate, Geddings Road, Hoddesdon, Hertfordshire, EN11 0NT Tel: (01992) 444428 Fax: (01992) 444428 E-mail: jpfabs@aol.com *Metal fabricators*

J P Filtration Ltd, 133-135 High Street, Stratford, London, E15 2RB Tel: (020) 8534 7431 Fax: (020) 8519 8768 *Filter cloth & bag manufrs*

J P Forrest & Son Ltd, Claylands Avenue, Worksop, Nottinghamshire, S81 7DJ Tel: (01909) 472031 Fax: (01909) 530124 E-mail: sales@jpforrest.com *Steel fabricators & machinery manufrs*

J & P Furniture Ltd, 5-8 Fenn Field Units, Homefield Road, Haverhill, Suffolk, CB9 8QU Tel: (01440) 702592 Fax: (01440) 707079 E-mail: sales@jpfurniture.co.uk *Furniture manufrs*

J P G Site Services Ltd, Kerry Road Works, Kerry Road, Newtown, Powys, SY16 1DX Tel: (01686) 624815 Fax: (01686) 629336 *Metal fabrication & fitters*

J & P Graphics International, 3, Lowerfold Drive, Shawclough, Rochdale, Lancashire, OL12 7JA Tel: (01706) 358055 Fax: 0845 280 2822 E-mail: jbrown5710@aol.com *Heidelberg Printers Engineers*

J P Griffiths, Newton Hall Farm, Saughall Massie Road, West Kirby, Wirral, Merseyside, CH48 1PQ Tel: 0151-625 5990 Fax: 0151-625 5775 *Agricultural contractors*

J P Hygiene Supplies, Britannia Estate, Leagrave Road, Luton, LU3 1RJ Tel: (01582) 488851 Fax: (01582) 410005 E-mail: sales@jphygiene.co.uk *Protective clothing suppliers, embroidery & cleaning chemicals*

J P J Business Services, 49 Whitefield Avenue, Liverpool, L4 1XJ Tel: 0151-284 1914 Fax: 0151-284 1914 *Computers & telephone cleaners*

J P J Installations Ltd, 8 Swinbourne Drive, Springwood Industrial Estate, Braintree, Essex, CM7 2YP Tel: (01376) 528111 Fax: (01376) 528222 E-mail: jpj@btconnect.com *Architectural aluminium*

▶ J P J Supplies, 9 Menmarsh Road, Worminghall, Aylesbury, Buckinghamshire, HP18 9JX Tel: (01844) 338312 Fax: (01844) 338312 *Janitorial suppliers*

J P Joinery, Portmanmoor Road Lane, Cardiff, CF24 5EQ Tel: (029) 2049 3661 Fax: (029) 2049 1592 *Joinery furniture manufrs*

J P Kelly, 34 Market Street, Chapel-en-le-Frith, High Peak, Derbyshire, SK23 0HY Tel: (01298) 813449 Fax: (01298) 813449 E-mail: kellyj45@btinternet.com *Joinery manufrs*

▶ J P Kennedy Construction Co. Ltd, Unit 5 Watling Gate, 297-303 Edgware Road, London, NW9 6NB Tel: (020) 8905 8942 Fax: (020) 8200 6124

J P Knight Ltd, Admirals Offices Main Gate Road, The Historic Dockyard, Chatham, Kent, ME4 4TZ Tel: (01634) 826633 Fax: (01634) 829093 E-mail: info@jpknight.com *Tug owners*

J P Knight & Sons Ltd, 98 Frindsbury Road, Rochester, Kent, ME2 4JB Tel: (01634) 723088 Fax: (01634) 722784 *Window blinds, awnings & canopies suppliers*

J P Knitwear, 36-38 Nansen Road, Leicester, LE5 5FX Tel: 0116-249 0991 Fax: 0116-249 0991 *Knitwear manufrs*

J P L Clothing Ltd, Victoria Street, Darwen, Lancashire, BB3 3HB Tel: (01254) 873922 Fax: (01254) 762362 *Clothing & fabric manufrs*

J P L Services, 15 High Street, Rampton, Cambridge, CB24 8QE Tel: (01954) 250851 Fax: (01954) 250543 *Power & lighting contractors*

▶ J P L Sound & Communications, 267 Holton Road, Barry, South Glamorgan, CF63 4HT Tel: (01446) 722711 Fax: (01446) 722711 E-mail: info@jplsound.com *Event sound contractors*

J P L Steel Stock Ltd, Pinfold Road, Thurmaston, Leicester, LE4 8AS Tel: 0116-260 6464 Fax: 0116-260 6808 E-mail: sales@jplsteelstock.co.uk *Steel stockholders*

J P Lennard Ltd, Hadrians Way, Glebe Farm Industrial Estate, Rugby, Warwickshire, CV21 1ST Tel: (01788) 544839 Fax: (01788) 541851 E-mail: sales@jpl.co.uk *Sporting goods distributors*

▶ J P Lifting Ltd, 95 Dover Avenue, Banbury, Oxfordshire, OX16 0JH Tel: (01295) 261126 Fax: (01295) 261126 E-mail: jclifting@btconnect.com *Crane hire services*

J P M Associates, 322 Upper Shoreham Rd, Shoreham-by-Sea, West Sussex, BN43 6BA Tel: (01273) 452305 Fax: (01273) 464228 E-mail: jpm_associates@compuserve.com *Computer consultants services*

J P M International, B4, South Point, Foreshore Road, Cardiff, CF10 4SP Tel: 0121-717 7111 Fax: (029) 2046 7399 E-mail: customerservices@jpm.co.uk *Amusement machine manufrs*

J P M Pressbrake Sections Ltd, Level Street, Brierley Hill, West Midlands, DY5 1UE Tel: (01384) 263691 Fax: (01384) 480126 *Steel & aluminium rain water goods manufrs*

J P Miles, Sophurst Wood Lane, Matfield, Tonbridge, Kent, TN12 7LH Tel: (01892) 724315 Fax: (01892) 724319 E-mail: jpmiles@seedersti.co.uk *Hose (hydraulic) assembly services*

J P Morgan Financial Investments Ltd, 60 Victoria Embkmt, London, EC4Y 0JP Tel: (020) 7600 2300 *Brokers*

J.P. Morgan Fleming Asset Management, 10 Aldermanbury, London, EC2V 7RF Tel: (020) 7742 6000 Fax: (020) 7742 8000 *Pension & investment consultants*

▶ J P Naylor Co., Woodside Business Park Beach Hay, Bayton, Kidderminster, Worcestershire, DY14 9NE Tel: (01299) 832726 Fax: (01299) 832779

J P Olives Ltd, 31a Heming Road, Redditch, Worcestershire, B98 0DH Tel: (01527) 516600 Fax: (01527) 516611 E-mail: sales@jpolives.co.uk *Tubular turned part manufrs*

J P Pine Ltd, Unit 8 Cci Business Pk, St. Asaph Av, Kinmel Bay, Rhyl, Clwyd, LL18 5HA Tel: 01745 369091 *Pine furniture suppliers*

J P Polymer Sheetings Ltd, Coneygre Industrial Estate, Tipton, West Midlands, DY4 8XP Tel: 0121-520 5020 Fax: 0121-522 4610 E-mail: sales@jppolymer.co.uk *Flooring & sheeting distributors*

J P Precision Engineering, Unit 14a Shrub Hill, Worcester, WR4 9EL Tel: (01905) 20319 Fax: (01905) 20319 *Precision machining*

▶ J P Price (Plumbers), Paragon House, 8 Milltown Street, Radcliffe, Manchester, M26 1WD Tel: 0161-723 2830 Fax: 0161-724 1020

▶ J & P Print Packaging Services Ltd, Unit 9 Ditchling Common, Ditchling, Hassocks, West Sussex, BN6 8SG Tel: (01444) 412510 Fax: (01444) 239039 E-mail: info@jpprintservicesltd.co.uk *Services to the print & packaging industry*

J P Prints & Signs, Pantone House, 124 Abertillery Road, Blaina, Gwent, NP13 3DR Tel: (01495) 291795 Fax: (01495) 291716 E-mail: john@jpprint.co.uk *Printers & sign manufrs*

J P Products (Chemicals) Ltd, 1-3 Evanton Place, Thornliebank Industrial Estate, Glasgow, G46 8SN Tel: 0141-638 0149 Fax: 0141-638 9388 *Janitorial goods suppliers*

J P Programming Ltd, 6 Lark Cl, Leicester Forest East, Leicester, LE3 3NX Tel: 0116-238 6758 *Computer programming*

J P Pumps Ltd, Meadow Brook Industrial Centre, Maxwell Way, Crawley, West Sussex, RH10 9SA Tel: (01293) 553495 Fax: (01293) 524635 E-mail: mailbox.uk@johnson-pump.com *Engines, pumps & rotating equipment*

J P R, Belmont Office Park, 232-240 Belmont Road, Belfast, BT4 2AW Tel: (028) 9076 0066 Fax: (028) 9076 0011 E-mail: mail@jprni.com *Public relations services*

J P R Structural Remedy, 59 New Dock Road, Llanelli, Dyfed, SA15 2EH Tel: (01554) 757549 *Builders*

J P S Lampshades, 1 Manchester Road, London, N15 6HP Tel: (020) 8800 1769 *Lampshade manufrs*

J P S Windings Ltd, 1a Shaftesbury Road, Reading, RG30 2QR Tel: 0118-959 9344 *Transformer manufrs*

J P Services, 39 Willow Drive, Airdrie, Lanarkshire, ML6 8AN Tel: (0800) 0730238 Fax: (01236) 603775 E-mail: jpservices39@yahoo.co.uk *Suppliers & fitters of quality conservatory blinds*

J P Services, 55a High Street, Marlow, Buckinghamshire, SL7 1BA Tel: (01628) 485533 Fax: (01628) 477606 E-mail: sales@jpscientific.com *Antivibration products*

J & P Supplies Ltd, Junction Road, Audnam, Stourbridge, West Midlands, DY8 4YH Tel: (01384) 393329 Fax: (01384) 440212 E-mail: info@jpsupplies.co.uk *Solenoid valves, expansion joints & industrial pipeline distributors*

▶ J P Tisdale Demolition Ltd, Dock Road, Liverpool, L19 2JN Tel: 0151-427 7906

J & P UK Ltd, 16 Hanover Street, London, W1S 1YL Tel: (020) 7493 6493 Fax: (020) 7493 0059 E-mail: sales@jandp.org *Services for construction & engineering industry*

▶ J & P Vehicle Deliveries Ltd, 1 Green Acre Park, Howard Street, Bolton, BL1 8HN Tel: (01204) 366464 Fax: (01204) 373465

▶ J P Wild Ltd, 149 Dewsbury Road, Leeds, LS11 5NW Tel: 0113-277 4944

J Parker & Son Ltd, The Weind, Great Eccleston, Preston, PR3 0ZU Tel: (01995) 670173 Fax: (01995) 671325 *Cooked meat manufrs*

J Parkinson & Sons Ltd, 3 Hampson Lane, Hampson, Lancaster, LA2 0HY Tel: (01524) 753301 Fax: (01524) 753302 E-mail: bcampbell@askam.co.uk *Building & civil engineers*

J Parlour & Son, South Otterington, Northallerton, North Yorkshire, DL7 9HJ Tel: (01609) 773607 Fax: (01609) 778405 E-mail: johns@jparlour.fslife.co.uk *Agriculture Engineers, Farm machinery hire, Fabrication, Repairs and Spares*

▶ J Pepper Plastering, 56A Tannery Drift, Royston, Hertfordshire, SG8 5DE Tel: 01763 247406 Fax: 01763 243888 E-mail: sales@jpepperplastering.co.uk *East Anglia's premier plasterers specialising in Plastering, Screeding, Dry Lining, Rendering, Pargetting and Pebble Dashing*

J Perkins, Ashford Road, Lenham, Maidstone, Kent, ME17 2DL Tel: (01622) 854300 Fax: (01622) 854301 E-mail: jpmail@jpmodels.co.uk *Model & hobby distributors*

J Pitchford & Son, Bolventure, Betley Lane, Bayston Hill, Shrewsbury, SY3 0HB Tel: (01743) 872155 *Carpentry & joinery*

J Pratley & Sons Ltd, Pingemead Farm, Pingewood, Reading, RG30 3UR Tel: 0118-975 7500 Fax: 0118-975 6787 E-mail: sales@j.pratleysons.co.uk *Steel & welding fabricators*

J Preedy & Sons Ltd, Lamb Works, North Road, London, N7 9DP Tel: (020) 7700 0377 Fax: (020) 7700 7579 E-mail: sales@preedyglass.com *Glass processors*

J Prescott, Lesser Marsh Farm, Station Road, Little Hoole, Preston, PR4 5LH Tel: (01772) 613688 Fax: (01772) 619561 *Horse box builders*

J Preston & Son, Pitt Street, Widnes, Cheshire, WA8 0TG Tel: 0151-424 3718 Fax: 0151-495 2360 E-mail: sales@prestonsofwidnes.co.uk *Steel fabricators & blacksmiths*

J Pullan & Sons Ltd, Sunnyview Gardens, Leeds, LS11 8QT Tel: 0113-271 7221 Fax: 0113-271 9238 E-mail: general@pullans.com *Building contractors*

J R B Enterprises Ltd, Dixies Development, High Street, Ashwell, Baldock, Hertfordshire, SG7 5NT Tel: (01462) 742157 Fax: (01462) 742088 E-mail: johnrbonnett@aol.com *We are an export consultancy & trading house specialising in FMCG's. Specialising in the Middle East & Africa*

J R Bourne Powder Coatings Ltd, Beckingham Road, Great Totham, Maldon, Essex, CM9 8EA Tel: (01621) 892972 Fax: (01621) 893299 E-mail: sales@jrbourne.co.uk *Drawing office equipment manufrs*

J R Camping Ltd, Egginton Road, Hilton, Derby, DE65 5FJ Tel: (01283) 733525 Fax: (01283) 734812 E-mail: derby@jrleisure.com *Camping equipment retailers*

J R Colston & Co., 119 Godstow Road, Wolvercote, Oxford, OX2 8PG Tel: (01865) 553483 Fax: (01865) 554043 *Electrical contractors*

J R Computer Services, 58 Elmroyd Avenue, Potters Bar, Hertfordshire, EN6 2EF Tel: (01707) 655185 Fax: (01707) 655185 *Computer consultants*

J R Concrete, Harcourt Street, Worsley, Manchester, M28 3GN Tel: (01204) 571004 *Concrete fencing*

J R Cooper Ltd, 39a Church Street, Gamlingay, Sandy, Bedfordshire, SG19 3JJ Tel: (01767) 650763 Fax: (01767) 651273 E-mail: sales@jrcooperltd.co.uk *Plastics injection mouldings manufrs*

J R Crompton U S A Ltd, 12th Floor, Sunlight House, Manchester, M3 3JZ Tel: 0161-817 6500 Fax: 0161-817 6506 E-mail: info@crompton.co.uk *Paper makers*

J R D Bipel Ltd, Unit 4 Merryhills House, Middlemore Lane West, Aldridge, Walsall, WS9 8BG Tel: (01922) 451245 Fax: (01922) 743040 E-mail: sales@jrdbipel.com *Manufacturer of high specification hydraulic presses*

▶ J R D Construction Ltd, Unit 2 65 South Street, Ilkeston, Derbyshire, DE7 5QQ Tel: 0115-944 7077 Fax: 0115-944 7859

▶ J R D Demolition Ltd, 7 Somervell Street, Cambuslang, Glasgow, G72 7EB Tel: 0141-641 7771 Fax: 0141-641 7771

J R D Engineers Ltd, 5 Willow Road, Poyle Trading Estate, Colnbrook, Slough, SL3 0BU Tel: (01753) 682665 Fax: (01753) 681475 *Marine diesel injection pumps manufrs*

J R E Dinnage Ltd, 158 Eltham Hill, London, SE9 5EA Tel: (020) 8850 5572 Fax: (020) 8850 2009 E-mail: jredinnage@hotmail.com *Heating & plumbing engineers*

▶ J & R Elliot Ltd, 30 Commercial Road, Hawick, Roxburghshire, TD9 7AD Tel: (01450) 372493 Fax: (01450) 377790

▶ J R Elliott, Rigg Farm, Auchinleck, Cumnock, Ayrshire, KA18 1RT Tel: (01290) 420000 Fax: (01290) 422113

J & R Engineering, 29 Willow Lane, Mitcham, Surrey, CR4 4NA Tel: (020) 8640 9028 *Precision engineering services*

J R F Chimney Specialists Ltd, 50 Nasmyth Road, Glenrothes, Fife, KY6 2SD Tel: (01592) 771199 Fax: (01592) 771135 E-mail: info@jrf-chimney-spec.co.uk *Chimney & gas vent distributors*

J R G Engineering Services Ltd, 7 Weaver St, Kirkstall Rd, Leeds, LS4 2AU Tel: 0113-263 8731 Fax: 0113-231 0294 *Effluent treatment plant manufrs*

▶ J R G Fire Surrounds Ltd, 214 Western Road, Kilmarnock, Ayrshire, KA3 1NJ Tel: (01563) 572111

J R H Bio Sciences Ltd, West Portway, Andover, Hampshire, SP10 3LF Tel: (01264) 333311 Fax: (01264) 332412 E-mail: info@jrheurope.com *Cell culture material manufrs*

▶ J R H Electrical Contractors Ltd, Unit A, Ashleigh Mews, Woodland Grove, Blackpool, FY3 9HD Tel: (01253) 390002 Fax: (01253) 390003 E-mail: info@jrh-electrical.com *Electrical installation contractor*

▶ J R H Enterprises, 33 Iveagh Close, Hackney, London, E9 7BW Tel: (020) 8525 0926 Fax: (020) 8525 0926 E-mail: sales@jrhenterprises.co.uk *Promotional/ Giftware printing*we specialise in sublimation printing. We also stock the Koolart range of transfers for mugs,t-shirts,polo shirts,mousemats,clocks,caps.We are the sole distributor of Bob Bonds Football Caricatures.*

continued

J & R Hall Joinery Ltd, Deanroyd Works, Deanroyd Road, Todmorden, Lancashire, OL14 6TX Tel: (01706) 810300 Fax: (01706) 810400 E-mail: jrhalljoinery@zen.co.uk *Manufacturers of wooden pallets & timber cases*

▶ J R Harding & Sons Frome Ltd, Manor Furlong, Frome, Somerset, BA11 4RJ Tel: (01373) 465581 Fax: (01373) 467352 E-mail: enquiries@jrhardings.co.uk

J & R Hateley Ltd, Lockside Tat Bank Road, Oldbury, West Midlands, B69 4NS Tel: 0121-544 6327 Fax: 0121-552 1150 *Window frame joinery & manufrs*

J R Hill & Sons Ltd, Broad Platt Croft, Broad Platt, Rotherfield Greys, Henley-on-Thames, Oxfordshire, RG9 4PD Tel: (01491) 628533 Fax: (01491) 628770 E-mail: jrhillwelding@aol.com *Contract welding & fabricators*

▶ J R Holland Food Services Ltd, 245 Dukesway, Team Valley Trading Estate, Gateshead, Tyne & Wear, NE11 0PZ Tel: 0191-491 0856 Fax: 0191-487 9021

J R Hood Ltd, Chesney Farm, Wansford Road, Driffield, North Humberside, YO25 5NW Tel: (01377) 252135 Fax: (01377) 252958 *General haulage*

J R I Ltd, Unit 18, Sheffield 35A Business Park, Churchill Way, Chapeltown, Sheffield, S35 2PY Tel: 0114-257 3200 Fax: 0114-257 3204 E-mail: manufacturing@jri-ltd.co.uk *Orthopaedic implant manufrs*

J R J Engineering, Ty Isaf, Llangennech, Llanelli, Dyfed, SA14 8UU Tel: (01554) 820464 Fax: (01554) 820070 E-mail: jrjengineering@btconnect.com *General engineers*

J R K & Co, Flat 61, Jepson Ho, Pearscroft Rd, London, SW6 2BG Tel: 020 77369012 *Computer services*

J R K Campbell & Co., Camling, Tynron, Thornhill, Dumfriesshire, DG3 4JS Tel: (01848) 330419 Fax: (01848) 330833 *Agricultural merchants*

▶ J R K Computer Supplies, Unit 27 Wombourne Enterprise Park, Bridgnorth Road, Wombourne, Wolverhampton, WV5 0AL Tel: (01902) 326426 Fax: (01902) 326323 E-mail: jrkkay@talk21.com *Computer systems, printers, consumables, toners & cartridges suppliers*

J & R Killick Ltd, 47 Station Approach, Hayes, Bromley, BR2 7EB Tel: (020) 8462 1009 Fax: (020) 8777 2744 *Property maintenance services* Also at: West Wickham

J R Leisure, 50 Oswin Road, Leicester, LE3 1HR Tel: 0116-247 0740 Fax: 0116-247 0865 *Camping & leisure suppliers*

▶ J R Livingstone & Co., Unit 6, Montgomery Place, Irvine, Ayrshire, KA12 8PN Tel: (01294) 275000

J R Lowry, Little Windsor Road, Southport, Merseyside, PR9 0RZ Tel: (01704) 537225 Fax: (01704) 537225 E-mail: ampdude@fsnet.co.uk *Joinery*

J & R M Richardson Construction Darlington Ltd, Trinity Hall, Portland Place, Darlington, County Durham, DL3 7BP Tel: (01325) 466688 Fax: (01325) 483311 E-mail: mail@richardson-construction.co.uk

J & R Marble Company Ltd, Unit 9, Period Works, London, E10 7QT Tel: (020) 8539 6471 Fax: (020) 8539 9264 E-mail: sales@jrmarble.co.uk *Slate, marble & granite merchants*

J R Marriott Collingham Ltd, Brunel Drive, Newark, Nottinghamshire, NG24 2EG Tel: (01636) 703800 Fax: (01636) 605254 *Road transport, haulage & freight services*

J R Marshall Farmer, Lower Mead Farm, Newton Abbot, Devon, TQ13 7LJ Tel: (01364) 652466 Fax: 01364 652466 *Floral & plant displays*

J R Nobbs & Sons Ltd, Rembrandt House, King Georges Avenue, Watford, WD18 7PW Tel: (01923) 234176 Fax: (01923) 211146 E-mail: sales@imp-engineering.co.uk *Fine limit sheet metalworkers*

J R Parkin Ltd, Whiteheads Mill, Young St, Bradford, West Yorkshire, BD8 9RQ Tel: (01274) 498567 Fax: (01274) 482023 E-mail: ian@jrparkin.wanadoo.co.uk *Bag & tarpaulin manufrs* Also at: Melton Constable

J R Pitchers Ltd, Selby Place, Great Yarmouth, Norfolk, NR30 3LG Tel: (01493) 843947 Fax: (01493) 857172 E-mail: jrpitchersltd@btconnect.com *Motor vehicle repair services & mot testing station*

J R Plant Services Ltd, 6 Cedar Ave, Connah's Quay, Deeside, Clwyd, CH5 4BE Tel: (01244) 810306 *Concrete batching plant & fabrication maintenance*

J & R Plastics Ltd, 30 Montipilier Rise, Golders Green, London, NW11 9DS Tel: (07957) 627143 E-mail: jrplastics@hotmail.com *Plastic vacuum form services*

J R Powell, Rectory Farm, Poundon, Bicester, Oxfordshire, OX27 9BE Tel: (01869) 278877 Fax: (01869) 278067 *Mechanical engineers*

J R Power Transmission Scotland Ltd, Faraday Street, Dryburgh Industrial Estate, Dundee, DD2 3QQ Tel: (01382) 813677 Fax: (01382) 833925 E-mail: info@jrpower.co.uk *Industrial power equipment distributors & conveyor belt manufrs*

▶ J R Press, 29 Brunel Close, Drayton Fields Industrial Estate, Daventry, Northamptonshire, NN11 8RB Tel: (01327) 301566 Fax: (01327) 301410 E-mail: sales@jrpress.co.uk

▶ J R R Engineering Ltd, 37 Highmeres Road, Leicester, LE4 9LZ Tel: 0116-276 8801 Fax: 0116-246 0015 *Metal fabrications*

J R Rix & Sons Ltd, 45 Spyvee Street, Hull, HU8 7JJ Tel: (01482) 222250 Fax: (01482) 338590 *Ship owners & fuel oil distributors*

J R Roberts & Sons, 67 Eagle Road, Wembley, Middlesex, HA0 4SL Tel: (020) 8903 1884 Fax: (020) 8903 1884 *Vehicle security systems installation & servicing*

J R Roofing Co. Ltd, 5 Swinburne Avenue, Hitchin, Hertfordshire, SG5 2RG Tel: (01462) 422300 Fax: (01462) 421342 E-mail: services@jr-roofing.co.uk *Roofing contractors & merchants*

J R Rubber & Polyurethane Products Ltd, Unit 28, Meadows Road, Queensway Meadows Industrial Estate, Newport, Gwent, NP19 4SS Tel: (01633) 270088 Fax: (01633) 278232 E-mail: info@jr-rubber.com Principal Export Areas: Africa *Polyurethane, rubber, rubber mouldings & tank liner manufrs*

J R S Fabrication Engineers Ltd, 3 Vauxhall Industrial Estate, Greg Street, Stockport, Cheshire, SK5 7BR Tel: 0161-477 4313 Fax: 0161-477 4616 *Metal stair case manufrs*

J R S Packaging Ltd, Unit 6, The Vineyards Industrial Estate, Gloucester Road, Cheltenham, Gloucestershire, GL51 8NJ Tel: (01242) 226269 Fax: (01242) 261954 E-mail: jrspackaging@lineone.net *Shrink wrap packaging services*

J R S Rewinds, 71 Halifax Road, Maidenhead, Berkshire, SL6 5ES Tel: (01628) 628964 Fax: (01628) 672333 *Electric motor rewind specialists design services*

J R S Roller Shutter Doors, Unit B8 Valleys Enterprise Centre, Merthyr Tydfil Industrial Park, Pentrebach, Merthyr Tydfil, Mid Glamorgan, CF48 4DR Tel: (01443) 692962 Fax: (01443) 692912 *Rolling shutter manufrs*

▶ J & R Seating, 31 Heol Tir Coed, Penllergaer, Swansea, SA4 9QZ Tel: (01792) 899726

▶ J R Smith, 2 Cambuslea Road, Ayr, KA8 9HT Tel: (01292) 269499 Fax: (01292) 284631 E-mail: sales@johnrsmith.co.uk

J R Smith, East Redmyre Farm, Allanton Road, Shotts, Lanarkshire, ML7 5AH Tel: (01501) 821517 Fax: (01501) 821517 *Steel fabrication*

▶ J R Smith Transport Ltd, Langdon Street, Tring, Hertfordshire, HP23 6DJ Tel: (0844) 3578282 Fax: (0870) 0664380 E-mail: info@jrsmith.co.uk

J R Spalding, 55 Mill Street, Kingston upon Thames, Surrey, KT1 2RG Tel: (020) 8546 0363 Fax: (020) 8546 0363 E-mail: jrspalding.joinery@amserve.net *Specialist woodworkers*

J & R Starbuck, Chandlery House, Warrior Way, Pembroke Dock, Dyfed, SA72 6UB Tel: (01474) 350671 Fax: (01474) 536788 E-mail: sales@jrstarbuck.co.uk *Ship chandlers*

J & R Steel Fabrications Ltd, Unit 5a Caxton Trading Estate, Printing House Lane, Hayes, Middlesex, UB3 1BE Tel: (020) 8569 0129 Fax: (020) 8569 0139 *Steel fabricators*

J R Stones, 4 Rose Hill, Dorking, Surrey, RH4 2EG Tel: (01306) 886754 Fax: (01306) 886754 *Computer consultants*

J & R Stores Ltd, Catfoot Lane, Lambley, Nottingham, NG4 4QG Tel: 0115-920 4152 Fax: 0115-920 4152 E-mail: lanley@grleisure.com *Camping equipment*

J R Technology Ltd, 81 North End, Meldreth, Royston, Hertfordshire, SG8 6NU Tel: (01763) 260721 Fax: (01763) 260809 E-mail: enquiries@jrtech.co.uk *Plastics, composite & adhesive metal bonded workshop services*

J R Trolleys Ltd, Hartwell Farm, 25 Court Road, Cranfield, Bedford, MK43 0DX Tel: (01234) 751188 Fax: (01234) 750193 E-mail: info@jrtrolleys.co.uk *Steel & non-ferrous metal fabricators*

J R Tusting & Co. Ltd, The Tannery Warehouse, 29-31 Olney Road, Lavendon, Olney, Buckinghamshire, MK46 4EU Tel: (01234) 712266 Fax: (01234) 713545 E-mail: info@tusting.co.uk *Leather goods manufrs*

J R Tyson & Sons Ltd, 5 Rawreth Industrial Estate, Rawreth Lane, Rayleigh, Essex, SS6 9RL Tel: (01268) 783555 Fax: (01268) 782655 *Stove enamellers services*

J R Webster, Unit 1 Prince William Avenue, Sandycroft, Deeside, Clwyd, CH5 2QZ Tel: (01244) 534747 Fax: (01244) 535866 E-mail: kwalker.jrw@cuk.com *Special fastener distributors* Also at: Ellesmere Port, Flint, Knowsley, Wallesey, Widnes & Wrexham

J R Wooddisse & Co. Ltd, Dale Street, Bilston, West Midlands, WV14 7LE Tel: (01902) 494336 Fax: (01902) 354953 *Approved wheelchair repairers*

J Reid Engineering Ltd, Factory Road, Sandycroft, Deeside, Clwyd, CH5 2QJ Tel: (01244) 520688 Fax: (01244) 525921 E-mail: linda@jreidtrading.demon.co.uk *Shot blast equipment manufrs*

▶ J Revis & Sons, Southfield Lane, Tockwith, York, YO26 7QP Tel: (01423) 358181 Fax: (01423) 358051

J Roberts & Son Ltd, 22 Wyvil Road, London, SW8 2TG Tel: (020) 7622 1131 Fax: (020) 7627 4442 E-mail: shop@jroberts-gunmakers.co.uk *Sporting shotguns & rifle manufrs*

▶ J Robertson, 1 Edinburgh Road, Cleghorn, Lanark, ML11 7RW Tel: (01555) 665084 Fax: (01555) 673819

J Robertson, Mill Lane, Walton on the Naze, Essex, CO14 8PF Tel: (01255) 672855 Fax: (01255) 850487 *Steel fabricators*

J Robinson Engineering Ltd, 12 Clarence Road, Fleet, Hampshire, GU51 3RZ Tel: (01252) 621312 Fax: (01252) 819100 E-mail: jim@jrobinsoneng.fsnet.co.uk *Diesel & petrol generator suppliers*

J Rosenfeld & Sons, 11 Hatton Garden, London, EC1N 8AH Tel: (020) 7831 3470 Fax: (020) 7430 1137 *Precious stone merchants & jewellery manufrs*

J Rostron Engineering Ltd, Lindred Road, Brierfield, Nelson, Lancashire, BB9 5SR Tel: (01282) 611110 Fax: (01282) 619961 E-mail: sales@rostron.co.uk *Industrial drying equipment suppliers*

▶ J Rutherford Contractors Hutton Ltd, Hutton Crofts, Hutton, Berwick-upon-Tweed, TD15 1TS Tel: (01289) 386226 Fax: (01289) 386256

J Rutherford Earlston Ltd, Swinton Mill Farm, Coldstream, Berwickshire, TD12 4JS Tel: (01890) 840458 Fax: (01890) 840461 E-mail: smill@rutherford-earlston.co.uk *Agricultural engineers*

J S A Mechanical Services Ltd, Unit 28 Croft Road Industrial Estate, Croft Road, Newcastle, Staffordshire, ST5 0TW Tel: (01782) 635517 Fax: (01782) 630485 *Heating, plumbing & industrial pipework*

J S B (Metals) Ltd, Factory Road, Blaydon-on-Tyne, Tyne & Wear, NE21 5RZ Tel: 0191-414 8989 Fax: 0191-414 1191 *Scrap metal merchants*

▶ J S B Plastics, Unit 2a Knighton Junction Lane, Leicester, LE2 6AR Tel: 0116-244 8049 Fax: 0116-270 2032 *Injection moulding manufrs*

J S B Tarbert Ltd, 24 Harbour Street, Tarbert, Argyll, PA29 6UD Tel: (01880) 820180 Fax: (01880) 820180 *Ship builders, repairs & fittings*

▶ J S B Training & Consulting, Dove House, Arcadia Avenue, London, N3 2JU Tel: (020) 8371 7000 Fax: (020) 8371 7001 E-mail: enquiries@jsbonline.com *Management training & consulting*

J S Bamforth & Co. Ltd, Top Vale Works, Colne Vale Road, Huddersfield, HD3 4NY Tel: (01484) 652777 Fax: (01484) 461460 *Scrap metal merchants*

▶ J. S. Bruce Engineering, 5 French Street, Ashton-under-Lyne, Lancashire, OL6 9PP Tel: 0161 3399476 Fax: 0161 3399476 E-mail: john@jsbruceengineering.co.uk *UK agent for Somex automation equipment. Northern distributor for Vacmagic vacuum pallet changer and work holding units. *Tw-in pro magnetic drill vice. Special purpose machine tools. Machine re-building and re- engineering.*

J S Burgess Engineering Ltd, Units 18-20, Bingswood Trading Estate, Whaley Bridge, High Peak, Derbyshire, SK23 7LY Tel: (01663) 719300 Fax: (01663) 719301 *Steel pallets manufrs*

▶ J S C Installations, Charlton Avenue, Eccles, Manchester, M30 0JQ Tel: 0161-211 9842 E-mail: enquiries@jscinstallations.co.uk *Installations of all kinds from telecommunications to access control*

▶ J S C International Ltd, Simpson House 11 Windsor Court, Clarence Drive, Harrogate, North Yorkshire, HG1 2PE Tel: (01423) 520245 Fax: (01423) 520297 E-mail: enquires@jsci.co.uk *Regulatory & environmental risk assessment to government & authorities*

J S Cantrill Designs & Manufacturing Holdings Ltd, Chosen View Road, Cheltenham, Gloucestershire, GL51 9LT Tel: (01242) 515794 Fax: (01242) 579265 E-mail: sales@cantrillmanufacturing.com *Manufacturers of aerospace items & precision engineers*

J S Clayton Ltd, Chiddingstone Causeway, Tonbridge, Kent, TN11 8JP Tel: (01892) 871111 Fax: (01892) 871122 E-mail: info@claytonfirstaid.com *Manufacturers of the CLAYTON first aid kit. Distributors of allied medical brands for the healthcare market.*

▶ J S Clayton Plant Hire Ltd, Unit 1a Sefton La Industrial Estate, Liverpool, L31 8BX Tel: 0151-531 1210 Fax: 0151-531 9600 E-mail: jsclaytonplanthire@hotmail.com *Plant Hire.*

J S Cleaning Supplies, 12 Charles Berrington Road, Liverpool, L15 9HQ Tel: 0151-722 3966 *Cleaning materials suppliers*

J S Computer Services Ltd, 61 Pinnocks Lane, Baldock, Hertfordshire, SG7 6DD Tel: (01462) 641556 Fax: (01462) 641557 E-mail: jscomputerservices@yahoo.co.uk *Computer maintenance for hardware & software*

▶ J & S Computing, 114 Abbey Street, Nuneaton, Warwickshire, CV11 5BX Tel: (024) 7675 7672 Fax: (024) 7638 5178

▶ J S Crawford Contracts (Borders) Ltd, Priorwood, Melrose, Roxburghshire, TD6 9EG Tel: (01896) 822030 Fax: (01896) 823359 E-mail: sales@jscrawford.co.uk

J S D Polishers Ltd, 19-21 Hatchett Street, Hockley, Birmingham, B19 3NX Tel: 0121-359 4880 Fax: 0121-359 4880 *Polishing services*

J S D Products (UK) Ltd, 84 Tippendell Lane, Park Street, St. Albans, Hertfordshire, AL2 2HD Tel: (01727) 875660 Fax: (01727) 875659 E-mail: info@jsdproducts.co.uk *Providers of high quality Lemon Wraps and elasticated Lemon Wedge Bags.*

J S Drew, 856 Plymouth Road, Slough, SL1 4LP Tel: (01753) 568181 Fax: (01753) 568121 E-mail: jsdrewengravers@aol.com *Machine & hand engravers*

▶ J S Electrics Bookham, 36 Strathcona Avenue, Bookham, Leatherhead, Surrey, KT23 4HP Tel: (01372) 452617 *electrical domestic appliance repairs surrey*

J S Engineering, 102 Commercial Road, Skelmanthorpe, Huddersfield, HD8 9DS Tel: (01484) 866254 Fax: (01484) 866255 E-mail: jsengineeringuk@aol.com *Nuclear instrumentation in industry*

▶ J S F Installations, 185 Garth Twentyfour, Killingworth, Newcastle Upon Tyne, NE12 6DJ Tel: 0191-268 5375 Fax: 0191-268 5375 *Curtain walling & doors manufrs*

J S Fire Protection Ltd, 4 Mews Road, St. Leonards-on-Sea, East Sussex, TN38 0EA Tel: (01424) 428174 *Fire extinguishers & alarms suppliers & installation services*

J S Fishdirect, 25 Princes Street, Pembroke Dock, Dyfed, SA72 6XT Tel: (07876) 715409 Fax: (01646) 680041 E-mail: info@jsfishdirect.co.uk *Wet fish & shell fish merchants*

J & S Franklin Holdings & Management Services Ltd, Franklin House, 151 Strand, London, WC2R 1HL Tel: (020) 7836 2762 Fax: (020) 7836 2784 E-mail: defence@franklin.co.uk *Military & civil equipment suppliers*

J S Fraser (Oxford) Ltd, Cotswold Dene, Standlake, Witney, Oxfordshire, OX29 7PL Tel: (01865) 303014 Fax: (01865) 303015 E-mail: sales@jsfraser.com *Commercial vehicle bodybuilders & repairers*

J S G Engineering, Unit 3/4, Wren Centre, Westbourne Road, Emsworth, Hampshire, PO10 7SU Tel: (01243) 379698 Fax: (01243) 379857 E-mail: jim@jsgeng.fsnet.co.uk *Plastic & rubber mould manufrs*

J S G Hydraulics, Unit E2 Enterprise Way, Bradford Road, Idle, Bradford, West Yorkshire, BD10 8EW Tel: (01274) 615800 Fax: (01274) 615552 *Hydraulic pump maintenance & repair services*

J & S Horn Consultants Ltd, 24 Henderson Drive, Skene, Westhill, Aberdeenshire, AB32 6RA Tel: (01224) 744330 Fax: (01224) 744330 E-mail: training@peakperformance.tv *Bookkeeping & admin services, training services*

J S Hubbuck Ltd, Anick Road, Hexham, Northumberland, NE46 4JS Tel: (01434) 601673 Fax: (01434) 605609 E-mail: catherine@hubbucks.freeserve.co.uk *Agricultural feed & fertiliser suppliers*

J & S Industrial Coatings Ltd, Unit 16 17 Old Mill Park, Kirkintilloch, Glasgow, G66 1SS Tel: 0141-775 2233 Fax: 0141-775 1999 *Decorative & industrial finishes*

J S J Precision, Milburn Road, Stoke-on-Trent, ST6 2QF Tel: (01782) 269694 Fax: (01782) 279138 *Precision sheet metal, folding, fabrication & welding services*

J S M Business Gifts, 9 St. Albans Road, Gloucester, GL2 5FW Tel: (01452) 310030 Fax: (01452) 304454 *Promotional & business gift house*

J S M Deeside Ltd, Station Road, Sandycroft, Deeside, Flintshire, CH5 2PT Tel: (01244) 535827 Fax: (01244) 535635 *General engineers*

J S M Engineering Ltd, Units 5-7 Humber Works, Humber Road, Beeston, Nottingham, NG9 2ET Tel: 0115-922 3849 Fax: 0115-922 3865 E-mail: sales@jsmeng.com *Architectural metalworkers*

J S M Joinery, 390 Sydenham Road, Croydon, CR0 2EA Tel: (0800) 7316345 Fax: (020) 8683 0404 E-mail: info@slhardwoods.co.uk *Joinery manufrs*

J S M Signs Ltd, Unit 24a Daniels Industrial Estate, Bath Road, Stroud, Gloucestershire, GL5 3TJ Tel: (01453) 751812 Fax: (01453) 751999 E-mail: jsm.signs@btconnect.com *Sign manufrs*

J & S Marine Ltd, Riverside Road, Pottington Business Park, Barnstaple, Devon, EX31 1LY Tel: (01271) 337500 Fax: (01271) 337501 E-mail: sales@jsmarine.co.uk *Acoustic systems, sensors, data network systems design & developers*

J S Marketing, 7 Wheler Road, Seven Stars Industrial Estate, Coventry, CV3 4LJ Tel: (024) 7651 1155 Fax: (024) 7651 8877 E-mail: sales@jsmarketing.com *Importers & distributors of mens trousers & jackets*

▶ J S P Ltd, Cotswold Innovation Centre, Rissington Business Park, Upper Rissington, Cheltenham, Gloucestershire, GL54 2QB Tel: (01451) 822534 Fax: (01451) 822304

▶ J & S Plumbing, 14 Cranmoor Crescent, Halesowen, West Midlands, B63 3TD Tel: 0121 503 0411 E-mail: enquiries@numberoneplumber.co.uk *General Plumbing, Bathrooms, Guttering, Pumps, Radiators, Showers, Outside Taps*

J S Precision Engineering, Spelthorne Lane, Ashford, Middlesex, TW15 1UX Tel: (01784) 246726 Fax: (01784) 423213 E-mail: info@jsprecisionengineering.co.uk *Precision engineers*

J & S Precision Engineering, 14a Shuttleworth Road, Elm Farm Industrial Estate, Bedford, MK41 0EP Tel: (01234) 268959 Fax: (01234) 268960 E-mail: jsengltd@btclick.com *Precision engineers*

J S Ramsbottom, Park Lane, Keighley, West Yorkshire, BD21 4QQ Tel: (01535) 605445 Fax: (01535) 602218 E-mail: sales@jsramsbottom.com *Gun rifle & revolver merchant*

J S Ridgway & Sons, The Oaklands Broadhay Lane, Lower Heath, Prees, Whitchurch, Shropshire, SY13 2BJ Tel: (01948) 840355 Fax: (01948) 840355 *Agricultural contractors*

J & S Sheet Metal Products, Unit 30 South Hampshire Industrial Park, Totton, Southampton, SO40 3SA Tel: (023) 8087 2827 Fax: (023) 8086 0033 E-mail: sales@jssheetmeta1.com *Laser cutting & sheetmetal fabrication*

J & S Simcox Ltd, Pikehelve Street, West Bromwich, West Midlands, B70 0TU Tel: 0121-557 3076 Fax: 0121-520 9674 *Steel drum merchants*

J S T Forklifts Ltd, 5 Higham Ferrers Road, Chelveston, Wellingborough, Northamptonshire, NN9 6AN Tel: (01933) 624215 Fax: (01933) 622393 E-mail: sales@jst-forktrucks.co.uk *Fork lift trucks sales & hirers & service*

▶ J S T International Transport, Room 101-102, Building 309, World Freight Terminal, Manchester Airport, Manchester, M90 5PH Tel: 0161-498 8882

J S T U K Ltd, Blyth Road, Halesworth, Suffolk, IP19 8EW Tel: (01986) 874131 Fax: (01986) 874276 E-mail: sales@jst.co.uk *Electronic connection manufrs*

J & S Tackle, 59 West Street, Arnold, Nottingham, NG5 7DB Tel: 0115-926 2644 *Fishing tackle retailers*

J & S Taylor Ltd, Corporation Mill, Corporation Street, Sowerby Bridge, West Yorkshire, HX6 2QQ Tel: (01422) 832616 Fax: (01422) 833686 E-mail: jands.taylor@btinternet.com *Woollen manufrs*

J S Tool & Gauge Co., Unit 4 Victoria Buildings, Newhall St, Willenhall, West Midlands, WV13 1LQ Tel: (01902) 636028 Fax: (01902) 608187 E-mail: jstool@live1.net *General engineers & press tool manufrs*

J S Trophies, 2 Rood Hill, Congleton, Cheshire, CW12 1LG Tel: (01260) 272505 Fax: (01260) 272505 E-mail: jstrophies@tiscali.co.uk *Trophies & engraving services retailers*

▶ J & S Upholstery, 43 Askern Industrial Estate Moss Road, Askern, Doncaster, South Yorkshire, DN6 0DD Tel: (01302) 709926 Fax: (01302) 789112 E-mail: joanne@thetrimshack.fsnet.co.uk *volkswagen /motorhome upholstery, coachtrimming*

J S W Inflatables, Unit 8, Church Hill Road, Thurmaston, Leicester, LE4 8DH Tel: 0116-264 0162 Fax: 0116-269 6814 E-mail: inflatafun@aol.com *Bouncy castles & soft play kiddies rides manufrs*

▶ J S W & Son (Coachbuilders), Northallerton Business Park, Thurston Rd, Northallerton, North Yorkshire, DL6 2NA Tel: (01609) 772449 Fax: (01609) 777995

continued

Company Information

continuation
E-mail: info@jswhorseboxes.co.uk *Horsebox manufrs*

▶ J S Wilson, 23 Pitheavlis Terrace, Perth, PH2 0JZ Tel: (01738) 624704

J S Wright & Sons Ltd, Boreham Road, Great Leighs, Chelmsford, CM3 1PR Tel: (01245) 361639 Fax: (01245) 361882 E-mail: jsw@cricketbatwillow.com *Cricket bat willow merchants*

J Scadding & Son Ltd, Eugene Street, St. Judes, Bristol, BS5 0TW Tel: 0117-955 6032 Fax: 0117-941 4536 E-mail: timber@scadding-son-ltd.co.uk *Timber merchants*

J Scott Thrapston Ltd, Bridge Street, Thrapston, Kettering, Northamptonshire, NN14 4LR Tel: (01832) 732366 Fax: (01832) 733703 E-mail: julia@scottsofthrapston.co.uk *Timber structures & buildings*

▶ J Shalev Diamonds, 100 Hatton Garden, London, EC1N 8NX Tel: (020) 7404 4022 Fax: (07900) 563551 E-mail: jacob@shalev.co.uk *Diamond Merchants*

J Sharples, Banastres at Bank, Nook Lane, Bamber Bridge, Preston, PR5 6BD Tel: (01772) 628644 Fax: (01772) 628644 *Demolition contractors*

J Shiner & Sons Ltd, 8 Windmill Street, London, W1T 2JE Tel: (020) 7636 0740 Fax: (020) 7580 0740 E-mail: info@j-shiner.co.uk *Wholesale & retail cabinet brassware*

▶ J Sinclair, 1 Eglinton, Kelliebank, Alloa, Clackmannanshire, FK10 1NT Tel: (01259) 212657 Fax: (01259) 213277

▶ J Smart & Co. (Contractors) P.L.C., 46 Redbraes Place, Edinburgh, EH7 4LL Tel: 0131-554 6418

J Smith Metals Ltd, Parkfield Road, Wolverhampton, WV4 6EL Tel: (01902) 492120 Fax: (01902) 353398 E-mail: chris@jsmithmetals.com *Non-ferrous scrap metal merchants*

J Smith & Sons, 2a Hawthorne Road, Blyth, Northumberland, NE24 3DT Tel: (01670) 352185 Fax: (01670) 352185 E-mail: davidblacksm@aol.com *Fire escape manufrs*

J Sperry & Son Ltd, 204 Prestbury Road, Cheltenham, Gloucestershire, GL52 3ER Tel: (01242) 244677 Fax: (01242) 244677 *Sign & poster writers & screen printers*

J Spindler & Sons Ltd, Joma Roma, The Common, Metfield, Harleston, Norfolk, IP20 0LP Tel: (01986) 785335 Fax: (01986) 785472 E-mail: martin@srts.fsnet.co.uk *Commercial vehicle dismantlers*

J Stevens, Hull Road, Eastrington, Goole, North Humberside, DN14 7XL Tel: (01430) 410333 Fax: (01430) 410354 E-mail: gdae@uk2.net *Conveyors & fabrications manufrs*

J Stimler Ltd, Martin House, Downs Road, London, E5 8QJ Tel: (020) 7254 8499 Fax: (020) 7254 1270 *Textile merchants*

J Stoddard & Sons Ltd, Pinsley Green, Wrenbury, Nantwich, Cheshire, CW5 8HE Tel: (01270) 780996 Fax: (01270) 780027 *Silica sand merchants or producers*

J Storey & Co. Ltd, Heron Chemical Works, Moor Lane, Lancaster, LA1 1QQ Tel: (01524) 63252 Fax: (01524) 381805 E-mail: sales@samuelbanner.co.uk *Chemical manufrs*

J Stott & Son Ltd, 56 Tontine Street, Blackburn, BB1 7ED Tel: (01254) 56616 Fax: (01254) 682780 E-mail: tony@stotts.fsbusiness.co.uk *Clothing manufrs*

J Strefford & Son, Atcham Grange, Atcham, Shrewsbury, SY5 6QF Tel: (01743) 761567 Fax: (01743) 761570 *Agricultural contractors*

J T Atkinsons Ltd, Ullswater Road, Penrith, Cumbria, CA11 7EH Tel: (01768) 865561 Fax: (01768) 890111 *Builders merchants*

▶ J T B Electronic Services, 19 Glenmore Road, Brixham, Devon, TQ5 9BT Tel: (01803) 856875 Fax: (01803) 856875 E-mail: mail@jtbelectronics.co.uk *Language Laboratory Services, Specialising in Sanako & Tandberg Products in England & Wales*

J T Barker & Sons Ltd, Leeds Foundries, Westland Square, Leeds, LS11 5SS Tel: 0113-271 6837 Fax: 0113-270 6901 *Brass founders*

J T Batchelor Ltd, 9-10 Culford Mews, London, N1 4DZ Tel: (020) 7254 2962 Fax: (020) 7254 0357 *Leather merchants, factors, distributors & agents*

J & T Beaven, The Midlands, Holt, Trowbridge, Wiltshire, BA14 6RJ Tel: (01225) 782245 Fax: (01225) 783155 E-mail: sales@beaven.com *Chamois leather producer*

J & T Blacksmiths Ltd, 23-29 Kelvin Avenue, Hillington Industrial Estate, Glasgow, G52 4LT Tel: 0141-882 9528 Fax: 0141-883 7110 *Blacksmiths*

J T Blythe Ltd, Kings Mill Lane, Redhill, RH1 5JY Tel: (01737) 823314 Fax: (01737) 822937 E-mail: harry@jtblythe.co.uk *Welding & sheet metalwork*

▶ J T Building Contractors, 12-14 Somerset House Suite 20 Hussar Court, Westside View, Waterlooville, Hampshire, PO7 7SG Tel: (023) 9225 9258 Fax: (023) 9225 9260 E-mail: info@jtbuilders.co.uk

J T Commercials, Wareham Road, Holton Heath, Poole, Dorset, BH16 6JW Tel: (01202) 632122 Fax: (01202) 621099 *Commercial vehicle dealers*

J T Computer Training Solutions, 16 Longpark Hill, Maidencombe, Torquay, TQ1 4TL Tel: (01803) 313386 Fax: (01803) 313376 E-mail: jt_training@msn.com *Software trainers*

▶ J T Dove Ltd, Northumberland Road, Tweedmouth, Berwick-upon-Tweed, TD15 2AS Tel: (01289) 304211 Fax: (01289) 306497

J T Dove Ltd, Orchard Street, Newcastle upon Tyne, NE1 3NB Tel: 0191-232 6151 Fax: 0191-222 1870 E-mail: newcastle@jtdove.co.uk *Builders' & plumbers' merchants* Also at: Ashington, Berwick, Carlisle, Hexham & Stockton-on-Tees

J T & E Castings Ltd, Leyland Mill Lane, Wigan, Lancashire, WN1 2SA Tel: (01942) 241966 Fax: (01942) 492136 E-mail: enquiries@jte-castings.co.uk *Iron founders*

J T Electrons, 42 Torridge Road, Thornton Heath, Surrey, CR7 7EY Tel: (020) 8665 6595 Fax: (020) 8665 6595 E-mail: istc@istc.org.uk *Engineering (specialised) services & consulting engineers*

▶ J T Feather Haulage Ltd, Black Dyke Mills, Brighouse Road, Queensbury, Bradford, West Yorkshire, BD13 1QA Tel: (01274) 889921

J T Griffiths & Co. Ltd, Ticking Supplies, 61 Stockport Road, Ashton-under-Lyne, Lancashire, OL7 0LE Tel: 0161-330 5665 Fax: 0161-343 1684 *Ticking fabric manufrs*

J & T Group Ltd, Victoria Works, 153 Victoria Street, Hartshill, Stoke-on-Trent, ST4 6HA Tel: (01782) 349440 Fax: (01782) 349449 E-mail: sales@storagebins.co.uk *Storage bin, bolts, nuts & industrial fasteners distributors*

J T Grout Ltd, Albert Road, Braintree, Essex, CM7 3JQ Tel: (01376) 320702 Fax: (01376) 349912 E-mail: jtgrout@btclick.com *General engineers*

J T Harrison, Druary, Back Lane, Holme-on-Spalding-Moor, York, YO43 4AU Tel: (01430) 860252 Fax: (01430) 860252 *Motor & agricultural engineers*

J T Hickinbottom Dudley Ltd, Unit 22 Thornleigh, Trading Estate, Dudley, West Midlands, DY2 8UB Tel: (01384) 234468 Fax: (01384) 254075 E-mail: jthickinbottom.dudley@zoom.co.uk *Aluminium & non-ferrous founders*

J & T James, Cilpostau, Cilycwm, Llandovery, Dyfed, SA20 0HH Tel: (01550) 720716 *Farming contractors*

J T Knitting Ltd, Dobroyd Mills, New Mill, Holmfirth, HD9 1AF Tel: (01484) 685415 Fax: (01484) 686119 *Knitted fabric manufrs*

J T L Systems Ltd, Unit 41, Kingfisher Court, Hambridge Road, Newbury, Berkshire, RG14 5SJ Tel: (01635) 263646 Fax: (01635) 263647 E-mail: sales@jtl.co.uk *Refrigeration control & temperature manufrs*

J & T Locks Bolts & Bars Ltd, Victoria Works, Victoria Street, Stoke-On-Trent, ST4 6HA Tel: (01782) 349440 Fax: (01782) 349449 E-mail: sales@storagebins.co.uk *Storage equipment & architectural ironmongery*

▶ J T M Skip Hire, 73 High Street, Blaenavon, Pontypool, Gwent, NP4 9PZ Tel: (01495) 791380 Fax: (01495) 791380 E-mail: john@jmahoney399.freeserve.co.uk *Skip Hire/Haulage*

▶ J T Mclaughlin Ltd, 362 Leach Place, Walton Summit Centre, Bamber Bridge, Preston, PR5 8AS Tel: (01772) 322777 Fax: (01772) 315569

J T Morgan, 128 Railway Arches, Behind Macfarlane Road, London, W12 7LA Tel: (020) 8222 6711 Fax: (020) 8969 2260 E-mail: jtmorgan@amserve.net *Wholesale haberdashery merchants*

J T Nex Ltd, Griffin Industrial Estate, Rowley Regis, West Midlands, B65 0SN Tel: 0121-559 1777 Fax: 0121-561 5945 E-mail: alan@jtnex.co.uk *Glass tube processors*

J T P (Non-Ferrous Stockholders) Ltd, Rope Street, Shelton New Road, Hartshill, Stoke-on-Trent, ST4 6DJ Tel: (01782) 711755 Fax: (01782) 717301 E-mail: dgreer@jtpnonferrous.co.uk *Non-ferrous metal stockholders*

J & T Partnership, Red House Barn, Mickfield Road, Stownham Aspal, Stowmarket, Suffolk, IP14 5LT Tel: (01449) 711010 Fax: (01449) 711010 *Specialist manufrs*

J T Pearce Springs Ltd, Arrow Road North, Redditch, Worcestershire, B98 8NT Tel: (01527) 61123 Fax: (01527) 61124 *General presswork services*

J T Pegg & Sons Ltd, The Garage, Bigsbys Corner, Saxmundham, Suffolk, IP17 1RP Tel: (01728) 604668 Fax: (01728) 604120 *Engineering small retailers*

▶ J T Projects Ltd, 32 Bellevue Terrace, Edinburgh, EH7 4DS Tel: (07980) 750040 Fax: E-mail: info@jtprojects.com *E-business consultants services*

J T R Controls Ltd, Bank Street, Walshaw, Bury, Lancashire, BL8 3AZ Tel: 0161-764 3829 Fax: 0161-764 3829 *Web guiding unit manufrs*

J T S Datacom Ltd, 2 Crossfields Close, Shinfield, Reading, RG2 9AY Tel: (0845) 6443193 Fax: (0845) 6448195 E-mail: info@jtsdata.com *Local & wide area networks*

J T S Engravers, 30-34 Aire Street, Leeds, LS1 4HT Tel: 0113-242 2158 Fax: 0113-242 8903 E-mail: jtsengravers@hotmail.co.uk *Engravers & sign makers*

J T Sawyer, 9 Pennine Industrial Estate, Modder Place, Armley, Leeds, LS12 3ES Tel: 0113-231 1255 Fax: 0113-231 1238 *Pneumatic & hydraulic engineers*

J T Services Ltd, 99 Reindeer Road, Fazeley, Tamworth, Staffordshire, B78 3SP Tel: (01827) 250280 Fax: (01827) 281363 *Steel tank & chimney manufrs*

J T Shakespeare & Co. Ltd, Hot Lane, Hot Lane Industrial Estate, Stoke-on-Trent, ST6 2BN Tel: (01782) 839311 Fax: (01782) 835783 E-mail: floors@jtshakespeare.com *General flooring contractors*

J T Simkins & Son, Chapel Farm, Chapel Road, Meppershall, Shefford, Bedfordshire, SG17 5NG Tel: (01462) 813330 *Agricultural contractors*

▶ J T Skillicorn Ltd, Second Avenue, Onchan, Isle of Man, IM3 4LT Tel: (01624) 621110 Fax: (01624) 611015

J & T Steel Shearing, 37 The Bridge Trading Estate, Bridge Street North, Smethwick, West Midlands, B66 2BZ Tel: 0121-565 2886 Fax: 0121-558 9670 E-mail: jtsteel@hotmail.co.uk *Steel sheet shearers & stockholders*

J & T Systems Ltd, 6 Northlands Road, Southampton, SO15 2LF Tel: (023) 8023 5280 Fax: (023) 8023 3358 *Computer training services*

J T Ward, 2 Station Street, Holbeach, Spalding, Lincolnshire, PE12 7LF Tel: (01406) 423517 Fax: (01406) 425805 E-mail: ltwardmd@aol.com *Joinery manufrs*

▶ J Tech Suffolk Computer Systems Ltd, 27-29 Orwell Road, Felixstowe, Suffolk, IP11 7DD Tel: (01394) 271555 Fax: 05600 766700 E-mail: sales@jtechsuffolk.com *Computer retailers & maintenance services*Hardware*software*data recovery*bespoke systems*anti virus software*

J Thackray & Sons Ltd, Brawby, Malton, North Yorkshire, YO17 6PY Tel: (01653) 668246 Fax: (01653) 668592 *Agricultural buildings & plant hire*

J Thibouville Lamy & Co. Ltd, Gilbert House, 406 Roding La South, Woodford Green, Essex, IG8 8EY Tel: (020) 8551 1282 Fax: (020) 8550 8377 E-mail: sales@jtlamy.co.uk *Musical instrument importers & wholesalers*

J Thompson, 78a Pall Mall, Liverpool, L3 7EN Tel: 0151-227 3600 Fax: 0151-231 1160 *Office furniture retailers*

J Thomson Colour Printers Ltd, 14-16 Carnoustie Place, Glasgow, G5 8PB Tel: 0141-429 1094 Fax: 0141-429 5638 *Colour & lithographic printers*

J Thwaites Ltd, 31 Bretton Street, Dewsbury, West Yorkshire, WF12 9BJ Tel: (01924) 460480 Fax: (01924) 460607 E-mail: info@tufgrip.com *Textile & conveyor roller covering manufrs*

J Todd & Son, Summerbridge, Harrogate, North Yorkshire, HG3 4JN Tel: (01423) 780319 Fax: (01423) 780431 E-mail: jtoddshop@aol.com *Agricultural merchants*

J U L Services, 53 Canons Drive, Edgware, Middlesex, HA8 7RG Tel: (020) 8951 5199 Fax: (020) 8905 6448 *Microwave repair services*

J UK E Services Ltd, Cratfield, Halesworth, Suffolk, IP19 0QL Tel: (01986) 785315 E-mail: jukeservicesltd@aol.com *Juke box services*

J V C Forex UK Ltd, JVC House, JVC Business Park, London, NW2 7BA Tel: (020) 8450 3282 Fax: (020) 8208 4385 *Audio hi-fi equipment systems, digital versatile disk products manufrs*

J V C Manufacturing U K Ltd, 2 Glenburn Road, East Kilbride, Glasgow, G74 5BA Tel: (01355) 241166 Fax: (01355) 265231 E-mail: enquiries@jvc.co.uk *Television receiver manufrs*

J V C UK Ltd, Gelderd Lane, Leeds, LS12 6AL Tel: 0113-279 5741 Fax: 0113-263 3987 *Audio/ hi-fi & VCR manufrs*

J & V Dalton Ltd, Dalmark House, Eye, Peterborough, PE6 7UD Tel: (01733) 222391 Fax: (01733) 223246 E-mail: sales@dalmark.co.uk *Agricultural merchants*

▶ J V F Consultants Ltd, 4 Loughborough Road, Mountsorrel, Loughborough, Leicestershire, LE12 7AT Tel: 0116-230 2880 Fax: 0116-237 6115 E-mail: sales@jvf.co.uk *Data & part finder & identifier parts identification*

J V Fabrication & Engineering, 5a Station Road, Langley Mill, Nottingham, NG16 4BG Tel: (01773) 530524 Fax: (01773) 530524 *Steel fabricators*

▶ J V Geer & Sons Ltd, 51 London Road, Sevenoaks, Kent, TN13 1AU Tel: (01732) 454082 Fax: (01732) 454728

▶ J V Price Ltd, Unit 2 Tower Hill, Chipperfield, Kings Langley, Hertfordshire, WD4 9LH Tel: (01442) 831777 Fax: (01442) 831888 E-mail: enquiries@jvprice.co.uk *Industrial window cleaners*

J V Trading Ltd, Unit 4a Brooke Business & Industrial Park, Heath Road, Lowestoft, Suffolk, NR33 9LZ Tel: (01502) 539631 Fax: (01502) 515400 E-mail: info@jvtrading.com *Beer, wines & spirits wholesalers*

J Vickers & Co., 6 Birchfield, Bolton, BL2 4AH Tel: (01204) 301092 Fax: (01204) 301092 *Conveyor belt retailers*

J W Alarms, 17 Crayke Road, Stockton-on-Tees, Cleveland, TS18 4EY Tel: (01642) 601131 Fax: (01642) 601131 *Security equipment supplier*

J W Andrews Ltd, Derby Road, Swanwick, Alfreton, Derbyshire, DE55 1BG Tel: (01773) 602191 Fax: (01773) 541492

J W B Print & Design, Dixon Court, Dixon Street, Lincoln, LN6 7DA Tel: (01522) 560760 Fax: (01522) 567272 E-mail: sales@jwbprint.co.uk *Commercial printers*

J W Baker & Sons Bradford Ltd, Premier Works, Newman Street, Bradford, West Yorkshire, BD4 9NT Tel: (01274) 651650 Fax: (01274) 681984 E-mail: bakerfabrications@btconnect.com *Steel fabricators*

J W Barrett Steel Fabrications, 55 High Street, Feckenham, Redditch, Worcestershire, B96 6HU Tel: (01527) 893866 Fax: (01527) 893866 E-mail: james@artmetal.co.uk *Artistic blacksmith*

J W Barrow & Co., Griffiths Road, Lostock Gralam, Northwich, Cheshire, CW9 7NU Tel: (01606) 331222 Fax: (01606) 331333 E-mail: jwbarrow@btinternet.com *Tank trailer rental agents*

▶ J W Bennie & Son, 6 Dundas Street, Grangemouth, Stirlingshire, FK3 8BX Tel: (01324) 482815 Fax: (01324) 665805

J W Blake & Son, 159 Brooker Road, Waltham Abbey, Essex, EN9 1JH Tel: (01992) 713756 Fax: (01992) 713756 *Commercial motor body builders & repair service*

J W Bowkett Electrical Installations Ltd, 2a Rugby Road, Newport, Gwent, NP19 0BS Tel: (01633) 254222 Fax: (01633) 213378 E-mail: jw.bowkett@virgin.net *Electrical contractors*

▶ J W Brown (Printers) Ltd, 77a Blackheath Road, London, SE10 8PD Tel: (020) 8469 0808 Fax: (020) 8691 6556 E-mail: sales@darwinpress.co.uk

J W Burford Metals, Russell Gardens, Wickford, Essex, SS11 8BH Tel: (01268) 732112 Fax: (01268) 573080 *Scrap metal merchant & skip hire*

▶ J W Cannon Co. Ltd, William St, Carshalton, Surrey, SM5 2RB Tel: (020) 8647 5584

J W Cooper Joinery, 6 Sea Lane, Rustington, Littlehampton, West Sussex, BN16 2RB Tel: (01903) 776941 Fax: (01903) 776941 E-mail: sales@cooperjoinery.co.uk *Architectural joiners*

J W Cooper UK Limited, 25 Glenmore Road, Minehead, Somerset, TA24 6GA Tel: 0845 8380394 Fax: 0871 9942178 E-mail: info@jwcgroup.co.uk *Total IT Solutions for Business, covering the Southern and Midlands regions of the UK Including LAN & WAN Network Infrastructure, Server and Client Hardware & Software Installations, Telephone, Remote and On Site Pro-Active Support, Professional Web Design and E-Commerce, Bespoke Software Development, High End Microsoft Technical Training Courses. Please contact our sales team on 0845 838 0394*

J.W.D. Rainwater Systems Ltd, Captain Clarke Road, Broadway Industrial Estate, Hyde, Stockport, Cheshire, SK1 4QG Tel: 0161-351 9990 Fax: 0161-351 9992 E-mail: info@rainwatergoods.co.uk *Rainwater goods distributors manufrs*

J W & E Morris & Son Ltd, South Road, Bridgend Industrial Estate, Bridgend, Mid Glamorgan, CF31 3RB Tel: (01656) 653705 Fax: (01656) 767187 E-mail: sales@jwmorris.co.uk *Electrical & mechanical engineering solutions to industry & commerce*

J W Engineering Ltd, Barker Gate, Ilkeston, Derbyshire, DE7 8DS Tel: 0115-877 0444 Fax: 0115-877 0791 E-mail: steelwork@jwestructures.co.uk *Structural steelwork*

J W Entwistle Co. Ltd, 41 Cobden Street, Salford, M6 6WF Tel: 0161-736 2297 Fax: 0161-745 7897 E-mail: adam@jwentwistle.com *Sheet metalworkers & roof flashings services*

J W Evans & Sons Ltd, 52-57 Albion Street, Birmingham, B1 3EA Tel: 0121-236 1775 Fax: 0121-236 7966 *Silversmiths*

J W F (UK) Ltd, 2 Stevenson Road, Sheffield, S9 3XG Tel: 0114-244 8821 Fax: 0114-244 4084 *Catering equipment suppliers*

J & W Fencing Ltd, Pecks Hill, Nazeing, Waltham Abbey, Essex, EN9 2NY Tel: (01992) 893352 Fax: (01992) 893324 *Fencing suppliers*

J W Fidler & Sons, Nile Street, Bolton, BL3 6BW Tel: (01204) 529948 Fax: (01204) 365263 *Food & wholesales suppliers*

J W H Group Ltd, War Industrial Estate, Church Road, Lydney, Gloucestershire, GL15 5EL Tel: (01594) 842406 Fax: (01594) 842232 E-mail: enquire@petlon.co.uk *Polymer products manufrs*

J W Hill Precision Engineers Ltd, 22-26 Bath Road, Worcester, WR5 3EL Tel: (01905) 356712 Fax: (01905) 763155 E-mail: info@jwhill-engineering.co.uk *Precision engineers & machinists*

J W Hinchliffe Tanks Ltd, Weaver Street, Kirkstall Road, Leeds, LS4 2AU Tel: 0113-263 5163 Fax: 0113-263 5164 E-mail: jwhinchliffetanks.ltd@yahoo.co.uk *Tank cleaning services*

J W Holdings, 4th Floor, Regant Centre, Regant Road, Aberdeen, AB11 5NS Tel: (01224) 890022 Fax: (01224) 582734 *Holding company*

▶ J W Housden Ltd, 1 Margetts Road, Kempston, Bedford, MK42 8DS Tel: (01234) 852033 Fax: (01234) 841226

J.W Hydraulics, Springvale Industrial Park, Unit 33, Bilston, West Midlands, WV14 0QL Tel: (01902) 408771 Fax: (01902) 354448 *Mobile hose services*

J W Instruments, 1 Church Lane, Normanton, West Yorkshire, WF6 2DE Tel: (01924) 891049 Fax: (01924) 220846 E-mail: j.wilson@jwinstruments.co.uk *Electric meter manufrs*

J W J Car & Commercial Repairs, 113-115 Codicote Road, Welwyn, Hertfordshire, AL6 9TY Tel: (01438) 820351 *Motor vehicle repair services*

▶ J W Jones & Son, 3-5 Bay View Road, Colwyn Bay, Clwyd, LL29 8DW Tel: (01492) 531414 Fax: (01492) 532336 E-mail: office@jwjones-son.co.uk

J W L Ltd, 1 Mundells, Welwyn Garden City, Hertfordshire, AL7 1EU Tel: (01707) 338410 Fax: (01707) 338731 E-mail: info@jwl.co.uk *Lithographic printers to the trade*

▶ J W Lewis & Sons Ltd, Bojea Industrial Estate, Trethowel, St. Austell, Cornwall, PL25 5RJ Tel: (01726) 72764 Fax: (01726) 65858 E-mail: enquiries@jwlewisandsons.sagenet.co.uk *Roofing contract services, slate & tile*

J W Lister Ltd, Clifton Road, Brighouse, West Yorkshire, HD6 1SL Tel: (01484) 712925 Fax: (01484) 715314 E-mail: sales@jwlister.co.uk Sales Contact: M.A. Wardingley *Manufacturers of wire goods & welded wire mesh products, industrial, domestic & plastic coated*

J W Lovitt, Station Road, Tempsford, Sandy, Bedfordshire, SG19 2BA Tel: (01767) 640934 Fax: (01767) 640839 E-mail: jwlrefrigeration@aol.com *Refrigeration buy & sell*

J W Machinery Services, Claytile Workshop, Fairy Hall Lane, Rayne, Braintree, Essex, CM77 6SZ Tel: (01376) 328034 Fax: (01376) 551676 E-mail: info@jwmservices.co.uk *Woodwork machinery service & Repair*

J W Martin Ltd, Prince Regent Road, Belfast, BT5 6QR Tel: (028) 9070 2021 Fax: (028) 9070 5566 E-mail: mail@jwmartin.co.uk *Sack & oven glove manufrs*

J & W Milligan, Galston Road, Hurlford, Kilmarnock, Ayrshire, KA1 5HS Tel: (01563) 527572 Fax: (01563) 536758 E-mail: sales@millicabin.com *Portable building & shed manufrs*

J W Mortimer, Horseshoe Inn, Egton, Whitby, North Yorkshire, YO21 1TZ Tel: (01947) 895520 Fax: (01947) 895520 *Agricultural engineering services*

▶ J W Munnings Ltd, Harfreys Road, Great Yarmouth, Norfolk, NR31 0LS Tel: (01493) 603328 Fax: (01493) 442424

▶ J W Munro, 18 Bogmoor Place, Glasgow, G51 4TQ Tel: 0141-445 4339 Fax: 0141-445 5511

J W O'Pray & Sons Ltd, Gillane Works, Wassand Street, Hull, HU3 4AL Tel: (01482) 323014 Fax: (01482) 215944 E-mail: sales@oprays.com *Lifting gear specialists*

continued

▶ indicates data change since last edition

J W Oxby & Son, The Big Red Shed, Cherry Tree Road, Doncaster, South Yorkshire, DN4 0BJ Tel: (01302) 361666 Fax: (01302) 323023 E-mail: sales@oxby.demon.co.uk *Catering Equipment Distributors.*

J W Plant & Co. Ltd, 39 Ashley Road, Leeds, LS9 7AJ Tel: 0113-248 0454 Fax: 0113-235 0118 E-mail: sales@jwplant.co.uk *Flag & banner makers*

J & W Robinson Glasgow Ltd, 719 South Street, Glasgow, G14 0BX Tel: 0141-950 1812 Fax: 0141-950 1944 *Metal recyclers*

J.W.Rudge & Co.Limited, Anne Road, Smethwick, West Midlands, B66 2NZ Tel: 0121-558 5519 Fax: 0121-558 0053 E-mail: millssteve@btconnect.co.uk *Electroplating services*

▶ J W S Import Ltd, Unit 1 Haven Business Park, Slippery Gowt Lane, Wyberton, Boston, Lincolnshire, PE21 7AA Tel: (01205) 363999 Fax: (01205) 358713 E-mail: sales@doorsandmore.biz *Import doors*

J W S Wardrobes Ltd, 5 Eastgate, Worksop, Nottinghamshire, S80 1RH Tel: (01909) 486715 Fax: (01909) 486715 *Fitted bedrooms and kitchens*

J W Services, 31 Woodview Avenue, Baildon, Shipley, West Yorkshire, BD17 7LG Tel: (01274) 530928 Fax: (01274) 530928 E-mail: jwservices999@hotmail.com

J W Stamp & Son LLP, Holydyke, Barton On Humber, Barton-upon-Humber, South Humberside, DN18 5PS Tel: (01652) 632421 Fax: (01652) 635878 *Welding fabricators*

J W Stead & Son Ltd, Preserve Works, Thackley Old Road, Shipley, West Yorkshire, BD18 1QB Tel: (01274) 597814 Fax: (01274) 532177 E-mail: info@jwstead.com *Textile engineers & manufacturer of industrial brushes*

▶ J W Steele & Sons Ltd, 264 Baddow Road, Chelmsford, CM2 9QT Tel: (01245) 352487 Fax: (01245) 283617

▶ J W Suckling Transport Ltd, Manor Road, West Thurrock, Grays, Essex, RM20 4BA Tel: (01708) 861234 Fax: (01708) 861483

J W T, 1 Knightsbridge Green, London, SW1X 7NW Tel: (020) 7656 7000 Fax: (020) 7656 7010 *Advertisers*

J & W Tait Ltd, Sparrowhawk Road, Hatston Industrial Estate, Kirkwall, Orkney, KW15 1GE Tel: (01856) 872490 Fax: (01856) 873076 *Farm equipment supplies & car sales*

J W Taylor & Son, Les-Osiers, Ings Road, Ulleskelf, Tadcaster, North Yorkshire, LS24 9SS Tel: (01937) 832138 *Basket manufrs*

J W Thompson & Sons, 5 Mile Hill, Mansfield Road, Hasland, Chesterfield, Derbyshire, S41 0JN Tel: (01246) 234940 Fax: (01246) 557425 *Scrap dealers*

J & W Whewell Ltd, Newbridge Chemical Works, York Street, Radcliffe, Manchester, M26 2GL Tel: 0161-796 6333 Fax: 0161-766 3017 E-mail: sales@jwwhewell.co.uk *Textile industry chemical manufrs*

J Wardle & Son Ltd, Boothferry Road, Howden, Goole, North Humberside, DN14 7DZ Tel: (01430) 430388 Fax: (01430) 423049 *Agricultural engineers*

J Webber, Coles Lane Farm, Shaftesbury, Dorset, SP7 0PY Tel: (01747) 851717 Fax: (01747) 855635 *Agricultural engineers*

J White Fabrications, South Cowton, Northallerton, North Yorkshire, DL7 0JB Tel: (01325) 378207 Fax: (01325) 378271 *Steel fabricators*

J White & Co Tde Ltd, Meadow Bank Road, Rotherham, South Yorkshire, S61 2NF Tel: (01709) 740099 Fax: (01709) 740438 E-mail: jwhite-tde@jwhite-tde.co.uk *Transport, excavation & demolition contractors services*

J Williams, Unit 2 Freeman Street, Birkenhead, Merseyside, CH41 1BR Tel: 0151-647 6532 Fax: 0151-647 6532 *Wholesale rag merchants*

J Wilmer, Signal Way, Swindon, SN3 1PD Tel: (01793) 522535 *Coal merchant*

J Wilson & Co., 96 David Street, Glasgow, G40 2UH Tel: 0141-551 0268 Fax: 0141-554 4620 E-mail: info@jwilsongroup.co.uk *Industrial power tool distribs*

J Wilson Agriculture, 75 Drumcroon Road, Garvagh, Coleraine, County Londonderry, BT51 4ED Tel: (028) 7086 8430 Fax: (028) 7086 8803 E-mail: cowcomfort@wilsonagri.co.uk *Dairy farm equipment suppliers & dairy housing specialists*

▶ J Wright Electrical, Quantas House, Rooley Lane, Bradford, West Yorkshire, BD4 7SJ Tel: (01274) 689696

J Wyllie, Towerhill Industrial Estate, Crosshouse Road, Kilmaurs, Kilmarnock, Ayrshire, KA3 2SA Tel: (01563) 539621 Fax: (01563) 539621 E-mail: gimwylliеplant@aol.com *Plant sale & repairers*

J&B, 7 Cambridge Road, Granby Industrial Estate, Weymouth, Dorset, DT4 9TJ Tel: (01305) 775377 Fax: (01305) 780443 *Precision engineers*

J&J, Unit 1 20 Paynes Lane, Rugby, Warwickshire, CV21 2UH Tel: (01788) 568217 Fax: (01788) 547125 E-mail: jjsheetmetal@dialstart.net *Sheet metalwork engineers & fabricators*

J&R Designs Ltd, 5-7 Shepherds Lane, London, E9 6JJ Tel: (020) 8985 0717 Fax: (020) 8985 7987 *Handbag frames, fittings, soft furnishings*

J&T Group Ltd, PO Box 5 Victoria Works, Stoke-on-Trent, ST4 6HA Tel: (01782) 202545 Fax: (01782) 349449 E-mail: sales@storagebins.co.uk *Architectural hardware/ironmongery/ironmongers metalwork*

J2G Ltd, Unit 16, Robjohns House, Navigation Road, Chelmsford, CM2 6ND Tel: (01245) 346290 Fax: (01245) 280800

▶ JA Architectural Ltd, Enterprise Park, Swansea, SA6 6ZW Tel: 07071 222455 Fax: 07071 222355 E-mail: enquiries@jaarchitectural.co.uk *Glazed fire rated systems*Steel security applications*Specialist doors*

▶ JAB Web Solutions, Suite 145, Cardiff, CF24 3DG Tel: (0777) 9633038 E-mail: andrew@jabwebsolutions.co.uk *UK web hosting*

Jabb Technical Graphics, 17 Crown Lane, Thurlby, Bourne, Lincolnshire, PE10 0EZ Tel: (01778) 421412 Fax: (01778) 421412 E-mail: andybaker@jtechg.fsnet.co.uk *Technical illustrators & publications*

Jabez Barker, Coneygre Industrial Estate, Tipton, West Midlands, DY4 8XP Tel: 0121-520 7058 Fax: 0121-522 3229 *New & used caravans suppliers*

Jabez Cliff & Co. Ltd, Globe Works, Lower Forster Street, Walsall, WS1 1XG Tel: (01922) 621676 Fax: (01922) 722575 E-mail: saddlery@barnsby.com *Saddlery & leather goods manufrs*

▶ Jabil Circuit, 1 Mosshill Industrial Estate, Ayr, KA6 6BE Tel: (01292) 885000 Fax: (01292) 885198

Jabil Circuit Ltd, Oakbank Park Drive, Mid Calder, Livingston, West Lothian, EH53 0TJ Tel: (01506) 432266 Fax: (01506) 442000 *Printed circuit board repairers*

Jable Ltd, Burnley Road, Altham, Accrington, Lancashire, BB5 5TX Tel: (01254) 237035 Fax: (01254) 872343 *Precision engineers*

Jac & Co., Failsworth Mill, Ashton Road West, Failsworth, Manchester, M35 0FR Tel: 0161-934 4070 Fax: 0161-683 2074 *Commission rollers & slitters*

▶ Jacamast Services Ltd, Colne Bridge Works, Bradley, Huddersfield, HD5 0RH Tel: (01484) 426190 Fax: (01484) 427682

Jacaranda Productions Ltd, Felgate Mews Studland Street, London, W6 0LY Tel: (020) 8741 9088 Fax: (020) 8748 5670 E-mail: creatives@jacaranda.co.uk *TV & film production & interactive media services*

Jacarem Ltd, 78 Asheridge Road, Chesham, Buckinghamshire, HP5 2PY Tel: (01494) 791336 Fax: (01494) 792336 E-mail: sales@jacarem.co.uk *Jacarem have developed a reputation as a reliable supplier of connectors, cables, cable assemblies/harnesses and panel wiring. Privately owned and founded in 1987, Jacarem"s large levels of stock carried for our distribution business also supports our in house cable assembly division ensuring prompt delivery of 100% tested cables. *We are a franchised distributor of a wide variety of connectors. Please find the following few examples: *Emulation Technology: Programming Adaptors, Prototyping Adaptors, Test Clips. *ERNI: DIN 41612, 2mm Hard Metric Connectors, High Density (0.8mm) Mezzanine Connectors, 1.27mm Connectors-SMT, Solderless Pressfit, IDC. Right Angle and Straight Surface Mount D-Types, Backplanes-Compact PCI, Advanced TCA and VME. *ODU: Modular connectors, Miniature Cylindrical connectors, specialist cylindrical connectors for the medical industry, Single Power Contacts (2000 A).***

Jacee Contracts Ltd, 2 Station Road, Cottingham, North Humberside, HU16 4LL Tel: (01482) 840167 Fax: (01482) 875467 E-mail: paul@jc.fsnet.co.uk *Exhibition contractors*

Jacee Print & Promotions Ltd, Publicity House, Station Road, Cottingham, East Yorkshire, HU16 4LL Tel: (01482) 842117 Fax: (01482) 875239 E-mail: sales@jaceeprint.co.uk *Lithographic, screen printers & embroidery*

Jacetts Ltd, 18 Hope Road, Deal, Kent, CT14 7DF Tel: (01304) 381990 Fax: (01304) 381991 E-mail: sales@jacetts.co.uk *Sportswear manufrs*

Jack Elam, Barton Road, Wisbech, Cambridgeshire, PE13 4TP Tel: (01945) 419090 Fax: (01945) 419088 E-mail: sales@jack-elam.co.uk *Electrical contractors & air conditioning engineers*

▶ Jack Green Engineering Ltd, 9c Station Yard, Thame, Oxfordshire, OX9 3UH Tel: (01844) 260010 Fax: (01844) 260020

James Jack Lifting Services Ltd, 7-13 South Esplanade West, Aberdeen, AB11 9AA Tel: (01224) 897535 Fax: (01224) 897299 E-mail: sales@james-jack.co.uk *Crane hire*

Jack Kaye Ltd, 1143 London Road, Leigh-on-Sea, Essex, SS9 3JE Tel: (01702) 476268 Fax: (01702) 476268 *Hairdressing equipment supplier*

Jack Lunn Construction Ltd, Progress House, 99 Bradford Road, Stanningley, Pudsey, West Yorkshire, LS28 6AT Tel: 0113-236 2777 Fax: 0113-236 2888 E-mail: admin@jacklunn.co.uk *Building contractors*

Jack Morton Europe Ltd, 16-18 Acton Park Industrial Esta, The Vale, London, W3 7QE Tel: (020) 8735 2000 Fax: (020) 8735 2020 *Conference & event organisers*

Jack Nadel, 23 Pembridge Square, London, W2 4DR Tel: (020) 7535 3400 Fax: (020) 7353 4310 E-mail: jn-ap@activepromotions.com *Sales promotion & business gifts*

Jack Oldman Textiles, Station Approach, Whaley Lane, Whaley Bridge, High Peak, Derbyshire, SK23 7AF Tel: (01663) 734334 Fax: (01663) 734334 E-mail: jill@jackoldhamtextiles.co.uk *Industrial cleaning cloths.*

Jack Russell Collections & Investigations, Bayleaf House, 10 York Road, Northampton, NN1 5QG Tel: (01604) 634170 Fax: (01604) 635507 E-mail: jrnorth@debtcollect.co.uk *Detective agency & private investigation on nationwide basis*

Jack Sharkey & Co. Ltd, 2 Middlemore Road, Smethwick, West Midlands, B66 2DR Tel: 0121-558 7444 Fax: 0121-558 9810 *Metal merchants*

▶ Jack Stock Essex Fencing, The Old Bakery, Hawk Lane, Battlesbridge, Wickford, Essex, SS11 7RL Tel: (01268) 732184 Fax: (01268) 761675

Jack Tighe Decorating Ltd, Redbourne Mere, Kirton Lindsey, Gainsborough, Lincolnshire, DN21 4NW Tel: (01652) 649215 Fax: (01652) 648159 *Commercial & industrial decorating* Also at: Doncaster & Scunthorpe

▶ Jack Trathen Carpentry and Building Services, 52 Reeds Avenue, Earley, Reading, RG6 5SR Tel: 0118-954 7544 E-mail: jack@jacktrathen.co.uk *Builders and carpenters based in Reading, we provide a wide range of building, carpentry and fitting services*

continued

to homes across Berkshire and beyond. With years of experience in quality refurbishment and building we will ensure that your work is completed with maximum satisfaction and minimum disruption to your lifestyle - all at very reasonable prices.

Jackdaw Tools Ltd, Leveson Street, Willenhall, West Midlands, WV13 1DB Tel: (01902) 366551 Fax: (01902) 634983 E-mail: jackd@ukindustry.co.uk *Engineers merchants*

Jackel International Ltd, Dudley Lane, Cramlington, Northumberland, NE23 7RH Tel: 0191-250 1864 Fax: 0191-250 1727 E-mail: mail@jackel.co.uk *Baby accessory distributors & manufrs*

▶ Jackie Lunn Ltd, Unit 7, Galabank Business Park, Galashiels, Selkirkshire, TD1 1TR Tel: (01896) 753877 Fax: (01896) 755709 E-mail: info@jackielunnltd.com *Bakery products*

▶ Jackpot, 20-21 Broad Street, Barry, South Glamorgan, CF62 7AD Tel: (01446) 749400

Jackpots, Frith Farm, Frith Lane, Wickham, Fareham, Hampshire, PO17 5AW Tel: (01329) 832902 *Vegetable preparation*

Jack's Glass, 41-43 Princes Road, Hull, HU5 2QS Tel: (01482) 491989 Fax: (01482) 444581 *Glass merchants*

Thomas Jacks Ltd, Unit B/2, The Bridge Business Centre, Timothys Bridge Road, Stratford Enterprise Park, Stratford-upon-Avon, Warwickshire, CV37 9HW Tel: (01789) 264100 Fax: (01789) 264200 E-mail: info@thomasjacks.co.uk *Distributors of night vision devices & lighting products*

Jackson & Allen Ltd, 244 Chingford Mount Road, London, E4 8JP Tel: (020) 8529 7014 Fax: (020) 8520 8040 *Builders' merchants*

Arthur Jackson & Co. Ltd, Rastrick Common, Brighouse, West Yorkshire, HD6 3DR Tel: (01484) 713345 Fax: (01484) 718150 E-mail: aj@ajack.demon.co.uk *Pattern makers*

Cliff Jackson, 97 Cottage Lane, Ormskirk, Lancashire, L39 3NF Tel: (07946) 434999 Fax: (01695) 571114 E-mail: cliffjackson@btinternet.com *Manufacturing agent for engineering products & end of line packaging*

Jackson Consultants, 9 Forest Court, Barlborough, Chesterfield, Derbyshire, S43 4UW Tel: (01246) 810155 Fax: (01246) 810155 *Mechanical engineers*

▶ Den Jackson Solutions Ltd, 5 Ames Court, Cawston, Norwich, NR10 4QD Tel: (01603) 879999 *Security group cctv access controllers*

E.S. Jackson, The Dees, Doddington, Lincoln, LN6 4RR Tel: (01522) 692921 Fax: (01522) 696314 E-mail: info@jacksonpine.co.uk *Pine furniture wholesaler & distributors*

Edward Jackson Ltd, Red Hall, Red Hall Lane, Southburgh, Thetford, Norfolk, IP25 7TG Tel: (01362) 820145 Fax: (01362) 820192 E-mail: info@edwardjacksonltd.com *Paint roller manufacturing machinery/paint brushes*

▶ Jackson Engine Auto Spares, 36 Dundrod Road, Nutts Corner, Crumlin, County Antrim, BT29 4ST Tel: (028) 9082 5396 *Suppliers of engine parts*

Jackson Engineering Stoke On Trent Ltd, Scott Lidgett Road, Stoke-on-Trent, ST6 4LX Tel: (01782) 812139 Fax: (01782) 824374 E-mail: sales@jacksonengineering.co.uk *Specialists in food/bakery plant & equipment manufr*

Ernest Jackson & Co. Ltd, High Street, Crediton, Devon, EX17 3AP Tel: (01363) 636000 Fax: (01363) 636063 E-mail: crediton.reception@csplc.com *Pastilles & lozenges manufrs*

Jackson Evans Ltd, 9 Market St, Rhyl, Clwyd, LL18 1RL Tel: (01745) 331257 *Bakery & confectionery distributors & manufrs*

Geoffrey Jackson, Blacksmiths Buildings, Langley-on-Tyne, Hexham, Northumberland, NE47 5LA Tel: (01434) 688977 Fax: (01434) 684487 *Cabinet manufrs*

▶ Jackson Glass, 25 Robinson Road, High Wycombe, Bucks, HP13 7BL Tel: 01494 812207 Fax: 0870 1367557 E-mail: enquiries@jacksonglass.co.uk

Jackson & Gocher Hire Centre, Harrow Lane, Farncombe Street, Godalming, Surrey, GU7 3LP Tel: (01483) 527000 Fax: (01483) 415523 *Construction plant or equipment hire*

Jackson Group Properties 11 Ltd, Jackson House, 86 Sandyhill Lane, Ipswich, IP3 0NA Tel: (01473) 335000 Fax: (01473) 219939 E-mail: enquiries@jackson-building.co.uk *Civil engineering contractors*

Harold Jackson Screenprint Ltd, 986 Pollokshaws Road, Glasgow, G41 2HE Tel: 0141-649 1783 Fax: 0141-649 6087 E-mail: enquiries@jacksonscreenprint.co.uk *Screen printers*

J. Jackson (Transport) Ltd, 31-33 Midland Road, Scunthorpe, North Lincolnshire, DN16 1DQ Tel: (01724) 856925 Fax: (01724) 859835 *Road transport specialists*

Jackson Joinery Manufacturing Ltd, 619 Liverpool Street, Salford, M5 5HQ Tel: 0161-281 9770 Fax: 0161-745 9217 *Joinery & window frame manufrs*

▶ Jackson & Keay Ltd, Private Road No. 7, Colwick Industrial Estate, Colwick, Nottingham, NG4 2JW Tel: 0115-961 7113 Fax: 0115-961 8664 *Gas cylinder services*

Jackson & Kelly Ltd, Wernolau Fawr, Llanboidy, Whitland, Dyfed, SA34 0EN Tel: (01994) 448245 Fax: (01994) 448722 *Catering equipment manufrs*

Jackson Kent Associates, 112 Harpenden Road, St. Albans, Hertfordshire, AL3 6DA Tel: (01727) 834690 Fax: (01727) 834678 E-mail: robk@jka.co.uk *Computer consultants*

L.E. Jackson (Coachworks) Ltd, Vehicle Body Centre, Queens Road, Loughborough, Leicestershire, LE11 1HD Tel: (01509) 230811 Fax: (01509) 230812 *Commercial motor body builders & accident repair center*

Jackson Lifts Ltd, Unit 4-19, Ropery Business Park, London, SE7 7RX Tel: (020) 8293 4176 Fax: (020) 8305 0274 E-mail: sales@jacksonlifts.com *Lift, escalator installation & services*

▶ Jackson Lloyd (D B M) Ltd, 2 Kilshaw Street, Wigan, Lancashire, WN5 8EA Tel: (01942) 620990

▶ Jackson Media Services Ltd, Hillside Centre, Upper Green Street, High Wycombe, Buckinghamshire, HP11 2RB Tel: (01494) 443600 Fax: (01494) 451414 E-mail: d.jackson@jms-ltd.co.uk

P. Jackson, 8 Robin Royd Grove, Mirfield, West Yorkshire, WF14 0LB Tel: (01924) 492388 Fax: (01924) 492388 *Alarm systems services*

Jackson Precision Gear Services Ltd, Elmtree Street, Belle Vue, Wakefield, West Yorkshire, WF1 5EQ Tel: (01924) 299866 Fax: (01924) 299338 E-mail: j.s.j@btinternet.com *Gear grinding & cutters*

Jackson Production Services Ltd, Grangefield Road, Town Street, Stanningley, Leeds, LS28 6JP Tel: 0113-236 3366 Fax: 0113-236 3339 E-mail: salesjps@aol.com *Machine tool merchants*

Jackson Refrigeration, Unit 19, Cossall Industrial Estate, Solomon Road, Ilkeston, Derbyshire, DE7 5UA Tel: 0115-944 4898 Fax: 0115-944 4981 E-mail: katejackson@jacksonrefrigeration.co.uk *Refrigeration & Air Conditioning Engineers*

Jackson Rich & Co., 9 Earn Avenue, Righead Industrial Estate, Bellshill, Lanarkshire, ML4 3LW Tel: (01698) 849661 Fax: (01698) 844036

Jackson Rich & Co. Ltd, Unit 4A, Faraday Court, Buckley Road Industrial Estate, Rochdale, Lancashire, OL12 9EF Tel: (01706) 650510 Fax: (01706) 647622 E-mail: mail@jackson-rich.com *Electrical contractors*

▶ Jackson Rundle (Rec2Rec), 2 Sheen Road, ., Richmond, Surrey, TW9 1AE Tel: 020 8943 2669 E-mail: kellysearch@jacksonrundle.com *Jackson Rundle Associates specialise in the placement of professional recruiters into a wide range of verticals and across all levels. Concentrating on London and the South-East, we offer a high quality service to both clients and candidates.*

▶ John Jackson & Sons Joiners Ltd, Victoria Building, 82 Hammond Street, Preston, PR1 7NU Tel: (01772) 881696

Jackson Steel Structures Ltd, Densfield Works, Tannadice Street, Dundee, DD3 7QP Tel: (01382) 858439 Fax: (01382) 833964 E-mail: sales@jacksonsteel.co.uk *Structural engineers*

William Jackson & Son Ltd, 40 Derringham Street, Hull, HU3 1EW Tel: (01482) 224939 Fax: (01482) 588237 E-mail: sales@wjs.co.uk *Bakers wholesale manufrs*

Jackson Yacht Services Ltd, Le Boulevard, St. Aubin, Jersey, JE3 8AB Tel: (01534) 743819 Fax: (01534) 745952 E-mail: sales@jacksonyatch.com *Boat builders & yacht brokers & life raft services*

Jacksons, Victory House, Cox Lane, Chessington, Surrey, KT9 1SG Tel: (020) 8391 5555 Fax: (020) 8391 5333 E-mail: info@jacksonscg.co.uk *Hotel table & glassware wholesalers*

Jacksons The Baker Ltd, New Hall Road, Chesterfield, Derbyshire, S40 1HE Tel: (01246) 274165 Fax: (01246) 200908 E-mail: jacksonsbakeries@hotmail.co.uk *Wholesale bakery supplier*

Jacksons Building Centres Ltd, Newbold Road, Chesterfield, Derbyshire, S41 7PB Tel: (01246) 203201 Fax: (01246) 208985 E-mail: paulbullivant@jacksonbc.co.uk *Builders & plumbers merchants*

Jacksons Fork Trucks, Rosenheath, Norwich Road, Barham, Ipswich, IP6 0PA Tel: (01473) 830691 Fax: (01473) 831492 *Forklift trucks hire*

Jacksons Garden Centre, 426-430 Stockfield Road, Yardley, Birmingham, B25 8JJ Tel: 0121-707 5066 Fax: 0121-707 5028 E-mail: martin@jacksons20.fsnet.co.uk *Prefabricated concrete garages & concrete sheds manufrs*

Jacksons Metal Spinners, 1 Noke Lane Business Centre, Noke Lane, St. Albans, Hertfordshire, AL2 3NY Tel: (01727) 846038 Fax: (01727) 846658 E-mail: gaallen@freenet.co.uk *Metal spinners, spinnings manufrs*

▶ Jackson's Online Garden Centre, Jackson's Nurseries, Bagnall, Stoke-on-Trent, ST9 9LD Tel: (01782) 504931 Fax: (01782) 504931 E-mail: luke@jacksonsnurseries.co.uk *Mail order delivery website offering a massive selection of plants and garden items online. Order through our secure server with a satisfaction guarantee!*

Jacksons Tool & Plant Hire & Industrial Supplies, Dormagen, Laurencekirk, Kincardineshire, AB30 1UP Tel: (01561) 377060 Fax: (01561) 377016 *Industrial suppliers*

Jackson's (Upholsterer's Supplies) Ltd, 359 Argyle Street, Glasgow, G2 8LT Tel: 0141-221 0178 Fax: 0141-204 2792 E-mail: jacksonsltd@tiscali.co.uk *Suppliers to the upholstery trade*

▶ Jacky Norton, 41 Greek Street, Stockport, Cheshire, SK3 8AX Tel: 0161-480 1480 Fax: (0870) 4445495 E-mail: Sales@njfpets.wanadoo.co.uk *Suppliers of hand made pure wool dog coats, Dog Beds and accessories.*

▶ Jaco Tooling Company Ltd, 41-42 Nutwood Trading Estate, Limestone Cottage Lane, Sheffield, S6 1NJ Tel: 0114-285 2422 Fax: 0114-285 2424 E-mail: sales@jacotooling.co.uk *Machine knife manufrs*

Jacob Fencing & Garden Supplies, 6 New Park Road, Ashford, Middlesex, TW15 1EG Tel: (01784) 256930 *Fencing & garden suppliers*

Jacob Pickwell & Co. Ltd, Pickwell House, Immingham Dock, Immingham, South Humberside, DN40 2LZ Tel: (01469) 572415 Fax: (01469) 572897 E-mail: j.pickwell@cargohandling.uk *Stevedoring contractors*

Jacob, White (Hospital Equipment) Ltd, Unit I4, Riverside Industrial Estate, Riverside Way, Dartford, DA1 5BX Tel: (01322) 223267 Fax: (01322) 288278 E-mail: jacobwhite@jacobwhite-hoftquip.co.uk *Hospital equipment manufrs*

Company Information

Jacob White Packaging Ltd, Riverside Industrial Estate, Dartford, DA1 5BY Tel: (01322) 272531 Fax: (01322) 270692 E-mail: jwhiteuk@aol.com *Cartoning machinery manufrs*

Jacobi Carbons, 3 Moss Industrial Estate, St. Helens Road, Leigh, Lancashire, WN7 3PT Tel: (01942) 670600 Fax: (01942) 670605 E-mail: infouk@jacobi.net *Manufacturers of carbons & associated filtration equipment*

Jacobs Builder Centre, Loguestown Industrial Estate, Coleraine, County Londonderry, BT52 2NS Tel: (028) 7034 4751 Fax: (028) 7035 5963 E-mail: jacobs@macblair.com *Timber merchants & building supplies*

Jacobs Engineering Ltd, 95 Bothwell Street, Glasgow, G2 7HX Tel: 0141-240 4700 Fax: 0141-226 3109 *Technical & management consultants*

▶ Jacobs Engineering UK Ltd, Fairbairn House, 23 Ashton Lane, Sale, Cheshire, M33 6WP Tel: 0161-905 5853 Fax: 0161-905 5855 *Technical & management consultants*

Jacobs Young & Westbury, Bridge Road, Haywards Heath, West Sussex, RH16 1UA Tel: (01444) 412411 Fax: (01444) 457662 E-mail: sales@jyw-uk.com Principal Export Areas: Worldwide *Furniture import/export merchants*

Jacobson Chemicals Ltd, Unit 4, Newman Lane, Alton, Hampshire, GU34 2QR Tel: (01420) 86934 Fax: (01420) 549574 E-mail: sales@jacobsonchemicals.co.uk *Specialist chemical distributors*

Jacon Ltd, 1 Brickfield Industrial Estate, New Road, Gillingham, Dorset, SP8 4LT Tel: (01747) 825858 Fax: (01747) 825634 E-mail: info@jacon.co.uk *Bags & holdall manufrs*

Jacopo Pandolfi Photography, 145-157, St John Street, London, EC1V 4PY Tel: 07946 860678 E-mail: info@jacopopandolfi.com *Jacopo Pandolfi is a freelance photographer working in London, United Kingdom. Trained in photography at the LCCm his reportage images of British youth subcultures, together with his portraits and music photogrpahs, are sold by photo agencies Getty Images, Camera Press, Retna and PYMCA. His work has been published/broadcasted on MTV Networks, The Economist, Picador Books, Elle and Time Out. His studio is located in South London.*

Jaco-Sumal Ltd, 8 Edwards Road, Birmingham, B24 9EP Tel: 0121-373 6988 Fax: 0121-384 7525 E-mail: jacosumal@yahoo.com *Lubrication public transport service equipment manufrs*

Jacowe Joinery Ltd, Clyde Yard, Cambridge Street, Godmanchester, Huntingdon, Cambridgeshire, PE29 2AT Tel: (01480) 457682 Fax: (01480) 434212 E-mail: jacowejoineryltd.@btconnect.com *Joinery manufrs*

Jacques Products, Greengate Industrial Estate, Greenside Way, Middleton, Manchester, M24 1SW Tel: 0161-688 7744 Fax: 0161-688 6060 *Drum dealers, reconditioners & suppliers*

▶ Jacques Vert (Retail) Ltd, Webber Pavilion, Seaham Grange Industrial Estat, Seaham, County Durham, SR7 0PZ Tel: 0191-521 3555 *Retail*

▶ Jacquet UK Ltd, Rockingham House, Wentworth Way, Tankersley, Barnsley, South Yorkshire, S75 3DH Tel: (01226) 745000 Fax: (01226) 746000 E-mail: j.uk@myjacquet.com *Stainless steel profiling company*

Jacquet Weston Engineering, Tower Works, Membury Airfield Industrial Estate, Lambourn Woodlands, Hungerford, Berkshire, RG17 7TJ Tel: (01488) 674400 Fax: (01488) 674405 E-mail: sales@jweltd.com *Manufacturers of plant equipment*

Jacuzzi UK, Woodlands, Roydsdale Way, Euroway Industrial Estate, Bradford, West Yorkshire, BD4 6ST Tel: (01274) 654700 Fax: (01274) 654750 *Bathroom fitting manufrs*

▶ Jad Filters, Unit 6, 1-3 Fairfield, Christchurch, Dorset, BH23 1QX Tel: (01202) 487618 Fax: (01202) 484786

Jade 2000 Ltd, 38 Dukewood Road, Clayton West, Huddersfield, HD8 9HF Tel: (01484) 863752 Fax: (01484) 862573 *Freight forwarding, air freight & haulage*

Jade Air P.L.C., Hanger 1, Shoreham Airport, Shoreham-by-Sea, West Sussex, BN43 5FF Tel: (01273) 464013 Fax: (01273) 465184 E-mail: info@jadeair.co.uk *Aeronautical designing & engineering services*

Jade Cushions, Gisburn Road, Barrowford, Nelson, Lancashire, BB9 6JD Tel: (01282) 615780 *Furnishings manufrs*

Jade Design Services, 17 St. James Drive, Brinsley, Nottingham, NG16 5DB Tel: (01773) 780391 E-mail: brian@jadedesign.demon.co.uk *Printed circuit artwork services*

Jade Engineering (Coventry) Ltd, 70 Bayton Road Industrial Estate, Exhall, Coventry, CV7 9EJ Tel: (024) 7636 5336 Fax: (024) 7664 4308 E-mail: sales@jade-eng.co.uk *General engineers*

Jade Non Ferrous Metals Ltd, Metallum House, Arthur Drive, Hoo Farm Industrial Estate, Kidderminster, Worcestershire, DY11 7RA Tel: (01562) 746454 Fax: (01562) 820465 E-mail: sales@metalwarehouse.com *Aluminium bar & plate stockholders*

Jade Press Ltd, Eagle House, Torre Road, Leeds, LS9 7QL Tel: 0113-248 0929 Fax: 0113-248 4609 E-mail: sales@jadepress.co.uk *Commercial & colour printers*

Jade Screen Supplies Ltd, 153 Upper Aughton Road, Southport, Merseyside, PR8 5EX Tel: (01704) 563186 Fax: (01704) 563186 *Screen printing & ink supplies*

Jadealto Ltd, Sagana Lodge, Scotton Road, Scotter, Gainsborough, Lincolnshire, DN21 3SB Tel: (01724) 764747 Fax: (01724) 764352 *Manufacture & repair glass tube heat exchange*

Jades Components Ltd, Derby Road, Kingsbridge, Devon, TQ7 1JL Tel: (01548) 853377 Fax: (01548) 856820 E-mail: jades@jadescomponents.co.uk *Coil, component & transformer manufrs*

▶ Jade's Entertainment Disco Mobile, 201 Union Street, Torquay, TQ1 4BY Tel: (0871) 7110627

Jaeger Casings, Irthlingborough Road, Wellingborough, Northamptonshire, NN8 1RA Tel: (01933) 222466 *Sausage casing*

Leon Jaeggi & Sons, Helcetia House, Austin Road, Ashford, Kent, TN23 6JR Tel: (01233) 634635 Fax: (01233) 633311 E-mail: leon@jaeggi.com *Catering equipment suppliers*

Jafco Tools Ltd, Access House, Great Western Street, Wednesbury, West Midlands, WS10 7LE Tel: 0121-556 7700 Fax: 0121-556 7788 E-mail: sales@jafco-tools.com *Glass fibre & hand tool manufrs*

Jaffa International Marketing Ltd, Mullany Business Park, Deanland Road, Golden Cross, Hailsham, East Sussex, BN27 3RP Tel: (01825) 872875 Fax: (01825) 872877 E-mail: jim@jaffa-international.co.uk *Hair accessory wholesalers*

Jaffabox Ltd, Starley Way, Birmingham, B37 7HB Tel: 0121-250 2000 Fax: 0121-250 2001 E-mail: sales@jaffabox.com *Carton & packaging materials manufrs*

Jaftextil Ltd, Unit 18, Hillgate Business Centre, Swallow Street, Higher Hillgate, Stockport, Cheshire, SK1 3AU Tel: 0161-480 2342 Fax: 0161-480 2397 E-mail: info@jaftextil.co.uk *Textile manufrs*

Jag Precision Engineering, 1 J A S Industrial Park, Titford Lane, Rowley Regis, West Midlands, B65 0PY Tel: 0121-561 4902 Fax: 0121-561 1181 E-mail: jagprecision@btconnect.com *Precision engineers*

Jag Signs Supplies, Mitre Ct, Winterland La, Holsworthy, Devon, EX22 6NF Tel: (01409) 254370 *Sign writing*

Jaguar Alarm Co., Jaguar House, 191 Old Oak Road, London, W3 7HH Tel: (020) 8743 1358 Fax: (020) 8743 1358 *Install security alarms & maintain*

Jaguar Axle Supplies, 23 Spencer Walk, Tilbury, Essex, RM18 8XH Tel: (01375) 846986 Fax: (01375) 408017 E-mail: ed@ward-engineering.co.uk *Jaguar spares*

Jaguar Business Forms, 9-17 Crompton Way, Crawley, West Sussex, RH10 9QG Tel: (01293) 512688 Fax: (01293) 551703 E-mail: sales@jagforms.co.uk *Business forms, digital printing & mailing services*

▶ Jaguar Design & Print, Philpot House, Station Road, Rayleigh, Essex, SS6 7HH Tel: (01268) 776741 Fax: (01268) 776741 E-mail: sales@jaguar-design-print.co.uk *Digital printing services*

▶ Jaguar Freight Services Ltd, The Linen House, 253 Kilburn Lane, London, W10 4BQ Tel: (020) 8964 2621 Fax: (020) 8964 1055 E-mail: sales@jaguarfreight.com

Jai Electronics, 155 High Street, London, NW10 4TR Tel: (020) 8965 5080 Fax: (020) 8961 2924 E-mail: jai@beeb.net *Sales, service & repairs to TV, hifi, video, microwaves & computers*

▶ Jaire Consultants, 398 Long Lane, Bexleyheath, Kent, DA7 5JN Tel: (020) 8303 2196 Fax: (020) 8298 9782

▶ Jaivel Europe Ltd, Mansfield i-centre, Hamilton Way, Oakham Business Park, Mansfield, Nottinghamshire, NG18 5BR Tel: 01623 600630 Fax: 01623 600601 E-mail: barrylomas@jaivel.com *Jaivel Europe operates a Dual Shore "Engineering Services" business model providing complete engineering turnkey solutions for those companies involved in the machining of components for the Aerospace and Power Generation sectors.*

Jakar International Ltd, Hillside House, 2-6 Friern Park, London, N12 9BX Tel: (020) 8445 6376 Fax: (020) 8445 2714 E-mail: info@jakar.co.uk *Art & craft distributors*

Jaketone Ltd, 44 Millhouse Lane, Wirral, Merseyside, CH46 6HN Tel: 0151-677 6620 Fax: 0151-677 6620 *Suspended ceiling contractors*

▶ Jakk, Unit 17 Granary Business Centre, North Street, Hellingly, Hailsham, East Sussex, BN27 4DU Tel: (01323) 847115 Fax: (01323) 833040 E-mail: jakkuk@aol.com *Manufacturers of hardwood memorial benches, gates and specialised joinery.*

Jak-Pak, Spring Bank Buildings, Every St, Nelson, Lancashire, BB9 7BS Tel: (01282) 698654 Fax: (01282) 611330 *Contract packaging & shrink wrapping*

▶ Jalee First Aid Training, Woodlands, 41 Behind Berry, Somerton, Somerset, TA11 6JS Tel: (0870) 7871043 Fax: (01458) 270116 E-mail: info@jaleefirstaid.co.uk *Providing first aid training*

Jalite plc, Wins House, Bentalls, Basildon, Essex, SS14 3BS Tel: (01268) 242300 Fax: (01268) 274148 E-mail: sales@jalite.com *Manufacturers of high performance photo luminescent materials*

Jallatte SAS Ltd, Unit C, Riverside Industrial Estate, Atherstone Street, Fazeley, Tamworth, Staffordshire, B78 3RW Tel: (01827) 831260 Fax: (01827) 831261 *Safety footwear distributors & manufrs*

Jaltek Systems, Unit 13 Sundon Business Park, Dencora Way, Luton, LU3 3HP Tel: (01582) 578170 Fax: (01582) 578171 E-mail: marketing@jaltek.com *Electronic contract manufacturing services*

Jamak Fabrication Europe Ltd, 52-53 Oakhill Industrial Estate, Devonshire Road, Worsley, Manchester, M28 3PT Tel: (01204) 794554 Fax: (01204) 574521 E-mail: mail@jamak.co.uk Principal Export Areas: Africa *Manufacturers of silicone & rubber mouldings*

Jamels Hairdressers' Equipment, 140 Queensway, Agora Shopping Centre, Bletchley, Milton Keynes, MK2 2RS Tel: (01908) 366636 Fax: (01908) 366636 *Hair products retailers*

James A Bruce, 1-5 Cameron Street, Stonehaven, Kincardineshire, AB39 2BL Tel: (01569) 762507 Fax: (01569) 762507 *Commercial printers*

Albert E. James & Son Ltd, Barrow Mill, Barrow Street, Barrow Gurney, Bristol, BS48 3RU Tel: (01275) 463496 Fax: (01275) 463791 *Agricultural feed merchants services*

▶ Andy James Roadshows, The Ashes, Chargrove, Bristol, BS30 5NT Tel: 0117-960 6738 E-mail: info@andyjames.co.uk *Wedding entertainment*

James Bedford & Co. Ltd, Pennine View, Birstall, Batley, West Yorkshire, WF17 9NF Tel: (01924) 442048 Fax: (01924) 472117 E-mail: sales@jbedford.co.uk Principal Export Areas: Worldwide *Steel workbenches & storage cabinet manufrs*

James & Beeching, Bartons Yard, Dunleys Hill, Odiham, Hook, Hampshire, RG29 1DP Tel: (01256) 701987 Fax: (01256) 701301 *Visual aid suppliers*

▶ James Bell & Sons Ltd, 2 Lower Auchingramont Road, Hamilton, Lanarkshire, ML3 6HW Tel: (01698) 282720 Fax: (01698) 283548 E-mail: sales@bellprinters.co.uk

James & Bloom Ltd, Blenheim Place, Gateshead, Tyne & Wear, NE11 9HF Tel: 0191-461 0088 Fax: 0191-461 0146 *Vehicle building supplies*

▶ James Booth Bolton Ltd, Manchester Road, Westhoughton, Bolton, BL5 3QH Tel: (01942) 818800 Fax: (01942) 818484 E-mail: sales@jamesbooth.co.uk

James Brothers (Hamworthy) Ltd, 19 Blandford Road, Hamworthy, Poole, Dorset, BH15 4AW Tel: (01202) 673815 Fax: (01202) 684033 E-mail: inquiries@james-bros.co.uk *Structural engineers*

▶ James Brown Construction Ltd, 10 Eglinton Street, Irvine, Ayrshire, KA12 8AS Tel: (01924) 272780 Fax: (01563) 573370

James Bruce & Co London Ltd, Great Oddynes, Cinder Hill Lane, Horsted Keynes, Haywards Heath, West Sussex, RH17 7BA Tel: (01825) 791123 Fax: (01825) 791411 E-mail: *Export trader*

James C Brett, 30-34 Clyde Street, Bingley, West Yorkshire, BD16 2NT Tel: (01274) 569381 Fax: (01274) 566851 *Knitting yarn suppliers*

▶ James Cargo Services Ltd, 9 Galleymead Road, Colnbrook, Slough, SL3 0EN Tel: (01753) 687722 Fax: (01753) 687723

James Chan & Co., 37 Ludgate Hill, London, EC4M 7JN Tel: (020) 7236 8880 Fax: (020) 7236 8883 E-mail: law@chanlegal.com *Solicitors*

▶ James D Philbin Ltd, Chapel Lane, Wigan, Lancashire, WN3 5DH Tel: (01942) 246690 Fax: 01942 825920 E-mail: sales@philbin-glassrecycling.co.uk *We are a bottle recyling company based in in Wigan and cover the Northwest of England.*

Daniel James Furnishings Ltd, Hilltop Works, Old Oak Common Lane, London, NW10 6DY Tel: (020) 8961 1070 E-mail: info@daniel-james.com *Soft manufacturer for furnishing to the trade*

David James, Grove Cottage, Blounts Court Road, Peppard Common, Henley-on-Thames, Oxfordshire, RG9 5EU Tel: 0118-972 4945 Fax: 0118-972 4946 *Food ingredients distributors*

James Drewitt & Son Ltd, 865 Ringwood Road, West Howe, Bournemouth, BH11 8IW Tel: (01202) 575757 Fax: (01202) 582500 *Property owning & managing holding company*

James E Hatch & Son, 9 Old School Lane, Adlington, Chorley, Lancashire, PR7 4DX Tel: (01257) 480064 Fax: (01257) 481213 *Machinery repairers*

James Engineering Ltd, Prenton Way, North Cheshire Trading Estate, Prenton, Merseyside, CH43 3DU Tel: 0151-609 1000 Fax: 0151-609 0741 E-mail: sales@jameseng.com *Engineers & profile company*

James Engineering Construction, Wood Street, Alfreton, Derbyshire, DE55 7JW Tel: (01773) 832425 Fax: (01773) 831000 E-mail: jamesengineering@btinternet.com *Steel fabricators & installers*

▶ James F Stephen, Backdykes, Glamis, Forfar, Angus, DD8 1RG Tel: (01307) 475000 Fax: (01307) 475001

James Fisher Inspection & Measurement Services Ltd, Factory Road, Sandycroft, Deeside, Clwyd, CH5 2QJ Tel: (01244) 520058 Fax: (01244) 535440 E-mail: sales@ndt-inspection.co.uk *Non destructive testing manufrs*

James French, Balloo Avenue, Bangor, County Down, BT19 7QT Tel: (028) 9147 3436 Fax: (028) 9145 1793 E-mail: info@french-eng.co.uk *Ventilation contractors*

▶ James Frew Ltd, 4 Lawmoor Avenue, Dixons Blazes Industrial Estat, Glasgow, G5 0XN Tel: 0141-429 4000

James Gibb & Co. Ltd, Royston Works, Royston Avenue, Southend-on-Sea, SS2 5JY Tel: (01702) 614927 Fax: (01702) 601382 *Engineers & ship store merchants*

James Gibbons Format Ltd, Vulcan Road, Bilston, West Midlands, WV14 7JG Tel: (01902) 405500 Fax: (01902) 385915 E-mail: sales@jgf.co.uk *Door furniture manufrs*

James Gilbert & Son Ltd, 129 The Vale, London, W3 7RQ Tel: (020) 8743 1566 Fax: (020) 8746 1393 E-mail: metalforest@hotmail.com *Wire goods manufrs*

James Gill Ltd, 8 Donkin Road, 2 District Armstrong Industrial Estate, Armstrong, Washington, Tyne & Wear, NE37 1PF Tel: 0191-416 9357 Fax: 0191-415 5338 *Bolt & nut distributors*

James Gordon Engineers Ltd, Dalbeattie Road, Castle Douglas, Kirkcudbrightshire, DG7 1HZ Tel: (01556) 502338 Fax: (01556) 504178 E-mail: admin@jgordon.co.uk *Agricultural machinery agents*

James Gordon Engineers Ltd, Heathhall Industrial Estate, Heathhall, Dumfries, DG1 3PH Tel: (01387) 261024 Fax: (01387) 272640 E-mail: dfsales@jgordon.co.uk *Agricultural engineers*

▶ James H, Redditch, Worcestershire, B97 Tel: 0845 6446570 Fax: 0845 6446570 E-mail: info@jameshuk.com *Providing mobile disco, karaoke, race nights & audio & visual services*

James H Heal & Co. Ltd, Richmond Works, Lake View, Halifax, West Yorkshire, HX3 6EP Tel: (01422) 366355 Fax: (01422) 352440 E-mail: info@james-heal.co.uk *Textile testing equipment manufrs*

James Hamilton & Co Lurgan Ltd, 1 Moores Lane, Lurgan, Craigavon, County Armagh, BT66 8DW Tel: (028) 3832 3727 Fax: (028) 3831 2312 E-mail: sales@jameshamilton.co.uk *Printers & packaging*

James Harvey UK Ltd, 2 The Lane, 1121 Cathcart Road, Glasgow, G42 9BD Tel: 0141-636 5514 Fax: 0141-636 5518 *Pillow & cushion*

▶ James Howard, Carrs Industrial Estate, Commerce Street, Haslingden, Rossendale, Lancashire, BB4 5JT Tel: (01706) 833511 Fax: (01706) 833550 E-mail: sales@james-howard.co.uk *We provide a wide range of equestrian products all at great prices. FREE UK DELIVERY on all orders. Order either online or through our catalogue.*

James Hoyle & Son, 50 Andrews Road, London, E8 4RL Tel: (020) 7254 2335 Fax: (020) 7254 8811 E-mail: jameshoyle@btclick.com *Architectural metalworkers*

James Hugh Group Ltd, 5 Hampstead West, 224 Iverson Road, London, NW6 2HL Tel: (020) 7328 3121 Fax: (020) 7328 5888 *Thermometer manufrs*

James Industrial & Aviation Supplies Ltd, Stowmarket, Suffolk, IP14 2EU Tel: (01449) 673902 Fax: (01449) 677394 *Cranes & crane spares*

James J Carrick & Co. Ltd, 450 Petershill Road, Glasgow, G21 4PB Tel: 0141-558 6008 Fax: 0141-557 0318 E-mail: enquiries@jamesjcarrick.com *Steel & plastic manufrs*

James Jack Lifting Services Ltd, Old Coal Yard, South Shore Road, Grangemouth, Stirlingshire, FK3 8TQ Tel: (01324) 664777

James Jack Listing Services Ltd, Oilfield Support Base, Shore Road, Invergordon, Ross-Shire, IV18 0EX Tel: (01349) 853000 Fax: (01349) 853416 E-mail: invergordon@james-jack.co.uk *Mobile & dock crane hire & haulage services*

▶ James Jones & Sons, Kinnoir, Huntly, Aberdeenshire, AB54 7XY Tel: (01466) 792372 Fax: (01466) 794393

▶ James Kemball Ltd, 1 Hodgkinson Road, Felixstowe, Suffolk, IP11 3QT Tel: (01394) 601500 Fax: (01394) 673006

▶ James King Plant Ltd, Northampton Road, Blisworth, Northampton, NN7 3DW Tel: (01604) 858558 Fax: (01604) 859204

James Kinnear Thornton Ltd, 91 Main Street, Thornton, Kirkcaldy, Fife, KY1 4AQ Tel: (01592) 774352 Fax: (01592) 771411 *Haulage contractors*

James Laird Gold Leaf Ltd, 18 Craig Road, Glasgow, G44 3DR Tel: 0141-637 8288 Fax: 0141-637 8288 E-mail: goldleaf@jameslaird.com *Gold leaf manufacturers & suppliers of all gilding & sign writing sundries*

James Langford, 81-83 Adelaide Street, Belfast, BT2 8FE Tel: (028) 9032 0610 Fax: (028) 9032 0610 *Industrial engravers*

James Latham, Longlands, Milner Way, Ossett, West Yorkshire, WF5 9JE Tel: (01924) 276111 Fax: (01924) 275156 E-mail: panels.ossett@lathams.co.uk *Timber importers & distribs*

James Latham, 13 Chartwell Drive, Wigston, Leicestershire, LE18 2FN Tel: 0116-288 9161 Fax: 0116-281 3806 E-mail: panels.wigston@lathams.co.uk *Timber importers*

James Latham Sales plc, Unit 2 Swallow Park, Finway Road, Hemel Hempstead Industrial Estate, Hemel Hempstead, Hertfordshire, HP2 7QU Tel: (01442) 849000 Fax: (01442) 239287 E-mail: marketing@lathams.co.uk *Timber merchants*

James Lawrence, 22-28 Tower Street, Brightlingsea, Colchester, CO7 0AL Tel: (01206) 302863 Fax: (01206) 305858 *Sail makers*

Lee James Graphic Systems Ltd, Unit 700 Thorp Arch Estate, Wetherby, West Yorkshire, LS23 7BJ Tel: (01937) 849000 Fax: (01937) 849999 E-mail: info@leejames.co.uk *Supplies a range of press consumables to the printing industry*

James Lister, 2 Miller Street, Birmingham, B6 4NF Tel: 0121-359 3774 Fax: 0121-333 3021 E-mail: birmingham@lister.co.uk *Industrial supplies*

▶ James Listers, 3 Riverside Industrial Estate, Meir Road, Redditch, Worcestershire, B98 7SY Tel: (01527) 500878 Fax: (01527) 510579 E-mail: redditch@lister.co.uk *Engineers*

James Lock & Co. Ltd, 6 Saint James's Street, London, SW1A 1EF Tel: (020) 7930 2421 Fax: (020) 7930 6616 E-mail: sales@lockhatters.co.uk *Hat retailers & wholesalers*

▶ James Long Masons Ltd, Timbrell Street, Trowbridge, Wiltshire, BA14 8PN Tel: (01225) 763074 Fax: (01225) 774654

James M Brown Ltd, Boving Works, Napier Street, Stoke-on-Trent, ST4 4NX Tel: (01782) 744171 Fax: (01782) 744473 E-mail: sales@jamesmbrown.co.uk *Inorganic pigment & oxide manufrs*

James M Green & Co. Ltd, 186b Drews Lane, Birmingham, B8 2SL Tel: 0121-327 8777 Fax: 0121-328 7076 E-mail: jamesmgreen@btconnect.com *Roofing contractors*

▶ James M Joiner (Macduff) Ltd, 14 Low Shore, Macduff, Banffshire, AB44 1RE Tel: (01261) 832526

James Mcgowan Engineering Ltd, Dechmont Works, Hamilton Road, Cambuslang, Glasgow, G72 7XS Tel: 0141-641 3648 Fax: 0141-641 5147 E-mail: info@mcgowaneng.co.uk *Mechanical engineering contractors*

James Mcgregor & Sons Ltd, 49 Sydenham Road, Belfast, BT3 9DR Tel: (028) 9045 1244 Fax: (028) 9045 6433 E-mail: sales@hardwoodni.com *Hardwood merchants & importers*

▶ James Mchugh Contracts Ltd, West End, 127a Main Street, Cairneyhill, Dunfermline, Fife, KY12 8QX Tel: (01383) 881390 Fax: (01383) 881390

▶ James Mackie Ltd, 1 Tams Brig, Ayr, KA8 8DF Tel: (01292) 269053

James Mcnaughton Paper Group, Jaymac House, Church Manorway, Erith, Kent, DA8 1DF Tel: (020) 8320 3200 Fax: (020) 8311 4162 E-mail: marketing@mcnaughton-paper.com *Paper merchants* Also at: Branches throughout the U.K.

James & Maja Ltd, 1a Rydens Grove, Walton-on-Thames, Surrey, KT12 5RX Tel: (01932) 228301 Fax: (01932) 228301 *Tool manufrs*

Mark James Ltd, 9 Churchill Close, Streatley, Luton, LU3 3PJ Tel: (01582) 881534 Fax: (01582) 883486 *Marine cargo, goods in transit & surplus stock*

James Maxton & Co, Calor Gas Building, Airport Road West, Belfast, BT3 9EE Tel: (028) 9045 8238 Fax: (028) 9045 6428 E-mail: jmaxton@aol.com *Consulting engineers*

▶ James Maxwell Building Contractors Ltd, Midbrae, Kirkwynd, Langholm, Dumfriesshire, DG13 0JD Tel: (01387) 381352 E-mail: sales@maxwellthebuilders.co.uk *Building contractors*

▶ James Mearchent & Sons Ltd, 104 Pollokshaws Road, Glasgow, G41 1PZ Tel: 0141-644 3414

▶ James Meffan Ltd, Parkend Farm, Kirriemuir, Angus, DD8 4PD Tel: (01575) 572152 Fax: (01575) 572130

▶ James Moffat & Sons Cardenden Ltd, Fulmar Way, Donibristle Industrial Park, Hillend, Dunfermline, Fife, KY11 9JY Tel: (01383) 821888 Fax: (01383) 821880

James Murphey Of Falkirk Ltd, Lochlands Industrial Estate, Unit 45, Larbert, Stirlingshire, FK5 3NS Tel: (01324) 562029 Fax: (01324) 621245 E-mail: sales@jamesmurphy-falkirk.co.uk *Wire workers & sieve & riddle makers*

▶ James & Nicholas Ltd Liability Partnership, Grove House, Grove Place, Port Talbot, West Glamorgan, SA13 1XA Tel: (01639) 885431 Fax: (01639) 891687

▶ James Nuttall Transport Ltd, Royle Barn Road, Rochdale, Lancashire, OL11 3DT Tel: (01706) 356255 Fax: (01706) 354806 E-mail: sales@jamesnuttall.co.uk

James O Flanagan Ltd, 110 Broad Street, Coventry, CV6 5AZ Tel: (024) 7668 9325 Fax: (024) 7666 2632 *Builders.*

James Orr, Room 17 Dalziel Workspace, Mason Street, Motherwell, Lanarkshire, ML1 1YE Tel: (01698) 267408 Fax: (01698) 259567 *Sheriff officers*

James P Maginnis Ltd, 1 St. Peters Road, Portslade, Brighton, BN41 1LS Tel: (01273) 417016 *Printing & photocopying services*

James P Wilson & Sons, Millmannoch Farm, Drongan, Ayr, KA6 6HF Tel: (01292) 570239 Fax: (01292) 570239 *Agricultural contractors*

James Packaging Ltd, Unit 24A, Park Avenue Industrial Estate, Sundon Park, Luton, LU3 3BP Tel: (01582) 561333 Fax: (01582) 561444 *Corrugated case manufrs*

▶ James Paterson Plumbing & Heating Ltd, 23 Winchester Avenue Industrial, Denny, Stirlingshire, FK6 6QE Tel: (01324) 823613 Fax: (01324) 822342

James Payne, 28-29 Vaughan Street, Llandudno, Gwynedd, LL30 1AB Tel: (01492) 876705 Fax: (01492) 860903 E-mail: jamespaynellandudno@hotmail.com.uk *Plumbers' & builders merchants*

James Pearson & Co West Bromwich Ltd, Mount Pleasant Street, West Bromwich, West Midlands, B70 7DL Tel: 0121-553 3580 Fax: 0121-553 7903 *Metal & plastic window servicing*

James Petre & Co. Ltd, Bentley Avenue, Cowpen Lane Industrial Estate, Billingham, Cleveland, TS23 4BU Tel: (01642) 563800 Fax: (01642) 564947 *Industrial roofing contractors*

▶ Andrew James Photography, Southlands, 26 Longlands Road, Lapal, Halesowen, West Midlands, B62 0AZ Tel: (07811) 171970 E-mail: enquiry@andrewjames-photography.co.uk *Specialist in photos of people, weddings & portraits*

▶ James Potter, Camps Industrial Estate, Kirknewton, Midlothian, EH27 8DF Tel: (01506) 881592 Fax: (01506) 884499

James & Powell, Little Ton Farm, Tredunnock, Usk, Gwent, NP15 1LY Tel: (01633) 450550 Fax: (01633) 450424 *Farm machinery distributors*

James Pringle, Unit 1 Mill Lane, Pitlochry, Perthshire, PH16 5BH Tel: (01796) 472315 *Retail*

James R Georgeson, Guidibest, Latheron, Caithness, KW5 6DQ Tel: (01593) 741300 Fax: (01593) 741300 *Agricultural Contractor*

James R Knowles, Suite 1a Cameron Court, Cameron Street, Hillington Industrial Estate, Glasgow, G52 4JH Tel: (0870) 7530820 Fax: 0141-883 9134 E-mail: glasgow@jrknowles.com *Construction contract consultants* Also at: Edinburgh & Stirling

James R Knowles, 2 Amber Business Village, Amber Close, Tamworth, Staffordshire, B77 4RP Tel: (0870) 7530830 Fax: (0870) 7530835 E-mail: tamworth@jrknowles.com *Construction consultants*

James Ramsey Glasgow Ltd, 85 Dykehead Street, Queenslie Industrial Estate, Glasgow, G33 4AQ Tel: 0141-774 2602 Fax: 0141-774 4321 E-mail: jamesramseyltd@btconnect.com *Boiler installation & repair services*

Richard James International Ltd, 48 Davis Street, Bristol, BS11 9JW Tel: 0117-982 8575 Fax: 0117-982 6361 E-mail: mail@richard-james.co.uk Principal Export Areas: Worldwide *Export merchants*

James Rickwood & Co.,Limited, 12 Ladybarn Crescent, Bramhall, Stockport, Cheshire, SK7 2EZ Tel: 0161-439 3778 Fax: 0161-439 7823 *Textile agents*

James Ronbinson Fibes Ltd, Wharfedale Road, Euroway Industrial Estate, Bradford, West Yorkshire, BD4 6SG Tel: (01274) 689400 Fax: (01274) 685986 E-mail: sales@jrfibres.co.uk *Textile merchants*

▶ James Ryan Thornhill Ltd, 41 Wollaton Road, Beeston, Nottingham, NG9 2RN Tel: 0115-876 0298 Fax: 0115-922 4212 E-mail: chris@jrtltd.co.uk *Independent Financial Advisers providing unbiased advice in a friendly and professional manner.*

James Scientific Instruments Ltd, PO Box 18134, London, EC1R 4WD Tel: (020) 7837 1154 Fax: (020) 7278 7293 E-mail: sales@jamessciinst.com *Thermometer manufacturers including industrial, digital & mercury*

Scott James Commercial Ltd, 10-12 Armstrong Close, St. Leonards-on-Sea, East Sussex, TN38 9ST Tel: (0500) 441066 Fax: (01424) 853911 E-mail: sales@scott-james.freeserve.co.uk *Aluminium fabricators*

James Smellie Fabrications Ltd, F Leona Trading Estate, Nimmings Road, Halesowen, West Midlands, B62 9JQ Tel: 0121-561 1167 Fax: 0121-559 0336 *Sheet metal fabricators*

▶ James Smith Denny Ltd, Boghead Garage, Broad Street, Denny, Stirlingshire, FK6 6EA Tel: (01324) 823823 Fax: (01324) 825476

▶ James Smith Denny Ltd, Boghead Garage, Broad Street, Denny, Stirlingshire, FK6 6EA Tel: (01324) 823823 Fax: (01324) 825476

James Smith & Son Redditch Ltd, 22-24 Bromsgrove Road, Redditch, Worcestershire, B97 4QY Tel: (01527) 62034 Fax: (01527) 68826 *Mild steel wire stockists & manufrs*

James Smith & Sons Ltd, 53 New Oxford Street, London, WC1A 1BL Tel: (020) 7836 4731 Fax: (020) 7836 4730 E-mail: jsmith.umbrellas@virgin.net *Umbrella & walking stick manufacturers & retailers*

▶ Steven James Jewellery, 22 Barleylands Road, Billericay, Essex, CM11 2UD Tel: (01268) 280488 Fax: (01268) 280488 *Jewellery repairers & services*

James Stevenson Quarries Ltd, Clinty Quarry, 215 Doury Road, Ballymena, County Antrim, BT43 6SS Tel: (028) 2565 6302 Fax: (028) 2564 6495 *Quarry owners & road contractors*

Stuart James Systems Ltd, 69 Trent Valley Road, Lichfield, Staffordshire, WS13 6EZ Tel: (01543) 256979 Fax: (01543) 251516 *Computer researchers & developers*

▶ James Swinton & Co., 11 Noble Place, Hawick, Roxburghshire, TD9 9QF Tel: (01450) 372470 Fax: (01450) 378967

James Tainsh & Sons, Drummondernoch Farm, Comrie, Crieff, Perthshire, PH6 2JB Tel: (01764) 670337 Fax: (01764) 670397 *Agricultural merchants & contractors*

James Technical Services, 3 Talgarth Business Park, Trefecca Road, Talgarth, Brecon, Powys, LD3 0PQ Tel: (01874) 711209 Fax: (01874) 712010 E-mail: sales@jts-test-chambers.co.uk *Environmental test equipment*

James Thornbeer Ltd, Holmes Mill, Greenacre Street, Clitheroe, Lancashire, BB7 1EB Tel: (01200) 423601 Fax: (01200) 429332 E-mail: sales@jamesthornber.com *Textile manufrs*

▶ James Timms Transport Ltd, 5 Quedgeley Trading Estate West, Bristol Road, Hardwicke, Gloucester, GL2 4PA Tel: (01452) 722880 Fax: (01452) 722992

▶ James Tobin & Son Ltd, Martland Industrial Estate, Smarts Heath Lane, Woking, Surrey, GU22 0RQ Tel: (01483) 233084

Tony James Component Wiring Ltd, Unit E10 Speedwell Way, Harleston Industrial Estate, Harleston, Norfolk, IP20 9EH Tel: (01379) 854485 Fax: (01379) 852718 E-mail: enquires@tonyjames.co.uk *Cable assembly, harness, electrical & electronic manufrs*

▶ James Upholstery, 3 Booth Road, Little Lever, Bolton, BL3 1JY Tel: (01204) 408993 E-mail: jamesupholstery@ntlworld.com *Re-upholstery of dental chairs, ergonomic seating*

James W Parsons Ltd, 5 Printing House Yard, Hackney Road, London, E2 7PR Tel: (020) 7739 0768 Fax: (020) 7739 1258 E-mail: jamesw@parsonslimited.fsnet.co.uk *International freight forwarders*

James Walker & Sons Blankets Ltd, Station Road, Mirfield, West Yorkshire, WF14 8NA Tel: (01924) 492277 Fax: (01924) 480263 E-mail: sales@jwalker.co.uk *Hospital textile suppliers*

▶ James Walton, Leyshon Road, Wheatley, Oxford, OX33 1XF Tel: 01865 875519 E-mail: contact@acdisco.com *ACDisco Light and PA Hire. Oxford. Supplies lighting and sound equipment systems to a variety of different events from to 2000 people.*

▶ James West Ltd, 1 Office Block 1 Southlink Business Park, Hamilton Street, Oldham, OL4 1DE Tel: 0161-624 1956 Fax: 0161-628 4474

James Whiteside & Co., 141 Church Lane, East Peckham, Tonbridge, Kent, TN12 5JJ Tel: (01622) 871513 Fax: (01622) 871992 E-mail: jameswhitesideco@btopenworld.com *Catering equipment manufrs*

▶ James Wilson & Son Auchmillan Ltd, Auchmillan, Mauchline, Ayrshire, KA5 6HD Tel: (01290) 550253 Fax: (01290) 550253

Jameson Curtains Ltd, 320 Cheapside, Birmingham, B5 6AX Tel: 0121-622 6620 Fax: 0121-622 6779 E-mail: furnishings@jamesons.demon.co.uk *Manufacturers of custom made contract curtains*

David Jameson Ltd, 116a High Street, Epping, Essex, CM16 4AF Tel: (01992) 560660 Fax: (01992) 577945 E-mail: russell@davidjameson.co.uk *Independent financial advisors*

Jameson Press, 21 The Fairways, New River Trading Estate, Cheshunt, Waltham Cross, Hertfordshire, EN8 0NL Tel: (01992) 635836 Fax: (01992) 636865 E-mail: info@jamesonpress.co.uk *Lithographic printers*

W.E. Jameson & Son Ltd, Foxholme Lane Mill, Masham Ripon, N Yorkshire, Ripon, North Yorkshire, HG4 4EL Tel: (01765) 689666 Fax: (01765) 689662 *Animal feed manufrs*

▶ Louis James-Parker, Cedars East, Chapel Road, West Row, Bury St. Edmunds, Suffolk, IP28 8PA Tel: (01638) 713350 E-mail: Louisjp@gmail.com *Photography services*

▶ James's Gourmet Coffee Co. Ltd, Cropper Row, Haigh Industrial Estate, Ross-on-Wye, Herefordshire, HR9 5LA Tel: (0870) 7870233 Fax: (01989) 566244 E-mail: peter@jamesgourmetcoffee.com *Craft coffee roasters.*"Coffees of excellence from farm to cup.*

Jamestan Engineering Ltd, Kynochs, Nuttaberry, Bideford, Devon, EX39 4DT Tel: (01237) 471878 Fax: (01237) 471370 *Precision engineers*

▶ Jamie Ambler Studio, 34 Headlands, Kettering, Northamptonshire, NN15 7HP Tel: (01536) 525467 Fax: 01536 312535 E-mail: sales@bluemoonstudios.uk.com *Bluemoon Studios Ltd is a design driven, promotional merchandising comany with over 25 years experience. We are located in the heart of England and provide promotional products from a-z.*

Jamies Tiles, Wear Street, Sunderland, SR5 2BH Tel: 0191-548 5678 Fax: 0191-548 2906 E-mail: sales@jamiestiles.co.uk *Ceramic tiles distributors*

▶ Jamie's Trophies, 31 Westgate, Ripon, North Yorkshire, HG4 2BQ Tel: (01765) 692233

Jamieson & Allan Construction, Unit 8, Bourtree Technology Park, Minto Drive, Altens Industrial Estate, Aberdeen, AB12 3LW Tel: (01224) 895333

▶ Jamieson Contracting Co. Ltd, Pitreavie Business Park, Queensferry Road, Dunfermline, Fife, KY11 8PU Tel: (01383) 721827 Fax: (01383) 721927

▶ Jamieson (Environmental Services) Ltd, 142 Busby RF, Clarkston, Glasgow, G76 8BG Tel: 0141-644 5191 Fax: 0141-644 1696 E-mail: sales@jamiesonenvironmental.co.uk *Industrial ventilation & dust & fume control, filter plant maintenance & COSHH survey reporting. Specialists in ventilation & air treatment. Years of experience, an enthusiasm & commitment to do the job right first time combined with the highest standards of equipment & service mean that we are a name you can trust*

Jamieson-Macgregor Ltd, Kelliebank, Alloa, Clackmannanshire, FK10 1NU Tel: (01259) 722725 Fax: (01259) 217165 E-mail: admin@jmark.co.uk *Engineers & fabricators*

Jamieson's Blinds, 54 Exley Lane, Elland, West Yorkshire, HX5 0SW Tel: (01484) 402299 Fax: (01422) 377363 *Blind retailers suppliers*

▶ Jami-Q's T-Shirt Printers, Unit 6, Wrexham Indust Estate, Wrexham, Clwyd, LL13 9RF Tel: (01978) 660220 Fax: (01978) 664604 E-mail: sales@jamiqs.co.uk *Suppliers of work & leisurewear, embroiderers printers & re-labellers*

Jamison & Green Ltd, 102-108 Ann Street, Belfast, BT1 3HU Tel: (028) 9032 2444 Fax: (028) 9033 0491 E-mail: sales@jamisonandgreen.co.uk *Hardware & tool merchants*

Jammal Trust Bank, 80 Berkeley Court, London, NW1 5ND Tel: (020) 7486 1314 Fax: (020) 7486 1315 *Financial services*

Jammers - Chalkboard artist and signwriter, Trinity Grange, Kidderminster, Worcestershire, DY10 2BJ Tel: (07866) 565081 E-mail: jammersart@googlemail.com *Professional Chalkboard and Blackboard Artist. Chalkboard, Blackboard, A-board and poster signwriting. midlands based nationwide travel.*

▶ Jammin Entertainments, Queen Street, Swaffham, Norfolk, PE37 7BZ Tel: (01760) 722247 E-mail: enquiry@jamminentertainments.co.uk *Bouncy castle, Slide,Adult inflatables,rodeo bull hire, Fairground rides*

Jammy Badge Co., Claimont, Victoria Street, Combe Martin, Ilfracombe, Devon, EX34 0JR Tel: (01271) 882524 *Badge manufrs*

Jammy Kids, Roseville House, Roseville Road, Leeds, LS7 1BQ Tel: 0113-244 6780 Fax: 0113-244 6780 *Childrens clothing*

Jampel Davison & Bell, 210a Tufnell Park Road, London, N7 0PZ Tel: (020) 7272 0562 Fax: (020) 7263 4005 E-mail: info@jamdavbell.co.uk *Structural consulting engineers*

▶ Jan De Vries Health Care Ltd, Auchenkyle, South Wood Road, Troon, Ayrshire, KA10 7EL Tel: (01292) 317485

Jan Engineering Ltd, Cheethams Mill, Park Street, Stalybridge, Cheshire, SK15 2BT Tel: 0161-338 6024 Fax: 0161-338 6024 *General engineers*

Jana International Ltd, 4 Benson Road, Nuffield Industrial Estate, Poole, Dorset, BH17 0GB Tel: (01202) 673636 Fax: (01202) 675701 E-mail: janaint@btconnect.com *Electronics consultants & designers*

Janal Bindings, Unit 11 Mahal Business Centre, 270 St. Saviours Road, Leicester, LE5 4HG Tel: 0116-273 1155 *Cloth binding distribution*

Jancy Engineering Inc, New Hall Hey Road, Rossendale, Lancashire, BB4 6HR Tel: (01706) 229490 Fax: (01706) 830496 E-mail: sales@jancy.com *Portable magnetic drilling machine manufrs*

Janda Barcode Label Services, Unit 17 Progress Business Park, Orders Lane, Kirkham, Preston, PR4 2TZ Tel: (01772) 686651 Fax: (01772) 684106 E-mail: sales@jandadigital.co.uk *Barcode labels*

▶ Jandle Supplies, 87 White Horse Lane, London Colney, St. Albans, Hertfordshire, AL2 1JW Tel: (01727) 824518 Fax: (01727) 824518 E-mail: desmondodonnell@hotmail.com *Janitorial products, cleaning chemicals & paper supplies*

Jane Chantler Ltd, Clifford House, Market Street, Brough, Kirkby Stephen, Cumbria, CA17 4AX Tel: (01768) 341296 E-mail: jane@touchstone2000.freeserve.co.uk *Designers & manufacturers of small runs of silver & gold items*

Jane Packer Ltd, 32-34 New Cavendish Street, London, W1G 8UE Tel: (020) 7486 1300 E-mail: sales@janepacker.com *Florist*

▶ Jane Phillips, The Quadrant, Parkway Avenue, Sheffield, S9 4WG Tel: 0114 227 0022

Jane's Information Group, 163 Brighton Road, Coulsdon, Surrey, CR5 2YH Tel: (020) 8700 3700 Fax: (020) 8763 1005 E-mail: info@janes.com *Publishers*

▶ Jangi Electronics, 10 The Bramblings, Bicester, Oxfordshire, OX26 6SU Tel: (07851) 425703 E-mail: sales@jangielectronics.co.uk *Jangi Electronics specialise in the Design of Electrical and Electronic Bespoke Interfaces for the Industrial market. We also offer Electronic Design, Assembly and Test of Prototype Units.*

▶ Jangro Janitorial Equipment, James House Worsley Road Industrial Estate, Worsley Road, Farnworth, Bolton, BL4 9NL Tel: (01204) 795955 Fax: (01204) 576801 *Janitorial suppliers*

Janilec : Cleaning & Janitorial Supplies, Kingswood House, 26a St. Dunstans Hill, Sutton, Surrey, SM1 2UE Tel: (020) 8641 9996 Fax: (020) 8641 9997 E-mail: sales@janilecsupplies.co.uk *Suppliers of cleaning and janitorial products including dry & wet cleaners, dispensers and machines, hygiene & cosmetics. We supply health clubs, schools, restaurants, hotels and offices.*

Janitorial Express, 3 Brewery Road, London, N7 9QJ Tel: (020) 7700 3322 Fax: (020) 7700 2299 E-mail: info@janitorialexpress.co.uk *Janitorial products manufrs*

▶ Janitorial Supplies Huntly Ltd, Bogside Cottage, West Adamston, Drumblade, Huntly, Aberdeenshire, AB54 6AJ Tel: (01466) 740335 Fax: (01466) 740335 E-mail: hall@jslhuntley.fsnet.co.uk *Toiletries wholesalers*

Jannock Cleaning Services, Captiva House, Queensway, Banbury, Oxfordshire, OX16 9NF Tel: (01295) 277737 Fax: (01295) 277732 *Commercial cleaning suppliers & contractors*

Janome Group UK Ltd, Southside, Bredbury, Stockport, Cheshire, SK6 2SP Tel: 0161-430 6011 Fax: 0161-494 0179 *Sewing machine & scissor distributors*

Janousek Racing Boats Ltd, 1a Abbot Close, Byfleet, West Byfleet, Surrey, KT14 7JN Tel: (01932) 353421 Fax: (01932) 336381 *Racing boats sales & manufrs*

▶ Jansoft Computer Consultants, 5 Penrwyn Court, Eynesbury, St. Neots, Cambridgeshire, PE19 2SU Tel: (01480) 218536 *IT consultancy*

▶ Janson Bridging (UK) Ltd, Charles House, Toutley Rd, Wokingham, Berkshire, RG41 1QN Tel: 0845 5262050 Fax: 0118-979 5472 E-mail: sales@jansonbridging.co.uk Principal Export Areas: Worldwide *Janson Bridges (UK) Ltd: covering the United Kingdom & Ireland are suppliers of Temporary Bridges, Panel Bridges, Footbridges, Pontoons and Linkspans. We offer a service which includes delivery, installation and commissioning. In addition to the above services we offer a full design service through an associate company of chartered consulting engineers. We are familiar with Highway and Railway requirements and our products are designed to meet European Standards and regulations. Whether it is highways, off-highways, private or port use, Janson Bridging (UK) has a solution and a proven track record to back it up.*

Janssen Animal Health, PO Box 79, High Wycombe, Buckinghamshire, HP12 4EG Tel: (01494) 567555 Fax: (01494) 567556 E-mail: ahealth@jacgb.jnj.com *Market ovals for farms & vets*

Janus Alarms Ltd, 95 Malvern Road, Worcester, WR2 4LJ Tel: (01905) 428971 Fax: (01905) 428866 E-mail: j.carvill@which.net *Alarm system installers*

▶ Jany, St. James Buildings, 79 Oxford Street, Manchester, M1 6FQ Tel: 0161-228 2798 Fax: 0161-237 9429 E-mail: sales@jany.co.uk *Vehicle seating manufrs*

Japanese Computer Services, Suffolk House, George Street, Croydon, CR0 1PE Tel: (020) 8662 4450 Fax: (020) 8662 4455 E-mail: info@japancs.com *Computer services*

Japanese Water Gardens, 251 Toton Lane, Stapleford, Nottingham, NG9 7JA Tel: 0115-939 7926 Fax: 0115-949 0451 *Aquatic suppliers*

Japhlin Computer Repairs, 77 Weeping Cross, Stafford, ST17 0DQ Tel: (01785) 663400 Fax: (01785) 665807 E-mail: phil@japhlin.co.uk *Computer maintenance repair & consultancy*

Japinda Products Ltd, Constellation Works, Fernhurst Street, Chadderton, Oldham, OL1 2RN Tel: 0161-620 4231 Fax: 0161-627 0914 E-mail: sales@japinda.co.uk *Luggage importers*

Jaques International, Orchard End, Shobdon, Leominster, Herefordshire, HR6 9NE Tel: (01568) 708644 Fax: (01568) 708166 E-mail: sales@jacquesint.com *Agricultural construction*

Jara Tube Manipulators Ltd, Unit 4 Block 3, Wednesbury Trading Estate, Wednesbury, West Midlands, WS10 7JN Tel: 0121-556 6141 Fax: 0121-556 6854 E-mail: sales@jaratube.co.uk *Tube manipulation & tubular fabrications*

▶ Jardak Services Ltd, PO Box 187, Welwyn Garden City, Hertfordshire, AL8 6AL Tel: (01707) 321225 Fax: (01438) 820004 E-mail: info@jardak.co.uk *Office cleaners*

Jardin Corrugated Cases Ltd, Elean Business Park, Sutton, Ely, Cambridgeshire, CB6 2QE Tel: (01353) 778522 Fax: (01353) 777708 E-mail: jcc.enquiries@jccltd.com *Cardboard corrugated boxes & horticultural packing products manufrs*

Jardine & Associates Ltd, Scottish Technology Park, James Watt Avenue, East Kilbride, Glasgow, G75 0QD Tel: (01355) 581150 Fax: (01355) 581151 *Computer consultants*

Jardine Lloyds Underwriting Agents Ltd, Jardine House, 6 Crutched Friars, London, EC3N 2HT Tel: (020) 7528 4444 Fax: (020) 7528 4488 *Holding company*

Jarmac Ltd, Stanton House, 6 Eastham Village Road, Eastham, Wirral, Merseyside, CH62 0BJ Tel: 0151-327 7511 Fax: 0151-327 7866 E-mail: sales@jarmac.u-net.com *Lubricant additive manufrs*

▶ Jarman Design Associates Ltd, The Barn Churchill Farm, Church Hill, Whaddon, Milton Keynes, MK17 0LZ Tel: (01908) 867398 Fax: (01908) 503884 E-mail: info@jdadesign.co.uk

Jaro Screens Ltd, Unit 20 Shaftmoor Industrial Estate, 226 Shaftmoor Lane, Hall Green, Birmingham, B28 8SP Tel: 0121-702 2157 Fax: 0121-778 6995 E-mail: sales@jaroscreensltd.co.uk *Screen printing services*

Company Information

Jaroken Sheet Metal Ltd, 502-503 Ipswich Road, Trading Estate, Slough, SL1 4EP Tel: (01753) 578728 Fax: (01753) 578730 E-mail: sales@jarokensheetmetal.co.uk *Sheetmetal work, punching, forming, welding & fabricators*

Jarrards Ltd, The Old Cobblers, 52A Great North Road, Stanborough, Welwyn Garden City, Hertfordshire, AL8 7TL Tel: (01707) 323239 Fax: (01707) 336116 E-mail: jarrardsltd@aol.com *Electrical contractors*

Jarrett & Lawson Ltd, 5 The Old Quarry, Nene Valley Business Park, Oundle, Peterborough, PE8 4HN Tel: (01832) 275551 Fax: (01832) 275553 E-mail: jarrettlawson@pgrconstructions.co.uk *Joinery manufrs*

Jarretts Transport Ltd, 115-121 Waterworks Road, Norwich, NR2 4DE Tel: (01603) 621862 Fax: (01603) 629087 E-mail: info@jarrettsremovals.co.uk *Removal contractors services*

Jarrobs Ltd, Units 1-5, Excalibur Industrial Estate, Fields Road, Alsager, Stoke-on-Trent, ST7 2LX Tel: (01270) 878711 Fax: (01270) 882464 E-mail: sales@jarrobs.co.uk Principal Export Areas: Central/East Europe, West Europe & North America *Jarrobs Ltd provide the ultimate precision sheet metal solution. Manufacturing the complete range, from simple brackets to large fabrications. We offer a full service from engineering drawings, laser profiling, cnc punching, welding & fabrication. We are specialists in sheet metal finishes, powder coating, stove enamelling and painting and we offer a wide range of finishes, colours and textures both stoved or air dried.*

Jarrold & Sons Ltd, Whitefriars, Norwich, NR3 1SH Tel: (01603) 660211 Fax: (01603) 630162 E-mail: info@njp.co.uk *Web offset printing* Also at: Thetford

Jarroy Importers Ltd, Unit 8 Heron Industrial Estate, Barbers Road, London, E15 2PE Tel: (020) 8519 7780 Fax: (020) 8519 7265 E-mail: info@jarroy.com *Novelty importers & exporters*

▶ Jarvey Stone Ltd, 15a Edinburgh Road, Bathgate, West Lothian, EH48 1BA Tel: (01506) 632565 Fax: (01506) 634566

▶ Jarvie Plant Ltd, Craigentinny Avenue North, Edinburgh, EH6 7LJ Tel: 0131-553 6994 Fax: 0131-553 6982 E-mail: sales@jarvieplant.co.uk

▶ Jarvie Plant Ltd, 295 Edmiston Drive, Glasgow, G51 3RN Tel: 0141-445 2121 Fax: 0141-440 2847

▶ Jarvie Plant Ltd, Dalgrain Road, Grangemouth, Stirlingshire, FK3 8ET Tel: (01324) 496500 Fax: (01324) 665117 E-mail: info@jarvieplant.co.uk

W. & A. Jarvie, Wester Auchenrivoch, Banton, Kilsyth, Glasgow, G65 0QZ Tel: (01236) 823297 Fax: (01236) 823297 E-mail: walter@wajarvie.freeserve.co.uk *Scientific instrument services*

Jarvis, Eynsford Road, Swanley, Kent, BR8 8EJ Tel: (01322) 615963 Fax: (01322) 667154 E-mail: jarvisexhibition@btconnect.com *Exhibition & conference organisers*

▶ Jarvis Couriers, 109 Oakridge Road, Basingstoke, Hampshire, RG21 5RW Tel: (01256) 884103 Fax: (01256) 361753 *Sameday nationwide Courier service.*

Jarvis Engineering Ltd, Oakridge Road, High Wycombe, Buckinghamshire, HP11 2PA Tel: (01494) 530123 Fax: (01494) 472864 E-mail: jarvis.engineering@virgin.net *Precision engineering services*

Jarvis & Evered Ltd, Priorswood Industrial Estate, Taunton, Somerset, TA2 8DG Tel: (01823) 337141 Fax: (01823) 323475 E-mail: jon@jarvisevered.com *Electrical engineers*

Jarvis H Son Joinery Ltd, Longbeck Trading Estate, Redcar, Cleveland, TS11 6HH Tel: (01642) 482366 Fax: (01642) 484015 E-mail: admin@jarvis.co.uk *Joinery manufrs*

Jarvis Heating Ltd, Jarvis House, 212 Station Road, Harpenden, Hertfordshire, AL5 4EH Tel: (01582) 761211 Fax: (01582) 764100 E-mail: info@jarvisheating.co.uk *Plumbing & heating engineers*

Jarvis Homes Ltd, No.1 Waterside, Station Road, Harpenden, Hertfordshire, AL5 4US Tel: (01582) 761211 Fax: (01582) 764100 *Property investment services*

Jarvis Infrastructure Services, Holbeck Depot, Nineveh Road, Leeds, LS11 9QG Tel: (01904) 712712 Fax: 0113-389 3134 *Rail service*

Jarvis Manufacturing Ltd, 22b Hawthorn Road, Eastbourne, East Sussex, BN23 6QA Tel: (01323) 411993 Fax: (01323) 649662 E-mail: info@jarvismanufacturing.co.uk *Textile products manufrs*

Jarvis Piccadilly, Portland Street, Manchester, M1 4PH Tel: 0161-236 8414 Fax: 0161-228 1568 E-mail: jshaw@jarvis.co.uk *Conference centre & hotel services*

Jarvis Print Ltd, Unit 2-19 Lakeside Business Park, Pinfold Road, Thurmaston, Leicester, LE4 8AT Tel: 0116-260 3026 Fax: 0116-264 0222 E-mail: jarvis.print@btinternet.com *Jarvis Print offer a comprehensive range of silk screen printing services including point of sale, vehicle livery, boat livery, shop frontage, cosmetic displays, exhibition stands, banners and signs to specification. With over 29 years experience in the industry we offer a comprehensive service from design to print.*

▶ Jary & Greensides, The Street, Framingham Pigot, Norwich, NR14 7QJ Tel: (01508) 493891 Fax: (01508) 495116

Jarzon Plastics Ltd, Golden Cresent, Hayes, Middlesex, UB3 1AQ Tel: (020) 8573 1537 Fax: (020) 8756 0138 E-mail: sales@jarzonplastics.co.uk *Manufacturers of (plastic) injection mouldings*

Jas Bolland Engineering Ltd, Blantyre Industrial Estate, Blantyre, Glasgow, G72 0TT Tel: (01698) 821009 Fax: (01698) 820011 E-mail: sales@bolland-eng.co.uk *Jig & fixture manufrs*

Jas Print Ltd, 12 Tower Road, Washington, Tyne & Wear, NE37 2SH Tel: 0191-417 6766 Fax: 0191-415 1351 E-mail: john@jasprint.com *Technical publication printers*

Jasco UK Ltd, 18 Oak Industrial Park, Chelmsford Road, Dunmow, Essex, CM6 1XN Tel: (01371) 876988 Fax: (01371) 875597 E-mail: inbox@jasco.co.uk *Sales & service analytical (scientific) instrument distributors*

Jaser Electronics Ltd, 1 Castle Mews, Rugby, Warwickshire, CV21 2XL Tel: (01788) 574796 Fax: (01788) 561352 E-mail: sales@jaser.co.uk *Electronic designers, consultants & engineers*

Jason Abbot Gunmakers Ltd, The Swan, 5 High Street, Tetsworth, Thame, Oxfordshire, OX9 7AB Tel: (01844) 281765 Fax: (01844) 281815 E-mail: jasonabbott@bicksnet.co.uk *Gunsmiths*

Jason Engineering Ltd, 27-33 High Street, Totton, Southampton, SO40 9HL Tel: (023) 8066 3535 Fax: (023) 8066 3531 *Using an Integrated approach from design through to final inspection Jason Engineering provides a mechanical machining service approved to ISO 9001. This includes qualified material selection, production methodology with all CNC machining, a turning capacity up to 1.4m diameter or 3m milling. Full lot traceability and bonded materials control.*

Jason Hydraulics Ltd, Burford Road, Minster Lovell, Witney, Oxfordshire, OX29 0RD Tel: (01993) 705565 Fax: (01993) 776856 E-mail: sales@jasonhydraulics.co.uk *Hydraulic cylinder service, repair & ram manufrs*

Jason Industrial Ltd, Unit 29 Normanby Park Workshops, Normanby Road, Scunthorpe, North Lincolnshire, DN15 8QZ Tel: (01724) 861006 Fax: (01724) 869846 *Vulcanising services & conveyor manufrs* Also at: Redcar

Jason Plastics Ltd, Prettywood, Bury New Road, Heap Bridge, Bury, Lancashire, BL9 7HZ Tel: 0161-763 8000 Fax: 0161-763 8052 E-mail: sales@jasonpackaging.co.uk *Polythene & polyethylene carrier bag manufrs*

Jason Steel Fabrications, 1 Bangley Farm, Hints Road, Mile Oak, Tamworth, Staffordshire, B78 3DJ Tel: (01827) 287207 Fax: (01827) 287207 *Steel fabricators*

Jasons Food Trade Supplies, 1a Edward Street, Stone, Staffordshire, ST15 8HN Tel: (01785) 819317 Fax: (01785) 811278 *Food trade suppliers*

Jasper Covers Ltd, The Mews, Heathfield Road, Portsmouth, PO2 8AG Tel: (023) 9271 1358 Fax: (023) 9261 2085 *Boat cover manufrs*

Jaspers Treburley Ltd, Treburley, Launceston, Cornwall, PL15 9PU Tel: (01579) 370461 Fax: (01579) 370192 E-mail: admin@jaspersbeef.co.uk *Abattoir retailers*

Jastac, 341 Court Road, Orpington, Kent, BR6 9BZ Tel: (01689) 873175 Fax: (01689) 873175 *Solder tag & terminal manufactures & stockholders*

Jasun Filtration plc, Riverside House, Parrett Way, Bridgwater, Somerset, TA6 5LB Tel: (01278) 452277 Fax: (01278) 450873 E-mail: info@jfilters.com *Carbon & air filter manufrs*

Jaswal Fashions, Gas Street, Back of Kempton Building, Leicester, LE1 3XL Tel: 0116-253 1625 Fax: 0116-251 2204 *Childrens wear manufrs*

Jat Airways, 7 Dering Street, London, W1S 1AE Tel: (020) 7629 6629 Fax: (020) 7629 6500 E-mail: sales@jatlondon.com *Airline company*

Jatech Ltd, 2 Springfield Business Centre, Brunel Way, Stroudwater Business Park, Stonehouse, Gloucestershire, GL10 3SX Tel: (01453) 791909 Fax: (01453) 828893 E-mail: info@jatech.co.uk *Computer consultants*

Jaten Fashion Manufacturing Co, Monemore Green Site, Bilston Road, Wolverhampton, WV2 2HT Tel: (01902) 455009 Fax: (01902) 455004 E-mail: jatenfashion@aol.com *Army surplus & work wear manufrs*

Jaton, Patriot Drive, Rooksley, Milton Keynes, MK13 8PB Tel: (01908) 690055 Fax: (01908) 690401 E-mail: milton.keynes@outlet-jaton.com *Fastener distributors*

Javac UK Ltd, 6 Drake Court, Middlesbrough, Cleveland, TS2 1RS Tel: (01642) 232880 Fax: (01642) 232870 E-mail: info@javac.co.uk *Vacuum pump & refrigeration manufrs*

Javah Ltd, Warwick Mills, Howard Street, Batley, West Yorkshire, WF17 6JH Tel: (01924) 452156 Fax: (01924) 455015 E-mail: sales@javah.com *Specialist suppliers of Steel, Polyester, Woven, PP Strapping, Seals & Buckles, Stretch film, Packaging Staples & Tapes, Hand Tools & Machines. Edge Protection, Dunnage Air Bags and much more*

Javaria Textiles Ltd, 4 Bay Street, Blackburn, BB1 5NJ Tel: (01254) 680777 Fax: (01254) 261688 *Textiles manufrs*

Javelin Computers, Unit C, Varis Business Park, Challenge Way, Blackburn, BB1 5QB Tel: (01254) 505505 Fax: (01254) 691466 E-mail: purchasing@javelincomputers.com *Computer hardware & software mail-orders*

▶ Javelin Controls Ltd, 10 Warbleton Road, Chineham, Basingstoke, Hampshire, RG24 8RF Tel: 01256 812557 Fax: 01256 812557 E-mail: sales@javelin-controls.com *Javelin Controls Ltd, based in Berkshire, design systems for special purpose machinery & process automation control, including electrical design, instrumentation, PLC software programming & HMI & SCADA design*

Javelin Irrigation Systems Ltd, The Pump House, Belvoir Way, Fairfield Industrial Estate, Louth, Lincolnshire, LN11 0YA Tel: (01507) 607175 Fax: (01507) 607521 E-mail: mail@javelinirrigation.co.uk *Importers of irrigation & pumping equipment*

Javelin Plastics & Tools, Unit 1M Albany Park Industrial Estate, Frimley Road, Camberley, Surrey, GU16 7PE Tel: (01276) 64446 Fax: (01276) 691174 E-mail: enquries@javelinplastics.co.uk *Plastics mould toolmakers*

Jawads Frozen Foods, 51 Ayres Road, Manchester, M16 9NH Tel: 0161-227 1786 Fax: 0161-227 1786 *Frozen foods distributors*

▶ Jaxpal Ltd, Unit 37 Planetary Industrial Estate, Planetary Road, Willenhall, West Midlands, WV13 3XB Tel: (01902) 721066 Fax: (01902) 865839

Jaxpal Ltd, Unit 37 Planetary Industrial Estate, Planetary Road, Willenhall, West Midlands, WV13 3XB Tel: (01902) 721066 Fax: (01902) 865839 E-mail: sales@jaxpal.co.uk *Corrugated box manufacturers containers*

▶ Jay, 59 Grove Gardens, Southampton, SO19 9QZ Tel: (07840) 183969 E-mail: graftersinfo@hotmail.co.uk *Window cleaner based in Southampton, Hampshire, domestic and commercial, reach and wash system*

Jay Be Ltd, Spen Lane, Gomersal, Cleckheaton, West Yorkshire, BD19 4PN Tel: (01924) 517820 Fax: (01924) 517910 E-mail: sales@jaybe.co.uk *Bed manufrs*

▶ Jay Cee Lichfield Engineering Ltd, Coppice Side Industrial Estate, Brownhills, Walsall, WS8 7EX Tel: (01543) 377633 Fax: (01543) 374100 E-mail: jc@jaycee-eng.co.uk *Engineering*

Darren Jay Entertainments, 31, Colonial Road, Bordesley Green, Birmingham, B9 5NR Tel: 0121-247 2332 Fax: 0121-247 2332 E-mail: sjservices@blueyonder.co.uk *Mobile dj services*

Jay & Davies (Crane Hire), 14 Sweetmans Yard, Harrow Road, Plough Lane, Hereford, HR4 0EE Tel: (01432) 267043 Fax: (01432) 270754 *Crane hire*

▶ Jay Dee Windows, Unit 32a Westminster Industrial Park, Rossfield Road, Ellesmere Port, CH65 3DU Tel: 0151-357 2112 Fax: 0151-357 2122 *Window frame manufrs*

Jay Engineering Consultancy Ltd, 178 Aldridge Road, Streetly, Sutton Coldfield, West Midlands, B74 3TP Tel: 0121-353 6400 Fax: 0121-353 9600 E-mail: john.butler@iee.org *Engineering consultants*

Jay House Ltd, Unit 6/B, Park Lane Trading Estate, Park Lane, Corsham, Wiltshire, SN13 9LG Tel: (01249) 714555 Fax: (01249) 714999 E-mail: sales@fotospeed.com *Photo chemicals*

Peter Jay & Partners, 176A Sutherland Ave, London, W9 1HR Tel: (020) 7286 6011 Fax: (020) 7286 6088 *Building service engineers*

Jay Rubber Linings Ltd, 132 Queen Street, Crewe, CW1 4AU Tel: (01270) 254655 Fax: (01270) 254526 E-mail: sales@jayrubberlinings.co.uk *Pipe, pump & tank linings*

Jay Shah, 56 Portland Cres, Stanmore, Middx, HA7 1NB Tel: (020) 8954 9441 Fax: (020) 8357 8391 E-mail: jayshah2002@hotmail.com *Fresh produce distribs*

Jay Stores, 130 Lower Road, London, SE16 2UG Tel: (020) 7237 2410 Fax: (020) 7237 2410 *Industrial clothing distributors*

Jay Tooling Co., Pindar Road, Hoddesdon, Hertfordshire, EN11 0DA Tel: (01992) 462875 Fax: (01992) 451422 E-mail: jaytool@btinternet.com *Toolmaking services*

Jaybeam Ltd, Rutherford Drive, Park Farm South, Wellingborough, Northamptonshire, NN8 6AX Tel: (01933) 408408 Fax: (01933) 408404 E-mail: sales@jaybeamwireless.com *Antenna manufacturers & designers*

Jaybee Engineering Co Brighton Ltd, Avis Way, Newhaven, East Sussex, BN9 0DS Tel: (01273) 514623 Fax: (01273) 513702 E-mail: sales@jaybee-eng.co.uk *CNC engineering services or machinists & precision engineers*

Jaybee Plastic Products, 10 Pywell Court, Willowbrook East Industrial Estate, Corby, Northamptonshire, NN17 5WA Tel: (01536) 266288 Fax: (01536) 266370 *Plastic products manufrs*

Jaycare Ltd, New York Way, New York Industrial Park, Newcastle Upon Tyne, NE27 0QF Tel: 0191-296 0303 Fax: 0191-296 1842 *Injection mouldings manufrs*

Jaycee Packaging Ltd, 8 Fairefield Crescent, Glenfield, Leicester, LE3 8EH Tel: 0116-231 4994 Fax: 0116-231 4989 *Manufacturers of cardboard boxes, cases & containers*

Jayclem Products Ltd, Newbold Road, Kirkby Mallory, Leicester, LE9 7QG Tel: (01455) 823560 Fax: (01455) 824846 E-mail: jclem@webleicester.co.uk *Steel cutting services*

Jayco Welding Supplies, 10 Old Bridge Close, Bursledon, Southampton, SO31 8AX Tel: (023) 8040 2025 Fax: (023) 8040 5812 E-mail: gloves@jaycowelding.freeserve.co.uk *Suppliers of welding & industrial leather gloves*

Jaycotts Sewing Centre, Unit 14 Brierley Business Centre, Mirion Street, Crewe, CW1 2AZ Tel: (01270) 617171 E-mail: info@jaycotts.co.uk *Sewing machine sales service*

Jaydee Aquatics, Mold Road, Cefn-y-Bedd, Wrexham, Clwyd, LL12 9UR Tel: (01978) 854254 Fax: (01978) 762051 *Tropical fish & equipment*

Jaydee Heating Ltd, Nobel Road, Wester Gourdie Industrial Estate, West Gourdie Industrial Estate, Dundee, DD2 4XE Tel: (01382) 611118 Fax: (01382) 400540 *Heating engineers*

▶ Jaydee Heating Ltd, 78 Jane Street, Edinburgh, EH6 5HG Tel: 0131-555 0388 Fax: 0131-555 2826

Jayem Blinds, 3 Scotter Road, Bournemouth, BH7 6LY Tel: (01202) 422525 Fax: (01202) 422525 E-mail: sales@jayemblinds.co.uk *Blind contractors & manufrs*

▶ Jayen Ltd, Goose Green Marsh, St Peter, Jersey, JE3 7BU Tel: (01534) 871086

Jayess Tools, 11 Star Road, Partridge Green, Horsham, West Sussex, RH13 8RA Tel: (01403) 711006 Fax: (01403) 711345 E-mail: enquiries@jayesstools.co.uk *Carbide cutter manufrs*

Jayex Technology Ltd, Unit 13 Sovereign Park, Coronation Road, London, NW10 7QP Tel: (020) 8838 6222 Fax: (020) 8838 3222 E-mail: sales@jayex.com *LED suppliers*

Jayfour Packaging, 93 Charles Henry Street, Birmingham, B12 0SJ Tel: 0121-622 4451 Fax: 0121-666 6502 E-mail: sales@jayfourpkg.com *Packaging material manufrs*

▶ Jaylec Electrical Contractors Ltd, 23 Burrowfield, Welwyn Garden City, Hertfordshire, AL7 4SS Tel: (01707) 333647 Fax: (01707) 391288

Jaylew Engineering Ltd, Unit 12a Autumn Park, Dysart Road, Grantham, Lincolnshire, NG31 7DD Tel: (01476) 565986 Fax: (01476) 562540 E-mail: enquiries@jaylew.com *Precision engineers*

Jaylyn Services (Midlands) Ltd, Unit 5 Shilton Industrial Estate, Coventry, CV7 9QL Tel: (024) 7661 9298 Fax: (024) 7660 2623 *Machine tool agents & engineers*

Jaymar Freight Services Ltd, Container Base Box Lane, Renwick Road, Barking, Essex, IG11 0SQ Tel: (020) 8984 8030 Fax: (020) 8984 7379 E-mail: shipping@jaymarfreight.co.uk *Freight forwarders*

Jaymar Packaging Ltd, Jaymar House First Avenue, Crew Gates Industrial Estate, Crewe, CW1 6XS Tel: (01270) 500711 Fax: (01270) 580837 E-mail: sales@jaymar.co.uk *Carton manufrs*

Jaymark Mould & Tool Co. Ltd, Unit 1, Capital Place, Lovet Road, The Pinnacles, Harlow, Essex, CM19 5AS Tel: (01279) 427945 Fax: (01279) 641063 E-mail: jaymark@btinternet.com *Plastics mould toolmakers & diecast manufrs*

Jaymart Rubber & Plastics Ltd, Woodlands Trading Estate, Eden Vale Road, Westbury, Wiltshire, BA13 3QS Tel: (01373) 864926 Fax: (01373) 858454 E-mail: matting@jaymart.net Principal Export Areas: Africa *Mats, matting & anti-slip flooring manufacturers including antifatigue, dust barrier, fibre/coir/coconut & rubber*

Jaymig Engineering, Unit 6 Redland Close, Aldermans Green Industrial Estate, Coventry, CV2 2NP Tel: (024) 7661 8630 Fax: (024) 7661 4412 *Welding equipment manufrs*

▶ Jaynies of London, 28 Upper Road, London, E13 0DH Tel: (07876) 343938 E-mail: jaynie@jayniesof london.com *One off handmade underwear manufrs*

Jay-Pee Workwear, Unit 1, Thomas Street, Congleton, Cheshire, CW12 1QU Tel: (01260) 299706 Fax: (01260) 299757 E-mail: sales@jaypeeworkwear.co.uk *We are a family run business with almost seventy years of manufacturing experience. Our success is based on the traditions of quality, value for money and a genuine care for our customers. We are very proud of our collections of chefs wear and workwear, many of which are made in our own factory.*

Jayprint, 2a Douglas Road, Luton, LU4 8EB Tel: (01582) 490906 Fax: (01582) 490906 *Printers & lithographers*

▶ JayrConsulting Ltd Freelance Training Consultants, 33 Ixworth Close, Watermeadow Estate, Northampton, NN3 8TW Tel: 01604 642041 Fax: 01604 642041 E-mail: john.roberts@jayrconsulting.co.uk *Freelance training consultants specialising in supplying a freelance trainer for bespoke training services on clients projects, systems, applications, product implementations and roll-outs. Unix and VMS operating systems also catered for.Training needs analysis carried out where required. Courses and documentation developed and delivered uk wide*

▶ Jay's Designer Boutique Ltd, 48 Trinity House, Heather Park Drive, Wembley, Middlesex, HA0 1SU Tel: (020) 8903 7230 Fax: (0870) 7052998 E-mail: armine@jaysboutique.com *A name that invokes fashion, style and trust. Dealing with the most exclusive range of traditional and modern fashion. Providing cutting edge fashion combined with outstanding customer satisfaction is amongst our strongest strengths.**We strive to attain maximum customer satisfaction and attend to all individual requirements by taking customised orders to specification.**Our exclusive range of fashion products will enhance every individual's unique characteristics.**

▶ Jays Information Systems, 384 Baring Road, London, SE12 0EF Tel: (020) 8857 8200 Fax: (020) 8857 8200

Jays Racewear, Throstle Nest Mill, Leeds Road, Nelson, Lancashire, BB9 7QZ Tel: (01282) 677907 Fax: (01282) 697319 E-mail: sales@jaysracewear.co.uk *Flameproof clothing manufrs*

Jay's Refractory Specialists Ltd, Callywhite Lane, Dronfield, Derbyshire, S18 2XR Tel: (01246) 410241 Fax: (01246) 290221 E-mail: info@jrsuk.com *Refractory stockists & distributors*

Jays Of Yorkshire, Green Lane, Featherstone, Pontefract, West Yorkshire, WF7 6EH Tel: (01977) 792431 Fax: (01977) 600334 E-mail: info@jaysofyorkshire.co.uk *Vandal & demolition protection, steel design & fabrication service*

▶ Jaystock Distribution, Unit A3 Empress Park, Empress Road, Southampton, SO14 0JX Tel: (023) 8063 9000 Fax: (023) 8023 5325 *Motor vehicle parts & accessories*

Jaytec Glass Ltd, Jaytec House, 1 Burgess Road, Hastings, East Sussex, TN35 4NR Tel: (01424) 424181 Fax: (01424) 721224 E-mail: enquiries@jaytecglass.co.uk *We manufacture scientific glassware, producing general volumetric equipment and more specialist items for the dairy, pharmaceutical, oil & gas, sugar and educational markets. We are able to turn out new products on a short timescale, and have a wide experience in producing custom calibrated items to order.*

Jaytec Systems, 1 Woodside View, Daisy Hill, Sacriston, Durham, DH7 6BP Tel: 0191-371 0867 Fax: 0191-371 9969 E-mail: info@jaytecsystems.com *Industrial computer systems manufrs*

Jaytee Biosciences Ltd, Units 171-172, John Wilson Business Park, Chestfield, Whitstable, Kent, CT5 3RB Tel: (01227) 265333 Fax: (01227) 265331 E-mail: sales@jaytee.com *Chromatography equipment service & sales providers*

Jaytrade Cleaning Materials, Store 1 Brocks Farm, Russell Lane, Danbury, Chelmsford, CM3 4PG Tel: (01245) 224646 Fax: (01245) 225078 *Janitorial equipment suppliers*

Jaytrix Rosettes, Bryncam Farm, Argoed Road, Ammanford, Dyfed, SA18 2PR Tel: (01269) 593195 Fax: (01269) 593195 *Rosette manufrs*

Jayville Engineering Ltd, Unit A2 Halesfield 24, Telford, Shropshire, TF7 4NS Tel: (01952) 583041 Fax: (01952) 586342 *General fabrications*

▶ JayWolfe, 64 Kingsley Road, Northampton, NN2 7BL Tel: 01604 821066 E-mail: jay.wolfe@ntlworld.com *Metal fabrication*

Jaywood Joineries Ltd, Andmar House, Tondu Road, Bridgend, Mid Glamorgan, CF31 4LJ Tel: (01656) 652831 .

▶ JB Locksmith, 33 Park Road, Conisbrough, Doncaster, South Yorkshire, DN12 2EQ Tel: (01709) 867361 Fax: (01709) 867361 E-mail: john@jblocksmithdoncaster.co.uk *Locksmiths*

▶ JBC Scotland, St. Ronans Drive, Kinross, KY13 8AF Tel: (01577) 864136 Fax: (01577) 864136

▶ JBES, The Cottage, Sackville Street, Winterborne Kingston, Blandford Forum, Dorset, DT11 9BJ Tel: (01929) 471114 Fax: (01929) 472521 E-mail: jbes@supanet.com *Computer aided design and draughting specialising in As Builts and Architectural visualisations.*Plotting service available*

Jbi Technology Ltd, Unit 2-3 Bond Street, West Bromwich, West Midlands, B70 7DQ Tel: 0121-553 0500 Fax: 0121-553 5333 E-mail: info@jbitech.co.uk *A specialist in the machining of large precision components in both exotic & conventional materials. Fabrications & structures can be constructed in 5 tonnes sections, as with precision components, from samples, drawings or sketches. Where your particular requirement is for the production of non-standard components, equipment, structures & machinery, JTL has the vital expertise to assist you.*

JBL Office, 168-170 Cumnor Road, Boars Hill, Oxford, OX1 5JS Tel: (01865) 739056 Fax: (01865) 326754 E-mail: sales@jbl.co.uk *Office equipment suppliers*

▶ JBP Royalty Free, 40 Rempstone Drive, Chesterfield, Derbyshire, S41 0YB Tel: 01246 540341

▶ JBP Transport Ltd, Oakmills, Lower Mill Street, Tillicoultry, Clackmannanshire, FK13 6BP Tel: (01259) 750459 Fax: (01259) 750459

JC Fluid Power, 5 Readmans Industrial Estate, Station Road, East Tilbury, Tilbury, Essex, RM18 8QR Tel: (01375) 843995 Fax: (01375) 859010 E-mail: info@jcfluidpower.co.uk *Hydraulic engineers*

▶ JC Inflatables, 32 Lilac Avenue, Scunthorpe, South Humberside, DN16 1JG Tel: (01724) 862015 E-mail: info@jcinflatables.co.uk *Bouncy Castle Hire in Scunthorpe*

JC Trophies, The Business Centre, 21 James Road, Tyseley, Birmingham, B11 2BA Tel: 0121-707 0606 Fax: 0121-707 0609 E-mail: jdcmanufacturing@blueyonder.co.uk *Die cast manufrs*

▶ JC2 (UK) Ltd, 12 Camelot Way, Gillingham, Dorset, SP8 4SY Tel: (01747) 821900 Fax: (01747) 821088 E-mail: justinc@jc2uk.com

▶ JCB Insurance Services Ltd, Rocester, Uttoxeter, Staffordshire, ST14 5BW Tel: (01889) 590219 Fax: (01889) 590742 E-mail: insurance@jcb.com *All types of Construction related Insurance arranged including :- Owned & Hired-In Plant, Liability, Contract Works, Motor Fleet. Unique schemes for Liability and Plant All Risks.*

JCC Engineering Ltd, 50 Adderley Street, Birmingham, B9 4ED Tel: 0121-773 6900 Fax: 0121-766 7760 E-mail: jccengineering@btconnect.com *Structural steelwork fabricators*

▶ JCC Property Care Ltd, 6 Mid Street, Rosehearty, Fraserburgh, Aberdeenshire, AB43 7JS Tel: 0800 4582372 Fax: 0704 3301765 E-mail: solutions@goJCC.net *Integrated Property Care Solutions provided by John C. Crook (Part of JCC Property Care Ltd) are helping to lower the cost and raise expectations of property tenants and owners. Being based in Rosehearty, Scotland, we are able to cater for any eventuality your property may happen to experience. We aim to respond to any queries with a workable solution within 24 hours of your first call.*

JCD Electronics Ltd, 4a Oakwood Parade, Oakwood Hill, Loughton, Essex, IG10 3EL Tel: (020) 8508 3355 Fax: (020) 8508 3355 *Printed circuit assembly*

▶ JCM Electrical Services Ltd, 108 Yardley Road, Acocks Green, Birmingham, B27 6LG Tel: 0121-764 4911 Fax: 0121-707 4448

JC-One, Lomia House, Falmouth Crescent, Normanton, West Yorkshire, WF6 2SW Tel: (01924) 891793 Fax: (01924) 223681 E-mail: sales@jc-one.co.uk *Personalised business & promotional products*

JCP Consulting, Lomond House, 85 - 87 Holywood Road, Belfast, BT4 3BD Tel: (028) 9065 9299 Fax: (028) 9022 1101 E-mail: consult@jcpconsulting.co.uk *Quantity & building surveyors*

JD & MFS Wood Ltd, 3 Townfield, Rickmansworth, Hertfordshire, WD3 7DD Tel: (01923) 441644 Fax: (01923) 441644 E-mail: jon@wood-ltd.fsnet.co.uk *Computer consultancy*

JD Pipes Ltd, Green Lane, Heywood, Lancashire, OL10 2EU Tel: (01706) 364115 Fax: (01706) 366402 E-mail: heywood@jdpipes.co.uk *Plastic tube fitting distributors & manufrs* Also at: Berkhamstead, Elmstead Market, Godstone & Skipton

JD Plastics, Unit 7 The Match Factory, Speke Road, Garston, Liverpool, L19 2RF Tel: 0151-427 1500 Fax: 0151-427 1539 E-mail: sales@jdplastics.com *Plastic fabricating & machining services*

JD Profile Extrusion, 30 Balmer Cut, Buckingham Industrial Estate, Buckingham, MK18 1UL Tel: (01280) 822693 Fax: (01280) 824003 E-mail: sales@jdprofile.co.uk *Plastic extrusion manufrs*

JD Vulcanising Services Ltd, Apple Orchard House, Skelton-in-Cleveland, Saltburn-by-the-Sea, Cleveland, TS12 2AZ Tel: (01287) 651194 Fax: (01287) 651194 *Rubber & conveyor belting & vulcanising*

▶ Jdisoftware Computer Consultants, 2 Hillside Cottage, Soot Hill, Anderton, Northwich, Cheshire, CW9 6AA Tel: (01606) 871110 E-mail: sales@jdisoftware.co.uk *Computer systems consultants*

JDL For Leather Ltd, PO Box 32, Stoke-on-Trent, ST8 7DU Tel: (01782) 518564 Fax: (01782) 522264 *Leather clothing & accessory suppliers*

JDP Ltd, 65-69 Ellingham Industrial Centre, Ellingham Way, Ashford, Kent, TN23 6JU Tel: (01233) 618323 Fax: (01233) 618324 *Plastics pipe manufrs*

JDR, 131 Grenfell Road, Maidenhead, Berkshire, SL6 1EX Tel: (01628) 629450 Fax: (01628) 625459 E-mail: ralph@jdrmhead.fsnet.co.uk *Electronic instrument case manufrs*

▶ JDR Reactive Ltd, 31 Harcote Street, London, W1H 4HU Tel: (020) 7724 9361 Fax: (020) 7723 9034 E-mail: jdreactive@aol.com *CORGI registered heating & plumbing services*

JDS Plaswood Ltd, Threxton House, Threxton Road Industrial Estate, Watton, Thetford, Norfolk, IP25 6NG Tel: (01953) 881799 Fax: (01953) 884774 *Shop fitting manufrs*

Jdsu, Spinnaker House, Lime Tree Way, Chineham, Basingstoke, Hampshire, RG24 8GG Tel: (01256) 891400 Fax: (01256) 891439 E-mail: sales.uk@jdsu.com *Communication test equipment suppliers*

Jeakins Motor Ltd, Noble House, Wrexham Road, Basildon, Essex, SS15 6PX Tel: (01268) 542464 Fax: (01268) 493593 E-mail: jeakins@lineone.net *Commercial vehicle repairs & rental*

Jeakins Removals Ltd, Charles House, Denbigh Road, Basildon, Essex, SS15 6PY Tel: (01268) 417320 Fax: (01268) 414443 E-mail: enquiries@jeakins-removals.co.uk *Removal contractors, storage & haulage*

▶ Jeakins Weir Ltd, Unit 5, Lynch Road, Berkeley, Gloucestershire, GL13 9TA Tel: (01453) 810695

Jeakins Weir Ltd, Iceland House, Corporation Street, Corby, Northamptonshire, NN17 1NQ Tel: (01536) 265181 Fax: (01536) 400650 *Building contractors*

Jeaton Tapes & Abrasives Ltd, Unit 1, Manchester Mill Industrial Estate, Geoffrey St, Preston, PR1 5NR Tel: (01772) 703636 Fax: (01772) 701271 E-mail: sales@jeaton.co.uk *Self-adhesive tape & abrasive distributors*

Jebb Metals Newcastle Ltd, Station Road, Walker, Newcastle upon Tyne, NE6 3PN Tel: 0191-262 7099 Fax: 0191-262 5458 E-mail: jebbmetals@btconnect.com *Scrap metal merchants*

Jebron Ltd, Bright Street, Wednesbury, West Midlands, WS10 9HX Tel: 0121-526 2212 Fax: 0121-568 2131 E-mail: sales@jebron.co.uk *Door closer manufrs*

Jeckells & Son Ltd, 128 Bridge Road, Lowestoft, Suffolk, NR33 9JT Tel: (01502) 565007 Fax: (01502) 565606 E-mail: sales@jeckellschandlers.co.uk *Yacht chandlers*

Jeckells & Son Ltd, Riverside Road, Hoveton, Norwich, NR12 8UQ Tel: (01603) 784488 Fax: (01603) 783234 E-mail: jeckellstrimmers@ukgateway.net *Boat cover & upholstery manufrs* Also at: Oulton Broad

Jeckells Of Wroxham Ltd, Station Road, Hoveton, Norwich, NR12 8UT Tel: (01603) 782223 Fax: (01603) 784023 E-mail: sails@jeckells.co.uk *Yacht sails & rigging manufrs*

Jectabore Ltd, East Side Road, Chesterfield, Derbyshire, S41 9AT Tel: (01246) 456124 Fax: (01246) 455289 E-mail: sales@jectabore.co.uk *Drill heads refurbishing*

Jede North East, Unit B4, Benfield Business Park, Benfield Road, Newcastle Upon Tyne, NE6 4NQ Tel: 0191-238 8000 Fax: 0191-238 8001 E-mail: jede.uk@jede.com *Vending machine suppliers*

▶ Jeevan Technologies Pvt Ltd, 79 St. Marys Wharf, Blackburn, BB2 3AF Tel: (01225) 335477 Fax: E-mail: v.sathish@jeevantechnologies.com,d.kannan@jeevantechnologies.com *Jeevan offers onsite technology consulting, software solutions and Business Process Outsourcing . All functional area quality system processes are defined and implemented based on the SEI CMMI Model*

▶ Jefberry Ltd, Bridgeman House, Pindar Road, Hoddesdon, Hertfordshire, EN11 0DA Tel: (01992) 442133

Jefco Services Ltd, Queens Road, Immingham, South Humberside, DN40 1QR Tel: (01469) 574888 Fax: (01469) 574224 *Building & civil engineering contractors*

▶ Jefco Services Ltd, 1 Colin Road, Scunthorpe, South Humberside, DN16 1TT Tel: (01724) 845626 Fax: (01724) 289784

Jeffark Engineering & Metal Pressings Ltd, 2 Lane End Road, Sands Industrial Estate, High Wycombe, Buckinghamshire, HP12 4HG Tel: (01494) 471454 Fax: (01494) 471131 E-mail: enquiries@jeffark.co.uk *Pressings & general engineers*

Jefferson Air Photography, Hawarden Airport, Flint Road, Saltney Ferry, Chester, CH4 0GZ Tel: (01244) 520892 Fax: (01244) 520894 E-mail: sales@aerial-photography.net *Aerial photography services*

▶ Jefferson Computer Services, 21-23 Hollands Road, Haverhill, Suffolk, CB9 8PU Tel: (01440) 762569 Fax: (0870) 4601859 E-mail: sales@jcs.gb.net *Service & support for home & business*

Emma Jefferson, 16 Cross Bank, Great Easton, Market Harborough, Leicestershire, LE16 8SR Tel: (01536) 772074 Fax: (01536) 772134 *Nursery products*

Tom Jefferson, Far Long Park Farm, Long Park, Carlisle, CA6 4JP Tel: (01228) 675451 Fax: (01228) 675363 *Agricultural engineers & suppliers*

▶ Jeffery & Pengelly, Unit 4 Fatherford Farm, Okehampton, Devon, EX20 1QQ Tel: (01837) 52277 Fax: (01837) 55379

Jeffrey Graham Ltd, 1 Crompton Avenue, Bolton, BL2 6PG Tel: (01204) 412721 Fax: (01204) 435274 *Suspended partitions & ceilings*

Jeffrey Walton Jewellery Ltd, 62 Albion Street, Leeds, LS1 6AD Tel: 0113-246 8010 Fax: 0113-242 3751 *Jewellery repairers & manufrs*

Lincoln Jeffries Ltd, Summer Lane, Birmingham, B19 3TH Tel: 0121-359 3343 Fax: 0121-359 3343 *Airgun ammunition & lead products*

▶ Jeftex Ltd, Red Brook Mill, Bury Road, Rochdale, Lancashire, OL11 4EE Tel: (01706) 645464 E-mail: jeftex@zen.co.uk *Computer software textile machinery agents*

Jegs Electrical Ltd, 20 Progress Road, Eastwood, Leigh-On-Sea, Essex, SS9 5LW Tel: (01702) 421555 Fax: (01702) 420363 E-mail: mail@jegs.co.uk *Electrical wholesalers*

Jekyll Electronic Technology Ltd, Unit 3 Zephyr House, Calleva Park, Aldermaston, Reading, RG7 8JN Tel: 0118-981 7321 Fax: 0118-981 4743 E-mail: mail@jekyll-electronic.co.uk *Electronic equipment designers & manufrs*

▶ Jeld Wen UK Ltd, Grosvenor House, 112-114 Prince of Wales Road, Norwich, NR1 1NS Tel: (01603) 697800 Fax: (01603) 697809 E-mail: info@jeld-wen.co.uk *Manufactures of timber*

Jeld Wen UK Ltd, Retford Road, Woodhouse Mill, Sheffield, S13 9WH Tel: 0114-254 2000 Fax: 0114-269 6696 *Joinery manufrs*

▶ Jeld-Wen UK Ltd, 169 Watch House Lane, Doncaster, South Yorkshire, DN5 9LR Tel: (01302) 394000 Fax: (01302) 787383 E-mail: customer-services@jeld-wen.co.uk *Manufacturers of doors*

▶ Jell Systems, 1 Fairways View, Talbot Green, Pontyclun, Mid Glamorgan, CF72 8JG Tel: (07791) 909689 E-mail: contact@jell-systems.co.uk *IT support & services to home & business users*

Jellybean Creative Ltd, 58 Copson Street, Ibstock, Leicestershire, LE67 6LB Tel: (01530) 263025 E-mail: jellybeancreative@tiscali.co.uk *Creative design consultancy providing outstanding retail interiors,exhibition stands,pos unitry,graphic and web communication. We provide conceptual design on the latest CAD systems, from brief to build with total satisfaction.*

▶ Jellyfish, 33 Buckland Road, Newton Abbot, Devon, TQ12 4DQ Tel: (01626) 205134 E-mail: jellyfish.uk@virgin.net *Professional,Friendly,Reliable Window Cleaning Service.*Insured. Window Cleaning (frames inc), Conservatory Cleaning, Gutter and Facia Cleaning.*Domestic Homes, Residential/ Retirement Homes, Pubs and Shops.*Inside Cleans.*FREE Quotes.*Daily, Weekly, 4 Weekly, 8 Weekly Cleans.*Working Throughout the Whole Year Rain or Shine.*Traditional and Pure Water Pole Technology Methods Used.*Most work has come from Recomendation.**

Jelmead Ltd, Units 1 & 4 Francis Works, Geddings Road, Hoddesdon, Hertfordshire, EN11 0NT Tel: (01992) 442751 Fax: (01992) 463739 *Corrugated & cardboard box manufrs*

Jem Ltd, Springfield Mills, Spa Street, Ossett, West Yorkshire, WF5 0HW Tel: (01924) 277626 Fax: (01924) 270759 E-mail: jayne@jemltd.co.uk *Shop fitting manufrs & installers*

▶ Jem Business Systems, Abbey Lakes Hall, Orrell Road, Orrell, Wigan, Lancashire, WN5 8QZ Tel: (01695) 627217 *Computer software developers*

Jem Sheet Metal & Engineering Ltd, Borron Street, Portwood, Stockport, Cheshire, SK1 2JD Tel: 0161-480 2347 Fax: 0161-480 6210 E-mail: info.jem@btinternet.com *Sheet metal fabrications & engineering services*

Jemcare Training, Churchill House, Stirling Way, Borehamwood, Hertfordshire, WD6 2HP Tel: (020) 8736 0536 Fax: (020) 8736 0535 E-mail: mslyper@kinetictraining.com *Computer training/consultancy*

Jemco, The Street, Manor Farm, Calthorpe, Norwich, NR11 7QR Tel: (01263) 761798 Fax: (01263) 768142 E-mail: jim@jemco.fsnet.co.uk *Safety signs & notices suppliers*

▶ Jemco Associates, 128 Elderslie Street, Glasgow, G3 7AW Tel: 0141-564 3906

▶ JemCraft Memories, 20 Metcalfe Avenue, Stubbington, Fareham, Hampshire, PO14 2HY Tel: 07733 452151 E-mail: queries@jemcraftmemories.com *Online retailer of craft products for cardmaking and scrapbooking.*Free UK P&P and up to 65% off.*

▶ Jemelec Ltd, Unit 16 Vanguard Trading Estate, Britannia Road, Chesterfield, Derbyshire, S45 9DX Tel: (0870) 7871769 *Electrical engineering services*

The Jemma Tools Group Ltd, Bell Lane, Bayton Road Industrial Estate, Uckfield, East Sussex, TN22 1QL Tel: (01825) 761711 Fax: (01825) 767568 E-mail: info@jemmatools.co.uk *Engineers' tools distributors*

Jemma Tools Kent Ltd, 16 Willesborough Industrial Park, Willesborough, Ashford, Kent, TN24 0TD Tel: (01233) 639600 Fax: (01233) 637300 E-mail: sales@jemma-kent.co.uk *Engineers & industrial abrasive products distributor*

JEMO Ltd, 11 Willowbank, Cepen Park, Chippenham, Wiltshire, SN14 6QG Tel: (01249) 447544 Fax: (01249) 661478 E-mail: jefftrain@jemoltd.plus.com *Training services*

Jempsons Ltd, Slade Yard, Rye, East Sussex, TN31 7DG Tel: (01797) 228500 Fax: (01797) 225080 E-mail: commercials@jempsons.co.uk *Commercial vehicle/plant repairs/maintenance*

Jemtech Designs Ltd, 18 Invincible Road, Farnborough, Hampshire, GU14 7QU Tel: (01252) 513556 Fax: (01252) 376168 E-mail: jemtech@globalnet.co.uk *Electronic consultants designers & manufrs*

Jen Advisory Services, 14 Briar Road, Harrow, Middlesex, HA3 0DR Tel: (020) 8907 1300 Fax: (020) 8907 5088 *Computer consultants*

Jenco Control & Export Ltd, Roebuck Road Trading Estate, 41-43 Roebuck Road, Ilford, Essex, IG6 3TU Tel: (020) 8501 5522 Fax: (020) 8501 5533 E-mail: info@jenco.co.uk Principal Export Areas: Worldwide *Ancillary equipment manufrs*

Jencol Engineering Ltd, 1 Somersham Road, St. Ives, Cambridgeshire, PE27 3LN Tel: (01480) 492922 Fax: (01480) 492926 E-mail: sales@jencolengineering.co.uk *Jencol Engineering comprises of 6 staff and operates as a family run business. From design, through prototype to completion, we can offer a complete service to match the customers' requirements.*We pride ourselves on our level of customer care. Each product is quality checked before despatch to ensure our high standards are adhered to. A large proportion of our turnover is as a result of referrals by existing customers.*

Jencons (Scientific) Ltd, Cherrycourt Way Industrial Estate, Stanbridge Road, Leighton Buzzard, Bedfordshire, LU7 4UA Tel: (01525) 372010 Fax: (01525) 379547 E-mail: export@jencons.co.uk *Laboratory apparatus & instruments distributors*

Jendee Trading Ltd, Kebbell House, Delta Gain, Watford, WD19 5EF Tel: (020) 8421 4235 Fax: (020) 8421 4236 E-mail: info@jendee.co.uk *Electronic exporters & importers*

Jenelec Ltd, Fuller Road, Harleston, Norfolk, IP20 9EA Tel: (01379) 853666 Fax: (01379) 854414 E-mail: sales@jenelec.co.uk *Manufacturers of battery chargers & dc power systems*

Jenkins, 26 Caxton Street, London, SW1H 0RJ Tel: (020) 7931 7141 Fax: (020) 7222 4660 *Law firm*

B. Jenkins & Sons Ltd, Watton Saw Mills, Brecon, Powys, LD3 7EN Tel: (01874) 622853 Fax: (01874) 622750 E-mail: sales.bjenkins@btconnect.com *Timber & builders' merchants*

Jenkins & Davies (Engineering) Ltd, Waterloo Industrial Estate, Pembroke Dock, Dyfed, SA72 6BS Tel: (01646) 685895 Fax: (01646) 621030 E-mail: stephensmedley@jenkinsanddavies.com *Steel pipe fabricators & erectors*

▶ Jenkins Engineering Services, Waldeck House, Waldeck Road, Maidenhead, Berkshire, SL6 8BR Tel: (01628) 674080 Fax: (01628) 776648 E-mail: jenkinseng@btconnect.com *Provide precision engineering services*

Jenkins & Hustwit Ltd, 3b Laurel Way, Bishop Auckland, County Durham, DL14 7NF Tel: (01388) 605005 Fax: (01388) 605005 *Fruitcake manufrs*

R.A. Jenkins, Gower Engineering Works, Station Road, Penclawdd, Swansea, SA4 3XN Tel: (01792) 851224 Fax: (01792) 851588 *Gear drive & gear box overhauls manufrs*

▶ Jenkinson Consulting, Deramore House, 76 Main Street, Moira, Craigavon, County Armagh, BT67 0LQ Tel: (028) 9261 9929 Fax: (028) 9256 2003 E-mail: martin@jenkinsonconsulting.com

Jenkinson Marshall & Co. Ltd, 103 Neepsend Lane, Sheffield, S3 8AT Tel: 0114-272 1311 Fax: 0114-276 6240 *Manufacturing printers & stationers*

Jenks & Cattell Engineering Ltd, Neachells Lane, Wolverhampton, WV11 3PU Tel: (01902) 305530 Fax: (01902) 305529 E-mail: sales@jenks-cattell.co.uk *General pressing manufrs*

Jenners Princes Street Edinburgh Ltd, 47 Princes Street, Edinburgh, EH2 2YJ Tel: 0131-225 2442 Fax: 0131-260 2218 E-mail: info@jenners.com *Retail store*

Jennersons Ltd, 17a Highfield Road, Dartford, DA1 2JS Tel: (01322) 275255 Fax: (01322) 225710 *Heating & plumbing service*

Jennic Ltd, Furnival Street, Sheffield, S1 4QT Tel: 0114-281 2655 Fax: 0114-281 2951 E-mail: sales@jennic.com *Chipless semiconductor designers*

▶ Jennings, Stream Cottages, Staunton-on-Arrow, Leominster, Herefordshire, HR6 9HR Tel: (01544) 388816 Fax: (01544) 388816 E-mail: peterjennings@farmmanagement.co.uk *Agricultural consultants*

Jennings Ltd, Unit 3 Sentry Lane, Newtownabbey, County Antrim, BT36 4XX Tel: (028) 9083 7799 Fax: (028) 9083 7762 *Engine spares distributors*

Jennings Computer Engineering Ltd, 24-28 Gain Lane, Bradford, West Yorkshire, BD3 7LS Tel: (01274) 637867 Fax: (01274) 633197 E-mail: info@jencomp.co.uk *Computer dealerships*

Hugh Jennings Ltd, Prior Farm, Muggleswick, Consett, County Durham, DH8 9DW Tel: (01207) 255365 Fax: (01207) 255628 E-mail: info@winsund.com *Wind & solar energy systems*

Jennings Winch & Foundry Co. Ltd, Tatham Street, Sunderland, SR1 2AG Tel: 0191-567 4408 Fax: 0191-510 1549 E-mail: jwf.co.ltd@aol.com *Grey & alloy iron casting manufrs*

Jennor Electrical, 57-59 Brynn Street, St. Helens, Merseyside, WA10 1JB Tel: (01744) 730717 Fax: (01744) 759657 E-mail: general@jennor.co.uk *Office refurbishers*

Jennor Timber Co. Ltd, Lockfield Avenue, Enfield, Middlesex, EN3 7QL Tel: (020) 8805 2121 Fax: (020) 8804 2292 *Timber merchants*

Jennychem, Jennychem House, Sort Mill Road, Mid Kent Business Park, Snodland, Kent, ME6 5UA Tel: (01634) 290770 Fax: (01634) 245777 E-mail: jenny@jennychem.com *Steam cleaning & chemical manufrs*

▶ Jennychem Industrial Chemicals, Mid Kent Business Park, Sortmill Road, Snodland, Kent, ME6 5UA Tel: (01634) 245666 Fax: (01634) 245777 *Suppliers of power washers*

Jen's Face Painting, 123 Repton Road, Bristol, BS4 3LY Tel: 0117-985 9258 E-mail: crackerjacks@blueyonder.co.uk *Professional Face Painting for all occasions. Fantastic for childrens parties and corporate events a speciality. Crackerjacks is based in Bristol and covers the whole of the South West*

Jensa Distribution Ltd, Unit 3-5 Manton Centre, Manton Lane, Manton Industrial Estate, Bedford, MK41 7PX Tel: (01234) 782679 Fax: (01234) 349918 *Road transport & haulage contractors*

▶ Jensen Barker Technical Services Ltd, Fowlswick Industrial Estate, Fowlswick Lane, Allington, Chippenham, Wiltshire, SN14 6QE Tel: (01249) 783844 Fax: (01249) 783306

continued

Company Information

continuation
E-mail: info@jensen-barker.com *Paper machinery distributors & industrial machine vision*

▶ Jensen Construction Ltd, Portberry House, Portberry Street, South Shields, Tyne & Wear, NE33 1QX Tel: 0191-454 4083 Fax: 0191-454 7232

Jensen & Son, 366-368 Old Street, London, EC1V 9LT Tel: (020) 7613 0280 Fax: (020) 7613 0267 E-mail: mail@jensens.co.uk *Patent agents*

Jenstar Ltd, Sturmi Way, Village Farm Industrial Estate, Pyle, Bridgend, Mid Glamorgan, CF33 6BZ Tel: (01656) 745818 Fax: (01656) 745818 E-mail: sales@jenstar.co.uk *Transformers*

Jentech Computers Ltd, Whitburn Street, Bridgnorth, Shropshire, WV16 4QP Tel: (01746) 761458 Fax: (01746) 768710 E-mail: alan@jentech.co.uk *Information technology consultants*

Jenter Engraving Ltd, Unit 4F, Lansbury Estate, 102 Lower Guildford Road, Knaphill, Woking, Surrey, GU21 2EP Tel: (01483) 289100 Fax: (01483) 289200 *Sign manufrs*

Jenton International Ltd, Unit 9 10 Evingar Industrial Estate, Ardglen Road, Whitchurch, Hampshire, RG28 7BB Tel: (01256) 892194 Fax: (01256) 896486 E-mail: sales@jenton.co.uk *Packaging equipment/machine/sysyems merchants or agents, ultaviolet curing equipment manufacturers, packaging equipment distributor or agents; polyethylene /polythene, converting machinery & ultraviolet industrial equipment manufrs*

Jenton International Ltd, Unit 9 10 Evingar Industrial Estate, Ardglen Road, Whitchurch, Hampshire, RG28 7BB Tel: (01256) 892194 Fax: (01256) 896486 E-mail: sales@jenton.co.uk *Sterilizes ultraviolet retailers, service providers & manufrs*

Jeol UK Ltd, Silver Court, Watchmead, Welwyn Garden City, Hertfordshire, AL7 1LT Tel: (01707) 377117 Fax: (01707) 373254 E-mail: uk.sales@jeoleuro.com *Electron microscope & scientific instrument manufrs*

Jeppesen Heaton Ltd, 17 Church Street, Epsom, Surrey, KT17 4PF Tel: (01372) 745678 Fax: (01372) 724111 E-mail: ian@jeppesen.freeserve.co.uk *Ship brokers* Also at: Hull & Tilbury

Jeppesen UK Ltd, Alteon House, Crawley Business Quarter, Manor Royal, Crawley, West Sussex, RH10 9AD Tel: (01293) 842400 E-mail: david.forsythe@jeppesen.com *Aviation navigation services & products*

Jepson Bolton & Co. Ltd, Suite 1, 186 St Albans Road, Watford, WD24 4AS Tel: (020) 8386 6853 Fax: (020) 8386 5130 E-mail: sales@jepbol.com Principal Export Areas: Worldwide *Scientific & laboratory supply services instruments*

Jepson Signs Ltd, Unit 2 North Road Industrial Estate, Meynell Road, Darlington, County Durham, DL3 0YQ Tel: (01325) 463547 Fax: (01325) 381172 *Car number plate manufrs*

Jepson Signs Ltd, 2 Morley Road, London, SE13 6DQ Tel: (020) 8318 5528 Fax: (020) 8297 9121 *Numberplate manufrs*

Jepsons Signs Ltd, 124A King William Street, Stourbridge, West Midlands, DY8 4EU Tel: (01384) 444588 Fax: (01384) 444589 *Number plates sales & manufrs*

▶ Jeremy Rendell Photography, Florin Court, 8 Dock Street, London, E1 8JR Tel: 07860 277411 E-mail: jeremy.rendell@btbconnect.com *Professional Freelance Photographer, specialising in photography for use in Advertising, Design, Corperate, Architectural and Stock photography. Specifically in the field of portraiture and life style imagery.* *

▶ Jeremy Uglow, Unit 5 Blacknest Industrial Estate, Blacknest Road, Blacknest, Alton, Hampshire, GU34 4PX Tel: (01420) 520009 Fax: (01420) 520463 E-mail: sales@jeremyuglow.com *Conservatories*

Jerome Engineering Ltd, Unit 30 Globe Industrial Estate, Rectory Road, Grays, Essex, RM17 6ST Tel: (01375) 898400 Fax: (01375) 898401 E-mail: tsmith@jeromeuk.com *Pipe work fabricators installer*

Jerram Developments Ltd, 14 Anning Street, London, EC2A 3LQ Tel: (020) 7729 2424 Fax: (020) 7739 9108 E-mail: hennessy@jerramfalkus.co.*Building contractors*

Jerrards, Marks Farm, Frating Road, Great Bromley, Colchester, CO7 7JN Tel: (0870) 7304050 Fax: (01206) 257524 E-mail: jerrards@btinternet.com *Plastic crates & removals boxes manufrs*

Jerrards plc, Arcadia House Cairo New Road, Croydon, CR0 1XP Tel: (020) 8251 5522 Fax: (020) 8251 5500 *Fluorescent lighting-gear trays-control boxes-P O P display lighting-lighting components-high frequency ballast-electronic starter switches*

Jersey Chamber of Commerce & Industry Inc., Chamber House, 25 Pier Road, St. Helier, Jersey, JE1 4HF Tel: (01534) 724536 Fax: (01534) 734942 E-mail: admin@jerseychamber.com *Chamber of commerce*

▶ Jersey Demolition Contractors, La Route Des Genets, St. Brelade, Jersey, JE3 8DB Tel: (01534) 498994 Fax: (01534) 498995

▶ Jersey Double Glazing, 1 St. Peters Technical Park, St. Peter, Jersey, JE3 7ZN Tel: (01534) 484459 Fax: (01534) 483309 E-mail: windows@jerseymail.co.uk

Jersey Electricity Co. Ltd, PO Box 45, Jersey, JE4 8NY Tel: (01534) 505000 Fax: (01534) 505011 E-mail: jec@jec.co.uk *Electric & utility suppliers*

Jersey Farmers (Trading) Union Ltd, 20 Commercial Buildings, St. Helier, Jersey, JE2 3NB Tel: (01534) 733277 Fax: (01534) 768916 E-mail: jstusth@jasonmiles.co.uk *Agricultural & horticultural merchants* Also at: St. John

Jersey Monumental Co, 82 New Street, St. Helier, Jersey, JE2 3TE Tel: (01534) 730252 Fax: (01534) 731374 E-mail: jmco@jerseymail.co.uk *Masonry services*

Jerusalem Farm Riding School, Skipton Old Road, Colne, Lancashire, BB8 7EW Tel: (01282) 865888 Fax: (01282) 869900 *Saddlery*

Jervis B Webb Co. Ltd, Swan Valley Way, Northampton, NN4 8BD Tel: (0845) 1270222 Fax: (0845) 1270221 E-mail: sales@jervisbwebb.co.uk *Manufacturers of conveyor systems*

Sharon Jervis Illustrations, Farndon Grange, East Farndon, Market Harborough, Leics, LE16 9SL Tel: (01858) 434344 Fax: (01858) 434181 *Cards & picture manufacturer*

▶ Jes Ltd, Phoenix Wharf, The Docks, Port Talbot, West Glamorgan, SA13 1RA Tel: (01639) 898166 Fax: (01639) 899454

Jespro 2000 Ltd, Central Mills, Raymond Street, Bradford, West Yorkshire, BD5 8DT Tel: (01274) 735446 Fax: (01274) 394909 E-mail: sales@jespro.com *Hydraulic equipment manufrs*

▶ Jesscam Transport, Gannow Lane, Burnley, Lancashire, BB12 6HY Tel: (01282) 423366

▶ Jessica Claire Designs, 133 Unicorn Avenue, Coventry, CV5 7FB Tel: (024) 7646 5577 E-mail: k.stewardson@btinternet.com *Hire chair covers*

Jessop & Smith Ltd, Albert Works, Sidney Street, Sheffield, S1 4RG Tel: 0114-272 1515 Fax: 0114-276 1733 *Cutlery drop forge stamping*

Jessops plc, 257 High Street, Cheltenham, Gloucestershire, GL50 3HJ Tel: (0845) 4587074 Fax: (01242) 228054 *Photographic shop*

▶ Jester Bounce, 83 Honeybourne, Bishop's Stortford, Hertfordshire, CM23 4ED Tel: (01279) 831559 E-mail: infojester@yahoo.co.uk *Bouncy Castles,Fun inflatables,Adult Sumo Suits,Giant Games And Airbrush Bodyart. Available For Parties, Weddings, Christenings, Fetes, Corporate & All Other Functions New Castles & Latest Themes.*

▶ Jesters, 36 Grantham Drive, York, YO26 4TZ Tel: (01904) 787893 Fax: 01904 787893 E-mail: jesters@ntlworld.com *Rosettes for all occasions*

Jet Blades & Engineering, Maguire Industrial Estate, 219 Torrington Avenue, Coventry, CV4 9HN Tel: (024) 7646 6841 Fax: (024) 7647 4215 E-mail: info@jetblades.com *Precision machinists*

▶ Jet Engineering Scotland Ltd, Unit 13d4, Anniesland Industrial Estate, Glasgow, G13 1EU Tel: 0141-958 0208 Fax: 0141-959 2688 E-mail: sales@jetengineering.co.uk *Jet engineering manufacture*

Jet Lube UK Ltd, Reform Road, Maidenhead, Berkshire, SL6 8BY Tel: (01628) 631913 Fax: (01628) 773138 E-mail: uksales@jetlube.com *Lubricant & grease manufrs.* *

Jet Removal Services, Plantation Road, Burscough Industrial Estate, Burscough, Lancashire, L40 8JT Tel: (01704) 895206 Fax: (01704) 896890 E-mail: sales@jetremovals.co.uk *Removal & storage contractors* Also at: Burscough

Jet Repro Print, 101 Peckham High St, London, SE15 5RS Tel: (020) 7732 4565 Fax: (020) 7635 9098 *General printers*

▶ Jet Resin Flooring Ltd, 1 Defender Drive, Aylesby Park, Grimsby, South Humberside, DN37 9PS Tel: (01472) 310203 Fax: (01472) 310203 *Industrial resin floor applicators*

Jet Security Ltd, 28 Horsenden La North, Greenford, Middlesex, UB6 0PA Tel: (020) 8422 5552 Fax: (020) 8422 5552 *Burglar alarm installers*

Jetform Services Ltd, Heath Road, Ramsden Heath, Billericay, Essex, CM11 1HU Tel: (01268) 711700 Fax: (01268) 711600 E-mail: sales@jetformservices.co.uk *Swimming pool contractors*

Jetmarine Ltd, 1 National Trading Estate, Bramhall Moor Lane, Hazel Grove, Stockport, Cheshire, SK7 5AA Tel: 0161-487 1648 Fax: 0161-483 7820 E-mail: sales@jetmarine.co.uk *Glass fibre laminators*

▶ Jetmedia UK Ltd, Metro House, 57 Pepper Road, Leeds, LS10 2RU Tel: 0113-276 1720 Fax: (0870) 1373013 E-mail: sales@jetmedia.co.uk *Jetmedia supplies inkjet cartridges, laser toners, paper, labels, CD media, compact flash, smartmedia and more.*

Jetpacks, 39 Stockport Road, Marple, Stockport, Cheshire, SK6 6BD Tel: 0161-449 5657 Fax: 0161-484 5420 E-mail: info@jetpacks.com *Drink machine suppliers*

Jetpatcher UK Ltd, Unit 10a Woodbine Street Hendon, Sunderland, SR1 2NL Tel: 0191-565 4400 Fax: 0191-564 1096 E-mail: info@jetpatcher.co.uk *Road repair machine hire & manufrs*

Jetseal Ballvalves Manufacturers, Unit 71, Cobham Road, Ferndown Industrial Estate, Wimborne, Dorset, BH21 7QE Tel: (01202) 897427 Fax: (01202) 890292 E-mail: office@jetseal.co.uk *Jetseal Floatvalves are a specialist supplier of plumbing products and maintenance saving float valves, including; high pressure float valves, chemical resistant float valves, high flow rate float valves, brass float valves, plastic float valves, insulated header tanks and expansion tanks, syphons and WC syphons. Join the ranks of the major Housing Authorities and Associations, Hotel Chains, Hospitals and many others saving on costly ongoing maintenance and unnecessary replacements. There is no longer the need to purchase plumbing products with a built-in ongoing maintenance factor. Jetseal is the simple patented answer, giving enormous savings on maintenance as well as superior performance. For labour saving, value for money products that also conserve water, specify Jetseal Float valves, Maintenance Saver WC cisterns, syphons and Eco-System pre-insulated water storage tanks. Full details of our unique products can be found via the website.*

▶ Jetstream, 15 Somerset Road, East Preston, Littlehampton, West Sussex, BN16 1BZ Tel: 01903 772804 E-mail: jetstream@firstcheckpoint.com *All aspects of high pressure cleaning work undertaken including graffiti and chewing gum removal. Domestic and commercial projects - patios, driveways, forecourts, carparks, facades, walls, upvc. Paint stripping and re-pointing. Jetstream is a registered RESIBLOCK installer for all aspects of hard surface sealing. A friendly reliable service covering West Sussex. Hot cold and steam systems. Fully insured*

▶ Jetstream Products Ltd, 206 Farnborough Road, Farnborough, Hampshire, GU14 7JL Tel: (01252) 545006 Fax: (01252) 372670 E-mail: info@jetstreamuk.com *Suppliers & distributors for a range of swimming pool equipment*

Jetter Distributors Ltd, Leighswood House, 43 Leighswood Road, Walsall, WS9 8AH Tel: (01922) 745200 Fax: (01922) 745045 E-mail: jetteruk@btinternet.com *Starter & control systems distribs*

Jetwin Precision Engineering Ltd, Enavant House, Reform Road, Maidenhead, Berkshire, SL6 8BT Tel: (01628) 625884 Fax: (01628) 771209 *Precision & production engineer services*

Jevons Brown LLP, 31-41 Worship Street, London, EC2A 2DX Tel: (020) 7065 7100 E-mail: mail@jevonsbrown.co.uk *Print management*

Jewel Abrasives, Stanley Street, Worksop, Nottinghamshire, S81 7HX Tel: (01909) 472650 Fax: (01909) 532186 *Grinding & abrasive wheel manufrs*

The Jewel Blade Co. Ltd, 442 Penistone Road, Sheffield, S6 2FU Tel: 0114-234 3533 Fax: 0114-285 2473 E-mail: sales@jewelblade.co.uk *Knives, industrial blades, shaving, trimming & slitting blade manufacturers. We also manufacture food processing blades*

▶ Jewell Pak Ltd, Unit 1, Barton Industrial Estate, Faldo Road, Barton-le-Clay, Bedford, MK45 4RP Tel: (01582) 882543 Fax: (01582) 882548 E-mail: jewellpak@btconnect.com *Manufacturers of polystyrene & boxes*

Jewellers Workshop, 164 Fleetwood Market, Adelaide Street, Fleetwood, Lancashire, FY7 6AB Tel: (01253) 776076 *Jewellers*

Jewellery Quarter Ltd, 91 Vyse Street, Hockley, Birmingham, B18 6JZ Tel: 0121-554 1965 Fax: 0121-515 4619 *Jewellery manufacturers & wholesalers*

Jewellery Trade Repairs, 9 Castle Lane, Lurgan, Craigavon, County Armagh, BT67 9BD Tel: (028) 3834 1005 *Jewellery repair, rental & manufrs*

Jewellery Trade Workshops, 17 St Giles Street, Norwich, NR2 1JL Tel: (01603) 625905 *Jewellery manufrs*

▶ Jewellery TV, Leeds, LS17 6WY Tel: (0870) 7447371 Fax: (0870) 1342096 E-mail: sales@jewellery.tv *Internet jewellery retailers*

Jewellery Work Shop, 38 High Street, Renfrew, PA4 8QP Tel: 0141-885 2560 Fax: (01505) 874277 *Make & repair classic jewellery*

Jewellery Workshop, 3 Windsor Street, Burbage, Hinckley, Leicestershire, LE10 2EE Tel: (01455) 611848 Fax: (01455) 632820 *Jewellery manufacturers & repairers*

Jewellery Workshop, 5 Kirk Wynd, Kirkcaldy, Fife, KY1 1EH Tel: (01592) 642950 *Jewellery repairs & manufrs*

▶ Jewellerybuymail.com, PO Box 3236, Rustington, West Sussex, BN16 2YT Tel: (07971) 989332 E-mail: sales@jewellerybuymail.com *Internet jewellery retailers*

Jewson Ltd, 4 Beeching Road, Bexhill-on-Sea, East Sussex, TN39 3LG Tel: (01424) 731414 Fax: (01424) 731887 *Timber & builders merchants*

▶ Jewson Ltd, Nuttaberry Works, Bideford, Devon, EX39 4DU Tel: (01237) 473421 Fax: (01237) 474987

Jewson Ltd, Nelson Way, Boston, Lincolnshire, PE21 8UA Tel: (01205) 362451 Fax: (01205) 365898 *Timber & builders merchants*

Jewson Ltd, Lyons Lane, Chorley, Lancashire, PR6 0PH Tel: (01257) 276211 Fax: (01257) 260098 *Builders, timber & plumbers merchants* Also at: Blackpool, Bolton, Morecambe, Preston & Wigan

Jewson, St. Peg Works, St. Peg Lane, Cleckheaton, West Yorkshire, BD19 3SH Tel: (01274) 872549 Fax: (01274) 864532 *Builders merchants*

Jewson Ltd, Merchant House Binley Business Park, Harry Weston Road, Coventry, CV3 2TT Tel: (024) 7643 8400 Fax: (024) 7643 8401 *Builders merchants*

▶ Jewson Ltd, 265 Godstone Road, Kenley, Surrey, CR8 5BP Tel: (020) 8763 9440 Fax: (020) 8763 9445

Jewson Ltd, 25 Bakewell Road, Loughborough, Leicestershire, LE11 5QY Tel: (01509) 212121 Fax: (01509) 610218 *Builders, plumbers & timber merchants* Also at: Long Eaton

Jewson Ltd, 10 Mason Road, Norwich, NR6 6RR Tel: (01603) 410411 Fax: (01603) 789031 *Builders' materials merchants* Also at: Dereham, Diss, King's Lynn, Lowestoft & Wymondham

Jewson Ltd, 3 Lamarsh Road, Oxford, OX2 0HF Tel: (01865) 249821 Fax: (01865) 241831 *Builders merchants*

Jewson Ltd, 89-105 High Street, Rowley Regis, West Midlands, B65 0EH Tel: 0121-559 1207 Fax: 0121-561 2461 *Builders merchants*

Jewson Ltd, Orchard Road, Royston, Hertfordshire, SG8 5HA Tel: (01763) 241561 Fax: (01763) 247759 *Builders' merchants* Also at: Branches throughout the U.K.

Jewsons Ltd, Cefndy Road, Rhyl, Denbighshire, LL18 2EU Tel: (01745) 334402 Fax: (01745) 344483 *Builders' merchants & DIY store*

Jewsons, Unit 6, Priory Industrial Estate, Tetbury, Gloucestershire, GL8 8HZ Tel: (01666) 502405 Fax: (01666) 505655 *Builders merchants*

▶ Jex Engineering Co. Ltd, Adam Smith Street, Grimsby, South Humberside, DN31 1SJ Tel: (01472) 361311 Fax: (01472) 240218 E-mail: phill.bodsworth@jexengineering.com

continued

Principal Export Areas: Africa *The complete solution for engineering & design services*

Jeyes Group Ltd, Brunel Way, Thetford, Norfolk, IP24 1HF Tel: (01842) 757575 Fax: (01842) 757812 *Household product manufrs* Also at: Borough Bridge, Cheltenham, East Kilbride & Wigan

Jeytec Services, 17 Silverwell Park, Modbury, Ivybridge, Devon, PL21 0RJ Tel: (01548) 830322 Fax: (01548) 830322 *Electrical contractors*

▶ Jfa Surveys, 36 High Street, Ashford, Kent, TN24 8TE Tel: (01233) 898439 Fax: (01233) 629300 E-mail: jfasurveys@johnfloydd.co.uk *Land and Measured Building Surveys, producing elevations, sections and sectional elevations.*

JFC Plastics Ltd, 6 Goldicote Business Park, Banbury Road, Goldicote, Stratford-upon-Avon, Warwickshire, CV37 7NB Tel: (01789) 740102 Fax: (01789) 740037 E-mail: info@delleve.co.uk *Plastic container recovery & recycling services*

▶ JFL Automotive Ltd, Frankley Industrial Park, Tay Road, Rubery, Rednal, Birmingham, B45 0LD Tel: 0121-453 1061 Fax: 0121-460 1144 *Furnace brazing, metal spinning, precision press work, tube manipulation, small/medium sized metallic assemblies. Products: fabricated fuel rails, oil pick up pipes, oil strainers, spun pulleys, vent pipe tubes, oil separator chambers*

J-Flex Rubber Products Ltd, Unit 1, London Road Business Park, Retford, Nottinghamshire, DN22 6HG Tel: (01777) 712400 Fax: (01777) 712409 E-mail: john@j-flex.co.uk Principal Export Areas: Worldwide *Manufacturers & distributors of silicone products*

▶ JFP Consulting, 9 Little Fallow, Lychpit, Basingstoke, Hampshire, RG24 8UN Tel: 01256 330318 Fax: 0870 705 2130 E-mail: Contact@JFPConsulting.co.uk *Change management consultancy*

▶ JH Acounting Services, 15 Lunt Place, Bilston, West Midlands, WV14 7AH Tel: (07801) 429827 E-mail: enquiries@jh-accounting.co.uk *accounting& payroll services for small to medium sized businesses*

▶ JH Training Services Ltd, 7 Baron Court, Peterborough, PE4 7ZE Tel: (07752) 847195 *On-site or off-site forklift, plant & instructor training*

JHH Contracts Ltd, 1 Italy Street, Middlesborough, Middlesbrough, Cleveland, TS2 1DP Tel: (01642) 240070 Fax: (01642) 241393 E-mail: sales@jhhcontracts.com *Suspended ceilings & decorative finished floors suppliers*

JHP Design, 2 6 Erskine Road, London, NW3 3AJ Tel: (020) 7722 3932 Fax: (020) 7586 7048 E-mail: jhp@jhp-design.co.uk *Graphic design consultants*

JHP Training Sheffield, 40 Castle Square, Sheffield, S1 2GF Tel: 0114-275 7286 Fax: 0114-279 7503 E-mail: sheffield.business.centre@jhp-group.com *Training provider*

JHP Training Wales, Sophia House, 28 Cathedral Road, Cardiff, CF11 9LJ Tel: (029) 2063 6137 Fax: (029) 2063 6138 E-mail: cardiff.business.centre@jhp-group.com *National training provider delivering a wide range of courses and programmes, including Apprenticeships and NVQs. JHP offers businesses skills training and recruitment solutions, and individuals the chance of career success.*

JHR Moulders Witney Ltd, Avenue Four, Witney, Oxfordshire, OX28 4BN Tel: (01993) 705059 Fax: (01993) 775949 *Injection moulding & toolmakers*

Jiffy Packaging Co. Ltd, Road Four, Winsford Industrial Estate, Winsford, Cheshire, CW7 3QR Tel: (01606) 551221 Fax: (01606) 592634 E-mail: sales@jiffy.co.uk *Packaging products manufrs*

Jiffy Trucks Ltd, Unit 26 Jubilee Way, Shipley, West Yorkshire, BD18 1QG Tel: (01274) 596000 Fax: (01274) 596444 E-mail: jiffy@jiffytrucks.co.uk *Truck manufrs*

▶ Jig Boring Services Ltd, Ordnance Street, Blackburn, BB1 3AE Tel: (01254) 680143

Jighand Ltd, 5c Thames Road, London, E16 2EZ Tel: (020) 7473 1400 Fax: (020) 7473 1372 E-mail: patsy@jighand.com *Aluminium founders manufrs*

Jigs & Fixtures, Station Yard, Rigg Street, Stewarton, Kilmarnock, Ayrshire, KA3 5AG Tel: (01560) 483512 Fax: (01560) 485160 E-mail: sales@jigsandfixtures.uk.com *Precision engineers*

▶ Jigsaw Business Interiors Limited, RVL House, 6 Elphinstone Square, Deans South West Industrial Estate, Livingston, West Lothian, EH54 8RG Tel: 01506 417177 Fax: 01506 418970 E-mail: info@jigsawbi.com

▶ Jigsaw Confex Ltd, Events Office - Raincliffe Manor, Lady Ediths Drive, Scarborough, North Yorkshire, YO12 5RJ Tel: (07951) 164820 Fax: (07092) 399780 E-mail: office@jigsaw-confex.co.uk *Experience in the planning & delivery of conferences,*

Jigsaw Consultancy, 272 Bath Street, Glasgow, G2 4JR Tel: 0141-353 9460 Fax: 0141-353 9386 E-mail: dorothy@westfieldtraining.co.uk *Providing personal licence training as well as other courses benefiting managers and staff at all levels.,*

▶ Jigsaw Executive Ltd, Regus House, Herald Way, Pegasus Business Park, Castle Donington, DE74 2TZ Tel: 01332 638046 Fax: 01332 638001 E-mail: info@JigsawExecutive.com *Helps business professionals break down the barriers to success*

▶ Jigsaw Innovations Ltd, 27 High Street, Hoddesdon, Hertfordshire, EN11 8SX Tel: (01992) 450550 Fax: (01992) 450551 E-mail: info@jigsawinnovations.co.uk *Audio equipment suppliers*

▶ Jigsaw Logistics Ltd, Unit 1a, Higher Bochym, Cury Cross Lanes, Helston, Cornwall, TR12 7AZ Tel: (01326) 241355 Fax: (0871) 2470904 E-mail: stuart.naish@jiglog.co.uk *Logistics consultants*

▶ Jigsaw public relations, Tower Court, Oakdale Road, Clifton Moor, York, YO30 4XL Tel: 01904 557673 E-mail: sarah@jigsawpr.co.uk *Jigsaw Public Relations Limited delivers a cost effective, comprehensive PR service with creativity and flair. We adapt our services to ensure*

continued

continuation
organisations communication goals are achieved above and beyond expectation. We deliver with total commitment and reliability.

Jigsaw Systems Ltd, The Old Mill, High Church Street, Nottingham, NG7 7JA Tel: (0870) 7306868 Fax: (0870) 7306850 E-mail: sales@jigsaw24.com *Computer mail order services*

▶ Jigsaw Training & Consultancy Services Ltd, Premier House, 50-52 Cross Lances Road, Hounslow, TW3 2AA Tel: (020) 8572 6388 E-mail: enquiries@outcomes4u.com *Providers of organisational development and performance improvement solutions to the public and private sectors.*

Jigtools Supplies Ltd, Unit A1, Trecenydd Industrial Estate, Caerphilly, Mid Glamorgan, CF83 2RZ Tel: (029) 2088 3066 Fax: (029) 2088 9763 E-mail: info@jigtools.co.uk *Engineers' merchants & tool distribs* Also at: Tredegar

▶ Jileon Ltd, 17 Kingston Drive, Hinckley, Leicestershire, LE10 1TX Tel: (01455) 891905 E-mail: sales@jileon.com *Jileon Ltd is a family run business operating from Hinckley in Leicestershire.**Registered Company Number: 5548774. **Our mission is to offer the very best in terms of customer service and satisfaction; we also aim to give value for money.*Our aim is to positively delight our customers, offering,quality products at realistic prices.***We offer a variety of products for personal and household use.**Products include, Laptop Bags, Pet Carriers, Chocolate Fountains, Wellington Boots and many more.**We also specialise in Wholesale and all our products are available on a Wholesale basis at Wholesale prices, please feel free to contact us for detailed prices, which are of course dependant upon quantity ordered.****

Jilks Plastics Ltd, 31 Trowers Way, Redhill, RH1 2LH Tel: (01737) 779799 Fax: (01737) 779800 E-mail: sales@jilksplasticsltd.co.uk *Manufacturers of vacuum formed products*

Jill Leonard, Unit 2, Machins Industrial Estate Nottingham Road, Gotham, Nottingham, NG11 0HG Tel: 0115-983 1084 Fax: 0115-983 1074 *Lace napery manufrs*

▶ Jill Paton Contemporary Jewellery, 24 Aubery Crescent, 'Glenogle', Largs, Ayrshire, KA30 8AP Tel: (01475) 672914 E-mail: jill@jillpaton.co.uk *Contemporary hand made jewellery. Unique designs from silver, gold and fresh water pearls. Bespoke commissions for galleries and individuals. Retail jewellery from an award winning silversmith.*

Jim Barlow Stationers Ltd, 18 Park Road, Worsley, Manchester, M28 7DA Tel: 0161-799 9558 Fax: 0161-703 8789 E-mail: sales@jimbarlows.co.uk *Stationers, printers, office furnishers & computer suppliers*

▶ Jim Brackenridge Transport Ltd, Unit 10 Hareness Park, Hareness Circle, Altens Industrial Estate, Aberdeen, AB12 3QY Tel: (01224) 899677 Fax: (01224) 899692

▶ Jim Brackenridge Transport Ltd, Old Inns, Wardpark Industrial Estate, Cumbernauld, Glasgow, G68 0DA Tel: (01236) 458908 Fax: (01236) 735205

Jim Brackenridge Transport Ltd, Unit 1 Dalcross Industrial Estate, Inverness, IV2 7XB Tel: (01667) 462999 Fax: (01667) 462788 E-mail: robert@jbt.co.uk *Refrigerated transport & distribution*

▶ Jim Ennis Construction Ltd, Ennis House, Sorby Road, Irlam, Manchester, M44 5BA Tel: 0161-777 9977 Fax: 0161-777 9205 E-mail: sales@ogara.co.uk

Jim Hall, Jacksoms Lane, Langley Burrell, Chippenham, Wiltshire, SN15 5LU Tel: (01249) 750291 Fax: (01249) 750291 *Agricultural merchants*

Jim Jack, 16-18 Tannoch Place, Cumbernauld, Glasgow, G67 2XU Tel: (01236) 738484 Fax: (01236) 725597 E-mail: ind_friction@cqm.co.uk *Industrial friction specialists*

Jim Mccoll Associates, 6a Mill Lane, Edinburgh, EH6 6TJ Tel: 0131-555 0721 Fax: 0131-555 0723 E-mail: enquiries@mccollassoc.co.uk *Consulting & civil engineers*

Jim Watts Signs, 27 Abbey Street, Market Harborough, Leicestershire, LE16 9AA Tel: (01858) 467763 Fax: (01858) 434826 E-mail: sales@jwsigns.co.uk *Sign manufrs*

▶ Jimminson Packaging Services Ltd, 4 Ashville Close, Queens Drive Industrial Estate, Nottingham, NG2 1LL Tel: 0115-986 6456 Fax: 0115-986 6516 E-mail: royatwork@jimminsom.co.uk *Carton finishers specialists*

▶ Jimmy Jackson Heating & Plumbing Engineers, 44 Rainford Road, Billinge, Wigan, Lancashire, WN5 7PF Tel: (01744) 892629 Fax: (01744) 892626

Jindal Europe, 4 The Street, Wallington, Baldock, Hertfordshire, SG7 6SN Tel: (01763) 288515 Fax: (01763) 288412 E-mail: jindal@dial.pipex.com *Polyester film suppliers*

▶ Jiq Jaq Gallery, 112 Heath Street, London, NW3 1DR Tel: (020) 7435 9300 Fax: E-mail: gallery@jiqjaq.com *Jiq Jaq is an innovative fine art gallery with contemporary Giclee prints by Jacqueline Crofton, superior quality at exceptional prices. Jaqueline's paintings are ebullient figurative and abstract colour compositions.*

Jiskoot Ltd, 85 Goods Station Road, Tunbridge Wells, Kent, TN1 2DJ Tel: (01892) 518000 Fax: (01892) 518100 E-mail: sales@jiskoot.com *Process automation engineers*

Jit Pak, Unit 14 Pages Industrial Park, Eden Way, Leighton Buzzard, Bedfordshire, LU7 4TZ Tel: (01525) 374412 Fax: (01525) 374416 E-mail: info@jitpak.co.uk *Plastic case suppliers & manufrs*

JJ Engineering (Birmingham) Ltd, Granby Avenue, Garretts Green, Birmingham, B33 0TJ Tel: 0121-784 9990 Fax: 0121-784 8588 E-mail: enquiries@jjeng.co.uk *JJ Engineering combines traditional craftsmanship with the latest technology and operates within an all-embracing culture of continuous improvement, quality and service. Since 1973, the company has seen continual growth and development in response to the need for complex metal-formed components for the automotive and other manufacturing sectors. Design, engineering and production of volume presswork, predominantly from low carbon steel up to 10mm thickness, but also in aluminium, copper and zinc galvanised steels, is complimented by secondary operations and surface treatments. Pressings, presswork, automotive pressings, metal pressings, power press, welding, tooling.*

continued

JJR, 13-15 Ward Street, Willenhall, West Midlands, WV13 1EP Tel: (01902) 637847 Fax: (01902) 637847 E-mail: jan@jjrtoolmakers.co.uk *Tools makers*

▶ JJS Cleaning, 27 Lavers Oak, Martock, Somerset, TA12 6HG Tel: 01793 636359 Fax: 01935 825885 E-mail: info@jjscleaning.co.uk *Contract Cleaning "One Stop Facilities Shop"*

▶ JK Assist, Lingley House, Commissioners Road, Rochester, Kent, ME2 4EE Tel: 01634 712171 E-mail: info@jk-assist.co.uk *Book keeping & support*

▶ JK Consultants, 110 The Brook, Chatham, Kent, ME4 4LB Tel: (01634) 818163 Fax: (01634) 818164 *Computer systems consultants*

▶ JK Seafoods, Fish Market Building, The Harbour, Kilkeel, Newry, County Down, BT34 4AX Tel: (07754) 462654 Fax: (028) 4176 1110 E-mail: kierantrimble@mfn.com *Seafood merchants*

▶ JKME, Cromer House, B5/3 Caxton Way, Stevenage, Hertfordshire, SG1 2DF Tel: (0845) 1080660 *Recordable media format distributors*

JKN Digital Ltd, 13e Chain Caul Road, Ashton-on-Ribble, Preston, PR2 2PD Tel: (01772) 722735 Fax: (01772) 760560 E-mail: sales@jkndigital.co.uk *Sign manufacturers & installers*

JL 2007 Realisations Ltd, Hastings House, Park Industrial Estate, St. Albans, Hertfordshire, AL2 2DR Tel: (01727) 875369 Fax: (01727) 875367 *Shirt importers*

JM Accident Repair Centre, 9 St Machar Drive, Aberdeen, AB24 3YJ Tel: (01224) 488441 Fax: (01224) 497989 *Motor body builders & repairers*

▶ JM Fabrications Electrical, 18 Green Hill Holt, Leeds, LS12 4HY Tel: 0113-263 1924 E-mail: jason@jmfabrications.co.uk *Domestic electrician installers & suppliers of gate alarms cctv*

▶ JM Network Products Ltd, 185 Halstead Road, Mountsorrel, Loughborough, Leicestershire, LE12 7HE Tel: 0116-237 4792 Fax: 0116-237 5736 E-mail: sales@jmnetworks.co.uk *Computer network, local area network, cables & back boxes*

▶ JM Workwear, Unit 11 Premier Building, Newport Road, Bedwas, Caerphilly, Mid Glamorgan, CF83 8YE Tel: (029) 2086 5530 Fax: (029) 2086 5110 E-mail: sales@jmworkwear.co.uk *Uniform clothing manufrs*

▶ JMC PARCELS T/A FASTWAY COURIERS, 37 SOUTHFIELD RD, CUMBERNAULD, G68 9DZ Tel: 01236 732016 E-mail: paul@paul474.wanadoo.co.uk *courier service offering £2.95 central scotland and from £4.95 nationwide up to 25kg next day and sameday deliveries*

▶ JMC Recycling Systems, Harrimans Lane, Lenton Lane Industrial Estate, Nottingham, NG7 2SD Tel: 0115-940 9630 Fax: 0115-979 1478 E-mail: neil@jmcrecycling.com

▶ JMCWD.com, 8 Dunevly Road, Portaferry, Newtownards, County Down, BT22 1NB Tel: (028) 4272 9738 E-mail: misc@jmcwd.com *Web Design and Other PC Services in Portaferry, Newtownards, County Down, Northern Ireland.*

▶ JMD It Training, 12 Northcote Road, Twickenham, TW1 1PA Tel: (020) 8892 7497 E-mail: jdonbavand@btinternet.com *IT training & consultancy*

JMJ, 10 Abbey Court, Liverpool, L25 5HS Tel: 0151-428 7857 Fax: 0151-428 7857 *Courier services*

JMR Section Benders Ltd, Unit 8 Sterling Industrial Estate, Rainham Road South, Dagenham, Essex, RM10 8TX Tel: (020) 8593 7324 Fax: (020) 8595 6139 E-mail: sales@jmrsectionbenders.co.uk Purchasing Contact: R. Jeffries Sales Contact: R. Jeffries *Manufacturers of rings (flanged or angle), steel, section bending services to the trade & steel fabricators. Also tube manipulation bending, metal bending/forming & plate rolling (metal) services*

JMS Coatings Ltd, Units 8-9, Harlaw Business Centre, Inverurie, Aberdeenshire, AB51 4FR Tel: (01467) 622385 Fax: (01467) 624431 *Industrial painting & grit blasting*

▶ JMS Cricket Ltd, Parkside Works, Parkwood Street, Keighley, West Yorkshire, BD21 4PJ Tel: (01535) 606777 Fax: (01535) 606777

JND Technologies Ltd, Thrumpton Lane, Retford, Nottinghamshire, DN22 7AN Tel: (01777) 706777 Fax: (01777) 713192 E-mail: info@jnd.co.uk *Process plant equipment manufacturers*

▶ JNV Security, 79 Stockiemuir Avenue, Bearsden, Glasgow, G61 3LL Tel: 0141-943 2174

Jo Bird & Co. Ltd, Factory Lane, Bason Bridge, Highbridge, Somerset, TA9 4RN Tel: (01278) 785546 Fax: (01278) 780541 E-mail: info@jobird.co.uk Principal Export Areas: Worldwide *Storage cabinets design & manufrs*

▶ Jo Howard, 2 Linnet Close, Hightown, Ringwood, Hampshire, BH24 3RE Tel: (01425) 476364 E-mail: info@coverrad.co.uk *Stainless Steel Radiator Covers made to measure. For Home or Offices.*

▶ Jo Talbot & Sue Young, 6m Hyde Park Mans, Cabbell Street, London, NW1 5BJ Tel: 0207 262 0189 Fax: 0207 262 2160 E-mail: joandsue@btconnect.com *Jo Talbot and Sue Young are London UK based photographers agents. With over years experience they have supplied portrait, landscape, reportage, still life, cars, celebrity*photography and related services to a wide range of commercial clients.*

Joal Engineering, 13 Orchard Road, Melbourn, Royston, Hertfordshire, SG8 6HL Tel: (01763) 245490 Fax: (01763) 247582 *Injection moulders & mould makers & general engineers*

Job Earnshaw & Bros.Limited, Main Offices Stocksmoor Road, Midgley, Wakefield, West Yorkshire, WF4 4JG Tel: (01924) 830099 Fax: (01924) 830080 E-mail: john@job-earnshaw.co.uk *Timber merchants & fencing centre*

Jobec UK Ltd, Stonnall House Farm, Mill Lane Lower Stonnall, Stonnall, Walsall, WS9 9HN Tel: (01543) 483172 Fax: (01543) 483173 E-mail: jobec@tinyworld.co.uk *Portable toilet, manufacturers & hirers*

▶ Jobero Ltd, 4 New Lane Galleries, New Street, Alfreton, Derbyshire, DE55 7BP Tel: (01773) 521500 E-mail: sales@jobero.com *Computer accessory suppliers*

Ernie Jobling, 25 St Pauls Drive, Brompton on Swale, Richmond, North Yorkshire, DL10 7HQ Tel: (01748) 818550 Fax: (01748) 818550 *Agricultural merchants*

Jobling Purser Ltd, Paradise Works, Scotswood Road, Newcastle Upon Tyne, NE15 6BZ Tel: 0191-273 2331 Fax: 0191-226 0129 E-mail: info@joblingpurser.com *Bituminous compound & sealant manufrs*

▶ Jobmaster Ltd, Intake Lane, Cromford, Matlock, Derbyshire, DE4 3RH Tel: (01629) 56363 Fax: (01629) 580469 E-mail: general@jobmaster.co.uk *Software for Contractors - Appropriate for 8 users or more, accounting, estimating or post-contract.*

Jobmatch Ltd, 159 High St, London, SE20 7EN Tel: (020) 8778 8322 Fax: (020) 8659 1324 *Recruitment company*

▶ Job-Recruit, PO Box 139, Thornton-Cleveleys, Lancashire, FY5 4WU Tel: (07834) 986958 E-mail: admin@job-recruit.co.uk

Jobs In Marketing Ltd, Dale House, 35 Dale Street, Manchester, M1 2HF Tel: 0161-950 8901 Fax: 0161-950 8903 E-mail: enquiries@jobs-in-marketing.co.uk *Marketing recruitment*

Jobsearch Employment Agency, 25 Bridge Street, Burnley, Lancashire, BB11 1AD Tel: (01282) 412212 Fax: (01282) 412212 E-mail: sales@jobsearch-employment.co.uk *Recruitment agency*

▶ Jobsearch Northern Ireland, PO Box 05, Ballymena, County Antrim, BT44 9YF Tel: 028276 41743 *Northern Irelands Online Jobs Newspaper - advertising current job vacancies from every sector and business type.*

Jobson Sewing Machines Ltd, 337 St. Saviours Road, Leicester, LE5 4HH Tel: 0116-273 3338 Fax: 0116-273 3339 *Sewing machines repairs & rental*

▶ Jobtrain Solutions, Sandpiper House, No.1 Modwen Road, Salford Quays, Salford, M5 3EZ Tel: 0161-875 1406 E-mail: jason.tye@jobtrain.co.uk *Experts in online recruitment and applicant tracking solutions. We allow companies to take control of their recruitment, by delivering innovative, robust and flexible online recruitment management/applicant tracking solutions.*

Jockey, Crown House, Manchester Road, Wilmslow, Cheshire, SK9 1BH Tel: (01625) 419600 Fax: (01625) 419601 E-mail: sales@jockeyuk.com *Distribution of underwear*

Jode Systems Technology Ltd, 37 High Street, Lutterworth, Leicestershire, LE17 4AY Tel: (01455) 559626 Fax: (01455) 559676 E-mail: sales@jodesystems.co.uk *Machine tool control equipment & systems suppliers & assemblers*

Jody Blinds, 34 Garrett Road, Lynx Trading Estate, Yeovil, Somerset, BA20 2TJ Tel: (01935) 420777 Fax: (01935) 434046 *Blinds manufrs*

▶ Joe Black Building Contractor, 11 Crannog Lane, Oban, Argyll, PA34 4HB Tel: (01631) 564623 Fax: (01631) 566799

Joe Davies Ltd, 149 Broadstone Road, Stockport, Cheshire, SK5 7GA Tel: 0161-975 6300 Fax: 0161-975 6301 *Giftware importers & distributors*

Joe Public Screen Print, Gables House, Bristol Road, Falfield, Wotton-under-Edge, Gloucestershire, GL12 8DL Tel: (01454) 260304 Fax: (01454) 261682 *Screen printers*

Joe Smokes Ribs, 50 Monier Road, London, E3 2ND Tel: (020) 8533 3373 Fax: (020) 8533 3833 *Frozen food manufrs*

Jo-El Electric Ltd, Stafford Park 5, Telford, Shropshire, TF3 3AS Tel: (01952) 209001 Fax: (01952) 209645 E-mail: info@jo-el.com *Fixing materials*

Jo-El Electric Ltd, Stafford Park 5, Telford, Shropshire, TF3 3AS Tel: (01952) 209001 Fax: (01952) 238090 E-mail: info@jo-el.com *Cable reel & trailing socket distributors*

Jofson Ltd, 25 Enterprise Drive, Sutton Coldfield, West Midlands, B74 2DY Tel: 0121-353 2721 Fax: 0121-353 6573 E-mail: info@jofson.com *Fork lift truck dealers*

Jogo Associates Ltd, Marlsbro House, 52 Newton St, Manchester, M1 1ED Tel: 0161-236 7132 Fax: 0161-236 1616 *Fashion casual manufrs*

Johanson Dielectrics Ltd, Acorn House, Old Kiln Road, Flackwell Heath, High Wycombe, Buckinghamshire, HP10 9NR Tel: (01628) 531154 Fax: (01628) 532703 *Chip manufrs*

C.E. Johansson Ltd, Metrology House, Halesfield 13, Telford, Shropshire, TF7 4PL Tel: 0870 4462667 Fax: 0870 4462668 E-mail: enquiry@hexmet.co.uk *Manufacturers of co-ordinate measuring machines, portable measuring devices and large scale measurement with laser trackers**

▶ John A Bates Contractors Ltd, Chance House, Crystal Drive, Smethwick, West Midlands, B66 1RD Tel: 0121-558 3823 Fax: 0121-555 5942

▶ John A Bros Ltd, 100 Fen Road, Watlington, King's Lynn, Norfolk, PE33 0HY Tel: (01553) 810255

▶ John A Russell Joinery Ltd, 8 Dilwara Avenue, Glasgow, G14 0QS Tel: 0141-958 0444 Fax: 0141-958 0333

John A Seale Ltd, New Barn Offices, Quin Hay Farm, Froxfield, Petersfield, Hampshire, GU32 1BZ Tel: (01730) 827416 Fax: (01730) 827207 E-mail: info.jasealeltd@virgin.net *Agricultural engineers*

John Abbott Flooring Contractors Ltd, Wallshaw House, Wallshaw Street, Oldham, OL1 3XD Tel: 0161-624 8246 Fax: 0161-627 1779 E-mail: sales@johnabbottflooring.co.uk *Commercial flooring sub contractor services*

▶ John Adams Ltd, Atlas Industrial Estate, Edgefauld Avenue, Glasgow, G21 4UR Tel: 0141-557 0007 Fax: 0141-558 9564 E-mail: sales@jadams.ibcos.net *Commercial vehicle body builders supplies*

John Adams, 8 Granville Road, Ilford, Essex, IG1 4JY Tel: (020) 8554 8019 Fax: (020) 4784 7927 E-mail: jadamsdesign@aol.com *Exhibition & display designers*

John Anslow Ltd, Stafford Street, Wednesbury, West Midlands, WS10 7JX Tel: 0121-556 1125 Fax: 0121-556 5414 *Hardware manufrs*

John B Akroyd Excavation Ltd, Albion Business Centre, 4 Albion Street, Halifax, West Yorkshire, HX1 1DU Tel: (01422) 381471 Fax: (01422) 321594 E-mail: enquires@jba-excavations.com *Excavationists & groundworkers*

▶ John B Mcbean (Haulage) Ltd, Mid Camp Industrial Estate, Kirknewton, Midlothian, EH27 8DF Tel: (01506) 881325

▶ John Bain (Contractors) Ltd, Unit 1, 5 Kyle Road, Irvine Industrial Estate, Irvine, Ayrshire, KA12 8JF Tel: (01294) 277568

John Baker & Partners, 35 Whitecross Road, Weston-super-Mare, Avon, BS23 1EN Tel: (01934) 627767 Fax: (01934) 616319 E-mail: jbandptns@btinternet.com *Stained glass windows contractors*

▶ John Beavan, Kyre, Tenbury Wells, Worcestershire, WR15 8RW Tel: (01885) 410549 Fax: (01885) 410563 E-mail: info@johnbeavan.com *Fitted furniture & cabinet makers*

John Bell Pipeline Caspian, Units 3/4 Camiestone Road, Thainstone Industrial Park, Inverurie, Aberdeenshire, AB51 5GT Tel: (01224) 716079 Fax: (01224) 716079 E-mail: sales@jbpipeline.co.uk *Tube fittings, actuators & valve stockists*

John Bennison, 10a Clarence Road, Sutton Coldfield, West Midlands, B74 4AE Tel: 0121-323 2370 *Microcomputer systems peripherals & software suppliers & maintanance*

John Benton Harris, 25 Morland Avenue, Croydon, CR0 6EA Tel: (020) 8656 0055 Fax: (020) 8656 0055 *Photographers*

John Blackburn Group Ltd, Old Run Road, Leeds, LS10 2AA Tel: 0113-277 7711 Fax: 0113-277 4009 E-mail: sales@jblackburn.co.uk *Printers & direct marketing*

John Bold & Co., 1 Willow Street, London, E4 7EG Tel: (020) 8524 9090 Fax: (020) 8524 9191 E-mail: johnboldandco@btconnect.com *Precision engineers*

John Bourne & Co. Ltd, Rye Road, Newenden, Cranbrook, Kent, TN18 5QG Tel: (01797) 252298 Fax: (01797) 253115 E-mail: enquiries@bourne.uk.com *Agricultural, construction & sporting industry landscaping product suppliers*

John Bradley Engineering Ltd, 5 Broadfield Road, Seymour St, Heywood, Lancashire, OL10 3AJ Tel: (01706) 366794 Fax: (01706) 620270 E-mail: jbe@johnbradleygroup.co.uk *Gears & precision engineers*

▶ John Brailsford Ltd, 30 Rawmarsh Hill, Rotherham, South Yorkshire, S62 6EU Tel: (01709) 523980 Fax: (01709) 523100 E-mail: sales@brailsfordprinters.co.uk

John Brooke & Sons Ltd, Yorkshire Technology & Office Park, Armitage Bridge, Huddersfield, HD4 7NR Tel: (01484) 340000 Fax: (01484) 340001 E-mail: office@yorkspark.com *Trading estate administrator*

▶ John Brown (Printers) Ltd, Glaisdale Parkway, Bilborough, Nottingham, NG8 4JQ Tel: 0115-928 0991

▶ John Brown (Strone) Ltd, Tyneshandon, Strone, Dunoon, Argyll, PA23 8TA Tel: (01369) 840387

John Bryson Keswick Ltd, 38-42 Main Street, Keswick, Cumbria, CA12 5JD Tel: (01768) 772257 Fax: (01768) 775456 *Bakery*

John Buckley Dudley Ltd, Alma Place, Dudley, West Midlands, DY2 8QH Tel: (01384) 252554 Fax: (01384) 456172 E-mail: sales@buckleybrass.co.uk *Hot brass pressings & stampings (hot-brass & hot non-ferrous)*

John Burke Associates, 117 Belgrave Avenue, Romford, RM2 6PS Tel: (01708) 770770 Fax: (01708) 770759 E-mail: office@jba.uk.com *Chartered surveyors*

John Burn & Co Birmingham Ltd, 74 Albert Road, Stechford, Birmingham, B33 9AJ Tel: 0121-508 4144 Fax: 0121-508 4145 E-mail: info@johnburn.co.uk Principal Export Areas: Worldwide *Engineers patternmakers suppliers*

John C Brow Ltd, Prince Regent Road, Belfast, BT5 6SA Tel: (028) 9079 8171 Fax: (028) 9040 1095 E-mail: sales@browpack.com *Polyethylene bag & sack manufrs*

John C Hadjipateras & Sons Ltd, 24 Baltic Street West, London, EC1Y 0UR Tel: (020) 7490 4010 Fax: (020) 7253 4043 *Ships agents*

John C Laurie Textile Engineers Ltd, Teviot CR, Hawick, Roxburghshire, TD9 9RE Tel: (01450) 373149 Fax: (01450) 373091 E-mail: kjohnson@johnclaurie.com *Knitting machinery engineers*

John C Lillywhite Ltd, Gravel Lane, Chichester, West Sussex, PO19 8PQ Tel: (01243) 781911 Fax: (01243) 780168 E-mail: jcl.builders@virgin.net *Building & maintenance services*

John C Wheeler International Ltd, Fishers Way, Belvedere, Kent, DA17 6BS Tel: (020) 8310 2032 Fax: (020) 8312 1913 E-mail: info@johncwheeler.co.uk *Freight forwarding services*

▶ John Cameron Ltd, Unit 5 & 6, 55 Maclellan Street, Glasgow, G41 1RR Tel: 0141-427 5353 Fax: 0141-427 4422 E-mail: sales@jcpbm.co.uk

John Carter Salt Lane Ltd, 6-10 Salt Lane, Salisbury, SP1 1EE Tel: (01722) 322407 Fax: (01722) 412146 E-mail: enquiry@john-carters.co.uk *Heating, ventilation & air conditioning engineers*

▶ John Catlow & Son Leeds Ltd, Scotch Park Trading Estate, Forge Lane, Leeds, LS12 2PT Tel: 0113-263 0526 Fax: 0113-263 0526

▶ John Caven, Offerance Farm, Gartmore, Stirling, FK8 3RZ Tel: (01877) 382244 Fax: (01877) 389023

▶ John Clark Ltd, Portrack Grange Road, Stockton-on-Tees, Cleveland, TS18 2PH Tel: (01642) 602288 Fax: (01642) 603388 *Valves stockists & distributor*

John Clark Ltd, Portrack Grange Road, Stockton-on-Tees, Cleveland, TS18 2PH Tel: (01642) 602288 Fax: (01642) 603388 E-mail: sales@jcvltd.com *Valve stockholders & distributors*

John Clayden & Partners Lubysil Ltd, 9 Frensham Road, Sweet Briar Road Industrial Estate, Norwich, NR3 2BT Tel: (01603) 789924 Fax: (01603) 417335 E-mail: claydenlubysil@aol.com *Specialists in cutting fluids*

John Cook Corn Merchants Ltd, Rushton Mills, Rushton Spencer, Macclesfield, Cheshire, SK11 0RT Tel: (01260) 226233 Fax: (01260) 226363 *Animal feeds manufrs*

▶ John Corbett Construction Ltd, The Pier, Brodick, Isle of Arran, KA27 8AU Tel: (01770) 302537 Fax: (01770) 302748

John Cotton, 111 Pallance Road, Cowes, Isle of Wight, PO31 8LS Tel: (01983) 299722 Fax: (01983) 299722 *Road transport/haulage/ freight services*

John Crane, Nash Road, Trafford Park, Manchester, M17 1SS Tel: 0161-872 2484 Fax: 0161-872 1654 *Mechanical seal manufrs*

John Crossley, Tan Yard Road, Catterall, Preston, PR3 0HP Tel: (01995) 606058 Fax: (01995) 606058 E-mail: sharonhenriques@btconnect.com *Flange & ring manufrs*

John D Campbell, Jacks Cottage, Okewood Hill, Dorking, Surrey, RH5 5PU Tel: (01306) 627545 Fax: (01306) 628149 *Building*

John D Dunlop, 3 Kyle Road, Irvine Industrial Estate, Irvine, Ayrshire, KA12 8JF Tel: (01294) 273475 Fax: (01294) 274297 E-mail: kdylanalexander@btconnect.com *Brass founders & engineers*

John D Hotchkiss Ltd, Main Road, West Kingsdown, Sevenoaks, Kent, TN15 6ER Tel: (01474) 853131 Fax: (01474) 853288 E-mail: sales@hotchkiss-engineers.co.uk *General & consulting engineers*

John D Wood, Warnford Court, 29 Throgmorton Street, London, EC2N 2AT Tel: (020) 7588 0557 Fax: (020) 7588 7277 E-mail: paul.kennerley@johndwood.com *Property consultants & surveyor services*

John D Wood & Co., 2 Jewry Street, Winchester, Hampshire, SO23 8RZ Tel: (01962) 863131 Fax: (01962) 841789 E-mail: sales@win.johndwood.co.uk *Estate agent*

John Darvell, 1 Westfield Farm, Henley Road, Medmenham, Marlow, Buckinghamshire, SL7 2TA Tel: (01491) 575286 Fax: (01491) 579617 E-mail: johndarvellpackaging@tiscali.co.uk *Packaging material manufrs*

John De Stefano & Co. Ltd, 13 Stratford Place, London, W1C 1BD Tel: (020) 7493 9999 Fax: (020) 7493 1200 *Commercial property agents*

John Dennis Coach Builders Ltd, Westfield Road, Slyfield Industrial Estate, Guildford, Surrey, GU1 1RR Tel: (01483) 506678 Fax: (01483) 579488 E-mail: sales@jdcfire.co.uk *Fire appliance vehicle manufrs*

John Dent Engineering Co. Ltd, 1432a Clock Tower Road, Isleworth, Middlesex, TW7 6DT Tel: (020) 8560 4414 Fax: (020) 8847 4582 E-mail: info@johndentengineering.com *Sheet metalwork engineers or fabricators*

John Devlin & Son Dukinfield Ltd, 1 Platt Street, Dukinfield, Cheshire, SK16 4QZ Tel: 0161-330 5074 Fax: 0161-330 5074 *Building contractors & steeplejacks*

▶ John Dewer & Sons Ltd, Macduff Distillery, Banff, AB45 3JT Tel: (01261) 812612 Fax: (01261) 818083 *Manufacture spirits*

John Dobson Milnthorpe Ltd, Bela Mill, Milnthorpe, Cumbria, LA7 7QP Tel: (01539) 563528 Fax: (01539) 562481 E-mail: enquiries@combs.co.uk *Manufacture plastic combs, sell chemist sundries* Also at: Dublin, Glasgow, Southport, St. Albans & Wheathamstead

▶ John Donaldson Builders, Abercorn Street, Paisley, Renfrewshire, PA3 4AY Tel: 0141-889 5190 Fax: 0141-848 6888

John Downs Hull Ltd, 13 Unit Factory Estate, Boulevard, Hull, HU3 4AY Tel: (01482) 329099 Fax: (01482) 329099 *Curtain accessories & haberdashery wholesaler*

▶ John Duncan Construction Services, The Duncan Centre, March Road Industrial Estate, Buckie, Banffshire, AB56 4BU Tel: (01542) 833501 Fax: (01542) 833614

▶ John Duncan Removals, Polton House, Polton Road, Lasswade, Midlothian, EH18 1BW Tel: 0131-654 1200 Fax: 0131-654 1006

John Dwyer, 5 Arches Business Centre, Mill Road, Rugby, Warwickshire, CV21 1QW Tel: (01788) 536332 Fax: (01788) 546313 *Bakery*

John Dylan Roberts, Pen Y Graig Fawr, Llansannan, Denbigh, Clwyd, LL16 5HE Tel: (01745) 870347 Fax: (01745) 870555 E-mail: dylanpencraig@aol.com *Steel fabricators*

John E Dale & Son, Fletchers Yard, Wellowgate, Grimsby, South Humberside, DN32 0RG Tel: (01472) 354662 *Sheet metalwork engineers*

▶ John E Griggs & Sons Ltd, London Road, Shenley, Radlett, Hertfordshire, WD7 9EN Tel: (01923) 852322 Fax: (01923) 852324

John E Hitchings Hereford Ltd, Twyford Road, Rotherwas Industrial Estate, Hereford, HR2 6JR Tel: (01432) 272584 Fax: (01432) 353072 E-mail: enquiries@hitchingsofhereford.co.uk *Tractor renovators*

John E Wright & Co Ltd, 9-11 Marble Street, Leicester, LE1 5XB Tel: 0116-255 6030 E-mail: leicester@johnewright.com *Large format photocopying & graphic arts services*

John E Wright & Co. Ltd, 3 Oxford Business Centre, Osney Lane, Oxford, OX1 1TB Tel: (01865) 244455 Fax: (01865) 793921 *Printers*

John Eccles & Co Blackheath Ltd, Holt Road, Halesowen, West Midlands, B62 9HQ Tel: 0121-559 1753 Fax: 0121-559 1753 *Welded steel fabricators*

John Eley, 17-18 Leofric Square, Peterborough, PE1 5TU Tel: (01733) 344293 Fax: (01733) 344293 E-mail: eleysigns@johneleysigns.com *Screen printing sign services*

▶ John Elliott Ltd, Great Clifton Farm, The Pow, Great Clifton, Workington, Cumbria, CA14 1TZ Tel: (01900) 603881 Fax: (01900) 603151

John Evans & Sons Llanelli Ltd, Sandy Road, Llanelli, Dyfed, SA15 4DP Tel: (01554) 773332 Fax: (01554) 759215 *Warehousing & storage*

John Ewans Design, Westbourne Street, High Wycombe, Buckinghamshire, HP11 2PZ Tel: (01494) 473441 Fax: (01494) 473442 E-mail: design@john-ewans-design.co.uk *Product designers*

John F White Cabinet Makers, Unit 6 Veasey Close, Attleborough Fields Industrial Estate, Nuneaton, Warwickshire, CV11 6RT Tel: (024) 7634 7347 Fax: (024) 7638 2077 E-mail: enquiries@jfw-cabinet.com *Industrial cabinet makers & joiners.*

John Farrah & Harrogate Toffee, Camwal Road, Harrogate, North Yorkshire, HG1 4PY Tel: (01423) 883000 Fax: (01423) 883029 E-mail: sales@farrahs.com *Confectionery manufrs*

John Fenwick Rossendale Ltd, Vine Grove Works, Commerce Street, Haslingden, Rossendale, Lancashire, BB4 5JT Tel: (01706) 210300 Fax: (01706) 210325 E-mail: dwrudd@lineone.net *Bearing & power transmission equipment*

▶ John Ferguson Spares Ltd, Unit 11 All Saints Industrial Estate, All Saints Avenue, Margate, Kent, CT9 5TJ Tel: (01843) 571717 Fax: (01843) 230801 E-mail: john@jfspares.com *Retailers of spare parts for amusement machines*

John Foad & Co., 30 Westbere Lane, Westbere, Canterbury, Kent, CT2 0HH Tel: (01227) 713333 Fax: (01227) 712600 *Agricultural merchants*

John Francis Ltd, 18 Lammas Street, Carmarthen, Dyfed, SA31 3AJ Tel: (01267) 233111 Fax: (01267) 235430 E-mail: carmarthen@johnfrancis.co.uk *Estate agents, auctioneers*

▶ John Fyfe Ltd, 41 Westview Terrace, Stornoway, Isle of Lewis, HS1 2HP Tel: (01851) 702482

▶ John G Macintosh, 20-22 Nelson Street, Edinburgh, EH3 6LJ Tel: 0131-557 2971

▶ John G Russell Ltd, Deanside Road, Glasgow, G52 4XB Tel: 0141-810 8200

▶ John G Russell Transport, 6-7 Salamander Street, Edinburgh, EH6 7JZ Tel: 0131-553 1225

John Gardiner Airfreight Ltd, 14 Mount Road, Feltham, Middlesex, TW13 6AR Tel: (020) 8894 3537 Fax: (020) 8894 3542 E-mail: john@johngardinerfreight.com Sales Contact: J. Gardiner *Air freight forwarders & general freight forwarding*

John Gargan Chartering Ltd, Trident House, 105 Derby Road, Bootle, Merseyside, L20 8LZ Tel: 0151-922 0066 Fax: 0151-922 5006 E-mail: john@johngargan.co.uk *Ships agents & brokers*

▶ John Gibbins (Contractors) Ltd, Crimond Airfield, Fraserburgh, Aberdeenshire, AB43 8QQ Tel: (01346) 532400 Fax: (01346) 532200

▶ John Gibson Projects Ltd, Sotherby Road, Middlesbrough, Cleveland, TS3 8BS Tel: (01642) 292299 Fax: (01642) 242004 E-mail: enqiries@johngibsonprojects.com

John Gibson & Sons Ltd, Unit 215 Heathhall Industrial Estate, Heathhall, Dumfries, DG1 3PH Tel: (01387) 254764 Fax: (01387) 266005 E-mail: gibsonblacksmith@aol.com *Blacksmiths & steel fabricators*

▶ John Gilbert Training, Broadfold Road, Bridge of Don, Aberdeen, AB23 8EE Tel: (01224) 825644

▶ John Gilbert Training, 162 Barleyknowe Road, Gorebridge, Midlothian, EH23 4PS Tel: (01875) 823364

John Glossop Model Makers, The Corner House, Coles Lane, Cambridge, CB21 4JS Tel: (01223) 892444 Fax: (01223) 894211 *Model makers*

▶ John Good Holbrook, 3 4 Elm Place, Old Witney Road, Eynsham, Witney, Oxfordshire, OX29 4BD Tel: (01993) 777700 Fax: (01865) 885401

John Good & Sons London Ltd, Northfleet Hope House Site 41, Tilbury Docks, Tilbury, Essex, RM18 7HX Tel: (01375) 859841 Fax: (01375) 850343 E-mail: tilbury@johngood.co.uk *Shipping forwarding & transport company*

John Good Ltd Trading As Cantate, Building B Parkfield Industrial Estate, Culvert Place, Battersey, London, SW11 5DZ Tel: (020) 7622 3401 Fax: (020) 7498 1497 E-mail: enquiries@cantate.biz *Colour printers*

John Gosnell & Co. Ltd, North Street, Lewes, East Sussex, BN7 2QG Tel: (01273) 473772 Fax: (01273) 472217 E-mail: info@johngosnell.com *Soap, cosmetic & perfume manufrs*

▶ John Gow & Sons, Graygoran House, Graygoran, Sauchie, Alloa, Clackmannanshire, FK10 3EH Tel: (01259) 722501

John Graham Dromore Ltd, Lagan Mills, Dromore, County Down, BT25 1AS Tel: (028) 9269 2291 Fax: (028) 9269 3412 E-mail: info@graham.co.uk *Building contractors civil engineering contractors*

John Gray Paper & Twine Ltd, 48 Thomas Street, Manchester, M4 1ER Tel: 0161-832 3313 Fax: 0161-839 7068 E-mail: sales@johngray-packaging.co.uk *Paper merchants service*

John Grout & Co. Ltd, Dallow Street, Burton-on-Trent, Staffordshire, DE14 2PQ Tel: (01283) 813454 *Industrial unit & office letting agents*

John Guest, Horton Road, West Drayton, Middlesex, UB7 8JL Tel: (01895) 449233 Fax: (01895) 420321 E-mail: sales@johnguest.co.uk *Push-in fittings manufrs*

John H King & Co. Ltd, 3 Sheaf Street, Leeds, LS10 1HD Tel: 0113-243 8890 Fax: 0113-242 2144 *Belts & waistbands manufrs*

John H Place Steels Ltd, 44 Black Park Road, Toomebridge, Antrim, BT41 3SL Tel: (028) 7965 0481 Fax: (028) 7965 0175 E-mail: sales@johnhplace.com *Steel stockholders & wrought ironmongers*

John H Rundle Ltd, Main Road, New Bolingbroke, Boston, Lincolnshire, PE22 7LN Tel: (01205) 480431 Fax: (01205) 480132 E-mail: jhrundle@globalnet.co.uk *Engineers services*

John H. Smith (Engineers) Ltd, Birds Royd Lane, Brighouse, West Yorkshire, HD6 1LQ Tel: (01484) 715295 Fax: (01484) 710253 *Wire working machinery manufrs*

John H Thomson, Merlwood, Kirkgunzeon, Dumfries, DG2 8JR Tel: (01387) 760270 Fax: (01387) 760655 *Forest & garden machinery services & retail services*

John H Whitaker Holdings, Crown Dry Dock, Tower Street, Hull, HU9 1TY Tel: (01482) 595300 Fax: (01482) 226270 *Transport gas oil*

John H Whitaker Holdings, Crown Dry Dock, Tower Street, Hull, HU9 1TY Tel: (01482) 595300 Fax: (01482) 226270 *Coastal tanker operators*

John Hall Ltd, 9 Piries Place, Horsham, West Sussex, RH12 1EH Tel: (01403) 269430 Fax: (01403) 269451 E-mail: info@jhal.com *Energy consultants*

John Hall Ltd, Selby Place, Stanley Industrial Estate, Skelmersdale, Lancashire, WN8 8EF Tel: (01695) 51875 Fax: (01695) 51863 E-mail: johnhall@enta.net *Fertiliser manufrs*

John Handley, Unit 2 Heath Mill Bus Centre, Wombourne, Wolverhampton, WV5 8AP Tel: (01902) 898560 Fax: (01902) 898561 E-mail: sales@johnhandleybearings.com *Bearing distributors*

John Hatcher Co. Ltd, Walton House, 218 High Street, Felixstowe, Suffolk, IP11 9DS Tel: (01394) 274321 Fax: (01394) 278600 E-mail: sales@hatcher.co.uk *Fertiliser suppliers*

John Heathcoat & Co Holdings Ltd, Westexe, Tiverton, Devon, EX16 5LL Tel: (01884) 254949 Fax: (01884) 252897 E-mail: email@heathcoat.co.uk *Textiles factory*

John Hellyar & Co. Ltd, Tyler Way, Whitstable, Kent, CT5 2RX Tel: (01227) 813200 Fax: (01227) 792203 E-mail: sales@hellyar.co.uk *Plastic compound manufrs*

John Hemsley Ropes & Lifting Equipment Ltd, Unit 19 Sapcote Industrial Estate, 20 James Road, Tyseley, Birmingham, B11 2BA Tel: 0121-706 5748 Fax: 0121-706 6703 *Manufacturers of rope slings*

▶ John Hill Building Contractor, 11 Goslipgate, Pickering, North Yorkshire, YO18 8DQ Tel: (07890) 942046 Fax: (01751) 477975 E-mail: info@countrywidedecorators.co.uk *painting contractors.*comercial, industrial & domestic*

John Hill & Son (Walsall) Ltd, Wolverhampton Road, Park Brook, Walsall, WS2 8TB Tel: (01922) 622309 Fax: (01922) 622309 *Iron, steel & metal merchants*

John Hinde UK Ltd, Unit 12b-D, Cardrew Industrial Estate, Redruth, Cornwall, TR15 1SS Tel: (01209) 211111 Fax: (01209) 210088 E-mail: sales@johnhinde.co.uk *Pictorial postcard & calendar publishers*

John Hogg, Mellors Road, Trafford Park, Manchester, M17 1PB Tel: 0161-872 5611 Fax: 0161-848 8206 E-mail: info@johnhogg.co.uk *Oil industry liquid dye & marker suppliers*

John Holdsworth & Co. Ltd, Shaw Lodge Mills, Halifax, West Yorkshire, HX3 9ET Tel: (01422) 433000 Fax: (01422) 433300 E-mail: sales@holdsworth.co.uk *Pile upholstery fabric weavers*

John Hood & Son Sculptors Ltd, Station Road, Wick, Caithness, KW1 5LB Tel: (01955) 603102 Fax: (01955) 603102 *Monumental sculptures manufrs*

John Horsfall & Sons Greetland Ltd, West Vale Works, Halifax, West Yorkshire, HX4 8BB Tel: (01422) 372237 Fax: (01422) 310105 E-mail: sales@johnhorsfall.com *Blanket manufrs*

John Howard & Sons Ltd, Mullineux Street, Worsley, Manchester, M28 3DZ Tel: 0161-790 2149 Fax: 0161-703 8253 *Steel fabricators*

▶ John Howitt Group Ltd, Oddicroft Lane, Sutton-in-Ashfield, Nottinghamshire, NG17 5FB Tel: (01623) 448000 Fax: (01623) 448001

John Innes Gilkes Ltd, Bugbrooke Road, Kislingbury, Northampton, NN7 4AY Tel: (01604) 830098 Fax: (01604) 832190 *Plant hire & steel fabrication contractors*

John Jaques & Sons Ltd, House of Jaques, 1 Fircroft Way, Edenbridge, Kent, TN8 6EL Tel: (01732) 500200 Fax: (01732) 500111 E-mail: gameon@jaques.co.uk *Sports & games manufrs*

John Jerram, Alfreton Road, Derby, DE21 4AL Tel: (01332) 205295 Fax: (01332) 205295 *Plastic moulding services*

▶ John Johnstone Dalbeattie Ltd, Millisle, Dalbeattie, Kirkcudbrightshire, DG5 4AX Tel: (01556) 610226

John Jones Excavation Ltd, Norjon House, Newby Road, Stockport, Cheshire, SK7 5DU Tel: 0161-483 9316 Fax: 0161-483 8006 *Civil engineering & excavations*

John K Cathcart Ltd, Trory, Ballinamallard, Enniskillen, County Fermanagh, BT94 2FH Tel: (028) 6632 4325 Fax: (028) 6632 5939 E-mail: general@cathcart.co.uk *Power equipment & machinery retailers sales & distributors*

John Kesson Lifting Equipment Ltd, Unit 1 Hawick Crescent Industrial Estate, Newcastle upon Tyne, NE6 1AS Tel: 0191-265 2593 Fax: 0191-265 0498 *Lifting equipment manufrs*

John Kesson Lifting Equipment Ltd, Unit 1 Hawick Crescent Industrial Estate, Newcastle upon Tyne, NE6 1AS Tel: 0191-265 2593 Fax: 0191-265 0498 E-mail: sales@johnkessonlifting.com *Lifting gear suppliers & manufrs*

▶ John Kettlewell & Son, Warehouse, Newdown Road, Scunthorpe, South Humberside, DN17 2TX Tel: (01724) 281881 Fax: (01724) 270358 *Packaging & haulage specialists*

John Knibbs, Hillside, Shawbury Lane, Coleshill, Birmingham, B46 2RR Tel: (01675) 481006 Fax: (01675) 481984 E-mail: enquiries@airgunspares.com *Guns & spare parts distributors & repairers*

John L Brierley Ltd, Turnbridge Mills, Huddersfield, HD1 6QT Tel: (01484) 435555 Fax: (01484) 435159 E-mail: sales@johnlbrierley.com *Yarn, spinners & doublers manufrs*

▶ John L McLellan, 59 Main Street, Prestwick, Ayrshire, KA9 1JN Tel: (01292) 478630

John L R James & Co. Ltd, Victoria Road Industrial, Estate, Skegness, Lincolnshire, PE25 3SW Tel: (01754) 768521 Fax: (01754) 768936 E-mail: sales@jlrjames.com *Continuous stationery to the trade*

John Laing, Gate 14, Basin South, London, E16 2QY Tel: (020) 7055 2450 Fax: (020) 7055 2451 E-mail: info@jlaingtraining.co.uk *Construction Training Provider based in London providing accredited training across the industry. We can provide recognised qualifications or tailor-made courses dependent on your needs. Includes CSCS, apprenticeships ,trade skills and Health and Safety. John Laing Training has been providing construction based training for over 15 years. We can deliver accredited training at various levels from taster days to apprenticeships at Level 2. Based in London we deliver across the South East to learners of all ages from 14 to 64. Our dedicated training centres operate throughout the year and offer regular start dates. Training includes bricklaying, carpentry, painting and decorating, plastering, dry-lining, multi-skills, health and safety, basic skills and CSCS. Our ability to be flexible means we can design and deliver courses specifically tailored to individual and business needs*

▶ John Langley, Sedgway Industrial Estate, Common Road, Witchford, Ely, Cambridgeshire, CB6 2HY Tel: (01353) 667777 Fax: (01353) 666866

John Lawrie Aberdeen Ltd, Forties Road, Montrose, Angus, DD10 9ET Tel: (01674) 672005 Fax: (01674) 677911 E-mail: sales@johnlawrie.com *Steel stockholders* Also at: Aberdeen, Evanton & Montrose

▶ John Lawrie Demolition Ltd, Hareness Road, Altens Industrial Estate, Aberdeen, AB12 3LE Tel: (01224) 871844 Fax: (01224) 898053 E-mail: info@johnlawrie.com *Marine & oil services*

John Leighton C N C Services Ltd, 13 Valley Road, Keighley, West Yorkshire, BD21 4LZ Tel: (01535) 607941 Fax: (01535) 691177 E-mail: johnleightoncnc@aol.com *CNC servicing*

▶ John Leitch Building Contractors, Midfield Road, Mitchelston Industrial Estate, Kirkcaldy, Fife, KY1 3NL Tel: (01592) 654306 Fax: (01592) 655545

▶ John Lewis plc, 2 Mercury Drive, Brackmills Industrial Estate, Northampton, NN4 7PN Tel: (01604) 767676 Fax: (01604) 767775

John Lord Holdings Ltd, Wellington Cement Works, Ainsworth Road, Bury, Lancashire, BL8 2RS Tel: 0161-764 4617 Fax: 0161-763 1873 E-mail: enquiries@john-lord.co.uk *Specialist flooring manufacturers and installers*

John Lund Gisburn Ltd, Unit 1c & 1d Mill Lane, Gisburn, Clitheroe, Lancashire, BB7 4LN Tel: (01200) 445263 Fax: (01200) 445155 *Steel fabricators*

▶ John M Allen Transport Ltd, Cuckoo Bridge Farm, Cuckoo Bridge, Spalding, Lincolnshire, PE11 3JY Tel: (01775) 722428

John M Carter Ltd, Winchester Road Industrial Estate, Kimbell Road, Basingstoke, Hampshire, RG22 4AB Tel: (01256) 324434 Fax: (01256) 816209 E-mail: info@johnmcarterltd.co.uk *Hirers of traditional marquees & aluminium structures*

John M Davis & Associates, East Riding Small Business Centre, Annie Reed Road, Beverley, North Humberside, HU17 0LF Tel: (01482) 865766 Fax: (01482) 865766 E-mail: pr@nilspin.com *Public relations & marketing*

John M Henderson & Co. Ltd, Kings Works, Sir William Smith Road, Kirkton Industrial Estate, Arbroath, Angus, DD11 3RD Tel: (01241) 870774 Fax: (01241) 875559 E-mail: contracts@johnmhenderson.co.uk *Mechanical handling equipment designers & manufrs*

John M Sykes & Sons, 98 Long Row, Horsforth, Leeds, LS18 5AT Tel: 0113-258 3881 Fax: 0113-258 0080 E-mail: jsykes@btconnect.com *Building contractors*

John M Warbeck, Glenburn, Canonbie, Dumfriesshire, DG14 0YF Tel: (01387) 372218 *Agricultural contractors*

▶ John Mcdonald Airfreight Forwarding, Units 1 & 2 Cargo Terminal, Glasgow Airport, Abbotsinch, Paisley, Renfrewshire, PA3 2SG Tel: 0141-887 7722 Fax: 0141-889 3761

▶ John Macdonald Consultancy Ltd, Forest View, 62 Loughborough Road, Coleorton, Coalville, Leicestershire, LE67 8HG Tel: (01530) 223456 Fax: 01530 223456 E-mail: john@johnmaccon.freeserve.co.uk *The company can offer both a professional Interim Management Service or Management Consultancy targeted at either performance improvement, or the management of projects We have extensive experience in Food Manufacture as well as experience in several other manufacturing sectors.*

John Mcgavigan Information Technology Ltd, 111 Westerhill Road, Bishopbriggs, Glasgow, G64 2QR Tel: 0141-302 0000 Fax: 0141-302 0290 E-mail: enquiries@mcgavigan.com *Instrument dial & plastic nameplate manufrs*

▶ John Mack (Haulage) Ltd, Greens Road, Yaxham Road Industrial Estate, Dereham, Norfolk, NR20 3TG Tel: (01362) 691150

John Mckinlay Ltd, 11 King Street, Perth, PH2 8HR Tel: (01738) 625627 Fax: (01738) 628226 E-mail: mckinlayprinters@aol.com *Printing services*

▶ John Mackinnon Building Contractor, Torlundy, Fort William, Inverness-Shire, PH33 6SW Tel: (01397) 704802

▶ John Maclachlan Quarries Ltd, Soroba, Oban, Argyll, PA34 4SB Tel: (01631) 566295 Fax: (01631) 566758

John Mcmurtry & Co. Ltd, 42 Douglas Terrace, Ballymena, County Antrim, BT42 3AP Tel: (028) 2564 8116 Fax: (028) 2564 2519 *Timber suppliers & builders merchants*

John Mcnicol & Co Electrical Engineers Ltd, 123 Elliot Street, Glasgow, G3 8EY Tel: 0141-221 0725 Fax: 0141-248 4569 E-mail: info@johnmcnicol.co.uk *Industrial electrical engineers & contractors*

John Madeley Machinery Ltd, Firs Industrial Estate, Kidderminster, Worcestershire, DY11 7QN Tel: (01562) 69955 Fax: (01562) 746304 E-mail: madeleyj@aol.com *Polythene extruder manufrs*

John Maden & Sons Ltd, Market Street, Bacup, Lancashire, OL13 0AU Tel: (01706) 873544 Fax: (01706) 879130 E-mail: info@johnmaden.com *Overall & hospital clothing manufrs*

▶ John Marshall Armour Systems Ltd, 578 Coldhams Lane, Cambridge, CB1 3JR Tel: (01223) 516814 Fax: (01223) 516813 E-mail: sales@marshallarmour.com *Body armour & personal protection equipment*

John Mason London Ltd, 35 Wilson Road, Huyton, Liverpool, L36 6AE Tel: 0151-449 3938 Fax: 0151-449 2690 E-mail: sales@johnmason.com *International removal specialists* Also at: London & Manchester

▶ John Medlicott & Company Ltd, Ninevah Farm, Lothersdale, Keighley, West Yorkshire, BD20 8HN Tel: (01535) 637740 Fax: (01535) 637740 E-mail: johnmedlicott@btconnect.com *Wholesale wine merchants & importers*

▶ John Michael Interiors, New Road, Dudley, W. Midlands, DY2 8TA Tel: (01384) 455520 Fax: (01384) 455521

The John Mills Group, 11 Hope Street, Liverpool, L1 9BJ Tel: 0151-709 9822 Fax: 0151-709 6585 E-mail: sales@johnmillsgroup.com *Video production, photography & exhibition services*

▶ John Mitchell Grangemouth Ltd, Earls Road, Grangemouth, Stirlingshire, FK3 8XA Tel: (01324) 486511 Fax: (01324) 665116

John Monaghan (Midlands) Ltd, Unit 5 Cavendish, Lichfield Road Industrial Estate, Tamworth, Staffordshire, B79 7XH Tel: (01827) 302480 Fax: (01827) 62164 E-mail: info@monaghanmidlands.co.uk *Access control systems supplier*

▶ JOHN MONAGHAN (southern) Ltd, Units 24/25, Mount Pleasant Industrial Estate, Northam, Southampton, SO14 0SP Tel: (023) 8023 2238 Fax: (023) 8021 1218 E-mail: info@monaghansouthern.co.uk *Architectural Ironmongers,*Sliding & Pivoting Door Fittings & Systems*

John Morgan Conveyors Ltd, 1 Purbrook Road, Wolverhampton, WV1 2EJ Tel: (01902) 455755 Fax: (01902) 452245 E-mail: jmconveyors@btinternet.com *Conveyor manufrs*

John Morris Developments Ltd, Stanton House, 6 Eastham Village Road, Eastham, Wirral, Merseyside, CH62 0DE Tel: 0151-326 2275 Fax: 0151-326 2276 E-mail: i.lee@tiscali.co.uk *Brickwork & Blockwork Subcontractor. Thin joint technology specialists (Substantial time & cost savings over traditional blockwork). Based in Merseyside serving the North West and North Wales regions.*

▶ John Mowlem (Midlands) Ltd, Priory Court, 1 Derby Rd, Beeston, Nottingham, NG9 2SZ Tel: 0115-968 3400 Fax: 0115-943 6069

▶ John N Dunn Scotland Ltd, 6b Dunnet Way, West Mains Industrial Estate, Broxburn, West Lothian, EH52 5NN Tel: (01506) 854831 Fax: (01506) 852565 E-mail: info@laxcon.com

▶ John N Dunns, Phoenix House Kingfisher Way, Silverlink Business Park, Wallsend, Tyne & Wear, NE28 9NX Tel: 0191-295 2900 Fax: 0191-295 2901

John Newbery Ltd, The Chalet, Eaton Road, Hove, East Sussex, BN3 3AF Tel: (01273) 775770 Fax: (01273) 775899 E-mail: enquiries@newbery.co.uk *Cricket bat retailer & manufrs*

John Nicholas Reproduction, Emblem House, Manor Hall Road, Southwick, Brighton, BN42 4NH Tel: (01273) 424876 Fax: (01273) 424876 E-mail: jnicholasreproductions@mistral.co.uk *Furniture manufrs*

John Nicol Fabrications Welding & Fabrications, 4 Laygate, South Shields, Tyne & Wear, NE33 1SH Tel: 0191-454 5803 Fax: 0191-454 5803 *Iron fabricators*

▶ John Nixon Ltd, Unit 6-6b, Greendykes Industrial Estate, Broxburn, West Lothian, EH52 6PG Tel: (01506) 859666 Fax: (01506) 859777

▶ John Nixon Ltd, Water Street, Newcastle upon Tyne, NE4 7AX Tel: 0191-226 0666 Fax: 0191-272 2176

John Norton & Son Ltd, 169 Rutland Road, Sheffield, S3 9PT Tel: 0114-272 1294 Fax: 0114-276 6336 E-mail: sales@nortons.co.uk *Kitchen, bathroom designers & installers*

▶ John Nunn & Co (Builders), Retreat, Cliff Road, Waldringfield, Woodbridge, Suffolk, IP12 4QL Tel: (01473) 736383 Fax: (01473) 736427

John O Groats Crafts Ltd, John O' Groats, John O' Groats, Wick, Caithness, KW1 4YR Tel: (01955) 611371 Fax: (01955) 611326 *Ladies, men & children clothing manufrs*

John Owen Aggregates Ltd, Unit 11 Monksbridge Trading Estate, Outgang Lane, Dinnington, Sheffield, S25 3QZ Tel: (01909) 564191 Fax: (01909) 564234 *Aggregate suppliers & haulers*

David John Papers Ltd, Unit 1A, Middlegreen Trading Estate, Middlegreen Road, Langley, Slough, SL3 6DF Tel: (01753) 570424 Fax: (01753) 512702 *Paper merchants*

John Perkins Bristol Ltd, 4 Ridgeway Industrial Centre, Chapel Lane, Clay Hill, Bristol, BS5 7EY Tel: 0117-965 3970 Fax: 0117-965 3980

▶ John Phillips & Sons Haulage Ltd, Borland, Cumnock, Ayrshire, KA18 4PQ Tel: (01290) 420831

John Pipe Ltd, 380 Ringwood Road, Poole, Dorset, BH12 3LT Tel: (01202) 715888 Fax: (01202) 743707 E-mail: david.pipe@johnpipe.co.uk *Export packers*

John Pipkin Control Panel Manufacturers, Uveco Business Centre, Dock Road, Birkenhead, Merseyside, CH41 1FD Tel: 0151-630 5577 Fax: 0151-630 5577 E-mail: johnpipkin@tiscali.co.uk *Control panel manufrs*

▶ John Plank Ltd, 17-18 Haywards Place, Clerkenwell Green, London, EC1R 0EQ Tel: (020) 7608 0074 Fax: (020) 7608 0075 E-mail: sales@johnplanck.co.uk *Architectural ironmongers, sliding & pivoting door fittings & systems*

John Preston & Co Belfast Ltd, Blaris Industrial Estate, Altona Road, Lisburn, County Antrim, BT27 5QB Tel: (028) 9267 7077 Fax: (028) 9267 7099 E-mail: info@jphealthcare.co.uk *Medical supplies & hospital equipment manufrs*

▶ John Quinn & Sons Car Transport Ltd, Kiveton Park Station, Sheffield, S26 6NQ Tel: (01909) 772519 Fax: (01909) 773897

John R Adam & Sons Ltd, Riverside Berth, King George V Dock, Renfrew Road, Glasgow, G51 4SD Tel: 0141-440 0424 Fax: 0141-440 0874 E-mail: sales@jradam.co.uk Principal Export Areas: Worldwide *Scrap metal merchants*

John R Boone Ltd, 18 Silk Street, Congleton, Cheshire, CW12 4DH Tel: (01260) 272894 Fax: (01260) 281128 E-mail: sales@jrboone.com *Manufacturers of mixer & pressure vessels*

John R Boone Ltd, 18 Silk Street, Congleton, Cheshire, CW12 4DH Tel: (01260) 272894 Fax: (01260) 281128 E-mail: sales@jrboone.com *Mixers chemical industry, mixers industrial process services*

John R Gow Ltd, 12 Union Street, Dundee, DD1 4BH Tel: (01382) 225427 Fax: (01382) 225427 E-mail: sales@scotland-fishing.co.uk *Fishing-tackle/gun retailers/equestrian accessories, outdoor wear*

John R Oliver Ltd, St James Works, Stourbridge Road, Bridgnorth, Shropshire, WV15 6AQ Tel: (01746) 762337 Fax: 01746 762317 E-mail: jroliver@btinternet.com *Precision engineers*

John R Weir Ltd, Hareness Road, Altens Industrial Estate, Aberdeen, AB12 3LE Tel: (01224) 871234 Fax: (01224) 894848 E-mail: sales@commercials.johnrweir.co.uk *Vehicle dealer*

John Raymond Transport Ltd, South Road, Bridgend Industrial Estate, Bridgend, Mid Glamorgan, CF31 3PU Tel: (01656) 666800 Fax: (01656) 666801 E-mail: customers@jrt.co.uk *Road transport, haulage & freight services*

▶ John Reeve Plant Hire Ltd, Old Chalk Pit, Heronden Road, Eastry, Sandwich, Kent, CT13 0ET Tel: (01304) 611288 Fax: (01304) 614462

▶ John Reid & Sons Ltd, Structural House, 6-106 Reid St, Christchurch, Dorset, BH23 2BT Tel: (01202) 483333 Fax: (01202) 470103 E-mail: sales@reidsteel.co.uk *Structural engineers*

John Reynolds Group Ltd, Stamford House, Northenden Road, Sale, Cheshire, M33 2DH Tel: 0161-905 5500 Fax: 0161-905 5510 E-mail: sales@john-reynolds.co.uk *Insurance brokers*

John Rhodes & Son Ltd, Hightown Foundry, Rhodes Street, Castleford, West Yorkshire, WF10 5LN Tel: (01977) 552324 Fax: (01977) 668011 E-mail: richardshaw@johnrhodes.co.uk *Iron casting manufrs*

▶ John Rich Fabrications Ltd, Unit 2-3 Lakeside Works, Oare Road, Faversham, Kent, ME13 7TJ Tel: (01795) 591178 Fax: (01795) 538889 E-mail: john.rich@eurotellonline.com

John Richardson & Son, Roper Street, Penrith, Cumbria, CA11 8HS Tel: (01768) 895000 Fax: (01768) 895007 *Joiners & timber merchants*

John Richmond & Co. Ltd, 18-20 Carnoustie Place, Scotland Street, Glasgow, G5 8PA Tel: 0141-429 7441 Fax: 0141-420 1406 E-mail: sales@richmond-phm.co.uk *Plumbers' merchants*

▶ John Roberts Associates, Amy Johnson Way, Blackpool, FY4 2RP Tel: (01253) 340240 Fax: (01253) 340250 E-mail: sales@johnrobertsassociates.com

▶ John Roberts Ffestiniog Ltd, Bont Newydd, Cwm Cynfal, Blaenau Ffestiniog, Gwynedd, LL41 4PT Tel: (01766) 762768 Fax: (01766) 762403

▶ John Ruck Construction, Longmead, Elms Green, Leominster, Herefordshire, HR6 0NS Tel: (01568) 615807

John Rudkin Refrigeration Ltd, 91, Catherine Street East, Horwich, Bolton, BL6 7JZ Tel: (01204) 697662 Fax: (01204) 669762 *Refrigeration engineers*

John S Braid & Co. Ltd, Maritime House, 143 Woodville Street, Glasgow, G51 2RQ Tel: 0141-445 2525 Fax: 0141-440 1238 E-mail: ddarroch@braidco.com *Shipping agents*

John S Burns Ltd, 107 Coltness Lane, Queenslie Industrial Estate, Glasgow, G33 4DR Tel: 0141-766 3355 Fax: 0141-766 1991 E-mail: sales@johnsburn.co.uk *Lithographic & screen printers*

▶ John S Burns & Sons Ltd, 25 Finlas Street, Possilpark, Glasgow, G22 5DS Tel: 0141-336 8678

▶ John S Feather Ltd, Cherry Street Works, Cherry Street, Keighley, West Yorkshire, BD21 4JX Tel: (01535) 662693 Fax: (01535) 662693

John S Shackleton Sheffield Ltd, 4 Downgate Drive, Sheffield, S4 8BU Tel: 0114-244 4767 Fax: 0114-242 5965 *Steel stockholders*

John Scott Precision, Unit 4a Star Industrial Estate, Bodmin Road, Coventry, CV2 5DB Tel: (024) 7661 0300 Fax: (024) 7661 7233 E-mail: john@johnscottprecision.co.uk *Precision engineering services*

▶ John Shaw Engineering Ltd, Kilbane Street, Fleetwood, Lancashire, FY7 7PF Tel: (01253) 875732 Fax: (01253) 771163 E-mail: office@jshaweng.co.uk *3D laser cutting, pressed parts & tooling*

John Sheridan & Sons, 72 Old Rossorry Road, Enniskillen, County Fermanagh, BT74 7LF Tel: (028) 6632 2510 Fax: (028) 6632 3895 E-mail: shaunsheridan@email.com *Bedroom & office furniture specialist*

▶ John Sisk & Sons Ltd, Unit 1740 1750, Solihull Parkway, Birmingham Business Park, Birmingham, B37 7YD Tel: 0121-329 0600 Fax: 0121-329 0606

John Skinner Manufacturing Ltd, 82b Chesterton Lane, Cirencester, Gloucestershire, GL7 1YD Tel: (01285) 657410 Fax: (01285) 650013 E-mail: sales@john-skinner.co.uk *Classic car trim manufrs*

John Smith & Co., PO Box 8, Aberdeen, AB11 5EA Tel: (01224) 586868 Fax: (01224) 590768 E-mail: sales@johnsmithaberdeen.co.uk *Wholesale ironmongers manufrs* Also at: Glasgow

John Smith & Son, The Abbey, 2 High Street, Auchterarder, Perthshire, PH3 1DF Tel: (01764) 662126 Fax: (01764) 662773

John Spencer Textiles Ltd, Ashfield Mill, Active Way, Burnley, Lancashire, BB11 1BS Tel: (01282) 423111 Fax: (01282) 416283 E-mail: sales@johnspencer.com *Woven textile fabric manufrs. Weavers of spun yarns for industry, the home and apparel*

John Stacey & Son Ltd, Stacey Industrial Park, Silchester Road, Tadley, Hampshire, RG26 3PZ Tel: 0118-981 3531 Fax: 0118-981 3458 E-mail: info@john-stacey.co.uk *Specialist sub-contracting, materials movement, site clearance, demolition, excavation, groundworks, earth moving, recycling concrete products, waste management, landfill operators, waste disposal, plant hire.*

John Stayte, Puddlesworth Lane, Eastington, Stonehouse, Gloucestershire, GL10 3AH Tel: (01453) 822859 Fax: (01453) 821298 E-mail: sales@johnstayteservices.co.uk *Bottled gas & animal feed merchants* Also at: Cheltenham, Cirencester, Gloucester, Stroud & Weston-Super-Mare

John Stedeford & Sons Ltd, Unit 68b Sapcote Trading Centre, Wyrley Road, Birmingham, B6 7BN Tel: 0121-328 3218 Fax: 0121-327 4965 *Commercial & industrial painting & decorating*

John Stokes Ltd, 60 High Street, Princes End, Tipton, West Midlands, DY4 9HP Tel: 0121-520 6301 Fax: 0121-557 7191 E-mail: stokeschrome@hotmail.com *Electroplating suppliers*

John Strand MK Ltd, 12-22 Herga Road, Harrow, Middlesex, HA3 5AS Tel: (020) 8930 6006 Fax: (020) 8930 6008 E-mail: enquirey@johnstrand-mk.co.uk *Mini-kitchen specialists*

John Stronach Ltd, The Docks, Silloth, Wigton, Cumbria, CA7 4JQ Tel: (01697) 331456 Fax: (01697) 332808 *Shipping agents*

John Sutcliffe & Son Grimsby Ltd, Alexandra Chambers, Flour Square, Grimsby, South Humberside, DN31 3LS Tel: (01472) 359101 Fax: (01472) 241935 E-mail: admin@jsutcliffe.co.uk *Freight forwarders & stevedores* Also at: Boston, Colchester, Immingham

John Sylvester Fasteners & Plastics Ltd, Vulcan Street, Bradford, West Yorkshire, BD4 9QU Tel: (01274) 684040 Fax: (01274) 684240 E-mail: sales.fp@btconnect.com *Bolt & nut distributors*

▶ John T Evans Haulage Contractors, Atlantic Way, Barry, South Glamorgan, CF63 3RA Tel: (01446) 420800 Fax: (01446) 421015

John Tate & Co. Ltd, 3 Captain Street, Bradford, West Yorkshire, BD1 4HA Tel: (01274) 724426 Fax: (01274) 737117 *Upholsterers warehousemen*

▶ John Taylor Plumbers Ltd, Mitchell Industrial Estate, Orebridge, Thornton, Kirkcaldy, Fife, KY1 4DT Tel: (01592) 771264 Fax: (01592) 630626

John Teire & Co. Ltd, 180 Rimrose Road, Bootle, Merseyside, L20 4QS Tel: 0151-944 1027 Fax: 0151-922 6739 E-mail: info@teire.co.uk *Lifting equipment manufrs*

John Teuton Garage Door Specialists, Unit 8, Bankside, Kidlington, Oxfordshire, OX5 1JE Tel: (01865) 373270 Fax: (01865) 842009 E-mail: info@john-teuton.co.uk *Garage door specialists*

▶ John Thomson Construction Ltd, Park Terrace, Lamlash, Isle of Arran, KA27 8NB Tel: (01770) 600242 Fax: (01770) 600714 E-mail: office@thomsonconstruction.co.uk

John Tinnelly & Sons, Forkhill Road, Cloughoge, Newry, County Down, BT35 8LZ Tel: (028) 3026 5331 Fax: (028) 3026 8491 E-mail: info@tinnelly.com *Demolition contractors scrap metal merchants*

John Trafford, Unit 16 Phoebe La Industrial Estate, Halifax, West Yorkshire, HX3 9EX Tel: (01422) 345575 Fax: (01422) 356300 E-mail: spintraff@aol.com *Metal spinning services*

▶ John Truswell & Sons Garages Ltd, Fall Bank Industrial Estate, Dodworth, Barnsley, South Yorkshire, S75 3LS Tel: (01226) 289471 Fax: (01226) 249402

John Truswell & Sons Garages Ltd, Fall Bank Industrial Estate, Dodworth, Barnsley, South Yorkshire, S75 3LS Tel: (01226) 289471 Fax: (01226) 249402 E-mail: traffic@truswell.co.uk *Road transport contractors*

▶ John Unwin Electrical Contractors Ltd, Contact House, 20 Jubilee Drive, Loughborough, Leicestershire, LE11 5XS Tel: (01509) 236313 Fax: (01509) 231862 E-mail: sales@john-unwin.com

John W Doubleday Ltd, Jekils Bank, Holbeach, Spalding, Lincolnshire, PE12 8SQ Tel: (01406) 540344 Fax: (01406) 540262 E-mail: graham.collishaw@btclick.com *Sales & repair.agricultural machinery*

W. Harold John & Co. Ltd, Adelaide Street, Crindau, Newport, Gwent, NP20 5RR Tel: (01633) 855273 Fax: (01633) 854778 E-mail: scrap@haroldjohn.com *Non ferrous metal merchants*

▶ John Walker Engineering Co. Ltd, Owens Road, Skippers Lane Industrial Estat, Middlesbrough, Cleveland, TS6 6HE Tel: (01642) 456621 Fax: (01642) 456522

John Walsh & Co Inserts Ltd, 183 High Street, Wealdstone, Harrow, Middlesex, HA3 5EA Tel: (020) 8863 9133 Fax: (020) 8427 3307 E-mail: thinsheetfastner@btinternet.com *Fastener manufrs*

▶ John Weaver Transport, Unit 3 15-17 Willis Way, Poole, Dorset, BH15 3SS Tel: (01202) 673089 Fax: (01202) 678256

▶ John White Printers Ltd, Station Road, Alford, Lincolnshire, LN13 9JA Tel: (01507) 466892 Fax: (01507) 463374

John Wigfull & Co Ltd, First Hangings, Blaby Road, Enderby, Leicester, LE19 4AQ Tel: 0116-286 2287 Fax: 0116-275 1232 E-mail: wigfullr@btinternet.com *LPG & liquid fuel engineers services*

John Williams & Co. Ltd, Stone Street, Lympne, Hythe, Kent, CT21 4LD Tel: (01303) 265198 Fax: (01303) 261513 E-mail: sales@johnwilliamsroofing.co.uk *Roofing contractors*

John Williams & Co Crwbin Quarries Ltd, Pantyrathro Manor, Llangain, Carmarthen, Dyfed, SA33 5AJ Tel: (01267) 241226 Fax: (01267) 241630 *Macadam & asphalt surfacing contractors*

▶ John Wilson, Ground Floor, 6 Madeira Road, London, SW16 2DF Tel: 020 8516 9582 E-mail: info@jcwilson.net *Panoramic photography services for print and web.*

▶ John Wylie Building Ltd, 9 Aitkenhead Road, Uddingston, Glasgow, G71 5RG Tel: (01698) 818480 Fax: (01698) 307001

▶ John Young Ltd, 2 Johnstone Street, Bellshill, Lanarkshire, ML4 1DE Tel: (01698) 748221

John Young, 7 Cranbrook Court, Avenue Two, Witney, Oxfordshire, OX28 4YP Tel: (01993) 700337 Fax: (01993) 778123 E-mail: john-young1@btconnect.com Principal Export Areas: Worldwide *Fastener distributors*

John Young Foam Consultants Ltd, 97 Cote Green Road, Marple Bridge, Stockport, Cheshire, SK6 5EN Tel: 0161-427 3734 Fax: 0161-449 0982 E-mail: jyfc@btconnect.com *Industrial consultants*

John Zink Division KCTG Ltd, 140 Windmill Road, Dolphin House, Sunbury-on-Thames, Middlesex, TW16 7HT Tel: (01932) 769830 Fax: (01932) 787471 *Combustion engineering services*

▶ Johns Of Essex, 86 High Street, Earls Colne, Colchester, CO6 2QX Tel: (01787) 221940 Fax: (01787) 221940 E-mail: nicholspongo@aol.com *Fishing tackle retailers*

Johns Manville, Unit 4 Roundwood Drive, Sherdley Road Industrial Estate, St. Helens, Merseyside, WA9 5JD Tel: (01744) 762500 Fax: (01744) 451076 E-mail: jeff.nash@jm.com Principal Export Areas: Worldwide *Manufacturers of glass fibre fabric, wall covering & tape. Also glass textiles*

Johnsen & Jorgensen Group Ltd, Newtons Court, Crossways Business Park, Dartford, DA2 6QL Tel: (01332) 291111 Fax: (01322) 293501 E-mail: info@jjpack.com *Suppliers of glass & plastic containers & packaging*

Johnson & Co., Chapel Square, Deddington, Banbury, Oxfordshire, OX15 0SG Tel: (01869) 338275 Fax: (01869) 337014 E-mail: office@johnsonsofdeddington.co.uk *Timber & builders' merchants*

▶ Adam Johnson, 57 The Cross Way, Montagu Estate, Kenton, Newcastle upon Tyne, NE3 4SW Tel: (07709) 445676 E-mail: adamshotdogs@yahoo.co.uk *We supply a professional building service, ranging from full extensions to rewiring, plumbing, tiling, and joinery. No job too big or small.*

Johnson & Akam Ltd, Old Park Court, Harris Street, Bradford, West Yorkshire, BD1 5HW Tel: (01274) 726375 Fax: (01274) 307946 E-mail: general@johnsonandakam.co.uk *Timber & corrugated packaging*

Johnson & Allen Ltd, Neocol Works, Smithfield, Sheffield, S3 7AR Tel: 0114-273 8066 Fax: 0114-272 9842 E-mail: info@johnsonandallen.co.uk *Johnson & Allen Ltd based in Sheffield are manufacturers of non-destructive test equipment & transformers. They provide a quality service that satisfies the most demanding of customers. These include Aerospace, Government and Military establishments and the Automotive, Offshore and Construction Industries.Their products include current flow equipment, electro magnets, permanent magnets, MPI accessories, inks, paints and many more.*

Johnson Apparelmaster, 15 Pixmore Avenue, Letchworth Garden City, Hertfordshire, SG6 1JW Tel: (01462) 686355 Fax: (01462) 671006 E-mail: sales@apparelmaster.co.uk *Textile rentals*

Ben Johnson Office Equipment Ltd, Sterling Park, York, YO30 4WU Tel: (01904) 698698 Fax: (01904) 698699 E-mail: info@benjohnson.co.uk *Office equipment retailers*

Johnson & Cawley Ltd, Moston Road, Sandbach, Cheshire, CW11 3HL Tel: (01270) 765661 Fax: (01270) 766542 E-mail: philpeters@btconnect.com *Electrical contractors*

Charles Johnson, 3 Beech Drive, Norwich, NR6 6RN Tel: (01603) 485429 Fax: (01603) 485459 *Breaks & clutch componants manufrs*

Johnson Cleaners UK Ltd, Kingsway, Team Valley Trading Estate, Gateshead, Tyne & Wear, NE11 0HB Tel: 0191-482 0088 Fax: 0191-482 1750 *Textile manufrs*

Johnson Cleaners UK Ltd, Ruthvenfield Road, Perth, PH1 3SW Tel: (01738) 623456 Fax: (01738) 635160 *Cleaning & workwear rental*

Johnson Control, Cherry Blossom Way, Sunderland, SR5 3TW Tel: 0191-415 6000 Fax: 0191-415 3857 E-mail: sales@ikedahoover.com *Car seat manufrs*

Johnson Control Telford Interiors, Unit E, Halesfield 10, Telford, Shropshire, TF7 4QP Tel: (01952) 686000 Fax: (01952) 686001 *Interior automotive trim designers & manufrs*

Johnson Controls, 14-16 St. Martins Avenue, Fieldhead Business Centre, Bradford, West Yorkshire, BD7 1LG Tel: (01274) 737070 Fax: (01274) 765301 E-mail: mike.metcalfe@jci.com *Industrial refrigeration manufacturers & contractors*

▶ Johnson Controls Ltd, Unit 17, Royal Portsbury, Bristol, BS20 7XE Tel: (01275) 375713 Fax: (01275) 375714 *Air conditioning & refrigeration & building services*

Johnson Controls Ltd, Tachbrook Park Drive, Tachbrook Park, Warwick, CV34 6RH Tel: (01926) 885288 Fax: (01926) 426119 *In vehicle entertainment systems manufrs*

Johnson Controls Automotive UK Ltd, Unit B Stafford Park 6, Telford, Shropshire, TF3 3BQ Tel: (01952) 209300 *Automotive component suppliers*

Johnson Controls UK Automotive Ltd, 10 Hedera Road, Redditch, Worcestershire, B98 9EY Tel: (01527) 507100 Fax: (01527) 507101 *Car interior trim manufrs*

Johnson Controls UK Automotive Ltd, 10 Hedera Road, Redditch, Worcestershire, B98 9EY Tel: (01527) 507100 Fax: (01527) 507101 *Manufacturers of seats*

Johnson Diversey Ltd, 1/117 Dargan Road, Bushmills, County Antrim, BT57 8XQ Tel: (028) 9078 1636 Fax: (028) 9037 0456 *Hygiene chemical manufrs*

Johnson Elevanja Ltd, Bath Road, Bridgwater, Somerset, TA6 4YQ Tel: (01278) 456411 Fax: (01278) 429949 E-mail: sales@jbrakes.com *Industrial brake maintenance & repair specialist*

Johnson Engineering Co., 319 Kennington Road, London, SE11 4QE Tel: (020) 7735 1412 Fax: (020) 7582 1161 *Electric motors & repairers*

▶ F. Johnson & Co. Heating (1983) Ltd, Chapel Street, Halstead, Essex, CO9 2LS Tel: (01787) 472382 Fax: (01787) 477563 E-mail: info@johnsonheating.co.uk *Design and Installation of domestic and commercial heating systems and general plumbing services.**

Johnson Fellowes Ltd, 32 Audit Hall Road, Empingham, Oakham, Leicestershire, LE15 8PH Tel: (01780) 460057 E-mail: idlyon@btinternet.com *Aerospace quality management services*

Fred Johnson, Unit D2, Imperial Business Centre, West Mill, Gravesend, Kent, DA11 0DL Tel: (01474) 569919 Fax: (01474) 533261 E-mail: info@fjpaper.co.uk *Paper merchants*

H & R Johnson Tiles Ltd, Harewood Street, Tunstall, Stoke-on-Trent, ST6 5JZ Tel: (01782) 575575 Fax: (01782) 577377 E-mail: sales@johnson-tiles.com *Ceramic tile manufrs*

Johnson Hall Services Ltd, 93 Gorof Road, Ystradgynlais, Lower Cwmtwrch, Swansea, SA9 1DS Tel: (01639) 849564 Fax: (01639) 845348 *Floating deck distributors*

Johnson Hospitality Services Ltd, Unit 5, Martinbridge Trading Estate, Lincoln Road, Enfield, Middlesex, EN1 1QL Tel: (020) 8443 3333 Fax: (020) 8805 8710 *Catering & furniture hire*

Johnson & Johnson, Glenthorne, Uxbridge Road, Uxbridge, Middlesex, UB10 0LF Tel: (01895) 270411 Fax: (01895) 270411 *Building contractors*

Johnson & Johnson Finance Ltd, Coronation Road, Ascot, Berkshire, SL5 9EY Tel: (01344) 864140 Fax: (01344) 871133 E-mail: enquiries@johnsonandjohnson.com *Surgical dressings manufrs*

Johnson & Johnson Furniture plc, Unit 12-19 Guinness Road Trading Estate, Guinness Road, Trafford Park, Manchester, M17 1SB Tel: 0161-872 7041 Fax: 0161-872 7351 E-mail: mail@jjff.co.uk *Fitted furniture manufrs*

Johnson Machine & Tool, Westbourne Road, Wednesbury, West Midlands, WS10 8BJ Tel: 0121-568 8013 Fax: 0121-526 4984 E-mail: jmt@johnson-group.co.uk *Machinery for the fastener industry*

Johnson Machine & Tool, Westbourne Road, Wednesbury, West Midlands, WS10 8BJ Tel: 0121-568 8013 Fax: 0121-526 4984 E-mail: jmt@johnson-group.co.uk *Manufacture tools for fastener industry*

Marcus Johnson Studios, 8 Ladywood Drive, Aboyne, Aberdeenshire, AB34 5HA Tel: (01339) 886066 Fax: (01339) 886636 *Photography*

Johnson Matthey Plc, 40-42 Hatton Garden, London, EC1N 8EE Tel: (020) 7269 8400 Fax: (020) 7269 8433 E-mail: jmpr@matthey.com *Specialist advanced chemicals precious metals auto catalysts manufrs*

Johnson Matthey Plc, York Way, Royston, Hertfordshire, SG8 5HJ Tel: (01763) 253200 Fax: (01763) 253168 E-mail: webbp@matthey.com *Silver brazing alloys, brazing fluxes, braze pastes manufrs*

Johnson Matthey plc, Orchard Road, Royston, Hertfordshire, SG8 5HE Tel: (01763) 253000 Fax: (01763) 253492 E-mail: nobleuk@matthey.com *Precious metals dealers*

Johnson Matthey P.L.C., King Street, Fenton, Stoke-On-Trent, ST3 4DF Tel: (01782) 590000 Fax: (01782) 339955 *Ceramic & raw material suppliers & manufrs*

Johnson Motor Accessories, 29 Central Parade, New Addington, Croydon, CR0 0JB Tel: (01689) 842151 Fax: (01689) 842151 *Motor accessories*

N.G. Johnson Ltd, Oldbury Road Industrial Estate, Oldbury Road, West Bromwich, West Midlands, B70 9DD Tel: 0121-525 3333 Fax: 0121-525 3366 *Refractory contractors*

Neville Johnson Ltd, 4 Broadoak Business Park, Ashburton Road West, Trafford Park, Manchester, M17 1RW Tel: 0161-873 8333 Fax: 0161-873 8335 E-mail: info@nevillejohnson.co.uk *Fitted office & home study furniture manufrs*

Johnson Packaging, Manor Farm, Main Street, Fenton, Newark, Nottinghamshire, NG23 5PX Tel: (01636) 626949 Fax: (01636) 626911 E-mail: sales@johnsonpackaging.biz

▶ Paul Johnson, 28 Werrington Drive, Callington, Cornwall, PL17 7TF Tel: (01579) 384764 *Blacksmiths*

Johnson Polymers Ltd, The Slough, Studley, Warwickshire, B80 7EN Tel: (01527) 850525 Fax: (01527) 850595 E-mail: sales@johnsonpolymers.co.uk *Plastics raw materials suppliers*

Johnson Porter Industrial Services, Attwood Street, Stourbridge, West Midlands, DY9 8RY Tel: (01384) 897080 Fax: (01384) 897170 *General engineers casting & fabricators*

Johnson Pump UK Ltd, Highfield Industrial Estate, Edison Road, Eastbourne, East Sussex, BN23 6PT Tel: (01323) 509211 Fax: (01323) 507306 E-mail: sales@johnsonpump.com *Pump manufacturers including rotary*

Richard Johnson Ltd, Northacre House, 80B High Street, Northwood, Middlesex, HA6 1BJ Tel: (01923) 835930 Fax: (01923) 836045 E-mail: info@relianceplumbing.co.uk *Heating engineers*

Johnson Security Ltd, Orchard Industrial Estate, Toddington, Cheltenham, Gloucestershire, GL54 5EB Tel: (01242) 621362 Fax: (01242) 621554 E-mail: sales@johnson-security.co.uk *Commercial vehicle body builders*

Johnson Service Group, Johnson House, Monks Way, Preston Brook, Runcorn, Cheshire, WA7 3GH Tel: 0151-933 6161 Fax: (01928) 704620 *Workwear, washroom products & dry cleaning*

Johnson & Starley Ltd, Brackmills Indust Estate, Brackmills Industrial Estate, Northampton, NN4 7HR Tel: (01604) 762881 Fax: (01604) 767408 E-mail: sales@johnsonandstarley.co.uk *Heating apparatus equipment manufrs*

Johnson Stevens Agencies Ltd, Johnson Stevens House, 2 Abbey Road, Barking, Essex, IG11 7AX Tel: (020) 8591 6200 Fax: (020) 8594 2161 E-mail: sales@j-s-agencies.co.uk *Liner shipping, husbanding agents services* Also at: Belfast, Bristol, Cork, Dublin, Felixstowe, Glasgow, Liverpool, Southampton & Tilbury

Johnson Systems International Ltd, Little Lane, Ilkley, West Yorkshire, LS29 8HY Tel: (01943) 607550 Fax: (01943) 609463 Principal Export Areas: Worldwide *Rotary joint manufrs*

▶ Johnson Technical Systems, Unit 6 Essex Technology Centre, The Gables, Ongar, Essex, CM5 0GA Tel: (01277) 364530 E-mail: mail@jtechnical.net *IT consultancy*

Terry Johnson Ltd, Cranmore Lane, Holbeach, Spalding, Lincolnshire, PE12 7HT Tel: (01406) 422286 Fax: (01406) 426356 *Agricultural crop equipment manufrs*

Johnson Walsh Engineering Ltd, 47 Newford Crescent, Stoke-on-Trent, ST2 7EB Tel: (01782) 544555 Fax: (01782) 544116 E-mail: jwesshot@btclick.com *Shot blasting contractors*

Johnson Window Films UK Ltd, 3 Mitchell Point, Ensign Way, Hamble, Southampton, SO31 4RF Tel: (023) 8045 4593 Fax: (023) 8045 4594 E-mail: jwsinstall@btconnect.co.uk *Window film wholesalers & installers*

Johnson & Wood, Lower Voe, Voe, Shetland, ZE2 9PX Tel: (01806) 588245 Fax: (01806) 588245 *Bakers*

Johnsons Apparel Master Ltd, Mill Road, Fishersgate, Portslade, Brighton, BN41 1PX Tel: (01273) 412111 Fax: (01273) 414056 *Textile workwear rental*

Johnsons Apparel Master, Cowley Bridge Road, Exeter, EX4 5AA Tel: (01392) 271291 Fax: (01392) 422078 *Laundry services*

Johnsons Apparelmaster P.L.C., Aldridge Road, Perry Barr, Birmingham, B42 2EU Tel: 0121-356 4512 Fax: 0121-344 3520 *Textile rental services*

Johnsons Apparelmaster Ltd, Rugby Road, Hinckley, Leicestershire, LE10 2NE Tel: (01455) 891191 Fax: (01455) 619056 E-mail: enquiries@johnsonapparemaster.com *Uniform suppliers*

Johnsons Apparelmaster, 150 Stoney Rock Lane, Leeds, LS9 7BL Tel: 0113-249 5755 Fax: 0113-249 7036 *Towel & workwear suppliers*

Johnsons Apparelmaster UK Ltd, Unit 6, Curlew Park, Threemilestone, Truro, Cornwall, TR4 9LE Tel: (01872) 260506 *Uniform distributor*

Johnsons (Burscough) Ltd, 3 Red Cat Lane, Burscough, Ormskirk, Lancashire, L40 0RD Tel: (01704) 893103

Johnsons Cartons, West Morland House, 160 Clifton Dr South, Lytham St. Annes, Lancashire, FY8 1HG Tel: (01253) 721766 Fax: (01253) 780200 E-mail: sales@johnsons-cartons.co.uk *Carton dealers*

Johnsons Catering Equipment Ltd, G/3, Unit, Cowlairs, Bulwell, Nottingham, NG5 9RA Tel: 0115-976 1621 Fax: 0115-979 4639 E-mail: paul@johnsonsce.co.uk *One of East Midlands Leading Suppliers to the Catering Industry. We offer an extensive range of light to heavy equipment, with over 50,000 products to choose from at discounted prices. Finance Leasing,Premier Customer Service, Sales and Design are provided as standard.**We can deliver nationwide to your door.**Website accessable 24 hours a day, office opening times 9.00am - 5.00pm Mon - Friday ***

Johnson's Chopwell Ltd, Tollbridge Road, Blaydon-on-Tyne, Tyne & Wear, NE21 5TB Tel: 0191-414 2455 Fax: 0191-414 1640 E-mail: johnsonschopwell@b&k.co.uk *Materials handling engineers*

Johnson's Engineering & Electrical Co., 61 High Street, Standlake, Witney, Oxfordshire, OX29 7RH Tel: (01865) 300270 Fax: (01865) 300911 *Engineering, machining & welding service & steel fabricators*

Johnsons Health Tech, 27-61 City Road, Stoke-on-Trent, ST4 1DP Tel: (01782) 749100 Fax: (01782) 572000 *Leisure equipment distribs*

▶ Johnsons Innovations Ltd, 14 Vale Walk, Woodhill, Bishopbriggs, Glasgow, G64 1LG Tel: 0141 5636475 E-mail: support@disc2drive.com *DiscDrive, The Ultimate In-Car Driver Training Programme, 1st of it's kind in the U.K. A must have for any learner driver. Professional Driving Lessons in C.D. format.*

Johnson's Insulation Supplies Ltd, 16 Victoria Way, Burgess Hill, West Sussex, RH15 9NF Tel: (01444) 243133 Fax: (01444) 871053 *Insulation contractors*

▶ Johnsons (Printers) Ltd, Oat Market, Nantwich, Cheshire, CW5 5AP Tel: (01270) 625207

Johnsons Veterinary Products Ltd, 5 Reddicap Trading Estate, Sutton Coldfield, West Midlands, B75 7DF Tel: 0121-378 1684 Fax: 0121-311 1758 E-mail: info@johnsons-vet.com *Pet care products*

Johnsons Wellfield Quarries Ltd, Crosland Hill, Huddersfield, HD4 7AB Tel: (01484) 652311 Fax: (01484) 460007 E-mail: sales@johnson-wellfield.co.uk *Quarriers*

Johnstech Interconnect Ltd, 1-2 Usk Street, Newport, Gwent, NP19 7BE Tel: (01633) 674452 Fax: (01633) 674453 E-mail: info@johnstech.com *Semi-conductor test equipment sales*

▶ Johnston Builders, Unit 17-18, Mayfield Industrial Estate, Dalkeith, Midlothian, EH22 4AD Tel: 0131-454 0796 Fax: 0131-454 0796 E-mail: sales@johnstonbuilders.co.uk

Johnston & Bulman Ltd, Lancaster Street, Carlisle, CA1 1TD Tel: (01228) 534131 Fax: (01228) 548188 E-mail: sales@johnstonbulman.co.uk *Engineers merchants*

D. Johnston & Co. (Laphroaig) Ltd, Laphroaig Distillery, Laphroaig, Port Ellen, Isle Of Islay, PA42 7DU Tel: (01496) 302418 Fax: (01496) 302496 E-mail: robin.shields@adsweu.com *Malt distillers*

▶ Johnston Engineering (Falkirk) Ltd, Dunipace Mill, Denovan Road, Larbert, Stirlingshire, FK5 4RY Tel: (01324) 821122 Fax: (01324) 821122 *Lift engineers*

Graham Johnston, 2 Baird Street, Stonehaven, Kincardineshire, AB39 2SP Tel: (01569) 762293 Fax: (01569) 767449 E-mail: graham.johnston4@btopenworld.com *Kitchen manufrs*

▶ Judith Johnston Lampwork Beads, 21 Kendal Road, Hove, East Sussex, BN3 5HZ Tel: (01273) 776985 *Handcrafted glass beads for jewellery*

Johnston Lightning Filler Ltd, K Prescot Trade Centre, Oliver Lyme Road, Prescot, Merseyside, L34 2SH Tel: 0151-430 0900 Fax: 0151-430 7350 E-mail: sales@jlf-packaging.co.uk *Sealing & packaging machine manufrs*

M. Johnston, Killard Sq, Ballyhornan, Downpatrick, Co. Down, BT30 7PW Tel: (028) 4484 1196 Fax: (028) 4484 2228 *Seafood processors*

▶ Johnston Mailing Ltd, 42-46 Watt Road, Hillington Industrial Estate, Glasgow, G52 4RY Tel: 0141-810 4433 Fax: 0141-810 4993 E-mail: sales@johnstonmailing.co.uk *As one of the fastest growing mailing houses in Scotland, we at Johnston Mailing feel you should get the chance to benefit from our cost effective direct mailing solutions as so many already have.*Only in our first year of trading and already accredited by the Direct Marketing Association, we have the on site capacity to exceed most of our competitors, in terms of speed, efficiency, accuracy and our customer service is second to none.**We offer fulfilment as standard and our prices won't be beaten!!!!!!!*We can offer our clients:*High-Speed Digital Overprinting of envelopes, postcards or virtually anything, any finish from the size of a credit card to an A3 sheet with the newest technology around,*Mono Laser Printing simplex/duplex at a resolution of 600dpi in A3-A6 sizes and various thicknesses,*Folding/Inserting of multiple letters/ inserts up to a maximum of 8 into mainly C5, C5+, DL and DL+ sizes with the only machine of its kind in Scotland,**

Malcolm Johnston, 156 Woodville Park Industrial Estate, Woodville Street, Glasgow, G51 2RL Tel: 0141-445 2368 Fax: 0141-445 2368 *Wholesale beds*

▶ Niall Johnston, 22 Berens Road, Shrivenham, Swindon, SN6 8EG Tel: (08709) 502012 Fax: (01793) 783769 E-mail: info@stretched4u.com *West Country Superior Stretched Limousines*We are one of UK""s finest limousine hire companies offering limo hire in Swindon and Wiltshire.**Other areas covered include Bristol, Oxford, Basingstoke, Winchester, Southampton, London, Salisbury, Newbury and much of Berkshire. Call us for more details.**Our jaw dropping Infiniti FX45 limo is one of the world""s most impressive stretched limousines with more glitz than a Vagas casino. If you want a truly magnificent limousine for your special occasion then look no further.**Your limo will be accompanied by a smartly attired, professional chauffeur. You are guaranteed a friendly and professional VIP service.**We can cater for anything from birthdays to corporate hire, and hen nights to a day at the races.***

Johnston Pine, 9b Main Street, Guardbridge, St. Andrews, Fife, KY16 0UG Tel: (01334) 838783 Fax: (01334) 838783 *Pine furniture shop & manufrs*

Johnston Pre-Cast Ltd, Doseley, Telford, Shropshire, TF4 3BX Tel: (01952) 630300 Fax: (01952) 501537 *Concrete manufrs*

Johnston Printing Ltd, Mill Road, Kilrea, Coleraine, County Londonderry, BT51 5RJ Tel: (028) 2954 0312 Fax: (028) 2954 1070 E-mail: service@johnston-printing.co.uk *General printers*

Johnston Reid & Co., 224 Hardgate, Aberdeen, AB10 6AA Tel: (01224) 212255 Fax: (01224) 211146 E-mail: sales@johnstonreid.co.uk *Office Furniture Supplies*

Johnston Sweepers Ltd, Curtis Road, Dorking, Surrey, RH4 1XF Tel: (01306) 884722 Fax: (01306) 884151 E-mail: enquiries@johnstonsweepers.com *Road sweepers manufrs* Also at: Redhill & Sheerness

Johnston Sweepers Ltd, 3 Heron Square, Deans Industrial Estate, Deans, Livingston, West Lothian, EH54 8QY Tel: (01506) 460563 Fax: (01506) 460564 E-mail: livingston@johnstonesweepers.com *Regional parts & service centre*

William Johnston & Company Ltd, 9 Spiersbridge Terrace, Thornliebank Industrial Estate, Glasgow, G46 8JH Tel: 0141-620 1666 Fax: 0141-620 1888 E-mail: sales@williamjohnston.co.uk *William Johnston & Company supplies gaskets and nuts, bolts and washers throughout the UK, Europe, the Middle East and the Far East. Our water gaskets, gas gaskets, pump gaskets and flange sets which have BSI, WRC and FDA approvals are used by utilities worldwide. For engineering and industrial applications we supply jointing materials including commercial rubber, SBR, EPDM, Neoprene, Nitrile , Viton, sponge , silicone, oil tan paper and graphite all of which are cut as gaskets or strip to suit customers' requirements. Suppliers include Novus, Klinger and Teadit. To these sectors we also supply metal ring gaskets, spiral wound gaskets, camprofile gaskets, PTFE envelopes, O rings and a full range of pump and valve packings in pure 24B PTFE. We supply the automotive sector with mudflaps, snowplough blades, antislip walkways and matting. Our fasteners are finished in Rilsan, Sheraplex Zinc and BZP.* Also at: Inverness

Johnstone Metal Works, 2a Park Road, Ramsgate, Kent, CT11 7QE Tel: (01843) 593451 Fax: (01843) 850615 *Sheet metalwork engineers*

Johnstons, Eastfield Mills, Mansfield Road, Hawick, Roxburghshire, TD9 8AA Tel: (01450) 360500 Fax: (01450) 378532 *Knitwear manufrs*

Johnstons, Eastfield Mills, Mansfield Road, Hawick, Roxburghshire, TD9 8AA Tel: (01450) 360500 Fax: (01450) 378532 E-mail: enquiries@johnstonscashmere.com *Knitwear manufrs*

Johnstons Of Elgin Ltd, Newmill, Elgin, Morayshire, IV30 4AF Tel: (01343) 554000 Fax: (01343) 554055 E-mail: elgin@johnstoncashmere.com *Knitted clothing manufrs*

▶ Johnston's PC Clinic, 98 Black Bull Road, Folkestone, Kent, CT19 5QX Tel: (01303) 244500 Fax: (01303) 244500 *Computer retailers*

Joinery Construction & Maintenance Ltd, 14 Fullarton Drive, Glasgow East Investment Park, Glasgow, G32 8FA Tel: 0141-646 3800 Fax: 0141-646 3888

▶ Joinery Crew, Unit 1, 70 Bell Lane, Uckfield, East Sussex, TN22 1QL Tel: 01825 766777 Fax: 01825 766755 *Joiners*

Joinery Shop, Unit 16 Dockray Hall Industrial Estate, Dockray Hall Road, Kendal, Cumbria, LA9 4RU Tel: (01539) 731857

Joint Arab British Chamber Of Commerce, 43 Upper Grosvenor Street, London, W1K 2NJ Tel: (020) 7235 4363 Fax: (020) 7245 6688 E-mail: bims@abcc.org.uk *Government agency*

▶ JOINT Design, Brescia, Main Road, St Pauls Cray, Kent, Orpington, Kent, BR5 3ET Tel: 07780 695492 E-mail: oliversdesign@gmail.com *Commercial & Domestic design & build service. Kitchen installation. Project Management. Carpentry & Joinery - which includes bespoke furniture, partitioning, with plastering. *Interior Design & planning - Decorating.*Qualified Architect, Plumber & Electrician on Board.*

Joint Replacement Instrumentation Ltd, 8 Broadstone Place, London, W1U 7EP Tel: (020) 7487 4477 Fax: (020) 7224 2862 E-mail: jri@jri-ltd.co.uk *Hip implants suppliers*

▶ Jojet Ltd, Ashley House,, 2, Lower Park Terrace, Pontypool, Torfaen, NP4 6LB Tel: (07183) 944621 *Jojet is an Internet consultancy owned by Joel Hughes based in South Wales able to offer web development expertise over a wide array of disciplines (e.g. PHP, Perl, ASP & .Net).**Experience across a variety of platforms (e.g. Windows, Linux & Solaris) is enhanced by excellent technical configuration knowledge (e.g. Apache, IIS, PHP, WorldPay, firewalls).**Proven communication and project management skills allow Jojet to seamlessly integrate with client"s in house development resources whilst coordinating remote working to project manage client"s developments.*

Jola Ltd, Sprinfield Works, Lloyd St, Hopwood, Heywood, Lancs, OL10 2BP Tel: (01706) 366339 Fax: (01706) 366382 E-mail: bernie.mjola@tinyworld.co.uk *Manufacturers of level controllers for all liquid applications & leakage detectors. Products include float switches & immersion probes & magnetically activated reed switch level controls. We also welcome any specials & offer full advice*

Jolibar Metal Works Ltd, Howe Moss Drive, Dyce, Aberdeen, AB21 0GL Tel: (01224) 770445 Fax: (01224) 770019 E-mail: sales@jolibarmetalworks.co.uk *Sheet metal & steel fabricators*

Jolley Engineering, Unit 4, Milbank, Storridge, Malvern, Worcestershire, WR13 5EN Tel: (01886) 880101 Fax: (01886) 880101 E-mail: sales@classicheads.com *Electronic ignitions for classic cars*

Gordon Jolly, Belvedere, Harray, Orkney, KW17 2LQ Tel: (01856) 771440 Fax: (01856) 771440 *Air compressor sets distributors*

John Jolly, P O Box 2, Kirkwall, Orkney, KW15 1HS Tel: (01856) 872268 Fax: (01856) 875002 E-mail: operations@johnjolly.co.uk *Ship brokers*

Jolly Roger (Amusement Rides) Ltd, College View Works, Manby Road, Grimoldby, Louth, Lincolnshire, LN11 8HE Tel: (01507) 328856 Fax: (01507) 327060 E-mail: roger@jolly-roger.co.uk *Glass fibre amusement ride manufrs*

Jolly's Transport, Irongate Arches, Copeland Rd, London, SE15 3SH Tel: 020 76394450 *Cold storage*

Joloda International, Joloda Hydraroll Division, Gaerwen, Gwynedd, LL60 6BH Tel: (01248) 421454 Fax: (01248) 421748 E-mail: sales@transpotech.co.uk *Vehicle loading, unloading & curtain slider kits manufrs*

Joloda (International) Ltd, 51 Speke Road, Liverpool, L19 2NY Tel: 0151-427 8954 Fax: 0151-427 1393 E-mail: info@joloda.com *Loading technology manufrs*

Jomac Engineering Ltd, The Airfield, Martin Moor, Metheringham, Lincoln, LN4 3BQ Tel: (01526) 378278 Fax: (01526) 378329 E-mail: sales@jomacengineering.sageweb.co.uk *Agricultural engineers & food processors*

Jomar Engineering, 119 Sandycombe Road, Richmond, Surrey, TW9 2ER Tel: (020) 8332 6692 Fax: (020) 8948 4269 *Sheet metalworkers & steel fabricators*

▶ Jon George Ltd, Unit 33-34 The Washford Industrial Estate, Heming Road, Redditch, Worcestershire, B98 0DP Tel: (01527) 515775 Fax: (01527) 502448

Jon Macrae, Lynjon, Lundy Green, Hempnall, Norwich, NR15 2NU Tel: (01508) 499400 *Agricultural contractors*

Jonathan Dean Textiles Ltd, The Old Coach House, Wharncliffe Road, Loughborough, Leicestershire, LE11 1SN Tel: (01509) 235251 Fax: (01509) 611121 E-mail: jonathan.dean@yahoo.co.uk *Equestrian textiles*

Jonathan Kaye Jewellery, James Binney House, 52 Cross Street, Manchester, M2 7AR Tel: 0161-839 6138 Fax: 0161-839 5895 E-mail: j.kaye01@ntlworld.com *Jewellery retailers & manufrs*

▶ Jonathan Mayers Services Ltd, 11 Newman Road, Trevethin, Pontypool, Gwent, NP4 8HQ Tel: (08701) 160821 Fax: (08701) 160821 E-mail: sales@j-m-s.co.uk *Plumbing & heating gas leak gas cookers fires servicing and repairs*

▶ Jones, Ryehill Court, Lodge Farm Industrial Estate, Northampton, NN5 7EU Tel: (01604) 588811

Jones, PO Box 141, Wallingford, Oxfordshire, OX10 6AF Tel: (01491) 835032 Fax: (01491) 834765 *Heating & mechanical engineers*

Jones & Co., Severn Road, Welshpool, Powys, SY21 7AR Tel: (01938) 555340 Fax: (01938) 552592 E-mail: ifan@jones-co.co.uk *Agricultural timber & building product suppliers*

Jones & Andrews Ltd, Melrose Close, Swansea Enterprise Park, Swansea, SA6 8QE Tel: (01792) 701797 Fax: (01792) 701793 *Shop fitters*

Ansell Jones, Unit 1 Satellite Industrial Estate, Neachells Lane, Wolverhampton, WV11 3PQ Tel: (01902) 722117 Fax: (01902) 725533 E-mail: sales@anselljones.com *Water tight door & hatch manufrs*

Jones & Baker, 1 Spring Lane, Swannington, Coalville, Leicestershire, LE67 8QR Tel: (01530) 837803 Fax: (01530) 837803 *Joinery manufrs*

Jones Baker Engineering Co., Love Lane, London, N17 8HG Tel: (020) 8808 8196 Fax: (020) 8365 0180 *Structural steelwork engineers*

Barry Jones & Son, Rotherwood, 235 Botley Rd, Southampton, SO19 0NL Tel: 023 80406396 *Boat builders & repairers*

Brian Jones Engineering (Fabrications), Heulwen, Penrhyndeudraeth, Gwynedd, LL48 6AH Tel: (01766) 770731 Fax: (01766) 770731 *Industrial building contractors*

Jones & Brooks Ltd, Duchess Street Industrial Estate, Shaw, Oldham, OL2 7UX Tel: (01706) 843121 Fax: (01706) 882985 E-mail: sales@jones-brooks.co.uk *Printer of hospital forms*

▶ Jones Bros (Henllan) Ltd, Unit 17, Cross Hands Business Centre, Heol Parc Mawr, Cross Hands Industrial Estate, Llanelli, Dyfed, SA14 6RE Tel: (01269) 844275

Jones Bros & Warriss Ltd, 104 Mary St, Sheffield, S1 4RU Tel: 0114-272 0820 Fax: 0114-272 9011 E-mail: warriss@gxn.co.uk *Silversmiths*

▶ Jones Bros Weston Rhyn Ltd, Garden Croft, Weston Rhyn, Oswestry, Shropshire, SY10 7SG Tel: (01691) 772091 Fax: (01691) 774325

C.H. Jones Ltd, Premier Business Park, Queen Street, Walsall, WS2 9PB Tel: (01922) 615231 Fax: (01922) 704441 E-mail: info@keyfules.co.uk *Fuel management service*

Jones & Clark (Burton-on-Trent) Ltd, 77-80 Waterloo Street, Burton-On-Trent, Staffordshire, DE14 2NE Tel: (01283) 541771 Fax: (01283) 542466 E-mail: sales@jonesandclark.co.uk *Tool merchants*

▶ Craig Jones, 2 Russell Avenue, High Lane, Stockport, Cheshire, SK6 8DT Tel: (01663) 762181

D.J. Jones, Maes Y Gwrdy, Llanarth, Dyfed, SA47 0QL Tel: (01545) 580353 Fax: (01545) 580353 *Joinery manufrs*

Jones & Edwards Agricultural Engineers Ltd, Bausley House Farm Coedway, Crew Green, Shrewsbury, SY5 9AS Tel: (01743) 884363 *Agricultural engineers*

F.A. Jones & Son, 57 West Road, Shoeburyness, Southend-On-Sea, SS3 9DR Tel: (01702) 292320 Fax: (01702) 294501 *Removal & storage specialists*

Frederick Jones (Belfast) Ltd, 17 Napier Street, Belfast, BT12 5FE Tel: (028) 9032 4467 Fax: (028) 9032 5252 E-mail: sales@fjones.com *Packing & corrugated case manufrs*

George Jones & Bros, 1-7 Lower Ashley Road, St. Agnes, Bristol, BS2 9QA Tel: 0117-955 6201 Fax: 0117-955 5503 *Plumbers & builders' merchants*

George Jones Engineering Services Ltd, Lionel Works, 89-91 Rolfe Street, Smethwick, West Midlands, B66 2AY Tel: 0121-558 1884 Fax: 0121-558 0017 E-mail: sales.georgejonesengservices@zyworld.com *Design & manufacturer of hydraulic systems*

Jones & Gough Electrical Ltd, 22 Horton Court, Hortonwood 50, Telford, Shropshire, TF1 7GY Tel: (01952) 606080 Fax: (01952) 608197 *Electrical engineers*

Graham Jones Crane Hire Ltd, 6-10 Haygate Road, Wellington, Telford, Shropshire, TF1 1QA Tel: (01952) 245455 Fax: (01978) 310573 *Crane hire*

Gwili Jones & Sons, Maesyfelin Business Park, Lampeter, Dyfed, SA48 8LS Tel: (01570) 423777 Fax: (01570) 423355 *Agricultural machinery retailers*

Henry Jones & Sons Ltd, Wyvern, 1 Brynhedydd Road, Rhyl, Denbighshire, LL18 3UH Tel: (01745) 351314 Fax: (01745) 351314 E-mail: office@hjs1923.f9.co.uk *Building maintenance services*

J S Jones, Glenside Bungalow, Blackvein Road, Cross Keys, Newport, Gwent, NP11 7NU Tel: (01633) 263458 Fax: (01633) 263458 *Plant hire*

James Jones & Sons Ltd, Garmouth Road, Mosstodloch, Fochabers, Morayshire, IV32 7LH Tel: (01343) 821421 Fax: (01343) 821299 E-mail: mosstodloch@jamesjones.co.uk *Sawmill & timber merchants*

James Jones & Sons Ltd, Broomage Avenue, Larbert, Stirlingshire, FK5 4NQ Tel: (01324) 562241 Fax: (01324) 558755 E-mail: sales@jamesjones.com *Timber merchants*

Jeff Jones, 7 Hannah Street, Porth, Mid Glamorgan, CF39 9PU Tel: (01443) 681626 *Jewellery repairers*

Jones Joinery, 144 Hornby Boulevard, Liverpool, L21 8HQ Tel: 0151-933 0442 *Joinery*

▶ Jones & Jones, Goole Road, Moorends, Doncaster, South Yorkshire, DN8 4JX Tel: (01405) 812413 Fax: (01405) 816363

Joshua Jones, White Mill Farm, Sturminster Marshall, Wimborne, Dorset, BH21 4BX Tel: (01258) 858470 *Cabinet makers*

Michael Jones & Associates, Crossway House, 8 London Road, Reigate, Surrey, RH2 9HY Tel: (01737) 245610 Fax: (01737) 241142 E-mail: info@mjassociates.co.uk *Mechanical & electrical engineering consultants*

Jones & Palmer Ltd, 95 Carver Street, Birmingham, B1 3AR Tel: 0121-236 9007 Fax: 0121-236 5513 E-mail: info@jonesandpalmer.co.uk *Printers*

Philip Jones Construction Materials Ltd, 40 Wood Lane, Hawarden, Deeside, Clwyd, CH5 3JE Tel: (01691) 626262 Fax: (01244) 520944 E-mail: philip.jones@tggroup.co.uk *Distributor of steel fibres for concrete reinforcement*

R.A. Jones Europak, Unit 30 Concourse House, Leeds, LS11 7DF Tel: 0113 2765842 *Packaging machinery manufrs*

R.C. Jones (Motor Bodies) Ltd, Claycliffe Road, Barugh Green, Barnsley, South Yorkshire, S75 1HS Tel: (01226) 205123 Fax: (01226) 292202 E-mail: reception@rcjones.net *Repairing vehicles*

R. Jones & Son, Greenhill Farm, Elson, Ellesmere, Shropshire, SY12 9EZ Tel: 01691 690252 *Agricultural contractors*

Jones & Shipman Precision Ltd, Murrayfield Road, Braunstone Frith Industrial Estate, Leicester, LE3 1UW Tel: 0116-201 3000 Fax: 0116-201 3002 E-mail: sales@jonesshipman.com *Jones & Shipman is an acknowledged world leader in sophisticated abrasive machine tool technology. We deliver complete solutions from single stand-alone machines to fully automated multi-machine systems. Every Jones & Shipman installation is backed by our unique philosophy of total quality, reliability and responsibility. Working in close association with customers, we are able to ensure that our grinding machines are manufactured to meet each individual's needs. Our in depth customer support includes application studies, demonstrations, consultancy and training whenever and wherever you require it. Face the challenges of the new millennium with increased confidence. Enjoy the benefits of increased productivity and enhanced quality. Our world of experience in abrasive machine tool technology is yours to command*

Shirley Jones & Associates Ltd, C The Courtyard, Lonesome Lane, Reigate, Surrey, RH2 7QT Tel: (01737) 244844 Fax: (01737) 243266 *Packaging components & aerosol filling*

Jones & Shufflebottom Ltd, Lytton Street, Stoke-on-Trent, ST4 2AG Tel: (01782) 846881 Fax: (01782) 414812 E-mail: stoke@shuffs.co.uk *Plumbers' merchants*

Simon Jones Superfreight Ltd, 1-2 Grant Road, London, SW11 2NU Tel: (020) 7924 3933 Fax: (020) 7223 1293 E-mail: simonjones@superfreight.fsnet.co.uk *Freight forwarders*

Jones Springs Engineering Ltd, Gladstone Street, Wednesbury, West Midlands, WS10 8BE Tel: 0121-568 7575 Fax: 0121-568 7692 E-mail: sales@jones-springs.co.uk *Laminated spring manufrs*

Jones Stroud Insulations, Queen Street, Longridge, Preston, PR3 3BS Tel: (01772) 783011 Fax: (01772) 784200 E-mail: info@krempel-group.com *Electrical insulation manufrs*

Jones Tim Carpentry Joinery Shopfitting, Trevanson Street, The Workshop, Wadebridge, Cornwall, PL27 7AR Tel: (01208) 814755 Fax: (01208) 814755 *Joinery manufacturers & bar refurbishes*

W.G. Jones Ltd, 24 Blackmore Road, Verwood, Dorset, BH31 6BD Tel: 01202 825467 *Precision engineer services*

W.I.S. Jones, Birds Hill Factory, Llandeilo, Dyfed, SA19 6SG Tel: 01558 822691 *Agricultural contractors*

Jonesco (Preston) Ltd, Pittman Way, Fulwood, Preston, PR2 9ZD Tel: (01772) 704488 Fax: (01772) 702209 E-mail: sales@jonesco-plastics.com *Jonesco was established in 1967 to manufacture steel mudguards for commercial vehicles. Jonesco plastic products are leading brand names with a high reputation and market share. They are widely fitted as original equipment and first installation. High quality, durability, competitiveness, service, high supply performance and support of a loyal distribution chain have gained this position. Our range of products include Durable mudguards, Durable mudguard, Tandem, Tridem, Tandem mudgaurds, Tridem mudguards, Fire boxes, Fire box, Front loader, Top Loader, Spray suppression, Integrated spray suppression, Quarter fender, High Density mudguard, Medium Density mudguard, Small Trailer mudguards, Adjustable mudguard fixings, adjustable fixings, Steel mudguards, Spats, Spill Pallets, Workfloors, Drum Trolley IBC bunds, Workfloor Ramp, Drum Rack, Drum Rack Base, DIBt, Safety boxes, Safety cabinets, Storage boxes, Storage cabinets, Spill Kits, Spill absorbents, absorbents, Spill prevention, Oil absorbent granules, granules, new safety tread, Multizorb, Fire extinguishers, Powder extinguishers. For more information on Jonesco products please visit www.jonesco-plastics.com, where all three catalogues can be downloaded. Alternatively call /e-mail +44 (0) 1772 706888 / sales@jonesco-plastics.com.*

JonesMarine, Cumberland House, 1 Kensington Road, London, W8 5NX Tel: (020) 7938 3046 Fax: (020) 7938 3015 E-mail: jerry@jonesmarine.com *Anti corrosion services*

Jongor Hampshire & Dorset Ltd, Copnor Road, Portsmouth, PO3 5LA Tel: (01202) 536306 Fax: (023) 9267 7417 E-mail: sales@jongor.com *Catering equipment distributors*

Jonic Engineering Ltd, Speedwell Road, Yardley, Birmingham, B25 8EU Tel: 0121-707 8222 Fax: 0121-706 7303 E-mail: sales@jonicengineering.co.uk *Designing & manufacturing quality hydraulic cylinders*

▶ Jonk Design & Film Boutique, 30 High Street, Eton, Windsor, Berkshire, SL4 6AX Tel: (07793) 122586 Fax: (01753) 840240 E-mail: info@jonkproductions.com *Full creative and management service, tailor made to fit their needs. *Alternative branding & marketing solutions, giving brands their cool. *Using strategically based creative solutions.*Jonk - creative thinkers. **

Joplings, John Street, Sunderland, SR1 1DP Tel: 0191-510 2105 Fax: 0191-510 5510 *Department store*

▶ Jorade Commercial Services Ltd, 16 Hartley Court Road, Three Mile Cross, Reading, RG7 1NS Tel: 0118-988 2852 Fax: 0118-988 3703 E-mail: debbie@byrne1718.fsnet.co.uk *Specialist vehicle ramps suppliers*

Jordan Ltd, Apollo, Lichfield Road Industrial Estate, Tamworth, Staffordshire, B79 7TA Tel: (01827) 55558 Fax: (01827) 53558 *Printing components manufrs*

▶ Jordan (Building & Joinery Contractors) Ltd, Lochlands Industrial Estate, Larbert, Stirlingshire, FK5 3NS Tel: (01324) 555844

Jordan Concrete Ltd, 10 Sheepwalk Road, Lisburn, County Antrim, BT28 3RD Tel: (028) 9264 8648 Fax: (028) 9264 8775 E-mail: sales@jordanconcrete.co.uk *Precast concrete manufacturers & suppliers*

Jordan & Cook, Ivy Arch Road, Worthing, West Sussex, BN14 8BX Tel: (01903) 235701 Fax: (01903) 824245 E-mail: phremovals@aol.com *Removal contractors, storers & shippers*

Jordan Cylinders, Little Folley, Eardisland, Leominster, Herefordshire, HR6 9BS Tel: (01544) 388227 *Hydraulic systems & equipment manufrs*

Jordan Division Ltd, Millbrook Road, Yate, Bristol, BS37 5PB Tel: (01454) 328300 Fax: (01454) 325866 E-mail: sales@jordanengineering.co.uk *Nuclear plant equipment & skid package units. Also stainless steel pipework*

Jordan Engineering Services Ltd, Hardley Industrial Estate, Hardley, Hythe, Southampton, SO45 3NQ Tel: (023) 8084 9988 Fax: (023) 8042 3779 E-mail: enquiries@chb-jordan.co.uk Principal Export Areas: Worldwide *Pipe work & pipeline contractors & pipe work fabricators*

▶ Jordan Engineering UK Ltd, Pillar Building, The Dockyard, Pembroke Dock, Dyfed, SA72 6TD Tel: (01646) 681999 Fax: (01646) 681998 E-mail: info@jordanengineering.co.uk *Engineering*

Jordan IT Services, 28 Carter Ave, Broughton, Kettering, Northants, NN14 1LZ Tel: (01536) 790425 Fax: (08701) 367829 E-mail: info@jordanitservices.com *Internet company constructing websites design*

Jordan Marine, High Bank, Moorland Road, Birch Vale, High Peak, Derbyshire, SK22 1BS Tel: (01663) 743885 Fax: (01663) 743885 *Fire safety consultants*

Michael Jordan Caravans Ltd, Station Approach, Gomshall, Guildford, Surrey, GU5 9NX Tel: (01483) 203335 Fax: (01483) 202780 E-mail: sales@michaeljordancaravans.co.uk *Caravan sales*

Neil Jordan Grills & Doors, 8E, 8E Sweechbridge Rd, Herne Bay, Kent, CT6 6TE Tel: (01227) 749991 Fax: (01227) 749991 *Grills & doors manufr*

Jordan Plastics Ltd, 109 Summerisland Road, Portadown, Craigavon, County Armagh, BT62 1SJ Tel: (028) 3885 3111 Fax: (028) 3885 3112 E-mail: sales@jordanplastics.com *Flexible plastic product manufrs*

Jordan Publishing Ltd, 21 St Thomas Street, Bristol, BS1 6JS Tel: 0117-923 0600 Fax: 0117-925 0486 E-mail: customersupport@jordans.co.uk *International company formation agents* Also at: Cardiff, Edinburgh & London

Jordan Reflectors Ltd, 9-10 Seax Way, Basildon, Essex, SS15 6SW Tel: (01268) 415828 Fax: (01268) 410985 E-mail: sday@jordonreflectors.co.uk *Manufacturers of lighting, louvres & reflectors*

Robert Jordan & Associates, 10 Alderley Road, Wilmslow, Cheshire, SK9 1JX Tel: (01625) 250000 Fax: (01625) 250005 E-mail: wilmslow@robertjordan.co.uk *Residential letting & management agents*

C.D. Jordans & Sons Ltd, Dundas Spur, Dundas Lane, Copnor, Portsmouth, PO3 5NX Tel: (023) 9266 1391 Fax: (023) 9267 9503 E-mail: michelle@cdjordan.co.uk *Scrap metal processors*

Jordans Garage Ltd, Flambard Way, The Wharf, Godalming, Surrey, GU7 1JF Tel: (01483) 415201 Fax: (01483) 424533 *Motor vehicle repair*

Jordans Sunblinds Ltd, York St, Hull, HU2 0QW Tel: (01482) 326657 Fax: (01482) 212486 E-mail: enquiries@jordansofhull.co.uk *Tarpaulin, sunblinds & security shutters manufrs*

Jordison Ltd, Tralee, Kirkleatham Business Park, Redcar, Cleveland, TS10 5SG Tel: (01642) 495270 Fax: (01642) 495271 *Outdoor advertising & promotion print* Also at: Perivale

Jorgar Ltd, Lockwood House, 81 Mawson Road, Cambridge, CB1 2DZ Tel: (01223) 504427 Fax: (01223) 504427 E-mail: jh@jorgar.co.uk *Chairs & tables manufrs*

Joro Abrasives Ltd, Holly Farm, Holly Lane, Styal, Wilmslow, Cheshire, SK9 4JL Tel: (01625) 524558 Fax: (01625) 539330 *Diamond blade manufrs*

Jorosa Ltd, 22 The Hive Industrial Estate, Hockley, Factory Road, Birmingham, B18 5JU Tel: 0121-507 1313 Fax: 0121-507 1440 E-mail: sales@jorosa.com *Hardware & roller shutter accessories*

Joseph Ash, North Road, Bridgend Industrial Estate, Bridgend, Mid Glamorgan, CF31 3TP Tel: (01656) 668735 Fax: (01656) 767139 E-mail: bend@josephash.co.uk *Galvanizers & rust proofing services*

Joseph Ash, Mortimer Road, Hereford, HR4 9SY Tel: (01432) 277722 Fax: (01432) 359091 *Complete galvanizing processors or services*

Joseph Ash, Stafford Park 6, Telford, Shropshire, TF3 3AT Tel: (01952) 290201 Fax: (01952) 290113 E-mail: telford@josephash.co.uk *Galvanisers*

Joseph Ash Galvanising, Seven Stars Road, Oldbury, West Midlands, B69 4JS Tel: 0121-552 1682 Fax: 0121-511 1125 E-mail: albion@josephash.co.uk *Galvanizes to the trade*

Joseph Ash London, Glaucus Works, Leven Road, London, E14 0LP Tel: (020) 7987 5070 Fax: (020) 7515 7498 E-mail: enquiries@josephash.co.uk *Complete galvanizing services*

Joseph Ash Walsall, Briteon Street Off Pleck Road, Walsall, WS2 9HW Tel: (01922) 628141 Fax: (01922) 623451 E-mail: walsall@josephash.co.uk *Galvanisers*

Joseph Braddell & Sons, 11 North Street, Belfast, BT1 1NA Tel: (028) 9032 0525 Fax: (028) 9032 2657 E-mail: fishing@braddells.fsnet.co.uk *Retailers & repairers of guns & fishing tackle*

Joseph Bros Textiles Ltd, 15 Gruneisen Road, Finchley, London, N3 1LS Tel: (020) 8346 0851 Fax: (020) 8343 1773 E-mail: mjfabrics@aol.com *Linings & interlinings manufrs*

Joseph Dixon Tool Company Ltd, Unit 2 Charles Street, Town Wharf Business Park, Walsall, WS2 9LZ Tel: (01922) 622051 Fax: (01922) 721168 E-mail: sales@josephdixon.co.uk *Gasket, press knife or cutter, label cutter, leather working tools & cutter (forme) (print/packaging) manufrs*

▶ Joseph Gallagher, Stanford Road, Orsett, Grays, Essex, RM16 3BX Tel: (01375) 672070 Fax: (01375) 673073 E-mail: atasker@josephgallagher.co.uk *Civil engineering contractors*

Joseph H Lines & Sons Ltd, Eagle Road, Moons Moat North Industrial Es, Redditch, Worcestershire, B98 9HF Tel: (01527) 63078 Fax: (01527) 63294 E-mail: j.h.lines@dial.pipex.com *Specialised case manufrs*

Joseph H Wood & Son Ltd, 15 Hemmons Road, Manchester, M12 5ST Tel: 0161-248 9814 Fax: 0161-225 2044 E-mail: wood@steamforindustry.freeserve.co.uk *Boiler engineers*

Joseph Hirst Huddersfield Ltd, 29 Byram Street, Huddersfield, HD1 1DY Tel: (01484) 435324 Fax: (01484) 435469 *Worn & trimming merchants*

Joseph & Jesse Siddons Ltd, Howard Street, Hill Top, West Bromwich, West Midlands, B70 0TB Tel: 0121-556 0218 Fax: 0121-556 3843 E-mail: info@jjsiddons.co.uk Principal Export Areas: Worldwide *Iron steel & SG casting manufrs*

Joseph Lavian, Oriental Carpet Centre, 105 Eade Road, London, N4 1TJ Tel: (020) 8800 0707 Fax: (020) 8800 0404 E-mail: lavian@lavian.com *Oriental carpet merchants*

Joseph Maxwell, 1 Galabreck Road, Thornhill, Dumfriesshire, DG3 4LP Tel: (01848) 330365 Fax: (01848) 331734 *Steel fabricators*

Joseph Newman, Highgate Business Centre, 1h Greenwood Place, London, NW5 1LB Tel: (020) 7482 1769 Fax: (020) 7482 1766 E-mail: jnewmantext@aol.com *Textile agents*

Joseph Parr Alco Ltd, Higginshaw Lane, Royton, Oldham, OL2 6JD Tel: 0161-633 1264 Fax: 0161-620 0866 E-mail: aellis@josephparr.co.uk *Builders & timber merchants*

Joseph & Pearce Ltd, 6th Floor 63-66 Hatton Garden, London, EC1N 8LE Tel: (020) 7405 4604 Fax: (020) 7242 1902 E-mail: info@josephpearce.co.uk *Jewellery suppliers & manufrs*

Joseph Thompson, Hendon Lodge Sawmills, Moor Terrace, Sunderland, SR1 2PA Tel: 0191-514 4663 Fax: 0191-514 3251 *Timber merchants*

Joseph Thoueiri, 30 Shrewsbury Walk, Isleworth, Middlesex, TW7 7DE Tel: (020) 8560 6945 *Coffee shop*

▶ Andrew Josephs, 16 South Terrace, Sowerby, Thirsk, North Yorkshire, YO7 1RH Tel: (01743) 343322 E-mail: ritaw18@hotmail.com *Enviornmental Consultant, specialist in Archaeology and EIA*

▶ Joseph's Well Office Space, Josephs Well, Hanover Walk, Leeds, LS3 1AB Tel: 0113-271 7221 Fax: 0113-246 1454 E-mail: mtaylor@pullans.com *Office rentals*

Josery Textiles Ltd, Unit 3 Benneworth Close, Hucknall, Nottingham, NG15 6EL Tel: 0115-963 2200 Fax: 0115-964 0223 E-mail: sales@josery.co.uk *Leisurewear fabric & garment suppliers & manufrs*

continued

B.L. Joshi UK Ltd, 212-214 Ealing Road, Wembley, Middlesex, HA0 4QG Tel: (020) 8903 0653 Fax: (020) 8902 2702E-mail: bljoshiuk@aol.com *Knitwear & textiles*

▶ Joss Aberdeen Ltd, Rigifa, Cove, Aberdeen, AB12 3LR Tel: (01224) 774422 Fax: (01224) 772444

Jost Great Britain Ltd, B7, Broadlands, Heywood Distribution Park, Heywood, Lancashire, OL10 2TS Tel: 0161-763 0200 Fax: 0161-763 0234 *Fifth wheel couplings*

▶ Jot Automation UK Ltd, 55 Beauly Crescent, Wishaw, Lanarkshire, ML2 8EG Tel: (01698) 376951

Jotika Midlands Software Ltd, Carmichael House, Village Green, Inkberrow, Worcester, WR7 4DZ Tel: (01386) 793415 Fax: (01386) 793407 E-mail: sales@jotika.com *Glass processing software*

Joto Ltd, 1c North Cresent, London, E16 4TG Tel: (020) 7511 4411 Fax: (020) 7511 5266 *Bookbinding machine manufrs*

Jotron (UK) Ltd, Crossland Park, Cramlington, Northumberland, NE23 1LA Tel: (01670) 712000 Fax: (01670) 590265 E-mail: salesair@jotron.com *Marine distress equipment suppliers*

▶ Jotun Paints Ltd, Stather Road, Flixborough, Scunthorpe, South Humberside, DN15 8RR Tel: (01724) 400000 Fax: (01724) 400100 E-mail: enquiries@jotun.co.uk *Marine, protective & decorative paint manufrs*

Jotun Paints Europe Ltd, 1 Altens Trade Centre, Hareness Circle, Altens Industrial Estate, Aberdeen, AB12 3LY Tel: (01224) 895238 Fax: (01224) 879174 E-mail: sales@jotun.co.uk *Paint distributors & manufrs*

▶ Jotun Paints (Europe) Ltd, 142 Minories, London, EC3N 1LB Tel: (020) 7481 2741 Fax: (020) 7265 1836 E-mail: enquiries@jotun.co.uk *Paint manufrs*

Joule Electronics Ltd, Bryn, Burn Lane, Newton Aycliffe, County Durham, DL5 4PG Tel: (01325) 310278 *Car security services*

Joules Signs, Philomel, 542 Abbott Street, Pamphill, Wimborne, Dorset, BH21 4EF Tel: (01202) 885847 Fax: (01202) 885847 *Sign makers*

Jourdan plc, Elm House, Elmer St North, Grantham, Lincolnshire, NG31 6RE Tel: (01476) 403456 Fax: (01476) 403458 E-mail: jda@jourdanplc.fsnet.co.uk *Industrial holding company*

Jourdans Sheet Metal Work, Marsh End, Lords Meadow Industrial Estate, Crediton, Devon, EX17 1DN Tel: (01363) 773562 Fax: (01363) 773365 E-mail: pluxton@jourdansmetal.co.uk *Wire & tube manufrs*

▶ Jovia Ltd, 3 Linden Crescent, Great Ayton, Middlesbrough, Cleveland, TS9 6AF Tel: (01642) 723211 Fax: (01642) 724681 *Mineral & chemical dealers*

Jovic Plant Ltd, Mayes Lane, Sandon, Chelmsford, CM2 7RP Tel: (01245) 224211 Fax: (01245) 224258 E-mail: sales@jovicplant.co.uk *Plant hire contractors*

▶ Joy & Co., PO Box 1968, Ilford, Essex, IG2 6DU Tel: (020) 8554 2389 Fax: (0871) 6617776 E-mail: mail@joyandco.co.uk *Do you want an accountant you can actually get hold of and who speaks to you in plain English? Joy & Co provides accountancy and taxation services to individuals and owner-managed businesses. Based in Ilford Essex we are within easy reach of London and the South East. Contact us today for a free no obligation initial consultation.*

Joy Mining Machinery Ltd, Kirkby La, Pinxton, Nottingham, NG16 6HX Tel: (01773) 515200 Fax: (01773) 515300 E-mail: rbailey@joy.co.uk *Engineering, mining, plant installation, erection & dismantling*

Joy Mining Machinery Ltd, Seaman Way, Ince, Wigan, Lancashire, WN1 3DD Tel: (0870) 2526000 Fax: (0870) 2526888 E-mail: rbailey@joy.co.uk *Manufacturers of underground mining equipment*

Joy Mining Machinery Ltd, Meco Works, Bromyard Road, Worcester, WR2 5EG Tel: (01905) 422291 Fax: (0870) 2521888 E-mail: worcester@joy.co.uk *Mining & quarry plant equipment manufrs*

Joy Steel Structures (London) Ltd, London Industrial Park, 1 Whitings Ways, East Ham, London, E6 6LR Tel: (020) 7474 0550 Fax: (020) 7473 0158 E-mail: info@joysteel.co.uk *Steel Fabricators*

Joyce, Speedwell Road, Yardley, Birmingham, B25 8HH Tel: 0121-773 6821 Fax: 0121-772 4941 E-mail: joycecomputers@btconnet.com *Civil engineers*

J.B. Joyce & Co., Station Road, Whitchurch, Shropshire, SY13 1RD Tel: (01948) 662817 Fax: (01948) 665068 E-mail: sales@jbjoyce.com *Clock manufrs*

Joyce & Co Printing Materials Ltd, 6 Cam Square, Wilbury Way, Hitchin, Hertfordshire, SG4 0TZ Tel: (01462) 420930 Fax: (01462) 421180 E-mail: sales@joyce-pm.com *Printers equipment suppliers*

▶ Joyce V'Soske UK Ltd, 168 Lavender Hill, London, SW11 5TF Tel: (020) 7801 6221 Fax: (020) 7801 6201 E-mail: chris@csdc.co.uk *Carpet & interior designers*

W. & M. Joyce Engineers (Taurus Equipment) Ltd, Steele Road, London, NW10 7AR Tel: (020) 8965 2521 Fax: (020) 8961 0242 E-mail: barry@taurus-equipment.co.uk *Precision engineers & toolmakers, picture framing equipment*

Joyce-Loebl Ltd, 390 Princesway, Team Valley Trading Estate, Gateshead, Tyne & Wear, NE11 0TU Tel: 0191-420 3000 Fax: 0191-420 3030 E-mail: andy.kevins@joyce-loebel.com *Communication & security electronic engineers*

Malcolm Joynes Consultancy, 7 Bracken Hall, Bracken Place, Chilworth, Southampton, SO16 3ET Tel: (023) 8076 7442 Fax: (0870) 7051038 E-mail: malcolm@malcolm-joynes.co.uk *Consultancy & Solutions for Small and Medium Sized Businesses · Covering Hampshire and Dorset · General consultancy - Analysing business and recommending/implementing needed changes · Innovation, IP (intellectual property) and business growth · Training and mentoring · Marketing and business development · Please email or phone for a no-charge, no commitment initial review. Use a friendly external advisor to help you look anew at your business and bring a fresh perspective to those pressing problems.*

Joynson Holland Ltd, Abercromby Avenue, High Wycombe, Buckinghamshire, HP12 3AZ Tel: (01494) 530274 Fax: (01494) 473387 E-mail: sales@joynsonholland.co.uk *Furniture manufrs*

▶ JP Electrical Services Ltd, 10 Lovedean Lane, Waterlooville, Hampshire, PO8 8HH Tel: (023) 9257 1333 Fax: (023) 9257 1999 E-mail: sales@jpelec.co.uk

JP Glass & Decor Ltd, 3 Eastcote Industrial Estate, Field End Road, Ruislip, Middlesex, HA4 9XG Tel: (020) 8429 2999 Fax: (020) 8868 4314 E-mail: sales@jpglass.com *Manufacturers of Toughened tabletops,display shelving,straight and shape bevelling,mirrors,tabletops.*Bespoke shower doors and enclosures.brilliant cutting,sandblasting.*

JP Morgan, Finsbury Dials, 20 Finsbury Street, London, EC2Y 9AQ Tel: (020) 7742 4000 Fax: (020) 7880 3486 *Investment bankers*

JP Soft Furnishings, Hitherford Workshop, Hitherford Lane, Over, Cambridge, CB24 5NY Tel: (01954) 230651 E-mail: mje@pjsoftfurnishings.co.uk *Re-upholstery specialists*

▶ JP taping & jointing, 57 Huntington terrace road, Cannock, Staffordshire, WS11 5HB Tel: 07976 284152 Fax: 01543 428578 E-mail: phasey@tiscli.co.uk *We are very experienced drylining contractors with a large team of CSCS registered operatives.All the work force are experianced in machine & hand applied taping which is carred out to a very high standard.Our reputation is built on reliabiility,excellent workmanship and honesty*

JPB Trading Ltd, Martindale, Cannock, Staffordshire, WS11 7XN Tel: (01543) 462676 Fax: (01543) 571368 E-mail: sales@eurospection.co.uk *Non-destructive testing services*

▶ JPM Manufacturing, 4 Admin Road, Knowsley Industrial Park, Liverpool, L33 7TZ Tel: 0151-549 1123 Fax: 0151-549 1124

Jpmorgan Cazenove, 20 Moorgate, London, EC2R 6DA Tel: (020) 7588 2828 Fax: (020) 7155 9000 *Investment banking*

▶ JP's, Unit 12 Corinium Business Park, Speculation Road, Forest Vale Industrial Estate, Cinderford, Gloucestershire, GL14 2YD Tel: (01594) 825057 Fax: (01594) 825057 E-mail: prtcja@aol.com *Suppliers of hair & beauty products*

JPS, 7 Radway Industrial Estate, Radway Road, Shirley, Solihull, West Midlands, B90 4NR Tel: 0121-711 2115 Fax: 0121-711 2584 E-mail: soltaujpsengineering@btinternet.com *Fuel flow meters manufrs*

JPS Stationery, 5 Arena Parade, Letchworth Garden City, Hertfordshire, SG6 3BY Tel: (01462) 480223 Fax: (01462) 480223 *Commercial stationery suppliers*

▶ Jpsa Manufacturing, 28 Castleham Road, St. Leonards-on-Sea, East Sussex, TN38 9NS Tel: (01424) 852221 Fax: (01424) 852135 E-mail: jpsa@btconnect.com *Sub-contract mechanical engineering*

▶ JPW, 302-304 Derby Road, Bootle, Merseyside, L20 8LN Tel: 0151-922 7070 Fax: 0151-922 7049

JRK Consultants, Silverdale, Leatherhead Road, Bookham, Leatherhead, Surrey, KT23 4RR Tel: (01372) 457134 Fax: (01372) 381499 E-mail: sales@jrkconsultants.co.uk *Training & organization development consultants*

▶ JRS, 47 Ridley Avenue, Howden, Wallsend, Tyne & Wear, NE28 0DY Tel: 0191-209 6565 E-mail: johnsansom00@hotmail.com *J R S building services offers a low price on all types of work,no job to small,free quotes on all building work*

▶ JRS Logistics, Unit D Mid Cragie Trading Estate, Mid Craigie Road, Dundee, DD4 7RH Tel: (01382) 450404 Fax: (01382) 450506

JS Auto Repairs, 137 Picasso Way, Shoeburyness, Southend-on-Sea, SS3 9UY Tel: (07779) 799027 Fax: (01702) 316137 E-mail: cs@jsautorepairs.co.uk *Mobile mechanical vehicle repairs*

▶ JS Bloor Winslow Ltd, 85 Adlington Road, Wilmslow, Cheshire, SK9 2BT Tel: (01625) 539762 Fax: (01625) 546809 E-mail: wilm@bloorhomes.com

▶ JSB Plumbing & Sons, 6 Carron Place, Edinburgh, EH6 7RE Tel: 0131-555 1230 Fax: 0131-467 2555

▶ JSD Construction Ltd, 1 The Chappel, Mill Moor Road, Meltham, Holmfirth, HD9 5JU Tel: (01484) 854900 Fax: (01484) 300960 E-mail: john@jsdconstruction.co.uk *Main Contractors for all building works, new build, extensions, disabled adaptations etc.*

▶ JSH Energy Solutions Ltd, Ardennais House, 6 Sorrel Horse Mews, Grimwade Street, Ipswich, IP4 1LN Tel: 0845 050 5830 Fax: 01473 232137 E-mail: andrew.lashley@jshipswich.co.uk *JSH Energy Solutions Ltd is an independent consultancy which specialises in advising industrial, commercial and public sector organisations of all sizes on reducing their energy consumption via energy surveys, training and consultation services*

JSL Bearbreak Ltd, Arcown House, Peartree Lane, Dudley, West Midlands, DY2 0XR Tel: (01384) 455777 Fax: (01384) 456184 E-mail: dudley@bearbreak.co.uk *Engineers merchants*

▶ JSM, 56 Boldmere Road, Sutton Coldfield, West Midlands, B73 5TJ Tel: 0121-250 1550 Fax: 0121-250 1552 E-mail: enquiries@jsmmodelmakers.co.uk *Jewellery manufrs*

▶ JSM Industrial Model Making, Unit 5 Home Farm House Works, Mildenhall, Marlborough, Wiltshire, SN8 2LR Tel: (01672) 512305 Fax: (01672) 512305 E-mail: studio@jsmmodelmakers.freeserve.co.uk *All areas of industrial modelmaking, prototyping, test rigs, vacuum forming, vacuum casting, sculpting, engineering models, exhibiton props etc*

JST Steel Fabrications Ltd, The Small Cord Workshop, The Fordrough Hay Mills, Birmingham, B25 8DW Tel: 0121-772 5460 *Steel fabricators*

JT Displays Ltd, Rear of, 211-213 High Town Road, Luton, LU2 0BZ Tel: (01582) 723295 Fax: (01582) 417600 *Sign makers*

▶ JT (Fencing) Services Ltd, Beech House, Gosditch, Ashton Keynes, Swindon, SN6 6NZ Tel: (01285) 861710 *Specialist fencing contractors.*

Jta Construction Huddersfield Ltd, 246 Lockwood Road, Huddersfield, HD1 3TG Tel: (01484) 303204 Fax: (01484) 303207

Jtag Technologies, Cople Road, Cardington, Bedford, MK44 3SN Tel: (01234) 831212 Fax: (01234) 831616 E-mail: sales@jtag.com *Boundary scan system manufrs*

Jtekt Automotive UK Ltd, New Factory, Neath Vale Supplier Park, Resolven, Neath, West Glamorgan, SA11 4SP Tel: (01639) 713100 Fax: (01639) 713128 *Power steering manufrs*

JTH Patternmakers Ltd, Players Foundry, Clydach, Swansea, SA6 5BQ Tel: (01792) 842363 Fax: (01792) 845275 E-mail: enquiries@jthpatternmakers.co.uk *Plastics fabricators & moulders*

▶ J-tronics Ltd, 1 Granger Avenue, Acomb, York, YO26 5LF Tel: (01904) 795690 Fax: (01904) 790887 E-mail: jt@j-tronics.fsnet.co.uk *Electronic component distributors*

JTT Equipment Services Ltd, 6 Factory Units, Belton Lane, Grantham, Lincolnshire, NG31 9HN Tel: (01476) 576704 Fax: (01476) 576217 E-mail: sales@jttltd.co.uk *Industrial cleaning equipment*

Jubilee Engineering Co., 5 Runnings Road Kingsditch Trading Estate, Cheltenham, Gloucestershire, GL51 9NQ Tel: (01242) 584883 Fax: (01242) 226855 *Press tool manufrs*

Jubilee Engineering Ltd, Unit 10b, Miry Lane Industrial Estate, Wigan, Lancashire, WN6 7TG Tel: (01942) 247111 Fax: (01942) 247333 *Precision engineering services*

Jubilee Joinery Hull Ltd, Eagle House, Cleveland Street, Hull, HU8 7AU Tel: (01482) 224275 Fax: (01482) 217672 E-mail: jubilee@sagehost.co.uk *Joinery manufrs*

Jubilee Machine Tools, Nuns Street, Derby, DE1 3LS Tel: (01332) 348749 Fax: (01332) 342416 E-mail: sales@jubileemactools.co.uk *Machine tool merchants*

Jubilee Plastics, Regency Mews, 219 Willesden High Road, London, NW10 2SA Tel: (020) 8459 2065 Fax: (020) 8459 0832 *Polystyrene products distributors*

Jubilee Press Ltd, 22-24 Abercromby Avenue, High Wycombe, Buckinghamshire, HP12 3AZ Tel: (01494) 533061 Fax: (01494) 462596 E-mail: sales@jubs.co.uk *Printers & stationers*

Jubilee Printers, 430 Edgware Road, London, W2 1EG Tel: (020) 7724 1094 Fax: (020) 7706 0518 E-mail: info@jubileeprinters.co.uk *Business stationery printers services*

Gerald Judd Sales Ltd, 47-51 Gillingham Street, London, SW1V 1HS Tel: (020) 7828 8821 Fax: (020) 7828 0840 E-mail: sales@geraldjudd.co.uk *Paper merchants*

Judd Medical Ltd, Highfield House, 53 Worcester Road, Bromsgrove, Worcestershire, B61 7DN Tel: (01527) 559010 Fax: (01527) 559080 *Manufactures & distributors of medical supplies*

Judds Of Hillingdon Ltd, 3 Westbourne Parade, Uxbridge Road, Hillingdon, Uxbridge, Middlesex, UB10 0NY Tel: (020) 8573 0196 Fax: (020) 8756 1766 *Fishing tackle retailers*

Judds Of Ruislip, 524-526 Victoria Road, Ruislip, Middlesex, HA4 0HD Tel: (020) 8841 7194 Fax: (020) 8841 7195 *Fishing equipment distributors*

▶ Judds Transport Ltd, Allers Back Lane, Kingston, Hazelbury Bryan, Sturminster Newton, Dorset, DT10 2DT Tel: (01258) 817394

Jude Engineering, Saxon Way East, Corby, Northamptonshire, NN18 9EY Tel: (01536) 460470 Fax: (01536) 460470 *Engineering subcontract services*

Judge & Dalton, 6 College Road, Northfleet, Gravesend, Kent, DA11 9AU Tel: (01474) 564504 Fax: (01474) 535809 E-mail: knjudg@aol.com *Marine & general engineers*

Judge & Priestley Ltd, Justin House, 6 West Street, Bromley, BR1 1JN Tel: (020) 8290 0333 Fax: (020) 8464 3332 E-mail: info@judge-priestley.co.uk *Debt recovery services*

Judges Postcards Ltd, 176 Bexhill Road, St. Leonards-on-Sea, East Sussex, TN38 8BN Tel: (01424) 420919 Fax: (01424) 438538 E-mail: sales@judges.co.uk *Publishers & printers services*

Judson Blinds, 11 St. Davids Road North, Lytham St. Annes, Lancashire, FY8 2BB Tel: (01253) 727715 Fax: (01253) 727715 E-mail: blinds@judsonblinds.freeserve.co.uk *Blinds manufrs*

Judson Signs Ltd, Unit 4C, Gibbons Road, Sheepbridge Lane, Mansfield, Nottinghamshire, NG18 5DZ Tel: (01623) 659444 Fax: (01623) 659222 E-mail: judson.signs@btconnect.com *Signs manufrs*

Jueson Ltd, 318-326 Southbury Road, Enfield, Middlesex, EN1 1TT Tel: (020) 8804 8244 Fax: (020) 8804 2876 E-mail: email@cakebreads.co.uk *Sanitary wear, electrical & building merchants* Also at: Branches throughout the S.E.

▶ Juice Master, 22 Moseley Gate, Birmingham, B13 8JJ Tel: (0845) 1302829 Fax: 0121-449 5392 E-mail: sales@thejuicemaster.com *Healthy living juice specialists*

Juke Box Services Ltd, Electroline House, 15 Lion Road, Twickenham, TW1 4JH Tel: (020) 8288 1700 E-mail: enquiries@jukeboxservices.co.uk *Juke box repairs & sales*

Jukebox Parts, 42 Eastcote Lane, Northolt, Middlesex, UB5 5RG Tel: (07986) 074574 E-mail: sales@jukeboxparts.co.uk *Jukebox hire*

Jukes Boxes Unlimited, The Paddocks, Back Lane, East Langton, Market Harborough, Leicestershire, LE16 7TB Tel: (01858) 545307 Fax: (01858) 545307 E-mail: fred@jukeboxes-uk.com *Jukebox restoration & sales*

▶ Julana Ltd, Millers Avenue, Brynmynach Industrial Estate, Aberenfig, Bridgend, Mid Glamorgan, CF32 9DT Tel: (01656) 725525 Fax: (01656) 724454 *Furniture producers*

Julian Designs Ltd, 25 Southfield Road, Hinckley, Leicestershire, LE10 1UA Tel: (01455) 615800 Fax: (01455) 615800 *Furniture manufrs*

▶ Julian Graves Ltd, 57-58 High Street, Taunton, Somerset, TA1 3PT Tel: (01823) 288197 Fax: (01384) 297707 *Grocery retail*

Julian Mousley, Llwyncelyn Uchaf, Llangynin, St. Clears, Carmarthen, SA33 4LA Tel: (01994) 230550 Fax: (01994) 230235 *Plant contractors*

▶ Julie Bell, The Dog House, Nomansland Farm, Wheathampstead, Herts, AL4 8EY Tel: 01582 834400 Fax: 01582 834400 E-mail: julie.bell@can-do.co.uk *Consultants to the insurance industry*

▶ Julie Martin, 10 Oakwood, Flackwell Heath, High Wycombe, Buckinghamshire, HP10 9DW Tel: (01628) 523235 Fax: (01628) 523235 E-mail: jglenister56@hotmail.com *Patient Female Driving Instructor*Beginner refresher Pass Plus and Motorway lessons*New dual controlled Mitsubishi Colt 1.5 Sport*

Juliette Designs, 90 Yerbury Road, London, N19 4RS Tel: (020) 7263 7878 Fax: (020) 7281 7326 E-mail: juliettedesigns@hotmail.com *Jewellery manufrs*

Julius A Meller Holdings plc, Meller House, 42-43 Chagford Street, London, NW1 6EB Tel: (020) 7724 5222 Fax: (020) 7724 3898 *Toiletries, gifts & accessory suppliers*

Julius Cee, 65-69 County Street, London, SE1 4AD Tel: (020) 7407 7273 Fax: (020) 7923 1794 E-mail: juliuscee@btconnect.com *Fasteners & fixing devices manufrs*

July Packaging, Unit 8 Manford Industrial Estate, Manor Road, Erith, Kent, DA8 2AJ Tel: (01322) 342123 Fax: (01322) 334479 E-mail: charlesdavies@zyworld.com *Packaging suppliers & corrugated case manufrs*

Jumbo Inflatables Ltd, 1 Harrowbrook Road, Hinckley, Leicestershire, LE10 3DJ Tel: (01455) 636478 Fax: (01455) 251275 E-mail: sales@jumbo.co.uk *Inflatables & indoor play manufrs*

▶ Jump 4 Joy, 92 Ackworth Road, Pontefract, West Yorkshire, WF8 4NQ Tel: (01977) 703867 *Inflatable bouncy castle hire services*

▶ The Jump Shop, C/o Skydive UK Ltd, Dunkeswell Airfield, Dunkeswell, Honiton, Devon, EX14 4LG Tel: (07939) 030339 Fax: (01246) 203487 E-mail: sales@thejumpshop.co.uk *Parachute equipment manufrs*

Jumpstart Ltd, 3 Medway Road, Birkenhead, Merseyside, CH42 2BD Tel: 0151-645 9398 Fax: 0151-645 9999 E-mail: nigel.birchenough@jumpstart.co.uk *Web design consultants*

▶ Jumpzone, Maritime House, Basin Road North, Hove, East Sussex, BN41 1WR Tel: 01273 384995 E-mail: info@jumpzone.org *Jumpzone Bungy Trampoline, UK manufactured bungy trampolines for corporate hire and sponsorship opportunities*

Junckers Ltd, Wheaton Court Commercial Centr, Wheaton Road, Witham, Essex, CM8 3UJ Tel: (01376) 517512 Fax: (01376) 514401 E-mail: sales@junckers.co.uk *Hardwood flooring manufrs*

Junction News, 169 Conway Road, Llandudno Junction, Gwynedd, LL31 9EG Tel: (01492) 573266 Fax: (01492) 573266 *Newsagents*

Jungheinrich (G B) Ltd, Orpen Park, Ash Ridge Road, Almondsbury, Bristol, BS32 4QD Tel: (01454) 616898 Fax: (01454) 616206 E-mail: trevorw@jungheinrich.co.uk *Fork lift truck manufrs*

Jungheinrich GB Ltd, Sherbourne House, Sherbourne Drive, Tilbrook, Milton Keynes, MK7 8HX Tel: (01908) 363100 Fax: (01908) 363180 E-mail: info@jungheinrich.co.uk *Fork lift truck sales services*

Jungheinrich GB Ltd, 620 Europa Boulevard, Westbrook, Warrington, WA5 7TX Tel: (01925) 625400 Fax: (01925) 230891 E-mail: info@jungheinrich.co.uk *Fork lift truck sales services* Also at: Birmingham, Bourne End, Bristol, Cumbernauld, Grays, Heston, Sheffield & Warring ton

▶ Jungle Gym Play & Party, 12 Chetham Court, Winwick Quay, Warrington, WA2 8RF Tel: (01925) 659995 E-mail: info@thejunglegym.co.uk *A fantastic jungle themed play centre for children up to 4"9" - with a separate toddler area. 2 great party rooms and The Jungle Express Cafe offering a relaxing area for parents/guardians and serving range of beverages, tasty snacks and healthy options. Situated next door to LA Bowl in Warrington.*

▶ Jungle I T Ltd, 2 Drury Lane, Horsforth, Leeds, LS18 4BQ Tel: 0113-258 4433 Fax: 0113-258 4499 *Computer software manufrs*

Jungle Junction Ltd, 35 Aveley La, Farnham, Surrey, GU9 8PR Tel: (01252) 747940 Fax: (01252) 747941 *Software development*

▶ Junglesale, Aizlewoods Mill, Nursery Street, Sheffield, S3 8GG Tel: (0871) 2501271 E-mail: raj@junglesale.com

▶ Juni Design & Artwork, 16 Manea Close, Lower Earley, Reading, RG6 4JN Tel: 0118-986 8064 Fax: 0118-986 8064 E-mail: ashton_dave@hotmail.com *We would like to introduce our Lower Earley based company. Offering Design and artwork services for Packaging, Corporate Identity, Business cards, Brochures, Promotional Literature, Advertising, Annual Reports, Exhibition Panels and anything else you can think of.**From a simple leaflet to a full corporate pack, we have the creativity and experience to surpass your expectations as well as answer your brief. **Please see our website for work examples and more information*http://www.juni.org.uk*

Juniper Trading Ltd, Mayfayre House, London Road, Denington Industrial Estate, Wellingborough, Northamptonshire, NN8 2QH Tel: (01933) 222495 Fax: (01933) 274077 E-mail: sales@juniperproducts.co.uk *Promotional item retailers & manufrs*

Juno Glass Ltd, 50 Lydden Road, London, SW18 4LR Tel: (020) 8874 8949 Fax: (020) 8877 1353 E-mail: chris@junoglass.co.uk *Glass merchants*

Juno Installations, 8 Carlton Park Avenue, London, SW20 8BL Tel: (020) 8543 1697 Fax: (020) 8543 1697 E-mail: harlea0@aol.com *PVC window frame & conservatories doors manufrs*

Jupitar Ltd, 68 Great Eastern Street, London, EC2A 3JT Tel: (020) 7729 8626 Fax: (020) 7729 8628 E-mail: info@jupitar.com *IT training*

Jupiter B2B Marketing, 82 Beech Farm Drive, Macclesfield, Cheshire, SK10 2ER Tel: (01625) 431166 Fax: (01625) 431177 E-mail: karriegrant@jupiterb2b.co.uk *Market research & telephone marketing*

▶ Jupiter It Soultions, 205-207 West End Road, Haydock, St. Helens, Merseyside, WA11 0AW Tel: (01744) 20085 Fax: (01744) 20085 *Sign manufrs*

▶ Jupiter Safety Management Ltd, 36 Shelley Road, Reddish, Stockport, Cheshire, Stockport, Cheshire, SK5 6JG Tel: 0161 442 4359 Fax: 0161 442 4359 E-mail: ccork-jupitersafety@fsmail.net *Jupiter Safety Management has combined years of experience to produce training that works. Our team have all been at the thick end of industry and therefore fully understand and appreciate the problems companies can face.**This ensure your staff development is exactly that, our training safety training programmes can be structured to your requirements and delivered in such a way that your staff will learn, enjoy and foremost remember what they have been taught.*

Jupiter Security, Twitten House, Furners Green, Uckfield, East Sussex, TN22 3RR Tel: (01825) 740557 Fax: (01825) 740406 E-mail: manager@jupitersecurity.co.uk *Install security systems*

Jupiter Signs, 20 Singer Way, Kempston, Bedford, MK42 7AE Tel: (01234) 854577 Fax: (01234) 841401 E-mail: sales@jupitersigns.com *Sign manufrs*

Jupiter Systems, 82 Meadrow, Godalming, Surrey, GU7 3HT Tel: (01483) 410001 Fax: (01483) 422866 E-mail: info@jupitersystems.net *Veterinary software developers*

Jupp & Sons, Fattings Hovel, Ditchling Road, Haywards Heath, West Sussex, RH17 7RE Tel: (01444) 471102 Fax: (01444) 471152 *Fencing suppliers*

Juraise (Springs) Ltd, Sugarbrook Mill, Buntsford Hill, Stoke Pound, Bromsgrove, Worcestershire, B60 3AR Tel: (01527) 878811 Fax: (01527) 877537 E-mail: adrian@juraise.com *Springs, pressings & wire shapes*

▶ Jura-Spray Ltd, Wandle Trading Estate, Goat Road, Mitcham Junction, Mitcham, Surrey, CR4 4HW Tel: (020) 8640 1775

Jury's Cardiff Hotel, Mary Ann Street, Cardiff, CF10 2JH Tel: (029) 2034 1441 Fax: (029) 2022 3742 *Hotel & conference centre*

Just Accountancy Ltd, 5 Crwys Place, Plasnewydd Cardiff, Cardiff, CF24 4NS Tel: (029) 2045 0874 Fax: (029) 2045 0874 E-mail: justyn.withey@justaccountancy.com *Independent Accountancy Recruitment Agency specialising in all levels of Accounting and Payroll, whether a Finance Director or Accounts clerk we are able to work with you*

Just Balloons, 2 The Steadings, Greenside, Ryton, Tyne & Wear, NE40 4JF Tel: 0191-413 6912 Fax: 0191-413 1185 E-mail: sales@just-balloons.co.uk *Balloon decorators*

Just Beds, 76 Broadway, Didcot, Oxfordshire, OX11 8AE Tel: (01235) 819188 Fax: (01235) 817978 *Bedding manufrs*

▶ Just Blinds, Unit 1 Monastery Lane, St. Helens, Merseyside, WA9 3SW Tel: (01942) 213600 Fax: (01744) 818002 E-mail: steve@just-blinds.co.uk *Manufacturer & installer of blinds, trade & retail*

Just Blinds & Curtains, 13 Market Place, Dereham, Norfolk, NR19 2AW Tel: (01362) 695437 Fax: (01362) 691465 *Blinds distributors & manufrs*

▶ Just Bonds, 1546 Stratford Road, Hall Green, Birmingham, B28 9HA Tel: 0121-682 1401 E-mail: justbonds@blueyonder.co.uk *Stunning hair extensions with 0% human hair using new fusion technique. Free consultation.*Get pampered in luxury.*

▶ Just C R M, Garden Cottage, Elsfield, Oxford, OX3 9UH Tel: (01865) 351771 E-mail: jonbowen@personal-computer-services.co.uk *JustCRM is a pioneering Contact Relationship Management system for Charities. Aimed at organisations with a turnover up to £3M. This will revolutionise the way you keep your branches & home workers & international offices up to date with Diary Events, Contact Information, Projects, Key Documents, etc.*

▶ Just Catering Ltd, Jessop Avenue, Norwood Green, Southall, Middlesex, UB2 5UY Tel: (0845) 0034271 Fax: (0845) 0034271 E-mail: sales@justcatering.com *Catering equipment manufrs*

Just Cold Services Ltd, 117 Old Farleigh Road, South Croydon, Surrey, CR2 8QD Tel: (020) 8657 2334 Fax: (020) 8651 1580 *Air conditioning engineers*

▶ Just Desserts, 1 Station Road, Shipley, West Yorkshire, BD18 2JL Tel: (01274) 590698 Fax: (01274) 590698 E-mail: just-desserts@dsl.pipex.com *Dessert manufrs*

▶ Just Desserts & Pastries, Unit 5b 193-205 Mayfair Business Centre, Garvaghy Road, Portadown, Craigavon, County Armagh, BT62 1HA Tel: (028) 3835 1593

Just Developments, 4 Sunnybank, Holly Road, Wilmslow, Cheshire, SK9 1ND Tel: (01625) 530752 Fax: (01625) 530752 E-mail: jurgstaubli@hotmail.com *Brick cleaning, pointing & tool manufrs*

Just Engraving, 138 St. Neots Road, Eaton Ford, St. Neots, Cambridgeshire, PE19 7AL Tel: (01480) 472715 Fax: (01480) 386716 E-mail: engraving@endersby.com *Machine engravers*

Just Fabrics, 29-30 Colemeadow Road, Moons Moat North Industrial Estate, Redditch, Worcestershire, B98 9PB Tel: (01527) 63246 Fax: (01527) 63247 *Curtains, blinds & track manufrs*

Just Fasteners, 4 Alpha Centre, 10 South Douglas Street, Clydebank, Dunbartonshire, G81 1PD Tel: (01236) 429444 Fax: 0141-941 0088 E-mail: sales@justfasteners.co.uk *Specialised fasteners distributors*

▶ Just Film, 7 Barnsway, Kings Langley, Hertfordshire, WD4 9PW Tel: (01923) 269599 E-mail: info@justfilm.co.uk *A low cost video production facility for charities, world development agencies, youth offending teams, human rights campaigners, environmental organisations, those engaged in mediation, restorative justice and victim support - in fact anyone promoting peace and social justice.*

Just Fittings Ltd, 122 Sydenham Road, Sparkbrook, Birmingham, B11 1DQ Tel: 0121-773 8730 Fax: 0121-766 7012 *Prototypes & presswork machinists*

▶ Just Forms Ltd, 72 Hammonds Drive, Eastbourne, East Sussex, BN23 6PW Tel: (01323) 732000 Fax: (01323) 732101

▶ Just Good Food Ltd, Ouseley Farm House, Hinxhill, Ashford, Kent, TN25 5NP Tel: (01233) 624886 Fax: (01233) 636367 *Frozen food manufrs*

▶ Just Great Events, Deerings, Shaw Lane, Holywell Green, Halifax, West Yorkshire, HX4 9DW Tel: (01422) 312816 E-mail: enquiries@justgreatevents.co.uk *Just Great Events is a FREE Venue Finding service for individuals who need to organise meetings, conferences, teambuilding, gala dinners, accommodation, residential training to name a few. We offer a Free service to find you a venue in the UK or worldwide for all of your business needs. We also offer many support services including, Event Management, Event & Delegate Marketing, Hospitality services, and full Technical support services. For more information visit www.justgreatevents.co.uk*

▶ Just Hom.Com, 44 High Street, Shrewsbury, SY1 1ST Tel: (01743) 247246 Fax: E-mail: sales@justhom.com *Stockist's of the HOM underwear brand, we stock past season ranges as well as new seasons.*Specialising in Men's thongs, Briefs and Maxi styles*

▶ Just Home Improvements Ltd, 181A Barrack Road, Christchurch, Dorset, BH23 2AR Tel: (01202) 479001

▶ Just I T Training Ltd, The Dragon House, 37 Artillery Lane, London, E1 7LP Tel: (020) 7655 4600 E-mail: recruitment@justit.co.uk *IT Recruitment specialists focusing on Network, Technical Support and Development in London and Home Counties.*

▶ Just Insulation, 27 Massetts Road, Horley, Surrey, RH6 7DQ Tel: (0845) 2606232 Fax: (0845) 2606242 E-mail: purchases@just-insulation.com *Heat reflective insulation, thermo reflective foil, multi-foil insulation and traditional dry insulation products & materials*

'Just Jax' Dinner Parties & Buffets, 27 Birch Street, Fleetwood, Lancashire, FY7 6TW Tel: 01253 772336 E-mail: info@justjax.co.uk *For Dinner Parties & Buffets, Where & When You Want, plus the added luxury of Chocolate Fountain Hire, Let "Just Jax" take the hard work out of your parties, for more info just ring Jax, go on spoil someone you love..*

▶ Just Kids, 3 Corney Square, Penrith, Cumbria, CA11 7PX Tel: (01768) 892783 Fax: (01697) 473009

Just Knitwear Ltd, Evington Business Centre, Chesterfield Road, Leicester, LE5 5LG Tel: 0116-273 4383 Fax: 0116-273 0554 *Knitwear manufrs*

Just Lighting Ltd, 21 Kenyon Road, Brierfield, Nelson, Lancashire, BB9 5SP Tel: (01282) 698507 Fax: (01282) 695588 *Lighting fittings manufrs*

Just Mugs Ltd, Unit 5, Hanley Business Park, Cooper Street, Stoke-On-Trent, ST1 4DW Tel: (01782) 274888 Fax: (01782) 202181 E-mail: info@justmugs.com *Bone china & earthenware mugs manufrs*

Just Paper, Foxlea House, Cliffe-Cum-Lund, Selby, North Yorkshire, YO8 6PE Tel: (01757) 630226 Fax: (01757) 630227 E-mail: sales@justpapertubes.co.uk *Label & tape cores manufrs*

Just PC, Milton House, Christchurch Road, New Milton, Hampshire, BH25 6QB Tel: (01425) 622776 Fax: (01425) 622665 E-mail: sales@just-pc.net *Computer hardware & software suppliers*

Just Plastics Ltd, The Maltings, Wayford, Norwich, NR12 9LL Tel: (01692) 581000 Fax: (01692) 581848 E-mail: martin@justplastics.co.uk *Laboratory plastics ware manufactures*

▶ Just Rachel, The Old Dairy, Churches Farm, Bromsberrow, Ledbury, Herefordshire, HR8 1SA Tel: (01531) 650639 Fax: (01531) 650639 E-mail: info@justrachel.com *Ice cream & desserts suppliers*

Just Rams plc, 6 Iron Bridge Close, Great Central Way, London, NW10 0UF Tel: (020) 8451 8700 Fax: (020) 8459 6301 E-mail: sales@justrams.co.uk *Computer camera & industrial memory distributors*

▶ Just Recruit (UK) Ltd, Viking Industrial Park, Tedco Business Centre, Jarrow, Tyne & Wear, NE32 3DT Tel: 0191-428 3336 Fax: 0191-428 3356 E-mail: mark@justrecruit.co.uk *Tailored recruitment services*

Just Rollers P.L.C., Somerset Industrial Estate, Cwmbran, Gwent, NP44 1QX Tel: (01633) 869436 Fax: (01633) 860046 E-mail: iain.sinclair@justrollers.com *Roller & roller covering manufrs*

Just Seating International Ltd, Croxdale, Durham, DH6 5HT Tel: (01325) 300123 Fax: (01388) 812416 E-mail: sales@justseating.co.uk *Office seating manufrs*

▶ Just Skips, The Portergate, Ecclesall Road, Sheffield, S11 8NX Tel: (0845) 4508863 Fax: (08454) 508864 E-mail: sales@justskips.co.uk *UK Skip Hire for residential, commercial/business and industrial waste. National coverage.*

▶ Just Stairlifts, Woodside, Crowhurst Lane End, Oxted, Surrey, RH8 9NT Tel: (0800) 0830513 Fax: (01342) 893466 E-mail: enquiries@juststairlifts.co.uk *Stair lifts supply, installation & servicing*

▶ Just Valve Amps, 14 Woodridge, Haywards Heath, West Sussex, RH16 3EP Tel: 07860 303545 E-mail: admin@justvalveamps.co.uk *Specialist in the repair & refurbishment of valve guitar amplifiers*

▶ Just Weddings Ltd, Buck Farm Willington, near Malpas, Willington, Malpas, Cheshire, SY14 7LX Tel: (08707) 577227 E-mail: info@just-wed.com *Just Weddings provide high quality linen chair covers and organza bows for hire.*

▶ Just William UK, Unit 31, 19b Moor Road, Broadstone, Dorset, BH18 8AZ Tel: (07775) 658148 Fax: (0871) 6614691 E-mail: sales@jwuk.com *T-shirt printing & embroidery service*

▶ Just-clips, Harrogate, North Yorkshire, HG3 2ZL Tel: (0845) 2300060 Fax: (0845) 2300080 E-mail: sales@just-clips.co.uk *Suppliers of pipe clips & plumbing products*

Justcroft International Ltd, Justcroft House, High Street, Staplehurst, Tonbridge, Kent, TN12 0AH Tel: (01580) 893333 Fax: (01580) 893399 E-mail: sales@justcroft.com *Oil & gas industries financial software developers service*

Justell Precision Engineers, Unit 2 & 17 Manor Park, 35 Willis Way, Poole, Dorset, BH15 3SZ Tel: (01202) 680500 Fax: (01202) 680510 E-mail: enquires@justellengineering.co.uk *CNC machining manufrs*

▶ just-endfeed, PO Box, 473, Harrogate, North Yorkshire, HG3 2ZL Tel: 0845 300060 Fax: 0845 300080 E-mail: sales@just-endfeed.co.uk *Suppliers of end feed fittings and plumbing products.*

Justengineers.Net, York House, 76 Lancaster Road, Morecambe, Lancashire, LA4 5QN Tel: (0845) 0502000 Fax: (0845) 0502001 E-mail: info@justengineers.net *Engineering Employment Job Board /Job Site*

▶ Justerini & Brooks Scotland Ltd, Auchroisk Distillery, Mulben, Keith, Banffshire, AB55 6XS Tel: (01542) 885000 Fax: (01542) 885039

▶ Justice Laboratory Services, JLS House, 25 - 27 Low Road, Auchtermuchty, Auchtermuchty, Fife, KY14 7BB Tel: (01337) 828404 *Computers & chromatography*

Justice Security Systems Ltd, Prestige House, Kingsbury Close, Minworth, Sutton Coldfield, West Midlands, B76 9DH Tel: 0121-313 1330 Fax: 0121-313 0909 E-mail: sales@justicesecurity.co.uk *Security alarms*

Justin Case Co., 23 Water Street, Edinburgh, EH6 6SU Tel: 0131-555 4466 Fax: 0131-555 9601 *Flight cases manufrs*

Justina Of London Ltd, 6 Lockwood Industrial Park, Mill Mead Road, London, N17 9QP Tel: (020) 8801 3663 Fax: (020) 8808 4578 E-mail: info@justinaoflondon.biz *Ladies fashion manufrs*

Justinor Products Ltd, St. Johns Business Park, St. Johns Grove, Hull, HU9 3RL Tel: (01482) 799321 Fax: (01482) 799470 E-mail: sales@justinor.co.uk *Specialised cardboard box manufrs*

▶ Justkarndean, 85 Blewitt Street, Brierley Hill, West Midlands, DY5 4AL Tel: (07981) 878863 E-mail: justkarndean@blueyonder.co.uk *Preparation & fitting of karndean & amtico design floor coverings*

▶ just-solder-ring, PO Box, 473, Harrogate, North Yorkshire, HG3 2ZL Tel: 08452 300060 Fax: 08452 300080 E-mail: sales@just-solder-ring.co.uk *Suppliers of solder ring fittings & plumbing products*

Justwise Group Ltd, Shire Hill, Saffron Walden, Essex, CB11 3AP Tel: (01799) 513466 Fax: (01799) 525657 E-mail: mail@justwise.demon.co.uk *Furniture*

▶ Jute Bags, 8 Dalston Gardens, Stanmore Industrial Park, Stanmore, Middlesex, HA7 1BU Tel: 0701 0704731 E-mail: sales@jutebag.co.uk *We are a leading supplier of eco-friendly jute bags in the UK. All our bags are bio-degradable and environmentally friendly. We customise bags as per each customer''s requirements such as logo printing. We won''t be beaten on price, quality and service.*

Juwel Aquarium UK Ltd, Gateway 11 Business Park, Penfold Drive, Wymondham, Norfolk, NR18 0WZ Tel: (01953) 606363 Fax: (01953) 603839 E-mail: info@juwel-aquarium.co.uk *Aquarium manufrs*

JVC Professional Europe Ltd, JVC House, 12 Priestley Way, London, NW2 7BA Tel: (020) 8208 6200 Fax: (020) 8208 6260 E-mail: sales@jvcpro.co.uk *Professional video equipment manufrs* Also at: Branches throughout the U.K.

▶ JW Blinds, 2 Hollyhill Road, Forest Vale Industrial Estate, Cinderford, Gloucestershire, GL14 2YA Tel: (01594) 829299 Fax: (01594) 829233 *Blind suppliers*

▶ JWC Services Ltd, 54 Cairnlee Avenue East, Cults, Aberdeen, AB15 9NH Tel: 01224 861507 Fax: 0709 2006687 E-mail: jw@dairyconsultant.co.uk *Dairy factory design, dairy factory interim management, dairy process design, dairy acquisitions, mergers & disposals, dairy joint ventures, dairy sales*

▶ JX Web Design, JXWD House, 23 Richmond Park Avenue, Bournemouth, BH8 9DL Tel: (01202) 315437 Fax: (07733) 462499 E-mail: contact@jxwd.co.uk *Complete web design solutions*

▶ K 4 Komputers, 21 London Street, Larkhall, Lanarkshire, ML9 1AQ Tel: (01698) 889123 *Computer maintenance & repair services*

K A B Systems Ltd, Lansdowne Road, Chadderton, Oldham, OL9 9EG Tel: 0161-678 6367 Fax: 0161-678 6979 E-mail: sales@kabsystems.co.uk *Instrument & control panel manufrs*

K A C Builders Merchants, 46 Stoke Newington Church Street, London, N16 0LU Tel: (020) 7254 0272 Fax: (020) 7254 0272 *Builders merchants*

K A D Detection Systems Ltd, Units 4-5, Barrmill Road, Galston, Ayrshire, KA4 8HH Tel: (01563) 820148 Fax: (01563) 820163 E-mail: sales@kad-detection.com *Fire, gas & environmental health monitoring equipment suppliers*

▶ K A D Metal Work Ltd, Studio 101, 7-10 Riverside Yard, London, SW17 0BB Tel: (020) 8946 2429 Fax: (020) 8946 0684

K A D Metal Work Ltd, Studio 101, 7-10 Riverside Yard, London, SW17 0BB Tel: (020) 8946 2429 Fax: (020) 8946 0684 E-mail: info@kadmetalworks.co.uk *Fabricators*

K A D Roofing Ltd, 14 Dongan Road, Warwick, CV34 4JW Tel: (01926) 400044 Fax: (01926) 494775 E-mail: nick@kadroofing.co.uk *Roofing contractors*

K & A Day Builders Ltd, The Builders Yard, Holtonwood Road, Stratford St. Mary, Colchester, CO7 6NE Tel: (01206) 231247 Fax: (01206) 231247 *Builders & contractors*

K & A Furness Ltd, Trent Industrial Estate, Duchess Street, Shaw, Oldham, OL2 7UT Tel: (01706) 843411 Fax: (01706) 882289 E-mail: sales@jet-vac.co.uk *Sheet metal fabricators & jet vac manufrs*

▶ K A Ingram, Quarry Ridge, Dallas, Forres, Morayshire, IV36 2RY Tel: (01343) 890369

K A Javid, 49 Hydepark Street, Glasgow, G3 8BW Tel: 0141-248 8666 Fax: 0141-248 7555 E-mail: sales@kajavid.com *Accountants*

K A Moon & Co., 29 Bingley Grove, Woodley, Reading, RG5 4TT Tel: 0118-969 1683 Fax: 0118-969 1683 *Office refurbishment*

K A P Blinds, 6 Lower Grange, Peterhead, Aberdeenshire, AB42 2AT Tel: (01779) 474949 Fax: (01779) 474949 *Blind sales & manufrs*

K & A Polystyrene, 30 Lavell Mews, Bradford, West Yorkshire, BD2 3HW Tel: (01274) 631341 Fax: (01274) 641781 *Packaging material suppliers*

K A R Alarms, 4 Lindsey Road, Denham, Uxbridge, Middlesex, UB9 5BP Tel: (01895) 834217 Fax: (01895) 835725 *Car security installation*

K A S Lighting Services Ltd, 39 Morton Way, London, N14 7HS Tel: (020) 8882 2500 Fax: (020) 8882 2605 *Lighting consultants*

K A S Paper Systems Ltd, Brewers Hill Road, Dunstable, Bedfordshire, LU6 1AD Tel: (01582) 662211 Fax: (01582) 664222 E-mail: mail@kaspapersystems.com *Mail handling equipment manufrs*

K A Welding & Fabrications, Deptford Trading Estate, Blackhorse Road, London, SE8 5HY Tel: (020) 8691 2771 Fax: (020) 8691 2771 *Kitchen furniture manufrs*

K A Wing Ltd, 13 Stapledon Road, Orton Southgate, Peterborough, PE2 6TD Tel: (01733) 370448 Fax: (01733) 370488 E-mail: kawing@btinternet.com *Mechanical engineering contractors*

▶ K Associates, 30 Niagara Avenue, London, W5 4UD Tel: 020 31329392 Fax: 020 31329392 E-mail: tim.slorick@kagroup.net *K Associates are procurement consultants who specialise in delivering savings and efficiencies in purchasing and the associated supply chain.**Benefitting from many years" experience in larger procurement consulting firms, the K Associates team have a track record in delivering real savings to the bottom line. In addition, we are a member of K Consulting Group, a European purchasing and operations consultancy offering similar services to ourselves, covering the main European markets.*

K.Azmeh (Textiles) Ltd, Richmond House, Richmond Grove, Manchester, M13 0LN Tel: 0161-274 4827 Fax: 0161-274 4815 E-mail: info@katuk.com *Textile & yarn merchants*

▶ K B A (U K) Ltd, Unit 5, Tolpits Lane, Watford, WD18 9PX Tel: (01923) 699535

K B Benfield Group Holdings Ltd, 88 Paynes Lane, Coventry, CV1 5LJ Tel: (024) 7622 7557 Fax: (024) 7622 1217 E-mail: mail@benfieldgroup.co.uk *House builders & property investment*

K B Catering Ltd, Unit 15, Craven Way, Newmarket, Suffolk, CB8 0BW Tel: (01638) 667994 Fax: (01638) 665970 E-mail: sales@kb-catering.co.uk *Internet based catering suppliers*

K B Design & Promotion Ltd, City Business Centre, Brighton Road, Horsham, West Sussex, RH13 5BA Tel: (01403) 262499 Fax: (01403) 261932 E-mail: sales@kb-design.com *Promotional gift specialists*

K B Door Sales, Chester Road, Gresford, Wrexham, Clwyd, LL12 8NT Tel: (01978) 855599 Fax: (01978) 855599 *Door sales*

K B Electrical, 7 Wentworth Drive, Lancaster, LA1 3RJ Tel: (01524) 37822 E-mail: kbelectrical@yahoo.com *Electrical & plumbing contractors*

▶ K B Elsmore & Sons Ltd, Brookfield Street, Syston, Leicester, LE7 2AE Tel: 0116-260 6036 Fax: 0116-260 5630 E-mail: sales@kbelsmoreandsons.co.uk *Engineering company*

K B Engineering Co. Ltd, Fowlswick Industrial Estate, Fowlswick Lane, Allington, Chippenham, Wiltshire, SN14 6QE Tel: (01249) 783186 Fax: (01249) 782603 *Food processing machinery manufrs*

K B Engineering Supplies Ltd, 7 Bloomfield Road, Tipton, West Midlands, DY4 9EU Tel: 0121-520 0003 Fax: 0121-520 5554 E-mail: frank.kendrick@ukonline.co.uk *Gaskets manufrs*

K B L Event Hire, Unit 4 Banters Lane Industrial Estate, Great Leighs, Chelmsford, CM3 1QX Tel: (01245) 360920 Fax: (01245) 360442 *Event equipment hire services*

K & B Machine Tool Services Ltd, 1 Farrier Road, Lincoln, LN6 3RU Tel: (01522) 687878 Fax: (01522) 687879 E-mail: service@kandbmts.com *CNC service & suppliers of ancillary equipment*

K B Packaging Ltd, Merlin Way, Quarry Hill Industrial Estate, Ilkeston, Derbyshire, DE7 4RA Tel: 0115-944 1600 Fax: 0115-932 7460 E-mail: enquiries@totalboxpack.co.uk *Clothes tags & packers*

K B Packaging & Insulation, The Warehouse, Foggathorpe, Selby, North Yorkshire, YO8 6PR Tel: (01757) 289131 Fax: (01757) 289142 E-mail: enquiries@kbpackagingandinsulation.co.uk *K B Packaging & Insulation are specialists in the provision of [ESP] expanded and extruded polystyrene products for a diverse range of applications. Established since 1983, we have over 20 years experience in the polystyrene industry. By using a variety of hot wire cutting techniques, we are able to provide bespoke solutions to individual customer requirements.**Our product range includes K B Loosefill which is a finer packaging material, similar to that found in bean bags. It is also 100% recycled and available in 6 cubic feet bags. We are also stockists of Bubblewrap and Polyethylene Foam (Cell-Aire), in varying thicknesses, splits and with or without perforations.**Based North East of Selby we are able to service and deliver nationwide.*

K B Pearson Servicing, 100 Ashkirk, Dudley, Cramlington, Northumberland, NE23 7DG Tel: 0191-250 0623 Fax: 0191-250 0623 *Hydraulic engineers & safety equipment*

K & B Profiles Ltd, Hatton Street, Bilston, West Midlands, WV14 0TD Tel: (01902) 409495 Fax: (01902) 353211 E-mail: kevin.sefton@tesco.net *Grinders & profile cutters*

K B Reinforcements (Northern) Ltd, Chaddock Lane, Boothstown, Worsley, Manchester, M28 4DR Tel: 0161-790 8635 Fax: 0161-799 7083 E-mail: sales@kb-northern.co.uk *Reinforcing steel manufrs*

K B S Computer Supplies Ltd, Unit 3a West Bank Business Park, 5 West Bank Drive, Belfast, BT3 9LA Tel: (028) 9037 0088 Fax: (028) 9077 4767 E-mail: sales@kbs-computer-supplies.co.uk *Computer consumable sales*

K B S Fabrications, 2b Vulcan Works, Leckhampton Road, Cheltenham, Gloucestershire, GL53 0AL Tel: (01242) 572507 Fax: (01242) 572507 *Architectural metalwork fabrication & steel fabricators*

K B S Group, 41 Marsh Green Road West, Marsh Barton Trading Estate, Exeter, EX2 8PN Tel: (01392) 208208 Fax: (01392) 208200 E-mail: sales@kbs-group.com *Sign manufrs*

K B S Group, 41 Marsh Green Road West, Marsh Barton Trading Estate, Exeter, EX2 8PN Tel: (01392) 208208 Fax: (01392) 208200 E-mail: sales@kbs-group.com *Sign writers & sign manufrs*

K B Supplies Astral Ltd, 126 Weeland Road, Knottingley, West Yorkshire, WF11 8DB Tel: 01977 671345 Fax: 01977 636004 *Chemical distributors*

K Bassam, Chambers, Court Street, Stourbridge, West Midlands, DY8 1EF Tel: (01384) 444028 Fax: (01384) 835028 E-mail: sales@jeweller.com *Jewellery repairs & sales*

K Bell, 3 Sunnyside Farm Trading Estate, Martcombe Road, Easton-in-Gordano, Bristol, BS20 0QQ Tel: (01275) 373238 *Agricultural farming*

K Binks Heating Ltd, Environment House, Witty Street, Hull, HU3 4BH Tel: (01482) 328979 Fax: (01482) 213897 E-mail: enquiries@binksheating.co.uk *Heating engineers*

K Brotherton, Unit 23 Honeybourne Airfield Trading Estate, Honeybourne, Evesham, Worcestershire, WR11 7QF Tel: (01386) 833429 Fax: (01386) 833429 *Accident repair & re-spray service*

K C A Deutag Drilling Ltd, Minto Drive, Altens Industrial Estate, Aberdeen, AB12 3LW Tel: (01224) 299600 Fax: (01224) 895813 E-mail: info@kcadeutag.com *Drilling & engineering contractors*

▶ K & C Building Contractors Ltd, Enterprise House, Enterprise Park, Kinmel Bay, Rhyl, Clwyd, LL18 5JZ Tel: (01745) 334591

K C C, 20-21A Harbour Court, Heron Road, Sydenham Business Park, Belfast, BT3 9LE Tel: (028) 9046 9914 Fax: (028) 9046 9915 E-mail: sales@kcchardware.com *Architectural ironmongers*

K C C Ltd, TLM Ho, Percy St, Eastwood, Nottingham, NG16 3EP Tel: (01773) 760900 Fax: (01773) 760985 E-mail: emsales@flomerics.co.uk *Computer Software Developers*

K C Carpets Ltd, 2 High Street, Moreton-in-Marsh, Gloucestershire, GL56 0AP Tel: (01608) 650331 Fax: (01608) 650829 *Carpet supply & fitters*

K C E Europe, Ashcombe House, Queen Street, Godalming, Surrey, GU7 1BA Tel: (01483) 528080 Fax: (01483) 528090 E-mail: sales@kce-europe.com *Printed circuit multilayer & through hole plated*

K C Engineering Ltd, Hownsgill Drive, Consett, County Durham, DH8 9HU Tel: (01207) 583100 Fax: (01207) 581900 E-mail: sales@kceng.com *White metal bearing specialists*

K & C Engineering, Unit 7 Three Elms Trading Estate, Hereford, HR4 9PU Tel: (01432) 351612 Fax: (01432) 342290 *Precision engineers*

K C Engineering, R/O 89 Upper Brockley Road, London, SE4 1TF Tel: (020) 8691 0219 Fax: (020) 8691 0219 *Sheet metalworkers*

▶ K C G Installations Ltd, 20 Burrish Street, Droitwich, Worcestershire, WR9 8HX Tel: (01905) 770531 E-mail: enquiries@kcg-installations.com *K.C.G Installations Ltd is run by the two day to day working directors of the company who have both been working in the industry for the last ten years. We have worked all over the UK and Europe in many various fields such as foundry plant installation, ductwork(both air con & industrial) and also machine installation & relocation.*

K C Glass Ltd, Unit 23 Central Trading Estate, Cable Street, Wolverhampton, WV2 2RJ Tel: (01902) 457765 Fax: (01902) 456417 E-mail: sales@kcglass.co.uk *Glass picture frames*

K C H Drilling Supplies Ltd, 35 York Place, Aberdeen, AB11 5FW Tel: (01224) 211820 Fax: (01224) 213065 E-mail: mudvac@ifb.co.uk *Drilling equipment distributors*

K C H Fibrous Plasters, Unit 13 Brickfields, Great Burches Road, Benfleet, Essex, SS7 3ND Tel: (01268) 741911 Fax: (01268) 414897 *Plaster manufrs*

▶ K C Handling, 47 Kirkwood Close, New Springs, Aspull, Wigan, Lancashire, WN2 1DZ Tel: (01942) 230054 Fax: (01942) 230054 E-mail: kc.handling@lycos.co.uk *Material handling equipment suppliers*

K C Hickson Ltd, 89-91 Rolfe Street, Smethwick, West Midlands, B66 2AY Tel: 0121-558 1884 Fax: 0121-558 0017 E-mail: kchickson@george-jones-engineering.co.uk *Industrial & commercial electrical installation contractors*

K.C. Inks Ltd, Unit 13 Blackhall Yard, Kendal, Cumbria, LA9 4LU Tel: (01539) 738200 Fax: (01539) 738822 E-mail: sales@kc-inks.co.uk *Computer consumables merchants*

K C M Packaging Ltd, Units 17-18 Etherow Industrial Estate, Woolley Bridge Road, Hadfield, Glossop, Derbyshire, SK13 2GA Tel: (01457) 862617 Fax: (01457) 861540 E-mail: sales@kcmpackaging.co.uk *Corrugated carton manufrs*

K C M Services Ltd, Mill View, Daisy Hill, Burstwick, Hull, HU12 9HE Tel: (01482) 227953 Fax: (08456) 445547 E-mail: info@kcmservices.com Principal Export Areas: Worldwide *Enhancing reliability by the bespoke application of predictive maintenance technology. 20 years experience in using Vibration Monitoring and Thermal Imaging within all sectors of Industry including Marine, Offshore, Oil and Gas, Manufacturing, Food etc. Example reports available, please see our catalogue*

K & C Machinery Ltd, Midland Trading Estate, Sparta Close, Rugby, Warwickshire, CV21 1PS Tel: (01788) 576381 Fax: (01788) 570182 E-mail: sales@kc-machinery.com *Machine tool merchants & exporters*

▶ K C Mobility Services Ltd, Unit 2, Carlinghow Mills, 501 Bradford Road, Batley, West Yorkshire, WF17 8LL Tel: (01924) 442386

K & C Mouldings (England) Ltd, Spa House, Shelfanger, Diss, Norfolk, IP22 2DF Tel: (01379) 642660 Fax: (01379) 650304 E-mail: kcmouldings@kcmouldings.co.uk *Glass fibre molding machine & concrete*

K C Office Services Ltd, The Relocation Centre, Blenheim Road, Lancing, West Sussex, BN15 8UQ Tel: (01903) 600400 Fax: (01903) 607082 E-mail: ops@kcos.co.uk *Business & industrial removals*

K C Precision Ltd, Armoury Works, Armoury Road, Birmingham, B11 2PP Tel: 0121-766 6217 Fax: 0121-693 9448 *Precision engineers*

K C S Electronics Ltd, First Avenue, Crewe Gates Industrial Estate, Crewe, CW1 6BG Tel: (01270) 588733 Fax: (01270) 583472 *Printed circuit board assemblers*

K C S Management Systems Ltd, Royal Oak Centre, Brighton Road, Purley, Surrey, CR8 2PG Tel: (020) 8660 2444 Fax: (020) 8668 8196 E-mail: sales@kcsconnect.com *Computer software producers*

K C & Son Construction Ltd, Amberley Way, Hounslow, TW4 6BH Tel: (020) 8577 2222 Fax: (020) 8577 2323 *Kitchens, bedrooms distributors & manufrs*

K C Tooling Ltd, Unit 22, Hayhill Industrial Estate, Sileby Road, Barrow Upon Soar, Loughborough, Leicestershire, LE12 8LD Tel: (01509) 814724 Fax: (01509) 816076 *Cutting tools manufrs*

▶ K C W International Ltd, 394A Wingletye Lane, Hornchurch, Essex, RM11 3DB Tel: (01708) 455224 Fax: (0871) 6614761 E-mail: kcwinternational@btinternet.com *Representative of Oversea Supplier of Digital Pushbutton Locks, Hardware Furniture, and Abrasive products.*

▶ K Carriers, Continental House, Avis Way, Newhaven, East Sussex, BN9 0DH Tel: (01273) 514599 Fax: (01273) 515939 *Furniture logistics services*

K Controls Ltd, Stone Close, West Drayton, Middlesex, UB7 8JU Tel: (01895) 449601 Fax: (01895) 448586 E-mail: sales@k-controls.co.uk *Control solutions valves & actuators manufrs*

K D Computers, 38 Borough Road, Middlesbrough, Cleveland, TS1 5DW Tel: (01642) 244477 Fax: (01642) 242415 E-mail: kdc@themail.co.uk *Computer consultants*

▶ K D Decorating Ltd, 5 Constable Court, Andover, Hampshire, SP10 3PX Tel: (01264) 394194 E-mail: karl@k-d-decorating.co.uk *Painting, decorating, plaster repairs, artexing, interior and exterior*

K D Design, Unit 2 Yonder Hill, Chard Junction, Chard, Somerset, TA20 4QR Tel: (01460) 221745 Fax: (01460) 221746 E-mail: kddf01@aol.co.uk *Steel fabricators*

K D Electrical Co. Ltd, Lyde Green, Halesowen, West Midlands, B63 2PG Tel: (01384) 560333 Fax: (01384) 560423 *Electrical contractors*

K D Engineering Merseyside Ltd, Unit 33b-33c Garston Industrial Estate, Blackburne Street, Liverpool, L19 8JB Tel: 0151-427 8996 Fax: 0151-427 9397 E-mail: kengine@mersinet.co.uk *Metal fabrication & welding, presswork services*

▶ K & D Haulage, Unit 9 Star Trading Estate, Ponthir, Newport, Gwent, NP18 1PQ Tel: (01633) 422896

K & D Joinery Ltd, Joinery House, 69 Chequers Lane, Dagenham, Essex, RM9 6QJ Tel: (020) 8526 7020 Fax: (020) 8526 7030 E-mail: info@kandd.org *Based in Dagenham with 25 years of experience offering all aspects of specialist joinery to commercial and private clients, and using the latest techniques and equipment.*

K D Optics Ltd, New Forest Farm, Walshford, Wetherby, West Yorkshire, LS22 5JJ Tel: (01937) 587003 Fax: (01937) 587002 *Optical electrical equipment manufrs*

K D P Electronic Systems Ltd, Station Road, Gamlingay, Sandy, Bedfordshire, SG19 3HB Tel: (01767) 651058 Fax: (01767) 651144 E-mail: sales@kdpes.co.uk *Manufacturing engineers electronic instrument manufrs*

▶ K D Partnership, 12-16 Clerkenwell Road, London, EC1M 5PQ Tel: (020) 7324 6343 E-mail: info@kdpartnership.co.uk *KD Partnership provides coaching and facilitation for strong leadership, effective change and high performance through skilful management. The company offers trainers who can make a difference and bring wisdom, good judgment, energy and fun. It helps companies and organisations find the right pace; make the most of business cycles; up the pace of staff performance; get in touch or in tune with their clients and increase managers' self-awareness and confidence.*

▶ K D Products Ltd, Redwither Tower, Redwither Business Park, Wrexham, Clwyd, LL13 9XT Tel: (01978) 661797 Fax: (01978) 661848 E-mail: sales@kdproducts.co.uk

▶ K D's, 38 North Point Shopping Centre, Goodhart Road, Bransholme, Hull, HU7 4EE Tel: (01482) 879489 *Nursery & young children's retailers*

▶ K & E Co. Ltd, 40 Strathmore Road, Glasgow, G22 7DW Tel: 0141-336 6111

K E Automatics Ltd, 39 Rosslyn Street, Kirkcaldy, Fife, KY1 3HS Tel: (01592) 652323 Fax: (01592) 655720 *Suppliers of fruit machines*

K E B Fabrications Ltd, 170 Rolfe St, Smethwick, West Midlands, B66 2AU Tel: 0121-555 5533 Fax: 0121-555 5193 E-mail: sales@kebfabrications.co.uk *Window & door manufrs*

K E B Packaging Ltd, Mills Hill Road, Middleton, Manchester, M24 2FT Tel: 0161-655 3464 Fax: 0161-655 3460 E-mail: sales@keb.co.uk *Specialised packaging manufrs*

K E F Audio UK Ltd, Eccleston Road, Tovil, Maidstone, Kent, ME15 6QP Tel: (01622) 672261 Fax: (01622) 750653 E-mail: enquiries@kef.com *High-fidelity loudspeaker manufrs*

K & E K Sports Trophies, 16 Holderness Road, Hull, HU9 1EG Tel: (01482) 212138 Fax: (01482) 212138 *Sports trophy manufrs*

K E M Fashions, 71-73 Powerscroft Road, London, E5 0PT Tel: (020) 8985 9387 Fax: (020) 8985 9387 *Fabric manufrs*

K E P Engineering Ltd, Mosley Street, New Basford, Nottingham, NG7 7FQ Tel: 0115-978 0616 Fax: 0115-942 2280 E-mail: info@kepengineering.com *Steel fabricators*

▶ K E P Print Group Ltd, Unit 21 Two Gates Trading Estate, Watling Street, Two Gates, Tamworth, Staffordshire, B77 5AE Tel: (01827) 280880 Fax: (01827) 285660

▶ K E Precision, Robey Close, Linby, Nottingham, NG15 8AA Tel: 0115-963 1880 Fax: 0115-963 8789 *Precision material manufrs*

▶ K E R Plant Co Ownership Ltd, Hannington Grange Farm, Redhouse Lane, Hannington, Northampton, NN6 9SZ Tel: (01604) 780180 Fax: (01604) 780129

K E R Videos, Chapel Buildings, Plainspot Road, Brinsley, Nottingham, NG16 5BQ Tel: (01773) 530315 Fax: (01773) 530315 E-mail: ker.videos@talk21.com *Amusement machine suppliers*

K E S Safetycutters, 147 Portland Road, London, SE25 4UX Tel: (020) 8656 6811 Fax: (020) 8656 6814 E-mail: sales@safetycutters.net *Forme, print & packaging cutter manufrs*

▶ K E S Translate, 6 Midland Cottages, Nightingale Road, Hitchin, Hertfordshire, SG5 1RW Tel: (01462) 458846 Fax: (01462) 458309 E-mail: info@kestranslate.co.uk *French to English translation, proofreading & editing services to businesses & individuals*

K Eardley, Cockpit Yard, Northington Street, London, WC1N 2NP Tel: (020) 7916 5941 Fax: (020) 7916 2455 *Ceramic manufrs*

▶ K Electrics, 20 Barnton Park Drive, Edinburgh, EH4 6HF Tel: 0131-336 3533

K Engineering, Unit 29 Parkrose Industrial Estate, Middlemore Road, Smethwick, West Midlands, B66 2DZ Tel: 0121-558 4367 Fax: 0121-565 1129 E-mail: sales@k-engineering.co.uk *Bolt & nut distributors*

K.F. Ltd, 36 Bolina Road, London, SE16 3LF Tel: (020) 7232 2266 Fax: (020) 7232 2288 E-mail: kabletie@btinternet.com *Automotive fuse manufrs*

K F Alliance Engineering Ltd, Units 28-29, Enfield Industrial Estate, Redditch, Worcestershire, B97 6BY Tel: (01527) 63331 Fax: (01527) 591191 E-mail: kfa@btconnect.com *Design & manufacture of special purpose materials handling equipment*

K F C Co., PO Box 55, Gloucester, GL14 3YB Tel: (01594) 822025 Fax: (01594) 822195 E-mail: info@kfcco.com *Weighing services*

K F C Engineering Ltd, Unit 6 Little Forge Road, Redditch, Worcestershire, B98 7SF Tel: (01527) 520371 Fax: (01527) 520346 E-mail: kevin@kfcengineering.co.uk *Jig & fixtures manufrs*

K F Lever (Precision Engineering) Ltd, 56 Ash Tree Road, Southampton, SO18 1LX Tel: (023) 8055 2351 Fax: (023) 8055 3574 E-mail: klseverltd@yiscalli.co.uk *Precision milling & drilling engineers*

K F Supplies, York Road, Market Weighton, York, YO43 3EE Tel: (01430) 872017 Fax: (01430) 874195 E-mail: kfsupplies@aol.com *Builders merchants & suppliers*

K F T Ltd, Baliscate, Tobermory, Isle of Mull, PA75 6QA Tel: (01688) 302113 Fax: (01688) 302113 *Fish tackle manufrs*

K Freeman Ltd, Westgate, North Newbald, South Newbald, York, YO43 4SN Tel: (01430) 827671 Fax: (01430) 827649 E-mail: kfreemanltd@aol.com *Steel framed building manufrs*

K G A Ltd, 8 Attenburys Park Estate, Attenburys Lane, Timperley, Altrincham, Cheshire, WA14 5QE Tel: 0161-962 5076 Fax: 0161-962 5312 *Crane erection services*

▶ K G B Car Valeting, 12 Stuchbury Close, Aylesbury, Buckinghamshire, HP19 8GD Tel: (01296) 436444 Fax: (01296) 436444 E-mail: info@kgbcarvaleting.co.uk *Car valeting services*

K G Business Centre, KG Business Centre, Kingsfield Way, Northampton, NN5 7QS Tel: (01604) 750777 Fax: (01604) 580011 E-mail: sales@kgbc.co.uk *Business property letting agents*

K G Christys & Co. Ltd, Helmet Street, Manchester, M1 2NT Tel: 0161-274 4339 Fax: 0161-274 4322 E-mail: sales@kgchristys.co.uk *Textile merchants & manufrs*

K G Coating Ltd, Unit 8-9 Canal Wood Industrial Estate, Chirk, Wrexham, LL14 5RL Tel: (01691) 778070 Fax: (01691) 778303 E-mail: sales@kgcoating.co.uk *Metal finishing & polishing services*

K G Consultants Ltd, Cessford, Kelso, Roxburghshire, TD5 8EG Tel: (01573) 440218 Fax: (01573) 440372 *Agricultural consultants*

K G D Industrial Services, Willow Court, Netherwood Road, Rotherwas Industrial Estate, Hereford, HR2 6JU Tel: (01432) 374374 Fax: (01432) 353419 E-mail: sales@kgdprocess.com *Offshore fluid handling systems manufrs*

K G Diecasting Weston Ltd, Tudor Centre, 264 Milton Road, Weston-super-Mare, Avon, BS22 8EN Tel: (01934) 412665 Fax: (01934) 412886 E-mail: kgdiecasting@btclick.com *Pressure die castings services*

▶ K G Drain Services Ltd, Woodlands Drive, Hoddesdon, Hertfordshire, EN11 8AZ Tel: (01992) 470203 Fax: (01992) 470204 E-mail: mail@kgdrains.co.uk *Drainage consultants*

▶ K G Haynes, 2 Ashford Industrial Estate, Dixon Street, Wolverhampton, WV2 2BX Tel: (01902) 870011 Fax: (01902) 459714 E-mail: kghaynesengineering@fsnet.co.uk *Metalworking & fabrication services*

K G J Price Railway Contractors Ltd, Penygroes Farm, Llantrisant, Pontyclun, Mid Glamorgan, CF72 8LP Tel: (029) 2088 9220 Fax: (029) 2045 1959 *Railway contractors*

K G Mccoll & Co. Ltd, Kilmelford Yachthaven, Kilmelford, Oban, Argyll, PA34 4XD Tel: (01852) 200248 Fax: (01852) 200343 E-mail: info@kilmelfordyachthaven.co.uk *Boat builders & repairers*

K.G. Products, 247 City Road, Stoke-on-Trent, ST4 2PX Tel: (01782) 844866 Fax: (01782) 744162 E-mail: enquiries@kgproducts.co.uk *Manufacture & supply of tanks & water gardens*

K G Projects, 40 Trenance Road, St. Austell, Cornwall, PL25 5AN Tel: (01726) 61119 Fax: (01726) 871110 *Air conditioning distributors & agents*

K G Smoke Dispersal, 3 Foundry Lane, Horsham, West Sussex, RH13 5PX Tel: (01403) 242299 Fax: (01403) 255577 E-mail: kgsmoke@hotmail.co.uk *Smoke window ventilation equipment*

K G Smoke Dispersal, 3 Foundry Lane, Horsham, West Sussex, RH13 5PX Tel: (01403) 242299 Fax: (01403) 255577 E-mail: kgsmoke@hotmail.co.uk *Aluminium automatically opening smoke ventilation window manufrs*

K G Sprayers Aldershot Ltd, 3a Holder Road, Aldershot, Hampshire, GU12 4RH Tel: (01252) 324309 Fax: (01252) 345895 *Shot blasting contractors & powder coating industrial finishers*

▶ K G Wagstaff & Sons, 136-138 Upminster Road, Hornchurch, Essex, RM12 6PL Tel: (01708) 442666 Fax: (01708) 437334 E-mail: info@wagstaffheating.co.uk

▶ K Guard UK Ltd, 6 Arlesey Business Park, Mill Lane, Arlesey, Bedfordshire, SG15 6RF Tel: (01462) 834834 Fax: (01462) 834835 E-mail: info@kguard.co.uk *Manufacturers of edge protection systems for the construction industry*

K H & D Bosomworth, The Forge, Melmerby, Ripon, North Yorkshire, HG4 5HH Tel: (01765) 640270 Fax: (01765) 640880 *Agricultural engineers & calor gas suppliers*

K & H Engineering, 5 Morris Road, Newtongrange, Dalkeith, Midlothian, EH22 4ST Tel: 0131-663 0564 Fax: 0131-654 2699 *Industrial roof rack manufrs*

K H Hedley, The Forge, Invershin, Lairg, Sutherland, IV27 4ET Tel: (01549) 421234 Fax: (01549) 421263 E-mail: khhedley@aol.com *Farrier*

K & H Packaging Ltd, Unit 7 Crayside Industrial Estate, Thames Road, Crayford, Dartford, DA1 4RF Tel: (01322) 521512 Fax: (01322) 553102 E-mail: rmarkrussell2@aol.com *Printers & packagers.*

K H S Ltd, 14 Spenlow Drive, Chelmsford, CM1 4UQ Tel: (01245) 440873 Fax: (01245) 422242 *Pest control services*

K H S Engineering Co., 31 Froysell Street, Willenhall, West Midlands, WV13 1QH Tel: (01902) 608784 Fax: (01902) 634466 E-mail: kasengineering@btconnect.com *Precision machinists*

▶ K Hayton, Units 2-3 Dumfries Enterprise Park, Tinwald Downs Road, Heathhall, Dumfries, DG1 3SJ Tel: (01387) 263435 Fax: (01387) 279523

K Home International Ltd, Ingram House, Allensway, Stockton-on-Tees, Cleveland, TS17 9HA Tel: (01642) 765421 Fax: (01642) 760721 E-mail: enquiry@khomeint.co.uk *Engineering design, project, construction management*

K & I Ltd, Hardengreen Coachworks, Dalkeith, Midlothian, EH22 3LD Tel: 0131-663 4545 Fax: 0131-654 2373 E-mail: info@k-and-i.co.uk *Motor body builders & repairers* Also at: Edinburgh

K I Fasteners Blackburn Ltd, Unit 8 Pearson Street, Blackburn, BB2 2ES Tel: (01254) 678017 Fax: (01254) 678018 *Fastener distributors*

K International plc, Carina Building, Sunrise Parkway, Milton Keynes, MK14 6PW Tel: (01908) 670399 Fax: (01908) 670170 E-mail: info@k-international.com *Language translation services*

K J B Engineering (West Tanfield) Ltd, Unit 2 The Sawmills, West Tanfield, Ripon, North Yorkshire, HG4 5JU Tel: (01677) 470511 Fax: (01677) 470811 E-mail: sales@kjblaser.co.uk Sales Contact: T. Birkbeck *LASER CUTTING SERVICES in North Yorkshire; Specialists in precision steel, stainless steel, aluminium & sheet metal fabrication. Press brake work. Punch press cutting services. TIG/MIG welding. Quality finishing, rumbling, powder coating services & paint finishing. CAD design. KJB are able to produce incredibly detailed profiles and components to exacting requirements at highly competitive rates.*

K & J Brakes & Hoses Ltd, Alamein Road, Morfa Industrial Estate, Landore, Swansea, SA1 2HY Tel: (01792) 460582 Fax: (01792) 642675 *Hydraulic hose distributors & motor factors services*

K J Bridgewater, 6 Jarvis Close, Hinckley, Leicestershire, LE10 1PG Tel: (01455) 635363 Fax: (01455) 635363 *Furniture fitters*

▶ K J Bryan Builders Ltd, 5 John Davies Workshops, Main Street, Huthwaite, Sutton-in-Ashfield, Nottinghamshire, NG17 2LQ Tel: (01623) 553997 Fax: (01623) 552815

K & J Cooked Meats, Unit 12 Phoenix Int Industrial Estate, Charles Street, West Bromwich, West Midlands, B70 0AY Tel: 0121-557 8430 Fax: 0121-522 3368 *Sliced & cooked meat product manufrs*

K J Engineering Ltd, Unit 4, 55 Albert Road North, Reigate, Surrey, RH2 9EL Tel: (01737) 223392 Fax: (01737) 224365 E-mail: kj.engineering@talk21.com *Ductwork services*

▶ K J Evans Electrical Ltd, 29 Spingate Close, Hornchurch, Essex, RM12 6SW Tel: (01708) 470570

▶ K J H, Woodpeckers, Wildcroft Drive, Wokingham, Berkshire, RG40 3HY Tel: (07932) 671564 Fax: 0118-977 5957 E-mail: kjhcom@btinternet.com *Website design & implementation for individuals & small businesses*

▶ K J H, Woodpeckers, Wildcroft Drive, Wokingham, Berkshire, RG40 3HY Tel: (07932) 671564 Fax: 0118-977 5957 E-mail: aardy@btinternet.com *Computer services & web site designers*

▶ K J Hire Centre, Kemys Way, Swansea Enterprise Park, Swansea, SA6 8QF Tel: (01792) 790953 Fax: (01792) 781803

K J Howells, Cobbs Quay, Poole, Dorset, BH15 4EL Tel: (01202) 665724 Fax: (01202) 665724 E-mail: sales@kjhowells.com *Marine products retail*

K J Joinery, Regent House, 15-21 Adam Street, Cardiff, CF24 2FH Tel: (029) 2049 5395 Fax: (029) 2049 5395 *Joinery manufrs*

K J Joyce, Canaan, Chale Green, Ventnor, Isle of Wight, PO38 2JN Tel: (01983) 551381 Fax: (01983) 551440 *Plant hirers*

K J K Plastics Ltd, 51 Knowl Piece, Wilbury Way, Hitchin, Hertfordshire, SG4 0TY Tel: (01462) 420422 Fax: (01462) 420242 E-mail: sales@kjkplastics.co.uk *Plastic injection mouldings to specification*

K J M Replacement Windows Ltd, 4 Sterling Park, Andover, Hampshire, SP10 3TZ Tel: (01264) 359355 Fax: (01264) 353441 E-mail: sales@kjmgroup.com *PVC window, doors, conservatories & hardwood & aluminium services*

K & J Moxham, Laburnum Road, Stonehouse, Gloucestershire, GL10 2NS Tel: (01453) 822368 Fax: (01453) 827432 *Educational books distributors*

K J N Automation Ltd, 5 Peckleton Lane Business Park, Peckleton Common, Peckleton, Leicester, LE9 7RN Tel: (01455) 823304 Fax: (01455) 828186 E-mail: sales@kjnltd.co.uk *We offer a wide range of high strength anodised extrusions, connectors and accessories for low cost modular structures which can be used to manufacture a variety of applications such as: Protective Enclosures, Machine guards, Work Stations, Conveyors, Robot Stands, Tightening Systems, Linear, Benches with Worktops, Support Frames, Test Rigs etc. There is no welding and more importantly no waiting. It is totally flexible and can easily be reconstructed or modified to accommodate your needs. The system can be supplied flat packed (no charge for cutting) or as a constructed unit. Also available is our fully equipped machine shop ideal for special requirements such as bespoke machine parts or bulk quantities.*

▶ K J Pheysey, 1 Albert Street, Redditch, Worcestershire, B97 4DA Tel: (01527) 64404

▶ K & J Plant Hire, West Park, Yarnscombe, Barnstaple, Devon, EX31 3LZ Tel: (01271) 858540 Fax: (01271) 858574 E-mail: training@ctacentre.co.uk

K J Roberts, 4 Abington Square, Northampton, NN1 4AA Tel: (01604) 635099 *Jewellery manufrs*

▶ K J Samson Construction Kent Ltd, 1 Granville Cottages, The Crescent, Boughton-under-Blean, Faversham, Kent, ME13 9AY Tel: (01227) 750701 Fax: (01227) 752400

K J Services Ltd, Capital Valley Industrial Estate, Rhymney, Tredegar, Gwent, NP22 5PT Tel: (01685) 841449 Fax: (01685) 840746 E-mail: sales@kjservices.co.uk *Construction plant & equipment hire*

K J Shepherd, Unit 27 Bancombe Trading Estate, Bancombe Road, Somerton, Somerset, TA11 6SB Tel: (01458) 273990 Fax: (01458) 273990 *Joinery*

▶ K & J Storton Contractors Ltd, 146 Cleveland Way, Stevenage, Hertfordshire, SG1 6BY Tel: (01438) 230671 Fax: (01438) 880449 E-mail: jimstorton@msn.com *brickwork specialists*contractors to new builds&private builders*residential&commercial***

K J T Plastics Ltd, Unit 4-5 Happy Valley Industrial Estate, Primrose Hill, Kings Langley, Hertfordshire, WD4 8HD Tel: (01923) 267913 Fax: (01923) 261853 *Plastics, mould & tool manufrs*

K J Thermosets Ltd, Unit 8 & 9 Victoria Industrial Estate, Victoria Road, Bradford, West Yorkshire, BD2 2DD Tel: (01274) 626627 Fax: (01274) 626800 E-mail: sales@kjthermosets.co.uk *Thermoset manufrs*

K J Thulborn Ltd, New Yard, Totnes Road, Paignton, Devon, TQ4 7HD Tel: (01803) 551217 Fax: (01803) 663722 *Agricultural contractors*

▶ K & J Travel Direct, 15 Beechcombe Close, Pershore, Worcestershire, WR10 1PW Tel: (01386) 553243 Fax: 01386 553653 E-mail: knewbury@traveldirect-pershore.co.uk *Taxi & private hire service*

K J W Alarms, 26A Church Road, Lilleshall, Newport, Shropshire, TF10 9HE Tel: (01952) 604757 *Alarms installers & engineers*

K J Water Treatments Ltd, 19 Hardings La, London, SE20 7JJ Tel: 020 86597216 Fax: 0208 6760138 *Water treatment*

K J Wykes Ltd, Goosey Lodge, Wymington Lane, Wymington, Rushden, Northamptonshire, NN10 9LU Tel: (01933) 315818 Fax: (01933) 355808 *Process engineers*

K Johnstone, Rear of, 351 Loxley Road, Sheffield, S6 4TH Tel: 0114-234 2131 Fax: 0114-234 2131 *Wooden furniture frames for upholstering trade*

K K Beds & Pine, 72-75 Lower Bristol Road, Bath, BA2 3HB Tel: (01225) 481818 Fax: (01225) 481818 *Furniture retailers*

K & K Computers, 1 Baker Street, Weston-super-Mare, Avon, BS23 3AA Tel: (01934) 419324 Fax: (01934) 419469 *Computer repair, maintenance & writing consultants*

▶ K & K Industrial Services Ltd, Unit 10-12, 10 Sugar House Lane, London, E15 2QS Tel: (020) 8519 4307 Fax: (020) 8522 0232

K & K Mouldings Ltd, Bridge Road, Ely, Cambridgeshire, CB7 4DY Tel: (01353) 663726 Fax: (01353) 668766 E-mail: sales@bridgeboatyard.com *Fibre glass manufacture & tourism*

K K S (Stainless Steels) Co. Ltd, Unit 2A, Charlton Mead Lane South, Hoddesdon, Hertfordshire, EN11 0DJ Tel: (01992) 445222 Fax: (01992) 446887 *Stainless steel stockholders*

K & L Commercials, 2 Shelah Road, Halesowen, West Midlands, B63 3PG Tel: 0121-585 1349 *Springs, automotive & suspension*

K L Engine Centre, Horsleys Fields, King's Lynn, Norfolk, PE30 5DD Tel: (01553) 772422 Fax: (01553) 769372 *Engine recondition, repairers & mot centre services* Also at: Norwich

K L G Glass Ltd, Lenton Lane, Nottingham, NG7 2NR Tel: 0115-942 3000 Fax: 0115-942 3444 E-mail: info@klg-glass.co.uk *Upvc doors, window suppliers & manufrs*

K L Goddard, 1 Lambton Road, London, SW20 0LW Tel: (020) 8946 9494 Fax: (020) 8947 5675 *Stationers & printers manufrs*

K.L Joinery, Little Trenance Farm, Trenance Road, St. Austell, Cornwall, PL25 5RF Tel: (01726) 64680 Fax: (01726) 70668 *Joinery manufrs*

K L Labels Ltd, 26 Skyline Drive, Lisburn, County Antrim, BT27 4HH Tel: (028) 9266 0366 Fax: (028) 9266 0366 *Label manufacturers & distributors*

K L M Steels Ltd, Unit 2a/172, 172 Argyle Street, Birmingham, B7 5TE Tel: 0121-327 0600 Fax: 0121-327 4575 E-mail: klmsteels@virgin.net *Steel stockholders & temporary security fencing manufacturer*

K L M Storage Ltd, Rushock Trading Estate, Droitwich, Worcestershire, WR9 0NR Tel: (01299) 250885 Fax: (01299) 251450 E-mail: info@klmstorage.com *General & bonded warehouses*

K L M Trophy Centre, 2-3 The Parade, Southfields, Letchworth Garden City, Hertfordshire, SG6 4NB Tel: (01462) 684242 Fax: (01462) 684242 E-mail: klmengravers@aol.com *Trophy manufrs*

K L Precision Engineering Ltd, Athelney Way, Cheltenham, Gloucestershire, GL52 6RT Tel: (01242) 244847 Fax: (01242) 244847 *Injection mould toolmakers*

K L S Ltd, 22-23 Austin Fields, King's Lynn, Norfolk, PE30 1PH Tel: (01553) 772935 Fax: (01553) 769118 E-mail: sales@klsonline.co.uk *Commercial catering & refrigeration supplies distributors*

▶ K & L Sewing Machines, PO Box 1305, Oxford, OX4 3BN Tel: (01865) 721915 Fax: (01865) 721915 *Sewing machine sales & repairs - top brands include bernina, singer, brother, toyota reconditioned machines all makes of sewing machines repaired*

K & L Tackle, Farfield House, 127 North Street, Keighley, West Yorkshire, BD21 3AB Tel: (01535) 667574 Fax: (01535) 661805 *Fishing tackle distributors*

▶ K L Uphill, Barclays Bank, 28b Station Road, New Milton, Hampshire, BH25 6JX Tel: (01425) 611187 Fax: (01425) 611187 E-mail: sales@kluphill.co.uk *Soft furnishings suppliers & manufrs*

K Line Air Service UK Ltd, Building 100 Beverley Road, East Midland Int Airport, Castle Donington, Derby, DE74 2SA Tel: (01332) 850888 Fax: (01332) 812185 E-mail: ema@uk.klinelogistics.com *Freight forwarders* Also at: Feltham

K Line LNG Shipping UK Ltd, River Plate House, 7-11 Finsbury Circus, London, EC2M 7EA Tel: (020) 7382 6500 *Shipping line*

▶ K Lumsden, Little Kings Ash Farm, Kings Ash, Great Missenden, Buckinghamshire, HP16 9NP Tel: (01494) 837666

K M A Grinding, Unit 62 Western Business Park, Great Western Close, Birmingham, B18 4QF Tel: 0121-554 5537 Fax: 0121-554 1933 *Ejector & punch pin manufrs*

K M Allerfeldt, Chapple Farm, Chapple Road, Bovey Tracey, Newton Abbot, Devon, TQ13 9JX Tel: (01626) 832284 Fax: (01626) 832284 *Livestock arable fruit & vegetable farmers*

K & M Arrowsmith, 81 West Street, Alford, Lincolnshire, LN13 9HT Tel: (01507) 463258 Fax: (01507) 462312 E-mail: steve@kandmarrowsmith.fsnet.co.uk *Agricultural & structural engineers*

K M B Shipping Ltd, Lower Church Lane, Tipton, West Midlands, DY4 7PH Tel: 0121-557 3352 Fax: 0121-520 0936 E-mail: info@onestopshipping.co.uk *Shipping & exporting services*

K M Birch Security Systems, 25 Corville Road, Halesowen, West Midlands, B62 9TJ Tel: 0121-421 5874 Fax: 0121-421 5874 *Alarm installation services*

K M C Electronics Ltd, Farcroft, Doley Gate, Gnosall, Stafford, ST20 0EH Tel: (01785) 822777 *Electronic consultants*

K M Construction North Wales Ltd, Lower Denbigh Road, St. Asaph, Clwyd, LL17 0EL Tel: (01745) 583752 Fax: (01745) 584705 *Civil engineering contractors & plant hire services*

K M Engineering Ltd, Unit 7b Parnall Road Trading Estate, Parnall Road, Bristol, BS16 3JQ Tel: 0117-965 9336 Fax: 0117-958 3673 E-mail: enquiries@km-engineering.co.uk *Precision engineers*

K & M Engineering Shropshire Ltd, Sarn Works, Westbury, Shrewsbury, SY5 9DA Tel: (01743) 884340 Fax: (01743) 884021 E-mail: kmeng@halfwayhse.fsnet.co.uk *Construction engineers & civil engineers*

K M F Quality Bridles, 4a Ablewell Street, Walsall, WS1 2EQ Tel: (01922) 621773 Fax: (01922) 621773 *Bridle manufrs*

▶ K M Furniture Ltd, Newton House, Pottery La West, Chesterfield, Derbyshire, S41 9BN Tel: (01246) 260123 Fax: (01246) 260221 E-mail: sales@efmchesterfield.co.uk *Manufacturers of educational furniture*

▶ K M Furniture Ltd, Newton House, Pottery La West, Chesterfield, Derbyshire, S41 9BN Tel: (01246) 260123 Fax: (01246) 260221 *Educational & office furniture manufrs*

K M G Systems Ltd, Station Road, Gamlingay, Sandy, Bedfordshire, SG19 3HE Tel: (01767) 650760 Fax: (01767) 651622 E-mail: admin@kmgsystems.com *Conveyor systems, vibratory & food industry*

K M H Powder Coating & Shotblasting, 10b Radnor Road, Wigston, Leicestershire, LE18 4XY Tel: 0116-277 0050 Fax: 0116-277 7229 E-mail: hackmower@aol.com *Shot blasting & powder coatings services*

K & M Hauliers Ltd, The Aerodrome, Watnall Road, Hucknall, Nottingham, NG15 6EN Tel: 0115-963 0630 Fax: 0115-968 0126 E-mail: traffic@kmhauliers.co.uk *Transport contractors & warehousing* Also at: Lincoln

K M Industrial Products Ltd, Unit 23, Mackintosh Road, Rackheath Industrial Estate, Rackheath, Norwich, NR13 6LJ Tel: (01603) 720792 Fax: (01603) 721192 E-mail: kmindustrial@fsmail.net *Precision engineers & light assembly*

K & M Model Trees, 4 North Street, Beaminster, Dorset, DT8 3DZ Tel: (01297) 21542 Fax: (01308) 363420 *Model trees manufrs*

▶ K & M Mowers, Poolbank Lane, Welton, Brough, North Humberside, HU15 1PX Tel: (01482) 667004 Fax: (01482) 666520 E-mail: mlowe@kmmowers.co.uk *Lawn mowers*

K M P Crusader Manufacturing Co. Ltd, Oldmedow Road, King's Lynn, Norfolk, PE30 4LD Tel: (01553) 817200 Fax: (01553) 691909 E-mail: sales@kmp-uk.co.uk *Computer consumable manufrs*

K M Packaging Services Ltd, 44 West Street, Oundle, Peterborough, PE8 4EF Tel: (01832) 274944 Fax: (01832) 274898 E-mail: louise@kmpack.co.uk *Packaging services*

K & M Precision Engineering, Knowl Piece, Wilbury Way, Hitchin, Hertfordshire, SG4 0TY Tel: (01462) 422115 Fax: (01462) 436223 *Precision engineers*

K M Pressings Ltd, 37B Copenhagen Road, Sutton Field Industrial Estate, Hull, HU7 0XQ Tel: (01482) 877900 Fax: (01482) 877909 E-mail: jonathon@kmpressing.karew.co.uk *Sheet metal pressing manufrs*

▶ K M R Pipelines Ltd, 7 mount view Gardens, Norton Lees, Sheffield, S8 8PY Tel: 0114 2551447 Fax: 0114 2551447 E-mail: lawrence@kmrpipelines.co.uk *Drain cleaning services and equipment supplies, Drain surveys, Culvert Cleaning*

▶ K M S 1996, 100 Ross Walk, Leicester, LE4 5HH Tel: 0116-261 1311 Fax: 0116-261 1313 *Injection molding*

K M S Adhesives, Hamlin Way, King's Lynn, Norfolk, PE30 4NG Tel: (01553) 774100 Fax: (01553) 774165 *Adhesive distributors*

K M S Hardrange, Unit 5 Manor Industrial Estate, Flint, Clwyd, CH6 5UY Tel: (01352) 732291 Fax: (01352) 762886 E-mail: kmshardrange01@btconnect.com *Welding engineers & ductwork manufrs*

K M Services Ltd, 16 Bourne Industrial Estate, Wrotham Road, Borough Green, Sevenoaks, Kent, TN15 8DG Tel: (01732) 882280 Fax: (01732) 886011 *Air conditioning & refrigeration engineers*

▶ K M T Waterjet Systems, Alexander House, Foxlands Drive, Wolverhampton, WV4 5NB Tel: (01902) 340140 Fax: (01902) 340544 E-mail: peter_longman@kmt-waterjet.co.uk *Innovative & professional water jet system manufrs*

K & M Welding & Fabrication Engineers Ltd, Unit 3, Dunton Trading Estate, Mount Street, Birmingham, B7 5QL Tel: 0121-327 4771 Fax: 0121-328 9203 E-mail: kmwelding@yahoo.com *Steel fabricators*

K & M Wholesale Suppliers Ltd, Unit 24 Lion Park New Street, Holbrook Industrial Estate, Holbrook, Sheffield, S20 3GH Tel: 0114-247 4733 Fax: 0114-247 5335 *Educational equipment wholesaler*

▶ K Martin Builders Ltd, 2a Sidney Road, Beckenham, Kent, BR3 4QA Tel: (020) 8650 4477 Fax: (020) 8650 5398

▶ K Mayhew Publishing Ltd, Buxhall, Stowmarket, Suffolk, IP14 3BW Tel: (01449) 737978 Fax: (01449) 737834 E-mail: info@kevinmayhewltd.com *Publishing services*

▶ K Morrison & Son Ltd, 1 Station Road, Braughing, Ware, Hertfordshire, SG11 2PB Tel: (01920) 822121

K Motors LTD, K Motors Ltd, 9f Centurion Court, Farington, Leyland, PR25 3UQ Tel: (01772) 613329 Fax: (0870) 4601296 E-mail: enquiries@kmotors.co.uk *Replacement parts for land rovers distributors*

K Murray & Co. Ltd, 29 Windsor Street, Cheltenham, Gloucestershire, GL52 2DG Tel: (01242) 521774 Fax: (01242) 227137 *General engineers*

K & N Coatings Ltd, 7 Bellingham Close, Bury, Lancashire, BL8 2TU Tel: 0161-797 2909 Fax: 0161-764 2810 *Ptfe & silicone coatings for bakeware*

K & N Filters Europe Ltd, John Street, Warrington, WA2 7UB Tel: (01925) 636950 Fax: (01925) 418948 E-mail: kn@knfilters.com *Air filter manufrs*

▶ K & N Finishers Southern Ltd, Castle Trading Estate, Fareham, Hampshire, PO16 9SF Tel: (023) 9237 0591 Fax: (023) 9238 0130 E-mail: kandnfinishers@bt.com *Metal finishers*

K N G Developments, North East Sector, Bournemouth Int Airport, Hurn, Christchurch, Dorset, BH23 6NE Tel: (07074) 581856 Fax: (01202) 581856 E-mail: keith.gilson@btinternet.com *Glass fibre moulders*

K & N International Office Systems Ltd, 52 Britton Street, London, EC1M 5UQ Tel: (020) 7490 9340 Fax: (020) 7490 9349 E-mail: sales@kn-international.co.uk *Office furnisher systems*

K N P Finishing Ltd, Unit 10, Commerce Way, Leighton Buzzard, Bedfordshire, LU7 4RW Tel: (01525) 850478 Fax: (01525) 850479 E-mail: andykendall@btconnect.com *Powder coating & stove enamelling services*

K & N Press Ltd, Unit 10, 19 Lyon Road, Walton-On-Thames, Surrey, KT12 3PU Tel: (01932) 232307 Fax: (01932) 232350 *General printing*

K N Transmissions, Slater House Farm, Haighton Green Lane, Preston, PR2 5SQ Tel: (01772) 655550 Fax: (01772) 655520 E-mail: kntransmissions@btopenworld.com *Gearbox & axle specialist services*

K N Wheels Ltd, Holyhead Road, Ketley, Telford, Shropshire, TF1 5DS Tel: (01952) 613757 Fax: (01952) 613757 E-mail: knwheels@bt.co.uk *Alloy wheel manufrs*

▶ K O Engineering Services, 1 Daniels Farm, Wash Road, Basildon, Essex, SS15 4AZ Tel: (01268) 281500 Fax: (01268) 281500 E-mail: info@koengineeringservices.com *Steel fabricators*

K O Imports, 78 Cadogan Avenue, West Horndon, Brentwood, Essex, CM13 3TX Tel: (01277) 810870 Fax: (01277) 810772 *Fishing & angling merchants*

▶ K O J Group, Unit 6atingley Bar Industrial Estate, Tingley Common, Morley, Leeds, LS27 0HE Tel: 0113-252 3220 Fax: 0113-238 0007 E-mail: k0j@btconnect.com

K O S Lift Trucks, Unit 2, Shuttleworth Court, Shuttleworth Road, Bedford, MK41 0EN Tel: (01234) 216993 *Fork lift truck sales & repairs*

▶ K O Scaffolding Services Ltd, 25 Derwent Road, Whitmore Park, Coventry, CV6 2HB Tel: (024) 7633 7803 Fax: (024) 76366727 E-mail: info@koscaffolding.co.uk *Sub-contract scaffolding, specializing in the event industry*

K P Badges & Trophies, 4 Antrim Road, Bristol, BS9 4BS Tel: 0117-962 0191 Fax: 0117-975 4264 E-mail: sales@trophiesuk.biz *Trophy distributors*

K P Electromech, Unit 3 Cross Hill, Codnor, Ripley, Derbyshire, DE5 9SQ Tel: (01773) 748270 Fax: (01773) 743612 *Control system manufrs*

K P Engineering Components, Barlow Road, Aldermans Green Industrial Estate, Coventry, CV2 2LD Tel: (024) 7660 3333 Fax: (024) 7660 4444 E-mail: sales@kpecltd.com *Hydraulic cylinder, ram repairers & manufrs*

K P Equipe Communications Ltd, 1-3 Faraday Close, Drayton Fields Industrial Estate, Daventry, Northamptonshire, NN11 8RD Tel: (01327) 871187 Fax: (01327) 871188 *Communication equipment supplier*

K P Foods, Macklin Avenue, Cowpen Lane Industrial Estate, Billingham, Cleveland, TS23 4DU Tel: (01642) 373600 Fax: (01642) 561590 *Biscuits retail & manufrs*

K P G Europe Ltd, Holkham Road, Orton Southgate, Peterborough, PE2 6TE Tel: 01733 235533 Fax: 01733 235117 E-mail: info@kpgeurope.com *RFID tagging, label printing machines & press suppliers*

K & P Heating & Plumbing, Saxon House, Edward Street, Cambridge, CB1 2LS Tel: (01223) 364129 Fax: (01223) 313886 E-mail: sales@kpheatingplumbing.co.uk *Heating & plumbing engineers*

▶ K P I Transport Ltd, Unit 4, Mckay Trading Estate, Blackthorne Road, Slough, SL3 0AH Tel: (01753) 682362 Fax: (01753) 682535 E-mail: sales@kpitransport.co.uk

▶ K P Joinery Ltd, Unit J Chantry Industrial Estate, Storrington, Pulborough, West Sussex, RH20 4AD Tel: (01903) 745929 Fax: (01903) 746037 *Joinery manufrs*

K P K (Sheet Metal) Ltd, Parkwood Works, Brooklands Close, Sunbury-On-Thames, Middlesex, TW16 7DX Tel: (01932) 789866 Fax: (01932) 789794 E-mail: sales@kpk-sheetmetal.co.uk *Precision sheet metalworkers*

K P Litho Ltd, 38 Gloucester Road, Brighton, BN1 4AQ Tel: (01273) 570173 *Lithographic printers*

K P M Engineering, Premier Partnership Estate, Leys Road, Brierley Hill, West Midlands, DY5 3UP Tel: (01384) 75567 Fax: (01384) 75567 *Precision engineers & precision/general machining services*

K P M Moisture Meters Aqua Boy, Manndalin, Harrogate View, Leeds, LS17 8AZ Tel: 0113-268 5054 Fax: 0113-268 5054 E-mail: kpmmeters@aol.com *Moisture meters, refract meters manufrs*

K P M Trophies & Engraving, 88 Duke Street, St. Helens, Merseyside, WA10 2JN Tel: (01744) 603021 *Trophy engraving*

K P P Converters Ltd, Site 72, Units 1-4, Manners Industrial Estate, Ilkeston, Derbyshire, DE7 8EF Tel: 0115-930 5777 Fax: 0115-932 9184 E-mail: enquiries@kpptissue.co.uk *Paper converters*

K P Packaging, Eastwood Avenue, Grimsby, South Humberside, DN34 5BE Tel: (01472) 750006 Fax: (01472) 349975 *Packaging materials stockists* Also at: Manchester

K P Plastics (Bletchley) Ltd, Ward Road, Bilton Industrial Estate, Bletchley, Milton Keynes, MK1 1JA Tel: (01908) 374811 Fax: (01908) 270238 E-mail: sales@kpplastics.co.uk *Injection mouldings manufrs*

K P S Ltd, 3 Lyon Close, Woburn Road Industrial Estate, Kempston, Bedford, MK42 7SB Tel: (01234) 852915 Fax: (01234) 840124 E-mail: sales@kpssheetmetal.co.uk *Precision sheet metalwork services*

K P Service Group, 12 Hammond Drive, Northleach, Cheltenham, Gloucestershire, GL54 3JF Tel: (01451) 860087 Fax: (01451) 860087 E-mail: ken@kpsg.net *Computers consultancy*

K P Thomas & Son, Templeton, Narberth, Dyfed, SA67 8SR Tel: (0800) 3286033 Fax: (01834) 861686 E-mail: kpthomas@templeton22.fsnet.co.uk *Fuel oil distributors, wholesale & retailers*

K Pilcher Engineering, Unit D1 Guy Motors Industrial Park, Park Lane, Wolverhampton, WV10 9QF Tel: (01902) 728820 Fax: (01902) 304769 E-mail: kpeng@waverider.co.uk *Press tool manufrs*

K & R Fabrications Ltd, Old Station Close, Shepshed, Loughborough, Leicestershire, LE12 9NJ Tel: (01509) 506996 Fax: (01509) 506996 E-mail: kandrfabs@btconnect.com *Steel fabricators*

K R G Industries Ltd, Russellcolt Street, Coatbridge, Lanarkshire, ML5 2BN Tel: (01236) 435659 Fax: (01236) 434812 E-mail: sales@krgindustries.com *Precision engineers & purpose machine manufrs*

K R Graphics Ltd, 121 University Street, Belfast, BT7 1HP Tel: (028) 9033 3792 Fax: (028) 9033 0549 E-mail: studio@krgraphics.co.uk *Graphic design & advertising*

K R L Concrete Ltd, Manor Nurseries, Kenilworth Road, Hampton-in-Arden, Solihull, West Midlands, B92 0LR Tel: (01675) 443157 Fax: (01675) 443316 *Ready mixed concrete manufrs*

K & R Laser Services, Unit 60A, Blackpole Trading Estate West, Worcester, WR3 8TJ Tel: (01905) 757548 Fax: (01905) 754571 E-mail: kr.lasers@virgin.net *Laser cutting services*

K R M Engineering, Marshlands Road, Farlington Industrial Estate, Farlington, Portsmouth, PO6 1SS Tel: (023) 9237 2141 Fax: (023) 9264 2288 *General engineers*

K R P Power Source UK Ltd, 2 The Galloway Centre, Express Way, Newbury, Berkshire, RG14 5TL Tel: (01635) 32510 Fax: (01635) 32510 E-mail: sales@krp.co.uk *Power supplies & DC-DC converters distributors*

K R Snoxell & Sons Ltd, 24-26 Clarendon Road, Luton, LU2 7PQ Tel: (01582) 724704 Fax: (01582) 452928 E-mail: snoxell-headwear@lineone.net *Lining, labels & ladies hats manufrs*

▶ K R Venning Ltd, Castle Farm, Raisbeck, Penrith, Cumbria, CA10 3SG Tel: (01539) 624481 Fax: (01539) 624483

K Russell, Brackenwood, Collinswood Road, Farnham Common, Slough, SL2 3LH Tel: (01753) 645569 Fax: (01753) 645230 E-mail: kr@keithrussell.com *Computer database designers*

▶ K S A Underwater Ltd, Unit 10 Skellgillside Workshops, Nenthead Road, Alston, Cumbria, CA9 3TR Tel: (01434) 382122 Fax: (01434) 382574 E-mail: ksauw@aol.com *Diver transportation systems manufrs*

K & S Aluminium Ltd, Bent Street, Kearsley, Bolton, BL4 9DH Tel: (01204) 577769 Fax: (01204) 579340 E-mail: info@ksaluminium.co.uk *Aluminium fabricators*

K & S Commercial Photos Ltd, 90 Commercial Square, Leicester, LE2 7SR Tel: 0116-247 0270 Fax: 0116-247 1026 E-mail: sales@kands.co.uk *Digital & photographic imaging*

K S Computers, 3 Dyneley Road, Blackburn, BB1 3AB Tel: (01254) 505500 Fax: (01254) 691466 E-mail: purchasing@javelincomputers.co.uk *Computer hardware & software mail-order*

▶ K S Distribution, Kearsley Mill, Crompton Road, Radcliffe, Manchester, M26 1RH Tel: (01204) 702338 Fax: (01204) 573394

K & S Engineering, 10 Wadsworth Road, Greenford, Middlesex, UB6 7JX Tel: (020) 8991 0073 Fax: (020) 8997 7786 *Precision grinding services*

K & S Engineering & Scientific Ltd, 18 Clifton Gardens, London, NW11 7EL Tel: (020) 8731 7461 Fax: (020) 8731 8604 E-mail: seedetails@www.kse-sci.com *Cable fault locators & manufacturers of control systems & electronic equipment (industrial)*

K S Interiors Ltd, School Road, Nomansland, Salisbury, SP5 2BY Tel: (01794) 390683 Fax: (01794) 390683 *Partitioning & suspended ceilings*

▶ K & S J Harvey & Sons, Old Hall St, Farnworth, Bolton, BL4 8HJ Tel: (01204) 791563

K S M Ltd, Unit 2 Eldon Road Industrial Estate, Attenborough, Beeston, Nottingham, NG9 6DZ Tel: 0115-968 3540 Fax: 0115-922 9500 E-mail: sales@madaboutcable.com *Supplying cables, connectors, cabinets, tools and accessories to the audio visual, data networking, security and telecommunications industries since 1991*

K S M Metal Finishing Ltd, Newhall Street, Willenhall, West Midlands, WV13 1LQ Tel: (01902) 607176 Fax: (01902) 607176 *Metal finishing & polishing services*

▶ K & S Metal Polishers, Unit G10 Rudford Industrial Estate, Ford Road, Ford, Arundel, West Sussex, BN18 0BD Tel: (01903) 718180 Fax: (01903) 718180 E-mail: ksmetal@talk21.com *K & S Metal polishers is a Sussex based company that has over 25 years experience in the business. Their quality service is unrivalled and they offer an individual metal polishing service from dull satin to a bright mirror finish. With so many years in the business they are the first choice for polishing services. We also offer a Lacquering & grit blasting service. Although a small family run business our experience is vast and we offer a professional service that is unrivalled*

▶ K & S Packaging, 33-37 Garman Road, London, N17 0UL Tel: (020) 8885 6677 Fax: (020) 8885 6678 E-mail: info@kspackaging.com *Plastic bag manufrs*

K S R Kuebler (UK) Level Measurement & Control Ltd, 43 Cherry Orchard Rd, West Molesey, Surrey, KT8 1QZ Tel: (020) 8941 3075 Fax: (020) 8979 4386 E-mail: ksruk@ksr-kuebler.com Principal Export Areas: Worldwide *Level control equipment & liquid level control equipment manufrs*

K S S Ltd, 122 Redriff Rd, London, SE16 6QD Tel: (020) 7232 2260 Fax: (020) 7232 2288 E-mail: kabletie@btinternet.com *Cable accessories*

K S Security Ltd, Units 2-6, Warsop Trading Estate, Hever Road, Edenbridge, Kent, TN8 5LD Tel: (01732) 867199 Fax: (01732) 867102 E-mail: info@ks-security.co.uk *Security counter screen & grille manufrs*

▶ K & S Services, Dam House, Astley Hall Drive, Tyldesley, Manchester, M29 7TX Tel: (01942) 881222 Fax: (01942) 881222 E-mail: enq@ksservices.com *Refrigeration & air conditioning engineers*

K S W Engineering Ltd, 7 Stirling Road, Glenrothes, Fife, KY6 2ST Tel: (01592) 774822 Fax: (01592) 772891 E-mail: stewart@kswengineering.com *Sub-contract machining services*

▶ K Seabourne, 17 Bath Road, Worcester, WR5 3AA Tel: (01905) 350234 Fax: (01905) 350234 E-mail: info@bassurgery.com *Bass guitar manufrs*

K Sime Machines, 14 Parkhills Road, Bury, Lancashire, BL9 9AX Tel: 0161-797 6723 Fax: 0161-797 6727 E-mail: office@tournament.co.uk *Amusement machine installation*

▶ K Stewart (Strathpeffer) Ltd, Blairninich, Strathpeffer, Ross-Shire, IV14 9AB Tel: (01997) 421333

K Supplies Ltd, Unit 14 Harwood Street, Blackburn, BB1 3BS Tel: (01254) 679025 Fax: (01254) 677010 E-mail: salesblackburn@ksupplies.co.uk *Nut & bolt stockists*

K Supplies Ltd, Hill End Lane, Rossendale, Lancashire, BB4 7PP Tel: (01706) 217441 Fax: (01706) 831772 E-mail: sales@ksupplies.co.uk *Engineers' supplies factors* Also at: Blackburn, Burnley & Rochdale

K T B Engineering Ltd, 14 Northwood Road, Thornton Heath, Surrey, CR7 8HQ Tel: (020) 8771 9541 Fax: (020) 8771 3896 E-mail: sales@ktbengineering.co.uk *Steam energy specialists* Also at: Hitchin

K T D Colourcraft Ltd, 7 Lowther Street, Carlisle, CA3 8ES Tel: (01228) 528559 Fax: (01228) 819799 *Computer, art & graphic agents & dealers*

▶ K.T. Electrical Services, 26 Waverley Crescent, Grangemouth, Stirlingshire, FK3 8RB Tel: 07876 345366 Fax: 01324 875727 *service all central scotland, Falkirk, Stirling, Fife, etc.*

K T Fabrications Ltd, Unit B Heath Place, Bognor Regis, West Sussex, PO22 9SL Tel: (01243) 861426 Fax: (01243) 826108 *Sheet metalwork engineers*

K T Hydraulic Ltd, Hope Hall Mill, Union Street South, Halifax, West Yorkshire, HX1 2LA Tel: (01422) 358885 Fax: (01422) 359512 *Pumps & flow meter distributors*

K T Ivory plc, Harper Lodge Farm, Harper Lane, Radlett, Hertfordshire, WD7 7HU Tel: (01923) 856081 Fax: (01923) 852470 E-mail: ivorys1@btconnect.com *Sand & ballast merchants*

K T Joinery Ltd, 9 Auckland New Business Centre, St. Helen Auckland Industrial Estate, Bishop Auckland, County Durham, DL14 9TX Tel: (01388) 458660 Fax: (01388) 606494 E-mail: office@ktjoinery.co.uk *contract joiners, corporate joiners, corporate contract joiners, best contract joiners, best corporate contract joiners, ktjoinery, kt joinery, uk joiner, uk joiners, uk joinery, contract joinery, corporate joinery, corporate contract joinery, best contract joinery, best contract joiners, wood joinery, woodworking joinery, first fix, first fix joiners, first fix joinery, second fix joiners, second fix joinery, first and second fix, first and second fix joiners, first and second fix joinery, company joinery, company joiners, fitters, joinery fitters, shop fitters, uk joiner, uk joiners, uk joinery, joiner uk, joinery uk, joiners uk, carpentry, joinery, joiners, second fix, carpenters, woodwork*

K T Mcpartlin & Sons, The Barrocks, Ramsey Road, Farcet, Peterborough, PE7 3DR Tel: (01733) 844557 *Agricultural contractors*

K T Moulds, 27 Westbury Close, Townsend Industrial Estate, Houghton Regis, Dunstable, Bedfordshire, LU5 5BL Tel: (01582) 699721 Fax: (01582) 699721 *Plastic mould manufrs*

K T R Couplings Ltd, Robert House Unit 7, Acorn Business Park, Woodseats Close, Sheffield, S8 0TB Tel: 0114-258 7757 Fax: 0114-258 7740 E-mail: ktr-uk@ktr.com *Couplings & hydraulic components*

▶ K T R Environmental Solutions Ltd, 1 Close Barn, Coberley Road, Coberley, Cheltenham, Gloucestershire, GL53 9QY Tel: (01242) 870134 Fax: (01242) 870134 E-mail: sales@ktrworld.com *Swimming Pool Safety Covers*Swimming Pool Debris Covers*Pool Winter Covers* Child Proof Fencing* Pool Alarms*Pond Safety Covers* Safety Nets* Pool Fencing*Pond Safety systems*

K T S L Ltd, PO Box 2637, Corsham, Wiltshire, SN13 0RP Tel: (0870) 0275587 Fax: (01249) 700650 E-mail: sales@ktsl.com *Computer systems & software (development)*

K T S Wire Industries Ltd, Park Mills, South Street, Morley, Leeds, LS27 8AT Tel: 0113-253 2421 Fax: 0113-307 6868 E-mail: mail@ktswire.com *Cold rolled flat wire manufrs*

K & T Sports Ltd, Po Box 183, Ashford, Kent, TN23 4ZY Tel: 01233 631447 Fax: 01233 611845 *Sports equipment import & export*

K T Tank Lining Services, Building 43, Kingsnorth Industrial Estate, Kingsnorth, Hoo, Rochester, Kent, ME3 9ND Tel: (01634) 846824 Fax: (01634) 845441 *Tank lining & tank refurbishment*

K & T Tilts, Readmans Industrial Estate, Station Road, East Tilbury, Tilbury, Essex, RM18 8QR Tel: (01375) 840880 Fax: (01375) 840740 E-mail: info@kandttilts.co.uk *Taurpaulin & side curtain manufrs*

▶ K Tools International Ltd, 1 Abbey La Industrial Estate, Abbey Lane, Burscough, Ormskirk, Lancashire, L40 7SR Tel: (01704) 895595 Fax: (01704) 895695 E-mail: info@ktools.co.uk *Distributors of air tools & air tools repair services*

K Toys, Second Avenue, Westfield Industrial Estate, Midsomer Norton, Radstock, BA3 4BH Tel: (01761) 411299 Fax: (01761) 411522 E-mail: mail@ktoys.co.uk *Educational wheeled toy suppliers & manufrs*

K UK Ltd, Suite 1, Homestead Farm, North Houghton, Stockbridge, Hampshire, SO20 6LG Tel: (01264) 810044 Fax: (01264) 810044 *DATA acquisition equipment to motor distribution*

K V Ltd, Lunar House, Crownhill, Milton Keynes, MK8 0HB Tel: (01908) 561515 Fax: (01908) 561227 E-mail: marketing@kvautomation.co.uk *Pneumatic equipment manufrs*

▶ K V A Power Ltd, Unit 12, Spring Mill Industrial Estate, Avening Road, Nailsworth, Stroud, Gloucestershire, GL6 0BS Tel: (01453) 832358

K V Computer Services Ltd, North Sands Business Centre, Dame Dorothy Street, Sunderland, SR6 0QA Tel: 0191-510 9566 Fax: 0191-510 0686 E-mail: kvinfo@kvcomputerservices.co.uk *Software house*

K V Rollers Ltd, Unit 1-3 Claenwern, Avondale Industrial Estate, Pontrhydyrun, Cwmbran, Gwent, NP44 1TY Tel: (01633) 871919 Fax: (01633) 877250 E-mail: kbrollers@tiscali.co.uk Principal Export Areas: Worldwide *Roller manufrs*

K W Barnett, 88 Main Street, Hutton Buscel, Scarborough, North Yorkshire, YO13 9LL Tel: (01723) 864375 Fax: (01723) 864375 *Agricultural contractors*

▶ K & W Brick Haulage Ltd, 21 Commerce Way, Highbridge, Somerset, TA9 4AG Tel: (01278) 792623 Fax: (01278) 785950

▶ K W Construction (Aberdeen) Ltd, 55 Constitution Street, Aberdeen, AB24 5ET Tel: (01224) 641190 Fax: (01224) 648329

▶ K W Curtain Designs, 59 Holt Drive, Loughborough, Leicestershire, LE11 3HZ Tel: (01509) 210585 E-mail: kwalmsley@kwdesigns.fsnet.co.uk *Made to measure curtains, cushions & blinds suppliers*

K W Engineering Poole Ltd, 5 Ency Park, 7 Abingdon Road, Nuffield Industrial Estate, Poole, Dorset, BH17 0UH Tel: (01202) 677990 Fax: (01202) 666355 E-mail: keith.ward@kw-eng.co.uk *Precision engineering specialists*

K & W Fabrications Ltd, Brighton Road, Handcross, Haywards Heath, West Sussex, RH17 6BZ Tel: (01444) 401144 Fax: (01444) 401188 E-mail: user@kw-fabrication.prestel.co.uk *Thermoplastic fabricators*

▶ K W Fire Protection Ltd, Unit 39, The Acorn Centre, Barry Street, Oldham, OL1 3NE Tel: 0161-628 9379 Fax: 0161-620 5354 E-mail: enquiries@kwfire.co.uk *Service & sales of fire extinguishers, fire blankets, safety equipment*

K W Geere Engineering, 4 Lady Bee Marina Industrial Units, Albion Street, Southwick, Brighton, BN42 4EG Tel: (01273) 596211 Fax: (01273) 592196 *Precision machining services & steel fabricators*

K W H Plast UK Ltd, Brunleys, Kiln Farm, Milton Keynes, MK11 3EW Tel: (01908) 566166 Fax: (01908) 568538 E-mail: sales@kwhplast.com *PVC, plastic, polypropylene sheeting manufrs*

K W O Tools (UK) Ltd, 4 Strawberry Vale, Vale Road, Tonbridge, Kent, TN9 1SJ Tel: (01732) 364444 Fax: (01732) 351144 E-mail: sales@kwo.co.uk *Wood tool specialists distributors*

K & W Services, Unit 15, Waterloo Park Industrial Estate, Bidford-on-Avon, Alcester, Warwickshire, B50 4JG Tel: (01789) 491492 Fax: (01789) 491493 E-mail: sales@kwservice.co.uk *Based in Warwickshire, K & W Services provide total UK coverage. We are an independent supplier of most type's generators including: generator hire, generator installation, generator sales, standby generators, generator repairs, generator service, generators form 5 KVA to 1500 KVA. K & W Services provides an excellent service in both the technical advice given and the supply of the correct product for your specific needs.*

K W Signs, 11 Burnside Road, Bolton, BL1 6EP Tel: (01204) 491487 Fax: (01204) 491488 *Sign manufrs*

K W Tilt & Sons, Whitehouse Farm, Hockley Brook Lane, Belbroughton, Stourbridge, West Midlands, DY9 0AH Tel: (01562) 730375 *Agricultural contractors & ploughing*

K W Timmins, The Cottage, Tillbridge Road, Sturton by Stow, Lincoln, LN1 2BP Tel: (01427) 788009 Fax: (01427) 787374 *Agricultural & industrial engineers*

▶ K W Training Services Ltd, High Street, Alfriston, Polegate, East Sussex, BN26 5SZ Tel: (01323) 870392 Fax: (01323) 870392

K W Wait Reinforcing Services, 2 Hill View, Soundwell, Bristol, BS16 4RW Tel: 0117-975 3610 *Steel fixing fabricators*

K W Welding & Fabrication, 60k Gorse Industrial Estate, Barnham, Thetford, Norfolk, IP24 2PH Tel: (01842) 890606 Fax: (01842) 890889 E-mail: kevinwhittred@aol.com *Steel fabricators*

K W Windows, Plumbe Street, Burnley, Lancashire, BB11 3AG Tel: (01282) 448387 Fax: (01282) 416017 *Window manufrs*

K Weiss Ltd, PO Box 78, Radlett, Hertfordshire, WD7 9ZT Tel: (01923) 855237 Fax: (020) 7504 8100 E-mail: handmade@weiss.co.uk *Goldsmiths*

▶ K Young & Sons (Stroud) Ltd, Gaineys Wells, Stroud, Gloucestershire, GL5 1LQ Tel: (01453) 764503

K&S, 1 Hardess Street, London, SE24 0HN Tel: (020) 7274 2215 Fax: (020) 7738 4531 *General engineering*

k1 Yarns Knitting Boutique, 6 Queen Margaret Drive, Glasgow, G20 8NY Tel: 0141 576 0113 E-mail: info@k1yarns.com

K2 Associates Ltd, 6 Haselmere Industrial Estate, Pig Lane, Bishop's Stortford, Hertfordshire, CM23 3HG Tel: (01279) 508305 Fax: (01279) 755530 E-mail: ken.day@k2a.co.uk Principal Export Areas: Worldwide *Acrylic laser cutting and fabrication*

K2 Catering Ltd, PO Box 49808, London, NW5 2YA Tel: (07970) 425285 Fax: (020) 7284 1325 E-mail: ian@k2catering.com *Specialists to construction side catering*

▶ K2 Communications & Structured Cabling Services, 1 Muirhall Road, Larbert, Stirlingshire, FK5 4RF Tel: (01786) 810801 Fax: (01786) 810802 E-mail: sales@k2comms.co.uk

K2 Glass Ltd, Sett End Road, Shadsworth Business Park, Blackburn, BB1 2PT Tel: (01254) 260040 Fax: (01254) 692389 E-mail: enquiry@k2glassltd.com *Glass units & double glazing manufrs*

K2 International Trading Ltd, The Kdo Business Park, Little Witley, Little Witley, Worcester, WR6 6LR Tel: (01299) 896959 Fax: (01299) 896965 E-mail: info@kdo.co.uk *Flexographic & label printing equipment manufrs*

K2 Kommunications, 37 Moulton Street, Manchester, M8 8FQ Tel: 0161-833 9952 Fax: 0161-833 9951 *Mobile telephone dealers*

K3 Business Technology Group, 1 Tavern Lane, Dereham, Norfolk, NR19 1PX Tel: (01362) 691999 Fax: (01362) 691710 *Computer software developers*

▶ K3 Secretarial Services, Blenheim Court, 17 Beulah Hill, London, SE19 3LJ Tel: (07786) 923079 Fax: (020) 8771 3651 E-mail: info@kzvirtualassistant.com *Bookkeeping, Secretarial Services, Word-processing, Spreadsheets,Invoicing, Sage line 50, Mail merges*

▶ K4 Contract Ltd, Tong Park, Baildon, Shipley, West Yorkshire, BD17 7QD Tel: (01274) 531617 Fax: (01274) 531718 E-mail: info@k4contracts.co.uk *Furniture manufrs*

▶ K8T Ltd, 8 Simmonds Buildings, Bristol Road, Bristol, BS16 1RY Tel: 0117-956 8477 E-mail: paulkingston@k8t.ltd.uk *Micro climate studies*Wind Studies*CFD*Thermography*Fluid flow *Heat transfer*Virtual Engineering**

K9 Euro Ltd, PO Box 133, Wigan, Lancashire, WN1 1AA Tel: 0151-548 4562 Fax: 0151-548 1918 E-mail: martinfarmer@k9euro.co.uk *Pest & vermin control services*

K9 Pet Foods, 44 Station Road, Framlingham, Woodbridge, Suffolk, IP13 9EE Tel: (01728) 621054 Fax: (01728) 621122 *Pet food wholesalers & retailers*

Kab Metal Works, Rospeath Industrial Estate, Crowlas, Penzance, Cornwall, TR20 8DU Tel: (01736) 740803 Fax: (01736) 740803 *Sheet metal workers*

Kab Seating Ltd, Stone Circle Road Round Spinney Indust Estate, Round Spinney Industrial Estat, Northampton, NN3 8RF Tel: (01604) 790500 Fax: (01604) 790155 E-mail: marketing@kabseating.com

KAB Seating Ltd, Round Spinney, Northampton, NN3 8RS Tel: (01604) 790500 Fax: (01604) 648176 E-mail: gailthompson@kabseating.com *Suspension seating manufrs*

Kaba Door Systems Ltd, Crow Arch La Industrial Estate, Crow Arch Lane, Ringwood, Hampshire, BH24 1PD Tel: (0870) 0005225 Fax: (0870) 0005226

Kaba Garog, 9 Eagle Park Drive, Warrington, WA2 8JA Tel: (01925) 401555 Fax: (01925) 401551 E-mail: sales@kgw.kaba.co.uk *Barrier distributors & automatic gates*

Kaba Hufcor Operable Partitions, Trent Lane, Castle Donington, Derby, DE74 2NP Tel: (0870) 0005250 Fax: (01332) 811059 E-mail: hufcoruk@dial.pipex.com *Partitioning constructors & manufrs*

▶ Kabam Computer Services, 248 Broadlands Drive, Lawrence Weston, Bristol, BS11 0PN Tel: (07876) 250434 E-mail: sales@kabam.co.uk *Computer maintenance, repairs, upgrades, virus removal, with no fix no fee, and no callout charge at very competitive rates!*

Kabel Electro Ltd, Saddleworth Business Centre, Huddersfield Road, Delph, Oldham, OL3 5DF Tel: (01457) 819800 Fax: (01457) 819801 E-mail: sales@kabelelectro.com *Cable distributors*

▶ Kabel Management Services Ltd, Georges Row, Dinas Powys, South Glamorgan, CF64 4LF Tel: (029) 2051 1099 Fax: (029) 2051 1098

Kabin Hire Ltd, Caerphilly Industrial Park, Van Road, Caerphilly, Mid Glamorgan, CF83 3EL Tel: (029) 2088 3079 Fax: (029) 2088 4518 E-mail: kabinhire@breathemail.net *Cabin hire & sale*

Kabooki (UK), Old Engine Shed, Westfield Road, Wells, Somerset, BA5 2HS Tel: (01749) 677044 Fax: (01749) 677055 *Children's wear agents*

▶ Kaboura Training, Business & Technology Centre, Bessemer Drive, Stevenage, Hertfordshire, SG1 2DX Tel: (01438) 310153 Fax: (01438) 310054 E-mail: sales@kabouratraining.co.uk *Kaboura Training specialises in designing and delivering challenging and innovative team building and training opportunities. Kaboura's services include unique community challenges, themed events,*

continued

*continuation residential experiences and a wide range of other team building and training activities. **With an extensive portfolio of activities and clients, Kaboura Training has established a strong reputation for providing high-quality team building events and services. Whatever the situation, whatever the brief, our friendly and dedicated team are here to ensure that we meet your training and event needs and provide you with a memorable and worthwhile experience. Please do contact us for further details and to find out how we can help.*

Kaby Engineers Ltd, 14-16 Upper Charnwood Street, Leicester, LE2 0AU Tel: 0116-253 6353 Fax: 0116-251 5237 E-mail: kb@kb.kaby.co.uk *Sub-contract machining*

Kaby Engineers Ltd, 14-16 Upper Charnwood Street, Leicester, LE2 0AU Tel: 0116-253 6353 Fax: 0116-251 5237 E-mail: kaby@kaby.co.uk *Precision & sub-contract engineers services*

Kac Alarm Co. Ltd, Kac House, Thorn Hill Road, Moons Moat North Industrial Es, Redditch, Worcestershire, B98 9ND Tel: (01527) 406655 Fax: (01527) 406677 E-mail: marketing@kac.co.uk *Manufacturers break glass call points*

George Kaccouris, 74 Aubert Pk, London, N5 1TS Tel: (020) 7704 1900 *Sewing machine industrial supply & repair*

Kadant UK Ltd, PO Box 6, Bury, Lancashire, BL8 1DF Tel: 0161-764 9111 Fax: 0161-797 1496 E-mail: sales@kadant.co.uk *Paper makers' engineers*

▶ Kadett Car, 7 Peacock Yard, Iliffe Street, London, SE17 3LH Tel: (020) 7701 5511 Fax: (020) 7701 5511

Kadocourt Ltd, The Gateway, Gatehouse Road, Aylesbury, Buckinghamshire, HP19 8ED Tel: (01296) 486192 Fax: (01296) 334655 E-mail: astron@kadocourt.co.uk *Book binding & finishing services*

▶ Kage Express Delivery, 24 Japonica Gardens, St. Helens, Merseyside, WA9 4WP Tel: (07841) 112210 E-mail: info@samedaynationwide.co.uk *Sameday nationwide delivery specialist courier service based in St.Helens, Merseyside.*

KAG-Kiln-formed Architectural Glass, The Post Office, Wick Road, Ewenny, Bridgend, Vale of Glamorgan, CF35 5BL Tel: (01656) 657744 Fax: (01656) 651061 E-mail: info@kag.uk.com *Kag-Kiln-formed Architectural Glass are based in Bridgend, South Wales covering the whole of the UK. KAG specialise in the design & manufacture of handmade, textured glass splashbacks, glass tiles, frameless shower screens, kiln formed architectural glass panels & textured glass kitchenware. Kag's unique kiln forming process produces a tactile, undulating, textured glass which refracts, reflects and magnifies the light, forming fascinating lighting effects at different viewing angles. The result of the process is a lively three dimensional illusion which appears to move with you. Products include balustrade, counter top, worktop, textured glass panel, partition, dividing wall, frameless textured glass door, door panel, floor tiles, lighting, decorative textured glass shelving, shower screen, signage, glass splashback, tabletop, glass tile, kitchenware, kitchen accessory, textured glass garden feature and many other glass products*

Kahn Displays Ltd, Unit 5-6 Eleys Estate, Angel Road, London, N18 3BH Tel: (020) 8803 0800 Fax: (020) 8803 0412 E-mail: kahn_displays@btconnect.com *PVC & pp ring binders, clip-boards & badge holders manufrs*

Kahrs, Unit 2 68 Bognor Road, Chichester, West Sussex, PO19 8NS Tel: (01243) 784417 Fax: (01243) 531237 E-mail: sales@kahrs.se *Parquet floor suppliers*

KAI Consulting, 7C Bayham Street, London, NW1 0EY Tel: (020) 7383 3700 E-mail: sales@kaiuk.co.uk *Computer consultants & specialist in film & TV industrial production management software & finance*

Kaid Ltd, 36B Sandbed Lane, Belper, Derbyshire, DE56 0SH Tel: (01773) 882461 Fax: (0870) 7062237 *Garage services*

Kaiku Ltd, Greenheys Business Centre, Pencroft Way, Manchester, M15 6JJ Tel: 0161-227 8900 Fax: 0161-227 8902 E-mail: sales@kaiku.co.uk *Instrumentation products & services*

Kail & Co. Ltd, 1 Castletown Road, Sunderland, SR5 3HT Tel: 0191-548 7712 Fax: 0191-549 6942 E-mail: sales@kai1.co.uk *Precision engineers*

▶ Kaill & Co Chimney Sweeping, 57 Oakhampton Road, Mill Hill, London, NW7 1NG Tel: (07910) 412751 E-mail: austen@akaill.wanadoo.co.uk *Services: *Comprehensive Chimney Sweeping Service and Maintenance including;*Smoke test for Solid Fuel & Gas Chimneys,*Diagnosis of Problem Flues,*Advice on Chimney Re-lining,*Removal of Vermin, Squirrels & Birds,*Issue of Chimney Sweeping Certificate,*Fully Insured & HETAS Approved.**

▶ Kair Ventilation, Unit 6, Chiltonian Industrial Estate, Manor Lane, London, SE12 0TX Tel: (0845) 1662240 Fax: (0845) 1662250 *Ventilation equipment & fitting services*

▶ Kai's Surprises, 5 Oliver Road, Bletchley, Milton Keynes, MK2 2SF Tel: (01908) 646008

Kaisertech, Unit 12, M3 Trade Park, Eastleigh, Hampshire, SO50 9YA Tel: (023) 8065 0065 Fax: (023) 8065 0060 E-mail: sales@kaisertech.co.uk *Suppliers & distributors of electronic production equipment*

▶ Kaizen Furniture Makers Ltd, Twelvetrees CR, London, E3 3JH Tel: (020) 7987 2777 Fax: (020) 7987 2077 *Furniture manufrs*

Kalamazoo Secure Solutions Ltd, Northfield, Birmingham, B31 2NY Tel: 0121-256 2222 Fax: 0121-256 2249 E-mail: kalamazoo@ksp.co.uk *Kalamazoo Secure Solutions is a leading supplier of secure print and secure solutions and bespoke business administration products to UK and oversears businesses. Core business solutions include security cheques, ticketing and visitor management solutions and staff ID systems.*

▶ Kalas Gemini Ltd, 17a Redstone Industrial Estate, Redstone Road, Boston, Lincolnshire, PE21 8EA Tel: (01205) 311185 Fax: (01205) 366069 *Printers*

John Kaldor Fabric Maker UK Ltd, Portland House, 4 Great Portland Street, London, W1W 8QJ Tel: (020) 7631 3557 Fax: (020) 7580 8628 E-mail: info@johnkaldor.co.uk *Fabric wholesalers & converters*

Kaleidoscope, 84 Parkwood Road, Bournemouth, BH5 2BL Tel: (01202) 431691 Fax: (01202) 429669 E-mail: sales@ksl-online.co.uk *Disco equipment distributors*

▶ Kalestead Ltd, Network House, Cressing Road, Braintree, Essex, CM7 3PG Tel: (01376) 349036 Fax: (01376) 348976 E-mail: sales@kalstead.co.uk *Manufactures cable*

Kalestead Ltd, Network House, 300-302 Cressing Road, Braintree, Essex, CM7 3PG Tel: (01376) 349036 Fax: (01376) 348976 E-mail: sales@kalestead.co.uk Principal Export Areas: Africa & North America *Electronic cable, temperature probe & cable assembly manufacturers.*

Kalfab Engineering, 25 Long Lane, Chapel-En-Le-Frith, High Peak, Derbyshire, SK23 0TF Tel: (01298) 816250 Fax: (01663) 733555 *Steel fabricators*

Kal-Gard UK Ltd, Canalwood Industrial Estate, Chirk, Wrexham, LL14 5RL Tel: (01691) 772070 Fax: (01691) 778303 E-mail: tony@kal-gard.co.uk *Manufacturers of functional surface coatings including: Corrosion preventative thin film coatings. Anti-galvanic corrosion coatings. Dry lubrication /low friction coatings based on molybdenum disulphide and PTFE. Non-stick (PTFE) coatings for domestic cookware and appliances. Non-stick /release coatings for bakery and food processing industries based on PTFE, PFA, FEP, silicone and other resins. Release coatings for the plastics, rubber, and packaging manufacturing industries. Conductive coatings and RFI /EMI shielding coatings for the electronics, electrical, automotive and aerospace industries. A fully comprehensive rangs of specialised coatings for the aerospace, defence, automotive, marine, electronics, and general light engineering industries.*

Kalico Products Ltd, Panty Buarth, Gwernaffield, Mold, Clwyd, CH7 5ER Tel: (01352) 742100 Fax: (01352) 742102 E-mail: info@kalico.co.uk *Commercial packaging manufrs*

▶ The Kaliko Group, Unit 3, Bowlers Yard, High Street, Earls Barton, Northampton, NN6 0JG Tel: (01604) 812040 Fax: (01564) 778012 E-mail: plm@kaltek.co.uk *Single ply membrane designers & suppliers.*

Kalimex Ltd, Unit 3, Plumpton Green Studios, St. Helena Lane, Plumpton Green, Lewes, East Sussex, BN7 3DQ Tel: (01273) 891162 Fax: (01273) 890704 E-mail: enquiries@kalimex.co.uk *Repair materials importers & distributors*

▶ Kall Kwik Ltd, 48 Clifton Road, Cambridge, CB1 7ED Tel: (01223) 502502 Fax: (01223) 508510

▶ Kall Kwik Printing, 252 Upper Richmond Road, London, SW15 6TQ Tel: (020) 8785 2299 Fax: (020) 8780 9261 E-mail: john@kkputney.co.uk *Kall Kwik Putney are specialists in providing a unique range of tailor made solutions for all print and design requirements.**

▶ Kall Kwik UK Ltd, 11 The Promenade, Gloucester Road, Bristol, BS7 8AL Tel: 0117-923 2036

▶ Kall Kwik UK Ltd, 1-2 Pegler Way, Crawley, West Sussex, RH11 7AG Tel: (01293) 611116 Fax: (01293) 611119

▶ Kall Kwik UK Ltd, 95 Golders Green Road, London, NW11 8EN Tel: (020) 8458 8771 Fax: (020) 8458 9665

▶ Kall Kwik UK Ltd, Sovereign House, 13-14 Queen Street, London, W1J 5PS Tel: (020) 7491 1973 Fax: (020) 7629 0316

▶ Kall Kwik UK Ltd, 358 Kings Road, London, SW3 5UZ Tel: (020) 7351 3133 Fax: (020) 7352 5858

Kall Kwik UK Ltd, Kall Kwik House, 106 Pembroke Road, Ruislip, Middlesex, HA4 8NW Tel: (0500) 872060 Fax: (01895) 872111 E-mail: info@kallkwik.co.uk *Holding company*

▶ Kall Kwik UK Ltd, Kingfisher Court, 201-203 Broadway, Salford, M50 2UE Tel: 0161-876 5111 Fax: 0161-876 5333

Kall Kwik UK Ltd, Heaton Mersey Industrial Estate, Battersea Road, Stockport, Cheshire, SK4 3EA Tel: 0161-486 1911 Fax: 0161-431 8069 E-mail: sales@kallkwik.uk.com *Window making machinery stockists*

▶ Kall Kwik UK Ltd, 71 High Street, Winchester, Hampshire, SO23 9DA Tel: (01962) 864900 Fax: (01962) 864649

▶ Kall Kwik UK Ltd, 29 Warwick Street, Worthing, West Sussex, BN11 3DQ Tel: (01903) 820400 Fax: (01903) 821432

Kalle UK Ltd, Perry Road, Industrial Estate East, Witham, Essex, CM8 3YY Tel: (01376) 531800 Fax: (01376) 518522 E-mail: sales@kalle.co.uk *Food packaging manufrs*

Kalmar Ltd, Siskin Drive, Middlemarch Business Park, Coventry, CV3 4FJ Tel: (024) 7683 4500 Fax: (024) 7683 4523 E-mail: sales@kalmarind.com *Truck importers & distributors*

Kalms Associates, 17 Lyon Road, London, SW19 2RL Tel: (020) 8286 6066 Fax: (020) 8547 7668 E-mail: sales@kalms-associates.com *Computer services, repairers & manufrs*

Kalon Pension Trustees Ltd, Huddersfield Road, Birstall, Batley, West Yorkshire, WF17 9XA Tel: (01924) 354000 Fax: (01924) 354001 E-mail: sales@kalon.co.uk *Paint*

Kaloric Heater Co. Ltd, 31 33 Beethoven Street, London, W10 4LJ Tel: (020) 8969 1367 Fax: (020) 8968 8913 E-mail: admin@kaloricheater.co.uk *Space heater manufrs*

Kalsep UK, Unit 2f Albany Park, Frimley Park, Camberley, Surrey, GU16 7PL Tel: (01276) 675675 Fax: (01276) 676276 E-mail: sales@kalsep.co.uk *Ultrafiltration & water treatment equipment manufrs*

Kalstan Engineering Ltd, Cavendish Road, Stevenage, Hertfordshire, SG1 2ET Tel: (01438) 745588 Fax: (01438) 360579 E-mail: sjkalmar@kalstanengineering.co.uk *CNC engineering services*

Kalvex Engineering Ltd, 4A Canal Estate, Station Road, Langley, Slough, SL3 6EG Tel: (01753) 548324 Fax: (01753) 549570 *Tube manipulation & bending manufrs*

Kalvin Tyre Co. Ltd, 259 High Road, Broxbourne, Hertfordshire, EN10 6PZ Tel: (01992) 462728 *Motor tyre distribs*

Kam Computers Ltd, 509 Finchley Road, London, NW3 7BB Tel: (020) 7431 1223 Fax: (020) 7431 3804 E-mail: sales@kamcomputers.co.uk *Computer consultants*

Kam Farming Ltd, Forston Farm, Forston, Dorchester, Dorset, DT2 7AB Tel: (01305) 257795 Fax: (01305) 889906 E-mail: kamfarming@aol.com *Contract farming*

Kamech Engineering Services, 7 4-6 Abingdon Road, Nuffield Industrial Estate, Poole, Dorset, BH17 0UG Tel: (01202) 669452 Fax: (01202) 669453 *Sub-contract machining services*

Kami Office Supplies, 620 Western Avenue, London, W3 0TE Tel: (020) 8896 9399 *Office equipment suppliers*

▶ Kamino Ltd, 3b Gatwick Metro Centre, Balcombe Road, Horley, Surrey, RH6 9GA Tel: (01293) 874444 Fax: (01293) 874454 *Freight management & logistics services*

Kammac plc, Gladden Place, Skelmersdale, Lancashire, WN8 9SY Tel: (01695) 727272 Fax: (01695) 720854 E-mail: info@kammac.com *Road transport, haulage & freight services*

▶ KaMo UK, I-Centre House, Hamilton Way, Oakham Business Park, Mansfield, Nottinghamshire, NG18 5BR Tel: (01623) 422006 Fax: (01623) 422003 E-mail: info@kamouk.com *Manufacturers of underfloor heating manifold systems*

Kamway Engineering Ltd, Fircroft Way, Edenbridge, Kent, TN8 6EN Tel: (01732) 862028 Fax: (01732) 866868 E-mail: enquires@kamway.co.uk *Subcontract precision engineers*

Kanbay Europe Ltd, Regus House, 1010 Cambourne Business Park, Cambourne, Cambridge, CB3 6DP Tel: (01223) 597836 Fax: (01223) 598062 *IT consultants*

Kandaprint Printers, 9 Oakley Hay Lodge, Great Fold Road, Corby, Northamptonshire, NN18 9AS Tel: (01536) 460890 Fax: (01536) 460890 E-mail: kandaprint@aol.com *Photocopying, frames, digital & lithographic printing services*

Kandel & Jacobs Ltd, Water Street, Northwich, Cheshire, CW9 5HP Tel: (01606) 43105 Fax: (01606) 40063 E-mail: kandel.jacobs@btopenworld.com *Ladies clothing manufrs*

Kandela Lighting Ltd, 200 Nottingham Road, Spondon, Derby, DE21 7NP Tel: (01332) 662793 Fax: (01332) 663525 E-mail: barry.kandela@gmail.com *manufacturers of fine silk lampshades , wire forms and powder coating*

▶ Kando Business Finance Ltd, 15 Mary Rose Close, Chafford Hundred, Grays, Essex, RM16 6LY Tel: (0870) 8034863 Fax: (0870) 8034867 E-mail: kbf@kandobusinessfinance.com *Finance broker*

Kandu Table Care, Sudden Mill, Manchester Road, Rochdale, Lancashire, OL11 4QR Tel: (01706) 868983 Fax: (01706) 868797 *Domestic furniture manufrs*

Kandys Patisserie, Unit 6-7, Clay Lane, Fishbourne, Chichester, West Sussex, PO18 8AH Tel: (01243) 575166 *Patisserie*

D. Kane Bacon, 493 Huddersfield Road, Oldham, OL4 2JG Tel: 0161-626 8464 Fax: 0161-626 4387 *Bacon & ham curers*

Kane Bros, 4 Divis Road, Hannahstown, Belfast, BT17 0NG Tel: (028) 9061 8235 Fax: (028) 9062 0067 *Shelving suppliers*

Kane Computing Ltd, 7 Theatre Court, London Road, Northwich, Cheshire, CW9 5HB Tel: (01606) 351006 Fax: (01606) 351007 E-mail: kane@kanecomputing.com *Image processing services* Also at: Northwich

Kane Engineering Ltd, Glenford Road, Newtownards, County Down, BT23 4AU Tel: (028) 9181 4465 Fax: (028) 9181 8900 E-mail: info@kane-engineering.co.uk *Electrical control panels manufrs*

Kane Group Ltd, Kane House, Swallowfield, Welwyn Garden City, Hertfordshire, AL7 1JG Tel: (01707) 375550 Fax: (01707) 393277 E-mail: sales@kane.co.uk *Energy management instrumentation manufrs*

▶ Kane Haulage Ltd, Construction House, Porters Wood, Valley Road Industrial Estate, St. Albans, Hertfordshire, AL3 6NW Tel: (01727) 733600 Fax: (01727) 733607 E-mail: info@kanehaulage.co.uk *Demolition, bulk earthworks, contract crushing, heavy plant hire & aggregate merchants*

Kane Mailing Systems Ltd, Glamorgan House, 47 Penallta Road, Ystrad Mynach, Hengoed, Mid Glamorgan, CF82 7AN Tel: (01443) 813588 Fax: (01443) 813587 E-mail: info@kanemailing.com *Mailing machine sales*

Sam Kane Ltd, 40 Howard Business Park, Howard Close, Waltham Abbey, Essex, EN9 1XE Tel: (01992) 712746 Fax: (01992) 700211 E-mail: helen@samkane.ltd.uk *Computer support services*

Kaneb Terminals Ltd, 3rd Floor Sierra House, St Marys Walk, Maidenhead, Berkshire, SL6 1QZ Tel: (01628) 687601 Fax: (01628) 771678 E-mail: mcloughlin@kneb.co.uk *Bulk liquid storage & distributors* Also at: Avonmouth, Belfast, Eastham, Glasgow, Grays, Leith, Runcorn, Sealsands & Wymondham

Kanection Computer Systems, 27... Stoke-on-Trent, ST3 5LQ Tel: (0... Fax: (01782) 595939 E-mail: male@kanection.co.uk *Co... development, maintenance & cons...*

Kanematsu Europe plc, Dashwood Ho... Broad Street, London, EC2M 1NS T... 7456 6300 Fax: (020) 7256 2850 *Ja... goods import & export agent*

Kaniko Computing, 23 Edward Road, Har... Middlesex, HA2 6QB Tel: (020) 8861 65... Fax: (020) 8861 6543 E-mail: kanikoc@a... *Software developers*

Kanor Chemicals, 12-14 Wharf Street, Warrin... WA1 2HT Tel: (01925) 639509 Fax: (01925) 445914 *Car wash chemicals*

Kansai Paint Europe Ltd, Wembley Point, 1 Har... Road, Wembley, Middlesex, HA9 6DE Tel: (02... 8900 5933 Fax: (020) 8900 5966 E-mail: info@kansaipaint.co.uk *Automotive & protective coatings*

Kanthal Ltd, Ruthvenfield Road, Inveralmond Industrial Estate, Perth, PH1 3ED Tel: (01738) 493300 Fax: (01738) 493301 E-mail: info.ukperth@sandvik.com *Industrial heating elements*

Kanthal Ltd, Canal Arm, Festival Way, Stoke-on-Trent, ST1 5UR Tel: (01782) 224800 Fax: (01782) 224820 E-mail: info.uk@kanthal.se *Heating element manufrs*

Kaotic Design, Unit 8, Priest Court, Springfield Business Park, Grantham, Lincolnshire, NG31 7BG Tel: (0870) 0633015 Fax: (0870) 0633017 E-mail: sales@kaoticdesigns.co.uk *Embroidery & printwear*

Kapok 1988 Ltd, Unit 13 Normanton Air Field, Long Bennington, Newark, Nottinghamshire, NG23 5FF Tel: (01949) 843020 Fax: (01949) 843719 E-mail: annable.kapok88@btclick.com *Protective lift drape manufrs*

Kappa Corby Corlon Packaging, Arnsley Road, Weldon North Industrial Estate, Corby, Northamptonshire, NN17 5QW Tel: (01536) 406784 Fax: (01536) 400320 E-mail: sales@kappa-corby.co.uk *Solidboard boxes, cases & container manufrs*

Kappa Corrugated UK, London Road, Purfleet, Essex, RM19 1QY Tel: (01708) 861776 Fax: (01708) 861910 *Solid fibre partition manufrs*

Kappa Corrugated UK Ltd, Knowl Street, Stalybridge, Cheshire, SK15 3AR Tel: 0161-338 3711 Fax: 0161-303 2647 *Corrugated container manufrs*

Kappa Lambda Squared Ltd, Erskine House, 53 London Road, Maidstone, Kent, ME16 8JH Tel: (01622) 670095 Fax: (01622) 200119 E-mail: sales@kl2.com *Computer software*

Kappa Paper Recycling, Private Road 2, Colwick Industrial Estate, Nottingham, NG4 2JR Tel: 0115-961 1753 Fax: 0115-940 0102 *Waste paper recycling*

Kappa SSK Ltd, Mount Street, Birmingham, B7 5RE Tel: 0121-327 1381 Fax: 0121-322 6300 E-mail: sales@sskpaper.co.uk *Recycled paper & corrugated case manufrs*

Kappler Europe Ltd, Unit 1 Crown Farm Way, Forest Town, Mansfield, Nottinghamshire, NG19 0FT Tel: (01623) 416200 Fax: (01623) 416250 E-mail: sales@kappler.com *Protective clothing manufrs*

▶ Kaptive Animation Studios, 73 Attlee Road, Walsall, WS2 0EX Tel: (01922) 867443 E-mail: kris@kaptive.co.uk *TV, film, video & print 3d animation & graphics*

Karachi Pine Ho, 161 Dickenson Rd, Manchester, M14 5HZ Tel: 0161-224 9444 Fax: 0161-225 1333 *Audio visual merchants*

Karaglow Ltd, 32 The Spires, Dromore, County Down, BT25 1QE Tel: (028) 9269 3641 *Motor vehicle repairers*

Kar-Aid, Barclays Bungalow, West Chiltington Lane, Coneyhurst, Billingshurst, West Sussex, RH14 9DN Tel: (01403) 783999 *Motor vehicle repair services*

Karakal U K, The Old Tanks, Penpole Lane, Bristol, BS11 0EA Tel: 0117-982 9057 Fax: 0117-982 9004 E-mail: sales@karakal.com *Sports warehouse*

Karalex Ltd, The Clock House 4 Russley Park Mews, Russley Park, Baydon, Marlborough, Wiltshire, SN8 2JY Tel: (01672) 540934 Fax: (01672) 540934 E-mail: tech@karalex.co.uk *Manufacturers Of Dehumidifiers*

Karaoke Direct, Starlaw Road, Bathgate, West Lothian, EH47 7BW Tel: (01506) 636107 Fax: (01506) 653730 E-mail: sales@karaokedirect.co.uk *Karaoke machine wholesalers*

Karcher UK, Lion court, Staunton Harold Hall, Melbourne Road, Staunton Harold, Ashby-de-la-Zouch, Leicestershire, LE65 1RT Tel: (01332) 695035 Fax: (01332) 695036 E-mail: enquiries@karcheruk.co.uk *Industrial & domestic cleaning equipment manufrs* Also at: Grays & Warrington

Kardex Systems UK Ltd, Kestrel House Falconry Court, Bakers Lane, Epping, Essex, CM16 5LL Tel: (0870) 2422224 Fax: (0870) 2400420 E-mail: moreinfo@kardex.co.uk *Office systems & industrial storage systems* Also at: Aberdeen, Birmingham, Edinburgh, Glasgow & Manchester

Kardex Sysytems, 26, Regency Park, Newtownards, County Down, BT23 8ZG Tel: (028) 9181 4242 Fax: (028) 9181 5599 *Storage (industrial)*

▶ Kardon Kontracts Ltd, 20 Birchwood Drive, Wilmslow, Cheshire, SK9 2RL Tel: (01625) 521101 E-mail: gmcgruer@kardonkontracts.com *Contract rental*

Kardwell Hobs Ltd, Sunrise House, Sunrise Business Park, Higher Shaftsbury Road, Blandford Forum, Dorset, DT11 8ST Tel: (01258) 452125 Fax: (01258) 486709 E-mail: hobbs.blandford@virgin.net *Wholesale stationers* Also at: Enfield

▶ Kare Orthopaedic Ltd, Gareloch Road, Port Glasgow, Renfrewshire, PA14 5XH Tel: (01475) 730020 Fax: (01475) 730040

Karen Parker Photography, 87 Wolverton Road, Stony Stratford, Milton Keynes, MK11 1EH Tel: (01908) 566366 E-mail: HeadMoose@PetStockBoys.com *Award winning photography-people, products & pets. Kodak Pets Photographer of the Year. Private studio with inhouse digital retouching*

▶ Karens Blinds, 38 Kenilworth Drive, Leicester, LE2 5LG Tel: 0116-271 7090 Fax: 0116-271 4086 E-mail: karen@karensblinds.co.uk *Suppliers & fitters of blinds*

Karib Kemi-Pharm Ltd, 63-65 Imperial Way, Croydon, CR0 4RR Tel: (020) 8688 5550 Fax: (020) 8688 6119 *Pharmaceutical generic manufrs*

Karim & Sons, 152 Bradford Road, Dewsbury, West Yorkshire, WF13 2HA Tel: (01924) 458131 *Knitwear manufrs*

Karimjee Jivanjee & Co UK Ltd, Hanging Sword House, 21 Whitefriars Street, London, EC4Y 8JJ Tel: (020) 7583 3768 Fax: (020) 7583 3916 E-mail: carol@karimjee.com *Import & export merchants*

Karimor Products UK Ltd, Phoebe La Mills, Halifax, West Yorkshire, HX3 9EX Tel: (01924) 830203 Fax: (01924) 848315 *Wire product manufrs*

Karl Construction Ltd, 92 Old Ballyrobin Road, Muckamore, Antrim, BT41 4TJ Tel: (028) 9442 5600 Fax: (028) 9442 5605 E-mail: sales@kar1.co.uk *Property development*

▶ Karl Fiala SBF Ltd, Levetts Barn, Bardfield Road, Thaxted, Dunmow, Essex, CM6 2LR Tel: (01371) 832002 Fax: (01371) 832005 E-mail: sales@karlfiala-sbf.com *Print & direct mail specialist*

▶ Karlan Digital Ltd, 76 Howdale Road, Hull, HU8 9JZ Tel: (07841) 870659 E-mail: enquiries@karlandigital.co.uk *Tide gauges, monitors, weather stations, data loggers, remote displays*

▶ Karlin Timber Frame, 9 Maple Way, Aycliffe Industrial Park, Newton Aycliffe, County Durham, DL5 6BF Tel: (0845) 3454277 Fax: (0845) 3454299 E-mail: info@karlintimberframe.co.uk *Design, manufacture & structural erection of timber frame buildings**

Karma, 26 Ysguthan Road, Port Talbot, West Glamorgan, SA12 6LY Tel: (01639) 896299 *Art material suppliers*

▶ Karma Times Limited, PO Box 9066, Chelmsford, CM3 8WU Tel: 07963 844171 E-mail: enquires@karma-times.co.uk *We offer a selection of items for the relief of physical and mental stress in gemstones, crystals, ceramics, jewellery, wood, hot packs, stress balls and wands. We look forward to healing from you soon.*

Karman Shipping Ltd, Timber Lodge, Plantation Road, Leighton Buzzard, Bedfordshire, LU7 3JB Tel: (01525) 851545 Fax: (01525) 850996 E-mail: sales@karmanshipping.com Principal Export Areas: Worldwide *Car shipping services*

Karnac (Books) Ltd, 6 Pembroke Buildings, London, NW10 6RE Tel: (020) 8969 4454 Fax: (020) 8969 5585 E-mail: shop@karnacbooks.com *Booksellers & publishers*

▶ Karraway Waste Paper Ltd, 1 Folly Close, Radlett, Hertfordshire, WD7 8DR Tel: (020) 8236 0108 Fax: (01753) 279301 E-mail: info@karraway.demon.co.uk

Karrimor Ltd, Petre Road, Clayton Le Moors, Accrington, Lancashire, BB5 5JZ Tel: (01254) 893000 Fax: (01254) 893100 E-mail: webmaster@karrimor.co.uk *Sports equipment manufrs*

▶ Karris Engineering, Stephenson Way, Thetford, Norfolk, IP24 3RE Tel: (01842) 755204 Fax: (01842) 755380 E-mail: karris@btconnect.com *Steel fabricators & machining*

Karrylite, PO Box 3, Markfield, Leicestershire, LE67 9ZR Tel: (01530) 817555 Fax: (01530) 244471 E-mail: karrylite@aol.com *Canine collectables & gifts distributors*

Karson 2002 Engineering Ltd, Tram Way, Oldbury Road, Smethwick, West Midlands, B66 1NR Tel: 0121-558 4852 Fax: 0121-558 4852 E-mail: sales@karson.co.uk *Press tool manufrs*

Kart Propulsion Co. Ltd, Bank Chambers, 70 Pier Road, Erith, Kent, DA8 1BA Tel: (01322) 346346 Fax: (01322) 347346 E-mail: info@kortpropulsion.com *Ducted propeller manufrs/suppliers of marine propulsion equipment*

Karters Joinery Ltd, 96 Vallentin Rd, London, E17 3JH Tel: 020 85217815 Fax: 020 85217815 *Window manufrs*

Karva Furniture, Widdrington, Morpeth, Northumberland, NE61 5DW Tel: (01670) 790325 Fax: (01670) 790325 *Furniture designers & manufrs*

▶ Kas Designs, 2 Langley Business Park, Station Road, Langley Mill, Nottingham, NG16 4DG Tel: (01773) 530444 Fax: (01773) 719600 E-mail: itskasdesign@aol.com *Contract upholstery suppliers*

▶ Kasdon Electronics, Unit 27 Strawberry La Industrial Estate, Strawberry Lane, Willenhall, West Midlands, WV13 3RS Tel: (01902) 606068 Fax: (01902) 606088 E-mail: sales@kasdon.co.uk *Suppliers PCB's of all technologies & volume requirements*

Kashif Export Company (International) Ltd, 2 Livesey Hill, Shenley Lodge, Milton Keynes, MK5 7EG Tel: (01908) 674758 Fax: (01908) 678139 E-mail: sales@kashifexport.co.uk *Renewable energy sugar plant specialists*

Kashket & Partners Ltd, 35 Hoxton Square, London, N1 6NN Tel: (020) 7739 3737 Fax: (020) 7729 0107 *Uniform clothing manufrs*

Kasmani Enterprises, Unit 6 43 Lancaster Street, Leicester, LE5 4GD Tel: 0116-274 2804 *Childrens clothing & baby wear manufrs*

Kason Corporation Europe, Unit 12-13 Parkhall Business Village, Parkhall Road, Stoke-on-Trent, ST3 5XA Tel: (01782) 597540 Fax: (01782) 597549 E-mail: sales@kasoneurope.co.uk *Manufacturer of vibratory, centrifugal and static sieving/screening/separation equipment. Fluid bed dryers and processing equipment for all industries*

Kason Hardware (UK) Ltd, Unit 3, Monmore Park Industrial Estate, Ettingshall Road, Wolverhampton, WV2 2LQ Tel: (01902) 409431 Fax: (01902) 353939 E-mail: kasonukltd@tiscali.co.uk *Refrigerator components suppliers*

Kaspersky Lab UK Ltd, Orwell Ho, Cowley Rd, Cambridge, CB4 0PP Tel: 01223 500450 Fax: 01223 470072 *Computer anti virus suppliers*

Kassero Edible Oils Ltd, 6-8 Albert Road, St. Philips, Bristol, BS2 0XA Tel: 0117-971 4331 Fax: 0117-972 4183 E-mail: sales@kassero.co.uk *Edible oil, fats & wholesalers*

Kassner Associated Publishers Ltd, 11 Wyfold Road, London, SW6 6SE Tel: (020) 7385 7700 Fax: (020) 7385 3402 E-mail: songs@kassner-music.co.uk *Music publishers*

Kastle Engineering Ltd, Longbeck Trading Estate, Marske By The Sea, Redcar, Cleveland, TS11 6HR Tel: (01642) 485506 Fax: (01642) 488601 E-mail: kastle10@btinternet.com *Steel manhole covers & frames*

▶ Kasway Ltd, 1 Conyers Avenue, Southport, Merseyside, PR8 4SZ Tel: 01704 551212 Fax: (01704) 551212 E-mail: mohammadi@kasway.co.uk *Providing consultancy services in relation to the Disability Discrimination Act and carrying out Disability Access Audit to ensure inclusivity of services.*Design and Architectural services and Project Management.*

▶ Katalyst Learning Ltd, Butterthwaite House, Jumble Lane, Ecclesfield, Sheffield, S35 9XJ Tel: 0114 257 6722 Fax: 0114 257 6733 E-mail: info@katalystlearning.co.uk *Supplier of learning resource materials from producers such as Video Arts, The BBC Worldwide, Fenman, Skills Boosters, Gower, etc. We have a free to use preview room and access to over 4000 training resource titles.**Katalyst are also a business support agency dedicated to supporting SME"s obtain expansion finance in the form of grants, soft loans, and invoice factoring.*

Katana Installations, 20 Muirfield Avenue, Swinton, Mexborough, South Yorkshire, S64 8SX Tel: (01709) 590678 Fax: (01709) 590678 *Security installers*

Kate Negus, Maidstone Road, Sidcup, Kent, DA14 5BG Tel: (020) 8302 3597 Fax: (020) 8309 5188 E-mail: sales@katenegus.com *Saddlery retail*

Kathglade Ltd, 20 Aston Road, Waterlooville, Hampshire, PO7 7XE Tel: (023) 9226 9777 Fax: (023) 9226 2190 *Precision engineeris & milling services*

Kathrina Fashions (Marketing) Ltd, 41-45 Little Donegall Street, Belfast, BT1 2JD Tel: (028) 9032 6963 Fax: (028) 9023 3427 E-mail: kathrina@tinyonline.co.uk *Blouse & skirt manufrs*

Katie Bard Executive Secretaries Ltd, Neville House, 14 Waterloo Street, Birmingham, B2 5TX Tel: 0121-633 4443 Fax: 0121-633 4746 E-mail: info@katiebardrecruitment.com *Employment agency*

Kato Entex Ltd, Glaisdale Dr East, Nottingham, NG8 4JY Tel: 0115-929 3931 Fax: 0115-929 5773 E-mail: springs@kato-entex.co.uk *Spring manufrs*

Katoll Metals & Industrial Products Ltd, Central Avenue, Cradley Heath, West Midlands, B64 7BY Tel: (01384) 634001 Fax: (01384) 410776 E-mail: sales@katollmetals.co.uk *Steel coil processing & shearing*

Katon Ingram Ltd, Vittlefields Industrial Estate, Forest Road, Newport, Isle of Wight, PO30 4LY Tel: (01983) 822180 Fax: (01983) 822181 E-mail: katoningram@aol.com *Electronic consultants or designers*

▶ Katrina's Cards, Unit 20 Century Business Centre, Century Park, Manvers, Rotherham, South Yorkshire, S63 5DA Tel: (01709) 300206 Fax: (01709) 300201 E-mail: contact@katrinascards.co.uk *Wedding stationery service*

Katron Engineering Precision Ltd, Park Mews Works, Lypiatt Street, Cheltenham, Gloucestershire, GL50 2UB Tel: (01242) 234040 Fax: (01242) 228224 E-mail: denman-groves@tiscali.co.uk *Precision engineers*

Katz & Co. (Folkestone) Ltd, 331-333 Cheriton Road, Folkestone, Kent, CT19 4BQ Tel: (01303) 271001 Fax: (01303) 279959 E-mail: sales@katzltd.com *Government surplus & camping equipment wholesaler*

▶ Kauerner Oilfield Products, Howe Mossavenue, Kirkhill Ind Estate Dyce, Aberdeen, AB21 0NZ Tel: (01224) 255000

Kautex Textron CVS Ltd, Dyffryn Business Park, Ystrad Mynach, Hengoed, Mid Glamorgan, CF82 7RJ Tel: (01443) 621800 Fax: (01443) 621940 Principal Export Areas: Worldwide *Automobile wash systems manufrs*

Kautex Unipart Ltd, Renown Avenue, Coventry, CV5 6UD Tel: (024) 7667 1100 Fax: (024) 7667 1101 *Plastic blown molding tanks*

▶ Kavado, 191, Randolph Avenue, London, W9 1DJ Tel: (020) 7604 4466

▶ Kavanagh, Bollin House, Bollin Walk, Wilmslow, Cheshire, SK9 1DP Tel: (01625) 543630 Fax: (01625) 538890 E-mail: info@kavanagh.co.uk *Computer systems consultants*

Kave Theatre Services, 15 Western Road, Hurstpierpoint, Hassocks, West Sussex, BN6 9SU Tel: (01273) 835880 Fax: (01273) 834141 E-mail: sales@kave.co.uk *Supply & install theatrical lighting, sound equipment, stage materials*

▶ Kaverner Oilfield Products, Howe Moss Avenue, Kirkhill Ind Est, Dyce, Aberdeen, AB21 0NA Tel: (01224) 255708

Kavia Mouldings Ltd, Unit 8, Balderstone Close, Heasandford Industrial Estate, Burnley, Lancashire, BB10 2BS Tel: (01282) 423935 Fax: (01282) 426105 E-mail: kavia.mouldingsltd@virgin.net *Thermoset & plastic injection moulders*

Kavlico Corporation, 11-15 Columbus Walk, Brigantine Place, Cardiff, CF10 4BZ Tel: (029) 2046 3449 Fax: (029) 2045 0852 E-mail: kavlico@btinternet.co.uk *Pressure & position sensor producers*

Kavo Dental Ltd, Corinium Industrial Estate, Raans Road, Amersham, Buckinghamshire, HP6 6JL Tel: (01494) 733000 Fax: (01494) 431168 E-mail: sales@kavo.com *Dental equipment manufrs* Also at: Bristol, Glasgow & Manchester

Kawasaki Motors UK, 1 Dukes Meadow, Millboard Road, Bourne End, Buckinghamshire, SL8 5XF Tel: (01628) 856750 Fax: (01628) 856796 E-mail: customerservice@kawasaki.co.uk *Sales & marketing company*

Kawasaki Precision Machinery UK Ltd, Ernesettle Lane, Plymouth, PL5 2SA Tel: (01752) 364394 Fax: (01752) 364816 E-mail: sales@kpm-uk.co.uk *Hydraulic pumps, motors & control valve suppliers*

Kawneer UK Ltd, Astmoor Industrial Estate, Runcorn, Cheshire, WA7 1QQ Tel: (01928) 502500 Fax: (01928) 502501 E-mail: sales@kawneereurope.com *Architectural aluminium systems.*

Kay Bangham Partnership, Birch House, 3 Myrtle Street, Bolton, BL1 3AH Tel: (01204) 362364 Fax: (01204) 363992 *Chartered quantity surveyors*

Kay Cee Blinds, 305 Whitmore Way, Basildon, Essex, SS14 2NW Tel: (01268) 293583 Fax: (01268) 293583 E-mail: kencarey@kayceeblinds.fsnet.co.uk *Blinds & awning installation*

Kay Dee Engineering Plastics Ltd, 2 Jubilee Court, Thackley Old Road, Shipley, West Yorkshire, BD18 1QF Tel: (01274) 590824 Fax: (01274) 531409 E-mail: info@kaylan.co.uk *Polyurethane elastomer products, sheet manufrs*

Kay Electrical Swansea Ltd, 345 Llangyfelach Road, Brynhyfryd, Swansea, SA5 9LQ Tel: (01792) 461753 Fax: (01792) 460470 E-mail: kay.electrical@virgin.net *Industrial electrical equipment distribs*

Kay Electronics & Materials, 52 Albany Park Road, Kingston Upon Thames, Surrey, KT2 5SU Tel: (020) 8546 3235 Fax: (020) 8549 5712 E-mail: jaqueline_babinet@hotmail.com *High precision metal tubes wires tapes manufrs*

▶ Kay Garage Doors, Unit 1, Phoenix Industrial Estate, Kerse Road, Stirling, FK7 7SG Tel: (01786) 474709 Fax: (01786) 451540 E-mail: info@kaygaragedoors.co.uk *We are a family run business and supply the best garage doors Scotland has to offer to builders, local authorities, private householders and shop owners within a 60 mile radius.**Our friendly and personal service ensures you get outstanding quality at very affordable prices. Get your ideal garage doors in Scotland ordered on time, fitted to very high standards and receive local after service care every year.**Whatever your needs, you can buy new garage doors for your home or business.**

▶ Kay Jay Print Ltd, Park Road, Cross Hills, Keighley, West Yorkshire, BD20 8AB Tel: (01535) 632921 Fax: (01535) 636155 E-mail: sales@kjprint.co.uk

Kay Metzeler Ltd, Wellington Road, Bollington, Macclesfield, Cheshire, SK10 5JJ Tel: (01625) 573366 Fax: (01625) 574075 E-mail: info@kay-metzeler.co.uk *Polyurethane foam manufrs* Also at: Alperton

▶ Kay (Newton Mearns) Ltd, 55 Barrhead Road, Newton Mearns, Glasgow, G77 6BB Tel: 0141-639 2462

Kay Oneill Ltd, Unit 6, Horton Road, Colnbrook, Slough, SL3 0AT Tel: (01753) 684606 Fax: (01753) 682241 E-mail: lhr@kayoneill.com *International freight & logistics services*

Kay & Stemmer, Stamford Works, Gillett Street, London, N16 8JH Tel: (020) 7503 2105 Fax: (020) 7275 7495 *Furniture design & manufrs*

Stephen Kay Printers, 236 Park Lane, Poynton, Stockport, Cheshire, SK12 1RQ Tel: (01625) 876229 Fax: (01625) 858399 *Commercial printing service*

Kay Trailers, 27 Stirling Road, Milnathort, Kinross, KY13 9XS Tel: (01577) 862493 Fax: (01577) 864864 E-mail: dropbox@kaytrailers.co.uk *Agricultural trailer manufrs*

▶ Kayani Systems Consultancy Ltd, 6 Ladbrooke Road, Slough, SL1 2SR Tel: (01753) 550888 Fax: (01753) 550333 *IT Consultants*

Kaybee Door Sales Ltd, 52-60 St. Anne Street, Liverpool, L3 3DX Tel: 0151-207 2131 Fax: 0151-298 1004 E-mail: sales@kaybeedoors.co.uk *Door manufacturers & distributors*

Kaybee Engineering, Station Street, Bromsgrove, Worcestershire, B60 2BS Tel: (01527) 870845 Fax: (01527) 870845 E-mail: andy.knight@kpe.demon.co.uk *Small press tools & pressworkers*

Kaybee Pneumatics, 6 Shaw Drive, Burntwood, Staffordshire, WS7 2JE Tel: (01543) 675309 Fax: (01543) 677743 *Hydraulic & pneumatic equipment suppliers*

▶ Kaybridge Construction Barnet Ltd, 24 Cecil Road, Enfield, Middlesex, EN2 6TG Tel: (020) 8366 3361 Fax: (020) 8363 1128 E-mail: enquiries@kaybridge.com *Groundwork services*

Kaycee Veterinary Products, Unit 14 Lindfield Enterprise Park, Lewes Road, Lindfield, Haywards Heath, West Sussex, RH16 2LH Tel: (01444) 482888 Fax: (01444) 483383 E-mail: tds@kaycee.co.uk *Livestock vaccinators suppliers*

Kaydee Web Design, 2 Meadow Close, Shipton-under-Wychwood, Chipping Norton, Oxfordshire, OX7 6BY Tel: 07769 970021 Fax: 01993 831072 E-mail: design@kaydee.net *Internet solutions to help you through the process of getting on the net, from reserving & hosting a domain name, web design & promoting your finished site on the web.*

Kaye Instruments, Unit 1 Apollo House, Calleva Park, Aldermaston, Reading, RG7 8TN Tel: 0118-981 7100 Fax: 0118-981 7102 *Computer support*

Kaye Presteigne, Harper Lane, Presteigne, Powys, LD8 2AH Tel: (01544) 267551 Fax: (01544) 267032E-mail: reception@kayepresteigne.co.uk *High pressure aluminium die casting*

Kaye & Stewart, Rashcliffe Mills, Albert Street, Lockwood, Huddersfield, HD1 3PE Tel: (01484) 423231 Fax: (01484) 435313 E-mail: headoffice@taylor-and-lodge.co.uk *Worsted cloth manufrs*

Kayel Engineering Ltd, Guildford Road, Broadbridge Heath, Horsham, West Sussex, RH12 3JR Tel: (01403) 261026 Fax: (01403) 217340 E-mail: kayel@talk21.com *Manufrs of stillage equipment for brewing industry*

▶ Kayes & Co Electrical Contractors Ltd, 355 Bank Street, Coatbridge, Lanarkshire, ML5 1EJ Tel: (01236) 440882

Kayfern Tools, Manchester Road, Mossley, Ashton-under-Lyne, Lancashire, OL5 9AT Tel: (01457) 832747 Fax: (01457) 832747 *Precision engineers & engineering subcontractors*

Kayfoam Ltd, Unit 3A Pegasis Business Park, Cameron Street, Hillington, Glasgow, G52 4TY Tel: 0141-810 4333 Fax: 0141-810 1424 *Manufrs of foam for packing industries*

Kayfoam Woolson, Unit 4B, Newline Industrial Estate, Bacup, Lancashire, OL13 9RW Tel: (01706) 875075 Fax: (01706) 872505 E-mail: kaywool@kayfoam.co.uk *Bed distribs*

Kaygee Engineering, 55 Great Union Street, Hull, HU9 1AG Tel: (01482) 326281 Fax: (01482) 219240 E-mail: info@kaygee.co.uk *General engineers*

Kayjay Hairdressers' Equipment, 6 Old Hall Industrial Estate, Revival Street, Walsall, WS3 3HJ Tel: (01922) 400001 Fax: (01922) 400001 *Wholesale hairdressing suppliers*

Kaylee Transfers Ltd, New Tythe Street, Long Eaton, Nottingham, NG10 2DP Tel: 0115-973 5247 Fax: 0115-946 0801 E-mail: sales@kayleetransfers.uk *Transfers, label manufacturers & screen printers & digital manufrs*

Bernard Kaymar Ltd, Kaymar Industrial Estate, Trout Street, Preston, PR1 4DL Tel: (01772) 562211 Fax: (01772) 257813 E-mail: sales@bernard-kaymar.co.uk *Printing services*

Kay-Metzeler Ltd, Brook Street, Chelmsford, CM1 1UQ Tel: (01245) 342100 Fax: (01245) 342123 E-mail: epssales@kay-metzeler.co.uk *Expanded polystyrene products manufrs*

Kaypul Optics Ltd, Unit 4 West Docks, Harbour Place, Burntisland, Fife, KY3 9DW Tel: (01592) 874140 Fax: (01592) 874140 E-mail: kaypulltd@aol.com *Manufacturer of optical substrates from glass & crystal materials - e.g. filters, windows & mirrors etc*

Kays Electronics Ltd, 85 Cavendish Street, Ipswich, IP3 8AX Tel: (01473) 214040 Fax: (01473) 214060 E-mail: enquiries@kayselectronics.com *Technical liaison consultant*

Kays Electronics of Chesterfield, 195 Sheffield Road, Chesterfield, Derbyshire, S41 7JQ Tel: (01246) 205361 E-mail: jk@kayselectronics.co.uk *Sound & lighting equipment installers, consultants & suppliers*

Kays Medical, 3-7 Shaw Street, Liverpool, L6 1HH Tel: 0151-482 2830 Fax: 0151-207 3384 E-mail: kays@kaysmedical.com *Stainless steel flanges*

Kays Ramsbottom Ltd, Britannia Works, Kenyon Street, Ramsbottom, Bury, Lancashire, BL0 0AE Tel: (01706) 824010 Fax: (01706) 828615 E-mail: sales@kays-soap.com *Soap manufrs*

Kays Of Scotland, 9 Barskimming Road, Mauchline, Ayrshire, KA5 5AJ Tel: (01290) 550256 Fax: (01290) 552438 E-mail: sales@kaysofscotland.co.uk *Curling stones & granite manufrs*

Kayson Green Ltd, 9 Commerce Park, Commerce Way, Colchester, CO2 8HX Tel: (01206) 751500 Fax: (01206) 791916 E-mail: abrasives@kaysongreen.co.uk *Bonded & coated abrasive product distributors*

Kaytu Systems Ltd, 6A & 6B Throckley Way, Middlefields Industrial Estate, South Shields, Tyne & Wear, NE34 0NU Tel: 0191-456 2046 Fax: 0191-456 1971 E-mail: kaytusystems@kaytu-systems.co.uk *General engineers*

▶ Kaywood Cabinet Makers, Unit 2b Westthorpe Fields Road, Killamarsh, Sheffield, S21 1TZ Tel: 0114-247 7700 Fax: 0114-247 7700 E-mail: kaywoodsfurniture@hotmail.com *Cabinet manufrs*

▶ Kaz Training, 575, Charminster Road, Bournemouth, BH8 9RG Tel: (01202) 515553

Kazzbar - The Moroccan Experience, Unit 3a, Hamlyn House, Mardle Way, Buckfastleigh, Devon, TQ11 0NS Tel: (0800) 2888624 Fax: (0871) 7334251 E-mail: sales@kazzbar.co.uk *Importers of Moroccan furniture and design-led accessories for both indoors & out.**We stock a huge range of Moroccan items: for outdoors, wrought iron tables and chairs, terracotta garden pots, copper basins & mosaic fountains; for indoors ceramics from Safi, wrought iron screens, pouffes, henne candles, Moroccan leather boho belts and bags, Moroccan kilims and rugs, leather slippers and shoes, lanterns, teapots, glasses and more. Wholesale and retail.*

KB Fabrications (Dewsbury) Ltd, Ravenswharfe Road, Dewsbury, West Yorkshire, WF13 3RD Tel: (01924) 438803 Fax: (01924) 438803 *Sheet metal work manufrs*

KBC Process Technology Ltd, 42-50 Hersham Road, Walton-on-Thames, Surrey, KT12 1RZ Tel: (01932) 242424 Fax: (01932) 224214 E-mail: info@kbcat.com *Process engineering consultancy providing specialised consultancy & support services to oil refineries*

▶ KBC Wood Floors Ltd, 135 Banbury Road, Brackley, Northamptonshire, NN13 6AX Tel: (01280) 700305 Fax: (01280) 700305 E-mail: kev@kbcwoodfloors.com *Supply & installation of wood floors*

KBR, Wellheads Place, Wellheads Industrial Estate, Aberdeen, AB21 7GB Tel: (01224) 777000 Fax: (01224) 777710

KBR, Hill Park Court, Springfield Drive, Leatherhead, Surrey, KT22 7NL Tel: (01372) 865000 Fax: (01372) 864400 *Consulting engineers & designers*

▶ KC Instrument Repairs, The Chapel, Lord Street, Crawshawbooth, Rossendale, Lancashire, BB4 8AD Tel: (01706) 230050 Fax: (01706) 229158 E-mail: kencurry@kcir.co.uk *Service & repair to all types of mechanical measuring equipment*

KCC Global, Global House, Adlington Indust Estate, Prestbury, Macclesfield, Cheshire, SK10 4BF Tel: (01625) 874111 Fax: (0845) 3459006 E-mail: enquiries@kccglobal.co.uk *Telecommunications consultants*

KCG Services Ltd, Neptune Close, Medway City Estate, Rochester, Kent, ME2 4LT Tel: (01634) 294787 Fax: (01634) 714111 *Metal fabricators*

KCG-Electronics Ltd, 15 LAGONDA DRIVE, IPSWICH, IP1 5QE Tel: (01473) 435346 Fax: (01473) 435346 E-mail: admin@kcg-electronics.com *MARINE INDUSTRIAL OFFSHORE KCG Electronics has been involved in control/monitoring systems and the supply of LV/MV switchgear since 1984. We have supplied components and systems to many major UK and European customers including defence industry clients. The company has gradually expanded its product range to include battery charging and optical products such as endoscopes for medical, law enforcement and inspection applications*

▶ Kcp.Co.Uk, 159 Heathhall Industrial Estate, Heathhall, Dumfries, DG1 3PH Tel: (01387) 256532 Fax: (01387) 256532

▶ KCR Transport & Removals, 447 Burton Road, Midway, Swadlincote, Derbyshire, DE11 7NB Tel: (0800) 4488839 Fax: 01283 211934 E-mail: kevin@kcrtransport.co.uk *Light haulage / courier service, domestic and commercial, deliveries, collections, light removals, any where any time, fully insured, visit our website for a quote online.*

KCS Herr-Voss UK Ltd, Glassworks House, Park Lane, Halesowen, West Midlands, B63 2QS Tel: (01384) 568114 Fax: (01384) 568115 E-mail: ukdrawingoffice@kcsherrvossuk.com *Coil processors*

KD Engraving, 37 Boston Road, Leicester, LE4 1AW Tel: 0116-234 0131 Fax: 0116-234 0131 *Engravers & screen printers*

Kddi, Atlas House, 1-7 King Street, London, EC2V 8AU Tel: (020) 7397 1111 Fax: (020) 7600 3088 *Telecommunications systems design*

KDG Instruments, Crompton Way, Crawley, West Sussex, RH10 9YZ Tel: (01293) 525151 Fax: (01293) 533095 E-mail: sales@mobrey.com Principal Export Areas: Worldwide *Pressure & flow measurement*

▶ KDH Construction, KDH House, Millfield Road, Donington, Spalding, Lincolnshire, PE11 4UR Tel: 01775 822888 Fax: 01775 822891 E-mail: sales@kdhconstruction.co.uk *We are a growing group of companies specialising in providing the needs large or small of the food industry-Construction, Project Management, Electrical & Mechanical and Refrigeration.* We have a quality team of people well known in the food industry and only carryout projects within the food Industry.*

KDM Events Ltd, Crowcrofts Road, Barlaston, Stoke-on-Trent, ST12 9BA Tel: (01782) 646300 Fax: (01782) 646060 E-mail: info@kdmevents.co.uk *Event organisers*

KDM International plc, The Havens, Ransomes Europark, Ipswich, IP3 9SJ Tel: (01473) 276900 Fax: (01473) 276911 E-mail: sales@kdm.co.uk *Forest products importers & exporters*

KDS Appliances Ltd, 33-35 Beehive Lane, Ilford, Essex, IG1 3RG Tel: (020) 8518 1988 *Domestic appliances*

Kea Flex Mouldings Ltd, Woolmer Way, Bordon, Hampshire, GU35 9QE Tel: (01420) 473645 Fax: (01420) 487498 E-mail: sales@kea-flex-mouldings.co.uk *Rubber bonded products manufrs*

▶ Keane Computer Services, 50 Kenmore Crescent, Coalville, Leicestershire, LE67 4RQ Tel: (01530) 451663 E-mail: mark@keaneservices.com *Keane Computer Services provides all aspects of computer related services, including upgrades, repairs, new and refurbished computer sales, service, training and support. **Based in Coalville in the Heart of the National Forest, we operate throughout Leicestershire, Derbyshire, Nottinghamshire and the Midlands. **A fast, friendly, professional service is always assured!*

▶ Keane Construction, 1 Springfield, Oxted, Surrey, RH8 9JL Tel: (01883) 722992 Fax: (01883) 722664

Keanes Ltd, 4 Iverson Road, London, NW6 2HT Tel: (020) 7625 5555 Fax: (020) 7624 8444 E-mail: office@ballyholmeps.bangor.ni.sch.uk *Suppliers of building materials*

▶ Kearns & Co. Ltd, 8 Hamilton Road, St. Albans, Hertfordshire, AL1 4PZ Tel: (01727) 865981

▶ Kearse & Boys, 2 Caberston Road, Walkerburn, Peeblesshire, EH43 6AU Tel: (01896) 870441 Fax: (01896) 870441 E-mail: info@kearse-boys.com *Scottish Designer Knitwear - Based in the Scottish Borders, Kearse & Boys produce a collection of Designer Knitwear. We employ traditional craft skills including,machine knitting,embroidery,crochet, weaving and our own unique felting process producing an unmistakably Scottish but also elegant and fashionable look. Jackets,cardigans,tunics, sweaters & accessories are individually knitted in lambswool,Shetland,Boucle and Donegal yarns in vibrant colours as well as soft countryside shades.They are finished with hand dyed Boucle"s and subbed wools to create their own special look.The designs by Virginia Kearse evolve season to season and are sold worldwide to various outlets.*

Kearsley Airways Ltd, Romeera House, London Stansted Airport, Stansted, Essex, CM24 1QL Tel: (01279) 871000 Fax: (01279) 871187 E-mail: sales@kalair.co.uk *Aircraft component repair & overhaul services*

Kearsley Airways Holdings Ltd, 8 Temple Gardens, London, NW11 0LL Tel: (020) 8458 7299 Fax: (020) 8458 9945 E-mail: mehta@kalair.co.uk *Aeronautical engineers*

Keating Gravure Systems (U K) Ltd, Unit 4, Bromfield Industrial Estate, Mold, Clwyd, CH7 1HE Tel: (01352) 755800 Fax: (01352) 756757 *Gravure engravers* Also at: Bristol

▶ Keating & King, Unit 13-14, The Bridge, Narberth, Dyfed, SA67 8QZ Tel: (01834) 861676 Fax: (01834) 861858 E-mail: keatingjoinery@aol.com *Joinery & staircase manufrs*

Thomas Keating Ltd, Station Mills, Daux Road, Billingshurst, West Sussex, RH14 9SH Tel: (01403) 782045 Fax: (01403) 785464 E-mail: m.clack@terahertz.co.uk *Precision press tool manufrs*

John Keatley (Metals) Ltd, 33-35 Shadwell Street, Birmingham, B4 6HD Tel: 0121-236 4300 Fax: 0121-236 8576 E-mail: lynley@johnkeatleymetals.com *Non-ferrous metal stockholders*

C. Keay Ltd, 21 Leopold Street, Birmingham, B12 0UP Tel: 0121-440 1894 Fax: 0121-440 2500 *Scrap metal merchants*

Keble Light Ltd, Bourton Industrial Park, Bourton-on-the-Water, Cheltenham, Gloucestershire, GL54 2HQ Tel: (01451) 822442 Fax: (01451) 822412 E-mail: keblelight.export@virgin.net *Sanitoryware & plumbing exporters*

Kebrell Nuts & Bolts Ltd, Imperial Works, Lockfield Avenue, Enfield, Middlesex, EN3 7PY Tel: (020) 8805 8510 Fax: (020) 8805 1553 E-mail: kebrell@montal-internet.co.uk *Nut & bolt & nut distributors/agents/stockholders. Also fastener (industrial) manufrs.* Also at: Bolton, Bristol, Coventry, Thetford & Wednesbury

Kec Ltd, Orpheus House, Calleva Park, Aldermaston, Reading, RG7 8TA Tel: 0118-981 1571 Fax: 0118-981 1570 E-mail: sales@kec.co.uk *Connectors & cable assembly manufrs*

Kecol Pumps Ltd, Faraday Drive, Bridgnorth, Shropshire, WV15 5BJ Tel: (01746) 764311 Fax: (01746) 764780 E-mail: sales@kecol.co.uk *Manufacturers & distributors of pumps & spare parts*

▶ Keda Plumbing Co. Ltd, 912A Bury Road, Bolton, BL2 6NX Tel: (01204) 414545

Keddie Saucemasters Ltd, Prince of Wales Industrial Estate, Abercarn, Newport, Gwent, NP11 5AR Tel: (01495) 244721 Fax: (01495) 244626 *Sauce, pickle & condiment manufrs*

Kedon Industrial Supplies, Oaklands Farm Industrial Estate, Goatsmoor Lane, Stock, Ingatestone, Essex, CM4 9RS Tel: (01277) 636346 Fax: (01277) 636356 E-mail: enquiries@kedonengravers.com *Facia panel manufrs*

Kee Engineering, Unit 14a Miller Business Park, Station Road, Liskeard, Cornwall, PL14 4DA Tel: (01579) 344285 Fax: (01579) 348635 E-mail: chris@kee.co.uk *Press machines & sheet metalworking manufrs*

▶ Kee Engineering Services Ltd, Limehurst Works, 3 Oaken Street, Ashton-under-Lyne, Lancashire, OL7 9PB Tel: 0161-343 7133 Fax: 0161-343 7311 *Manufacture recycling frames*

Kee Systems Ltd, 11 Thornsett Road, London, SW18 4EW Tel: (020) 8874 6566 Fax: (020) 8874 5726 E-mail: sales@keesystems.com *Tube & fittings merchants*

Kee Valves, The Old School, Outclough Road, Brindley Ford, Stoke-on-Trent, ST8 7QD Tel: (01782) 523388 Fax: (01782) 523399 E-mail: sales@keevalves.co.uk *Valve distributors of ball, butterfly, check, control & knife*

▶ Keeble Bros, Eastern Industrial Estate, Bancrofts Road, South Woodham Ferrers, Chelmsford, CM3 5UG Tel: (01245) 321930 Fax: (01245) 321930 *General engineers*

Keeble Heating & Air Conditioning, 41 Rectory Grove, Wickford, Essex, SS11 8ER Tel: (01268) 735830 Fax: (01268) 735973 Principal Export Areas: Central/East Europe *Air conditioners specialists*

Keeble Paper Recycling Ltd, Paper Recycling Centre, Ferry Lane, Rainham, Essex, RM13 9DB Tel: (01708) 528000 Fax: (01708) 521991 E-mail: recycle@kpr.co.uk *Waste paper recycling collecting & processing*

Keegal Engineering Ltd, The Link Centre, Unit G Oldmixon CR, Weston-super-Mare, Avon, BS24 9AY Tel: (01934) 419659 Fax: (01934) 641185 E-mail: peter@keegal.co.uk *General engineers*

▶ Keela (International) Ltd, 53 Nasmyth Road, Glenrothes, Fife, KY6 2SD Tel: (01592) 771241

Keeler Ltd, Clewer Green Works, Clewer Hill Road, Windsor, Berkshire, SL4 4AA Tel: (01753) 857177 Fax: (01753) 830247 E-mail: info@keeler.co.uk *Medical instrument manufrs*

Keeley & Lowe Ltd, 38 The Oval, London, E2 9DT Tel: (020) 7729 3350 Fax: (020) 7739 5654 E-mail: keeleylowe@btconnect.co.uk *Commercial printers & stationers*

Keeling & Walker Ltd, Whieldon Road, Stoke-on-Trent, ST4 4JA Tel: (01782) 744136 Fax: (01782) 744126 E-mail: sales@keelingwalker.co.uk *Tin oxide manufrs*

▶ Keelsupply Plaster Suppliers, 1 Tomlinson Business Park, Tomlinson Road, Leyland, PR25 2DY Tel: (01772) 641495 Fax: (01772) 641844 *Plasters*

Keely Machinery Ltd, Unit 11 Ronald Close, Woburn Road Industrial Estate, Kempston, Bedford, MK42 7SH Tel: (01234) 857744 Fax: (01234) 854219 E-mail: sales@keelymachinery.co.uk Principal Export Areas: Worldwide *Machinery hiring company*

▶ Keemac Bakery, 2 Block 5, Whiteside Industrial Estate, Bathgate, West Lothian, EH48 2RX Tel: (01506) 655303 Fax: (01506) 655303 *Wholesale bakers*

▶ Keemlaw Ltd, Super Abbey Estate, Beddow Way, Aylesford, Kent, ME20 7BH Tel: (01732) 870078 Fax: (01732) 870068 E-mail: info@keemlaw.co.uk *Supply, manufacture & service catering equipment*

▶ Keemlaw Catering, 755 London Road, Larkfield, Aylesford, Kent, ME20 6DE Tel: (01732) 522419 Fax: (01622) 790348 E-mail: info@keemlaw.co.uk

Keen IT Solutions Limited, 79 Ansell Road, Frimley, Camberley, Surrey, GU16 8DH Tel: 0845 0940320 E-mail: info@keenit.co.uk *Keen IT Solutions specialises in providing onsite IT Support and Consultation services to all types of Home and Business users.**We are based in Camberley and provide our services to the surrounding areas including Surrey, Berkshire, Hampshire, Sussex and London.* * *

Phillip W. Keen Ltd, 284 High Road, Northweld, Epping, Essex, CM16 6EG Tel: (01992) 524824 Fax: (01992) 524239 *Ballast merchants* Also at: Ongar

▶ Keen Photo Supplies Ltd, Keen House Fleckney Road, Kibworth, Leicester, LE8 0HJ Tel: (01858) 431122 Fax: 0116-279 1275 E-mail: gary@keenphoto.co.uk *Specialists in the supply of plastic ID card systems and consumables. Best prices on all identification accessories including custom printed Lanyards and card holders.*

Keen World Marketing Ltd, 1 Northbrook Street, Newbury, Berkshire, RG14 1DJ Tel: (01635) 34600 Fax: (01635) 33360 E-mail: info@keen-newport.com *Exports aerosol products & smokers requisites*

Keenan Research Ltd, Victoria House, 15 Gay Street, Bath, BA1 2PH Tel: (01225) 336569 Fax: (01225) 442685 E-mail: kmkeenan@keenan-research.com *Occupational health and safety including managing stress related illness, violence, alcohol, drug and substance abuse training, workplace stress management coaching and help tackling stress at work to help with reducing absence and sickness.**

Keenans Steel Fabricators, 197-199 Highland Road, Southsea, Hampshire, PO4 9EZ Tel: (023) 9282 6841 Fax: (023) 9285 1401 *Steel fabricators & stockholders*

Keene Printing Co. Ltd, 33-41 Dallington St, London, EC1V 0BB Tel: (020) 7251 2722 Fax: (020) 7490 8736 E-mail: info@keenes.co.uk *Printers & colour printing services* Also at: Andover

Keenedge Ltd, Unit 7 Summerlands Industrial Estate, Endmoor, Kendal, Cumbria, LA8 0FB Tel: (01539) 561800 Fax: (01539) 561799 E-mail: info@cutting.co.uk *Textile slitting contract services*

Keenpac Ltd, Centurion Way, Meridian Business Park, Leicester, LE19 1WH Tel: 0116-289 0900 Fax: 0116-289 3757 E-mail: info@keenpac.co.uk *Paper & polythene carrier bag manufrs*

Keens Guns, 117 Bridgend Road, Aberkenfig, Bridgend, Mid Glamorgan, CF32 9AP Tel: (01656) 720807 Fax: (01656) 724889 E-mail: sales@keenstackleandguns.co.uk *Fishing tackle & guns retailers*

Keep Clean Drain Services, E2-E3 Unit, Jaggard Way, London, SW12 8SG Tel: (020) 8772 9388 Fax: (020) 8772 9389 E-mail: sales@kcdrains.co.uk *Drain cleaning contractors*

John T. Keep & Sons Ltd, PO Box 78, Beckenham, Kent, BR3 4BL Tel: (020) 8658 2299 Fax: (020) 8658 8672 E-mail: sales@bollom.com Purchasing Contact: E.E. Hartley Sales Contact: E.E. Hartley Principal Export Areas: Africa *Manufacturers of screen printing ink*

Keep Keen Controls Ltd, 8 Churchfield Croft, Rothwell, Leeds, LS26 0RX Tel: 0113-282 5387 Fax: 0113-288 0695 E-mail: john@keepkeen.co.uk *Heating control systems manufrs*

▶ Keep Me Promotions, 2 New Concordia Wharf, Mill Street, London, SE1 2BB Tel: (020) 7231 0001 Fax: (0870) 7605511 E-mail: steve@keepmepromotions.com *Leader in promotional merchandise and custom printed bags.**

Keeping Storage Systems, Beaufoys Avenue, Ferndown, Dorset, BH22 9RJ Tel: (01202) 894122 Fax: (01202) 891642 *Storage installers*

Keetch Factors 1984 Ltd, Alexandra Road, Mablethorpe, Lincolnshire, LN12 1BJ Tel: (01507) 477177 Fax: (01507) 473878 E-mail: keetchfactors@aol.com *Lighting & electrical wholesalers*

Keeton,Sons & Co.,Limited, Keetona House, Acres Hill Lane, Sheffield, S9 4LR Tel: 0114-242 0328 Fax: 0114-261 8860 E-mail: keetons@keetons.com *Deep Hole Boring, Associated Bar & Tube Processing, & Other Specialised Engineering Services*

▶ Kegless Ltd, Moffat Centre, 219 Colinton Road, Edinburgh, EH14 1DJ Tel: (07838) 241700 E-mail: info@kegless.co.uk *Beer delivery service*

▶ Kegmaster.Co.Uk, 77 Warwick Road, Sparkhill, Birmingham, B11 4RB Tel: 0121-247 5347 Fax: 0121-247 5347 E-mail: sales@kegmaster.co.uk

Kegworth Marine, Kingston Lane, Kegworth, Derby, DE74 2FS Tel: (01509) 672300 Fax: (01509) 672300 *Boat repairers services*

▶ Kehoe Contractors Ltd, Rear of, 102 Vandyke Road, Leighton Buzzard, Bedfordshire, LU7 3HA Tel: (01525) 852588 Fax: (01525) 852570

Keihan Systems, Unit 24 Padgets Lane, Redditch, Worcestershire, B98 0RB Tel: (01527) 518525 Fax: (01527) 518526 E-mail: info@keihan.co.uk *Tube manipulation & bending services*

▶ Keillor Graphics, 290 High Street, Arbroath, Angus, DD11 1JF Tel: (01241) 876722 Fax: (01241) 871558 E-mail: colin@keilorgraphics.com *Sign manufrs*

Keiper UK Ltd, Woodgate Business Park, Clapgate Lane, Birmingham, B32 3BZ Tel: 0121-423 2828 Fax: 0121-423 2561 *Motor car & vehicle seat manufrs*

Edward Keirby & Co. Ltd, Vine Works, Chichester Street, Rochdale, Lancashire, OL16 2BG Tel: (01706) 645330 Fax: (01706) 352882 E-mail: info@edwardkeirby.co.uk *Manufacturers*

continued

of insulating materials including high temperature & thermal

Keiss Contracts (UK) Ltd, 9-10 Cooper Drive, Braintree, Essex, CM7 2RF Tel: (01376) 326962 Fax: (01376) 322555 E-mail: keiss-contracts@btconnect.com *Sheet metalwork engineers*

Keith & A M Singleton, Nethertown, Egremont, Cumbria, CA22 2UQ Tel: (01946) 820412 Fax: (01946) 824091 *Horticultural equipment manufrs*

Keith Ashby Print Finishing Ltd, 12-14 Clothier Road, Brislington, Bristol, BS4 5PS Tel: 0117-972 8882 Fax: 0117 9728884 E-mail: keith@kapf.wanadoo.co.uk *Print Finishers - Specialist hand finishers. Experienced staff and knowledgeable team who understand all aspects of print, design and make up. Automated finishing: MBO and stayl folding machines, gate folds, concertinas, roll folds, section folding for the trade, Stitching on new Heidelberg ST300, including 4 head loop stitching, guillotining, drilling, shrinkwrapping, collating,point of sale, bookwork - cutting out, tipping in, envelope inserting, polybbagging, etc. We are also able to offer a full print management service should that be required.*

Keith Audio Ltd, North End, Ditchling, Hassocks, West Sussex, BN6 8TG Tel: (01273) 843232 Fax: (01273) 843232 *Audio equipment manufrs*

Keith Bryan, 13a Lime Street, Walsall, WS1 2JL Tel: (01922) 628325 Fax: (01922) 628325 *Saddlery manufrs*

Keith Ceramic Materials Ltd, Fishers Way, Belvedere, Kent, DA17 6BS Tel: (020) 8311 8299 Fax: (020) 8311 8238 *Raw materials manufrs*

Keith Collier Engineering, Riverview Farm, Overcote Road, Over, Cambridge, CB24 5NT Tel: (01954) 231760 Fax: (01954) 231979 *Steel fabricators*

▶ Keith Day, Unit 51 Van Alloys Industrial Estate, Busgrove Lane, Stoke Row, Henley-on-Thames, Oxfordshire, RG9 5QW Tel: (01491) 680040 Fax: (01491) 682123 E-mail: keithdayprinters@btinternet.com *Lithographic printers*

Keith Evans Contract Furnisher Ltd, Brackla Industrial Estate, Bridgend, Mid Glamorgan, CF31 2AE Tel: (01656) 655015 Fax: (01656) 658162 E-mail: sales@keithevans.com *Contract furnishers & bar fitters*

Keith Martin Jewellery, 25 Chapel Ash, Wolverhampton, WV3 0TZ Tel: (01902) 424742 Fax: (01902) 424742 *Jewellery manufacturers & repairers*

Keith Prosser, Unit 22 Victoria Business Centre, Victoria Street, Accrington, Lancashire, BB5 0PJ Tel: (01254) 384898 Fax: (01254) 384898 E-mail: kpcast@prosser.fslife.co.uk *Aluminium casting manufrs*

Keithley Instruments Ltd, 2 Commerce Park, Brunel Road, Theale, Reading, RG7 4AB Tel: 0118-929 7500 Fax: 0118-929 7519 E-mail: enquiries@keithley.com *Test & measurement equipment manufrs*

▶ Keiton Engineering Ltd, 2 William Burton Works, St. James Street, Wednesbury, West Midlands, WS10 7DY Tel: 0121-556 9919 Fax: 0121-556 1398

Kejan Sheet Metal Work, 9 Railway St Industrial Estate, Railway Street, Gillingham, Kent, ME7 1YQ Tel: (01634) 571016 Fax: (01634) 575789 E-mail: alan@kejan.f2s.com *Steel fabricators*

Kel Air Plastics Ltd, Holme Mills, Britannia Road, Huddersfield, HD3 4QF Tel: (01484) 461083 Fax: (01484) 461084 E-mail: tands@fsbdial.co.uk *Plastic tanks & systems*

Kelan Circuits Ltd, Wetherby Road, Boroughbridge, York, YO51 9UY Tel: (01423) 321100 Fax: (01423) 321107 E-mail: sales@kelan.co.uk *Printed circuit board manufrs*

▶ Kelburne Construction Ltd, 8 Inkerman Place, Kilmarnock, Ayrshire, KA1 2LL Tel: (01563) 539116 Fax: (01563) 535911

Kelcamp Ltd, St. Albans Road Industrial Estate, Stafford, ST16 3DR Tel: (01785) 259415 Fax: (01785) 258022 *Pre-cast concrete post manufrs*

Kelcoat Engineering Plastics Ltd, Barnfield Road Industrial Estate, Leek, Staffordshire, ST13 5QG Tel: (01538) 383547 Fax: (01538) 387918 *Corrosion prevention processors*

Keldrigg Shutters & Grilles Ltd, Keldrigg House, Woodhouse, Milnthorpe, Cumbria, LA7 7NQ Tel: (01539) 564550 Fax: (01539) 564681 *Roller shutter maintenance & installation*

Kelectronic, 1 Waterworks Road, Portsmouth, PO6 1NG Tel: (023) 9237 2077 Fax: (023) 9237 2077 E-mail: kelectronic.uk@aol.com *Machine tool maintenance services*

Kelher Supplies, 46 Fairfax Road, Birkenhead, Merseyside, CH41 9EJ Tel: 0151-647 9595 Fax: 0151-647 4077 E-mail: info@kelhersupplies.co.uk *Cleaning bar & hygiene suppliers*

▶ Kelicomp Computing Ltd, 2a Croham Road, South Croydon, Surrey, CR2 7BA Tel: (020) 8760 9220 Fax: (0845) 1669072 *Computer systems consultants*

Kelk Engineering, Unit 4 Kelleythorpe Industrial Estate, Kellythorpe, Driffield, North Humberside, YO25 9DJ Tel: (01377) 252313 Fax: (01377) 232846 E-mail: enquiries@kelkeng.co.uk *Bulk material handling specialists*

Kelland Precision Tooling, Quebec Street, Elland, West Yorkshire, HX5 9BX Tel: (01422) 370715 Fax: (01422) 370523 E-mail: sales@kellandtools.co.uk *Toolmakers for the plastic moulding industry*

Kellands Holdings Ltd, Salmon Parade, Bridgwater, Somerset, TA6 5JY Tel: (01278) 451601 Fax: (01278) 446381 E-mail: terry@kellandsplantsales.co.uk *Industrial plant sales, maintenance & supply services*

Kellands Plant Sales Ltd, High Street, Delabole, Cornwall, PL33 9AE Tel: (01840) 212393 Fax: (01840) 212120 E-mail: sales@kellands.com *Plant & machinery dealers*

Company Information

Kellars Ltd, Unit 14, Rugby Park, Bletchley Road, Stockport, Cheshire, SK4 3EJ Tel: 0161-443 0970 Fax: 0161-432 7453 E-mail: tonybates@aol.com *Carpet wholesalers & contractors*

Keller Ltd, Oxford Road, Ryton on Dunsmore, Coventry, CV8 3EG Tel: (024) 7651 1266 Fax: (024) 7630 5230 E-mail: marketing@keller-ge.co.uk *Ground engineering contractors*

Keller Bryant & Co. Ltd, Swan Centre, Fishers Lane, London, W4 1RX Tel: (020) 8996 9525 E-mail: mail@keller-bryant.co.uk *Freight forwarders*

Keller Bryant Shipping Ltd, Ibex House, Minories, London, EC3N 1DY Tel: (020) 7481 8833 Fax: (0870) 4104312 E-mail: keller-bryant@dial.pipex.com *Ship repair services*

Keller Ground Engineering, Thorp Arch Trading Estate, Thorp Arch, Wetherby, West Yorkshire, LS23 7BJ Tel: (01937) 541118 Fax: (01937) 541371 E-mail: info@keller-ge.co.uk *Specialist geotechnical engineers*

Keller UK Ltd, Winfrith Technology Centre, Winfrith Newburgh, Dorchester, Dorset, DT2 8ZB Tel: (01929) 401200 Fax: (07000) 329535 E-mail: sales@keller-pressure.co.uk *Pressure sensor manufrs*

Kellett Engineering Co. Ltd, Hill Top Road, Leeds, LS12 3PX Tel: 0113-263 9041 Fax: 0113-231 0717 E-mail: klt@btconnect.co.uk *Vehicle windows consultants & manufrs*

▶ Kelleway Media, Unit 8 Thesiger Close, Worthing, West Sussex, BN11 2RN Tel: (01903) 218111 Fax: (01903) 288659 E-mail: sales@kellewaymedia.com *Lithographic quality digital print. **Affordable colour printing in low volumes from as little as 1 print is now posible without any compromise in quality. ** print only what you need * no costly set up charges **Its quick, its quality, its revolutionary...*

Kellforms Woodmasters Ltd, Derehams Lane, Loudwater, High Wycombe, Buckinghamshire, HP10 9RH Tel: (01494) 472233 Fax: (01494) 462269 E-mail: kevin@kellforms.com *Special tool designers & manufrs*

Kelly & Barratt Ltd, Scotch Park Trading Estate, Forge Lane, Leeds, LS12 2PS Tel: 0113-231 1322 Fax: 0113-231 1883 *Shade card & pattern book manufrs*

Kelly Bros Road Markings Ltd, 15 Station Road, Yate, Bristol, BS37 5HT Tel: (01454) 312675 Fax: (01454) 320425

▶ Kelly Communications Ltd, Kelly House, 8 Headstone Road, Harrow, Middlesex, HA1 1PD Tel: (020) 8424 0909 Fax: (020) 8424 0509

D.P. Kelly (Holdings) Ltd, Nether Handley, Sheffield, S21 5RP Tel: (01246) 451167 Fax: (01246) 451167 *Plant hire contractors & waste disposal*

Kelly Freight, C Cedars Transport Depot, Church Manorway, Erith, Kent, DA8 1DE Tel: (01322) 430231 Fax: (01322) 463446 E-mail: upn55scott@aol.com *Road haulage & storage services*

Kelly Freight, C Cedars Transport Depot, Church Manorway, Erith, Kent, DA8 1DE Tel: (01322) 430231 Fax: (01322) 463446 E-mail: upn55scott@aol.com *Road transport & haulage*

Kelly Fuels, Railway Yard, Railway Street, Ballymena, County Antrim, BT42 2AF Tel: (028) 2564 9811 Fax: (028) 2564 0099 *Oil company*

Kelly Fuels, 1 Lombard Street, Belfast, BT1 1BN Tel: (028) 9026 1500 Fax: (028) 9033 0032 *Coal importers & oil distributors* Also at: Ballymeno, Carrickfergus, Coleraine, Londonderry & Portadown

Kelly Fuels, Brownstown Business Centre, Brownstown Road, Portadown, Craigavon, County Armagh, BT62 4EA Tel: (028) 3835 0360 Fax: (028) 3835 0356 *Oil & coal distributors*

▶ Kelly Hydraulics Ltd, 67 Amhurst Gardens, Isleworth, Middlesex, TW7 6AN Tel: (020) 8847 3414 Fax: (020) 8847 3414 E-mail: raymondkelly50@hotmail.com *Mobile hydraulic hose repair services*

▶ Kelly Mcevoy & Brown, 1-5 Castle Avenue, Castlewellan, County Down, BT31 9DX Tel: (028) 4377 0141 Fax: (028) 4377 0141

Nigel Kelly (Joinery Division) Ltd, The Old Chapel, Main Street, Garton-On-The-Wolds, Driffield, East Yorkshire, YO25 3ET Tel: (01377) 241113 Fax: (01377) 241113 E-mail: info@collectiondisplays.com *Joiners*

Pat Kelly Machine Rentals Ltd, 5 Glencoe Business Park, Warne Road, Weston-super-Mare, Avon, BS23 3TS Tel: (01934) 620703 Fax: (01934) 642306 *Amusement machine contract hire*

Kelly Plant Hire, Fowberry Road, Newcastle upon Tyne, NE15 6XP Tel: 0191-275 3339 Fax: 0191-275 3304 E-mail: tele.planthire@virgin.net *Plant hire*

Kelly Services, 22 Hanover Buildings, Southampton, SO14 1JU Tel: (023) 8023 5835 Fax: (023) 8023 6519 E-mail: southampton@kellyservices.co.uk *Industrial recruitment agency office based staff*

Simon Kelly Partnership, 12 Argyle Road, Clevedon, Avon, BS21 7BP Tel: (01275) 875569 Fax: (01275) 875509 E-mail: simon_kelly@btinternet.com *Business performance improving specialists*

▶ Kelly Technical Services, 21 St Petersgate, Stockport, Cheshire, SK1 1EB Tel: 0161-429 9853 Fax: 0161-429 9867 E-mail: ker_manchester@kellyservices.co.uk *Kelly Engineering Resources TM specialises in recruiting the most talented engineers and providing companies with high calibre candidates. From Electrical, Process and Chemical to Automotive and service engineers, whether permanent or contract staff, we work quickly and efficiently to match engineering skills to employers" needs across a range of industries*

▶ Kellylink Ltd, Unit 2, Arrow Road North, Lakeside, Redditch, Worcestershire, B98 8NT Tel: (01527) 62222 Fax: (01527) 62222 E-mail: info@kellylink.co.uk *KellylinK , Redditch, Parcels delivery , courier , couriers , sameday , nextday , Nationwide , Worldwide , TEL:0800 2989242 Worcestershire*

Kelly's Of Aberdeen, 22-24 South Mount Street, Aberdeen, AB25 2TB Tel: (01224) 638689 Fax: (01224) 649009 E-mail: enquiries@kellyscopiers.co.uk *Photocopiers & office equipment suppliers*

Kelly's Blinds, 115b Claude Road, London, E10 6NF Tel: (020) 8556 4147 Fax: (020) 8584 2299 E-mail: sales@kellysblinds.co.uk *We supply & fit all types of window blinds. Venetian blinds, Roller blinds, Vertical blinds & Wooden blinds. To offices & homes.*

Kelly's Industrial Clothing Ltd, 22a Allport Lane, Wirral, Merseyside, CH62 7HP Tel: 0151-334 2318 *Industrial clothing distributor*

Kelmat Ltd, Unit 13, Penarth Centre, Penarth Street, London, SE15 1TR Tel: (020) 7277 5167 Fax: (020) 7277 6601 E-mail: kelmet@btconnect.com *Electrical contractors*

▶ Kelo & Co. Ltd, Market Hill, St. Ives, Cambridgeshire, PE27 5AL Tel: (01480) 466805 Fax: (01480) 495173 E-mail: mail@kelopipelines.com

Kelpie Boats, Hobbs Point, Pembroke Dock, Dyfed, SA72 6TR Tel: (01646) 683661 Fax: (01646) 621398 E-mail: martin@kelpieboats.com *Boat, outboard engine sales & service*

Kelpie Marine Boat Yard, Kelpie Marine, Great North Road, Roxton, Bedford, MK44 3DS Tel: (01234) 870249 *Private moorings*

Kelsea Assembly, 55 Eastlea Avenue, Bishop Auckland, County Durham, DL14 6HD Tel: (01388) 450489 Fax: (01388) 450489 *Electronic manufrs*

Kelsey Roofing Industries Ltd, Kelsey House, Paper Mill Drive, Church Hill South, Redditch, Worcestershire, B98 8QJ Tel: (01527) 594400 Fax: (01527) 594444 *Industrial, commercial roofing & cladding contractors* Also at: Branches throughout the U.K.

▶ Kelson Interiors, Topcliffe Lane, Morley, Leeds, LS27 0HW Tel: 0113-252 7900 Fax: 0113-252 7977 E-mail: info@kelson.co.uk *Special interior design, build & refurbishment service of commercial & office buildings*

Kelston Precisions Gears Ltd, Crews Hole Road, Bristol, BS5 8BB Tel: 0117-955 8671 Fax: 0117-935 0023 E-mail: sales@kelstongears.co.uk *Gear manufrs*

Keltbray Ltd, Wentworth House, Dormay Street, London, SW18 1EY Tel: (020) 7643 1000 Fax: (020) 7643 1001 E-mail: office@keltbray.com *Demolition & excavator contrators*

Keltec Ltd, Unit 2 Bracknell Enterprise Centre, Bracknell, Berkshire, RG12 1NF Tel: (01344) 306700 Fax: (01344) 306800 E-mail: sales@keltec.co.uk *Hardware & software resellers*

Kelvin Conference Centre, The West Of Scotland Science Park, 2317 Maryhill Road, Glasgow, G20 0TH Tel: 0141-330 3939 Fax: 0141-330 2828 E-mail: kcc@gla.ac.uk *Conference centre*

Kelvin Diesels Ltd, 133 Helen Street, Glasgow, G51 3HD Tel: (01698) 810666 Fax: (01698) 810999 E-mail: sales@britishpolarengines.co.uk *Diesel engine maintenance & manufrs*

Kelvin Fuel Control Systems Ltd, Fordrough, Birmingham, B25 8DW Tel: 0121-772 0972 Fax: 0121-772 0972 *Furnace engineers*

Kelvin Steels Ltd, Spiersbridge Lane, Thornliebank Industrial Estate, Thornliebank, Glasgow, G46 8JT Tel: 0141-638 7988 Fax: 0141-638 1097 E-mail: info@kelvinsteels.com *Steel & non-ferrous stockholders*

Kelwood Exports, 70 Blover Road, Lindley, Huddersfield, HD3 3HR Tel: (01484) 653053 Fax: (01484) 658934 *Polyester & worsted cloth manufrs*

▶ KEM Kueppers UK, 2 Highfield Drive, Ickenham, Uxbridge, Middlesex, UB10 8AL Tel: (01895) 233552 Fax: (01895) 230312 E-mail: service@kueppers.co.uk *Suppliers of industrial flow meters*

Kemach Services, 34 Singer Way, Woburn Road Industrial Estate, Kempston, Bedford, MK42 7AF Tel: (01234) 857340 Fax: (01234) 857340 E-mail: tworr46530@aol.com *Shot blasting contractors & shot blasting equipment distributors*

M Kember Groundworks, 20 Knottesford Close, Studley, Warwickshire, B80 7RL Tel: (01527) 854254 *Groundwork*

Kembery Group Ltd, 67-69 Sutherland Road, London, E17 6BH Tel: (020) 8527 1520 Fax: (020) 8527 1524 *Heating installation engineers*

Kembrey Wiring Systems Ltd, Garrard Way, Greenbridge, Swindon, SN3 3HY Tel: (01793) 693361 Fax: (01793) 614298 E-mail: sales@kembrey.co.uk *Cable harness assembly manufrs*

▶ Kemco Technology, Acorn House, Tonbridge Road, Bough Beech, Edenbridge, Kent, TN8 7AU Tel: (01892) 870077 Fax: (01892) 870777 E-mail: info@kemcotech.com *Photo luminescent materials manufrs*

Kemet International Ltd, Sutton Road, Maidstone, Kent, ME15 9NJ Tel: (01622) 755287 Fax: (01622) 670915 E-mail: sales@kemet.co.uk *World leaders in surface finishing technology using diamond superabrasives. We have 5 main divisions: Flat Lapping Machines, Metallographic Machines, Mould & Die /Toolroom consumables, Ultrasonic Cleaning & Coated Abrasives*

▶ Kemira Growhow UK Ltd, Ince, Chester, CH2 4LB Tel: 0151-357 2777 Fax: 0151-357 1755 E-mail: kemira-growhow.uk@kemira-growhow.com *Fertiliser & chemical manufrs*

Kemkill Pest Control & Hygiene Services, 14 Whilton Close, Sutton-in-Ashfield, Nottinghamshire, NG17 3BF Tel: (01623) 552284 Fax: (01623) 552284 *Pest controllers*

Kemlite Ltd, 25 Caker Stream Road, Alton, Hampshire, GU34 2QF Tel: (01420) 86512 Fax: (01420) 541124 *Plastic nab fact grp manufrs*

Kemlows Diecasting Products Ltd, Charlton Mead Lane, Hoddesdon, Hertfordshire, EN11 0HB Tel: (01992) 460671 Fax: (01992) 446889 E-mail: sales@kemlows.co.uk *Aluminium die-casting manufrs*

Kemmel Ltd, Unit 6, Cradle Hill Industrial Estate, Seaford, East Sussex, BN25 3JE Tel: (01323) 899024 Fax: (01323) 893149 E-mail: sales@kemmel.co.uk *Sub contract engineers*

▶ Kemnay T V Sales & Service, 20 Aquithie Road, Kemnay, Inverurie, Aberdeenshire, AB51 5SS Tel: (01467) 642282 Fax: (01467) 643397 *Retail white goods*

Kemo Ltd, 3 Brook Co, Blakeney Road, Beckenham, Kent, BR3 1HG Tel: (020) 8658 3838 Fax: (020) 8658 4084 E-mail: technical@kemo.com *Electronic filter manufrs*

Kemp Commercial Bodybuilders Ltd, 30 Brunel Road, Manor Trading Estate, Benfleet, Essex, SS7 4PS Tel: (01268) 792491 Fax: (01268) 795121 E-mail: kempbodybuilders@tesco.net *Commercial vehicle body builders*

▶ Kemp Randles Consulting Ltd, Trenowyth House Mullion Cove, Mullion, Helston, Cornwall, TR12 7EP Tel: (01326) 240274 E-mail: enquiries@kemprandles.co.uk *Providing specialist advisory services to primary and secondary healthcare providers, maximising financial and business efficiency, also providing litigation support to minimise professional negligence compensation claims.*

▶ Roger Kemp Associates, River View, High Street, Loxwood, Billingshurst, West Sussex, RH14 0RE Tel: (01403) 752370 E-mail: mattkemp70@hotmail.com *Installers of Quality kitchens and bathrooms. Project managment from concept to completion. Trade discounts offered. Portfolio and references available.*

Kemps Neon Ltd, 2 Matrix Court, Leeds, LS11 5WB Tel: 0113-271 5777 Fax: 0113-271 5666 E-mail: sales@kempsneon.com *Cold cathode lighting systems & general signage manufrs*

Kemps Publishing Ltd, 11 Swan Courtyard, Charles Edward Road, Birmingham, B26 1BU Tel: 0121-765 4144 Fax: 0121-706 6210 E-mail: enquiries@kempspublishing.co.uk *Directory & information publishers*

Kempster Engineering Ltd, 1 Astra Centre, Royle Barn Road, Rochdale, Lancashire, OL11 3DT Tel: (01706) 345599 Fax: (01706) 657396 E-mail: sales@kempsteruk.com *Knife gate valves & rotary joint manufacturers & distributors*

Kempston Ltd, Brunel Road, Bedford, MK41 9TG Tel: (01234) 341144 Fax: (01234) 348281 *Sheet metalworkers & stove enamellers*

Kempston Controls, Shirley Road, Rushden, Northamptonshire, NN10 6BZ Tel: (01933) 414500 Fax: (01933) 410211 E-mail: sales@kempstoncontrols.co.uk Principal Export Areas: Worldwide *Distributors of control gear, fuses, sensors & circuit breakers*

Kemtec Manufacturing, 1a Caddick Road, Knowsley Business Park, Prescot, Merseyside, L34 9HP Tel: 0151-549 1559 Fax: 0151-549 1729 E-mail: enquiries@kemtec.co.uk *Cleaning chemicals, powders & aerosols manufrs*

Kemtile Ltd, Unit C3, Taylor Business Park, Risley, Warrington, WA3 6BL Tel: (01925) 763045 Fax: (01925) 763381 E-mail: all@kemtile.co.uk *Suppliers & applicators of industrial floorings*

Kemtronix UK Ltd, Churn Road, Compton, Newbury, Berkshire, RG20 6PP Tel: (01635) 578779 Fax: (01635) 578983 E-mail: ljw@kemtronix.com *Suppliers of laboratory equipment*

▶ Kemutec Group, St Blazey Road, Par, Cornwall, PL24 2HY Tel: (01726) 812201 Fax: (01726) 818510 E-mail: info@kemutec.com *Manufactures*

▶ Kemutec Powder Technologies Ltd, Springwood Way, Macclesfield, Cheshire, SK10 2ND Tel: (01625) 412000 Fax: (01625) 412001 E-mail: sales@kemutec.com *Powder Processing & Handling Equipment*

Kemwall Engineering Co., 52 Bensham Grove, Thornton Heath, Surrey, CR7 8DA Tel: (020) 8653 7111 Fax: (020) 8653 9669 E-mail: sales@kemwall.co.uk *Cosmetic filling machinery manufrs*

Kemwell Thermal Ltd, Roma Road, Birmingham, B11 2JH Tel: 0121-708 1188 Fax: 0121-706 3390 E-mail: enquiries@kemwellthermal.com *Metal heat treatment services*

Ken Abrahams (Concrete) Ltd, Pool Industrial Estate, Pool, Redruth, Cornwall, TR15 3RH Tel: (01209) 218550 Fax: (01209) 314881 *Ready-mixed concrete manufrs* Also at: Indian Queens

▶ Ken Abram Ltd, Stanley Way, Skelmersdale, Lancashire, WN8 8EA Tel: (01695) 50177

▶ Ken Barbour, Fitmacan, Boyndie, Banff, AB45 2LA Tel: (01261) 861455

Ken G Lundy, 38 Annaboe Road, Portadown, Craigavon, County Armagh, BT62 4HW Tel: (028) 3887 0681 Fax: (028) 3887 0861 *Agricultural contractors*

▶ Ken Girvan Printers, 90 Peterborough Road, Farcet, Peterborough, PE7 3BN Tel: (01733) 562372 Fax: (01733) 897988

▶ Ken Hall, Newman Street, Kettering, Northamptonshire, NN16 0TG Tel: (01536) 522468 Fax: (01536) 410373 E-mail: enquiries@kenhall.co.uk *Orthopedic footwear manufrs*

Ken Hughes, 4 Keston Fruit Farm Cottages, Blackness Lane, Keston, Kent, BR2 6HR Tel: (07778) 285135 Fax: (01689) 855524 E-mail: kenhugheswoodfls@onetel.net.uk *Wood flooring*

Ken Langford Saddlers, Eaton Road, Appleton, Abingdon, Oxfordshire, OX13 5JH Tel: (01865) 863774 Fax: (01865) 863774 *Saddlery distributors*

▶ Ken Mallinson & Sons Ltd, Clough Green, Lane Head Road, Cawthorne, Barnsley, South Yorkshire, S75 4AD Tel: (01226) 792250 Fax: (01226) 792235

Ken Rooms Ltd, Cumberland Street, Hull, HU2 0PU Tel: (01482) 320129 Fax: (01482) 586040 E-mail: name@ken-rooms.co.uk *Steel drum suppliers & cleaners*

Ken Taylor Ltd, Unit 1-2 Crown Business Centre, George Street, Failsworth, Manchester, M35 9BW Tel: 0161-682 9400 Fax: 0161-682 6833 E-mail: sales@kpsupplies.com *First class distribution of contractors tools, protective*

continued

clothing, janitorial products & road safety equipment, free next day delivery service

▶ Ken Ware Engineers Ltd, Brailwood Road, Bilsthorpe, Newark, Nottinghamshire, NG22 8UA Tel: (01623) 871173 Fax: (01623) 871904 *Engineering*

Kenard Engineering Co. Ltd, Green Street Green Road, Dartford, DA1 1QE Tel: (01322) 421200 Fax: (01322) 421220 E-mail: info@kenard.co.uk *CNC machinists*

▶ Kenard Engineering (Tewkesbury) Ltd, Newtown Trading Estate, Green Lane, Tewkesbury, Gloucestershire, GL20 8SJ Tel: (01684) 271400

Kenbe Binders, Unit 25, City Industrial Park, Southern Road, Southampton, SO15 1HG Tel: (023) 8022 8976 Fax: (023) 8022 2491 E-mail: binders@kenbe.co.uk *Printing trade finishing services*

Kenbe Reproductions Ltd, 25 City Industrial Park, Southern Road, Southampton, SO15 1HG Tel: (023) 8022 5020 Fax: (023) 8022 2491 E-mail: calenders@kenbe.co.uk *Calendar publishers*

Kenburn Waste Management, Kenburn House, Porters Wood, St. Albans, Hertfordshire, AL3 6HX Tel: (01727) 844988 Fax: (01727) 844778 E-mail: info@kenburn.co.uk *Waste management equipment suppliers*

Kencom Computer Services, Aberfoyle Road, Dumgoyne, Glasgow, G63 9LA Tel: (01360) 550085 E-mail: sales@kencom.co.uk *Computer consultants*

Kenda Knitwear Ltd, 7 Water Row, Glasgow, G51 3UW Tel: 0141-445 2231 Fax: 0141-445 5114 *Knitwear manufrs*

Kendal Business Equipment Ltd, Kendal House, The Street, Shadoxhurst, Ashford, Kent, TN26 1LU Tel: (01233) 733267 Fax: (01233) 733221 E-mail: kendalbusinessequipment@hotmail.com *Office equipment suppliers*

Kendal Joinery Co. Ltd, Dockray Hall Road, Kendal, Cumbria, LA9 4RY Tel: (01539) 722629 Fax: (01539) 740891 *Industrial units rental services*

Kendal Metal Works Ltd, Mintsfeet Road, Kendal, Cumbria, LA9 6NN Tel: (01539) 722050 Fax: (01539) 741190 *Sheet metal engineers services*

Kendall Bros Portsmouth Ltd, Kendalls Wharf, Eastern Road, Portsmouth, PO3 5LY Tel: (023) 9266 2801 Fax: (023) 9267 0889 E-mail: sales@kendalls.co.uk *Concrete aggregate merchants*

Charles Kendall Freight Ltd, Spur Road, Feltham, Middlesex, TW14 0SL Tel: (020) 8384 9494 Fax: (020) 8384 9403 E-mail: ckf@charleskendallfreight.com *Export packers & freight forwarders*

▶ Charles Kendall Freight Ltd, Unit 3 4, Severnside Trading Estate, Textilose Road, Trafford Park, Manchester, M17 1WA Tel: 0161-877 5881 Fax: 0161-877 8072 E-mail: admin@charleskendallfreight.com

Kendall Electrical Services Telford Ltd, Stafford Park 6, Telford, Shropshire, TF3 3AT Tel: (01952) 290830 Fax: (01952) 291027 E-mail: sales@kendal-group.co.uk *Electrical engineers & contractors*

▶ Kendall Press Ltd, Crown House, Trafford Park Road, Trafford Park, Manchester, M17 1HG Tel: 0161-872 9808 Fax: 0161-877 9085

Kendall's Ices, Denholme Gate Road, Hipperholme, Halifax, West Yorkshire, HX3 8JQ Tel: (01422) 202246 Fax: (01422) 202246 *Ice cream manufrs*

Kendata Services Ltd, Nutsey Lane, Totton, Southampton, SO40 3NB Tel: (023) 8086 9922 Fax: (023) 8086 0800 E-mail: kpsales@kenda.co.uk *Specialised systems manufrs*

Kendlebell, 236 Nantwich Road, Crewe, CW2 6BP Tel: (01270) 219500 Fax: (01270) 219500 E-mail: heleng@kendlebell.co.uk *UK's number one telephone answering and virtual office service, call handling, virtual office, virtual office uk, answering services, telephone answering service, virtual office service, telephone answering, answering services, call handling services, virtual office services, telephone answering and virtual office service.*

Kendley Ltd, Old Goods Yard, Station Road, Talacre, Holywell, Clwyd, CH8 9RD Tel: (01745) 887412 Fax: (01745) 888290 E-mail: kendley@btconnect.com *Steel fabricators & erectors*

▶ Kendon Packaging, 37 Wigman Road, Nottingham, NG8 4PA Tel: 0115-916 0055 Fax: 0115-916 0056 E-mail: sales@kendonpackaging.co.uk *Packaging products*

Kendon Packaging Group, Bow Paper Works, Bridgwater Road, London, E15 2JZ Tel: (020) 7249 9645 Fax: (020) 8519 4333 E-mail: sales@kendon.co.uk *Packaging material manufacturers & distributors*

Kendrick Homes Ltd, Tasker Street, Walsall, WS1 3QW Tel: (01922) 622263 Fax: (01922) 721632 E-mail: feedback@kendrick.co.uk *Building contractors*

Kendrick Sheet Metal, 3 Peacocks Estate, Providence Street, Cradley Heath, West Midlands, B64 5DG Tel: (01384) 638363 Fax: (01384) 637881 *Sheet metalworks engineers*

Kendrion Binder Magnete (UK) Ltd, Huddersfield Road, Low Moor, Bradford, West Yorkshire, BD12 0TQ Tel: (01274) 601111 Fax: (01274) 691093 E-mail: sales@kendrion-binder.co.uk *Electromagnetic, solenoid & industrial valves & vibrator distributors*

Kenex Electro Medical Ltd, 24 Burnt Mill Industrial Estate, Elizabeth Way, Harlow, Essex, CM20 2HS Tel: (01279) 417241 Fax: (01279) 443749 E-mail: kenex@kenex.co.uk *X-ray protection equipment suppliers & manufrs*

Kenfield Ltd, 23-25 Prince Road, Kings Norton Business Centre, Norton, Birmingham, B30 3HB Tel: 0121-451 3051 Fax: 0121-433 3247 E-mail: info@pvc-strip-doors.co.uk *The website of Kenfield Ltd. Manufacturers of insulation products including K-Flex PVC doors, PVC strip curtains and PVC rolls. Kenfield Ltd are the largest manufacturer and distributor of PVC*

continued

continuation
strips, PVC rolls and PVC curtains in the UK and have been in business since 1983.

Kenfield Recovery Southern Ltd, 124-126 Nathan Way, London, SE28 0AU Tel: (020) 8855 5544 Fax: (020) 8317 2471 *Car, commercial recovery & repairs*

Kengate Products Ltd, Littleton Lane, Shepperton, Middlesex, TW17 0NF Tel: (01932) 568672 Fax: (01932) 567171 *Tiles manufrs*

Kenilworth Printers, Unit 9b Princes Dr Industrial Estate, Coventry Road, Kenilworth, Warwickshire, CV8 2FD Tel: (01926) 851180 Fax: (01926) 851173

Kenira, Ince Marshes, Ince, Chester, CH2 4LB Tel: 0151-357 1010 Fax: 0151-357 1755 *Fertiliser manufrs*

▶ Kenley Warehousing & Distribution, Darwen Mill, Hilton Street, Darwen, Lancashire, BB3 2AY Tel: (01254) 701633 Fax: (01254) 703378 *Storage & distribution*

Kenlowe Accessories & Co. Ltd, Burchetts Green, Maidenhead, Berkshire, SL6 6QU Tel: (01628) 823303 Fax: (01628) 823451 E-mail: sales@kenlowe.com *Transport equipment manufrs*

▶ Kenmac Haulage Ltd, Building 76 Greenfield Business Park, Bagillt Road, Greenfield, Holywell, Clwyd, CH8 7HJ Tel: (01352) 715425 Fax: (01352) 712704

Kenmac (U K) Ltd, Unit D Wigan Hall Road, Good Yard, Wigan Hall Road, Watford, WD18 0EZ Tel: (01923) 218998 Fax: (01923) 818454 E-mail: enquiries@kenmacuk.com *Cleaning & hygiene products & industrial workwear distributors*

Kennametal UK Ltd, PO Box 29, Kingswinford, West Midlands, DY6 7NP Tel: (01384) 401000 Fax: (01384) 408015 E-mail: kingswinfold.service@kennametal.com *Cutting tool materials equipment manufrs*

Kennedy Asphalt, Downs Road, Willenhall, West Midlands, WV13 2PF Tel: 0121-568 7903 Fax: 0121-526 7265 *Surfacing contractors & associated civil engineering works* Also at: Manchester

Kennedy Demolition Ltd, 219 Wickham Road, Croydon, CR0 8TG Tel: (020) 8655 1111 Fax: (020) 8655 1123 *Demolition contractors*

Kennedy Grinding Ltd, Commerce Park, Commerce Way, Colchester, CO2 8HX Tel: (01206) 790407 Fax: (01206) 793113 *Machine knives & grinders service*

Kennedy Grinding Ltd, Shrewsbury Road, Craven Arms, Shropshire, SY7 9QH Tel: (01588) 672289 Fax: (01588) 673504 E-mail: kennedygrinding@btconnect.com *Regrinding services* Also at: Bristol & London SE1

The Kennedy Group Ltd, Wigston Works, Victoria St, Wigston, Leicestershire, LE18 1AJ Tel: 0116-288 8777 Fax: 0116-288 8222 E-mail: overseas@cromwell-kennedy-group.co.uk *Workshop contractors*

Michael Kennedy, 43 Hillbeck Crescent, Nottingham, NG8 2EZ Tel: 0115-913 8167 Fax: (0870) 7120591 E-mail: kennedy@grantsuk.fsbusiness.co.uk *Finance consultants*

Kennedy & Morrison Ltd, Boucher Road, Belfast, BT12 6QF Tel: (028) 9087 0870 Fax: (028) 9087 0871 E-mail: sales@kandm.co.uk *Engineering suppliers*

Kennedy Print, 11a Wilson Road, Liverpool, L36 6AN Tel: 0151-449 2984 Fax: 0151-449 3270 *Digital printing services*

S.J. Kennedy Group, 25 Main Street, Cambuslang, Glasgow, G72 7EX Tel: (0845) 6588899 Fax: (0845) 6588898 *Computer consumables*

Kennedy Transmission Ltd, Station Road, Facit Whitworth, Rochdale, Lancashire, OL12 8LJ Tel: (01706) 853021 Fax: (01706) 852217 E-mail: kennedytransmissions@hotmail.com *Reconditioned industrial tranmissions, pumps & electric motor distribs*

Kennedys Fine Chocolates Ltd, The Old School, Orton, Penrith, Cumbria, CA10 3RU Tel: (01539) 624781 Fax: (01539) 624781 E-mail: kennedys.chocolates@btinternet.com *Handmade chocolates manufacturer & supplier*

Kennering Transmission Ltd, Grendon Road, Polesworth, Tamworth, Staffordshire, B78 1NX Tel: (01827) 892517 Fax: (01827) 893914 E-mail: steve@ktl.org.uk *Precision engineers*

Kennet Croft Contractors, Islandstone Lane, Hurst, Reading, RG10 0RJ Tel: 0118-934 1921 Fax: (01889) 344305 *Agricultural machinery contractors*

Kennet Plastics, Unit A, Aerial Business Park, Lambourn Woodlands, Hungerford, Berkshire, RG17 7RZ Tel: (01488) 72055 Fax: (01488) 71122 E-mail: sales@kennet-pack.co.uk *Cardboard & postal tube manufrs* Also at: Haslingden

Kenneth Elliott & Rowe Solicitors, 162 South Street, Romford, RM1 1RA Tel: (01708) 757575 Fax: (01708) 766674 E-mail: sales@ker.co.uk *Solicitors*

▶ Kenneth Grubb Associates Ltd, Wessex House, St Leonards Road, Bournemouth, BH8 8QS Tel: (01202) 311766 Fax: (01202) 318472 E-mail: email@kgal.co.uk *Consulting engineers for moving bridges, marina gates, floodgates, dock equipment*

Kenneth Mackenzie Holdings Ltd, Sandwick Road, Stornoway, Isle of Lewis, HS1 2SJ Tel: (01851) 702772 Fax: (01851) 705271 E-mail: sales.kennethmckenzie@fsmail.net *Harris tweed manufrs*

Kenneth Whitehouse, Mill Lane, Fazeley, Tamworth, Staffordshire, B78 3QD Tel: (01827) 261678 Fax: (01827) 251469 E-mail: kenw@clara.co.uk *Pallet/stillages*

Kennicott Water Systems Ltd, Kennicott House, Well Lane, Wolverhampton, WV11 1XR Tel: (01902) 721212 Fax: (01902) 721333 E-mail: sales@kennicott.co.uk *Water treatment plants designers & contractors*

Kennington Motors, Unit 52 Sandford Lane, Kennington, Oxford, OX1 5RP Tel: (01865) 739064 Fax: (01865) 730007 *MOT's, servicing & crash repairs*

▶ Kenny Bros Civil Engineering Ltd, 8 Dales Lane, Whitefield, Manchester, M45 7RL Tel: 0161-766 7555

Archibald Kenrick & Sons Ltd, Union Street, Kenrick Way, West Bromwich, West Midlands, B70 6DB Tel: 0121-553 2741 Fax: 0121-500 6332 E-mail: enquiries@kenricks.co.uk *Die casting manufrs*

Kenrix Builders Merchants Ltd, 27 Wickham Lane, London, SE2 0XJ Tel: (020) 8265 4413 Fax: (020) 8265 4413 *Builders merchants & diy suppliers*

▶ Kenro Ltd, The Oppenheimer Centre, Greenbridge Road, Swindon, SN3 3LH Tel: (01793) 615836 Fax: (01793) 530108 E-mail: sales@kenro.co.uk *Photographic*

Kenross Containers Ltd, Kippax Mill, Goodshawfold Road, Rossendale, Lancashire, BB4 8QW Tel: (01706) 228381 Fax: (01706) 831523 E-mail: sales@kenross.co.uk *Corrugated case manufrs*

Kenroy Thompson Ltd, 25 Cobourg Street, Plymouth, PL1 1SR Tel: (01752) 227693 Fax: (0800) 7836322 E-mail: sales@kenroythompson.co.uk *Retail stationers*

▶ Kensa Creative Solutions, Tamar House, Moorlands Ind Estate, Saltash, Cornwall, PL12 6LX Tel: 01752 846686 E-mail: k.seldon@kensa.co.uk *Kensa Creative Solutions is a full-service agency based in South West England but with a growing international reputation.**Services provided include branding, website design, internet marketing, technical copywriting, promotional items, multimedia cd"s, database development, telesales & packaging design.*

Kensa Engineering Ltd, Tin Pit, Mabe Burnthouse, Penryn, Cornwall, TR10 9JH Tel: (01326) 377627 Fax: (01326) 374470 E-mail: info@kensaengineering.com *Air conditioning installers & ground force heat pumps manufrs*

Kensal Handling Systems Ltd, Kensal House, President Way, Luton, LU2 9NR Tel: (01582) 425777 Fax: (01582) 425776 E-mail: sales@kensal.com *Conveyor systems manufrs*

Kensett Ltd, 196 Old Shoreham Road, Hove, East Sussex, BN3 7EX Tel: (01273) 725627 Fax: (01273) 724867 *Book binders & print finishers*

Kensey Foods, Pennygillam Industrial Estate, Launceston, Cornwall, PL15 7AF Tel: (01566) 778300 Fax: (01566) 778333 *Food manufrs*

Kensington Engineering, Burton Street, Leek, Staffordshire, ST13 8DA Tel: (01538) 387578 Fax: (01538) 387578 *Steel fabricators & erectors*

▶ Kensington Flowers, 3 Launceston Place, London, W8 5RL Tel: (020) 7937 0268 Fax: 020 7937 0268 E-mail: info@kensingtonflowers.co.uk *Bespoke florist*

▶ Kensingtons Ltd, 2 Dixon Place, Collage Milton, East Kilbride, Glasgow, G74 5JF Tel: (0845) 2722845 Fax: E-mail: enquiry@kensingtons-catering.co.uk *Corporate hospitality wedding & event catering services*

Kensworth Sawmills Ltd, Dovehouse Lane, Kensworth, Dunstable, Bedfordshire, LU6 2PQ Tel: (01582) 873124 Fax: (01582) 873024 E-mail: kensworthsawmillsltd@hotmail.com *Timber fence distributors*

Kent Alarms Ltd, 37 Main Street, South Hiendley, Barnsley, South Yorkshire, S72 9BS Tel: (0800) 0854999 Fax: (01226) 717075 E-mail: sales@kentalarms.co.uk *Burglar alarm installation services*

Kent Balloons UK Ltd, Unit 2a Underlyn Industrial Estate, Underlyn Lane, Marden, Tonbridge, Kent, TN12 9AT Tel: (01622) 832213 Fax: (01622) 832388 E-mail: sales@kentballoon.com *Balloon suppliers*

Kent Bearings, John Wilson Business Park Harvey Drive, Unit 128a, Chestfield, Whitstable, Kent, CT5 3QY Tel: (01227) 772111 Fax: (01227) 771444 *Bearing, power transmissions distributors & engineers* Also at: Ashford

Kent Blaxill & Co. Ltd, 129-139 Layer Road, Colchester, CO2 9JY Tel: (01206) 216000 Fax: (01206) 762981 E-mail: sales@kentblaxill.co.uk *Builders & glass merchants* Also at: Bury St. Edmunds, Ipswich, Kirby Cross, Norwich, Sudbury & Woodbridge

Kent Builders, 39 Ellingham, Hemel Hempstead, Herts, HP2 5LE Tel: (01442) 251425 *Building contractors*

▶ Kent Car Imports Ltd, 39 Maritime Gate, Northfleet, Gravesend, Kent, DA11 9EH Tel: (01474) 320859 Fax: (01474) 569159 E-mail: admin@kc-imports.com *Importing American Pickup trucks. We specialise in supplying the Ford F150 and Ford Mustang for UK buyers*

Kent Car Panel & Paint Ltd, Units 2-3, Willow Industries, Tyland Lane, Sandling, Maidstone, Kent, ME14 3BN Tel: (01622) 752821 Fax: (01622) 754254 E-mail: kentcarpanels@aol.com *Auto-refinishing suppliers & auto-body panel* Also at: Bexleyheath

Kent Coin Automatics, 6 Tontine Street, Folkestone, Kent, CT20 1JU Tel: (01303) 256047 Fax: 01303 850424 *Fruit machine hire*

▶ Kent Connection Ltd, Factory Road, Blaydon-on-Tyne, Tyne & Wear, NE21 5RU Tel: 0191-414 0055

▶ Kent Cosmetics Ltd, Kent House, Ashford Road, Harrietsham, Maidstone, Kent, ME17 1BW Tel: (01622) 859898

▶ Kent Ductwork Ltd, Unit 7-9 Crayford Industrial Estate, Swaisland Drive, Crayford, Dartford, DA1 4HS Tel: (01322) 558887 Fax: (01322) 559991

Kent Edwards Litho Ltd, 29 Woolmer Trading Estate, Bordon, Hampshire, GU35 9QE Tel: (01420) 475666 Fax: (01420) 489004 E-mail: sales@kentedwards.co.uk *Lithographic printers*

Kent Express Ltd, Medcare House, Centurion Close, Gillingham Business Park, Gillingham, Kent, ME8 0SB Tel: (01634) 878750 Fax: (01634) 878788 E-mail: sales@kentexpress.co.uk *Suppliers of dental equipment*

Kent Grouting Services Ltd, 10 Gun Lane, Rochester, Kent, ME2 4UB Tel: (01634) 717554 Fax: (01634) 711396 E-mail: martinstromsoy@freenetname.co.uk *Grouting contractors, hire & sales*

Kent Harvest Centre, Bayley Wood, Great Chart, Ashford, Kent, TN26 1JJ Tel: (01233) 822300 Fax: (01233) 822301 E-mail: steve_lewis@southernharvesters.co.uk *Agricultural machinery suppliers*

Howard Kent, 5 Brighton Road, Shoreham-by-Sea, West Sussex, BN43 6RN Tel: (01273) 871871 Fax: (01273) 870970 E-mail: howardkent@ukonline.co.uk *Plant handling self storage services*

Kent Hydraulic & Garage Eqt, The Range, Clement Street, Swanley, Kent, BR8 7PQ Tel: (01322) 666432 Fax: (01322) 666532 *Garage equipment suppliers*

Kent Link Transport & Storage, Unit 18 Henwood Business Centre, Henwood, Ashford, Kent, TN24 8DH Tel: (01233) 638889 Fax: (01233) 635869 E-mail: sales@kentlink.com *Transport & warehousing logistics*

P.B. Kent & Co. Ltd, Alexandra Road South, Immingham Dock, Immingham, North East Lincolnshire, DN40 2QW Tel: (01469) 563980 Fax: (01469) 571444 E-mail: michael.dickinson@pbkent.co.uk *Fertiliser manufrs*

▶ Kent P H K Ltd, Hermitage Way, Mansfield, Nottinghamshire, NG18 5ES Tel: (01623) 421202 Fax: (01623) 421302 E-mail: nottingham@kentphk.co.uk

Kent Pest Control, 5 Birling Park Estate, Birling, West Malling, Kent, ME19 5JD Tel: (01732) 845178 *Pest control service providers*

Kent Pharmaceuticals Ltd, Wotton Road, Ashford, Kent, TN23 6LL Tel: (01233) 638614 Fax: (01233) 646899 E-mail: sales@kentpharm.co.uk *Pharmaceutical distributors*

Kent Plastics UK Ltd, Derrychara Rd, Enniskillen, County Fermanagh, BT74 6JG Tel: (028) 6632 3131 Fax: (028) 6632 7410 *Plastics injection moulders*

Kent Refrigeration Ltd, 6 Yew Tree Industrial Estate, Mill Hall, Aylesford, Kent, ME20 7ET Tel: (01622) 792228 Fax: (01622) 790530 E-mail: sales@kentrefrigeration.com *Refrigeration equipment suppliers & maintenance providers*

▶ Kent Refurbishment, 216 Lower Twydall Lane, Gillingham, Kent, ME8 6QB Tel: (01634) 318626 E-mail: info@kent-refurbishment.co.uk *Commercial and Domestic Referbishment Specialist, Loft Conversion, Small work and Service*

Kent Superior Pictures, Fred Martin Studio Barton Road, Dover, Kent, CT16 2ND Tel: (01304) 202827 Fax: (01384) 213824 *Audio & video production services*

▶ Kent & Sussex Scales Ltd, Wilderwick Road, East Grinstead, West Sussex, RH19 3NT Tel: (01342) 870221 Fax: (01342) 870104 E-mail: sales@kentandsussexscales.co.uk *Scale manufrs*

Kent & Sussex Truck Centre Ltd, Longfield Road, Tunbridge Wells, Kent, TN2 3EY Tel: (01892) 515333 Fax: (01892) 531813 E-mail: vehicles@kst.co.uk *Commercial vehicle repair services*

Kent & Sussex Vending, K S V Business Park, Nan Tucks Lane, Buxted, Uckfield, East Sussex, TN22 4PN Tel: (01825) 732772 Fax: (01825) 732696 E-mail: info@ksv.co.uk *Vending machine distribs*

▶ Kent Sweepers Ltd, Station Yard, Nightingale Road, Horsham, West Sussex, RH12 2NW Tel: (01403) 249499 Fax: (01403) 254354

▶ Kent Sweepers Ltd, Tenter Street, Rotherham, South Yorkshire, S60 1LB Tel: (01709) 555153 Fax: (01709) 555013

Kent Technical, 10 High Street, Snodland, Kent, ME6 5DF Tel: (01634) 248900 Fax: (01634) 248901 *Contract drawing services*

Kent Transmissions Centre, Unit 1 Skein Enterprise Park, Hodsoll Street, Sevenoaks, Kent, TN15 7LB Tel: (01732) 824618 *Gearbox reconditioners*

▶ Kent Transport, Archers Fields, Burnt Mills Industrial Estate, Basildon, Essex, SS13 1DN Tel: (01268) 530805 Fax: (01268) 530811

Kent & Co Twines Ltd, Long Lane, Walton, Liverpool, L9 7DE Tel: 0151-525 1601 Fax: 0151-523 1410 E-mail: kenttwines@aol.com *Rope & twine merchants*

Kent United Contractors Ltd, Unit 4 Regis Business Park, New Road, Sheerness, Kent, ME12 1NB Tel: (01795) 583475 Fax: (01795) 583476 E-mail: kuc@lineone.net *Stevedoring services*

William Kent Memorials (March) Ltd, 11 Upwell Rd, March, Cambs, PE15 9DT Tel: (01354) 652030 Fax: (01354) 652030

Kent Wire Ltd, Chatham Docks, Chatham, Kent, ME4 4SW Tel: (01634) 830964 Fax: (01634) 830967 *Reinforcement steel producers*

▶ Kentec, Unit 25 Fawkes Avenue, Dartford Trade Park, Dartford, DA1 1JQ Tel: (01322) 222121 Fax: (01322) 291794 E-mail: sales@kentec.co.uk

▶ Kentec Building Services Ltd, 34 Nightingale Way, London, E6 5JR Tel: (020) 7474 4774 Fax: (020) 7474 4775

▶ Kentec Power Systems Ltd, Unit 18 Cannel Road, Chasetown Industrial Estate, Burntwood Business Park, Burntwood, Staffordshire, WS7 3FU Tel: (01543) 677802 Fax: (01543) 677508 E-mail: sales@kentec.uk.com *Authorised Caterpillar Olympian Dealer, supplier of new Olympian and Olympiad generator sets. Supply and installation packages offered. Our services include:- Sales of Olympian & Olympiad Generators Installations: Commissioning: Workshop Repairs: Onsite Service of Diesel, Petrol Generator Sets, including Marine.*

Kenter Plastics, Finches Yard, Eastwick Road, Bookham, Leatherhead, Surrey, KT23 4BA Tel: (01372) 456487 Fax: (01372) 450475 *Plastic mouldings manufrs*

Kenthorp Supplies Wholesale Ltd, 83 Palmerston Road, Bournemouth, BH1 4HW Tel: (01202) 302030 Fax: (01202) 396000 E-mail: enquiries@kenthorpsupplies.co.uk *Catering disposal wholesalers*

▶ Kentish Sign Writers, 139 Ballens Road, Chatham, Kent, ME5 8PG Tel: (01634) 309295 Fax: E-mail: sales@kentishsigns.com *Signwriters & sign manufrs*

Kenton Leather Products, Windmill Road, Rushden, Northamptonshire, NN10 9TN Tel: (01933) 312160 Fax: (01933) 412185 *Leather goods manufrs*

Kenton Research Ltd, Unit 19 Bourne Road Industrial Park, Bourne Road, Dartford, DA1 4BZ Tel: (01322) 552000 Fax: (01322) 552020 E-mail: info@kentonresearch.co.uk *Telecommunication equipment system manufrs*

Kentone Plastics Ltd, Town Farm, Campton Road, Gravenhurst, Bedford, MK45 4JB Tel: (01462) 711797 Fax: (01462) 711031 E-mail: kentoneplastics@hotmail.com *Injection mould toolmakers*

Kentra Grain Systems Ltd, Station Road, Kirk Hammerton, York, YO26 8DN Tel: (01423) 330085 Fax: (01423) 331347 E-mail: kentra@graindriers.com *Agricultural machinery manufrs*

▶ Kentvale Transport Ltd, Beacon Hill Industrial Estate, Botany Way, Purfleet, Essex, RM19 1SR Tel: (01708) 868833 Fax: (01708) 860901

Kenval Precision Grinding, 204 St Andrews Road, Northampton, NN2 6DA Tel: (01604) 622960 Fax: (01604) 630435 *Grinding services*

Charles Kenward Motors Ltd, 14 Sherwood Road, Bromsgrove, Worcestershire, B60 3DR Tel: (01527) 875432 Fax: (01527) 570088 *Motor vehicle repair & recovery*

Kenward Precision & Gear, Unit 1b & 13 Perseverance Mills, Lockwood Scar, Huddersfield, HD4 6BW Tel: (01484) 512355 Fax: (01484) 420793 E-mail: kenward@mywebpage.net *Precision engineering services*

▶ Kenward Pullen Ltd, Head Office & Works, York Road, St. Leonards-on-Sea, East Sussex, TN37 6PU Tel: (01424) 435900 Fax: (01424) 422500

Kenwell Precision Die Casting Ltd, 1 Smallbridge Industrial Park, Riverside Drive, Rochdale, Lancashire, OL16 2SH Tel: (01706) 640412 Fax: (01706) 711894 E-mail: sales@kenwellprecisiondiecastings.co.uk *High pressure zinc die casting manufrs*

Kenwood Appliances plc, New Lane, Havant, Hampshire, PO9 2NH Tel: (023) 9247 6000 Fax: (023) 9239 2400 E-mail: enquiries@kenwood.co.uk *Domestic electrical appliances*

Kenwood UK Ltd, Kenwood House, Dwight Road, Watford, WD18 9EB Tel: (01923) 816444 Fax: (01923) 819131 E-mail: comms@kenwood-electronics.co.uk *Communications equipment suppliers*

Kenworth Engineering Ltd, Jackson Place, Wilton Road Industrial Estate, Humberston, Grimsby, North East Lincolnshire, DN36 4AS Tel: (01472) 210678 Fax: (01472) 210912 E-mail: rob@kenworthengineering.co.uk *Precision engineers*

Kenyon Group Ltd, Regent House, Regent Street, Oldham, OL1 3TZ Tel: 0161-633 6328 Fax: 0161-627 5072 E-mail: sales@gluegunsdirect.com *Fluid mixers & pumping equipment conveyors*

Kenyon Road Haulage Ltd, Thornley Avenue, Blackburn, BB1 3HJ Tel: (01254) 503600 Fax: (01254) 503601 E-mail: sales@kenyon-haulage.com *Road haulage*

Robert Kenyon Ltd, PO Box 18, Bolton, BL3 6NH Tel: (01204) 523810 Fax: (01204) 364819 *Stationers & printers*

S.W. Kenyon, PO Box 71, Cranbrook, Kent, TN18 5ZR Tel: (01580) 850770 Fax: (01580) 850225 E-mail: swkenyon@btinternet.com *Photographic dulling spray manufrs*

William S Kenyon Ltd, 131 Town Street, Sandiacre, Nottingham, NG10 5DS Tel: 0115-939 8800 Fax: 0115-939 1404 E-mail: info@turnedparts.co.uk *CNC engineers*

Keplens Ltd, 94 Chester Road, Buckley, Clwyd, CH7 3AH Tel: (0870) 7418860 Fax: (0870) 7418861 E-mail: info@keplens.co.uk *Computer builders & sellers of software & internet*

Kepston Holdings Ltd, Unit 2 Coppice Lane, Walsall, WS9 9AA Tel: (01922) 743133 Fax: (01922) 743130 E-mail: sales@kepston.co.uk Principal Export Areas: Africa *Precision Grinding* Also at: Wednesbury & Whitburn

▶ Keramag Waveney Ltd, London Road, Beccles, Suffolk, NR34 8TS Tel: (01502) 716600 Fax: (01502) 717767 E-mail: kerrina@waveneybaths.co.uk *Bath manufrs*

▶ Keramag Waveney Ltd, London Road, Beccles, Suffolk, NR34 8TS Tel: (01502) 716600 Fax: (01502) 717767 E-mail: ian@keramagwaveney.co.uk *Bathroom distribution*

Keramikos Ltd, Lumsdale Mill, Lower Lumsdale, Matlock, Derbyshire, DE4 5EX Tel: (01629) 580033 Fax: (01629) 582234 E-mail: info@keramikos.co.uk *Decorative promotional mug manufrs*

Keraplate Ltd, 46 Holton Road, Holton Heath Trading Park, Poole, Dorset, BH16 6LT Tel: (01202) 622882 Fax: (01202) 632438 E-mail: sales@keraplate.co.uk *Nameplate & control panel manufrs*

Kerb Konus, Unit B5 Hortonwood 10, Telford, Shropshire, TF1 7ES Tel: (01952) 677388 Fax: (01952) 677488 E-mail: kkuk@pipex.com *Fastener thread locking, sealing conversion & insert manufrs*

Kered Engineering Ltd, 32-34 Carron Place, Kelvin, East Kilbride, Glasgow, G75 0YL Tel: (01355) 237016 Fax: (01355) 264366 E-mail: sales@nesso.co.uk *Engineers cutting tool manufrs*

continued

▶ indicates data change since last edition

Kerensa Systems Ltd, Unit 4, Mercers Road, Bury St. Edmunds, Suffolk, IP32 7HX Tel: (01284) 767334 Fax: (01284) 767335 E-mail: bsmith@kerensasystems.co.uk *Electrical engineers*

▶ Keridwen Crafts, Unit 4 - 6 Tyock Industrial Estate, Tyock Industrial Estate, Elgin, Morayshire, IV30 1XZ Tel: (01343) 551353

▶ Kerio Technologies Ltd, Sheraton House, Castle Park, Cambridge, CB3 0AX Tel: (01223) 370136 Fax: (01223) 370040

▶ Kerlectables, Lambshear Lane, Lydiate, Liverpool, L31 2LA Tel: 07985 905717 E-mail: kerlectables@tiscali.co.uk *Quality antique gifts, ceramics and novelty items at affordable prices. From the Victorian period and through the Art nouveau and Art deco eras to the present. Specialising in Royal Doulton figures, Clarice Cliff, perfume bottles and much more.*

Kern Ltd, Unit 5 Concorde Close, Fareham, Hampshire, PO15 5RT Tel: (01489) 564141 Fax: (01489) 565009 E-mail: info@kern.co.uk *Mailing equipment distributors*

Kerndale Ltd, Pontygwindy Industrial Estate, Caerphilly, Mid Glamorgan, CF83 3HU Tel: (029) 2086 5152 Fax: (029) 2088 7742 E-mail: tonydoel@kerndale.demon.co.uk *Precision engineers*

Kern-Liebers Ltd, Corringham Road Industrial Estate, Gainsborough, Lincolnshire, DN21 1QB Tel: (01427) 612085 Fax: (01427) 610301 E-mail: kl-uk@kern-liebers.com *Constant torque & clock type manufrs*

T. & A. Kernoghan Ltd, 5 Blackwater Road, Newtownabbey, County Antrim, BT36 4TZ Tel: (028) 9084 2311 Fax: (028) 9084 3107 E-mail: info@aol.com *Building contractors*

▶ Kernon Countryside Consultants, Brook Cottage, Purton Stoke, Swindon, SN5 4JE Tel: (01793) 771333 Fax: (01793) 778384 E-mail: sales@kernon.co.uk *Rural planning consultants*

Kernow Coatings Ltd, Kernick Road, Penryn, Cornwall, TR10 9DQ Tel: (01326) 373147 Fax: (01326) 376614 E-mail: kc@sensitisers.com *Sensitised coating specialists*

Kernow Fixings, Manfield Way, Holmbush Industrial Estate, St. Austell, Cornwall, PL25 3HQ Tel: (01726) 624600 Fax: (01726) 624604 *Fixing equipment manufrs*

Kernow Oils, Hayle Industrial Park, Hayle, Cornwall, TR27 5JR Tel: (01736) 757002 Fax: (01736) 757979 E-mail: sales@kernowoils.co.uk *Lubricating oils manufrs*

Kernow Plusfile, Winship Road, Milton, Cambridge, CB24 6BQ Tel: (01223) 425003 Fax: (01223) 425120 *Diaries & Personal Organisers*

Keronite Ltd, 26 Aintree Road, Keytec 7 Business Park, Pershore, Worcestershire, WR10 2JN Tel: (01386) 552032 Fax: (01386) 561261 E-mail: ics.systems@btconnect.com *Electroplating plant & equipment manufrs*

Kerr Fire Fighting Chemicals Ltd, Ashcroft Road, Knowsley Industrial Park, Kirkby, Liverpool, L33 7TS Tel: 0151-548 6424 Fax: 0151-548 7263 E-mail: info@kfp.co.uk Principal Export Areas: Worldwide *Fire fighting chemicals manufrs*

▶ John Kerr & Son (Dairymen) Ltd, Unit M 207, Strathmartine Road, Dundee, DD3 8PH Tel: (01382) 825018 *Dairy services*

▶ Kerr Multilingual, 41-42 Haven Green, Ealing, London, W5 2NX Tel: (020) 8810 7839 Fax: (020) 8998 0388 E-mail: info@kerr-recruitment.co.uk *Kerr Multilingual is a language recruitment specialist supplying skilled bilingual and trilingual candidates to businesses across London. Thorough registrations and language tests are carried out in-house to provide only talented linguists with relevant work histories.** **Kerr Multilingual has extensive experience in fulfilling staffing needs within the customer service, call centre, sales support, secretarial /administration, logistics and import /export markets. An extensive database ensures swift, appropriate response to recruitment requests.** **All of our consultants are bilingual or trilingual with international experience of different markets and educational systems therefore understand the challenges and cultural differences involved in recruiting multinational teams.*

Kerr & Noble Ltd, Welford Barn, Binton Road, Welford On Avon, Stratford-Upon-Avon, Warwickshire, CV37 8PT Tel: (01789) 751075 Fax: (01789) 751089 *Disposable paper product manufrs*

▶ Kerr Timber Products Ltd, Hecklegirth Works, Annan, Dumfriesshire, DG12 6SN Tel: (01461) 201622 Fax: (01461) 201633

Kerri Engineering, South March, Long March Industrial Estate, Daventry, Northamptonshire, NN11 4PH Tel: (01327) 876944 Fax: (01327) 300713 *General presswork manufacturers & tooling*

▶ Kerry D Ltd, 12 North Street, Pinxton, Nottingham, NG16 6LP Tel: (07971) 439487

Kerry Engineering, Unit 12 Isis Trading Estate, Swindon, SN1 2PG Tel: (01793) 423333 Fax: (01793) 423888 *Mechanical engineers & machinists*

Kerry Foods Ltd, Corinium Industrial Estate, Raans Road, Amersham, Buckinghamshire, HP6 6HU Tel: (01494) 721552 Fax: (01494) 432394 *Food distributors*

Kerry Foods Ltd, Rookery Farm, Attleborough Road, Little Ellingham, Attleborough, Norfolk, NR17 1JH Tel: (01953) 851076 Fax: (01953) 851441 *Food processing plant*

Kerry Foods Ltd, 76 Mosley Street, Burton-on-Trent, Staffordshire, DE14 1DS Tel: (01283) 561661 Fax: (01283) 511048 *Meat (processed & cooked) products manufrs*

▶ Kerry Foods Ltd, 69 Colvilles Place, Kelvin Industrial Estate, East Kilbride, Glasgow, G75 0PZ Tel: (01355) 247549 Fax: (01355) 247553 *Chilled foods distribution*

▶ Kerry Foods Ltd, Horsfield Way, Bredbury Park Industrial Estate, Bredbury, Stockport, Cheshire, SK6 2TE Tel: 0161-406 4500 Fax: 0161-406 4515

▶ Kerry Foods Direct Sales, Gravel Hill, Shirrell Heath, Southampton, SO32 2JQ Tel: (01329) 832542 Fax: (01329) 834786

Kerry Foodservice, Gatehouse Road, Gatehouse Industrial Area, Aylesbury, Buckinghamshire, HP19 8HH Tel: (01296) 318000 Fax: (01296) 338425 E-mail: info@kerry-foodservice.co.uk *Food ingredient suppliers*

Kerry Holdings UK Ltd, Thorpe Lea Manor, Thorpe Lea Road, Egham, Surrey, TW20 8HY Tel: (01784) 430777 Fax: (01784) 479597 E-mail: enquiries@kerryfoods.co.uk *Consumer food product distributor & manufrs*

Kerry Ingredients Ltd, Portbury Way, Royal Portbury Dock, Portbury, Bristol, BS20 7XN Tel: (01275) 378500 Fax: (01275) 378555 *Food ingredient producers*

Kerry Ingredients UK Ltd, Equinox South, Great Park Road, Bradley Stoke, Bristol, BS32 4QL Tel: (01454) 201666 Fax: (01454) 620711 E-mail: info@kerry-ingredients.co.uk *Food ingredients manufrs*

Kerry Ingredients UK Ltd, Carr Lane, Gainsborough, Lincolnshire, DN21 1LG Tel: (01427) 613927 Fax: (01427) 811805 *Bread crumb dressing products*

▶ Kerry Services Ltd, 6 The Walks East, Huntingdon, Cambridgeshire, PE29 3AP Tel: (01480) 391504 Fax: (01480) 386467 E-mail: info@kerrytrans.com *Technical translation service in all European and Far Eastern languages. Specialising in engineering and radio communications.*

▶ Kerry Ultrasonics, Snagill Industrial Estate, Keighley Road, Skipton, North Yorkshire, BD23 2QR Tel: (01756) 799911 Fax: (01756) 790213 E-mail: sales@guyson.co.uk *Ultrasonic cleaning equipment manufrs*

Kerryredd Surveying Equipment Ltd, 1206 London Road, London, SW16 4DN Tel: (020) 8679 7233 Fax: (020) 8679 9147 *Engineering & surveying consultants*

▶ Kerry's Castles, 18 Long Cliffe Close, Shafton, Barnsley, South Yorkshire, S72 8WJ Tel: (01226) 712975

Kershaw & Co. Ltd, Hixon Industrial Estate, Church Lane, Hixon, Stafford, ST18 0PY Tel: (01889) 270556 Fax: (01889) 271295 E-mail: sales@kershaw-engineering.co.uk *Precision turned parts manufrs*

Kershaw Insulation Ltd, Willowcroft Works, Broad Lane, Cottenham, Cambridge, CB4 8SW Tel: (01954) 250155 Fax: (01954) 251628 E-mail: sales.office@kershaw-insulation.co.uk *Insulation contractors*

Joshua Kershaw & Co. Ltd, Water Street, Stockport, Cheshire, SK1 2BP Tel: 0161-480 3423 Fax: 0161-480 8106 E-mail: office@kershawleather.com *Tanners, leather dressers & finishers*

▶ Kershaw Mechanical Services Ltd, Beadle Trading Estate, Ditton Walk, Cambridge, CB5 8PD Tel: (01223) 715800 Fax: (01223) 411061 E-mail: enquiries@kershaw-grp.co.uk Purchasing Contact: I. Greenstock *Building engineering (mechanical) services, heating & ventilation engineers, installation or service, ventilation engineers installation or service. In house ductwork, manufacturer and full maintenance facility. Over 50 years expertise*

Kershaw Signs, 31 Harrowby Road, Leeds, LS16 5HX Tel: 0113-278 5873 *Signwriters & sign manufacturers*

Thomas Kershaw Ltd, Unit 10, Walnesley Court, Accrington, Lancashire, BB5 5JQ Tel: (01254) 875550 Fax: (01254) 875551 E-mail: tkfabrics@hotmail.com *Textile merchant laminators & converters*

Kershaw's Health Foods, 127 Queen Street, Whitehaven, Cumbria, CA28 7QF Tel: (01946) 66627 Fax: (01946) 599237 *Health food merchants*

Kershaw's Rubber Stamps, Cotton Hall Street, Darwen, Lancashire, BB3 0DW Tel: (01254) 703040 Fax: (01254) 703373 E-mail: info@planetree.co.uk *Rubber stamp manufrs*

Kerstar Ltd, 10-16 St. Georges Street, Northampton, NN1 2TR Tel: (01604) 637531 Fax: (01604) 620796 E-mail: sales@kerstar.co.uk *Vacuum cleaner manufrs*

Kerswell Tooling Services Ltd, Britannic Lodge, Britannic Way, Llandarcy, Neath, West Glamorgan, SA10 6EL Tel: (01792) 812101 Fax: (01792) 814575 E-mail: sales@kerswelltoolingservices.com *Engineers' tool distributors*

Kerton Plastics Ltd, Unit 2 Phoenix Way, Gorseinon, Swansea, SA4 9WF Tel: (01792) 897779 Fax: (01792) 896668 E-mail: enquiries@kerton.co.uk *Plastic & glass fibre fabricators*

Kes, 262 Ashley Road, Poole, Dorset, BH14 9BZ Tel: (01202) 742393 Fax: (01202) 722042 *Power tool services & retailers*

KES Power & Light Ltd, Stanton Road, Southampton, SO15 4HU Tel: (023) 8070 4703 Fax: (023) 8070 1430 E-mail: sakes@kes.co.uk *Electrical manufrs*

Kespar Engineering Ltd, Johnson House Bilston Industrial Estate, Oxford Street, Bilston, West Midlands, WV14 7EG Tel: (01902) 353848 Fax: (01902) 494939 E-mail: andywalker@kespar.co.uk *Die & tool treatment reclamation*

Kesslers International Ltd, 11 Rick Roberts Way, London, E15 2NF Tel: (020) 8522 3000 Fax: (020) 8522 3129 E-mail: kesslers@kesslers.com *Point of sale unit manufrs*

Kesson Engineering Co., Manor Drive North, New Malden, Surrey, KT3 5PN Tel: (020) 8337 0800 Fax: (020) 8335 3047 *Precision engineers*

Kesta At David Barry Ltd, 7-9 Solebay Street, London, E1 4PW Tel: (020) 7790 2525 Fax: (020) 7790 5656 E-mail: sales@kesta.co.uk *Ladies coat wholesalers & manufrs*

Kesteven Plastics Ltd, Unit 3, Moorland Way, Tritton Road, Lincoln, LN6 7JW Tel: (01522) 695977 Fax: (01522) 695977 E-mail: george@kestevenplasticsltd.co.uk *Plastics fabricators*

Kestlin Diesel Services Ltd, Bar Lane, Waddington, Lincoln, LN5 9SA Tel: (01522) 722900 Fax: (01522) 722922 E-mail: kestlin.diesel@virgin.net *Marine diesel engineers*

Kestmark Precision Engineering, 3 Winster Grove Industrial Estate, Winster Grove, Birmingham, B44 9EG Tel: 0121-360 8850 Fax: 0121-360 8850 E-mail: eng@kestmark.fsnet.co.uk *Precision engineers*

Keston Boilers Ltd, 34 West Common Road, Bromley, BR2 7BX Tel: (020) 8462 0262 Fax: (020) 8462 4459E-mail: info@keston.co.uk *Boilers*

Kestral Controls Ltd, 3 Garrell Road, Kilsyth, Glasgow, G65 9JX Tel: (01236) 821564 Fax: (01236) 825676 E-mail: sales@kestralcontrols.co.uk *Control panel manufrs*

Kestrel, Heaton Road, Bradford, West Yorkshire, BD9 4SH Tel: (01274) 360404 Fax: (01274) 360401 E-mail: sales.kestrel@haddowholdingsplc.com *Curtain accessories, fabrics & soft furnishing retailers*

Kestrel Building Services Ltd, George Street, High Wycombe, Buckinghamshire, HP11 2RZ Tel: (01494) 474398 Fax: (01494) 472540 E-mail: info@kestreloffice.com *Office interior designers*

▶ Kestrel Electrical Systems Ltd, 85-86 High Street, Rowley Regis, West Midlands, B65 0EH Tel: 0121-559 2929 Fax: 0121-559 9933 E-mail: info@keslimited.co.uk

Kestrel Electronic Components Ltd, 178 Brighton Road, Purley, Surrey, CR8 4HA Tel: (020) 8668 7522 Fax: (020) 8668 4190 *Electronic components distributors*

Kestrel Engineering, School Works, School Lane, Coleorton, Coalville, Leicestershire, LE67 8HT Tel: (01530) 223100 Fax: (01530) 223100 E-mail: kestrelengineering@btinternet.com *Hand tool manufrs*

Kestrel Engineering, 9 Dartmouth Buildings, Fort Fareham Industrial Site, Fareham, Hampshire, PO14 1AH Tel: (01329) 233443 Fax: (01329) 284148 E-mail: alan.s.walker@talk21.com Sales Contact: A.S. Walker *Manufacturers of cycle stands & cycle display equipment. Also, display metal equipment & shop fittings manufrs*

Kestrel Equipment Ltd, 21-23, Scott Road, Luton, LU3 3BF Tel: (01582) 563600 Fax: (01582) 563323 E-mail: info@kestrelequipment.co.uk *Pneumatic tools distributors*

Kestrel Group Ltd, Unit 1-2 York Street, St. Werburghs, Bristol, BS2 9XT Tel: 0117-955 7524 Fax: 0117-955 8157 *Continuous stationery & commercial printers*

▶ Kestrel Mechanical Services Ltd, Betsom Farm, 2 Pilgrims Way, Westerham, Kent, TN16 2DS Tel: (01959) 564269 Fax: (01959) 564387

Kestrel Pest Control, Rooks Ridge, Up Somborne, Stockbridge, Hampshire, SO20 6RB Tel: (01794) 388346 Fax: (01794) 388608 *Pest controllers*

Kestrel Powered Access Ltd, 5 Victoria Terrace, St. Philips, Bristol, BS2 0TD Tel: 0117-958 8888 Fax: 0117-972 4125 E-mail: sales@kestrelaccess.co.uk *Access equipment hire*

▶ Kestrel Press Irvine Ltd, 25 Whittle Place, South Newmoor Industrial Estate, Irvine, Ayrshire, KA11 4HR Tel: (01294) 222222 Fax: (01294) 222219 E-mail: sales@kestrelpress.com

Kestrel Printing Ltd, Journeymans Way, Temple Farm Industrial Estate, Southend-On-Sea, SS2 5TF Tel: (01702) 444888 Fax: (01702) 444880 E-mail: sales@kestrel-printing.co.uk *Commercial printers* Also at: Cambridge

▶ Kestrel Thermoplastics Ltd, 3 High Street, Prescot, Merseyside, L34 3LD Tel: 0151-426 9969 Fax: 0151-430 6633 E-mail: sales@kestrelplastics.com *Road marking materials*

Keswick Trays, Forest View Farm, Peckleton Lane, Desford, Leicester, LE9 9JU Tel: (01455) 828990 Fax: (01455) 828999 E-mail: david@keswicktrays.f9.co.uk *Glass fibre tray manufrs*

Ketchum, 35-41 Folgate Street, London, E1 6BX Tel: (020) 7611 3500 Fax: (020) 7611 3501 *Public relations services*

Ketech Systems, Glaisdale Dr East, Nottingham, NG8 4GR Tel: 0115-900 5600 Fax: 0115-900 5601 E-mail: enquiry@ketech.com *Industrial design systems engineers*

Keter U.K Ltd, 12-14 Kettles Wood Drive, Birmingham, B32 3DB Tel: 0121-422 6633 Fax: 0121-422 0808 E-mail: sales@outstanding-keter.com *Plastics injection moulders*

Ketlon Ltd, Paddock Wood Distribution Centre, Paddock Wood, Tonbridge, Kent, TN12 6UU Tel: (01892) 835555 Fax: (01892) 832389 E-mail: sales@ketlon.co.uk *General engineers & automotive component manufrs*

Kettering Bodycraft Ltd, Henson Way, Telford Way Industrial Estate, Kettering, Northamptonshire, NN16 8PX Tel: (01536) 483739 Fax: (01536) 511500 *Vehicle accident repairs*

Kettering Compressed Air Services Ltd, 16 Cross Street, Kettering, Northamptonshire, NN16 9DQ Tel: (01536) 516482 Fax: (01536) 411842 E-mail: sales@kcas.co.uk *Air compressor distributors*

Kettering Koi & Ponds Ltd, 63-65 Field Street, Kettering, Northamptonshire, NN16 8EW Tel: (01536) 515304 Fax: (01536) 515304 *Aquarium center*

Kettering Surgical Appliances Ltd, 73 Overstone Road, Northampton, NN1 3JW Tel: (01604) 622886 Fax: (01604) 629689 E-mail: paul@ketteringsurgical.com *Orthopaedic product manufrs*

R.E. & P. Kettle Ltd, 11 Ruston Road, Grantham, Lincolnshire, NG31 9SW Tel: 01476 563473 *Welders & fabricators*

▶ The Kettlebell Company Ltd, 4 Lockers Park Lane, Hemel Hempstead, Hertfordshire, HP1 1TH Tel: (01442) 247218 E-mail: sales@kettlebell.co.uk *Kettlebells for exercise and competition*

Kettler (GB) Ltd, Merse Road, North Moons Moat, Redditch, Worcestershire, B98 9HL Tel: (01527) 591901 Fax: (01527) 62423 E-mail: sales@kettler.co.uk *Garden furniture & fitness equipment distributors*

Kevin Johnson Contracting, 4 Church Road, Wittering, Peterborough, PE8 6AG Tel: (01780) 782924 Fax: (01780) 782924 E-mail: info@sandhill-gardencentre.co.uk *Agricultural contractors*

Kevington Building Products Ltd, Unit 7 Ludgershall Business Park, New Drove Road, Ludgershall, Andover, Hampshire, SP11 9RN Tel: (01264) 790400 Fax: (01264) 791762 *Prefabricated GRP chimney systems.*

Kevington Building Products Ltd, Rowfant Bus Centre, Wallage Lane, Turners Hill, Crawley, West Sussex, RH10 4NG Tel: (01342) 718899 Fax: (01342) 718528 E-mail: sales@kevingtonbrick.com *Brick Wall Cladding Panels.*

Kevington Building Products Ltd, Unit 27 Creeting Road, Stowmarket, Suffolk, IP14 5AY Tel: (01449) 770200 Fax: (01449) 771199 *Brick arches with lintels.*

Kevin's Cloth Emporium, 39 Victoria Road, Ruislip, Middlesex, HA4 9AB Tel: (01895) 624333 Fax: (01895) 623114 *Pool & snooker distributors*

Kew Computers, 78 Woolmer Way, Bordon, Hampshire, GU35 9QF Tel: (01420) 479666 Fax: (01420) 488348 E-mail: info@kewcomputers.com *Computer maintenance & repairers*

▶ Kew Electrical Distributor Ltd, 2 Chapel Road, Portslade, Brighton, BN41 1PF Tel: (01273) 420452 Fax: (01273) 418060 E-mail: darren@kewelectrical.co.uk *Lighting equipment suppliers*

▶ Kew Health and Beauty Ltd, Wallace House, New Abbey Court, 51 - 53 Stert Street, Abingdon, Oxfordshire, OX14 3JF Tel: (0870) 7607586 Fax: (0870) 7607598 E-mail: info@kewhb.co.uk *Luxury health, beauty, cosmetic & personal care products*

Kew Technik Ltd, Rankine Road, Basingstoke, Hampshire, RG24 8PP Tel: (01256) 864100 Fax: (01256) 864164 E-mail: sales@kewt.co.uk *Hand tool distributors & manufrs*

Kewal Brothers Textiles Ltd, Unit 51/52 Bridge Trading Estate, Bridge Street North, Smethwick, West Midlands, B66 2BZ Tel: 0121-555 8080 Fax: 0121-555 8081 *Coat & anorak manufrs*

▶ Keweld Ltd, 109 Sadler Road, Lincoln, LN6 3RS Tel: (01522) 691723 Fax: (01522) 500855 E-mail: keweldltd@btconnect.com *Specialists welders*

Kewell Converters Ltd, 60 Holmethorpe Avenue, Redhill, RH1 2NL Tel: (01737) 771710 Fax: (01737) 769732 E-mail: sales@kewell-converters.co.uk Principal Export Areas: Central/East Europe, West Europe & North America *One of the UK's leading converters/fabricators of polyethylene foam, and other cellular foams and rubbers, for use in all areas of industry, not just packaging! Products include foam sheets and strips, gaskets, case inserts, end caps, foam display/presentation units, expansions joint fillers. In house fabrication facilities include 5 axis CNC routing, high-pressure water jet cutting, die cutting (automatic), and vertical & horizontal NC cutting.*

Kewmill Construction Ltd, Dagnall Road, High Wycombe, Buckinghamshire, HP12 4AN Tel: (01442) 843333 Fax: (01442) 842297 *Suspended ceilings suppliers*

Kewtube Ltd, 63 Bideford Avenue, Perivale, Greenford, Middlesex, UB6 7PT Tel: (020) 8991 0062 Fax: (020) 8991 2883 E-mail: info@kewtube.com *Kewtube Ltd, specialising in Tube Bending and Tube manipulation services covering the whole of the UK and Europe. We offer a complete range of welding including MIG welding, TIG welding and brazing as well as hydraulic pressure testing of welding fabrications. Our services also include CNC bending, coiling, end forming, flaring and rolling ,CNC Milling, Turning and Drilling. We are able to work in all different types of metal including mild steel tube bending, stainless steel tube bending, aluminium tube bending, brass tube bending and copper tube bending. Kewtube Ltd are also able to offer powder coated tubular products or pain t ing in our in house facilities. The company produces tubes for use in a wide variety of applications: compressors, agricultural machinery, dishwashers, shop fitting and heat exchangers, among others. We also produce architectural metalwork, point of sale display frames, exhaust, compressor and hydraulic pipes.*

▶ Key Associate Group, Orbit House Second Floor, Albert Street, Eccles, Manchester, M30 0BL Tel: 0161-707 9448 Fax: (0870) 2320090 E-mail: Natasha.Karimi@Keyassociategroup.com *Key Associate Group is a highly reputable executive resource consultancy. Delivering high caliber and exceptional recruitment solutions for candidates and clients alike. Covering a comprehensive and highly professional range of sectors with particular care in making sure that we match your defined criteria through a professional selection process. **Our strength's lie in the expertise that resides in our individual specialist divisions, with each offering a different focus and sector experience. We deliver speedy services with creative and innovative solutions. We strongly believe our success is built around our commitment, knowledge & expertise within our specialist market sectors.***

Key Audio Visual Services, Black Tower Studios, 15 Bracondale, Norwich, NR1 2AL Tel: (01603) 616661 Fax: (01603) 616668 E-mail: sales@keyav.com *Conference organising services*

Key Catering plc, 33-34 Eastbury Road, London, E6 6GP Tel: (020) 7511 4100 Fax: (020) 7511 0417 E-mail: sales@keycatering.co.uk *Catering vending & hygiene products distributors* Also at: Birmingham, Manchester, Portsmouth & Scotland

Key Coatings, 288 Aberdeen Avenue, Slough, SL1 4HG Tel: (01753) 537775 Fax: (01753) 570869 *Stove enamelling & powder coating*

Key Communication Systems Ltd, Key House, 21 Bourne Road, Bexley, Kent, DA5 1LW Tel: (01322) 555522 Fax: (01322) 555227 E-mail: info@keycoms.co.uk *Specialised dealing equipment manufrs*

Key Computer Applications, Cavern House, Ellesmere Street, Leigh, Lancashire, WN7 4LQ Tel: (01942) 261671 Fax: (01942) 260262 *Computer support*

Key Consultancy Ltd, 277 Birmingham Road, Bromsgrove, Worcestershire, B61 0EP Tel: (01527) 575182 Fax: (01527) 576288 E-mail: sales@thekeyconsultancy.co.uk *We provide health, safety & environmental training/ consultancy at practitioner, manager, supervisor, operative & specialist levels. We are an accredited provider of the NEBOSH Certificate, Diploma Parts 1 & 2, Level 4 Diploma, & Specialist Diploma in Environmental Management; we also deliver IEMA, IOSH & short topical courses at our training venue in the Midlands. All of our courses can be delivered at client premises worldwide & from April 2005 we will be offering many of our accredited courses through a training organisation in the Middle East.*

Key Controls Ltd, Unit 6 Spring Street, Keighley, West Yorkshire, BD21 3LE Tel: (01535) 604133 Fax: (01535) 604341 *Process control systems manufrs*

Key Data Group Ltd, Lincoln Street, Old Basford, Nottingham, NG6 0FT Tel: 0115-942 2266 Fax: 0115-942 0065 E-mail: info@keydatagroup.co.uk *Market research*

Key Electronic Components, 4 Kitwood Drive, Lower Earley, Reading, RG6 3TA Tel: 0118-935 1546 Fax: 0118-966 0294 E-mail: sales@keyelectronic.com *Specialist cooling fan distributors*

▶ Key Enterprises, Ravenscraig Hospital, Inverkip Road, Greenock, Renfrewshire, PA16 9HA Tel: (01475) 727722 Fax: (01475) 727722

Key Factors, 11 Cannon Grove, Fetcham, Leatherhead, Surrey, KT22 9LG Tel: (01372) 376904 Fax: (01372) 376904 E-mail: sales@keyfactors.co.uk *Manufacturers of domed emblems*

Key Health Care Ltd, Key Health Care, Ashpoole House, Sandy Lane, Lowton, Warrington, WA3 1BG Tel: (01942) 673315 Fax: (01942) 673315 *Janitorial products supply*

Key Information Systems Ltd, P O Box 7283, Tamworth, Staffs, B77 1QQ Tel: 01827 250807

Key It Systems Ltd, Brake Lane, Boughton, Newark, Nottinghamshire, NG22 9HQ Tel: (01623) 863556 Fax: (01623) 863203 E-mail: brian@keyits.co.uk *Computer consultants*

Key Joinery Ltd, Peveril House, Alfreton Road, Derby, DE21 4AG Tel: (01332) 331457 Fax: (01332) 206434 E-mail: sales@key-joinery.co.uk *Specialist joinery item manufrs*

▶ Key Lighting, 37 Dulverton Road, Birmingham, B6 7EQ Tel: 0121-322 2300 Fax: 0121-328 5050 *Lighting distributors*

▶ Key Networks Ltd, 10 Imperial Square, Cheltenham, Gloucestershire, GL50 1QB Tel: (01242) 245340 E-mail: info@keynetworks.co.uk *Complete it outsourcing & consultancy services*

Key Note Ltd, Field House, 72 Oldfield Road, Hampton, Middlesex, TW12 2HQ Tel: (020) 8481 8750 Fax: (020) 8783 0049 E-mail: sales@keynote.co.uk *Market information services & publishers*

Key Paint Ltd, 1 Eldon Road, Luton, LU4 0AZ Tel: (01582) 572627 Fax: (01582) 593489 *Automotive paint distributors*

Key Safety Systems UK Ltd, Norfolk Street, Carlisle, CA2 5HX Tel: (01228) 591711 Fax: (01228) 546994 E-mail: reception@keysafetyinc.com *Car safety belt manufrs*

▶ The Key Shop Ltd, 14D High Street, Lutterworth, Leicestershire, LE17 4AD Tel: (01455) 554999 E-mail: ian@thekeyshop.co.uk *Locksmiths & security safe services*

▶ The Key Shop Lutterworth Ltd, 14 High Street, Lutterworth, Leicestershire, LE17 4AD Tel: (01455) 554999 Fax: (01455) 554999 E-mail: ian@thekeyshop.co.uk *24 hr lock & door opening service*

Key Steering System Ltd, Unit 2675 Kings Court, The Crescent, Birmingham Business Park, Birmingham, B37 7YE Tel: 0121-717 5230 Fax: 0121-717 5236 E-mail: aston.c@keysafetyinc.com *Steering wheel & leather goods distributors*

Key Vehicle Solutions, 80a Main Street, Cherry Burton, Beverley, North Humberside, HU17 7RF Tel: (0845) 1662405 Fax: (0845) 1662406 E-mail: sales@key-vehicle-solutions.co.uk *Vehicle leasing & contract hire*

▶ Key Wear, 9 Frances Street, Truro, Cornwall, TR1 3DN Tel: (01872) 242233 Fax: (01872) 262390 *Uniform clothing manufrs*

▶ Key3 Partners, 12 Davy Court, Central Park, Rugby, Warwickshire, CV23 0WE Tel: 01788 540550 Fax: 01788 575484 E-mail: enquires@key3partners.com *Key3 Partners is a dynamic team of experts delivering logistics efficiency through operational and systems improvements. Six Sigma improvement tools give us the unique edge to drive out more savings than traditional logistics consultants. Our aim is to partner with clients from start to finish; from the business case creation through to full delivery of the benefits, demonstrating independence and neutrality in our approach.*

Keycare Midlands Ltd, High Edge Court, Church Street, Heage, Belper, Derbyshire, DE56 2BW Tel: (01773) 854141 Fax: (01773) 856203 E-mail: enquiries@keycare-midlands.co.uk *Building contractors*

▶ Keycraft Nottingham, 24 West Street, Hucknall, Nottingham, NG15 7BY Tel: 0115-963 0323 Fax: 0115-963 0323

Keyence UK Ltd, Avebury House, 219-225 Avebury Boulevard, Milton Keynes, MK9 1AU Tel: (01908) 696900 Fax: (01908) 696777 E-mail: ukinfo@keyence.co.uk *Supplier of advanced factory automation products*

Keyford Precision Engineering (Frome) Ltd, Olympic House, Whitworth Road, Marston Trading Estate, Frome, Somerset, BA11 4BY Tel: (01373) 463455 Fax: (01373) 452050 E-mail: sales@keyford.co.uk *Precision & electronic engineers*

Keyford Silverware, Roundabout Cottage, Hanch, Lichfield, Staffordshire, WS13 8HQ Tel: (01543) 264275 Fax: (01543) 257076 *Jewellery manufrs*

▶ Keyframe (UK) Ltd, Unit 32, Lyon Industrial Estate, Moss Lane, Kearsley, Bolton, BL4 8NB Tel: (01204) 705718 Fax: (01204) 705812 *UPVc window fabricators*

Keyland Services Ltd, 7 Timbertop Road, Biggin Hill, Westerham, Kent, TN16 3QR Tel: (01959) 540670 Fax: (01959) 540670 E-mail: sales@keylandservices.com *Special lubrication services*

Keylighting Ltd, Northbrook Works, Alkincote Street, Keighley, West Yorkshire, BD21 5JT Tel: (01535) 616300 Fax: (01535) 616301 E-mail: sales@keylighting.co.uk *Lighting manufrs*

Keyline Ltd, Bentinck Street, Ashton-under-Lyne, Lancashire, OL7 0PT Tel: 0161-330 2214 Fax: 0161-343 2158 *Builders merchants* Also at: Stalybridge

Keyline Ltd, Scotia Business Park, Scotia Road, Stoke-on-Trent, ST6 4HG Tel: (01782) 811999 Fax: (01782) 813999 *Timber, builders & plumbers merchants*

Keyline Associates Ltd, High Meres Road, Leicester, LE4 9LZ Tel: 0116-276 1371 Fax: 0116-274 1570 E-mail: display@keline.co.uk *Point of purchase & display manufrs*

Keyline Brick & Builders Merchant, Beaufort Road, Plasmarl, Swansea, SA6 8HR Tel: (01792) 792264 Fax: (01792) 796279 E-mail: swanseavea@keyline.co.uk *Building materials merchants* Also at: Kilgetty & Pontypool

Keyline Brick & Builders Merchant, Beaufort Road, Plasmarl, Swansea, SA6 8HR Tel: (01792) 792264 Fax: (01792) 796279 *Builders merchants* Also at: Cardiff

Keyline Builders Merchant, 2A Hospital Road, Haddington, East Lothian, EH41 3BH Tel: (01620) 822472 Fax: (01620) 825689 *Building materials distributors*

Keyline Builders Merchants Ltd, Station Lane, Birtley, Chester le Street, County Durham, DH2 1AW Tel: 0191-410 2708 Fax: 0191-492 2104 E-mail: angela.mcrobbie@keyline.co.uk *Builders merchants*

Keyline Builders Merchants Ltd, 1 Bath Road, Edinburgh, EH6 7BB Tel: 0131-519 5000 Fax: 0131-519 5051 *Kitchen furniture & building materials* Also at: Branches throughout the U.K.

Keyline Builders Merchants Ltd, 130 Salkeld Street, Glasgow, G5 8HD Tel: 0141-429 5141 Fax: 0141-429 4992 *Timber & joinery sales*

Keyline Builders Merchants Ltd, 1 Strathkelvin Place, Kirkintilloch, Glasgow, G66 1XH Tel: 0141-777 8979 Fax: 0141-775 1420 E-mail: welcome@keyline.co.uk *Builders merchants* Also at: Branches throughout the U.K.

Keyline Builders Merchants Ltd, Moulton Park Industrial Estate, Northampton, NN3 6TE Tel: (01604) 643622 Fax: (01604) 790353 E-mail: welcome@keylineco.uk *Builders merchants* Also at: Branches throughout the U.K.

Keyline Windows, K Key Industrial Park, Fernside Road, Willenhall, West Midlands, WV13 3YA Tel: (01902) 307685 Fax: (01902) 865800 E-mail: enquiries@keylinewindows.com *Windows, doors & conservatories manufrs*

▶ Keylock Mobile Locksmiths, 30 Caernarvon Way, Rumney, Cardiff, CF3 1RY Tel: (029) 2021 3446 Fax: (029) 2021 3446 E-mail: keylockuk@ntlworld.com *24 hours emergency call out locksmith*

Keymax International Ltd, West Road, Templefields, Harlow, Essex, CM20 2AL Tel: (01279) 454455 Fax: (01279) 445550 E-mail: ttrsales@keymax.co.uk *Carbon paper & laser cartridge exporters*

Keymed Ltd, Keymed House, Stock Road, Southend-on-Sea, SS2 5QH Tel: (01702) 616333 Fax: (01702) 465677 E-mail: keymed@keymed.co.uk *Optical & medical equipment manufrs*

Keymer Tiles Ltd, Nye Road, Burgess Hill, West Sussex, RH15 0LZ Tel: (01444) 232931 Fax: (01444) 871852 E-mail: info@keymer.co.uk *Hand made clay roof tiles*

Keymesh Ltd, Premier Business Centre, Attwood Street, Stourbridge, West Midlands, DY9 8RY Tel: (01384) 898899 Fax: (01384) 898775 E-mail: sales@keymesh.com Principal Export Areas: Africa *Packaging material distributors*

Keynes Controls, PO Box 7828, Crowthorne, Berkshire, RG45 7NE Tel: (01344) 752036 Fax: (01344) 752233 E-mail: sales@keynes-controls.com *Data acquisition*

Keynote Business Services Ltd, Unit 46 Alpha Business Centre, 60 South Grove, London, E17 7NX Tel: (020) 8926 9216 Fax: (020) 8926 9216 E-mail: info@keynotes.co.uk *Web design*

Keypaint Ltd, 329 London Road, Hemel Hempstead, Hertfordshire, HP3 9AL Tel: (01442) 262915 Fax: (01442) 267734 E-mail: eurocolour@auto-net.co.uk *Supplies to automotive & refinishes trade*

Keyplan Shopfitting Ltd, Wharfside, Festival Way, Stoke-on-Trent, ST1 5PU Tel: (01782) 285596 Fax: (01782) 204365 E-mail: mike@keyplanshopfit.co.uk *Shop fitters*

Keypower Consultants Ltd, Kingswood House, Baxter Avenue, Southend-on-Sea, SS2 6BG Tel: (01702) 431666 Fax: (01702) 353825 E-mail: mail@kpcl.com *Computer consultants*

▶ Keyreels UK Ltd, 20 New Road, Trimley St Mary, Trimley St. Mary, Felixstowe, Suffolk, IP11 0TQ Tel: (01394) 213306 Fax: (020) 7117 3271 E-mail: shop@keyreels.com *Retractable key chain wholesalers, promotional & security products*

Keys Electrical Wholesalers, 4 Elder Road, Leeds, LS13 4DL Tel: 0113-236 1486 Fax: 0113-236 1487 E-mail: keysdata@nildram.co.uk *Computer wholesales*

Keys Mcmahon, 15 Bay Road, Londonderry, BT48 7SH Tel: (028) 7136 6321 Fax: (028) 7136 4388 E-mail: info@rkeys.com *Timber & builders merchants*

Keys of Steel Ltd, Stringes Lane, Willenhall, West Midlands, WV13 1LF Tel: (01902) 606816 Fax: (01902) 636733 E-mail: sales@willenhall-locks.co.uk *Key, lock & hardware manufrs*

W.H. Keys Ltd, Hall End Works, Church Lane, West Bromwich, West Midlands, B71 1BN Tel: 0121-553 0206 Fax: 0121-500 5820 E-mail: sales@wh-keys.fsnet.com *Bituminous preparations & solution manufrs*

Keysecure UK Ltd, 39-40 Seymour Road, Nuneaton, Warwickshire, CV11 4JD Tel: (024) 7637 4888 Fax: (024) 7637 4666 E-mail: info@keysecure-uk..com *Roof edge protection*

Keyspace Ltd, Raven Street, Hull, HU9 1PP Tel: (01482) 326565 Fax: (01482) 216337 E-mail: sales@keyspace.co.uk *Port cabin & building hire*

▶ Keystone, 204 Duggins Lane, Coventry, CV4 9GP Tel: (024) 7642 2580 *Natural stone floor layer & designer*

Keystone Computers, 17 Perry Vale, London, SE23 2NE Tel: (020) 8699 4546 Fax: (020) 8473 8361 *Computer building system manufrs*

▶ Keystone Creative Ltd, 7A London Road, Alderley Edge, Cheshire, SK9 7JT Tel: (01625) 865611 Fax: (01625) 865775 E-mail: info@keystonecreative.co.uk *Marketing agency - business development & management consultancy*

Keystone Media, Units 4 & 5, The Old Creamery, Highbridge, Somerset, TA9 3DF Tel: (01278) 780438 Fax: (01278) 793858 *Computer accessories distributors*

▶ Keystone Restoration Ltd, 39 Station Road, Longfield, Kent, DA3 7QD Tel: (01474) 703600 Fax: (01474) 703100 E-mail: mail@kystm.co.uk *Stone restoration & tiling & restoration*

Keystone Software Developments Ltd, 84 Commercial Road, Grantham, Lincolnshire, NG31 6DB Tel: (01476) 562447 E-mail: info@keystonesoftware.co.uk *Authors of Khaos Control, leading UK sales order processing and stock control software application with integrated financials and CRM capabilities. Khaos Control has been specially adapted to address the business needs of two distinct market sectors, which are MAIL-ORDER companies and FOOD /MEAT /FRESH PRODUCE businesses.*

▶ Keytech, Inter Scot House, Midfield Road, Mitchelston Industrial Estate, Kirkcaldy, Fife, KY1 3NL Tel: (01592) 597734 Fax: (01592) 597719

▶ Keytel International, 402 Edgware Road, London, W2 1ED Tel: (020) 7616 0300 Fax: (020) 7616 0317 E-mail: enquiries@keytel.co.uk *Keytel is the only official UK booking agent for Spanish paradors. Over 00 high standard European hotels. Personal service, competitive prices, online reservation system.*

Keytons, Newton Road, Sudbury, Suffolk, CO10 6RN Tel: (01787) 882338 *Car mechanics*

Keytronics, 88 Hadham Road, Bishop's Stortford, Hertfordshire, CM23 2QT Tel: (01279) 505543 Fax: (01279) 757656 E-mail: pk@keytronics.co.uk *Buying & selling integrated circuits*

▶ Keyway Gloucester, The Luther Challis Business Centre, Barnwood Road, Gloucester, GL4 3HX Tel: (01452) 300567 Fax: (01452) 381381 E-mail: sales@keyway.co.uk

Keyways Security Systems Ltd, Keyways House, 337 Hale Road, Hale Barns, Altrincham, Cheshire, WA15 8SX Tel: 0161-980 6655 Fax: 0161-904 0768 E-mail: info@keyways.co.uk *CCTV installers, locksmiths, access control fitters*

▶ Keyword Typesetting Services Ltd, 30 Stafford Road, Wallington, Surrey, SM6 9AA Tel: (020) 8773 2433 Fax: (020) 8669 4963 *Typesetting for publishing industry*

Keyzone Computer Products Ltd, 497 Sunleigh Road, Wembley, Middlesex, HA0 4LY Tel: (020) 8900 1525 Fax: (020) 8903 1486 E-mail: enquiries@keyzone.com *Computer peripheral equipment manufrs*

Kezvale Ltd, 5 Johnsons Industrial Estate, Silverdale Road, Hayes, Middlesex, UB3 3BA Tel: (020) 8569 2731 Fax: (020) 8569 2790 E-mail: info@kezvale.co.uk *PCB control manufrs*

▶ KFL Leisure, Prospecthill, Falkirk, FK1 5LD Tel: 01324 410987 Fax: 01324 410987 E-mail: info@kflleisure.com *Uk Retailer of Table Tennis Tables and Accessories*

▶ KG Contractors Ltd, 184 Avenue Farm, Sutton Bridge, Spalding, Lincolnshire, PE12 9QF Tel: (01406) 359115 Fax: (01406) 359114

KGM Roofing, Glenside South, Glenside, Pinchbeck, Spalding, Lincolnshire, PE11 3SA Tel: (01775) 717800 Fax: (01775) 717829 *Roofing & cladding contractors*

Khan Consultants Ltd, 7 Beech Drive, Woodville, Swadlincote, Derbyshire, DE11 7DA Tel: (01283) 552994 Fax: (01283) 558209 E-mail: info@khanconbsultants.co.uk *Software development*

▶ Khan Fashion Studio, Unit 4, 344-346 St. Saviours Road, Leicester, LE5 4HJ Tel: 0116-273 6882 Fax: 0116-273 6882

▶ Khaydor Ltd, Yr Hen Swyddfa Bost, Waunfawr, Aberystwyth, Dyfed, SY23 3QD Tel: (01970) 611320 *Computer software developers*

▶ Khipu Networks Ltd, Infineon House, Minley Road, Fleet, Hampshire, GU51 2RD Tel: (01252) 773184 Fax: (01252) 629008 E-mail: sales@khipu-networks.com *Advanced systems integrator providing secure networks*

▶ Khusvinder Gill, The Chestnuts, Long Eaton, NG10 3QB Tel: 0115 9468725 *Here at group8.org.uk we offers a wide range of free online project management facilities that provide customers with an easy to use interface and traceability of communications, issues and*

continued

versions of project files demanded by many international standards.

Kia, 2 The Heights, Brooklands, Weybridge, Surrey, KT13 0NY Tel: (0800) 775777 E-mail: pcarter@kia.co.uk *Importers & concessionaries*

Kibmore Electronics, Bramble Cottage, Axes Lane, Redhill, RH1 5QN Tel: (01737) 765424 *Printed circuit manufrs*

Anthony Kidd Agencies Ltd, Halford House, 2 Colvall Lane, Chelmsford, CM1 1TZ Tel: (08702) 411271 Fax: (08702) 874285 *Insurance underwriters company*

Archie Kidd (Thermal) Ltd, Pullshot, Devizes, Wiltshire, SN10 1RT Tel: (01380) 828490 Fax: (01380) 828186 *Central heating boilers manufrs*

Kidd Services (Yorkshire), International House, Cliff Road, Hornsea, North Humberside, HU18 1JB Tel: (01964) 537000 Fax: (01964) 537111 E-mail: user@kidds.co.uk *Household effects removals*

Kidde Fire Protection Services Ltd, 400 Dallow Road, Luton, LU1 1UR Tel: (01582) 413694 Fax: (01582) 402339 E-mail: kiddefps@kiddefps.com *Suppliers of fire protection & detection equipment*

Kidde Fire Protection Services, Unit 3, Orchard Business Centre, Steer Place, Salfords, Redhill, RH1 5EL Tel: (01293) 778700 Fax: (01293) 825365 E-mail: kiddefps@kiddefps.com *Supply, Install, Maintain a range of fire detection equipment.*

Kidde Fire Protection Services Ltd, PO Box 318, Sunbury-on-Thames, Middlesex, TW16 7YX Tel: (0845) 6003909 Fax: (01582) 402339 E-mail: kiddefps@kiddefps.co.uk *Kidde Fire Protection Services is a leading supplier of fire safety services including fire detection and alarms, fire extinguishers, fire suppression systems and fire safety training in the UK. *We set the benchmark in providing and maintaining an unrivalled range of fire protection equipment and services. By working closely with you, we are able to provide the most effective fire safety solutions to meet your fire protection needs. *Fire Products and Services *Kidde provide fire extinguishers, fire detection and alarm systems, fixed fire suppression, fire safety training, and fire risk assessment services to meet all your fire protection needs.*

Kidde Fire Protection Services Ltd, Unit 12 Llwyn' Y' Graig, Garngoth Industrial Estate, Gorsenion, Swansea, SA4 9WG Tel: (01792) 898884 Fax: (01792) 891808 E-mail: kfpfswansea@kiddefps.com *Supply, install maintain fire protection equipment*

Kidde Fire Training Ltd, M1 Markham Lane, Duckmanton, Chesterfield, Derbyshire, S44 5HS Tel: (01246) 242700 Fax: (01246) 242701 *Fire training products*

Kidde Products, Unit 2, Blair Way, Dawdon, Seaham, County Durham, SR7 7PP Tel: 0191-513 6100 Fax: 0191-513 6102 *Smoke detection equipment manufrs*

▶ Kidderminster Fencing, 9 mayfield close, kidderminster, Worcestershire, DY11 5NG Tel: 01562 745427 E-mail: kidderminsterfencing@yahoo.co.uk *we suuply and install all types of fencing to domestic properties.we offer excellent rates and free quotes.*

Kidderminster Mirror, 86-88 Blackwell Street, Kidderminster, Worcestershire, DY10 2DZ Tel: (01562) 823117 Fax: (01562) 743592 *Glass merchants*

Kiddies Kastles, Fish Pond Trading Estate, Foundry Lane, Bristol, BS5 7UZ Tel: 0117-955 5544 Fax: 0117-955 0786 *Bouncing castles manufrs*

Kiddies World, Roseville House, Grant Avenue, Leeds, LS7 1QB Tel: 0113-243 5003 Fax: 0113-243 5004 *Baby clothing suppliers*

Kidds Stuff Ltd, 1 Danby Avenue, Old Whittington, Chesterfield, Derbyshire, S41 9NH Tel: (01246) 453055 *Bouncy castle hire*

Kiddy Care, 25 Hockley, Nottingham, NG1 1FH Tel: 0115-950 5169 Fax: 0115-950 6107 E-mail: sales@kiddycare.co.uk *Nursery equipment suppliers*

Kiddy & Partners 2007 Ltd, 74a Charlotte Street, London, W1T 4QH Tel: (020) 7486 6867 Fax: (020) 7486 6863 E-mail: info@kpl.co.uk *Business psychologists* Also at: Bristol

Kidlington Joinery, The Old Builders Yard, High Street, Islip, Kidlington, Oxfordshire, OX5 2RX Tel: (01865) 374880 Fax: (01865) 379246 *Joinery manufrs*

Kidman & Sons Ltd, 68 Victoria Road, Cambridge, CB4 3DY Tel: (01223) 352476 Fax: (01223) 351519 *Building contractors*

▶ Kids Industries, 65 Leonard Street, London, EC2A 4QS Tel: (020) 7684 3795 Fax: 020 7684 3801 E-mail: bertie@kidsindustries.co.uk

Kidsgrove Tropicals, 6 Hardingswood Road, Kidsgrove, Stoke-On-Trent, ST7 1EF Tel: (01782) 775947 *Aquatic suppliers*

▶ Kidz Bedroom Depot Ltd, Apt 6 Littlemere Court, 42 Ashley Road, Altrincham, Cheshire, WA14 2LZ Tel: 0161-929 1103 Fax: 0161-929 9488 E-mail: info@kidzbedroomdepot.com *Retail of nursery & children's bedroom furniture*

▶ Kidzone South West Ltd, Bradley Mill, Bradley Lane, Newton Abbot, Devon, TQ12 1LZ Tel: (01626) 353081 Fax: (01626) 357516 E-mail: aquaticssouthwest@hotmail.com *O.A.T.A qualified staff. aquarium maintenance also aquarium maintenanceinstallations rentals and maintenance. All at a low price without compromising on the quality.*

Kidzstuff, 60 Lansdown Crescent Lane, Cheltenham, Gloucestershire, GL50 2LD Tel: (01242) 232521 Fax: (0870) 1643904 E-mail: sales@kidzstuff.uk.com *Amusement machine service & support*

▶ Kiel Pharma Ltd, 95b Belfast Road, Carrickfergus, County Antrim, BT38 8BX Tel: (028) 9335 0880 Fax: (028) 9335 0890 E-mail: info@keilpharma.co.uk *Pharmaceutical manufrs*

▶ Kielder Plumbing & Heating Contracts Ltd, Unit 6a Colliery Lane, Hetton-le-Hole, Houghton le Spring, Tyne & Wear, DH5 0BG Tel: 0191-526 2222 Fax: 0191-526 6622

Kier Caribbean Ltd, Tempsford Hall, Sandy, Bedfordshire, SG19 2BD Tel: (01767) 640111 Fax: (01767) 641179 E-mail: david.parr@kier.co.uk *Constructors*

Kier Managed Services Ltd, Conway House, St. Mellons Business Park, Fortran Road, Cardiff, CF3 0EY Tel: (029) 2036 1616 Fax: (029) 2036 2303 E-mail: enquiries@kier.co.uk *Facilities management services*

Kier North West, Yardley Road, Knowsley Industrial Park, Liverpool, L33 7ST Tel: 0151-546 3341 Fax: 0151-548 6039 *Building contractors*

Kier (Scotland), Buchanan Business Park, Cumbernauld Road, Stepps, Glasgow, G33 6HZ Tel: 0141-779 3020

▶ Kier Sheffield, Lift Services, Manor Lane, Sheffield, S2 1TR Tel: 0114 2736714 Fax: 0114 2735210 E-mail: paul.hastings@kier.co.uk *Lift maintenance*

Kier Southern, St. Andrews House, West Street, Havant, Hampshire, PO9 1LB Tel: (023) 9248 4343 Fax: (023) 9245 5414 E-mail: lisa.haywood@kier.co.uk *Construction & property management services*

Kier Western, 27-37 Martin Street, Plymouth, PL1 3NQ Tel: (01752) 201123 Fax: (01392) 261789 E-mail: info.plymouth@kier.co.uk *Building contractors & shopfitters*

Kierbeck Ltd, Kierbeck Business Complex, North Woolwich Road, London, E16 2BG Tel: (020) 7474 0055 Fax: (020) 7474 7778 E-mail: sales@kierbeck.com *Kierbeck Ltd is the largest independent fabricator of Cut & Bent, Prefabricated steel reinforcement supplying the U.K construction industry. The company has a 25 year history of supplying he leading main contractors on some of the most prestigious building & civil engineering projects.*

Paul Kiernan Associates Ltd, PO Box 120, London, SW3 4LU Tel: (020) 7352 5562 *Management selection consultants*

Kigass Aero Components Ltd, Montague Road, Warwick, CV34 5LW Tel: (01926) 493833 Fax: (01926) 401456 E-mail: enquiries@kigassaero.co.uk *Aero engine component manufrs*

Josef Kihlberg Ltd, The Bridgewater Complex, Canal Street, Bootle, Merseyside, L20 8AH Tel: 0151-550 0085 Fax: 0151-550 0086 E-mail: reception.ltd@kihlberg.co.uk *UK distributors & manufacturers for industrial fastening systems*

Kilbey Cleaning & Maintenance Services, 104 Mansfield Road, London, NW3 2HX Tel: (020) 7267 8829 Fax: (020) 7284 4525 *Office cleaning contractors*

Kilbrandon Oysters, Cuan Road, Oban, Argyll, PA34 4RB Tel: (01852) 300586 Fax: (01852) 300584 E-mail: scott.glen@kilbrandon-oysters.co.uk *Catering suppliers*

▶ Kilbride Industrial Services, New Road, Cambuslang, Glasgow, G72 7PU Tel: 0141-646 1411 Fax: 0141-646 1422

Kilburn & Strode, 20 Red Lion Street, London, WC1R 4PJ Tel: (020) 7539 4200 Fax: (020) 7539 4299 E-mail: ks@kstrode.co.uk *European & chartered patent attorneys*

▶ Kilco Chemicals Ltd, 1a Trench Road, Newtownabbey, County Antrim, BT36 4TY Tel: (028) 9084 4344 Fax: (028) 9034 2494 E-mail: info@kilcogroup.com *Chemical manufrs*

▶ Kildonan Homes Ltd, Bandeath Industrial Estate, Stirling, FK7 7NP Tel: (01786) 815656 *Timber tip company*

Kildress Joinery Works, 4 Dunnamore Road, Cookstown, County Tyrone, BT80 9NR Tel: (028) 8675 1292 Fax: (028) 8675 1007 *Joinery & building suppliers*

Kiley & Clinton, 52-53 Birchall Street, Birmingham, B12 0RP Tel: 0121-772 8000 Fax: 0121-772 3215 E-mail: kileyclinton@btconnect.com *Manufacturers of power assisted & manual steering systems*

Kilgour, 7-8 Savile Row, London, W1S 3PE Tel: (020) 7734 6905 Fax: (020) 7287 8147 E-mail: kilgour@8savilerow.com *Men & ladies tailors*

Kilhallon Quality Meats Ltd, The Abattoir, Kilhallon, Par, Cornwall, PL24 2RL Tel: (01726) 814926 Fax: (01726) 812800 E-mail: info@kittowsbutchers.co.uk *Meat processors*

Kilhey Court Hotel, Chorley Road, Standish, Wigan, Lancashire, WN1 2XN Tel: (01257) 472100 Fax: (01257) 422401 *Conference centre/hotel/ leisure facilities*

▶ Kilkie Paper Mill Services, Lovesta, Gowanlea Road, Comrie, Crieff, Perthshire, PH6 2HD Tel: (01764) 670141 Fax: (0870) 1301570 E-mail: sales@kilkie.com *Suppliers of paper making equipment*

Kilkie Paper Mill Services, Lovesta, Gowanlea Road, Comrie, Crieff, Perthshire, PH6 2HD Tel: (01764) 670141 Fax: (0870) 1301570 E-mail: sales@kilkie.com Principal Export Areas: Worldwide *Paper making machinery services*

Killan Structural Ltd, 626 Huddersfield Road, Lees, Oldham, OL4 3NL Tel: 0161-624 2033 Fax: 0161-627 0793 E-mail: info@killan.co.uk *Structural repairs*

Killby & Gayford Ltd, 30 Radford Way, Billericay, Essex, CM12 0DA Tel: (020) 7498 9898 Fax: (01277) 630193 E-mail: sales@killbygayford.com *Building engineering services*

Killby & Gayford Group Ltd, Osborne House, 9 - 11 Macauley Road, London, SW4 0QP Tel: (020) 7498 9898 Fax: (020) 7498 0838 E-mail: info@killbygayford.co.uk *Building maintenance & restoration services*

▶ Killeavy Wood Products, 25 Ballintemple Road, Killeavy, Newry, County Down, BT35 8LQ Tel: (028) 3084 9374 Fax: (028) 3084 9375 E-mail: technatab@fsmail.net *Suppliers & manufacturers of pallets*

James Killelea & Co. Ltd, Stoneholme Road, Crawshawbooth, Rossendale, Lancashire, BB4 8BA Tel: (01706) 229411 Fax: (01706) 228388 E-mail: info@killelea.co.uk *Specialists in design, fabrication & erection service of all types of steel*

Killick Martin & Co. Ltd, Bowden Freight Terminal, Luckyn Lane, Pips Hill Industrial Estate, Basildon, Essex, SS14 3AX Tel: (01268) 274382 Fax: *Ship brokers & liner agents* Also at: Birmingham, Felixstowe, Hull, Leeds, Manchester & Southampton

▶ Killigrew King, 13 Calico Row, London, SW11 3YH Tel: (020) 7350 5900 Fax: (020) 7350 5909

Killin Outdoor Centre, Dreadnought Place, Main Street, Killin, Perthshire, FK21 8UJ Tel: (01567) 820652 Fax: (01567) 820116 E-mail: shop@killinoutdoor.co.uk *Outdoor activity gear hire & sales centre*

Killiney Properties Ltd, 207 Barkby Road, Leicester, LE4 9HZ Tel: 0116-276 7554 Fax: 0116-246 0447 *Property investors & builders*

Killingholme Animal Feeds, Town Street, South Killingholme, Immingham, South Humberside, DN40 3DD Tel: (01469) 540793 Fax: (01469) 540793 *Animal food & equipment suppliers*

Killyleagh Box Co. Ltd, 39 Shrigley Road, Killyleagh, Downpatrick, County Down, BT30 9SR Tel: (028) 4482 8708 Fax: (028) 4482 1222 E-mail: sales@killyleaghbox.co.uk *Corrugated plastic box manufrs*

Kilmarnock Engineers, Spittalhill Works, Ayr Road, Kilmarnock, Ayrshire, KA1 5NX Tel: (01563) 830198 Fax: (01563) 830692 *Architectural & general metalworkers*

▶ Kilmarnock Removals International, 9-15 West Netherton Street, Kilmarnock, Ayrshire, KA1 4BU Tel: (01563) 520001 Fax: (01563) 536939

▶ T. Kilmister Ltd, 83A Stakes Road, Purbrook, Waterlooville, Hampshire, PO7 5NP Tel: (023) 9225 1393 Fax: (023) 9226 1273 *Plumbing & heating contractors*

Kilmore Agencies, 8 Keadybeg Road, Mountnorris, Armagh, BT60 2UQ Tel: (028) 3750 7440 Fax: (028) 3750 7294 *Bakery equipment*

▶ Kiln Maintenance Ltd, 4 Florida Close, Hot Lane Industrial Estate, Stoke-on-Trent, ST6 2DJ Tel: (01782) 816383 Fax: (01782) 575651 E-mail: sales@kilnmaintenance.co.uk *Kiln design, construction, repair & maintenance*

Kiln Refractory Services Ltd, 221 Birches Head Road, Stoke-on-Trent, ST1 6NB Tel: (01782) 851685 Fax: (01782) 768949 E-mail: krs@cwcom.net *Kiln manufrs*

Kiln Saddlery, Park House, Layer Road, Kingsford, Colchester, CO2 0HT Tel: (01206) 734695 Fax: (01206) 734688 E-mail: kiln.saddlery@tiscali.co.uk *Saddlery & riding wear*

▶ Kiln Services Ltd, Burnham Business Park, Springfield Road, Burnham-on-Crouch, Essex, CM0 8TE Tel: (01621) 785935 Fax: (01621) 785937

▶ Kilncare Ltd, The Kiln Works, 907 Leek New Road Baddeley Green, Stoke-on-Trent, ST2 7HQ Tel: (01782) 535915 Fax: (01782) 535338 E-mail: sales@kilncare.co.uk *Kilns for all trades and applications including pottery, glass, jewellery and dentistry. The Glasscare range is the largest glass kiln range by a single U.K. manufacturer. Kilns, lehrs and furnaces. Now suplying cold working glass tools ranging from gloves and diamond hand pads, to Kristal grinders and sand blasters.******

Jack Kilner & Son Ltd, Slaithwaite Road, Meltham, Holmfirth, HD9 5NY Tel: (01484) 850784 Fax: (01484) 852655 *Iron castings suppliers*

▶ Kilngrove, Ivory House, Cockfield, Bury St. Edmunds, Suffolk, IP30 0LN Tel: 01284 827474 Fax: 01284 827475 E-mail: enquiries@kilngrove.co.uk *Structural Engineers working with Residential extensions & Alterations, Restoration, Historic Buildings, Individual houses, Education & Leisure, Commercial offices and Industrial.*

Kilns & Furnaces Ltd, 1 Cinderhill Industrial Estate, Weston Coyney Road, Stoke-on-Trent, ST3 5JU Tel: (01782) 344620 Fax: (01782) 344621 E-mail: sales@kilns.co.uk *Industrial kilns for ceramics*

Kilnstruct, Walley St, Stoke-on-Trent, ST6 2AH Tel: (01782) 833383 Fax: (01782) 833411 *Flint manufrs*

Kilnwick Sprayers Ltd, Thorpefield Farm, Thorpe le Street, York, YO42 4LN Tel: (01430) 871222 Fax: (01430) 871333 E-mail: sales@kilnwkk.sagehost.co.uk *Agricultural machinery & crop sprayer specialists*

▶ Kilo Electrical, 1 Stackpool Road, Southville, Bristol, BS3 1NX Tel: 07903 243918 E-mail: nick-walsh@lycos.com *Domestic and commercial electrical contractor covering Bristol and the South West.*

▶ Kilo75 Ltd, Round Foundry Media Centre, Foundry Street, Leeds, LS11 5QP Tel: 0113 394 4606 E-mail: info@kilo75.com ***kilo75 is a web design agency based in Leeds, West Yorkshire. We love working with ideas, design and technology. Since 2000 we have been lucky enough to win web site design commissions from people who like that stuff too. We hope you find what you''re looking for in our website and perhaps something more besides.*

Kiloheat Ltd, The Industrial Estate, Enterprise Way, Edenbridge, Kent, TN8 6HF Tel: (0870) 0435207 Fax: (01732) 866370 E-mail: sales@kiloheat.co.uk Principal Export Areas: Worldwide *Fans manufrs*

Chris Kilpin Machinery, 20 Bridgwater Court, Oldmixon Cresent, Weston-super-Mare, Avon, BS24 9AY Tel: (01934) 625850 Fax: (01934) 412816 E-mail: sales@ckmachinery.com *Window industry machinery & services*

Kilrot, 928 Foleshill Road, Coventry, CV6 6GS Tel: (024) 7668 9998 Fax: (024) 7663 7562 E-mail: dickdixon@kilrot.fsbusiness.co.uk *Damp proofing*

Kiltex Fashions Ltd, Rear Of 72 Queen St, Maidenhead, Berks, SL6 1HY Tel: (01628) 673367 Fax: (01753) 868608 *Fashion clothing manufrs*

Kiltox Contracts Ltd, 6 Chiltonian Industrial Estate, Manor Lane, London, SE12 0TX Tel: (020) 8463 9690 Fax: (0845) 1662050 E-mail: info@kiltox.co.uk *Condensation control services & remedial for timber & damp*

Kilworth Agricultural Machinery, Annwell Lane, Smisby, Ashby-de-la-Zouch, Leicestershire, LE65 2TA Tel: (01530) 412690 Fax: (01530) 560002 E-mail: sales@kilworthmachinery.co.uk *Machinery importers & distributors*

Kilwuddie Construction, 5 Wilson Place, East Kilbride, Glasgow, G74 4QD Tel: (01355) 266700 Fax: (01355) 261962 *Excavation & groundwork contractors*

▶ Kim Developments Ltd, Lower Farm, Warrington, Olney, Buckinghamshire, MK46 4HN Tel: (01234) 711797

▶ Kim Software Solutions Ltd, 1 The Square, Sawbridgeworth, Hertfordshire, CM21 9AE Tel: (01279) 600171 Fax: (01279) 600557 E-mail: mikepj@kimsp.com *Bespoke software developers*

Kim Systems Ltd, 4 Brook Road, Bicton Industrial Park, Kimbolton, Huntingdon, Cambridgeshire, PE28 0LR Tel: (01480) 860730 Fax: (01480) 861251 *Control panel manufrs*

Kimal plc, Sherwood Road, Bromsgrove, Worcestershire, B60 3DR Tel: (01527) 572300 Fax: (01527) 579936 E-mail: sales@kimal.co.uk *Hospital disposable product manufrs*

Kimal P.L.C., Arundel Road, Uxbridge Industrial Estate, Uxbridge, Middlesex, UB8 2SA Tel: (01895) 270951 Fax: (01895) 274035 Principal Export Areas: Worldwide *Medical disposables & procedure packs*

Kimber Allen Ltd, Broomfield Works, London Road, Swanley, Kent, BR8 8DF Tel: (01322) 663234 Fax: (01322) 668318 E-mail: ka@kimberallen.freeserve.co.uk *Pressings manufacturers & light engineers*

Kimber Engineering Ltd, Arisdale Avenue, South Ockendon, Essex, RM15 5DP Tel: (01708) 852469 Fax: (01708) 853228 E-mail: info@kimbereng.co.uk *Balustrading & railing manufrs*

▶ Kimberley Couriers, 35 Cotswold Road, Stourbridge, West Midlands, DY8 4UW Tel: (0800) 7833681 Fax: (01384) 443396 E-mail: info@kimberleycouriers.com *We provide a Sameday Nationwide Courier Delivery Service.*We are professional, trustworthy and competitively priced.*Conveniently based in Stourbridge, West Midlands - within easy reach of the M5, M6, M42 and all points beyond.*We deliver to anywhere in the UK.*Your goods are protected by our Goods in Transit insurance.*Whilst specialising in small van deliveries, we can provide vehicles of all sizes to suit your requirements.*Call us for a free no-obligation quote.*

Kimberley Distribution Ltd, Wanlip Road, Syston, Leicester, LE7 1PD Tel: 0116-260 2224 *Warehousing (storage) contractors, facilities & services*

▶ Kimberley Scaffolding Ltd, Park Road, Bestwood Village, Nottingham, NG6 8TQ Tel: 0115-927 8222 Fax: 0115-927 8333

Kimberly Clark Ltd, 1 Tower View, Kings Hill, West Malling, Kent, ME19 4HA Tel: (01732) 594000 Fax: (01732) 594001 *Disposable paper product manufrs*

Kimberly-Clark Finance Ltd, Thames House, Crete Hall Road, Gravesend, Kent, DA11 9AD Tel: (01474) 336000 Fax: (01474) 336478 E-mail: sales@kimberley-clark.com *Andrex manufrs*

Kimbermatics Ltd, Cheethams Mill, Park Street, Stalybridge, Cheshire, SK15 2BT Tel: 0161-368 4891 Fax: 0161-304 8152 E-mail: kimbermatics@aol.com *Conveyor manufrs*

Kimbolton Fireworks (Displays) Ltd, 7 High Street, Kimbolton, Huntingdon, Cambridgeshire, PE28 0HB Tel: (01480) 860988 Fax: (01480) 861277 E-mail: info@kimboltonfireworks.co.uk *Firework manufrs*

Kimco Hot Foil Printers, 1 Waterside Court, Bone Lane, Newbury, Berkshire, RG14 5SH Tel: (01635) 30154 Fax: (01635) 32245 E-mail: petekimco@aol.com *Hot foil printing services & supplies*

Ernest F. Kime & Son Ltd, Commonside, Old Leake, Boston, Lincolnshire, PE22 9PP Tel: (01205) 870482 *Road transport, haulage & freight services*

Kimlyn Products Ltd, 28 Armstrong Road, Tamworth, Staffordshire, B79 7TA Tel: (01827) 66933 Fax: (01827) 66323 *Plastic injection moulders*

▶ Kims Computers, 223 Maiden Lane, Dartford, DA1 4PL Tel: (01322) 310492

Kim's Food, 284-288 Western Road, London, SW19 2QA Tel: (020) 8640 4018 Fax: (020) 8640 4018 E-mail: kimsfood@yahoo.com *Food manufrs*

J.B. Kind Ltd, Shobnall Street, Burton-On-Trent, Staffordshire, DE14 2HP Tel: (01283) 564631 Fax: (01283) 511132 *Door retailers, pallet & packing case manufrs*

G.R. Kinder (Ceilings) Ltd, Unit 1 Rochdale Road Industrial Estate, Church Street, Middleton, Manchester, M24 2PY Tel: (0161) 654 8084 Fax: (0161) 655 3762 E-mail: paul@kinderinteriors.co.uk *Interior refurbishers*

Kinder Janes Engineers Ltd, Porters Wood, St. Albans, Hertfordshire, AL3 6HU Tel: (01727) 844441 Fax: (01727) 844247 E-mail: info@kinder-janes.co.uk *Pump distributors*

Kinder Marketing, Unit D Roe Cross Indust Park, Old Road, Mottram, Hyde, Cheshire, SK14 6LG Tel: (01457) 762758 Fax: (01457) 776547 *Speciality chemical manufrs*

Kinder Roofing Ltd, Conservation House, 116 Darwen Road, Bromley Cross, Bolton, BL7 9BQ Tel: (01204) 592200 Fax: (01204) 597700 E-mail: roofing@kinders.co.uk *Roofing & slating contractors*

▶ Kindon Textiles Ltd, 31 Belmont Way, Rochdale, Lancashire, OL12 6HR Tel: (01706) 656951 Fax: (01706) 345496 E-mail: g-kindon@msn.com *Textile merchants & converters*

Kindplace Ltd, 45 Fitzroy Street, London, W1T 6DY Tel: (020) 7383 7277 Fax: (020) 7388 7227 *Casual wear & leather garment manufrs*

▶ Kindunique Ltd, Grieves Buildings, Front Street, New Herrington, Houghton le Spring, Tyne & Wear, DH4 7AU Tel: 0191-512 0052 Fax: 0191-512 0543 E-mail: holtkindunique@dsi.pipex.com *Control consoles manufrs*

Kindways.Com, 4 Trinity Avenue, Llandudno, Gwynedd, LL30 2NQ Tel: (01492) 879312 Fax: (01492) 873811 *Computer services*

▶ Kinegar Quarry, Glenfin Quarry, Neuk Farm, Cockburnspath, Berwickshire, TD13 5YH Tel: (01368) 830457

▶ Kinetic plc, Duckworth House, Talbot Road, Stretford, Manchester, M32 0FP Tel: 0161-872 2333 Fax: 0161-872 2444 E-mail: info@kinetic-plc.co.uk *Kinetic specialise in providing flexible workforce and high calibre search and selection permanent recruitment solutions to U.K companies working in the Engineering, Manufacturing, Production and Technical industries. Full payroll & HR services are also handled on behalf of new and existing clients.*

Kinetic plc, Duckworth House, Talbot Road, Stretford, Manchester, M32 0FP Tel: 0161-872 2333 Fax: 0161-872 2444 E-mail: info@kinetic-plc.co.uk *Since 1983, Kinetic plc has been committed to supplying flexible workforce personnel and high calibre permanent recruitment solutions to companies based in the Engineering, Manufacturing, Production, Technical, Rail and Nursing industries. Full payroll & HR services are also handled on behalf of new and existing clients.* Also at: Preston, Queensferry, Rochdale, Runcorn, Stockport, Stoke-on-Trent & Wrexham

Kinetic Concepts Ltd, 18 Voases Lane, Anlaby, Hull, HU10 7BH Tel: (01482) 829292 Fax: (01482) 837997 E-mail: bill@kinetic.gbservices.co.uk *Manufacturers of laboratory furniture & fume cupboards. We provide a complete service from design through to installation. We carry out modifications to existing laboratory furniture including maintenance & repairs*

▶ Kinetic Electrical, Pump House Farm, Ongar Road, Brentwood, Essex, CM15 0LA Tel: 01277 365622 Fax: 01277 365689 E-mail: info@kineticelectrical.com *Kinetic Electrical is a firm of general electrical contractors and hi-tech specialists. It''s our wide capability and our unique approach to your work, which make us different.**At Kinetic we have experience in a number of work areas. Please feel free to contact us for further information or for help with any specific project you may have.*

Kinetic Products Ltd, Unit B1, Brookside Business Park, Greengate Middleton, Manchester, M24 1GS Tel: 0161-654 9595 Fax: 0161-654 9596 E-mail: sales@kinetic-security.co.uk *Security lighting & cctv product importers*

Kinetic Special Vehicles Ltd, Kings Cross Centre, Weel Road, Tickton, Beverley, North Humberside, HU17 9RY Tel: (01964) 543398 Fax: (01964) 543845 E-mail: sales@kinetic.uk.com *Special vehicle manufrs*

Kinetico UK Ltd, Bridge House, Park Gate Business Centre, Park Gate, Southampton, SO31 1FQ Tel: (01489) 566970 Fax: (01489) 566976 E-mail: info@kinetico.co.uk Sales Contact: G. Audemard *Manufacturers of water purification systems, industrial water softening equipment, water demineralisation plant & water treatment plant & equipment including reverse osmosis systems*

Kinetrol Ltd, Farnham Trading Estate, Farnham, Surrey, GU9 9NU Tel: (01252) 733838 Fax: (01252) 713042 E-mail: sales@kinetrol.com Principal Export Areas: Worldwide *Actuators manufrs*

King A & A Building Contractors, Brook Road Industrial Estate, Brook Road, Wimborne, Dorset, BH21 2BH Tel: (01202) 881819 Fax: (01202) 882514 E-mail: aaking@mpz.co.uk *Building restoration specialists*

▶ A. & L. King (Builders) Ltd, Hunter Street, Auchterarder, Perthshire, PH3 1PA Tel: (01764) 662688

King Bros, Cross Lane, Salterforth, Barnoldswick, Lancashire, BB18 5UD Tel: (01282) 813118 Fax: (01282) 851984 E-mail: peter.kingbros@btconnect.com *Agricultural contractors*

King Bros (Burnham) Ltd, 53 Huntercombe Lane North, Slough, SL1 6DX Tel: 01628 661481 Fax: 01628 667466 *Wooden packing cases manufrs*

King Cole Ltd, Merrie Mills, Old Souls Way, Crossflatts, Bingley, West Yorkshire, BD16 2AX Tel: (01274) 561331 Fax: (01274) 551095 E-mail: enquiries@kingcole.co.uk *Knitting wool spinners*

King Communication Services, 19 Coatbank Street, Coatbridge, Lanarkshire, ML5 3SP Tel: (01236) 429445 Fax: (01236) 429445 E-mail: info@kingcoms.com *Business telephone systems & cctv retailers*

King Engineering, Bell Farm, Royston, Hertfordshire, SG8 8ND Tel: (01763) 848899 Fax: (01763) 848899 *Manufacturer of turned parts & precision engineering*

George. W. King Ltd, Blackhorse Road, Letchworth Garden City, Hertfordshire, SG6 1GE Tel: (01462) 481180 Fax: (01462) 675847 E-mail: george.king@gwkgroup.com *Automotive parts manufrs*

H. King & Sons Ltd, Acreman Street, Sherborne, Dorset, DT9 3PA Tel: (01935) 812185 Fax: (01935) 812034 *Mechanical engineers & contractors*

King Highway Products Ltd, Riverside, Market Harborough, Leicestershire, LE16 7PX Tel: (01858) 467361 Fax: (01858) 467161 E-mail: sales@skyking.co.uk *Incorporating SkyKing aerial access platforms, with a reach of up to 85 metres, and Traiload traffic management and safety equipment, including crash cushions and mobile lane closure vehicles.*

King Industrial Products Ltd, Unit 12, Techno Trading Estate, Brambell Road, Swindon, SN2 8HB Tel: (01793) 491606 Fax: (01793) 530461 E-mail: sales@kingindustrial.co.uk *Rubber & PVC hose distributors*

▶ King IT Solutions, 65 Mayfield Park South, Fishponds, Bristol, BS16 3NF Tel: 07766 088035 Fax: 08716 618564 E-mail: info@KingITSolutions.com *IT consultancy & support company*

John King Chains Ltd, Lancaster Close, New Climax Works, Sherburn In Elmet, Leeds, LS25 6NS Tel: (01977) 689442 Fax: (01977) 681899 E-mail: admin@johnking-chain.com *Conveyor chain suppliers*

King & Johnston Building Contractors Ltd, 380 New Hythe Lane, Larkfield, Aylesford, Kent, ME20 6RZ Tel: (01622) 792255 Fax: (01622) 792266

M.B. King, 109 Gladstone St, Darlington, County Durham, DL3 6LA Tel: 01325 252088 *Computer repairs*

▶ Mrs Elizabeth King Ltd, 30 High Hazles Road, Cotgrave, Nottingham, NG12 3GZ Tel: 0115-989 4101 Fax: 0115-989 4101 *Food processors*

Paul King, Keepers Cottage, Tilmanstone, Tilmanstone, Deal, Kent, CT14 0JN Tel: (01304) 832545 Fax: (01304) 830370 *Excavation & groundwork contractors*

King Plastics, Unit 11 Foxwood Industrial Park, Chesterfield, Derbyshire, S41 9RN Tel: (01246) 260300 Fax: (01246) 260321 E-mail: kingplas@supanet.com *Plastic stockholders services*

King & Rawlings, 278-284 High Street, Waltham Cross, Hertfordshire, EN8 7EA Tel: (01992) 623575 Fax: (01992) 640570 *Metal spinners & sheet metalworkers*

King Salmon Co., 54 Kinloch Drive, London, NW9 7LH Tel: (020) 8205 1550 Fax: (020) 8205 1550 *Fish smokers & curers*

King Sliding Doors Gear, Invest House, Bruce Road, Fforestfach, Swansea, SA5 4HS Tel: (01792) 583555 Fax: (01792) 587046 E-mail: enquiries@kingslidingdoorgear.com *Roller shutters manufrs*

▶ King Stag Ltd, 6 Hartfoot Close, Melcombe Bingham, Dorchester, Dorset, DT2 7TY Tel: (01963) 363611 Fax: (08700) 940778 E-mail: sales@kingstag.com *Marine control systems manufrs*

King Sturge, 30 Warwick Street, London, W1B 5NH Tel: (020) 7493 4933 Fax: (020) 7409 0469 E-mail: firstname.surname@kingsturge.com *Chartered surveyors & property consultants*

King Trailers Ltd, Riverside, Market Harborough, Leicestershire, LE16 7PX Tel: (01858) 467361 Fax: (01858) 467161 E-mail: info@kingtrailers.co.uk Principal Export Areas: Worldwide *Manufacturers of a wide range of heavy duty specialist trailer, including Stepframes, Lowloaders, Plant Bodies and Plant Drawbars, capable of carrying payloads of up to 150 tonnes. The company also offers Swingthru, an innovative Container Handling System, Road/ Rail vehicles and full project management services.*

King UK Ltd, Unis 1-3 Conquest Industrial Estate, Knight Road, Rochester, Kent, ME2 2AL Tel: (01634) 290913 Fax: (01634) 716739 *Disposable consumer goods manufrs*

James Kingan & Sons Ltd, Townhead Sawmill, New Abbey, Dumfries, DG2 8DU Tel: (01387) 850282 Fax: (01387) 850492 *Timber merchants*

▶ Kingate Press Ltd, Unit 8 South Hartland Indust Park, Devon Street, Vauxhall, Birmingham, B7 4SL Tel: 0121-333 6533 Fax: 0121-333 6544 E-mail: sales@kingate.co.uk *Printing services*

Kingcome Sofas Ltd, 24 Old Newton Road, Heathfield Industrial Estate, Heathfield, Newton Abbot, Devon, TQ12 6RA Tel: (01626) 834800 Fax: (01626) 835866 E-mail: sales@kingcomesofas.co.uk *Bespoke upholstered furnish manufrs*

▶ KINGconsultancy, Gherraidh, Churchend Cottages, Churchend, Charfield, Wotton-under-Edge, Gloucestershire, GL12 8LJ Tel: (01454) 261722 E-mail: donald@kingconsultancy.com *Cost effective safety consultancy based in Gloucerstershire offering user friendly policies and procedures to ensure compliance with Legislation.**FREE safety inspection of your workplace.**NO travel charges in the UK and low cost charges to work in Europe.*

Kingdom Agribusiness, 7 Douglas Cresent, Kinross, KY13 8TJ Tel: (01577) 863396 *Chemicals*

Kingdom Computers, 129 High Street, Staines, Middlesex, TW18 4PD Tel: (01784) 466800 Fax: (01784) 466899 *Computer network services*

▶ Kingdom Industrial Supplies Ltd, Kingdom House, Bancrofts Road, South Woodham Ferrers, Chelmsford, CM3 5UQ Tel: (01245) 322177 Fax: (01245) 325878 E-mail: sales@kingdomgroup.com *Tape specialists manufrs*

Kingdom Office Supplies Ltd, 150 Means Court, Glenrothes, Fife, KY7 6XP Tel: (01592) 620525 Fax: (08707) 624291 E-mail: sales@kingdomofficesupplies.co.uk *National supplier of low cost, high quality office supplies, stationery, machines and furniture, discounts to 90%. No hassle return basis. Deliveries 2-48 hours. Furniture up to 5 days. From depots in England: London, Rochdale, West Midlands, Birmingham, Scotland: Glasgow, Fife.*

▶ Kingdom Scaffolding Ltd, Building 11, Forties Commercial Campus, Rosyth, Dunfermline, Fife, KY11 2XB Tel: (01383) 420212 Fax: (01383) 420304

Kingdom Storage, 14 Faraday Road, Glenrothes, Fife, KY6 2RU Tel: (01592) 630882 Fax: (01592) 630892

Kingdons Holdings Ltd, North Street, South Molton, Devon, EX36 3AP Tel: (01769) 573204 Fax: (01769) 573200 E-mail: sales@kingdons.co.uk *Builders merchants & ironmongers*

▶ Kingerlee Ltd, Langford Locks, Kidlington, Oxfordshire, OX5 1HR Tel: (01865) 840000 Fax: (01865) 840048

Kingfield Cotswold, Cotswold House, St. Philips Road, Bristol, BS2 0JZ Tel: 0117-900 6000 Fax: 0117-900 6100 *Stationary wholesalers*

Kingfield Electronics Ltd, Carrwood House, Carrwood Road, Chesterfield Trading Estate, Chesterfield, Derbyshire, S41 9QB Tel: (01246) 451701 Fax: (01246) 572390 E-mail: d.bailey@kingfield-electronics.co.uk *Contract electronic manufacturing services*

Kingfield Heath Ltd, 17 Trench Road, Hydepark Industrial Estate, Newtownabbey, County Antrim, BT36 4TY Tel: (028) 9084 3511 Fax: (028) 9083 5133 *Stationery wholesale*

Kingfisher P.L.C, 3 Sheldon Square, London, W2 6PX Tel: (020) 7372 8008 Fax: (020) 7644 1001 *Holding company*

Kingfisher Angling Centre, 9 New Street, Shrewsbury, SY3 8JN Tel: (01743) 240602 Fax: (01743) 240602 *Fishing equipment*

▶ Kingfisher Aquaculture, Owls Hall, Blackmore End, Braintree, Essex, CM7 4DF Tel: (01371) 850360 Fax: (01371) 850360 E-mail: kfa@fishculture.co.uk *Fish farm design & engineering*

Kingfisher Associates UK Ltd, Nine Yews, Cranborne, Wimborne, Dorset, BH21 5PW Tel: (01725) 517744 Fax: (01725) 517766 E-mail: sales@kfa.co.uk *Computer software developers*

Kingfisher Blinds, The Woodlands, Heol Creigiau, Efail Isaf, Pontypridd, Mid Glamorgan, CF38 1BG Tel: (01443) 208300 Fax: (01443) 208300 E-mail: enquiries@kingfisherblinds.com *Blinds manufrs*

Kingfisher Blinds Bath Ltd, Unit C The Hawthorns, Old Pit Road, Midsomer Norton, Radstock, BA3 4BQ Tel: (01761) 417807 Fax: (01761) 417807 *Blinds manufrs*

Kingfisher Blinds & Curtains Ltd, Kingfisher Court, The Oaks, Coldfield Drive, Redditch, Worcestershire, B98 7ST Tel: (01527) 544844 Fax: (01527) 544648 *Blinds & curtains*

Kingfisher Building Products Ltd, Cooper Lane, Bardsea, Ulverston, Cumbria, LA12 9RA Tel: (01229) 869100 Fax: (01229) 869101 E-mail: sales@kingfisherchem.com *Building product manufrs*

Kingfisher Construction Services Ltd, Kempton Park Close, Derby, DE24 8QB Tel: (01332) 382088 Fax: (01332) 294902

▶ Kingfisher Exchange, Kingfisher House, Walton Street, Aylesbury, Buckinghamshire, HP21 7AY Tel: (01296) 468510 Fax: (01296) 468511 E-mail: aylesbury@redstone-bc.com *Kingfisher Exchange offers serviced offices, strategically located with easy access to London and to national and international transport links. **Tenants receive high quality services, not just high quality business environments, and the complete service offered includes the maintenance and repairs of the serviced offices as well as providing critical services businesses need. **The centre provides a fully managed and secured internet service, telephony, as well as the essential office services of daily cleaning, office furnishings and meeting room availability. **www.redstone-bc.com**(Aylesbury serviced offices flexible managed office space to rent, to lease or to let business centres Aylesbury HP21 UK)*

Kingfisher Facilities Group, Kingfisher House, Rowan Way, New Balderton, Newark, Nottinghamshire, NG24 3AU Tel: (01636) 610776 Fax: (01636) 610150 E-mail: kingfisher.graphics@ntlworld.com *Manufacturers of safety signs, traffic signs & fire signs*

Kingfisher Industrial, Rushock Trading Estate, Droitwich, Worcestershire, WR9 0NR Tel: (01299) 251121 Fax: (01299) 251021 E-mail: enquiries@kingfisher-industrial.co.uk *Wear resistant linings suppliers*

▶ Kingfisher Landscaping, 3 Higham Rd, Rushden, Northants, NN10 6DS Tel: 01933 353159

Kingfisher Lighting, Ratcher Way, Forest Town, Mansfield, Nottinghamshire, NG19 0FS Tel: (01623) 415900 Fax: (01623) 415910 E-mail: sales@kingfisher-lighting.co.uk *Industrial lighting systems & fittings*

Kingfisher (Lubrication) Ltd, 136 Meanwood Road, Leeds, LS7 2BT Tel: 0113-209 8989 Fax: 0113-237 4027 E-mail: enquiries@kingfisherlub.co.uk Principal Export Areas: Asia Pacific, Middle East, Africa, North America & South America *Grease fittings manufrs*

▶ Kingfisher Print & Design Ltd, Wills Road, Totnes, Devon, TQ9 5XN Tel: (01803) 867087 Fax: (01803) 867088

Kingfisher Rubber & Plastics, Unit 1alfred Court Saxon Business Park, Hanbury Road, Stoke Prior, Bromsgrove, Worcestershire, B60 4AD Tel: (01527) 570570 Fax: (01527) 575200 E-mail: marklewis.kingfisher@virgin.net *Rubber & plastic moulding suppliers*

Kingfisher Sales & Marketing, PO Box 100, Aberdare, Mid Glamorgan, CF44 8YX Tel: (01685) 879879 *Skincare & cleansing products importers & distributors*

Kingfisher Tapes Ltd, Unit 3 Kents Avenue, Hemel Hempstead, Hertfordshire, HP3 9XH Tel: (01442) 212624 Fax: (01442) 241057 *Packaging material distributors*

Kingfisher Windows & Joinery, 296 Bolton Road, Hawkshaw, Bury, Lancashire, BL8 4JN Tel: (01204) 888595 Fax: (01204) 888595 E-mail: geoffside@hotmail.com *Joiners*

Kingfob, 4 John Street, Walsall, WS2 8AF Tel: (01922) 722561 Fax: (01922) 722442 E-mail: artwork@keyfob.co.uk *Suppliers of advertising gifts & small leather goods*

▶ Kingford Transport Ltd, 7 Silverwood, Snow Hill, Crawley Down, Crawley, West Sussex, RH10 3EN Tel: (01342) 714113 Fax: (01342) 715195

Kinghorn Davies Advertising Ltd, 35-39 Blandford Street, Newcastle upon Tyne, NE1 4HW Tel: 0191-261 8666 Fax: 0191-232 3635 E-mail: sales@kinghorn-davies.co.uk *Public relations consultancy & advertisers*

Kinglea Plant Centre Coffee Shop, Meadgate Road, Nazeing, Waltham Abbey, Essex, EN9 2PB Tel: (01992) 467775 Fax: (01992) 892967 E-mail: sales@kingsboilerhire.com *Industrial hire & boiler sale*

Kingpak Plastic Sheeting Supplies, Unit 11-12, Waterside Business Park, Hadfield, Glossop, Derbyshire, SK13 1BE Tel: (01457) 862521 Fax: (01457) 862138 E-mail: enquiries@kingpak.co.uk *Manufacturers of packaging materials goods products*

Kingpin Tyres Ltd, C8 Wem Industrial Estate, Soulton Road, Wem, Shrewsbury, SY4 5SD Tel: (01939) 232156 Fax: (01939) 233889 E-mail: enquiries@kingpin-tyres.com *Tyre re-treading & recycling*

Kings Cross Truck, 41 Leighlands, Crawley, West Sussex, RH10 3DN Tel: (01293) 873767 Fax: (01293) 873767 E-mail: sales@kingscrosstruck.co.uk *Truck, trolley & barrow manufrs*

Kings Hill Forest Glade, Newmains, Wishaw, Lanarkshire, ML2 9PJ Tel: (01501) 823085 Fax: (01501) 822161 E-mail: sales@kmwl.co.uk *Mineral water bottling for water cooling industry*

Kings Land Colour Ltd, Unit 2, Roslin Square, Roslin Road, Acton, London, W3 8DH Tel: (020) 8993 7111 Fax: (020) 8993 2243 E-mail: sales@kingslandcolour.co.uk *General printers*

Kings Lynn Blinds, The Lodge, King's Lynn, Norfolk, PE33 0DR Tel: (01366) 348009 E-mail: enquiries@norfolksunblinds.co.uk *Blind manufrs*

▶ Kings Lynn Joinery Ltd, Austin Fields, King's Lynn, Norfolk, PE30 1QH Tel: (01553) 777747 Fax: (01553) 771170 *Joiners*

Kings Norton Engineering Co. Ltd, Facet Road, Birmingham, B38 9PT Tel: 0121-458 3538 Fax: 0121-458 3886 E-mail: jharper@kingsnortonengineering.co.uk *Precision & general engineers*

▶ Kings Road Sporting Club Ltd, 40-42 Kings Road, London, SW3 4UD Tel: (020) 7589 5418 *Snow+Rock King's Road, specialising in women's clothing and accessories and offering a small range of styles for men, is a dedicated clothing store with a strong bias towards our female customers. Operating within the King's Road Sporting Club in Chelsea, snowsports fashion comes to the King's Road.*

Kings Road Tyres & Repairs Ltd, Pump Lane, Hayes, Middlesex, UB3 3NB Tel: (020) 8561 3737 Fax: (020) 8561 4012 E-mail: info@kingsroadtyres.co.uk *Tyre sales*

King's School of English, 25 Beckenham Road, Beckenham, Kent, BR3 4PR Tel: (020) 8650 5891 Fax: (020) 8663 3224 E-mail: info@kingslon.co.uk *Language school*

Kings Security Systems Ltd, Security House, Bob Hardisty Drive, Bishop Auckland, County Durham, DL14 7AL Tel: (01388) 451433 Fax: (01388) 451269 *Installation*

▶ Kings Transport Devon Ltd, Durham Way, Heathpark Industrial Estate, Honiton, Devon, EX14 1SQ Tel: (01404) 44555 Fax: (01404) 47555 E-mail: kingoffice@cs.com

Kings Worldwide Ltd, 34 Junction Rd, London, N19 5RE Tel: (020) 7263 0963 Fax: (020) 7281 3966 E-mail: info@kingsww.com *Manufacturers' agents - building materials & finishes*

Kingsbury Engineering Birmingham Ltd, 842 Kingsbury Road, Erdington, Birmingham, B24 9PS Tel: 0121-377 6383 Fax: 0121-377 6694 E-mail: cad@kingsbury-eng.com *Engineering company, press toolmakers services*

Kingsdown, Brook Street, Snodland, Kent, ME6 5BB Tel: (01634) 249555 Fax: (01634) 249550 E-mail: sales@kingsdownuk.com *Exporter services of spare parts for trucks & tractors*

▶ Kingsdown Commercial Stationers & Printers, Unit A Dean Street, Bristol, BS2 8SF Tel: 0117-924 4443 Fax: 0117-924 4881

Kingsfield Computer Product Ltd, Kingsfield Centre, Moulton Park, Northampton, NN3 6RB Tel: (0870) 8888410 Fax: (0870) 8888460 E-mail: purchase@kingsfieldcomputers.co.uk *Computer product suppliers*

Kingsford Services Ltd, Bromley Road, Elmstead, Colchester, CO7 7BY Tel: (01206) 827653 Fax: (01206) 827654 E-mail: enquiries@kingsfordservices.co.uk *Heating & air conditioning installers*

Kingsforth Landscape & Construction Ltd, Mangham Way, Rotherham, South Yorkshire, S61 4RL Tel: (01709) 378977 Fax: (01709) 838992 E-mail: enquiries@kingsforthfencing.co.uk *Fencing contractors*

▶ Kingsgate Furniture Sales Ltd, Unit 4 Oakwood Industrial Estate, Broadstairs, Kent, CT10 3JL Tel: (01843) 860686 Fax: (01843) 860456 E-mail: kingsgate@kingsgate.co.uk *Manufactures of leather furniture*

▶ Kingshall Furniture, 5 Millennium Point, Broadfields, Aylesbury, Buckinghamshire, HP19 8ZU Tel: (01296) 339925 Fax: (01296) 392900 E-mail: info@kingshallfurniture.com *Furniture suppliers*

Kingsland, The Winery, Fairhills Road, Irlam, Manchester, M44 6BD Tel: 0161-333 4300 Fax: 0161-333 4301 E-mail: info@kingsland-wines.com *Wine merchants bottlers & equipment suppliers*

Kingsland Construction Ltd, 8 Cookley Wharf, Leys Road, Brierley Hill, West Midlands, DY5 3UP Tel: (01384) 482945 Fax: (01384) 482955 E-mail: sales@kingslandaluminium.co.uk *Manufacturers of shopfronts, windows, curtain walling & automatic doors*

Kingsland Engineering Co. Ltd, Weybourne Road, Sheringham, Norfolk, NR26 8HE Tel: (01263) 822153 Fax: (01263) 825667 E-mail: info@kingsland.com *Sheet metal machinery manufrs*

Kingsland Engineering, Eagle Industrial Estate, Bagnall Street, Great Bridge, Tipton, West Midlands, DY4 7BS Tel: 0121-522 4929 Fax: 0121-522 3174 E-mail: sales@kingsland.com *Sheet metalworking machinery manufrs*

Kingsland Saw Mills Ltd, Kingsland, Leominster, Herefordshire, HR6 9SF Tel: (01568) 708206 Fax: (01568) 708258 E-mail: info@kingslandstabling.com *Timber buildings manufacturers & suppliers*

Kingsley, Tregoniggie Industrial Estate, Falmouth, Cornwall, TR11 4SN Tel: (01326) 373531 Fax: (01326) 372965 E-mail: kingsley_falmouth@hotmail.com *Cleaning & hygiene products supplier*

▶ Kingsley Commercial, Chenil House, 181-183 Kings Road, London, SW3 5EB Tel: (020) 7352 3130 Fax: (020) 7352 5111 E-mail: sales@kingsleycommercial.co.uk *Commercial property agents. Sales, lettings and acquisitions of commercial property, offices, shops and industrial property in Central London.*

Kingsley Commercial Components Ltd, Oak Hill Works, Broad Street, Guildford, Surrey, GU3 3BJ Tel: (01483) 303092 Fax: (01483) 572242 *Hydraulic component supply & repair. Hydraulic hose & fittings counter service. Hydraulic power packs. Van delivery & collection in the South East*

Kingsley Farrington, Whitlingham Lane, Trowse, Norwich, NR14 8TR Tel: (01603) 666545 Fax: (01603) 666545 *Boat building & boat transport services*

Kingsley Garage Doors, Unit 3 Eastman Way, Hemel Hempstead Industrial Est, Hemel Hempstead, Hertfordshire, HP2 7DU Tel: (01442) 257111 Fax: (01442) 257111 E-mail: jason@swrgaragedoors.com *Manufacturers of garage door accessories*

Kingsley Security, 1 Town Street, Farsley, Pudsey, West Yorkshire, LS28 5EN Tel: 0113-255 6996 Fax: 0113-255 6919 E-mail: sales@kingslysecurity.co.uk *Alarm installers*

Kingsley & Talboys, 4 Sinclair House, Hastings Street, London, WC1H 9PZ Tel: (020) 7387 8897 Fax: (020) 7387 8714 E-mail: info@kingsleytalboys.com *Patent, trademark & research consultants*

Kingsmead Carpets Ltd, Caponacre Industrial Estate, Cumnock, Ayrshire, KA18 1SH Tel: (01290) 421511 Fax: (01290) 424211 *Carpet manufrs*

▶ Kingsmede Ltd, 18 Warbreck Drive Bispham, Blackpool, FY2 9RZ Tel: (01253) 358827 E-mail: handymen@kingsmede.co.uk *Skilled, mature local handymen available for all types of handyman work from leaking taps to building flat pack furniture.**Fixed rates from just £24.99 inc VAT.**All work guarenteed with £5m insurance backing.*

Kingsmill Industries UK Ltd, Unit 14 Hermitage Way, Mansfield, Nottinghamshire, NG18 5ES Tel: (01623) 621111 Fax: (01623) 621211 E-mail: sales@kingsmillearthing.co.uk *Kingsmill Industries are a leading manufacturer and distributor of earthing and lighting protection products for the UK and Export markets. We specialise in earthing products.*

Kingsmoor Packaging Ltd, Cary Court, Bancombe Road, Somerton, Somerset, TA11 6SB Tel: (01458) 273001 Fax: (01458) 273350 *Plastic pack manufrs*

Kingsoak Homes, Eagle Close, Chandler's Ford, Eastleigh, Hampshire, SO53 4NF Tel: (023) 8046 1000 Fax: (023) 8046 1007

▶ Kingsoak South Midlands Ltd, Unit 4-5 Elm Court, Copse Drive, Coventry, CV5 9RG Tel: (01676) 525900 Fax: (01676) 525901

Kingspan Ltd, Greenfield Business Park 2, Greenfield, Holywell, Flintshire, CH8 7GJ Tel: (01352) 716100 Fax: (01352) 710161 E-mail: sales@kingspanpanels.com *Roof & wall cladding manufacturers.*

Kingspan Access Floors Ltd, Marfleet Lane, Hull, HU9 5SG Tel: (01482) 781701 Fax: (01482) 799272 E-mail: enquiries@kingspanaccessfloors.co.uk *Raised access floors* Also at: Enfield

Kingspan Contoled Environments, Hanger 1A, Wrights Lane, Burtonwood, Warrington, WA5 4DB Tel: (01925) 711157 Fax: (01925) 711158 *Manufacturers of panels for cold storage*

Kingspan Industrial Insulation Ltd, PO Box 3, Glossop, Derbyshire, SK13 8LE Tel: (0870) 8508555 Fax: (0870) 8508444 E-mail: enquires.uk@insulation.kingspan.com *Thermal heat suppliers*

Kingston Communications Ltd, Elmbank Mill, Menstrie, Clackmannanshire, FK11 7BU Tel: (01259) 768700 Fax: (01259) 768709 *Telecommunications*

Kingston Communications Hull plc, 35-37 Carr Lane, Hull, HU1 3RE Tel: (01482) 602100 Fax: (01482) 320652 E-mail: publicrelations@kcom.com *Telecommunications & directory publishers* Also at: Edinbugh, Leeds, London & Sidcup

Kingston Masonry, 19 Cambridge Road, Kingston upon Thames, Surrey, KT1 3NG Tel: (020) 8546 3504 Fax: (020) 8547 3493 *Monumental memorial manufrs*

Kingston Ornate Plaster, 23 Saner Street, Hull, HU3 2TR Tel: (01482) 320536 Fax: (01482) 320536 *Plaster manufrs*

▶ Kingston Partnership, The Prairie, Astwood Lane, Astwood Bank, Redditch, Worcestershire, B96 6HA Tel: (01527) 893793 Fax: (01527) 894029 E-mail: info@kingstonpartnership.com *Executive search and selection, the provision of Interim Managers and Executive Outplacement. Clients range from SMEs to major listed groups within the manufacturing sector. Firm has been in business for over 20 years. Specialists in fmcg manufacture*

Kingston Printers Ltd, 52 Kingsgate Road, Kingston upon Thames, Surrey, KT2 5AA Tel: (020) 8549 3311 Fax: (020) 8546 4365 *Printers*

▶ Kingston Publishing Services, Broadway House, 105 Ferensway, Hull, HU1 3UN Tel: (01482) 602600 Fax: (01482) 216816 E-mail: sue.brightman@kcom.com *Specialist directory publisher. Contract publishing solutions*

Kingston Theatre, Kingston Square, Hull, HU2 8DA Tel: (01482) 225828 Fax: (01482) 587969 E-mail: gary@kingstontheatrehotel.com *Business accommodation, conference facilities & corporate functions*

▶ Kingston Timber Frame Ltd, 14 Mill Hill Drive, Huntington, York, YO32 9PU Tel: (01904) 766686 Fax: (01904) 766686 E-mail: info@kingstontimberframe.co.uk *Timber frame homes*

Kingston U P V C Ltd, Todmorden Road, Littleborough, Lancashire, OL15 9EQ Tel: (01706) 378824 Fax: (01706) 372138

Kingston Windows & Conservatories, Melbourne House, Caxton Road, Elm Farm Industrial Estate, Bedford, MK41 0HU Tel: (01234) 271625 Fax: (01234) 327797 E-mail: sales@kingstonwindows.fsnet.co.uk *Doors, windows & conservatory manufacturers & installers*

▶ Kingstone (London) Ltd, Unit 37A, Grace Business Centre, Willow Lane, Mitcham, Surrey, CR4 4TU Tel: (020) 8640 3560 Fax: (020) 8640 3160 E-mail: martin@optionsmarble.demon.co.uk *Stone manufrs*

▶ Kingstone & Mortars, Monkredding Works, Kilwinning, Ayrshire, KA13 7QN Tel: (01294) 559888

Kingstonian Paints Ltd, Sculcoates Lane, Hull, HU5 1DR Tel: (01482) 342216 Fax: (01482) 493096 E-mail: info@kpaints.co.uk *Industrial & decorative finishes manufrs*

Kingstonian Quality Ice Cream Co., 2 Glenville Road, Kingston upon Thames, Surrey, KT2 6DD Tel: (020) 8541 0585 Fax: (020) 8541 0585 E-mail: mail@kingstonianicecream.com *Ice cream manufrs*

Kingstonian Storage Equipment Ltd, 1 Phoenix Enterprise Park, Grovehill Road, Beverley, North Humberside, HU17 0JG Tel: (01482) 868055 Fax: (01482) 872558 E-mail: paul@kingsstorage.fsnet.co.uk *Storage & locker stockists*

Kingstons Homes Ltd, The Estate Office West Hall, Parvis Road, West Byfleet, Surrey, KT14 6EP Tel: (01932) 340111 Fax: (01932) 352602 *Property developers*

▶ Kingstown Furniture Ltd, Victoria House, Leads Road, Hull, HU7 0BZ Tel: (01482) 701173 Fax: (01482) 706248 E-mail: enquiries@kingstown.co.uk *Furnishing manufrs*

Kingsway Amusement Machines Co., Unit 1 Harper Lodge Farm, Harper Lane, Radlett, Hertfordshire, WD7 7HU Tel: (01923) 711700 *Gaming machines & amusements machines hire services*

Kingsway Cane Furniture Ltd, 119 Parker Drive, Leicester, LE4 0JP Tel: 0116-235 0419 Fax: 0116-236 6724 E-mail: sales@kingswaycane.co.uk *Cane furniture importers & manufacturers outdoor all weather furniture*

Kingsway Engineering Ltd., Hanham Road, Bristol, BS15 8PX Tel: 0117-961 3168 Fax: 0117-960 4718 E-mail: sales@kingswayengineering.co.uk *Manufacturers of gears, bevel, helical & spur. Also gear cutters*

Kingsway English Centre Language School, 40 Foregate Street, Worcester, WR1 1EE Tel: (01905) 619877 Fax: (01905) 613388 E-mail: info@kingsway-english.com *English language training schools*

Kingsway Press Ltd, Seventh Avenue, Team Valley Trading Estate, Gateshead, Tyne & Wear, NE11 0SL Tel: 0191-491 0455 Fax: 0191-491 0454 E-mail: sales@kingswaypress.co.uk *Screen process printers*

Kingsway Print, The Old Chapel, Peterborough Road, Whittlesey, Peterborough, PE7 1PJ Tel: (01733) 350550 *Pad Printer/Plastic Printing Services*

▶ Kingsway Stairs Ltd, Castle Court, 377 Station Road, London, E7 0AB Tel: (020) 8519 0166 Fax: (020) 8519 6636

Kingsway TV & Video, 28 Greenheys Road, Wallasey, Merseyside, CH44 5UP Tel: 0151-630 4071 *Video repairs*

Kingswinford Engineering Co. Ltd, Shaw Road, Dudley, West Midlands, DY2 8TS Tel: (01384) 253411 Fax: (01384) 258107 E-mail: kfordengcoltd@aol.com *Mild & stainless steel fabrication services*

▶ Kingswood Cabinets, HCS Workshops, Binders Industrial Estate, Cryers Hill, High Wycombe, Buckinghamshire, HP15 6LJ Tel: 07966 263491 E-mail: Mat@KingswoodCabinets.com *Maker of bespoke items of fine furniture and high class joinery to order.*

Kingswood Canvas Ltd, Unit 8-9 Douglas Road Industrial Park, Douglas Road, Kingswood, Bristol, BS15 8PD Tel: 0117-960 1281 Fax: 0117-935 2632 E-mail: kingswoodcanvas@btconnect.com *Canvas & pvc goods manufrs*

▶ Kingswood Construction UK Ltd, Unit 2 Stanton Court, Stirling Road, Swindon, SN3 4YH Tel: (01793) 822449 Fax: (01793) 829436 E-mail: info@kingswoodgroup.co.uk *Market leaders in PRC reinstatement, big enough to cope small enough to care*

▶ Kingswood Interiors, 26 Kingswood Drive, Walsall, WS6 6NX Tel: (01922) 417041 *Bathroom furniture, built in services*

Kingswood Leisure Ltd, 9 Graiseley Row, Wolverhampton, WV2 4HJ Tel: (01902) 713303 Fax: (01902) 713117 E-mail: info@kwlonline.com Principal Export Areas: Worldwide *Provides new and reconditioned pool tables, snooker, billiard and football tables.*UK.*

Kingswood Plastics Ltd, 9 Corbetts Passage, London, SE16 2BD Tel: (020) 7237 6181 Fax: (020) 7252 2842 E-mail: sales@kingswood-plastics.co.uk *Plastic packaging (vacuum formed)packaging services & product development, blister packs, clam packs, point of sale, trays, transit trays, prototypes*

Kingswood Tools & Mouldings, Victoria Avenue Industrial Estate, Swanage, Dorset, BH19 1BJ Tel: (01929) 425330 Fax: (01929) 424279 *Plastic injection mouldings*

▶ KingswoodSaddlery.co.uk, Barleycorn Cottage, Babylon Lane, Lower Kingswood, Tadworth, Surrey, KT20 6XD Tel: (01737) 249121 Fax: (01737) 249121 E-mail: sales@kingswoodsaddlery.co.uk *We are*

continued

a family run business specialising in buying and selling top brand used saddles. We offer quality saddles at affordable prices with first class service. At Kingswood Saddlery we understand the importance of selling the right saddle to both horse and rider. The service we offer allows customers to buy with peace of mind and confidence in their choice.

▶ Kingsword Ltd, Unit 5, The Boundary Business Park, Wheatley Road, Garsington, Oxford, OX44 9EJ Tel: (01865) 361840 Fax: (01865) 361850 E-mail: sales@cssg.co.uk *Financial advisers*

Kingsworthy Foundry Co. Ltd, London Road, Kingsworthy, Winchester, Hampshire, SO23 7QG Tel: (01962) 883776 Fax: (01962) 882925 E-mail: kwf@fsbdial.co.uk *Fireplaces & cane furniture retailers*

Kington Forge, 2 The Old Foundry, Victoria Road, Kington, Herefordshire, HR5 3DA Tel: (01544) 231690 Fax: (01544) 231690 *Wrought ironwork*

John Kington, The Larches, Four Oaks, Newent, Gloucestershire, GL18 1LU Tel: (01531) 890445 Fax: (01531) 890770 *Saddler, & manufacturers of bridlery & leather*

▶ Kington Process Ltd, 38-44 St. Andrews Road, Birmingham, B9 4LN Tel: 0121-772 3000 Fax: 0121-772 7000

Kingtools Power Tools, Norris Way, Rushden, Northamptonshire, NN10 6BP Tel: (01933) 410900 Fax: (01933) 350471 E-mail: sales@kingtools.co.uk *Industrial safety equipment distributors service*

▶ Kingwood Building Services Ltd, Rainbow Industrial Park, Station Approach, London, SW20 0JY Tel: (020) 8946 1556 Fax: (020) 8946 1585

Kingwood Stud, Lambourn Woodlands, Lambourn Woodlands, Hungerford, Berkshire, RG17 7RS Tel: (01488) 71657 Fax: (01488) 73434 *Veterinary suppliers*

▶ Kinkajou Accessories, 58 Allaston Road, Lydney, Gloucestershire, GL15 5ST Tel: 01594 840312 *Fabulous handmade fascinators and hair accessories, Suitable for all special occasions*

▶ Kinko's Ltd, 1 Curzon Street, London, W1J 5HD Tel: (020) 7717 4900 Fax: (020) 7717 4901

Kinkz Love Store, 45 Banister Way, Wymondham, Norfolk, NR18 0TY Tel: (01953) 857517 E-mail: sales@kinkz.co.uk

Kinloch Anderson Ltd, 4 Dock Street, Leith, Edinburgh, EH6 6EY Tel: 0131-555 1355 Fax: 0131-555 1392 E-mail: enquiries@kinlochanderson.com *Quality clothing in tartans & tweeds*

Kinmel Paper Supplies, 180 Wellington Road, Rhyl, Clwyd, LL18 1LL Tel: (01745) 354589 Fax: (01745) 354589 *Continuous stationery suppliers & printers*

Kinnarps UK Ltd, 8 Lindsay Square, Deans Industrial Estate, Deans, Livingston, West Lothian, EH54 8RL Tel: (01506) 415885 Fax: (01506) 411447 E-mail: sales@kinnarps.co.uk *Contract office furniture systems services*

Kinnes Shipping Ltd, Fish Dock Road, Dundee, DD1 3LZ Tel: (01382) 462858 Fax: (01382) 462870 E-mail: general@kinnes-shipping.co.uk *Shipping & cargo forwarding agents*

Kinnoull Bacon Co. Ltd, 32 Main Street, Almondbank, Perth, PH1 3NJ Tel: (01738) 583292 Fax: (01738) 583292 E-mail: jharty@fsnet.com *Bacon & ham curers*

▶ Kinpars Industrial Plastics Ltd, Whitlaw Indust Estate, Lauder, Berwickshire, TD2 6QA Tel: (01578) 718855 Fax: (01578) 718844 E-mail: admin@kinpars.co.uk *Glass fibre manufrs*

Kinross & Render Ltd, 192-198 Vauxhall Bridge Road, London, SW1V 1DX Tel: (020) 7592 3100 Fax: (020) 7931 9640 E-mail: info@kinrossrender.com *Public relations consultants*

Kinshofer (UK) Ltd, 4 Milton Industrial Court, Horsfield Way, Bredbury, Stockport, Cheshire, SK6 2TA Tel: 0161-406 7046 Fax: 0161-406 7014 E-mail: info@kinshofer.com *Crane attachment manufacturers & distributors*

▶ Kinsman Water Features & Fountains, 56a Priory Road, Reigate, Surrey, RH2 8JB Tel: (01737) 222040 Fax: (01737) 222040 E-mail: mark@moesmoulds.co.uk *Manufacture & sale of water features & fountains*

Kinswood Electronic Services, 2 4 Josselin Court, Josselin Road, Burnt Mills Industrial Estate, Basildon, Essex, SS13 1QE Tel: (01268) 455100 Fax: (01268) 455103 *Electronic contract manufrs*

▶ Kintore Business Park, Cairnhall, Kintore, Inverurie, Aberdeenshire, AB51 0YG Tel: (01467) 632670 *Kintore Business Park offers affordable industrial premises at the heart of Aberdeenshire. Excellent parking facilities are available on-site. Unit sizes vary from 2,500 square feet to 10,000 square feet. Contact us now for competitive rates!*

Kintyre Of Scotland Ltd, Victoria Rd, Hawick, Roxburghshire, TD9 7AH Tel: (01450) 72788 Fax: (01450) 360207 E-mail: info@pringlescotland.com *Knitted fabrics*

▶ Kinv Property Maintenance, 6 High Street, Princes Risborough, Buckinghamshire, HP27 0AX Tel: (01844) 274876 Fax: (01844) 274876 E-mail: info@kinv.co.uk *Property maintenance, all types of work undertaken painting, electrics etc*

Kiosk, No. 2, 43 High Street, Leamington Spa, Warwickshire, CV31 1LN Tel: (01926) 776282 *Design & print studio*

Kiosk Knitwear & Textiles, 134-146 Curtain Road, London, EC2A 3WB Tel: (020) 7729 6101 Fax: (020) 7729 6101 E-mail: sales@kioskuk.com *Knitwear designers*

Kiosk World, 21 Fownhope Road, Sale, Cheshire, M33 4RF Tel: 0161-969 3005 Fax: 0161-969 3966

▶ Kip Mcgrath Education Centre (Southall), The Arches, Merrick Road, Southall, Middlesex, UB2 4AU Tel: (020) 8574 7338 E-mail: enquiries@kmgsouthall.com *Educational tuition ages 6 -16 in Maths, English, Reading and Spelling. We offer free assessments and individual programmes. All tuition is given by qualified professional teachers only.*

Kipling Motorist Centre, 76 Ifield Road, Crawley, West Sussex, RH11 7BQ Tel: (01293) 612211 Fax: (01293) 612444 *Tyre, battery & exhaust distributors*

Kipp & Zonen Ltd, PO Box 819, Lincoln, LN6 0WY Tel: (01522) 695403 Fax: (01522) 696598 E-mail: kipp.uk@kippzonen.com *Distribution Of Testing/Measuring Equipment*

H.G. Kippax & Sons Ltd, Upper Bankfield Mills, Almondbury Bank, Huddersfield, HD5 8HF Tel: (01484) 426789 Fax: (01484) 541799 E-mail: sales@hgkippax.co.uk *Screen printing machinery & printed circuit manufrs*

Kira Supplies, Holt Lane, Lea, Matlock, Derbyshire, DE4 5GQ Tel: (01629) 534934 Fax: (01629) 534933 E-mail: admin@kira.co.uk *Computer suppliers*

Kirans London Ltd, 69 St. John Street, London, EC1M 4AN Tel: (020) 7608 0299 Fax: (020) 7608 3150 E-mail: info@kiranlondon.co.uk *Export finance house*

▶ Bruce Kirby, Sycamore Cottage, Hemsford, Littlehempston, Totnes, Devon, TQ9 6NE Tel: (01803) 762136 E-mail: bruce@acanthus.org.uk *Stone masonry*

Kirby Devon Ltd, Elm Tree House, Yealmbury Hill, Yealmpton, Plymouth, PL8 2JH Tel: (01752) 881717 Fax: (01752) 881710 E-mail: sales@kirbydevon.freeserve.co.uk *Electronics design services*

Kirby Electrical Ltd, 4 Storforth La Trading Estate, Hasland, Chesterfield, Derbyshire, S41 0QD Tel: (01246) 220202 Fax: (01246) 208638 *Security system installers* Also at: Birmingham, Edinburgh, London, Manchester & Sheffield

Kirby MacLean Ltd, Roman House, 159 Ravenscroft Road, Beckenham, Kent, BR3 4TN Tel: (020) 8778 9282 Fax: (020) 8676 8575 E-mail: kirby.maclean@messages.co.uk *Contract decorators services*

Kirby Security (UK) Ltd, Southbank House, Black Prince Road, London, SE1 7SJ Tel: (020) 7834 6714

Kirby & Wells Ltd, 6 Benner Road, Pinchbeck, Spalding, Lincolnshire, PE11 3TZ Tel: (01775) 766886 Fax: (01775) 766885 *Architectural hardware retail & trade*

Kirby's Produce, Unit B56-B59, Fruit & Vegetable Market, New Covent Garden, Nine Elms Lane, London, SW8 5JB Tel: (020) 7622 4494 Fax: (020) 7720 5352 E-mail: info@kirbysproduce.com *Kirbys Fresh Produce, fruit and vegetable suppliers in New Covent Garden, London, UK. In London, one of the world's leading gastronomic centres, Kirby's Produce has created a benchmark in the supply of fresh produce. Our business has been nurtured over many years through careful and steady growth, constantly adapting to meet the requirements of our diverse range of clients. Within a crowded marketplace we have been able to offer our customers the competitive edge by taking a fresh approach, aiming to never let you down.*

Kiremko Food Processing Equipment UK Ltd, Armstrong House, First Avenue, Doncaster Finningley Airport, Doncaster, South Yorkshire, DN9 3GA Tel: (01302) 772929 Fax: (01302) 770548 E-mail: sales@kiremko.com *Food preparation machinery manufrs*

▶ Kiren Foods, 3 Smallbridge Industrial Park, Riverside Drive, Rochdale, Lancashire, OL16 2SH Tel: (01706) 526732 Fax: (01706) 869749 E-mail: enquiries@kirenfoods.com *Food processors & manufrs*

▶ Kiren Foods, 3 Smallbridge Industrial Park, Riverside Drive, Rochdale, Lancashire, OL16 2SH Tel: (01706) 526732 Fax: (01706) 869749 *Pizza manufacturer*

Francis Kirk & Son Ltd, Denton Hall Farm Road, Denton, Manchester, M34 2QN Tel: 0161-336 2631 Fax: 0161-335 0043 E-mail: sales@franciskirk.com *Engineers merchants*

▶ Kirk Hallam Building Co. Ltd, 1 Langley Park Industrial Estate, North Street, Langley Mill, Nottingham, NG16 4BS Tel: (01773) 532000 Fax: (01773) 531010

Kirk John Design, 18 Hayhill, Barrow upon Soar, Loughborough, Leicestershire, LE12 8LD Tel: (01509) 817100 Fax: (01509) 817101 E-mail: accounts@johnkirkdesign.co.uk *Exhibition stand consultants*

John Kirk Supplies Ltd, 145 Guildford Road, Ash, Aldershot, Hampshire, GU12 6DF Tel: (01252) 334774 Fax: (01252) 315946 E-mail: sales@johnkirksupplies.com *Cutting edge suppliers*

▶ Kirk Natural Stone Ltd, Bridgend, Fyvie, Turriff, Aberdeenshire, AB53 8LL Tel: (01651) 891891 Fax: (01651) 891891 E-mail: info@kirknaturalstone.com *Natural stone suppliers*

▶ Kirk Scaffolding Ltd, Greenbank Works, Gorse Street, Blackburn, BB1 3EU Tel: (01254) 672337 Fax: (01254) 667711

▶ Kirkaldy Fencing & Dyking, 64 Feus, Auchterarder, Perthshire, PH3 1DG Tel: (01764) 663115 E-mail: kirkaldyfencinganddyking@msn.com *Services available:*All types of fences supplied and erected.*All stone work eg. dry stone dyking, cement dykes, retaining walls.*

Kirkbride Sheet Metal Work, 47 Wenlock Way, Leicester, LE4 9HU Tel: 0116-276 0131 Fax: 0116-246 1001 E-mail: kirkmfabs@aol.com *Sheet metalworkers*

▶ Kirkby Blinds, St. Chads Parade, Liverpool, L32 8RH Tel: 0151-547 3677 Fax: 0151-548 8006 E-mail: kirkby.blinds@merseymail.com *Blind retailers & manufrs*

Charles Kirkby & Sons Ltd, 84 Sidney Street, Sheffield, S1 4RH Tel: 0114-272 1327 Fax: 0114-275 6506 *Cutlery & instrument case manufrs*

Kirkby Jig & Tool Co. Ltd, Bradman Road, Knowsley Industrial Park, Liverpool, L33 7UR Tel: 0151-546 2681 Fax: 0151-546 4937 *Toolmakers & precision engineers*

Kirkby Lindsey Electrical Engineering Ltd, Crowle Street, Hull, HU9 1RH Tel: (01482) 223937 Fax: (01482) 218261 E-mail: sales@kirkby-lindsey.co.uk *Electric motor stockists & repairers*

Kirkby Precision Engineering Ltd, Ashcroft Road, Liverpool, L33 7TW Tel: 0151-549 1007 Fax: 0151-549 2400 E-mail: kirkbyprecision@btclick.com *CNC machining services & precision engineers*

Kirkby Steel Tubes Ltd, Abbotsfield Road, Reginald Road Industrial Estat, St. Helens, Merseyside, WA9 4HU Tel: (01744) 830600 Fax: (01744) 830609 E-mail: mail@kst.uk.com *Stockholders & suppliers of steel tubes*

Kirkby (Tyres) Ltd, Speke Hall Avenue, Speke, Liverpool, L24 1UU Tel: (07734) 870892 Fax: 0151-486 5391 E-mail: sales@kirkbytyres.co.uk *Tyre suppliers*

▶ Kirkcaldy Print Ltd, Waverley Road, Mitchelston Industrial Estate, Kirkcaldy, Fife, KY1 3NH Tel: (01592) 655590

Kirker Europe Ltd, Davidson Drive, Castle Avenue Industrial Estate, Invergordon, Ross-Shire, IV18 0SA Tel: (01349) 856000 Fax: (01349) 852255 *Cosmetics manufrs*

Kirkfield Ltd, Unit 1/2 Schofield Business Park, Sugarbrook Road, Bromsgrove, Worcestershire, B60 3DN Tel: (01527) 559345 Fax: (01527) 835690 E-mail: sales@kirkfield.co.uk *Specialist in mouse mats, sheet, strip pads & rolls*

Ray Kirkham & Partners, 13 High Street, Prestwood, Great Missenden, Buckinghamshire, HP16 9EE Tel: (01494) 863423 E-mail: raykirkham@clara.co.uk *Computer consultants*

▶ Kirkham Young Ltd, Suite 4, 17 High Street, Battle, East Sussex, TN33 0AE Tel: (0870) 7873134 Fax: (01424) 777746 E-mail: info@kirkhamyoung.co.uk *Kirkham Young is a highly specialist recruitment agency*dedicated to the commercial healthcare market * * We provide a diverse range of companies operating in,the*healthcare arena with permanent sales, marketing, management*and technical /clinical support staff * * Kirkham Young benefits from having two directors, Sam Kirkham*and Tina Young, who are both highly motivated, professionally qualified and*have extensive industry knowledge providing strong contacts*with both clients and candidates in this niche market. **

Kirkholme Collectables, Main Street, Brandesburton, Driffield, North Humberside, YO25 8RL Tel: (01964) 543686 Fax: (01964) 543895 E-mail: sales@kirkholmecollectables.co.uk *Ceramics production*

Kirkland Ltd, 95 Main Street, Golspie, Sutherland, KW10 6TG Tel: (01408) 633079 Fax: (01408) 634468 E-mail: webad@kirkland.ltd.uk *IT consultancy*

▶ Kirkland Kitchens & Joinery Co. Ltd, The Old Cooperage, Gatebeck, Kendal, Cumbria, LA8 0HW Tel: (01539) 566999 Fax: (01539) 567733 E-mail: info@kirkland-kitchens.co.uk *Handcrafted bespoke furniture mainly kitchens*

Kirklands Ltd, Kirkland House, Main Cross Road, Great Yarmouth, Norfolk, NR30 3NZ Tel: (01493) 843060 Fax: (01493) 853001 E-mail: sales@kirkgroup.co.uk *Safety equipment (industrial) distributors & tarpaulin manufrs* Also at: Aberdeen

▶ Kirklees Plumbing & Heating Wigan Ltd, Unit H2 Belle Green Industrial Estate, Belle Green Lane, Ince, Wigan, Lancashire, WN2 2EP Tel: (01942) 324058 Fax: (01942) 491273

Kirkman & Jourdain Holdings Ltd, 150 Brooker Road, Waltham Abbey, Essex, EN9 1JH Tel: (01992) 788588 Fax: (01992) 788643 E-mail: k.j@kirkmanandjourdain.com *Building contractors, shopfitters, term maintenance contracts*

Kirkpatrick Ltd, PO Box 17, Walsall, WS2 9NF Tel: (01922) 620026 Fax: (01922) 722525 E-mail: sales@kirkpatrick.co.uk *Builders ironmongery manufrs*

Kirkpatrick Holdings Ltd, 88 Arthur Street, Redditch, Worcestershire, B98 8JY Tel: (01527) 522384 Fax: (01527) 507065 E-mail: sales@kirkpatrickcarriers.com *Haulage contractors*

Kirkstons Packaging Insulation(E Midlands) Ltd, Unit 16, Corringham Road Industrial Estate, Gainsborough, Lincolnshire, DN21 1QB Tel: (01427) 612007 Fax: (01427) 810952 E-mail: kirkston@packaging.fsworld.co.uk *Conversion of expanded polystyrene*

Kirkton Engineering, The Works, Station Road, Monymusk, Inverurie, Aberdeenshire, AB51 7HJ Tel: (01467) 651276 Fax: (01467) 651616 E-mail: kirktoneng@lineone.net *Steel fabricators*

Kirkvale Ltd, 18 Orchard Street, Burton-on-Trent, Staffordshire, DE14 3SJ Tel: (01283) 568692 Fax: (01283) 210961 *Lorry repairs*

Alexander Kirkwood & Son, 13 Albany Street, Edinburgh, EH1 3PY Tel: 0131-556 7843 Fax: 0131-556 4779 *Medallists, silversmiths & engravers*

▶ Kirkwood Homes Ltd, Woodside, Sauchen, Inverurie, Aberdeenshire, AB51 7LP Tel: (01330) 833595 Fax: (01330) 833625 E-mail: sales@kirkwoodhomes.co.uk

Kirmell Ltd, Eyre Street, Birmingham, B18 7AA Tel: 0121-456 3141 Fax: 0121-456 3151 E-mail: sales@kirmell.co.uk *Press work tool making*

Kirolite Products, 34-35 Dawkins Road, Poole, Dorset, BH15 4JW Tel: (01202) 676500 Fax: (01202) 681922 E-mail: info@kirolite.com *General wood machining*

Kirtek Industries Ltd, Thorney Road, Crowland, Peterborough, PE6 0AL Tel: (01733) 211290 Fax: (01733) 212331 E-mail: gkerk01@fsmail.net *Kirteks UK offer a professional service as a UK based company specialising in exterior textured wall coating, professional commercial painter decorator services, rising damp treatment and rising damp solutions, acting as patio cleaning contractors in the UK. Our driveway cleaning company offers driveway cleaning and power jet washing services, independent external protective wall coating and roof coating as well as exterior textured wall coating and protective wall coating sealers. If you require any kind of exterior decoration or high pressure water cleaning or industrial and house painting services from our company, in or around Cambridgeshire,*

continued

continuation Lincolnshire or Norfolk, from Lincoln to Peterborough and Kingslynn, as far as Boston, Skegness and Oundle, to Spalding and Wisbeach visit our UK company website www.kirteks.co.uk today

▶ Kirtlington Park Polo School, Park Farm Technology Centre, Akeman Street, Kirtlington, Kidlington, Oxfordshire, OX5 3JQ Tel: (01869) 350083 Fax: (01869) 350083 E-mail: melissawadley@hotmail.com *polo tuition,corporate days,polo holidays,team bulding,team managment,pony livery,pony hire,private or group lessons one hour from london*

Kirton Healthcare Group Ltd, 23 Rookwood Way, Haverhill, Suffolk, CB9 8PB Tel: (01440) 705352 Fax: (01440) 706199 E-mail: info@kirtonhealthcare.demon.co.uk *Specialist seating manufrs*

Kirton Kayaks Ltd, Marsh Lane, Lords Meadow Industrial Estate, Crediton, Devon, EX17 1ES Tel: (01363) 773295 Fax: (01363) 775908 E-mail: sales@kirton-kayaks.co.uk *Kayak manufrs*

Kirwin Airconditioning Ltd, B Riffa Business Park, Harrogate Road, Leathley, Otley, West Yorkshire, LS21 2RZ Tel: 0113-284 3667 Fax: 0113-284 3093 *Air conditioning design & contractors*

▶ Kisa Engineering Ltd, 45 Lady La Industrial Estate, Hadleigh, Ipswich, IP7 6BQ Tel: (01473) 823152 Fax: (01473) 828165 *Engineering sheet metalwork, fabricators*

Kisgap, Unit 7/8 Clifton House, 14 Wells Terrace, London, N4 3JU Tel: (020) 7272 8333 Fax: (020) 7272 8102 *Ladies wear retailer*

Kishorn Mechanical, Russel Workshop, Kishorn, Strathcarron, Ross-Shire, IV54 8XF Tel: (01520) 733261 Fax: (01520) 733261 *General engineering & marine engineers*

▶ Kisska Design, 36 Woodside Avenue, Chislehurst, Kent, BR7 6BU Tel: (020) 8467 5421 Fax: (020) 8467 5490 E-mail: info@kisska.com *Specialists in e-commerce & web catalogue publication systems*

Kistler Instruments Ltd, Murrell Green Business Park, London Road, Hook, Hampshire, RG27 9GR Tel: (01256) 741550 Fax: (01256) 741551 E-mail: sales.uk@kistler.com *Transducer & sensor supplier*

Kit Speakman, Witham Road, Little Braxted, Witham, Essex, CM8 3EU Tel: (01376) 515164 Fax: (01376) 515165 E-mail: kit@ksmltd.co.uk *Agricultural suppliers*

The Kitchen Accessory Company Ltd, Invicta House, 1 Claytonbrook Road, Openshaw, Manchester, M11 1AL Tel: 0161-223 5223 Fax: 0161-223 1149 E-mail: kitacco@aol.com *Kitchen furniture suppliers*

▶ Kitchen Concepts, 2 Anson Close, Aylesbury, Buckinghamshire, HP21 8AT Tel: (01296) 395558 Fax: (01296) 395558 E-mail: quainton@fsbdial.co.uk *Kitchen retailers*

Kitchen Deep Cleaning, 9 High Street, Orpington, Kent, BR6 0JE Tel: (01689) 828233 Fax: (01689) 828233 *Industrial kitchen deep cleaning*

Kitchen Design Centre, 789 Lisburn Road, Belfast, BT9 7GX Tel: (028) 9038 1265 Fax: (028) 9068 2452 E-mail: info@kdckitchendesign.com *Fitted kitchen installation*

▶ Kitchen Heaven, 26 Nibley Lane, Iron Acton, Bristol, BS37 9UP Tel: (01454) 228100 E-mail: sales@kitchenheaven.co.uk *Quality fitted kitchens*

Kitchen La Frenais Morgan, 1 Tenterden Street, London, W1S 1TA Tel: (020) 7317 3700 Fax: (020) 7317 3701 E-mail: info@klmproperty.co.uk *Commercial property agents*

Kitchen Master, Unit 8 Ashurst Drive, Stockport, Cheshire, SK3 0RY Tel: 0161-428 7777 Fax: 0161-428 7755 *Catering & industrial chemicals* Also at: Belfast, Bristol, Dublin, Glasgow & Nottingham

Kitchen Range Foods Ltd, Kingfisher Way, Hinchingbrooke Business Park, Huntingdon, Cambridgeshire, PE29 6FJ Tel: (01480) 445900 Fax: (01480) 434555 E-mail: krf@kitchenrangefoods.co.uk *Frozen food processors & products manufrs*

Kitchen Tech, 123 The Vale, London, W3 7RQ Tel: (020) 8749 7606 Fax: (020) 8746 7616 *Kitchen appliance suppliers*

Kitchen Vent Company, 3 Boydfield Avenue, Prestwick, Ayrshire, KA9 2JL Tel: (01292) 671333 Fax: (01292) 671171 E-mail: info@kvcayr.com *Ventilation, air conditioning & refrigeration services*

Kitchen Warehouse, Appleton Village, Widnes, Cheshire, WA8 6EQ Tel: 0151-424 5991 Fax: 0151-423 3357 *Kitchen makers*

▶ The Kitchen Workshop, Norwich, Tel: 01603 702344 E-mail: enquiries@the-kitchen-workshop.co.uk *Using 30 years of experience in kitchen production. We can design, build and install your new kitchen to your requirements.*

Kitcheneers Ltd, Monarch House, Honeywell Lane, Oldham, OL8 2LY Tel: 0161-665 5800 Fax: 0161-627 4507 E-mail: sales@kitcheneers.co.uk *Catering equipment agents & engineers*

Kitchens & Bedrooms Ltd, Whitehall Industrial Estate, Whitehall Road, Leeds, LS12 5JB Tel: 0113-263 9888 Fax: 0113-203 8917 *Kitchen & bedroom manufrs*

▶ Kitchens By Design, 41-43 Bell Street, Wigston, Leicestershire, LE18 1AD Tel: 0116-281 0440 *Built in furniture sales & installers*

▶ Kitchens Unlimited, Bridge Farm, High Halden, Ashford, Kent, TN26 3HZ Tel: (01233) 851199 Fax: (01233) 850066 E-mail: sales@whatkitchen.com

Kitchner 2000, Gec Business Park, Blackburn Road, Clayton le Moors, Accrington, Lancashire, BB5 5JW Tel: (01254) 239194 Fax: (01254) 232873 E-mail: info@kitchener2000.co.uk *Portable appliance electrical testing & inspection services*

Kite International Ltd, 4 Low March Industrial Estate, Low March, Daventry, Northamptonshire, NN11 4SD Tel: (01327) 314200 Fax: (01327) 314201 *Precision machinists*

Kite Packaging, PO Box 50, Blackwood, Gwent, NP12 2XF Tel: (01495) 230976 Fax: (01495) 230080 E-mail: southwales@packwithkite.com *Packaging material distributors*

Kite Packaging, 2 Newbridge Road Industrial Estate, Pontllanfraith, Blackwood, Gwent, NP12 2XF Tel: (01495) 230976 Fax: (01495) 230080 *Packaging materials distributors*

Kite Packaging, 186 Torrington Avenue, Coventry, CV4 9AJ Tel: (024) 7642 0088 Fax: (024) 7642 0062 E-mail: sales@packwithkite.com *Packaging materials*

Kite Packaging, H Park 34, Collett, Didcot, Oxfordshire, OX11 7WB Tel: (01235) 815615 Fax: (01235) 750760 E-mail: thamesvalley@packwithkite.com *Packaging materials distributors*

Kite Packaging, 8 Stirling Road, Glenrothes, Fife, KY6 2ST Tel: (01592) 630536 Fax: (01592) 630936 *Packers*

Kite Packaging, 2 Crammond Park, Lovet Road, Harlow, Essex, CM19 5TF Tel: (01279) 406160 Fax: (01279) 406161 E-mail: southeast@packwithkite.com *Distribution of packaging materials*

Kite Packaging, Unit 24-28, Stakehill Industrial Estate, Middleton, Manchester, M24 2RW Tel: 0161-643 1001 Fax: 0161-643 1122 E-mail: manchester@packwithkite.com *Packaging materials distributors*

Kite Packaging, Portfield Road, Portsmouth, PO3 5SF Tel: (023) 9265 2676 Fax: (023) 9265 2677 E-mail: southcoast@packwithkite.com *Packaging distributor*

Kite Packaging Ltd (Sheffield), Unit 3, Grange Mill Lane, Sheffield, S9 1HW Tel: (01709) 565010 Fax: (01709) 565011 E-mail: sheffield@packwithkite.com *Packaging materials distributors*

Kite Press Ltd, 3 Central Trading Estate, Signal Way, Swindon, SN3 1PD Tel: (01793) 436452 Fax: (01793) 487192 E-mail: sales@kite-press.co.uk *General stationery printers*

Kitech Services, 38 Saddleston Close, Hartlepool, Cleveland, TS26 0EZ Tel: (01429) 276114 Fax: (01429) 276114 E-mail: alison@kitech.co.uk *Laboratory equipment manufrs*

Kitel C S, Welldon, Askham, Penrith, Cumbria, CA10 2PG Tel: (01931) 712870 *Telecommunications installers*

Kitney & Co., Unit 12 Crystal Business Centre, Sandwich, Kent, CT13 9QX Tel: (01304) 611968 Fax: (01304) 614642 E-mail: sales@kitneyandco.com *Sterling silver & white metal gifts manufrs*

Kitpac Buildings Ltd, Shares Hill, Great Saredon, Wolverhampton, WV10 7LN Tel: (01922) 415425 Fax: (01922) 414246 E-mail: lisa@kitpac.freeserve.co.uk Principal Export Areas: Worldwide *Kitpac Buildings Ltd System Manufacturers Wolverhampton UK Temporary Buildings Folding Modular Buildings Relocatable Buildings Installations Wolverhampton UK Pakaway Modular Architectural Services Mezzanine Floors Temporary Buildings Wolverhampton UK.*

▶ Kitronik Ltd, Unit 18, Lenton Business Centre, Lenton Boulevard, Nottingham, NG7 2BY Tel: (0845) 8380781 Fax: (0845) 8380782 E-mail: sales@kitronik.co.uk *Specialists in curriculum based electronic project kits*

Kits & Bits, Reform Street, Sutton-in-Ashfield, Nottinghamshire, NG17 5DB Tel: (01623) 442524 Fax: (01623) 442545 E-mail: kitsandbitsltd@aol.com *Valve mounting kits & valve accessories manufrs*

Kitson Insulation Products Ltd, Cwmdu Industrial Estate, Carmarthen Road, Gendros, Swansea, SA5 8JF Tel: (01792) 588461 Fax: (01792) 583849 E-mail: swansea@kitsonsthermal.co.uk *Refractory & installation & fire protection stockists*

Kitson Trade Windows Ltd, South Road, Alnwick, Northumberland, NE66 2PD Tel: (01665) 606150 Fax: (01665) 606382 E-mail: enquiries@kitson.co.uk *Window suppliers & manufrs*

Kitsons, 139 Scudamore Road, Leicester, LE3 1UQ Tel: 0116-232 5000 Fax: 0116-232 5001 *Distributors of thermal insulation*

Kitsons Thermal Supplies, Broadfold Road, Bridge of Don, Aberdeen, AB23 8EE Tel: (01224) 771566 Fax: (01224) 770319 *Insulation distributors*

Kitto Joinery Ltd, 174a Cheltenham Road, Bristol, BS6 5RE Tel: 0117-942 0315 Fax: 0117-942 0405 E-mail: sales@kitto-group.co.uk *Joinery manufrs*

Kitto Laboratories Ltd, Christy House, Church Lane, Braintree, Essex, CM7 5RX Tel: (01376) 552554 Fax: (01376) 552923 *Metallurgical analysts*

▶ Kiuger Incorparated, Royce Trading Estate, Ashburton Road West, Trafford Park, Manchester, M17 1RY Tel: 0161-874 7300 Fax: 0161-874 7320 *Paper manufrs*

Kiveton Park Holdings Ltd, Kiveton Park, Sheffield, S26 6NQ Tel: (01909) 770252 Fax: (01909) 772949 E-mail: sales@kpsteel.co.uk *Steel wire metal heat treatment services & bright steel bar manufrs*

▶ Kiwanda, Unit B4, Bolney Road, Cowfold, Horsham, West Sussex, RH13 8AZ Tel: (01403) 864848 *Woodwork furniture manufrs*

Kiwi Canoes, 72 Hartley Rd, Radford, Nottingham, NG7 3AD Tel: 0115-978 4149 *Canoe manufrs*

Kiwi Craftsmen In Wood, 13 Rea Barn Close, Brixham, Devon, TQ5 9EA Tel: (01803) 858093 Fax: (01803) 858093 *Joinery manufrs*

Kiwi Products Dartford Ltd, 12 Dickens Court, Enterprise Close, Medway City Estate, Rochester, Kent, ME2 4LY Tel: (01634) 718484 Fax: (01634) 718484 E-mail: enquiries@kiwiproducts.co.uk *CNC precision engineers & breathing equipment manufrs*

Kiwiplan, Unit 5, Crompton Court, Burntwood Business Park, Burntwood, Staffordshire, WS7 3GG Tel: (01543) 273073 Fax: (01543) 273074 E-mail: info@kiwiplan-europe.com *Software house*

▶ Kizza Business Consultants Ltd, Seaton Close, Plaistow, London, E13 8JJ Tel: (020) 7511 8187 E-mail: pollykidza@yahoo.com *we clean computer keyboards,LCDs and Monitor screens professionally*We also clean all other office equipment and specialise in computer rooms.*please call for a free quote*

▶ KJH Digital, Forest Hill, Yeovil, Somerset, BA20 2PE Tel: 07955 154433 E-mail: production@kjhdigital.com *KJH Digital are experienced producers of web sites for small and medium businesses.*

▶ KJH - Solutions By Design, Holmlea, St Marys Road, Meare, Glastonbury, Somerset, BA6 9SS Tel: 07944 114235 E-mail: kevin@hann.freeserve.co.uk *Design engineers*

▶ KJW Resources Ltd, 12 Main Street, Scarcliffe, Chesterfield, Derbyshire, S44 6SZ Tel: (01246) 827703 E-mail: info@kjw-resources.com *Specialist organization providing management services*

KK Systems Ltd, PO Box 2770, Brighton, BN45 7ED Tel: (01273) 857185 Fax: (01273) 857186 E-mail: sales@kksystems.com *Data communications equipment suppliers*

Kkeil Construction, 26 Station Road, Cuxton, Rochester, Kent, ME2 1AB Tel: 01634 727275 Fax: 01634 727265 E-mail: info@kkeilconstruction.co.uk *Kkeil Construction is a Company formed in 2003 comprising of experienced tradesmen who have worked with one another for a combined 50 years on projects as diverse as erecting Conservatories to £6million commercial property restoration projects. Based in Medway, Kent, Kkeil Construction can undertake projects of any size in any UK location.*

KKK Limited, 7 Regent Park, Park Farm Industrial Estate, Off Booth Drive, Wellingborough, Northants, NN8 6GR Tel: (01933) 671480 Fax: (01933) 671470 E-mail: kkk.limited@agkkk.de *Manufacturers of compressors (gas), generating sets & steam turbines*

KL Nuts & Bolts, 4 Oldmedow Road, King's Lynn, Norfolk, PE30 4JL Tel: (01553) 763487 Fax: (01553) 774097 *Engineering supplies*

KLA Plastics (NI) Ltd, Unit 17 Comber Road Industrial Estate, Comber Road, Newtownards, County Down, BT23 4QP Tel: (028) 9181 8187 Fax: (028) 9181 1410 E-mail: info@klaplastics.co.uk *Reprocess plastics compounding & granulation crumbing contractors*

Klaremont Foods Service Products Ltd, 67 Weir Road, London, SW19 8UG Tel: (020) 8971 2012 Fax: (020) 8971 2005 E-mail: sales@klaremont.com *Catering equipment suppliers*

Klargester Environmental Ltd, College Road, Aston Clinton, Aylesbury, Buckinghamshire, HP22 5EW Tel: (01296) 633000 Fax: (01296) 633001 E-mail: sales@kingspanec.com *Sewage treatment plant & equipment manufrs*

Klark Teknik Group UK plc, Coppice Industrial Trading Estate, Walter Nash Road, Kidderminster, Worcestershire, DY11 7HJ Tel: (01562) 741515 Fax: (01562) 745371 *PA & recording equipment manufrs*

Klasp Prosthesis Laboratory, 110 Church Street, Westhoughton, Bolton, BL5 3SF Tel: (01942) 819979 Fax: (01942) 812080 *Dental technology suppliers*

Klassic Computers Services Ltd, 9 Church Meadow, Long Ditton, Surbiton, Surrey, KT6 5EP Tel: (020) 8398 3504 E-mail: sales@klassic.co.uk *Buy & sell computers*

Klaus Union (UK) Ltd, Charles Industrial Estate, Stowmarket, Suffolk, IP14 5AH Tel: (01449) 677645 Fax: (01449) 678136 E-mail: peter@klausunionltd.demon.co.uk *Magnetic drive pump manufrs*

Kle Audio Equipment, 218 Main Road, Goostrey, Crewe, CW4 8PE Tel: (01477) 533255 Fax: (01477) 533750 *Audio visual consultants*

Kleaning Equipment Western Ltd, Park Road, Dawley Bank, Telford, Shropshire, TF4 2BE Tel: (01952) 502600 Fax: (01952) 504703 E-mail: enquiries@cleaning-equipment.co.uk *Washers, pressure*

▶ Kleanstone Floor Maintenance Equipment, 204 Duggins Lane, Coventry, CV4 9GP Tel: (024) 7642 2609 Fax: (024) 7669 5794 *Floor cleaning machines retailer*

Kleen Tex Industries Ltd, Causeway Mill Express Trading Estate, Stone Hill Road, Farnworth, Bolton, BL4 9TP Tel: (01204) 863000 Fax: (01204) 863001 E-mail: sales@kleentexuk.com *Cleaning material manufrs*

▶ Kleeneze Ltd, 1A St Georges Avenue, Herne Bay, Kent, CT6 8JU Tel: (01227) 360903 Fax: (0870) 4325666 E-mail: julie@kleeneze-option.co.uk *Suppliers & distributors of home shopping items*

▶ Kleeneze Ltd, 80 Conniburrow Boulevard, Conniburrow, Milton Keynes, MK14 7DA Tel: (01908) 664153 E-mail: britishbiz@yahoo.co.uk *Catalogue Home Shopping Business. Part and Full time opportunities. Distributors and Business Builders required UK, Holland, and Ireland.*

▶ Kleeneze Ltd, 21 Bridle Close, Bradville, Milton Keynes, MK13 7EW Tel: (01908) 226025 Fax: (01908) 226025 E-mail: peacheybigbucks@aol.com *Network Marketing Professionals/Trainees required by major British plc for European expansion. Car, cash and travel incentives available.*

Kleerex Group UK Ltd, River Way, Temple Bank, Harlow, Essex, CM20 2DY Tel: (01279) 451103 Fax: (01279) 451104 E-mail: solutions@kleerex.co.uk *Point of sale display manufrs*

Kleiberit Adhesives UK, Brunel Way, Stephenson Industrial Estate, Coalville, Leicestershire, LE67 3HF Tel: (01530) 836699 Fax: (01530) 836677 E-mail: sales@kleiberit.com *Industrial adhesives*

Kleinmichel, Birds Hill, Letchworth Garden City, Hertfordshire, SG6 1JE Tel: (01462) 677611 Fax: (0870) 7626539 E-mail: uk-sales@kleinmichel.com *Manufacturers of automated adhesive dispensing systems*

Kleinwort Benson Gilts Ltd, 20 Fenchurch St, London, EC3M 3BY Tel: (020) 7623 8000 Fax: (020) 7623 4069 *Private investment bank*

John Kleis Car Hi-Fi Communications, 248 Basingstoke Road, Reading, RG2 0HN Tel: 0118-986 6224 Fax: (0870) 7702870 E-mail: sales@johnkleis.com *Retailers of car hi-fi, alarms, security & hands free car kits*

Klemetric Displays Ltd, Old Airfield Industrial Estate, Warboys Airfield, Warboys, Huntingdon, Cambridgeshire, PE28 2SH Tel: (01487) 824015 Fax: (01487) 823746 E-mail: sales@klemetricdisplays.co.uk *Point of sale & display equipment*

▶ Klempner Heiz, 52 Bruntsfield Avenue, Kilwinning, Ayrshire, KA13 6RZ Tel: (01294) 551949 Fax: (01294) 551949 E-mail: mjmcdonald@klempner-heiz.co.uk *Project & commercial management, mechanical & electrical engineering, plumbing & heating engineering, fabricators*

Klenzan Ltd, 2 Cameron Court, Winwick Quay, Warrington, WA2 8RE Tel: (01925) 234696 Fax: (01925) 234693 E-mail: info@klenzan.co.uk *Chemical manufrs*

Kler Knitwear, 46 Jellicoe Road, Leicester, LE5 4FN Tel: 0116-274 0199 Fax: 0116-276 0327 E-mail: info@kler.co.uk *Knitwear manufrs*

▶ Klere Lighting, 16 Church Lane, London, SW17 9PP Tel: (020) 8772 4081

▶ Klew Gets Wed, Unit 3, Millbrook Business Park Hoe Lane, Nazeing, Waltham Abbey, Essex, EN9 2RJ Tel: (01992) 890378 Fax: 01992 890378 E-mail: info@klew.co.uk *Klew Clothing Designs has created a unique collection of cutting-edge clothing for men and women. Each garment features an original, hand-printed design. Available wholesale and retail. *We also provide a bespoke print and embroidery service for promotional wear.**

▶ Klick Solutions, Pinfold Lane, Penkridge, Stafford, ST19 5AP Tel: (0845) 2620052 Fax: (01785) 716829 E-mail: enquiries@klicksolutions.co.uk *Full service marketing agency*

Klick Technology Ltd, Claverton Road, Roundthorn Industrial Estate, Manchester, M23 9FT Tel: 0161-998 9726 Fax: 0161-946 0419 E-mail: sales@klicktechnology.co.uk *Education furniture manufrs*

Kliklok Woodman International Ltd, Western Drive, Bristol, BS14 0AY Tel: (01275) 836131 Fax: (01275) 891754 E-mail: sales@kliklok-woodman-int.com Principal Export Areas: Worldwide *Packaging machine manufrs*

Kliko Environmental Systems, 23 Gladstone House, High Street, Hadley, Telford, Shropshire, TF1 5NF Tel: (01952) 641366 Fax: (01952) 641766 E-mail: info@kliko.co.uk

Klinger Ltd, Klinger Building, Wharfedale Road, Euroway Industrial Estate, Bradford, West Yorkshire, BD4 6SG Tel: (01274) 688222 Fax: (01274) 688962 E-mail: enquiries@klingeruk.co.uk *Manufacturers of metallic, semi metallic, soft cut gaskets, compression packings & jointing* Also at: Aberdeen, Middlesborough, Runcorn & Wilton

Klingspor Abrasives Ltd, Dukeries Close, Worksop, Nottinghamshire, S81 7DN Tel: (01909) 504400 Fax: (01909) 504405 E-mail: sales@klingspor.co.uk *Abrasive coated products/component manufrs*

▶ Klosters Chalet, 19 Blakesley Avenue, LONDON, W5 2DN Tel: 020 8810 5657 E-mail: chalet@klosterschalet.com *Luxury self-catering Swiss alpine Chalets, bases for skiing, winter sports, walking, hiking, trekking, sailing and paragliding. E.g. Chalet Rhaetia in Klosters. Sleeps 8 in luxury. set in beautiful natural landscape, stunning views.**

KLP, 109 Wardour Street, London, W1F 0UH Tel: (020) 7478 3400 Fax: (020) 7478 3578 E-mail: sales@klpeuroscd.co.uk *Marketing & events services*

Kluber Lubrication, Bradford Road, Halifax, West Yorkshire, HX3 7BN Tel: (01422) 319149 Fax: (01422) 206073 E-mail: info@uk.klueber.com *Lubricant distributors*

Kluman & Balter Ltd, 8 The I O Centre Waltham Cross, New Ford Road, Waltham Cross, Hertfordshire, EN8 7PG Tel: (01992) 704000 Fax: (01992) 768171 E-mail: customerservice@kaybeefoods.com *Bakers ingredient & prepared material producers*

Kluthe, 314 Midsummer Boulevard, Milton Keynes, MK9 2UB Tel: (01908) 440120 Fax: (01908) 440121 E-mail: info@kluthe.co.uk *Chemical manufrs*

Klyne Tugs Lowestoft Ltd, Cumberland Place, Whapoad Road, Lowestoft, Suffolk, NR32 1UQ Tel: (01502) 515250 Fax: (01502) 500225 E-mail: enquiries@klyne-tugs.demon.co.uk *Tug operators & brokers towage salvage services*

▶ KM Products Europe Ltd, The Forum, Unit B, Hanworth Lane Business Park, Hanworth Lane, Chertsey, Surrey, KT16 9JX Tel: (01932) 571991 Fax: (01932) 571994 E-mail: sales@kmpuk.com *Engine parts for bulldozers retailers & distributor*

KMC, 7 Old Park Lane, London, W1K 1QR Tel: (020) 7317 4600 Fax: (020) 7317 4620 E-mail: london@kmcinternational.com *Recruitment consultants*

▶ KMD, 109a Whippingham Road, Brighton, BN2 3PF Tel: (01273) 679700 Fax: (01273) 605057 *Carpentry*

KMD Investors Ltd, 140 Queens Road, Leicester, LE2 3FX Tel: 0116-270 9221 Fax: 0116-270 2334 E-mail: steve@kmd-company.co.uk *Carton folded manufrs*

KME UK Ltd, Severn House, Prescott Drive, Warndon Business Park, Worcester, WR4 9NE Tel: (01905) 751816 Fax: (01905) 751801 E-mail: info@kme.com *Non-ferrous metal stockholders & manufrs*

▶ Kmi, Unit 17-19 Chiltern Court Asheridge Road Industrial Estate, Asheridge Road, Chesham, Buckinghamshire, HP5 2PX Tel: (01494) 783066 Fax: (01494) 783088

Kmi Petrol Injection Engineers, Unit 2a Farm La Trading Estate, Farm Lane, London, SW6 1QJ Tel: (020) 7385 7138 Fax: (020) 7610 0884 *Fuel injection engineering services*

▶ KMS, 63 Tanner Street, London, SE1 3PL Tel: (020) 7939 0740 Fax: (020) 7407 2810 E-mail: rachelb@kms-software.com *Software suppliers & distributors*

Knaggs Furniture Fittings, Ash Industrial Estate, Flex Meadow, Harlow, Essex, CM19 5TJ Tel: (01279) 641199 Fax: (01279) 641133 E-mail: enquiries@knaggs4fittings.co.uk *Furniture suppliers*

▶ Knapman & Sons Builders Ltd, 139 North Cray Road, Sidcup, Kent, DA14 5HE Tel: (020) 8302 2233 Fax: (020) 8302 6060

Knaresborough Engineering, Sandbeck Way, Wetherby, West Yorkshire, LS22 7DN Tel: (01937) 589000 Fax: (01937) 585566 *Sheet metal fabrication engineers*

Knauf Drywall Ltd, Sittingbourne, Kent, ME10 3HW Tel: (01795) 424499 Fax: (01795) 428651 E-mail: info@knauf.co.uk *Manufacture plaster & plasterboard*

Knebworth Fire Protection, 22 Doncaster Close, Stevenage, Hertfordshire, SG1 5RY Tel: (01438) 712642 Fax: (01438) 861759 *Fire protection*

Knee Agricultural Machinery, Ashton Mills, West Ashton Road, Trowbridge, Wiltshire, BA14 7BB Tel: (01225) 753894 Fax: (01225) 762208 E-mail: info@kamengineering.co.uk *Steel fabricators*

▶ Wendy Knee Life Coach, Yew Tree Cottage, Foghamshire Lane, Trudoxhill, Frome, Somerset, BA11 5DG Tel: (01373) 837247 *Live the life you love, love the life you live!*Wendy offers personal, co-active life coaching: she will work with you to help you get the most out of life, realise your dreams and give you the perspective and motivation to take the first steps to achieve them.*

Kneeshaw C C M Ltd, Manchester House, 48 High Street, Stokesley, Middlesbrough, Cleveland, TS9 5AX Tel: (01642) 711583 Fax: (01642) 711678 E-mail: mail@kccm.co.uk *Chartered quantity surveyors* Also at: Durham, London & Middlesbrough

▶ Knew Image Ltd, 33 Hampton Road, Twickenham, TW2 5QE Tel: (020) 8893 9661 Fax: (020) 8893 9662 E-mail: sales@knewimage.co.uk *Exhibition stand Designers and suppliers of modular displays and accessories*

Knibbs Computer Services Ltd, Suite 1 Falmer Court, London Road, Uckfield, East Sussex, TN22 1HN Tel: (01825) 749416 Fax: (0870) 7051341 E-mail: info@knibbs.com *Computer systems consultants*

Knicat Ltd, 64 Railway Road, Downham Market, Norfolk, PE38 9EL Tel: (01366) 383708 *Bakery suppliers*

Knight Andy Ltd, 2-6 Occupation Road, London, SE17 3BE Tel: (020) 7252 5252 Fax: (020) 7252 5111 E-mail: info@andyknight.co.uk *Model makers & TV advertising*

Knight Architechtural Design, 181 Kathleen Road, Southampton, SO19 8GX Tel: (023) 8042 0938 Fax: (023) 8042 0938 E-mail: ian.kad@lineone.net *Architectural consultants*

Knight & Butler Ltd, 2 High Street, East Grinstead, West Sussex, RH19 3AW Tel: (01342) 318650 Fax: (01342) 318651 E-mail: email@knightandbutler.com *Structural engineers*

Knight Chapman Psychological Ltd, 1 The Friars, High Street, Lewes, East Sussex, BN7 2AD Tel: (01273) 487333 Fax: (01273) 471475 E-mail: service@kcpltd.com *Occupational test publishers*

▶ D.W. Knight Engineering Co. Ltd, Unit 1, Sywell Airport, Sywell, Northampton, NN6 0BN Tel: (01604) 647689 Fax: (01604) 494637 E-mail: d-w-knight@tiscali.co.uk *Fabrication engineers*

Knight Engineering, Unit 22 Thruxton Industrial Estate, Thruxton, Andover, Hampshire, SP11 8PW Tel: (01264) 773291 Fax: (01264) 773075 E-mail: sales@knightengineering.co.uk *Engineering subcontractor*

Knight Frank Property Company, Knight Frank 20 Hanover Square, London, W1S 1HZ Tel: (020) 7408 1100 Fax: (020) 7493 4114 E-mail: farms.estates@knightfrank.com *Commercial, industrial & shop property agents*

Knight & Gibbins Ltd, Windham Road, Chilton Industrial Estate, Sudbury, Suffolk, CO10 2XD Tel: (01787) 377264 Fax: (01787) 378258 E-mail: sales@knightandgibbins.co.uk *Clock & clock case manufrs*

▶ J.P. Knight Caledonian Ltd, Invergordon Boat Yard, 37 Shore Road, Invergordon, Ross-Shire, IV18 0EH Tel: (01349) 852611 Fax: (01349) 853087 E-mail: info@jpknight.co.uk

Leigh Knight Ltd, 82 Arnos Grove, London, N14 7AR Tel: (020) 8886 9806 Fax: (020) 8447 8332 E-mail: sales@leighknight.com *Woolen piece goods wholesalers*

Knight Motors, Unit G, Bakers Wharf, Millbank Street, Southampton, SO14 5QQ Tel: (023) 8023 4008 Fax: (023) 8023 4008 E-mail: richard@knightmotors.com *Vehicle repairs & gearbox specialists*

Knight Plastics Ltd, 1 Clydesmuir Industrial Estate, Clydesmuir Road, Cardiff, CF24 2QS Tel: (029) 2048 8129 Fax: (029) 2048 9132 E-mail: knight@kplastics.fsnet.co.uk *Plastic injection moulding to the trade and industry*

Knight Precision Wire, Hadley Works, Cranborne Road, Potters Bar, Hertfordshire, EN6 3JL Tel: (01707) 645261 Fax: (01707) 649225 E-mail: kpw.sales@knight-group.co.uk *Manufacturers and stockholders of precision wire for over 70 years.*Round, flat and square wires.*Stainless steel, high carbon spring steel,*

continued

*copper, brass, beryllium copper, phosphor bronze, nickel, cupro-nickel, nickel alloys.*Also wire straightening and cutting, spooling/ rewinding, wire cleaning.* Certified to ISO 9001:2000, also aerospace AS9100 and AS9120.*

▶ Knight Projects Group Ltd, Station App, Atherton, Manchester, M46 9LJ Tel: (01942) 874171 Fax: (01942) 897482

Knight Sound & Light, 98 Uxbridge Road, London, W7 3SU Tel: (020) 8579 0144 Fax: (020) 8579 8222 E-mail: info@knightsoundandlight.com *Sound & lighting equipment sale, hire & installation service*

Knight Strip Metals Ltd, Saltley Business Park, Cumbria Way, Saltley, Birmingham, B8 1BH Tel: 0121-322 8400 Fax: 0121-322 8401 E-mail: kms.sales@knight-group.co.uk *Slitting, rotary, metal; coil slitting, non ferrous & steel slitting*

▶ Knight Systems, 43 Thornbury Drive, Uphill, Weston-Super-Mare, Avon, BS23 4YA Tel: (01934) 625089 E-mail: info@knightsystems.org *Door entry intruder alarms manufrs*

Knight Thermal Insulation, 54 Factory Estate, College Road, Perry Barr, Birmingham, B44 8BS Tel: 0121-356 3980 Fax: 0121-356 1688 *Thermal insulation & asbestos removal*

Knight UK Ltd, Unit 15 The Brunel Centre, Newton Road, Crawley, West Sussex, RH10 9TU Tel: (01293) 615570 Fax: (01293) 615585 *Chemical pump retailers*

W.G. Knight & Son, 18 Main Ridge, Boston, Lincolnshire, PE21 6SS Tel: 01205 363084 *Sheet metalworkers*

W. Knight Watson & Co. Ltd, Mandal House, South Shore Road, Grangemouth, Stirlingshire, FK3 8AE Tel: (01324) 486721 Fax: (01324) 473096 E-mail: enquiries@wkwat.co.uk *Ship brokers*

T.H. Knightall, Hawksley Avenue, Sheffield, S6 2BG Tel: 0114-234 8886 Fax: 0114-285 4753 E-mail: thkltd@aol.com *Sportswear manufrs*

Knighthood Security Systems Ltd, 132 Talbot Road, London, W11 1JA Tel: (020) 8541 4725 Fax: (020) 8255 9190 E-mail: sales@knighthoodsecurity.co.uk *Security system maintenance & installation services*

▶ Knighton Haulage, Station Yard, Station Road, Knighton, Powys, LD7 1DT Tel: (01547) 529500 Fax: (01547) 529236

Knights Design & Manufacturer, Trident Business Park, 6 Park Street, Nuneaton, Warwickshire, CV11 4NS Tel: (024) 7634 4822 Fax: (024) 7634 4822 *Design & manufacture of jigs & fixtures*

Norman Knights Ltd, 1 Russell Court, Russell Gardens, Wickford, Essex, SS11 8QU Tel: (01268) 733722 Fax: (01268) 764537 E-mail: sales@normanknights.com *Polypropylene bag & transparent film manufrs*

Knights Photographers, 51 Bear Street, Barnstaple, Devon, EX32 7DB Tel: (01271) 371776 *Commercial photographers*

▶ Knights Saddlery, Unit 1e Utility Savings Centre, Station Road, Docking, King's Lynn, Norfolk, PE31 8LT Tel: (01485) 518080 E-mail: annettezera@aol.com *QUALITY EQUESTRIAN GOODS AT VERY COMPETITIVE PRICES*

▶ Knights Templar Events, PO Box 740, Warrington, WA4 2WT Tel: (01925) 267658 Fax: (01925) 267658 E-mail: info@knightstemplarevents.co.uk *professional corporate event entertainment company and service provider specilising in murder mystery events, fun casino nights, corporate entertainment and party planning.*

Knights Warner Kings Lynn Ltd, Austin Fields, King's Lynn, Norfolk, PE30 1PL Tel: (01553) 773929 Fax: (01553) 691532 E-mail: knights-warner@btconnect.com *Building services engineers*

Knightsbridge Ltd, 191 Thornton Road, Bradford, West Yorkshire, BD1 2JT Tel: (01274) 731442 Fax: (01274) 736641 E-mail: sales@knightsbridge-furniture.co.uk *Furniture manufrs*

Knightsbridge Importers Ltd, 5 Oakwood Road, London, NW11 6QU Tel: (020) 8458 3898 Fax: (020) 8201 9992 *Toiletries & sundries wholesalers*

Knightsbridge Lighting Ltd, Unit 9 Station Road Industrial Estate, Attleborough, Norfolk, NR17 2NP Tel: (01953) 452323 Fax: (01953) 453037 E-mail: sales@lightingforall.com *Lighting manufacturers & distributors*

▶ Knightsbridge Mechanical Handling Ltd, Newby Road Industrial Estate, Newby Road, Hazel Grove, Stockport, Cheshire, SK7 5DA Tel: 0161-456 0123 Fax: 0161-456 8683 E-mail: knightsbridgemechanical@btconnect.com *Sales, hire rental, training - forklift trucks*

▶ Knightsbridge Property Services Ltd, Knightsbridge House, 42 Willow Lane, Mitcham, Surrey, CR4 4NA Tel: (020) 8287 3838 Fax: (020) 8287 3737 E-mail: enquiries@knightsbridgeproperty.co.uk *Knightsbridge Property Services Ltd(KPS)offer complete repair, maintenance & refurbishment services for all types of domestic, retail, commercial & industrial buildings. Based in South London since 1985 we cover South East England & employ fully qualified engineers. We also offer a 24 hour emergency call-out facility, our Call Centre is experienced to handle all types of queries and can arrange for on site quotations. Our services range from General Building, Electrical, Plumbing, Roofing, Air Conditioning and Refrigeration Services. We are Corgi and NICEIC Registered and members of professional bodies.*We are acredited to CONSTRUCTIONLINE, CHAS, SAFECONTRACTOR AND EXOR.*

Knightsbridge Reproduction, Unit 14 Greenside Trading Centre, Greenside Lane, Droylsden, Manchester, M43 7AJ Tel: 0161-370 2999 Fax: 0161-371 1991 *Manufacturers of reproduction leather furniture*

Knightsridge Engineering Services Ltd, 10 Nettlehill Road, Houstoun Industrial Estate, Livingston, West Lothian, EH54 5DL Tel: (01506) 430605 Fax: (01506) 440380 E-mail: kesl@btconnect.com *CNC contractors*

Knightwatch Ltd, PO Box 319, Sevenoaks, Kent, TN15 8JL Tel: (01732) 886777 Fax: (01732) 886888 E-mail: sales@autowatch.co.uk *Car security suppliers*

▶ Knitted Trimmings, 3 Fosse Way, Syston, Leicester, LE7 1NF Tel: 0116-327 0336 Fax: 0116-327 0336 E-mail: info@uk-trims.co.uk

Knitter Switch UK Ltd, Grove House, Lutyens Close, Lychpit, Basingstoke, Hampshire, RG24 8AG Tel: (01256) 338670 Fax: (01256) 338671 E-mail: ksuk@knitter-switch.com *Switch manufrs*

Knitting Industries Federation, 12 Beaumanor Road, Leicester, LE4 5QA Tel: 0116-266 3332 Fax: 0116-266 3335 E-mail: directorate@knitfed.co.uk *National trade federation*

Knitwire Products, Dalton Court, Chadwick Road, Runcorn, Cheshire, WA7 1PU Tel: (01928) 566996 Fax: (01928) 566996 E-mail: sales@knitwire.com *Knitted wire mesh demister, mist eliminator & filter manufrs*

Knobs, Leone Works, John Street, New Basford, Nottingham, NG7 7HL Tel: 0115-942 0006 Fax: 0115-970 2106 E-mail: sales@knobs.uk.com *Industrial knobs & handles available off-the-shelf from one of the UK's largest suppliers*

▶ Knockout, 115 Vale Road, Worcester Park, Surrey, KT4 7EB Tel: (020) 8337 4491 E-mail: knockoutpcs@aol.com *Pest controllers*

Knockout Colour Ltd, Unit 6 Shore Business Centre, 14-16 Shore Rd, London, E9 7TA Tel: (020) 8533 1177 Fax: (020) 8533 5895 *Reprographic house*

▶ Knockout Pest Control Services, 33 Pennington Road, Chalfont St. Peter, Gerrards Cross, Buckinghamshire, SL9 9PH Tel: (01753) 882182 *Pest controllers*

▶ Knockout Show Ltd, Holly House Barn Bradkirk Lane, Bamber Bridge, Preston, PR5 6ZQ Tel: (01772) 335544 Fax: (01772) 746678 E-mail: Dave@itsaknockout.com *Road show suppliers*

Knoll International, 1 Lindsey Street, London Central Markets, London, EC1A 9PQ Tel: (020) 7236 6655 Fax: (020) 7248 1744 *Furniture*

Knorr Bremse Systems for Commercial Vehicles Ltd, Century House, Follybook Road, Emerald Park East, Emmersons Green, Bristol, BS16 7SE Tel: 0117-984 6100 Fax: 0117-984 6101 Principal Export Areas: Worldwide *Air braking component manufrs*

Knorr-Dremse Systems UK Ltd, Westinghouse Way, Hampton Park East, Bowerhill, Melksham, Wiltshire, SN12 6TL Tel: (01249) 442000 Fax: (01225) 898705 E-mail: sales@westbrake.com *Railway brakes manufrs*

Knotbox, 47A High Street, Witney, Oxfordshire, OX28 6JA Tel: (01993) 778772 Fax: (01993) 701184 *Hardwood furniture suppliers*

▶ The Knotty Wood Co., The Ward, Strathaven, Lanarkshire, ML10 6AS Tel: (01357) 523366 Fax: (01357) 523366

▶ Knotweed Creations, 6 High Street, Bluntisham, Huntingdon, Cambridgeshire, PE28 3LD Tel: (01487) 842033 E-mail: andrea@knotweedcreations.co.uk *Artist*

▶ Know I.T. Consulting Ltd, 1st Floor, 17 Station Road, Kettering, Northamptonshire, NN15 7HH Tel: (0845) 8382645 E-mail: info@knowitconsulting.co.uk *It services*

Knowhow Consulting, Elmbridge House, Elmbridge Lane, Woking, Surrey, GU22 9AF Tel: (01483) 776000 Fax: (01483) 433317 E-mail: info@knowhowconsultinglco.uk *IT consultants*

Knowle Nets Ltd, 20 East Road, Bridport, Dorset, DT6 4NX Tel: (01308) 424342 Fax: (01308) 458186 E-mail: sales@knowlenets.co.uk *Net manufrs*

Knowledge Ability, 48 St. Dennis Road, Malmesbury, Wiltshire, SN16 9BH Tel: (01666) 826654 *Internet consultants*

Knowledge Solutions UK Ltd, 4b The Lanterns, Melbourn Street, Royston, Hertfordshire, SG8 7BX Tel: (01763) 257100 Fax: (01763) 257112 E-mail: sales@knowledgeuk.com *Computer consultants & software developers*

▶ Knowledge Train, 30 Mildenhall Road, London, E5 0RU Tel: 020 8986-5430 E-mail: info@knowledgetrain.co.uk *Project management training courses*

▶ Knowledgepoint Ltd, 5 Cutbush Park, Danehill, Lower Earley, Reading, RG6 4UT Tel: 0118-918 1500 Fax: 0118-918 1501 E-mail: sales@knowledgepoint.co.uk

Knowles Europe, York Road, Burgess Hill, West Sussex, RH15 9TT Tel: (01444) 235432 Fax: (01444) 248724 E-mail: info@knowles.com *Transducer manufrs*

Knowles Transport Ltd, New Road, Wimblington, March, Cambridgeshire, PE15 0RG Tel: (01354) 740233 Fax: (01354) 741333 E-mail: sales@knowles-transport.co.uk *Road transport contractors*

Knowlsons Of Blackpool, 20 Boome Street, Blackpool, FY4 2JX Tel: (01253) 406555 Fax: (01253) 406606 *Bakery wholesalers*

Knowlton & Newman, Belvidere Terrace, Southampton, SO14 5QR Tel: (023) 8022 5869 Fax: (023) 8063 1969 E-mail: sales@knsoton.co.uk *Electric motor rewinds & repairers*

Knowlton & Newman (Portsmouth) Ltd, Unit 4, Admiral Park, Portsmouth, PO3 5RQ Tel: (023) 9265 0100 Fax: (023) 9265 1097 E-mail: sales@knports.co.uk *Electrical installation services*

▶ Knowsley Engineering Services, 6 Peel Road, Skelmersdale, Lancashire, WN8 9PT Tel: (01695) 556108 Fax: (01695) 556649 E-mail: mail@knowsleyengineeringservices.co.uk *Fabrications & sheet metal ware*

Knowsley Instrument Services Ltd, Ashcroft Road, Knowsley Industrial Park North, Liverpool, L33 7TW Tel: 0151-548 8099 Fax: 0151-548 6599 E-mail: sales@kis-liverpool.co.uk *Manufacture pressure & temperature equipment*

▶ Knowsley Lift Services Ltd, Cotton Exchange Building, Old Hall Street, Liverpool, L3 9LQ Tel: 0151-286 1322 Fax: 0151-286 2400 E-mail: info@knowsleylifts.com *Lift & escalators engineers, installers & repairers*

Knox Industries Ltd, Clearview, Scholague Road, Abbeylands, Isle of Man, IM4 5BU Tel: (01624) 674434 Fax: (01624) 674434 *Fencing manufrs*

John Knox Ltd, 55 Rosebank Street, Leek, Staffordshire, ST13 6AG Tel: (01538) 399733 Fax: (01538) 399985 E-mail: jknox1066@aol.com *Business development specialists*

Knurr UK Ltd, Burrel Road, St. Ives, Cambridgeshire, PE27 3LE Tel: (01480) 496125 Fax: (01480) 496373 E-mail: knuerr.uk@knuerr.com Principal Export Areas: Worldwide *Electronic cabinet & consoles*

▶ Kobelco Cranes Europe Ltd, 9 The Felbridge Centre, Imberhorne Lane, East Grinstead, West Sussex, RH19 1XP Tel: (01342) 301122 Fax: (01342) 326987 *Crane manufrs*

Kobi, Unit 19 Seax Court, Southfields Industrial Estate, Basildon, Essex, SS15 6SL Tel: (01268) 416335 Fax: (01268) 542148 E-mail: cradles@kobi.co.uk *Building access equipment manufrs* Also at: Edinburgh

Kobo (UK) Ltd, Ketten House, Leestone Road, Sharston Industrial Area, Manchester, M22 4RH Tel: 0161-491 9840 Fax: 0161-428 1999 E-mail: info@kobo.co.uk *International power transmission manufrs and Anti-vibration Products, Vibratory Motors.*

▶ Kobu Ltd, 3 Manor Farm Offices, Northend Road, Fenny Compton, Southam, Warwickshire, CV47 2YY Tel: (01295) 771182 Fax: (01295) 771185 E-mail: info@kobu.co.uk *Graphic design services*

Koch Glitsch (U K), Hobson Lane, Kirkby Stephen, Cumbria, CA17 4RN Tel: (01768) 374400 Fax: (01768) 374401 *Mass transfer equipment, oil & petrol*

Koch Heat Transfer Company, PO Box 790, Wimborne, Dorset, BH21 5BQ Tel: (01258) 840776 Fax: (01258) 840961 E-mail: bftuk@kochind.com *Heat exchangers manufrs*

Koch Membrane Systems, The Granary, Telegraph Street, Stafford, ST17 4AT Tel: (01785) 272500 Fax: (01785) 223149 *Filtration equipment distributors*

Kochane Bros Ltd, 29 Whitechapel Road, London, E1 1DU Tel: (020) 7247 9148 Fax: (020) 7247 2937 *Textile merchants*

Kodak Ltd, Hemel One, Boundary Way, Hemel Hempstead, Hertfordshire, HP2 7YU Tel: (01442) 261122 E-mail: gb-ei-orders@kodak.com *Imaging photographic systems suppliers*

Kodak Graphic Communications Ltd, Axis 1, Rhodes Way, Watford, WD24 4FD Tel: (01923) 233366 Fax: (01923) 227802 Principal Export Areas: Worldwide *Printing plate manufrs* Also at: Atherstone & Leeds

Kodak Polychrome Graphics, Howley Park Estate, Morley, Leeds, LS27 0QT Tel: 0113-253 7711 E-mail: sales@kpgraphics.com *Printing plate manufrs* Also at: Branches throughout the U K

▶ Kodela Computer Consultants, 433 Porters Avenue, Dagenham, Essex, RM9 4ND Tel: (020) 8984 0606 Fax: 020 89840606 *Computer systems consultants*

▶ Koehler Chemie Ltd, Astley Way, Astley La Industrial Estate, Swillington, Leeds, LS26 8XT Tel: 0113-287 1122 Fax: 0113-287 3087

▶ Koenig & Wiegand, 45 Sarisbury Close, Tadley, Hampshire, RG26 3SZ Tel: 0118-981 9481 Fax: (020) 7117 3273 E-mail: s.hewett@koenig-wiegand.de *Suppliers & traders in food ingredients & chemicals*

▶ Koga, 323 Filton Avenue, Horfield, Bristol, BS7 0BB Tel: (0789) 1284705 E-mail: zinapromotion@o2.pl *Koga is a manufacturer of products from GRP (glass reinforced polyester). We make rowing boats, kayaks, canoes, motor boats, garden ponds, auto body parts, containers, covers, shower cabins, toilets, and so on.*

Kohler Daryl Ltd, Alfred Road, Wallasey, Merseyside, CH44 7HY Tel: 0151-606 5000 Fax: 0151-638 0303 E-mail: daryl@daryl-showers.co.uk *Shower doors, screens enclosures & related products* Also at: Skelmersdale

▶ KOI Furniture, PO Box 449, Harpenden, Herts, AL5 9AF Tel: 0845 2268271 Fax: 0870 7626151 E-mail: enquiries@koifurniture.co.uk *KOI Furniture offers an online range of antique Chinese furniture as well as contemporary reproduction furniture for Oriental living*

Koi Joy, 14 Norwich Road, Lowestoft, Suffolk, NR32 2BW Tel: (01502) 564479 Fax: (01502) 564479 *Wholesale fish & reptiles service & installers*

Koi Joy Pet, 60-61 Nile Road, Gorleston, Great Yarmouth, Norfolk, NR31 6AS Tel: (01493) 442703 Fax: (01493) 441393 *Ponds, fish, aquariums & pets suppliers*

▶ Koi Logic, Forest View Nursery, St. Marys Lane, North Ockendon, Upminster, Essex, RM14 3PA Tel: (01708) 226699 E-mail: sales@koilogic.co.uk *Koi filtration manufrs*

Koi Plus, Newton Chambers Road, Thorncliffe Park Estate, Chapeltown, Sheffield, S35 2PH Tel: 0114-257 7525 Fax: 0114-257 7525 E-mail: sales@koiplus.force9.co.uk *Aquarium & pond suppliers*

Koi Pool, Fleetwood Road South, Thornton-Cleveleys, Lancashire, FY5 5NS Tel: (01253) 856411 Fax: (01253) 828610 *Importers*

Koi Water Garden, Lower Morden Lane, Morden, Surrey, SM4 4SJ Tel: (020) 8337 3337 Fax: (020) 8335 3979 E-mail: sales@koiwatergarden.com *Koi carp specialists & aquatic & water garden features*

▶ Koiman Enterprises, 10 Main Road, Duston, Northampton, NN5 6JB Tel: (01604) 581074 E-mail: koiman.geff@btinternet.com *Koi carp fish farming & sales*

▶ Kolb Components, 60 Vernon Avenue, London, SW20 8BW Tel: (07833) 695330 E-mail: sam.franz@kolbcomponents.co.za *Manufactures the Kolb engine monitoring*

continued

continuation
system, a protection module that protects engines, gearboxes, hydraulic systems, radiators, batteries & more

Kolbus UK Ltd, 35 Heathfield, Stacey Bushes, Milton Keynes, MK12 6HR Tel: (01908) 317878 Fax: (01908) 310863 E-mail: sales@kolbus.co.uk Bookbinders machinery, parts & services suppliers

▶ Kolectric Research, 41 Couching Street, Watlington, Oxfordshire, OX49 5PX Tel: (01491) 613523 Fax: (01491) 613339 E-mail: enquiries@kolectric.com Metal detector suppliers

▶ Kollmorgen Lift Control, Barnsole Road, Gillingham, Kent, ME7 4JH Tel: (01634) 280077 Fax: (01634) 280346 Manufacturer of control systems for lifts

Kolon Imperial Graphics plc, Erico House, 93/99 Upper Richmond Road, London, SW15 2TG Tel: (020) 8780 1585 Fax: (020) 8785 7004 E-mail: junelee21@kolonuk.net Import & export merchants

Kolorcraft Ltd, Concept House, Mortimer Rise Milner Way, Ossett, West Yorkshire, WF5 9JE Tel: (01924) 780780 Fax: (01924) 262586 Litho & digital screen printers services

Kolorgraphic Ltd, Unit 3a Stag Industrial Estate, Atlantic Street, Broadheath, Altrincham, Cheshire, WA14 5DW Tel: 0161-928 6014 Fax: 0161-928 7299 E-mail: kolorgraphic01@hotmail.com Display materials & vehicle graphic appliers & manufrs

Kolorpik UK, 58 Cowper Crescent, Hertford, SG14 3EA Tel: (01992) 581979 Fax: (01992) 550142 E-mail: kolorpik.uk@ntlworld.com Marker pens, highlighter, permanent, whiteboard, colouring suppliers

▶ Kolorplast Coatings Ltd, Radley House, Hawksworth, Didcot, Oxfordshire, OX11 7PJ Tel: (01235) 511414 Fax: (01235) 516701

Komac, Unit 17-18, Narrowboat Way, Blackbrook Valley Indusrial Estate, Dudley, West Midlands, DY2 0XQ Tel: (01384) 481396 Fax: (01384) 481397 Office seating manufrs

Komatsu UK Ltd, Durham Road, Birtley, Chester le Street, County Durham, DH3 2QX Tel: 0191-410 3155 Fax: 0191-410 8156 E-mail: enquiries@komatsuuk.com Earth moving equipment manufrs

Komfort, 96 Hopewell Drive, Chatham, Kent, ME5 7PY Tel: (01634) 829290 Fax: (01634) 831213 Office furniture

Komfort Office Crate Hire, 7 Sipson Lane, Hayes, Middlesex, UB3 5EH Tel: (020) 8897 0414 Fax: (020) 8476 1370 Office crate hire & building maintenance services

Komfort Office Environments Plc, Units 1-10, Whittle Way, Crawley, West Sussex, RH10 9RW Tel: (01293) 592500 Fax: (01293) 553271 E-mail: general@komfort.com Partition component manufrs

Komfort Office Environments P.L.C., Unit T Gildersome Spur Industrial Estate, Wakefield Road, Morley, Leeds, LS27 7JX Tel: 0113-201 3700 Fax: 0113-238 0447 Partitions & ceiling distributors

Komfort Workspace P.L.C., Reith Way, West Portway Industrial Estate, Andover, Hampshire, SP10 3TY Tel: (01264) 332166 Fax: (01264) 333560 E-mail: velosity@komfort.com Manufacturers of open plan office screens & furniture

▶ Komodo Recordings, 79 Magheraconluce Road, Hillsborough, County Down, BT26 6PR Tel: (028) 9268 8285 Fax: (028) 9268 9581 E-mail: info@komodorecordings.com Studio and mobile recording, ALL styles of music, from Singer/Songwriters through Classical to Heavy Rock, offering hassle-free recording deals that involve no upfront charge. Also mastering, duplication, graphic design, printing, sound reinforcement, drum tuition etcEquipment: Pro Tools, Soundfield, Focusrite, AKG 414s, Valve Compressors, 2 Drumkits, 3 Basses, Ampeg, 5 Guitars, Marshall, Weighted Keyboard, all for use during recording sessions free of charge.*Call 02892688285 for friendly advice and more details.*

Komori UK Ltd, Kirkstall Industrial Park, Kirkstall Road, Leeds, LS4 2AZ Tel: 0113-279 9944 Fax: 0113-279 9922 E-mail: info@komori-europe.com Printing machine distributors & manufrs

▶ Kompan, 21 Roebuck Way, Knowlhill, Milton Keynes, MK5 8HL Tel: (01908) 201002 Fax: (01908) 201007 E-mail: kompan.uk@kompan.com Playground equipment manufacturer

Kompass Publishers, Windsor Court, East Grinstead House, East Grinstead, West Sussex, RH19 1XA Tel: (0800) 0185882 Fax: (01342) 335747 E-mail: sales@kompass.co.uk Global business information provider with over 40 years experience in delivering accurate, detailed company information to assist in sales, marketing, purchasing and research activities. Specialists in the provision of Industrial and commercial information online, via CD-Rom, bespoke list rental and printed directories.

▶ Kompress Holdings Ltd, 34 Dalziel Road, Hillington Industrial Estate, Glasgow, G52 4NN Tel: 0141-883 0228 Fax: 0141-883 6123 E-mail: sales@kompress.com Terminals, copper, cable accessories

Kompress Holdings Ltd, Unit 5 Little Tennis Street, Nottingham, NG2 4EL Tel: 0115-958 1029 Fax: 0115-958 4180 E-mail: info@kompress.com Electrical connector manufrs Also at: Birmingham, Glasgow & Sunderland

Kompressors Ltd, Southgate Avenue, Mildenhall, Bury St. Edmunds, Suffolk, IP28 7AT Tel: (01638) 715361 Fax: (01638) 510762 Compressor manufrs

▶ Komputrak Ltd, Redhill House, 41 Hope Street, Chester, CH4 8BU Tel: (01244) 671800 Fax: (01244) 671880 Bar code products

▶ KOMS 17 Ltd, 18 Nursery Close, Combwich, Bridgwater, Somerset, TA5 2JB Tel: 01278 651274 Fax: 01278 651274 E-mail: kevin@koms17.com Consultancy and Auditing services specialising in ISO9001:2000 (Quality, ISO27001 (Information Security), ISO20000 (IT Service Management, BS25999 (Business Continuity Management. we also provide software development, website design and hosting services.

continued

Konaflex Ltd, Unit 2 Northcote Road, Stechford, Birmingham, B33 9BE Tel: 0121-783 9778 Fax: 0121-784 8026 E-mail: konaflex@aol.com Galvanised steel pipe work manufrs

Koncar, Unit 43, Brittania Way, Enterprise Industrial Pk, Lichfield, Staffs, WS14 9UY Tel: (01543) 255995 Fax: (01543) 250316 AC electric motors

Kone Ltd, 31 Clarendon Road, Belfast, BT1 3DD Tel: (028) 9031 2180 Fax: (028) 9024 6604 E-mail: info@kone.com Lift manufrs

Kone plc, 137-145 South Liberty Lane, Bristol, BS3 2TL Tel: 0117-966 2741 Fax: 0117-963 6310 Lift control equipment manufrs

Kone plc, Global House Station Place, Fox La North, Chertsey, Surrey, KT16 9HW Tel: (0870) 7701122 Fax: (0870) 7701122 E-mail: salesandmarketing.uk@kone.com Electric lift manufrs

Kone plc, 86 Broad Street, Glasgow, G40 2PX Tel: 0141-554 7604 Fax: 0141-554 6762 Manufacturing, installing & servicing of lifts

KONE PLC, Blisworth Hill Farm, Stoke Road, Blisworth, Northampton, NN7 3DB Tel: 08451 999 999 Fax: 0870 7701144 E-mail: sales.marketinguk@kone.com Purchasing Contact: D. Pearce Sales Contact: D. Pearce Manufacturers of materials handling equipment & dock/loading bay equipment. In addition lift (hydraulic), lift (scissor) & lift (goods) manufrs

Konecranes Service Ltd, Albion Road, West Bromwich, West Midlands, B70 8AX Tel: 0121-569 1000 Fax: 0121-569 1099 Crane maintenance & services

▶ Konect Electrical Services, 207 Bramhall Lane, Stockport, Cheshire, SK2 6JA Tel: 0161-456 1362 Fax: 0161-483 9473

Konematic Bolton Brady, 14 Robin Hood Industrial Estate, Alfred St South, Nottingham, NG3 1GE Tel: 0115-950 3262 Fax: 0115-958 9032 E-mail: nttinghm@boltonbrady.co.uk Door, barrier & gate installation, maintenance & repairers

Kongsberg Auto Motive, Christopher Martin Road, Basildon, Essex, SS14 3ES Tel: (01268) 522861 Fax: (01268) 282994 E-mail: m.dickason@morse-controls.co.uk Remote control & cable systems equipment

Kongsberg Automotive, Callister Way, Burton-on-Trent, Staffordshire, DE14 2SY Tel: (01283) 492000 Fax: (01283) 492003 E-mail: info@ka-group.com Automotive component suppliers

▶ Kongsberg Simrad, Campus 1 Balgownie Road, Aberdeen Science & Technology Park, Bridge of Don, Aberdeen, AB22 8GT Tel: (01224) 226500 Fax: (01224) 226501 Underwater cameras manufrs

Kongsberg Simrad, Campus 1 Balgownie Road, Aberdeen Science & Technology Park, Bridge of Don, Aberdeen, AB22 8GT Tel: (01224) 226500 Fax: (01224) 226501 Marine technology underwater cameras manufrs

▶ Kongsberg Simrad Ltd, Airport Industrial Estate, Wick Airport, Wick, Caithness, KW1 4QS Tel: (01955) 603606 Fax: (01955) 607520 Manufacture underwater visual equipment

▶ Kongskilde UK Ltd, Hempstead Road, Holt, Norfolk, NR25 6EE Tel: (01263) 713291 Fax: (01263) 712922 E-mail: mail@kuk.kongskilde.com Process waste handling for plastic, paper, corregated industries

Konica Business Machines UK Ltd, 2 Wharfside, Oldbury, West Midlands, B69 2BU Tel: 0121-544 3344 Fax: 0121-544 3130 E-mail: info@bs.konicaminolta.co.uk Photocopier distributors

Konica Minolta Business Solutions (UK) Ltd, 84-86 Bradley Road, Wrexham, Clwyd, LL13 7TP Tel: (01978) 356772 Fax: (01978) 361560 E-mail: info@bs.konicaminolta.co.uk Photocopiers distributors

▶ Konrad Chemicals, Manchester Road, Wilmslow, Cheshire, SK9 2JW Tel: (01625) 531581 Fax: (01625) 529906 E-mail: konradchemicals@ntlworld.com Suppliers chemicals & pharmaceuticals

Kontact Engineering Services, Court Lodge Farm, Kenward Road, Yalding, Maidstone, Kent, ME18 6JP Tel: (01622) 817966 Repairers, service & sales of fork lift trucks

▶ Konteaki Furniture Importers, Unit C Aisecome Way, Weston-super-Mare, Avon, BS22 8NA Tel: (01934) 425050 Fax: (01934) 425050 E-mail: steve@hattrick-furniture.co.uk Mexican & indian furniture importers

Kontron UK Ltd, 9 Ben Turner Industrial Estate, Oving Road, Chichester, West Sussex, PO19 7ET Tel: (01243) 523500 Fax: (01243) 532949 E-mail: uksales@kontron.com Laptop computers

▶ Kontur Cabinet Makers, 13 Rectory Lane, Radcliffe, Manchester, M26 2QU Tel: 0161-723 2603 Fax: 0161-723 3373 E-mail: kontur@btconnect.com Cabinet manufrs

▶ Konvekta Ltd, Knowsley Road Industrial Estate, Haslingden, Rossendale, Lancashire, BB4 4RR Tel: (01706) 227018 Fax: (01706) 831124 Dampers, grills & air ventilation suppliers

Kood International Ltd, 6 Wellington Road, London Colney, St. Albans, Hertfordshire, AL2 1EY Tel: (01727) 823812 Fax: (01727) 827338 E-mail: info@koodinternational.com Purchasing Contact: J. Sherwood Sales Contact: J. Sherwood Batteries, camera accessories & printing accessories

Kookaburra Reader Ltd, Unit 25, The Alders, Seven Mile Lane, Mereworth, Maidstone, Kent, ME18 5JG Tel: (01622) 812230 Fax: (01622) 814224 E-mail: sales@alfredreader.co.uk Sports equipment manufrs

▶ Kookaburra Sport, 3 Brakey Road, Weldon North Industrial Estate, Corby, Northamptonshire, NN17 5LU Tel: (01536) 209210 Fax: (01536) 209211 E-mail: sales@kookaburra.co.uk Cricket equipment

▶ Kooka-Kleen, 27 Hayman Road, Ipswich, IP3 0HB Tel: (01473) 429485 E-mail: chris@kookakleen.com We provide a proffesional domestic oven cleaning service in the Ipswich area.

Kool It Services Ltd, 85-87 Wellington Road, Eccles, Manchester, M30 9GW Tel: 0161-707 2580 Fax: 0161-288 0135 Air conditioning & refrigeration sales & service

▶ Koolatron International, Unit C3 Knights Park, Knight Road Strood, Rochester, Kent, ME2 2LS Tel: (01634) 297383 Fax: (01634) 297374 Coolbox distributors

Kooltech Ltd, 433 Hillington Road, Hillington Industrial Estate, Glasgow, G52 4BL Tel: 0141-883 0447 Fax: 0141-883 5642 E-mail: sales@kooltech.co.uk Air conditioning & refrigeration equipment distributors

Kooltech Refrigeration Equipment, 53 Wharton St Industrial Estate, Wharton Street, Birmingham, B7 5TR Tel: 0121-327 6565 Fax: 0121-327 6868 Refrigeration & air conditioning wholesalers

Koopmans Surveyors, 34 Watling Street, Radlett, Hertfordshire, WD7 7NN Tel: (01923) 853749 Fax: (01923) 854493 E-mail: .property@koopmans.co.uk Surveyors

Kopak-Walker Ltd, PO Box 65, Hitchin, Hertfordshire, SG4 0TW Tel: (01462) 452487 Fax: (01462) 452249 E-mail: sales@kopak-walker.co.uk Principal Export Areas: Worldwide Manufacturers of gaskets, electrical matting, rubber extrusions, rubber mouldings & sponge rubber products

Kopex International Ltd, 3rd Floor Crossbow House, 40 Liverpool Road, Slough, SL1 4QZ Tel: (01753) 502502 Fax: (01753) 693521 E-mail: jaustin@kopex.co.uk Electrical conduit manufrs

▶ Kopo Greenwood, Unit 3, Trident Industrial Estate, Blackthorne Road, Colnbrook, Slough, SL3 0AX Tel: (01753) 682828 Fax: (01753) 687338

Koppen & Lethem Ltd, 6 Glenholm Park, Brunel Drive, Newark, Nottinghamshire, NG24 2EG Tel: (01636) 676794 Fax: (01636) 671055 E-mail: sales@koppen-lethem.co.uk Hydraulic equipment, hoists & winches

Koppers UK Ltd, Normanby Gateway, Lysaghts Way, Scunthorpe, North Lincolnshire, DN15 9YG Tel: (01724) 281555 Fax: (01724) 281343 E-mail: kuk@koppers-eu.com Tar distillers Also at: Middlesbrough, Newport (Gwent) & Southampton

Koppert, Unit 8, 53 Hollands Road, Haverhill, Suffolk, CB9 8PJ Tel: (01440) 704488 Fax: (01440) 704487 E-mail: info@koppert.co.uk Biological control product for horticulture manufrs

▶ Kopy Kats Karaoke & Disco, PO Box 8486, Prestwick, Ayrshire, KA9 2JJ Tel: (01292) 476708 Fax: (01292) 471938 E-mail: kopykatskaraoke@tiscali.co.uk Available for pubs.hotels. parties and corporate events. Over 3000 songs from the 50's to current chart hits

Kopykat Printing Ltd, 76c Rivington Street, London, EC2A 3AY Tel: (020) 7739 2451 Fax: (020) 7729 5925 E-mail: print@kopykat.co.uk Kopykat provides a design, printing, copying and direct mail service specialising in comapny stationery and marketing material such as leaflets, postcards and newsletters

Kor, Pynes Hill, Exeter, EX2 5JL Tel: (01392) 266870 Fax: (01392) 445400 E-mail: admin@kor.uk.com Offices in Exeter and Wokingham covering mainland UK, we specialise in construction project management, quantity surveying and project planning. Contractor and client sectors, tender contract and post contract works undertaken.

Korean Air, 67-68 Piccadilly, London, W1J 0HJ Tel: (020) 7495 2299 Fax: (020) 7495 1616 E-mail: sales@koreanair.com Airline companies

KOREC, 34-44 Mersey View, Waterloo, Liverpool, L22 6QB Tel: 0845 6031214 Fax: 0151 9315559 E-mail: info@korecgroup.com Surveying equipment, Machine Control and GIS Mapping equipment. Trimble"s largest distributor, for sale, hire, service, repair and training.

KO-REC-TYPE, Unit 4, Beta House, Orchard Industrial Estate, Toddington, Cheltenham, Gloucestershire, GL54 5EB E-mail: sales@korectype.co.uk Printer Cartridge Sales and Cartridge/mobile phone recycling.*Inkjet cartridges- compatible & remanufactured, Remanufactured Laser toner cartridges, Thermal ribbons, Typewriter and Printer ribbons.

Korg UK Ltd, 9 Newmarket Court, Kingston, Milton Keynes, MK10 0AU Tel: (01908) 857100 Fax: (01908) 857199 E-mail: info@korg.co.uk Musical instrument distributors

Korker Sausages Ltd, High Street, Rolvenden, Cranbrook, Kent, TN17 4LN Tel: (01580) 241307 Fax: (01580) 240092 E-mail: enquiries@korker-sausages.co.uk Sausages manufrs

Koronka Agriculture & Tanks Ltd, Bridgend, Kinross, KY13 8EN Tel: (01577) 862189 Fax: (01577) 864773 E-mail: sales@koronka.co.uk Tank manufrs

Korporate Creations Ltd, 151 Utney Bridge Road Shire Place, Swaffield Road, London, SW15 2NZ Tel: (020) 8870 2070 Fax: (020) 8870 2012 E-mail: info@korporate-creations.com Business gifts

▶ Korsch Pharmaceutical Distributors, Stoney Bottom, Grayshott, Hindhead, Surrey, GU26 6HB Tel: (01865) 400424 Fax: (01428) 608728 E-mail: sales@horsch.de Pharmaceutical manufrs

Korsnas Packaging Ltd, Priory Road, Rochester, Kent, ME2 2BD Tel: (01634) 716701 Fax: (01634) 717468 Paper sack manufrs

Korva Ltd, 2 Maxwelltown Industrial Estate, Glasgow Road, Dumfries, DG2 0NW Tel: (01387) 268572 Fax: (01387) 268657 E-mail: cdoyle@korva.co.uk Roll containers & trolley suppliers

▶ Kosco Interiors Ltd, 500b Knutsford Road, Warrington, WA4 1DX Tel: (01925) 242555 Fax: (01925) 242818 E-mail: koscointeriors@aol.com Ceiling manufrs

Koshka Knitwear, 250 Canongate, Edinburgh, EH8 8AA Tel: 0131-557 4757 E-mail: koshka@btconnect.com Knitwear manufrs

Koso Kent Introl Ltd, Armytage Road, Brighouse, West Yorkshire, HD6 1QF Tel: (01484) 710311 Fax: (01484) 407407 E-mail: control.valve@kentintrol.com Control valve manufrs

Kosran ECV (UK) Ltd, No. 6 The Glenmore Centre, Grove Technology Park, Wantage, Oxfordshire, OX12 9FA Tel: (0870) 7875687 Fax: (0870) 7875633 E-mail: sales@kosran.com Construction plant immobilization system manufrs

Kossway Automatics Distributors Ltd, 8 The Ridgeway, Iver, Buckinghamshire, SL0 9HJ Tel: (01753) 655400 Fax: (01753) 630278 E-mail: sales@kosswayautomatics.co.uk Rent gaming & amusement machines

Kotschy Pauline Associates, 83 Mansel Street, Swansea, SA1 5TY Tel: (01792) 472725 Fax: (01792) 479828 E-mail: info@paulinek.com Recruitment selection

Kountry Kit Ltd, 22-23 West Street, Tavistock, Devon, PL19 8AN Tel: (01822) 613089 Fax: (01822) 615798 E-mail: enquires@kountrykit.fsnet.co.uk Outdoors equipment

▶ Kover-It, Bath Road, Hare Hatch, Reading, RG10 9SB Tel: 0118-940 6095 Fax: (0871) 9895598 Awning & sun blind retailers

▶ Koyanagi Worlwide Ltd, Units 8 & 9, Crystal Way, Harrow, Middlesex, HA1 2HP Tel: (020) 8427 6355

Koyo Bearings (Europe) Ltd, PO Box 101, Barnsley, South Yorkshire, S75 3TA Tel: (01226) 733200 Fax: (01226) 204029 E-mail: kbe@kbe.co.uk Bearings manufrs

Koyo (UK) Ltd, Whitehall Avenue, Kingston, Milton Keynes, MK10 0AX Tel: (01908) 289300 Fax: (01908) 289333 E-mail: info@koyo.co.uk Ball & roller bearing manufrs

▶ KP Couriers (Cambs) Ltd, Keepers Lodge, Gamlingay Road, Waresley, Sandy, Bedfordshire, SG19 3DD Tel: (01767) 651717 Fax: (01767) 652062 E-mail: kpcambs@hotmail.co.uk Same day/next day courier services,documents to large loads, dedicated and shared load rates.

KP Fire, 283 Dinas, Newtown, Powys, SY16 1NW Tel: (01686) 626312 Fax: (01686) 626312 Fire extinguisher sales & services

▶ KP Technology Ltd, Burn Street, Wick, Caithness, KW1 5EH Tel: (01955) 602777 Fax: (01955) 605122 E-mail: iain@kptechnology.ltd.uk Manufacturers of surface analysis equipment

KPC Engineering Company Ltd, KPC House, Coventry Road, Yardley, Birmingham, B26 1DD Tel: 0121-707 0004 Fax: 0121-706 0065 E-mail: kpcengineering@btclick.com Export merchants & agents

▶ KPH Environmental Services Ltd, 4 Paddock Barn Farm, Godstone Road, Caterham, Surrey, CR3 6RE Tel: (01883) 346604

KPK Building & Joinery Contractors, Burncoose Nursery, Burncoose, Gwennap, Redruth, Cornwall, TR16 6BJ Tel: (01209) 860472 Fax: (01209) 860213 Building contractors

▶ KPL Cosmetics Ltd, 22a Union Street, Ryde, Isle of Wight, PO33 2DT Tel: (01983) 813900 Fax: (01983) 618431

KPMG UK Ltd, Peat House, 1 Waterloo Way, Leicester, LE1 6LP Tel: 0116-256 6000 Fax: 0116-256 6050 Accountants & business advisors Also at: Leeds & London EC4

▶ K-Point Internet Solutions Ltd, 1 Osborne Promenade, Warrenpoint, Newry, County Down, BT34 3NQ Tel: (028) 4175 4836 E-mail: info@kpoint.co.uk Bespoke web based software solution providers

▶ Kraft Stop Ltd, 60 Eastway, Maghull, Liverpool, L31 6BS Tel: 0151-526 1298 Fax: 0151-526 1298 E-mail: lynn@kraftstop.co.uk Paper craft sales

Kram Sheet Metal, Whitacre Road Industrial Estate, Nuneaton, Warwickshire, CV11 6BZ Tel: (024) 7664 1272 Fax: (024) 7635 2520 Sheet metal workers & laser cutting services

Kramba Associates Ltd, 6 Lynwood Close, Darwen, Lancashire, BB3 0JY Tel: (01254) 776616 Fax: (01254) 776616 E-mail: kramba@tiscali.co.uk Business improvement consultants selling of safety equipment

Kramer Lee & Associates Ltd, Vermont House, Chrisy Close, Southfields Business Park, Basildon, Essex, SS15 6EA Tel: (01268) 494500 Fax: (01268) 494555 E-mail: info@kramerlee.com I T consultancy developers

Kramer Westfield, Old Pound House, London Road, Sunningdale, Ascot, Berkshire, SL5 0DJ Tel: (01344) 875087 Fax: (01344) 874877 E-mail: enquiries@kramwest.com Recruitment consultants

Kramp UK Ltd, Station Business Park, London Road, Biggleswade, Bedfordshire, SG18 8QB Tel: (01767) 602602 Fax: (01767) 602620 E-mail: info.agri.uk@kramp.com Kramp UK supply a wide range of farming and forestry equipment and accessories.

Krams Ugo Ltd, 18 Deans Drive, Edgware, Middlesex, HA8 9NU Tel: (020) 8906 8656 Fax: (020) 8906 8822 E-mail: enquiries@kramsugo.co.uk Tergal voiles, sheers & flame retardant net curtain wholesalers

Krane Ltd, Unit 9 Broomers Hill Park, Broomers Hill Lane, Pulborough, West Sussex, RH20 2RY Tel: 0845 4941750 Fax: (01798) 872100 E-mail: kraneltd@aol.com Principal Export Areas: Worldwide Heavy industrial machinery spare parts, specialising in mobile crane spares worldwide, in the following makes: Grove, Grove/ Coles, Coles, Jones Cranes, PPM cranes, Hyster Forklift truck, Massey Ferguson, Cummins & Deutz. Exporting Worldwide

Krantz Systems Ltd, 61-67 Rectory Road, Wivenhoe, Colchester, CO7 9ES Tel: (01206) 827171 Fax: (01206) 826936 E-mail: kjr@d4s.co.uk Principal Export Areas: Worldwide Air conditioning equipment services

Kratos Analytical Ltd, Trafford Wharf Road, Trafford Park, Manchester, M17 1GP Tel: 0161-888 4400 Fax: 0161-888 4401 E-mail: sales@kratos.co.uk *Instruments for the advancement of science*

Krauss Maffei U K Ltd, 410 Europa Boulevard, Westbrook, Warrington, WA5 7TR Tel: (01925) 644100 Fax: (01925) 234284 E-mail: sales@kraussmaffei.co.uk *Plastic machinery manufacturers & suppliers*

▶ Krazy Bobs, Chester Road, Heswall, Wirral, Merseyside, CH60 3SE Tel: 0151-342 4700 *Fencing manufrs*

KRC, Kings Road, New Haw, Addlestone, Surrey, KT15 3BG Tel: (01932) 353851 Fax: (01932) 353851 *Precision engineers*

Kreative Bunting Ltd, 35 Charter Gate, Quarry Park Close, Moulton Park Industrial Estate, Northampton, NN3 6QB Tel: (01604) 790077 Fax: (01604) 643773 E-mail: sales@kreativebunting.com *Bunting manufrs*

▶ Kreative Innovative Technology Ltd, Sheepbridge Works, Dunston, Chesterfield, Derbyshire, S43 2PE Tel: (01246) 268506 Fax: (01246) 269246 E-mail: sales@kitinfo.co.uk *Manufactures & suppliers of specialist clothing & equipment*

▶ Kreative Juice, 24 Martholme Close, Blackburn, BB6 7TZ Tel: (01254) 884917 E-mail: info@kreativejuice.co.uk *Graphic design company*

▶ Kremena Krumova Ltd, 1 Percy Road, North Finchley, London, N12 8BY Tel: (020) 8445 2267 E-mail: keme@abv.bg *professional cleaning services*-houses -honest*-offices -reliable* -affordable*

Kremer Signs Ltd, Units 18, East Road Industrial Estate, Sleaford, Lincolnshire, NG34 7EQ Tel: (01529) 415511 Fax: (01529) 415444 E-mail: sales@kremersigns.co.uk *Screen printers & sign makers*

Kremer Signs, 300 New Greenham Park, Greenham, Thatcham, Berkshire, RG19 6HN Tel: (01635) 46125 Fax: (01635) 523170 E-mail: sales@kremersigns.co.uk *Sign manufrs*

Kridan Forklifts Garth House, Scarborough Road, East Heslerton, Malton, North Yorkshire, YO17 8RW Tel: (01944) 728301 Fax: (01944) 728301 *Forklift trucks service, repair, hire & sales*

Kris Motors, Withy Road, Ladymore, Bilston, West Midlands, WV14 0RX Tel: (01902) 492995 Fax: (01902) 494626 *Used motor parts exporters*

Krisco Engineering Ltd, Unit B2 Oldmixon Cresent, Weston-super-Mare, Avon, BS24 9AY Tel: (01934) 413800 Fax: (01934) 412620 E-mail: sales@kriscoengineering.co.uk *Sheet metalwork & fabrication*

▶ Krispy Kreme UK Ltd, Albany Park, Camberley, Surrey, GU16 7PQ Tel: (01276) 601170 Fax: (01276) 601180 E-mail: office@krispykreme.co.uk *Bakers*

▶ Krissiis Klips, 1 Hawkshead Avenue, Chaddesden, Derby, DE21 4EA Tel: (07891) 615724

Krohne Ltd, Rutherford Drive, Park Farm Industrial Estate, Wellingborough, Northamptonshire, NN8 6AE Tel: (01933) 408500 Fax: (01933) 408501 E-mail: info@krohne.co.uk *Innovative instrumentation services*

▶ Kroll, 49 Azura Close, Woolsbridge Industrial Est/Three Legg, Three Legged Cross, Wimborne, Dorset, BH21 6SZ Tel: (01202) 822221 Fax: (01202) 822222 E-mail: sales@krolluk.com *Oil burner manufrs & waste oil heaters distrs*

Kromex Ltd, Shepherds Grove Industrial Estate, Stanton, Bury St. Edmunds, Suffolk, IP31 2AR Tel: (01359) 250565 Fax: (01359) 250561 E-mail: sales@kromex.co.uk *Screen printing ink & paint manufrs*

Kromschroder UK Ltd, Unit 15a Frederick Road, Hoo Farm Industrial Estate, Kidderminster, Worcestershire, DY11 7RA Tel: (01562) 747756 Fax: (01562) 744129 *Gas control distributors*

Kronology Ltd, Unit 20 Lochshot Place, Livingston, West Lothian, EH54 6SJ Tel: (07967) 136061 *Bar scanner distributor*

▶ Kronons, 25-27 Wateny Market, Watney Street, London, E1 9PP Tel: (020) 7790 7144 Fax: (0870) 7062842 E-mail: info@kronons.com *Computer maintenance & repair services*

Kronos Ltd, Barons Court, Manchester Road, Wilmslow, Cheshire, SK9 1BQ Tel: (01625) 547200 Fax: (01625) 533123 E-mail: kronos.sales.uk@nli-usa.com *Titanium dioxide pigments distributors*

Kronos Systems Ltd, 2 Carey Road, Wokingham, Berkshire, RG40 2NP Tel: 0118-978 9784 Fax: 0118-978 2214 E-mail: ukinfo@kronos.com *Time & attendance systems*

Krouse Precision Engineering Ltd, Carterton Industrial Estate, Black Bourton Road, Carterton, Oxfordshire, OX18 3EZ Tel: (01993) 843683 Fax: (01993) 840539 E-mail: sales@jdkrouse.co.uk *Precision sub-contract engineering*

Kroy (Europe) Ltd, Worton Drive, Worton Grange Ind Estate, Reading, RG2 0LZ Tel: 0118-986 1411 Fax: 0118-986 5205 E-mail: hamilton@kroy.com *Labelling machine systems manufrs*

Kroyair Ltd, 262 Moseley Road, Birmingham, B12 0BX Tel: 0121-440 5383 Fax: 0121-446 4236 E-mail: info@kroyair.fsnet.co.uk *Air conditioning contractors*

KRS Ltd, Westfield House, Broad Lane, Leeds, LS13 3HA Tel: 0113-239 3088 Fax: 0113-257 7582 *Commercial printers & rubber stamp manufrs*

Kruger Tissue Industrial Division, Penygroes Industrial Estate, Penygroes, Caernarfon, Gwynedd, LL54 6DB Tel: (01286) 880969 Fax: (01286) 880026 *Industrial clothing*

Kruger Tissue Industrial Division, Penygroes Industrial Estate, Penygroes, Caernarfon, Gwynedd, LL54 6DB Tel: (01286) 880969 Fax: (01286) 880026 E-mail: customer.service@kruger.co.uk *Paper converters*

Krupa Bros & Son Ltd, 14 Brook Street, Bury, Lancashire, BL9 6AH Tel: 0161-797 4499 Fax: 0161-764 8722 *Press knives, press studs machines & tools manufrs*

Krusty Loaf, Bakery, 2 Crescent Road, Hunstanton, Norfolk, PE36 5BU Tel: (01485) 533457 *Bakery suppliers*

Kruuse UK Ltd, 14A Moor Lane Trading Estate, Sherburn In Elmet, Leeds, LS25 6ES Tel: (01977) 681523 Fax: (01977) 683537 E-mail: kruuse.uk@kruuse.com *Animal health equipment suppliers*

▶ Kruze Driving Academy Ltd, 79 Blandford Waye, Hayes, Middlesex, UB4 0PB Tel: (020) 8561 6617 E-mail: info@kruzedrivingacademy.co.uk *Learn to drive: Block bookings available, Pass Plus courses, Based in London - Middlesex. KRUZE to SUCCESS!!!! ADI"s wanted.*

Kryle Technical Services, Ivory Buildings, Madeley Street, Stoke-on-Trent, ST6 5AT Tel: (01782) 838877 Fax: (01782) 866457 E-mail: sales@kryle.com *Designer & builder service repair*

Krylite Ltd, 80a Newton Road, Rushden, Northamptonshire, NN10 0HQ Tel: (01933) 312745 Fax: (01933) 410484 *Lamp & light colours manufrs*

▶ Krystal Upvc Windows, Newton Place, Bradford, West Yorkshire, BD5 7JW Tel: (01274) 683622 Fax: (01274) 681228 *Window installers*

▶ Krysteline Group, One Thorne Way, Three Legged Cross, Wimborne, Dorset, BH21 6FB Tel: (0870) 6000033 Fax: (0870) 6003014 E-mail: enq@krysteline.net

▶ KS Associates, 3c Priory Business Park, Fraser Road, Bedford, MK44 3WH Tel: (01234) 838811 Fax: (01234) 838811 E-mail: admin@ks-associates.co.uk *We provide Quantity Surveying Services to the constuction industry*

Ksa, Tippons Strawberry Gardens, Mill Hill Lane, Tavistock, Devon, PL19 8NH Tel: (01822) 614894 Fax: (01822) 614800 *Service & repair of garage equipment & sales*

▶ KSK Belts, Woodburn Road, Smethwick, West Midlands, B66 2PU Tel: 0121-565 0808 Fax: 0121-565 0808 *Leather belts*

KSM Property Maintenance South East Ltd, PO Box 8002, Harlow, Essex, CM20 3XA Tel: (01279) 439777 Fax: (01279) 439750 E-mail: sales@ksm-maintenance.co.uk *Property maintenance specialists, insurance claims works*

▶ KSN Northage & Co. Ltd, Vulcan House, Goliath Road, Coalville, Leicestershire, LE67 3FT Tel: (01530) 513599 Fax: (01530) 513594

KSS Hire Services, Russell Gardens, Wickford, Essex, SS11 8BH Tel: (01268) 769531 Fax: (01268) 561034 *Diamond drilling, plant contractors, power tool & excavator hire*

KTC Office Stationery Supplies, 21 Pudding Lane, Maidstone, Kent, ME14 1TY Tel: (01622) 758853 Fax: (01622) 753741 E-mail: ktcoffice@btconnect.com *Office supplies retailers*

K-Tech, 1 Brighton Crescent, Langley, Macclesfield, Cheshire, SK11 0DL Tel: 01260 252156 Fax: 01260 253156 E-mail: karl@ktechplastics.co.uk *Plastic machinery agents*

KTSX, 2 Eastgate, Llanboidy, Whitland, Carmarthenshire, SA34 0EJ Tel: (01994) 448771 Fax: (01994) 448771 E-mail: info@ktsx.co.uk *KTSX (business & home solutions) provide all your IT needs, from supply of hardware, supply & creation of software, networks, maintenance and troubleshooting to web design, domain and e-mail management.*

Kubach & Sambrook (Metals) Ltd, 57 Manor Park Crescent, Edgware, Middlesex, HA8 7LY Tel: (020) 8951 0688 Fax: (020) 8951 4540 E-mail: info@kubach.co.uk *Import & export merchants*

Kubiak Creative Ltd, 1 Farleigh Court, Old Weston Road, Flax Bourton, Bristol, BS48 1UR Tel: (01275) 464836 Fax: (01275) 461295 E-mail: sales@kubiakcreative.com *We are a Bristol based design and marketing agency. We offer the full spectrum of services, working with a wide range of companies to attract and engage an audience, utilising both print and digital media*

Kubota (UK) Ltd, Dormer Road, Thame, Oxfordshire, OX9 3UN Tel: (01844) 214500 Fax: (01844) 216685 E-mail: sales@kubota.co.uk *Ground care construction & engine suppliers*

Kudlian Soft, 8a Nunhold Business Centre, Dark Lane, Hatton, Warwick, CV35 8XB Tel: (01926) 842544 *Software house*

Kudos Computer Supplies, 7 Orwell Court, Hurricane Way, Wickford, Essex, SS11 8YJ Tel: (01268) 571122 Fax: (01268) 570771 E-mail: sales@kudos-supplies.com *Computer consumer boards*

▶ Kudos Fencing Supplies Ltd, Unit 23, Oaklands Trading Estate, Braydon, Swindon, SN5 0AN Tel: (01793) 855282 *Fencing & gate suppliers & installers*

Kudos Software Ltd, Cliff House, Cliff Road, Salcombe, Devon, TQ8 8JQ Tel: (01548) 843586 Fax: (01548) 843503 E-mail: kudos@kudos-software.co.uk *Computer software developers*

Kudos Solutions Ltd, The Manor, Main Street, Tur Langton, Leicester, LE8 0PJ Tel: (01858) 545976 Fax: (01858) 545977 *IT consultants*

▶ Kudos Systems UK Ltd, Unit 17 Louis Pearlman Centre, Goulton Street, Hull, HU3 4DL Tel: (01482) 321210 Fax: (01482) 322019 E-mail: info@kudos-systems.com *Computer system consultants*

Kudos U K, Dimension House, Cundell Drive, Cottenham, Cambridge, CB24 8RU Tel: (01954) 252000 Fax: (01954) 250956 *Automated products*

Kudos Visions Ltd, The White House, Main Road, Gwaelod-y-Garth, Cardiff, CF15 9HJ Tel: (08707) 605325 E-mail: info@kudosvisions.com *Kudos Visions Ltd Cardiff web design Company was formed in South Wales in 2002. *Our experience in providing successful web site design and development along with e-commerce software development services has helped many SMEs in Cardiff South Wales produce affordable and professional web sites. Kudos Visions Ltd offers*

continued

*complete services for web design, hosting, domain name, pre designed website"s and logo templates.**So if you are looking for a professional web site, contact our Cardiff web design team to discuss the right web site solution for your business!***

Kue Engineering Ltd, Unit 6, Birksland Street, Bradford, West Yorkshire, BD3 9SU Tel: (01274) 669516 Fax: (01274) 720088 *Steel surface preparation service providers*

Kue Group Ltd, Dick Lane, Bradford, West Yorkshire, BD4 8JW Tel: (01274) 669516 Fax: (01274) 665356 *Blasting & coating service*

Kue Software Ltd, 28 Ashpole Spinney, Northampton, NN4 9QB Tel: (01604) 592121 Fax: (01604) 592120 E-mail: simonk@kueservices.co.uk *Computer Consultants*

Kuehne + Nagel Ltd, Hays House, Sunrise Parkway, Linford Wood, Milton Keynes, MK14 6BW Tel: (01908) 255000 Fax: (01908) 255200 *Distribution agents*

Kuehne & Nagel Ltd, St.Andrews House, St.Andrews Road, Avonmouth, Bristol, BS11 9DQ Tel: 0117-982 7101 Fax: 0117-982 4606 E-mail: knbrs.fa@kuehne-nagel.com *Freight forwarders*

Kuehne & Nagel Ltd, B6 Broadlands, Heywood Distribution Park, Heywood, Lancashire, OL10 2TS Tel: 0161-761 8000 Fax: 0161-761 8001 *Warehousing & distribution contractors*

Kuehne & Nagel Ltd, Building 317, World Freight Terminal, Manchester Airport, Manchester, M90 5NA Tel: 0161-436 9400 Fax: 0161-436 9429 E-mail: manfa@kuehne-nagel.com *Freight forwarding services*

Kuehne & Nagel Ltd, Worton Drive Industrial Estate, Imperial Way, Reading, RG2 0TH Tel: 0118-986 5865 Fax: 0118-986 5801 E-mail: knrdg.dx@kuehne-nagel.com *Road transport*

Kuehne & Nagel UK Ltd, Old Bath Road, Colnbrook, Slough, SL3 0NW Tel: (01895) 552000 Fax: (01753) 762401 *Freight forwarding, warehouse & distribution providers* Also at: Birmingham, Bradford, Bristol, Leeds, Manchester, Paisley & Plymouth

Kuhmichel U K, Friars Mill, Friars Terrace, Stafford, ST17 4AU Tel: (01785) 252200 Fax: (01785) 252100 E-mail: andrew.shepphaerd@kuhmichel.com *Distributor of abrasive materials*

Kuhn Farm Machinery (UK) Ltd, Stafford Park 7, Telford, Shropshire, TF3 3BQ Tel: (01952) 239300 Fax: (01952) 290091 E-mail: infouk@kuhn.co.uk *Farm machinery distributors*

Kuhn Rikon (UK) Ltd, Landport Road, Wolverhampton, WV2 2QJ Tel: (01902) 458410 Fax: (01902) 458160 E-mail: gourmets@kuhnrikon.demon.co.uk *Cookware distributors*

Kuhr Engineering Ltd, Ivy Arch Road, Worthing, West Sussex, BN14 8BX Tel: 0845 5314280 Fax: (01903) 205208 E-mail: ralf.kuhr@kuhr-engineering.co.uk *Kuhr Engineering Ltd provides first class quality precision engineering services, specialising in small or large batch fine limit sheet metal fabrication and welding. To ensure the highest levels of service and product quality, Kuhr Engineering has BS EN ISO 9002 approval. Stringent quality control is applied throughout all processes from order receipt through to delivery, ensuring that your product is not only correct, but delivered on time. Finishing services, such as painting, plating, polishing and screening can be provided to special requirements. Extensive range of power press, CNC and fabrication plant*

Kuka Automation & Robotics, Hereward Rise, Halesowen, West Midlands, B62 8AN Tel: 0121-585 0800 Fax: 0121-585 0900 E-mail: sales@kuka.co.uk *KUKA range of industrial robots manufrs*

Kuka Automation & Robotics Ltd, Hereward Rise, Halesowen, West Midlands, B62 8AN Tel: 0121-585 0800 Fax: 0121-585 0900 E-mail: sales@kuka.co.uk *Manufacturers of controllers (computer) (industrial robot); press automation equipment; robots (industrial); robot (industrial) systems; welded automated systems. Also automation special purpose equipment/ systems manufacturers/constructors. In addition, welding equipment, spot*

▶ Kukri Sports Ltd, Ranglet Road, Walton Summit Centre, Bamber Bridge, Preston, PR5 8AR Tel: (01772) 338899 Fax: (01772) 330055 *Sports clothing & equipment suppliers*

▶ Kulfi Kids, 7 Market place, Camelford, Cornwall, PL32 9PB Tel: 01840 211144 E-mail: orders@kulfikids.co.uk

Kulite Sensors Ltd, Kulite House, Stroudley Road, Basingstoke, Hampshire, RG24 8UG Tel: (01256) 461646 Fax: (01256) 479510 E-mail: sales@kulite.co.uk *Electronic miniature pressure transducer manufrs*

Kullasigns Sign Writers, 1 Benham Water Farm, Ashford Road, Newingreen, Hythe, Kent, CT21 4JD Tel: (01303) 261279 Fax: (01303) 261280 E-mail: sales@legendsigns.co.uk *Sign makers & screen printers*

Kultronic Security Systems Ltd, 28 Ennerdale Avenue, Liverpool, L31 9BU Tel: 0151-531 6429 Fax: 0151-531 6429 *Closed circuit television installers*

▶ Kumar & Co., 255-261 Horn Lane, London, W3 9EH Tel: (020) 8993 7771 Fax: (020) 8993 0057 E-mail: anil@kumar.co.uk *We are an enthusiastic, responsive and experienced firm of Chartered Accountants dedicated to the achievement of total client satisfaction (If we fail you don't pay!). Highly experienced in all aspects of taxation, accountancy, business and profit growth strategies and business consultancy*

Kumarlo Bodyworks Ltd, 22 Ivanhoe Road, Finchampstead, Wokingham, Berkshire, RG40 4QQ Tel: 0118-973 3077 Fax: 0118-973 4787 E-mail: enquiries@kumarlobodyworks.co.uk *Commercial vehicle repairers*

Kumho Tyre (U.K.) Ltd, 6th Floor 9 Sutton Court Road, Sutton, Surrey, SM1 4SZ Tel: (020) 8661 6112 Fax: (020) 8661 2771 E-mail: sales@kumho-euro.com *Tyre import merchants*

Kuretake UK Ltd, 14 Broad Ground Road, Redditch, Worcestershire, B98 8YP Tel: (01527) 523799 Fax: (01527) 523815 E-mail: zig33uk@kuretake.ne.jp *Writing instruments & inks wholesalers*

Kurion Technologies Ltd, 43 Brunel Close, Drayton Fields Industrial Estate, Daventry, Northamptonshire, NN11 8RB Tel: (01327) 876600 Fax: (01327) 705131 E-mail: sales@kurion.co.uk *Waste water treatment & acid recovery*

Kuros Ltd, 38-42 Church Street, Ballymena, County Antrim, BT43 6DF Tel: (028) 2565 6732 Fax: (028) 2565 2798 *Wholesale chemist*

Kurt J Lesker Co. Ltd, Ivyhouse Lane, Hastings, East Sussex, TN35 4NN Tel: (01424) 719101 Fax: (01424) 421160 E-mail: sales@lesker.com *Vacuum science research & distributors*

Kurvers International Supply Services Ltd, Unit 14 Northfields Prospect Business Centre, Northfields, London, SW18 1PE Tel: (020) 8877 1355 Fax: (020) 8874 7266 E-mail: info@ukkurvers.com *Pipeline supplies & distribs*

Kustom Sport, 1 2 & 3 Carlton Industrial Estate, Albion Road, Carlton, Barnsley, South Yorkshire, S71 3HW Tel: (01226) 203347 Fax: (01226) 203357 E-mail: Kustomsport@tiscali.co.uk *Carpet manufrs*

Kutana Computer Systems, The Old Mill, Mill Street, Wantage, Oxfordshire, OX12 9AB Tel: (0870) 2202275 E-mail: info@kutana.co.uk *Software developers*

Kutting UK Ltd, 16 Tanners Drive, Blakelands, Milton Keynes, MK14 5BN Tel: (01908) 218100 Fax: (01908) 218666 E-mail: info@kuttinguk.co.uk *Hose manufrs*

Kuwait Petroleum International Lubricants UK Ltd, Knowsthorpe Gate, Cross Green Industrial Estate, Leeds, LS9 0NP Tel: 0113-235 0555 Fax: 0113-248 5026 E-mail: marketing@q8oils.com *Industrial & automotive lubricant manufrs*

Kvaerner P.L.C., Kvaerner House, 68 Hammersmith Road, London, W14 8YW Tel: (020) 7339 1082 Fax: (020) 7339 1100 *Holding company*

Kvaerner E & C, 68 Hammersmith Road, London, W14 8YW Tel: (020) 7339 1000 Fax: (020) 7339 1100 *Process & petrol-chemical engineers*

Kverneland Group UK Ltd, Walkers Lane, Lea Green, St. Helens, Merseyside, WA9 4AF Tel: (01744) 853200 Fax: (01744) 853400 E-mail: sales@kvernelandgroup.com *Agricultural implement manufrs*

KVJ Computers, 5 Ashley Road, Gillingham, Kent, ME8 6TT Tel: (01634) 263786 Fax: (01634) 263787 E-mail: sales@kvjcomputers.co.uk *Computer suppliers*

▶ KVM, 1 Southern Court, South Street, Reading, RG1 4QS Tel: (0870) 2202370 Fax: (0870) 2202371 E-mail: sales@kvmpartnership.co.uk *IT*

▶ KW Electrics Southern Ltd, Rosedeane, Easthampstead Road, Wokingham, Berkshire, RG40 3AF Tel: 0118-979 2939 Fax: 0118-989 1174

KWC UK Ltd, 149 Balham Hill, London, SW12 9DJ Tel: (020) 8675 9335 Fax: (020) 8675 8568 E-mail: kwcuk@globalnet.co.uk *Kitchen & bathroom tap distributors service*

Kween B Ltd, 29 Dalkeith Road, Sutton Coldfield, West Midlands, B73 6PW Tel: 0121-355 2662 E-mail: info@kweenb.co.uk *Plastics processing machinery* Also at: Small Heath

Kwick Key & Lock Service, Sherman Road, Bromley, BR1 3JN Tel: (020) 8464 3249 Fax: (020) 8464 5332 *Locksmiths*

Kwick Key & Lock Service, 16 Westow Street, Upper Norwood, London, SE19 3AH Tel: (020) 8653 8272 Fax: (020) 8768 1214 E-mail: guythompson@yahoo.com *Locksmiths*

Kwik Kook, 73 Main Street, Hillend, Dunfermline, Fife, KY11 9ND Tel: (01383) 410041 Fax: (01383) 414817 *Microwave maintenance*

Kwik Kook, 56 Higher Road, Liverpool, L25 0QQ Tel: 0151-448 1201 Fax: 0151-281 2508 E-mail: howie@kwikkook.co.uk *Electric oven repairers*

▶ Kwik Kook (We Mend Microwaves), Rossendale Place, Shipley, West Yorkshire, BD18 3PP Tel: (01274) 530456 Fax: (01274) 533125 E-mail: kwik.kook@virgin.net *Sales/Service/ Repair of ALL MAKES of Commercial/Domestic Microwave Ovens. FREE CALL OUT & Estimate.*

Kwik Snax Ltd, John Hillhouse Ind Est, Cambuslang Rd, Cambuslang, Glasgow, G72 7TS Tel: 0141-643 2111 Fax: 0141 647 5614 *Food manufrs*

▶ Kwik Tools, Hamilton Close, Feltham, Middlesex, TW13 4PS Tel: 020 8123 7173 E-mail: info@kwiktools.co.uk *Specialists in Fast Track High Quality Extrsuion Tooling*

Kwik Turn Engineering, Unit 4 The Hayes Trading Estate, Folkes Road, Stourbridge, West Midlands, DY9 8RN Tel: (01384) 898011 Fax: (01384) 896869 *Precision turned parts manufrs*

▶ Kwikbuild, Peasiehill Road, Elliot Industrial Estate, Arbroath, Angus, DD11 2NJ Tel: (01241) 879751

Kwikfill Ltd, Bullock Street, West Bromwich, West Midlands, B70 7HE Tel: 0121-553 0433 Fax: (0121) 553 0433 E-mail: sales@quickfill.co.uk *Contract packaging services & silk screen printers*

Kwik-Fit GB Ltd, 216 West Main Street, Broxburn, West Lothian, EH52 5AS Tel: (01506) 864000 Fax: (01506) 864141 E-mail: info@kwik-fit.com *Car part repair & replacement*

▶ Kwikgrip Ltd, Denaby Main Industrial Estate, Denaby Main, Doncaster, South Yorkshire, DN12 4LH Tel: (01709) 772422 E-mail: sales@kwikgrip.co.uk *Adhesive tape, carpet protectors & carpet metals services*

Kwikspace Portables, Whitesmith, Lewes, East Sussex, BN8 6JG Tel: (01825) 872000 Fax: (01825) 872999 *Portable building hire*

▶ Kwintessential Ltd, 75 Northwood Avenue, Purley, Surrey, CR8 2ES Tel: (020) 8406 9288 Fax: 0208 4069288 E-mail: info@kwintessential.co.uk *London based Cross Cultural Communication Consultants proving training and management solutions for UK business sector. We provide cross cultural awarenes briefings, language tuition and translation/interpretation services.*

KWR UK Ltd, KWR (Uk) Ltd Whessoe Road, Darlington, County Durham, DL3 0QP Tel: (01325) 284422 Fax: (01325) 284422 E-mail: kevin@kwr.biz *Motor vehicle repair*

KWTJ Products Ltd, 155A Hampton Road, Southport, Merseyside, PR8 5DJ Tel: (01704) 534798 Fax: (01704) 534798 *Sausage manufrs*

Kyal Machine Tools Ltd, Foundry Road, Stamford, Lincolnshire, PE9 2PP Tel: (01780) 765965 Fax: (01780) 765877 E-mail: office@kyalmachinetools.co.uk *Machine tool import merchants*

▶ Kye Systems UK Ltd, Unit 4 131 Beddington Lane, Croydon, CR0 4TD Tel: (020) 8664 2700 Fax: (020) 8664 2721

▶ Kyle Freight & Distribution Services Ltd, Unit B, Horton Trading Estate, Stanwell Road, Slough, SL3 9PF Tel: (01753) 687171

▶ Kyle Tarmacadam Ltd, 2 Murdoch Place, Oldhall West Industrial Estate, Irvine, Ayrshire, KA11 5DG Tel: (01294) 279206

Kyme Packaging Ltd, The Dairy, 2, Culverthorpe, Grantham, Lincolnshire, NG32 3NQ Tel: (01529) 455777 Fax: (01529) 455787 E-mail: kyme.packaging@virgin.net *Suppliers of paper bags & carrier bags*

▶ Kyndal Warehousing Ltd, Tomnavoulin, Ballindalloch, Banffshire, AB37 9JA Tel: (01807) 590285 Fax: (01807) 590497

Kyocera Mica UK Ltd, Beacontree Plaza, Gillette Way, Reading, RG2 0BS Tel: 0118-931 1500 Fax: 0118-931 1108 E-mail: kyocera@kyoceramita.co.uk *Printer & copier manufrs*

Kyoto Futons Ltd, Hards Lane, Frognall, Deeping St. James, Peterborough, PE6 8RP Tel: (01778) 380555 Fax: (01778) 380444 *Futon manufr*

Kypol Ltd, Suven House, 55 Gosforth Close, Middlefield Industrial Estate, Sandy, Bedfordshire, SG19 1RB Tel: (01767) 682424 Fax: (01767) 681180 E-mail: info@kypol.co.uk *Electroplating & anodising services*

Kyron, Oak Cottage, Benty Heath Lane, Willaston, Neston, CH64 1SB Tel: 0151-327 1957 Fax: 0151-327 7410 E-mail: john.hardman@kyron.co.uk *Engineering consultancy services*

▶ Kysen Design Consultants, Orwell House, 16-18 Berners Street, London, W1T 3LN Tel: (020) 7323 3230 Fax: (020) 7436 9103 E-mail: enquiries@kysen.co.uk *A specialist consultancy providing PR expertise to law firms and other professional services organisations. We provide the full range of media relations and marketing services.*

L 4 Lease Ltd, Keystone House, 30 Exeter Road, Bournemouth, BH2 5AR Tel: (0870) 4462407 Fax: (07005) 804365 E-mail: info@myfleet.co.uk *Specialist vehicle leasing company*

L A B Engineering, White City Road, Fforestfach, Swansea, SA5 4EE Tel: (01792) 587363 Fax: (01792) 585370 E-mail: labengineering@btinternet.com *Precision engineers*

L A Brook Ltd, Royds Mill, Leeds Road, Ossett, West Yorkshire, WF5 9YA Tel: (01924) 277026 Fax: (01924) 262074 E-mail: sales@labrook.com *Cleaning & hygiene product suppliers*

L A C Conveyors Ltd, Unit 3, Charles Park, Cinderhill Road, Bulwell, Nottingham, NG6 8RE Tel: 0115-975 3300 Fax: 0115-975 3384 E-mail: sales@lacconveyors.co.uk *Industrial conveyor systems manufrs*

L A Computers, 12 Magister Road, Bowerhill, Melksham, Wiltshire, SN12 6FE Tel: (01225) 793337 Fax: (01225) 793335 *Computer suppliers*

L A D Fish Exporters, Dales Industrial Estate, Peterhead, Aberdeenshire, AB42 3JF Tel: (01779) 479327 Fax: (01779) 474891 E-mail: rafael@ladfish.freeserve.co.uk *Fish merchants*

L A Drinks, 3 College Grove, Lurgan, Craigavon, County Armagh, BT66 6DA Tel: (028) 3832 6601 Fax: (028) 3832 9937 E-mail: sales@ladrinks.com *Drink suppliers to public houses*

▶ L A G A T, Ariazne House, 25 Tentercroft Street, Lincoln, LN5 7DB Tel: (01522) 513227 Fax: (01522) 545533 E-mail: enquiries@lagat.co.uk *Training providers*

L A H Signs, 47 Gaol Lane, Sudbury, Suffolk, CO10 1JJ Tel: (01787) 373073 Fax: (01787) 373073 *Vinyl graphics*

L A Hall (Hull) Ltd, 19-27 Lime Street, Hull, HU8 7AB Tel: (01482) 320367 Fax: (01482) 320367 *Roofing contractors & merchants*

L A International, International House, Festival Way, Stoke-on-Trent, ST1 5UB Tel: (01782) 203000 Fax: (01782) 203050 E-mail: mail@lainternational.co.uk *Recruitment agency computing*

▶ L A Label, 10 Penvale Close, Barripper, Camborne, Cornwall, TR14 0QP Tel: (01209) 718440 Fax: (01209) 718440 E-mail: artwork@lalabels.co.uk *Label manufrs*

L A Marketing Ltd, The Old Chapel, Lane End, Chapeltown, Sheffield, S35 2UH Tel: 0114-284 4484 Fax: 0114-286 9447 E-mail: info@la-mktg.demon.co.uk *Marketing consultants*

L A Metals Ltd, Roebuck Lane, Smethwick, West Midlands, B66 1BY Tel: 0121-553 6846 Fax: 0121-553 3270 *Aluminium extrusion stockholders*

▶ L A Moore Ltd, Old Railway Yard, Haybridge, Wells, Somerset, BA5 1AH Tel: (01749) 672870 Fax: (01749) 672072 E-mail: sales@lamoore.co.uk

L A Overseas Co., 50 Northampton St, Hockley, Birmingham, B18 6DX Tel: 0121 2366671 Fax: 0121 2334513 E-mail: laoverseas1@yahoo.co.uk *Gemstone dealers*

L A P Electrical Ltd, 52 Enterprise Drive, Aldridge Road, Sutton Coldfield, West Midlands, B74 2DZ Tel: 0121-353 5181 Fax: 0121-353 5206 *Car Component manufrs*

L & A Personal Searches Ltd, 31 Corsham Street, London, N1 6DR Tel: (020) 7250 1410 Fax: (020) 7250 1973 E-mail: searches@landa.ltd.uk *Personal local authority searches*

L A Recruitment & Management Services Ltd, 173 Union St, Aberdeen, AB11 6BB Tel: (01224) 212929 Fax: (01224) 573845 E-mail: info@larecruitment.co.uk *Personnel recruitment*

L A Reed & Son Haulage Ltd, 47 Low Street, Swinefleet, Goole, North Humberside, DN14 8DF Tel: (01405) 704351 Fax: (01405) 766654 *Road transport contractors*

L A Richardson & Son Ltd, Putney Bridge Arches, 75-76 Station Approach, London, SW6 3UH Tel: (020) 7736 1566 Fax: (020) 7736 1566 *Metal & forge workers*

L A S Aero Ltd, Oakhampton Point, Exeter Road Industrial Estate, Okehampton, Devon, EX20 1UA Tel: (01837) 658081 Fax: (01837) 658080 E-mail: sales@lasaero.com *Aircraft component distribs*

L A Sarb Engineering, Unit 6b, George Street, West Bromwich, West Midlands, B70 6NH Tel: 0121-525 2569 Fax: 0121-525 2459 *Industrial fastener manufrs*

▶ L A T Access Ltd, Creech Mills Industrial Estate, Taunton, Somerset, TA3 5PX Tel: (01823) 413327 Fax: (01823) 413383 E-mail: lataccess@btopenworld.com *Access equipment hire*

L A Tooling Ltd, Toronto Place, Gosport, Hampshire, PO12 4UZ Tel: (023) 9250 1331 Fax: (023) 9252 0807 *Precision engineers*

L A Wiles & Sons, The Conifers, Aisthorpe, Lincoln, LN1 2SG Tel: (01522) 730351 Fax: (01522) 730900 E-mail: sales@wilestanks.co.uk *Storage tanks manufrs*

L B Bentley Ltd, Fromehall Mill, Lodgemore Lane, Stroud, Gloucestershire, GL5 3EH Tel: (01453) 761500 Fax: (01453) 761505 E-mail: sales@lb-bentley.com *Compressed air, gas dryer & filter manufrs*

L B Freight Ltd, 36 Prescott Street, Halifax, West Yorkshire, HX1 2QW Tel: (01422) 351217 Fax: (01422) 330209 E-mail: sales@lbfreight.co.uk *Shipping & freight forwarding*

L B L Finishers, Gunstore Road, Portsmouth, PO3 5HL Tel: (023) 9269 2020 Fax: (023) 9267 0379 E-mail: sales@tomburn.co.uk *Stove enamellers* Also at: Chichester

L B Lighting Ltd, Unit 6E, Southbourne Business Park, Courtlands Road, Eastbourne, East Sussex, BN22 8UY Tel: (01323) 430047 Fax: (01323) 732356 E-mail: sales@lblighting.co.uk *Specialist lighting manufrs*

L B Litho, 15 Tait Road, Croydon, CR0 2DT Tel: (020) 8683 4205 Fax: (020) 8683 4193 *Printers*

L B M Office Supplies Ltd, 88 Bancroft, Hitchin, Hertfordshire, SG5 1NG Tel: (01462) 431201 Fax: (01462) 420476 *Stationers distributors*

L B Parkes Co. Ltd, Station Street, Walsall, WS2 9JZ Tel: (01922) 720720 Fax: (01922) 723400 E-mail: sales@lbparkes.co.uk *Anodising & powder coating of aluminium & steel products suppliers*

L B Plastics Ltd, Firs Works, Heage Firs, Nether Heage, Belper, Derbyshire, DE56 2JJ Tel: (01773) 852311 Fax: (01773) 857080 E-mail: sheerframe@lbplastics.co.uk *UPVC systems manufrs*

▶ L B Stone, Hatton Court, Hatton Close, Moulton Park Industrial Estate, Northampton, NN3 6SU Tel: (01604) 670333 Fax: (01604) 648764

L B Technologies Ltd, 42 Medley Road, Rayne, Braintree, Essex, CM77 6TQ Tel: (01376) 345041 E-mail: bullimores@aol.com *Lighting manufrs*

L B Tyres & Dropshafts, Unit 4a Station Yard, Tolladine Road, Worcester, WR4 9PT Tel: (01905) 612391 Fax: (01905) 612391 *Tyres & prop shafts suppliers*

L Bennett & Son Ltd, 43 Normandy Road, St. Albans, Hertfordshire, AL3 5PR Tel: (01727) 855879 Fax: (01727) 847409 E-mail: enquiries@bennetts.com *Motor part distributors*

L Bingham Ltd, 36 Malinda Street, Sheffield, S3 7EJ Tel: 0114-272 1525 Fax: 0114-249 3397 E-mail: lbinghamltd@aol.com *Scissors manufacturers & metal polishers*

▶ L Blackstock, Threeply Farm, Torr Road, Bridge of Weir, Renfrewshire, PA11 3RT Tel: (01505) 612375 Fax: (01505) 612425 *Blacksmiths*

L C A Controls Ltd, 1 Boleyn Court, Manor Park, Runcorn, Cheshire, WA7 1SR Tel: (01928) 579677 Fax: (01928) 579086 E-mail: lcacontrols@btinternet.com Principal Export Areas: Worldwide *Control panel manufrs*

L.C. Automation Ltd, LC Automation Ltd Duttons Way, Shadsworth Business Park, Blackburn, BB1 2QR Tel: (0870) 8501708 Fax: (01254) 685901 E-mail: sales@lca.co.uk *Machinery safety, automation & motion control solutions technical distributors*

L C Davis & Sons Ltd, 6 Prince Georges Road, London, SW19 2PX Tel: (020) 8648 3113 Fax: (020) 8640 8282 E-mail: info@lcdavis.com *Commercial motor factors*

L C Davis & Sons Ltd, Drury Lane, St. Leonards-on-Sea, East Sussex, TN38 9BA Tel: (01424) 430787 Fax: (01424) 721006 E-mail: hastings@lcdavis.com *Motor component suppliers*

L C Designs Co. Ltd, Sheldon Way, Larkfield, Aylesford, Kent, ME20 6SE Tel: (01622) 716000 Fax: (01622) 791119 E-mail: enquiries@londonclock.co.uk *Gift retailer*

▶ L C E Archimed, 164-165 Western Road, Brighton, BN1 2BB Tel: (01273) 206710 Fax: (01273) 206891 E-mail: info@lcearch.com *Architectural, design, consultancy & project management services*

▶ L C H Generators, 3 Telford Road, Bayton Road Industrial Estate, Exhall, Coventry, CV7 9ES Tel: (024) 7636 1333 Fax: (024) 7636 3633 *Generator & generating sets, maintenance & repair*

L C Kittow Ltd, 34 Spear Road, Southampton, SO14 6UH Tel: (023) 8032 2650 Fax: (023) 8032 2651 E-mail: info@lckittow.com Principal Export Areas: Africa *Electronic motor rewinds & repairs AC-DC & pump unit manufrs*

L C L Castings Ltd, Showfield Lane, Malton, North Yorkshire, YO17 6BT Tel: (01653) 694436 Fax: (01653) 600224 E-mail: sales@lcl-castings.co.uk *Pressure diecasting manufrs*

L C M I T Cleaning Specialists, Main Road, Boreham, Chelmsford, CM3 3AJ Tel: (01245) 450320 Fax: (01245) 462020 *Cleaning services*

L C P Automotive Components, Unit 3 Ebbsfleet Industrial Estate, Northfleet, Gravesend, Kent, DA11 9DZ Tel: (01474) 320300 Fax: (01474) 320595 *Motor component distributors*

L C P Developments Ltd, L C P House, The Pensnett Estate, Kingswinford, West Midlands, DY6 7NA Tel: (01384) 400123 Fax: (01384) 400862 *Industrial & commercial property development*

L C R Ltd, 197 Church Street, Blackpool, FY1 3NY Tel: (01253) 628020 Fax: (01253) 621718 E-mail: sales@lcrbpl.co.uk *Cash registers sales & service*

L C R Capacitors Eu Ltd, Unit 18 Rassau Industrial Estate, Rassau, Ebbw Vale, Gwent, NP23 5SD Tel: (01495) 307070 Fax: (01495) 306965 E-mail: sales@lcrcapacitors.co.uk *Capacitor manufrs*

L C S Group Ltd, 7-9 Alexandra Road, Grimsby, South Humberside, DN31 1RD Tel: (01472) 501234 Fax: (01472) 501501 E-mail: info@lcsgroup.com *Hardware & software developers*

L C S London Ltd, 65-85 Grosvenor Road, Hanwell, London, W7 1HR Tel: (020) 8567 4884 Fax: (020) 8567 2803 *Packaging services*

L C Switchgear Ltd, Unit 2, Hove Technology Centre, St Josephs Close, Hove, East Sussex, BN3 7ES Tel: (01273) 770540 Fax: (01273) 770547 *Switchgear engineering design & manufacture*

L C Teague, Colliers Hill, Little Rissington, Cheltenham, Gloucestershire, GL54 2ND Tel: (01451) 820591 Fax: (01451) 822449 *Agricultural contractors*

▶ L C V Leasing & Finance Ltd, Unit 1a Basepoint Enterprise Centre, Stroudley Road, Basingstoke, Hampshire, RG24 8UP Tel: (0845) 4665599 Fax: (01256) 406739 E-mail: info@lcvleasing.co.uk *Lcv leasing*

L Clancey & Sons, Murton Lane, Murton, York, YO19 5UF Tel: (01904) 489169 Fax: (01904) 489508 E-mail: clancey.l@btconnect.com *Metal merchant specialists*

L D A, Abbeygate House, East Road, Cambridge, CB1 1DB Tel: (01223) 357744 Fax: (01223) 460557 *Educational aids & equipment manufrs*

L D C Racing Sail Boats, Trafalgar Close, Chandler's Ford, Eastleigh, Hampshire, SO53 4BW Tel: (023) 8027 4500 Fax: (023) 8027 4800 E-mail: info@ldcracingsailboats.co.uk *Marine retailers*

▶ L D D, Wira House, Ring Road, Leeds, LS16 6EB Tel: 0113-224 2222 Fax: 0113-224 2234 E-mail: sales@ldd.co.uk *Computer hardware & software retailers*

L D Engineering Ltd, Great Northern Works, Hartham Lane, Hertford, SG14 1QW Tel: (01992) 584049 Fax: (01992) 584927 E-mail: ldeng@tiscali.co.uk *Welding services, steel fabricators & welded fabrication manufrs*

L D H Plant Ltd, South Dock, Alexandra Docks, Newport, Gwent, NP20 2NQ Tel: (01633) 263936 Fax: (01633) 264013 E-mail: sales@ldhplant.co.uk *Plant dealers*

L & D Mortimer, Birch Street, Bury, Lancashire, BL9 5AL Tel: 0161-764 1362 Fax: 0161-761 6836 *Scrap metal merchants*

L & D Precision Engineers Ltd, Peace Mills, Perry Road, Nottingham, NG5 3AL Tel: 0115-962 4116 Fax: 0115-969 1354 E-mail: sales@ldprecision.co.uk *Sub contracting engineers*

L D S Test & Measurement Ltd, Heath Works, Baldock Road, Royston, Hertfordshire, SG8 5BQ Tel: (01763) 242424 Fax: (01763) 249711 E-mail: sales@lds-group.com *Vibration test equipment manufrs*

L D Supplies, 166 Kylepark Drive, Uddingston, Glasgow, G71 7DB Tel: (01698) 810440 Fax: 01698 810440 *Janitorial supplies*

L Doble Ltd, Newdowns, West Polberro, St. Agnes, Cornwall, TR5 0ST Tel: (01872) 552121 Fax: (01872) 553797 E-mail: sales@doble.foods.co.uk *Frozen & chilled food product distribution*

L E G Electrical Ltd, 83 High St South, London, E6 6EJ Tel: (020) 8471 8229 Fax: (020) 8472 1817 *Electrical contractors*

L E Haslett & Co., 21 Ballagh Road, Clogher, County Tyrone, BT76 0JY Tel: (028) 8554 8285 Fax: (028) 8554 8683 E-mail: lehasslet@hotmail.com *Sectional building manufrs*

L E S Engineering Ltd, Armstrong Street, Grimsby, South Humberside, DN31 1XD Tel: (01472) 320200 Fax: (01472) 345337 E-mail: info@les-engineering.co.uk *Engineering contractors*

L E T S S, The Lodge, Crown Woods School, Riefield Road, London, SE9 2QL Tel: (020) 8850 0100 Fax: (020) 8850 0400 E-mail: letss@compuserve.com *Computer repair services*

L E Talbot Plant Hire Ltd, Holyhead Road, Oakengates, Telford, Shropshire, TF2 6DJ Tel: (01952) 610456 Fax: (01952) 619050 *Contractors plant hire*

L E W Diecastings Ltd, Trows Lane, Rochdale, Lancashire, OL11 2UF Tel: (01706) 632218 Fax: (01706) 643714 E-mail: alan@lew.co.uk *Aluminium alloy diecastings*

L E W Diecastings Ltd, Trows Lane, Rochdale, Lancashire, OL11 2UF Tel: (01706) 632218 Fax: (01706) 638473 E-mail: alan@lew.co.uk *Alloy iron & steel, investment lost wax process & non ferrous metal casting manufacturers. In addition, gravity, aluminium/bronze & aluminium/ alloy diecastings*

L E Went Ltd, 52-56 Burlington Road, New Malden, Surrey, KT3 4NU Tel: (020) 8949 0626 Fax: (020) 8715 1116 E-mail: iew.paint@virgin.net *Automotive paint specialists* Also at: Byfleet

L F C DespatchLine, Grange House, 2 Geddings Road, Hoddesdon, Hertfordshire, EN11 0NT Tel: (01992) 454500 Fax: (01992) 448989 E-mail: enquiries@lfcdespatch.co.uk *LFC DespatchLine offers a comprehensive range of innovative products to attract youngsters to a world of learning. With 13 years experience serving the needs of teachers and librarians we can help you make the learning experience more valuable and rewarding. You will find hundreds of new and innovative products designed to create inspiring learning environments. Our range includes exclusive reading promotions and BCI library shelving together with a comprehensive selection of curriculum based educational resources for Literacy, Numeracy, Arts & Crafts, PHSE, and Science. With an extensive range of educational and classroom furniture, kinderboxes, media display, audio visual equipment, book coverings, book trolleys and returns, library equipment, storage and filing cabinets. By providing the best possible service, with same-day despatch for stocked items, 30 days no-quibble guarantee and easy ways to order you can rely on LFC.*

▶ L F Dangerfield Ltd, Church Street, Kings Stanley, Stonehouse, Gloucestershire, GL10 3HT Tel: (01453) 822540 Fax: (01453) 828277

L F E Material Handling, Units 3-5 Hibberd House, Curriers Close, Charter Avenue Industrial Esta, Coventry, CV4 8AW Tel: (024) 7647 0170 Fax: (024) 7669 4521 E-mail: lfemh@btconnect.com *Material handling equipment manufrs*

L F F Scotland Ltd, Peregrine Road, Westhill Business Park, Westhill, Aberdeen, AB32 6JL Tel: (01224) 747636 Fax: (01224) 747637 E-mail: a.mitchell@aberdeen.lff.co.uk *Pipeline fitting & flange agents*Carbon, stainles, duplex and full range of exotic materials*

L F & H F Harrison, Brandon Parva, Norwich, NR9 4DY Tel: (01603) 759281 Fax: (01603) 759420 *Agricultural engineers*

L F Moon Ltd, Unit 12 Brickfields, Liverpool, L36 6HY Tel: 0151-480 5848 Fax: 0151-480 8339 *Glazers & mirror specialists*

▶ L F Nugent Ltd, High Street, Handcross, Haywards Heath, West Sussex, RH17 6BN Tel: (01444) 401097 Fax: (01444) 401103 E-mail: info@lfnugentgroup.co.uk *Ground workers*

L F Nugent Ltd, High Street, Handcross, Haywards Heath, West Sussex, RH17 6BN Tel: (01444) 401097 Fax: (01444) 401103 E-mail: lenn@nugentgroup.co.uk *Groundwork contractors*

▶ L F P (UK) Ltd, LFP House, 1 Grange Meadows, Elmswell, Bury St. Edmunds, Suffolk, IP30 9GE Tel: (01359) 242900 Fax: (01359) 242121 E-mail: info@lfpuk.co.uk *MDF, chipboard, plywood, veneered panels, hardwood agents*

L & F Plant Hire Company Ltd, 36-44 London Lane, London, E8 3PR Tel: (020) 8985 1472 Fax: (020) 8986 3518 *Commercial vehicle hire*

L F Smith, Pink Road, Lacey Green, Princes Risborough, Buckinghamshire, HP27 0PG Tel: (01844) 343901 *Small holding farmers*

L G Ball Valves Ltd, Units 5-6, Westgate Trading Estate, Aldridge, Walsall, WS9 8EX Tel: (01922) 459999 Fax: (01922) 458688 E-mail: sales@lgball-valves.co.uk *Manufacturers of ball valves, high temperature; block & bleed*

L G C Promochem Ltd, Queens Road, Teddington, Middlesex, TW11 0LY Tel: (020) 8943 8480 Fax: (020) 8943 7554 E-mail: uksales@lgcpromochem.com *Pharmaceutical reference supplier*

▶ L G Electronics, Imperial Park, Newport, NP10 8ZY Tel: (01633) 683000

L G G, 67 Smithbrook Kilns, Cranleigh, Surrey, GU6 8JJ Tel: (01483) 277574 Fax: (01483) 277888 E-mail: info@lgg.org.uk *Training centre*

L G Harris & Co. Ltd, Hanbury Road, Stoke Prior, Bromsgrove, Worcestershire, B60 4AE Tel: (01527) 575441 Fax: (01527) 575366 E-mail: enquiries@lgharris.co.uk Principal Export Areas: Worldwide *Brush (general), paint brush, paint roller & decorators' tool manufrs*

L G International (U K) Ltd, Profile West, 950 Great West Road, Brentford, Middlesex, TW8 9ES Tel: (020) 8326 1400 Fax: (020) 8560 5601 E-mail: bmsuh@lgi.co.kr *Import & export merchants*

L G K Industries Ltd, Station Approach, Pulborough, West Sussex, RH20 1AY Tel: (01798) 873663 Fax: (01798) 873722 E-mail: sales.logikontrol@btinternet.com *Electronic design consultants*

L G L Protectaseal Ltd, Unit 8 & 9, Hitchin Road Industrial Estate, Oxen Road, Luton, LU2 0DZ Tel: (01582) 422976 Fax: (01582) 404082 E-mail: contact@protectaseal.com *Self-adhesive security seals & substrates*

L G Leisure Ltd, Old Station Yard, Tenby, Dyfed, SA70 7NG Tel: (01834) 845383 Fax: (01834) 845157 *Leisure industry services*

L G M Ltd, Coppice Trading Estate, Kidderminster, Worcestershire, DY11 7QY Tel: (01562) 823700 Fax: (01562) 68237 E-mail: acook@lgm-ltd.co.uk *Soft furnishing contractors & floor coverings*

L G Optical (Mfg) Ltd, 25 Brunel Road, St. Leonards-on-Sea, East Sussex, TN38 9RT Tel: (01424) 851878 Fax: (01424) 853368 E-mail: info@lgoptical.co.uk *Optical engineers*

L G Prout & Sons Ltd, Swann Street, Hull, HU2 0PH Tel: (01482) 329600 Fax: (01482) 216296 E-mail: andy@lgprout.co.uk *General & precision engineers*

L G S A Marine, The White House, Clifton Marine Parade, Gravesend, Kent, DA11 0DY Tel: (01474) 357181 Fax: (01474) 569037 E-mail: gravesned@lgsamarine.co.uk *International cargo surveyors*

L G S A Marine, 67-83 Mariners House Queens Dock Commercial Centre, Norfolk S, Liverpool, L1 0BG Tel: 0151-707 2233 Fax: 0151-707 2170 E-mail: liverpool@lgsamarine.co.uk *Marine & cargo surveyors* Also at: Leicester

L & G Signs Ltd, Unit B9 Larkfield Trading Estate, New Hythe Lane, Larkfield, Aylesford, Kent, ME20 6SW Tel: (01732) 783640 Fax: (01622) 715758 E-mail: sales@landgsigns.co.uk *Sign manufrs*

L Gent Ltd, 54 Syston Street East, Leicester, LE1 2JW Tel: 0116-253 8727 Fax: 0116-251 4761 E-mail: info@lgent.co.uk *Automated sewing machine systems manufrs*

▶ L H Castles, 57 Forelands Square, Deal, Kent, CT14 9DT Tel: (01304) 367247 *Bouncy castle hire services*

▶ L & H Computers Ltd, 207 High Street, London, SE20 7PF Tel: (020) 8778 8883 Fax: (020) 8778 0555 E-mail: sales@itsyourpc.net *Computer engineers*

L H Jones & Son Ltd, Low Road, St. Ives, Cambridgeshire, PE27 5ET Tel: (01480) 494040 Fax: (01480) 495280 E-mail: info@jonesboatyard.co.uk *Marina operators*

L H Nichols Ltd, Nautilus Works, Reckleford, Yeovil, Somerset, BA21 4EL Tel: (01935) 476288 Fax: (01935) 431474 E-mail: office@lhnichols.com *Lambskin merchants*

L H Plastics Ltd, Allenby House, Rees Way, Bradford, West Yorkshire, BD3 0DZ Tel: (01274) 736330 Fax: (01274) 736332 E-mail: sales@lhplastics.co.uk *Plastic injection moulders*

▶ L H Plumbing & Heating Services Ltd, 132 Vaughan Road, Harrow, Middlesex, HA1 4ED Tel: (020) 8864 2311 Fax: (020) 8423 2020

L & H Promotional Ltd, 1A Barton Heys Road, Formby, Liverpool, L37 2EZ Tel: (01704) 873550 Fax: (01704) 878812 E-mail: pual@lhapm.com *Promotional & premium product designers*

L H R Marine Ltd, Unit 3a Deemouth Business Centre, South Esplanade East, Aberdeen, AB11 9PB Tel: (01224) 248821 Fax: (01224) 248831 E-mail: info@lhrmarine.com *Marine safety equipment suppliers*

L H Safety Ltd, Greenbridge Works, Fallbarn Road, Rossendale, Lancashire, BB4 7NX Tel: (01706) 235100 Fax: (01706) 235150 E-mail: enquiries@lhsafety.co.uk Principal Export Areas: Worldwide *Safety footwear distributors*

▶ L H Stainless Ltd, Towieburn, Keith, Banffshire, AB55 5JA Tel: (01466) 792222 Fax: (01466) 795329 E-mail: sales@l-h-s.co.uk

L H T Anodisers, Wallingford Road, Uxbridge, Middlesex, UB8 2SR Tel: (01895) 817700 Fax: (01895) 274275 E-mail: sales@lhtanodisers.co.uk *Anodising processors*

▶ L H T Timber Ltd, Rotherham Road, Parkgate, Rotherham, South Yorkshire, S62 6EZ Tel: (01709) 527501

L H W Engineering Ltd, Iremonger Road, London Road, Nottingham, NG2 3HU Tel: 0115-986 1247 Fax: 0115-986 0684 E-mail: sales@lhw.co.uk *Light engineering services*

L H Wilson Ltd, Unit 1 Sandbeck Trading Estate, Sandbeck Lane, Wetherby, West Yorkshire, LS22 7TW Tel: (01937) 583563 Fax: (01937) 584500 E-mail: pw@lubeoilsystems.com *Engineering & pump stockist company*

L Hardy, Timeside, Salisbury Street, Mere, Warminster, Wiltshire, BA12 6HF Tel: (01747) 860125 *Cabinet makers*

▶ L Harvey & Son Ltd, Binders Yard, Cryers Hill, High Wycombe, Buckinghamshire, HP15 6LJ Tel: (01494) 711925

L J A Miers & Co. Ltd, Hawkesden Road, St. Neots, Cambridgeshire, PE19 1QS Tel: (01480) 211177 Fax: (01480) 211190 E-mail: sales@ljamiers.co.uk *Rubber & plastic distribution*

▶ L J B Construction Ltd, 30 Southsea Road, Patchway, Bristol, BS34 5DY Tel: 0117-969 5777 Fax: 0117-969 5777

L J Bearing & Engineering Services, Unit A5 Imex Business Park, Kings Rd, Tyseley, Birmingham, B11 2AL Tel: 0121-604 7131 Fax: 0121-604 7122 E-mail: enquiries@bearings-uk.com *Bearing distributors/agents/stockholders*

L J Constructions (Plastics) Ltd, Ashford Road, Ashford, Middlesex, TW15 1XB Tel: (01784) 421112 Fax: (01784) 427050 E-mail: plastics@ljc.co.uk Purchasing Contact: Minett *Fabricators and distributors of industrial plastic systems including pressure pipe and fittings, sheet and rod plastics in PVC, PP, Polycarbonate, PETG, Polyethene, Acrylic. Values, flow monitoring equipment, flexible hose and pumps. Approved stockist of George Fisher (GF) piping systems. Please quote Kellysearch upon calling.*

L J Dennison, 94 Leopold Street, Birmingham, B12 0UD Tel: 0121-772 8871 Fax: 0121-772 8871 *Precision turned parts manufrs*

L J F UK Ltd, Centurion Way, Meridian Business Park, Leicester, LE19 1WH Tel: 0116-289 1888 Fax: 0116-289 2283 E-mail: sales@ljf-uk.com *Distributors of industrial adhesives*

L J H Group Ltd, Leigh Road, Chantry, Frome, Somerset, BA11 3LR Tel: (01373) 836451 Fax: (01373) 836879 E-mail: sales@ljhgroup.co.uk *Fabricators of quarry plant manufrs*

L J Hydleman & Co. Ltd, Marton Street, Skipton, North Yorkshire, BD23 1TF Tel: (01756) 706700 Fax: (01756) 798083 E-mail: sales@hydleman.co.uk *Hand tool importers & distributors*

L & J Mechanical Services Swindon Ltd, Unit 7, Lyndon Road, Cheney Manor, Swindon, SN2 2QJ Tel: (01793) 541419 Fax: (01793) 495759 E-mail: owen.bignenn-ljms@btinternet.com *Dust extraction & fume extraction engineers, installation or service*

L J Monks Process Ltd, Thorn Lane, Long Sandall, Doncaster, South Yorkshire, DN2 4NN Tel: (01302) 329090 Fax: (01302) 341399 E-mail: enquiries@ljmonks.co.uk *Electrical installation engineer contractors*

L J Ruskin & Son, Sibsey Lane, Boston, Lincolnshire, PE21 6HB Tel: (01205) 362380 Fax: (01205) 362380 *General printers*

▶ L J & S Services, 87 Westminster Gardens, Eye, Peterborough, PE6 7SP Tel: (01733) 222235 Fax: (01733) 223743

L J Solomon, Little Laniley Farm, Bodrean, Truro, Cornwall, TR4 9AG Tel: (01872) 273909 Fax: (01872) 273909 *Dairy farmers*

L J Technical Systems Ltd, 5-6 Francis Way, Bowthorpe Employment Area, Norwich, NR5 9JA Tel: (01603) 740421 Fax: (01603) 746340 E-mail: uksales@ljgroup.com *Education training system*

L J W Air Conditioning Ltd, 2 Post Office Lane, Rugeley, Staffordshire, WS15 2UP Tel: (01889) 582422 Fax: (01889) 583423 E-mail: hvac@ljw.co.uk *Air conditioning installers*

L & J Wilcock, 10 Walnut Avenue, Wigan, Lancashire, WN1 3XE Tel: (01942) 242705 *Potato merchants*

▶ L Jenkins, 18 Beeches Drive, Bayston Hill, Shrewsbury, SY3 0PQ Tel: (01743) 871000 Fax: 01743 871000 *NICEIC PART P APPROVED CONTRACTOR.*SERVICES OFFERED:REWIRES,TEST&INSPECTION,FIRE ALARMS,EMERGENCY LIGHTING,NEW INSTALLATIONS*

▶ L K F Ltd, Unit 4 Technology Centre, White Oak Square, London Road, Swanley, Kent, BR8 7AG Tel: (01322) 614621

L K Metals, 37 Hollinhall Street, Oldham, OL4 3EH Tel: 0161-633 3536 Fax: 0161-633 3536 *Scrap metal merchants & processors*

▶ L L G Solutions, 21 Kings Avenue, Prestatyn, Clwyd, LL19 9AA Tel: (01745) 886954 *Computer systems consultancy*

L L Morgan, Dolidrey, Llanddewi, Llandrindod Wells, Powys, LD1 6SE Tel: (01597) 851378 Fax: 01597 851378 *Agricultural contracting & farming*

L L P, Office 1, Arkwright Suite Coppull Enterprise Centre, Mill La, Coppull, Chorley, Lancs, PR7 5BW Tel: (01257) 470111 Fax: (01257) 470111 E-mail: diagseervol@aol.com *Engineering maintenance*

L L P, Watson House, London Road, Reigate, Surrey, RH2 9PQ Tel: (01737) 241144 Fax: (01737) 241496 *Actuarial & consultants*

L L Pneumatic & Engineering Supplies Ltd, Unit 1, Turner Street, Dudley, West Midlands, DY1 1TX Tel: (01384) 230123 Fax: (01384) 456146 *Pneumatic equipment distribs*

L L Potter & Sons Taplow Ltd, Taplow Road, Marshgate Trading Estate, Taplow, Maidenhead, Berkshire, SL6 0ND Tel: (01628) 667167 Fax: (01628) 667801 E-mail: potters@globalnet.co.uk *Sheet metalworkers*

▶ L & L Welding, Unit E 1, St. Davids Industrial Estate, Pengam, Blackwood, Gwent, NP12 3SW Tel: (01443) 832000 Fax: (01443) 832000 E-mail: marklewiswales@yahoo.co.uk *Wrought iron specialists, gates & railings, furniture manufrs*

L Littlewood & Son Exports Ltd, 3 Edwin Road, Beswick, Manchester, M11 3ER Tel: 0161-273 1344 Fax: 0161-273 3013 E-mail: l-littlewood@btconnect.com *Textile merchants*

L M A Ltd, LMA House, Third Avenue, Southampton, SO15 0LD Tel: (023) 8077 2888 Fax: (023) 8077 2999 E-mail: create@lma.co.uk *Advertising, design & marketing agents*

L M C Audio Systems Ltd, Unit 10 Acton Park Industrial Estate, The Vale, London, W3 7QE Tel: (020) 8743 4680 Fax: (020) 8749 9875 E-mail: sales@lmcaudio.co.uk *Audio equipment dealers & distributors*

L M C Technik Ltd, Cherry Way, Dubmire Industrial Estate, Houghton le Spring, Tyne & Wear, DH4 5RJ Tel: 0191-385 8500 Fax: 0191-385 7819 E-mail: sales@lmctechnik.com *Reaction injection moulders*

L M Computers Ltd, Arcade Chambers, Little Wellington Street, Aldershot, Hampshire, GU11 1EE Tel: (01252) 406323 Fax: (01252) 406324 E-mail: sales@lmcomputers.co.uk *Computer network & software suppliers*

L M D Associates, Leicester Road, Earl Shilton, Leicester, LE9 7TJ Tel: (01455) 840000 Fax: (01455) 840266 E-mail: sales@lmdassociates.co.uk *Point of sale display manufrs*

L M D Farms, Kirton Road, Blyton, Gainsborough, Lincolnshire, DN21 3PE Tel: (01427) 628059 *Maggot breeders*

L M D Frames Ltd, Unit 45 Burton Indust Est, Petford St, Cradley Heath, Cradley Heath, West Midlands, B64 6DJ Tel: 01384 410909 Fax: 01384 634344 *Furniture manufrs*

▶ L & M Engineering, Garthspool, Lerwick, Shetland, ZE1 0NY Tel: (01595) 692522 Fax: (01595) 693601 *Marine & general electrical engineers*

L M Engineering Services Ltd, Unit 226D, Redwither Industrial Complex, Wrexham, Clwyd, LL13 9XU Tel: (01978) 660111 Fax: (01978) 660227 E-mail: steel@lmeng.fsbusiness.co.uk *Steel & stainless steel fabricators*

L & M Food Group Ltd, Trelawney House, 454-456 Larkshall Road, Highams Park, London, E4 9HH Tel: (020) 8531 7631 Fax: (020) 8531 8607 *Food traders*

L M Form Tools Precision Grinding, Unit 18 Canalside Industrial Estate, Brettell Lane, Brierley Hill, West Midlands, DY5 3JU Tel: (01384) 78738 Fax: (01384) 78738 E-mail: sales@formtools.co.uk *Form tool manufrs*

▶ L & M Hosting, Internet House, 64 Haig Street, Grangemouth, Stirlingshire, FK3 8QF Tel: (0845) 3312898 Fax: (0845) 6443809

L & M Nutt, 418 Chester Road, Sutton Coldfield, West Midlands, B73 5BS Tel: 0121-373 5497 Fax: 0121-373 5497 *Sewing machine sales & repairs*

L M P Market Supplies, 4 Marine Industrial Estate, Marine Street, Cwm, Ebbw Vale, Gwent, NP23 7TB Tel: (01495) 370052 Fax: (01495) 370052 *Market stall & wrought iron gate manufrs*

L & M Phoenix Luggage UK Ltd, Middlesex House, 29-45 High Street, Edgware, Middlesex, HA8 7UU Tel: (020) 8905 6678 Fax: (020) 8905 6644 E-mail: sales@phoenixint.net *Luggage & travel goods*

L M Products Ltd, Unit 10, Union Road, Oldbury, West Midlands, B69 3EX Tel: 0121-552 8622 Fax: 0121-544 4571 E-mail: sales@lmproducts.co.uk *Specialist supplies constructions industry*

L M R Computer Repairs, 2 North Parade, Norris Road, Sale, Cheshire, M33 3JS Tel: 0161-962 8872 Fax: 0161-962 8872 *Computer services for schools*

▶ L & M Refrigeration, Unit 3, Thesiger Close, Worthing, West Sussex, BN11 2RN Tel: (0871) 2882665 Fax: (01903) 214296 E-mail: admin@lmrefrigeration.co.uk *Air conditioning & refrigeration sales, service, maintenance*

L M S Constructional Engineers Ltd, 8 Swinton Meadows Industrial Estate, Meadow Way, Swinton, Mexborough, South Yorkshire, S64 8AB Tel: (01709) 571001 Fax: (01709) 571021 E-mail: sales@lmskan.co.uk *Manufacturers of storage-materials*

▶ L M S Music Supplies, PO Box 7, Exeter, EX1 1WB Tel: (01392) 428108 Fax: (01392) 412521 E-mail: lmsmusic@compuserve.com *Mail order for schools*

L M S Precision Engineering, 44 Wassage Way, Hampton Lovett, Droitwich, Worcestershire, WR9 0NX Tel: (01905) 779783 Fax: (01905) 779041 E-mail: roger@lmsprecision.co.uk *Precision machined parts*

L & M Signs, Unit 1 Highlands Close, St Helens Way, Thetford, Norfolk, IP24 1HG Tel: 01842 821990 Fax: 01842 750706 E-mail: trevor@lmsigns.co.uk *Sign Makers & Screen Printers*

L M Software Ltd, Apak House Badminton Court, Station Road, Yate, Bristol, BS37 5HZ Tel: (01454) 871060 Fax: (01454) 871199 E-mail: enquiries@lmsoft.co.uk *Database software suppliers*

▶ L M T S, 36 Ocean Street, Plymouth, PL2 2DJ Tel: (07968) 113070 Fax: (01752) 597 69 E-mail: daveking@cncengineers.com *Machine Tools Services. CNC Electronic and Mechanical specialists offering Machine recovery, Installations and routine servicing.*

L M W Electronics Ltd, L M W House Merrylees Industrial Estate, Lee Side, Desford, Leicester, LE9 9FS Tel: (01530) 231141 Fax: (01530) 231143 E-mail: sales@lmw.co.uk *Radio designers & manufrs*

L & M Window Cleaning Co. Ltd, 7-9 Summer Hill Terrace, Birmingham, B1 3RA Tel: 0121-236 1448 Fax: 0121-233 0037 E-mail: info@londonandmidland.co.uk *Industrial cleaning contractors*

▶ L MS Plastering, 21 Hillside Close, Bartley Green, Birmingham, B32 4LT Tel: 0121-585 6773 E-mail: pokernext99126@aol.com *dry-lining,rending,ceilings, boarding, skimming*

L.Nicot & Company Ltd, 7 Beeches Avenue, Carshalton Beeches, Carshalton, Surrey, SM5 3LB Tel: (020) 8773 8050 Fax: (020) 8773 8070 *Mat, cane & basket importers*

L O T-Oriel Ltd, 1 Mole Business Park, Randalls Road, Leatherhead, Surrey, KT22 7BA Tel: (01372) 378822 Fax: (01372) 375353 E-mail: sales@lotoriel.co.uk *Scientific instrument distributors*

L P A Niphan Ltd, P O Box 15, Saffron Walden, Essex, CB11 4AN Tel: (01799) 512800 Fax: (01799) 512828 E-mail: sales@lpa-niphan.com *Industrial plug & socket manufrs* Also at: Caldicot, Pontefract & Stockport

L P B Contracts, 4 Matthews Green Road, Wokingham, Berkshire, RG41 1JU Tel: 0118-978 3424 Fax: 0118-978 3424 *Office interior refurbishes*

L P C Computer Solutions, Unit 2 Buslingthorpe Green, Leeds, LS7 2HG Tel: 0113-262 2626 Fax: 0113-262 6622 E-mail: len@lpconline.co.uk *Computer parts retail*

L P C Properties Ltd, Waterside Road, Hamilton Industrial Park, Leicester, LE5 1TZ Tel: 0116-246 0888 Fax: 0116-246 0222 E-mail: info@lpcgroup.co.uk *Disposable paper product manufrs*

L P Dawe, Meneer House, 22 Berkeley Vale, Falmouth, Cornwall, TR11 3PA Tel: (01326) 312405 Fax: (01326) 316233 E-mail: lpdawe@btconnect.com *Insurance brokers*

L P E Ltd, Russell St, Johnstone, Renfrewshire, PA5 8BZ Tel: (01505) 331165 Fax: (01505) 328606 E-mail: make@linellengservices.co.uk *Precision engineers*

▶ L & P Flooring, Victoria Road, Bradford, West Yorkshire, BD2 2BH Tel: (01274) 634455 Fax: (01274) 634455 *Floor suppliers*

L P Hangers, Units 5-9, Parker Paul Trading Estate, Sunbeam Street, Wolverhampton, WV2 4PF Tel: (01902) 420653 Fax: (01902) 714716 E-mail: info@lphangers.co.uk *Plastics injection moulders*

L P K F Laser & Electronics Ltd, Coppid Beech Lane, Wokingham, Berkshire, RG40 1PD Tel: (01344) 455046 Fax: (01344) 860547 E-mail: sales@lpkf.co.uk *Laser & electronics*

L P L Ltd, 19 Thorndale Croft, Wetwang, Driffield, North Humberside, YO25 9XZ Tel: (01377) 236282 Fax: (01377) 236303 E-mail: info@lpl.co.uk *Website designers*

L P L Commercial Investigations, 890-900 Eastern Avenue, Ilford, Essex, IG2 7HH Tel: (020) 8597 2229 Fax: (020) 8597 1180 E-mail: info@lplgroup.com *Debt recovery services*

L P R Services Ltd, 6 Cantors Way, Minety, Malmesbury, Wiltshire, SN16 9QZ Tel: (01666) 860992 Fax: (01666) 860992 E-mail: info@lprservices.co.uk *Shop fitters*

▶ L P S South, 10 Brunel Road, Gorse La Industrial Estate, Clacton-on-Sea, Essex, CO15 4LU Tel: (01255) 221369 Fax: (01255) 476754 E-mail: lpsouth@aol.com *Lightning protection system installations*

L & P Security & Electrical Services Ltd, Suite F1 St James House, 6 Overcliffe, Gravesend, Kent, DA11 0EF Tel: (01474) 351038 Fax: (01474) 353880 *Alarm system engineers*

L & P Springs UK Ltd, Ravenscroft Way, Barnoldswick, Lancashire, BB18 6JA Tel: (01282) 814054 Fax: (01282) 814064 E-mail: sales@leggett.com *Spring manufrs*

▶ L P Tooling, Brooklands Approach, Romford, RM1 1DX Tel: (01708) 755300

L Parry & Sons, Gorse Hall New Farm, Promised Land Lane, Rowton, Chester, CH3 6AZ Tel: (01244) 335880 Fax: (01244) 335856 *Agricultural machinery suppliers*

L Person & Son Ltd, 33 Hollands Road, Haverhill, Suffolk, CB9 8PU Tel: (01440) 702811 Fax: (01440) 702711 E-mail: david@personhaverhill.freeserve.co.uk *Press tool manufrs*

L & R, 69 Rockingham Rd, Uxbridge, Middx, UB8 2UA Tel: (01895) 272523 Fax: (01895) 273664 *Air conditioning engineers*

▶ L R B Consulting Ltd, 2 Fairmeadows Way, Loughborough, Leicestershire, LE11 2QT Tel: (01509) 550023 Fax: (01509) 550023 E-mail: enquiries@lrbconsulting.co.uk *Health and Safety Consultancy.*Training Consultancy.*

L R Centre, Bridge Industrial Estate, Speke Hall Road, Speke, Liverpool, L24 9HB Tel: 0151-486 9800 Fax: 0151-486 5986 E-mail: info@lrparts.net *Motor vehicle accessories & parts*

L R D Systems Ltd, 37 Robert Moffat, High Legh, Knutsford, Cheshire, WA16 6PS Tel: (01925) 758700 Fax: (01925) 758700 E-mail: enquiries@lrd.co.uk *Computer consultants & web developers*

L R Engineering, Milton Farm Workshop, West End Gardens, Fairford, Gloucestershire, GL7 4JB Tel: (01285) 713163 Fax: (01285) 713632 E-mail: lrengineering@btconnect.com *Welding fabricators*

L & R Engineering Ltd, 53 Colvilles Place, Kelvin Industrial Estate, East Kilbride, Glasgow, G75 0PZ Tel: (01355) 241744 Fax: (01355) 241744 *General light engineers*

L R G Sound & Vision Ltd, 171-175 Albertbridge Road, Belfast, BT5 4PS Tel: (028) 9045 1381 Fax: (028) 9073 1478 E-mail: lrg@btconnect.com *Retailing hi-fi equipment*

▶ L & R Loft Services, 8 Stonehill Crescent, Bognor Regis, West Sussex, PO21 3PQ Tel: (0800) 2984350 E-mail: enq@loftservices.co.uk *Loft ladders & velux windows suppliers & installers*

▶ L & R Products, 2A Ham Lane, Kingswinford, West Midlands, DY6 7JU Tel: (01384) 293042 *Manufacturing plastic products*

▶ L & R Roadlines Ltd, 24-32 Forth Street, Liverpool, L20 8JW Tel: 0151-933 6293

L & R Saddles Ltd, Clifford House, 10-14 Butts Road, Walsall, WS4 2AR Tel: (01922) 630740 Fax: (01922) 721749 E-mail: landrsaddles@btconnect.com *Riding saddle manufrs*

L R & Sons, Laindon Common Road, Little Burstead, Billericay, Essex, CM12 9SY Tel: (01277) 652381 Fax: (01277) 652381 E-mail: lrandsons@aol.com *Agricultural contractors*

L Rampling Plant Hire, 6 Victory Rd, West Mersea, Colchester, CO5 8LY Tel: (01206) 382989 Fax: (01206) 384782 *Building contractors & plant hire*

▶ L Razec, 82 Oakdale Road, Poole, Dorset, BH15 3LQ Tel: (07716) 529694 E-mail: contact@razec.co.uk *LRAZEC offers a reliable efficient and cost effective solution to the busy homeowner. Our courteous and friendly staff will ensure that you are delighted with their efforts. If you"re looking for a reliable contract cleaning company to put a smile on your place, e-mail or call for a free quotation*

L Rifkin (Liverpool) Ltd, Marsh Street, Kirkdale, Liverpool, L20 2BL Tel: 0151-922 3004 Fax: 0151-922 0780 E-mail: dhale.rifkin@cybase.co.uk *Scrap metal merchants, demolition contractors & skip hire*

▶ L S C Services Ltd, Unit 7, Brampton Centre, Brampton Road, Wath-Upon-Dearne, Rotherham, South Yorkshire, S63 6BB Tel: (01709) 879555

L & S Carpet Co. Ltd, 48 Central Road, Morden, Surrey, SM4 5RU Tel: (020) 8648 6131 Fax: (020) 8648 6193 *Carpet & floor contractors*

L & S Design, 11-13 Hatton Garden, London, EC1N 8AN Tel: (020) 7404 2302 Fax: (020) 7404 2321 *Jewellery manufrs*

L S Direct Ltd, 44 Holcombe Crescent, Kearsley, Bolton, BL4 8JY Tel: (01204) 862776 Fax: (01204) 707865 E-mail: pat@lsdirect.co.uk *Lighting installations service*

L S E Storage Equipment Ltd, 15 Aintree Road, Bootle, Merseyside, L20 9PL Tel: 0151-476 2478 Fax: 0151-476 2482 E-mail: sales@lsestorage.com *Storage system suppliers*

L & S Engineers Ltd, Unit 5 West Coppice Road, Walsall, WS8 7HB Tel: (01543) 378189 Fax: (01543) 370006 *Engineers/general engineering*

▶ L & S Engineers Calberto Ltd, Spire Road, District 10, Washington, Tyne & Wear, NE37 3ES Tel: 0191-416 8339 Fax: 0191-415 4615 E-mail: calberto@btopenworld.co.uk *Metalworking & fabrication services*

▶ L S Fabrications Ltd, Swallowfields, Welwyn Garden City, Hertfordshire, AL7 1JD Tel: (01707) 885885

L & S Fire Protection Systems Ltd, 7a Rathbone Square, 28 Tanfield Road, Croydon, CR0 1AL Tel: (020) 8240 4456 Fax: (020) 8240 4457 E-mail: landsfire@ssbdial.co.uk *Fire protection engineers & designers*

L S Francis, Unit 12a Mayfair Industrial Area, Maldon Road, Latchingdon, Chelmsford, CM3 6LF Tel: (01621) 740924 Fax: (01621) 740924 *Self-adhesive label manufrs*

L & S Hardware, The Stabes, Victoria House, Banknock, Bonnybridge, Stirlingshire, FK4 1UE Tel: (01324) 849992 Fax: (01324) 849993 *Bolt fastener & socket screw distributors*

L & S Joinery, 98 Lower Bedfords Road, Romford, RM1 4DQ Tel: (01708) 755966 Fax: (01708) 730748 *Joinery manufrs*

L & S Litho Printers & Designers Ltd, 15-27 Arrol Place, Glasgow, G40 3NY Tel: 0141-556 2837 Fax: 0141-554 2590 E-mail: bill.livingstone@btlslitho.com *Printers & graphic designers*

L & S Middleton Paper Co., Eagle Works, Somerford Place, Willenhall, West Midlands, WV13 3EA Tel: (01902) 635551 Fax: (01902) 636728 E-mail: middletonpaper@compuserve.com *Paper converters & merchants*

L S N, 1 Wheldon Road, Castleford, West Yorkshire, WF10 2SE Tel: (01977) 604461 Fax: (01977) 604461 *Powder coating suppliers*

L S P Ltd, 168 Blackfen Road, Hawthorn Terrace, Sidcup, Kent, DA15 8PT Tel: (020) 8859 8877 Fax: (020) 8859 8787 E-mail: sales@lspuk.com *Rubber products manufrs*

▶ L S Patterns, Unit 2 Stonebroom Industrial Estate, Stonebroom, Alfreton, Derbyshire, DE55 6LQ Tel: (01773) 591777 Fax: (01773) 875777 E-mail: len@lspatterns.com *Supply of coach parts*

L & S Printing Co. Ltd, Unit 10 Hazelwood Trading Estate, Hazelwood Close, Worthing, West Sussex, BN14 8NP Tel: (01903) 821005 Fax: (01903) 821006 E-mail: sue.m@ls-printing.com *Printing services*

L & S Prints, Export House, West Lane, Keighley, West Yorkshire, BD21 2LH Tel: (01535) 690030 Fax: (01535) 690133 *Textile printers*

▶ L S Printworks, Unit 4, Amlwch Industrial Estate, Amlwch, Gwynedd, LL68 9BX Tel: (01407) 830059

L S Rumble, 5 Hatton Place, London, EC1N 8RU Tel: (020) 7242 5845 *Jewellery manufrs*

▶ L S S International Ltd, E 206 Manchester Road, Mossley, Ashton-under-Lyne, Lancashire, OL5 9AY Tel: (01457) 833170 Fax: (01457) 834087 *Precision engineers*

L & S Schofield Ltd, Unit 11-13, Haigh Avenue, Stockport, Cheshire, SK4 1NU Tel: 0161-480 3570 Fax: 0161-480 0836 E-mail: steve@dowelpins.fsnet.co.uk *Wood turners & moulding manufrs*

L S Starrett Co. Ltd, Oxnam Road, Jedburgh, Roxburghshire, TD8 6LR Tel: (01835) 863501 Fax: (01835) 863018 E-mail: sales@starrett.co.uk Principal Export Areas: Worldwide *Band saw blading, band saw, hacksaw & saw blade manufrs*

L & S Sun Blinds Ltd, 2 Holme Street, Grimsby, South Humberside, DN32 9AD Tel: (01472) 351855 Fax: (01472) 251011 E-mail: enquiries@blinds4sale.co.uk *Manufacturers of made to measure roller, vertical, venetian, perfect fit, conservatory, wooden and pleated blinds.*

L S UK Ltd, 124 Anlaby Road, Hull, HU3 2JH Tel: (01482) 610977 Fax: (01482) 219818 E-mail: kvssales@aol.co.uk *Alarm & battery distributors*

L S UK Rewind, 12 Bucklands Road, Penmill Trading Estate, Yeovil, Somerset, BA21 5EA Tel: (01935) 476255 Fax: (01935) 433627 E-mail: rewind@rgillard.wannado.co.uk *Motor rewind service*

▶ L Shailer, Hafod School House, Llanerfyl, Welshpool, Powys, SY21 0JH Tel: (01938) 820110 Fax: (01938) 820118 E-mail: info@lynshailer.co.uk *Exclusive designs of bed linen & linens*

L Swanick, 9-11 Market Street, Uttoxeter, Staffordshire, ST14 8JA Tel: (01889) 569808 Fax: (01889) 566567 E-mail: swan@electrics.sagehost.co.uk *Electrical contractors*

L T E Scientific Ltd, Greenbridge Lane, Greenfield, Oldham, OL3 7EN Tel: (01457) 876221 Fax: (01457) 870131 E-mail: info@lte-scientific.co.uk *Laboratory equipment manufrs*

L T H Electronics Ltd, Eltelec Works, Chaul End Lane, Luton, LU4 8EZ Tel: (01582) 593693 Fax: (01582) 598036 E-mail: sales@lth.co.uk *Analysis equipment & analyser manufr*

L T Industrial Training, 99 Desborough Road, Rothwell, Kettering, Northamptonshire, NN14 6JQ Tel: (01536) 711183 Fax: (01536) 711961 *Industrial training*

L T M Furnaces Ltd, 21 Fenlow Avenue, Stoke-on-Trent, ST2 9NE Tel: (01782) 501441 Fax: (01782) 598676 *Manufacturer of furnaces*

L T Printing, Alfred Road, Wallasey, Merseyside, CH44 7HY Tel: 0151-647 8006 Fax: 0151-666 1704 E-mail: post@ltprintgroup.co.uk *Designers & printers*

▶ L T S, 8 Ashgrove Crescent, Ecclefechan, Lockerbie, Dumfriesshire, DG11 3EA Tel: (01576) 300589 E-mail: enquiries@anchortesting.co.uk *LTS specialises in the installation and testing of personal protective anchors*

L T S S Print Finishers Ltd, 329 Stean Street, London, E8 4ED Tel: (020) 7923 3155 Fax: (020) 7923 3562 *Finishers to the printing trade*

L Tec Control Engineers Ltd, 125 Deerdykes View, Westfield, Cumbernauld, Glasgow, G68 9HN Tel: (01236) 727766 Fax: (01236) 733903 *Control system manufrs*

L U K A S (Hereford) Ltd, Holme Lacy Road, Rotherwas, Hereford, HR2 6LA Tel: (01432) 265265 Fax: (01432) 275146 *Clutch & motor suppliers*

L V S I M A S Ltd, Swansey Mill, Swansey Lane, Whittle-le-Woods, Chorley, Lancashire, PR6 7NR Tel: (01257) 263666 Fax: (01257) 241821 E-mail: sales@rubberbelts.co.uk *Conveyor belt sales & service*

L V S Rubber Mouldings Ltd, Robins Rd, Chasetown Industrial Estate, Burntwood, Staffordshire, WS7 3FX Tel: (01543) 673989 Fax: (01543) 683823 E-mail: sales@lvsrubber.com Principal Export Areas: Central/East Europe, Central America & South America *Manufacture and supply of rubber mouldings, rubber hoses, rubber mountings, grommets, rubber gaskets, seals, bonded rubber components, rubber to metal bonding, TPE mouldings, plastic mouldings and rubber extrusions. We have rubber injection moulding, compression rubber moulding and flashless rubber moulding capabilities. Tool making facilities and prototyping abilities. We supply low cost, high quality precision rubber mouldings for automotive industry, white goods industry, hydraulic applications, pneumatic seals, construction industry and specialist engineering. Processing EPDM, Natural Rubber NR, Neoprene, Viton, Vamac, Silicone, SBR, Nitrile PVC .*

L V Shipping Ltd, Walton Avenue, Felixstowe, Suffolk, IP11 3AL Tel: (01394) 278784 Fax: (01394) 284498 E-mail: felixstowe@lvshipping.com *Freight forwarders* Also at: Aberdeen, London, Middlesbrough & Sheerness

L V Tomlinson & Son Ltd, Catwick Lane, Brandesburton, Driffield, North Humberside, YO25 8RY Tel: (01964) 542969 Fax: (01964) 543431 *Steel fabricators*

L V Transport Ltd, Norfolk Road, Gravesend, Kent, DA12 2PS Tel: (01474) 567361 Fax: (01474) 564455 E-mail: lv.transport@btopenworld.com *Road transport contractors & storage contractors*

▶ L V V Services Ltd, 31 Preswylfa Court, Merthyrmawr Road, Bridgend, Mid Glamorgan, CF31 3NX Tel: (01656) 658195 Fax: (01656) 658195 E-mail: stevemagill@btopenworld.com *Mobile Repair and Restoration to Motor Vehicles Minor Paint Damage Dings and Dents Seat Burns and Trim Repair Bumpers Repaired ,Air Conditioning Parts and Service Automotive Diagnostics ,ABS and Air Bag systems and Engine Managment Systems and Lights.*

L V W Auto Motive Components Ltd, 118 Cleveland Street, Birkenhead, Merseyside, CH41 3QP Tel: 0151-666 2000 Fax: 0151-647 7220 E-mail: precision@senareng.demon.co.uk *Precision engineers services*

L W Cole Distributors Ltd, Castle Vale Industrial Estate, Maybrook Road, Minworth, Sutton Coldfield, West Midlands, B76 1BE Tel: 0121-313 1199 Fax: 0121-313 1560 *Kitchen & electric appliance distributors* Also at: Bristol & Nottingham

L W Safety Ltd, Unit 12, Derby Road, Greenford, Middlesex, UB6 8UJ Tel: (020) 8575 9000 Fax: (020) 8575 0600 *Fire equipment sales & services*

L W Vass Holdings Ltd, Station Road, Ampthill, Bedford, MK45 2RB Tel: (01525) 403255 Fax: (01525) 404194 E-mail: sales@vass.co.uk *Government surplus dealers services*

L W Waller & Son Ltd, Waller Building, Fish Market, Lowestoft, Suffolk, NR32 1BU Tel: (01502) 573236 *Fish merchants*

▶ L & W Wilson Ltd, Gatebeck Road, Endmoor, Kendal, Cumbria, LA8 0HL Tel: (01539) 567601 Fax: (01539) 567775 E-mail: office@landwwilson.co.uk

L W Yates, Cooke Street Forge, Cooke Street, Bentley, Doncaster, South Yorkshire, DN5 0DD Tel: (01302) 874330 Fax: (01302) 874330 *Steel fabricators*

L Whitaker & Sons 1983 Ltd, Unit 4-5 Rochdale Industrial Centre, Albion Road, Rochdale, Lancashire, OL11 4HN Tel: (01706) 655611 Fax: (01706) 655611 E-mail: sales@lwhitaker.co.uk *Cotton goods wholesalers*

L Wynne & Co Manchester Ltd, Unit A7 The Dresser Centre, Whitworth Street, Openshaw, Manchester, M11 2NE Tel: 0161-223 2640 Fax: 0161-231 1367 *Industrial thermal insulation contractors*

▶ L X R Web Design, Po Box 601, Altrincham, Cheshire, WA14 1WE Tel: (01925) 753629 E-mail: studio@lxrwebdesign.co.uk *LXR is a web development company based in South Manchester, we provide original and creative web design, multilingual web sites, search engine optimisation, e-commerce solutions, develop advanced web media and video*

▶ L2H Jewellery, Birchgrove, Castleton Road, Auchterarder, Perthshire, PH3 1JW Tel: (01764) 661130 E-mail: john@sundialcreative.com *Beautiful handmade jewellery from Love2have - supporting UK based designers and modern jewellery makers.*

L3 Comunnications Ltd, Astro House, Brants Bridge, Bracknell, Berkshire, RG12 9HW Tel: (01344) 477900 Fax: (01344) 477901 E-mail: matthew.woodman@l-3.com *Security metal detectors & x-ray equipment distributors & manufrs*

La Baguette, 17 Picardy Street, Belvedere, Kent, DA17 5QQ Tel: (020) 8311 1113 Fax: (020) 8310 5179 *Bakery & confectionary suppliers*

La Bourse Ltd, 15 Harley House, 28-32 Marylebone Road, London, NW1 5HE Tel: (020) 7487 4745 Fax: (020) 7486 0055 *Financial advisers*

La Conch Lighting, Cranborne Industrial Estate, Cranborne Road, Potters Bar, Hertfordshire, EN6 3JN Tel: (01707) 644440 Fax: (01707) 644446 E-mail: info@laconch.co.uk *Lighting distributors*

▶ La Deliveries, 3 Beacon Farm, Moor Road, Great Staughton, St. Neots, Cambridgeshire, PE19 5BW Tel: (01234) 378861

La Galinette Ltd, Legacy Centre, Hanworth Trading Estate, Hampton Road West, Hanworth, Feltham, Middlesex, TW13 6DH Tel: (020) 8755 5858 Fax: (020) 8755 5878 E-mail: sales@lagalinette.co.uk *La Galinette manufacture and wholesale the finest fresh French patisserie in the London area, catering to the top end of the market. All patisseries are* *continued* *fresh and made with authentic ingredients. The patisseries is sold to through coffee shops, patisseries shops, top class restaurants, five star hotels and first/business class of some airlines. Accredited with High Level of BRC Global Standard - Food.*

La Jana Ltd, 34-35 Hatton Garden, London, EC1N 8DX Tel: (020) 7242 6668 Fax: (020) 7242 1991 *Wholesale jewellers pearl & coral*

La Patisserie Supreme, Unit 18 Avonbank Industrial Centre, West Town Road, Bristol, BS11 9DE Tel: 0117-982 0687 Fax: 0117-982 0687 E-mail: lapatisserie@btconnect.com *La Patisserie Supreme based in Bristol are manufacturers of frozen and chilled desserts.*

La Riche, PO Box 2093, Southend-on-Sea, SS3 9QP Tel: (01702) 297532 Fax: (01702) 297533 E-mail: laricheltd@aol.com *Hair cosmetics manufrs*

La Rondine, 12 Queen Street, Bedford, MK40 2HA Tel: (01234) 400990 Fax: (01234) 219443 *Catering suppliers*

▶ La Serve, The Old Station, Coastal Road, Hest Bank, Lancaster, LA2 6HN Tel: (01524) 825603 Fax: (01524) 825615 E-mail: office@laserve.co.uk *Marketing services, website design & telemarketing*

La Tea Doh Ltd, 136 Nithsdale Road, Glasgow, G41 5RB Tel: 0141-424 3224 Fax: 0141-424 3224 E-mail: info@lateadoh.co.uk *Food retailers*

Lab 3 Ltd, 1 Dragon Court, Crofts End Road, Bristol, BS5 7XX Tel: (0870) 1260333 Fax: (0870) 1260349 *Laboratory equipment suppliers*

Lab 3 Ltd, 1 The Business Centre, Ross Road, Weedon Road Industrial Estate, Northampton, NN5 5AX Tel: (0870) 4445553 Fax: (0870) 1260350 E-mail: sales@lab3.co.uk *Laboratory instruments & chemical supplies*

Lab Craft Ltd, 22b King Street, Saffron Walden, Essex, CB10 1ES Tel: (01799) 513434 Fax: (01799) 513437 E-mail: sales@labcraft.co.uk Principal Export Areas: Worldwide *Light fitting equipment suppliers(24v)* Also at: Harold Wood

Lab Engineering, Bowood Lane, Wendover, Aylesbury, Buckinghamshire, HP22 6PY Tel: (01296) 624222 Fax: (01296) 624222 *Precision engineers*

Lab Furnishings Group, Unit 2 Malmo Park, Stockholm Road, Sutton Fields Industrial Estate, Hull, HU7 0XW Tel: (01482) 827999 Fax: (01482) 827995 E-mail: p.moran@lfplc.co.uk Principal Export Areas: Worldwide *The Lab Furnishings Group & its associate companies offer a comprehensive range of school furniture, laboratory furniture, fume cupboards, healthcare furniture & modular buildings to the educational, healthcare & industrial market sectors*

▶ Lab Med, Unit 4 Brunel Way, Thetford, Norfolk, IP24 1HP Tel: (01842) 762513 Fax: (01842) 753927 E-mail: labmedemail@yahoo.co.uk *Laboratory & medical equipment suppliers*

Lab Systems Furniture Ltd, Rotary House, Bontoft Avenue, Hull, HU5 4HF Tel: (01482) 444650 Fax: (01482) 444730 E-mail: office@lab-systems.co.uk *Laboratory furniture manufrs*

▶ Lab Tek Instruments, Star House, The Drive, Hellingly, Hailsham, East Sussex, BN27 4EP Tel: (01323) 840584 Fax: (01323) 840583 E-mail: tom.howe@footfallcounters.com *Automated footfall, customer counting equipment suppliers & manufrs*

Lab UK Furniture Ltd, Coal Pit Lane, Atherton, Manchester, M46 0RL Tel: (01942) 893223 Fax: (01942) 894141 *Laboratory furniture manufrs*

Labco, Brow Works, Copyground Lane, High Wycombe, Buckinghamshire, HP12 3HE Tel: (01494) 459741 Fax: (01494) 465101 E-mail: sales@labco.co.uk *Laboratory glassware manufrs*

Labdon Building Supplies, Palmers Bridge, Station Road, Cullompton, Devon, EX15 1BQ Tel: (01884) 33405 Fax: (01884) 35405 *Builders merchants & diy supplies*

Label Apeel Ltd, James House, Murrayfield Road, Leicester, LE3 1UW Tel: 0116-231 4555 Fax: 0116-231 4552 E-mail: info@labelapeel.co.uk *Label printers & manufrs*

▶ Label Innovations, Enfield Industrial Estate, Redditch, Worcestershire, B97 6BN Tel: (01527) 597774 Fax: (01527) 597775 E-mail: sales@label-innovations.com *Bar code system manufrs multi-coloured labels, cartons glue & folding*

Label Link, The Old Bakery, High Street, Angmering, Littlehampton, West Sussex, BN16 4AG Tel: (01903) 782588 Fax: (01903) 782588 E-mail: sales@label-link.co.uk *Label makers/silk screen printers*

The Label Makers Ltd, Labmak House, Prince Street, Bradford, West Yorkshire, BD4 6HQ Tel: (01274) 681151 Fax: (01274) 651090 E-mail: info@labmak.co.uk *Self-adhesive label printers*

Label Spec, Unit 2, Drummond Crescent, Riverside Business Park, Irvine, Ayrshire, KA11 5AN Tel: (01563) 550990 Fax: (01563) 550991 E-mail: sales@labelspec.co.uk *Label manufrs*

▶ Label Studio Ltd, 171 Waterside Road, Hamilton, Leicester, LE5 1TL Tel: 0116-276 3569

Label Supply Eastbourne Ltd, North Street, Eastbourne, East Sussex, BN21 3HG Tel: (01323) 645264 Fax: (01323) 727488 E-mail: enquiries@labelsupply.co.uk *Labels suppliers*

Label Talk, 145a Gallery Chambers, Connaught Avenue, Frinton-on-Sea, Essex, CO13 9AH Tel: (01255) 850110 Fax: (01255) 850043 E-mail: labeltalk@teliaco.co.uk *Labelling consultants*

▶ Label Technology Ltd, 15 Walton Road, Pattinson North, Washington, Tyne & Wear, NE38 8QA Tel: 0191-416 7038

▶ Labelcraft Engraving, Abbey Farm, Gulpher Road, Felixstowe, Suffolk, IP11 9RD Tel: (01394) 285354 Fax: (01394) 670902 *Label & sign production to order*

Label-Form Ltd, Reform Road, Maidenhead, Berkshire, SL6 8BY Tel: (01628) 782082 Fax: (01628) 770879 E-mail: sales@label-form.co.uk Principal Export Areas: Africa, Central/East Europe & West Europe *Printers & suppliers of labels*

▶ Labelling & Packaging Systems Ltd, 1 Telford Place, South Newmoor Industrial Estate, Irvine, Ayrshire, KA11 4HW Tel: (01294) 215058 E-mail: info@lpsltd.co.uk *Packaging machines*

Labelman Labels & Tags, 52b Salop Road, Oswestry, Shropshire, SY11 2RQ Tel: (01691) 679333 Fax: (01691) 679444 E-mail: sales@1abelman.demon.co.uk *Self adhesive labels & labelling System distributors*

▶ Labelnet Ltd, Labelnet House Hallsford Bridge Industrial Estate, Stondon Road, Ongar, Essex, CM5 9RB Tel: (01277) 364964 Fax: (01277) 365965

Labelon Sales Ltd, Unit 10 Chilford Court, Rayne Road, Braintree, Essex, CM7 2QS Tel: (01376) 553030 Fax: (01376) 349437 E-mail: sales@labelon.co.uk *Self woven garment labels*

Labelpower Ltd, 6 Kingsbury Trading Estate, Church Lane, London, NW9 8AU Tel: (020) 8205 8255 Fax: (020) 8200 1769 E-mail: sales@labelpower.co.uk *Self-adhesive label manufrs*

Labelprint Identification Cards, 73 Imperial Drive, Harrow, Middlesex, HA2 7DU Tel: (020) 8424 9413 Fax: (020) 8424 9413 *Thermal printers*

▶ Labels, 7 City Court Trading Estate, Poland Street, Manchester, M4 6AL Tel: 0161-205 5711 Fax: 0161-205 5722

Labels & Data Systems (UK) Ltd, 9 Cresswell Close, Pinchbeck, Spalding, Lincolnshire, PE11 3TY Tel: 0161-929 8828 Fax: 0161-929 8518 E-mail: labelsdata@aol.com *Label & labelling machine manufacturers ribbons printer*

▶ Labels Galore, PO BOX 114, Newcastle upon Tyne, NE20 9ZQ Tel: (07739) 960871 E-mail: info@labelsgalore.co.uk *Printed labels at affordable prices! Address labels, barcode labels & numbered labels. Create your own with a wide range of clipart or even your own image/logo! Free delivery within 5 days!*

Labels 'N' Signs, 254 Rake Lane, Wallasey, Merseyside, CH45 1JR Tel: 0151-630 2337 Fax: 0151-691 2001 E-mail: sales@labelsnsigns.co.uk *Sign manufrs*

Labels Plus Ltd, Unit 3, River Side Industrial Estate, Bordercot Lane, Wickham Market, Woodbridge, Suffolk, IP13 0TA Tel: (0870) 7705161 Fax: (01728) 745385 *Self-adhesive labels*

Labels Symbology Ltd, 22 Froghall Lane, Warrington, WA2 7JR Tel: (01925) 415135 Fax: (01925) 415775 *Bar coded labels manufrs*

▶ Labels4U, Bingswood Industrial Estate, Whaley Bridge, High Peak, Derbyshire, SK23 7SP Tel: (0870) 4282283 Fax: (0870) 4282283 E-mail: sales@labels4u.co.uk *Labels manufrs*

Labelsco, 29 Moat Way, Barwell, Leicester, LE9 8EY Tel: (01455) 852400 Fax: (01455) 841444 E-mail: sales@labelsco.co.uk *Labelsco are one of the UK's largest, privately owned printers of high quality labels, sachets and laminates. Accredited with BRC/IOP, ISO9001:2000, ISO14001, and PS9000, we have a dedicated pharmaceutical division who have also developed complaint quality management systems, to ensure consistently high standards are met. We are equipped with an extensive in-house studio and colour management laboratory, supported by a team with specialist knowledge in the complexities of transferring concepts and designs to final print. Our production facility is modern and well organised, equipped to print up to 10 colours including UV and water-based flexo, rotary screen and on-line/off-line foil blocking. We also have a dedicated team running our finishing department, using high-level inspection equipment and a computer-controlled inventory.*

Lablogic Systems Ltd, Paradigm House, 3 Melbourne Avenue, Sheffield, S10 2QJ Tel: 0114-266 7267 Fax: 0114-266 3944 E-mail: solutions@lablogic.com *Scientific software & instruments*

Labman Automation Ltd, Stokesley Industrial Park, Middlesbrough, Cleveland, TS9 5JZ Tel: 0845 4941644 Fax: (01642) 710667 E-mail: mailroom@labman.co.uk *Manufacturers of assembly & industrial robot systems*

Laboratories For Applied Biology Ltd, 91 Amhurst Park, London, N16 5DR Tel: (020) 8800 2252 Fax: (020) 8809 6884 E-mail: labltd@dircon.co.uk *Pharmaceutical manufrs*

Laboratory Facilities Ltd, 24 Britwell Road, Burnham, Slough, SL1 8AG Tel: (01628) 604149 Fax: (01628) 667920 E-mail: officelabfacs@btconnect.com *Cosmetics suppliers & contract packers*

Laboratory Precision Ltd, Unit 30 Lanchester Way, Royal Oak Industrial Estate, Daventry, Northamptonshire, NN11 8PH Tel: (01327) 877774 Fax: (01327) 877444 E-mail: sales@crimpers-and-decappers.com *Crimping & decapping tool manufrs*

Laboratory Supplies & Instruments Ltd, 13b-14a Rathenraw Industrial Estate, Antrim, BT41 2SJ Tel: (028) 9446 3070 Fax: (028) 9446 8642 E-mail: info@labsuppliesltd.co.uk *Laboratory supply services*

Labour Ready Temporary Services UK Ltd, 2 Pilot Industrial Estate, Manchester Road, Bolton, BL3 2ND Tel: (01204) 525306 Fax: (01204) 525367 E-mail: sales@labouready.com *Temporary labour*

Labro Tools & Gas Supply Co., 42-42a Nunhead Lane, London, SE15 3TU Tel: (020) 7639 9739 Fax: (020) 7252 8943 *Butane gas & appliance distributors & hardware*

▶ Labrys Multimedia, 179 Meltham Road, Huddersfield, HD4 7BG Tel: (01484) 662448 E-mail: jane@labrysmm.co.uk *Web development, bespoke content management, database driven website, asp programming.*

Company Information

Labtech Ltd, Broadaxe Business Park, Presteigne, Powys, LD8 2UH Tel: (01544) 267099 Fax: (01544) 260310E-mail: ptfe@labtech.ltd.uk *Printed circuit manufrs*

Labtech International Ltd, 1 Finger Post Cottages, The Broyle, Ringmer, Lewes, East Sussex, BN8 5NN Tel: (01273) 814888 Fax: (01273) 814999 *Laboratory equipment distribution*

Labtech Modular Engineering, Blackness Road, Altens Industrial Estate, Aberdeen, AB12 3LH Tel: (01224) 337777 Fax: (01224) 337770 E-mail: sales@labtech.co.uk *Accommodation module hire & rental services, refurbishment contractors & manufrs*

▶ Labtos Ltd, Unit 3, Abbey Park Industrial Estate, Abbey Road, Barking, Essex, IG11 7BT Tel: (0870 2407269 Fax: 01268 693600 E-mail: info@labtos.co.uk *Labtos Ltd is one of the leading suppliers of good quality charcoal imported from West Africa to various destinations in Europe. Our company is well known for its quality products and satisfying the growing demands of its domestic and international customers.*We import in large quantities, minimum of 20 tons per 40ft container, which can come loose or bagged in the container depending on customers specification, our retail outlet offers charcoal from 5kg to 20kg at a very competitive prices to our local customers, we also offer free delivery on all orders from 20kg to in and around london and essex.*

Laburnum House Educational, Carlisle Street, Gainsborough, Lincolnshire, DN21 2HZ Tel: (01427) 811109 Fax: (01427) 811109 E-mail: sales@laburnumhouse.co.uk *Educational books suppliers*

Labute Colour Printers Ltd, Cambridge Printing Park, Milton, Cambridge, CB4 6AZ Tel: (01223) 420000 Fax: (01223) 420860 E-mail: info@labute.co.uk *Lithographic printers*

▶ Labyrinth Computers Ltd, Unit 3 Lufton Heights Commerce Park, Boundary Way, Lufton, Yeovil, Somerset, BA22 8UY Tel: (01935) 421299 Fax: (01935) 421887 E-mail: sales@labyrinth-computers.com *IT solution specialists*

Lace Hire Altrincham Ltd, 203 Woodhouse La East, Timperley, Altrincham, Cheshire, WA15 6AS Tel: 0161-905 1652 Fax: 0161-905 1652 E-mail: altcaterhire@tisacali.co.uk *Catering hire, hirers of china, cutlery, glassware, furniture & linen.*

Lace Mechanics Ltd, Atlas Mills, Birchwood Avenue, Long Eaton, Nottingham, NG10 3ND Tel: 0115-973 2852 Fax: 0115-946 5917 E-mail: lacemechanics@btconnect.com *General engineers & security products*

Lacegold Electrical & Mechanical Services, 1 Aerial House, School Aycliffe, Newton Aycliffe, County Durham, DL5 6QF Tel: (01325) 315316 Fax: (01325) 329940 E-mail: lacegoldems@upexgroup.co.uk *Electrical engineers, plumbing & pipework services*

Lacey's Hair & Beauty Supplies, Unit 5 The Markham Centre, Station Road, Theale, Reading, RG7 4PE Tel: 0118-930 2338 *Hair & beauty products supplier*

Laceys I O W Ltd, 42 High Street, Bembridge, Isle of Wight, PO35 5SF Tel: (01983) 872663 Fax: (01983) 872575 E-mail: sales@laceysremovals.co.uk *Removal & warehousing contractors*

Lachenmeier (UK) Ltd, Wilsons Park, Monsall Road, Newton Heath, Manchester, M40 8PA Tel: 0161-205 3666 Fax: 0161-205 3777 E-mail: kl@lachenmeier.com *Shrink, stretch & sleeve wrapping machines manufrs*

Lachlan Macgregor Feeds, 1 Cross Street, Callander, Perthshire, FK17 8EA Tel: (01877) 331218 Fax: (01877) 331414 *Agricultural feed merchants*

John Lack Equipment, 6 Denington Court, Denington Industrial Estate, Wellingborough, Northamptonshire, NN8 2QR Tel: (01933) 441646 Fax: (01933) 441476 E-mail: johnlackequipment@tiscali.co.uk Principal Export Areas: Worldwide *Converting & finishing machinery suppliers*

Lacron UK Ltd, Radfield, London Road, Teynham, Sittingbourne, Kent, ME9 9PS Tel: (01795) 521733 Fax: (01795) 522085 E-mail: info@lacron.co.uk *Water filter & pumps manufrs*

▶ Lad Construction Ltd, 16 Gorst Road, London, NW10 6LE Tel: (020) 8961 1342 Fax: (020) 8961 1649 E-mail: info@lad.co.uk

Lada Engineering Services, Vickers House, Vickers Business Centre Priestley Road, Basingstoke, Hampshire, RG24 9NP Tel: (01256) 333571 Fax: 01256 353130 E-mail: info@ladaengineering.co.uk *Lada Engineering offer CNC milling, CNC turning and precision engineering sheetmatal fabrication services including CNC laser cutting, CNC robotic welding, assembly services, bonding, welding, and metal finishing.*

Ladbrook & Langton, Hill Farm, Watling Street, Radlett, Hertfordshire, WD7 7HP Tel: (01923) 854639 Fax: (01923) 856530 E-mail: cal303@aol.com *Gun repairers*

Ladco, Sir William Smith Road, Kirkton Industrial Estate, Arbroath, Angus, DD11 3RD Tel: (01241) 434444 Fax: (01241) 434411 E-mail: enquiries@macintyre.co.uk *We manufacture for UK & overseas customers with manufacturing facilities in both Scotland & Germany , we supply machinery & components to 135 countries.*

The Ladder Man, City Ladder Works, Victoria Road, Fenton, Stoke-On-Trent, ST4 2HS Tel: 0800 197 3839 Fax: (01782) 410172 E-mail: info@theladderman.co.uk *As a family run firm of ladder manufacturers established in 1953, we are able to offer advice backed by a comprehensive product range, that is available from stock for delivery throughout the UK Mainland. Quality Products, Quality Service, Qualified Advice Gained from over 50 years experience. Being centrally located in England we ideally positioned to distribute our products throughout the UK mainland. We offer a full range of trade, industrial & domestic ladders & steps in aluminium, timber & glass fibre. In*

continued

addition we also stock complete range of professional window cleaning equipment. A delivery service is available throughout the UK Mainland. Our comprehensive range of stock is backed by friendly knowledgeable advice and a traditional level of service

Ladds Concrete Products, Wilson Way, Pool, Redruth, Cornwall, TR15 3RY Tel: (01209) 213132 Fax: (01209) 314441 E-mail: sales@laddsconcrete.co.uk *Manufacturers of precast concrete products*

Ladenall Ltd, Diesel House 5 Humber Trading Estate, Humber Road, London, NW2 6DW Tel: (020) 8452 1552 Fax: (020) 8452 8471 E-mail: enquiries@ladenall.com *Fuel injection spares distribs*

▶ Ladesigns.Co.Uk, 20 Hartfield Road, Eastbourne, East Sussex, BN21 2AR Tel: (07801) 421368 E-mail: info@ladesigns.co.uk *ladesigns.co.uk interior design from conception to completion.Services offered:A one-off thought session. Impartial advise on any project. House Doctoring Service to help you move quickly. Re-vamps of existing rooms. Sourcing Service for any product or contractor saving you time. New designs for any property or room. Oversee projects and contractors.*

Ladkin Hosiery Ltd, Seagrave Road, Sileby, Loughborough, Leicestershire, LE12 7TT Tel: (01509) 813344 Fax: (01509) 816663 *Socks manufrs*

Ladwa Engineering Ltd, Sanders Lodge Industrial Estate, Rushden, Northamptonshire, NN10 6BQ Tel: (01933) 359204 Fax: (01933) 410583 E-mail: info@ladwaengineering.co.uk *Sheet metalwork engineers*

The Lady Ltd, 39-40 Bedford Street, London, WC2E 9ER Tel: (020) 7379 4717 Fax: (020) 7497 2137 E-mail: info@thelady.co.uk *Magazine publishers*

Lady 1, 154 West Green Road, London, N15 5AE Tel: (020) 8802 3201 E-mail: sales@try1clothing.co.uk *Clothing distributors & manufrs*

▶ Lady Care, 67 Main Street, Garforth, Leeds, LS25 1AF Tel: 0113-287 1197 *Toiletries retailers*

Lady Clare Ltd, Oldends Lane Industrial Estate, Oldends, Stonehouse, Gloucestershire, GL10 3RQ Tel: (01453) 824482 Fax: (01453) 827855 E-mail: info@lady-clare.com *Lady Clare offer the finest handcrafted placemats and accessories. Their collections include tablemats, coasters, fine trays and waste bins. They are based in Stonehouse, Gloucestershire and look forward to dealing with your requests.*

▶ Lady Royd Garage, 507 Thornton Road, Bradford, West Yorkshire, BD8 9RB Tel: (01274) 545304 Fax: (01274) 498176 E-mail: fiona@ladyroyd.co.uk *Garage repairs*

Ladybank Tyres Ltd, Commercial Road, Ladybank, Cupar, Fife, KY15 7JS Tel: (01337) 830932 Fax: (01337) 831156 E-mail: ladybank.tyres@virgin.net *Tyres & exhausts suppliers*

Ladybridge Systems, 17b Coldstream Lane, Hardingstone, Northampton, NN4 6DB Tel: (01604) 709200 Fax: (01604) 709200 E-mail: sales@ladybridge.com *Development & servicing of software*

▶ Ladymead Joinery Ltd, Denham, Quainton, Aylesbury, Buckinghamshire, HP22 4AN Tel: (01296) 655770 Fax: (01296) 655377 E-mail: info@ladymeadjoinery.co.uk *Joinery work*

Laerdal Medical Ltd, Laerdal House, Goodmead Road, Orpington, Kent, BR6 0HX Tel: (01689) 876634 Fax: (01689) 873800 E-mail: customer.service@laerdal.co.uk *Resuscitation equipment & training aid manufrs*

Lafarge Aggregates Ltd, Marsh Lane, Easton-in-Gordano, Bristol, BS20 0NF Tel: (0800) 373636 Fax: (01275) 377700 *Plasterboard manufrs*

Lafarge Aggregates Ltd, Riverside House, Upper Quay, Fareham, Hampshire, PO16 0LY Tel: (01329) 235717 Fax: (01329) 822697 *Aggregate suppliers*

Lafarge Aggregates Ltd, Knowsthorpe Gate, Leeds, LS9 0NP Tel: 0113-240 0034 *Concrete & aggregate suppliers*

Lafarge Aggregates Ltd, Whisby Quarry, Thorpe Road, Whisby, Lincoln, LN6 9BT Tel: (01522) 694342 Fax: (01522) 694226 *Sand & gravel suppliers*

Lafarge Aluminates Ltd, Dolphin Way, Purfleet, Essex, RM19 1NZ Tel: (01708) 863333 Fax: (01708) 861033 *Concrete aggregate merchants & cement manufrs*

Lafarge Cement Ltd, Manor Court, Chilton, Didcot, Oxfordshire, OX11 0RN Tel: (01235) 448400 Fax: (01235) 448600 *Holding company*

Lafarge Cement Ltd, New Edinburgh Road, Uddingston, Glasgow, G71 6NE Tel: (01698) 812261 Fax: (01698) 814980 *Cement distribution*

Lafarge Cement UK, At Watling Street, Bean, Dartford, DA2 8AH Tel: (01474) 833551 Fax: (01474) 834325 *Cement manufrs*

Lafarge Readymix Ltd, Barrington Road Industrial Estat, Bedlington, Northumberland, NE22 7AL Tel: (01670) 823336 Fax: (01670) 823336 *Ready mixed concrete suppliers*

Lafarge Readymix Ltd, Dobs Wier Pit, Nazeing New Road, Broxbourne, Hertfordshire, EN10 6TD Tel: (01992) 465865 *Ready mixed concrete distributor & manufr*

Lafarge Readymix Ltd, Sandall Stones Road, Kirk Sandall Industrial Estate, Doncaster, South Yorkshire, DN3 1QR Tel: (01302) 883941 *Ready mixed concrete manufrs*

Lafarge Readymix Ltd, Jeffreys Road, Enfield, Middlesex, EN3 7XD Tel: (020) 8805 8150 *Ready mixed concrete manufrs*

Lafarge Readymix Ltd, Harper Lane, Radlett, Hertfordshire, WD7 7HX Tel: (01923) 852302 *Concrete & mortar ready mixed*

Lafarge Readymix Ltd, Cheltenham Road, Stockton-on-Tees, Cleveland, TS18 2SA Tel: (01642) 673335 Fax: (01642) 679507 *Concrete & mortar ready mixed suppliers*

Lafarge Readymix Ltd, Pocklington Industrial Estate, Pocklington, York, YO42 1NP Tel: (01759) 305767 *Concrete suppliers*

Lafarge Redland Aggregates Ltd, The Business Centre, Watermead Business Park, Syston, Leicester, LE7 1WA Tel: (01509) 882088 Fax: (01707) 356141 *Concrete & mortar ready mixed*

Lafarge Roofing Technical Centers Ltd, Sussex Manor Business Park, Gatwick Road, Crawley, West Sussex, RH10 9NZ Tel: (01293) 618418 Fax: (01293) 614548 *Mechanical engineers & roofings specialists*

Lafford Buildbase, Arrowhead Road, Theale, Reading, RG7 4AH Tel: 0118-932 3700 Fax: 0118-932 3202 E-mail: theale@buildbase.co.uk *Buildbase is one of the UK's fastest growing builders merchants. All of our branches are long established companies which have been serving local trades people for many years, with knowledge and experience to match. We believe strongly in understanding the needs of trades professional and our business has been developed specifically to meet those demands. Massive stocks, top quality products, competitive pricing, reliable delivery, specialist staff and exceptional customer service.*

Lafford & Leavey, Arrowhead Road, Reading, RG7 4XB Tel: 0118-930 3333 Fax: 0118-932 3707 E-mail: sales@1afford.com *Window & conservatory installers* Also at: Banbury

Lafford & Moore, Power House, Powerscroft Road, Sidcup, Kent, DA14 5EA Tel: (020) 8309 4224 Fax: (020) 8309 4222 E-mail: sales@laffordandmoore.co.uk *Timber importers*

Lagan Cement Co., Mccaughey Road, Belfast, BT3 9AG Tel: (028) 9074 3293 Fax: (028) 9074 9340 *Cement suppliers*

Lagan Construction Ltd, Rosemount House, 21-23 Sydenham Road, Belfast, BT3 9HA Tel: (028) 9045 5531 Fax: (028) 9045 8940 E-mail: charles.brand@lagan-group.com *Civil engineers*

Laganside Computer Consultants Ltd, Studio A, Hollywood Road, Belfast, BT4 3D Tel: (028) 9065 3006 Fax: (028) 9065 3005 *Software suppliers*

Lagenes UK Ltd, 8 Anglers Lane, London, NW5 3DG Tel: (020) 7485 3778 Fax: (020) 7284 1251 *Ladies dresses & separates manufrs*

▶ Lager, Holywell House, Parsons Lane, Hinckley, Leicestershire, LE10 1XT Tel: (01455) 238725

Lagerstedt & Krantz (UK) Ltd, Unit 3, Metana House, Priestley Way, Crawley, West Sussex, RH10 9NT Tel: (0870) 2424873 Fax: (0870) 2424874 E-mail: info@lagerstedt-krantz.co.uk *Manufactures of warm water under floor heating*

▶ Lagoonal.com, Princes House, Wright Street, Hull, HU2 8HX Tel: 07815 865051 E-mail: info@lagoonal.com *The new way to source and compare promotional items on one page from multiple suppliers. FastQuotes allows you to request a quote from multiple companies, it is quick and free.*

Lagrove Ltd, 51-53 The Green, Southall, Middlesex, UB2 4AR Tel: (020) 8574 4656 Fax: (020) 8843 0605 E-mail: lagrove@cs.com *Insurance brokers*

▶ Lagta Group Training Ltd, 3 Dryden Place, Loanhead, Midlothian, EH20 9HP Tel: 0131-440 2922 Fax: 0131-440 3933 E-mail: sales@lagta.co.uk

Lahoma Engineers Ltd, Manning Road Industrial Estate, Bourne, Lincolnshire, PE10 9HW Tel: (01778) 423942 Fax: (01778) 393136 E-mail: production@lahomaengineers.co.uk *Precision engineers & subcontract engineering services*

Laidlaw Architectural Hardware, 7 Dakota Avenue, Salford, M50 2PU Tel: 0161-848 1700 Fax: 0161-872 9313 E-mail: info@laidlaw.net *Architectural wholesale ironmongers* Also at: Salford

▶ Laidlaw Scott Ltd, 46 Queen Elizabeth Avenue, Hillington Industrial Estate, Glasgow, G52 4NQ Tel: 0141-848 6262 Fax: 0141-889 7800

Laidlaw Solutions Ltd, 4-5 Bonville Road, Bristol, BS4 5NF Tel: 0117-316 0460 Fax: 0117-316 0491 E-mail: gateshead@laidlaw.net *Architectural hardware* Also at: Cheadle

Laidlaw Solutions Ltd, T Y Cefnfar, Ocean Way, Cardiff, CF24 5PE Tel: (029) 2047 1808 Fax: (029) 2049 0250 *Architectural ironmongers*

Laidlaw Solutions Ltd, PO Box 15, Perth, PH1 3DU Tel: (01738) 620581 Fax: (01738) 633262 *Architectural ironmongers* Also at: Dundee & Glasgow

Laidler Products, 35 Fairfield Rise, Stourbridge, West Midlands, DY8 3PQ Tel: (01384) 442815 Fax: (01384) 441065 E-mail: mail@laidlerproducts.co.uk *Self cleaning spray nozzle manufrs*

Laidler Steels Ltd, Stallings Lane, Kingswinford, West Midlands, DY6 7LE Tel: (01384) 400442 Fax: (01384) 294295 *Steel stockholders*

▶ Laidrite Construction Ltd, Unit 4 Fynney Fields, Basford Lane Industrial Estate, Leek, Staffordshire, ST13 7QG Tel: (01538) 373648 Fax: (01538) 386210

Laig Engineering Ltd, 1 Bunting Road, Bury St. Edmunds, Suffolk, IP32 7BX Tel: (01284) 763852 Fax: (01284) 706866 E-mail: info@laig.uk.com *CNC machining services*

Lailey Ltd, 25 Harewood Avenue, Bournemouth, BH7 6NJ Tel: (01202) 388840 Fax: (01202) 417748 E-mail: martinking@layley.co.uk *Computer consultants*

Laindon Metals, Roberts Works, Wrexham Road, Laindon, Basildon, Essex, SS15 6PX Tel: (01268) 543741 Fax: (01268) 491766 *Scrap merchants*

▶ D Laing & Co. Ltd, Douglas House, 18 Lynedoch Crescent, Glasgow, G3 6EQ Tel: 0141-333 9242 *Spirits*

▶ Laing Homes North Thames, Premiere House, Elstree Way, Borehamwood, Hertfordshire, WD6 1JH Tel: (020) 8236 3700 Fax: (020) 8236 3801

John Laing P.L.C., Allington House, 150 Victoria Street, London, SW1E 5LB Tel: (020) 7901 3200 Fax: (020) 7901 3520 E-mail: enquiries@equion.ltd.uk *Investment company*

▶ Laing O'Rourke Northern, Curtin House 6 Columbus Quay, Riverside Drive, Liverpool, L3 4DB Tel: 0151-726 2420 Fax: 0151-727 6748

Lainiere De Picardie UK Ltd, 5 Danbury Court, Sunrise Parkway, Linford Wood, Milton Keynes, MK14 6PL Tel: (0870) 1213160 Fax: (0870) 1213161E-mail: lpuk@chargeurs-interlining.com *Interlining to clothing industry warehousing*

▶ Laird Bros Forfar Ltd, Old Brechin Road, Lunanhead, Forfar, Angus, DD8 3NQ Tel: (01307) 466577 Fax: (01307) 468642

Laird Group Ltd, 3 St. James's Square, London, SW1Y 4JU Tel: (020) 7468 4040 Fax: (020) 7839 2921 E-mail: info@laird-plc.co.uk *Holding company*

▶ Laird Security, 18 Burnbank Road, Falkirk, FK2 7PE Tel: (01324) 633889 Fax: (01324) 633767 E-mail: sales@lairdsecurity.co.uk *Hardware for the fenestration industry*

Laird Security Hardware, Bloomfield Park, Bloomfield Road, Tipton, West Midlands, DY4 9AP Tel: 0121-224 6131 Fax: 0121-520 1039 E-mail: sales@saracen-secure.co.uk *Hardware for the fenestration industry*

▶ T. Laird Plumbers & Electrical Contractors, Unit 1, Woodilee Industrial Estate, Kirkintilloch, Glasgow, G66 3TY Tel: 0141-776 2843

▶ Lairdside Laser Engineering Centre, Campbeltown Road, Birkenhead, Merseyside, CH41 9HP Tel: 0151-650 2305 Fax: 0151-650 2304 E-mail: info@llec.co.uk *Laser engineering services*

▶ Laishley Ltd, B300 The Grange, Michelmersh, Romsey, Hampshire, SO51 0AE Tel: (01794) 368283 Fax: (01794) 367543

Lait Storage & Distribution Ltd, Northern Road, Chilton Industrial Estate, Sudbury, Suffolk, CO10 2ZB Tel: (01787) 376493 Fax: (01787) 312707 E-mail: admin@lait-storage.co.uk *Storage & distribution contractors*

Lake Financial Systems, Stable Mews Beechwoods Estate, Elmete Lane, Leeds, LS8 2LQ Tel: 0113-273 7788 Fax: 0113-273 9300 E-mail: info@lake.co.uk *Software solution providers*

Lake, Muckley & Co. Ltd, The Stable, Lillyfee Farm, Lillyfee Farm Lane, Wooburn Green, High Wycombe, Buckinghamshire, HP10 0LL Tel: (01494) 673632 Fax: (01494) 673632 *Architectural metalworkers & ornamental ironwork*

Lake & Nicholls Engineering, 4 Cornish Way, North Walsham, Norfolk, NR28 0AW Tel: (01692) 404602 Fax: (01692) 406723 E-mail: enquiries@lakeandnicholls.co.uk *Welding & general engineers*

▶ Lakefield Trading, Flat 6 Bearstead House, Abbey Park, Beckenham, Kent, BR3 1PP Tel: (020) 8650 2341 Fax: (0870) 8912953 *Grain suppliers*

▶ Lakehaven Ltd, 179 Milton Park, Abingdon, Oxfordshire, OX14 4SD Tel: (01235) 832281 E-mail: sales@lakehaven-removals.co.uk

▶ Lakehaven, Unit K2, Eagle Road, Langage Business Park, Plymouth, PL7 5JY Tel: (01752) 231881 Fax: (01752) 231882

▶ Lakehouse Contracts Ltd, 1 King George Close, Romford, RM7 7LS Tel: (01708) 758800 Fax: (01708) 758888 E-mail: info@lakehouse.uk.com *Building contractors, roofing & concrete repairs*

Lakeland Agri Care, Agri House, Main Street, Lisnaskea, Enniskillen, County Fermanagh, BT92 0JG Tel: (028) 6772 2377 Fax: (028) 6772 3655 *Agricultural farmers*

Lakeland Carbons Ltd, Flusco, Penrith, Cumbria, CA11 0JB Tel: (01768) 483726 Fax: (01768) 483610 E-mail: info@lakelandcarbons.co.uk *Blast cleaning abrasives*

Lakeland Concrete Products Ltd, Flusco House, Flusco, Penrith, Cumbria, CA11 0JB Tel: (01768) 483617 Fax: (01768) 483890 E-mail: info@lakelandconcrete.co.uk *Blocks & block paving manufrs*

▶ Lakeland for Fundraising & Bingo Supplies, Suite 16 Regent House, Skinner Lane, Leeds, LS7 1AX Tel: (0870) 1283166 Fax: (0870) 1283177 E-mail: sales@lakelandfundraising.co.uk *Fundraising & bingo supplies, information, advice & suggestions*

Lakeland Investments Ltd, Estate Office, Lowtheriu Trust, Penrith, Cumbria, CA10 2HG Tel: (01931) 712577 Fax: (01931) 712679 E-mail: john.r@lowther.co.uk *Holding company*

▶ Lakeland Leisure, The Old Brewery, Shore Street, Barrow-in-Furness, Cumbria, LA14 2UB Tel: (01229) 870770 Fax: (01229) 434140 *Amusement machine & pool table manufrs*

Lakeland Mouldings, Soulby, Penrith, Cumbria, CA11 0JE Tel: (01768) 486989 Fax: (01768) 486989 E-mail: ann@lakelandmouldings.co.uk *Mould & resin casters manufrs*

Lakeland Skirts, Unit 1b Boundary Bank, Kendal, Cumbria, LA9 5RR Tel: (01539) 725341 Fax: (01539) 741403 *Skirt manufrs*

Lakeland Spring Soft Drinks Ltd, Red Lonning Industrial Estate, Whitehaven, Cumbria, CA28 6SJ Tel: (01946) 690777 Fax: (01946) 690888 E-mail: lakelandspring@aol.com *Soft drink & spring water manufrs*

Lakeland Windows, Holme Mills Industrial Estate, Holme, Carnforth, Lancashire, LA6 1RD Tel: (01524) 781800 Fax: (01524) 781800 *UPVC window manufrs & installers*

Lakes Buildbase, Parcel Terrace, Derby, DE1 1LQ Tel: (01332) 349083 Fax: (01332) 290178 E-mail: derbybuilding@buildbase.co.uk *Buildbase is one of the UK's fastest growing builders merchants. All of our branches are long established companies which have been serving local trades people for many years, with knowledge and experience to match. We believe strongly in understanding the needs of trades professional and our business has been developed specifically to meet those demands. Massive stocks, top quality products, competitive pricing, reliable delivery, specialist staff and exceptional customer service.*

Lakes Consultants Ltd, Flecket House, Helton, Penrith, Cumbria, CA10 2QA Tel: (01931) 712232 Fax: (01931) 712336 *Network specialists*

Lakes & Greens Ltd, Ketches Lane, Sheffield Park, Uckfield, East Sussex, TN22 3RY Tel: (01825) 790483 Fax: (01825) 790271 *Golf Course Irrigation contractors*

Lakeside Leisure Park, Trunch Lane, Chapel St. Leonards, Skegness, Lincolnshire, PE24 5TU Tel: (01754) 872631 Fax: (01754) 872631 *Leisure complex including fishing, camping & boats*

Lakeside Security Shutters, Bruce Road, Fforestfach, Swansea, SA5 4HS Tel: (01792) 561117 Fax: (01792) 587046 E-mail: sails@lakesidesecurity.co.uk *Up & over garage door manufacturers,*

▶ Lakeside Water & Building Services, Unit 2 St. Marys Road Industrial Estate, Ramsey, Huntingdon, Cambridgeshire, PE26 2SW Tel: (01487) 815914 Fax: (01487) 815070 E-mail: elaine@lakesidewater.co.uk *Water treatment plant & equipment servicing & manufrs*

Lakeway Filtration Ltd, 7 North Street, North Tawton, Devon, EX20 2DE Tel: (01837) 82777 Fax: (01837) 82777 *Water purification equipment manufrs*

Lakey & Co., Saxon House, Crown Road, Old Buckenham, Attleborough, Norfolk, NR17 1SD Tel: (01953) 861180 Fax: (01953) 861060 *Business transfer agents*

▶ Lakey & Co Yorkshire, Barugh Close, Melmerby, Ripon, North Yorkshire, HG4 5NB Tel: 01765 640064 E-mail: sales@lakey-yorkshire.co.uk *Business Transfer Agents*

▶ Lakin Accounting Services Ltd, Manor Lodge, Teeton, Northampton, NN6 8LH Tel: (01604) 505563 Fax: 01604 505563 E-mail: louise@lakinltd.go-plus.net *Accounting and taxation service for individuals and small business. *Services include tax returns, management and statutory accounts, VAT, payroll, business planning and bookkeeping*

Lak-Ler (Builders) Ltd, Aintree Close, Red Lane Industrial Estate, Coventry, CV6 5QB Tel: (024) 7668 1907 Fax: (024) 7663 8678 *Building contractors*

Lakshmi Collison Care, 290a Ampthill Road, Bedford, MK42 9QL Tel: (01234) 261930 Fax: (01234) 353372 *Car repair service agents*

Lal & Co. (Glasgow), Laltex House, 12-18 Coburg Street, Glasgow, G5 9JF Tel: 0141-429 0935 Fax: 0141-429 8036 *General wholesalers & importers*

Lalcrest Ltd, Woods Lane, Flintham, Newark, Nottinghamshire, NG23 5LR Tel: (01636) 525584 E-mail: enquiries@lalcrest.co.uk *Software measurement specialists*

Laleham Healthcare Ltd, Sycamore Park, Mill Lane, Alton, Hampshire, GU34 2PR Tel: (01420) 566500 Fax: (01420) 566566 Purchasing Contact: D. Liddle Sales Contact: B.W. Sills *Filling (contract) services, packaging services/ contract packaging, pharmaceutical manufacturers/contract manufacturing & toiletries manufrs*

Laleham Products, Unit H Heath Place, Bognor Regis, West Sussex, PO22 9SL Tel: (01243) 826270 Fax: (01243) 829325 E-mail: sales@lalehamproducts.com *PVC welded product manufrs*

Lall Engineering Ltd, 343 Bedworth Road, Longford, Coventry, CV6 6BN Tel: (024) 7636 4904 Fax: (024) 7636 2083 *Sheet metal fabricators*

Lalpac, 8 The Causeway, Chippenham, Wiltshire, SN15 3BT Tel: (01249) 660088 Fax: (01249) 660099 *Computer consultants*

Laltex & Co. Ltd, Leigh Commerce Park, Green Fold Way, Leigh, Lancashire, WN7 3XH Tel: (01942) 687000 Fax: (01942) 687070 E-mail: mail@laltex.com Principal Export Areas: Worldwide *Importers & exporters*

LAM Electronics Ltd, Unit 6/A, Mercury House, Calleva Park, Aldermaston, Reading, RG7 8PN Tel: 0118-981 1717 Fax: 0118-981 7475 E-mail: almelecinfo@almelec.co.uk *Electronics manufrs*

Lam Plas Durham Ltd, Pont Factory, Pont Lane, Leadgate, Consett, County Durham, DH8 6LA Tel: (01207) 502474 Fax: (01207) 500407 E-mail: jimdeath@lamplas.co.uk *Comprehensive glass fibre mouldings manufrs*

Lama Petroleum Ltd, 14 Ensign House, Admirals Way, London, E14 9YR Tel: (020) 7538 2603 Fax: (020) 7515 9780 E-mail: info@ammora.com *Aluminium extrusions, petroleum oil suppliers*

Lam-art Dundee Ltd, 122 Liff Road, Dundee, DD2 2TL Tel: (01382) 612222 Fax: (01382) 612233 E-mail: lamartdundee@btopenworld.com *Laminate fabricators*

Lamb Commercials Ltd, 126 Tamnamore Road, Dungannon, County Tyrone, BT71 6HW Tel: (028) 8772 2111 Fax: (028) 8773 7393 E-mail: lambsales@erf.com *Bulk container manufacturers & vehicle dealership*

John Lamb Media Ltd, 2 Dairy Cottages, Wolterton, Norwich, NR11 7LX Tel: (01263) 768572 *Publishers of IT materials*

Lamb Macintosh Ltd, The Ten Building, 10 Wellcroft Road, Slough, SL1 4AQ Tel: (01753) 522369 Fax: (01753) 517216 E-mail: sales@lambmacintosh.com *Wooden & laminate office furniture manufrs*

Lamb Signs, 62 West Harbour Road, Edinburgh, EH5 1PW Tel: 0131-552 3900 Fax: 0131-552 1093 *Sign manufrs*

W.T. Lamb & Sons Ltd, Nyewood Court, Brookers Road, Billingshurst, West Sussex, RH14 9RZ Tel: (01403) 785141 Fax: (01403) 784663 E-mail: sales@lambsbricks.com *Brick merchants & manufrs*

W.T Lamb & Sons Ltd, Pitsham Brickyard, Midhurst, West Sussex, GU29 9QJ Tel: (01403) 785141 Fax: (01730) 816836 *Brick manufrs*

Lamba Welding Systems, 31 Racecourse Road, Gallowfields Trading Estate, Richmond, North Yorkshire, DL10 4SU Tel: (01748) 850292 Fax: (01748) 850343 *Welding, bronzing & wire machines manufrs*

Lambda Calibration Ltd, Chorley Business & Technology Centre, Euxton Lane, Euxton, Chorley, Lancashire, PR7 6TE Tel: (01257) 246020 Fax: (01257) 246023 E-mail: mail@lambda-cal.co.uk *Calibration*

continued

Laboratory, UKAS accredited to ISO/IEC 17025, operating in the fields of: Dimensional, Electrical, Force, Mass, Pressure, Temperature & Torque.

Lambda Photometrics Ltd, Lambda House, Batford Mill, Lower Luton Road, Harpenden, Hertfordshire, AL5 5BZ Tel: (01582) 764334 Fax: (01582) 712084 E-mail: info@lambdaphoto.co.uk *Laser for science industry medicine distributors*

Lambda UK, Kingsley Avenue, Ilfracombe, Devon, EX34 8ES Tel: (01271) 856600 Fax: (01271) 864894 E-mail: powersolutions@lambda-europe.com Principal Export Areas: Worldwide *Power supply converters*

Lamberhurst Engineering Ltd, Priory Farm, Parsonage Lane, Lamberhurst, Tunbridge Wells, Kent, TN3 8DS Tel: (0845) 6121141 Fax: (0845) 6121142 E-mail: info@lameng.com *Agricultural engineers*

Lambert & Blaber Ltd, 25 Kings Road, Haslemere, Surrey, GU27 2QA Tel: (01428) 658534 Fax: (01428) 658341 E-mail: sales@lambertblaber.co.uk *Distributors of catering equipment & sundries*

Lambert Brothers Holdings Ltd, Woodside Avenue, Boyatt Wood Industrial Estate, Eastleigh, Hampshire, SO50 4ZR Tel: (023) 8061 7331 Fax: (023) 8062 9261 E-mail: info@lambro.co.uk *Road haulage & warehousing*

Lambert Contracts & Coatings Ltd, Hamilton House, Blackhall Lane, Paisley, Renfrewshire, PA1 1TA Tel: 0141-840 1444 Fax: 0141-848 9593 E-mail: sales@lambertcontracts.co.uk *Building maintenance contractors*

Derek Lambert (Polythene) Ltd, Keighley Road, Bingley, West Yorkshire, BD16 2RD Tel: (01274) 560423 Fax: (01274) 561833 E-mail: sales@dereklambert.co.uk *Manufacturers of pallet cover & polythene bags*

Lambert Engineering Ltd, Station Estate, Tadcaster, North Yorkshire, LS24 9SG Tel: (01937) 832921 Fax: (01937) 835604 E-mail: le@lamberteng.com *Special purpose machinery manufrs*

Lambert Howarth Group P.L.C., Healeywood Road, Burnley, Lancashire, BB11 2HL Tel: (01282) 471200 Fax: (01282) 471279 *Shoe distributors*

Lambert Machine Tool Co. Ltd, Luton Street, Keighley, West Yorkshire, BD21 2LE Tel: (01535) 611996 Fax: (01535) 610771 E-mail: ray@lambertmt.co.uk *Lambert Machine Tool Company Limited was formed in 1992 to specialise in grinding machine re-precisioning, rebuilding and as required re-engineering to update to CNC controls. We also have a wide range of new and used grinding machines. The application of machines completed is varied and range from the production of crankshafts for Formula One racing engines to Aircraft Engine/ Landing Gear Overhaul & Repair, Aerospace bearings to Carbide dies for the Canning Industry.*

Lambert Metals International Ltd, Laburnum House, 1 Spring Villa Road, Edgware, Middlesex, HA8 7EB Tel: (020) 8951 4844 Fax: (020) 8951 1151 E-mail: howardmasters@lambert-metals.co.uk *Minor metal traders*

R.W. Lambert, 1 Woodlands Terrace, Threshfield, Skipton, North Yorkshire, BD23 5EU Tel: 01756 752208 *Agricultural engineers*

Lambert Roper & Horsefield, The Old Woolcombers Mill, 12-14 Union St South, Halifax, West Yorkshire, HX1 2LE Tel: (01422) 360788 Fax: (01422) 380201 E-mail: mail@lrh.co.uk *Chartered accountants* Also at: Truro & Wakefield

Lambert Smith Hampton, 79 Mosley Street, Manchester, M2 3LQ Tel: 0161-228 6411 Fax: 0161-228 7354 E-mail: manchester@lsh.co.uk *Property investment agents*

Lambert Smith Hampton Group Ltd, Regent Arcade House, 19-25 Argyle Street, London, W1F 7TS Tel: (020) 7494 4000 Fax: (020) 7414 0866 E-mail: westend@lsh.co.uk *Property investment agents* Also at: Manchester

Lambert Timber, Stanworth Road, Nelson, Lancashire, BB9 7DS Tel: (01282) 613333 Fax: (01282) 613933 *Timber merchants & importers*

Lamberton Ltd, Block G, West Way, Porterfield Road, Renfrew, PA4 8DJ Tel: 0141-889 1660 Fax: 0141-887 4829 *Mechanical engineers*

Lamberts.Co.Uk Industrial Distributor, Whiffler Road, Norwich, NR3 2AY Tel: (01603) 422100 Fax: (01603) 422130 E-mail: nr.sales@lamberts.co.uk *Suppliers of pipe, valves fittings, work wear, tools, fasteners, lubricants*

Lambeth Commutators, Brassmill Lane Trading Estate, Bath, BA1 3JF Tel: (01225) 426250 Fax: (01225) 445372 E-mail: david.fearn@wyco.co.uk Principal Export Areas: Worldwide *Electric commentator & slip ring manufrs*

Lambie Gilchrist Consultancy, Wamphray Mill, Wamphray, Moffat, Dumfriesshire, DG10 9NP Tel: (01576) 470880 Fax: (01576) 470881 *Tourism training*

Lamboard Ltd, 228 Leads Road, Hull, HU7 0DQ Tel: (01482) 701143 Fax: (01482) 712332 *Panel product laminators*

L.W. Lambourn & Co. Ltd, 27 Citypoint, 1 Ropemakers Street, London, EC2Y 9ST Tel: (020) 7775 3600 Fax: (020) 7775 3829 E-mail: info@stemcor.com *Brokers in steel*

Lambourn Valley Projects Ltd, 13 Prospect Road, Hungerford, Berkshire, RG17 0JL Tel: (01488) 680680 Fax: (01488) 681258 E-mail: sales@dock-levellers.co.uk *Loading bay equipment & systems*

Lambourne Clothing International, 18 Dunlop Road, Hadleigh Road Industrial Estate, Hadleigh Road, Ipswich, IP2 0UG Tel: (01473) 250404 Fax: (01473) 222282 E-mail: lambourneint3@aol.com *Country clothing manufrs*

Lambourne's Ltd, White Post Hill, Farningham, Dartford, DA4 0LB Tel: (08700) 362436 Fax: (01322) 865491 E-mail: sales@lambournes.co.uk *24 hour tail lift commercial vehicle repair services*

Lamb's Signs, Unit B3 Sapphire Way, Rhombus Business Park, Norwich, NR6 6NN Tel: (01603) 410400 Fax: (01603) 410700 E-mail: lambsigns@talk21.com *Sign contractors*

Lambson Ltd, Avenue D, 603 Thorp Arch Estate, Wetherby, Leeds, LS23 7FS Tel: (01937) 840150 Fax: (01937) 840171 E-mail: sales@lambson.com *Fine chemicals manufrs*

▶ Lambton Tailoring, Unit 25g Springfield Commercial Centre, Bagley Lane, Farsley, Pudsey, West Yorkshire, LS28 5LY Tel: 0113-257 0841 Fax: 0113-239 4472 *Suit manufrs*

Lamby Engineering Ltd, East Moors Road, Cardiff, CF24 5EE Tel: (029) 2049 7716 Fax: (029) 2049 7701 *Structural engineers*

Lamco Design, 35A Cardigan Road, Bournemouth, BH9 1BD Tel: (01202) 530724 Fax: (01202) 530724 *Furniture manufrs*

Lamda Polytech Ltd, 1 Lincoln Park, Borough Road, Buckingham Road Industrial Est, Brackley, Northamptonshire, NN13 7BE Tel: (01280) 705500 Fax: 01280 706868 E-mail: sales@lamdapolytech.co.uk *Contact lens material manufrs*

▶ Lameduck Enterprises, 27 Duxford Close, Redditch, Worcestershire, B97 5BY Tel: (01527) 542269 Fax: (01527) 540299 E-mail: lameduck@hotmail.com *Manufacturer of parts & accessories, for the motorcycle trade*

▶ Lamerholm Electronics Ltd, Pixmore Centre, Pixmore Avenue, Letchworth Garden City, Hertfordshire, SG6 1JG Tel: (01462) 481396 Fax: (01462) 473942 E-mail: web@lamerholm.com *ShockLog shock recorders and ShockWatch indicator labels from Lamerholm Electronics Ltd. Innovative development solutions to your sensor based problems, talk to the sensor experts at Lamerholm Electronics.*

Lamez Ltd, 56C Minerva Road, London, NW10 6HJ Tel: (020) 8357 1300 Fax: (020) 8357 1600 E-mail: lamezltd@aol.com *Iron on patches suppliers*

▶ Lamin 8 Ltd, Unit 71 Clywedog Road East, Wrexham Industrial Estate, Wrexham, Clwyd, LL13 9XE Tel: (01978) 660400 Fax: (01978) 660401

Lamina Dielectrics Ltd, Daux Road, Billingshurst, West Sussex, RH14 9SJ Tel: (01403) 783131 Fax: (01403) 782237 E-mail: sales@lamina.uk.com *Insulating material manufrs*

Lamina Keyboards Ltd, 32 Southridge Rise, Crowborough, East Sussex, TN6 1LG Tel: (01892) 664633 Fax: (01892) 603928 E-mail: sales@lamina-keyboards.com *Membrane keyboard manufrs*

▶ Laminated Supplies Ltd, Valletta House, Valletta Street, Hedon Road, Hull, HU9 5NP Tel: (01482) 781111 Fax: (01482) 701185 E-mail: sales@laminatedsupplies.com Principal Export Areas: Worldwide *Insulated core laminated sandwich & wall cladding insulated composite panel manufrs*

Laminating East Midlands, 26 Low Farm Place, Moulton Park Industrial Estate, Northampton, NN3 6HY Tel: (01604) 642823 Fax: (01604) 790423 E-mail: postmaster@eml.uk.com *Film laminating services & specialised print finishing*

▶ The Laminator Flooring Company Ltd, 53 Warwick Road, Cliftonville, Margate, Kent, CT9 2JU Tel: 0800 1955196 E-mail: a1jonathanweston@hotmail.com *Supplier and fitter of quality laminate and hardwood floorinf, offering services in and around kent, canterbury, hernbay, ramsgate, margate, thanet*

▶ James Lammond Ltd, 32 Market Street, Brechin, Angus, DD9 6BB Tel: (01356) 622072 Fax: (01356) 622350 E-mail: sales@jameslammondltd.com

Lamond & Murray Ltd, Burnside, Inverkeithing, Fife, KY11 1HT Tel: (01383) 413541 Fax: (01383) 414548 E-mail: gears@lamondandmurray.co.uk *Gear wheel & gearing manufrs*

Lamonde Automation Ltd, Project House, Morris Road, South Nutfield, Redhill, RH1 5SA Tel: (01737) 824600 Fax: (01737) 821431 E-mail: sales@lamonde.com *Manufacturers & suppliers of programmable control systems*

▶ Lamp Post, 101 High Street, Hythe, Kent, CT21 5JH Tel: (01303) 265982 Fax: 0871 221517 E-mail: pets@lamp-post.co.uk *Lamp-Post Pet Supplies was established in 1989 and is a UK based family pet shop offering secure online shopping for all your pet requirements.*

▶ Lampard & Partners, Little London, Albury, Guildford, Surrey, GU5 9DG Tel: (01483) 203741 Fax: (01483) 203445 E-mail: info@lampardandpartners.co.uk

Lampion & Co. Ltd, Unit 36 Hortonwood 33, Telford, Shropshire, TF1 7EX Tel: (01952) 608600 Fax: (01952) 608700 E-mail: sales@lampion.co.uk *Auto lamp bulb importers & distributors*

▶ Lamplan Industries Ltd, Unit 5, Pettings Court Farm, Hodsoll Street, Sevenoaks, Kent, TN15 7LH Tel: (01732) 824829 Fax: (01732) 824828 E-mail: jbroad@lamsplan.com *Diamond polishing service*

▶ Lamp-Light, 49 Catley Road, Sheffield, S9 5JF Tel: (01142) 430406 Fax: (01142) 430602 E-mail: sales@lamp-light.co.uk *Indoor & outdoor lighting suppliers*

▶ Lamps & Candles Ltd, 42 Manasty Road, Orton Southgate, Peterborough, PE2 6UP Tel: (01733) 237720 Fax: (01733) 237725 E-mail: info@lampsandcandles.co.uk *Lighting manufrs*

Lamps & Lighting, Bridgewater Court, Network 65 Business Park, Hapton, Burnley, Lancashire, BB11 5ST Tel: (01282) 448666 Fax: (01282) 417705 E-mail: sales@lamps-lighting.co.uk *Lighting*

Lamps & Tubes Illuminations Ltd, Unit 1, Springfield Road Industrial Estate, Chesham, Buckinghamshire, HP5 1PW Tel: (01494) 783541 Fax: (01494) 773972

continued

E-mail: enquires@ltilluminations.co.uk *Specialist lighting suppliers*

Lampshade Designs Ltd, 11-12 Sapcote Trading Centre, High Road, London, NW10 2DH Tel: (020) 8459 0367 Fax: (020) 8451 7907 E-mail: jt@lampshadedesigns.co.uk *Lampshade manufrs*

▶ Lampshades UK, Park Road, Rhosymedre, Wrexham, LL14 3YP Tel: (01691) 774409 E-mail: sales@lampshades.uk.com *Visit our online lighting shop where you can browse through an ever changing selection of exquisite lampshades in sumptious silks, rich brocades and other exciting fabrics, all lavishly trimmed with elegant fringing and tassels or exclusive Italian beading. The lampshades can be ordered from the display or e-mail us with your specific requirements. If you treasure your old lampshade we will do our utmost to recover it for you in your chosen fabric and trimming or you may prefer to supply your own fabric.*

▶ Lamri, The Aske Stables, Aske, Richmond, North Yorkshire, DL10 5HG Tel: (01748) 821824 E-mail: marketing@lamri.com *Computer systems consultants*

▶ Lamtha2 Telecom, Fairford Leys Way, Aylesbury, Buckinghamshire, HP19 7FQ Tel: (0871) 9190134 *UK non-geographic numbers - 0800 Freephone, 0845 Local, 0870, 0871, 09xx and fax2email. Advanced services include create your own switchboard,voicemail, divert to mobile or international and online realtime control panel.*

▶ Lamtha2 Web Solutions, Fairford Leys Way, Aylesbury, Buckinghamshire, HP19 7FQ Tel: (0845) 1294912 E-mail: info@lamtha2.co.uk *Web design services for start ups & small businesses*

Lan 2 Lan Ltd, 5 Genises Park, Woking, Surrey, GU21 5RW Tel: (01483) 594100 Fax: (01483) 594101 *Computer consultants*

Lan Com International Ltd, Birchwood, Main Road, Curbridge, Witney, Oxfordshire, OX29 7NT Tel: (01993) 776543 Fax: (01993) 776899 E-mail: jc.lancom@btinternet.com *Computer cable installation & computer network services*

Lan Electronics, Unit 5 50, Rother Valley Way, Holbrook, Sheffield, S20 3RW Tel: 0114-251 1066 Fax: 0114-251 1067 E-mail: sales@lanelectronicsltd.co.uk *Manufacturers of high quality bespoke single & 3 phase transformers*

Lanark Chainsaw Service, 13 Westbank Holdings, Ravenstruther, Lanark, ML11 8NL Tel: (01555) 870259 Fax: (01555) 870259 *Chainsaw & lawn mowers services*

Lanarkshire Welding Co. Ltd, John Street, Wishaw, Lanarkshire, ML2 7TQ Tel: (01698) 264271 Fax: (01698) 265711 E-mail: johnhett@lanarkshirewelding.co.uk *Steel fabricators*

Lancare Engineering, Lancare Park, Pelynt, Looe, Cornwall, PL13 2LT Tel: (01503) 220209 Fax: (01503) 220144 E-mail: ellott@lancarefarmfsnet.com *Agricultural contractors & engineers*

Lancashire Board & Paper Co. Ltd, Balderstone Lane, Heasandford Industrial Estate, Burnley, Lancashire, BB10 2AL Tel: (01282) 835033 Fax: (01282) 835044 E-mail: sales@lancsboard.co.uk *Packaging material/products & cartons*

Lancashire Cash Registers T P Data, 30 The Crescent, Maghull, Liverpool, L31 7BL Tel: 0151-531 6667 Fax: 0151-531 0066 *Cash registers & EPOS suppliers*

▶ Lancashire Cast Stone Ltd, Unit 35 Lune Industrial Estate, Lancaster, LA1 5QP Tel: (01524) 388501 Fax: (01524) 845007

Lancashire & Cheshire Garage Equipment Services, Progress House, 7 Longshut Lane West, Stockport, Cheshire, SK2 6RX Tel: 0161-477 6715 Fax: 0161-477 6151 E-mail: enquiries@garageequipment.biz *Car & commercial vehicle equipment specialists*

▶ Lancashire College, Southport Road, Chorley, Lancashire, PR7 1NB Tel: (01257) 276719 Fax: (01257) 241370 E-mail: dawn.shelton@ed.lancscc.gov.uk *Business language training & conference venue*

Lancashire County Cricket Club, Talbot Road, Old Trafford, Manchester, M16 0PX Tel: 0161-282 4040 Fax: (0870) 0624614 E-mail: enquiries@lccc.co.uk *Cricket professional*

Lancashire County Engineering Services, Dewhurst Row, Bamber Bridge, Preston, PR5 6BB Tel: (01772) 628323 Fax: (01772) 532343 E-mail: hq@lces.lancscc.gov.uk *Sign manufacturers & highway grounds maintenance*

Lancashire Daf Ltd, Four Oaks Road, Walton Summit Centre, Bamber Bridge, Preston, PR5 8BW Tel: (01772) 338111 Fax: (01772) 332665 E-mail: enquiries@lancashiredaf.co.uk *Daf truck dealers* Also at: Warrington

Lancashire Electric Lamp Co. Ltd, 121-123 St James Street, Liverpool, L1 5HE Tel: 0151-709 1122 Fax: 0151-709 8872 *Wholesale lighting suppliers*

Lancashire Fittings Ltd, 16 Back Devonshire Place, Harrogate, North Yorkshire, HG1 4AF Tel: (01423) 522355 Fax: (01423) 506111 E-mail: sales@lancashirefittings.com Principal Export Areas: Worldwide *Manufacturers of stainless steel tube fittings*

▶ Lancashire Hill Joinery, 215 Chestergate, Stockport, Cheshire, SK3 0AN Tel: 0161-480 6928 Fax: 0161-476 3345

Lancashire Hygiene, 12 Forest Road, Southport, Merseyside, PR8 6ST Tel: (01704) 535363 Fax: (01704) 514800 *Cleaning material suppliers*

Lancashire Motor Radiator Co Ltd, 2-28 Great Homer Street, Liverpool, L5 3LE Tel: 0151-207 1048 Fax: 0151-207 0996 E-mail: nell@chemdirect.co.uk *Car radiators*

▶ Lancashire Printing Co. Ltd, Pleasington Street, Blackburn, BB2 1UF Tel: (01254) 673431 Fax: (01254) 680050

▶ Lancashire PVC-U Trade Frames Ltd, Unit 7, Meadow Business Park, Meadow Lane, Breightmet, Bolton, BL2 6PT Tel: (01204) 548899 Fax: (01204) 548890 E-mail: info@lancashiretradeframes.co.uk *PVC windows, doors & conservatories manufrs*

Company Information

Lancashire Saw Co. Ltd, Imperial Mill, Gorse Street, Blackburn, BB1 3EU Tel: (01254) 51116 Fax: (01254) 672046 E-mail: info@lancashiresaw.co.uk *Woodworking machine manufrs*

Lancashire Security Systems, 90 Ings Lane, Rochdale, Lancashire, OL12 7DX Tel: (01706) 655253 *Burglar alarms installers*

Lancashire Spring Company, Meadowhead Spring Works, Off Dale Street, Milnrow, Rochdale, Lancashire, OL16 4HG Tel: (01706) 715800 Fax: (01706) 715801 E-mail: info@lancashire-spring.co.uk *Spring manufrs*

Lancashire Stone Cutters Ltd, Unit 3, Ramsbottom Mill Crow Lane, Ramsbottom, Bury, Lancashire, BL0 9BR Tel: (01706) 827799 Fax: (01706) 827799 *Architectural store merchants*

Lancashire Tippers, Kirkhall Workshops, Bilbao Street, Bolton, BL1 4HH Tel: (01204) 493750 Fax: (01204) 847966 E-mail: lanctip@masseytruckengineering.co.uk *Commercial vehicle body builders*

Lancashire Transmissions & Conveyor Engineers Ltd, PO Box 33, Bolton, BL1 2QS Tel: (01204) 382241 Fax: (01204) 362275 E-mail: gary@ltce.co.uk *Industrial & chain conveyor systems*

Lancaster & Co. (Bow) Ltd, Hancock Road, London, E3 3DF Tel: (020) 8980 2827 Fax: (020) 8981 7815 E-mail: info.grahamwelding@btconnect.com *Galvanizers*

Lancaster City Council, 4-5 Dalton Square, Lancaster, LA1 1PJ Tel: (01524) 582000 Fax: (01524) 582161 E-mail: llogan@lancaster.gov.uk *Economic development*

Lancaster Communications Ltd, Tarn View, Denny Beck, Lancaster, LA2 9HG Tel: (01524) 846900 Fax: (01524) 846900 E-mail: enq@lancastercomms.co.uk *Data communication systems installation services*

Lancaster Fastener Co. Ltd, Middlegate, White Lund Industrial Estate, Morecambe, Lancashire, LA3 3BN Tel: (01524) 62645 Fax: (01524) 66367 E-mail: enquiries@lancasterfastener.co.uk *Importers & distributors of industrial threaded fasteners*

▶ Lancaster & Gibbings, H The Scope Complex, Wills Road, Totnes, Devon, TQ9 5XN Tel: (01803) 868181 *Gift ware manufrs*

Lancaster GTB Systems Ltd, 32 Europa Way, Lund Industrial Estate, Lancaster, LA1 5QP Tel: (01524) 599600 Fax: (01524) 599699 E-mail: info@lancastergtb.com *Thermal & acoustic insulation suppliers*

Lancaster & Tomkinson, Unit 10, Brock Way, Newcastle, Staffordshire, ST5 6AZ Tel: (01782) 614156 Fax: (01782) 622334 E-mail: contact@lancaster-tomkinson.com *Cabinet makers*

Lancaster & Winter Ltd, Brownroyd Street, Bradford, West Yorkshire, BD8 9AE Tel: (01274) 546303 Fax: (01274) 481143 E-mail: lancaster.winter.ltd@themail.co.uk *Steel stockholders*

Lancastria Roofing Distributors, Fairhills Industrial Estate, Woodrow Way, Irlam, Manchester, M44 6ZQ Tel: 0161-777 9009 Fax: 0161-777 7557 *Roofing, tooling & equipment*

Lancastrian Labels Ltd, 183 Great Howard Street, Liverpool, L3 7DL Tel: 0151-298 1212 Fax: 0151-298 1432 E-mail: sales@lancastrian.co.uk Principal Export Areas: Africa, Central/East Europe, West Europe & North America *Labels, self adhesive, tag label manufacturers, lithographic printers*

Lance Leathers, 14 Bedford Road, Stagsden, Bedford, MK43 8TP Tel: (01234) 823200 Fax: (01234) 826110 E-mail: david@lanceleathers.co.uk *Leather goods & accessories distributors*

▶ Lance Paragon Ltd, Owlerton Green, Sheffield, S6 2BJ Tel: 0114- 255 1063 E-mail: info@lance-paragon.co.uk Purchasing Contact: J. Hawkins Sales Contact: M. Cutter Principal Export Areas: Worldwide *Manufacturers & suppliers of surgical blades & handles to the medical industry.*

▶ Lancebox Ltd, Block O Kent Kraft Industrial Estate, Lower Road, Northfleet, Gravesend, Kent, DA11 9SR Tel: (01322) 427482 Fax: (01322) 427397 E-mail: lancebox@fsmail.net *Demolition contractors*

▶ Lanceni Press Ltd, 1 Garrood Drive, Fakenham, Norfolk, NR21 8NN Tel: (01328) 851578 Fax: (01328) 851298 E-mail: lanceni@clara.net *Commercial printers*

Lancer Labels, Riverview, Blackburn Road, Ribchester, Preston, PR3 3ZQ Tel: (01254) 878744 Fax: (01254) 878280 E-mail: admin@ancerlabelsuk.com *Label designers & printers*

Lancer UK Ltd, 1 Pembroke Avenue, Waterbeach, Cambridge, CB25 9QP Tel: (01223) 861665 Fax: (01223) 861990 E-mail: info@lancer.co.uk *Industrial washing machines & laboratory glassware washing machines*

Lancereal Ltd, Springfield Mills, Springfield Lane, Kirkburton, Huddersfield, HD8 0NZ Tel: (01484) 606040 Fax: (01484) 609911 E-mail: sales@lancereal.com *Engineering power transmission*

Lancewich Promotional Items, Unit 14 Wellington Business Park, Dukes Ride, Crowthorne, Berkshire, RG45 6LS Tel: (01344) 753550 Fax: (01344) 753551 E-mail: sales@lancewich.co.uk *Promotional items & advertising gifts suppliers*

Lancing Marine, 51 Victoria Road, Portslade, Brighton, BN41 1XY Tel: (01273) 411765 Fax: (01273) 430290 E-mail: mail@lancingmarine.com *Marine engine suppliers & manufrs*

Lancopak Ltd, Central Indust Estate, St.Marks Street, Bolton, BL3 6NR Tel: (01204) 395959 Fax: (01204) 383161 E-mail: barrie@lancopak.co.uk *Stretch wrapping machines suppliers*

▶ Land Clean Ltd, The Street, South Harting, Petersfield, Hants, GU31 5QB Tel: (01730) 890432 Fax: (01730) 890436 E-mail: info@landclean.net *Nationwide contractor specialising in providing creative environmental solutions for the clean up of contaminated land and water.*

▶ Land of Leather Ltd, Unit 15 Crescent Link Retail Park, Londonderry, BT47 6SA Tel: (028) 7134 7877 Fax: (028) 7131 8938

Land & Marine, Lawrence House, Lower Bristol Road, Bath, BA2 9ET Tel: (01225) 331116 Fax: (01225) 445057 E-mail: steveholton@landandmarine.co.uk *Civil engineering & public works contractors*

Land & Marine Products Ltd, 32 Woolmer Way, Bordon, Hampshire, GU35 9QF Tel: (01420) 474484 Fax: (01420) 489002 E-mail: sales@landandmarine.co.uk *Recovery equipment manufrs*

Land & Marine Project Engineering, Dock Road North, Wirral, Merseyside, CH62 4TQ Tel: 0151-641 5600 Fax: 0151-644 9990 E-mail: matthew.osullivan@landandmarine.com *Design, supply, fabrication & contruction of fixed & floating roof storage tanks vapour recovery systems, floating roof tank seals & floating cover*

Land Securities Finance Ltd, 5 Strand, London, WC2N 5HR Tel: (020) 7413 9000 Fax: (020) 7920202 E-mail: landsecurities@landsecurites.com *Property investment developers*

▶ Land Sheriffs, The Yard, PO Box 5854, Harlow, Essex, CM18 7FB Tel: 07921 100100 E-mail: info@landsheriffs.co.uk *Certificated Bailiffs tackling gypsy eviction and removing illegal encampments from private and public land.*Clearing vacant building plots etc of illegal encampments*

Land Technology Ltd, Playing Fields, Gunters La, Bexhill-on-Sea, E. Sussex, TN39 4EN Tel: (01424) 214082 Fax: (01424) 214082 *Grounds maintenance*

▶ Land Unit Construction Ltd, Hartwell Road, Hanslope, Milton Keynes, MK19 7BX Tel: (01908) 510414 Fax: (01908) 511056

Land Use Consultancy Services, 16 Springdale Road, Market Weighton, York, YO43 3JT Tel: (01430) 871489 Fax: (01430) 871489 E-mail: skinglucs@aol.com *Land use consultants*

Land Use Consultants, 43 Chalton Street, London, NW1 1JD Tel: (020) 7383 5784 Fax: (020) 7383 4798 *Environmental planning & management*

▶ Landalow P.L.C., Spectrum House, Inveralmond Place, Inveralmond Industrial Estate, Perth, PH1 3TS Tel: (01738) 633674

Landauer Inc, Unit 12 North Oxford Business Centre, Lakesmere Close, Kidlington, Oxfordshire, OX5 1LG Tel: (01865) 373008 Fax: (01865) 373017 *Radiation monitor suppliers*

Landauer Ltd, 25 Beaufort Court, Admirals Way, London, E14 9XL Tel: (020) 7538 5383 Fax: (020) 7538 2007 E-mail: trading@landauerseafood.com *International traders*

Landauer Honey Ltd, Top Barn, Fowlmere Road, Newton, Cambridge, CB22 7PG Tel: (01223) 872444 Fax: (01223) 872512 *Honey refiners & wax trading*

▶ Land-Drill Geotechnics Ltd, Drilling & Exploration Centre, Pardovan Estate, Philipstoun, Linlithgow, West Lothian, EH49 7RX Tel: (01506) 830044 Fax: (01506) 830055 E-mail: info@land-drill.com *Drilling services*

Lander Automotive Ltd, Woodgate Business Park, 174 Clapgate Lane, Birmingham, B32 3ED Tel: 0121-423 1110 Fax: 0121-423 2220 E-mail: enquiries@lander.co.uk *Wireworkers & tube manipulators*

J.B. Landers, 6 Stonebridge Centre, 51 Rangemoor Rd, London, N15 4LP Tel: (020) 8808 0066 Fax: (020) 8808 0066 *Machine pleating*

Landers Quarries Ltd, Kingston Road, Worth Matravers, Swanage, Dorset, BH19 3JP Tel: (01929) 439205 Fax: (01929) 439268 E-mail: landers@purbeckstone.co.uk *Stone merchants & masons*

▶ Landesk Software UK Ltd, Theale House, Brunel Road, Theale, Reading, RG7 4AQ Tel: (0845) 2305580 Fax: 0118-902 6201 *Security network company*

Landfall Scaffolding Ltd, 77 Whitecraigs Road, Glenrothes, Fife, KY6 2RX Tel: (01592) 771345 Fax: (01592) 630349 E-mail: sales@landfallscaffolding.co.uk *Scaffolding contractors* Also at: Grangemouth

▶ Landfill Services, Lyneburn Industrial Estate, Halbeath Place, Dunfermline, Fife, KY11 4JT Tel: (01383) 739073 Fax: (01383) 739073

▶ Landford Stone Ltd, Giles Lane, Landford, Salisbury, SP5 2BG Tel: (01794) 324232 Fax: (01794) 324242 E-mail: sales@landfordstone.co.uk *Granite worktop supply & installation*

Landia UK Ltd, Waymills Indust Estate, Waymills, Whitchurch, Shropshire, SY13 1TT Tel: (01948) 661200 Fax: (01948) 661201 E-mail: info@landia.co.uk *Landia, manufacturers of high quality precision engineered submersible pumps, mixers flowmakers and aerators for the waste water industry. Professional dimensioning of all equipment supplied by Landia, with a no compromise attitude, guarantees the correct solution every time. We also manufacture long shaft dry installed seal less pump along side out range of dry installed cutter pumps and externally mounted air-jets for tank mixing and aerating. Landia UK offer the service of complete installation of all equipment supplied including the supply and fit of pump pipe work and controls. We carry a large stock of spares and complete units in our purpose built premises in north Shropshire. Also we have complete fabrication facilities which enable us to fabricate special brackets for the non -standard situation. Our motto is 'quality in every detail', from quote stage right through to after sales and service; we will always try to accommodate every situation how ever arisen*

▶ Landlab Scotland, Lilac Grove, Laurieston, Castle Douglas, Kirkcudbrightshire, DG7 2PW Tel: (01556) 505970 Fax: (01556) 505975 E-mail: mail@landlab.co.uk *Chartered Landscape Architects*

Landline Ltd, 1 First Avenue, Halstead, Essex, CO9 2EX Tel: (01787) 476699 Fax: (01787) 472507 E-mail: sales@landline.co.uk *Geomembrane insulation manufrs*

▶ Landline Phones, 27-29A New Broadway, Tarring Road, Worthing, West Sussex, BN11 4HP Tel: (0870) 7707191 Fax: (0870) 7707191 E-mail: info@landlinephones.co.uk *Telecommunications retailer*

▶ Landmark Builders Ltd, Unit 12 St Andrews Industrial Estate, Sydney Road, Birmingham, B9 4QB Tel: 0121-245 0575 Fax: 0121-245 0576

▶ Landmark Environmental Ltd, Myerscough Hall, St. Michaels Road, Bilsborrow, Preston, PR3 0RY Tel: (01995) 642109 Fax: (01995) 642108 E-mail: info@land-mark.co.uk *Natural resources management solutions*

Landmark Surgical Ltd, 21 Woodland Road, Birkenhead, Merseyside, CH42 4NT Tel: 0151-643 1323 Fax: 0151-643 9312 E-mail: landmarksurgical@btconnect.com *Surgical instrument & equipment distributors*

Landmark Systems Ltd, Unit 6, Swan Court, Station Road, Pulborough, West Sussex, RH20 1RL Tel: (01798) 877100 Fax: (01798) 875392 E-mail: info@landmarksystems.co.uk *Agriculture & rural business software house*

Landmec Ltd, Redlake Trading Estate, Ivybridge, Devon, PL21 0EZ Tel: (01752) 891285 Fax: (01752) 891392 E-mail: info@landmecpottinger.co.uk *Agricultural spray equipment distributors*

Landmec-Pottinger Ltd, Cantrell Works, Bittaford, Ivybridge, Devon, PL21 0EZ Tel: (01752) 891285 Fax: (01752) 891392 E-mail: info@landmecpottinger.co.uk *Agricultural machinery distributors* Also at: Bearley

Landor Ltd, Riverside House, River Way, Harlow, Essex, CM20 2DW Tel: (01279) 441411 Fax: (01279) 423729 E-mail: paul@landor-hawa.co.uk *Luggage & travel goods distributors*

Landor Cartons Ltd, Church Manorway, Erith, Kent, DA8 1NP Tel: (01322) 435426 Fax: (01322) 445830 E-mail: erithsales@landorcartons.co.uk *Folding carton manufrs*

▶ Landour Ltd, 27 Old Gloucester Street, London, WC1N 3XX Tel: (0870) 3213858 Fax: (0870) 1354533 E-mail: info@landourcom.net *Software developers & website services*

▶ Landreflections, Running Waters, Dorstone, Hereford, HR3 6AD Tel: (01981) 550465 E-mail: landreflections@hotmail.co.uk *Framed pictures*

Lands End Pine Ltd, Lower Leha, St. Buryan, Penzance, Cornwall, TR19 6EJ Tel: (01736) 810211 Fax: (01736) 810211 E-mail: landsendpine@yahoo.co.uk *Pine furniture manufrs*

Lands Improvement Co., 1 Buckingham Place, London, SW1E 6HR Tel: (020) 7222 5331 Fax: (020) 7630 7034 E-mail: enquiries@lih.co.uk *Land investment & finance*

▶ Landscapes Of Bath, York Buildings, Bath, BA1 2EB Tel: (07739) 462855 Fax: (01225) 462358 E-mail: sales@landscapesofbath.co.uk *Hard and Soft Landscaping to complement you home, Block drives and turfing also catered for. Dry-stone-walling a speciality.*www.landscapesofbath.co.uk/web for more details*

▶ Landscope Engineering Ltd, Wrentnall Stables, Wrentnall Farm, Pulverbatch, Shrewsbury, SY5 8ED Tel: (01743) 719204 Fax: (01743) 719215 E-mail: enquiries@land-scope.com *Land surveyors*

Landsdown & Angrove, 68 Llandaff Road, Cardiff, CF11 9NL Tel: (029) 2038 2034 Fax: (029) 2039 4377 *Electrical contractors*

Landtecnics Ltd, Unit18, Orchard Place Business, Comp Road, Wrotham Heath, Sevenoaks, Kent, TN15 8QX Tel: (01732) 885700 Fax: (01732) 882255 E-mail: landtecnics@btconnect.com *Agricultural machinery services*

Landworth Product Ltd, 555 London Road, Hadleigh, Benfleet, Essex, SS7 2EA Tel: (01702) 558373 *Pre-cast concrete & fencing manufrs*

Landywood Concrete Products Ltd, Stafford Road, Wolverhampton, WV10 7EG Tel: (01902) 786696 *Concrete distributor & manufrs*

Lane Business Systems Ltd, 7 Denbigh Street, London, SW1V 2HF Tel: (020) 7828 6767 Fax: (020) 7828 2211 E-mail: enquiries@lanebus.com *Computer reselling*

Lane Electronics, Slinfold Lodge, Stane Street, Slinfold, Horsham, West Sussex, RH13 0RN Tel: (01403) 790661 Fax: (01403) 790849 E-mail: sales@fclane.com *Approved assemblers & distributors of connectors (electrical) & cable ties. In addition, connectors; CECC specification, BS 9000 specification, ATEX rated (previously BASEEFA), QPL approved, audio, circular multi-pin, waterproof/splashproof, miniature, subminiature, environmentally sealed, co-axial, RF, IDC interconnection, MIL-C specification, mains voltage, crimp, electric, subsea/ underwater, filter, hermetic & high voltage*

Lane Electronics, Slinfold Lodge, Stane Street, Slinfold, Horsham, West Sussex, RH13 0RN Tel: (01403) 790661 Fax: (01403) 790849 E-mail: sales@wealdelectronics.com Purchasing Contact: M. Lewis Sales Contact: R. Lane Principal Export Areas: Worldwide *Electrical connector manufacturers. Also connector accessories, BS9000 specification & CECC specification*

Lane Farm Country Foods, Lane Farm, Brundish, Woodbridge, Suffolk, IP13 8BW Tel: (01379) 384593 Fax: (01379) 384934 *Specialty butchers*

George Lane & Sons Ltd, Bannerley Road, Birmingham, B33 0SL Tel: 0121-784 5525 Fax: 0121-783 6988 E-mail: info@georgelane.co.uk *Manufacturers of wire belting, conveyor belting & safety curtains*

Lane Mechanical Services Ltd, 5 Tudor Industrial Estate, Wharfdale Road, Birmingham, B11 2DG Tel: 0121-706 8454 Fax: 0121-706 3144 E-mail: lanemech@fsbdial.co.uk *Pipework design & installation services*

Norman Lane Ltd, 1 Wiggenhall Road, Watford, WD18 0FH Tel: (01923) 235231 Fax: (01923) 222569 E-mail: normanlane@easynet.co.uk *Printing suppliers*

Lane Punch Tech Ltd, 1 Apex Business Park, Diplocks Way, Hailsham, East Sussex, BN27 3JU Tel: (01323) 844777 Fax: (01323) 849091 E-mail: michelle.thompson@lanepunch.co.uk *Press tool component manufrs*

▶ Lane Roofing, Walsall House, 167 Walsall Road, Perry Barr, Birmingham, B42 1TX Tel: 0121-331 4407 Fax: 0121-344 3782 E-mail: info@laneroofing.co.uk *Roofing & asbestos*

Lane Signs, Peartree Farm, Welwyn Garden City, Hertfordshire, AL7 3UW Tel: (01707) 326084 Fax: (01707) 372366 *Sign contractors*

Lane Telecommunications Ltd, Lane House, Priors Way, Maidenhead, Berkshire, SL6 2XJ Tel: (01628) 785351 Fax: (01628) 781611 E-mail: pfincham@lanetelecom.com *Independent software vendor for communications systems*

▶ Lanes Ltd, 16 Patricia Way, Pysons Road Industrial Estate, Broadstairs, Kent, CT10 2LF Tel: (01843) 861314 Fax: (01843) 860919

▶ Lanes For Drains Ltd, Sandleheath Industrial Estate, Old Brickyard Road, Sandleheath, Fordingbridge, Hampshire, SP6 1PA Tel: (01425) 656116 Fax: (01425) 657563

Lanes Engineering & Construction, 189 New Road, Rainham, Essex, RM13 8SH Tel: (01708) 553555 Fax: (01708) 630523 *High pressure cleaning services*

Lanes Pellets Ltd, The Raylor Centre, James Street, York, YO10 3DW Tel: (01904) 430051 Fax: (01904) 765483 *Air gun pellet manufrs*

▶ Lanes Storage & Removals, Greenbottom, Chacewater, Truro, Cornwall, TR4 8QW Tel: (01872) 560147 Fax: (01872) 561051

Lanes Trophies, 121 Higher Parr Street, St. Helens, Merseyside, WA9 1AG Tel: (01744) 732229 Fax: (01744) 732293 *Trophy supply services*

C.J. Lang & Son Ltd, 78 Longtown Road, Dundee, DD4 8JU Tel: (01382) 512000 Fax: (01382) 508222 E-mail: info@cjlang.co.uk *C.J. Lang & Son Ltd based in Scotland are suppliers of food products and catering equipment.*

▶ Langage Farm Dairy Produce, Langage Farm, Higher Chalonsleigh, Smithaleigh, Plymouth, PL7 5AY Tel: (01752) 337723 E-mail: sales@langagefarm.com *Produce ice cream*

Langbow Ltd, 222 Wolseley Court Towers Plaza, Wheelhouse Road, Rugeley, Staffordshire, WS15 1UW Tel: (01889) 575380 Fax: (01889) 578872 E-mail: sales@langbow.com *Machine suppliers*

Langdale Bros, Weatherhill Works, Hathersham Close, Smallfield, Horley, Surrey, RH6 9JE Tel: (01342) 843164 Fax: (01342) 843164 E-mail: langdalebros@aol.com *Press tool, injection moulding & credit card tooling manufrs*

Langdean Manufacturing Ltd, 3 Thames Industrial Estate, High St South, Dunstable, Bedfordshire, LU6 3HD Tel: (01582) 696369 Fax: (01582) 666658 E-mail: langdean@btconnect.com *Rubber product manufrs*

Langdon Group Ltd, Wallfird Cross, Taunton, Somerset, TA2 8QP Tel: (01823) 412800 Fax: (01823) 412678 E-mail: sales@langdons.co.uk Principal Export Areas: Africa *Haulage, road transport, freight services*

Langdon Systems Ltd, Westward House, King Street West, Wigan, Lancashire, WN1 1LP Tel: (01942) 202202 Fax: (01942) 206000 *Software developers*

▶ Langdons Industry Ltd, Skimpot Road, Luton, LU4 0JB Tel: (0870) 0008363 Fax: (0870) 0008365

Frank Langfield Ltd, Hollins Mill Lane, Sowerby Bridge, West Yorkshire, HX6 2RF Tel: (01422) 835388 Fax: (01422) 834452 E-mail: sales@langfieldwelding.com *Welding supplies distributors*

Langfields Ltd, 158 Liverpool Street, Salford, M5 4LJ Tel: 0161-736 4506 Fax: 0161-745 7108 E-mail: sales@langfields.com *Process plant fabricators*

Langford & Hill Ltd, Unit 17 Kings Exchange, Tileyard Road, London, N7 9AH Tel: (020) 7619 0527 Fax: (020) 7619 9856 E-mail: info@langfordhill.co.uk *Graphic equipment suppliers*

Langford Lodge Engineering Co. Ltd, 97 Largy Road, Crumlin, County Antrim, BT29 4RT Tel: (028) 9445 2451 Fax: (028) 9445 2161 E-mail: enquiries@rlc-langford.com *Precision engineers*

Langford Performance Engineering Ltd, 17 Bradfield Close, Finedon Road Industrial Estate, Wellingborough, Northamptonshire, NN8 4RQ Tel: (01933) 441661 Fax: (01933) 441549 E-mail: sales@lpengines.demon.co.uk *High performance engine builders*

Langham Lifts Ltd, 28 Sidney Road, London, N22 8LS Tel: (020) 8881 3337 Fax: (020) 8889 3381 E-mail: enquiries@langham-lifts.co.uk *Lift engineers*

Langham Products Ltd, Willow Road, Castle Donington, Derby, DE74 2NP Tel: (01332) 850277 Fax: (01332) 850366 E-mail: enquiries@langhamproducts.co.uk *Disability aids manufacturers & suppliers*

Langholm Dyeing Co Ltd, Waterside Mill, Langholm, Dumfriesshire, DG13 0DG Tel: (01387) 381188 Fax: (01387) 381177 *Textile dyers*

Langlands & Mcainsh (Packaging) Ltd, 133 Seagate, Dundee, DD1 2HP Tel: (01382) 224657 Fax: (01382) 201969 *Packing case manufrs*

Langley Alloys Ltd, Campbell Rd, Stoke-on-Trent, ST4 4ER Tel: (01782) 847474 Fax: (01782) 847476 E-mail: chris@meighs.co.uk Sales Contact: C. Halliday *Corrosion resistant alloy stockholders*

Langley Business Systems Ltd, 29 Junction Street South, Oldbury, West Midlands, B69 4TA Tel: 0121-552 2570 Fax: 0121-511 1317 E-mail: sales@lbswholesale.demon.co.uk *Cash registers & scale distributors* Also at: Birmingham

Langley Components Maidenhead Ltd, Fullers Yard, Sheephouse Road, Maidenhead, Berkshire, SL6 8HA Tel: (01628) 623809 Fax: (01628) 623809 *Precision machinists*

▶ Langley Designs, 12 Ray Park Lane, Maidenhead, Berkshire, SL6 8PY Tel: (01628) 771224 Fax: (01628) 771224 E-mail: info@langleydesigns.co.uk *Langley Designs manufacture fine bespoke furniture, including fitted and free standing furniture for domestic or commercial environments, handmade wardrobes & kitchens, & home office furniture.*

Langley Labels Ltd, Harthall Lane, Kings Langley, Hertfordshire, WD4 8JJ Tel: (01923) 263777 Fax: (01923) 270392 E-mail: info@langleylabels.com *Self adhesive label printers manufrs*

Langley London Ltd, Calver Quay, Calver Road, Warrington, WA2 8UD Tel: (0845) 2301515 Fax: (0845) 2301516 E-mail: mail@langleylondon.co.uk *Floor, wall & tile distribs*

Langley Mill Boat Yard Ltd, Derby Road, Langley Mill, Nottingham, NG16 4AA Tel: (01773) 760758 *Boat building & moorings*

Langley Sound & Light, 104 Meadfield Road, Langley, Slough, SL3 8HR Tel: (01753) 543389 Fax: (01753) 549690 *Sound & lighting equipment retailers*

Langley-Smith & Co. Ltd, 36 Spital Square, London, E1 6DY Tel: (020) 7247 7473 Fax: (020) 7375 1470 E-mail: sales@langley-smith.co.uk *Chemical Agents.*

Langner Parry, 52-54 High Holborn, London, WC1V 6RR Tel: (020) 7242 5566 Fax: (020) 7405 1908 E-mail: ip@langnerparry.com *International patent & trademark agents*

Lango Ltd, 101 Greenfield Road, London, E1 1EJ Tel: (020) 7247 8376 Fax: (020) 7247 3282 *Textile merchants*

Langpark Ltd, 93 Manthorpe Road, Grantham, Lincolnshire, NG31 8DE Tel: (01476) 574509 *Industrial property owners for rent*

Langrex, Unit 4, Daux Road, Billingshurst, West Sussex, RH14 9SJ Tel: (01403) 785600 Fax: (01403) 785656 E-mail: langrex@aol.com *Electronic valves, tubes, component & semiconductor distributors*

Langridge Homes Ltd, 17-21 Clumber Avenue, Sherwood Rise, Nottingham, NG5 1AG Tel: 0115-962 6626 Fax: 0115-969 1340

Langridge Scaffolding Sussex Ltd, Unit M1 Rudford Industrial Estate, Ford Road, Ford, Arundel, West Sussex, BN18 0BF Tel: (01903) 725873 Fax: (01903) 723468 E-mail: enquiries@langridgescaffolding.co.uk *Scaffolding hire & rental*

▶ Langsett Computers, 334 Langsett Road, Sheffield, S6 2UF Tel: 0114-234 4422 *Net workers*

William Langshaw & Sons Ltd, Abbey Works, Back King Street, Whalley, Clitheroe, Lancashire, BB7 9SP Tel: (01254) 824518 Fax: (01254) 823830 E-mail: enquiries@wmlangshaw.co.uk *Joiners & building contractors*

Langside Linde Servernside Ltd, 4 Britannia Road, Patchway, Bristol, BS34 5TA Tel: 0117-906 3000 Fax: 0117-906 3001 E-mail: enquiries@linde.severnside.co.uk *Fork lift truck manufrs*

▶ Langside Storage & Distribution, Unit 5 70 Strathclyde Street, Glasgow, G40 4JR Tel: 0141-550 3200

Langstane Press Ltd, Palmerston Road, Aberdeen, AB11 5QJ Tel: (01224) 212212 Fax: (01224) 210066 E-mail: sales@langstane.co.uk *Office products & services*

Langston Jones & Co. Ltd, Station St West Business Park, Coventry, CV6 5BP Tel: (024) 7666 8592 Fax: (024) 7666 8593 E-mail: sales@langston-jones.co.uk *Electrical testing specialists*

Langstone Engineering Ltd, Units 1-3 Beaver Industrial Est., Southmoor Lane, Havant, Hampshire, PO9 1JW Tel: (023) 9245 2430 Fax: (023) 9245 2440 E-mail: corporate@langstone-engineering.co.uk *Toolmaking and Precision Engineering services, prototype engineering and component manufacture for F1/Motor Sports, Medical, Automotive, Rubber/Plastic, Aeronautical, Marine & Defence Industries etc. Full hands-on fast-track supply service with full CAD/CAM suite specialising in 3, 4 and 5-Axis 3D CNC milling and turning, plus spark erosion, mould polishing, fitting etc. Accredited to BS EN ISO 9001:2000, supported by CMM technology with Strict non-disclosure & confidentiality undertaking.*

Langstone Safetywear Ltd, 1 St. Johns Court, Upper Forest Way, Swansea Enterprise Park, Swansea, SA6 8QR Tel: (01792) 535500 Fax: (01792) 535509 E-mail: info@langstone.co.uk *Industrial protective clothing & personal protective equipment*

Langtec Ltd, 1 Calder Court, Altham, Accrington, Lancashire, BB5 5YB Tel: (01282) 772544 Fax: (01282) 772740 E-mail: info@langtec.co.uk *Langtec Limited have been manufacturers and suppliers of a wide range of electrical and thermal insulating materials in sheet, processed to drawing and in tubular form for over fifty years. We are specialist manufacturers of micapaper, phenolic and glass fabric tubes in various resin systems, plus processed laminates in phenolic and glass. Products include micapaper, phenolic and glass fabric tubes in various resin systems, plus processed laminates in phenolic and glass. Electrical insulation, thermal insulation, glass tubes, fabric tubes, processed laminates, latex glass, lantex paper, filamic sheet, muscovite, phlogopite, mica paper and epoxy glass laminate.*

Langton Engineering, Denmark Street, Maidenhead, Berkshire, SL6 7BN Tel: (01628) 632764 Fax: (01628) 776183 *Prototype engineers*

▶ Langton House, 46 Alma Road, Windsor, Berkshire, SL4 3HA Tel: 01753 858299 Fax: 01753 858299 E-mail: paul@langtonhouse.co.uk *Family run Bed and Breakfast in the centre of Royal Windsor. All rooms are ensuite/private. Great location for business traveller or holiday, being close to Slough, Heathrow and London. ETB 4 Diamond rating.*

Langton Signs & Graphics, 499a Saffron Lane, Leicester, LE2 6UJ Tel: 0116-283 4484 Fax: 0116-283 4484 *Sign company*

Langton Software Ltd, Holly Road, Twickenham, TW1 4EG Tel: (0845) 1235714 Fax: (020) 8831 7522 E-mail: admin@langton.com *Computer software house*

Tom Langton & Son, Knowsthorpe Lane, Leeds, LS9 0AT Tel: 0113-249 9440 Fax: 0113-240 2287 E-mail: chris@tomlangtons.com *Builders merchants*

▶ The Language Company, The Thistles, 9 Ramblers Close, Colwick, Nottingham, NG4 2DN Tel: 0115 8449369 E-mail: info@thelanguagecompany.co.uk *The Language Company provides a first class service in language training, interpreting, translating and consulting acorss the East Midlands and further afield. All our language courses are tailor-made to suit each individual or group. Sign up for a business course and we will send a trainer to your company. Sig up for a private course and learn from the comfort of your own home. All our trainers are bi-lingual native speakers and highly qualified in their field of expertise.*

Language Connect, Unit 9, Empire Square, Tabard Street, London, SE1 4NA Tel: 0207 940 8108 Fax: 0870 787 7560 E-mail: info@languageconnect.net *Operating from a central London location, Language Connect is a passionate company offering translation, interpreting, website localisation, voiceovers and other language services in over 120 languages and dialects to clients worldwide. Set-up in 2003 the company has 5 years experience in the language services sector and provides a wide range of specialist language services which are delivered by their strong global network of professional and talented linguists.*

▶ Language Direct, 3 92 Matlock Road, London, E10 6DJ Tel: (020) 8539 5142 Fax: (020) 8539 9588 E-mail: languagedirect@btinternet.com *Interpreters, translators, websites, languages, localization dialects*

▶ Language Link UK, Mooregate House, 7B Station Road West, Oxted, Surrey, RH8 9EE Tel: (020) 7484 0999 Fax: (020) 7830 9331 E-mail: london@languagelinkuk.com *Translation & interpretation services*

Language Studies International, 19-21 Ridgmount Street, London, WC1E 7AH Tel: (020) 7467 6500 Fax: (020) 7323 1736 *Language school*

Language Technology Centre, 5&7 Kingston Hill, Kingston Upon Thames, Surrey, KT2 7PW Tel: (020) 8549 2359 Fax: (020) 8974 6994 E-mail: admin@langtec.co.uk *Software consultants*

▶ Language Company UK Ltd, 32 Pentire Avenue, Shirley, Southampton, SO15 7RS Tel: (023) 80570014 E-mail: client.services@language.co.uk *Easy to use, high quality translation, interpretation and language learning courses and resources.*

Langwith Metal Finishers, Unit 21 Doublegate Lane, Rawreth, Wickford, Essex, SS11 8UD Tel: (01268) 570020 Fax: (01268) 570700 E-mail: enquiries@langwithmetal.com *Shot blasting contractors*

Lanier UK Ltd, Eskdale Road, Winnersh, Wokingham, Berkshire, RG41 5TS Tel: (08702) 202012 Fax: (08702) 202018 *Manufacturers & repair photocopiers*

▶ Lanka Kade, 1 South Folds Road, Corby, Northamptonshire, NN18 9EU Tel: (01536) 461188 Fax: (01536) 461100 *Wooden toys suppliers*

Lanlee Supplies Ltd, Red Scar Works, Burnley Road, Colne, Lancashire, BB8 8ED Tel: (01282) 868204 Fax: (01282) 870116 E-mail: sales@lanleesupplies.co.uk *Fencing specialists*

Lanmar Pipework Engineering Ltd, 35 Lightburn Road, Cambuslang, Glasgow, G72 8UB Tel: 0141-646 2233 Fax: 0141-641 7838 *Pipework fabricators*

▶ Lanmarc Ltd, 5 Beechwood Business Park, Burdock Close, Cannock, Staffordshire, WS11 7GB Tel: (01543) 467477 Fax: (01543) 467699

Lanmark Technical Services Ltd, 30-32 Thames Street, Hampton, Middlesex, TW12 2DX Tel: (020) 8783 3260 Fax: (020) 8783 3270 E-mail: sales@lanmark.co.uk *IT consultants*

▶ Lanner Manufacturing Ltd, J Telford Road, Basingstoke, Hampshire, RG21 6YU Tel: (01256) 464288 Fax: (01256) 464209

Lans & Addison, 3 Rose Cottage, Wappenshall, Telford, Shropshire, TF6 6DE Tel: (01952) 255109 Fax: (01952) 255109 *Central heating engineers*

Lans Fine Furnishings, 1717 London Road, Leigh-on-Sea, Essex, SS9 2SW Tel: (01702) 480591 Fax: (01702) 480591 *Licensed bar fitters & furnishers*

Lansa UK Ltd, 4-5 The Big Peg, Warstone Lane, Birmingham, B18 6NA Tel: 0121-233 4588 Fax: 0121-233 4655 *Jewellery display, pricing systems*

Lansdale Engineering Ltd, Norfolk House, Drake Avenue, Staines, Middlesex, TW18 2AP Tel: (01784) 460793 Fax: (01784) 440628 E-mail: jason@lansdaledirect.fsnet.co.uk *Army gear distributors*

▶ Lansdale Health and Safety Services, 1 Pennine Way, Kettering, Northants, NN16 9AX Tel: 01536 500840 Fax: 01536 500840 E-mail: lansdalehs@ntlworld.com *Health and Safety consultancy. Health & Safety accredited and non-accredited training. CIEH: Risk Assessment, Stress, Manual Handling, COSHH, Foundation certificate. IOSH: Managing and Working Safely. Bespoke training*

Lansdowne Bakery, 16 Lansdown Road, Bude, Cornwall, EX23 8BH Tel: (01288) 352777 Fax: (01288) 352777 *Bakers*

Lansdowne Cartmel Ltd, 3e West Way, Andover, Hampshire, SP10 5AS Tel: (01264) 353234 Fax: (01264) 359025 E-mail: lansdownecartmel@aol.com *Electroplating services*

▶ Lansdowne Studio (Newcastle) Ltd, 35 Moorland Way, Nelson Park, Cramlington, Northumberland, NE23 1WE Tel: (01670) 590011

▶ Lansford Access Ltd, 10 Chancel Close, Gloucester, GL4 3SN Tel: (01452) 520144 Fax: (01452) 308369 E-mail: sales@lansfordaccess.co.uk

▶ Lanteeh Network Solutions, 24 Ribble Avenue, Southport, Merseyside, PR9 8LZ Tel: (0870) 3505268 Fax: (0870) 7066048 E-mail: info@lantechnetworks.co.uk *At Lantech Network Solutions we pride ourselves on offering a comprehensive range of IT services to suit every business.**We realise that most small and medium size businesses cannot afford to have there own in-house IT department. To assist with the development of these businesses we offer a full range of IT services. We will become your 'Virtual IT Department', enabling you to have all the benefits afforded a large organisation but without the associated costs.**Some of the key services we provide are:*** Network design, installation and maintenance ** Managed Security products to protect your network ** Backup solutions to safeguard your valuable data ** Anti-virus software ** Support when you need it most*

Lantern Engineering Ltd, Hamilton Road, Maltby, Rotherham, South Yorkshire, S66 7NE Tel: (01709) 813636 Fax: (01709) 817130 E-mail: sales@lantern.co.uk *Impact sockets & mobile container ramps manufrs*

Lantonpark Ltd, Clipper Close, Medway City Estate, Rochester, Kent, ME2 4QP Tel: (01634) 724108 Fax: (0870) 7052305 E-mail: sales@lantonpark.co.uk *Concrete mixing & batching plant manufrs*

Lantor (UK) Ltd, 73 St. Helens Road, Bolton, BL3 3PP Tel: (01204) 855000 Fax: (01204) 61722 E-mail: sales@lantor.co.uk *Hospital disposable & non-woven industrial fabric manufrs*

▶ Lantrix Internet Solutions Ltd, Willowbrook House, Chemical Lane, Stoke-on-Trent, ST6 4PB Tel: (01782) 577888 E-mail: info@lantrix.co.uk *Internet*

Lanway Ltd, PO Box 3568, Bewdley, Worcestershire, DY12 1ZU Tel: (01299) 861733 Fax: (0871) 7333899 E-mail: sales@lanway.ltd.uk Principal Export Areas: Africa *Manufacturers of Lanway Rotary Hammermills, Spare Parts & Servicing for Quarry, Mining & Recycling applications. We also supply very high quality "dissimilar" type welding electrodes for maintenance applications*

Lanway Corporate Business Systems Ltd, Network 65 Business Park, Burnley, Lancashire, BB11 5TE Tel: (01282) 418888 Fax: (01282) 418861 E-mail: sales@lanway.co.uk *IT consultancy*

Lanxess Ltd, Lichfield Road, Branston, Burton-On-Trent, Staffordshire, DE14 3WH Tel: (01283) 714200 Fax: (01283) 714201 E-mail: info@hawley.edi.co.uk *Pigment manufrs*

Lanz Transport Ltd, Galleymead House, Old Bath Road, Colnbrook, Slough, SL3 0NT Tel: (01753) 682005 Fax: (01753) 682040 *Skips & haulage suppliers*

Lap Tab Ltd, 205 Tyburn Road, Birmingham, B24 8NB Tel: 0121-328 1697 Fax: 0121-328 9787 E-mail: sales@lap-tab.co.uk *Specialist plastic finishers & stone enamellers*

▶ Laplace Electrical Ltd, Unit 26 42 Dalsetter Avenue, Glasgow, G15 8TE Tel: 0141-949 0099 Fax: 0141-949 1154 *Metalworking & fabrication services*

Laplace Instruments Ltd, Unit 3b Middlebrook Way, Holt Road, Cromer, Norfolk, NR27 9JR Tel: (01263) 515160 Fax: (01263) 512532 E-mail: tech@laplace.co.uk *Electromagnetic compatibility compliance test equipment manufrs*

Laporta Office Furniture & Equipment, 26-30 Prescott Place, London, SW4 6BU Tel: (020) 7720 6006 Fax: (020) 7720 6116 E-mail: info@laporta.co.uk *Office furniture suppliers*

Laporte Doors, 31 Winchester Avenue, Winchester Trading Estate, Denny, Stirlingshire, FK6 6QE Tel: (01324) 820082 Fax: (01324) 820141 E-mail: info@la-porte.co.uk *Hinged steel door system manufrs*

Lapp Ltd, 3 Perivale Park, Horsenden La South, Greenford, Middlesex, UB6 7RL Tel: (020) 8758 7800 Fax: (020) 8758 7880 E-mail: sales@lappgroup.com *Manufacturers of high quality cables*

S. Lappin, 191 Granemore Road, Tassagh, Armagh, BT60 2RD Tel: (028) 3753 8634 Fax: (028) 3753 8634 *Fertilizer*

LapSafe(R) Products, Unit 3, Wakes Hall Business Centre, Colchester Road, Wakes Colne, Colchester, CO6 2DY Tel: (0845) 2301010 Fax: (0845) 2301020 E-mail: sales@lapsafe.com *Suppliers of laptop trolleys, laptop security solutions & interactive kiosks*

Paul Lapsley Photography Ltd, 3-4 25 Somers Road, Rugby, Warwickshire, CV22 7DG Tel: (01788) 561511 Fax: (01788) 540781 E-mail: plpphoto@btconnect.com *Industrial & commercial photographers*

▶ Laptop Specialists, Lane End House, Green Lane, Tansley, Matlock, Derbyshire, DE4 5FJ Tel: (01629) 584456

▶ Laptop Support, No. 1 Factory Road, Poole, Dorset, BH16 5SJ Tel: (0800) 1977665 E-mail: repairs@testlink.co.uk

▶ Laptopshop IT Ltd, 12-14 Valley Bridge Road, Clacton-on-Sea, Essex, CO15 4AD Tel: (01255) 422033 Fax: (01255) 470300 E-mail: sales@laptopshop.co.uk *Laptop manufrs*

▶ Lapwing Computers, Cowshill, Bishop Auckland, County Durham, DL13 1DA Tel: (01388) 537337 E-mail: info@lapwing.net *Computer sales, service & support for businesses, schools, charities, voluntary & community groups*

The Lapworth Consultancy Ltd, The Barn, Hambridge Farm, Hambridge Road, Newbury, Berkshire, RG14 2QG Tel: (01635) 567777 Fax: (01635) 550067 E-mail: tlc@tlc-ltd.com *Computer consultants*

Lara Marketing, 1st Floor, 93 East Street, Chichester, West Sussex, PO19 1HA Tel: (01243) 788006 Fax: (01243) 701347 E-mail: sales@laramarketing.co.uk *Labels & tags*

Laranca Engineering Ltd, Earlswood Trading Estate, Poolhead Lane, Earlswood, Solihull, West Midlands, B94 5EW Tel: (01564) 702651 Fax: (01564) 702341E-mail: sales@laranca.com *Precision engineers*

Larchbank Supplies, 210 Holbrook Lane, Coventry, CV6 4DD Tel: (024) 7666 7079 Fax: (0560) 0492708 E-mail: larchbankdoors@btconnect.com *Garage door suppliers & installers*

Larchbond Facilities Ltd, Ongar Hall Farm, Brentwood Road, Orsett, Grays, Essex, RM16 3HU Tel: (01375) 892929 Fax: (01375) 892624 E-mail: sales@larchbond.co.uk *Office furniture installation & removals & sales*

Larchfield Ltd Graphics Division, 18-20 East Street, Tonbridge, Kent, TN9 1HA Tel: (01732) 369757 Fax: (01732) 369767 E-mail: sales@larchfieldgraphics.net *Suppliers of aerospace accessories*

Larchfield Services, 30 Spruce Road, Woodley, Reading, RG5 4BB Tel: 0118-944 1239 Fax: 0118-944 2495 E-mail: larchfield@ntlworld.com *Refrigeration repairs & services*

Larchwood Machine Tools Ltd, 61 Blue Lake Road, Dorridge, Solihull, West Midlands, B93 8BH Tel: (01564) 776234 Fax: (01564) 779270 E-mail: sales@larchwoodltd.co.uk *Machine tool merchants or agents*

Larcombes Memorials, 14-16 Mount Charles Road, St. Austell, Cornwall, PL25 3LD Tel: (01726) 73618 Fax: (01726) 69900 *Memorial supplies & fireplaces*

▶ Lareine Engineering, Unit 1 Armadale Industrial Estate, Armadale, Bathgate, West Lothian, EH48 2ND Tel: (01501) 731600 Fax: (01501) 733828 E-mail: lareine@btconnect.com *Manufacturers of roof lights*

Lark Computers Ltd, 65 James Carter Road, Mildenhall, Bury St Edmunds, Suffolk, IP28 7DE Tel: (01638) 716423 Fax: (01638) 716779 *Computer manufrs*

Lark Electrical Ltd, Woolpit Business Park, Windmill Avenue, Woolpit, Bury St. Edmunds, Suffolk, IP30 9UP Tel: (01359) 243500 Fax: (01359) 244405 E-mail: info@lark-technology.co.uk *Electrical contractors*

Larkbeare Holdings Ltd, The Talewater Mill, Talaton, Exeter, EX5 2RT Tel: (01404) 850833 Fax: (01404) 850246 E-mail: finishing@larkbeare.com *Trade print finishers & binders*

Larkshill Engineering Ltd, 8 Bond Street, Hockley, Birmingham, B19 3LB Tel: 0121-236 2617 Fax: 0121-236 6963 E-mail: frankmurphy@larkshilleng.com *Press tools to specification manufrs*

Larkswood Ltd, Care Of Courts, Orchard Retail Pk, London Rd, Coventry, CV3 4EU Tel: 024 76303020 *Furniture manufrs*

Larkswood Ltd, Bedford Road, Aspley Guise, Milton Keynes, MK17 8DJ Tel: (01908) 583897 Fax: (01908) 583317 E-mail: sales@larkswood.f2s.com *Furniture reproducers*

Larmar Engineering Co. Ltd, Main Road, Margaretting, Ingatestone, Essex, CM4 9JD Tel: (01277) 352058 Fax: (01277) 356447 E-mail: info@larmar.co.uk *Precision engineers & fabricators*

Larn Ltd, Unit 5 The Stable Block, Brewer Street, Bletchingley, Redhill, RH1 4QP Tel: (01883) 744033 Fax: (01883) 743844 *Light box manufrs*

Larne Enterprise Development Co. Ltd, Ledcom Industrial Estate, Bank Road, Larne, County Antrim, BT40 3AW Tel: (028) 2827 0742 Fax: (028) 2827 5653 E-mail: davidgillespie@ledcom.org *Business advisers & local enterprise agency*

Larne Harbour Ltd, 9 Olderfleet Road, Larne, County Antrim, BT40 1AS Tel: (028) 2887 2100 Fax: (028) 2887 2209 E-mail: info@portoflarne.co.uk *Port authority & stevedores*

Larner Pallets Recycling Ltd, Jute Lane, Brimsdown, Enfield, Middlesex, EN3 7PJ Tel: (020) 8804 1494 Fax: (020) 8804 1164 E-mail: admin@larnerpallets.com *Pallet recovery & supply services*

▶ Larner Sing Architectural & Building Design, 29 Lower Street, Rode, Frome, Somerset, BA11 6PU Tel: (01373) 830836 Fax: (01373) 830527 E-mail: ian@larner-sing.co.uk *Architectural practice dealing with all aspects of architectural design and planning matters. We design new buildings, extensions, and carry out works on conversions and listed property. Our clients range from the private individual to the medium sized developer. We specialise in small to mediul sized schemes.*

▶ Larner & Weeks (Printers) Ltd, 32 Mill Green Road, Mitcham, Surrey, CR4 4HY Tel: (020) 8646 8400

Laroc (Coventry) Ltd, Curriers Close, Charter Avenue Industrial Estate, Coventry, CV4 8AW Tel: (024) 7646 6085 Fax: (024) 7646 6085 *Sheet metalwork engineers or fabricators*

Larousse Foods Ltd, 24 Finaghy Road South, Belfast, BT10 0DR Tel: (028) 9043 2522 Fax: (028) 9062 3492 E-mail: sales@laroussefoods.co.uk *Catering retailers*

Larsens, 4 West Bank Road, Belfast, BT3 9JL Tel: (028) 9077 4000 Fax: (028) 9077 6945 E-mail: p.duffy@larsenbuildingproducts.com *Manufacture building products*

Larssen Engineering Ltd, Globe Industrial Estate, Rectory Road, Grays, Essex, RM17 6ST Tel: (01375) 371909 Fax: (01375) 390582 E-mail: sales@larssen.com *Marine engineers*

Las Manchester Ltd, 91 Heaton Street, Denton, Manchester, M34 3RY Tel: 0161-336 3444 *Audio*

Company Information

▶ Lasa Development UK Ltd, Little Manor, Itlay, Daglingworth, Cirencester, Gloucestershire, GL7 7HZ Tel: (01285) 643469 E-mail: info@lasadev.com *LASA helps you to improve your creativity and business effectiveness through developing leadership and innovation. Using Appreciative Inquiry helps your organisation develop by making clear how you need to implement and integrate the change.*

Lasarge Concrete Products, Newlands Road, Charing, Ashford, Kent, TN27 0AS Tel: (01233) 712267 Fax: (01233) 713720 *Concrete building block manufrs*

Lascar Electronics Ltd, Module House, Whiteparish, Salisbury, SP5 2SJ Tel: (01794) 884567 Fax: (01794) 884616E-mail: sales@lascar.co.uk *Electronic readout systems manufacturers including custom solutions*

▶ Lascells Scientific Apparatus, Walkmill Business Park, Market Drayton, Shropshire, TF9 2HT Tel: (01630) 657801 Fax: (01630) 656726 E-mail: sales@lascells.co.uk *Science equipment manufacturers for education*

▶ Laser Ltd, West House, 115 West Street, Faversham, Kent, ME13 7JB Tel: (01795) 590683 Fax: (01795) 533019

Laser 2000 UK Ltd, Britannia House, Denford Road, Ringstead, Kettering, Northamptonshire, NN14 4DF Tel: (01933) 461666 Fax: (01933) 461699 E-mail: sales@laser2000.co.uk *Laser & fibre optics distributors*

Laser Alarms, 23 The Lane, Awsworth, Nottingham, NG16 2QP Tel: 0115-932 4658 *Alarms installers*

▶ Laser Build, Findel House, Excelsior Road, Ashby-de-la-Zouch, Leicestershire, LE65 1NT Tel: (01530) 410280 Fax: (01530) 410281

Laser Byte Ltd, Burstow Park, Antlands Lane, Shipley Bridge, Horley, Surrey, RH6 9TF Tel: (01293) 772201 Fax: (01293) 774694 E-mail: support@lazerbyte.com *Software house*

Laser Cartridge Recycling Co., Lower Kingsdown Road, Kingsdown, Corsham, Wiltshire, SN13 8BG Tel: (01225) 740022 Fax: (01225) 740092 *Computer accessories recycler*

Laser Civil Engineering Ltd, Bredon House, Worcester, WR2 4SQ Tel: (01905) 832900 Fax: (01905) 832901 *Civil engineers*

Laser Claddings Ltd, Lowndes Road, Stourbridge, West Midlands, DY8 3ST Tel: (01384) 376200 Fax: (01384) 372737 E-mail: laser.cladding@blueyonder.co.uk *Industrial cladding & window installers*

Laser Crystal Ltd, 3 Ariel Park, Uddens Trading Estate, Wimborne, Dorset, BH21 7NL Tel: (01202) 875657 Fax: (01202) 861438 E-mail: laser_profiles@compuserve.com *For over 20 years Laser Profiles have provided an advanced laser cutting job shop service to all manufacturing sectors. Our skilled and experienced workforce cut components used for a diverse range of products that utilise many different types of materials. We supply laser cut parts manufactured from flat sheet and plate, and tube material formed in square, round, oval and rectangular sections. From our 15,000sq/ft premises Laser Profiles offers a full in-house production facility. A team of dedicated CAD/CAM programmers will create component programs from sheet and tube materials, and large profiles and tube bundles can be easily and safely handled utilizing our 5ton and 3 ton overhead cranes. Our continued investment in the latest in the latest automated laser cutting equipment and materials handling technology ensures we remain at the cutting edge of the industry, and allows our customers to benefit from the many advantages that laser cutting can offer* Also at: Basildon

Laser Cutting Ceramics Ltd, Wide Range Works, Catley Road, Sheffield, S9 5JF Tel: 0114-249 4005 Fax: 0114-242 5194 E-mail: info@lasercutting-ceramics.co.uk *Laser cutting services*

Laser Cutting Services, Flanders Moss, Station Road, Buchlyvie, Stirling, FK8 3NB Tel: (01360) 850389 Fax: (01360) 850565 E-mail: sarahgleave@yahoo.com *Laser cutting, stencils & home decorating*

Laser Electrical Services, Rochester House, 275 Baddow Road, Chelmsford, CM2 7QA Tel: (01245) 492823

▶ Laser Experience, 10 Elder Close, Bilton, Rugby, Warwickshire, CV22 7TJ Tel: (01788) 814288 Fax: (01788) 521705 E-mail: peter@laserexperience.com *Industrial laser applications & training consultants services*

▶ Laser Friend, Unit 14 15 Station Lane Industrial Estate, Station Lane, Old Whittington, Chesterfield, Derbyshire, S41 9QX Tel: (01246) 266010 Fax: (01246) 266011 E-mail: tony@laserfriend.com *Re-manufacture cartridges laser printers, photocopiers & fax machines*

▶ Laser Fume Extraction Guidance, Unit 11 Solent Industrial Estate, Hedge End, Southampton, SO30 2FX Tel: 01489 782262 Fax: 01661 833010 E-mail: info@laser-fume-extraction.com *We provide a wide range of manufacturing, development and packaging services to meet your clinical trial needs." "As a truly special clinical trial service provider delivering small scale and specialist services we can adapt to meet your requirements." "Based on client feedback over recent years, our vision is now very much your reality. We have built a reputation for offering an excellent manufacturing capability and extremely efficient operating systems that deliver outstanding quality. Combined withour uncompromisingly professional attitude and uniquely flexible approach to meet deadlines, Specials Clinical Manufacturing endeavours to provide the solution to your clinical trial conundrum." "Whatever your requirements, whether for manufacturing, packaging, filling, analytical and microbiological testing or anything else relating to Phase I - III studies, we invite you to challenge us.*

▶ Laser Graphics Services Ltd, 40 Wates Way, Mitcham, Surrey, CR4 4HR Tel: (020) 8646 8877

Laser Instrumentation Ltd, 11 Jubilee lane, Farnham, Surrey, GU10 4SZ Tel: (01252) 794918 Fax: (01252) 792810 E-mail: p.hurley@farn-ct.ac.uk *Laser device & component manufrs*

Laser Leisure Ltd, Rugby Road, Brandon, Coventry, CV8 3GH Tel: (024) 7654 4095 Fax: (024) 7654 4095 *Coin operated amusement machine suppliers*

Laser Lifeline UK Ltd, 2 Cavendish Enterprise Centre, Brassey Street, Birkenhead, Merseyside, CH41 8BY Tel: 0151-651 2037 Fax: 0151-651 2037 *Printer cartridge suppliers*

Laser Line Engineering Ltd, Unit 14 Avon Business Park, Lodge Causeway, Bristol, BS16 3JP Tel: 0117-965 7002 Fax: 0117-965 7004 E-mail: sales@laser-line.net *Laser & profile cutting services*

Laser Plane Ltd, 6 Devonshire Business Park, Knights Park Road, Basingstoke, Hampshire, RG21 6XE Tel: (01256) 460161 Fax: (01256) 363283 E-mail: laserplaneltd@tiscali.co.uk *Laser survey equipment suppliers*

Laser Process Ltd, Upper Keys, Keys Park Road, Hednesford, Cannock, Staffordshire, WS12 2GE Tel: (01543) 495000 Fax: (01543) 495001 E-mail: sales@laserprocess.co.uk *Laser Process is at the leading edge of laser cutting. Based in the West Midlands we offer nationwide coverage and in most cases, next day delivery. **Utilizing the latest laser cutting technology and a skilled, experienced workforce, we help our customers to: *Increase productivity *Improve profitability *Maintain quality levels **Laser Process provides an outstanding laser cutting service, using a range of the most powerful laser systems, to support customers. **Making continual investment in the latest laser cutting systems, allows us to supply the standards required by almost every manufacturing sector. **Please view our website or call the number below for further information.*

▶ Laser Products UK Ltd, Phoenix Works, Hope Bank Honley, Holmfirth, HD9 6PR Tel: (01484) 665870 Fax: (01484) 663581 E-mail: sales@laserproductsuk.com *Laser cutting services*

Laser S O S Ltd, 3 Burrel Road, St. Ives, Cambridgeshire, PE27 3LE Tel: (01480) 460990 Fax: (01480) 469978 E-mail: sales@lasersos.com *Laser accessory & system manufrs*

Laser Services Cartridge Master, 2 Woodview Business Centre, Lockwood Close, Nottingham, NG5 9JN Tel: 0115-967 3445 Fax: 0115-967 3899 E-mail: sales@laserservices.co.uk *Specialist laser toner*

Laser Sport International Ltd, Building 19 Stanmore Industrial Estate, Bridgnorth, Shropshire, WV15 5HR Tel: (01746) 767186 Fax: (01746) 761312 E-mail: sales@lasersport.biz *Laser games manufrs*

Laser Steel Ltd, Chartwell Drive, Wigston, Leicestershire, LE18 2FL Tel: 0116-288 4933 Fax: 0116-288 4966 *General sheetmetal work*

Laser Support Services Ltd, School Drive, Ovenstone, Anstruther, Fife, KY10 2RR Tel: (01333) 311938 Fax: (01333) 312082 E-mail: enquiries@laser-support.com *Laser component & optics distributors*

Laser Surveys Ltd, Brockamin House, Leigh, Worcester, WR6 5JU Tel: (01886) 833173 Fax: (01886) 833485 E-mail: worcester@lasersurveys.com *Land surveys & underground services* Also at: London

Laser Systems (UK) Ltd, Unit 9, Arc Progress, Mill Lane, Stotfold, Hitchin, Hertfordshire, SG5 4NU Tel: (01462) 735333 Fax: (01462) 732510 E-mail: gbowler@lasersystems.ltd.uk *Suppliers of Laser Cutting & marking systems.**

Laser Techniques Ltd, Unit 11 Shaw Crescent, Hutton, Brentwood, Essex, CM13 1JD Tel: (01277) 228194 Fax: (01277) 232840 E-mail: sales@laser-techniques.com *Engravers*

Laser Traders, 83 Horton Road, Datchet, Slough, SL3 9LY Tel: (01753) 580082 Fax: (01753) 580082 *Computer cartridges suppliers*

Laser Transport International Ltd, Lympne Industrial Estate, Lympne, Hythe, Kent, CT21 4LR Tel: (01303) 260471 Fax: (01303) 264851 E-mail: sales@laserint.co.uk *Freight forwarding agents*

Laser Vision, 52 North Street, Bedminster, Bristol, BS3 1HJ Tel: 0117-963 2963 E-mail: laservisioncouk@aol.com *Home cinema equipment*

Lasercare Bristol Ltd, 8 Bromley Heath Avenue, Bristol, BS16 6JS Tel: 0117-908 3463 Fax: 0117-907 7538 E-mail: sales@lasercarebristol.co.uk *IT printers consumables & electronic office equipment suppliers*

Lasercharge UK Ltd, 70 Main Street, Garforth, Leeds, LS25 1AA Tel: 0113-286 4535 Fax: 0113-287 4232 E-mail: laserchargeuk@btinternet.com *Printer consumables suppliers*

▶ Lasercomb Dies Ltd, 2 Meir Road, Old Forge Drive, Redditch, Worcestershire, B98 7SY Tel: (01527) 516665 Fax: (01527) 516700

Lasercroft Ltd, 9 Hedon Road, Hull, HU9 1LL Tel: (01482) 229119 Fax: (01482) 223077 E-mail: info@lasercroft.com Principal Export Areas: Worldwide *Floor coatings, protective or non slip manufrs*

Laseread Software Ltd, 10 Medway Close, Newport Pagnell, Buckinghamshire, MK16 9DT Tel: (01908) 211116 Fax: (01908) 211120 E-mail: sales@laseread.com *Software house*

Laserflex Ltd, J Balthane Industrial Estate, Balthane, Ballasalla, Isle of Man, IM9 2AG Tel: (01624) 822155 Fax: (01624) 824573 E-mail: sales@laserflex.co.uk *Printing roller engravers & rotary screen engravers* Also at: Oldham

Laserform International Ltd, Higher Lane, Lymm, Cheshire, WA13 0RZ Tel: (01925) 750000 Fax: (01925) 750021 E-mail: admin@laserform.co.uk *Legal software house maunfrs*

Laserit Ltd, Unit 26 Beeches Industrial Estate, Lavenham Road, Yate, Bristol, BS37 5QX Tel: (01454) 318585 Fax: (01454) 318541 E-mail: sales@laserit.co.uk Purchasing Contact:

continued

K. Bowden Sales Contact: D. Holtom *Laser, profile & stainless steel profile cutting services, as well as Bending/Forming, Sheetmetalwork and Fabrications and a Powder Paint facility.*

▶ Laserite Promotional Items, Unit 14 Childerditch Hall Drive, Little Warley, Brentwood, Essex, CM13 3HD Tel: (01277) 811137 Fax: (01277) 811450 E-mail: info@laserite.co.uk *Laser cutting, marking equipment & services*

Laserline Computer Systems, 5a The Crescent, Dunston, Gateshead, Tyne & Wear, NE11 9SJ Tel: 0191-421 1899 Fax: 0191-420 2954 *Manufacturers of laser toner cartridges*

Laserline Dies Ltd, 6 Northumberland Court, Chelmsford, CM2 6UW Tel: (01245) 461117 Fax: (01245) 461366 E-mail: aldersc@laserlinedies.com *Laser cut die manufrs*

▶ Lasermatrix, 87 Ludlow Road, Woolston, Southampton, SO19 2ET Tel: (07734) 206005 Fax: (07005) 938915 E-mail: chris.priest@lasermatrix.co.uk *Laser Hire Services, Custom Animations and Shows, Beam Shows, Outdoor events or indoor events.*

Lasermet Ltd, 67 Portchester Road, Bournemouth, BH8 8JX Tel: (01202) 770740 Fax: (01202) 770730 E-mail: sales@lasermet.com *World experts in laser safety offering advice and equipment including, consultancy, training, laser and LED product testing, interlock systems, protective eyewear, signs, labels, safety screens, curtains, enclosures, LaserSafe PC software, filter windows and beam shutters.*

Laserpack Cartons & Cases Ltd, Unit 4, Llandygai Industrial Estate, Bangor, Gwynedd, LL57 4YH Tel: (0845) 2575758 Fax: (0845) 2575759 E-mail: sales@laserpack.co.uk *Manufacturers of corrugated cases & die cut containers & fitments. Supplier of packaging materials.*

Laserprint Software International, 23 Townmead Business Centre, William Morris Way, London, SW6 2SZ Tel: (020) 7610 9697 Fax: (07000) 486226 E-mail: info@laserprintsoftware.com *Computer software publishers & developers*

Laserus Cartridges, 24 Whellock Road, London, W4 1DZ Tel: (020) 8723 3116 Fax: (020) 8995 8653 *Computer cartridges manufrs*

Laserweld 2000 Ltd, Walsall Road, Norton Canes, Cannock, Staffordshire, WS11 9TA Tel: (01543) 450099 Fax: (01543) 450098 E-mail: laserweld@aol.com *Laser welding & profile cutting services*

Laserworld Engineering Co. Ltd, Brownside Mill, Brun Terrace, Burnley, Lancashire, BB10 3JR Tel: (01282) 425999 Fax: (01282) 426739 E-mail: info@laserworldengineering.co.uk *Laser cutting cnc machining milling manufrs*

▶ Lasso Computer Consultants, 2 Kingsfield Road, Biggleswade, Bedfordshire, SG18 8AT Tel: (01767) 600288 Fax: (01767) 600289 *Computer systems consultants*

Last Bros Ltd, Delamare Road, Cheshunt, Waltham Cross, Hertfordshire, EN8 9TE Tel: (01992) 638283 Fax: (01992) 638286 E-mail: sales@lastbros.co.uk *Printers & label manufrs*

Last Engineering Ltd, St. Thomas Place, Ely, Cambridgeshire, CB7 4EX Tel: (01353) 669000 Fax: (01353) 668999 E-mail: mail@lastengineering.com *Precision engineers*

Last & Mazin, 21 Welbeck Street, London, W1G 8EE Tel: (020) 7763 7763 Fax: (020) 7763 7764 E-mail: post@lastandmazin.com *General practice & building chartered surveyors*

▶ Last Minute Cottages, Pondmead, Seldon Farm, Monkokehampton, Winkleigh, Devon, EX19 8RY Tel: (01837) 811150 E-mail: enquiries@lastminute-cottages.co.uk

Last Party, 7 Carlingnose Park, North Queensferry, Inverkeithing, Fife, KY11 1EX Tel: (01383) 415022 E-mail: sales@lastparty.co.uk *Embedded software for engineering & defence industries*

▶ Lasting Impressions Ltd, Unit E3-E4 Barwell Business Park, Leatherhead Road, Chessington, Surrey, KT9 2NY Tel: (020) 8944 0808

Lastolite Ltd, 1 Atlas Road, Coalville, Leicestershire, LE67 3FQ Tel: (01530) 813381 Fax: (01530) 830408 E-mail: sales@lastolite.com *Photographic equipment manufrs*

Laston Partnership, Laston House, Barnstaple Road, Ilfracombe, Devon, EX34 9NT Tel: (01271) 866557 Fax: (01271) 867754 *Hotel*

▶ lastseason.com, 12 Myton Crescent, Warwick, CV34 6QA Tel: (01926) 313175 E-mail: info@lastseason.com *lastseason.com is a high street online clothing shop specializing in discounted styles. with up to 60% off great brands, lastseason is a great place for all your wardrobe needs.*

▶ Latch & Batchelor, Hay Mills, Birmingham, B25 8DW Tel: 0121-772 1386 Fax: 0121-772 0762 E-mail: sales@latchandbatchelor.co.uk *Specialist manufacturers, stockists, and global distributors of high quality steel wire ropes and fittings. Latch & Batchelor Ltd was founded in 1888 and are based in Birmingham.*

Latches Ltd, 24 Hebden Road, Scunthorpe, South Humberside, DN15 8DT Tel: (01724) 270660 Fax: (01724) 271750 *Glass fibre manufacturers & moulders*

Latchford Farm Aquatics, Latchford Farm, St. Marys Lane, Upminster, Essex, RM14 3PB Tel: (01708) 641363 *Aquatics & animal feed distributors*

Latchfords Timber Merchants, 24-28 Warner Street, London, EC1R 5EX Tel: (020) 7837 1461 Fax: (020) 7837 1462 *Timber merchants*

▶ Latens Systems, 1-3 Upper CR, Belfast, BT7 1NT Tel: (028) 9057 1500 *Technology services*

▶ Lateral Blue Ltd, 9 Columba Road, Edinburgh, EH4 3QZ Tel: 0131-332 5152 Fax: 0870 1329471 E-mail: info@lateralblue.co.uk *Lateral Blue Limited specialises in computer services and consulting, network set up support and consultancy wireless networks and computer installation in Edinburgh uk scotland*

A.H. Latham Marine, Highfield Business Centre, 1 Simmonds Road, Wincheap Industrial Estate, Canterbury, Kent, CT1 3RA Tel: (01227) 472822 Fax: (01227) 768597 E-mail: sales@zincsmart.com *Cathodic protection systems manufrs*

Latham Finishers Ltd, P O Box 794, Luton, LU1 4YA Tel: 01582 455322 Fax: 01582 455322 *Bar code labels, scanners & library systems*

Latham International Ltd, Rowhurst Close, Rowhurst Industrial Estate, Newcastle, Staffordshire, ST5 6BD Tel: (01782) 565364 Fax: (01782) 564886 E-mail: info@lathaminternational.com Principal Export Areas: Worldwide *Filter press manufrs*

James Latham, Badminton Road Trading Estate, Badminton Road, Yate, Bristol, BS37 5JX Tel: (01454) 315421 Fax: (01454) 323488 E-mail: panels.yate@lathams.co.uk *Timber merchants*

James Latham Ltd, Nest Road, Felling Industrial Estate, Gateshead, Tyne & Wear, NE10 0LU Tel: 0191-469 4211 Fax: 0191-469 2615 E-mail: denis@lathams.co.uk *Plywood merchants & importers*

Latham Jenkins Ltd, Brown Street, Wigan, Lancashire, WN3 4DH Tel: (01942) 821414 Fax: (01942) 821432 *Furniture manufrs*

▶ R. Latham Computer Consultants, 2 Albion Road, Chesterfield, Derbyshire, S40 1NB Tel: (07904) 120638 E-mail: richardlatham@ntlworld.com *Computer consultants*

Samuel Latham Ltd, 475 Evesham Rd, Crabbs Cross, Redditch, Worcs, B97 5JQ Tel: (01527) 543238 Fax: (01527) 550824 *Paint & household brush manufrs*

Latham & Sons Beckenham Ltd, Latham House, Kangley Bridge Road, London, SE26 5BA Tel: (020) 8778 9008 Fax: (020) 8659 2360 *Skip hire contractors*

Lathe Trays Fabricators Ltd, Station Road, Rowley Regis, West Midlands, B65 0JX Tel: 0121-559 1115 Fax: (0870) 4202912 E-mail: admin@lathetrays.co.uk *Fabrications in all metals*

Lathom Motorcraft, 15 Briars Lane, Lathom, Ormskirk, Lancashire, L40 5TG Tel: (01704) 893284 Fax: (01704) 893284 E-mail: enquiries@catchup2000.com *Exhaust, catalyst systems distributors & manufrs*

Lati UK Ltd, West Wing, The Quadrangle, Crewe Hall, Weston Road, Crewe, CW1 6UA Tel: (01270) 501713 Fax: (01270) 509713 E-mail: mfreestone@uk.lati.com *Engineering thermoplastic compounds sale & distributors*

Latimer Trend Printing Group, Estover Road, Plymouth, PL6 7PY Tel: (01752) 201930 Fax: (01752) 201760 E-mail: systems@trends.co.uk *Printers*

Latitude Communications, 50 Regent St, London, W1B 5RD Tel: (020) 7470 7125 Fax: (020) 7470 7113 *Telecommunication services*

▶ Latrave Paper & Cardboard Products, Unit 2 Edison Close, Park Farm Industrial Estate, Wellingborough, Northamptonshire, NN8 6AH Tel: (01933) 678548 Fax: (01933) 678987 *Adhesive tape manufrs*

Latter's Pine Furniture, 18 Crescent Road, London, N22 7RS Tel: (020) 8888 7477 *Kitchen suppliers*

Lattice Semiconductors UK Ltd, 1st Floor, River Mead House, Hamm Moor Lane, Addlestone, Surrey, KT15 2SF Tel: (01932) 825700 Fax: (01932) 825701 E-mail: neursales@latticesemi.com *Semiconductors suppliers*

Lattimer Engineering Ltd, 79-83 Shakespeare Street, Southport, Merseyside, PR8 5AP Tel: (01704) 535040 Fax: (01704) 541046 E-mail: sales@lattimer.com *Precision engineers & cnc turning - parts for the glass industry*

Lattis Ltd, New Loom Ho, 101 Back Church La, London, E1 1LU Tel: (020) 7366 6666 Fax: (020) 7366 1122 *IT management*

Lauderdale Coachworks, Kirk Wynd, Lauder, Berwickshire, TD2 6ST Tel: (01578) 722227 Fax: (01578) 722227 E-mail: jim@rabbittrap.co.uk *Steel fabricators*

▶ Laugh Out Loud, Fox Moss, Pewit Lane, Hunsterson, Nantwich, Cheshire, CW5 7PP Tel: (07970) 295258 Fax: (01270) 520127

▶ Laugharne Pottery & Glass, King Street, Laugharne, Carmarthen, Dyfed, SA33 4RY Tel: (01994) 427476 Fax: (01994) 427770

▶ Laundry Creative Consultants, 35a Stoneleigh Broadway, Epsom, Surrey, KT17 2JE Tel: (020) 7870 8330 *UK based design consultants*

Laundry Supplies Ltd, Vulcan Road, Lode Lane Industrial Estate, Solihull, West Midlands, B91 2JY Tel: 0121-705 4645 Fax: 0121-711 2051 E-mail: sales@slmarketing.co.uk *Laundry & dry cleaning suppliers*

Launer London Ltd, 86 Clarendon Road, Croydon, CR0 3SG Tel: (020) 8681 3573 Fax: (020) 8681 3530 E-mail: sales@launer.com *Ladies' handbag & leathergoods manufrs*

▶ Launton Press Ltd, Telford Road, Bicester, Oxfordshire, OX26 4LF Tel: (01869) 242124 E-mail: sales@launtonpress.co.uk

Laura Ashley Ltd, Design Centre, 27 Bagleys Lane, London, SW6 2QA Tel: (020) 7880 5100 Fax: (020) 7880 5200 *Clothing garment manufrs*

Laurel Bank Forge, Woodway Lane, Claybrooke Parva, Lutterworth, Leicestershire, LE17 5BH Tel: (01455) 209379 Fax: (01455) 209379 *Blacksmiths & farriers*

▶ Laurel Cottage Ltd, 15 Ballyhay Road, Donaghadee, County Down, BT21 0NG Tel: (028) 9188 8033 Fax: (028) 9188 8063 E-mail: info@cottagepublications.com *Book Publishers specialising in high quality full colour books*

▶ The Laurel Property Co. Ltd, The Laurels, Sling, Coleford, Gloucestershire, GL16 8JJ Tel: (01594) 833049

Laurel Signs, Bankfield Works, Chapel Street, Stanningley, Pudsey, West Yorkshire, LS28 6BW Tel: 0113-236 1219 Fax: 0113-236 3697 E-mail: bwaller@btconnect.com *Sign makers*

Lauren Industries, Loxley Green, Uttoxeter, Staffordshire, ST14 8QF Tel: (01889) 568000 Fax: (01889) 567116 E-mail: info@laurenindust.co.uk *Office interiors*

Gilbert Laurence Ltd, 1 Union Buildings, Wallingford Road, Uxbridge, Middlesex, UB8 2FR Tel: (01895) 455980 Fax: (01895) 455999 E-mail: sales@gilbertlaurence.co.uk *Fastener distributors*

Laurence Industrial Oil Services Ltd, Gardner & Son, Bowerland Lane, Lingfield, Surrey, RH7 6DF Tel: (01342) 836143 Fax: (01342) 836375 *Fuel oil & lubricant distribs*

Laurence, Scott & Electromotors Ltd, Po Box 25, Norwich, NR1 1JD Tel: (01603) 628333 Fax: (01603) 610604 E-mail: sales@laurence-scott.com Principal Export Areas: Worldwide *Manufacturers of gear boxes & units, including custom built, epicyclic, helical, planetary, reversible, right angle, shaft mounted, slow speed, to specification, speed reducing, turbine, variable speed & worm. Also electric motors, including battery powered, braked, DC, fractional HP DC, low power DC, fractional horse power, permanent magnet & split capacitors, printed, pump, reversible, shaded pole, shunt wound, soft start, synchronous, three phase squirrel cage, torque, traction, two & variable speed, DC drives, repair & rewind specialist services & adjustable speed couplings. AC motors, including brushless, fractional, HP, high efficiency, high voltage & to specification. Electric, fractional horse power & helical geared motor manufacturers & refurbishment services. In addition, electric & mechanical variable speed power transmission equipment manufacturers, maintenance & repair services & electric drive systems manufrs*

▶ Laurie Pest Control Ltd, Hunters Moon, The Street, Raydon, Ipswich, IP7 5LW Tel: (01473) 310807 Fax: (01473) 312030 *Pest controllers*

▶ Lauriston Park Guest House, 6 Lauriston Park, Edinburgh, EH3 9JA Tel: 0131-228 5557 E-mail: info@lauristonpark.com *Edinburgh Bed and Breakfast Accommodation - Comfortable*guest house located in the city centre of Edinburgh. Bed and Breakfast accommodation in the capital of Scotland close to the Kings Theatre and the Edinburgh Castle. Our location is in the in the West End of the city and not far from the busy and famous shopping centre of Princes Street probably the premier shopping street in Scotland. Close at hand are numerous good retaurants , theatres and the world famous Usher hall. Only a five minute walk from here is the Edinburgh International Conference Centre which is located in the main financial district of the city.*

Lauriston Pine, 319 Torquay Road, Paignton, Devon, TQ3 2EY Tel: (01803) 664077 Fax: (01803) 664077 *Pine furniture sales, distribution & manufrs*

▶ Laurmar Storage & Distribution, Units 1-3, Heathhall Industrial Estate, Heathhall, Dumfries, DG1 3PH Tel: (01387) 250738 Fax: (01387) 259464

J.H. Lavender & Co. Ltd, Hall Green Works, Crankhall Lane, West Bromwich, West Midlands, B71 3JZ Tel: 0121-588 2273 Fax: 0121-588 7936 E-mail: lavender-diecast@city2000.net *Aluminium castings manufrs*

Lavendersblue Florists, 4 York Street, Ramsgate, Kent, CT11 9DS Tel: (01843) 595953 E-mail: lavenders36@aol.com *Florists*

Lavenham Leisure Ltd, 24-25 Churchfield Road, Sudbury, Suffolk, CO10 2YA Tel: (01787) 379535 Fax: (01787) 880096 E-mail: info@lavenhamhorserugs.com *Country clothing & horse rug manufrs*

Arnold Laver Birmingham Board Timberworld, Dudley Road, Oldbury, West Midlands, B69 3DA Tel: 0121-552 7788 Fax: 0121-544 7186 E-mail: sales@birminghamtimberworld.co.uk *Timber importers & merchants*

Laver Publishing, PO Box 7, Liverpool, L19 9EN Tel: 0151-475 7949 *Publishers*

Lavers Transport Ltd, North Downs Business Park, Limepit Lane, Dunton Green, Sevenoaks, Kent, TN13 2TL Tel: (01732) 462320 Fax: (01732) 740133 *Road transport, haulage & freight services*

Laverty Plant Hire, 24 Limavallaghan Rd, Clough, Ballymena, Co. Antrim, BT44 9RX Tel: (028) 2175 8613 *Plant hire*

▶ Lavery Transport, 14 Derryvore Lane, Portadown, Craigavon, County Armagh, BT63 5RS Tel: (028) 3835 0231 Fax: (028) 3836 8258 E-mail: info@laverytransport.co.uk *Road Haulage & distribution throughout Ireland & the UK*

Law & Accountancy Agency Services Ltd, 31 Corsham Street, London, N1 6DR Tel: (020) 7250 1410 Fax: (020) 7250 1973 E-mail: searches@landa.ltd.uk *Company registration agents*

Law Debenture Corporation Plc, 100 Wood St, London, EC2V 7EX Tel: (020) 7606 5451 Fax: (020) 7606 0643 E-mail: finance@lawdeb.co.uk *Investment trust company services*

George Law Ltd, 35 Mill Street, Kidderminster, Worcestershire, DY11 6XB Tel: (01562) 820421 Fax: (01562) 829205 *Building & civil engineers*

James Law (Chemicals) Ltd, Crossley Street Works, Royal Street, Smallbridge, Rochdale, Lancashire, OL16 2QA Tel: (01706) 644940 Fax: (01706) 644037 *Janitorial supplies manufrs*

Law Leisure & Learning, Community Hall, 2-10 Queens Head Road, Birmingham, B21 0QG Tel: 0121-551 5115 Fax: 0121-554 6417 *Computer training & consultants*

Law Security Systems, 9 Deal Avenue, Burntwood, Staffordshire, WS7 2EU Tel: (01543) 683036 Fax: (01543) 683036 *Burglar alarm fittings*

▶ Lawcris Panel Products Ltd, Unit C Cross Green Close, Leeds, LS9 0RY Tel: 0113-217 7177 Fax: 0113-240 5588 E-mail: sales@lawcris.co.uk *Panel distributors*

Lawday Engineering Ltd, Grafton Road, West Bromwich, West Midlands, B71 4EH Tel: 0121-553 4892 Fax: 0121-500 5842 E-mail: sales@lawday.co.uk *Die casting engineers & toolmakers services*

Law-Denis Engineering Ltd, Fengate, Peterborough, PE1 5PE Tel: (01733) 563000 Fax: (01733) 563300 E-mail: info@lawdenis.com *Manufacturers of bulk materials handling equipment & grain processing*

Lawford & Sons Ltd, Graham Park Way, London, NW9 5PQ Tel: (020) 8200 6622 Fax: (020) 8905 9400 *Builders merchants*

▶ Lawie Ltd, Midmill Business Park, Tumulus Way, Kintore, Inverurie, Aberdeenshire, AB51 0TG Tel: (01467) 633064 Fax: (01467) 633207

Lawlor Construction Ltd, Unit 12 Bentinck Street Industrial Estate, Manchester, M15 4LN Tel: 0161-839 3087 Fax: 0161-839 3010 E-mail: lawlorconstruct@btconnect.com *Civil engineering contractors*

▶ Lawlor Office Supplies Ltd, 2 Agecroft Enterprise Park, Shearer Way, Swinton, Manchester, M27 8WA Tel: 0161-737 0100 Fax: 0161-737 9944 E-mail: sales@lawloroffice.co.uk *Office supplies, furniture & lithographic printing services*

Lawmax Electrical Contractors Ltd, Lawmax House, 30-32 Nottingham Road, Stapleford, Nottingham, NG9 8AA Tel: 0115-939 4248 Fax: 0115-939 9412 E-mail: sales@lawmaxelec.co.uk *Electrical & computer installation contractors*

▶ Lawn Mower Leisure, 40 Field Acre Way, Long Stratton, Norwich, NR15 2WE Tel: (01508) 536793 E-mail: sales@lawnmowerleisure.co.uk *Lawn mowers specialists*

▶ Lawn3 (Bristol North) Ltd, 1 Amberley Close, Calne, Wiltshire, SN11 9UP Tel: (0800) 2889846 E-mail: bristolnorth@lawn3.co.uk *Want a green weed-free lawn? Lawn3 provide regular lawn treatment services for domestic and commercial lawns. We use the highest quality weedkillers and fertilizers to produce the greenest weed-free lawn you"ve ever seen. Try us today - call 0800 288 9846*

Lawncourt Harvest Ltd, Unit 6a Eastlands Industrial Estate, Leiston, Suffolk, IP16 4LL Tel: (01728) 833003 Fax: (01728) 833005 E-mail: sales@munchyseeds.co.uk *Health food manufrs*

▶ Lawncraft Ltd, 17 Holywell Hill, St. Albans, Herts, AL1 1DT Tel: 01727 856777 Fax: 01727 830087 E-mail: info@lawncraft.co.uk *Lawncraft provides a professional and affordable lawn and grass cutting service for domestic and commercial customers. A garden maintenance service is also available.*

Lawrayne Clothing Mnfrs, 13 Lockett Street, Manchester, M8 8EE Tel: 0161-839 1084 Fax: 0161-839 1084 *Rainwear & casual clothing manufrs*

▶ Lawrence & Co., 17 Cook Street, Leigh, Lancashire, WN7 4BT Tel: (01942) 674785 Fax: (01942) 674785 E-mail: enquires@lawcoflooring.co.uk *Refurbishments of terrazzo marble, granite & all other stone floorings*

Charles Lawrence International Ltd, Jessop Way, Newark, Nottinghamshire, NG24 2ER Tel: (01636) 610680 Fax: (01636) 610222 E-mail: sales@clgplc.co.uk *Scrap tyre recycling*

Lawrence Creative Ltd, 1 Newton Place, Glasgow, G3 7PR Tel: 0141-333 9009 Fax: 0141-333 9495 E-mail: design@lawrencecreative.com *Graphic designers*

▶ David Lawrence Lighting, Unit 7, New Lydenburg Commercial Estate, New Lydenburg Street, London, SE7 8NF Tel: (020) 8858 2820 Fax: (020) 8858 2820 E-mail: david@davidlawrencelights.co.uk *Lighting & consumables for video & photographic trade*

▶ Lawrence & Foster Ltd, Unit B5 Whitwood Enterprise Park, Whitwood Lane, Whitwood, Castleford, West Yorkshire, WF10 5PX Tel: (01977) 604440 Fax: (01977) 604442

Lawrence Group Ltd, 63-66 Hatton Garden, London, EC1N 8LE Tel: (020) 7242 6521 Fax: (020) 7404 0551 *Precious metal dealers & jewellery shop*

Lawrence & Hayward, 148 Abercromby Avenue, High Wycombe, Buckinghamshire, HP12 3BJ Tel: (01494) 520329 Fax: (01494) 520329 *Precision engineers*

Lawrence Industries Ltd, Lawrence House, Apollo, Tamworth, Staffordshire, B79 7TA Tel: (01827) 314151 Fax: (01827) 314152 E-mail: sales@l-i.co.uk *Chemical distributors & merchants*

J.C. Lawrence & Sons, 44 Elmhurst Road, Gosport, Hampshire, PO12 1PQ Tel: (023) 9258 1445 *Commercial photographer*

Lawrence Joinery Pine Specialists, Unit 15b Greenhill Mills, Grange Road, Batley, West Yorkshire, WF17 6LH Tel: (01924) 422088 Fax: (01924) 422088 *Pine furniture manufrs*

Lawrence M Barry & Co., Britannia Mill, North Cresent, London, E16 4TG Tel: (020) 7473 2898 Fax: (020) 7473 1381 E-mail: sales@1mb.co.uk *Textile recycling*

Lawrence & Tester Ltd, Property Services House, George Summers Close, Medway City Estate, Rochester, Kent, ME2 4NS Tel: (01306) 886313 Fax: (01634) 290777 E-mail: reception@lawrenceandtester.co.uk *Office cleaning contractors*

Laws Glass, 22 Marston Lane, Bedworth, Warwickshire, CV12 8DH Tel: (024) 7664 0030 Fax: (024) 7664 0777 E-mail: info@shopfronts-midlands.com *Glazing contractors*

Lawson Bros, 7 Snoll Hatch Road, East Peckham, Tonbridge, Kent, TN12 5EE Tel: (01622) 872816 *Canvas goods manufrs*

Lawson Distributors Ltd, Scotshaw Brook House, Scotshaw Brook Estate, Lower Darwen, Darwen, Lancashire, BB3 0PR Tel: (01254) 677121 Fax: (01254) 665922 E-mail: sales@johnlawsondist.co.uk *Industrial fastener & engineers tool distributors*

Lawson Engineers Ltd, Barras Lane, Dalston, Carlisle, CA5 7ND Tel: (01228) 711470 Fax: (01228) 711255 E-mail: sales@lawson-engineers.com *Mechanical handling equipment manufrs*

Lawson Fuses Ltd, Meadowfield, Ponteland, Newcastle upon Tyne, NE20 9SW Tel: (01661) 823232 Fax: (01661) 824213 E-mail: sales@lawson-fuses.co.uk *Fuses & fuse holder manufrs*

▶ Grant Lawson Ltd, Albany House, 14 Shute End, Wokingham, Berkshire, RG40 1BJ Tel: 0118-979 6023 Fax: (07092) 382965 *Professional accountancy recruitment*

H.I.S. Lawson Ltd, 84-88 Millbrook Road East, Southampton, SO15 1BG Tel: (023) 8063 2927 Fax: (023) 8033 9878 E-mail: enquiries@lawson-his.co.uk *Industrial supplies distributors*

▶ Harry Lawson Ltd, Balunie Drive, Dundee, DD4 8UU Tel: (01382) 738100 Fax: (01382) 480275

Lawson Model Makers, 21 Viking Way, Metheringham, Lincoln, LN4 3DW Tel: (01526) 321628 Fax: (01526) 322140 E-mail: john@jlawson.com *Model makers & engineering industry*

Lawson Products Ltd, 300 Quadrant, Ash Ridge Road, Bradley Stoke, Bristol, BS32 4QA Tel: (01454) 202223 Fax: (01454) 618510 Principal Export Areas: Central/East Europe *Maintenance consumables suppliers*

▶ Lawson Richard Motor Co., Rossfield Road, Ellesmere Port, CH65 3BS Tel: 0151-355 2155 Fax: 0151-357 1229

Lawson Software, Building C Trinity Court, Wokingham Road, Bracknell, Berkshire, RG42 1PL Tel: (01344) 360273 Fax: (01344) 868351 *Human resource services*

Lawson Timber Ltd, White Hart Road, London, SE18 1DH Tel: (020) 8855 7621 Fax: (020) 8854 6552 *Timber merchants*

Lawson Ward & Gammage Ltd, 4 Berry Street, London, EC1V 0AE Tel: (020) 7253 4146 Fax: (020) 7253 4944 E-mail: info@lwandg.com *Jewellery manufacturers & suppliers*

Lawson Wood Ltd, 4 Heliport Estate, Lombard Road, London, SW11 3RE Tel: (020) 7228 9812 Fax: (020) 7738 2499 *Household furniture manufrs*

Lawsons Builders Merchants, 164 Collier Row Road, Romford, RM5 2BD Tel: (01708) 767716 Fax: (01708) 746354 E-mail: sales@lawsons.co.uk *Builders merchants*

Lawsons Gibbs & Co. Ltd, 46-47 Dorset Street, London, W1U 7ND Tel: (020) 7580 9000 Fax: (020) 7935 5166 E-mail: sales@lawson-gibbs-co.demon.co.uk *Social, press & commercial photographers*

Lawsons Whetstone Ltd, Woodcote Grove Road, Coulsdon, Surrey, CR5 2AG Tel: (020) 8660 0807 Fax: (020) 8668 4847 *DIY & timber merchants*

Andrew Lawton Furniture, Goatscliff Workshops, Grindleford, Hope Valley, Derbyshire, S32 2HG Tel: (01433) 631754 Fax: (01433) 631754 E-mail: andrewlawton@btinternet.com *Bespoke furniture manufrs*

Edwin Lawton Ltd, Old Quarry, Uttoxeter Road, Blythe Bridge, Stoke-on-Trent, ST11 9ND Tel: (01782) 393631 Fax: (01782) 388221 E-mail: pallets@edwinlawton.com *Manufacturers of wooden pallets & packing cases*

Fred Lawton & Son Ltd, Meltham Mills, Meltham, Holmfirth, HD9 4AY Tel: (01484) 852573 Fax: (01484) 852737 E-mail: enquiries@fredlawton.com *Carpet yarn spinners*

Lawton Precision Engineers Ltd, 1 25a Hanworth Road, Sunbury-on-Thames, Middlesex, TW16 5DA Tel: (01932) 789001 Fax: (01932) 789003 *Precision engineers*

Lawton Tools Ltd, Manor Street, Stoke-on-Trent, ST4 2UF Tel: (01782) 747007 Fax: (01782) 413983 E-mail: sales@lawtontools.co.uk *Engineer merchants*

▶ Lawtons Group Ltd, 60 Vauxhall Road, Liverpool, L3 6DL Tel: 0151-479 3000 Fax: 0151-479 3001 E-mail: info@lawtonsgroup.co.uk Principal Export Areas: Worldwide *Wholesalers*

Lawtronic Ltd, Hamlin Way, King's Lynn, Norfolk, PE30 4NG Tel: (01553) 765247 Fax: (01553) 692147 *Control system engineers*

Laxbrin Ltd, York House, Empire Way, Wembley, Middlesex, HA9 0QL Tel: (020) 8900 0243 Fax: (020) 8900 1804 E-mail: laxbrin@aol.com *Import & export confirming house*

Laxford Steels, 21 Load Street, Bewdley, Worcestershire, DY12 2AE Tel: (01299) 400144 Fax: (01299) 400144 *Steel stockholders*

Laxmi Investments Ltd, 123 Barkby Road, Leicester, LE4 9LG Tel: 0116-276 6625 Fax: 0116-246 0787 *Knitted fabric manufrs*

R.A. Laxton Ltd, Unit 3k The Stormall Industrial Estate, Liddicoat Road, Lostwithiel, Cornwall, PL22 0HE Tel: (01208) 872224 Fax: (01208) 871070 *Swimming nose clip manufrs*

Laxton Tool Supplies Ltd, Royal Leamington Spa, Leamington Spa, Warwickshire, CV32 5GN Tel: (01239) 820212 Fax: (01239) 820763 E-mail: laxtontool@aol.com *Hand & machine tool sales*

▶ Lay Construction Ltd, 1 Eastcott Hill, Swindon, SN1 3JG Tel: (01793) 616677 Fax: (01793) 488428 E-mail: post@whitehorse.co.uk

Laybond Products Ltd, Riverside, Chester, CH4 8RS Tel: (01244) 674774 Fax: (01244) 682218 E-mail: sales-info@laybond.com *Manufacturers of bitumen compounds, adhesives, floor coverings & roofing*

Laycast Ltd, Sheffield Road, Woodhouse Mill, Sheffield, S13 9ZD Tel: 0114-288 9995 Fax: 0114-288 9500 E-mail: info@laycast.com *General engineers & iron casting manufrs*

E.G. Laycock & Sons Ltd, Layco Works, Smithfield, Sheffield, S3 7AR Tel: 0114-272 0880 Fax: 0114-276 8519 E-mail: chefcutler@aol.com *General engineers*

Laycock International Ltd, Stanley Mills, Whitley Street, Bingley, West Yorkshire, BD16 4JH Tel: (01274) 562563 Fax: (01274) 562823 E-mail: mohair@legend.co.uk *Speciality top makers*

Laycocks Agricultural Chemists, Gargrave Road, Skipton, North Yorkshire, BD23 1UD Tel: (01756) 792166 Fax: (01756) 701008 E-mail: info@laycocks.co.uk *Agricultural veterinary medicine retailers & wholesalers*

Laycocks Animal Health, Showfield Lane, Malton, North Yorkshire, YO17 6BT Tel: (01653) 600328 Fax: (01653) 690338 *Agricultural chemists*

▶ Layfix Flooring Ltd, PO Box 2764, Calne, Wiltshire, SN11 9QY Tel: (01249) 816713 Fax: (01249) 816713 E-mail: enquiries_layfix@hotmail.com *Flooring specialists*

Layher Ltd, Works Road, Letchworth Garden City, Hertfordshire, SG6 1WL Tel: (01462) 475100 Fax: (01462) 475101 E-mail: info@layher.com *Scaffolding manufacture, hire & rental*

Layton Blackham Insurance Brokers Ltd, Weston House, 246 High Holborn, London, WC1V 7EX Tel: (0870) 1600201 Fax: (020) 7415 3910 *General insurance*

Layton Technologies, Parkhall Business Park, Parkhall Road, Weston Coyney, Stoke-on-Trent, ST3 5XA Tel: (01782) 370400 Fax: (01782) 333202 E-mail: webenquiries@laytontechnologies.com *Manufacturers of component cleaning systems*

Layton-Fine Machine Technologies Ltd, Units E8-E9, Park La, Castle Vale, Birmingham, B35 6LJ Tel: 0121-776 8883 Fax: 0121-776 8884 E-mail: enquiries@layton-fine.co.uk *Spark erosion & wire erosion machine distributors or agents. Also spark erosion machine (used/secondhand) dealers & machine tool merchants*

▶ Laytrad, Fith Floor Northway House, 1379 High Road, London, N20 9LP Tel: (020) 8492 3604 Fax: (020) 8446 5944 E-mail: sales@1aytrad.co.uk

Laywell Beds Ltd, Cordingley Street, Bradford, West Yorkshire, BD4 0PP Tel: (01274) 681000 Fax: (01274) 681666 *Bed manufrs*

▶ Lazar Signs, 4 Period Works, 1 Lammas Road, London, E10 7QT Tel: (020) 8558 5656 Fax: (020) 8556 4725 E-mail: sales@lazarsigns.co.uk *Sign manufacture & installation*

Lazawood Ltd, 79 Farleigh Road, Warlingham, Surrey, CR6 9EJ Tel: (01883) 622151 Fax: (01883) 624533 Principal Export Areas: Worldwide *Manufacturers of shop fitting display cabinets*

La-z-Boy, Centurion Building, Lancashire Enterprises Business Park, Leyland, PR26 6JW Tel: (01772) 450100 Fax: (01772) 453511 E-mail: sales@centurion.tellme.com Principal Export Areas: North America, Central America & South America *Furniture suppliers*

Lazdan Builders Merchants Ltd, 218 Bow Common Lane, London, E3 4HH Tel: (020) 8980 2213 Fax: (020) 8980 5395 *Reclaimed building materials suppliers*

▶ Lazenby Design Associates, Coach Cottage, Riverside Lane, Summerbridge, Harrogate, North Yorkshire, HG3 4JP Tel: (01423) 781781 E-mail: info@lazenbydesign.com *Designers of habitats and immersive environments for zoos, aquaria, nature centres and museums.*

Lazenby Metal Services, Unit 34 Calder Wharf Mills, Huddersfield Road, Dewsbury, West Yorkshire, WF13 3JW Tel: (01924) 457777 Fax: (01924) 457755 E-mail: enquiries@lazenbymetal.com *Stockholders, metal finishing & polishing services*

Lazenbys Ltd, Main Street, Hull, HU2 0LF Tel: (01482) 329519 Fax: (01482) 216152 *CNC sheet metal engineers*

Lazer Kits Ltd, Lissadel Street, Salford, M6 6GG Tel: 0161-743 1400 Fax: 0161-743 1411 E-mail: info@lazerkits.co.uk *Sportswear & kit manufrs*

Lazer Partitions & Ceilings, 119a Tarring Road, Worthing, West Sussex, BN11 4HE Tel: (01903) 205719 Fax: (01903) 204041 E-mail: lazer@mistral.co.uk *Partitions, suspended ceilings, mezzanine floors, office interiors, air conditioning, project management, shop fitting, small and large projects undertaken, nationwide and overseas service.*

Lazer Printing, 65 Coniston Road, Peterborough, PE4 7UL Tel: (01733) 324404 Fax: (01733) 324404 *General & promotional printers*

Lazer Promotions, Unit 26 Midland Oak Trading Es, Marlissa Dr, Coventry, CV6 6HQ Tel: 024 76661213 Fax: 024 76661213 *Kitchens & exhibitions*

▶ Lazer Security Ltd, DMB House, 2 Beckett Road, Doncaster, South Yorkshire, DN2 4AA Tel: (01302) 344773

Lazer Vix Ltd, Turner Buildings, Russell Road, Birkenhead, Merseyside, CH42 1LU Tel: 0151-644 8860 Fax: 0151-643 1204 *Nail & screw distributors*

Lazerbuilt Ltd, 20 Gunnels Wood Park, Gunnels Wood Road, Stevenage, Hertfordshire, SG1 2BH Tel: (01438) 743753 Fax: (01438) 720077 E-mail: enquiries@lazerbuilt.co.uk *Telephone equipment & mobile accessories*

Lazgill Ltd, 1 Vicarage Road, Hampton Wick, Kingston Upon Thames, Surrey, KT1 4EB Tel: (020) 8977 2125 Fax: (020) 8943 3248 E-mail: sales@lazgill.co.uk *Precision engineers*

▶ LB Computer Solutions, 6 Whitelees Road, Cleghorn, Lanark, ML11 7SP Tel: (01555) 870394 *Computer maintenance & repair*

LB Ford Ltd, Park Lane, Nottingham, NG6 0DT Tel: 0115-927 2821 Fax: 0115-976 1041 E-mail: lb@ford.co.uk *Electrical contractors*

▶ Lba International Ltd, 2 Caxton Close, Drayton Fields Industrial Estate, Daventry, Northamptonshire, NN11 8RT Tel: (01327) 311020 Fax: (01327) 311030 E-mail: sales@lbainternational.com *Ballistic body armour manufacturers*

▶ LBBC Ltd, Beechwood Street, Pudsey, West Yorkshire, LS28 6PT Tel: 0113-205 7400 Fax: 0113-256 3509 E-mail: sales@lbbc.co.uk *Autoclave manufacturing services*

LBS Builders Merchants Ltd, Station Road, Llandeilo, Dyfed, SA19 6NL Tel: (01558) 822385 Fax: (01558) 822145 E-mail: mdavies@lbs-buildersmerchants.co.uk *Building materials & civil merchants*

LBS South West Ltd, 29 Amberley Way, Wickwar, Wotton-under-Edge, Gloucestershire, GL12 8LW Tel: 0117-956 3004 Fax: (01454) 299209 E-mail: sales@lbscashregisters.co.uk *Cash registers*

▶ LBVALETING, 55 Walnut Crescent, Kettering, Northamptonshire, NN16 9PX Tel: (01536) 501217 E-mail: lbvaleting@hotmail.com *ALL VALETING AT ONE SET PRICE AT TRADE PRICES WE COME TO YOU LOOK AT WEB SITE FOR MORE HELP*

▶ LCH Generators, 13 Main Street, Milngavie, Glasgow, G62 6BJ Tel: 0141-956 7111 Fax: 0141-956 7222 E-mail: headoffice@speedygenerators.co.uk *Generators retail & hire services*

LCI Ltd, 55 Merthyr Terrace, Barnes, London, SW13 8DL Tel: (020) 8741 5747 Fax: (020) 8748 9879 E-mail: contact@lci-uk.com *Laser & water screen display shows & multimedia productions*

LCP, 3 Mill Road, Portslade, Brighton, BN41 1PD Tel: (01273) 430730 Fax: (01273) 430901 E-mail: sales@lcp-automotive.co.uk *Motor component distributors*

LCP Automotive Components, Bridge Road, Ashford, Kent, TN23 1BB Tel: (01233) 623113 Fax: (01233) 631366 *Motor component distributors*

LCP Automotive Components, Prospect House, Broad Oak Road, Canterbury, Kent, CT2 7PX Tel: (01227) 766001 Fax: (01227) 769425 *Motor components sales* Also at: Ashford, Brighton, Dartford, Gillingham, Maidstone, Norfleet & Tunbridge Wells

LCP Automotive Components, 15 Acorn Industrial Park, Crayford Road, Dartford, DA1 4AL Tel: (01322) 557825 Fax: (01322) 557829 *Motor components*

LCP Automotive Components, 555 Canterbury Street, Gillingham, Kent, ME7 5LF Tel: (01634) 575506 Fax: (01634) 855573 *Motor component distributors*

LCP Automotive Components, St. Peter Street, Maidstone, Kent, ME16 0SN Tel: (01622) 672222 Fax: (01622) 672227 *Motor component distributors*

LCP Automotive Components, 3 Lamberts Road, Tunbridge Wells, Kent, TN2 3EH Tel: (01892) 544829 Fax: (01892) 548131 *Motor component distributors*

▶ LCP Packaging Materials, Unit 4a Tanfield Lea Industrial Estate South, Tanfield Lea, Stanley, County Durham, DH9 9QX Tel: (01207) 237666 Fax: (01207) 238666 E-mail: enquiries@lcp.linst.ac.uk

LCT, 7 Acorn Mews, Harlow, Essex, CM18 6NA Tel: (01279) 411331 Fax: (01279) 412864 E-mail: sales@lctinternational.com *Management & training consultants*

LCW, 56 Norfolk Street, Liverpool, L1 0BE Tel: 0151-709 7034 Fax: 0151-708 6022 *Carpet underlay rubber*

▶ LD Sussex Decoration, Bexhill Road, Eastbourne, East Sussex, BN22 7JJ Tel: (01323) 646721 Fax: (01323) 646721 E-mail: demiralplevent@hotmail.com *INTERIOR EXTERIOR PAINTING AND DECORATING SERVICE, FLOORING,TILING,RENDERING,GENERAL MAINTENANCE*

▶ LD Trailer Sales Ltd, Munroe House, Ringtail Court, Burscough Industrial Estate, Burscough, Lancashire, L40 8LB Tel: 01704 893009 Fax: 01704 896660 E-mail: sales@ldtrailersales.co.uk *Supply and purchase second hand Trailers and commercial vehicles. Assist with refurbishments, renewals and repairs of all commercial vehicles.*

▶ LDA Chain Specialists, Unit 11, Bamford Business Park, Stockport, Cheshire, SK4 1PL Tel: 0161-477 5252 Fax: 0161-477 9559 E-mail: lda.transmission@btconnect.com *Established in 1980 LDA is a leading specialist in the supply of a diverse range of transmission and conveyor chain and associated accessories. The 'Climax' range of Quality Roller Chain with over 100 years experience in supplying world markets, available in both BS and Ansi standards have been developed to provide the user with manufacturing design that formulate such factors as fatigue and wear resistance, high tensile strength giving the best solution to long chain life. LDA manufacture in house attachment chains K/M and extended pins on a very fast turn round. Special attachments are also available; many designed and manufactured to meet individual applications. From agriculture to heavy machinery, food processing and packaging we have the right chain for you. We are the number one UK stockist of Agricultural chains, Hollow Pin chains, Extended Pin chains, Rubber Top chains, Accumulation chains, ISO and Metric Conveyor chains, available plated or in stainless steel.*

LDJ, Bridge Works, Iver Lane, Uxbridge, Middlesex, UB8 2JG Tel: (01895) 231880 Fax: (01895) 271825 *Sheet metalwork engineers*

Le Baron Marketing, 16 Maddox Street, London, W1S 1PH Tel: (020) 7499 5343 Fax: (020) 7493 7331 E-mail: elena@cxd.co.uk *Marketing & pr (cashmere)*

Le Carbone Great Britain Ltd, South Street, Portslade, Brighton, BN41 2LX Tel: (01273) 415701 Fax: (01273) 415673 *Manufacturers of carbon brush*

Le Carousel, 35 Easter Park, Benyon Road, Silchester, Reading, RG7 2PQ Tel: 0118-970 0228 Fax: 0118-970 1944 *Stove enamelling & metal spraying services*

Le Computer, School Road, Rayne, Braintree, Essex, CM77 6SR Tel: (01376) 348886 Fax: (01376) 349996 E-mail: info@lecomputer.co.uk *Supply & installation of computer cabling & hardware*

Le Craft Products, Unit 10-11 Ebblake Industrial Estate, Forest Close, Ebblake Industrial Estate, Verwood, Dorset, BH31 6DE Tel: (01202) 827171 Fax: (01202) 813020 *Spark erosion machining services*

Le Creuset (UK) Ltd, 4 Stephenson Close, East Portway, Andover, Hampshire, SP10 3RU Tel: (01264) 343900 Fax: (01264) 356396 *Cast iron cookware*

Le Guellec, Stone Road, Tittensor, Stoke-On-Trent, ST12 9HA Tel: (01782) 374111 Fax: (01782) 373488 E-mail: info@wlmetals.co.uk *Manufacturers of precision tubes*

Le Maitre Fireworks Ltd, Unit 6 Forval Close, Mitcham, Surrey, CR4 4NE Tel: (020) 8646 2222 Fax: (020) 8646 1955 E-mail: info@lemaitreltd.com *Stage effects manufrs* Also at: Peterborough

Le Mark Self Adhesives Ltd, Houghton Hill Industries, Houghton Hill Farm, Houghton, Huntingdon, Cambridgeshire, PE28 2DH Tel: (01480) 494540 Fax: (01480) 494206 E-mail: info@lemark.co.uk *Adhesive tape distributors & self adhesive labels*

Le Marquand Bros, 5-6 Peirson Road, St. Helier, Jersey, JE2 3PD Tel: (01534) 723261 Fax: (01534) 768971 *Pet shop retailers*

Le Meridien, North Terminal, London Gatwick Airport, Gatwick, West Sussex, RH6 0PH Tel: (01293) 567070 Fax: (01293) 567739 E-mail: sales@1emeridien-gatwick.com *Hotel with conference facilities*

▶ Le Missey Ltd, 18-20 Grosvenor Street, Manchester, M1 7JJ Tel: 0161-273 1777 Fax: 0161-273 7778 *Knitwear manufrs*

▶ Le Moulin, Mill Walk, Wheathampstead, St. Albans, Hertfordshire, AL4 8DT Tel: (01582) 831988 Fax: (01582) 831988 E-mail: julie.bell@can-do.co.uk *Gourmet Meals expertly cooked from the finest fresh ingredients to your exact requirements - for dinner parties at home or our restaurant.*

Le Pain De Paris, Unit 1/2 Off Mill Yard, Kendal, Cumbria, LA9 4QR Tel: (01539) 822102 Fax: (01539) 822420 *Bakery & food distribution*

Le Pla & Co Automation Ltd, Riverside Works, Neepsend Lane, Sheffield, S3 8AU Tel: 0114-273 1020 Fax: 0114-273 9331 E-mail: engineers@le-pla.com *Precision engineer services*

▶ Le Rule Originals, 2 Selsey Close, Hayling Island, Hampshire, PO11 9SX Tel: 02392 463845 Fax: 02392 463845 E-mail: louise@leruleoriginals.co.uk *Handmade fashion jewellery & rosary*

Le Software Man Ltd, Aberdeen House, 22 Highbury Grove, London, N5 2EA Tel: (020) 7354 8414 Fax: (020) 7226 2015 E-mail: sales@answersthatwork.com *Computer consultants*

Le Strange Arms, Golf Course Road, Hunstanton, Norfolk, PE36 6JJ Tel: (01485) 534411 Fax: (01485) 534724 *Hotel with conference facilities, banqueting, restaurant & bar*

Le Vigneron, 26 Lion Road, Bexleyheath, Kent, DA6 8NR Tel: (020) 8303 3534 Fax: (020) 8303 3534 E-mail: sales@levigneron.co.uk *Wine importers*

▶ LE16 Communications, 3 Corby Road, Cottingham, Market Harborough, Leicestershire, LE16 8XH Tel: 01536 770821 Fax: 01536 770827 E-mail: jane@LE16.com *LE16 is a regionally based communications agency with the national experience to help you make headlines. Whatever the size of your company, we"ll show you how public relations can raise your profile and generate sales efficiently and cost effectively.**We can also help you to develop internal communications that place your employees at the heart of your success and truly add value to your business.**Our services include media campaigns, communications audits, change and crisis communications, newsletters, marketing materials, copywriting, video and audio production. Whatever level of support you require - from strategic planning to practical implementation - LE16 can make communications work for you. ***

Lea Boxes Ltd, 38 Camford Way, Luton, LU3 3AN Tel: (01582) 505561 Fax: (01582) 490352 E-mail: maria@leaboxes.co.uk *Cardboard box & carton manufrs*

Lea Manufacturing Co., Tongue Lane, Buxton, Derbyshire, SK17 7LN Tel: (01298) 25335 Fax: (01298) 79945 E-mail: sales@lea.co.uk *Abrasive & buff manufrs* Also at: Birmingham & Sutton

Leabank Coatings Ltd, Wycombe Road, Stokenchurch, High Wycombe, Buckinghamshire, HP14 3RJ Tel: (01494) 483737 Fax: (01494) 484239 E-mail: info@leabank.net *Decorative & protective coating services*

Leach Bros, Old Market Field Industrial Estate, Witheridge, Tiverton, Devon, EX16 8TA Tel: (01884) 861120 Fax: (01884) 860902 E-mail: leachbrothers@aol.com *Agricultural engineers*

Leach & Clegg, Lily Street, Milnrow, Rochdale, Lancashire, OL16 3NQ Tel: (01706) 642757 Fax: (01706) 658369 *Joinery manufrs*

Leach Glass & Catering Equipment Hire Service, Unit 3, Switch Hill, School Yard, Horbury, Wakefield, West Yorkshire, WF4 6NA Tel: (01924) 278516 Fax: (01924) 274399 *Catering equiptment hire services*

Leach Lewis Ltd, Victoria House, Britannia Road, Waltham Cross, Hertfordshire, EN8 7NU Tel: (01992) 704100 Fax: (01992) 704170 E-mail: enquiries@leachlewis.co.uk *Construction Equipment Sales - Parts - Aftersales Services & Repairs - Finance ..Brands include Thwaites, Bomag, Kubota, Manitou, Atlas Copco, Clipper, Honda, Partner, Stihl.* Also at: Oxford

Leach Pottery, Higher Stennack, St. Ives, Cornwall, TR26 2HE Tel: (01736) 799703 *Pottery manufacturing*

R.E. Leach (Engineers) Ltd, Brockles Way, Garstang, Preston, PR3 0PZ Tel: 01995 640133 *Structural engineers*

Leach & Thompson Ltd, Chapel Foundry, Dalton Lane, Keighley, West Yorkshire, BD21 4JU Tel: (01535) 602452 Fax: (01535) 669183 E-mail: info@smallcasting.co.uk *Iron founders. Small castings, high technical specification*

Leach's Lawnmower Centre, Unit 2 Ford Street, Stockport, Cheshire, SK3 0BT Tel: 0161-477 5688 Fax: 0161-477 5688 E-mail: leachs.lawnmowers@virgin.net *Lawn mower sales & service*

Leaco Ltd, Lamberhead Industrial Estate, Leopold Street, Wigan, Lancashire, WN5 8DH Tel: (01942) 221188 Fax: (01942) 226682 E-mail: sales@leaco.ltd.uk *Injection moulders & pressworkers*

▶ Leacy Construction Contractors, 93 London Road, Sawbridgeworth, Hertfordshire, CM21 9JJ Tel: (01279) 723455

Lead Precision Machine Tools Ltd, Calamine House, Calamine Street, Macclesfield, Cheshire, SK11 7HU Tel: (01625) 434990 Fax: (01625) 434996 E-mail: sales@leadmachinetools.co.uk *CNC machine tool specialists*

Leadatom Europe Ltd, 1 Shamrock Enterprise Centre, Wingate Road, Gosport, Hampshire, PO12 4DP Tel: (023) 9252 3973 Fax: (023) 9252 3973 E-mail: sales@leadatom.co.uk *LeadAtom Europe Ltd based in Gosport, Hampshire are manufacturers of radiation shielding equipment & all types of lead castings, weights & stampings*

▶ Leadbitter Construction, Grange Court Abingdon Science Park, Barton Lane, Abingdon, Oxfordshire, OX14 3NB Tel: (01235) 544500 Fax: (01235) 544600

▶ Leadbitter Construction, 4 Ivanhoe Road, Finchampstead, Wokingham, Berkshire, RG40 4QQ Tel: 0118-973 7541 Fax: 0118-973 1901

Leader Sound, Causeway End, Church Causeway, Potton, Sandy, Bedfordshire, SG19 2RL Tel: (01767) 262880 Fax: (01767) 262888 E-mail: info@leadersound.com *Professional audio equipment service & maintenance*

Leaders 89 Ltd, Cable Harnesses, 6 Union Road, Chippenham, Wiltshire, SN15 1HW Tel: (01249) 651180 Fax: (01249) 651180 *Manufacturers of cable looms & electrical assemblies*

▶ Leadership Development Centre, Technology House, University of Salford, Lissadell Street, Salford, M6 6AP Tel: 0161 2782413 E-mail: enquires@ldc-uk.com *Conflict management training. door supervisor training qualifications licensing team Leadership Development Centre door staff licensing supervisor team training qualifications BII BIIAB NCL NLC Licensing Act 2003 licensing Reform Workshops National Certificate for Licensees On-License Off-License PartIV license National Certificate for Door Supervisors Licensed Premises Professional barperson"s Qualification National Barperson"s Qualification Approved Centre Salford Manchester North West communcation customer service hospitality management professional personal development business development doormen conflict CPD continuing personal development training education assistant intermediate cellar beer quality food hospitality catering reception quality licensing authority magistrates police sergeant permits new legislation Security guarding, vehicle immobilisation,*

The Leadership Trust Training Ltd, Weston Under Penyard, Weston under Penyard, Ross-on-Wye, Herefordshire, HR9 7YH Tel: (01667) 455811 Fax: (01989) 768133 E-mail: enquiries@leadership.co.uk Principal Export Areas: Africa *Project managers*

▶ Lead-In Research, Walton Road, 13-14 Wellesbourne House, Wellesbourne, Warwick, CV35 9JB Tel: (01789) 471555 Fax: (01789) 471550 E-mail: info@leadinresearch.co.uk *Providers of exclusive business leads. Get the latest info on companies planning to relocate, refurbish or invest in new products and services. Free trial available*

Leading Computer Ltd, 27 Vesta Avenue, St. Albans, Hertfordshire, AL1 2PG Tel: (01727) 867705 Fax: (01727) 867705 *Computer repair consultants*

Leading Edge Systems Ltd, 203 High La West, West Hallam, Ilkeston, Derbyshire, DE7 6HP Tel: 0115-944 7994 *System & software suppliers*

▶ Leading Health & Safety Consultants Ltd, 26 Chaplin Walk, Great Cornard, Sudbury, Suffolk, CO10 0YT Tel: (01787) 377265 Fax: (01787) 883190 E-mail: info@leadinghealthandsafety.co.uk *Occupational health & safety consultants*

Leading Labels Ltd, 1 Main Street, Alexandria, Dunbartonshire, G83 0UG Tel: (01389) 607101 Fax: (01389) 607104 *Men's & women's retail outlet*

Leadline Services Ltd, 54 New Street, Worcester, WR1 2DL Tel: (01905) 724000 Fax: (01905) 726888 E-mail: sales@leadline.co.uk *Leadline is an established call centre offering Telephone Answering, IVR, Database Cleansing and Customer Satisfaction Surveys.**

Leaf & Carver Electrical Services Ltd, 323 Kennington Road, London, SE11 4QE Tel: (020) 7735 8434 Fax: (020) 7735 0552 E-mail: leaf_carver@btconnect.com *Electrical contractors*

Leaf Clothing, 1 Niphon Works, 43-68 Lower Villiers Street, Wolverhampton, WV2 4NA Tel: (01902) 427946 *Children's clothing manufr*

▶ Leaf (U K) Ltd, 66 Virginia St, Southport, Merseyside, PR8 6RX Tel: (01704) 502400

▶ Leafcutter Design, 119 Penn Hill Avenue, Poole, Dorset, BH14 9LY Tel: (01202) 716969 Fax: (01202) 716969 E-mail: sales@leafcutterdesign.co.uk *Retail of tiles*

Leafe & Hawkes Ltd, 5 Merrick Street, Hull, HU9 1NF Tel: (01482) 325951 Fax: (01482) 225406 E-mail: s.leafe@leafeandhawkes.co.uk *Ship brokers & freight forwarders* Also at: Grimsby & Scarborough

Leafield Engineering Ltd, Leafield Industrial Estate, Corsham, Wiltshire, SN13 9SS Tel: (01225) 810771 Fax: (01225) 810614 E-mail: lel@leafield.co.uk *Pyrotechnics & valve engineers*

Leaflike Floral & Plant Displays, Wallingford Road, Uxbridge, Middlesex, UB8 2RW Tel: (01895) 810910 Fax: (01895) 233609 *Contract plant suppliers for commercial businesses*

Leak Repairs UK, Kings Road, Immingham, South Humberside, DN40 1FN Tel: (01469) 550527 Fax: (01469) 576293 E-mail: sales@leakrepairs.co.uk *On-line leak sealing services*

Leakes Masonry Ltd, James Street, Louth, Lincolnshire, LN11 0JW Tel: (01507) 604828 Fax: (01507) 600826 E-mail: info@leakes-masonry.com *Stone masonry contractors*

Le-Al (Associates) Ltd, Zenith House, Cromwell Road, Bredbury, Stockport, Cheshire, SK6 2RF Tel: 0161-406 9899 Fax: 0161-406 9880 E-mail: info@le-al.co.uk *Executive office furniture manufrs*

Le-Al (Associates) Ltd, Zenith House, Cromwell Road, Bredbury, Stockport, Cheshire, SK6 2RF Tel: 0161-406 9899 Fax: 0161-406 9880 *Furniture manufrs*

Keith Lealand Services, 50 Village Farm Road, Village Farm Industrial Estate, Pyle, Bridgend, Mid Glamorgan, CF33 6BN Tel: (01656) 742555 Fax: (01656) 744261 *Pipework bellows & pipe tool hire*

Leamington Pine Workshop, Unit 2 Court Street, Milverton House, Leamington Spa, Warwickshire, CV31 2BB Tel: (01926) 312229 Fax: (01926) 312229 *Wooden furniture manufrs*

▶ Leamore Contracts Ltd, 2-3 Walsall Road, Willenhall, West Midlands, WV13 2EH Tel: (01902) 601559 Fax: (01902) 637591

Leander Architectural, Hallsteads Close, Dove Holes, Buxton, Derbyshire, SK17 8BP Tel: (01298) 814941 Fax: (01298) 814970 E-mail: sales@1eanderarch.demon.co.uk *Cast metal sign manufrs*

▶ Leap Coaching Associates, 7 Hopewell Way, Crigglestone, Wakefield, West Yorkshire, WF4 3PU Tel: (01924) 254173 *Personal one-to-one performance and career coaching/ mentoring for managers and professionals in organisations, life coaching and HR consulting solutions.*

▶ Leapfrog Properties, Sutton Court Road, Chiswick, London, W4 4NN Tel: (0845) 6066919 Fax: (020) 8742 1170 E-mail: info@leapfrog-properties.com *Specialist French property agency with online database of up to 200,000 properties for sale. Provides personal service from fluent French speakers to help clients find, view and buy their property*

▶ Leapfrogg Ltd, Tower Point, 44 North Road, Brighton, BN1 1YR Tel: 01273 669450 E-mail: jody.mason@leapfrogg.co.uk

Leapwade International Training Ltd, Jordangate House, Jordangate, Macclesfield, Cheshire, SK10 1EQ Tel: (01625) 500694 Fax: (01625) 500696 *Human resources, health & safety training*

Lear Browne & Dunsford, Waterbridge Court, Matford Park Road, Marsh Barton Trading Estate, Exeter, EX2 8FD Tel: (01392) 822510 Fax: (01392) 823270 E-mail: sales@lbd-harrisons.com *Woollen & trimming merchants*

Lear Corporation UK Ltd, Glaisdale Parkway, Nottingham, NG8 4GP Tel: 0115-901 2200 Fax: 0115-928 9688 *Wiring assembly manufrs*

Lear Seating UK Ltd, Gielgud Way, Cross Point Business Park, Coventry, CV2 2SA Tel: (024) 7686 7200 Fax: (024) 7686 7235 *Car seats manufrs*

Lear Stationers & Printers, 17 High Street, Bilston, West Midlands, WV14 0EH Tel: (01902) 408660 Fax: (01902) 408660 *Stationers & printers*

▶ Learn 247 online, 1 Dawney Drive, Four Oaks, Birmingham, B75 5JA Tel: 0121-323 2224 Fax: 0121-323 2224 E-mail: sales@learn247online.com *Online learning packages for individuals and corporate clients*

▶ Learning 4 Business, Fromehall Mill, Lodgemore Lane, Stroud, Gloucestershire, GL5 3EH Tel: (01453) 756000 Fax: (01453) 751148 E-mail: info@safety4business.com *Online learning*

▶ Learning 4 Business, Fromehall Mill, Lodgemore Lane, Stroud, Gloucestershire, GL5 3EH Tel: (01453) 756000 Fax: (01453) 751148 *Online and CDROM based learning in the areas of Workplace legislation and management training*

▶ Learning Expanse Ltd, Technology House, Lissadel Street, Salford, M6 6AP Tel: 0161 2782595 E-mail: info@learning-expanse.co.uk *learning expanse provides educatioal audit and learning management solution for education and training organizations*

Learning Materials Ltd, Dixon Street, Wolverhampton, WV2 2BX Tel: (01902) 454026 Fax: (01902) 457596 E-mail: learning.materials@btinternet.com *Educational publishers for pupils with special needs*

▶ Learning Partnership, Unit 8 The Old Power Station, 121 Mortlake High Street, London, SW14 8SN Tel: (020) 8876 9322 Fax: (020) 8876 9322 E-mail: info@tlp.org *Training services*

▶ The Learning Path, Bordesley Hall, The Holloway, Alvechurch, B48 7QA Tel: (01527) 585310 E-mail: ellen@thelearningpath.co.uk *The Learning Path delivers professional Neuro-Linguistic Programming courses such as Introduction to NLP, NLP for Business Excellence and Hearts and Minds.**We also offer excellent training and development capabilities in many people-development topics, including, Presentational skills, Training Needs Analysis, Leadership and Interpersonal Skills. **All training courses include practical "hands on" workshops. **The Learning Path offer quality, cost effective training. Our training courses allow beginners and professionals to expand skills. Small classes allow clients plenty of individual assistance from our experienced trainers. **We also offer bespoke training. Courses can be tailor-made to the clients"" businesses, interests and skill level. They can be delivered at the clients"" offices or at a local training facility. .**If you have any questions about any of the training courses please call 01527 5853 or email us at info@thelarningpath.co.uk*

Learning & Skills Council Co Durham, Allergate House, Belmont Business Park, Durham, DH1 1TW Tel: (0845) 0194174 Fax: 0191-376 2302 E-mail: ask@lsc.gov.uk *Training & business support agency service*

Learning & Teaching Scotland, 58 Robertson Street, Glasgow, G2 8DU Tel: 0141-282 5000 Fax: 0141-282 5050 E-mail: equiries@ltscotland.org.uk *Educational software, training & website development*

W.H. Leary Ltd, Bentalls, Basildon, Essex, SS14 3BX Tel: (01268) 535800 Fax: (01268) 535808 E-mail: sales.europe@whleary.com *Adhesive application & coating machine manufrs*

▶ indicates data change since last edition

Lease Products Ltd, 165 Bath Road, Slough, SL1 4AA Tel: (01753) 802000 Fax: (01753) 791447 E-mail: marketing.lpgb@leaseplan.co.uk *Fleet management consultants*

▶ Leasing Quote, c/o Able It, Atlantic Business Centre, 111 Marlowes, Hemel Hempstead, Hertfordshire, HP1 1BB Tel: (0800) 0198836 E-mail: inbox@leasingquote.co.uk *Submit your details and receive up to 6, no obligation, car leasing quotes. Free of charge.*

Leather Grace, 80 Nelson Street, London, E1 2DY Tel: (020) 7790 8000 Fax: (020) 7790 9000 E-mail: info@lloydbaker.com *Leather goods importer*

Leather Studio, 5 Almond Road, Burnham, Slough, SL1 8HX Tel: (01628) 667279 Fax: (01628) 666389 E-mail: info@leatherstudio.co.uk *Leather goods merchants & manufrs*

Leatherhead Food International Ltd, Randalls Road, Leatherhead, Surrey, KT22 7RY Tel: (01372) 376761 Fax: (01372) 386228 E-mail: enquiries@lfra.co.uk *Research consultants*

Leathertex Ltd, 143 Bethnal Green Road, London, E2 7DG Tel: (020) 7613 4251 Fax: (020) 7613 4252 E-mail: leathertexltd@aol.com *Leather garment suppliers & manufrs*

▶ Leaves Green Garage, Biggin Hill Garage, Leaves Green Road, Keston, Kent, BR2 6DU Tel: (01959) 571903 *Motor vehicle repairers*

Leavesley Container Services, Lichfield Rd, Branston, Burton-on-Trent, Staffordshire, DE14 3HD Tel: (01283) 537382 Fax: (01283) 511740 E-mail: sales@leavesley-containers.com Principal Export Areas: Worldwide *Leavesley Containers operate a container storage and repair depot at Branston, near Burton on Trent, Staffs. A range of containers, new and second hand, are available for purchase. A rental service is also offered, with units delivered by Hiab self off-load vehicle to customers premises for short or long term temporary storage use. Customers can hire a storage container for self-access storage on site at either Branston or Fazeley, Tamworth. Prices start at £0.95 pence (+VAT) per day (minimum 30days), for a 50sq ft unit. All units are at ground level with easy vehicle access direct to the doors. Containers can be converted in the on site workshop facility to provide site offices, workshops, machinery housing units etc, with over 25 years experience we can do wonders with the metal box, we even supply certified containers for their original design use, shipping goods around the world.*

Leax Lighting Controls, Unit 11 Mandeville Courtyard, 142 Battersea Park Road, London, SW11 4NB Tel: (020) 7501 0880 Fax: (020) 7501 0890 *Lighting control systems*

Leay Ltd, Unit 3 Lake Road, Quarry Wood, Aylesford, Kent, ME20 7TQ Tel: (01622) 882345 Fax: (01622) 882208 E-mail: enquiries@leay.com *Curtain walling systems, aluminium doors & windows*

Le-Belle International, 248 Lewisham High Street, London, SE13 6JU Tel: (020) 8852 3604 Fax: (020) 8852 3604 *Cosmetic retailer & wholesalers*

Lebury Metals, The Fields, Kingsland Road, Shrewsbury, SY3 7AF Tel: (01743) 233215 Fax: (01743) 233215 *Marketing consultants*

Lebus International Engineers Ltd, Dane Works, Crown Quay Lane, Sittingbourne, Kent, ME10 3HU Tel: (01795) 475324 Fax: (01795) 428004 E-mail: enquiries@lebusintengineers.com *Underwater winches, crane manufrs*

Lec Refrigeration, Unit Dundonald Enterprise Park, Carrowreagh Road, Dundonald, Belfast, BT16 1QT Tel: (028) 9041 9400 Fax: (028) 9041 9229 *Refrigeration repairs seals & services*

Lechler Ltd, 1 Fell Street, Sheffield, S9 2TP Tel: 0114-249 2020 Fax: 0114-249 3600 E-mail: info@lechler.com Sales Contact: C. Lawton Principal Export Areas: Worldwide *Lechler is one of the leading manufacturers of spray nozzles & associated products. With an offering in excess of 25,000 different spray products. For more information please click the image to visit out website*

Lechler Coatings UK Ltd, Unit 42 Pochin Way, Middlewich, Cheshire, CW10 0GY Tel: (01606) 738600 Fax: (01606) 738517 E-mail: sales@lechler.it *Automotive & industrial paint distributors*

▶ Lechley Recruitment, The Rural Business Centre, Bilsborrow, Preston, PR3 0RY Tel: 01995 642260 Fax: 01995 642258 E-mail: scott@lechley.com *Construction Recruitment Specialist*

Leck Construction Ltd, Leck House, Ironworks Road, Barrow-in-Furness, Cumbria, LA14 2PQ Tel: (01229) 820394 Fax: (01229) 811414 E-mail: leckcon.bar@btinternet.com *Building contractors & developers* Also at: Kendal & Manchester

Leck Curphey Ltd, 6 Gloucester Road, Anfield, Liverpool, L6 4DS Tel: 0151-260 0096 *Engineers merchants*

Leckhampton Computers Ltd, Leckhampton House, Lund House Green, Harrogate, North Yorkshire, HG3 1QG Tel: (01423) 879202 Fax: (01423) 870741 E-mail: pkl@leckhampton.com *Computer software services*

▶ Leckie, Allanshaw Industrial Estate, Wellhall Road, Hamilton, Lanarkshire, ML3 9BG Tel: (01698) 283754 Fax: (01698) 281037 *Plant hire*

Leckmill Ltd, 3 Norman Road, Rochdale, Lancashire, OL11 4HS Tel: (01706) 353737 Fax: (01706) 358577 *Expanded metal product manufrs*

Leco Accessories Ltd, London Road, Brandon, Suffolk, IP27 0NG Tel: (01842) 810456 Fax: (01842) 815151 *Point of sale equipment*

Leco Computer Supplies Ltd, Unit 1, Ashwellthorpe Industrial Estate, Ashwellthorpe, Norwich, NR16 1ER Tel: (01508) 489535 Fax: (01508) 489331 E-mail: sales@leco.co.uk *Computer accessory distributors & wholesalers*

Leco Instruments (U K) Ltd, Newby Road Industrial Estate, Hazel Grove, Stockport, Cheshire, SK7 5DA Tel: 0161-487 5900 Fax: 0161-456 0969 E-mail: general@lecouk.com *Analytical instrument distributors*

Lecol Engineering Ltd, 123 Barr Street, Birmingham, B19 3DE Tel: 0121-523 0404 Fax: 0121-523 2372 *Production engineers, capstan milling & drilling*

Lecrafern Pools, Eastcourt Yard, Lower Higham Road, Gravesend, Kent, DA12 2NZ Tel: (01474) 824151 Fax: (01474) 822486 E-mail: lecrafernpools@aol.com *Swimming pool installers*

Lectroheat Industrial Heating Ltd, Unit 16 Pantglas Industrial Estate, Bedwas, Caerphilly, Mid Glamorgan, CF83 8DR Tel: (029) 2088 9300 Fax: (029) 2086 1872 E-mail: info@lectroheat.com *Heating Elements for the plastics industry*

▶ LED Colour Solutions Ltd, Titus House, 29 Saltaire Road, Shipley, West Yorkshire, BD18 3HH Tel: (01274) 609605 Fax: (01274) 531966 E-mail: samantha.crabtree@spacekraft.co.uk *LED lighting domestic & industrial, bar, nightclub installation*

Leda Suspension Ltd, Unit 1 Park Drive, Braintree, Essex, CM7 1AP Tel: (01376) 326531 Fax: (01376) 326530 E-mail: info@leda.com *Race suspension manufrs*

Leda-Lite International Ltd, The Briars, Mayes Lane, Sandon, Chelmsford, CM2 7RP Tel: (01245) 227500 Fax: (01245) 221673 E-mail: leda-lite-international@aol.com *Low level lighting & safety escape lighting manufrs* Also at: Dundee

▶ Ledan Windows Ltd, 25-27 Concorde Road, Norwich, NR6 6BJ Tel: (01603) 482428 Fax: (01603) 488428 E-mail: sales@ledan.co.uk *Window frames manufrs*

Ledbury Welding & Engineering Ltd, New Mills Industrial Estate, Leadon Way, Ledbury, Herefordshire, HR8 2SR Tel: (01531) 632222 Fax: (01531) 634718 E-mail: sales@lweltd.co.uk *Steel tank fabricators*

▶ Ledge Associates (North West) Ltd, Warwick House Green Lane, Featherstone, Pontefract, West Yorkshire, WF7 6EH Tel: (01977) 709698 E-mail: info@ledge-associates.co.uk *We can provide the full range of project and commercial management services from conception through to completion of all projects*

▶ Ledingham Chalmers, Critchton House, Critchton Close, Edinburgh, EH8 8DT Tel: 0131-200 1000 Fax: 0131-200 1080

Ledingham Chalmers Solicitors Estate Agents, 1st, Rose Street, Aberdeen, AB10 1UB Tel: (01224) 408408 Fax: (01224) 408400 E-mail: mail@ledinghamchalmers.com *Solicitors*

Ledlite Glass Ltd, 168 London Road, Southend-on-Sea, SS1 1PH Tel: (01702) 345893 Fax: (01702) 435099 E-mail: sales@ledlite-glass.co.uk *Glazing contractors & glass merchants*

Ledra Steels Ltd, Ledra Works, Reservoir Pl, Walsall, WS2 9SN Tel: (01922) 621542 Fax: (01922) 637755 *Bright drawn steel bar stockholders*

Ledwell Plastics Ltd, 33 Cannock Street, Leicester, LE4 9HR Tel: 0116-276 6221 Fax: 0116-246 0134 E-mail: sales@ledplasticsgroup.co.uk *Injection mouldings manufrs*

Lee, Crossley Hall Works, York Street, Bradford, West Yorkshire, BD8 0HR Tel: (01274) 496487 Fax: (01274) 487081 *Transmission engineers breakdown service*

Lee Air Conditioning Services Ltd, Lee House, Lower Road, Kenley, Surrey, CR8 5NH Tel: (020) 8660 5022 Fax: (020) 8668 0296 E-mail: nick.taylor@leeac.co.uk *Air conditioning, heating, ventilation, plumbing services*

▶ Lee Associates, Denmark House, 3b High Street, Willingham, Cambridge, CB24 5ES Tel: (01954) 262120 Fax: (01954) 262129 E-mail: info@willwriting-services.co.uk

▶ Lee Associates, Denmark House, 3b High Street, Willingham, Cambridge, CB24 5ES Tel: (01954) 262120 Fax: (01954) 262129 E-mail: info@lee-associates.co.uk *Financial consultants pensions, wills, inheritance tax, trusts*

Lee Beesley Ltd, Merthyr Tydfil Industrial Estate, Dowlais, Merthyr Tydfil, CF48 2SS Tel: (01685) 385524 Fax: (01685) 723006 E-mail: enq@leebeesley.co.uk *Mechanical handling equipment manufrs*

Lee Beesley Ltd, 69 Sorby Street, Sheffield, S4 7LA Tel: 0114-272 8621 Fax: 0114-273 0586 E-mail: sfiddall@lbd.co.uk *Electrical contractors* Also at: Hatfield

▶ Lee Broadbent, 1-3 Bosley Arcade, Clifton Street, Blackpool, FY1 1JP Tel: 01253 623330 E-mail: info@locksmenswear.co.uk *Discount Designer Clothing, Paul and Shark, Evisu, Hugo Boss, D&G, Fake London, Stone Island, Diesel, Armani, Etienne Ozecki, CP Company, Paul Smith, Thomas Burberry and Lacoste all available at Locks Designer Menswear*

Lee Brothers Construction Supplies, Spring Road, Ettingshall, Wolverhampton, WV4 6JT Tel: (01902) 491911 Fax: (01902) 353228 E-mail: sales@leebrothers.co.uk *Construction supplies*

▶ Lee & Broughton Ltd, Homestead Workshop, Skitham Lane, Out Rawcliffe, Preston, PR3 6BE Tel: (01995) 672599 Fax: (01995) 672599 *Joiners*

Lee Colourplan Ltd, Crompton Road, Ilkeston, Derbyshire, DE7 4BG Tel: 0115-944 1500 Fax: 0115-944 1481 E-mail: sales@leecolourplan.com *Pattern book manufrs*

Lee Cooper Group Ltd, Lee Cooper House, 17 Bath Road, Slough, SL1 3UF Tel: (01753) 771908 Fax: (01753) 779299 E-mail: lcuk@aol.com *Jeans manufrs*

E.H. Lee Ltd, Holly House, New Road, Woodston, Peterborough, PE2 9HB Tel: (01733) 554853 Fax: (01733) 897024 E-mail: info@ehlee.co.uk *Road transport & freight services*

Lee Fencing, Lidsey Road, Woodgate, Chichester, West Sussex, PO20 3SU Tel: (01243) 542345 Fax: (01243) 542345 *Fencing manufrs*

Lee Filters, Unit 1-2 Kingsway, Andover, Hampshire, SP10 5LQ Tel: (01264) 364112 Fax: (01264) 355058 E-mail: sales@leefilters.com *Lighting & camera filter manufrs*

Lee Floorstok Ltd, Unit B1 The Dresser Centre, Whitworth Street, Openshaw, Manchester, M11 2NE Tel: 0161-231 8080 Fax: 0161-231 8787 E-mail: leefloor@aol.com *Carpet fitting accessory merchants* Also at: Liverpool

▶ Lee Heating, 63 Carshalton Road, Sutton, Surrey, SM1 4LH Tel: (020) 8661 0171 Fax: (020) 8661 0424

John Lee Sacks Ltd, Old Wharf Road, Grantham, Lincolnshire, NG31 7AA Tel: (01476) 565501 Fax: (01476) 590580 E-mail: *Manufacturers of flexible intermediate bulk containers & sacks, including valve type, woven & hessian*

Lee Lighting Ltd, 110 Lancefield Street, Glasgow, G3 8JD Tel: 0141-221 5175 Fax: 0141-248 2751 E-mail: mark@lee.co.uk *Studio lighting contractors* Also at: London

Lee Packaging Ltd, Bull Lane Industrial Estate, Bull Lane, Acton, Sudbury, Suffolk, CO10 0BD Tel: (01787) 372874 Fax: (01787) 376707 E-mail: sales@leepackaging.co.uk *Corrugated cardboard box manufrs*

Lee Plastics Ltd, Stapleton House, 6 High Street, Fleckney, Leicester, LE8 8AJ Tel: 0116-240 2798 Fax: 0116-240 2394 E-mail: bob@leeplastics.co.uk *Plastic pallets & containers.*

Lee Spring Ltd, Latimer Road, Wokingham, Berkshire, RG41 2WA Tel: 0118-978 1800 Fax: 0118-977 4832 E-mail: abinding@leespring.co.uk Principal Export Areas: Central/East Europe & West Europe *Manufacturers of springs including springs, compression; springs, extension; springs, torsion & springs, die*

Lee Taylor, Unit A10 Barton Industrial Estate, Faldo Road, Barton-le-Clay, Bedford, MK45 4RP Tel: (01582) 882518 Fax: (01582) 882518 E-mail: leetayloorplastics@metronet.co.uk *Plastic injection moulding service*

William Lee Ltd, Callywhite Lane, Dronfield, Derbyshire, S18 2XU Tel: (01246) 416155 Fax: (01246) 292194 E-mail: sales@wmlee.co.uk Principal Export Areas: West Europe & North America *Components in spheroidal graphite iron, austempered ductile iron & grey iron either as raw castings or f ully finished components.*

Lee Zak, The Workshop, Fair View, Blackwood, Gwent, NP12 3NS Tel: (01443) 835049 *Joinery manufrs*

Leech & Son, 4a Church Road, Boreham, Chelmsford, CM3 3EF Tel: (01245) 465249 Fax: (01245) 261130 *Gunsmiths*

W. J. Leech & Sons Ltd, 275 Derby Road, Bootle, Merseyside, L20 8PL Tel: 0151-933 9334 Fax: 0151-933 5005 E-mail: david@wjleech.com *Tarpaulin side curtain manufrs* Also at: Carlisle, Cwmbran, Glasgow, Luton & Worcester

▶ Leed Recruitment Ltd, The Manor House, 6-10 St. Margaret's Green, Ipswich, IP4 2BS Tel: (01473) 289000 E-mail: info@leedrecruitment.com *Leed Recruitment Limited are a skilled specialist recruitment consultancy in Marketing, Sales, Advertising, PR, Design, IT, New Media and Print. We provide a comprehensive and highly professional range of recruiting services for clients and applicants in the East of England, London and the home counties.*

▶ Leedan Packaging Ltd, 6 Hampton Lovett Industrial Estate, Lovett Road, Hampton Lovett, Droitwich, Worcestershire, WR9 0QG Tel: (01905) 794703 Fax: (01905) 794704 E-mail: leedan.packaginglimited@virgin.net *Manufacture of polythene bags*

Lee-Dickens Ltd, Rushton Rd, Desborough, Kettering, Northamptonshire, NN14 2QW Tel: (01536) 760156 Fax: (01536) 762552 E-mail: sales@lee-dickens.co.uk Sales Contact: R Gee Principal Export Areas: Worldwide *Based in Desborough, Northamptonshire, Lee-Dickens is a private limited company, involved in the design and manufacture of high integrity industrial and military process monitoring and control systems. We have an enviable reputation for product design, innovation and quality established over a wide customer base. Our product range includes: sensors - level, relative humidity and temperature; signal conditioning equipment - trip amplifiers, isolating signal converters, maths functions, frequency to current /voltage converters, signal integrators, instrument power supplies; power measuring equipment - watt meters, VAR meters, power factor meters, watt-watt-hour meters; and digital process indicators. Our Systems Division provides systems design, manufacture, supply, installation, commissioning and setting to work of Telemetry, SCADA (Supervisory Control and Data Acquisition), and, Remote Control and Monitoring Systems.*

Leeds Bearings Ltd, Unit 14, Castleton Close, Armley Road, Leeds, LS12 2DS Tel: 0113-234 1919 Fax: 0113-245 0037 *Bearing distributors*

▶ Leeds Car Hire, Sheepscar St South, Leeds, LS7 1AD Tel: 0113-244 5244 Fax: 0113 399 3281 E-mail: amjid@leedscarhire.com *Car hire. Quality cars at very competitive rates. Short and Long term rentals. 24 hour booking service. includes insurance, breakdown cover, vat and unlimited mileage. Cheap daily, weekly and weekend rates. Fast, friendly service.*

▶ Leeds Galvanizing Co. Ltd, Albion Park, Armley Road, Leeds, LS12 2EJ Tel: 0113-243 1111

▶ Leeds Graphic Press Ltd, 24-40 Pontefract Lane, Leeds, LS9 8HY Tel: 0113-248 9262 Fax: 0113-248 9264

Leeds Leisure Ltd, Unit 12 Springhead Mills, Springfield Road, Guiseley, Leeds, LS20 9BL Tel: (01943) 877888 Fax: (01943) 876192 *Amusement machines supplier*

Leeds Training Trust, Mitchell House, 139 Richardshaw Lane, Stanningley, Pudsey, West Yorkshire, LS28 6AA Tel: 0113-255 2417 Fax: 0113-236 1004 E-mail: admin@ltt.co.uk *Training organisation*

Leeds Transformer Co. Ltd, Larchfield Road, Leeds, LS10 1QP Tel: 0113-270 5596 Fax: 0113-272 1458 E-mail: sales@leedstransformer.co.uk *Transformer manufacturers*

Leeds Vacuum Formers Ltd, 4 National Road, Hunslet Business Park, Leeds, LS10 1TD Tel: 0113-277 3800 Fax: 0113-277 5263 E-mail: sales@leedsvacform.com *Plastic vacuum formed products manufrs*

Leeds Valve Co. Ltd, Caledonia Road, Batley, West Yorkshire, WF17 5NH Tel: (01924) 428000 Fax: (01924) 428001 E-mail: sales@leedsvalve.com Principal Export Areas: Worldwide *Butterfly, actuated & control valves*

Leeds Welding Co. Ltd, Westland Square, Leeds, LS11 5SS Tel: 0113-271 1000 Fax: 0113-271 1023 E-mail: sales@leedswelding.co.uk *Steel fabricators*

Leedsheath Ltd, Westfield Road, Slyfield Industrial Estate, Guildford, Surrey, GU1 1RR Tel: (01483) 503248 Fax: (01483) 575627 E-mail: tonycoker@btconnect.com *Sheet metalwork engineers & fabricators*

Leedum Ltd, Stanley Works, Church Street, Eyam, Hope Valley, Derbyshire, S32 5QH Tel: (01433) 630838 Fax: (01433) 631888 E-mail: mail@leedum.co.uk *Plastic extrusion &automotive trim manufrs*

Leegem Angling Centre, 81 Sheffield Road, Chesterfield, Derbyshire, S41 7LT Tel: (01246) 559480 Fax: (01246) 559420 *Fishing & angling equipment manufrs*

Lee-Healey, Manchester, M24 2XH Tel: 0161-655 0303 Fax: 0161-655 0304 E-mail: info@lee-healey.com *Rubber goods manufrs*

Leek Bearings, 13-15 Burton Street, Leek, Staffordshire, ST13 8BU Tel: (01538) 381489 Fax: (01538) 387672 *Bearing distributors*

Charles Leek & Sons Ltd, Springfield Works, Ashbourne Road, Leek, Staffordshire, ST13 5AY Tel: (01538) 382066 Fax: (01538) 373153 E-mail: sales@leekgears.co.uk *Gear cutters, manufacturers & general machining services*

Leek Signs & Graphics, Unit 10 Town Yard Industrial Estate, Station Street, Leek, Staffordshire, ST13 8BF Tel: (01538) 385262 Fax: (01538) 385262 *Signs & graphics manufrs*

Harry Leeks Freight Ltd, St. Leonard's Street, Bedford, MK42 9BS Tel: (01234) 359402 Fax: (01234) 348891 *International freight forwarding agents* Also at: Bridgwater & Somerset

Leemicks Business Equipment, Image House, Lancashire Hill, Stockport, Cheshire, SK4 1UB Tel: 0161-480 4001 Fax: 0161-480 2428 *Photocopier services*

Leeming Nelson Ltd, Bankhall Works, Juniper Street, Liverpool, L20 8EL Tel: 0151-922 7019 Fax: 0151-922 0795 *Mild steel & stainless steel fabricators*

Leeming & Peel Ltd, Duncombe Street Works, Bradford, West Yorkshire, BD8 9AJ Tel: (01274) 491464 Fax: (01274) 481690 E-mail: lpsprings@aol.com Principal Export Areas: Worldwide *Coil & flat spring manufrs*

Leemo (Partitions) Ltd, Essex House, Kelfall Street, Oldham, OL9 6HR Tel: 0161-665 4666 Fax: 0161-624 4376 *Dry construction partition erectors*

Leen Valley Engineering Ltd, Station Terrace, Hucknall, Nottingham, NG15 7TQ Tel: 0115-963 3822 Fax: 0115-968 0131 *Palletised container handling*

Leengate Valves, Grange Close, Clover Nook Industrial Estate, Somercotes, Alfreton, Derbyshire, DE55 4QT Tel: (01773) 521555 Fax: (01773) 521591 E-mail: info@leengatevalves.co.uk *Major distributor and stockist for some of Europes leading manufacturers. - Alfa Valvole, RIV, Belgicast-Iprosa, Crane, Peglers, Castflow, Polix, Maran-Peracinini, Diaval, MaxAir, Effebi, TIS, Watergates. -Valve types include Ball, Butterfly, Gate, Globe, Ball Check, Disc Check, Duel Plate, Swing Check, Knife Gate, Pressure Gauges, Cocks, Pneumatic & Electric Actuators, Strainer, Regulating, Relief, Reducing, Float,Diaphragm, Needle, Flow indicators, Site Glasses, Solenoid. -Material Types Cast Iron, Ductile Iron, Brass, Bronze, Ali-Bronze, Cast Steel, Forged Steel, Stainless Steel. Valves for, Marine, Oil,Gass, Petrochemical, Steam, Air,Water,Sewage,Heating, AirConditioning.*

Leerco Engineering Ltd, Full Sutton Industrial Estate, Stamford Bridge, York, YO41 1HS Tel: (01759) 371128 Fax: (01759) 371034 E-mail: leercoeng@aol.com *Industrial ovens, furnaces & enamelling*

▶ Christina Lees, Cocoa Court, 21a Pillory Street, Nantwich, Cheshire, CW5 5BZ Tel: (01270) 611142 Fax: (01270) 842822 *full curtain makeing service, interior design service,stock fabrics,wallpaper,tracks,re-covering sofas.and full fitting service.*

Lees Newsome Ltd, Ashley Mill, Ashley Street, Oldham, OL9 6LS Tel: 0161-652 1321 Fax: 0161-627 3362 E-mail: sales@leesnewsome.co.uk *Textile goods manufrs*

Lees Of Scotland Ltd, North Caldeen Road, Coatbridge, Lanarkshire, ML5 4EF Tel: (01236) 441600 Fax: (01236) 441601 E-mail: sales@leesofscotland.co.uk *Bakers wholesale confection manufrs*

William Lees & Sons Ltd, Unit 4A Peacock Cross Estate, 32 Burnbank Road, Hamilton, Lanarkshire, ML3 9AQ Tel: (01698) 426662 Fax: (01698) 429919 *Manufacturers of aircraft industry fasteners & tooling for aircraft*

▶ Leeson Designs Ltd, Brook St, Nelson, Lancs, BB9 9PU Tel: (01282) 696009 Fax: (01282) 411728 E-mail: sales@leesondesigns.co.uk

Leeson Polyurethanes Ltd, Hermes Close, Tachbrook Park, Warwick, CV34 6NW Tel: (01926) 833367 Fax: (01926) 881469 E-mail: sales@lpultd.com *Polyurethane adhesive manufrs*

▶ Lees-Smith Computing, 9A Marshall Parade, Coldharbour Road, Pyrford, Woking, Surrey, GU22 8SW Tel: (0845) 2570546 E-mail: info@thelscgroup.com *Computer accessories & engineering services*

Company Information

▶ Leete & French, Unit 1 Reginald Street, Stoke-on-Trent, ST6 1DU Tel: (01782) 575710 Fax: (01782) 835363 E-mail: tapes@leeteandfrench.co.uk *Adhesive tape distributors**

Leetex Wipers & Disposables Ltd, Unit 4, Hollis Road, Earlesfield Lane Industrial Estate, Grantham, Lincolnshire, NG31 7QH Tel: (01476) 577777 Fax: (01476) 577774 *Cleaning & wiping cloth manufrs*

▶ Leeward Coachbuilders Ltd, Richards Street, Wednesbury, West Midlands, WS10 8AJ Tel: 0121-526 4709 Fax: 0121-526 4718 E-mail: sales@leewardcoachbuilders.co.uk *Specialist commercial vehicle bodybuilders & engineers*

▶ Leeward Properties Ltd, Brickwall House, Birch Road, Layer-de-la-Haye, Colchester, CO2 0EL Tel: 01206 734319 E-mail: nigel@sail-east.co.uk *NICEIC Domestic Installer. All domestic electrical work undertaken. Only in the Colchester area.*

Leeways Packaging Services Ltd, Lobstock, Churcham, Gloucester, GL2 8AN Tel: (01452) 750487 Fax: (01452) 750653 E-mail: info@leeways.co.uk *Contract packaging specialists services*

Leewood Hotel, 13 Manchester Road, Buxton, Derbyshire, SK17 6TQ Tel: (01298) 23002 Fax: (01298) 23228 E-mail: sales@leewoodhotel.co.uk *Hotel with conference facilities*

Legend Engineering Ltd, Unit B1, Meadow Lane Industrial Estate, Alfreton, Derbyshire, DE55 7EZ Tel: (01773) 520192 Fax: (01773) 830267 E-mail: legend@fsbdial.co.uk *Special purpose machinery manufrs*

Legend Signs Ltd, 1 Benham Business Park, Ashford Road, Newingreen, Hythe, Kent, CT21 4JD Tel: (01303) 261278 Fax: (01303) 261280 E-mail: info@kullasigns.co.uk *Signs for interior or exterior installation services & manufrs*

Legendary Property Company (Aberdeen) 2002 Ltd, Optimum House, Clippers Quay, Salford, M50 3XP Tel: 0161-872 2622 Fax: 0161-872 2633 E-mail: debbie@lpc1.co.uk *Property developers*

Legg Brothers Holdings Ltd, Spring Road, Ettingshall, Wolverhampton, WV4 6JT Tel: (01902) 408188 Fax: (01902) 408228 E-mail: mail@leggbrothers.co.uk *Hot rolled small steel sections manufrs*

Legg Mason Investments, 32 Harbour Exchange Square, London, E14 9JX Tel: (020) 7537 0000 Fax: (020) 7070 7505 *Financial services company*

Leggat Plant Ltd, Crossmill, Glasgow Road, Glasgow, G78 1TG Tel: 0141-881 8104 Fax: 0141-881 8334 *Crane hire*

▶ Legge Associates Ltd, Annfield House, Eskbank Toll, Dalkeith, Midlothian, EH22 3DY Tel: 0131 654 0101 Fax: 0131 654 9596 E-mail: Symon@leggeassociates.demon.co.uk *Chartered Quantity Surveyors and Planning Supervisors*

F. Legge Thompson & Co., 1 Norfolk Street, Liverpool, L1 0BE Tel: 0151-709 7494 Fax: 0151-709 3774 *Iron cement*

Leggett Freightways (European) Ltd, 102 East Duck Lees Lane, Ponders End, Enfield, Middlesex, EN3 7SS Tel: (020) 8805 4791 Fax: (020) 8443 5100 E-mail: michaellinney@leggettgroup.co.uk *Freight forwarding agents* Also at: Birmingham, Glasgow, Manchester, Nottingham & Swindon

Legion Security, 351-353 Newmarket Road, Cambridge, CB5 8JG Tel: (01223) 352328 Fax: (01223) 355223 *Security services*

Lego Company Ltd, 33 Bath Road, Slough, SL1 3UF Tel: (01753) 495000 Fax: (01753) 495100 E-mail: sales@lego.com *Toy brick manufrs*

Legrand Electric Ltd, Great King Street North, Birmingham, B19 2LF Tel: 0121-515 0515 Fax: 0121-515 0516 E-mail: legrand.sales@legrand.co.uk *Electrical wiring accessories manufrs*

Legris Ltd, Unit 1210, Lansdowne Court, Brockworth, Gloucester, GL3 4AB Tel: (01452) 623500 Fax: (01452) 623501 E-mail: salesuk@legris.com *Pipeline fittings manufrs*

▶ Legsun (W E Jeffreys) Ltd, 51 Springvale Industrial Estate, Cwmbran, Gwent, NP44 5BB Tel: (01633) 483073 Fax: (01633) 863560 E-mail: neil-jedd@legsun.fsbusiness.co.uk

Leguard Scaffolding Co. Ltd, 53 Gunnersbury Lane, London, W3 8ED Tel: (020) 8992 6306 Fax: (020) 8992 9617 *Scaffolding contractors*

▶ Legume Technology Ltd, Eastwood Farm, Hagg Lane, Epperstone, Nottingham, NG14 6AX Tel: 0115-966 3679 Fax: 0115-966 3679 E-mail: bruce@legumetechnology.co.uk *Agricultural services*

Lehman Brothers (Indonesia) Ltd, 25 Bank Street, London, E14 5LE Tel: (020) 7102 1000 Fax: (020) 7102 2999 *Stock brokers & investment bankers*

Lehvoss UK Ltd, 20 West Road, Congleton, Cheshire, CW12 4ER Tel: (01260) 291000 Fax: (01260) 291111 E-mail: contact@lehvoss.co.uk *Magnesia suppliers*

Leica Geosystems Ltd, 83 Inglis Green Road, Edinburgh, EH14 2EZ Tel: 0131-443 6966 Fax: 0131-443 7825 *Surveying equipment manufrs*

Leica Geosystems Ltd, Davy Avenue, Knowlhill, Milton Keynes, MK5 8LB Tel: (01908) 256500 Fax: (01908) 609992 E-mail: uk.construction@leica-geosystems.com *Leica geo systems manufrs*

Leica Microsystems UK Ltd, Davy Avenue, Knowlhill, Milton Keynes, MK5 8LB Tel: (0800) 437 0492 Fax: (01908) 609992 E-mail: sales@leica-geosystems.com *Microscope manufrs*

Leicester Balustrading Co. Ltd, Unit 1, Ruding Street, Leicester, LE3 5BX Tel: 0116-299 2229 Fax: 0116-299 2122 *Balustrade & handrail manufrs*

Leicester Bar Fitting Co. Ltd, West Avenue, Wigston, Leicestershire, LE18 2FB Tel: 0116-288 4897 Fax: 0116-281 3122 E-mail: sales@leicesterbarfitting.co.uk *Laminated plastics fabricators*

Leicester Bearing Co Ltd, Tunnel Top, 10 Putney Road, Leicester, LE2 7TF Tel: 0116-254 9886 Fax: 0116-247 1182 E-mail: enquires@leicester-bearings.co.uk *Bearing distributors*

Leicester Compressor Services, 28 Boston Road, Leicester, LE4 1AU Tel: 0116-235 2906 Fax: 0116-235 2077 E-mail: leicestercompressors@fsnet.co.uk *Air compressor distributors*

Leicester Enamellers Ltd, Coventry Road, Narborough, Leicester, LE19 2GG Tel: 0116-275 1231 Fax: 0116-275 1330 *Stove enamelling, powder coating, architectural services*

Leicester Fabrications Ltd, Hazel Drive, Narborough Road South, Leicester, LE3 2JE Tel: 0116-289 8154 Fax: 0116-289 2768 *Structural steelwear*

Leicester Glass Co. Ltd, 119-125 Bridge Road, Leicester, LE5 3QP Tel: 0116-276 8316 Fax: 0116-246 0462 E-mail: enquires@leicesterglass.co.uk *Glass merchants & glaziers*

▶ Leicester Hose & Hydraulics, Unit 3-5 Abbey Court, Wallingford Road, Leicester, LE4 5RD Tel: 0116-266 7755 Fax: 0116-266 7707 E-mail: sales@leicesterhose.com *suppliers of all industrial hose and hydraulic products.*

Leicester Labels Ltd, 51-53 Baggrave Street, Leicester, LE5 3QW Tel: 0116-251 5625 Fax: 0116-251 5621 *Label manufrs*

▶ Leicester Machine Movers Ltd, 40 Great Central Street, Leicester, LE1 4JT Tel: 0116-253 6662 Fax: 0116-251 0631

▶ Leicester Marquee Hire, PO Box 7741, Leicester, LE5 2FD Tel: 0116-254 3879 E-mail: info@lmhire.co.uk *Hire of marquees, tables & chairs*

▶ Leicester Moulding Ltd, 10-12 Russell Square, Leicester, LE1 2DS Tel: 0116-233 0111 Fax: 0116-222 1110 *Injection mouldings*

Leicester Office Furnishers, 9-11 Cannock Street, Leicester, LE4 9HR Tel: 0116-246 3686 Fax: 0116-246 3681 E-mail: enquiries@leicesteroffice.com *Office furniture wholesalers & retailers*

Leicester Office Solutions, Optec House, Wigston, Leicestershire, LE18 1HY Tel: 0845 0940363 E-mail: info@losdesign.co.uk *We partner with new start-up and small to mid-size companies who desire an online web presence. With web site and online store development, using our expertise in marketing and logistics, we can expand your company online.**We also understand your budget constraints and need for various levels of technical support, that is why we offer complete management services, from development through to logistical support to ensure you are ready for the growth that the internet will bring.**

▶ Leicester Optical Ltd, Unit 9, Victoria Mills, Fowke Street, Rothley, Leicester, LE7 7PJ Tel: 0116-237 5646 Fax: 0116-237 6449 E-mail: info@leicesteroptical.co.uk *Manufacture lenses*

Leicester Plating Co. Ltd, Wesley Street, Leicester, LE4 5QG Tel: 0116-266 1344 Fax: 0116-266 2716 E-mail: office@leicesterplating.co.uk *Electroplaters*

Leicester Polythene Packaging Ltd, 93a Gwendolen Road, Leicester, LE5 5FL Tel: 0116-273 4235 Fax: 0116-273 4410 E-mail: sales@lppl.co.uk *Leicester Polythene has a long history of high quality and service. We are flexible enough to offer fast delivery and produce products to meet your specific needs, our staff are ready to answer your questions.*

Leicester Saw Blades Ltd, 6 Morris Road, Leicester, LE2 6BR Tel: 0116-270 9293 *Saw repairers & manufrs*

Leicester Sports Wear Co. Ltd, 92a Ashfordby St, Leicester, LE5 3QH Tel: 0116-253 9804 Fax: 0116-253 9804 *Tee shirt manufrs*

Leicester Switch & Control Co. Ltd, Ross Walk, Leicester, LE4 5HA Tel: 0116-299 9277 Fax: 0116-299 9278 E-mail: lsc@lsandc.co.uk *Control panel system manufrs*

Leicester Thread & Trimming Manufacturers Ltd, 105 Barkby Road, Leicester, LE4 9LG Tel: 0116-276 5858 Fax: 0116-246 0451 *Sewing thread & trimming manufrs* Also at: Derby

Leicester Trading Co. Ltd, 77-79 Chesterfield Road, Leicester, LE5 5LH Tel: 0116-273 0239 Fax: 0116-273 0237 *Children's, ladies' knitwear wholesalers & manufrs*

Leicester Ventilation Systems Ltd, 19 Batten Street, Leicester, LE2 7PA Tel: 0116-224 0244 Fax: 0116-224 0247 E-mail: leisvent@aol.com *Ventilation & air conditioning installers*

Leicester Water Jet Ltd, Unit B6 Troon Way Business Centre, Humberstone Lane, Leicester, LE4 9HA Tel: 0116-274 2551 Fax: 0116-274 2551 E-mail: info@leicesterwaterjet.co.uk *Water jet cutting services*

Leicester Wood Technique Ltd, Main Steet, Theddingworth, Lutterworth, Leicestershire, LE17 6QY Tel: (01858) 880643 *Woodworking Machinery*

Leicester Wrought Iron Co., 25-27 Thurcaston Road, Leicester, LE4 5PG Tel: 0116-266 3566 Fax: 0116-266 3566 *Railings & gates*

Leicestershire Chamber Of Commerce & Industry, 5 New Walk, Leicester, LE1 6TE Tel: 0116-247 1800 Fax: 0116-247 0430 E-mail: info@chamberofcommerce.co.uk *Chamber of commerce*

Leif Design, Lambton House, High Street, Rothbury, Morpeth, Northumberland, NE65 7UZ Tel: (01669) 621162 Fax: (01669) 621162 E-mail: jo@leif-design.com *Jewellery manufacturers, designers & retailers*

Leifield UK Ltd, The Estate Yard, Overbury, Tewkesbury, Gloucestershire, GL20 7NT Tel: (01386) 725721 Fax: (01386) 725736 E-mail: sales@leifeld.co.uk *Metal spinning & flow forming machinery manufrs*

Leigh Concrete Ltd, 30 Bridge Street, Heywood, Lancashire, OL10 1JF Tel: (01706) 366010 Fax: (01706) 366122 *Building materials merchants*

Leigh & G Joinery, Butlers Lands Farm, Mortimer, Reading, RG7 2AG Tel: 0118-933 2481 Fax: 0118-933 2455 *Specialised joinery manufrs*

Leigh Joinery Co. Ltd, Clifton Street, Leigh, Lancashire, WN7 5AD Tel: (01942) 608182 Fax: (01942) 608182 *Joinery*

Leigh & Letcher, Chequers Lane, Dagenham, Essex, RM9 6QD Tel: (020) 8984 1015 Fax: (020) 8984 1735 E-mail: sales@leighandletcher.co.uk *Pressings & general presswork manufrs*

Leigh Park Garden Machinery Ltd, Dunkirk Farm Estate, Frome Road, Southwick, Trowbridge, Wiltshire, BA14 9NJ Tel: (01225) 774202 Fax: (01225) 774303 E-mail: Enquiries@LeighParkGardenMachinery.co.uk *Ride on Mowers - Leigh Park Garden Machinery sellers of mowers, garden tools, machinery and maintenance based in wiltshire since 1982*

Leigh Pine, 73 Leigh Road, Leigh-on-Sea, Essex, SS9 1JN Tel: (01702) 477725 Fax: (01702) 477725 E-mail: enquiries@leighpine.co.uk *Pine furniture manufrs*

Leigh Precision Grinding, 132 Blyth Road, Hayes, Middlesex, UB3 1TD Tel: (020) 8573 0451 Fax: (020) 8561 6399 E-mail: leighgrinding@btinternet.co.uk *Precision grinding services*

Leigh Spinners Ltd, Park Lane, Leigh, Lancashire, WN7 2LB Tel: (01942) 676995 Fax: (01942) 261694 E-mail: carpets@leigh-spinners.demon.co.uk *Tufted & non-woven floor covering manufrs*

Leigh Timber Co. Ltd, 1388-1416 London Road, Leigh-on-Sea, Essex, SS9 2UJ Tel: (01702) 711366 Fax: (01702) 470993 *Timber merchants*

▶ Leighs Quarries, New Forres Quarry, Forres, Morayshire, IV36 2RQ Tel: (01309) 671144 Fax: (01309) 671199 *Quarry*

Leighton Carter Insulation Co. Ltd, 25 Argyle Street, Newport, Gwent, NP20 5NE Tel: (01633) 856624 Fax: (01633) 856178 *Insulation & sheet metal fabricators*

Leighton Coach Works, Buzzard Works, Billington Road, Leighton Buzzard, Bedfordshire, LU7 4TN Tel: (01525) 373365 Fax: (01525) 853365 *Car bodywork repairers*

Leighton Ironcraft Ltd, Unit 4, 39 Willow Lane, Mitcham, Surrey, CR4 4NA Tel: 0845 5314075 Fax: (020) 8971 5098 E-mail: sales@leightonironcraft.co.uk *About Leighton Ironcraft Limited - Leighton Ironcraft Limited is a family run business established in 1984. We specialise in metalwork and wrought iron gates, railings and staircases. We can offer a full installation service, our trained staff are on hand to assist you in the design of the railing and gates most suitable for your premises. We specialise in gates, railings, raileheads, fire baskets, metal staircases and metal stairs. We can cater for your every need. Why not call the team today quoting KELLYSEARCH!*

▶ Leighton Packaging Ltd, Leigh Commerce Park, Green Fold Way, Leigh, Lancashire, WN7 3XJ Tel: (01942) 601011 Fax: (01942) 601012 E-mail: info@leighton-packaging.co.uk *Boxes & containers*

Leighton Signs Ltd, Unit 2 3 Water Hall Farm, Wavendon Road, Salford, Milton Keynes, MK17 8AZ Tel: (01908) 282283 Fax: (01908) 282284 E-mail: info@leightonsigns.co.uk *Sign manufrs*

▶ Leighwill Engineering, 61c & 61d Gorse Industrial Estate, Barnham, Thetford, Norfolk, IP24 2PH Tel: (01842) 890686 Fax: (01842) 890686 *General engineering*

Leiper Engineering, Loamo Works, Brown Street, Dundee, DD1 5EE Tel: (01382) 200240 Fax: (01382) 200240 *General machining services*

Leipold (UK) Ltd, Unit D, Stafford Park 2, Telford, Shropshire, TF3 3AR Tel: (01952) 230100 Fax: (01952) 230111 E-mail: info@leipold-uk.com *Precision turned parts manufrs*

Leisure Control Systems, Clump Farm Industrial Estate, Shaftesbury Lane, Blandford Forum, Dorset, DT11 7TD Tel: (01258) 489075 Fax: (01258) 488526 E-mail: sales@wyvern-innleisure.co.uk Principal Export Areas: Worldwide *Coin operated & timer sun beds hair dryers & hand dryers distributor*

▶ Leisure Design, 35 Dunvegan Avenue, Gourock, Renfrewshire, PA19 1AE Tel: (01475) 520912

▶ Leisure Direct Ltd, Unit 21, Fleetway West Business Park, 14-16 Wadsworth Road, Perivale, Greenford, Middlesex, UB6 7LD Tel: (020) 8997 2266 Fax: (020) 8997 4334 E-mail: leisuredirect@yahoo.co.uk *Sale & hire, pinball's pool tables, fruit machines, jukeboxes*

Leisure Games, 13 St. Davids Road, Llandudno, Gwynedd, LL30 2UL Tel: (01492) 860100 E-mail: leisuregames@btconnect.com *Amusement game machine suppliers*

Leisure Link Ltd, Unit 10 Whitehall Trading Estate, Cooksley Road, Bristol, BS5 9DN Tel: 0117-955 6743 Fax: 0117-955 0725 *Fruit machines*

Leisure Link, Unit 8, Stafford Park 12, Telford, Shropshire, TF3 3BJ Tel: (01952) 292266 Fax: (01952) 292216 *Amusement machine equipment distributors* Also at: Bromsgrove

Leisure Link, Unit 10 Langford Way, Appleton, Warrington, WA4 4TZ Tel: (01925) 265888 Fax: (01925) 269229 E-mail: info@llg.co.uk *Leisure company*

Leisure Link Electronic Entertainment Ltd, Unit 4 Derwent Mills Commercial Park, Cockermouth, Cumbria, CA13 0HT Tel: (01900) 823029 Fax: (01900) 827691 E-mail: enquiries@leisure-link.com *Amusement machines distributors*

Leisure Repair, PO Box 613, Croydon, CR0 2XQ Tel: (020) 8665 4271 Fax: (020) 8665 4234 E-mail: leisurerepair@btconnect.com *Sauna, steam room repairers*

Leisure Systems International Ltd, Northfield Road, Kineton Road Industrial Estate, Southam, Leamington Spa, Warwickshire, CV47 0RD Tel: (01926) 811611 Fax: (01926) 816102 *Sports equipment manufrs*

▶ Leisure Tech GB Ltd, 11 Hasler Place, Haslers Lane, Great Dunmow, Dunmow, Essex, CM6 1AJ Tel: (01371) 872822 E-mail: enquiries@leisuretechgb.co.uk *Suppliers & installers of artificial grass*

Leisurelines Embroiderers, Unit 10 Staunton Court Business Park, Ledbury Road, Staunton, Gloucester, GL19 3QS Tel: (0800) 7318410 *Badge & tie manufrs*

Leisurequip Ltd, Longwood, The Mount, Headley, Bordon, Hampshire, GU35 8AG Tel: (01428) 713185 Fax: (01428) 713185 *Sauna suppliers & installers*

Leisuretec Distribution Ltd, Unit L3 Cherrycourt Way, Leighton Buzzard, Bedfordshire, LU7 4UH Tel: (01525) 850085 Fax: (01525) 852285 E-mail: vestax@leisuretec.co.uk *Audio, visual & lighting equipment distributors*

Leisureteq Swimming Pool Equipment, Unit 15 Innage Park, Holly Lane Industrial Estate, Atherstone, Warwickshire, CV9 2QX Tel: (01827) 715750 Fax: (01827) 715550 E-mail: mailbox@leisureteq.co.uk *Swimming pool equipment suppliers*

▶ Leisurewear-actecs, 6 Penhill Industrail Park, Beaumont Road, Banbury, Oxon, OX16 1RW Tel: (01295) 703165 Fax: (01295) 255059 E-mail: sales@actecs.co.uk *Health & safety product distributors*

▶ Leisurewood, Unit 22, Diss Business Centre, Dark Lane, Scole, Diss, Norfolk, IP21 4HD Tel: (01379) 652620 Fax: (01379) 640590

Leitch Europe Ltd, Holland Park House, Oldbury, Bracknell, Berkshire, RG12 8TQ Tel: (01344) 446000 Fax: (01344) 446100 E-mail: sales.europe@leitch.com *Professional broadcasting equipment*

Leith Agency Ltd, 37 The Shore, Edinburgh, EH6 6QU Tel: 0131-561 8600 Fax: 0131-561 8601

Leith Optical Co., Unit 12-14 Stewartfield, Edinburgh, EH6 5RQ Tel: 0131-554 8355 Fax: 0131-553 4318 *Opticians manufrs*

Leith (U K) Ltd, Pier Road, Berwick-upon-Tweed, TD15 1JB Tel: (01289) 307264 Fax: (01289) 330517 E-mail: enquiries@wleithmarquees.co.uk *Tent & marquee hire & manufrs*

Leithen Valley Plastics, Leithen Road, Innerleithen, Peeblesshire, EH44 6HX Tel: (01896) 830345 Fax: (01896) 830345 *Plastic ware & moulding manufrs*

Leiths Precast Concrete, Durris, Banchory, Kincardineshire, AB31 6DD Tel: (01330) 844444 Fax: (01330) 844417 *Pre-cast concrete manufrs*

▶ Leiths (Scotland) Ltd, Rigifa, Cove, Aberdeen, AB12 3LR Tel: (01224) 876333 *Quarrying, haulage, civil engineering supplies*

Leiths Scotland Ltd, Broomfield Industrial Estate, Broomfield Road, Montrose, Angus, DD10 8SY Tel: (01674) 677037 Fax: (01674) 672809 *Concrete pre-cast product manufrs*

Leitz Tooling UK Ltd, Flex Meadow, Harlow, Essex, CM19 5TN Tel: (01279) 454530 Fax: (01279) 454509 E-mail: sales@har.leitz.org *Woodworking tools manufrs*

Leivers Associates, 6 Clinton Avenue, Nottingham, NG5 1AW Tel: 0115-960 3548 Fax: 0115-969 1147 E-mail: sales@1eiversassociates.co.uk *Building engineers consulting services*

Louis Lejeune Ltd, The Rectory, 71 High Street, Wilburton, Ely, Cambridgeshire, CB6 3RA Tel: (01353) 740444 Fax: (01353) 741599 *Bronze sculpture & car mascots manufrs*

▶ Lek Trix Enterprises, The Barn, 15 Station Street, Whetstone, Leicester, LE8 6JS Tel: 0116-286 5956 Fax: 0116-286 5956 E-mail: lektrix@aol.com *Providing a repair service to the dj/nightclub industry. Servicing any make and any model of sound and lighting equipment.*

Lektrix Installations Ltd, 820 Garratt Lane, London, SW17 0LZ Tel: (020) 8672 6945 Fax: (020) 8672 8118 E-mail: lektrix56@hotmail.com *Electrical retailing & contractors*

Lektro Mechanical Handling, Shear House, Petersfield Avenue, Slough, SL2 5DY Tel: (0800) 0854245 Fax: (01753) 497859 E-mail: info@lektro.co.uk *Fork Lift storage equipment distributors*

▶ Lektron Services Ltd, Middleton Avenue, Strutherhill Industrial Estate, Larkhall, Lanarkshire, ML9 2TL Tel: (01698) 885333

▶ Lellers Valeting Centres Ltd, 159 Turners Hill, Cheshunt, Waltham Cross, Hertfordshire, EN8 9BH Tel: (01992) 641383 Fax: E-mail: valet@lellers.co.uk

Lelliotts Sunblinds Ltd, 80 Sopmting Road, Worthing, West Sussex, BN14 9ES Tel: (01273) 330077 Fax: (01903) 538052 E-mail: lelliottsblinds@btclick.com *Blind manufrs*

Lely (UK) Ltd, 1 Station Road, St. Neots, Cambridgeshire, PE19 1QH Tel: (01480) 226810 Fax: (01480) 226811 E-mail: ag.sales.uk@lely.com *Agricultural & professional turf care machinery distributors*

Lema Electronics, 1 Talisman Business Centre, Duncan Road, Park Gate, Southampton, SO31 7GA Tel: (01489) 572230 Fax: (01489) 578741 E-mail: sales@lemaelectronics.co.uk *Printed circuit assembly services*

LEMAC Ltd, Hospital Road, Haddington, East Lothian, EH41 3PD Tel: (01620) 828700 Fax: (01620) 828730 E-mail: info@lemac.com Principal Export Areas: Africa, Central/East Europe & West Europe *Manufacturers of electric motors*

Lemac Engineering, Pentrebach Road, Pontypridd, Mid Glamorgan, CF37 4BW Tel: (01443) 407777 Fax: (01443) 401720 E-mail: lemac.eng@btinternet.com *Manufacturers of excavator buckets*

Lemac Engineering, Block 3 Barnpark Drive, Tillicoulty, Clackmannanshire, FK13 6BZ Tel: (01259) 751573 Fax: (01259) 751196 *Engineering services*

Leman Ltd, New Works Road, Low Moor, Bradford, West Yorkshire, BD12 0QN Tel: (01274) 693231 Fax: (01274) 693190 E-mail: bradford@leman.co.uk *Freight forwarders* Also at: Basildon, Birmingham & Bristol

Lemar Engines Engine Reconditioners, Babbage Road, Totnes, Devon, TQ9 5JA Tel: (01803) 866548 Fax: (01803) 866548 *Engine reconditioning services*

Lemarc Display Systems, 55 Chiswick Avenue, Mildenhall, Bury St. Edmunds, Suffolk, IP28 7AY Tel: (01638) 714909 Fax: (01638) 712500 E-mail: mail@lemarc.co.uk *Metal slatwall, plain or perforated*

Lemark Office Equipment North Ltd, Unit 2-3 Universal Cresent, North Anston Trading Estate, North Anston, Sheffield, S25 4JJ Tel: (01909) 566328 Fax: (01909) 567771 *Office equipment*

Lemin & Co. Ltd, Unit 4 Albone Way, Biggleswade, Bedfordshire, SG7 5AN Tel: (01767) 600120 Fax: (01767) 600121 E-mail: enquiries@lemin.co.uk *Plastic & wood finishing services* Also at: Baldock

▶ Lemmeleg, 3 West Parade, Wakefield, West Yorkshire, WF1 1LT Tel: (01924) 211300 Fax: (01924) 215161 E-mail: sales@lemmeleg.co.uk

Lemo U K Ltd, 12 North Street, Worthing, West Sussex, BN11 1DU Tel: (01903) 234543 Fax: (01903) 206231 E-mail: uk.office.services@lemo.com *Electrical connector manufrs*

Clive C. Lemon, The Gun Room, Park Cottage, Upper Bentley, Redditch, Worcestershire, B97 5TD Tel: (01527) 550080 Fax: (01527) 550080 *Gun manufactures & repairs*

Lemon Groundwork Supplies, Russell Gardens, Wickford, Essex, SS11 8BH Tel: (01268) 571571 Fax: (01268) 571555 E-mail: sales@lemon-gs.co.uk *Manufacturers of cut & bent reinforcement and stockist of mesh reinforcement. Prefabrication specialists for Groundbeams, Pile Cages, Pile Caps. Delivery on our own HIAB off load vehicles. Major suppliers of Cellcore, Clayboard & Claymaster.*

▶ The Lemon Press Ltd, Pipers Road, Park Farm Industrial Estate, Redditch, Worcestershire, B98 0HU Tel: (01527) 500048 Fax: (01527) 253697 E-mail: info@lemonpress.co.uk

Lemon Steel Services Ltd, Russell Gardens, Wickford, Essex, SS11 8BL Tel: (01268) 571666 Fax: (01268) 571555 E-mail: phil@lemonsteel.co.uk *Steel fabricators & site installation services*

▶ Lemon Tree Interiors, 5 Cambridge Road, Ely, Cambridgeshire, CB7 4HJ Tel: (01353) 610585 Fax: (01353) 610466 E-mail: Design@LemonTreeInteriors.Co.Uk *Interior Designers for Homes, Hotels and Businesses. Complete Design Service. Fabrics available include Zoffany, Villa Nova, Harlequin, Swaffer.*

▶ Lemonpark Construction Ltd, Green Lane, Heywood, Lancashire, OL10 1NG Tel: (01706) 369008

Lemsford Mill Controls Ltd, 5 Alders Court, Welwyn Garden City, Hertfordshire, AL7 1LT Tel: (01707) 334833 Fax: (01707) 328266 *Manufacturers of electrical control systems*

Len Fowler Trophies Ltd, 55 Lambs Conduit Street, London, WC1N 3NB Tel: (020) 7405 6130 Fax: (020) 7405 6130 *Sports trophies suppliers & engravers*

Len Griffiths Fork Lift Services, Units 24-26 Station Industrial Estate, Worcester Road, Leominster, Herefordshire, HR6 8AR Tel: (01568) 611773 Fax: (01568) 615400 E-mail: lgfs27@aol.com *Fork lift services, hire & sales*

Len Lothian U Store, 11 Bankhead Broadway, Edinburgh, EH11 4DB Tel: 0131-538 8200 Fax: 0131-538 8210 E-mail: info@lenlothain.com *Professional warehousing & self storage services* Also at: Montrose

Lenack Engineering Co. Ltd, Thame Road Industrial Estate, Thame Road, Haddenham, Aylesbury, Buckinghamshire, HP17 8BY Tel: (01844) 292923 Fax: (01844) 292925 *Precision engineers*

Lenco Engineering (Hull) Ltd, Unit 1D Marfleet Lane Industrial Estate, Burma Drive, Hull, HU9 5SD Tel: (01482) 784988 Fax: (01482) 796661 E-mail: lenco98@hotmail.com *Coppersmiths, pipework & welding fabricators*

Lenesco Ltd, Grove Road, Northfleet, Gravesend, Kent, DA11 9AX Tel: (01474) 564692 Fax: (01474) 327329 *Sheet metalworkers & fabricators*

Lenham Storage Ltd, Ham Lane, Lenham, Maidstone, Kent, ME17 2LH Tel: (01622) 858441 Fax: (01622) 850469 E-mail: info@lenhamstorage.co.uk *Storage & distribution services*

Lenham Storage Southern Ltd, Fyfield Road, Weyhill, Andover, Hampshire, SP11 8DL Tel: (01264) 772166 Fax: (01264) 773431 E-mail: administration@lenhamstoragesouthern.co.uk *Storage distributors* Also at: Maidstone

Lenic Engineering Ltd, Unit 24 Cradle Hill Industrial Estate, Afriston Road, Seaford, East Sussex, BN25 3JE Tel: (01323) 896783 Fax: (01323) 491416 E-mail: info@metalpressings.co.uk *Toolmakers & metal pressings*

Leniks Motor Panels Ltd, Lenik House, Slingsby Close, Attleborough Fields Industrial Estate, Nuneaton, Warwickshire, CV11 6RP Tel: (024) 7638 4728 Fax: (024) 7638 4728 *Sheet metalwork engineers & fabricators*

Lennox Foundry Co. Ltd, Bredgar Road, Gillingham, Kent, ME8 6PN Tel: (01634) 386683 Fax: (01634) 386684 E-mail: lennox@kestner-eng.co.uk *High duty iron castings*

Lennox House Holdings Ltd, Beeding Close, Southern Cross Trading Estate, Bognor Regis, West Sussex, PO22 9TS Tel: (01243) 866565 Fax: (01243) 868301 E-mail: enquiries@ggcompacters.co.uk *Waste recycling & compaction system manufrs*

Lennox Industries, PO Box 174, Northampton, NN4 7EX Tel: (01604) 669100 Fax: (01604) 669150 E-mail: sales@lennoxuk.com *Providing Indoor climate comfort systems*

▶ Lennox Leisure, 14 Bradford Road, Guiseley, Leeds, LS20 8NH Tel: (01943) 876676 Fax: (01943) 870827 E-mail: sales@lennoxleisure.co.uk *Swimming pools*

The Lennox Partnership Ltd, Unit 1a Erskine House, North Avenue, Clydebank Business Park, Clydebank, Dunbartonshire, G81 2DR Tel: 0141-951 1131 Fax: 0141-952 0312 E-mail: info@thelennoxpartnership.org *Business development consultants*

Lennox Sewing Machines, 2 Red Lion Yard, Rotherham, South Yorkshire, S60 1PN Tel: (01709) 377797 Fax: (01709) 377797 *Sewing machines, steam presses, overlockers repairs & suppliers*

▶ Mike Lenny & Co., 35 Gondar Gardens, West Hampstead, London, NW6 1EP Tel: (020) 7794 3700 Fax: (020) 7443 9300 E-mail: m.lenny@btconnect.com *Mike Lenny & Co. Private Investigations. Matrimonial, employee background, missing persons, fraud investigation, process serving. 25 years of experience in Business and Private matters. Confidential and discreet. No Job too small. London, NW6, TEL: 0207-794-3700*

Henry Lenox Industrial Ltd, 9 Hanworth Road, Hampton, Middlesex, TW12 3DH Tel: (020) 8941 9274 Fax: (020) 8941 9374 E-mail: sales@henrylenox.co.uk *Thermoforming agents*

Lenpack Contract Packing & Warehousing, Pretoria Road, Chertsey, Surrey, KT16 9LW Tel: (01932) 567997 Fax: (01932) 564070 E-mail: sales@lenpack.co.uk *Contract packing & warehousing*

Lenrich Labs, 7 Shefton Rise, Northwood, Middlesex, HA6 3RE Tel: (01923) 826590 Fax: (01923) 841575 E-mail: bud@sheftonfreeserve.co.uk *Maintenance chemicals & hygiene products manufrs*

Lenser (UK) Ltd, Winton House, Stoke Road, Stoke-On-Trent, ST4 2RW Tel: (01782) 415414 Fax: (01782) 415757 E-mail: lenseruk@aol.com *Filtration engineers*

▶ Lensfast, Seath Road, Rutherglen, Glasgow, G73 1RW Tel: 0141-643 1135 Fax: 0141-643 1219 *Optical lenses manufrs*

Lenson Select UK Ltd, Brandon Way, West Bromwich, West Midlands, B70 8JA Tel: 0121-553 6699 Fax: 0121-553 6622 E-mail: sales@lenson-select.co.uk *Fixing systems & electrical supplies*

▶ Lenstec Ltd, Unit 8 Bedwas Business Centre, Bedwas, Caerphilly, Mid Glamorgan, CF83 8DU Tel: (029) 2088 3009 Fax: (029) 2088 9798 E-mail: sales@lenstec.co.uk *Optical lenses & instruments*

▶ Lenten Hall Antiques, Lenten Hall, Lenten Pool, Llansannan, Denbigh, LL16 3LG Tel: (01745) 870283 Fax: (01745) 870283 E-mail: sales@lentenhallantiques.com *We provide a full antiques export service; which consists of a complete container packing and shipping service worldwide. We specialize in furniture 1800s to 1900s, including selected bric-a-brac. The most appealing antique items at the most competitive of prices.*

Lentjes UK Ltd, Dukes Court, Duke Street, Woking, Surrey, GU21 5BH Tel: (01483) 730044 Fax: (01483) 729595 *Process plant contractors*

Lentoid Group, PO Box 21, Otley, West Yorkshire, LS21 1HA Tel: (01943) 461613 Fax: (01943) 464018 E-mail: sales@lentoid.com *Lens manufrs*

Lenton Brook, Unit D Hawthorns Industrial Estate, Middlemore Road, Middlemore Road, Birmingham, B21 0BH Tel: 0121-523 9390 Fax: 0121-523 9390 E-mail: graham@lentonbrook.freeserve.co.uk *Gravity die casting aluminium & zinc*

Lenton Treatment Holdings Ltd, 68 Cannock Street, Barkby Thorpe Road, Leicester, LE4 9HR Tel: 0116-276 7162 Fax: 0116 2767446 E-mail: mail@lentontreatments.co.uk *Sodium hydride metal treatment*

▶ Lentrol Ltd, Unit 22 Weaver Park Industrial Estate, Mill Lane, Frodsham, WA6 7JB Tel: (01928) 735345 Fax: (01928) 735300

Lenwade Hydraulic Service, 6 Emmerson Industrial Estate, Norwich Road, Lenwade, Norwich, NR9 5SA Tel: (01603) 872403 Fax: (01603) 872372 E-mail: lenhydser@aol.com *Hydraulic engineers*

▶ Lenwood Conservatories, 6 Poplar Road, Broadmeadow Industrial Estate, Broadmeadow Industrial Estate, Dumbarton, G82 2RQ Tel: (01389) 761133 E-mail: sales@1enwood.co.uk *PVC doors, conservatories & windows suppliers & fittters*

Lenzkes Clamping Tools, Universal House, Farfield Park, Manvers, Rotherham, South Yorkshire, S63 5DB Tel: (01709) 870000 Fax: (01709) 870010 *Work holding clamp distributors*

▶ Lenzman Photographers, 164 Grimston Road, South Wootton, King's Lynn, Norfolk, PE30 3PB Tel: (01553) 671524 E-mail: lenzman@lenzmanuk.com *Professional photographers*

Leo Burnett, Warwick Building, Avonmore Road, London, W14 8HQ Tel: (020) 7751 1800 Fax: (020) 7348 3855 *Advertising agents*

Leo Engineering Ltd, Bingswood Industrial Estate, Whaley Bridge, High Peak, Derbyshire, SK23 7LY Tel: (01663) 735344 Fax: (01663) 735352 E-mail: info@minibusoptions.co.uk *Minibus conversion services*

Leo Fittings Ltd, Lakes Road, Braintree, Essex, CM7 3QS Tel: (01376) 341616 Fax: (01376) 349427 E-mail: info@leofittings.co.uk *Pipe fittings distributors*

▶ Leo Max Ltd, 73 Church Leys, Harlow, Essex, CM18 6DB Tel: (0870) 1993525 Fax: 0870 1350272 E-mail: info@leomaxuk.com *Importers and suppliers of industrial safety equipments, Coveralls, Safety boots, uniforms, work wears, protective gloves, High quality Helmets. Visit our web site or give us a call to serve you in batter way*

Leo Pharma, Longwick Road, Princes Risborough, Buckinghamshire, HP27 9RR Tel: (01844) 347333 Fax: (01844) 342278 E-mail: enquiries@leo-pharma.com *Pharmaceutical product distributors*

▶ Leo Recruitment, 2 The Grand Union Office Park, Packet Boat Lane, Uxbridge, Middlesex, UB8 2GH Tel: (0870) 4214016 E-mail: jobs@leorecruitment.co.uk *Leo Recruitment has been established as a recruitment to recruitment and sales recruitment company that can provide an honest, ethical, professional, but most importantly a personal service. *Candidates will be given honest and consultative advice with regards to the most suitable opportunities within the market place, specifically tailored to match their individual requirements. We are committed to making the process of finding a new position as easy and enjoyable as possible. *Dedicated to our clients success, Leo Recruitment believe that this can only be achieved by establishing close working relationships with our clients so as to have a full and comprehensive understanding of their recruitment requirements and long term growth plans.*

▶ Leofric Structures, Merton Street, Banbury, Oxfordshire, OX16 4RN Tel: (01295) 266318 Fax: (01295) 271603 E-mail: sales@leofricstructures.com *Design, Manufacture and erection of steel framed industrial, commercial and agricultural buildings and all associated cladding.*

Leominster Construction Co. Ltd, Leominster Industrial Estate, Southern Avenue, Leominster, Herefordshire, HR6 0QF Tel: (01568) 612943 Fax: (01568) 612910 *Steel frame building manufrs*

Leominster Engineering Co., Southern Avenue, Leominster, Herefordshire, HR6 0QF Tel: (01568) 613284 Fax: (01568) 614734 *Specialising in precision machining*

Leominster Farm Supplies Ltd, 17 Broad Street, Leominster, Herefordshire, HR6 8DB Tel: (01568) 612277 Fax: (01568) 616993 E-mail: hintonscountry@btinternet.com *Garden & pet supplies*

Leonard Bowes Engineering Co. Ltd, 31 Mill Street, Brierley Hill, West Midlands, DY5 2RG Tel: (01384) 573000 Fax: (01384) 573000 *General engineers & machinists*

Leonard E Goode Ltd, 594 College Road, Kingstanding, Birmingham, B44 0HU Tel: 0121-373 7581 Fax: 0121-373 7585 E-mail: sales@legoode.co.uk *Advertising & industrial photographers*

Leonard Edward Dresses London Ltd, Unit 2 30a Borwick Avenue, London, E17 6RA Tel: (020) 8521 7155 Fax: (020) 8520 1444 *Gown manufrs*

Leonard Hall Patterns Ltd, 352 Loxley Road, Sheffield, S6 4TJ Tel: 0114-234 3571 Fax: 0114-234 3571 *Engineers pattern makers*

Leonard-Carter Communications Ltd, 113 Lavender Walk, London, SW11 1JS Tel: (020) 7738 0738 Fax: (020) 7738 0081 *Telecommunication equipment & services*

Leonardo Computer Systems, Woodlands Business Village, Woodlands Business Village C Oronation Road, Basingstoke, Hampshire, RG22 4BH Tel: (01256) 322445 E-mail: sales@leonardo-cad.co.uk *Computer aided design systems suppliers & manufrs*

▶ Leonardo Windows Ltd, Turncroft House Unit 3b, Turncroft Lane, Stockport, Cheshire, SK1 4AR Tel: 0161-480 5885 Fax: 0161-480 6005 *Manufacturing windows*

Leoni Temco Ltd, Whimsey Industrial Estate, Cinderford, Gloucestershire, GL14 3HZ Tel: (01594) 820100 Fax: (01594) 823691 E-mail: general@leonitemco.com *Manufacturers of wire including copper*

Leoni Wiring Systems Ltd, Lower Milehouse Lane, Newcastle, Staffordshire, ST5 9BT Tel: (01782) 563366 Fax: (01782) 604895 E-mail: sales@leoniwiring.com *Electrical wiring system manufrs*

Leopard Press UK Ltd, Foxoak Street, Cradley Heath, West Midlands, B64 5DP Tel: (01384) 410800 Fax: (01384) 410420 E-mail: enquiries@leopardpress.fsnet.co.uk *General printing & stationary services*

Leopold Grove Engineering Co. Ltd, Amy Johnson Way, Blackpool, FY4 2RP Tel: (01253) 342144 Fax: (01253) 349667 E-mail: office@leopoldeng.co.uk *Nuclear plant manufrs*

Leopold Professional Services, 57 Lancaster Road, Barnet, Hertfordshire, EN4 8AS Tel: (020) 8441 4310 Fax: (020) 8449 0317 E-mail: paul@leopold.co.uk *Digital processors*

Leo's Ice Cream, 1 Thomas Street, Wolverhampton, WV2 4JS Tel: (01902) 424363 Fax: (01902) 712436 *Ice cream manufrs*

Leotronics Ltd, London Road, Rake, Liss, Hampshire, GU33 7PQ Tel: (01730) 893838 Fax: (01730) 894442 E-mail: sales@leotronics.co.uk *Connectors & cable assemblies*

Lepol Fire Equipment, Hanson Lane Enterprise Centre, Halifax, West Yorkshire, HX1 5PG Tel: (01422) 359052 Fax: (01422) 365622 E-mail: enquiries@lepolfire.co.uk *Fire equipment service & suppliers*

▶ Lerch Bates Ltd, Media House, 1a Dunnswood Road, Wardpark South, Cumbernauld, Glasgow, G67 3EN Tel: (01236) 457750 *Consultancy*

Lericoat Ltd, Unit 18, Addington Park Industrial Estate, Little Addington, Kettering, Northamptonshire, NN14 4AS Tel: (01933) 651618 Fax: (01933) 652112 E-mail: rob.britten@lericoat.co.uk *Leather coatings manufrs*

Leroy Packaging Ltd, Heasandford Mill, Netherwood Road, Burnley, Lancashire, BB10 2EJ Tel: (01282) 438016 Fax: (01282) 430289 E-mail: learoyd@learoyd.co.uk *High performance flexible packaging manufacturer*

▶ Lerwick Building Centre Ltd, 5d Gremista Industrial Estate, Gremista, Lerwick, Shetland, ZE1 0PX Tel: (01595) 696373 Fax: (01595) 692802 E-mail: billy@lerwickbuildingcentre.co.uk *DIY shop*

▶ Lerwick Engineering & Fabrication Ltd, Greenhead, Lerwick, Shetland, ZE1 0PY Tel: (01595) 692349

Lerwick Hotel, 15 South Road, Lerwick, Shetland, ZE1 0RB Tel: (01595) 692166 Fax: (01595) 694419 E-mail: reception@lerwickhotel.co.uk *Hotel & conference facilities*

Les Owen Ltd, Brook Street, Welshpool, Powys, SY21 7NA Tel: (01938) 552229 Fax: (01938) 552229 *Dairy product suppliers*

▶ Les Podraza, PO Box 93, Redditch, Worcestershire, B96 6EN Tel: 01527 465117 E-mail: capricorndriverservices@yahoo.co.uk *Capricorn Driver Services provide a private transfer service to all Airport, Rail and Sea Port UK Destinations. Based in Redditch Worcestershire, we also provide private transportation for Corporate Trips, Sightseeing Tours and Social Occasions.*

▶ Les Searle Plant Hire & Sales Ltd, 16 Parsonage Road, Horsham, West Sussex, RH12 4AN Tel: (01403) 262033 Fax: (01403) 217060

▶ Les Taylor Group, Muir of Ord Industrial Estate, Great North Road, Muir Of Ord, Ross-Shire, IV6 7UA Tel: (01463) 870904 Fax: (01463) 870968

▶ Les Tuileries, Pixholme Cottage, Pixham Lane, Dorking, Surrey, RH4 1PF Tel: 01306 881252 Fax: 01306 881252 E-mail: info@lestuileries.co.uk *Offering creative & stylish interior design for residential clients*

▶ Les White & Partners, 832 Whittingham Lane, Goosnargh, Preston, PR3 2AX Tel: (01772) 865490 Fax: (01772) 865490

Lesjofors Springs (U K) Ltd, Unit J4, Lowfields Way, Lowfields Business Park, Elland, West Yorkshire, HX5 9DA Tel: (01422) 377335 Fax: (01422) 373336 E-mail: info.ell@lesjoforsab.com *Lesjofors are your supplier for standard stock springs, industrial springs, super alloy springs, wire forms, pressings & gas springs. Lesjofors are one of Europe's largest & most diverse spring manufacturers with over 150 years experience. Lesjöfors manufacturers and distributes gas springs into the industrial, medical, furniture, leisure and automotive sectors. Its gas springs are easy to use and install and perform a number of critical purposes such as balancing, unloading and lifting or lowering a heavy item easily. The range is made up of both conventional and lockable gas springs, many of which feature a stainless steel tube. We also offer variable, safety lock, traction, and friction gas springs Lesjöfors can supply its standard stock range of gas springs in three to four days. There are more than 700 references in its range and the company is able to meet special requirements*

Lesk Engineers Ltd, Carden Street, Worcester, WR1 2AX Tel: (01905) 23187 Fax: (01905) 612536 E-mail: company@leskengineers.co.uk *Precision machinists*

Leslie Atkins & Partners Ltd, 3 Airfield Road, Christchurch, Dorset, BH23 3TG Tel: (01202) 499444 Fax: (01202) 499223 E-mail: reception@latkins.co.uk *Shop fitting contractors, specialist joinery manfacture, joinery manufacture, shopfitting, commercial interiors, retail interiors*

Leslie Dick & Sons Ltd, Linkfield Farm, Airth, Falkirk, FK2 8QT Tel: (01324) 831335 Fax: (01324) 831335 *Farming agricultural contracting & land drainage*

Leslie Group Ltd, 198-202 Waterloo Road, Yardley, Birmingham, B25 8LD Tel: 0121-708 1123 Fax: 0121-707 7793 E-mail: sales@leslie.co.uk *Hot brass stampers & machining contractors*

Leslie J Plail, Unit 1+2 Furlongs Farm, Riverside, Eynsford, Dartford, DA4 0AE Tel: (01322) 865688 *Cabinet manufrs*

Leslie Powell & Co., Kay Street, Manchester, M11 2DU Tel: 0161-231 3231 Fax: 0161-230 6578 E-mail: sales@1esliepowell1.co.uk

Lesmac Fasteners Ltd, 73 Dykehead Street, Glasgow, G33 4AQ Tel: 0141-774 0004 Fax: 0141-774 2229 E-mail: sales@lesmac.co.uk *Bolt & nut distributors*

▶ Lesmar Ltd, 10 Spencer Street, St. Albans, Hertfordshire, AL3 5EG Tel: (01727) 732631 Fax: (01727) 732632 E-mail: online@lesmar.com *Suppliers of business gifts & promotions*

Lesney Industries Ltd, Norwood House, Temple Bank, River way, Harlow, Essex, CM20 2DY Tel: (01279) 260130 Fax: (01279) 413100 E-mail: *Precision die castings & plastic moulders*

▶ LeSoftCo Ltd, Carlson Suite, Vantage Point Business Village, Mitcheldean, Gloucestershire, GL17 0DD Tel: (01594) 546120 E-mail: info@lesoftco.co.uk *Lotus Notes/ Domino*Web services*Software development and related services*

Lesser & Pavey Ltd, Leonardo House Fawkes Avenue, Dartford Trade Park, Dartford, DA1 1JQ Tel: (01322) 279225 Fax: (01322) 279586 E-mail: sales@leonardo.co.uk *Glassware, china, fancy goods & figurines import service*

▶ Lessnoise Acoustic Engineers, Pheonix House, Sussex Close, Knaphill, Woking, Surrey, GU21 2RB Tel: (01483) 487575 Fax: (01483) 487575 E-mail: mail@lessnoise.net *Noise control engineering & consultancy*

Lesta Packaging plc, 21 Nedham Street, Leicester, LE2 0HD Tel: (0116) 2624448 Fax: (0116) 2624449 E-mail: enquiries@lestapackaging.co.uk *Manufacturers & importers of prestige printed paper carrier bags, boxes, polythene carrier bags and packaging products. Trading since 1974, Lesta Packaging is the world class packaging supplier. With expertise in producing complete marketing solutions through packaging and with regional sales offices we are the perfect partner for your packaging needs.**

▶ Andrew Lester & Associates, 9 Thames Park, Lester Way, Wallingford, Oxfordshire, OX10 9TA Tel: (01491) 824181 Fax: (01491) 824180 E-mail: marketing@andrew-lester.com *Market research agency services*

Lester Control Systems Ltd, Unit D, 18 Imperial Way, Croydon, CR9 4QP Tel: (020) 8288 0668 Fax: (020) 8288 0667 E-mail: info@lestercontrols.co.uk *Lift control systems manufrs*

▶ Lester Control Systems, Unit 3 Wycliffe Industrial Estate, Lutterworth, Leicestershire, LE17 4HG Tel: (01455) 557780

Lester Engineering Ltd, Rathdown Road, Lissue Industrial Estate, Lisburn, County Antrim, BT28 2RE Tel: (028) 9262 1681 Fax: (028) 9262 1681 *Aluminium fabricators*

continued

Lester & Lester Ltd, 1-9 Tennyson Road, London, SW19 8SH Tel: (020) 8540 8687 Fax: (020) 8543 4322E-mail: darren@lesters.ssworld.co.uk *Shop fitters & joinery manufrs*

Lester Lift Services Ltd, 2 Torridge View, Meddon St, Bideford, Devon, EX39 2EG Tel: (01237) 478055 *Lift repairs & manufrs* Also at: Thornton Heath

Lester Lift Services Ltd, 53b Winterbourne Road, Thornton Heath, Surrey, CR7 7QX Tel: (020) 8240 0059 Fax: (020) 8684 5381 *Lift engineering services*

Lestercast Ltd, 14-16 Ireton Avenue, Leicester, LE4 9EU Tel: 0116-276 7284 Fax: 0116-246 0401 E-mail: sales@lestercast.co.uk Principal Export Areas: Africa *Casting manufrs*

Lesterdale Ltd, Whitebirk Road, Blackburn, BB1 3JA Tel: (01254) 581607 Fax: (01254) 665425 *Textiles manufacturer*

Lesters, 13-14 George Street, Hove, East Sussex, BN3 3YA Tel: (01273) 734686 Fax: (01273) 734686 *Beds, sofa beds & bedroom furniture manufrs*

Leswidden, Leswidden, St. Just, Penzance, Cornwall, TR19 7RU Tel: (01736) 788644 Fax: (01736) 788644 *Concrete products manufrs*

Leta Telephone Training Equipment, Unit 1, Edolph Farm, Norwood Hill Road, Charlwood, Horley, Surrey, RH6 0EB Tel: (01293) 865019 Fax: (01293) 863971 *Telephone training equipment hire & sale*

Letchford Swifts Ltd, Leamore Lane, Walsall, WS2 7BU Tel: (01922) 402460 Fax: (01922) 402460 *Aluminium & stainless sheet metalworkers*

Letchworth Garden City Heritage Foundation, Suite 401 Spirella Buildings, Bridge Road, Letchworth Garden City, Hertfordshire, SG6 4ET Tel: (01462) 476000 Fax: (01462) 476050 E-mail: info@letchworth.com *Trading estate administrators & proprietors*

Letchworth Roofing Co. Ltd, Roof Centre, Works Road, Letchworth Garden City, Hertfordshire, SG6 1JY Tel: (01462) 755766 Fax: (01462) 755750 E-mail: sales@letchworthroofing.co.uk *Roofing contractors, industrial. Al so roofing materials, waterproof membrane, felts, slates, all roofing supplies* Also at: Grantham

Letchworth Steel Construction, 29 Jubilee Trading Estate, Jubilee Road, Letchworth Garden City, Hertfordshire, SG6 1NE Tel: (01462) 480080 Fax: (01462) 481191 E-mail: lesco@aol.com *Structural steel fabricators & erectors*

Lethaby Numbering Systems, Central Way, Walworth Industrial Estate, Andover, Hampshire, SP10 5AL Tel: (01264) 365951 Fax: (01264) 356303 E-mail: sales@atlanticzeiser.com *Numbering machine manufrs*

Lethenian Enterprises, Barnsurges, Mincombe Post, Sidbury, Sidmouth, Devon, EX10 0QP Tel: (01395) 597666 Fax: (01395) 222894 *horological and instrument glass specialist manufacturer e.g bevelled glass for watches clocks barometers caridge clocks hand mirrors compact mirrors hunters/half hunters and convex glasses ect.*

Leton Engineering, Unit 14 Cockshades Farm, Stock Lane, Wybunbury, Nantwich, Cheshire, CW5 7HA Tel: (01270) 841977 Fax: (01270) 569226 E-mail: sales@1eton.net *Sheet metalwork engineers*

Letraset Ltd, Kingsnorth Industrial Estate, Wotton Road, Ashford, Kent, TN23 6FL Tel: (01233) 624421 Fax: (01233) 658877 E-mail: info@letraset.com *Graphic arts production*

▶ Lets Party, 35 Saffron Road, Biggleswade, Bedfordshire, SG18 8DJ Tel: (01767) 312252 *Party suppliers*

▶ Lets Party Ruislip Ltd, 288 West End Road, Ruislip, Middlesex, HA4 6LS Tel: (01895) 633606 E-mail: letsparty@blueyonder.co.uk *Fancy Dress, Balloons, T-Shirt Printing*

▶ Letsrentaproperty, Castelnau, Barnes, London, SW13 8KH Tel: (020) 8741 6565 Fax: E-mail: tomco666@yahoo.co.uk *Search for property to rent in London and across the UK. Advertise your apartment or house. View our area guides and property news.*

Lettergold Plastics Ltd, 4 Hammond Close, Newmarket, Suffolk, CB8 0AZ Tel: (01638) 666888 Fax: (01638) 666999 E-mail: info@lettergold.co.uk *Injection moulders & central heating adjectives manufrs*

Lettergraph Ltd, Harvey Road, Basildon, Essex, SS13 1EP Tel: (01268) 728552 Fax: (01268) 728479 E-mail: mail@lettergraph.net Principal Export Areas: Worldwide *We are the leading suppliers of labelling machines and systems. Specializing in Kroy and Brother printers and consumables.*

Lettering Systems Unlimited, Imex Business Centre, Abbey Road Business Park, Pity Me, Durham, DH1 5JZ Tel: 0191-386 5222 Fax: 0191-386 5444 E-mail: sales@lsu.co.uk *Vinyl cutting systems*

Letters & Logos Ltd, Crow La Bus Park, Crow, Ringwood, Hampshire, BH24 3EA Tel: (01425) 477281 Fax: (01425) 480094 E-mail: team@lettersandlogos.co.uk *Sign manufrs*

▶ Letting Solutions, PO Box 3734, Leamington Spa, Warwickshire, CV31 3ZF Tel: (01926) 735754 E-mail: ask@nvh-letting.com *We are fully focused on the priorities and needs of Landlords and Tenants. Our professional standards, and low costs offer excellent value letting and property management and our effective marketing means property is let quickly. If you have property to let, contact us now and we will match your property to our extensive database of tenants.*

Letts Compute, Unit 1, 71 Kings Street, Derby, DE1 3GZ Tel: (01332) 386500 Fax: (01332) 386500 *Computer systems consultants*

Letts Swimming Pools Ltd, Semer, Ipswich, IP7 6HP Tel: (01473) 822375 Fax: (01473) 824223 *Swimming pool construction & equipment services*

Leuze Mayser Electronic Ltd, Generation Business Park, Barford Road, St. Neots, Cambridgeshire, PE19 6YQ Tel: (01480) 408500 Fax: (01480) 403808 E-mail: mail@leuzemayser.co.uk

continued

Manufacturers of bar code systems electronic safety guards

▶ Levant Office Interiors, Tedco Business Works, Henry Robson Way, South Shields, Tyne & Wear, NE33 1RF Tel: 0191-427 4692 Fax: 0191-427 4694 E-mail: enquiries@levantofficeinteriors.com *Office furniture distributors*

Level 7 Computers Ltd, 39 Eastover, Bridgwater, Somerset, TA6 5AW Tel: (01278) 444770 E-mail: mail@level7.co.uk *Computer maintenance & sales*

▶ Level Best Screeders, 17 Swallows Green Drive, Durrington, Worthing, West Sussex, BN13 2TS Tel: 01903 830126 Fax: 01903 261574 E-mail: floorscreeder@aol.com *Specialists in applying site mix & pre mix floor screeds.Sand & cement and also flow screeds, such as gyvlon.Clean, efficient and reliable*

▶ Level Best Solutions Ltd, Commerce Way, Edenbridge, Kent, TN8 6ED Tel: (01732) 868218 Fax: (01732) 860107 E-mail: info@levelbestsolutions.com *Office refurbishment manufrs*

▶ Level One Engineering Ltd, Birchill Road, Knowsley Industrial Park, Liverpool, L33 7TG Tel: 0151-547 1300 Fax: 0151-546 7877

Level Seven Communications Ltd, 10-16 Tiller Road, London, E14 8PX Tel: (020) 7345 5125 Fax: (020) 7345 9476 E-mail: sales@l7c.com *Software systems developers*

Levell Instruments, Four Hazels, Allard Way, Broxbourne, Hertfordshire, EN10 7ER Tel: (01992) 464248 Fax: (01992) 464248 E-mail: levellbcc@aol.com *Electronic test equipment manufrs*

▶ Leven Crest Ltd, Suite 90, 38 Queen Street, Glasgow, G1 3DX Tel: 0141-204 7819

Levenbridge Engineering Ltd, 50 Perry Avenue, Teesside Industrial Estate, Thornaby, Stockton-on-Tees, Cleveland, TS17 9LN Tel: (01642) 750456 Fax: (01642) 750567 E-mail: enquiries@levenbridge.com *Fabrication & steel erection engineering*

Levenshulme Karate Club, Klondyke Club, Burnage Range, Levenshulme, Manchester, M19 2UG Tel: 0161-221 2676 E-mail: shukokaikarate2000@yahoo.co.uk *jason olsen 1st dan in the tradiional japanese art of karate,is enrolling new beginners of all ages to join us and meet new friends have fun etc whilst learning and keeping fit.come along monday eve 7pm.*

Leventis Overseas Ltd, West Africa House, Ashbourne Road, London, W5 3QP Tel: (020) 8997 6651 Fax: (020) 8997 2621 E-mail: leventis@overseas.com *Import & export merchants*

Lever Faberge, PO Box 69, Wirral, Merseyside, CH62 4ZD Tel: 0151-641 4000 Fax: 0151-641 4029 *Detergent & soap manufrs* Also at: Kingston-upon-Thames

James Lever & Sons Ltd, Unit 26 Orient Works Morris Green, Business Park Prescott, Bolton, BL3 3PE Tel: (01204) 658154 Fax: (01204) 658154 E-mail: sales@jameslever.co.uk Principal Export Areas: Africa *Rope, twine, cordage & clothes line manufrs*

Levern Engineering Ltd, 30 Cogan Street, Barrhead, Glasgow, G78 1EJ Tel: 0141-881 9101 Fax: 0141-881 1888 E-mail: service@leverneng.co.uk *Electrical & mechanical engineers services*

LeverPress Ltd, 12-14 Goddard Road, Whitehouse Industrial Estate, Ipswich, IP1 5NP Tel: (01473) 461464 Fax: (01473) 240118 E-mail: sales@leverpress.co.uk *Lithographic & screen printing services*

Levertech Metal Finishing Services, Green Lane, Eccles, Manchester, M30 8JJ Tel: 0161-787 7247 Fax: 0161-789 6411 E-mail: levertech@levertech.fsnet.co.uk *Metal finishing specialists*

Levi (Europa), 44 Mill Street, Kidderminster, Worcestershire, DY11 6XB Tel: (01562) 69957 Fax: (01562) 824321 *Cookers & wood burning stoves*

▶ Nick Levi - Close Up Magic, 2 North Park Avenue, Norwich, NR4 7EG Tel: (07962) 252949 E-mail: nick@levimagic.com *Nick Levi is a rising talent in close-up magic. Coins appear out of thin air, ropes get restored in a blink, and cards don"t obey science anymore! When magic is so close to the eye, completely inexplicable, and used with great comedy, it never fails to entertain! Read more, watch clips and videos of live performance on Nick Levi"s Website, and get in touch!*

Levi Strauss UK Ltd, Swan Valley, Northampton, NN4 9BA Tel: (01604) 581501 Fax: (01604) 599815 *Jeans & casual wear distributors*

Levingstone Manufacturing Ltd, Cranmere House, 196 Upper Chobham Road, Camberley, Surrey, GU15 1HD Tel: (01276) 25915 Fax: (01276) 21251 E-mail: conroy@hendries.freeserve.co.uk *Medical suppliers*

Levington Cold Store Co., Levington Street, Grimsby, South Humberside, DN31 3HY Tel: (01472) 359140 Fax: (01472) 355523 *Cold storage fish processors*

Levolux Ltd, 1 Forward Drive, Harrow, Middlesex, HA3 8NT Tel: (020) 8863 9111 Fax: (020) 8863 8760 E-mail: info@levolux.com *Internal and external Solar shading, including blinds, brise soleil, fins, louvres, curtains and tracks and acoustic fabric walling.*

Levolux A T Ltd, Levolux House 24 Eastville Close, Eastern Avenue, Gloucester, GL4 3SJ Tel: (01452) 500007 Fax: (01452) 527496 E-mail: info@levolux.com *Curtains, blinds & louvres suppliers*

Levy Associates Ltd, Pilgrims Lodge Holywell Hill, St. Albans, Hertfordshire, AL1 1ER Tel: (01727) 792200 Fax: (01727) 868890 E-mail: mail@levynet.co.uk *IT recruitment*

B. Levy & Co. (Patterns) Ltd, 37 Churton Street, London, SW1V 2LT Tel: (020) 7834 1073 Fax: (020) 7630 8673 E-mail: sales@blevy.com *Architectural metalworkers fabricators*

Levy Gems Co., Minerva House, 26-27 Hatton Garden, London, EC1N 8BR Tel: (020) 7242 4547 Fax: (020) 7831 0102 E-mail: levey.gems@virgin.net *Gemstone & diamond suppliers*

Lewbuild Fence Products, Ashton Rd, Bardsley, Oldham, OL8 3HT Tel: 0161-633 2301 Fax: 0161-624 7525 *Security fencing contractors & manufrs*

Lewden Electrical Industries, Argall Avenue, London, E10 7QD Tel: (020) 8539 0233 Fax: (020) 8558 2718 E-mail: alan.green@lewden.co.uk *Industrial plug & socket manufrs*

▶ Lewden Metal Products Ltd, Argall Avenue, London, E10 7QD Tel: (020) 8539 0237 Fax: (020) 8558 2718 E-mail: info@lewden.com *Plugs & socket manufrs*

Lewes Design Contracts Ltd, The Mill, Glynde, Lewes, East Sussex, BN8 6SS Tel: (01273) 858341 Fax: (01273) 858200 E-mail: info@spiralstairs.co.uk *Spiral & helical staircase manufrs*

David Lewin Metal Craft, P O Box 753, St. Albans, Hertfordshire, AL2 3WU Tel: (01727) 868300 Fax: (01727) 868300E-mail: delewin@theiet.org *Metalworkers & wrought ironworkers*

▶ Lewis, Unit 92 Dolphin House Stephenson Way, Formby Business Park, Formby, Liverpool, L37 8EG Tel: (01704) 831142 Fax: (01704) 879767 E-mail: enquiries@ablewis.co.uk *Importer & distributor of sawn & further processed hardwoods*

Lewis & Co., Unit 5 Faraday Close, Washington, Tyne & Wear, NE38 8QJ Tel: 0191-419 2234 Fax: 0191-419 0724 *Upholsterers warehousemen*

Lewis & Co., Hinton Hall, Hinton, Whitchurch, Shropshire, SY13 4HB Tel: (01948) 662923 Fax: (01948) 667908 E-mail: lewisnco@btopenworld.com *Self drive plant hire & used equipment sales*

Lewis & Beddows Ltd, Windsor Court, 9-13 Olton Road, Shirley, Solihull, West Midlands, B90 3NF Tel: 0121-733 1246 Fax: 0121-733 1245 E-mail: info@lewis-beddows.co.uk

Lewis Bros, The Grove, Hollyhurst, Leebotwood, Church Stretton, Shropshire, SY6 7JP Tel: (01694) 751212 Fax: (01694) 751212 *Hay & straw merchants*

▶ Lewis Bros, Lilford Street, Warrington, WA5 0LJ Tel: (01925) 632994 Fax: (01925) 415588

▶ Lewis Builders Ltd, Rigs Road, Stornoway, Isle of Lewis, HS1 2RF Tel: (01851) 705015 Fax: (01851) 703718 E-mail: sales@lewis-builders.com

▶ Lewis Buxton Groundworks, Unit 2, Thurnscoe Business Park, Phoenix Lane, Rotherham, South Yorkshire, S63 0BH Tel: (01709) 890600

▶ Lewis & Clark Ltd, 33 Coldstream Street, Blantyre, G72 0SR Tel: (0792) 1818223 Fax: (01698) 305302 E-mail: pmccreadie@lewis-clark.com *Refurbished and Second-User Test and SMT Equipment*

▶ Lewis Conquer, 82 Heath Drive, Chelmsford, CM2 9HF Tel: (07973) 463120 Fax: (01245) 492910 E-mail: lewis@iso-9000-consultant.co.uk

▶ Lewis Craft, 47 Ajax Drive, Bury, Lancashire, BL9 8EF Tel: 0161-796 0235 Fax: 0161-796 0235 E-mail: lewiscraft@gmail.com *design and installation of bathroom suites and tiling. Boiler replacements. Installation of central heating systems. showers supplied and fitted. Leaks repaired.No call out charge.*

Lewis Crofters Ltd, Island Road, Stornoway, Isle Of Lewis, HS1 2RD Tel: (01851) 702350 Fax: (01851) 703077 *Agricultural cooperative*

Lewis Day Transport plc, 76 East Road, London, N1 6AB Tel: (020) 7014 1000 Fax: (020) 7014 1001 *Courier services*

Lewis Direct Mail Marketing Ltd, 433-435 Caledonian Road, London, N7 9BG Tel: (020) 7607 6505 Fax: (020) 7607 0932 E-mail: info@ldm.co.uk *Direct mail services*

Lewis Ductwork, 43a Hayes Road, Bromley, BR2 9AF Tel: (020) 7737 4435 *Metal work*

Lewis Ductwork, 450 Rathgar Road, London, SW9 7EP Tel: (020) 7737 4435 Fax: (020) 7737 4435 *Metalwork fabricators*

Lewis Equipment Ltd, Waterloo Road, Bidford-on-Avon, Alcester, Warwickshire, B50 4JH Tel: (01789) 773044 Fax: (01789) 490379 E-mail: sales@lewis-equipment.co.uk *Manufacturers of retrofit backhoe loaders*

Lewis & Co Fabrics Ltd, Sunbury House The Wallows Industrial Estate, Wallows Road, Brierley Hill, West Midlands, DY5 1QA Tel: (01384) 263313 Fax: (01384) 79019 *Upholstery fabric distributors*

Lewis & Co Fabrics Ltd, Sunbury House, 1 Andrews Road, London, E8 4QL Tel: (020) 7249 4967 Fax: (020) 7241 3163 E-mail: sales@sunburyfabrics.co.uk *Soft fabric distributors* Also at: Brierley Hill & Sunderland

Lewis Furniture Ltd, 3A Bridge Street, Halesworth, Suffolk, IP19 8AB Tel: (01986) 874002 Fax: (01986) 874002 *Pine, oak & beach furniture manufacturers & wholesalers*

Lewis Group Plc, Lawrence House, Riverside Drive, Cleckheaton, West Yorkshire, BD19 4DH Tel: (01274) 852000 Fax: (01274) 862602 *Debt recovery services*

Lewis & Hickey Ltd, 17 Dorset Square, London, NW1 6QB Tel: (020) 7724 1611 Fax: (020) 7724 2282 E-mail: all@lewishickeylondon.com *Architects, project managers & interior designers* Also at: Guildford

▶ Lewis Hygiene Ltd, Unit 8c Oldham Broadway Business Park, Chadderton, Oldham, OL9 9XA Tel: 0161-345 3444 Fax: 0161-345 3445 E-mail: info@lewishygiene.co.uk *Janitorial & cleaning products, hand towels & toilet roll suppliers*

Lewis Industrial Products, 25 Lichfield Close, New Arley, Coventry, Warwickshire, CV7 8PU Tel: (01676) 541792 Fax: (01676) 541184 E-mail: lewislip@aol.com *Self-adhesive tape distribs*

Lewis J C Maidenhead Ltd, 117 Blackamoor Lane, Maidenhead, Berkshire, SL6 8RQ Tel: (01628) 621013 Fax: (01628) 781009 *Crane hire & general haulage*

J. Lewis & Co. (Manchester) Ltd, Vulcan Works, Pollard Street, Manchester, M4 7AN Tel: 0161-273 3077 Fax: 0161-273 2044 E-mail: avijlewis@aol.com *Furnishing fabric merchants*

▶ Lewis & King Electrical Services Ltd, Unit 14 Waterloo Industrial Estate, Waterloo Road, Bidford-on-Avon, Alcester, Warwickshire, B50 4JH Tel: (01789) 490049 Fax: (01789) 778490

Lewis Marquees Westbourne Ltd, Unit 20 The Wren Centre, Westbourne Road, Emsworth, Hampshire, PO10 7SU Tel: (01243) 372242 Fax: (01243) 372265 E-mail: admin@lewismarquees.com *Marquee contractors*

Lewis & Mason Plastics, Unit 47 Business Development Centre, Stafford Park 4, Telford, Shropshire, TF3 3BA Tel: (01952) 210322 Fax: (01952) 292647 E-mail: info@lewis-mason-plastics.co.uk *As one of the first plastics distributors and fabricators formed in the U.K., Lewis & Mason have been suppliers to the industry since 1972. With over 29 years experience we recognise your need for quality products, durable in use, and supported by a reliable delivery service - all at competitive prices.*

Lewis Masonry, 14 The Barges, Tower Parade, Whitstable, Kent, CT5 2BF Tel: (01227) 280064 Fax: (01227) 280064 E-mail: lewismatanle@supanet.com *Stonemasonry, building restoration, conservation & alteration*

Lewis & Peat Produce Ltd, 79 Knightsbridge, London, SW1X 7RB Tel: (020) 7235 0099 Fax: (020) 7235 2055 E-mail: lewisandpeat@compuserve.com *Shipping agents & brokers*

Peter Lewis Ltd, Unit 14, Red Lion Business Centre, Surbiton, Surrey, KT6 7QD Tel: (020) 8391 5477 Fax: (020) 8974 1650 E-mail: sales@peter-lewis.co.uk *Small leather goods manufrs*

Lewis Plant Hire Ltd, Peacock Road, Newcastle, Staffordshire, ST5 9HY Tel: (01782) 623776 Fax: (01782) 614738 *Contractors' plant hire*

Lewis & Raby (Engineers) Ltd, Birchill Road, Knowsley Industrial Park, Liverpool, L33 7TG Tel: 0151-546 2882 Fax: 0151-549 1585 *General engineers services*

▶ Lewis Ronald, 5 Long Street, London, E2 8HN Tel: (020) 7033 9134 Fax:

▶ Lewis & Ross Contractors Ltd, Kings Head Yard, Kings Head Road, Gendros, Swansea, SA5 8DA Tel: (01792) 586664

Samuel Lewis Ltd, PO Box 65, Cradley Heath, West Midlands, B64 5PS Tel: 0121-561 2157 Fax: 0121-561 5273 *Agricultural hardware suppliers*

Lewis Security Group Ltd, 1 Hanlon Court, Royal Industrial Estate, Jarrow, Tyne & Wear, NE32 3HR Tel: 0191-496 2400 Fax: 0191-496 2401 E-mail: sales@lsgroup.com *Locksmiths, safe & security engineers*

Lewis & Sons, 8 Silver Street, Barnstaple, Devon, EX32 8HR Tel: (01271) 342336 Fax: (01271) 323330 *Removal & storage contractors*

Lewis T Davies, Brewery Road, Carmarthen, Dyfed, SA31 1TF Tel: (01267) 221746 Fax: (01267) 221776 E-mail: info@lewistdavies.co.uk *Paper & polythene merchants*

▶ Lewis Transport Services Ltd, Cavendish Lodge, Derby Road, Doveridge, Ashbourne, Derbyshire, DE6 5JU Tel: (01889) 568181 Fax: (01889) 568198 E-mail: mark@lewistransport.co.uk *Road transport & heavy haulage services*

▶ Lewis Ventilation & Ducting, 6 Manor Park Business Centre, Mackenzie Way, Swindon Village, Cheltenham, Gloucestershire, GL51 9TX Tel: (01242) 233825 *Ducting ventilation systems manufrs*

Lewis W O, 39 Howard Street, Birmingham, B19 3HP Tel: 0121-236 4240 Fax: 0121-233 3057 E-mail: sales@lewisbadges.co.uk *Badge manufrs*

Lewis & Wood Ltd, 5 The Green, Uley, Dursley, Gloucestershire, GL11 5SN Tel: (01453) 860080 Fax: (01453) 860054 E-mail: office@lewisandwood.co.uk *Wallpaper & fabrics manufrs*

Lewis's Medical Supplies, Broadoak House, Coronation Street, Stockport, Cheshire, SK5 7PG Tel: 0161-480 6797 Fax: 0161 4804787 E-mail: sales@lewis-plast.co.uk Principal Export Areas: Central/East Europe & West Europe *Manufacturers of first aid outfits & dressings. In addition, first aid supply services & suppliers of fire extinguishers & blankets*

Lewmar Ltd, Southmoor Lane, Havant, Hampshire, PO9 1JJ Tel: (023) 9247 1841 Fax: (023) 9248 5720 E-mail: info@lewmar.com *Yacht winches & hatch manufrs*

Lewmar Ltd, Crescent House, Latimer Road, Luton, LU1 3UZ Tel: (01582) 404400 Fax: (01582) 400331 E-mail: sales@whitlocksteering.com *Marine steering manufrs*

Lewmar Fencing Co., 11 Sutherland Street, Swinton, Manchester, M27 6AT Tel: 0161-793 7630 Fax: 0161-793 7630 E-mail: sales@lewmarfencing.co.uk *Fencing contractors & manufrs*

Lewmax Programming, Unit 1, Fowke Street, Rothley, Leicester, LE7 7PJ Tel: 0116-212 2133 Fax: 0116-212 2136 E-mail: sales@lewmax.co.uk *Semiconductor device programming & tape reeling services*

Lex Knitwear Ltd, 28 Knowsley Street, Manchester, M8 8HQ Tel: 0161-834 9005 Fax: 0161-834 9005 *School uniform manufrs*

Lex Transfleet Ltd, 17 Western Road, London, NW10 7LT Tel: (020) 8961 5225 Fax: (020) 8965 9214 *Commercial vehicle contract hire*

Lex Vehicle Leasing Ltd, Heathside Park, Heathside Park Road, Stockport, Cheshire, SK3 0RB Tel: (0870) 1124000 Fax: (0870) 1124400 *Vehicle contract hire*

Lexden Engineering Co. Ltd, 277 Crescent Drive, Petts Wood, Orpington, Kent, BR5 1AY Tel: (01689) 833366 Fax: (01689) 833366 E-mail: lexdenengineering@ntlworld.com *General engineers*

Lexicon Distribution, 11 Ackroyd St, Morley, Leeds, LS27 8QX Tel: 0113-252 2727 Fax: 0113-252 3177 E-mail: rob@xic.co.uk *Computer systems development*

Lexicon Lifeline Ltd, Unit 3, 78 Blandford Road, Corfe Mullen, Wimborne, Dorset, BH21 3HQ Tel: (01202) 657252 Fax: (01202) 657252 E-mail: office@lexiconlifeline.co.uk *IT consultants for schools*

▶ Lexicon Recruitment Ltd, 7th Floor, 120 Vyse Street, Jewellery Quarter, Birmingham, B18 6 NF Tel: 0845 130 6680 Fax: 0709 286 0437 E-mail: info@lexiconrecruitment.com *A Specialist IT/Telecommunications Recruitment Consultancy working with both Permanent, Contract & Interim candidates supplying to Blue Chip Clients throughout the UK. Specialising in the supply of CEO, CTO, IT/Technical, Programme, Project & Product Directors/Managers. Other specialist supply areas include Web Design & Development, Network Design & Support, Software/Internet development, Voice/Data Network Specialists, RDBMS administration & development etc. We also offer a full Vendor Management solution to clients in our marketplace.*

Lexington Payne Homes Ltd, Longbeck Estate, Marske-by-the-Sea, Redcar, Cleveland, TS11 6HD Tel: (01642) 490808 Fax: (01642) 488520 *Private house builders*

Lexisnexis, Halsbury House, 35 Chancery Lane, London, WC2A 1EL Tel: (020) 7400 2500 Fax: (020) 7400 2611 E-mail: marketingdepartment@lexisnexis.co.uk *LexisNexis® is a leading provider of comprehensive information and business solutions to professionals in a variety of areas legal, risk management, corporate, government, law enforcement, accounting and academic. A member of Reed Elsevier Group plc, LexisNexis helps customers achieve their goals in 100 countries through 13,000 employees dedicated to putting the Customer First.*

Lexisnexis UK, 2 Addiscombe Road, Croydon, CR9 5AF Tel: (020) 8662 2000 Fax: (020) 8662 2012 E-mail: sales@lexisnexis.co.uk *Publishing services*

Leyblend Manufacturing Ltd, Eastlands Industrial Estate, Leiston, Suffolk, IP16 4LL Tel: (01728) 831883 Fax: (01728) 833806 E-mail: leyblend@btconnect.com *Contract blenders & grinders*

Leyden Electrical Supplies Ltd, Leyden Road, Stevenage, Hertfordshire, SG1 2BP Tel: (01438) 316144 Fax: (01438) 364946 E-mail: info@leydenelectrical.co.uk *Electrical & lighting distributors*

▶ Leyden Kirby Associates Ltd, 49 Bury Business Centre, Kay Street, Bury, Lancashire, BL9 6BU Tel: 0161-763 7200 Fax: 0161-763 7318 E-mail: info@leydenkirby.co.uk *Environmental consultants, asbestos*

Leyden Transmissions Ltd, Roberttown Lane, Liversedge, West Yorkshire, WF15 7LQ Tel: (01924) 402820 Fax: (01924) 411350 E-mail: info@leyden-ptc.co.uk *Power transmission equipment manufrs*

Leyfos Plastics, Unit D1, Rosehill Industrial, Stoke Heath, Market Drayton, Shropshire, TF9 2JU Tel: (01630) 638557 Fax: (01630) 638651 E-mail: sales@leyfos.com *Plastic coating/ corrosion prevention services*

Leyland Filtration Ltd, Yarrow Road, Chorley, Lancashire, PR6 0LP Tel: (01257) 269292 Fax: (01257) 261056 E-mail: layland.filtration@talk21.com *Filter manufrs*

Leyland Furniture Frames, Altcar Lane, Leyland, PR25 1LE Tel: (01772) 434090 Fax: (01772) 434090 *Furniture frames specialists*

Leyland Trucks Ltd, Croston Road, Leyland, PR26 6LZ Tel: (01772) 621400 Fax: (01772) 625910 E-mail: sales@packar.com *Truck assemblers*

▶ Leylec Electrical Contractors, 26 Kennet Drive, Leyland, PR25 3QX Tel: (01772) 451172 Fax: (01772) 451172 E-mail: sales@leylec.co.uk *Electrician & security systems*

Leyletts Engineering Co. Ltd, Cornwallis Road, Lyng, West Bromwich, West Midlands, B70 7JF Tel: 0121-544 6669 Fax: 0121-544 8483 E-mail: sales@leyletts.co.uk *Steel fabricators*

Leyprint Ltd, Leyland Lane, Leyland, PR25 1UT Tel: (01772) 425000 Fax: (01772) 425001 E-mail: info@leyprint.co.uk *Carton manufrs*

Leysen Associates Ltd, Padmores Yard, St. Johns Mews, Woking, Surrey, GU21 7ZE Tel: (01483) 881188 Fax: (01483) 881189 *Computer consultants*

Leythorne Ltd, Hawthorns Business Centre, Halfords Lane, Smethwick, West Midlands, B66 1BB Tel: 0121-558 1181 Fax: 0121-555 4913 E-mail: sales@leythorne.co.uk *Producers of technical support documentation*

Leyton Engineering Services Ltd, Unit 8 Horndon Industrial Park, Station Road, West Horndon, Brentwood, Essex, CM13 3XL Tel: (01277) 812404 Fax: (01277) 810853 E-mail: sales@leytongroup.com *Industrial door & shutter manufrs*

Leyton Fasteners Ltd, 9-15 Cook Street, Ellesmere Port, CH65 4AU Tel: 0151-355 8045 Fax: 0151-356 1885 E-mail: sales@leytonfasteners.co.uk *Industrial fastener distributors*

Leyton Timber Merchants, 583-585 High Road, London, E10 6PY Tel: (020) 8539 6491 Fax: (020) 8539 6491 *Timber merchants*

Leytoner De Montfort Ltd, 8 Layton Road, Leicester, LE5 0PU Tel: 0116-276 7272 E-mail: leytoner@aol.com *General engineers fabrication & sheet metal*

▶ LFI Ladder & Fencing Industries (Newent) Ltd, Horsefair Lane, Newent, Glos, GL18 1RP Tel: (01531) 820541 Fax: (01531) 821161 E-mail: sales@lfi-ladders.co.uk *Manufacturers of wooden, aluminium & step ladders*

▶ LG Insurance Services Ltd, Unit C6, Seedbed Centre Davidson Way, Romford, RM7 0AZ Tel: (01708) 730830 Fax: (01708) 734505 E-mail: LGinsurance@aol.com *Insurance brokers*

LG International, Marsh Road, Lords Meadow Industrial Estate, Crediton, Devon, EX17 1EU Tel: (01363) 777500 Fax: (01363) 777501 *Dial thermometers & pressure instrumentation manufrs*

▶ LGI Consulting, 2nd Floor, 41A Church Street, Weybridge, Surrey, KT13 8DG Tel: 01932 856699 E-mail: info@lgiconsulting.co.uk *Arranging financial solutions for both Private and Business clients. *Contact us for a free mortgage review, and visit our website for a full list of services.*

LGM Products Ltd, 18 Riverside Park Industrial Estate, Dogflud Way, Farnham, Surrey, GU9 7UG Tel: (01252) 725257 Fax: (01252) 727627 E-mail: sales@lgmproducts.com *Audible warning signal distributors & alarm*

L'hotellier Montrichard (UK) Ltd, Balena Close, Poole, Dorset, BH17 7DU Tel: (01202) 693409 Fax: (01202) 658657 E-mail: sparkesc@lcn.ltd.uk *Plastic product manufrs*

▶ Liability Risk Services Ltd, 33 Burndale Drive, Sunnybank, Bury, Lancs, BL9 8EN Tel: 0161 2809269 E-mail: info@liability-risk.com *Liability Risk Services Ltd is a small, independent UK consultancy specialising in the management of safety and health along with the provision of specialised liability insurance underwriting information to insurers and brokers.**The principal consultant is David Bannister who has experience and qualifications in both occupational safety & health and occupational hygiene.**Our consulting activities are designed to assist clients achieve increased levels of productivity, quality and profitability. Our services increase performance in health & safety management resulting in fewer interruptions to normal operations and lower costs. Organisations with whom we work achieve a pro-active approach to risk by knowing precisely where their health & safety priorities lie, by implementing plans to progressively improve safety standards and assigning health & safety responsibilities, accountabilities and authorities from board level downwards.***

Liaison & Consultant Services (U K) Ltd, PO Box 56, Woking, Surrey, GU21 2PP Tel: (01483) 799322 Fax: (01483) 799311 E-mail: rclcsuk@aol.com *Export & import agents & consultants*

Lianda Business Services, Lianda House, Camphill Road, West Byfleet, Surrey, KT14 6EW Tel: (01932) 341444 Fax: (01932) 349220 E-mail: sales@lianda.co.uk *Stationary wholesalers*

▶ Liannes Mobile Hairdresser, 7 New Rectory Lane, Kingsnorth, Ashford, Kent, TN23 3LY Tel: (01233) 503226 E-mail: hair@liannes.co.uk *Mobile hair stylist providng hair care in the comfort of your own home.*

▶ Liant Software Ltd, 5-8 The Sanctuary, London, SW1P 3JS Tel: (020) 7799 2434 Fax: (020) 7799 2552 *Computer maintenance & repair services*

Libec Europe Ltd, Priory House Industrial Estate, Pitsford Street, Birmingham, B18 6LX Tel: (01527) 596955 Fax: (01527) 596788 E-mail: sales@libeceurope.com *Audio visual & broadcasting equipment*

Liber8 Ltd, Asher House, Barsbank Lane, Lymm, Cheshire, WA13 0ED Tel: (01925) 758283 Fax: (01925) 758470 E-mail: info@liber8.co.uk *Computer consultants*

Liberon, Mountfield Industrial Estate, Learoyd Road, New Romney, Kent, TN28 8XU Tel: (01797) 367555 Fax: (01797) 367575 *Wood care distributors*

▶ LibeRATE Estimating Software, 25B The Borough, Farnham, Surrey, GU9 7NJ Tel: (01252) 725513 Fax: (01252) 727828 E-mail: info@landpro.co.uk *Construction industry software suppliers*

▶ Liberte' Horsebox Hire, Unit 7, Greetby Place, East Gillibrands, Skelmersdale, Lancashire, WN8 9UL Tel: (01928) 740020 E-mail: info@libertehorseboxes.co.uk *We are a family based business based in thr North West supplying self-drive horseboxes to the growing equestrian market.*

Liberty Plc, 210-220 Regent St, London, W1B 5AH Tel: (020) 7734 1234 Fax: (020) 7573 9876 E-mail: info@liberty.co.uk *Departmental store* Also at: Branches throughout the UK

Liberty Bell Voice & Data Ltd, The Old Courthouse, Chapel Street, Dukinfield, Cheshire, SK16 4DT Tel: (0800) 5053373 Fax: (0800) 5053773 *Business telephone systems*

▶ Liberty Business Centres, Sybrig House, Ridge Way, Donibristle Industrial Park, Hillend, Dunfermline, Fife, KY11 9JN Tel: (01383) 823030 Fax: (01383) 820003 E-mail: info@libertybusinesscentres.co.uk *Provider of lettable office and storage Space. Also provide virtual offices, admin and telephone answering services.*

▶ Liberty Consulting, 8 Cromwell Road, Hove, East Sussex, BN3 3WB Tel: (0845) 0090044 Fax: (0845) 0090045 E-mail: vicky@liberty-consulting.co.uk *Liberty Consulting is the perfect recruitment solution and because of our innovative charging methods we are able help our clients to save thousands of pounds.**We recruit for all kinds of vacancies, including:**Administration, Customer Services, Telemarketing, Telesales, Account Manager, Sales, Marketing, Executive, Management, Technical/IT, programming and many other job roles.**Our clients use us for complete recruitment campaigns or select from the following services:**Develop full job descriptions *Write job advertisements *Place advertisements in the appropriate media *Monitor, manage and filter all response *Telephone interview candidates *Arrange all interviews *Write behavioural and situational interview formats *Carry out face-to-face interviews on your site *All recruitment administration *Salary negotiation and reference checking *Workshops and assessment days* ***

Liberty Plastics Ltd, Riversleigh Business Centre, 20 Harcourt Road, Dorney Reach, Maidenhead, Berkshire, SL6 0DU Tel: (01628) 773943 Fax: (01628) 788031 E-mail: tony@libertyplastics.freeserve.co.uk *Polythene manufacturers.*

Liberty Printers Ltd, Willett Road, Thornton Heath, Surrey, CR7 6AA Tel: (020) 8684 1486 Fax: (020) 8689 3202 E-mail: service@libertyprinters.co.uk *Bespoke printing*

Libra Audio, Unit 2, Buckhurst Farm, Buckhurst Park, Withyham, Hartfield, East Sussex, TN7 4BB Tel: (01892) 662700 Fax: (01892) 662700 E-mail: william@libraaudio.co.uk *Audio supplies & installation*

▶ Libra Management Consultants, Suite 14-15 Axwel House, Westerton Road, East Mains Industrial Estate, Broxburn, West Lothian, EH52 5AU Tel: 0845 1249342 Fax: 0707 5024394 E-mail: admin@libramanagement.com *Distance Learning Training courses in a wide variety of topics. Including Sales, Management, Stress Management, Domestic Appliance Repair. Also in-house bespoke courses for companies, we tailor the course to suit your requirements. E-courses available in many subjects. Visit site for full details.*

Libra Professional Broadcast, Chester House, 91-95 Alcester Road, Studley, Warwickshire, B80 7NJ Tel: (01527) 853305 Fax: (01527) 852086 E-mail: andy@libraproinfo.co.uk *Audio visual equipment services*

Libra Signs Ltd, Great Keelings, Lower Stock Road, West Hanningfield, Chelmsford, CM2 8UY Tel: (01277) 841944 Fax: (01277) 841629 E-mail: sales@librasigns.com *Sign manufrs*

Libra Solutions Ltd, 34 Furham Field, Pinner, Middlesex, HA5 4DZ Tel: (020) 8428 2776 Fax: (020) 8428 2776 E-mail: sales@librasolutions.co.uk *Broadcast systems designers & installation*

Libra Speciality Chemicals Ltd, Brinell Drive, Northbank Industrial Park, Irlam, Manchester, M44 5LF Tel: 0161-775 1888 Fax: 0161-777 9109 E-mail: sales@librachem.co.uk *Chemical and contract manufacturers*

Libraco Library Accessories, Filston Farm, Filston Lane, Sevenoaks, Kent, TN14 5JU Tel: (01959) 524074 Fax: (01959) 525218 E-mail: sales@1ibraco.uk.com *Library furniture equipment*

Libran Laminations Ltd, Coles Green Road, London, NW2 7HW Tel: (020) 8452 2006 Fax: (020) 8452 4456 E-mail: info@libranlaminations.co.uk *Lamination & encapsulation services*

Library Information Technology Centre, South Bank University, 103 Borough Road, London, SE1 0AA Tel: (020) 7815 7872 Fax: (020) 7815 7050 *Information technology consultancy*

Librex Educational Ltd, Colwick Road, Nottingham, NG2 4BG Tel: 0115-950 4664 Fax: 0115-958 6683 E-mail: sales@librex.co.uk *Library equipment suppliers*

Librios Research Ltd, 2 Chestnut Road, Towcester, Northamptonshire, NN12 7TW Tel: (01908) 543090 E-mail: info@librios.com *Computer consultants & software developers*

License to Frill Lingerie, 44 Fronhaul, Swiss Valle, Llanelli, Carmarthenshire, SA14 8LF Tel: (01554) 752277 E-mail: dawn@licensetofrill.co.uk *Online Lingerie shop selling a range of lingerie including camies, teddies, basques, corsets, costumes, hosiery. Free UK delivery*

Lichfield International Freight Terminal Ltd, Units 1,2 & 4, Wellington Road, Burton-on-Trent, Staffordshire, DE14 2TG Tel: (01283) 511888 Fax: (01283) 511900 E-mail: ops@lichfieldinternational.co.uk *Pallet distribution services*

Lichfield Side Saddle, Huckers Buildings, Long Acre Street, Walsall, WS2 8HP Tel: (01922) 646468 Fax: (01922) 628936 *Saddlery manufrs*

Lichfield Studio Glass Ltd, Boston Industrial Estate, Power Station Road, Rugeley, Staffordshire, WS15 2HS Tel: (01889) 575551 Fax: (01889) 575551 E-mail: lich@globalnet.co.uk *Glass manufrs*

Liddell's Cabinet Works Ltd, Marsh Lane, Lords Meadow Industrial Estate, Crediton, Devon, EX17 1ES Tel: (01363) 772032 Fax: (01363) 774838 E-mail: liddells@eclipse.co.uk *Educational furniture manufrs*

Liddle Doors, Wagonway Industrial Estate, Wagonway Road, Hebburn, Tyne & Wear, NE31 1SP Tel: 0191-483 5449 Fax: 0191-489 0698 E-mail: liddle@liddledoors.co.uk *Steel security door manures*

Liebherr Crane Hire, Stratton Business Park, Biggleswade, Bedfordshire, SG18 8QB Tel: (01767) 602100 Fax: (01767) 602110 E-mail: info.lgb@liebherr.com *Liebherr-Great Britain Ltd. is a subsidiary of Liebherr-International AG, Bulle (Switzerland), and provides national sales, service and spares for the Group's complete range of construction equipment throughout the whole of the British Isles. Liebherr-Great Britain is an integral part of the British construction, mining, materials handling, plant hire and associated industries, playing a leading role in providing these markets with state-of-the-art technology equipment and national spares and after-sales service from a well-established depot network Particular features to note include:- The biggest rolling road in the UK for mobile cranes, capable of handling up to 20 tonnes axles: Outdoor test facilities for all crane types up to 1000 tonnes capacity: Four separate workbays for cranes, earthmovers, concrete truckmixers and a welding area: Underfloor fume extraction ducting: Six strategically positioned and computerised oil delivery stations: Four 25 tonnes capacity overhead cranes.*

Liebig Bolts Ltd, Silica Road, Amington Industrial Estate, Tamworth, Staffordshire, B77 4DT Tel: (01827) 50547 Fax: (01827) 310524 E-mail: sales@liebigbolts.co.uk *We have been a market leader in manufacturing of heavy duty fixing bolts for more than 50 years. We specialise in producing anchors up to lengths of 1.5 metres in 8.8 and A4 80 stainless steel.*

Life Coach Associates, 19 Meadow Way, Kinoulton, Nottingham, NG12 3RE Tel: (01949) 81125 E-mail: gerard@life-coach-associates.com *Business and Personal Coaching.*Get results using an experienced and qualified coach.*Improve performance and have fun!*

▶ Life Foundation School of Therapeutics, Maristowe House, Dover Street, Bilston, West Midlands, WV14 6AL Tel: (01902) 409164 Fax: (01902) 497362 E-mail: chrision2000@yahoo.co.uk *Bowen tech therapist, yoga tutor, dvds, cds & books of yoga products*

▶ Life Healthcare, Freepost JE723, St. Helier, Jersey, JE1 1AF Tel: (0845) 1667070 E-mail: help@elixireurope.com *Dedicated to providing natural health solutions that work*

Life Insurance Corporation of India, 13th Floor, York House, Empire Way, Wembley, Middlesex, HA9 0PX Tel: (020) 8902 5294 Fax: (020) 8902 5281 E-mail: enquiries@liciuk.com *Insurance company* Also at: Birmingham

Life Science Products Ltd, 185l Milton Park, Milton, Abingdon, Oxfordshire, OX14 4SR Tel: (01235) 832111 Fax: (01235) 832129 E-mail: sales@lifescience.co.uk *Electronic water softener services*

Life Style, 1 Exeter Street, North Tawton, Devon, EX20 2HB Tel: (01837) 82824 Fax: (01837) 82824 *Pharmacy supplier*

▶ Life Tradings Ltd, 32 Mason St, Manchester, M4 5EY Tel: 0161-834 5838 Fax: 0161-834 4498 E-mail: lifetrading@yahoo.com *Manufacture clothing*

▶ Life Transition Consultants Ltd, Jasmine Cottage Tunbridge Road, Chew Magna, Bristol, BS40 8SP Tel: (01275) 331545 E-mail: info@lifetransition.co.uk *Business training consultants*

▶ Lifecare Hospital Supplies Ltd, Shenstone Drive, Aldridge, Walsall, WS9 8TP Tel: (01922) 455405 Fax: (01922) 749943 E-mail: rhall@hs-lifecare.com *Injection moulded medical & industrial components suppliers*

▶ Lifecote Damp Proofing, 5 Higher Beacon, Ilminster, Somerset, TA19 9AJ Tel: (01460) 52669 Fax: (01460) 52669 E-mail: info@lifecote.net *We are a Somerset based company offering professional and efficient solutions for damp proofing, rising damp, woodworm, dry rot, timber treatments, tanking and plastering. We are able to offer a totally free 30-year guarantee or for a small cost a third party insured guarantee which is approved and so recognized by all major banks, building societies and mortgage lenders.*

Lifecycle Software Ltd, Unit 2, Riverside House, Mill Lane, Newbury, Berkshire, RG14 5QS Tel: (01635) 553400 Fax: (01635) 37700 E-mail: info@lifecycle-software.com *Telecommunications software manufrs*

Lifeline Fire & Safety Systems Ltd, Burnsall Road Industrial Estate, Burnsall Road, Coventry, CV5 6BU Tel: (024) 7671 2999 Fax: (024) 7671 2998 E-mail: sales@lifeline-fire.co.uk *Automated fire suppression system manufrs*

▶ Lifeline Insurance Services, PO Box 2929, Blantyre, Glasgow, G72 9YZ Tel: (01698) 828866 Fax: (0870) 1308007 E-mail: sales@1ifelineinsuranceservices.co.uk *Independent Financial Advisers.**Life Assurance, Pensions, Savings, Investments and Mortgage Brokers.*

▶ Lifescales, Spectrum House, Dunstable Road, Redbourn, St. Albans, Hertfordshire, AL3 7PR Tel: (0845) 6381330 E-mail: info@workscales.co.uk *Outplacement consultants, performance/change management consultants*stress management*

Lifescan Scotland, Beechwood Park North, Inverness, IV2 3ED Tel: (01463) 721000 Fax: (01463) 722000 *Medical or surgical supplies*

▶ Lifestyle Assessment Ltd, 39 Watery Lane, Keresley, Coventry, CV6 2GF Tel: (0800) 2985521 Fax: 02476 722053 *We"re a provider of healthcare services and lifestyle assessments designed to improve the health of your workplace and reduce the huge cost impact of absenteeism on your business. At an average salary of almost £0 per day a reduction by anything more than one day per employee absent per annum, would have an immediate financial benefit to your company. In essence the assessments will pay for themselves. We are committed to working along side you, towards the reduction of absenteeism and increased productivity within your organisation.*

Lifestyle Ford, 3 Mount Ephraim, Tunbridge Wells, Kent, TN4 8AG Tel: (01892) 515666 Fax: (01892) 548441 E-mail: mail@lifestyleford.co.uk *Ford car dealers*

▶ Lifestyle Products Ltd, Talbot House, 17 Church Street, Rickmansworth, Hertfordshire, WD3 1DE Tel: (01923) 711832 Fax: (01923) 711831 E-mail: sales@life-style.co.uk

Lifestyle Products Direct, London Road, Osbournby, Sleaford, Lincolnshire, NG34 0DG Tel: (01529) 455666 Fax: (01529) 455646 E-mail: sales@lifestyleproductsdirect.com *Garden furniture distributors & manufrs*

Lifestyle Shutters, Unit 8 The Enterprise Centre, Bell Lane Industrial Estate, Uckfield, East Sussex, TN22 1QL Tel: (01825) 760722 Fax: (01825) 769305 E-mail: info@lifestyleshutters.co.uk *Design & install interior plantation window shutters,*

Lifetime Interiors Ltd, Unit D2, 86-102 King Street, Farnworth, Bolton, BL4 7AS Tel: (01204) 574166 Fax: (01204) 574263 E-mail: mail@lifetimeinteriors.co.uk *Suspended ceiling & partitions contractors*

▶ Lifetime Water, North East Suffolk Business Centre, Pinbush Road, Lowestoft, Suffolk, NR33 7NQ Tel: (01502) 515200

▶ Lift Care, 3 Sutton Hall Cottages, Elton Head Road, St. Helens, Merseyside, WA9 5BN Tel: (01744) 817189 Fax: (01744) 850035 *Lift installers & manufrs*

Lift Components Ltd, Units B13-14, Poplar Business Park, London, E14 9RL Tel: (020) 7515 5504 Fax: (020) 7538 2815 E-mail: sales@liftcomponents.co.uk *Lift component distributors*

Lift Control Ltd, 89 Spottiswoode Gardens, Mid Calder, Livingston, West Lothian, EH53 0JX Tel: (01506) 880043 Fax: (01506) 880043 *Lift manufrs*

Company Information

Lift & Engineering Services Ltd, 16 Portersfield Road, Cradley Heath, West Midlands, B64 7BN Tel: (01384) 633115 Fax: (01384) 633119 E-mail: mailbox@lift-engineering.co.uk *Bespoke lift manufacturers & contractors*

▶ Lift Maintenance Ltd, 12 Jordanvale Avenue, Glasgow, G14 0QP Tel: 0141-959 3601 Fax: 0141-959 3602 *Elevators & lift services*

Lift West Nissan Ltd, New Road, Seavington St Michael, Ilminster, Somerset, TA19 0QQ Tel: (01460) 242400 Fax: (01460) 240020 E-mail: info@liftwest.com *Provider of new & used lifting equipment, maintenance, service, hire & forklift driver training**

▶ Liftec Training Services, 66 Romford Road, Aveley, South Ockendon, Essex, RM15 4PP Tel: (07905) 426975 *Fork lift training service*

Liftech Engineering, 12d Tower Workshops, Riley Road, London, SE1 3DG Tel: (020) 7237 6580 Fax: (020) 7252 3785 *Steel fabricators & welders*

Liftequip Ltd, 64 Falcon Road, Battersea, London, SW11 2LR Tel: (020) 7223 9394 Fax: (020) 7228 2270 E-mail: liftequip@tiscali.co.uk *Lifts manufrs*

Lifting Equipment Services, 2 The Trailer Centre Cottismore Farm, Newbury Road, Kingsclere, Newbury, Berkshire, RG20 4SY Tel: (01635) 297804 Fax: (01635) 297803 *Repair services for lifting equipment*

Lifting Equipment & Services Ltd, B6 Foundry Way, Eaton Socon, St. Neots, Cambridgeshire, PE19 8TR Tel: (01480) 217605 Fax: (01480) 407108 E-mail: info@liftingequipmenthire.com *Lifting equipment distribution & manufrs*

Lifting Equipment Services Doncaster Ltd, Unit 3b Plumtree Farm Industrial Estate, Plumtree Road, Bircotes, Doncaster, South Yorkshire, DN11 8EW Tel: (01302) 711552 Fax: (01302) 719952 E-mail: sales@lesdoncaster.co.uk *Manufacturers in lifting gear*

Lifting Gear Hire plc, Hockley Way, Nixs Hill Industrial Estate, Alfreton, Derbyshire, DE55 7FA Tel: (01773) 608325 Fax: (01773) 540566 E-mail: sales@lgh.co.uk *Lifting gear hire*

Lifting Gear Hire Ltd, Avon Trading Estate, 20A Albert Road, Bristol, BS2 0XA Tel: 0117-977 9514 Fax: 0117-972 3076 *Lifting gear hire*

Lifting Gear Hire Ltd, Brunel Industrial Estate, Blyth Road, Harworth, Doncaster, South Yorkshire, DN11 8QA Tel: (01302) 743600 Fax: (01302) 750697 *Lifting gear hire services*

Lifting Gear Hire plc, 17 Rosscliffe Road, Ellesmere Port, CH65 3AS Tel: 0151-357 2906 Fax: 0151-357 2380 E-mail: info@lgh.co.uk *Lifting hire gear contractors*

Lifting Gear Hire plc, Unit D4 South Orbital Trading Park, Hedon Road, Hull, HU9 1NJ Tel: (01482) 223737 Fax: (01482) 219491 E-mail: hull-lifting@speedydepots.co.uk *Lifting gear hire services*

Lifting Gear Hire Ltd, Unit 27 Boston Road, Gorse Hill Industrial Estate, Beaumont Leys, Leicester, LE4 1AW Tel: 0116-234 0255 Fax: 0116-234 0254 E-mail: leicester@lgh.co.uk *Lifting gear hire*

Lifting Gear Hire plc, 74 Roding Road, London, E6 6LS Tel: (020) 7511 0233 Fax: (020) 7511 1784 *Lifting gear hire services*

Lifting Gear Hire plc, 120 Bolton Road, Atherton, Manchester, M46 9YZ Tel: (01942) 878081 Fax: (01942) 895018 E-mail: info@lgh.co.uk *Lifting gear hire*

Lifting Gear Hire Ltd, High Yard, Wincomblee Road, Newcastle upon Tyne, NE6 3PL Tel: 0191-295 5301 Fax: 0191-295 4311 E-mail: tyneside@lgh.co.uk *Lifting gear hire*

Lifting Gear Hire Ltd, Unit 1, Kings Parade, Newport, Gwent, NP20 2DU Tel: (01633) 243244 Fax: (01633) 243236 E-mail: newport@lgh.co.uk *Lifting gear hire*

Lifting Gear Supplies Ltd, 23 Anstey Lane, Leicester, LE4 0FF Tel: 0116-262 8023 Fax: 0116-251 4862 E-mail: sales@liftinggearsuppliesltd.co.uk *Lifting gear distributors*

Lifting Point, 8 Warren Road, Trafford Park, Manchester, M17 1QR Tel: 0161-872 5993 Fax: 0161-872 5994 E-mail: liftingplant@hirestation.co.uk *Lifting gear hire*

Lifting Systems, 60 Haytor Road, Wrexham, LL11 2PU Tel: (0870) 0114326 Fax: (0870) 7062999 E-mail: sales@liftingsystems.co.uk *Supply of specialist lifting products for the TV and Plasma servicing, manufacturing, rework and repair industries. Authorised UK and Ireland distributor for Dixon Lifting Systems Australia, and Lifting Logistics GmbH. Product patented names TeleLift and TV-Assist.*

Lift-It Ltd, Sendalls Way, Glacis Park Crownhill, Plymouth, PL6 5JT Tel: (01752) 771311 Fax: (01752) 788093 *Crane & transport hire*

Liftomatic International Ltd, 9 Farriers Way, Bootle, Merseyside, L30 4XL Tel: 0151-524 3066 Fax: 0151-524 3075 E-mail: liftomatic.ltd@btconnect.com *Drum handling specialists*

Liftruck Liftright, 49 Bankhall Street, Liverpool, L20 8JD Tel: 0151-933 6868 Fax: 0151-922 1110 *Fork lift trucks buy & sell*

Light Aircraft Engineering Elstree Ltd, Elstree Aerodrome, Elstree, Borehamwood, Hertfordshire, WD6 3AW Tel: (020) 8953 9341 Fax: (020) 8207 4540

Light Alloy Ltd, 85 Dales Road, Ipswich, IP1 4JR Tel: (01473) 740445 Fax: (01473) 240002 E-mail: sales@lightalloy.co.uk *Aluminium container sales & distribution*

Light Alloy Ltd, Barney Hayes Lane, Cadnam, Southampton, SO40 2ND Tel: (023) 8081 1180 Fax: (023) 8081 1197 *Packaging manufrs*

Light Car Co. Ltd, 1 White Horse Business Park, Faringdon Road, Stanford in the Vale, Faringdon, Oxfordshire, SN7 8NP Tel: (01367) 710377 Fax: (01367) 710219 *High performance car manufrs*

Light Engineering Services, 28 Rampton End, Willingham, Cambridge, CB4 5JB Tel: (01954) 260804 Fax: (01954) 260804 E-mail: lightengservices@lineone.net *Special purpose & custom built engineering, grinding, milling & repair services*

▶ Light Fantastic Ipl, Clattern House, 8-10 High Street, Kingston upon Thames, Surrey, KT1 1EY Tel: (020) 8546 6262 E-mail: lightfanlinks@yahoo.co.uk *We offer a range of hair removal and skin rejuvenation treatments including the removal of unwanted hair on any part of the body giving smooth clear skin.**The Light Fantastic IPL Beauty Clinic is a new breed of professional, professional Health and Beauty clinics, bringing to you the most up to date and affordable treatments.**We invest in the best, newest and most effective hair removal and skin rejuvenation treatments available, striving to be at the forefront of technology. **The Light Fantastic staff are CIBTAC qualified, and members of BABTAC, and we also have a registered laser care doctor- Dr Philip Dobson.**Light Fantastic IPL is registered with The Healthcare Commission.**Look great, feel great, and book now on 020 8546 6262*

▶ Light House Electrical, Unit 19f Number One Industrial Estate, Consett, County Durham, DH8 6SY Tel: (01207) 500599 Fax: (01207) 508154

Light Innovation Ltd, 362 Kingston Road, Epsom, Surrey, KT19 0DT Tel: (020) 8873 1582 Fax: (020) 8224 8949 *Lighting manufrs*

▶ The Light Lab, 20-22 Vestry Street, London, N1 7RE Tel: (020) 7427 2378 Fax: (020) 7427 2363 E-mail: info@thelightlab.com *Specialist lighting designers*

Light Matters, 6 Long Street, London, E2 8HQ Tel: (020) 7749 4770 Fax: (020) 7749 4771 E-mail: london@lightmatters.co.uk *Lighting design consultancy*

Light Solutions, Well House, Penn Street, Amersham, Buckinghamshire, HP7 0PY Tel: (01494) 717709 Fax: (01494) 891165 E-mail: sales@light-solutions.co.uk *Specialist lighting manufrs*

Light Stop Ltd, 52 Furze Platt Road, Maidenhead, Berkshire, SL6 7NN Tel: (01628) 632632 Fax: (01628) 686900 *Photographic & computer consultants*

▶ Lightbody Of Hamilton Ltd, 73 Bothwell Road, Hamilton, Lanarkshire, ML3 0DW Tel: (01698) 285227 Fax: (01698) 891600 E-mail: info@lightbody.co.uk

▶ Lightbox Photography, 19 Lynton Drive, Southport, Merseyside, PR8 4QP Tel: (01704) 566066 E-mail: sales@the-lightbox.com *Aerial photographers*

Lightbulb Co. (UK) Ltd, Thomas Edison House, 74-77 Magdalen Road, Oxford, OX4 1RE Tel: (01865) 794500 Fax: (01865) 203996 E-mail: sales@thelightbulb.co.uk *Lightbulb wholesalers*

Lightech Sound & Light Ltd, Bramhall Hill Farm, Bank Lane, North Rode, Congleton, Cheshire, CW12 2PJ Tel: (01260) 223666 Fax: (01260) 223777 E-mail: mail@lightech.fsnet.co.uk *Lighting hire, fireworks atmospheric lighting suppliers*

▶ Lightening Computers, 107 Duke Street, St. Helens, Merseyside, WA10 2JG Tel: (01744) 751110 Fax: (01744) 882746 *Computer maintenance consultants*

Lightfactor Sales, 20 Greenhill Crescent, Watford Business Park, Watford, WD18 8JA Tel: (01923) 698090 Fax: (01923) 698081 E-mail: info@lightfactor.co.uk *Lighting & sound equipment sales*

Lightfoot Bros Ltd, 32 Castle Street, Aylesbury, Buckinghamshire, HP20 2RA Tel: (01296) 482855 Fax: (01296) 482855 *Electrical & heating contractors*

Charles Lightfoot Ltd, Heywood Road, Sale, Cheshire, M33 3WB Tel: 0161-973 6565 Fax: 0161-962 5335 E-mail: clightfootltd@aol.com *Leaded lights manufrs*

Lightfoot Refrigeration Co. Ltd, Unit D2, Premier Business Centre, Newgate Lane, Fareham, Hampshire, PO14 1TY Tel: (01329) 237272 Fax: (01329) 237276 E-mail: office@lightfootrefrigeration.com *Marine refrigeration, design, maintain & installation services*

Lightfoot Windows Ltd, 31 Crouch Hill, London, N4 4AS Tel: (020) 7272 1622 Fax: (020) 7281 1404 *Window frame distributors or agents* Also at: Beckenham

Lightfoot Windows Ltd, 31 Crouch Hill, London, N4 4AS Tel: (020) 7272 1622 Fax: (020) 7281 1404 *Distributors or agents of window fittings*

Lighthouse, 7 Belgrave Terrace, Aberdeen, AB25 2NR Tel: (01224) 627396 Fax: (01224) 621115 *Graphic & web designers*

The Lighthouse, 14 Station Road, Swinton, Manchester, M27 6AF Tel: 0161-727 8742 Fax: 0161-794 3562 E-mail: markalin2003@yahoon.co.uk *Retail & wholesale lighting supplies*

▶ Lighthouse Electrical, 26 Sandwood Road, Glasgow, G52 2PP Tel: (01418) 830069 Fax: 0141-883 0069

Lighthouse Images, 2 Fords Court Cottages, Budlake, Exeter, EX5 3JS Tel: (01392) 882345 Fax: (01392) 882858 *Commercial & industrial photographers*

▶ Lighthouse Printing, 1 Anglesey Street, Cardiff, CF5 1QZ Tel: (029) 2034 4899 Fax: (029) 2034 4899 E-mail: lighthouseprint@ntlworld.com *Promotional printers suppliers*

Lighting & Ceiling Louvres Ltd, 7-13 Cutlers Road, South Woodham Ferrers, Chelmsford, CM3 5WA Tel: (01245) 321561 Fax: (01245) 325034 E-mail: sales@lcll.co.uk *Lighting & ceiling louvres manufrs*

▶ Lighting for Gardens Ltd, 20 Furmston Court, Letchworth Garden City, Hertfordshire, SG6 1UJ Tel: (01462) 486777 Fax: (01462) 480344 E-mail: sales@lightingforgardens.com *Garden lighting retailers*

Lighting Industry Federation Ltd, Swan Ho, 207 Balham High Rd, London, SW17 7BQ Tel: (020) 8675 5432 Fax: (020) 8673 5880 E-mail: info@lif.co.uk *Trade association*

▶ Lighting Infocus, The Old Rectory, Jacobstowe, Okehampton, Devon, EX20 3RQ Tel: (01837) 851436 E-mail: judy@lawsondev.com

▶ The Lighting & Interiors Group Ltd, Cobden Mill, Bentinck Street, Farnworth, Bolton, BL4 7EP Tel: (01204) 707277 Fax: (01204) 861890

Lighting Motions, 2 Slater Street, Oldham, OL9 6ES Tel: 0161-628 0098 Fax: 0161-620 7298 E-mail: sales@lightingmotions.com *Lighting manufrs*

Lighting & Sound Equipment, 118 Cowley Road, Oxford, OX4 1JE Tel: (01865) 722027 Fax: (01865) 202454 *Hire & sale of lighting & sound equipment*

Lightiq Ltd, 1 Rylett Studios 77 Rylett Crescent, London, W12 9RP Tel: (020) 8749 1900 Fax: (020) 8749 1999 E-mail: abby@lighting.com *Light IQ is an independent lighting and home automation consultancy; we design, supply and install inspirational and innovative lighting schemes for residential or commercial properties within the UK and Europe. As an esteemed lighting and AV design consultancy we believe that the realisation of the ultimate design solution is achieved through insight, imagination and meticulous attention to details. The desire for an exact and seamless experience is our key goal, one which is apparent through our entire approach. Simplicity and ease of use is guaranteed within our lighting and home automation schemes, and once you see the results you'll never look back!*

Lightique Ltd, 7 Bayton Way, Exhall, Coventry, CV7 9ER Tel: (024) 7636 5665 Fax: (024) 7636 5520 E-mail: lightique@btinternet.com *Lighting fixtures suppliers & manufrs*

Lightline Electrical Services Ltd, 40a Dryden Avenue, Ashton-in-Makerfield, Wigan, Lancashire, WN4 0JZ Tel: (01942) 713394 Fax: (01942) 713394

▶ Lightmasters UK Ltd, 3 Little End Road, Eaton Socon, St. Neots, Cambridgeshire, PE19 8JH Tel: (01480) 407727 Fax: (01480) 407757

Lightning Aerospace Ltd, Falkland Close, Charter Avenue Industrial Estate, Coventry, CV4 8AU Tel: (024) 7646 1238 Fax: (024) 7646 4745 E-mail: info@lightningaerospace.co.uk *Precision Sheet Metal Work, Cable Harness Design and Manufacture, Coded Welding, CNC Machining, Laser Cutting, Water Jet Cutting, Cable, Connector, RF Cable Stockist*

▶ Lightning Connection.biz, 35 Underbank Lane, Moulton, Northampton, NN3 7HH Tel: (0776) 2771290 E-mail: info@lightningconnection.biz *Speed business networking events services*

Lightning Consultants UK Ltd, 12 Longue Drive, Calverton, Nottingham, NG14 6QF Tel: 0115-965 4124 Fax: 0115-965 4754 E-mail: sales@prevectron.com *Lightning conductor suppliers*

Lightning Protection Services, Cove Farm, Kirkpatrick Fleming, Lockerbie, Dumfriesshire, DG11 3AT Tel: (01461) 800323 Fax: (01461) 800269 *Lightning conductor engineers*

▶ Lightning Technology Ltd, 38 Stafford Road, Wallington, Surrey, SM6 9AA Tel: (0800) 3288727 Fax: (020) 8647 1115 E-mail: kevin@lightningofficesupplies.co.uk *Supplier of office stationery & printer consumables*

▶ Lightning Transport Group, P Acorn Industrial Estate, Strawberry Street, Hull, HU9 1EN Tel: (01482) 327070 Fax: (01482) 586712

▶ Lightning Transport Group, Parkside Commercial Centre, Terry Avenue, York, YO23 1JP Tel: (01904) 610415 Fax: (0871) 8710028

Lightowlers Yarns Ltd, Brigg House Mills, 7 The Cobbles, Meltham, Holmfirth, HD9 5QQ Tel: (01484) 850908 Fax: (01484) 850424 E-mail: lighthowlersyarns@aol.com *Woollen spun yarns*

Lightpipe Co. Ltd, 116B High Street, Cranfield, Bedford, MK43 0DG Tel: (0870) 2416680 Fax: (01234) 751144 *Sell sky lights*

▶ Lightside Ltd, 2 Cardwell Terrace, Cardwell Road, London, N7 0NH Tel: (020) 7607 5640 Fax: (020) 7607 5240

▶ Lightsmith's Photography, Lightsmith's Studios, Telford, Shropshire, TF3 2NN Tel: (01952) 660013 Fax: (01952) 660013 E-mail: images@lightsmith.me.uk

Lightsource Data Presentations, Fox Studio, King Street, Much Wenlock, Shropshire, TF13 6BL Tel: (01952) 727715 Fax: (0870) 4204316 E-mail: lights@lightsource.co.uk *Business presentations services*

▶ Lightspeed Entertainments, 108 Quay Road, Bridlington, East Yorkshire, YO16 4JB Tel: (07831) 192740 Fax: (01262) 679735 E-mail: lightspeed@trancefixed.fsnet.co.uk *Sound & lighting installation, hire & service*

Lightways (Contractors) Ltd, Lochlands Industrial Estate, Larbert, Stirlingshire, FK5 3NS Tel: (01324) 553025 Fax: (01324) 557870 E-mail: head.office@lightways.co.uk *Road surfacing contractors*

Lightwood plc, Hangar 2, North Weald Airfield, North Weald, Epping, Essex, CM16 6AA Tel: (01992) 524237 Fax: (01992) 524501 E-mail: store@lightwoodplc.demon.co.uk *Contract packers, storage, distribution & case manufrs*

▶ Lightwood Contracts Ltd, Lightwood Road, Longton, Stoke-on-Trent, ST3 4JG Tel: (01782) 599600 Fax: (01782) 330753 E-mail: stevehill@plattsgarage.com *Contract hire cars & commercial van leasing*

Lignacite Ltd, Meadgate Works, Meadgate Road, Nazeing, Waltham Abbey, Essex, EN9 2PD Tel: (01992) 464441 Fax: (01992) 445713 E-mail: info@lignacite.co.uk *Concrete block manufrs*

Lignacite Brandon Ltd, Norfolk House, High Street, Brandon, Suffolk, IP27 0AX Tel: (01842) 810678 Fax: (01842) 814602 E-mail: info@lignacite.co.uk *Building & concrete block manufrs*

Likeprod Engineers Ltd, 37 Furlong Road, Bourne End, Buckinghamshire, SL8 5AF Tel: (01628) 522055 Fax: (01628) 524599 *Precision engineers*

▶ Liko Ltd, Units 2A-2B, Brunel Centre, Brunel Way, Stonehouse, Gloucestershire, GL10 3RU Tel: (01453) 827272 Fax: (01453) 828844 *Lifting equipment manufrs*

▶ Lilco Ltd, Diamond House, Stenness, Stromness, Orkney, KW16 3JX Tel: (01856) 850179 Fax: (01856) 851291 E-mail: mail@lilco.co.uk *Manufacturers of talent broadband*

Lillechurch Farms & Contracting Ltd, Lillechurch Road, Higham, Rochester, Kent, ME3 7HW Tel: (01634) 222332 Fax: (01634) 222344 *Agricultural contractors*

Lilleker Bros Ltd, 30 Moorgate Road, Rotherham, South Yorkshire, S60 2AG Tel: (01709) 374073 Fax: (01709) 364517 E-mail: info@lillekerbros.com *Electrical engineers & installations*

Lilleker Engineering Co. Ltd, Unit 3b Lincoln Street, Rotherham, South Yorkshire, S60 1RP Tel: (01709) 829541 Fax: (01709) 829542 E-mail: sales@lilleker.co.uk *Stainless steel fabricators*

Lilleshall Steel Services Ltd, Steel House, 1 Bristol Road, Gloucester, GL1 5TF Tel: (01452) 526821 Fax: (01452) 300430 E-mail: sales@lilleshall-steel.co.uk *Steel stockholders*

Lilleson Engineering Ltd, Unit 12 Brookside Court, Parkgate, Rotherham, South Yorkshire, S62 6NX Tel: (01709) 371188 Fax: (01709) 378232 E-mail: sales@lilleson.co.uk *Electrical & mechanical engineers*

▶ Lilley Information Systems Ltd, 16 Kingsway, Hayes, Middlesex, UB3 2TY Tel: (020) 8573 3911 E-mail: vlilley@lilleyinfosys.co.uk *Information systems consultants*

John Lilley & Gillie Ltd, Clive Street, North Shields, Tyne & Wear, NE29 6LF Tel: 0191-257 2217 Fax: 0191-257 1521 E-mail: sales@lilleyandgillie.co.uk *Compass & nautical instrument manufrs*

William Lillico & Son Ltd, Wonham Mill, Betchworth, Surrey, RH3 7AD Tel: (01737) 247666 Fax: (01737) 246783 *Bio technology agents*

Lilliput Aquarium, 16 St Annes Road, Blackpool, FY4 2AN Tel: (01253) 408824 Fax: (01253) 408824 *Aquarium & pond supplies*

Lilliput UK, 20-21 Worcester Street, Wolverhampton, WV2 4LD Tel: (01902) 688886 Fax: (01902) 399915 E-mail: sales@ucs.co.uk *Computer builders, maintenance & repair*

Eli Lilly & Co. Ltd, Erl Wood Manor, Sunninghill Road, Windlesham, Surrey, GU20 6PH Tel: (01276) 483000 *Medical research centre*

▶ Lilo Leisure Products Ltd, Cupola Way, Scunthorpe, South Humberside, DN15 9YJ Tel: (01724) 872202 Fax: (01724) 270041 *Distributors of christmas gifts & decorations*

▶ Lily Design, 23 Bracken Road, North Baddesley, Southampton, SO52 9FP Tel: 07855 869318 E-mail: enquiries@lilydesign.co.uk *Unique handcrafted sterling silver jewellery*

Lilyplan Ltd, 31 Franklynn Road, Haywards Heath, West Sussex, RH16 4DQ Tel: (01444) 451215 *Hair dresser's laundry services*

Lilytone Ltd, 74 Laneside Road, New Mills, High Peak, Derbyshire, SK22 4LX Tel: (01663) 747335 Fax: (01663) 747393 E-mail: sales@plastic-boxes.co.uk *Plastic box suppliers*

Lilyville Screen Entertainment Ltd, 7 Lilyville Road, London, SW6 5DP Tel: (020) 7371 5940 Fax: (020) 7736 9431 E-mail: tony.cash@btclick.com *TV programme production*

Lima Networks, 5-6 Carolina Way, Quays Reach, Salford, M50 2ZY Tel: 0161-743 3000 Fax: (0845) 3451220 E-mail: sales@lima.com *Computer networkers*

Limar Solutions Ltd, Imperial Works, King Street, Enderby, Leicester, LE19 4NT Tel: 0116-284 9019 Fax: 0116-275 0564 E-mail: steve@limarsolutions.co.uk *Acrylic sheet fabricators*

Limavady Concrete Products, 68 Carlaragh Road, Limavady, County Londonderry, BT49 9LF Tel: (07886) 022597 Fax: (028) 7776 7816 *Concrete products*

Limavady Printing Co. Ltd, 26C Catherine Street, Limavady, County Londonderry, BT49 9DB Tel: (028) 7776 2051 Fax: (028) 7776 2132 E-mail: print@limprint.com *Commercial & colour printers*

Limbrick Jig & Tool Co., Unit 14 Wilden Industrial Estate, Stourport-on-Severn, Worcestershire, DY13 9JY Tel: (01299) 823139 Fax: (01299) 823139 *Precision engineers*

▶ Limbs & Things Ltd, Sussex Street, Bristol, BS2 0RA Tel: 0117-311 0500 Fax: 0117-311 0501

Lime Bright Ltd, 29B Marlborough Road, Newport, Gwent, NP19 0BX Tel: (01633) 244225 Fax: (01633) 665777 *Shop fittings manufrs*

Lime Green Products Ltd, The Coates Kiln, Stretton Road, Much Wenlock, Shropshire, TF13 6DG Tel: (01952) 728611 Fax: (01952) 728361 E-mail: enquire@lime-green.co.uk

Lime Grove Services, Edison Road, Elm Farm Industrial Estate, Bedford, MK41 0HU Tel: (01234) 348709 Fax: (01234) 271724 *Fastener & fixing sales*

Lime Guard UK, PO Box 2796, Calne, Wiltshire, SN11 9ZY Tel: (01249) 816749 Fax: (01249) 816838 E-mail: enquiries@limeguard.com *High water pressure systems services*

Lime Kiln Narrow Boats, 4 Bridgnorth Road, Wolverhampton, WV6 8AA Tel: (01902) 751147 Fax: (01902) 753853 *Narrow boat builders*

▶ Lime P M Ltd, Unit 1A, Gresham Industrial Estate, Eastern Road, Aldershot, Hampshire, GU12 4TE Tel: (01252) 322252 Fax: (01252) 322315

▶ Limegreentangerine, 57 Cowbridge Road East, Cardiff, CF11 9AE Tel: (029) 2046 2544 E-mail: info@limegreentangerine.co.uk *Graphic design company & print*

Limehouse Boardmills Ltd, 26 Crittall Road, Witham, Essex, CM8 3DR Tel: (01376) 519519 Fax: (01376) 514520 E-mail: sales@limehouse-board.co.uk *Boarding converters*

Limel Engines & Generators, Unit 54 The Bluebird Centre, Park Lane, Wolverhampton, WV10 9QQ Tel: (01902) 739903 Fax: (01902) 739903 *Suppliers of engines, generators industrial & reconditioned*

Limelight, 107 George Lane, London, E18 1AN Tel: (020) 8989 6106 Fax: (020) 8989 7163 E-mail: contact@limelightdesign.co.uk *Exhibition stand designers & contractors*

▶ Limelight, 4 High Beech, Lowestoft, Suffolk, NR32 2RY Tel: 01502 568021 Fax: 07050 600176 E-mail: info@limelight.org.uk *Limelight design and manufacture quality PA loudspeaker cabinets and guitar and bass loudspeakers. Custom finishes and individual designs. Special designs made to order.*

Limelight Signs Ltd, Plantation Works, Heys Street, Bacup, Lancashire, OL13 9QL Tel: (01706) 873866 Fax: (01706) 879102 E-mail: sales@limelight-signs.co.uk *Sign maker*

Limetree Marketing, Unit 1, Warboys Road, Old Hurst, Huntingdon, Cambridgeshire, PE28 3AL Tel: (01487) 823823 Fax: (01487) 823898 E-mail: earl@limetreemarketing.co.uk *Computer consumable supplies*

Limitless Communications Ltd, 43 St Mour Road, London, SW6 4DR Tel: (020) 7371 5224 Fax: (020) 7371 9048 E-mail: enquiries@limitlesscommunications.com *Theatrical agents*

▶ Limpet Labels UK Ltd, Russell House, Abbey Road North, Wrexham Industrial Estate, Wrexham, Clwyd, LL13 9RX Tel: (01978) 664411 Fax: (01978) 661662 E-mail: sales@limpetlabels.co.uk *Specialist label supplier to the chemical hygiene & oils industries*

Limpet Printed Tapes Ltd, The Causeway, Bassingbourn, Royston, Hertfordshire, SG8 5JB Tel: (01763) 252420 Fax: (01763) 252421 E-mail: print@limpettapes.com *Printed tape manufrs*

Limrose Group Ltd, Aerial Road, Llay Industrial Estate, Llay, Wrexham, Clwyd, LL12 0TU Tel: (01978) 855555 Fax: (01978) 855556 E-mail: limrose@aol.com *Software & educational aid manufrs*

▶ Linacre Locksmiths, 41 Linacre Avenue, Norwich, NR7 8JZ Tel: (01603) 408528 E-mail: linacrelocks@aol.com *24 hour locksmith service locks replaced, key cutting*

LINAK UK Ltd, Actuation House, Crystal Drive, Sandwell Business Park, Smethwick, West Midlands, B66 1RJ Tel: 0121-544 2211 Fax: 0121-544 2552 E-mail: sales@linak.co.uk *LINAK is a world leader in electric linear actuation, developing electric linear actuators, actuator control systems, and lifting columns that are used in many applications, from height adjustable desks to hospital beds to replacing hydraulics & pneumatics on bespoke machinery. We provide innovative actuation solutions that improve people's quality of life & working environment. LINAK is an international company, founded on a simple principle - electric linear actuation. *Partnership *Multilevel cooperation with our customers is extremely important, for the benefit of both LINAK & the customer. Partnership is the driving force behind R&D, after-sales, logistics, manufacturing and marketing. *Values *The results LINAK has achieved throughout the years are based on a set of values, which make us unique & define what we stand for. The values are: Customer orientation, Creativity, The will to change, Loyalty, Openness & honesty, Enthusiasm and individual efficiency & Job satisfaction.*

Linatex Ltd, Wilkinson House Galway Road, Blackbushe Business Park, Yateley, Hampshire, GU46 6GE Tel: (01252) 743000 Fax: (01252) 743030 E-mail: info@linatex.com *Mineral processing industry rubber products manufrs*

▶ Linburn Technology Ltd, Sybrig House Ridge Way, Donibristle Industrial Park, Hillend, Dunfermline, Fife, KY11 9JN Tel: (01383) 820680 Fax: (01383) 824393

▶ Linburn Technology Ltd, Sybrig House Ridge Way, Donibristle Industrial Park, Hillend, Dunfermline, Fife, KY11 9JN Tel: (01383) 820680 Fax: (01383) 824393

Linc Fabrication & Welding, Dawsons Lane Unit 14, The Enterprise Centre, Barwell, Leicester, LE9 8BE Tel: (01455) 840870 Fax: (01455) 840870 E-mail: kevbriggs@btconnect.com *Pipeline maintenance equipment*

Linc Freight Management, 8 Capital Industrial Centre, Fulmar Way, Wickford, Essex, SS11 8YW Tel: (01438) 746766 Fax: (01438) 369125 E-mail: linc@lincfreight.co.uk *Linc Freight Management offers you: - Complete reliability Total flexibility Savings between 5 and 15% Improved buying power Shipment by Road, Rail, Sea or Air Part or Full Loads Logistic Consultancy Agency Partners World-wide Implants Letters of Credit We believe that we are the best people to form a co-ordinated logistics plan for you as we have done so for all of our customers*

Linc It, North Street, Gainsborough, Lincolnshire, DN21 2HS Tel: (01427) 811770 Fax: (01427) 811780 E-mail: office@lincit.com *Computer retail outlet & repairers*

Linco Components, 2 Redstone Industrial Estate, Redstone Road, Boston, Lincolnshire, PE21 8EA Tel: (01205) 352516 Fax: (01205) 310205 *Motor vehicle spares distributors*

Linco Engineering Co. Ltd, 108 Park Street, Motherwell, Lanarkshire, ML1 1PF Tel: (01698) 254541 Fax: (01698) 276178 *Gear manufrs*

▶ Linco Engineering, 88 Heming Road, Redditch, Worcestershire, B98 0EA Tel: (01527) 518333 Fax: (01527) 518666 E-mail: linco@btconnect.com *Aluminium weather loathers manufrs*

Lincon PC Ltd, Edge Lane Street, Royton, Oldham, OL2 6DS Tel: 0161-624 7098 Fax: 0161-678 6162 E-mail: info@lincopc.com *Mezzanine flooring suppliers & manufrs*

▶ Lincoln, Barnett Way, Barnwood, Gloucester, GL4 3RZ Tel: (01452) 374500 Fax: (01452) 634300 E-mail: sales@lincoln-financialuk.com *Life assurance & pensions company*

Lincoln Castings Ltd, Station Road, North Hykeham, Lincoln, LN6 9XB Tel: (01522) 681515 Fax: (01522) 692021 E-mail: info@licolncasting.com *Iron casting manufrs*

Lincoln Concrete Products, Leckwith Bridge, Leckwith, Cardiff, CF11 8AS Tel: (029) 2022 5974 Fax: (029) 2031 8696 *Concrete products supplier & manufrs*

▶ Lincoln Co-Operative Society Ltd, Moorland Way, Lincoln, LN6 7TN Tel: (01522) 500588 Fax: (01522) 500489

Lincoln Diesels plc, Great Northern Terrace, Lincoln, LN5 8HJ Tel: (01522) 511512 Fax: (01522) 512935 E-mail: ld@lincolndiesels.com *Diesel engine spares & services*

Lincoln Equipment Ltd, Cash Register Centre, Moorland Way, Lincoln, LN6 7JW Tel: (01522) 814555 Fax: (01522) 814556 E-mail: enquiries@lsepos.co.uk *Cash register suppliers*

Lincoln Gaming, 495 Newark Road, North Hykeham, Lincoln, LN6 9NG Tel: (01522) 878697 Fax: (01522) 793008 *Amusement machines*

Lincoln & Hull Marine Contractors Ltd, 100 Lime Street, Hull, HU8 7AR Tel: (01482) 320727 Fax: (01482) 320727 E-mail: noel@siggle.fsnet.co.uk *Ship repairers & dry dock owners*

Lincoln Industrial Ltd, Unit 2 Canada Close, Banbury, Oxfordshire, OX16 2RT Tel: (01295) 256611 Fax: (01295) 275771 E-mail: sales@lincolnindustrial.co.uk *Manufacturers of lubrication systems & ink pumps*

Lincoln Metalcraft, 2 Branston Business Park, Lincoln Road, Branston, Lincoln, LN4 1NT Tel: (01522) 795000 Fax: (01522) 794444 *Wrought iron workers*

Lincoln Security Ltd, 79-83 High Street, Lincoln, LN5 8AA Tel: (01522) 532038 Fax: (01522) 536060 E-mail: enquiries@lincolnsecurity.co.uk *Security equipment suppliers & master locksmiths*

Lincoln Timber & Fencing, Unit 3 Great Northern Way, Lincoln, LN5 8XF Tel: (01522) 514448 Fax: (01522) 514448 *Timber & fencing manufrs*

Lincolnshire Chamber Of Commerce & Industry, Outer Circle Road, Lincoln, LN2 4HY Tel: (01522) 523333 Fax: (01522) 546667 E-mail: enquiries@lincs-chamber.co.uk *Chamber of commerce.*

Lincolnshire Drainage Co. Ltd, Fen Road, Frampton Fen, Boston, Lincolnshire, PE20 1SD Tel: (01205) 311800 Fax: (01205) 360726 *Land drainage contractors*

Lincolnshire Fastener Co., Hadley Road, Sleaford, Lincolnshire, NG34 7EG Tel: (01529) 306443 Fax: (01529) 306168 *Industrial fastener distributors*

Lincolnshire Fork Lifts, Fen Farm, Stickney, Boston, Lincolnshire, PE22 8BJ Tel: (01205) 480336 Fax: (01205) 366408 *Fork lifts agents*

Lincolnshire Koi Fish Health Consultants, Thornimans Lane, Frampton, Boston, Lincolnshire, PE20 1AJ Tel: (01205) 723413 Fax: (01205) 724267 E-mail: koidoc@globalnet.co.uk *Fish laboratory*

▶ Lincolnshire Limestone Flooring, Stamford Road, Marholm, Peterborough, PE6 7HX Tel: (01780) 740852 Fax: (01780) 740970 E-mail: sales@lincolnshirelimestoneflooring.co.uk *Producer of natural english limestone flooring tiles.*

Lincolnshire Machinery Ring Ltd, Cannon St House, Cannon Street, Louth, Lincolnshire, LN11 9NL Tel: (01507) 600888 Fax: (01507) 611888 *Agricultural contractors & suppliers*

Lincolnshire Motors Ltd, Windsor Road, Fairfield Industrial Estate, Louth, Lincolnshire, LN11 0LF Tel: (01507) 604061 Fax: (01507) 605609 E-mail: sales@lincsmotors.co.uk *Agricultural engineers*

Lincolnshire Rewinds, Long Leys Road, Lincoln, LN1 1DX Tel: (01522) 524283 Fax: (01522) 521122 *Electrical rewind services*

Lincon Batteries Ltd, Faraday Works, 25-26 Faraday Road, Leigh-On-Sea, Essex, SS9 5JU Tel: (01702) 528711 Fax: (01702) 421362 E-mail: batteries@lincon.co.uk *Lead acid batteries*

Linconshire Office Friends Ltd, Unit 1 Viking Court, Gilbey Road, Grimsby, North East Lincolnshire, DN31 2UJ Tel: (01472) 341493 Fax: (01472) 341600 E-mail: sales@officefriends.com *Office equipment distributors* Also at: Lincoln

▶ Linc's 2 Drivers, Unit 2, Earlesfield Lane, Grantham, Lincolnshire, NG31 7NT Tel: (01476) 570601 Fax: (01476) 570268 E-mail: info@links2drivers.co.uk

Lincs Auto Services 1986 Ltd, 136-140 Roman Bank, Skegness, Lincolnshire, PE25 1SE Tel: (01754) 767463 Fax: (01754) 762290 E-mail: rrsbfm@aol.com *Car mechanical repairers & car parts sales services*

▶ Lincs Electrical Services, 6 Buttler Way, Sleaford, Lincolnshire, NG34 7PA Tel: (01529) 309505 E-mail: lincelectrical@tiscali.co.uk *Electrical contractors*

Lincs Mini-mix, R M C House, Long Lane, Attenborough, Nottingham, NG9 6BL Tel: (01205) 353035 Fax: 0115-925 6268 *Ready mixed concrete suppliers*

Lincs Pumps & Pipeline, Water Gate, Quadring, Spalding, Lincolnshire, PE11 4PY Tel: (01775) 821163 Fax: (01775) 821613 *Light civil engineers*

Lincs Radio Engineering, 211-213 Cleethorpe Road, Grimsby, South Humberside, DN31 3BE Tel: (01472) 241418 Fax: (01472) 352099 E-mail: lincsradio@btconnect.com *Radio communication systems contractor services*

▶ Linctec, 81 Saxon Way, Bourne, Lincolnshire, PE10 9QY Tel: (01778) 393757 E-mail: info@linctec.co.uk

Lind Wood Components Ltd, River Mill, Park Road, Dukinfield, Cheshire, SK16 5LR Tel: 0161-330 2624 Fax: 0161-343 1094 E-mail: info@lindwood.co.uk *Wooden component manufrs*

▶ Linda Abrahams, 27 Chelwood Drive, Leeds, LS8 2AT Tel: 0113-295 0098 Fax: 0113-295 6697 E-mail: Linda@lindaabrahams.co.uk *Designers of wedding & event invitations & accessories*

Lindab Ltd, 98 Roding Road, London, E6 6LS Tel: (020) 7474 5102 Fax: (020) 7476 8001 *Ventilation equipment suppliers & manufrs*

Lindab Ltd, 8 Deans Road Industrial Estate, Deans Road, Swinton, Manchester, M27 0RD Tel: 0161-727 5200 Fax: 0161-727 5201 *Heating & ventilation products manufrs*

Lindab Ltd, Unit 9 - 10 Carousel Way, Riverside Business Park, Northampton, NN3 9HG Tel: (01604) 788350 Fax: (01604) 788351 *Air diffusion & damper-ducting manufrs*

Lindal Valve Co. Ltd, Cherrycourt Way, Leighton Buzzard, Bedfordshire, LU7 4UH Tel: (01525) 381155 Fax: (01525) 383304 *Aerosol valve manufrs*

▶ Lindale Building Services Ltd, Hallcourt House, Hallcourt CR, Cannock, Staffordshire, WS11 0AB Tel: (01543) 506606 Fax: (01543) 570445

Lindapter International, Brackenbeck Road, Bradford, West Yorkshire, BD7 2NF Tel: (01274) 521444 Fax: (01274) 521130 E-mail: enquiries@lindapter.com *Established in 1934, Lindapter is the world's innovator of steelwork clamping systems, eliminating the requirement to drill or weld steel. In comparison to traditional connection methods, Lindapter solutions allow rapid installation, significantly reduced costs whilst preserving the integrity of the steelwork. The range of independently approved products includes steelwork, cavity, decking, support, and floor fixings.*

▶ Lindars Electrical Contractors, 74-77 Magdalen Road, Oxford, OX4 1RE Tel: (01865) 794433 Fax: (01865) 203997

Linde Castle Ltd, Linde Way, Aycliffe Industrial Park, Newton Aycliffe, County Durham, DL5 6HR Tel: (01325) 311526 Fax: (01325) 315860 E-mail: castle@lansinglinde.co.uk *Fork lift truck distributors*

Linde Cryoplants Ltd, Blackwater Way, Aldershot, Hampshire, GU12 4DR Tel: (01252) 331351 Fax: (01252) 343062 E-mail: info@linde-lcl.com *Cryogenic engineers*

Linde Gas UK Ltd, 160 Leyton Road, London, E15 1DT Tel: (020) 8555 5544 Fax: (020) 8519 8627 *Gas producers & suppliers*

Linde Gas UK Ltd, Newfield Industrial Estate, High Street, Stoke-on-Trent, ST6 5PD Tel: (01782) 822058 Fax: (01782) 822350 *Gas (industrial, medical & special) producers & suppliers*

Linde Jewsbury's Ltd, Units 5-7 Deans Trading Estate, Deans Road, Swinton, M27 0RD Tel: 0161-794 6101 Fax: 0161-794 1592 E-mail: enquiries@linde-jewsburys.co.uk *Fork lift truck distributors*

Linde Material Handeling (Scotland) Ltd, Unit 9, Riverside Drive, Dundee, DD2 1UH Tel: (01382) 644301 Fax: (01382) 644243 *Fork lift hire supplies & services*

Linde Material Handling East Ltd, Unit 1 Charlton Mead Lane, Hoddesdon, Hertfordshire, EN11 0DJ Tel: (01992) 443121 Fax: (01992) 468050 *Fork lift truck manufrs* Also at: Norwich

Linde Material Handling Scotland, Unit 11 Barrett Trading Estate, Denmore Road, Bridge of Don, Aberdeen, AB23 8JW Tel: (01224) 707020 Fax: (01224) 707066 E-mail: enquiries@linde-mh-scotland.co.uk *Fork lift manufrs* Also at: Dundee, Edinburgh & Glasgow

Linde Material Handling Scotland Ltd, 3 Milton Road, East Kilbride, Glasgow, G74 5DH Tel: (01355) 233601 Fax: (01355) 235833 E-mail: enquiries@linde-mh-scotland.co.uk *Fork lift truck manufrs*

Linde Material Handling (South East) Ltd, Affinity Point, Glebeland Road, Camberley, Surrey, GU15 3DB Tel: (01276) 403400 Fax: (01276) 403499 *Fork lift truck ssuppliers*

▶ Linde Material Handling (South East) Ltd, Affinity Point, Glebeland Road, Camberley, Surrey, GU15 3DB Tel: (01276) 403400 Fax: (01276) 403499 *Material handling services*

Linde Material Handling UK Ltd, Kingsclere Road, Basingstoke, Hampshire, RG21 6XJ Tel: (01256) 342000 Fax: (01256) 342921 E-mail: sales@lansinglinde.co.uk *Fork lift truck suppliers & manufrs* Also at: Warrington

Linde Refrigeration & Retail Systems Ltd, Meridian House, Peter's Way, Oxford, OX4 6HQ Tel: (01865) 337700 Fax: (01865) 337799 Principal Export Areas: Worldwide *Manufacturers of refrigerated display cabinets* Also at: Belfast & Dublin

Linden Bauer Ltd, Mid Kent Business Park, Sortmill Road, Snodland, Kent, ME6 5UA Tel: (01634) 243137 Fax: (01634) 249306 E-mail: christian@lindenbauer.freeserve.co.uk *Specialist joiners & cabinet makers*

Linden Computer Services, Laverham House, 77 St Georges Place, Cheltenham, Gloucestershire, GL50 3PP Tel: (01242) 269369 Fax: (01242) 231341 *Computer maintenance & repairers*

Linden Group Ltd, 1 Leaside North, Aycliffe Industrial Estate, Aycliffe Industrial Park, Newton Aycliffe, County Durham, DL5 6DU Tel: (01325) 311331 Fax: (01325) 300128 E-mail: sales@lindengroup.co.uk *Hydraulic products suppliers*

▶ Linden Homes Ltd, 14 Bartram Road, Totton, Southampton, SO40 9PP Tel: (023) 8066 5100 Fax: (023) 8066 5155

Linden Textiles Ltd, Linden Court House, 52 Liverpool Street, Salford, M5 4LT Tel: 0161-745 9268 Fax: 0161-737 6061 E-mail: zedfred@aol.com *Household textiles merchants*

▶ Linden Upholstery Ltd, Clay Flatts Trading Estate, Workington, Cumbria, CA14 2TQ Tel: (01900) 64787 Fax: (01900) 870630 E-mail: linden.upholstery@btinternet.com *Manufacturers of three-piece suites*

Lindfield Communications, 134 Islingword Road, Brighton, BN2 9SH Tel: (01273) 609008 E-mail: sales@1ndfieldcomms.co.uk *Telecommunication equipment distributor*

Lindfield Rover, 2 Bridge Road, Haywards Heath, West Sussex, RH16 1UA Tel: (01444) 458641 Fax: (01444) 458644 *Car dealers*

Lindisposables Ltd, King Street, Kirton, Boston, Lincolnshire, PE20 1HZ Tel: (01205) 724444 Fax: (01205) 722818 *Catering, janitorial & cleaning distributors*

Lindner Publications, Unit3a, Hayle Industrial Park, Hayle, Cornwall, TR27 5JR Tel: (01736) 751914 Fax: (01736) 751911 E-mail: info@prinz.co.uk *Coin & stamp accessories mail order*

Lindon Environmental Air Services Ltd, Stoke Heath Terminal, Warrant Road, Market Drayton, Shropshire, TF9 2JH Tel: (01630) 655100 Fax: (01630) 654675 *Industrial heating & ventilation engineers*

▶ Lindon Lewis Marine Ltd, Shepperton Marina, Felix Lane, Shepperton, Middlesex, TW17 8NS Tel: 01932 247427 Fax: 01932 223934 E-mail: info@pushtheboatout.com *Largest chandlery, service centre and boat sales team on the River Thames.*

William Lindop Ltd, PO Box 46, Manchester, M60 3DP Tel: 0161-832 9467 Fax: 0161-833 1961 E-mail: info@lindopsports.co.uk *Sports wholesalers*

Lindow Leisure Lines, 15 Windsor Avenue, Wilmslow, Cheshire, SK9 5HE Tel: (01625) 533737 *Playground equipment manufrs*

Lindsay Ellacott UK Ltd, Newton Farm Boyton, Boyton, Launceston, Cornwall, PL15 9RL Tel: (01566) 772208 Fax: (01566) 777228 E-mail: lellacott@aol.com Principal Export Areas: Worldwide *Spraying equipment manufrs*

▶ Lindsay Saddlery & Riding Wear, Solway Trading Estate, Maryport, Cumbria, CA15 8NF Tel: (01900) 819955 *Equestrian supplies*

Lindsey Fabrication & Engineering, 4 Pytchley Lodge Road, Kettering, Northamptonshire, NN15 6JQ Tel: (01536) 485770 Fax: (01536) 410730 E-mail: sales@1indseyfabs.co.uk *Stainless steel & steel fabricators*

Lindsey Welding Supply Co., Warwick Road, Fairfield Industrial Estate, Louth, Lincolnshire, LN11 0YB Tel: (01507) 604083 Fax: (01507) 604083 E-mail: sales@lindseyweldings.sagehost.co.uk *Welding equipment & consumables suppliers*

Lindum Auto Electrical Ltd, 136 Dixon Street, Lincoln, LN6 7TX Tel: (01522) 522294 Fax: (01522) 533457 E-mail: lindumauto@aol.com *Auto electrical & wholesalers*

Lindum BMS Grimsby, 1 Alexandra Road, Grimsby, South Humberside, DN31 1RD Tel: (01472) 355171 Fax: (01472) 236667 E-mail: ew@lindumgroup.co.uk *Design & construction*

Lindum Group Ltd, Lindum House, Station Road, North Hykeham, Lincoln, LN6 3QX Tel: (01522) 500300 Fax: (01522) 500377 *Builders & civil engineers*

Lindy Electronics Ltd, Sadler Foster Way, Teesside Industrial Estate, Stockton-on-Tees, Cleveland, TS17 9JY Tel: (01642) 754000 Fax: (01642) 754027 E-mail: postmaster@lindy.co.uk *Computer cables & accessories distributors*

Lindy Lou, 33 George Street, Hove, East Sussex, BN3 3YB Tel: (01273) 732770 *Retail leather goods*

G.Y. Line (Agency) Ltd, East Quay, 51 South Denes Road, Great Yarmouth, Norfolk, NR30 3PR Tel: (01493) 852411 Fax: (01493) 857583 E-mail: gyline@gywc.uk *Ship agents*

Line Casting Machinery Ltd, Unit 34 John Wilson Business Park, Chestfield, Whitstable, Kent, CT5 3QT Tel: (01227) 770665 Fax: (01227) 277300 E-mail: linecasting@btconnect.com *We are a family owned company with over 40 years experience in supplying equipment, spare parts, and technical advice worldwide to the printing industry. We are based in Whitstable, Kent. Our reputation has been built on attention to detail and thoroughness in all aspects of our business, whether it is our rebuilding of machinery, or our assistance in sourcing the right equipment for your needs you can be assured of our professionalism in every facet. Originally supplying only Linotype and Intertype hotmetal typesetting, we now supply machines and spares from a whole range of leading manufacturers, including Heidelberg, Polar, Wohlenberg, Stahl, MBO, Muller Martini, Duplo, Horizon, and Sulby.*

▶ Line Markings Ltd, Brownsburn Industrial Estate, Airdrie, Lanarkshire, ML6 9SE Tel: (01236) 755114 Fax: (01236) 751880

Line Out, Fosse Art Centre, Mantle Road, Leicester, LE3 5HG Tel: 0116-262 1265 *Film & video organisation*

Line Packaging & Display, Centre 2000, St. Michaels Road, Sittingbourne, Kent, ME10 3DZ Tel: (01795) 429986 Fax: (01795) 439748 *Packaging distributors & manufrs*

Line Performance Improvement Ltd, The Granary, Stoke Mills, Mill Road, Bedford, MK44 1NN Tel: (01234) 782333 *Industrial engineering*

Line Scan, Unit 2, Seeking Road, Bartlett Court, Lynx Trading Estate, Yeovil, Somerset, BA20 2NZ Tel: (01935) 471440 Fax: (01935) 475285 E-mail: enquiries@linescan.co.uk *Document scanning & microfilm bureau services*

Line X, Unit 6, Fells Road, Team Valley Trading Estate, Gateshead, Tyne & Wear, NE11 0NN Tel: 0191-491 3010 Fax: 0191-491 3010 E-mail: andrew@linexgateshead.co.uk *Spray-on polyurethane protective coatings*

Linear Ltd, Coatham Avenue, Aycliffe Industrial Park, Newton Aycliffe, County Durham, DL5 6DB Tel: (01325) 310151 Fax: (01325) 307200 E-mail: enquiries@linear-ltd.com *Weather stripping manufrs*

Linear Blue Ltd, 400 Thames Valley Park Drive, Thames Valley Park, Reading, RG6 1PT Tel: (0870) 351 6594 E-mail: info@linearblue.com *File maker database & lasso website developers*

Linear Composites Ltd, Vale Mills, Oakworth, Keighley, West Yorkshire, BD22 0EB Tel: (01535) 643363 Fax: (01535) 643605 E-mail: mail@linearcomposites.com *Synthetic rope & webbing manufrs*

Linear Motion, Park St South, Wolverhampton, WV2 3JH Tel: (01902) 425588 Fax: (01902) 425504 *Engineers tables, linear, to specification*

Linear Photographics Ltd, Unit 17 Magreal Industrial Estate, Freeth Street, Ladywood, Birmingham, B16 0QZ Tel: (0121) 454 5864 *Commercial photographers*

Company Information

▶ Linear Scaffolding Solutions, 71 Denmark Street, Bedford, MK40 3TH Tel: (01234) 295164 Fax: (01234) 295164 E-mail: linearscaff@hotmail.com *Specialists in the hire and supply of scaffolding to all areas of construction, especially roofing and handrails. we are fully insured.*

Linear Software Ltd, 17 Pulborough Road, London, SW18 5UN Tel: (020) 8877 0159 Fax: (020) 8877 0552 *Software consultants*

Linear Systems & Equipment Ltd, 9 Sampson House, Arterial Road, Laindon, Basildon, Essex, SS15 6DR Tel: (01268) 419558 Fax: (01268) 417034 E-mail: linsys@btconnect.com *Special purpose custom built machinery constructors*

Linear Technology Ltd, 3 The Listons, Liston Road, Marlow, Buckinghamshire, SL7 1FD Tel: (01628) 477066 Fax: (01628) 478153 *Linear integrated circuits*

Linear Tools Ltd, 1 Clock Tower Road, Isleworth, Middlesex, TW7 6DT Tel: (020) 8400 2020 Fax: (020) 8400 2021 E-mail: sales@lineartools.co.uk *Tool importers*

Lineartron Cabling Systems Ltd, Unit 5 Slader Business Park, Witney Road, Nuffield Industerial Estate, Poole, Dorset, BH17 0GP Tel: (01202) 672689 Fax: (01202) 672457 E-mail: sales@lineartron.co.uk *Computer cable installers*

Lineartron Maintenance Ltd, Lineartron House, 7 Black Moor Road, Ebblake Industrial Estate, Verwood, Dorset, BH31 6AX Tel: (01202) 828001 Fax: (01202) 828089 E-mail: sales@lineartron.co.uk *Fibre optic cable maintenance services*

Linecross Group Ltd, Station Road, South Luffenham, Oakham, Leicestershire, LE15 8NG Tel: (01780) 720720 Fax: (01780) 722333 E-mail: kgday@linex.uk.com *Plastics thermo-forming manufrs*

Linen Room, 482 Wilbraham Road, Manchester, M21 9AS Tel: 0161-860 4979 Fax: 0161-860 4979 E-mail: info@2tlr.co.uk *Textiles manufrs*

Linenfabrics.Co.Uk, 96 Northway, Maghull, Liverpool, L31 5NF Tel: 0151-526 0508 Fax: 0151-526 0508 E-mail: info@linenfabrics.co.uk *Wholesaler of linen fabrics*

Lineplex Ltd, PO Box 590, Guildford, Surrey, GU5 9YL Tel: (01306) 731395 Fax: (01306) 731240 E-mail: lineplex@cix.co.uk *Telecommunication products design & manufrs*

Lineprint Screen Process Printers, 6 Woodside Industrial Park, Works Road, Letchworth Garden City, Hertfordshire, SG6 1LA Tel: (01462) 672914 Fax: (01462) 681124 E-mail: lineprint@hotmail.com *Screen process printers*

Linertech Ltd, Wellington Mills, Quebec Street, Elland, West Yorkshire, HX5 9BX Tel: (01422) 377551 Fax: (01422) 311636 E-mail: sales@linertech.co.uk *Container liner manufrs*

Linetex Clothing Co. Ltd, 56-58 Nelson Street, London, E1 2DE Tel: (020) 7790 0916 Fax: (020) 7790 9760 E-mail: linetex@hotmail.com *Ladies wear manufrs*

Linford Furniture, Mill Lane, Stony Stratford, Milton Keynes, MK11 1EW Tel: (01908) 261521 *Furniture designers & manufrs*

Linford-Bridgeman Ltd, Quonians, Lichfield, Staffordshire, WS13 7LB Tel: (01543) 414234 Fax: (01543) 258250 E-mail: clare.millington@linfordgroup.co.uk *Building specialist restoration* Also at: Cannock

Henry Ling Ltd, 23 High East Street, Dorchester, Dorset, DT1 1HD Tel: (01305) 251066 Fax: (01305) 251908 E-mail: production@henryling.co.uk *Printers*

Ling Marketing, Stones House, Lower Broad Oak Road, West Hill, Ottery St. Mary, Devon, EX11 1XH Tel: (01404) 811111 Fax: (01404) 811345 *Food service marketing consultants*

Lingcroft Associates Ltd, Park House, Brooke Street, Cleckheaton, West Yorkshire, BD19 3RY Tel: (01274) 876500 Fax: (01274) 876125 E-mail: richard@lingcroft.co.uk *Fabrics including uniform, protective & waterproof*

▶ Lingfield Roofing, 52 Saxbys Lane, Lingfield, Surrey, RH7 6DR Tel: (01342) 833018 *Established since 1970. Lingfiled Roofing are able to supply a complete, reliable and fully insured roofing service.***

▶ Lingfield Warehousing Ltd, Lingfield Point, Mcmullen Road, Darlington, County Durham, DL1 1RW Tel: (01325) 359795

Lingley Control Systems Ltd, Lingley House, Lingley Road, Great Sankey, Warrington, WA5 3ND Tel: (01925) 729933 Fax: (01925) 791331 E-mail: caloffice@cal.uk *Computer control company*

▶ LingoTec Translations, 4 Edith Cottages, Hansford Lane, St. Helier, Jersey, JE2 3JL Tel: 01534 498604 E-mail: info@lingotec.co.uk *We provide translation services of the highest quality at competitive prices and are experienced in German to English and English to German in a wide variety of subject matters.*Our translators are all professionally qualified and fully experienced in the language and subject matters they cover.*Our sworn-in translators have been duly authorised by a German regional court to translate and certify documents.*

Linguarama Ltd, New London Bridge House, 25 London Bridge Street, London, SE1 9SG Tel: (020) 7939 3200 Fax: (020) 7939 3230 E-mail: london@linguarama.com *Language training consultancy* Also at: Bath, Birmingham, Manchester, Nottingham, Stratford & Winchester

▶ Linguarama Language Services, PO Box 341, Leeds, LS17 7AL Tel: 0113 2619030 E-mail: learn@linguarama.org *Based in Leeds, West Yorkshire, U.K. Linguarama offers: first-rate, affordable tuition in the language of your choice including French, Italian, Spanish, German, Greek and English as a Foreign Language; corporate in-house language training; customised language courses - either in the comfort of your own home or join a lively group at one of our modern teaching venues; language support for GCSE and "A" level; assistance with buying a property abroad; voice overs;*

continued

*interpreting and translation; cultural awareness seminars **

Lingwood Fitted Furniture, Sawmills Road, Diss, Norfolk, IP22 4GG Tel: (01379) 650040 Fax: (01379) 650813 E-mail: woodstyle@btopenworld.co.uk *Kitchen & bedroom furniture manufrs*

Lingwood Steels Ltd, Unit 1-2 Brymill Industrial Estate, Brown Lion Street, Tipton, West Midlands, DY4 9EG Tel: 0121-520 6161 Fax: 0121-522 2967 E-mail: paul@lingwoodsteels.co.uk *Steel stockholders*

Linhill Associates Ltd, Dunston House, Portland Street, Lincoln, LN5 7NN Tel: (01522) 535022 Fax: (01522) 518185 *Software house*

▶ Linian North West Ltd, Unit 9 Shaw Street, St. Helens, Merseyside, WA10 1DQ Tel: (01744) 736330 Fax: (01744) 22013 E-mail: sales@linian.co.uk *Structural steelwork fabricators*

Lining Systems Ltd, Unit 8 Woodcock Trading Estate, 277 Barton Street, Gloucester, GL1 4JE Tel: (01452) 387771 Fax: (01452) 387771 E-mail: sales@liningsystems.co.uk *Suspended ceiling & partiton installers*

Linings & Hoses Ltd, 95 Cooperative Street, Stafford, ST16 3DA Tel: (01785) 254634 Fax: (01785) 222802 E-mail: peterjackson@liningsandhoses.co.uk *Motor factors*

The Link, 15 Market Centre, Crewe, CW1 2NG Tel: (01270) 254747 Fax: (01270) 254712 *Mobile communications*

▶ The Link, 43-45 Fishergate, Preston, PR1 2AD Tel: (01772) 562396 Fax: (01772) 562409

Link 51 Ltd, Link House, Halesfield 6, Telford, Shropshire, TF7 4LN Tel: (0800) 515600 Fax: (01952) 682452 E-mail: enquiries@link51.co.uk Principal Export Areas: Middle East, Africa, Central/East Europe & West Europe *Pallet rack/racking manufrs*

Link 51 (Shelving Storage) Ltd, 16 Mill St, Brierley Hill, West Midlands, DY5 2TB Tel: (01384) 472500 Fax: (01384) 472599 E-mail: shelving@link51.co.uk *Storage equipment systems manufrs*

▶ The Link Aberdeen, 105 Union Street, Aberdeen, AB11 6BD Tel: (01224) 586811

Link Cable Assemblers Ltd, North Caldeen Road, Coatbridge, Lanarkshire, ML5 4EF Tel: (01236) 423005 Fax: (01236) 449118 E-mail: sales@linkcableassemblies.co.uk *Electronic assemblies manufrs*

Link CCTV Systems, Unit 2, Campus 5, Letchworth Garden City, Hertfordshire, SG6 2JF Tel: (01462) 682300 Fax: (01462) 678382 E-mail: service@linkcctv.co.uk *CCTV installation & services maintenance*

Link Contract Supplies Ltd, Unit 1, 172-174 Mile Cross Lane, Norwich, NR6 6RY Tel: (01603) 415355 Fax: (01603) 401921 *Chemical cleaning product distributors*

Link Controls Ltd, Stuart Road, Manor Park, Runcorn, Cheshire, WA7 1TS Tel: (01925) 222436 Fax: (01928) 579259 E-mail: sales@linkcontrols.co.uk *Door control systems manufrs*

Link Design Development, 17 Brownfields, Welwyn Garden City, Hertfordshire, AL7 1AN Tel: (01707) 331991 Fax: (01707) 327918 *Packaging designers*

Link Electrical Testing, Races Farm, Aston Street, Aston Tirrold, Didcot, Oxfordshire, OX11 9DJ Tel: (01235) 850813 Fax: (01235) 850672 E-mail: info@linktesting.co.uk *electrical inspection & testing portable appliances*

Link Engineering Services (Manchester) Ltd, Trafford Park Road, Trafford Park, Manchester, M17 1AN Tel: 0161-848 8039 Fax: 0161-872 3553 *Lifting equipment*

Link H R Systems, Normant House, 121-123 Long Lane, Upton, Chester, CH2 1JF Tel: (01244) 399555 Fax: (01244) 399666 E-mail: general@link-hrsystems.com *Management consultants*

Link Hamson Ltd, 6 York Way, Lancaster Road, Cressex Business Park, High Wycombe, Buckinghamshire, HP12 3PY Tel: (01494) 439786 Fax: (01494) 526222 E-mail: sales@linkhamson.com *Thermal profiling equipment & computer label systems*

Link Hydraulic Services Ltd, 38 Sherwood Road, Bromsgrove, Worcestershire, B60 3DR Tel: (01527) 579145 Fax: (01527) 576555 E-mail: link.hydraulics@btconnect.com *Hydraulic engineers*

Link Level Services Ltd, Business & Technology Centre, Radway Green, Crewe, CW2 5PR Tel: (01270) 886113 Fax: (01270) 886237 E-mail: sales@linklevel.co.uk *Computer repair & service providers*

Link Lockers, Link House, Halesfield 6, Telford, Shropshire, TF7 4LN Tel: (01952) 682380 Fax: (01952) 684312 E-mail: sales@linklockers.co.uk *Manufacturers of lockers including aluminium & steel*

Link Logistics Scotland Ltd, 9 Limekilns Road, Cumbernauld, Glasgow, G67 2RN Tel: (01236) 457789 Fax: (01236) 457944 *Road transport/ haulage/freight services*

▶ Matthew Link Ltd, PO Box 313, Knutsford, Cheshire, WA16 8YT Tel: 01565 650031 Fax: 01565 650755 E-mail: mjl@matthewlink.co.uk *Product design service*

Link Microtek Ltd, Intec 4.1, Wade Road, Basingstoke, Hampshire, RG24 8NE Tel: (01256) 355771 Fax: (01256) 355118 E-mail: sales@linkmicrotek.com *RF & microwave products*

Link Packaging Ltd, Tingley Bar Industrial Estate, Tingley Mills, Morley, Leeds, LS27 0HE Tel: 0113-252 7011 Fax: 0113-238 0069 E-mail: linkltd@aol.com *Carton & box manufrs*

Link Project Services Ltd, 12 The Parks, Haydock Park, Newton-Le-Willows, Merseyside, WA12 0JQ Tel: (01942) 408440 Fax: (01942) 408450 E-mail: uk@link-projects.com *International personnel service providers*

▶ Link Radio Services, Europa Way, Martineau Lane, Norwich, NR1 2EN Tel: (01603) 765477 Fax: (01603) 765272 E-mail: info@linkradioservices.co.uk *Radio communications & car hands free provider*

Link Recruitment Services, 86a London Road, East Grinstead, West Sussex, RH19 1EP Tel: (01342) 313234 Fax: (01342) 313052 E-mail: linkrecruitment@talk21.com *Employment agency & recruitment consultants*

Link Southern Heating Supplies, Bridge House, 283 Kingsland Road, London, E2 8AS Tel: (020) 7729 9328 Fax: (020) 7739 4336 *Heating & plumbing merchants*

Link Systems, The Farmhouse, Steeple View Farm, Dunton Road, Basildon, Essex, SS15 4DB Tel: (0845) 2302940 Fax: (01268) 496029 E-mail: sales@link-systems.co.uk *Business software solutions providers*

Link Systems Ltd, 15 Greenfields, Adstock, Buckingham, MK18 2JA Tel: (0800) 7311450 Fax: (01296) 714664 *Fire alarm manufrs*

▶ Link Tool & Plant Sales, 3 Old Station Yard, Station Road, Petworth, West Sussex, GU28 0JF Tel: (01798) 342342 Fax: (01798) 343555 E-mail: linktoolplantsales@btconnect.com *Tool & plant suppliers*

Link-A-Bord, The Colliery Industrial Estate, Main Road, Morton, Alfreton, Derbyshire, DE55 6HL Tel: (01773) 590566 Fax: (01773) 590681 E-mail: sales@link-a-bord.co.uk *Based in the East Midlands we specialise in Link-A-Bord which is a unique modular system. We supply standard and one off garden compost bins, vegetable or flower beds, plant containers, whelping boxes, pet runs, fumigated plastic pallets, garden furniture, plastic plant tubs, plastic containers, garden plant trays, potting boxes,*

Linkam Scientific Instruments Ltd, 8 Epsom Downs Metro Centre, Waterfield, Tadworth, Surrey, KT20 5HT Tel: (01737) 363476 Fax: (01737) 363480 E-mail: info@linkam.co.uk *Scientific instrument manufrs*

Linkbridge Ltd, 173 Quemerford, Calne, Wiltshire, SN11 8JX Tel: (01249) 811476 Fax: (01249) 811854 E-mail: lars@linkbridge.co.uk *We specialise in Customer Satisfaction Surveys for companies with ISO 9000 and for businesses who want to improve Quality and strengthen Customer Relationship and Loyalty. We do both local work and international, in 45 different countries. We have backgrounds in international industry and business management and fully understand our clients' situation. Over many years we have developed a good understanding of customer behaviour. Each survey is developed together with the client to suit his specific needs. We assist with communications from client to customers about the survey, before and after, a very powerful tool for building strong customer relationships. Customers are surveyed by phone, the only way to get good quality responses. Our survey reports are detailed. Results are specific and actionable and we offer advice on what the client should do next. Structured Customer Feedback provides an effective Management Tool. Our clients will testify to that.*

Linkcare Ltd, Unit 15 Chiltern Business Village, Arundel Road, Uxbridge, Middlesex, UB8 2SN Tel: (01895) 232626 Fax: (01895) 251001 E-mail: linkcare@hotmail.com *Automation & access control equipment & aluminium gates retailer*

Linkester Chemical & Supply Co. Ltd, Gaw End Lane, Macclesfield, Cheshire, SK11 0LB Tel: (01260) 252116 *Steel fabrications*

Linkester Fire Protection, 4-6 Cross Street, Macclesfield, Cheshire, SK11 7PG Tel: (01625) 511272 Fax: (01625) 511272 *Sprinkler systems installers*

Linkgain Services, 14 Larksfield Close, Carterton, Oxfordshire, OX18 3SY Tel: (01993) 844589 Fax: (01993) 212801 E-mail: linkgain@ntlworld.com *Dishwasher suppliers*

Linkhill Marketing Ltd, 4 The Linen House, 253 Kilburn Lane, London, W10 4BQ Tel: (020) 8964 3990 Fax: (020) 8964 3910 E-mail: sales@uniformsjohnmarks.com *Ladies & men's clothing, uniform design & manufrs*

▶ Linklan Solutions Ltd, The Lodge, 66 St. Leonards Road, Windsor, Berks, SL4 3BY Tel: (01753) 621660 Fax: (01753) 621690

Linklater Engineering, Stenness, Stenness, Stromness, Orkney, KW16 3JZ Tel: (01856) 851000 Fax: (01856) 851080 E-mail: enquiries@linklaterengineering.co.uk *Agricultural machinery distributor*

▶ Links Construction Services Ltd, 47C Bridge Street, Musselburgh, Midlothian, EH21 6AA Tel: 0131-665 2595

Links Engraving, 150 Duke Street, Edinburgh, EH6 8HR Tel: 0131-554 5156 Fax: 0131-553 6827 E-mail: sales@linksengraving.co.uk *General engravers & metal nameplate manufrs*

Links Labels & Tapes Ltd, Pinfold Road, Bourne, Lincolnshire, PE10 9HT Tel: (01778) 426282 Fax: (01778) 425003 E-mail: enquiries@linkslabels-tapes.co.uk *Adhesive label & tape manufrs*

▶ Links Screens Ltd, 36 Parker Road, Hastings, East Sussex, TN34 3TT Tel: (01424) 729444 Fax: (01424) 729555 E-mail: info@linksscreens.co.uk *Screen & digital printers, sign*makers*

▶ Linktip, Rainbow Business Park, Stringes Lane, Willenhall, West Midlands, WV13 1HH Tel: (01902) 365880 Fax: (01902) 365889 *Commercial vehicle body builders*

Linkup Mailing Houses, 107 New Greenham Park, Greenham, Thatcham, Berkshire, RG19 6HN Tel: (01635) 552022 Fax: 01635 550857 E-mail: sales@1ink-up-project.org.uk *mailshots*light packaging and assembly*shrink wrapping*

Linkweld Engineering & Construction Ltd, 56 High Street, Edenbridge, Kent, TN8 5AJ Tel: (01732) 862339 *Site welding & fabrications*

Linland Ltd, 34 36 Fratton Road, Portsmouth, PO1 5BX Tel: (023) 9282 3037 Fax: (023) 9286 1615 *Amusement arcade*

▶ Linmark Scaffolding Ltd, Compass Road, Rose Dock, Cardiff, CF10 4LT Tel: (029) 2046 0999 Fax: (029) 2046 1999

Linn Products Ltd, Glasgow Road, Eaglesham, Glasgow, G76 0EQ Tel: 0141-307 7777 E-mail: helpline@linn.co.uk *Audio hi-fi equipment manufrs*

▶ Linn Tech Scotland Ltd, Unit 15 Tartraven Place, East Mains Industrial Estate, Broxburn, West Lothian, EH52 5LT Tel: (01506) 858999 Fax: (01506) 858444 *Aluminium window & door fabricators*

Linnell Bros Ltd, Silverstone Fields Farm, Silverstone, Towcester, Northamptonshire, NN12 8TB Tel: (01327) 354422 Fax: (01327) 355840 E-mail: info@linnellbros.co.uk *Timber merchants*

Linnet Technology Ltd, 3 Darby Gate, West Portway, Andover, Hampshire, SP10 3LF Tel: (01264) 366812 Fax: (01264) 366778 E-mail: sales@linnet-tec.co.uk *Suppliers of uninterruptible power supplies*

Linnhoff March Ltd, Targeting House, Gadbrook Park, Northwich, Cheshire, CW9 7UZ Tel: (01606) 815100 Fax: (01606) 815151 *Process design consultants*

LINPAC Allibert, Road One Industrial Estate, Winsford, Cheshire, CW7 3RA Tel: (01606) 561900 Fax: (01606) 561998 E-mail: *Manufacturers of plastic injection mouldings*

Linpac Automotive Southend, Thornford Gardens, Southend-on-Sea, SS2 6PU Tel: (01702) 349481 Fax: (01702) 343982 *Plastics mouldings manufrs*

LINPAC Environmental, Leafield Way, Leafield Industrial Estate, Corsham, Wiltshire, SN13 9UD Tel: (01225) 816500 Fax: (01225) 816501 E-mail: paxton@linpac.com Principal Export Areas: Worldwide *Manufacturers & designers of plastic mould*

▶ Linpac Filmco, Salters Lane, Sedgefield, Stockton-on-Tees, Cleveland, TS21 3EE Tel: (01740) 620751 Fax: (01740) 625825 E-mail: gary.trotter@linpak-filmco.co.uk *Plastics manufrs*

Linpac Materials Handling, Newfield Close, Walsall, WS2 7PB Tel: (01922) 726060 Fax: (01922) 643422 E-mail: lmhsolutions@linpac.com *Plastics container manufrs*

LINPAC Moulded Foams Ltd, 5-7 Menasha Way, Queensway Industrial Estate, Brigg Road, Scunthorpe, North Lincolnshire, DN16 3RT Tel: (01724) 868153 Fax: (01724) 270021 *Packaging material manufrs*

Linpac Moulded Foams, Unit 4 Dinas Isaf Industrial Estate, Williamstown, Tonypandy, Mid Glamorgan, CF40 1NY Tel: (01443) 441491 Fax: (01443) 441453 *Moulded foam packaging manufrs*

Linpac Packaging Ltd, Caldicot Decorating Works, Caldicot, Monmouthshire, NP26 5XG Tel: (0870) 2426280 Fax: (01291) 307646 *Printed tinplate lithographics*

Linpac Plastics Ltd, Pegrams Road, Harlow, Essex, CM18 7QU Tel: (01279) 451148 Fax: (01279) 451187 *Plastics manufrs*

Linpac Plastics, Wakefield Road, Featherstone, Pontefract, West Yorkshire, WF7 5DE Tel: (01977) 692111 Fax: (01977) 692450 *Food packaging products*

Linpharma Ltd, PO Box 13511, Linlithgow, West Lothian, EH49 7YH Tel: (01506) 848649 Fax: (01506) 848775 E-mail: info@linpharma.com *Herbal medicine distributors*

Linread Northbridge, Crossgate Road, Redditch, Worcestershire, B98 7TD Tel: (01527) 525719 Fax: (01527) 526881 E-mail: info@linreadnorthbridge.co.uk *Fasteners for the aircraft industry*

Linread Northbridge, Viking Road, Wigston, Leicestershire, LE18 2BL Tel: 0116-288 1192 Fax: 0116-257 2901 *Manufacturers of industrial fasteners & fasteners for the aircraft*

Linscert UK Ltd, 25 Osborne Avenue, Aston, Sheffield, S26 2BY Tel: 0114-269 2513 Fax: 0114-287 7816 *Fume extractor service & install*

Linseal International Ltd, 11-13 The Green, Bilton, Rugby, Warwickshire, CV22 7LZ Tel: (01788) 814334 Fax: (01788) 521726 E-mail: sales@linseal.com *Fibre & latex free tire sealant manufrs*

Linsley Bros Established 1780 Ltd, 55 Tower Street, Harrogate, North Yorkshire, HG1 1HS Tel: (01423) 505677 Fax: (01423) 563673 *Registered gunsmiths*

▶ Lint Free Wipes, Dawsons Lane, Barwell, Leicester, LE9 8BE Tel: (01455) 845855 Fax: E-mail: sales@hainesbrothers.co.uk *Manufacturers of lint free wipes, wipes for printing machinery*

▶ Lintaprint Ltd, Midland Road, Swadlincote, Derbyshire, DE11 0AN Tel: (01283) 221536 Fax: (01283) 550273 E-mail: sales@lintaprint.co.uk

▶ Lintarealm Plastic Moulding Co. Ltd, Garth Industrial Estate, Gwaelod-y-Garth, Cardiff, CF15 9JN Tel: (029) 2081 3157 Fax: (029) 2081 1988 *Trade plastic moulding manufrs*

Lintarealm Plastic Moulding Co. Ltd, Garth Industrial Estate, Gwaelod-y-Garth, Cardiff, CF15 9JN Tel: (029) 2081 3157 Fax: (029) 2081 1988 *Plastics injection moulders*

Lintec Antennas, Unit 22 Woods Way, Goring-by-Sea, Worthing, West Sussex, BN12 4QY Tel: (01903) 242243 Fax: (01903) 242588 E-mail: sales@lintec-antennas.co.uk *Communication aerials design & manufrs*

Lintec Systems Ltd, Unit 11 Maguire Industrial Estate, Torrington Avenue, Coventry, CV4 9HN Tel: 0121-442 4434 Fax: 0121-442 4160 E-mail: peter@justhandling.fsnet.co.uk *Material handling & storage equipment distributors shelving*

▶ Lintel International Ltd, 7 The Caxton Centre, Porters Wood, St. Albans, Hertfordshire, AL3 6XT Tel: (01727) 842345

L'Interieur Furniture, 4a Little Aston Lane, Sutton Coldfield, West Midlands, B74 3UF Tel: 0121-353 2525 Fax: 0121-353 4314 E-mail: info@linterieur.co.uk *Kitchen showroom supplier & fitters*

▶ Linthorpe Frames, Rear of Haymore Street, Middlesbrough, Cleveland, TS5 6JD Tel: (07841) 944417 Fax: (01642) 816596 Frame manufrs

Linton Brick Ltd, James Nasmyth Way, Eccles, Manchester, M30 0SF Tel: 0161-787 3700 Fax: 0161-787 3711 E-mail: sales@lintonbrick.co.uk Brick manufrs

Linton Design & Manufacture Ltd, 6a Bessemer CR, Rabans Lane Industrial Area, Aylesbury, Buckinghamshire, HP19 8TF Tel: (01296) 429179 Fax: (01296) 392290 E-mail: linton.design@btinternet.com Precision engineers

▶ Linton Electrical Contractors Kent Ltd, Arnold Businesss Park, Branbridges Road, East Peckham, Tonbridge, Kent, TN12 5HD Tel: (01622) 873333 Fax: (01622) 873344

Linton Handcrafts, 213 Milton Road, Weston-super-Mare, Avon, BS22 8EG Tel: (01934) 642849 Fax: (01934) 642849 E-mail: sales@lintonhandcrafts.co.uk Pine furniture manufacturers & retailers

Norman Linton Ltd, Linton House, 39-51 Highgate Road, London, NW5 1RS Tel: (020) 7267 0921 Fax: (020) 7267 0928 E-mail: email@normanlinton.co.uk Dress importers, exporters & manufrs

Linton Plastic Moulders Ltd, Unit 3, The Grip, Linton, Cambridge, CB21 4XN Tel: (01223) 892143 Fax: (01223) 894618 E-mail: info@lintonplasticmoulders.co.uk Principal Export Areas: Worldwide Manufacturers of injection moldings

Linton Tweeds Ltd, Shaddon Mills, Shaddongate, Carlisle, CA2 5TZ Tel: (01228) 527569 Fax: (01228) 512062 E-mail: info@lintontweeds.co.uk Woollen & worsted manufrs

Lintott Control System Ltd, Units 3, 5, 7, &9, Jarrold Way, Bowthorpe Industrial Estate, Norwich, NR5 9JD Tel: (01603) 201201 Fax: (01603) 749118 Process control solution providers

▶ LinuSoft, 10 Silfield Road, Wymondham, Norfolk, NR18 9AU Tel: (01953) 601294 E-mail: enquiries@linusoft.co.uk Linux service provider, maintenance support, software development

▶ The Linux Consultancy, 6 Kendal Avenue, Shinfield, Reading, RG2 9AR Tel: 0118 988 3071 Fax: 0870 051 6027 E-mail: keith@TheLinuxConsultancy.co.uk Anything Linux. Servers, support, troubleshooting, configuration, training, consultancy, shoulder to cry on.

Linvic Engineering Ltd, Hickman Avenue, Wolverhampton, WV1 2DW Tel: (01902) 456333 Fax: (01902) 455856 E-mail: sales@linvic.co.uk Flange & fittings manufrs

▶ LinWin Computer Services, 123 Tradewinds, Wards Wharf Appproach, London, London, E16 2ER Tel: 079 71695701 Fax: 0870 7064637 E-mail: info@linwin.co.uk We provide a 0% IT service for our business and individual clients in London area. We cater for all IT needs specialising in systems development, technical and software support, hardware, networking, security, web design, training and retail.** Network Design and support* PC setup and troubleshooting* Web Design and maintenance**We specialise in diagnosing and repairing all computer problems. If you"re having problems upgrading or your machine is slow, or even dead, we can help!**We know that keeping a PC running can be frustrating sometimes, and that is why we have a comprehensive list of PC repair/maintenance tasks that we can carry out for you at a price that won"t disappoint! **Our latest price list is available in pricing section . If you don"t see the service you require, please call us. We offer quotations for any PC work.

▶ Linx Recruitment, Archway House, Norton Way North, Letchworth Garden City, Hertfordshire, SG6 1BH Tel: (01462) 677669 E-mail: keith@linxrecruitment.co.uk Engineering & construction

Lion Alarms, Castle Street, Chorley, Lancashire, PR7 3BU Tel: (01257) 266102 Fax: (01257) 249355 Alarm installation services

▶ Lion Barn Electrical Ltd, Unit 3, Lion Lane, Ipswich, IP6 8NT Tel: (01449) 722221

Lion Bridge, Copthall Terrace, Coventry, CV1 2FP Tel: (024) 7622 2844 Fax: (024) 7625 8892 Technical publishing & translation services Also at: Chipping Sodbury, Edinburgh & Preston

▶ Lion Consultancy Services, Woodpecker Cottage, Talwrn Road, Legacy, Wrexham, LL14 4ES Tel: (01978) 844397 Fax: (01978) 844397 E-mail: mike@lionconsultancy.com We are a company who specialise in environmentally friendly cleaning products and water reduction services

Lion Engineering Services Ltd, Gapton Hall Road, Great Yarmouth, Norfolk, NR31 0NL Tel: (01493) 653642 Fax: (01493) 653353 E-mail: sales@lion-oil-tools.demon.co.uk Machinists engineers & downhole tool manufrs

Lion F P G Ltd, Oldbury Road, West Bromwich, West Midlands, B70 9DQ Tel: 0121-585 0000 Fax: 0121-503 0419 E-mail: sales@lionfpg.co.uk Computer stationery printers

Lion House UK Ltd, 1 Old Parsonage Yard, Horton Road, Horton Kirby, Dartford, DA4 9BN Tel: (01322) 868606 Fax: (01322) 866441 E-mail: howardelkins@lionhouse.co.uk Office equipment suppliers

Lion Hudson P.L.C., Mayfield House, 256 Banbury Road, Oxford, OX2 7DH Tel: (01865) 302750 Fax: (01865) 302757 E-mail: enquiries@lionhudson.com Publishers

▶ Lion Instruments Ltd, Unit 2C East Gores Farm, Salmons Lane, Coggeshall, Colchester, CO6 1RZ Tel: (0845) 2300030 Fax: (01376) 564923 E-mail: sales@lioninstruments.co.uk Process Instrumentation Distributors - representing, Siemens, Barksdale, Fluke Test & measurement, Camille Bauer, London Electronics, Turck Banner, Watson Smith, Yokogawa, Lee Dickens

▶ Lion Labels & Packaging, Regent House, Regent Street, Coppull, Chorley, Lancashire, PR7 5AX Tel: (01257) 793335 Fax: (01257) 471530

Lion Lift Controls Ltd, Littleton Mill, Chew Road, Winford, Bristol, BS40 8HJ Tel: (01275) 332515 Fax: (01275) 333085 E-mail: sales@lionliftcontrols.co.uk Control panel manufrs

Lion Picture Framing Supplies Ltd, 148 Garrison Street, Birmingham, B9 4BN Tel: 0121-773 1230 Fax: 0121-771 2540E-mail: sales@lionpic.co.uk Picture frame equipment & materials distributors

▶ The Lion Press, 19 Market Square, Sandy, Bedfordshire, SG19 1EH Tel: (01767) 680368

Lion Safety Products, Jackson Avenue, Grangemouth, Stirlingshire, FK3 8JU Tel: (01324) 474744 Safety equipment & protective clothing suppliers

Lion Springs Ltd, Summer Street, Rochdale, Lancashire, OL16 1SY Tel: (01706) 861352 Fax: (01706) 657863 E-mail: sales@lionsprings.co.uk Compression, tension & torsion spring manufrs

Lion Steel Equipment Ltd, Johnson Brook Road, Hyde, Cheshire, SK14 4RB Tel: 0161-368 4286 Fax: 0161-367 8214 E-mail: sales@lionsteel.co.uk Steel office furniture manufrs

▶ Lion Watch Security Services Ltd, 143 High Street, Chesterton, Cambridge, CB4 1NL Tel: (07903) 960665 E-mail: info@lionwatch.co.uk Security services

Lion Witch & Lampshade, Birmingham House, High Street, Blakeney, Gloucestershire, GL15 4EB Tel: (01594) 516552 Fax: (01594) 516422 Lampshade manufacturers & retailers

Lionkent Ltd, Unit 18 Serl Industrial Estate, London Road, Baldock, Hertfordshire, SG7 6NG Tel: (01462) 892870 Fax: (01462) 893981 Cardboard box manufrs

Lions Equipment Ltd, 1 Little Balmer, Buckingham Industrial Estate, Buckingham, MK18 1TF Tel: (01280) 822655 Fax: (01280) 822656 E-mail: lionsequipment@aol.com Garage & workshop equipment distributors

Lionweld Kennedy Ltd, Marsh Road, Middlesbrough, Cleveland, TS1 5JS Tel: (01642) 245151 Fax: (01642) 224710 E-mail: sales@lk-uk.com Access engineering products manufrs

Lipco Engineering Ltd, Hightown Industrial Estate, Crow Arch Lane, Ringwood, Hampshire, BH24 1ND Tel: (01425) 476036 Fax: (01425) 475527 Precision engineers

Liphook Coachworks Ltd, Unit 3, Bleachers Yard Industrial Estate, Station Road, Liphook, Hampshire, GU30 7DR Tel: (01428) 722363 Fax: (01428) 725255 E-mail: lee@liphookcoachworks.freeserve.co.uk Accident repair centre

Lipman & Sons, 22 Charing Cross Road, London, WC2H 0HR Tel: (020) 7379 3872 Fax: (020) 7497 8733 Menswear wholesalers & distribs

▶ Liquid Alternative Ltd, 2/4 Arran Mall, Ayr, KA7 1SQ Tel: 01292 886779 Fax: 01292 886602 E-mail: info@labeds.com Scotlands largest waterbed specialist. First for quality and service. Quality bedroom furniture and flooring. Full range of waterbed accessories and spares.Waterbed sheets and bedding.

Liquid Control Ltd, Stewarts Road, Finedon Road Industrial Estate, Wellingborough, Northamptonshire, NN8 4RJ Tel: (01933) 277571 Fax: (01933) 440273 E-mail: sales@liquidcontrol.co.uk Purchasing Contact: J. Haines Sales Contact: D. Bridgeman Principal Export Areas: Worldwide Manufacturers of adhesive application/coating equipment, dispensing (polyurethane/resin etc) equipment, encapsulating machine/system, robot (industrial) systems, sealant application equipment & filling machines. Also mixers, fluid/liquid

▶ Liquid It Ltd, 22 Heron Court Road, Bournemouth, BH9 1DG Tel: (08707) 547843 Fax: 08707 627843 Liquid IT is a provider of leading edge, integrated IT Solutions and Services for small business throughout the United Kingdom.

Liquid Measure, Gelli-Hirion Industrial Estate, Pontypridd, Mid Glamorgan, CF37 5SX Tel: (01443) 844622 Fax: (01443) 844623 E-mail: liquidmeasure@treforest.wannadoo.co.uk Alcohol & soft drinks wholesalers

Liquid Metering Instruments Ltd, L M I House, West Dudley Street, Winsford, Cheshire, CW7 3AG Tel: (01606) 550583 Fax: (01606) 550485 E-mail: sales@lmipumps.co.uk Chemical metering pumps & dosing systems suppliers & manufrs

Liquid Plastics Ltd, PO Box 7, Preston, PR1 1EA Tel: (01772) 255017 Fax: (01772) 255671 E-mail: info@liquidplastics.co.uk Protective coating & paint manufrs Also at: Glasgow

Liquid Software Solutions Ltd, 2 Wilsons Road, Knowle, Solihull, West Midlands, B93 0HZ Tel: (01564) 779090 Fax: (01564) 776161 E-mail: info@liquid-soft.com Supply, support & develop Application software for Wholesalers & Distributors

Liquified Gas Pumping Services Ltd, 18 Abbotsinch Road, Grangemouth, Stirlingshire, FK3 9UX Tel: (01324) 485475 Fax: (01324) 485677 E-mail: sales@lgpservices.co.uk Petroleum gas equipment maintenance

Liquitech Ltd, Old Post Office House, East Street, Pembridge, Leominster, Herefordshire, HR6 9HA Tel: (0845) 6449020 Fax: (0845) 6449021 E-mail: andrew@liquitech.co.uk Tank refurbishment services, water tanks

Liquor Bottle Ltd, 7 Elsinore House, 77 Fulham Palace Road, London, W6 8JA Tel: (020) 8748 0008 Fax: (020) 8741 1701 Bottle suppliers

Liric Associates, Jericho Farm House, Worton, Witney, Oxfordshire, OX29 4SZ Tel: (01865) 880366 Fax: (01865) 882054 E-mail: sales@1iric.co.uk Communication services consultants

▶ Lisa Bakery Ltd, 40 Coldhurst Street, Oldham, OL1 2BQ Tel: 0161-652 1595 Cake makers

▶ Lisa J Fine Art Ltd, 4 Albion Parade, Kingswinford, West Midlands, DY6 0NP Tel: (01384) 401117 Fax: (01384) 294984 E-mail: sales@lisaj.biz Limited Edition prints and Original Art.*Specialists in Doug Hyde, Sarah Jane Szikora, Peter Smith and Alexander Millar.

▶ Lisa Pitchford, Hollies Close, Dronfield, Derbyshire, S18 1TY Tel: (07713) 123606 E-mail: lisa.pitchford@btinternet.com Portrait, Wedding, Legal and Event Photography

Lisburn Security Services Ltd, Security House, Lissea Industrial Estate East, Lisburn, County Antrim, BT28 2RD Tel: (028) 9260 5859 Fax: (028) 9262 2423 E-mail: gsmith@lisburnsecurityservices.co.uk Security guard services & CCTV monitoring

John Liscombe Ltd, Mariner Way, Felnex Industrial Estate, Newport, Gwent, NP19 4PQ Tel: (01633) 284100 Fax: (01633) 284125 E-mail: sales@liscombe.co.uk Purchasing Contact: S. Grant Sales Contact: R. Seabury Industrial glove & protective clothing/footwear & safety equipment (industrial) distributors or agents

Lisega Ltd, Unit3, Washington Centre, Hales Owen Road, Netherton, West Midlands, DY2 9RE Tel: (01384) 458660 Fax: (01384) 213301 E-mail: sales@lisega.co.uk Pipework, clamp & shock absorber manufrs

Liskeard Metal Finishers, 6 Iskeard Enterprise Centre, Station Road, Liskeard, Cornwall, PL14 4BT Tel: (01579) 348251 Fax: (01579) 348258 Powder coating

Liskeard Signs & Trophies, 8 Pike Street, Liskeard, Cornwall, PL14 3JE Tel: (01579) 347098 Fax: (01579) 347098 Sign makers & engravers

Lisland Ltd, St. Chads, Fisher Street, Brindley Ford, Stoke-on-Trent, ST8 7QJ Tel: (01782) 522544 Fax: (01782) 522255 Industrial kiln manufrs

▶ Lisle Design, 50 Lade Braes, St. Andrews, Fife, KY16 9DA Tel: (01334) 471435

Lismore Instruments Ltd, 2 Tristar Business Centre, Star Road, Partridge Green, Horsham, West Sussex, RH13 8RA Tel: (01403) 713121 Fax: (01403) 713141 E-mail: sales@intercall.com Staff safety attack system manufrs

Lissan Harper International Ltd, Unit B4 Stafford Park 4, Telford, Shropshire, TF3 3BA Tel: (01952) 292408 Fax: (01952) 292419 E-mail: info@lissan-harper.co.uk Import & distribution of leather handbags

List Design Group Ltd, Manby Road By Passage, Immingham, South Humberside, DN40 2DW Tel: (01469) 571888 Fax: (01469) 571450 E-mail: ldgltd@aol.com Consulting engineers Also at: Branches throughout the U.K.

List Design Group Ltd, Unit 2, Avon Terrace, Salisbury, SP2 7BX Tel: (01722) 335112 Fax: (01722) 412521 E-mail: engineering@listgroup.co.uk Based in Salisbury - List Design Group offer a complete package in engineering design and recruitment.

Lista (UK) Ltd, 17 Alston Drive, Bradwell Abbey, Milton Keynes, MK13 9HA Tel: (01908) 222333 Fax: (01908) 222433 E-mail: info.uk@lista.com Storage equipment/systems distributors

Listan Paper Converters Ltd, Old Wharf Industrial Estate, Old Wharf Road, Grantham, Lincolnshire, NG31 7AA Tel: (01476) 570052 Fax: (01476) 565542 E-mail: sales@listan.freeserve.co.uk Paper merchants & paper converters

Lister & Durling Printers, 69 Station Road, Flitwick, Bedford, MK45 1JU Tel: (01525) 713770 General printers

Lister Engineering Ltd, 164 Harris Street, Bradford, West Yorkshire, BD1 5JA Tel: (01274) 721855 Fax: (01274) 721251 E-mail: sales@listerengineering.co.uk Precision engineers

Lister Gases, Bridge Street, Wednesbury, West Midlands, WS10 0AW Tel: 0121-556 7181 Fax: 0121-505 1744 E-mail: gasses@lister.co.uk Wholesale liquefied petroleum gas equipment

Lister Gases, Bridge Street, Wednesbury, West Midlands, WS10 0AW Tel: 0121-556 7181 Fax: 0121-505 1744 E-mail: primuslimited@smsuppliers.btinternet.com Liquefied petroleum gas appliance & fittings distributors or agents

James Lister & Sons Ltd, Spon La South, Smethwick, West Midlands, B66 1QJ Tel: 0121-553 2949 Fax: 0121-525 6116 E-mail: tools@lister.co.uk Tool factors distributors

Lister Lutyens Co. Ltd, 6 Alder Close, Eastbourne, East Sussex, BN23 6QF Tel: (01323) 431177 Fax: (01323) 639314 E-mail: sales@listerteak.com Garden furniture manufrs

Lister Machine Tools Ni Ltd, Unit 10 Boucher Business Centre, Apollo Road, Belfast, BT12 6HP Tel: (028) 9066 3804 Fax: (028) 9066 3801 E-mail: sales@listermachinetools.co.uk Machine tool distributors

Lister Precision Components Ltd, 27 Benedict Square, Werrington, Peterborough, PE4 6GD Tel: (01733) 573700 Fax: (01733) 326224 E-mail: keith@listerprecision.co.uk CNC machining services

Listers, 3 Gloddaeth Street, Llandudno, Gwynedd, LL30 2DD Tel: (01492) 871940 Soft furnishing retailers

Listgrove Ltd, 16 The Courtyard, Timothys Bridge Road, Stratford-upon-Avon, Warwickshire, CV37 9NP Tel: (01789) 207070 Fax: (01789) 207096 E-mail: contact@listgrove.co.uk Recruitment consultants plastic packaging sectors

Litchfield Bros Ltd, Ripley Road, Ambergate, Belper, Derbyshire, DE56 2EP Tel: (01773) 852435 Fax: (01773) 852661 E-mail: aksimmons@lbplastics.co.uk Spring manufrs

Lite On Ltd, North Seaton Industrial Estate, Ashington, Northumberland, NE63 0YB Tel: (01670) 813648 Fax: (01670) 853787 E-mail: sales@liteon.co.uk Design & manufacture of power supplies

Lite Tec, 507 Ashingdon Road, Rochford, Essex, SS4 3HE Tel: (01702) 540187 Fax: (01702) 541049 E-mail: sales@lite-tec.co.uk Principal Export Areas: Worldwide Manufacturers of fibre-optics

▶ Litecraft, 95 Seaward Street, Kinning Park, Glasgow, G41 1HJ Tel: 0141-429 0000 Lighting sales

Liteon Automotive Electronics Ltd, 11 Ptarmigan Place, Attleborough Fields Industrial Estate, Nuneaton, Warwickshire, CV11 6RX Tel: (024) 7637 4222 Fax: (024) 7637 5444 Automated electronic suppliers

▶ Litetask Ltd, 1 The Courtyards, Victoria Road, Leeds, LS14 2LB Tel: 0113-265 2651 Fax: 0113-265 2652 Distributors of commercial lighting

Litex Design, Unit 4 Empire Centre, Imperial Way, Watford, WD24 4YH Tel: (01923) 247254 Fax: (01923) 226772 E-mail: joshea@litex.demon.co.uk Exterior & interior lighting equipment suppliers

▶ Lithgo Press Ltd, Unit 10, Ashville Way, Whetstone, Leicester, LE8 6NU Tel: 0116-284 1414 Fax: 0116-286 2302 E-mail: sales@lithgopress.co.uk

Lithgow Factoring Ltd, Langbank, Port Glasgow, Renfrewshire, PA14 6YG Tel: (01475) 540692 Fax: (01475) 540558 E-mail: admin@lithgows.co.uk Holding company

▶ Lithium Systems, Unit 4 Block 1 Crookaridge Way, Alloa, Clackmannanshire, FK10 3LP Tel: (01259) 727847 Fax: (01259) 729963 Computer maintenance & repair services

Litho Supplies Ltd, Longmoor Lane, Breaston, Derby, DE72 3BQ Tel: (01332) 873921 Fax: (01332) 875103 Printing trade suppliers Also at: Basingstoke, Cardiff, Derby, Maidstone & Plymouth

Litho Supplies, Flagship Square, Shaw Cross Business Park, Dewsbury, West Yorkshire, WF12 7TH Tel: (01924) 486130 Fax: (01924) 460502 E-mail: dewsbury@litho.co.uk Electronic printing equipment

Litho Supplies, Flagship Square, Shaw Cross Business Park, Dewsbury, West Yorkshire, WF12 7TH Tel: (01924) 486130 Fax: (01924) 460502 E-mail: dewsbury@litho.co.uk Print & graphic suppliers

Litho Supplies Midlands Region, 1 Tamebridge Industrial Estate, Aldridge Road, Perry Barr, Birmingham, B42 2TX Tel: 0121-344 4222 Fax: 0121-344 4494 E-mail: midlands@litho.co.uk Printers & printing suppliers

Litho Supplies Scotland Ltd, 8 Elphinstone Square, Deans Industrial Estate, Deans, Livingston, West Lothian, EH54 8RG Tel: (01506) 462555 Fax: (01506) 465678 E-mail: scotland@litho.co.uk Print & press room products

Litho Supplies (Wessex), Unit 22, Metropolitan Centre, Darby Road, Greenford, Middlesex, UB6 8UJ Tel: (020) 8578 5787 Fax: (020) 8575 6252 E-mail: greenford@litho.co.uk Printing supplies

Lithoflow Ltd, 32 Aylesbury St, London, EC1R 0ET Tel: (020) 7017 8660 Fax: (020) 7364 6433 E-mail: info@lithoflow.co.uk Litho printer manufrs

Lithographics Ltd, Bromyard Road, Worcester, WR2 5HN Tel: (01905) 429011 Fax: (01905) 748257 E-mail: info@lithographics.co.uk Printing services

Lithograve (Birmingham) Ltd, 8-10 Lawford Close, Birmingham, B7 4HJ Tel: 0121-359 3350 Fax: 0121-359 3119 E-mail: dave@lithograve.com Trade printers & plate makers

Lithoprint Ltd, 4 Earl Haig Road, Hillington Park, Glasgow, G52 4RP Tel: 0141-891 8000 Fax: 0141-810 5496 Colour printer manufrs

Lithotech Print Services, Unit 12, The Grove, Parkgate Industrial Estate, Knutsford, Cheshire, WA16 8XP Tel: (01565) 633703 Fax: (01565) 633703 E-mail: bryan@lithotech.freesurf.co.uk General printers & stationers

Litre Meter Ltd, Unit 50 Rabans Close, Rabans Lane Industrial Area, Aylesbury, Buckinghamshire, HP19 8RS Tel: (01296) 420341 Fax: (01296) 436446 E-mail: sales@litremeter.com Principal Export Areas: Asia Pacific, Africa, North America & South America Flow measurement systems & flow meter manufacturers

▶ Little Angels, 54-58 Frodingham Road, Scunthorpe, South Humberside, DN15 7JN Tel: (01724) 843366 Fax: (01724) 843366 E-mail: les@littleangelsonline.wanadoo.co.uk Showroom, baby equipment, prams, car seats, highchairs, cots,

Little Brown Book Group Ltd, Brettenham House, Lancaster Place, London, WC2E 7TL Tel: (020) 7322 1400 Fax: (020) 7911 8100 E-mail: emailuk@twbg.co.uk Book publishers

▶ Little Cherubs, Unit 2, Charlotte Court, Old Milton Road, New Milton, Hampshire, BH25 6DT Tel: (01425) 621316

▶ Little Devils, 188 Sidbury Circular Road, Tidworth, Hampshire, SP9 7EX Tel: (07900) 675667 Inflatable bouncing castles manufrs

Little Dreams Ltd, Campbell Road, Stoke-on-Trent, ST4 4ES Tel: (01782) 413600 Fax: (01782) 413601 E-mail: info@littledreams.co.uk Educational furniture & display stand manufrs

▶ Little Gems Handmade Cards, 63 Wentworth Road, Southend-on-Sea, SS2 5LF Tel: (01702) 613945 Handmade cards for all occasions

▶ Little Green Nursery, 117 Middlehill Road, Wimborne, Dorset, BH21 2HL Tel: (01202) 884527 E-mail: info@little-green-nursery.co.uk Manufacturer and supplier of organic skin care, organic essential oils (rosehip/rosa mosquota, lavender, hemp etc).

▶ Jonathon Little, 9 James Reckitt Avenue, Hull, HU8 7TJ Tel: (01482) 715345 E-mail: mjlimited@hotmail.co.uk

Little & Little, 16 St Marks Road, Henley-on-Thames, Oxfordshire, RG9 1LJ Tel: (01491) 572533 Agricultural contractors

Little Miss Clothing, Unit 1 Church Street, Moxley, Wednesbury, West Midlands, WS10 8RD Tel: 0121-556 4870 Fax: 0121-556 2259 Womens clothing manufrs

▶ Little Monsters, 14 Fern Drive, Havant, Hampshire, PO9 2YH Tel: (023) 9278 8427 E-mail: littlemonsters@ntlworld.com Bouncy Castle Hire for havant, Fareham, Portsmouth, Eastleigh, Southampton, Lee on the Solent, gosport, waterlooville, Hampshire & The south Coast. Book Your Bouncy Castle, sumo"s, assault course, gladiator joust, slides and many more inflatables today

▶ indicates data change since last edition

Company Information

The Little Packaging Company Ltd, Unit 10, Athena Avenue, Elgin Industrial Estate, Swindon, SN2 8HH Tel: (01793) 693179 Fax: (01793) 693945 E-mail: littlepackagingco@unidsl.co.uk *Solutions, Fulfilment, Warehousing, Container Work, Distribution, Repackaging, Case Shipments, Rework, Contract Packing, Import, Stacking, Picking, Bulk Containers, Logistics, Haulage, Pallet Shipments, Collating, Palletising, Pallet Storage, Packing, Freight Containers, Pick And Pack, Transportation, Labelling, Break Bulk Palletisation, Assembly, Strapping, Freight Forwarding, e-Commerce.*

▶ Little Press Book, 159 Mellish street, London, E14 8PJ Tel: (020) 7531 6127

▶ Little Rascals Bouncy Castles, 55 Kingsway, Kingswood, Bristol, BS15 8AJ Tel: 0117-904 1801 E-mail: kerrybird@littlerascalsbouncycastles.co.uk *Childrens bouncy castle hire in Bristol and Bath. We have an extensive range of bouncy castles, ball ponds and inflatable slides. We have full public liability insurance*

Little Tikes Commercial Playstems, 3 Cross Green, Liverpool, L37 4BH Tel: (01704) 833123 Fax: (01704) 833888 *Designers of play equipment*

Little Town Farm Ltd, Burlington Cresent, Goole, North Humberside, DN14 5EQ Tel: (01405) 720198 Fax: (01405) 720365 E-mail: littletownfarm@btconnect.com *Dairy products wholesalers & suppliers*

Little Whiting & Tedford Ltd, Princes Dock, 14 Clarendon Road, Belfast, BT1 3BG Tel: (028) 9053 3302 Fax: (028) 9053 3222 E-mail: agency@hamiltonshipping.com *Freight forwarding agents*

Littlebrook Power Services Ltd, Littlebrook Complex, Manor Way, Dartford, DA1 5PU Tel: (01322) 280038 Fax: (01322) 284835 E-mail: general@littlebrookservices.co.uk *Calibrating laboratories*

Littledown Products Ltd, 7a Wincombe Business Park, Shaftesbury, Dorset, SP7 9QJ Tel: (01747) 851177 *Specialist lighting manufrs*

Littlefairs Builders Merchants, Littlefairs, Hobson Lane, Kirkby Stephen, Cumbria, CA17 4RN Tel: (01768) 371216 Fax: (01768) 372234 E-mail: enquiries@littlefairs.co.uk *Builders' merchants* Also at: Appleby & Hawes

▶ LittleFish Web Design, 79 King George Avenue, Horsforth, Leeds, LS18 5ND Tel: 0113 2170419 E-mail: contact@littlefishwebdesign.com *LittleFish Web Design offers a range of fast, friendly and affordable web design and associated services to small businesses.*

Littlehampton Welding Ltd, S Riverside Industrial Estate, Bridge Road, Littlehampton, West Sussex, BN17 5DF Tel: (01903) 721555 Fax: (01903) 726805 E-mail: lhw@lhwelding.co.uk *Architectural & structural metalworkers*

Littleline Ltd, 41 West Road, Tottenham, London, N17 0RE Tel: (020) 8880 3790 Fax: (020) 8880 3830 *Furniture reproduction*

Littleport Timber Buildings, 5a Saxon Business Park, Littleport, Ely, Cambridgeshire, CB6 1XX Tel: (01353) 861707 *Timber building manufrs*

Littler Co. Ltd, 2 Greaves Way Industrial Estate, Stanbridge Road, Leighton Buzzard, Bedfordshire, LU7 4UB Tel: (01525) 373310 Fax: (01525) 381371 *Precision engineers*

James Littler & Sons Ltd, Barons Quay Sawmills, Leicester Street, Northwich, Cheshire, CW9 5LD Tel: (01606) 46112 Fax: (01606) 43844 E-mail: sales@timbermerchantuk.com *Timber merchants*

Albert Littlewood Garage Equipment Ltd, 1 Westfield Lane, Barlborough, Chesterfield, Derbyshire, S43 4TP Tel: (01246) 811268 Fax: (01246) 811268 *Garage equipment suppliers service & repairers*

▶ Littlewoods Successors Ltd, Paddock Foot, Huddersfield, HD1 4RY Tel: (01484) 423960 Fax: (01484) 450172

Littner Hampton Ltd, Unit 30 Forest Business Park, South Access Road, London, E17 8AD Tel: (020) 8520 8474 Fax: (020) 8520 4464 E-mail: littnerhampton@aol.com *Carpet wholesalers* Also at: Netherton

Litton Furniture, Bonslea House, White Lane Close, Sturminster Newton, Dorset, DT10 1EJ Tel: (01258) 472359 Fax: (01258) 473512 *Furniture makers & specialist joiners*

Litton Group Ltd, 38 Young Street, Lisburn, County Antrim, BT27 5EB Tel: (028) 9267 2325 Fax: (028) 9260 7473 E-mail: mechanical@litton.co.uk *Mechanical engineers*

Live Devices, Atlas House, Link Business Park, Osbaldwick, Link Road, York, YO10 3JB Tel: (01904) 562580 Fax: (01904) 562581 *Embedded systems software developers*

▶ Live Solutions, 51 Conway Road, Colwyn Bay, Clwyd, LL29 7AW Tel: (01492) 534393 *Web site design, networking, office equipment supply & integration*

▶ Live Sound Hire, Unit 4, The Paddocks, Gambles Lane, Ripley, Woking, Surrey, GU23 6HS Tel: (07870) 857004 E-mail: mike@surreyav.co.uk *Sound equipment hire*

Livedale Foam & Sundries Ltd, Albert Road, Farnworth, Bolton, BL4 9EL Tel: (01204) 573566 Fax: (01204) 705672 E-mail: sales@1ivedale.co.uk *Foam polyethylene converters*

▶ Livefoods Direct Ltd, Houghton Road, North Anston Trading Estate, North Anston, Sheffield, S25 4JJ Tel: (01909) 518888 Fax: (01909) 568666 E-mail: sales@livefoodsdirect.co.uk

Liveline Fishing Tackle & Guns, 41 West Main Street, Armadale, Bathgate, West Lothian, EH48 3PZ Tel: (01501) 733150 Fax: (01501) 733150 *Fishing tackle & guns retail*

Live-Link Communications Ltd, 6 Milrig Cottage, Kirknewton, Midlothian, EH27 8DE Tel: (01506) 884404 Fax: (01506) 884406 E-mail: nursecallalarms@aol.com *Radio nurse call equipment*

Livenet Computing Ltd, 214 School Rd, Sheffield, S10 1GL Tel: 0114-268 7030 *Pc repairs*

Liver Grease Oil & Chemical Company Ltd, 11 Norfolk Street, Liverpool, L1 0BE Tel: 0151-709 7494 Fax: 0151-709 3774 E-mail: sales@livergrease.co.uk *Bituminous solution makers*

Livermead Art Glass Ltd, Greenwich Industrial Estate, Greenwich High Rd, London, SE10 8JF Tel: (020) 8858 6441 Fax: (020) 8858 7119 *Decorative glass manufrs*

Liverpool Auto Service, Unit 12b Weaver Industrial Estate, Blackburne Street, Liverpool, L19 8JA Tel: 0151-427 5707 Fax: 0151-427 5707 *Welding services & paint spraying contractors & services*

Liverpool Bulk Bags, 35a Seaforth Vale North, Liverpool, L21 3TR Tel: 0151-920 2280 Fax: 0151-922 4076 E-mail: info@bulkbagsuk.com *FIBCs, recycled & flexible bulk containers suppliers*

Liverpool Chamber Of Commerce & Industry, 1 Old Hall Street, Liverpool, L3 9HG Tel: 0151-227 1233 Fax: 0151-236 0121 E-mail: info@liverpoolchamber.org.uk *Business support services*

▶ Liverpool Cubicles & Washroom Systems Ltd, Unit 5-7 Luton Street, Liverpool, L5 9XR Tel: 0151-298 1509 Fax: 0151-298 2276 E-mail: liverpoolcubicle@aol.com *Manufacturers of toilet cubicles & washroom systems*

▶ Liverpool Data Research Associates Ltd, Monks Ferry, Portside, Birkenhead, Merseyside, CH41 5LH Tel: 0151-649 9300 Fax: 0151-649 9666 E-mail: info@ldra.co.uk *Software testing*

▶ Liverpool Electronics Ltd, 6 Brunel Road, Bromborough, Wirral, Merseyside, CH62 3NY Tel: 0151-343 9980 Fax: 0151-343 9985 *Electronic equipment manufrs*

▶ Liverpool Gate Co., 73, Henry Street, Liverpool, L1 5BS Tel: 0151-709 7172 Fax: 0151-709 7172

▶ Liverpool Locksmith, 46 Merlin Street, Liverpool, L8 8HZ Tel: 0151-281 5392 Fax: 0151-281 5392 E-mail: locksmith@safe-mail.net *24 HOUR EMERGENCY LOCKSMITHS *FREE SECURITY CHECK,SUPPLY/FIT SAFES,LOCKS,DOORS,STEEL BARS, GRILLS,ACCESS CONTROL,DIGI LOCKS,KEY CUTTING, AUTO CAR ENTRY,*

Liverpool & London P & I Management Ltd, Royal Liver Building, Pier Head, Liverpool, L3 1QR Tel: 0151-236 3777 Fax: 0151-236 0053 E-mail: info@livlon.co.uk *Mutual marine insurance company*

Liverpool & London Trade Protection Society Ltd, 9 Hillview Close, Purley, Surrey, CR8 1AU Tel: (020) 8763 8807 Fax: (020) 8645 0601 E-mail: mail@lltps.co.uk *Debt recovery & credit insurance services, reporting*

Liverpool R.X. Co. Ltd, Liverpool, L69 1UZ Tel: 0151-709 1643 Fax: 0151-709 1643 *Optical manufrs*

Liverpool Steel Services, 31-32 Byng Street, Millers Bridge Industrial Estate, Millers Bridge Industrial Esta, Bootle, Merseyside, L20 1EE Tel: 0151-922 4265 Fax: 0151-922 0400 E-mail: liverpool@bmsteel.co.uk *Steel stockholders*

Liverpool Victoria Financial Advice Services Ltd, County Gates, Bournemouth, BH1 2NF Tel: (0845) 6020690 Fax: (01202) 292253 E-mail: sales@liverpoolvictoria.co.uk *Insurance company*

Liverpool Water Witch Marine Engineering Co. Ltd, 4 Lightbody Street, Liverpool, L5 9UZ Tel: 0151-207 4874 Fax: 0151-298 1366 E-mail: sales@waterwitch.demon.co.uk *Pollution control equipment manufrs*

Liversidge Windows & Double Glazing Ltd, Belgrave Mill, Fitton Hill Road, Oldham, OL8 2LU Tel: 0161-620 4525 Fax: 0161-627 0082 E-mail: liversidge@belgravemill.snet.co.uk *Window manufrs*

Livesey Ltd, Longden Road, Shrewsbury, SY3 9EB Tel: (01743) 235651 Fax: (01743) 232944 E-mail: info@liveseyltd.co.uk *Commercial printing services*

Livesey Business Systems, 95 Princes Avenue, Hull, HU5 3QR Tel: (01482) 343453 E-mail: sales@livbiz.com *Software solutions distributor & manufrs*

Livewire Digital Ltd, 14-15 First Quarter, Blenheim Road, Epsom, Surrey, KT19 9QN Tel: (01372) 731400 Fax: (01372) 731420 E-mail: enquirie@livewire.co.uk *Satellite communications*

Livewire Electronic Components Ltd, CWM Farm Barn, Llantrisant, Usk, Gwent, NP15 1LG Tel: (01291) 673003 Fax: (01291) 671001 E-mail: info@livewire.uk.com *Electronic component distributors & agents*

Livewire Telecommunication, Kineton Road, Gaydon, Warwick, CV35 0HB Tel: (01926) 640634 *Telecommunication consultants & equipment installation*

▶ Living Flames, 751 Pollokshaws Road, Glasgow, G41 2AX Tel: 0141-422 1540

Living Fountains Detox Clinic, 10 Hemlock Close, Oakwood, Derby, DE21 2NZ Tel: 0870 027 3656 Fax: 0870 1334836 E-mail: info@livingfountains.org *Residentia; detox clinic helping people loose weight and build up their immune system.*

Living In Style, Unit 1, 162 Coles Green Road, London, NW2 7HW Tel: (020) 8450 9555 Fax: (020) 8450 7565 E-mail: sales@livinginstyle.co.uk *Kitchen & bedroom designers*

Livingdale Ltd, 4 Candleby Lane, Cotgrave, Nottingham, NG12 3JG Tel: 0115-989 9070 Fax: 0115-989 4763 E-mail: sales@livingdale.co.uk *Industrial sewing*

Livingston & Doughty Ltd, 17 Mandervell Road, Oadby, Leicester, LE2 5LR Tel: 0116-271 4221 Fax: 0116-271 6977 E-mail: orders@shoenet.co.uk *Shoe bottom fillers & shoe supplies*

▶ Livingston Mechanical Services, Nettlehill Road, Houstoun Industrial Estate, Livingston, West Lothian, EH54 5DL Tel: (01506) 442669 Fax: (01506) 442671

Livingston Precision (Engineering) Ltd, 28 Firth Road, Houstoun Industrial Estate, Livingston, West Lothian, EH54 5DJ Tel: (01506) 435281 Fax: (01506) 433973 *Sheet metalwork engineers*

Livingston Services plc, Livingston House, 2-6 Queens Road, Teddington, Middlesex, TW11 0LR Tel: (020) 8943 1142 Fax: (020) 8977 6431 E-mail: info@livingston.co.uk *Computer leasing, rental & hire services*

Livingwood Floorcoverings, The Mount, Flimwell, Wadhurst, East Sussex, TN5 7QP Tel: (01580) 879888 Fax: (01580) 879444 E-mail: sales@livingwood.net *Supply & installation of timber products*

Lixmere Ltd, Lixmere House, 211 Kenton Road, Harrow, Middlesex, HA3 0HD Tel: (020) 8907 1177 Fax: (020) 8909 2777 E-mail: enquiries@lixmere.co.uk *Automotive spares exporters*

▶ LJ Occasions, 70a King Street, Norwich, NR1 1PG Tel: (01603) 613788 E-mail: info@ljoccasions.co.uk *Card making, greeting cards, fresh flowers, gifts, bags & wraps*

Llandaff Engineering Co. Ltd, Paper Mill Road, Canton, Cardiff, CF11 8PH Tel: (029) 2083 8300 Fax: (029) 2056 5125 E-mail: majenkins@llandaffeng.com *Manufacturers of contact (electrical components) & switchgear components. Also aluminium fabricators & punching (CNC) services*

Llandissilio Garage, Modyrllys, Llandissilio, Clynderwen, Dyfed, SA66 7TG Tel: (01437) 563225 Fax: (01437) 563709 *Agricultural machinery repairs & sales*

Llandudno Wholesale Ltd, 98 Trinity Avenue, Llandudno, Gwynedd, LL30 2YQ Tel: (01492) 876579 Fax: (01492) 860080 E-mail: sales@llandudnowholesale.co.uk *Wholesaler of catering equipment*

Llanelec Precision Engineering Co. Ltd, Jenkins Road, Skewen, Neath, West Glamorgan, SA10 7GA Tel: (01792) 817676 Fax: (01792) 818187 E-mail: sales@llanelec.co.uk *Specialist engineer manufrs*

Llangloffan Cheese Ltd, Prendergast, Castle Morris, Haverfordwest, Dyfed, SA62 5ET Tel: (01348) 891241 Fax: (0870) 0561043 E-mail: sales@welshcheese.co.uk *Cheese makers*

Llanharan Concrete Co. Ltd, Llanharry Road, Llanharan, Pontyclun, Mid Glamorgan, CF72 9RN Tel: (01443) 226212 Fax: (01443) 237685 *Concrete block manufrs*

Llanrad Distribution plc, Unit 26 Bookers Way, Dinnington, Sheffield, S25 3SH Tel: (01909) 550944 Fax: (01909) 568403 E-mail: cool@llanrad.co.uk *Motor vehicle accessories distributors*

Llansilin Tractors, Bwlch, Llansilin, Oswestry, Shropshire, SY10 7JW Tel: (01691) 791460 Fax: (01691) 791243 *Agricultural engineers*

Llewellyn Heating Ltd, Station Approach, Hereford, HR1 1BB Tel: (01432) 266413 Fax: (01432) 271493 *Central heating engineers*

Llewellyn Ryland Ltd, Haden Street, Birmingham, B12 9DB Tel: 0121-440 2284 Fax: 0121-440 0281 E-mail: sales@llewellyn-ryland.co.uk *Polyester colour paste suppliers*

▶ Llexia Art, 196 High Street, Brentford, Middlesex, TW8 8AH Tel: (020) 8560 5550 Fax: (020) 8560 5562 *Art supplies & frame retailers*

▶ Lloret Controls Systems Ltd, 24 Ullswater Crescent, Coulsdon, Surrey, CR5 2HR Tel: (020) 8410 4600 Fax: (020) 8660 5469

Lloyd Ltd, Vale Business Park, Llandow, Cowbridge, South Glamorgan, CF71 7PF Tel: (01446) 773231 Fax: (01446) 771039 E-mail: enquiries@plmortgages.co.uk *Wood handle & sporting goods manufrs*

Lloyd Ltd, Myers Lane, Penrith, Cumbria, CA11 9DP Tel: (01768) 863806 Fax: (01768) 865664 E-mail: lloyd.ltd@lineone.net *Agricultural & construction equipment main dealers*

▶ Lloyd Construction, 10a 42 Bayton Road, Exhall, Coventry, CV7 9EJ Tel: (0870) 7590898 Fax: (0870) 7590899

Lloyd Drilling Ltd, 72 Hutton Close, Crowther, Washington, Tyne & Wear, NE38 0AH Tel: 0191-419 0321 Fax: 0191-416 8863 E-mail: lloyddrill@msn.com *Diamond drilling, sawing, repairs & grooving services*

▶ Lloyd Fraser Ltd, Furnace Lane, Nether Heyford, Northampton, NN7 3LB Tel: (01327) 349111 Fax: (01327) 349288

Lloyd Furnishings, Albert Close Trading Estate, Whitefield, Manchester, M45 8EH Tel: 0161-796 1920 Fax: 0161-796 1921 E-mail: sales@curtains.co.uk *Furnishing fabric converters & importers*

Lloyd & Jones Engineers Ltd, Langton House, 74 Regent Road, Bootle, Merseyside, L20 1EJ Tel: 0151-955 4700 Fax: 0151-922 5418 E-mail: sales@lloyd-jones.com *Oil & gas industry supply services*

Kevin Lloyd Ltd, 2 Mickleton Road, Middlesbrough, Cleveland, TS2 1RQ Tel: (01642) 226950 Fax: (01642) 226951 *Pipework fabricators*

Lloyd Loaders MH Ltd, Hipperholme, Halifax, West Yorkshire, HX3 8PJ Tel: (01422) 201164 Fax: (01422) 205872 E-mail: muir-hill@lloydsmh.fsnet.co.uk *Loading shovels & tractors supply*

Lloyd Management Ltd, Maidhurst, Arundel, West Sussex, BN18 0NL Tel: (020) 7405 3499 E-mail: lloydmanagement@maidhurst.fsnet.co.uk *Recruitment consultancy*

▶ Lloyd Management Systems Ltd, 73 Arethusa Road, Rochester, Kent, ME1 2UR Tel: (01634) 846519 Fax: 01634 846519 E-mail: lloydmanagementsystems@blueyonder.co.uk *Provider of ISO 9001 quality certification services, ISO 14001 environmental certification services and OH&S 18001 health & safety certification services*

Lloyd Morris Electrical Ltd, Unit 1 Pandy Industrial Estate, Plas Acton Road, Wrexham, Clwyd, LL11 2UD Tel: (01978) 291505 Fax: (01978) 365433 E-mail: enquiries@lloydmorris.co.uk *Control panel manufrs*

▶ Peter Lloyd & Associates, 18 Demesne Road, Holywood, County Down, BT18 9NB Tel: (028) 9042 8080 Fax: (028) 9042 8063 E-mail: LloydSound@aol.com *Acoustic consultant. Architectural, environmental.*

Lloyd Research Ltd, 7-7A Brook Lane, Warsash, Southampton, SO31 9FH Tel: (01489) 885515 Fax: (01489) 885853 E-mail: progs@lloydres.co.uk *Device programmers & sale designers & manufrs*

Richard Lloyd Ltd, Cromwell Works, Tenbury Wells, Worcestershire, WR15 8LF Tel: (01584) 810381 Fax: (01584) 810080 E-mail: sales@galtona.co.uk *Milling cutters & thread tap manufrs*

Roy Lloyd Ltd, 1 Hall Street, Southport, Merseyside, PR9 0SF Tel: (01704) 537333 Fax: (01704) 548543 *Car body repairs*

Lloyd Savage Services Ltd, 25 The Green, Richmond, Surrey, TW9 1LY Tel: (020) 8332 7266 *Software house & computer developer*

Lloyd Signs Of Birkenhead, Units 7-10, Cavendish Enterprise Centre, Birkenhead, Merseyside, CH41 8BY Tel: 0151-653 8053 Fax: 0151-653 8053 *Sign manufrs*

Lloyd & Son, Copthall Farm, Breakspear Road South, Ickenham, Uxbridge, Middlesex, UB10 8HB Tel: (01895) 679000 Fax: (01895) 679000 E-mail: lloydandson640@btinternet.com *Metal spinners*

W.S. Lloyd Ltd, 7 Redgrove House, Stonards Hill, Epping, Essex, CM16 4QQ Tel: (01992) 572670 Fax: E-mail: jhogg@wslloyd.co.uk Principal Export Areas: Middle East, Africa, Central/East Europe & West Europe *Importers, processors & exporters of vegetable oils (castor & linseed) for all surface coatings industries*

W. Lloyd Williams & Sons, Poplar Terrace, Machynlleth, Powys, SY20 8BY Tel: (01654) 702106 Fax: (01654) 702106 *Abattoir*

Lloyd Worrall London, Unit F21, Riverside Business Centre, Haldane Place, London, SW18 4UQ Tel: (020) 8874 4755 Fax: (020) 8874 4624 E-mail: sales@london.lloydworrall.co.uk *Suppliers of architectural ironmongery*

Lloyd Worrall Sheffield Ltd, 10 Fell Road, Sheffield, S9 2AL Tel: 0114-244 3350 Fax: 0114-244 4219 E-mail: sales@sheffield.lloydworrall.co.uk *Suppliers of architectural ironmongery*

Lloydnorthove Ltd, Pulpit House, 1 The Sqaure, Abingdon, Oxfordshire, OX14 5SZ Tel: (01235) 554499 Fax: (01235) 532878 *Marketing design & brand consultancy services*

Lloyds & Co. Ltd, Birds Hill, Letchworth Garden City, Hertfordshire, SG6 1JE Tel: (01462) 683031 Fax: (01462) 481964 E-mail: sales@lloydsandco.com *Professional grass cutting equipment manufrs*

▶ Lloyds Animal Feeds Southern Ltd, Westover Trading Estate, Langport, Somerset, TA10 9RB Tel: (01458) 251170 Fax: (01458) 250073

▶ Lloyds Bedrooms Design, 4 Padstow Road, Coventry, CV4 9XB Tel: (024) 7669 4488 Fax: (024) 7669 5548

Lloyds Blinds, Elim Stores, Llanfachraeth, Holyhead, Gwynedd, LL65 4UP Tel: (0800) 435549 Fax: (01407) 741164 E-mail: sales@lloydsblindsdirect.co.uk *Blind manufrs*

▶ Lloyds British Testing plc, Bedlay View, Tannochside Drive, Uddingston, Glasgow, G71 5PD Tel: (01698) 812811 Fax: (01698) 813811

Lloyds British Testing plc, Wincomblee Road, Walker, Newcastle upon Tyne, NE6 3QQ Tel: 0191-262 9844 Fax: 0191-263 8868 E-mail: sales@lloydsgroup.co.uk *Lifting gear manufacturers & hiring*

Lloyds British Testing P.L.C., Fabian Way, Swansea, SA1 8PU Tel: (01384) 426900 Fax: (01792) 656998 *Rolling stock lifting equipment manufrs*

Lloyds British Testing Co. Ltd, Sneckyeat Road Industrial Estate, Whitehaven, Cumbria, CA28 8PF Tel: (01946) 64146 Fax: (01946) 695757 E-mail: sales.whitehaven@lloydsgroup.co.uk *Lifting equipment hire*

Lloyds Equipment Hire Ltd, 3 Arrol Place, Glasgow, G40 3NY Tel: (01324) 620620 Fax: 0141-554 6531 *Lifting equipment hire*

Lloyds Equipment Hire, Chain Works, Fabian Way, Crymlyn Burrows, Swansea, SA1 8PX Tel: (01792) 644460 Fax: (01792) 470559 *Lifting equipment*

Lloyds Equipment Hire, Chain Works, Fabian Way, Crymlyn Burrows, Swansea, SA1 8PX Tel: (01792) 644460 Fax: (01792) 470559 E-mail: swansea@lloydsbritish.com *Lifting manufrs*

Lloyds Fabrications, Unit 7, Star Trading Estate, Ponthir, Newport, Gwent, NP18 1PQ Tel: (01633) 430378 Fax: (01633) 430378 E-mail: sales@lloydsfabrications.co.uk *Gate railing & automation specialists, security grills & balconies suppliers*

Lloyds International Ltd, Station Road, Reddish, Stockport, Cheshire, SK5 6ND Tel: 0161-219 0909 Fax: 0161-431 5780 E-mail: vicky@thos-storey.co.uk *Baler/baling machine press manufacturers including paper & reconditioned & industrial.*

▶ Lloyds Konecranes, Unit 1e Brighouse Business Village, Brighouse Road, Middlesbrough, Cleveland, TS2 1RT Tel: (01642) 223411 Fax: (01642) 225587

Lloyd's Of London, 1 Lime Street, London, EC3M 7HA Tel: (020) 7327 1000 Fax: (020) 7626 2389 E-mail: alison.burnett@lloyds.com *Insurance market*

Lloyds Mastics Ltd, Lloyds House, 19-21 Kents Hill Road, Benfleet, Essex, SS7 5PN Tel: (01268) 792626 Fax: (01268) 792646 E-mail: info@lloydsmastics.co.uk *Sealant & mastic pointing abesailing concrete repairs*

Lloyds Motor Spares Ltd, 96 Bilton Road, Perivale, Greenford, Middlesex, UB6 7BN Tel: (020) 8902 1188 Fax: (020) 8795 1327 *Motor spares suppliers*

Lloyds Pharmacy Ltd, Sapphire Court, Walsgrave Triangle, Walsgrave, Coventry, CV2 2TX Tel: (024) 7643 2400 Fax: (024) 7643 2301 E-mail: enquiries@lloydspharmacy.com *Pharmacy*

Lloyds Recruitment Ltd, 15 Dane Street, Bishop's Stortford, Hertfordshire, CM23 3BT Tel: (01279) 507310 Fax: (01279) 507310 E-mail: lloyds'recruitment@ntlworld.com *Temporary & permanent staff*

Lloyds Refrigeration & Air Conditioning Ltd, 1 Wylds Road, Bridgwater, Somerset, TA6 4LF Tel: (01278) 422074 Fax: (01278) 429369 E-mail: lloydssales@lloydsrac.co.uk *Maintenance & repairers for air conditioning*

Lloyds Register, Denburn House, Union Terrace, Aberdeen, AB10 1NN Tel: (01224) 267400 Fax: (01224) 267401 E-mail: enquiries@lr.org *Non-destructive test inspection services*

Lloyds Register, 71 Fenchurch Street, London, EC3M 4BS Tel: (020) 7709 9166 Fax: (020) 7488 4796 E-mail: lloydsreg@lr.org *Independent risk assessment agents*

Lloyds T S B, St. William House, Tresillian Terrace, Cardiff, CF10 5BH Tel: (029) 2029 6000 Fax: (0870) 8503105 *Finance house* Also at: Branches throughout the U.K.

Lloyds T S B Development Capital Ltd, 45 Old Bond Street, London, W1S 4QT Tel: (020) 7499 1500 Fax: (020) 7647 2000 E-mail: info@ldc.co.uk *Development capital*

Lloyds TSB Autolease Ltd, Blake House, Hatchford Way, Birmingham, B26 3RZ Tel: (0870) 6006333 Fax: 0121-700 6030 *Company car leasing & contract hire*

Lloys TSB Commercial Finance, 1 Brookhill Way, Banbury, Oxfordshire, OX16 3EL Tel: (01295) 272272 Fax: (01295) 272246 E-mail: sue.baker@ltsbcf.co.uk *Financial advisors*

Lloytron Electronics Ltd, Laltex House, Leigh Commerce Park, Green Fold Way, Leigh, Lancashire, WN7 3XH Tel: (01942) 687000 Fax: (01942) 687070 E-mail: mail@laltex.com *Promotional gifts & electrical good suppliers*

Llumarlite Ltd, Unit 30, Anglo Business Park, Smeaton Close, Aylesbury, Buckinghamshire, HP19 8UP Tel: (01296) 436666 Fax: (01296) 435533 E-mail: info@llumarlite.co.uk *Lighting consultancy*

Llwynon Saddlery, Llwynon, Llywel, Brecon, Powys, LD3 8RG Tel: (01874) 638091 Fax: (01874) 638091 E-mail: enquiries@llwynonsaddlery.co.uk *Saddlery retail & manufrs*

▶ LM Matters, Unit 26 Daniels Industrial Estate, 104 Bath Road, Stroud, Gloucestershire, GL5 3TJ Tel: (0845) 1707700 Fax: (01453) 759950 *Computer training services*

▶ LMC Purchasing Solutions Ltd, 13 Hope Park Gardens, Bathgate, West Lothian, EH48 2QT Tel: (01506) 651276 Fax: (01506) 651276 *Purchasing services within the electronic industry, sourcing & costing*

LMJ Engineering Services, 379 Verity Cresent, Poole, Dorset, BH17 8TS Tel: (01202) 678688 Fax: (01202) 686457 E-mail: enquiries@lmjengineering.co.uk *LMJ supplies Pressure, Temperature, Flow and Level Instrumentation. *Pressure and Vacuum Gauges Standard brass and stainless steel wetted parts, diaphragm, low pressure, capsule and test gauges, electrical contact gauges. *Pressure Switches High and low pressure, stainless steel and hastalloy wetted parts. *Pressure Transducers and Transmitters Ranges from 40mBar to 700Bar, a range of outputs, electrical connections, industrial Din and cable to IP68, submersible process connections flush diaphragm, G1" and G¾", open end ¼G ¼NPT G½ and 7/16 -20 UNF. *Temperature Gauges Ranges; Bi-Metal -60 to + 500 DegC, gas filled -200 to +800 DegC, mounting type direct back, bottom and panel mounted, process connection ½ BSP, liquid expansion type, dimensions from 60mm to 150mm. *Flow Flow switches; paddle, piston plunger type, flow indicators and meters with various outputs. *Level Level switches, float type, level transmitters, ultrasonic, conductivity type, level indicators and controllers*

LMR Recruitment Agency, 58 Leazes Park Road, Newcastle upon Tyne, NE1 4PG Tel: 0191-232 6622 Fax: (0870) 9901839 E-mail: newcastle@lmr.co.uk *Employment & recruitment agency*

▶ Lng3 Ltd, 21 Albert Road, Rochester, Kent, ME1 3DG Tel: (01634) 405740 Fax: (01795) 411511 E-mail: steve.allen@lng3.com *LNG3 is a process analysis and simulation consultancy business specialising in the field of simulation modelling, risk assessment and risk management. **We help people explore their business process opportunities, manage their risks and optimise their performance through the knowledge and insight derived from effective process simulation. **Our analytical and simulation based methods make it possible to prove what can really be achieved. We are convinced that simulation is an excellent way to test ideas and solutions. Our methods enable you to see the effect of today's decisions tomorrow and in years to come.*

LNS Turbo UK Ltd, Waterside Park, Valley Way, Wombwell, Barnsley, South Yorkshire, S73 0BB Tel: (01226) 270033 Fax: (01226) 270044 E-mail: sales@lnsturbouk.com *Bar feed systems importers & distributors*

▶ Lo Call Security, 20 School Lane, Iwade, Sittingbourne, Kent, ME9 8SE Tel: (01795) 554047 E-mail: info@locallsecurity.co.uk *Lo-Call Security are installers of Burglar Alarms,CCTV and Access Control Systems, Based in Sittingbourne Kent.*

Lo Cost Packaging Ltd, 32 Stephenson Street, London, E16 4SA Tel: (020) 7474 3786 Fax: (020) 7474 5786 *Distributors of paper & polythene packaging*

▶ Lo Cost Tyre & Exhaust, Unit 6, Wotton Road, Ashford, Kent, TN23 6LL Tel: (01233) 666636 *Tyres & exhausts*

▶ Lo Cust Drillings Ltd, Hall Place, Penshurst Road, Leigh, Tonbridge, Kent, TN11 8HH Tel: (01732) 832223 Fax: (01732) 834442

Load Monitor (U K) Ltd, The Marchoness Building, Commercial Rd, Bristol, BS1 6TG Tel: 0117-925 2300 Fax: 0117-925 2300 E-mail: sales@loadmonitor.com *Crane/fork lift weighing systems*

Load Moving Systems, Pitts House, Grange Road, Duxford, Cambridge, CB2 4QE Tel: (01223) 839930 Fax: (01223) 839940 E-mail: info@loadmovingsystems.co.uk *Air skate hire & sales*

Loader Fluid Engineering, Unit 4 2 Willis Way, Poole, Dorset, BH15 3SS Tel: (01202) 675220 Fax: (01202) 666890 E-mail: sales@loadereng.co.uk *Fluid handling engineers*

John Loader (Wessex) Ltd, Station Mill, Ashford Road, Fordingbridge, Hampshire, SP6 1BY Tel: (01425) 652394 Fax: (01425) 652625 E-mail: info@wessex-feeds.co.uk *Agricultural merchants & manufrs*

Loades Dynamics Ltd, Abbey Industrial Estate, Bodmin Road, Coventry, CV2 5DB Tel: (024) 7661 6146 Fax: (024) 7662 2211 E-mail: sales@loades.com *Aircraft component manufrs*

▶ Loading Bay Service Ltd, Whiteheads Building, 26a Snow Hill, Wolverhampton, WV2 4AF Tel: (01902) 427472 Fax: (01902) 429374 E-mail: info@loadingbayservice.co.uk

Loading Bay Specialists Ltd, 4 Garnet Close, Watford, WD24 7JX Tel: (01923) 208888 Fax: (01923) 208899E-mail: info@saralbs.co.uk *Sara are established in 5 market sectors within the UK; Sprint High Speed Doors, Loading Bay Equipment, Industrial Doors, Aluminium Ramps and Drawbridge Levellers. Our business philosophy is High Quality, Good Service and a fair price. We are a Total Package supplier, not only in our product range, but also in the area of technical information. We employ more than 0 staff, including fully trained engineers operating from mobile workshops carrying tools, equipment and spare parts.*

▶ Loadlift Ltd, Winchester House, Winchester Road, Frinton-on-Sea, Essex, CO13 9JB Tel: (01255) 671187 Fax: (01255) 672236 E-mail: sales@loadlift.co.uk *Ladder & tower sales*

Loadpoint Ltd, Unit J Chelworth Industrial Estate, Chelworth Road, Cricklade, Swindon, SN6 6HE Tel: (01793) 751160 Fax: (01793) 750155 E-mail: sales@loadpoint.co.uk *Machine tool manufrs*

▶ Loafas Co Op, 12 Herring Market, Lowestoft, Suffolk, NR32 1BY Tel: (01502) 531755 Fax: (01502) 531596

▶ Loafdom Computers, Units 10-11, Stratford Antiques Centre, 60 Ely Street, Stratford-upon-Avon, Warwickshire, CV37 6LN Tel: (01789) 296515

Loake Bros Ltd, Wood Street, Kettering, Northamptonshire, NN16 9SN Tel: (01536) 415411 Fax: (01536) 410190 E-mail: enquiries@loake.co.uk *Men's shoe manufrs* Also at: Findon

▶ Loanhead Electrics, 111 The Loan, Loanhead, Midlothian, EH20 9AH Tel: 0131-440 0447 Fax: (01968) 670541

▶ Loanhead Engineering Ltd, Bankmill, Valleyfield Road, Penicuik, Midlothian, EH26 8LW Tel: (01968) 675577 *Steel fabrication*

Loblite International Ltd, 3rd Avenue, Team Valley Trading Estate, Gateshead, Tyne & Wear, NE11 0QQ Tel: 0191-487 8103 Fax: 0191-482 0270 E-mail: info@loblite.co.uk *Electric accessory manufrs*

Lobro Tools Ltd, Long Street, Premier Business Park, Walsall, WS2 9XP Tel: (01922) 623140 Fax: (01922) 648297 E-mail: sales@lobrotools.com *Press tools designer & manufrs*

▶ Loc, 100 Mildenhall Road, Fordham, Ely, Cambridgeshire, CB7 5NR Tel: (01638) 720653 Fax: (01638) 721376 E-mail: mmusridd@btconnect.com

▶ LOC LIMITED INTERNATIONAL HORSE TRANSPORT, 5 KETTLES COTTAGES, TRIG STREET, BEARE GREEN, DORKING, SURREY, RH5 4QF Tel: 01306 710100 E-mail: LIZ@LOCLTD.COM *NATIONAL AND INTERNATIONAL HORSE TRANSPORT. FLIGHTS ARRANGED WORLD WIDE. 24 HOUR EMERGENCY BREAK DOWN WORK UNDERTAKEN*CONTACT US ANY TIME ON 006 70*

▶ Local Books, 39 Scott Road, Lowton, Warrington, WA3 2HQ Tel: (0870) 7530717 Fax: (01942) 716755 *Book supplier*

Local Building Supplies, 112 Richardshaw Lane, Stanningley, Pudsey, West Yorkshire, LS28 6BN Tel: 0113-255 6921 Fax: 0113-236 0358 E-mail: info@localbuildingsupplies.co.uk *Builders' merchants*

Local Computing Ltd, The Old Bakery, Rosemary Lane, Bampton, Oxfordshire, OX18 2NF Tel: (01993) 851006 Fax: (01993) 851007 *Computer systems & software development*

▶ Local Farmers Markets, 29 Compton Street, Chesterfield, Derbyshire, S40 4TA Tel: 01246 230302

▶ Local Personnel, 26 High Street, Wetherby, Leeds, Leeds, LS22 6LT Tel: 01937 588111 Fax: 01937 588444 E-mail: john@localpersonnel.co.uk *Supply of staff, temp and perms.*Working for Yorkshire*

Local Telecom Service Ltd, The Business Communications Centre, 34 Auster Road, York, YO30 4XA Tel: (01904) 690550 Fax: (01904) 492064 E-mail: sales@lts.co.uk *Install & maintain business telephones*

Local Trading Co., 207 London Road, Sheffield, S2 4LJ Tel: 0114-255 1953 Fax: 0114-255 1953 *DIY upholstery suppliers*

Local Vending Ltd, The Old Vicarage, St Johns Road, Ilkeston, Derbyshire, DE7 5PA Tel: 0115-930 8550 *Vending machine services*

▶ Location Works UK Ltd, 42 Old Compton Street, London, W1D 4TX Tel: (020) 7494 0888 Fax: (020) 7287 2855 E-mail: info@locationworks.com *Location co-ordination services*

▶ Location25, 25 Clapham Common South Side, London, SW4 7AB Tel: (020) 7720 6514 Fax: (020) 7498 0040 E-mail: info@location25.com *One of the UK''s top location library companies based in London and dedicated to finding the best locations for film and photographic shoots. Also provides venues for all sorts of events. **

Loch Carron, Waverley Mill, Huddersfield Street, Galashiels, Selkirkshire, TD1 3AY Tel: (01896) 752091 Fax: (01896) 758833 E-mail: sales@1ochcarron.com *Woollen & cashmere fabric manufrs*

▶ Loch Lomond Distillery Co. Ltd, Lomond Industrial Estate, Alexandria, Dunbartonshire, G83 0TL Tel: (01389) 752781 Fax: (01389) 757977 E-mail: mail@lochlomonddistillery.com *Spirits*

▶ Loch Lomond Leisure, Main Road, Balmaha, Glasgow, G63 0JQ Tel: (01360) 870144 Fax: (01361) 870446 E-mail: info@llwf.co.uk *Self catering luxury lodges on waterside of Loch Lomond. Quiet site in National Park with fishing, bird watching, walking, sailing and restaurant.*

▶ Lochaber Kitchens, Unit 12e, Annat Industrial Estate, Fort William, Inverness-shire, PH33 7HR Tel: (01397) 702710 E-mail: info@lochaberkitchens.co.uk *Lochaber Kitchens Bathrooms & Conservatories is a Fort William based company run by Martin Bergin who has over 20 years of trade experience. We have created our good name by designing and fitting some of the finest Kitchens, Bathrooms, Conservatories and Double Glazing in the Lochaber Area and pride ourselves on the work that is carried out by our team of highly skilled local tradesman.*

▶ Lochavon Ltd, 12-14 Millerston Street, Glasgow, G31 1QE Tel: 0141-550 4422

Lochcarron Weavers, Lochcarron, Strathcarron, Ross-Shire, IV54 8YH Tel: (01520) 722212 Fax: (01520) 722634 *Woollen tartan manufrs*

Lochinvar Ltd, 7 Lombard Way, Banbury, Oxfordshire, OX16 4TJ Tel: (01295) 269981 Fax: (01295) 271640 E-mail: sales@lochinvar.ltd.uk *Heating & water heating equipment suppliers*

Lochinver Fish Selling Co., Culag Square, Lochinver, Lairg, Sutherland, IV27 4LG Tel: (01571) 844228 Fax: (01571) 844344 *Fish merchants*

Lochmaben Coal Co., Crofts Vennel, Queen Street, Lochmaben, Lockerbie, Dumfriesshire, DG11 1PP Tel: (01387) 810466 Fax: (01387) 810497 *Coal & smokeless fuel, haulage contractors*

Alan Richard Lock, Pathfields Industrial Estate, South Molton, Devon, EX36 3LH Tel: (01769) 572220 Fax: (01769) 574777 *Commercial vehicle testers & repairers*

Lock Alarm & Safe Co., 1 Edwin Road, Manchester, M11 3NQ Tel: 0161-273 8835 Fax: 0161-276 0035 E-mail: mike@commsec.co.uk *24 hour locksmiths service*

Lock Assist, 139 Royal George Road, Burgess Hill, West Sussex, RH15 9TD Tel: (01444) 244344 Fax: (01444) 241324 E-mail: info@lockassist.co.uk *Locksmiths & emergency callout*

Lock Bros, Rouses Farm, Calves Lane, Stoke By Nayland, Colchester, CO6 4RR Tel: (01206) 262340 *Agricultural Contractors*

▶ Lock Bros Plant Hire Ltd, Union Yard, Manor Road, Erith, Kent, DA8 2AD Tel: (01322) 350679 Fax: (01322) 351160

Lock Engineering Co Ltd, Western Trading Estate, 22 Trading Estate Road, London, NW10 7LY Tel: (020) 8961 6649 Fax: (020) 8961 1036 E-mail: ss@lockeng.co.uk *Metal pressings*

Lock Inspection Group Ltd, Lock House, Neville Street, Oldham, OL9 6LF Tel: 0161-624 0333 Fax: 0161-624 5181 E-mail: marketing@lockinspection.co.uk Principal Export Areas: Worldwide *Metal detectors, food process pharmaceutical, clothing, weigh systems specialists*

▶ Lock N Store Ltd, Walker Road, Newcastle upon Tyne, NE6 2HL Tel: 0191-224 3411 Fax: 0191-276 6476

▶ Lock Services Ltd, Unit 2e Queensway Enterprise Centre, Queensway, New Milton, Hampshire, BH25 5NN Tel: (01425) 623093 Fax: (01425) 638501 E-mail: sales@lock-services.co.uk *Mechanical & electrical lock design & manufrs*

Lock Studios Ltd, 32 Wates Way, Mitcham, Surrey, CR4 4HR Tel: (020) 8648 2381 Fax: (020) 8646 0542 *Screen process printers*

▶ Lock Way Plastics, Highfield Mills, Heaton Street, Cleckheaton, West Yorkshire, BD19 3TN Tel: (01274) 869439 Fax: (01274) 869428 E-mail: sales@lockway.co.uk *Injection moulders*

▶ Debbie Locke Health & Beauty, Frost Hill, Congresbury, Bristol, BS49 5AD Tel: (01935) 877700 E-mail: salon@debbielocke.co.uk *Quality treatments, electrolysis, skin care, colonic hydrotherapy. Gift vouchers, spa days, pamper packages.Products such as Matis and Jane Iredale.*

Locke Engineering Egham, Unit 19, Eversley Way, Thorpe Industrial Estate, Egham, Surrey, TW20 8RG Tel: (01784) 438120 Fax: (01784) 438120 *Specialist engineering services*

The Locke Group Ltd, Unit 2, Millshaw, Leeds, LS11 8EG Tel: 0113-237 9400 Fax: 0113-237 9419 E-mail: sales@lockeuk.com *Trouser waistband manufrs*

Locker Freight Ltd, Wilson Rd, Huyton, Liverpool, L36 6AN Tel: 0151-480 8922 Fax: 0151-480 3744 E-mail: general@locker-freight.co.uk *Freight forwarders*

Locker Philip Photographic Design Studios Ltd, 132 Bradford Street, Farnworth, Bolton, BL4 9JY Tel: (01204) 707725 Fax: (01204) 792575 E-mail: info@photographicdesign.com *Photography, graphics & print services*

Locker Wire Weavers, Farrell Street, Warrington, WA1 2WW Tel: (01925) 406600 Fax: (01925) 444386 E-mail: sales@lockerwire.co.uk *Woven wire mesh, wire gauze/cloth, screens & filters. Replacement screens for Locker Rotex vibratory screeners, hooked strip screens & bonded mesh screens. Architectural mesh, offshore radiant heat shielding, & synthetic mesh effluent clarifier screens.*

Lockerbie & Wilkinson Engineering Ltd, Alexandra Works, Locarno Road, Tipton, West Midlands, DY4 9SD Tel: 0121-557 1861 Fax: 0121-557 4804 E-mail: locwiltipton@aol.com *Meat plant engineers*

Lockertex, Church Street, Warrington, WA1 2SU Tel: (01925) 642709 Fax: (01925) 630431 E-mail: sales@lockertex.co.uk *Filter bag manufrs*

Lockhart Catering Equipment, 8 Fountain Court, New Leaze, Bradley Stoke, Bristol, BS32 4LA Tel: (01454) 202500 Fax: (01454) 202266 *Catering equipment distributors*

Lockharts Of Canterbury Ltd, Woodside House, Upper Harbledown, Canterbury, Kent, CT2 9AX Tel: (01227) 454990 Fax: (01227) 780940 *Garden shed manufrs*

▶ Lockheed Martin UK INSYS Ltd, Reddings Wood, Bedford, MK45 2HD Tel: (01525) 843883 Fax: (01525) 843446 E-mail: nigel.urquhart@lmco.com *Defense manufrs*

William Lockie & Co. Ltd, 27-28 Drumlanrig Square, Hawick, Roxburghshire, TD9 0AW Tel: (01450) 372645 Fax: (01450) 373846 E-mail: sales@williamlockie.com *Knitwear manufrs*

▶ Locks Express, Norland, Edenmount Road, Grange-over-Sands, Cumbria, LA11 6BN Tel: (0800) 7831104 *24 hour emergency call out service, british standard locks fitted*

Locks & Fittings Ltd, Unit 7-8 Rollingmill Business Park, Rollingmill Street, Walsall, WS2 9EQ Tel: (01922) 623200 Fax: (01922) 721086 E-mail: enquiries@locksandfittings.org.uk *Architectural ironmongers*

▶ Locksmiths, 235 Earls Court Road, London, SW5 9FE Tel: (0800) 6951908 E-mail: john@a-jlocksmiths.com *Locksmith*

▶ Locksmiths I/C Supplies Division, Unit B6, Rudford Industrial Estate, Ford, Arundel, West Sussex, BN18 0BF Tel: (01903) 735321 Fax: (01903) 732777 E-mail: sales@icsupplies.co.uk *Locksmiths*

Lockson Services Ltd, Heath Park Industrial Estate, Freshwater Road, Dagenham, Essex, RM8 1RX Tel: (020) 8597 2889 Fax: (020) 8597 5265 E-mail: enquiries@lockson.co.uk *Shipping & forwarding agents*

Lockstore Ltd, Unit 11 Greetby Place, Eastgillybrans, Skelmersdale, Lancashire, WN8 9UL Tel: (01744) 885757 Fax: (01695) 51413 *Structural steelwork engineers & erectors*

Locktec Ltd, Unit 7-11, Pentlandfield Business Park, Roslin, Midlothian, EH25 9RE Tel: 0131-445 7788 Fax: 0131-445 7527 E-mail: sales@locktec.net *Electronic locker systems & security products manufrs*

Lockwise Lock Smiths, Border Road, Wallsend, Tyne & Wear, NE28 6RX Tel: 0191-263 0003 Fax: 0191-263 0075 E-mail: enquiries@lockwise.co.uk *Locksmith & safe engineers*

▶ The Lockwood Window Company Ltd, 4 Perseverance Mills, Lockwood Scar, Huddersfield, HD4 6BW Tel: (01484) 519677 Fax: (01484) 519676 E-mail: lockwoodwindow@freeuk.com

Locom Engineering Ltd, Units 34-35 Cranswick Industrial Estate, Beverley Road, Cranswick, Driffield, North Humberside, YO25 9PF Tel: (01377) 271474 Fax: (01377) 271535 E-mail: info@locom.co.uk *Animal feed milling engineers*

Locpac Suppliers, 2 Queensway Business Centre, Waterloo Road, Widnes, Cheshire, WA8 0FD Tel: 0151-423 2828 Fax: 0151-495 2630 E-mail: enquiries@locpac.co.uk *Packaging material manufacturers servicing the U.K.*

Locton Ltd, Unit 6a Alfred Court Saxon Business Park, Hanbury Road, Stoke Prior, Bromsgrove, Worcestershire, B60 4AD Tel: (01527) 570977 Fax: (01527) 878990 E-mail: locton@spring-tooling.co.uk *Wire drawing manufrs*

Locum Fine Steels Ltd, Little London Road, Sheffield, S8 0UH Tel: 0114-255 7371 Fax: 0114-250 9114 E-mail: info@locumfinesteels.com *Steel stockholders*

Locwil Ltd, Unit 17 Spring Road Industrial Estate, Lanesfield Drive, Wolverhampton, WV4 6UB Tel: (01902) 404093 Fax: (01902) 497561 E-mail: info@locwil.com *Vending machine manufrs*

Lodent Precision, Colliers Close, Coppice Side Industrial Estate, Brownhills, Walsall, WS8 7EU Tel: (01543) 453700 Fax: (01543) 453800 E-mail: info@lodent.flyer.co.uk *Precision mould toolmakers*

Lodestar Technologies Ltd, The Coach House, Gymnasium Street, Ipswich, IP1 3NX Tel: (01473) 408888 Fax: (01473) 400336 E-mail: sales@lodestar.co.uk *Computer reseller*

Lodge Dental Laboratory, Unit 10 Station Industrial Estate, Oxford Road, Wokingham, Berkshire, RG41 2YQ Tel: 0118-989 0202 Fax: 0118-989 2009

▶ Lodge Engineering Doncaster Ltd, Queens Court, Doncaster, South Yorkshire, DN5 9QH Tel: (01302) 390665 Fax: (01302) 789140

George Lodge & Sons Ltd, P O Box 61, Hull, HU3 2DX Tel: (01482) 329553 Fax: (01482) 223317 E-mail: sales@georgelodge.co.uk *George Lodge & Sons Ltd are authorised distributors for leading manufacturers of bearings, lubricants, chain, oil Seal, pulleys and transmission products. We supply bearings, transmission products, lubricants, torque limiters, couplings, tools and many other products. The company also has ready access through Authorised channels to : Gearbox, motors & clutches.*

Lodge Radio Telephone Systems Ltd, Beccles Road, Raveningham, Norwich, NR14 6NX Tel: (01502) 717929 Fax: (01502) 712937 *Communications equipment*

▶ Lodge Scaffold Ltd, Crows Nest, Ashton Road, Billinge, Wigan, Lancashire, WN5 7XY Tel: (01744) 891717 Fax: (01744) 891718

Lodge Service International Ltd, Imperial Life House, 400 High Road, Wembley, Middlesex, HA9 6UD Tel: (020) 8903 3033 Fax: (020) 8902 6655 E-mail: info@lodgeservice.com *Retail security consultants*

Lodge Service (Midland) Ltd, Scala House, Holloway Circus, Queensway, Birmingham, B1 1EQ Tel: 0121-643 2400 Fax: 0121-643 1807 E-mail: lodgeserv@virgin.net *Security services*

Lodge Sheet Metal Ltd, Commerce Street, Haslingden, Rossendale, Lancashire, BB4 5JT Tel: (01706) 212606 Fax: (01706) 831417 *General fabricators*

Lodge Tyre Co. Ltd, 25-29 Lord Street, Birmingham, B7 4DE Tel: 0121-380 3206 Fax: 0121-359 0046 E-mail: sales@lodgetyre.com *Motor tyre distributors*

The LodgeTaylor's Shopfitters, 280 Birchanger Lane, Birchanger, Bishop's Stortford, Hertfordshire, CM23 5QP Tel: (01279) 817003 *Shop fitters & joinery manufrs*

▶ Lodgico Ltd, Unit 9 Taw Mill Business Park, Howard Avenue, Whiddon Valley Industrial Esta, Barnstaple, Devon, EX32 8QA Tel: (01271) 326343 Fax: (01271) 326425 E-mail: sales@lodgico.co.uk *Design & build log cabins & holiday lodges*

▶ LoewyBe, 147A Grosvenor Road, London, SW1V 3JY Tel: (020) 7798 2100 Fax: (020) 7798 2022 E-mail: enquire@loewybe.com *Marketing company*

▶ Loft Shop Ltd, 37 Westley Road, Birmingham, B27 7UQ Tel: 0121-707 7900 Fax: 0121-707 7933 *Suppliers of loft accessories*

▶ Loft Shop Ltd, 39 Littlehampton Road, Worthing, West Sussex, BN13 1QJ Tel: (01903) 694111 Fax: (01903) 738501 *Loft equipment distributors*

▶ Loft Tec Essex, 10-12 Second Avenue, Halstead, Essex, CO9 2SU Tel: (01787) 273600 E-mail: loft_tec@yahoo.co.uk *Specialists in loft conversions.**We offer a comprehensive service from concept to realization. Use of specialist architects, quantity surveyors and builders gives the most professional package available.**

Lofthouse Of Fleetwood Ltd, Maritime Street, Fleetwood, Lancashire, FY7 7LP Tel: (01253) 872435 Fax: (01253) 778725 E-mail: sales@fishermansfriend.com *Confectionery manufrs*

Lofthus Signs & Engraving Ltd, 5 St. Machar Drive, Aberdeen, AB24 3YJ Tel: (01224) 487377 Fax: (01224) 487580 *Sign makers*

▶ Lofting Services North West Ltd, Unit 7c-7d Arrow Trading Estate, Corporation Road, Audenshaw, Manchester, M34 5LR Tel: 0161-337 9111 Fax: 0161-337 9222 E-mail: sales@cncprecision.co.uk

Loftus Computer Consultancy, First Quarter, Blenheim Road, Epsom, Surrey, KT19 9QN Tel: (01372) 748874 Fax: (01372) 739307 E-mail: info@loftusitns.co.uk *Computer network consultants*

Log Onto Fires.Com, Colston Cross, Colston, Axminster, Devon, EX13 7NF Tel: (01297) 631669 Fax: (01297) 33007 *Stoves, log or wood burning suppliers*

Logan Air Ltd, Kirkwall Airport, Kirkwall Aerodrome, Kirkwall, Orkney, KW15 1TH Tel: (01856) 872420 Fax: (01856) 872420 *Aircraft services*

▶ Logan Construction, 121 Nuxley Road, Belvedere, Kent, DA17 5JX Tel: (01322) 443270 Fax: (01322) 437376

▶ Logan Ingles Ltd, 14 Dunnswood Road, Wardpark South, Cumbernauld, Glasgow, G67 3EN Tel: (01236) 729555 Fax: (01236) 782999 E-mail: sales@loganinglis.com *Supply & fit vehicle mounted equipment*

Logan Teleflex UK Ltd, Sutton Road, Kingston Upon Hull, Hull, HU7 0DR Tel: (01482) 785600 Fax: (01482) 785699 E-mail: marketing@loganteleflex.co.uk *Conveying systems & materials handling equipment manufrs*

▶ Logic Aluminium Systems Ltd, Unit12 Moorbridge Court, Hucknall Lane, Bulwell, Nottingham, NG6 8AJ Tel: 0115-975 0800 Fax: 0115-975 0822 E-mail: info@logicaluminium.co.uk *Aluminium Fabricators*

▶ Logic Business Systems Ltd, Logic House, Allenbrook Road, Rosehill Industrial Estate, Carlisle, CA1 2UT Tel: (01228) 527676 Fax: (01228) 515900 *Computer sales & support for business customers*

The Logic Group Enterprises Ltd, Logic House, Waterfront Business Park, Fleet Road, Fleet, Hampshire, GU51 3SB Tel: (01252) 776755 Fax: (01252) 776738 E-mail: marketing@the-logic-group.com *Communication consultants & services*

▶ Logic Handling Systems Ltd, Hill View House, Littley Green, Chelmsford, CM3 1BU Tel: (01245) 362962 Fax: 01245 362962 E-mail: info@logichandling.co.uk *Suppliers and Distributors of all Types of racking, shelving and storage systems. Annual inspections of installations conducted and recorded. All types of Security safes supplied and inspected.*

Logic Office Group, Vestry Industrial Estate, Vestry Road, Sevenoaks, Kent, TN14 5EL Tel: (01732) 457636 Fax: (01732) 740706 E-mail: contracts.admin@logic-office.co.uk *Office fitting out contractors* Also at: Hounslow

▶ Logic Office Interiors Ltd, 748 London Road, Hounslow, TW3 1PD Tel: (020) 8572 7474 *Office furniture manufrs*

Logic Systems Consultants Ltd, Logic House, Central Street, St. Helens, Merseyside, WA10 1TP Tel: (01744) 455000 Fax: (01744) 453300 E-mail: sales@logicsystems.co.uk *Control systems*

Logica P.L.C., Hamilton House, Church Street, Altrincham, Cheshire, WA14 4DQ Tel: 0161-927 7888 Fax: 0161-927 7889 Principal Export Areas: Worldwide *IT consultants*

Logica Engineering Ltd, 2 Firbank Court, Firbank Way, Leighton Buzzard, Bedfordshire, LU7 4YJ Tel: (01525) 373377 Fax: (01525) 853377 *Machine component specialists*

Logica UK Ltd, Stephenson House, 75 Hampstead Road, London, NW1 2PL Tel: (020) 7637 9111 Fax: (020) 7468 7006 E-mail: webmaster@logicacmg.com *Independent computer systems consultants*

Logical Ltd, Unit 5 Avis Way, Newhaven, East Sussex, BN9 0DS Tel: (01273) 514146 Fax: (01273) 514146 E-mail: enquiries@logical-grp.co.uk *Glass fibre & grp custom mouldings manufrs*

Logical Computers Ltd, 25 Henley Street, Stratford-upon-Avon, Warwickshire, CV37 6QW Tel: (01789) 296200 Fax: (01789) 261250 E-mail: pancho@logical-computers.co.uk *Computer retailers & services*

▶ Logical Innovations, 24 Castle View, Airth, Falkirk, FK2 8GE Tel: (01324) 832333 E-mail: enquiries@logicalinnovations.co.uk *Recruitment software solutions from the award winning TalentTracker range. From a straighforward applicant tracking system to highly customised end to end recruitment solutions, we have the products, people and know how to deliver.*

▶ Logical Minds Ltd, Leigh House, Varley Street, Stanningley, Pudsey, West Yorkshire, LS28 6AN Tel: 0113-236 1199 Fax: 0113-236 1188 E-mail: mail@logicalminds.co.uk *Bespoke software applications*

▶ Logical Resources Ltd, 22 Regent Street, Leeds, LS2 7QA Tel: 0113-212 0000 Fax: (0870) 9906959 E-mail: info@logicalresources.co.uk *Recruitment agents*

Logical Software Ltd, 143 Clitherow Avenue, London, W7 2BU Tel: (020) 8579 7795 Fax: (020) 8579 7795 *Software duplication*

▶ Logicall Results, 5 Beacontree Plaza, Gillette Way, Reading, RG2 0BS Tel: 0118-922 4400 Fax: 0118 922 4401 E-mail: info@logicallresults.co.uk *Logicall Results is one of the UK's leading IT telemarketing Agencies, Generating Qualified Results on behalf of an impressive list of clients ranging from small start ups through to global PLCs.**

Logicol Technical Services Ltd, Units 15-17 Abenbury Way, Wrexham Industrial Estate, Wrexham, LL13 9UZ Tel: (01978) 664482 E-mail: sales@logicol.co.uk *Our services include, IT system support, installation, computer repairs, upgrades and maintenance as well as portable appliance testing, website design, database development and bespoke software applications. Whether you require bespoke or industry standard solutions, Logicol can accommodate.*

▶ Logicomm 2000 Ltd, 174 Watling Street, Bridgtown, Cannock, Staffordshire, WS11 0BD Tel: (0845) 2255816 Fax: (0845) 2255817 E-mail: sales@logicomm-2000.com *Computer supply & support*

Logicscope Realisations Ltd, 64 Great Eastern Street, London, EC2A 3QR Tel: (020) 7880 5950 Fax: (020) 7880 5999 E-mail: info@logicscope.com *Software house*

▶ Logicus Technologies Ltd, 16 The Drive, Wembley, Middlesex, HA9 9EG Tel: (0870) 0637010 Fax: (0870) 0638010 E-mail: sme@logicus-technologies.com *Web Design*Domain Hosting and Registration*Email Marketing*Consultancy*Export*

Logicware Ltd, 16 Northfield Park Avenue, Annan, Dumfriesshire, DG12 5EX Tel: (01461) 204913 Fax: (0870) 7051744 E-mail: info@logic-ware.com *Programming services, scada systems*

▶ Logie Building Services, Unit 4-5 Riverside Court, Mayo Avenue, Dundee, DD2 1XD Tel: (01382) 669669 Fax: (01382) 642111

Logik Copying Systems Ltd, 644 Wimborne Rd, Bournemouth, BH9 2EH Tel: (01202) 518444 Fax: (01202) 516444 *Photocopier equipment suppliers (cannon)*

Logistech Ltd, Exchange House, 494 Midsummer Boulevard, Milton Keynes, MK9 2EA Tel: (01908) 255985 E-mail: info@logistech.co.uk *Management & logistics consultants*

Logis-Tech Associates, 140 Boyd Street, Crosshill, Glasgow, G42 8TP Tel: 0141-423 6911 Fax: (0870) 1276102 E-mail: hugo@logis-tech.co.uk *Learning engineering courses suppliers of industrial equipment*

Logistic Fasteners (UK) Ltd, Unit 2A Odell House, Summerleys Road, Princes Risborough, Buckinghamshire, HP27 9DT Tel: (01844) 275816 Fax: (01844) 342880 E-mail: logfast@aol.com *Fasteners & rivets distributors*

▶ Logistic Packaging Return, The Oaks, Clews Road, Redditch, Worcestershire, B98 7ST Tel: (01527) 523311 Fax: (01527) 517166 *Logistic services*

▶ Logistical Services Limited, 58 Hellesdon Park Road, Drayton High Road, Norwich, NR6 5DR Tel: 01603 484569 Fax: 01603 427100 E-mail: simon.feilden@comment.uk.net *We specialise in mail services contracts, and local collections and deliveries covering Norfolk, Suffolk, and North Essex. If you're looking for local value and local service, you've found it!*

Logistics Business, 17 The Crescent, Bromsgrove, Worcestershire, B60 2DF Tel: (01527) 889060 Fax: (01527) 559192 E-mail: info@logistics.co.uk *Logistics consultancy & software development services*

▶ Logistics International plc, 5 Lion Park Avenue, Chessington, Surrey, KT9 1ST Tel: (020) 8974 1144 Fax: (020) 8974 2999 *IT service solutions*

Logistics Simulation Ltd, The Capstan House, Middlewood Road, Poynton, Stockport, Cheshire, SK12 1SH Tel: (01625) 850919 Fax: (01625) 850377 E-mail: info@logsim.co.uk *Warehouse consultants*

▶ Log-It Systems Ltd, 12 Sycamore Close, Retford, Nottinghamshire, DN22 7JP Tel: (0800) 7834625 Fax: (0800) 3281240 E-mail: sales@logitsystems.com *Health & safety device manufrs*

▶ Logitech Ltd, Erskine Ferry Road, Old Kilpatrick, Glasgow, G60 5EU Tel: (01389) 875444 Fax: (01389) 879042 *Export lapping & polishing machines*

Logitrans UK Ltd, Unit 5 Ascot Industrial Estate, Icknield Way, Letchworth Garden City, Hertfordshire, SG6 1TD Tel: (01462) 678444 Fax: (01462) 678555 *Materials handling equipment manufrs*

Logix Computer Service, 2 Mill Road, Harpley, King's Lynn, Norfolk, PE31 6TT Tel: (01485) 520338 Fax: (01485) 520889 *Computer supplies & service*

▶ Logix Retail Display & Design Consultancy, Unit 15, Arlington Way, Dalton, Huddersfield, HD5 9TF Tel: (01484) 533548 E-mail: logix_gareth@fsmail.net

Logma Systems Design Ltd, 27 Victoria Street, Chorley, Lancashire, PR7 2TX Tel: (01257) 233123 Fax: (01257) today 273215 E-mail: sales@logma.net *Software and hardware solutions for business. Sage Manufacturing/Line 50/Line 100/MMS accredited developer. IT Maintenance and support contracts. Consultancy. Servers, Laptops, Workstations, Thin Client Terminals, networking, wireless, firewall, security, VPN remote access, Terminal Services. Bespoke software development. Based in Northwest, UK.*

Logmasters Fence Suppliers, Mystycroft, Burtons Green, Halstead, Essex, CO9 1RH Tel: (01787) 473450 Fax: (01787) 472299 *Fencing equipment manufrs*

Logo Bugs Plus Ltd, 9 Airfield Way, Christchurch, Dorset, BH23 3PE Tel: (01202) 588500 Fax: (01202) 487177 E-mail: sales@tpd.co.uk *Manufacturers of logo bugs & adman mop heads*

Logo Leisurewear, Unit 22, Caddsdown Industrial Estate, Clovelly Road, Bideford, Devon, EX39 3HN Tel: (01237) 459393 Fax: (01237) 459393 E-mail: sales@logoleisurewear.co.uk *Printed leisurewear suppliers*

Logo Leisurewear, 111 Hubert Road, Birmingham, B29 6ET Tel: 0121-472 5300 Fax: 0121-472 8017 E-mail: peter@rsfarmah.freeserve.co.uk *Badge & emblem makers*

Logo Systems, 8 Greenwich Quay, Clarence Road, London, SE8 3EY Tel: (020) 8469 2222 Fax: (020) 8469 2211 E-mail: service@logosystems.co.uk *Computer consultants*

Logomotif Embroiderers, 2 Eagle Close, Arnold, Nottingham, NG5 7FJ Tel: 0115-920 0777 Fax: 0115-920 0888 E-mail: logomotif@aol.com *Commissioned embroiderers*

Logstrup (UK) Ltd, Units 3H & 4H Lyntown Trading Estate, Lynwell Road, Manchester, M30 9QG Tel: 0161-788 9811 Fax: 0161-789 0063 E-mail: sales@logstrupuk.co.uk *Modular casing system manufrs*

Logsys, Ebor Court, Westgate, Leeds, LS1 4ND Tel: 0113-384 0400 Fax: 0113-245 4798 *IT services*

Logsys, Logsys House, Ashville Way, Wokingham, Berkshire, RG41 2PL Tel: 0118-979 4121 Fax: 0118-977 2506 E-mail: info@logsys.org *Application systems developers security consultancy*

Logtek C N C Cut, 12a Church Road, Formby, Liverpool, L37 8BQ Tel: (01704) 873222 Fax: (01704) 873222 E-mail: deslogan@supanet.com *Cutting tool distributors*

Logue Casings Ltd, Flying Horse Industrial Estate, Brannish Road, Downpatrick, County Down, BT30 6LL Tel: (028) 4461 4700 *Sausage casing manufrs*

Lohan Ceilings Ltd, 120 Ashton Road, Denton, Manchester, M34 3JE Tel: 0161-336 0954 Fax: 0161-337 8727 E-mail: lohanceiling@tiscali.co.uk *Suspended ceilings & partitions*

▶ Lohmacs Ltd, 24 Linton Court, Glenrothes, Fife, KY6 1JF Tel: (01592) 758113

▶ Lohmann Adhesive Tape Systems, Cane End Lane, Bierton, Aylesbury, Buckinghamshire, HP22 5BH Tel: (01296) 337888 Fax: (01296) 337772 E-mail: info@lohmann-tapes.co.uk Sales Contact: Kathy Hutchinson *Double sided & industrial adhesive tapes, stereo plate mounting & print tapes. Also adhesive tape & self-adhesive tape convertors & manufacturers of self-adhesive die cut shapes*

Lohmeier-Comat UK Ltd, 1 Dunston Pl, Dunston Rd, Chesterfield, Derbyshire, S41 8XA Tel: (01246) 264300 Fax: (01246) 264301 E-mail: sales@edlcomat.co.uk *Manufacturers of industrial relays, time switches*

Lojer Products Ltd, 56 The Broadway, Thatcham, Berkshire, RG19 3HP Tel: (01635) 865882 Fax: (01635) 871087 E-mail: sales@lojerproducts.co.uk *Electric motors, fans & heating elements*

Lokfast Special Fasteners Ltd, Audley Street, Mossley, Ashton-under-Lyne, Lancashire, OL5 9NH Tel: (01457) 837514 Fax: (01457) 832213 E-mail: lokfast@aol.com *Bolt & nut distributors & stockists*

Lokring Southern (UK), 5 Owls Gardens, Cottenden Road, Stonegate, Wadhurst, East Sussex, TN5 7DZ Tel: (07802) 871688 Fax: (01580) 200465 E-mail: rlansdowne@lokring.com *Lokring is a mechanical pipe and tube connection that is equivalent to a weld but DOESN'T require HOT-WORK. Each connection is a permanent, metal-to-metal hydraulically formed seal and is completely tamper-proof. The Lokring fittings are quick and easy to install, giving you significant cost saving compared to welded systems.**Lokring connections have become commonplace within Pulp & Paper, Metal Industries, Offshore Production & Refineries, Shipbuilding & Repair, Power, Automotive, Chemical Processing Industries, Medical Gas & Vacuum and Railroad.**Technical approvals/ qualifications include: ANSI/ASME B31.1 & B31.3, Lloyd's Register, American Bureau of Shipping (ABS), NAVSEA, U.S. Coast Guard, Association of American Railroads, API -607 Rev 4 Fire Test, & CARB.**

Loks Plasma Services, Unit 10 11 Walker Road Industrial Park, Blackburn, BB1 1BG Tel: (01254) 689111 Fax: (01254) 689222 E-mail: sales@loksplasma.co.uk *Stainless steel profile cutting services*

Loks Profiling Services Ltd, Westhoughton Industrial Estate, James Street, Westhoughton, Bolton, BL5 3QR Tel: (01942) 816108 Fax: (01942) 814757 *Profiling services* Also at: Wakefield

Loks Profiling Services Ltd, Calder Vale Road, Horbury Junction Industrial Estate, Horbury, Wakefield, West Yorkshire, WF4 5ER Tel: (01924) 271978 Fax: (01924) 280006 E-mail: wakesales@locksprofiling.co.uk *Profile cutting & surface grinding* Also at: Bolton

Lol Summers Joinery Ltd, Barlow Road, Aldermans Green Industrial Estate, Coventry, CV2 2LD Tel: (024) 7661 9644 Fax: (024) 7661 6012 *Joinery manufacturers contractors suppliers*

Lola Cars Ltd, 12 Glebe Road, St Peters Hill, Huntingdon, Cambridgeshire, PE29 7DY Tel: (01480) 456722 Fax: (01480) 482970 E-mail: lola@lolacars.com *Racing car design manufrs*

Lollipop Bouncy Castles, Galley Lane, Great Brickhill, Milton Keynes, MK17 9AA Tel: (0800) 3892088 *Bouncy castle hire*

▶ Lolly's Loft, Sale, Cheshire, M33 Tel: 0161-976 6071 E-mail: lollysloft@btinternet.com *Handcrafted Wedding and Christening Stationery. Traditional and contemporary Invitations, Table Plans, Guest Books and Photo Albums.*

Lomas & Thorpe Ltd, Bentley Avenue, Stakehill, Middleton, Manchester, M24 2RW Tel: 0161-653 9310 Fax: (0161) 655 3648 E-mail: enquiries@lomas-thorpe.co.uk *CAD, Design & Reprographic services*

Lomax Demolition & Timber Yard, Albion Street, Bury, Lancashire, BL8 2AD Tel: 0161-764 5845 *Reclaimed slate & timber merchant*

Lomax Mobility Ltd, Chalmers Building, Charles Bowman Avenue, Claverhouse Industrial Park, Dundee, DD4 9UB Tel: (01382) 503000 Fax: (01382) 503550 E-mail: sales@lomaxmobility.com *Wheel chair manufrs*

Lombard Cleaning Services Ltd, Kemp House, 152-160 City Road, London, EC1V 2NP Tel: (020) 7251 2182 Fax: (020) 7251 2444 *Commercial cleaning*

Lombard Facilities Ltd, 3 Princess Way, Redhill, RH1 1NP Tel: (01737) 774111 Fax: (01737) 760031 *Finance & banking company*

Lombard Shipping & Forwarding Ltd, Lombard Centre, Link Road, Huyton, Liverpool, L36 6AP Tel: 0151-449 3535 Fax: 0151-489 1229 E-mail: sales@1ombardshipping.co.uk *Freight forwarding agents*

Lombards Of Cheshunt Ltd, 25 High Street, Cheshunt, Waltham Cross, Hertfordshire, EN8 0BS Tel: (01992) 623160 Fax: (01992) 622422 *Glass & double glazing manufrs*

Lombardy Consulting Group, 17 Bedford Sq, London, WC1B 3RA Tel: (020) 8343 0101 Fax: (020) 8343 1666 *Management consultants*

Lomond Electrical Ltd, Poplar Road, Glenrothes, Fife, KY7 4AA Tel: (01592) 757176 Fax: (01592) 757210 E-mail: admin@cfelectricalservices.com *Electrical contractors*

Lomond Electronic Services, 8 Silverston Avenue, Bognor Regis, West Sussex, PO21 2RB Tel: (01243) 842520 Fax: (01243) 842520 E-mail: lomondpsu@btclick.com *Power supply units*

▶ Lomond Homes Ltd, Unit 2 Strathenry Mill, Leslie, Glenrothes, Fife, KY6 3HU Tel: (01592) 742030

Lonco Retail Services Ltd, 168-170 Upminster Road, Upminster, Essex, RM14 2RB Tel: (01708) 462000 Fax: (01708) 462002 E-mail: enquiries@lisl.co.uk *Service engineers*

London Aerial Photo Library, Chobham, Woking, Surrey, GU24 8HU Tel: (01276) 855997 Fax: (01276) 855455 E-mail: info@londonaerial.co.uk *Aerial photographers & surveys*

▶ London Apartment Rentals, 17 Queensborough Terr, Bayswater, London, W2 3SS Tel: (020) 7727 2828 Fax: (020) 7229 9816 E-mail: brian@london-apartment-rentals.com *Central London apartment lettings & rentals*

London Bearings (Kent) Ltd, Unit 2, Sabre Court, Gillingham Business Park, Gillingham, Kent, ME8 0RW Tel: (01634) 235335 Fax: (01634) 230268 E-mail: lbk.uk@btinternet.com *Bearings & power transmission distributors*

London Binder Manufacturers Ltd, Units 11-12, Bestwood Road, Brookhill Industrial Estate, Pinxton, Nottingham, NG16 6NT Tel: (01773) 813807 Fax: (01773) 580497 *Manufacturers of loose leaf*

▶ London Black Cab, Faircross Avenue, Romford, RM5 3UB Tel: (07956) 808896 E-mail: alan.smith222@virgin.net *Traditional London black cab service, all airport and seaport transfers, also online booking service and all major credit cards taken, fill free to ask for a quote on your journey.*

London Blind Co., 205a Long Lane, Bexleyheath, Kent, DA7 5AF Tel: (020) 8303 7964 Fax: (020) 8301 3586 *Blind & awning manufrs*

▶ London Bread & Cake Co., Angel Road Works, Advent Way, London, N18 3AH Tel: (020) 8807 6773 Fax: (020) 8803 5229 E-mail: sales@londonbread.com

London Bread & Cake Co., Angel Road Works, Advent Way, London, N18 3AH Tel: (020) 8807 6773 Fax: (020) 8803 5229 E-mail: sales@londonbread.com *Wholesale bakers*

London Burger Co Ltd, Redlands, Lower Street, Great Addington, Kettering, Northamptonshire, NN14 4BL Tel: (01536) 330551 Fax: (01536) 330552 E-mail: info@londonburger.fsnet.co.uk *Burger manufrs*

London Business Equipment, 529 High Road Leytonstone, London, E11 4PB Tel: (020) 8558 0024 Fax: (020) 8556 4865 E-mail: sales@1ondonbusinessequipment.com *Office equipment manufrs*

▶ London Canal Museum, 12-13 New Wharf Road, London, N1 9RT Tel: (020) 7713 0836 Fax: (020) 7689 6679 E-mail: hire@canalmuseum.org.uk *London's accessible venue for business conferences (up to 140), small meetings (up to 12), and corporate hospitality. Only 5 minutes walk from king's Cross station in an attractive setting beside the Regent's Canal.*

The London Car Alarm Co, 14 Pennine Drive, London, NW2 1PB Tel: (020) 8264 7227 E-mail: londoncaralarmco@yohoo.co.uk *Car security services*

London Catering Disposables, 43 Southfields Road, London, SW18 1QW Tel: (020) 8874 7951 Fax: (020) 8877 1806 E-mail: lcd43@btinternet.com *Tableware disposables*

London Central Communications, 81 Southwark Street, London, SE1 0HX Tel: (020) 7401 3122 Fax: (020) 7357 8480 *Telecommunications systems & equipment manufrs*

▶ London Chemicals & Resources Ltd, Studio V, Trinity Buoy Wharf, 64 Orchard Place, London, E14 0JY Tel: (020) 7183 0651 Fax: (020) 7987 7980 E-mail: info@lcrl.net Principal Export Areas: Worldwide *Distributors & suppliers of chemicals & metals*

London & City Carriage Co., 18-20 Laystall Street, London, EC1R 4PG Tel: (020) 7880 4880 Fax: (020) 7250 0851 *Courier & car service*

London Cleaning Supplies, 180-182 Brownhill Road, London, SE6 2DJ Tel: (020) 8697 3444 Fax: (020) 8461 5713 *Industrial cleaning equipment suppliers*

▶ London & Coastal Properties, 37 Bench Manor Crescent, Chalfont St. Peter, Gerrards Cross, Buckinghamshire, SL9 9HL Tel: (01753) 882899 Fax: (01753) 400217 *Residential Property Management and Building Maintenance. A local service for private landlords and residential block management companies.*

London College Of Business & Computing, 206 Cambridge Heath Road, London, E2 9NQ Tel: (020) 8983 4193 Fax: (020) 8983 4286 E-mail: lcbc@compuserve.com *Education*

London Colney Anodising Co. Ltd, Lyon Way, St. Albans, Hertfordshire, AL4 0LB Tel: (01727) 834231 Fax: (01727) 834232 E-mail: sales@lca.uk.com *Anodises, anodising & metal finisher*

London Communications plc, 134 Gloucester Avenue, Regents Park, London, NW1 8JA Tel: (020) 7586 9851 Fax: (020) 7483 6401 E-mail: clive.waylett@londoncomms.com *Radio communications*

London Concrete Ltd, 77 Boston Manor Road, Brentford, Middlesex, TW8 9JQ Tel: (020) 8380 7300 Fax: (020) 8380 7301 E-mail: london.concrete@aggregate.com *Suppliers of readymade concrete*

London Concrete Ltd, Station Yard, Approach Road, Purley, Surrey, CR8 2AL Tel: (020) 8668 2111 Fax: (020) 8668 4532 *Concrete distributors*

London Contracts Interiors Ltd, 88 Gillespie Road, London, N5 1LN Tel: (020) 7354 0077 Fax: (020) 7354 0077 E-mail: londoncontractsinteriors@hotmail.com *Contract blinds & curtains service*

▶ London Cooling, 50 Northbourne Road, Gillingham, Kent, ME8 6QH Tel: (01634) 372345 *Supplying Air Conditioning Services to Offices and Homes*

London Copier Machine, 244 Blackhorse La, London, E17 6AD Tel: 020 89253019 *Photocopier service maintenance*

London Cutlery Co., 6 Plantagenet Road, Barnet, Hertfordshire, EN5 5JQ Tel: (020) 8441 9505 *Grinders & sharpeners*

▶ London Demolition Co. Ltd, 65 Church Street, Chalvey, Slough, SL1 2NN Tel: (01753) 572262

London Displays, Railway Arch 69, Enid Street, London, SE16 3RA Tel: (020) 7500 7699 Fax: (020) 7237 9444 E-mail: sales@london-displays.com *Branding services, corporate logos & websites*

▶ London Domestic Cleaners, 41 Grovebury Court, London, N14 4JR Tel: (020) 8374 3020 E-mail: info@london-domestic-cleaners.co.uk

London Door Co., 153 St Johns Hill, London, SW11 1TQ Tel: (020) 7801 0877 Fax: (020) 7223 7296 E-mail: sales@londordoor.co.uk *Door manufrs*

London Electronics Ltd, Warren Court, Chicksands, Shefford, Bedfordshire, SG17 5QB Tel: (01462) 850967 Fax: (01462) 850968 E-mail: support@london-electronics.com *Manufacturers of digital read out systems*

London Engineering Co. Ltd, 9-13 Valentia Place, London, SW9 8PJ Tel: (020) 7738 7338 Fax: (020) 7924 0331 E-mail: londonendco@aol.com *Steel fabricators & guillotine cutting*

London Essential Maintenance Ltd, 62 Rainham Road, London, NW10 5DJ Tel: (0800) 0191363 Fax: (0870) 7621371 E-mail: sales@londonessential.co.uk *Longstanding Corgi registered commercial plumbing, heating and air conditioning company, We offer servicing, repair and installation, and cover all London areas. *Air conditioning All air conditioning systems are serviced and repaired, from the smallest office split system to large VRF units, so when it all starts to warm up, give us a call to discuss your requirements, however small. All makes are catered for - whatever age. *Heating We are competent in the repair and servicing of all current and old systems - from the smallest combination boiler up to and including large semi industrial boiler units. We also deal with all types and sizes of warm air heating. *Gas All gas works are catered for from small gas leaks up to industrial gas pipes, purging, tightness testing and the like. *Plumbing All plumbing works are undertaken - from small drips to total refits *At all stages we are able to keep clients informed through detailed job reporting. All works are carried out in accordance with industry regulations, and engineers are competent in all works they attend. *Overall we are competitive without sacrificing on quality, and our customer service is second to none. *Call us to discuss your requirements, any time*

▶ London & Essex Interiors Ltd, 30 Sawney Brook, Writtle, Chelmsford, CM1 3JH Tel: (07863) 349830 Fax: (01245) 423074 E-mail: londonandessex@btinternet.com *Partitioning ceiling & carpentry specialists services*

London & Essex Power Washers Ltd, 2 North Drive, Chelmsford, CM2 7EU Tel: (01245) 472227 Fax: (01245) 477498 E-mail: bramigk@aol.com *Repairs, maintenance & sales of pressure washers & cleaning equipment*

London Fan Co. Ltd, 75-81 Stirling Road, London, W3 8DJ Tel: (020) 8992 6923 Fax: (020) 8992 6928 E-mail: sales@londonfan.co.uk *Axial fan manufrs*

The London Fancy Box Company Ltd, Poulton Close, Coombe Valley, Dover, Kent, CT17 0XB Tel: (01304) 242001 Fax: (01304) 240229 E-mail: a.darrall@londonfancybox.co.uk *Packaging designers-manufacturers contract packaging*

London Financial Group, 19 Hillcroft Crescent, Ealing, London, W5 2SG Tel: (020) 8810 8801 Fax: (020) 8663 9087 E-mail: info@londonfinancial.co.uk *Corporate finance*

London Fire & Pump Co. Ltd, 11 Bridle Road, Pinner, Middlesex, HA5 2SL Tel: (020) 8866 6342 Fax: (020) 8866 6342 *Fire Protection*

The London Floor Spring Co., PO Box 6888, London, N1 8EX Tel: (020) 7253 2538 Fax: (01268) 514940 *Floor springs services*

London Fluid Systems Technologies Ltd, Unit 11, Kingley Park, Station Road, Kings Langley, Hertfordshire, WD4 8GW Tel: (01923) 272000 Fax: (01923) 272027 E-mail: info@london.swagelok.com *Valve & tube fittings distributors*

▶ London Foam, Unit 14 38-40 Upper Clapton Road, London, E5 8BQ Tel: (020) 8442 9327 Fax: (020) 8806 6188 E-mail: sales@cutfoam.co.uk *Foam conversions*

▶ The London Gallery, 24 Scott Court, Battersea, London, SW8 3HD Tel: 0207450 4729 *Photo Gallery of London with Prints and Framed Prints for sale*

London General Holdings Ltd, Combined House, 15 Wheatfield Way, Kingston Upon Thames, Surrey, KT1 2PA Tel: (020) 8247 9888 Fax: (020) 8549 5584 *Insurance services*

▶ London Graphic Centre, 16-18 Shelton Street, London, WC2H 9JL Tel: (020) 7759 4500 Fax: (020) 7759 4585 E-mail: matt@londongraphicsystems.co.uk *Photocopying & printing equipment suppliers & services*

London Graphic Centre, 16-18 Shelton Street, London, WC2H 9JL Tel: (020) 7759 4500 Fax: (020) 7759 4585 E-mail: mailorder@londongraphics.co.uk *Graphic art equipment supplies*

▶ London Hermetics P.L.C., Unit 42, Weir Road, Durnsford Industrial Estate, London, SW19 8UG Tel: (020) 8947 0886 Fax: (020) 8947 1007 E-mail: sales@lh-plc.co.uk *Compressed air or gas equipment*

London Hoist Ltd, Rifle Street, London, E14 6PB Tel: (020) 7538 4833 Fax: (020) 7515 3593 E-mail: info@londonhoist.co.uk *Hoist & goods lift manufrs*

London House Signs, 28 High Street, Bluntisham, Huntingdon, Cambridgeshire, PE28 3LD Tel: (01480) 453922 Fax: (01480) 411077 E-mail: john@londonhousesigns.com *Sign contractors*

London Independent Office Cleaning Ltd, 32-38 Scrutton Street, London, EC2A 4RQ Tel: (020) 7377 8487 Fax: (020) 7655 8444 *Office cleaning contractors*

▶ London Intercom, 119-123 Sandycombe Road, Richmond, Surrey, TW9 2EP Tel: 07790 145376 E-mail: londonintercom@yahoo.co.uk *Installation, Service and repairs of Audio and Video Entryphone/Intercom systems. Please call for a free no obligation quotation.*

London Kbe, 562 Lordship Lane, London, N22 5BY Tel: (020) 8889 9709 *Vacuum cleaner repairers & sales*

London Labels Ltd, 20 Oval Road, London, NW1 7DJ Tel: (020) 7267 7105 Fax: (020) 7267 1165 *Label printers*

London & Lancashire Rubber Company Ltd, Unit 15 Decimus Park, Kingstanding Way, Royal Tunbridge Wells, Tunbridge Wells, Kent, TN2 3GP Tel: (01892) 515919 Fax: (01892) 615353 E-mail: sales@londonandlancs.com *DIY manufacturers & wholesalers*

▶ London Law Agency Ltd, 67-69 Southampton Row, London, WC1B 4ET Tel: (020) 7436 5880 Fax: (020) 7583 1531 E-mail: info@londonlaw.co.uk *Company registration agents*Company formation agents*Agents for Service of Process*Company Secretarial Services*Company Searches*

▶ London Leafletters, 23 Castalia Square, Docklands, London, E14 3NG Tel: 0207 261 1257 E-mail: info@londonleafletters.co.uk *Door to door leaflet distribution in london. From £25 per 00.*Minimum order 4000 leaflets per postcode.*

London Life Ltd, Spectrum Building, Bond Street, Bristol, BS1 3AL Tel: 0117-984 7777 Fax: 0117-984 7700 E-mail: sales@amp-online.co.uk *Life assurance & pension schemes* Also at: Branches throughout the U.K.

London Lifting Gear, Buzzard Creek Industrial Estate, River Road, Barking, Essex, IG11 0EL Tel: (020) 8594 8794 Fax: (020) 8594 8795 E-mail: sales@londonliftinggear.co.uk *Manufacture, hire, repair and supply of all forms of lifting, pulling and materials handling equipment from standard chain hoists to custom designed lifting solutions for the railway, power generation, mining, petro-chemical, steel and construction industries. Light Engineering and fabrication.*

The London & Local Manufacturing Co. Ltd, 312B Kingston Road, London, SW20 8LX Tel: (020) 8644 5951 Fax: (020) 8641 4119 E-mail: londonandlocal1@aol.co.uk *Double glazing installers & manufrs*

London Lock & Safe Co., 10 Great Eastern Street, London, EC2A 3NT Tel: (020) 7241 3535 Fax: (020) 7650 8999 E-mail: londonlocksafe7@btconnect.com *Safe suppliers & locksmith services*

▶ London Martial Arts Club, Miles St, London, SW8 1SD Tel: 0207 352 7716 *The London Martial Arts Club offers instruction to men and women of all levels in martial arts.*

London Metal Exchange Ltd, 56 Leadenhall Street, London, EC3A 2DX Tel: (020) 7264 5555 Fax: (020) 7680 0505 E-mail: info@lme.co.uk *Commodity market*

▶ London Millwrights, The Forge, Stonehill Green, Dartford, DA2 7HJ Tel: (01322) 667373 Fax: (01322) 662544 *Maintenance company*

London Money Market Association, 2 Gresham Street, London, EC2V 7QP Tel: (020) 7597 4485 Fax: (020) 7597 4491 E-mail: richard.vardy@investec.co.uk *Association representing interests of members*

London Navaids Ltd, Unit 29 Sheraton Business Centre, 20 Wadsworth Road, Greenford, Middlesex, UB6 7JB Tel: (020) 8997 6599 Fax: (020) 8997 6899 *Non-directional beacon & transmitter exporters*

London Net Solutions UK Ltd, 4 Mead Way, Bromley, BR2 9EU Tel: 0208 4622655 Fax: 0208 4626389 E-mail: info@wsiworldclassnetsolutions.com *a) Business plans, Business Finance*b) Web design, Hosting and Ecommerce solutions*

▶ London News Distribution, 1 Dockley Road Industrial Estate, Dockley Road, London, SE16 3SF Tel: (020) 7231 2065 Fax: (020) 7231 1866

London North Learning & Skills Council, Dumayne House, 1 Fox Lane, London, N13 4AB Tel: (0845) 0194158 Fax: (020) 8882 5931 E-mail: post@nltec.co.uk *Funders of training schemes*

London Offices & Properties Ltd, 35 Piccadilly, London, W1J 0DW Tel: (020) 7734 7282 Fax: (020) 7734 4561 E-mail: offices@35piccadilly.co.uk *Serviced office accommodation*

London Offshore Consultants Ltd, 20 St Dunstans Hill, London, EC3R 8NP Tel: (020) 7283 5544 Fax: (020) 7600 0562 E-mail: loc@londonoffshore.co.uk *Marine & engineering consultants*

London Oil Refining Co., Richardshaw Road, Grangefield Industrial Estate, Stanningley, Pudsey, West Yorkshire, LS28 6QZ Tel: 0113-236 0036 Fax: 0113-236 0038 E-mail: info@astonish.co.uk *Household cleaning products*

London & Overseas Supplies, Unit G, Crackley Way, Peartree Lane, Dudley, West Midlands, DY2 0UW Tel: (01384) 246230 Fax: (01384) 246240 E-mail: landos@wyko.co.uk *Export merchants*

▶ The London Plant Co., Unit 16b Tower Workshops, 58 Riley Road, London, SE1 3DG Tel: (0800) 1691198 Fax: (020) 7394 0333 E-mail: sales@londonplant.co.uk *Tropical office plants suppliers, rental & maintenance*

London Plastercraft Ltd, 314 Wandsworth Bridge Road, London, SW6 2UA Tel: (020) 7736 5146 Fax: (020) 7736 7190 E-mail: info@londonplastercraft.com *Fibrous plaster installers & manufrs*

The London Pottery Company Ltd, 54 Weir Road, London, SW19 8UG Tel: (020) 8944 9738 Fax: (020) 8944 0400 E-mail: info@london-pottery.co.uk *Pottery ware distribs*

London Property Maintenance Cleaning Ltd, 245 Main Road, Sidcup, Kent, DA14 6QS Tel: (020) 8269 8480 Fax: (020) 8269 8481 E-mail: lpm@lpm-cleaning.co.uk *Cleaning contractors*

▶ London Property Management Services Ltd, 2 Hall Place, Sutton Square, London, E9 6EG Tel: (0800) 1078760 Fax: (020) 8533 7756 E-mail: wireless@additional-knowledge.com *Wireless network monitoring, security, site survey, configuration and support for 802.11 voice and data wireless networks.*

▶ London Quilting Co., Unit C 25 Stable Way, London, W10 6QX Tel: (020) 8964 5782 Fax: (020) 8964 5782

The London Safe Deposit Co. Ltd, 20 Regent Street, London, SW1Y 4PH Tel: (020) 7930 8846 Fax: (020) 7976 1250 *Safe deposit hire*

London & Scandinavian Metallurgical Co. Ltd, Fullerton Road, Rotherham, South Yorkshire, S60 1DL Tel: (01709) 828500 Fax: (01709) 833772 E-mail: enquiries@lsm.co.uk *Metallurgical analysts, assayers, metallurgists & samplers*

London Screen Printing, St. Clare Business Park, Holly Road, Hampton, Middlesex, TW12 1PZ Tel: (020) 8941 8285 Fax: (020) 8941 8806 *Screen printing & durable outdoor sign manufrs*

London Screw Co. Ltd, Park Lane, Halesowen, West Midlands, B63 2QY Tel: (01384) 569832 Fax: (01384) 410296 E-mail: sales@londonscrew.com *Screws manufrs*

London Shopfitters Ltd, 6 Blackwater Close, Rainham, Essex, RM13 8UA Tel: (01708) 552225 Fax: (01708) 557567 *Shopfitters*

London Silver Vaults, Chancery House, 53-64 Chancery Lane, London, WC2A 1QT Tel: (020) 7242 3844 Fax: (020) 7405 5648 *Silver & safe deposit facility service providers*

▶ London Stainless Steel Exhaust Centre Ltd, Coopers Place, Combe Lane, Wormley, Godalming, Surrey, GU8 5SZ Tel: (01428) 687722 Fax: (01428) 687790 E-mail: info@quicksilverexhausts.com *Stainless steel exhaust systems manufrs*

London Stone Conservation, 42 Sekforde Street, Clerkenwell, London, EC1R 0HA Tel: (020) 7251 0592 Fax: (020) 7251 0592 E-mail: lsc@londonstoneconservation.co.uk *London Stone Conservation is a small London based company of master craftsmen specialising in the conservation, repair and replacement of carving and masonry on historic and contemporary buildings, the conservation and repair of stone sculptures and the manufacturing of new sculptural commissions in stone*

London Style Ltd, 7 Putney Hill, London, SW15 6BA Tel: (020) 7480 5705 Fax: (020) 7480 5705 *Ladies garments*

London Taxis (International) Plc, Holyhead Road, Coventry, CV5 8JJ Tel: (024) 7657 2000 Fax: (024) 7657 2001 E-mail: exports@lti.co.uk *Pressings contractors*

▶ The London Tiffin Co, Unit Cu533 St Martins Square Middle Mall, Bullring, Birmingham, B5 4BE Tel: 0121-616 2407 Fax: 0121-616 1448 E-mail: bullring@tiffinbite.com *Catering equipment wholesalers*

London Tools Ltd, 1 Gatton Road, London, SW17 0EX Tel: (020) 8672 1086 Fax: (020) 8672 0248 E-mail: londontools@hotmail.com *Protective clothing manufrs*

London Tower Service Ltd, Unit 16 London Industrial Park, Eastbury Road, Beckton, London, E6 6LP Tel: (020) 7511 2090 Fax: (020) 7511 8060 E-mail: hire@londontowerservice.co.uk *Access tower specialists suppliers*

London Transport Ltd, 55 Broadway, London, SW1H 0BD Tel: (020) 7222 5600 Fax: (020) 7918 4093 *Public passenger transport operation*

London Trimmings Wholesale Ltd, 26-28 Cambridge Heath Road, London, E1 5QH Tel: (020) 7790 2233 Fax: (020) 7265 8946 E-mail: ykk@aol.com *Trimmings, buttons & zips distributors*

The London Upholstery Co., 245a Coldharbour Lane, London, SW9 8RR Tel: (0845) 2262178 Fax: (020) 7095 9919 E-mail: info@thelondonupholsterycompany.co.uk *Upholstery company*

London Weekend Television Ltd, The London Television Centre, Upperground, London, SE1 9LT Tel: (020) 7620 1620 Fax: (020) 7928 7825 *Broadcast, production & facilities house*

London Woodturners, 45 Hackney Road, London, E2 7NX Tel: (020) 7739 2296 Fax: (020) 7729 7270 E-mail: lwt@blueyonder.co.uk *Stair case part manufacturers & wood turning services*

Londonderry Chamber Of Commerce, 1 St Columbs Court, Londonderry, BT48 6PT Tel: (028) 7126 2379 Fax: (028) 7128 6789 E-mail: info@londonderrychamber.co.uk *Chamber of commerce*

Londonderry Farriers & Blacksmiths, The Forge, Londonderry, Northallerton, North Yorkshire, DL7 9NE Tel: (01677) 422587 Fax: (01677) 426587 E-mail: sales@forgesupplies.co.uk *Farriers & blacksmiths*

Londonderry Garage Ltd, New Garage, Londonderry, Northallerton, North Yorkshire, DL7 9NB Tel: (01677) 422185 Fax: (01677) 428311 *Municipal vehicle sales*

▶ LondonHandyman, LNP, Hammersmith, London, W6 Tel: (07092) 338064 Fax: (07092) 338064 E-mail: info@londonhandyman.com *London Handyman performs home and commercial property repairs, maintenance and improvements in London. All work carried out is to a very high standard by an experienced tradesman.**Taking pride in our attention to detail, we offer a skilled handyman to take care of those awkward odd jobs, ranging from furniture assembly, hanging pictures, shelving, painting and decorating and general property repairs.*

▶ London-Locksmiths.co.uk, Stanley Road, Woodford, London, E18 Tel: (0800) 0151552 E-mail: safesecure@btinternet.com

▶ Londons Cheapest Locksmith, 9 Hurstfield Crescent, Hayes, Middlesex, UB4 8DN Tel: (0808) 1661066 E-mail: robertwells99@hotmail.co.uk *londons cheapest locksmith, no cll out fee, no vat, all lock problems solved, for your best quote call free 080816666*

▶ London's Flying Chef, 38 Great Suffolk Street, London, SE1 0UE Tel: (020) 7633 0099 Fax: (020) 7633 0999 E-mail: sales@flyingchef.co.uk *London"s Flying Chef offer an efficient, reliable business catering service to over two thousand of London"s companies. London"s Flying Chef are corporate and events caterers in London catering for meetings and events at various venues.**We offer; Corporate catering, Private catering and the opportunity of ordering food on delivery.*

Lones (UK) Ltd, Middlemore Lane West, Aldridge, Walsall, WS9 8BG Tel: (01922) 743833 Fax: (01922) 743760 E-mail: sales@workplace-products.co.uk *Products for the workplace, shelving systems, lockers, distributors*

▶ Long Clawson Dairy, 7 Langar Lane, Harby, Melton Mowbray, Leicestershire, LE14 4BL Tel: (01949) 860405 Fax: (01949) 860259 *Cheese manufrs*

Long Eaton, 76a Derby Road, Long Eaton, Nottingham, NG10 4LB Tel: 0115-972 1111 *Beds bedding & blankets*

▶ The Long Eaton Fan Co., 152, Newthorpe Common, Newthorpe, Nottingham, NG16 2EN Tel: (01773) 768343 Fax: (01773) 771083

▶ Long Eaton Plant Hire Ltd, Crompton Road Industrial Estate, Crompton Road, Ilkeston, Derbyshire, DE7 4BG Tel: 0115-932 7121 Fax: 0115-930 5230

Long Engineering Ltd, Wood Road, Kingswood, Bristol, BS15 8DX Tel: 0117-960 0193 Fax: 0117-935 3203 E-mail: admin@longengineering.co.uk *Engineering services*

George Long Ltd, New Close Works, Easingwold, York, YO61 3DG Tel: (01347) 821657 *Agricultural engineers*

Long Island Products (Fashion) Ltd, Unit 3 Westmoreland House, Cumberland Park, Scrubs Lane, London, NW10 6RE Tel: (020) 8962 8688 Fax: (020) 8960 4481 *Costume jewellery manufrs*

Long & Co Kent Ltd, Bybow Farm, Orchard Way, Dartford, DA2 7ER Tel: (01322) 273028 Fax: (01322) 228818 *Engineering designers*

▶ Long Life Windows Ltd, Derby Road, Burton-on-Trent, Staffordshire, DE14 1RX Tel: (01283) 545287 Fax: (01283) 566898 E-mail: johnmarson@longlifewindows.co.uk *Plastic products manufacturer for double glazing*

Long & Marshall Ltd, 2 Downley Road, Havant, Hampshire, PO9 2NJ Tel: (023) 9248 0141 Fax: (023) 9245 3368 E-mail: sales@longmar.com *Precision machinists*

Long Neck Enterprises Ltd, 4 Leacroft Close, Kenley, Surrey, CR8 5EX Tel: 07092 887252 Fax: 07092 887252 E-mail: kwalexander@longneck.co.uk *Manufacturer or custom designed rubber stamps. For quantities as small as one or large orders.*

▶ Long Neck Stamps, 4 Leacroft Close, Kenley, Surrey, CR8 5EX Tel: 0709 288 7252 Fax: 0709 288 7252 E-mail: kwalexander@longneck.co.uk *Manufacturer of custom designed pre inked rubber stamps. Order online or by phone to 0709 288 7252 or fax 0709 288 7252. Rubber stamps can contain signature, clip art or digital logo. Rubbers stamps can be used for addresses, both business and domestic, company names, return address, etc. Rubber*

continued

▶ indicates data change since last edition

*continuation stamps can promote websites, email id""s, chase payment etc. Rubber stamps can contain your photo, signature, national flag etc. Rubber stamps are available in single colour, choice of blue, black or red.**

Long Reach Irrigation Ltd, Unit 6, Furnham Close, Furnham Road, Chard, Somerset, TA20 1AX Tel: (01460) 261255 Fax: (01460) 261266 E-mail: sales@xlreach.com *Irrigation equipment & dust suppression services*

Long Technology Ltd, 1 Richmond Lane, Huntly, Aberdeenshire, AB54 8FJ Tel: (01466) 794646 Fax: (01466) 794111 E-mail: sales@longtechnology.com *Spring distributors*

Longacres Nursery, London Road, Bagshot, Surrey, GU19 5JB Tel: (01276) 476778 Fax: (01276) 452779 E-mail: landscape@longacres.co.uk *Garden design & landscape*

Longar Industries Ltd, Unit 25 Glenmore Business Park, Colebrook Way, Andover, Hampshire, SP10 3GZ Tel: (01264) 332993 Fax: (01264) 332994 E-mail: enquires@longar.co.uk *Expanded metal products & air filter manufrs*

▶ Longborough Concrete Ltd, The Sitch, Moreton Road, Longborough, Moreton-in-Marsh, Gloucestershire, GL56 0QJ Tel: (01451) 830140 Fax: (01451) 870065

Longbottom & Co Keighley Ltd, Dalton Mills, Dalton Lane, Keighley, West Yorkshire, BD21 4JH Tel: (01535) 604007 Fax: (01535) 609947 *Pipe clip & bracket manufrs*

▶ Longbottom Wright, Mullany Business Park, Deanland Road, Golden Cross, Hailsham, East Sussex, BN27 3RP Tel: (01825) 872900 Fax: (01825) 873399

Longbridge Tool & Gauge Ltd, Unit 74, Heming Road, Washford Industrial Estate, Redditch, Worcestershire, B98 0EA Tel: (01527) 520706 Fax: (01527) 510170 *Precision gauge manufrs*

Longcliffe Quarries Ltd, Longcliffe, Brassington, Matlock, Derbyshire, DE4 4BZ Tel: (01629) 540284 Fax: (01629) 540569 E-mail: sales@longcliffe.co.uk *Lime & limestone producers & suppliers*

Longcroft Engineering Ltd, Rochdale Road Industrial Estate, Walsden, Todmorden, Lancashire, OL14 6UD Tel: (01706) 819955 Fax: (01706) 819966 E-mail: paul@longcroftengineering.co.uk Principal Export Areas: Worldwide *General presswork & spring manufrs*

▶ Longcrofts Transport Services Ltd, Cutlers House, Lumen Road, Royston, Hertfordshire, SG8 7AG Tel: (01763) 247386 Fax: (01763) 249352

▶ Longday Foods Ltd, 98 Pottergate, Norwich, NR2 1EQ Tel: (01603) 612000 Fax: (01603) 664777 E-mail: mike@longday.co.uk *Processed poultry & meat importers*

Longden Engineering, The Farriers, Annscroft, Shrewsbury, SY5 8AN Tel: (01743) 860131 Fax: (01743) 860315 *General engineering services*

Longden & Jones, Wharf Road, Whaley Bridge, High Peak, Derbyshire, SK23 7AD Tel: (01663) 734273 Fax: (01663) 719156 *Joinery company*

Longdon Truck Equipment Ltd, Chapel Street, New Mills, High Peak, Derbyshire, SK22 3JL Tel: (01663) 747101 Fax: (01663) 747561 *Trailer rental & sales*

Longfield Chemicals Ltd, Hawthorne Farm, Tarvin Road, Frodsham, WA6 6UZ Tel: (01928) 739977 Fax: (01928) 739553 E-mail: enquiries@longchem.co.uk *Plastics polymers & additives distributors*

Longfield Coating & Engineering Products Ltd, 21 Humes Avenue, London, W7 2LJ Tel: (020) 8567 1852 Fax: (020) 8579 3399 E-mail: ans@longfield-coating.com *Paper coating equipment manufrs*

Longfield Instruments Ltd, East Portway, Andover, Hampshire, SP10 3LU Tel: (01264) 323949 Fax: (01264) 355353 E-mail: eddy@longfield-instruments.co.uk *Precision engineers*

Longford Bearings Engineering Sales Ltd, Transmission House, 10a Lady Lane, Longford, Coventry, CV6 6AZ Tel: (024) 7636 0666 Fax: (024) 7636 0759 *Bearing & castor distributors*

Longford Gear Cutting Co Ltd, Bayton Road Industrial Estate, Bayton Road, Exhall, Coventry, CV7 9EL Tel: (024) 7636 5777 Fax: (024) 7636 5727 E-mail: sales@longford-gear.co.uk *Gear manufrs*

Longhope Welding Engineers, Church Road, Longhope, Gloucestershire, GL17 0LA Tel: (01452) 830572 Fax: (01452) 830983 *Welding & general steel work*

Longleat Forestry, Picket Post, Warminster, Wiltshire, BA12 7JS Tel: (01985) 213507 Fax: (01985) 847438 *Woodchips, mulch, rustic poles & timber suppliers*

▶ Longlife Exhausts, 7 Denvale Trade Park, Galdames Place, Cardiff, CF24 5PF Tel: (029) 2048 9657 Fax: (029) 2048 6812 *Exhaust system suppliers*

Longpre Furniture Ltd, Station Road, Bruton, Somerset, BA10 0EH Tel: (01749) 813966 Fax: (01749) 813977 E-mail: furniture@longpre.co.uk *Home & office furniture manufrs*

Longridge Teaching Centre, Berry Lane, Longridge, Preston, PR3 3JA Tel: (01772) 786668 Fax: (01772) 784578 *Computer training*

▶ Longrow Builders Ltd, 2D Edna Road, London, SW20 8BT Tel: (020) 8543 1227

Longs Ltd, Hanworth Lane Business Park, Chertsey, Surrey, KT16 9LZ Tel: (01932) 561241 Fax: (01932) 567391 E-mail: sales@longs.co.uk Principal Export Areas: Worldwide *Rubber rollers, coverings, services & processors manufrs*

Longs Packaging Ltd, 5-8 Rutherford Close, Leigh-on-Sea, Essex, SS9 5LQ Tel: (01702) 524342 Fax: (01702) 420257 E-mail: peterwood145@supanet.com *Packaging material goods products manufrs*

▶ Longservice.com Ltd, The Granary, Ryehurst Lane, Binfield, Bracknell, Berkshire, RG42 5QZ Tel: (0870) 7705445 Fax: (0870) 7770536 E-mail: sales@longservice.com *Promotional & incentives specialists*

▶ Longshawe Packaging Ltd, Leekbrook Industrial Estate, Cheadle Road, Leek, Staffordshire, ST13 7AP Tel: (01538) 373683 Fax: (01538) 372265

▶ Longshore Systems Engineering Ltd, Pentire Workshops, High Street, Delabole, Cornwall, PL33 9AH Tel: (01840) 212122 Fax: (01840) 212173 E-mail: info@longshores.co.uk *CNC machining, 3d cad, systems design, development engineering services*

Sam Longson (Buckston) Ltd, Town End Garage, Chapel-En-Le-Frith, High Peak, Derbyshire, SK23 0PF Tel: (01298) 812301 Fax: (01298) 815013 *Road transport, haulage & freight services*

Longton Crane Hire Ltd, Clarence Road, Longton, Stoke-On-Trent, ST3 1AZ Tel: (01782) 310911 Fax: (01782) 599411 *Crane hire & transport*

Longton Light Alloys Ltd, Foxley Lane, Stoke-on-Trent, ST2 7EH Tel: (01782) 536615 Fax: (01782) 533415 E-mail: info@aluminium-castings.com *Casting aluminium, alloy & bronze manufrs*

Longulf Ltd, Prince Albert House, 2 Kingsmill Terrace, London, NW8 6BN Tel: (020) 7722 7733 Fax: (020) 7722 9028 E-mail: info@longulf.com *Overseas purchasing agents*

Longvale Ltd, The Grain Warehouse, Derby Street, Burton-On-Trent, Staffordshire, DE14 2JJ Tel: (01283) 510108 Fax: (01283) 510910 E-mail: rdear@longvale.co.uk *Proximity & explosion proof switches*

Longville, 119 Burcott Road, Bristol, BS11 8AD Tel: 0117-982 7657 Fax: 0117-938 4109 E-mail: bristol@sldpumps.com *Pump & generators, hire & sales*

Longville S L D Ltd, Unit B, Colima Avenue, Sunderland Enter Park, Sunderland, SR5 3XE Tel: 0191-516 5500 Fax: 0191-516 5501 *Pump suppliers, air conditioning, generators*

Longwater Gravel, Longwater Industrial Estate, Dereham Road, New Costessey, Norwich, NR5 0TX Tel: (01603) 743767 Fax: (01603) 747302 *Sand, gravel producers & retailers*

▶ Longwood Engineering Co. Ltd, Silver Street, Huddersfield, HD5 9BS Tel: (01484) 424545 Fax: (01484) 437379 E-mail: email@longwoodengineering.co.uk *Effluent screening equipment manufrs* Also at: Basingstoke

Longwood Joinery Ltd, 656 Thorp Arch Trading Estate, Thorp Arch, Wetherby, West Yorkshire, LS23 7BJ Tel: (01937) 843072 Fax: (01937) 541110 E-mail: sales@longwood-joinery.co.uk *Speciality joinery designers & manufrs* Also at: Harrogate & York

Longworth Ltd, Leltex House, Longley Lane, Manchester, M22 4SY Tel: 0161-945 1333 Fax: 0161-946 0026 E-mail: sales@longworth.co.uk *Industrial glove & clothing manufrs*

A. Longworth & Sons Ltd, 55 Waverley Road, Sale, Cheshire, M33 7AY Tel: 0161-973 8398 Fax: 0161-905 1095 *Heating & ventilation engineers*

▶ Longworth Consulting Worldwide Ltd, 12 Fairbairn Road, Livingston, West Lothian, EH54 6TS Tel: (01506) 414167 Fax: (01506) 414147 E-mail: admin@longworthconsulting.co.uk *Longworth Consulting offer legal advice to the UK building & construction industry. Consultancy services include: contract claim preparation and management, health & safety law, dispute resolution methods, adjudication, arbitration, mediation, conciliation and construction law training.*

▶ Longworth Consulting Worldwide Ltd, 12 Fairbairn Road, Livingston, West Lothian, EH54 6TS Tel: (01506) 414167 Fax: (01506) 414147 E-mail: NickLongworth@compuserve.com *Longworth IT Contracts provide it project contracts dispute and contract law services to companies based in Scotland and the UK.*

Lonmin plc, 4 Grosvenor Place, London, SW1X 7YL Tel: (020) 7201 6000 Fax: (020) 7201 6100 E-mail: contact@lonmin.com *Mining contractors*

Lonsdale Commercial Body Builders Ltd, Unit2, Gulf Works, Off Penarth Road, Cardiff, CF11 8TW Tel: (029) 2034 3077 Fax: (029) 2023 7506 E-mail: lee@lonsdalej.fsnet.co.uk *Commercial vehicle body builders*

Lonsdale Health Products Ltd, Unit 4 Ingleton Industrial Estate, Ingleton, Carnforth, Lancashire, LA6 3NU Tel: (01524) 241007 Fax: (01524) 241971 E-mail: info@lonsdalehealth.com *Health food manufrs*

Lonsdale Metal Industries, Unit 40 Milmead Industrial Centre, Mill Mead Road, London, N17 9QU Tel: (020) 8801 4221 Fax: (020) 8801 1287 E-mail: info@lonsdalemetal.co.uk *Glazing unit & systems fabricators, contractors or manufrs*

Lonsdale Print Solutions Ltd, Denington Road, Denington Industrial Estate, Wellingborough, Northamptonshire, NN8 2RA Tel: (01933) 228855 Fax: (01933) 442405 E-mail: info@lonsdaleps.co.uk *Stationery manufrs*

Lonsdale Revision Guides, Elmsfield Park, Holme, Carnforth, Lancashire, LA6 1RJ Tel: (01539) 565920 Fax: (01539) 564167 E-mail: enquiries@lonsdalesrg.co.uk *Producers of educational guides*

▶ Lontex Design Ltd, 6 The Court Yard, Holding Street, Gillingham, Kent, ME8 7HE Tel: (01634) 300041 Fax: 01634 300041 E-mail: info@lontexdesignltd.co.uk *PAINTING & DECORATING & BUILDING/PROPERTY MAINTENANCE*RESIDENTIAL COMMERCIAL INDUSTRIAL*CITY & GUILDS TRAINED*CITB REGISTERED*FULLY INSURED*COMPREHENSIVE GUARANTEED SERVICE FREE ESTIMATES*TOTAL BUILD-EXTENSIONS-GARAGES-PATIOS-PORCHES*DECORATING-INTERNAL-EXTERNAL *WALLPAPER HANGING-PAINTING-SPRAYING-TEXTURED COATINGS- SPRAYING- WEATHER PROOF COATINGS*WINDOW CARE*TIMBER RESIN REPAIR SPECIALISTS*ALL AREAS COVERED**

continued

Lonton & Gray Sailmakers, 61c High Street, Burnham-on-Crouch, Essex, CM0 8AH Tel: (01621) 786200 Fax: (01621) 786201 E-mail: dicklonton@clara.net *Sail makers*

Lonza Biologics plc, Bath Road, Slough, SL1 4DX Tel: (01753) 777000 Fax: (01753) 777001 *Pharmaceutical production plant & equipment manufrs*

▶ Looby Lou's Miniatures, 3 Brookside, Calcot, Reading, RG31 7PJ Tel: 0118-941 9500 E-mail: karen@loobylousminiatures.co.uk *Online retail of 1/12th scale Dolls House and Shop kits and miniature accessories including Heidi Ott, Wonham, Dolls House Workshop and Blackwells.*

▶ Looe Enterprise Centre, Enterprise House, Higher Market Street, Looe, Cornwall, PL13 1BN Tel: (01503) 265947 Fax: (01503) 265947 E-mail: looe.centre@btconnect.com *Computer & business training services*

Look C, Unit 3c The Waterfront, Goldcrest Way, Newcastle upon Tyne, NE15 8NY Tel: 0191-229 5720 Fax: 0191-229 5730 *CCTV equipment*

Look CCTV Ltd, Aldon Road, Poulton Industrial Estate, Poulton-le-Fylde, Lancashire, FY6 8JL Tel: (01253) 891222 Fax: (01253) 891221 E-mail: enquiries@lookcctv.com *CCTV installation & services*

Look Now Optical, 5 Skinner Street, Gillingham, Kent, ME7 1HD Tel: (01634) 852600 Fax: (01634) 852600 E-mail: sales@easylenses.co.uk *Optical & telephones*

▶ The Look Signs & Graphics Ltd, Unit B, Little Moor Lane, Loughborough, Leicestershire, LE11 1SF Tel: (01509) 232614 Fax: (01509) 232617 E-mail: info@thelook.co.uk *Sign contractors*

Look Systems, 1 The Grouse, 52 High Street, Gargrave, Skipton, North Yorkshire, BD23 3RB Tel: (01756) 749922 Fax: (01756) 749933 E-mail: sales@1ooksystems.co.uk *Computing consultants*

Lookers plc, 776 Chester Road, Stretford, Manchester, M32 0QH Tel: 0161-291 0043 Fax: 0161-864 2363 E-mail: administrator@lookers.co.uk *Holding company*

Looking Glass Design Ltd, 95 High Street, Crowthorne, Berkshire, RG45 7AD Tel: (020) 7384 1322 E-mail: info@lookinglassdesign.com *Design & multimedia*

▶ lookingforaproperty.com, 18 Grosvenor Wharf Road, Isle of Dogs, London, E14 3EF Tel: (020) 7538 1915 Fax: (01322) 226 047 E-mail: info@lookingforaproperty.com *Residential Letting Agents*

▶ Loop Design, 399 Castlereagh Road, Belfast, BT5 6QP Tel: 02890 400200 Fax: 02890 400226 E-mail: info@loopdesign.co.uk *Packaging carton construction design, graphic & multimedia design*

▶ Loopy, 10 Jacob's Yard, Middle Barton, Chipping Norton, Oxfordshire, OX7 7BY Tel: (01869) 347726 Fax: (01869) 347726 E-mail: loopydesign@aol.com *Loopy -Original designer clothing , furnishings and decorative accessories for children, designed and made in England. Vintage inspired handmade dresses and knitwear. Ballet inspired party wear for Special occasion,Perfect for bridesmaids and flower girls. Garden /Party Bunting made from Antique textiles. Introducing a new range of children's chairs.*

▶ Loose Ends Fabrics & Workshop, Unit 8 Priory Place, Hankerton, Malmesbury, Wiltshire, SN16 9JZ Tel: (01666) 575300 Fax: (01666) 575300 E-mail: info@looseendsfabrics.co.uk *Curtain makers & custom made curtains services*

▶ Looseleaf Design, The Coach House, Balkerne Close, Colchester, CO1 1NZ Tel: (01206) 545495 Fax: (01206) 545495 E-mail: paul@looseleafdesign.co.uk *Creative design company. Specialising in creative design for marketing communications services including: brand design, re-branding, corporate identity, identity guidelines and web site design based in Colchester, Essex, East Anglia.*

Loraine Shaw, 602a Liverpool Road, Irlam, Manchester, M44 5AA Tel: 0161-776 2360 Fax: 0161-776 2360 E-mail: info@loraineshawdesign.co.uk *Soft furnishings manufrs*

Alan Lord (Industrial Tools) Ltd, Unit 21 Bordesley Trading Estate, Bordesley Green Road, Birmingham, B8 1BZ Tel: 0121-328 6033 Fax: 0121-328 1842 *Power tool repairs, sales & distributors*

Lord Communications Ltd, 2 Thelby Cl, Luton, LU3 2UF Tel: 01582 494600 Fax: 01582-583383 *Communications phone lines*

Lord Corporation Ltd, Stretford Motorway Estate, Barton Dock Road, Stretford, Manchester, M32 0ZH Tel: 0161-865 8048 Fax: 0161-865 0096 Principal Export Areas: Africa *Chemical, mechanical, adhesives & mechanical parts distributors*

The Lord Group Ltd, Oak Mill Mellor Street, Rochdale, Lancashire, OL12 6UY Tel: (01706) 341311 Fax: (01706) 861810 E-mail: info@thelordgroup.co.uk *Building refurbishment & painting services* Also at: Leeds, Widnes & Wigan

Lord Hire Centre, Shields Road, Newcastle upon Tyne, NE6 2UD Tel: 0191-224 0044 E-mail: lord@lordhire.co.uk *Tool hire company*

Lord & Midgley, Harrow Street, Hull, HU3 4LB Tel: (01482) 320324 Fax: (01482) 328211 *Non-ferrous scrap metal merchants*

Lord & Midgley, Reservoir Road, Hull, HU6 7QH Tel: (01482) 342394 Fax: (01482) 441301 *Scrap iron & steel merchants*

▶ Lordan (UK) Ltd, Unit 1 North Road, Penallta Industrial Estate, Hengoed, Mid Glamorgan, CF82 7QZ Tel: (01443) 812222 Fax: (01443) 812312 E-mail: rob@lordan-uk.com *Heat exchanger coils manufrs*

▶ Lords College Ltd, 53 Manchester Road, Bolton, BL2 1ES Tel: (01204) 523731 Fax: (0870) 4299706 E-mail: principal@lordscollege.co.uk *Privet education for 11 to 16 year old children*

▶ Lordswood Litho Ltd, Unit 10, Lordswood Industrial Estate, Revenge Road, Chatham, Kent, ME5 8UD Tel: (01634) 660611

L'Oreal Luxury Products Ltd, 255 Hammersmith Road, London, W6 8AZ Tel: (020) 8762 4000 Fax: (020) 8762 4001 E-mail: sales@1orea1.com *Cosmetic manufrs*

▶ Lorena Massoni Mico, 4 Croydon Road, Caterham, Surrey, CR3 6QD Tel: (01883) 349205 E-mail: lorena@buylabels4less.com *Provides Spanish and English tuition for Business Executives and individuals in the London area. Six week intensive courses are available. One on one tuition also available as well as small classes to suit client.*

▶ Lorica Ltd, 12c Main Road, Radcliffe-on-Trent, Nottingham, NG12 2FH Tel: 0115-933 6304 Fax: (0871) 9902184 E-mail: info@loricasystems.com *Internet security, support & installation services*

▶ Lorica Ltd, 12c Main Road, Radcliffe-on-Trent, Nottingham, NG12 2FH Tel: 0115-933 6304 Fax: (0871) 9902184 E-mail: info@loricasystems.com *IT security services*

Lorien Group plc, Leadenhall Street, London, EC3A 4AF Tel: (020) 7654 1000 Fax: (020) 7654 1010 E-mail: asqfor@lorien.co.uk *I.T. management & consultants* Also at: Glasgow, Leeds, London, Sale & Solihull

Lorient Holdings Ltd, Fairfax Road, Heathfield Industrial Estate, Newton Abbot, Devon, TQ12 6UD Tel: (01626) 834252 Fax: (01626) 833166 E-mail: admin@lorient.co.uk *Fire protection manufrs*

Lorlec Ltd, Horninglow Road North, Burton-on-Trent, Staffordshire, DE13 0SF Tel: (01283) 531191 Fax: (01283) 538113 E-mail: sales@lorlec.com *Premium quality surface finishers to the trade electroplating services*

Lorlin Electronics, Enterprise Unit A-C, Harwood Road, Littlehampton, West Sussex, BN17 7AT Tel: (01903) 725121 Fax: (01903) 723919 E-mail: lorlin@btconnect.com *Manufacturers electro-mechanical switches*

Lormay Ltd, Lormay House, Main Street, Westbury, Brackley, Northamptonshire, NN13 5JR Tel: (01280) 700570 Fax: (01280) 705201 *Printed circuit manufrs*

▶ Lorne Stewart P.L.C., PO Box 7, Dumfries, DG2 8NE Tel: (01387) 254251

Lorne Stewart plc, Phillips House, Sandgate Industrial Estate, Hartlepool, Cleveland, TS25 1UB Tel: (01429) 268116 Fax: (01429) 860244 E-mail: hartlepool@lornestewart.co.uk *Mechanical electrical building services engineers*

Lorne Stewart plc, Barley House, Duncan Road, Park Gate, Southampton, SO31 1ZT Tel: (01489) 885444 Fax: (01489) 885606 E-mail: soton@lornestewart.co.uk *Building services engineers* Also at: Branches throughout the U.K.

Lorraine Electronics Surveillance, 716 Lea Bridge Road, London, E10 6AW Tel: (020) 8558 4226 Fax: (020) 8558 1338 E-mail: info@lorraine.co.uk *Audio & video surveillance product suppliers*

Lorraines Curtains Ltd, 15 Acacia Business Centre, Howard Road, London, E11 3PJ Tel: (020) 8558 5599 Fax: (020) 8558 5599 *Curtain & blind manufrs*

Lo's Noodle Co. Ltd, 6 Dansey Place, London, W1D 6EZ Tel: (020) 7734 3885 *Food product manufrs*

Losberger Walter UK, 27 High Street, Collingham, Collingham, Newark, Nottinghamshire, NG23 7LA Tel: (01636) 893776 Fax: (01636) 893774 E-mail: losbergeruk@losberger.com *Warehouse fabricators, structural; temporary warehouse*

Lossie Seafoods Ltd, 2 March Road Industrial Estate, Buckie, Banffshire, AB56 4BY Tel: (01542) 831000 Fax: (01542) 833300 E-mail: tracy@lossieseafoods.demon.co.uk *Fish processors*

▶ The Lost Connection, 13 Gordon Crescent, Brierley Hill, West Midlands, DY5 1HS Tel: (01384) 347597 *Computer maintenance & repair services*

▶ Lost It Productions Ltd, Crossland Court, Czar Street, Leeds, LS11 9PR Tel: 0113-245 7773 Fax: 0113-245 7773 *Hire services*

Lost Wax Castings Ltd, 23 Tithe Cl, Codicote, Hitchin, Herts, SG4 8UX Tel: (01438) 820822 Fax: (01438) 820822 E-mail: sjm3753735@gsk.com *Castings (stainless steel), castings(steel), castings (investment/lost wax process). Also steel fabricators & services*

Lost Wax Development, Firs Industrial Estate Ricketts Close, Off Oldington Lane, Kidderminster, Worcestershire, DY11 7QN Tel: (01562) 822100 Fax: (01299) 877352 E-mail: sales@lwd.co.uk *Investment castings in all metals*

Lostock Tackle Box, 16 Watkin Lane, Lostock Hall, Preston, PR5 5RD Tel: (01772) 626585 Fax: (01772) 626585 *Fishing tackle distribution*

▶ Lostyourpet.net, Atterton Road, Haverhill, Suffolk, CB9 7SR Tel: (07813) 888442 E-mail: jason@pitcher.freeserve.co.uk *National lost & found pet register*

Lothbury Software Ltd, Suite 1 Warnford Court, 29 Throgmorton Street, London, EC2N 2AT Tel: (020) 7256 8734 Fax: (020) 7256 9026 *Software consultants*

Lothian Alarms, Cooper Business Park, Buchan Lane, Broxburn, West Lothian, EH52 5QD Tel: (01506) 855978 Fax: (01506) 855666 *Security*

Lothian Communications Ltd, Unit 3 15 Marine Crescent, Glasgow, G51 1HD Tel: 0141-429 2929 Fax: 0141-429 6789 E-mail: mail@mxpower.co.uk *Radio communication equipment hire*

▶ Lothian Electric Machines Ltd, Hospital Road, Haddington, East Lothian, EH41 3PD Tel: (01620) 828700 Fax: (01620) 828730 *Engineering*

Lothian Engineering Co Whitburn Ltd, 1 Burnhouse Industrial Estate, Whitburn, Bathgate, West Lothian, EH47 0LQ Tel: (01501) 740624 Fax: (01501) 741831 E-mail: lothian.eng@btinternet.com *Machining & steel fabricators & general engineering*

Lothian Harvesters Ltd, 2c Hospital Road, Haddington, East Lothian, EH41 3BH Tel: (01620) 825738 Fax: (01620) 824224 *Agricultural dealership*

▶ Lothian Heating Services Ltd, Edgefield Road Industrial Estate, Edgefield Road, Loanhead, Midlothian, EH20 9TB Tel: 0131-440 2958 Fax: 0131-440 4244

Lothian Mechanical Handling Ltd, 8 Mosshall Industrial Estate, Blackburn, Bathgate, West Lothian, EH47 7LY Tel: (01506) 655535 Fax: (01506) 634799 E-mail: lmh@lothianmechanicalhandling.co.uk *Fork lift truck specialists*

▶ Lothian Print, 7 New Lairdship Yards, Edinburgh, EH11 3UY Tel: 0131-444 2344

Lothian Printers, 109 High Street, Dunbar, East Lothian, EH42 1ES Tel: (01368) 863785 Fax: (01368) 864908 E-mail: lothian.printers@virgin.net *Printers & stationers*

Lothian Projects 2000 Ltd, Methilhaven Road, Methil, Leven, Fife, KY8 3LA Tel: (01333) 429134 Fax: (01333) 423582 E-mail: info@stegroup.com *Design engineers*

Lothian Steel Services Ltd, Whitburn Road, Bathgate, West Lothian, EH48 2HR Tel: (01506) 633500 Fax: (01506) 633648 E-mail: sales@lothiansteels.co.uk *Steel stockholders*

▶ Lotus Ltd, Gambrel Road, Westgate Industrial Estate, Northampton, NN5 5BB Tel: (01604) 755211 Fax: (01604) 759061

▶ Lotus Cars Ltd, Potash Lane, Hethel, Norwich, NR14 8EZ Tel: (01953) 608000 Fax: (01953) 608300 E-mail: engineering@lotuscars.co.uk *Consulting specialist in vehicle systems & vehicle engineering services*

Lotus Fashions, Matlock Road, Coventry, CV1 4JR Tel: (024) 7668 0091 Fax: (024) 7663 7084 E-mail: sales@lotusfashions.com *Ladies wear manufrs*

Lotus Jewellery, Alexandra House, Chartwell Drive, Wigston, Leicestershire, LE18 2EZ Tel: (0870) 8508200 Fax: (0870) 8508201 E-mail: apollo.sales@timeproducts.co.uk *Cultured pearl importers*

▶ Lotus Sales & Marketing Ltd, 35 Windsor Avenue, Sutton, Surrey, SM3 9RR Tel: (020) 8644 2717 Fax: (020) 8641 3082 *Importers & distributors of nutritional supplements*

Lotus Water Garden Products Ltd, Stewart House, Purley Way, Croydon, CR9 4HS Tel: (020) 8686 2231 Fax: (020) 8688 3857 *Injection moulders*

Loubec Sheet Metal Ltd, Throstle Nest Mill, Leeds Road, Nelson, Lancashire, BB9 9XG Tel: (01282) 604737 Fax: (01282) 611897 *General sheet metalwork engineers & fabricators*

▶ Loud & Clear Graphics Ltd, 14 Langport Close, Fulwood, Preston, PR2 9FE Tel: (01772) 461457 Fax: (07092) 003982 *Sign manufacturers & advertising displays*

Loud Mastering Audio Post Production, Whitehall, Taunton, Somerset, TA1 1PG Tel: (01823) 353123 Fax: (01823) 353055 E-mail: info@loudmastering.com *Sound mastering producers*

▶ Loudmouth Postcards, 5 Hendon Street, Sheffield, S13 9AX Tel: (0845) 2309805 Fax: 0114-288 0044 E-mail: chet@loudworld.co.uk *Printers of postcards, business cards, leaflets, catalogues & brochures*

▶ Loud-N-Clear Com Ltd, 29 Castle Crescent, Reading, RG1 6AQ Tel: 0118-967 7693 Fax: 0118-954 2756 E-mail: enquiries@loud-n-clear.com *Website implementation & hosting*

Loughboro Designs Ltd, Sandy Lane North, Wallington, Surrey, SM6 8JX Tel: (020) 8640 4343 Fax: (020) 8647 2855 E-mail: sales@loughboro-designs.co.uk *Architectural metalworkers*

▶ Loughborough Sheet Metal Specialists, 2 Royal Way, Loughborough, Leicestershire, LE11 5XR Tel: (01509) 233874 Fax: (01509) 241277 E-mail: sales@lborosheetmetal.co.uk *Fabrication & sheet metal manufrs*

B. & R. Loughlin, 19 Meadowcourt Road, Oadby, Leicester, LE2 2PD Tel: 0116-271 2373 Fax: 0116-272 0239 *Energy saver heat insulation*

Loughlin Engineering, 10a Woodham Lane, New Haw, Addlestone, Surrey, KT15 3NA Tel: (01932) 855250 Fax: (01932) 859623 *Engineering subcontracting services*

Louis Dreyfus Investment Co. Ltd, Queensbury House, 3 Old Burlington Street, London, W1S 3LD Tel: (020) 7596 1000 Fax: (020) 7529 9000 E-mail: ldbeijing@louisdreyfus.com *Commodity traders*

Louise Products Antrim Ltd, 18 Ballycraigy Road, Antrim, BT41 1PW Tel: (028) 9446 4088 Fax: (028) 9442 8276 *Protective clothing manufrs*

Louise's Balloon Co, Willow Lodge, Weston Colville Rd, Brinkley, Newmarket, Suffolk, CB8 0SG Tel: 01638 508217 Fax: 01638 508217 *Party decorator*

▶ Loum Bookkeeping Services, Flat 2, 20 - 21 Richmond Place, Brighton, BN2 9NA Tel: 01273 570453 E-mail: salina.loum@ntlworld.com *We offer the following services: accounts, payroll, VAT and advice*

▶ Loungearound, 33 Station Road, New Milton, Hampshire, BH25 6HR Tel: (01425) 639212 Fax: (01425) 639213 E-mail: sales@loungearound.co.uk *Supply quality furniture, beds, mattresses, settees, suites, divans , contract furniture*

▶ Loungearound Furniture, 40-42 Ashley Road, Bournemouth, BH1 4LJ Tel: (01202) 720777 Fax: (01202) 720888 E-mail: Sales@loungearound.co.uk *Supplier of quality furniture*

▶ Lounsdale Electric Ltd, Glasgow Road, Renfrew, PA4 8XZ Tel: 0141-885 4466 E-mail: enquiry@lounsdale.com

Louth Transformer Co. Ltd, Belvoir Way, Fairfield Industrial Estate, Louth, Lincolnshire, LN11 0LQ Tel: (01507) 606436 Fax: (01507) 600168 E-mail: info@louthtransformers.co.uk *Transformer manufacturers made to specification*

Louver-Lite Ltd, Ashton Road, Hyde, Cheshire, SK14 4BG Tel: 0161-882 5000 Fax: 0161-882 5009 E-mail: enquiries@louver-liteltd.co.uk *Blind production cloth & fabric accessories*

Lovair, The Old Stables, Brook Street, Macclesfield, Cheshire, SK11 7AA Tel: (0845) 1302907 Fax: (0845) 1302908 E-mail: sales@lovair.co.uk *Stainless steel washroom accessories*

▶ M. Lovatt Electrical, 6 The Crescent, Mitcheldean, Gloucestershire, GL17 0SB Tel: (01594) 543907 E-mail: martin@mlovatt.co.uk *Industrial and Domestic Electrician. Registered for part p of building regs*

▶ Love The Planet, 124 Crown Street, Aberdeen, AB11 6HQ Tel: (01224) 594411 Fax: (01224) 594411 E-mail: sales@1ovetheplanet.co.uk *Cosmetics manufacturers & distributors*

▶ Loveday & Loveday Removal Co., 2 Wilkinson Road, Love Lane Industrial Estate, Cirencester, Gloucestershire, GL7 1YT Tel: (01285) 651505 Fax: (01285) 640363

Loveden Computer Services Ltd, Lovedon Beck, Casthorpe Road, Denton, Grantham, Lincolnshire, NG32 1JT Tel: (01476) 870000 E-mail: info@loveden.co.uk *Computer services*

▶ Lovell Ltd, Churchwood House, 116 Cockfosters Road, Barnet, Hertfordshire, EN4 0DR Tel: (020) 8370 6300 Fax: (020) 8370 6330

D. & P. Lovell Quarries Ltd, Downs Quarry, Kingston Road, Langton Matravers, Swanage, Dorset, BH19 3JP Tel: (01929) 439255 Fax: (01929) 439324 *Stone merchants & producers*

Lovell Johns Ltd, 10 Hanborough Business Park, Lodge Road, Long Hanborough, Witney, Oxfordshire, OX29 8RU Tel: (01993) 883161 Fax: (01993) 883096 E-mail: enquiries@lovelljohns.com *Maps & related services*

▶ Lovell Partnerships, Bell Heath Way, Birmingham, B32 3BZ Tel: 0121-421 8300 Fax: 0121-421 8210 E-mail: enquiries@lovellpartnerships.co.uk

Lovell Partnerships Ltd, Marston Park, Tamworth, Staffordshire, B78 3HN Tel: (01827) 305600 Fax: (01827) 305601 E-mail: enquiries@lovell.co.uk *Builders & developers*

Lovell Sport Ltd, Unit 3 Alvis Court, Billingham, Cleveland, TS23 4JG Tel: (01642) 566444 Fax: (01642) 651022 *Cycle clothing manufrs*

Lovells Solicitors, Atlantic House, 50 Holborn Viaduct, London, EC1A 2FG Tel: (020) 7296 2000 Fax: (020) 7296 2001 E-mail: information@lovells.com *Solicitors*

J.M. Loveridge Ltd, Southbrook Road, Southampton, SO15 1BH Tel: (023) 8022 2008 Fax: (023) 8063 9836 E-mail: admin@jmloveridge.com *Chemist manufrs*

J.M. Loveridge P.L.C., Higher Merley Lane, Corfe Mullen, Wimborne, Dorset, BH21 3EQ Tel: (01202) 882306 Fax: (01202) 880059 *Pharmaceutical wholesaler*

▶ Loveshaw Europe, 9 Brunel Gate, Andover, Hampshire, SP10 3SL Tel: (01264) 357511 Fax: (01264) 355964 E-mail: sales@loveshaw-europe.co.uk *Distributors of packaging equipment*

Lovewell Blake, Wrenrock House, The Street, Felthorpe, Norwich, NR10 4AB Tel: (01603) 755389 Fax: (01760) 725070 *Air filter distributors & manufrs*

Lovibond Water Testing, Waterloo Road, Salisbury, SP1 2JY Tel: (01722) 327242 Fax: (01722) 412322 E-mail: sales@tintometer.com *Water/colour testing products manufrs*

▶ Lovie Ltd, Blackhill Quarry, Tyrie, Fraserburgh, Aberdeenshire, AB43 7DR Tel: (01346) 541212 Fax: (01346) 541424 *Quarry & concrete products suppliers*

Lovie Ltd, Cowbog, New Pitsligo, Fraserburgh, Aberdeenshire, AB43 6PR Tel: (01771) 653777 Fax: (01771) 653527 E-mail: sales@lovie.co.uk *Quarry & concrete product manufrs*

▶ Low Cost Airport Transfers, 36 Walters Road, Ogmore Vale, Bridgend, Mid Glamorgan, CF32 7DN Tel: (01656) 841353 E-mail: info@low-cost-airport-transfers.co.uk *Chauffuer driven executive cars available for airport tranfers to all UK airports*

▶ Low Cost Beds, The Barn, Aldern House, Horsted Lane, Sharpthorne, East Grinstead, West Sussex, RH19 4HX Tel: (08700) 270107

Low Cost Communications, 4 Hillcrest Avenue, Leigh, Lancashire, WN7 5HH Tel: (01942) 603812 Fax: (01942) 603812 *Telecommunication installation service*

Low Cost Signs, 250 Upminster Road North, Rainham, Essex, RM13 9JL Tel: (01708) 500123 Fax: (01708) 500900 *Sign making*

▶ Low Fell Removals, Ropery Works, Sunderland, SR6 0DN Tel: 0191-514 0282 Fax: 0191-565 6769

Low Power Radio Solutions Ltd, Two Rivers Industrial Estate, Station Lane, Witney, Oxfordshire, OX28 4BH Tel: (01993) 709418 Fax: (01993) 705415 E-mail: sales@lprs.co.uk *Low power radio module distributors & manufrs*

Low Quote Limited, 2a Alton House Office Park, Gatehouse Way, Gatehouse Industrial Area, Aylesbury, Bucks, HP19 8YF Tel: (07834) 542976 E-mail: admin@low-quote.net *Committed to helping you find competitive insurance cover*

Low Temp Refrigeration, Unit 13 Robert Davies Court, Nuffield Road, Cambridge, CB4 1TP Tel: (01223) 426067 Fax: (01223) 426067 *Refrigeration designers & retailers service*

Lowara UK Ltd, Weycroft Avenue Millwey Rise Indust Estate, Axminster, Devon, EX13 5HL Tel: (01297) 630200 Fax: (01297) 630270 E-mail: lowara@itt.com *Pump manufrs*

▶ Lowcost IT, Suites 1-2, Caxton House, 243 South Coast Road, Peacehaven, East Sussex, BN10 8NN Tel: (01273) 589222 E-mail: info@lowcost-it.com *Computer consultants*

Lowden Metals Ltd, 7 Harvey Works Industrial Estate, Shelah Road, Halesowen, West Midlands, B63 3PG Tel: 0121-501 3596 Fax: 0121-585 5162 E-mail: enquiries@metals26.freeserve.co.uk *Low melting alloy stockholders*

Lowdens, 42 Duncrue Crescent, Belfast, BT3 9BW Tel: (028) 9037 0357 Fax: (028) 9037 1207 *Builders merchants*

Lowe Aston Partnership, Moorlands Lane, Saltash, Cornwall, PL12 4HL Tel: (01752) 842233 Fax: (01752) 848060 E-mail: info@loweaston.co.uk *Manufacturers of promotional paper*

Chas Lowe & Sons (Builders' Merchants) Ltd, 156 London Road, Knebworth, Hertfordshire, SG3 6HA Tel: (01438) 812740 Fax: (01438) 814324 E-mail: peter@chaslowe.co.uk *Builders & timber merchants service*

Edwin Lowe Ltd, Perry Bridge Works, Aldridge Road, Perry Barr, Birmingham, B42 2HB Tel: 0121-356 5255 Fax: 0121-344 3172 E-mail: sales@edwinlowe.com *Conveyor component specialists*

Lowe Electronics Ltd, Bentley Bridge, Chesterfield Road, Matlock, Derbyshire, DE4 5LE Tel: (01629) 580800 Fax: (01629) 580020 E-mail: info@lowe.co.uk *Radio communications importers* Also at: Bournemouth, Bristol, Cambridge, Glasgow & London

Lowe Engineering Midland Ltd, Stone Road, Bramshall, Uttoxeter, Staffordshire, ST14 8SH Tel: (01889) 563244 Fax: (01889) 563554 E-mail: sales@loweengineering.co.uk *Steel fabricators*

Lowe Of Loughborough, 37-40 Churchgate, Loughborough, Leicestershire, LE11 1UE Tel: (01509) 217876 *Executive office furniture manufrs*

Lowe Paddock Wood Paddock Wood Cold Storage Ltd, Transfesa Road, Paddock Wood, Tonbridge, Kent, TN12 6UT Tel: (01892) 832436 Fax: (01892) 835028 E-mail: lowepaddockwood@btconnect.com *Cold storage service*

Lowe Refrigeration Ltd, 101 Ballynahinch Road, Carryduff, Belfast, BT8 8DP Tel: (028) 9081 2248 Fax: (028) 9081 2608 E-mail: mail@loweref.co.uk *Refrigeration equipment sales & hire*

Russell Lowe Ltd, Unit 37, Broomhills Industrial Estate, Braintree, Essex, CM7 2RW Tel: (01245) 351599 Fax: (01376) 345825 *Wooden lighting*

Stephen D. Lowe, The Forge, 49 Claverham Road, Yatton, Bristol, BS49 4LD Tel: (01934) 834907 Fax: (01934) 876568 *Steel fabricators*

Lower Park Marina Ltd, Kelbrook Road, Barnoldswick, Lancashire, BB18 5TB Tel: (01282) 815883 Fax: (01282) 816421 *Boat builders & repairs*

Lower Quinton Garages Ltd, Back Lane, Lower Quinton, Stratford-upon-Avon, Warwickshire, CV37 8SX Tel: (01789) 720265 Fax: (01789) 721489 E-mail: lqg@lqgltd.co.uk *Agricultural motor service & sales*

Lower Swell Chemicals Ltd, Sunnydale, Naunton, Cheltenham, Gloucestershire, GL54 3AD Tel: (01451) 850456 Fax: (01451) 810707 E-mail: enquiries@lscltd.fsnet.co.uk *Institutional cleaning products* Also at: Bourton-on-the-Water

Lowes, Unit 8-9 Owen Road Industrial Estate, Willenhall, West Midlands, WV13 2PY Tel: 0121-526 2601 Fax: 0121-526 2612 *Steel & wood fabricators*

▶ Lowestoft Electrical Co. Ltd, Service House, Wildes Street, Lowestoft, Suffolk, NR32 1XH Tel: (01502) 565484 Fax: (01502) 588933 E-mail: enquiries@lowestoftelectricalgroup.co.uk *Electrical contractors*

Lowestoft Ice Co. Ltd, Battery Green Road, Lowestoft, Suffolk, NR32 1DQ Tel: (01502) 565565 Fax: (01502) 514382 *Suppliers of flake ice*

Lowestoft Sign Centre Design Manufacture Installation, Ellough Industrial Estate, Ellough, Beccles, Suffolk, NR34 7TD Tel: (01502) 710717 Fax: (01502) 717233 E-mail: sales@lowestoftsigns.co.uk *Sign manufrs*

▶ Lowhall Motors, Woodbottom Mills, Low Hall Road, Horsforth, Leeds, LS18 4EF Tel: 0113-250 4411 *Garage services*

Lowland Ensor Doors Ltd, 9 Pickering Works, Netherton Road, Wishaw, Lanarkshire, ML2 0EQ Tel: (01698) 376444 Fax: (01698) 376888 E-mail: sales@lowlandensor.co.uk *Roller shutter manufrs*

Lowland Sheet Metal Ltd, Unit 2 Coppice Trading Estate, Kidderminster, Worcestershire, DY11 7QY Tel: (01562) 743215 Fax: (01562) 863436 *Sheet metalwork engineers & fabricators*

▶ Lowlands Gas Ltd, Wellwood Service Centre, Ettrick Terrace, Selkirk, TD7 4JS Tel: (01750) 23054 Fax: (01750) 22160

Lowley Engineering Ltd, Unit B3 Pennygillam Way, Pennygillam Industrial Estate, Launceston, Cornwall, PL15 7ED Tel: (01566) 773998 Fax: (01566) 777137 E-mail: lowleyeng@aol.com *Precision turned parts suppliers & manufrs*

Brian Lowndes Print Ltd, Graphichouse, Portland Street, Walsall, WS2 8BE Tel: (01922) 725282 Fax: (01922) 720981 E-mail: mail@blprint.co.uk *Printers*

Lowood Garage Ltd, 12 Kings Avenue, London, SW4 8BQ Tel: (020) 7622 7174 Fax: (020) 7720 9095 *Motor repairs*

▶ lowquote.me.uk, Rosebank, Lymm, Cheshire, WA13 0JH Tel: (01925) 758984 E-mail: please@lowquote.me.uk *HOME EXPERTS**Interior and exterior Design for: -**Loft Conversions*Garden Decking*Impressed Driveways*Stoneworks*Brickwork*****

▶ Lowrey Contractors Ltd, 200 South Liberty Lane, Bristol, BS3 2TY Tel: 0117-963 7111 Fax: 0117-963 7111

Lowrie Bros, The Yard, Kenardington, Ashford, Kent, TN26 2LX Tel: (01233) 733833 Fax: (01233) 733899 E-mail: heather@lowriebros.co.uk *Mobile buildings distributors*

▶ Eve Lowrie Props, 12 Aaron Lodge, 144 Burnt Ash Hill, London, SE12 0HU Tel: (07919) 411872 E-mail: evelowrie@hotmail.com *Specialist props and sculptures for Theatre, TV, Film, corporate & private clients. **I am a qualified freelance prop maker based in London with a wide range of experience. My skills and creative approach have been applied to a variety of project requirements, from high-finish theatrical props to model making, sculpting, specialist costume making, scenery construction and painting.***Please browse my website for a portfolio of selected works.**

Lowrie Foods Ltd, 153 Brinkburn Street, Newcastle upon Tyne, NE6 2BU Tel: 0191-265 9161 Fax: 0191-224 0019 E-mail: sales@lowriefoods.co.uk *Fresh frozen food processors & products distributors*

Lowther Manufacturing Ltd, Nest Road, Felling, Gateshead, Tyne & Wear, NE10 0ES Tel: 0191-438 6936 Fax: 0191-495 0428 *Storage tanks & metal fabricators*

Lowther Rolton International Ltd, The Charles Parker Building, Midland Road, Higham Ferrers, Rushden, Northamptonshire, NN10 8DN Tel: (01933) 411837 Fax: (01933) 411887 *Heavy lifting consultants*

▶ Daniel Lowton Designs, Rochester Avenue, Rochester, Kent, ME1 2DS Tel: (01634) 880754 E-mail: daniel@dldesigns.biz *Graphic design services*

Loxam Access Ltd, Unit 12a, Glaisdale Point, Glaisdale Parkway, Nottingham, NG8 4GP Tel: 0115-900 8855 Fax: 0115-900 8880 E-mail: abishop@loxam-access.co.uk *Access equipment hirer*

Loxford Timber Supplies, 332 Ilford Lane, Ilford, Essex, IG1 2LT Tel: (020) 8553 0362 Fax: (020) 8594 7956 *Wooden timber manufrs*

▶ Loxley Equestrian, 39 Chesterfield Road, Ashford, Middlesex, TW15 2NE Tel: (01784) 229641 E-mail: info@loxleyequestrian.co.uk *Online Tack Shop. Everything for Horse & Rider. Quality items at extremely competitive prices. Regular Special Offers. Join our loyalty scheme. Secure, easy to use website. Friendly, family run business.*

William Loxley Ltd, 1 Weoley Avenue, Birmingham, B29 6PP Tel: 0121-472 0834 Fax: 0121-472 8658 *Monumental masons & marble workers*

Loxton Installations Ltd, Unit 14 Mill Hall Business Estate, Mill Hall, Aylesford, Kent, ME20 7JZ Tel: (01622) 716131 Fax: (01622) 719217 E-mail: info@loxtons.com *Electrical sub-contractors*

Loxwood Contacts Ltd, Unt 11 Cardiff Road Industrial Estate, Cardiff Road, Watford, WD18 0DG Tel: (01923) 254521 Fax: (01923) 818027 E-mail: sales@loxwoodcontacts.co.uk *Electrical contact manufrs*

▶ Loy Surveys Ltd, 1 Paisley Road, Renfrew, PA4 8JH Tel: 0141-885 0800 Fax: 0141-885 1202 E-mail: survey@loy.co.uk *Surveying services*

▶ Loyal E, 39 Stonewell Park Road, Congresbury, Bristol, BS49 5DP Tel: (01934) 832143 Fax: (01934) 832143 E-mail: enquiries@loyal-e.com *Web design & consultancy*

Loyal & Sons Ltd, 50 Kenilworth Drive, Oadby, Leicester, LE2 5LG Tel: 0116-271 8235 Fax: 0116-271 8235 E-mail: ajitloyal@aol.com *Leisure wear fabric manufrs*

LP Marketing Ltd, Millenium House, Junction Road, Sheffield, S11 8XB Tel: 0114-268 2812 Fax: 0114-268 2812 *Business gift & incentive products*

LPA Haswell Engineers Ltd, Oakwood Business Park, Stephenson Road West, Clacton-On-Sea, Essex, CO15 4TL Tel: (01255) 253900 Fax: (01255) 432963 E-mail: enquiries@lpa-haswell.com *Sheet metalworkers*

LPC Caravan Dealers, 7 South Circular Business Park, Newtownards Road, Bangor, County Down, BT19 7AG Tel: (028) 9146 5551 Fax: (028) 9146 8815 *Camping & caravan centre*

LPC Contracts Ltd, 370 Coventry Road, Hinckley, Leicestershire, LE10 0NH Tel: (01455) 635816 Fax: (01455) 615329 *Roofing contractors*

LPC Holdings Ltd, Coundon Industrial Estate, Coundon, Bishop Auckland, County Durham, DL14 8NR Tel: (01388) 608270 Fax: (01388) 450048 E-mail: enquiries@lpcholdings.co.uk *Heating element, rheostat & resistor manufrs*

LPC Printing Co. Ltd, Hardley Industrial Estate, Hardley Hythe, Southampton, SO45 3ZX Tel: (023) 8084 6334 Fax: (023) 8084 0389 E-mail: enquiries@lpcprinting.com *Commercial printers*

▶ Lpe Medical Ltd, Gordleton Industrial Estate, Hannah Way, Pennington, Lymington, Hampshire, SO41 8JD Tel: (01590) 681258 Fax: (01590) 681251 E-mail: sales@lpemedical.com

▶ LPG Auto Conversions, Island Cottage, Stone, Tenterden, Kent, TN30 7JL Tel: (01233) 758014 E-mail: lpg@uk2.net *OMVL dream system fitting & conversion services*

LRS, Unit 7 New Way Estate, Dunkeswell Industrial Estate, Honiton, Devon, EX14 4LD Tel: (01404) 891521 Fax: (01404) 891521 E-mail: lrsgroup@fsbdial.co.uk *Industrial washing equipment manufrs*

LS Controls, 270 Abbey Road, Leeds, LS5 3ND Tel: (01943) 872025 Fax: 0113-259 0243 E-mail: ls.lee@amserve.com *Tachometer counter manufrs*

LS Forklifts, 12 Clonmakate Road, Portadown, Craigavon, County Armagh, BT62 1LR Tel: (028) 3885 1728 Fax: (028) 3885 1234 E-mail: sales@lsforklifts.co.uk *Forklift suppliers*

▶ LS UK Ltd, Riverside Terrace, Aberystwyth, Dyfed, SY23 1PN Tel: (01970) 617013 Fax: (01970) 612443

LSH Ltd, Western Road, Silver End, Witham, Essex, CM8 3QB Tel: (01376) 507507 Fax: (01376) 584687 E-mail: sales@lairdsecurity.co.uk *Window & door security hardware*

Lsi Logic Europe Ltd, Greenwood House, London Road, Bracknell, Berkshire, RG12 2UB Tel: (01344) 413200 Fax: (01344) 413329 *Data preparation consultants*

LT Mumford, 223 Gascoigne Road, Barking, Essex, IG11 7LN Tel: (020) 8594 1187 *Steel merchant non-ferrous metal*

▶ LTG Couriers, Unit B12, Parkside Commercial Centre, Terry Avenue, York, YO23 1JP Tel: 08000 191211 Fax: 0871 8710028 E-mail: info@ltg-ltd.com *Express sameday courier service. Delivering throughout the UK and Europe. 24hrs a day 7 days a week. Bikes and Vans. Over 20 years experience delivering in the UK Sameday Couriers industry*

LTG Mailaender (UK) Ltd, 55 Winter Hey Lane, Horwich, Bolton, BL6 7NT Tel: (01204) 668606 Fax: (01204) 668450 E-mail: sales@ltguk.co.uk *Industrial air purification equipment suppliers*

▶ LTL, Pear Mill Industrial Estate, Stockport Road West, Bredbury, Stockport, Cheshire, SK6 2BP Tel: 0161-406 8601 Fax: 0161-406 8073 E-mail: info@fresh-air.co.uk *Manufacture distributors, installation service, air purifier equipment, air cleaning equipment*

▶ LTR, 3 Newtown Grange Farm Business Park, Desford Road, Newtown Unthank, Leicester, LE9 9FL Tel: (01455) 821999 Fax: (01455) 821949 E-mail: sales@ltrtech.co.uk *Time recorder systems*

LTR Lifts & Escalator Ltd, Graphic House, Druid Street, Hinckley, Leicestershire, LE10 1QH Tel: (01455) 633760 Fax: (01455) 636005 E-mail: sales@ltr-lifts.co.uk *Lifts & escalators suppliers, fitters & service providers*

Lubepack Ltd, Cow Lane, Oldham, OL4 1HS Tel: 0161-620 0440 Fax: 0161-621 0801 E-mail: info@lubepack.co.uk *Packaging services*

▶ Lubina Kitchen Co. Ltd, Unit 2, Hythe Quay, Colchester, CO2 8JB Tel: (01206) 792807 Fax: (01206) 863728 E-mail: emmarose@lubina.co.uk *Kitchen & bedroom manufrs*

Lubkowski Saunders & Associates Designs & Exports Ltd, E Dolphin Estate, Windmill Road West, Sunbury-on-Thames, Middlesex, TW16 7HE Tel: (01932) 789721 Fax: (01932) 789793 E-mail: sales@lsa-international.co.uk *Cookware & glass distributors*

Lubrication Engineers UK Ltd, Latton Bush Business Ctr, Southern Way, Harlow, Essex, CM18 7BH Tel: (01763) 274253 Fax: (01763) 274253 E-mail: sales@le-lubricants.co.uk *Lubricant manufrs*

Lubrication Services, 152 Oxford Road, Banbury, Oxfordshire, OX16 9BA Tel: (01295) 251821 Fax: (01295) 251821 *Lubrication systems*

Lubrizol Advanced Materials UK Ltd, Carlton Industrial Estate, Albion Road, Carlton, Barnsley, South Yorkshire, S71 3HW Tel: (01226) 723661 Fax: (01226) 728298 *Textile coating manufrs*

Lubron UK Ltd, 14 Commerce Way, Colchester, CO2 8HH Tel: (01206) 866444 Fax: (01206) 866800 E-mail: joe.austin@lubron.co.uk *Lubron UK Limited is the UK operation of Lubron Holding - a European market leader in the provision of water treatment equipment, plant and services for clean water applications since 1978, with sister companies in Holland , Germany and Belgium. Lubron designs and manufactures complete pre-engineered water treatment systems for numerous process applications and healthcare requirements as well as key elements for third parties and other OEMs. Lubron work with a wide customer base, from specifiers and consultants to contractors and end users, we provide turnkey solutions wherever needed. To compliment our engineering, design and manufacturing capabilities we also have a strong service support network offering cost effective planned maintenance contracts and a chemicals supply service for all aspects of chemical water treatment. In the Pharmaceutical market we offer fully validated systems compliant with cGMP, GAMP, CFR 21 part 11 and the ISPE Base Line Guide. We are an approved Ionpure CEDI supplier and service provider.*

Lubysil UK Ltd, Suite 401 Langham House, 302 Regent Street, London, W1B 3AT Tel: (020) 7580 6491 Fax: (020) 7580 4729 E-mail: info@swindens-vices.co.uk *High performance lubricant distributors*

Lucas Aftermarket Operations, Stratford Road, Shirley, Solihull, West Midlands, B90 4LA Tel: 0121-506 5000 Fax: 0121-506 5001 E-mail: enquiries@lucasestateagents.co.uk Principal Export Areas: Worldwide *Manufacturers of brakes, autoelectrical & electronic equipment*

▶ Lucas Express Couriers, 11 Benbow Close, Hinckley, Leicestershire, LE10 1RQ Tel: (01455) 634705 E-mail: rich@lucasexpress.co.uk *National 24 hour sameday delivery service*

G.G. Lucas & Company Ltd, 17-18 Old Bond Street, London, W1S 4PT Tel: (020) 7629 1680 Fax: (020) 7629 7309 E-mail: shipping@gglucas.com *Ship broking*

Lucas Sectional Buildings, The Row, West Dereham, King's Lynn, Norfolk, PE33 9RH Tel: (01366) 500502 Fax: (01366) 501005 E-mail: info@fjlucas.com *Sectional timber buildings manufacturer*

Lucas Software Solutions, 95 Tilehouse St, Hitchin, Hertfordshire, SG5 2DW Tel: (01462) 440885 Fax: (01462) 440954 E-mail: sales@lucas-software.co.uk *Software solution*

Lucas & Steen Ltd, Castle Works, 88 Hill Street, Ardrossan, Ayrshire, KA22 8HE Tel: (01294) 468671 Fax: (01294) 604018 *Ducting installation & manufrs*

Lucchini UK Ltd, Ashburton Road West, Trafford Park, Manchester, M17 1GU Tel: 0161-872 0492 Fax: 0161-872 2895 *Machine railway manufrs*

Lucebay Plant Hire Ltd, Drough Duil, Dunragit, Stranraer, Wigtownshire, DG9 8QA Tel: (01581) 400248

▶ Lucent Design Ltd, 9 Portrea Close, Davenport, Stockport, Cheshire, SK3 8RU Tel: 0161-612 2585 E-mail: paulbell@lucentdesign.co.uk *Web design/development & hosting solutions.*

Lucent Lighting (UK) Ltd, Old Station House, 7A Coppetts Road, London, N10 1NN Tel: (020) 8442 0880 Fax: (020) 8444 6998 *Lighting distributors*

Lucent Technologies Holdings UK, Optimus, Windmill Hill Business Park, Swindon, SN5 6PP Tel: (01793) 883333 Fax: (01793) 883236 *Computer software suppliers*

▶ Luciano's Foods, 17b Olympia Food Court, East Kilbride, Glasgow, G74 1PG Tel: (01355) 579922 Fax: (01355) 612508

▶ Luciant Consulting, 72 New Bond Street, London, W1S 1RR Tel: (020) 7514 1789 Fax: (020) 7348 0699 E-mail: info@hbcl.co.uk *Quantity Surveying, Cost and Project Management*

▶ Lucid Innovation Group, PO Box 180, Manchester, M21 9XW Tel: 0161-860 0058 E-mail: ideas@lucidinnovation.com *Product design consultancy, industrial design consultants, research and innovation services. We create ideas that inspire people and develop them into practical, profitable products. Lucid's team are product and industrial designers who specialise in new product development for structural packaging, technology products, security, medical device design, beauty, food and drinks promotion and dispense. Our people have over 20 years of design and manufacturing management experience in the UK and Far East. Lucid Group ISO 9001 - 2000 accredited business, we work with small, specialist businesses and major multi-nationals.*

▶ Lucid It Ltd, 26 St. Leonards Way, Ashley Heath, Ringwood, Hampshire, BH24 2HS Tel: (01425) 475060 E-mail: info@lucidit.co.uk **Tailored IT Services include: Consultancy, Design, Development, Infrastructures, Facilities Management, Project Management, Open Source, Linux, Remote Support, IntraNet & ExtraNet creation, LANs & WANS, VOIP, virtual offices.*Clients include Thomas Cook Tour Operators* Lucid IT is fair, fast, flexible and focussed.*

▶ Lucid Optical Services Ltd, Lucid Training Centre, Garsdale, Sedbergh, Cumbria, LA10 5PE Tel: (01539) 621219 Fax: (01539) 621205 E-mail: annette@lucidos.co.uk *Training & consultancy in fibre optics, laser safety & cabling*

Lucite International Speciality Polymers & Resins Ltd, Horndale Avenue, Aycliffe Industrial Estate, Aycliffe Industrial Park, Newton Aycliffe, County Durham, DL5 6YE Tel: (01325) 300990 Fax: (01325) 314925 *Dental & surface coating polymers*

▶ Lucite International UK Ltd, P O Box 34, Darwen, Lancashire, BB3 3GB Tel: (01254) 874444 Fax: (01254) 874202 *Perspex manufrs*

Martin Luck Ltd, Rowdown House Rowdown Close, Langage Business Park, Plympton, Plymouth, PL7 5EY Tel: (01752) 336699 Fax: (01752) 330022 E-mail: sales@martinluck.co.uk *Office supplies & furniture*

V.A. Luck Ltd, 414 Shaftmoor Lane, Hall Green, Birmingham, B28 8TA Tel: 0121-777 3366 Fax: 0121-778 5888 *Timber merchants*

Luckett Investigation, 14 Barnfield Way, Stafford, ST17 4NB Tel: 01785 602075 Fax: 01785 602075 E-mail: info@luckett-investigation.co.uk *Professional, qualified accident and personal injury investigation, private investigation and claims management.*

▶ Lucking & Holder, 33 Baker Close, Llantarnam Industrial Park, Cwmbran, Gwent, NP44 3AX Tel: (01633) 480408 Fax: (01633) 480407

Luckshmee Ltd, Woodside End, Wembley, Middlesex, HA0 1UR Tel: (020) 8900 1990 Fax: (020) 8900 9890 *Indian sweets & snacks manufrs*

Luckswitch Ltd, Unit 1b St Columbe Industrial Estate, St. Columb Road, St. Columb, Cornwall, TR9 6PZ Tel: (01726) 862994 Fax: (01726) 862995 *Lighting consultants, importers & distributors & wholesalers*

Lucky Knitwear Ltd, 53 Marshall Street, Manchester, M4 5FU Tel: 0161-832 1715 *Knitwear manufrs*

▶ Lucra Garden & Leisure, Culver Garden Centre, Cattlegate Road, Enfield, Middlesex, EN2 9DS Tel: (020) 8363 2628

Lucy Art, 178b Batley Road, Alverthorpe, Wakefield, West Yorkshire, WF2 0AJ Tel: 01924 362009 Fax: 0870 1227055 E-mail: sales@lucyart.co.uk *Canvas art to suit your space. Canvas prints and photos to canvas also available. Any size or colour, modern art for everyone.*

▶ Lucy Locketts, 10 Stafford Street, Market Drayton, Shropshire, TF9 1HY Tel: 01630 657900

Lucy Switchgear, Howland Road, Thame, Oxfordshire, OX9 3UJ Tel: (01844) 267222 Fax: (01844) 267223 E-mail: sales.switchgear@wlucy.co.uk *Lucy Switchgear designs & manufactures medium voltage ring main units (RMUs) for urban development and major infrastructure projects. Additionally it offers overhead line equipment for rural electrification projects. Lucy Switchgear has developed its Gemini range of automation and remote control solutions that can be supplied with Lucy equipment along with OEM products.*

▶ Luddon Construction Ltd, Balmore House, 1497 Balmore Road, Glasgow, G23 5HD Tel: 0141-945 2233 Fax: 0141-946 5400 E-mail: enquiries@luddon.co.uk *Building contractors, civil engineers & public works contractors*

▶ Luddon Construction Ltd, Bo'ness Road, Grangemouth, Stirlingshire, FK3 9UQ Tel: (01324) 485456

Ludgate Office Equipment Ltd, 7 Stevens Lane, Claygate, Esher, Surrey, KT10 0TD Tel: (01372) 466091 Fax: (01372) 464960 E-mail: sales@ludgateoe.co.uk *Office equipment suppliers* Also at: London SE1

Ludham Bridge Services, Ludham Bridge, Ludham, Great Yarmouth, Norfolk, NR29 5NX Tel: (01692) 630486 *Boat builders & repairers*

Ludlow, 6 Prospect View, Rock Lane, Ludlow, Shropshire, SY8 1ST Tel: (01584) 875096 *Toolmakers & contract presswork*

Frank Ludlow Ltd, 71 Windmill Road, Luton, LU1 3XL Tel: (01582) 414441 Fax: (01582) 483618 *Motor vehicle body refinishing*

P.M. Luft, Essex House, Astra Centre, Edinburgh Way, Harlow, Essex, CM20 2BN Tel: (01279) 416087 Fax: (01279) 416076 *Air conditioning unit manufrs*

Lugg Facilities Ltd, 99-107 Hill Top, West Bromwich, West Midlands, B70 0RY Tel: 0121-556 1551 Fax: 0121-556 1552 E-mail: sales@lugg-tools.co.uk *Ironmongers & engineers merchants*

▶ Lugsys Plant, Bridge Meadow Stadium, Bridge Meadow Lane, Haverfordwest, Dyfed, SA61 2EX Tel: (01437) 779427

Luhrfilter Ltd, 58a Thornhill Road, Sutton Coldfield, West Midlands, B74 3EN Tel: 0121-353 8703 Fax: 0121-353 4066 E-mail: sales@luhrgb.demon.co.uk *Dust & fume extraction services*

Luk Aftermarket Service Ltd, Holme Lacy Road, Hereford, HR2 6BQ Tel: (01432) 264264 Fax: (01432) 275146 E-mail: sales@luk.co.uk *Agricultural vehicle components*

Luk UK Ltd, Waleswood Road, Wales Bar, Sheffield, S26 5PN Tel: (01909) 510500 Fax: (01909) 515151 E-mail: info@luk.co.uk *Automotive & agricultural clutch manufrs*

Luke Jones, Greinan Farm, Tower Hill, Chipperfield, Kings Langley, Hertfordshire, WD4 9LU Tel: (01442) 832891 Fax: (01442) 831115 *Furniture makers*

Luma Automation, Technology House, Blackpole Trading Estate West, Worcester, WR3 8TJ Tel: (01905) 753700 Fax: (01905) 753701 E-mail: sales@rglumagroup.co.uk *Special purpose machines, Industrial automation, Robot integration, Control systems, Automated assembly and test equipment*

Luma Automation, Technology House, Blackpole Trading Estate West, Worcester, WR3 8TJ Tel: (01905) 753700 Fax: (01905) 753701 E-mail: sales@rgautomation.co.uk *Control panel builders & manufrs*

Luma Plastic Engineering, 4 Baltimore Trading Estate, Baltimore Road, Birmingham, B42 1DD Tel: 0121-344 4414 Fax: 0121-344 4414 E-mail: krysplas@hotmail.com *Plastic engineering manufrs*

Lumalite Ltd, Unit 2 Greenhill Industrial Estate, Mytholmroyd, Hebden Bridge, West Yorkshire, HX7 5QF Tel: (01422) 884879 Fax: (01422) 882366 E-mail: sales@lumalite.co.uk *Outdoor & indoor decor lighting manufrs*

▶ Lumasign Ltd, Unit 7, Crewe Close, Blidworth, Mansfield, Nottinghamshire, NG21 0TA Tel: (01623) 491136 Fax: (0845) 2300288 E-mail: info@lumasign.com *Lighting manufrs*

Lumatic Ga Ltd, Theaklen Drive, St. Leonards-on-Sea, East Sussex, TN38 9AZ Tel: (01424) 436343 Fax: (01424) 429926 E-mail: sales@lumatic.co.uk *Lubricating system distributors & manufrs*

Lumber Mill Somerset, Haselbury Plucknett, Crewkerne, Somerset, TA18 7PH Tel: (01460) 73201 *Timber merchants*

Lumenglow Ltd, 335 Underhill Road, London, SE22 9EA Tel: (020) 8693 8919 Fax: (020) 8693 9847 E-mail: sole@lumenglow.co.uk

▶ Lumier Ltd, County Park Road, Barrow-in-Furness, Cumbria, LA14 4BQ Tel: (01229) 821104 Fax: (01229) 821104 *Manufacturers of electronic components*

Luminaire UK Ltd, 9-15 Henley Street, Birmingham, B11 1JB Tel: 0121-766 1490 Fax: 0121-766 1491 E-mail: sales@luminaireuk.com *Lighting fittings manufrs*

Luminars Lighting Mnfrs, 68 Miskin Street, Cardiff, CF24 4AR Tel: (029) 2022 8878 Fax: (029) 2022 8878 *Micro process developments*

Luminescence Incorporated, The Fairway, Bush Fair, Harlow, Essex, CM18 6NG Tel: (01279) 453711 Fax: (01279) 421142 E-mail: sales@luminescence.co.uk *Security inks for printing manufrs*

Luminite Security Equipment, 2a Bellevue Road, London, N11 3ER Tel: (020) 8368 7887 Fax: (020) 8368 3952 E-mail: sales@luminite.co.uk *Security lighting manufrs*

▶ Lumino Ltd, Lumino House, Lovet Road, Harlow, Essex, CM19 5TB Tel: (01279) 635411 Fax: (01279) 626101 E-mail: info@lumino.co.uk *Lighting design & sales*

Luminose Escape Routes, 75 Birkmyre Road, Glasgow, G51 3JH Tel: 0141-445 6655 Fax: 0141-425 1511 *Fire escape & evacuation equipment*

Lumitron Ltd, Park House, 15-23 Greenhill Crescent, Watford Business Park, Watford, WD18 8PH Tel: (01923) 226222 Fax: (01923) 211300 E-mail: sales@lumitron.co.uk *Industrial lighting fitters*

Lumley Letsure Ltd, Hargrave House, Belmont Road, Maidenhead, Berkshire, SL6 6TB Tel: (01628) 581500 Fax: (01628) 581401 *Holding company*

▶ Lumleytech, 46 Kinloss Park, Cupar, Fife, KY15 4ER Tel: (07891) 313274

▶ Lumos Lighting, 8 Brentwood Avenue, Jesmond, Newcastle upon Tyne, NE2 3DH Tel: 0191-281 5050 Fax: 0191-281 5161 E-mail: sales@lumoslighting.co.uk *Retail providers of home, garden, and outdoor lighting. UK Based supplier. Provides information & advise on all aspects of lighting your home and garden.*

Lumsden Security, 128-130 John Street, Aberdeen, AB25 1LE Tel: (01224) 632428 Fax: (01224) 645656 E-mail: sales@lumsdensecurity.co.uk *Locksmiths & safe dealers*

Lunar Freezing & Cold Storage Co. Ltd, East Quay, The Harbour, Peterhead, Aberdeenshire, AB42 1JF Tel: (01779) 477446 Fax: (01779) 476599 *Fish product manufrs*

▶ Lunar Interactive Multimedia Design, 2 Robincroft, Gressingham, Lancaster, LA2 8LP Tel: (01524) 222335 E-mail: john@lunar.co.uk *Creative new media design for cd-roms, dvd & kiosks*

Lunar Refrigeration Ltd, Unit 5 Forestgate, White Lund Industrial Estate, Morecambe, Lancashire, LA3 3PD Tel: (01524) 64273 Fax: (01524) 846357 E-mail: lunar.refrig@virgin.net *Refrigeration engineering services & air conditioning*

Lund Bros & Co. Ltd, Brookside Avenue, Rustington, Littlehampton, West Sussex, BN16 3LF Tel: (01903) 784242 Fax: (01903) 787126 E-mail: sales@lunds.co.uk *Sheet metalwork & precision fine limit engineers or fabricators*

Lund Engineering Co. Ltd, Clayton Street, Nelson, Lancashire, BB9 7ES Tel: (01282) 695641 Fax: (01282) 602496 *Tooling & machines specialists*

Lund Precision Reeds Ltd, St. Andrews House, Russell Street, Keighley, West Yorkshire, BD21 2JU Tel: (01535) 662580 Fax: (01535) 608428 *Reed makers*

Lund Roberts Engineers Ltd, 1 Barbon Close, London, WC1N 3JX Tel: (020) 7405 8507 Fax: (020) 7831 7974 E-mail: engineers@lundroberts.co.uk *Electrical contracting engineers*

Lundbeck Pharmaceuticals Ltd, Seal Sands, Middlesbrough, Cleveland, TS2 1UB Tel: (01642) 546574 Fax: (01642) 546085 *Pharmaceutical chemical manufrs*

▶ Lund-Conlon Removers & Storers, Remstore House, Wolseley Road, Kempston, Bedford, MK42 7EF Tel: (01234) 404411 Fax: (01234) 404422

Lundie Bros Ltd, 15 Tait Road, Croydon, CR0 2DP Tel: (020) 8683 4451 Fax: (020) 8683 4193 E-mail: print@lundiebros.co.uk *Commercial & general printers*

Lunn Engineering Co. Ltd, Manor Road Industrial Estate, Atherstone, Warwickshire, CV9 1RB Tel: (01827) 713228 Fax: (01827) 717624 E-mail: info@lunnengineering.co.uk *General, special purpose engineering services*

Luntri (UK) Ltd, Trinity House, Foxes Parade, Sewardstone Road, Waltham Abbey, Essex, EN9 1PH Tel: (01992) 653065 Fax: (01992) 653165 E-mail: luntri@wxs.wl.com *Laboratory furniture manufrs*

Lunt's Castings Ltd, Hawthorns Industrial Estate, Middlemore Road, Handsworth, Birmingham, B21 0BJ Tel: 0121-551 4301 Fax: 0121-523 7954 E-mail: info@luntscastings.co.uk *Sculpture & fine art castings*

Lupton Fabrications Ltd, Unit A Aquatite House, Water Lane, Leeds, LS11 9UD Tel: 0113-242 6872 Fax: 0113-242 6874 E-mail: sales@lupton.uk.com *Sheet metal fabricators for the roofing & construction industry*

▶ Lupus Engineering Services Ltd, Abergeldie Cottage, Ballater, Aberdeenshire, AB35 5SY Tel: (01339) 742073

Lurejumbo Ltd, Unit 2 Darwin Road, Off Steel Road, Corby, Northamptonshire, NN17 5XZ Tel: (01536) 401971 Fax: (01536) 401972 E-mail: info@metalico.org.uk *Office furniture manufrs*

▶ Lurgan Mail, 4a High Street, Lurgan, Craigavon, County Armagh, BT66 8AW Tel: (028) 3832 7777 Fax: (028) 3832 5271

Lusas Computer Systems, 66 High Street, Kingston upon Thames, Surrey, KT1 1HN Tel: (020) 8541 1999 Fax: (020) 8549 9399 E-mail: info@lusas.com *Software house*

▶ Lush Hand Made Cosmetics, 73 Broadmead, Bristol, BS1 3DX Tel: 0117-925 7582 Fax: 0117-934 9150 *Cosmetics manufrs*

Lush Heat Treatment Ltd, 128 Great North Road, Hatfield, Hertfordshire, AL9 5JN Tel: (01707) 264104 Fax: (01707) 274850 *Heat treatment specialists*

▶ Lush Manufacturing Ltd, 61-65 Nuffield Road, Nuffield Industrial Estate, Poole, Dorset, BH17 0RD Tel: (01202) 661777 Fax: (01202) 683434 E-mail: jet@lush.co.uk

Lush Signs, 64 Old Milton Road, New Milton, Hampshire, BH25 6DX Tel: (01425) 616905 Fax: (01425) 628830 E-mail: lushsigns@newmilton.fsbusiness.co.uk *Sign manufrs*

W.S. Lusher & Son Ltd, School Lane, Sprowston, Norwich, NR7 8TH Tel: (01603) 426363 Fax: (01603) 787669 *Building & church restoration contractors*

Lusso Sportswear, 1 Withins Street, Radcliffe, Manchester, M26 2RX Tel: 0161-724 5222 Fax: 0161-724 9393 E-mail: sales@lusso.co.uk *Cycle ware manufrs*

Lustalux Ltd, Unit A3 Anchorage Business Park, Chain Caul Way, Ashton-on-Ribble, Preston, PR2 2YL Tel: (01772) 726622 Fax: (01772) 726644 E-mail: sales@lustalux.co.uk *Solar control & safety window film*

▶ Lusted Consulting Ltd, 5 Alliance Way, Paddock Wood, Tonbridge, Kent, TN12 6TY Tel: (01892) 835937 E-mail: info@lustedconsulting.ltd.uk *Lusted Consulting Ltd offers specialist advice in all aspects of oil and gas industry geotechnics. This ranges from offshore facilities to onshore and nearshore petrochemical and LNG projects worldwide. The primary service is targeted at provision of support for Operators and designers.*

Lustre Anodising Co. Ltd, Units 22-24, Cannon Business Park, Gough Road, Coseley, Bilston, West Midlands, WV14 8XR Tel: (01902) 494455 Fax: (01902) 494411 E-mail: info@lustre-anodising.co.uk *Component anodises & powder coaters*

G. Lusty Ltd, Hoo Lane, Chipping Campden, Gloucestershire, GL55 6AU Tel: (01386) 841333 Fax: (01386) 841322 E-mail: geoffreylusty@aol.com *Woven fibre furniture importers & manufrs*

▶ Luta Ltd, 106 Beecham Berry, Basingstoek, Basingstoke, Hampshire, RG22 4QN Tel: 0778 0993697 Fax: 01256 814135 E-mail: info@luta.co.uk *Luta Ltd mainly deals with imports and exports between the UK and China. We have contacts with more than 300 factories in mainland China. And we can help the UK companies to find Chinese suppliers and manufacturers at unbeatable prices.*Save more with Luta!*

Lutley Manufacturing Ltd, Unit H, 100 Dudley Road East, Oldbury, West Midlands, B69 3DY Tel: 0121-552 2456 Fax: 0121-544 3545 E-mail: richardsweeney.lutley@btinternet.com *Tube manipulation, bending services & fabricators*

continued

Luton Ceramic Tile Co. Ltd, 6 Britannia Estate, Leagrave Road, Luton, LU3 1RJ Tel: (01582) 412121 Fax: (01582) 413061 E-mail: enquiries@lutonceramics.co.uk *Ceramic tile retailers*

Luton Electrical Services, 29 Upper Luton Road, Chatham, Kent, ME5 7BH Tel: (01634) 845413 *Power tool repairers*

Luton Fabrications Ltd, Tring Road, Dunstable, Bedfordshire, LU6 2JX Tel: (01582) 663330 Fax: (01582) 662333 *Steel fabricators*

Luton Glass, 2b Miller Road, Bedford, MK42 9NY Tel: (01582) 726000 Fax: (01582) 480980 E-mail: info@allregionsglazing.co.uk *Glazing contractors & shutter fitters*

Luton Jig & Tool Co. Ltd, Unit 3 Chase Street, Luton, LU1 3QZ Tel: (01582) 725591 Fax: (01582) 735211 E-mail: david@ljtco.co.uk *Press tool & general engineering services & manufrs*

Luton Metal Castings, 3b Holly Street Trading Estate, Holly Street, Luton, LU1 3XG Tel: (01582) 451817 Fax: (01582) 723798 *Non-ferrous founders*

Luton Steels, Wharley Farm, College Road, Cranfield, Bedford, MK43 0AH Tel: (01234) 750003 Fax: (01234) 750084 E-mail: sales@lutonsteels.co.uk *Steel stockholders & fabricators*

Luton Swimming Pool Supplies, 86 Old Bedford Road, Luton, LU2 7PD Tel: (01582) 731819 Fax: (01582) 611054 E-mail: sales@lutonpools.com *Swimming pool services*

Luton Travel Lodge, 641 Dunstable Road, Luton, LU4 8RQ Tel: (01582) 575955 Fax: (01582) 490065 *Hotel with conference facilities*

Lutterworth Electrical Services, 1a Market Street, Lutterworth, Leicestershire, LE17 4EJ Tel: (01455) 552511 Fax: (01455) 557812 E-mail: enquiries@lutterworthelectrical.co.uk *Electrical contractors*

Lutz (UK) Ltd, Gateway Estate, West Midlands Freeport, Birmingham, B26 3QD Tel: 0121-782 2662 Fax: 0121-782 2680 E-mail: lutzpump@aol.com Purchasing Contact: J. McGurk Sales Contact: R. Gooch Principal Export Areas: Middle East, Africa, Central/East Europe, West Europe & South America *Distributors/agents/stockholders of pumps; acid, barrel, chemical. corrosion resistant & drum*

▶ Luv It Furniture, Unit 6, Deacon Trading Estate, Earle Street, Newton-Le-Willows, Merseyside, WA12 9XD Tel: (01925) 298788 Fax: (01925) 298736 *Manufacturers of furniture*

Luvaca Wolverhampton Ltd, Unit B, Smeston Bridge Industrial Estate, Bridgnorth Road, Wombourne, Wolverhampton, WV5 8AY Tel: (01902) 324747 Fax: (01902) 324501 E-mail: sales@thatcher-alloys.com Principal Export Areas: Asia Pacific, Central Asia, Middle East, Africa, Central/East Europe, West Europe & South America *Stockholders of copper, alloy & non-ferrous metal*

Luvata Sales Oy (UK), Regency Chambers Regency Arcade, 154-156 Parade, Leamington Spa, Warwickshire, CV32 4BQ Tel: (01689) 825677 Fax: (01926) 459149 E-mail: enquiries@outokumpu.com *Manufacturers of copper strip, copper sheet and electrical and power components.*

Luwa UK Ltd, Wrigley Street, Oldham, OL4 1HN Tel: 0161-624 8185 Fax: 0161-626 4609 E-mail: service@luwa.co.uk *Industrial air conditioning systems manufrs*

Lux Lighting Ltd, 100 Icknield Street, Hockley, Birmingham, B18 6RU Tel: 0121-236 7595 Fax: 0121-236 6548 E-mail: luxlight@aol.com *Lighting fittings distributors*

Luxcrete Ltd, Premier House, Disraeli Road, London, NW10 7BT Tel: (020) 8965 7292 Fax: (020) 8961 6337 E-mail: sales@luxcrete.co.uk *Glass block panels*

Luxfer Gas Cylinders, Colwick Industrial Estate, Nottingham, NG4 2BH Tel: 0115-980 3800 Fax: 0115-980 3899 E-mail: info@luxfercylinders.com *Aluminium extrusion manufrs*

▶ Luxmore Lighting, Unit 5 Shawlands Court, Newchapel Road, Lingfield, Surrey, RH7 6BL Tel: (01342) 836420 Fax: (01342) 836420 E-mail: luxmore@btconnect.com *Lighting designers*

Luxomation Ltd, 5 Worton Hall Industrial Estate, Worton Road, Isleworth, Middlesex, TW7 6ER Tel: (020) 8568 6373 Fax: (020) 8847 2603 *Sheet metalwork engineers*

Luxtrade Ltd, Unit C5 Hilton Trading Estate, Hilton Road, Lanesfield, Wolverhampton, WV4 6DW Tel: (01902) 353182 Fax: (01902) 404628 E-mail: sales@luxtrade.co.uk *Expanded metal sheets & fabrication service*

▶ Luxtravel Ltd, Tenterden Road, Biddenden, Ashford, Kent, TN27 8BH Tel: (01580) 292970 Fax: (01622) 750751 E-mail: enquiries@luxtravel.co.uk *We provide luxury coaches and minibuses from 6 to 53 seats for UK and continental travel. **From private hire to short breaks, school trips, airport transfers, weddings and holidays at affordable prices.**The name we want you to remember when booking your next adventure is LuxTravel.*

▶ Luxury Beds, Town Street, Batley Carr, Dewsbury, West Yorkshire, WF13 2HG Tel: (01924) 437392 Fax: (01924) 437825 *Bed manufrs*

LWD Precision Engineering Co Ltd, 169 Elland Road, Leeds, LS11 8BY Tel: 0113-271 3097 Fax: 0113-271 8655 E-mail: sales@lwdeng.com *CNC machining services*

Lyall Willis & Co. Ltd, 49 Cooden Sea Road, Bexhill-on-Sea, East Sussex, TN39 4SL Tel: (01424) 848388 Fax: (01424) 848399 E-mail: info@lyallwillis.co.uk *Supplies of surgical instruments*

Lyalvale Ltd, Express Estate, Fisherwick Road, Lichfield, Staffordshire, WS13 8XA Tel: (01543) 434400 Fax: (01543) 434420 E-mail: sales@lyalvaleexpress.com *Sporting ammunition*

Lycett Fabrications Ltd, Mariner, Lichfield Road Industrial Estate, Tamworth, Staffordshire, B79 7UL Tel: (01827) 53231 Fax: (01827) 69650 E-mail: mckd@lycettfab13.freeserve.co.uk *Steel fabricators*

Lycetts Insurance Brokers, Milburn House, Dean Street, Newcastle upon Tyne, NE1 1PP Tel: 0191-232 1151 Fax: 0191-232 1873 E-mail: info@lycetts.co.uk *Insurance brokers*

Lydfield Construction Ltd, Meadow House, Cooks Lane, Calmore, Southampton, SO40 2RU Tel: (023) 8081 4466 Fax: (023) 8081 3785 *Groundwork contractors*

Lydford Precision Engineering Ltd, Sutherland Avenue, Monmore Green, Wolverhampton, WV2 2JH Tel: (01902) 351353 Fax: (01902) 351616 E-mail: sales@lydford-eng.co.uk *Manufacturers of bolts & nuts, non-standard & special specification*

▶ Raymond Lydiard Engineering Services, Industrial Estate, 16 Willow Road, Yaxley, Peterborough, PE7 3HT Tel: (01733) 245532 Fax: (01733) 245534

Lydney Containers Ltd, Unit 14 Lydney Industrial Estate, Harbour Road, Lydney, Gloucestershire, GL15 4EJ Tel: (01594) 842378 Fax: (01594) 843213 E-mail: info@lydneycontainers.co.uk *Secure steel site stores & offices manufrs*

Lydney Containers Ltd, Unit 29-30 Vulcan Works, Wargrave Road, Newton-le-Willows, Merseyside, WA12 8RN Tel: 01695 731890 Fax: 01925 229484 E-mail: info@lydneycontainers.co.uk *Portable container manufrs*

Lydwood Ltd, Lower Lydbrook, Lydbrook, Gloucestershire, GL17 9NB Tel: (01594) 860374 Fax: (01594) 861312 E-mail: nick@lydwood.co.uk *CNC woodworking*

Lye Commutators, The White House, Pearson Street, Stourbridge, West Midlands, DY9 8BB Tel: (01384) 893025 Fax: (01384) 422398 *Commutator manufrs*

Lye Engineers Supplies Ltd, Roetan House, Thorns Road, Brierley Hill, West Midlands, DY5 2PF Tel: (01384) 424420 Fax: (01384) 424906 *Machine tool merchants*

Lye Panels Ltd, 41 Delph Road, Brierley Hill, West Midlands, DY5 2TW Tel: (01384) 70032 Fax: (01384) 70032 *Motor vehicle body panels manufrs*

Lye Valley Windows & Doors, 4 Stour Vale Road Industrial Estate, Stour Vale Road, Stourbridge, West Midlands, DY9 8PN Tel: (01384) 892952 Fax: (01384) 422626 *Window & door manufrs*

Lykiardopulo & Co. Ltd, 2-3 Gough Square, London, EC4A 3DE Tel: (020) 7353 6633 Fax: (020) 7353 6645 E-mail: office@lykiardopulo.co.uk *Ship agents*

▶ LYLLOY Co.,LTD, Unit 60, 3-9 Hyde Road, Ardwick Green, Manchester, M12 6BQ Tel: 0773 0383126 *LYLLOY is a trading company importing Dolls House, Mini*Furnitures, Radio Remote Control Toys (Helicopter, Plane, Boat), Mini*Moto/Quad/Dirt Bike/ATV, etc. And we run an online store offering*retail, dropship and wholesale servies as well in the UK. We are also officed in China, helping our customers sourcing the best cost*effective products with high quality. Please feel free to contact us,all enquiries are welcome.*

▶ Lymburn Contractors Ltd, Macmanniston Cottage, Dalrymple, Ayr, KA6 6BT Tel: (01292) 560369 Fax: (01292) 560643 E-mail: enquiries@lynburn.co.uk

Lymington Precision Engineers, Gosport Street, Lymington, Hampshire, SO41 9EE Tel: (01590) 677944 Fax: (01590) 647000 *Engineering subcontract services*

Lymington Yacht Haven Ltd, Kings Saltern Road, Lymington, Hampshire, SO41 3QD Tel: (01590) 677071 Fax: (01590) 678186 E-mail: admin@havenboatyard.com *Boat repair & refitting services*

Lymm Engraving, 199 Liverpool Road, Cadishead, Manchester, M44 5XH Tel: 0161-775 7625 Fax: 0161-775 7247 E-mail: enquires@lymmengraving.co.uk *Industrial engravers*

Lympsham Concrete Supplies, Wharfside, Lympsham, Weston-super-Mare, Avon, BS24 0EZ Tel: (01934) 750257 Fax: (01934) 750257 *Ready mix concrete suppliers*

Lyn Plan Ltd, 43 Imperial Way, Croydon, CR9 4LP Tel: (020) 8681 1833 Fax: (020) 8680 5727 E-mail: sales@lynplan.com *Furniture manufrs*

Lynbond 2000 Ltd, St. Davids House, 8 Blenheim Court Brownfields, Welwyn Garden City, Hertfordshire, AL7 1AD Tel: (01707) 259996 Fax: (01707) 259997 E-mail: solutions@lynbond2000.com *Clean room & controlled environment apparel suppliers*

Lynbrook Reprographic Ltd, Unit 15A, Boxer Place, Leyland, PR26 7QL Tel: (01772) 452125 Fax: (01772) 622304 E-mail: sales@lynbrookreprographic.co.uk *Laser equipment & photocopier suppliers*

▶ Lynch Ltd, 45 Neptune Street, London, SE16 7JP Tel: (020) 7394 8811 Fax: (020) 7394 8844

Gerry Lynch, 29 Kingsland Bridge Mansions, Murivance, Shrewsbury, SY1 1JF Tel: (01743) 353254 Fax: (01743) 248296 E-mail: gerry.lynch@talk21.com *Woodwork machines importer & distributor*

Lynch Truck Services Ltd, Barnfield Way, Altham, Accrington, Lancashire, BB5 5YT Tel: (01282) 773377 Fax: (01282) 779933 E-mail: enquiries@lynchtrucks.com *Commercial vehicle repairs, sales & rental services*

▶ Lynco, 110a Fenlake Road, Bedford, MK42 0EU Tel: (01234) 272425 Fax: (01234) 213141 E-mail: johncuthbert@ntlworld.com *Injection moulding services*

Lyncolec Ltd, 2 Abingdon Road, Nuffield Industrial Estate, Poole, Dorset, BH17 0UG Tel: (01202) 679797 Fax: (01202) 684530 E-mail: pcb@lyncolec.co.uk *Printed circuit board manufrs*

Lyndale Engines Peterborough Ltd, Fengate, Peterborough, PE1 5XB Tel: (01733) 345256 Fax: (01733) 553920 *General machining & reconditioning services*

▶ Lyndale Stairs, 1 Mount Road, Burntwood, Staffordshire, WS7 0AJ Tel: (01543) 677780

The Lyndann Group, Broadmeadows, Padstow Road, St. Breock, Wadebridge, Cornwall, PL27 7LS Tel: (01208) 815040 Fax: E-mail: daveharring@btconnect.com *Contract cleaning services*

▶ Lyndees, 105 Burnham Road, Dartford, DA1 5AZ Tel: (01322) 225147 E-mail: shop@lyndeesflorist.co.uk *Flowers for all occasions, local delivery available*

Lynden Tooling Services, 1 Main Road, Gilberdyke, Brough, North Humberside, HU15 2SW Tel: (01430) 449438 Fax: (01430) 449118 E-mail: sales@lyndentooling.co.uk *PCD tooling manufrs*

Lyndex Recycling Systems Ltd, Stafford Park 10, Telford, Shropshire, TF3 3BP Tel: (01952) 290333 Fax: (01952) 290229 E-mail: info@lindexrecycling.com *Recycling equipment manufrs*

Lyndhurst Precision Engineering Ltd, Weir Mill, Crosse Hall Street, Chorley, Lancashire, PR6 0UH Tel: (01257) 267876 Fax: (01257) 260724 E-mail: sales@lyndhurst-precision.co.uk *Precision engineers*

Lyndon Co., Unit 14 Saxon Business Centre, Windsor Avenue, London, SW19 2RR Tel: (020) 8543 9969 Fax: (020) 8543 9765 E-mail: sales@lydongroup.co.uk *Computer retailers*

▶ Lyndon Design Ltd, 342 Swindon Road, Cheltenham, Gloucestershire, GL51 9JZ Tel: (01242) 224295

Lyngrade Lancashire Ltd, Unit 23 Hardmans Business Centre, New Hall Hey Road, Rossendale, Lancashire, BB4 6HH Tel: (01706) 212780 Fax: (01706) 212816 E-mail: info@lyngrade.co.uk *Street furniture manufrs*

▶ Lynic Industrial Designs Ltd, 138 Main Street, Billinge, Wigan, Lancashire, WN5 7PD Tel: (01744) 895949 Fax: (01744) 892714 E-mail: info@lynicindes.co.uk *Pipework design consultants, pipework design, engineering & stress analysis services, pipe support engineering, 3-D piping design modelling & associated virtualisations, orthorgrphic layouts & isometric drawings, bills of materials & piping specifications. 3D-Cad models & drawing services for mechanical components & assemblies, skids, modules, etc. All these services related to the Oil, gas, chemical & pharmaceuticall processing, water treatment, fossil-fuel & hydro power generation industries*

Lynn & Jones Storefitters Ltd, Falcon House, Kenneth Street Off Ingram Road, Holbeck, Leeds, LS11 9RF Tel: 0113-234 0737 Fax: 0113-245 6130 E-mail: enquiries@lynnandjones.co.uk *Shop fitters*

Lynn Road Motors Ltd, 28-30 Lynn Road, Ilford, Essex, IG2 7DS Tel: (020) 8554 5670 Fax: (020) 8518 2426 *Car body repairers*

Lynnet Packaging, Unit E1, Neath Vale Business Park, Resolven, Neath, West Glamorgan, SA11 4SR Tel: (01639) 711122 Fax: (01639) 711166 E-mail: lynnet-packaging@btconnect.com *Vacuum packaging manufrs*

Lynnmoore Engineering Co. Ltd, Horsleys Fields, King's Lynn, Norfolk, PE30 5DD Tel: (01553) 771122 Fax: (01553) 777105 E-mail: tech@lynnmooreeng.co.uk *Manufacturer of high quality stainless steel*

Lynrose Engineering, Unit 12 Shrub Hill Industrial Estate, Worcester, WR4 9EL Tel: (01905) 729795 Fax: (01905) 729798 E-mail: mhlynrosesales@aol.com *Flame cutters manufrs*

Lyntech Systems Ltd, Unit 11 Maguire Industrial Estate, Torrington Avenue, Coventry, CV4 9HN Tel: (024) 7646 8710 Fax: (024) 7646 6111 E-mail: sales@lyntech-systems.ltd.uk *Ceiling, partition component suppliers & installers*

Lynton Clothes (1997) Ltd, Unit 1, Camart House, 15-19 Cowper Road, Leeds, LS9 7HR Tel: 0113-248 2111 Fax: 0113-248 1137 *Clothing manufrs*

Lynton Shopfitters Ltd, Hose Street, Stoke-on-Trent, ST6 5AL Tel: (01782) 819902 Fax: (01782) 839919 E-mail: admin@lynton-shopfitters.co.uk *Shop fitters*

Lynton Trailers UK Ltd, Constable Street, Manchester, M18 8GJ Tel: 0161-223 8211 Fax: 0161-223 0933 E-mail: lyntonmail@aol.com Principal Export Areas: Worldwide *Mobile exhibition unit manufrs*

Lyntons Ceiling & Partitions, 32-34 Albion Road, Sutton, Surrey, SM2 5TF Tel: (020) 8661 7875 *Suspended ceilings & partitioners*

Lynvale Ltd, Unit 6, Lime Grove Estate, Falconer Road, Haverhill, Suffolk, CB9 7XU Tel: (0870) 1609255 Fax: (0870) 1609256 E-mail: info@lynvale.co.uk *Manufacturing single & double-sided self adhesive foams & tapes, fabrics, felt, cork & magnetic products*

Lynwood Engineering, Albert House, High Street, Tipton, West Midlands, DY4 9HG Tel: 0121-522 6600 Fax: 0121-522 6601 E-mail: lynwoodengineering@qualtronyc.co.uk *Motor vehicle component manufrs*

Lynx Ltd, 269 Banbury Road, Oxford, OX2 7JF Tel: (01865) 310150 Fax: (01865) 310499 *Computer services*

Lynx Automotive Systems Ltd, Delta 500, Delta Business Park, Welton Road, Swindon, SN5 7XE Tel: (01793) 645300 Fax: (01793) 645301 E-mail: enquiries@mmi-automotive.co.uk *Computer hardware & software suppliers*

Lynx Computing, 171 Junction Road, London, N19 5PZ Tel: (020) 7263 6232

▶ Lynx Copiers, Unit 10 Lufton Heights Commerce Park Boundary Way, Lufton Tra, Lufton, Yeovil, Somerset, BA22 8UY Tel: (01935) 706914 Fax: (01935) 477110 E-mail: sales@lynxcopiers.co.uk *Supply & maintenance of digital colour & black & white copiers*

Lynx D P M Ltd, Unit 35a Monument Industrial Park, Warpsgrove Lane, Chalgrove, Oxford, OX44 7RW Tel: (01865) 891989 Fax: (01865) 891164 E-mail: sales@lynxdpm.com *Litho printers*

Lynx Engineering Kent Ltd, 2 Denton Slipways Site, Wharf Road, Gravesend, Kent, DA12 2RU Tel: (01474) 328877 Fax: (01474) 327744 *Specialists in front end applications, making sure you get the most effective use from your tractor, no matter what the make or model*

▶ Lynx Express Ltd, Stephenson Road, Durranhill Industrial Estate, Carlisle, CA1 3NX Tel: (01228) 529483 Fax: (01228) 592368

▶ Lynx Express Ltd, Unit 60, Dalcross Industrial Estate, Inverness, IV2 7XB Tel: (01667) 461303 Fax: (01667) 460185

Lynx Express Ltd, Pentland Industrial Estate, Loanhead, Midlothian, EH20 9QH Tel: 0131-448 2625 Fax: 0131-448 2621 *Parcel courier* Also at: Branches throughout the U.K.

Lynx Express Ltd, Coppetts Road, London, N10 1JR Tel: (020) 8365 2222 Fax: (020) 8883 7284 *Couriers*

▶ Lynx Express Ltd, Scotia Road, Stoke-on-Trent, ST6 4HG Tel: (01782) 814403 Fax: (01782) 814343

Lynx Lighting Ltd, 3 Oxford Road, Pen Mill Trading Estate, Yeovil, Somerset, BA21 5HR Tel: (01935) 429290 Fax: (01935) 845045 E-mail: sales@lynxlighting.co.uk *Special lighting*

Lynx Motors (International) Ltd, 68 Castleham Road, St. Leonards-on-Sea, East Sussex, TN38 9NU Tel: (01424) 851277 Fax: (01424) 853771 E-mail: enquiries@lynxmotors.co.uk *Motor vehicle designers, restorers & manufrs*

Lynx Security, The Old Pump Station, Furnace Lane, Finedon, Wellingborough, Northamptonshire, NN9 5NZ Tel: (01604) 621727 Fax: (01536) 724666 E-mail: enquiries@lynxsecurity.net *Electronic security installers*

Lynx Systems (West), Beaconfield, Pitts Lane, West Melbury, Shaftesbury, Dorset, SP7 0BU Tel: (01747) 855999 Fax: (01747) 852871 E-mail: sales@lynxssytems.co.uk *Computer systems & software development*

Lynx Technology Ltd, 3 Midland Way, Barlborough, Chesterfield, Derbyshire, S43 4XA Tel: (01246) 574000 Fax: (01246) 819401 E-mail: enquiries@lynxtec.co.uk *Computer systems & it solutions specialists*

Lynxcourt Ltd, Unit 9 Victoria Way, Newmarket, Suffolk, CB8 7SH Tel: (01638) 669214 Fax: (01638) 660209 E-mail: kiteley@lynxcourt.freeserve.co.uk *Bulk commercial builders*

▶ Lynxdiesels, 405 Finchampstead Road, Finchampstead, Wokingham, Berkshire, RG40 3RL Tel: 0118-973 4469 Fax: 0118-973 4026 E-mail: alandarby@lynxdiesels.com *Diesel fuel injection specialist*

Lyon Cole Insurance Management Ltd, King Harold Court, Sun Street, Waltham Abbey, Essex, EN9 1ER Tel: (01992) 787477 Fax: (01992) 787479 E-mail: carol.deal@lyoncole.com *Insurance brokers*

▶ Lyon Computer Solutions, 62, Lyon Road, Crowthorne, Berkshire, RG45 6RT Tel: (01344) 750147 *Computer solutions services*

Lyons, 206 Lylehill Road, Belfast, BT14 8SN Tel: (028) 9082 5688 Fax: (028) 9082 5688 *Signs manufrs*

Lyons Associates, 98 Wick Lane, Bournemouth, BH6 4LB Tel: (01202) 433379 Fax: (01202) 419676 E-mail: info@l-a.co.uk *IT strategic & market research consultants*

▶ Lyons Electrical, 7 Deacon Trading Centre, Knight Road, Rochester, Kent, ME2 2AU Tel: (01634) 290000 Fax: (01634) 290006

Lyons Seafoods Ltd, 3 Fairfield Road, Warminster, Wiltshire, BA12 9DA Tel: (01985) 217214 Fax: (01985) 847117 E-mail: info@lyons-seafoods.com *Sea food processors & products manufrs*

Lyontech Engineering Ltd, Unit 16 Manor Industrial Estate, Flint, Clwyd, CH6 5UY Tel: (01352) 730710 Fax: (01352) 730320 *Fire protection engineers*

Lyquidity Solutions, Ground Floor Office Suite, 16 Lynton Road, New Malden, Surrey, KT3 5EE Tel: (020) 7043 2777 Fax: (0870) 1373744 E-mail: sarah.seddon@lyquidity.com *ComplyXL from Lyquidity is the market leading solution for the compliance and control of spreadsheets within an organization. ComplyXL ensures changes are tracked, users roles and rights are controlled and all spreadsheets are managed in line with your company"s policy, so ensuring Sarbanes Oxley compliance.*

Lyras Financial Services Ltd, 24 26 Baltic Street, London, EC1Y 0RP Tel: (020) 7251 1313 Fax: (020) 7608 1783 E-mail: all@lyras-maritime.demon.co.uk *Ship brokers*

Lyrical Computing Ltd, 21 Chriswick High Road, London, W4 2ND Tel: (0844) 4822250 Fax: (0844) 4822251 *Consultants*

Lysis UK Ltd, 334 Chiswick High Road, London, W4 5TA Tel: (020) 8742 7719 Fax: (020) 8742 8397 *IT digital broadcasting systems*

Lyster & Associates, The Coach House, Ashford Lodge, Sudbury Road, Halstead, Essex, CO9 2RR Tel: (01787) 477777 Fax: (01787) 477377 E-mail: postmaster@lyster-assoc.co.uk *Communication device installation services*

Lytchett Minster Joinery, 14-16 Holton Road, Holton Heath Trading Park, Poole, Dorset, BH16 6LT Tel: (01202) 622441 Fax: (01202) 622441 *Joinery manufrs*

Lyte Ladders & Towers, Wind Road, Ystradgynlais, Swansea, SA9 1AF Tel: (01639) 846816 Fax: (01639) 841541 E-mail: sales@lyteladders.co.uk *Access equipment manufrs*

Lyten Ltd, 1-3 Inchview Road, Wallyford, Musselburgh, Midlothian, EH21 8JZ Tel: 0131-653 2400 Fax: 0131-665 0040 E-mail: sales@lyten.co.uk *Windows, doors & conservatories manufrs*

Lyteze Products Ltd, 8 Colne Road, Brightlingsea, Colchester, CO7 0DL Tel: (01206) 302699 Fax: (01206) 302699 E-mail: annecook@lyteze.com *Heated cutting & sealing handtool manufrs*

Lytham Garden Funiture, 63 Rossall Rd, Lytham St. Annes, Lancs, FY8 4BY Tel: (01253) 795544 Fax: (01253) 795544 *Garden & patio furniture manufacturer & distribs*

▶ M 3 Associates Ltd, 70 High Street, Houghton Regis, Dunstable, Bedfordshire, LU5 5BJ Tel: (01582) 866800 Fax: (01582) 866446 E-mail: sales@m3associates.co.uk *Consulting, asbestos, health & safety*

M A & C E Hathaway, 7 Blackmoor Road, Ebblake Industrial Estate, Verwood, Dorset, BH31 6AX Tel: (01202) 824067 Fax: (01202) 821301 *Packing case manufacturers & joinery*

M A C Electrical & Heating Engineers Ltd, Sites, 6-7 Back O Hill Road Industrial Estate, Stirling, FK8 1SH Tel: (01786) 464782 Fax: (01786) 450658

▶ M A C Motors Ltd, Unit E, Curzon Business Centre, Curzon Street, Burton-on-Trent, Staffordshire, DE14 2DH Tel: (01283) 534230 E-mail: sales@macmotors.co.uk *Vehicle repairs*

M.A.C.-Rk Precision Engineering Ltd, Unit A1, Bridge Road Industrial Estate, Southall, Middlesex, UB2 4AB Tel: (020) 8843 1999 Fax: (020) 8843 1666 E-mail: office@macfittings.co.uk *CNC machining hydraulic hose fitting manufrs*

M A C Services Ltd, 23 Blandford Street, London, W1U 3DL Tel: (020) 7486 9075 Fax: (020) 7224 1459 E-mail: mail@mac-services.co.uk *M A C Services are electrical contractors, engineers and wholesalers based in Westminster for over 30 years. Some of the services we provide are as follows: Test and Inspection, Emergency Lighting, Maintenance, Fire Alarms, Security Systems, Data Wiring, Contracting, Access Control Systems, Wiring /Rewiring 24 hour emergency Service and Free Quotation Service*

M A C Tool Hire, 25 Park Street, Congleton, Cheshire, CW12 1EG Tel: (01260) 299751 Fax: (01260) 299698 *Builders, DIY & garden tool hire*

M A C Tools, Gowerton Road, BlackMills, Northampton, NN4 7BW Tel: (01604) 827351 Fax: (01604) 661654 *Industrial power tool manufrs*

▶ M A C Transport, Albion Parade, Gravesend, Kent, DA12 2RN Tel: (01474) 320999

▶ M A Carpets, 401 Kenton Lane, Harrow, Middlesex, HA3 8RZ Tel: (020) 8909 1373 *Carpet retailers*

▶ M & A City Kitchen Equipment, 214 Century Building, Tower Street, Brunswick Business Park, Liverpool, L3 4BJ Tel: 0151-709 6303 Fax: 0151-709 6324 E-mail: salesliverpool@ma-enviro.co.uk *Catering equipment suppliers*

M A Computing Ltd, 52A Church Street, Broughty Ferry, Dundee, DD5 1HB Tel: (01382) 770044 Fax: (0870) 0557796 E-mail: ian@macomputing.demon.co.uk *Computer services solutions*

M A Consultant, 87 Cobham Road, Ilford, Essex, IG3 9JL Tel: (020) 8599 1421 Fax: (020) 8599 1421 E-mail: ma_afzal@btinternet.com *Rubber waste & scrap consultants*

▶ M & A Couriers, 6 Stanley Close, Sherburn, Durham, DH6 1JS Tel: 0191-372 1210 Fax: 0191-372 1210 E-mail: info@maac.co.uk *uk sameday courier service*24/7 fragile goods specialist*fully tracked vehicles with sat nav*

M A Culshaw, School Farm, Back La East, Mawdesley, Ormskirk, Lancashire, L40 3TA Tel: (01704) 821076 Fax: (01704) 821986 E-mail: sales@furniture-bespoke.co.uk *Bespoke furniture manufrs*

M A Distributors Ltd, Industrial House, Conway Street, Hove, East Sussex, BN3 3LW Tel: (01273) 720129 Fax: (01273) 820915 E-mail: ash@ma-d.net *In-car entertainment accessories & car alarms distributors*

▶ M A Engineering, Boughton Farm, Stoke Ferry, King's Lynn, Norfolk, PE33 9ST Tel: (01366) 502205 *Engineers*

M & A Environmental Ltd, Unit 3 Gidleys Meadow, Christow, Exeter, EX6 7QB Tel: (01647) 252855 Fax: (01647) 252882 E-mail: sales@ma-enviro.co.uk *Distribution of cleaning, catering, equipment*

▶ M & A Environmental Ltd, PO Box 479, Harrogate, North Yorkshire, HG3 4WW Tel: (01423) 781330 Fax: (01423) 780709 E-mail: Simon@ma-enviro.co.uk

M & A Environmental Northern Ltd, 2 Royd Business Park, Dye House Lane, Brighouse, West Yorkshire, HD6 1LL Tel: (01484) 475100 Fax: (01484) 475103 E-mail: sales@brook-industrial.fsnet.co.uk *Safety clothing distributors & janitorial*

▶ M A G Scaffolding Services Ltd, 170 Bitterne Road West, Southampton, SO18 1BG Tel: (023) 8021 1393

▶ M.A.G. Scotland Ltd, 9 Gladstone Avenue, Barrhead, Glasgow, G78 1QT Tel: (0870) 0276977 E-mail: sales@magscotland.com *Plastics fabrication, welding, design CNC machining*

M A Hadfield, 57 Commercial Street, Norton, Malton, North Yorkshire, YO17 9HX Tel: (01653) 694095 E-mail: mhadfield@lineone.net *Saddlery & horse clothing manufrs*

M A J Electronics, Stallings Lane, Kingswinford, West Midlands, DY6 7HU Tel: (01384) 278646 Fax: (01384) 298877 E-mail: sales@majelectronic.co.uk *Amplifier/ speaker enclosure manufrs*

M A J Hi Spec Ltd, 1 Scott St, Keighley, West Yorkshire, BD21 2JJ Tel: (01535) 606524 Fax: (01535) 610255 *Electroplating services*

M A Jordan (Transportation), Jordans Compound, Merrylees Road, Leicester, LE9 9FE Tel: (01455) 828333

M A K Drums & Containers, Unit 16 Garston Industrial Estate, Blackburne Street, Liverpool, L19 8JB Tel: 0151-494 3331 Fax: 0151-494 9580 E-mail: sales@makdrums.co.uk *Drum reconditioners & suppliers*

M A Kelly, 284 Councillor Lane, Cheadle Hulme, Cheadle, Cheshire, SK8 5PN Tel: 0161-485 2255 Fax: 0161-442 1617 *Up & over door specialists*

M A L (Meauctore), PO Box 2286, Swindon, SN4 7BA Tel: (01793) 849911 Fax: (01793) 848847 E-mail: info@mal-it.co.uk *Fire service radio equipment suppliers*

▶ M & A Locksmiths, 31 Nelson Road, Uxbridge, Middlesex, UB10 0PU Tel: (0800) 6954195 E-mail: john@a-jlocksmiths.com *Locksmiths*

M A Majid, Swan La Mill, Higher Swan Lane, Bolton, BL3 3BJ Tel: (01204) 657442 Fax: (01204) 855314 *Ladies underwear manufrs*

M A N E R F UK Ltd, Frankland Road, Blagrove, Swindon, SN5 8YU Tel: (01793) 448000 Fax: (01793) 448260 *Suppliers of commercial & armoured military vehicles*

▶ M A Networks Ltd, 171 Warley Hill, Great Warley, Brentwood, Essex, CM13 3AG Tel: 07802 481688 Fax: 0870 706 2516 E-mail: info@manetworks.co.uk *IT Auditing, Project Management and IT Support. Specialising in all areas of IT Auditing, Security Administration, oeprations, problem nad change management plus vendor management processes. IBM mainframe, AS/400, UNIX platforms, VMS, Windows, Firewalls, content filtering etc.*

M & A Office Supplies Ltd, Unit 12 Westwood Court, Brunel Road, Totton, Southampton, SO40 3WX Tel: (023) 8066 7110 Fax: (023) 8066 7136 E-mail: simon@maoffice.demon.co.uk *Commercial & office stationers suppliers*

M A P A Spontex UK Ltd, Berkeley Business Park Berkeley Business Park, Wainwright Road, Worcester, WR4 9ZS Tel: (01905) 450300 Fax: (01905) 450350 *Cellulose sponge & cloth manufrs*

M A P Structual Steel Manufacturing, Cross Pipes Road, Alverthorpe, Wakefield, West Yorkshire, WF2 8BG Tel: (01924) 367447 Fax: (01924) 366593 E-mail: info@mapss.com *Structural steelwork & steel fabricators*

M A P Systems, Unit 51, Bergen Way, North Lynn Industrial Estate, King's Lynn, Norfolk, PE30 2JG Tel: (01553) 764314 Fax: (01553) 769388 E-mail: eng@mapsystems.co.uk *Food packaging material manufrs & engineers*

M A P Systems Ltd, Unit 22 Sarum Complex, Salisbury Road, Uxbridge, Middlesex, UB8 2RZ Tel: (01895) 811234 Fax: (01895) 238681 *Packaging machines & materials distributors*

M A P Woodcraft (Caerphilly) Ltd, The Rhos, Bedwas Road, Caerphilly, Mid Glamorgan, CF83 3AU Tel: (029) 2088 2339 Fax: (029) 2086 8315 *Wooden components manufrs*

M & A Packaging Services Ltd, Spring Lane North, Malvern, Worcestershire, WR14 1BU Tel: (01684) 560099 Fax: (01684) 560095 E-mail: info@mapexinspection.co.uk *Coding & printing equipment manufrs*

M & A Pharmachem Ltd, Allenby Laboratories, Wigan Road, Westhoughton, Bolton, BL5 2AL Tel: (01942) 816184 Fax: (01942) 813937 E-mail: info@mapharmachem.co.uk *Pharmaceutical manufrs*

M A Platt Ltd, St. James Street, Accrington, Lancashire, BB5 1NU Tel: (01254) 234743 Fax: (01254) 238884 *Furniture manufrs*

M A Products Ltd, 36 Hirst Lane, Malthouse Road, Tipton, West Midlands, DY4 9AE Tel: 0121-520 7077 Fax: 0121-520 9677 *Architectural joinery, countering & woodwork*

M A S Co., Church Road Studios, 56-62 Church Road, London, E12 6AF Tel: (020) 8553 5594 E-mail: sy@skillwork.com *Property investment services*

M A S Business Systems Ltd, 8 Crown Court, Clough Road, Severalls Industrial Park, Colchester, CO4 9TZ Tel: (01206) 852827 Fax: (01206) 855009 E-mail: sagesales@masbs.co.uk *Software development services*

M A S Furniture Contracts Ltd, Welham House, Travellers Lane, North Mymms, Hatfield, Hertfordshire, AL9 7HF Tel: (01707) 272737 Fax: (01707) 260124 E-mail: sales@masfurniture.co.uk *Hotel & restaurant furniture*

M A S S Computers Ltd, 53 Dereham Road, Norwich, NR2 4HZ Tel: (01603) 630768 Fax: (01603) 610657 E-mail: sales@masscomputers.co.uk *Computer repairs & manufrs*

M A Samad, 105 Eade Road, London, N4 1TJ Tel: (020) 8802 2929 Fax: (020) 8802 2777 *Oriental carpet importer*

M A Taylor Engineering Ltd, Orchard Street, Redditch, Worcestershire, B98 7DP Tel: (01527) 62138 Fax: (01527) 68600 E-mail: micktaylorj@tiscali.co.uk *Precision & production engineers*

M & A Thomson Litho Ltd, 10 Colvilles Place, East Kilbride, Glasgow, G75 0SN Tel: (01355) 233081 Fax: (01355) 245439 *General & commercial printers*

▶ M Adams, 77 Colvend Street, Glasgow, G40 4DU Tel: 0141-556 2915

▶ M Albutt Electrical Contractors Ltd, 39a Birmingham Road, Blakedown, Kidderminster, Worcestershire, DY10 3JW Tel: (01562) 700242 Fax: (01562) 701242

▶ M AND M DOMESTIC SERVICES, 5 Prudden Close, Elstow, Bedford, MK42 9EB Tel: 01234 219924 E-mail: mandmservices@fsmail.net *High quality domestic cleaning at realistic prices for every home.Serving Bedford and the surrounding villages*

M B A Michael Bailey Associates plc, 12 Brook House, Chapel Place, London, EC2A 3SJ Tel: (020) 7739 2022 Fax: (020) 7739 4280 *IT recruitment*

M B A Systems Ltd, Staple House, Staple Gardens, Winchester, Hampshire, SO23 8SR Tel: (01962) 841494 Fax: (01962) 864770 *IT developers & web designers*

M B Aerospace Ltd, Unit 9, P O Box 11, Heasandford Industrial Estate, Burnley, Lancashire, BB10 2TG Tel: (01282) 446600 Fax: (01282) 439318 *Aeronautical engineers*

M B Air Systems Ltd, Unit 13b Enterprise Court, Seaham Grange Industrial Estate, Seaham, County Durham, SR7 0PS Tel: 0191-521 4111 Fax: 0191-521 1616 E-mail: sales@mbairsystems.co.uk *Air products supply services* Also at: Barrow-in-Furness, Billingham, Carlisle & Kelso

M B Air Systems, 149 Glasgow Road, Wishaw, Lanarkshire, ML2 7QJ Tel: (01698) 355711 Fax: (01698) 359299 E-mail: sales@mbairsystems.co.uk *Distributors of compressed air*

M B Audio Visual Ltd, Unit 2c Thirsk Industrial Park, York Road, Thirsk, North Yorkshire, YO7 3BX Tel: (01845) 522322 Fax: (01845) 522322 E-mail: info@mbaudiovisual.co.uk *Located in Thirsk North Yorkshire, MB Audio Visual ltd are specialists in all areas of audio and visual equipment for both sale and hire. Covering North Yorkshire, West Yorkshire, East Yorkshire, Middlesbrough and Teeside for av, projectors, Plus Ben Q etc, plasma screens, LCD screens, speakers, microphones, smart boards, lighting effects professional cameras we deal with all the major suppliers Sony, Electro Voice, JVC, Panasonic, Pro-light, Numark, and many more, we specialise in hire for conferences, with stage sets built to order. We are supplier projector screens from fast fold rear projection, to tripod. Also outdoor PA for your show or event from two horns to thirty, with caravan and presenter if required, our main PA system goes up to 8000watts. Whatever you require in the audiovisual field MB Audio Visual are completely dedicated to your total satisfaction.*

M & B Brakepress Ltd, Bellotts Road, Bath, BA2 3RT Tel: (01225) 317788 Fax: (01225) 448395 *Press brake facilities*

M & B Brick Cutting Services, Old Canal Yard, 52 Reuben Street, Stockport, Cheshire, SK4 1PS Tel: 0161-476 6939 Fax: 0161-429 7896 *Brick cutting services*

M B C Signs London Ltd, Unit 33 Leyton Industrial Village, Argall Avenue, London, E10 7QP Tel: (020) 8532 8321 Fax: (020) 8518 7676 *Sign manufrs*

M B C Signs London Ltd, Unit 33 Leyton Industrial Village, Argall Avenue, London, E10 7QP Tel: (020) 8532 8321 Fax: (020) 8518 7676 E-mail: mcassanova@btconnect.com *Sign contractors & manufrs*

M B Carwash, The Mardy, Llandenny, Usk, Gwent, NP15 1DN Tel: (01291) 690404 Fax: (01291) 639503 E-mail: mb'carwash@onet.co.uk *Lease car washing services*

M B Controls & Installation, 3 White Swan Industrial Estate, Derker Street, Oldham, OL1 3LY Tel: 0161-628 5026 Fax: 0161-628 5027 E-mail: mikeholt@mbcontrols.fsnet.co.uk *Electric control systems manufrs*

M & B Diesel Glasgow Ltd, 31 Queensferry Street, Glasgow, G5 0XR Tel: 0141-429 2000 Fax: 0141-429 3130 E-mail: mbdiesel@btconnect.com *Diesel fuel injection repairers*

M B Distribution Cleveland Ltd, Wallis Road, Skippers Lane Industrial Estate, Middlesbrough, Cleveland, TS6 6JB Tel: (01642) 455945 Fax: (01642) 455504 E-mail: sales@mb-distribution.co.uk *Window & door fitting distributors or agents*

▶ M & B Edible Oil, 2 Cannon Road, Heathfield, Newton Abbot, Devon, TQ12 6SH Tel: (01626) 836280 Fax: (01626) 836280 E-mail: mboils@btconnect.com *Collectors of used cooking oil/fats*

M B Electronics, Clayfield Industrial Estate, Tickhill Road, Doncaster, South Yorkshire, DN4 8QG Tel: (01302) 855229 Fax: (01302) 855229 *Cathode ray tube stockists*

M & B Engineering Ltd, Bellotts Road, Bath, BA2 3RT Tel: (01225) 333944 Fax: (01225) 448395 *Steel fabricators*

M & B Engineering, 62-63 John Wilson Business Park, Thanet Way, Whitstable, Kent, CT5 3QT Tel: (01227) 261917 Fax: (01227) 770809 E-mail: robertacros@tiscali.co.uk *Precision & production engineering services*

M B Engineering Services Ltd, Lancaster Approach, North Killingholme, Immingham, South Humberside, DN40 3JZ Tel: (01469) 540478 Fax: (01469) 540548 *Plant engineers services*

M B Engineering Solutions Ltd, Logans Road, Motherwell, Lanarkshire, ML1 3NP Tel: (01698) 266111 Fax: (01698) 269774 E-mail: info@mbgroup.com *Project engineering, construction, specialist services*

M B F Business Forms Ltd, 20 Rectory Road, West Bridgford, Nottingham, NG2 6BG Tel: 0115-981 3786 Fax: 0115-945 5249 E-mail: info@mbf-business-forms.co.uk *Business forms & systems printers manufrs*

M & B Fencing Supplies Ltd, Unit 49, Boughton Industrial Estate, Boughton, Newark, Nottinghamshire, NG22 9LD Tel: (01623) 861184 Fax: (01623) 862820 E-mail: sales@mbfence.co.uk *Container hire & fence manufrs*

M & B Fuel Injection Service Ltd, Unit 22 Parham Drive, Eastleigh, Hampshire, SO50 4NU Tel: (023) 8061 9655 Fax: (023) 8062 9524 *Diesel fuel injection repair services*

M & B Haulage & Waste Paper Co. Ltd, Low Mill Lane, Dewsbury, West Yorkshire, WF13 3LX Tel: (01924) 494240 Fax: (01924) 480574 *Waste management & transport logistics*

▶ M B Heating Ltd, Unit 1 Darby Lane, Hindley, Wigan, Lancashire, WN2 3DW Tel: (01942) 520100 Fax: (01942) 523173

M B Inspection Ltd, Wellhead Way, Wellhead Industrial Estate, Aberdeen, AB21 7DG Tel: (01224) 772161 Fax: (01224) 772156 E-mail: operations@mbinspection.co.uk *Difficult access engineers*

M B Inspections Ltd, PO Box 4, Motherwell, Lanarkshire, ML1 3NP Tel: (01698) 262277 Fax: (01698) 269774 *Materials testing & metallurgical analysts* Also at: Aberdeen

M B K Motor Rewinds Ltd, 10a Lythalls Lane, Coventry, CV6 6FG Tel: (024) 7668 9510 Fax: (024) 7666 2944 E-mail: sales@mbk-rewinds.co.uk *Coil winders, coil (electrical) manufacturers or services*

M B M Clothing Ltd, 90 Freer Road, Aston, Birmingham, B6 6NB Tel: 0121-554 7522 Fax: 0121-554 7522 *Rally coats & casual wear manufrs*

M B M UK, Eurotec Building, New Road, Newhaven, E. Sussex, BN9 0DR Tel: (01273) 472554 Fax: (01273) 476100 *Catering equipment manufrs & suppliers*

M B Motors, Wedglen Park, Midhurst, West Sussex, GU29 9RE Tel: (01730) 813000 Fax: (01730) 812227 E-mail: mbmotors@pchowne.freeserve.co.uk *Car repairers & services*

M B O Tools Ltd, 50 North Street, Steeple Bumpstead, Haverhill, Suffolk, CB9 7DP Tel: (01440) 730475 Fax: (01440) 730475 E-mail: jhall.mbotools@virgin.net *Sales of tooling, materials, electronic production specialists*

M B O (U K) Ltd, Mill End, Standon, Ware, Hertfordshire, SG11 1LR Tel: (01920) 823999 Fax: (01920) 823631 E-mail: sales@mbouk.co.uk *Solders, electronics industry*

M B Plant Hire, 14 Wilson Street, Peterhead, Aberdeenshire, AB42 1UD Tel: (01224) 575255 Fax: (01779) 479236 *Van & plant hire agents*

M B Plastics Ltd, Bridge Lane, Woolston, Warrington, WA1 4BA Tel: (01925) 822811 Fax: (01925) 818907 E-mail: sales@mbplastics.co.uk *GRP products design & manufacture & install*

▶ M B Plumbing, 18 Westend Court, Law, Carluke, Lanarkshire, ML8 5SL Tel: (01698) 375968

▶ M B Plumbing & Heating, 189 Ashgate Road, Chesterfield, Derbyshire, S40 4AP Tel: (01246) 555161

M B Products Ltd, Parkgate Works, Coleman Street, Parkgate, Rotherham, South Yorkshire, S62 6EL Tel: (01709) 528215 Fax: (01709) 710796 E-mail: roger@mbpgroup.freeserve.co.uk *Waterproof clothing & healthcare products manufrs*

M B Pumps Ltd, 2 Royle Park, Congleton, Cheshire, CW12 1JJ Tel: (01260) 299438 Fax: (01260) 297595 E-mail: sales@mbpumps.co.uk *Cutter pumps, submersible & dry well specialists*

M B R Group Ltd, Beezon Road, Kendal, Cumbria, LA9 6EL Tel: (01539) 796400 Fax: (01539) 796499 *Photocopier suppliers*

M & B Radio (Leeds), 86 Bishopgate Street, Leeds, LS1 4BB Tel: 0113-243 5649 Fax: 0113-242 6881 *Electronic test & measurement distributors*

▶ M B Roche & Sons Ltd, 28 The Weir, Hessle, North Humberside, HU13 0RU Tel: (01482) 648731 Fax: (01482) 649273

M B S, Nowhurst Lane, Broadbridge Heath, Horsham, West Sussex, RH12 3PJ Tel: (01403) 263303 Fax: (01403) 263839 *Survey software*

M B S Window Systems Ltd, Corringham Road Industrial Estate, Gainsborough, Lincolnshire, DN21 1QB Tel: (01427) 615050 Fax: (01427) 614436 *UPVc & aluminium window & door installers & manufrs*

M B Spanier, 22 Hatton Garden, London, EC1N 8BA Tel: (020) 7242 2586 Fax: (020) 7405 1472 *Jewellery manufrs*

M & B Spraying, 2b Radnor Road, Wigston, Leicestershire, LE18 4XY Tel: 0116-277 8740 Fax: 0116-277 8740 *Paint spraying services*

M B Techniques Ltd, Douglas Street, Hamilton, Lanarkshire, ML3 0BU Tel: (01698) 457222 Fax: (01698) 891924 *CNC machining, press parts & turned parts tooling manufrs*

M B Technology, Benfieldside, Milton Road, Wokingham, Berkshire, RG40 1DD Tel: 0118-977 6039 Fax: 0118-978 9386 *Precision equipment for science/industry*

▶ M B W Doors, Unit 8, Dale Street Industrial Estate, Radcliffe, Manchester, M26 1AD Tel: 0161-723 5577 Fax: 0161-723 5577 E-mail: mbwdoors1@btconnect.com *Doors retailers*

M B W Training, Unit 2-5 Princess Street Enterprise Centre, Princess Street, Blackpool, FY1 5BZ Tel: (01253) 291110 Fax: (01253) 291110 *Training & resource centre, IT, job search, career guidance*

▶ M B Wellclad, PO Box 4, Motherwell, Lanarkshire, ML1 3NP Tel: (01698) 266111 Fax: (01698) 275487 E-mail: info@mbgroup.com *Oil, tanks, plastic & steel*

▶ M Barnwell Services Ltd, Reginald Road, Smethwick, West Midlands, B67 5AS Tel: 0121-429 6448 Fax: 0121-434 3016 E-mail: sales@barnwell.co.uk *Stockists & distributors of sealing products*

M Bielby Ltd, 4 Cave Street, Hull, HU5 2TZ Tel: (01482) 342653 Fax: (01482) 447366 E-mail: info@mbielby.com *Heating & mechanical engineering services*

▶ M Bliss Ltd, 1 Mallard Close, Earls Barton, Northampton, NN6 0JF Tel: (01604) 811122 Fax: (01604) 811198

M Brigstock, Stallings Lane, Kingswinford, West Midlands, DY6 7HT Tel: (01384) 293817 Fax: (01384) 279357 *Dairy products merchant*

M Brittain York Ltd, 8 Moneybroom Road, Lisburn, County Antrim, BT28 2QP Tel: (028) 9262 2270 Fax: (028) 9262 2280 *Steel stockholders*

M Brittain York Ltd, 29 Hospital Fields Road, Fulford Industrial Estate, York, YO10 4FZ Tel: (01904) 636021 Fax: (01904) 611627 E-mail: sales@mbrittainyork.co.uk *Steel processors*

M C A (Aston) Ltd, 38-50 Victoria Road, Aston, Birmingham, B6 5HF Tel: 0121-554 6644 Fax: 0121-554 7854 *Motor cycle spares & accessories wholesalers*

M & C (Agricultural) Ltd, Norwich Road, Swaffham, Norfolk, PE37 8DD Tel: (01760) 722607 Fax: (01760) 725435 E-mail: itaylor@mcagri.co.uk *Agricultural engineers* Also at: Bunwell

M C Air Filtration Ltd, Motney Hill Road, Gillingham, Kent, ME8 7TZ Tel: (01634) 388333 Fax: (01634) 379384 E-mail: sales@mcaf.co.uk *Manufacturers of air filters & air filtration equipment*

M C B Imaging Services Ltd, 14 Fraser Road, Erith, Kent, DA8 1QJ Tel: (01322) 333062 Fax: (01322) 441654 E-mail: info@mcbimaging.co.uk *Document Management, Scanning & Microfilm bureau services*

M C Brick Cutting Services Ltd, Unit 4 Sir Francis Ley Industrial Park, Derby, DE23 8XA Tel: (01332) 203332 Fax: (01332) 203335 *Brick cutting services*

M C Building Chemicals, Stechford Trading Estate Lyndon Road, Unit 17, Stechford, Birmingham, B33 8BU Tel: 0121-789 8333 Fax: 0121-789 8595 E-mail: sales@mc-bauchemie.de *Construction chemicals*

▶ M C Clark Ltd, 3 Norwich Road, Hethersett, Norwich, NR9 3DD Tel: (01603) 501071 Fax: (01603) 811748 E-mail: mailbox@mcclarkbuilders.co.uk

▶ M C Control Systems, Rayner House, Stockport, Cheshire, SK1 3ER Tel: 0161 4771266 *Lift control systems manufrs*

▶ M C D Electrical Services Ltd, Unit 24b Chapelhall Industrial Estate, Chapelhall, Airdrie, Lanarkshire, ML6 8QH Tel: (01236) 771440 Fax: (01236) 771441

M C D Engineering Ltd, 4 Smiths Forge, North End Road, Yatton, Bristol, BS49 4AU Tel: (01934) 835450 Fax: (01934) 876427 *Precision engineer services for induct specialist in nuclear industry*

M C Electronics Ltd, 61 Grimsdyke Road, Pinner, Middlesex, HA5 4PP Tel: (020) 8428 2027 Fax: (020) 8428 2027 E-mail: sales@mcelectronics.co.uk *Safety equipment suppliers for railway industry*

M & C Engineering, Unit 12 West Bowhouse Workshops, Girdle Toll, Irvine, Ayrshire, KA11 1BU Tel: (01294) 215986 Fax: (01294) 215986 *Precision component manufrs*

M C Engineering Services, Unit 3b The Lays Farm, Charlton Road, Keynsham, Bristol, BS31 2SE Tel: 0117-986 4196 Fax: 0117-986 4196 E-mail: info@kagemforge.co.uk *Welding fabricators*

▶ M & C Environmental Services, Teresa Gavin House, Southend Road, Woodford Green, Essex, IG8 8FA Tel: (020) 8550 3838 Fax: (020) 8551 7995

M C F Services Ltd, Units 4-5, Camden Drive, Hockley, Birmingham, B1 3LR Tel: 0121-236 8956 Fax: 0121-236 8048 *Milling engineering joinery & aluminium profiles*

▶ M C Freeze Refrigeration & Air Conditioning, Barrs Court Road, Hereford, HR1 1EG Tel: (01432) 355164 Fax: (01432) 273612

M & C Furnishing Pine Centre, 115-117 Albert Road, Colne, Lancashire, BB8 0BT Tel: (01282) 869072 Fax: (01282) 869072 *Pine furniture retailers*

M C G Applications Ltd, 150 Hastings Road, Battle, East Sussex, TN33 0TW Tel: (01424) 774748 Fax: (01424) 777190 E-mail: gill@mcg-applications.co.uk *Book keeping, payroll & computer consultancy*

M C G Systems Ltd, The Hayloft, Condover Mews, Condover, Shrewsbury, SY5 7BG Tel: (01743) 875150 Fax: (01743) 875155 E-mail: info@mcgsystems.co.uk *Software development services*

M C H Design & Shopfitting Ltd, 27 Fergusson Drive, Knockmoore Hill Industrial Park, Lisburn, County Antrim, BT28 2EX Tel: (028) 9266 8000 Fax: (028) 9267 8008 E-mail: ask@makeit-fit.com *Design & shopfitting*

M C H Eletrical Systems Ltd, Unit 7, Woodall Street, Bloxwich, Walsall, WS3 3HG Tel: (01922) 404050 Fax: (01922) 404045 E-mail: sales@mchlet.co.uk *Switchgear (low voltage)*

▶ M C I, Bridge Park, Merrow Lane, Guildford, Surrey, GU4 7BF Tel: (01483) 306500 Fax: (01483) 455378

M C I, Reading International Business Park, Reading, RG2 6DA Tel: 0118-905 5000 Fax: 0118-905 5711 *Telecommunications & Internet providers*

▶ M C I Electrotechnics Ltd, Unit E26 Wellheads Crescent, Wellheads Industrial Estate, Dyce, Aberdeen, AB21 7GA Tel: (01224) 772211

M C Insulation Supplies Ltd, Unit 3 Brandon Way, West Bromwich, West Midlands, B70 9PQ Tel: 0121-525 0444 Fax: 0121-525 0440 E-mail: marycarthy@aol.com *Insulation distributors*

M C Kelly Ltd, Elston Farm, Copplestone, Crediton, Devon, EX17 5PB Tel: (01363) 84545 Fax: (01363) 84060 E-mail: sales@mckelly.co.uk *Food wholesaler's, turkey producers*

M C L Software Ltd, Hesketh Mount, Lord Street, Southport, Merseyside, PR8 1JR Tel: (01704) 501001 Fax: (01704) 533003 E-mail: info@mclsoftware.co.uk *Computer software developers*

M C L Unitex Ltd, Adams Close, Heanor, Derbyshire, DE75 7SW Tel: 01773 535365 *Passive fire protection systems*

M C M, 26 Donisthorpe Street, Leeds, LS10 1PL Tel: 0113-245 1020 Fax: 0113-243 1971 E-mail: info@mcmpos.co.uk *Sign distributors & manufrs*

M C M Direct Mail, Unit 10 Solent Industrial Estate, Shamblehurst Lane, Hedge End, Southampton, SO30 2FX Tel: (01489) 796611 Fax: (01489) 795511 E-mail: sales@mcmdirect.com *MCM Direct Mail provides its customers with a quality, reliable direct mail and mailing partner. We offer you exceptional database services, mailing, data processing and direct mail all under one roof. Our strategy is one of quality and consistency, building trust and long term relationships with our clients and suppliers. We aim to carry out your mailing in the most environmentally friendly way, minimising the impact on our world, maximising our future, One - stop mailing solutions, Fulfilment, Database Services, 15 years in Direct Mail, QMP Accredited, Clients that stay. Find out how MCM Direct can help you make the most of your database and mailing activity.*

M C M Machine Sales Ltd, 22 Bancrofts Road, South Woodham Ferrers, Chelmsford, CM3 5UQ Tel: (01245) 322545 Fax: (01245) 329468 E-mail: mc.m@talk21.com *Plastic injection mouldings manufrs*

M C Mills & Co. Ltd, Lower Castlereagh St, Barnsley, South Yorkshire, S70 1AR Tel: (01226) 732566 Fax: (01226) 285446 E-mail: mc.mills@virgin.net *Bolts, nuts & engineers supplies distributors & agents*

▶ M C Plumbing, Unit 7, Ermine Point Business Park, Westmill Road, Ware, Hertfordshire, SG12 0EF Tel: (01920) 465111

M C Products, Unit 1-2 Yardley Centre, Yardley Road, Knowsley Industrial Park, Liverpool, L33 7SS Tel: 0151-548 0144 Fax: 0151-549 2283 E-mail: sales@mcproducts.co.uk *Police & security suppliers & promotional items specialists*

M C R Electrical Services, 2 Factory Estate, English Street, Hull, HU3 2BE Tel: (01482) 589062 Fax: (01482) 589525 E-mail: mcr@unit2.fslife.co.uk *Electrical engineers*

▶ M C Research, 28 Hornsby Square, Southfields Business Park, Basildon, Essex, SS15 6SD Tel: (01268) 490242 Fax: (01268) 410595 E-mail: info@mcresearch.co.uk *Data publishing specialists services*

▶ M C Resources, Lune Industrial Estate, Lancaster, LA1 5QP Tel: (01524) 847272 Fax: (01524) 847878 E-mail: mcresources@tiscali.co.uk *Glass fibre processing plant*

M & C Roofing Contractors, Brunswick Industrial Estate, Brunswick Village, Newcastle upon Tyne, NE13 7BA Tel: 0191-236 7901 Fax: 0191-236 2086 *Roofing contractors*

M C S, 134 Stanney Lane, Ellesmere Port, CH65 9AQ Tel: 0151-355 1935 Fax: 0151-355 6253 E-mail: mcs@mcsbowling.com *Computer consultants*

M C S Control Systems Ltd, Unit 4 Phoenix Park, Bayton Road Industrial Estate, Coventry, CV7 9QN Tel: (024) 7636 0211 Fax: (024) 7636 8219 E-mail: sales@mcscs.co.uk *Control systems design consultants*

M C S Technical Products Ltd, Factory 1, Cheney Manor Industrial Estate, Swindon, SN2 2PN Tel: (01793) 538308 Fax: (01793) 522324 E-mail: sales@mcstechproducts.co.uk *MCS Technical Products are distributors of catering equipment based in Swindon, Wiltshire and are specialists in bringing the latest designs in energy efficient cooking solutions and innovative food safety technology to your kitchen, together with superior aftersales support.*

▶ M C Services, 21a New Road, Earby, Barnoldswick, Lancashire, BB18 6UY Tel: (01282) 844801 Fax: (01282) 843159 *Welders & fabricators*

▶ M C Squared Ltd, Old Kings Head Court, 11 High Street, Dorking, Surrey, RH4 1AR Tel: (01306) 876505 Fax: (01306) 877508 E-mail: studio@mvsquared.co.uk *Designers exhibitions services*

▶ M C T Ltd, Liss Business Centre, Station Road, Liss, Hampshire, GU33 7AW Tel: (01730) 894834 Fax: (01730) 892641 E-mail: info@mctl.co.uk *IT services*

M C T Ltd, 129 London Rd, Ongar, Essex, CM5 9PP Tel: (01277) 362112 Fax: (01277) 362112 *Computer consultants*

M C Truck & Bus Ltd, Maymac House Unit 2 Yeoman Industrial Park, Test Lane, Southampton, SO16 9JX Tel: (023) 8066 3500 Fax: (023) 8087 3160 *Commercial vehicle service,sales and rental of any make or model.*

M C W Group, Wrexham Technology Park, Wrexham, Clwyd, LL13 7YP Tel: (01978) 340340 Fax: (01978) 340345 *IT Solutions*

M C W Group, Wrexham Technology Park, Wrexham, Clwyd, LL13 7YP Tel: (01978) 340340 Fax: (01978) 340345 E-mail: admin@mcwgroup.co.uk *IT solutions, providers of hardware, software & networking*

M C2 Micrographic, 19 Heron Road, Belfast, BT3 9LE Tel: (028) 9046 6337 Fax: (028) 9046 6397 *Micro film distributors*

M Camilleri & Sons Roofing Ltd, Sully Moors Road, Sully, Penarth, South Glamorgan, CF64 5RP Tel: (01446) 721450 Fax: (01446) 749710 E-mail: general@camilleri.co.uk *Roofing contractors*

M Computer Technologies, Stirling House, 226 St. Vincent Street, Glasgow, G2 5RQ Tel: (0845) 4753695 Fax: (0845) 4753694 E-mail: info@mcomputer.com *PC consultants, manufacturers & software developers*

M Courts Ltd, 31 Commercial Road, London, N18 1TP Tel: (020) 8884 0999 Fax: (020) 8884 4666 E-mail: mcourtsltd@btconnect.com *Trimmings & harberdashery wholesalers*

M Criscuolo & Co. Ltd, Crisco House, 169 Godstone Road, Kenley, Surrey, CR8 5BL Tel: (020) 8660 7949 Fax: (020) 8668 5334 E-mail: sales@crisco.co.uk *Hair fashion accessories*

▶ M D A Security Systems Ltd, 10, Elm Lane, Tongham, Farnham, Surrey, GU10 1BX Tel: (01252) 342225

M D A Technical Personnel Ltd, Millbank House, North Way, Runcorn, Cheshire, WA7 2SX Tel: (01928) 734222 Fax: (01928) 739666 E-mail: info@millbank.com *Employment agency* Also at: Salford, Warrington, Whitehaven & Winnington

▶ M D B Software, 26 Adbolton Grove, West Bridgford, Nottingham, NG2 5AR Tel: 0115-981 9986

▶ M D & B W Buxton, 80 Derby Road, Heanor, Derbyshire, DE75 7QJ Tel: (01773) 714804 Fax: (01773) 531113

▶ M D Clarke (Contractors) Ltd, Midland House, Brent, Ninian Way, Tame Valley Industrial Estate, Tamworth, Staffordshire, B77 5DF Tel: (01827) 282323

M & D Cleaning Supplies Ltd, Grove Road, Upholland, Skelmersdale, Lancashire, WN8 0LH Tel: (01695) 632765 Fax: (01695) 632760 E-mail: sales@mandd.co.uk *Janitorial supply services*

M & D Commerical Kitchens, 1A Union Street, Royton, Oldham, OL2 5JD Tel: 0161-620 5556 Fax: 0161-620 5556 *Catering equipment manufrs*

M D Distribution Ltd, 167 London Road, Stoke-on-Trent, ST4 7QE Tel: (01782) 746693 Fax: (01782) 746695 *Computer systems & hardware manufrs*

▶ M D Electronics, 9 Quarry Fields, Leek Wootton, Warwick, CV35 7RS Tel: (01926) 850315 Fax: (01926) 850315 E-mail: info@mdelectronics.co.uk *Design and manufacture of custom electronic devices.*

M & D Engineering, 4 Pritchett Street, Birmingham, B6 4EH Tel: 0121-359 1134 Fax: 0121-333 5165 *Precision engineers*

M D F Designs, 153 Barton Lane, Eccles, Manchester, M30 0HN Tel: 0161-789 6602 Fax: 0161-789 6715 E-mail: sales@mdfdesign.com *Door manufrs*

M D Fabrications, 9 Marlow Road, Leicester, LE3 2BQ Tel: 0116-282 6771 Fax: 0116-282 6771 E-mail: md.fabrications@globaluk.net *Steel fabricators*

M D Fasteners Ltd, 129 Smiths Lane, Windsor, Berkshire, SL4 5PF Tel: (01753) 855773 Fax: (05600) 759015 E-mail: mdkfateners@yahoo.co.uk Principal Export Areas: Worldwide *Bolt & nut distributors*

▶ M D Flooring, Tenterfield Road, Ossett, West Yorkshire, WF5 0RU Tel: (07876) 350823 E-mail: mdflooring@fsmail.net *Approved Karndean & Capets installer*

▶ M & D Foundations & Building Services, 6 Holmeroyd Road, Adwick-le-Street, Doncaster, South Yorkshire, DN6 7BH Tel: (01302) 337711 Fax: (01302) 330335 E-mail: sales@mdfoundations.com

M D G Crest Ltd, Malvern View Business Park, Stella Way, Bishops Cleeve, Cheltenham, Gloucestershire, GL52 7DQ Tel: (01242) 675778 Fax: (01242) 676999 *Jig & fixture construction engineers*

▶ M D G Property Services, 60 Sandholme Drive, Bradford, West Yorkshire, BD10 8EY Tel: (01274) 200078 E-mail: mikegreasley@blueyonder.co.uk *Joiners, roofing, cladding & fencing*

M D Heard, Tregatreath Yacht Yard, Tregatreath, Mylor Bridge, Falmouth, Cornwall, TR11 5NS Tel: (01326) 374441 Fax: (01326) 372469 *Boat building & repairs*

M D Hotel Interiors Ltd, 2 Station Road Industrial Estate, Latchford, Warrington, WA4 1LB Tel: (01925) 650412 Fax: (01925) 656538 *Furniture contractors*

M D Hughes & Partners, 52 High Street, Stonehouse, Gloucestershire, GL10 2NA Tel: (01453) 824551 Fax: (01453) 828624 E-mail: mdhp@btconnect.com *Consulting civil & structural engineers*

M D International Ltd, 45 Circus Road, St. John's Wood, London, NW8 9JH Tel: (020) 7266 2939 Fax: (020) 7286 8291 *Metal traders*

M & D Joinery Ltd, 56 Stanworth Street, London, SE1 3NY Tel: (020) 7231 2965 Fax: (020) 7231 2965 *Joinery manufrs*

M D Laundry Machines (Kendal) Ltd, Parkside Business Park, Parkside Road, Kendal, Cumbria, LA9 7EN Tel: (01539) 729090 Fax: (01539) 728298 E-mail: sales@mdlaundrymachines.com *Manufacturers of drying & finishing equipment for the laundry industry*

M D M Leisure Ltd, 7 Battisford Park, Plympton, Plymouth, PL7 5AT Tel: (01752) 342589 Fax: (01752) 342589 *Fruit machine distributors*

M D M Leisure Ltd, 56 Seaview Drive, Great Wakering, Southend-on-Sea, SS3 0BE Tel: (01702) 217917 Fax: (01702) 217917 *Amusement Machines*

▶ M D P Engineering Ltd, Unit 21, Cornton Business Park, Cornton Road, Stirling, FK9 5AT Tel: (01786) 449600

▶ M D P Windows Ltd, 9 Hattersley Industrial Estate, Stockport Road, Hyde, Cheshire, SK14 3QT Tel: 0161-367 9265 Fax: 0161-367 9802 *Window manufrs*

M D Phillips Appliances, 44 Hackenden Close, East Grinstead, West Sussex, RH19 3DS Tel: (01342) 314670 Fax: (01342) 325445 *Domestic appliance repairs*

M D Plating Ltd, 21 Wedgewood Gate Industrial Estate, Wedgewood Way, Stevenage, Hertfordshire, SG1 4SU Tel: (01438) 350527 *Electroplating services*

M & D Precision Grinding, Unit 8 North Weylands Industrial Estate, Molesey Road, Walton-on-Thames, Surrey, KT12 3PL Tel: (01932) 246270 Fax: (01932) 246270 *Precision grinders*

▶ M D Printers Ltd, 7 Phoenix Park, Coldred Road, Maidstone, Kent, ME15 9XN Tel: (01622) 755222 Fax: (01622) 752052

M & D Russell Haulage Ltd, Myothill Mains, Denny, Stirlingshire, FK6 5HH Tel: (01324) 822734 Fax: (01324) 829301

M D S Architectural Fabrications Ltd, Unit 3a Brandon Way, West Bromwich, West Midlands, B70 8JB Tel: 0121-525 3338 Fax: 0121-525 3348 *Commercial aluminium window door manufrs*

M D S Wedgloking Services, Unit 6, Alpha Business Park, Deedmore Road, Coventry, CV2 1EQ Tel: (024) 7661 4577 Fax: (024) 7660 4975 *Fastener wedge locking services*

M & D Tooling, 12a Carvers Trading Estate, Southampton Road, Ringwood, Hampshire, BH24 1JS Tel: (01425) 489945 Fax: (01425) 489946 *Precision engineering services*

▶ M D Totco Instruments Ltd, Badentoy Way, Badentoy Industrial Estate, Aberdeen, AB12 4YF Tel: (01224) 343650

▶ M & D Transport, Burtonhead Road, St. Helens, Merseyside, WA9 5EA Tel: (01744) 25900 Fax: (01744) 453574

▶ M & D Wright Devlopment Ltd, 46 Park Lane, Bedhampton, Havant, Hampshire, PO9 3HL Tel: (023) 9247 5595 Fax: (023) 9247 6697 E-mail: dgolf@tiscali.co.uk *Construction & refurbishment, conservatories & double glazing*

M Davies, Tyrafon, Pentrefelin, Sennybridge, Brecon, Powys, LD3 8TU Tel: (01874) 638124 Fax: (01874) 638124 *Agricultural engineers*

▶ M & Dee, 34 Farley Hill, Luton, LU1 5HQ Tel: 07768 626141 E-mail: m.and.dee@lycos.co.uk *Deep carpet cleaning and cleaning services that will suit your requirements*

▶ M Denyer & R Tribble, Unit 2 New Mill End, Luton, LU1 3TS Tel: (01582) 460035 Fax: (01582) 460035 *Cabinet manufrs*

M Donald, Unit A Kingmoor Park Heathlands Estate, Carlisle, CA6 4RE Tel: (01228) 672050 Fax: (01228) 672025 E-mail: sales@weldtech-uk.com *Engineering machinery prototype design & manufacture*

▶ M Douglas, 1-3 West Street, Worsbrough, Barnsley, South Yorkshire, S70 5PG Tel: (01226) 205623 Fax: (01226) 205628 *Manufacture prefabricated bricks*

▶ M Dunnigan, 44 Race Road, Bathgate, West Lothian, EH48 2AP Tel: (01506) 652751

M & E Alarms Ltd, Lower Charlecott, Tawstock, Barnstaple, Devon, EX31 3JY Tel: (01271) 858550 Fax: (01271) 858423 E-mail: sales@m-and-e.co.uk *Closed circuit television distributors*

M E C Air Conditioning, 60 Chatterley Drive, Kidsgrove, Stoke-on-Trent, ST7 4LL Tel: (01782) 785721 *Air conditioning repairers & installers*

M E C Signs Ltd, Boxshall Court, Pound Street, Newbury, Berkshire, RG14 6AB Tel: (01635) 41745 Fax: (01635) 31923 E-mail: sales@mecsigns.co.uk *Sign manufrs*

M E C-Air (Pneumatics & Hydraulics) Ltd, Unit 5c, Enterprise Way, Five Lane Ends, Bradford, West Yorkshire, BD10 8EW Tel: (01274) 621037 Fax: (01274) 621230 *Pneumatic & hydraulic equipment hire*

▶ M & E Civil Engineering & Groundwork Ltd, Unit 2 Evegate Park Barn, Ashford, Kent, TN25 6SX Tel: (01303) 814444 E-mail: sales@mecivilengineering.co.uk

M E Electronics, St Marys Works, 115 Burnmoor Street, Leicester, LE2 7JL Tel: 0116-254 8918 Fax: 0116-254 8918 *Leisure equipment & repairers*

M E H Group Services P.L.C., 1 Thornham Grove, Stratford, London, E15 1DN Tel: (020) 8534 4441 Fax: (020) 8519 1933 E-mail: mwood@mehltd.co.uk *Mechanical & electrical building services engineers*

M E I, Eskdale Road, Winnersh Triangle, Wokingham, Berkshire, RG41 5AQ Tel: 0118-969 7700 Fax: 0118-944 6412 *Coin acceptor mechanism manufrs*

M E I Unitech Ltd, PO Box 457, Sheffield, S9 3UU Tel: 0114-243 7296 Fax: 0114-242 5958 *Power tool importers*

M & E James, Unit 2 Hare Street, Bilston, West Midlands, WV14 7DX Tel: (01902) 408030 Fax: (01902) 490166 E-mail: saws@supanet.com *Gearbox reconditioners*

M E L Aviation Ltd, Lawrence Walter House, Addison Road, Chilton Industrial Estate, Sudbury, Suffolk, CO10 2YW Tel: (01787) 373282 Fax: (01787) 310812 E-mail: info@melaviation.co.uk *Aerospace equipment service, repair & manufrs*

M E L Chemicals, PO Box 6, Manchester, M27 8LS Tel: 0161-911 1066 Fax: 0161-911 1090 E-mail: melchemsales@melchemicals.com *Speciality zirconium chemical producers*

M E L Research, 8 Holt Court North, Heneage St West, Birmingham, B7 4AX Tel: 0121-604 4664 Fax: 0121-604 6776 E-mail: info@m-e-l.co.uk *Environment researchers*

▶ M E M Group Plc, Edward House, Dallis Road, Ocean Park, Cardiff, CF24 5TW Tel: (029) 2049 8111 Fax: (029) 2048 4775 E-mail: info@memgroup.co.uk *Services Provided by the Group include:**Buildings and property maintenance, offering services in building, plumbing. plastering and bricklaying, with expertise also available in the mechanical, electrical, heating and ventilation engineering fields.*Landscape and sports field management*Commercial and industrial cleaning*Janitorial Supplies*Environmental and waste management*Asbestos monitoring, surveys, removal and re-insulation*Laboratory testing facilities (UKAS accredited)*COSHH and Health & Safety advice and training*I. T. Management, web design and broadband configuration and connection*Production personnel and specialist plant hire**

M E P Ltd, PO Box 1824, Salisbury, SP2 0AH Tel: (01722) 744799 Fax: (0870) 7052951 E-mail: enquiries@mep.uk.com *Minerals process plant*

M E P Mineral Engineers Processors Ltd, Unit 4 PWS Industrial Estate, Tunstall Road, Knypersley Viddleph, Stoke-On-Trent, ST8 7BE Tel: (01782) 511244 Fax: (0870) 7052951 *Mineral processing engineers*

M E P Services Ltd, 3 Catsash Rd, Langstone, Newport, Gwent, NP18 2LZ Tel: (01633) 211995 Fax: (01633) 213131 E-mail: enq@mepfreight.com *Freight forwarders & export packers*

M E R Electrical & Mechanical, The Broadway, Mansfield, Nottinghamshire, NG18 2RL Tel: (01623) 621522 Fax: (01623) 627719 E-mail: sales@mer-electrical.co.uk *Electrical rewinders, repair, motor & stockists*

M E S International Ltd, 11 Copdale Road, Leicester, LE5 4FG Tel: 0116-249 0333 Fax: 0116-249 0142 E-mail: sales@mesinternational.uk.com *Quarry & mining equipment suppliers*

▶ M E S L Group, Cordwallis House, Cordwallis Street, Maidenhead, Berkshire, SL6 7BG Tel: (01628) 771717 Fax: (01628) 770427

M E T Steel Ltd, 51 Mallusk Road, Newtownabbey, County Antrim, BT36 4RU Tel: (028) 9083 7311 Fax: (028) 9084 3548 *Corrugated steel sheet manufrs*

M E V Ltd, Baxall Business Centre Adswood Industrial Estate, Adswood Road, Stockport, Cheshire, SK3 8LF Tel: 0161-477 1898 Fax: 0161-718 3587 E-mail: sales@mev.co.uk *Software & hardware design service*

▶ M E Willis Sales & Hire Ltd, 38 Long Street, Easingwold, York, YO61 3HT Tel: (01347) 822368 Fax: (01347) 821655

M F B Manufacturing Ltd, 7a The Stirling Centre, Market Deeping, Peterborough, PE6 8EQ Tel: 01778 343110 Purchasing Contact: N. Scotney Sales Contact: N. Scotney *Sheet metalworkers/fabricators, architectural metalwork engineers or fabricators, engineering subcontract services, machinists engineers/general machining services, stainless steel fabricators & stud welding services*

M F Bailey, Hartwell Stud Farm, Hartwell Lane, Stone, Staffordshire, ST15 8TL Tel: (01782) 372523 *Horse transporters*

M F Business Services, 10 Bodington Road, Sutton Coldfield, West Midlands, B75 5ET Tel: (07973) 639660 Fax: 0121-308 3003 E-mail: enquiries@mfbusiness.co.uk *Consultants*

▶ M F C Barcoding Ltd, 1 Fir Trees, Anlaby, Hull, HU10 7DQ Tel: (0845) 8386130 Fax: (0845) 8386131 E-mail: sales@mfcbarcoding.co.uk *We supply thermal printers, scanners, RFID*

continued

continuation
Equipment, ID card printers , replacement printheads and repairs to all Barcoding equipment. "Our range includes: Datacard, Datamax, HHP, Intermec, Metrologic, Opticon, Paxar, Sato, Toshiba & Zebra

M F C Partnership, 21 Bedford Square, Brighton, BN1 2PL Tel: (01273) 821084 Fax: (01273) 202350 E-mail: info@mfcpartnership.co.uk *Computer consultants*

M F C Patterns & Castings, Unit 6 Broomhouse Lane, Edlington, Doncaster, South Yorkshire, DN12 1ET Tel: (01709) 864305 *Patterns engineers*

M & F Components, Marlbrough Road, Accrington, Lancashire, BB5 5BE Tel: (01254) 301121 Fax: (01254) 391416 E-mail: ucount@mafcobell.co.uk *Automotive tools & car spares merchants*

▶ M F Compton & Son, Grovebury Road, Leighton Buzzard, Bedfordshire, LU7 4TS Tel: (01525) 371707 Fax: (01525) 851891 E-mail: enquiries@tankers-r-us.com *Suppliers of secondhand & new road tankers in aluminium, stainless steel & mild steel*

M F D Capacitors (1991) Ltd, Lion Lane, Penley, Wrexham, LL13 0LY Tel: (01978) 710551 Fax: (01978) 710501 E-mail: sales@mfdcapacitors.co.uk *MFD is an independent manufacturer supplying customers in all fields of electronics. The company was established in 1969 as the first producer of close tolerance plastic film capacitors in the UK, & continues to operate from its purpose built base in North East Wales. We have numerous general purpose ranges & routinely produces thousands of different special designs for UK & international customers. Examples of specials include large suppression capacitors for most of the UK's power filter manufacturers, close tolerance polycarbonate for communications & defence, & fail-safe capacitors for railway signalling, polypropylene, polyester & polycarbonate capacitors. The speciality of one of our custom designs could be extremely close tolerance, high voltage rating, high current rating or could be as simple as a special size to fit in a confined situation. Our typical production time is three to four weeks from receipt of order.*

M F D Ductwork Installations Ltd, 16a York Road, Earls Colne, Colchester, CO6 2RN Tel: (01787) 222745 Fax: (01787) 222182 *Heating & ventilation*

M F Fire & Safety Equipment, The Safety Centre, 198 Cator Lane, Beeston, Nottingham, NG9 4BE Tel: 0115-925 2261 *Fire & safety equipment suppliers*

M F Furnishings, 5 Richmond St, Walsall, WS1 2JX Tel: 01922 624040 Fax: 01902 368282 *Manufacture Furniture*

M F G Machinery, 6 Climax Works, Station Road, Reddish, Stockport, Cheshire, SK5 6YZ Tel: 0161-431 9125 Fax: 0161-432 2440 *Machinery building & repair services*

M F H Contract Engineering Services (Leicester) Ltd, Service Works, 2 Highmeres Road, Troon Industrial Estate, Leicester, LE4 7LZ Tel: 0116-276 3807 Fax: 0116-246 0198 E-mail: eng@mfhgroup.co.uk *Engineering subcontract services*

M F H Engineering Holdings Ltd, Charlotte House, 500 Charlotte Road, Sheffield, S2 4ER Tel: 0114-279 9999 Fax: 0114-279 7501 E-mail: eng@mfhgroup.co.uk *Maintenance management consultants*

M F Hire Ltd, 2 Highmeres Road, Leicester, LE4 9LZ Tel: 0116-276 3807 Fax: 0116-246 0198 E-mail: enquiries@mfhgroup.co.uk *Tool hire, leasing & rental* Also at: Leeds, Nottingham & Sheffield

M F Hire Ltd, 2-3 Colwick Road, Nottingham, NG2 4BG Tel: 0115-958 1505 Fax: 0115-950 3846 E-mail: eno@mfhgroup.co.uk *Tool hire*

M F Hydraulics Ltd, Unit 2, Pony Rd, Horspath Industrial Estate, Oxford, OX4 2RD Tel: (01865) 714126 Fax: (01865) 748140 E-mail: sales@mfhydraulics.co.uk *Hydraulic hose distributors*

M F I UK Ltd, Southon House, 333 The Hyde, Edgeware Road, London, NW9 6TD Tel: (020) 8200 8000 Fax: (020) 8200 8636 *Furniture retailers*

M F Induction Heating, Martindale Trading Estate, Martindale, Cannock, Staffordshire, WS11 7XL Tel: (01543) 570642 Fax: (01543) 574460 E-mail: sales@mfinduction.com *Induction heating equipment manufrs*

▶ M F J Homes, Red Craig Cottage, Burghead, Elgin, Morayshire, IV30 5XX Tel: (01343) 831100

M F K Group Ltd, 23-25 Gunnels Wood Park, Gunnels Wood Road, Stevenage, Hertfordshire, SG1 2BH Tel: (01438) 312777 Fax: (01438) 317789 *Typesetting services & data manipulation services*

M F Manufacturing Ltd, Unit 1 Foundry Lane, Bristol, BS5 7XH Tel: 0117-965 1100 Fax: 0117-965 1188 E-mail: sales@mf-manufacturing.co.uk *Polystyrene packaging manufrs*

M F R Consultancy Services Ltd, Dunelm Ho, 33 Greenfields Rise, Whitchurch, Shropshire, SY13 1EP Tel: (01948) 666778 Fax: (01948) 666775 E-mail: mfrose@mfrcsl.co.uk *Epoxy resin/Polyurethane products consultants*

M F S Checkland, 29 Hartfield Road, London, SW19 3SG Tel: (020) 8543 9166 Fax: (020) 8540 8977 *Insurance brokers*

M F S Electro Plating Co., Clifton Road, Huntingdon, Cambridgeshire, PE29 7EJ Tel: (01480) 459966 *Electroplating services*

M F S Reprographics, 15 Blackmoor Gate, Furzton, Milton Keynes, MK4 1DS Tel: (01908) 504550 Fax: (01908) 504550 E-mail: mfsrepro@btinternet.com *Architects, construction, design & information* Also at: Cambridge & Leighton Buzzard

▶ M F Sealing Systems Ltd, 2C Brighouse Business Village, Brighouse Road, Middlesbrough, Cleveland, TS2 1RT Tel: (01642) 253253 Fax: (01642) 257980 *Engineering services*

M F T Co Ltd, 22 Bedford Road, Lower Stondon, Henlow, Bedfordshire, SG16 6EA Tel: (01462) 850536 Fax: (01462) 851522 E-mail: sales@mftsat.co.uk *Aerial & satellite erectors & electrical wholesalers*

M F & T, 22 Dawkins Road Industrial Estate, Hamworthy, Poole, Dorset, BH15 4JY Tel: (01202) 666456 Fax: (01202) 685545 E-mail: steve.hunt@porvairfilteration.com *Engineering services*

▶ M F T M, 12 Knightsbridge Avenue, Northwich, Cheshire, CW9 8GE Tel: (01606) 352306 Fax: (0870) 7627906 E-mail: mail@mftm.co.uk *UK and European Registered Trade Mark Attorney for friendly, professional and cost-effective trade mark advice, trade mark searching and trade mark registration in the UK, European Community and worldwide. Initial no-obligation consultations are free.*

M F Tofield & Sons, 14 Barton Road, Bletchley, Milton Keynes, MK2 3JG Tel: (01908) 274527 Fax: (01908) 371395 E-mail: enquiries@tofield.com *Builders & joiners*

M Fairclough, 41-42 Centurion Industrial Estate, Centurion Way, Farington, Leyland, PR25 4GU Tel: (01772) 436184 Fax: (01772) 436184 *Steel fabricators*

M Fairnington, A Berwick Road, Wooler, Northumberland, NE71 6AH Tel: (01668) 282027 Fax: (01668) 282439 *Agricultural, general engineering services & distributors*

M Forker, 8 Maghery Road, Portadown, Craigavon, County Armagh, BT62 1SZ Tel: (028) 3885 1268 Fax: (028) 3885 1017 *Compost manufrs*

M G A Corporation Ltd, Unit 6 Britannia Business Park, Mills Road Quarrywood, Quarry Wood, Aylesford, Kent, ME20 7NT Tel: (01622) 717332 Fax: (01622) 715508 E-mail: goldstaruk@ukonline.co.uk *Contract t-shirt & sweatshirt printing services*

M G A Fencing, 8 Bottomley Yard, Bottomley Street, Nelson, Lancashire, BB9 9SW Tel: (01282) 449100 Fax: (01282) 449100 *Fencing contractors*

M G Agricultural Ltd, Innage Park, Abeles Way, Holly Lane Industrial Estate, Atherstone, Warwickshire, CV9 2QX Tel: (01827) 712703 Fax: (01827) 718800 *Agricultural sales, repairs & spares*

▶ M G Associates Construction Consultancy Ltd, 11 The Quadrant, Manor Park CR, Edgware, Middlesex, HA8 7LU Tel: (020) 8381 1429 Fax: (020) 8381 1425 E-mail: info@mg-assoc.co.uk *Civil Engineering and Building Consultants, construction materials testing, project management and supervision, technical training for contractors and Engineers*

M G Automation Ltd, 16 Stratfield Park, Elettra Avenue, Waterlooville, Hampshire, PO7 7XN Tel: (023) 9226 7727 Fax: (023) 9226 7747 E-mail: sales@mgautomation.co.uk *Distributors of bosch rexroth automation equipment & manufrs*

M G B Press Break Sections Ltd, Dawley Brook Road, Kingswinford, West Midlands, DY6 7BD Tel: (01384) 400717 Fax: (01384) 400747 *Aluminium & architectural metalworkers & fabricators*

M G Bennett & Associates Ltd, Bennett House, Pleasley Road, Whiston, Rotherham, South Yorkshire, S60 4HQ Tel: (01709) 373782 Fax: (01709) 363730 E-mail: mgb@bennettmg.co.uk *Consulting engineers services*

M G Building Services Engineers Ltd, 31a High Street, Alcester, Warwickshire, B49 5AF Tel: (01789) 400270 Fax: (01789) 400396 E-mail: mgbse@globalnet.co.uk *Heating & air conditioning*

M G C Engineering Ltd, Bradfords Quay, Wadebridge, Cornwall, PL27 6DB Tel: (01208) 812585 Fax: (01208) 814066 E-mail: mgceng@tiscali.co.uk *Structural engineers*

M G C Systems Ltd, Power Transmission House, Redcliffe Road, Mansfield, Nottinghamshire, NG18 2QH Tel: (01623) 635150 Fax: (01623) 635125 E-mail: sales@mgcsystems.com *Importers & distributors of power transmission products*

M G Cases Ltd, Unit 8 Neills Road, Bold Industrial Park, St. Helens, Merseyside, WA9 4TU Tel: (01744) 821630 Fax: (01744) 821630 *Export packers & case manufrs*

M & G Catering, 69/79 Hadfield Street, Old Trafford, Manchester, M16 9FE Tel: 0161-848 0959 Fax: 0161-848 0959 E-mail: mg-catering@ntlworld.com *Catering equipment*

M G Communications, 24 Durant Street, London, E2 7BP Tel: (020) 7729 2628 Fax: (020) 7729 2628 *Telecommunications*

▶ M & G Construction Ltd, Gilbert House, Stanley Road, Ilford, Essex, IG1 1RB Tel: (020) 8514 2981 Fax: (020) 8553 0262

M & G Engineering, 1 James Chalmers Road, Kirkton Industrial Estate, Arbroath, Angus, DD11 3LR Tel: (01241) 870874 Fax: (01241) 870874 *General engineers*

M G Engraving, 135 Somerset Road, Coventry, CV1 4EF Tel: (024) 7622 5110 Fax: (024) 7663 2894 E-mail: mg@mgengineering.fsnet.co.uk *Engravers, signs, graphic design*

▶ M G Event & Sound, 147 Main Road, Sheepy Magna, Atherstone, Warwickshire, CV9 3QU Tel: (01827) 714772 Fax: (01827) 714772 E-mail: info@mgeventandsound.co.uk *Sound and Lighting engineering, hire, Event Management and system installation for conferences, concerts, exhibitions and outdoor events. Conveniently located for Birmingham NEC, Coventry, Leicester, Nottingham, Tamworth, and Nuneaton.*

M & G Express, M & G House, Head Road, Douglas, Isle Of Man, IM1 5BF Tel: (01624) 623841 Fax: (01624) 623004 E-mail: postmaster@mcb.net *Road transport contractors*

M G F Trench Construction Systems Ltd, Redbrook Lane Industrial Estate, Redbrook Lane, Rugeley, Staffordshire, WS15 1QU Tel: (01889) 574777 Fax: (01889) 574794 E-mail: info@mgf.ltd.uk *Ground construction*

M & G Fire Protection, Colchester Road, Maldon, Essex, CM9 4NN Tel: (01621) 840999 Fax: (01621) 842322 E-mail: mgfireessex@aol.com *Supply, service & refill of portable fire extinguishers, supply of health & safety signs, fire risk assessments*

M G Framing, Unit 8 Islwyn Workshops, Pontymister Industrial Estate, Risca, Newport, Gwent, NP11 6NP Tel: (01633) 612034 Fax: (01633) 612034 E-mail: mgframing@btinternet.com *Framing services*

M & G Group Plc, Governors House, 5 Laurence Pountney Hill, London, EC4R 0HH Tel: (020) 7626 4588 Fax: (020) 7623 8615 E-mail: sales@mandg.co.uk *Financial company*

M G H Industries Ltd, Lancaster House, Old Wellington Road, Eccles, Manchester, M30 9QG Tel: 0161-707 7690 Fax: 0161-707 7701 E-mail: sales@nultz-boltz.co.uk *Fasteners, industrial*

M G H Reclaim Ltd, Unit 23 Common Bank Industrial Estate, Ackhurst Road, Chorley, Lancashire, PR7 1NH Tel: (01257) 279999 Fax: (01257) 279797 E-mail: neil@mgh-group.co.uk *IT asset management of computer equipment disposal & roll out*

▶ M & G Haulage Container Service Ltd, 9 Arcade Workshops, Atlantic Trading Estate, Barry, South Glamorgan, CF63 3RF Tel: (01446) 738212 Fax: (01446) 735294

M G Joinery, 375 Stoney Stanton Road, Coventry, CV6 5DT Tel: (024) 7661 2330 Fax: (024) 7663 7916 *Joiners*

M G K Engineering (Northern) Ltd, Polbeth Industrial Estate, Polbeth, West Calder, West Lothian, EH55 8TJ Tel: (01506) 871757 Fax: (01506) 873400 E-mail: sales@mgkscot.co.uk *Storage & metal handling specialists*

M G Knife Services, 8 Avon Business Park, Lodge Causeway, Bristol, BS16 3JP Tel: 0117-958 3974 Fax: 0117-958 3997 *Machine knives manufrs*

M.G.L. Demolition Ltd, Davison House Rennys Lane, Dragonville Industrial Estate, Durham, DH1 2RS Tel: 0191-374 0789 Fax: 0191-383 9911 E-mail: enquiries.mgl@sheal.co.uk

M G M Precision Engineering Ltd, M G M House, Newburn Bridge Road, Newburn, Newcastle upon Tyne, NE15 8NR Tel: 0191-499 0005 Fax: 0191-499 0007 E-mail: mgm@mgmplc.com *Engineering sub-contract services*

▶ M G M Trading Ltd, Second Avenue, Centrum Business Park, Burton-On-Trent, Staffordshire, DE14 2WF Tel: (01283) 740774 Fax: (01283) 492511 E-mail: sales@mgm-trading.co.uk *Furnishings*

M G Mathews, Homefield, Westlands Road, Lacey Green, Princes Risborough, Buckinghamshire, HP27 0QP Tel: (07768) 574573 Fax: (01844) 344819 *Mini excavator hire*

M G Non-Ferrous Products Ltd, 2 Station Road, Stratford St Mary, Colchester, CO7 6WZ Tel: (01206) 337429 Fax: (01206) 337413 E-mail: mgnf@dial.pipex.com *Traders of aluminium*

M G P Photography Ltd, 36-37 Featherstone St, London, EC1Y 8QZ Tel: (020) 7608 1066 Fax: (020) 7336 8338 *Commercial photographers*

M G Plastics Ltd, Progress Mill, Marsh House Lane, Darwen, Lancashire, BB3 3JB Tel: (01254) 703930 Fax: (01254) 774472 E-mail: sales@mgplastics.com *Plastic injection moulders*

M G Production Engineering, The Paddocks, Rowley Lane, Barnet, Hertfordshire, EN5 3HW Tel: (020) 8441 3380 Fax: (020) 8441 3432 *Vacuum forming & light engineering*

M G R Foamtex Ltd, 10 Jefferson Way, Thame, Oxfordshire, OX9 3SZ Tel: (01844) 260005 Fax: (01844) 260157 E-mail: sales@mgrfoamtex.co.uk *Aircraft interior designers*

M G R Welding Ltd, Unit 13 Churchill Way, Fleckney, Leicester, LE8 8UD Tel: 0116-240 3215 Fax: 0116-240 3215 *Metalwork steel fabricators*

M G R Wood & Clark Ltd, 133 Neilston Road, Paisley, Renfrewshire, PA2 6QL Tel: 0141-884 2000 Fax: 0141-884 4443 E-mail: mgrscotlandltd@lineone.net *Lifting gear distributors*

M G Rubber Co. Ltd, Moorbridge Road, Bingham Industrial Estate, Nottingham, NG13 8GG Tel: (01949) 839112 Fax: (01949) 831357 E-mail: sales@mgrubber.com *Protective clothing manufrs*

▶ M G S Consultancy, Desford Hall, Leicester Lane, Desford, Leicester, LE9 9JJ Tel: (01455) 828220 Fax: (01455) 828490

M G S Signs Ltd, Quickjay House, Bilston Street, Willenhall, West Midlands, WV13 2AW Tel: (01902) 366223 Fax: (01902) 366340 *Sign writing contractors*

M G Sanders Co. Ltd, Newcastle Street, Stone, Staffordshire, ST15 8JU Tel: (01785) 815544 Fax: (01785) 815642 E-mail: sales@mgsanders.co.uk *CNC engineering machinists & heavy metal manufrs*

▶ M & G Sheds & Fencing, Unit J9 Dudley Trading Estate, Shaw Road, Dudley, West Midlands, DY2 8QX Tel: (01384) 240956 Fax: (01384) 255741 *Sheds fencing pigeon lofts manufrs*

▶ M G Shopfronts Ltd, Units 5f-2c Albion Works, Moor Street, Brierley Hill, West Midlands, DY5 3SZ Tel: (01384) 571227 Fax: (01384) 573006 E-mail: sales@mgshopfronts.com *Shop fronts & roller shutter suppliers*

M G Signs Ltd, Pond Wood Close, Moulton Park Industrial Estate, Northampton, NN3 6RT Tel: (01604) 493226 Fax: (01604) 790288 E-mail: sales@mgsigns.com *Sign contractors & manufrs*

M G Steel Products, Morthen Road, Wickersley, Rotherham, South Yorkshire, S66 1DX Tel: (01709) 709545 Fax: (01709) 709546 *Precision steel fabricators*

M G Steels Ltd, Phoenix House, Dudley Road West, Tividale, Oldbury, West Midlands, B69 2PJ Tel: 0121-522 4520 Fax: 0121-520 0191 *Steel stockholders*

▶ M G Supplies Ltd, Unit Y Smarden Business Estate, Smarden, Ashford, Kent, TN27 8QL Tel: (01233) 770500 Fax: (01233) 770100 E-mail: sales@mgsupplies.com *Stockholders of aluminium, stainless steel, brass, copper & bronze*

▶ M G Sutton, Grendon House Farm, Warton Lane, Grendon, Atherstone, Warwickshire, CV9 3DT Tel: (01827) 892295 Fax: (01827) 892432 E-mail: lee.sutton@btinternet.com *Arable farming business*

▶ M G T Ltd, P O Box 200, Kirkcaldy, Fife, KY2 6WD Tel: (0870) 8407000 Fax: (0870) 8407001

M G Tools, 158 Charles Street, Sheffield, S1 2NE Tel: 0114-272 2281 Fax: 0114-278 7157 E-mail: info@mgtools.co.uk *Pocket knife, pattern, modelling & hobby tools*

M & G Trailers Ltd, Hayes Lane, Stourbridge, West Midlands, DY9 8PA Tel: (01384) 424200 Fax: (01384) 424452 E-mail: mandgtrailers@lyeone.net *Road trailer manufrs*

M & G Transport, Highlands Road, Shirley, Solihull, West Midlands, B90 4ND Tel: 0121-705 2323 Fax: 0121-705 9163 E-mail: sales@storage-removals.co.uk *Domestic & office removers*

M G Trevett Ltd, Winterborne Stickland, Blandford Forum, Dorset, DT11 0NT Tel: (01258) 880490 Fax: (01258) 880470 *Horsebox manufacturers & steel fabricators*

M G Visual C C T V Ltd, 1 3 Wigan Road, Skelmersdale, Lancashire, WN8 8NB Tel: (01695) 558591 Fax: (01695) 558591 E-mail: sales@mgvisual.co.uk *Closed circuit television designers & installation*

M Gaze, Thurlton, Norwich, NR14 6NZ Tel: (01508) 548910 Fax: (01508) 548920 *HGV maintenance*

▶ M Glover, Dalbeattie Road, Castle Douglas, Kirkcudbrightshire, DG7 1HZ Tel: (01556) 503303 Fax: (01556) 502028

M Golunski & Co., Moor Street Trading Estate, Brierley Hill, West Midlands, DY5 3SS Tel: (01384) 78326 Fax: (01384) 841737 E-mail: golunski@lineone.net *Leather goods importers & manufrs* Also at: Bloxwich

▶ M Goodey, 9 Cameron Avenue, Abingdon, Oxfordshire, OX14 3SR Tel: (01235) 532875 Fax: (01235) 532875 E-mail: info@goodeyplumbingandheating.co.uk

M Greenaway & Son Ltd, Hayward Industrial Park, Vigo Place, Walsall, WS9 8UG Tel: (01922) 743322 Fax: (01922) 743163 E-mail: sales@greenaways.co.uk *Pipe clips & brackets manufrs*

M Grovic & Son Ltd, Adelaide Road, Reading, RG6 1PE Tel: 0118-926 2491 Fax: 0118-935 2364 E-mail: mgrovic@ulc.co.uk *Sack & bag merchants*

▶ M & G's Disco, 7 Gregory Close, Bow, Crediton, Devon, EX17 6LR Tel: (0800) 0754082 E-mail: mark@djbesty.co.uk *Disco*

▶ M H 4 Draines, 38 Moss Avenue, Rochdale, Lancashire, OL16 4AA Tel: (01706) 868886 E-mail: mh4drains@btconnect.com *Pipe cleaning, CCTV surveys, Excavation & repair, pipe lining*

▶ M H Automation International Ltd, 8 Swift Business Centre East Moors Industrial Estate, Keen Road, Cardiff, CF24 5JR Tel: (029) 2025 3300 Fax: (029) 2025 3303 E-mail: mail@mhai.co.uk *Electrical control system specialists*

M & H Builders Merchants Ltd, 72-74 Wood Street, Walthamstow, London, E17 3HT Tel: (020) 8521 5900 Fax: (020) 8509 1933 *Timber merchants*

M H C Industrials Ltd, Wetmore Road, Burton-On-Trent, Staffordshire, DE14 1QN Tel: (01283) 564651 Fax: (01283) 511526 E-mail: sales@mhcind.co.uk *Woodworking machinery suppliers*

▶ M & H Coachworks Ltd, New Princess Street, Leeds, LS11 9BA Tel: 0113-244 1671 Fax: 0113-243 8959 E-mail: paul@mhcoachworks.wanadoo.co.uk *Bus & coach repairs & refurbishment services*

M H Connectors Ltd, Darwin Road, Willowbrook East Industrial Es, Corby, Northamptonshire, NN17 5XZ Tel: (01536) 200963 Fax: (01536) 201963 E-mail: info@mhconnectors.com *Connectors services*

▶ M H Cragg & Sons Ltd, Ingleside, 11 Lee Lane, Horwich, Bolton, BL6 7BP Tel: (01204) 697157 Fax: (01204) 699113 *Central heating, plumbing & air conditioning contractors*

M H Electrical Distributors Ltd, 2 Station House, Lowlands Road, Runcorn, Cheshire, WA7 5TQ Tel: (01928) 591888 Fax: (01928) 591555 E-mail: mhelec001@aol.com *Electrical distributors*

M H Group plc, Dickinson Place, Bognor Regis, West Sussex, PO22 9QU Tel: (01243) 822963 Fax: (01243) 830398 E-mail: mhg@mh-group.co.uk *Plastics injection moulding manufrs*

M H Group, M H House, Madeley Street, Hull, HU3 2AH Tel: (01482) 328896 Fax: (01482) 225867 E-mail: sales@mhindustrial.co.uk *M H Group provide cost effective & versatile storage solutions suitable for any environment - industrial, retail or commercial. We can supply a range of products including - mezzanine floors for retail or industrial use. Racking & shelving systems. Forklift trucks for sale service and hire.*

M H I Ltd, 10 Appleton Gate, Newark, Nottinghamshire, NG24 1JY Tel: (01636) 704814 Fax: (01636) 671113 E-mail: enquiries@mhidesign.co.uk *Architecture, Civil & Structural Engineering and Project Management*

▶ M H L Corporate, Claremont CR, Edinburgh, EH7 4HX Tel: 0131-557 4633

▶ M H M, 2 Boswell Park, Ayr, KA7 1NP Tel: (01292) 263625 Fax: (01292) 265081

▶ M H Plasterers Ltd, 3 The Pleasance, Swillington, Leeds, LS26 8ED Tel: 0113-287 7144 Fax: 0113-287 7144 E-mail: mhplasterers@fsmail.net *we plasterer from bed sits to mansion quality without question*

M & H Plastics, London Road, Beccles, Suffolk, NR34 8TS Tel: (01502) 715518 Fax: (01502) 712581 E-mail: sales@mhplastics.com *M&H Plastics is one of the leading suppliers of plastic packaging and has set the benchmarks in design and manufacturing for plastic bottles, jars, closures and flexible tubes. M&H's expertise is in developing packaging solutions for markets where quality and style are critical to a products success, these include personal care products, pharmaceutical, food and household products, and for a variety of unique promotion projects.*

M & H Print Finishers, Hazel Lane, Walsall, WS6 6AA Tel: (01922) 419323 Fax: (01922) 419323 *Print finishers*

M H S Ltd, 35 Nobel Square, Burnt Mills Industrial Estate, Basildon, Essex, SS13 1LT Tel: (01268) 591010 Fax: (01268) 728202 E-mail: sales@modular-heating-group.co.uk *Commercial heating distributors*

M H Southern & Co. Ltd, Church Bank Sawmills, Jarrow, Tyne & Wear, NE32 3EB Tel: 0191-489 8231 Fax: 0191-428 0146 E-mail: sales@mhsouthern.co.uk *Timber merchants*

M H Spencer Ltd, Charter Avenue, Coventry, CV4 8AF Tel: (024) 7646 4044 Fax: (024) 7669 4011 E-mail: james.evans@mhspencer.co.uk Principal Export Areas: Worldwide *Welding services*

M H Spencer Ltd, Charter Avenue, Coventry, CV4 8AF Tel: (024) 7646 4044 Fax: (024) 7669 4011 E-mail: sales@weavingreeds.com *Textile accessories/textile export merchants/agents*

M H Systems Ltd, 12 Tunbridge Chambers, Dembery Road, Tonbridge, Kent, TN9 2HZ Tel: (01732) 367227 Fax: (01732) 367447 E-mail: tech@gcgold.co.uk *Computer software specialists*

▶ M H T Group, 10 Arkwright Road, Reading, RG2 0LU Tel: 0118-975 5557 Fax: 0118-920 5180

M H V Products Ltd, 33 Woodthorpe Road, Ashford, Middlesex, TW15 2RP Tel: (01784) 241628 Fax: (01784) 255610 E-mail: sales@mhvproducts.co.uk *Sheet metalworkers & prototype machining services*

M H Weltronic Systems Ltd, Unit 1 Crowles Ash Business Centre, Crowles Ash, Bromyard, Herefordshire, HR7 4SW Tel: (01885) 400777 Fax: (01885) 400777 E-mail: weltronic_sysltd@lineone.net *Temperature controller manufrs*

M Hasson & Sons Ltd, 17 Glebe Road, Rasharkin, Ballymena, County Antrim, BT44 8SS Tel: (028) 2957 1281 Fax: (028) 2957 1575 E-mail: sales@hassons.com *Structural steel engineers*

M Hibbert, Windmill Farm, Dale, Haverfordwest, Dyfed, SA62 3QX Tel: (01646) 636428 E-mail: sheila.hibbert@tesco.net *Farm contractors*

M Honour, Mead Farm, Mead Road, Barford St. John, Banbury, Oxfordshire, OX15 0PW Tel: (01295) 721809 Fax: (01295) 721809 *Agricultural engineers*

M I B International Ltd, Sun Alliance House, Little Park Street, Coventry, CV1 2JZ Tel: (024) 7622 5202 Fax: (024) 7622 1752 E-mail: sales@mibinternational.com *Emergency equipment manufrs*

M I C Engineering, 1a-B Unit, Dans Castle, Tow Law, Bishop Auckland, County Durham, DL13 4BB Tel: (01388) 731347 Fax: (01388) 731348 E-mail: info@mic-valves-eng.co.uk *Precision engineers & butterfly valve manufrs*

M I D A International Ltd, Bordesley Hall, The Holloway, Alvechurch, Birmingham, B48 7QA Tel: (01527) 585505 Fax: (01527) 585575 E-mail: enquiries@mida.co.uk *Buying consortium for electrical wholesalers*

M I D Services, Kilworthy Hill, Tavistock, Devon, PL19 0EP Tel: (01822) 615625 Fax: (01822) 615625 *Machinery removal & installation contractors*

M I Diesel Products, Chorley North Industrial Park, Chorley, Lancashire, PR6 7BX Tel: (01257) 239200 Fax: (01257) 241726 E-mail: sales@midiesel.co.uk *Diesel fuel injection spare parts*

M I Drilling Fluids Ltd, Pocra Quay, Aberdeen, AB11 5DQ Tel: (01224) 584336 Fax: (01224) 576119 *Chemicals for oil production*

M I E Medical Research Ltd, 6 Wortley Moor Road, Leeds, LS12 4JF Tel: 0113-279 3710 Fax: 0113-231 0820 E-mail: sales@mie-uk.com *Physiological monitoring equipment distributors & manufrs*

M I Edwards Engineers Ltd, Mundford Road, Weeting, Brandon, Suffolk, IP27 0PL Tel: (01842) 813555 Fax: (01842) 811595 *Woodchipper suppliers*

M I Engineering Ltd, Bromley Street, Stourbridge, West Midlands, DY9 8HU Tel: (01384) 894156 Fax: (01384) 894151 *Coil process machine manufrs*

M I F Filter Systems Ltd, M I F Ho, Waterfall Lane Trading Estate, Cradley Heath, West Midlands, B64 6PU Tel: 0121-561 5380 Fax: 0121-561 3711 E-mail: sales@mif-filters.com *Filter systems*

M I G Pattern Cutting Services Ltd, 3 D Mackenzie Road, London, N7 8QZ Tel: (020) 7700 6164 Fax: (020) 7700 6687 E-mail: sales@migpatterncutting.com *Pattern cutters*

M I H Welding Supplies Ltd, Unit E Rio Works, Polesdon Lane, Ripley, Woking, Surrey, GU23 6JX Tel: (01483) 225409 Fax: (01483) 224242 *Welding equipment, supplies & repairs*

M I J Technology, PO Box 158, Deal, Kent, CT14 9GZ Tel: (01304) 360223 Fax: (0870) 7061577 *Computer hardware maintenance & web site designer*

M I K Engineering, 5 Cannock Street, Leicester, LE4 9HR Tel: 0116-233 3740 Fax: 0116-233 3740 *Machine tool reconditioning & repairers*

M I P Ltd, Park Lane, Halesowen, West Midlands, B63 2RE Tel: (01384) 637711 Fax: (01384) 410104 *Plastic packaging manufrs*

M I S Cooperate Defence Solutions, Hermitage Lane, Maidstone, Kent, ME16 9NT Tel: (0800) 243649 Fax: (01622) 728690 E-mail: webmaster@mis-cds.com *Computer consultants*

M I S Fuel Monitoring Ltd, Horseley Works, Walsall Street, Wolverhampton, WV1 3LN Tel: (01902) 870037 Fax: (01902) 871661 E-mail: info@merridale.co.uk Principal Export Areas: Africa *Fleet (vehicle) management specialists/consultants*

M I S UK Ltd, Lime House, The Quadrant, 135 Salusbury Road, London, NW6 6RJ Tel: (020) 7625 9900 Fax: (020) 7625 9901 E-mail: info@misag.com *Accountancy computer software producers*

▶ M I Swaco Specialist Tools, Endeavour Drive, Arnhall Business Park, Westhill, Aberdeenshire, AB32 6UF Tel: (01224) 742200 Fax: (01224) 742288 E-mail: fmuirhead@miswaco.com *Oil & gas servicing*

M & I Tunk, 16 Heathland Road, London, N16 5NH Tel: (020) 8800 1949 Fax: (020) 8809 6783 *Casting jewellers*

M I W Fabrications Ltd, Marmi Works, 23 Grafton Road, Croydon, CR0 3RP Tel: (020) 8681 5435 Fax: (020) 8681 2839 E-mail: info@miwfabrication.co.uk *Metalwork*

M J Agar Steel Fabricators & Engineers 2004 Ltd, Weirhead Works, 1 Hobson Avenue, Sheffield, S6 2GR Tel: 0114-234 2911 Fax: 0114-232 3885 *Steel fabricators*

M J Andrew, Tamsquite House, St. Tudy, Bodmin, Cornwall, PL30 3PU Tel: (01208) 850261 Fax: (01208) 850261 *Contract mechanic & engineer*

M J B Engineering Ltd, 133 Barkers Lane, Bedford, MK41 9RX Tel: (01234) 358454 Fax: (01234) 273423 E-mail: sales@mjbengineering.co.uk *Precision engineers*

M J B Engineering (2000) Ltd, 20 Dodwells Bridge Industrial Estate, Jacknell Road, Hinckley, Leicestershire, LE10 3BS Tel: (01455) 615906 Fax: (01455) 633206 E-mail: m.j.bengltd@btconnect.com *Sub-contract precision engineers*

M J B Engineering Services, Greg Street, Stockport, Cheshire, SK5 7BU Tel: 0161-476 5811 Fax: 0161-476 5844 E-mail: sales@mjb-engineering-services.com *Precision engineering services*

▶ M & J Ballantyne Ltd, 24 Shedden Park Road, Kelso, Roxburghshire, TD5 7AL Tel: (01573) 224255 Fax: (01573) 225603

▶ M J Berry, 1 Freeland Way, Erith, Kent, DA8 2LQ Tel: (01322) 351139 Fax: (01322) 351137

M J Beskeen, 1872 Melton Road, Rearsby, Leicester, LE7 4YS Tel: (01664) 424799 Fax: (01664) 424799 *Plant hire*

M J Blinds, 45 Castle Street, Tyldesley, Manchester, M29 8FP Tel: (01942) 882181 Fax: (01942) 882181 *Roller & venetian blind suppliers*

M & J Bowers, Lucott, Limington, Yeovil, Somerset, BA22 8EQ Tel: (01935) 840308 Fax: (01935) 841544 *Data destruction services*

M J Bradshaw & Sons, Glaston Road, Uppingham, Oakham, Leicestershire, LE15 9EU Tel: (01572) 822727 Fax: (01572) 822727 *Joinery*

▶ M J Brown Ltd, Fallow House, Farm Close, Warnham, Horsham, West Sussex, RH12 3QT Tel: (01403) 252252 Fax: (01403) 252000 E-mail: thomas@therryansweb.co.uk *Portable toilet hire*

M J Brown Joinery, Hewitt Street, Crewe, CW2 6DZ Tel: (01270) 211518 Fax: (01270) 211941 *Joinery & glass manufrs*

M J C Distribution, 50 Icknield Street, Hockley, Birmingham, B18 5AY Tel: 0121-551 3549 Fax: 0121-554 9097 *Meat distribution*

M J C Technical Ltd, 12 York Street, Stourport-on-Severn, Worcestershire, DY13 9EF Tel: (01299) 827272 Fax: (01299) 827273 *Photocopier retail & servicing*

▶ M J Construction, Ivy Cottage, Monkwood Green, Hallow, Worcester, WR2 6NX Tel: (07896) 948686 E-mail: ayers_67@hotmail.com *General builders and specialists in renovations.also all general building work undertaken.please contact for free quotes and a reliable service.*

M J Curwood, Wards Cross, Broadclyst, Exeter, EX5 3DB Tel: (01404) 822264 Fax: (01404) 822264 *Agricultural contractors*

▶ M J D & Sons Ltd, White Cliff Park, Manor Way, Swanscombe, Kent, DA10 0LL Tel: (01322) 370700 Fax: (01322) 427424

▶ M & J Distributors, Unit A Hanix Building, Windmill Lane, Denton, Manchester, M34 3SP Tel: 0161-337 9600 Fax: 0161-337 0482 *Cycle wholesalers*

M J Dowson, Station House, Station Road, Tollerton, York, YO61 1RD Tel: (01347) 838272 Fax: (01347) 838957 *Joinery manufrs*

M J Electronics Services (International) Ltd, Unit 19B, Sedgemount Industrial Park, Bristol Road, Bridgwater, Somerset, TA6 4AR Tel: (01278) 422882 Fax: (01278) 453331 E-mail: sales@mjelectronics.freeserve.co.uk Principal Export Areas: Worldwide *Distributors of electrical inverters & power supplies*

M J Ellis Manufacturing, Forest Extra, Up Somborne, Stockbridge, Hampshire, SO20 6RA Tel: (01794) 388384 *Steel fabricators*

M J Engineering Ltd, Unit E6, Market Harborough, Leicestershire, LE16 7PS Tel: 01858 410620 *Precision engineers*

M & J Enterprises, Cuckoo Lane, Winterbourne Down, Bristol, BS36 1AG Tel: 0117-957 2440 Fax: (01454) 318710 *Wooden pallet manufrs*

M & J (Europe) Ltd, Tafarnaubach Industrial Estate, Tafarnaubach, Tredegar, Gwent, NP22 3AA Tel: (01495) 723444 Fax: (01495) 723555 *Conveyor systems, & ancillary equipment suppliers & manufrs*

M & J Evans Construction, 44 Hall Lane, Walsall Wood, Walsall, WS9 9BB Tel: (01543) 373766 Fax: (01543) 379018 *Civil engineers*

M J F Interdec Ltd, Greenford, Middlesex, UB18 9YS Tel: (01895) 909090 Fax: (01895) 909010 E-mail: hotline@interdec.co.uk *Office relocation & refurbishment services*

M J Farmer, 50 Wolverhampton Road, Wednesfield, Wolverhampton, WV11 1UJ Tel: (01902) 728827 Fax: (01902) 728827 *Office stationery & furniture suppliers*

M J Farrington Ltd, Locks Farm, Main Road, Dibden, Southampton, SO45 5TD Tel: (023) 8084 0755 Fax: (023) 8084 4588 *Plant & machinery repairers*

M & J Flat Roofing Ltd, Triumph Way, Kempston, Bedford, MK42 7QB Tel: (01234) 854890 Fax: (01234) 840776 E-mail: mj@mjroofing.com *Roofing contractors*

M J Fry Ltd, 1-2 Allens Lane, Poole, Dorset, BH16 5DA Tel: (01202) 622863 Fax: (01202) 624127 *Glass fibre moulding manufrs*

M J Garage Equipment Services Ltd, The Meadows, Bristol, BS15 3PB Tel: (07957) 855505 Fax: 0117-967 2994 *Garage equipment repairs & sales*

M J Gilbert & Co., Mill Road, Barnstaple, Devon, EX31 1JQ Tel: (01271) 343442 Fax: (01271) 343442 *Electric motor rewinders*

M J Gleeson Group plc, Unit 7-9 Callendar Business Park, Callendar Road, Falkirk, FK1 1XR Tel: (01324) 678460 Fax: (01324) 623741 *Civil engineering contractors*

▶ M J Green Navenby Ltd, Highfields, High Dyke, Navenby, Lincoln, LN5 0BQ Tel: (01522) 810295 Fax: (01522) 811263

M J H Engineering Services, Maycot, Quay Lane, Kirby-le-Soken, Frinton-on-Sea, Essex, CO13 0DP Tel: (01255) 675515 E-mail: info@mjh-engineering.co.uk *Software development & support & sales*

M J & H J Mills, 53 Livesey Street, Wateringbury, Maidstone, Kent, ME18 5BQ Tel: (01622) 812204 *Chestnut fencing manufrs*

M J & H M Roberts, The Smithy Bungalow, Bromyard Road, Bringsty, Worcester, WR6 5TA Tel: (01885) 482775 *Agricultural engineers*

▶ M J Impressions, Priory House, 25 St. John's Lane, London, EC1M 4HD Tel: (020) 7336 0880 Fax: (020) 7336 0890 E-mail: copy@mj.uk.com *Printing machine services*

M J Joinery, Swift Farm, Hensting Lane, Fishers Pond, Eastleigh, Hampshire, SO50 7HH Tel: (023) 8069 2184 *Joinery manufrs*

▶ M J K Acrylics, Unit 8b Whinfield Industrial Estate, Rowlands Gill, Tyne & Wear, NE39 1EH Tel: (01207) 549999 Fax: (01207) 549999 E-mail: mjkacrylics@btinternet.com *mjk acrylics design and manufacture acrylic encapsulations for business gifts awards and point of sale*

▶ M J & K Speck, The Gables, Northside Road, Hollym, Withernsea, North Humberside, HU19 2RS Tel: (01964) 613356 Fax: (01964) 613354

▶ M J Leisure, 9 Heene Road, Worthing, West Sussex, BN11 3RL Tel: (01903) 213214 E-mail: sales@mj-leisure.co.uk

▶ M J Leisure, Miners Park, Llay Industrial Estate, Llay, Wrexham, Clwyd, LL12 0PQ Tel: (0870) 1417373 Fax: (0870) 1417373 E-mail: info@mjleisure.com *Suppliers of appliances, parts & accessories for caravans*

M & J Lossos Co. Ltd, 31 Beethoven St, London, W10 4LJ Tel: (020) 8969 1367 Fax: (020) 8968 8913 E-mail: admin@kaloricheater.co.uk *Heating & air conditioning engineers*

M J M Engineering Ltd, 14 Rydal Avenue, Droylsden, Manchester, M43 6HH Tel: 0161 3717902 *Chemical machinery dealers*

▶ M J M Engineering Services Ltd, 26 Poplar Road, Glenrothes, Fife, KY7 4AA Tel: (01592) 610771 Fax: (01592) 610088

M.J.M Marine Ltd, 10 Loughbrickland Road, Rathfriland, Newry, County Down, BT34 5AA Tel: (028) 4063 8396 Fax: (028) 4063 8973 E-mail: sales@mjmmarine.com *Ship refurbishment & shop fitters*

M J M Software Ltd, 217-219 Hamstel Road, Southend-On-Sea, SS2 4LB Tel: (01702) 300441 Fax: (01702) 300115 E-mail: sales@mjm-ltd.com *Computer software*

M J M Suspended Ceilings, Melville Road, Sidcup, Kent, DA14 4LX Tel: (020) 8300 8400 E-mail: smarks.mjm@ntlworld.com *Ceiling installers*

M J M Toolmaking Ltd Ltd, Farfield Park, Manvers, Rotherham, South Yorkshire, S63 5DB Tel: (01709) 873131 Fax: (01709) 873131 *Tool making & injection moulders*

M J Macaulay, 4 Webster Place, Rosyth, Dunfermline, Fife, KY11 2TU Tel: (07708) 854378 E-mail: mac@macaulay2560.freeserve.co.uk *Mobile car valeting and forensic cleaning service, from a simple wash and wax to a full valet to return your car to the condition it was when you first bought it*

▶ M J McCabe & Sons Ltd, Emerald House, Myrtle Lane, Billingshurst, West Sussex, RH14 9SG Tel: (01403) 785855

M J Mccleave & Co., 3 Hannahstown Hill, Hannahstown, Belfast, BT17 0LT Tel: (028) 9061 3377 Fax: (028) 9060 0001 *Steel erectors*

M J Madkins, Thornborough Road, Nash, Milton Keynes, MK17 0HN Tel: (01296) 712938 Fax: (01296) 712938 *Agricultural consultants*

M J Maillis UK Ltd, Monarch House, Chrysalis Way, Eastwood, Nottingham, NG16 3RY Tel: (01773) 539000 Fax: (01773) 539090 E-mail: info@mallis.co.uk *Stretch wrap film & machninery manufacturers.*

M J Metalcraft Ltd, 32-34 Sampson Road North, Birmingham, B11 1BL Tel: 0121-771 3711 Fax: 0121-771 3766 E-mail: enquiries@mjmetalcraftltd.co.uk *Electric cabinets, consoles & control panel enclosures (metal) manufrs*

M J Milward Printing Ltd, 21 Nottingham South & Wilford Industrial Estate, Nottingham, NG11 7EP Tel: 0115-981 3378 Fax: 0115-981 2386 E-mail: mgmprint@compuserve.com *Printers*

M J N Ltd, Davis House, 69-73 High Street, Croydon, CR9 1PY Tel: (020) 8686 5577 Fax: (020) 8681 3114 E-mail: jhipwell@mjncolston.co.uk *Air conditioning engineers* Also at: Bridgend, Bristol, Exeter & Norwich

▶ M J N C Jesney, 648 Chesterfield Road, Sheffield, S8 0SB Tel: 0114-249 3436 *Bakery*

▶ M J N Colston, 9 Bridgend Business Park, Bennett Street, Bridgend Industrial Estate, Bridgend, Mid Glamorgan, CF31 3SH Tel: (01656) 661808 Fax: (01656) 660473 E-mail: bridgend@mjncolston.co.uk

M J Nelmes, Cornworthy, Coombe Road, Salisbury, SP2 8BT Tel: (01722) 324351 *Road transport, haulage & freight services*

M & J Nuttall, Unit 14 Pearlbrook Industrial Estate, Chorley New Road, Horwich, Bolton, BL6 5PX Tel: (01204) 691311 *Joiners*

M J P Ltd, 9 Alpha Business Park, Travellers Close, North Mymms, Hatfield, Hertfordshire, AL9 7NT Tel: (01707) 261179 Fax: (01707) 272470 E-mail: mike.player@virgin.net *Welding equipment supplies & service*

M J P Electronics Ltd, Unit 1, Gore Cross Business Park, Corbin Way, Bradpole, Bridport, Dorset, DT6 3UX Tel: (01308) 425800 Fax: (01308) 455770 E-mail: murry@mjpelectronics.com *Printed circuit assembly services*

M J P Tube & Fittings Ltd, Regil Lane, Winford, Bristol, BS40 8AX Tel: (01275) 474758 Fax: (01275) 472753 *General fabricators*

▶ M J Partridge Ltd, Builders Yard, Birdlip, Gloucester, GL4 8JH Tel: (01452) 862555 Fax: (01452) 864363

M J Pawsey Refrigeration, 129 Parkway, Dorking, Surrey, RH4 1ET Tel: (01306) 884121 *Refrigeration services*

M J Pringle, Main Street, Radcliffe, Morpeth, Northumberland, NE65 0JB Tel: (01665) 711702 Fax: (01665) 711702 *Agricultural engineers*

M & J Products, 20 Gresley Close, Drayton Fields Industrial Estate, Daventry, Northamptonshire, NN11 8RZ Tel: (01327) 872885 Fax: (01327) 300706 E-mail: mjproducts@btconnect.com *DIY products wholesalers*

M J Q Ltd, 52 Heronsgate Road, Chorleywood, Rickmansworth, Hertfordshire, WD3 5BB Tel: (01923) 285266 Fax: (01923) 285168 E-mail: sales@mjq.co.uk *Recording equipment suppliers & retailers*

▶ M J Quinn Integrated Services Ltd, Gormley House, Waxlow Road, London, NW10 7NU Tel: (020) 8453 0450 Fax: (020) 8453 0455

M J R Controls Ltd, Unit 85, Willows Court, Thornaby, Stockton-on-Tees, Cleveland, TS17 9PP Tel: (01642) 762151 Fax: (01642) 762502 E-mail: enquiries@mjrcontrols.com *Established in 1971, MJR Controls is a marine & industrial electronic, electrical and automation engineering company. We specialise in PCB & Electronic System Repair; Control System, PLC & SCADA Design; Osolete Equipment Re-engineering; Custom Electronic Design; Electrical Engineering.*

M J R Fabrications, B Cranborne Industrial Estate, Cranborne Road, Potters Bar, Hertfordshire, EN6 3JN Tel: (01707) 646825 Fax: (01707) 649089 *Sheet metal workers, engineers, fabricators & precision engineering*

M J Raven & Son Ltd, Unit 22 Patricia Way, Pysons Road Industrial Estate, Broadstairs, Kent, CT10 2LF Tel: (01843) 866676 Fax: (01843) 866070 E-mail: sales@mjraven.co.uk *Sub-contract engineering services*

▶ M J Refrigeration Transport Ltd, Treetops, Holyhead Road, Nesscliffe, Shrewsbury, SY4 1AY Tel: (01743) 741658 Fax: (01743) 741766

M J Richardson, Newholme Farm, High Street, Hatfield, Doncaster, South Yorkshire, DN7 6RS Tel: (01302) 840518 *Agricultural contractants*

M & J Seafoods Wholesale Ltd, 1 Crescent Wharf, North Woolwich Road, London, E16 2BG Tel: (020) 7540 4800 Fax: (020) 7540 4809 *Fish wholesalers*

M J Sections Ltd, Unit 5 Marriott Road Industrial Estate, Netherton, Dudley, West Midlands, DY2 0JZ Tel: (01384) 230444 Fax: (01384) 456086 E-mail: sales@mjsections.co.uk *Rolled ring section manufrs*

M J Security Systems Ltd, 46 Edward Street, Dunstable, Bedfordshire, LU6 1HF Tel: (01582) 665022 Fax: (01582) 477754 *Security alarms installation*

M J Security Systems Ltd, PO Box 6, Nottingham, NG10 4PN Tel: 0115-946 1280 Fax: (0870) 7482040 *Security alarm systems*

M J Security UK Ltd, Tudor Walk, Berry Hill, Coleford, Gloucestershire, GL16 7AE Tel: (01594) 834585 E-mail: enquiries@mjsecuritysystems.com *Security systems installers*

M J Sheet Metal Co., 158 Crow Lane, Romford, RM7 0ES Tel: (01708) 737050 Fax: (01708) 737096 *Sheet metalworkers*

M J Sherwin, Unit 16 Lord Nelson Industrial Estate, Commercial Road, Stoke-on-Trent, ST1 3QF Tel: (01782) 213289 Fax: (01782) 204587 *Joinery manufrs*

M J Spencer, The Range, Hawkesbury Road, Hillesley, Wotton-under-Edge, Gloucestershire, GL12 7RE Tel: (01453) 843059 Fax: (01453) 843059 *Ground workers*

M J T Controls Ltd, Unit 10, Novers Hill Trading Estate, Novers Hill, Bedminster, Bristol, BS3 5QY Tel: 0117-963 7142 Fax: 0117-963 2332 E-mail: mjtcontrols@btinternet.com *HVAC controls distribs*

▶ M J T Electrical Services, 40 First Avenue, Galley Hill, Waltham Abbey, Essex, EN9 2AL Tel: (0797) 1252699 Fax: (01992) 701412 E-mail: mjtelectricalservices@fsmail.net *Electrical, testing service*

M J Taylor King Ltd, 1 Cowper Road, Harpenden, Hertfordshire, AL5 5NF Tel: (01582) 763430 Fax: (01582) 461156 E-mail: tailorking@ukonline.co.uk *Building services*

M & J Timber Ltd, 32 Union Street, Greenock, Renfrewshire, PA16 8DJ Tel: (01475) 723737 Fax: (01475) 722537 *Timber & builders merchants*

M J Visual Systems Ltd, Unit 1, New Bury Park, Easthampnett, Chichester, West Sussex, PO18 0JY Tel: (01243) 780816 Fax: (01243) 783562 E-mail: sales@mjvisual.co.uk *Audio visual sales & hire*

▶ M J Wilson Ltd, Charlton Street, Grimsby, South Humberside, DN31 1SQ Tel: (01472) 345361 Fax: (01472) 340172 E-mail: sales@dcmarshinstruments.co.uk *Instrumentation & fastenings suppliers*

M J Wilson Ltd, Charlton Street, Grimsby, South Humberside, DN31 1SQ Tel: (01472) 345361 Fax: (01472) 340172 E-mail: sales@dcmarshinstruments.co.uk *Industrial fastener & instrumentation manufrs*

M K Aero Support Ltd, Andrews Field, Stebbing, Dunmow, Essex, CM6 3TH Tel: (01371) 856796 Fax: (01371) 856855 E-mail: mkaerosupport@btconnect.com *Aircraft maintenance & leasing services*

M K Contracts Ltd, 50 Buntingbridge Road, Ilford, Essex, IG2 7LR Tel: (020) 8518 2100 Fax: (020) 8518 2984 *Interior refurbishments*

M K Electric, The Arnold Centre, Paycocke Road, Basildon, Essex, SS14 3EA Tel: (01268) 563000 Fax: (01268) 563405 E-mail: mkorderingenquires@hornywell.com *Manufacturers of bulbar distribution electrical systems*

M K Electric Ltd, Glascoed Road, St. Asaph, Clwyd, LL17 0ER Tel: (01745) 532000 Fax: (01745) 532127 *Electric equipment manufrs*

▶ M K Electrical, 537 Blairdardie Road, Glasgow, G15 6JQ Tel: 0141-944 7020 Fax: 0141-944 7030 E-mail: info@mkelectrical.co.uk *Electrical maintenance commercial, industrial electrical installations service*

▶ M K Engines Ltd, 6 Clarke Road, Bletchley, Milton Keynes, MK1 1LG Tel: (01908) 366566 Fax: (01908) 366566

M & K Fabrication, Hillsdene, Clockhouse Lane, Romford, RM5 2RR Tel: (01708) 769004 Fax: (01708) 769005 *Architectural metalworkers*

M K Fire Ltd, 65-69 Queens Road, High Wycombe, Buckinghamshire, HP13 6AH Tel: (01494) 769774 Fax: (01494) 465378 E-mail: info@mkfire.co.uk *Fire protection equipment suppliers* Also at: Sheffield

M K G Food Products Ltd, Westgate, Aldridge, Walsall, WS9 8DE Tel: (01922) 459311 Fax: (01922) 743077 E-mail: sales@mkgfoods.co.uk *Frozen food distributors*

M K H Ltd, 5 Gloster Drive, Kenilworth, Warwickshire, CV8 2TU Tel: (01926) 850555 Fax: (01926) 850888 E-mail: mkh.ltd@virgin.net *MKH Limited offers the complete solution for creating stylish office environments that work for your business. We liaise with our clients to ensure that both technically and logistically all projects are implemented efficiently by our team. Our standards are high - the majority of new business we receive is from personal recommendation - so our reputation for excellence is important to us.*

▶ M K Leslie Ltd, Staneyhill Quarry, Staneyhill, Lerwick, Shetland, ZE1 0QW Tel: (01595) 695060 Fax: (01595) 697239

M K M Agriculture, Sun Valley Works, Woodend, Marston Moretaine, Bedford, MK43 0NJ Tel: (01234) 768889 Fax: (01234) 767935 E-mail: info@mkmagri.com *Quad bikes & agricultural engineers*

▶ M & K Mcleod, Kilmory Industrial Estate, Kilmory, Lochgilphead, Argyll, PA31 8RR Tel: (01546) 602989 Fax: (01546) 603789 E-mail: sales@mkmacleod.co.uk

M K Marking Systems Ltd, 22 Carters Lane, Kiln Farm Industrial Estate, Kiln Farm, Milton Keynes, MK11 3HL Tel: (01908) 561676 Fax: (01908) 562551 E-mail: sales@mkmarking.co.uk *Signs, rubber stamp & badge manufrs*

▶ M & K Pine Co, Fisher Street, Newcastle upon Tyne, NE6 4LT Tel: 0191-263 0274

M K Powder Coaters Ltd, 33 Blundells Road, Bradville, Milton Keynes, MK13 7HD Tel: (01908) 318484 Fax: (01908) 322253 *Powder coaters*

▶ M K Powder Coatings, 5 Cordingley Street, Bradford, West Yorkshire, BD4 0PP Tel: (01274) 680099 Fax: (01274) 680099 *We can spray any colour on any metal; gates shop fixtures, shutters railings or grilles, shotblasting and galvanising services are availiable. We can accomodate even the largest of jobs, we can offer a 24hr turnaround to suit your needs and we offer very competitive prices. We can arrange pickup and delivery*

M K R Electronic Services, Unit 1 Havannah Street, Congleton, Cheshire, CW12 2AH Tel: (01260) 271553 Fax: (01260) 275750 *Electronic contract manufrs*

M K S Instruments UK, 10 Delta House, Carmondean Centre, Livingston, West Lothian, EH54 8PT Tel: (01506) 440004 Fax: (01506) 430004 E-mail: sales@mksinst.co.uk *Instrumentation suppliers*

M K Services Ltd, Unit 24 Pages Industrial Park, Eden Way, Leighton Buzzard, Bedfordshire, LU7 4TZ Tel: (01525) 382333 Fax: (01525) 850073 E-mail: sales@mkservices.co.uk *Geophysical equipment distributors*

M K Services, 199 Middlewood Road, Sheffield, S6 4HD Tel: 0114-232 6394 Fax: 0114-285 2189 *Floor cleaning equipment sales & services*

M K Services, 23 St Johns Way, Knowle, Solihull, West Midlands, B93 0LE Tel: (01564) 779976 *Portable air conditioning fans*

M & K Sewing Machines, 257-259 Barlow Road, Levenshulme, Manchester, M19 3HQ Tel: 0161-225 2074 Fax: 0161-257 3057 *Sewing machine sales & repairs*

M K Site Services, Carillion Building, Loaninghill, Uphall, Broxburn, West Lothian, EH52 5NT Tel: (01506) 433435 Fax: (01506) 433438 E-mail: enquiries@mksiteservices.com

M & K Storage & Handling Supplies, 4a Armoury Road, Lufton Trading Estate, Lufton, Yeovil, Somerset, BA22 8RL Tel: (01935) 476555 Fax: (01935) 433700 E-mail: sales@mk-shelving.co.uk *Supplier of new storage & handling products, shipping containers*

M K Test Systems Ltd, Orchard Court, West Buckland, Wellington, Somerset, TA21 9LE Tel: (01823) 661100 Fax: (01823) 661160 E-mail: sales@mktest.com *Test equipment manufrs*

M K Tool & Die Ltd, 19 Spackmans Way, Slough, SL1 2SA Tel: 01753 539159 *Gravity die toolmakers*

▶ M & K Trading Ltd, Unit 26 Earith Business Park, Meadow Drove, Earith, Huntingdon, Cambridgeshire, PE28 3QF Tel: (01487) 840155 Fax: (01487) 843976 E-mail: sales@mandktrading.co.uk *Machinery equipment manufrs*

M K Trophies, 21 Scott Drive, Newport Pagnell, Buckinghamshire, MK16 8PW Tel: (01908) 615326 Fax: (01908) 615326 *Trophies & rosettes manufrs*

M K Trueman, 4 Murphys Yard, Railway Road, Idle, Bradford, West Yorkshire, BD10 9RJ Tel: (01274) 612492 *Metal work*

▶ M & K Units, 4 Lisburn Street, Hillsborough, County Down, BT26 6AB Tel: (028) 9268 3085 Fax: (028) 9268 3739 E-mail: mk_units@hotmail.com *Furniture manufrs*

M K W Engineering Ltd, Stargate Industrial Estate, Ryton, Tyne & Wear, NE40 3EX Tel: 0191-413 0000 Fax: 0191-413 2736 E-mail: sales@mkw.co.uk *General engineers & fabricators*

M K Wheeler Ltd, Nine Lock Works, Mill Street, Brierley Hill, West Midlands, DY5 2SX Tel: (01384) 487600 Fax: (01384) 487619 E-mail: sales@vanleeuwenwheeler.co.uk *Steel tube stockholders* Also at: Bury, East Kilbride & Iver

M L Accessories Ltd, 5A-5B Kings Street, Houghton Regis, Bedfordshire, LU5 5DF Tel: (01582) 868903 Fax: (01582) 868830 *Wiring accessory manufrs*

M L B Engineering, 1a Belle Eau Park, Bilsthorpe, Newark, Nottinghamshire, NG22 8TX Tel: (01623) 871991 Fax: (01623) 871991 *Construction*

M L Banfield & Sons Ltd, 1-2 Little Western Street, Brighton, BN1 2QH Tel: (01273) 737622 Fax: (01273) 720950 E-mail: philip@banfields.co.uk *Builders & ironmongers*

M L C Monsoon Ltd, Northfield Business Park, London Road, Lower Dicker, Hailsham, East Sussex, BN27 4BZ Tel: (01323) 440422 Fax: (01323) 845705 *Vehicle accessories manufrs*

▶ M & L Carpets Ltd, 54 Crouch End Hill, London, N8 8AA Tel: (020) 8341 0914 Fax: (020) 8341 0914 E-mail: info@mlcarpets.com *One of Londons leading suppliers and fitters oif carpets and flooring.*

▶ M L Carpets & Flooring Ltd, 223 Salisbury Road, Totton, Southampton, SO40 3PF Tel: (023) 8036 7098 Fax: (023) 8036 7098 E-mail: mike@mlcarpets.co.uk *Carpets & flooring retailers*

M & L Crane Plant Services Ltd, 50 Holme Hall Avenue, Scunthorpe, South Humberside, DN16 3PZ Tel: (01724) 281621 Fax: (01724) 281621 E-mail: mlcrane@aol.com *Crane servicing & plant inspection*

M & L Engravers, 14 Ravenswood Industrial Estate, Shernhall Street, London, E17 9HQ Tel: (020) 8520 5144 Fax: (020) 8509 3803 *Engraving services*

▶ M & L Foods, 5 First Avenue, Halstead, Essex, CO9 2EX Tel: (01787) 472048 Fax: (01787) 474110 *Bakers*

M L G Engineering, Unit 26 Small Business Centre, Penmaen Road, Pontllanfraith, Blackwood, Gwent, NP12 2DZ Tel: (01495) 220695 Fax: (01495) 220695 *General fabricators*

M & L Homestyle Ltd, Lupin Works, Worcester Road, Kidderminster, Worcestershire, DY10 1JR Tel: (01562) 755333 Fax: (01562) 745559 *PVC & aluminium window & doors assemblers & installers*

M L Hughes, Bryn Olwen, Llanfair Road, Abergele, Clwyd, LL22 8PB Tel: (07850) 401762 Fax: (01745) 832243 *Agricultural contractors*

▶ M L I T C, 40 Roman Way, Felixstowe, Suffolk, IP11 9NP Tel: (01394) 671579 E-mail: mark@mlconsultancy.co.uk

M.L.P.S., PO Box 27, Grantham, Lincs, NG31 6SJ Tel: (01476) 590400 Fax: (01476) 590400 E-mail: sales@mlps.co.uk *Lettering systems/ printing machine distributors*

M & L Promotional Products Ltd, 5 Queen Street, Mirfield, West Yorkshire, WF14 8AH Tel: (01924) 498500 Fax: (01924) 497200 E-mail: sales@mlbadges.com *Badge manufrs*

M L Propagators, Fairview, Shucknall Hill, Hereford, HR1 3SW Tel: 01432 850213 Fax: 01432 850213 *Irrigation equipment manufrs*

▶ M L Quinn Construction Ltd, 108 Carrickgallogly Road, Belleeks, Newry, County Down, BT35 7QS Tel: (028) 3087 9300

M L R Networks Ltd, St. Michaels House, Hale Road, Widnes, Cheshire, WA8 8XL Tel: 0151-423 3633 Fax: 0151-495 1665 E-mail: pmorris@mlrnetworks.co.uk *Computer installation engineers*

▶ M L R Surveyors Ltd, 8 Newton Place, Glasgow, G3 7PR Tel: 0141-333 1594 Fax: 0141-333 1586 E-mail: glasgow@mlr.uk.com *Quantity surveyors planning supervisors*

M L Signs, 3a Bessemer Road, Cardiff, CF11 8BA Tel: (029) 2022 7694 Fax: (029) 2038 8148 *Sign makers*

▶ M L System Services Ltd, Glenfield Park, 1 Philips Road, Blackburn, BB1 5PF Tel: (01254) 691444 E-mail: sales@mlsystemservices.com *Computer system consultants*

M L (UK) Ltd, Kettering Terrace, Mile End, Portsmouth, PO2 7AE Tel: (023) 9281 9114 Fax: (023) 9282 3386 E-mail: martin@mluk.co.uk *Steel fabricators*

M Lambe Construction Ltd, Newton House, Newton Place, Birmingham, B18 5JY Tel: 0121-523 0666 Fax: 0121-554 8896 *Ground workers & civil engineers*

M Latchford, 10 Alstone Lane, Cheltenham, Gloucestershire, GL51 8EG Tel: (01242) 584588 Fax: (01242) 529251 E-mail: sales@marklatchford-screenprint.co.uk *Screen printing*

M.Laurier & Sons Ltd, Unit 10 Triumph Trading Estate, Tariff Road, London, N17 0EB Tel: (020) 8365 9000 Fax: (020) 8365 9005 E-mail: info@laurier.co.uk *Polythene & hessian suppliers, scaffold sheeting & accessories* Also at: Birmingham & Bristol

M Leach Jewellers, 98 Worcester Road, Malvern, Worcestershire, WR14 1NY Tel: (01684) 573673 Fax: (01684) 573673 *Jewellery repairers & suppliers*

M Lord & Sons, Florence Mill, Whalley New Road, Blackburn, BB1 9SR Tel: (01254) 661002 Fax: (01254) 661002 *Carpet retailers*

M M A Insurance plc, 2 Norman Place, Reading, RG1 8DA Tel: 0118-955 2222 Fax: 0118-955 2211 E-mail: info@mma-insurance.com *Insurance company*

M & M Bell, Techmuiry, Fraserburgh, Aberdeenshire, AB43 7BD Tel: (01346) 541289 Fax: (01346) 541454 *Agricultural contractor*

M M C Ltd, 2ND Floor, Guide Bridge Mill, South Street, Ashton-Under-Lyne, Lancashire, OL7 0HU Tel: 0161-343 1740 Fax: 0161-343 1741 E-mail: pats@mmc93.co.uk *Display stands & shop fittings installers & manufrs*

M & M Computing Services Ltd, Dial Post Court, Horsham Road, Rusper, Horsham, West Sussex, RH12 4QX Tel: (01293) 871971 Fax: (01293) 871796 E-mail: sales@mm-computing.com *Computer dealers, brokers & distributors*

M M D (Shipping Services) Ltd, Flathouse Quay, Prospect Road, Portsmouth, PO2 7SP Tel: (023) 9282 6351 Fax: (023) 9229 1910 *Shipping agents*

M M Digital Ltd, Haig Road, Parkgate Industrial Estate, Knutsford, Cheshire, WA16 8DX Tel: (01565) 755356 Fax: (01565) 755357 E-mail: sales@mmdigital.co.uk *Ink jet printers suppliers*

M & M Ducksbury, 95 Newcastle Street, Tuxford, Newark, Nottinghamshire, NG22 0LN Tel: (01777) 870289 Fax: (01777) 872932 *Agricultural contractors*

▶ M M E Engineering Ltd, Unit 3 Faversham Shipyard, Upper Brents, Faversham, Kent, ME13 7DZ Tel: (01795) 535559 Fax: (01795) 536374 *Ship manufrs*

M M Electrical Services, 17 Reddicap Trading Estate, Sutton Coldfield, West Midlands, B75 7BU Tel: 0121-378 4565 Fax: 0121-378 3541 E-mail: info@mmelec.co.uk *Electrical engineers & contractors*

▶ M & M Embroidery, 39 Hutton Close, Crowther, Washington, Tyne & Wear, NE38 0AH Tel: 0191-415 3552 Fax: 0191-415 0514 E-mail: enquiries@mandm-embroidery.demon.co.uk *Embroidered garments, online embroidery service, promotional items, we embroider football boots, school wear suppliers, badges and emblems. anything that can be embroidered we do it*

M & M Engineering Construction, 66 Templepatrick Road, Ballyclare, County Antrim, BT39 9AL Tel: (028) 9335 2891 Fax: (028) 9335 2891 *Steel fabricators*

M M F Ltd, 55 Woodburn Road, Smethwick, West Midlands, B66 2PU Tel: 0121-555 6555 Fax: 0121-555 6816 E-mail: sales@fluepipes.com *Flue & chimney specialists*

M & M Fabrications Ltd, Disraeli Street, Aylestone, Leicester, LE2 8LX Tel: 0116-245 2800 Fax: 0116-245 2801 E-mail: mandm@b-on-line.com *Punching & sheet metalwork services*

M M Fork Truck Services, Greenhill Farm, Dunstable Road, Tilsworth, Leighton Buzzard, Bedfordshire, LU7 9PU Tel: (01525) 210605 Fax: (01525) 384864 *Fork lift trucks service, sales & hire*

M M G (Construction) Ltd, Crighton Wynd, Bellshill, Lanarkshire, ML4 3NF Tel: (07855) 314856 *Offering top quality, reliable joinery services in the central Scotland area. All types of work undertaken including kitchens, flooring, doors, decking, timber kits and many other services. Contact us for a free no obligation quote.*

M M G Guards, 1 Station Street, Holbeach, Spalding, Lincolnshire, PE12 7LF Tel: 01406 426047 *Guards manufrs*

M & M International UK Ltd, 12 Railton Road, Kempston, Bedford, MK42 7PW Tel: (01234) 855888 Fax: (01234) 856999 E-mail: sales@mmint.co.uk *Solenoid valves, pressure switches & timers*

M M & K Ltd, 1 Bengal Court, London, EC3V 9DD Tel: (020) 7283 7200 Fax: (020) 7283 4119 E-mail: info@mm-k.com *Tax & investment planning services*

M M K Express Ltd, 4 Antrim Business Park, Sentry Lane, Newtownabbey, County Antrim, BT36 4XX Tel: (028) 9083 8388 Fax: (028) 9084 8822 E-mail: sales@mmkexpress.co.uk *Freight forwarders*

M, M & M Ltd, 102 Seymour Place, London, W1H 1NF Tel: (020) 7724 5117 Fax: (020) 7724 5087 E-mail: mmm@mmmltd.com *Assembly & sale of computers*

▶ M M Marketing Ltd, Devonshire Road, Heathpark Industrial Estate, Honiton, Devon, EX14 1SD Tel: (01404) 44446 Fax: (01404) 42484 E-mail: info@mmmarketing.net *Computer printer & cartridge suppliers*

▶ M M P Polishers, Clovelly Road, Southbourne, Emsworth, Hampshire, PO10 8PE Tel: (01243) 379204 Fax: (01243) 378145 *Metal polishing services*

▶ M M P S Plumbing Services Ltd, 9 McLennan Street, Glasgow, G42 9DH Tel: 0141-632 6622

M M Palmer Ltd, 3-5 Capital Place, Harlow, Essex, CM19 5AS Tel: (01279) 439023 Fax: (01279) 635940 E-mail: sales@palmersprint.co.uk *Commercial printers*

M & M Patterns, Unit 11 Park Farm Buildings, Cranfield Road, Wavendon, Milton Keynes, MK17 8HA Tel: (01908) 585164 Fax: (01908) 585164 *Pattern making*

M & M Paving Slabs, Old Manor Farm, Leigh Road, Wimborne, Dorset, BH21 2BT Tel: (01202) 840455 Fax: (01202) 840455 *Paving slabs, fencing & garden ornaments manufacturers & timber products*

▶ M & M Picture Frames Mouldings Ltd, Humber Road, Barton-upon-Humber, South Humberside, DN18 5BN Tel: (01652) 632632 Fax: (01652) 660451 E-mail: sales@pinewrap.co.uk *Manufactures mouldings*

M & M Precision Engineering, 24-25 Saville Road Industrial Estate, Saville Road, Peterborough, PE3 7PR Tel: (01733) 332117 Fax: (01733) 264424 E-mail: sales@mmpe.co.uk *Precision engineers*

M M Production Services Ltd, Londonderry Farm Workshops, Keynsham Road, Willsbridge, Bristol, BS30 6EL Tel: 0117-932 6255 Fax: 0117-932 6256 *Sale of machine tool equipment*

▶ M M R Ltd, Cash Feus, Strathmiglo, Cupar, Fife, KY14 7QT Tel: (01337) 860212 Fax: (01337) 860716

▶ M M R Ltd, Cash Feus, Strathmiglo, Cupar, Fife, KY14 7QT Tel: (01337) 860212 Fax: (01337) 860716

M M R International Ltd, 32 Station Approch, West Byfleet, Surrey, KT14 6NF Tel: (01932) 351733 Fax: (020) 7482 3518 *Medical marketing researchers*

M & M Rewinds, 15 Dinsdale Road, Croft Business Park, Bromborough, Wirral, Merseyside, CH62 3PY Tel: 0151-334 6808 Fax: 0151-334 6808 E-mail: mandmrew@amserve.com *Electric motor repair services*

▶ M & M Road Surfacing, 9A Bankhead Medway, Edinburgh, EH11 4BY Tel: (07860) 388272

M M S Ship Repair & Dry Dock Co. Ltd, Alexandra Dock, Hull, HU9 1TA Tel: (01482) 219278 Fax: (01482) 588061 E-mail: sales@mms-shiprepair.co.uk *Marine engineering services*

M & M Secure Services Ltd, Station Yard, Whitehaven, Moor Row, Cumbria, CA24 3JP Tel: (01946) 815957 Fax: (01946) 815957 *Confidential data destruction*

▶ M & M Services Ltd, 662 Holburn Street, Aberdeen, AB10 7JQ Tel: (01224) 589222

M & M Steel Stockholders & Fabricators, Riverside Works Trevor St Industrial Estate, Trevor Street, Birmingham, B7 5RG Tel: 0121-327 1695 Fax: 0121-327 1708 E-mail: mmsteel@btconnect.com *Stockholders & fabricators*

M & M Studios, Millers Yard, Hayseech Road, Halesowen, West Midlands, B63 3PD Tel: 0121-501 3868 Fax: 0121-585 5377 *Advertising & industrial photography*

M M T Services Ltd, 31 Vicarage Lane, Shrivenham, Swindon, SN6 8DT Tel: (01793) 784685 Fax: (01793) 784730 E-mail: andrew@mmtservicesltd.co.uk *Dairy engineers*

M & M Technical Services Ltd, Ebberns Road, Hemel Hempstead, Hertfordshire, HP3 9RD Tel: (01442) 213602 Fax: (01442) 242152 E-mail: glford@tiscali.co.uk *Process engineering consultants*

M M Textiles, 65 Anderton Road, Birmingham, B11 1LZ Tel: 0121-773 7522 Fax: 0121-773 7522 *Textile distributors*

M & M Timber Ltd, Hunt House Sawmills, Clows Top, Kidderminster, Worcestershire, DY14 9HY Tel: (01299) 832611 Fax: (01299) 832536 E-mail: sales@mmtimber.co.uk *Timber merchants & manufrs*

▶ M M W Welding Ltd, Gremista, Lerwick, Shetland, ZE1 0PX Tel: (01595) 695600 Fax: (01595) 695474

M Marcus, 7 Blackbrook Industrial Estate, Peartree Lane, Dudley, West Midlands, DY2 0XW Tel: (01384) 457900 Fax: (01384) 457903 E-mail: info@m-marcus.com *Door fittings importers*

M Michaels, 69 St. Marks Road, London, W10 6JG Tel: (020) 8964 5555 Fax: (020) 8964 5929 *Food photographer*

▶ M Miller, 55 Macrae Street, Wick, Caithness, KW1 5QW Tel: (01955) 602746 Fax: (01955) 605927

▶ M & M's Metalwork, Winchester, Hampshire, SO21 3NT Tel: 01962 761663 Fax: 01962 761663 *Steel fabricators*

M Musgrove Ltd, 1 Gunnersbury Mews, London, W4 4AP Tel: (020) 8994 2941 Fax: (020) 8994 4484 *Timber specialists*

M N B Precision Ltd, Falkland Close, Charter Avenue Industrial Estate, Coventry, CV4 8AU Tel: (024) 7669 5959 Fax: (024) 7669 5909 E-mail: sales@mnbprecision.com *Sub-contract precsion engineers*

M & N Canvas Services Ltd, Butterthwaite Lane, Ecclesfield, Sheffield, S35 9WA Tel: 0114-246 1293 Fax: 0114-257 0311 *Tarpaulins, nets, ropes & straps manufrs*

▶ M & N Electrical & Mechanical Services Ltd, Unit 12, Southwell Business Park, Portland, Dorset, DT5 2JS Tel: (01305) 821142 Fax: (01305) 821268

M & N Fabrications Ltd, Wharf Road, Woodston, Peterborough, PE2 9PS Tel: (01733) 342408 Fax: (01733) 342408 E-mail: deegeorge@aol.com *Tube, key clamps & timber distributors*

M & N Group Ltd, 118 London Road, Kingston upon Thames, Surrey, KT2 6QJ Tel: (020) 8974 5252 Fax: (020) 8974 5588 E-mail: sales@mn-group.com *Company formation (UK & off shore registration agents)*

M & N Pool Table Services, Leisure House, Billington Road, Leighton Industrial Park, Leighton Buzzard, Bedfordshire, LU7 4TN Tel: (01525) 381133 Fax: 01525 381133 *Pool table repairs & supplies*

▶ M & N Self Adhesive Labels Ltd, Mossneuk Estate, Gleniffer Braes, Neilston, Glasgow, G78 3AL Tel: (01505) 815892 Fax: (01505) 812740 E-mail: mn.labels@talk21.com *Label printing services*

M & N Sewing Machines, 41 Tennyson Road, Kettering, Northamptonshire, NN16 0DD Tel: (01536) 514880 Fax: (01536) 411169 *Sewing machines sales, service & rental*

▶ M N Stewart, Ashlea Cottage, Dunecht, Westhill, Aberdeenshire, AB32 7EQ Tel: (01330) 860363 Fax: (01330) 860939

M & N Textiles Ltd, Wrengate House, 221 Palatine Road, Didsbury, Manchester, M20 2EE Tel: 0161-438 1050 Fax: 0161-438 1021 E-mail: mandn@wrengate.co.uk *Grey cloth & cotton fabric merchants*

continued

M O J Machines Ltd, Unit 6-190-192 Beverley Trading Estate, Garth Road, Morden, Surrey, SM4 4LU Tel: 0118-973 7004 Fax: 0118-932 8262 Principal Export Areas: Worldwide *Bar & tube chamfering machine manufrs*

M O S Cold Cutting Systems Ltd, Acorn Park Industrial Estate, Charlestown, Shipley, W. Yorkshire, BD17 7SW Tel: (01274) 588066 Fax: (01274) 588077 E-mail: stm@constructionplus.net *Cold cutting systems for sale & contracting*

▶ M O S Group Ltd, Unit 2, Newby Road Industrial Estate, Newby Road, Hazel Grove, Stockport, Cheshire, SK7 5DA Tel: 0161-484 0444

The M O T Welding Service (Auto Weld) Of Worthing, Unit 14 Ivy Arch Road, Worthing, West Sussex, BN14 8BX Tel: (01903) 230634 *General welding services & repairs*

M P Alarms, 21 Bailey Lane, Clenchwarton, King's Lynn, Norfolk, PE34 4AY Tel: (01553) 772991 Fax: (01553) 776587 *Alarms & security systems installers*

▶ M P Automation Ltd, 46 Europa Business Park, Bird Hall Lane, Stockport, Cheshire, SK3 0XA Tel: 0161-428 7452 Fax: 0161-428 7304 *Industrial cutting Lasers for Metal,Dieboards,Aclrylic,*Comprehensive range of engraving systems.*Full team of qualified uk engineers for service and support.*

M P B Industries Ltd, Unit 1, Branbridges Industrial Estate, East Peckham, Tonbridge, Kent, TN12 5HF Tel: (01622) 872401 Fax: (01622) 871294 E-mail: mail@mpbflowmeters.com *Flow meter manufrs*

▶ M P B Photographic, 21-22 Old Steyne, Brighton, BN1 1EL Tel: (01273) 648348 E-mail: sales@mpbphotographic.co.uk *Photographic equipment retailers*

▶ M P Brothers Ltd, Unit 14 London Group Business Park, 715 North Circular Road, London, NW2 7AQ Tel: (020) 8208 1988 Fax: (020) 8208 0162

M P C Plastics Ltd, Unit 61, Enfield Industrial Estate, Redditch, Worcestershire, B97 6DE Tel: (01527) 584949 Fax: (01527) 61351 *Thermoplastics injection mouldings*

M P Calibration Services Ltd, A1 Romany Centre, Wareham Road, Holton Heath, Poole, Dorset, BH16 6JL Tel: (01202) 624468 Fax: (01202) 625132 E-mail: info@mpcalibration.co.uk *Mechanical calibrating*

M & P Carriage Works (Coventry) Ltd, Torrington Avenue, Coventry, CV4 9BL Tel: (024) 7642 1515 Fax: (024) 7642 1818 *Commercial vehicle body builders*

M P D Offset Ltd, Unit 5 Rivergate, Westlea, Swindon, SN5 7ET Tel: (01793) 495522 Fax: (01793) 495515

M P E Ltd, Hammond Road, Knowsley Industrial Park, Liverpool, L33 7UL Tel: 0151-632 9100 Fax: 0151-632 9112 E-mail: sales@mpe.co.uk *Electric/electronic capacitor manufrs*

M P E Alarms & Security Systems, 22 Fennfields Road, South Woodham Ferrers, Chelmsford, CM3 5RZ Tel: (0870) 8505862 Fax: (01245) 320350 *Fire & intruder alarm installers*

M P E Systems Ltd, 1 Manor Farm, Culham, Abingdon, Oxfordshire, OX14 4NP Tel: (01235) 554771 Fax: (01235) 550656 *Design & supply of processing systems for food industry*

M P Engineering, 7 Locke Place, Birmingham, B7 4HH Tel: 0121-359 5854 Fax: 0121-359 5854 *General engineering services*

M & P (Engineering) Ltd, Wharfside Way, Trafford Park, Manchester, M17 1AN Tel: 0161-872 8378 Fax: 0161-872 9250 E-mail: info@mp-engineering.co.uk *Manufacturers of packaging equipment, filling machines & food processing plant & machinery*

M P Engineering Stalybridge Ltd, Park View Works, Park Street, Stalybridge, Cheshire, SK15 2BT Tel: 0161-303 9988 Fax: 0161-303 9988 *Sub-contract engineering*

M P G Accessories Ltd, 3 278 Alma Road, Enfield, Middlesex, EN3 7RS Tel: (020) 8804 0123 Fax: (020) 8804 6821 *Fashion jewellery importers*

M P G Books Ltd, Victoria Square, Bodmin, Cornwall, PL31 1EB Tel: (01208) 73266 Fax: (01208) 73603 E-mail: print@mpg-books.co.uk *Book printers & specialist bookbinders*

M P Harvey, 119-123 Middle Watch, Swavesey, Cambridge, CB24 4RP Tel: (01954) 206113 Fax: (01954) 206113 *Power tool repairs*

M & P Hydraulic Ltd, Unit 3c Bergen Way, Hull, HU7 0YQ Tel: (01482) 820701 Fax: (01482) 823101 *Engineers*

M P I Ltd, Suite 1 Syer House, Stafford Court, Telford, Shropshire, TF3 3BD Tel: (01952) 290862 Fax: (01952) 290864 E-mail: telford@mpi.ltd.uk *Aviation industry employment agency*

M & P Joinery Joinery, 39a Shaftesbury Avenue, Bristol, BS6 5LT Tel: 0117-941 3210 Fax: 0117-941 3210 *Window consultants*

M P L Fabrications, Dutton Road, Aldermans Green Industrial Estate, Coventry, CV2 2LE Tel: (024) 7661 0778 Fax: (024) 7661 9499 E-mail: sales@mplfabrications.com *Sheet metalwork fabricators*

M P M Engineering Services Ltd, Unit 2 192 Camford Way, Luton, LU3 3AN Tel: (01582) 582811 Fax: (01582) 491865 E-mail: enquiries@mpm-eng.co.uk *Kitchen furniture & components suppliers*

M P M (Moulds Patterns & Models) Ltd, 1 Centre St, Bradford, West Yorkshire, BD5 9DB Tel: (01274) 572515 Fax: (01274) 571880 *Glass fibre manufrs*

M P M Presstools, 1 Chancel Way Industrial Estate, Chancel Way, Birmingham, B6 7AU Tel: 0121-356 7600 Fax: 0121-356 9766 E-mail: mpm.presstools@btconnect.com *Presstool making,wire eroding,CNC milling, jigs & fixtures, prototyping and development.*

M P M Scales & Fabrications, Unit 3 Millbuck Way, Sandbach, Cheshire, CW11 3HT Tel: (01270) 768470 Fax: (01270) 762992 E-mail: info@mpmscales.co.uk *Weighing equipment manufrs*

M P Manipulated Tubes Ltd, 40 Bracebridge Street, Aston, Birmingham, B6 4PJ Tel: 0121-359 0478 Fax: 0121-333 3082 *Bending services or fabricators*

▶ M P Moran & Sons Ltd, Worthington House, 449-451 High Road, London, NW10 2JJ Tel: (020) 8459 9000 Fax: (020) 8451 4776 E-mail: sales@mpmoran.co.uk *We are a large London based builders merchant stocking over 25,000 products including sand,cement,bricks,block,timber, doors,mdf,ply,building chemicals plumbing & electrical etc*

▶ M P S Ltd, 57 Woodroffe Drive, Basingstoke, Hampshire, RG22 6NH Tel: (01256) 817933 Fax: (08707) 625402E-mail: sales@mpsintl.com *Purchasing & selling of electronic components*

M P S, 45a Claremont Street, Cradley Heath, West Midlands, B64 6HH Tel: (01384) 413933 *Precision engineers*

M P S Garden Machinery, 288 Frome Road, Trowbridge, Wiltshire, BA14 0DT Tel: (01225) 776667 Fax: (01225) 776667 *Lawn mowers distributors*

M P S Group, 207 Desborough Road, High Wycombe, Buckinghamshire, HP11 2QL Tel: (01494) 452600 Fax: (01494) 449122 E-mail: bbi@bbi.co.uk *Marketing agency & website design services*

M P S Labels Ltd, The Brick Store, Gallants Farm, Gallants Lane, East Farleigh, Maidstone, Kent, ME15 0LD Tel: (01622) 727510 Fax: (01622) 725210 E-mail: sales@mpslabels.co.uk *Self adhesive labels manufacturers & printers*

▶ M & P SPECIALISTS LEAD ROOFING CONTRACTORS, 57 RINGMER DRIVE, LOWER FALMER, BRIGHTON, BN1 9HW Tel: 07887 818478 Fax: 01273 702752 E-mail: macbha@ntlworld.com *1: Family run Firm*2: Fully Insured*3: Friendly & Reliable*4: We only take on Lead projects*

▶ M P T Colour Graphics Ltd, Thames Park Business Centre, Thame, Oxfordshire, OX9 3XA Tel: (01844) 216888

M P T Products, 14 Malmesbury Road, Kingsditch Trading Estate, Cheltenham, Gloucestershire, GL51 9PL Tel: (01594) 825438 Fax: (01242) 227071 E-mail: tom@mptproducts.demon.co.uk *Industrial & specialised fastener manufrs*

M P V Packaging Ltd, Swan Lane, Hindley Green, Wigan, Lancashire, WN2 4HA Tel: (01942) 522522 Fax: (01942) 522523 E-mail: mpvpackaging@aol.com *Corrugated box, case, container & cardboard*

M P Vineis Ltd, 34 Henry Road, Barnet, Hertfordshire, EN4 8BD Tel: (020) 8449 4206 Fax: (020) 8449 4206 E-mail: vineis@btconnect.com *Engineering & tool making*

M P Welding Fabrications, Wareley Road, Peterborough, PE2 9PF Tel: (01733) 344455 Fax: (01733) 561628 *Steel fabrication & welding*

M & P Williams, Little Toldish Farm, Moorland Road, Indian Queens, St. Columb, Cornwall, TR9 6HJ Tel: (01726) 860664 Fax: (01726) 860401 *Farm contractors*

M Power Tools Ltd, Manor Farm, Newton Tony, Salisbury, SP4 0HA Tel: (01980) 629526 *Tools & tool manufrs*

M Q Metal Fabrication Ltd, Unit 11 Shaftesbury Industrial Centre, Bull Lane, London, N18 1SX Tel: (020) 8807 0098 Fax: (020) 8807 7318 *Steel stockholders & welding services*

M R A Cutting Tools, Unit 29 Lythalls La Industrial Estate, Lythalls Lane, Coventry, CV6 6FL Tel: (024) 7668 5813 Fax: (024) 7668 5813 *Foam manufrs*

M & R Bedding Ltd, Marshfield Mills, Marsh Street, Bradford, West Yorkshire, BD5 9NE Tel: (01274) 730004 Fax: (01274) 273008 E-mail: sales@mrbedding.co.uk *Furnishings*

M R C Publications Ltd, 5 Worcester Street, Oxford, OX1 2BX Tel: (01865) 200202 Fax: (01865) 200509 E-mail: sales@mrc.info.com *Directory publishers*

▶ M R C T Ltd, Potash Lane, Mid Suffolk Business Park, Eye, Suffolk, IP23 7HE Tel: (01379) 871500 Fax: (01379) 872985

M & R Coatings, 18a ST. Nicholas Street, Bristol, BS1 1UB Tel: 0117 9257247 *Protective coatings, refinishing & repairers*

M & R Communications Ltd, 7 Bell Industrial Estate, Cunnington Street, London, W4 5HB Tel: (020) 8995 4714 Fax: (020) 8995 5136 E-mail: office@m-rcom.com *Interpreting services, equipment hire & sales*

M R Consultants, Greshop Industrial Estate, Forres, Morayshire, IV36 2GW Tel: (01309) 675605 Fax: (01309) 678909 *Computer consultants*

M R Couriers, 45 Homefield, Shortwood, Nailsworth, Stroud, Gloucestershire, GL6 0SP Tel: (01453) 835868 *Courier & private hire services*

M R D C Ltd, PO Box 5745, Epping, Essex, CM16 4LE Tel: (01992) 577377 Fax: (01992) 577377 E-mail: calvert@mrdcnet.com *Plastic product design & development*

▶ M R D The Ice Zone, MRD House, Glasgow Road, Bathgate, West Lothian, EH48 2QW Tel: (01506) 630575 Fax: (01506) 630575 E-mail: sales@mrdbathgate.com *Car audio retailers & installers*

M R Designs, 6 Lower Farm, 130 High Street, Irchester, Wellingborough, Northamptonshire, NN29 7AB Tel: (01933) 410016 Fax: (01933) 419929 E-mail: mr-designs@btconnect.com *Packaging designers & sample manufrs*

▶ M R E Electrical Services, 21 Carnation Road, Farnworth, Bolton, BL4 0DT Tel: (01204) 709007 E-mail: mre_electrical@btinternet.com *Domestic Commercial And Industrial Electrical Contractors*

▶ M R Engineering Ltd, 107-125 Bridge Street, Birkenhead, Merseyside, CH41 1BD Tel: (01625) 524925 E-mail: sales@mrengineering.co.uk *We specialise in motor rewinds, precision & mechanical engineering, condition monitoring, electronics, motor controls, bearings & power transmission, we are also a supplier of Danfoss Drives*

▶ M R Engineering, Well Meadow Street, Sheffield, S3 7GS Tel: 0114-272 0077 Fax: 0114-279 9277 E-mail: mr_engineering@yahoo.com *Manufacturers of precision ground tool steel. Surface grinding of most ferrous metals to customer requirements. CAD Water jet profile cutting service.*

▶ M R F, 40 St Judes Road West, Wolverhampton, WV6 0DA Tel: (01902) 568037 Fax: (01902) 650410 E-mail: sales@mrfdesign.co.uk *Designers and suppliers of contemporary contract furniture to architects, specifiers and interior designers.**Our service to the hospitality industry includes a range of catalogue contract furniture as well as a bespoke design and manufacture service to client specification.**We currently supply to bar, club, restaurant, hotel and reception. More details and an up to date portfolio of our products can be found on our website.*

M R F Fabrications Ltd, Unit 6, Holton Road, Poole, Dorset, BH16 6LT Tel: (01202) 631877 Fax: (01202) 631841 E-mail: larry@mrffabs.fsnet.co.uk *Pipework steelwork fabricators*

▶ M & R Facilities Management Ltd, Unit 11, 13 Telford Road Thornton, Ellesmere Port, CH65 5EU Tel: 0151-357 1901 Fax: 0151-357 1902 E-mail: sales@mrfm.co.uk *Facilities Management Services.*Building, Construction and Civil Engineering.*Mechanical & Electrical Maintenance and Engineering.*Industrial & Cleaning Services*Specialist Cleaning Services*Airconditiong and Refrigeration Engineering and Installation**

M R G Systems Ltd, Willow Court, Beeches Green, Stroud, Gloucestershire, GL5 4BJ Tel: (01453) 751871 Fax: (01453) 753125 E-mail: sales@mrgsystems.co.uk *Television broadcasting equipment & display systems manufrs*

▶ M R Gas Services, 6 Elm Grove, Plympton, Plymouth, PL7 2BW Tel: (01752) 346482 Fax: *Offering general plumbing work, Gas installations and servicing throughout the Plymouth area.*

▶ M & R Heating Services, 9 St John Street, Stranraer, Wigtownshire, DG9 7HS Tel: (01776) 706655 Fax: (01776) 706655

M & R Hydraulics Ltd, Unit 13, Thornton Industrial Estate, Ellesmere Port, CH65 5EU Tel: 0151 3571901 *Hydraulic & hose distributors*

M & R Joinery Ltd, The Barn, Nine Yews, Cranborne, Wimborne, Dorset, BH21 5PW Tel: (01725) 517220 *Specialised wooden furniture manufrs*

M R K Services, Unit 97 Northwick Business Centre, Northwick Park, Blockley, Moreton-in-Marsh, Gloucestershire, GL56 9RF Tel: (01386) 700912 Fax: (01386) 700922 E-mail: sales@mrkservices.co.uk *Welding*

▶ M R L Signs, 23 Finkle Hill, Sherburn in Elmet, Leeds, LS25 6EB Tel: (01977) 682168 E-mail: enquiries@mrlsigns.com *Vehicle graphics, sign & banner manufrs*

M R M Engineering Ltd, Units 15-16, Enterprise Drive, Westhill Industrial Estate, Westhill, Aberdeenshire, AB32 6TQ Tel: (01224) 742383 Fax: (01224) 742326 E-mail: sales@mrmengineering.co.uk *Grain, coffee grading equipment & fabrication*

▶ M R M Fabrications, Unit 2, Bowbank House Farm, Kirk Merrington, Spennymoor, County Durham, DL16 7HY Tel: (01740) 656889 E-mail: mrmfabrications@talktalk.net *Root iron fabrication*

M R M Graphics Ltd, 61 Station Road, Winslow, Buckingham, MK18 3DZ Tel: (01296) 712364 Fax: (01296) 713733 E-mail: keith@mrmgraphics.co.uk *Reprographic printers*

M R M International Generators Ltd, PO Box 78, Ipswich, IP9 2WZ Tel: (01473) 310000 Fax: (01473) 310011 E-mail: generators@mrmint.co.uk *Industrial water & air cooled generators from 2 to 5000KVA*

M R P Control Ltd, 4 Crown Avenue, Dukestown, Tredegar, Gwent, NP22 4EE Tel: (01495) 726430 Fax: (01495) 718623 *Control panel manufrs*

M R P Electronics plc, 59 Brunel Road, Bedford, MK41 9TJ Tel: (01234) 216222 Fax: (01234) 219000 E-mail: sales@mrpplc.co.uk *Surface mounted assembly services*

M R P Trucks & Trolleys, 40 Horringer Road, Bury St. Edmunds, Suffolk, IP33 2DR Tel: (01284) 766300 Fax: (01284) 766500 E-mail: sales@mrptruckstrolleys.co.uk *Industrial trailer, trolley & hand operated truck manufrs*

M R S Communications Ltd, Viaduct Road, Gwaelod Y Garth, Cardiff, CF10 9JN Tel: (029) 2081 0810 Fax: (029) 2081 3755 *Two way radio communication*

▶ M R S J C Altham, Anchor Building, Penrod Way, Heysham, Morecambe, Lancashire, LA3 2UZ Tel: (01524) 862010

M R S Scientific Ltd, Brocks BSNS Park, Hodgson Way, Wickford, Essex, SS11 8YN Tel: (01268) 730777 Fax: (01268) 560241 E-mail: sales@mrs-scientific.com *Export merchants service*

▶ M R Scaffolding Anglia Ltd, Harfreys Road, Great Yarmouth, Norfolk, NR31 0LS Tel: (01493) 665066 Fax: (01493) 664050

M R (Site Services) Ltd, Unit 6, Worcester Trading Estate, Blackpole, Worcester, WR3 8HR Tel: (01905) 755055 Fax: (01905) 755053 E-mail: info@mrsiteservices.com *Welding services for aluminium roofing*

▶ M R Studio, Liverpool, L12 0WW Tel: (07876) 518390 E-mail: info@mrstudio.biz *Mobile sound recording*

M R Tool (Atherstone) Ltd, Unit 1, Netherwood Industrial Estate, Ratcliffe Road, Atherstone, Warwickshire, CV9 1HY Tel: (01827) 713097 Fax: (01827) 718518 E-mail: mrtoolsales@btconnect.com *HSS cutting tool manufrs*

M Rocker Associates Ltd, 54 Home Close, Greens Norton, Towcester, Northamptonshire, NN12 8AY Tel: (01327) 358044 Fax: (01327) 358044 *Computer consultants*

M S A Ltd, Wassalls Hall, Bishops Wood Road, Wickham, Hampshire, PO17 5AT Tel: (01329) 835440 Fax: (01329) 835430 E-mail: sales@msaltd.com *Catering equipment servicing*

M S A Britain Ltd, Shawhead Industrial Estate, Coatbridge, Lanarkshire, ML5 4TD Tel: (01236) 424966 Fax: (01236) 440881 E-mail: sales@msabritain.co.uk *Manufacturers of industrial safety equipment. In addition, breathing apparatus, gas detection equipment/ systems & industrial/safety respirator manufrs*

M S A Engineering Services Ltd, Sub-Station Road, Felixstowe, Suffolk, IP11 3JB Tel: (01394) 675108 Fax: (01394) 673311 *Commercial vehicle repair & services*

M S A In Print, 115 Graingers Lane, Cradley Heath, West Midlands, B64 6AD Tel: (01384) 568790 Fax: (01384) 410320 E-mail: msainprint@fsb.dial.co.uk *Print & stationery services*

M S A Wheels & Casters Ltd, 10 Maclure Road, Rochdale, Lancashire, OL11 1DN Tel: (01706) 516640 Fax: (0870) 7590160 E-mail: sales@msawhhelsandcasters.co.uk *Stockholders, wheels & casters*

M & S Accident Repair Centre, Unit 21 Slingsby Close, Attleborough Fields Industrial Estate, Nuneaton, Warwickshire, CV11 6RP Tel: (024) 7632 8239 Fax: (024) 7632 8239 *Motor vehicle repair & restoration services*

M S Air Movement, Unit 2a Hexton Manor Stables, Hexton, Hitchin, Hertfordshire, SG5 3JH Tel: (01582) 883662 Fax: (01582) 881009 E-mail: info@msairmovement.co.uk *Air Conditioning/ductwork/ventilation.*

M & S Aluminium Systems Ltd, Unit 19 Van Alloys Industrial Estate, Busgrove Lane, Stoke Row, Henley-on-Thames, Oxfordshire, RG9 5QW Tel: (01491) 680600 Fax: (01491) 680700 E-mail: sales@ms-ali.com Principal Export Areas: Asia Pacific, Africa, Central/East Europe, West Europe & North America *Supply aluminum shop frontage*

M S B Enginnering Ltd, Head Dyke Lane, Pilling, Preston, PR3 6SJ Tel: (01253) 790009 Fax: (01253) 790790 *Steel fabrications*

M S Bodies (Bristol) Ltd, 152a Soundwell Rd, Bristol, BS16 4RT Tel: 0117-940 6886 Fax: 0117-976 0910 *Commercial body repairs*

M S C A Ltd, The Seedbed Centre, Vanguard Way, Shoeburyness, SS3 9QY Tel: (01702) 382338 Fax: (01702) 382391 E-mail: ldmtt@ldn.xm.mitsui.co.jp *Distributor of textiles*

M S C Copperflow Ltd, 28 Hulme Street, Bolton, BL1 2SX Tel: (01204) 528206 Fax: (01204) 366877 *Bronze, chrome, copper & nickel platers*

▶ M & S Carriers, Unit 24, Charnley Fold Industrial Estat, School Lane, Bamber Bridge, Preston, PR5 6PS Tel: (01772) 696555

▶ M & S Carriers, 60 Causewayhead Road, Stirling, FK9 5EZ Tel: (01786) 470072 Fax: (01786) 470072

M & S Commercials Ltd, Bealey Industrial Estate, Dumers Lane, Radcliffe, Manchester, M26 2BD Tel: 0161-724 1311 Fax: 0161-724 1322 E-mail: mandscommercials@aol.com *Commercial vehicle repairs*

M S Contract Carpets, Carr House Lane, Shelf, Halifax, West Yorkshire, HX3 7RB Tel: (01274) 691511 Fax: (01274) 693474 *Carpet tile distributors*

▶ M S D L, Unit 32 Wirral Business Centre, Dock Road, Birkenhead, Merseyside, CH41 1JW Tel: 0151-630 1020 Fax: 0151-630 5544 E-mail: sales@msdl.net *Computer system developers*

M & S Developments, 9 Brittania Court, Basildon, Essex, SS13 1EU Tel: (01268) 728988 Fax: (01268) 724034 *Special purpose machinery design services*

M S E Consultants Ltd, North House, 31 North Street, Carshalton, Surrey, SM5 2HW Tel: (020) 8773 4500 Fax: (020) 8773 4600 E-mail: enquiries@mse.co.uk *Oil & gas consultants services* Also at: Rugby

M & S Engineering Ltd, East Road, Eastriggs, Annan, Dumfriesshire, DG12 6TD Tel: 01461 40111 *Steel fabricators & erecters*

M S Engineering, PO Box 255, Bedford, MK41 9BH Tel: (01234) 772255 Fax: (01234) 772266 E-mail: info@msengineering.co.uk Principal Export Areas: Africa *Vehicle components manufrs*

M S Engineering, Unit 49 Silicon Business Centre, Wadsworth Road, Greenford, Middlesex, UB6 7JZ Tel: (020) 8991 1444 Fax: (020) 8991 1444 *Precision & prototype engineers*

▶ M & S Fabrication, 1 Corunna Place, Edinburgh, EH6 5JG Tel: 0131-553 7134 Fax: 0131-554 4171

M & S Fire Protection Glasgow Ltd, 50 Waddell Street, Glasgow, G5 0LU Tel: 0141-429 7991 Fax: 0141-429 2958 *Hand-held fire-fighting equipment services*

▶ M S Furnishings, 14 Canning Road, London, E15 3NW Tel: (020) 8555 3928 Fax: (020) 8519 7672 E-mail: msfurnishingsuk@yahoo.co.uk *Wholesale, home furnishings*

M S G Business Systems Ltd, 18 Harrowby Street, Cardiff, CF10 5GA Tel: (029) 2091 1700 Fax: (029) 2029 1171 *Software developers*

M S G Computer Services, 4 Uplands Court, London Road, Luton, LU1 3RQ Tel: (01582) 731848 Fax: (01582) 484430 E-mail: sales@msgcomp.co.uk *Computer re-selling specialists*

M S G Computers, Summit Chambers, Castle Hill Terrace, Maidenhead, Berkshire, SL6 4JP Tel: (01628) 671621 Fax: (01628) 623953 *Write software for solicitor & hardware manufacturers & estate agents*

▶ M & S Hairdressing Supplies, Unit 5 United Business Park, Lowfields Road, Leeds, LS12 6UB Tel: 0113-244 5581 Fax: 0113-247 1082 *Suppliers of hairdressing accessories*

M S Hammond, 38 Manor Bridge Court, Tidworth, Hampshire, SP9 7NH Tel: (01980) 847500 Fax: (01980) 847500 *Plastics & raw material suppliers & manufrs*

▶ M & S Hire Ltd, Unit 11c Dolphin Park, Cremers Road, Sittingbourne, Kent, ME10 3HB Tel: (01795) 429731 Fax: (01795) 427790

M S I Alarms Ltd, Communications House, 9 Llewelyn Avenue, Llandudno, Gwynedd, LL30 2ER Tel: (01492) 860050 Fax: (01492) 870009 E-mail: solutions@msi.uk.net *Security systems & burglar alarms*

continued

M S I Defence Systems Ltd, Salhouse Road, Norwich, NR7 9AY Tel: (01603) 484065 Fax: (01603) 415649 E-mail: contact@msi-dsl.com *Naval gun & general defense engineers & manufrs*

M S I Forks Ltd, Carr Hill, Doncaster, South Yorkshire, DN4 8DH Tel: (01302) 366961 Fax: (01302) 340663 *Fork lift truck attachment manufrs*

M S I Oilfield Products, Units 5-6 Murcar Industrial Estate, Denmore Road, Bridge of Don, Aberdeen, AB23 8JW Tel: (01224) 708011 Fax: (01224) 708022 E-mail: bherd@msiproducts.com *Oilfield equipment suppliers, composite polyurethane protector manufrs*

M S I - Quality Forgings Ltd, Balby Carr Bank, Balby, Doncaster, South Yorkshire, DN4 8DH Tel: (01302) 325906 Fax: (01302) 760511 E-mail: sales@msi-forge.com *Steel forgings manufrs*

M S I Visual Displays Ltd, 11 Fairway Business Centre, Airport Service Road, Portsmouth, PO3 5NU Tel: (023) 9265 4525 Fax: (023) 9269 8797 E-mail: sales@display-it.co.uk *Audio visual equipment hire*

M S Instruments P.L.C., Unit 4, Ravens Quay Business Centre, Cray Avenue, Orpington, Kent, BR5 4BQ Tel: (01689) 883020 Fax: (01689) 871392 E-mail: sales@msinstruments.co.uk *Electronic defence equipment manufrs*

▶ M S (International) Plc, Balby Carr Bank, Doncaster, South Yorkshire, DN4 8DH Tel: (01302) 322133 *Metalworking & fabrication services*

M S K Packaging Ltd, 13 Prince William Road, Loughborough, Leicestershire, LE11 5GU Tel: (01509) 264338 Fax: (01509) 233427 *Packaging & shrink wrap machinery suppliers*

M & S Kitchens, 352 Oxford Road, Cleckheaton, West Yorkshire, BD19 4JR Tel: (01274) 813005 E-mail: sales@mandsinteriors.com *Quality kitchens & bedrooms supplied & fitted*

M S L Ltd, 101 Smithycroft Road, Glasgow, G33 2RH Tel: 0141-770 4366 Fax: 0141-770 4084 E-mail: msl.quality@virgin.net *Chemical manufrs*

▶ M S L Ltd, 81 Highmarsh Crescent, Newton-Le-Willows, Merseyside, WA12 9WE Tel: (01925) 223666 Fax: (01925) 223666 E-mail: contracts@managementservicesnw.co.uk *Professional installers of industrial & commercial roofing*

M S L Oilfield Services LTD, Unit 14 Brickfield Trade Estate, Brickfield Lane, Chandler's Ford, Eastleigh, Hampshire, SO53 4DP Tel: (023) 8027 5100 Fax: (023) 8027 5200 E-mail: sales@msluk.net *Load cells & load monitoring systems design & manufrs*

M S L Woodworking Machinery Ltd, Burnley Road, Mytholmroyd, Hebden Bridge, West Yorkshire, HX7 5QL Tel: (01422) 886542 Fax: (01422) 886542 *Servicing & repair of woodworking machinery*

M S Laboratories Ltd, 33 Sanders Road, Finedon Road Industrial Estate, Wellingborough, Northamptonshire, NN8 4NL Tel: (01933) 276668 Fax: (01933) 273841 E-mail: enquiries@mslabs.co.uk *Analytical & testing services*

M & S Lift Trucks, 1240 Dewsbury Road, Tingley, Wakefield, West Yorkshire, WF3 1LX Tel: 0113-259 7909 Fax: 0113-252 9072 *Forktruck sales, forktruck hire, forktruck servicing, any make of forktruck serviced. All aspects of health & safety work undertaken. Insurance work undertaken. Chain tests, fork, tyres, flashing becons, seatbelts, REV bleepers, lights etc.*

M S M Group of Companies, Spring Vale Works, Middleton, Manchester, M24 2HS Tel: 0161-643 2462 Fax: 0161-643 3490 E-mail: info@msmgroup.org *Aerospace fabricators*

M & S Mailing & Support Ltd, Unit 17 18, Royce Road, Crawley, West Sussex, RH10 9NX Tel: (01293) 527711 Fax: (01293) 527713 *Direct mail & print services*

M S Michael & Co. Ltd, 4 Batchelor Street, Chatham, Kent, ME4 4BJ Tel: (01634) 844994 Fax: (01634) 844995 *Cricket & school cap manufrs*

M S Midlands Ltd, Unit 9, Oak Street Trading Estate, Quarry Bank, Brierley Hill, West Midlands, DY5 2JQ Tel: (01384) 262252 Fax: (01384) 484951 *Manufacturers of wardrobe doors*

M S N Network Power Ltd, Fourth Avenue, Globe Park, Marlow, Buckinghamshire, SL7 1YG Tel: (01628) 403200 Fax: (01628) 403203 E-mail: sales@emersonnetworkpower.com *Manufacturers of air conditioning & uninterruptible power supplies*

M S P Ltd, Roman Way, Coleshill, Birmingham, B46 1HG Tel: (01675) 469100 Fax: (01675) 463699 E-mail: daphne@msp.ltd.uk *Multi-spindle retailers*

M S P Ltd, Roman Way, Coleshill, Birmingham, B46 1HG Tel: (01675) 469100 Fax: (01675) 463699 E-mail: sales@msp.ltd.uk *Precision turned parts manufrs*

▶ M S P Construction, Northfield Road, Rotherham, South Yorkshire, S60 1RR Tel: (01709) 838472 Fax: (01709) 838586

M S P (Scotland) Ltd, 1 Telford Road, Cumbernauld, Glasgow, G67 2AX Tel: (01236) 729591 Fax: (01236) 721859 E-mail: helenshaw@mspscot.co.uk *Industrial cladding & roofing materials products*

M S Precision Ltd, 3 Bristows Brickfield, Walters Ash, High Wycombe, Buckinghamshire, HP14 4UX Tel: (01494) 564200 Fax: (01494) 564200 *Special purpose machinery design services*

M & S Products Ltd, Unit 16 Riverside Industrial Estate, Thames Road, Barking, Essex, IG11 0ND Tel: (020) 8507 3940 Fax: (020) 8594 7033 *Manufacturers & distributors of industrial doors & door spring barrels*

M S Quirke, 171 St Agnells Lane, Hemel Hempstead, Hertfordshire, HP2 6LH Tel: (01442) 244603 *Construction ground workers contractors*

M S R Kirk, Leagate Road, Gipsey Bridge, Boston, Lincolnshire, PE22 7BU Tel: (01205) 280516 *Agricultural contractors*

M & S Reprographics Ltd, 48 Chorley New Road, Bolton, BL1 4AP Tel: (01204) 371188 Fax: (01204) 370737 *Photocopier & fax suppliers*

M S S Clean Technology, Castle House, The Industrial Estate, York Road, York, YO60 6RZ Tel: (01347) 878877 Fax: (01347) 878878 E-mail: postbox@mss-ct.co.uk *York based MSS CleanTechnology specialises in the design, development, manufacture and installation of cleanrooms and controlled environments. Operating worldwide, they provide a range of modular cleanroom systems to meet the needs of the pharmaceutical, biological, micro-electronic, containment and associated industries where environmental considerations are absolutely critical.*

M S S L Systems, Albany Road, Gateshead, Tyne & Wear, NE8 3AT Tel: 0191-477 3518 Fax: 0191-490 0264 E-mail: info@mssl.com Principal Export Areas: Central/East Europe, West Europe & North America *Wire & harness manufrs*

M & S Security Systems, 11 Houlson Street, Penywern, Dowlais, Merthyr Tydfil, CF48 3NW Tel: (01685) 389143 Fax: (01685) 389143 *Installation*

M S Services, 18 Esk Place, Aberdeen, AB16 6SQ Tel: (01224) 691742 Fax: (01224) 691742 E-mail: msservices@fsmai8l.net *Locksmiths, joiners & plumbers*

M & S Shipping International Ltd, Enterprise House, 34 Faringdon Avenue, Romford, RM3 8SU Tel: (01708) 340034 Fax: (01708) 373787 E-mail: logistics2000@msshipping.com *Freight forwarders*

M S Shirts Box Ltd, 45 Finchwell Road, Sheffield, S13 9AS Tel: 0114-244 2591 Fax: 0114-244 3909 E-mail: msshirtsbox@ssbdial.co.uk *Wooden packing cases & pallets*

M & S Shutter Services Ltd, 8 Alexandra Industrial Estate, Locarno Road, Tipton, West Midlands, DY4 9SJ Tel: 0121-520 6505 Fax: 0121-520 9011 E-mail: mandsshutters@hotmail.com *Rolling shutters & rolling shutters maintenance & repair*

M S Souch, 55 Brize Norton Road, Minster Lovell, Witney, Oxfordshire, OX29 0SG Tel: (01993) 775386 Fax: (01993) 709635 *Suppliers of farming equipment*

M S Storage Equipment Ltd, 78 Park Lane, Poynton, Stockport, Cheshire, SK12 1RE Tel: (01625) 858555 Fax: (01625) 858262 E-mail: sales@msstorage.co.uk *Archive storage, industrial racking, shelving, cabinets & lockers*

M & S Sub Aqua Supplies Ltd, 1 Hackenden Close, East Grinstead, West Sussex, RH19 3DR Tel: (01342) 300162 Fax: (01342) 322500 *Diving, swimming & snorkeling equipment wholesalers*

M & S Supplies Liverpool Ltd, Haigh Avenue, Stockport, Cheshire, SK4 1NU Tel: 0161-477 5479 Fax: 0161-480 5505 *Hairdressers equipment & suppliers*

M & S Systems Ltd, 21 Excelsior Grove, Pelsall, Walsall, WS3 4PX Tel: (01922) 685615 E-mail: simon@mandssys.demon.co.uk *Computer systems & IT training services*

M S T Interiors, 27 Gelli Gwyn Road, Morriston, Swansea, SA7 9TF Tel: 0870 803 4847 E-mail: info@partitionsandceilings.co.uk *the industry & we are ready to complete projects of any scale, anywhere in the UK.*All of our team are fully CIS & CSCS registered & have vast experience in the industry. In addition we have certification in scissor lifts, telescopic boom & fork lift. We have full liability insurance & fully comply with health & safety requirements.*The services we offer are :*Partition Walls, *Suspended Ceilings, *Firewalls, *Fireblankets, *Dry Lining, *Mezzanine Floors, *Pallet Racking, *Tennon Partitioning.**

M S Tech Ltd, 9 St. Marys Avenue, Northwood, Middlesex, HA6 3AY Tel: (07956) 317392 E-mail: sales@mstech.org.uk *Software consultants*

M & S Toiletries Ltd, Express Way, Wakefileds, Euro Port, Normanton, West Yorkshire, WF6 2TZ Tel: (01924) 244200 Fax: (01924) 244222 *Toiletries distribs*

M S W Machinery (International) Ltd, 84 St James Lane, London, N10 3RD Tel: (020) 8883 0734 Fax: E-mail: michael@mswmc.co.uk *Distributors/merchants or agents of agricultural machinery/equipment/implement, construction equipment spare parts, exports, machinery exports & tractor spare parts/wearing*

▶ M S Wayman & Sons, Chalk Lane, Sutton Bridge, Spalding, Lincolnshire, PE12 9YF Tel: (01406) 350216 Fax: (01406) 351622

M S West & Son, Swiss Cottage, Westminster Lane, Newport, Isle of Wight, PO30 5DP Tel: (01983) 522472 Fax: (01983) 825538 *Ready mixed concrete manufrs*

▶ M Saltmarsh, 32 Monson Road, Tunbridge Wells, Kent, TN1 1LU Tel: (01892) 527512 Fax: (01892) 545592 *Art & craft material suppliers*

M Sedgwick & Co. Ltd, Swinnow Lane, Leeds, LS13 4QG Tel: 0113-257 0637 Fax: 0113-239 3412 E-mail: sales@sedgewicks.co.uk *Woodworking machines manufrs*

▶ M Spiller, 43 Linmere Walk, Houghton Regis, Dunstable, Bedfordshire, LU5 5PS Tel: (01582) 866363 Fax: 01582 656046 E-mail: mike@michaelspiller.co.uk *Michael Spiller Training is an ITTSAR accredited training provider offering training in*the safe opperation of:**Forklift Trucks,*Overhead Gantry Cranes,*Banksman/Slinger,*Abrasive Wheels, and*Manual Handling.**We can also offer a full Health and Safety package inc:**Risk Assessment,*Audit, and*PAT Testing*

M Squared Instrumentation, Copse Business Centre, Hounsdown Business Park, Bulls Copse Road, Totton, Southampton, SO40 9LR Tel: (023) 8086 8393 Fax: (023) 8066 7720 E-mail: sales@msquaredinst.co.uk *Industrial engineers*

M T Box, 8 Plough Estate, Blandford Heights, Blandford Forum, Dorset, DT11 7UG Tel: (01258) 459837 Fax: (01258) 480132 *Packaging suppliers*

M T Buxton Industrial Services Ltd, 237 Station Road, Langley Mill, Nottingham, NG16 4AD Tel: (01773) 714339 Fax: (01773) 535251 E-mail: enquiries@mtbuxton.com *Heating & ventilation engineers*

M T Developments Lancashire Ltd, Cornfield Cliffe, Industry Street, Darwen, Lancashire, BB3 0HA Tel: (01254) 873837 Fax: (01254) 775268 E-mail: info@aprons.co.uk *Workwear manufrs*

M & T Engineering, 42b Gloucester Road, Croydon, CR0 2DA Tel: (020) 8683 3696 Fax: (020) 8665 5185 *Precision engineers*

M T H Ltd, 42 Queens Road, Farnborough, Hampshire, GU14 6DT Tel: (01252) 519251 Fax: (01252) 524494 E-mail: mthltd@nildram.co.uk *Custom built electronic equipment consultants*

▶ M T I Instruments & Calibration, Littleburn Industrial Estate, Langley Moor, Durham, DH7 8HJ Tel: 0191-378 3990 Fax: 0191-378 3973 E-mail: enquiries.mtisales@hstdgroup.com

M T I Instruments & Calibration, Littleburn Industrial Estate, Langley Moor, Durham, DH7 8HJ Tel: 0191-378 3990 Fax: 0191-378 3973 *Test instruments & calibration*

M T M Construction Ltd, Blackburn Industrial Estate, Kinellar, Aberdeen, AB21 0RX Tel: (01224) 790888 Fax: (01224) 790922 E-mail: info@mtmconstructionltd.co.uk *Civil engineering contractors*

M T M Plant Hire & Sales Ltd, Milner Road, Chilton Industrial Estate, Sudbury, Suffolk, CO10 2XG Tel: (01787) 312007 Fax: (01787) 883395 E-mail: mtm.plantlesltd@virgin.net *Plant hire, diggers & building materials*

M T M Products Ltd, Dunston Trading Estate, Foxwood Road, Sheepbridge, Chesterfield, Derbyshire, S41 9RF Tel: (01246) 450228 Fax: (01246) 455635 E-mail: sales@mtmlabels.co.uk *Plastic labels, metal & plastic nameplate manufrs*

M T M Promotional, 287 Palatine Road, Northenden, Manchester, M22 4ET Tel: 0161-946 9200 Fax: 0161-946 9209 E-mail: info@mtmpromotional.co.uk *Promotional product & advertising gift designers*

M T M Specialists, Unit 2 Westminster Industrial Estate, Station Road, North Hykeham, Lincoln, LN6 3QY Tel: (07843) 657181 Fax: (01522) 689989 E-mail: mtmspec@fsbdial.co.uk *Gear box reconditioners*

M T Mechanical Handling, Unit B6 Chasewater Estate, High Street, Burntwood Business Park, Burntwood, Staffordshire, WS7 3XD Tel: (01543) 675573 Fax: (01543) 674590 E-mail: sales@mtmechanical.co.uk *New & Used equipment. LPG, Diesel & Electric to suit all budgets. Hire - Worry free/full maintenance packages short or long term. Service - Latest health/safety checks, all repairs/service on or off site. Our range includes: Forklift trucks, Used forklift trucks, Forklift truck forks, Forklift truck servicing, Forklift truck repairs, Forklift truck hire, Forklift truck arms, Diesel Forklift trucks, Electric powered forklift trucks, Gas powered forklift trucks, Forklift truck spare parts, Forklift truck batteries, Petrol forklift trucks, Forklift truck accessories, Forklift truck attachments, Forklift truck wheels, Forklift truck tyres, Hand operated forklift trucks,Fork lift truck sales and much more.*

M T Perry Ltd, 5 Rawcliffe House, Howarth Road, Maidenhead, Berkshire, SL6 1AP Tel: (01628) 630330 Fax: (01628) 630330 E-mail: enquiries@perryfabs.co.uk *Sheet metalworking fabricators, stainless steel*

M T R Ltd, 58 Cross Road, Watford, WD19 4DQ Tel: (01923) 234050 Fax: (01923) 255746 E-mail: mtrltd@aol.com *Audio company & sound*

M T S (GB) Ltd, M T S Building, Hughenden Avenue, High Wycombe, Buckinghamshire, HP13 5FT Tel: (01494) 755600 Fax: (01494) 459775 E-mail: info@chaffoteaux.co.uk *Gas water heaters & boilers*

▶ M.T.S Nationwide Ltd, Unit 2, Flanshaw Way, Wakefield, West Yorkshire, WF2 9LP Tel: (01924) 387007 Fax: (01924) 384011 E-mail: mtsnationwidelimited@btinternet.com *Plant hire services*

M T S Power Tools, 97 St James Mill Road, Northampton, NN5 5JP Tel: (01604) 751688 Fax: (01604) 759041 E-mail: sales@mts.co.uk *Tool & equipment stockists*

M T S (Sales) Ltd, Midland House, Hayes Lane, Lye, Stourbridge, West Midlands, DY9 8RD Tel: (01384) 424823 Fax: (01384) 422819 E-mail: sales@gearbox-mts.com *Transmission reconditioning services*

M T S Systems Ltd, Brook House Somerford Court, Somerford Road, Cirencester, Gloucestershire, GL7 1TW Tel: (01285) 648800 Fax: (01285) 658052 *Test equipment manufrs*

M T W Pritchard, Yew Tree Cottage, Hillgates, Hereford, HR2 8JG Tel: (01981) 540828 *Hay & straw merchants*

M Tech Engineering, Plot 16 Tufthorn Industrial Estate, Stepbridge Road, Coleford, Gloucestershire, GL16 8PJ Tel: (01594) 837172 Fax: (01594) 832999 *Light fabricators & machiners*

M Tech UK Ltd, 913a Uppingham Road, Bushby, Leicester, LE7 9RR Tel: 0116-241 5791 *CNC advanced machine tools suppliers*

M Thornley, 12a High Street, Waltham, Grimsby, South Humberside, DN37 0LL Tel: (01472) 827019 *Saddler distributor*

M U C L, Suite 10, Berkeley House, Barnett Road, London Colney, St. Albans, Hertfordshire, AL2 1BD Tel: (01727) 822520 Fax: (01727) 822008 E-mail: eras@muscl.co.uk *Oil & gas procurement services*

M V A Consultancy, Sunley Tower, Piccadilly Plaza, Manchester, M1 4BT Tel: 0161-236 0282 Fax: 0161-236 0095

▶ M V Components Ltd, Hayseech Road, Halesowen, West Midlands, B63 3PD Tel: 0121-550 6441

M V I Systems Ltd, Appian House, 4 Wessex Road, Bourne End, Buckinghamshire, SL8 5TD Tel: (01344) 426844 *Licence plates recognition systems design & produce*

M V M Holdings Ltd, M V M House, 2 Oakfield Road, Bristol, BS8 2AL Tel: 0117-974 4477 Fax: 0117-970 6897 E-mail: mvm@mvm.co.uk *Software consultants*

M V M Sheet Metal Fabrications Ltd, 7-9 Dawkins Road Industrial Estate, Poole, Dorset, BH15 4JP Tel: (01202) 677244 Fax: (01202) 679762 E-mail: enquiries@mvm-uk.com *Established in 1966, MVM Group based in Bournemouth, Dorset, have over 40 years manufacturing experience specializing in mechanical engineering design, CAD services, street furniture installations, steel and aluminium sheet metal fabrications, castings, extrusions, welding services and injection mouldings. Our plan is simple; to offer the most complete manufacturing solution to our customers from the moment we receive an enquiry through to manufacture, delivery and installation. MVM are an ISO9001 approved company and with a continual investment into new plant and equipment, MVM can give the best price with the highest quality, while our own MRP system ensures full traceability of customer's orders from initial order to delivery. From one off prototypes to volume production, no order is too big or too small. We offer competitive pricing with the highest quality while ensuring on time deliveries. Please quote Kellysearch when calling.*

▶ M V P UK, Castle Court, Carnegie Campus, Castle Drive, Dunfermline, Fife, KY11 8PB Tel: (01383) 629960 Fax: (01383) 629979 *Installation equipment, printed circuits*

M V Shepherd, Sibson Lane, Shenton, Nuneaton, Warwickshire, CV13 6DD Tel: (01455) 212670 Fax: (01455) 213707 *Agricultural contractors*

M W A International Ltd, PO Box 17, Wednesbury, West Midlands, WS10 0AB Tel: 0121-556 6366 Fax: 0121-556 5566 E-mail: info@mwa-international.com *Manufacturers & suppliers of welding electrodes*

M W Amusements, 26 Marine Parade, Worthing, West Sussex, BN11 3PT Tel: (01903) 210888 Fax: (01903) 214538 *Amusement machine arcade manufrs*

M W Brunsdon, 25 Buckstone Lea, Edinburgh, EH10 6XE Tel: 0131-445 5182 *Two-way radio sales, service & hire*

M & W Contractors (Pensnett) Ltd, Morgan House, Folkes Road, Lye, Stourbridge, West Midlands, DY9 8RG Tel: (01384) 424411 Fax: (01384) 892425 E-mail: david@mwcontractors.co.uk *Steel fabricators*

▶ M W Cripwell Ltd, 6 Victoria Road, Burton-on-Trent, Staffordshire, DE14 2LU Tel: (01283) 564269 Fax: (01283) 569537 E-mail: info@mvcripwell.co.uk

▶ M W Crowe Ltd, Fen Road, Owmby-by-Spital, Market Rasen, Lincolnshire, LN8 2HP Tel: (01673) 878303 Fax: (01673) 878740

M W Encap Ltd, Oakbank Park Way, Mid Calder, Livingston, West Lothian, EH53 0TH Tel: (01506) 448080 Fax: (01506) 448081 E-mail: enquiries@encapdrugdelivery.com *Filling liquids into gelatine capsules*

▶ M & W Engineering Ltd, Sea View Business Park, North Road Industrial Estate, Berwick-upon-Tweed, TD15 1UP Tel: (01289) 330524 Fax: (01289) 303595 E-mail: mwengineering@btconnect.com *Sheet metalwork engineers or fabricators*

M W F Services, Kelsey Close, Attleborough Fields Industrial Estate, Nuneaton, Warwickshire, CV11 6RS Tel: (024) 7634 7774 Fax: (01858) 571196 E-mail: david_jeffrey@btopenworld.com *CNC forming manufrs*

M W Farm Supplies, 61 Holme Road, Market Weighton, York, YO43 3EW Tel: (01430) 872899 Fax: (01430) 872093 *Farm suppliers*

M W Furlong & Co., Ridley Farm, Bardon Mill, Hexham, Northumberland, NE47 7BP Tel: (01434) 344531 Fax: (01434) 344531 *Agricultural contractors*

M & W Grinding Services, Unit 10 Annwood Lodge, Arterial Road, Rayleigh, Essex, SS6 7UA Tel: (01268) 590059 Fax: (01268) 590058 E-mail: mwgrinding@btconnect.com *M & W Grinding Services based in Rayleigh, Essex offer sharpeners & saws and grinding services. Products include; TCT saws, circular saws & grinders, planner irons, guillotine blades, router cutters and band saws. Covering all areas of Essex including Basildon, Canvey, Pitsea, Southend, Shoeburyness, Rayleigh, Rochford, Chelmsford, South Woodham Ferrers, Colchester, Halstead, Braintree and Maldon.*

M W H, Kirk Wynd House, Montgomery Place, The Village, East Kilbride, Glasgow, G74 4BF Tel: (01355) 260540 Fax: (01355) 279191 E-mail: stephen.friend@mwhglobal.com *MWH is a global leader in providing Environmental Engineering and Programme Management. With more than $1 billion in revenue worlwide, our 6,500 specialists in 36+ countries provide premiere solutions to municipalities, government agencies, multinational companies, industrial concerns and military organizations worldwide.*

▶ M W H UK, Melbourne House, Melbourne Street, Newcastle Upon Tyne, NE1 2JQ Tel: 0191-261 5588 Fax: 0191-261 6688 *MWH is a global leader in providing Environmental Engineering and Programme Management. With more than $1 billion in revenue worlwide, our 6,500 specialists in 36+ countries provide premiere solutions to municipalities, government agencies, multinational companies, industrial concerns and military organizations worldwide.*

M & W Motors Hayes Ltd, Printing House Lane, Hayes, Middlesex, UB3 1AP Tel: (020) 8573 1082 Fax: (020) 8561 9330 *Petrol sales & car repairers*

M W Nash & Partners, Smoky Farm, Staplegrove, Taunton, Somerset, TA2 6SL Tel: (01823) 451298 Fax: (01823) 451870 *Farming*

M W Partridge & Co. Ltd, 60 High Street, Hadleigh, Ipswich, IP7 5EE Tel: (01473) 822333 Fax: (01473) 828009 E-mail: sales@partridgemw.co.uk *Agricultural engineers, garden machinery retailers & ironmongers*

M W Polymer Products Ltd, The Old Brewery, Duffield Road, Little Eaton, Derby, DE21 5DS Tel: (01332) 835001 Fax: (01332) 835051 *Pipe leaking sealing kit suppliers*

▶ M W T International Ltd, Great North Way, York, YO26 6RB Tel: (01904) 789880 Fax: (01904) 693192 E-mail: sales@mwtsafestyle.co.uk *Importers of industrial clothing, gloves & safety footwear*

M & W Toyota Handling, The Luther Challis Business Centre, Barnwood Road, Gloucester, GL4 3HX Tel: (01452) 523490 Fax: (01452) 523491 *Fork lift truck sales & service*

M W White Ltd, Station Lane, Hethersett, Norwich, NR9 3AZ Tel: (01603) 812898 Fax: (01603) 812838 E-mail: enquiries@mwwhite.co.uk *Waste paper merchants*

M Waldman Ltd, 8 224 Iverson Road, London, NW6 2HL Tel: (020) 7624 6527 Fax: (020) 7625 7326 E-mail: contactus@waldmanskirts.com *Ladies' skirt & separates manufrs*

M Walsh & Sons Ltd, 190 Malvern Com, Poolbrook, Malvern, Worcestershire, WR14 3JZ Tel: (01684) 572247 Fax: (01684) 574465 *Civil engineering contractors*

▶ M Webb, Oakdale Trading Estate, Ham Lane, Kingswinford, West Midlands, DY6 7JH Tel: (01384) 401067 Fax: (01384) 294880

M Wellings Engineering, Unit 38 Premier Partnership Estate, Leys Road, Brierley Hill, West Midlands, DY5 3UP Tel: (01384) 74927 Fax: (01384) 74927 E-mail: mick@mwellings.fsnet.co.uk *Dye manufrs*

▶ M Williams, Hortonwood 8, Telford, Shropshire, TF1 7GR Tel: (01952) 606023 Fax: (01952) 603334

M Williams & Sons Ltd, Llys, Clawddnewydd, Ruthin, Clwyd, LL15 2NB Tel: (01824) 750750 Fax: (01824) 750357 *Refrigeration & electrical retailers*

▶ M X Digital, Dunley Hill Court, Ranmore Common, Dorking, Surrey, RH5 6SX Tel: (01483) 286650 Fax: (01483) 286658 E-mail: sales@mxdigital.co.uk *Call centre solutions provider*

M & Y Air Systems Ltd, Twickenham Trading Centre, Rugby Road, Twickenham, TW1 1DN Tel: (020) 8892 8893 Fax: (020) 8891 6175 E-mail: sales@myairsystems.fsnet.co.uk *Waste extraction systems manufrs*

▶ M Y Boiler Services, Thieves Lane, Attleborough, Norfolk, NR17 2AP Tel: (01953) 497177 Fax: (01953) 456531 E-mail: sales@myboilerservices.co.uk

M Y Cartons Ltd, Grosvenor Road, Gillingham Business Park, Gillingham, Kent, ME8 0SA Tel: (01634) 388777 Fax: (01634) 377733 E-mail: sales@mypackaging.com *Litho carton packaging manufacturers.*

M Y Cartons-Leeds, Cockburn Fields, Middleton Grove, Leeds, LS10 1AR Tel: 0113-276 0730 Fax: 0113-276 0165 Principal Export Areas: Worldwide *Cartons*

M Y Fans Ltd, Westend Street, Oldham, OL9 6AJ Tel: 0161-628 3337 Fax: 0161-627 4153 E-mail: m.y.fans@mmp-ltd.co.uk *Industrial fans & centrifugal fans*

M Y Healthcare, E Railway Triangle, Walton Road, Portsmouth, PO6 1TY Tel: (023) 9221 0229 Fax: (023) 9221 9263 E-mail: sales@mypackaging.com *Health care packaging manufrs*

▶ M&A, Blue House Point Road, Stockton-on-Tees, Cleveland, TS18 2PQ Tel: (01642) 670379 Fax: (01642) 654055

M&B, Blaby Industrial Park, Winchester Avenue, Blaby, Leicester, LE8 4GZ Tel: 0116-277 6363 Fax: 0116-278 7871 E-mail: enquiries@mbgears.co.uk Principal Export Areas: Africa & North America *CNC engineering & gear manufrs*

▶ M&G-GB Ltd, Caxton Way, Stevenage, Hertfordshire, SG1 2DF Tel: (01438) 747999 Fax: (01438) 747070 E-mail: mg.gb@mailbox.as *Metal & aluminium tubing manufrs*

M&M, Unit 4-5 Phoenix Centre, Road One, Winsford Industrial Estate, Winsford, Cheshire, CW7 3PZ Tel: (01606) 861869 Fax: (01606) 861497 *Pallet suppliers*

▶ M&N Photography, Studio 25 @ Martello Street, London Fields, London, UK, E8 3PE Tel: (020) 7241 2816 E-mail: info@mn-photo.co.uk *We are a professional photographic company with our own large studio in the heart of London city. We offer portraiture, fashion and portfolio photography.*

M/A-com Ltd, Featherstone Road, Wolverton Mill, Milton Keynes, MK12 5EW Tel: (01908) 574200- Fax: (01908) 574300 Principal Export Areas: Worldwide *Microwave component manufrs*

M1 Engineering Ltd, 5 Commondale Way, Bradford, West Yorkshire, BD4 6SQ Tel: (01274) 416000 Fax: (01274) 420307 *Cryogenic equipment manufrs*

▶ M1 Plastics, Unit 6, Holly BSNS Park, Belfast, BT11 9DT Tel: (028) 9030 0555 Fax: (028) 9030 0555 *Plastics ancillary equipment suppliers*

M1 Sport Ltd, Phoenix House, Waller Avenue, Luton, LU4 9RS Tel: (01582) 580000 Fax: (01582) 580040 *Bag retailers*

▶ M1 Trade Frames, Units 1 & 2 Intake Road Intake Industrial Estate, Bolsover, Chesterfield, Derbyshire, S44 6BD Tel: (01246) 240225 Fax: (01246) 240230 *PVC doors, widows & conservatories manufrs*

M12 Solutions, The Bellfry, Solent Business Park, Fareham, Hampshire, PO15 7FJ Tel: (0845) 4081212 Fax: (0845) 4081213 E-mail: info@m12solutions.co.uk *Business telecommunications services*

M2, Unit 3, City Commerce Centre, Marsh Lane, Southampton, SO14 3EW Tel: (023) 8063 4437 Fax: (023) 8022 5011 E-mail: sale@movement.com *Disco equipment supplier*

M2 Digital Ltd, PO Box 2000, Manchester, M16 9EB Tel: 0161-877 0222 Fax: 0161-877 0220 E-mail: sales@m2digital.co.uk *Photocopier manufacturing services*

M2 Refrigeration Services Ltd, Ivy Farm, Lidsing, Gillingham, Kent, ME7 3NL Tel: (01634) 263636 Fax: (01634) 263636 *Refrigeration equipment distributors*

M2 Technical Services Ltd, 18 Glebe Street, Glasgow, G4 0ET Tel: 0141-552 3877 Fax: 0141-552 3896E-mail: admin@m2ltd.co.uk *Computer maintenance & repairs*

M25 Security Systems Ltd, 276 New Road, Croxley Green, Rickmansworth, Hertfordshire, WD3 3HH Tel: (01923) 721222 Fax: (01923) 441118 *Security systems fitters & sales*

▶ M2s Media Consultancy, Twyford Place, Wellington, Somerset, TA21 8BZ Tel: (01823) 663146 Fax: (01823) 663146 E-mail: m2smedia@btconnect.com *Providing affordable and flexible PR and media support, ideal for SMEs and charitible organisations.*

M3 Signs, 3 Hursley Road, Chandler's Ford, Eastleigh, Hampshire, SO53 2FW Tel: (023) 8025 3632 Fax: (023) 8025 4444 *Sign contractors*

M5 Data Ltd, Mendip Court, Bath Road, Wells, Somerset, BA5 3DG Tel: (01749) 679222 Fax: (01749) 673928 *Data systems researchers*

M6 Paper Group Ltd, Motorway House, Charter Way, Macclesfield, Cheshire, SK10 2NY Tel: (01625) 610044 Fax: (01625) 511144 E-mail: info@m6papers.co.uk *Paper merchants & converters*

▶ M8 Design, 102 Bath Street, Glasgow, G2 2EN Tel: (0870) 7460424 Fax: (0870) 7420745

▶ M81, 95 Willowbank Road, Aberdeen, AB11 6XD Tel: 01224 591274

▶ Ma Horne Ltd, Unit 9 Enterprise Park, Black Moor Road, Ebblake Industrial Estate, Verwood, Dorset, BH31 6YS Tel: (01202) 822770 Fax: (01202) 827583 E-mail: admin@m-a-horne.co.uk *Motor racing manufrs*

Ma Interiors, St Jude's Church, Dulwich Road, London, SE24 0PB Tel: (020) 7737 1371 Fax: (020) 7274 2023 E-mail: sales@mainteriors.co.uk *Office furniture & equipment distributors*

Ma Rich, 50 Sunnymead Road, London, NW9 8BU Tel: (020) 8205 3172 Fax: (020) 8205 2642 *Computer suppliers*

▶ Maag Pumps, PO Box 193, Evesham, Worcestershire, WR11 2WY Tel: (01386) 423756 Fax: (01386) 423862 E-mail: info@suurmond.co.uk *Advising & engineering company*

▶ Maal Transport Ltd, Crossley Park, Crossley Road, Heaton Chapel, Stockport, Cheshire, SK4 5BF Tel: 0161-431 1030

Maars Software International Ltd, 7 High Street, Maidenhead, Berkshire, SL6 1JN Tel: (01628) 633115 Fax: (01628) 633114 *Computer software manufrs*

▶ Mab Environment & Ecology Ltd, The Old Chapel, Knayton, Thirsk, North Yorkshire, YO7 4AZ Tel: (01845) 537845 E-mail: Giles@mab.uk.com *Environmental consultancy services including bat surveys, HLS and ELS applications, protected species surveys, vegetation surveys, grant applications, wildflower meadow creation, ponds, woods, stewardship, farming and environmental advice.*

Mabanaft Ltd, Malta House, 36-38 Piccadilly, London, W1J 0DP Tel: (020) 7470 7600 Fax: (020) 7447 0077 E-mail: enquiry@mabanaft.co.uk *Oil company*

Mabbett & Associates Ltd, Mabbett House, 11 Sandyford Place, Glasgow, G3 7NB Tel: 0141-227 2300 Fax: 0141 227 2301 E-mail: bradley@mabbett.com *Environmental, Health & Safety Consultants & Engineers - we provide a wide and comprehensive range of services to include: Building Services Engineering Consulting & Design; Energy Auditing & Consulting; Environmental Compliance & Permitting; EHS Management Systems; Environmental Monitoring; Environmental Pollution Control Systems Consulting & Design; Industrial Hygiene; Occupational Health & Safety; On-site Technical Professional Services; Resource Efficiency & Waste Minimisation Solutions; Site Assessment & Remediation, and Training. Please see www.mabbett.com for further details.*

▶ Mabey Hire Ltd, Stag Industrial Estate, Oxford Street, Bilston, West Midlands, WV14 7HZ Tel: (01902) 404512 Fax: (01902) 494942

▶ Mabey Hire Ltd, Harris Road, Calne, Wiltshire, SN11 9PT Tel: (01249) 821193 Fax: (01249) 821535

▶ Mabey Hire Ltd, Travellers Lane, North Mymms, Hatfield, Hertfordshire, AL9 7HN Tel: (01707) 267171 Fax: (01707) 268971

▶ Mabey Hire Ltd, Oakwood Grange, Robbinetts Lane, Cossall, Nottingham, NG16 2RX Tel: 0115-930 1154 Fax: 0115-944 0195

▶ Mabey Hire Ltd, Commissioners Road, Rochester, Kent, ME2 4EQ Tel: (01634) 722465 Fax: (01634) 723976 E-mail: group@mabey.co.uk

▶ Mabey Hire Ltd, Cupernham Lane, Romsey, Hampshire, SO51 7LF Tel: (01794) 515666 Fax: (01794) 524196

▶ Mabey Hire Ltd, 198 Gibbons Road, Ashton-in-Makerfield, Wigan, Lancashire, WN4 0YA Tel: (01942) 725341 Fax: (01942) 721243

Mabey & Johnson Ltd, Floral Mile, Twyfors, Reading, RG10 9SQ Tel: 0118-940 3921 Fax: 0118-940 3941 E-mail: sales@mabey.co.uk Principal Export Areas: Worldwide *Steel bridge constructors*

Mablethorpe Joinery Services, Unit 2, Golf Road Indust Estate, Mablethorpe, Lincolnshire, LN12 1NB Tel: (01507) 478594 Fax: (01507) 478594 *Joinery contractors & manufrs*

Mabro Trading Ltd, Rebond House, 98-124 Brewery Road, London, N7 9PG Tel: (020) 7609 4181 Fax: (020) 7607 4828 E-mail: mail@mabro.co.uk *Men's outerwear clothing wholesalers & manufrs*

Mabron Plastics Ltd, Unit 28 Mount Street, Accrington, Lancashire, BB5 0PJ Tel: (01254) 385619 Fax: (01254) 231496 E-mail: mabronplastics@aol.com *Plastic sheet manufacturers, stockholders & suppliers*

Mac Air Conditioning Ltd, Unit 11 Maple Park, Essex Road, Hoddesdon, Hertfordshire, EN11 0EX Tel: (01992) 478000 Fax: (01992) 478200 E-mail: sales@macair.co.uk *Installation & maintenance of air conditioning*

Mac Anodising Ltd, Unit 8 Harebridge Lane, Halton, Aylesbury, Buckinghamshire, HP22 5PF Tel: (01296) 621194 Fax: (01296) 621174 E-mail: macanodising@btconnect.com *Black and Clear Anodising, Alochrom 0, 1200 and soon 00, Bead Blasting. Engineering Facility providing cnc and manual milling and turning plus more...*

Mac Automatics Ltd, 38 Station Road, Kennett, Newmarket, Suffolk, CB8 7QD Tel: (01638) 750335 Fax: (01638) 552197 *Amusement caterers*

Mac Cartridges, Unit 11 Pinfold Lane, Llay Industrial Estate, Llay, Wrexham, Clwyd, LL12 0PX Tel: (01978) 853669 Fax: (01978) 853500 *Cartridge manufacturers & printers*

Mac Computers & Communications Centre, 20 Western Av, London, W3 7TZ Tel: 020 87491438 *Computer communications*

Mac Fabrication, Tregarth Farm, Camelford, Cornwall, PL32 9TX Tel: (01840) 212234 E-mail: aaron_macleod@hotmail.com *Metal fabricators & agricultural engineering services*

Mac Farr Engineering Co. Ltd, Garn Road, Blaenavon, Pontypool, Gwent, NP4 9RT Tel: (01495) 790648 Fax: (01495) 790648 *Commercial roof rack manufacturers & tow bar fitters*

Mac Machining Ltd, Unit 26, Hoobrook Enterprise Centre, Worcester Road, Kidderminster, Worcestershire, DY10 1HY Tel: (01562) 67619 Fax: (01562) 861243 E-mail: morris@macmachining.freeserve.co.uk *Precision turning, milling & CNC milling*

Mac Marney Refrigeration & Air Conditioning Ltd, The Old Forge, Stone Street, Crowfield, Ipswich, IP6 9SZ Tel: (01449) 760560 Fax: (01449) 760590 E-mail: sales@macmarney.co.uk *Refrigeration & air conditioning contractors*

▶ Mac Millan, 46A Wardo Avenue, Fulham, London, SW6 6RE Tel: 0207 731 8784 Fax: 0207 731 8622 E-mail: info@mac-millan.com *Fashion design*

▶ Mac Mole, East Sutton Road, Headcorn, Ashford, Kent, TN27 9PS Tel: (01622) 891366 Fax: (07836) 250549 mobile *Established in 1981. Waterboard approved contractors. Installing water supplies & services. Impact moling under roads/drives & lawns etc with no ground disturbance. Iron pipes replaced with plastic, improving flow. Narrow chaintrenching 150mm wide*

▶ Mac Pac, Units 1 & 2, Baillieston Distribution Centre, Baillieston, Glasgow, G69 6UL Tel: 0141-781 4888 Fax: 0141-781 4788

Mac Pac Ltd, 5 Barton Road, Stockport, Cheshire, SK4 3EG Tel: 0161-442 1642 Fax: 0161-442 1643 E-mail: sales@macpac.co.uk *Plastic & blister packaging specialists*

▶ Mac PC Solutions Ltd, 53 Shirley Gardens, Barking, Essex, IG11 9XB Tel: (07956) 168242 E-mail: info@macpcsolutions.co.uk *Computer hardware maintenance support*

Mac Plant Services Ltd, 1 Mernan Road, Bonnybridge, Stirlingshire, FK4 2BW Tel: (01324) 815330 Fax: (01324) 815305 *Plant repairs*

▶ Mac Signs & Graphics, 49 Long Lane, Holbury, Southampton, SO45 2LG Tel: (023) 8089 2228 Fax: (023) 8089 9268 E-mail: info@mac-signs.co.uk *Sign makers*

▶ Mac Steels, Woodhouse Farm, Robeys Lane, Alvecote, Tamworth, Staffordshire, B78 1AS Tel: (01827) 896699 Fax: (01827) 897799 *Steel fabricators*

Mc2 Data Innovation Ltd, 9 Barn Road, Broadstone, Dorset, BH18 8NH Tel: (01202) 657434 E-mail: enquiries@mc2data.co.uk *Computer consultants*

Mca, 1 Millers Way, Wirral, Merseyside, CH46 6EH Tel: 0151-678 6663 Fax: 0151-678 6663 *Burglar alarm installation*

Mca Consulting Engineers Ltd, Newhouse Farm Business Centre, Horsham, West Sussex, RH12 4RU Tel: (01293) 851490 Fax: (01293) 852156 E-mail: sales@mcaltd.co.uk *Building services consulting engineers*

Mcadams Confectionery, Unit 15 Cocker Trading Estate, Cocker Street, Blackpool, FY1 2EP Tel: (01253) 296516 Fax: (01253) 296516 *Confectionery manufrs*

▶ Mcadie & Reeve Ltd, Crowness Road, Hatston, Kirkwall, Orkney, KW15 1RG Tel: (01856) 872101 Fax: (01856) 876087

Mcaleer & Rushe Ltd, 24 Dungannon Road, Cookstown, County Tyrone, BT80 8TL Tel: (028) 8676 3741 Fax: (028) 8676 5265 E-mail: info@mcaleer-rushe.co.uk *Building & design contractors*

Mcaleer & Teague, Camderry Road, Dromore, Omagh, County Tyrone, BT78 3AP Tel: (028) 8289 8535 Fax: (028) 8289 8244 E-mail: info@mactni.co.uk *Building contractors*

Mcalerney Brian Farmer, 20 Clanmaghery Road, Ballyward, Castlewellan, County Down, BT31 9RR Tel: (028) 4065 0281 Fax: (028) 4065 0653 *Tractor & machinery sales*

D. Macalister, Chruch Hill Quarry Stores, Tarbert, Argyll, PA29 6YA Tel: (01880) 820845 *Fish merchants*

Mcallister's Confectionery Products, Unit 14 Thistle Business Pk, Ayr Rd, Cumnock, Ayrshire, KA18 1EQ Tel: 01290 426464 *Confectionery manufrs*

McAlonan Oils, 3 Mill Street, Ballycastle, County Antrim, BT54 6ES Tel: (028) 2076 2233 Fax: (028) 2076 8939 *Oil retailers*

Mcalpine & Co. Ltd, 45 Kelvin Avenue, Hillington Industrial Estate, Glasgow, G52 4LF Tel: 0141-882 3213 Fax: 0141-891 5065 *Plastic plumbing product manufrs*

Alfred McAlpine Slate Ltd, Penrhyn Quarry, Bethesda, Bangor, Gwynedd, LL57 4YG Tel: (01248) 600656 Fax: (01248) 601171 E-mail: slate@mcalpineplc.co.uk *Roofing slate & granule manufrs*

McAlpine Grant Ilco, Osney Mead Industrial Estate, Oxford, OX2 0ER Tel: (01865) 251225 Fax: (01865) 791877 E-mail: info@mglitd.co.uk *Established in 1981, McAlpine Grant Ilco is an*

continued

environmental temperature control company solely focused on providing the best in cooling, air-conditioning, refrigeration and heating solutions for businesses and public organisations. With wide-ranging experience of installations across all types of commercial environments, we offer the very best in air-conditioning, comfort cooling and heating solutions. With over 20 years of expertise, we provide a wide variety of first-rate services for the development of secure cold rooms, refrigerators and freezers for our clients. Air conditioning in Oxford Oxfordshire. Refrigeration in Oxford Oxfordshire. Oxfordshire specialist in temperature controlled environments.

▶ McAlpine Infrastructure Services, Palmer Mount Works, Kilmarnock Road, Dundonald, Kilmarnock, Ayrshire, KA2 9DR Tel: (01563) 850333

▶ Mcandrew & Co., 44 Hanover Street, Stranraer, Wigtownshire, DG9 7RP Tel: (01776) 704324 Fax: (01776) 704329

Macandrews, Lancaster House Mercury Court, Tithebarn Street, Liverpool, L2 2QP Tel: 0151-479 5555 Fax: 0151-236 2644 E-mail: reservations@aws.co.uk *Ship owners, agents & air cargo logistics* Also at: Birmingham, Bradford, Glasgow & London

McAndrews Textiles Ltd, West Scholes Mill, West Scholes, Queensbury, Bradford, West Yorkshire, BD13 1NQ Tel: (01274) 881111 Fax: (01274) 883311 E-mail: info@mcandrewtextiles.co.uk *Textile yarns & fibres - distribution of*

Steve Macare Photography, 59 Dragon Avenue, Harrogate, North Yorkshire, HG1 5DS Tel: (01423) 561809 Fax: (01423) 561809 E-mail: stevemacare@ntlworld.com *Commercial photography & exhibitions*

▶ Macarron Electroplaters, Orchardbank Industrial Estate, Forfar, Angus, DD8 1UQ Tel: (01307) 460999 Fax: (01307) 469810 *Metal finishing equipment manufrs*

Macart Textiles Machinery Ltd, Macart House, Farnham Road, Bradford, West Yorkshire, BD7 3JG Tel: (01274) 525900 Fax: (01274) 525901 E-mail: enquiries@macart.com *Textile machinery distribs*

▶ Mcarthur, 198-202 Broomhill Road, Bristol, BS4 5SF Tel: 0117-977 3311 Fax: 0117-977 6164 *Manufacturing*

▶ McArthur, Waverley Street, Court Bridge, Coatbridge, Lanarkshire, ML5 2BE Tel: (01236) 449266 Fax: (01236) 442100 *Fencing & building products suppliers*

▶ Mcarthur, 12 Station Road, Kilsyth, Glasgow, G65 0AB Tel: (01236) 821480 Fax: (01236) 824480

McArthur Fencing Ltd, Udimore Road, Broad Oak, Brede, Rye, East Sussex, TN31 6BX Tel: (01424) 882888 Fax: (01424) 882559 *Wooden fence manufrs*

Mcarthur Group Ltd, 27 Perimeter Road, Pinefield Industrial Estate, Elgin, Morayshire, IV30 6AF Tel: (01343) 548694 Fax: (01343) 541688 E-mail: marketing@mcarthur-group.com *Sales fencing, roofing & building materials*

Mcarthur Group Ltd, Arctic House, Goulton Street, Hull, HU3 4DL Tel: (01482) 506907 Fax: (01482) 351558 E-mail: enquiries@mcarthur-group.com *Wire product distributors*

Mcarthur Group Ltd, Economy House Copley Hill Trading Estate, Whitehall Road, Leeds, LS12 1HE Tel: 0113-245 7557 Fax: 0113-242 1150 E-mail: marketing@mcarthur-group.com *Protective clothing, footwear distributors*

Mcarthur Group Ltd, Brunswick Indust Estate, Brunswick Village, Hazlerigg, Newcastle upon Tyne, NE13 7DX Tel: 0191-236 5911 Fax: 0191-217 0581 E-mail: marketing@mcarthur-group.com *Fencing distributors*

Peter Macarthur & Co. Ltd, 17 Station Road, Biggar, Lanarkshire, ML12 6BW Tel: (01899) 221933 Fax: (01899) 221353 E-mail: petermacarthur@aol.com *Textile manufrs*

▶ McArthurs Mechanical & Electrical Services Ltd, 55 Colvilles Place, Kelvin Industrial Estate, Glasgow, G75 0PZ Tel: (01355) 266630

▶ Macaskill Fuels, 14 Inaclete Road, Stornoway, Isle of Lewis, HS1 2RB Tel: (01851) 702569 Fax: (01851) 702639

▶ R. Macaskill Ltd, Ardhasaig, Isle Of Harris, HS3 3AJ Tel: (01859) 502066

▶ Macaulay Askernish Ltd, Hillside Office, Lochboisdale, Isle of South Uist, HS8 5TH Tel: (01878) 700278 Fax: (01878) 700310

▶ McAuley, 14B Stone Row, Coleraine, County Londonderry, BT52 1EP Tel: (028) 7032 9104 Fax: (028) 7034 4246

▶ Mcauley, 26 Strawmore Road, Draperstown, Magherafelt, County Londonderry, BT45 7JE Tel: (028) 7962 8859 Fax: (028) 7962 7843

Mcausbyrne Tools Ltd, 10 Westbourne Place, Hove, East Sussex, BN3 4GN Tel: (01273) 776318 Fax: (01273) 776318 E-mail: david.austin@btconnect.com *Plastics mould toolmakers*

▶ Mcausland & Co, 112 Mid Wharf Street, Glasgow, G4 0LD Tel: 0141-333 0700 Fax: 0141-332 7817

Mcavoy Group Ltd, 76 Ballynakilly Road, Dungannon, County Tyrone, BT71 6HD Tel: (028) 8774 0372 Fax: (028) 8774 8175 E-mail: gilliand@mcavoygroup.com *Prefabricated building manufrs*

MACAW Engineering Ltd, 1 Park Road, Gosforth Business Park, Newcastle upon Tyne, NE12 8DG Tel: 0191-216 4930 E-mail: info@macawengineering.com *Engineering consultants*

Mcbain George & Co., 2 Whitemyres Avenue, Aberdeen, AB16 6HQ Tel: (01224) 683921 Fax: (01224) 685562 *Sheetmetal fabrications manufrs*

Mcbain Refrigeration, Fremington, Barnstaple, Devon, EX31 2NT Tel: (01271) 371774 Fax: (01271) 321199 *Domestic appliance repair services*

▶ Mcbean Contracts Ltd, 2a Gardenhall, East Kilbride, Glasgow, G75 8SP Tel: (01355) 248463 Fax: (01355) 241309

Mcbeth Joinery, Cardiff Bay Workshops, Brindley Road, Cardiff, CF11 8TX Tel: (029) 2038 7676 Fax: (029) 2038 7676 *Purpose made joinery cabinets*

Mcbraida plc, Bridgeyate Eng Works, Bath Road, Bridgeyate, Bristol, BS30 5JW Tel: 0117-961 3103 Fax: 0117-960 1417 E-mail: admin@mcbraida.plc.uk *Precision engineers*

McBride P.L.C., McBride House, Penn Road, Beaconsfield, Buckinghamshire, HP9 2FY Tel: (01494) 607050 Fax: (01494) 607056 *Bleach & detergent manufrs* Also at: Bradford & Hull

Mcbride Signs & Engraving Services, 2 Henderson Drive, Inverness, IV1 1TR Tel: (01463) 237303 Fax: (01463) 713373E-mail: mcbsigns@aol.com *Sign contractors*

Macbrown Fork Truck Services Ltd, 95 Wakefield Road Ossett, Wakefield, Ossett, West Yorkshire, WF5 9JY Tel: (01924) 278609 Fax: (01924) 261220 E-mail: info@macbrown.co.uk *Fork lift truck repairers, sales & hire*

▶ Mcburney Civils, Brittannia Indust Estate, Blackwood, Gwent, NP12 3SP Tel: (01443) 835305 Fax: (01443) 831055

▶ Mcburney Transport, East Lakes Business Park, Gilwilly Industrial Estate, Penrith, Cumbria, CA11 9BB Tel: (01768) 895636 Fax: (01768) 895637

▶ Macburnie International Transport Ltd, Supergas Industrial Estate, Downs Road, Witney, Oxfordshire, OX29 0SZ Tel: (01993) 708882 Fax: (01993) 708884

Macc International, Unit Q, Camilla Court, Nacton, Ipswich, IP10 0EU Tel: (01473) 655127 Fax: (01473) 655098 E-mail: macc@macc-eod.com *"Seriously Competitive, Safe and Secure" ISO9001:2000 Accredited Bomb Disposal and Security Company*

McCabe Safety Air Services Ltd, 7 Centre Way, Claverings Industrial Estate, London, N9 0AP Tel: (020) 8884 0222 Fax: (020) 8884 0333 *Safety equipment services*

Maccaferri Ltd, 7600 The Quorum, Oxford Business Park North, Garsington Road, Oxford, OX4 2JZ Tel: (01865) 770555 Fax: (01865) 774550 E-mail: oxford@maccaferri.co.uk *Retaining Structures,*Erosion Protection,*Slope Reinforcement,*Pavements,*Basal Platforms.**

▶ Mccaffrey Concrete Products, Ummera, Derrylin, Enniskillen, County Fermanagh, BT92 9PZ Tel: (028) 6774 8738 Fax: (028) 6774 8282 *Co*

▶ Mccaig John Electric Contractors, 3 Old Farm Road, Ayr, KA8 9ST Tel: (01292) 283018

Mccain Foods G B Ltd, Havers Hill, Eastfield, Scarborough, North Yorkshire, YO11 3BS Tel: (01723) 584141 Fax: (01723) 581230 E-mail: info@mccain.com *Frozen food processors & products manufrs*

Mccain Foods GB Ltd, Heath Mill Road, Wombourne, Wolverhampton, WV5 8AE Tel: (01902) 894022 Fax: (01902) 897998 *Frozen food processors & products manufrs*

Mccall Promotional Products Ltd, Gorse Farm, Lutterworth Road, Bramcote, Nuneaton, Warwickshire, CV11 6QL Tel: (024) 7637 2835 *Suppliers & manufacturers of pennant, banners, fundraising tabards & sashes*

Mccallum Bagpipes, Moorfield Indus Estate, Troon Road, Kilmarnock, Ayrshire, KA2 0BA Tel: (01563) 527002 Fax: (01563) 530260 *Bagpipe makers*

▶ Mccallum & Craig Builders Ltd, 48 Strathmore Road, Glasgow, G22 7DW Tel: 0141-336 6300 Fax: 0141-336 5868

McCallum Water Heating, Glen Works, Barrhead, Glasgow, G78 1ND Tel: 0141-881 1051 Fax: 0141-881 8275 E-mail: info@mccallumwaterheating.co.uk *Coppersmiths & cylinder manufrs*

H.J. Mccammon, Hebbross, Perridge Close, Exeter, EX2 9PX Tel: (01392) 259111 *Suspended ceilings*

▶ Mccann, Albert House, Park Street, Motherwell, Lanarkshire, ML1 1PT Tel: (01698) 263625 Fax: (01698) 250238

▶ Colm McCann, 49 Lisnagowan Road, Carland, Dungannon, County Tyrone, BT70 3LH Tel: (028) 8776 1774 Fax: (028) 8776 9465 E-mail: colm@cangirr.com *Engineering company*

▶ McCann Groundworks Ltd, Rear Office, 2 London Road, East Grinstead, West Sussex, RH19 1AQ Tel: (01342) 312519 Fax: (01342) 312535

Mccann's Concrete Products, 256 Whitebridge Road, Sixmilecross, Omagh, County Tyrone, BT79 9HH Tel: (028) 8076 1257 Fax: (028) 8076 1239 *Concrete products manufrs*

Mccarthy Design, Ladygrove Court, Preston, Hitchin, Hertfordshire, SG4 7SA Tel: (01462) 440957 Fax: (01462) 440961 E-mail: peter@mccarthydesign.co.uk *Furniture*

Mccarthy Developments 2000 Ltd, Systems House, Broad Lane, Coventry, CV5 7AX Tel: (024) 7646 8866 Fax: (024) 7669 4486 E-mail: sales@mccarthygroup.co.uk *Design, project management & office refurbishment*

▶ Mccarthy & Stone Developments Ltd, Hartington House, Hartington Road, Altrincham, Cheshire, WA14 5LX Tel: 0161-941 6255 Fax: 0161-928 2803

▶ Mccarthy & Stone Developments Ltd, Emerald House, 30-38 High St, Byfleet, West Byfleet, Surrey, KT14 7QG Tel: (01932) 336099

Mccarthy & Stone Quest Trustees Ltd, 26-32 Oxford Road, Bournemouth, BH8 8EZ Tel: (01202) 292480 Fax: (01202) 557261 E-mail: info@mccarthyandstone.co.uk *Building & selling retirement homes*

▶ McCarthy Surfacing Ltd, Beckton Works, Jenkins Lane, Barking, Essex, IG11 0AD Tel: (020) 8594 1966 Fax: (020) 8594 7244

Mccarthy's, 1 Dundonald Road, Broadstairs, Kent, CT10 1PE Tel: (01843) 600053 Fax: (01843) 600048 E-mail: mccarthysreproductions@virgin.net *Furniture & mirror manufrs*

Mccash's Country Store, 1 Feus Road, Perth, PH1 2AS Tel: (01738) 623245 Fax: (01738) 451011 E-mail: info@mccash.uk.com *Agricultural merchants*

Mccaskie Farm Supplies Ltd, Fossowey Garage, Crook of Devon, Drum, Kinross, KY13 0PR Tel: (01577) 840272 Fax: (01577) 840694 *Agricultural suppliers*

Mccaskie Farm Supplies Ltd, 4 Munro Road, Springkerse Industrial Estate, Stirling, FK7 7UU Tel: (01786) 474481 Fax: (01786) 464099 E-mail: admin@mccaskie.co.uk *Agricultural engineering services & animal feed supplements* Also at: Ayr

James McCaughey (Boatbuilders) Ltd, Harbour Quay, Wick, Caithness, KW1 5EP Tel: (01955) 602858 Fax: (01955) 602858 *Boat builders & repairers*

J. Mccaughry Ltd, Harbour Quay, Wick, Caithness, KW1 5EP Tel: 01955 603701 *Boat builders & repairers*

Samuel McCausland Ltd, Commecial Road, Banbridge, County Down, BT32 3ES Tel: (028) 4066 2277 Fax: (028) 4066 2288 E-mail: sales@mccauslands.co.uk *Seed & pet food merchants*

McCaw Allan & Co. Ltd, Victoria Street, Lurgan, Craigavon, County Armagh, BT67 9DU Tel: (028) 3834 1412 Fax: (028) 3834 3095 E-mail: sales@mccaw-allan.com *Household textile manufrs*

▶ Macclesfield Joinery Ltd, R/O Artillery House, Heapy Street, Macclesfield, Cheshire, SK11 7JB Tel: (01625) 617428

Clusky McCloskey International Ltd, 47 Moor Road, Coalisland, Dungannon, County Tyrone, BT71 4QB Tel: (028) 8774 0926 Fax: (028) 8774 7242 *Waste recycling treatment plant service*

Mccloskey & O'Kane Building Co. Ltd, 16 Windyhill Road, Limavady, County Londonderry, BT49 0RA Tel: (028) 7772 2711 Fax: (028) 7776 8505 E-mail: info@mccloskeyandokane.com *Building contractors*

▶ McCloud, Unit 4, Metro Business Centre, Kangley Bridge Road, London, SE26 5BW Tel: (020) 8778 4254 Fax: (020) 8776 9196

Mccluskey (Joinery) Ltd, Unit 7 Hamilton Road Industrial Estate, Strathaven, Lanarkshire, ML10 6UB Tel: (01357) 522264 Fax: (01357) 521729 E-mail: shaun@mcclusky joinery.co.uk *Construction*

Mccluskey Pottery, 11 Gortgarn Road, Limavady, County Londonderry, BT49 0QW Tel: (028) 7776 4579 Fax: (028) 7776 4579 *Pottery manufrs*

Mcclymont Intruder Alarms, 106 Essex Road, Liverpool, L36 1XP Tel: 0151-482 1527 Fax: 0151-482 1527 *Intruder alarms installers*

Mccollin Furniture, 39 Urlwin Street, London, SE5 0NF Tel: (020) 7703 2262 Fax: (020) 7703 2262 E-mail: mccollinbryan@aol.com *Clockmaker & furniture manufrs*

McCollins, Boynton Hall, Boynton St, Hull, HU3 3BZ Tel: (01482) 329634 Fax: (01482) 329634 *Glass bevelling services processing & toughening*

J.C. McCollom, 2 Carew Street, London, SE5 9DF Tel: (020) 7733 7025 Fax: (020) 7733 7025 *Catering equipment repair & refurbishment*

▶ Mccoll's Control System Equipment, 81 High Street, Forres, Morayshire, IV36 1AA Tel: (01309) 672693 Fax: (01309) 672787

Mccomb Coachwork, 22 Market Place, Tattershall, Lincoln, LN4 4LJ Tel: (01526) 342292 Fax: (01526) 344411 E-mail: mail@mccombcoachwork.co.uk *Commercial vehicle body builders & painting services*

Mccombe Bros Antrim Ltd, Springfarm Industrial Estate, Antrim, BT41 4NT Tel: (028) 9446 2611 Fax: (028) 9446 2794 E-mail: info@mccombebros.co.uk *Building contractors*

The Mccombie Napier Company Ltd, Newburgh, Ellon, Aberdeenshire, AB41 6BW Tel: (01358) 789987 Fax: (01358) 789877 E-mail: mccombienapier@aol.com *Naval architecture/designing/fishing & research ferries*

McConnel Ltd, Temeside Works, Ludlow, Shropshire, SY8 1JL Tel: (01584) 873131 Fax: (01584) 876463 E-mail: sales@mcconnel.com *Agricultural equipment*

McConnell Equipment Ltd, 16 Ballycraigy Road, Antrim, BT41 1PL Tel: (028) 9446 3921 Fax: (028) 9446 7102 E-mail: macquip@btinternet.com *Food/general industry conveyors*

Mcconomy & Co. Ltd, 1f Columbus Quay, Riverside Drive, Liverpool, L3 4DB Tel: 0151-726 1942 Fax: 0151-728 9935 E-mail: mccon@mcconomy.com *Hide & skin traders* Also at: Irthlingborough

Mcconville Bros, 55-57 Kilvergan Road, Lurgan, Craigavon, County Armagh, BT66 6LJ Tel: (028) 3834 1452 Fax: (028) 3834 8892 *Protective clothing manufrs*

J.P. McCool, Artasooley, Maydown Road, Dungannon, County Tyrone, BT71 7LN Tel: (028) 3754 8074 *Software development*

William McCormac & Henderson & Co. Ltd, 9 Broomhead Drive, Dunfermline, Fife, KY12 9DR Tel: (01383) 721882 *Scrap iron merchants*

▶ Mccormack Developments Ltd, Main Street, Cowie, Stirling, FK7 7BN Tel: (01786) 813144 Fax: (01786) 813144

▶ McCormack & Kent Consulting Ltd, PO Box 49, Ashford, Kent, TN24 9WF Tel: (0845) 0573257 Fax: (01622) 338900 E-mail: team@mccormack-kent.co.uk *Business and risk management consultants including online risk auditing programmes.*

Alan McCormick & Co. Wholesale, 84A Locking Road, Weston-super-Mare, Somerset, BS23 3ET Tel: (01934) 626635 Fax: (01934) 645042 E-mail: alanmccormickco@aol.com *Wholesalers of zip fasteners*

Mccormick Macnaughton Ni Ltd, Blaris Industrial Estate, Altona Road, Lisburn, County Antrim, BT27 5QB Tel: (028) 9266 1221 Fax: (028) 9266 1355 E-mail: sales@mccormickmacnaughton.com *Constructional engineers*

▶ McCormick Site Services Ltd, Park House, 56 Trench Road, Mallusk, Newtownabbey, County Antrim, BT36 4TY Tel: (028) 9084 8381

McCormick Tractors International Ltd, Wheatley Hall Road, Doncaster, South Yorkshire, DN2 4PE Tel: (01302) 366631 Fax: (01302) 733491 E-mail: bridget.kenny@mccormick-intl.com *Agricultural implement manufrs* Also at: Branches throughout the U.K.

McCormick Weeks Ltd, Unit 2, Springfield Farm, Perrotts Brook, Cirencester, Gloucestershire, GL7 7DT Tel: (01285) 831771 Fax: (01285) 831881E-mail: enquiries@mccormickweeks.com *Curtain poles manufrs*

Mccornack Country Knitwear, 55 Scotts Street, Annan, Dumfriesshire, DG12 6JH Tel: (01461) 204244 Fax: (01461) 204244 *Hand made knitwear manufrs*

McCorquodale Confidential Print Ltd, South Portway Close, Round Spinney, Northampton, NN3 8RH Tel: (01604) 790234 Fax: (01604) 790880 E-mail: sales@theprintfactory.co.uk *Commercial printers*

Mccoy Bros Ltd, 1 Ebenezer Street, Birkenhead, Merseyside, CH42 1NH Tel: 0151-645 7720 Fax: 0151-643 8964 *Scrap metal merchants*

Mccoy Saddlery & Leathercraft, High Street, Porlock, Minehead, Somerset, TA24 8QD Tel: (01643) 862518 Fax: (01643) 863088 E-mail: sales@mccoysaddlery.co.uk *Saddlery services*

Maccravats Ltd, Byrons Lodge, Byrons Lane, Macclesfield, Cheshire, SK11 7JW Tel: (01625) 422079 Fax: (01625) 614641 E-mail: maccravats@yahoo.com *Club, corporate tie & scarf manufrs*

Mccready's Sailboats Ltd, Priory Park, Holywood, County Down, BT18 0LG Tel: (028) 9042 1821 Fax: (028) 9042 2998 E-mail: sales@mccreadysailboats.co.uk *Sailing dinghies & equipment manufrs*

Mccroft Lighting, 54a Woods Lane, Derby, DE22 3UD Tel: (01332) 299100 Fax: (01332) 200365 *Suppliers of lamps & motor vehicle lighting equipment.*

Mccroy Engineering, 49b Armaghlughey Road, Aughnacloy, County Tyrone, BT69 6DN Tel: (028) 8555 7790 Fax: (028) 8555 7790 *Plant & machinery manufrs*

▶ Mccue plc, Unit 27, Shamblehurst Lane, Hedge End, Southampton, SO30 2FY Tel: (01489) 795668 Fax: (01489) 795670 *Manufacturers of medical equipment*

▶ Mccue International, Mount House, Bond Avenue, Bletchley, Milton Keynes, MK1 1SF Tel: (01908) 365511 Fax: (01908) 365527 E-mail: sales@mccuecorp.co.uk

▶ Mccue's Food Packers, Pelham Road, Cleethorpes, South Humberside, DN35 7JZ Tel: (01472) 291999 Fax: (01472) 291999 *Food manufacturers & packaging*

Mccullagh Farm Machinery, 206 Derrylin Road, Bellanaleck, Enniskillen, County Fermanagh, BT92 2BA Tel: (028) 6634 8213 Fax: (028) 6634 8013 *Agricultural machinery services*

▶ Alan Mcculloch Associates, 49 Virginia Street, Glasgow, G1 1TS Tel: 0141-572 5969 Fax: 0141-572 2992 *Civil engineers*

▶ McCulloch European Transport, Unit 1, Loch Park Industrial Estate, Stonehouse, Larkhall, Lanarkshire, ML9 3LS Tel: (01698) 791367

Macculloch & Wallis Ltd, 25-26 Dering Street, London, W1S 1AT Tel: (020) 7629 0311 Fax: (020) 7629 8097 E-mail: macculloch@psilink.co.uk *Haberdashery, silk fabric merchants & sewing machines suppliers*

▶ W.J. McCullough Services Ltd, Units 5-6, Brighton, BN1 4GD Tel: 01273 675487 *Sheet metalwork engineers, stainless steel & aluminium bespoke metal works*

Mccurdy & Co. Ltd, Manor Farm, Stanford Dingley, Reading, RG7 6LS Tel: 0118-974 4866 Fax: 0118-974 4375 E-mail: jobs@mccurdyco.com *Timber frame buildings*

McDade Neckware Ltd, Unit 20, Imex Bussiness Centre, 198 Swanston Street, Glasgow, G40 3HH Tel: 0141-554 0448 Fax: 0141-556 2403 E-mail: mcdadeties@cwcom.net *Necktie manufrs*

MacDermid P.L.C., Palmer St, Bordesley, Birmingham, B9 4EU Tel: 0121-606 8100 Fax: 0121-606 8300 E-mail: cs@macdermid.com *Mechanical plating chemistry*

Macdermid plc, Cale Lane, New Springs, Wigan, Lancashire, WN2 1JR Tel: (01942) 501000 Fax: (01942) 501110 E-mail: wigansales@macdermid.com *Offshore industry production control fluids suppliers & manufrs*

Macdermot Autotype Ltd, Grove Road, Wantage, Oxfordshire, OX12 7BZ Tel: (01235) 771111 Fax: (01235) 771196 E-mail: feedback@autotype.com *Screen printing chemical manufrs*

H. McDermott & Sons, 49 Rivulet Road, Wrexham, Clwyd, LL13 8DU Tel: (01978) 262489 *Scrap metal merchants*

Mcdevitt Electrical Engineers, 212-218 Upper Newtownards Road, Belfast, BT4 3ET Tel: (028) 9047 2626 Fax: (028) 9047 3636 E-mail: info@vhmcdevitt.co.uk *Electrical engineers & contractors*

Macdonald Associates Ltd, 6 Cecil Aldin Drive, Tilehurst, Reading, RG31 6YP Tel: 0118-945 2862 Fax: 0118-962 4854 E-mail: info@macd.com *Computer software consultants*

Macdonald Bower Hotel, Hollinwood Avenue, Chadderton, Oldham, OL9 8DE Tel: 0161-682 7254 Fax: 0161-683 4605 E-mail: admin@macdonaldhotels.co.uk *Hotel with conference rooms*

McDonald Diecasting Ltd, Unit 21a Coneygre Industrial Estate, Birmingham New Rd, Tipton, West Midlands, DY4 8XP Tel: 0121-520 1177 Fax: 0121-557 0677 E-mail: info@mcdonald-diecasting.co.uk *Specialists in providing castings suitable for plating finishes and has a reputation for providing high quality products including: McDonalds own range of cistern levers and bathgrips, Bathroom and shower components from customers own tooling, Automotive components, Window furniture components, General Engineering castings, Castings for model engineers, Furniture handle components.*

continued

Mcdonald Engineers Ltd, Flemington Road, Glenrothes, Fife, KY7 5QF Tel: (01592) 611123 Fax: (01592) 611166 E-mail: info@mcdonald-engineers.com *Hot water system manufrs*

Macdonald Fabrication, Unit 2 Glebe Industrial Estate, Douglas, Lanark, ML11 0RH Tel: (01555) 851948 Fax: (01555) 851174 *Installers of freezers*

Macdonald Fire Equipment, 3 Building 24, Stevenston Industrial Estate, Stevenston, Ayrshire, KA20 3LR Tel: (01294) 601989 Fax: (01294) 602688 *Fire equipment suppliers*

▶ Gerald McDonald & Co. Ltd, Cranes Farm Road, Basildon, Essex, SS14 3GT Tel: (01268) 244900 *Herb spices & juices manufrs*

Macdonald Hotel Group, Paternoster Row, Winchester, Hampshire, SO23 9LQ Tel: (01962) 861611 Fax: (01962) 849617 *Hotel & conference facilities*

Macdonald Humfrey Automation Ltd, 29-35 Bolton Road, Luton, LU1 3HY Tel: (01582) 405741 Fax: (01582) 453237 E-mail: sales@mhaltd.co.uk Principal Export Areas: Worldwide *Control systems design consultants*

Mcdonald Insulation & Maintenance Ltd, 7 Eastbury Road, London, E6 6LP Tel: (020) 7511 8899 Fax: (020) 7473 1133 E-mail: info@mcdonaldbrownltd.co.uk *Sheet metalwork engineers & facility management services*

▶ Macdonald Linda, Laigh Barrs, Main Road, Cardross, Dumbarton, G82 5PX Tel: (01389) 841848 Fax: (01389) 849094 E-mail: sales@lindamacdonaldjewellery.com *Jewellery*

Macdonald Mailing, Staplehurst Road, Sittingbourne, Kent, ME10 2NH Tel: (01795) 439513 Fax: (01795) 439551 *Direct mailing & promotions*

▶ Macdonald Pneumatique, Peel Park Place, East Kilbride, Glasgow, G74 5LS Tel: (01355) 249507 Fax: (01355) 220091 *Pneumatic tools suppliers*

▶ Macdonald Pneumatique, Peel Park Place, East Kilbride, Glasgow, G74 5LS Tel: (01355) 249507 Fax: (01355) 220091 E-mail: info@macdonaldairtools.co.uk *Pneumatic tool manufrs* Also at: Calne

▶ McDonald Transport Services, Unit 4a Wrexham Enterprise Park, Ash Road North, Wrexham, LL13 9JT Tel: (0845) 0547544 *McDonald Transport Services provides a nationwide next day parcel delivery service for*small businesses and private users based within a 20 mile radius of Wrexham town centre. Storage, picking and packing operation available on request at an extra charge. Ebay users welcome.*

Macdonald's Engineers Ltd, 11-13 Linden Walk, Louth, Lincolnshire, LN11 9HT Tel: (01507) 603566 Fax: (01507) 603565 *Agricultural & general engineers*

▶ Mcdougall Group, 3 Telford Court, 11 South Avenue, Clydebank Business Park, Clydebank, Dunbartonshire, G81 2NR Tel: 0141-951 1900 Fax: 0141-951 1900

▶ Mcdougall Group, Charlotte Dundas House, Dalgrain Road, Grangemouth, Stirlingshire, FK3 8EL Tel: (01324) 471797 Fax: (01324) 483544 E-mail: sales@themcdougallgroup.com

Macdougalls Blinds, 4 Wisteria Drive, Healing, Grimsby, South Humberside, DN41 7JB Tel: (01472) 887049 Fax: (01472) 887049 *Blind manufrs*

Mcdowall Air Conditioning, Middlemore La West, Walsall, WS9 8EJ Tel: (01922) 454955 Fax: (01922) 454815 E-mail: sales@mcdowalls.co.uk *Air conditioning systems installations*

▶ McDowell Contractors Ltd, 5-6 Parkend Industrial Estate, Stornoway, Isle of Lewis, HS2 0AN Tel: (01851) 701558

William McDowell & Partners, Aldersgate House, 13-19 University Road, Belfast, BT7 1NA Tel: (028) 9024 5444 Fax: (028) 9024 5916 *Civil & structural engineers*

Macduff Shipyards Ltd, The Harbour, Macduff, Banffshire, AB44 1QT Tel: (01261) 832234 Fax: (01261) 833541 E-mail: macduffshipyards@btconnect.com *Shipbuilding & repair services*

▶ Andy Mace Locksmith, 67 West Hill, Portishead, Bristol, BS20 6LG Tel: (01275) 844879 E-mail: andenash@aol.com *Locksmiths offering 24 hour service, domestic & commercial customers*

▶ Macedonia Steel Ltd, 93-99 Upper Richmond Road, London, SW15 2TG Tel: (020) 8780 5577 Fax: (020) 8780 5455 E-mail: macsteel@onetel.net.uk *Trading in raw non-ferrous metals, ores & concentrates*

Macelloy Ltd, Hawke Street, Sheffield, S9 2LN Tel: 0114-242 6704 Fax: 0114-243 1324 E-mail: info@macalloy.com *Steel production & manufrs*

Macemain Engineering Ltd, Boyle Road, Willowbrook East Indust, Corby, Northamptonshire, NN17 5XU Tel: (01536) 401331 Fax: (01536) 401298 E-mail: sales@macemainamstad.com *Street furniture manufrs*

▶ Mcevoy Engineering Ltd, 5b Harbour Industrial Estate, Montgomerie Street, Ardrossan, Ayrshire, KA22 8EG Tel: (01294) 467677 Fax: (01294) 467677 E-mail: chris@mcevoyengineering.co.uk

Mcewan Bros Kirkintilloch Ltd, The Smithy House, Old Duntiblae Road, Glasgow, G66 3LG Tel: 0141-776 1880 Fax: 0141-776 1040 E-mail: mcewansfencing@aol.com *Fencing contractors*

Mcewan Layne Soft Furnishings, 83 Canal Street, Long Eaton, Nottingham, NG10 4GA Tel: 0115-973 6330 Fax: 0115-973 6330 *Soft furnishers*

Macey & Macey Ltd, 50 Cutlers Place Colehill, Wimborne, Dorset, BH21 2HU Tel: (01202) 882400 E-mail: enquiries@maceyandmacey.co.uk *Customer satisfaction surveys; lost customer surveys, telemarketing project work; business consultancy.*

Macfaction, Tew Lane, Wootton, Woodstock, Oxfordshire, OX20 1HA Tel: (01993) 811197 Fax: (01993) 812686 E-mail: info@macfaction.co.uk *IT consultants*

▶ McFadyen Conservatories, Crossford, Carluke, Lanarkshire, ML8 5QF Tel: (01555) 860123

▶ McFadyen Conservatories, Unit 3, Meadow Road, Motherwell, Lanarkshire, ML1 1QB Tel: (01698) 268862

▶ McFadyen's Contractors (Campbeltown) Ltd, Glebe Street, Campbeltown, Argyll, PA28 6JJ Tel: (01586) 552961

▶ Mcfadyens Transport Ltd, Glebe Street, Campbeltown, Argyll, PA28 6LR Tel: (01586) 551111 Fax: (01586) 552000

Macfarlan Smith Ltd, Wheatfield Road, Edinburgh, EH11 2QA Tel: 0131-337 2434 Fax: 0131-337 9813 E-mail: msl@macsmith.com *Alkaloids & fine chemicals*

▶ Mcfarlane, Ravenshill Drive, Cleland, Motherwell, Lanarkshire, ML1 5QL Tel: (01698) 862324

MacFarlane Environmental Ltd, Unit 20, East Belfast Enterprise Park, Belfast, BT5 4GX Tel: (028) 9045 7961 Fax: (028) 9045 9275 E-mail: macfarlane@btinternet.com *Heating & ventilation engineers & suppliers*

▶ Macfarlane Gray Group, 15 Gladstone Place, Stirling, FK8 2NX Tel: (01786) 451745 Fax: (01786) 472528

Macfarlane Group Ltd, Siskin Parkway East, Middlemarch Business Park, Coventry, CV3 4PE Tel: (024) 7651 1511 Fax: (024) 7651 1302 E-mail: enquiries@national-packaging.co.uk *Packaging material supplier*

Macfarlane Group plc, 21 Newton Place, Glasgow, G3 7PY Tel: 0141-333 9666 Fax: 0141-333 1988 *Holding company*

Macfarlane Group UK Ltd, Unit 2, Concorde Road, Patchway, Bristol, BS34 5TB Tel: (0870) 8500542 Fax: (0870) 8500543 E-mail: bristol@macfarlanegroup.net *Packaging material distributors*

Macfarlane Group Ukltd, 22 Bentinck Street, Kilmarnock, Ayrshire, KA1 4AS Tel: (01563) 525151 Fax: (01563) 539963 E-mail: kwoodhouse@macfarlanelabels.com *Quality self-adhesive label manufrs* Also at: Slough

Macfarlane Packaging P.L.C., The Water Front, Kingfisher Boulevard, Mewburn Riverside, Newcastle Upon Tyne, NE15 8NZ Tel: (0870) 6086100 Fax: (0870) 6086101 *Packaging material, goods & products*

Macfarlane Shipping Co. Ltd, Grianan, Thurlow Road, Nairn, IV12 4HJ Tel: (01667) 451671 Fax: (01667) 455383 E-mail: macship@btinternet.com *Ship brokers*

▶ Macfarlene Group, Unit A2, The Waterfront, Kingfisher Boulevard, Newcastle Upon Tyne, NE15 8NZ Tel: (0870) 6086100 Fax: (0870) 6086101 *Packaging material manufrs*

Mcfeggan Brown Ltd, Unit 1, 38 Midland Road, Staplehill, Bristol, BS16 4NW Tel: 0117-957 3355 Fax: 0117-956 7221 *Interior office designers*

▶ Mcfletch Ltd, The Barn, The Street, Pebmarsh, Halstead, Essex, CO9 2NH Tel: (01787) 269964 Fax: (01787) 269909 E-mail: mcfletch@demo-ltd.fsnet.co.uk

▶ Mcfletch Waste Management, The Barn, The Street, Pebmarsh, Halstead, Essex, CO9 2NH Tel: (01787) 882200 Fax: (01787) 269909 E-mail: sales@mcfletch.co.uk

▶ Macform Ltd, Avalon, Wishaw, Lanarkshire, ML2 0RS Tel: (01698) 355585 Fax: (01698) 355585

▶ Mcgarrie's Ltd, Latherford Close, Four Ashes, Wolverhampton, WV10 7DY Tel: (01902) 791661 Fax: (01902) 791644

Mcgarrigle Signs, Aubery Street, Londonderry, BT48 6RX Tel: (028) 7126 0699 Fax: (028) 7126 0699 *Sign makers*

▶ Mcgarry Moon Architects Ltd, 17 Drumimerick Road, Kilrea, Coleraine, County Londonderry, BT51 5SY Tel: (028) 2954 2323 Fax: (028) 2954 2323 E-mail: info@mcgarry-moon.com

▶ McGarvey Construction, 86 Clark Street, Paisley, Renfrewshire, PA3 1RB Tel: 0141-848 7555

▶ Mcgawn Bros, Thistle House, Alloway Road, Maybole, Ayrshire, KA19 8AA Tel: (01655) 882119

▶ John McGeady Ltd, 17 South Annandale Street, Glasgow, G42 7LB Tel: 0141-422 1524

Mcgeoch Marine Ltd, 38 Loanbank Quadrant, Glasgow, G51 3HZ Tel: 0141-445 5353 Fax: 0141-445 5164 E-mail: sales@m-m-l.com *Marine doors manufrs*

▶ Mcgeown's Transport International, 67a Rathfriland Road, Newry, County Down, BT34 1LD Tel: (028) 3025 1616 Fax: (028) 3025 1617 E-mail: info@mcgeowninternational.com

Mcgill, Harrison Road, Dundee, DD2 3SN Tel: (01382) 884488 Fax: (01382) 828777 E-mail: sales@mcgill-electrical.co.uk *Electrical contractors & security engineers & heating contractors*

Mcgill Services Ltd, Vinci House Macklin Avenue, Cowpen Lane Industrial Estate, Billingham, Cleveland, TS23 4HF Tel: (01642) 379400 Fax: (01642) 379429 E-mail: mcgill@mcgillservices.co.uk *Insulation contractors*

▶ Mcgirr Engineering, Lurganbuoy, Sixmilecross, Omagh, County Tyrone, BT79 9EJ Tel: (028) 8075 8694 Fax: (028) 8075 8694

▶ Mcgoff & Vickers Ltd, 47 Canal Street, Bootle, Merseyside, L20 8AQ Tel: 0151-922 6441 Fax: 0151-944 1528

▶ Mcgougan & Co., The Roading, Campbeltown, Argyll, PA28 6LU Tel: (01586) 552531

▶ Mcgougan & Co., Glebe Street, Campbeltown, Argyll, PA28 6LR Tel: (07721) 753650 Fax: (01586) 552531

Mcgowan & Co (Contractors) Ltd, 28 Cramond Road South, Edinburgh, EH4 6AB Tel: 0131-336 2181 Fax: 0131-336 4037 E-mail: sales@jsmart.co.uk *Public works contractors*

Mcgowan Signs Ltd, 42 Marriner Road, Keighley, West Yorkshire, BD21 5LW Tel: (01535) 210011 Fax: (01535) 210012 *Sign manufrs*

McGown Snowden, 14-18 Emerald Street, London, WC1N 3QA Tel: (020) 7242 2412 Fax: (020) 7242 0460 E-mail: office@mcgowensnowden.co.uk *Design consultants*

Mcgrath Bros Ltd, 71 Broadgate Lane, Horsforth, Leeds, LS18 5AB Tel: 0113-259 0888 Fax: 0113-259 0888

Mcgrath Bros (Engineering) Ltd, Lisnagarvagh House, Lissue Road, Lisburn, County Antrim, BT28 2SU Tel: (028) 9262 1186 Fax: (028) 9262 1955 E-mail: cmccann@mcgrath-group.com *Steel fabricators & specialist metalworkers*

▶ McGrath Regional Publications Ltd, 23 Bolton Road, Farnworth, Bolton, BL4 7JN Tel: (01204) 796494 Fax: (01204) 791494 E-mail: mcgrathartwork@aol.com

Mcgraw-Hill International UK Ltd, Mcgraw-Hill House, Shoppenhangers Road, Maidenhead, Berkshire, SL6 2QL Tel: (01628) 502500 Fax: (01628) 770224 E-mail: info@mcgraw-hill.com *Publishers*

Macgregor Associates Consulting, Sherwood House, 7 Gregory, Nottingham, NG7 6LB Tel: 0115-962 0222 Fax: 0115-962 2144 E-mail: info@macgregorassociates.co.uk *Management consultants*

Mcgregor Business Equipment, Unit 2 Fence Avenue, Macclesfield, Cheshire, SK10 1LT Tel: (01625) 618182 Fax: (01625) 618545 E-mail: officesupplies@mcgregors.co.uk *Office equipment suppliers*

▶ McGregor Construction Highlands Ltd, Seafield Road, Longman, Inverness, IV1 1SG Tel: (01463) 222791 Fax: (01463) 236657

MacGREGOR (GBR) Ltd, Grampian House, 59 Palmerston Road, Aberdeen, AB11 5QJ Tel: (01224) 583300 Fax: (01224) 583450 E-mail: sales@macgregor-group.com *Hydraulic hose & equipment distributors* Also at: Ellon, Fraserburgh & Peterhead

Macgregor GBR Ltd, Powerhouse, Silverlink, Wallsend, Tyne & Wear, NE28 9ND Tel: 0191-295 2180 Fax: 0191-295 2188 E-mail: info@macgregor-group.com *Marine engineers*

▶ Mcgregor International Ltd, 12 Oakfield House, Oakfield Road, Altrincham, Cheshire, WA15 8EW Tel: 0161-942 4800 Fax: 0161-942 4808 E-mail: office@mcgregor-mc.co.uk *Clothing manufrs*

MacGregor & Moir, Unit 4, 95 Westburn Drive, Cambuslang, Glasgow, G72 7NA Tel: 0141-643 3636 Fax: 0141-641 8505 E-mail: info@macgregorandmoir.com *Abrasive product & refractory distribs*

Mcgregor Polytunnels Ltd, Winton Farm, Petersfield Road, Monkwood, Alresford, Hampshire, SO24 0HB Tel: (01962) 772368 Fax: (01962) 772471 E-mail: sales@mcgregorpolytunnels.co.uk *Polytunnel & swimming pool enclosure manufrs*

Macgregor Radio Control Ltd, Macgregor House, Cordwallis Street, Maidenhead, Berkshire, SL6 7GF Tel: (01628) 760341 Fax: (01628) 760435 *Plastics machinists*

Mcgruther & Marshall Shipping, Shore Road, Invergordon, Ross-Shire, IV18 0ER Tel: (01349) 853073 Fax: (01349) 853678 E-mail: dave@mmagency.co.uk *Shipping services*

Mcguinness Feeds, 65a Liverpool Road, Penwortham, Preston, PR1 9XD Tel: (01772) 745139 Fax: (01772) 752261 *Animal feed merchants*

McGuinness (P.) Co. Ltd, Romdin House, Romdin Road, Ardwick, Manchester, M12 6BF Tel: 0161-273 5272 Fax: 0161-274 3884 E-mail: demolition@pmcguinness.com *Demolition contractors*

▶ Mcguire Builing Maintenence Ltd, Unit 17 Dumbryden Industrial Estate, Dumbryden Road, Edinburgh, EH14 2AB Tel: 0131-467 7806 Fax: 0131-467 7808

▶ Mcgurk Studios Ltd, 2-3 Burleigh Street, Hull, HU8 8SS Tel: (01482) 587117 Fax: (01482) 589995 E-mail: mark.richardson@mcgurkstudios.com *Packaging Concept to Completion - Design, Photography, Artwork Reprographics, Colour Proofing, plate making. Project & process management tools. Managing the packaging origination process.*

▶ McGurran Construction, Main Street, Derrygonnelly, Enniskillen, County Fermanagh, BT93 6HW Tel: (028) 6864 1222 Fax: (028) 6864 1515 E-mail: info@mcgurranconstruction.com

Mach Agencies International UK Ltd, 265 Fullwell Avenue, Barkingside, Ilford, Essex, IG5 0RD Tel: (020) 8550 8177 *Video presentation equipment supplier*

Mach Aire Ltd, Bridge Street, Horwich, Bolton, BL6 7BT Tel: (01204) 668905 Fax: (01204) 668906 E-mail: sales@machaire.co.uk *Fume cupboards manufrs*

Mach One Design Equipment Ltd, Columbia House, Columbia Drive, Worthing, West Sussex, BN13 3HD Tel: (01903) 525100 Fax: (01903) 525155 E-mail: sales@machone.co.uk *Mackintosh computers*

▶ Mach One (Holdings) Ltd, Unit 8 Norfolk Business Park, Foley Street, Sheffield, S4 7YW Tel: 0114-270 0545 Fax: 0114-276 7438 E-mail: sales@mach-int.com *Steel fixings suppliers & manufrs*

▶ Mach Vehicle & Finance Ltd, 12 High Street, Madeley, Telford, Shropshire, TF7 5AQ Tel: (01952) 277700 Fax: (01952) 277703 E-mail: terry.mvf@virgin.net *Contract hire & leasing of motor vehicles & commercial vehicles*

▶ Machan Consulting, 1 Belvedere Close, Keyworth, Nottingham, NG12 5JF Tel: 07780 646142 Fax: 0115 9375407 E-mail: enquiries@machan.co.uk *Manufacturing and Supply Chain Consultancy for the Food and Healthcare sector*

▶ McHardy Media Ltd, The Media Centre, 6 North Isla Street, Dundee, DD3 7JQ Tel: (01382) 423248 E-mail: sales@mchardymedia.co.uk *Scottish design group*

▶ Machine Condition Monitoring, Unit 6 Clwydfro Business Centre, Lon Parcwr Industrial Estate, Ruthin, Clwyd, LL15 1NJ Tel: (01824) 705333 Fax: (020) 7681 1861 E-mail: info@mcm-ltd.co.uk *Machine Condition Monitoring (MCM) Ltd is an UK-based company, dedicated to providing advanced condition monitoring PRODUCTS & SERVICES & have formed alliances with some of the world's leading names in condition monitoring thus enabling us to provide a range of products for a myriad of applications, Intrinsically Safe (IS or ATEX approved), submersible, direct PLC or DCS 4-20 mA interface as well as general purpose vibration monitoring within a Predictive Maintenance programme. We supply a wide range of products such as vibration sensors or accelerometers, Infra Red (IR) fixed & portable Non Contact Temperature Monitoring products, a wide range of temperature & process Data logging units, Portable Sound Level Meters (which could be used for Environmental Noise Measurement or Noise at Work), Individual Noise doseBadges (to ensure the Health and safety of employees), Encoders & speed sensors. Our services include Infra Red Thermography, Vibration Analysis & Ultrasonic Leak detection.*

Machine Control Engineers Ltd, Unit A1, Block 9a South Avenue, Blantyre Industrial Estate, Glasgow, G72 0XB Tel: (01698) 829566 Fax: (01698) 821608E-mail: sales@mce.uk.com *Electrical & mechanical engineers*

Machine Electrics Ltd, Unit 6 The Timberyard, East Moors Road, Cardiff, CF24 5ES Tel: (029) 2049 8840 Fax: (029) 2048 0469 *Fork lift truck parts manufrs*

Machine Electrics Ltd, Whitefield Road, Bredbury, Stockport, Cheshire, SK6 2RW Tel: 0161-430 6825 Fax: 0161-494 8954 E-mail: sales@machineelectrics.com *Industrial electronic engineers*

Machine Mart Ltd, 71-73 Manchester Road, Altrincham, Cheshire, WA14 4RJ Tel: 0161-941 2666 *Tools & equipment distribution*

Machine Mart Ltd, Hay Mills, 1152 Coventry Road, Sheldon, Birmingham, B26 3EA Tel: 0121-771 3433 Fax: 0121-771 3262 *Automotive retailers*

Machine Mart Ltd, Machine Mart House, Derwent Street, Derby, DE1 2ED Tel: (01332) 290931 Fax: (01332) 366531 E-mail: sales@machinemart.co.uk *Machinery tool sales*

Machine Mart Ltd, 50 Lobley Hill Road, Gateshead, Tyne & Wear, NE8 4XA Tel: 0191-493 2520 Fax: 0191-493 2212 *Machine retailers*

Machine Mart Ltd, 8-10 Holderness Road, Hull, HU9 1EG Tel: (01482) 223161 Fax: (01482) 225085 *Industrial machinery*

Machine Mart Ltd, 211 Lower Parliament Street, Nottingham, NG1 1GN Tel: (0870) 7707830 Fax: (0870) 7707811 E-mail: sales@machinemart.co.uk *Air compressor & spare part distribs* Also at: Branches throughout the U.K.

Machine Mart Ltd, Middleway, Thornaby, Stockton-on-Tees, Cleveland, TS17 6BZ Tel: (01642) 677881 Fax: (01642) 679896 *Machinery sales*

Machine Mart Ltd, Ryhope Road, Sunderland, SR2 9SX Tel: 0191-510 8773 Fax: 0191-514 7389 *General tool manufrs*

Machine Mart Ltd, 17-21 Victoria Road, Swindon, SN1 3AL Tel: (01793) 491717 Fax: (01793) 514787 *Power tools retailers*

▶ Machine Networks, PO Box 69, Immingham, South Humberside, DN40 1PL Tel: (0870) 7607750 Fax: (0870) 7607750 E-mail: info@machinenetworks.co.uk *UK web hosting provider, domain name registration services*

▶ Machine Resources Ltd, 77 Poplars Close, Mardy, Abergavenny, Monmouthshire, NP7 6LQ Tel: (01873) 857093 Fax: (01873) 857093 E-mail: machine-resources@tiscali.co.uk *Supply, maintenance & fault rectification of fuel powered generators*

Machine Sales & Services Ltd, 23 Cowley Road, Nuffield Industrial Estate, Poole, Dorset, BH17 0UJ Tel: (01202) 686238 Fax: (01202) 686661 E-mail: enquiries@machinesalesandservices.co.uk *Distributors of power tools & wood working machinery*

Machine Techniques Ltd, Unit 3-5 Court Yard Workshops, Bath Street, Market Harborough, Leicestershire, LE16 9EW Tel: (01858) 434059 Fax: (01858) 433638 E-mail: sales@mactec.co.uk Principal Export Areas: Worldwide *manufacturers of plastic welding equipment, welding equipment (laser), plastic welding high frequency/radio frequency equipment & ultrasonic welding equipment*

Machine Technology Ltd, 22-23 Arcadia Avenue, London, N3 2JU Tel: (020) 8349 4814 Fax: (020) 8346 6251E-mail: machinetech@btconnect.com *Heat sealing machinery manufrs*

Machine Tool Attachments, 123 Kedleston Road, Derby, DE22 1FS Tel: (01332) 346948 Fax: (01332) 342360 E-mail: tony@machinetoolattachments.fsnet.co.uk *Hydraulic copy system manufrs*

Machine Tool & Engineering Services Ltd, Unit 14 Quay Lane Industrial Estate, Hardway, Gosport, Hampshire, PO12 4LJ Tel: (023) 9251 1666 Fax: (023) 9251 1164 E-mail: info@mtes.co.uk *Service & repair special purpose machines*

▶ Machine Tool Technologies Ltd. (MTT), 307 Ecroyd Suite, Turner Road, Lomeshaye Business Village, Nelson, Lancashire, BB9 7DR Tel: (01282) 607854 Fax: (01282) 607894 E-mail: info@mtt.uk.com *CNC machine tool technical support specialists*

Machineair Engineering Ltd, 70 Colliers Water Lane, Thornton Heath, Surrey, CR7 7LB Tel: (020) 8684 4849 Fax: (020) 8683 4635 *Valve & hose equipment distribs*

Machined Component Systems plc, 2-5 Madeley Road, Moons Moat North Industrial Estate, Redditch, Worcestershire, B98 9NB Tel: (01527) 65208 Fax: (01527) 585048 E-mail: sales@machined-components-systems.plc.uk *Turned parts manufrs*

Machined Components Ltd, 11 Ailsa Road, Irvine Industrial Estate, Irvine, Ayrshire, KA12 8LR Tel: (01294) 278112 Fax: (01294) 277698

Machined Fabrications Ltd, 20 Blowers Green Road, Dudley, West Midlands, DY2 8UP Tel: (01384) 257681 Fax: (01384) 241571 E-mail: machfabs@aol.com *Steel fabrications & cnc machining services*

Machinery Development Services, Bristol Road, Whitminster, Gloucester, GL2 7NY Tel: (01452) 740112 Fax: (01452) 740511 E-mail: enq@mds-uk.com *Paper converting machinery manufrs*

Machinery Installations (Birmingham) Ltd, Unit 12A, Middlemore Lane West, Aldridge, Walsall, WS9 8BG Tel: (01922) 743187 Fax: (01922) 743206 E-mail: mibham@aol.com *Contractors for factory removal/relocation & machinery removal. Plant installation*

▶ Machinery Movements & Crane Hire Ltd, Queen Alexandra Dock, Cardiff, CF10 4LT Tel: (029) 2048 8360

Machinery Products UK Ltd, Four Trees, Main Road, South Elkington, Louth, Lincolnshire, LN11 0RU Tel: (01507) 610108 Fax: (01507) 610044 E-mail: johnny.walker@btconnect.com *VISIT OUR WEBSITE TO FIND A VAST NUMBER OF GOOD, USED PLASTIC AND RUBBER MACHINES, MACHINE TOOLS, CONVERTING MACHINERY FOR THE PAPER INDUSTRY - A HUGE SELECTION AT YOUR FINGERTIPS. WE COVER A VERY WIDE RANGE OF INDUSTRIES - CONTACT US FOR USED INJECTION MOULDERS, EXTRUDERS, VACUUM FORMERS, BLOW MOULDERS, BLOWN FILM, ALL TYPES OF MIXERS, MILLS, CALENDERING LINES ALSO MANY COMPLETE PLANTS (E.G. STEEL WORKS, BOTTLING FACTORIES, CONDOM PLANTS, BREWERIES AND MANY MORE). WE ALSO OFFER A RANGE OF NEW INJECTION MOULDERS AND CUTTING PRESSES. PLEASE CONTACT US IF YOU DO NOT SEE WHAT YOU NEED ON OUR WEBSITE. WE HAVE A CONSTANT STREAM OF MACHINERY COMING AVAILABLE ALL THE TIME, WHICH MAY NOT YET HAVE APPEARED ON OUR WEBSITE, SO WE MAY JUST HAVE IT, OR KNOW WHERE IT IS. WE HAVE WORLDWIDE CONNECTIONS BUILT UP OVER THE YEARS AND HAVE HELD EXHIBITIONS IN VIRTUALLY EVERY COUNTRY IN THE WORLD.*

Machining Centre Ltd, Pembroke Lane, Milton, Abingdon, Oxfordshire, OX14 4EA Tel: (01235) 831343 Fax: (01235) 834708 E-mail: info@machiningcentre.co.uk *Precision engineers*

Machtech Press Tool Distributors, Brown Lion Street, Tipton, West Midlands, DY4 9EG Tel: 0121-522 4340 Fax: 0121-522 3860 E-mail: chris.pring@tiscali.co.uk *Toolmaking services*

Macinnes Joiners, Unit 10 C Coal Wynd, Kirkcaldy, Fife, KY1 2RA Tel: (01592) 597085 Fax: (01592) 597085 *Carpenters & joiners*

Macintosh Ltd, Unit 10a Blairlinn Industrial Estate, Cumbernauld, Glasgow, G67 2TW Tel: (01422) 846953 Fax: (01236) 723924 E-mail: sales@mackintosh-scotland.com *Waterproof clothing manufrs*

▶ Andrew McIntosh, Craggan Cottage, Grantown-on-Spey, Morayshire, PH26 3NT Tel: (01479) 872489 E-mail: andmcandtosh@hotmail.com

McIntosh Enterprises, 227 Kilsyth Road, Banknock, Bonnybridge, Stirlingshire, FK4 1UF Tel: (01324) 841674 Fax: (01324) 841674 *Car accessories (CB radio) distributors*

▶ Mcintosh & Robertson, Broompark Terrace, Murthly, Perth, PH1 4HJ Tel: (01738) 710255 Fax: (01738) 710598

Mcintyre Caravans, Hempsted Bridge, Bristol Road, Gloucester, GL2 5DH Tel: (01452) 520737 Fax: (01452) 309970 E-mail: info@goldencastle.co.uk *Caravan distributors*

Mcintyre Leisure, Whitehouse Farm, Britwell Road, Watlington, Oxfordshire, OX49 5JY Tel: (01491) 613284 Fax: (01491) 614778 *Sauna steam spa suppliers*

▶ Mcintyre UK Ltd, Holywell Green, Holywell Green, Halifax, West Yorkshire, HX4 9HZ Tel: (01422) 312200 Fax: (01422) 312214

▶ McIvor Tutorials, 6 Bushfield Mills, Feeny, Londonderry, BT47 4TL Tel: (0784) 3146283 Fax: E-mail: mcivortdr@yahoo.co.uk *This Business Provides specialist tution in science or Mathematics. The tuition can be carried out via Emails through distance tutoring and Student Support packs being sent to the homes to further enrich the students understanding of the Curriculum material.*The following Subjects are offered to A Level(or UK equivalent) or the International Equivalent in*Chemistry*Biology*Mathematics. *This Specialist Tuition is carried out by an experience tutor eight years in the field.*

B.W. Mack (Machinery) Ltd, Barroway Drove, Downham Market, Norfolk, PE38 0AL Tel: (01366) 324256 Fax: (01366) 324431 E-mail: info@bwmack.co.uk *Agricultural machinery suppliers*

Mack Engineering, Montrose Avenue, Hillington Industrial Estate, Glasgow, G52 4LA Tel: 0141-882 1030 Fax: 0141-882 7330 E-mail: mackengineering@btinternet.com *Marine & industrial pump suppliers*

Alf McKay, Manor Barn, Crewkerne, Somerset, TA18 8QT Tel: (01460) 78916 Fax: (01460) 78916 *Cabinet maker & restorer*

Mackay Boatbuilders Arbroath Ltd, The Boatyard, Old Shore Head, Arbroath, Angus, DD11 1BB Tel: (01241) 872879 Fax: (01241) 872879 E-mail: mackayboatbuilders@connectfree.co.uk *Boat building repairs & joinery services*

Mackay Bros, Culag Square, Lochinver, Lairg, Sutherland, IV27 4LE Tel: (01571) 844298 Fax: (01571) 844598 *Fish processors*

Company Information

▶ Mackay Bros The Joinery Specialists, Showroom, 127 Eastbank Street, Southport, Merseyside, PR8 1DQ Tel: (01704) 540772 E-mail: mackaybrothers@btinternet.com *Joinery, door canopies, porches, windows, doors*

Mackay Decorators Perth Ltd, 1 Riverside, Perth, PH2 7TR Tel: (01738) 623227 Fax: (01738) 623228 E-mail: enquiries@mackaydecorators.co.uk *Painting contractors*

▶ Mckay Flooring Ltd, 123 Harmony Row, Glasgow, G51 3NB Tel: 0141-440 1586 Fax: 0141-425 1020 E-mail: enquires@mckay.co.uk *Hardwood flooring*

▶ Mackay & Inglis Ltd, 19 Polmadie Street, Glasgow, G42 0PQ Tel: 0141-423 8866

▶ Mackay & Pearson, 46a High Street, Horbury, Wakefield, West Yorkshire, WF4 5LE Tel: (01924) 273122 Fax: (01924) 273122 E-mail: info@mackayandpearson.co.uk *Manufacturers & retail jewellery*

▶ Mackay Plant Hire Ltd, 39 High Meadow, Tollerton, Nottingham, NG12 4DZ Tel: 0115-937 2890 Fax: 0115-937 2889

McKay Signs & Graphics, Unit 7 Chipping Edge Estate, Hatters Lane, Chipping Sodbury, Bristol, BS37 6AA Tel: (01454) 319483 Fax: (01454) 312912 *Sign manufrs*

William McKay Ltd, 34 Singer Road, Kelvin Industrial Estate, Glasgow, G75 0XS Tel: (01355) 229756 Fax: (01355) 238106 E-mail: stuart1@s.mckay.free-online.co.uk *Precision engineers*

Mackays Ltd, James Chalmers Road Kirkton Indust Estate, Kirkton Industrial Estate, Arbroath, Angus, DD11 3LR Tel: (01241) 432500 Fax: (01241) 432444 E-mail: info@mackays.com *Confectionery & jam manufrs*

Mckay's Bakery, 9 High Street, Brechin, Angus, DD9 6ES Tel: (01356) 623664 Fax: (01356) 623061 *Bakery*

Mackays Of Cambridge Ltd, 120 Church End, Cambridge, CB1 3LB Tel: (01223) 508222 Fax: (01223) 510222 E-mail: engineering@mackay.co.uk *Architectural fabricators*

Mackays Of Chatham Ltd, Badger Road, Chatham, Kent, ME5 8TD Tel: (01634) 864381 Fax: (01634) 867742 E-mail: macays@cpi-group.co.uk *Printers & bookbinders*

▶ Mckay's Transport, 9 Broomfield Industrial Estate, Broomfield Road, Montrose, Angus, DD10 8SY Tel: (01674) 673020 Fax: (01674) 673409

McKean & Co. (Glasgow) Ltd, 48 Kelvingrove Street, Glasgow, G3 7RZ Tel: 0141-332 1822

▶ Mckean & Company (Glasgow) Ltd, 21/27 Woodville Street, Glasgow, G51 2RY Tel: 0141-445 0123 E-mail: enquiries@mckean-group.co.uk

Mckeand Smith Co. Ltd, Station Road, Albrighton, Wolverhampton, WV7 3EA Tel: (01902) 373426 Fax: (01902) 373469 *Building & public works contractors*

▶ Mckeating Ltd, 4 Wykeham Road, Glasgow, G13 3YT Tel: 0141-434 1117 Fax: 0141-954 2987

F.B. McKee & Co. Ltd, 62-66 Duncrue Street, Belfast, BT3 9AY Tel: (028) 9035 1071 Fax: (028) 9035 4103 E-mail: fbmckee@btconnect.com *Civil engineering & public works contractors*

▶ Mackellar Ltd, Strathspey Industrial Estate, Woodlands Terrace, Grantown-on-Spey, Morayshire, PH26 3NB Tel: (01479) 872577 Fax: (01479) 872436 E-mail: enquiries@mackellars.co.uk

Mckellars Slipway Ltd, Shore Road, Kilcreggan, Helensburgh, Dunbartonshire, G84 0JL Tel: (01436) 842334 *Wintering storage & repairs*

Mckelvey Bros, 34-36 Lisburn Street, Ballynahinch, County Down, BT24 8BD Tel: (028) 9756 5680 Fax: (028) 9756 5680 Principal Export Areas: Central/East Europe *Retailers of farm supplies*

▶ McKenna Demolition Ltd, Sheetings Farm, Salt Box Hill, Biggin Hill, Westerham, Kent, TN16 3EE Tel: (01959) 571512 Fax: (01959) 572439 E-mail: mckennademo@btconnect.com *Demolition contractors*

A.D. Mackenzie, THe Old Saddlery, Cladach, Brodick, Isle Of Arran, KA27 8DE Tel: (01770) 302311 E-mail: sales@mckenzieleather.co.uk *Leather bags retail & manufrs*

▶ Mckenzie Engineering, 32 Cutlers Road, South Woodham Ferrers, Chelmsford, CM3 5XJ Tel: (01245) 425413 *Precision engineers*

Mackenzie Glass, Grace Road, Marsh Barton Trading Estate, Exeter, EX2 8QE Tel: (01392) 258538 Fax: (01392) 420096 E-mail: mackenzieglass@btinternet.com *Glazing contractors*

Mckenzie Martin Ltd, Eton Hill Works, Eton Hill Road, Radcliffe, Manchester, M26 2US Tel: 0161-723 2234 Fax: 0161-725 9531 E-mail: general@mckenziemartin.co.uk *Industrial ventilator & roof light manufrs*

Ritchie MacKenzie & Co. Ltd, Broomhill Industrial Estate, Kirkintilloch, Glasgow, G66 1TQ Tel: 0141-776 6274 Fax: 0141-776 0285 E-mail: sales@ritmac.co.uk *Pump distributors, installers & contractors*

▶ Mackenzie & Son Transport, 86 Cloglands, Forth, Lanark, ML11 8DY Tel: (01555) 811635 Fax: (01555) 812071

MacKenzie Tribbeck Associates & (Computer Consultants) Ltd, Suite 2 92 Gloucester Place, London, W1H 3DA Tel: (020) 7224 3146 *Computer consultants*

Mckenzie-Midlane Ltd, PO Box 35, Whitby, North Yorkshire, YO21 3EZ Tel: (01947) 820243 Fax: (01947) 820488 E-mail: sales@mckmid.com *Underwater technology consultancy*

▶ McKerron & Milne Ltd, Fisherton Yard, Aberlour, Banffshire, AB38 9LB Tel: (01340) 871410

▶ Mckerron & Milne, 35 New Street, Rothes, Aberlour, Banffshire, AB38 7BQ Tel: (01340) 831523 Fax: (01340) 831804

▶ Mackey Software Design Ltd, Parnella House, 23 Market Place, Devizes, Wiltshire, SN10 1JQ Tel: (01380) 724688 E-mail: info@mackeysoftware.co.uk

Mackie Automotive Systems UK Ltd, North Road, Ellesmere Port, CH65 1BL Tel: 0151-356 4004 Fax: 0151 356 3281 E-mail: sales@mackieautomotive.com *Subassembly services*

Mckiernan Group Ltd, Crown St Works, Crown Street, Accrington, Lancashire, BB5 0RW Tel: (01254) 398532 Fax: (01254) 392157 E-mail: design@themckiernangroup.co.uk *Industrial heating & ventilating engineers* Also at: Liverpool & Newport

Mckillop Dental Equipment Ltd, 45a Derby Road, Southport, Merseyside, PR9 0TZ Tel: (01704) 538221 Fax: (01704) 538353 E-mail: office@mckillopdental.co.uk *Dental equipment suppliers*

P.P. Mackingdale Ltd, Claymore, Tame Valley Industrial Estate, Tamworth, Staffordshire, B77 5DQ Tel: (01827) 261100 Fax: (01827) 281223 *Chain conveyor parts suppliers*

▶ McKinlay & Blair Ltd, Burnbank, Campbeltown, Argyll, PA28 6JD Tel: (01586) 552012

McKinlay Electrical Manufacturing Co. Ltd, 62 Weir Rd, Wimbledon, London, SW19 8UG Tel: (020) 8879 1141 Fax: (020) 8946 3047 E-mail: mckinlayelec@aol.com *McKinlay Electrical Manufacturing Co. Ltd, London was formed over 50 years ago, and has forged a reputation for expertise in resin castings and encapsulations. A wide customer base includes the Ministry of Defence; major defence subcontractors; marine, water, oil and gas, aerospace, automotive, electronic, mining and high voltage Industries. The Company offers a full turn-key facility for the design, development and manufacture of finished components in epoxies, super epoxies, silicone rubbers and polyurethanes. Additional in-house facilities include a tool room for the manufacture of mould tools, jigs and fixtures; precision engineering for the finishing of epoxy castings, metal and plastic components; coil-winding facilities for the manufacture of transformers, power supplies, fine wire potentiometers and general electronic sub-assemblies and a multi-task assembly line facility for the manufacture of light electromechanical components.*

Mackinnon & Saunders Ltd, 146-148 Seamons Road, Altrincham, Cheshire, WA14 4LJ Tel: 0161-929 4441 Fax: 0161-929 1441 *Models animation for film & television*

Mackinnon Of Scotland, Kirkshaws Road, Coatbridge, Lanarkshire, ML5 4SL Tel: (01236) 423231 Fax: (01236) 433482 *Knitted outerwear manufrs*

▶ Mackinnons, Plasterfield, Stornoway, Isle of Lewis, HS1 2UR Tel: (01851) 702804 *Bakery*

Mackin's Concrete & Building Supplies, 27 Hilltown Road, Newry, County Down, BT34 2LJ Tel: (028) 3026 3384 Fax: (028) 3026 0514 *Concrete products & building suppliers*

Mckinsey & Co. (UK), 1 Jermyn Street, London, SW1Y 4UH Tel: (020) 7839 8040 Fax: (020) 7339 5000 *Management consultants*

Alistair Mackintosh Ltd, Bannerley Road, Garretts Green Industrial Estate, Birmingham, B33 0SL Tel: 0121-784 6800 Fax: 0121-789 7068 E-mail: info@alistairmackintosh.co.uk *Stockists of Limestone, marble, granite travertine for floors and walls.Granite worktops to specification.Large Showrooms*

▶ Mackintosh Highland, Braeview Clava, Culloden Moor, Inverness, IV2 5EL Tel: (01463) 790779 Fax: (01463) 792290

▶ Mackintosh Joinery, 64 Haugh Road, Inverness, IV2 4SD Tel: (01463) 250160 Fax: (01463) 250180

Mackintosh & Partners (Properties) Ltd, The Sawmills, Small Dole, Henfield, West Sussex, BN5 9XG Tel: (01273) 497100 Fax: (01273) 497139 E-mail: sales@mackintosh.co.uk *Timber importers & merchants*

Mackintosh & Partners (Timber) Ltd, Coopers Lane, Northaw, Potters Bar, Hertfordshire, EN6 4NE Tel: (01707) 642361 Fax: (01707) 646341 E-mail: jpaige@mackintosh.co.uk *Timber merchants & importers*

▶ McKinty Marketing Services, 56 Stoke Fields, Guildford, Surrey, GU1 4LS Tel: (01483) 852815 E-mail: alexandra@mckinty.com *Marketing Services for business and education. We specialize in Marketing Communications, Market Research and Marketing for schools and colleges. A marketing mentoring service is also offered to small organisations without their own marketing personnel.*

Mackley & Co. Ltd, Chatham Street, Sheffield, S3 8EJ Tel: 0114-272 3991 Fax: 0114-272 1004 *Sheet metalworkers*

J.T. Mackley & Co. Ltd, Bankside House, Henfield Road, Small Dole, Henfield, West Sussex, BN5 9XQ Tel: (01273) 492212 Fax: (01273) 494328 E-mail: construct@mackley.co.uk *Civil engineering contractors*

Macklow Industrial Ltd, The Mill, Station Road, Salhouse, Norwich, NR13 6NY Tel: (01603) 720950 Fax: (01603) 720033 E-mail: info@macklow.co.uk *Ventilation ductwork & ducting & duct contractors*

▶ Mackman Ltd, Twinkle Star House, 11 West Stockwell Street, Colchester, CO1 1HN Tel: (01787) 376687 E-mail: marketing@mackmanltd.co.uk *Mackman Marketing acts as an extension of your company, providing a complete range of professional marketing services at affordable rates. From start-ups and micro businesses through to large organisations we collaborate to develop marketing that makes a difference. We also specialise in gathering business information and research services. Call us today to find out more.*

▶ Macks Toiletries, Unit 29 Watford Metro Centre, Dwight Road, Watford, WD18 9SB Tel: (01923) 831931 Fax: (01923) 831932

Macksons London Ltd, 270 Kilburn High Road, London, NW6 2BY Tel: (020) 7624 7133 Fax: (020) 7625 6091 E-mail: enquiries@macksons.co.uk *Footwear*

continued

exporters, retailers & distributors Also at: London W2

Mackwell Electronics Ltd, Hayward Industrial Park, Vigo Place, Walsall, WS9 8UG Tel: (01922) 458255 Fax: (01922) 451263 E-mail: sales@mackwell.com *Manufacturers of inverters, lighting components & modules*

Mclaggan Smith Mugs Ltd, Jamestown, Alexandria, Dunbartonshire, G83 8BS Tel: (01389) 755655 Fax: (01389) 754260 E-mail: polly@msmugs.com *Mug decorators, retail & specially commissioned services*

Maclan Plastics, Unit Ba Keighley Business Centre, South Street, Keighley, West Yorkshire, BD21 1AG Tel: (01535) 680127 Fax: (01535) 680222 E-mail: info@maclanplastics.co.uk *Plastic consultants, moulders & toolmakers*

▶ Mclanachan Transport Ltd, 12a Garrell Road, Kilsyth, Glasgow, G65 9JX Tel: (01236) 823539 Fax: (01236) 826347 E-mail: sales@mtltransport.com

Mclaren Cars Ltd, Horsell Common, Woking, Surrey, GU21 4YH Tel: (01483) 261500 Fax: (01483) 261502 E-mail: mcl.reception@mclaren.com *Car manufrs*

Maclaren Europe Ltd, Station Works, Station Road, Long Buckby, Northampton, NN6 7PF Tel: (01327) 842662 Fax: (01327) 844133 E-mail: info@maclaren.co.uk *Baby buggies*

Nigel McLaren, 29 Clifton Court, Northwick Terrace, London, NW8 8HT Tel: (07866) 769268 Fax: (020) 7289 3003 E-mail: nigelmclaren@aol.com *Software development, web site building, web hosting & marketing*

McLaren Plastics Ltd, Pentland Industrial Estate, Loanhead, Midlothian, EH20 9QH Tel: 0131-448 2200 Fax: 0131-448 2221 E-mail: sales@mclaren-plastics.co.uk Sales Contact: C. McLaren *Based 3 miles south of Edinburgh, covering the whole of the U.K. and some of Europe, we are a plastic injection moulding company supplying a wide range of companies and industries. We have shown below some of the ranges of products we supply - Plastic carry handles, carton carry handles, tube end plugs, plastic tube end plugs, plastic closures, plastic core plugs, core plugs for tubes, injection moulding, plastic moulding, plastic moulded components, injection moulded components, shower curtain rings, curtain rings, plastic reels, plastic rings, plastic pipe clips, plastic tumblers, in-house mould making, tool making. As a trade/custom injection moulder we supply a large number of electronics, engineering and various other manufacturing companies with hundreds, thousands or millions of parts to their design. Accredited to ISO9002 and ISO14001. Established in 1960 - we are experienced, capable and expanding. We would be pleased to quote you for your requirements*

▶ Mclaren Tractors Ltd, Strathpeffer Road, Dingwall, Ross-Shire, IV15 9QF Tel: (01349) 867210 Fax: (01349) 866738 *Agricultural machinery distributors*

▶ Maclarty, Galvelmore Street, Crieff, Perthshire, PH7 3QY Tel: (01764) 652892

▶ McLaughlan Construction Ltd, Burnside Cottage, Old Glasgow Road, Kilwinning, Ayrshire, KA13 7QJ Tel: (01294) 550533

▶ McLaughlan Transport, 10 Almswall Road, Kilwinning, Ayrshire, KA13 6BN Tel: (01294) 559224

▶ Mclaughlin Fitted Furniture, Unit 15 Glenshane Enterprise Centre, 441a Ballyquin Road, Dungiven, Londonderry, BT47 4NQ Tel: (028) 7774 2681 Fax: (028) 7774 2681 *Bathroom, kitchen & bedroom furniture manufrs*

McLay Ltd, Glentanar Road, The Balmore Industrial Estate, Glasgow, G22 7XS Tel: 0141-336 6543 Fax: 0141-336 4857 E-mail: meat@mclay.co.uk *Frozen food processors & products manufrs*

Maclay Civil Engineering Ltd, 38 Stirling Road, Airdrie, Lanarkshire, ML6 7JA Tel: (01236) 768388 Fax: (01236) 748425

Mclay Furniture, Little Trodgers Lane, Mayfield, East Sussex, TN20 6PN Tel: (01435) 872877 Fax: (01435) 872817 *Furniture manufrs*

Mclean Aviation, Rufforth Airfield, Rufforth, York, YO23 3NA Tel: (01904) 738653 Fax: (01904) 738146 *Fiber glass aircraft repairs & services*

Mclean Buchanan & Wilson Glasgow Ltd, 250 Helen Street, Glasgow, G51 3JG Tel: 0141-445 3045 Fax: 0141-440 1225 E-mail: sales@mbw.co.uk *Structural fastener distributors*

▶ Maclean Environmental, Beeby Road, Scraptoft, Leicester, LE7 9SJ Tel: 0116-276 9592 Fax: 0116-276 9373 *Pest control services*

Maclean & Speirs Group Ltd, East Fulton Farm, Darluith Road, Linwood, Paisley, Renfrewshire, PA3 3TP Tel: (01505) 324777 Fax: (01505) 335482 E-mail: info@macleanandspeirs.co.uk *Decorators & painting contractors*

Maclean's Bakery Benbecula Ltd, Maclean Bakery, Uachdar, Isle of Benbecula, HS7 5LY Tel: (01870) 602659 Fax: (01870) 603121 E-mail: macleansbakery@tiscali.co.uk *Bakery suppliers*

Macleans Foils Ltd, Essex Works, Kenway, Southend-On-Sea, SS2 5DY Tel: (01702) 463566 Fax: (01702) 616954 E-mail: sales@macleansfoils.co.uk *Aluminum foil printers*

▶ Mcleish Sales & Services Ltd, Endeavour Drive, Arnhall Business Park, Westhill, Aberdeenshire, AB32 6UF Tel: (01224) 279955 Fax: (01224) 279966 E-mail: graeme@mcleishsales.co.uk *Instrumentation distributors*

▶ Mclellan Harris & Co., Waterloo Chambers, 19 Waterloo Street, Glasgow, G2 6AY Tel: 0141-221 0631 Fax: 0141-204 4019 *Accountancy*

MacLellan International Ltd, 110 Birmingham Road, West Bromwich, West Midlands, B70 6RP Tel: 0121-500 5000 Fax: 0121-524 8815 E-mail: enquiries@maclellan-int.com *Integrated facilities & support services providers*

Mclellan & Partners Ltd, 7 Station Approach, West Byfleet, Surrey, KT14 6NL Tel: (01932) 343271 Fax: (01932) 348037 E-mail: mclellan_uk@compuserve.com *Project management consulting engineers* Also at: Stockton

Maclellan Rubber, Neachells Lane, Wolverhampton, WV11 3QG Tel: (01902) 725515 Fax: (01902) 305201 E-mail: sales@maclellanrubber.com *Manufacturers of anti-vibration mounting & rubber sheeting* Also at: Birmingham

Mclellan Software Design Ltd, 18 Carlton Business Centre, Carlton, Nottingham, NG4 3AA Tel: 0115-961 7676 Fax: 0115-961 6866 E-mail: sales@msdmagic.co.uk *Software accountants*

▶ Mclelland Cheese Packaging, Commerce Road, Stranraer, Wigtownshire, DG9 7DA Tel: (01776) 706790 Fax: (01776) 707629 *Dairy products*

▶ McLellans Transport, 6 Wellington Road, Bishopbriggs, Glasgow, G64 2SA Tel: 0141-772 7757

Mcleman Forklift Services Ltd, 15 Andover Street, Birmingham, B5 5RG Tel: 0121-643 1788 Fax: 0121-631 3725 E-mail: dgillespie@mclemanforklifts.co.uk *Forklift sales & hire*

Mclennan Servo Supplies Ltd, Unit 1, The Royston Centre, Lynchford Road, Ash Vale, Aldershot, Hampshire, GU12 5PQ Tel: (0870) 7700700 Fax: (0870) 7700699 E-mail: sales@mclennan.co.uk *Mclennan Servo Supplies are a UK based company, manufacturer and distributor of precision motion control. Products include stepper, servo and brushless motors, drives and controls and complete turn-key systems.*

▶ Mcleod, Glengarnock Technology Centre Caledonia Road, Lochshore Industrial Estate, Glengarnock, Beith, Ayrshire, KA14 3DD Tel: (01505) 684922 Fax: (01505) 684922

▶ Macleod Building Services Contracts, 39 Turnhouse Road, Edinburgh, EH12 0AE Tel: 0131-339 2680 Fax: 0131-339 5829 *Builders*

Mcleod Cabins Ltd, The Saw Mill, Ipsden, Wallingford, Oxfordshire, OX10 6AS Tel: (01491) 871502 Fax: (01491) 871504 *Cabin hire*

Macleod Engineering, North Street Industrial Estate, Droitwich, Worcestershire, WR9 8JB Tel: (01905) 794578 Fax: (01905) 794965 *Precision toolmakers*

▶ John Mcleod, Whitehouse, Alford, Aberdeenshire, AB33 8DQ Tel: (01975) 562507 *Agricultural & industrial supplies*

▶ Macleod & Mitchell (Contractors) Ltd, Unit 4, Cliffton, Poolewe, Achnasheen, Ross-Shire, IV22 2JU Tel: (01445) 781380

▶ Mcleod Plant Hire, Naurcris, Dyce, Aberdeen, AB21 0EY Tel: (01224) 723718 Fax: (01224) 772877

Macloch Construction, Unit 3 Zetland School, Middle St Lane, Grangemouth, Stirlingshire, FK3 8EH Tel: (01324) 486279 Fax: (01324) 473500

▶ Macloch Construction, Unit 3 Zetland School, Middle St Lane, Grangemouth, Stirlingshire, FK3 8EH Tel: (01324) 486279 Fax: (01324) 473500

Mcluckie Engineering Ltd, 54 Barterholm Road, Paisley, Renfrewshire, PA2 6PF Tel: 0141-887 2201 Fax: 0141-889 5970 E-mail: sales@mcluckie.co.uk *Dust extraction equipment manufrs*

▶ Mcmahon Air Conditioning, The Popples, Clifford Road, Bramham, Wetherby, West Yorkshire, LS23 6RN Tel: (01937) 844203 Fax: (01937) 844203

Mcmahon Contractors Services Ltd, Old Station Yard, Station Road, Stratford-upon-Avon, Warwickshire, CV37 8RP Tel: (01789) 720836 Fax: (01789) 721048 E-mail: sales@mcmahon-holdings.co.uk *Civil engineers*

▶ McManus Joinery, 343 Dowling Road, Clonliff, Enniskillen, County Fermanagh, BT92 3BP Tel: (028) 6634 8161 Fax: (028) 6634 8601 E-mail: mcmanus_joinery@hotmail.com *Joinery services*

Mcmaster Garages, 55 Trent Road, Boughton, Newark, Nottinghamshire, NG22 9ZB Tel: (01623) 836230 Fax: (01623) 836230 *Buildings portable*

McMillan Ltd, Prestonpans Industrial Estate, Mid Road, Prestonpans, East Lothian, EH32 9JB Tel: (01875) 811110 Fax: (01875) 814022 E-mail: sales@mcmillanltd.co.uk *Distillery plant & equipment manufrs*

Mcmillan Communications, 198b Newhouse Road, Blackpool, FY4 4PA Tel: (01253) 698885 Fax: (01253) 798474 E-mail: info@mcmillan-communications.co.uk *Data sockets installers*

McMillan Conroy Machinery, PO Box 3081, Walsall, WS2 9SS Tel: (01922) 725444 Fax: (01922) 640336 E-mail: sales@mcmillanconroy.co.uk *Used rolling mills*

▶ Mcmillan Contracting, Unit 27 New Albion Industrial Estate, Halley Drive, Glasgow, G13 4DJ Tel: 0141-952 0444 Fax: 0141-952 0777

Macmillan Davies Consultants Ltd, Salisbury House, Bluecoats Avenue, Hertford, SG14 1PU Tel: (01992) 552552 Fax: (01992) 514101 E-mail: contact@hodes.co.uk *Advertising agents & recruitment consultants*

Macmillan Distribution Ltd, Howard Road, St. Neots, Cambridgeshire, PE19 8EZ Tel: (01480) 212666 *Book distributors* Also at: London WC1

Mcmillan & Co. (Electrical Engineers) Ltd, 49 Scrutton Street, London, EC2A 4XJ Tel: (020) 7729 1919 Fax: (020) 7729 0174 E-mail: rec@mcmh.clara.net *Electrical engineers*

Mcmillan Plant, Aird Quarry, Castle Kennedy, Stranraer, Wigtownshire, DG9 8RX Tel: (01776) 707241 Fax: (01776) 707264 *Concrete production*

Macmillan Publishers Ltd, Brunel Road, Houndmills, Basingstoke, Hampshire, RG21 6XS Tel: (01256) 329242 Fax: (01256) 479476 *Publishers*

Mcmillan Scott plc, Quay House, Quay Street, Manchester, M3 3JE Tel: 0161-832 6000 Fax: 0161-832 1166 *Publishers & consultants*

McMillan-Scott Ltd, Trelawney House, Chestergate, Macclesfield, Cheshire, SK11 6DW Tel: (01625) 613000 Fax: (01625) 511446 *Publishers* Also at: Lancaster & Manchester

Mcmillen UK Ltd, 60 Nelson St, Aberdeen, AB24 5ES Tel: 01224 645366 Fax: 01224 624097 *Audio visual equipment*

Macmillian Publishers Ltd, Brunel Road, Houndmills, Basingstoke, Hampshire, RG21 6XS Tel: (01256) 464481 Fax: (01256) 479496 *Publishing*

Macmurchie Bagpipe Makers, 47e West End, West Calder, West Lothian, EH55 8EJ Tel: (01506) 872333 Fax: (01506) 885220 E-mail: sales@macmurchiebagpipes.co.uk *Bagpipe manufrs*

Macnab, Stringes Lane, Willenhall, West Midlands, WV13 1LD Tel: (01902) 631159 Fax: (01902) 606922 *Bar & shaft straightening services*

Mcnair Engineering Ltd, 11-12 Lovat Place, Glasgow, G52 4XE Tel: 0141-883 0496 Fax: 0141-882 7823 E-mail: enquiries@mcnair-engineering.co.uk *Hydraulic maintenance engineers*

Mcnally Crane Hire Ltd, Drumrainy, Newtownbutler, Enniskillen, County Fermanagh, BT92 6LY Tel: (028) 6773 8830 *Crane hire*

▶ Mcnally Electrics, 19 Turnavall Road, Newry, County Down, BT34 1LZ Tel: (028) 3026 5760 Fax: (028) 3026 0881

John Macnamara & Co. Ltd, 19a Bush Road, London, SE8 5AR Tel: (020) 7237 1591 Fax: (020) 7231 5173 *Plant & tool hire*

Rudd Macnamara Ltd, Holyhead Road, Birmingham, B21 0BS Tel: 0121-523 8437 Fax: 0121-551 7032 E-mail: rudd@nameplates.co.uk *Nameplate & label manufrs*

Mcnaughton Dynamics Ltd, 9 Carters Lane, Long Crendon, Aylesbury, Buckinghamshire, HP18 9DE Tel: (01844) 208333 Fax: (01844) 201552 E-mail: sales@mcnaughton.co.uk *Aircraft ground support equipment distributors*

James McNaughton Paper Group Ltd, Unit 3, Maxted Court, Maxted Road, Hemel Hempstead, Hertfordshire, HP2 7BY Tel: (01442) 270104 Fax: (01442) 217390 E-mail: gskelton@mcnaughton-paper.com *Paper merchants*

Mcnaughton & Watson Ltd, 423 Gallowgate, Glasgow, G40 2EA Tel: 0141-554 2757 Fax: 0141-551 9809 *Food trade supplier*

Charles McNeil (Engineers), PO Box 4, Motherwell, Lanarkshire, ML1 3NP Tel: (01698) 266111 Fax: (01698) 269774 E-mail: lpowell@mbgroup.com *Pressure vessel door manufrs*

▶ Mcneil Marine, 1 Tan Y Banc, Graig, Burry Port, Dyfed, SA16 0DT Tel: (01554) 833233 E-mail: surveys@mcneilmarine.com *Marine surveyors*Yacht and Small Craft Surveys Pre-Purchase, Insurance, Valuation, Osmosis Inspection, and Consultancy*

Mcneill Associates Ltd, 14 Well Hall Parade, London, SE9 6SP Tel: (020) 8294 1565 Fax: (020) 8859 4562 E-mail: post@mcneill.co.uk *Provide outsourced it support services*

▶ Macneill Consultancy, 8 Old Coach Mews, Templepatrick, Ballyclare, County Antrim, BT39 0JS Tel: (028) 9443 9129 E-mail: info@macneillconsultancy.com *Marketing & management consultancy*

McNeill-McManus Ltd, Hydepark Industrial Estate, Mallusk, Newtownabbey, County Antrim, BT36 4PX Tel: (028) 9084 2611 Fax: (028) 9034 2317 E-mail: mailbox@mcneill-mcmanus.com *Suppliers of glass, designers & glaziers*

Mcnelis Workshop Machinery & Steel Supplies, 122 Curr Road, Beragh, Sixmilecross, Omagh, County Tyrone, BT79 0QT Tel: (028) 8075 8225 Fax: (028) 8075 8225 *Workshop machinery suppliers*

▶ McNicholas P.L.C., Victoria Road, Ashford, Kent, TN23 7HE Tel: (01233) 666159

Mcnicholas Construction Holdings Ltd, Lismirrane Industrial Park, Elstree Road, Borehamwood, Hertfordshire, WD6 3EA Tel: (020) 8953 4144 Fax: (020) 8953 1860 E-mail: sales@mcnicholas.co.uk *Utility, building & civil engineering (public works) contractors*

Mcnulty Offshore Ltd, 16-17 Corstorphine Town, South Shields, Tyne & Wear, NE33 1RZ Tel: 0191-401 5800 Fax: 0191-401 5802 E-mail: mcnulty@mcnultyoffshore.com *Offshore fabricators*

Mcnulty Wray, 4-6 Bypass Park Estate, Sherburn in Elmet, Leeds, LS25 6EP Tel: (01977) 681133 Fax: (01977) 681177 E-mail: sales@mcnultywray.co.uk *Paper napkins manufrs*

▶ Maco Door & Window Hardware UK Ltd, Eurolink Industrial Centre, Castle Road, Sittingbourne, Kent, ME10 3LY Tel: (01795) 433900 Fax: (01795) 433901

Maco Manufacturing Co. Ltd, 6d The St Industrial Estate, Heybridge Street, Maldon, Essex, CM9 4XT Tel: (01621) 856789 Fax: (01621) 851358 E-mail: info@maco.uk.com *Tarpaulin & safety equipment manufrs*

Maco Refrigeration Ltd, 106 Havelock Street, Kettering, Northamptonshire, NN16 9QA Tel: (01536) 514105 Fax: (01536) 415645 E-mail: mail@maco-ltd.demon.co.uk *Refrigeration engineers & contractors services*

Mcof Ltd, 3 Station Road, Brompton on Swale, Richmond, North Yorkshire, DL10 7SN Tel: (01748) 812612 Fax: (01748) 812618 E-mail: thomaslinckh@btconnect.com *Office interior supplier*

Macola UK, 4 The Potteries, Wickham Road, Fareham, Hampshire, PO16 7ET Tel: (01329) 235846 Fax: (01329) 221425 E-mail: sales@macola.co.uk *Integrated accountants*

▶ Macom Technologies Ltd, 17 Glasgow Road, Paisley, Renfrewshire, PA1 3QS Tel: 0141-849 6287 Fax: 0141-849 6497 E-mail: info@macomtech.net *Suppliers of condition monitoring equipment*

Maconochies of Kilmarnock Ltd, 22-26 Campbell Street, Riccarton, Kilmarnock, Ayrshire, KA1 4HW Tel: (01563) 522681 Fax: (01563) 541297 *Property agents*

▶ McPhedran Co. UK, 23 Carriage Drive, Kettering, Northamptonshire, NN16 9EN Tel: (07778) 211855 *Executive, leadership, management, personal and career coaching. Training and development for the creative industries and innovative team building.*

▶ McPhee Bros (Blantyre) Ltd, 58 John Street, Blantyre, Glasgow, G72 0JF Tel: (01698) 823422 Fax: (01698) 823853 E-mail: lorna@mcfeemixers.co.uk *Lorry mounted concrete mixer unit manufrs*

▶ Mcpherson Ltd, Fisherton Garage, Aberlour, Banffshire, AB38 9LB Tel: (01340) 871401 Fax: (01340) 871721

▶ Mcpherson Document Solutions, 102-112 Main Road, Elderslie, Johnstone, Renfrewshire, PA5 9AX Tel: (01505) 331534 Fax: (01505) 328266 E-mail: sales@trmcpherson.co.uk *Based near Glasgow, Scotland, McPherson Document Solutions supply document management and document scanning solutions to companies, local authorities and service providers throughout Scotland and the UK. We offer full-service solutions in the field of document management and document scanning, including: Document consultancy, Digital document management , Document hard storage ,Mass document scanning , Large format scanning , Microfilm scanning , On-site scanning , CD Duplication , Hard Copy and PDF Service Manual Duplication, Media Storage, Hard Storage, Large Format Printing, High Quality Imaging, Service Manual Duplication, Microfilm, Supply and maintenance of microfilm and document scanners, printers, readers, cameras and document management software, and much more. Please visit our website or call us for more information.*

Geoffrey E. Macpherson Ltd, Unit 8, The Midway, Lenton, Nottingham, NG7 2TS Tel: 0115-986 8701 Fax: 0115-986 4430 E-mail: gem@macphersons.co.uk *Distributors & reconditioned embroidery machines* Also at: Ireland, London, Manchester, Scotland & Taunton

Macphie, E Tannochside Drive, Tannochside Park, Uddingston, Glasgow, G71 5PD Tel: (01698) 328200 Fax: (01698) 328201 *Food manufrs*

Macphie of Glenbervie Ltd, Glenbervie, Stonehaven, Kincardineshire, AB39 3YG Tel: (01569) 740641 Fax: (01569) 740677 E-mail: cservice@macphie.com *Food ingredient manufrs*

▶ Mcphillips Wellington Ltd, Horton House, Hortonwood 50, Telford, Shropshire, TF1 7FG Tel: (01952) 670440 Fax: (01952) 670388 E-mail: mcphilps@mcphilips.co.uk

Macpower Ltd, 167 Cheviot Gardens, London, NW2 1PY Tel: (020) 8458 2793 Fax: (020) 8458 8484 *International merchandising*

Macqueen Air Conditioning Ltd, 39-41 Carrholm Road, Leeds, LS7 2NQ Tel: 0113-393 0287 Fax: 0113-393 0284 E-mail: sales@macqueen-ac.co.uk *Air conditioning*

James M. McQueen & Son, 180 West Regent Street, Glasgow, G2 4RU Tel: 0141-248 4865 Fax: 0141-221 4114 *Chamois leather dressers & janitorial supplies*

▶ Mcqueen-Simon Consultancy, PO Box 50663, London, SW6 7QN Tel: (07957) 296196 Fax: (020) 7384 5415 E-mail: info@mcqueen-enterprises.com *Secretarial Services - audio typing, word processing, in-person dictation, databases graphs, mail merges, spreadsheets, tables, virtual assistance and office support.*

Mcquillan Civil Engineers, 11 Ballinderry Road, Lisburn, County Antrim, BT28 2SA Tel: (028) 9266 8831 Fax: (028) 9266 8832 E-mail: john@johnmcquillan.com *Civil engineering & road surfacing*

Mcquillan Signs, Cleves, Keymer Road, Burgess Hill, West Sussex, RH15 0AP Tel: (01444) 471847 Fax: (01444) 248592 E-mail: johntmcquillan@fsnet.co.uk *Signwriters & lettering services*

▶ Macrae Bros, Laide, Achnasheen, Ross-Shire, IV22 2NB Tel: (01445) 731315 Fax: (01445) 731138

D.M. Macrae, Sky Telematic Centre, 3 Broom Place, Portree, Isle Of Skye, IV51 9HL Tel: (01478) 613576 Fax: (01478) 613080 E-mail: shop@3dk.co.uk *Computer repair & manufrs*

Macrete Ireland Ltd, 50 Creagh Road, Toomebridge, Antrim, BT41 3SE Tel: (028) 7965 0471 Fax: (028) 7965 0084 E-mail: info@macrete.com *Macrete are one of the few truly independent precast concrete manufacturers within the United Kingdom and Ireland. Having over thirty years experience in the design and manufacture of a wide range of reinforced and pre-stressed concrete products and systems, Macrete are established at the forefront of the precast concrete industry. *Many types of precast concrete solutions are designed and supplied to the civil, rail, water, stadia, marine and agricultural markets. Using a superior distribution network Macrete successfully export products anywhere in the UK and Ireland. *Macrete believe in developing strong long-term partnerships with their client base. The majority of clients that work with Macrete do so on a repeat basis and their satisfaction is the fundamental objective. Macrete continually endeavour to evaluate the market place to increase market share and have experienced a steady increase in sales.*

Macro 4 plc, The Orangery, Turners Hill Road, Worth, Crawley, West Sussex, RH10 4SS Tel: (01293) 872000 Fax: (01293) 872001 E-mail: market@macro4.com *Software development services*

▶ Macro Art Ltd, 3 Hardwick Road, Great Gransden, Sandy, Bedfordshire, SG19 3BJ Tel: (01767) 677946 Fax: (01767) 677916

▶ Macro Business Equipment (UK) Ltd, 10 Clarke Street, Derby, DE1 2BU Tel: (01332) 227630 Fax: (0870) 7412899

Macro Marine Ltd, Unit 33 Station Road Industrial Estate, Estate, Hailsham, East Sussex, BN27 2ER Tel: (01323) 842331 Fax: 01323 842980 *Pump manufrs*

Mcrobb Display, 70 Montgomery Street, Edinburgh, EH7 5JA Tel: 0131-556 9633 Fax: 0131-556 7657 E-mail: info@mcrobb.co.uk *Exhibition display graphic producers*

MacRobins P.L.C., 40 Great Portland Street, London, W1W 7ND Tel: 08456 300740 Fax: 08456 300750 E-mail: postmaster@macrobins.co.uk *Insurance brokers & independent financial advisors*

Macrodyne Electronics Ltd, The Birches, Birches Lane, Newent, Gloucestershire, GL18 1DN Tel: (01531) 828010 Fax: (01531) 821153 E-mail: mailbox@macrodyne.com Principal Export Areas: West Europe & North America *Electronics design developments & manufacture - hardware, software & analogue*

Macron Safety Systems UK Ltd, Woodlands Road, Guildford, Surrey, GU1 1RN Tel: (01483) 572222 Fax: (01483) 302180 E-mail: info@macron-safety.com Principal Export Areas: Worldwide *Fire protection engineers*

▶ Mcrostie Leather Goods, The Harness Room, Bowfield Road, Howwood, Johnstone, Renfrewshire, PA9 1DB Tel: (01505) 705030 Fax: (01505) 705010 E-mail: sales@mcrostie.co.uk *Handmade leather goods manufrs*

Macrovision Europe Ltd, 14-18 Bell Street, Maidenhead, Berkshire, SL6 1BR Tel: (01628) 786100 Fax: (0870) 8711161 E-mail: info@macrovison.com *Software specialists*

Macs, Unit 5 Ashburton Park, Wheelforge Way, Trafford Park, Manchester, M17 1EH Tel: (0845) 2607711 Fax: 0161-272 7449 E-mail: support@macs-solutions.com *Garage & gate automation services, access control, barriers*

▶ Mac's Removals (Dorset) Ltd, Suite 7, Space Maker House, 518 Wallisdown Road, Bournemouth, BH11 8PT Tel: (01202) 535044

▶ Macs Sports, 4 Bridge Street, Cushendall, Ballymena, County Antrim, BT44 0RP Tel: (028) 2177 2121 Fax: (028) 2177 2315 *Sports goods equipment accessory manufrs*

Macsalvors Plant Hire Ltd, Newham Road, Truro, Cornwall, TR1 2SU Tel: (01872) 277123 Fax: (01872) 223340 E-mail: caneron@macsalvors.co.uk *Mobile crane hire services & machinery removal & heavy haulage* Also at: Plymouth & Redruth

Macscott Bond Ltd, PO Box 1, Loanhead, Midlothian, EH20 9SW Tel: 0131-448 2950 Fax: 0131-448 2941 *Hydraulic equipment suppliers*

Macsteel International UK Ltd, 1 Harbour Exchange Square, London, E14 9GE Tel: (020) 7971 5678 Fax: (020) 7531 9187 E-mail: admin@miuk.co.uk *Metal merchants & agents*

▶ Mactabilis, 26B Ramsay Ind Est, Glasgow Rd, Kirkintilloch, Glasgow, G66 1SH Tel: 0845 838 5573 Fax: 0845 838 5574 E-mail: kal@mactabilis.com *Mactabilis has over 17 years experience, training and qualifications in industrial; commercial; criminal; civil; investigation and security. We have worked with Corporate and Private clients, Public bodies and Authorities at the highest levels of clearance. With the onset and upsurge of technology, Mactabilis maintains a modern approach, comprising of the training, equipment and methods employed in all operations and consultancy.*

Mactac UK Ltd, Unit 4-6 Britannia Trade Centre, Ryehill Close, Lodge Farm Industrial Estate, Northampton, NN5 7UA Tel: (01604) 756521 Fax: (01604) 758150 E-mail: bridings@bemis.com *Manufacturers of self adhesive materials.*

▶ Mactaggart Bros, Oakwell Road, Castle Douglas, Kirkcudbrightshire, DG7 1LE Tel: (01556) 503791 Fax: (01556) 504003

Mactaggart Scott (Holdings) Ltd, PO Box 1, Loanhead, Midlothian, EH20 9SP Tel: 0131-440 0311 Fax: 0131-440 4493 *Hydraulic & marine engineers*

Mctaggart Shipping & Management Co. Ltd, 1 Great Cumberland Place, London, W1H 7AL Tel: (020) 7468 8500 Fax: (020) 7468 8625 E-mail: chadring@macnav.com *Ship brokers*

Mactapes Ltd, Heatherside, Stalybridge, Cheshire, SK15 2QN Tel: 0161-303 2244 Fax: 0161-303 2244 *Curtain tape manufrs*

▶ Mactavish Consulting Ltd, Unit L13 South Fens Business Centre Fenton Way, Chatteris, Cambridgeshire, PE16 6TT Tel: (01354) 694073 Fax: (01354) 694073 E-mail: mactavishconsult@btconnect.com *Consulting agents*

Mctavish Ramsay & Co. Ltd, Fowler Road, West Pitkerro Industrial Estate, Broughty Ferry, Dundee, DD5 3RN Tel: (01382) 737722 Fax: (01382) 480054 E-mail: sales@mctavish-ramsay.com *Timber door manufrs*

Mactherapy Consulting Ltd, Unit 41 Kings Exchange, Tileyard Road, London, N7 9AH Tel: (020) 7700 0044 Fax: (020) 7700 7071 *Computer consultants*

▶ Macuncle.Com, 2a Blakeney Road, Beckenham, Kent, BR3 1HA Tel: (07740) 796183 Fax: E-mail: eamon@macuncle.com *Repair & advices services for apple mac computers*

Mcveigh Parker & Co Ltd, Southend Road, Southend, Reading, RG7 6HA Tel: (0845) 1207755 Fax: 0118-974 4123 E-mail: sales@mcveighparker.co.uk *Agricultural fencing retailers*

Mcveigh Technical Solutions Ltd, PO Box 407, Leicester, LE3 8ZA Tel: 0116-232 1181 Fax: 0116-232 1186 *Air conditioning & ventilation*

Mcveigh-Parker & Co. Ltd, Six Acre Farm, Stane Street, Adversane, Billingshurst, West Sussex, RH14 9JR Tel: (01403) 784250 Fax: (01403) 786394 E-mail: sales@mcveighparker.co.uk *Agricultural, landscaping & fencing equipment*

Mcvities, Victoria Biscuit Works, 35 Clydeford Drive, Glasgow, G32 8YW Tel: 0141-550 6800 Fax: 0141-554 8601 *Manufacturer of biscuits*

Mcvities Cake Co., Kingston Mills, Hopwood Lane, Halifax, West Yorkshire, HX1 4EY Tel: (01422) 360697 Fax: (01422) 330284 *Cake manufrs*

Mcvities Group Ltd, Waxlow Road, London, NW10 7NY Tel: (020) 8965 5787 Fax: (020) 8965 8496 *Manufacturer of biscuits*

Macward Steel Slitting Services Ltd, Unit 3 Polo Grounds, New Inn, Pontypool, Gwent, NP4 0TW Tel: (01495) 751122 Fax: (01495) 762369 E-mail: salesoffice@macwards.co.uk *Steel stockholders*

Macwhirter Ltd, 5 Stoke View Business Park, Stoke View Road, Bristol, BS16 3AE Tel: 0117-939 6661 Fax: 0117-939 6662 E-mail: sales@macwhirter.co.uk *Air conditioning engineers* Also at: Cardiff

▶ Macwilliam, Hollandhurst Road, Coatbridge, Lanarkshire, ML5 2EG Tel: (01236) 421222 Fax: (01236) 422025

Mcwilliam Sailmakers Ltd, Cowes Yacht Haven, Vectis Yard, Cowes, Isle of Wight, PO31 7AY Tel: (01983) 281100 Fax: (01983) 281101 E-mail: keith@mcwsales.co.uk *Sail makers*

Mcwiltons Ltd, 4 Basin Road North, Portslade, Brighton, BN41 1WA Tel: (01273) 423733 Fax: (01273) 430836 *Export packers*

MacXperts Ltd, London, W4 3UW Tel: (0871) 5504050 Fax: (020) 8181 7798 E-mail: info@macxperts.com *Computer consultants*

▶ Mad About Wheels, Grange Road, Basildon, Essex, SS13 2LW Tel: (01268) 725656

The Mad Cow Puzzles Ltd, 2 Weycroft Avenue, Axminster, Devon, EX13 5HU Tel: (01297) 35577 Fax: (01297) 33883 E-mail: info@madcowpuzzles.co.uk *Logic puzzles manufrs*

Maday Automatics, 42 Boyslade Road East, Burbage, Hinckley, Leicestershire, LE10 2RQ Tel: (01455) 636848 Fax: (01455) 617516 *Gaming machine hire*

Madden Construction & Display Ltd, Unit 26-27 Watery La Industrial Estate, Watery Lane, Willenhall, West Midlands, WV13 3SU Tel: (01902) 366234 Fax: (01902) 366500 *Exhibition contractors shopfitters*

Madden & Layman, Unit C2, 20 Theaklen Drive, Ponswood Industrial Estate, St. Leonards-On-Sea, East Sussex, TN38 9AZ Tel: (01424) 715977 Fax: (01424) 715320 *Contact lens manufrs*

▶ Maddison, 25 Hatton Garden, London, EC1N 8BQ Tel: (020) 7831 8122 Fax: (020) 7242 1988 E-mail: info@madisondiamondrings.co.uk *Madison Diamond & Wedding Ring Specialist*Specialists in certified diamonds, quality engagement and wedding rings in gold and platinum. Highly recommended, our professional salesteam will make your visit an enjoyable and memorable occasion.*Open Mon - Sat 9am - 5pm, Sun am - 2pm**

Maddison Commercial Printers, Knaves Beech Business Centre, Knaves Beech Indust Estate Knaves Beech Way, Loudwater, High Wycombe, Buckinghamshire, HP10 9QY Tel: (01628) 530717 Fax: (01628) 819459 E-mail: sales@worldofenvelopes.com *Envelope printing services*

Maddison Water Technology, 39 Cley Hall Drive, Spalding, Lincolnshire, PE11 2EB Tel: (01775) 725131 Fax: (01775) 760730 E-mail: sales@maddisonwatertech.co.uk *Irrigation contractors*

Maddox Ford Ltd, Rosedale House, Rosedale Road, Richmond, Surrey, TW9 2SZ Tel: (020) 8939 9048 Fax: (020) 8939 9090 *IT consultancy*

Made in Portugal, Unit 4, Mews House, Princes Lane, Muswell Hill, London, N10 3LU Tel: (0845) 232 0001 Fax: (0845) 232 0007 E-mail: info@madeinportugal.co.uk *B2B Portal for products made from Portugal **Connecting Buyers with Portuguese Suppliers*

Madeira Engineering, Queens Road, Southall, Middlesex, UB2 5BA Tel: (020) 8571 4627 Fax: (020) 8843 0292 *General engineering services*

Madeley Brass Castings, Unit B8 Court Works Industrial Estate, Bridgnorth Road, Madeley, Telford, Shropshire, TF7 4JB Tel: (01952) 583004 Fax: (01952) 583004 *Brass casting manufrs*

Madeley & Glaze Ltd, 8 The Benyon Centre, Walsall, WS2 7NQ Tel: 01922 407717 *Precision toolmakers*

▶ Maden Design & Build, Old Schoolhouse, North Greenwich Road, Spittal, Berwick-Upon-Tweed, TD15 1RG Tel: (01289) 332204

Howard Maden Machine Tools, 23 High Street, Rawcliffe, Goole, East Yorkshire, DN14 8QQ Tel: (01405) 839376 Fax: (01405) 839008 *Machine tool reconditioners*

Maderite Designers, 102 Greenheath Business Centre, Three Colts Lane, London, E2 6JB Tel: (020) 7739 6602 Fax: (020) 7739 6602 E-mail: victorsims@macumltd.net *Clothing manufrs*

Madewell Products Ltd, Sandy Way, Tamworth, Staffordshire, B77 4DS Tel: (01827) 67721 Fax: (01827) 67721 E-mail: sales@madewellproducts.co.uk *Industrial gates, rail & laser manufrs*

Madico Graphic Films Ltd, 9 Cordwallace Park, Clivemont Road, Maidenhead, Berkshire, SL6 7BU Tel: (01628) 777766 Fax: (01628) 776666 E-mail: info@madico.co.uk *Self adhesive plastic film distributors*

▶ Madison Avenue, 5 Stanford House, Princess Margaret Road, East Tilbury, Tilbury, Essex, RM18 8YP Tel: (01375) 840022 E-mail: enquires@madavesalon.co.uk *pharmacology anti-aging scars inch loss anti-wrinkle Danne skin revision treatment sun damage rehydration fine lines enzymes, toxins styling cutting Harley street trained staff*Hair straightening opti-smooth wedding specialists matrix clear skin spots face peels permenant beauty Danne Crystal Clear skin resurfacing waxing manicure pedicure massage and body sculpting East Tilbury Essex*hair styling extensions replacement Mane connection cellulite removal*acne scarring frown lip lines pigmentation marks stretch marks exfoliation body wrap micro epidermal skin system rejuvenation human hair tuition replacement extensions pigmentation, microdermabrasion*

Company Information

Madison Filter, Knowsley Road Industrial Estate, Haslingden, Rossendale, Lancashire, BB4 4EJ Tel: (01706) 213421 Fax: (01706) 221916 E-mail: info@madisonfilter.com *Dust & liquid solid filtration*

Madison Grant, Freightmaster Estate, Ferry Lane, Rainham, Essex, RM13 9BJ Tel: (01708) 477377 Fax: (01708) 456552 E-mail: madisongrant@freeserve.co.uk *Manufacturing of stainless steel*

Madison Hosiery, Mill Green, Leeds, LS12 6HE Tel: 0113-244 3434 Fax: 0113-242 5634 *Hosiery distributors & wholesalers*

Madison Wire (Europe) Ltd, Madison House, Davyfield Road, Roman Road Industrial Estate, Blackburn, BB1 2LU Tel: (01254) 663555 Fax: (01254) 663222 E-mail: info@madison-wire.co.uk *Wire & cables manufrs*

Maelor Feeds Ltd, Pandy Farm, Whitchurch Road, Bangor-on-Dee, Wrexham, Clwyd, LL13 0BL Tel: (01978) 780280 Fax: (01978) 780150 *Agricultural feed merchants*

Maelor Pharmaceuticals Ltd, Riversdale, Cae Gwilym Road, Newbridge, Wrexham, Clwyd, LL14 3JG Tel: (01978) 810153 Fax: (01978) 810169 E-mail: enquiries@maelor.plc.uk *Pharmaceutical device development designers*

Maelor-Trafflex Ltd, Wrexham Industrial Estate, Abbey Road, Wrexham, Clwyd, LL13 9RF Tel: (01978) 661040 Fax: (01978) 661450 E-mail: orders@maelortrafflex.co.uk *Street litter bins & vandal resistant lighting*

▶ Maersk Contractors, Maersk House, Greenbank Road, East Tullos Industrial Estate, Aberdeen, AB12 3BR Tel: (01224) 216600 Fax: (01224) 216609 *Shipping of oil & gas*

Maersk Line (UK), 58 Robertson Street, Glasgow, G2 8DU Tel: 0141-275 6380 Fax: 0141-248 3496 *Shipping line*

Maersk Logistics, Unit 6 Orwell House, Ferry Lane, Felixstowe, Suffolk, IP11 3AQ Tel: (01394) 614600 Fax: (01394) 614636 *Shipping company*

▶ Maersk Logistics UK Ltd, Blowfield Road, Felixstowe, Suffolk, IP11 4XQ Tel: (01394) 613206 Fax: (01394) 613207 E-mail: gbrlogsal@maersk-logistics.com

Maersk Sealand (UK), Silkhouse Court, Tithebarn Street, Liverpool, L2 2LZ Tel: (08703) 330804 Fax: 0151-236 4199 E-mail: lplmng@maersk.com *Shipping*

The Maersk Company UK Ltd, Maersk House, Brayham Street, London, E1 8EP Tel: (020) 7441 1439 Fax: (020) 7712 5100 E-mail: gbrmkt@maersk.com *Ship owners & liner agents*

Maestro Computer Services Ltd, 5 Smitham Bottom Lane, Purley, Surrey, CR8 3DE Tel: (020) 8763 9513 Fax: (020) 8763 0027 E-mail: mail@maestrocompserv.co.uk *Computer consultants*

Maestro International Ltd, 11-17 Powerscroft Road, Sidcup, Kent, DA14 5NH Tel: (020) 8302 4035 Fax: (020) 8302 8933 E-mail: info@maestrointl.co.uk *Drinking water coolers & fountains suppliers*

Maestro Solutions Ltd, 5 Woodland Road, Maple Cross, Rickmansworth, Hertfordshire, WD3 9ST Tel: (01923) 770856 Fax: (01923) 771143 E-mail: maestrosoloutions@aol.com *Computer software & hardware consultants*

▶ Mag Surveys, Europa Business Park, 46 Bird Hall Lane Unit F-10, Stockport, Cheshire, SK3 0XA Tel: 0161-718 8213 Fax: 0161-718 8213 E-mail: greg@magsurveys.co.uk *Land surveyors*

Magals Solutions Ltd, 258, Kingsland Road, London, E8 4DG Tel: (020) 7254 6481 Fax: (020) 7503 7959

Magazine Printing Co. P.L.C, 1082 Mollison Avenue, Brimsdown, Enfield, Middlesex, EN3 7NT Tel: (020) 8805 5000 Fax: (020) 8804 2432 E-mail: mpc@magprint.co.uk *Short run magazine printers*

Magchucks (UK), 16-22 Lodge Road, Hockley, Birmingham, B18 5PN Tel: 0121-551 1566 Fax: 0121-523 9188 *Milling & grinding engineers*

Magee Clothing Ltd, Unit 5-25 Woodside Road Industrial Estate, Woodside Road, Ballymena, County Antrim, BT42 4QJ Tel: (028) 2564 6211 Fax: (028) 2564 5111 E-mail: mageesales@aol.com *Menswear manufrs*

Magel Engineering Ltd, Headley Road East, Woodley, Reading, RG5 4SN Tel: 0118-969 2351 Fax: 0118-927 2307 Principal Export Areas: Worldwide *Manufacturer of car parts*

Magellan Aerospace Bournemouth, 510 Wallisdown Road, Bournemouth, BH11 8QN Tel: (01202) 517411 Fax: (01202) 530886 *Precision engineers*

▶ Magellan Capital, 51 Lowther Road, London, SW13 9NT Tel: (07976) 878417 Fax: (020) 8741 7702 E-mail: info@magellan-capital.com

▶ Magenta Chemicals, Golf Course Road, Southampton, SO16 7LE Tel: (023) 8076 8842 Fax: (023) 8076 6460 E-mail: magentachemicals@btclick.com *Chemical distributor*

Magenta Electronic Ltd, 135 Hunter Street, Burton-on-Trent, Staffordshire, DE14 2ST Tel: (01283) 565435 Fax: (01283) 546932 E-mail: sales@magenta2000.co.uk *Electronic kits & parts designers & providers*

Magenta Technology Ltd, 36 Holme Lacy Road, Hereford, HR2 6BY Tel: (01432) 278296 Fax: (01432) 340388 E-mail: enquiries@magenta-tech.com *Photocopiers & fax machines supplies & services*

▶ Maggie Carol Ltd, Unit 1 & 2, Fallbarn Road, Rossendale, Lancashire, BB4 7NT Tel: (01706) 228879

▶ Maggot Inn, 193 Upminster Road South, Rainham, Essex, RM13 9BB Tel: (01708) 526652 *Fishing tackle retailers*

Maghera Joinery Works Ltd, 100 Glen Road, Maghera, County Londonderry, BT46 5JG Tel: (028) 7964 2501 Fax: (028) 7964 4181 E-mail: info@beavercabinets.co.uk *Kitchen housing & doors contract kitchen manufrs*

Magiboards Ltd, Unit F, Stafford Park 12, Telford, Shropshire, TF3 3BJ Tel: (01952) 292111 Fax: (01952) 292280 E-mail: sales@magiboards.co.uk *Manufacturers & Suppliers of Presentation & Display equipment*

▶ Magic Bean & Cow Ltd., 93-97 Gowe Street, London, WC1E 6AD Tel: 07841 841319 Fax: 0207 9169686 E-mail: info@magicbeanandcow.co.uk *Professional cleaning for properties across London and Manchester. Regular domestic and end of tenancy cleans. Carpet shampooing and offices.*

▶ Magic Box Products Ltd, The Grange, Market Square, Westerham, Kent, TN16 1AR Tel: (01959) 562220 *Telecommunication equipment suppliers*

▶ Magic Breaks, Linotype House, Norman Road, Altrincham, Cheshire, WA14 1LP Tel: 0161 927 4777 E-mail: holidays@magicbreaks.com *Magic Breaks is an award-winning, call centre and web based travel agency, specialising in world-wide leisure travel. Magic Breaks can discount every tour operator's brochure price guaranteeing the best deals on the market.*

▶ Magic Maids, 7 Charmian Avenue, Stanmore, Middlesex, HA7 1LL Tel: (020) 8931 8921 E-mail: sales@magic-maids.co.uk *Professional cleaning company serving NW London area. We do;*** Domestic and Office cleaning** Regular or One off cleans** Spring /Carpet cleans** Pre / Post Tenancy cleans** Builders Cleans**A company with over twenty years of cleaning experience!*

▶ Magic Man Ltd, Gordon House, 15 Gordon Road, Portslade, Brighton, BN41 1GL Tel: (01273) 417110 Fax: (0845) 4581011 E-mail: info@magicman.ltd.uk *Repair specialist*

Magic Mitre Ltd, 3 Newton Court, Basingstoke, Hampshire, RG24 8GF Tel: 01256 478498 *D I Y tool retailers*

▶ Magic Pencil, 16 Upper Meadow Road, Birmingham, B32 1NX Tel: (0870) 2863881 Fax: (0870) 2863882 E-mail: creative@magicpencil.co.uk *Graphic design & illustration services for business stationery*

▶ Magic Signs, 167 Ash Hill Road, Ash, Aldershot, Hampshire, GU12 5DW Tel: (01252) 337776 Fax: (01252) 337776 E-mail: sales@magicsigns.co.uk *Sign manufrs*

Magic Systems Ltd, Unit 3 Sandridge Park, Porters Wood, St. Albans, Hertfordshire, AL3 6PH Tel: (01727) 855511 Fax: (01727) 864351 E-mail: sales@magicgroup.com *Computer consultancy*

▶ Magic Touch, 63 Barnton Street, Stirling, FK8 1HH Tel: (01786) 445992 Fax: (01786) 434922

Magic Video Co., 17 The Moat, Puckeridge, Ware, Hertfordshire, SG11 1SJ Tel: (01920) 821003 Fax: (01920) 821003 E-mail: robert-hamilton@btconnect.com *Video production service providers*

Magical Marking Ltd, Roall, Goole, North Humberside, DN14 0NA Tel: (01977) 662500 Fax: (01977) 663000 *Playground marking equipment suppliers*

▶ Magicboxgifts, Optec House, Westfield Avenue, Wigston, Leicester, LE18 1HY Tel: 0116-229 0232 Fax: 0116-229 0232 E-mail: sales@magicboxgifts.co.uk *UK Trade cards, paper, ephemera, rare toys and collectible specialists including Postcards, Royal memorabilia, Limited edition toys and many sought after newspapers and magazines.*

Magictype Computer Consumables, 22 Swallow Rise, Knaphill, Woking, Surrey, GU21 2LG Tel: (01483) 888813 Fax: (01483) 888814 E-mail: magictype@ntlworld.com *Printer cartridge distributors*

Magill Menswear, 45 Ashgrove Road, Newry, County Down, BT34 1QN Tel: (028) 3026 1311 Fax: (028) 3026 2930 E-mail: magillgroup@btconnect.com *Clothing wholesale distributors*

▶ Maginus Software Solutions, Dallimore Road, Roundthorn Industrial Estate, Manchester, M23 9NX Tel: 0161-953 0000 Fax: 0161-945 3806 E-mail: mail@maginus.com *Software suppliers*

Magisco Valves Ltd, 53 Limes Road, Wolverhampton, WV6 8RD Tel: (01902) 561111 *Control valve distributors*

Magma Fabrication (Glenrothes) Ltd, 21 Faraday Road, Southfield Industrial Estate, Glenrothes, Fife, KY6 2RU Tel: (01592) 773046 Fax: (01592) 773046 E-mail: admin@magmafabrication.co.uk *Stainless steel fabricators*

Magna Colours Ltd, 3 Dodworth Business Park, Upper Cliffe Road, Dodworth, Barnsley, South Yorkshire, S75 3SP Tel: (01226) 731751 Fax: (01226) 731752 E-mail: sales@magnacolours.com *Textile printing chemical producers services*

Magna Display Systems Ltd, Unit 13 Alliance Close, Attleborough Fields Industrial Estate, Nuneaton, Warwickshire, CV11 6SD Tel: (024) 7632 0032 Fax: (024) 7635 0213 E-mail: info@magnadisplaysystems.co.uk *Complete sign & display service*

Magna Electronics Ltd, 9 Harrow Road, Hereford, HR4 0EH Tel: (01432) 353434 Fax: (01432) 278749 E-mail: mark@magna-electronics.co.uk *Printed circuit assembly manufrs*

Magna Frequency Management Ltd, Magna House Dales Manor Business Park, Grove Road, Sawston, Cambridge, CB2 4TJ Tel: (01223) 834800 Fax: (01223) 834600 E-mail: sales@magnafrequency.com *Crystal & quartz crystal suppliers & crystal oscillator manufrs*

Magna Machinery, Parrotts Grove Works, Aldermans Green Rd, Coventry, CV2 1NP Tel: (024) 7664 5084 Fax: (024) 7664 5085 *Machine tools*

▶ Magna Safety Products Ltd, Unit 1, Industrial Estate, London Road, Pampisford, Cambridge, CB22 3EE Tel: (01223) 836643 Fax: (01223) 834648 E-mail: info@magnasafety.co.uk *Manufactures of anti slip products*

Magna Systems Ltd, Oakridge House, Plane Tree Way, Woodstock, Oxfordshire, OX20 1PG Tel: (01993) 811282 Fax: (01993) 813330 E-mail: pidoux1@aol.com *Canopies manufrs*

Magnacom Ltd, Crossford Mill, Beith Road, Kilbarchan, Johnstone, Renfrewshire, PA10 2NS Tel: (01505) 706000 Fax: (01505) 706067 E-mail: office@magnacom.co.uk *Computer systems manufrs*

▶ Magnadata International Ltd, Norfolk Street, Boston, Lincolnshire, PE21 6AF Tel: (01205) 310031 Fax: (01205) 312612 E-mail: sales@magnadata.co.uk *Ticketing tagging, magnetic tickets, parking, leisure & bespoke*

Magnaflux, Faraday Road, Dorcan, Swindon, SN3 5HE Tel: (01793) 524566 Fax: (01793) 619498 E-mail: sales@magnaflux.co.uk Principal Export Areas: Worldwide *Crack detection systems. In addition, magnetic particle inspection machinery & non-destructive test equipment/ systems manufrs*

Magnapower Equipment Ltd, 11 North Street Industrial Estate, Droitwich, Worcestershire, WR9 8JB Tel: (01905) 779157 Fax: (01905) 779867 E-mail: info@magnapower.co.uk *The Magnapower group has been established for over thirty years and has been supplying magnetic separation equipment to a wide variety of industries including the recycling industry, metals recovery (both ferrous and non ferrous), food processing and mineral processing.**We supply:**Eddy Current Separator, Overband Magnet, Drum Magnet, Magnetic Head Pulley, Can Sorter, Tyre Wire Separation Plant, WEEE Processing Plant and Material Recycling Facilities**

Magnasign Ltd, Orchard Hill, Rudgwick, Horsham, West Sussex, RH12 3EQ Tel: (01403) 822280 E-mail: languagelabsuk@aol.com *Telesales digital language laboratories*

▶ Magnate Grey Box Ltd, Airport Business Centre, 10 Thornbury Road, Estover, Plymouth, PL6 7PP Tel: (0845) 0702490 Fax: (0845) 0702495 E-mail: enquires@mgbl.co.uk *Provider of fully integrated solutions for electrical control housing*

Magnatec Ltd, Coventry Road, Lutterworth, Leicestershire, LE17 4JB Tel: (01455) 554711 Fax: (01455) 558843 E-mail: sales@semelab.co.uk *Semi-conductor components distributors*

Magne-Flo Excess Flow Valves Ltd, Alcester Road, Portway, Birmingham, B48 7HX Tel: (01564) 822383 Fax: (01564) 824712 E-mail: enquiries@magne-flo.co.uk *Safety shut-off gas valves manufrs*

▶ Magnel Ltd, Unit 11 Mercury Units, Tir Llwyd Enterprise Park, Kinmel Bay, Rhyl, Clwyd, LL18 5JZ Tel: (01745) 338000 Fax: (01745) 338000 E-mail: sales@magnel.com *Moulders (GRP)*

Magnet Ltd, 12 St Machar Road, Aberdeen, AB24 2UU Tel: (01224) 492894 Fax: (01224) 488276 *Joiners*

Magnet Ltd, Units 6 & 7 Pines Way Industrial Estate, Ivo Peters Road, Bath, BA2 3QS Tel: (01225) 335659 Fax: (01225) 448684 *Home improvement & manufrs*

▶ Magnet Ltd, Victoria House Corner, 24 London Road, Hadleigh, Benfleet, Essex, SS7 2QP Tel: (01702) 553112 Fax: (01702) 551892 E-mail: hadliegh.branch@magnet.co.uk *Kitchen sales*

Magnet Ltd, 1581 Pershore Road, Stirchley, Birmingham, B30 2JF Tel: 0121-451 3001 Fax: 0121-458 5750 *Doors, windows & kitchens distributor & manufrs*

Magnet Ltd, Spa Road, Bolton, BL1 4SL Tel: (01204) 521611 Fax: (01204) 364779 *Joinery manufrs*

Magnet Ltd, 390 Newport Road, Cardiff, CF23 9AE Tel: (029) 2047 3366 Fax: (029) 2048 0170 E-mail: sales@magnetexpress.com *Joinery centre, kitchen & bedroom showroom*

Magnet Ltd, 253-255 Old Heath Road, Colchester, CO2 8BN Tel: (01206) 794233 Fax: (01206) 798832 *Kitchen & joinery resellers*

Magnet Ltd, Allington Way, Darlington, County Durham, DL1 4XT Tel: (01325) 481177 Fax: (01325) 744379 *Diy distributors & joinery manufrs*

Magnet Ltd, 60 Grieve Street, Dunfermline, Fife, KY12 8DW Tel: (01383) 720155 Fax: (01383) 620615 *Kitchen & joinery manufrs*

Magnet Ltd, 66 Twyford Road, Eastleigh, Hampshire, SO50 4HN Tel: (023) 8061 3581 Fax: (023) 8061 2791 *Kitchen planners or installation, joinery manufrs*

Magnet Ltd, Ambley Road, Gillingham Business Park, Gillingham, Kent, ME8 0PU Tel: (01634) 377242 Fax: (01634) 379047 *Joinery*

Magnet Ltd, Woodbridge Road, Guildford, Surrey, GU1 1DP Tel: (01483) 565411 Fax: (01483) 536522 *Kitchen & bedroom door sales & manufrs*

Magnet Ltd, 2a Hillbottom Road, Sands Industrial Estate, High Wycombe, Buckinghamshire, HP12 4HJ Tel: (01494) 445243 Fax: (01494) 538685 E-mail: highwycombe@magnettrade.co.uk *Kitchen units manufrs*

Magnet Ltd, Rotterdam Road, Hull, HU7 0XD Tel: (01482) 825451 Fax: (01482) 830241 *Joinery & kitchen manufrs*

Magnet Ltd, 78 Wigmore Street, London, W1U 2SL Tel: (020) 7486 8711 Fax: (020) 7486 3264 E-mail: wigmorestreet.branch@magnet.co.uk *Fitted kitchens*

Magnet Ltd, 593-613 Old Kent Road, London, SE15 1LA Tel: (020) 7639 2128 Fax: (020) 7252 8117 *Kitchens & joinery products distributors*

Magnet Ltd, 153 Hurlingham Road, London, SW6 3NN Tel: (020) 7731 7304 Fax: (020) 7384 2217 *Kitchen joinery & fitting*

Magnet Ltd, 5 Leagrave Street, London, E5 9QX Tel: (020) 8985 6382 Fax: (020) 8986 0489 *Joinery manufrs*

Magnet Ltd, 65-67 Holmes Road, London, NW5 3AN Tel: (020) 7267 1149 Fax: (020) 7267 1149 E-mail: kentish.branch@magnet.co.uk *Kitchen manufrs*

Magnet Ltd, 2 Salter Street, London, NW10 6UN Tel: (020) 8960 4333 Fax: (020) 8964 0271 E-mail: willesden.branch@magnet.co.uk *Appliance wholesalers & joiners*

Magnet Ltd, 2 Morley Street, Nottingham Road, Loughborough, Leicestershire, LE11 1EW Tel: (01509) 610484 Fax: (01509) 235990 E-mail: loughbroug.branch@magnet.co.uk *Kitchen & bedroom joiners*

Magnet Ltd, Sutton Road, Mansfield, Nottinghamshire, NG18 5HT Tel: (01623) 622359 Fax: (01623) 421049 E-mail: mansfield.branch@magnet.co.uk *Joinery products manufrs*

Magnet Ltd, 108h Market Street, Musselburgh, Midlothian, EH21 6QA Tel: 0131-665 2451 Fax: 0131-653 3302 *Joiners suppliers*

Magnet Ltd, Leeway Industrial Estate, Newport, Gwent, NP19 4SL Tel: (01633) 274795 Fax: (01633) 277276 *Kitchen manufrs*

Magnet Ltd, 171 Mile Cross Lane, Norwich, NR6 6RE Tel: (01603) 429428 Fax: (01603) 406658 *Joinery kitchens suppliers & manufrs*

Magnet Ltd, Dunkeld Road, Perth, PH1 3AA Tel: (01738) 634007 Fax: (01738) 643764 *Home improvements, joinery*

Magnet Ltd, Fengate, Peterborough, PE1 5PE Tel: (01733) 558211 Fax: (01733) 563664 *Kitchen & joinery product manufrs*

Magnet Ltd, Transit Way, Plymouth, PL5 3TW Tel: (01752) 703755 Fax: (01752) 766804 *Fitted furniture*

Magnet Ltd, 45-51 Barnet Road, Potters Bar, Hertfordshire, EN6 2QY Tel: (01707) 651213 Fax: (01707) 650159 *Kitchen & home improvement services*

Magnet Ltd, Newington Road, Ramsgate, Kent, CT12 6ED Tel: (01843) 583147 Fax: (01843) 596276 *Joiners & kitchen manufrs*

Magnet Ltd, Unit 3a Redhill Distribution Centre, Salbrook Road, Redhill, RH1 5DY Tel: (01293) 824277 Fax: (01293) 824287 *Joinery manufrs*

Magnet Ltd, King George Close, Romford, RM7 7PN Tel: (01708) 755388 Fax: (01708) 746349 *Kitchens & joinery*

Magnet Ltd, Midland Sawmills, Broughton Road, Skipton, North Yorkshire, BD23 1RT Tel: (01756) 798011 Fax: (01756) 700408 *Kitchen manufrs*

Magnet Ltd, Polebarn Road, Trowbridge, Wiltshire, BA14 7EG Tel: (01225) 763058 Fax: (01225) 768254 E-mail: trowbridge.branch@magnet.co.uk *Joinery manufrs*

Magnet Ltd, Rosehill, Willenhall, West Midlands, WV13 2AR Tel: (01902) 366330 Fax: (01902) 602328 *Joiners*

Magnet Ltd, 2 Tebay Road, Wirral, Merseyside, CH62 3QJ Tel: 0151-334 6169 Fax: 0151-334 6122 *Kitchen, window & bedroom fittings*

Magnet Ltd, Kettlestring Lane, York, YO30 4XF Tel: (01904) 691962 Fax: (01904) 693134 *Joinery manufrs*

Magnet Kitchens, Longfield Road, Tunbridge Wells, Kent, TN2 3UR Tel: (01892) 514427 Fax: (01892) 539215 *Kitchen retail & building joinery suppliers*

Magnet Retail, Phoenix House, 315-323 High Street, Sutton, Surrey, SM1 1NH Tel: (020) 8643 1234 Fax: (020) 8770 7115 *Kitchens manufrs*

Magnet Sales & Service Ltd, Unit 31, Blackworth Industrial Estate, Highworth, SN6 7NA Tel: (01793) 862100 Fax: (01793) 862101 E-mail: sales@magnetsales.co.uk *Manufacturers of industrial, assembly, permanent & separators magnetic*

▶ Magnet Works Ltd, 10 Wentworth Close, Worthing, West Sussex, BN13 2LQ Tel: (01903) 260035 Fax: (01903) 260035 E-mail: j.fletcher@magnet-works.co.uk *Advertising gifts & business*

Magnetex Sign Systems, 20 Junction Road, Saintfield, Ballynahinch, County Down, BT24 7JU Tel: (028) 9751 0093 Fax: (028) 9751 1044 *Sign installation & manufrs*

Magnetic Component Engineering (U K) Ltd, 1 Union Street, Luton, LU1 3AN Tel: (01582) 735226 Fax: (01582) 734226 E-mail: eurosales@mceproducts.com *Industrial magnet manufrs*

Magnetic Separations Ltd, 14 Meadowside Road, Sutton, Surrey, SM2 7PF Tel: (020) 8642 4413 Fax: (020) 8642 9476 E-mail: info@magneticseparations.com *Magnet (industrial) manufacturers & distributors or agents*

Magnetic Shields Ltd, Headcorn Road, Staplehurst, Tonbridge, Kent, TN12 0DS Tel: (01580) 891521 Fax: (01580) 893345 E-mail: sales@magneticshields.co.uk *Magnetic shield/sheet metal manufrs*

Magnetic Solutions, Unit B7, Crabtree Road, Thorpe Industrial Estate, Egham, Surrey, TW20 8RN Tel: (01784) 438666 Fax: (01784) 438777 E-mail: trushton@magsol.co.uk Principal Export Areas: Worldwide *Electromagnet & solenoid manufrs*

Magnetrol International UK Ltd, 1 Regent Business Centre, Jubilee Road, Burgess Hill, West Sussex, RH15 9TL Tel: (01444) 871313 Fax: (01444) 871317 E-mail: sales@magnetrol.co.uk *Manufacturers of flow switches*

▶ Magnetron Catering Equipment, 5-21 Carrock Road, Croft Business Park, Bromborough, Wirral, Merseyside, CH62 3RA Tel: (0870) 8400720 Fax: (08708) 740721 E-mail: sales@catmag.fsnet.co.uk *Catering equipment suppliers*

▶ Magnets4Life - Bioflow / Ecoflow Distributor, Manorcroft, School Road, Rayne, Braintree, Essex, CM77 6SR Tel: 01376 349993 Fax: 01376 349991 E-mail: vanessa@magnets4life.com *Bioflow magnotherapy bracelets & wrist bands. Magnetic collars, boots and coats for animals. Magnetic Fuel savers. Organic and fragrance free skincare range.*

Magnetto Topy Wheels UK Ltd, Holbrook Lane, Coventry, CV6 4QZ Tel: (024) 7666 7738 Fax: (024) 7666 7401 *Motor vehicle component manufrs*

Magnex Scientific Ltd, Oxford Industrial Park, 6 Mead Road, Yarnton, Oxford, OX5 1QU Tel: (01865) 853800 Fax: (01865) 842466 E-mail: sales@magnex.com *Cryogenic equipment design & manufrs*

Magnum Aluminium Products (1993) Ltd, Units 3-4 Blackwater Close, Marsh Way, Rainham, Essex, RM13 8RH Tel: (01708) 522417 Fax: (01708) 525840 E-mail: gary@magnumaluminium.co.uk *Curtain walling systems fabricators*

Magnum Materials Ltd, Globe Lane Indust Estate Broadway, Dukinfield, Cheshire, SK16 4UU Tel: 0161-343 1131 Fax: 0161-343 1132 E-mail: sales@magnum-uk.com *Self-adhesives label stock suppliers*

Magnum Office Products, 4-5 Priestley Way, Crawley, West Sussex, RH10 9NT Tel: (01293) 547220 Fax: (01293) 543572 E-mail: ray.butler@magnumoffice.co.uk *Office furniture, equipment & stationary retailers*

Magnum Security Ltd, 50 Alexandra Rd, Acocks Green, Birmingham, B27 6HE Tel: 0121-706 0087 Fax: 0121-243 2712 *Security, alarm & cctv suppliers*

Magnum Venus Platech Ltd, MTC, Chilsworthy Beam, Gunnislake, Cornwall, PL18 9AT Tel: (01822) 832621 Fax: (01822) 833999 E-mail: rtm@plastech.co.uk *Injection equipment manufrs*

Magnum Venus Products, Stambermill Industrial Estate, Timmis Road, Stourbridge, West Midlands, DY9 7BJ Tel: (01384) 898589 Fax: (01384) 898394 E-mail: sales@mvpeurope.co.uk *Supply fibreglass equipment & release agents*

Magog Industries Ltd, Swains Mill, Crane Mead, Ware, Hertfordshire, SG12 9PY Tel: (01920) 465201 Fax: (01920) 463345 E-mail: enquiries@magog.co.uk *Screws, plastic extrusion & injection moulding services*

Magpie Computer Developments Ltd, The Old Telephone Exchange, Gnosall, Stafford, ST20 0EX Tel: (01785) 823315 E-mail: dtweed@magpieed.co.uk *Embedded micro-controllers*

Magpie Services, Derwent Howe Indust Estate, Adams Road, Derwent Howe Industrial Estate, Workington, Cumbria, CA14 3YS Tel: (01900) 872892 Fax: (01900) 67765 E-mail: magpie@thismove.com *Removals & delivery services*

Magpies Nest, 58 Tong Lane, Whitworth, Rochdale, Lancashire, OL12 8BE Tel: (01706) 853081 *Business & business systems*

Magson Stationery, Bluestem Road, Ransomes Industrial Estate, Ipswich, IP3 9RR Tel: (01473) 727667 Fax: (01473) 727863 *Stationery & card wholesalers*

Magtek Europe, Unit 25-26, Shrivenham Hundred Business Park, Majors Road, Watchfield, Swindon, SN6 8TZ Tel: (01793) 786070 Fax: (01793) 786076 E-mail: sales@magtek.co.uk *Credit & cheque reading specialists*

Maguire Boss, 24 East Street, St. Ives, Cambridgeshire, PE27 5PD Tel: (01480) 301588 Fax: (01480) 464405 E-mail: tmark@maguires.co.uk *European patent attorneys*

▶ Magzs Group, 13 Woodhouse Grove, London, E12 6SR Tel: 0794 0549770 Fax: 0208 4716016 E-mail: sales@magzs.com *High quality & innovative design sportswear*

▶ Mahan Fod, 21 Dragor Road, London, NW10 6JN Tel: (020) 8963 0012 Fax: (020) 8963 0090 *Food manufrs*

Maheono Alternative Therapies, 99 Reading Road, Yateley, Hampshire, GU46 7LR Tel: (01252) 861351 Fax: E-mail: info@maheono.com *Bowen Therapy Technique is a gentle yet powerful complementary therapy for treating shoulder pain, back pain, neck pain, frozen shoulder, chronic pain, shoulder pain, musculoskeletal, hip pain and sporting injuries in hampshire, berkshire, surrey, uk,*

Maher, 131 Canwick Road, Lincoln, LN5 8EY Tel: (01522) 885727 *Plant hire civil & engineers*

Maher Ltd, 2 Brightside Way, Sheffield, S9 2RQ Tel: 0114-290 9200 Fax: 0114-290 9290 E-mail: sales@maher.co.uk Principal Export Areas: Worldwide *Nickel alloy stockholders*

MAHLE Power Train Ltd, Costin House, St. James Mill Road, Northampton, NN5 5TZ Tel: (0870) 1573000 Fax: (0870) 1573100 E-mail: sales@gb.mahle.com *Design engine develop -high performance gasoline engine-car engines manufacturers. Also high performance road engines and high performance car engines.*

Mahler Investments Ltd, Mahler Ho, 130 Worcester Rd, Droitwich, Worcs, WR9 8AN Tel: (01905) 770024 Fax: (01905) 795233 *Property investment company*

Mahoney Associates Ltd, Stapleton Road, Bristol, BS5 0RB Tel: 0117-955 6800 Fax: 0117-935 0556 *Homological material supplier & wholesalers of clock & watch parts*

H.R. Maiden & Sons, Overley, Telford, Shropshire, TF6 5HD Tel: (01952) 740281 Fax: (01952) 740496 *Road transport, haulage & freight services*

Harry Maiden Ltd, Lowfield, Croft Road, Montrose, Angus, DD10 9NL Tel: (01674) 673222 Fax: (01674) 673299 E-mail: info@harrymaiden.co.uk *Steel fabricators*

Maidenbury Ltd, 360 Blackfen Road, Sidcup, Kent, DA15 9NY Tel: (020) 8303 4253 Fax: (020) 8303 4253 E-mail: kenhillard@maidenbury.co.uk *Printed circuit design services*

Maidenhead Aquatic Centre, Bourne End Garden Centre, Hedsor Road, Bourne End, Buckinghamshire, SL8 5EE Tel: (01628) 528882 Fax: (01628) 850429 *Supply fish, pond, & dry goods*

Maidenhead Aquatics Morden Water World, Morden Hall Road, Morden, Surrey, SM4 5JG Tel: (020) 8646 1066 Fax: (020) 8648 1414 E-mail: info@fishkeeper.co.uk *Aquatics equipment retailers*

Maidenhead Machine Tool Co. Ltd, PO Box 833, Bourne End, Buckinghamshire, SL8 5YR Tel: (01628) 526345 Fax: (01628) 810732 E-mail: mmtools@msn.com *Machine tool merchants*

Maidenhead Plating, 3 Martin Road, Maidenhead, Berkshire, SL6 7DE Tel: (01628) 783747 Fax: (01628) 778717 *Electroplating*

▶ Maidenhead Tile Centre, 20 Cannon Court Road, Maidenhead, Berkshire, SL6 7QN Tel: (01628) 776333 Fax: (01628) 789206 E-mail: sales@maidenheadtiles.co.uk *Tile retailers*

▶ Maids for You, 120 Mow Lane, Gillow Heath, Stoke-on-Trent, ST8 6RJ Tel: (01782) 515541 E-mail: avrily@aol.com *Domestic Services With A Difference!*Domestic Cleaning Packages*Friendly Dog Walking Services*Free Collection & Delivery Ironing Service*

Maidstone & Mid Kent Chamber Of Commerce Industry Training, Westree Road, Maidstone, Kent, ME16 8HB Tel: (01622) 695544 Fax: (01622) 682513 E-mail: sales@inmaidstone.com *Chamber of commerce*

Maidstone Trimming Co., 12 The Downs, Chatham, Kent, ME5 9RA Tel: (01622) 690707 E-mail: maidstonetrim@aol.com *Motor vehicle trimmers & upholsterer*

Mail Marketing International Ltd, Springfield House, West Street, Bedminster, Bristol, BS3 3NX Tel: 0117-966 6900 Fax: 0117-963 6737 E-mail: sales@formpromm.co.uk *Direct communications & printing company*

Mail Marketing (Scotland) Ltd, 42 Methil Street, Glasgow, G14 0SZ Tel: 0141-950 2222 Fax: 0141-950 2726 E-mail: glasgow@mailmarkscot.com *Circular distribution services*

Mail News & Media Ltd, Blundells Corner, Beverley Road, Hull, HU3 1XS Tel: (01482) 327111 Fax: (01482) 584314 *Book, magazine & newspaper publisher*

▶ Mail Order Systems Ltd, Unit 3, Mercia Business Village, Torwood Close, Westwood Business Park, Coventry, CV4 8HX Tel: (024) 7688 3434 Fax: (024) 7688 3773

▶ Mail Shot International Ltd, Unit 2 Park House, Greenhill Crescent, Watford Business Park, Watford, WD18 8PH Tel: (01923) 800422 Fax: (01923) 800433 E-mail: info@mailshotinternational.co.uk *Mail Shot International is a UK based mailing house providing laser printing,full data management and mailing services for a successful direct mail project.*

Mail Source, 3a St Leonards Industrial Estate, Aston Road, Bedford, MK42 0LJ Tel: (01234) 405555 Fax: (01234) 363025 *Microfilm, scanning services & document management*

▶ Mailboosters, The Gables, Holt Hill, Beoley, Redditch, Worcestershire, B98 9AT Tel: (0870) 4421862 Fax: (0870) 0664267 E-mail: enquiries@responsegeneration.co.uk *We generate sales for business using the techniques of direct marketing*

Mailbox Mouldings International Ltd, Bayley Street, Stalybridge, Cheshire, SK15 1QQ Tel: 0161-330 5577 Fax: 0161-330 5576 E-mail: ch@mailboxmouldings.co.uk *The Swift Division offers one of Europe's most comprehensive ranges of materials-handling containers in addition to an ever-increasing number of products for other market areas. This Mailbox E-catalogue represents industrial mail-order at its very best. We have taken into account the time pressures of today's busy buyers and responded to them with a mail-order system which offers simplicity of ordering coupled with first-class products.*

Mailboxes Etc (UK) Ltd, 8 Camp Road, Farnborough, Hampshire, GU14 6EW Tel: (01252) 371711 Fax: (01252) 371811 E-mail: info@mbefarnborough.co.uk *International couriers*

Mailboxes Etc (UK) Ltd, 19-21 Crawford Street, London, W1H 1PJ Tel: (020) 7224 2666 Fax: (020) 7224 2777 E-mail: peter@mailboxes-etc.co.uk *Business services*

Mailcom P.L.C., Snowdon Drive, Winterhill, Milton Keynes, MK6 1HQ Tel: (0870) 5888222 Fax: (0870) 1261335 E-mail: info@mailcom.co.uk *Direct marketing services*

Mailflight Ltd, Unit 2 Central Way, Feltham, Middlesex, TW14 0RX Tel: (020) 8893 1477 Fax: (020) 8893 1459 E-mail: ops@mfcourier.com *International courier & mail specialist*

Mailing & Mechanisation UK Ltd, Thistle House, Baird Close, Drayton Fields Industrial Estate, Daventry, Northamptonshire, NN11 8RY Tel: (01327) 315031 Fax: (01327) 315231 E-mail: info@mailingandmech.com *Mail house equipment distributors*

▶ Mailing Solutions UK Ltd, Trident House, Anchor Court, Commercial Road, Darwen, Lancashire, BB3 0DB Tel: (0845) 3311007 Fax: (0845) 3311008 E-mail: enquiries@mailingsolutionsuk.co.uk *Mail room equipment sales*

Mailings International Ltd, Unit 10, The Demcora Centre, Campfield Road, St. Albans, Hertfordshire, AL1 5HN Tel: (01727) 836062 Fax: (01727) 848863 *Overseas mailing & distribs*

Mailord Mail Order Services Ltd, 115 Park Avenue, Potters Bar, Hertfordshire, EN6 5EW Tel: (01707) 662442 Fax: (01707) 664180 E-mail: mike@mailord.co.uk *Computer services, consultants & computer software house*

Mailshot Services, 21 Upper Priory Street, Grafton Street Industrial Estate, Northampton, NN1 2PT Tel: (01604) 622290 Fax: (01604) 622290 *Mailing services*

Mailtime Services Ltd, 490 Gorton Road, Reddish, Stockport, Cheshire, SK5 6PP Tel: 0161-223 0044 Fax: 0161-223 0055 *Mailing house, direct & international mailing services*

Mailway Northern Holdings Ltd, 12-16 Pitcliffe Way, West Bowling, Bradford, West Yorkshire, BD5 7SG Tel: (01274) 720019 Fax: (01274) 370132 E-mail: reception@mailway.co.uk *Packaging case manufrs*

▶ Mailworkshop, Unit31 Criftin Enterprise Centre, Oxton Road, Epperstone, Nottingham, NG14 6AT Tel: 0115-965 4446 Fax: 0115-965 4033 E-mail: sales@mailworkshop.co.uk *Mail Workshop provide international and UK direct mail and distribution services, marketing support, magazine distribution, laser printing and copying, machine fulfilment and specialist hand enclosing*

▶ Main Ltd, Shawclough Road, Shawclough, ROCHDALE, LANCASHIRE, OL12 6LN Tel: 01706 655131 Fax: 01706 655132 E-mail: wendy@mainltd.co.uk *Manufacturers and suppliers of IBC Approved Bunded Diesel bowsers and plastic and galvanised water bowsers.*

Main Cabinet Works, 687 Melton Road, Thurmaston, Leicester, LE4 8ED Tel: 0116-269 3078 *Window manufrs*

Main Event Sales & Hire, Unit 25, Coleshill Industrial Estate, Station Road, Coleshill, Birmingham, B46 1JP Tel: (01675) 464224 Fax: (01675) 466082 E-mail: sales@mainevent.co.uk Purchasing Contact: Cowen *Display hire, display board hire, display boards hire, display boards rental, display panel hire, display panel rent, display panels hire, display systems hire, display stands hire, exhibition hire, poster board hire, poster boards hire, exhibition boards hire, rope and post hire, rope barrier hire, rope barrier hire, barrier rope hire, rope barriers, barrier ropes, rope and post, ropes & posts, ropes and poles, rope and post, ropes and post, ropes and posts, post and rope, posts & rope, posts & ropes, posts and rope, posts and ropes, security rope, security ropes, queuing systems, barriers, barrier rent, barrier rental, barrier systems, barriers rent, barriers rental, security barrier, security barriers, portable barriers, tensa barriers, tensa barriers, rope post hire, crowd control, crowd control barriers, rope and stand, rope and stands, ropes stands, notice board, notice boards, red carpet. Located in Birmingham, West Midlands nr. The NEC.*

Main Ford Car Dealership, Hopping Hill, New Duston, Northampton, NN5 6PD Tel: (01604) 581121 Fax: (01604) 582969 *Ford vehicle dealers*

J.A. Main Ltd, 20 Portway Road, Oldbury, West Midlands, B69 2BY Tel: 0121-552 2941 Fax: 0121-511 1401 E-mail: info@jamain.co.uk *Jewellery manufrs*

Main Line Bearing Co. Ltd, Chatsworth Industrial Estate, Percy Street, Leeds, LS12 1EL Tel: 0113-263 3321 Fax: 0113-279 1434 E-mail: sales@mainlinebearings.com *Bearing distributors*

Main Line Patterns, Unit 20b, Alliance Industrial Estate Dodsworth Street, Darlington, County Durham, DL1 2NS Tel: (01325) 483462 Fax: (01325) 483462 *Engineering pattern makers*

Main Line Products Richards, Attwood Street, Stourbridge, West Midlands, DY9 8SL Tel: (01384) 422661 Fax: (01384) 423163 *Galvanized hollow-ware manufrs*

Main Line Timber Ltd, Station Yard Caravan, Station Road, Woodford Halse, Daventry, Northamptonshire, NN11 3RB Tel: (01327) 262124 *Fencing manufrs*

▶ Main & Main, 252a Finney Lane, Heald Green, Cheadle, Cheshire, SK8 3QD Tel: 0161-498 9009 Fax: 0161-498 9280 *Apartment management services*

▶ Main Maintenance Ltd, Pikehelve Street, West Bromwich, West Midlands, B70 0TU Tel: 0121-557 0777 Fax: 0121-557 1666

Main Man Supplies, Station Approach, Adisham, Canterbury, Kent, CT3 3JE Tel: (01304) 842030 Fax: (01304) 841312 E-mail: mnshydra@hotmail.com *Safety clothing distributors*

▶ Main Pro, 51 Waybridge Industrial Estate, Daniel Adamson Road, Salford, M50 1DS Tel: (0870) 7774595 Fax: (0870) 7774596 E-mail: manchester@main-pro.co.uk

Main Road Ground Works, Unit 22 Coniston Road, Kitty Brewster Industrial Esta, Blyth, Northumberland, NE24 4RF Tel: (01670) 353049

Main Stream Publications, 139 Thomas Street, Portadown, Craigavon, County Armagh, BT62 3BE Tel: (028) 3833 4272 Fax: (028) 3835 1046 E-mail: andrewcrozier@mainstreammagazines.co.uk *Trade magazine publishers*

Main Street Marketing, 1-3 Bachelors Walk, Lisburn, County Antrim, BT28 1XJ Tel: (028) 9268 2059 Fax: (028) 9267 1555 *Marketing company*

Main Systems Ltd, Beach Road, Newhaven, East Sussex, BN9 0BX Tel: (01273) 612000 Fax: (01273) 514324 E-mail: newhaven@main-systems.co.uk *Electric control gear manufrs* Also at: Brentwood, Derby & Winsford

Main Tel Ne Ltd, Bassleton Lane, Thornaby, Stockton-on-Tees, Cleveland, TS17 0LD Tel: (01642) 762202 Fax: (01642) 762573 E-mail: admin@main-tel.co.uk *Telecommunications*

Main Tool Co. Ltd, Old Edinburgh Road, Bellshill, Lanarkshire, ML4 3HL Tel: 01698 749473 *Precision toolmakers*

▶ Main Train Transmissions LTD, 143 Coppermill Lane, Walthamstow, London, E17 7HD Tel: 0845 8380599 E-mail: sales@maintrainltd.com *At Main Train Transmissions LTD, we offer our customers quality and branded Gearbox, Differential and Axle components. We supply authentic bearings, gaskets and oil seals that are necessary to rebuild the transmission unit ensuring that we provide the highest quality service to our customers in terms of professional advice and assistance regarding their product. ***

Main Welding Co. Ltd, Shawclough Road, Shawclough, Rochdale, Lancashire, OL12 6LN Tel: (01706) 655131 Fax: (01706) 655135 E-mail: enquiries@mainltd.co.uk *Steel fabricators, bowser, mezzanine floor & platform manufrs*

William Main, 9 West Port, Dunbar, East Lothian, EH42 1BT Tel: (01368) 863258 Fax: (01368) 865336 *Garden centre & giftware*

Maina Freight Forwarders plc, 5 Featherstone Industrial Estate, Dominion Road, Southall, Middlesex, UB2 5DP Tel: (020) 8843 1977 Fax: (020) 8571 5628 E-mail: info@maina.com *Freight forwarders*

▶ Mainbell, Unit 4B, Bridge Farm Industries, Botley Road, Curbridge, Southampton, SO30 2HB Tel: (01489) 799444 Fax: (01445) 821949 E-mail: admin@mainbell.free-online.co.uk

▶ Maincolour, Hammond House, Heapy Street, Macclesfield, Cheshire, SK11 7JB Tel: (01625) 667400 Fax: (01625) 424888 E-mail: sales@maincolour.co.uk

Maindec Computer Engineering Ltd, Maindec House, Holtspur Lane, Wooburn Green, High Wycombe, Buckinghamshire, HP10 0AB Tel: (01628) 810977 Fax: (01628) 810733 E-mail: roger.timms@maindec.co.uk *Computer maintenance services & solutions*

▶ Maine Business Systems Plc, 81 Gloucester Road, Croydon, CR0 2DN Tel: 08709 088099 Fax: 08709 088098 E-mail: service@printerrepair.co.uk *Fast laser printer repairs & maintenance. No call out charge. All makes - UK coverage. Call Freephone 0800-526-716.*

Maine Business Systems P.L.C., Hanover Park House, Merebank Lane, Croydon, CR0 4NP Tel: (020) 8688 8855 Fax: (020) 8688 8897 E-mail: post@maine-plc.com *Office equipment*

Maine Engineering Services Ltd, West Line Industrial Estate, Birtley, Chester le Street, County Durham, DH2 1AU Tel: 0191-410 0004 Fax: 0191-410 2053 E-mail: mick.main@dsl.pipex.com *Dust & fume control*

Maine Furniture Company Manufacturers, The Goods Yard, Railway Street, Ballymena, County Antrim, BT42 2AF Tel: (028) 2564 7507 Fax: (028) 2564 7507 E-mail: maineupholsterers@irishtrade.net *Manufacture lounge suites*

The Maine Group, Home Park Industrial Estate, Station Road, Kings Langley, Hertfordshire, WD4 8LZ Tel: (01923) 260411 Fax: (01923) 267136 E-mail: sales@maine.co.uk *Metal furniture & filing manufrs*

Maine Soft Drinks Ltd, 35 Ballymena Road, Ballymoney, County Antrim, BT53 7EX Tel: (028) 2766 2088 Fax: (028) 2766 6112 E-mail: bruce@mainesoftdrinksltd.co.uk *Soft drink manufrs*

Maineport Ltd, Rossmore Industrial Estate, Ellesmere Port, CH65 3BS Tel: 0151-355 0111 Fax: 0151-356 1093 E-mail: sales@uecnet.co.uk *Pipe fabrication supports fittings flanges*

Mainetti (U K) Ltd, Oxnam Road, Jedburgh, Roxburghshire, TD8 6NN Tel: (01835) 865000 Fax: (01835) 863879 E-mail: jwilde@uk.mainetti.com *Plastics moulders & garment hanger production*

Mainframe Communications Ltd, Network House, Journeymans Way, Temple Farm Industrial Estate, Southend-On-Sea, SS2 5TF Tel: (01702) 443800 Fax: (01702) 443801 E-mail: sales@mainframecomms.co.uk *Fibre optics communication systems manufrs*

Mainframe Data Ltd, 7 Oakwood Court, 122 Bromley Road, Beckenham, Kent, BR3 6PD Tel: (020) 8658 3928 E-mail: support@londondatabases.com *I.T Consultants*

Mainframe Fabrications Hereford Ltd, Unit 6A Thorn Business Park, Rotherwas, Hereford, HR2 6JT Tel: (01432) 353703 Fax: (01432) 340588 *Metal fabricators*

▶ MainFrameDirect (MFD Limited), 3 Fieldside, High Street, West Lavington, Devizes, Wiltshire, SN10 4HQ Tel: (01380) 818782 Fax: (01380) 818782 E-mail: mfd@mainframedirect.net *MainFrame is a modular system for building garden structures to support netting or fleece. It is lightweight and can be re-structured to allow different uses as the seasons change.*

Maingate Ltd, PO Box 330, Woking, Surrey, GU22 9XS Tel: (0845) 2306585 Fax: (0845) 2307585 *UK agent & distributor for fort wheelbarrows*

Maingrade Ltd, 9 Oakland Industrial Estate, Lower Road, Cannock, Staffordshire, WS12 2UZ Tel: (01543) 426155 Fax: (01543) 426155 E-mail: conductag@aol.com *Electrically conductive fillers & aggregates*

Mainland Car Deliveries Ltd, Mainland House, Bootle, Merseyside, L20 3EF Tel: 0151-933 9612 Fax: 0151-933 4751 E-mail: contactus@mcd-ltd.co.uk *Motor car distributors & storage* Also at: Branches throughout the U.K.

Mainland Catering Equipment Ltd, Unit 1a Fountain Mill, Rakefoot, Haslingden, Rossendale, Lancashire, BB4 5RE Tel: (01706) 244810 Fax: (01706) 244811 E-mail: sales@mainlandcatering.co.uk *Suppliers of catering equipment*

Mainline Ceilings & Partitioners, The Stables Pickerings Farm, Halegate Road, Widnes, Cheshire, WA8 8LY Tel: 0151-425 2412 Fax: 0151-425 4342 *Ceilings & partition installations*

▶ Mainline Construction, The Grove, Bognor Regis, West Sussex, PO22 7EY Tel: (01243) 863138 Fax: (01243) 870568

▶ Mainline Haulage Ltd, Neachells Park Distribution C, Neachells Lane, Willenhall, West Midlands, WV13 3RR Tel: (01902) 631127

Mainline Screens, 19 Medway Drive, Chandler's Ford, Eastleigh, Hampshire, SO53 4SR Tel: (023) 8026 7846 Fax: (023) 8026 7869 E-mail: info@mainlinescreens.co.uk *PVC flexible door/curtain manufrs*

Mainline Security Systems, 39 Wrawby Street, Brigg, South Humberside, DN20 9BS Tel: (01652) 650567 Fax: (01652) 658818 *Security services*

Mainline Surplus Sales, Unit 1A, Cutters Close, Coventry Road, Harborough, Leicester, LE19 2FR Tel: (0116) 286 5303 Fax: (0116) 2867797 E-mail: sales@mainlinegroup.co.uk *Electronic component distributors*

Mainline (Water Solutions) Ltd, Unit 4 Brickfields Indust Est, Finway Rd, Hemel Hempstead, Hertfordshire, HP2 7QA Tel: (01442) 211121 Fax: (01442) 211171 E-mail: sales@mainlinewater.co.uk *Water cooler distribution*

continued

Mainport Engineering (1990) Ltd, Pembroke Dock, Dyfed, SA72 6WD Tel: (01646) 621563 Fax: (01646) 621305 E-mail: mpe@my-office.co.uk *Steel fabricators & pressure vessel manufrs*

▶ Mainport Training, Lanrick Road, London, E14 0JF Tel: (020) 7537 7449 Fax: (020) 7987 8193

▶ Mains Distribution Ltd, Union Street, Pendlebury, Swinton, Manchester, M27 4HL Tel: 0161-727 9996 Fax: 0161-727 9998

▶ Mainsail Ltd, Medina Yard, Arctic Road, Cowes, Isle of Wight, PO31 7PG Tel: (01983) 200901 Fax: (01983) 200902 E-mail: beth@mainsail.co.uk *Mainsail is an event management, marketing, design and sponsorship company.*

Mainstream Maintenance Group, 256 High Street, Potters Bar, Hertfordshire, EN6 5DB Tel: (01707) 662774 Fax: (01707) 653382 E-mail: sales@mainstreamgroup.com *At Mainstream we pride ourselves on our ability to make the desirable affordable and are delighted to give you an insight into what we can offer. We are proud to present to you the very best in European kitchen, bedroom and dining furniture. Be it English, French or German made our striking, traditional or contemporary designs will compliment any home adding a touch of class and sophistication. Crafted in the most desirable materials with outstanding workmanship and expertise we believe that our furniture will make an impression in any environment. Not only can we provide you with beautiful furniture but all the accessories as well. From kitchen appliances and bathroom ceramics to flooring and granite / marble. With our in-house designers nothing is left to chance. We also provide a complete building and kitchen /bathroom installation service carrying all CIS certification, full health and safety compliant, registered carries of waste and are fully CORGI gas registered engineers.*

▶ Mainstream Printing Services, 16-22 Pritchards Road, London, E2 9AP Tel: (020) 7729 4564 Fax: (020) 7739 5567

Mainstream Software Solutions, 43 Longway Avenue, Charlton Kings, Cheltenham, Gloucestershire, GL53 9JH Tel: (01242) 227377 Fax: (01242) 251319 E-mail: mainstream@bitstream.com *Computer software developers*

▶ Maintel Europe Ltd, 61 Webber Street, London, SE1 0RF Tel: (0870) 5002244 Fax: (0870) 5113399 E-mail: info@maintel.co.uk *Our mission is to ensure your telephone system is operating fully, enabling you to concentrate on running your business and if it fails we respond quickly and professionally to fix it. *Our solution is simple: a one-stop shop offering everything from systems maintenance, consultancy and equipment sales to network services, software upgrades and network carrier management. **

Maintenance Direct Ltd, 50c Coldharbour Lane, Hayes, Middlesex, UB3 3EP Tel: (0870) 7494044 Fax: (020) 8569 0399 E-mail: sales@maintenance-direct.com *Computer maintenance & repairs*

F S R Maintenance, 8 Arnside Road, Waterlooville, Hants, PO7 7UP Tel: (023) 9226 3222 Fax: (023) 9223 0946 E-mail: fsr@shaftfield.co.uk *Industrial relocation specialists*

▶ Maintenance Service Direct Ltd, Birmingham Road, Alvechurch, Birmingham, B48 7AJ Tel: 0121-447 8464 Fax: 0121-447 8463 E-mail: msd-ltd@btconnect.com *Air conditioning installers*

Maintenance Supply Co. Ltd, Codham Hall, Codham Hall Lane, Great Warley, Brentwood, Essex, CM13 3JT Tel: (01277) 200520 Fax: (01277) 225378 E-mail: maintenancesupply@jangro.net *Janitorial supplies*

Maisonneuve & Co., 29 Newman Street, London, W1T 1PS Tel: (020) 7636 9686 Fax: (020) 7436 0770 E-mail: enq@maisonneuve.co.uk *Furnishing fabric agents*

Maisun Blinds, 17 High Street, Wall Heath, Kingswinford, West Midlands, DY6 0HB Tel: (01384) 402800 Fax: (01384) 402900 *Blind manufrs*

Majenta Audio Visual Ltd, Unit 2, Wills Industrial Estate, Salmon Parade, Bridgwater, Somerset, TA6 5JT Tel: (01278) 433700 Fax: (01278) 433131 E-mail: sales@majenta-av.co.uk *Sound lighting & audio visual installation & servicing*

Majenta Solutions, Coptfold Road, Brentwood, Essex, CM14 4BN Tel: (01277) 263244 Fax: (01277) 263245 E-mail: info@majentasolutions.co.uk *Computer service repair & installation*

Majestic, Queen Street, Walsall, WS2 9NU Tel: (01922) 628596 Fax: (01922) 628597 E-mail: info@majestics.org.uk *Anodising aluminium services*

▶ Majestic Corrugated Cases Ltd, Unit 30 Parkrose Industrial Estate, Middlemore Road, Smethwick, West Midlands, B66 2DZ Tel: (01902) 733330 Fax: 0121-558 7000 E-mail: kavi.jundu@majesticbox.com

▶ Majestic Corrugated Cases Ltd, Unit 30 Parkrose Industrial Estate, Middlemore Road, Smethwick, West Midlands, B66 2DZ Tel: (01902) 733330 Fax: 0121-558 7000

Majestic Crystal Ltd, The Old Chapel, High Street, Martin, Lincoln, LN4 3QY Tel: (01526) 378676 Fax: (01526) 378633 E-mail: sales@majesticcrystal.co.uk *Glass engravers*

▶ Majestic Events Ltd, Majestic House, 1 Roberts Close, Eaton Socon, Cambs, PE19 8YE Tel: 01480 390325 Fax: 01480 390325 E-mail: majestic.eventsltd@ntlworld.com *Keep your training fresh, sharpe and fun. Management and Leadership, Team building & corporate fun days at our stimulating lakeside venue or a venue of your choice. On Site personal services*

▶ Majestic Floors, Corner Glades, 16 Elmton Close, Leeds, LS10 3UD Tel: 0113-270 9921 E-mail: majesticfloors@hotmail.com *Supply, fit flooring*

▶ Majestic Gates, Unit 1 Temple Street, Hull, HU5 1AD Tel: (01482) 441466 Fax: (01482) 441466 E-mail: sales@majesticgates.com *Wrought iron gate & railing manufrs*

Majestic Shower Co. Ltd, 1 North Place, Edinburgh Way, Harlow, Essex, CM20 2SL Tel: (01279) 443644 Fax: (01279) 635074 E-mail: info@majesticshowers.com *Shower door manufrs*

Majestic Towels Ltd, 72 Alfred Street, Sparkbrook, Birmingham, B12 8JP Tel: 0121-772 0936 Fax: 0121-766 8029 E-mail: info@majestictowels.co.uk *Towel manufrs*

Majestic Trophies Ltd, David Lane, Nottingham, NG6 0JU Tel: 0115-970 8509 Fax: 0115-942 0712 *Trophies & engraving*

▶ Majestic Window Cleaning Services, 36 Darbishire Road, Fleetwood, Lancashire, FY7 6QA Tel: (01253) 777584 E-mail: thegarnetts2003@yahoo.co.uk

▶ Majic Solutions, 15 Swanwick Walk, Broughton, Milton Keynes, MK10 9LJ Tel: (01908) 236678 E-mail: sales@majic.co.uk *Computer software developers*

▶ Majic Systems Ltd, Hine Lodge, Ransom Road, Mapperley, Nottingham, NG3 5HN Tel: 0870 753 3641 Fax: 0870 753 3651 E-mail: enquiries@majicsystems.co.uk *Cremator, abatement plant and ancillary crematorium equipment manufacture, sales, servicing, parts and repairs. Also animal cremators, gas detection systems and associated services.*

Major Air Systems Ltd, Union Works, Andover Street, Birmingham, B5 5RG Tel: 0121-634 1580 Fax: 0121-643 2320 *Ventilation ductwork contractors*

Major Equipment Ltd, Middleton Road, Middleton, Morecambe, Lancashire, LA3 3JJ Tel: (01524) 850501 Fax: (01524) 850502 E-mail: ukinfo@major-grasscare.com *Agricultural engineers*

Major Fabrications Kent Ltd, Broad Lane, Betteshanger, Deal, Kent, CT14 0LX Tel: (01304) 614541 Fax: (01304) 614544 E-mail: enquiries@majorfabrications.com *Sheet metalwork fabrication specialists*

Major Gold, Harbour House, Coldharbour Lane, Rainham, Essex, RM13 9YB Tel: (01708) 523233 Fax: (01708) 559818 E-mail: j.majorgold@btclick.com *Software house*

Harry Major Machine UK Ltd, 3 Gosforth Close, Middlefield Industrial Estate, Sandy, Bedfordshire, SG19 1RB Tel: (01767) 689500 Fax: (01767) 680893 E-mail: sales@hmm-uk.com *Conveyor manufrs*

▶ Major Hire Co. Ltd, 48 Burbage Road, London, SE24 9HE Tel: (020) 7326 5221 Fax: (020) 7978 8874

Major Machine Tools Ltd, Poyntz House, Harlestone Road, Chapel Brampton, Northampton, NN6 8AW Tel: (01604) 844665 Fax: (01604) 821108 E-mail: sales@majormachinetools.com *Machine tool merchants*

Major Pine Trade Suppliers Ltd, Unit H2 Beckingham Business Park, Beckingham Street, Tolleshunt Major, Maldon, Essex, CM9 8LZ Tel: (01621) 868722 Fax: (01621) 869543 *Pine furniture manufrs*

Major Refrigeration & Air Conditioning Services Ltd, 6 Broadway Road, Evesham, Worcestershire, WR11 1BH Tel: (01386) 49342 Fax: (01386) 45232 E-mail: info@majorcooling.co.uk *Refrigeration & air conditioning engineers*

Major Sheet Metals, 483 Bradford Road, Batley, West Yorkshire, WF17 8LB Tel: (01924) 441610 Fax: (01924) 420535 *Stainless steel, aluminium sheet metalworking & fabricators*

Major Signs, 189 Meanwood Road, Leeds, LS7 1NB Tel: 0113-243 8792 Fax: 0113-243 8792 *Sign manufrs*

Major Travel plc, Fortress Grove, 28-34 Fortress Road, London, NW5 2HB Tel: (020) 7393 1088 Fax: (020) 7393 1096 E-mail: info@majortravel.co.uk *Flight bookings for flights, hotels, car hire & car insurance*

Majorfax Ltd, Charles Street, Walsall, WS2 9LZ Tel: (01922) 645815 Fax: (01922) 620500 E-mail: castings@majorfax.co.uk *Ferrous & non-ferrous castings manufrs*

Majorsell International Ltd, Unit G Springhill Business Park, 111 Steward Street, Birmingham, B18 7AF Tel: 0121-455 0200 Fax: 0121-455 0272 E-mail: sales@majorsell.co.uk *Commercial air brake equipment distributors*

Majortek Components Ltd, Netley Firs, Kanes Hill, Southampton, SO19 6AJ Tel: (023) 8040 5276 Fax: (023) 8040 2873 E-mail: sales@majortek.co.uk Purchasing Contact: M. Renshaw Sales Contact: R. Renshaw *Cable accessories, fibre optics component/equipment/instrument & heat shrinkable sleeving manufacturers. Also cable tie distributors or agents*

MAKA Machinery UK Ltd, Unit 19 Queensway Link Industrial Estate, Stafford Park 17, Telford, Shropshire, TF3 3DN Tel: (01952) 270006 Fax: (01952) 270007 E-mail: info@makauk.com *MAKA - Max Mayer Maschinenbau GmbH manufacture a comprehensive range of precision 3, 4 and 5 axis CNC machining centres for the plastics, wood and aluminium industries. Offering single and multi head configurations with a wide range of tool changers, spindles and clamping options - MAKA provide custom specific solutions for each application.*

Make A Dye Laser, 2 Abbey Road, London, E15 3LG Tel: (020) 8519 8161 Fax: (020) 8534 3248 *Die cutters (packaging & display industry)*

Make Em & Break Em, Penybont Road, Pencoed, Bridgend, Mid Glamorgan, CF35 5LE Tel: (01656) 862070 Fax: (01656) 862070 *Plant & machinery repairers*

Make Fast Ltd, 31 Mochdre Industrial Estate, Mochdre, Newtown, Powys, SY16 4LE Tel: (01686) 629010 Fax: (01686) 626700 E-mail: sales@makefast.com *Marine & safety hardware*

Make It With Lasers, T W I, Granta Park, Great Abington, Cambridge, CB1 6AL Tel: (01223) 891162 Fax: (01223) 890661 E-mail: miwl@twi.co.uk *Research instruments*

▶ Make Me A Princess Tiaras, 16 Quartz Avenue, Mansfield, Nottinghamshire, NG18 4XB Tel: (01623)627257 E-mail: enquiries@makemeaprincess.co.uk *A beautiful selection of tiaras and headdresses for brides and bridesmaids to suit all budgets. Visit our secure online shop to browse our products.*

▶ Make Space Mezzanine Floors Ltd, 1-5 Mill Field Road, Donington, Spalding, Lincolnshire, PE11 4UR Tel: (01775) 822060 Fax: (01775) 822061

▶ Makein & Mcnab, Unit 3 Riverside Court, Cupar, Fife, KY15 5JY Tel: (01334) 654422 Fax: (01334) 656590

Makers, Egerton Street, Nottingham, NG3 4GQ Tel: 0115-941 9290 Fax: 0115-948 1834 E-mail: makers@fsbdial.co.uk *MAKERS is a highly creative model making company operating in the UK with an excellent reputation of producing top-flight work for companies of all sizes. From conception to creation we use highly experienced teams to generate exactly what you want, fitting your specifications, time-scale and budget*

▶ Makers UK Finance Ltd, Rye Hill Office Park, Birmingham Road, Allesley, Coventry, CV5 9GT Tel: (024) 7640 5600 Fax: (024) 7640 5629 *Car part refurbishment services*

Makesafe Ltd, 34 Balls Road, Prenton, Merseyside, CH43 5RE Tel: 0151-653 8404 Fax: 0151-653 8404 *Locksmiths*

▶ MakeUpMadness, 44 Barnard Avenue, Ludworth, Durham, DH6 1LS Tel: (01429) 821343 E-mail: chris@makeupmadness.co.uk *Cosmetics retail website*

▶ Makeupworld, 5 Maes Street, St. Thomas, Swansea, SA1 8ES Tel: (07851) 734820 E-mail: customerservice@makeupworld.co.uk *Discount makeup and skincare. Wholesale and retail customers welcome*

Makewell & Skinner, 4 The Forest, Hatfield Broad Oak, Bishop's Stortford, Hertfordshire, CM22 7BT Tel: (01279) 718114 Fax: (01279) 718115 *Tool & cutter grinders suppliers & manufrs*

Makin Metal Powers Ltd, Buckley Road, Rochdale, Lancashire, OL12 9DT Tel: (01706) 717317 Fax: (01706) 717303 E-mail: mmp@makin-metals.com *Manufacturers of non-ferrous irregular*

Makin Rochard Ltd, 5 Union Court, Richmond, Surrey, TW9 1AA Tel: (020) 8948 7757 Fax: (020) 8948 5981 E-mail: solutions@makinrochard.co.uk *IT computer software developers*

Makinson & Worsley, Era Street, Bolton, BL2 6JB Tel: (01204) 523606 Fax: (01204) 388058 *Joinery manufrs*

Makita UK Ltd, Vermont Place, Michigan Drive, Tongwell, Milton Keynes, MK15 8JD Tel: (01908) 211678 Fax: (01908) 211400 E-mail: info@makitauk.com *Electric power tool distributors & manufrs*

Makkipak Ltd, Mallard Close, Earls Barton, Northampton, NN6 0JF Tel: (01604) 812755 Fax: (01604) 812413 E-mail: sales@makkipak.com *Packaging suppliers manufrs*

Mala Electrical Ltd, 126 Petherton Road, London, N5 2RT Tel: (020) 7359 3925 Fax: (020) 7359 4672 E-mail: mala@mala.co.uk *Building services*

Malbern Windows & Doors Ltd, 3 Malbern Industrial Estate, Holland Street, Denton, Manchester, M34 3WE Tel: 0161-320 5801 Fax: 0161-335 0986 E-mail: sales@malbernwindows.co.uk *Upvc door & window manufrs*

Malbrook, C.S. Ltd, 8 Millbank Court, Millbank Way, Bracknell, Berkshire, RG12 1RP Tel: (01344) 424458 Fax: (01344) 424459 E-mail: support@csmb.co.uk *Computer consultants*

▶ Malby, Zylo Works, Sussex Street, Brighton, BN2 0HH Tel: (01273) 607028 Fax: (01273) 571214 *Name plates & labels suppliers & manufrs*

▶ Malc Firth, Fairview, Rainwalls Lane, Sutterton, Boston, Lincolnshire, PE20 2HY Tel: (01205) 460293 Fax: (01205) 460933 E-mail: info@malcfirthlandscapes.co.uk *We are able to carry out all aspects of landscaping from commercial to domestic with a friendly and efficient service.As a natural turf specialist, we are able to construct a high performance sports field or upgrade existing worn patches.*Being able to offer a full drainage service for new or existing pitches. **

Malcolm Clarke Haulage Ltd, Jubilee Works, Clifton St Miles, Manchester, M40 8HN Tel: 0161-205 7280 Fax: 0161-205 8473 E-mail: sales@clarke-steel.co.uk *Steel plate stockholders*

Malcolm Electrical Ltd, 657-661 High Road, London, E10 6RD Tel: (020) 8556 1838 Fax: (020) 8556 1352 *Electrical wholesalers*

Malcolm Enamellers Midlands Ltd, Lawley Middleway, Birmingham, B4 7XT Tel: 0121-359 7553 Fax: 0121-359 8309 E-mail: sales@malcolms.co.uk *Metal finishers, powder coating services & electrophoretic painting/lacquering services*

Malcolm Engineering Co. Ltd, Banks Road, McMullen Industrial Estate, Darlington, County Durham, DL1 1YF Tel: (01325) 461549 Fax: (01325) 381196 E-mail: malco@malcolm-eng.co.uk *Precision & repetition machinists*

Malcolm Insulation Ltd, 59 Beardmore Way, Clydebank, Dunbartonshire, G81 4HT Tel: 0141-941 2204 Fax: 0141-951 1487 *Insulating material distributors*

▶ Malcolm Plant, PO Box 1, Irvine, Ayrshire, KA12 8JA Tel: (01294) 272314 Fax: (01294) 222288

Malcolm Plant, Murray Street, Paisley, Renfrewshire, PA3 1QQ Tel: 0141-889 8711 Fax: 0141-889 7510 E-mail: contact@whm.co.uk *Contractors plant hire*

▶ Malcolm Power Systems, Unit 15, Spurryhillock Industrial Estate, Broomhill Road, Stonehaven, Kincardineshire, AB39 2NH Tel: (01569) 762416 Fax: (01569) 767071

continued

E-mail: enquiries@malcolmpower.co.uk *Supply & maintenance services of power systems*

Malcolm Robertson and Sons Ltd, Unit 2 Church Street, Caldewgate, Carlisle, CA2 5TJ Tel: (01228) 521018 Fax: (01228) 542458 *Industrial pipe manufrs.*

Malcolm Rose & Karin Richter, English Passage, Lewes, East Sussex, BN7 2AP Tel: (01273) 481010 Fax: (01273) 481010 E-mail: info@malcolm-rose.com *Harpsichord manufrs*

▶ Malcolm Smith Contracts Ltd, 6 Drumaline Ridge, Worcester Park, Surrey, KT4 7JT Tel: (020) 8337 4421 Fax: (020) 8337 4431

Malcolm West Fork Lifts Immingham Ltd, Bridge House, Goulton Street, Hull, HU3 4DD Tel: (01482) 327681 Fax: (01482) 226116 E-mail: info@malcolmwest-nissan.co.uk *Fork lift sales & service*

▶ MalcolmEWhite&Son, 28 Brick Hill, Bromham, Chippenham, Wiltshire, SN15 2JL Tel: (01380) 850562 Fax: (01380) 850562 E-mail: info@malcolmewhiteandson.co.uk *Creators of bespoke geometrical staircases*

▶ Malcolmson & Co., 74 Commercial Road, Lerwick, Shetland, ZE1 0NL Tel: (01595) 693027 Fax: (01595) 696086 *Bakery retail*

Malcro Lighting Ltd, Unit 13 College Fields Industrial Estate, Prince Georges Road, London, SW19 2PT Tel: (020) 8640 1001 Fax: (020) 8640 9248 *Lighting wholesalers & distributors*

Malden Plating Works Ltd, 32 Wates Way, Mitcham, Surrey, CR4 4HR Tel: (020) 8640 1272 Fax: (020) 8640 1372 *Anodising services-metal plating*

Maldon Chandlery Ltd, North Street, Maldon, Essex, CM9 5HL Tel: (01621) 854280 Fax: (01621) 843849 E-mail: chandlers@marinestore.co.uk *Chandlers*

Maldon Crystal Salt Co. Ltd, Wycke Hill Business Park, Wycke Hill, Maldon, Essex, CM9 6UZ Tel: (01621) 853315 Fax: (01621) 858191 E-mail: sales@maldonsalt.co.uk *Salt merchants & manufrs*

Maldon Marine Ltd, 16 West Station Yard, Spital Road, Maldon, Essex, CM9 6TW Tel: (01621) 859000 Fax: (01621) 858935 E-mail: info@maldon-marine.co.uk *Steel fabrication, design & erection*

Maldon Printing Co. Ltd, Unit 2-14 Wycke Hill Business Park, Wycke Hill, Maldon, Essex, CM9 6UZ Tel: (01621) 853904 Fax: (01621) 859565 *General printers*

▶ Maldon Rail Centre Ltd, 8 Silver Street, Maldon, Essex, CM9 4QE Tel: (01621) 858188 Fax: (01621) 855527 *Model rail track manufrs*

B.J. Male & Son Ltd, Uints 4-10, Ellis Square, Selsey, Chichester, West Sussex, PO20 0AY Tel: (01243) 602231 Fax: (01243) 602770 *Structural steel engineers*

Malek Joinery Ltd, 16 Belsham Street, London, E9 6NG Tel: (020) 8985 2222 Fax: (020) 8985 2223 *Joinery manufrs*

▶ Malev Hungarian Airlines P.L.C., 22-25A First Floor, Sackville St, London, W1S 3DR Tel: (0870) 9090577 Fax: (020) 7734 8116 E-mail: london@malev.hu *Airline*

Malhi Trimmings Ltd, Excelda Works, 36 Rookery Road, Handsworth, Birmingham, B21 9NB Tel: (0121) 554 5731 Fax: (0121) 554 5733 E-mail: sales@mahligroup.co.uk *Clothes suppliers*

Maliksons Logistics, Building B, Source Road, Trafford Park, Manchester, M17 1PY Tel: 0161-872 6565 Fax: 0161- 872 6566 E-mail: sales@maliksons.co.uk *Warehousing, storage, transport, distribution, freight consolidation, groupage, handling, cargo*

Malin Bridge Engineering Ltd, 40 Worthing Road, Sheffield, S9 3JJ Tel: 0114-275 0860 Fax: 0114-275 0405 *General engineering*

Malisa Lighting Ltd, Unit 4 Conqueror Court, Spilsby Road, Harold Hill, Romford, RM3 8SB Tel: (01708) 372221 Fax: (01708) 381354 E-mail: malisa@mabeys.co.uk *Lighting equipment designers & distributors*

Malken Gauge & Tool Co. Ltd, 260 Summer Lane, New Town, Birmingham, B19 2PX Tel: 0121-333 3808 Fax: 0121-333 3617 E-mail: enquiries@malkengauge.co.uk *Precision gauge manufrs*

Mall Galleries, 17 Carlton House Terrace, London, SW1Y 5BD Tel: (020) 7930 6844 Fax: (020) 7839 7830 E-mail: info@mallgalleries.co.uk *Organisation of art exhibitions*

Mallaband Motor Factors Ltd, Unit 2, Lansell Industrial Estate, Caton Road, Lancaster, LA1 3PD Tel: (01524) 60861 Fax: (01524) 843556 *Suppliers of automotive refinishing products*

Mallaig Boatbuilding & Engineering Co. Ltd, Harbour Slipways, Mallaig, Inverness-Shire, PH41 4QS Tel: (01687) 462304 Fax: (01687) 462378 *Boat engineering*

Mallalieu's Of Delph Ltd, Valley Mill, Millgate, Delph, Oldham, OL3 5DG Tel: (01457) 874811 Fax: (01457) 870231 E-mail: sales@mallalieus.com *Woollen manufrs*

Mallard Models & Effects, 133 Dorset Road, London, SW19 3EQ Tel: (020) 8540 4430 Fax: (020) 8715 7301 *Models for advertising & photography*

Mallards Interiors, Peter James Lane, Fairlight, Hastings, East Sussex, TN35 4AH Tel: (01424) 813853 Fax: (01424) 813853 *Curtain makers*

Mallatite Ltd, Hardwick View Road, Holmewood, Chesterfield, Derbyshire, S42 5SA Tel: (01246) 593280 Fax: (01246) 593281 E-mail: info@mallatite.co.uk *Sign post lighting column manufrs*

▶ Mallatite Ltd, Units 5-6 Creswell Industrial Estate, Colliery Road, Creswell, Worksop, Nottinghamshire, S80 4BX Tel: (01909) 724465 Fax: (01909) 724198

▶ Mallatite (Scotland), 1 McMillan Road, Wishaw, Lanarkshire, ML2 0LA Tel: (01698) 352888 Fax: (01698) 352777 *Lighting manufrs*

Malletts Home Hardware, 6-7 Victoria Square, Truro, Cornwall, TR1 2RT Tel: (01872) 274441 Fax: (01872) 240664 E-mail: sales@mallettshomehardware.co.uk *Wholesale ironmongers & products*

Malling Press, Unit 4b Diplocks Way, Hailsham, East Sussex, BN27 3JF Tel: (01323) 847157 Fax: (01323) 847457 *General printers*

Malling Products Ltd, Fiddlers Reach, Wouldham Road, Grays, Essex, RM20 4YB Tel: (01375) 486300 Fax: (01375) 372642 E-mail: malling@laingrourke.com *Pre-cast concrete products manufrs*

Mallinson's Of Oldham Ltd, Trent Industrial Estate, Duchess Street, Shaw, Oldham, OL2 7UT Tel: (01706) 299000 Fax: (01706) 299700 *Frying range suppliers*

R.D. Mallory Milking Machine & Dairy Supplies Ltd, Unit 3, Strensham Business Park, Strensham, Worcester, WR8 9JZ Tel: (01684) 275040 Fax: (01684) 275020 *Dairy equipment suppliers*

Mallusk Security Services Ltd, 495 Upper Newtownards Road, Belfast, BT4 3LL Tel: (028) 9047 1394 Fax: (028) 9047 2227 E-mail: mallusksecurity@hotmail.com *Manned guarding & security guards*

Malmesbury Farm Supplies Ltd, Whitewalls, Easton Grey, Malmesbury, Wiltshire, SN16 0RD Tel: (01666) 822254 Fax: (01666) 826129 *Agricultural merchants*

Malmic Lace Ltd, Malmic House, Brookside Road, Ruddington, Nottingham, NG11 6AT Tel: 0115-940 5151 Fax: 0115-984 5706 E-mail: info@malmiclace.co.uk *Lace & elastic braid manufrs*

Malone Associates, Fordham House, 46 Newmarket Road, Fordham, Ely, Cambridgeshire, CB7 5LL Tel: (01638) 721770 Fax: (01638) 721771 E-mail: sean@malones.co.uk *Conference & live events organizer*

Malordale Engineering Ltd, Unit 10E, Britannia Estate, Leagrave Road, Luton, LU3 1RJ Tel: (01582) 421138 Fax: (01582) 412894 E-mail: tonyfuller@malordale.co.uk *Prototype engineering & production sheet metal services*

▶ Malpas Tractors, Middlewich Road, Holmes Chapel, Crewe, CW4 7ET Tel: (01477) 549800 Fax: (01477) 549900 E-mail: info@malpastractors.co.uk *Agricultural services*

Malro Ltd, Malro House, 245 Wood Street, London, E17 3NT Tel: (020) 8521 5137 Fax: (020) 8521 6862 *Corporate clothing suppliers*

Malrod Insulations Ltd, Glebe Mill, Library Street, Westhoughton, Bolton, BL5 3AU Tel: (01942) 811591 Fax: (01942) 814411 E-mail: enquiries@malrod.co.uk *Insulation & asbestos removal contractors*

Malroy Products Dudley Ltd, Shaw Road, Dudley, West Midlands, DY2 8TR Tel: (01384) 254178 Fax: (01384) 230126 E-mail: info@malroy.co.freeserve.co.uk *Housewares manufrs*

Malt Mill Engineering Co. Ltd, 4 Kinwarton Workshops, Kinwarton Farm Road, Kinwarton, Alcester, Warwickshire, B49 6EH Tel: (01789) 764497 Fax: (01789) 400161 E-mail: maltmill@aol.com *Precision engineers services*

Maltaward Ltd, Wellingham House Holmbush Potteries, Crawley Road, Faygate, Horsham, West Sussex, RH12 4SE Tel: (01293) 854930 Fax: (01293) 854939 E-mail: gtreacy@maltaward.co.uk *Civil engineering & public works contractors*

▶ Maltby Engineering Co. Ltd, Denaby Industrial Estate, Old Denaby, Doncaster, South Yorkshire, DN12 4JJ Tel: (01709) 862076

Maltby Punch & Die Ltd, 17a Blyth Road, Maltby, Rotherham, South Yorkshire, S66 8HX Tel: (01709) 816206 *Tool manufrs*

▶ Maltech UK Ltd, 1 Newgate, Malton, North Yorkshire, YO17 7LF Tel: (01653) 697092 Fax: (01653) 692486 *Construction engineers*

Malthouse Engineering Co. Ltd, 3 Hainge Road, Tividale, Oldbury, West Midlands, B69 2NL Tel: 0121-557 8455 Fax: 0121-520 2034 *Steel profilers*

Maltings Hotel, The Street, Weybourne, Holt, Norfolk, NR25 7SY Tel: (01263) 588731 Fax: (01263) 588240 *Hotel*

Malton Laser Ltd, Unit E3 The Pyramid Estate, Showfield Lane, Malton, North Yorkshire, YO17 6BT Tel: (01653) 697770 Fax: (01653) 690970 E-mail: info@maltonlaser.co.uk *Malton Laser Ltd provide the highest quality sheet and tube metal component manufacture, the most modern of engineering solutions and a rapid turnaround - all at a very competitive price. They manufacture a wide variety of items from steel, stainless steel and aluminium, ranging from components and parts right through to finished assemblies. They are located in Malton, North Yorkshire.*

Malton Plastics UK Ltd, Enterprise Way, Thornton Road Industrial Estate, Pickering, North Yorkshire, YO18 7NA Tel: (01751) 477760 Fax: (01751) 477760 E-mail: sales@maltonplastics.com *Manufacturers of plastic mouldings*

Maltron International Ltd, PO Box 15, Rayleigh, Essex, SS6 9SN Tel: (01268) 778251 Fax: (01268) 745176 E-mail: maltron@msn.com *Ultrasonic detectors*

Malvern Blinds, The Old Fire Station, Howsell Road, Malvern, Worcestershire, WR14 1TF Tel: (01684) 574047 Fax: (01684) 892729 E-mail: info@malvernblinds.co.uk *Blind manufrs*

Malvern Boilers Ltd, Spring Lane North, Malvern, Worcestershire, WR14 1BW Tel: (01684) 893777 Fax: (01684) 893776 E-mail: sales@malvernboilers.co.uk *Domestic boiler manufrs*

▶ Malvern Cooling Services Ltd, Unit 21B, Oak Road, West Chirton North Industrial, North Shields, Tyne & Wear, NE29 8SF Tel: 0191-296 1766

▶ Malvern Instruments Ltd, Enigma Business Park, Grovewood Road, Malvern, Worcestershire, WR14 1XZ Tel: (01684) 892456 Fax: (01684) 892789 E-mail: info@malvern.co.uk *Malvern Instruments develops, manufactures and markets advanced analytical systems that deliver industrially relevant particle characterization, rheological and chemical composition data. Laboratory, on-line and in-line solutions are proven in sectors from cement production to pharmaceutical drug discovery, and provide*

continued

information that supports the understanding, improvement and optimization of many industrial processes.

Malvern Lapidary, 39 Broadlands Drive, Malvern, Worcestershire, WR14 1PW Tel: (01684) 561537 Fax: (01684) 891611 *Tool manufrs*

▶ Malvern Packaging, Unit 24 Bourne Road Industrial Park, Bourne Road, Dartford, DA1 4BZ Tel: (01322) 524780 Fax: (01322) 524780 E-mail: enquiries@malvernpackaging.co.uk *Packaging distributors*

Malvern Press Ltd, 71 Dalston Lane, London, E8 2NG Tel: (020) 7249 2991 Fax: (020) 7254 1720 E-mail: admin@malvernpress.com *Colour printers & holography*

Malvern Tubular Components Ltd, Spring Lane, Malvern, Worcestershire, WR14 1DA Tel: (01684) 892600 Fax: (01684) 892337 E-mail: sales@mtc.uk.com Purchasing Contact: Paul Sauntson Sales Contact: Mike Welburn *Tube Manipulation and Fabrication services. Processes include: Cutting, CNC Bending, End Forming, Flaring, Drilling, Threading, Beading,Flanging, Machining, MIG and TIG Welding, and Brazing. Surface treatments include: Painting, Plating, Anodising, etc. We work in Mild Steel, Stainless, Aluminium and Copper.Products designed and manufactured to customers specific reqirements and include water transfer tubes, water inlet/outlet pipes, breather tubes, charge air pipes, exhaust pipework, injector pipework, fuel supply tubes and oil tubes.*

MAM Software Ltd, 1 Station Road, Deepcar, Sheffield, S36 2SQ Tel: (0870) 7667012 Fax: (0870) 7667023 *Computer software suppliers motor industry*

Mamba Signs, 9 Wyndham Lane, Plymouth, PL1 5ED Tel: (01752) 227434 Fax: (01752) 260310 *Sign manufrs*

▶ Mambo's UK Tanning Supplies, 434 Preston Old Road, Blackburn, BB2 5LY Tel: (0800) 8496359 Fax: (01254) 209621 E-mail: info@iso-italia.co.uk

▶ Mamco Ltd, 6 Vernon Road, Porthcawl, Porthcawl, Mid Glamorgan, CF36 5LN Tel: (0845) 1668509 Fax: 0871-242 6223 E-mail: admin@mamco.co.uk *'Identification, assessment & management of asbestos-containing materials. Asbestos Surveys, Asbesto Consultancy, Asbestos Awareness Training, Asbestos Remediation & Removal, Industrial & Commercial Asbestos Surveying. FREEPHONE 0800 019 0396'*

Mamelok Holdings Ltd, Northern Way, Bury St. Edmunds, Suffolk, IP32 6NJ Tel: (01284) 762291 Fax: (01284) 703689 E-mail: sales@mamelok.com *Publishers, printers & paper product manufrs*

Mamod Ltd, Unit 1a Summit Crescent, Smethwick, West Midlands, B66 1BT Tel: 0121-500 6433 Fax: 0121-500 6309 E-mail: accommodation@mamod.co.uk *Pressworkers & model steam engines*

Man Ltd, 4-5 Grosvenor Place, London, SW1X 7DG Tel: (020) 7201 3366 Fax: (020) 7235 9450 E-mail: manfred.stelz@man-ltd.co.uk *Engineers, diesel engine & compressors manufrs*

Man Acoustics, Walrow Industrial, Commerce Way, Highbridge, Somerset, TA9 4AG Tel: (01278) 789335 Fax: (01278) 735385 *Acoustics consultants*

▶ MAN Audio Services, Catherine Court Farm, Coppershell, Gastard, Corsham, Wiltshire, SN13 9PZ Tel: (01249) 701363 Fax: (01249) 701236 E-mail: matt@manaudio.co.uk *MAN Audio Services Limited is a small, dynamic company that can provide equipment and expertise for most of your live audio, sound installation and sound production needs. We have many years of experience in the audio industry.*

MAN B & W Diesel Ltd, Hythe Hill, Colchester, CO1 2HW Tel: (01206) 795151 Fax: (01206) 797869 E-mail: sales@manbwltd.com *Manufacturers & distributors of diesel*

Man Diesel Ltd, Bramhall Moor Lane, Hazel Grove, Stockport, Cheshire, SK7 5AQ Tel: 0161-483 1000 Fax: 0161-487 1465 *Market manufrs*

▶ MAN Hydraulics & Engineering Ltd, Unit 9, Thurnscoe Business Centre, Princess Drive, Thurnscoe, Rotherham, South Yorkshire, S63 0BL Tel: (01709) 880520 Fax: (05601) 165945 E-mail: manhydeng@yahoo.co.uk *Suppliers & manufacturers of quality hydraulic components*

▶ Man Mat, Matrix House Balthane Industrial Estate, Balthane, Ballasalla, Isle of Man, IM9 2AJ Tel: (01624) 828603 Fax: (01624) 823966 E-mail: sales@manmat.com *Plastic product manufrs*

Man Shuen Hong London, 4 Tring Close, Ilford, Essex, IG2 7LQ Tel: (020) 8554 3838 Fax: (020) 8554 3883 *Teas & royal jelly suppliers*

▶ Man With A Van!!, 27 Banners walk, Kingstanding, Birmingham, B44 0TB Tel: 0121 3508269 *Man with A Van for hire*Removals, Household clearances,Ect**No job too small!!**West midlands and surrounding areas***

Managed Networks, 6-8 Bonhill Street, London, EC2A 4BX Tel: (020) 7496 8000 E-mail: info@managednetworks.co.uk *IT networks managers*

▶ Managed Security Solutions, 1 Goodmans Yard, London, E1 8AT Tel: (020) 7953 1270 Fax: (020) 7953 1388 E-mail: info@mssuk.com *I.T security solution services*

Management Advisory Ltd, 5 - 8 Edwards Centre, The Horsefair, Hinckley, Leicestershire, LE10 0AN Tel: (01455) 444222 Fax: (01455) 891251 E-mail: admin@managementadvisory.net *Management consultants*

Management Archives, Parkside House, Parkside Lane, Leeds, LS11 5TD Tel: 0113-277 2525 Fax: 0113-387 7690 E-mail: guymanarch@aol.com *Document storage services*

▶ Management Consultancy 4 Limited, 7-111 Fleet Street, London, EC4A 2AB Tel: 0 870 770 9116 Fax: 0 870 770 9117 E-mail: info@mc4.co.uk *MC4 provide Recruitment solutions in the following market sectors:***Investment*

continued

*Banking*Retail Banking *Finance *Technology *Energy & Commodity Trading *Insurance & Re-Assurance *Fast-Moving Consumer *Retail *Healthcare & Pharmaceutical *Manufacturing *Legal *Media *Government**

Management Horizons Europe Ltd, Europa House, Church Street, Isleworth, Middlesex, TW7 6DA Tel: (020) 8560 9393 Fax: (020) 8580 8310 E-mail: info@mheurope.com *Specialist retail management consultants*

▶ Management Introductions, 50 Gordon Street, Glasgow, G1 3PU Tel: 0141-248 5066 Fax: 0141-248 5086 *Training services*

Management Process Development Ltd, 30 Chantreys Drive, Elloughton, Brough, North Humberside, HU15 1LH Tel: (01482) 665675 E-mail: richard-grafton@supanet.com *Management & business consultants, customer relationship management, marketing, sales team training & business plans*

▶ Management Services 2000 Ltd, Middleton House, 38 Monkgate, York, YO31 7PF Tel: (01904) 659009 E-mail: enquiries@ms2m.com *Bespoke software for financial services companies*

Management Technology Services Ltd, 29 Bleasdale Avenue, Greenford, Middlesex, UB6 8LB Tel: (020) 8991 8066 Fax: (020) 8904 8055 E-mail: sramos@mtsl-net.co.uk *Computer consultants*

Manager Group Ltd, Claymore House, Claymore, Tame Valley Industrial Estate, Wilnecote, Tamworth, Staffordshire, B77 5DQ Tel: (0800) 0370120 Fax: (01827) 255367 E-mail: phil.richards@pergroup.co.uk *Accountants & business support for IT contractors & local business*

▶ manageyourbiz.com, Old Castle Farm, Llangain, Carmarthen, SA33 5BD Tel: (07810) 090268 E-mail: steve.williams@manageyourbiz.co.uk *We offer Professional Services to your Company in the following areas : *Business Process Re-Engineering, CAD/CAM, Continuous Improvement, SPC, Decision Analysis, Design, Design management, Electronic Communications, Environmental Management, Facilities Planning /Management, Finance and Management /Budgetary Controls, Health and Safety, Information Systems, People management, Performance Management and Appraisal, Process Analysis, Problem Solving, Product Design, Project management, Plastic Products, Situation Appraisal, Systems Development /Implementation, Systems Integration, Technology.*

Manas Ltd, PO Box 26273, London, W3 6FN Tel: (0870) 7335000 Fax: (0870) 7336000 E-mail: mail@manas.co.uk *Computer consultants*

Manbat Ltd, Water Street, Abergele, Clwyd, LL22 7SL Tel: (01745) 832174 Fax: (01745) 833503 E-mail: sales@manbat.co.uk *Batteries, motor vehicle & automotive distributors & agents* Also at: Chesterfield, Hereford, Manchester & Shrewsbury

Manbat Ltd, Unit 4D, Temple Gate Distribution Centre, Mead Street, Bristol, BS3 4RP Tel: 0117-977 6477 Fax: 0117-977 8481 E-mail: bristol@manbat.co.uk *Battery distributors*

Manbat Ltd, Foxwood Industrial Park, Chesterfield, Derbyshire, S41 9RN Tel: (01246) 452522 Fax: (01246) 452511 E-mail: chesterfield@manbat.co.uk *Battery distributors*

Manbat Ltd, Unit 1-5 Chancel Place, Store Street, Manchester, M1 2WB Tel: 0161-273 2235 Fax: 0161-273 7368 E-mail: sale@manbat.co.uk *Battery distributors*

Manbat Ltd, Lancaster Road, Shrewsbury, SY1 3LG Tel: (01743) 460792 E-mail: sales@manbat.co.uk *Battery distributors*

Joe Manby Ltd, Hook Stone Park, Harrogate, North Yorkshire, HG2 7DB Tel: (01423) 814730 Fax: (01423) 814760 E-mail: info@joemanby.co.uk *Exhibition stand contractors*

Mancells Marfleet Ltd, Erimus Works, Valletta Street, Hull, HU9 5NU Tel: (01482) 375231 Fax: (01482) 706545 E-mail: sales@mancells.co.uk *Steel stockholders*

Manches & Co., Aldwych House, 81 Aldwych, London, WC2B 4RP Tel: (020) 7404 4433 Fax: (020) 7430 1133 *Solicitors* Also at: Oxford

▶ Manchester Beds & Appliances, 342 Oldham Road, Manchester, M40 7NS Tel: 0161-205 9922 Fax: 0161-205 1717

Manchester Brick Services, Haigh Avenue, Whitehill Indust Estate, Reddish, Stockport, Cheshire, SK4 1NU Tel: 0161-480 2621 Fax: 0161-480 0108 *Concrete products & brick products manufrs*

Manchester Cabins Ltd, Tweedale Way, Oldham, OL9 7LD Tel: 0161-684 3333 Fax: 0161-684 1111 E-mail: info@manchestercabins.co.uk *Portable building & container hire*

Manchester Calorifiers Ltd, Lund Street, Manchester, M16 9EJ Tel: 0161-872 3613 Fax: 0161-872 3027 *Copper fabricators & heat exchanger manufrs*

▶ Manchester College Of Draughting & Technology, 2 Hellidon Close, Ardwick, Manchester, M12 4AH Tel: 0161-272 8900 Fax: 0161-230 6613

Manchester Drums Ltd, Bower Street, Newton Heath, Manchester, M40 2AS Tel: 0161-203 4611 Fax: 0161-203 5404 *Drum re-conditioners & refurbishment specialists*

Manchester Hosiery Ltd, Queens Road, Hinckley, Leicestershire, LE10 1EE Tel: (01455) 632161 Fax: (01455) 635390 E-mail: sales@palmunderwear.co.uk *Underwear manufrs*

Manchester Knitwear Manufacturing Ltd, 20 Stamford Road, Manchester, M13 0SN Tel: 0161-224 5313 *Knitwear & fabrics manufrs*

Manchester Paper Co. Ltd, Victoria Works, Williams Road, Gorton, Manchester, M18 7AY Tel: 0161-223 9363 Fax: 0161-223 9291 E-mail: sales@manchester.com *Paper products manufrs*

Manchester Paper Box Ltd, 2 Bird Hall Lane, Stockport, Cheshire, SK3 0SZ Tel: 0161-428 4225 Fax: 0161-428 0797 E-mail: c@mpbox.co.uk *Corrugated container manufrs*

Manchester Pin Mill Textiles Ltd, Dreamscene House, Park House Bridge Estate, Langley Road, Salford, M6 6JQ Tel: 0161-737 3300 Fax: 0161-737 3100 E-mail: info@pinmill.com *Domestic textile importers & distributor*

▶ Manchester Print Co., 8 Lower Ormond Street, Manchester, M1 5QF Tel: 0161-228 0775 E-mail: msctshirt@yahoo.co.uk *T-shirt printers*

The Manchester Rubber Stamp Company Ltd, 63 Red Bank, Manchester, M8 8RD Tel: 0161-834 1988 Fax: 0161-835 1529 E-mail: geoff@mrsengravers.co.uk *Rubber stamp & nameplate manufrs*

Manchester Safety Services Ltd, Fir Street, Heywood, Lancashire, OL10 1NW Tel: (01706) 364943 Fax: (01706) 360026 E-mail: sales@manchestersafety.co.uk *Industrial & road safety equipment distributors*

Manchester Seals, Hilmar House, 5 Girton Street, Salford, M7 1UR Tel: 0161-832 7922 Fax: 0161-833 1637 E-mail: sally@manchesterseals.co.uk *Hydraulic seal distributors*

Manchester Slate Ltd, 1119 Ashton Old Road, Manchester, M11 1AA Tel: 0161-223 5031 Fax: 0161-220 8925 *Building & plumbing material suppliers*

Manchester Sports Ltd, Unit G5, Newton Business Park, Talbot Road, Hyde, Cheshire, SK14 4UQ Tel: 0161-366 1212 Fax: 0161-366 1177 E-mail: sales@manchestersports.co.uk *Sportswear & equipment sales*

Manchester Toiletries & Food Wholesale, 173-175 Cheetham Hill Road, Manchester, M8 8LG Tel: (0161) 839 7086 Fax: (0161) 839 7084 E-mail: zabarimports@aol.com *Wholesalers of food & toiletries*

▶ Manchester Towbar Trailer & Roofrack Centre Ltd, Baring St (off Fairfield St), Ardwick, Manchester, M12 6HJ Tel: 0161-273 5816 Fax: 0161-273 6678 E-mail: info@manchestertowbars.co.uk *Manufacturers and suppliers of towbars trailers and roofracks*

Manchester Training Ltd, Greengate, Middleton, Manchester, M24 1RU Tel: (0800) 3895283 Fax: 0161-653 3536 E-mail: mail@manchestertraining.com *Training centre, vehicle & transportation trainers*

Manchester Umbrella Co. Ltd, Unit 10 Brook St Works, Adcroft Street, Stockport, Cheshire, SK1 3HZ Tel: 0161-480 5328 Fax: 0161-477 7884 E-mail: sales@manchesterumbrellas.co.uk *Promotional & sports umbrella manufrs*

Manchester Vehicle Painters, Unit 2 Reliance Trading Estate, Manchester, M40 3AG Tel: 0161-682 2556 Fax: 0161-682 0090 *Vehicle painters*

Manchester Vending Services Ltd, Alpha Point, Bradnor Road, Manchester, M22 4TE Tel: 0161-945 2030 E-mail: info@manvend.com *Vending machine services*

▶ Manchester Wholesale Tools, 5 Sagar Street, Manchester, M8 8EU Tel: 0161-834 1123 Fax: 0161-834 1123

Manco, Garland Works, Bennett Street, Ardwick, Manchester, M12 5BW Tel: 0161-223 0303 Fax: 0161-231 6558 *Coppersmiths*

Mandair Textiles Ltd, 175 Hockley Hill, Hockley, Birmingham, B18 5AN Tel: 0121-554 9506 Fax: 0121-554 3663 E-mail: mantexltd@hotmail.com *Trousers manufrs*

▶ Mandalay Venue Finding, East Wing, Stourton, Shipston-on-Stour, Warwickshire, CV36 5HJ Tel: (0870) 0201610 Fax: (0870) 0201611 E-mail: look@mandalaypartners.co.uk *Corporate conferences, conference venue, free venue finding service, hotel booking & complete event management, incentive travel, training & seminar locations found & compared for you for free.*

Mandale Engraving Co. Ltd, 11-12 Bissell Street, Birmingham, B5 7HQ Tel: 0121-622 3906 Fax: 0121-622 1817 E-mail: email@mandaleengraving.co.uk *Control & fascia panels, commercial engraving services*

▶ Mandco Ltd, 50 Watson Road East, Nechells, Birmingham, B7 5SB Tel: 0121-327 5026 Fax: 0121-328 0610 E-mail: enquiries@mandco.co.uk

Manderstam International Group Ltd, Douglas House, 16-18 Douglas Street, London, SW1P 4PB Tel: (020) 7730 9224 Fax: (020) 7823 3056 E-mail: migl@manderstam.com *Consulting engineers*

Manderwood Timber Engineering Ltd, Unit 5, Great Honeyborough Trading Estate, Milford Haven, Dyfed, SA73 1SE Tel: (01646) 600621 Fax: (01646) 600784 E-mail: mwoodnyl@aol.com *Timber roof truss manufrs* Also at: Baglan & Highbridge

Mandeville Medicines, Mandeville Road, Aylesbury, Buckinghamshire, HP21 8AL Tel: (01296) 394142 Fax: (01296) 397223 E-mail: manmed@bucksnet.co.uk *Pharmaceuticals manufrs*

Mando Brand Assurance Ltd, 27-28 Faraday Road, Rabans La Industrial Area, Aylesbury, Buckinghamshire, HP19 8TY Tel: (01296) 717900 Fax: (01296) 394273 *Fixed fee sales promotion consultants*

Mandor Engineering Ltd, Units 1 & 2 93 Oxford Street, West, Ashton-under-Lyne, Lancashire, OL7 0LZ Tel: 0161-330 6837 Fax: 0161-308 3336 E-mail: info@mandor.co.uk *Mandor provides cutting edge products within the industrial & commercial door market by combining the latest in technology with the highest quality in manufacture & assembly. Some of these products include the manufacture of automatic entrance doors, high speed doors & roller shutters. We offer a 24 hour service throughout the UK. Call us on 0161 330 6837 or take a look at our website www.mandor.co.uk*

▶ Maneline Coachworks, Basil Road, West Dereham, King's Lynn, Norfolk, PE33 9RP Tel: (01366) 502254 Fax: (01366) 502254

Company Information

▶ Manesis Search & Selection, 1 Lower Bar, Newport, Shropshire, TF10 7BE Tel: (01952) 811550 E-mail: recruit@manesis.co.uk *A specialist recruitment consultant focusing on Sales & Marketing Management positions within the building products and industrial manufacturing markets.*

Manesty Fabrication Services, Holmfield Industrial Estate, Holmfield, Halifax, West Yorkshire, HX2 9TP Tel: (01422) 241122 Fax: (01422) 241100 E-mail: chris.clarke@manesty.com *Stainless steel fabricators*

Mangar International Ltd, Presteigne Industrial Estate, Presteigne, Powys, LD8 2UF Tel: (01544) 267674 Fax: (01544) 260287 E-mail: sales@mangar.co.uk *Disabled equipment manufrs*

▶ Mangini Stairlifts, 48 Dunkerley Avenue, Failsworth, Manchester, M35 0EB Tel: (07960) 012276 Fax: 0161-681 0329 E-mail: mangini.stairlifts@virgin.net *Supply & install & repair stair lifts & other mobility equipment*

Mango Electronics, Mango House, 1 Buckhurst Road, Bexhill-On-Sea, East Sussex, TN40 1QF Tel: (01424) 731500 Fax: (01424) 731502 E-mail: colin@mango-electronics.co.uk *Designers of custom built electronic equipment*

▶ Mango Media, 49 Carnaby Street, London, W1F 9PY Tel: (020) 7292 9000 Fax: (020) 7434 1077 E-mail: info@mangomedia.net *Graphic design marketing consultants*

▶ Manhattan Blinds, 121 Brookfield Drive, Liverpool, L9 7AJ Tel: 0151-525 1166 Fax: 0151-525 1144 *Manufacturers of blinds*

Manhattan Design Studio, 25a Harrington Street, Pear Tree, Derby, DE23 8PE Tel: (01332) 776464 Fax: (01332) 776464 *Clothing manufrs*

Manhattan Electronics, 4 Cooksey Lane, Birmingham, B44 9QN Tel: 0121-605 2957 Fax: 0121-605 3031 E-mail: manhattanelec@hotmail.com *Computer repairs*

Manhattan Products Ltd, 89 Steward Street, Birmingham, B18 7AF Tel: 0121-454 6404 Fax: 0121-454 1497 E-mail: sales@manhattanproducts.com *One of the leading manufacturers of high quality prestige promotional products*

Manhattan Properties, 1147 Greenford Road, Greenford, Middlesex, UB6 0DP Tel: (020) 8423 8161 Fax: (020) 8423 8165 *Investment & financial consultants*

Manhattan Skyline Ltd, 5 Bracknell Business Centre, Downmill Road, Bracknell, Berkshire, RG12 1QS Tel: (01344) 307733 Fax: (01344) 307744 E-mail: sales@mansky.co.uk *Electronic displays import, distributors*

▶ Manhatten Heights, 108 Buckstones Road, Shaw, Oldham, OL2 8DN Tel: (01706) 849752 Fax: (01706) 299209 E-mail: sales@manheights.co.uk *Design, installation, maintenance & repair of air conditioning*

Manhick Engineering Ltd, 7 Wise Street, Leamington Spa, Warwickshire, CV31 3AP Tel: (01926) 332323 Fax: (01926) 315950 E-mail: dick.hickman@manhick.co.uk *Engineering services*

▶ Maniac Films Ltd, 6 Lorna Doone, Croyde, Braunton, Devon, EX33 1NU Tel: (01271) 891140 E-mail: info@maniacfilms.com *DVD production company & independent digital film*

▶ Manifax Engineering Ltd, 8 Coppen Road, Dagenham, Essex, RM8 1HJ Tel: (020) 8592 8849 Fax: (020) 8592 2553

▶ Manifest Communications, The Media Centre, Northumberland Street, Huddersfield, HD1 1RL Tel: (01484) 483088 Fax: (01484) 483089 E-mail: info@manifestcomms.co.uk *Manifest is a creative communications agency. Covering all marketing disciplines from advertising to pr, we work strategically with clients to provide effective campaigns to actively boost thier bottom line perfromance.*

▶ Manifest Station, Unit 8, Burstow Park Business Centre, Antlands Lane, Shipley Bridge, Horley, Surrey, RH6 9TF Tel: (01293) 823673 Fax: (01293) 821462 E-mail: station@manifeststation.co.uk *Window film & manifestation applied on glass nationally*

Maniflow Exhaust Centre, Mitchell Road, Salisbury, SP2 7PY Tel: (01722) 335378 Fax: (01722) 320834 E-mail: maniflow@lineone.net *Exhaust systems manufrs*

Manitowoc Europe Holdings Ltd, 1 Azure Court, Doxford International Business Park, Sunderland, SR3 3BE Tel: 0191-522 2000 Fax: 0191-522 2053 E-mail: info@manitowoc.com Principal Export Areas: Worldwide *Cranes sale & service*

Manitowoc Potain Ltd, Unit 2c Tomo Industrial Estate, Packet Boat Lane, Uxbridge, Middlesex, UB8 2JP Tel: (01895) 430053 Fax: (01895) 459500 *Excavator & crane manufrs*

Manjet Electronics, Longmeadow Works, Ringwood Road, Three Legged Cross, Wimborne, Dorset, BH21 6RD Tel: (01202) 823013 Fax: (01202) 823013 *Electronic equipment manufrs*

▶ Manjit Morjaria - Life Coaching, 14 Millennium Way, Wolston, Coventry, CV8 3PE Tel: (07968) 130980 Fax: (0870) 0671850 E-mail: m_morjaria@yahoo.co.uk *Life Coaching and mentoring individuals to achieve their goals. Working on a 1 to 1 basis, professional life coaching with a qualified individual who"se very personable and easy to talk to. Anything"s possible as long as you...1} know what you want, 2} when you want it by 3} how you"re going to do it. Sessions to suit the individual with fixed price, transparent pricing.*

Manjits Ltd, 304-310 Alcester Road, Birmingham, B13 8LJ Tel: 0121-449 5759 Fax: 0121-449 8925 *Builders & plumbers merchants*

▶ Manley Hill Plumbing & Heating Contractors, Unit 7, 8-10 Marlborough Hill, Harrow, Middlesex, HA1 1UX Tel: (020) 8863 0373 Fax: (020) 8424 8500 E-mail: enquiries@manleyhill.co.uk

Manley Summers Ltd, 49-50 The Hop Exchange, 24 Southwark St., London, SE1 1TY Tel: (020) 7403 7588 Fax: (020) 7403 0535 E-mail: mjcmanleysummers@aol.com *Employment agency*

Mann Aviation Group Engineering Ltd, Fairoaks Airport, Chobham, Woking, Surrey, GU24 8HX Tel: (01276) 857888 Fax: (01276) 857510 E-mail: engineering@alanmann.co.uk *Helicopter charter & maintenance*

Mann Bros Ltd, 142 High Street, West Bromwich, West Midlands, B70 6JJ Tel: 0121-553 7156 Fax: 0121-553 1961 E-mail: info@mannbros.co.uk *Casual wear suppliers & manufrs*

▶ Mann Crane Hire Ltd, Unit 1 Balthane Industrial Estate, Ballasalla, Isle Of Man, IM9 2AJ Tel: (01624) 835758 Fax: (01624) 836040 E-mail: mancranehire@manx.net

▶ Mann & Hummel, 70 Churchill Square, Kings Hill, West Malling, Kent, ME19 4YU Tel: (01732) 523533 Fax: (01732) 523534 E-mail: sales@mann-hummel.com *Filtering manufrs*

Mann Mcgowan Fabrications Ltd, 4 The Brook Trading Estate, Deadbrook Lane, Aldershot, Hampshire, GU12 4XB Tel: (01252) 333601 Fax: (01252) 322724 E-mail: sales@mannmcgowan.co.uk *Passive fire protection products manufrs*

Mann & Overton Ltd, 39-41 Brewery Road, London, N7 9QH Tel: (020) 7700 0888 Fax: (020) 7700 6676 E-mail: info@mannandoverton.com *Vehicle retailers*

▶ Mann Restoration, 30 Gloucester Place, Witney, Oxfordshire, OX28 6LA Tel: (01993) 704679 E-mail: sales@mannrestoration.com *Specialist cleaning of all masonry & timber beam cleaning*

Mann & Son London Ltd, The Navel House, Kings Quay Street, Harwich, Essex, CO12 3JJ Tel: (01255) 245200 Fax: (01255) 245219 E-mail: enquiries@manngroup.co.uk *Ship, liner agents & freight forwarders*

Manned Precision, Lower Wield, Alresford, Hampshire, SO24 9RX Tel: 01256 389258 *Precision engineers*

Manner UK Ltd, 13 Station Road, Cam, Dursley, Gloucestershire, GL11 5NS Tel: (01453) 546333 Fax: (01453) 549222 E-mail: sales@manner.co.uk *UK distributor for market leading wheels & castors. Excellent performance & visual. Supplied for wide range of mobile equipment utilised in many different product-market sectors. Key brands includes: 'Tango' - new generation of castor & 'WHEEL 2000' - innovative design.*

▶ Simon Manners, The Street, Croxton, Thetford, Norfolk, IP24 1LN Tel: (01842) 755922 Fax: (01842) 755922 *Furniture manufrs*

Manning Construction, Coychurch, Bridgend, Mid Glamorgan, CF35 5BU Tel: (01656) 862333 Fax: (01656) 861439

▶ Manning & Norman Ltd, 11 Harvest Court, Harvest Drive, Lowestoft, Suffolk, NR33 7NB Tel: (01502) 572957

Manning Selvage & Lee, Pembroke Building, Avonmore Road, London, W14 8DG Tel: (020) 7878 3000 Fax: (020) 7878 3030 E-mail: sales@mslpr.com *Public relations consultancy*

Mannings, 347 Footscray Road, London, SE9 2EH Tel: (020) 8859 3908 Fax: (020) 8859 3908 *Leaded lights & window contractors*

Manningtree Engineering Ltd, Riverside Avenue West, Manningtree, Essex, CO11 1UN Tel: (01206) 395636 Fax: (01206) 391209 E-mail: peter.spurgeon@btconnect.com *Plastics injection moulders*

Mannion Contractors Ltd, High Oak Road, Wicklewood, Wymondham, Norfolk, NR18 9QP Tel: (01953) 601156 *Demolition contractors*

Mannofield Electrical Ltd, Unit 11a Spires Business Units, Mugiemoss Road, Bucksburn, Aberdeen, AB21 9NY Tel: (01224) 682244 Fax: (01224) 680044 E-mail: mannofieldelectrical@aol.com *Electrical*

Mannor Blinds & Curtains, Unit 1 Cavendish Court, Lawkholme Lane, Keighley, West Yorkshire, BD21 3DY Tel: (01535) 665520 Fax: (01535) 691919 *Blind manufrs*

▶ Mann's Fireplaces, 96-98 Scotland Road, Nelson, Lancashire, BB9 7XJ Tel: (01282) 614789 Fax: (01282) 614789 E-mail: info@mannsfireplaces.co.uk *Stone, slate & marble, wood & brick fireplaces*

Manor Aquatics Centre, 653-657 Romford Road, London, E12 5AD Tel: (020) 8478 4478 Fax: (020) 8514 1400 E-mail: enquiries@manoraquatics.co.uk *Aquatics wholesalers*

Manor Bakeries Ltd, Fish Dam Lane, Barnsley, South Yorkshire, S71 3HQ Tel: (01226) 286191 Fax: (01226) 291003 *Cake manufrs*

▶ Manor Bakeries, Bellshill Road, Uddingston, Glasgow, G71 6NP Tel: (01698) 811738 Fax: (01698) 818783 *Photographers & printers*

Manor Bakeries Ltd, Brisbane Street, London, SE5 7NL Tel: (020) 7703 0291 *Cake distributors*

▶ Manor Bakeries Ltd, Newcastle Road, Stoke-on-Trent, ST4 6PH Tel: (01782) 621161 Fax: (01782) 623031 *Cake making specialists*

Manor Bakeries Ltd, 110 Reeds Lane, Wirral, Merseyside, CH46 1PR Tel: 0151-488 4800 Fax: 0151-488 4809 E-mail: cristianname.surname@manor-bakeries.co.uk *Bakery suppliers*

▶ Manor Beauty, Hove Manor, Hove Street, Hove, East Sussex, BN3 2DF Tel: (01273) 748483 E-mail: admin@blakeneymanor.co.uk *Beauty treatments suppliers*

▶ Manor Builders (Yeovil) Ltd, Manor Road, Yeovil, Somerset, BA20 1UF Tel: (01935) 474429

The Manor Cabinet Company Public Ltd Company, Kelvin Road, Swindon, SN3 3JW Tel: (01793) 423314 Fax: (01793) 423312 E-mail: info@manorcabinets.co.uk *Kitchen furniture manufrs*

Manor Coating Systems Ltd, Otley Road, Baildon, Shipley, West Yorkshire, BD17 7DP Tel: (01274) 587351 Fax: (01274) 531360 E-mail: info@manorcoatingsystems.co.uk *Industrial paint manufrs*

Manor Creative Ltd, 7-8 Edison Road, Eastbourne, East Sussex, BN23 6PT Tel: (01323) 514400 Fax: (01323) 509306 *Printers & lithographers*

▶ Manor Direct Ltd, 27-31 Francis Street, Hull, HU2 8DT Tel: (01482) 586312 Fax: (01482) 585310 E-mail: sales@manorglass.co.uk *Design planning & installation of commercial kitchens, catering equipment distributor* Also at: Hull

Manor Doors Ltd, Manor House, 6-8 Creek Road, Barking, Essex, IG11 0TA Tel: (020) 8591 3300 Fax: (020) 8591 3338 E-mail: enquiries@manordoors.com *Door & doorset manufrs*

Manor Enterprises, 3 Beacon Court, Birmingham Road, Kidderminster, Worcestershire, DY10 3JT Tel: (01562) 700375 Fax: 0121-358 1105 *Badge suppliers & manufrs*

Manor Forklift Services, 18 Harvesters Road, Willenhall, West Midlands, WV12 4AG Tel: (01902) 633390 Fax: (01902) 633390 *Fork lift trucks services*

Manor Foundry Ilkeston Ltd, Lower Granby Street, Ilkeston, Derbyshire, DE7 8DJ Tel: 0115-932 0097 Fax: 0115-930 4548 E-mail: john@manor-foundry.wanadoo.co.uk *Non-ferrous metal founders*

Manor House, Portland House, Reading, RG7 4YJ Tel: 0118-981 9333 Fax: 0118-981 9025 E-mail: manor.reservations@compass-group.co.uk *Country house conference centre*

▶ Manor House Care Services Ltd, 1 Queensmount, Five Ashes, Mayfield, East Sussex, TN20 6LH Tel: (01825) 830755 Fax: (01825) 830755 E-mail: admin@manorhousecareservices.co.uk *We provide mandatory training to small business- First Aid and Manual Handling, as well as providing a comprehensive Health and Safety service, comprising H&S Policies and Technical Manuals and general advice and help*

▶ Manor House Music String Quartet, 6 Goose Acre, Cheddington, Leighton Buzzard, Bedfordshire, LU7 0SR Tel: (01296) 663744 E-mail: info@manorhousemusic.co.uk *String Quartet available for corporate events, product launches, weddings, parties and functions. Able to supply full classical repertoire, pop and rock hits or special requests by arrangement.*

▶ Manor House Produce Ltd, 2 Daish Way, Newport, Isle of Wight, PO30 5XB Tel: (01983) 527327 Fax: (01983) 522187 E-mail: sales@manorhouseproduce.co.uk *Fruit & veg merchants*

Manor Industries Sa, Westwood, Dobbin Lane, Barlow, Dronfield, Derbyshire, S18 7SU Tel: 0114-289 1305 Fax: 0114-289 9264 E-mail: manoiruk@globlenet.co.uk *Steel founders*

▶ Manor Interiors, 86 High Street, Evesham, Worcestershire, WR11 4EU Tel: (01386) 422222 Fax: (01386) 48816 E-mail: sales@manor-interiors.co.uk *Retailers of curtains, carpets, rugs & blinds*

▶ Manor Lodge Dairy Products, 157a Sefton Street, Southport, Merseyside, PR8 5DA Tel: (01704) 538537 Fax: (01704) 501211 *Chilled goods wholesale & distribution*

Manor Marketing Label Supplies, 11 Manor Drive, Fenstanton, Huntingdon, Cambridgeshire, PE28 9QZ Tel: (01480) 462443 Fax: (01480) 359015 *Self adhesive labeling services*

The Manor Optical Co. Ltd, Manor House, Dudley Road, Halesowen, West Midlands, B63 4LS Tel: 0121-550 2609 Fax: 0121-550 5915 E-mail: sales@manor-optical.co.uk *Manufacturing opticians*

▶ Manor Packaging Ltd, 30-31 Maxwell Road, Peterborough, PE2 7JN Tel: (01733) 233884 Fax: (01733) 233885 E-mail: sales@manorpackaging.co.uk *Manufacturers, corrugated boxes, regular, plain & printed*

Manor Park Blinds Ltd, The Spinney, 5A Rectory Lane, Castle Bromwich, Birmingham, B36 9DH Tel: 0121-748 6900 Fax: 0121-747 9254 *Blind manufrs*

Manor Park Homes Ltd, Finedon Sidings Industrial Estate, Furnace Lane, Finedon, Wellingborough, Northamptonshire, NN9 5NY Tel: (01536) 726009 Fax: (01536) 726203 E-mail: manorparkhomes@lineone.net *Mobile homes producers*

▶ Manor Press Ltd, 36-38 Normanton Spring Road, Sheffield, S13 7BB Tel: 0114-269 5755 Fax: 0114-269 5755 E-mail: manorpress@tiscali.co.uk *Printers*

▶ Manor Printing Services (Wotton) Ltd, The Abbey Business Park, Charfield Road, Kingswood, Wotton-Under-Edge, Gloucestershire, GL12 8RL Tel: (01453) 843891

Manor Signs, 62 Knighton Lane, Leicester, LE2 8BE Tel: (0116) 283 5007 Fax: (0116) 283 8946 *House Sign Manufrs*

▶ Manor Sound Systems, 8 The Manor Way, Wallington, Surrey, SM6 7PJ Tel: (020) 8773 3793 E-mail: manorsound@btopenworld.com *installation/design/& repair to sound systems in pubs/clubs/bars/churchs.*

Manor Supplies Incorporating Manor Blinds, The Old Forge, Hall Lane, Upminster, Essex, RM14 1TT Tel: (01708) 377518 Fax: (01708) 343003 *Hospital cubicle track & insect screen manufacturers. Load-release system, to reduce risk of self-harm by patients. Curtain tracks, coat hooks, wardrobe rails, towel rails. Discreet protection for psychiatric areas.*

Manorhouse Stone, School Lane, Normanton le Heath, Coalville, Leicestershire, LE67 2TH Tel: (01530) 262999 Fax: (01530) 262515 *Reconstituted stone manufrs*

Manorway Fabrications Ltd, 9 Parsons Road, Manor Trading Estate, Benfleet, Essex, SS7 4PU Tel: (01268) 565565 Fax: (01268) 565761 *Steel fabricators*

Manoucher Food & Co UK Ltd, 4 Wilton Mews, London, SW1X 7AR Tel: (020) 7823 2345 Fax: (020) 7245 1202 E-mail: sales@manoucher.com *Bread suppliers*

Manpower UK Ltd, 12 Hall Quay, Great Yarmouth, Norfolk, NR30 1HP Tel: (01493) 853222 Fax: (01493) 330366 E-mail: great.yarmouth@manpower.co.uk *Specialist recruitment services*

Manpower UK Ltd, Capital Court, 30 Windsor Street, Uxbridge, Middlesex, UB8 1AB Tel: (01895) 205200 Fax: (01895) 205201 *Recruitment agency*

▶ Manrochem Ltd, 18 New North Parade, Huddersfield, HD1 5JP Tel: (01484) 453868 Fax: (01484) 453884 E-mail: rih@manrochem.co.uk *Chemical plant & process plant contractors or designers*

Manrose Manufacturing Ltd, Albion House, Albion Close, Slough, SL2 5DT Tel: (01753) 691399 Fax: (01753) 692294 E-mail: sales@manrose.com *Ventilation fans & equipment manufrs*

Mansam Products Ltd, 49-51 Broughton Lane, Manchester, M8 9UE Tel: 0161-834 1356 Fax: 0161-835 1024 E-mail: sales@mansam.co.uk *Welcome to Mansam Products Fabric and Trimmings suppliers to the trade based in Manchester. We stock a large supply of coated fabrics, vinyls and synthetic leather products in a wide variety of colours and finishes. We also supply PVC Sheeting and Linings including water resistant fabrics, suedettes, nonwoven breathable linings and plastic and padded foam linings. *We also stock a large stock of Trimmings including plastic and metal fittings, hook and look fasteners, zips, webbings, bindings, fasteners, threads, cords, elastic, tapes, pipings, press studs, eyelets, rivets, tags and locks for the textile markets. We supply nationally and internationally so please call us with your requirements or visit our website.*

Manse Furniture, 7 Curran Business Park, Portland Road, Larne, County Antrim, BT40 1DH Tel: (028) 2827 7744 Fax: (028) 2827 9137 *Kitchen furniture manufrs*

Mansel Construction Services Ltd, Lawrence House, River Front, Enfield, Middlesex, EN1 3SY Tel: (020) 8367 2999 Fax: (020) 8370 2992 E-mail: mansellenfield@mansell.plc.uk *Building contractors*

Mansell, Roman House, Granitehill Road, Aberdeen, AB16 7AW Tel: (01224) 717700 Fax: (01224) 698262 E-mail: info@mansell.plc.uk *Building contractors & joinery manufrs* Also at: Edinburgh, Elgin, Fraserburgh, Glasgow & Perth

▶ Mansell, Wards Road, Elgin, Morayshire, IV30 1NL Tel: (01343) 543974 Fax: (01343) 541045

▶ Mansell Construction General Works Division, 269d Queensway South, Team Valley Trading Estate, Gateshead, Tyne & Wear, NE11 0SD Tel: 0191-487 0004 Fax: 0191-482 5982

Mansell Construction Services Ltd, 522 Derby Road, Nottingham, NG7 2GW Tel: 0115-978 0788 Fax: 0115-942 0808 E-mail: midlands@mansell.plc.co.uk *Building contractors* Also at: Derby & Market Harborough

Mansell Construction Services Ltd, Roman House, Salisbury Road, Totton, Southampton, SO40 3XF Tel: (023) 8058 0400 Fax: (023) 8058 0401 E-mail: southampton@mansell.plc.uk *Building contractors & maintenance* Also at: Ashford

Mansell Construction Services Ltd, Wollaston Road, Stourbridge, West Midlands, DY8 4HP Tel: (01384) 440330 Fax: (01384) 440169 E-mail: stourbridge@mansell.plc.uk *Building & civil engineering*

Mansell Construction Services Ltd, Roman House, Turbine Way, Swaffham, Norfolk, PE37 7XD Tel: (01760) 721388 Fax: (01760) 724693 E-mail: swaffham@mansell.plc.uk *Building contractors*

▶ Mansell Watson (Builders) Ltd, Willow Bank, Insch, Aberdeenshire, AB52 6XJ Tel: (01464) 820488 Fax: (01464) 820371 E-mail: info@mansellwatsonbuildersltd.co.uk

Mansells Ltd, 20 Vanguard Way, Shoeburyness, Southend-on-Sea, SS3 9RA Tel: (01702) 294222 Fax: (08708) 722750 E-mail: man@oppenheimers.co.uk *Wooden furniture & instrument box makers & CNC router services*

Manser Precision Engineering, Unit 2, 216 Barnes Lane, Sarisbury Green, Southampton, SO31 7BG Tel: (01489) 564646 Fax: (01489) 564647 E-mail: jigboremanser@onetel.com *Jig boring specialists*

Mansfield Anodisers Ltd, 3 Kings Mill Way, Mansfield, Nottinghamshire, NG18 5ER Tel: (01623) 627700 Fax: (01623) 628800 E-mail: sales@mansfield-anodisers.co.uk *Decorative anodising manufrs*

Mansfield Board Machinery Ltd, 2 Horsley Road, Northampton, NN2 6LJ Tel: (01604) 713656 Fax: (01604) 791132 E-mail: sales@mansfieldboard.co.uk *Machine tool merchants*

Mansfield Brick Co. Ltd, Sandhurst Avenue, Mansfield, Nottinghamshire, NG18 4BE Tel: (01623) 622441 Fax: (01623) 420904 *Brick manufrs*

▶ Mansfield core supply, 53, Willowbridge lane, Sutton-in-ashfield, Nottinghamshire, NG17 1DW Tel: 01623 477583 E-mail: ianvardy@yahoo.com *Suppliers of Caliper and Clutch core to the remanufacturing industry.Also new parts available.*

Mansfield, Pollard & Co. Ltd, Edward House, Parry Lane, Bradford, West Yorkshire, BD4 8TL Tel: (01274) 774050 Fax: (01274) 775424 E-mail: admin@manpo.co.uk *Ventilation engineers*

Mansfield Refrigeration & Air Conditioning Co. Ltd, Dallas Street, Mansfield, Nottinghamshire, NG18 5SZ Tel: (01623) 626168 Fax: (01623) 420915 *Air conditioning & refrigeration suppliers*

Mantarun Systems Ltd, 310 Green La, Ilford, Essex, IG1 1XT Tel: (020) 8599 9980 Fax: (020) 8599 2498 E-mail: mantarun@btconnect.com *Computer consultants*

▶ Mantaur Ecommerce Solutions, Crombie Close, Hawkinge, Folkestone, Kent, CT18 7QR Tel: (01303) 894451 Fax: (01303) 894451 E-mail: contact@mantaur.co.uk *First and foremost we strive to understand your business and its objectives, and from there determine how the Internet would benefit you.**We can supply you with effective and efficient solutions to bring higher satisfaction and usability to both you and the end user. We will work with you to help grow your business, utilising Internet technologies to increase your customer base, visit frequency and spend, and simultaneously reduce your*

continued

continuation
*operating costs.**We have successfully undertaken a broad spectrum of web design projects. In our portfolio we include projects ranging from online brochures to full-blown database-driven Ecommerce sites.*

Mantaya Beverages Systems (MBS) Ltd, Unit 3 Blakenhall Farm, Linton Road, Caldwell, Swadlincote, Derbyshire, DE12 6RU Tel: (01283) 762867 Fax: (01283) 763859 E-mail: sales@mantaya.com *Mantaya Beverage Systems Ltd, Swadlincote, Derbyshire Only the best machines make the best coffee and our machines are designed and constructed to provide a great cup of coffee every time. We offer a wide range of coffee and beverage machines from fully automatic bean-to-cup, to the highest quality traditional and high volume commercial infusion brewers. Whatever your need we have a commercial coffee machine to suit. Machines can be purchased outright or leased as required. We also supply the full range of consumable items including specialist cleaning materials for grinders and expresso machines, filter papers and water filters. Full installation and training is available on all our machines backed up by our nationwide dealer network.*

Mantec Engineering Ltd, Unit 1-2 City Course Trading Estate, Whitworth Street, Openshaw, Manchester, M11 2DW Tel: 0161-223 8166 Fax: 0161-223 1084 E-mail: mail@mantec.org.uk *Mantec Engineering Ltd are based in Manchester and specialise in the CNC machining of both turned and milled components on our 8 and 9 axis turning centres, and twin pallet horizontal and vertical machining centres with 4th axis capabilities. With our quality approvals to ISO 9001, new CNC machines, Edge Cam programming and inspection department with a CMM, we have one of the best machining facilities in the North of England delivering quality assured components made to your exacting standards. Manchester, Northwest, UK.*

Mantells, A, 2 Holland Road, London, SE25 5RF Tel: (020) 8654 3163 Fax: (020) 8654 3163 *Plumbing & heating contractors*

Mantex International Ltd, Millbank House, Bollin Walk, Wilmslow, Cheshire, SK9 1BJ Tel: (01625) 530555 Fax: (01625) 528323 E-mail: mantex@mantexintl.co.uk *Textile agents & brokers*

Mantid Ltd, Unit 16 Klondyke Trading Estate, Rushenden Road, Queenborough, Kent, ME11 5HB Tel: (01795) 580558 *Crane hire & marine services*

Manton Engineering, 4-5 13 Murdock Road, Manton Industrial Estate, Bedford, MK41 7PE Tel: (01234) 345554 Fax: (01234) 272710 *Precision engineers*

Manton Office Equipment Ltd, 4 Clipstone Brook Industrial Estate, Cherrycourt Way, Leighton Buzzard, Bedfordshire, LU7 4GP Tel: (01525) 852350 Fax: (01525) 852352 E-mail: info@mantonoffice.com *Office equipment & stationery suppliers*

▶ Manton Transport Ltd, Springfield Farm Cold Cotes Road, Kettlesing Head, Felliscliffe, Harrogate, North Yorkshire, HG3 2LW Tel: (01423) 770520

Mantra Consultancy Group, 25 Ellington Street, London, N7 8PN Tel: (020) 7609 9055 Fax: (020) 7609 9447 *Management consultancy & training services*

Mantra Information Services Ltd, 12 Ash Close, Abbots Langley, Hertfordshire, WD5 0DN Tel: (01923) 266572 Fax: (01923) 351394 E-mail: nkg@mantra95.freeserve.co.uk *IT consultants*

Mantracourt Electronics Ltd, The Drive, Farringdon, Exeter, EX5 2JB Tel: (01395) 232020 Fax: (01395) 233190 E-mail: info@mantracourt.co.uk *Electronic instrument manufrs*

Mantsbrite Ltd, 19F Spital Road, Maldon, Essex, CM9 6DY Tel: (01621) 853003 Fax: (01621) 850877 E-mail: sales@mantsbrite.com Principal Export Areas: Worldwide *Marine electronic equipment distributor*

Manual Handling Solutions, 58, Paige Close, The Meadows, Watlington, King's Lynn, Norfolk, PE33 0TQ Tel: (01553) 811977 Fax: (01553) 811004 E-mail: sales@manualhandlingsolutions.co.uk *Manual handling & materials handling equipment.*Stair Climbers mobility and commercial*

Manuals Sewing Services Ltd, Unit 3-4, London Road Industrial Estate, Baldock, Hertfordshire, SG7 6NG Tel: (01462) 491828 Fax: (01462) 491829 E-mail: mail@manualz.co.uk *Industrial sewing services*

Manuel Engineering Co. Ltd, Unit 33 Barking Industrial Park, Alfreds Way, Barking, Essex, IG11 0TJ Tel: (020) 8594 9264 Fax: (020) 8594 5507 *Toolmakers & general engineers*

Manuel Lloyd Ltd, 20 Bull Lane, London, N18 1SX Tel: (020) 8807 4303 Fax: (020) 8807 3839 *Cardboard carton merchants or agents*

Manufacturers Supplies Acton Ltd, 2 Langley Wharf, Railway Terrace, Kings Langley, Hertfordshire, WD4 8JE Tel: (01923) 260845 Fax: (01923) 260847 E-mail: manusupplies@aol.com *Protective clothing Manufacturing*

Manufacturing Excellence Ltd, Round Foundry Media Centre, Foundry Street, Leeds, LS11 5QP Tel: (0870) 4202460 E-mail: Roger.lees@manufacturingexcellence.co.uk *Lean and Agile Manufacturing Consultancy. We are a DTI accredited Centre of Expertise in Manufacturing. We are a leading deliverer of Manufacturing Advisory Service supported projects in Yorkshire and Humberside and operate primarily throughout the North of England and Midlands. We are also approved by EAL as NVQ Assessors for PMO and BIT.*

▶ Manufacturing Executive Ltd, Ivy House 90 Town Street, Lound, Retford, Nottinghamshire, DN22 8RX Tel: (01777) 818280 E-mail: info@manufacturingexecutive.com *Provides assistance amd support to just manufacturing companies, coaching, advice,*

continued

consultancy or interim management - whatever is needed to help the business survive or meet its objectives

Manufacturing Techniques Corporation UK Ltd, Units 5-6 North Avon Business Centre, Dean Road, Yate, Bristol, BS37 5NH Tel: (01454) 318491 Fax: (01454) 318575 *Computer disk production machinery*

The Manufacturing Technologies Association, 62 Bayswater Road, London, W2 3PS Tel: (020) 7298 6400 Fax: (020) 7298 6430 E-mail: info@mta.org.uk *Representatives of companies in the manufacturing technologies sector*

Manufacturing Technology Partnership Ltd, 1b Millennium Way, Belfast, BT12 7AL Tel: (028) 9027 9860 Fax: (028) 9027 9869 E-mail: sales@mtpltd.com *Help smaller manufacturers increase revenue through appropriate technology*

Manufax Engineering Ltd, Cromer Street, Stockport, Cheshire, SK1 2NP Tel: 0161-480 2855 Fax: 0161-474 7159 E-mail: manufax@manufax.co.uk *Precision engineers & toolmakers*

Manuli-hydraulics UK Ltd, Unit C Nasmyth Business Centre, Green Lane, Patricroft, Eccles, Manchester, M30 0SN Tel: 0161-787 8085 Fax: 0161-787 8086 *Hydraulic hose manufrs*

Manumit Computers Ltd, Scope House, Weston Road, Crewe, CW1 6DD Tel: (01270) 250022 Fax: (01270) 250033 E-mail: contact@manumit-computers.com *Computer consultants*

Manumold Ltd, Lawrence Burns Ltd, Griffin Lane, Aylesbury, Buckinghamshire, HP19 8BP Tel: (01296) 435424 *Injection moulding machine manufrs*

Manuplastics Ltd, Lombard Road, London, SW19 3TZ Tel: (020) 8542 3421 Fax: (020) 8540 0594 E-mail: sales@manuplastics.co.uk *Plastic packaging products manufrs*

Manuscript Holdings Ltd, Moorswater, Moorswater, Liskeard, Cornwall, PL14 4LG Tel: (01579) 340340 Fax: (01579) 340341 E-mail: sales@manuscript.co.uk *Framed print & mirror manufrs*

Manuscript Pen Co. Ltd, New Road, Highley, Bridgnorth, Shropshire, WV16 6NN Tel: (01746) 861236 Fax: (01746) 862737 E-mail: manuscript@calligraphy.co.uk *Fountain pen sales, marketing & manufrs*

▶ Manusoft UK Ltd, The Groveange, Welford Road, Long Marston, Stratford-upon-Avon, Warwickshire, CV37 8RH Tel: (01789) 721930 Fax: (01789) 721901 E-mail: sales@menusoft.co.uk *IT solutions manufacturing industry development installation support*

Manx Computer Beureu Ltd, M & G House, Head Road, Douglas, Isle Of Man, IM1 5BF Tel: (01624) 623841 Fax: (01624) 623004 E-mail: postmaster@mcb.net *Computers, administration & payroll services*

Manx Engineers Ltd, Wheel Hill, Laxey, Isle of Man, IM4 7NL Tel: (01624) 861362 Fax: (01624) 861914 *Precision engineers & precision turned parts manufrs* Also at: Colne

Manx Petroleums, Battery Pier, Douglas, Isle of Man, IM99 1DE Tel: (01624) 691691 Fax: (01624) 662313 E-mail: info@manx-petroleums.co.im *Petroleum products distribs*

Manx Seafoods Ltd, Mill Road, Peel, Isle of Man, IM5 1TA Tel: (01624) 842415 Fax: (01624) 842342 E-mail: manxseafoods@manx.net *Fish processors*

Manx Security, 27 Regent Square, Belvedere, Kent, DA17 6EP Tel: (01322) 439333 Fax: (01322) 408331 E-mail: brian.manx@ntlworld.com *Vehicle security*

▶ Manx Workshop For The Disabled, Victoria Avenue, Douglas, Isle of Man, IM2 4AW Tel: (01624) 620149 Fax: (01624) 662516

▶ Manxboats.com, Unit 5,, Balderton Court, Balthane Industrial Estate, Ballasalla, Isle Of Man, IM9 2AJ Tel: (01624) 825040 E-mail: manxboats@manx.net *Boat sales*

Map Marketing Ltd, 92-104 Carnwath Road, London, SW6 3HW Tel: (020) 7526 2322 Fax: (020) 7371 0473 E-mail: sales@mapmarketing.com *Encapsulated business map suppliers*

▶ Map Marketing Limited, Suite 23,, Hardmans Business Centre, New Hall Hey Road, Rawtenstall, Lancashire, BB4 6HH Tel: 01706 220444 E-mail: glen@mapmarketing.com *Map Marketing Limited provide Ordnance Survey maps for planning applications, building regulations & land registry searches to a level of detail that shows individual building shapes.*

▶ Map Plant, Brunswick House, Ripple Road, Barking, Essex, IG11 0SL Tel: (020) 8592 7070 Fax: (020) 8592 8080

Mapal Ltd, Swift Park, Old Leicester Road, Rugby, Warwickshire, CV21 1DZ Tel: (01788) 574700 Fax: (01788) 569551 *Precision tooling manufrs*

Mapat Group Ltd, Unit 6, Mowat Trading Estate, Sandon Road, Watford, WD24 7UZ Tel: (01923) 255525 Fax: (01923) 250737 *School equipment suppliers*

Mapex UK Ltd, Unit 9 Pulloxhill Business Pk, Greenfield Rd, Pulloxhill, Bedford, MK45 5EU Tel: (01525) 719979 Fax: (01525) 719339 E-mail: info@mapex.demon.co.uk *Extrusion systems*

Mapgale Ltd, 1 Peppin Lane, Fotherby, Louth, Lincolnshire, LN11 0UW Tel: (01507) 600635 Fax: (01507) 600635 *Suspended ceilings & partitioning*

Maple Aggregates UK Ltd, 50 Preston Road, Brighton, BN1 4QF Tel: (01273) 699001 Fax: (01273) 670977 *Pumice stone & mineral importers*

▶ Maple Arenas, 41 Newlands Road, Riddings, Alfreton, Derbyshire, DE55 4EQ Tel: (01773) 606068 Fax: (01773) 606068 E-mail: info@maneges.co.uk *Equestrian arenas & gallops*

▶ Maple Computer Components, 37 Measham Way, Lower Earley, Reading, RG6 4ES Tel: 0118-987 5522

Maple Fleet Services Ltd, Maple House, High Street, Slamannan, Falkirk, FK1 3EY Tel: 0161-477 3476 Fax: 0161-477 6377 E-mail: sales@mapletechnology.co.uk Principal Export Areas: Worldwide *Commercial vehicles security systems & lock manufrs*

Maple Leaf Design Ltd, 4 Queen Street, Leicester, LE1 1QW Tel: 0116-262 6326 Fax: 0116-222 8919 *Menswear manufacturers.*

Maple Leaf Insulations Conservatories, Maple Leaf House, Canterbury Road, Worthing, West Sussex, BN13 1AW Tel: (01903) 692122 Fax: (01903) 831570 *Home improvements*

Maple Systems, 5 Mercia Business Village, Torwood Close, Westwood Business Park, Coventry, CV4 8HX Tel: (024) 7669 4489 Fax: (024) 7669 4474 E-mail: sales@maplesys.com Principal Export Areas: Worldwide *IBM compatible machine suppliers/manufrs*

▶ Maple Systems - Euro Reps Ltd., 155 Regents Park Road, (Main European Office), London, United Kingdom, NW1 8BB Tel: 0207 6649121 *European Representation for Maple Systems USA.*

▶ Maple Timber Frame, Tarnacres Hall Business Park, Tarnacre Hall Mews, Preston, PR3 0SZ Tel: (01995) 679444 Fax: (01995) 679769 *Prefabricated timber houses & buildings*

Maple Worcester Ltd, Stanier Road, Warndon, Worcester, WR4 9FE Tel: (01905) 754567 Fax: (01905) 756334 E-mail: sales@mapleworcester.com *Precision Engineering.*

▶ Maplecroft Joinery, Unit 26 Limestone Cottage Lane, Sheffield, S6 1NJ Tel: 0114-231 4490 Fax: 0114-231 4490

Maplin Electronics P.L.C., National Distribution Centre, Valley Road, Wombwell, Barnsley, South Yorkshire, S73 0BS Tel: (0870) 4296000 Fax: (0870) 4296001 E-mail: sales@maplin.co.uk *Electrical components distributors*

Mappin & Webb Ltd, 170 Regent Street, London, W1B 5BQ Tel: (020) 7734 3801 Fax: (020) 7494 3766 *Silversmiths* Also at: London EC3

▶ Mapra Technik Co., Unit D13, The Seedbed Centre, Langston Road, Loughton, Essex, IG10 3TQ Tel: (020) 8508 4207 Fax: (020) 8502 5107 E-mail: info@mapra.co.uk *MAPRA Technik Co. have launched their own range of MAPRA "High Quality - Low Cost" digital precision measuring instruments (including digital calipers with Absolute ABS, High Precision, IP67, Left-Hand, Metal Casing versions; digital height gauges; digital outside micrometers; digital thickness gauges; digital depth gauges; digital indicators). MAPRA Technik Co. are also the exclusive agents in the U.K. and Eire for the entire range of products manufactured by: MARCEL AUBERT S.A. of Switzerland ("non contact" optical metrology products, video measuring and inspection systems, centering microscopes, profile projectors) and BAREISS GmbH of Germany (SHORE and IRHD hardness testers, abrasion testers, resilience elasticity testers, hardness testers for gelatine capsules, Vickers Testers and other materials testers). Official agents for: KÄFER GmbH of Germany (dial gauges, dial indicators and thickness gauges.*

Maprac (UK) Ltd, 57-59 High Street, Hoddesdon, Hertfordshire, EN11 8TQ Tel: (01992) 440880 Fax: (01992) 442422 E-mail: info@mapracuk.co.uk *Importer & distributor of plastics*

Mapsoft Computer Services Ltd, Idstone, Loddiswell, Kingsbridge, Devon, TQ7 4EJ Tel: (01548) 550047 E-mail: impdeved@mapsoft.com *Computer software consultants*

▶ Maq Air Conditioning, Hillhouse Community Workshop, Argyle CR, Hillhouse Industrial Estate, Hamilton, Lanarkshire, ML3 9BQ Tel: (01698) 286721 Fax: (01698) 200426

Marah Timms & Sons Scaffolding Ltd, 6 High Street, New Whittington, Chesterfield, Derbyshire, S43 2DX Tel: (01246) 450673 Fax: (01246) 452262 *Scaffolding contractors*

Marandy Computers Ltd, 21 Lowswater Drive, Loughborough, Leicestershire, LE11 3RR Tel: 0115-911 8808 Fax: 0115-958 2400 E-mail: info@marandy.com *Computer consultants*

Marann Blinds, 18 Ferndale Cresent, Kidderminster, Worcestershire, DY11 5LL Tel: (01562) 67522 *Blinds resellers*

Marasu's Petits Fours Ltd, 8 Powergate Business Park, Volt Avenue, London, NW10 6PW Tel: (020) 8961 3399 Fax: (020) 8963 0088 E-mail: sales@marasu.co.uk *Chocolate manufrs*

Marathon Belting Ltd, Healey Mill, Whitworth Road, Rochdale, Lancashire, OL12 0TF Tel: (01706) 657052 Fax: (01706) 525143 E-mail: sales@marathonbelting.co.uk *Marathon Belting Limited was formed in 1976 to fill a small niche in the woven belting market. Since that time our market research, development and innovation has taken us into the field of heavy industrial textiles. We believe that we have the most diverse range of looms, the majority of which are shuttle looms, in the textile industry, having the ability to weave from 50mm to 3000mm in width from a single ply construction up to 40mm thick woven as a nine ply. Our company is now a market leader in many areas of specialised heavy weaving where durable and precise textile constructions are needed to fulfil difficult operating requirements often at high temperatures. Other products and services include rope and chain slings, rope and chain prectection, roller sleeves, press pads, high temperature conveyor belt textiles, cotton and polyester webbing for the biscuit industry, impression fabric for the rubber industry, metallised weave Colourmesh which is a radically new architectural material using stainless steel in the weave which is used for wall coverings, screens and many more applications. As a leader in export we have many representatives in upto 100 countries who are happy to assist you in proving a quality service*

Marathon Electric, 6 Thistleton Road, Market Overton, Oakham, Leicestershire, LE15 7PP Tel: (01572) 768206 Fax: (01572) 768217 E-mail: meuk@btinternet.com *Alternator & motor distributors*

Marathon Electronics Ltd, Sovereign Park, Cleveland Way, Hemel Hempstead, Hertfordshire, HP2 7DA Tel: (01442) 232324 Fax: (01442) 243656 E-mail: salse@marathonelectronics.couk *Electronic components distributors*

Marathon Engineering, Unit 15 Chiltern Trading Estate, Earl Howe Road, Holmer Green, High Wycombe, Buckinghamshire, HP15 6QT Tel: (01494) 715528 Fax: (01494) 715528 *Precision engineers*

Marathon Equipment, PO Box 102, Bexhill-on-Sea, East Sussex, TN40 2ZT Tel: (01424) 223700 Fax: (01424) 223800 *Garage equipment distributors*

Marathon International Petroleum G B Ltd, Capital House, 25 Chapel Street, London, NW1 5DQ Tel: (020) 7298 2500 Fax: (020) 7298 2501 *Oil, gas exploration & production*

Marathon Microfilming Ltd, St. Marys Place, Southampton, SO14 3HY Tel: (023) 8022 0481 Fax: (023) 8023 0452 E-mail: sales@marathonmicro.com *CD duplication services, document scanning, microfilm & scanning*

Marathon P R Ltd, 2 West Street, Epsom, Surrey, KT18 7RG Tel: (01372) 727030 Fax: (01372) 744150 E-mail: ray@marathonpr.co.uk *Business telephone system manufrs*

Marathon Window Co. Ltd, 35 Upper High Street, Epsom, Surrey, KT17 4RA Tel: (01372) 740706 Fax: (01372) 722857 *Double glazing installers* Also at: Purley

Marawise Treatments Ltd, Unit 17 Relton Mews, Eden Street, Coventry, CV6 5HE Tel: (024) 7668 7121 Fax: (024) 7668 7121 *Blast cleaning metal treatments*

Marbaix Holdings Ltd, Marbaix House, Wella Road, Basingstoke, Hampshire, RG22 4AG Tel: (01256) 473141 Fax: (01256) 462352 *Holding company*

Marbal Pre Packing, 22-28 Clough Road, Rotherham, South Yorkshire, S61 1RD Tel: (01709) 553900 Fax: (01709) 553803 E-mail: sales@marbal.com *Pre-packaged hardware & contract packers*

▶ Marbank Construction Ltd, Unit 3, Silver Court, Welwyn Garden, Welwyn Garden City, Hertfordshire, AL7 1TS Tel: (01707) 338844 Fax: (01707) 323322

Marbco Fire & Safety, Barrington Industrial Estate, Bedlington, Northumberland, NE22 7DQ Tel: (01670) 828488 Fax: (01670) 828315 *Sales & service of fire equipment*

Marben Engineering Ltd, 3 Cobham Road, Ferndown Industrial Estate, Wimborne, Dorset, BH21 7PE Tel: (01202) 895980 Fax: (01202) 891416 E-mail: marben123@aol.com *Production & precision engineers & fabrication*

Marber Promotions & Marketing Ltd, 30b Park Road, Hale, Altrincham, Cheshire, WA15 9NN Tel: 0161-927 9085 Fax: 0161-927 9087 E-mail: enquiries@marber.co.uk *Promotional marketing case manufrs*

Marbill Developments Sabden Ltd, Victoria Mill, Watt Street, Clitheroe, Lancashire, BB7 9ED Tel: (01282) 778031 Fax: (01282) 779507 E-mail: sales@marbill.co.uk *Polyurethane products, rollers manufacturer & spray coating services*

▶ Marble Building Products Ltd, The Airfield, Full Sutton, York, YO41 1HS Tel: (01759) 373352 Fax: (01759) 373394 E-mail: ethurlow@mbpltd.uk.com *Marble granite work surfaces supply & manufrs*

▶ Marble Recruitment Ltd, Dominions House, Queen Street, Cardiff, CF10 2AR Tel: (029) 2038 3837 Fax: (029) 2038 3847 E-mail: paul@marblerecruitment.co.uk *Marble Recruitment is one of Cardiff's newest and most progressive recruitment agencies. We aim to provide clients with the right people to grow their business and candidates the right job to develop their career. Our focus areas are admin & secretarial, sales & marketing and construction & Technical.*

Marble Warehouse, Unit 1 Maritime Industrial Estate, Pontypridd, Mid Glamorgan, CF37 1NY Tel: (01443) 408548 Fax: (01443) 480344 *Fireplaces manufrs*

▶ Marbles Ltd, 9 South Street, Bromley, BR1 1RH Tel: (020) 8313 3467 Fax: (020) 8313 3509 E-mail: graham@marbellimited.com *Stone products*

Marbonyx Ltd, Welton Way, Purdeys Indust Estate, Purdeys Industrial Estate, Rochford, Essex, SS4 1LA Tel: (01702) 543235 Fax: (01702) 543266 E-mail: sales@marbonyx.com *Marble, stone & granite specialist merchants - monumental masons*

Marc Containers Ltd, Unit 33b Westerton Road, East Mains Industrial Estate, Broxburn, West Lothian, EH52 5AU Tel: (01506) 852804 Fax: (01506) 857083 *Storage container manufrs*

Marc Five Ltd, Maydown Industrial Estate, Carrakeel Drive, Maydown, Londonderry, BT47 6UQ Tel: (028) 7186 1288 Fax: (028) 7186 1285 E-mail: marc_fiveltd@hotmail.com *Joinery manufrs*

▶ Marc Stapleford, Unit A39 The Springboard Centre, Mantle Lane, Coalville, Leicestershire, LE67 3DW Tel: (0870) 7417314 E-mail: marc@msld.co.uk *Commercial & private landscape design*

Marcalex Insulation Services, Hampstead Mill, Lake Street, Great Moor, Stockport, Cheshire, SK2 7NU Tel: 0161-456 7455 Fax: 0161-483 2529 E-mail: sales@marcalexservices.co.uk *Insulation contractors*

▶ Marcegaglia UK Ltd, New Road, Dudley, West Midlands, DY2 8TA Tel: (01384) 242812 Fax: (01384) 242813 E-mail: uk@marcegaglia.com *Steel tube manufrs*

March Designs & Measurements, 11 Alfred Street, Dunstable, Bedfordshire, LU5 4HZ Tel: (01582) 600016 Fax: (01582) 600016 E-mail: info@marchdesigns.com *Electronic gauging equipment designers & manufrs*

▶ Marchant Design Associates, 28/29 Woodside Close, Amersham, Buckinghamshire, HP6 5EF Tel: 01494 725093 E-mail: business@marchantassociates.com *Award-winning product design from concept to production*

▶ Marchant Joinery, Unit 21 Park Farm, Hundred Acre Lane, Wivelsfield Green, Haywards Heath, West Sussex, RH17 7RU Tel: (07753) 821124 Fax: (01273) 891977 *Joinery manufrs*

Marchant Manufacturing Co. Ltd, Piperell Way, Haverhill, Suffolk, CB9 8QW Tel: (01440) 705351 Fax: (01440) 762593 E-mail: sales@marchant.co.uk *Glass fibre mouldings manufrs*

▶ Marchaven Consulting Ltd, 8 Daisy Lane, Overseal, Swadlincote, Derbyshire, DE12 6JH Tel: (01283) 761813 E-mail: jarvis.whitehead@marchaven.co.uk *Financial services*

▶ Marcher Chemicals Ltd, Rock Road, Rhosymedre, Wrexham, Clwyd, LL14 3YF Tel: (01978) 821245 Fax: (01978) 821169 E-mail: sales@aquatecpaint.co.uk *Timber preservatives*

▶ Marches Architectural Hardware, Ddole Road Industrial Estate, Llandrindod Wells, Powys, LD1 6DF Tel: (01597) 823822 Fax: (01597) 823821

Marchwood Scientific Services, Unit 4G, Marchwood Industrial Pk, Marchwood, Southampton, SO40 4PB Tel: (023) 8066 9126 Fax: (023) 8066 9127 E-mail: enquiries@marchwood-scientific.co.uk *Analysis services*

Marchwood Technologies Ltd, Unit 9, 7 Black Moor Road, Ebblake Industrial Estate, Verwood, Dorset, BH31 6AX Tel: (01202) 810770 Fax: (01202) 820770 E-mail: norma@marchwood.co.uk *Industrial engineers*

▶ Marcle Leisure .Co.Uk, Huntleys Farm Lane, Much Marcle, Ledbury, Herefordshire, HR8 2NB Tel: (01531) 660797 Fax: (01531) 660462 E-mail: mail@marcleleisure.co.uk *Specialty supplier & installer of semi air suspension systems*

Marcmoor Computer Systems, 5a Church Sq, Market Harborough, Leics, LE16 7HB Tel: (01858) 465746 Fax: (01858) 434628 E-mail: paul@marcmoor.co.uk *Software house*

▶ Marco Electrical, 22 Tresillian Street, Cattedown, Plymouth, PL4 0QW Tel: (01752) 256243 Fax: (01752) 256249 *Electrical contractors*

Marco Joinery Ltd, 17-19 Downing Street, Sutton-in-Ashfield, Nottinghamshire, NG17 4EF Tel: (01623) 556684 Fax: (01623) 556664 *Joinery manufrs*

▶ Marco Specialist Interiors, 2 Boughton Road, London, SE28 0AG Tel: (020) 8331 0066 Fax: (020) 8317 3161 E-mail: info@marcointeriors.co.uk *Lift construction & installation services*

Marco Trading Co. Ltd, Marco House, Tariff Street, Manchester, M1 2FF Tel: 0161-228 6765 Fax: 0161-236 3611 E-mail: info@marco-uk.com *Ladieswear & school clothes for children*

Marcol Fabrications Ltd, Unit 10 Southfield Road Trading Estate, Nailsea, Bristol, BS48 1JJ Tel: (01275) 810022 Fax: (01275) 810033 E-mail: sales@marcolplastics.co.uk Sales Contact: Mark. Godfrey *Design-manufacture-service-repair. Plastic fabrication, including the manufacture/installation of bulk storage chemical tanks, on site pipe-work for chemical & fluid handling. Scrubber/fume extraction engineers, ventilation ductwork to DW 154 & BS7258 & supplier of plastic fans. Also manufacturers of industrial machine guards. A full CAD design service available*

▶ Marcol Plant Services Ltd, 57 Pentstemon Drive, Swanscombe, Kent, DA10 0NL Tel: (07973) 781118 Fax: (01322) 384504 E-mail: martin@marcolplant.com *Suppliers of vacuum lifting systems for the safe handling of any object for all industries, highways & associated civil engineering contractors*

Marcon Concepts Ltd, Building 16a, Greenwich Road, Newport, Gwent, NP20 2NN Tel: (0870) 0853790 Fax: (0870) 0853799 E-mail: enq@marconconcepts.co.uk *Industrial engraving & hot foil labelling*

Marcon Diamond Products Ltd, Marcon House, 131 High Street, Codicote, Hitchin, Hertfordshire, SG4 8UB Tel: (01438) 820581 Fax: (01438) 821352 *Diamond tool manufrs*

▶ Marcote (UK), Unit 2 Greenhough Trading Estate, Greenhough Road, Lichfield, Staffordshire, WS13 7AU Tel: (01543) 419904 Fax: (01543) 415752 E-mail: sales@marcote.co.uk *Surface coating contractors*

Marcrist International Limited, Marcrist House, Kirk Sandall Industrial Estate, Doncaster, S. Yorkshire, DN3 1QR Tel: (01302) 890888 Fax: (01302) 883864 E-mail: info@marcrist.com *Marcrist, we create success for our customers by providing world-class cutting edge products and services. Our product portfolio includes the design and manufacture of Diamond Blades, Diamond Cores, Surface Preparation Equipment, Dust Management Systems and Bonded Abrasives.*

Marcroft Engineering Ltd, Whieldon Road, Stoke-on-Trent, ST4 4HP Tel: (01782) 844075 Fax: (01782) 843579 *Build, re-furbish & maintain all types of rail freight rolling stock* Also at: Stoke-on-Trent & Swansea

Marcus Ltd, 39 Outram Street, Darlington, County Durham, DL3 7DP Tel: (01325) 353882 Fax: (01325) 358408 E-mail: sales@newpc.co.uk *Computer manufrs*

▶ Marcus (Bradford) Ltd, Low Fold Farm, Back Heights Road, Thornton, Bradford, West Yorkshire, BD13 3RP Tel: (01274) 835232

▶ Marcus (Bradford) Ltd, Unit 10, Northside Industrial Estate, Northside Road, Bradford, West Yorkshire, BD7 2QT Tel: (01274) 573488

Edward Marcus Ltd, Unit 3 Marrtree Business Park, Kirkwood Close, Oxspring, Sheffield, S36 8ZP Tel: (01226) 764082 Fax: (01226) 764082 E-mail: sales@edwardmarcus.co.uk *Ophthalmic instrument distributors*

Marcus Hearn & Co. Ltd, 65 Shoreditch High Street, London, E1 6JL Tel: (020) 7739 3444 Fax: (020) 7739 7888 E-mail: mail@marcushearn.co.uk *Insurance brokers*

Marcus Wilkinson The Time House, Bluecourt, Guildhall Street, Grantham, Lincolnshire, NG31 6NJ Tel: (01476) 560400 Fax: (01476) 568791 E-mail: sales@thetimehouse.com *Jewellery repairs & retailers*

▶ Marcus Worthington & Co. Ltd, Claughton Industrial Estate, Brockholes Way, Claughton-on-Brock, Preston, PR3 0PZ Tel: (01995) 640690 Fax: (01995) 640771 E-mail: enquiries@worthingtons.co.uk

▶ Mardale Clothing Ltd, Unit 101 Oystons Mill, Strand Road, Preston, PR1 8UR Tel: (01772) 722513 Fax: (01772) 726715 E-mail: sales@mardale.com

Mardale Pipes Plus Ltd, PO Box 86, Runcorn, Cheshire, WA7 1PX Tel: (01928) 580555 Fax: (01928) 591033 E-mail: sales@mardale-pipes.com *Pipe flange manufrs*

Mardec Joinery Distributors Sussex Ltd, Unit 16 Swan Barn Business Centre, Old Swan Lane, Hailsham, East Sussex, BN27 2BY Tel: (01323) 449028 Fax: (01323) 449024 *Fitted furniture joinery distributors & manufrs*

Marden Edwards Ltd, 2 East Dorset Trade Park, Nimrod Way, Wimborne, Dorset, BH21 7SH Tel: (01202) 861200 Fax: (01202) 861400 E-mail: sales@mardenedwards.com Purchasing Contact: P. Daniel Sales Contact: M Patey Principal Export Areas: Worldwide *Designers and manufacturers of overwrapping, stretchbanding, shrink wrapping, product handling machines and conveying systems. Based in both the UK and Germany we manufacture and supply packaging machinery to over 150 countries around the world. We supply a large range of film wrapping machines, ranging from chamber L sealers, manual I sealers, automatic L sealers, automatic two reel sleevewrappers through to individual and multipacking overwrappers. Our large design team enables both bespoke and turnkey projects to be supplied, including special purpose machinery. Please contact us whatever product it is that you wish to wrap.*

Marden Engineering, 1 Priestley Way, Crawley, West Sussex, RH10 9NT Tel: (01293) 530530 Fax: (01293) 530537 *Machine parts manufrs*

▶ Marden Homes Ltd, 275 Prince Avenue, Westcliff-On-Sea, Essex, SS0 0JP Tel: (01702) 437100 *Property Developers /Builders*

Mardix Automatic Controls Ltd, Westmorland Business Park, Gilthwaiterigg Lane, Kendal, Cumbria, LA9 6NS Tel: (01539) 720161 Fax: (01539) 724384 E-mail: switchgear@mardix.co.uk *Electrical switch gears manufrs*

Mardon Engineering Co. Ltd, Ditton Priors Trading Estate, Station Road, Ditton Priors, Bridgnorth, Shropshire, WV16 6SS Tel: (01746) 712616 Fax: (01746) 712349 *Extraction equipment manufrs*

Mardyke Miniature Railway, 1 Imperial Trading Estate, Lambs La North, Rainham, Essex, RM13 9XL Tel: (01708) 520264 Fax: (01708) 553395 *Narrow gauge railway constructors*

Marel Food Systems Ltd, The Warrens Industrial Park, Enderby, Leicester, LE19 4JS Tel: 0116-284 3500 Fax: 0116-284 9339 *Weighing equipment retail*

Marell Electronic Systems Ltd, Coldwell Street, Linthwaite, Huddersfield, HD7 5QN Tel: (01484) 843142 Fax: (01484) 843177 E-mail: info@marell.co.uk *Electronic equipment for the film & television industry*

Marenda Lindsey Ltd, Station Road, South Willingham, Market Rasen, Lincolnshire, LN8 6JQ Tel: (01507) 313301 Fax: (01507) 313513 E-mail: enquiries@marendalindsey.co.uk *Bathroom & kitchen equipment sales*

Maresco Ltd, 2 The Alcorns, Cambridge Road, Stansted, Essex, CM24 8DF Tel: (01279) 817333 Fax: (01279) 817334 *Flooring specialists & contractors*

Marex Carlton Ltd, Gossard House, Savile Row, London, W1S 3PE Tel: (020) 7491 6700 Fax: (020) 7491 6799 *Commodity brokers & dealers*

Marex Financial Ltd, Ground & 1St Floor Trinity Tower, Thomas Moore Square, London, E1W 1YH Tel: (020) 7488 3232 Fax: (020) 7265 3959 *Commodity & financial brokers services*

Marflow Engineering Ltd, Austin Way, Hampstead Industrial Estate, Birmingham, B42 1DU Tel: 0121-358 1555 Fax: 0121-358 1444 E-mail: sales@marflow.co.uk *Plumbing & heating equipment distributors*

Margaret Ann Baby Wear, Ayr Street, Nottingham, NG7 4FX Tel: 0115-942 0384 Fax: 0115-970 4967 *Baby wear suppliers*

▶ Margaret Hall Ltd, Scar Bank, Warwick, CV34 5DB Tel: (01926) 492574 Fax: (01926) 400796 *Bakery*

Margin Services Ltd, Brookside Business Park, Brookside Avenue, Littlehampton, West Sussex, BN16 3LF Tel: (01903) 856123 Fax: (01903) 786062 E-mail: martin@marginservices.co.uk *Electrical contractors*

Marglen Engineering Co. Ltd, 50a Bunyan Road, Kempston, Bedford, MK42 8HL Tel: (01234) 853270 Fax: (01234) 857179 E-mail: marglen@btconnect.com *Precision engineers*

Margnor Fasteners Ltd, 36 Stringers Avenue, Guildford, Surrey, GU4 7NW Tel: (01483) 536800 Fax: (01483) 536801 *Bolt & nut stockists*

Margolis Business Systems, Unit 4.02 Crayfield Business Park, New Mill Road, Orpington, Kent, BR5 3QA Tel: (01689) 891000 Fax: (01689) 890555 E-mail: sales@margolis.co.uk *Office equipment, partitioning designers & builders*

Margolis Technology, Laser House, 132-140 Goswell Road, London, EC1V 7DY Tel: (020) 7251 7000 Fax: (020) 7251 7600 E-mail: tdwyer@margolistechnology.com *Complete office solutions providers*

Margot Steel, Johnstonebridge, Lockerbie, Dumfriesshire, DG11 1HD Tel: (01576) 470258 Fax: (01576) 470640 E-mail: sales@margotsteel.com *Giftware manufrs*

▶ maria clark, Acacia house, lordship road, london, london, united kingdom, N16 0px Tel: 0207 502 1592 E-mail: maria@mariaclark.com *handmade bespoke soap beautifully created and gift wrapped can also be personalised*

Marian Engineering Ltd, First Avenue, Team Valley Trading Estate, Gateshead, Tyne & Wear, NE11 0NU Tel: 0191-482 2891 Fax: 0191-491 0891 E-mail: admin@mariandoors.co.uk *Industrial door manufrs*

Maricom Ltd, Hamble Point Marina, School Lane, Hamble, Southampton, SO31 4JD Tel: (023) 8045 4263 Fax: (023) 8045 6910 E-mail: sales@maricom.co.uk *Marine electronic engineers*

Maridian Engineers Ltd, Unit 14 Vincent Works, Vincent Lane, Dorking, Surrey, RH4 3HW Tel: (01306) 881250 Fax: (01306) 887415 *Press tool manufrs*

Marigold Health Foods Ltd, 102 Camley Street, London, NW1 0PF Tel: (020) 7388 4515 Fax: (020) 7388 4516 E-mail: info@marigoldhealth.co.uk *Chilled vegetarian products manufrs*

Marigold Industrial Ltd, B2 Vantage Park, Old Gloucester Road, Hambrook, Bristol, BS16 1GW Tel: (01454) 323633 Fax: (0845) 0753356 E-mail: sales@marigold-industrial.com *Industrial glove manufrs*

Marilake Instruments Ltd, Building 97, Bournemouth International Airport, Christchurch, Dorset, BH23 6SE Tel: (01202) 570055 Fax: (01202) 581369 E-mail: phil@mailake.com *Aircraft instrument repair services*

Marime Ltd, 47 Ryhill Way, Lower Earley, Reading, RG6 4AZ Tel: 0118-986 9685 Fax: 0118-975 6196 *Ventilation engineers*

MARINA SPA, 40 Portsmouth Road, Camberley, Surrey, GU15 1JU Tel: 01276 686682 Fax: 01276 686682 E-mail: info@marinaspa.co.uk *Hot tubs, Spa, gazebo, Canadian Spa Dealer, Canadian Spa Dealer in Surrey, ®Visscher speciality products dealer, champion chemicals, canadian spa chemicals, garden design, cheap spas.*

Marine Aid, Tidesreach Convent Meadows Caravan Park, The Quay, Christchurch, Dorset, BH23 1BD Tel: (01202) 477484 Fax: (01202) 477484 *Water treatment equipment & service*

▶ Marine Current Turbines, The Court, The Green, Stoke Gifford, Bristol, BS34 8PD Tel: 0117-979 1888 Fax: 0117-906 6140 E-mail: sales@marineturbines.com

▶ Marine Decor, Castle Street, Trowbridge, Wiltshire, BA14 8AY Tel: (01225) 768802 Fax: (01225) 768822 E-mail: kerryjohns@aol.com *Cruise ship consultants*

▶ Marine Dental Practice, 36 Marine Parade, Worthing, West Sussex, BN11 3QA Tel: (01903) 234136 Fax: (01903) 216195 *Dentist*

Marine Electronic Supplies, Unit 14 Westwood Court, Brunel Road, Totton, Southampton, SO40 3WX Tel: (023) 8066 3316 Fax: (023) 8066 3241 E-mail: sales@mesuk.com *Supply & servicing of marine navigation & communication electronics*

Marine Engineering Pipworks, Leechmere East Industrial Estate, Sunderland, SR2 9TE Tel: 0191-521 1941 Fax: 0191-523 6954 E-mail: info@mepsun.com Principal Export Areas: Worldwide *Distributors, agents & stockholders of tube fittings*

Marine Equipment Supply Co. Ltd, Enterprise House, Harveys Lane, Seething, Norwich, NR15 1EN Tel: (01508) 483702 Fax: (01508) 482710 E-mail: enquiries@marine-equipment.co.uk *Marine equipment specialists*

Marine Equipment Supply, Enterprise House, Harveys Lane, Seething, Norwich, NR15 1EN Tel: (01508) 483703 Fax: (01508) 482710 E-mail: sales@fendercare.com *Marine equipment manufrs*

Marine & General Engineers Ltd, PO Box 470, Guernsey, GY1 6AT Tel: (01481) 245808 Fax: (01481) 248765 *General engineers, welding & fabrication*

Marine & General Mutual Life Assurance Society, M G M House, Heene Road, Worthing, West Sussex, BN11 2DY Tel: (01903) 836000 Fax: (01903) 836001 E-mail: customer.centre@mgm-assurance.co.uk *Life pensions & assurance*

Marine Harvest Scotland Ltd, Ratho Park, 88 Glasgow Road, Newbridge, Midlothian, EH28 8PP Tel: (01397) 701550 Fax: 0131-336 1199 *Salmon farming & frozen food processors*

Marine & Industrial Plastics Ltd, Unit D/1, Segensworth Business Centre, Segensworth Road, Fareham, Hampshire, PO15 5RQ Tel: (01329) 847443 Fax: (01329) 847451 E-mail: sales@mipltd.co.uk *Glove box systems manufrs*

▶ Marine & Industrial Transmissions Ltd, Weeland Road, Hensall, Goole, North Humberside, DN14 0QE Tel: (01977) 661467 Fax: (01977) 662099 *Engineering*

Marine Lighting UK Ltd, 80 Dunster Road, Chelmsley Wood, Birmingham, B37 7UU Tel: 0121-770 8522 Fax: 0121-770 0505 E-mail: marlux@btconnect.com *Offshore marine & lighting manufrs*

▶ Marine Mechanical Services, 5 Ballybryan Road, Greyabbey, Newtownards, County Down, BT22 2RB Tel: (028) 4278 8697 Fax: (0870) 7065677 E-mail: garry@mmsni.co.uk *Marine engine seal suppliers*

Marine & Offshore Consultants Ltd, Magellan House, James Watt Close, Great Yarmouth, Norfolk, NR31 0NX Tel: (01493) 440166 Fax: (01493) 658490 E-mail: support@modgy.co.uk *Marine surveyors & consultants*

Marine & Offshore Consultants Ltd, Magellan House, James Watt Close, Great Yarmouth, Norfolk, NR31 0NX Tel: (01493) 440166 Fax: (01493) 658490

continued

E-mail: support@modgy.co.uk *Survey & rig positioning services*

Marine Power Ltd, Deacons Boatyard, Bridge Road, Bursledon, Southampton, SO31 8AW Tel: (023) 8040 3918 Fax: (023) 8040 4491 E-mail: peter@marine-power.co.uk *Marine engine sales & service*

Marine Radio Services Ltd, 50 Merton Way, West Molesey, Surrey, KT8 1PQ Tel: (020) 8979 7979 E-mail: marineradio@f2s.com *Marine electronic contractors*

▶ Marine Representation, Southon House, Station Approach, Edenbridge, Kent, TN8 5LP Tel: (01732) 867722 Fax: (01732) 868222 E-mail: info@activitymarine.com *Specialist suppliers of WATER SAFETY EQUIPMENT Buoys, Housings Floating lines and including SAFETY SIGNAGE for lakes, ponds, rivers etc.,"Specialist distributors of Marine Life Saving Equipment including Life Jackets, Life Buoys, Life Rafts, Buoyancy aids, EPIRB"s SART"S Reflecive Tape and much more*

▶ Marine Security Worldwide, 41 Burnley Road, Newton Abbot, Devon, TQ12 1YD Tel: (01626) 200515 *Marine security services*

▶ Marine Surveys, 8 Queens Park Gardens, Seaford, East Sussex, BN25 2QE Tel: 01323 873267 E-mail: info@marine-surveys.org *Yacht and commercial craft surveys for insurance, pre-purchase, damage assessment.*

Marine Trimming Service, Penton Hook Marina, Mixnams Lane, Chertsey, Surrey, KT16 8QR Tel: (01932) 563779 Fax: (01932) 570540 *Boat repairs*

Marine Ventures Ltd, Marven House, 1 Field Road, Reading, RG1 6AP Tel: 0118-950 3707 Fax: 0118-950 4066 E-mail: info@marineventures.co.uk Principal Export Areas: Worldwide *Marine equipment distributors*

▶ Mariner Computer Services Ltd, 23 Grey Friars, Wybers Wood, Grimsby, North East Lincolnshire, DN37 9QT Tel: (01472) 233105 E-mail: trevor@marinercomputerservices.com *IT consultancy*

▶ Mariners Building Contractors, 7 West Street, Selsey, Chichester, West Sussex, PO20 9AA Tel: (01243) 603468 Fax: (01243) 606405

Marinetronix Ltd, Unit 1, Airside Business Park, Dyce Drive, Kirkhill Industrial Estate, Dyce, Aberdeen, AB21 0GT Tel: (01224) 774423 Fax: (01224) 724396 E-mail: info@marinetronix.co.uk *Marine navigation, offshore data logging & remote controlled vehicles*

▶ Mario Nova, 1 Southmead Road, London, SW19 6SS Tel: (07788) 505205 E-mail: mario_venetianplaster@yahoo.co.uk *Mario Nova specializes in the application of OIKOS - Italian paints, polished plasters and innovative surface finishes As the specialist in we bring the atmosphere of old world for your, to explore a rich visual finish and the depth of substance, that have outstand the time.*

▶ Mariposa Alternative Bodycare, 15A Shelldale Road, Portslade, BN41 1LE Tel: (01273) 242925 Fax: (01273) 242925 E-mail: enquiries@mariposa-alternative-bodycare.co.uk *Cosmetic retail*

Marish Packaging Ltd, Riverside Way, Cowley, Uxbridge, Middlesex, UB8 2YF Tel: (01895) 256885 Fax: (01895) 256905 E-mail: sales@marishpackaging.co.uk *Multipurpose boxes manufrs*

Marita (Diamond Tooling) Ltd, 8 Longacre Way, Holbrook, Sheffield, S20 3FS Tel: 0114-248 8194 Fax: 0114-251 0667 E-mail: info@mdt.eu.com *Diamond tooling manufrs*

Maritech Consultants Ltd, 10 South Quay, Great Yarmouth, Norfolk, NR30 2QH Tel: (01493) 331822 Fax: (01493) 331687 E-mail: sales@maritech.co.uk *Geophysical consultants*

Maritime Consulting Associates Ltd, Owl Building, Battery Green Road, Lowestoft, Suffolk, NR32 1DH Tel: (01502) 730791 Fax: (01502) 508001 E-mail: marineconsult@compuserve.com *Marine surveyors management & consultancy services*

Maritime Progress Ltd, 3-5 Holmethorpe Avenue, Redhill, RH1 2LZ Tel: (01737) 763400 Fax: (01737) 782818 E-mail: info@maritimeprogress.com *Precision engineering services design & manufrs*

Maritime Rescue Institute Lifeboat Station, Old Pier, Stonehaven, Kincardineshire, AB39 2JU Tel: (01569) 765768 Fax: (01569) 764066 *Advisory & training*

Maritime Solutions, 87 Cauldwell Hall Road, Ipswich, IP4 4QG Tel: (0777) 6347360 E-mail: info@maritimesolutionsipswich.com *Marine Engineering and Diving Services*

Maritime Surveyors Ltd, 27 Acton Road, Lowestoft, Suffolk, NR33 7LG Tel: (01502) 563081 Fax: (01502) 586650 E-mail: lesleyholland@maritimesurveyors.fsnet.co.uk *Marine survey services*

▶ Maritime Transport Ltd, C/O Freight Liners, Millbrook Road East, Southampton, SO15 1JS Tel: (023) 8077 6851

Maritime Workshop, 50 Ferrol Road, Gosport, Hampshire, PO12 4UG Tel: (023) 9252 7805 Fax: (023) 9258 6822 E-mail: maritimeworkshop@btconnect.com *Boat repair*

Maritz Europa Ltd, Alexander House, Globe Park, Marlow, Buckinghamshire, SL7 1YW Tel: (01628) 486011 Fax: (01628) 475737 *Marketing services company*

▶ Mark 1 Hire, Purdeys Way, Rochford, Essex, SS4 1ND Tel: (01702) 545454 Fax: (01702) 546372 *Tool & Equipment Hire*

▶ Mark 1 Locks, 6 Ascot Road, Gravesend, Kent, DA12 5AL Tel: (01474) 747660 E-mail: 24hr@mark1locks.com *Locksmiths*

▶ Mark 1 Signs, Charleston, Nigg, Aberdeen, AB12 3LN Tel: (01224) 899311 Fax: (01224) 899311 E-mail: info@mark1signs.co.uk *Sign contractors*

▶ Mark Andrew Smith Limited, Unit 23 Millingford Ind Est, Bridge Street, Golborne, Warrington, WA3 3QE Tel: 01942 722518 E-mail: sales@markandrewsmith.co.uk *PC*

continued

continuation
support, server support, wireless, network wiring, ADSL, IT security, server, pc, help desk support, computer hire, disaster recovery bata backup servers

Mark Barlow, 4 Buxton Street, Gatley, Cheadle, Cheshire, SK8 4NW Tel: 0161-428 6389 *Jewellery repairers & manufrs*

Mark Brazier Jones, Hyde Hall Barn, Sandon, Buntingford, Hertfordshire, SG9 0RU Tel: (01763) 273599 Fax: (01763) 273410 E-mail: studio@braizer-jones.com *Furniture designers & manufrs*

▶ Mark C Brown Ltd, PO Box 69, Hull, HU2 8HS Tel: (01482) 218172 Fax: (01482) 214999 E-mail: info@markcbrown.co.uk *Rubber & pre-inked stamp manufrs*

Mark Clegg & Co., Lower Road, Longridge, Preston, PR3 2YJ Tel: (01772) 785655 Fax: (01772) 784681 E-mail: mark@markclegg.co.uk *Cheese & dairy supplier*

Mark Evans Electrical & Security, 165c Soundwell Road, Bristol, BS16 4RS Tel: 0117-956 0695 Fax: 0117-956 0695 *Electrical alarms installations*

Mark Griffiths Furniture Maker, Unit 4 Sewells Farm, Barcombe, Lewes, East Sussex, BN8 5TJ Tel: (01273) 401611 Fax: (01273) 628290 *Furniture manufrs*

Mark Haigh Dairy Products, 19 Church Lane, Cayton, Scarborough, North Yorkshire, YO11 3SA Tel: (01723) 583192 *Milk produce distributor*

Mark Handford & Co., 78 Coleswood Road, Harpenden, Hertfordshire, AL5 1EQ Tel: (01582) 762065 Fax: (01582) 623317 *Badge embroiderers & ties*

Mark Hellier Tractors Se Ltd, Thousand Acre Farm, Biddenden, Ashford, Kent, TN27 8BF Tel: (01580) 291271 Fax: (01580) 292432 E-mail: mail@markhellier.co.uk *Tractor & combine harvester dealers*

Mark II Ltd, Unit S3B Westcott Venture Park, Aylesbury, Buckinghamshire, HP18 0XB Tel: (01296) 653088 Fax: (01296) 653089 E-mail: mail@mark-two.co.uk *Commercial & domestic refurbishment*

Mark Insulation Ltd, 4 Ravenhurst Court, Birchwood, Warrington, WA3 6PN Tel: (01925) 822882 Fax: (01925) 819292 *Insulation contractor*

▶ Mark James Distribution Ltd, March Way, Battlefield Enterprise Park, Shrewsbury, SY1 3JE Tel: (01743) 460500 Fax: (01743) 441222

▶ Mark Lee Construction Ltd, Unit 1-15 Greys Green Farm, Greys Green, Rotherfield Greys, Henley-on-Thames, Oxfordshire, RG9 4QG Tel: (01491) 629083 E-mail: info@tvpres.demon.co.uk

Mark Metals Ltd, Seven Stars Road, Oldbury, West Midlands, B69 4JR Tel: 0121-552 7479 Fax: 0121-552 9088 *Foundry suppliers*

Mark Milton, Baird House, 15-17 St. Cross Street, London, EC1N 8UW Tel: (020) 7405 5402 Fax: (020) 7406 6858 *Jewellery importers*

▶ Mark One Limousines, 75 Merrivale Road, Portsmouth, PO2 0TH Tel: (023) 9266 9062 Fax: (023) 9267 7755 E-mail: markone.limousines@ntlworld.com *We are a family owned business established in February 2003 offering stretched limousine hire throughout the UK Southern Region and beyond.*We pride ourselves in offering a professional and reliable service with attention to detail. Our Chauffeurs are courteous and professional, dedicated to providing you with a premier limousine service. *Based in Portsmouth, UK, our luxury Superstretch limousines are for hire in the Southern UK Region, for Weddings, Airportlinks, Proms, Hen&Stag, Birthdays, etc. Experience the affordable luxury of travelling in a MARK ONE LIMOUSINE. **

▶ Mark R Bennett, The Estate Office, 2a Bridge Street, Stourport-on-Severn, Worcestershire, DY13 8XD Tel: (01299) 871701

Mark Scott Construction Ltd, 434 Chartridge Lane, Chesham, Buckinghamshire, HP5 2SJ Tel: (01494) 794545 *Building & construction contractors*

▶ Mark Two Distributors, Basai Dai, Prestleigh Road, Evercreech, Shepton Mallet, Somerset, BA4 6LN Tel: 0117-982 2531 Fax: 0117-982 2531

Mark Wilkinson (Furniture) Ltd, Overton House, High St, Bromham, Chippenham, Wiltshire, SN15 2HA Tel: (01380) 850004 Fax: (01380) 850184 E-mail: info@mws.com *Furniture manufrs*

Mark Williams Associates Ltd, 6 Bute Crescent, Cardiff, CF10 5AN Tel: (029) 2048 8488 Fax: (029) 2049 7776 E-mail: info@thinkmwa.co.uk *Advertising, marketing services*

▶ Mark1 Quality Assurance, 53 Cedarway, Bollington, Macclesfield, Cheshire, SK10 5NR Tel: 0800 4589630 E-mail: mark@mark1qa.co.uk *We provide a professional quality assurance management advice and systems to the manufacturing and service industries, This includes ISO9000 and the outsourcing of Quality Management (internal and Supplier auditing, management reviews, Continuous Improvements, Customer Satisfaction etc)We also carry out "hands on"training sessions.*

Markall Machines Ltd, PO Box 1948, Loughton, Essex, IG10 2BE Tel: (01992) 575355 Fax: (01992) 575553 *Marking machine manufrs*

Markapac, 37-41 Finchley Park, London, N12 9JY Tel: (0800) 2300301 Fax: (0800) 2300302 E-mail: info@detsafe.co.uk *Printed bags & packaging*

Marked & Sparkling, 201a West Street, Fareham, Hampshire, PO16 0EN Tel: (01329) 827678 Fax: (01329) 825365 E-mail: markbiz@btconnect.com *Glass & industrial engravers*

▶ Markell Computer, 47 Greygoose Park, Harlow, Essex, CM19 4JW Tel: (01279) 441000 Fax: (01279) 441110 E-mail: sales@marcelcomputers.com *Computer sales, repairs, upgrades*

Markes International Ltd, Unit D3 Llantrisant Business Park, Llantrisant, Pontyclun, Mid Glamorgan, CF72 8YW Tel: (01443) 230935 Fax: (01443) 231531 E-mail: enquiries@markes.com *Laboratory equipment manufrs*

Market Developer Ltd, Bourne House, 10 Windmill Road, Hampton Hill, Middlesex, TW12 1RH Tel: (020) 8979 1122 Fax: (020) 8941 7595 E-mail: simon.davis@marketdeveloper.com *Database management services*

Market Focus Research Ltd, Holt Barns, The Kilns, Frith End, Bordon, Hampshire, GU35 0QW Tel: (01420) 488355 Fax: (0845) 1309220 E-mail: admin@marketfocus.com *Information & research services*

Market Intelligence Ltd, Market Towers, 1 Nine Elms Lane, London, SW8 5NQ Tel: (020) 7501 3700 Fax: (020) 7498 6472 E-mail: info@fruitnet.com *Publishers*

▶ Market Link Creative Marketing Ltd, 30 St Georges Square, Worcester, WR1 1HX Tel: (01905) 726575 Fax: (01905) 726090 E-mail: sales@marketlink-uk.com *A public relations consultancy specialising in effective media relations for a wide range of clients in a broad spectrum of sectors including: education; heating and plumbing products; new build housing; social housing; hotels and conference centres; healthcare; the environment; commercial property; technology transfer; water and wastewater treatment; automotive etc etc. Visit our website, email us or call us for more information*

Market Metals, Unit 1 Senate Place, Whitworth Road, Stevenage, Hertfordshire, SG1 4QS Tel: (01438) 740512 Fax: (01438) 740513 E-mail: sales@marketmetals.co.uk *Marine aluminium stockists*

Market Place Merchandising, The Design Building Hewetts Kilns, Tongham Road, Farnham, Surrey, GU10 1PJ Tel: (01252) 781115 Fax: (01252) 781116 E-mail: info@marketplace-merchandising.com *Creative designers*

Market Press & Paper Co., 25 Holywell Row, London, EC2A 4XE Tel: (020) 7247 0920 Fax: (020) 7729 1442 E-mail: baileyprintgroup@talk21.com *Commercial printers*

Market Research (Northern Ireland) Ltd, 44-46 Elmwood Avenue, Belfast, BT9 6AZ Tel: (028) 9066 1037 Fax: (028) 9068 2007 E-mail: info@mrni.co.uk *Market researchers*

Market Research Society, 15 Northburgh Street, London, EC1V 0JR Tel: (020) 7490 4911 Fax: (020) 7490 0608 E-mail: sales@mrs.org.uk *Professional body*

The Market Shop, 48 Bridge Street, Berwick-upon-Tweed, TD15 1AQ Tel: (01289) 307749 Fax: (01289) 307749 *Health food retailers & arts suppliers*

▶ Market Synergies Ltd, 65 Cannon Court Road, Maidenhead, Berkshire, SL6 7QP Tel: (0790) 9993682 E-mail: enquiries@marketsynergies.co.uk *Short and Long Term Contract Sales Consultancy and New Business Development. Need to get your new business development kick started? Worried if your first full time salesperson is upto it? Consider a short term contract with an experienced sales development consultant!*

▶ Marketforce (UK) Ltd, Fifth Floor Low Rise Bldg, Kings Reach Tower, Stamford Street, London, SE1 9LS Tel: (020) 7633 3300 Fax: (020) 7633 3565 E-mail: ecommerce@marketforce.co.uk *Magazine distribution and sales and marketing services.*

Marketing Assistance Ltd, Grange Road, Tiptree, Colchester, CO5 0QQ Tel: (01621) 818555 Fax: (01621) 810884 E-mail: sales@marketing-assistance.co.uk *Research based marketing consultancy with 15 years experience of growing sales and profits for our clients.*

▶ Marketing Direct, 26 Makendon Street, Hebburn, Tyne & Wear, NE31 1RF Tel: 0191 4836090 E-mail: md_marketingdirect@yahoo.co.uk *DESIGN PRINT AND DISTRIBUTION OF ADVERTISING MATERIAL, PUBLISHER OF ADVERTISING PUBLICATIONS.*

▶ Marketing Direct, Northfield Road, Princes Risborough, Buckinghamshire, HP27 0HY Tel: (07734) 951179 *Circular distributors*

▶ Marketing Force Ltd, Cliff House, Chevalier Road, Felixstowe, Suffolk, IP11 7EJ Tel: (01394) 672467 Fax: (01394) 672468 E-mail: marketingforce@digitalflair.co.uk *Marketing services*

▶ Marketing Outsourced, 15 Heaven Tree Close, London, N1 2PW Tel: (020) 7354 5657 *Marketing Outsourced is a well established marketing consultancy delivering expert marketing advice and a wide range of marketing communications services on a project, monthly or daily basis. Specialise in IT companies and B2B SME's in growth mode.*

Marketing for Profits Ltd, Top Floor, 33 Southbourne Grove, Southbourne, Bournemouth, BH6 3QT Tel: 01202 257423 Fax: 01202 257423 E-mail: accounts@consultancymarketing.co.uk *Web site marketing & search engine consultancy services*

Marketing Services Travel & Tourism Ltd, High Holborn House, 52-54 High Holborn, London, WC1V 6RB Tel: (020) 7242 3131 Fax: (020) 7242 2838 E-mail: info@supereps.com *Travel marketing consultants*

Marketing Solutions, 51 Castleton Road, Ilford, Essex, IG3 9QW Tel: (020) 8590 2703 Fax: (020) 8597 4911 E-mail: mktsolutions@hotmail.com *Advertising gift suppliers*

▶ Marketing Team, Sensor House, Wrexham Technology Park, Wrexham, LL13 7YP Tel: (0870) 3501539 E-mail: info@marketing-team.co.uk *The Marketing Team are a North Wales based technology lead agency for professionals *who need to outsource marketing communications projects including strategic reviews, corporate image design, website design and management, internet marketing SEM and SEO campaigns, public relations, advertising and direct mail work.*

▶ Market-IT Direct Ltd, The Meridian, 4 Copthall House, Station Square, Coventry, CV1 2FL Tel: (0870) 8502365 E-mail: info@marketitdirect.com *Discover How to make a significant , secure income working on-line - Let the experts fast track you to unlimited success!*

▶ Marketmicrostructure.org, Buchanan Gardens, The Scores, St. Andrews, Fife, KY16 9LY Tel: (01334) 424598 E-mail: query@marketmicrostructure.org *An empirical market microstructure firm that specialized in providing econometric modeling and microstructure analysis for European derivatives.*

Marketmix, Unit 12, Leigh Indoor Market Hall, Albion Street, LEIGH, Lancashire, WN7 4PG Tel: (01942) 677777 Fax: (07902) 045895 E-mail: rob@marketmix.co.uk *Computers for sale also repairs,upgrades,and networking*over 20 years experience*tel 01942 677777*www.marketmix.co.uk*

▶ Marketwise Strategies Ltd, Adamson House, 65 Westgate Road, Newcastle upon Tyne, NE1 1SG Tel: 0191-261 4426 E-mail: info@marketwisestrategies.com *Delivering high quality market research & strategy development in UK & international markets***

D.R. Markey & Sons, Adcroft Street, Higher Hillgate, Stockport, Cheshire, SK1 3HZ Tel: 0161-480 1440 Fax: 0161-480 6164 *Engineers tool manufrs*

Mar-Key Marquees Ltd, 427c Aviation Park West, Bournemouth Int Airport, Hurn, Christchurch, Dorset, BH23 6NW Tel: (01202) 577111 Fax: (01202) 573014 E-mail: sales@mar-key.com *Marquee manufacture & rental*

Markfield Services, Trent Works, Felton Road, Nottingham, NG2 2EH Tel: 0115-985 0400 Fax: 0115-985 0252 E-mail: markfield@trentworks.demon.co.uk *Engineering services*

Markham Marquees, Morrow House, Morrow Lane, Ardleigh, Colchester, CO7 7NG Tel: (01206) 231084 Fax: (01206) 230713 E-mail: info@markham-marquees.co.uk *Marquee hire, leasing & rental*

Markham (Sheffield) Ltd, Marspal House, Lawn Road Industrial Estate, Carlton-In-Lindrick, Worksop, Nottinghamshire, S81 9LB Tel: (01909) 730861 Fax: (01909) 733584 E-mail: sales@markham-sheffield.co.uk *Specialist hire company*

Marking Service Signs Ltd, King Street Works, King Street, Drighlington, Bradford, West Yorkshire, BD11 1EJ Tel: 0113-285 2745 Fax: 0113-285 4748 E-mail: marserve@fsnet.co.uk *Sign & nameplate manufrs*

Markit Precision Engineering, 1 The Oaks Industrial Estate, Ravenstone Road, Coalville, Leicestershire, LE67 3NB Tel: (01530) 834435 Fax: (01530) 834438 E-mail: sales@markitprecisionengineering.sagenet.co.uk *Precision engineers*

Markland Advertising & Marketing Ltd, The Old Chapel, 13 Victoria Road, Chester, CH2 2AX Tel: (01244) 651951 Fax: (01244) 651952 *Advertising & graphic design agency*

Markmaid Ltd, 55 Beechwood Rd, Swansea, SA2 0JL Tel: (01792) 280610 Fax: (01792) 281414 E-mail: markmaid@btconnect.com *Marketing advertising public relations consultancy*

▶ Marknine Networks, 19 Crabtree Walk, Broxbourne, Hertfordshire, EN10 7NH Tel: (07075) 055577 Fax: (07075) 055577 E-mail: tonym@marknine.net *Web site developers*

▶ Markon Ltd, Marcon, Inchneuk Road, Glenboig, Coatbridge, Lanarkshire, ML5 2QX Tel: (01236) 875134 Fax: (01236) 875525 E-mail: enquiries@markon.co.uk

▶ Marks 4 Cars, Hall Farm Cottage, The Hill, Worlaby, Brigg, North Lincolnshire, DN20 0NP Tel: (01652) 618317 E-mail: sales@marks4cars.co.uk *Large choice of Cherished and Personalised number plates for immediate transfer. Low Prices*

Marks & Clarke, 5 The Quadrant, Coventry, CV1 2EL Tel: (024) 7622 2756 Fax: (024) 7625 6197 E-mail: ip@marks-clarke.com *Patent & trade mark agents* Also at: Leicester, London & Nottingham

Marks & Clerk, 27 Imperial Square, Cheltenham, Gloucestershire, GL50 1RQ Tel: (01242) 524520 Fax: (01242) 579383 E-mail: cheltonham@marks-clerk.com *Patent & trade mark attorneys*

▶ Marks & Clerk, 19 Royal Exchange Square, Glasgow, G1 3AE Tel: 0141-221 5767 Fax: 0141-221 7739 E-mail: glasgow@marks-clerk.com *Patent & trade mark agents* Also at: Edinburgh

Marks & Clerk, 90 Long Acre, London, WC2E 9RA Tel: (020) 7420 0000 Fax: (020) 7836 3339 *Chartered patent agents*

Marks Of Distinction, 55 Central Avenue, West Molesey, Surrey, KT8 2QZ Tel: (020) 8941 5533 Fax: (020) 8941 5575 E-mail: lbrind@chelsea.co.uk *Promotional & incentive items*

Marks Heeley & Brothwell Ltd, The Stables, Cannons Mill Lane, Bishop's Stortford, Hertfordshire, CM23 2BN Tel: (01279) 465900 Fax: (01279) 465999 E-mail: general@mhb.co.uk *Consulting structural & civil engineers* Also at: Southampton

Marks N Clarke, Cliffords Inn, Fetter Lane, London, EC4A 1BX Tel: (020) 7405 4916 Fax: (020) 7831 0343 *Chartered patent agents*

Marks Shutters, 189 Church End, Harlow, Essex, CM19 5PE Tel: (01279) 445282 E-mail: marksshutters@hotmail.co.uk *Industrial doors manufrs*

Stephen Marks (London) Ltd, Unit B, Dolphin Way, Purfleet, Essex, RM19 1NZ Tel: (020) 7036 7000 Fax: (020) 7036 7001 *Men's, ladies & childrens wear*

Marks Tey Products, Church Lane, Marks Tey, Colchester, CO6 1LN Tel: (01206) 210744 Fax: (01206) 210744 *Fencing equipment suppliers*

▶ Markus Products, Murray Way, Wincanton Business Park, Wincanton, Somerset, BA9 9RX Tel: (01963) 435270 Fax: (01963) 435271 E-mail: info@markusproducts.co.uk *Food manufrs*

Markwell Ltd, 24-25 Littlewood Lane, Hoveton, Norwich, NR12 8DZ Tel: (01603) 783053 Fax: (01603) 783053 *General precision & marine engineers*

Marl Bank Sheet Metal Co. Ltd, Newtown Road, Worcester, WR5 1HA Tel: (01905) 22801 Fax: (01905) 726235 E-mail: marlbank@marlbank77.wannadoo.co.uk *Sheet metalworkers & stainless steel fabricators*

Marl International Ltd, Morcambe Road, Ulverston, Cumbria, LA12 7RY Tel: (01229) 582430 Fax: (01229) 585155 E-mail: sales@marl.co.uk *LED optic electronic designers services*

Marla Tube Fittings Ltd, Units 1-2, Kinwarton Farm Road, Kinwarton, Alcester, Warwickshire, B49 6EH Tel: (01789) 761234 Fax: (01789) 761205 E-mail: alcester@hpf-energy.com *Pipeline, tube fittings & flange stockholders*

Marland Fabrications Ltd, 3 Addison Street, Sunderland, SR2 8BL Tel: 0191-565 6010 Fax: 0191-565 6010 *Steel fabricators*

Marland Paper & Plastics Ltd, Whiteleather Square, Billingborough, Sleaford, Lincolnshire, NG34 0QP Tel: (01529) 240637 Fax: (01529) 240638 E-mail: sales@marland.co.uk *Packaging suppliers*

▶ Marlaw Pallet Services Ltd, Carlisle Road, Airdrie, Lanarkshire, ML6 8RL Tel: (01236) 750000 Fax: (01236) 750011

▶ Marlaw Pallet Services Ltd, Camps Industrial Estate, Kirknewton, Midlothian, EH27 8DF Tel: (01506) 882061

Marlboro' Motors Ltd, 10 Watson, 10 Watsons Walk, St. Albans, Hertfordshire, AL1 1PA Tel: (01727) 850601 Fax: (01727) 844245 *Motor vehicle servicing*

Marlborough Constructional Engineers Ltd, Winston Avenue, Croft, Leicester, LE9 3GQ Tel: (01455) 283500 Fax: (01455) 285147 E-mail: enquiries@marlboroughltd.com *Fume extraction equipment manufrs*

Marlborough Data Systems Ltd, 2 The Parade Mews, The Parade, Marlborough, Wiltshire, SN8 1NE Tel: (01672) 511198 Fax: (01672) 511836 E-mail: sales@mdsltd.org *Computer maintenance repair services*

Marlborough Engineering Ltd, 67 Sydenham Road, Belfast, BT3 9DJ Tel: (028) 9073 2181 Fax: (028) 9073 2798 E-mail: marlborough@dnet.co.uk *Precision engineers*

Marlborough Four Wheel Drive, Unit B, Smiths Yard, Axford, Marlborough, Wiltshire, SN8 2EY Tel: (01672) 516041 Fax: (01672) 519189 *Engineering repairs & commercial vehicle engineering services*

▶ Marlborough Joinery Ltd, Ivy House Farm, Fyfield, Marlborough, Wiltshire, SN8 1PU Tel: (01672) 861292 Fax: (01672) 861611

Marlborough Leathers, Unit A Bury Close, Higham Ferrers, Rushden, Northamptonshire, NN10 8HQ Tel: (01933) 411314 Fax: (01604) 790946 E-mail: ml@witmore-bacon.co.uk *Leather import & export merchants*

▶ Marlborough Marble & Stone Work Ltd, 30 Welbeck Road, Glasgow, G53 7SD Tel: 0141-881 8200 Fax: 0141-880 4468 *Stone manufacture & retail*

Marlborough Radio Services, 9-11 Kildare Terrace, Leeds, LS12 1DB Tel: 0113-243 1626 Fax: 0113-246 1838 E-mail: andy@marlboroughradio.com *Radio communication equipment distributors*

Marlborough Tools Ltd, 315 Summer Lane, Birmingham, B19 3RH Tel: 0121-359 3491 Fax: 0121-359 3491 E-mail: marlborotools@supanet.com *Precision engineers*

Marldon, Scout Lane, London, SW4 0LA Tel: (020) 7627 7600 Fax: (020) 7627 7601 E-mail: mdb@marldon.demon.co.uk *Property developers*

▶ Marldon Marquees, 111 Winner Street, Paignton, Devon, TQ3 3BP Tel: (01392) 433633 Fax: (01803) 666888 E-mail: info@marldonmarquees.co.uk *Marquee hire*

▶ Marlec Marine Ltd, 11 Military Road, Ramsgate, Kent, CT11 9LG Tel: (01843) 852452 Fax: (01843) 596280 E-mail: alan@marlecmarine.com *Marine engineering & supplies*

Marleton Cross Ltd, Alpha Close, Tewkesbury, Gloucestershire, GL20 8JF Tel: (01684) 293311 Fax: (01684) 293900 E-mail: rhj@mxgroup.demon.co.uk *Shower & bathroom accessory manufrs*

Marley Building Materials Ltd, Station Road, Coleshill, Birmingham, B46 1HP Tel: (01675) 468400 Fax: (01675) 468485 *Roof tile manufrs* Also at: Manchester, Newbury, Newcastle upon Tyne, Purfleet, South Alloa & Thetford

Marley Eternit Ltd, Lichfield Road, Branston, Burton-on-Trent, Staffordshire, DE14 3HD Tel: (01283) 722588 Fax: (01283) 722219 E-mail: profile@marleyeternit.co.uk *Building materials.*

Marley Plumbing & Drainage Ltd, Rannoch Road, Uddingston, Glasgow, G71 5PA Tel: (01698) 815231 Fax: (01698) 810307 *Distribute plumbing & drainage equipment*

Marley Plumbing & Drainage, Dickley Lane, Lenham, Maidstone, Kent, ME17 2DE Tel: (01622) 858888 Fax: (01622) 858725 E-mail: marketing@marleyext.com *Manufacturers of pvc plumbing & draining products*

Marlin Agency Ltd, 68-70 Surrey Street, Belfast, BT9 7FS Tel: (028) 9066 8233 Fax: (028) 9068 2033 E-mail: marlinni@aol.com *Audio visual services*

continued

▶ indicates data change since last edition

▶ Marlin Design (MD) Ltd, 24 North Street, Chichester, West Sussex, PO19 1LB Tel: (01243) 773552 Fax: (01243) 787227 E-mail: marlindesign@btconnect.com *Component & tool designers*

Marlin Group Holdings, Marlin House Johnson Road, Fernsode Business Park, Ferndown Industrial Estate, Wimborne, Dorset, BH21 7SE Tel: (01202) 862900 Fax: (01202) 862901 E-mail: sales@marlin-ltd.co.uk Principal Export Areas: Worldwide *Automation special purpose equipment, systems designers & manufrs*

Marlin Products Ltd, Boundary Road, Buckingham Road Industrial Estate, Brackley, Northamptonshire, NN13 7ES Tel: (01280) 705484 Fax: (01280) 700242 E-mail: marlinproducts@btconnect.com *Plastic injection moulders*

▶ Marlow Air Conditioning, N Rose Business Estate, 54 Marlow Bottom Road, Marlow, Buckinghamshire, SL7 3ND Tel: (01628) 472250 Fax: (01628) 487760 E-mail: enqs@marlowaircon.co.uk *Air conditioning installation services*

Henry Marlow & Co. Ltd, 133 Rendlesham Road, London, E5 8PA Tel: (020) 8985 4158 Fax: (020) 8985 4301 *Fancy linen wholesalers*

Marlow Industries Europe, Aberdeen House, South Road, Haywards Heath, West Sussex, RH16 4NG Tel: (01444) 443404 Fax: (01444) 443334 E-mail: support@marlow-europe.co.uk *Thermal management*

Marlow Marketing, Electron House, Unit 2, Everglade Close, Longfield, Kent, DA3 7EZ Tel: (01474) 700121 Fax: (01474) 700122 E-mail: new.world@dial.pipex.com *Electronic component surplus dealers*

Marlow Ropes Ltd, Rope Maker Park, Dipilocks Way, Hailsham, East Sussex, BN27 3GU Tel: (01323) 444444 Fax: (01323) 444455 E-mail: sales@marlowropes.com *Manufacturers of rope & elastic cord*

Marlowe Graphic Services Ltd, Marlowe House, 346 High Street, Berkhamsted, Hertfordshire, HP4 1HT Tel: (01442) 878785 Fax: (01442) 878828 E-mail: sales@marlowe.co.uk *Prepress*

Marlows Carpet, 67 East Hill, London, SW18 2QE Tel: (020) 8871 1169 Fax: (020) 8877 9425 E-mail: marlows@dsl.pipex.com *Carpet suppliers, fitters*

▶ The Marmalade Cat Co., Ingles Meadow, Castle Hill Avenue, Folkestone, Kent, CT20 2RD Tel: (0870) 0634868 Fax: (0870) 0634869 E-mail: info@marmaladecat.com *Supplying the best of British Food to expats throughout the world. We have all your favourite brands, Cadburys, PGTips and Nescafe along with many more items for you to purchase within our simple and friendly to use site. A reliable, friendly and secure service shipping traditional British Food.*

Marmerstein Ltd, 10-14 Hewett Street, London, EC2A 3RL Tel: (020) 7247 1483 Fax: (020) 7539 1111 E-mail: fein@kimpton.co.uk *Property & equity investment services*

▶ Marmic Solutions, 6 Pathfields Road, Clacton-on-Sea, Essex, CO15 3JH Tel: (01255) 425676 *Web design & authoring.*Computers supplied, serviced and repaired.*

Marmon Contracts Ltd, 8 Boundary Street, Liverpool, L5 9UF Tel: 0151-207 2491 *Cleaning contractors*

Marmorit UK Ltd, 1 Port View Road, Avonmouth, Bristol, BS11 9LF Tel: 0117-982 1042 Fax: 0117-982 3025 E-mail: enquires@marmorit.co.uk *Insulation materials & external render suppliers & manufrs*

Marmox UK Ltd, 3 Rochester Airport Industrial Estate, Laker Road, Rochester, Kent, ME1 3QX Tel: (01634) 862277 Fax: (01634) 864223 E-mail: sales@marmox.com *Insulation Boards & Tile-backer boards. Floor & wall tiles.*

Marneon Signs Ltd, 11 Pontyglasdwr Street, Swansea, SA1 2BH Tel: (01792) 646949 Fax: (01792) 652227 E-mail: andrew-cotford@marneonsigns.com *Neon sign manufrs*

Marnic P.L.C., Armstrong Road, London, SE18 6RS Tel: (020) 8312 7200 Fax: (020) 8312 7250 E-mail: tapes@marnic.com *Adhesive tape & scrim (plastering) distributors*

Marnic Technology Ltd, Station Road, Reddish, Stockport, Cheshire, SK5 6ND Tel: 0161-431 3662 E-mail: sales@marnict.demon.co.uk *Industrial control systems manufrs*

Marnol Precision Engineering, Unit 9 Bee-Hive Trading Estate, 72-78 Crews Hole Road, St. George, Bristol, BS5 8AY Tel: (01275) 50095 *Sub-contract CNC machining*

▶ Marpal Ltd, Room 34, College Business Centre, The College, Uttoxeter New Road, Derby, DE22 3WZ Tel: (01332) 869290 Fax: (01332) 869291 E-mail: info@marpal.co.uk *Planning supervision*

Marpet Fabrications Ltd, Unit 04 Clyde Workshops, Fullarton Road, Glasgow East Investment Park, Glasgow, G32 8YL Tel: 0141-641 1778 Fax: 0141-641 7118 E-mail: marpetfabs@aol.com *Stainless steel fabricators*

Marplas Ltd, Martineau Lane, Norwich, NR1 2HU Tel: (01603) 667303 Fax: (01603) 764089 *Glass fibre material suppliers*

Marple Laboratories Birmingham Ltd, 19 Northampton Street, Birmingham, B18 6DU Tel: 0121-233 1504 Fax: 0121-236 3287 E-mail: info@marplelabs.co.uk *Gold & silver assayers & refiners*

Marple Polymer Processors Ltd, Primrose Mill, Mill Brow, Marple Bridge, Stockport, Cheshire, SK6 5AS Tel: 0161-427 2534 Fax: 0161-427 7872 *Manufacturers of custom rubber compounds*

▶ Joseph Marples Ltd, York Works, Valley Road, Sheffield, S8 9FT Tel: 0114-250 1166 Fax: 0114-250 1177 E-mail: enquiry@marples.co.uk *Manufacturers of joiners hand tools*

▶ Marpol Security, 47 Second Drove Industrial Estate, Peterborough, PE1 5XA Tel: (01733) 319402 Fax: (01733) 565483 *Security services & equipment.*

Marposs Ltd, Leofric Business Park, Progress Way, Binley Industrial Estate, Coventry, CV3 2TJ Tel: (024) 7688 4950 Fax: (024) 7663 6622 E-mail: sales@uk.marposs.com Principal Export Areas: Worldwide *Electronic gauging systems manufrs*

▶ Marquee Malarkey, 1 Great Buckmans Farm, Lower Howsell Road, Malvern, Worcestershire, WR14 1UX Tel: (07868) 750480 E-mail: info@marqueemalarkey.com *Temporary structures, suitable for weddings etc*

Marquee Print, 2 Wharfdale Road, Bournemouth, BH4 9BT Tel: (01202) 769077 Fax: (01202) 752858 E-mail: info@marqueeprint.com *Office stationery suppliers*

Marquees Ltd, Keens Lane, Guildford, Surrey, GU3 3JS Tel: (01483) 232394 Fax: (01483) 236420 E-mail: sales@guildfordshades.co.uk *Rolling blind manufrs*

Marquesman Sports Services Ltd, 11c Salamanca Road, Tharston, Norwich, NR15 2PF Tel: (01508) 531010 Fax: (01508) 530660 *Rugby equipment manufrs*

Marquin Engineering Co. Ltd, Alma Street, Wolverhampton, WV10 0EY Tel: (01902) 456904 Fax: (01902) 453089 *CNC repetition & precision machinists*

Marr Engineering Ltd, Green Acres Farm, Old Gloucester Road, Winterbourne, Bristol, BS36 1RZ Tel: (01454) 777150 Fax: (01454) 777152 *Steel fabricators*

▶ Marr Vessel Management Ltd, St Andrews Dock, Hull, HU3 4PN Tel: (01482) 327873

▶ Marrakesh Trading, 14a Pottergate, Norwich, NR2 1DS Tel: (01603) 610092 E-mail: thetinmine@hotmail.com *Supplier of quality hand-crafted Moroccan merchandise at affordable prices. Based in Norwich city centre we also supply wholesale as well as retail. Specialists in furniture, ceramics, lighting and textiles.*

▶ Marray & Mcintyre, Hawthorn House, 1 Medlicott Close, Corby, Northamptonshire, NN18 9NF Tel: (01536) 747888 Fax: (01536) 747744 E-mail: mail@marrayandmcintyre.co.uk *Chartered Accountants providing full range of accounting, taxation and business services*

▶ The Marriage Carriage Co., 85 Hay Green Road South, Terrington St. Clement, King's Lynn, Norfolk, PE34 4PU Tel: (01553) 827198 Fax: (01553) 829758 E-mail: tony@themarriagecarriagecompany.co.uk *Vintage jaguar wedding cars provider*

Marrill Engineering Co. Ltd, Waterman Road, Coventry, CV6 5TP Tel: (024) 7668 9221 Fax: (024) 7666 8114 E-mail: sales@marrill.co.uk *Machine tool rebuilders & CNC tooling*

▶ Marriott & Co., 19 East Street, Farnham, Surrey, GU9 7SD Tel: (01252) 712083 Fax: (01252) 737613 E-mail: mail@marriott.co.uk *Plant machinery valuers & auctioneers*

Marriott Breadsall Priory, Moor Road, Morley, Ilkeston, Derbyshire, DE7 6DL Tel: (01332) 832235 Fax: (01332) 833509 *Hotel & country club*

Marriott Construction, Marriott House, Brindley Close, Rushden, Northamptonshire, NN10 6EN Tel: (01933) 357511 Fax: (01933) 356746 *Building contractors* Also at: Shepshed

Marriott Dalmahoy Hotel & Country Club, Kirknewton, Kirknewton, Midlothian, EH27 8EB Tel: 0131-333 1845 Fax: 0131-333 1433 E-mail: salesadmin.dalmahoy@marriotthotels.co.uk *Hotel group*

Marriott Design, St James House, 3 Lower St. James Street, Newport, Isle of Wight, PO30 5HE Tel: (01983) 529039 Fax: (01983) 821544 E-mail: studio@marriott-design.co.uk *Print & internet designers*

Marriott & Price Ltd, Station House Station Yard, Waterhouse Lane, Kingswood, Tadworth, Surrey, KT20 6EN Tel: (01737) 352735 Fax: (01737) 359192 E-mail: info@marriottandprice.co.uk *Terrazzo marble & tiling contractors*

Marriott St Pierre Hotel & Country Club, St. Pierre Park, Hayesgate, Chepstow, Gwent, NP16 6YA Tel: (01291) 635208 Fax: (01291) 629975 E-mail: mhrs.cwlgs.frontdesk@marriothotels.com *Hotel & conference facilities*

Marriott Security Ltd, 18 Ridgeway, Peterborough, PE2 8HQ Tel: (01733) 894334 *CCTV Installers*

Marriott Sprowston Manor Golf Club, Wroxham Road, Norwich, NR7 8RP Tel: (01603) 254292 Fax: (01603) 788884 E-mail: sprowstonmanor@marriotthotels.co.uk *Hotel with conference facilities*

Marrs Cross & Wilfrid Fairbairns Ltd, Hardwood House, 1 Oglander Road, London, SE15 4EH Tel: (020) 7639 5106 Fax: (020) 7639 5106 E-mail: mxf@ukgateway.net *Timber protection & decoration*

Marrs Of Methlick, Methlick, Ellon, Aberdeenshire, AB41 7DS Tel: (01651) 806910 Fax: (01651) 806911 E-mail: marrsofmethlick@btconnect.com *Agricultural engineers*

▶ Stephen Marrs Bike Art, 9 loan road, Cullybackey, Ballymena, County Antrim, BT42 1er Tel: (028) 2588 1865 E-mail: stephen@marrs101.freeserve.co.uk *Motorbike & scooter paintwork services ,plastic welding,lambretta paint work,vespa paint work,northern ireland*

Marrutt Ltd, Unit 9 Bellbrook Industrial Estate, Uckfield, East Sussex, TN22 1QL Tel: (01825) 764057 Fax: (01825) 768841 E-mail: digital@marrutt.com *Revolving darkroom door manufrs*

Mars Hall Consultancy & Training, Cheshire House, 164 Main Road, Goostrey, Crewe, CW4 8JP Tel: (01477) 534209 Fax: (01477) 537170 E-mail: enquiries@techsafeconsultants.co.uk *Safety & environment management consultants*

Marsden Crane Hire Ltd, 12 Ince Lane, Eccleston, Chorley, Lancashire, PR7 5TH Tel: (01257) 452689 Fax: (01257) 453776 *Crane hire with operators*

Marsden Dive Centre, Diving Centre, 6 Fallow Road, South Shields, Tyne & Wear, NE34 7AG Tel: 0191-427 7820 Fax: 0191-427 7820 E-mail: sales@marsdendivecentre.co.uk *Scuba diving instruction & supplies*

Lynne Marsden, Heatherdean, Llwynygroes, Tregaron, Dyfed, SY25 6PY Tel: (01974) 821271 Fax: (01974) 821271 E-mail: lynne.marsden@btopenworld.com *Soft furnishings manufrs*

Marsden Metal Products Ltd, Cedar Works, Ryebourne Street, Oldham, OL4 2BP Tel: 0161-624 9217 E-mail: info@marsdenmetal.co.uk *Sheet metal engineers*

▶ Marsden Motor Rewinds Ltd, Unit 19 Clayton St Industrial Estate, Nelson, Lancashire, BB9 7PH Tel: (01282) 694544 Fax: (01282) 694544 E-mail: phllppck2@ntlworld.com *Repair electric motors*

P.S. Marsden (Precision Engineers) Ltd, Private Road No 8, Colwick Industrial Estate, Nottingham, NG4 2JX Tel: 0115-987 9026 Fax: 0115-940 0805 E-mail: precision@psmarsden.co.uk *Sub contract machining services*

Marsden Packaging Ltd, Peter Street, Blackburn, BB1 5LW Tel: (01254) 56453 Fax: (01254) 581090 *Contract packaging services*

Marsden Weighing Machine Group, 47 Market Place, Henley-on-Thames, Oxfordshire, RG9 2AD Tel: (0845) 1307330 Fax: (0845) 1307440 E-mail: sales@marsdengroup.demon.co.uk *Scales retailers & manufrs*

Marsden's Computer Systems, Unit 168 Glenfield Park Lomeshaye Business Village, Turner Road, Nelson, Lancashire, BB9 7DR Tel: (01282) 616176 Fax: (01282) 616152 E-mail: info@marsdens.net *Computer consultants*

▶ Marsel Display Marketing, Marsel House, Belton Road, Silsden, Keighley, West Yorkshire, BD20 0EE Tel: (01535) 650000 Fax: (01535) 650001 E-mail: marsel@marsel.co.uk *Display stand manufrs*

Marsh Ltd, 48 St. Vincent Street, Glasgow, G2 5TR Tel: 0141-304 4300 Fax: 0141-221 5409 *Insurance broker*

Marsh Barton Coachworks Ltd, Grace Road, Marsh Barton, Exeter, EX2 8PU Tel: (01392) 202224 Fax: (01392) 423576 E-mail: admin@marshbartoncoachworks.co.uk *Motor body builders & repairers*

Marsh Environmental, Unit 8, 69 St. Marks Road, London, W10 6JG Tel: (020) 8962 0111 Fax: (020) 8962 0486 E-mail: enquiries@marshltd.co.uk *Air quality measurement & water treatment*

Marsh Forge Blacksmiths, Chapel House Farm, Offley Marsh, Bishops Offley, Stafford, ST21 6HE Tel: (01785) 280487 Fax: (01785) 280487 E-mail: info@marshforge.co.uk *Blacksmiths*

Marsh Labels Ltd, 6 Lady Bee Marina Industrial Estate, Albion Street, Southwick, Brighton, BN42 4EP Tel: (01273) 595744 Fax: (01273) 870425 E-mail: sales@marshlabels.co.uk *Printed self-adhesive labels*

Marsh Mclennan & Companies, 1 Tower Place West, London, EC3R 5BU Tel: (020) 7357 1000 Fax: (020) 7929 2705 *Holding company*

N.& G. Marsh, Unit 12, Meadow Industrial Estate, Reach Road, Burwell, Cambridge, CB25 0GH Tel: (01638) 741354 Fax: (01638) 743424 *Agricultural engineers*

Peter Marsh & Sons Ltd, Dundee Works, 47 Canal Street, Bootle, Merseyside, L20 8AE Tel: 0151-922 1971 Fax: 0151-922 3804 E-mail: sales@petermarsh.co.uk *Corrugated box, case, container & paper sac manufrs*

▶ Marsh Plant Ltd, Leabrook Road, Wednesbury, West Midlands, WS10 7LZ Tel: 0121-556 2158

Marsh Plant Hire Ltd, 67 New Lane, Havant, Hampshire, PO9 2LZ Tel: (023) 9248 2323 Fax: (023) 9245 3813 E-mail: info@marshplant.com *Contractors plant & crane hire*

Marsh Plant Hire Ltd, Wallingford Road, Uxbridge, Middlesex, UB8 2SS Tel: (01895) 231291 Fax: (01895) 811650 *Plant & crane hire*

Marshall, 18 Johnson Street, Sheffield, S3 8GT Tel: 0114-276 7071 Fax: 0114-273 8084 E-mail: sales@geomarshall.co.uk *Power tool distributors or agents*

Marshall Aerospace International Services Ltd, Airport House, Newmarket Road, Cambridge, CB5 8RX Tel: (01223) 373737 Fax: (01223) 321032 E-mail: sales@marshallaerospace.com *Maintenance & service*

Marshall Amplifications plc, Denbigh Road, Bletchley, Milton Keynes, MK1 1DQ Tel: (01908) 375411 Fax: (01908) 376118 E-mail: jtait@marshallamps.com *Audio amplifier manufrs*

Marshall Barry (Lincoln) Ltd, Camp Road, Witham St. Hughes, Lincoln, LN6 9TW Tel: (01522) 868844 Fax: (01522) 868855 E-mail: marshall.barry@dial.pipex.com *Road transport, haulage & freight services*

▶ Marshall Belting Supplies Limited, 11 Cedar Avenue, Spixworth, Norwich, NR10 3PB Tel: 01603 897405 Fax: 01603 897405 E-mail: mbs@tesco.net *Norfolks largest Conveyor Belt Distributor, based in Norwich supplying East anglia with, PU, PVC, MODULAR, TRANSMISSION and STEEL BELTING.BDL DRUM MOTORS and Full on site fitting service available.*We also have a stainless and mild steel fabrication and design, CONVEYORS, TABLES, GENERAL MAINTENANCE AND INSTALLATION.**

▶ Marshall Brass, Keeling Hall Road, Foulsham, Dereham, Norfolk, NR20 5PR Tel: (01362) 684105 Fax: (01362) 684280 E-mail: sales@marshall-brass.com *Foundry & iron brass manufrs*

Marshall Brewson Ltd, 6 Westside Industrial Estate, South Humberside Industrial Estate, Grimsby, South Humberside, DN31 2TG Tel: (01472) 359001 Fax: (01472) 359954 E-mail: sales@marshallbrewson.co.uk *Compressed air specialists, sales*

Marshall Building Contractors Ltd, Huddersfield Road, Elland, West Yorkshire, HX5 9BW Tel: (01422) 375533 Fax: (01422) 310811 *Constructors*

Marshall Cavendish International Ltd, 119 Wardour Street, London, W1F 0UW Tel: (020) 7734 6710 Fax: (020) 7734 6221 *Publishers*

Marshall Coppin Ltd, Unit 5 Chingford Industrial Centre, Hall Lane, London, E4 8DJ Tel: (020) 8524 1018 Fax: (020) 8524 8978 *Shoe repair trade suppliers & wholesalers*

Marshall Deacon Knitwear Ltd, 122 Fairfax Road, Leicester, LE4 9EL Tel: 0116-246 1260 Fax: 0116-274 3528 E-mail: info@marshalldeacon.com *Mens & ladies knitwear manufrs*

Marshall Drills Ltd, Metrology House, Dukinfield Road, Hyde, Cheshire, SK14 4SD Tel: 0161-882 9618 Fax: 0161-366 9800 E-mail: sales@marshalldrills.co.uk *Drill bit engineers & tool merchants*

Marshall Engineering Services, Kendrick House, Mere View Industrial Estate, Yaxley, Peterborough, PE7 3HS Tel: (01733) 240045 Fax: (01733) 241821 *Valve repair & refurbishing services*

Marshall Farm Machinery, Rugby Road, Leicester, LE9 7TB Tel: (01788) 832300 Fax: (01455) 888179 E-mail: sales@marshallfarmmachinery.co.uk *Agricultural spare parts & horticultural suppliers*

Marshall Group Ltd, Cader House, Cader Avenue, Kinmel Bay, Rhyl, Clwyd, LL18 5HU Tel: (01745) 343131 Fax: (01745) 345223 E-mail: mmar@dialstart.net *Toys, gifts & beach goods distributors*

James A. Marshall Ltd, 50 Crownpoint Road, Bridgeton, Glasgow, G40 2QE Tel: 0141-556 1626 Fax: 0141-556 4630 E-mail: enquiries@jamesamarshall.com *Printers & bookbinders*

▶ K. Marshall & Associates, School House, Rushall, Pewsey, Wiltshire, SN9 6EN Tel: (01980) 630688 Fax: (01980) 630549 E-mail: kma@consult.screaming.net *Quality management consultancy, auditing & interim management services*

▶ Marshall Langston Ltd, Marlan House, Lower Tuffley Lane, Gloucester, GL2 5DT Tel: (01452) 529717 Fax: (01452) 309994 E-mail: sales@marshalllangston.co.uk *Packaging manufrs*

Marshall Law, Estate House, 2 Pembroke Road, Sevenoaks, Kent, TN13 1XR Tel: (01732) 458062 Fax: (01732) 458609 E-mail: vpl@marshall-law.co.uk *Trade mark agents* Also at: West Wickham

Marshall Marquees, Watercress Farm, Upton Lane, Dundry, Bristol, BS41 8NS Tel: 0117-964 6528 E-mail: info@marshallmarquees.co.uk *Marquee manufrs*

Marshall & Parsons Ltd, 1111 London Road, Leigh-on-Sea, Essex, SS9 3JL Tel: (01702) 470100 Fax: (01702) 471160 E-mail: marshallandparsons@ancatown.co.uk *Hand power tool distributors*

Marshall Pump Systems Ltd, 4 Rhodes Bank, Oldham, OL1 1UA Tel: 0161-678 6111 Fax: 0161-627 0913 E-mail: info@marshallpumps.co.uk *Pump agents, stockists & distributors*

Robert Marshall Marketing Consultancy, 194 Richmond Road, Kingston Upon Thames, Surrey, KT2 5HE Tel: (020) 8546 1711 Fax: (020) 8974 6120 E-mail: rmarshal@netcomuk.co.uk *Market research*

Marshall Specialist Joinery Ltd, The Old Railway Station, Sampford Courtenay, Okehampton, Devon, EX20 2SN Tel: (01837) 54189 Fax: (01837) 54808 *Specialist joinery manufacturer*

Marshall Specialist Vehicles Ltd, The Airport, Cambridge, CB5 8RX Tel: (01223) 373900 Fax: (01223) 373064 E-mail: info@marshallsv.com *MSV forms the Vehicle Division of the Marshall Group. MSV are a market leader in the design, integration and supply of Rapid Deployment Mobility Systems and Sub-Systems. Benefiting from extensive inter-group facilities, resources and technical expertise, resulting in a broad range of capabilities, MSV is an ISO 9001:2000 accredited company with an emphasis on continual product development.*MSV specialise in:*Homeland Security including Command and Control Infrastructure, Mass decontamination systems, Urban search and rescue, Rapid Deployment Systems, Incident Management Complexes, Secure Data and Communications.*Military Systems including Vehicle Platform Integration, Airportable Mobile Ground stations, Tactical Shelters, Rapid Deployment Systems, NBC, EMP, RFI and TEMPEST Protected Systems.*Product Support including Fleet management for Homeland Defence & Military systems, Contractor and Integrated Logistics Support, Post Design Services, Training Services, Spares Management.**

▶ Marshall Surfacing Contracts Ltd, 249 Godstone Road, Whyteleafe, Surrey, CR3 0EN Tel: (01883) 622241 Fax: (01883) 627265

▶ Marshall Thermo King Ltd, Units 7-8, Willment Way, Bristol, BS11 8DJ Tel: 0117-982 1455 Fax: 0117-982 2899

Marshall Thermo King Ltd, Teversham House, Newmarket Road, Teversham, Cambridge, CB5 8AA Tel: (01223) 377800 Fax: (01223) 377819 E-mail: sales@marshall-thermoking.co.uk *Transport refrigeration Company*

Marshall Thermo King Ltd, Cemetery Road, Houghton Regis, Dunstable, Bedfordshire, LU5 5BZ Tel: (01582) 867847 Fax: (01582) 866648 E-mail: houghtonregis@marshallthermoking.co.uk *Refrigeration engineers*

Marshall Thermo King Ltd, 3b Andes Road, Nursling, Southampton, SO16 0YZ Tel: (023) 8073 9944 Fax: (023) 8073 9090 E-mail: southampton@marshall-thermoking.co.uk *Transportation & refrigeration repairs*

Marshall Tufflex Ltd, Churchfields Industrial Estate, Sidney Little Road, St. Leonards-on-Sea, East Sussex, TN38 9PU Tel: (0870) 2403200 Fax: (0870) 2403201

continued

continuation
E-mail: sales@marshall-tufflex.com *Plastic extrusions & mouldings manufrs*

Marshall Wilson, Units 4 a-c Blochairn Industrial Estate, 16-24 Siemens Place, Glasgow, G21 2BN Tel: 0141-552 7577 Fax: 0141-552 5434 *Packaging material distributors*

▶ Marshalls plc, Birkby Grange, Birkby Hall Road, Huddersfield, HD2 2TJ Tel: (01484) 438900 Fax: (01484) 438944

Marshalls, Eastern Dry Dock, Corporation Road, Newport, Gwent, NP19 4RE Tel: (01633) 284600 Fax: (01633) 284612 E-mail: suebell@marshalls.co.uk *Block paving slab manufrs*

Marshalls, Llay Road, Llay, Wrexham, Clwyd, LL12 0TL Tel: (01978) 858200 Fax: (01978) 858212 *Building services*

▶ Marshalls The Bakers Ltd, Tower Road, Glover Industrial Estate, Washington, Tyne & Wear, NE37 2SH Tel: 0191-416 8100 *Bakers*

Marshalls Clay Products Ltd, Quarry Lane, Dewsbury, West Yorkshire, WF12 7JJ Tel: 0113-220 3500 Fax: 0113-220 3555 *Clay products manufrs*

Marshalls Clay Products, 4 Park Terrace, Glasgow, G3 6BY Tel: 0141-333 0985 Fax: 0141-332 6877 *Builders bricks manufrs*

Marshalls Hard Metals Ltd, Windsor Street, Sheffield, S4 7WB Tel: 0114-275 2282 Fax: 0114-273 8499 E-mail: sales@hardmet.com *Tool manufrs*

Marshalls Industrial Ltd, Hithercroft Road, Wallingford, Oxfordshire, OX10 9DG Tel: (01491) 834666 Fax: (01491) 839777 E-mail: sales@marshalls-industrial.co.uk *Automotive components, industrial engines & diesel engine manufrs*

Marshalls Mono Ltd, Landscape House, Premiere Way, Housefield Business Park, Elland, West Yorkshire, HX5 9HT Tel: (01422) 306400 Fax: (0870) 6002426 Principal Export Areas: Asia Pacific & Africa *Manufacturers of bollards & municipal street furniture*

Marshalls Mono Ltd, Landscape House, Premiere Way, Housefield Business Park, Elland, West Yorkshire, HX5 9HT Tel: (01422) 306400 Fax: (01422) 312999 *Precast concrete & landscape product manufrs*

Marshalls Sheetmetal Blackrow Barns, Short Thorn Road, Blackrow Barns, Felthorpe, Norwich, NR10 4DE Tel: (01603) 755473 Fax: (01603) 754040 E-mail: enquiries@marshallssheetmetal.co.uk *Heating vitalization manufacturer*

Marshall's Transport (Evesham) Ltd, Long Lane, Throckmorton, Pershore, Worcestershire, WR10 2JH Tel: (01386) 556808 Fax: (01386) 556760 E-mail: brian@marshallsofevesham.co.uk *Road transport contractors storage distributors*

▶ Marshalls Transport Services Ltd, Glenfoot Farm, Tillicoultry, Clackmannanshire, FK13 6BT Tel: (01259) 750631

Marshbeck Reproduction Furniture, 60e High Street, Lavenham, Sudbury, Suffolk, CO10 9PY Tel: (01787) 247548 Fax: (01787) 249498 E-mail: enquiries@marshbeck.co.uk *Furniture reproduction*

Marshcouch, 14 Robinsfield, Hemel Hempstead, Hertfordshire, HP1 1RW Tel: (01442) 862210 Fax: (01442) 866786 E-mail: nigel@marshcouch.com *Manufacturer of treatment couches*

Marske Fabrication & Engineering Ltd, Longbeck Estate, Marske-by-the-Sea, Redcar, Cleveland, TS11 6HB Tel: (01642) 482123 Fax: (01642) 470463 *Steel fabrications services*

Marske Site Services Ltd, Suite 311, The Innovation Centre, Vienna Court, Kirkleatham Business Park, Redcar, Cleveland, TS10 5SH Tel: (01642) 777993 Fax: (01642) 777994 E-mail: tim.mccullagh@marske.com *Mechanical, structural services & personnel*

Marsland & Co. Ltd, Commerce Way, Station Road, Edenbridge, Kent, TN8 6EE Tel: (01732) 862501 Fax: (01732) 866737 E-mail: sales@marsland-windows.co.uk *PVC & aluminium windows manufrs & installers*

Marson, Unit 8 Kings Exchange, Tileyard Road, London, N7 9AH Tel: (020) 7619 6500 Fax: (020) 7619 6501 Principal Export Areas: West Europe *Textile merchant converters*

▶ The Marstan Press Ltd, Princes Street, Bexleyheath, Kent, DA7 4BJ Tel: (020) 8301 5900 Fax: (020) 8298 1612 E-mail: sales@themarstanpress.co.uk *Environmentally conscious Colour Printers*

Marston Agricultural Services Ltd, Toll Bar Road, Marston, Grantham, Lincolnshire, NG32 2HT Tel: (01400) 250226 Fax: (01400) 250540 E-mail: sales@mas-trailers-group.co.uk *Trailer manufrs*

W. Marston Ltd, 70 Fazeley Street, Birmingham, B5 5RD Tel: 0121-643 0852 Fax: 0121-643 9534 E-mail: info@williammarstonltd.co.uk *Motor car trimmings suppliers*

Marsworth Computing, 34 Byron Hill Road, Harrow, Middlesex, HA2 0HY Tel: (020) 8864 4842 Fax: (020) 8864 4842 E-mail: sales@marsworth.net *Computer consultants*

Martec Engineering, Grange Road, Tipree, Colchester, CO5 0QQ Tel: (01621) 819673 Fax: (01621) 817297 E-mail: marteng@aol.com *General & precision engineers & gear manufrs*

▶ Martec Engineering Group Ltd, Block 7 20 Clydesmill Drive, Cambuslang Investment Park, Clydesmill Industrial Estate, Glasgow, G32 8RG Tel: 0141-646 5220 Fax: 0141-646 1056 E-mail: martec@martecengineering.co.uk *Steel security doors & stainless & structural steel*

Martec Environmental Consultants Ltd, Waterbrow Wood, Gressingham, Lancaster, LA2 8LX Tel: (01524) 222000 Fax: (07970) 137469 E-mail: sales@noise.sh *Consulting engineers*

Martech, 21 Church Street, Sawtry, Huntingdon, Cambridgeshire, PE28 5SZ Tel: (01487) 832288 Fax: (01487) 832739 E-mail: techinical@martech.co.uk

Martech Design Services, 109 London Road, Bagshot, Surrey, GU19 5DH Tel: (01276) 476922 Fax: (01276) 451622 E-mail: office@martechds.co.uk *Design engineering services to the building services industry*

Martech UK Ltd, Conway House, Thornhill Road, Dewsbury, West Yorkshire, WF12 9QQ Tel: (01924) 482700 Fax: (01924) 438388 E-mail: sales@martech-uk.com

Martek, Unit 12b, Ridings Park, Eastern Way, Cannock, Staffordshire, WS11 7FJ Tel: (01543) 502202 Fax: (01543) 467726 E-mail: info@martekonline.co.uk *Ink jet printers*

▶ Martek Composites, Park Works, Park Road, Crosland Moor, Huddersfield, HD4 5DD Tel: (01484) 431527 Fax: (01484) 431522 E-mail: enquiries@martek-composites.co.uk *Fibre glass moulding services & manufrs*

Martel Electrical Contractors, Tamworth Business Centre, 23 Amber Close, Tamworth, Staffordshire, B77 4RP Tel: (01827) 316533 Fax: (01827) 316568 *Industrial & commercial installers*

Martel Instruments Holdings Ltd, Stanelaw Way, Tanfield Lea Industrial Estate, Tanfield Lea, Stanley, County Durham, DH9 9XG Tel: (01207) 290266 Fax: (01207) 290239 E-mail: info@martelinstruments.com *Printer digital panel meters manufrs*

▶ Martel Wessex Composites Ltd, Unit 4 Williams Way Indust Estate, Irchester, Wellingborough, Northamptonshire, NN29 7AN Tel: (01933) 664060 Fax: (01933) 664605 E-mail: enquiries@martel-wessex.co.uk *Make interiors for luxury yachts*

Martello Ltd, 14 Allens Lane, Hamworthy, Poole, Dorset, BH16 5DA Tel: (01202) 628470 Fax: (01202) 628471 E-mail: sales@martello.co.uk *Rapid prototyping engineers and low volume production of plastic parts specialists*

▶ Martello Bay Tele Consultants Ltd, 5 Stephenson Road, Clacton-on-Sea, Essex, CO15 4XA Tel: (01255) 221110

Martello Plant Hire Ltd, Potts Marsh Industrial Estate, Westham, Pevensey, East Sussex, BN24 5NA Tel: (01323) 761887 Fax: (01323) 461933 *Plant hire contractors*

Martells Of Sutton Ltd, Unit 3, 4, Charlwoods Road, East Grinstead, West Sussex, RH19 2HG Tel: (01342) 321303 Fax: (01342) 302145 E-mail: removals@martells.co.uk *Retail, removal, storage & shipping services*

Marten Walsh Cherer Ltd, Midway House, 27-29 Cursitor Street, London, EC4A 1LT Tel: (020) 7405 5010 Fax: (020) 7405 5026 E-mail: martinwc@aol.com *Legal & conference reporting*

Martens Conveyor Belting Ltd, 72 Wheathead Lane, Keighley, West Yorkshire, BD22 6NN Tel: (01535) 609028 Fax: (01535) 605425 E-mail: sales@martensbelt.co.uk *Conveyor belting manufrs*

Martex Boat Equipment, Hillside, Church Minshull, Nantwich, Cheshire, CW5 6EA Tel: (01270) 522251 Fax: (01270) 522616 *Boat equipment & accessories suppliers*

Martham Boat Building & Development Co. Ltd, Cess Road, Martham, Great Yarmouth, Norfolk, NR29 4RF Tel: (01493) 740249 Fax: (01493) 740065 E-mail: info@marthamboats.com *Boat builders, repairers & hire services*

Martin Co. Ltd, 160 Dollman Street, Duddeston, Birmingham, B7 4RS Tel: 0121-359 2111 Fax: 0121-359 4698 E-mail: sales@martin.co.uk *Cabinet hardware suppliers*

▶ Martin, 8 Walnut Tree Avenue, Martham, Great Yarmouth, Norfolk, NR29 4QS Tel: (01493) 740746 E-mail: martin@procleaning-office.co.uk *Established in 1995 Procleaning are a specialist office cleaning company covering Norwich & Gt Yarmouth*

A. Martin Bunzl Ltd, 27 London Road, Bromley, BR1 1DF Tel: (020) 8464 4141 Fax: (020) 8460 2035 E-mail: sales@martinbunzl.co.uk *Raw materials for textile industry*

Martin Aerospace Ltd, 2 Block 6, Caldwellside Industrial Estate, Lanark, ML11 7SR Tel: (01555) 664751 Fax: (01555) 665860 E-mail: sales@martinaerospace.com *Precision engineers*

▶ Martin Aitken Associates, Aspire Business Centre, 16 Farmeloan Road, Rutherglen, Glasgow, G73 1DL Tel: 0141-647 0101 Fax: 0141-647 0107 E-mail: martinaitkenassociates@btconnect.com *Chartered surveyors, quantity surveyors, building surveyors services*

Martin Audio Ltd, 2 Century Point, Halifax Road, Cressex Business Park, High Wycombe, Buckinghamshire, HP12 3SL Tel: (01494) 535312 Fax: (01494) 438669 E-mail: info@martin-audio.com Principal Export Areas: Worldwide *Loudspeaker manufacturer*

Brett Martin Ltd, 24 Roughfort Road, Newtownabbey, County Antrim, BT36 4RB Tel: (028) 9084 9999 Fax: (028) 9083 6666 E-mail: sales@brettmartin.com *Plastic down pipes, guttering & sheets manufrs*

C.A. Martin & Son, Upper Bell Clive, Hartcliff Road, Penistone, Sheffield, S36 9FE Tel: (01226) 764444 Fax: (01226) 762336 E-mail: sales@camartinandson.co.uk *Plaster air ventilators manufrs*

C.S. Martin (Alford) Ltd, 33 West Street, Alford, Lincolnshire, LN13 9DQ Tel: (01507) 463427 Fax: (01507) 466942 *Precision engineers*

Martin Cox, Jacksons Lane, Wellingborough, Northamptonshire, NN8 4LB Tel: (01933) 276935 Fax: (01933) 277127 E-mail: sales@martincoxchamois.com *Chamois & stockinet manufrs*

Martin Dawes Solutions Ltd, Martin Dawes House, Europa Boulevard, Westbrook, Warrington, WA5 7WH Tel: (01925) 555000 Fax: (01925) 494835 *Electrical retailers*

Martin Edwards, 16a Limerick Road, Redcar, Cleveland, TS10 5JU Tel: (01642) 494688 Fax: (01642) 494688 E-mail: dave.atkinson@me-ff.com *Fish frying range manufrs*

Martin Fasteners Ltd, 5 Saddlers Court, Fryers Road, Walsall, WS2 7LZ Tel: (01922) 712169 Fax: (01922) 416452 *Industrial fastener manufrs*

Martin & Frost, Kinnaird Park, Newcraighall Road, Edinburgh, EH15 3HP Tel: 0131-657 0820 Fax: 0131-657 0821 *House furnishers*

Gordon Martin & Son, The Chalet, Tresarrett, Bodmin, Cornwall, PL30 4QF Tel: (01208) 850405 Fax: (01208) 851405 *Haulage*

▶ Martin Group N W Ltd, Bouthwood Road, Sowerby Woods Industrial Estate, Barrow-in-Furness, Cumbria, LA14 4RD Tel: (01229) 813428 Fax: (01229) 430330

H. & J. Martin Ltd, Ulster Building Works, 163 Ormeau Road, Belfast, BT7 1SP Tel: (028) 9023 2622 Fax: (028) 9023 3104 E-mail: info@hjmartin.co.uk *Building & civil engineering services*

G.F.K. Martin Hamblin, Ludgate House, 245 Blackfriars Road, London, SE1 9UL Tel: (020) 7222 8181 Fax: (020) 7890 9001 E-mail: info@gfk.com *Market researchers*

Martin Hopkins Partnership, 31 The Parade, Roath, Cardiff, CF24 3AD Tel: (029) 2046 1233 Fax: (029) 2049 7208 E-mail: info@martinhopkins.co.uk *Graphic design consultants*

Martin Instrument Co. Ltd, 160 Darlaston Road, Wednesbury, West Midlands, WS10 7TA Tel: 0121-568 7755 Fax: 0121-568 7744 E-mail: mic.ltd@virgin.net *Plastics test equipment*

Irvine Martin Ltd, Kenton Road, Debenham, Stowmarket, Suffolk, IP14 6LA Tel: (01728) 860909 Fax: (01728) 861056 E-mail: info@irvine-martin.co.uk *Plastic moulding manufrs*

J.G. Martin Plant Hire Ltd, 95 Orbiston Street, Motherwell, Lanarkshire, ML1 1PX Tel: (0870) 8536100 Fax: (0870) 8536099 E-mail: gail@martinplanthire.co.uk *Tool equipment hire, sales & repair* Also at: Dundee, Edinburgh, Falkirk, Kirkaldy, Motherwell & Perth

Martin Jenkins Engineering Co. Ltd, Nicholls Road, Tipton, West Midlands, DY4 9LG Tel: 0121-557 3663 Fax: 0121-557 9517 E-mail: a7vos@aol.com *CNC engineers*

John Martin Ltd, PO Box 28, Havant, Hampshire, PO9 2UB Tel: (023) 9249 2969 Fax: (023) 9249 2968 E-mail: jmelectronics@havant366.freeserve.co.uk *Electronic starter switch manufrs*

▶ Martin Jolly Ltd, Calgow Farm, Newton Stewart, Wigtownshire, DG8 7AN Tel: (01671) 402161 Fax: (01671) 402161

Martin Land Sewing Machine Co. Ltd, Mulberry House, Hall Lane, Morley St. Botolph, Wymondham, Norfolk, NR18 9TB Tel: (01953) 603139 *Industrial sewing machine repairs & suppliers*

Martin Leighfield, Main Street, Checkendon, Reading, RG8 0SP Tel: (01491) 681444 Fax: (01491) 681155 *Cabinet makers*

Martin Manufacturing UK plc, Belvoir Way, Fairfield Industrial Estate, Louth, Lincolnshire, LN11 0LQ Tel: (01507) 604399 Fax: (01507) 601956 E-mail: sales@martin.dk *Smoke generating equipment manufrs*

Murray Martin Services Ltd, Unit 3 Block 2 River Place, Paddockholm Industrial Estate, Kilbirnie, Ayrshire, KA25 7EN Tel: (01505) 684822 Fax: (01505) 683005 E-mail: enquiries@murraymartinservices.co.uk *Air conditioning & electrical contractors*

Martin & Partners Ltd, 10-11 Regent Square, Northampton, NN1 2NQ Tel: (01604) 639466 Fax: (01604) 620552 E-mail: martin.partners@virgin.net *Builders merchants*

Percy Martin Ltd, Church Hill Road, Thurmaston, Leicester, LE4 8DJ Tel: 0116-260 5582 Fax: 0116-264 0227 E-mail: info@percymartin.co.uk *Used machine tool distributors*

▶ Martin Plant Hire Ltd, B Etna Road, Falkirk, FK2 9EG Tel: (01324) 612842 Fax: (01324) 622116

▶ Martin Plant Hire Ltd, 17 Lancefield Street, Glasgow, G3 8HZ Tel: (0800) 9756851 Fax: 0141-248 8357

▶ Martin Plant Hire Ltd, Unit 12 Howard Court, Nerston Industrial Estate, East Kilbride, Glasgow, G74 4QZ Tel: (01355) 245600 Fax: (01355) 244066 *Construction materials suppliers*

▶ Martin Plant Hire Ltd, Unit 7 Carberry Place, Mitchelston Industrial Estate, Kirkcaldy, Fife, KY1 3NQ Tel: (01592) 655535

▶ Martin Rees, Brewery Field, Victoria CR, Llandovery, Dyfed, SA20 0YE Tel: (01550) 721198 Fax: (01550) 721180 E-mail: enquiries@martinrees.co.uk

Martin Reprographics Ltd, Wrightsway, Lincoln, LN2 4JY Tel: (01522) 526268 Fax: (01522) 546514 E-mail: martinrepro@talk21.com *Commercial stationers & office equipment*

Martin Scott, 2 Hollies Industrial Estate, Graiseley Row, Wolverhampton, WV2 4HE Tel: (01902) 428381 Fax: (01902) 711222 *Bolt & nut distributors*

▶ Martin & Sons, 103-109 Efford Road, Plymouth, PL3 6NG Tel: (01752) 771586 Fax: (01752) 706388 E-mail: martinsandsons@plymstonewannado.co.uk *Memorials, flooring, fireplaces in granite, slate, marble, stone suppliers*

▶ Martin Tool Makers, Unit 32 Herons Gate Trading Estate, Paycocke Road, Basildon, Essex, SS14 3EU Tel: (01268) 272240 Fax: (01268) 272097 *Injection moulding & tool making manufrs*

Martin Trucks Ltd, 61 Battlefield Road, Shrewsbury, SY1 4AD Tel: (01743) 440205 Fax: (01743) 440205 *Machine manufrs*

Martin Ward Anderson Ltd, 7 Savoy Court, The Strand, London, WC2R 0EL Tel: (020) 7240 2233 Fax: (020) 7240 8818 E-mail: info@martinwardanderson.com *Executive recruitment consultants*

Martin Woolman Ltd, Unit 12 Martinfield Business Centre, Martinfield, Welwyn Garden City, Hertfordshire, AL7 1HG Tel: (01707) 373181 Fax: (01707) 373174 E-mail: sales@martinwoolman.co.uk *Electronic sub-contract manufrs*

Martin Works, 271 Lynn Road, Wisbech, Cambridgeshire, PE13 3DZ Tel: (01945) 589005 Fax: (01945) 474694 *Agricultural, industrial blacksmiths & ornamental ironwork services*

Martin-Baker Aircraft Co. Ltd, Lower Road, Higher Denham, Uxbridge, Middlesex, UB9 5AJ Tel: (01895) 832214 Fax: (01895) 832587 E-mail: amartin@martin-baker.co.uk *Aircraft ejection seat manufrs*

Martindale Electric Co. Ltd, Metrohm House, Penfold Trading Estate, Imperial Way, Watford, WD24 4YY Tel: (01923) 441717 Fax: (01923) 446900 E-mail: sales@martindale-electric.co.uk *Electrical test equipment & training*

Martindales Polythene Packaging Ltd, Block D, St. Michaels Industrial Estate, Widnes, Cheshire, WA8 8TL Tel: 0151-420 5355 Fax: 0151-420 5356 E-mail: sales@martindalespps.com *Polythene bag manufrs*

Martineau Johnson, St.Philips House, St. Phillips Place, Birmingham, B3 2PP Tel: 0121-200 3300 Fax: 0121-200 3300 E-mail: marketing@martjohn.com *International lawyers*

Martingale Associates Ltd, 64 Cliffords Inn, Fetter Lane, London, EC4A 1BX Tel: (020) 7242 0064 Fax: (020) 7404 1862 E-mail: sales@martingale.com *Computer consultants*

Martins Ltd, 11b Roderick Road, London, NW3 2NN Tel: (020) 7485 5922 *Refrigeration equipment distributors*

Martins Feeds & Farm Supplies, Nutts Corner Road, Aldergrove, Crumlin, County Antrim, BT29 4BT Tel: (028) 9082 5239 Fax: (028) 9082 5239 *Animal food & medicine suppliers*

Martins Instrumentation, Wellington Road, Tharston Industrial Estate, Long Stratton, Norwich, NR15 2PE Tel: (01508) 531813 Fax: (01508) 531758 *Metal diaphragm manufrs*

Martin's International, Kirkby Road, Sutton In Ashfield, Nottingham, NG17 1GZ Tel: (01623) 441122 Fax: (01623) 492083 E-mail: post@cooperandroe.co.uk *Knitwear manufrs* Also at: Sutton in Ashfield

Martins Mill Packaging, Unit 2 Reflecting Roadstuds Induxtrial Estate, Mill Lane, Booth Town, Halifax, West Yorkshire, HX3 6TR Tel: (01422) 363935 Fax: (01422) 300800 E-mail: rmatmmp@aol.com *Packaging materials & polypropylene bags manufrs*

Martins Plant, 10a Hayes Road, Deanshanger, Milton Keynes, MK19 6HW Tel: (01908) 563437 Fax: (01908) 262429 *Plant hire & ground work*

▶ Martins Removal Service Ltd, 198 Colinton Road, Edinburgh, EH14 1BP Tel: 0131-443 1056

Martin's Rubber Co. Ltd, Orchard Place, Southampton, SO14 3PE Tel: (023) 8022 6330 Fax: (023) 8063 1577 E-mail: sales@martins-rubber.co.uk *Manufacturers of rubber mouldings*

▶ Martin's Services & Supplies, 81 Elmers End Road, London, SE20 7UU Tel: (020) 8289 9910 Fax: (020) 8289 2100 E-mail: ptpmartin@btinternet.com *DIY & plumbing supplies*

▶ Martins Shop & Bar Fitters Ltd, 2-8 West Bowling Green Street, Edinburgh, EH6 5PQ Tel: 0131-553 4777

Martintrux Dover, Lord Warden Square, Dover, Kent, CT17 9EQ Tel: (01304) 213122 Fax: (01304) 213247 E-mail: clearance@martintrux.co.uk *Forwarding agents*

▶ Martland Ltd, Unit 1D, Cricket Street Business Centre, Cricket Street, Wigan, Lancashire, WN6 7TP Tel: (01942) 497064 Fax: (01942) 497075 E-mail: martland-ltd@tiscali.co.uk *Rubber products & fabricators*

Martlet Technological Ltd, 57 Blatchington Road, Hove, East Sussex, BN3 3YJ Tel: (01273) 722305 Fax: (01273) 321915 E-mail: martlettechno@btconnect.com *Overseas project contractors*

Martlets Machinery Ltd, Winnell Manor Road, Winnell Trading Estate, Winchester, Hampshire, SO23 0RF Tel: (01962) 856655 Fax: (01962) 841683 E-mail: enquiries@martletsairpower.com *Compressed air engineers*

Martock Waste Paper Co. Ltd, Great Western Road, Martock, Somerset, TA12 6HB Tel: (01935) 823101 Fax: (01935) 826612 E-mail: martockwp@aol.com *Waste paper merchants*

Marton Dump Trucks Ltd, Oxford Road, Marton, Rugby, Warwickshire, CV23 9RU Tel: (01926) 632241 Fax: (01926) 633421 E-mail: sales@martondumptrucks.com *Marton Dump Trucks is a leading provider of artic, rigged and rear dump trucks spares, equipment and servicing. It also stocks reconditioned plant for quarrying, mining and the construction industry, including machinery manufactured by Aveling Barford, Euclid, Haulmatic, Moxey, Terex and Lancerboss.*

Marton Gateway Engineers, 96 Vicarage Lane, Blackpool, FY4 4EL Tel: 01253 692611 *Gate manufrs*

Marton Geotechnical Services Ltd, Heyford Close, Aldermans Green Industrial Estate, Coventry, CV2 2QB Tel: (024) 7660 2323 Fax: (024) 7660 2116 E-mail: sales@mgf.co.uk *Civil engineers*

Martor Direct UK Ltd, Ahed House, Sandbeds Trading Estate, Ossett, West Yorkshire, WF5 9ND Tel: (01924) 281333 Fax: (01924) 281444 E-mail: dennis@martor-uk-demon.co.uk Principal Export Areas: Worldwide *Knife distributors*

Martract, Ardent Link, Humber Bridge Industrial Estate, Humber Bridge Industrial Estat, Barton-upon-Humber, South Humberside, DN18 5RN Tel: (01652) 632172 Fax: (01652) 660295 E-mail: info@martract.co.uk *Ball valve machining services & precision engineers*

▶ Martrans Bodies Ltd, Blyborough, Gainsborough, Lincolnshire, DN21 4EY Tel: (01427) 667600 Fax: (01427) 667612 E-mail: martronstrailers@btconnect.com *Commercial vehicle body builders & trailer manufrs*

Martyn Price Ltd, PO Box 48, Stourbridge, West Midlands, DY9 8QF Tel: (01384) 424767 Fax: (01384) 424833 E-mail: sales@martynprice.com *Stainless steel bolt & nut distributors*

Company Information

continued

Martyn Pugh Ltd, Unit 8 Winyates Centre, Redditch, Worcestershire, B98 0NR Tel: (01527) 502513 Fax: (01527) 502513 *Precious jewellery, silverware designers & manufrs*

▶ Martyn Wilson & Associates, 52 Abbotswood Road, London, SW16 1AW Tel: 0844 484 9727 Fax: 0870 855 5365 E-mail: Kelly@martynwilson.co.uk *Business to business marketing services; copywriting for advertising, press relations, websites, direct marketing and internal communications. Backed by 35 years of business-to-business marketing communications experience*

Marubeni Komatsu Ltd, Church Farm, Gransden Road, Papworth Everard, Cambridge, CB23 3PL Tel: (01954) 719755 Fax: (01954) 719639 E-mail: sales@marubeni-komatsu.co.uk *Earth moving equipment manufrs*

Marubeni Komatsu Ltd, The Close, Horley, Surrey, RH6 9EB Tel: (01293) 822500 Fax: (01293) 822189 *Construction equipment suppliers*

Marvelfairs Ltd, Suite 44-45, Level 7 Westec House, Westgate, Ealing, London, W5 1YY Tel: (020) 8998 9052 Fax: (020) 8991 0995 E-mail: general@marvelfairs.com *Uniform equipment manufrs*

The Marvellous Media Company, Unit 1 GMS House, Boundary Road, Woking, Surrey, GU21 5BX Tel: 01483 740800 Fax: 01483 656810 E-mail: info@marvellousmedia.com *The Marvellous Media Company provides high quality, bespoke web design, cd-rom production, dvd authoring and print design services to businesses, organisations and educational establishments. Our approach is friendly yet professional, using plain language and avoiding unnecessary techno-babble.*

Marven Ltd, 3 Farm La, London, SW6 1PU Tel: (020) 7386 9445 Fax: (020) 7386 9775 *Web development*

Marvic Joinery Ltd, Millers Road, Warwick, CV34 5AN Tel: (01926) 491990 Fax: (01926) 400673 *Timber bending & joinery manufrs*

Marvic Textiles Ltd, Chelsea Harbour Design Centre, London, SW10 0XE Tel: (020) 7352 3119 Fax: (020) 8879 3448 *Precision milling services*

Marwaha Textiles Ltd, 7 Brays Lane, Coventry, CV2 4DT Tel: (024) 7644 1216 *Schoolwear manufrs*

Marwel Conveyors Ltd, 108 Dudley Road East, Oldbury, West Midlands, B69 3EB Tel: 0121-552 4418 Fax: 0121-552 4018 E-mail: sales@marwel.com *Conveyor systems, power operated loaders, distributors & manufrs*

Marwill Tools & Fasteners Ltd, Units 4 & 5 Thomas Street, Whalley Banks Trading Estate, Blackburn, BB2 2HZ Tel: (01254) 264879 Fax: (01254) 680636 E-mail: marwill.uk@btopenworld.com *Fixings & fastener suppliers*

Marwood Group Ltd, Fengate Eastern Industrial Area, Peterborough, PE1 5BN Tel: (01733) 311444 Fax: (01733) 349974 E-mail: enquire@marwoodgroup.co.uk *Plant hire specialists*

▶ Mary Ann, Acton Place Industrial Estate, Melford Road, Acton, Sudbury, Suffolk, CO10 0BB Tel: (01787) 377978 *Curtain making & alterations*

▶ Mary Rose Bakery Ltd, 10, The Nelson Centre, 3100 Blueprint, Portsfield Road, Portsmouth, PO3 5SF Tel: (023) 9266 0385 Fax: (023) 9266 0385 *Manufacturers of bakery*

Maryland Farm, Main Road, Whissendine, Oakham, Leicestershire, LE15 7ER Tel: (01664) 474155 Fax: (01664) 474155 *Agricultural contractors*

Marylebone Cleaning Co. Ltd, Sherlock Mews, Baker St, London, W1U 6DW Tel: (020) 7581 9847 Fax: (020) 7581 9847 *Cleaning services*

Marylebone Commercial Finance Ltd, Sovereign House, P O Box 302, Manchester, M60 4AL Tel: 0161-833 2222 Fax: 0161-953 3333 *Finance*

▶ MAS Computers, 310 Ruislip Road East, Greenford, Middlesex, UB6 9BH Tel: (020) 8575 0777 Fax: (020) 8575 0777 E-mail: arifsiddiqi@hotmail.com *Computer maintenance & repair services*

Mascolo Support Systems, 6 Dean Park Crescent, Bournemouth, BH1 1HL Tel: (01202) 311826 Fax: (01202) 311830 E-mail: support@salongenius.com *Software & management systems for the hair & beauty industry suppliers*

Mascot Letting Agent, 351 A Whitehorse Road, Croydon, CR0 2HS Tel: (020) 8665 6683 Fax: (020) 8665 6683 E-mail: mascot.croydon@btinternet.com *Property managers & letting agents*

Mascot UK, PO Box 2090, Salisbury, SP2 2BH Tel: (01722) 504853 Fax: (01264) 396402 E-mail: andrew.parrish@mascot.no *Manufacturer of battery chargers, inverters, DC/DC converters & power supplies*

Masdar International Ltd, Masdar House, 1 Reading Road, Hook, Hampshire, RG27 0RP Tel: 0118-973 0750 Fax: 0118-973 0002 E-mail: masdar@masdar.com *Management consultants*

▶ Masefield Epson Ltd, Coneygre Road, Tipton, West Midlands, DY4 8XF Tel: 0121-557 3433

Maselec Ltd, Unit A2 The Courtyard, Lonesome Lane, Reigate, Surrey, RH2 7QT Tel: (01737) 225335 Fax: (01737) 225559 E-mail: sales@maselec.co.uk *Distributors or agents of hydraulic systems*

Masher Bros, 97-103 Florence Road, London, SE14 6QL Tel: (020) 8691 1632 Fax: (020) 8691 1496 E-mail: sales@masherbros.com *Joinery manufrs*

Mashford Bros Ltd, Shipbuilding Yard, Cremyll, Torpoint, Cornwall, PL10 1HY Tel: (01752) 822232 Fax: (01752) 823059 E-mail: mashfords@btconnect.com *Boat builders & ship repairers*

Mashlin Friction Ltd, 404-408 Cricket Inn Road, Sheffield, S2 5AX Tel: 0114-272 5650 Fax: 0114-265 1665 *Industrial brake recliner distributors*

Maskame & Tait, 9-11 St. Peter Street, Peterhead, Aberdeenshire, AB42 1QB Tel: (01779) 473661 Fax: (01779) 481482 E-mail: info@maskameandtait.co.uk *Manufacturing joiners & shop fitters*

Maskold Ltd, Unit 70 Wimbledon Stadium Business Centre, Riverside Road, London, SW17 0BA Tel: (020) 8946 0483 Fax: (020) 8947 8782 E-mail: service@maskold.co.uk *Air conditioning & refrigeration engineers*

Phil Masland, Coxs Yard, Taunton Road, Wellington, Somerset, TA21 9HG Tel: (01823) 666160 Fax: (01823) 666160 *Agricultural machinery repairers*

Maslands Ltd, Unit 12 Howden Industrial Estate, Tiverton, Devon, EX16 5HW Tel: (01884) 242767 Fax: (01884) 257103 E-mail: mail@maslands.co.uk *Commercial & general printers*

Mason Albums Two Trees Press Ltd, Grey Street, Denton, Manchester, M34 3RU Tel: 0161-336 2002 Fax: 0161-335 0346 E-mail: print@twotreespress.co.uk *Lithographic colour printers*

Mason & Ball & Associates Ltd, Bourn House, Park Street, Bagshot, Surrey, GU19 5AQ Tel: (01276) 472774 Fax: (01276) 451520 E-mail: mail@mba-uk.co.uk *Independent financial advisers & insurance brokers*

▶ Mason Bros Transport Ltd, Fairfield Farm, Blackjack Road, Swineshead, Boston, Lincolnshire, PE20 3HG Tel: (01205) 820236 Fax: (01205) 821085

Mason Coatings P.L.C., Nottingham Rd, Derby, DE21 6AR Tel: (01332) 295959 Fax: (01332) 295252 E-mail: mason@masoncoatings.com *Paint manufrs* Also at: Derby, Kirkaldy, Peterborough & Wakefield

David Mason Design Ltd, Snowline Houseware, Foxwood Road, Sheepbridge Industrial Estate, Chesterfield, Derbyshire, S41 9RN Tel: (01246) 260500 Fax: (01246) 260520 E-mail: sales@davidmasondesign.co.uk *House ware manufrs*

David Mason Textiles Ltd, 2-4 Frog Island, Leicester, LE3 5AG Tel: 0116-253 9929 Fax: 0116-253 8458 E-mail: greg.dmt@btinternet.com *Sock manufrs*

Harry Mason Ltd, 217 Thimble Mill Lane, Birmingham, B7 5HS Tel: 0121-328 5900 Fax: 0121-327 7257 E-mail: gt@harrymason.co.uk *Beer dispenser & cellar bar equipment*

Ian Mason, Station Road, Hillington, King's Lynn, Norfolk, PE31 6DH Tel: (01485) 600496 Fax: (01485) 601412 *Agricultural contractors*

Mason & Jones Packaging, Unit 7, Aston Road, Aston Fields Industrial Estate, Bromsgrove, Worcestershire, B60 3EX Tel: (01527) 577123 Fax: (01527) 577248 E-mail: sales@masonandjones.com *Manufacturers & importers of polypropylene, hessian & polythene sacks, tubing & fabric. Distributors worldwide. We carry extensive stocks & specialise in cutting, re-rolling & slitting of fabrics. Plus in-house printing facilities are available.*

Mason & King Ltd, 11 Birstall Street, Leicester, LE1 2HJ Tel: 0116-253 6491 Fax: 0116-251 2403 E-mail: ray@masonking.co.uk *Sheet metal laser cutting services & paint finishing services*

Mason Land Surveys Ltd, Dickson Street, Dunfermline, Fife, KY12 7SL Tel: (01383) 727261 Fax: (01383) 739480 E-mail: sales@mason.co.uk *Land & hydrographic surveyors*

Mason Metals Ltd, Two Woods Lane, Mill Street, Brierley Hill, West Midlands, DY5 1TA Tel: (01384) 79841 Fax: (01384) 76414 E-mail: info@masonmetals.co.uk *Non-ferrous scrap metal contractors*

Mason Morley Ltd, Spray Quip House, St Pauls Street, Morley, Leeds, LS27 9EP Tel: 0113-253 8681 Fax: 0113-252 3179 E-mail: info@masonmorley.co.uk *Spray equipment maintenance & grit blasting service*

Mason & Morton (Electronics) Ltd, 24 Ullswater Crescent, Ullswater Business Park, Coulsdon, Surrey, CR5 2HR Tel: (020) 8410 4610 Fax: (020) 8660 5469 *Electronic assembly equipment*

Mason Pearce Ltd, Canterbury Road, Worthing, West Sussex, BN13 1AW Tel: (01903) 264231 Fax: (01903) 830175 E-mail: masonpearce@hotmail.com *Screen printing services*

Mason Pearson Bros Ltd, 37 Old Bond Street, London, W1S 4AB Tel: (020) 7491 2613 Fax: (020) 7499 2635 E-mail: sales@masonpearson.com Principal Export Areas: Worldwide *Hair brush manufrs*

Peter Mason Associates, New Street, Mawdesley, Ormskirk, Lancashire, L40 2QP Tel: (01704) 823245 Fax: (01704) 823246 E-mail: steve.douglas@btinternet.com *Consulting civil & municipal engineers*

Mason Philips, 33 Great Portland Street, London, W1W 8QG Tel: (020) 7436 1212 Fax: (020) 7436 1350 E-mail: property@masonphilips.co.uk *Property investment agents*

Mason Pinder Tool Makers Ltd, Coulman Street, Thorne, Doncaster, South Yorkshire, DN8 5JS Tel: (01405) 814778 Fax: (01405) 814977 *Plastic injection moulding manufrs*

Mason Shipbrokers Ltd, Unit 5-6 Blake House, Admirals Way, London, E14 9UJ Tel: (020) 7538 5366 Fax: (020) 7538 4677 E-mail: masonshp@globalnet.co.uk *Ship brokers*

Wilson Mason & Partners, 3 Chandos Street, London, W1G 9JU Tel: (020) 7637 1501 Fax: (020) 7631 0325 E-mail: enquiries@wilsonmason.co.uk *Architects & interior designers*

Masona Plastics, Avis Way, Newhaven, East Sussex, BN9 0DH Tel: (01273) 612440 Fax: (01273) 611495 E-mail: ken@masona.co.uk *Injection moulders*

▶ MasonHost - Web Site Builders, Blairquhosh Farm, Blanefield, Glasgow, G63 9AJ Tel: 0800 019 4565 Fax: 01360 771470 E-mail: kelly@masonhost.com *Web site designers, Scotland, offering a comprehensive professional service. Flat fee based services include shopping cart installation, customisation and maintenance, copywriting, graphics design, logos, stationery and image editing. Design services, from £350, include consultation, basic search engine optimisation plus directory*

continued

submission and are complemented by managed hosting from £7 per month including updating, support and multiple email addresses.

Masonlite Ltd, 36 Second Avenue, Chatham, Kent, ME4 5AX Tel: (01634) 812751 Fax: (01634) 811883 E-mail: neon@masonlite.com *Lighting component manufrs*

Masonry Cleaning Services, 1a Allpits Road, Calow, Chesterfield, Derbyshire, S44 5AU Tel: (01246) 209926 Fax: (01246) 211620 E-mail: mike@masonrycleaningservices.com *Stone & brick cleaning contractors*

Masons, 1-4 Portland Square, Bristol, BS2 8RR Tel: 0117-924 5678 Fax: 0117-924 6699 E-mail: enquiries@pinsentmasons.com *Full service law firm and trade mark attorneys with offices in Birmingham, Bristol, Edinburgh, Glasgow, Leeds, London, Manchester, Brussels, Hong Kong and Shanghai offering services in the areas of construction, major projects, energy and utilities, employment, litigation, outsourcing and technology, corporate finance, mergers and acquisitions, intellectual property, insurance and pensions, property and tax.*

▶ Masons, 123 St. Vincent Street, Glasgow, G2 5EA Tel: 0141-248 4858 Fax: 0141-248 6655 E-mail: enquiries@pinsentmasons.com *UK based international full service law firm and trade mark attorneys with offices in Birmingham, Bristol, Edinburgh, Glasgow, Leeds, London, Manchester, Brussels, Hong Kong and Shanghai offering services in the areas of construction, major projects, energy and utilities, employment, litigation, outsourcing and technology, corporate finance, mergers and acquisitions, intellectual property, insurance and pensions, property and tax*

Masons, Cornmarket, Louth, Lincolnshire, LN11 9QD Tel: (01507) 350500 Fax: (01507) 600561 E-mail: info@patricia-williams.com *Agricultural services*

Masons Fasteners Ltd, 3-4 Doris Road, Bordesley Green, Birmingham, B9 4SJ Tel: 0121-766 7500 Fax: 0121-766 8551 Principal Export Areas: Central/East Europe & West Europe *Manufacturers of fasteners (*

Masons Moving Group Ltd, Storage House, Priority Business Park, Barry, South Glamorgan, CF63 2BG Tel: (01446) 733330 Fax: (01446) 733827 E-mail: enquiries@masonsmovinggroup.co.uk *Removal & storage contractors*

Masons Paper, 107 Elkington Street, Birmingham, B6 4SL Tel: 0121-359 5601 Fax: 0121-359 5600 *Paper merchants*

Mason's Paper Ltd, 1 Island House, Bluestem Road, Ipswich, IP3 9RR Tel: (01473) 711123 Fax: (01473) 270109 Principal Export Areas: Worldwide *Paper merchants* Also at: Cambridge & Hornchurch

▶ Masons Print Group Ltd, Viscount House, River Lane, Saltney, Chester, CH4 8RH Tel: (01244) 674433

Mason's Products, 2 Schofield Street, Littleborough, Lancashire, OL15 0JS Tel: (01706) 379817 Fax: (01706) 379817 E-mail: sales@dogoil.co.uk *Pharmaceutical manufrs*

Mason's Textiles Ltd, Cricketers Close, Carleton New Road, Skipton, North Yorkshire, BD23 2AZ Tel: (01756) 799333 Fax: (01756) 700182 E-mail: sales@masonsdesign.demon.co.uk *Silk & polyester tie fabric manufrs*

Masplas Mouldings, 8 Williams Way Industrial Estate, Industrial Estate, Wollaston, Wellingborough, Northamptonshire, NN29 7RQ Tel: (01933) 665577 Fax: (01933) 665680 E-mail: jmitchinson@btclick.com *Plastic injection moulder manufrs*

Mass Measuring Systems, 149 Holland Street, Denton, Manchester, M34 3GE Tel: 0161-304 5700 Fax: 0161-336 4383 E-mail: enquiries@mass-measuring.com *Industrial weighing equipment manufrs*

Mass Sectrometry International Ltd, Unit C, Tudor Road, Broadheath, Altrincham, Cheshire, WA14 5RZ Tel: 0161-929 7583 Fax: 0161-941 5540 *Scientific instrument manufrs*

Mass Spec UK Ltd, Regal House, Highfield Street, Oldham, OL9 6DT Tel: 0161-785 0828 Fax: 0161-785 0838 E-mail: service@massspecuk.ltd.uk *Spectrometers services*

Mass Spectrometry Solutions, 19 Lawrence Close, Cranage, Crewe, CW4 8FA Tel: (01477) 532540 Fax: (01477) 532541 E-mail: jim.speakman@mass-spectrometry-solutions.co.uk *Formed in 2003 by a senior engineer from Micromass/Waters, specialising in service and repair of mass spectrometers, new and not so new. Based in Cheshire, covering the whole world, we are an approved supplier of service for Waters Micromass products. We have access to a large number of new and used parts, to keep you up and running with minimum downtime. Through a network of other independent service providers and manufacturers, we can deliver a complete service solution for all your instruments and accessories. We can also remanufacture parts in our associated workshop, with turning, milling and vacuum brazing facilities. We are European Service Agents for Ionspec Corporation Fourier Transform Mass Spectrometers. We also represent Research Scientific Services Inc in Europe. We particularly specialise in repair of Quattro, Trio, Platform LC, Platform ICP and ZMD instruments and we also supply multipliers, filaments, source heaters and ICP consumables.*

Massey Bros Feeds Ltd, Cranage Mill, Knutsford Road, Cranage, Crewe, CW4 8EE Tel: (01477) 533312 Fax: (01477) 533556 E-mail: enquiries@masseyfeeds.co.uk *Animal feed manufrs*

▶ Massey Coldbeck, Lyntown Trading Estate, Eccles, Manchester, M30 9QG Tel: 0161-789 8867 Fax: 0161-787 7790 *Pump repairs & engineers & motor rewinds*

Massey Engineering Ltd, Ludlow Business Park, Orleton Road, Ludlow Business Park, Ludlow, Shropshire, SY8 1XF Tel: (01584) 875210 Fax: (01584) 874089 *Hydraulic equipment maintenance*

Massey & Harris Engineering Ltd, Cook Street Works, King Street West, Stockport, Cheshire, SK3 0AF Tel: 0161-480 5243 Fax: 0161-476 0151 E-mail: masseyharris@btconnect.com *Playground & sports ground equipment manufrs*

MasseyFforgeing Ltd, Unit F, Joseph Adamson Industrial Estate, Croft Street, Hyde, Cheshire, SK14 1EE Tel: 0161-351 7364 Fax: 0161-351 7365 E-mail: sales@masseyforgeing.com *Hot forging machinery sales, spares, refurbished plant*

▶ Massie Consulting Ltd, 20 Upper Olland Street, Bungay, Suffolk, NR35 1BH Tel: 01986 895030 E-mail: harold@massieconsulting.co.uk *Business Continuity Management Consultancy*

Massmould Ltd, Cosgrove Way, Luton, LU1 1XL Tel: (01582) 728285 Fax: (01582) 723166 *Injection moulders* Also at: Eaton Socon & Flitwick

Massmould Holdings Ltd, Maulden Road, Flitwick, Bedford, MK45 5BZ Tel: (01525) 718718 Fax: (01525) 712111 *Plastic mouldings manufrs*

Masson Joinery Ltd, The Joinery Works, The Green, Frant, Tunbridge Wells, Kent, TN3 9DE Tel: (01892) 750351 Fax: (01892) 750695 *Joinery manufrs*

Masson Seeley & Co. Ltd, Rouses Lane, Downham Market, Norfolk, PE38 9AN Tel: (01366) 388000 Fax: (01366) 385222 E-mail: sales@masson-seeley.co.uk *Sign makers*

Masstech, 9 Valley Road, Markfield, Leicestershire, LE67 9QS Tel: (01530) 244467 Fax: (01530) 244467 E-mail: masstech@bigfoot.com *Casting & forging component company*

Masstock Arable UK Ltd, Station Road, Andoversford, Cheltenham, Gloucestershire, GL54 4LZ Tel: (01242) 821100 Fax: (01242) 820807 *Chemical manufrs*

Masstock Arable (Uk) Ltd, Moreton Mill, Moreton, Ongar, Essex, CM5 0DP Tel: (01277) 899700 Fax: (01277) 898206 E-mail: jane.cable@masstock.co.uk *Agricultural merchants*

Mast Group Ltd, Mast House, Derby Road, Bootle, Merseyside, L20 1EA Tel: 0151-933 7277 Fax: 0151-944 1332 E-mail: sales@mastgrp.com *Medical diagnostics kit manufrs*

Mast International Group plc, Hermitage House, Bath Road, Taplow, Maidenhead, Berkshire, SL6 0AR Tel: (01628) 784062 Fax: (01628) 773061 E-mail: info@mast.co.uk *Management consultants*

Mastclimbers (Scotland) Ltd, Denmark Street Industrial Estate, 97a Hawthorn Street, Glasgow, G22 6HY Tel: 0141-336 3344 Fax: 0141-336 3355 E-mail: sales@mastclimbers.co.uk *Suppliers of specialist access solutions to the construction industry*

Mastek UK Ltd, Crown House, 1a High Street Theale, Theale, Reading, RG7 5AH Tel: 0118-930 5190 Fax: 0118 -932-3354 *I.T solution consultants*

Master Alarms, Unit 1, The Arcade, Leagrave Road, Luton, LU4 8JE Tel: (01582) 484477 Fax: (01582) 413800 *Alarm engineers*

Master Badge, 306 Gloucester Road, Cheltenham, Gloucestershire, GL51 7AG Tel: (01242) 580430 Fax: (01242) 580430 E-mail: info@masterbadge.co.uk *Personalised corporate badge manufrs*

▶ Master Blaster Disco's, 20 Pinewood, Forest Hill, Skelmersdale, Lancashire, WN8 6UZ Tel: (07769) 734126 E-mail: masterblasterdiscos@hotmail.co.uk

Master Chemical Europe Ltd, Maitland Road, Lion Barn Business Park, Needham Market, Ipswich, IP6 8NZ Tel: (01449) 726800 Fax: (01449) 721719 E-mail: info@masterchemical.co.uk *Chemical manufrs*

▶ Master Clean, 41 Willows Lane, Rochdale, Lancashire, OL16 4BQ Tel: (01706) 710426 Fax: (01706) 710426 E-mail: master_clean@walla.com *A carpet and upholstery cleaning service specially targeted at the domestic market, offering superior cleaning at a really superior price. PROTECTIVE TREATMENTS including stainguard are also available. We cover all of the North West of England and include 24 Hr emergency call out, Floods and insurance work.*

Master Cleaning Supplies, Middlemore La West, Aldridge, Walsall, WS9 8BG Tel: (01922) 453682 Fax: (01922) 458687 *Cleaning suppliers*

Master Control UK Ltd, Loughborough Motorway Trading Estate, Gelders Hall Road, Shepshed, Loughborough, Leicestershire, LE12 9QX Tel: (01509) 650750 Fax: (01509) 600075 E-mail: info@mastercontrol.co.uk *Control panel manufrs*

Master Filtration Ltd, 7 Arden Press Way, Letchworth Garden City, Hertfordshire, SG6 1LH Tel: (01462) 675844 Fax: (01462) 480852 E-mail: sales@master-filtration.co.uk *Air oil, fuel filtration equipment & accessories & distributors*

▶ Master Houses Ltd, Newlands, Kirknewton, Midlothian, EH27 8LR Tel: (01506) 885588 Fax: (01506) 885588

Master Rope Makers Ltd, The Historic Dockyard, Chatham, Kent, ME4 4TG Tel: (01634) 827812 Fax: (01634) 827217 E-mail: sales@master-ropemakers.co.uk *Rope manufrs*

Masterange Business Services Ltd, 9 East Road, Harlow, Essex, CM20 2BJ Tel: (01279) 300600 Fax: (01279) 306911 E-mail: services@masterange.co.uk *Printers & stationers distributors & manufrs*

Masterblock, Nether Kellet, Carnforth, Lancashire, LA6 1EA Tel: (01524) 736636 Fax: (01524) 736635 *Concrete product manufrs*

Masterbuild Plastics, Unit 8 Henley Business Park, Trident Close, Medway City Estate, Rochester, Kent, ME2 4FR Tel: (01634) 291277 Fax: (01634) 291278 *Plastic & building material suppliers*

Mastercool Southern Ltd, 7a Baker Street, Ampthill, Bedford, MK45 2QE Tel: (01525) 840689 Fax: 01525 840699 E-mail: mastercool15@btopenworld.com *Refrigeration & air-conditioning equipment suppliers*

Mastercote Ltd, Wendover Road, Rackheath Industrial Estate, Rackheath, Norwich, NR13 6LH Tel: (01603) 720326 Fax: (01603) 721805 *Industrial finishes & powder coatings services*

Mastercraft Joinery Works Ltd, 24 Honey Hill Road, Bristol, BS15 4HQ Tel: 0117-947 7171 Fax: 0117-947 7171 *Joinery*

Mastercut Cutting Systems Ltd, 8 Bridge St Industrial Estate, Bridge Street, Clay Cross, Chesterfield, Derbyshire, S45 9NU Tel: (01246) 860811 Fax: (01246) 866928 E-mail: info@mastercut.co.uk *Manufacturers of granulating machine blades, paper guillotines & machine knifes.Also blade (guillotine) sharpening/maintenance/repair services*

Masterfil Ltd, Olympus House, Mill Green Road, Haywards Heath, West Sussex, RH16 1XQ Tel: 01444 472300 Fax: 01444 472329 E-mail: sales@masterfil.com *Liquid filling & bottle capping machinery*

Masterflex Technical Hoses Ltd, Unit G & H Prince Of Wales, Vulcan St, Oldham, OL1 4ER Tel: 0161 6268066 *Manufacturers of flexible ducting*

Masterflo Valve Co (U K) Ltd, Blackness Road, Altens Industrial Estate, Altens, Aberdeen, AB12 3LH Tel: (01224) 878999 Fax: (01224) 878989 E-mail: info@masterflo.co.uk *Valve & actuator manufrs*

Masterfoods, Oakwell Way, Birstall, Batley, West Yorkshire, WF17 9LU Tel: (01924) 427000 Fax: (01924) 427427 *Manufacturer of animal foods*

Masterfoods, Hansa Road, King's Lynn, Norfolk, PE30 4JE Tel: (01553) 692222 Fax: (01553) 697920 E-mail: sales@unclebens.co.uk *Food product manufrs*

Masterford Ltd, Lyon Road, Bletchley, Milton Keynes, MK1 1EX Tel: (01908) 373106 Fax: (01908) 377181 E-mail: john-forder@btconnect.com *Sheet metalwork engineers or fabrications; sheet metalwork precision fine limit engineers or fabricators; steel fabricators & metal fabricators*

Masterguard Security & Fire Services, The Paddocks, Greenacres Drive, Uttoxeter, Staffordshire, ST14 7EB Tel: (01889) 566040 Fax: (01889) 566040 *Security & fire consultants*

Masterguard Security Services Ltd, Masterguard House, 1 Ipsley Street, Redditch, Worcestershire, B98 7AR Tel: (01527) 65344 Fax: (01527) 63888 E-mail: mastergaurd_2000@yahoo.co.uk *Security guard services & alarm installations*

Masterkey Systems Ltd, 27a Queens Road, Southend-on-Sea, SS1 1LT Tel: (01702) 437146 *Computer programmers to travel agencies*

▶ Masterlink Management Ltd, Hearts Court, Wearish Lane, West Houghton, Bolton, BL5 2DG Tel: (0845) 2701212 Fax: (0845) 2701210 *Software support services*

▶ Mastern Patterns, 17 Murraysgate Industrial Estate, Whitburn, Bathgate, West Lothian, EH47 0LE Tel: (01501) 744554 Fax: (01501) 743561

▶ Masterpart, 4 Grainger Road, Southend-on-Sea, SS2 5BZ Tel: (01702) 310031 Fax: (01702) 312000 E-mail: sales@masterpart.com *Domestic appliance wholesalers*

▶ Masterplay Leisure Services Ltd, 16 Deanway Trading Estate, Wilmslow Road, Handforth, Wilmslow, Cheshire, SK9 3HW Tel: (01625) 533392 Fax: (01625) 524471

Masterpoint Communication Systems Ltd, 15 Tresham Street, Kettering, Northamptonshire, NN16 8RS Tel: (01536) 417744 Fax: (0870) 4428855 *Telecommunication engineers*

Masterpower Electronics Ltd, Badentoy Cresent, Badentoy Industrial Estate, Portlethen, Aberdeen, AB12 4YD Tel: (01224) 783700 Fax: (01224) 783701 E-mail: sales@masterpower.co.uk *Power supply systems manufrs*

Masters Choice Ltd, 4 Carrive Road, Silverbridge, Newry, County Down, BT35 9LJ Tel: (028) 3086 1032 Fax: (028) 3086 1693 E-mail: chenjian80515@163.com *Sliding acoustic panels & moveable walls*

John Masters, Trenay, Two Waters Foot, Liskeard, Cornwall, PL14 6HX Tel: (01208) 821248 *Agricultural contractors services*

Julian Masters, Newbridge House, Chew Road, Winford, Bristol, BS40 8HL Tel: (01275) 331080 Fax: (01275) 331080 E-mail: info@newbridgefurniture.com *Retail furniture*

Masters Vehicle Security, 57 Anerley Road, London, SE19 2AS Tel: (020) 8289 9835 Fax: (020) 8289 8188 *Stockist of car Hi-fi & alarm systems*

Masterswitch (UK) Ltd, 184 Walpole Rd, Tottenham, London, N17 6BW Tel: (020) 8881 3918 Fax: (020) 8881 3918 E-mail: pells@masterswich.prestel.co.uk *Personal alarms*

▶ Masterton Dismantling Contractors, Boyd Street, Falkirk, FK2 7BL Tel: (01324) 637816 Fax: (01324) 612142

Mastervent Ventilation Systems, 2 Engine Street, Smethwick, West Midlands, B66 3DT Tel: 0121-558 1559 Fax: 0121-565 4047 E-mail: home@masterventltd.go-plus.net *Dust & fume ductwork fabricators*

Mastervolt UK Ltd, Winchester Hill, Romsey, Hampshire, SO51 7ND Tel: (01794) 516443 Fax: (01794) 516453 E-mail: sales@mastervolt.com *Distributors of battery chargers & batteries including marine*

Masterwaves, 131 Maiden Lane, Dartford, DA1 4NF Tel: (020) 8312 1000 Fax: (01322) 525488 E-mail: masterwaves@aol.com *Supply & service microwaves*

Masterwood UK Ltd, St Andrews, 13 East Abercromby Street, Helensburgh, Dunbartonshire, G84 7SP Tel: (01436) 675000 Fax: (01436) 678999 *Woodwork machinery*

Masthead Printers Ltd, 6 Menin Works, Bond Road, Mitcham, Surrey, CR4 3HG Tel: (020) 8640 6559 Fax: (020) 8646 7133 E-mail: peter@mastheadprinters.demon.co.uk *Commercial printers* Also at: Mitcham

▶ Mastif Supplies Ltd, M90 Lathalmond, Dunfermline, Fife, KY12 0SJ Tel: (01383) 725544

▶ Mastooplast Tool Design, Westwood Farm, 34 Highcross Road, Southfleet, Gravesend, Kent, DA13 9PH Tel: (01474) 834455 Fax: (01474) 834457 E-mail: ne1@mundy-side.prestel.co.uk *Toolmaking services*

▶ MAT Network Express Ltd, Euroterminal, Unit 5 Westinghouse Circle, Trafford Park, Manchester, M17 1PY Tel: 0161-872 3222 Fax: 0161-848 9261 E-mail: bill.wyman@mat-group.com

Matador Co. Ltd, Unit 6, Top Angel, Buckingham Industrial Park, Buckingham, MK18 1TH Tel: (01280) 823824 Fax: (01280) 817717 E-mail: wipers@matador.co.uk *Windscreen wipers & washers manufrs*

Matain Ltd, 39 Ludgate Hill, London, EC4M 7JN Tel: (020) 7236 0096 Fax: (020) 7236 3957 E-mail: reprocopy@lithoprinting.co.uk *General printing services*

Matalan Ltd, Gillibrands Road, Skelmersdale, Lancashire, WN8 9TB Tel: (01695) 552400 Fax: (01695) 552401 *Fashion retailers*

Matann Metal Fabrication Ltd, 5 Blatchford Road, Horsham, West Sussex, RH13 5QR Tel: (01403) 249994 Fax: (01403) 249355 *Sheet metal workers & welders*

Matano, Units 14-15 Whinfield Industrial Estate, Whinfield Way, Rowlands Gill, Tyne & Wear, NE39 1EH Tel: (01207) 549448 Fax: (01207) 549447 E-mail: james.harlend@metano.com *IBC rental (stainless steel) services*

Matatec, Station Road, Seaton Delaval, Seaton Delaval, Whitley Bay, Tyne & Wear, NE25 0PT Tel: 0191-237 9900 Fax: 0191-237 9999 E-mail: msl@matatec.co.uk *Ship repair services*

Match-It Ltd, 95 Stansted Road, Bishop's Stortford, Hertfordshire, CM23 2DU Tel: (0845) 1300510 Fax: (01279) 757447 E-mail: enquiries@match-it.com *Software*

▶ Matchless Ltd, Gilbert Wakefield Lodge, 65 Bewsey Street, Warrington, WA2 7JQ Tel: (01925) 231900 Fax: (01925) 415423

Matchless Mouldings, Stonebridge Mill, Stonebridge Lane, Oswaldtwistle, Accrington, Lancashire, BB5 3HX Tel: 0845 5260333 Fax: (01254) 356151 E-mail: david.rowbottom@ashleyengineering.com *Injection moulders*

Matchmaker CNC, 8 Woodland Studios, Brook Willow Farm, Woodlands Road, Leatherhead, Surrey, KT22 0AN Tel: (01372) 844999 Fax: (01372) 844998 E-mail: sales@matchmakermc.co.uk *Supplier of CNC Machine Tools*

Matchmakers International Ltd, Park View Mills, Wibsey Park Avenue, Wibsey, Bradford, West Yorkshire, BD6 3SR Tel: (01274) 711011 Fax: (01274) 711030 E-mail: reception@matchmakers.co.uk *Saddlery agents*

Matchmakers International, Richmond Street, Sheepfolds Industrial Estate, Sunderland, SR5 1BQ Tel: 0191-514 4199 Fax: 0191-565 6416 E-mail: matchfactory@edward-thompson.com *Bookmatch manufrs*

Matchtech Group plc, 1450 Parkway, Solent Business Park, Fareham, Hampshire, PO15 7AF Tel: (01489) 898150 E-mail: jdean@Matchtech.com *Technical & IT recruitment consultants*

Matcom, 140 Windsor Road, Maidenhead, Berkshire, SL6 2DW Tel: (01628) 626352 Fax: (01628) 631757 E-mail: postbox@matcom.co.uk *Internet services & web developers*

Matcon Group Ltd, Matcon House, London Road, Moreton-in-Marsh, Gloucestershire, GL56 0HJ Tel: (01608) 651666 Fax: (01608) 651635 E-mail: matcon@matcon.co.uk *Materials handling equipment manufrs*

Matech Computers, North Quay, Great Yarmouth, Norfolk, NR30 1RE Tel: (01493) 331591 Fax: (01493) 851852 *Software engineers*

Matek Business Media Ltd, 4 Field Place Estate, Field Place, Broadbridge Heath, Horsham, West Sussex, RH12 3PB Tel: (01403) 276300 Fax: (01403) 276311 E-mail: sales@matek.net *Media & forensics system integration service providers & manufrs*

▶ Mateleco UK Ltd, Northgate Close, Mansell Way, Middlebrook, Bolton, BL6 6PQ Tel: (01204) 673040 Fax: (01204) 693209 E-mail: sales@mateleco.co.uk *Electronic component distributors*

Mateline Engineering Ltd, 42 Walkers Road, Moons Moat North Industrial Estate, Redditch, Worcestershire, B98 9HD Tel: (01527) 63213 Fax: (01527) 584530 E-mail: mateline.engineering@tiscali.co.uk *Food processing plant service producers*

▶ Material Edge Ltd, High Moss House, 9 Wheat Moss, Chelford, Macclesfield, Cheshire, SK11 9SP Tel: (01625) 861808 Fax: 0161-332 8200 E-mail: chris@materialedge.co.uk *Construction material suppliers*

Material Handling Devices Ltd, Lindeth House, 563 Bradford Road, Cleckheaton, West Yorkshire, BD19 6BU Tel: (01274) 874164 Fax: (01274) 852233 E-mail: sales.mathandlin@btclick.com *Lifting equipment manufrs & distributors*

Material Inspection Ltd, Wincomblee Road, Walker, Newcastle upon Tyne, NE6 3QQ Tel: 0191-295 4733 Fax: 0191-295 4723 E-mail: office@materialinspection.co.uk *Non-destructive testing & inspection*

▶ Material Managers, 28a London Road, Grays, Essex, RM17 5XY Tel: (01375) 390202 Fax: (01375) 390201 E-mail: info@materialmanagers.com *Procurement & supply of machinery, equipment & materials*

Material Matters, 2 Ninian Park, Ninian Way, Wilnecote, Tamworth, Staffordshire, B77 5ES Tel: (01827) 262527 Fax: (01827) 262530 *Interior designers*

Material Measurements Ltd, Avenue One, Witney, Oxfordshire, OX28 4XS Tel: (01993) 778522 Fax: (01993) 708673 E-mail: ph@material-measurements.co.uk *Non-destructive test & inspection services*

Material Measurements Group Ltd, 61 Albert Road North, Reigate, Surrey, RH2 9RS Tel: (01737) 222211 Fax: (01737) 224333 E-mail: enquiries@material-measurements.co.uk *Non-destructive test services*

▶ Material Resources, Kingstable Street, Eton, Windsor, Berkshire, SL4 6AB Tel: (01753) 624120 Fax: (01803) 732073

▶ Materials Handling Services (UK) Ltd, Unit 3, Thornley Station Industrial Estate, Shotton Colliery, Durham, DH6 2QA Tel: (01429) 838113 Fax: (01429) 838103 E-mail: mhsuk1@aol.com *Fabricators*

Materials Science, Victoria House, 15 Craven Terrace, Kirkgate, Settle, North Yorkshire, BD24 9DB Tel: (01729) 822327 Fax: (01729) 824500 E-mail: edward.hindle@btinternet.com *Scientific instrument manufrs*

Materials Testing Equipment Ltd, Gilwilly Industrial Estate, Penrith, Cumbria, CA11 9BQ Tel: (01768) 865302 Fax: (01768) 890954 E-mail: mte@materialstestingequip.com *Test equipment manufrs*

Matform Ltd, Matform Business Centre, Terminus Road, Chichester, West Sussex, PO19 8UL Tel: (01243) 780157 Fax: (01243) 789029 E-mail: pdown@matform.net *Screenprinters & engravers*

Matglen Ltd, Unit 48 Milmead Industrial Centre, Mill Mead Road, London, N17 9QU Tel: (020) 8801 7799 Fax: (020) 8801 7985 E-mail: sales@matglen.demon.co.uk *Abrasive products, hand tools & metals*

Matglobe Ltd, 7-9 Davenant Street, London, E1 5NB Tel: (020) 7375 2877 Fax: (020) 7479 9414 *Women & children's clothing manufrs*

Mathbirk Ltd, Mansfield Road, Sutton-in-Ashfield, Nottinghamshire, NG17 4HE Tel: (01623) 559333 Fax: (01623) 552109 *Textile engineers*

David Mather Supplies Ltd, 6 Knowsley Street, Manchester, M8 8GF Tel: 0161-834 6606 Fax: 0161-832 5066 E-mail: info@davidmather.com *Household textile merchants*

Mather Engineering Co. Ltd, 73 River Road, Barking, Essex, IG11 0DR Tel: (020) 8594 1092 Fax: (020) 8594 9247 E-mail: email@mather-engeering.co.uk *Expanded polystyrene tool manufrs*

Mather K.G Office Supplies, 1a Higher Common Way, Buckley, Clwyd, CH7 3PW Tel: (01244) 548393 Fax: (01244) 548393 *Office equipment suppliers*

Mathesons & Co. Ltd, 3 Lombard Street, 1 Undershaft, London, EC3V 9AQ Tel: (020) 7816 8100 Fax: (020) 7816 8182 *Investment house*

Mathew C Blythe & Son Ltd, The Green, Tredington, Shipston-on-Stour, Warwickshire, CV36 4NJ Tel: (01608) 662295 Fax: (01608) 662006 E-mail: sales@matthewcblythe.co.uk *High voltage electrical engineers*

Martin Mathew & Co. Ltd, Riverdene House, 140 High Street, Cheshunt, Waltham Cross, Hertfordshire, EN8 0AW Tel: (01992) 641641 Fax: (01992) 641888 E-mail: sales@martinmathew.co.uk *Food importers & distribs*

Mathewson & Rosemond Ltd, Union Mills, 9 Dewsbury Road, Leeds, LS11 5DE Tel: 0113-245 7983 Fax: 0113-242 6986 E-mail: salesmandrleeds@btconnect.com *Plumbers suppliers*

Mathmos, Sterte Avenue West, Poole, Dorset, BH15 2BE Tel: (01202) 644600 Fax: (01202) 669440 *Decorative lighting manufrs*

The Mathworks Ltd, Matrix House 10 Cowley Park, Cowley Road, Cambridge, CB4 0HH Tel: (01223) 423200 Fax: (01223) 423289 E-mail: sales@mathworks.co.uk *Engineering consultants*

Mathys & Squire, 120 Holborn, London, EC1N 2SQ Tel: (020) 7830 0000 Fax: (020) 7830 0001 E-mail: sales@mathys-squire.com *Patent & trade mark agents*

Matki Public Ltd Company, Churchward Road, Yate, Bristol, BS37 5PL Tel: (01454) 322888 Fax: (01454) 315284 E-mail: sales@matki.co.uk *Shower surrounds & shower manufrs*

▶ Matlock Trading & Supply Co., Northwood Lane, Darley Dale, Matlock, Derbyshire, DE4 2HQ Tel: (01629) 732231 Fax: (01629) 732176

▶ Matlock Transport Ltd, Northwood Lane, Darley Dale, Matlock, Derbyshire, DE4 2HQ Tel: (01629) 733357 Fax: (01629) 732176

MATO Ltd, Church Bank Works, Kirk Road, Church, Accrington, Lancashire, BB5 4JW Tel: (01254) 235411 Fax: (01254) 238023 E-mail: info@mato.co.uk *Conveyor belt fastener manufrs*

Matravers Engineering Ltd, Isle Moor Works, Fivehead, Taunton, Somerset, TA3 6PA Tel: (01460) 281544 Fax: (01460) 281735 E-mail: info@matravers.co.uk *Steel fabricators & general engineers*

Matric Services & Supplies Ltd, Unit 25-26 Essington Light Industrial Estate, Bognop Road, Essington, Wolverhampton, WV11 2BJ Tel: (01922) 479132 Fax: (01922) 494450 E-mail: matric@amserve.com *Protective clothing suppliers*

Matrica, Unit 30 Cannon Wharf Business Park, 35 Evelyn Street, London, SE8 5RT Tel: (020) 7536 2950 Fax: (020) 7237 0044 *Software suppliers*

Matrice, Hawthorn Cottage, Hadham Road, Bishop's Stortford, Hertfordshire, CM23 2QT Tel: (01279) 501955 E-mail: info@matrice.co.uk *Software training & consultants*

Matrikon, 81 Dale Road, Matlock, Derbyshire, DE4 3LU Tel: (01629) 580886 Fax: (01629) 582104 E-mail: info@ics-ltd.co.uk *Software house*

▶ Matrix Aluminium Fabrications, 4 Robert Leonard Industrial Site, Stock Road, Southend-on-Sea, SS2 5QD Tel: (01702) 613490 Fax: (01702) 619406

▶ Matrix Building Services, Highfields, Weedon Road, Nether Heyford, Northampton, NN7 3LF Tel: (01327) 341506 E-mail: matrixbuildingservices@hotmail.co.uk *General Builders. Extensions, stone work, renovations, patios, UPVC windows and doors, any building work undertaken.*

Matrix Catering Systems Ltd, Victoria Court, Hurricane Way, Wickford, Essex, SS11 8YY Tel: (01268) 574001 Fax: (01268) 574004 *Vending machines manufrs*

Matrix Computer Services, Matrix Buildings, Darenth Road, Dartford, DA1 1LU Tel: (01322) 292391 Fax: (01322) 229908 E-mail: matrixcomputers@compuserve.com *Computer dealers & repair services*

▶ Matrix Control Solutions Ltd, Littlemoss Road, Droylsden, Manchester, M43 7EF Tel: 0161-371 0111 Fax: 0161-371 0880 *Control systems installers*

Matrix Controls, 4 Zan Industrial Park, Crewe Road, Wheelock, Sandbach, Cheshire, CW11 4QD Tel: (01270) 753066 Fax: (01270) 753066 E-mail: sales@matrixcontrols.co.uk *Marine control system manufrs*

Matrix Design Services, Unit 331e Vauxhall Industrial Estate, Greg Street, Stockport, Cheshire, SK5 7BR Tel: 0161-480 5610 Fax: 0161-474 1845 E-mail: office@matrixdesigns.co.uk *Corporate clothing*

Matrix Educational Furniture Ltd, Unit 10 Shawbridge Industrial Estate, 237-239 Shawbridge Street, Glasgow, G43 1QN Tel: 0141-636 5700 Fax: 0141-649 0909 E-mail: matrixed@ukonline.co.uk *Educational furniture distributors*

Matrix Engineered Systems Ltd, Eastmill Road, Brechin, Angus, DD9 7EP Tel: (01356) 602000 Fax: (01356) 602060 E-mail: sales@matrix-international.com Purchasing Contact: D. Robertson Sales Contact: F Logan Principal Export Areas: Worldwide *Engineering sub-contract services. Also friction brakes, friction clutches & gear tooth couplings*

▶ Matrix Flooring Solutions Ltd, 471 Ranglet Road, Walton Summit Centre, Bamber Bridge, Preston, PR5 8AR Tel: (01772) 330033 Fax: (01772) 330053 E-mail: sales@matrixflooring.net *Carpet suppliers & distributors*

▶ Matrix Information Technology Ltd, Imperial Chambers, 41-43 Longsmith Street, Gloucester, GL1 2HT Tel: (01452) 387002 Fax: (01452) 309693 E-mail: sales@matrixinfotech.co.uk *Computer training services*

Matrix Information Technology Ltd, Imperial Chambers, 41-43 Longsmith Street, Gloucester, GL1 2HT Tel: (01452) 387002 Fax: (01452) 309693 E-mail: sales@matrixinfotech.co.uk *Computer training*

Matrix Interior Systems Ltd, Crombie Mews, Abercrombie Street, London, SW11 2JB Tel: (020) 7924 7574 Fax: (020) 7924 7270 E-mail: matrixinteriors@aol.com *Office refurbishment contractors*

Matrix Lasers North East Ltd, 5 Trafalgar Court, South Nelson Industrial Estate, Cramlington, Northumberland, NE23 1WF Tel: (01670) 739222 Fax: (01670) 739333 *Laser cutting & profiling services*

Matrix Machinery, Bermar House Unit 38 Rumer Hill Business Estate, Rumer Hill Road, Cannock, Staffordshire, WS11 0ET Tel: (01543) 466256 Fax: (01543) 466320 E-mail: jpl@matrixmachinery.fsnet.co.uk *Food machinery repair & refurbishment*

▶ Matrix Media World, 5-9 Vernon Street, Bolton, BL1 2QB Tel: (01204) 522066 Fax: (0870) 0113694 *Trade warehouse for computer consumables*

▶ Matrix Memory Technology, Burlyns Coach House, Ball Hill, Newbury, Berkshire, RG20 0NU Tel: (01635) 255039

▶ Matrix Microscience Ltd, Lynx Business Park, Fordham Road, Snailwell, Newmarket, Suffolk, CB8 7NY Tel: (01638) 723110 Fax: (01638) 723111

Matrix Moulds & Models Ltd, Glover Street, St. Helens, Merseyside, WA10 3LF Tel: (01744) 24333 Fax: (01744) 27999 E-mail: mmm@rapid.co.uk *Wooden mould & pattern makers*

▶ Matrix Network Services Ltd, Unit 20, Exchange Road, Lincoln, LN6 3JZ Tel: (01522) 682333 Fax: (01522) 689868 E-mail: sales@matrixns.co.uk *Cabling systems design, structured*

▶ Matrix PCs, 5 Willow Drive, Wimborne, Dorset, BH21 2RA Tel: (01202) 840902 E-mail: info@matrix-pcs.co.uk *Computer and network services in the Bournemouth and Poole area to include; diagnosis & repair, maintenance, virus and spyware removal, low noise computer build, software and hardware upgrades, wired and wireless networks (home and office),tuition and video to DVD editing /copying.*

Matrix Plastics Ltd, 141 Edinburgh Avenue, Slough, SL1 4SS Tel: (01753) 551177 Fax: (01753) 551166 E-mail: sales@matrix-plastics.co.uk *Plastics compound manufrs*

Matrix Security UK, Ingles Manor, Castle Hill, Folkestone, Kent, CT20 RD Tel: 01304 207372 Fax: 01304 207395 E-mail: info@matrixsecurityuk.com *Event Management Services, Event security/stewards, Manned Guarding, Close Protection, Tour Security, TV & Film Location, CCTV Systems, Investigations, Auditing. We cover the whole of the UK. Call and quote "kellysearch".*

▶ Matrix Technologies, Sheldon House, 29 Morley Street, Bradford, West Yorkshire, BD7 1AG Tel: (01274) 394111 *Computer consultants*

Matrix Technology Services Ltd, North Street, Maldon, Essex, CM9 5HL Tel: (01621) 841000 Fax: (01621) 843849 E-mail: sales@matrix-ts.com *Data communications system suppliers*

▶ Matrix World, 14 New Street, Dudley, West Midlands, DY1 1LP Tel: (01384) 242867 Fax: (01384) 239585 E-mail: sale@matrixworld.co.uk *Computer hardware suppliers & mobile phones*

▶ Matrixgrade Ltd, Matrix House, Meadow Road, Netherfield, Nottingham, NG4 2FF Tel: 0115-987 0871

Matrox Vite Ltd, C Sefton Park, Bells Hill, Stoke Poges, Slough, SL2 4JS Tel: (01753) 665500 Fax: (01753) 665599 *Computer peripherals manufrs*

▶ Mat's Castles, 51 Upper Field Close, Redditch, Worcestershire, B98 9LE Tel: (07870) 833269 *Inflatable bouncy castle hire services*

Matt Aminoff & Co., 26-27 Hatton Garden, London, EC1N 8BR Tel: (020) 7405 3587 Fax: (020) 7430 1073 E-mail: enquiries@mattaminoff.com *Cultured pearl importers*

▶ Matt Purdie & Sons Ltd, 48-54 East Main Street, Blackburn, Bathgate, West Lothian, EH47 7QS Tel: (01506) 652792 Fax: (01506) 632370

Mattacott Dairy Engineers, 4 Collaford Farm Business Units, Plympton, Plymouth, PL7 5BD Tel: (01752) 881000 Fax: (01752) 881000 *Agricultural services*

Mattalex Lighting Ltd, Unit C, 13-2 The Acacia Buliding, Vantage Point Business Village, Mitcheldean, Gloucestershire, GL17 0DD Tel: (01594) 546368 Fax: (01594) 546373 E-mail: sales@mattalex.co.uk *Emergency lighting manufrs & electrical engineers*

Matten Ltd, Market Street, Whitworth, Rochdale, Lancashire, OL12 8PW Tel: (01706) 341197 Fax: (01706) 342580 E-mail: john@mattenltd.co.uk *Hand press manufrs*

▶ Matter Solutions, 51 Back Church Lane, London, E1 1DQ Tel: (020) 7702 2200 *E business & web consultants*

Matterson Cranes, 45 Regent Street, Rochdale, Lancashire, OL12 0HQ Tel: (01706) 649321 Fax: (01706) 657452 *Electric crane & hoist block manufrs*

Matterson King Cranes, PO Box 31, Glasgow, G15 8TE Tel: 0141-944 4000 Fax: 0141-944 0111 E-mail: pct@pctgroup.co.uk *Electric crane & hoist block manufrs*

Mattersons Ltd, Kingfield Road, Coventry, CV6 5AS Tel: (024) 7670 3713 Fax: (024) 7666 8156 E-mail: sales@matterson.co.uk *Steel stockholders*

▶ Matthew Aerial & Satellite Systems, 57a Glencoe Road, Bushey, WD23 3DP Tel: (020) 8950 2213 Fax: (020) 8950 4262

Matthew Clark, Holford Way, Holford, Birmingham, B6 7AX Tel: 0121-344 3773 Fax: 0121-331 8506 *Wine, spirit & beer wholesalers*

▶ Matthew Cornish Transport Ltd, Sub Station Road, Felixstowe, Suffolk, IP11 8JB Tel: (01394) 676134

▶ Matthew Investments Ltd, 45-47 High Street, Potters Bar, Hertfordshire, EN6 5AW Tel: (01707) 655550 Fax: (01707) 664595 E-mail: sales@matthew-homes.co.uk

▶ Matthew James Ltd, 6 Poyntell Cresent, Chislehurst, Kent, BR7 6PJ Tel: (020) 8467 6292 Fax: (01322) 437508

▶ Matthew Noble, Yew Grange, Wykeham, Scarborough, North Yorkshire, YO13 9QP Tel: (01723) 865384 E-mail: matthew@matthewnoble.co.uk *Commercial and Industrial Photographer specilaising in food, catalogues, web sites. Contact for a no obligation free quote.*

▶ Matthews, Home Farm, Hatfield Park, Hatfield, Hertfordshire, AL9 5NH Tel: (01707) 262351 Fax: (01707) 264813 E-mail: brian@buildingconservation.co.uk

Bernard Matthews Foods Ltd, Great Witchingham Hall, Norwich, NR9 5QD Tel: (01603) 872611 Fax: (01603) 871118 *Frozen food processors*

David Matthews Ltd, Clayton Tinplate Works, Pontardulais, Swansea, SA4 8SN Tel: (01792) 882766 Fax: (01792) 885195 E-mail: inquiries@dmlltd.demon.co.uk *Tinplate stockholders & metal packaging manufrs* Also at: Birmingham

E.F.G. Matthews Ltd, Northfield Drive, Milton Keynes, MK15 0DQ Tel: (01908) 665643 Fax: (01908) 609948 *Business furniture manufacturers & retailers*

Matthews Engineering, Whieldon Industrial Estate, Whieldon Road, Stoke-on-Trent, ST4 4JP Tel: (01782) 849534 Fax: (01782) 849534 *Precision machinists*

F.W.P. Matthews Ltd, Station Road, Shipton-Under-Wychwood, Chipping Norton, Oxfordshire, OX7 6BH Tel: (01993) 830342 Fax: (01993) 831615 *Flour millers*

▶ Geoff Matthews Engineers, Unit 17 Pavilion Workshops, Holmewood Industrial Park, Park Road, Holmewood, Chesterfield, Derbyshire, S42 5UY Tel: (01246) 851118 Fax: (01246) 855502 E-mail: enquiries@gmengineers.co.uk *Distributor of tractor parts*

▶ Matthews Haulage Ltd, Mead Lane, Hertford, SG13 7BB Tel: (01992) 553737 Fax: (01992) 551360

▶ Matthews International Transport, Claylands Avenue, Worksop, Nottinghamshire, S81 7DJ Tel: (01909) 485555

James Matthews, 17 Glebe Road, Downpatrick, County Down, BT30 7AW Tel: (028) 4488 1619 Fax: (028) 4488 1619 *Metal fabrication manufrs*

John Matthews Clothing Ltd, Building 62, Third Avenue, Pensnett Trading Estate, Kingswinford, West Midlands, DY6 7PP Tel: (01384) 401071 Fax: (01384) 401840 *Schoolwear*

Matthews Of Keynsham Ltd, Keynsham Road, Keynsham, Bristol, BS31 2DE Tel: 0117-986 4356 Fax: 0117-986 7491 E-mail: sales@matthewsofkeynsham.com *Industrial roofing material suppliers*

Neil Matthews Engineering Ltd, Units 8-9, Newton Close, Park Farm Industrial Estate, Wellingborough, Northamptonshire, NN8 6UW Tel: (01933) 401038 Fax: (01933) 401039 E-mail: sales@neilmatthewsengineering.co.uk *Precision engineers*

Paul Matthews Ltd, 47 Arbrook Lane, Esher, Surrey, KT10 9EG Tel: (01372) 470234 *Knitwear & textiles distributors*

▶ Matthews Print, The Courtyard, 19 Tamworth Street, Lichfield, Staffordshire, WS13 6JP Tel: (01543) 263112

Matthews & Son Hanley Ltd, Howson Street, Stoke-on-Trent, ST1 3LG Tel: (01782) 213866 Fax: (01782) 213866 *Metal fabrications*

Matthews Sussex Ltd, Stephenson Place, Stephenson Way, Crawley, West Sussex, RH10 1TN Tel: (01293) 617014 Fax: (01293) 617018 *Transport & civil engineers*

Matthews Transport, Greengate, Middleton, Manchester, M24 1RU Tel: 0161-653 5441 Fax: 0161-655 3956 E-mail: sales@matthewstransport.com *Road transport, haulage & freight services*

Matthews & Wilson Ltd, Forest Road, Charlbury, Chipping Norton, Oxfordshire, OX7 3HH Tel: (01608) 811539 Fax: (01608) 811834 *Cosmetics manufrs*

Matthieson Bros, 177 Yardley Road, Acocks Green, Birmingham, B27 6LZ Tel: 0121-706 4915 Fax: 0121-764 5202 *Glazing contractors*

Mattress Production Technology Ltd, New Line Industrial Estate, The Sidings, Bacup, Lancashire, OL13 9RW Tel: (01706) 878558 Fax: (01706) 878288 E-mail: enquiries@mptg.demon.co.uk *Mattress Production Technology Group (MPT Group), formed in 1999, is one of the leading providers of automated & stand alone machinery for the mattress industry. MPT Groups comprehensive product range meets all the demands of the mattress production process, offering a first point of call for any company in the Mattress Industry. Our range of products include: Tape Edge Systems, Automatic & Manual Spring Coiling & Assembly machinery, Quilting Systems & a comprehensive range of Border & Handle Machinery.*

Mattrix Ltd, 23 Trowlock Avenue, Teddington, Middlesex, TW11 9QT Tel: (020) 8977 5453 Fax: (020) 8977 8337 E-mail: mattrix@btconnect.com *Irrigation consultants services*

Matts Business Centre, Station Crescent, Llandrindod Wells, Powys, LD1 5BD Tel: (01597) 827940 E-mail: info@matts.co.uk *Computer software & hardware supply engineering maintenance support to corporate sector*

Charles Matts, Manor Farm, Thurgarton, Norwich, NR11 7PG Tel: (01263) 761422 Fax: (01263) 768748 *Furniture manufrs*

▶ Matts & Jenkins Ltd, Garland Street, Birmingham, B9 4DE Tel: 0121-772 4718 Fax: 0121-773 0023 E-mail: sales@mattsandjenkins.co.uk

Matt's Sheet Metal, Whitefield Mill, St. Marys Street, Nelson, Lancashire, BB9 7BA Tel: (01282) 602228 Fax: (01282) 602228 *Sheet metal work engineers & powder coating specialists services*

▶ Mattvac Carpet & Upholstery Cleaning, 45 Hallidale Crescent, Renfrew, PA4 0YA Tel: 0141-562 3873 E-mail: sales@mattvac.co.uk *Carpet cleaners*

Maturi A & Sons Ltd, 8 Whitmore Road, Small Heath, Birmingham, B10 0NP Tel: 0121-772 4919 E-mail: andrew@mowerspares.co.uk *Lawn mower retailers & services*

▶ M-audio, Floor 6, Gresham House, 53 Clarendon Road, Watford, WD17 1LA Tel: (01923) 204010 Fax: (0871) 7177101 *Audio equipment specialists*

G.H. Maughan Ltd, Bella Street Industrial Estate, Bolton, BL3 4DU Tel: (01204) 653516 Fax: (01204) 657362 E-mail: ghmaughan@lineone.net *Plastic & nylon bearing manufrs*

Roger Maughfling Engineering Ltd, Station Works, Knucklas, Knighton, Powys, LD7 1PN Tel: (01547) 528201 Fax: (01547) 520392 E-mail: supersprox@supersprox.demon.co.uk *Sprocket manufrs*

Maul Technology, 13 Bridge House, Bridge Street, Sunderland, SR1 1TE Tel: 0191-514 0611 Fax: 0191-565 5309 E-mail: sales@maultechnology.co.uk *General engineers*

Maun Hosiery Ltd, Intake Business Centre, Kirkland Avenue, Mansfield, Nottinghamshire, NG18 5QP Tel: (01623) 621860 Fax: (01623) 621860 E-mail: nightwear@maunhosiery.co.uk *Nightdress manufrs*

Maun Industries Ltd, Moor Lane, Mansfield, Nottinghamshire, NG18 5SE Tel: (01623) 624525 Fax: (01623) 659969 E-mail: maun.industries@btinternet.com *Hand tool manufrs*

Maunder & Sons Ltd, Scarne Industrial Estate, Launceston, Cornwall, PL15 9HS Tel: (01566) 773079 Fax: (01566) 776823 *Agricultural merchants*

Maurer (UK) Ltd, Unit 4 Field End, Crendon Industrial Estate, Aylesbury, Buckinghamshire, HP18 9EJ Tel: (01844) 201481 Fax: (01844) 201355 E-mail: sjb@maurer.co.uk *Mechanical bridge expansion joints*

Mauri Products Ltd, Stockholm Road, Sutton Fields Industrial Estate, Hull, HU7 0XW Tel: (01482) 833133 Fax: (01482) 838460 E-mail: sue.fox@mauri.co.uk Principal Export Areas: Africa *Bakers, distillers & yeast manufrs*

Maurice D Spencer & Co., Faircharm Trading Estate, Evelyn Drive, Leicester, LE3 2BU Tel: 0116-289 1313 Fax: 0116-289 3484 E-mail: mdspencer@ic24.net *Cutting form*

Maurice Gill Blacksmith, 42 Lydia Road, Walmer, Deal, Kent, CT14 9JX Tel: (01304) 362771 Fax: (01304) 362771 *Blacksmith*

▶ Maurice Hood Dental Laboratory Ltd, Houghton Street, Oldbury, West Midlands, B69 2BB Tel: 0121-544 8855 Fax: 0121-544 8835 E-mail: sales@mauricehood.co.uk *Full service quality dental laboratory with delivery service throughout the Midlands. We also operate a free postal/courier service for the rest of the country. Denture repairs and Twice @ copy denture direct to the public.*

Maurice Lay Ltd, Fourth Way, Bristol, BS11 8DW Tel: 0117-938 1900 Fax: 0117-938 2446 E-mail: sales@mlay.co.uk *Kitchen, bedroom furniture & accessories distributors*

Maurice Payne Colour Print Ltd, 12 Exeter Way, Theale, Reading, RG7 4PF Tel: 0118-930 3678 Fax: 0118-930 3759 *Brochure & poster printers*

▶ Maurice Pierce Ltd, 1d The Maltings, Station Road, Sawbridgeworth, Hertfordshire, CM21 9JX Tel: (01279) 306633 Fax: (01279) 306644

Maury Sewing Machine Co., Unit 12 Peterley Business Centre, Hackney Road, London, E2 9EQ Tel: (020) 7729 7328 Fax: (020) 7729 7534 E-mail: maurysew@aol.com *All types of industrial sewing machines bought & sold, agents for new prosew machines, export & import of sewing machines & parts trade & dealer enquiries welcome*

Mauve Furniture Ltd, Arnlie, 79 Edinburgh Road, Dumfries, DG1 1JX Tel: (01387) 248889 Fax: (01387) 248889 E-mail: info@mauvefurniture.co.uk *Supplier of quality contract furniture to hotels, restaurants, bars and leisure venues.*

Mauville Servicing Ltd, Baird Way, Thetford, Norfolk, IP24 1JA Tel: (01842) 755363 Fax: (01842) 765085 *Commercial vehicle servicing*

Maval Ltd, Skippers Lane, Skippers Lane Industrial Estat, Middlesbrough, Cleveland, TS6 6HA Tel: (01642) 455101 Fax: (01642) 458507 E-mail: maval@talk21.com *Electrical contractors*

Maverick Presentation Products Ltd, 3 Wellington Industrial Estate, Basingstoke Road, Spencers Wood, Reading, RG7 1AW Tel: 0118-988 6266 Fax: 0118-988 6233 *Presentation equipment distribs*

▶ Mavero Recruitment, 145-157 St John Street, London, EC1V 4PY Tel: 0207 8710727 Fax: 0207 7882992 E-mail: info@mavero.co.uk *Professional recruitment agency specialising in the recruitment and relocation of candidates from Poland to work in the UK. We cover variety of sectors including healthcare, IT and construction.*

▶ Mavisat Ltd, 2 Wokingham Road, Reading, RG6 1JG Tel: (0870) 4450111 Fax: (0870) 4450112 E-mail: sales@mavisat.com *Communications*

Mawby & King Ltd, Upperton Road, Leicester, LE2 7AY Tel: 0116-204 6000 Fax: 0116-204 6001 E-mail: sales@mawbyandking.co.uk *Glass processors & mirror manufrs*

Mawdsley Yorkshire Ltd, 7 Parkway One, Parkway Drive, Sheffield, S9 4WU Tel: 0114-244 0321 Fax: 0114-243 6054 *Pharmacy products wholesalers*

Mawdsley's Bristol Electrical Repairs, Barton Manor, Midland Road, Bristol, BS2 0RL Tel: 0117-955 2481 Fax: 0117-955 2483 E-mail: info@mawdsleys.com *Electric motor repair contractors*

Maws Pies, 7 St. Lukes Terrace, Pallion, Sunderland, SR4 6NQ Tel: 0191-510 0822 *Bakery food distribution & pie manufrs*

Mawson Triton Mouldings Ltd, 4-8 Waterside Industrial Estate, Doulton Road, Rowley Regis, West Midlands, B65 8JG Tel: (01384) 633321 Fax: (01384) 565782 E-mail: sales@mawsontriton.co.uk *Manufacturers of composite components*

Mawsons, 57 George Street, Oldham, OL1 1LT Tel: 0161-624 8182 Fax: 0161-624 8182 *Herbalist*

Max Access Ltd, Unit 17 Bankside, Station Approach, Kidlington, Oxfordshire, OX5 1JE Tel: (01865) 373566 Fax: (01865) 378021 E-mail: info@maxaccess.co.uk *Spider access platform hire, sales & services*

Max Appliances Ltd, Kingfisher House, Wheel Park, Westfield, Hastings, East Sussex, TN35 4SE Tel: (01424) 751666 Fax: (01424) 751444 E-mail: sales@max-appliances.co.uk *Food waste disposal units*

The Max Distribution Co., The Old Bakery, High Street, East Malling, West Malling, Kent, ME19 6AJ Tel: (01732) 840845 E-mail: sales@the-max.co.uk *Distribution agents*

Max E Ott Ltd, 1a Southcote Road, London, N19 5BJ Tel: (020) 7607 1384 Fax: (020) 7607 3506 *Cabinet makers*

Max Fordham & Partners, 42-43 Gloucester Cresent, London, NW1 7PE Tel: (020) 7267 5161 Fax: (020) 7482 0329 E-mail: post@maxfordham.com *Consulting engineers & designers*

▶ Max Lift Trucks, Tumbletrees, Cannock, Staffordshire, WS12 4DX Tel: 01543 279879 *Suppliers of new and high quality used forklift trucks and materials handling equipment.*

Max Stone, Unit 3 Jubilee Trade Centre, Pershore Street, Birmingham, B5 6ND Tel: 0121-666 6704 Fax: 0121-622 2247 E-mail: sales@maxstone.co.uk *General engineering services*

Maxam Pneumatics Ltd, Walkmill Lane, Bridgtown, Cannock, Staffordshire, WS11 0LR Tel: (01543) 456000 Fax: (01543) 456001 E-mail: mkemp@parker.com Principal Export Areas: Worldwide *Pneumatic actuators & valves manufrs*

▶ Maxcess Scaffolding Erectors, 2 Albert Road, Edinburgh, EH6 7DP Tel: 0131-555 5645 Fax: 0131-555 5997

▶ Maxcroft Securities Ltd, 632 Eastern Avenue, Ilford, Essex, IG2 6PG Tel: (020) 8518 1828 Fax: 020 85547296 E-mail: enquiries@maxcroft.co.uk *Unsecured loans. Pawnbrokers lending against jewellery, watches, electricals, cars and more. Cheque cashing. Payday advances.Log book loans.*

Maxdean, PO Box 19, Manchester, M25 9JP Tel: 0161-796 6696 Fax: 0161-796 6400 E-mail: maxdean@uk2.net *Gift boxes & gift wrap papers*

▶ Maxella Ltd, Cypress House, Coburg Road, London, N22 6TP Tel: (020) 8889 4686 Fax: (020) 8889 3231

▶ Maxfield Services Ltd, Brook Farm, Stapleford Road, Stapleford Abbotts, Romford, RM4 1EJ Tel: (01708) 688600 E-mail: enquiries@maxfieldservices.co.uk *Photocopiers, faxes, printers sales & service*

Maxhunt Ltd, Yelverton Road, Bristol, BS4 5HP Tel: 0117-977 9001 Fax: 0117-971 5971 E-mail: sales@maxhunt.com *Security systems manufrs*

▶ MAXi COIN, PO BOX 1, Cramlington, Northumberland, NE23 7WU Tel: (0870) 2072077 E-mail: Info@MaxiCoin.co.uk *Suppliers of coin operated equipment.*

▶ Maxi Construction Ltd, Firth Road, Houstoun Industrial Estate, Livingston, West Lothian, EH54 5DJ Tel: (01506) 442233 Fax: (01506) 442010

Maxi Haulage Ltd, Macadam Way, West Portway Industrial Estate, Andover, Hampshire, SP10 3LF Tel: (01264) 361888 Fax: (01264) 332206 *Road haulage & warehouse keepers*

▶ Maxi Haulage Ltd, 3 Belgrave Street, Bellshill Industrial Estate, Bellshill, Lanarkshire, ML4 3NP Tel: (01698) 748444 Fax: (01698) 745364

Maxi Haulage Ltd, Maxi Haulage Ltd, Oldham Road, Manchester, M40 5AF Tel: 0161-205 9000 Fax: 0161-205 9191 *Road transport, haulage & freight services*

Maxi Haulage Ltd, Hawkes Drive, Heathcote Industrial Estate, Warwick, CV34 6LX Tel: (01926) 881192 Fax: (01926) 881937 E-mail: action@maxihaulage.co.uk *Haulage contractors & warehouse keepers*

Maxi Million Ltd, 21a Whitmore Street, Whittlesey, Peterborough, PE7 1HE Tel: (01733) 208283 Fax: (01733) 208366 E-mail: peterborough@maxi-million.co.uk *Telesales*

Maxi Storage Systems Ltd, Walkley Mills, Spen Vale Street, Heckmondwike, West Yorkshire, WF16 0PS Tel: (01924) 411706 Fax: (01924) 411711 E-mail: keith@maxistorage.co.uk *Industrial racking systems & Mezzanine Floor Manufactures.*

Maxibrite Ltd, Mwyndy Industrial Estate, Mwyndy, Pontyclun, Mid Glamorgan, CF72 8PN Tel: (01443) 224283 Fax: (01443) 227085 E-mail: sales@maxibrite.co.uk *Manufacture of anthracite briquettes*

Maxicrop (UK) Ltd, Corby, Northamptonshire, NN17 1ZH Tel: (08700) 115117 Fax: (08700) 115118 E-mail: info@maxicrop.co.uk *Fertiliser manufrs*

▶ Maxiflo Technologies Ltd, Unit 208 Tedco Business Works, Henry Robson Way, South Shields, Tyne & Wear, NE33 1RF Tel: 0191-427 4723 Fax: 0191-427 4724 E-mail: sales@maxiflo.co.uk *Air operated liquid pumps, high pressure valves, fittings manufrs*

▶ Maxilin Ltd, Sharples Vale, Bolton, BL1 6NR Tel: (01204) 309111 Fax: (01204) 596596

Maxilusta Ltd, 24A Main Road, Radcliffe-On-Trent, Nottingham, NG12 2FH Tel: 0115-933 4966 Fax: 0115-933 5974 *Yarn winders merceriser & dyers*

Maxim Group Ltd, The New Mill, 16 Gateforth Lane, Hambleton, Selby, North Yorkshire, YO8 9HP Tel: (01757) 228822 Fax: (01757) 228844 E-mail: info@themaximgroupltd.com *Alco foil agents & distributors*

Maxim Industries Ltd, Bankfield Road, Tyldesley, Manchester, M29 8QH Tel: 0161-703 2244 Fax: 0161-702 6454 E-mail: info@themssgroup.co.uk *Non-ferrous metal stockholders*

Maxim Integrated Products Ltd, 612 Reading Road, Winnersh, Wokingham, Berkshire, RG41 5HE Tel: 0118-900 6300 Fax: 0118-900 6400 *Printed intergrated circuits*

Maxim Integrated Products (UK) Ltd, 612 Reading Road, Winnersh, Wokingham, Berkshire, RG41 5HE Tel: 0118-930 3388 Fax: 0118-900 6400 E-mail: maximdallasdirect_sales@maximhq.com *Electronic distributors*

Maxim Power Tools (Scotland) Ltd, Couper Street, Glasgow, G4 0DL Tel: 0141-552 5591 Fax: 0141-552 5064 E-mail: info@maxim-power.com *Power tools distributors*

Maxim Recruitment, 45 Bromley Road, London, E17 4PR Tel: (0870) 2430446 E-mail: contact@maximrecruitment.co.uk *Maxim Recruitment can help you find the latest jobs for Quantity Surveyors, Project Managers and Consulting Professionals in the building and construction sector.*

Maxim Training Knowledgepool, 42 Bond Street, Brighton, BN1 1RD Tel: (01273) 827751 Fax: (01273) 738829 E-mail: tracy.capaldi-drewett@knowledgepool.com *Computer training services*

Maxima, 2 Bell Business Park, Smeaton Close, Aylesbury, Buckinghamshire, HP19 8JR Tel: (01296) 318060 Fax: (01296) 318089 *Computer systems software consultants*

Maxima, Stonepail Court, Stonepail Road, Gatley, Cheadle, Cheshire, SK8 4EX Tel: 0161-491 3700 Fax: 0161-491 2859 *Accounting software writers & maintenance*

Maxima, 84 Coombe Road, New Malden, Surrey, KT3 4QS Tel: (020) 8336 8800 Fax: (020) 8336 8899 *Software supplier to the construction industry*

Maximach Ltd, Gorton Crescent, Windmill Industrial Estate, Denton, Manchester, M34 3RB Tel: 0161-320 3216 Fax: 0161-337 8162 E-mail: helensmax@aol.com *Woodworking tools & machinery distributors*

Maximesh Ltd, Unit 6A, Morelands Trading Estate, Bristol Road, Gloucester, GL1 5RZ Tel: (01452) 561156 Fax: (01452) 544005 E-mail: sales@maximesh.co.uk *Elegant Security Door Grilles with unique integrated insect mesh. Also suppliers of Attractive and functional driveway and path gates, full height side gates, decorative modular fencing and architectural/load bearing products.*

▶ Maximeyes Security Ltd, Unit 2, Dalewood Road, Lymedale Business Park, Newcastle, Staffordshire, ST5 9QH Tel: (01782) 566611 Fax: (01782) 566616 E-mail: maximeyes2003@yahoo.co.uk *Static security, key holding & alarm response service*

▶ Maximillion, Halesfield 20, Telford, Shropshire, TF7 4QU Tel: (01952) 585100 Fax: (01952) 585332 *IT re-sellers*

Maximotive Design Ltd, 70 River Way, Christchurch, Dorset, BH23 2QR Tel: (01202) 565713 Fax: (01202) 565713 E-mail: mylne@maximotive.com *Control system designers*

▶ Maximum Security, 60 Skylark Rise, Plymouth, PL6 7SN Tel: (01752) 695569 Fax: (01752) 548020 E-mail: safeandsecure@maximum-security.co.uk *Providers of Manned Guarding services. Established since 1983*

Maximus Operandi Ltd, Unit 3b Sanders Lodge Industrial Estate, Rushden, Northamptonshire, NN10 6BQ Tel: (01933) 413113 Fax: (01933) 413114 E-mail: info@maximusuk.com *Exhibition stands, roll ups, popups, exhibition systems, display stands, exhibitions, ultima displays, banner stands, bannerstands, pop-up display*

continued

continuation
systems, panel systems, folding panel stands, portable exhibition stands, exhibition accessories, large format graphics, display systems, out door banners, PVC banners, flag systems, building wraps. The specialists in Portable Banner Stands and Pop up Display Systems. Quality printing, On time, On Budget.

Maxiroach Ltd, Unit 2 Crowarch Lane Industrial Estate, Ringwood, Hampshire, BH24 1PG Tel: (01425) 480408 Fax: (01425) 480996 E-mail: sales@easyreef.com *Yacht sails manufrs*

Maxit Ltd, A46 The Heath Business & Technical Park, Runcorn, Cheshire, WA7 4QX Tel: (01928) 515656 Fax: (01928) 576792 E-mail: sales@maxit.co.uk *Brick manufrs*

▶ Maxitherm Heating Ltd, Unit 6 Ford La Business Park, Ford, Arundel, West Sussex, BN18 0UZ Tel: (01243) 558885 Fax: (01243) 558886

Maxknit Fabrics Ltd, 9 Bath Street, Leicester, LE4 7QE Tel: 0116-266 4793 Fax: 0116-266 1348 *Knitted fabric*

▶ Maxoil Solutions, Riverview Business Centre Centurion Court, North Esplanade We, Aberdeen, AB11 5QH Tel: (01224) 726810 Fax: (01224) 726805 E-mail: contact@maxoilsolutions.com *Consultancy oil & gas industry*

Maxol Oil, 48 Trench Road, Mallusk, Newtownabbey, County Antrim, BT36 4TY Tel: (028) 9050 6000 Fax: (028) 9050 6500 E-mail: info@maxoldirect.com *Suppliers of Home Heating Oil in Belfast and Northern Ireland. For our cheapest oil price and best value, use our low cost online ordering service. Depots in Belfast, Londonderry and Enniskillen.******

Maxon Combustion Systems Ltd, Chantry House, High Street, Coleshill, Birmingham, B46 3BP Tel: (01675) 464334 Fax: (01675) 467285 E-mail: kp@maxon.be *Manufacturers of gas burners, burners (dual fuel) (gas/oil), oxy-fuel, oil burners (industrial) & combustion systems. Also valves, control & safety shut-off*

maxon motor uk ltd, Maxon House, Hogwood Lane, Finchampstead, Wokingham, Berkshire, RG40 4QW Tel: 0118-973 3337 Fax: 0118-973 7472 E-mail: salesuk@maxonmotor.com *Miniature electric motors manufrs*

Maxpower Automotive Ltd, Bank Street, West Bromwich, West Midlands, B71 1HB Tel: 0121-567 0200 Fax: 0121-588 6828 E-mail: jgarner@maxaut.co.uk *Ferrous, non-ferrous & plastic tube manipulation manufrs*

Maxresponse Ltd, 55 Linkside Avenue, Oxford, OX2 8JE Tel: (01865) 316251 Fax: (0870) 0518845 E-mail: sales@maxresponse.co.uk *Macintosh service providers*

Maxspeed Engineering Ltd, Foxoak Street, Cradley Heath, West Midlands, B64 5DE Tel: (01384) 564999 Fax: (01384) 564888 *Precision engineers*

Maxsym Engine Technology Ltd, 5b Brailes Industrial Estate, Winderton Road, Lower Brailes, Banbury, Oxfordshire, OX15 5JW Tel: (07740) 404574 Fax: (01608) 685156 E-mail: sales@maxsym.com *Petrol engines*

▶ Maxtag (UK) Ltd, 8 Suttons Bussiness Park, Reading, RG6 1AZ Tel: 0118-935 6180 Fax: 0118-935 6181 E-mail: sales@maxtag.com *Sellers & fitters of security systems*

▶ Maxtar Ltd, 14 Chanctonbury View, Henfield, West Sussex, BN5 9TW Tel: (07714) 850950 Fax: (01273) 491848 E-mail: juergen.brinner@maxtar.co.uk *web design, web site hosting, internet consulting, internet training, professional skill development training, marketing, sales, e-commerce development*

Maxtor (Europe) Ltd, Langwood House, 63-81 High Street, Rickmansworth, Hertfordshire, WD3 1EQ Tel: (01923) 712448 Fax: (01923) 712888 *Computer hard drive manufrs*

Maxtrack Sports Equipment, New Rock House, Kempley Road, Dymock, Gloucestershire, GL18 2BB Tel: (01531) 890955 Fax: (01531) 890950 E-mail: sales@maxtrack.com *Sport equipment distribution*

▶ Maxview Ltd, Common Lane, Setch, King's Lynn, Norfolk, PE33 0AT Tel: (01553) 813300 Fax: (01553) 813301 E-mail: sales@maxview.ltd.uk *TV & FM aerials & signal booster manufrs*

Maxwell Concrete, 22 Folliard Road, Castlederg, County Tyrone, BT81 7JW Tel: (028) 8167 1326 Fax: (028) 8167 1157 *Precast concrete slabs*

Maxwell Emsworth Ltd, Elsted Station, Elsted, Midhurst, West Sussex, GU29 0JT Tel: (01730) 812662 Fax: (01730) 813560 *Agricultural machinery & tractor exporters*

Maxwell Engineering Co. Ltd, Waterloo Road, Llandrindod Wells, Powys, LD1 6BH Tel: (01597) 822414 Fax: (01597) 823067 E-mail: sales@maxwell-engineering.co.uk *Industrial fasteners & bolts manufrs*

Maxwell Jones Studios Ltd, 58K Arthur Street, Redditch, Worcestershire, B98 8JY Tel: (01527) 502900 Fax: (01527) 510265 E-mail: sales@maxwelljones.com *Sign makers*

Maxwell Labels, Unit 8, Moorbridge Road, Bingham Industrial Estate, Nottingham, NG13 8GG Tel: (01949) 837831 Fax: (01949) 831128 *Label manufrs*

Maxwell Stamp Group plc, Abbots Court, 34 Farringdon Lane, London, EC1R 3AX Tel: (020) 7251 0147 Fax: (020) 7251 0140 E-mail: london@maxwellstamp.com *Maxwell Stamp is one of the world"s leading international economics consultancies. Established in 1959, we have over 45 years of experience in over 165 countries and territories."*

▶ Maxwell W (Glasgow) Ltd, PO Box 3, Bellshill, Lanarkshire, ML4 1EH Tel: (01698) 747549

Wayne Maxwell Designs, Unit6, Resolution Way, Deptford, London, SE8 4NT Tel: (020) 8691 3000 E-mail: designs@waynemaxwell.com *Wayne Maxwell Design is a design studio and contemporary furniture showroom offering a dynamic and fresh approach to modern living. Designing a collection of modern furniture and offering a bespoke fitted furniture service.*

Maxwood, Bodmin Road, Wyken, Coventry, CV2 5DB Tel: (024) 7662 1122 *WC cubicles & washroom system manufrs*

Maxxis International, 9 Farthing Road Industrial Estate, Sproughton Road, Ipswich, IP1 5AA Tel: (01473) 742333 Fax: (01473) 742414 *Motorcycle tyre wholesalers*

▶ Maxxraxx Trading, Unit 10 Hays Bridge Farm, Brickhouse Lane, South Godstone, Godstone, Surrey, RH9 8JW Tel: (01342) 841989 Fax: (01342) 844150 E-mail: info@maxxraxx.co.uk *Sales & marketing services of bike racks & related products*

May Gurney Ltd, Ringland Lane, Costessey, Norwich, NR8 5BG Tel: (01603) 744440 Fax: (01603) 747310 *Fencing*

May Gurney Construction Ltd, Haden House, Argyle Way, Stevenage, Hertfordshire, SG1 2AD Tel: (01438) 363900 Fax: (01438) 363945 *Civil engineering contractors*

May Gurney (Highways), Chalk Lane, Snetterton, Norwich, NR16 2LB Tel: (01953) 888828 Fax: (01953) 888846 *Civil engineering contractors*

William May Ltd, Cavendish Street, Ashton-under-Lyne, Lancashire, OL6 7QW Tel: 0161-330 3838 Fax: 0161-339 1097 E-mail: mwm@william-may.com *Parflu flue systems manufrs*

Mayalls of Wigan, Woodhouse Lane, Wigan, Lancashire, WN6 7TH Tel: (01942) 241711 Fax: (01942) 241271 E-mail: maywigan@travisperkins.co.uk *Plumbing & decorating merchants* Also at: Chorley & Wallasey

Mayan Experience Latin American Crafts, 7 Castle Sq, Swansea, SA1 1DW Tel: 01792 472874 *Importer of Latin & American furniture & crafts*

▶ Mayantex Garden Furniture, Trenton House, 4- 5 Imperial Way, Croydon, CR0 4RR Tel: (020) 8686 2144

Maybole Coachworks, 3 Barns Terrace, Maybole, Ayrshire, KA19 7EP Tel: (01655) 883911 Fax: (01655) 740458 *Coach repair*

Mayborn Group P.L.C., Dylon House, Worsley Bridge Road, London, SE26 5HD Tel: (020) 8663 4801 E-mail: dylonimp@dylon.co.uk *Holding company*

Maybrey Reliance, Worsley Bridge Road, Lower Sydenham, London, SE26 5BE Tel: (01322) 315370 Fax: (01322) 550724 E-mail: sales@maybrey.co.uk *Castings manufrs*

Maybridge Electronics Ltd, 10 Godstone Road, Purley, Surrey, CR8 2DA Tel: (020) 8763 8778 E-mail: purley@aol.com *Process control equipment manufrs*

Mayburn Design Ltd, 117 Piersfield Terrace, Edinburgh, EH8 7BS Tel: 0131-661 0590 Fax: 0131-652 1603 *Recruitment agency*

Maybury Sports Ltd, 139 Northwood Road, Thornton Heath, Surrey, CR7 8HX Tel: (020) 8653 5440 Fax: (020) 8771 3497 E-mail: sales@mayburysports.co.uk *Sportswear suppliers*

Maycast Nokes Precision Engineering Ltd, Factory La West, Halstead, Essex, CO9 1EX Tel: (01787) 472500 Fax: (01787) 474264 E-mail: enquiries@maycast.co.uk *Manufacturers of Investment/lost wax castings and precision sand castings in a wide range of aluminium alloys. CNC machining facilities and non destructive test facilities all on site.*

▶ Maycoil Ltd, 3 Wilton Road, Ramsgate, Kent, CT12 5HG Tel: (01843) 570044 Fax: (01843) 570055 *Elevator shaft builders*

Mayday Commercial Catering Services, 21 Walmley Ash Road, Sutton Coldfield, West Midlands, B76 1HY Tel: 0121-313 0301 *Commercial equipment repairs & maintenance*

▶ Mayday Graphic Products, Graphic House, Cratfield Road, Bury St. Edmunds, Suffolk, IP32 7DF Tel: (01284) 701571 Fax: (01284) 750553 E-mail: sales@maydaygraphics.co.uk *Supply to printing trade*

▶ Mayday Plant Hire, 19 Woodville Road, Thornton Heath, Surrey, CR7 8LH Tel: (020) 8771 7333 Fax: (020) 7771 7336 *Plant hire*

Maydencroft Aquatic Nurseries, Maydencroft Lane, Gosmore, Hitchin, Hertfordshire, SG4 7QD Tel: (01462) 456020 Fax: (01462) 422652 *Aquatic nurseries*

Maydown International Tours Ltd, Mercury Park, Amber Close, Tamworth, Staffordshire, B77 4RP Tel: (01827) 309700 Fax: (01827) 309719 *Manufacturing carbide cutting tools*

Maydown Precision Engineering Ltd, 11 Carrakeel Drive, Maydown, Londonderry, BT47 6UH Tel: (028) 7186 0531 Fax: (028) 7186 0496 E-mail: info@maydown.com *Precision engineers*

Mayer Cohen Industries Ltd, Newtown Industrial Estate, Cross Keys, Newport, Gwent, NP11 7PZ Tel: (01495) 272777 Fax: (01495) 271270 *Warehousing services*

Mayer Enviromental Ltd, Transport Avenue, Brentford, Middlesex, TW8 9HA Tel: (020) 8847 3637 Fax: (020) 8847 3638 E-mail: info@mayer-enviro.com *Environmental consultants specialising in contaminated land*

Mayer International (UK) Ltd, 18 Monnach Way, Winchester, Hampshire, SO22 5QU Tel: (01962) 625618 E-mail: johnmayer@tunnel-lighting-control.com *Road tunnel lighting control*

Karl Mayer Textile Machinery Ltd, Kings Road, Shepshed, Loughborough, Leicestershire, LE12 9HT Tel: (01509) 502056 Fax: (01509) 508065 E-mail: mhyeabsley@karlmayer.co.uk *Textile machinery manufrs*

Mayer Services (UK) Ltd, The Springboard Centre, Mandle Lane, Coalville, Leicestershire, LE67 3DW Tel: (0845) 0093542 Fax: (0871) 5972419 *Wood working machinery manufrs*

C.J.D. Mayers & Co. Ltd, Unit 6, Speedwell Close Industrial Estate, Speedwell Road, Yardley, Birmingham, B25 8HT Tel: 0121-773 0101 Fax: 0121-773 0104 E-mail: mayers@madasafish.com *Fastener, fixings & industrial consumables distributors*

Mayers & Shaw Ltd, Unit 6 Bunns Bank, Old Buckenham, Attleborough, Norfolk, NR17 1QD Tel: (01953) 453225 Fax: (01953) 456055 E-mail: sales@mayersandshaw.co.uk *Importers of occasional tables & furniture*

▶ Mayes Self Drive, 155 Chingford Road, London, E17 4PN Tel: (020) 8531 1123 Fax: (020) 8531 1330 E-mail: sales@mayesselfdrive.co.uk *Self Drive Vehicle Rental, inc van hire and also tippers, dropsides, trucks, minibuses, MPVs and car hire*

Mayes & Warwick Ltd, 5 Mount Road, Burntwood Industrial Estate, Burntwood, Staffordshire, WS7 0AJ Tel: (01543) 682561 Fax: (01543) 686232 E-mail: sales@mayesandwarwick.com *Precision engineers & tooling manufrs*

Mayfair Blinds, 94 Old Church Street, Manchester, M40 2JF Tel: 0161-684 9960 *Blind manufrs*

Mayfair Business Systems Ltd, 85 Market Street, Watford, WD18 0PT Tel: (01923) 800800 Fax: (01923) 800810 E-mail: info@mayfairbs.co.uk *Computer systems*

The Mayfair Cleaning Company Ltd, 374 Wandsworth Road, London, SW8 4TD Tel: (020) 7720 6447 Fax: (020) 7498 8246 E-mail: info@mayfaircleaning.co.uk *Office & window cleaning contractors*

Mayfair School Of English, 61-65 Oxford Street, London, W1D 2EL Tel: (020) 7437 9941 Fax: (020) 7494 3611 E-mail: info@mayfairschool.co.uk *Language school*

Mayfair Security, Adelaide House Vivars Way, Canal Road, Selby, North Yorkshire, YO8 8BE Tel: (01757) 701596 Fax: (01757) 212442 E-mail: sales@mayfairsecurity.co.uk *Alarm systems services*

Mayfair Security Ltd, 62 Hillside Road, Southminster, Essex, CM0 7AL Tel: (01621) 772580 Fax: (01621) 774580 *Security & intruder alarm installers*

▶ The Mayfield Group UK Ltd, Bournemouth, BH1 9GR Tel: (01202) 233959 Fax: (01202) 732853 E-mail: enquiries@themayfieldgroup.co.uk *Caravan accessories, pvc fencing & decking manufrs*

Mayfield Leisure Ltd, 26-32 Cobham Road, Wimborne, Dorset, BH21 7NP Tel: (01202) 855222 Fax: (01202) 732853 E-mail: enquiries@themayfieldgroup.co.uk *Holiday home accessories manufrs*

Mayfield Systems Ltd, 89 Mayfield Gardens, Brentwood, Essex, CM14 4UN Tel: (01277) 200292 Fax: (01277) 200292 E-mail: malcolmcree@msn.com *Computer consultants*

Mayflex Middle East Ltd, Excel House, Junction Six Industrial Park, Birmingham, B6 7JJ Tel: 0121-326 7557 Fax: (0800) 3892270 E-mail: sales@mayflex.com *Mayflex is a distributor of: CCTV, IP Surveillance, cat5e and cat6 structured cabling, fibre optic cable, kvm switches, voice cabling, 19 inch cabinets, wall cabinets, remote control management, remote access management, open rack systems, ethernet switches, wireless lan, power over ethernet, network testers We sell products from manufacturers: Excel, LevelOne, Mobotix, Minicom, Extreme Networks, Belden, Brand-Rex, Fluke, Rose to name but a few.*

Mayflower Arosoft Systems Ltd, Mayflower House, Herbert Road, Stafford, ST17 9BH Tel: (01785) 240073 Fax: (01785) 245266 E-mail: b.bartlett@mfc-group.co.uk *Security*

Mayflower Ceiling Services, 107 Lawn Lane, Hemel Hempstead, Hertfordshire, HP3 9HS Tel: (01442) 242005 Fax: (01442) 268555

Mayflower Ceiling Services, 107 Lawn Lane, Hemel Hempstead, Hertfordshire, HP3 9HS Tel: (01442) 242005 Fax: (01442) 268555 *Suspended ceilings*

Mayflower Computing Consultants, Spindrift, West Looe Hill, West Looe, Looe, Cornwall, PL13 2HE Tel: (01503) 263688 Fax: (0870) 7407649 E-mail: sales@mayflower-cc.com *Computing consultants*

▶ Mayflower Control Ltd, Mayflower House, Herbert Road, Stafford, ST17 9BH Tel: (01785) 245263 Fax: (01785) 245266

Mayflower Engineering Ltd, Coleridge Road, Sheffield, S9 5DA Tel: 0114-244 1353 Fax: 0114-244 5977 E-mail: sales@mayflower-engineering.co.uk *Steelworkers plant & general engineers*

Mayflower Glass Ltd, Moor Lane, East Boldon, Tyne & Wear, NE36 0AQ Tel: 0191-536 0343 Fax: 0191-536 8099 E-mail: sales@mayflower-glass.com *Manufacturers of glass giftware*

Mayflower Hydraulics Ltd, Castlefields Trading Estate, Symons Way, Bridgwater, Somerset, TA6 4DR Tel: (01278) 450226 Fax: (01278) 446678 *Hydraulic equipment distributors*

Mayfly Containers Ltd, Bridge St Industrial Estate, Bridge Street, Clay Cross, Chesterfield, Derbyshire, S45 9NU Tel: (01246) 862456 Fax: (01246) 862711 *Waste & offshore steel container manufrs*

Mayfran (U K) Ltd, Orchard Court Binley Business Park, Harry Weston Road, Coventry, CV3 2TQ Tel: (024) 7645 9000 Fax: (024) 7645 9690 E-mail: sales@mayfran-europe.com *Scrap handling conveyors*

▶ Maygray Graphics Ltd, Graphics House, Arundel Road, Uxbridge, Middlesex, UB8 2JX Tel: (01895) 812525

Mayhan & Co. Ltd, 24 Tenby Street, Birmingham, B1 3EE Tel: 0121-236 3284 Fax: 0121-236 1981 E-mail: andrew.mayor@btclick.com *Precious metal services*

▶ Mayhew Flowers, 6 Cockpit Hill, Cullompton, Devon, EX15 1DF Tel: (01884) 839826 Fax: 01884 839826 E-mail: info@mayhewflowers.co.uk *Professional Florist based in Cullompton Devon. Weddings, Special Occasions, Funerals*

Mayhill Contracts Ltd, 11 Mucklow Hill Trading Estate, Mucklow Hill, Halesowen, West Midlands, B62 8DF Tel: 0121-550 0016 Fax: 0121-550 0017 *Precision engineers*

Maylan Engineering Co., Crucible Road, Corby, Northamptonshire, NN17 5TS Tel: (01536) 261798 Fax: (01536) 200957 E-mail: maylan@maylan.com *Precision engineers & machine tool accessories manufrs*

Maylin Clasps, Century Buildings, 35-38 Summerhill Road, Birmingham, B1 3RB Tel: 0121-236 4641 Fax: 0121-455 6430 E-mail: abros@jeweller.co.uk *Clasps & snaps for necklets*

▶ Mayling Transport Ltd, Broadwater Lane, Harefield, Uxbridge, Middlesex, UB9 6AH Tel: (01895) 822541 Fax: (01895) 823184

▶ Mayne Computer Technology Ltd, 13b Dalewood Road, Lymedale Business Park, Newcastle, Staffordshire, ST5 9QH Tel: (01782) 562522 Fax: (01782) 562299 E-mail: cathy-lou@maynetechnology.co.uk *IT software services*

Mayne Pharma Euro Finance Co. Ltd, Queensway, Leamington Spa, Warwickshire, CV31 3RW Tel: (01926) 820820 Fax: (01926) 821041 *Pharmaceutical distributors*

▶ Mayoh Press Ltd, Preston Street, Carnforth, Lancashire, LA5 9BY Tel: (01524) 732579

Mayor & Son Ltd, 1 Brierley Street, Ashton-on-Ribble, Preston, PR2 2AU Tel: (01772) 254488 Fax: (01772) 259897 *Tarpaulin manufrs*

▶ Mayor's Sportswear & Menswear, 1606 Dumbarton Road, Glasgow, G14 9DB Tel: 0141-959 0959 Fax: 0141-959 0959

Maypole Ltd, 54 Kettles Wood Drive, Birmingham, B32 3DB Tel: 0121-423 3011 Fax: 0121-423 3020 E-mail: maypole@maypole.ltd.uk *Towing, trailer parts & accessories manufrs*

▶ Maypole Frozen Foods Ltd, Sandleas Way, Crossgates, Leeds, LS15 8AW Tel: 0113-260 4455 Fax: 0113-260 4455 E-mail: sales@maypolefrozenfoods.com *Ice cream & lollipop wholesaler*

Mayr Melnhof Packaging UK Ltd, Fourth Avenue, Deeside Industrial Park, Deeside, Clwyd, CH5 2NR Tel: (01244) 289885 Fax: (01244) 281223 E-mail: sales@mm-packaging.com *Carton manufrs*

Mayr Melnhof UK Ltd, Bourne House, Bourne Close, Calcot, Reading, RG31 7BS Tel: 0118-942 5504 Fax: 0118-942 0750 *Carton board supplier*

Mayridge Ltd, Atherstone Hill Farm, Atherstone on Stour, Stratford-upon-Avon, Warwickshire, CV37 8NF Tel: (01789) 450898 Fax: (01789) 450855 E-mail: info@mayridge.com *Exhibition consultancy, graphics, stand design & event management services* Also at: London

▶ Mayrise Ltd, The Wheelhouse Bonds Mill, Stonehouse, Gloucestershire, GL10 3RF Tel: (01453) 827400 Fax: (01453) 853753 E-mail: office@mayrise.co.uk *Computer software developers*

Mayrock Fabrications, Old Airfield, Crail, Anstruther, Fife, KY10 3XL Tel: (01333) 450980 Fax: (01333) 450980 *Steel & aluminium fabricators*

▶ Mays Estate Agents, 290 Sandbanks Road, Poole, Dorset, BH14 8HX Tel: (01202) 709888 Fax: (01202) 707648 E-mail: poole@maysestateagents.co.uk *Estate Agents in Poole, Dorset. , Property for sale in Poole, Sandbanks, Canford Cliffs, Branksome Park, Lower Parkstone. Property Sales, Valuations, Property in Poole.*

Wally Mays (Contractors) Ltd, 57 Spyvee Street, Hull, HU8 7JJ Tel: (01482) 324077 Fax: (01482) 589596 E-mail: info@wallymays.karoo.co.uk *Electrical contractors*

▶ Maysair Ductwork Ltd, 7 Rycote Farm, Rycote Lane, Milton Common, Thame, Oxfordshire, OX9 2NZ Tel: (01844) 279635 Fax: (01844) 278980 E-mail: maysir1@aol.com

Maysmith Engineering Co Ltd, Unit 9, Woodlands Business Park, Woodlands Park Avenue, Maidenhead, Berkshire, SL6 3UA Tel: (01628) 828494 Fax: (01628) 829779 *Jig fixtures/press tools/precision engineering*

Charles Mayson Ltd, The Old Rectory, Byford, Hereford, HR4 7LD Tel: (01981) 590218 Fax: (01981) 590499 *Agricultural merchants*

Maytex Fabrics Ltd, Curzon Works, Curzon Street, Leicester, LE1 2HH Tel: 0116-262 4422 Fax: 0116-262 4447 E-mail: maytexfab@aol.com *Knitted fabric manufrs*

▶ Maythorn Construction Ltd, Compton Wharf, Bridgnorth Road, Wolverhampton, WV6 8AA Tel: (01902) 746181 Fax: (01902) 746388

▶ Maytree Associates Ltd, 17 Maytree Drive, Kirby Muxloe, Leicester, LE9 2LP Tel: 0116-239 4275 Fax: (0870) 7515096 E-mail: maytreeass@btconnect.com *Import & export agents*

Maytyne Engineering, Gardner Street, Herstmonceux, Hailsham, East Sussex, BN27 4LE Tel: (01323) 833200 Fax: (01323) 833200 *Precision turned parts manufrs*

Mayview Packaging, 41 Oak Walk, Hockley, Essex, SS5 5AR Tel: (01702) 207560 Fax: (01702) 207560 *Outwork assemblers*

▶ Mayway Construction Ltd, 2 Burbages Lane, Longford, Coventry, CV6 6AY Tel: (024) 7636 7714 Fax: (024) 7664 4462

Mayweld Engineering Co. Ltd, Banners Lane, Halesowen, West Midlands, B63 2SD Tel: (01384) 560285 Fax: (01384) 411456 *Domestic & industrial fuel tanks distributors & manufrs*

Maywick Ltd, Unit 7, Hawk Hill, Battlesbridge, Wickford, Essex, SS11 7RJ Tel: (01268) 573165 Fax: (01268) 573085 E-mail: sales.maywick@btconnect.com *Industrial oven parts & spares & agricultural heater suppliers*

Maywood Equipment Group Ltd, Larkfield Trading Estate, Larkfield, Aylesford, Kent, ME20 6SW Tel: 01622 718044 *Garage equipment distributors, vehicle lifts*

Mazak, Willenhall La Industrial Estate, Willenhall Lane, Bloxwich, Walsall, WS3 2XN Tel: (01922) 714430 Fax: (01922) 714433 E-mail: sales@mazak-limited.co.uk *Alloy, zinc & pigment distributors*

Maziak Compressor Services Ltd, 1 Stanton Close, Finedon Road Industrial Estate, Wellingborough, Northamptonshire, NN8 4HN Tel: (01933) 222000 Fax: (01933) 222200 E-mail: sales@maziak.co.uk *Air compressor distribs*

▶ Mazza Confectionery, Unit 1a Cranleigh Gardens Industrial Estate, Southall, Middlesex, UB1 2BZ Tel: (020) 8571 6272 Fax: (020) 8571 6281 E-mail: mazzaconf@aol.com *Confectionery manufrs*

continued

MB Careers Ltd, 8 High Street, Berkhamsted, Herts, HP4 2BL Tel: 0845 2263478 E-mail: info@mb-careers.co.uk *Consultancy specialising in HR advice for SME and technical recruitment (Engineers, Fitters, Mechanics). UK and Europe.*

MB Engineering Services, Midland Road, Leeds, LS10 2RP Tel: (01924) 877860 Fax: 0113-276 0372 E-mail: sales@clayton-walker.co.uk *Design & supervise construction of gas holders*

▶ MB Fabrications, Unit 18, Yeoman Business Estate, Wharf Road, Burton-on-Trent, Staffordshire, DE14 1PZ Tel: 01283 516026 Fax: 01283 516026

MB Fire Protection, Unit 22 Bourne Road Industrial Park, Bourne Road, Dartford, DA1 4BZ Tel: (01322) 523399 Fax: (01322) 528883 *Fire fighting equipment distributors* Also at: Erith

▶ MB Sign Design, 4 Newtown Grange Farm Business Centre, Desford Road, Newtown Unthank, Leicester, LE9 9FL Tel: (01455) 824102 Fax: (01455) 824102 *Sign manufrs*

▶ Mba Businessense Ltd, Skiers Hall Farm, Elsecar, Barnsley, South Yorkshire, S74 8EU Tel: (01226) 748338 Fax: (01226) 748338 E-mail: info@mbabusinessense.co.uk *Business consultancy*

Mbe Computer Systems, 3 Fair View Industrial Estate, Kingsbury Road, Curdworth, Sutton Coldfield, West Midlands, B76 9EE Tel: (01675) 470061 Fax: (01675) 470889 E-mail: phil.cowtan@morrisonplc.com Principal Export Areas: Africa *Building contractors*

Mbe Fabrications Ltd, 1 Town Drove, Quadring, Spalding, Lincolnshire, PE11 4PU Tel: (01775) 821222 Fax: (01775) 820914 E-mail: sales@mbefabs.com *Fabrication & garage pit manufrs*

Mbe Fasteners, Unit D1 Bearsted Green Business Centre, The Green, Bearsted, Maidstone, Kent, ME14 4DF Tel: (01622) 736868 Fax: (01622) 730111 *Major stockists & distributors of industrial fasteners*

MBG Management Consultants Ltd, 50 Greenhill Road, Moseley, Birmingham, B13 9SS Tel: 0121-449 5434 Fax: 0121-449 5844 E-mail: mbgmb@globalnet.co.uk *Human resources & management training*

MBM, Unit 7 Gibson Square, Talbot Street, Golborne, Warrington, WA3 3NN Tel: (01942) 721126 Fax: (01942) 276410 *Forklift truck parts service exchange*

MBM Group, 11 Railway Street, Newcastle, County Down, BT33 0AL Tel: (028) 4372 2257 Fax: (028) 4372 2257 E-mail: sales@thembmgroup.com *Hardware, networks, software, web design, training, repairs & epos*

MBN Fabrications Ltd, Units 2-3, Northbridge Road, Berkhamsted, Hertfordshire, HP4 1EF Tel: (01442) 877888 Fax: (01442) 877862 *Goods in cheap metal manufrs*

▶ MBP Precision Products, 8 Stocks Lane, Barnsley, South Yorkshire, S75 2BL Tel: (01226) 202918 Fax: (01226) 770400

Mbptv, Saucelands Barn, Coolham, Horsham, West Sussex, RH13 8QG Tel: (01403) 741620 Fax: (01403) 741647 E-mail: sales@mbptv.com *Audio-visual production services*

MBS, 53-59 Southcote Road, Bournemouth, BH1 3SH Tel: (01202) 589314 Fax: (01202) 587974

▶ MBS, 4 Bush Industrial Estate, Standard Road, London, NW10 6DF Tel: (020) 8453 1166 Fax: (020) 8963 0128 E-mail: marketing@mbsgroupcompanies.com *Your one stop shop for your dream house. Manufacturers of quality bedrooms and kitchen units, marble, granite, limestone work surfaces. Also cuto to customers specifications. Suppliers of sanitary and plumbing goods, ceramic and natural stone tiles.**

MBS, 24 Hanson Close, Middleton, Manchester, M24 2HD Tel: 0161-643 6151 Fax: 0161-643 6151 *Industrial refrigeration & air conditioning engineers*

MBS Foam Products Ltd, Unit 6A & 6B George Street, Handsworth, Birmingham, B21 8LE Tel: 0121-500 5455 Fax: 0121-500 4040 *Foam & fibre suppliers to upholsterers*

MBS International Marketing, Olympic House, 142 Queen Street, Glasgow, G1 3BU Tel: 0141-221 3298 Fax: 0141-221 3409 E-mail: sales@mbs-int-marketing.com *International marketing*

MBT Buildbase, 3 Dunnswood Road, Wardpark South, Cumbernauld, Glasgow, G67 3EN Tel: (01236) 454454 Fax: (01236) 454054 E-mail: cumbernauld@buildbase.co.uk *Buildbase is one of the UK's fastest growing builders merchants. All of our branches are long established companies which have been serving local trades people for many years, with knowledge and experience to match. We believe strongly in understanding the needs of trades professional and our business has been developed specifically to meet those demands. Massive stocks, top quality products, competitive pricing, reliable delivery, specialist staff and exceptional customer service*

▶ MC Technical Services, Unit 4 A6 Business Centre, Telford Way Telford Industrial, Telford Way Industrial Estate, Kettering, Northamptonshire, NN16 8UN Tel: (01536) 410201 Fax: (01536) 412189 E-mail: sales@mctechnicalservices.com *Suppliers of machines, service & breakdown cover & spare parts*

▶ MCB Roads, 54 Ronaldstone Road, Sidcup, Kent, DA15 8QU Tel: (020) 8850 6428

▶ MCB Supplies Veneers, Court Cottage, Porthpean, St. Austell, Cornwall, PL26 6AY Tel: (01726) 75653 E-mail: sales@mcb-supplies.co.uk *Trade & retail supplies of wood veneers,bandings Boxwood & Ebony lines, marquetry,chess & backgammon lay on panels,glue film, veneer tape & sundries.*

MCC Ltd, 2 Milford Road, Sherburn in Elmet, Leeds, LS25 6AF Tel: (01977) 682880 Fax: (0870) 0518693 E-mail: tim@mccltd.org.uk *Computer consultants*

MCG Graphics Ltd, Citadel Trading Park, Citadel Way, Hull, HU9 1TQ Tel: (01482) 225835 Fax: (01482) 215077 E-mail: webmaster@mcg-graphics.com *Pre press*

▶ MCL Cadcam Ltd, Block 2 Office 5 Nortonthorpe Industrial Estate, Wakefield Road, Scissett, Huddersfield, HD8 9LA Tel: (01484) 866311 Fax: (01484) 866575 E-mail: sales@mclsolutions.com *Computer maintenance services*

MCP, 8 Whitebridge Industrial Estate, Whitebridge Lane, Stone, Staffordshire, ST15 8LQ Tel: (01785) 815651 Fax: (01785) 812115 E-mail: equipment@mcp-group.co.uk Principal Export Areas: Worldwide *Plastic injection moulding machines & spraying equipment manufrs*

▶ MCP Consulting, Griffin House, West Street, Woking, Surrey, GU21 6BS Tel: (01483) 881270 Fax: (01483) 881290 E-mail: pmg@mcpconsulting.com *Building Services Consulting Engineers*

MCP Microsystems, 369 Warrington Road, Rainhill, Prescot, Merseyside, L35 8LD Tel: 0151-431 0133 Fax: 0151-431 0072 E-mail: admin@mcpmicro.co.uk *Computer reseller*

▶ MCPP, Unit H2 Hilton Main Industrial Estate, Bognop Road, Essington, Wolverhampton, WV11 2BE Tel: (01902) 736893

▶ MCPS Ltd, Tedco BSNS Works, Tedco Business Works, Henry Robson Way, South Shields, Tyne & Wear, NE33 1RF Tel: 0191-454 4444 Fax: 0191-427 4607 E-mail: sales@mcpsltd.com *Corrosion protection equipment*

▶ MCS Flooring & Fabric Cleaning, Rundells, Harlow, Essex, CM18 7HB Tel: (01279) 866838 E-mail: chamois.leathers@ntlworld.com *Carpet & upholstery cleaning service*

MD Instruments Ltd, 31 Yarmouth Close, Toothill, Swindon, SN5 8LL Tel: (01793) 433595 Fax: (01793) 644244 E-mail: sales@mdinstruments.co.uk *Water quality monitoring instruments & control manufrs*

▶ MD Welding Services, Unit 1-3 MBJ Business Park, Kenny Hill, Bury St. Edmunds, Suffolk, IP28 8DS Tel: (01353) 675599 Fax: (01353) 675599

▶ MDB Group, Cavendish House, Cavendish Rd, Stevenage, Hertfordshire, SG1 2EQ Tel: 01438 365451 E-mail: sales@mdbgroup.co.uk *MDB Group (Becker Transport) provide specialised transport services for laboratory removals, removal, relocation, engineering, services, supplies, installation and equipment distribution.*

▶ MDBXPRESS, 9 Flax Gardens, Kings Norton, Birmingham, B38 9QY Tel: (07917) 784210 Fax: 0121-451 3272 E-mail: enquiries@mdbxpress.co.uk *We offer a same day, next day and european courier service. We can also offer a next day service to any where in Ireland.*

▶ MDF Powder Coating Ltd, Bonlea Trading Estate, Thornaby, Stockton-on-Tees, Cleveland, TS17 7AQ Tel: (01642) 603399 *Powder coaters*

▶ Mdi-Digital, 130 Mansfield Lane, Norwich, NR1 2LT Tel: (01603) 632005 Fax: (01603) 632005 E-mail: info@mdi-digital.com *Illustration & 3D visualisation*

MDLogistics, MDL House, 151 Mead Way, Old Coulsdon, Coulsdon, Surrey, CR5 1PR Tel: (0845) 4561914 E-mail: info@mdlogistics.co.uk *Communications specialists*

▶ MDM Specialist Trades Ltd, 36 Watt Road, Hillington, Glasgow, G52 4RY Tel: 0141-891 4981 Fax: 0141-891 4230 E-mail: info@mdmspecialisttrades.co.uk

▶ MDN Contractors Limited, 12 Burnham Road, Owston Ferry, Doncaster, South Yorkshire, DN9 1AY Tel: 01427 728744 Fax: 01427 728744 E-mail: mdn.contractors@btinternet.com *Plant Operators available nationwide*

MDS Consultants, Tribune Avenue, Broadheath, Altrincham, Cheshire, WA14 5RX Tel: 0161-927 7744 Fax: 0161-927 7612 *Technical recruitment consultants*

MDS Interiors Ltd, Willows, St.James's Place, Cranleigh, Surrey, GU6 8RR Tel: (01483) 276206 Fax: (01483) 278227 E-mail: mail@mds-services.demon.co.uk *Interior office contractors*

MDS Petrochemical Supplies, Unit 48b Premier Partnership Estate, Leys Road, Brierley Hill, West Midlands, DY5 3UP Tel: (01384) 485055 Fax: (01384) 480053 E-mail: sales@mdspetrochemical.co.uk *Pipe fittings & flange manufrs*

MDTS UK Ltd, 65 Redwood Drive, Laindon, Basildon, Essex, SS15 4AF Tel: (0870) 2427319 Fax: 07092 043571 E-mail: enquiries@mdts.uk.com *Business Internet Solutions - MDTS UK Limited provide Internet Solutions to Businesses throughout England, UK. Services include E-Commerce Solutions, Online Business Systems, WebSite Design and Internet Strategy Consultancy.*

▶ Meachers Transport, East Side Park East Service Road, Raynesway, Spondon, Derby, DE21 7BF Tel: (01332) 666670 Fax: (01332) 666690

A.H. Mead & Son (Engineering) Ltd, Martel Works, High Easter Road, Dunmow, Essex, CM6 1NB Tel: (01371) 873907 Fax: (01371) 876703 *General engineers*

▶ Mead Building Services Ltd, Tomo Industrial Estate, Packet Boat Lane, Uxbridge, Middlesex, UB8 2JP Tel: (01895) 460057 Fax: (01895) 460058

▶ Mead Construction (Cambridge) Ltd, Liberty Barns, Heath Road, Swaffham Prior, Cambridge, CB5 0LA Tel: (01638) 742463

Mead Grove Export Ltd, 25 Curzon Street, London, W1J 7TG Tel: (020) 7629 5886 Fax: (020) 7408 0849 E-mail: info@meadoil.com *Chemicals, plastics & pharmaceutical services*

Meade Bros Ltd, Eckersall Road, Birmingham, B38 8SS Tel: 0121-486 2291 Fax: 0121-486 2276 E-mail: meadebrothersltd@aol.com *Electrical equipment enclosures suppliers*

Meade King Robinson & Company Ltd, 501 Tower Building, 22 Water Street, Liverpool, L3 1BL Tel: 0151-236 3191 Fax: 0151-236 4431 E-mail: info@mkr.co.uk *Chemical distributors*

Meaden Civil Engineering, 71 Micheldever Road, Whitchurch, Hampshire, RG28 7JH Tel: (01256) 893270 *Groundwork's*

Meadex Mouldings Ltd, Units 1-2, Tanyard Lane, Ross-On-Wye, Herefordshire, HR9 7BH Tel: (01989) 567999 Fax: (01989) 768022 E-mail: sales@meadex.co.uk *Rubber mouldings manufrs*

Meadhams Lawnmowers Sales & Service, 12 Bankside, Kidlington, Oxfordshire, OX5 1JE Tel: (01865) 378010 Fax: (01865) 378010 E-mail: meadhams@btinternet.com *Garden equipment*

Meadow Designs Ltd, Church Farm Rural Workshops, Stanton Lacy, Ludlow, Shropshire, SY8 2AE Tel: (01584) 856562 *Garden furniture manufrs*

▶ Meadow Engineering & Patterns, 53 Kenilworth Drive, Oadby, Leicester, LE2 5LT Tel: 0116-271 1763 Fax: 0116-271 6022

Meadow Industrial Electronics, Newcastle Enterprise Centre, High Street, Knutton, Newcastle, Staffordshire, ST5 6BX Tel: (01782) 714200 Fax: (01782) 714204 E-mail: info@meadowindustrial.co.uk *Electronic designers*

Meadow Lane Scrap Co. Ltd, Grainger Street, Nottingham, NG2 3HA Tel: 0115-986 3884 Fax: 0115-986 4050 *Scrap metal merchants, contractors, processors & services*

▶ Meadow Line Services Ltd, Cameron Court, Cameron Street, Hillington Industrial Estate, Glasgow, G52 4JX Tel: 0141-883 7722

▶ Meadowcraft Flowers Of Scotland Ltd, Clettyden, Woodhead, Turriff, Aberdeenshire, AB53 8PL Tel: (01651) 891799 Fax: (01651) 891799 E-mail: sales@flowersofscotland.com *Florists*

Meadows Lift Trucks, Ridley Road, Burnt Mills Industrial Estate, Basildon, Essex, SS13 1EG Tel: (01268) 724422 Fax: (01268) 725282 *Fork lift trucks*

Meadows Wye Container Groupage, Castlebank House, Oak Road, Leatherhead, Surrey, KT22 7PG Tel: (01372) 370066 Fax: (01372) 370077 *Shipping & forwarding agents*

▶ Meads Ltd, 3 90a Tideswell Road, Eastbourne, East Sussex, BN21 3RT Tel: (01323) 726425 Fax: (01323) 726425

Meadsway Construction Ltd, 8 Sunbeam Road, Woburn Road Industrial Estate, Kempston, Bedford, MK42 7BY Tel: (01234) 856023 Fax: (01234) 841450 *Building contractors*

E.& R. Meakes Ltd, Forge Works, Lane End, High Wycombe, Buckinghamshire, HP14 3HJ Tel: (01494) 881262 Fax: (01494) 883279 *Industrial steel fabrication manufrs*

Meakin & Son, 270 Abbey Street, Derby, DE22 3SX Tel: (01332) 344144 Fax: (01332) 292420 E-mail: metalwork@dial.pipex.com *Sheet metalworkers*

Meakins & Son Ltd, 17 St. James Industrial Estate, Westhampnett Road, Chichester, West Sussex, PO19 7JU Tel: (01243) 774343 Fax: (01243) 780223 E-mail: meakins@fsmail.net *MOT'S & car repair services*

Meakins Transport Ltd, The Garage, Back Lane, Spencers Wood, Reading, RG7 1JB Tel: 0118-988 2134 Fax: 0118-988 4150 *Haulage contractors & vehicle repair*

Mealbox Ltd, 235 Farnham Road, Slough, SL2 1DE Tel: (01753) 554391 E-mail: enq@mealbox.com *Call centre*

Mealey Horgan plc, 16 Park Street, London, W1K 2HZ Tel: (020) 7499 4902 Fax: (020) 7499 4903 E-mail: mealyhorgan@btclick.com *Financial & property consultants*

Mealham Metal Products, Orchard Buildings, Chilmington Green, Great Chart, Ashford, Kent, TN23 3DL Tel: (01233) 621150 Fax: (01233) 621150 *Steel fabricators & stockholders*

Colin Mealing Ironworks, Mealings Yard, 55 High Street, Westbury-on-Trym, Bristol, BS9 3ED Tel: 0117-950 6262 *Manufactures of iron gates & security griddles*

Mealor-Clarke Cycle Spares, Unit 4 St. Johns Road, Saxmundham, Suffolk, IP17 1BE Tel: (01728) 605970 Fax: (0560) 0751879 E-mail: ray@mealorclarkecyclespares.com *Wholesale bicycle component suppliers*

Meals on the Move, Fearby Road, Masham, Ripon, North Yorkshire, HG4 4ES Tel: (01765) 689595 E-mail: graham.thornton@danbys.biz

Means 2 Consulting Ltd, Hattons Farm, The Street, Rumburgh, Halesworth, Suffolk, IP19 0JU Tel: (01986) 781252 E-mail: aidan.ward@means2.com *Logistics consultants specialising in distribution solutions, notably warehouse operations for manufacturers, retailers and distributors. Key competencies encompass, warehouse solution design incorporating full resource modelling; operations benchmarking and re-engineering exploiting industrial engineering techniques; tendering solutions for outsourcing distribution operations reinforced by long term internal experience of 3rd party logistics sector.*

Meap Ltd, 1 Bath Road, Stonehouse, Gloucestershire, GL10 2JD Tel: (01453) 828088 Fax: (01453) 828980 E-mail: roger.hughes@softlogic.co.uk *Computer consultants*

Colin Mear Engineering Ltd, Combe Wood, Combe St Nicholas, Chard, Somerset, TA20 3NL Tel: (01460) 67351 Fax: (01460) 65661 E-mail: cme@cme-ltd.com *Precision engineers*

M.H. Mear & Co. Ltd, 56 Nettleton Road, Huddersfield, HD5 9TB Tel: (01484) 648181 Fax: (01484) 485408 E-mail: kath@mhmear.com *Calculation machine manufrs*

▶ Mearchent Sons Builders, Glenwood Business Park Block C, Glenwood Place, Glasgow, G45 9UH Tel: 0141-634 5731 Fax: 0141-634 5731

Mearns & Gill Advertising Ltd, 7 Carden Place, Aberdeen, AB10 1PP Tel: (01224) 646311 Fax: (01224) 631882 E-mail: info@mearns-gill.com *Public relations services*

Mearns Trophy Centre, 60 Riverside Drive, Stonehaven, Kincardineshire, AB39 2GP Tel: (01569) 764762 Fax: (01569) 764762 *Trophies & engraving services*

▶ Measham Heating Air Conditioning Ltd, 142 Birmingham Road, Aldridge, Walsall, WS9 0AH Tel: (01922) 456567 Fax: (01922) 456446 E-mail: reception@measham.co.uk *Heating & air- conditioning*

▶ Measured DJ, 77 Whyke Lane, Chichester, W. Sussex, PO19 7PD Tel: 07811 276529 E-mail: info@measured-dj.co.uk *Tailor made Tuxedos, DJs, dinner suits /jackets for only £99. Home visits in Sussex, Hampshire or organised measured days.*

Measurement Aids Ltd, 90-92 Tontine Street, Folkestone, Kent, CT20 1JW Tel: (01303) 850722 Fax: (01303) 220380 *Electronic systems developers*

Measurement Devices Ltd, Silverburn Crescent, Bridge of Don Industrial Estate, Aberdeen, AB23 8EW Tel: (01224) 246700 Fax: (01224) 824987 E-mail: info@mdl.co.uk *Laser measurement manufrs*

Measurement Technology Ltd, 18 Power Court, Luton, LU1 3JJ Tel: (01582) 723633 Fax: (01582) 422283 E-mail: enquiry@mtl-inst.com *Intrinsically safe instruments*

Measure-Rite Ltd, Great Central Way Industrial Estate, Great Central Way, Rugby, Warwickshire, CV21 3XH Tel: (01788) 577512 Fax: (01788) 560864 E-mail: sales@measure-rite.com *Calibrating & measuring equipment*

Measuring Machines Ltd, 9 Oban Court, Hurricane Way, Wickford, Essex, SS11 8YB Tel: (01268) 560999 Fax: (01268) 561222 E-mail: info@measuringmachines.co.uk *Fabric measuring machine manufrs*

Measuring & Process Control Ltd, Unit 2, Tabrums Farm, Tabrums Lane, Battlesbridge, Wickford, Essex, SS11 7QX Tel: (01245) 322855 Fax: (01245) 328922 *Process controller systems manufrs*

Meath Engineering Tools Ltd, Black Bourton Road, Carterton, Oxfordshire, OX18 3EZ Tel: (01993) 841041 *Press tool manufrs*

Meatingpoint A.B., 27 The Business Exchange, Rockingham Rd, Kettering, Northants, NN16 8JX Tel: (01536) 526477 Fax: (01536) 526478 E-mail: malcolm.morrison@meatingpoint.com *Supply chain management solutions for the meat industry*

MEB Equipment Ltd, Broadwater Lane, Harefield, Uxbridge, Middlesex, UB9 6AH Tel: (01895) 821002 Fax: (01895) 824845 E-mail: sales@mebequipment.co.uk *Truck mounted forklifts distributors*

Meba Saw Co Ltd, 27 Palmer Road, Retford, Nottinghamshire, DN22 6SS Tel: (01777) 860102 Fax: (01777) 860306 E-mail: mebasaw@btconnect.com *Sawing equipment distributors*

Mec A Tec Services Ltd, Boleness Road, Wisbech, Cambridgeshire, PE13 2RB Tel: (01945) 474685 Fax: (01945) 474687 E-mail: mecatec@aol.com *Manufacture of conveyors & systems*

Mec Com Ltd, St. Leonards Works, St. Leonards Avenue, Stafford, ST17 4LT Tel: (01785) 273708 Fax: (01785) 273777 E-mail: sales@mec-com.ltd.uk *Mechanical component manufrs*

▶ Mec Sail Ltd, Mount Lee Lodge, Egham, Surrey, TW20 0EU Tel: (01784) 436113 Fax: (01784) 436945 E-mail: davidmccarthy@mec-sail.com *Mec Sail is a yacht charter company based in Southampton. We specialise in corporate sailing charters with yachts from 31' - 86'. Private charter, hen and stag parties catered for.*

Mecc Alte UK Ltd, Lands End Way, Oakham, Leicestershire, LE15 6RF Tel: (01572) 771160 Fax: (01572) 771161 E-mail: sales@meccalte.it *Alternator manufrs*

Mecca Engineering, 13 Farrington Court, Burnley, Lancashire, BB11 5SS Tel: (01282) 452290 Fax: (01282) 452290 *Production engineering*

Mecdine Instruments Ltd, 7 Sherborne Road, Burbage, Hinckley, Leicestershire, LE10 2BE Tel: (01455) 250220 Fax: (01455) 238541 *Instrument designers & manufrs*

Mecelex & Co, 19a Nottingham Road, Daybrook, Nottingham, NG5 6JW Tel: 0115-967 0665 Fax: 0115-967 0665 E-mail: mecelex@aol.com *Printed circuit manufrs*

Co Mech Ltd, Victory House, Victory Road, Derby, DE24 8EL Tel: (01332) 275820 Fax: (01332) 275817 E-mail: sales@comech.co.uk *Scientific services*

Mech Tool Engineering Ltd, Whessoe Road, Darlington, County Durham, DL3 0QT Tel: (01325) 355141 Fax: (01325) 487053 E-mail: info@mechtool.co.uk *Successful Global Supplier of Industrial Noise Control Products, Packaged Equipment Modules and Passive Fire & Explosion Protection Solutions*

Mechagryl Ltd, Unit 7, London Group Business Park, 715 North Circular Road, London, NW2 7AQ Tel: (020) 8208 4677 Fax: (020) 8903 2802 E-mail: mechagryl@btclick.com *Export merchants*

▶ Mechaid Magazine, 41 High Street, Morcott, Oakham, Leicestershire, LE15 9DN Tel: (01572) 747472 E-mail: mechaid@mechaid.com *UK's leading tools, plant & equipment magazine*

Mechalloy Ltd, 4 Orgreave Cresent, Sheffield, S13 9NQ Tel: 0114-269 3945 Fax: 0114-269 8099 *Special alloy machinists & drilling*

Mechan Controls Ltd, 14 Seddon Place, Stanley Industrial Estate, Skelmersdale, Lancashire, WN8 8EB Tel: (01695) 722264 Fax: (01695) 729664 E-mail: info@mechancontrols.co.uk *Safety & machine guard interlock manufrs*

Mechandling Ltd, 11b Greenfield Farm Industrial Estate, Congleton, Cheshire, CW12 4TR Tel: (01260) 299411 Fax: (01260) 299032 E-mail: sales@mechandling.co.uk *Materials handling & mechanical handling equipment manufrs*

Mechanelec Ltd, 10 Waterloo Road, Widnes, Cheshire, WA8 0PY Tel: 0151-495 1739 Fax: 0151-495 1227 E-mail: enquiries@mechanelec.co.uk *Power supply systems*

Mechanical Air Supplies Ltd, Crouch Indust Estate, Barnett Wood Lane, Leatherhead, Surrey, KT22 7DG Tel: (01372) 370084 Fax: (01372) 370085 *Ventilation ductwork, ducting service*

Mechanical Cleansing Services Ltd, Unit G, Salford Street Industrial Estate, Aston, Birmingham, B6 7SH Tel: (0845) 5314243 Fax: 0121-327 3105 E-mail: droemcsltd@aol.com *Oil tank cleansing, petrol tank cleansing, oil tank removal, petrol tank removal, foam filling of tanks, 24 hour emergency oil spill response, degassing & removal of oil tanks, Interceptor, Washbay and Bund Wall Cleaning. Cesspit, Interceptor emptying, Septic Tank & Grease trap uplifts, oils spills clean ups, high pressure drain jetting. 24 hour call out, ISO 14001 registered. ISO 18001.*

Mechanical Engineering Services, Unit 32n The Washford Industrial Estate, Heming Road, Redditch, Worcestershire, B98 0DH Tel: (01527) 510930 Fax: (01527) 529992 *Maintenance engineers*

Mechanical & Ferrous Ltd, 1 Church Road, Erith, Kent, DA8 1PG Tel: (01322) 447714 Fax: (01322) 436228 E-mail: mechferrous@aol.com *Mechanical fabricators & engineering services*

Mechanical Installations International Ltd, Richmond House, 468 Chepstow Road, Newport, Gwent, NP19 8JF Tel: (01633) 282115 Fax: (01633) 290159 *Heavy engineering installation & maintenance*

Mechanical & Pipework Fabrications Ltd, Racecourse Road, Pershore, Worcestershire, WR10 2EY Tel: (01386) 554048 Fax: (01386) 556695 E-mail: sales@mpf-ltd.co.uk *Pipe work fabricators*

Mechanical Seals, Swinton, Manchester, M27 8UJ Tel: 0161-3 516666

D A T Mechanical Services, 19 Waldorf Heights, Blackwater, Camberley, Surrey, GU17 9JQ Tel: (01276) 35801 Fax: (01276) 36515 E-mail: datforktrucks@aol.com *Fork lift trucks retailers & repairers*

Mechanical Services (Luton) Ltd, 158A Beechwood Road, Luton, LU4 9RY Tel: (01582) 494747 Fax: (01582) 494749 E-mail: mechservluton@aol.com *Machinery removal contractors, factory removal & relocation contractors*

Mechanical Workshop, 45 Station Road, Littlethorpe, Leicester, LE19 2HS Tel: 0116-286 3896 Fax: 0116-286 3962 *Automatic transmission engineers*

Mechatherm International Ltd, Hampshire House, High Street, Kingswinford, West Midlands, DY6 8AW Tel: (01384) 279132 Fax: (01384) 291211 E-mail: milcom@mechatherm.co.uk *Furnace & foundry equipment designers*

Mechatronic Production Systems Ltd, 2267 Coventry Road, Sheldon, Birmingham, B26 3PD Tel: 0121-742 7206 Fax: 0121-743 6882 E-mail: sales@mechatronic.co.uk *Automated assembly system manufrs*

Mechelec Building Services Ltd, Poulton Close, Dover, Kent, CT17 0HL Tel: (01304) 205559 Fax: (01304) 242068 *Mechanical, plumbing & electrical contractors* Also at: Ashford

Mechfast Ltd, Unit 3 & 4 Dalehouse La Industrial Estate, Cotton Drive, Kenilworth, Warwickshire, CV8 2UE Tel: (01926) 858698 Fax: (01926) 858051 E-mail: *Mechanical fastenings stockists*

▶ Mechplant Plant & Machinery Hire, Schofield Street, Littleborough, Lancashire, OL15 0JS Tel: (01706) 370111 Fax: (01706) 377634

▶ Mechserv Ltd, Sir William Smith Road, Kirkton Industrial Estate, Arbroath, Angus, DD11 3RD Tel: (01241) 439070 Fax: (01241) 439074 *Designing & fabricating parts for oil fields*

▶ Mechshop Ltd, 9 Arden Business Centre, Arden Road, Alcester, Warwickshire, B49 6HW Tel: (01789) 763963 Fax: (01789) 400882

Mechtech Valves Services, The Stenders, Mitcheldean, Gloucestershire, GL17 0ZE Tel: (01594) 541717 Fax: (01594) 541716 *Valve distributors & agents*

Mechtronic Industries Ltd, Innovation Centre, Kirton Lane, Stainforth, Doncaster, South Yorkshire, DN7 5DA Tel: (01302) 845000 Fax: (01302) 844440 E-mail: mechtro@aol.com Principal Export Areas: Worldwide *Manufacturers for Mechtronic laser cut profile systems, Stanzform.*

Mec-Lon, 1 Enterprise Park, Etna Road, Bury St. Edmunds, Suffolk, IP33 1JZ Tel: (01284) 706334 Fax: (01284) 706334 E-mail: sales@mec-lon.co.uk *Machining services*

Mecnov Products Ltd, Unit 3, Arlesey Business Park, Mill Lane, Arlesey, Bedfordshire, SG15 6RF Tel: (01462) 832282 Fax: (01462) 735127 E-mail: phill@flingprom.com *Pop up promotions services*

Meco Pak (UK) Ltd, Greenway House, Sugarswell Business Park, Shenington, Banbury, Oxfordshire, OX15 6HW Tel: (01295) 688910 Fax: (01295) 688911 E-mail: info@mecopak.co.uk Principal Export Areas: Africa *Packaging equipment/machine/ systems manufacturers, packaging: wraparound, case/tray, shrink wrap sleeve wrapping machine, pick & place handling systems manufacturers*

Mecon Ltd, 5a Pound Hill, Cambridge, CB3 0AE Tel: (01223) 355990 Fax: (01223) 354297 E-mail: enquiries@mecon.ltd.uk *Contract R & D designers*

Meconic P.L.C., 10 Wheatfield Road, Edinburgh, EH11 2QA Tel: 0131-313 1416

Mecright Contractors Ltd, Unit 10 Prospect Business Park, Longford Road, Cannock, Staffordshire, WS11 0LG Tel: (01543) 469222 Fax: (01543) 469444 E-mail: patrick@mecright.co.uk *Steel fabricators. Also steel & metal staircases*

Mectech Services, Place Farm, Place Farm Lane, Doddinghurst, Brentwood, Essex, CM15 0JA Tel: (01277) 372848 Fax: (01277) 374942 *Plant maintenance services*

Mectronic Instruments Ltd, West Chirton Trading Estate, North Shields, Tyne & Wear, NE29 7TY Tel: 0191-296 0183 Fax: 0191-296 1163 E-mail: sales@mectronic.co.uk Principal Export Areas: Worldwide *Precision engineers*

Mecwash Systems Ltd, Unit A 64 Hundred, 7 Drive, Tewkesbury Business Park, Tewkesbury, Gloucestershire, GL20 8TB Tel: (01684) 271600 E-mail: paulyoung@mecwash.co.uk Principal Export Areas: Central/East Europe & South America *Degreasing plant & equipment manufacturers & washing equipment manufrs for metal components*

Med Tech, Riverside Works, Miller Row, Edinburgh, EH4 3BQ Tel: 0131-225 4295 Fax: 0131-220 4065 E-mail: med-tech@tiscali.co.uk *Oxygen therapy equipment*

Meda Plastics Ltd, Unit 23 Siddons Factory Estate, Howard Street, West Bromwich, West Midlands, B70 0SU Tel: 0121-502 0463 Fax: 0121-505 3248 *PVC compound manufrs*

▶ Medaes Ltd, Telford Cresent, Speedwell Industrial Estate, Staveley, Chesterfield, Derbyshire, S43 3PF Tel: (01246) 474242 Fax: (01246) 472982 E-mail: sales@medaes.co.uk *Medical gas systems, bedhead trunking, pendant systems, booms, bedhead services, headwalls* Also at: Sunbury-on-Thames & Washington (Tyne & Wear)

Medasil (Surgical) Ltd, Medasil House, Hunslet Road, Leeds, LS10 1AU Tel: 0113-243 3491 Fax: 0113-242 9276 E-mail: medasil@dial.pipex.com *Surgical product manufrs*

Medc Ltd, Colliery Road, Pinxton, Nottingham, NG16 6JF Tel: (01773) 864111 Fax: (01773) 582800 E-mail: sales@medc.com *Hazardous area equipment manufrs*

Medcalf & Co. (Coachbuilders) Ltd, Fordwater Trading Estate, Fordwater Road, Chertsey, Surrey, KT16 8HG Tel: (01932) 563026 Fax: (01932) 571086 *Motor car repairers & restorers*

Medcrest Ltd, Valley Road, Wombwell, Barnsley, South Yorkshire, S73 0BS Tel: (01226) 759360 Fax: (01226) 757392 E-mail: general@medcrest.co.uk *Radiographic examination of castings*

Meddings Machine Tools, Kingsley Close, Lee Mill Industrial Estate, Ivybridge, Devon, PL21 9LL Tel: (01752) 313323 Fax: (01752) 313333 E-mail: sales@meddings.co.uk *Machine tool manufrs*

Medeci Rehab Ltd, Hallsford Bridge Industrial Estate, Stondon Road, Ongar, Essex, CM5 9RB Tel: (01277) 364449 Fax: (01277) 364962 E-mail: sales@ponting.co.uk *Disabled persons aid designers*

Medella Manufacturing Ltd, 1 Palmer Street, Leicester, LE4 5PT Tel: 0116-233 3299 Fax: 0116-233 3431 E-mail: jgarner-socks@aol.com *Sock manufrs*

Meden Vale Engineering Co. Ltd, Meden Square, Pleasley, Mansfield, Nottinghamshire, NG19 7SQ Tel: (01623) 810601 Fax: (01623) 812190 *Precision engineers*

Medex Scientific (UK) Ltd, 4 Denne Road, Horsham, West Sussex, RH12 1JE Tel: (01403) 218999 *Slimming & dietary products by mail order*

Medezine & Medica, 7 Station Approach, Stoneleigh, Epsom, Surrey, KT19 0QZ Tel: (020) 8873 3033 Fax: (020) 8873 3034 E-mail: medimed@easynet.co.uk *Medical equipment manufr*

Medforth & Co. Ltd, 190 Hilderthorpe Road, Bridlington, North Humberside, YO15 3HD Tel: (01262) 673003 Fax: (01262) 679706 E-mail: johnbifton@btconnect.com *Agricultural merchants*

Medi UK, Plough Lane, Hereford, HR4 0EL Tel: (01432) 373500 Fax: (01432) 373510 E-mail: enquiries@mediuk.co.uk *Surgical stocking distributors*

▶ The Media Agency, 1 Brewery Hill, Arundel, West Sussex, BN18 9DQ Tel: 01903 882836 Fax: 01903 882836 E-mail: themediaagency@hotmail.co.uk *The Media Agency is a recruitment consultancy specialising in all media, including film, TV, radio, publishing, advertising, design, PR, marketing, events and exhibitions. We supply technical, creative and sales staff from juniors to directors.*

Media Cards, 108 Davies Road, West Bridgford, Nottingham, NG2 5HY Tel: 0115-914 2369 E-mail: sales@media-cards.co.uk *Interactive & electronic business cards manufrs*

Media Communications Ltd, Research House, Fraser Road, Greenford, Middlesex, UB6 7AQ Tel: (020) 8998 1517 Fax: (020) 8566 8290 E-mail: info@mclweb.co.uk *IT development services*

▶ Media Control Ltd, Matrix House, Victoria Road, Dartford, DA1 5AJ Tel: (01322) 272822 Fax: (01322) 291909

▶ Media Control UK Ltd, 69 Dartmouth Middleway, Birmingham, B7 4UA Tel: 0121-333 3333 Fax: 0121-333 3347 E-mail: info@mcl-birmingham.com *Audio visual conference & exhibition services*

▶ Media Heaven Ltd, 12 Castleton Close, Leeds, LS12 2DS Tel: 0113-244 3550 Fax: 0113-244 3994 E-mail: info@mediaheaven.co.uk *CD & DVD printing & duplication, replication & packaging*

Media Information Solutions Ltd, 32 Ballmoor, Buckingham Industrial Estate, Buckingham, MK18 1RQ Tel: (01280) 824488 Fax: (01280) 824489 E-mail: info@m-i-s.co.uk *PC & macintosh consultants*

▶ Media Link Europe Ltd, Unit 13, Roman Way Small Business Park Lon, Godmanchester, Huntingdon, Cambridgeshire, PE29 2LN Tel: (01480) 453288 Fax: 01480 451088 E-mail: wayne@caseonline.co.uk *Here at Media Link we manufacture CD carry cases and also Laptop cases. We also manufacture USB products and all of the above can also be branded to you specifercation.*

Media Logic Ltd, PO Box 3214, Sheffield, S10 5WT Tel: 0114-230 3758 Fax: 0114-263 0868 E-mail: info@medialogic.net *Computer consultants*

Media Magic Computers, Media House, 196a Abbey Road, Leeds, LS5 3NG Tel: 0113-228 9911 Fax: 0113-228 9933 *Computer maintenance, consultants & networking*

Media Market Ltd, 24 Gordon Avenue, Stanmore, Middlesex, HA7 3QD Tel: (020) 8954 5994 Fax: (020) 8954 1624 *Imports end of line items*

Media Masters, Bernard Street, Uplands, Swansea, SA2 0HT Tel: (01792) 464441 Fax: (01792) 651356 *Electronic equipment*

▶ Media Merge Ltd, 20 Ditton Fields, Cambridge, CB5 8QL Tel: (01223) 573449 E-mail: info@mediamerge.co.uk *Media production*

Media Plastics, 8 Merrylees Industrial Estate, Lee Side, Desford, Leicester, LE9 9FS Tel: (01455) 292110 Fax: (01455) 292190 E-mail: sales@mediaplastics.co.uk *Manufacturers of binders (plastic), loose leaf binders & wallets (packet plastic)*

Media Resources, Church Croft House, Station Road, Rugeley, Staffordshire, WS15 2HE Tel: (01889) 503100 Fax: (01889) 503100 E-mail: info@media-resources.co.uk *Computer & backup media suppliers*

▶ The Media Services Co., 106 Tappesfield Road, London, SE15 3EZ Tel: (020) 7635 3459 Fax: (020) 7635 3459 E-mail: info@themediaservicescompany.com *Audio visual hire for conferences & events*

Media Services Group Ltd, 64 Charlotte Street, London, W1T 4QD Tel: (020) 7436 0070 Fax: (020) 7580 5706 E-mail: hbrantley@msgl.com *Software house for events*

The Media Shop (Scotland) Ltd, 5 Royal Exchange Square, Glasgow, G1 3AH Tel: 0141-221 0280 Fax: 0141-204 0722 E-mail: info@the-media-shop.co.uk *Advertising agents*

▶ Media Stations, 86 Smithbrook Kilns, Cranleigh, Surrey, GU6 8JJ Tel: (01483) 277765 E-mail: enquiries@mediastation.co.uk *Advanced interactive & video solutions providers*

▶ Media9, 4 West Park Grove, Broxburn, West Lothian, EH52 6ET Tel: (08707) 480407 Fax: (08707) 480418 E-mail: info@media9.co.uk *Graphic Design & Print, Large Format Printing, Vehicle Graphics, Web Design.*

Mediacomm, Unit 10, Riverside Business Centre, Brighton Road, Shoreham-By-Sea, West Sussex, BN43 6RE Tel: (01273) 465664 Fax: (01273) 465665 E-mail: sales@media-comm.co.uk *Telephone installers*

Mediamax, 25A Chertsey Road, Chobham, Woking, Surrey, GU24 8PD Tel: (01276) 856144 Fax: (01276) 855958 E-mail: sales@mediamax.co.uk *Computer media*

▶ Median Enterprises, PO Box 32, Southampton, SO31 6UH Tel: (01489) 885174 Fax: (01489) 574847 E-mail: info@median.co.uk *Median Enterprises specialise in the purchase and sale of all types of concrete plant and machinery, including Schwing + Putzmeister concrete pumps, Steelfield, Elba, Liebherr + Stetter concrete plants and aggregate storage + conveyor systems.*

Median Systems Ltd, Unit 26 Bailey Gate, Sturminster Marshall, Wimborne, Dorset, BH21 4DB Tel: (01258) 858999 Fax: (01258) 857714 *Distribution of medical equipment*

▶ Mediascene Ltd, A-D Unit, Bowen Industrial Estate, Aberbargoed, Bargoed, Mid Glamorgan, CF81 9AB Tel: (01443) 821877 Fax: (01443) 822055 E-mail: hi@mediascene.co.uk *Direct mail services*

Mediatech Ltd, 3 Ferndale Close, Thornton-Cleveleys, Lancashire, FY5 4PD Tel: (01253) 825251 Fax: (01253) 863839 *Computer consultancy*

Medical Air Technology, Mars Street, Oldham, OL9 6LY Tel: 0161-621 6200 Fax: 0161-624 7547 E-mail: sales@medicalairtechnology.com *Clean air equipment manufrs*

▶ Medical Case Notes Assessment, 47-48 Hawley Square, Margate, Kent, CT9 1NY Tel: (01843) 209645 Fax: 01843 209646 E-mail: webmaster@medicalcasenotes.co.uk *Medical Case Notes Assessment Ltd provide medical expert reports to solicitors in Britain and Ireland for medical negligence cases.*

Medical & Cosmetic Mouldings Ltd, Gas Road, Sittingbourne, Kent, ME10 2QD Tel: (01795) 426452 Fax: (01795) 421495 E-mail: informationmcm@aol.com Purchasing Contact: N.E. Plumb Sales Contact: D. Wise *Cosmetic container (packaging), injection mouldings (BS clean room environment), injection mouldings (plastic), plastic cap & plug (protective) & plastic mouldings manufrs*

Medical Device Consultancy, 6 Bessborough Drive, Cardiff, CF11 8NE Tel: (029) 2022 1640 Fax: (029) 2022 1579 E-mail: lewlink@btclick.com *Medical devices consultants*

Medical Export Co. Ltd, Woolleys Farm, Naseby, Northampton, NN6 6DP Tel: (01858) 575065 Fax: (01858) 575095 E-mail: medexuk@aol.com *Pharmaceutical product exports*

Medical Gases Ltd, Aztex House, Perrywood Business Park, Salfords, Redhill, RH1 5DZ Tel: (01737) 378000 Fax: (01737) 378055 E-mail: rsmith@medicalgases.uk.com Sales Contact: R. Smith *Laboratory & medical pipeline installation contractors*

Medical & Industrial Manufacturing Co. Ltd, Broadway, Dukinfield, Cheshire, SK16 4UU Tel: 0161-339 6028 Fax: 0161-330 0944 E-mail: mimcoltd@compuserve.com *Medical equipment manufrs*

Medical Marine Computing Ltd, 9b Bowthorpe Road, Wisbech, Cambridgeshire, PE13 2DX Tel: (01945) 580021 Fax: (01945) 580044 E-mail: support@medicalmarine.co.uk *Software suppliers*

Medical Sickness Pensions Administration Ltd, Colmore Circus Queensway, Birmingham, B4 6AR Tel: (08081) 001884 Fax: 0121-200 9140 *Insurance company* Also at: Manchester & Swindon

Medical Technology Ltd, Parkway Close, Parkway Industrial Estate, Sheffield, S9 4WH Tel: 0114-273 8764 Fax: 0114-273 8764 Principal Export Areas: Worldwide *Investment casting.*

Medical Wire & Equipment Co Bath Ltd, Unit 29 Leafield Industrial Estate, Leafield Way, Corsham, Wiltshire, SN13 9RT Tel: (01225) 810361 Fax: (01225) 810153 E-mail: sales@mwe.co.uk *Medical supplies & laboratory equipment manufrs*

Medicell International Ltd, 239 Liverpool Road, London, N1 1LX Tel: (020) 7607 2295 Fax: (020) 7700 4156 E-mail: all@medicell.co.uk *Laboratory equipment supply & manufrs*

Medici Ltd, 17-18 Margaret Street, London, W1W 8RP Tel: (020) 7436 2882 Fax: (020) 7631 0168 E-mail: mediciltd@aol.com *Ladieswear manufrs*

Medico-Biological Laboratories Ltd, Kingsend House, 44 Kingsend, Ruislip, Middlesex, HA4 7DA Tel: (01895) 632724 Fax: (01895) 622736 *Pharmaceutical preparation manufrs*

Medico-Oil Co, 29 Penhale Road, Eastbourne, East Sussex, BN22 7JX Tel: (01323) 646777 Fax: (01323) 646777 E-mail: sales@medico-oil.fsnet.co.uk *Oil importers, exporters & distributors*

▶ Medics Recruitment Agency, Banchory Business Centre, Burn O' Bennie Road, Banchory, Kincardineshire, AB31 5ZU Tel: (01330) 826700 Fax: (01330) 820670 E-mail: sam@triowise.com *TrioWise offer unique recruitment and HR services to the health and medical sector throughout the UK and overseas.*

Medifix Adhesive Products Ltd, Cosgrove Way, Luton, LU1 1XL Tel: (01582) 488499 Fax: (01582) 488100 E-mail: medifix@btinternet.com *Dressings/tapes for medical use*

Medigen Telecommunications Ltd, 186 High Road, Ilford, Essex, IG1 1LR Tel: (020) 8477 0807 Fax: (020) 8478 3349 *Telecommunications equipment distributors*

Medilink, 5 Greenfield Crescent, Birmingham, B15 3BE Tel: 0121-452 5630 Fax: 0121-454 2325 E-mail: info@medilinkwm.co.uk *Membership trade association for medical markets*

Medimpex UK Ltd, 127 Shirland Road, London, W9 2EP Tel: (020) 7266 2669 Fax: (020) 7266 2702 E-mail: enquiries@medimpexuk.com *Importers & exporters pharmaceuticals*

Medina Packaging, 123 Station Road, Kings Heath, Birmingham, B14 7TA Tel: 0121-444 1425 Fax: 0121-624 3956 E-mail: medinapackaging@blueyonder.co.uk *Polythene & paper bag manufrs*

Medina Yacht Services, Marvel Lane, Newport, Isle of Wight, PO30 3DT Tel: (01983) 822691 Fax: (01983) 822692 E-mail: s@mys.com *Marine consultants*

▶ Medion Karaoke Entertainment, 13 Hill Top View, Normanton, West Yorkshire, WF6 1LZ Tel: (01924) 211848

Medipost (UK) Ltd, 17 Surrey Close, Granby Industrial Estate, Weymouth, Dorset, DT4 9TY Tel: (01305) 760750 Fax: (01305) 776917 E-mail: info@medipost.co.uk *Medical equipment & nursing suppliers*

Medirex Opticans, 28-29 Wilcox Close, London, SW8 2UD Tel: (020) 7622 1893 Fax: (020) 7652 0033 E-mail: *Pharmacy & opticians*

Medisafe UK Ltd, The Snap Factory, Twyford Road, Bishop's Stortford, Hertfordshire, CM23 3LJ Tel: (01279) 461641 Fax: (01279) 461643 E-mail: info@medisafe.uk.com *Ultrasonic equipment manufrs*

Medisavers Ltd, Southgate Way, Orton, Peterborough, PE2 6YQ Tel: (01733) 361414 Fax: (01733) 230030 E-mail: sales@medisavers.co.uk *Distributors of disposable products*

Medisco Medical Systems Ltd, Unit 13, Isis Trading Estate, Strutton Road, Swindon, SN1 2PG Tel: (01793) 692781 Fax: (01793) 491688 E-mail: jim@redman-sheet-metal.co.uk *Hospital & medical dispensing trolley manufrs*

▶ Mediscot Online, 65 Oakbank Drive, Cumnock, Ayrshire, KA18 1BA Tel: (01290) 426438 Fax: (01563) 521077 E-mail: info@mediscot.co.uk *supplier of quality health, safety, medical, sports injury and related products amd services*

Medisponge, 35 Water Drive, Standish, Wigan, Lancashire, WN6 0EH Tel: (01257) 473175 Fax: (01257) 473175 *Natural sponges merchants or agents*

Medisure Group, 100 Temple Street, Bristol, BS1 6EN Tel: (0870) 3331174 Fax: (0870) 3330077 E-mail: natalie.delphin@medisure.co.uk *Healthcare administration services*

Meditech Veterinary Pharmacies, 2 Upper Russell Street, Wednesbury, West Midlands, WS10 7AR Tel: 0121-505 6370 Fax: 0121-505 3564 *Pigeon pharmaceuticals manufrs*

▶ Mediterranean Ices, 1a Riverside Road, London, SW17 0BA Tel: (020) 8879 6122 Fax: (020) 8879 6122 *Ice cream manufrs*

▶ Mediterranean Pantry, PO Box 12465, Sutton Coldfield, West Midlands, B73 9BE Tel: 0121-351 4202 Fax: 0121-351 4202 E-mail: info@medpantry.co.uk *Suppliers of Authentic Culinary Products.*

Mediterranean Shipping Company UK Ltd, The Havens, Ipswich, IP3 9SJ Tel: (01473) 277777 Fax: (01473) 277700 E-mail: enquiries@medite.co.uk *Shipping agency*

▶ Meditrax, Group House, Bowling Hill Business Park, Quarry Road, Chipping Sodbury, Bristol, BS37 6JL Tel: (01454) 318373 Fax: (01454) 322792 E-mail: enquiries@meditrax.co.uk *Designs & supplies medical tracking*

Medivance Instrumnets Ltd, Barretts Green Road, London, NW10 7AP Tel: (020) 8965 2913 Fax: (020) 8963 1270 E-mail: enquiries@velopex.com Principal Export Areas: Worldwide *X-ray film processors & chemicals*

▶ MediVisas UK, 1 Harley Street, London, W1G 9QD Tel: (020) 7307 8761 Fax: (020) 7307 8762 E-mail: chris.fysh@medivisas.com *UK Immigration Services.**Family and work permit advice and representation.*

Company Information

▶ Mediwatch Ltd, Swift House, Cosford Lane, Swift Valley Industrial Estate, Rugby, Warwickshire, CV21 1QN Tel: (01788) 547888 Fax: (01788) 538434 E-mail: info@mediwatch.com *Medical equipment production*

▶ Mediwin Pharmaceutical Distributors, Unit 12-13 Martello Enterprise Centre, Courtwick Lane, Wick, Littlehampton, West Sussex, BN17 7PA Tel: (01903) 725628 E-mail: contact@mediwin.co.uk *Pharmaceutical wholesaler*

Mediworld Ltd, 444 - 446 Streatham High Road, London, SW16 3PX Tel: (020) 8764 1806 Fax: (020) 8679 2489 E-mail: sales@mediworld.co.uk *Surgical instrument manufrs*

Mediwrap, Birchwood House, 55 Vanguard Way, Shoeburyness, Southend-On-Sea, SS3 9QY Tel: (01702) 291878 Fax: (01702) 290013 E-mail: sales@mediwrap.com *High protection products*

Med-Lab International Ltd, Copeland Street, Derby, DE1 2PU Tel: (01332) 349094 Fax: (01332) 371237 E-mail: sales@med-lab.co.uk *Aircraft overhaul materials*

▶ Medline Scientific Ltd, Tower Estate, Warpsgrove Lane, Stadhampton, Oxford, OX44 7XZ Tel: (01865) 400321 Fax: (01865) 400736 *Medical equipment distributors & manufrs*

Medlock Construction Ltd, Greengate Street, Oldham, OL4 1FN Tel: 0161-621 5200 *Bar fitters & building contractors*

Medlock Electric Ltd, 605-609 Green Lanes, London, N8 0RE Tel: (020) 8348 5191 Fax: (020) 8348 3854 E-mail: sales@medlocks.demon.co.uk *Electrical distrbutors* Also at: Basingstoke, Clacton, Crayford, Fareham, London SE10, E8 & N8, Southend-on-Sea, Sutton, Waltham Cross & Ware

Medontic, Medontic LTD., Spencer House, Northampton, NN1 5AA Tel: (01604) 633457 Fax: (01604) 633457 E-mail: info@medontic.co.uk *Medical & dental equipment supplier*

▶ Medrad UK Ltd, Unit 25 Lancaster Way Business Park, Ely, Cambridgeshire, CB6 3NW Tel: (01353) 645024 E-mail: info@medrad.com

▶ Medrock Training, 2 Carr Gate, Billinghay, Lincoln, LN4 4HD Tel: (07789) 530222 Fax: (01526) 861889 E-mail: info@medrocktraining.co.uk *Medrock Training is a company based in Lincolnshire specialising in 4 Day FAAW recommended and approved First Aid Training Courses . Although Lincolnshire based, the services of MRT are available throughout the UK and beyond if necessary.""All experienced instructors in the field of First Aid whose past military background [Royal Air Force] has ensured they have all seen service all over the UK and the world. Their real life experiences whilst serving in several of the world""s trouble spots are used to demonstrate that sometimes the book doesn""t have all the answers.*

Medscope Ltd, 68 Hardy Street, Maidstone, Kent, ME14 2SJ Tel: (01622) 204743 Fax: (01622) 202362 *Medscope supplies quality medical equipment to doctors, nurses, osteopaths, chiroprators, veterinary surgeons and other medical practitioners. Specialists in supplying medical students. We also supply diagnostic equipment for domestic use. Both wholesale and retail.*

Medtap International, 20 Bloomsbury Square, London, WC1A 2NS Tel: (020) 7299 4550 Fax: (020) 7299 4555 *Research organisation*

Medtec Design Services Ltd, Unit 34, JS White Eastate, Cowes, Isle Of Wight, PO31 7LP Tel: (01983) 294974 Fax: (01983) 290255 E-mail: design@medtec.co.uk *Design engineering consultants*

Medtex Ltd, 9 139 Oldbury Road, Smethwick, West Midlands, B66 1JE Tel: 0121-558 1398 Fax: 0121-565 1910 *Medical mould manufrs*

▶ Medusa, 95 Albion Road, Broadstairs, Kent, CT10 2UT Tel: (01843) 602500 *Hairdressing suppliers*

▶ Medusa Creations, Unit 2b Carnaby Industrial Estate, Lancaster Road, Carnaby, Bridlington, North Humberside, YO15 3QY Tel: (01262) 605222 Fax: (01262) 605654 *Manufacturers of granite & marble worktops*

▶ Medusa Media Creations, 35 Tyndale Street, Leicester, LE3 0QQ Tel: 0116-291 2365 E-mail: medusa@medusamediacreations.co.uk *Creative media company*

Medway Computer Supplies, 2-11 Enterprise Close, Medway City Estate, Rochester, Kent, ME2 4LY Tel: (01634) 297575 Fax: (01634) 723227 E-mail: sales@medwaycomputers.fsnet.co.uk *Computer supplies & system builders*

Medway Cutters, Joseph Wilson Industrial Estate, Millstrood Road, Whitstable, Kent, CT5 3PS Tel: (01227) 273138 Fax: (01227) 770344 E-mail: sales@medwaycutters.co.uk *Print finishers*

Medway Engraving Products, 62 High Street, Newington, Sittingbourne, Kent, ME9 7JL Tel: (01795) 842617 Fax: (01795) 843782 *Signs, prespaced lettering, vinyl engravers & screen printers*

Medway Fibre-Glass Ltd, 8 Trinity Trading Estate, Tribune Drive, Sittingbourne, Kent, ME10 2PG Tel: (01795) 435535 E-mail: medwayfibreglass@btconnect.com *Glass fibre plastics manufrs*

Medway Office Interiors Ltd, 10 Sherwood Close, Herne Bay, Kent, CT6 7DX Tel: (01227) 363505 Fax: (01227) 363505 *Suspended ceiling & partitioning manufrs*

▶ Medway Portable Appliance Testing Ltd, 70 Ellison Way, Rainham, Gillingham, Kent, ME8 7PG Tel: (01634) 388966 Fax: (01634) 388966 E-mail: sales@medwaypattesting.co.uk *SPECIALIST PORTABLE APPLIANCE TESTING COMPANY,TRAINED TO CITY&GUILDS 2377,FULLY COMPLIES WITH THE "IEE CODE OF PRACTICE"USEING THE LATEST TEST EQUIPMENT,OUT OF HOURS WORKING.FREE ADVICE GIVERN.*

Medway Portable Buildings, 29 Stoke Road, Hoo, Rochester, Kent, ME3 9BE Tel: (01634) 250890 Fax: (01634) 250890 *Sale & hire of portable buildings*

Medway Powder Coatings, 4 Sextant Park, Neptune Close, Medway City Estate, Rochester, Kent, ME2 4LU Tel: (01634) 290992 Fax: (01634) 720073 *Metal powder coating services*

Medway Sling Co. Ltd, Knight Road, Rochester, Kent, ME2 2AH Tel: (01634) 726400 Fax: (01634) 726420 E-mail: sales@medwayslingcompany.co.uk *Lifting gear manufrs*

Medway T & G Services Ltd, 2 & 3 Victory Park, Medway City Estate, Rochester, Kent, ME2 4ER Tel: 01634 717766 *Design, development & manufrs*

Samuel S. Mee Ltd, 5 Museum Square, Leicester, LE1 6UF Tel: 0116-255 2756 Fax: 0116-247 1083 E-mail: samuel.mee@btconnect.com *Yarn agents*

T.J. Mee Contracts, 11 Tyler Road, Ratby, Leicester, LE6 0NQ Tel: 0116-238 7628 Fax: 0116-238 7628 *Partition constructors*

Meech Air Technology, 2 Network Point, Range Road, Witney, Oxfordshire, OX29 0YN Tel: (01993) 706700 Fax: (01993) 776977 E-mail: sales@meech.com *Eliminate static services*

Meech S C T Ltd, 2 Network Point, Range Road, Witney, Oxfordshire, OX29 0YD Tel: (01993) 706700 Fax: (01993) 776977 E-mail: sales@meech.com *Manufacturers of printing machine cleaning equipment*

Meeching Boats, Denton Island, Newhaven, East Sussex, BN9 9BA Tel: (01273) 514907 Fax: (01273) 514907 *Boat building & moorings suppliers & repair services*

▶ Meehan Handbuilt Furniture, Drumsillagh One, Springfield, Enniskillen, County Fermanagh, BT74 9DX Tel: (028) 6634 1111 Fax: (028) 6634 1100 E-mail: sales@meehanhandbuilt.com *Bathroom, kitchen & office furniture manufrs*

▶ Peter Meehan, 151 Cliftonville Road, Belfast, BT14 6JR Tel: (028) 9074 9944 E-mail: info@bigrockdesigns.com *Web design & microsoft training*

Angus Meek Partnership Ltd, 60 Arley Hill, Bristol, BS6 5PP Tel: 0117-942 8286 Fax: 0117-942 0495 E-mail: admin@angusmeek.co.uk *Project management consultants & architects*

Meek The Furnishers, 13-14 Market Place, Penzance, Cornwall, TR18 2JL Tel: (01736) 367890 Fax: (01736) 363071 *Foam & filling service*

▶ Meesha Graphics Ltd, 37 Orchard Street, Leicester, LE1 3UG Tel: 0116-242 6300 Fax: 0116-242 6301 E-mail: raj@meeshagraphics.com *Textiles screen printing*

MeesPierson Securities (UK) Ltd, 23 Camomile St, London, EC3A 7PP Tel: (020) 7444 8000 Fax: (020) 7444 8888

Meetens Industrial Engines Ltd, Unit 2, Eclipse Trading Estate, 30 West Hill, Epsom, Surrey, KT19 8JD Tel: (08456) 340295 Fax: (08000) 150707 E-mail: sales@meetens.com *Engine suppliers*

Meg Wire Ltd, 139 Gatley Road, Gatley, Cheadle, Stockport, Cheshire, SK8 4PD Tel: 0161-282 2805 E-mail: sales@megwire.co.uk *Supplier of electronic wires*

▶ Mega Bites, 4 Cross Buildings, Woodfield Street, Morriston, Swansea, SA6 8DR Tel: (01792) 516220 Fax: (01792) 516220

Mega Bonus, 101 Ock Street, Abingdon, Oxfordshire, OX14 5DQ Tel: (01235) 550776 E-mail: sales@megabonus.co.uk *Electrical appliances distributors & repairs domestic appliances*

Mega Creations Ltd, Mega House, The Grip, Linton, Cambridge, CB21 4XN Tel: (01223) 897057 Fax: (01223) 893 94 E-mail: info@megacreations.co.uk *Metal stone engraving services.*

Mega Electronics Ltd, Unit 4, The Grip, Linton, Cambridge, CB21 4XN Tel: (01223) 893900 Fax: (01223) 893894 E-mail: sales@megauk.com *Printed circuit board equipment & PCB prototype production equipment manufrs* Also at: Leeds

Mega International Group, Block C4, Ford Airfield Industrial Estate, Ford, Arundel, West Sussex, BN18 0HY Tel: (01903) 717150 Fax: (01903) 717150 E-mail: info@mega-kayaks.co.uk *Canoes & kayaks manufrs*

▶ Mega Marble, 5 Premier Park Road, London, NW10 7NZ Tel: (020) 8965 5007 Fax: (020) 8965 8552 E-mail: info@megamarble.co.uk *Manufacture, trade fabricators, stone products*

▶ Mega Mould Ltd, Unit 8, Savile Business Centre, Mill Street East, Dewsbury, West Yorkshire, WF12 9AH Tel: (01924) 485585

Mega Company Services P.L.C., Business Information House, Farmoor Court, Cumnor Road, Oxford, OX2 9LU Tel: (01865) 865666 Fax: (01865) 865465 E-mail: info@mega.co.uk *Business information & credit reporting agency*

Mega U K, Wheldon Road, Castleford, West Yorkshire, WF10 2SE Tel: (01977) 556531 Fax: (01977) 519980 *Fork lift trucks service & sales & repairs*

Megabaits, 16 Brue Avenue, Bridgwater, Somerset, TA6 5LT Tel: (01278) 424614 Fax: (01278) 424615 *Fishing ground bait manufrs*

Megabytes, 90 Central Road, Worcester Park, Surrey, KT4 8HU Tel: (020) 8335 4224 Fax: (020) 8715 0914 E-mail: sales@megabytes.co.uk *Computer upgrades*

Megacon Controls Ltd, 21 Oldends Industrial Estate, Oldends, Stonehouse, Gloucestershire, GL10 3RQ Tel: (01453) 824471 Fax: (01453) 825234 E-mail: sales@megacon.co.uk *Control systems, generator, earth leakage/insulation monitoring equipment (electrical) manufacturers & relays, motor protection* Also at: Falmouth

Megadyne U K Ltd, Gildersome Spur, Gildersome, Leeds, LS27 7JZ Tel: 0113-238 2910 Fax: 0113-238 3870 E-mail: sales@megadyne.co.uk *Polyurethane, belting & food industry belting manufacturers. In addition, transmission belting distributors/agents/ stockholders*

Megaframe, Bridge Inn Yard, League Street, Rochdale, Lancashire, OL16 5RT Tel: (01706) 649111 Fax: (01706) 649111 *PVCu window frame manufrs*

▶ Megalist Associates, PO Box 23, Petersfield, Hampshire, GU31 4XF Tel: (0777) 5851261 E-mail: lists@megalist.co.uk *Business & Consumer Lists, Email Marketing, Telemarketing*

Megaplant Ltd, Wyke Street, Hull, HU9 1PA Tel: (01482) 323800 Fax: (01482) 223864 *Contractors plant hire service providers*

Megaplas (Peterlee) Ltd, Fiennes Road, North West Industrial Estate, Peterlee, County Durham, SR8 2QH Tel: 0191-518 5900 Fax: 0191-518 5909 *Plastic injection moulding*

Mega-Quartz UK Ltd, 25 Boshers Gardens, Egham, Surrey, TW20 9NZ Tel: (01784) 437072 Fax: (01784) 435793 E-mail: megaquartzuk@aol.com *Clock component/barometer/thermometer distributors*

Megar Ltd, Archcliffe Road, Dover, Kent, CT17 9EN Tel: (01304) 502100 Fax: (01304) 241491 E-mail: uksales@megger.com *Electrical test equipment manufrs*

▶ Megatech Ltd, Littleton Drive, Cannock, Staffordshire, WS12 4TS Tel: (01543) 500044 Fax: (01543) 500066 E-mail: web@megatechlimited.co.uk *Thin film suppliers*

Megator Ltd, Hendon Street, Sunderland, SR1 2NQ Tel: 0191-567 5488 Fax: 0191-567 8512 E-mail: info@megator.co.uk *Pump manufrs*

Megatron Ltd, Unit 24f1, 784-788 High Road, London, N17 0DA Tel: (020) 8365 9797 Fax: (020) 8808 6186 E-mail: sales@megatron.co.uk *Manufacturers of light meters & photometers*

Megatronics Group Ltd, 240 Wellesley Road, Methil, Leven, Fife, KY8 3BW Tel: (01333) 421116 Fax: (01333) 307004 E-mail: info@megatronicsgroup.com *Computer sales, repairs & installation*

Megatype, Unit 6, Genesis Business Centre, Redkiln Way, Horsham, West Sussex, RH13 5QH Tel: (01403) 217613 Fax: (01403) 217612 E-mail: sales@megatype.demon.co.uk *Typing fonts suppliers*

Meggitt P.L.C., Atlantic House, 3 Aviation Park West, Bournemouth International Airport, Hurn, Christchurch, Dorset, BH23 6EW Tel: (01202) 597597 Fax: (01202) 597555 *Aerospace engineers*

▶ Meggs Costoya Attfield, 3 Warberry Road, London, N22 7TQ Tel: (020) 8826 0044 Fax: (020) 8829 0441 *Computer training services*

Megtec Systems Ltd, Unit 4, Bell St, Maidenhead, Berkshire, SL6 1BL Tel: 01628 776244 *Ancillary equipment suppliers*

Mehdi & Ward Information Systems, 23 Aldermans Hill, London, N13 4YD Tel: (020) 8245 4545 Fax: (020) 8245 0151 E-mail: sales@mehdiward.com *Bespoke software & software consultants*

Meibel Fitted, Unit 43 Elms Business Park, Cranfield Park Road, Wickford, Essex, SS12 9EP Tel: (01268) 561661 Fax: (01277) 650602 E-mail: sales@meibel.co.uk *Furniture - fitted beds*

Meiji Techno UK Ltd, The Vineyard, Hillside, Axbridge, Somerset, BS26 2AN Tel: (01934) 733655 Fax: (01934) 733660 E-mail: enquiries@meijitechno.co.uk *Microscope importers & distributors*

▶ Meikle Construction, 87 Coalburn Road, Coalburn, Lanark, ML11 0LU Tel: (01555) 820699 Fax: (01555) 820700

Meiklejohn Chef & Work Wear, 198 Swanston Street, Glasgow, G40 4HH Tel: 0141-554 2709 Fax: 0141-554 4645 E-mail: sales@meilkejohns.co.uk *Clothes manufrs*

Meiller Maintenance Service Ltd, 99 Saffron Drive, Oakwood, Derby, DE21 2SW Tel: (01332) 678334 Fax: (01332) 727736 E-mail: meiller@oakwood.fs.business.co.uk *Waste handling machinery services*

Meister Abrasives UK Ltd, High March Industrial Estate, Daventry, Northamptonshire, NN11 4PG Tel: (01327) 703813 Fax: (01327) 871617 E-mail: sales@master-abrasives.co.uk *Abrasive products converters, retailers & manufrs*

Meister Abrasives UK Ltd, High March Industrial Estate, Daventry, Northamptonshire, NN11 4PG Tel: (01327) 703813 Fax: (01327) 871617 E-mail: sales@meister-abrasives.co.uk *Abrasive converters*

Mejdaf Europe Ltd, 196 Preston Road, Wembley, Middlesex, HA9 8PA Tel: (020) 8933 0727 Fax: (020) 8930 0944 *Computer system & software developers*

Mekanag, Shepards Grove, Stanton, Bury St. Edmunds, Suffolk, IP31 2AR Tel: (01359) 250415 Fax: (01359) 250464 E-mail: neio.smith@shelbourne.com *Agricultural engineering*

Mekko Technologies, Matrix House, Unit 20, Leicester, LE1 1PL Tel: 0116-251 4648 E-mail: enquiries@mekko.co.uk *Surface mount production equipment suppliers*

Mekvale Envelopes P.L.C., Grange Mills, Weir Road, London, SW12 0NE Tel: (020) 8673 4367 Fax: (020) 8675 7178 E-mail: mekvale@btclick.com *Envelope printers & manufrs*

▶ Mel Aviation Ltd, Morley Avenue, Mapperley, Nottingham, NG3 5FW Tel: 0115-962 3499 Fax: 0115-969 3125

Mel Cleaning Chemicals, Bank Top Industrial Estate, St. Martins, Oswestry, Shropshire, SY10 7HB Tel: (01691) 774300 Fax: (01691) 770001 E-mail: gemma@laws3311.fsbusiness.co.uk *Cleaning chemical product distributors & manufrs*

▶ Mel Wake Joinery Ltd, 4 Squire Drive, Brynmenyn, Bridgend, CF32 9TX Tel: (01656) 722500 Fax: (01656) 722723

Melamaster, Bodmin Road, Coventry, CV2 5DB Tel: (024) 7672 4919 Fax: (024) 7672 4920 E-mail: sales@melamaster.co.uk *Plastic trays & ashtray manufrs*

Melandra Cable Installation & Maintenance Co. Ltd, Unit 2-3, Dinting Trading Estate, Dinting Lane, Glossop, Derbyshire, SK13 7NU Tel: (01457) 855200 Fax: (01457) 863391 E-mail: melandracables@btopenworld.com *Cable laying & jointing contractors*

▶ Melavid Ltd, 39 Chesnut Grove, Birkenhead, Merseyside, CH42 0LB Tel: 0151-650 0074 Fax: 0151-647 3058

Melayway Glass Assemblies Ltd, Centennium House, Pyrford Road, West Byfleet, Surrey, KT14 6LD Tel: (01932) 349404 Fax: (01932) 349405 E-mail: info@melayway.co.uk *Structural glass, curtain walling, structural glazing*

MelbaSwintex Ltd, Derby Works, Manchester Road, Bury, Lancashire, BL9 9NX Tel: 0161-761 4933 Fax: 0161-797 1146 E-mail: sales@swintex.co.uk *Plastic container & sign manufrs*

Melborha Engineering Co. Ltd, Unit B, Cradock Road, Luton, LU4 0JF Tel: (01582) 494387 *Precision turned parts manufrs*

Melbourne Sun Rooms Ltd, 25 Victoria Street, Melbourne, Derby, DE73 8FR Tel: (01332) 863811 E-mail: melbournesunroom@aol.com *Tanning salon*

Melbray Chemicals Ltd, Chemical House, Durham Lane Industrial Park, Stockton-on-Tees, Cleveland, TS16 0RG Tel: (01642) 790483 Fax: (01642) 790486 E-mail: melbraychemicals@btconnect.com *Chemicals & oilfield technology*

▶ Melbro Ltd, 109 London Road, Crayford, Dartford, DA1 4DS Tel: (01322) 523645 Fax: 01322 523257 E-mail: brian.morgan@melbro.net *Contract Furnishing- Desking; Seating;Storage furniture including all types of steel shelving:Floorcoverings: Window treatment including bomb blast protection: Bedding: Notice & Visual display boards: Desk & Freestanding Screening: Interior & external Signs: Basic to Executive Furniture. Site surveys. Supply only or supply and full installation.*

Melcom Electronics, Elliott House, Gogmore Lane, Chertsey, Surrey, KT16 9AP Tel: (01932) 565544 Fax: (01932) 569988 E-mail: melcomsales@melcom.co.uk *Electronic components distributors*

▶ Melcombe Regis Construction Ltd, The Old Forge, Wyke Square, Weymouth, Dorset, DT4 9XP Tel: (01305) 773239 Fax: (01305) 773239 E-mail: info@buildersdorset.co.uk

Melcon (Hereford) Ltd, 8 St Martins St, Hereford, HR2 7RE Tel: (01432) 265195 Fax: (01432) 269623 E-mail: enquiries@melconltd.co.uk *Electrical engineers & contractors*

Meldan Fabrications Ltd, St Marys Works, Marsh Lane, Barton-upon-Humber, South Humberside, DN18 5HB Tel: (01652) 632075 Fax: (01652) 660389 E-mail: sales@meldan.co.uk *Steel & pipework fabricators*

Meldon Gears 1967 Ltd, Lees Road, Knowsley Industrial Park, Liverpool, L33 7XP Tel: 0151-546 9787 Fax: 0151-546 2861 E-mail: sales@meldongears.co.uk *Gear manufrs*

Meldrum Mailing Ltd, Units 1-2 Hainault Works, Hainault Road, Little Heath, Romford, RM6 5NF Tel: (020) 8597 3218 Fax: (0845) 6445675 *Mail handling services*

Meldrum Motors Ltd, 3 Market Square, Oldmeldrum, Inverurie, Aberdeenshire, AB51 0AA Tel: (01651) 872247 Fax: (01651) 872247 *MOT station repairers*

Thomas Meldrum Ltd, Freedom Works, John Street, Sheffield, S2 4QT Tel: 0114-272 5156 Fax: 0114-272 6409 E-mail: sales@thomasmeldrumltd.co.uk *Hand tool distributors & manufrs*

Melec Trading, 24 Parkshiel, South Shields, Tyne & Wear, NE34 8BU Tel: 0191-454 5585 E-mail: ka@melec.co.uk *Marine personnel contracting services*

Melecular Control Systems Ltd, 1 Greetby Place, Skelmersdale, Lancashire, WN8 9UL Tel: (01695) 566700 Fax: (01695) 50329 E-mail: sales@porpoise.co.uk Sales Contact: A. George Principal Export Areas: Worldwide *World leaders in Rheology based plant control systems. With a combination of class leading rheometry equipment and wide ranging understanding of plant control and polymer chemistry, Porpoise specialise in creating solutions for reaction and quality control in the polymer and process industries.*

Melford Electronics Ltd, 14 Blenheim Road, Cresses Business Park, Cressex Business Park, High Wycombe, Buckinghamshire, HP12 3RS Tel: (01494) 638069 Fax: (01494) 463358 E-mail: sales@melford-elec.co.uk *Manufacturers of electronic info display devices*

Melford Pests, Melford House, Stevenage Road, Little Wymondley, Hitchin, Hertfordshire, SG4 7JA Tel: (01438) 722393 Fax: (01438) 722395 *Pest control services*

Melhuish & Bateman Ltd, 5 Flowers Hill Close, Bristol, BS4 5LF Tel: 0117-977 1450 Fax: 0117-971 7388 E-mail: melhuishbateman@aol.com *Sheet metalwork engineers*

▶ Melia Smith & Jones Ltd, Vinery Court, 58 Cardigan Lane, Leeds, LS4 2LD Tel: 0113-230 6080 Fax: 0113-220 8900 E-mail: admin@msj.co.uk *Melia Smith & Jones Ltd,"Consulting Engineers, "Chartered Civil & Structural Engineers*

▶ Meliar Design, Lower Cwm Barns, Llanafan Fawr, Builth Wells, Powys, LD2 3SG Tel: 01597 860291 E-mail: info@meliar.com *Architectural software*

Melingey Smoked Fish & Trout Farm, St. Issey, Wadebridge, Cornwall, PL27 7QU Tel: (01841) 540551 Fax: (01841) 540476 *Fish smokers & curers*

Melitta System Service, Unit 21 Grove Park Industrial Estate, Waltham Road, White Waltham, Maidenhead, Berkshire, SL6 3LW Tel: (01628) 829888 Fax: (01628) 825111 *Coffee making appliances & catering manufrs*

Meller Flowtrans Ltd, 12 Millersdale Close, Euroway Industrial Estate, Bradford, West Yorkshire, BD4 6RX Tel: (01274) 687687 Fax: (01274) 687744 E-mail: info@mellerflowtrans.co.uk *Specialist*

continued

continuation
providers loading & discharge for trucks & road tanks

Mellersh & Harding, 43 St. James'S Place, London, SW1A 1NS Tel: (020) 7499 0866 Fax: (020) 7522 8501 E-mail: info@mellersh.co.uk *Office agents & property consultants & chartered surveyors*

Melles Griot Ltd, Sovereign Court, Lancaster Way, Ermine Business Park, Huntingdon, Cambridgeshire, PE29 6XU Tel: (01480) 420800 Fax: (01480) 420811 E-mail: info@mellesgriot.com *Optical components & coatings*

▶ Melling Roofing, 2 Fowler Street, Fulwood,, Preston, PR2 2LT Tel: 01772 461878 E-mail: mellingmark@blueyonder.co.uk *Local Roofing firm with a decade"s experience. Call for more details..*

Mellingey Mill Willowcraft Centre, Mellingey Mill, St. Issey, Wadebridge, Cornwall, PL27 7QU Tel: (01841) 540604 Fax: (01841) 540604 *Willowcraft & basket makers*

Iain Mellis, 492 Great Western Road, Glasgow, G12 8EW Tel: 0141-339 8998 Fax: 0141-339 6006 E-mail: sales@ijmellischeesemonger.co.uk *Cheese retailers & wholesalers*

Mellish (Engineering), Unit 28, Mitchell Close, Segensworth Industrial Estate, Fareham, Hampshire, PO15 5SE Tel: (01489) 582393 Fax: (01489) 885823 *Precision engineers*

Mellish Engineering, Unit 14 Merchants Way, Aldridge, Walsall, WS9 8SW Tel: (01922) 457799 E-mail: mellishengineering@btopenworld.com *Fasteners manufrs*

Melliss & Partners, Boundary House The Pines Business Park, Broad Street, Guildford, Surrey, GU3 3BH Tel: (01483) 567879 Fax: (01483) 574616 E-mail: mail@melliss.com *Consulting engineers*

▶ Mello Ltd, 86 Church Lane, Arlesey, Bedfordshire, SG15 6UX Tel: 01462 733993 Fax: 01462 733993 E-mail: mello@hmlc.fsnet.co.uk *Importers/ Wholesalers of Contemporary Ceramic and Glass Homeware items.*

Mellor Bromley, 141 Barkby Road, Leicester, LE4 9LW Tel: 0116-276 6636 Fax: 0116-246 0426 E-mail: dbloxam@mellorbromley.co.uk *Mechanical services contractors*

David Mellor Design Ltd, The Round Building, Leadmill, Hathersage, Hope Valley, Derbyshire, S32 1BA Tel: (01433) 650220 Fax: (01433) 650944 E-mail: sales@davidmellordesign.com *Cutlery manufrs*

Mellor Electrics Ltd, Sett End Road, Shadsworth Business Park, Blackburn, BB1 2NW Tel: (01254) 53854 Fax: (01254) 678625 E-mail: info@mellorelectrics.co.uk *Gear manufrs*

Mellorsons Manufacturing Ltd, George Street, West Bromwich, West Midlands, B70 6NH Tel: 0121-580 0520 Fax: 0121-580 0521 *Repetition work engineers*

Melloy Ltd, Main Avenue, Unit C10, Treforest Industrial Estate, Pontypridd, Mid Glamorgan, CF37 5UD Tel: (01443) 824880 Fax: (01443) 844797 E-mail: enquiries@melloy.co.uk Principal Export Areas: Central/East Europe & West Europe *Diecastings including gravity, low & high pressure. Contact Francis at enquiries@melloy.co.uk or Terry Ryan at terry@melloy.co.uk.*

▶ Melmar Stone, Hallcroft Industrial Estate, Aurilac Way, Retford, Nottinghamshire, DN22 7PX Tel: (01777) 870444 Fax: (01777) 860060

Melnei Engineering, Unit F4 Heath Place, Bognor Regis, West Sussex, PO22 9SL Tel: (01243) 829103 Fax: (01243) 829103 E-mail: melnei@melneiengineering.co.uk *Compression fitting manufrs*

▶ Melody Group Ltd, L'Islet, St. Sampson, Guernsey, GY2 4XN Tel: (01481) 245596 Fax: (01481) 249801

Melpack Ltd, 79 Huddersfield Road, Meltham, Holmfirth, HD9 4AF Tel: (01484) 850940 Fax: (01484) 850940 *Cardboard box manufrs*

Melrose Packaging, 6 Lyon Close, Woburn Road Industrial Estate, Kempston, Bedford, MK42 7SB Tel: (01234) 841144 Fax: (01234) 841166 E-mail: info@melrosepackaging.co.uk *Polythene bag manufrs*

Melson And Co, 125 High St, West Bromwich, W. Midlands, B70 6NY Tel: 0121-525 2226 Fax: 0121-525 2226 *Clothing manufrs*

▶ Melsystech, 1 Victoria Street, Portrush, County Antrim, BT56 8DL Tel: (0870) 8504309 Fax: (020) 8708 2490 *Web design consultants*

Meltcharm Ltd, 4 Enterprise Works, Lockfield Avenue, Enfield, Middlesex, EN3 7PX Tel: (020) 8804 5779 Fax: (020) 8443 3814 *Non-ferrous founders supplier*

Meltech Ltd, 185 Cannock Road, Westcroft, Wolverhampton, WV10 8QL Tel: (01902) 722588 Fax: (01902) 730142 E-mail: steve@induction-furnaces.co.uk *Metal melting furnaces to the foundry & metallurgical industries*

Meltek, 5 Spring Village, Horsehay, Telford, Shropshire, TF4 2LY Tel: (01952) 505207 E-mail: meltek@tesco.net *Electronic control system maintenance or repair*

▶ Meltemi Co Clothing Ltd, Barnard Road, Bowthorpe Employment Area, Norwich, NR5 9JB Tel: (01603) 731330 Fax: (0870) 7871759 E-mail: sales@meltemi.co.uk

Meltham Carbide Precision Co., Bent Ley Mill, Bent Ley Road, Meltham, Holmfirth, HD9 4AP Tel: (01484) 850998 Fax: (01484) 854808 E-mail: mcp.co@btinternet.com *Manufacturers of tungsten carbide plug gauges*

Melton Pets Direct Ltd, Unkit 3 Top End Industrial Estate, Thistleton Road, Oakham, Leicestershire, LE15 7PP Tel: (01572) 768444 Fax: (01572) 767123 E-mail: sales@meltonpets.com *Pet products for birds importers*

Melton Printers of Lincoln, Unit 3, Sleaford Road, Bracebridge Heath, Lincoln, LN4 2ND Tel: (01522) 541827 Fax: (01522) 528237 E-mail: sales@meltonprinters.co.uk *General printers*

▶ Melville Craig, Harbourside House, Ocean Square, 110 Commercial Street, Edinburgh, EH6 6NF Tel: 0131-555 4321 Fax: 0131-555 4224

▶ Melville & Whitson, 22a Edinburgh Road, Dalkeith, Midlothian, EH22 1JR Tel: 0131-660 1480 Fax: 0131-654 2687

Melvin Bros, Unit 3 Baird Avenue, Strutherhill Industrial Estate, Larkhall, Lanarkshire, ML9 2PJ Tel: (01698) 887605 Fax: (01698) 884871 E-mail: melvinbrothers@aol.com *Steel fabricators & fencing contractors*

Melzone Plastic Products, 11 Sandgate High Street, Sandgate, Folkestone, Kent, CT20 3BD Tel: (01303) 248545 Fax: (01303) 248545 *Chemical bleaching & bottle manufrs*

Mem Saab World Of Fabric, 89 Erleigh Road, Reading, RG1 5NN Tel: 0118-966 6037 *Clothing distributors*

▶ Memflex, Calder House, Saville Road, Castleford, West Yorkshire, WF10 1HH Tel: (01977) 669690 Fax: (01977) 669693 E-mail: sales@memflex.co.uk *Memory foam mattress.Memflex advanced memory foam beds,mattresses and pillows.*

Memory House Ltd, Technology House Glaisher Drive, Wolverhampton Science Park, Wolverhampton, WV10 9RU Tel: (01902) 824190 Fax: (01902) 824191 E-mail: enquiries@memoryhouse.co.uk *Computer systems & software sales*

Memory Lane Prints, 43 Park Road, Hartlepool, Cleveland, TS24 7PW Tel: (01429) 234268 Fax: (01429) 281007 *Picture framers & suppliers*

Memory Lane Productions, Shalford, Ricksons Lane, West Horsley, Leatherhead, Surrey, KT24 6HU Tel: (01483) 284409 E-mail: maclanep56@btinternet.com *Photographic restoration*

Memotrace Controls, 13 The Avenue, Spinney Hill, Northampton, NN3 6BA Tel: (01604) 642808 Fax: (01604) 642808 E-mail: memotrace@lineone.net *Electronic consultants & designers*

▶ Memprotech, 9, Crane Way,, Woolsbridge Industrial Estate,, Three Legged Cross, Wimborne, Dorset, BH21 6FA Tel: (01202) 823699 Fax: (01202) 813863 E-mail: info@memprotech.com *An enzymatic-based cleaning system*

Mems Power Generation, Beechings Way, Gillingham, Kent, ME8 6PS Tel: (01634) 264666 Fax: (01634) 263666 E-mail: sales@memsgen.co.uk *Dealer for cummins power generation*

Mem's Travel, Unit 27 Market Hall Wood Green Shopping City, High Road, London, N22 6YE Tel: (020) 8889 2631 Fax: (020) 8882 9873 *Retailers*

Menai Blinds, Cibyn Industrial Estate, Caernarfon, Gwynedd, LL55 2BD Tel: (01286) 672595 Fax: (01286) 673937 E-mail: sales@menaiblinds.co.uk *Window blinds supply, fit & manufrs*

▶ Menai Electrical Ltd, Station House, Treborth, Bangor, Gwynedd, LL57 2NX Tel: (01248) 353855 Fax: (01248) 361356

Menallack Farm, Treverva, Penryn, Cornwall, TR10 9BP Tel: (01326) 340333 *Cheese makers*

Mend-All Catering Services Ltd, 24 Cromwell Road, Hove, East Sussex, BN3 3EB Tel: 01273 777200 *Repair catering equipment repairers & distributors*

Mendip Engineering Ltd, Mendip House, Pows Orchard, Midsomer Norton, Radstock, BA3 2HY Tel: (01761) 413698 Fax: (01761) 416172 E-mail: enquiries@mendipengineering.co.uk *Electronic design contractors*

▶ Mendip Metalcraft, Unit 28 Underwood Business Park, Wells, Somerset, BA5 1AF Tel: (01749) 674590 Fax: (01749) 674590 E-mail: nigel.stewart@btconnect.com

Mendip Signs, Unit 14 Keyford Court, Manor Furlong, Frome, Somerset, BA11 4BD Tel: (01373) 461460 Fax: (01373) 461305 E-mail: sales@mendipsigns.co.uk *Sign manufrs*

Mendit Rug & Tack, Unit 2 Enterprise Park, Piddlehinton, Dorchester, Dorset, DT2 7UA Tel: (01305) 849070 Fax: (01305) 849070 E-mail: info@menditsaddery.co.uk *Rug & tack suppliers*

Mendz Industrial Move Ltd, Abbey Meadows, Back Lane, Cotes, Loughborough, Leicestershire, LE12 5TA Tel: (01509) 212711 Fax: (01509) 212722 *Machinery removal contractors*

Meniscus Systems Ltd, Blotts Barn, Brooks Road, Raunds, Wellingborough, Northamptonshire, NN9 6NS Tel: (01933) 625900 Fax: (01933) 625800 E-mail: sales@meniscus.co.uk *Data processors*

Menlow Worldwide, Unit 19 Airlinks Industrial Estate, Spitfire Way, Heston, Hounslow, TW5 9NR Tel: (020) 8260 6000 Fax: (020) 8260 6170 E-mail: stewartinnes@menlowworldwide.com *Air freight forwarders*

Menos Lighting Equipment, 225-227 High Street, London, W3 9BY Tel: (020) 8993 7013 Fax: (020) 8992 8588 *Lighting retailers*

Menrad Optics Ltd, Unit 4, Bone Lane, Newbury, Berkshire, RG14 5SH Tel: (01635) 32123 Fax: (01635) 38442 E-mail: jenny@menrad.co.uk *Optical supplies*

Menrica Engineering Ltd, 17 Paynes Lane, Rugby, Warwickshire, CV21 2UH Tel: (01788) 572434 *Precision, general engineering & toolmakers*

▶ Mental Solutions Ltd, 1 The Arcade, Northgate, Bridgnorth, Shropshire, WV16 4ER Tel: (01746) 761133 Fax: (07092) 262950 E-mail: info@mentalsolutions.com *Computer systems consultants*

Mentat Systems Ltd, 21 Porthleven Crescent, Astley, Tyldesley, Manchester, M29 7FZ Tel: (01942) 749444 E-mail: sales@mentat.co.uk *Software developers*

Mentat Systems Ltd, 3 Rutland Road, Southport, Merseyside, PR8 6PB Tel: (01704) 514506 E-mail: sale@mentat.co.uk *Software developers*

Mentha & Halsall (Shopfitters) Ltd, 95a Linaker St, Southport, Merseyside, PR8 5BU Tel: (01704) 530800 Fax: (01704) 500601 E-mail: info@mentha-halsall.com *Shop & office fitters*

Mentmore Foods Ltd, The Corner House, 9 The Green, Cheddington, Leighton Buzzard, Bedfordshire, LU7 0RJ Tel: (01296) 668117 Fax: (01296) 662737 *Dairy products distributor*

Mentmore Smithy, Stagg Hill, Mentmore, Leighton Buzzard, Bedfordshire, LU7 0QG Tel: (01296) 661760 Fax: (01296) 662502 *Blacksmiths*

Mentor Communications Ltd, PO Box 21, Wellingborough, Northamptonshire, NN8 1PB Tel: (08454) 581552 Fax: (08708) 401553 E-mail: mentor.comms@fsbdial.co.uk *Software & telephone systems*

Mentor Computer Consultants, 18 Old Stack Yard, Village Road, Great Barrow, Chester, CH3 7JE Tel: (01829) 740794 *Computer consultancy*

Mentor Graphic UK Ltd, Rivergate Newbury Business Park, London Road, Newbury, Berkshire, RG14 2QB Tel: (01635) 811411 Fax: (01635) 810108 *Electronic design automation software manufrs*

Menu Shop, 38 High Street, Warminster, Wiltshire, BA12 9AF Tel: (01985) 217000 Fax: (01985) 218000 E-mail: sales@menushop.co.uk *Catering industry menu suppliers*

Menzel UK, Preston Road, Charnock Richard, Chorley, Lancashire, PR7 5JZ Tel: (01257) 791503 Fax: (01257) 793980 *Textile manufrs*

Andreas Menzies Associates, 14 Kestrel Road, Oakham, Leicestershire, LE15 6BU Tel: (01572) 770653 Fax: (01572) 722575 E-mail: andreas@amanet.co.uk *Computer consultants*

Menzies Engineering Design Ltd, Dornoch, Sutherland, IV25 3RW Tel: (01862) 810788 Fax: (01862) 810171 *Computer systems & software developers*

▶ Menzies Nunn Ltd, The Wallows Industrial Estate, Fens Pool Avenue, Brierley Hill, West Midlands, DY5 1QA Tel: (01384) 262148 Fax: (01384) 265136 E-mail: sales@menzies-nunn.co.uk *Colour printers*

▶ Menzies Travel, 93a Glaisnock Street, Cumnock, Ayrshire, KA18 1JP Tel: (01290) 423636 Fax: (01290) 423737 *USA & cruise specialist travel agents*

Menzolit, Perseverance Works, Halifax Road, Todmorden, Lancashire, OL14 6EG Tel: (01706) 814714 Fax: (01706) 814717 E-mail: sales@menzolit-uk.co.uk *Polyester moulding compound & glass fibre moulding manufrs*

Meopham Welding Supplies, Railway Sidings, Station Approach, Meopham, Gravesend, Kent, DA13 0LT Tel: (01474) 812050 Fax: (01474) 813714 *Welding equipment wholesalers*

▶ MEP ASSOCIATES, Pegasus, London Road, Crowborough, East Sussex, TN6 2TX Tel: 01892 669978 Fax: 08712 425325 E-mail: lbassett@mepa.co.uk *Production of Paper Based and Electronic Building Services Operating and Maintenance Manuals*

Mepc Milton Park Ltd, 6g Milton Park, Milton, Abingdon, Oxfordshire, OX14 4RR Tel: (01235) 865555 Fax: (01235) 865560 E-mail: enquiries@miltonpark.co.uk *Property surveyors services*

▶ Merac Computer Systems, 10 King Street, Exeter, EX1 1BQ Tel: (01392) 679653 Fax: (01392) 491008 E-mail: sales@merac.co.uk *Computer systems for retail*

Merc Serono, Bedfont Cross, Bedfont, Feltham, Middlesex, TW14 8NX Tel: (01895) 452200 Fax: (01895) 420605 E-mail: info@merckpharma.co.uk *Pharmaceuticals lab supplies*

Mercado Belfast, 101B Airport Road West, Belfast, BT3 9ED Tel: (028) 9046 7680 Fax: (028) 9046 7699 E-mail: sales@merbelfast.co.uk *Carpet distribs*

Mercantile Met-Tech Ltd, Plumpton House, Plumpton Road, Hoddesdon, Hertfordshire, EN11 0LB Tel: (01992) 445709 Fax: (01992) 467217 E-mail: info@mercantilemettech.co.uk *Sheet metal fabricators & cnc machining*

▶ Mercaston Food Co., Express Works, Luke Lane, Brailsford, Ashbourne, DE6 3BY Tel: (01335) 361400 Fax: (01335) 361188 E-mail: enquiries@mercastonfood.com

▶ Mercaston Tree Co., Ednaston, Ednaston, Ashbourne, Derbyshire, DE6 3AE Tel: (01335) 360947 Fax: (01335) 360394 E-mail: enquiries@mercastontreecompany.com *Tree nursery*

Mercatron International Ltd, 15 Johnson Way, Park Royal, London, NW10 7PF Tel: (020) 8961 1973 Fax: (020) 8961 2016 E-mail: info@mercatron.co.uk *Tungsten filament manufrs*

Mercedes Benz (UK) Ltd, Tongwell, Delaware Drive, Milton Keynes, MK15 8BA Tel: (01908) 245000 *Car & commercial vehicle importers*

Mercedes Benz UK Ltd, Quarry Road, Brixworth, Northampton, NN6 9UB Tel: (01604) 880100 Fax: (01604) 882800 E-mail: reception@mercedes-benz-hpe.com *High performance racing engines manufrs*

Frank Mercer & Sons Ltd, Chequerbent Works Manchester Road, Chequerbent, Westhoughton, Bolton, BL5 3JF Tel: (01942) 841111 Fax: (01942) 842388 E-mail: mercer@toughsheet.co.uk *Polyethylene manufrs*

▶ Mercer Leyton (Building) Ltd, The Joinery Works, Ware Road, Tonwell, Ware, Hertfordshire, SG12 0HN Tel: (01920) 461972 Fax: (01920) 468889

Mercer & Sons Ltd, Pump Street Warehouses, Blackburn, BB2 1PG Tel: (01254) 587000 Fax: (01254) 680875 E-mail: info@mercer-sons.co.uk *Steel stockholders & ironmongers*

▶ The Company Merchant Ltd, Redditch, Worcestershire, B98 0NU Tel: (0870) 4323232 Fax: (0870) 4323295 E-mail: mail@thecompanymerchant.co.uk *Same day limited company formation service*

Merchant Ferries, North Quay, Heysham Harbour, Heysham, Morecambe, Lancashire, LA3 2UL Tel: (01542) 865050 Fax: (01524) 865070 E-mail: will.conderbank@northmerchantferries.com

Merchants Systems, 11 Paul Street, Liverpool, L3 6DX Tel: 0151-236 2253 Fax: 0151-236 0861 E-mail: sales@merchants-systems.co.uk *NHS documents, continuous business form & stationery manufrs*

Mercia Flooring Ltd, 59 The Square, Dunchurch, Rugby, Warwickshire, CV22 6NU Tel: (01788) 522168 Fax: (01788) 811847 E-mail: sales@merciaflooring.co.uk *Supply, installation & maintenance of hardwood flooring*

▶ Mercia Gas Ltd, Mercia House, 63 Holyhead Road, Coventry, CV1 3AA Tel: (024) 7652 5150 Fax: (024) 7652 5800 E-mail: service@merciagas.co.uk

▶ Mercia Image Ltd, 8 Perkins Industrial Estate, Mansfield Road, Derby, DE21 4AW Tel: (01332) 291555 Fax: (01332) 291400

▶ Mercia Instant Print Ltd Trading As Prontaprint, 34 Chapel Ash, Wolverhampton, WV3 0TN Tel: (01902) 771177 Fax: (01902) 422255

Mercia Interiors, 8 Victoria Buildings, Newhall Street, Willenhall, West Midlands, WV13 1LN Tel: (01902) 636685 Fax: (01902) 637086 E-mail: info@mimltd.freeserve.co.uk *Specialist joinery & bar fitters*

Mercia International Fragrances Ltd, Station Road, Elmswell, Bury St. Edmunds, Suffolk, IP30 9HD Tel: (01359) 242459 Fax: (01359) 242129 E-mail: sales@merciaif.co.uk *Fragrance manufrs*

Mercia Lifting Gear Ltd, Dukesway, Teesside Industrial Estate, Stockton-on-Tees, Cleveland, TS17 9LT Tel: (01642) 760990 Fax: (01642) 761200 *Lifting gear distributors*

Mercia Machinery Sales Ltd, Unit 9 Orchard Industrial Estate, Toddington, Cheltenham, Gloucestershire, GL54 5EB Tel: (01242) 621237 Fax: (01242) 621303 E-mail: mercia@toddingtonglos.fsnet.co.uk *Plastics machinery engineers*

Mercia Mechanical Handling Ltd, Unit C4-C6, Guy Motors Industrial Park, Park Lane, Wolverhampton, WV10 9QF Tel: (01902) 739852 Fax: (01902) 739547 E-mail: merciamech@btconnect.com *A Wolverhampton based company who offer standard and bespoke manufacturing and engineering services for conveyor systems, material handling equipment and industrial equipment including: Belt conveyors, Roller conveyors, Chain driven conveyors, Gravity roller conveyor systems, Industrial conveyor systems, Slat conveyor systems, Roller belt conveyor systems, Horizontal chain conveyor systems, Modular conveyor systems, Material handling industrial turntables, Conveyor systems design, and much more. We have been established for over 25 years and pride ourselves in our continued good service history within the industry.*

Mercia Radio Telephones, Unit 1 Groveandstand Business Centre, Westfields Trading Estate, Hereford, HR4 9NS Tel: (01432) 267864 Fax: (01432) 279953 E-mail: sales@merciaradio.co.uk *Two way radio systems service, hire & distributors*

Mercia Security, 4 Redhill, Telford, Shropshire, TF2 9PA Tel: (01952) 610894 Fax: (01952) 610894 *Man guards services*

Mercian Developments Ltd, Mercian House 9-10 Darwin Court Clayton Way, Oxon Business Park, Bicton Heath, Shrewsbury, SY3 5AL Tel: (01743) 352415 Fax: (01743) 232349 E-mail: mail@merciandev.co.uk *Property developers*

Mercian Electric, 79-93 Ratcliffe Road, Sileby, Loughborough, Leicestershire, LE12 7PU Tel: (01509) 816181 Fax: (01509) 816060 *Electric heater & control panel manufrs*

Mercian Lifting Gear Ltd, Unit 15 Trench Lock 3, Telford, Shropshire, TF1 5ST Tel: (01952) 261851 Fax: (01952) 222028 *Lifting gear manufrs*

Mercian Preservation Ltd, 74 Cinder Bank, Dudley, West Midlands, DY2 9BH Tel: (01384) 250154 Fax: (01384) 456068 *Damp proofing & timber contractors* Also at: Gloucester, Stafford & Stoke-on-Trent

Mercian Toolmaking Co Tamworth Ltd, 6 Felspar Road, Amington Industrial Estate, Tamworth, Staffordshire, B77 4DP Tel: (01827) 69484 Fax: (01827) 310153 E-mail: sales@merciancut.co.uk Principal Export Areas: West Europe & North America *Specialised cutting tools engineers*

Merck Sharp & Dohme Ltd, Shotton Lane, Cramlington, Northumberland, NE23 3JU Tel: (01670) 716211 Fax: (01670) 593001 E-mail: sales@merck.com Principal Export Areas: Worldwide *Pharmaceutical services*

Mercol (Office Furniture) Ltd, Primrose Mill, Ratcliffe Street, Darwin, Blackburn, BB3 2BZ Tel: (01254) 775500 Fax: (01254) 774911 *Office furniture manufrs*

▶ Mercolour Graphics Ltd, Cherrywell House, Tamian Way, Hounslow, TW4 6BL Tel: (020) 8572 2260 Fax: (020) 8572 2262

Mercom, 5 Cowley Road, Nuffield Industrial Estate, Poole, Dorset, BH17 0UJ Tel: (01202) 661210 Fax: (01202) 661216 E-mail: kevin.hockney@mercom.org *Electronic test & repair services*

Mercuri International UK Ltd, 6 Olton Bridge, 245 Warwick Road, Solihull, West Midlands, B92 7AH Tel: 0121-706 3400 Fax: 0121-706 3900 E-mail: admin.london@mercuri.co.uk *Management consultants*

▶ Mercury Architectural Projects Ltd, 2 Shrike Close Clayton Heights, Bradford, West Yorkshire, BD6 3YG Tel: (01274) 816105 Fax: 01274 816105 E-mail: info@mercuryarchitectural.com *We provide the following services:**High quality sub-contract installation labour resources for the curtainwall, window and cladding sector. *Drafting, supply and installation of quality aluminium glazing solutions. *Quantity surveying and claims consultancy services. *On site project management services.*

▶ Mercury Architectural Projects Ltd, 2 Shrike Close Clayton Heights, Bradford, West Yorkshire, BD6 3YG Tel: (0800) 695 7595 E-mail: info@mercurygardens.co.uk *Specialising in the supply magnificent timber garden buildings, offices, garages and climbing frames.*

▶ indicates data change since last edition

Company Information

Mercury Control Ltd, The Cottage, Back Dawson Terrace, Harrogate, North Yorkshire, HG1 2AJ Tel: (01423) 566613 Fax: (01423) 566614 *Heating & air conditioning control systems suppliers*

Mercury Despatch Ltd, Unit 14 Central Business Centre, Great Central Way, London, NW10 0UR Tel: (020) 8459 8022 Fax: (020) 8451 6722 E-mail: sales@mercurydespatch.co.uk *Courier service & mail room*

Mercury Engraving & Diesinking Ltd, Unit A5 Up Ringway, Bounds Green Industrial Estate, London, N11 2UD Tel: (0800) 1077118 Fax: (020) 8368 9018 E-mail: sales@mercuryengraving.co.uk *Nameplates, plaques & signs manufrs*

▶ Mercury Express, 8 Ashley Park, Uddingston, Glasgow, G71 6LU Tel: (01698) 811010

▶ Mercury Facilities Management (UK) Ltd, 17 Camp Road, Rutherglen, Glasgow, G73 1EU Tel: 0141-613 6132 Fax: 0141-613 3411 E-mail: enqiries@mercuryfacilities.co.uk

Mercury Instruments Ltd, Station Yard, Station Road, St. Ives, Cambridgeshire, PE27 5BH Tel: (01480) 494471 Fax: (01438) 367711 E-mail: mil@cwcom.net *Process controller/ control instrumentation manufrs*

Mercury Labels Ltd, Foxtam House, Watts Street, Oldham, OL9 9LQ Tel: 0161-633 2984 Fax: 0161-725 8376 E-mail: accounts@mercurylabels.com *Label manufrs*

▶ Mercury Material Management, Units 14 & 15 Rosevale Road, Parkhouse Industrial Estate West, Newcastle, Staffordshire, ST5 7EF Tel: (01782) 576385 Fax: (01782) 565279 *Tyre assembly & distribution services*

Mercury Motors Ltd, 5-7 Strawberry Vale, Twickenham, TW1 4RX Tel: (020) 8892 4604 Fax: (020) 8892 4454 E-mail: enquiries@mercurymotors.co.uk *Motor vehicle repair garage*

Mercury Panel Products Ltd, 132 Sculcoates Lane, Hull, HU5 1DP Tel: (01482) 441400 Fax: (01482) 441500 *Composite panel manufrs*

Mercury & Phillips, 51-59 Waterworks Road, Norwich, NR2 4DA Tel: (01603) 666699 Fax: (01603) 616781 E-mail: sales@mercuryphillipssigns.co.uk *Sign manufrs*

Mercury Precision, Unit 22 The Hayes Trading Estate, Folkes Road, Stourbridge, West Midlands, DY9 8RG Tel: (01384) 424110 Fax: (01384) 422311 *Precision engineers*

▶ Mercury Print & Packaging, The Print Factory, Wood Lane, Off Whitehall Road, Leeds, LS12 6JY Tel: 0113-263 4463

Mercury Products South Ltd, 36 Carpenters, Billingshurst, West Sussex, RH14 9RB Tel: (01403) 786639 Fax: (01403) 786637 E-mail: merprod@yahoo.co.uk *Composite cylinders & medical equipment manufrs*

Mercury Rewinds, Unit E3 Greenwood Court, Cartmel Drive, Shrewsbury, SY1 3TB Tel: (01743) 446936 Fax: (01743) 460099 *Electric motor repairers*

▶ Mercury Safety & Security Group Ltd, 461 London Road, High Wycombe, Buckinghamshire, HP11 1EL Tel: (01494) 510131 Fax: (01494) 474706 E-mail: info@mercurysafetyandsecurity.com *Wireless security systems installers, suppliers & manufrs*

▶ Mercury Search & Selection Ltd, Redhill House, Hope Street, Chester, CH4 8BU Tel: (01244) 677219 Fax: (01244) 682710 E-mail: info@mercurysearch.co.uk

▶ Mercury Signs & Designs, 2 Carseview Road, Forfar, Angus, DD8 3BT Tel: (01307) 469555 Fax: (01307) 468618

▶ Mercury Signs Designs, South Street, Perth, PH2 8PD Tel: (01738) 451450 Fax: (01738) 451412 E-mail: ian@mercurysigns-design.com *Sign manufrs*

Mercury Sports Equipment Ltd, Victoria Road, Stoke-on-Trent, ST4 2HS Tel: (01782) 845577 Fax: (01782) 744998 E-mail: mercurysports@clara.net *Sports equipment manufrs*

Mercury Spring Ltd, Unit 2 Leamore Enterprise Park, Wall End Close, Walsall, WS2 7PH Tel: (01922) 712271 Fax: (01922) 409947 E-mail: mercuryspring@mail.net *Spring manufacturers & distributors*

Mercury Switch Manufacturing Co. Ltd, 26 Greenhill Cres, Watford Business Pk, Watford, WD18 8XG Tel: (01923) 240272 Fax: (01923) 228796 *Level control equipment manufrs*

Mercury Systems Engineers Ltd, Unit G2 Liners Industrial Estate, Pitt Road, Southampton, SO15 3FQ Tel: (023) 8033 6620 Fax: (023) 8033 6630 E-mail: verna@mercury-systems.co.uk *Network installation and maintenance services including VoIP, email and internet solutions, IT support, plus pc and network hardware supply in Hampshire, Wiltshire, Sussex, Dorset and the Home Counties. Mercury Systems are based in Southampton.*

Mercury Thread Gauges, 182-186 Fletchamstead Highway Industrial Estate, Fletchamstead Highway, Coventry, CV4 7BB Tel: (024) 7671 4185 Fax: (024) 7669 1234 E-mail: sales@mercurygauges.co.uk *Gauge inspection equipment & manufrs*

▶ Mercury Trade, 55 Lady Croft Walk, Stanmore, Harrow, Middlesex, HA7 1PD Tel: (020) 89511669 E-mail: mercurytrade@btinternet.com *We are leading Traders for re-usable Ship Machinery and Equipments. Our main trade is in Radars; Gyros; Generators; Main engines; Governors; Life Rafts; Hydraullics; Pumps; Chilling compressors and Steel.*If you have any kind of requirment just give us an email and your query would be answered within 24 hours.*Thanking you*

Mercury Welding Supplies, 6-7 Jubilee Estate, Horsham, West Sussex, RH13 5UE Tel: (01403) 260200 Fax: (01403) 217544 E-mail: sales@mercurywelding.com *Welding consumables suppliers*

▶ Merdean Ltd, Chester House, 2-6 Mansfield Road, Eastwood, Nottingham, NG16 3AQ Tel: (01773) 719844 Fax: (01773) 712669 E-mail: enquiries@merdean.co.uk *Autoclave Engineers*

Mere Developments, Tangley Mere, New Road, Chilworth, Guildford, Surrey, GU4 8LZ Tel: (01483) 562631 Fax: (01483) 532022 *Computer consultants*

Meredith & Eyre Ltd, Broadway, Hyde, Cheshire, SK14 4QF Tel: 0161-368 6414 Fax: 0161-367 8702 E-mail: sales@meredithandeyre.co.uk *Trailer manufrs*

Meredith Jones, Parry Road, Llanrwst, Gwynedd, LL26 0DG Tel: (01492) 640348 Fax: (01492) 640348 E-mail: rwroberts@enterprise.net *Monumental masons*

▶ Merediths Maids, 15 Crescent Road, Kidderminster, Worcestershire, DY11 6RN Tel: (07891) 815232 E-mail: tracey@merediths maids.com *Meredith"s Maids will provide you with a thorough cleaning package to suit your requirements and needs. **Services include:*One off cleans *Regular cleans (weekly, fortnightly, monthly, quarterly) *Home owner house move cleans *End of tenancy cleans *Pre orPost party clean ups !! *Shopping services *Let us know your needs and we will happily discuss and solve all your cleaning problems! ***

▶ Merge Design Consultancy, 37 Dinorben Avenue, Fleet, Hampshire, GU52 7SQ Tel: (07980) 626443 E-mail: nick.green@mergedc.co.uk *Merge Design Consultancy is a Hampshire-based company with a diverse range of clients with the techniques to match. Our multi-disciplinary structure offers services in brand identity and development, interior and exhibition design and design for print.*

Meridale Plastics Ltd, Meridale Works, Linford Road, Grays, Essex, RM16 4JS Tel: (01375) 850009 Fax: (01375) 851113 E-mail: sales@buildwithplastics.co.uk *Plastic stockholders*

Meriden Paper Ltd, 38 Meriden Street, Digbeth, Birmingham, B5 5LS Tel: 0121-643 2168 Fax: 0121-631 3378 E-mail: admin@meridenpaper.co.uk *Paper roll manufrs*

▶ Meridian, Spring La North, Malvern, Worcestershire, WR14 1BU Tel: (01684) 578441 Fax: (01684) 578442 *Cardboard cartons & pvc manufacturers & distributors*

Meridian Audio Ltd, Stonehill, Stukeley Meadows Industrial Es, Huntingdon, Cambridgeshire, PE29 6EX Tel: (01480) 445678 Fax: (01480) 445686 *Hi-fi equipment manufrs*

Meridian Azimuth, 51 Watson Crescent, Edinburgh, EH11 1EW Tel: (07876) 127164 E-mail: alain.grangeret@meridianaz.co.uk *Combustion engineers, low NOx technology*

▶ Meridian Colour Co., Unit 3g Black Dyke Mills, Brighouse Road, Queensbury, Bradford, West Yorkshire, BD13 1QA Tel: (01274) 884900 Fax: (0871) 2216425 E-mail: info@meridiancolour.com *Manufacturer of pigment dispersions*

▶ Meridian Colour Repro Ltd, 8 The Old Mill, Reading Road, Pangbourne, Reading, RG8 7HY Tel: 0118-984 4719 Fax: 0118-984 4135

Meridian Computer Stationery, 9-17 Crompton Way, Crawley, West Sussex, RH10 9QG Tel: (01293) 400210 Fax: (01293) 551703 *Computer stationery printers*

Meridian Controls Ltd, 38 Galloway Close, South Ham, Basingstoke, Hampshire, RG22 6SX Tel: 0845 5314080 Fax: (01256) 324209 E-mail: sales@meridian-controls.co.uk *Meridian Controls is an experienced provider of Pulsejet Cleaning Systems on Dust Arrestment Plant and specialise in supplying a complete range of equipment necessary for an effective cleaning system on both bag filters and cartridge filters. *Supported by our technical capability to undertake computer based calculations for accurate sizing of Pulse Valves, Header Tanks, Blow Tube Nozzles and Cartridges to ensure the correct selection of equipment to suit the application. *Meridian Controls are the sole authorised distributor for the TURBO range of Dust Filter Components in the UK, Ireland and Belgium and also authorised distributor for the ESA range of electronic Pulse Controllers and Dust Emission Monitors and the ASCO JOUCOMA range of Dust Filters. Call Jason Williams for more information about the products and services of Meridian Controls.*

Meridian Doors Ltd, The Croft, High Street, Whetstone, Leicester, LE8 6LQ Tel: 0116-275 0666 Fax: 0116-275 0606 E-mail: meridiandoors@webleicester.co.uk *Industrial door manufrs*

▶ Meridian Electrical (Eastern) Ltd, 775 Southchurch Road, Southend-On-Sea, SS1 2PP Tel: (01702) 466604

Meridian Foods, The Estate Office, Stockbridge Road, Sutton Scotney, Winchester, Hampshire, SO21 3JW Tel: (01962) 761935 Fax: (01962) 761860 E-mail: info@meridianfoods.co.uk *Health food producers*

Meridian Leisure Services, Unit 5b 46 Holton Road, Holton Heath Trading Park, Poole, Dorset, BH16 6LT Tel: (01202) 632333 Fax: (01202) 620036 E-mail: sales@meridianleisure.co.uk *Amusement machines*

▶ Meridian Lifts European Ltd, Unit 7, Benridge Business Park, Holyrood Close, Poole, Dorset, BH17 7BD Tel: (01202) 659530 Fax: (01202) 775850

Meridian Services Ltd, 94a Ash Road, Aldershot, Hampshire, GU12 4EY Tel: (01252) 318893 Fax: (01252) 336969 *Lighting contractors*

Meridian Technology Ltd, Unit 24 Park Gate Business Centre Chandlers Way, Park Gate, Southampton, SO31 1FQ Tel: (01489) 577599 Fax: (01489) 579472 E-mail: sales@19inchracks.com *Manufacturers of 19 inch enclosures*

Meridian Tooling Co. Ltd, Unit 6, Exis Court, Veasey Close, Attleborough Fields Industrial Estate, Nuneaton, Warwickshire, CV11 6RT Tel: (024) 7634 0187 Fax: (024) 7664 1301

continued

E-mail: meridian@netcomuk.co.uk *Press tool manufrs*

▶ Meridian Welded Structures, 4b Station Road, Harrietsham, Maidstone, Kent, ME17 1JA Tel: (01622) 853533 Fax: (01622) 853534

Merit, Alloa Business Centre, The Whins, Alloa, Clackmannanshire, FK10 3SA Tel: (01259) 726640 Fax: (01259) 726620 E-mail: info@merit-at.com *Software, performance, functional testing & automated test tools*

Merit Badge & Regalia Co. Ltd, Merit House, Stanhope Street, Highgate, Birmingham, B12 0UX Tel: 0121-440 6861 Fax: 0121-440 1037 E-mail: sales@fcparry.com *Badge & regalia manufacturers.*High quality Cufflinks and fashion accessories*

Merit Display, 8-10 Maudslay Road, Coventry, CV5 8EL Tel: (024) 7667 6700 *Display equipment, sale & hire*

▶ Merit Ice Cream Ltd, Postford Mill, Mill Lane, Chilworth, Guildford, Surrey, GU4 8RT Tel: (01483) 209700 Fax: (01483) 209777

Merit Lowson & French Ltd, The Barn, Wharfe Bank Terrace, Tadcaster, North Yorkshire, LS24 9AN Tel: (01937) 835225 Fax: (01937) 530225 E-mail: lowson@mlfltd.fsbussines.co.uk *Ultrasonic test services* Also at: Faversham & Tadcaster

Merit Machine Tools, Coronation Road, Cressex Business Park, High Wycombe, Buckinghamshire, HP12 3RP Tel: (01494) 522072 Fax: (01494) 529552 *Machine tool stockists or agents*

▶ Merit Marketing, Cedar Terrace, Dalrymple, Ayr, KA6 6DT Tel: (01292) 560638 E-mail: bertilotti@btinternet.com *information products*

Merit Plastic Mouldings Ltd, Vinces Road, Diss, Norfolk, IP22 4YE Tel: (01379) 644321 Fax: (01379) 644236 E-mail: mpm@meritplastics.co.uk *Trade injection moulders*

Merit Process Engineering Ltd, Cumberland House, Cumberland Road, North Balkwell Farm Industrial Estate, North Shields, Tyne & Wear, NE29 8RD Tel: 0191-257 2788 Fax: 0191-257 2784 E-mail: enquiries@meritpe.co.uk *Pipework installations & fabricators*

Merit Technology Europe Ltd, 935bsittingbourne Research Centre, Cornforth Drive, Sittingbourne, Kent, ME9 8PX Tel: (01795) 418900 Fax: (01795) 418929 E-mail: sales@mtel.co.uk *Software consultants*

Meritor HVS Ltd, Rackery Lane, Llay, Wrexham, Clwyd, LL12 0PB Tel: (01978) 852141 Fax: (01978) 856173 E-mail: thomas.hughes@arvinmeritor.com *Manufacturers of axles, breakpads & car parts*

Meritor Light Vehicle Systems (U K) Ltd, Roof Systems, Fordhouse Lane, Birmingham, B30 3BW Tel: 0121-459 1166 Fax: 0121-459 9808 E-mail: marco.foley@arvinmeritor.com *Automotive component*

Meritronics Ltd, Otterden Place, Otterden, Faversham, Kent, ME13 0BT Tel: (01795) 890341 Fax: (01795) 890341 E-mail: contact@meritronics.co.uk *Non-destructive test equipment apparatus manufrs* Also at: Dunstable & Tadcaster

▶ Merkaba, 17 Brook Street, Polegate, East Sussex, BN26 6BQ Tel: (01323) 848414 Fax: (01323) 848414 *Interior designers & manufrs*

Merkle-Korff, Treetops House, Gillotts Lane, Henley-On-Thames, Oxfordshire, RG9 1PT Tel: (01543) 255995 Fax: (01491) 412211 E-mail: sales@acdcsystems.com *Permanent split capacitors & reversible electric motors*

Merlett Plastics (UK) Ltd, Unit 2, Waverley Road, Beeches Industrial Estate, Yate, Bristol, BS37 5QT Tel: (01454) 329888 Fax: (01454) 324499 *Hose distributors & manufrs*

▶ Merley Paper Converters Ltd, Merley House, Pilot Road, Corby, Northamptonshire, NN17 5YH Tel: (01536) 274274 Fax: (01536) 200338 E-mail: headoffice@merley.com

Merlin Accessories Ltd, Unit G, St. Martins Trade Park, Nickel Close, Winchester, Hampshire, SO23 7RJ Tel: (01962) 842002 Fax: (01962) 842420 E-mail: sales@merlinaccessories.com *Fastener & fixings distributors*

Merlin Chemicals Ltd, Passfield Mill Business Park, Mill Lane, Passfield, Liphook, Hampshire, GU30 7QU Tel: (01428) 751122 Fax: (01428) 751133 E-mail: sales@merlinchemicals.co.uk *Cleaning chemicals.*

Merlin Circuit Technology Ltd, Unit 1, Hawarden Industrial Park, Hawarden, Deeside, Clwyd, CH5 3PZ Tel: (01244) 520510 Fax: (01244) 520721 E-mail: sales@merlincircuit.co.uk *Manufacturers of P.C.B.'s*

▶ Merlin Consultancy, 2 Upper Cosmeston Farm, Penarth, South Glamorgan, CF64 5UB Tel: (029) 2070 0045 Fax: (029) 2070 0045 E-mail: sales@merlinconsultancy.com

▶ Merlin Corporate Services, 34 Hatton Lane, Stretton, Warrington, WA4 4NG Tel: (01925) 730077 Fax: (01925) 730659 E-mail: info@merlin.uk.net *Merlin Corporate Services provides high quality print design, web design, e-commerce solutions & top Search Engine ranking for businesses in NW UK. See our portfolio of clients' work on our website*

Merlin Diesel Systems Ltd, Unit 3-4 Lincoln Place, Walton Summit Centre, Bamber Bridge, Preston, PR5 8NA Tel: (01772) 627676 Fax: (01772) 626220 E-mail: sales@merlindiesel.com Principal Export Areas: Worldwide *Fuel injection test equipment distributors & manufrs*

▶ Merlin Electrical, 6 Border Place, Saltcoats, Ayrshire, KA21 5NL Tel: (01294) 468753 E-mail: merlinelectrical@sbmbroadband.com *Electrical installation, inspection & testing service*

Merlin Electro-Plating Ltd, Newhouse Industrial Estate, Newhouse, Motherwell, Lanarkshire, ML1 5RX Tel: (01698) 734038 Fax: (01698) 834847 E-mail: info@merlinep.co.uk *Electroplating contractors*

Merlin Engineering, Wallows Road, Brierley Hill, West Midlands, DY5 1HQ Tel: (01384) 571936 Fax: (01384) 793436 E-mail: sales@merlinengineering.co.uk *Precision engineers*

Merlin Equipment, Unit 4, Cabot Business Village, Holyrood Close, Cabot Lane, Poole, Dorset, BH17 7BA Tel: (01202) 697979 Fax: (01202) 691919 E-mail: sales@merlinequipment.com *Mobile power system manufrs*

Merlin Extrusion Services, 11 & 12 Walkers Road, Moons Moat North Industrial Estate, Redditch, Worcestershire, B98 9HE Tel: (01527) 64833 Fax: (01527) 66021 E-mail: ron@merlinextrusionservices.freeserve.co.uk *Tool makers*

Merlin Fireworks Ltd, Sunnyside View, Stockbridge Road, Kings Somborne, Stockbridge, Hampshire, SO20 6PH Tel: (01794) 389111 Fax: (01794) 389051 *Professional firework displays services*

Merlin Forms Ltd, Unit 3, 222 London Road Business Park, St. Albans, Hertfordshire, AL1 1PN Tel: (01727) 845077 Fax: (01727) 845013 E-mail: sales@merlinformsltd.co.uk *Printing services*

Merlin Glass, Barn Street, Liskeard, Cornwall, PL14 4BJ Tel: (01579) 342399 Fax: (01579) 345110 E-mail: info@glassdoorhandles.com *Door handles suppliers & manufrs*

Merlin Industrial Services, 55 Merlin Way, East Grinstead, West Sussex, RH19 3XG Tel: (01342) 300818 Fax: (01342) 324562 *Dust extraction services*

▶ Merlin International Projects Ltd, 115a High Street, Selsey, Chichester, West Sussex, PO20 0QB Tel: (01243) 606876

Merlin It Ltd, 4 Main Road, Long Hanborough, Witney, Oxfordshire, OX29 8BE Tel: (01993) 880002 Fax: 01993 880002 *Computer consultants*

▶ Merlin Leisure, Ladds Garden Centre, Bath Road, Hare Hatch, Reading, RG10 9SB Tel: 0118-940 1444 E-mail: sales@advantagespas.co.uk

Merlin Leisure Group, Bloomfield Garden Centre, 241 Berechurch Hall Road, Colchester, CO2 9NP Tel: (01206) 766402 Fax: (01206) 766406 *Swimming pool installers*

Merlin Motor Co. Ltd, 3 Lodge Estate, Withybush Road, Haverfordwest, Dyfed, SA62 4BW Tel: (01437) 764928 Fax: (01437) 769628 *General engineers*

▶ Merlin Network Ltd, Merlin Way, Hillend, Dunfermline, Fife, KY11 9JY Tel: (01383) 821182 Fax: (01383) 824682 *Manufactures of pick windows & conservatries*

▶ Merlin Office Equipment, 1-7 Glasgow Street, Dumfries, DG2 9AF Tel: (01387) 257027 Fax: (01387) 250037 E-mail: service@merlinofficeequipment.co.uk

Merlin Office Supplies, 7-8 Northbrook Close, Worcester, WR3 8BP Tel: (01905) 24240 Fax: (01905) 726747 E-mail: merlinoffice@aol.com *Office stationery suppliers*

Merlin Plastics, Charity Farm, Baxterley, Atherstone, Warwickshire, CV9 2LN Tel: (01827) 874572 Fax: (01827) 874898 *Plastic mould toolmakers*

▶ Merlin Polyurethanes, Camelot House, Claylake, Spalding, Lincolnshire, PE12 6BL Tel: (01775) 722208 Fax: (01775) 722298 *Polyurethane molding*

Merlin Software International Ltd, 6 Bancombe Road, Somerton, Somerset, TA11 6SB Tel: (01458) 271300 Fax: (01458) 224044 E-mail: info@caliburn-software.com *Software sales*

Merlin Software International Ltd, PO Box 27, Somerton, Somerset, TA11 6SB Tel: (01458) 271300 Fax: (01458) 224044 E-mail: info@caliburn-software.com *Computer software consultants*

Merlin Solutions, 5 Gaskells End, Tokers Green, Reading, RG4 9EW Tel: 0118-972 4666 Fax: 0118-972 4535 E-mail: terriw@mersol.co.uk *PC consultants*

Merlin Systems Ltd, Pandy Industrial Estate, Ty Gwyn Lane, Wrexham, Clwyd, LL11 2UA Tel: (01978) 313911 Fax: (01978) 313811 E-mail: sales@merlin-systems.ltd.uk *Industrial process control systems manufrs*

Merloni Domestic Appliances Ltd, Merloni Ho, 3 Cowley Business Pk, High St, Cowley, Uxbridge, Middx, UB8 2AD Tel: (01895) 858200 Fax: (01895) 858270 *Domestic appliances*

Merlyn Electronics, Bridge Mills, Holland Street, Salford, M6 6EL Tel: 0161-745 7697 Fax: 0161-737 5615 E-mail: sales@merlyn-electronics.co.uk *Electric motor control systems*

Mermaid Marine Ltd, 70-72 Cobham Road, Ferndown Industrial Estate, Wimborne, Dorset, BH21 7RN Tel: (01202) 891824 Fax: (01202) 895882 E-mail: engines@mermaid-marine.co.uk *Diesel & marine engine manufrs*

Mermaid Marine Management Ltd, Hoopers Hill, Lymington Road, New Milton, Hampshire, BH25 5PZ Tel: (01425) 619262 Fax: (01425) 619237 E-mail: mermaid.marine@btinternet.com *Ship management consultants*

Mermaid Panels Ltd, DBC House, Grimsby Road, Laceby, Grimsby, South Humberside, DN37 7DP Tel: (01472) 279940 Fax: (01472) 752575 E-mail: sales@mermaidpanels.com *Wall panelling marketing & distribution*

Merpro Leisure Ltd, Brent Avenue, Forties Road Industrial Estate, Montrose, Angus, DD10 9JA Tel: (01674) 662200 Fax: (01674) 662266 E-mail: sales@merpro.com *Computer aided design services*

Merrell Casting Ltd, 70-71 Warstone Lane, Birmingham, B18 6NG Tel: 0121-236 3767 Fax: 0121-236 8439 *Precision casting jewellers*

Phillip Merrell Agency, 51 Cleave Road, Sticklepath, Barnstaple, Devon, EX31 2DU Tel: (01271) 322175 Fax: (01271) 325414 *Agents for catering equipment manufrs*

Merrick & Heath, Rolfe Street, Smethwick, West Midlands, B66 2AW Tel: 0121-558 1291 Fax: 0121-558 1291 *Builders merchants*

Merrick Loggin Trailers, College Farm, Bicester Hill, Evenley, Brackley, Northamptonshire, NN13 5SD Tel: (01280) 702725 Fax: (01280) 702060 E-mail: loggin@freeuk.com *Trailer manufrs*

Merricknits, 80 Queen St, Newton Stewart, Wigtownshire, DG8 6JL Tel: (01671) 403842 *Knitwear manufrs*

Merridale Polishing & Plating Co. Ltd, Friar Street, Wednesbury, West Midlands, WS10 0RE Tel: 0121-556 3636 Fax: 0121-556 8886 *Finishers in the metal finishing industry*

Merriefield Engineering Ltd, 7 Willis Way, Poole, Dorset, BH15 3SS Tel: (01202) 680644 Fax: (01202) 684389 E-mail: sales@merriefield.co.uk *Subcontract fabrication*

Merrill Brown Ltd, Trent Lane, Nottingham, NG2 4DS Tel: 0115-950 6669 Fax: 0115-950 3486 E-mail: sales@merrillbrown.co.uk *Sign manufrs*

Merriman Mineral Processing, Charnwood Edge, Syston Road, Cossington, Leicester, LE7 4UZ Tel: 0116-269 5137 Fax: 0116-269 2261 E-mail: sales@merrimans.com *Plant hire, repairs & refurbishment & property development*

Merriott, Tail Mill Lane, Merriott, Somerset, TA16 5PG Tel: (01460) 72457 Fax: (01460) 74481 E-mail: sales@merriott.com *Plastic moulders*

Merris Development Engineers Ltd, Howarth Road, Maidenhead, Berkshire, SL6 1AP Tel: (01628) 785371 Fax: (01628) 670339 E-mail: brendan@merris.co.uk Principal Export Areas: Worldwide *Manufacturers of paint tinting equipment & mixing machines*

Merritt Air Conditioning, 44 Birchwood Drive, Dartford, DA2 7NF Tel: (01322) 525485 Fax: (01322) 524203 E-mail: fredmerrittac@aol.com *Air conditioning contractors*

Merritt & Fryers Ltd, Firth Street Works, Firth Street, Skipton, North Yorkshire, BD23 2PX Tel: (01756) 792485 Fax: (01756) 700391 E-mail: info@merrittandfryers.co.uk *Building & timber merchants*

Joseph Merritt Group P.L.C., Byron Ave, Lowmoor Business Park, Kirkby-in-Ashfield, Nottingham, NG17 7LA Tel: (01623) 759737 Fax: (01623) 758826 E-mail: enquiries@merrittgroupplc.co.uk *Factory removal relocation contractors, machinery removal contractors, machinery engineers dismantling/erecting, installing & plant installation/erection/dismantling engineers*

Merritt Plastics Ltd, 5 Winster Buildings, Manners Avenue, Manners Industrial Estate, Ilkeston, Derbyshire, DE7 8EF Tel: 0115-944 7661 Fax: 0115-944 1864 E-mail: simon@merrittplastics.fsnet.co.uk *Plastic & PVC extrusion & plastic tube manufrs*

Merrivale IT Resourcing, Coborn House Suite 210, 3 Coborn Road, London, E3 2DA Tel: (0800) 1077850 Fax: (0871) 6619084 E-mail: mvit@mvit.co.uk *Specialist IT recruitment consultancy*

Merrow Sales UK Ltd, 17 Glebe Road, Groby, Leicester, LE6 0GT Tel: 0116-232 1779 Fax: 0116-287 8099 *Industrial sewing machine distributors*

▶ Merrows Ltd, 50b Inverness Avenue, Westcliff On Sea, Westcliff-on-Sea, Essex, SS0 9DY Tel: (01702) 347493 *Online retailer, mainly bathrooms*

Merrychef, 5E Langley Business Centre, Station Road, Langley, SL3 8DS Tel: 01753 485 900 (01753) 485900 Fax: (01753) 485901 E-mail: info@enodis.com *Merrychef are based in Aldershot, Hampshire and are manufacturers of commercial microwave ovens.*

▶ Merryfield Associates, Newcott Cottage, Newcott Near Honiton, Honiton, Devon, EX14 9ND Tel: (01404) 861587 E-mail: barriebc@btopenworld.com *Innovation, licensing, technology transfer & IPR*

▶ Merryfields, Merryfields, Church Road, Partridge Green, Horsham, West Sussex, RH13 8JS Tel: (07732) 437628 Fax: (07876) 892851 *Computer services ,hardware & software*

Merryhill Envirotec Ltd, Merryhill House, Budds Lane, Romsey, Hampshire, SO51 0HA Tel: (01794) 515848 Fax: (01794) 524386 E-mail: enquiries@merryhill-idm.co.uk *Asbestos removal, asbestos surveys, disaster recovery & hazardous material remediation*

Merrythought Ltd, Dale End, Iron Bridge, Telford, Shropshire, TF8 7NJ Tel: (01952) 433116 Fax: (01952) 432054 E-mail: sales@merrythought.co.uk *Toy makers*

Merryworth Joinery Ltd, 21-23 Girton Street, Cambridge Industrial Area, Salford, M7 1UR Tel: 0161-839 3321 Fax: 0161-839 3321 *Joinery manufrs*

Mersey Can Ltd, 12-14 Ebenezer Street, Birkenhead, Merseyside, CH42 1NH Tel: 0151-645 8511 Fax: 0151-644 6749 *Tinplate can manufrs*

Mersey Equipment Co. Ltd, Arcade Housed, 82-90 Taylor Street, Birkenhead, Merseyside, CH41 1BQ Tel: 0151-647 9751 Fax: 0151-647 3343 E-mail: admin@merseq.fssbusiness.co.uk *Safety & welding equipment distributors* Also at: Liverpool

Mersey Forwarding Co Shipping Services Ltd, Mersey House, 1 Church Street, Bootle, Merseyside, L20 1AF Tel: 0151-933 2000 Fax: 0151-933 0883 E-mail: tlennonmfss@btconnect.com *Freight forwarders & shipping agents*

Mersey Mirror Ltd, The Foundry, 36 Henry Street, Liverpool, L1 5BS Tel: 0151-709 7567 E-mail: post@merseymirror.com *Publishing, printing & multi media*

Mersey Pattern Ltd, Unit 7-9 & 11, Edwards La Industrial Estate, Liverpool, L24 9HX Tel: 0151-486 9500 Fax: 0151-448 1171 *Pattern & sample manufrs*

▶ Mersey Scientific, Redstones, Mill Lane, Rainhill, Prescot, Merseyside, L35 6NH Tel: (07732) 176739 Fax: 0151-426 2876 E-mail: sales@merseyscientific.com *Laboratory suppliers for equipment, consumables,*

▶ Mersey Signs, Unit 24, Junction 8 Business Park, Ross Cliffe Road, Ellesmere Port, CH65 3AS Tel: 0151-355 0478 Fax: 0151-356 5352 E-mail: info@merseysigns.co.uk *Illuminated, promotional, reflective & vehicle livery signs manufrs*

Mersey Weigh Ltd, Unit 48 Canal Bridge Enterprise Centre, Meadow Lane, Ellesmere Port, CH65 4EH Tel: 0151-356 5274 Fax: 0151-356 5274 *Weighing system suppliers*

Merseyflex Ltd, 46 Mason Street, Edge Hill, Liverpool, L7 3EW Tel: 0151-707 1652 Fax: 0151-708 0128 E-mail: sales@merseyflex.co.uk *Hose oil & petroleum industry manufrs*

▶ Merseyside Compressor Services, 3 Atherton Road, Liverpool, L9 7EL Tel: 0151-523 2160 Fax: 0151-523 2413 E-mail: mikefoley.mcs@tiscali.co.uk *Compressed air engineers*

Merseyside Galvanising Ltd, Weaver Industrial Estate, Blackburne Street, Liverpool, L19 8JA Tel: 0151-427 1449 Fax: 0151-427 2690 E-mail: merseyside@wedge-galv.co.uk *Merseyside Galvanizing at Garston gives you access to hot dip galvanizing organisation, part of nation-wide Wedge Group*

Merseyside Hydraulics & Pneumatics, Unit C5 Kingfisher Business Park, Hawthorne Road, Bootle, Merseyside, L20 6PF Tel: 0151-944 2668 Fax: 0151-944 2669 *Hydraulic engineers services*

Merseyside Industrial Supplies, 241 Rake Lane, Wallasey, Merseyside, CH45 5DJ Tel: 0151-639 7382 Fax: 0151-637 1396 E-mail: sales@misuk.com *Protective clothing distributors*

Merseyside Metalwork Ltd, Cotton Street, Liverpool, L3 7DY Tel: 0151-236 7349 Fax: 0151-236 6397 *Sheet metal & ductwork specialists* Also at: London

Merseyside Multi Glazing Ltd, St Michaels Industrial Estate, Widnes, Cheshire, WA8 8TL Tel: 0151-424 7070 Fax: 0151-420 6944 E-mail: contact@multiglazing.co.uk *Window installers & glaziers*

▶ Merseyside & North Wales Fencing, Mold Road, Alltami, Mold, Clwyd, CH7 6LG Tel: (01352) 780373 Fax: (01244) 548184 *Fencing manufrs*

Merseyside Pipeline Supplies Ltd, Baltic Road, Bootle, Merseyside, L20 1AW Tel: 0151-933 3835 Fax: 0151-933 4166 E-mail: merseypipes@aol.com *Pipeline fittings & flange stockholders*

Merseyside Road Springs, 97 Rimrose Road, Bootle, Merseyside, L20 4HN Tel: 0151-922 3603 Fax: 0151-944 1996 *Laminated & multileaf spring manufrs*

Merseyside Rustproofing Co., 84 Seel Street, Liverpool, L1 4BH Tel: 0151-709 2409 *Rust proofing services*

Mersh Brothers Lewisham Ltd, 16a Algernon Road, London, SE13 7AT Tel: (020) 8692 2844 Fax: (020) 8692 2804 E-mail: sales@mershbros.co.uk *MOT testing*

▶ Merson Signs Ltd, 12 Merlin Centre, County Oak Way, Crawley, West Sussex, RH11 7XA Tel: (01293) 408728 Fax: (01293) 403010 E-mail: sales@merson-signs.com

Mersona Ltd, PO Box 12, Halesowen, West Midlands, B62 8AP Tel: 0121-559 5683 Fax: 0121-559 7487 *Ophthalmic lense manufrs*

Mertech Pumps Ltd, 39 Hastings Street, Luton, LU1 5BE Tel: (01582) 422622 Fax: (01582) 422922 E-mail: mail@mertech.co.uk *Switch board control manufrs*

▶ Mertek Engineering Ltd, 7 Baylys Road, Plymouth, PL9 7NQ Tel: (01752) 480497 Fax: (01752) 480497 *Metalworking & fabrication services*

▶ Merthe Logistics, 62-82 Greystone Road, Antrim, BT41 1NU Tel: (028) 9446 8300 Fax: (028) 9446 8338

Merthyr Electroplating Co. Ltd, Unit 23a Merthyr Tydfil Industrial Estate, Dowlais, Merthyr Tydfil, CF48 2SR Tel: (01685) 723677 Fax: (01685) 379343 E-mail: martin.sullivan@merthyrelectroplating.com *Electroplating services*

Merton & Falcon Ltd, 18 Commercial Road, London, N18 1TU Tel: (020) 8884 2150 Fax: (020) 8803 8887 E-mail: merton@falconltd.freeserve.co.uk *Tobacco, pipe & accessory distributors*

Merton Timber, Rowfant Sawmills, Wallage Lane, Rowfant, Crawley, West Sussex, RH10 4NQ Tel: (01342) 716633 Fax: (01342) 716655 E-mail: sales@merton-timber.co.uk *Timber & builders merchants*

Merton Timber Ltd, 65-71 Grove Vale, London, SE22 8EQ Tel: (020) 8299 4131 Fax: (020) 8693 4136 E-mail: sales@mertontimber.co.uk *Builders merchants*

Merton Timber, 28 Goat Road, Mitcham, Surrey, CR4 4HU Tel: (020) 8687 0055 Fax: (020) 8648 5663 E-mail: sales@merton-timber.co.uk *Builders merchants*

Merton Timber, Central House, Murray Road, Orpington, Kent, BR5 3QY Tel: (01689) 890044 Fax: (01689) 890066 E-mail: sales@merton-timber.co.uk *Builders merchants*

Merton Timber Ltd, 102 Rose Hill, Sutton, Surrey, SM1 3HB Tel: (020) 8644 7884 Fax: (020) 8641 0943 E-mail: sales@merton-timber.co.uk *Power tools/accessories distributors or agents*

Merton Timber & Builders Merchants, Unit E 2 Endeavour Way, London, SW19 8UH Tel: (020) 8879 0626 Fax: (020) 8947 6061 E-mail: sales@mertontimber.com *Timber & builders' merchants*

Merula Ltd, 25-31 Huntingdon Street, St. Neots, Cambridgeshire, PE19 1BG Tel: (01480) 222940 Fax: (01480) 222941 E-mail: info@merula.net *Internet providers*

Merv Hutchings Workwear, 169 Pinhoe Road, Exeter, EX4 7HZ Tel: (01392) 412376 *Protective clothing manufrs*

Mervian Label Co., 27 Alexandra Road, Skegness, Lincolnshire, PE25 3QY Tel: (01754) 767178 Fax: (01754) 762219 E-mail: sales@mervian.co.uk *Label manufrs*

Mervyn Cyril Clothier, Marston Mains Farm, Marston Bigot, Frome, Somerset, BA11 5BY Tel: (01373) 836276 *Dairy farming*

▶ Mes High Access, 22 Dale Drive, Brighton, BN1 8LD Tel: (01273) 557711 Fax: (01273) 557711 E-mail: mark@mes-window-cleaning.co.uk *Commercial & Domestic Properties, windows up to 60' high safely & Professionally cleaned from the safety of the ground using the "Reach & Wash System". Registered Member of "National Federation Of Master Window & General Cleaners", Health & Safety Compliant, Fully Insured. Free quotes & Advice Given, We can also be contacted on 07743 741852 (Mark)*

Meshtex Ltd, Second Avenue, Poynton Industrial Estate, Poynton, Stockport, Cheshire, SK12 1ND Tel: (01625) 876949 Fax: (01625) 879529 E-mail: info@meshtex.com *Rotary screen engravers*

▶ Meson Solutions, B9 Bicester Innovation Centre, Telford Road, Bicester, Oxfordshire, OX26 4LD Tel: (01869) 255777 Fax: (01869) 255801 E-mail: sales@mesonsolutions.com *Development sales & consultancy of software*

Messages On Hold Ltd, P O Box 55, Barnet, Hertfordshire, EN4 0HF Tel: 020-8441 4920 Fax: 020-8449 2626 E-mail: moh@london.com *Audio-visual production & distributors*

▶ Messaging Warehouse UK, Paragon House, 48 Seymour Grove, Manchester, M16 0LN Tel: 0161-888 3333 Fax: 0161-877 7991 E-mail: sales@messagingwarehouse.com *Messaging Warehouse (UK) is one of the fastest growing audio production houses in the UK today, specialising in telephone 'on-hold' marketing messages and music for telephone systems.*

Messider Plastics, 101 Villiers Road, London, NW2 5QB Tel: (020) 8459 3017 Fax: (020) 8830 1787 *Plastic moulding manufrs*

Messier-Dowty Ltd, Cheltenham Road East, Gloucester, GL2 9QH Tel: (01452) 712424 Fax: (01452) 713821 E-mail: peter.hall@messier-dowty.com *Aircraft landing gear manufrs*

Messmer Instruments Ltd, Unit F1 Imperial Business Estate, West Mill, Gravesend, Kent, DA11 0DL Tel: (01474) 566488 Fax: (01474) 560310 E-mail: sales@messmerinstruments.com Principal Export Areas: Worldwide *Plastic paper & board test instrument manufrs*

Messrs G Owen & Co., Owen House, Barking, Essex, IG11 9HY Tel: (0845) 0958225 Fax: (0845) 0958235 E-mail: gowenandco@yahoo.com *Voluntary, Not-for-Profit Sector & Fundraising Consultants'**

Met Anglia Ltd, Unit 2 Garrod Drive Industrial Estate, Fakenham, Norfolk, NR21 8NN Tel: (01328) 862026 Fax: (01328) 855961 *Refrigeration & air conditioning installers*

▶ Met Engineering Ltd, Unit 3, Mode Wheel Road, Salford, M5 5DQ Tel: 0161-737 2627 Fax: 0161-737 2628 E-mail: info@metenguk.com *Suppliers of professional quality meteorological instrumentation*

Met Spec Roofing Services Ltd, 252 Peel Green Road, Eccles, Manchester, M30 7BU Tel: 0161-787 8821 Fax: 0161-707 0070 *Industrial roofing contractors*

Meta Skill P.L.C., 7 Fortuna Court, Aldermaston, Reading, RG7 8UB Tel: 0118-981 9316 Fax: 0118-981 7958 E-mail: rsmith@metaskill.com *IT staff services*

Meta System UPS Ltd, Oakmoore Court, Kingswood Road, Hampton Lovett, Droitwich, Worcestershire, WR9 0QH Tel: (01905) 791700 Fax: (01905) 791701 E-mail: ruggieroannunziata@metasystemups.co.uk *Meta System UPS Ltd is part of Meta System SPA, an electronics company totally dedicated to the design, manufacture and supply of high technology products. Our UPS products are backed with thirty years of experience in designing and developing power solutions.**We manufacture a complete product range, ranging from 400 VA up to kVA Single Phase, and from 8 kVA up to 30kVA Three Phase. **

▶ Meta Vision Systems Ltd, Oakfield House Oakfield Industrial Estate, Stanton Harcourt Road, Eynsham, Witney, Oxfordshire, OX29 4TH Tel: (01865) 887900 Fax: (01865) 887901

Metadata Ltd, 39 Pemberton Terrace, London, N19 5RX Tel: (020) 7272 3726 *Computer consultancy*

Metafab Solutions, Marine Shed, Cu Lighting Estate, Broadwell, Coleford, Gloucestershire, GL16 7EG Tel: (01594) 839220 Fax: (01594) 827878 E-mail: sales@metafabs.com *Bespoke architectural steel fabrications*

Metafin Group Holdings Ltd, Green Lane, Walsall, WS2 8JG Tel: (01922) 626073 Fax: (01922) 720673 *Stove enamelling & powder coating specialists*

Metaflake Ltd, Station Road, Anstruther, Fife, KY10 3JA Tel: (01333) 313440 Fax: (01333) 313044 E-mail: enq@metaflake.com *Aluminium pigments & pastes, paint inks & powder coating manufrs*

▶ Metaflex Ltd, Milltown Industrial Estate, Greenan Road, Warrenpoint, Newry, County Down, BT34 3FN Tel: (028) 4177 3604 Fax: (028) 4177 3266 *Ceiling systems contractors & manufrs*

Metaform Ltd, 12 Trading Estate Road, London, NW10 7LU Tel: (020) 8961 0999 Fax: (020) 8965 3319 *Manufacturers security bars & gates*

Metal Acadamy, National Metalforming Centre, 47 Birmingham Road, West Bromwich, West Midlands, B70 6PY Tel: 0121-601 6357 Fax: 0121-553 3143 E-mail: enquiries@metskill.co.uk *Apprenticeship offers for metal industry services*

Metal Agencies, Cobb House, 2 Oyster Lane, Byfleet, West Byfleet, Surrey, KT14 7DU Tel: (01932) 331111 Fax: (01932) 331190 E-mail: ngould@metalagencies.vionet.gr *Copper tube manufrs*

Metal Art Co., Cadgerhill, Glendaveny, Peterhead, Aberdeenshire, AB42 3DY Tel: (01779) 838888 Fax: (01779) 838333 E-mail: info@classicmetalart.co.uk *Wrought iron products interior & exterior**

Metal Bulletin Journals Ltd, Park House, 3 Park Terrace, Worcester Park, Surrey, KT4 7HY Tel: (020) 7827 9977 Fax: (020) 8337 8943 E-mail: books@metalbulletin.co.uk *Directory publishers*

Metal Cabinets Sales Ltd, Moorfield Road Estate, Yeadon, Leeds, LS19 7BN Tel: 0113-250 8082 Fax: 0113-250 5138 E-mail: person@metalcabinets.co.uk *Cabinet, console & desk manufrs*

Metal Casements Ltd, Birch St, Walsall, WS2 8JB Tel: (01922) 724032 Fax: (01922) 723048 *Steel window manufrs*

Metal Castings Ltd, Droitwich Road, Worcester, WR3 7JX Tel: (01905) 754400 Fax: (01905) 754347 E-mail: sales@metalcastingsltd.com *Aluminium alloy pressure diecasting manufrs*

Metal Closures Ltd, Po Box 32, West Bromwich, West Midlands, B70 7HY Tel: (0870) 7605553 *Aluminium bottle top manufrs*

Metal Closures Huddersfield Ltd, Tandem Industrial Estate, Wakefield Road, Tandem, Huddersfield, HD5 0BL Tel: (01484) 533216 Fax: (01484) 543203 E-mail: sales@metal-closures.co.uk *Aluminium tin closures manufrs*

Metal Coating Services Ltd, Hamburg Road, Off Rotterdam Road, Hull, HU7 0XD Tel: (01482) 820202 Fax: (01482) 820150 E-mail: gareth@metalcoatingservices.com *Powder coating specialists*

Metal Craft Industries UK Ltd, Allen House, 17-21 Paterson Road, Finedon Road Industrial Estate, Wellingborough, Northamptonshire, NN8 4BZ Tel: (01933) 440573 Fax: (01933) 440574 E-mail: sales@store-equipment.co.uk *Stainless steel manufacturers for the catering & supermarket industry*

Metal Crystals & Oxides Ltd, Unit B4 Button End Industrial Estate, Harston, Cambridge, CB22 7GX Tel: (01223) 872072 Fax: (01223) 872517 E-mail: sales@metal-crystals.com *Crystal growers*

Metal Detection Ltd, Burntmeadow Road, Redditch, Worcestershire, B98 9PA Tel: (01527) 65858 Fax: 0121-522 2013 E-mail: info@mastermagnets.co.uk *Check weighers & metal detectors*

Metal Developments Ltd, The Workshop, Wheatcroft Farm, Cullompton, Devon, EX15 1RA Tel: (01884) 35806 Fax: (01884) 35505 *Wood burning stove, multi-fuel manufrs*

Metal Enterprises & Co. Ltd, 150 Buckingham Palace Road, London, SW1W 9TR Tel: (020) 7730 6134 Fax: (020) 7730 0740 *Metal merchants* Also at: Sedgley

Metal Fabrication, Unit 13 Waterside Business Park, Waterside, Hadfield, Glossop, Derbyshire, SK13 1BE Tel: (01457) 862043 Fax: (01457) 868961 *Metal fabricators*

Metal Fabrication Co (Cardiff) Ltd, East Moors Road, Cardiff, CF24 5EE Tel: (029) 2048 9767 Fax: (029) 2048 0407 E-mail: sales@metal-fab.co.uk *Heating & ventilating engineers*

Metal Fabrication Services, Unit 3-4 Soaphouse Industrial Estate, Howard Street, Bristol, BS5 7AZ Tel: 0117-955 4132 Fax: 0117-935 0185 E-mail: enquries@wcltd.co.uk *Sheet metal fabricators*

Metal Fabrications Darwen Ltd, Taylor Street, Darwen, Lancashire, BB3 1DQ Tel: (01254) 701829 Fax: (01254) 701829 *Steel fabricators*

▶ Metal Fabrications Systems, Metal House, Hobson Industrial Estate, Hobson, Newcastle upon Tyne, NE16 6EA Tel: (01207) 271199 Fax: (01207) 272299 E-mail: john@metal-fabrication.co.uk *Steel fabrication manufrs*

▶ Metal Fast, Unit 11, Cirrus Court, Glebe Road, Huntingdon, Cambridgeshire, PE29 7DL Tel: (01480) 451144 Fax: (01480) 420910 E-mail: sales@metalfast.co.uk *Aluminium stockholders*

Metal Finishers Llandudno Ltd, Central Place, Llandudno, Gwynedd, LL30 2SZ Tel: (01492) 879183 Fax: (01492) 874695 *Electroplating services*

Metal Finishing Ltd, Station Street, Town Wharf Business Park, Walsall, WS2 9JZ Tel: (01922) 720720 Fax: (01922) 723400 E-mail: sales@lbparkes.net *Anodize processors, metal finishing, polishing, powder coating*

Metal Finishing & Coatings Ltd, Sweet Street Foundry, Derwent View, Leeds, LS11 9TJ Tel: 0113-244 6686 Fax: 0113-234 0842 E-mail: coating@btconnect.com *Electroplating services*

Metal Finishing Supplies Ltd, 99a North Street, Cannock, Staffordshire, WS11 0AZ Tel: (01543) 505771 Fax: (01543) 466011 *Electrochemical, chemical products distributors & agents*

Metal Goods Wales Ltd, North Road, Bridgend Industrial Estate, Bridgend, Mid Glamorgan, CF31 3TP Tel: (01656) 647755 Fax: (01656) 647744 E-mail: sales@metalgoods.co.uk *Stockholders of aluminium, stainless steel & other metals*

Metal Improvement Company, European Corporate Office, Hambridge Lane, Newbury, Berkshire, RG14 5TU Tel: (01635) 279621 Fax: (01635) 279629 E-mail: eurosales@metalimprovement.com *Metal Improvement (MIC) provides metal treatment services including controlled shot and laser peening and coatings which enhance the performance and extend the life of critical components, prevent premature fatigue and corrosion failures and enable component designs to achieve their maximum potential. Our metal treatment services are used by the aerospace, automotive, power generation, chemical processing, medical and other general engineering industries through a network of over 60 operating facilities in Europe and North America. The services we offer are: - Shot peening - Laser peening - Shot peen forming - Heat treating - Engineered Coatings We pride ourselves on being able to offer a superior reliable and quality assured service tailored to our customers needs. MIC has over 60 years experience and are committed to the continued development of existing and new technology.* Also at: Chester, Derby & Sunderland

Metal Injection Mouldings Ltd, Davenport Lane, Broadheath, Altrincham, Cheshire, WA14 5DS Tel: 0161-928 4247 Fax: 0161-927 7023 *Metal Injection Moulding enables the production of small components in steels, stainless and other high strength metals with complex shapes, close*

continued

Company Information

continuation
tolerances, smooth surface finish and finely reproduced detail. The principles of metal injection moulding are similar to plastic injection moulding - fine metal powder mixed with binder, is injection moulded in a die and the binder is then removed, to give an injection moulding in pure metal. This is sintered at high temperature to produce the finished metal injection moulding. Metal injection moulding is ideal for producing small, complex-shaped parts and fine detail, combined with excellent mechanical strengths. Metal injection mouldings can be treated like any other metal - "MIM" parts can be bent, riveted, welded, heat treated etc. MATERIALS: Low Alloy Steel Metal Injection Mouldings Stainless Steel Metal Injection Mouldings Tool Steel Metal Injection Mouldings Nickel & Cobalt based Metal Injection Mouldings Pure Iron Metal Injection Mouldings

Metal Mouldings Ltd, Unit 6, North Street, Walsall, WS2 8AU Tel: (01922) 615225 Fax: (01922) 632763 *Aluminium & aluminium extrusion stockholders*

Metal Office Equipment Ltd, 52a Chiswick Avenue, Mildenhall, Bury St. Edmunds, Suffolk, IP28 7AY Tel: (01638) 716960 Fax: (01638) 717875 *Office storage & desk systems manufrs*

Metal & Plastics Products Fabrication Ltd, 2 Astley Park Estate Chaddock Lane, Astley, Tyldesley, Manchester, M29 7JY Tel: (01942) 894657 Fax: (01942) 897483 E-mail: sales@metalandplastics.co.uk *Plastic injection mouldings manufrs*

Metal Prefabrications Dartford Ltd, Dewlands Estate, London Road, Stone, Dartford, DA2 6AS Tel: (01322) 220171 Fax: (01322) 288089 *Stainless steel fabricators*

Metal Pressings Group Ltd, Howard Road, Redditch, Worcestershire, B98 7SE Tel: (01527) 526933 Fax: (01527) 510009 E-mail: cmp@metal-pressings.com Principal Export Areas: Central/East Europe & West Europe *Press tool manufrs*

Metal Products Arden Ltd, Prospect Road, Burntwood, Staffordshire, WS7 0AE Tel: (01543) 682627 Fax: (01543) 671901 E-mail: enquiries@metalproducts.co.uk Purchasing Contact: S. Heart Sales Contact: R. Ward *Manufacturers of materials handling equipment; pallet/stillage, steel fabrications*

Metal Railing Co. Ltd, Unit 28 Point Pleasant Industrial Estate, Wallsend, Tyne & Wear, NE28 6HA Tel: 0191-295 1685 Fax: 0191-262 2882 *Steel fabrication*

Metal Scan Ltd, 16 The Brunel Centre, Newton Road, Manor Royal, Crawley, West Sussex, RH10 9TU Tel: (01293) 513123 Fax: (01293) 521507 E-mail: sales@aruntechnology.com Principal Export Areas: Worldwide *Optical emission spectrometers manufrs*

Metal Sections Ltd, Broadwell Road, Oldbury, West Midlands, B69 4HE Tel: 0121-601 6000 Fax: 0121-601 6121 E-mail: metsecplc@metsec.com *Manufacture bespoke sections*

► Metal Solutions South West Ltd, B Estover Trading Estate, Estover Road, Plymouth, PL6 7PY Tel: (01752) 770555 Fax: (01752) 775444 *Metal fabricators*

Metal Spinners Group Ltd, Clough Road, Manchester, M9 4FP Tel: 0161-205 2286 Fax: 0161-203 4376 E-mail: msg@metal-spinners.co.uk *Metal spinning services*

Metal Spinners Group Ltd, Newburn Industrial Estate, Shelley Road, Newcastle upon Tyne, NE15 9RT Tel: 0191-267 1011 Fax: 0191-264 7137 E-mail: sales@metal-spinners.co.uk Purchasing Contact: Simon Robson Sales Contact: Joe Butler *Metal spinners up to 4m diameter. In addition, deep drawn pressings & stainless & aluminium fabrications. Additional services include water jet cutting & polishing*

Metal Stitching Services Ltd, The Old Court Yard, Warwick Street, Prestwich, Manchester, M25 3HN Tel: 0161-773 6919 Fax: 0161-798 7352 *Casting repairs & restoration services*

Metal Supermarket, 10 Madeley Road, Moons Moat North Industrial Estate, Redditch, Worcestershire, B98 9NB Tel: (01527) 68818 Fax: (01527) 68414 E-mail: mscredditch@aol.com *Special steel supplier*

Metal Supermarkets, Unit 381a Jedburgh Court, Team Valley Trading Estate, Gateshead, Tyne & Wear, NE11 0BQ Tel: 0191-487 2144 Fax: 0191-487 2155 E-mail: gateshead@metalsupermarkets.org.uk *Steel stockholders*

Metal Supermarkets, 1 Overland Trading Estate Gelderd Road, Gildersome, Morley, Leeds, LS27 7JN Tel: 0113-238 0900 Fax: 0113-238 0060 E-mail: headoffice@metalsupermarkets.com *Special Steel Supplier, branches nationwide inc, Coventry, Gateshead, Govan, Leeds, Livingston, Manchester, London, Redditch, Southampton and West Bromwich. Steel specification include Stainless Steel, Carbon and Alloy steels, ground flat stock, cast iron and many other's. Also Nylons and High Grade materials. Call our branches for a friendly and professional response to your requirement. Our Product is Metal, Our Business is Service*

Metal Supermarkets Ltd, Trafford Park Way, Trafford Park, Trafford Park, Manchester, M17 1AN Tel: 0161-872 1199 Fax: 0161-872 8021 E-mail: mscmanchester@aol.com *Steel supplier, stainless steel, carbon & alloy steels*

Metal Supermarkets, 37 Trading Estate, Kelvin Way, West Bromwich, West Midlands, B70 7TP Tel: 0121-553 4424 Fax: 0121-525 2001 E-mail: info@metalsupermarkets.co.uk *Steel supplier, stainless, carbon & alloy steels & high grade*

Metal Supermarkets Coventry, Bayton Road, Exhall, Coventry, CV7 9EJ Tel: (024) 7636 6567 Fax: (024) 7636 6320 E-mail: msccoventry@aol.com *Special Steel Supplier, branches nationwide inc, Coventry, Gateshead, Govan, Leeds, Livingston, Manchester, London, Redditch, Southampton and West Bromwich. Steel specification include*

continued

Stainless Steel, Carbon and Alloy steels, ground flat stock, cast iron and many other's. Also Nylons and High Grade materials. Call our branches for a friendly and professional response to your requirement. Our Product is Steel, Our Business is Service

Metal Supermarkets Govan, Unit 8-9 Orton Place, Glasgow, G51 2HF Tel: 0141-440 1300 Fax: 0141-440 1308 E-mail: msgovan@aol.com *Special steel supplier*

Metal Supermarkets Park Royal, Unit 11 Hanover Industrial Estate, Acton Lane, London, NW10 7NB Tel: (020) 8961 1414 Fax: (020) 8961 1419 E-mail: parkroyal@metalsupermarkets.org.uk *Stainless, carbon & alloy steels, ground flat stock & cast iron*

Metal Supermarkets Southampton, Unit 16 Mount Pleasant Industrial Estate, Mount Pleasant Road, Southampton, SO14 0SP Tel: (023) 8022 0999 Fax: (023) 8023 3449 E-mail: southampton@metalsupermarkets.org.uk *Stainless steel*

Metal Technology Ltd, Steeple Road Industrial Estate, Antrim, BT41 1AB Tel: (028) 9448 7777 Fax: (028) 9448 7878 E-mail: info@metaltechnology.com *Metal stockholders*

Metal Technology, 9 Viking Way, Bar Hill, Cambridge, CB23 8EL Tel: (01954) 781729 Fax: (01954) 789901 *General & precision engineering*

Metal & Waste Recycling, Powke Lane, Cradley Heath, West Midlands, B64 5PT Tel: 0121-559 1156 Fax: 0121-561 5371 E-mail: enquires@nbrookes.co.uk *Scrap iron & metal merchants*

Metal & Waste Recycling, Kenninghall Road, London, N18 2PD Tel: (020) 8807 4268 Fax: (020) 8884 0381 *Metal merchants & recyclers*

Metal Work Ltd, Blackhill Drive, Wolverton Mill, Milton Keynes, MK12 5TS Tel: (01908) 222288 Fax: (01908) 222824 E-mail: sales@metalwork.co.uk *Industrial pneumatic equipment manufrs*

Metal Work Supplies, Unit 15 Grandstand Business Centre, Westfields Trading Estate, Hereford, HR4 9NS Tel: (01432) 266621 Fax: (01432) 270323 *Engineers merchants*

Metal Working Lubricant Services, Threshing Barn, Pillaton, Penkridge, Stafford, ST19 5RZ Tel: (01785) 716465 Fax: 01785 711043 E-mail: help@metalworkinglubricantservices.co.uk *Metalworking Lubricant Services (MLS) are one of the UK's leading independent suppliers of cutting fluids. With access to the world''s leadind coolants, Our team of Consultant Engineers recommend products on an engineering performance basis, showing cost effective results by eliminating coolant related problems and issues.*

► Metal Works UK Ltd, Greenman Yard, Boreham Street, Hailsham, East Sussex, BN27 4SF Tel: (01323) 833333 Fax: (01323) 833740 *Metal fabricators*

Metalas UK Ltd, White Cottages, Fuller Street, Fairstead, Chelmsford, CM3 2AY Tel: (01245) 233715 Fax: (01245) 381866 E-mail: admin@metalas.co.uk *Industrial Cleaning machines*

Metalcote Wire Products Mnfrs, Unit 14 Bromyard Road Industrial Estate, Ledbury, Herefordshire, HR8 1NS Tel: (01531) 633704 Fax: (01531) 635085 E-mail: enquiries@metalcote.co.uk *Metalcote - Wire mesh Cat Baskets from only £18.22. Specialists in plastic coated wire goods, The original wire cat basket manufacturer, veterinary restrainers, animal rescue equipment, i.e. cat traps, fold flat kennels,*

► Metalcraft Architectural Engineering Co. Ltd, Unit 1 Ravenscroft Way, Barnoldswick, Lancashire, BB18 6JA Tel: (01282) 817517 Fax: (01282) 851300 *Metalwork engineers*

Metalcraft Plastic Coatings Ltd, Back Wellington Street, Accrington, Lancashire, BB5 2NW Tel: (01254) 871727 Fax: (01254) 871168 E-mail: claudeen1@btconnect.com *Corrosion resistant coatings*

Metalcraft Tottenham Ltd, 6-40 Durnford Street, London, N15 5NQ Tel: (020) 8802 1715 Fax: (020) 8802 1258 E-mail: sales@makingmetalwork.com *Architectural metalworkers, sheet metalwork engineers & balustrade manufrs*

Metalcraft Willenhall Ltd, Ezekiel Lane, Willenhall, West Midlands, WV12 5QX Tel: (01922) 476954 Fax: (01922) 409588 *Sheet metalworkers & fabricators*

Metalcrafts 1991 Ltd, 22 St Helens Road, Prescot, Merseyside, L34 6HR Tel: 0151-430 6078 Fax: 0151-430 6078 *Metal workers*

► Metalduct Nottingham Ltd, C12 Haydn Road, Nottingham, NG5 1DG Tel: 0115-962 3482 Fax: 0115-969 2881

Metalen Products Ltd, The Winnowing Barn, Sherington, Newport Pagnell, Buckinghamshire, MK16 9QP Tel: (01908) 327100 Fax: (01908) 327101 E-mail: sales@metalen.co.uk *Hospitality furniture manufrs*

Metalflake Motor Factors, 15d Oakcroft Road, Chessington, Surrey, KT9 1RH Tel: (020) 8397 6198 Fax: (020) 8974 2850 E-mail: sales@metalflake.co.uk *Paint distributors or factors*

Metalflex Industrial Supplies Ltd, Unit 9 Adlington Court, Birchwood, Warrington, WA3 6PL Tel: (01925) 814999 Fax: (01925) 838999 E-mail: john.milsom@metalflex.co.uk *Metallic hose tubing & hose assembly manufrs*

Metalfold Engineering Ltd, Riverside Works, London Road Terrace, Macclesfield, Cheshire, SK11 7RN Tel: (01625) 511598 Fax: (01625) 618838 *Steel sheet metalwork engineers or fabricators*

Metalform Inc Ltd, Stratford St North, Birmingham, B11 1BP Tel: 0121-771 4432 Fax: 0121-766 6911 *Machinery reconditioning services*

Metalion Ltd, North Acton Road, London, NW10 6PD Tel: (020) 8965 4677 Fax: (020) 8965 3142 *Syntha pulvin powder coaters*

Metalised Products Ltd, Pontygwindy Industrial Estate, Caerphilly, Mid Glamorgan, CF83 3HU Tel: (029) 2088 5988 Fax: (029) 2086 3718 *Film paper & board manufrs*

Metalite Ltd, 121 Barkby Road, Leicester, LE4 9LU Tel: 0116-276 7874 Fax: 0116-233 0337 *Sprocket, gear & pulley manufrs*

Metalite Aviation Lighting, Winster Grove, Great Barr, Birmingham, B44 9EJ Tel: 0121-360 2222 Fax: 0121-366 6003 E-mail: sales@metaliteaviation.com *Portable airfield lighting manufrs*

Metallic Construction Co. Ltd, Alfreton Road, Derby, DE21 4AQ Tel: (01332) 831296 Fax: (01332) 833712 *Steel fabricators*

Metallic Extractors (Non-Ferrous) Ltd, Marsh Lane, Water Orton, Birmingham, B46 1NS Tel: 0121-747 3611 Fax: 0121-749 3769 E-mail: srap@beavermetals.com *Metal refiners & recycling services*

Metallic Fabrications Ltd, 212 Thorp Arch Trading Estate, Wetherby, West Yorkshire, LS23 7BJ Tel: (01937) 843485 Fax: (01937) 845517 E-mail: metfabs@aol.com *Architectural metal workers*

► Metallic Mango CD Duplication, 30 Water Street, Birmingham, B3 1HL Tel: 0121-604 0302 Fax: E-mail: info@metallicmango.co.uk *Audio CD Duplication for djs, producers, recording artists, record labels, event promoters, club brands, dj agencies, bands, demos, promos - music industry specialists. Data CD Duplication for businesses, advertising, models, photographers, showcases, modelling agencies. On-Disc Printing. CD Packaging.*

Metallic Wool Co. Ltd, Bredgar Road, Gillingham, Kent, ME8 6PL Tel: (01634) 239444 Fax: (01634) 239888 E-mail: enquiries@metallic-wool.co.uk *Steel wool products manufrs*

Metallics Metal Finishing Services, Unit 7 Sparkbrook Street, Coventry, CV1 5ST Tel: (024) 7663 3229 Fax: (024) 7625 2200 *Electro plating services*

Metallifacture Ltd, Mansfield Road, Redhill, Nottingham, NG5 8PY Tel: 0115-966 0200 Fax: 0115-967 0133 E-mail: mail@metallifacture.co.uk *Jack manufrs* Also at: Birmingham

► Metalliform Holdings, Chambers Road, Hoyland, Barnsley, South Yorkshire, S74 0EZ Tel: (01226) 350555 Fax: (01226) 350112 E-mail: sales@metalliform.co.uk *Educational furniture & stadium seating manufrs*

Metalline Signs Ltd, Barton Hill Trading Estate, Maze Street, Bristol, BS5 9TE Tel: 0117-955 5291 Fax: 0117-955 7518 E-mail: sales@metalline-signs.co.uk *Sign manufrs*

Metallink Fluid Power Systems, Prospect Road, Crook, County Durham, DL15 8JG Tel: 01388 761200 *Hydraulic tube & tubing fabricators & manipulators*

Metallizers (Heckmondwike) Ltd, Old White Lee Colliery, Leeds Road, Heckmondwike, West Yorkshire, WF16 9BH Tel: (01924) 473840 Fax: (01924) 473794 *Metal spraying & finishing contractors*

Metallon Ltd, Unit D Lea Road Trading Estate, Lea Road, Waltham Abbey, Essex, EN9 1AE Tel: (01992) 715737 Fax: (01992) 767607 E-mail: sales@metallon.co.uk *Display stand manufrs*

Metalltechnik UK Ltd, 8 Mere Close, Shifnal, Shropshire, TF11 9QA Tel: (01952) 461242 Fax: (01952) 417489 E-mail: metuk@dialstart.net *Shot blasting material suppliers*

► Metalmesh Ltd, PO Box 138, Marlborough, Wiltshire, SN8 1XE Tel: (01672) 841404 Fax: (01672) 841484 E-mail: sales@meshpartitions.com *Security partitions, machine guards & fencing specialists*

Metalocast Ltd, 58-60 Duncrue Street, Belfast, BT3 9AR Tel: (028) 9074 7433 Fax: (028) 9074 8017 E-mail: metalocast@aol.com *Engineers merchants & supplies*

Metalock Engineering, Hamilton, Glasgow, Tel: 0141-641 3368 E-mail: sales@metalock.co.uk *Casting repairs, onsite machining & maintenance*

Metalock Engineering UK Ltd, Paragon Way, Bayton Road Industrial Estate, Coventry, CV7 9QS Tel: (01322) 290090 Fax: (01322) 290088 E-mail: sales@metalock.co.uk *Specialists in casting repairers* Also at: Bristol, Cleveland, Dartford, Glasgow

Metalogic plc, Orbit House, Albert Street, Eccles, Manchester, M30 0BL Tel: 0161-707 1234 Fax: 0161-707 1304 E-mail: info@metalogicplc.com *Information communication technology suppliers*

Metalogics Sheet Metal Work, Whitehorse Industrial Estate, Bodmin Parkway, Bodmin, Cornwall, PL30 4BB Tel: (01208) 73696 Fax: (01208) 73696 *Structural steelworkers*

Metalor Technologies (UK) Ltd, 74 Warstone Lane, Birmingham, B18 6NG Tel: 0121-236 3241 Fax: 0121-236 3568 E-mail: electrotechnics@metalor.com Principal Export Areas: Worldwide *Based in Birmingham we are precious metal specialists and we work in the following markets; electrical contact material , watches, jewellery, metal refining, gold refining, silver refining, and advanced coatings. We supply, precious metal wire strips, rivet tips, and contact assemblies, Metalor are also respected Bullion dealers. Metalor provides an excellent service in both the technical expertise and excellent customer service*

Metalpacks Ltd, Old Parsonage Works, High Street, Farningham, Dartford, DA4 0DG Tel: (01322) 862727 Fax: (01322) 865580 E-mail: metalpacks@usa.net *Profile milling services*

Metalpoint Ltd, Factory D, Western Approach, South Shields, Tyne & Wear, NE33 5NN Tel: 0191-455 6086 Fax: 0191-455 2447 E-mail: sales@arndale.co.uk *Bolt & nut & general engineering supplies distributors*

Metalprint Signs & Nameplates, 37 The Pentlands, Kintbury, Hungerford, Berkshire, RG17 9XB Tel: (01488) 658670 Fax: (01488) 658670 E-mail: fp@metalplaques.co.uk *Commemorative metal plaques, metal labels*

Metalrax, Bordesley Green Road, Birmingham, B9 4TP Tel: 0121-772 8151 Fax: 0121-772 6135 E-mail: sales@metalrax-storage.co.uk *Designers, manufacturers and installers of storage and material handling systems including static and mobile shelving, pallet racking, mezzanine floors, small parts containers, gravity conveyors and rollers. We supply lockers, cupboards, steps, and trucks to industrial and commercial environments.*

Metalrax Group plc, Ardath Road, Birmingham, B38 9PN Tel: 0121-433 3444 Fax: 0121-433 3325 E-mail: info@toolspec.co.uk *Holding company*

Metals Group Ltd, Units 10-11 Walker Industrial Park, Guide, Blackburn, BB1 2QE Tel: (01254) 586700 Fax: (01254) 692063 E-mail: sales@metalsuk.com *Metals stock holder services*

Metals Research Ltd, Newton Hall, Town Street, Newton, Cambridge, CB2 5PE Tel: (01223) 872822 Fax: (01223) 872983 E-mail: info@newtonhall.co.uk *Fibre optic cabling equipment manufrs*

Metals South West, 10 Bradley Lane, Newton Abbot, Devon, TQ12 1LZ Tel: (01626) 362026 Fax: (01626) 332220 *Non-ferrous stockholders*

Metals Technology (Testing) Ltd, Unit 1 Byron House, 6 Finchwell Close, Sheffield, S13 9DF Tel: 0114-243 7271 Fax: 0114-243 7288 E-mail: sales@metalstechnology.co.uk *Metallurgical analysts/assayers/metallurgists*

► Metalskills Wrought Ironwork, 85 Seawall Road, Cardiff, CF24 5TH Tel: (029) 2048 2500 Fax: (029) 2048 2500 *Wrought iron services*

Metalsolv Software, A1 House, Kengington Village, Avonemoor Rd, London, W14 8TS Tel: (020) 7348 1500 Fax: (020) 7348 1501 *Internet developers*

Metalstyle Fabrications Ltd, Unit 25, Harvest Drive, South Lowestoft Industrial Estate, Lowestoft, Suffolk, NR33 7NJ Tel: (01502) 515758 Fax: (01502) 589927 E-mail: metalstylefab@btconnect.com *Steel fabricators*

Metaltec Ltd, Unit 5 Hurricane Close, Old Sarum, Salisbury, SP4 6LG Tel: (01722) 339090 Fax: (01722) 321311 E-mail: metal_tec@btconnect.com Principal Export Areas: West Europe *Metal fabricators*

Metaltech, Bonsall Street, Mill Hill, Blackburn, BB2 4DD Tel: (01254) 691488 *Cable & wire machinery manufrs*

Metaltech Ltd, Hownsgill Drive, Consett, County Durham, DH8 9HU Tel: (01207) 501085 Fax: (01207) 580743 E-mail: gf@metaltech.co.uk *Heat treatment materials manufrs*

Metaltech Consulting Services, 2 Talisman Business Centre, Duncan Road, Park Gate, Southampton, SO31 7GA Tel: (01489) 885483 Fax: (01489) 589372 E-mail: info@metaltechconsulting.co.uk *Metallurgical consultancy services*

► Metaltech Sheet Metal Work, Arundel Street, Halifax, West Yorkshire, HX1 4LE Tel: (01422) 355760 Fax: (01422) 344294 E-mail: sales@metaltech.org *Stainless steel fabrication supplies*

Metaltex UK Ltd, Brunleys, Kiln Farm, Milton Keynes, MK11 3HR Tel: (01908) 262062 Fax: (01908) 262162 E-mail: info@metaltex.com *Kitchen tool & utensil distributors*

Metaltreat Ltd, 359 Canal Road, Bradford, West Yorkshire, BD2 1AN Tel: (01274) 221500 Fax: (01274) 221520 E-mail: metaltreat@wedge-galv.co.uk *Hot dip galvanizing organisation*

Metalways Ltd, 20 Churchill Way, Fleckney, Leicester, LE8 8UD Tel: 0116-240 3148 Fax: 0116-240 3013 E-mail: erica@metalwaysltd.com *Fabricators & sheet metalworkers*

Metalweb, Unit 9, Trident Industrial Estate, Pindar Road, Hoddesdon, Hertfordshire, EN11 0WZ Tel: (020) 8804 4032 Fax: (01992) 450557 E-mail: info@metalweb.co.uk *Aluminium stockholders*

Metal-Woods Ltd, 14 Church Street, Market Harborough, Leicestershire, LE16 7AB Tel: (01858) 462641 Fax: (01858) 431616 E-mail: sales@metal-woods.co.uk *Cutting & creasing rule suppliers, distributors & manufrs*

Metalwork Structures, St Annes House, 399 Lees Hall Road, Dewsbury, West Yorkshire, WF12 9HB Tel: (01924) 461355 Fax: (01924) 450291 E-mail: sales@metalworkgroup.co.uk *Metalworking & hi-fi units*

Metamix Concrete, Purdy Road, Bilston, West Midlands, WV14 8UB Tel: (01902) 493626 Fax: (01902) 497418 *Ready mixed concrete merchants & floor screed*

► Metamorphicycles, The Old Foundry, Chawston Lane, Chawston, Bedford, MK44 3BH Tel: (01480) 216510 Fax: (01480) 216510 *Trike manufrs*

Metanet Engravers, Unit 10 Threeways Farm, Melton Road, Queniborough, Leicester, LE7 3FN Tel: 0116-264 0567 Fax: 0116-264 0567 *General engravers*

► Metaphorix Ltd, 3 Temple Court, Temple Way, Coleshill, Birmingham, B46 1HH Tel: (01675) 432400 Fax: (01675) 465571 E-mail: enquiries@metaphorix.co.uk *Financial accounting solutions*

Metascybe Systems Ltd, 89 Hartfield Road, London, SW19 3TJ Tel: (01937) 543500 Fax: (020) 8544 0700 E-mail: info@metascybe.co.uk *Computer software development house services*

Metasmith Edinburgh Ltd, Unit 12 Bilston Glen Industrial Estate, Dryden Road, Loanhead, Midlothian, EH20 9LZ Tel: 0131-440 7002 Fax: 0131-440 7003 *Sheet metalwork engineers & fabricators*

Metax Ltd, 77 Capital Business Centre, Carlton Road, South Croydon, Surrey, CR2 0BS Tel: (020) 8916 2077 Fax: (01689) 889994 E-mail: sales@metax.co.uk *Scientific instruments suppliers*

▶ Joseph Metcalf Ltd, Nook Lane, Lower Green, Astley, Manchester, M29 7LW Tel: (01942) 896668 Fax: (01942) 897485 E-mail: rgrice@gemweb.co.uk *Fertilisers & compost suppliers*

Metcalf Leenside Ltd, 139-143 Canal Street, Nottingham, NG1 7HD Tel: 0115-958 0865 Fax: 0115-959 8934E-mail: sales@metcalf.co.uk *Tarpaulin & webbing manufrs*

Metcalfe J.J Fishing Tackle, 15 Newgate Street, Walton on the Naze, Essex, CO14 8DT Tel: (01255) 675680 Fax: (01255) 675680 *Fishing tackle retail, suppliers & manufrs*

▶ Metcalfe Plant Hire Ltd, 46 Gilwilly Road, Gilwilly Industrial Estate, Penrith, Cumbria, CA11 9BL Tel: (01768) 868686 Fax: (01768) 868688

▶ Met-Check Ltd, 9 Churchfield Road, Chilton Industrial Estate, Sudbury, Suffolk, CO10 2YA Tel: (01787) 883138 Fax: (01787) 883139 E-mail: sales@met-check.co.uk Sales Contact: J. West *Manufacturers of environmental monitoring equipment/systems, meteorological/ environmental instruments/systems, weather stations & wind indicators/wind socks (speed or direction)*

Metcraft Engineering Ltd, Unit 10 Fenn FLD Indust Estate, Homefield Road, Haverhill, Suffolk, CB9 8QP Tel: (01440) 712227 Fax: (01440) 712274 *Engineers*

Metcraft Lighting Ltd, Bourne Street, Chadderton, Oldham, OL9 7LX Tel: 0161-683 4298 Fax: 0161-688 8004 E-mail: info@metcraftlighting.com *Street lighting manufrs*

Metelec Ltd, Vulcan Industrial Estate, Walsall, WS2 7BZ Tel: (01922) 712665 Fax: (01922) 710919 E-mail: sales@metelec.co.uk *Suppliers of extruded copper section, together with copper components primarily for the switchgear industry, as a wholly owned subsidiary of Gindre SA. Metelec offer the largest range of copper extrusions & strip from stock, or made to order, now include a wide selection of brass extrusions together with copper & brass sheet* Also at: Rochdale

Meteor, 239 Drum Road, Cookstown, County Tyrone, BT80 9HP Tel: (028) 8675 1515 Fax: (028) 8672 8961 E-mail: sales@meteorelectrical.com *Electrical wholesalers*

Meteor Communications (Europe) Ltd, Hertfordshire Business Centre, Alexander Road, London Colney, St. Albans, Hertfordshire, AL2 1JG Tel: (01727) 828200 Fax: (01727) 828100 *Radio telemetry systems manufrs*

Meter Mix Systems Ltd, Unit 1 Brindley Close, Rushden, Northamptonshire, NN10 6EN Tel: (01933) 354500 Fax: (01933) 354506 *Sealant & adhesive mixing machine distributors & manufrs*

Metering Systems UK Ltd, Cross Edge, Oswaldtwistle, Accrington, Lancashire, BB5 3SD Tel: (01254) 395651 Fax: (01254) 237349 E-mail: john@meteringsystems.co.uk *Flow meter systems manufrs*

Metering Technology Solutions Ltd, Dogmore, Stoke Row, Henley-on-Thames, Oxfordshire, RG9 5PD Tel: (01491) 681688 Fax: (01491) 681076 E-mail: mts@meter.co.uk *Meter reading systems distributors*

▶ Meters Meter Suppliers, Whitegate, White Lund Industrial Estate, Morecambe, Lancashire, LA3 3BT Tel: (01524) 555929 Fax: (01524) 847009 E-mail: sales@meters.co.uk *Utility Meter Manufacturers.*Manufacturers Of Electricity, Gas, Heat,Oil & Water Meters*

Metex Engineering Ltd, 5 Holly Lane, Beeston, Nottingham, NG9 4AB Tel: 0115-943 0155 Fax: 0115-943 6365 *Sheet metal fabrications*

▶ Metfab Architectural Metalwork Rainham, Unit 8, Salamons Way, Rainham, Essex, RM13 9UL Tel: (01708) 550058 Fax: (01708) 526667 E-mail: iain@metfab.org

Metfab Design Ltd, Unit 220 Foley Industrial Estate, Kidderminster, Worcestershire, DY11 7DH Tel: (01562) 864129 Fax: (01562) 864129 *Sheetmetalwork engineers/fabricators*

▶ Metfab UK Ltd, Strode Road, Newnham Industrial Estate, Plympton, Plymouth, PL7 4AY Tel: (01752) 337208 Fax: (01752) 337209 *Steel fabrication*

Metfabs Ltd, Rope Walk, Littlehampton, West Sussex, BN17 5DE Tel: (01903) 717517 Fax: (01903) 713682 *Sheet & plate metal workers*

Metfix Ceilings Ltd, 40b Humber Avenue, Coventry, CV3 1AY Tel: (024) 7645 7343 Fax: (024) 7663 5915 *Suspended ceiling components*

Metflex, Queen Street, Great Harwood, Blackburn, BB6 7AU Tel: (01254) 884171 Fax: (01254) 887753 E-mail: sales@metlex.co.uk Principal Export Areas: Worldwide *Rubber diaphragms, gaskets & injection mouldings manufrs*

Methodist Insurance plc, Brazennose House West, Brazennose Street, Manchester, M2 5AS Tel: 0161-833 9696 Fax: 0161-833 1287 E-mail: enquiries@micmail.com *Insurance company*

Methods Application Ltd, 39 King Street, London, WC2E 8JS Tel: (020) 7240 1121 Fax: (020) 7379 8561 E-mail: central@methods.co.uk *IT consultants*

Metix (UK) Ltd, Saxon House, Henson Way, Telford Way Industrial Estate, Kettering, Northamptonshire, NN16 8PX Tel: (01536) 312990 Fax: (01536) 312985 E-mail: sales@metix.co.uk Sales Contact: A. Weatherley *Mixers, static, disposable static mixers manufrs*

Metklean Products Ltd, 23 Hailey Road, Erith, Kent, DA18 4AA Tel: (020) 8310 9882 Fax: (020) 8312 1336 *Cleaning products manufrs*

Metlab Supplies Ltd, Unit 7, Glendale Avenue, Sandycroft, Deeside, Clwyd, CH5 2QP Tel: (01244) 526300 Fax: (01244) 526301 E-mail: barry@metlabsupplies.co.uk *Laboratory equipment & chemical distributors*

Metmachex Engineering Ltd, 9 Monk Road, Alfreton, Derbyshire, DE55 7RL Tel: (01773) 836241 Fax: (01773) 520109 E-mail: sales@metmachex.com *Precision engineering manufrs*

Metnor Galvanising Ltd, Hardwick View Road, Holmewood, Chesterfield, Derbyshire, S42 5SA Tel: (01246) 854650 Fax: (01246) 850086 *Galvanizers & galvanizing services*

Metokote U K Ltd, Hackwood Road, High March Industrial Estate, Daventry, Northamptonshire, NN11 4ES Tel: (01327) 703745 Fax: (01327) 300141 *Volume metal finishing & electroplating*

Metool Products Ltd, Unit 1 Mercian Park, Mercian Close, Ilkeston, Derbyshire, DE7 8HG Tel: 0115-922 5931 Fax: 0115-925 8183 E-mail: postmaster@metool.com *Manufacturers of brakes, disc; cable/hose drag chain systems; cable reeling drum/reel & hose reel (automatic/ self-wind)*

Metprep Ltd, Curriers Close, Charter Avenue Industrial Estate, Coventry, CV4 8AW Tel: (024) 7642 1222 Fax: (024) 7642 1192 E-mail: sales@metprep.co.uk *Supply of metallographic equipment & suppliers*

Metra Martech Ltd, 7 Chiswick High Road, London, W4 2ND Tel: (020) 8742 7888 Fax: (020) 8742 8558 E-mail: research@metra-martech.com *Management consultants & market researchers*

Metra Non-Ferrous Metals Ltd, Pindar Road, Hoddesdon, Hertfordshire, EN11 0DE Tel: (01992) 460455 Fax: (01992) 451207 E-mail: enquiries@metra-metals.co.uk *Distributors of metal spraying wire, zinc sheet & zinc wire*

▶ Metrans Processing Ltd, Unit 5, North Orbital Trading Estate, Napsbury Lane, St. Albans, Hertfordshire, AL1 1XB Tel: (01727) 848160

Metreat Ltd t/a Applied Metal Finishers, Units 2-3, Prosper House, Padholme Road East, Peterborough, PE1 5XL Tel: (01733) 703030 Fax: (01733) 704040 E-mail: sales@appliedmetalfinishers.co.uk *Applied Metal Finishers are specialist metal coaters operating from 15000 sq ft premises, adjacent to the A1. Products processed include: point of sale, shop fittings, electrical cabinets, automotive and general engineering. Long term corrosion protection, pre-treatments prior to powder coating, including zinc phosphate, alocrom chromate conversion, anoding and nylon-coating. We offer a range of processes all to ISO9002 standard. Anodising Sulphuric acid, transparent coating. Hard Anodising, thicker & harder than sulphuric anodising. Yellow Chromate Coatings, For aluminium. Trade names - Alocrom, 1200 Golden appearance, 1000 Clear film. Good corrosion resistance, excellent paint adhesion on aluminium surfaces. Low electrical resistance, can be used as a final finish. Zinc Plating, Rust-proof finish, applied by electro deposition, Phosphating, Iron phosphate, Zinc Phosphate. Powder Coating. Other Finishes - details on request; blackodising, copper, chrome, tin.*

Metric Group Ltd, Metric House, 5 Love Lane, Cirencester, Gloucestershire, GL7 1YG Tel: (01285) 651441 Fax: (01285) 653944 E-mail: postmaster@metricgroup.co.uk *Special purpose machinery & electronic ticketing*

▶ Metric Group Ltd, Metric House Westmead Drive, Westmead Industrial Estate, Swindon, SN5 7AD Tel: (01793) 647800 Fax: (01793) 647802 E-mail: sales@metricgroup.co.uk *Manufacturer sell & maintain & repair parking equipment*

▶ Metric Scaffolding Co. Ltd, Stanley Works, Ampthill Road, Kempston Hardwick, Bedford, MK45 3JE Tel: (01234) 325005 Fax: (01234) 210933 *Supply, hire & erect of scaffolding Kwikstage, tube & fittings*

Metric Tool & Die Ltd, 10a Havant Road, Horndean, Waterlooville, Hampshire, PO8 0DT Tel: (023) 9257 1544 Fax: (023) 9257 1542 *Tool manufrs*

Metrik Office Supplies, 20 Market Square, Dumfries, DG2 7AB Tel: (01387) 253844 Fax: (01387) 257343 E-mail: scallender@metrik.co.uk *Office & stationery suppliers*

Metris UK Ltd, Argosy Road, Nottingham EMA, Castle Donnington, Derby, DE74 2SA Tel: (01332) 811349 Fax: (01332) 850149 E-mail: sales@lkuk.co.uk *Inspection equipment manufrs*

Metro Ltd, 13 Imperial Park, Rawreth Lane, Rayleigh, Essex, SS6 9RS Tel: (01268) 782084 Fax: (01268) 782653 E-mail: sales@metroltd.co.uk *Industrial & commercial lighting manufrs*

Metro Blinds, 4 Gosford Industrial Estate, Far Gosford Street, Coventry, CV1 5ED Tel: (024) 7652 0613 Fax: (024) 7652 0613 *Blind manufrs*

Metro Box Ltd, 25-30 Green Street, Birmingham, B12 0NB Tel: 0121-772 5411 Fax: 0121-771 4371 E-mail: ajf@metrobox.freeserve.co.uk *Corrugated box, case & container manufrs*

Metro Clothing Co. Ltd, 96 Fonthill Road, London, N4 3HT Tel: (020) 7263 0962 Fax: (020) 7263 0962 *Ladies fashion wholesalers*

▶ Metro Commercial Printing Ltd, 7 Mowat Industrial Estate, Sandown Road, Watford, WD24 7UY Tel: (01923) 252812 Fax: (01923) 818727

▶ Metro Digital Television, Unit D20-21 Fieldhouse Industrial Estate, Fieldhouse Road, Rochdale, Lancashire, OL12 0AA Tel: (01706) 358222 Fax: (01706) 350211 E-mail: sales@mdtv.co.uk *Maintain and Install Communal Aerial Television Systems Both IRS and DTT. Installers of Direct to Home Satellite Television reception systems and Digital Aerials.*

Metro Engineering Co., Unit 12 Chillington Fields, Wolverhampton, WV1 2BY Tel: (01902) 455254 Fax: (01902) 455254 *Engineers*

Metro Leisure Developments Ltd, 13 Hylton Street, North Shields, Tyne & Wear, NE29 6SQ Tel: 0191-258 3677 Fax: 0191-295 4926 E-mail: johnkelly@metroleisure.co.uk *Products for the leisure market & glass fibre manufrs*

Metro Plan Ltd, Lake District Business Park, Mint Bridge Road, Kendal, Cumbria, LA9 6NH Tel: (01539) 730103 Fax: (01539) 730765 E-mail: sales@metroplan.co.uk *Visual aids & planning equipment*

▶ Metro Press Ltd, 64-66 Albion Road, Edinburgh, EH7 5QZ Tel: 0131-661 8984

▶ Metro Rentals Limited, Unit 2, Colne Way, Colne Way Court, Watford, WD24 7NE Tel: 01923 630630 Fax: 01923 639191 E-mail: enquiries@metrorentals.co.uk *At Metro Rentals, we offer self-drive van and minibus hire at very competitive rates. Our pricing is clear with no hidden extras.**We ensure that our vehicles are regularly maintained and we take particular care to ensure that they are clean, both inside and out prior to hiring them out. All our vans and minibuses come with full AA coverage and comprehensive insurance protection as well as unlimited mileage. **We pride ourselves on providing a personalised and professional service in the North London and Southwest Hertfordshire area especially in Harrow, Wembley, Ruislip, Watford, Hemel Hempstead, St. Albans and Hatfield.**If you are thinking about van hire or minibus hire either for a day or up to a month we would be pleased to provide you with a competitive quote, without obligation. Please visit us online at www.metrorentals.co.uk or call us on 01923 630 630.**

▶ Metro Research Ltd, 118 The Chandlery, 50 Westminster Bridge Road, London, SE1 7QY Tel: (0870) 9979777 Fax: (020) 7953 7450 E-mail: vinesh@metroresearch.com *Market research services*

Metro Rod P.L.C., East Barnet, Barnet, Hertfordshire, EN4 8WR Tel: (020) 8449 8477 Fax: (020) 8449 8466 E-mail: ascriven@sgaservices.co.uk *Drain & pipe cleaning specialists* Also at: Branches throughout the U.K.

Metro Sales, Unit 1 Crathie Road, Off Western Road, Kilmarnock, Ayrshire, KA3 1NG Tel: (01563) 574481 Fax: (01563) 533537 E-mail: sales@metrosales.biz *Plastic pocket & wallet manufrs*

Metro Security, 5 Ashton Road, Harold Hill, Romford, RM3 8UJ Tel: (0870) 6090095 Fax: (0870) 6090096 E-mail: info@metrosecurity.co.uk *Burglar alarms & security systems services*

▶ Metro Security Services, Liverpool, L28 1YX Tel: (0845) 2269185 E-mail: metrosecurity@lycos.co.uk *Static & Mobile security, sinage, Gate House security, Reception Security, Events & Concert Security, Close Protection Security, 24 Hours 7 Days A week,Merseyside, Liverpool, North West Areas, North Wales,*

Metro Shipping Ltd, 50 Cliveland Street, Birmingham, B19 3SH Tel: 0121-333 4455 Fax: 0121-333 4021 E-mail: enquiries@metroshipping.co.uk *Freight management*

Metrodata Ltd, Blenheim House Crabtree Office Village, Eversley Way, Egham, Surrey, TW20 8RY Tel: (01784) 744700 Fax: (01784) 477423 E-mail: sales@metrodata.co.uk Principal Export Areas: Worldwide *Data communication manufacturers network services*

Metrode Products Ltd, Hanworth Lane, Chertsey, Surrey, KT16 9LL Tel: (01932) 566721 Fax: (01932) 565168 E-mail: info@metrode.com *Manufacturers and suppliers of alloyed welding consumables in the UK.*

Metrodent Ltd, Lowergate Works, Huddersfield, HD3 4EP Tel: (01484) 461616 Fax: (01484) 462700 E-mail: admin@metrodent.com *Dental care equipment distributors & manufrs*

Metrohm UK Ltd, 2 Buckingham Industrial Park, Top Angel, Buckingham Industrial Estate, Buckingham, MK18 1TH Tel: (01280) 824824 Fax: (01280) 824800 E-mail: enquiry@metrohm.co.uk *Chemical analysis equipment manufrs*

Metrol Springs Ltd, 75 Tenter Road, Moulton Park Industrial Estate, Northampton, NN3 6AX Tel: (01604) 499332 Fax: (01604) 493390 E-mail: sales@metrol.com *Spring manufrs*

Metrol Technology Ltd, Unit 24 Kirkhill Place, Dyce, Aberdeen, AB21 0GU Tel: (01224) 772771 Fax: (01224) 772660 *Oil services*

Metrology Instrument Solutions, 94 Repton Road, Hartshorne, Swadlincote, Derbyshire, DE11 7AE Tel: (01283) 223800 E-mail: metrology@mcmail.com *Engineering instrumentation*

Metrology Systems Wales, 21 Bessant Close, Cowbridge, Vale of Glamorgan, CF71 7HP Tel: (01446) 772926 Fax: (01446) 772926 *Roll calliper gauges - manual roll caliper gauges - manual roll calliper gauges - electronic roll caliper gauges - electronic roll trotter roll shop management software rollshop management system*

Metromold Ltd, Oak Road, West Chirton North Industrial Estate, North Shields, Tyne & Wear, NE29 8SF Tel: 0191-296 3303 Fax: 0191-296 3303 E-mail: sales@metromold.co.uk *Specialist medium, small & micro moulders*

Metron Energy Management Ltd, PO Box 190, Winsford, Cheshire, CW7 9AH Tel: (01606) 882722 Fax: (01606) 889440 E-mail: enquiries@demmetron.co.uk *Design & manufacture of energy saving lighting controls for factories & schools*

Metron Technology (UK) Ltd, 2 Gregory Road, Livingston, West Lothian, EH54 7DR Tel: (01506) 403000 Fax: (01506) 403037 *Electronic component distribs*

Metronet Rew Ltd, 130 Bollo Lane, London, W3 8BZ Tel: (020) 7918 6525 Fax: (020) 7918 6525 E-mail: chris.skuse@metronetrail.com *Railway transport repair services*

Metropes Metals Ltd, Estate Road 3, South Humberside Industrial Estate, Grimsby, South Humberside, DN31 2TB Tel: (01472) 342440 Fax: (01472) 267815 *Steel stockists*

Metropolis, Grange Business Centre, Belasis Avenue, Billingham, Cleveland, TS23 1LG Tel: (01642) 361255 Fax: (01642) 365700 E-mail: sales@metropolisdevelopments.co.uk *Scale & industrial model makers*

▶ Metropolis Modern Art, 29 Compton Street, Chesterfield, Derbyshire, S40 4TA Tel: (01246) 233568

Metropolitan Coffee Co. Ltd, 28-30 Telford Way, London, W3 7XS Tel: (020) 8743 8959 Fax: (020) 8743 4929 E-mail: sales@metropolitancoffee.co.uk *Coffee is our speciality. To enjoy the Segafredo Zanetti coffee experience, Europe's number one espresso, please get in touch or see our website. We also proudly supply Integrity Fairtrade coffees and Caffe Amada espresso beans. As the main importer of La San Marco espresso machinery, since 1920 the leader in quality, reliability, technological innovation and Italian design we can offer machines, serving and training. We always have time for coffee, how about you?*

▶ Metropolitan Fencing, Prothero Works, Bilport Lane, Wednesbury, West Midlands, WS10 0NT Tel: 0121-502 6600 Fax: 0121-502 0303 E-mail: chrisw@tangorail.com *Steel palisade manufacturers of both d & w section & security gates*

▶ Metropolitan Security Services Group Ltd, 384 Poynters Road, Luton, LU4 0TW Tel: (0870) 2424557 Fax: (01582) 570001 E-mail: sales@metropolitansecurity.co.uk *Security services*

Metropolitan Stone, 5 Wells Place, Merstham, Redhill, RH1 3DR Tel: (01737) 644111 Fax: (01737) 648300 *Stone restoration*

Metropolitan Weighing Machine Co. Ltd, Metro Weighing Machines, Foxton Road, Grays, Essex, RM20 4XX Tel: (01375) 390140 Fax: (01375) 390140 E-mail: enquiries@metroweigh.com *Manufacturers of weighing systems*

Metropolitano Ltd, Communications House, 26 York Street, Westminster, London, W1U 6PZ Tel: (020) 7060 2501 Fax: (020) 7060 6031 E-mail: info@metropolitano.co.uk *Staff recruitment, managers, programmers, sales & marketing*

Metrovac Co., 1016 Harrow Road, Kensal Green, London, NW10 5NS Tel: (020) 8969 4522 *Industrial & kitchen cleaning*

Metsec plc, Broadwell Works, Birmingham Road, Oldbury, West Midlands, B69 4HE Tel: 0121-552 1541 E-mail: windows@metsec.com Principal Export Areas: Africa, Central/East Europe & West Europe *Steelwork support manufrs*

Metso Automation Ltd, 2 Lindenwood, Crockford Lane, Chineham, Basingstoke, Hampshire, RG24 8QY Tel: (0870) 6061478 Fax: (01256) 707661 E-mail: sales@metso.com *Control valves manufrs*

▶ Metso Minerals (UK) Ltd, Parkfield Road, Rugby, Warwickshire, CV21 1QJ Tel: (01788) 532100 Fax: (01788) 560442 E-mail: ukenquiries@metso.com *Bulk materials, handling equipment & mineral processing*

Metso Paper Ltd, Birchwood One, Duehurst Road, Birchwood, Warrington, WA3 7GB Tel: (01925) 286850 Fax: (01925) 286868 E-mail: info@metsopaper.com *Paper making plant manufrs*

Metsol Engineering, Ridgacre Enterprise Park, Ridgacre Road, West Bromwich, West Midlands, B71 1BW Tel: 0121-553 2189 Fax: 0121-525 3375 E-mail: metsolcnc@aol.com *Precision engineers services*

Metspin Ltd, Clovelly Road, Southbourne, Emsworth, Hampshire, PO10 8PF Tel: (01243) 378401 Fax: (01243) 374219 E-mail: sales@metspin.com Sales Contact: N. Cousins *We are one of the few Specialist Metal Spinning Companies in the UK that have the knowledge and wealth of expertise and technical knowhow in the art of Metal Spinning. We are equipped with the latest state of the art PNC Liefeld programmable Automatic Spinning Machines that enable us to manufacture precision spun Aerospace components in most materials - hastelloy, nimonic, inconel, titanium, mu-metal, tantalum and aerospace alloys and steels etc - max. diameter 1100mm x 12mm thick. In addition to our Power Forming Division we have one of the most experienced assembled team of time served manual craftesmen who between them cover the whole spectrum from engineering precision spinning to general commercial components -max. diameter 2100mm x 4mm thick. We design and manufacture Tooling up to 3 tons. We carry many Company Approvals such as Rolls Royce Approval No. 90130 and we are also fully ISO 9001-2000 Accredited. We offer a full manufacturing service*

▶ Metstrut, Unit 3 Granada Trading Estate, Off Park Street, Oldbury, West Midlands, B69 4LH Tel: 0121-601 6085 Fax: 0121-601 6177 E-mail: nsmith@metsec.com *Manufacturers of cable support systems*

Mettallicut, Deepdale Lane, Lower Gornal, Dudley, West Midlands, DY3 2AF Tel: (01384) 455115 Fax: (01384) 455015 *Engineers & toolmakers*

Mettech Ltd, Ramsden Road, Rotherwas Industrial Estate, Hereford, HR2 6LR Tel: 01432 341630 *Precision sheet metal & powder coating manufrs*

Mettis Aerospace Ltd, Windsor Road, Redditch, Worcestershire, B97 6EF Tel: (01527) 406400 Fax: (01527) 406401 E-mail: info@mettis-aerospace.com *Forging manufrs*

Mettler Toledo Safeline Ltd, Montford Street, Salford, M50 2XD Tel: 0161-848 8636 Fax: 0161-848 8595 *Metal detection systems manufrs*

Metwin Ltd, 1-5 Rosina Street, London, E9 6JH Tel: (020) 8985 4371 Fax: (020) 8985 6778 *Light engineering*

Metwin Ltd, 104 Chingford Mount Road, London, E4 9AA Tel: (020) 8523 2081 Fax: (020) 8531 8313 E-mail: metwin@btconnect.com *Metal window manufrs* Also at: London E9

Metwin Engineering, Unit 16 Charfleets Indust Estate, Charfleets Industrial Estate, Canvey Island, Essex, SS8 0PN Tel: (01268) 685959 Fax: (01268) 696208 *Sub-contract precision engineers*

Meura (Brewery Equipment) Ltd, 1 Park Farm, Buntingford, Hertfordshire, SG9 9AZ Tel: (01763) 272680 Fax: (01763) 272321 E-mail: info@meura.co.uk *Manufacturers of brewery equipment*

Mevagissey Shark & Angling Centre, West Wharf, Mevagissey, St. Austell, Cornwall, PL26 6UJ Tel: (01726) 843430 Fax: (01726) 843430 E-mail: sales@skua.org.uk *Retail outlet & fishing trips*

A.J. & R.J. Mew, 20 Mayfield Road, Ryde, Isle Of Wight, PO33 3TR Tel: (01983) 852835 Fax: (01983) 568758 *Removal & storage contractors*

▶ A.J. & R.J. Mew The Movers, 23 Little Preston Road, Ryde, Isle Of Wight, PO33 1DG Tel: (01983) 566664 E-mail: info@mewthemovers.co.uk *Removals & storage services*

Mexboro Concrete Ltd, Yalberton Tor Industrial Estate, Alders Way, Paignton, Devon, TQ4 7QQ Tel: (01803) 558025 Fax: (01803) 524717 E-mail: adc@mexboroconcrete.com *Pre-cast concrete & cast stone manufrs*

Mexmast Ltd, 2 Jubilee Road, Victoria Industrial Estate, Burgess Hill, West Sussex, RH15 9TL Tel: (01444) 247198 Fax: (01444) 246431 E-mail: sales@mexmast.co.uk *Fork lift truck dealers*

Meyn Poultry Equipment Ltd, 7 Bilton Industrial Estate, Bilton Road, Basingstoke, Hampshire, RG24 8LJ Tel: (01256) 466040 Fax: (01256) 841916 E-mail: peter.meyn@btconnect.com *Poultry processing equipment manufrs*

Meynell Paints Ltd, 400 Roding Lane South, Woodford Green, Essex, IG8 8EZ Tel: (020) 8550 9999 Fax: (020) 8551 8555 E-mail: gaye.brown@talk21.com *Industrial paint manufrs*

Meyrick & Powell Ltd, Llangenny, Llangenny, Crickhowell, Powys, NP8 1HD Tel: (01873) 812074 Fax: (01873) 812074 *Agricultural services*

William Meyrick Jones, Fronhaul, Cwm Golau, Cyfronydd, Welshpool, Powys, SY21 9EZ Tel: (01938) 810419 *Farming & contractors*

The Mezzanine Floor Co. Ltd, Unit 2B, 9 Cannon Lane, Tonbridge, Kent, TN9 1PP Tel: (01732) 356085 Fax: (01732) 361278 E-mail: sales@mezzanine.co.uk Principal Export Areas: Central/East Europe & West Europe *Mezzanine floor constructors*

▶ MF Home Typists, 34 Devon Avenue, Twickenham, Twickenham, TW2 6PW Tel: (020) 8755 4450 E-mail: farrm001@rgfl.org.uk *Typing services*

MFA/Como Drills, Felderland Lane, Worth, Deal, Kent, CT14 0BT Tel: (01304) 612132 Fax: (01304) 614696 E-mail: info@mfacomo.com *Manufacturer & distributor of motor gearboxes & drill equipment*

MFB Fabrications Ltd, High Street, Clay Cross, Chesterfield, Derbyshire, S45 9DX Tel: (01246) 861700 Fax: (01246) 861777 E-mail: sales@mfbfabs.co.uk *Steel fabricators*

Mfi Furniture Centre Ltd, Astmoor Road, Astmoor Industrial Estate, Runcorn, Cheshire, WA7 1PQ Tel: (01928) 581111 Fax: (01928) 573997 *Household furniture manufrs*

MG Auto Electrics, 1 Cherry Tree Avenue, Farnworth, Bolton, BL4 9SB Tel: (01204) 705905 Fax: (01204) 705900 E-mail: sales@mgautoelectrics.co.uk *Auto electrical repairs & fittings*

MG Micro, 41 Priest Meadow, Fleckney, Leicester, LE8 8TZ Tel: 0116-240 3157 Fax: 0116-240 3157 *CCTV cameras & burglar alarms installers*

▶ MG Site Services Ltd, 4 Oak Meadows, Tanyfron, Wrexham, Clwyd, LL11 5TH Tel: (01978) 752341 Fax: (01978) 754368 E-mail: info@asbestos-surveys-wales.co.uk *MG Site Services provide an independant Asbestos Survey service. We can provide professional advice on current regulations and survey your property or Business, advising on best options for any Asbestos issues.*

MG Stainless Ltd, Unit 1 & 2, Shaw Rd, Netherton, Dudley, West Midlands, DY2 8TS Tel: (01384) 232175 Fax: (01384) 232177 E-mail: mail@mgstainless.co.uk *MS Stainless are based in the heart of England, ideally located for serving the UK. We offer a comprehensive range of stainless steel sanitary ware, washroom and catering equipment, for projects requiring the durability and hygienic properties of stainless steel. Our product range includes: wash troughs, wash fountains, inset bowls, bucket/utility sinks, janitorial units, shower trays & cubicles, ice sinks, washroom accessories, grab rails, urinals, basins, drinking fountains, catering equipment, hospital equipment, WC pans/suites.*For more details on our product range, please look at our website which contains our online catalogue.*

▶ MGC Haulage Ltd, Mayfield Garage, 1 East Avenue, Carfin Industrial Estate, Motherwell, Lanarkshire, ML1 4UE Tel: (01698) 834146 E-mail: mgchaulage@btinternet.com *Dumptruck, tipper truck hire. Hiab crane lorry hire. Contact earth, tar, gravel, etc shifting /disposal.*

Mge Ups Systems Ltd, Orion House, 171-177 High Street, Wealdstone, Harrow, Middlesex, HA3 5EA Tel: (020) 8861 4040 Fax: (020) 8861 2812 E-mail: jason.koffler@mgeups.com *Power supply systems manufrs*

MGL Van Hire, Unit 8, Trench Lock Industrial Estate, Telford, Shropshire, TF1 5SW Tel: (01952) 252396 *Steel fabricators*

▶ MGM Du Verre Ltd, London Road, Dorking, Surrey, RH5 6AA Tel: (01306) 886222 Fax: (01306) 886222 E-mail: info@mgm-duverre.co.uk *Importers & exporters of glass containers to food & beverage industry*

▶ MGM Petrogas, 29 Hazeldown Road, TEIGNMOUTH, Devon, TQ14 8QR Tel: 01626 775803 Fax: 01626 775803 E-mail: mgmpetrogas@btinternet.com *Provider of all aspects of LP Gas training. Underground pipe systems,Leisure, Marine & Process Manufacturing.*Specialist "Ad Hoc" in house training for competency certifications.*Independant gas related incident investigations.*

MGN Electronics, Beaumont Enterprise Centre, Boston Road, Leicester, LE4 1HB Tel: 0116-235 4004 Fax: 0116-236 6584 E-mail: gush@mgnelect.co.uk *Electronic consultants*

MH CompuTech, 6 Blackwell Close, Higham Ferrers, Northamptonshire, NN10 8PJ Tel: (01933) 315900 E-mail: info@mhcomputech.co.uk *We are a professional IT company based in Higham Ferrers, Northants. For upgrades, repairs, installations of computers, broadband, servers and printers whether for home or businesses.*

▶ mh design, 6 Willand Court, Retford, Retford, Nottinghamshire, DN22 7GD Tel: 01777 704967 Fax: 01777 719517 E-mail: sales@mhdesign.co.uk *Suppliers of machinery and handling equipment to the PVCu and window fabrication industry*

Mha Computer Services, 42 Wheatsheaf Road, Alconbury Weston, Huntingdon, Cambridgeshire, PE28 4LF Tel: (01480) 891338 Fax: (01480) 891343 *Computer consultancy*

▶ MHA-Turnkey, 1 Roundwood House, Roundwood Road, High Wycombe, Buckinghamshire, HP12 4HE Tel: (01494) 528006 Fax: (01494) 445154 E-mail: mha-turnkey@supanet.com *Contractors, home extensions, interior design, conservatories*

Mho Trak Ltd, Blackhorse Road, Letchworth Garden City, Hertfordshire, SG6 1HB Tel: (01462) 480123 Fax: (01462) 480246 E-mail: data@mhotrak.co.uk *Printed circuit board manufrs*

MHS Highway Hire, Highway House, Station Road, Shirehampton, Bristol, BS11 9XA Tel: 0117-916 2400 Fax: 0117-916 2427 E-mail: info@mhs-hire.co.uk *Municipal vehicles hire & contract retailers* Also at: Bristol

Miba Tyzack Ltd, Green Lane Works, Green Lane, Sheffield, S3 8ST Tel: 0114-270 0254 Fax: 0114-276 8547 *Precision engineering products*

▶ Mica Glazing, 113-115 Cable Depot Road, Clydebank, Dunbartonshire, G81 1UY Tel: 0141-952 7069 Fax: 0141-951 1593 *Glaziers*

Micad Systems & F M Data Services, Lansdown House, 85 Buxton Road, Stockport, Cheshire, SK2 6LR Tel: 0161-474 7174 Fax: 0161-474 7163 E-mail: support@micad.co.uk *Computer data services bureau*

Micaline Electrical Systems Ltd, Unit 9, Block B Wednesbury Trading Estate, Darlaston Road, Wednesbury, West Midlands, WS10 7JN Tel: 0121-556 5194 Fax: 0121-556 4953 *Control systems-electric & control panel manufrs*

Gregory Micallef Associates, 63 Croydon Road, London, SE20 7TB Tel: (020) 8778 7759 Fax: (020) 8778 3090 E-mail: sales@gmal.co.uk *Computer consultants*

Mican Ltd, Oakmere, Horsemans Green, Whitchurch, Shropshire, SY13 3DY Tel: (01948) 830069 *Computer consultants*

Micas Solutions Ltd, Baldwin Road, Stourport-On-Severn, Worcestershire, DY13 9AX Tel: (01299) 825588 Fax: (01299) 828840 E-mail: info@micas.co.uk *Consultancy & software services*

Mice Kay Mar Ltd, Brookhill Industrial Estate, Pinxton, Nottingham, NG16 6NS Tel: (01773) 810107 Fax: (01773) 580286 E-mail: sales@micekaymar.com *Sheet metalwork engineers*

Michael Anthony & Partners, 54 Kingsbury, Aylesbury, Buckinghamshire, HP20 2JE Tel: (01296) 433666 Fax: (01296) 397686 E-mail: list@michaelanthony.co.uk *Property letting & sales agency*

▶ Michael Associates New Media Solutions, 1 Hazeldene Road, Hamilton, Leicester, LE5 1UA Tel: (0845) 8386888 Fax: (0871) 2424413 E-mail: info@michaelassociates.co.uk *Graphic designers*

Michael Barclay Partnership, 105 Strand, London, WC2R 0AB Tel: (020) 7240 1191 Fax: (020) 7240 2241 *Consulting structural engineers*

▶ Michael Brady Ltd, Trinity House, Heather Park Drive, Wembley, Middlesex, HA0 1SU Tel: (020) 8900 2345 Fax: (020) 8903 2345

Michael Brandon, 29 Royal Industrial Estate, Jarrow, Tyne & Wear, NE32 3HR Tel: 0191-428 6668 Fax: 0191-428 6066 E-mail: sales@brandonltd.co.uk *Electronic design & manufrs*

▶ Michael Eeley & Son, Hose Street Works, Hose Street, Stoke-on-Trent, ST6 5AL Tel: (01782) 813383 Fax: (01782) 813383 *Local French Polishers and Antique Restoration. Specialists in Pianos and other musical instruments.*

Michael Figgitt Upholstery Upholstery, Orleans Close, Unit 3, Four Pools Industrial Estate, Evesham, Worcestershire, WR11 2FP Tel: (01386) 45120 Fax: (01386) 45264 E-mail: sales@figgittupholstery.co.uk *Upholsterer*

Michael G Harris, Greenway, Rowden Mill Lane, Stourton Caundle, Sturminster Newton, Dorset, DT10 2JT Tel: (01963) 362302 *Agricultural contractors*

Michael Gerson Finance plc, Downland Close, Whetstone, London, N20 9LB Tel: (020) 8446 1300 Fax: (020) 8446 5088 E-mail: moving@michaelgerson.com *Overseas removal contractors*

Michael Graphics Ltd, 21 Bullivant Street, Nottingham, NG3 4AT Tel: 0115-950 3488 Fax: 0115-950 0447 *Process engravers*

▶ Michael Healey & Son, Francis House, Talbot Way, Market Drayton, Shropshire, TF9 3SJ Tel: (01630) 653366 Fax: (01630) 653372

Michael John Edwin Vernon, The Park, Edstaston, Wem, Shrewsbury, SY4 5RF Tel: (01939) 232070 Fax: (01939) 234897 *Refrigerator couriers*

▶ Michael Jordan Ltd, Pittwood Road, Lillyhall, Workington, Cumbria, CA14 4JP Tel: (01900) 601675 Fax: (01900) 66006

Michael Kinder Ltd, 1 Rectory Meadow, Bradwell, Braintree, Essex, CM77 8EX Tel: (01376) 561522 Fax: (01376) 561522 *Computer consultants*

Michael L Shaw Fabrications Ltd, 257 Hollin Lane, Middleton, Manchester, M24 5LU Tel: 0161-653 1081 Fax: 0161-655 4326 E-mail: m4@mlshawfabs.com *Extraction canopies manufrs*

Michael Lee Cheese Wholesalers, Wakefield Road, Ackworth, Pontefract, West Yorkshire, WF7 7AA Tel: (01977) 618828 Fax: (01977) 618828 *Cheese Wholesaler*

Michael Longland, 2 Church Way, Alconbury Weston, Huntingdon, Cambridgeshire, PE28 4JB Tel: (01480) 891034 Fax: (01480) 891034 *Saddlers & riding wear retailer*

▶ Michael Nutt, 80 College Road, Sittingbourne, Kent, ME10 1LD Tel: (07970) 956264 E-mail: michaelks@michaelnutt.com *Michael Nutt Decorators offer a complete interior and exterior decoration and renovation service covering Kent, London and the South-East.*

Michael Pepper Joinery, Ascot Drive, Derby, DE24 8GW Tel: (01332) 371133 Fax: (01332) 371132 E-mail: enquires@npeperjoinery.co.uk *Bespoke joinery*

Michael R Hawes, 18 Clovelly Road, Hayling Island, Hampshire, PO11 0SD Tel: (023) 9246 4470 Fax: (023) 9246 9472 E-mail: michael.hawes6@btinternet.com *Fencing & woodwork manufacturers & distributors*

Michael Rigby Associates, 15 Market Street, Wotton-under-Edge, Gloucestershire, GL12 7AE Tel: (01453) 521621 Fax: (01453) 521681 E-mail: results@521621.,com *Management & publ;ic relations consultants*

Michael Smith & Associates, Chemix Building, Dudley Road, Halesowen, West Midlands, B63 3NT Tel: 0121-585 0662 Fax: 0121-585 0649 E-mail: info@msasystems.co.uk *Computer software writers service*

Michael Thompson Ltd, Michael Thompsons Yard, St. Ninians Road, Carlisle, CA2 4LR Tel: (01228) 525314 Fax: (01228) 515022 E-mail: admin@michaelthompsonltd.co.uk *Building contractors*

Michael Thorne, Bishops Court, Bishops Court Lane, Clyst St. Mary, Exeter, EX5 1DH Tel: (01392) 261350 Fax: (01392) 261390 E-mail: info@michaelthorne.co.uk *Steel fabricators*

Michael Tyler Furniture Co. Ltd, Woodlands Way, The Ridge, Hastings, East Sussex, TN34 2RY Tel: (01424) 756675 Fax: (01424) 751436 *Furniture manufrs*

Michael Virden Ltd, Folgate Road, North Walsham, Norfolk, NR28 0AJ Tel: (01692) 404417 Fax: (01692) 406698 E-mail: sales@mvirden.com *Glass engraving services*

Michael W Hart, Inveresk Village, Musselburgh, Midlothian, EH21 7TD Tel: 0131-665 0764 Fax: 0131-665 0764 *Cabinet maker*

Michael Ward Refrigerated Transport, 5 Rookes Enterprise Park, Little Catterton Lane, Islington, Tadcaster, North Yorkshire, LS24 8EA Tel: (01937) 834808 Fax: (01937) 835025 E-mail: service@michealward.co.uk *Transport refrigeration*

Michael Weinig UK Ltd, 5 Blacklands Way, Abingdon, Oxfordshire, OX14 1DY Tel: (01235) 557600 Fax: (01235) 538070 E-mail: sales@weinig.co.uk *Woodworking machine distributors*

▶ Michael Williams Ltd, Wilbraham Road, Fulbourn, Cambridge, CB21 5ET Tel: (01223) 882222 Fax: (01223) 882598 E-mail: sales@mikewills.co.uk *We specialise in customised factory cleaning equipment. If you have a particular cleaning requirement that needs a particular Big Brute vacuum cleaner, talk to us. We can make machines in all shapes and sizes to meet your exact requirements*

▶ Michael Williams Agricultural Merchant, PO Box 1, Uttoxeter, Staffordshire, ST14 7SB Tel: (0870) 4324626 E-mail: agbiz@michaelwilliams.biz *Michael Williams (Agriculture) is an independent merchanting company that has been serving farmers in Staffordshire, Derbyshire, and Cheshire since 1981. We are now one of the leading suppliers of premier animal feeds, seeds and fertilisers in the Midlands.*

▶ Michael's Pitta Bread Bakery, 18 West Road, London, N17 0RP Tel: (020) 8808 5119 *D050*

Michael's Workwear, 56 Cricklade Road, Swindon, SN2 8AF Tel: (01793) 614721 Fax: (01793) 614721 E-mail: michaelsworkwear@aol.com *Retailers of industrial footwear & clothing*

Micheal Hope Sports, 7 High Street, Bathampton, Bath, BA2 6SY Tel: (01225) 464648 Fax: (01225) 464642 E-mail: sales@michaelhope.co.uk *Sports clubs & schools garments, embroidery & printing service*

Michel Hurel, Manor Farm, Church Street, Appleford, Abingdon, Oxfordshire, OX14 4PA Tel: (01235) 847200 Fax: (01235) 847888 E-mail: sales@michel-hurel.co.uk *Haulers & freight forwarders*

Michelin Tyre Plc, Campbell Road, Stoke-on-Trent, ST4 4EY Tel: (01782) 402000 Fax: (01782) 402253 E-mail: agr@uk.michelin.com *Tyre manufrs*

Michell Bearings, Scotswood Road, Newcastle upon Tyne, NE15 6LL Tel: 0191-273 0291 Fax: 0191-272 2787 E-mail: sales@michellbearings.com *Manufacturers of hydro-dynamic bearings*

Michelmersh Brick & Tile Co. Ltd, Hill View Road, Michelmersh, Romsey, Hampshire, SO51 0NN Tel: (01794) 368506 Fax: (01794) 368845 E-mail: sales@michelmersh.co.uk *Brick & tile manufrs*

Michie Charles Pharmaceutical Chemist, 391 Union Street, Aberdeen, AB11 6BX Tel: (01224) 585312 Fax: (01224) 574264 E-mail: info@michies.co.uk *Retail chemists*

Michill Engineering, Westcroft, Orton, Kettering, Northamptonshire, NN14 1LJ Tel: (01536) 710463 Fax: (01536) 710463 *Specialist engineers*

Michrome Electro Plating Ltd, Harrowbrook Road, Hinckley, Leicestershire, LE10 3DJ Tel: (01455) 637156 Fax: (01455) 637131 *Hard chrome plating services*

▶ Michton, Kingsway, Fforestfach, Swansea, SA5 4HD Tel: (01792) 561617 Fax: (01792) 561619 E-mail: sales@michton.com *Supplier of gourmet chocolate & sugar confectionery*

Micina Technologies Group, Regent House, 40 Nelson Street, Leicester, LE1 7BA Tel: 0116-233 9944 Fax: 0116-233 9945 E-mail: mike@micina.co.uk *Telephone installers*

Mick Furniss Agricultural Engineering, Higham Fields Farm, Basin Bridge Lane, Higham-on-the-Hill, Nuneaton, Warwickshire, CV13 6ET Tel: (01455) 213124 *Agricultural engineers*

Mickalan Ltd, 191 Granville Avenue, Long Eaton, Nottingham, NG10 4HE Tel: 0115-946 2761 Fax: 0115-973 3166 *Textile manufrs*

▶ Mickiewicz S, 4 Rectory Lane, Byfleet, West Byfleet, Surrey, KT14 7LL Tel: (01932) 347179

Mickle Laboratory Engineering Co. Ltd, Goose Green, Gomshall, Guildford, Surrey, GU5 9LJ Tel: (01483) 202178 Fax: (01483) 202178 E-mail: anthony@micklelab.freeserve.co.uk *Laboratory equipment technical manufrs*

▶ Micks Computer Clinic, 31 Milner Road, Long Eaton, Nottingham, NG10 1LB Tel: 0115-849 1797

Mico Signs & Blinds Ltd, 123 Kentish Town Road, London, NW1 8PB Tel: (020) 7284 2698 Fax: (020) 7267 5191 E-mail: sales@micosigns.co.uk *Sign & blind manufrs*

▶ Mico Trends, 4 Pendle Street, Nelson, Lancashire, BB9 7NH Tel: (01282) 447197 E-mail: info@micotrends.co.uk *Computer systems consultancy or services, software*

Micom Engineering Ltd, 7 Industrial Estate, The St, Heybridge, Maldon, Essex, CM9 4XB Tel: (01621) 856324 Fax: (01621) 858778 E-mail: sales@micomltd.co.uk *Subcontract engineers services*

▶ Micon Joinery, Charlotte Despard Avenue, London, SW11 5JE Tel: (020) 7627 8484 Fax: (020) 7720 8159

▶ Micor Ltd, Templewood, Stock Road, West Hanningfield, Chelmsford, CM2 8LL Tel: (01277) 841288 Fax: (01277) 841882

Micra Air Conditioning Services, 9 Vicarage Road, Woodford Green, Essex, IG8 8NH Tel: (020) 8505 0749 Fax: (020) 8504 5490 E-mail: micraair@tiscali.co.uk *Repair, service, maintenance & installation of all types & makes of air conditioning*

Micra Pattern Co. Ltd, 91 Sorby Street, Sheffield, S4 7LA Tel: 0114 2720724 *Pattern making & CNC services*

Micrafilter, Lake Road, Unit 4, Quarry Wood, Aylesford, Kent, ME20 7TQ Tel: (01622) 716616 Fax: (01622) 716606 E-mail: rod.fletcher@micrafilter.co.uk *Filter manufrs*

Micrex Profiles Ltd, Stamford Mill, Bayley Street, Stalybridge, Cheshire, SK15 1QQ Tel: 0161-330 6518 Fax: 0161-330 5576 E-mail: enquiry@micrex-profiles.co.uk *Plastic extrusion manufrs*

▶ Micro At Home, 4A South Street, Wincanton, Somerset, BA9 9DL Tel: (01963) 824808 E-mail: sales@microathome.biz *Computer software distributors*

▶ Micro B Pest Control, 3 Dalton House, 60 Windsor Avenue, London, SW19 2RR Tel: (020) 8540 6188 Fax: (020) 8540 7477 E-mail: admin@microbee.co.uk *Pest controllers*

Micro Business Maintenance Ltd, 8a Windmill Bank, Wombourne, Wolverhampton, WV5 9JD Tel: (01902) 324494 Fax: (01902) 324748 E-mail: nigel@twfinternet.com *Computer support maintenance services*

Micro Check, 75 North Street, Wellington, Somerset, TA21 8NA Tel: (01823) 664943 Fax: (01823) 665747 E-mail: sales@microcheckcomputers.co.uk *Computer retail*

Micro Clutch Developments Ltd, Unit 8-9 Kiln Park Industrial Estate, Searle CR, Weston-super-Mare, Avon, BS23 3XP Tel: (01934) 415606 Fax: (01934) 636658 E-mail: sales@microclutch.com *Gear box distributors*

▶ Micro Computer Forms Ltd, 9 Blackbrook Valley Industrial Estate, Narrowboat Way, Dudley, West Midlands, DY2 0XQ Tel: (01384) 455221 Fax: (01384) 455223 E-mail: lsm@mcforms.co.uk *General printing services*

Micro Computer Solutions, 10 Carn Industrial Area, Portadown, Craigavon, County Armagh, BT63 5YY Tel: (028) 3839 3839 Fax: (028) 3839 3838 E-mail: sales@mcsgroup.co.uk *Hardware manufrs*

Micro Data Systems Ltd, 65 Lower Olland Street, Bungay, Suffolk, NR35 1BY Tel: (01986) 895004 Fax: (01986) 896563 E-mail: sales@microdata.co.uk *Computer programming*

Micro Design Consultancy, Kenilworth Ho, 60 Kenilworth Rd, Leamington Spa, Warwickshire, CV32 6JY Tel: 01926 778899 Fax: 01926 778888 *Computer network support*

Micro Direct Ltd, 275a Upper Brook Street, Manchester, M13 0HR Tel: 0161-248 4949 Fax: (0870) 4444432 E-mail: sales@microdirect.co.uk *Distribution of computer components*

Micro Engineering Ltd, 155 Kingston Road, New Malden, Surrey, KT3 3NS Tel: (020) 8949 2191 Fax: (020) 8336 1127 E-mail: sales@microeng.co.uk *Computer dealers & networks*

Micro Focus Ltd, The Lawn, 22-30 Old Bath Road, Newbury, Berkshire, RG14 1QN Tel: (01635) 32646 Fax: (01635) 33966 E-mail: ukmarketing@microfocus.com *Computer software house & software publishers*

Micro Laser Designs, 105 Midford Road, Bath, BA2 5RX Tel: (01225) 833266 Fax: (01225) 832200 E-mail: sales@mld.co.uk *Stationery printing*

Micro Matic Ltd, Millington House, Stancliffe St Industrial Estate, Blackburn, BB2 2QR Tel: (01254) 671231 Fax: (01254) 682229 E-mail: mmltv@micro-matic.co.uk *Injection moulding manufrs*

Micro Metallic Ltd, 125 Bridge Street, Birkenhead, Merseyside, CH41 1BD Tel: 0151-647 4641 Fax: 0151-647 5012 E-mail: info@micromet.co.uk Principal Export

continued

continuation
Areas: Worldwide *Laser cutting services* Also at: Birmingham

▶ Micro Metalsmiths Ltd, Kirkdale Road, Kirkbymoorside, York, YO62 6PX Tel: 0845 2139030 Fax: (01751) 432061 E-mail: info@micrometalsmiths.co.uk *Micro Metalsmiths core technology is their precision investment casting foundry. This unique lost wax process results in superior surface finishes, thin sections, complex cast detail in non ferrous metals including aluminum LM25, A356, 40E and copper alloys/brass MB1, HTB3, AB2. This is complemented by an in-house specialist cast machining capability and well developed subcontracting range. Enabling finished components to be supplied direct to production lines.* Micro Metalsmiths uses its wide casting knowledge and world wide contacts to also supply finished ferrous castings.* The microwave radar division is a leading international design and manufacture facility offing power dividers and combiners, filters, waveguide components, diplexers, rotary joints, antenna, comparators, complete radar front end solutions and sub systems.*

Micro Milling, Johnsons Lane, Widnes, Cheshire, WA8 0SJ Tel: 0151-422 2970 Fax: 0151-495 1044 *Talcum powder & toiletries*

Micro Movements Ltd, Eversley Centre, Hook, Hampshire, RG27 0NB Tel: 0118-973 0200 Fax: 0118-9328872 E-mail: info@micromovements.co.uk *Manufacturers of data acquisition systems*

Micro Nav Ltd, Gild House, 64-68 Norwich Avenue West, Bournemouth, BH2 6AW Tel: (01202) 764444 Fax: (01202) 545079 E-mail: sales@micronav.co.uk *Providers of air traffic control simulation training products & services for civil & military users*

Micro Partners Ltd, Minavil House, Ealing Road, Wembley, Middlesex, HA0 4PZ Tel: (0871) 2502771 Fax: (020) 8903 0029 E-mail: eddie.m@micro-partners.co.uk *Epson products*

Micro Peripherals Ltd, Shorten Brook Way, Altham Business Park, Altham, Accrington, Lancashire, BB5 5YJ Tel: (01282) 776776 Fax: (01282) 770001 E-mail: sales@micro-p.com *Computer peripheral equipment distributors*

Micro Plastics (International) Ltd, Unit 2, Henley Industrial Park, Henley Road, Coventry, CV2 1SR Tel: (024) 7661 4320 Fax: (024) 7661 4831 E-mail: microplas@aol.com *Fastener (industrial) distributors*

Micro Plus Computers, 33 Bailey Street, Oswestry, Shropshire, SY11 1PX Tel: (01691) 656875 Fax: (01691) 671285 E-mail: chris@micro-plus.co.uk *Computer systems & software sales*

Micro Plus Software Ltd, Continental House, 497 Sunleigh Road, Alperton, Middlesex, HA0 4LY Tel: (020) 8733 8233 Fax: (020) 8733 8237 E-mail: sales@tollring.co.uk *Telecommunication systems*

Micro Pneumatics, 1 Palmer Street, Leicester, LE4 5PT Tel: 0116-261 1055 Fax: 0116-261 1066 E-mail: sales@micropneumatics.co.uk *Pneumatic work aids manufrs*

Micro Precision Ltd, Duxons Turn, Hemel Hempstead, Hertfordshire, HP2 4SB Tel: (01442) 241027 Fax: (01442) 268074 E-mail: enquiries@microprecision.co.uk *Precision engineers & precision grinding services*

Micro Precision Instruments Ltd, The Welsh Mill, Park Hill Drive, Frome, Somerset, BA11 2LE Tel: (01373) 461057 Fax: (01373) 451835 *Medical instrument designers & manufrs*

Micro Rent plc, 6 The Gateway Centre, Coronation Road, Cressex Business Park, High Wycombe, Buckinghamshire, HP12 3SU Tel: (01494) 768768 Fax: (01494) 768700 E-mail: sales@microrent.co.uk *Computer rental services*

Micro Robotics Ltd, 135 Ditton Walk, Cambridge, CB5 8QB Tel: (01223) 523100 Fax: (01223) 524242 E-mail: sales@microrobotics.co.uk Principal Export Areas: Worldwide *Control systems design consultants*

Micro Search Laboratories Ltd, Burnley Road, Mytholmroyd, Hebden Bridge, West Yorkshire, HX7 5LH Tel: (01422) 885087 Fax: (01422) 883721 E-mail: mail@micro-search.com *Microbiological consultants*

Micro Services, 293a Newark Road, Lincoln, LN5 8PE Tel: (01522) 522128 Fax: (01522) 522128 *Computer maintenance & repairs*

Micro Services (Eastern) Ltd, Unit 4 Craven Way Industrial Estate, Newmarket, Suffolk, CB8 0BW Tel: (01638) 661055 Fax: (01638) 664098 *Microfilm & fiche bureau services digital imaging*

Micro Spring & Presswork Co. Ltd, Enfield Industrial Estate, Redditch, Worcestershire, B97 6BW Tel: (01527) 69121 Fax: (01527) 61758 E-mail: email@microspring.co.uk *Spring manufrs*

Micro Supply Company Ltd, Kamarhatty 40 Lynedoch Road, Scone, Perth, PH2 6RJ Tel: (01738) 551250 Fax: (01738) 551156 E-mail: sales@microsupplies.co.uk *Computer consumables & stationary retailers*

Micro System Support, The Common East, Premier House, Bradley Stoke, Bristol, BS34 6BH Tel: (01454) 626463 Fax: 01454 626462 *Computer engineers*

Micro Technology Consultants, Unit 32 Business Centre, Main Street, Coatbridge, Lanarkshire, ML5 3RB Tel: (01236) 432205 Fax: (01236) 421933 *Software design & consultancy service providers*

Micro Warehouse Ltd, Horizon One, Studio Way, Borehamwood, Hertfordshire, WD6 5WH Tel: (020) 8327 5000 Fax: (020) 8953 7617 E-mail: sales@microwarehouse.co.uk *Computer reseller*

Micro Warehouse Ltd, Stuarts Road, Manor Park, Runcorn, Cheshire, WA7 1TH Tel: (01928) 595252 Fax: (01928) 579810 E-mail: derek.lloyd@inmac.co.uk *Computer accessories & consumables*

Micro-Analysis Consultants Ltd, Unit 19, Edison Road, St. Ives, Cambridgeshire, PE27 3LF Tel: (01480) 462626 Fax: (01480) 462901 E-mail: standards@dial.pipex.com *Elemental standards manufrs*

Microbial Developments Ltd, Spring La North, Malvern, Worcestershire, WR14 1BU Tel: (01684) 891055 Fax: (01684) 891060 E-mail: info@micdev.com Principal Export Areas: Worldwide *Agricultural & biological chemical manufrs*

The Microbiological Supply Co., PO Box 23, Dunstable, Bedfordshire, LU5 6DW Tel: (01525) 872515 Fax: (01525) 874967 *Sales supplies to laboratories*

Microblade Holdings Ltd, Sanderson Street, Sheffield, S9 2UA Tel: 0114-261 8855 Fax: 0114-261 9555 *Machine knife manufrs*

Microbus Designs Ltd, Treadaway Hill, Loudwater, High Wycombe, Buckinghamshire, HP10 9QL Tel: (01628) 537300 Fax: (01628) 537301 E-mail: microbus@microbus.co.uk *Hardware designers & manufrs*

Microcare Corporation, 34 Chantry Close, Harrow, Middlesex, HA3 9QZ Tel: (020) 8204 3630 Fax: (020) 8204 3638 E-mail: microcare@breathemail.net *Computer software sales*

Microchem Ltd, Unit 1 Belmont Industrial Estate, Durham, DH1 1TN Tel: 0191-386 9988 Fax: 0191-386 2722 E-mail: sales@microchem.co.uk *Industrial chemical manufrs*

Microcide Ltd, Shepherd's Grove, Stanton, Bury St. Edmunds, Suffolk, IP31 2AR Tel: (01359) 251077 Fax: (01359) 251545 E-mail: microcide@microcide.co.uk *Spraying equipment distributors*

Microclutch Ltd, Units 8-9, Kiln Park, Searle Crescent, Weston-super-Mare, Avon, BS23 3XP Tel: (01934) 415606 Fax: (01934) 636658 E-mail: info@microclutch.com *Electric motor distributors*

Microcomms Ltd, New Portreath Road, Redruth, Cornwall, TR16 4QL Tel: (01209) 843636 Fax: (01209) 843666 E-mail: sales@microcomms.co.uk *Data cable communication systems manufrs*

Microcraft Ltd, PO Box 3252, Tamworth, Staffs, B79 0BF Tel: (01827) 373551 Fax: (01827) 284667 E-mail: harryke@microcraft.ltd.uk *3rd/4th party computer maintenance, network cabling installations, workshop repair & on-site services.*

Microdat Automation Co Uk Ltd, Unit2, Benyon Park Way, Leeds, LS12 6DP Tel: 0113-244 5225 Fax: 0113-244 5226 E-mail: info@microdat.co.uk Principal Export Areas: Worldwide *Automated Machinery Manufactures*Brewery Keg & Cask Handling*Robot Palletiser*Conveyors*Sub Contract Stainless Steel Manuf*WaterJet,CNC Bending,CNC Turning*

Microdia Ltd, 16 Gloucester Street, Painswick, Stroud, Gloucestershire, GL6 6QW Tel: 01452 812501 *Microdia specialises in the supply & distribution of tungsten carbide burrs/tools, end mills, diamond files & precision instruments to both UK & international markets covering many different industry sectors*

▶ Microdrive (UK) Ltd, Passfield Business Centre, Lynchborough Road, Passfield, Liphook, Hants, GU30 7SB Tel: (01428) 751116 Fax: (01428) 751117

Microelectronics, Europa House, Havant Street, Portsmouth, PO1 3PD Tel: (023) 9230 3303 Fax: (023) 9230 2506 E-mail: processuk@pall.com *Manufacturers of filters including process cartridge, sheet, depth*

▶ Microexpert, Columbia House, Columbia Drive, Worthing, West Sussex, BN13 3HD Tel: (01903) 264252 Fax: (01903) 692616 *Smart card security manufrs*

Microfinance Systems Ltd, Milestone House, North Malvern Road, Malvern, Worcestershire, WR14 4LX Tel: (01684) 560141 Fax: (01684) 569186 *Software designers & developers*

Micro-Fix, Hemlock Place, Hyssop Close, Cannock, Staffordshire, WS11 7GA Tel: (01543) 467579 Fax: (01543) 469624 E-mail: info@on2net.co.uk *Computer maintenance repair services & internet*

▶ Microflex Software, 20a Eglinton Crescent, Edinburgh, EH12 5BY Tel: 0131-337 2821

▶ Microfloss, 61 Bromsgrove Road, Redditch, Worcestershire, B97 4RH Tel: (01527) 584959

Microflow Europe Ltd, Globe Square, Dukinfield, Cheshire, SK16 4RF Tel: 0161-343 1557 Fax: 0161-343 3762 E-mail: sales@microflowEurope.com *Beer dispenser services & manufrs*

Microforce Computer Systems, 327 Moseley Road, Birmingham, B12 0DX Tel: 0121-440 0440 Fax: 0121-440 1440 E-mail: info@microforce.co.uk *Computer consultants*

Microform Imaging Ltd, Main Street, East Ardsley, Wakefield, West Yorkshire, WF3 2AP Tel: (01924) 825700 Fax: (01924) 871005 E-mail: info@microform.co.uk *Microfilm publishers & scanners services*

Microformat UK Ltd, 344 High Street, Rochester, Kent, ME1 1JE Tel: (01634) 813751 Fax: (01634) 831557 E-mail: sales@microformat.co.uk *Document imaging bureau services*

▶ Microgaming Software Systems Ltd, M G S House, Circular Road, Douglas, Isle Of Man, IM1 1BL Tel: (01624) 647777 Fax: (01624) 647778 *Sell software to online casinos*

Microgas Systems Ltd, Aztec Ho, Perrywood Business Pk Honeycrock La, Salfords, Redhill, RH1 5DZ Tel: (01737) 378000 Fax: (01737) 378055 E-mail: rsmith@microgas.uk.com Sales Contact: R. Smith *High purity pipework erection contractors*

▶ Microgator Ltd, 15A Bramford Road, Ipswich, IP1 2LZ Tel: (0800) 2986258 E-mail: sales@microgator.biz *Computer resellers & service providers*

Microgen P.L.C., Fleet House Fleetwood Park, 3 Barley Way, Fleet, Hampshire, GU51 2QJ Tel: (01252) 772300 Fax: (01252) 772301 E-mail: marketing@microgen.co.uk *Manufacturers of computer output to microfilm (COM)*

Microgen Solutions P.L.C., 320 City Road, London, EC1V 2PT Tel: (020) 7239 8400 Fax: (020) 7239 8401 E-mail: enquiry@imagoqa.com *Software testing consultants*

Micrographic Techniques, Pennington House Unit 10, Commonwealth Close, Leigh, Lancashire, WN7 3BD Tel: (01942) 682562 Fax: (01942) 262867 E-mail: enquiries@paperscanning.co.uk *Document scanning & microfilming services*

Microguide Corporate Computer Consultants Ltd, Wyndham House, 82 Shortlands Road, Kingston upon Thames, Surrey, KT2 6HE Tel: (020) 8549 7152 Fax: (020) 8549 8112 E-mail: enquiry@microguide.co.uk *Management consultancy*

Microhelp Ltd, Unit 2a, Caldey Road, Roundthorn Industrial Estate, Manchester, M23 9GE Tel: 0161-946 0193 Fax: 0161- 945 4947 E-mail: sales@microhelp.co.uk *Computer software writers*

Micro-HELP (Scotland), 47 Parkhill Circle, Dyce, Aberdeen, AB21 7FN Tel: (01224) 773438 Fax: (01224) 773438 E-mail: dwh@mh-s.co.uk *Computer consultants*

Microkerf Ltd, 43 Boston Road, Leicester, LE4 1AW Tel: 0116-234 1500 Fax: 0116-234 1600 E-mail: sales@microkerf.com Principal Export Areas: Worldwide *Laser cutting, drilling & welding services*

Microlease plc, Unit 6 Whitefriars Trading Estate, Tudor Road, Harrow, Middlesex, HA3 5SS Tel: (020) 8420 0200 Fax: (020) 8420 0299 E-mail: info@microlease.com *Rental & second user sales of electronic test & measurement equipment*

Microlights Ltd, Elcot Lane, Marlborough, Wiltshire, SN8 2BG Tel: (01672) 515611 Fax: (01672) 513816 E-mail: sales@microlightsgroup.com *Lighting wholesalers*

Microlise Business Computing, Farrington Way, Eastwood, Nottingham, NG16 3AG Tel: (01773) 535111 Fax: (01773) 537373 E-mail: enquiries@microlise.co.uk *Provision of complete IT solutions and support for small and medium business in the East Midlands*

▶ Microlock Ltd, Unit 15 Parker Dr Business Centre, 47 Parker Drive, Leicester, LE4 0JP Tel: 0116-235 7777 Fax: 0116-235 6666 E-mail: amanda@microlock.co.uk *Create innovative & cost-effective pop*

Microlog Computer Software, 7 Stainland Road, Greetland, Halifax, West Yorkshire, HX4 8AD Tel: (01422) 310031 Fax: (01422) 371694 E-mail: sales@microlog.co.uk *Computer consultants, repair & retail services*

Micromark, Building 5, Waltham Road, White Waltham, Maidenhead, Berkshire, SL6 3TN Tel: (01628) 512900 Fax: (01628) 512999 E-mail: sales@micromark.net *Electronic components distributors*

Micromark Burglar Alarm Systems, Unit B1 Senator Point, South Boundary Road, Knowsley Industrial Park, Liverpool, L33 7RS Tel: (0870) 2413029 Fax: 0151-547 2266 *Security alarms research & developers*

Micromat International, Sanders Lodge Industrial Estate, Rushden, Northamptonshire, NN10 6BQ Tel: (01933) 313093 Fax: (01933) 319293 E-mail: sales@micromat.co.uk *Printed circuit equipment production*

▶ Micromatter Technology Solutions Ltd, 21 Victoria Terrace, Dunfermline, Fife, KY12 0LY Tel: (01383) 733467 E-mail: alan.craig@micromatter.co.uk *Software application development services*

Micromech Precision Tools, Wellfield Street, Rochdale, Lancashire, OL11 1AW Tel: (01706) 646505 Fax: (01706) 646505 *Precision toolmakers & diecasting mould manufrs*

Micromech Systems Ltd, Units 7 & 8, Chilford Court, Braintree, Essex, CM7 2QS Tel: (01376) 333300 Fax: (01376) 552600 E-mail: sales@micromech.co.uk *Control systems manufrs*

MicroMedia UK Ltd, 74 Gloucester Road, London, E17 6AE Tel: (07762) 660697 Fax: (020) 8527 3302 *Software & office supplies, stationery & machines*

▶ Micro-Membrane Systems Ltd, 9 Cork Terrace, Bath, BA1 3BE Tel: (01225) 444290 Fax: (01225) 461060 E-mail: info@micromembrane.co.uk *Micro-Membrane Systems are specialist water treatment membrane cleaning consultants and contractors. We also offer recycled or exchange membrane elements, sales of bulk deionised water and general technical consultancy in membrane water and wastewater treatment technology*

Micromeritics Ltd, Chestnut House, 178-182 High Street North, Dunstable, Bedfordshire, LU6 1AT Tel: (01582) 475248 Fax: (01582) 475252 E-mail: ussales@micromeritics.com *Particle size analyser distributors*

Micrometics Ltd, 26 Hollands Rd, Haverhill, Suffolk, CB9 8PR Tel: (01440) 707010 Fax: (01440) 762116 E-mail: info@micrometics.co.uk *Glass to metal seal manufacturers, connectors, hermetic, electroplating services, electroless (nickel) plating services & connectors, special purpose*

Micromix Solutions Ltd, Coachgap Lane, Langar, Nottingham, NG13 9HP Tel: (01949) 861087 Fax: (01949) 861061 E-mail: info@micromixsolutions.com *Chemical fertilizers & packers*

Micron Aluminium Doors Ltd, Micron House, 45 Leesons Hill, St. Mary Cray, Orpington, Kent, BR5 2LF Tel: (01689) 833501 Fax: (01689) 836188 E-mail: info@micronwindows.co.uk *Replacement windows & doors suppliers & fitters*

Micron Engineering Co., Dominion Works, Freshwater Road, Dagenham, Essex, RM8 1RX Tel: (020) 8983 8800 Fax: (020) 8983 8866 E-mail: micronengineering@unit5.freeserve.co.uk *Precision engineers*

Micron Engineering Ltd, Unit 5 Earls Way, Earl Way Industrial Estate, Thurmaston, Leicester, LE4 8DL Tel: 0116-264 0040 Fax: 0116-289 1402 E-mail: e.muddimer@btconnect.com *Precision engineers*

Micron Gauges Ltd, 1-3 Keyford Court, Manor Furlong, Frome, Somerset, BA11 4BD Tel: (01373) 461584 Fax: (01373) 461585 E-mail: sales@microngauges.co.uk *Dedicated measuring systems*

Micron Metrology 2000 Ltd, Eurolab House, Unit 10, Valepits Road, Garretts Green Industrial Estate, Birmingham, B33 0TD Tel: 0121-784 7498 Fax: 0121-783 6031 E-mail: alansmith@micron-metrology.co.uk *Micron is a UKAS Accredited Calibration Laboratory (0720) east of Birmingham providing an impressive range of calibration services including electrical, dimensional and torque at our permanent laboratory in the West Midlands together with electrical and dimensional calibrations at our clients' sites where required. Calibration services, UKAS calibration, thread gauge calibration, instrument calibration, West Midlands, Birmingham.*

Micron Precision Grinding, Unit 50 Haydon Industrial Estate, Radstock, BA3 3RD Tel: (01761) 437640 Fax: (01761) 437910 *Grinding contractors*

Micron Services Ltd, Baird Close, Drayton Fields Industrial Estate, Daventry, Northamptonshire, NN11 8RY Tel: (01327) 704921 Fax: (01327) 300013 *Machine tool spindle reconditioners*

Micron Software Ltd, 22 Lonsdale Road, Rackheath, Norwich, NR13 6QW Tel: (01603) 721600 Fax: (01603) 721607 E-mail: sales@micronds.com *Computer software*

Micron Sprayers Ltd, Bromyard Industrial Estate, Bromyard, Herefordshire, HR7 4HS Tel: (01885) 482397 Fax: (01885) 483043 E-mail: micron@micron.co.uk *Agricultural spraying machines manufrs*

Micron Techniques Ltd, 22 Ashley Walk, Mill Hill, London, NW7 1DU Tel: (020) 8343 4836 Fax: (020) 8343 4286 E-mail: micron@micronlondon.demon.co.uk *Electro-optical equipment*

Micron Technologies Ltd, Crossways Boulevard, Crossways, Dartford, DA2 6QY Tel: (01322) 425200 Fax: (01322) 425201 E-mail: info@microntech.com *Pharmaceutical milling service*

Micronair, Unit 17, Bradwell Works, Davenport Street, Stoke-on-Trent, ST6 4LL Tel: (01782) 816300 Fax: (01782) 790767 E-mail: kp@filter.co.uk *Environmental pollution control services*

Microclean (Newbury) Ltd, Faraday Road, Newbury, Berkshire, RG14 2AD Tel: (01635) 37901 Fax: (01635) 31528 E-mail: sales@microclean-newbury.co.uk *Clean room clothing supply services*

Micronics Ltd, Knaves Beech Business Centre, Davies Way, Loudwater, High Wycombe, Buckinghamshire, HP10 9QR Tel: (01628) 810456 Fax: (01628) 531540 E-mail: sales@micronicsltd.co.uk *Flow meter manufrs*

Micronics Filtration, Sandbach Road, Stoke-on-Trent, ST6 2DR Tel: (01782) 284385 Fax: (01782) 284987 E-mail: info@micronicsinc.com *Filters press retailers & manufrs*

Micronizing (UK) Co. Ltd, Charnwood Mill, Framlingham, Woodbridge, Suffolk, IP13 9PT Tel: (01728) 723435 Fax: (01728) 724359 E-mail: newton@micronizing.com *Food industry plant engineers*

Micropack Engineering Ltd, Fir Training Centre, Portlethen, Aberdeen, AB12 4RR Tel: (01224) 784055 Fax: (01224) 784056 E-mail: info@micropack.co.uk *Fire & gas detector systems manufrs*

▶ Micro-Pension Systems, 12 Burlington Place, Reigate, Surrey, RH2 9HT Tel: (01737) 237859 *Computer software*

Micropharm Ltd, Gernos, Maesllyn, Llandysul, Dyfed, SA44 5LP Tel: (01239) 858972 Fax: (01239) 710529 E-mail: enquiries@micropharm.co.uk *Biotechnology*

▶ Microphonic Ltd, Unit G25 Waterfront Studios Business Centre, Dock Road, London, E16 1AG Tel: (020) 7474 6696 E-mail: info@microphonic.biz *Record Company and Professional Audio Services.*

▶ Microplus Engineering Ltd, Unit 12 Gainsborough Trad Estate, Rufford Road, Stourbridge, West Midlands, DY9 7ND Tel: (01384) 442991 Fax: (01384) 441164 *Specialists in centreless grinding from 2mm to 90mm diameter, surface grinding, precision batch machining, ISO9001-2000 accredited firm. Ground Bar in all materials, stainless, duplex, aluminium, brass all ground to your specification. All batch sizes from 1 off to 100,000 off.*

Microplus Solutions Ltd, 7 66 Fazeley Road, Tamworth, Staffordshire, B78 3JN Tel: (01827) 68080 Fax: (01827) 64620 E-mail: info@mpsl.co.uk *Computer solution services*

Micropoint Plus Ltd, 22 Laurel Avenue, Slough, SL3 7DG Tel: (01753) 790829 Fax: (01753) 790830 E-mail: micropointplus@btconnect.com *Test equipment designers & programmers*

Micropol Ltd, Bayley Street, Stalybridge, Cheshire, SK15 1QQ Tel: 0161-330 5570 Fax: 0161-343 7687 E-mail: enquiry@micropol.co.uk *Plastics raw materials manufrs*

Micros For Managers Ltd, 149 Gloucester Road, London, SW7 4TH Tel: (020) 7565 2111 Fax: (020) 7565 2114 *Computer consultants*

Microscal Ltd, 79 Southern Row, London, W10 5AL Tel: (020) 8969 3935 Fax: (020) 8968 7302 E-mail: info@microscal.com *Flow micro calorimeters specialists*

MicroScope, Quadrant House, The Quadrant, Sutton, Surrey, SM2 5AS Tel: (020) 8652 3500 Fax: (020) 8652 8297 E-mail: microscope@rbi.co.uk *Newspaper publishers for computer manufacturers, distributors & retailers*

Microscopix Medical Equipment Mnfrs, Unit 18 Impressapark, Pindar Road, Hoddesdon, Hertfordshire, EN11 0DL Tel: (01992) 469085 Fax: (01992) 470541 E-mail: atrh@mx-l.com Principal Export Areas: Worldwide *Endoscope instruments suppliers & repairers*

Company Information

Microscopy Supplies & Consultants Ltd, Park House, 6a Carneil Road, Carnock, Dunfermline, Fife, KY12 9JH Tel: (01383) 851434 Fax: (01383) 851434 *Supply microscopes & optical equipment*

Microscribe, PO Box 738, Cambridge, CB2 5WY Tel: 0845 064 5555 E-mail: info@microscribe.co.uk *Hand-held rugged IP65 terminals and DOS/CE .NET computers.*

Microsec Computer Systems, 3b The Old Flour Mill, Queen Street, Emsworth, Hampshire, PO10 7BT Tel: (01243) 370073 Fax: (01243) 379997 E-mail: info@microsec.co.uk *Computer software house*

▶ Microshield Solutions Ltd, 1-1a Greenhill Avenue, Giffnock, Glasgow, G46 6QX Tel: 0141-639 1734 Fax: 0141-616 0503

Microsoft Ltd, 10 Great Pulteney Street, London, W1F 9NB Tel: (0870) 6010100 *Computer software distributors & manufrs*

Microsoft Research Ltd, 7 JJ Thomson Avenue, Madingley Road, Cambridge, CB3 0FB Tel: (01223) 479700 Fax: (01223) 479999 *Microsoft researchers*

▶ Microspec Computers Ltd, 90 Grahams Road, Falkirk, FK2 7DL Tel: (01324) 636147 Fax: (01324) 636148 E-mail: mail@microspec.co.uk *IT software suppliers*

Microspot Ltd, Concorde House, 10-12 London Road, Maidstone, Kent, ME16 8QA Tel: (01622) 687771 Fax: (01622) 690801 E-mail: microspot@microspot.co.uk *Computer reseller & software writers*

Micross Electronics Ltd, Units 4-5, Great Western Court, Ashburton Industrial Estate, Ross-on-Wye, Herefordshire, HR9 7XP Tel: (01989) 768080 Fax: (01989) 768163 E-mail: sales@micross.co.uk *Microprocessor applications manufrs*

Microstat, Unit 17, Crown Road, King Norton Business Centre, Birmingham, B30 3HY Tel: 0121-486 2020 Fax: 0121-486 2424 E-mail: enquiry@microstat.co.uk *Microstat, an authorised Canon scanning bureau, specialises in all aspects of Document Management. This includes document scanning, drawing scanning, book scanning, microfiche scanning, microfilm scanning, aperture cards scanning. Other services we offer include data entry, web hosting, full text search and document storage. We provide a complete and free consultancy service whereby we will assess your document management needs and provide a fully costed quotation and free sample images from your records. Documents can be scanned into many formats including Tiff, PDF and Jpeg. We have been scanning for 24 years and have scanned in excess of 300 million documents. FOR FURTHER INFORMATION, A QUOTATION, OR A FREE SAMPLE CD OF YOUR DOCUMENTS SIMPLE CALL TIM 0121 486 2020*

▶ Microstencil Limited, Starlaw Park, Starlaw Road, Livingston, West Lothian, EH54 8SF Tel: 01506 409190 Fax: 01506 409181 E-mail: n.gorman@microstencil.com *MicroStencil offers breakthrough stencil technology and interconnecting solutions for the microelectronics packaging industry.**The Company provides manufacturing, advice, service and training centred on stencil printing to incorporate smoothly its novel and readily adaptable technology. **We offer cost-effective tailor-made stencil designs with apertures and web spaces never achieved * *before. **Our technology is a quantum leap for achieving high-density electrical interconnects leading to higher portability and functionality in electronic systems. Mini-disk players, digital cameras, personal digital assistants, flat panel displays and mobile phones are examples that will directly benefit from MicroStencil technology.* *Microstencil also offers a low cost and high quality Photo Plotting service on both Emulsion Glass Plates and Acetate Films.*

Microsys Controls Ltd, Fennels Way, Flackwell Heath, High Wycombe, Buckinghamshire, HP10 9BY Tel: (01628) 532195 Fax: (01628) 532196 E-mail: microsyscontrols@aol.com *Control systems installers*

Microsystems Consultants, 26 Dunstall Way, West Molesey, Surrey, KT8 1PD Tel: (020) 8979 4099 Fax: (020) 8979 5898 E-mail: ivorhughes15@hotmail.com *Hardware consultants*

Microtec CNC Ltd, 370 Thurmaston Boulevard, Troon Industrial Area, Leicester, LE4 9LE Tel: 0116-246 0020 Fax: 0116-246 1006 E-mail: postmaster@microtec.uk.com *Precision engineers*

Microtec Ware Ltd, 146 Cherry Hinton Road, Cambridge, CB1 7AJ Tel: (01223) 416641 Fax: (01223) 413341 E-mail: purchasing@microtecware.com *Computer suppliers*

Microtech Ltd, Leicester Grange, Wolvey, Hinckley, Leicestershire, LE10 3JB Tel: (01455) 633016 Fax: (01455) 251588 E-mail: microtech@btconnect.com *Automated systems*

Microtech Business Systems, Units 1-3, 139A Moorland Road, Weston-Super-Mare, Avon, BS23 4HU Tel: (01934) 633875 Fax: (01934) 612011 *Computer manufrs*

Microtech Filters Ltd, The Lodge Factory, Kirkby Lane, Pinxton, Nottingham, NG16 6HW Tel: (01773) 862345 Fax: (01773) 863111 E-mail: info@microtechfilters.co.uk *Filters & filter element manufrs*

Microtech Precision Ltd, Unit D1 Bersham Enterprise Centre, Colliery Road, Rhostyllen, Wrexham, Clwyd, LL14 4EG Tel: (01978) 362295 Fax: (01978) 352043 E-mail: sales@microtechprecision.co.uk *Precision engineering & grinding manufrs, suppliers & distributors*

Microtech Services Ltd, 160 Westgate, Wakefield, West Yorkshire, WF2 9SR Tel: (01924) 332373 Fax: (01924) 216300 E-mail: sales@microtechservices.co.uk *Computer suppliers & networkers*

▶ Microtek Computer Consultants, 49 Cheylesmore Drive, Frimley, Camberley, Surrey, GU16 9BN Tel: (01276) 61940 Fax: (01276) 61940

Microtek Services Ltd, Gateway House, Gate Way Drive, Yeadon, Leeds, LS19 7XY Tel: 0113-238 7300 Fax: 0113-238 7320 E-mail: enquiries@microtek-services.co.uk *EPOS & it repair services & part sales*

Microtest Ltd, Technology House, 18 Normandy Way, Bodmin, Cornwall, PL31 1EX Tel: (01208) 73812 Fax: (01208) 77677 E-mail: sales@microtest.co.uk *IT services*

Micro-Till Systems, 172 Baddow Road, Chelmsford, CM2 9QW Tel: (01245) 347094 Fax: (01245) 347094 *Cash register retailers*

Microturbo Ltd, Concorde Way, Fareham, Hampshire, PO15 5RL Tel: (01489) 564848 Fax: (01489) 563905 E-mail: sales@microturbo.co.uk *Gas turbine engine manufacturers & repair services*

Microvitec Display Ltd, Drumhill Works, Clayton Lane, Bradford, West Yorkshire, BD14 6RF Tel: (01274) 816700 Fax: (01274) 817733 E-mail: sales@microvitec.co.uk *VDU systems manufrs*

Microvox Musical Instrument, 248 Huddersfield Road, Thongsbridge, Holmfirth, HD9 3JL Tel: (01484) 684049 Fax: (01484) 684049 E-mail: sales@microvox.co.uk *Musical instrument microphone manufr*

Microwave Amplifiers Ltd, 4 High Street, Nailsea, Bristol, BS48 1BT Tel: (01275) 853196 Fax: (01275) 858502 E-mail: sales@maltd.com *Microwave amplifier design & manufrs*

Microwave & Commercial Services, PO Box 145, Worksop, Nottinghamshire, S81 8YA Tel: (01909) 569000 Fax: (07976) 208744 E-mail: microwaveservices@yahoo.co.uk *Commercial & domestic microwave oven, vacuum cleaner & breadmaker repair, service, parts & accessories, mobile engineers carry out repairs on-site, Panasonic, Samsung, Sharp approved service agent.*

Microwave Hospital, 90 Oxford Road, Waterloo, Liverpool, L22 7RF Tel: 0151-931 4221 *Microwave repairers*

Mictell Hillpress, Victoria House, 18 Dalston Gardens, Stanmore, Middlesex, HA7 1BU Tel: (020) 8905 0008 Fax: (020) 8732 2848 *Control panel manufrs*

▶ Mid America (UK) Ltd, Hill House, Rockfield, Tain, Ross-Shire, IV20 1RF Tel: (01862) 871555 Fax: (01862) 871666 E-mail: fujismt@btconnect.com *Supply products for contract consumer electronic manufrs*

Mid Anglia Crane Hire Ltd, Shepherds Grove Industrial Estate, Stanton, Bury St. Edmunds, Suffolk, IP31 2AR Tel: (01359) 251451 Fax: (01359) 251313 E-mail: midangliacranehire@telco4u.net *Mobile crane hire service*

▶ Mid Beds Development Ltd, N Cradock Road, Luton, LU4 0JF Tel: (01582) 580327 Fax: (01582) 565248

▶ Mid Cheshire Construction Ltd, 206 Chester Road, Hartford, Northwich, Cheshire, CW8 1LG Tel: (01606) 871349 Fax: (01606) 871350

Mid Continent Great Yarmouth Ltd, Gapton Hall Road, Harfreys Industrial Estate, Great Yarmouth, Norfolk, NR31 0HX Tel: (01493) 655269 Fax: (01493) 601512 E-mail: sales@midcontinentgy.com *Oilfield equipment distributors* Also at: Aberdeen

Mid Cornwall Brokers Insurance, 68 Fore Street, Bodmin, Cornwall, PL31 2HR Tel: (01208) 72506 Fax: (01208) 72506 *Insurance consultants*

▶ Mid Cornwall Metal Fabrications, Treloggan Industrial Estate, Newquay, Cornwall, TR7 2SX Tel: (01637) 879474 Fax: (01637) 877278

Mid Cornwall Photographic, 11 Victoria Road, St. Austell, Cornwall, PL25 4QF Tel: (01726) 72695 Fax: (01726) 72695 E-mail: mc.photographic@btconnect.com *Wedding & Studio Photographers*

▶ Mid Cornwall Plumbing & Electrical Services, 24 Chyverton Close, Newquay, Cornwall, TR7 2AR Tel: (01637) 872727 Fax: (0870) 1350579 E-mail: mcpe@btconnect.com *Kitchens & hot tubs suppliers*

Mid Counties Handling Ltd, Unit 11 Haywoods Court, Garretts Green Trading Estate, Valepits Road, Birmingham, B33 0TD Tel: 0121-784 0704 Fax: 0121-789 7054 E-mail: sales@midcountieshandling.co.uk *Forklift trucks & examination services*

Mid England Agriculture Ltd, Hopyard Farm, Lubbesthorpe, Enderby, Leicester, LE19 4AZ Tel: 0116-263 0208 Fax: 0116-263 0121 *Grain merchants*

Mid Essex Fasteners Ltd, Beehive Lane Works, Beehive Lane, Chelmsford, CM2 9TE Tel: (01245) 257323 Fax: (01245) 252460 E-mail: midessexfasteners@btinternet.com *Fastener distributors*

Mid Fab Developments Ltd, 84 Cliveland Street, Birmingham, B19 3SN Tel: 0121-359 1641 Fax: 0121-333 3228 E-mail: sales@midfabdevelopments.co.uk *Sheet metalworkers*

Mid Glam Cash Registers, Croftmore, Gelliwion Woods, Maesycoed, Pontypridd, Mid Glamorgan, CF37 1QB Tel: 07957 566120 Fax: 01443 407738 E-mail: Paul.Suminski@midglamcashregisters.co.uk *Mid Glamorgan Cash Registers have been in the business for over 35 years and has over 35 years experience selling and maintaining Cash Registers. We pride ourselves in knowing your business so we can deliver a personalised experience to ensure you purchase the most suitable ECR or EPOS equipment. Your experience does not end with the purchase of your equipment. We ensure you have the correct maintenance and when your business grows we are there to reassess your requirements and if need be help you to upgrade your equipment.*

Mid Glam Packing Supplies Ltd, Unit 8 Nine Mile Point Industrial Estate, Ynysddu, Newport, Gwent, NP11 7HZ Tel: (01495) 200555 Fax: (01495) 200876 E-mail: sales@midglam-packing.co.uk *Packaging materials suppliers*

Mid Kent Electrical Engineering Co., The Street, Detling, Maidstone, Kent, ME14 3JT Tel: (01622) 735702 Fax: (01622) 734844 E-mail: pumpsales@mke.co.uk *Pump, motor rewinds repair & maintenance services*

▶ Mid Kent Recycling, 82 Columbine Road, Rochester, Kent, ME2 2YB Tel: (01634) 720099 E-mail: TONY@aalexander4.freeserve.co.uk *skip hire company in strood medway. waste transfer station, strood,kent.6-12yrd + ,full site/office/ house clearance, also 8 wheel tipper hire,*

The Mid Kent Steel Centre, Station Road, Harrietsham, Maidstone, Kent, ME17 1JA Tel: (01622) 859955 Fax: (01622) 858333 *Steel fabricators*

Mid Lancs Labels Ltd, 1 High Street, Standish, Wigan, Lancashire, WN6 0HA Tel: (01257) 400700 Fax: (01257) 422871 *Label retailers & carrier bag suppliers*

▶ Mid Lincs Generators, Spridlington Road, Faldingworth, Market Rasen, Lincolnshire, LN8 3SQ Tel: 01673 885296 Fax: 01673 885296 E-mail: gennyman.2@virgin.net *Generators*

Mid & North Wales Training Group Ltd, Myrick House, Hen-Domen, Montgomery, Powys, SY15 6EZ Tel: (01686) 668670 Fax: (01686) 668771 E-mail: myrick@btinternet.com *Management training & development services*

Mid Somerset Catering Hire, 8 Wireworks Estate, Bristol Road, Bridgwater, Somerset, TA6 4AP Tel: (01278) 422666 Fax: (01278) 420325 *Catering equipment hire*

▶ Mid Somerset Cleaning Supplies, Rear of Crest Home Improvement, Crown Trading Estate, Shepton Mallet, Somerset, BA4 5QQ Tel: (01749) 343243 E-mail: evmcs@aol.com *Janitorial suppliers, distributor of numatic vacuum cleaners*

Mid Sussex Timber Ltd, Ballards Yard, Park Road, Crowborough, East Sussex, TN6 2QS Tel: (01892) 652725 Fax: (01892) 653280 E-mail: mh@mstc.co.uk *Timber merchants*

Mid Sussex Timber Co. Ltd, Station Road, Forest Row, East Sussex, RH18 5EL Tel: (01342) 822191 Fax: (01342) 823052 E-mail: sales@mstc.co.uk *Timber merchants* Also at: Crowborough, East Grinstead & Haywards Heath

Mid Sussex Tyres, Wedglen Industrial Estate, Midhurst, West Sussex, GU29 9RE Tel: (01730) 815335 Fax: (01730) 816510 *Tyre & car battery retailer & wholesaler*

Mid Ulster Proteins Ltd, 47 Seagoe Industrial Estate, Craigavon, County Armagh, BT63 5QD Tel: (028) 3833 7217 Fax: (028) 3833 6114 E-mail: atrfood@btinternet.com *Oil, fat producers, refiners & merchants*

Mid Wales Signs, Llanbrynmair, Powys, SY19 7AA Tel: (01650) 521250 Fax: (01650) 521250 E-mail: ibwilliams88@hotmail.com *Suppliers of vinyl signs*

Mid Warwickshire Cleaning Supplies Ltd, Budbrooke Road Industrial Estate, Budbrooke Road, Budbrooke Industrial Estate, Warwick, CV34 5WQ Tel: (01926) 497272 Fax: (01926) 408407 E-mail: sales@mwcleaningsupplies.co.uk *Suppliers of cleaning materials*

▶ Mid West Displays, Laundry Lane, Shrewsbury, SY2 6ER Tel: (01743) 248095 Fax: (01743) 248096 E-mail: sales@midwestdisplays.co.uk *Supply of sign fixings & window display equipment, track lighting & poster displays*

The Mid Yorkshire Chamber Of Commerce & Industry Ltd, Commerce House, Wakefield Road, Huddersfield, HD5 9AA Tel: (01484) 438800 Fax: (01484) 514199 E-mail: post@chambercom6.bdx.co.uk *Training services, represent local businesses* Also at: Barnsley, Castleford, Dewsbury, Halifax, Huddersfield, Pontefract & Wakefield

Mida Sign Services UK Ltd, Gatefield House, Blandford Street, Ashton-under-Lyne, Lancashire, OL6 7DW Tel: 0161-830 0600 Fax: 0161-830 0601 E-mail: enquiries@midasignservices.co.uk *Sign installers*

▶ Midall Stones, 443 Sheffield Road, Chesterfield, Derbyshire, S41 8LT Tel: (01246) 456466 Fax: (01246) 456922 E-mail: admin@midallstones.com

▶ Midas, Unit 3 Singer Way, Kempston, Bedford, MK42 7AW Tel: (01234) 857770 Fax: (01234) 857771 *Manufacturers of metal products*

Midas, Trafford Wharf Road, Trafford Park, Manchester, M17 1EX Tel: 0161-877 3000 Fax: 0161-848 8638 E-mail: midas@midas.org.uk *Inward investment agency*

Midas, 4 Rectory Road, Newton, Sudbury, Suffolk, CO10 0QZ Tel: (01787) 373898 Fax: (01787) 374882 E-mail: billaldworth@midas-eastanglia.freeserve.co.uk *Jig & tool design*

Midas Computer Systems, Gilnockie Station Ho, Canonbie, Dumfriesshire, DG14 0SG Tel: (01387) 371526 Fax: (01387) 371526 *IT consultancy*

▶ Midas Contract Systems, 1 Airth Drive, Glasgow, G52 1JU Tel: 0141-849 1001 Fax: 0141-840 2112

Midas Floors Ltd, 20 Dollman Street, Birmingham, B7 4RP Tel: 0121-333 5846 Fax: 0121-333 6476 E-mail: midas.floors@dial.pipex.com *Flooring contractors*

Midas Leisure Cafe & Arcade, 148 High Street, Eston, Middlesbrough, Cleveland, TS6 9EN Tel: (01642) 454851 Fax: (01642) 505333 *Amusement arcade suppliers*

Midas Marine & Joinery Co., Eastlands Boatyard Eastlands, Coal Park Lane, Swanwick, Southampton, SO31 7GW Tel: (01489) 583310 Fax: (01489) 581869 E-mail: midasmaraine@fsbdial.co.uk *Boat building manufrs*

▶ Midas (NW) Ltd, Midas House, Porritt Street, Bury, Lancashire, BL9 6HJ Tel: 0161-764 6220 Fax: 0161-761 1293 *Suppliers to hotel, leisure, airline & healthcare industries*

Midas Plating & Engineering Co. Ltd, Woodend Mills, Hartshead St, Oldham, OL4 5EE Tel: 0161-620 0939 Fax: 0161-678 8614 *Electroplaters & engineers*

Midas Press, 3 Columbus Drive, Southwood Business Park, Farnborough, Hampshire, GU14 0NZ Tel: (01252) 517221 Fax: (01252) 516455 E-mail: sales@midaspress.co.uk *Lithographic printers*

▶ Midas Productions UK, Saracens House Business Centre, 25 St. Margarets Green, Ipswich, IP4 2BN Tel: (01473) 222260 Fax: (01473) 222260 E-mail: dave@midas-uk.co.uk *UKs First Eco Friendly Generator Hire and sales*

Midas Technologies, Unit A Roundhouse Close, Fengate, Peterborough, PE1 5TA Tel: (01733) 342600 Fax: (01733) 346672 E-mail: sales@midastech.co.uk *Stainless steel fabricators*

Mid-Blue International Ltd, Great Queen Street, Dartford, DA1 1TJ Tel: (01322) 407000 Fax: (07092) 364351 E-mail: nigel.scott@mid-blue.com *Computer engineering & consultants*

Mid-Bucks Machine Tools Ltd, PO Box 15, Chinnor, Oxfordshire, OX39 4AT Tel: (01844) 352329 Fax: (01844) 352348 E-mail: midbucks@nildram.co.uk *Buyers & suppliers of new & used machining centres*

Midcast Stampings Ltd, Enterprise Drive, Four Ashes, Wolverhampton, WV10 7DF Tel: (01902) 791971 Fax: (01902) 791030 *Hot brass stampings manufrs*

▶ Midco Print & Packaging Ltd, Chantry House Grange Business Park, Enderby Road, Whetstone, Leicester, LE8 6EP Tel: 0116-277 4244 Fax: 0116-277 0167 E-mail: sales@midco-pp.co.uk *Supply labels to the nhs*

Midd Engineering Coventry Ltd, Blackhorse Road, Exhall, Coventry, CV7 9FW Tel: (024) 7636 3033 Fax: (024) 7636 3044 E-mail: sales@midd-engineering.co.uk *Subcontract engineers services*

▶ Middle East International Advertising Co., Suite 31 Consort Rise House, 199-203 Buckingham Palace Road, London, SW1W 9TB Tel: (020) 7730 0055 Fax: (020) 7730 0056 E-mail: meiac@btconnect.com *Advertising*

Middleburn Ltd, 6 Bentley Park, Blacknest Road, Blacknest, Alton, Hampshire, GU34 4PX Tel: (01420) 520227 Fax: (01420) 23796 E-mail: bob@middleburn.co.uk *General engineering services*

Middledale Foods Ltd, 20 Abbey Road, Bourne End, Buckinghamshire, SL8 5NZ Tel: (01628) 521685 Fax: (01628) 521123 E-mail: sales@middledalefoods.co.uk *Dairy produce agents suppliers*

Middlehurst Ltd, 103 Boyn Valley Road, Maidenhead, Berkshire, SL6 4EA Tel: (01628) 628044 Fax: (01628) 773143 E-mail: office@middlehurstlimited.com *Shop fitting & trolley manufrs*

Middlesex Group Ltd, Telford Road, Houndmills Industrial Estate, Basingstoke, Hampshire, RG21 6YU Tel: (01256) 353711 Fax: (01256) 842613 E-mail: sales@middlesex.co.uk *Aerospace components manufacturers*

Middlesex Packaging Ltd, Middlesex House, Crown Trading Centre, Clayton Road, Hayes, Middlesex, UB3 1DU Tel: (020) 8756 0808 Fax: (020) 8848 1991 *Carton distributors*

Middlestown PCS Ltd, 52 High Street, Horbury, Wakefield, West Yorkshire, WF4 5LE Tel: (01924) 260615 Fax: (01924) 270245 E-mail: info@middlestownpcs.co.uk *Computer hardware maintenance services*

▶ Middleton Engineering Ltd, Ashcott Road, Meare, Glastonbury, Somerset, BA6 9SU Tel: (01458) 860264 Fax: (01458) 860311 E-mail: middletonadmin@btconnect.com *Waste paper balers & shredders*

Middleton Forge Ltd, Station Bank, Middleton-in-Teesdale, Barnard Castle, County Durham, DL12 0NG Tel: (01833) 640595 Fax: (01833) 640157 E-mail: enquiries@middleton-forge.co.uk *Steel fabricators*

Middleton Heat Treatments Ltd, 315 Whapload Road, Lowestoft, Suffolk, NR32 1UL Tel: (01502) 561721 Fax: (01502) 517712 *Metal heat treatment (including on site) & stress relieving services*

Middleton Maintenance Services Ltd, The London Centre, 99 Queensland, London, N7 7AJ Tel: (020) 7700 7070 Fax: (020) 7609 3223 E-mail: sales@middleton-maintenance.co.uk *Industrial door & shutter servicing* Also at: Bristol, Fareham, Grangemouth, Manchester, Plymouth, South Shields & Telford

▶ Middleton Maintenance Services Ltd, Unit B Peacock View, Fenton Industrial Estate, Stoke-on-Trent, ST4 2XJ Tel: 0121-326 7777 Fax: (01782) 274007

Middleton Metal Spinning, Clough Road, Manchester, M9 4FP Tel: 0161 2058687 *Metal spinning*

▶ Middleton On The Walds Natural Therapies, 2a Front Street, Middleton on the Wolds, Driffield, North Humberside, YO25 9UA Tel: (01377) 217623 E-mail: sales@middlemists.co *Middlemists sells unusual ethnic, costume and crystal jewellery, and also crystals i.e.gifts, display pieces, therapists working crystals, crystal night lights. The pieces are sourced with care by a crystal therapist, to find unique and unusual items.*

Middleton Sheet Metal Co. Ltd, Spring Vale, Middleton, Manchester, M24 2HS Tel: 0161-643 2462 Fax: 0161-643 3490 E-mail: info@msmgroup.org *Sheet metalwork engineers*

▶ Middletons Ltd, Compston Road, Ambleside, Cumbria, LA22 9DJ Tel: (01539) 432154

▶ Middlewich Food Trays Ltd, 4 Montgomery Close, Parkgate Industrial Estate, Knutsford, Cheshire, WA16 8XW Tel: (01565) 652668 Fax: (01565) 633136 *Catering disposable food service manufrs*

Mident Trading Co., Remmets House, Lord Street, Bury, Lancashire, BL9 0RE Tel: 0161-761 6060 Fax: 0161-763 1005 E-mail: midentuk@aol.com *Plastic product manufrs*

Mid-Essex Electrical Engineers Ltd, 37 Beehive Lane, Chelmsford, CM2 9TQ Tel: (01245) 262226 Fax: (01245) 495911 E-mail: midessex@aol.com *Electrical contractors*

Mid-Essex Gravel Ltd, Essex Regiment Way, Broomfield, Chelmsford, CM3 3PZ Tel: (01245) 440621 Fax: (01245) 442212 E-mail: info@midessexgravel.co.uk *Sand & gravel*

Midge & Flyscreen Co., Clearwater House, Glenuig, Lochailort, Inverness-Shire, PH38 4NB Tel: (01687) 470318 Fax: (01687) 470318 *Fly screen supplier & manufrs*

A. Midgley & Co., Unit 2 Heritage Acres, Wakefield Road, Fitzwilliam, Pontefract, West Yorkshire, WF9 5BP Tel: (01977) 613426 Fax: (01977) 616532 E-mail: david@amfoodmachinery.fsnet.co.uk *Food processing equipment suppliers & manufrs*

Midgley Design & Print, Unit 2c, York Road Industrial Park, Malton, North Yorkshire, YO17 6YA Tel: (01653) 695115 Fax: (01653) 690680 E-mail: dmidgley@fsbdial.co.uk *Photographic colour printers*

Midhope Products, Unit 26-27 Albion Mills, Miry Lane, Thongsbridge, Holmfirth, HD9 7HP Tel: (01484) 688646 Fax: (01484) 688648 E-mail: midprod@btinternet.com *Rubber mouldings, & rubber & metal bondings*

Midhurst Garage, Wedglen Industrial Estate, Midhurst, West Sussex, GU29 9RE Tel: (01730) 814032 Fax: (01730) 814032 E-mail: infomidhurst@motormouse.net *Car sales & repair*

Midland Abrasives Ltd, 8-9 Boulton Industrial Centre, Icknield Street, Hockley, Birmingham, B18 5AU Tel: 0121-687 1135 Fax: 0121-687 2442 E-mail: midlandabrasives@supanet.com *Abrasive wheel retailers*

Midland Air Conditioning Ltd, 253 Walsall Road, Perry Barr, Birmingham, B42 1TY Tel: 0121-356 1809 Fax: 0121-356 9478 E-mail: midlandaircon@btclick.com *Air conditioning installation*

Midland Audio Visual Ltd, 210 New Road, Rubery, Rednal, Birmingham, B45 9JA Tel: 0121-453 3141 Fax: 0121-453 4626 E-mail: sales@midlandaudiovisual.co.uk *Audio visual video hire*

Midland Automatic Transmissions Ltd, Unit A1M1 Business Centre, Kettering, Northamptonshire, NN16 8TD Tel: (01536) 517866 Fax: (01536) 517764 E-mail: sales@automaticgearbox.co.uk Principal Export Areas: West Europe *Gear box reconditioning services*

Midland Automatics, 10 Sheffield Street, Leicester, LE3 0GX Tel: 0116-254 5515 *Video repairs*

Midland Box Co. Ltd, Field Industrial Estate, Clover Street, Kirkby-in-Ashfield, Nottingham, NG17 7LH Tel: (01623) 758758 Fax: (01623) 757229 E-mail: sales@midlandbox.co.uk *Corrugated paper board & box manufrs*

Midland Brass Fittings Ltd, Wynford Industrial Trading Estate, Wynford Road, Birmingham, B27 6JT Tel: 0121-707 6666 Fax: 0121-708 1270 E-mail: sales@midbras.co.uk *Plumbers fittings manufrs*

▶ Midland Business Development (MBD), Radclyffe House, 66-68 Hagley Road, Birmingham, B16 8PF Tel: 0121-242 0022 Fax: 0121-242 0020 E-mail: mail@midbusdev.co.uk *UK Mailing Lists UK Lead Generation Telemarketing Business Development Direct Marketing Birmingham West Midlands UK Midland Business Development Co Provides Quality Direct Marketing Business Development UK Telemarketing Lead Generation Mailing Lists*

Midland Business Equipment Ltd, Unit 4 Highlands House, Stirling Road, Shirley, Solihull, West Midlands, B90 4NE Tel: (01675) 470061 Fax: 01675 470889 E-mail: info@m-b-e.co.uk *Office equipment & computer systems suppliers*

Midland Business Supplies Ltd, Midland House, Cross Street, Oadby, Leicester, LE2 4DD Tel: 0116-272 0044 Fax: 0116-272 0050 E-mail: info@mbs-sales.co.uk *Office equipment distributors*

Midland Cable Jointing Co., 16 Gretton Road, Nottingham, NG3 5JT Tel: 0115-960 3413 Fax: 0115-960 3413 *Cable laying & jointing contractors*

Midland Cam & Tool (1982) Co., 21 Nursery Road, Hockley, Birmingham, B19 2XN Tel: 0121-551 9922 Fax: 0121-551 9929 E-mail: tooling@centreless.com *Cams & cam blanks manufrs*

Midland Canal Centre, Stenson, Barrow-On-Trent, Derby, DE73 1HL Tel: (01283) 701933 Fax: (01283) 702818 E-mail: eddie@mccboats.co.uk *Boat builders*

Midland Carbides, Ivanhoe Indust Estate, Smisby Road, Willesley, Ashby-de-la-Zouch, Leicestershire, LE65 2UG Tel: (01530) 414949 Fax: (01530) 417039 *Tungsten carbide tip manufrs*

Midland Ceilings Ltd, 63 Chartwell Drive, Wigston, Leicestershire, LE18 2FS Tel: 0116-288 7721 Fax: 0116-288 7022 *Ceiling & partitioning contractors*

Midland Chromium Plating Co. Ltd, 116 Aldridge Road, Perry Barr, Birmingham, B42 2TP Tel: 0121-356 9431 Fax: 0121-356 5891 E-mail: info@midchrome.co.uk *Brass & chromium electroplaters*

▶ Midland Cleaning Services, 152 Falcon Lodge Crescent, Sutton Coldfield, West Midlands, B75 7NA Tel: (0845) 2260881 Fax: (0870) 0940775 E-mail: pwayt@midlandcleaningservice.co.uk *Office & commercial cleaning services*

Midland Control & Automation, 13 Industrial Estate, Sanders Road, Bromsgrove, Worcestershire, B61 7DG Tel: (01527) 574224 Fax: (01527) 574225 E-mail: johnmca@fsbdial.co.uk *Electrical control panel designers*

Midland Control Systems, Unit 13 West Cannock Way, Cannock Chase Enterprise Centre, Hednesford, Cannock, Staffordshire, WS12 0QW Tel: (01543) 879116 Fax: (01543) 422518 *Gate & barrier automation*

▶ Midland Counties Heating Services Ltd, Bridge House, Upper St. John Street, Lichfield, Staffordshire, WS14 9DT Tel: (01543) 251152 Fax: (01543) 414256

Midland Cranes Ltd, Church La, Seisdon, Wolverhampton, WV5 7EZ Tel: 01902 897018 Fax: 01902 898491 *Over head crane suppliers & manufrs*

Midland Diving Equipment Ltd, 57 Sparkenhoe Street, Leicester, LE2 0TD Tel: 0116-212 4262 Fax: 0116-212 4263 E-mail: info@midlanddiving.com *Air filtration equipment manufrs*

Midland Earthmoving Co. Ltd, Gibbs Road, Lye, Stourbridge, West Midlands, DY9 8SY Tel: (01384) 894488 Fax: (01384) 894489 *Earth moving contractors*

▶ Midland Electrial Supplies, 375 Tyburn Road, Birmingham, B24 8HJ Tel: 0121-328 6448 Fax: 0121-328 6448 E-mail: morris-i@btconnect.com *Electrical Wholesaler*

Midland Electrical Holdings Ltd, 14 Abbotsinch Road, Grangemouth, Stirlingshire, FK3 9UX Tel: (01324) 486817 Fax: (01324) 474834 E-mail: info@midlandgroup.co.uk *Electric motor & coil repairers*

Midland Electrical Services, 6 Moor Street Industrial Estate, Moor Street, Brierley Hill, West Midlands, DY5 3ST Tel: (01384) 262558 Fax: (01384) 480661 *Installation & repair of cranes & machinery*

Midland Elements Ltd, 58 Sutherland Road, Stoke-on-Trent, ST3 1HU Tel: (01782) 333377 Fax: (01782) 599940 *Making heating elements*

Midland Enamellers, 1 Pinfold Road, Thurmaston, Leicester, LE4 8AS Tel: 0116-269 7861 Fax: 0116-264 0739 *Stove enamellers*

Midland Engineering Services Ltd, Bathville Business Centre, Armadale Indust Estate, Armadale, Bathgate, West Lothian, EH48 2ND Tel: (01501) 739081 Fax: (01501) 739083 E-mail: sales@mes4thk.sageweb.co.uk *Midland Engineering Services Ltd is a bearing, power transmission and engineering supplies company, stocking various products for both local and national industries. Based in Armadale, West Lothian, our location affords us access to all main motorway networks, allowing us quick access to Glasgow and Edinburgh suppliers and customers, ensuring a speedy service.*We are the sole independent distributor for THK LM System linear guides in Scotland, looking after both the local business and the rest of the independent trade across the UK, and have full technical back-up from THK UK. We also have an on-site cutting facility which allows us to supply custom linear rail lengths on a same-day basis.*The company offers a fast and reliable local delivery service, saving customers money on machine downtime, and our partnership with our local Interlink depot ensures that our customers across the country receive urgent goods on a next-day basis.*

Midland Engineering Steels, Units 6-8 Eagle Industrial Estate, Bagnall St, Great Bridge, Tipton, W. Midlands, DY4 7BS Tel: 0121-522 3535 Fax: 0121-522 3737 E-mail: mes@niag.com *Producer and stockists of Steel bar. Specialists in bright steel bar, steel turned bar, polished carbon steel bar and alloy steel bars. Carbon and free cutting grades available from stock; Suppliers of large diameter leaded bars; Can produce bright bar from 100mm to 380mm in diameter; Black bar from90mm to 320mm available from stock.*

Midland Environmental Laboratories, Unit D17 Forge Lane, Minworth Industrial Park, Minworth, Sutton Coldfield, West Midlands, B76 1AH Tel: 0121-351 6469 Fax: 0121-351 6469 *Pollution & analytical services*

Midland Erection Ltd, Roetan House, Thorns Road, Brierley Hill, West Midlands, DY5 2PF Tel: (01384) 424227 Fax: (01384) 424906 E-mail: miderect1@btconnect.com *Structural engineers*

▶ Midland Fabrication & Welding Ltd, Unit 18 Gregston Industrial Estate, Birmingham Road, Oldbury, West Midlands, B69 4EX Tel: 0121-544 8668 *Steel & aluminium fabricators & repairers*

Midland Felt Roofing Ltd, Green Lane, Woodstock, Oxfordshire, OX20 1JP Tel: (01993) 811543 Fax: (01993) 813418 *Felt roofing contractors*

▶ Midland Finishing Ltd, Eel Street, Oldbury, West Midlands, B69 2BX Tel: 0121-544 9494 Fax: 0121-544 4540 E-mail: info@midlandfinishing.co.uk *Metal polishing stainless steel ferrous & nonferrous*

Midland Fire, Lido House, Sansome Road, Shirley, Solihull, West Midlands, B90 2BJ Tel: 0121-745 8444 Fax: 0121-745 4115 *Fire extinguisher services*

Midland Fire Protection Services Ltd, Unit 17 Courtaulds Industrial Estate, Foleshill Road, Coventry, CV6 5AY Tel: (024) 7668 5252 Fax: (024) 7663 7575 E-mail: info@midlandfire.co.uk *Fire protection supplies*

▶ Midland Fire & Safety, Summerwood, Symonds Yat, Ross-on-Wye, Herefordshire, HR9 6BP Tel: (01600) 891338 Fax: (01600) 891380 E-mail: info@morganrose.co.uk *Fire alarm systems installation services*

Midland Fireworks, 89 High Street, Burton-on-Trent, Staffordshire, DE14 1LJ Tel: (01332) 294043 Fax: (01332) 364206 *Fireworks mail-order company*

Midland Fixing Services Ltd, Unit 20 Bordesley Trading Estate, Bordesley Green Road, Birmingham, B8 1BZ Tel: 0121-327 5713 Fax: 0121-328 1842 *Wholesale ironmongers*

Midland Fixings (Manchester), 3 Rufford Parade, Rufford Drive, Whitefield, Manchester, M45 8PL Tel: 0161-766 2491 Fax: 0161-767 9023 *Trade wholesaler*

Midland Fork Lifts Ltd, Orion Way, Kettering Business Park, Kettering, Northamptonshire, NN15 6NL Tel: (01536) 482561 Fax: (01536) 511559 E-mail: sales@midlandforklifts.co.uk *Fork lift truck hire sales & service*

Midland Framing, 988 Tyburn Road, Birmingham, B24 0TL Tel: 0121-384 4831 Fax: 0121-384 4831 *Framed mirrors & prints*

▶ Midland Fuel Services Ltd, 62 Primrose Way, Kidderminster, Worcestershire, DY10 1NG Tel: 01562 748991 *-OIL FIRED HEATING ENGINEERS.**-SPECIALSTS IN FUEL STORAGE AND SUPPLY PIPEWORK TO APPLIANCES AND ALL RELATED EQUIPMENT.**-TANK INSTALLATIONS.**-TANK REMOVALS.*

Midland Garage Services, Stourport House, Stourport Road, Kidderminster, Worcestershire, DY11 7QL Tel: (01562) 752458 Fax: (01562) 752548 *Garage equipment sales, installation & service*

▶ Midland Glass Supplies Ltd, Lady Lea Works, Ladylea Road, Horsley Woodhouse, Ilkeston, Derbyshire, DE7 6AZ Tel: (01332) 782800 Fax: (01332) 782808

Midland Graphics Sign Depot, 14 Victoria Terrace, Leamington Spa, Warwickshire, CV31 3AB Tel: (01926) 452009 Fax: (01926) 470767 *Sign makers*

Midland Handling Equipment Ltd, Stretton Road, Great Glen, Leicester, LE8 9GN Tel: 0116-259 3175 Fax: 0116-259 2820 E-mail: sales@mhel.co.uk *Manufacturers of conveyor systems, overhead & belt*

Midland Heat Treatments Ltd, Chillington Works, Hickman Avenue, Wolverhampton, WV1 2BU Tel: (01902) 450757 Fax: (01902) 459093 E-mail: induction@midland-heat.co.uk *Metal & induction heat treatment services*

Midland Hydraulic Services, Unit 4 Ariane, Tamworth, Staffordshire, B79 7XF Tel: (01827) 59012 Fax: (01827) 60615 *Hydraulic engineers services*

Midland Independent Newspaper, 28 Colmore Circus Queensway, Birmingham, B4 6AT Tel: 0121-236 3366 Fax: 0121-236 9638 *Paper & magazine publisher*

Midland Industrial Designers Ltd, Common Lane, Watnall, Nottingham, NG16 1HD Tel: 0115-938 2154 Fax: 0115-938 6315 E-mail: sales@mid.uk.com *Valve manufrs*

Midland Interiors Ltd, Unit 58 G Arthur Street, Lakeside, Redditch, Worcestershire, B98 8JY Tel: (01527) 522566 Fax: (01527) 522562 E-mail: s.troth@midlandinteriors.co.uk *Ceilings & partition manufrs*

Midland Linen Services Ltd, 3 Klaxon Tysley Industrial Estate, 751 Warwick Road, Tyseley, Birmingham, B11 2HA Tel: 0121-708 1069 Fax: 0121-707 4686 E-mail: info@midlandlinen.co.uk *Linen hire & laundry services for catering trade*

Midland Machine Knives Ltd, Unit 17 Baltic Works, Effingham Road, Sheffield, S9 3QA Tel: 0114-244 8952 Fax: 0114-243 2437 *Machine knife manufrs*

Midland Machinery Heavy Lift Ltd, Heath Road, Wednesbury, West Midlands, WS10 8XE Tel: 0121-526 5511 Fax: 0121-526 6846 *Machine merchants & movers*

Midland Marble Ltd, Masonry Works, 80 Dollman Street, Birmingham, B7 4RP Tel: 0121-359 3699 Fax: 0121-333 3052 E-mail: enquiries@midlandmarbleltd.co.uk *Marble merchants*

Midland Materials Handling Co. Ltd, Reeves Street, Walsall, WS3 2DL Tel: (01922) 409887 Fax: (01922) 710253 E-mail: midlandmh@aol.com *Fork lift truck hire & rental, sales & service*

Midland Mercantile Export Company, 2 The Avenue, Bedford Park, London, W4 1HT Tel: (020) 8994 8111 Fax: (020) 8994 6856 *Exporters*

Midland Mobility Ltd, Torrington Avenue, Coventry, CV4 9BL Tel: (024) 7647 1124 Fax: (024) 7646 5288 E-mail: sales@midlandmobility.co.uk *Invalid chair distributors & repairs*

Midland Motor Rewinds, 6 Factory Road, Birmingham, B18 5JU Tel: 0121-551 2323 Fax: 0121-554 2295 *Construction, steel buildings & warehouses*

Midland Oil Refinery Ltd, Shelah Road, Halesowen, West Midlands, B63 3PN Tel: 0121-585 6006 Fax: 0121-585 5405 *Oil & solvent lubricant manufrs*

Midland Painting Contractors, 34 College Street, Kempston, Bedford, MK42 8LU Tel: (01234) 354097 Fax: (01234) 267478 E-mail: helen@midlandpainters.co.uk *Painting contractors*

▶ Midland Pallets Ltd, 12 Finedon Sidings Industrial Estate, Furnace Lane, Finedon, Wellingborough, Northamptonshire, NN9 5NY Tel: (01536) 722217 Fax: (01536) 726013

▶ MIDLAND PARROTS, 160 Crescent Road, Hugglescote, Coalville, Leicestershire, LE67 2BD Tel: 01530 451682 Fax: 01530 451682 E-mail: info@midland-parrots.com *We supply quality food for Parrots and smaller birds.*We also supply Toys and accessories for your feathered companion.*

▶ Midland Patrol Dogs Ltd, PO Box 12241, Birmingham, B31 5LZ Tel: 0121-475 2615 E-mail: midlandpatroldog@aol.com *Security dog patrols*

Midland Phone Services plc, Unit 6-7 Two Woods Lane, Brierley Hill, West Midlands, DY5 1TA Tel: (01384) 74888 Fax: (01384) 76888 *Telecommunications*

Midland Pipeline Supplies Ltd, 92 Old Eaton Road, Rugeley, Staffordshire, WS15 2HA Tel: (01889) 585054 Fax: (01889) 585194 *Valve suppliers*

Midland Plant Installations Ltd, Curriers Cl, Charter Avenue Industrial Estate, Coventry, CV4 8AW Tel: (024) 7646 1225 Fax: (024) 7669 4261 E-mail: info@mpi-uk.com *Machinery removal & factory removal/relocation contractors, also plant installation/erection/dismantling engineers*

Midland Plant & Scaffolding Ltd, 171 Gloucester Crescent, Wigston, Leicestershire, LE18 4YH Tel: 0116-278 6677 *Scaffolding, building equipment sales & hire*

▶ Midland Plastic Windows (Hinckley) Ltd, Sapcote Road, Burbage, Hinckley, Leicestershire, LE10 2AZ Tel: (01455) 234635 Fax: (01455) 612880 *PVC doors windows & conservatories manufrs*

Midland Power Machinery Distributors Ltd, Farrell House, Orchard Street, Worcester, WR5 3DW Tel: (01905) 763027 Fax: (01905) 354241 E-mail: info@midlandpower.co.uk *Power & garden machinery & parts distributors*

Midland Precision Ltd, Unit 3a Peckleton Lane Business Park, Peckleton, Leicester, LE9 7RF Tel: (01455) 828998 Fax: (01455) 828993 E-mail: sales@mid-precision.co.uk *Precision engineers*

Midland Precision Diamond Tools, 44 Hockley Street, Birmingham, B18 6BH Tel: 0121-515 2108 Fax: 0121-554 9674 *Diamond tipped tool manufrs*

Midland Precision Equipment Co. Ltd, Haslucks Green Road, Shirley, Solihull, West Midlands, B90 2LY Tel: 0121-744 2719 Fax: 0121-733 1296 E-mail: sales@midland-precision.co.uk *Precision engineers*

Midland Precision Tool Makers, 3 Cyclo Works, Lifford Lane, Birmingham, B30 3DY Tel: 0121-486 3346 Fax: 0121-486 3346 *Toolmakers/toolmaking services*

▶ Midland Printers, Unit3 & 4 Acre Ridge Industrial Estate, Salcombe Road, Alfreton, Derbyshire, DE55 7RG Tel: (01773) 521007 Fax: (01773) 521144

Midland Properties, Reeves Street, Walsall, WS3 2DL Tel: (01922) 404148 Fax: (01922) 400212 *Property development & lettings*

Midland Pump Manufacturing Co. Ltd, Tyseley Industrial Estate, Seeleys Road, Birmingham, B11 2LF Tel: 0121-773 8862 Fax: 0121-771 4363 E-mail: sales@midlandpump.co.uk Principal Export Areas: Asia Pacific, Central Asia, Middle East, Africa, Central/East Europe & West Europe *Manufacturers of pumps, gear pumps, oil pumps, rotary pumps, high pressure (suds) pumps. Also damp proofing spray & injection equipment manufrs*

Midland Pumps Ltd, 25 Colemeadow Road, Moons Moat North Industrial Es, Redditch, Worcestershire, B98 9PB Tel: (01527) 598556 Fax: (01527) 598557 E-mail: sales@midlandpumps.co.uk *Pumps & associated equipment installers*

Midland Quarry Products Ltd, Leicester Road, Whitwick, Coalville, Leicestershire, LE67 5GR Tel: (01530) 832244 Fax: (01530) 832299 E-mail: sales@mqp.co.uk *Suppliers of asphalt & aggregates*

Midland Regional Printers Ltd, Nottingham Road, Nottingham, NG7 7BT Tel: 0115-955 1000 Fax: 0115-955 1012 E-mail: sales@midlandregionalprinters.co.uk Principal Export Areas: Africa *Commercial printers*

▶ Midland Reprographics Ltd, The Old Church, Main Street, Kimberley, Nottingham, NG16 2LL Tel: 0115-938 2353 Fax: 0115-945 9748 E-mail: sales@midlandreprographics.com *Sales & service of new & refurbished photocopiers*

Midland Rubber Co. Ltd, Unit 8, Commerce Court, Challenge Way, Bradford, West Yorkshire, BD4 8NW Tel: (01274) 820268 *Rubber product suppliers*

Midland Safe, Halesfield 2, Telford, Shropshire, TF7 4QH Tel: (01952) 682000 Fax: (01952) 682009 E-mail: sales@midland-safe.co.uk *Safe, strong room & lock experts*

Midland Safe Load Indicators Ltd, Watling Street Works, Watling Street, Brownhills, Walsall, WS8 7JT Tel: (01543) 453166 Fax: (01543) 453167 *Crane test, lifting gear, & machinery maintenance & repair services*

▶ Midland Security & Surveillance, 14 Clarry Drive, Sutton Coldfield, West Midlands, B74 2RA Tel: 0121-323 2126 Fax: 0121-323 2165 *Suppliers of burglar alarm systems*

Midland Security Systems, 544a Burton Road, Littleover, Derby, DE23 6FN Tel: (01332) 296664 Fax: (01332) 298238 *Security installation services*

▶ Midland Shelving Ltd, 8 Coventry Road, Bulwell, Nottingham, NG6 8RA Tel: 0115-977 1400 Fax: 0115-977 1600 E-mail: sales@midlandshelving.com *Shelving & pallet racking wholesalers & floor manufrs*

Midland Signs Leicester Ltd, 15 Foxholes Road, Golfcourse Lane, Leicester, LE3 1TH Tel: 0116-254 4445 Fax: 0116-254 2020 E-mail: info@ggstreetnameplates.com *Road signs & street name plates manufrs*

Midland Signs Systems Ltd, 2 Stour Road, Weedon Road Industrial Estate, Northampton, NN5 5AA Tel: (01604) 580966 Fax: (01604) 581878 *Tradework sign suppliers*

Midland Snacks Ltd, 6 Park Village Industrial Estate, Bridge Street, Park Village, Wolverhampton, WV10 9DX Tel: (01902) 728394 Fax: (01902) 863335 E-mail: sales@midlandsnacks.co.uk *Pork scratchings manufrs*

Midland Spinanpress Co. Ltd, 5 Sydney Road, Bordesley Green, Birmingham, B9 4QB Tel: 0121-772 6804 Fax: 0121-766 8580 *Metal spinners*

Midland Steel Traders Ltd, 19 Hogg Street, Airdrie, Lanarkshire, ML6 9JH Tel: (01236) 767288 Fax: (01236) 747116 *Plant machinery repairs*

Midland Structural Holdings Ltd, Herald Business Park, Golden Acres Lane, Coventry, CV3 2RT Tel: (024) 7644 5584 Fax: (024) 7645 9995 E-mail: steel@mss-ltd.com *Structural steelworkers & fabricators*

Midland Surface Finishing, 42 Bayton Road, Exhall, Coventry, CV7 9EJ Tel: (024) 7636 0436 Fax: (024) 7636 0721 *Blast cleaners & paint sprayers*

Midland Tank & Ironplate Co. Ltd, 241-243 Heneage Street, Birmingham, B7 4LY Tel: 0121-359 0298 Fax: 0121-333 3035 E-mail: sales@mti.uk.com *Sheet metalwork engineers & steel fabrications & manufacturers of galvanised tanks*

▶ Midland Testing Services, 3 Hollis Meadow, East Leake, Loughborough, Leicestershire, LE12 6RU Tel: (01509) 854444 Fax: (01509) 854444 E-mail: kevinspencer@midlandstestingservices.co.uk *Electrical appliance testing services*

Midland Time Recorder Services Ltd, 324 Hob Moor Road, Small Heath, Birmingham, B10 9HJ Tel: 0121-784 3761 Fax: 0121-784 7461 *Time recording machines*

Midland Tool & Design Ltd, Units 19-20, Barnfield Road, Tipton, West Midlands, DY4 9DF Tel: 0121-520 1171 Fax: 0121-557 3410 E-mail: sales@mtdltd.co.uk *Tungsten carbide press toolmakers*

Midland Tool Manufacturing Co. Ltd, Unit 13, Belle Eau Park, Bilsthorpe, Newark, Nottinghamshire, NG22 8TX Tel: (01623) 870411 Fax: (01623) 871857 E-mail: midlandtoolmans@msn.com *Accessories for lathe chucks*

Midland Trade Stringing & Folding Services, 9-10 The Square, Earls Barton, Northampton, NN6 0NA Tel: (01604) 810420 Fax: (01604) 812509 E-mail: mail@midlandtradestringing.co.uk *Printing trade finishers*

Midland Transmissions Ltd, 887 Melton Road, Thurmaston, Leicester, LE4 8EF Tel: 0116-260 6200 Fax: 0116-260 2548 E-mail: fosse.bearings@btinternet.com *Industrial gear box repairs & sales*

Midland Tube & Fabrications, 4 Corngreaves Works, Corngreaves Road, Cradley Heath, West Midlands, B64 7DA Tel: (01384) 566364 Fax: (01384) 566365 E-mail: keithcadman@btconnect.com *We are based in the heart of the black country, but deal nationwide, with our own 7.5 tonne lorry. We have been trading since 1993 selling mainly down graded and second hand tubes which can be financially beneficial, we also supply tube and fittings to the sand and gravel quarries in the area, including on site work when required. To complement our stocks we sell new welding fittings, elbows, flanges, tees etc plus Victaulic joints and roll grooving also Viking Johnson joints. We have a fully qualified welder for any type of fabrication work, including aluminium and stainless steel. We have two large automatic band saws which can cut up to 18" od tube. Please contact Keith or jude for any enquiries you may have, however small we will be only too pleased to help.*

Midland Vacum Cleaner Services, 1477-1479 Pershore Road, Stirchley, Birmingham, B30 2JL Tel: 0121-458 7185 Fax: 0121-458 4226 E-mail: enquries@midlandvac.co.uk *Vacuum cleaners & cleaning equipment*

Midland Vehicle Components Ltd, Oban Road, Coventry, CV6 6HH Tel: (024) 7664 4255 Fax: (024) 7636 4747 *Motor factors*

▶ Midland Vending Supplies, Unit 46 Willan Industrial Estate, West Ashton Street, Salford, M50 2XS Tel: 0161-745 9966 E-mail: midlandvendingsupplys@yahoo.co.uk *Midland vending supplies supply a wide range of top quality novelty toys and confectionary vending machines. We also supply stock at low low prices. check out the website for more details.*27mm bouncy balls £22.50*90mm £1 capsules from just 0.26p each**

Midland Veneers Ltd, 3 The Hayes Trading Estate, Folkes Road, Stourbridge, West Midlands, DY9 8RG Tel: (01384) 424924 Fax: (01384) 424929 E-mail: sales@mid-ven.co.uk *Decorative veneered door & panel manufrs*

Midland Wallboards Ltd, Severn House, Western Road, Oldbury, West Midlands, B69 4LY Tel: 0121-552 9333 Fax: 0121-552 9330 E-mail: sales@midlandwallboards.co.uk *Sheet material* Also at: Birmingham

Midland Welding Supply Co. Ltd, Starley Way, Birmingham, B37 7HF Tel: 0121-782 1977 Fax: 0121-782 1921 *Welding consumables & plant supplies* Also at: Sutton Coldfield

▶ Midland Wheels and Castors, The Die-Pat Centre, Broad March, Daventry, Northamptonshire, NN11 4HE Tel: (01327) 313111 Fax: (01327) 871821 E-mail: rayh@die-pat.co.uk *Wheels & castors manufrs*

Midland Wiper Manufacturing Co. Ltd, Fletcher Street, Long Eaton, Nottingham, NG10 1JU Tel: 0115-973 5187 Fax: 0115-946 2012 E-mail: office@midlandwiper.co.uk *Manufacturers of industrial and hygiene cleaning cloths and non-woven wipers*

Midland Wire Cordage Co. Ltd, 2a Eagle Road, Moons Moat North Industrial Estate, Redditch, Worcestershire, B98 9HF Tel: (01527) 594150 Fax: (01527) 64322 E-mail: info@mid-cord.co.uk Principal Export Areas: Worldwide *Manufacturers of heat exchanger tube turbulators*

Midland Wire Mesh Ltd, Lodgefield Road, Halesowen, West Midlands, B62 8AX Tel: 0121-559 4020 Fax: 0121-561 4030 E-mail: waltmesh@aol.co.uk Sales Contact: D. Walters *Midland Wire Mesh have been a supplier of welded wire mesh and woven wire mesh to industry for over 30 years. A family run company based in the West Midlands supplying wire mesh for many uses, offering, from stock, mild steel, galvanised and stainless steel welded mesh also avairy & pet mesh, stainless steel filter mesh and insect screening mesh. We also offer our popular wire mesh cutting service giving reliable local and national delivery and we are available to offer advise on all your wire mesh requirements and welcome enquiries large or small.*

Midlands Ltd, Wincanton Close, Ascot Drive Industrial Estate, Derby, DE24 8NB Tel: (01332) 753453 Fax: (01332) 757292 *Precision machinists*

Midlands Area Rabbit Control, 59 Coventry Road, Bulkington, Bedworth, Warwickshire, CV12 9LZ Tel: (024) 7631 3632 *Pest control services*

Midlands Asbestos Survey Services, 184 Northumberland Court, Northumberland Road, Leamington Spa, Warwickshire, CV32 6HW Tel: (01926) 434444 Fax: (01926) 430280 E-mail: info@massltd.co.uk *Asbestos Survey Services (Midlands) are a Warwickshire based company providing specialist asbestos surveyors throughout the U.K. Our comprehensive surveys will assist you in complying with asbestos management laws and are carried out in compliance with the HSE document 'MDHS100'. All samples are independently tested at UKAS accredited laboratories. Call us on 01926 432040, we can help.*

Midlands Direct Mail & Packaging Services Ltd, Bellamy Road, Mansfield, Nottinghamshire, NG18 4LN Tel: (01623) 636337 Fax: (01623) 420917 E-mail: sales@mdmuk.co.uk *Direct mail services contract packers*

Midlands Electrical Installations Ltd, 51 Winpenny Road, Parkhouse Industrial Estate East, Newcastle, Staffordshire, ST5 7RH Tel: (01782) 566844 Fax: (01782) 566756 *Electrical engineers contractors*

Midlands Electrical Specialists Ltd, 3 Ariane, Tamworth, Staffordshire, B79 7XF Tel: (01827) 63293 Fax: (01827) 55588 *Electrical contractors*

Midlands Instrumentation Maintenance, Woodwards Place, Coppice Side, Swadlincote, Derbyshire, DE11 9AA Tel: (01283) 229000 Fax: (01283) 229111 E-mail: mimspeak@aol.com *Gas analysis & recalibration services*

Midleton Joinery, Midleton Industrial Estate, Guildford, Surrey, GU2 8XW Tel: (01483) 451994 Fax: (01483) 452110 E-mail: enquiries@midletonjoinery.co.uk *Joiners*

MidMos Solutions Limited, 29 Navigation Drive, Hurst Business Park, Brierley Hill, West Midlands, DY5 1UT Tel: (01384) 472930 Fax: (01384) 472911 E-mail: markgroobey@b-one.com *MidMos Solutions Limited provides complete biting insect (Mosquito, midge and others) solution packages.*

Midos Communications, 10 Heol-Y-Deri, Cardiff, CF14 6HG Tel: (029) 2069 1698 Fax: (029) 2069 1693 *PC's assembly, communications & mobile phones*

Midpoint Ltd, 18 Leeds Road, Harrogate, North Yorkshire, HG2 8AA Tel: (01423) 528520 Fax: (01423) 529484 E-mail: enquiries@midpoint.co.uk *CAD systems & web design for architects & to the construction industry*

Midshire Business Systems Northern Ltd, Jones Court, Jones Square, Stockport, Cheshire, SK1 4LJ Tel: 0161-477 3277 Fax: 0161-477 3340 E-mail: info@midshire.co.uk *Office equipment suppliers*

Midshires Radiator Services Ltd, 5 Orleton Road, Ludlow Business Park, Ludlow, Shropshire, SY8 1XF Tel: (01584) 874495 Fax: (01584) 874495 *Radiator repairs*

▶ Midshires Scaffolding Co. Ltd, Unit 22 Bilton Industrial Estate, Humber Avenue, Coventry, CV3 1JL Tel: (024) 7665 2901 Fax: (024) 7665 2902

Midsoft Computer Systems, Aston Lane, Aston, Stone, Staffordshire, ST15 0BW Tel: (01785) 818054 Fax: (01785) 817513 E-mail: sales@midsoft.co.uk *Software developers*

Midsomer Engineering, Coombend, Radstock, BA3 3AS Tel: (01761) 434929 Fax: (01761) 432271 *Steel fabricators*

Midsteel Pipeline Ltd, Building 67 Third Avenue, Pensnett Trading Estate, Kingswinford, West Midlands, DY6 7FA Tel: (01384) 400321 Fax: (01384) 400461 E-mail: sales@midsteel.co.uk Principal Export Areas: Central/East Europe, West Europe, North America & South America *Pipeline Fittings & Flanges*

▶ Midsummer House, Midsummer Common, Cambridge, CB4 1HA Tel: (01223) 369299 Fax: (01223) 302672 E-mail: reservations@midsummerhouse.co.uk *Midsummer House boasts a fabulous setting within its own secluded garden along the banks of the River Cam. It is an ideal venue for a host of occasions, from a romantic dinner for two to a corporate dinner party for fifty guests.**Since winning its second Michelin Star in January 2005, Midsummer House has enjoyed a wealth of publicity and has succeeded in placing East Anglia firmly on the culinary map.**Midsummer House boasts a fabulous setting within its own secluded garden along the banks of the River Cam. It is an ideal venue for a host of occasions, from a romantic dinner for two to a corporate dinner party for fifty guests. Throughout the year you can enjoy the pleasures of the light and airy conservatory dinning room. Inside it's charming, peaceful and perfect for any occasion. When you eat at Midsummer House it is not just dining it's an experience. **

Mid-thames Chandlery, Mill Green, Caversham, Reading, RG4 8EX Tel: 0118-948 4226 Fax: 0118-946 1371 *Chandlery*

Midvale Electrical Engineering Co. Ltd, 20 Butlers Leap, Rugby, Warwickshire, CV21 3RQ Tel: (01788) 543216 Fax: (01788) 540899 E-mail: sales@midvale-electrical.com *Control panel manufrs*

Midway Designs Ltd, Unit A1 Pear Mill Industrial Estate, Stockport Road West, Bredbury, Stockport, Cheshire, SK6 2BP Tel: 0161-430 7810 Fax: 0161-430 1714 E-mail: sales@midwaydesigns.co.uk *Sign design, manufacture & installation to the construction industry*

Midway Material Handling, 7 Pinewood Drive, Little Haywood, Stafford, ST18 0NX Tel: (01889) 882014 Fax: (01889) 882014 *Supplies of hoisting*

Midway Metalcraft, Ridgeway Court, Grovebury Rd, Leighton Buzzard, Bedfordshire, LU7 4SW Tel: (01525) 374861 Fax: (01525) 374082 E-mail: enquiries@midwaymetalcraft.com *Sheet metalwork manufrs*

Midway Precision Ltd, Pontygwindy Industrial Estate, Caerphilly, Mid Glamorgan, CF83 3HU Tel: (029) 2088 3552 Fax: (029) 2086 6410 E-mail: hjh@midwayprecisioneng.co.uk *Machine sub-contractors*

Midway Tools Ltd, 9a Walsall Street, West Bromwich, West Midlands, B70 7NX Tel: 0121-553 3819 Fax: 0121-500 5453 E-mail: sales@midwaytools.co.uk *Engineers suppliers & cutting tool distributors*

▶ Midwest Computer Consultants, The Old Coach House, Felton, Hereford, HR1 3PH Tel: (01432) 820033 Fax: (01432) 820044 *Recruitment consultants*

Midwest Displays, 22 Oxford Street, Birmingham, B5 5NR Tel: 0121-643 1746 Fax: 0121-616 1014 *Screen printers*

Midwest Forklift Services Ltd, Blackheath Trading Estate, Cakemore Road, Rowley Regis, West Midlands, B65 0QN Tel: 0121-561 2141 Fax: 0121-561 5931 *Forklift truck sales, service & hire*

Midwest Market Force Ltd, 46 Raddens Road, Halesowen, West Midlands, B62 0AN Tel: 0121-421 2333 Fax: 0121-421 3555 E-mail: mwmf@btconnect.com *Coffee machines & utensils importer*

▶ MidWinter Computer Services Ltd, 385 Cricklade Road, Swindon, SN2 1AQ Tel: (01793) 522175 Fax: (0871) 6616186 E-mail: enquiries@midwintercomputers.com *Obtain, no gimmick, cost effective solutions for all of your information and communication technology needs.*

Miele Co. Ltd, Fairacres, Marcham Road, Abingdon, Oxfordshire, OX14 1TW Tel: (0845) 3303618 Fax: (01235) 554477 E-mail: miele-professional@miele.co.uk *Miele Professional located in Abingdon, Oxford are manufacturers of laundry equipment, commercial dishwashers and thermal disinfectors. They have many specialist applications and look forward to dealing with your requests.*

Mifflin Construction Ltd, Worcester Road, Leominster, Herefordshire, HR6 8AY Tel: (01568) 613311 Fax: (01568) 614935 E-mail: sales@mifflin.co.uk *Structural steel fabricators*

▶ Mifflin Motors, Barrs Court Road, Hereford, HR1 1EG Tel: (01432) 356268 Fax: (01432) 357052

▶ Mig Antig Workshops, 28 Business Village, Wexham Road, Slough, SL2 5HF Tel: (01753) 529961 Fax: (01753) 529961 *Architectural welders & sheet metal fabricators*

Migatronic Welding Equipment Ltd, 21 Jubilee Drive, Loughborough, Leicestershire, LE11 5XS Tel: (01509) 211492 Fax: (01509) 231959 E-mail: sales@migatronic.co.uk *Welding equipment manufacturers & suppliers*

Mighton Products Ltd, PO Box 1, Saffron Walden, Essex, CB10 1QJ Tel: (01223) 497097 Fax: (01799) 531135 E-mail: sales@mighton.co.uk *Mighton is market leader in the design, manufacture and distribution of advanced hardware products for sash windows, with customers and offices in the UK and USA. Mighton has introduced a suite of innovative products to revolutionise the window industry: Ultrashoe, a patented adjustable pivotshoe, targets fabricators and installers, making adjusting the balances of sash windows a simple, three step operation. Ventlock, a restricted opening security device for timber and PVC-U sash windows. Fenestrator, a retro-fitted opening aid, and Powersash, a motorised aid, are both designed for the elderly and disabled markets, which are set to see much change following the Disability Discrimination Act 2004.*

The Mighty Fine Company Ltd, Quatro House, Lyon Way, Frimley, Surrey, GU16 7ER Tel: 0845 072 0090 E-mail: info@mightyfinecompany.com *Mighty Fine specialises in high quality, soft adventure travel experiences. Imagine the thrill of a wildlife safari in South Africa, swimming with wild dolphins in Australia or an exhilarating snowmobile safari in Scandinavia. Picture yourself soaking up the stunning natural beauty of the Norwegian fjords, seeing the sun rise at Ayers Rock or encountering the moving and heart-warming spirit of Soweto.**There's no end to the adventures that you can have and, whatever your own personal adventure, we want to offer you excitement, new experiences, ear-to-ear grins and a whole lot of fun! So let your adventure start here!*

Mighty Micro, 268 Wilmslow Road, Manchester, M14 6JR Tel: 0161-224 8117 Fax: 0161-257 2803 E-mail: info@mighty-micro.co.uk *Computer resellers*

Mightyhire Ltd, Unit 40, Foster Street Industrial Estate, Hull, HU8 8BT Tel: (01482) 325954 Fax: (01482) 325490 E-mail: ppwmightyhire@hotmail.com *Haulage contractors*

▶ Migra-Cap (UK) Ltd, Venture Wales, Merthyr Industrial Park, Pentrebach, Merthyr Tydfil, Mid Glamorgan, CF48 4DR Tel: (01443) 693464 Fax: (01443) 693511 E-mail: info@migracap.com *Therapy application for relief of migraine & headaches*

▶ Migrate Media, 96 Ethel Street, Hove, East Sussex, BN3 3LL Tel: (07966) 025392 E-mail: info@migratemedia.co.uk *Migrate Media, based in Brighton UK, offer a wide range of internet & design services including website design & development, search engine optimisation & online marketing. Web design & freelance designers at competitive rates.*

Scott Mihajlovic Associates Ltd, 25 Aden Gro, London, N16 9NP Tel: (020) 7690 9700 Fax: (020) 7690 9711 *Software development*

Mika Property Building Services, 6 Tern Road, Porthcawl, Mid Glamorgan, CF36 3TS Tel: (01656) 786150 Fax: (01656) 786158 E-mail: mikapbs@aol.com *Property maintenance services*

Mikado Computer Support, 38 Gravel Hill, Wimborne, Dorset, BH21 1RR Tel: (01202) 883808 Fax: (01202) 883808 E-mail: sales@mikado.co.uk *Computer teaching, training & engineer support*

Mikay Distributors, Unit 17 River Road Business Park, 33 River Road, Barking, Essex, IG11 0DA Tel: (020) 8507 7665 Fax: (020) 8507 7670 E-mail: sales@mikay.co.uk *Importers & distributors of electrical accessories, audio leads*

▶ Mike Beer Ltd, Port Zone, Old Park, Whitfield, Dover, Kent, CT16 2HQ Tel: (01304) 828600 Fax: (01304) 829255 E-mail: info@mikebeer.co.uk

Mike Brown, 21 Horsecroft, Stanford in the Vale, Faringdon, Oxfordshire, SN7 8LL Tel: (01367) 718993 Fax: (01367) 718993 *Sign manufrs*

Mike Brown Joinery Contractor, 1 Rainnieshill Road, Newmachar, Aberdeen, AB21 0XG Tel: (01651) 863086 Fax: (01651) 862832 *Joinery manufrs*

Mike Davies Bearings Ltd, Leamore Lane, Walsall, WS2 7DE Tel: (01922) 494940 Fax: (01922) 407760 E-mail: sales@mikedaviesbearings.com *Ball bearing stockists & distributors*

▶ Mike Goldrick Window Blinds Ltd, 13 Bramhall Lane, Stockport, Cheshire, SK2 6HT Tel: (01706) 625525 Fax: (01706) 625525 *Manufacturers of window blinds*

▶ mike hughes, 12, the acorns, upton, chester, CH2 1JL Tel: 07866469338 Fax: 01244 378702 E-mail: mikehistdservices@yahoo.co.uk *site maintenance work, full deep cleaning services for industrial,commercial. and residential.members of national federation of master window & general cleaners also members of british institute of cleaning science.*

Mike Nash, PO Box 43, Hayle, Cornwall, TR27 5BG Tel: (01736) 756277 E-mail: sales@mikenash.co.uk *Internet design & marketing.*

Mike O'Leary Cleaning Services, 181 Scribers Lane, Birmingham, B28 0PN Tel: 0121-745 4662 Fax: 0121-745 4662 *Industrial cleaning contractors*

▶ Mike Robertson Associates, 3 Old Ladies Court, High Street, Battle, East Sussex, TN33 0AH Tel: (01424) 777156 Fax: (01424) 775668 E-mail: mike.robertson@mraltd.com *Financial & business advisers*

Mike Tucker Autos, Millwood Street, Manselton, Swansea, SA5 9JZ Tel: (01792) 456287 *Automatic gear box repairs & services*

Mike's Boatyard Ltd, 17 High Street, Old Leigh, Leigh-On-Sea, Essex, SS9 2EN Tel: (01702) 713151 Fax: (01702) 480092 *Marine services, Boat Hire, Engineering, Commercial Marine contracts, Wharfage*

Mike's Uk's No 1 Dive Stores, 268-270 Hillmorton Road, Rugby, Warwickshire, CV22 5BW Tel: (01788) 551800 Fax: (01788) 551900 E-mail: sales@scubagear.co.uk *Scuba retailers, training & servicing*

Mike's Waterfront Warehouse, Unit 1 Wyatts View, St. Anne's Park, Bristol, BS4 4WW Tel: 0117-977 6227 *Diving equipment suppliers*

Mikes Waterfront Warehouse, 42 Lichfield Terrace, Upminster, Essex, RM14 3JX Tel: (01708) 227122 E-mail: info@waterfrontscuba.com *Diving equipment suppliers*

Mikina Engineering, Unit 40 Downton Industrial Estate, Batten Road, Downton Industrial Estate, Salisbury, SP5 3HU Tel: (01725) 513388 Fax: (01725) 513399 *Precision engineers*

Mi-King Ltd, Bentall Business Park, Glover District 11, Washington, Tyne & Wear, NE37 3JD Tel: 0191-415 5919 Fax: 0191-415 1300 E-mail: sales@mi-king.co.uk *Steel stockholders & slitting services*

Mikkimugs Screen Process Printers, Matravers Farm, Uploders, Bridport, Dorset, DT6 4PH Tel: (01308) 485300 Fax: (01308) 485542 E-mail: sales@mikkimugs.demon.co.uk *Promotional product manufrs*

Mikkis Mouse Mats, Flat 3, 34 Croft Road, Clacton-on-Sea, Essex, CO15 3EF Tel: (01255) 225301 Fax: (01255) 225311 E-mail: sales@mikkis.com *Promotional mouse mat manufrs*

▶ Miko Coffee South West (Exeter), 6 Orchard Court, Heron Road, Sowton Industrial Estate, Exeter, EX2 7LL Tel: (01392) 447272 Fax: (01392) 447373 E-mail: fhowell@miko.co.uk *Coffee company*

▶ Miko Cornwall, Miko House, New Portreath Road, Parc Erissey Industrial Estate, Redruth, Cornwall, TR16 4HZ Tel: (01209) 215555 Fax: (01209) 213333 E-mail: sales@cornishcoffee.co.uk *Office coffee machines & products suppliers*

▶ Miko.co.uk, Unit 2, Tweed Road, Clevedon, Somerset, BS21 6RR Tel: (01275) 874416 Fax: (01275) 342027 E-mail: info@mikocoffee.co.uk *Coffee & tea suppliers*

▶ Mikom Systems Ltd, 110 Parkgate, Darlington, County Durham, DL1 1RX Tel: (01325) 465683 Fax: (01325) 463930 E-mail: sales@mikom.co.uk *Computer maintenance & repairers*

Mikon, 15 Horwood Court, Bletchley, Milton Keynes, MK1 1RD Tel: (01908) 379333 Fax: (01908) 379900 *Special purpose machinery manufrs*

Mikris Finishers, Lower Dudbridge House, Dudbridge Road, Dudbridge, Stroud, Gloucestershire, GL5 3HF Tel: (01453) 763873 Fax: (01453) 763873 *Blast cleaning & paint finishing*

Mikrofill Systems Ltd, West Court, Buntsford Park Road, Bromsgrove, Worcestershire, B60 3DX Tel: (01527) 574574 Fax: (01527) 575565 E-mail: info@mikrofill.com *Heating & pressurisation specialists*

Mikrojet (UK), Unit 1 Leflaive Business Centre, Church Lane, Naphill, High Wycombe, Buckinghamshire, HP14 4US Tel: (01494) 565610 Fax: (01494) 565612 E-mail: info@mikrojet.co.uk *Inkjets distributors*

Miktek Ltd, 2 Wetherden Business Park, Wetherden, Stowmarket, Suffolk, IP14 3JU Tel: (01359) 241456 E-mail: mik@miktek.co.uk *Welders & fabricators*

Mikuni Heating UK Ltd, Unit 6 Second Avenue, Southampton, SO15 0LP Tel: (023) 8052 8777 Fax: (023) 8052 8800 E-mail: sales@mikuniheating.com Principal Export Areas: Worldwide *Air heaters & boat heating equipment manufrs*

Mil Tek Environmental Ltd, 3 Queens Close, Oswestry, Shropshire, SY11 2JA Tel: (01691) 670891 E-mail: sales@pressingsolutions.co.uk *Waste management equipment suppliers*

Mil Tek Scotland Ltd, 16 Monreith Road, Glasgow, G43 2NX Tel: 0141-571 3100 Fax: 0141-571 3200 *Waste processing machinery*

Mila Maintenance Services, Oaks Business Park, Oaks Lane, Barnsley, South Yorkshire, S71 1HT Tel: (01226) 203315 Fax: (01226) 249493 E-mail: sales@milamaintenance.co.uk *Window & door maintenance*

Milano Sports Ltd, 2-4 Winifred Street, Hucknall, Nottingham, NG15 7RX Tel: 0115-963 8945 Fax: 0115-963 8420 *School & leisure wear manufrs*

Milap Weekly, Masbro Centre, 87 Masbro Road, London, W14 0LR Tel: (020) 7385 8966 Fax: (020) 7385 8966 *Indian magazine publishers*

Milar Ltd, Minereva House, 1 Bilton Road, Rugby, Warwickshire, CV22 7NZ Tel: (01788) 551288 Fax: (01788) 552142 *Executive research organisation*

Milbank Industries, Brandon Central Depot, Mundford Road, Weeting, Brandon, Suffolk, IP27 0PL Tel: (01842) 819818 *Floors & trucks*

Milbank Industries Ltd, Airfield, Earls Colne, Colchester, CO6 2NS Tel: (01787) 223931 Fax: (01787) 220535 E-mail: estimating@milbank.co.uk *Pre-stressed concrete floor manufrs*

▶ Milbank Trucks Ltd, Airfield, Earls Colne, Colchester, CO6 2NS Tel: (01787) 224226 Fax: (01787) 220533

▶ Milbank Trucks Ltd, Denton Wharf, Mark Lane, Gravesend, Kent, DA12 2QD Tel: (01474) 364326

▶ Milbank Trucks Ltd, 15 The Old Depot, Bridge Street, Weedon, Northampton, NN7 4PS Tel: (01327) 342678 Fax: (01327) 342623

Milbor Engineering Co. Ltd, Belswains Lane, Hemel Hempstead, Hertfordshire, HP3 9XE Tel: (01442) 242945 Fax: (01442) 257308 E-mail: enquiries@nashmills.herts.sch.uk *Light & general precision engineering*

Milburn Boats, Bridge Grounds, Shuckburgh Road, Staverton, Daventry, Northamptonshire, NN11 6BG Tel: (01327) 702164 Fax: (01327) 702258 E-mail: enquiries@milburnboats.co.uk *Boat builders*

▶ Milcon Construction & Property Services Ltd, Enterprise House Wistaston Road Business Centre, Wistaston Road, Crewe, CW2 7RP Tel: (01270) 580000 Fax: (01270) 500041

Milden Steels Ltd, Unit 1 Park St Works, Kidderminster, Worcestershire, DY11 6TN Tel: (01562) 66615 Fax: (01562) 829293 E-mail: sales@milden-steels.fsnet.co.uk *Steel shearing & stockholding services*

Milequip Computer Maintenance Ltd, Hepworth House, 115 Southgate Street, Gloucester, GL1 1UT Tel: (01452) 305430 Fax: (01452) 411010 E-mail: mcmcomputers@freeuk.com *Computer sales & services*

Miles Better Software, 221 Cannock Road, Cannock, Staffordshire, WS11 5DD Tel: (01543) 466577 Fax: (01543) 466579 *Computer hard & software*

Miles Commercial Interiors, Broadoak, Newbury Road, Kingsclere, Newbury, Berkshire, RG20 5SH Tel: (01635) 297508 Fax: (01635) 299815 *Office interior refurbishment services*

▶ John Miles, 7 Halliwell Industrial Estate, Rossini Street, Bolton, BL1 8DL Tel: (01204) 844538 Fax: (01204) 848592 *Manufacturers of gaskets, washers & packaging*

Miles Platts Ltd, 39 Abbey Park Road, Leicester, LE4 5AN Tel: 0116-262 2593 Fax: 0116-253 7889 E-mail: enquiries@milesplatts.co.uk *Manufacturers of bobbins injection mouldings & plastic mouldings*

Miles Smith (Insurance Brokers), Birchin Court, 20 Birchin Lane, London, EC3V 9DU Tel: (020) 7283 0040 Fax: (020) 7220 0860 E-mail: mhartshorn@milessmith.co.uk *Miles Smith are an independent Insurance Broker based in the City of London, with direct and immediate access into Lloyd's and all other major underwriters and insurers. We can provide you with a tailored solution to meet all your specific requirements. For further information, please visit our website: www.milessmith.co.uk*

Miles Stone, Quarry Yard, Woodside Avenue, Eastleigh, Hampshire, SO50 9ES Tel: (023) 8061 3178 *Natural stone suppliers*

Walter Miles (Electrical Engineers) Ltd, 48 Hinckley Road, Leicester, LE3 0RB Tel: 0116-255 3131 Fax: 0116-254 9396 E-mail: office@waltermiles.co.uk *Electrical engineers & contractors*

Milestone Minitures Ltd, 25 West End, Redruth, Cornwall, TR15 2SA Tel: (01209) 218356 Fax: (01209) 217983 *Miniatures in metal manufrs*

▶ Milestone Technologies Ltd, 6 Jardine Cottages, Templewood Lane, Stoke Poges, Slough, SL2 4BQ Tel: 01753 662182 Fax: 0870 134 1924 E-mail: enquiries@milestonetechnologies.co.uk *We provide telecommunications network planning, capacity planning, project management*

Mileta Sports Ltd, Spen Vale Mills, Spen Vale Street, Heckmondwike, West Yorkshire, WF16 0NQ Tel: (01924) 409311 Fax: (01924) 409839 E-mail: email@tog24.com *Clothing manufrs*

Milfin Trade Finishers Ltd, Tonbridge Works, Tonbridge Road, Romford, RM3 8TS Tel: (01708) 377716 Fax: (01708) 377719 *Packaging trade finishers*

▶ Milford Haven Ship Repairers, The Docks, Milford Haven, Dyfed, SA73 3DJ Tel: (01646) 696320 Fax: (01646) 696321 E-mail: mhsr@milford-docks.co.uk *Marine and port service ship repairers.*

▶ Milford Homes Ltd, 850 Brighton Road, Purley, Surrey, CR8 2BH Tel: (020) 8763 3500 Fax: (020) 8763 8643

Milford Mouldings Ltd, Unit 36 38, Station Road Industrial Estate, Hailsham, East Sussex, BN27 2EY Tel: (01323) 440561 Fax: (01323) 449349 *Plastic component manufrs*

▶ Milford Plants, Common Lane, South Milford, Leeds, LS25 5BX Tel: (01977) 683623 Fax: (01977) 685944

▶ Milford Saddlery Ltd, Parknook Farm, Ranton, Stafford, ST18 9JU Tel: (01785) 282034

Milford Steel, Unit 18 Thornton Industrial Trading Estate, Milford Haven, Dyfed, SA73 2RZ Tel: (01646) 698821 Fax: (01646) 697403 E-mail: millfodd@ellissteelgroup.co.uk *The company commenced trading on 1st July 1970 as Ellis Steel Stockholders in Swansea. It grew in size gradually and opened Bristol Steel Stockholders in November 1977. The need for a specialist non-ferrous metal supplier saw the birth of Enterprise Metals which was followed by the acquisition of Milford Steel in West Wales. Logan & Allen was recently added to the group*

continued

*providing a source of imported steel for the group. More recently, the group acquired an established steel stockholder in Swansea, McArthur Faull which combined with the existing Ellis Steel became Ellis Faull Stockholders. Cutting & bending reinforcing bar to BS8666:2005, (Bristol Steel & Ellis Faull are CARES approved for reinforcing bar & mesh) *Sawing including mitre cuts on our in house band saw:- *Drilling, Painting, Welding, Fabrication to your drawings, Galvanising, Guillotining, Bending, Anodising, Plasma/Laser Cutting, PLUS DELIVERY SERVICE*

Milhench Painting Contractors Ltd, Lyceum Works, George Street, Chadderton, Oldham, OL9 9HY Tel: 0161-624 2868 Fax: 0161-628 5569 *Painting contractors*

Military Mart, 151 Throston Grange Lane, Hartlepool, Cleveland, TS26 0TX Tel: (01429) 868428 Fax: (01429) 299029 *Medals & militaries suppliers*

▶ militarybadges.co.uk, 27 Post House Wynd, Darlington, County Durham, DL3 7LP Tel: (01325) 489820 E-mail: diamondmerchants@btopenworld.com *THE SALE THROUGH MY WEBSITE AND SHOP OF MILITARY TIES, CUFFLINKS AND TIE SLIDES, BLAZER BADGES, FULL SIZE AND MINIATURE MEDALS. ANY BLAZER BADGES MADE TO ORDER WITH YOUR DESIGN. FROM ONE BADGE TO A THOUSAND. MEDAL MOUNTING THROUGH THE SHOP, INCLUDING FRAMING.* THE SHOP IS PRIMARILY CONCERNED WITH THE BUYING AND SELLING OF NEW AND SECONDHAND DIAMOND, GOLD AND SILVER JEWELLERY.**

Milk-Rite, PO Box 2, Melksham, Wiltshire, SN12 6NB Tel: (0870) 7315010 Fax: (01225) 896311 E-mail: sales@milk-rite.com *Polymer products manufrs*

Mill At Gordleton, Silver Street, Sway, Lymington, Hampshire, SO41 6DJ Tel: (01590) 682219 Fax: (01590) 683073 E-mail: sales@gordletonmill.co.uk *Paint stripping specialists*

▶ Mill Design & Marketing, Hilliard House, Lester Way, Wallingford, Oxfordshire, OX10 9TA Tel: (01491) 833822 Fax: (01491) 833002 E-mail: steve@millmarketing.co.uk *Business graphic design solutions services*

Mill Garage, Walkington, Beverley, North Humberside, HU17 8RT Tel: (01482) 868365 Fax: (01482) 865232 *Agricultural engineers*

Mill Garage Ltd, 19 Crown Road, Kings Norton Business Centre, Birmingham, B30 3HY Tel: 0121-486 3486 Fax: 0121-486 3486 *Motor vehicle repair service & MOT*

Mill Green Forge, Essendon Forge, Essendon Hill, Essendon, Hatfield, Hertfordshire, AL9 6AL Tel: (01707) 271141 Fax: (01707) 271141 E-mail: chris@penstone-smith.fsnet.co.uk *Blacksmith forge*

Mill Hill Supplies, Unit 37 Broton Trading Estate, Broton Drive, Halstead, Essex, CO9 1HB Tel: (01787) 472236 Fax: (01787) 477797 E-mail: mail@millhillsupplies.co.uk *Sell small engineering tools*

Mill House Manufacturing Design Ltd, Roughton Road, Kirkby-on-Bain, Woodhall Spa, Lincolnshire, LN10 6YL Tel: (01526) 354404 Fax: (01526) 354424 E-mail: sales@millhouse-md.co.uk *Educational furniture, toys, & equipment suppliers*

Mill Lane Engineering, 24 Mill Lane, Briston, Melton Constable, Norfolk, NR24 2JG Tel: (01263) 860711 Fax: (01263) 860711 *Hydraulic engineers*

Mill Road Properties Ltd, Pressing Room Dye Works, Hartley Street, Dewsbury, West Yorkshire, WF13 2HR Tel: (01924) 465323 Fax: (01924) 502662 *Textiles wholesaler & data storage*

Mill Shop Ltd, Tynwald Mills, St. Johns, Isle of Man, IM4 3AD Tel: (01624) 801213 Fax: (01624) 801893 E-mail: bobjeavons@manx.net *Retail & property*

The Mill Shops, Buckfast Road, Buckfast, Buckfastleigh, Devon, TQ11 0ED Tel: (01364) 643325 Fax: (01364) 643183 *Yarn manufrs*

▶ Mill Systems, Unit 4, Heritage Business Centre, Derby road, Belper, Derbyshire, DE56 1SW Tel: (01773) 824400 Fax: (0870) 0515380 E-mail: sales@millsystems.com *Computer software development*

Mill Tech Computers, 39c James Street, Whitehaven, Cumbria, CA28 7HZ Tel: (01946) 696200 Fax: (01946) 656208 *Software, hardware & computer repairers*

Adam Millar & Sons Ltd, 22 Muriel Street, Barrhead, Glasgow, G78 1QB Tel: 0141-881 6000 Fax: 0141-881 6060 E-mail: info@adammiller.com *Sheet metalworkers & steel fabricators*

▶ Millar Callaghan Engineering Services Ltd, 10 Arkwright Way, North Newmoor Industrial Estat, Irvine, Ayrshire, KA11 4JU Tel: (01294) 217711 Fax: (01294) 217722 *Metalworking & fabrication services*

▶ Millar International Freight Transport Ltd, Springkerse Road, Stirling, FK7 7SN Tel: (01786) 451409

Millar Mcdowell, 44 Lany Road, Moira, Craigavon, County Armagh, BT67 0NZ Tel: (028) 9262 1086 Fax: (028) 9262 1086 *Dairy engineer (servicing)*

Millbank, Westmorland Business Centre, 41-43 Westmorland Road, Newcastle Upon Tyne, NE1 4EH Tel: 0191-232 1301 Fax: 0191-232 1302 E-mail: enquiries@ampekko.com *Manufacture voice alarm systems & public address systems*

▶ Millbank Manufacturing Ltd, Yardley Works, Stourbridge Road, Stourbridge, West Midlands, DY9 7BD Tel: (01384) 896229

Millbride Products, 67 Fountain Road, Edgbaston, Birmingham, B17 8NP Tel: (0800) 281905 Fax: 0121-429 3231 E-mail: sales@klarit.com *Anti-mist treatment for glasses*

The Millbridge (Group) P.L.C., 43-43 Maddock Street, London, W1S 2PD Tel: (020) 7399 4343 Fax: (020) 7399 4349 E-mail: info@millbridgegroup.co.uk *Chartered surveyors & project managers*

Millbrook Engineering, Wesley Road, Cinderford, Gloucestershire, GL14 2JN Tel: (01594) 823822 Fax: (01594) 823222 *Welding & precision engineers*

Millbrook Furnishings Industries, Stephenson Road, Calmore Industrial Estate, Totton, Southampton, SO40 3RY Tel: (023) 8066 2221 Fax: (023) 8066 2264 E-mail: sales@mfil.co.uk *Furniture restoration & interior refurbishers*

Millbrook Instruments Ltd, Greenbank Business Park, Challenge Way, Blackburn, BB1 5QB Tel: (01254) 699606 Fax: (01254) 699610 E-mail: info@millbrook-instruments.com *Scientific Instrument design & manufrs*

▶ Millbrook Machine Tools, Park Road, Holmewood, Chesterfield, Derbyshire, S42 5UY Tel: (01246) 859999 Fax: (01246) 856069 E-mail: info@millbrookgroup.co.uk *Sub-contract machining & used machine sales & repairs*

Millbrook Proving Ground Ltd, Station Lane, Millbrook, Bedford, MK45 2JQ Tel: (01525) 404242 Fax: (01525) 403420 E-mail: test@millbrook.co.uk *Vehicle test, development & certification*

Millen Machine Tools Ltd, Hamilton House, 126 St. Georges Avenue, Northampton, NN2 6JF Tel: (01604) 721122 Fax: (01604) 721329 E-mail: harvey.millen@virgin.net *Machinery suppliers*

T.P. Millen Co. Ltd, 4 Stuart Way, East Grinstead, West Sussex, RH19 4RS Tel: (0787) 6658207 Fax: (01342) 335747 E-mail: tmillen@vodafone.net *Specialist precision engineers*

Millenium Brick Ltd, Unit B Levenshulme Trading Estate, Printworks Lane, Manchester, M19 3JP Tel: 0161-248 0882 Fax: 0161-248 5445 E-mail: sales@millenniumbrick.plus.com *Brick manufrs*

Millennium Au Pairs & Nannies, The Coach House, The CR, Belmont, Sutton, Surrey, SM2 6BP Tel: (020) 8241 9752 Fax: (020) 8643 1268 E-mail: sales@aupairchoice.com *Placement of livein in Au Pairs, Mothers Helps, Nannies & housekeepers in London and Home Counties. All applicants interviewed & vetted. We are full members of IAPA & BAPAA and offer a fast & efficient matching service.*

▶ Millennium Awards, Smithy Market Hill, Glass, Huntly, Aberdeenshire, AB54 4XX Tel: (01466) 700311 Fax: (01466) 700344 E-mail: info@onlinetrophies.co.uk *Trophies & medals suppliers*

Millennium Blinds Ltd, 3 Northern Buildings, Northern Road, Portsmouth, PO6 3DL Tel: (023) 9222 0204 Fax: (023) 9222 0204 *Blind manufrs*

Millennium Computer Systems Ltd, B11 The Seedbed Centre, Wyncolls Road, Colchester, CO4 9HT Tel: (01206) 855288 Fax: (01206) 855285 E-mail: info@millennium-computer.co.uk *Computer consultants*

▶ Millennium Coupling Co. Ltd, 72b Roman Way Industrial Estate, Ribbleton, Preston, PR2 5BE Tel: (01772) 653530 Fax: (01772) 653531 E-mail: sales@mcc-ltd.com *Hose coupling distributors*

Millennium Crane Hire Ltd, Rear Of 400 Edgware Road, Cricklewood, London, NW2 6ND Tel: (020) 8208 1444 Fax: (020) 8452 1248 *Crane hire services*

▶ Millennium Hygiene Services, Unit 20 Longton Business Park, Station Road, Little Hoole, Preston, PR4 5LE Tel: (0870) 7669119 Fax: (0870) 7665119 E-mail: office@mhsuk.com *Feminine hygiene specialists, sanitary bins,& washroom services*

▶ Millennium Lighting UK Ltd, 6 Balm Road Industrial Estate, Beza Street, Leeds, LS10 2BG Tel: 0113-277 9988 Fax: 0113-277 5697 E-mail: info@mlukltd.com *Light manufrs*

▶ Millennium Printing Services, 12 Barnsbury Close, New Malden, Surrey, KT3 5BP Tel: 020 89425488 Fax: 070 92300436 E-mail: barrymps@blueyonder.co.uk *Foil printing services*

▶ Millennium School Of Motoring Ltd, Unit 111 112, Springvale Industrial Estate, Cwmbran, Gwent, NP44 5BG Tel: (01633) 873022 Fax: (01633) 868181 E-mail: millenniumsom@aol.com *DRIVING TUITION. RESIDENTIAL DRIVING COURSES, DRIVING INSTRUCTOR TRAINING.*

Millennium Security Systems, 6 Kirkland Way, Mile Oak, Tamworth, Staffordshire, B78 3PL Tel: (01827) 288727 Fax: (01827) 288727 E-mail: info@millennium-securitysystems.co.uk *Millennium Security Systems install and maintain to European and British Standards. Intruder Alarms,Fire Alarms, C.C.T.V and Door Access Systems. And are members of S.S.A.I.B. Inspectorate*

Millennium Software Solutions Centre Scotland Ltd, Burnfield Avenue, Thornliebank, Glasgow, G46 7TP Tel: 0141-633 5885 Fax: 0141-633 5733 E-mail: amanda@milleniumsoftware2000.com *Computer training software manufrs*

▶ Miller, 24 Carsegate Road, Inverness, IV3 8EX Tel: (01463) 241000 Fax: (01463) 230130

▶ Miller Architects, The Studio, 11 Gage Ridge, Forest Row, East Sussex, RH18 5HL Tel: 01342 823553 E-mail: info@millerarchitects.net *Design led RIBA architects - architectural services include residential and commercial, architect designed new build houses, sustainability, conversion and extension, refurbishment and conservation. Plans and drawings for town planning and building regulations applications. Site visits.*

Miller Construction, Millenim Way East, Pheonix Centre, Nottingham, NG8 6AR Tel: (0870) 3364900 Fax: 0115-927 1255 E-mail: nottingham@miller.co.uk

▶ Miller Construction (UK) Ltd, Unit 4 Pitreavie Court, Pitreavie Business Park, Queensferry Road, Dunfermline, Fife, KY11 8UF Tel: (01383) 627550

▶ Miller Electrics Ltd, Unit 5, Thistle Business Park North, Ayr Road, Cumnock, Ayrshire, KA18 1EQ Tel: (01290) 420202

Miller Fluid Power, 3 Bailey Drive, Norwood Industrial Estate, Killamarsh, Sheffield, S21 2JF Tel: 0114-247 2936 Fax: 0114-247 8371 *Hydraulic & pneumatic cylinder*

▶ Miller Freeman & Sons Nottingham Ltd, Adco Business Centre, Bobbers Mill, Nottingham, NG8 5AH Tel: 0115-978 9895 Fax: 0115-978 9896

Miller Graphic UK Ltd, 2 Hollands Road, Haverhill, Suffolk, CB9 8PP Tel: (01440) 703001 Fax: (01440) 703421 E-mail: sales@millergraphics.com *Manufacturers of rubber rollers*

Herman Miller Ltd, 61 Aldwych, London, WC2B 4AE Tel: (0845) 226 7202 Fax: (0845) 430 9260 E-mail: info_uk@hermanmiller.com *Office furnishers & furniture distributors*

▶ Miller Homes, Unit 3630, Parkside, Birmingham Business Park, Birmingham, B37 7YG Tel: (0870) 3364800 Fax: 0121-779 5895 E-mail: sales@homes.miller.co.uk

Miller Homes, Miller House, 2 Lochside View, Edinburgh, EH12 9DH Tel: (0870) 3365000 Fax: 0131-315 6110 *Public works contractors* Also at: Altrincham, Glasgow, London, Rugby, Stockton-on-Tees, Wakefield & Winchester

Miller Insurance Services Ltd, Dawson House, 5 Jewry Street, London, EC3N 2PJ Tel: (020) 7488 2345 Fax: (020) 7265 1423 E-mail: sales@millerinsurance.co.uk *Insurance brokers*

J.H. Miller & Sons Ltd, Irlam Wharf Road, Irlam, Manchester, M44 5PN Tel: 0161-775 0005 Fax: 0161-775 0006 E-mail: sales@jhmiller.co.uk *Domestic light fittings wholesalers*

John Miller & Sons (Painters) Ltd, 52 Main Street, Barrhead, Glasgow, G78 1RE Tel: 0141-881 1516 Fax: 0141-880 8113 *Painting & decorating contractors* Also at: Airdrie

Joseph Miller & Sons Ltd, 1 Denver Close, Orpington, Kent, BR6 0SB Tel: (01689) 609901 Fax: (01689) 609901 E-mail: hsjmiller@aol.com *Industrial protective clothing & footwear suppliers*

Miller Methil Ltd, 40 Links Road, Lundin Links, Leven, Fife, KY8 6AU Tel: (01333) 422694 Fax: (01333) 426330 E-mail: millermethil@btconnect.com *Boat building & repairing*

Miller & Miller, Unit 3 15-17 Roebuck Road, Hainault Business Park, Ilford, Essex, IG6 3TU Tel: (020) 8500 6122 Fax: (020) 8500 6124 E-mail: info@millerandmillerchem.co.uk *Pharmaceuticals*

P.J. Miller Ltd, The Old Baths, Main Road, Far Cotton, Northampton, NN4 8EN Tel: (01604) 767710 Fax: (01604) 764884 *Blacksmith & steelworker*

Miller Pattison Ltd, 3 Eldon Way, Biggleswade, Bedfordshire, SG18 8NH Tel: (01767) 314444 Fax: (01767) 317601 E-mail: biggleswade@miller-patterson.co.uk *Insulation contractors*

Miller Pattison Ltd, 3 Park Square, Thorncliffe Park, Chapeltown, Sheffield, S35 2PH Tel: 0114-240 4370 Fax: 0114-240 4380 E-mail: sheffield@miller-pattison.co.uk *Insulation contractors*

Miller Plant, Woodside House, Pedmore Road, Dudley, West Midlands, DY2 0RL Tel: (01384) 262400 Fax: (01384) 350269 E-mail: millplant@aol.com *Miller plant specialise in the supply of new and quality used construction equipment for the UK and abroad. A family partnership established in the late 60's, they provide a full service backup and training*

Miller Plant, North Lurg, Midmar, Inverurie, Aberdeenshire, AB51 7NB Tel: (01330) 830033 Fax: (01330) 833478

Miller Plating Co., Unit 15 All Saints Industrial Estate, All Saints Street, Birmingham, B18 7RJ Tel: 0121-523 3348 Fax: 0121-515 3187 *Electroplating, zinc platers & plating services*

Miller Property Consultants, 17 Hogarth Avenue, Brentwood, Essex, CM15 8BE Tel: (01277) 233100 Fax: (01277) 233300 E-mail: advice@millerproperty.co.uk *Industrial & commercial property advisors*

Miller Signs, 52 Berry Street, Liverpool, L1 4JQ Tel: 0151-708 0072 Fax: 0151-708 0072 *Sign manufrs*

Thomas Miller & Co. Ltd, International House, 26 Creechurch Lane, London, EC3A 5BA Tel: (020) 7283 4646 Fax: (020) 7283 5614 *Marine insurance managers*

▶ Millers, 9 Cleveland Street, Wolverhampton, WV1 3HH Tel: (01902) 421215 *Rotary watches, jewellery suppliers*

Miller's, Borogate, Helmsley, York, YO62 5BN Tel: (01439) 771252 *Knitwear manufrs*

Millers Alarms Ltd, Moorley House, 539 Woodborough Road, Mapperly, Nottingham, NG3 5FR Tel: 0115-960 4232 Fax: 0115-955 2552 E-mail: millersalarms@ntlworld.com *Security system installation services*

Millers Catering Equipment, Unit 2 College Fields Business Centre, Prince Georges Road, Merton, London, SW19 2PT Tel: (020) 8687 5390 Fax: (020) 8687 5399 E-mail: sales@millerscatering.co.uk *Whatever you want in the way of commercial catering equipment, we can supply, install, repair, service, and fully maintain with an Individually Tailored Maintenance Contract. Don't buy elsewhere until you've sought our advice and a quotation - we know the business, are very competitive, and give excellent value for money. On this Web Site, each product section highlights some of our most popular products in our Current Catalogue. If you can't find what you want or are looking for something specific, or would like to arrange a meeting - click the "Contact Millers" icon to find our contact details and an inter-active request form. We are agents for all leading manufacturers and provide impartial advice and excellent service. With over 50 years in this industry, our expertise is virtually unrivalled.*

Don Millers Hot Bread Kitchens, 36 Cornmarket, Derby, DE1 2DG Tel: (01332) 371434 Fax: (01332) 371434 *Bakery manufrs*

▶ Millers Electrical & Building Services, 29 Portland Road, London, SE25 4UF Tel: (020) 8654 4440

Millers Oils Ltd, Hillside Oil Works, Rastrick, Brighouse, West Yorkshire, HD6 3DP Tel: (01484) 713201 Fax: (01484) 721263 E-mail: enquiries@millersoils.co.uk *Lubricant manufrs*

▶ Millers Publications Ltd, The Cellars, High Street, Tenterden, Kent, TN30 6BN Tel: (01580) 766411 Fax: (01580) 766100 *Publishing millers*

Millers Retail Design Ltd, Granby House, Greenwood Street, Salford, M6 6PD Tel: 0161-743 1026 Fax: 0161-743 1598 *Shop fitters*

▶ Millers Roofing & Roofline, Bourne House, Milbourne Street, Carlisle, CA2 5XF Tel: (0800) 0837641 E-mail: millers@roofing111.wanadoo.co.uk *millers roofing and replacement roofline, we are specialists in new roofs, re-roofs, tiling, slating, dry verge cappings, flat roofs, storm damage, pvcu roofline products for more info on all are services please go to are web site*

▶ Millertech, Unit 7 Bondor Business Centre, London Road, Baldock, Hertfordshire, SG7 6HP Tel: (01462) 896417 Fax: (01462) 490435 *Vehicle tracking & security services*

Millets, 33 Bridge Street, Evesham, Worcestershire, WR11 4SQ Tel: (01386) 446759 *Camping equipment retailers*

Millets (Camping & Countrywear) Ltd, 119 Broadway, Bexleyheath, Kent, DA6 7HF Tel: (020) 8303 5089 Fax: (020) 8301 4603 *Outdoor wear & camping equipment*

Millets (Camping & Countrywear) Ltd, 65 High Street, Bromley, BR1 1JY Tel: (020) 8460 0418 *Camping equipment suppliers*

Millets (Camping & Countrywear) Ltd, Unit 2b Sauchiehall Centre, Sauchiehall Street, Glasgow, G2 3ER Tel: 0141-332 5617 Fax: 0141-332 5617 *Outdoor specialists*

Millets (Camping & Countrywear) Ltd, 68 Northbrook Street, Newbury, Berkshire, RG14 1AE Tel: (01635) 40070 Fax: (01635) 40070 *Outdoor equipment suppliers*

Millets (Camping & Countrywear) Ltd, 4-5 St Marys Butts, Reading, RG1 2LN Tel: 0118-959 5228 *Camping equipment suppliers*

Millets (Camping & Countrywear) Ltd, 42-44 South Street, Romford, RM1 1RB Tel: (01708) 743751 Fax: (01708) 743751 *Camping retailer*

Millets (Camping & Countrywear) Ltd, 13 Gaolgate Street, Stafford, ST16 2BQ Tel: (01785) 251912 Fax: (01785) 259250 *Outdoor good suppliers*

Millets (Camping & Countrywear) Ltd, 24 Queen Street, Wrexham, Clwyd, LL11 1AL Tel: (01978) 261267 *Outdoor leisure retail*

▶ Millfield Associates, Unit 6, Keyes Way, Braintree, Essex, CM7 9TR Tel: 01376 349946 Fax: 01376 349946 E-mail: millfield@asbestos-specialist.co.uk *Independent asbestos surveyors providing professional asbestos surveys and consutations, NHS approved and MDHS 0 compliant, P402 & P405 qualified, using UKAS accredited testing; staff certification in Confined Spaces, available for specialist surveys; underground service ducting for example and all aspects of asbestos management.**

Millfield F R P Ltd, Newburn Industrial Estate, Shelley Road, Newcastle upon Tyne, NE15 9RT Tel: 0191-264 8541 Fax: 0191-264 6962 E-mail: mail@millfield-group.co.uk *Glass fibre mouldings & reinforced plastic & pattern making*

Millhouse Developments, Ravensworth House, 1 Ravensworth Street, Bedlington, Northumberland, NE22 7JP Tel: (01670) 530616 Fax: (01670) 829649 *Property developers*

Millies Cookies Ltd, Unit 32 The Merry Hill Centre, Brierley Hill, West Midlands, DY5 1SY Tel: (01384) 480864 *Cookie manufacturing services*

▶ Millies Cookies Ltd, Maritime Way, St. Marys Island, Chatham, Kent, ME4 3ER Tel: (01634) 893450 Fax: (01634) 893450 *Bakers*

▶ Millies Cookies Ltd, 13 The Liberty, Romford, RM1 3RL Tel: (01708) 735174 Fax: (01708) 735174 *Cookie retailers*

▶ Millies Cookies Ltd, 8 Park Lane, Meadowhall Centre, Sheffield, S9 1EL Tel: 0114-256 9065 Fax: 0114-256 9065 *Retail*

Millies Retail Ltd, Unit 62, The Merry Hill Centre, Brierley Hill, W. Midlands, DY5 1SY Tel: (01384) 75475 Fax: (01384) 75475 *Cookie manufr*

Brian Milligan Associates, 57 Wensley Road, Salford, M7 3GJ Tel: 0845 5314073 Fax: 0161-792 2269 E-mail: brian@brian-milligan.co.uk *Based in Greater Manchester, but covering the whole of the UK, we provide an occupational hygiene and environmental consultancy service to all industry sectors. We specialise in workplace air monitoring for toxic substances, mainly dust and fumes (such as welding fumes, wood dust, paper dust, flour dust, isocyanates, solvents, dyes and pigments, plastics extruder fumes, diesel engine exhaust fumes, etc.) and also in workplace noise exposure monitoring and environmental noise surveys. Other aspects of the business are the examination and testing of local exhaust ventilation systems and air sampling for harmful bacteria and fungi. We carry out risk assessment to ensure compliance with workplace legislation, principally the COSHH Regulations and the Noise at Work Regulations. Our clients are assured of the services of a highly qualified and experienced professional in the field.*

Milliken Industrials Ltd, Wellington Street, Bury, Lancashire, BL8 2AY Tel: 0161-764 2244 Fax: 0161-705 2148 E-mail: john.lancashire@milliken.com *Manufacturers of carpet tiles, felt (tennis ball), industrial fabric, matting/mat (dust barrier), table linen (coated), textile (fashion) fabric*

Milliken Industrials Ltd, Wellington Street, Bury, Lancashire, BL8 2AY Tel: 0161-764 2244 Fax: 0161-705 2148 E-mail: peter_janczyk@milliken.com *Industrial fabrics manufrs* Also at: Stroud & Wigan

Milliken Walk Off Mats, Hilton Fold Lane, Middleton, Manchester, M24 2HZ Tel: 0161-655 1380 Fax: 0161-655 1379 E-mail: mcse@milliken.com *Manufacturers of technical rubber compounds*

Milliken White & Co. Ltd, 6 Huss Row, Belfast, BT13 1EE Tel: (028) 9032 2076 Fax: (028) 9031 5350 E-mail: millikenwhite@hotmail.co.uk *Linen manufacturers & embroidery specialists*

Milliken Woolen Speciality, Lodgemore Mills, Stroud, Gloucestershire, GL5 3EJ Tel: (01453) 760800 Fax: (01453) 752919 E-mail: wsp-sales@milliken.com *Felt manufrs*

Milliken Woollen Speciality Products, Cam Woollen Mills, Everlands, Cam, Dursley, Gloucestershire, GL11 5NN Tel: (01453) 542258 Fax: (01453) 548540 *Textiles*

Millington & Ramstedt Ltd, 242-248 Bristol Road, Gloucester, GL1 5TA Tel: 0845 5260526 Fax: (01452) 306132 E-mail: sales@millingtonandramstedt.co.uk *Millington & Ramstedt, specialist timber merchant and hardware retailer, where you will find 1000's of items in stock. *Established for over 90 years, our family run business spread over 3 generations, has provided a friendly, personal service very much tailored to our customers needs. Our team have a wealth of knowledge and expertise with over 45 years in DIY, there's not a lot they don't know but don't take our word for it, why not come in and browse around and ask for some professional advice without obligation.*

Millington York Ltd, Leighswood Road, Walsall, WS9 8AL Tel: (01922) 454121 Fax: (01922) 743045 E-mail: richard@millington-york.co.uk *Drawing office materials & equipment*

Millington's Angling Equipment, 32 Steeley Lane, Chorley, Lancashire, PR6 0RD Tel: (01257) 272392 *Fishing tackle retailers, trophy & engraving service*

J.S. Millinton & Sons Ltd, Albert Buildings, Humberstone Road, Leicester, LE5 3AJ Tel: 0116-253 3333 Fax: 0116-251 4471 E-mail: webmaster@jsmillington.com *Builders merchants*

▶ Millipore (UK) Ltd, Gemini Crescent, Dundee Technology Park, Dundee, DD2 1SW Tel: (01382) 561600 Fax: (01382) 561601 *Bio-tech company*

Millipore UK Ltd, Fleming Road, Kirkton Campus, Livingston, West Lothian, EH54 7BN Tel: (01506) 404000 Fax: (01506) 404001 E-mail: *Bovine serum albumin & monoclonal blood type reagents*

Millipore (UK) Ltd, Units 3-5 The Court Yard, Hattes Lane, Watford, WD18 8YH Tel: (0870) 9004645 Fax: (0870) 9004646 E-mail: csr_uk@millipore.com *Filters & water purification manufrs*

▶ Millnet Financial Ltd, Stapleton House, 29-33 Scrutton Street, London, EC2A 4HU Tel: (020) 7375 2300 Fax: (020) 7422 8888 E-mail: help@efinancialcareers.com *Financial market recruitment specialists*

Millpac Ltd, Basepoint Business Centre, Marsh Way, Rainham, Essex, RM13 8EU Tel: (020) 8965 9204 Fax: (020) 8965 3826 E-mail: info@millpac.co.uk *Plastic bottle tops & mouldings manufrs*

Millpond (UK) Ltd, The Factory, Boswithian Rd, Tolvaddon, Camborne, Cornwall, TR14 0EJ Tel: 01209 714222 *Furniture manufrs*

▶ Millroad Joinery, Unit 5a, Ryehill Close, Lodge Farm Industrial Estate, Northampton, NN5 7UA Tel: (01604) 582200 Fax: (01604) 582200 *Bespoke joiners*

Mills, 13 Fairway Drive, Fairway Industrial Estate, Greenford, Middlesex, UB6 8PW Tel: (020) 8833 2626 E-mail: sales@millsltd.com *Mills Ltd is a distributor of high quality cable management products and specialist tooling for the communication industry. Originally established as an engineering distributor in 1918, Mills is still a family business, supplying a range of over 2000 products nationally for next day delivery from its headquarters in Greenford, West London.*

▶ The Mills, Third Way, Wembley, Middlesex, HA9 0EL Tel: (020) 8795 5400 Fax: (020) 8900 0301 E-mail: mike.simmonds@haymills.com *Joinery manufrs*

Mills Advertising & Publicity, North House, 5 North Road, Stokesley, Middlesbrough, Cleveland, TS9 5DU Tel: (01642) 713156 Fax: (01642) 713174 E-mail: enquiries@millsadvertising.co.uk *Advertising & publicity agency*

▶ Mills Arts & Crafts, 49 South Street, Bo'Ness, West Lothian, EH51 9HA Tel: (01506) 829982 *Artists material retailers*

Mills Computer Products International Ltd, 7 Amber Drive, Langley Mill, Nottingham, NG16 4BE Tel: (01773) 761246 Fax: (01773) 531246 E-mail: sales@millsimage.co.uk *Computer accessories manufrs*

Mills & Coombs, 95A Chaplin Road, Easton, Bristol, BS5 3JE Tel: 0117-961 3882 Fax: 0117-961 3887 *Press tool manufrs*

▶ Mills & Douglas Builders Ltd, Barrington Road, Orwell, Royston, Hertfordshire, SG8 5QP Tel: (01223) 208123 E-mail: sales@millsanddouglas.co.uk

Mills Forgings Ltd, Charterhouse Road, Coventry, CV1 2BJ Tel: (024) 7622 4985 Fax: (024) 7652 5453 E-mail: sales@millsforgings.co.uk *Mills Forgings Ltd is a private company, founded in 1919, producing small and high volume, quality, press closed die and upset forgings in carbon and alloy steels - please quote "kellysearch" when making your enquiry*

John Mills & Sons (Newcastle) Ltd, 509 Shields Road, Walkergate, Newcastle upon Tyne, NE6 4PX Tel: 0191-265 6550 Fax: 0191-265 1002 E-mail: sales@johnmillsnewcastleltd.co.uk *Valve manufrs*

Ken Mills Engineering Ltd, New Street Works, Shawclough, Rochdale, Lancashire, OL12 6NS Tel: (01706) 644698 Fax: (01706) 649285 E-mail: ken.mills@zen.co.uk *Manufacturers of baling presses & conveyor systems*

Mills Manufacturing Technology, Tachbrook Park Drive, Warwick, CV34 6RH Tel: (01926) 736736 Fax: (01926) 736737 E-mail: sales@millscnc.co.uk *Mills Manufacturing Technology supply CNC machine tools and high technology manufacturing solutions in the UK. Located in Royal Leamington Spa, Warwickshire Mills are exclusive distributors for Daewoo CNC lathes and machining centres, Kuraki CNC boring machines and OM CNC vertical turning machines. As well as being the factory approved providers of service support, spare parts and maintenance contracts for machines within these ranges. Mills CNC Finance assists clients with budgeting for their machine tool investment, minimising impact on cash flow whilst maximising the efficiency of tax planning, whether for outright purchase or through leasing or hire purchase schemes. Insurance backed collision and breakdown damage cover for up to 5 years is available on new and used machines sourced from Mills.*

continued

▶ Mills Media Limited, 2 Morpeth Wharf, Twelve Quays, Wirral, Merseyside, CH41 1LF Tel: 0151 649 3600 Fax: 0151 649 3700 E-mail: norman@millsmediagroup.com *Mills media provide a complete conference and live event production service.Offering free venue finding.set,stage design and build.audio visual hire and supply,video production.photography,graphic design and exhibition systems.Supported by in house technicians.Covering the U.K. and overseas.*

▶ Mills & Scott Ltd, Summit Works, Manchester Road, Burnley, Lancashire, BB11 5HG Tel: (01282) 431128 Fax: (01282) 457263 E-mail: sales@millsandscott.co.uk *Bespoke kitchen furniture*

Mills Signs Ltd, Unit 55 Queens Court Trading Estate, Greets Green Road, West Bromwich, West Midlands, B70 9EQ Tel: 0121-557 1722 Fax: 0121-557 5394 E-mail: millssigns@btconnect.com *Signs & lettering services*

Mills & Sons Longcases, 15 Townsend Lane, Long Lawford, Rugby, Warwickshire, CV23 9DQ Tel: (01788) 565268 *Long-case clock manufrs*

Mills & Wood, 18 Grosvenor Street, London, W1K 4QQ Tel: (020) 7499 0934 Fax: (020) 7408 0250 E-mail: sales@millsandwood.co.uk *Surveyors & valuers*

Millside Ltd, Niagra Works, Beeley Wood Road, Sheffield, S6 1NH Tel: 0114-233 3091 Fax: 0114-232 6776 *Pipe work installers & fabricators*

Millsigns Sign Writers, 26 Bell Street, Romsey, Hampshire, SO51 8GW Tel: (01794) 830088 *Signwriters*

Millsons Vending, 89 Pembury Road, Tonbridge, Kent, TN9 2JF Tel: (01732) 500599 Fax: (01732) 363318 E-mail: info@millsons.co.uk *Vending machine suppliers*

Millstone Studios Ltd, Works Road, Hollingwood, Chesterfield, Derbyshire, S43 2PE Tel: (01246) 477516 Fax: (01246) 281666 E-mail: millstone@lineone.net *Concrete stone merchants*

Millstore Fine Furniture, 12 Fysh House Farm, Cuckoo Hill, Bures, Suffolk, CO8 5LD Tel: (01787) 227770 Fax: (01787) 227007 *Cabinet makers & manufrs*

Millstream Services, Horn Street, Hythe, Kent, CT21 5SL Tel: (01303) 770777 Fax: (01303) 770888 E-mail: sales@millstreamtaximeters.com *Suppliers & distributors of custom made rotary transducers for the automotive industry*

Milltex Fabrics Ltd, 96 Brown Street, Newmilns, Ayrshire, KA16 9BP Tel: (01560) 322503 Fax: (01560) 323034 E-mail: sales@milltex.co.uk *Manufacturers of materials for blinds*

Millthorne Engineering Co., 82 Tewin Road, Welwyn Garden City, Hertfordshire, AL7 1BD Tel: (01707) 371695 Fax: (01707) 372141 *Precision engineers*

Millturn Engineering, 17 Burrel Road, St. Ives, Cambridgeshire, PE27 3LE Tel: (01480) 469644 Fax: (01480) 469342 *Precision engineers*

Millvale Ltd, Briar Close, Evesham, Worcestershire, WR11 4JT Tel: (01386) 446661 Fax: (01386) 442931 E-mail: sales@millvaleltd.co.uk *Manufacturers of printed packaging and the printed image.*

Millvale Engineering Ltd, Millvale House, Selsley Hill, Dudbridge, Stroud, Gloucestershire, GL5 3HF Tel: (01453) 766396 Fax: (01453) 759630 E-mail: clive.millward@millvaleltd.co.uk *Engineering products marketers*

Millview Saddlery, 1 Haxey Road, Misterton, Doncaster, South Yorkshire, DN10 4AA Tel: (01427) 890509 Fax: (01427) 890509 E-mail: sales@millviewsaddlery.com *Saddlery manufacture & retail*

Millward Brown UK Ltd, Olympus Avenue, Tachbrook Park, Warwick, CV34 6RJ Tel: (01926) 452233 Fax: (01926) 833600 E-mail: info@uk.millwardbrown.com *Market research*

Millway Stationery Ltd, Chapel Hill, Stansted, Essex, CM24 8AP Tel: (01279) 812009 Fax: (01279) 812741 *Office stationery suppliers*

Millwood Cabinet Makers, Bates Farm, Wittersham, Tenterden, Kent, TN30 7PL Tel: (01797) 270170 Fax: (01797) 270505 *Furniture*

D.E. Millwood, Queens Road, Malvern, Worcestershire, WR14 1RH Tel: (01684) 575002 Fax: (01684) 575002 *Electronic engineer*

Millwood Marketing, Fivefield House, Bennetts Road, Keresley End, Coventry, CV7 8HX Tel: (024) 7633 1433 Fax: (024) 7633 5663 *Disposables, janitorial supplies & hygiene products. A family owned & operated business providing a reliable & personal service for the benefit of all customers, offering a wide range of quality products at keen prices, delivered on time by our own transport*

▶ Millwood Servicing Ltd, 102 Stafford Road, Wallington, Surrey, SM6 9AY Tel: (020) 8669 0080 Fax: (020) 8669 2727 E-mail: tracey@millwood.co.uk *Fire & security sales services systems & products*

Millwood Stainless Fasteners, Unit 20 Lea Hall Enterprise Park, Rugeley, Staffordshire, WS15 1LH Tel: 01889 577712 *Industrial & stainless steel fastener distributors, agents & stockholders*

Millwrights Liverpool Ltd, 31-33 Naylor Street, Liverpool, L3 6DR Tel: 0151-236 0479 Fax: 0151-255 0198 *Ventilation contractors*

Milmega Ltd, Ryde Business Park, Nicholson Road, Ryde, Isle Of Wight, PO33 1BQ Tel: (01983) 616863 Fax: (01983) 616864 E-mail: sales@milmega.co.uk *Microwave electronics design & manufrs*

Milmont Marketing, 110 Montrose Avenue, Luton, LU3 1HS Tel: (01582) 418392 Fax: (01582) 418392 E-mail: sales@milmont.co.uk *Janitorial product suppliers*

Milne Friend & Partners, Suite 2-5 Renslade House, Bonhay Road, Exeter, EX4 3AY Tel: (01392) 430097 Fax: (01392) 218696 E-mail: rodmilne@milnefriend.co.uk *Insurance brokers & independent financial advisers*

▶ Milne Trucking, 501 Blackbyres Road, Barrhead, Glasgow, G78 1TN Tel: 0141-876 4188

William Milne (Tarpaulins) Ltd, 42a Seaforth Road, Aberdeen, AB24 5PU Tel: (01224) 631012 Fax: (01224) 631012 *Tarpaulin manufrs*

K.C. Milner Engineering Ltd, Unit 7 Shepherd Cross Street, Bolton, BL1 3DE Tel: (01204) 843540 Fax: (01204) 493480 *Steel fabricators & staircase manufrs*

Milnes Bros, Unit 9 Enterprise Close, Croydon, CR0 3RZ Tel: (020) 8665 9907 Fax: (020) 8665 9956 E-mail: milnesbros@aol.com *Dental laboratory equipment manufrs*

▶ Les Milnes Combustion Ltd, Geanlea, Blairadam Drive, Kelty, Fife, KY4 0JF Tel: (01383) 830697 Fax: (01383) 830697 E-mail: lmcltd@btinternet.com *Combustion engineers supply of industrial gas burners*

▶ Milo Web Designs, 34 Lifestyle House, 2 Melbourne Avenue, Sheffield, S10 2QH Tel: 0114 2678414 E-mail: miloweb@btinternet.com *Milo Web Designs is a website design company based in Sheffield, South Yorkshire. We specialise in creating websites for small businesses, individuals, clubs and organisations at competitive and very affordable costs***

Milsco Manufacturing Ltd, Harrington Way, Bermuda Park, Nuneaton, Warwickshire, CV10 7SH Tel: (024) 7658 0400 Fax: (024) 7658 0401 E-mail: info@milsco.co.uk *Designs & manufactures seating products for industrial vehicles*

Milsom Industrial Designs Ltd, 11 Kelso Place, Upper Bristol Road, Bath, BA1 3AU Tel: (01225) 444809 Fax: (01225) 444787 E-mail: enquiries@milsom.uk.com *Design engineers*

Milsted Langdon Ltd, Winchester House, Deane Gate Avenue, Taunton, Somerset, TA1 2UH Tel: (01823) 445566 Fax: (01823) 445555 E-mail: simonlmilsted@milsted-langdon.co.uk *Chartered accountants*

Milsteel, Monmouth Road, Abergavenny, Gwent, NP7 5HF Tel: (01873) 858295 Fax: (01873) 859808 *Steel fabricators*

Miltech International Ltd, Unit 3 Magellan Close, Walworth Industrial Estate, Andover, Hampshire, SP10 5NT Tel: (01264) 323233 Fax: (01264) 400905 E-mail: info@miltech-international.com *Stainless steel medical equipment specialists*

Miltech Stove Enamellers & Powder Coating, Unit 7 Leyton Avenue, Mildenhall, Bury St. Edmunds, Suffolk, IP28 7BL Tel: (01638) 717880 Fax: (01638) 717880 E-mail: anthonybrooks98@wannado.co.uk *Powder coaters & industrial coatings*

Miltek, Rectory Farm, Brandon Road, Stubton, Newark, Nottinghamshire, NG23 5BY Tel: (01636) 626796 Fax: (01636) 626905 E-mail: sales@miltekbalers.com *Compaction (refuse/scrap/waste) systems manufacturers & balrs, industrial*

▶ Mil-Tek Central, Unit 3 Easingwold Business Park, Birch Way, Easingwold, York, YO61 3FB Tel: (01347) 824900 Fax: (01347) 824901 *Waste system suppliers*

Mil-tek (GB) Ltd, Saville Court, Saville Place, Clifton, Bristol, BS8 4EJ Tel: (0800) 0835713 Fax: 0117-973 6797 E-mail: info@miltek-uk.co.uk *Providing balers to all business sectors to crush cardboard & plastics*

Milton Bridge Ceramic Colour Ltd, Unit 9 Trent Trading Park, Botteslow Street, Stoke-on-Trent, ST1 3NA Tel: (01782) 274229 Fax: (01782) 281591 *Ceramic colours & enamel manufrs*

Milton Furniture Ltd, Tourment Building, Smifby Road, Ashby-de-la-Zouch, Leicestershire, LE65 2UR Tel: (01530) 564287 Fax: (01530) 564723 E-mail: mfh@thefurniturehirepeople.com *Exhibition hire furnishers*

Milton Joinery, Unit 9 Ridge Way, Drakes Drive, Long Crendon, Aylesbury, Buckinghamshire, HP18 9BF Tel: (01844) 203630 Fax: (01844) 203635 *Office furniture manufrs*

Milton Keynes Blind Co. Ltd, 12 Wolseley Road Woburn Industrial Estate, Woburn Road Industrial Estate, Kempston, Bedford, MK42 7TN Tel: (01234) 841515 Fax: (01234) 840682 E-mail: sales@concordeblinds.com *Window blind & curtain manufrs*

Milton Keynes Buildbase, Simpson Road, Bletchley, Milton Keynes, MK1 1BB Tel: (01908) 369801 Fax: (01908) 270243 E-mail: miltonkeynes@buildbase.co.uk *Buildbase is one of the UK's fastest growing builders merchants. All of our branches are long established companies which have been serving local trades people for many years, with knowledge and experience to match. We believe strongly in understanding the needs of trades professional and our business has been developed specifically to meet those demands. Massive stocks, top quality products, competitive pricing, reliable delivery, specialist staff and exceptional customer service.*

Milton Keynes City Glaziers Ltd, Vicarage Road, Stony Stratford, Milton Keynes, MK11 1BN Tel: (01908) 563866 Fax: (01908) 560102 E-mail: jackie@mkcg.freeserve.co.uk *Glass & glazing company*

Milton Keynes Metals Ltd, Ridge Hill Farm, Nash, Milton Keynes, MK17 0EH Tel: (01296) 713631 Fax: (01296) 714155 E-mail: sales@mkmetals.co.uk *Webshop,small and large orders accepted trade counter,orders by phone ,fax ,email ,online webshop deliveries local,uk and internationally bright steel, black*

continued

continuation
- steel ,structural,stainless steel,brass,bronze,aluminium,copper,nickel silver,silver steel,ground flat stock,cast iron,steel chain,rounds ,squares,hexagons,flats,tubes,sheet,angles, channel,screws,nuts,washers,taps and dies,diestocks,tapwrenches ,engineering tools ,centre drills,milling cutters,drills,lowmelt casting metal , silver solder,casting equipment,solder pots,fine metals,model metals,half round,mesh,rivets,model engineering materials

Milton Keynes Paint & Equipment Ltd, Unit K, Lyon Road, Denbigh West, Bletchley, Milton Keynes, MK1 1EX Tel: (01908) 371441 Fax: (01908) 367030 E-mail: sales@mkpe.co.uk *Motor vehicle body refinishers*

Milton Keynes Vehicle Services, Unit 27 Harmill Industrial Estate, Grovebury Road, Leighton Buzzard, Bedfordshire, LU7 4FF Tel: (01525) 374633 Fax: (01525) 374633 *Fleet lorry & private vehicle maintenance*

Milton Keynes Workwear & Safety Co. Ltd, 15-16 Darin Court, Crownhill, Milton Keynes, MK8 0AD Tel: (01908) 566640 Fax: (01908) 566540 E-mail: sales@mkworkwear.com *Clothing & personal protective equipment distributors*

Milton Laboratory Furniture Ltd, Unit 17 Birksland Industrial Estate, Bradford, West Yorkshire, BD4 8TY Tel: (01274) 395110 Fax: (01274) 395111 E-mail: paul@miltonfurniture.com *Laboratory furniture manufrs*

Milton Lee Joinery, Unit 4 Rink Drive, Swadlincote, Derbyshire, DE11 8JL Tel: (01283) 225657 Fax: (01283) 225657 *Building contractors & joinery manufrs*

Milton Leicester Ltd, North Street, Wigston, Leicestershire, LE18 1PR Tel: 0116-288 5871 Fax: 0116-288 0116 E-mail: sales@miltons.ltd.uk *Textile merchants*

Milton Lloyd Ltd, 42-44 Norwood High Street, London, SE27 9NR Tel: (020) 8670 4433 Fax: (020) 8761 6130 E-mail: worldclass@milton-lloyd.co.uk Principal Export Areas: Worldwide *Perfume*

Milton Pipes Ltd, Cooks Lane, Sittingbourne, Kent, ME10 2QF Tel: (01795) 425191 Fax: (01795) 420360 E-mail: sales@miltonpipes.com *Concrete drainage product manufrs*

Milton Roy UK Ltd, Oaklands Business Centre, Oaklands Park, Wokingham, Berkshire, RG41 2FD Tel: 0118-977 1066 Fax: 0118-977 1198 E-mail: contact@dosapro.com *Distributors & servicing of metering pumps*

Milton Steel Ltd, 20 Queensway, Stem Lane Industrial Estate, New Milton, Hampshire, BH25 5NN Tel: (01425) 613582 Fax: (01425) 623929 E-mail: sales@miltonsteel.co.uk *Structural engineers manufrs/supplier/distributer*

Miltools Engineering Supplies, The Sanderson Centre, Lees Lane, Gosport, Hampshire, PO12 3UL Tel: (023) 9252 6551 Fax: (023) 9252 2559 *Engineering cutting tool suppliers*

Mil-Tu-Fit, 246 Broomhill Road, Bristol, BS4 5RG Tel: 0117-971 7234 Fax: 0117-971 4789 E-mail: miltofit@hotmail.com *General engineers*

Mil-Ver Metal Co., Coronel Avenue, Longford, Coventry, CV6 6AP Tel: (024) 7666 7098 Fax: (024) 7666 2299 E-mail: steve.miles@milver.co.uk *Aluminium ingot manufrs*

Milverton Motor Cycle Parts, 21-23 Kyotts Lake Road, Birmingham, B11 1JX Tel: 0121-772 4517 Fax: 0121-771 1904 *Motor cycle spares & parts*

Mimicks Face Painting, 5 Corinthian Road, Chandler's Ford, Eastleigh, Hampshire, SO53 2BA Tel: (023) 8025 5894 E-mail: mimicks@ntlworld.com *Face painting, party & corporate events*

Minatol Ltd, Mandarin House, 4 Manorgate Road, Kingston upon Thames, Surrey, KT2 7UB Tel: (020) 8549 9222 Fax: (020) 8547 1635 E-mail: sales@minatol.co.uk *Industrial cleaning materials distributors*

Minca Computing Ltd, 42 Main Street, Milngavie, Glasgow, G62 6BU Tel: 0141-956 2260 Fax: 0141-956 2234 E-mail: info@CUIS.co.uk *Computer consultants*

Minco Sampling-Techniques (UK) Ltd, Tofts Farm Industrial Estate, Brenda Road, Hartlepool, Cleveland, TS25 2BS Tel: (01429) 273252 Fax: (01429) 232611 E-mail: enquiries@mincouk.com *Expendable & re-usable thermocouples*

Mincost Trading, 15a High Street, Lydney, Gloucestershire, GL15 5DP Tel: (01594) 841014 Fax: (01594) 843341 E-mail: sales@mincost.co.uk *Garden machinery & diy tool distributors*

▶ Mind Machine, 69 Hutton Close, Crowther, Washington, Tyne & Wear, NE38 0AH Tel: 0191-417 9295 Fax: 0191-417 0643 E-mail: admin@mindmachine.co.uk *Printer & laptop repairs, suppliers of printers & spares*

▶ Mind Mapping Software Shop, 100 Vale Road, Windsor, Berkshire, SL4 5JL Tel: (01753) 621426 Fax: (01753) 621427 *Computer software services*

Minden Industrial Ltd, Saxham Business Park, Little Saxham, Bury St. Edmunds, Suffolk, IP28 6RX Tel: (01284) 760791 Fax: (01284) 702156 E-mail: sales@minden-ind.co.uk *Paint spraying equipment distributors*

Minder Alarm Co., 1 Market Place, Penistone, Sheffield, S36 6DA Tel: (01226) 370100 Fax: (01226) 764994 E-mail: minderalarmsltd@btconnect.com *Intruder alarms repairs maintenance*

Minderaty Solutions N I Ltd, 75 Belfast Road, Carrickfergus, County Antrim, BT38 8BX Tel: (028) 9335 7300 Fax: (028) 9335 7305 E-mail: infoni@mindready.com *Automatic test equipment manufrs ATE fixture manufrs*

Mindex Ltd, Melita House, Yattendon Road, Horley, Surrey, RH6 7BS Tel: (01293) 408123 Fax: (01293) 408125 E-mail: sales@mindex-ltd.co.uk *Safety belt distributors or agents*

▶ Mindgrade Ltd, 90 Plimsoll Road, London, N4 2EE Tel: (020) 7226 8004 Fax: (020) 7359 0434

▶ MindGrove Ltd, PO Box 729, Warrington, WA4 4WZ Tel: (01925) 732757 Fax: (01925) 732756 E-mail: enquiries@mindgrove.co.uk *Training & consultancy in risk awareness, internal audit, it security*

Mind's Eye Design Ltd, Carn Brea, Shutta Road, Looe, Cornwall, PL13 1HW Tel: (01503) 264422 Fax: (01503) 264422 *Mind''s Eye Design is a small, multi-disciplinary design company, providing a wide range of design services to businesses seeking a creative, personal and thoughtful approach. We have created an extensive portfolio of innovative work in the areas of website, corporate identity, brochure, packaging, promotion and book design as well as photography and illustration. You can find many examples of our work on our website. If you need a design company that is always prepared to go that extra length for you, please call Chris on +44 (0) 1503 264422 or email us via the contact page on our website. Thank you.*

▶ Mindset Communications, Nelson Close, Farnham, Surrey, GU9 9AR Tel: (07771) 870868 Fax: (01252) 316881 E-mail: info@mindsetcomms.co.uk *Specialists in the use of creative conference, exhibition and video production to provide integrated, strategic corporate communications programmes*

Mindshare, 140 Walcot Street, Bath, BA1 5BL Tel: (01225) 329577 Fax: (01225) 329675 E-mail: sales@mindsharesecurity.co.uk *Computer net workers*

Minehead Pine, E F South Road, Watchet, Somerset, TA23 0HF Tel: (01984) 639044 Fax: (01984) 639396 E-mail: enquiries@pineman.com *Pine furniture manufrs*

Minelco, 3 Riverside Business Centre, Brighton Road, Shoreham-by-Sea, West Sussex, BN43 6RE Tel: (01273) 452331 Fax: (01273) 464741 E-mail: info@minelco.com *Minerals & aggregates* Also at: Bristol & Stockton-on-Tees

▶ Mineral Crushing & Classification Ltd, Unit 5, Airfield Industrial Estate, Newport Road, Seighford, Stafford, ST18 9NR Tel: (01785) 281113 Fax: (01785) 281114 E-mail: info@mineralcrushing.co.uk *Abrasives importers & distributors*

Minerale Water Co., PO Box 2798, London, NW10 0DG Tel: (020) 8450 8082 Fax: (020) 8450 8083 E-mail: sales@minerale-water.co.uk *Mineral water suppliers*

▶ Minerva Accord Ltd, City Gates, 2-4 Southgate, Chichester, West Sussex, PO19 8DJ Tel: (01243) 779257 Fax: (01243) 753102

▶ Minerva Centre, Bradtrad House, Ripley Street, Bradford, West Yorkshire, BD5 7JW Tel: (01274) 726754 Fax: (01274) 722368

▶ Minerva Chocolates, 14 Cheap Street, Bath, BA1 1NA Tel: (01225) 464999 Fax: (01225) 464793 *Confectionery suppliers*

Minerva Dental Ltd, Courtney House Pacific Business Park, Pacific Road, Cardiff, CF24 5HJ Tel: (029) 2049 0504 Fax: (029) 2048 2139 E-mail: info@minervadental.co.uk *Dental, medical & surgical appliance distributors*

▶ Minerva Mill Innovation Centre, Station Road, Alcester, Warwickshire, B49 5ET Tel: 01789 400446 Fax: 01789 400447 E-mail: info@minervamill.co.uk *IT systems support & letting agents*

Minerva Software, Cedar Lodge, Mill Road, Peasenhall, Saxmundham, Suffolk, IP17 2LJ Tel: (01728) 660411 Fax: (01728) 660385 E-mail: sales@minervasoftware.com *Software accountancy distributors*

▶ MinEx & Associates, 114 Efford Road, Plymouth, PL3 6NQ Tel: (01752) 296451 E-mail: stevec@minex.org *Exploration, Mining, Mineral Processing and Minerals Marketing advice to all scales of projects.**Diamonds, gold and virtually all solid minerals.**Experience in many countries world wide. **Project Management and Production Enhancement of Hard rock, Alluvial (placer), Tailings Re-treatment.**Please visit our website and submit an enquiry, or associate with us.***

▶ Minford Ltd, Strawberry Lane, Willenhall, West Midlands, WV13 3RS Tel: (01902) 603030 Fax: (01902) 603069 E-mail: sales@minford.co.uk *Print finishing*

▶ Minghella Isle Of Wight Ltd, High Street, Wootton Bridge, Ryde, Isle of Wight, PO33 4PL Tel: (01983) 883545 Fax: (01983) 883242 E-mail: sales@minghella.co.uk *Cocktail sorbets & ice creams suppliers*

Mini Clipper Ltd, 7 Chartmoor Road, Leighton Buzzard, Bedfordshire, LU7 4WG Tel: (01525) 244700 Fax: (01525) 851445 E-mail: sales@miniclipper.co.uk *Road transport, storage & haulage service providers*

▶ Mini Media Ltd, Castagnia, St. Ives, Cornwall, TR26 2BF Tel: (01736) 797900 Fax: (01736) 799599 E-mail: sales@mini-media.co.uk *Print & production of miniature promotional & communicational products*

▶ Mini Moose, Moose Hall (Private address), 69 Hewarts Lane, Rose Green, Bognor Regis, West Sussex, PO21 3DW Tel: (07891) 420383 E-mail: samantha@minimoose.co.uk *On-Line Baby Store*Offering everything from nappies to parms to cots to birthing pool hire and sales. Some items free UK delivery*

Minianchor, 3 Toledo Works, Neepsend Lane, Sheffield, S3 8UL Tel: 0114-275 6211 Fax: 0114-249 6211 E-mail: info@minianchorltd.co.uk *Fabrication engineers*

Minibus Options Ltd, PO Box 1, High Peak, Derbyshire, SK23 7LY Tel: (01663) 735355 Fax: (01663) 735352 E-mail: sales@minibusoptions.co.uk *Minibus & wheelchair accessible vehicle converters*

Minicrete, Able House Billingham Reach Industrial Estate, Haverton Hill Road, Billingham, Cleveland, TS23 1PX Tel: (01642) 730000 Fax: (01642) 312126 *Concrete manufacturing & suppliers*

Minilco Specialities Ltd, Bowesfield Industrial Estate, Bowesfield Lane, Stockton-on-Tees, Cleveland, TS18 3HJ Tel: (01642) 674375 Fax: (01642) 614379 *Industrial mineral processors*

Minimould Ltd, Units 10A & 10B, Thame Road, Aylesbury, Buckinghamshire, HP17 8LJ Tel: 01844 292880 *Injection moulding & plastics manufrs*

Mining & Chemical Products Ltd, 1-4 Nielson Road, Finedon Road Industrial Estate, Wellingborough, Northamptonshire, NN8 4PE Tel: (01933) 225766 Fax: (01933) 227814 E-mail: info@mcp-group.co.uk Purchasing Contact: S.W. Davenhill Sales Contact: S. Fuller Principal Export Areas: Worldwide *Bismuth alloy producers or suppliers; bismuth salts producers or suppliers; fusible alloy producers; gallium producers or suppliers; indium producers or suppliers; selenium producers & tellurium metal alloy producers.*

▶ Minion A V, 44 Dunraven Parade, Belfast, BT5 6BT Tel: (07799) 558787 Fax: E-mail: nathanmateer@minionvideo.co.uk *Music video & visual effects, backing tracks & other musical needs provider*

▶ MiniscuLe of Motoring, 11 Cherry Orchard, Wotton-under-Edge, Gloucestershire, GL12 7HT Tel: (01453) 521543 E-mail: andrew.shell@btinternet.com

Minister Joinery, Riverside Barn, Bridport, Dorset, DT6 4PQ Tel: (01308) 485740 Fax: (01308) 485752 *Cabinet maker & joiners*

Ministry of Cake Ltd, Frobisher Way, Bindon Road, Taunton, Somerset, TA2 6AB Tel: (01823) 257922 Fax: (01823) 333328 E-mail: commercials@ministryofcake.co.uk *Frozen food processors, manufacturers & distributors*

Minitech Systems Ltd, Bridle Way, St. Vincents Close, Girton, Cambridge, CB3 0PB Tel: (01223) 277049 Fax: (01223) 277632 E-mail: sales@minitech-systems.com *Software house*

Minitek Mouldings Ltd, Pennard Close, Brackmills Industrial Estate, Northampton, NN4 7BE Tel: (01604) 767397 Fax: (01604) 706805 E-mail: info@minitekmouldings.co.uk *Injection mouldings manufrs*

Minium Tool Co. Ltd, Unit 1 & 2, Malmesbury Road, Kingsditch Trading Estate, Cheltenham, Gloucestershire, GL51 9PL Tel: (01242) 529352 Fax: (01242) 521737 E-mail: miniumtool@btconnect.com *Aluminium extrusion die manufrs*

▶ Minivator Benefit Trustee Ltd, Building 82, First Avenue, Pensnett Trading Estate, Kingswinford, West Midlands, DY6 7FJ Tel: (01384) 408700 E-mail: sales@minivator.co.uk *Disabled & elderly personal aids suppliers*

Minnie Business Systems Ltd, 65 London Wall, London, EC2M 5TU Tel: (020) 7638 3815 Fax: (020) 7638 1481 E-mail: ad@minniebusiness.co.uk *Software designers & computer systems suppliers*

Cyril Minns Engineering Ltd, Gladstone Road, Kingswood, Bristol, BS15 1SW Tel: 0117-967 1834 Fax: 0117-961 8638 E-mail: cyrilminns@dial.pipex.com *Engineering & precision toolmakers*

Minns (Oxford) Ltd, Willow Court, 7 West Way, Oxford, OX2 0JB Tel: (01865) 258600 Fax: (01865) 250123 E-mail: kevin.minns@minns.co.uk *Property developers*

Minoli Tiles, Watlington Road, Oxford, OX4 6LX Tel: (01865) 778225 Fax: (01865) 747642 E-mail: info@minoli.co.uk *Floor & wall tile importers & distributors*

Minortracts Builders Ltd, Sandown House, Auckland Road, Birmingham, B11 1RH Tel: 0121-772 2511 Fax: 0121-766 8243 E-mail: mail@minortracts.co.uk *Building contractors*

▶ Minotaur (UK) Ltd, Unit 14, Cariocca Business Park, Hellidon Close, Ardwick, Manchester, M12 4AH Tel: (0845) 2268232 E-mail: info@minotaur-uk.com *Anti-slip products for every type of pedestrian floor surfaces*

Minshall Brothers, Adderley Road, Market Drayton, Shropshire, TF9 3SX Tel: (01630) 657647 Fax: (01630) 657202 E-mail: info@minshallconstruction.com *Agricultural contractors*

Minster Alarms, Suncliffe House, 157 New Lane, Huntington, York, YO32 9NQ Tel: (01904) 466400 Fax: (01904) 466401 E-mail: sales@minsteralarms.co.uk *Security alarms installers*

Minster Cleaning Services, 1 Priors Gate, Priory Street, Ware, Hertfordshire, SG12 0DA Tel: (01920) 462261 Fax: (01920) 462265 E-mail: hertfordshire@minstergroup.co.uk *Cleaning services*

Minster Composite Products, Minster House, Private Road 2, Colwick Industrial Estate, Nottingham, NG4 2JR Tel: 0115-940 0644 Fax: 0115-940 0655 E-mail: minster@btclick.com *Specialist custom moulders*

Minster Distribution Ltd, Unit 11 Oldington Trading Estate, Stourport Road, Kidderminster, Worcestershire, DY10 1HE Tel: (01562) 747422 Fax: (01562) 60715 E-mail: minsterdist@aol.com *Hardware distributors*

Minster Engineering Co. Ltd, Ebor Industrial Estate, 74 Hallfield Road, York, YO31 7XD Tel: (01904) 717220 Fax: (01904) 717222 E-mail: gregallison@minstereng.freeserve.co.uk *Sheet metalwork engineers*

Minster Fuels Ltd, Three Cross Road, West Moors, Wimborne, Dorset, BH21 6QW Tel: (01202) 897771 Fax: (01202) 891155 E-mail: sales@minsterfuels.co.uk *Oil distributors*

Minster Lovell Construction Ltd, 57 Brize Norton Road, Minster Lovell, Witney, Oxfordshire, OX29 0SG Tel: (01993) 775355 Fax: (01993) 775409 *Groundwork contractors*

▶ Minster Weathervanes, 119 Middlehill Road Colehill, Wimborne, Dorset, BH21 2HL Tel: (01202) 881355 E-mail: bruceking20@tiscali.co.uk *Mobile welding services*

Minsterport Weighing Equipment, Baildon Mills, Northgate, Baildon, Shipley, West Yorkshire, BD17 6JX Tel: (01274) 580028 Fax: (01274) 583800 *Industrial weighing equipment suppliers*

Minsterstone Ltd, Harts Close, Ilminster, Somerset, TA19 9DJ Tel: (01460) 52277 Fax: (01460) 57865 E-mail: varyl@minsterstone.ltd.uk *Fireplace & garden ornament manufrs*

Minstrel Metalcraft Co., 300a Hillhead Road, Knockloughrim, Magherafelt, County Londonderry, BT45 8QT Tel: (028) 7964 4454 Fax: (028) 7964 4453 *Road iron work manufrs*

Minta Instrumentation Ltd, Caddick Road, Knowsley Business Park, Prescot, Merseyside, L34 9HP Tel: 0151-548 6818 Fax: 0151-548 5578 E-mail: sales@mintasensors.co.uk *Thermocouple connectors & cables*

Mintai, 14-16 Douglas Bldgs, Royal Stuart La, Cardiff, CF10 6EL Tel: 029 20489813 Fax: 029 20489784 *Television programme producer*

▶ Minta's The Printers Ltd, Palin Street, Nottingham, NG7 5AG Tel: (0808) 1550731 Fax: 0115-970 8856E-mail: sales@mintas.co.uk

Mintdale Engineering, Unit 8 Devonshire Industrial Hamlet, Station Road, Brimington, Chesterfield, Derbyshire, S43 1JU Tel: (01246) 550316 Fax: (01246) 550236 E-mail: mintdale.eng@virgin.net *Precision engineers*

Mintech Semiconductors Ltd, 2 Hellesdon Park Road, Drayton High Road, Norwich, NR6 5DR Tel: (01603) 788967 Fax: (01603) 788920 E-mail: sales@mintech.co.uk *Semi-conductor distributors*

Mintel Group Ltd, 18-19 Long Lane, London, EC1A 9PL Tel: (020) 7606 4533 Fax: (020) 7606 5932 E-mail: info@mintel.com *Market research analysts*

Minting Communications Ltd, Sebastopol Barn, Church Lane, Minting, Horncastle, Lincolnshire, LN9 5RS Tel: (01507) 578500 E-mail: collinrood@minting.ltd.co.uk *Telecommunications engineers*

▶ Minto D P Ltd, 66 Market Place, Inverurie, Aberdeenshire, AB51 3XN Tel: (01467) 620416 Fax: (01467) 621663 E-mail: sales@mintodp.co.uk

Minto Recruitment, 1 North Pallant, Chichester, West Sussex, PO19 1TL Tel: (01243) 787003 Fax: (01243) 787694 E-mail: info@mintorecruit.com *Minto Recruitment based in Chichester are an employment agency offering temporary and permanent recruitment solutions.*

Minton Treharne & Davies Ltd, Merton House The Avenue Industrial Park, Croescadarn Close, Cardiff, CF23 8HF Tel: (029) 2054 0000 Fax: (029) 2054 0111 E-mail: mtd@minton.co.uk *Metallurgical analysts*

Mintra Ltd, 963 Stockport Road, Manchester, M19 3NP Tel: 0161-256 4030 Fax: 0161-225 2848 E-mail: sales@mintra.com *Total solutions provider*

▶ Minty Designs, 1 New Buildings, Harbertonford, Totnes, Devon, TQ9 7SZ Tel: 01803 731077 Fax: (01803) 864649 E-mail: sales@mintydesigns.co.uk *Hand made & printed greetings cards*

Minui HandySitt (Cheeky Rascals Ltd), Stone Barn, 1 The Brows, Farnham Road, Liss, Hampshire, GU33 6JG Tel: (01730) 895761 Fax: (01730) 897549 E-mail: sales@cheekyrascals.co.uk *THE ONLY HIGHCHAIR YOU WILL EVER NEED!**The sleek new HandySitt® by Danish designers ®minui is a compact highchair for use in restaurant environments. Folding flat to store or carry between tables, it brings all the benefits of a conventional highchair with none of the drawbacks.**Redesigned to conform to EU safety standards for a 'free standing highchair'^ the HandySitt fits easily to virtually all dining chairs, allowing children to sit at the table and participate fully in family mealtimes, yet taking up little space....**^Conforms to BS EN 14988:2006**....SPACE SAVING, COST SAVING**Handmade in Denmark from solid birch, the HandySitt is a great investment. Suitable for children aged 6 months right through to 5 years, HandySitt can be used as a highchair and booster seat- thereby saving money as well as space.*

▶ Minuteman Press, 3/5 Highfield Road, Hall Green, Birmingham, B28 0EL Tel: 0121-777 0018 Fax: 0121-777 5810 E-mail: karl.mccabe@minutemanpress.com *Full service printing centre*

Mipa (UK) Ltd, 25 Robin Ride, Brackley, Northamptonshire, NN13 6PU Tel: (01280) 841190 Fax: (01280) 841191 E-mail: mipauk@aol.com *Manufacturers of packaging*

Miracle Astec Ltd, PO Box 119, Horsham, West Sussex, RH12 4YZ Tel: (01403) 255140 Fax: (01403) 260855 *Software development company*

▶ Miracle Design & Play Ltd, 14 Duncan Close, Moulton Park Industrial Estate, Northampton, NN3 6WL Tel: (01604) 591796 Fax: (01604) 591718 E-mail: sales@miracledandp.co.uk *Playground equipment manufrs*

Miracle Jewellery Ltd, 29 Shadwell Street, Birmingham, B4 6HB Tel: 0121-236 7456 Fax: 0121-233 1781 E-mail: miraclejewel@aol.com *Fashion jewellery manufrs*

Miracle Mills Ltd, Knightsdale Road, Ipswich, IP1 4LE Tel: (01473) 742325 Fax: (01473) 462773 E-mail: info@cristy-turner.com *Manufacturers of hammer mills, crushing industrial plant & waste recycling/processing plant*

Miracon Conveyors Ltd, Drayton Road, Shirley, Solihull, West Midlands, B90 4NG Tel: 0121-705 8468 Fax: 0121-711 2074 E-mail: sales@miracon.com *Conveyor & elevator manufrs*

▶ Mirada Solutions, Beaver House, 23-38 Hythe Bridge Street, Oxford, OX1 2ET Tel: (01865) 265500 Fax: (01865) 265501 *Medical equipment suppliers*

Mirage, The Old Bakery, 54 High Street, Methwold, Thetford, Norfolk, IP26 4NX Tel: (01366) 727777 Fax: (01366) 727778 *Pine mirrors*

▶ Mirage Blinds, The Birches, Nook Lane, Weston, Shrewsbury, SY4 5LP Tel: (01948) 840956 Fax: (01948) 840956 E-mail: sean@mirageblinds.co.uk *Manufacturing blinds*

Mirage Fashions Ltd, 313 Saffron Lane, Leicester, LE2 6UE Tel: 0116-283 7259 Fax: 0116-283 1523 E-mail: enquiries@mirage-fashions.co.uk *Ladies fashion*

Mirage Interiors Ltd, 12 Sand Road, Kewstoke, Weston-super-Mare, Avon, BS22 9UH Tel: (01934) 612439 Fax: (01934) 641900 E-mail: walls@mirage-interiors.com *Office refurbishment & partitioning*

Mirage R C Enterprises Ltd, 19 William Nadin Way, Swadlincote, Derbyshire, DE11 0BB Tel: (01283) 226570 Fax: (01283) 229401 *Remote control car parts distributor*

▶ Mirage Studios Ltd, Unit 10, Adam Business Centre, Henson Way, Kettering, Northamptonshire, NN16 8PX Tel: (01536) 417707

Mirage Television Production, 53 Newington Road, Edinburgh, EH9 1QW Tel: 0131-668 2010 Fax: 0131-668 2243 *Audio-visual producers*

Miranda Technologies Ltd, 1-2 Hithercroft Road, Wallingford, Oxfordshire, OX10 9DG Tel: (01491) 820000 Fax: (01491) 820001 *Broadcasting equipment manufrs*

Mircro Networks Ltd, Unit 5, Dorcan Bus Village, Murdoch Road, Swindon, SN3 5HY Tel: (01793) 613991 Fax: (01793) 613977 E-mail: sales@mnc.com *Microwave component manufrs*

Miric Engineering Ltd, Wigwam Lane, Hucknall, Nottingham, NG15 7SZ Tel: 0115-968 1163 Fax: 0115-968 1483 E-mail: janeyates@miricengineering.com *Hydraulic fitting & adaptor manufacturers. We hold stocks of Jic, Bsp, Orfs, Bspt, Npt,& Metric fittings. *We can make fittings straight or forged to suit your requirments.*

Mirific Services Ltd, Enterprise House, Cherry Orchard Lane, Salisbury, SP2 7LD Tel: (01722) 427270 Fax: (01722) 414165 E-mail: info@mirific.co.uk *Touch screen epos suppliers*

Mirj Hygiene Products Ltd, Unit 3, Antelope Industrial Park, Rhydymwyn, Mold, Clwyd, CH7 5JH Tel: (01352) 741919 Fax: (01352) 741920 E-mail: sales@mirjhygiene.co.uk *Industrial cleaning product manufrs*

Mirka Abrasives Ltd, 7 Holdom Avenue, Bletchley, Milton Keynes, MK1 1QU Tel: (01908) 375533 Fax: (01908) 376611 E-mail: sales.uk@mirka.com *Abrasive product distributors*

Mirlyn Ltd, 57 Coleridge Street, Hove, East Sussex, BN3 5AB Tel: (01273) 733404 Fax: (01273) 703330 *General fabricators*

Mirren Drawing Office Services Ltd, 13 Old Sneddon Street, Paisley, Renfrewshire, PA3 2AG Tel: 0141-561 7213 Fax: 0141-561 7213 *Reprographic duplicating & photocopying service*

Mirror Colour Print Watford Ltd, St. Albans Road, Watford, WD24 7RG Tel: (01923) 230455 Fax: (01923) 249861 E-mail: editor@mirror.co.uk *Printing newspapers*

▶ Mirror Finish Metal Polishing, 2 Fryers Road, Walsall, WS2 7LZ Tel: (01922) 402080

Mirrors & Glass Stockport Ltd, 84 Wellington Road North, Stockport, Cheshire, SK4 1HW Tel: 0161-480 1875 Fax: 0161-480 7008 E-mail: sales@mirrorsandglass.co.uk *Glass merchants & mirror manufrs*

Mirum Products Ltd, Station Road, Ardleigh, Colchester, CO7 7RT Tel: (01206) 230230 Fax: (01206) 231764 E-mail: mirum@talk21.com *Collapsible tube manufrs*

Mirus Plastics Ltd, Ridings Business Park, Hopwood Lane, Halifax, West Yorkshire, HX1 3TT Tel: (01422) 345227 Fax: (01422) 347524 *Plastic injection moulders*

Mis Shipping Ltd, 34 The Mall, London, W5 3TJ Tel: (020) 8567 4456 Fax: (020) 8567 5890 E-mail: misshipping@msn.com *Freight forwarding agents*

Misco, Darby Close, Park Farm South, Wellingborough, Northamptonshire, NN8 6GS Tel: (08707) 208720 Fax: (08707) 208686 E-mail: salesdesk@misco.co.uk *Computer products direct mail catalogue*

▶ Mishi Ltd, 42 Harvest Way, Witney, Oxfordshire, OX28 1EG Tel: (01993) 708719 Fax: (01993) 708719 E-mail: mishi.ltd@tiscali.co.uk *Product DesignEngineering Design*

Miskelly Bros Ltd, 29 Moss Road, Ballygowan, Newtownards, County Down, BT23 6JE Tel: (028) 9752 8218 Fax: (028) 9752 1792 *Quarry operators services*

Miskin Plant & Tool Hire Co. Ltd, Alban House, Brownfields, Welwyn Garden City, Hertfordshire, AL7 1BE Tel: (01707) 371858 Fax: (01707) 373073 *Tool hire & sales*

Mison Security Ltd, 5 Skyline, Lime Harbour, London, E14 9TS Tel: (020) 7093 1177 Fax: (020) 7923 0493 E-mail: mail@misonsecurity.com *Security sevices*

Miss Albion Ltd, Unit 4-5 St Francis Factory Estate, Thomas Street, West Bromwich, West Midlands, B70 6LY Tel: 0121-553 2505 Fax: 0121-525 8226 *Ladies fashion manufrs* Also at: West Bromwich

▶ Miss Maid Cleaning Services, Unit 19, 6 Millenium Way, London, E14 3QF Tel: (020) 7987 4158 Fax: 0870 446 0778 E-mail: mail@missmaid.co.uk *Cleaning services*

▶ Missiles & Space Batteries Ltd, Shawhead, Coatbridge, Lanarkshire, ML5 4UZ Tel: (01236) 437775 Fax: (01236) 436650

▶ Mississippi River Boat Horning Ltd, Poppyfields Barn, Shoals Road, Irstead, Norwich, NR12 8XR Tel: (01692) 630262 Fax: (01692) 631372

Mist-Air Environmental Systems, PO Box 10, Oswestry, Shropshire, SY10 9JF Tel: (07071) 666000 Fax: (01691) 828499 E-mail: info@mist-air.co.uk *Manufacturers of dust suppression (airborne) systems*

▶ Mister Bouncy, 20 Five Heads Road, Waterlooville, Hampshire, PO8 9NW Tel: (0800) 0280291 *Bouncy castle hire services*

▶ Mister Natural Leather & Luggage, 4 & 5 West Bute Street, Cardiff Bay, Cardiff, CF10 5FT Tel: (029) 2049 6813 Fax: (029) 2049 6813 E-mail: mister@natural.fsnet.co.uk *Leather*

continued

goods manufacture & sales, suitcase & leather repairs, luggage

Mister Steel Ltd, Stewarts La Depot, Dickens Street, London, SW8 3EP Tel: (020) 7738 8858 Fax: (020) 7738 8893 E-mail: info@mistersteel.co.uk *Steel stockholders*

Mister Tee's Rock Stop, 65 Blackwell Street, Kidderminster, Worcestershire, DY10 2EL Tel: (01562) 515291 *Promoters of premium products & advertising gift*

▶ Mistflex Ltd, 6 5 Fountayne Road, London, N15 4QL Tel: (020) 8808 3345 Fax: (020) 8808 3324

Mistley Quay & Forwarding, High Street, Mistley, Manningtree, Essex, CO11 1HB Tel: (01206) 394431 Fax: (01206) 393882 E-mail: enquiries@twlogistics.co.uk *Stevedores & forwarding agents* Also at: Branches throughout the U.K.

▶ Mistral Boilers Ltd, Unit C3, Halesfield 23, Telford, Shropshire, TF7 4NY Tel: (01952) 270082 Fax: (01952) 270086 E-mail: mistralboilers@aol.com *Manufacture central heating boilers*

Mistral LPM, Staplehurst Office Centre, Weston On The Green, Bicester, Oxfordshire, OX25 3QU Tel: (01869) 352720 Fax: (01869) 351519 *Public relations services*

Mistura Systems, 217 Kingsbury Road, London, NW9 9PQ Tel: (020) 8511 1854 Fax: (020) 8205 0055 E-mail: safety@mistura.co.uk *Safety interlocking systems for switchgear and machine safety applications*

▶ Misura Recruitment Services Ltd, PO BOX 625, Rotherham, South Yorkshire, S60 9BB Tel: (01709) 739278 Fax: (01709) 739278 E-mail: info@misurajobs.co.uk *Employment Agency and Business.*Sectors include Administration IT, Banking, Executive and Management, Engineering and Manufacturing, H.R,Legal Services, Logistics,Marketing, Purchasing, Retail and Sales.**

Misus Group, 1 St Georges Road, Wimbledon, London, SW19 4DR Tel: (020) 7757 6222 Fax: (020) 8944 7275 E-mail: sales@misys.com *Financial software & development systems services*

Miswa Chemicals Ltd, Caswell Road, Brackmills Industrial Estate, Northampton, NN4 7PW Tel: (01604) 701111 Fax: (01604) 701120 E-mail: sales@miswa.com *Industrial chemical manufrs*

Misys P.L.C., Burleigh House, Chapel Oak, Salford Priors, Evesham, Worcestershire, WR11 8SP Tel: (01386) 871373 Fax: (01386) 871045 *Computer software distributors for finance & health care industries*

▶ MiT, Church Lane, Middleton, Tamworth, Staffordshire, B78 2AN Tel: 0121- 308 1154 Fax: (0871) 239 9379 E-mail: mitltd@btinternet.com *Sales, hire & contract leasing of a wide range of vacuum tankers & equipment associated with liquid waste management, vehicles such as rigid vacuum tankers, Tri Axle Vacuum Tankers, Vactor, Disab & Whale, equipment, hoses, pumps, fittings & tools are also available*

Mita (U K) Ltd, Manor Farm Industrial Estate, Flint, Clwyd, CH6 5UY Tel: (01352) 792200 Fax: (01252) 792314 E-mail: info@mita.co.uk *Cable management systems manufrs*

Mitac Synnex UK Ltd, Synnex House, Nedge Hill, Telford, Shropshire, TF3 3AH Tel: (01952) 207200 Fax: (01952) 201216 Principal Export Areas: Worldwide *Industrial computer manufrs*

Andrew Mitchell & Co. Ltd, 15 Dunivaig Road, Glasgow, G33 4TT Tel: 0141-773 5454 Fax: 0141-773 5455 E-mail: info1@mitco.co.uk *Manufacturers of textiles*

Mitchell & Cooper Ltd, 140 Framfield Road, Uckfield, East Sussex, TN22 5AU Tel: (01825) 765511 Fax: (01825) 767173 E-mail: sales@mitchellcooper.co.uk *Internationally recognised by bar and catering professionals, Mitchell & Cooper manufacture and supply an extensive range of kitchen, bar, dispensing equipment and point of sale products.* The company is over 125 years old and has built an enviable reputation as the manufacturer of Bonzer brand kitchen and bar products. The Bonzer range continues to expand with the new product developments and acquisitions of Diamond Dispensers in 2002.* Since 1982 Mitchell & Cooper have also supplied quality products from other leading producers around the world, including the French brands Dynamic, Matfer, Bourgeat and the USA brands Zeroll, Katchall and San Jamar, and most recently the companies Barth, Hovicon and Pulltex.* The most recent addition to Mitchell & Cooper is our Point of Sale team, which has been up and running for 4 years now with much success. Our design skills have been appreciated by brand owners and marketing agencies alike. Many of our designs come into fruition and can be seen on our website. www.mitchellcooper.com*

Mitchell Cotts Transmissions, Winterstoke Road, Weston-super-Mare, Avon, BS24 9AT Tel: (01934) 428000 Fax: (01934) 428001 E-mail: andy.cook@gearboxes.com Principal Export Areas: Central/East Europe, West Europe, North America, Central America & South America *Transmission & engine manufrs*

▶ Mitchell Demolition, 1a Gunton Lane, Norwich, NR5 0AE Tel: (01603) 748060 Fax: (01603) 747170

Mitchell Diesel Ltd, Fulwood Road South, Sutton-in-Ashfield, Nottinghamshire, NG17 2JZ Tel: (01623) 550550 Fax: (01623) 551617 E-mail: sales@mitchells.co.uk *Diesel engines, components & spares*

Mitchell Dryers Ltd, Denton Holme, Carlisle, CA2 5DU Tel: (01228) 534433 Fax: (01228) 633555 E-mail: sales@mitchell-dryers.co.uk Principal Export Areas: Worldwide *Industrial drying equipment/sludge treatment/intensive rubber mixers*

Mitchell Engineering Ltd, 10 Bridge Street, Cambuslang, Glasgow, G72 7ED Tel: 0141-641 2177 Fax: 0141-641 5185 *General engineering & fabricators*

Mitchell Engineering Ltd, 10 Bridge Street, Cambuslang, Glasgow, G72 7ED Tel: 0141-641 2177 Fax: 0141-641 5185 E-mail: mail@mitchellengineering.co.uk *Brick-making machinery manufrs*

Mitchell Fox & Co. Ltd, 9 Whitehouse Street, Leeds, LS10 1AD Tel: 0113-246 1000 Fax: 0113-246 5000 E-mail: sales@mitchellfox.co.uk *Engineering services*

G.E. Mitchell Electrical Ltd, Springvale, Brookfoot, Brighouse, West Yorkshire, HD6 2RW Tel: (01484) 717607 Fax: (01484) 720484 E-mail: sales@gemitchell.co.uk *Automatic control system manufrs*

George Mitchell & Co. (Newcastle) Ltd, 8 Malmo Close, Tyne Tunnel Trading Estate, North Shields, Tyne & Wear, NE29 7SX Tel: 0191-296 3434 Fax: 0191-296 2978 *Wholesale chemists sundriesmen*

Mitchell Grieve Ltd, Wolsey Road, Coalville, Leicestershire, LE67 3TS Tel: (01530) 510565 Fax: (01530) 510458 E-mail: sales@mitchell-grieve.co.uk *Needle & element manufrs*

Mitchell & Hargreaves, Hough Side Works, Hough Side Road, Pudsey, West Yorkshire, LS28 9DD Tel: 0113-255 2861 Fax: 0113-239 3979 *Joinery manufrs*

Mitchell & Hewitt Ltd, Ascot Drive, Derby, DE24 8GZ Tel: (01332) 332177 Fax: (01332) 374769 E-mail: admin@mitchellandhewitt.co.uk *Control panel manufrs*

Mitchell Hire, 1 Lynch Road, Weymouth, Dorset, DT4 0SJ Tel: (01305) 770601 Fax: (01305) 761752 *Tool hire suppliers*

Mitchell Industries Ltd, Unit 18H, Hilton Business Park, The Mease, Hilton, Derby, DE65 5JD Tel: (01283) 731100 Fax: (01283) 734309 E-mail: danny.hall@mitchell-industries.co.uk *Agricultural engineers & industrial ground care* Also at: Coalville, Derby, Etwall, Nottingham & Sheffield

Mitchell Industries Ltd, Unit 1 Brindley Close, Tollgate Industrial Park, Stafford, ST16 3HS Tel: (01785) 242341 Fax: (01785) 222616 *Agricultural machinery repair services*

Mitchell Interflex Ltd, County Brook Mill, County Brook Lane, Foulridge, Colne, Lancashire, BB8 7LT Tel: (01282) 813221 Fax: (01282) 813633 E-mail: sales@mitchell-interflex.co.uk *Weaving manufrs*

Mitchell Machine Tool Services Ltd, Faraway, Church Road, Long Itchington, Southam, Warwickshire, CV47 9PR Tel: (01926) 817947 Fax: (01926) 817947 *Machine tools service & repair*

▶ Mitchell Maintenance Services, 33 Balkerach Street, Doune, Perthshire, FK16 6DE Tel: (01786) 842411 Fax: (01786) 842170 E-mail: bmscotland@yahoo.co.uk *Electrical services and more. Fully qualified electricans to carry out Portable Appliance Testing (PAT testing), electrical installation and data cabling. Contact us for any property maintenance needs such as painting & decorating, plumbing, roofing, building and landscaping.We'll project manage the finishing trades and make sure your project is finished on time - on budget. Most commercial & domestic work undertaken.*

Mitchell Oil Co. Ltd, Unit 4 Thornleigh Trading Estate, Dudley, West Midlands, DY2 8UB Tel: (01384) 233803 Fax: (01384) 456279 E-mail: mitchelloilltd@tiscali.co.uk *Grease lubricating products*

Mitchell & Partners, 13-15 Archway Road, London, N19 3TX Tel: (020) 7272 7661 Fax: (020) 7272 6628 E-mail: sales@mitch.co.uk *Insurance brokers*

Mitchell Sails, 28 North Street, Fowey, Cornwall, PL23 1DD Tel: (01726) 833731 Fax: (01726) 833731 E-mail: info@sailmakers.uk.com *Sail & cover manufrs*

▶ Mitchell Storage & Distribution Ltd, Unit 12 The Warren, East Goscote, Leicester, LE7 3XA Tel: 0116-260 4080 Fax: 0116-260 4081 E-mail: sales@ncexpress.com *Storage & distribution company local, nationwide & international*

▶ Mitchell Storage & Distribution Ltd, Unit 12 The Warren, East Goscote, Leicester, LE7 3XA Tel: 0116-260 4080 Fax: 0116-260 4081 E-mail: sales@ncexpress.com *Storage & distribution company*

▶ Mitchell & Struthers, Unit 6, Royal Elizabeth Yard, Kirkliston, West Lothian, EH29 9EN Tel: 0131-331 4971 Fax: 0131-331 4971

Mitchell Transformers Ltd, 12 Allens Lane, Poole, Dorset, BH16 5DA Tel: (01202) 622361 Fax: (01202) 624369 *Transformer manufrs*

▶ Mitchell Veneers & Components Ltd, 170 Folly Lane, St. Albans, Hertfordshire, AL3 5JG Tel: (01727) 763705 Fax: (01727) 867974 E-mail: paul.mitchell.com@ntlworld.com *Wood veneers components*

William Mitchell Ltd, Tram Way, Oldbury Road, Smethwick, West Midlands, B66 1NY Tel: 0121-558 2694 Fax: 0121-558 4239 E-mail: phil.bytheway@virgin.net *Fine blanking, pressing, general presswork*

Mitchells Millbrook Ltd, Manor Industrial Estate, Millbrook Road, Southampton, SO15 0LD Tel: (023) 8077 1004 Fax: (023) 8070 4736 E-mail: sales@mitchellsworktops.co.uk *Worktops distributors*

Mitchells Wool Fat Soap Ltd, 46 St Helena Road, Bradford, West Yorkshire, BD6 1QH Tel: (01274) 693063 Fax: (01274) 693057 E-mail: info@mitchellwoolfatsoap.co.uk *Soap Mnfct & Distributor*

Mitchinson Engineering, Airfield, Kirkbride, Wigton, Cumbria, CA7 5LF Tel: (01697) 351925 Fax: (01697) 352060 *Industrial & food industry drying equipment*

Mitec Computer Solutions, 2 Lesley Smith Drive, Faversham, Kent, ME13 7LE Tel: (01795) 533393 Fax: (01795) 533318 *Computer hardware & software repairs & building manufrs*

Mitech Communications Engineering, 4 Lower Mill Street, Cheltenham, Gloucestershire, GL51 8JN Tel: (01242) 224015 Fax: (01242) 223988 *Network software designers*

Mitech Joinery, 234 Derby Road, Denby, Ripley, Derbyshire, DE5 8NN Tel: (01773) 570577 Fax: (01773) 570577 E-mail: roberts@mitechjoinery.co.uk *Joinery*

▶ Mitech Storage Services, Vicarage Farmbrington Rdflore, Flore, Northampton, NN7 4NQ Tel: (01327) 341822 Fax: (01327) 341844

Mitech Telecom, Arenson Centre, Arenson Way, Houghton Regis, Dunstable, Bedfordshire, LU5 5UL Tel: (01582) 445000 Fax: (01582) 445060 *Microwave components manufrs*

Mitek Industries Ltd, Grazebrook Industrial Park, Peartree Lane, Dudley, West Midlands, DY2 0XW Tel: (01384) 451400 Fax: (01384) 451411 E-mail: sales@mitek.co.uk *Manufacturers of roofing products*

Mitel Networks, Mitel Business Park, Portskewett, Caldicot, Gwent, NP26 5YR Tel: (0870) 9092020 Fax: (0870) 9094040 E-mail: sales@mitel.com Principal Export Areas: Worldwide *Business telephone system manufrs*

▶ Miter Press Ltd, Miter House, 150 Rosebery Avenue, London, N17 9SD Tel: (020) 8808 9776 Fax: (020) 8885 4409 E-mail: sales@miter.co.uk

Mithril Racing Ltd, Goodwood Airfield, Goodwood, Chichester, West Sussex, PO18 0PH Tel: (01243) 528815 Fax: (01243) 771522 E-mail: chris@mithril.co.uk *Corporate entertainment operators*

▶ MiTi Co, Ford Mill farm, Woolsery, Bideford, Devon, EX39 5RF Tel: (01409) 241289 E-mail: mikeivory@miticompany.co.uk *Builders of the Conway Range of boats and leisure craft.*Rowing boats, angling craft, yacht tenders, punts and canoes*

▶ Mitie Engineering Maintenance, 22-30 Sturt Road, Frimley Green, Camberley, Surrey, GU16 6HY Tel: (01252) 836800 Fax: (01252) 832250 E-mail: phil.townsend@mitie.co.uk *Engineering maintenance*

Mitie Engineering Services Bristol Ltd, Novers House, Novers Hill, Bedminster, Bristol, BS3 5QY Tel: 0117-963 7361 Fax: 0117-966 9100 E-mail: helen.young@mitie.co.uk *Mechanical & electrical engineers*

▶ Mitie Engineering Services Scotland Ltd, Seafield House, Seafield Road, Inverness, IV1 1SG Tel: (01463) 715233

▶ Mitie Engineering Services (South East) Ltd, London Road, Hook, Hampshire, RG27 9BY Tel: (01256) 768768

Mitie Generation Ltd, Meriton Street, Bristol, BS2 0SZ Tel: 0117-972 4550 Fax: 0117-972 4502 E-mail: bristol@generationuk.co.uk *Access equipment distributors*

▶ Mitie Generation Ltd, Kingsfield Way, Kings Heath Industrial Estate, Northampton, NN5 7QN Tel: (01604) 580444 Fax: (01604) 580487

Mitie Mccartney Fire Protection Ltd, 8 Lawmoor Place, Glasgow, G5 0XW Tel: 0141-429 4646 Fax: 0141-429 4442 E-mail: charlesa@mccartney.co.uk *Fire protection consultants* Also at: Dumfries, Reading & St. Helens

▶ Mitie Mccartney Fire Protection Ltd, 3 Abbey Mead Industrial Park, Brooker Road, Waltham Abbey, Essex, EN9 1HU Tel: (01992) 761666 Fax: (01992) 761777 E-mail: paulas.waide@mitie.co.uk *Fire protection consultants*

Mitie Pest Control Ltd, Battledown Works, King Alfred Way, Cheltenham, Gloucestershire, GL52 6QP Tel: (01242) 696969 Fax: (01242) 696970 E-mail: info@eaglepest.co.uk *Pest control services environmental & estate*

▶ MITIE property services, 2 Enterprise Court, Crosland Park, Cramlington, Northumberland, NE23 1LZ Tel: (01670) 716111 E-mail: admin@mitie-property-services-northern.co.uk *Plasterers Screeders Dry Lining Contractors*

Mitie Property Services Eastern Ltd, Davey Close, Colchester, CO1 2XL Tel: (01206) 871954 Fax: (01206) 863818 E-mail: property.colchester@mitie.co.uk *Painting & maintenance contractors* Also at: Bournemouth, Bristol, Exeter, Newcastle, Plymouth, Preston, Southampton & Taunton

Mitie Property Services London Ltd, Mitie House, Eskdale Road, Uxbridge, Middlesex, UB8 2RT Tel: (01895) 206850 Fax: (01895) 206851 *Building & home refurbishment contractors*

Mitie Property Services (Midlands) Ltd, Coppice Side Industrial Estate, Brownhills, Walsall, WS8 7HF Tel: (01543) 375461 Fax: (01543) 378194 *Painting & maintenance contractors*

Mitie Property Services North East Ltd, 1 Redesdale Court, Middlesbrough, Cleveland, TS2 1RL Tel: (01642) 247956 Fax: (01642) 223378 E-mail: prop@mitie.co.uk *Painting & decorating contractors* Also at: Bishops Auckland & Gateshead

Mitie Property Services North West Ltd, 1-3 Rough Hey Road, Grimsargh, Preston, PR2 5AR Tel: (01772) 703328 Fax: (01772) 793257 E-mail: propertyservices@mitie.co.uk *Property services specialists* Also at: Birmingham, Glasgow, Leeds & Sheffield

Mitier Communications, 2 Rudgard Avenue, Cherry Willingham, Lincoln, LN3 4JG Tel: (01522) 754279 Fax: (01522) 751942 E-mail: info@radiolinc.co.uk *Data communication systems distributors*

▶ Mitime Office Refurbishment & Design, 12 Tanglewood, Finchampstead, Wokingham, Berkshire, RG40 3PR Tel: 0118-932 8235 E-mail: info@mitimedesign.co.uk *At Mitime Ltd we offer a refurbishment service, which is dedicated to Creating the Perfect Working Environment. We pride ourselves in offering a no nonsense approach to the design and refurbishment needs of our clients. Mitime offers a range of services including:**Interior Design *Space planning *Full office fit out *Suspended ceilings *Office decoration *Partitioning *Office furniture *and full Project Management. We can fit your office space with virtually everything you require. From start to finish we design, project manage and install your ideal office. Our managers are very experienced and undertake to deliver your projects in the manner that you would expect. That is reliably, effectively and efficiently - saving you time and money. **

Mito Construction & Engineering Ltd, Adams Wharf, 19 Yeoman Street, London, SE8 5DT Tel: (020) 7231 0918 Fax: (020) 7231 6307 E-mail: mitocons@aol.com Principal Export Areas: Middle East, Central/East Europe, West Europe, North America, Central America & South America *Iron & steel engineers*

▶ MitraWorks, Church Street, Monmouth, NP25 6BU Tel: (01600) 775576 E-mail: info@mitraworks.co.uk *Specialist developers of content managed websites for all levels of users*

Mitre Amusement Services, SWN Yr Afon, Seiont Mill Road, Caernarfon, Gwynedd, LL55 2YL Tel: (01286) 674313 *Fruit machine & arcade game hire*

Mitre Group Ltd, Molyneux Business Park, Whitworth Road, Darley Dale, Matlock, Derbyshire, DE4 2HJ Tel: (01629) 733900 Fax: (01629) 735666 E-mail: mail@mitregroup.co.uk *Consultancy, training, development & market researchers*

Mitre Plastics, Moss Way, Preston Farm Industrial Estate, Stockton-on-Tees, Cleveland, TS18 3TF Tel: (01642) 633366 Fax: (01642) 633377 *Plastic mould injections*

Mitre Sports International Ltd, Pentland Centre, Lakeside, Squires Lane, London, N3 2QL Tel: (020) 8346 2600 Fax: (020) 8970 2887 *Sportswear Manufrs*

Mitre Woodcraft, The Workshops, Market Street, Wells, Somerset, BA5 2DS Tel: (01749) 671266 Fax: (01749) 671266 *Furniture manufrs*

Mitrechoice Ltd, Haynes Garage, The Knoll, Sherington, Newport Pagnell, Buckinghamshire, MK16 9NZ Tel: (01908) 611054 Fax: (01908) 611054 *Ventilation contractors*

Mitregate Ltd, Slack Lane, Heanor, Derbyshire, DE75 7GX Tel: (01773) 762320 Fax: (01773) 530927 *Steel fabricators*

Mitreprize Ltd, Mitre House, 96-98 Braemar Avenue, South Croydon, Surrey, CR2 0QB Tel: (020) 8668 4999 Fax: (020) 8668 1487 E-mail: info@mitreprize.co.uk *Advertising gift producers*

Mitsubishi Carbide, Mitsubishi House, Galena Close, Amington Heights, Tamworth, Staffordshire, B77 4AS Tel: (01827) 312312 Fax: (01827) 312314 *Distributors of mitsubishi carbide tools*

Mitsubishi Corporation (UK) P.L.C., Mid City Place, 71 High Holborn, London, WC1V 6BA Tel: (020) 7025 3000 Fax: (020) 7025 3499 Principal Export Areas: Worldwide *Import & export merchants, including japanese goods import*

Mitsubishi Electric Europe, Unit 12 Mercury Park, Mercury Way, Urmston, Manchester, M41 7LY Tel: 0161-866 6060 Fax: 0161-866 6081

Mitsubishi Electric Finance Europe P.L.C., The Atrium, Uxbridge One, 1 Harefield Road, Uxbridge, Middlesex, UB8 1PH Tel: (01895) 276600 Fax: (01895) 276697 *Electronic component import or export*

Mitsubishi Electric UK Ltd, Air Conditioner Plant, Nettlehill Road, Livingston, West Lothian, EH54 5EQ Tel: (01506) 437444 Fax: (01506) 445511

▶ Mitsui Babcock Ltd, Torness Power Station, Torness, Dunbar, East Lothian, EH42 1QU Tel: (01368) 865188 Fax: (01368) 865183 *Engineering*

▶ Mitsui Babcock Services Ltd, PO Box 8, Tipton, West Midlands, DY4 8YY Tel: 0121-557 3451

Mitsui Fanuc Mitsui, 21 Brunel Close, Drayton Fields Industrial Esta, Daventry, Northamptonshire, NN11 8RB Tel: (01327) 706880 Fax: (01327) 706661 E-mail: uksales@mmte.de *Electric injection moulding machine suppliers*

Mitsui O S K Bulk Shipping Europe Ltd, Dexter House, Royal Mint Court, London, EC3N 4JR Tel: (020) 7265 7500 Fax: (020) 7265 7560 *Shipping company*

▶ Mitsui Osk Lines, Enterprise House, Ocean Way, Southampton, SO14 3XB Tel: (023) 8071 4500 Fax: (023) 8071 4509

Mitsukoshi, Dorland House, 14-20 Regent Street, London, SW1Y 4PH Tel: (020) 7930 0317 Fax: (020) 7839 1167 *Export merchants & department store*

Mitsumi (UK) Ltd, Bede Industrial Estate, Jarrow, Tyne & Wear, NE32 3HD Tel: 0191-428 0333 Fax: 0191-483 3333 E-mail: sales@mitsumi.co.uk *Electronic component sub-contractors & manufrs*

Mittens Vehicle Servicing, The Council Depot, Swindon Road, Cheltenham, Gloucestershire, GL51 9JZ Tel: (01242) 526445 Fax: (01242) 526445 *Car & commercial vehicle services*

Mitton & Holden Ltd, Floor 2 The Arsenel, Sutton Mill, Heapy Street, Macclesfield, Cheshire, SK11 7JL Tel: (01625) 869966 Fax: (01625) 869955 E-mail: sales@mnhltd.fsbusiness.co.uk *Ladies fashion manufrs*

▶ Miura Conference, The Malthouse, Factory Road, Llanblethian, Cowbridge, South Glamorgan, CF71 7JD Tel: (0845) 6447950 E-mail: info@miuraconference.co.uk *Miura Conference provides high quality audio and web conferencing solutions to businesses. We offer extremely competitive rates for Microsoft Live Meeting.*

▶ Miura Consulting Ltd, The Malthouse, Factory Road, Llanblethian, Cowbridge, South Glamorgan, CF71 7JD Tel: (0845) 2260793 E-mail: info@miuradesign.co.uk *Miura Design is a web development Company specialising in high quality web site design and ecommerce solutions for businesses. Our professional search engine optimisation (SEO) services deliver tangible results to ensure our client's sites are highly visible and cost effective.*

Mix It Stirrers, Little Chillaton, Loddiswell, Kingsbridge, Devon, TQ7 4EG Tel: (01548) 550298 *Agriculture machinery manufrs*

▶ Mix & Lay Concrete Supplies Ltd, Denver Site, Ferry Lane, Rainham, Essex, RM13 9BU Tel: (01708) 521414 *Ready mix supplier & distributor*

Mixamate Concrete, 1 Cambridge Grove, Clevedon, Avon, BS21 7BW Tel: (01275) 340804 Fax: (01225) 792204 *Ready mix concrete*

Mixamate Concrete, Head Office, Birkenhead Avenue, Kingston upon Thames, Surrey, KT2 6RP Tel: (020) 8547 0300 Fax: (020) 8547 0300 *Concrete ready mixed*

Mixamate Concrete, 11 West Down, Bookham, Leatherhead, Surrey, KT23 4LJ Tel: (01243) 860300 Fax: (0845) 7225555 *Concrete manufrs*

Mixamate Concrete, South Park, Sevenoaks, Kent, TN13 1EA Tel: (0800) 2888047 *Scientific equipment manufrs*

Mixamate Concrete, Martland Industrial Units, Smarts Heath Lane, Woking, Surrey, GU22 0RQ Tel: (01483) 810101 Fax: (01483) 810101 *Ready mixed concrete suppliers*

Mixamate Holdings, 11 West Down, Bookham, Leatherhead, Surrey, KT23 4LJ Tel: (01372) 456714 Fax: (01372) 456714 *Ready mixed concrete suppliers*

▶ Mixerman, 28 Marshall Avenue, Bridlington, North Humberside, YO15 2DS Tel: (01262) 401058 E-mail: info@mixerman.freeserve.co.uk *Karaoke and Disco Agency ,Hire, Sales, Service and Repair*

Mixing Solutions Ltd, Unit G Venture House, Bone Lane, Newbury, Berkshire, RG14 5SH Tel: (01635) 275300 Fax: (01635) 275375 E-mail: sales@mixingsolutions.com *Mixers fluid, liquid, slurry. Agitator /Mixer (industrial) manufrs*Side Entry, Top Entry, Bottom Entry Mixers*Large Process Mixers*

Miyano Machinery UK Ltd, 9A Navigation Drive, Hurst Business Park, Brierley Hill, West Midlands, DY5 1UT Tel: (01384) 489500 Fax: (01384) 489501 E-mail: sales@macrocnc.co.uk *CNC machine tool distributors*

Mizuho International plc, Bracken House, 1 Friday Street, London, EC4M 9JA Tel: (020) 7236 1090 *Investment bankers*

Mizzy's Sports, 10 Hall Road West, Liverpool, L23 8SY Tel: 0151-931 4955 Fax: 0151-931 5818 E-mail: mizzyssports2002@yahoo.co.uk *Sportswear manufrs*

▶ MJ Freight Solutions Ltd, 7 Bristol Close, Rayleigh, Essex, SS6 9RZ Tel: 01268 780637 Fax: 01268 780653 E-mail: Jo@mjfreightsolutions.co.uk *UK based freight agent, specialising in UK and European movements and express freight.*

▶ MJ Impressions, 1 Montagu Mews North, London, W1H 2JS Tel: (020) 7935 5569 Fax: (020) 7935 5198

MJ Lighting Technology Ltd, The Workshop, Peplow Hall Estate, Peplow, Market Drayton, Shropshire, TF9 3JP Tel: (01952) 840244 Fax: (01952) 840207 E-mail: sales@mjlighting.com *Led in ground lighting & led lighting suppliers*

▶ MJ Pat Services, 30 Northbank Crescent, Ormesby, Middlesbrough, Cleveland, TS7 9EU Tel: (01642) 326857 E-mail: mike@mjpatservices.co.uk *Portable appliance testing specialists*

▶ MJ Servicing, 60 Haytor Road, Wrexham, LL11 2PU Tel: 01978 310384 Fax: 0870 7062999 E-mail: support@mjservicing.co.uk *Professional printer repair - on and off site. **From the largest workgroup colour laser printer, to the humble desktop inkjet - we repair and service them all. **Call us for a free no obligation quotation. **We cover North Wales, The Wirral and Cheshire.*

▶ mjbaudio, 21 Camellia Close, Three Legged Cross, Wimborne, dorset, BH21 6UD Tel: 07818 402662 E-mail: sales@mjbaudio.co.uk *High quality manufacturer and supplier of hi-fi equipment including the Tubthumper garden planter speaker. Specialists in outdoor hi-fi speakers and waterproof speakers. Custom build available. Trade and Retail enquiries welcome.*

MJK Specialist Mould Polishers & Polishing Consultants, Pickering, North Yorkshire, Tel: (07946) 714777 E-mail: mjk1@sky.com *Mould polishers*

MJM Data Recovery, Unit B2, Pixmore Industrial Estate, Letchworth Garden City, Hertfordshire, SG6 1JJ Tel: (01462) 680333 Fax: (01462) 483648 E-mail: sales@mjm.co.uk *Raid recovery specialists ESD protected areas and clean air facilities, hard disks, floppy disks, memory cards, jazz disc, zip disc.*

MJM Fencing, Halebank Road, Widnes, Cheshire, WA8 8NA Tel: 0151-495 3948 Fax: 0151-495 3948 *Fencing suppliers & erectors*

▶ MJS It Services Ltd, Florida House, 13 Comberton Hill, Kidderminster, Worcestershire, DY10 1QG Tel: (01562) 748573 Fax: (01562) 753621 E-mail: enquiry@mjsits.co.uk *It consultants*

MK Air Controls Ltd, Vimy Road, Leighton Buzzard, Bedfordshire, LU7 1ED Tel: (01525) 374157 Fax: (01525) 374411 E-mail: sales@mkaircontrols.com *Control cabinets & control systems design & build*

MK Profile Systems, 9 Cowling Business Park, Canal Side, Chorley, Lancashire, PR6 0QL Tel: (01257) 263937 Fax: (01257) 271409 E-mail: info@mkprofiles.co.uk *Aluminium framework systems, conveyors & factory equipment manufrs*

MK Scales Ltd, Cherrycourt Way, Leighton Buzzard, Bedfordshire, LU7 4UH Tel: (01525) 375519 Fax: (01525) 377290 E-mail: sales@mkscales.co.uk *Scales manufrs*

MK Technology, 45 Bradgate Street, Leicester, LE4 0AW Tel: 0116-251 3001 Fax: 0116-251 7834 *Cutting & creasing die manufrs*

▶ MK Training, Sunningdale Avenue, Feltham, Middlesex, TW13 5JU Tel: (07976) 515095 E-mail: mk.training@virgin.net *MK Training, established in 1997. We can offer you various training programmes, especially in the area of IT. We offer a broad spectrum of training at all levels to suit your individual business needs. Training is offered on a one-to-one or group basis usually on-site.**All training programmes are offered with experienced, professional trainers. We also currently provide training to senior management on a one-to-one basis and fully understand the importance of applying discretion and empathy when training individuals or groups.**All training programmes are reinforced using jargon free course material, created over nearly a decade of training large and medium sized organisations. The costs are based on an hourly/daily basis, not per person, and so reducing overall training costs**

continued

▶ MK Virtual PA, 64 Trueman Place, Oldbrook, Milton Keynes, MK6 2HJ Tel: (07712) 353957 E-mail: info@mkvirtualpa.co.uk *Virtual PA - comprehensive administration service for small businesses and private individuals.*

MKA Projects Ltd, 15/20 Churchill Square, Kings Hill, West Malling, Kent, ME19 4YU Tel: (01732) 897917 Fax: (01732) 897927 E-mail: info@mka-projects.co.uk *Chartered Quantity Surveyors, Project Managers, Planning Supervisors, Capital Allowances Consultants, Building Surveying and Architecture*

MKG Motor Group Ltd, Cavendish Road, Stevenage, Hertfordshire, SG1 2ET Tel: (01438) 365663 Fax: (01438) 318318 *Motor vehicle accident repair services*

MKL Meats, 45b Saul Road, Downpatrick, County Down, BT30 6PA Tel: (028) 4461 2123 Fax: (028) 4461 7009 E-mail: mklmeat@btconnect.com *Meat products manufrs*

MKM Mansfelder Copper Ltd, 37-39 Compton, Ashbourne, Derbyshire, DE6 1BX Tel: (01335) 300585 Fax: (01335) 300577 *Manufacturers & suppliers of copper & copper alloy semis*

▶ MLK Music, 5 Madeline Grove, Ilford, Essex, IG1 2RG Tel: 07951 302734 E-mail: info@mlkmusic.co.uk *MLK Music is a UK based production team consisting of two producers, moody & luffa. We are specialist in all genres of urban music including RnB, Hip Hop and UKG. We have a fully functional digital studio which is available for hire. Please call for more information.*

MLM Fasteners Ltd, Building 81, The Pensnett Estate, Kingswinford, West Midlands, DY6 7FJ Tel: (01384) 276280 Fax: (01384) 276299 E-mail: sales@mlmfast.co.uk *Industrial fastener distributors, agents & stockholders*

▶ MLS Business Centres South West, 66 Queen Square, Bristol, BS1 4JP Tel: 0117-987 6200 Fax: 0117-987 6201 E-mail: tom.endacott@mlsbusinesscentres.com *MLS Business Centres operate flexible, affordable, quality serviced office space in Bristol, Bath and over 45 other locations.*

Mmapp Haulage Contractors Ltd, Railway Arch 501, Silwood Street, London, SE16 2TD Tel: (020) 7394 0099 Fax: (020) 7394 9997 *Road transport, haulage & freight services*

▶ Mmaxx Underfloor Heating Ltd, 2 Lenziemill Road, Cumbernauld, Glasgow, G67 2RL Tel: (01236) 787000

▶ MMC Precision Engineering, Unit 7a Stanley Green Industrial Estate, Stanley Green Crescent, Poole, Dorset, BH15 3TH Tel: (01202) 667321 E-mail: mmc-eng@ntlworld.com *Small precision component manufrs*

▶ MMK Solutions, 8 De Mandeville Road, Elsenham, Bishop's Stortford, Hertfordshire, CM22 6LR Tel: (01279) 816230 Fax: (01279) 816030 E-mail: sales@mmksolutions.co.uk *Freight forwarding services*

MMP UK Ltd, Dunnings Bridge Road, Bootle, Merseyside, L30 6TR Tel: 0151-522 2700 Fax: 0151-522 2747 *Packaging company*

▶ MMS Almac Print Ltd, Unit 4 Tyock Industrial Estate, Elgin, Morayshire, IV30 1XY Tel: (01343) 551353 Fax: (01343) 551962 E-mail: sales@mms-almac.co.uk *Design & print suppliers*

▶ MMS Scotland Ltd, Clyde Marina, The Harbour, Ardrossan, Ayrshire, KA22 8DB Tel: (01294) 604831 E-mail: info@mmsscotland.co.uk *Marine engineers, welding and fabrication. Authorised dealer for Caterpillar, Daewoo, Westerbeke, Beta Marine, Fischer Panda, and Johnson Pump. Sales, parts and service on all marine diesels, transmissions and generators.*

MMV Design, 30 Rosewood Court, Rothwell, LEEDS, LS26 0XG Tel: 0113 2825831 E-mail: enquiries@mmvdesign.co.uk *MMV Design is a small graphic design company dedicated to delivering inspirational, creative and effective design and print presentations.**Whether you're looking for logo design, brochure design or a basic leaflet, MMV Design will deliver an exceptional finished product.*

MMV Performance Ltd, 111 Drip Road, Raploch, Stirling, FK8 1RW Tel: (01786) 448800 Fax: (01786) 448808 *Motor & vehicle performance services*

Moat Bros, 391 Holywood Road, Belfast, BT4 2LS Tel: (028) 9065 5328 Fax: (028) 9065 7225 E-mail: rubberstamps@devans.co.uk *Rubber stamp manufrs*

Moat Plant Hire Ltd, 105 Town Street, Stanningley, Pudsey, West Yorkshire, LS28 6ES Tel: 0113-256 4890 *Contractors plant hire*

▶ Mobal Solutions, 20 Hop Garden, Church Crookham, Fleet, Hampshire, GU52 0YL Tel: (01252) 623499 E-mail: info@mobalsolutions.co.uk *Computer trainers*

▶ Mobarak, 1 Harrogate Road, Rawdon, Leeds, LS19 6HW Tel: 0113-250 0880 E-mail: info@mobarak.co.uk *Retailers for ladieswear*

Mobex Ltd, Unit 6 Rigestate Industrial Estate, Station Road, Berkeley, Gloucestershire, GL13 9RL Tel: (01453) 511210 Fax: (01453) 511226 E-mail: info@mobex.co.uk *Mobile exhibition equipment & sales*

Mobifax UK Ltd, Units 3-4 Ash Court, Crystal Drive, Sandwell Business Park, Smethwick, West Midlands, B66 1QG Tel: 0121-541 1604 Fax: 0121-541 1605 *IT hardware & services*

Mobil Oil Co. Ltd, ExxonMobil House, Ermyn Way, Leatherhead, Surrey, KT22 8UX Tel: (01372) 222000 Fax: (01372) 222556 *Lubricant manufrs*

Mobil Services Co. Ltd, Mobil Court, 3 Clements Inn, London, WC2A 2EB Tel: (020) 7412 4000 Fax: (020) 7412 4084 *Shipping & gas supplies*

Mobil Shipping Co. Ltd, St. Catherines House, 2 Kingsway, London, WC2B 6WJ Tel: (020) 7412 4000 Fax: (020) 7412 4084 *Oil company*

Mobile Audio, 56 Lowesmoor, Worcester, WR1 2SE Tel: (01905) 23315 Fax: (01905) 23315 E-mail: mobileaudio@ukonline.co.uk *Car security suppliers*

Mobile Base Co Shropshire Ltd, Unit E1 Stafford Park 15, Telford, Shropshire, TF3 3BB Tel: (01952) 200018 Fax: (01952) 291119 *Storage systems & storage equipment*

Mobile Communications Solutions Ltd, Unit 5-6, Station Yard, Llanrwst, Gwynedd, LL26 0EH Tel: (0845) 3626365 Fax: (0845) 3623616 E-mail: kevin.jones@mcs-cymru.co.uk *Supplier of test equipment & rental services to the wireless industry*

Mobile Concrete Supplies, Hethersett Road, East Carleton, Norwich, NR14 8HX Tel: (01603) 811492 Fax: (01603) 814328 *Concrete manufacturers & distributors*

Mobile Electrics, 2a Pwllmawr Avenue, Rumney, Cardiff, CF3 3HH Tel: (029) 2079 5689 Fax: (029) 2079 5689 *Electrical vehicle suppliers*

Mobile Electro Service Ltd, Units 1-2 Buntsford Park Road, Bromsgrove, Worcestershire, B60 3DX Tel: (01527) 579795 Fax: (01527) 579963 E-mail: sales@mesuk.co.uk *Control panel manufrs*

▶ Mobile Expertise Ltd, Unit B, Wooland Works, Water End Road, Potten End, Berkhamsted, Hertfordshire, HP4 2SJ Tel: (0870) 8508891 Fax: (0870) 0322744 E-mail: sales@mobile-expertise.co.uk *Design & manufacture of high quality communications devices*

Mobile Freezer Rentals Ltd, Greensbury Farm, Thurleigh Road, Bolnhurst, Bedford, MK44 2ET Tel: (01234) 376999 Fax: (01234) 376060 E-mail: julie@mfrltd.co.uk *Mobile Freezer Rentals Ltd based in Bedford offer refrigeration rental and crane hire.*

▶ Mobile Hygiene Services, Unit 12 John Hillhouse Industrial Estate, 211 Cambuslang Road, Cambuslang, Glasgow, G72 7TS Tel: 0141-647 5776 Fax: 0141-647 5776

Mobile M I G, Unit 4 Arnold Street, Lowestoft, Suffolk, NR32 1PU Tel: (01502) 512970 Fax: (01502) 512971 E-mail: sales@mobilemig.co.uk *Welders & fabricators on site & workshop*

Mobile Marine Models, Drinsey Nook, Lincoln, LN1 2JJ Tel: (01522) 704485 *Model manufrs*

▶ Mobile Movies, 28 High Street, Wymington, Rushden, Northamptonshire, NN10 9LS Tel: (01933) 411234 Fax: (01933) 411234 *Audio visual hire*

Mobile Music, Back Dawson Terrace, Harrogate, North Yorkshire, HG1 2AJ Tel: (01423) 565823 Fax: (01423) 508885 *Auto electrical suppliers*

Mobile Pallet Truck Services, The Watermill, Barton Mill Lane, Faldo Road, Barton-le-Clay, Bedford, MK45 4RF Tel: (01582) 769971 Fax: (01582) 763665 *Pallet trucks hire & distribution*

Mobile Pallets Ltd, 1 Woodend Mill, Manchester Road, Mossley, Ashton-under-Lyne, Lancashire, OL5 9AY Tel: (01457) 837725 Fax: (01457) 837804 *Packing & pallet case manufrs*

▶ Mobile PC Fix, 23 Norton Road, London, E10 7LQ Tel: (020) 8556 3044 *Computer maintenance & repair services*

▶ Mobile Phones 4U, 10 Langhurst Court, Wenlock Close, Loundsley Green, Chesterfield, Derbyshire, S40 4PE Tel: (01246) 237267 E-mail: dallsop@mobile-phones4u.net *Nokia, Orange & T Mobile: FREE Mobile Phones - Save Money Half Price Rental - Free and cheap mobile phones in the UK.*

▶ Mobile Racing & Equestrian Supplies, Nortons Piece, Bristol Road, Hardwicke, Gloucester, GL2 4RF Tel: (01452) 886398 E-mail: richardwardle@btinternet.com *Horse & riding equipment suppliers*

▶ Mobile Radio Services, Unit 23 City Industrial Estate, Haven Road, Exeter, EX2 8DD Tel: (01392) 273803 Fax: (01392) 495400 E-mail: sales@vehiclemultimedia.co.uk *Supply & install multi-media in car entertainment & security systems for both private & commercial use*

Mobile Seeds Ltd, Village Farm Buildings, Sheriffhales, Shifnal, Shropshire, TF11 8RD Tel: (01952) 463097 Fax: (01952) 463097 *Seed distributors*

Mobile Storage UK Ltd, Woodham Industrial Park, Creighton Road, Woodham, Aylesbury, Buckinghamshire, HP18 0QE Tel: (01296) 655411 Fax: (01296) 651894 E-mail: info@mobilestorage.com *Container hire services*

Mobile Storage UK, New Millerdam Industrial, Barnsley Road, Newmillerdam, Wakefield, West Yorkshire, WF2 6QW Tel: (01924) 254254 Fax: (01924) 249249 *Container & storage unit hire services*

▶ Mobile Systems Ltd, 1 Four Turnings Cottages, Preston Road, Wingham Canterbury, Canterbury, Kent, CT3 1EU Tel: (01227) 720011 E-mail: sales@mobilesystemsltd.co.uk *Car security & stereo navigation suppliers*

Mobile Systems, 2 Greaves Way Industrial Estate, Stanbridge Road, Leighton Buzzard, Bedfordshire, LU7 4UB Tel: (01525) 853267 Fax: (01525) 853268 E-mail: info@mobilesystems.co.uk *Car security & audio installers*

▶ Mobile Tracking Systems, 1-2 Kingdom Close, Fareham, Hampshire, PO15 5TJ Tel: (01489) 571600 E-mail: admin@mtsgroup.co.uk *Retailers of navigation & tracking systems for vehicles*

Mobile Welding & Fabrications Ltd, Unit 220 Alexandra Business Park, Sunderland, SR4 6UG Tel: 0191 5147985 *Welding fabricators*

▶ Mobileloo.com Ltd, 4 Carus Crescent, Highwoods, Colchester, CO4 9FU Tel: (07793) 144542 Fax: (020) 7691 7518 E-mail: info@mobileloo.co.uk *Mobile toilets, showers & hand wash stations suppliers & manufrs*

▶ Mobiletron Car Component Mnfrs, 80 Roman Way Industrial Estate, Ribbleton, Preston, PR2 5BE Tel: (01772) 693780 Fax: (01772) 693790 E-mail: sales@mobiletron.co.uk *Motor vehicle accessories or components or spare parts*

Mobilite International Ltd, PO Box 236, Oxford, OX2 6XU Tel: (0870) 2410729 Fax: (0870) 2410730 E-mail: david@mobiliteuk.com *Folding furniture suppliers*

▶ The Mobility Aids Centre Ltd, 88 South Street, Stanground, Peterborough, PE2 8EZ Tel: (01733) 344930 Fax: (01733) 312489

The Mobility Market Ltd, Dolphin House, 36 Liverpool Road, Eccles, Manchester, M30 0WA Tel: 0161-788 8676 Fax: 0161-788 8665 E-mail: admin@themobilitymarketusa.com *Mobility Aids Products Disability Aids Pre-Used Scooters Wheelchairs Adapted Vehicles House*

Mobilrax International Ltd, Arch Unit 1138 Bath Factory Estate, 41 Norwood Road, London, SE24 9AJ Tel: (020) 8674 0131 Fax: (020) 8678 6270 E-mail: info@mobilrax.com *Manufacturers of mobile racking*

Mobius IT Solutions Ltd, The Media Centre, 7 Northumberland St, Huddersfield, HD1 1RL Tel: (01484) 546053 Fax: (01484) 314483 E-mail: info@mobius-it.com *Software development, IT consultancy& services*

▶ Mobri Ltd, 35-37 St Marys Lane, Ecclesfield, Sheffield, S35 9YE Tel: 0114-246 0112 *Bakery*

Mockridge Labels (Sales) Ltd, Viaduct Works, Cavendish Street, Ashton-under-Lyne, Lancashire, OL6 7QL Tel: 0161-308 2331 Fax: 0161-343 1958 E-mail: mike.graham@mockridge.com *Manufacturers of labels, signs & nameplates. Also engravers & specialists in 3-D doming*

Mod Fix Ltd, Zygology House, Seawall Road, Cardiff, CF24 5ZY Tel: (029) 2049 9999 Fax: (029) 2049 1188 E-mail: info@modfix.com *Industrial fastener distributors*

Modatec, Unit 14 Orchard Business Park, Cottismore Farm, Kingsclere, Newbury, Berkshire, RG20 4SY Tel: (01635) 291968 Fax: (01635) 291970 E-mail: david-lancaster@btconnect.com *Control systems design & manufrs*

▶ Mode Associates Ltd, 8 Museum Place, Cardiff, CF10 3BG Tel: (029) 2035 9200 Fax: (0871) 6613854 E-mail: info@modestudio.co.uk *Design consultancy*

▶ Mode Designer PC's, 112 Deansgate, Bolton, BL1 1BD Tel: (01204) 366849 Fax: (01204) 366900 *Computer software retailers*

Mode Lifestyle, Winsham, Chard, Somerset, TA20 4BZ Tel: (0870) 2403606 E-mail: e@mode.co.uk *Indoor & outdoor furniture & furniture accessories*

Mode Lighting UK Ltd, Chelsing House, Mead Lane, Hertford, SG13 7AW Tel: (01992) 554566 Fax: (01992) 553644 E-mail: sales@modecontracts.com *Printed circuit assembly services & manufrs*

Mode Lighting (UK) Ltd, The Maltings, 63 High Street, Ware, Hertfordshire, SG12 9AD Tel: (01920) 462121 Fax: (01920) 466882 E-mail: sales@mode-lighting.co.uk *Electronic transformers, converters, & architectural lighting systems*

▶ The Model Academy Ltd, 1 Atworth Grove, Littleover, Derby, DE23 3WZ Tel: (01332) 540446 Fax: (01332) 549017 E-mail: ra@themodelacademy.co.uk *Model agency*

Model Branch Ltd, William Street, Bedworth, Warwickshire, CV12 9DS Tel: (024) 7631 4393 Fax: (024) 7631 4393 *Joinery contractors, suppliers & manufrs*

Model Engineering Supplies (Bexhill), Clifford Mews, Clifford Road, Bexhill-on-Sea, East Sussex, TN40 1QA Tel: (01424) 223702 Fax: (01424) 223702 E-mail: sales@model-engineering.co.uk *Model engineers & manufrs*

▶ Model Enthusiasts, Lower Station Road, Henfield, West Sussex, BN5 9UG Tel: (0870) 7552241 *Mamod engines and spares with free technical advice avaliable. Traction Engines, Steam Rollers and a full stock of parts and spares. The most specialised and Mamod focused retailer in the U.K.*

Model Making & Graphic Services Ltd, 9 Bath Buildings, Montpelier, Bristol, BS6 5PT Tel: 0117-944 6050 Fax: 0117-944 5973 E-mail: mmgsltd@aol.com *Prototype architectural engineers & model manufrs*

Model Productions Dover Ltd, Hollow Wood Road, Dover, Kent, CT17 0UB Tel: (01304) 206784 Fax: (01304) 215067 E-mail: enquiries@modelproductions.co.uk *Plastic injection moulders*

Model Technology Ltd, Unit 11 Speedgate Farm, Speedgate, Fawkham, Longfield, Kent, DA3 8NJ Tel: (01474) 879878 Fax: (01474) 874683 *Model manufrs*

Modelpower.co.uk, 3 Church Walk, Mancetter, Atherstone, Warwickshire, CV9 1PZ Tel: (01827) 711501 Fax: (01827) 700039 E-mail: internetsales@modelpower.co.uk *Rechargeable batteries, radio control models suppliers & manufrs*

Models & Computers Plus, 55-55a West Street, Boston, Lincolnshire, PE21 8QN Tel: (01205) 365102 Fax: (01205) 369949 E-mail: sales@modcomp.net *Computer software & hardware services & retailers*

Models London Manufacturing Ltd, 160 Dukes Road, London, W3 0SL Tel: (020) 8896 2440 Fax: (020) 8752 1391 E-mail: info@models-london.com *Display model manufrs*

Modern Air Systems Ltd, 219 Humberstone Lane, Leicester, LE4 9JT Tel: 0116-269 3485 Fax: 0116-269 3543 E-mail: sales@parkerplant.com *Dust collection*

Modern Baking Systems Bristol Ltd, 26 Clothier Road, Bristol, BS4 5PS Tel: 0117-977 9494 Fax: 0117-971 9926 *Bakery plant equipment & engineers*

▶ Modern Bathroom/Kitchen Services, 12 Paroma Road, Belvedere, Kent, DA17 5AA Tel: (020) 8306 1397 E-mail: modernbathservices@tiscali.co.uk *Complete bathroom/kitchen/bedroom installations. Central heating/boiler installations/ servicing. Plastering end electrics. Tiling. Free estimates.*

Modern Blinds, 11 Bottesford Road, Scunthorpe, South Humberside, DN16 3HA Tel: (01724) 862472 Fax: (01724) 862472 *Blind manufrs*

Modern Bookbinders Ltd, Pringle Street, Blackburn, BB1 1SA Tel: (01254) 59371 Fax: (01254) 59373 E-mail: binders@btclick.com *Magazine binder manufrs*

Modern Business Technology Ltd, Tregurtha Downs, Goldsithney, Penzance, Cornwall, TR20 9LD Tel: (01736) 711756 *Computer systems*

Modern Colour Solutions, 2 Bullsbridge Industrial Estate, Hayes Road, Southall, Middlesex, UB2 5NB Tel: (020) 8848 4577 Fax: (020) 8848 1513 E-mail: sales@moderncoloursolutions.co.uk *We are traditional Lithographic Printers with a full background in Design, Reprographic and Digital Pre-Press technologies.Environmentally friendly members of the Woodland Trust using recycled stocks*

Modern Computers Ltd, 181 Old Kent Road, London, SE1 5NA Tel: (020) 7231 1313 Fax: (020) 7231 3225 E-mail: sales@moderncomputers.com *Computer repairers & manufrs*

Modern Conditioning Services Ltd, Church Lane, West Bromwich, West Midlands, B71 1BX Tel: 0121-553 4001 Fax: 0121-500 5102 *Air conditioning equipment distribs*

Modern Door Closures, Lloyds Bank Chambers, High Street, Littlehampton, West Sussex, BN17 5AG Tel: (01903) 724003 Fax: (01903) 739806 E-mail: tradersnetwork@btconnect.com *Automatic door closure systems incorporated in the hinge*

Modern Drives & Controls Ltd, 5 Barrington Park, Leycroft Road, Leicester, LE4 1ET Tel: 0116-234 0234 Fax: 0116-236 6310 E-mail: modern.drives@connectfree.co.uk *Business of motion & control*

Modern Engraving Ltd, Leese Street, Stoke-on-Trent, ST4 1AL Tel: (01782) 849055 Fax: (01782) 744565 E-mail: sales@modernengraving.co.uk *The Complete Nameplate Service - Signs, Plaques, Die cutting, guards, Stencils, Mimic panels, Cake and tyre moulds, Badges, Labels, Tags, Switch membranes, Metal blanks, Artwork and design in-house. Precision engravers, Etchers and Screen Printers*

Modern Equipment & Foundry Engineering Ltd, 1 Dalton Lane, Keighley, West Yorkshire, BD21 4HW Tel: (01535) 605501 Fax: (01535) 602816 *Structural steelwork manufrs*

Modern Fabrications (Barnsley) Ltd, Modern House, Summer Lane, Barnsley, South Yorkshire, S70 2NP Tel: (01226) 733337 Fax: (01226) 730004 E-mail: sales@modern-fabrications.co.uk *PVCu fabrication & window manufrs*

▶ Modern Fordayne Fire Protection Ltd, Crofton Drive, Lincoln, LN3 4NJ Tel: (01522) 531711 Fax: (01522) 510291 E-mail: sales@rilmac.co.uk *Fire protection services*

Modern Handling Services Ltd, 21 George Street, Milnsbridge, Huddersfield, HD3 4JD Tel: (01484) 461043 Fax: (01484) 461042 E-mail: themhsltd@aol.com *Plastic materials & shelving agents & distributor*

Modern Images UK, P.O. Box 460, Rochdale, Lancashire, OL12 0WX Tel: (0870) 6091364 Fax: (01706) 354746 E-mail: enquiries@modern-imagesuk.com *Photographs or artwork can be transformed into gallery quality pictures for home or business and even gift products. Many options - from large-scale, full-colour reproduction framed canvas prints to scatter cushions, beach bags and holdalls. Any hard copy or digital image and any kind of photograph can be transformed by canvas printing into a remarkable artwork or an unusual gift. High quality image reproduction at our own studios with extreme resolution print technology.*

Modern Laminates, 179b Queens Road, Watford, WD17 2QJ Tel: (01923) 229029 Fax: (01923) 246308 *Worktop fabricators, distributors & retailers*

Modern Machinery Supplies Ltd, Rathdown Road, Lissue Industrial Estate West, Lisburn, County Antrim, BT28 2RE Tel: (028) 9262 2011 Fax: (028) 9262 2181 E-mail: sales@modernmachinerysupplies.co.uk *General Engineers*

Modern Maintenance Products International, Brunel Close, Park Farm Industrial Estate, Wellingborough, Northamptonshire, NN8 6QX Tel: (01933) 670870 Fax: (01933) 670800 E-mail: info@mmp-international.co.uk Principal Export Areas: Worldwide *Suppliers of protective coatings*

Modern Metal Finishes Ltd, Burstwick Industrial Estate, Ellifoot Lane, Burstwick, Hull, HU12 9EF Tel: (01964) 671040 Fax: (01964) 671040 E-mail: sales@mmfgold.co.uk *Electroplating & silver plating services or processors. In addition, gilding & gold plating services to the trade. Also electroless (nickel) plating services*

Modern Mix Concrete Supplies Ltd, Unit 1 Empson Street, London, E3 3LT Tel: (020) 7538 2266 Fax: (020) 7537 3256 *Ready mixed concrete merchants*

Modern Moulds Associates Ltd, Lightsfield, Oakley, Basingstoke, Hampshire, RG23 7BY Tel: (01256) 782333 Fax: (01256) 782915 *Injection moulders & toolmakers*

Modern Moulds & Tools, Commerce Way, Lancing, West Sussex, BN15 8TA Tel: (01903) 851905 Fax: (01903) 851907 E-mail: mail@modernmoulds.co.uk *Plastic mould toolmakers*

Modern Ornate Steel & Iron Crafts Mosaic, 19-25 Nelson Street, Nottingham, NG1 1DR Tel: 0115-910 0115 Fax: 0115 9100156 *Iron furnishings & staging*

Modern Packaging UK Ltd, Unit 26 Lansdown Industrial Estate, Gloucester Road, Cheltenham, Gloucestershire, GL51 8PL Tel: (01242) 262002 Fax: (01242) 261919 E-mail: sales@modern-packaging.co.uk *Flexible packaging & printing manufrs*

Modern Plant Hire, 6 Somers Road, Rugby, Warwickshire, CV22 7DE Tel: (01788) 565186 Fax: (01788) 579878 *Contractors plant & equipment hire*

Modern Plastics Moulding Co., Booth Street, Smethwick, West Midlands, B66 2PF Tel: 0121-565 3390 Fax: 0121-565 3390 *Disposable refuse sack manufrs*

Modern Rollers Ltd, Greengate, Salford, M3 7NS Tel: 0161-834 1539 Fax: 0161-835 3303 E-mail: modernrollers@davidbentley.co.uk Principal Export Areas: Worldwide *Rubber roller manufrs*

Modern Saddlery Ltd, Leamore Lane, Walsall, WS2 7NT Tel: (01922) 476166 Fax: (01922) 497958E-mail: enquiries@modernsaddlery.co.uk *Saddlery manufrs*

Modern Saddlery Ltd, Leamore Lane, Walsall, WS2 7NT Tel: (01922) 476166 Fax: (01922) 497958 E-mail: enquries@modernsaddlery.com *Manufacturers of riding equipment*

Modern Screws Ltd, 5 Dartford Road, Bexley, Kent, DA5 2BH Tel: (01322) 553224 Fax: (01322) 555093 E-mail: sales@modern-screws.co.uk Purchasing Contact: C.B. Minchinton Sales Contact: C.B. Minchinton Principal Export Areas: Worldwide *Bolt & nut, fastener (industrial) & screw distributors/agents/stockholders. Also screws, miniature, precision*

Modern Tool Hire Ltd, Minerva Lane Works, Walsall Street, Wolverhampton, WV1 3LX Tel: (01902) 453044 Fax: (01902) 453221 *Steam cleaning equipment*

Modern Typewriting Supplies Ltd, 69 Choumert Road, London, SE15 4AS Tel: (020) 7639 6317 Fax: (020) 7358 1079 E-mail: modern@btconnect.com *Office stationery suppliers & printers*

Modern Valves & Fittings, Unit 13A, Victoris Industrial Estate, Victoris Road West, Hebburn, Tyne & Wear, NE31 1UP Tel: 0191-250 2384 Fax: 0191-250 2247 *Valves & fittings, distributors*

▶ Modis, Swan House, 33 Queen Street, London, EC4R 1BR Tel: (020) 7383 3888 Fax: (020) 7038 6401 E-mail: info@modisintl.com Principal Export Areas: Worldwide *Modis is one of the world's largest and most respected providers of Information Technology Resource Management (ITRM) services and solutions. Modis has successfully operated throughout Europe for over 30 years, and today delivers world class IT & Engineering Services to over 2,500 clients in the United Kingdom, Europe, the United States and Canada. Through our work with leading companies and organisations around the world, Modis has developed strong areas of expertise that have propelled our clients to the leading edge of technology. By providing a full range of critical information technology services and solutions, Modis is a key partner for many of the world's premier companies. Our capabilities span a broad spectrum of IT services, including: Contract Recruitment Services, Project Management Services, Permanent Recruitment Services, and Managed Services We have built a strong track record in an extensive variety of business categories, which gives us a true advantage in meeting the needs of each client. Through our network of European Offices, we provide specialist help from offices local to both clients and candidates. A personal service in your locality with national and international connections.*

▶ Moduflex Ltd, Fourth Way, Bristol, BS11 8DX Tel: 0117-982 2882 Fax: 0117-982 2881 E-mail: info@moduflex.co.uk *Storage equipment system manufrs*

Modular, 103 Chatsworth Drive, Mansfield, Nottinghamshire, NG18 4QU Tel: (01623) 622144 Fax: (01623) 438308 E-mail: admin@modcompsys.demon.co.uk *Computer software suppliers*

Modular Automation International Ltd, Talbot Way, Small Heath Business Park, Birmingham, B10 0HJ Tel: 0121-766 7979 Fax: 0121-766 6385 E-mail: crampton@modular.co.uk *Assembly system manufrs*

Modular Environment, 31 Dalsholm Avenue, Glasgow, G20 0TS Tel: 0141-946 2222 Fax: 0141-946 2211 *Interior designers*

Modular Hydraulic Systems Ltd, 9 Redan Hill Estate, Redan Road, Aldershot, Hampshire, GU12 4SJ Tel: (01252) 333883 Fax: (01252) 343615 E-mail: sales@mhs.co.uk *Hydraulic equipment systems manufrs*

Modular Mouldings Ltd, Lower Quay, Gweek, Helston, Cornwall, TR12 6UD Tel: (01326) 221722 Fax: (01326) 221800 E-mail: mml@clara.net *Construction consultants*

▶ Modular Office & Storage Systems, Unit 321i, Mayoral Way, Team Valley Trading Estate, Gateshead, Tyne & Wear, NE11 0RT Tel: 0191-487 1212 Fax: 0191-487 7979 E-mail: info@modular-systems.co.uk *Manufacturer of partitioning*

Modular Robotic Systems Ltd, Cale Lane, Aspull, Wigan, Lancashire, WN2 1HQ Tel: (01942) 820088 Fax: (01942) 820431 E-mail: info@modular-ltd.co.uk *Structural engineers*

Modular Scaffolding & Building Equipment Ltd, 950 Grimesthorpe Road, Sheffield, S4 8EL Tel: 0114-243 6090 Fax: 0114-243 6046 E-mail: andy@modular.org.uk *Scaffolding contractors*

Modulex Systems Ltd, 9a North Portway Close, Round Spinney Industrial Estate, Northampton, NN3 8RQ Tel: (01604) 672100 Fax: (01604) 672161 E-mail: mxuk@modulex.co.uk *Interior & exterior sign manufrs*

Modulus Management Consultancy Ltd, 188 Washway Road, Sale, Cheshire, M33 6RN Tel: 0161-905 1089 Fax: 0161-905 3588 E-mail: mmc@modulus-ltd.co.uk *Training & consultancy providers for motor industry*

Modus Air Ltd, 75 Lifford Lane, Birmingham, B30 3JH Tel: 0121-459 3060 Fax: 0121-459 6417 E-mail: modusair@btinternet.com *Dust & fume extraction plant & equipment manufrs*

Modus Airtech Ltd, Airtech House, Eastmead Trading Estate, Ashford, Kent, TN23 7RX Tel: (01233) 638030

Modus Furniture Ltd, Unit 12-14, Rose Mills Industrial Estate, Hort Bridge, Ilminster, Somerset, TA19 9PS Tel: (01460) 57465 Fax: (01460) 57004

continued

E-mail: sales@modusfurniture.co.uk *Homes & gardens furniture*

▶ Modus Visual Communications, 85 Queens Park Avenue, Bournemouth, BH8 9LJ Tel: (01202) 422986 Fax: (01202) 394790 E-mail: sales@modusvisualcomms.co.uk *Audio visual equipment & accessories hire, sales & service*

Moduspace Ltd, Burts Wharf, Crabtree Manorway North, Belvedere, Kent, DA17 6LJ Tel: (020) 8311 7070 Fax: (020) 8312 9908 E-mail: moduspace@aol.com *Manufacturers of prefabricated modular & pod buildings*

Moduspec Engineering UK Ltd, 2 Craigshaw Road, West Tullos Industrial Estate, Aberdeen, AB12 3AQ Tel: (01224) 248144 Fax: (01224) 284125 E-mail: sales@moduspec.com *Drilling rig maintenance services*

Moeller Holding Ltd, PO Box 35 Gatehouse Close, Aylesbury, Buckinghamshire, HP19 8DH Tel: (01296) 393322 Fax: (01296) 421854 E-mail: marketingl@moeller.co.uk *Manufacturers of electrical control gear, motor control centres*

▶ Moe's Moulds, 56 Priory Road, Reigate, Surrey, RH2 8JB Tel: (01737) 222040 E-mail: mark@moesmoulds.co.uk *Mould manufacturer rubber, fibre glass*

▶ Moette Leisurewear Ltd, The Old Chapel, Quebec Street, Langley Park, Durham, DH7 9XA Tel: 0191-373 5995 Fax: 0191-373 6318 E-mail: mail@moette.co.uk *Embroidery services*

Mofast Ltd, Unit D1 Peartree Industrial Park Crackley Way, Peartree Lane, Dudley, West Midlands, DY2 0UW Tel: (01384) 455440 Fax: (01384) 458595 E-mail: mfast-sales@morgalv.pus.com *Bolt & nut distributors & importers*

Moffat Communications Ltd, 1 Bow Lane, London, EC4M 9EE Tel: (020) 7489 4567 Fax: (020) 7489 4568 *Computer project management*

E & R Moffat Ltd, Bonnymuir Works, Seabegs Road, Bonnybridge, Stirlingshire, FK4 2BS Tel: (01324) 812272 Fax: (01324) 814107 E-mail: sales@ermoffat.co.uk Principal Export Areas: Worldwide *Catering equipment manufacturers E&R Moffat are viewed as one of the most respected brand names in the catering industry, with an enviable reputation for quality and innovation built over 40 years.*

▶ Moffat Press Co. Ltd, 1-23 Queens Road West, London, E13 0PE Tel: (020) 8548 2966 Fax: (020) 8471 2494 E-mail: sales@retailweekly.com

Moffett & Sons Ltd, Seymour Hill Industrial Estate, Dunmurry, Belfast, BT17 9PW Tel: (028) 9030 1411 Fax: (028) 9061 0785 E-mail: enquiries@moffett.co.uk *Bedding manufrs*

Moffett Thallon & Co. Ltd, 143 Northumberland Street, Belfast, BT13 2JF Tel: (028) 9032 2802 Fax: (028) 9024 1428 E-mail: info@moffett.demon.co.uk *Door, ironmongery suppliers & manufrs*

Moflash Signalling, 18 Klaxon Tysley Industrial Estate, 751 Warwick Road, Tyseley, Birmingham, B11 2HA Tel: 0121-707 6681 Fax: 0121-707 8305 E-mail: uksales@moflash.co.uk *Manufacturers of signalling products including Rotating Beacons, Xenon Beacons, Obstacle Marking products, Air Horns, Hooters, Bells and Buzzers.*

▶ MOGdesign Ltd, Tilden House 5, 22 Comeragh Road, London, W14 9HP Tel: (020) 7386 8539 Fax: (020) 7381 1127 E-mail: info@mogdesign.co.uk *Manufacturers & installers high quality sliding door wardrobe systems*

Mogensen, Harlaxton Road, Grantham, Lincolnshire, NG31 7SF Tel: (01476) 566301 Fax: (01476) 590145 E-mail: sales@mogensen.co.uk *Vibratory screen manufrs*

Mogerley's Food Products, 49 Friars Vennel, Dumfries, DG1 2RQ Tel: (01387) 253590 *Butchers*

Mogul Engineers Ltd, Chesterton Road, Eastwood Trading Estate, Rotherham, South Yorkshire, S65 1SU Tel: (01709) 379293 Fax: (01709) 378869 E-mail: enquires@mogul-engineers.co.uk *CNC engineering services or machinists*

Mohling UK Ltd, Dudley Road, Halesowen, West Midlands, B63 3NR Tel: 0121-585 7222 Fax: 0121-501 6817 E-mail: info@mohling.co.uk *Cold formed equipment manufrs*

▶ Moidart Engineering, Mingarry, Acharacle, Argyll, PH36 4JX Tel: (07880) 706439 Fax: (01967) 431515 E-mail: jaz.maclellan@tiscali.co.uk *Marine & General Engineering,*Hydraulic sales & service,Hoses made to order. *Welding, fabrication of most metals. mig/ tig,mma,gas,plasma*Marine electrical installation & repair*

▶ Moisture Control & Measurement Ltd, Thorp Arch Trading Estate, Thorp Arch, Wetherby, West Yorkshire, LS23 7BJ Tel: (01937) 843927 Fax: (01937) 842524 E-mail: sales@mcm-moisture.com Principal Export Areas: Worldwide *World leaders in moisture technology services*

▶ Mojo Creation = Marketing & Graphic Design, 85 Boundary Crescent, Stony Stratford, Milton Keynes, MK11 1DH Tel: 01908 263023 Fax: 01908 263023 E-mail: info@mojocreation.com *Independent marketing, graphic*

Mokveld, Unit 2 Butts Courtyard, The Butts, Poulton, Cirencester, Gloucestershire, GL7 5HY Tel: (01285) 851225 Fax: (01285) 851342 E-mail: uk@mokveld.com *Valve manufrs*

Mold CB & Radio, 5 Daniel Owen Precinct, Mold, Clwyd, CH7 1AP Tel: (01352) 757934 *CB & radio retailers*

Mold Hygiene Chemicals Co. Ltd, Unit 3 Antelope Industrial Park, Rhydymwyn, Mold, Clwyd, CH7 5JH Tel: (01352) 741000 Fax: (01352) 740074 E-mail: sales@mirjhygiene.co.uk *Chemicals blending/mixing services*

Mold Systems, Millennium Way, Heighington Lane Business Park, Newton Aycliffe, County Durham, DL5 6JW Tel: (01325) 328700 Fax: (01325) 328707 E-mail: sales@moldsystems.com *Injection mould toolmakers*

Moldmet Ltd, Sandall Stones Road, Kirk Sandall Industrial Estate, Doncaster, South Yorkshire, DN3 1QR Tel: (01302) 888810 Fax: (01302) 880333 E-mail: ken@moldmet.com *Agents for polish mouldmakers*

Moldow Ltd, Unit 31 Britannia Way, Britannia Enterprise Park, Lichfield, Staffordshire, WS14 9UY Tel: (01543) 258844 Fax: (01543) 416311 *Dust extraction plant & equipment manufrs*

Moldsytems Plastics, 1 Edwardson Road, Meadowfield Industrial Estate, Durham, DH7 8RL Tel: 0191-378 0747 Fax: 0191-378 9255 *Plastic injection mould toolmakers*

Moldwell Products Ltd, John Street, Walsall, WS2 8AF Tel: (01922) 631252 Fax: (01922) 631225 E-mail: moldwel@aol.com *Manufacturers of parts in plastic specialising in health applications*

▶ Mole Architects Ltd, The Black House, Kingdon Ave, Prickwillow, Ely, Cambridgeshire, CB7 4UL Tel: 01353 688287 Fax: 01353 688287 E-mail: studio@molearchitects.co.uk *Award winning architects designing low energy contemporary buildings*

Mole Avon Trading Ltd, Station Yard, Axminster, Devon, EX13 5PF Tel: (01297) 32441 Fax: (01297) 35818 E-mail: axminster@moleavon.co.uk *Farm product retailers*

Mole Avon Trading Ltd, Mill Street, Crediton, Devon, EX17 1HL Tel: (01363) 774786 Fax: (01363) 773695 E-mail: admin@moleavon.co.uk *Agricultural requisites* Also at: Axminster & Okehampton

Mole Plumbers, 123 Arrowe Park Road, Wirral, Merseyside, CH49 5PB Tel: 0151-605 1469 Fax: 0151-605 1472 E-mail: sales@moleuk.com *Underground boring contractors & specialists*

▶ Mole Productions, Old Lion Court, High Street, Marlborough, Wiltshire, SN8 1HQ Tel: (0845) 1235725 E-mail: enquiries@moleproductions.com *Video production services including filming and editing. Production of corporate video for promotional, training and educational use.*

▶ Mole Storage, Aston Down, Frampton Mansell, Stroud, Gloucestershire, GL6 8HX Tel: (01285) 760444

Mole Valley Farmers Ltd, The Forge, Church Street, Witheridge, Tiverton, Devon, EX16 8AP Tel: (01884) 860478 Fax: (01884) 860769 *Engineers*

Molecular Devices Ltd, 135 Wharfedale Road, Winnersh, Wokingham, Berkshire, RG41 5RB Tel: 0118-944 8000 Fax: 0118-944 8001

Molecular Products Group plc, Mill End, Thaxted, Dunmow, Essex, CM6 2LT Tel: (01371) 830676 Fax: (01371) 830998 E-mail: sales@molprod.com *Chemicals & pollution control*

▶ Molecular Technologies, 2 Modular Court, Enterprise Drive, Four Ashes, Wolverhampton, WV10 7DF Tel: (01902) 797990 Fax: (01902) 798295 *Manufacturers of electrophoresis resins & coatings*

Molemax International Ltd, Tanglewood House, Murrayfield Loan, Crieff, Perthshire, PH7 3ET Tel: (0870) 4438355 Fax: (0870) 4438356 E-mail: info@molemax.co.uk *Specialist ploughs for the installation of very high voltage & underground power cables*

▶ Molenaar, 32, Buckingham Close, Northampton, NN4 0RR Tel: (01604) 701367 Fax: (01604) 701514

Molesey Metal Works, 22 Island Farm Avenue, West Molesey, Surrey, KT8 2UA Tel: (020) 8979 1772 Fax: (020) 8979 7337 *Sheet metalwork engineers*

Molex Premise Networks Ltd, Network House, Concorde Way, Fareham, Hampshire, PO15 5RL Tel: (01489) 572111 Fax: (01489) 559106 E-mail: sales@molexpn.co.uk Principal Export Areas: Worldwide *Cable systems manufrs*

Molex UK Ltd, The Millennium Centre, Crosby Way, Farnham, Surrey, GU9 7XX Tel: (01252) 720720 Fax: (01252) 720721 E-mail: mxuk@molex.com *Connectors for electronics*

Molins Tobacco Machinery Ltd, Haw Lane, Saunderton, High Wycombe, Buckinghamshire, HP14 4JE Tel: (01844) 343211 Fax: (01844) 342410 E-mail: enquiries@molins.co.uk *Special purpose machinery manufrs*

Mollart Engineering Ltd, Roebuck Road, Chessington, Surrey, KT9 1EU Tel: (020) 8391 2282 Fax: (020) 8391 6626 E-mail: info@mollart.co.uk *Drilling machine manufrs*

Mollertech UK Ltd, 1 Nine Mile Point Industrial Estate, Cwmfelinfach, Ynysddu, Newport, Gwent, NP11 7HZ Tel: (01495) 200044 Fax: (01495) 200055 *Automotive plastic injection moulders*

Mollington Farms Ltd, Grange Farm, Parkgate Road, Mollington, Chester, CH1 6NP Tel: (01244) 851982 Fax: (01244) 851226 *Cheese manufrs*

Moloney Automatics, 8 Factory Road, Bristol, BS36 1QN Tel: (01454) 776772 Fax: (01454) 776772 *Amusement equipment suppliers*

▶ Molplant Ltd, 43 Castle Street, Dumfries, DG1 1DU Tel: (01387) 253030 Fax: (01387) 266158 E-mail: sales@molplant.co.uk

▶ Moltech Power Systems Ltd, Unit 20, Loomer Road, Chesterton, Newcastle, Staffordshire, ST5 7LB Tel: (01782) 566622 Fax: (01782) 576640 E-mail: rob.phillips@moltechpower.co.uk *Rechargeable battery designers & manufacturers*

Molygran & Co. Ltd, 115-119 Bury Road, Radcliffe, Manchester, M26 2UT Tel: 0161-724 4771 Fax: 0161-724 8855 E-mail: sales@molygran.com *Flexible polystyrene packaging manufrs*

Molyneux Dust Control Ltd, 7 Leicester Avenue, Alsager, Stoke-on-Trent, ST7 2BS Tel: (01270) 879359 Fax: (01270) 879355 E-mail: johnmolydust@aol.com *Dust collection equipment & fume extraction plant & equipment manufrs*

Molyneux Engineering (Matlock) Ltd, Stancliffe Works, Molyneux Business Park, Darley Dale, Matlock, Derbyshire, DE4 2HJ Tel: (01629) 734823 Fax: (01629) 734822 E-mail: sales@molyneux-eng.co.uk *Laser cutting services*

Molyneux Press, Unit 102 Horton Kirby Trading Estate, Station Road, South Darenth, Dartford, DA4 9BD Tel: (01322) 861582 Fax: (01322) 861584 E-mail: molypress@aol.com *Printers*

Molyneux Rose Ltd, 143 New Bond Street, London, W1S 2TP Tel: (020) 7409 0130 Fax: (020) 7499 7636 E-mail: retail@molyrose.co.uk *Surveyors & valuers*

Molyslip Atlantic, Unit 1 Danebrook Court, Langford Lane, Kidlington, Oxfordshire, OX5 1LQ Tel: (01865) 370032 Fax: (01865) 372030 E-mail: enquiries@molyslip.co.uk *Manufacturers of general purpose lubricants*

Momart Ltd, 199-205 Richmond Road, London, E8 3NJ Tel: (020) 8986 3624 Fax: (020) 8533 0122 E-mail: enquiries@momart.co.uk *Fine art handlers, shippers & storage services*

Moments Calendars, Wayzgoose Drive, Derby, DE21 6ST Tel: (01332) 285911 Fax: (01332) 285912 E-mail: sales@moments.co.uk *Calendar & diary publishers*

▶ Momentum, Nisoft House, Ravenhill Business Park, Belfast, BT6 8AW Tel: (028) 9045 0101 Fax: (028) 9045 2123 *Trade association*

Momentum Ltd, Unit 27, Verey Road, Woodside Estate, Dunstable, Bedfordshire, LU5 4TT Tel: (01582) 607301 Fax: (01582) 607302 *Retail displays design & store refurbishments*

Momentum Ltd, Clarkson Place, Dudley Road, Stourbridge, West Midlands, DY9 8EL Tel: (01384) 896879 Fax: (01384) 424691 E-mail: sales@hangar51.co.uk *Design & development engineers*

Momentum Design Management Ltd, Robert Denholm House, Bletchingley Road Nutfield, Nutfield, Redhill, RH1 4HW Tel: (01737) 822555 E-mail: contact@momentum-dm.com *Sign consultancy & project management*

▶ Momentum Packaging Ltd, Enterprise Way, Lowton, Warrington, WA3 2BP Tel: (01942) 267211 Fax: (01942) 267200 E-mail: info@foilco.co.uk *Suppliers of decorative packaging including holographic, metallic, woodgrain and transparent effects. These can be supplied as paper, board or self adhesive label. Using our materials has continually led to increased customer sales and awareness.*

▶ Momentum Partnership Marketing Ltd, Unit 3, New Inn Bridge Estate, 998 Foleshill Road, Coventry, CV6 6EN Tel: (024) 7666 2004 Fax: (024) 7666 4700 E-mail: sales@momentumsalespartner.com *Business to business sales services*

Mona Lisa Of London plc, Zenith House, 69 Lawrence Road, London, N15 4EY Tel: (020) 8800 7747 Fax: (020) 8802 7807 E-mail: monalisa@zenithhouse.freeserve.co.uk *Ladies fashion manufrs*

Mona Precast Anglesey Ltd, Gaerwen Industrial Estate, Gaerwen, Gwynedd, LL60 6HR Tel: (01248) 421772 Fax: (01248) 421424 E-mail: monaprecast@aol.com *Concrete product manufrs*

Mona Tractor Co. Ltd, Gilfach Yard, Chwilog, Pwllheli, Gwynedd, LL53 6SL Tel: (01766) 810222 Fax: (01766) 810999 E-mail: monatractors@mtchwilog.fsnet.co.uk *Agricultural machinery distributors & services*

Mona Units, 56 Monadore Road, Claudy, Londonderry, BT47 4DP Tel: (028) 7778 1600 Fax: (028) 7778 1500 E-mail: tony@monaunits.com *Kitchen & fitted furniture manufrs*

Monad Precision Engineering Ltd, Montague House, 615-621 Kingston Road, London, SW20 8SA Tel: (020) 8543 1701 Fax: (020) 8443 2458 E-mail: admin@monadpe.co.uk *Precision engineers*

Monaghans Vinyl & Sunroof Services, 142 North Road, Darlington, County Durham, DL1 2EJ Tel: (01325) 357028 *Specialist car accessories*

Monarch Aircraft Engineering Ltd, London Luton Airport, Percival Way, Luton, LU2 9NU Tel: (01582) 424211 *Aircraft maintenance & repairers*

Monarch Airlines Ltd, Prospect House, Prospect Way, London Luton Airport, Luton, LU2 9NU Tel: (01582) 400000 Fax: (01582) 398323 E-mail: reservation@monarchairlines.com *Air charter services*

▶ Monarch Business Systems Ltd, Unit 7, Drumhill Works, Clayton Lane, Clayton, Bradford, W. Yorkshire, BD14 6RF Tel: (01274) 883000

Monarch Business Systems, 121 Allington Drive, Birstall, Leicester, LE4 4FF Tel: 0116-267 5956 Fax: 0116-267 5956 E-mail: info@monarch-ecr.co.uk *Service cash register*

Monarch Equestrian, King Street, Willenhall, West Midlands, WV13 1QT Tel: (01902) 605566 Fax: (01902) 633556 E-mail: sales@monarch-equestrian.co.uk *Equestrian products stabling & horse walkers*

Monarch Group Systems, 32-33 Monarch Parade, London Road, Mitcham, Surrey, CR4 3HA Tel: (020) 8648 3344 E-mail: sales@mgsonline.co.uk *Sales & service of digital photocopiers, printers, scanners & fax*

Monarch Ipswich Ltd, 5 Scrivener Drive, Ipswich, IP2 0SD Tel: (01473) 604010 Fax: (01473) 604011 E-mail: ed@monarchjoinery.co.uk *Joinery manufrs*

Monarch Knitting Machinery UK Ltd, 74 Boston Road, Beaumont Leys, Leicester, LE4 1BG Tel: 0116-235 1502 Fax: 0116-236 7201 E-mail: general@monarchknitting.co.uk *Knitting machinery distributors*

Monarch Lifts Ltd, 5 14-16 Shore Road, London, Greater London, E9 7TA Tel: 020 89866116 *Lift repairers & manufrs*

Monarch Machine Tools, Banbury Street, Birmingham, B5 5RH Tel: 0121-693 7051 Fax: (01543) 373888 E-mail: info@monarch-machine-tools.co.uk *Machine tool agents*

▶ Monarch Security Ltd, 20-24 Constitution Street, Edinburgh, EH6 7BT Tel: 0131-554 3553 Fax: 0131-555 2100

Monarch Shelving Ltd, Unit 7, Moss Lane Industrial Estate, Heyside, Oldham, OL2 6HR Tel: (01706) 880355 Fax: (0870) 7505477 E-mail: sales@monarchdirect.co.uk *Warehouse equipment*

Monarch Textiles, Lowmoor Business Park, Kirkby-in-Ashfield, Nottingham, NG17 7LF Tel: (01623) 750777 Fax: (01623) 720779 E-mail: enquiry@monarch-textiles.co.uk *High visibility manufrs*

Monarch Tubes Ltd, Autobase Industrial Estate, Tipton Road, Tividale, Oldbury, West Midlands, B69 3HU Tel: 0121-601 5039 Fax: 0121-601 5038 *Steel tube stockholders*

Monard Precision Engineering Ltd, Avon Industrial Estate, Butlers Leap, Rugby, Warwickshire, CV21 3UY Tel: (01788) 569998 Fax: (01788) 568434 E-mail: monard@avonrugby.freeserve.co.uk *Precision engineers*

Monarflex Ltd, Unit 23 North Orbital Commercial Park (Off Natsbury Avenue), St. Albans, Hertfordshire, AL1 1XB Tel: (01727) 830116 Fax: (01727) 868045 E-mail: geos.uk@icopal.com *Gas construction membranes*

Monark Diesel & Electrical Products UK Ltd, 19 Hanley Workshops, Hanley Swan, Worcester, WR8 0DX Tel: (01684) 311031 Fax: (01684) 311009 E-mail: sales@monarkdiesel.co.uk *Suppliers of spare parts for auto electrical & diesel fuel injection*

▶ Monarkle Couriers, 154 Cannock Road, Wednesfield, Wolverhampton, WV10 8PX Tel: (01902) 563354 E-mail: courier@monarkle.com *Courier & light haulage services*

Monax Glass Ltd, 22 Charles Jarvis Court, Cupar, Fife, KY15 5EJ Tel: (01334) 657800 Fax: (01334) 657857 E-mail: monax@sol.co.uk Principal Export Areas: Worldwide *Manufacturers of sight glass*

Monckton Coke & Chemical Company Ltd, PO Box 25, Barnsley, South Yorkshire, S71 4BE Tel: (01226) 722601 Fax: (01226) 700307 *Coke producers & suppliers*

John Moncrieff Ltd, The Glassworks, Scotlandwell Farmhouse, Main Street, Scotlandwell, Kinross, KY13 9JA Tel: (01592) 840064 Fax: (01592) 840065 E-mail: enquiries@jmoncrieff.co.uk *Glass manufrs*

▶ Mondi Board Ltd, Unit 2 Hilltop Industrial Park, Bardon Hill, Coalville, Leicestershire, LE67 1TT Tel: (01530) 510022 Fax: (01530) 510261 E-mail: *Corrugated Packaging*

Mondi Packaging, Harfreys Road, Harfreys Industrial Estate, Great Yarmouth, Norfolk, NR31 0LS Tel: (01493) 656431 Fax: (01493) 440235 *Cardboard box manufrs*

Mondi Packaging, Unit 10 Southside, Bredbury Park Industrial Estate, Bredbury, Stockport, Cheshire, SK6 2SP Tel: 0161-406 4200 Fax: 0161-406 7217 E-mail: manchester@boxesandpackaging.co.uk *Corrugated carton manufrs*

▶ Mondi Packaging Bux, Airfield Works, Pulham St. Mary, Diss, Norfolk, IP21 4QH Tel: (01379) 676531 Fax: (01379) 676275 E-mail: sales.bux@mondipackaging.com *Corrugated sheet board & cartons manufrs*

Mondi Packaging Eastern Region Ltd, 11 Uxbridge Road, Leicester, LE4 7ST Tel: 0116-266 2666 Fax: 0116-266 2555 E-mail: sales@boxesandpackaging.co.uk *Corrugated box manufrs*

▶ Mondi Packaging Stockport Ltd, Priory House, Ellesmere Avenue, Marple, Stockport, Cheshire, SK6 7AN Tel: 0161-449 9994 Fax: 0161-449 9948 E-mail: releaseliner@mondipackaging.com *Maufacturers of Silicone release papers*

Mondi Packaging UK Ltd, Mold Business Park, Mold, Clwyd, CH7 1XZ Tel: (01352) 750655 Fax: (01352) 750677 E-mail: mark.mccleery@mondipackaging.com *Corrugated board, boxes, containers & cases manufrs*

Mondi Packaging Wheatley Ltd, Atkinsons Way, Foxhills Industrial Estate, Scunthorpe, South Humberside, DN15 8QJ Tel: (01724) 295800 Fax: (01724) 854652 E-mail: wheatley@wheatleypackaging.com *Extrusion & food packaging printing*

Mondi Paper UK Ltd, Creams Mill, Mytham Road, Little Lever, Bolton, BL3 1AU Tel: (01204) 573811 Fax: (01204) 862574 *Paper*

Mondi Reprographics, 7 Glebe House, 110 Church La East, Aldershot, Hampshire, GU11 3HN Tel: (01252) 313830 *Office equipment suppliers*

Mondiale Car Co. Ltd, 9 Balloo Cresent, Bangor, County Down, BT19 7WP Tel: (028) 9145 2322 Fax: (028) 9145 0932 E-mail: mondiale@lagan.net *Racing car & spare parts manufrs*

Mondiboard, Carlisle Road, Larkhall, Lanarkshire, ML9 3PX Tel: (01698) 885848 Fax: (01698) 882421 *Cardboard packaging manufrs*

Mondo Foods Ltd, Station Road, Winslow, Buckingham, MK18 3DD Tel: (01296) 715007 Fax: (01296) 712575 *Quiche manufrs*

Mondside Ltd, Unit 22 Jubilee Trade Centre, Jubilee Road, Letchworth Garden City, Hertfordshire, SG6 1SP Tel: (01462) 682875 Fax: (01462) 686698 E-mail: mail@monside.com *Electric motor stockists distributors & agents*

Mondy Packaging & Bromborough, Old Hall Industrial Estate, Wirral, Merseyside, CH62 3QH Tel: 0151-334 1060 Fax: 0151-334 4443 *Cardboard box manufrs*

Money Controls Ltd, New Coin Street, Royton, Oldham, OL2 6JZ Tel: 0161-678 0111 Fax: 0161-626 7674 E-mail: sales@moneycontrols.com *Electronic coin & note handling equipment*

▶ Money For Old Rope, PO Box 332, Bushey, WD23 3XZ Tel: 07050 686012 Fax: 07050 686013 E-mail: john@solditonline.net *We now can offer a fantastic chance for you to purchase the terrific products available from the 'well known retailers' Natural Floorings Catalogue and take a 20% discount from the retail price! Often we will have a special promotion discount on selected products also. We can do this due to our high turnover discount and want to pass this on to you!This is how you get your discount**First you must decide which of 'well known retailers' Natural Floorings you wish to order, if you are not sure click on the 'well known retailers' button on the left, this will open 'well known retailers' page where you must click on the brochure request graphic.This will start your e-mail editor to enable you to request a Natural Floorings catalogue and retail price list from them direct.*

▶ Moneycorp, 100 Brompton Road, London, SW3 1ER Tel: (020) 7823 7500 Fax: (020) 7235 4250 E-mail: smaguire@receptional.com

Moneymore Manufacturing Co. Ltd, 7 Smith Street, Moneymore, Magherafelt, County Londonderry, BT45 7PF Tel: (028) 8674 7177 Fax: (028) 8674 7077 *Designer ladies wear manufrs*

Moneysoft Ltd, Enterprise House, Cherry Orchard Lane, Salisbury, SP2 7LD Tel: (01722) 327707 Fax: (020) 8743 8073 E-mail: info@moneysoft.co.uk *Software developers*

Moneywise Software, 1 Joanna House, 34 Central Road, Worcester Park, Surrey, KT4 8JB Tel: (020) 8337 0663 Fax: (020) 8715 9909 E-mail: itmltd@aol.com *Software house*

▶ Moneyworld Financial Advisers, 34 High Street, High Wycombe, Buckinghamshire, HP11 2AG Tel: (01494) 443806 Fax: (01494) 465511 E-mail: admin@moneyworld-ifa.co.uk *Massive discounts on - Life Insurance - Annuities - Investments - ISAs - Unit Trusts - PEP Transfers and Pensions.*

Mongoose Plastics Ltd, 57-58 Nasmyth Road, Glenrothes, Fife, KY6 2SD Tel: (01592) 774800 Fax: (01592) 775032 E-mail: george@mongoose-plastics.co.uk *Plastics vacuum formed products manufrs*

▶ Mongrel Clothing -T-Shirts, PO Box 44, Newtown, Powys, SY16 1WD Tel: (07791) 081943 E-mail: contact@mongrelclothing.co.uk *Sale of original hand-printed designs on organic cotton "t-shirts."*

Monica Jane, Ger Y Ffynnon, Maenygroes, New Quay, Dyfed, SA45 9TH Tel: 01545 561309 Fax: 01545 560296 *Soft furnishings manufrs*

Monier Ltd, 61 Largy Road, Crumlin, County Antrim, BT29 4RR Tel: (0870) 5601000 Fax: (028) 9442 2165 *Roof tile manufrs*

Monika, 10 Brook Park, Gaddesby Lane, Rearsby, Leicester, LE7 4YL Tel: (01664) 423900 Fax: (01664) 420033 E-mail: info@monika.com *Monika, based in Rearsby, Leicester, is a leading manufacturer of temperature probing, logging and monitoring systems. Their integrated solutions meet compliance needs for food, pharmaceuticals, biological samples and other temperature critical products. They offer simple hand held data collection for small operators through to continuous monitoring with remote data access for large and multi-site businesses.*

Monitor Audio Ltd, 2 Brook Road Industrial Estate, Brook Road, Rayleigh, Essex, SS6 7XL Tel: (01268) 740580 Fax: (01268) 740589 E-mail: info@monitoraudio.co.uk *Audio equipment hire*

Monitor Coatings Ltd, Monitor House 2 Elm Road, West Chirton Industrial Estate, North Shields, Tyne & Wear, NE29 8SE Tel: 0191-293 7040 Fax: 0191-293 7041 E-mail: info@monitorcoatings.co.uk *Plasma coating services*

▶ Monitor Computer Systems Ltd, Marlborough House, Westminster Place, Nether Poppleton, York, YO26 6RW Tel: (0870) 7551153 E-mail: sales@monitorsoft.com *Computer software development*

▶ Monitor Fire, 92 Hopewell Drive, Chatham, Kent, ME5 7PY Tel: (01634) 827127 Fax: (01634) 827128 E-mail: monfire@designsmartuk.com *Fire protection systems suppliers*

Monitor Shop, 574 Carlton Road, Nottingham, NG3 7AB Tel: 0115-911 0366 Fax: 0115-959 0932 *Retailers & distributors of electrical equipment*

MonitorMyBaby, 6 Pentney Road, London, SW12 0NX Tel: 0208 6750771 *MonitorMyBaby - Baby monitor specialists. All types of baby monitor in stock, including audio baby monitors - digital and analogue, audio/visual baby monitors and sensor baby monitors. Most with free delivery.*"

Monitran Ltd, 33 Hazlemere Road, Penn, High Wycombe, Buckinghamshire, HP10 8AD Tel: (01494) 816569 Fax: (01494) 812256 E-mail: sales@monitran.co.uk *Accelerometer & condition monitoring equipment manufrs*

Monix Ltd, 11 Solebay Street, London, E1 4PW Tel: (020) 7790 6404 Fax: (020) 7791 7296 *Ladies clothing manufrs*

Monk Bridge Construction Co., B2 Airfield Industrial Estate, York Road, Elvington, York, YO41 4AR Tel: (01904) 608416 Fax: (01904) 608759 *Structural steelwork engineers*

Monk Of Colne Ltd, 5 Sun Street, Newtown, Colne, Lancashire, BB8 0JJ Tel: (01282) 863122 Fax: (01282) 871121 E-mail: sales@monkofcolne.co.uk *Civil engineers services*

Monk Converyors, Unit 18 Woodside Park, Catteshall Lane, Godalming, Surrey, GU7 1LG Tel: (01483) 791700 Fax: (01483) 791701 E-mail: sales@monk-conveyors.co.uk *Automatic assembly systems & conveyor systems manufrs*

Monk Furniture, Cottage Street Mill, Cottage Street, Macclesfield, Cheshire, SK11 8DZ Tel: (01625) 425900 Fax: (01625) 503919 *Furniture manufrs*

Monk Marketing Partnership Ltd, Unit 11 Triangle Business Centre, Commerce Way, Lancing, West Sussex, BN15 8UP Tel: 0845 0700826 Fax: 0845 0700856 E-mail: sales@monkmarketing.com *Incentive gifts, promotional merchandise, business gifts, Corporate clothing, give-aways, fundraising items, Send for free catalogue or View/buy online at www.monkmarketing.com. Monk Marketing have over 25 years' experience of supplying branded promotional items such as incentive gifts, promotional merchandise, promotional clothing, corporate gifts, promotional giveaways and incentive merchandise to a wide range of organisations throughout the UK. We supply Items and services from incentive gifts and promotional merchandise, corporate gifts,*

continued

Company Information

continuation incentive merchandise, USB flash drives, pens, mouse mats, bags, golf umbrellas and desk top items to promotional giveaways and promotional clothing. We have offices in West Sussex (Head Office), Essex, Manchester and South East.

Monk Metal Windows Ltd, Hansons Bridge Road, Birmingham, B24 0QP Tel: 0121-351 4411 Fax: 0121-351 3673 E-mail: neil.holdings@monkmetal.co.uk *Steel frame window manufrs*

Monk Optics Ltd, Wye Valley Observatory, The Old School, Brockweir, Chepstow, Gwent, NP16 7NW Tel: (01291) 689858 Fax: (01291) 689834 E-mail: advice@monkoptics.co.uk *Binoculars*

Monk & Silvester Developments Ltd, The Nook, Burton End, Stansted, Essex, CM24 8UQ Tel: (01279) 816542 Fax: (01279) 816104 *Building contractors*

Monk Woodworkings, Boundary Way, Lufton Trading Estate, Lufton, Yeovil, Somerset, BA22 8HZ Tel: (01935) 425232 Fax: (01935) 431233 E-mail: info@monkwoodworking.fsnet.co.uk *Joinery manufrs*

▶ Monkey Gaming, 7 Church Street, Highbridge, Somerset, TA9 3AE Tel: (01278) 784790 *Leisure facility*

Monkhouse & Brown, Teams Street, Gateshead, Tyne & Wear, NE8 2RF Tel: 0191-460 0220 Fax: 0191-460 0334 *Steel stockholders*

Tony Monkhouse, Heatherview, Hill End, Frosterley, Bishop Auckland, County Durham, DL13 2SU Tel: (01388) 528726 *Livestock haulage hay & straw merchants*

Monkman Brass Founders, 3 Broom Street, Bradford, West Yorkshire, BD4 7AP Tel: (01274) 732117 Fax: (01274) 732117 *Brass founders & casting manufrs*

Monks & Crane Ltd, Seawall Road, Cardiff, CF24 5XG Tel: (029) 2043 6400 Fax: (029) 2048 9910 E-mail: mcinfo@mcrane.co.uk *Engineers* Also at: West Bromwich

Monks & Crane Holdings plc, Unit 2 Atlantic Way, Black Country New Road, Wednesbury, West Midlands, WS10 7WW Tel: 0121-506 4000 Fax: 0121-500 5001 E-mail: info@monks-crane.com *Tap & die, tool & fixing distributors* Also at: Nottingham, Preston & Telford

▶ Monks Maberly Ltd, Gibson St Works, Gibson St, Nelson, Lancashire, BB9 8RR Tel: (01282) 614974 Fax: (01282) 614977 E-mail: sales@interform-furniture.co.uk *Contract furniture manufrs*

▶ Monksview Demolition, 71 Narrow Lane, Leicester, LE2 8NA Tel: 0116-244 0590 Fax: (01406) 330323

Monmouthshire Timber Supplies Ltd, PO Box 20, Newport, Gwent, NP20 2YQ Tel: (01633) 213268 Fax: (01633) 257088 E-mail: mts@montimber.co.uk *Timber merchants & timber manures*

Monnickendam Diamonds Ltd, 9 Ely Place, London, EC1N 6RY Tel: (020) 7242 2333 Fax: (020) 7404 0223 *Diamond merchants*

Mono Alarm Installations, New Hall, Liverpool Road, Eccles, Manchester, M30 7LJ Tel: 0161-786 2649 Fax: 0161-786 2648 E-mail: sales@thewhitegroup.co.uk *Alarm installation services*

Mono Equipment, Queensway, Swansea West Industrial Park, Swansea, SA5 4EB Tel: (01792) 561234 Fax: (01792) 561016 E-mail: sales@monoequip.com *Founded more than 50 years ago, MONO is a dynamic engineering company committed to providing production and retailing solutions to a world-wide bakery and foodservice industry. Their product range includes bakery equipment, foodservice systems, industrial food making equipment, belshaw equipment, and much more.*

Mono Pumps Ltd, Martin St, Audenshaw, Manchester, M34 5JA Tel: 0161-339 9000 Fax: 0161-344 0727 E-mail: info@mono-pumps.com *Manufacturers of pumps & grinders*

Monochic Ltd, Canalside Unit, Staly Industrial Estate, Knowle Street, Stalybridge, Cheshire, SK15 3AJ Tel: 0161-338 8888 Fax: 0161-303 0970 *Engineers' tool merchants*

Monocon International Refractories Ltd, Denaby Lane, Old Denaby, Doncaster, South Yorkshire, DN12 4LQ Tel: (01709) 864848 Fax: (01709) 860481 E-mail: sales@monocon.com *Refractory materials manufrs*

Monode Ltd, Celtic House, 44 Ballmoor, Buckingham Industrial Estate, Buckingham, MK18 1RQ Tel: (01280) 814171 Fax: (01280) 814169 E-mail: sales@monode.co.uk *Electronic consultants*

Monofix Ltd, 4 Premier Trading Estate, Dartmouth Middleway, Birmingham, B7 4AT Tel: 0121-359 2117 Fax: 0121-359 2187 E-mail: sales@monofix.co.uk *Fasteners & fixings*

Monomet Ltd, 14 Eton Grove, Dacre Park, London, SE13 5BY Tel: (020) 8463 9300 Fax: (020) 8318 3594 *Geotextile membrane distributors*

Monometer Holdings Ltd, Monometer House, Rectory Grove, Leigh-on-Sea, Essex, SS9 2HN Tel: (01702) 472201 Fax: (01702) 715112 E-mail: sales@monometer.co.uk *Design of metal melting & heat treatment furnaces manufactures*

Monopol Holdings Ltd, Oakley House, Dennis Road, Widnes, Cheshire, WA8 0YQ Tel: 0151-424 4121 Fax: 0151-423 3417 E-mail: mail@monopol.co.uk *Holding company*

▶ Monori Wrought Iron, 14 PArk Place, Woking, Surrey, GU22 7NP Tel: 01483 723236 Fax: 01483 723236 *We sell quality hand made wrought iron products.Free UK delivery with all products!www.monoriron.co.uk Beds,Lamps,Lighting,accessories,candle holders,mirrors,seats,tables.Please visit our website.*

Monostar Ltd, Peggs Barn, Drinkstone, Bury St. Edmunds, Suffolk, IP30 9TW Tel: (01449) 736081 Fax: (01449) 736083 E-mail: info@monostar.co.uk *Computer aided designers*

Monowa Ltd, Gable House, 16 Lower Plantation, Loudwater, Rickmansworth, Hertfordshire, WD3 4PQ Tel: (01923) 897779 Fax: (01923) 897780 E-mail: sales@monowa.co.uk *Sliding partition suppliers, installers & manufrs*

J.F.C. Monro, Guildford Road Industrial Estate, Hayle, Cornwall, TR27 4QZ Tel: (01736) 755766 Fax: (01736) 755767 E-mail: sales@jfcmonro.co.uk *Horticultural wholesalers*

Monro South, Unit 1, Quarrywood Industrial Estate, Burntash Road, Maidstone, Kent, ME20 7XB Tel: (01622) 717373 Fax: (01622) 716339 E-mail: sales@monrosouth.co.uk *Horticultural sundriesmen* Also at: Aylesford & Goodwood

Monroe Exports (UK) Ltd, 39 Hartland Drive, Edgware, Middlesex, HA8 8RJ Tel: (020) 8958 9673 Fax: (020) 8357 2810 E-mail: jdhruve@btclick.com *Pharmaceuticals & chemical export merchants*

Monroe Systems, Tubs Hill House South, London Road, Sevenoaks, Kent, TN13 1BL Tel: (0845) 6003233 Fax: (0845) 6445733 E-mail: monroe@monroe.co.uk *Computer personnel recruitment agents*

Monsoon Ruggur Farm & Country Clothing Ltd, 63 Teignmouth Road, Clevedon, Avon, BS21 6DL Tel: (01275) 870220 Fax: (01275) 342272 E-mail: sales@monmark.co.uk *Industrial workwear manufrs*

Mont Blanc Industri UK Ltd, Eden Way, Pages Industrial Park, Leighton Buzzard, Bedfordshire, LU7 4TZ Tel: (01525) 850800 Fax: (01525) 850808 E-mail: sales@montblancuk.co.uk *Motor accessories manufrs*

Montage Design, 3 2 Sycamore House, Vantage Point Business Village, Mitcheldean, Gloucestershire, GL17 0DD Tel: (01594) 546100 Fax: (01594) 546200 E-mail: sales@montagedesigns.co.uk *Partitioning systems manufrs*

Montagne Jeunesse, Astral Court, Central Avenue, Baglan, Port Talbot, West Glamorgan, SA12 7AX Tel: (01639) 861550 Fax: (01639) 861660 E-mail: customerservices@montagnejeunesse.com *Natural toiletries designers*

Montague L Meyer, Lyncastle Road, Barley Castle Lane, Appleton, Warrington, WA4 4SN Tel: (01925) 211112 Fax: (01925) 211090 E-mail: sales.warrington@mlm.uk.com *Timber importers & merchants*

Montague L Meyer (Pension Trustee) Ltd, Rippleway Wharf, Barking, Essex, IG11 0DU Tel: (020) 8477 8000 Fax: (020) 8594 8255 E-mail: info@mlmuk.com *Timber import merchants & agents* Also at: London W1

Montague Tate Ltd, PO Box 179, Cirencester, Gloucestershire, GL7 7YT Tel: (0870) 4030007 Fax: (0870) 4030008 E-mail: admin@montague-tate.co.uk *Internet & network providers*

Montana Bakery Ltd, Blackthorne Road, Colnbrook, Slough, SL3 0AP Tel: (01753) 760800 Fax: (01753) 760801 *Bakery wholesalers*

Montaque L Meyer, Bromford Gate, Bromford Lane, Erdington, Birmingham, B24 8DW Tel: 0121-326 3200 Fax: 0121-326 3231 E-mail: sales.birmingham@mlmuk.com *Importer & distributor of wood-based panel products*

▶ Monterey Recruitment, Suite 8 Merlin House, Mossland Road, Hillington Park, Glasgow, G52 4XZ Tel: (0845) 4332211 Fax: (0845) 4332217 *Specialists in the rail, engineering, oil and gas and nuclear industries, Monterey can supply permanent, temporary and contract staff, throughout the whole of the UK.*

Monterpoint Ltd, 22 Belvedie Road, London, SE19 2HN Tel: (020) 8771 1666 Fax: (020) 8771 2249 E-mail: info@monterpoint.co.uk *Computer consultants*

Montessori Trading Co. Ltd, 13 Hewer Street, London, W10 6DU Tel: (020) 8960 7585 Fax: (020) 7328 5341 *Sell educational equipment & montessori*

Montex Ltd, 109 Clarence Gate Gardens, Glentworth Street, London, NW1 6AL Tel: (020) 7724 3207 Fax: (020) 7724 3831 E-mail: cmshah@marmon.co.uk *Drilling equipment distributors*

Montgomerie Feeds, Dryholme, Silloth, Wigton, Cumbria, CA7 4PZ Tel: (01697) 331396 Fax: (01697) 331272 *Agricultural merchants*

Montgomerie Steel & Co. Ltd, Glen Works, 4 Paisley Road, Barrhead, Glasgow, G78 1ND Tel: 0141-881 4500 Fax: 0141-881 8275 E-mail: info@montgomeriesteele.co.uk *Fencing contractors*

Audry Montgomery Ltd, 9 Manchester Square, London, W1U 9PL Tel: (020) 7886 3000 Fax: (020) 7886 3001 E-mail: mel@montex.co.uk *Trade exhibition organisers*

Montgomery Engravers Ltd, Red Doles Road, Huddersfield, HD2 1AT Tel: (01484) 429520 Fax: (01484) 435022 Sales Contact: M. Bell *Screen printing & nameplate manufacturing*

Montgomery Refrigerated Ltd, 111 Vicarage Road, Portadown, Craigavon, County Armagh, BT62 4HF Tel: (028) 3833 5544 Fax: (028) 3835 0777 *Road transport/haulage/freight services*

Montgomery Refrigeration Ltd, 5 Falcon Road, Adelaide Industrial Estate, Belfast, BT12 6RD Tel: (028) 9066 2111 Fax: (028) 9068 1130 E-mail: service@montgomery-ltd.co.uk *Refrigeration distributors*

Robert Montgomery & Partners, 3 Junction Mews, London, W2 1PN Tel: (020) 7439 1877 Fax: (020) 7434 1144 E-mail: info@creativetalentlimited.com *Photographers agents*

▶ Montgomery Swann Ltd, Scotts Sufferance Wharf, 1 Mill Street, London, SE1 2DE Tel: (020) 7237 0537 Fax: (020) 7237 2661 E-mail: s.bradshaw@montgomeryswann.com *Chartered certified accountants, auditors & tax advisers, specialising in growing business*

Montgomery Tank Services, 50 Trench Road, Newtownabbey, County Antrim, BT36 4TY Tel: (028) 9084 3723 Fax: (028) 9084 9111 E-mail: sales@montgomerytankservices.co.uk *Road tanker services*

▶ Montgomery Transport Ltd, 607 Antrim Road, Glengormley, Newtownabbey, County Antrim, BT36 4RF Tel: (028) 9084 9321

▶ Montgomery Transport Ltd, Unit 502 Green Place, Walton Summit Centre, Bamber Bridge, Preston, PR5 8AY Tel: (01772) 339818 Fax: (01772) 620517

William Montgomery & Sons, 79 Ladas Drive, Belfast, BT6 9FR Tel: (028) 9040 1593 Fax: (028) 9040 1593 *Packaging wholesale & printers*

Monton Fencing Ltd, Montonfields Road, Eccles, Manchester, M30 8AW Tel: 0161-788 7838 Fax: 0161-707 5525 *Fencing manufrs*

Montracon Ltd, Carr Hill, Doncaster, S. Yorkshire, DN4 8DE Tel: (01302) 739292 Fax: (01302) 730660 E-mail: enquiries@montracon.com *Trailer manufrs* Also at: Preston

▶ Montravia Fasteners & Fixing Devices, Unit 10 St. Augustines Business Park, Estuary Close, Whitstable, Kent, CT5 2QJ Tel: (01227) 791790 Fax: (01227) 791789E-mail: robknight@sky.com *Fixings & fastener retailers*

Montreal Associates Systems, Newbury House, 890 Eastern Avenue, Ilford, Essex, IG2 7HY Tel: (020) 8548 3500 Fax: (020) 8548 3501 E-mail: cvs@montreal.co.uk *Computer recruitment consultants*

Montrose Garden Supply Co., Paradise Avenue, Ballymena, County Antrim, BT42 3AE Tel: (028) 2565 3796 Fax: (028) 2564 8642 *Horticultural & garden sundry distributors*

Montrose Review Press Ltd, 59 John Street, Montrose, Angus, DD10 8QU Tel: (01674) 672605 Fax: (01674) 676232 E-mail: reviewnews@montrosereview.com *Editorial publishers*

Montrose Rope & Sail Co., 13 Bents Road, Montrose, Angus, DD10 8QA Tel: (01674) 672657 Fax: (01674) 675785 E-mail: neilpaton@montroseropeandsail.co.uk *Tarpaulin & kit bag merchants*

Monument Press Stirling Ltd, 42 Abbey Road, Stirling, FK8 1LP Tel: (01786) 474763 Fax: (01786) 451520 E-mail: gr@monpress.demon.co.uk *General, commercial & jobbing printers*

Monument Tools, Restmor Way, Hackbridge Road, Hackbridge, Wallington, Surrey, SM6 7AH Tel: (020) 8288 1100 Fax: (020) 8288 1108 E-mail: info@monument-tools.com Principal Export Areas: Worldwide *Plumbing tools & drain cleaning suppliers*

Monway Builders Supplies Ltd, Portway Road, Wednesbury, West Midlands, WS10 7EQ Tel: 0121-502 0911 Fax: 0121-556 9427 *Builders merchants*

Monwel Hankinson Signs & Services, Letchworth Road, Ebbw Vale, Gwent, NP23 6UZ Tel: (01495) 301333 Fax: (01495) 350323 *Sign makers*

Monwel Hankinson Signs & Services, Letchworth Road, Ebbw Vale, Gwent, NP23 6UZ Tel: (01495) 301333 Fax: (01495) 350323 E-mail: monwel@blaner-gwent.co.uk *Sign makers*

▶ Monx Electronic Engineers, County Park Road, Barrow-in-Furness, Cumbria, LA14 4BQ Tel: (01229) 837860 Fax: (01229) 837824

▶ Monzie Joinery Ltd, Monzie, Crieff, Perthshire, PH7 4HE Tel: (01764) 654877 *Bespoke kitchens*

▶ Moodsbydesign, The Technocentre Coventry University Technology Park, Puma Way, Coventry, CV1 2TT Tel: (07791) 119380 Fax: (024) 7623 6388 E-mail: info@moodsbydesign.co.uk *Design mirrors, decorative glass, corporate logos shower enclosures*

Moody plc, West Carr Road Industrial Estate, Retford, Nottinghamshire, DN22 7SN Tel: (01777) 701141 Fax: (01777) 709086 E-mail: paul.gregory@moodyplc.com *Suppliers to the dairy industry*

Moody plc, West Carr Road Industrial Estate, Retford, Nottinghamshire, DN22 7SN Tel: (01777) 701141 Fax: (01777) 709086 E-mail: info@moodyplc.com *Dairy equipment distributors*

▶ Moody Fastpack, 82 Horninglow Street, Burton-on-Trent, Staffordshire, DE14 1PN Tel: (01283) 510592 Fax: (01283) 510892 E-mail: sales@moodyplc.com *Packaging project services*

MOOG Components Group Ltd, 30 Suttons Park Avenue, Suttons Business Park, Reading, RG6 1AW Tel: 0118-966 6044 Fax: 0118-966 6524 E-mail: mcg@moog.com *Slip ring manufrs*

Moog Controls Ltd, Ashchurch, Tewkesbury, Gloucestershire, GL20 8NA Tel: (01684) 296600 Fax: (01684) 296760 E-mail: sales@moog.co.uk *Precision control solutions hydraulic & electric servo piston pumps specialists*

Abraham Moon & Sons Ltd, Netherfield Mills, Guiseley, Leeds, LS20 9PA Tel: (01943) 873181 Fax: (01943) 870182 E-mail: sales@moons.co.uk *Woollen & worsted manufrs*

Richard Moon Consulting, PO Box 425, Bedford, MK44 2ZW Tel: (01234) 772509 E-mail: richard@richardmoon.com *Software developers*

Moon Star Garments, S M B Ho, Gipsy La, Leicester, LE4 6RE Tel: 0116-268 2322 Fax: 0116-268 2322 *Childrens garments*

Moonbridge Air Project S A Freight Ltd, Unit 9, Ascot Road, Bedfont, Feltham, Middlesex, TW14 8QH Tel: (01784) 259555 Fax: (01784) 259599 E-mail: administrator@moonbridge.co.uk *Air, sea & road freight forwarders*

Mooncie Printing Services, 62 Evington Valley Road, Leicester, LE5 5LJ Tel: 0116-273 8882 E-mail: mooncieprinting@aol.com *Colour printing services*

Moonlight Bedrooms, Unit 4 Pocklington Industrial Estate, Pocklington, York, YO42 1NR Tel: (01759) 305620 Fax: (01759) 305620 *Fitted bedroom furniture manufrs*

▶ Moonlight Beds, 2 Byron Parade, Uxbridge Road, Uxbridge, Middlesex, UB10 0LZ Tel: (020) 8756 0999 Fax: (020) 8561 9774 *Bed retailers*

Moonlight Environmental Ltd, 48 Rommany Road, London, SE27 9PX Tel: (020) 8766 7587 Fax: (020) 8766 7587 E-mail: office@me-ltd.biz *Food safety consultancy services*

Moonlight Photographic Services, 80 Wollaston Way, Burnt Mills Industrial Estate, Basildon, Essex, SS13 1DJ Tel: (01268) 727789 Fax: (01268) 725777 E-mail: info@moonlight-uk.com *Exhibition display designers, producers & services*

Moon's Plant Hire, 3 Laureate Industrial Estate, Newmarket, Suffolk, CB8 0AP Tel: (01638) 662622 Fax: (01638) 660961 *Plant hire & civil engineering contracting*

Moons Of Selling 1982 Ltd, Grove Road, Sheldwich, Faversham, Kent, ME13 9RR Tel: (01227) 752217 Fax: (01227) 752217 *Agricultural contracting services*

▶ Moonshine Studio, 1 High Street, Penzance, Cornwall, TR18 2SX Tel: (01736) 330887 Fax: (01736) 330887 E-mail: info@frames.uk.com *Frames, picture mounts, custom mounts manufrs*

▶ Moor Insulation Ltd, Unit 29 Woodend Industrial Estate, Woodend Avenue, Speke, Liverpool, L24 9NB Tel: 0151-486 8272 Fax: 0151-486 8252 *Sheet metal installations services*

▶ Moor Leisure, Fingle Cottage, Moretonhampstead Road, Lustleigh, Newton Abbot, Devon, TQ13 9SN Tel: (01647) 277528 Fax: (01647) 277549 *Party equipment & hire services*

Moor 'N Dales, Chop Gate, Middlesbrough, Cleveland, TS9 7JB Tel: (01642) 778203 *Agricultural contractors*

Moor Park Homes Ltd, The Sawmills, Whitelees Road, Lanark, ML11 7RX Tel: (01555) 665087 Fax: (01555) 666244 E-mail: sales@moorparkhomes.co.uk *Timber frame house manufrs*

Bill Moore (Lifting Tackle) Ltd, 15 Woodlands Drive, Morecambe, Lancashire, LA3 1LZ Tel: (01524) 854692 Fax: (01524) 851566 E-mail: billmoreliftingtackleltd@gmail.com *Lifting gear hire, suppliers & repair*

Moore Bowman Services Ltd, 2 Glebe Road, Egham, Surrey, TW20 8BT Tel: (01784) 452387 Fax: (01784) 458500 *Plastics sheet welding equipment services*

Moore Bros Ltd, 12 Cashel Road, Birkenhead, Merseyside, CH41 1DY Tel: 0151-639 6252 Fax: 0151-639 6252 *Surgical footwear manufrs*

Moore Bros, Unit 19 Midland Oak Trading Estate, Marlissa Drive, Coventry, CV6 6HQ Tel: (024) 7668 2888 Fax: (024) 7668 0888 *General builders & architectural joinery*

Moore Bros, Finkle Street, Market Weighton, York, YO43 3JL Tel: (01430) 872521 *Agricultural engineers*

Moore Bros Surgical Ltd, Unit 8, The Headlands, Salisbury Road, Salisbury, SP5 3JJ Tel: (01725) 512551 Fax: (01725) 512699 E-mail: moore.bros@virgin.net *Surgical footwear manufrs*

Moore & Buckle Ltd, 3 Lancots Lane, St. Helens, Merseyside, WA9 3EX Tel: (01744) 733066 Fax: (01744) 451000 E-mail: info@mooreandbuckle.com *Flexible packaging & protective bags*

Chris Moore Transport Co. Ltd, Mill Court Barns, Binsted, Alton, Hampshire, GU34 4JF Tel: (01420) 23555 E-mail: chris_moore2000@hotmail.com *Civil engineering contractors*

Coleman Moore Partner Agency Network Ltd, 53A Main Road, Duston, Northampton, NN5 6JN Tel: (01604) 598989 Fax: (01604) 598979 E-mail: info@colemanmoore.com *Advertising, design & marketing consultants*

Moore Construction, 2 Longfield Road, Eglinton, Londonderry, BT47 3PY Tel: (028) 7181 0147 Fax: (028) 7181 1018 *Building contractors*

Moore David Photography, Missions House, Biddulph Common Road, Biddulph, Stoke-on-Trent, ST8 7SR Tel: (01782) 515588 E-mail: david@moorephoto.co.uk *Commercial & industrial photographers*

▶ Moore Electrical Services Ltd, Unit 1 Ryder Court, Corby, Northamptonshire, NN18 9NX Tel: (01536) 461616 Fax: (01536) 461010

Moore Eric T Books, 24 Bridge Street, Hitchin, Hertfordshire, SG5 2DF Tel: (01462) 450497 E-mail: booksales@erictmoore.co.uk *40th Anniversary 1965 - 2005**Secondhand, out-of-print & antiquarian books, maps & prints*

Moore Fans Ltd, 2-3 Claremont, Hastings, East Sussex, TN34 1HA Tel: (01424) 436815 Fax: (01424) 422789 E-mail: info@moorefans.com *Axial fan distributors & manufrs*

G.C. Moore (U.K.) Ltd, PO Box 6541, Burton-On-Trent, Staffordshire, DE13 8WY Tel: (01283) 712901 Fax: (01283) 716690 E-mail: grahamhughes@btconnect.com *Elastic tape manufrs*

Harold Moore & Son Ltd, 16 Rawson Spring Road, Sheffield, S6 1PD Tel: 0114-233 6161 Fax: 0114-232 6375 E-mail: admin@haroldmoorebaths.co.uk *Acrylic bath & shower tray manufrs*

Moore Industries Europe Inc, 1 Lloyds Court, Manor Royal, Crawley, West Sussex, RH10 9QU Tel: (01293) 514488 Fax: (01293) 536852 E-mail: sales@mooreind.com *Process control instrumentation manufrs*

John Moore Security Ltd, Glencoe House, 559 Anlaby Road, Hull, HU3 6HP Tel: (01482) 507507 Fax: (01482) 509109 E-mail: sallymoore@johnmooresecurity.co.uk *Security consultants*

Moore Large & Co. Ltd, Grampian Buildings, Sinfin Lane, Derby, DE24 9GL Tel: (01332) 274200 Fax: (01332) 270635 *Cycle & accessories importers*

Moore Machinery International Ltd, 68 Glover Street, Birmingham, B9 4EL Tel: (0845) 2307040 Fax: (0845) 2307050 E-mail: mooremac@globalnet.co.uk Principal Export Areas: Worldwide *Machine tools, used/secondhand; sheet metalworking machinery (used/secondhand); sheet metalworking machinery merchants or agents & machine tool merchants or agents*

▶ Moore & Mulheron Contracts Ltd, 36-38 Main Street, Stoneyburn, Bathgate, West Lothian, EH47 8AU Tel: (01501) 763099 Fax: (01501) 763150

Peter Moore, 20 Holland Close, Shorne, Gravesend, Kent, DA12 3EH Tel: (01474) 824177 Fax: (01474) 824177 *Noise & vibration specialists*

▶ Moore R D Ltd, Brunel Way, Stephenson Industrial Estate, Coalville, Leicestershire, LE67 3HF Tel: (01530) 510224 Fax: (01530) 836200 *Sheet metal work*

Moore Response Marketing, Studio 4, The Calls, Leeds, LS2 7EY Tel: 0113-222 3330 Fax: 0113-222 3331 *Direct mail production services*

Moore Scott & Co. Ltd, Knapp Lane, Cheltenham, Gloucestershire, GL50 3QJ Tel: (01242) 584400 Fax: (01242) 222388 E-mail: southern.sales@moorescott.co.uk *Brick & block factor*

Simon Moore Water Services, Unit 2, Poundbury West Industrial Estate, Dorchester, Dorset, DT1 2PG Tel: (01305) 251551 Fax: (01305) 257107 *Water engineers*

Moore & Sons Ltd, PO Box 407, Newcastle, Staffordshire, ST5 7EE Tel: (01782) 563470 Fax: (01782) 561796 *Clay sales*

Moore Stephens International Ltd, St Paul's, 8-12 Warwick Lane, London, EC4P 4BN Tel: (020) 7248 4499 Fax: (020) 7334 7976 E-mail: postmaster@moorestephens.com *Chartered accountants*

Moore & Tillyer Ltd, Metro House, Northgate, Chichester, West Sussex, PO19 1BE Tel: (01243) 784341 Fax: (01243) 785788 E-mail: enquiries@mooreandtillyer.co.uk *Printers*

▶ Moore Training Ltd, 17 Canterbury Close, Yate, Bristol, BS37 5TJ Tel: (01454) 321463 Fax: (0871) 6617479 E-mail: info@mooretraining.co.uk *Provider of all types of training from Operator to Instructor in Construction, Transport and Warehousing Industry*

Moore & Wright, Unit 15 Bordon Trading Estate, Old Station Way, Bordon, Hampshire, GU35 9HH Tel: 0114-225 0400 Fax: 0114-225 0410 E-mail: sales@moore-and-wright.com *Calibration laboratories, measuring equipment, precision tools & gauges*

▶ Mooreland Construction Ltd, Leabrook Road, Wednesbury, West Midlands, WS10 7LZ Tel: 0121-505 6248

Moorepine, 98 Moore St, Bootle, Merseyside, L20 4PL Tel: 0151-933 7141 *Pine furniture manufrs*

Moores Evic Glassworks Ltd, Evic Works, 143 Hersham Road, Walton-on-Thames, Surrey, KT12 1RR Tel: (01932) 222314 Fax: (01932) 243330 E-mail: sales@moores-glass.co.uk *Scientific & electronics glassware*

Moores Forklifts Ltd, Baythorne House, St. Luke's Square, London, E16 1HT Tel: (020) 7511 8696 Fax: (020) 7511 7636 *Retail & maintenance of forklifts*

Moores Furniture Group Ltd, Thorp Arch Estate, Thorp Arch, Wetherby, West Yorkshire, LS23 7DD Tel: (01937) 842394 Fax: (01937) 845396 *Kitchen bedroom & bathroom furniture manufrs*

Moores of London Ltd, Third Floor, Elizabeth House, 54-58 High Street, Edgware, Middlesex, HA8 7EJ Tel: (020) 8731 2120 Fax: (020) 8731 2121 E-mail: sales@mooreslondon.co.uk *Promotional & premium product designers*

▶ Mooreserve, 5 Castlecroft, Norton Canes, Cannock, Staffordshire, WS11 9WS Tel: (01543) 275300

Moorfield Associates, Moorfield, Plumley Moor Road, Plumley, Knutsford, Cheshire, WA16 9RS Tel: (01565) 722609 Fax: (01565) 722758 E-mail: sales@moorfield.co.uk *Distributors of scientific instruments*

Moorfield Control Systems Ltd, Unit 17/18 Ashbrooke Park, Parkside Lane, Leeds, LS11 5SF Tel: 0113-270 7177 Fax: 0113-270 0264 *Industrial motor control panel manufrs*

Moorfield Industries Ltd, Dover Mill, Chunal Lane, Glossop, Derbyshire, SK13 6LA Tel: (01457) 891520 Fax: (01457) 855157 E-mail: rodben@moorfieldin.co.uk *Car care products manufrs*

Moorfield Of Lancashire, Perseverence Mill, Olive Lane, Eccleshill, Darwen, Lancashire, BB3 3BA Tel: (01254) 704131 Fax: (01254) 704141 E-mail: donelana@aol.com *Dust sheets*

Moorgate Ltd, 2 Cedar Court, Taylor Business Park, Risley, Warrington, WA3 6BT Tel: (01925) 765432 Fax: (01925) 765422 E-mail: sales@moorgate.co.uk *Computer dealers, brokers, distributors & agents*

Moorgate Paper Co Ltd, Watercombe Lane, Lynx West Trading Estate, Yeovil, Somerset, BA20 2SU Tel: (01935) 426888 Fax: (01935) 847400 *Paper & board merchants*

Moorgate Precision Engineering, Polymer House, Admin Road, Knowsley Industrial Park, Liverpool, L33 7TZ Tel: 0151-548 7766 Fax: 0151-548 7788 E-mail: ian@moorgate-precison.com *Precision engineers*

▶ Moorhead Excavations, Westfield Court, Lower Wortley Road, Leeds, LS12 4PX Tel: 0113-279 6556 Fax: 0113-231 0096

▶ Moorhouse Construction Ltd, 111-113 Melton Road, Barrow Upon Soar, Loughborough, Leicestershire, LE12 8NT Tel: (01509) 620200 Fax: 01509 412612 E-mail: sales@moorhouse-construction.co.uk *Concrete foundations*Machine & Plant Bases*Concrete Paving*Building Contractors*Groundworks*Property Development*

Moorhouse Fasteners, 17 Malmesbury Road, Kingsditch Trading Estate, Cheltenham, Gloucestershire, GL51 9PL Tel: (01242) 690392 Fax: (01242) 690391 E-mail: peterhamer@hambury.fsnet.co.uk *Industrial fastener distributors & agents*

Moorhouse Group Limited, Barclay House, Pontygwindy Road, Caerphilly, Mid Glamorgan, CF83 2WJ Tel: (029) 2080 8949 E-mail: nmadhavan@moorhouseinsurance.co.uk *Commercial Insurance Brokers specialising in Liability Insurance, Commercial Vehicle & Fleet Insurance, Retail Insurance and Corporate Insurance for larger businesses. We also provide Personal Insurance to our existing customers.*

Moorhouse Software Services, Capital House, 45 The Broadway, West Ealing, London, W13 9BP Tel: (020) 8567 7817 Fax: (020) 8840 4153 *Computer value added resellers*

Moorings Knitwear, 11 Main Street, Largs, Ayrshire, KA30 8AA Tel: (01475) 686808 *Knitwear retailer*

Moorland Ltd, 1 Snells Wood Court, Cokes Lane, Amersham, Buckinghamshire, HP7 9QT Tel: (01494) 763965 Fax: (07890) 138190 E-mail: moorland.limited@btinternet.com *Water treatment services*

▶ Moorland Compound, 2 Power Wash Trading Estate, Tunstall Road, Knypersley, Stoke-on-Trent, ST8 7BE Tel: (01782) 515522 Fax: (01782) 515522 E-mail: miked@moorlandcompounds.co.uk *Fibreglass moulding manufrs*

Moorland Plastics Barnsley, Moorland Avenue, Barnsley, South Yorkshire, S70 6PQ Tel: (01226) 242753 Fax: (01226) 293401 E-mail: moorlandplastics@barnsley.gov.uk *Plastics injection mouldings manufrs*

▶ Moorland Tackle, 32a Russell Street, Leek, Staffordshire, ST13 5JF Tel: (01538) 372288

Moorland Woodturning Co. Ltd, Woodlands Mill, Luke Lane, Thongsbridge, Holmfirth, HD9 7TB Tel: (01484) 683126 *Wooden plugs for paper mills*

Moormead Leisure Ltd, Moormead House, Fosters Hill, Holwell, Sherborne, Dorset, DT9 5LQ Tel: (01963) 23622 Fax: (01963) 23622 *Swimming pools & spa's*

Moorside Marketing, 16 Moorside Drive, Drighlington, Bradford, West Yorkshire, BD11 1HD Tel: 0113-285 3102 Fax: 0113-285 3102 *Point of purchase product suppliers*

Moorside Pine, 3 Keighley Road, Steeton, Keighley, West Yorkshire, BD20 6RJ Tel: (01535) 656925 *Pine & oak furniture manufrs*

Moorside Wrought Iron, Piercy End, Kirkbymoorside, York, YO62 6DQ Tel: (01751) 432244 *Wrought iron*

▶ Moortown Construction, Clarall Cottage, Doncaster Road, Knottingley, West Yorkshire, WF11 8NY Tel: (01977) 676000 Fax: (01977) 679922

▶ Mops 'R' Us, 30 Princip Street, Birmingham, B4 6LE Tel: 0121-359 0629 Fax: 0121-359 3487 E-mail: sales@mopsrus.com *Suppliers of professional & commercial cleaning & polishing supplies*

Mor Brock Tool & Gauge Co., Maldon Road, Romford, RM7 0JB Tel: (01708) 706606 Fax: (01708) 740906 *Press tool manufrs*

▶ Andrew Moran & Son Ltd, Unit 6, Stuart Industrial Estate, Napier, Paisley, Renfrewshire, PA3 3AJ Tel: (01505) 382345 E-mail: sales@movewithmoran.com

Moran's, Retail Market, Bank Street, Warrington, WA1 2EN Tel: (01925) 576299

Moray Business & Computer Centre, 20 Commerce Street, Elgin, Morayshire, IV30 1BS Tel: (01343) 552000 Fax: (01343) 552020 E-mail: sales@moray-business.co.uk *Computer & office suppliers*

Moray Firth Blinds Ltd, 24-26 Millbank Road, Munlochy, Ross-Shire, IV8 8ND Tel: (01463) 811274 Fax: (01463) 811274 *Window blinds manufrs*

▶ Moray Glass & Glazing Co., Chanonry Road, Elgin, Morayshire, IV30 1XH Tel: (01343) 541023 Fax: (01343) 541137 *PVC windows manufrs*

▶ Moray I T Ltd, 10 Woodlands Crescent, Bishopmill, Elgin, Morayshire, IV30 4LY Tel: (01343) 551484

Moray Instruments, 1 Tyock Industrial Estate, Elgin, Morayshire, IV30 1XY Tel: (01343) 543747 Fax: (01343) 548390 *Radio sales, service & hire*

Moray Security, 7 Barwell Road, Forres, Morayshire, IV36 1FD Tel: (01309) 672117 E-mail: sales@moraysecurity.co.uk *Security alarms installers*

▶ Moray Stone Cutters, Ashgrove, Birnie, Elgin, Morayshire, IV30 8SW Tel: (01343) 860244 Fax: (01343) 860226

Moray Timber Ltd, 11 Perimeter Road, Elgin, Morayshire, IV30 6AF Tel: (01343) 545151 Fax: (01343) 549518 E-mail: roncameron@btconnect.com *Woodwork machinists & builders merchants*

▶ Morayvale Ltd, 9 Terrace Road, Greenock, Renfrewshire, PA15 1DJ Tel: (01475) 786655

Morco Fish Merchants, Cormorant House, 9 Raik Road, Aberdeen, AB11 5QL Tel: (01224) 594366 Fax: (01224) 588123 *Fish processing services*

Morco Products Ltd, Morco House, 59 Beverley Road, Hull, HU3 1XW Tel: (01482) 325456 Fax: (01482) 212869 *Caravan fitting distributors*

Morcon Foundations Ltd, 2 Duffield Road Industrial Estate, Duffield Road, Little Eaton, Derby, DE21 5DR Tel: (01332) 834055 Fax: (01332) 834101 E-mail: post@morcon.demon.co.uk *Pile driving & underpinning contractors*

▶ More Consultancy Group, Arena Business Centre 9 Nimrod Way, Ferndown Industrial Estat, Wimborne, Dorset, BH21 7SH Tel: (01202) 862555 Fax: (01202) 862666 E-mail: info@more-group.co.uk *Recruitment agency*

More Control (UK) Ltd, Control House, Mount Farm Industrial Estate, Clarke Road, Bletchley, Milton Keynes, MK1 1LG Tel: (01908) 364555 Fax: (01908) 364511 E-mail: more@more-control.com *Electrical distributors*

More Paid Ltd, North Wing Burlington House, Crosby Road North, Liverpool, L22 0LG Tel: 0151-949 0082 Fax: 0151-949 1027 *Processing payrolls*

▶ More Than Accounts Ltd, The Vision Centre, 5 Eastern Way, Bury St. Edmunds, Suffolk, IP32 7AB Tel: (01284) 704464 Fax: (01284) 701412 E-mail: info@morethanaccounts.co.uk *Chartered certified accountants*

▶ More Than Pine Ltd, 60-62 Friar Street, Reading, RG1 1DX Tel: 0118-951 0010 Fax: 0118-951 0038 E-mail: morethanpine@fsmail.net *Pine furniture & accessory manufrs*

▶ More than Words Media Ltd, 17 Greens Farm Lane, Billericay, Essex, CM11 2EZ Tel: (0783) 5001534 E-mail: info@morethanwordsmedia.com *Copywriting, marketing and public relations solutions for businesses across the world*

▶ Louis Moreau (The Quilters) Ltd, Unit 9G1 N17 Studios, 784/788 High Road, Tottenham, London, N17 0DA Tel: (020) 8808 1337 Fax: (020) 8365 0547 E-mail: moreau@smeuk.com *Quilters & bedspread manufrs*

Morecambe Metals Ltd, Northgate, White Lund Industrial Estate, Morecambe, Lancashire, LA3 3AZ Tel: (01524) 69191 Fax: (01524) 843987 E-mail: sales@morecambemetals.co.uk *Scrap metal merchants*

Morecheck Ltd, Unit 449, Walton Summit Centre, Bamber Bridge, Preston, PR5 8AU Tel: (01772) 629708 Fax: (01772) 629709 E-mail: sales@morecheck.com *Engineering pipework contractors & fabricators*

Morecroft Engineers Ltd, 14 Churchfield Road, Sudbury, Suffolk, CO10 2YA Tel: (01787) 374717 Fax: (01787) 881016 *Stainless steel manufrs*

Morelli Birmingham, 1 Stratford St North, Birmingham, B11 1BY Tel: 0121-772 7100 Fax: 0121-772 7713 E-mail: headoffice@morelli.co.uk *Automotive paint distribs* Also at: Branches throughout the U.K.

Morelli Central Ltd, 414 Stoney Stanton Road, Coventry, CV6 5DG Tel: (024) 7668 1143 Fax: (024) 7663 7464 E-mail: headoffice@morelli.co.uk *Body shop supply specialists*

Morelli Equipment Ltd, 1 City Road, Norwich, NR1 3AJ Tel: (01603) 760037 Fax: (01603) 760017 E-mail: headoffice@morelli.co.uk *Motor body refinishing products*

Morelli Group Ltd, Unit 2 Baird Road, Enfield, Middlesex, EN1 1SJ Tel: (07956) 385795 Fax: (020) 8351 5172 E-mail: headoffice@morelli.co.uk *Motor trade paint suppliers* Also at: Branches throughout the South East

Morells, 99 Mabgate, Leeds, LS9 7DR Tel: 0113-245 0371 Fax: (0845) 4501717 E-mail: leeds@morrells-woodfinishes.com *Wood finishes*

Morelock Signs Ltd, Morelock House, Strawberry Lane, Willenhall, West Midlands, WV13 3RS Tel: (01902) 605040 Fax: (01902) 637576 E-mail: mail@morelock.co.uk *Sign manufrs*

Morep Food Process Systems Ltd, 223a King Cross Road, Halifax, West Yorkshire, HX1 3JL Tel: (01422) 884761 Fax: (01422) 885140 E-mail: morepltd@aol.com *Food industry process machinery suppliers*

Moresecure Ltd, Haldane House, Halesfield 1, Telford, Shropshire, TF7 4EH Tel: (01952) 683900 Fax: (01952) 683982 E-mail: sales@moresecure.co.uk *Storage & handling equipment manufrs*

Moreton Alarm Supplies, Unit 1, Soveriegn Way, Maritime Business Park, Dock Road, Birkenhead, Merseyside, CH41 1DG Tel: 0151-630 0000 Fax: 0151-670 9888 E-mail: save@mas-uk.co.uk *Alarm & electrical suppliers*

Moreton Baker & Co. Ltd, March House, Keepers Gate, Sutton Coldfield, West Midlands, B74 2NL Tel: 0121-355 0049 Fax: 0121-355 0254 *Marketing consultants*

Moreton C Cullimore & Son Ltd, Fromebridge Lane, Whitminster, Gloucester, GL2 7PD Tel: (01452) 740436 Fax: (01452) 740866 *General haulage & aggregate sales*

Morework Fabrications, 4 Heath Road, Hounslow, TW3 2NH Tel: (020) 8577 5027 Fax: (020) 8572 5396 *Fence gate & barrier suppliers*

Moreys, Trafalgar Road, Newport, Isle of Wight, PO30 1RT Tel: (01983) 525111 Fax: (01983) 520815 *Timber frames & roof trusses distributors*

John Morfield Ltd, 10 Teal Court, Strathclyde Business Park, Bellshill, Lanarkshire, ML4 3NN Tel: (01698) 840888 Fax: (01698) 840234 *Filter distributors & agents*

John Morfield Ltd, Unit 98 Sadler Foster Way, Teeside Industrial Estate, Stockton-on-Tees, Cleveland, TS17 9JY Tel: (01642) 760555 Fax: (01642) 750391 E-mail: enquiries@johnmorfield.co.uk *Filter agents & distributors*

Morfitts Building Services, 16 St Michael's Lane, Leeds, LS6 3AJ Tel: 0113-275 8631 Fax: 0113-261 8701 E-mail: ajm@morfitts.co.uk *Heating, plumbing engineers & elect rical contractors* Also at: Harrogate & York

Morflin Precision Castings Ltd, 21 Northampton Street, Birmingham, B18 6DU Tel: 0121-233 9361 Fax: 0121-233 0713 E-mail: sales@morflin.com *Precious metal castings*

▶ Morgan, Vauxhall Industrial Estate, Ruabon, Wrexham, Clwyd, LL14 6HY Tel: (01978) 810456 Fax: (01978) 824303 E-mail: ruabon.sales@morganplc.com Principal Export Areas: Worldwide *Capacitors including fixed, ceramic, high power specialists*

Morgan Advanced Ceramics, Bewdley Road, Stourport-on-Severn, Worcestershire, DY13 8QR Tel: (01299) 827000 Fax: (01299) 827872 E-mail: webleads@morganadvancedceramics.com *Morgan Advanced Ceramics (MAC) has a comprehensive range of materials, from which its products are manufactured. Supplying to a variety of demanding markets, MAC has established an enviable reputation for providing value-added solutions through world-class ceramics and advanced materials research and development applied with innovative design.* Also at: Southampton

Morgan Advanced Materials & Technology, Unit 13, Madeley Road, North Moons Moat, Redditch, Worcestershire, B98 9NB Tel: (01527) 69205 Fax: (01527) 62195 *Ceramic machining & silicon carbide product manufrs*

Morgan Alarm Systems, 20 Fir Tree Close, Tamworth, Staffordshire, B79 8NL Tel: (07973) 238772 Fax: (01827) 54698 *Security systems installation*

Morgan Associates, Unit 15 Ilford Trading Estate, Paycocke Road, Basildon, Essex, SS14 3DR Tel: (01268) 288587 Fax: (01268) 288587 E-mail: info@ma4.co.uk *Exhibition lettering & display, general sign manufacturers*

Morgan Automation Ltd, Rake Heath House, Hill Brow, Liss, Hampshire, GU33 7NT Tel: (01730) 895900 Fax: (01730) 895922 E-mail: sales@morgan-automation.com *Electronic medical equipment manufrs*

Morgan Blacksmiths Ltd, Chase Forge, Upper Chase Road, Malvern, Worcestershire, WR14 2BT Tel: (01684) 573848 Fax: (01684) 573848 *Steel fabricators*

▶ Morgan Blair Ltd, 12 Abbey Park Place, Dunfermline, Fife, KY12 7PD Tel: (01383) 738088 Fax: (01383) 620120 E-mail: info@morganblair.co.uk

Morgan Bros, 95 Bethesda Road, Tumble, Llanelli, Dyfed, SA14 6LL Tel: (01269) 841576 Fax: (01269) 841576 *Bakery*

Morgan Bros, Colomendy, Church Stoke, Montgomery, Powys, SY15 6ST Tel: (01588) 620279 Fax: (01588) 620279 *Agricultural contractors*

Morgan Computer Co., 64-72 New Oxford Street, London, WC1A 1AX Tel: (020) 7255 2115 Fax: (020) 7436 6285 E-mail: info@morgancomputers.co.uk *Computer retailers*

Morgan Computer Co., 11-12 Gateway House, Piccadilly South, Manchester, M1 2GH Tel: 0161-237 1111 Fax: 0161-237 3146 E-mail: man@morgancomputers.co.uk *Computer brokers*

Morgan Cooper Ltd, Salmon Road, Great Yarmouth, Norfolk, NR30 3QS Tel: (01493) 843233 Fax: (01493) 844068 E-mail: info@morgan-cooper.co.uk *Profile cutting, fabrication & welding services*

The Morgan Crucible Co. P.L.C., Quadrant, 55-57 High Street, Windsor, Berkshire, SL4 1LP Tel: (01753) 837000 Fax: (01753) 850872 *Engineering company*

Morgan Engineering, The Workshop, Grange Farm, Whittington, King's Lynn, Norfolk, PE33 9TF Tel: (01366) 500947 Fax: (01366) 501554 *Outdoor pig equipment manufrs*

▶ Morgan Est plc, Morgan Estate House, Corporation Street, Rugby, Warwickshire, CV21 2DW Tel: (01788) 534500 Fax: (01788) 534579 E-mail: info@morganest.com *Tunnelling, civil engineering, water & utilities providers*

▶ Morgan Est Capital Projects, Harrier House, St. Albans Road East, Hatfield, Hertfordshire, AL10 0HE Tel: (01707) 272516 Fax: (01707) 272440 E-mail: sales@gleesonmcl.co.uk

Morgan Europe Ltd, Morgan House, Brompton Road, Sheffield, S9 2PA Tel: 0114-261 7177 Fax: 0114-261 7178 E-mail: lidgates@morganco.com *Rolling mill plant & equipment design engineers*

F.C. Morgan (Removals) Ltd, 30 Crosby Road North, Liverpool, L22 4QF Tel: 0151-928 3154 Fax: 0151-928 2848 *Removal & storage specialists*

Morgan Fire Protection Ltd, Hillgrove Business Park, Nazeing Road, Nazeing, Waltham Abbey, Essex, EN9 2HB Tel: (01992) 893498 Fax: (01992) 892098 *Fire protection services*

Morgan Fire Protection Ltd, Hillgrove Business Park, Nazeing Road, Nazeing, Waltham Abbey, Essex, EN9 2HB Tel: (01992) 893498 Fax: (01992) 892098 E-mail: info@totalprotectionservices.co.uk *Fire safety consultants*

▶ Morgan & Fone Ltd, Unit 1, Royston Road, Baldock, Hertfordshire, SG7 6PA Tel: (01462) 894455

Guy Morgan Design, 87 Maunsell Way, Wroughton, Swindon, SN4 9JF Tel: (01793) 814300 Fax: E-mail: guy@gmdesign.co.uk Principal Export Areas: Central/East Europe & West Europe *Exhibition stand fabricators & display hire services*

▶ Morgan Hamilton Chartered Certified Accountants, Sheridan House, 17 St Anns Road, Harrow, Middlesex, HA1 1JU Tel: (020) 8515 7970 Fax: (020) 8515 7979 E-mail: info@morganhamilton.com *Morgan Hamilton is a modern, forward thinking firm of Accountants, committed to providing clients with on-time, effective solutions to help their businesses move forward. Visit the firm"s website to learn more about what they can do for you.*

Morgan Lovell P.L.C., 16 Noel Street, London, W1F 8DA Tel: (020) 7734 4466 Fax: (020) 7734 2968 E-mail: info@morganlovell.co.uk *As the UK's leading office interior design, fit out and refurbishment specialist, Morgan Lovell can help you assess your needs, evaluate the right site, pinpoint the right style, then build it perfectly, down to the last detail. Our award-winning designers will make sure your office design is not only visually stunning, but will work in your day-to-day life too. Creating an office environment that will inspire your staff and impress your clients. Your dedicated project manager will manage every step of the office fit out or office relocation process on your behalf. You can be involved or removed as you like. Our Perfect Delivery? Pledge means you'll get exactly what you asked for. On time, on budget - guaranteed. And if you're looking for a more sustainable office design, you can benefit from our in-house LEED and BREEAM expertise.**Intrigued? Call us for an informal chat on 0800 028 0945*

Morgan & Marlow Ltd, 93 Buckingham Street, Birmingham, B19 3JB Tel: 0121-212 9755 Fax: 0121-212 9756 *Steel section manufrs*

Morgan Masonry Ltd, Marble Yard, Carnon Valley, Carnon Downs, Truro, Cornwall, TR3 6LG Tel: (01872) 870091 Fax: (01872) 870092 E-mail: enquiries@morganmasonry.co.uk *We are specialists in working all types of architectural natural stone. We also supply and fix marble fireplaces and granite countertops*

Morgan Materials Technology Ltd, Bewdley Road, Stourport-on-Severn, Worcestershire, DY13 8QR Tel: 01299 827557 Fax: 01299 827187 E-mail: mormetalloys@mormet.co.uk *Research & development in ceramics*

Morgan Motor Co. Ltd, Pickersleigh Road, Malvern, Worcestershire, WR14 2LL Tel: (01684) 573104 Fax: (01684) 892295 E-mail: sales@morgan-motor.co.uk *Motor car manufrs*

continued

Morgan & Power, 20 Hockley Street, Birmingham, B18 6BL Tel: 0121-693 5065 Fax: 0121-693 5065 E-mail: manddpower@btconnect.com *Jewellery repairers*

Morgan Rekofa Tinsley Division, 37 John Swains Way, Long Sutton, Spalding, Lincolnshire, PE12 9DQ Tel: (01406) 366400 Fax: (01406) 366626 E-mail: sales@morgan-rekofa.co.uk *Sliprings & cable drums design, supply & manufrs*

Morgan Rushworth Ltd, Bromley Street, Lye, Stourbridge, West Midlands, DY9 8HS Tel: (01384) 895491 Fax: (01384) 424448 E-mail: sales@morganrushworth.com *Sheet metal working machinery service & distribution*

▶ Morgan Signs, Fairoak House, Fairoak Road, Cardiff, CF24 4YA Tel: (029) 2023 2022 Fax: (029) 2023 2017 E-mail: ceri@morgan-signs.co.uk *Sign manufacturers & designers, digital prints*

Morgan Stanley Bank International Ltd, 25 Cabot Square, Canary Wharf, London, E14 4QA Tel: (020) 7425 8000 Fax: (020) 7425 8990 E-mail: info@morganstanley.com *Investment house*

Morgan & Co Strood Ltd, Knight Road, Rochester, Kent, ME2 2BA Tel: (01634) 290909 Fax: (01634) 290800 E-mail: info@morgantimber.co.uk *Timber merchants, importers & sawmillers*

Morgan (Timber & Boards), Park Lane Saw Mills, Kidderminster, Worcestershire, DY11 6TG Tel: (01562) 820620 *Timber importers & merchants* Also at: Burton & Coventry

▶ Morgan Utilities Ltd, Unit 14-17, Enterprise Centre, 1 Dryden Road, Loanhead, Midlothian, EH20 9LZ Tel: 0131-448 0900

▶ W B & A D Morgan Ltd, Presteigne Industrial Estate, Presteigne, Powys, LD8 2UF Tel: (0800) 5427613 Fax: (01544) 267981 E-mail: info@findingwater.co.uk *Drills bore holes*

Morgana Systems Ltd, Station Road, Ampthill, Bedford, MK45 2QY Tel: (01525) 403058 Fax: (01525) 404308 *Print finishing equipment manufrs* Also at: Milton Keynes

Morganite Crucible Ltd, Woodbury Lane, Norton, Worcester, WR5 2PU Tel: (01905) 728200 Fax: (01905) 767877 E-mail: marketing@morganitecrucible.com Principal Export Areas: Worldwide *Crucibles, foundry accessories & furnaces iservices* Also at: Wirral

Morganite Electrical Carbon Ltd, Upper Fforest Way, Swansea Enterprise Park, Swansea, SA6 8PP Tel: (01792) 763000 Fax: (01792) 763191 E-mail: sales@mecl.co.uk *Carbon products, components & brush manufrs*

Morganite Electro Carbon, Stanhope Street, Birmingham, B12 0UZ Tel: 0121-773 3738 Fax: 0121-771 4473 E-mail: sales@mecl.co.uk *Electrical carbon products distributors & manufrs*

Morgans, Mile End Business Park, Maesbury Road Industrial Estate, Oswestry, Shropshire, SY10 8NN Tel: (01691) 657700 Fax: (01691) 680681 E-mail: emailsales@morgans-machinery.co.uk *Agriculture machinery supplier*

Morgans, 102 Borstal Road, Rochester, Kent, ME1 3BD Tel: (01634) 370370 Fax: (01634) 370037 E-mail: sales@shopfitting.com *Shop fitters, designers & contractors*

Morgans Pomade Co. Ltd, Tyler Way, Swalecliffe, Whitstable, Kent, CT5 2RT Tel: (01227) 792761 Fax: (01227) 794463 E-mail: sales@morganspomade.co.uk *Hair preparation manufrs*

Morgans Products, 7 Myreside Drive, Inverkeilor, Arbroath, Angus, DD11 5PZ Tel: (01241) 830267 Fax: (01241) 830435 E-mail: dosher@inverkeilor.rapiddial.co.uk *Metering & chemical injection pump distributors*

Morgans UK Ltd, Roma Road, Birmingham, B11 2JH Tel: 0121-706 3216 Fax: 0121-765 4177 *Steel fabricators*

Morgantic Ltd, 71 Harehills Road, Harehills, Leeds, LS8 5HS Tel: (0845) 3000440 Fax: (0845) 3000441 *Fire protection engineers service*

Morglam Ltd, Burley Mills, 3 Navigation Street, Leicester, LE1 3UR Tel: 0116-299 2209 E-mail: alexmaher@morglam.com *Ladies & childrens clothing manufrs*

▶ Morgram Services Ltd, Staffordshire House, 28 New Road, Dudley, West Midlands, DY2 8TA Tel: (01384) 458880

Mori, 77-81 Borough Road, London, SE1 1FY Tel: (020) 7347 3000 Fax: (020) 7347 3800 E-mail: mori@mori.com *Market research analysis*

Mori Seiki (UK) Ltd, 4060 Lakeside, Solihull Parkway, Birmingham Business Park, Birmingham, B37 7YN Tel: (0870) 2409500 Fax: (0870) 2409539 *Machine tools*

Morison & Miller Engineering Ltd, 249 Glasgow Road, Rutherglen, Glasgow, G73 1SU Tel: 0141-647 0825 Fax: 0141-647 3133 E-mail: sales@morisonandmiller.co.uk *Suppliers of ventilation equipment*

Morite Winding Co. Ltd, Unit 10c Sand Road Industrial Estate, Great Gransden, Sandy, Bedfordshire, SG19 3AH Tel: (01767) 677811 Fax: (01767) 677812 E-mail: sales@morite.co.uk *Transformer & coil manufrs*

Moritex Europe Ltd, 14 Signet Court, Swann Road, Cambridge, CB5 8LA Tel: (01223) 301148 Fax: (01223) 301149 E-mail: moritex.europe@dial.pipex.com Principal Export Areas: Worldwide *Video inspection systems*

Morland, Cain Valley Trading Estate, Llanfyllin, Powys, SY22 5DD Tel: (01691) 648626 Fax: (01691) 648560 E-mail: toby.morris@morlandpanels.co.uk *Decorative laminated plastics & board panels*

▶ Morland Electrical Ltd, 134 Park View Road, Welling, Kent, DA16 1SJ Tel: (020) 8303 3083

Morland Jones Lotus Repairs, 226 Railway Arches, Trussley Road, London, W6 7PP Tel: (020) 8741 2303 Fax: (020) 8741 3116 E-mail: info@morlandjones.co.uk *Lotus vehicle repairers*

Morland Profiles Ltd, Henfaes Lane, Welshpool, Powys, SY21 7BE Tel: (01938) 554020 Fax: (01938) 554285 *Vinyl faced profile manufrs*

Morlands Glastonbury, 3 Creeches Lane, Walton, Street, Somerset, BA16 9RR Tel: (01458) 446969 Fax: (01458) 840108 E-mail: morlands@btinternet.com *Sheepskin manufrs*

▶ Morlands Lock Smiths, 581 Charminster Road, Bournemouth, BH8 9RQ Tel: (01202) 513787 Fax: (01202) 510500 E-mail: sales@morlands.demon.co.uk *Lock & key supplies. Also trade.*

Morley Bros, Yedingham, Malton, North Yorkshire, YO17 8SS Tel: (07855) 829094 Fax: (01944) 728280 *Sand & gravel quarrying*

The Morley Electrical Engineering Co. Ltd, Bradford Road, Stanningley, Pudsey, West Yorkshire, LS28 6QB Tel: 0113-257 1734 Fax: 0113-257 0751 E-mail: sales@morleymotors.com *Flameproof & AC electric motors. Also permanent magnet generators*

Morley Signs, Unit 5 Station Avenue, Bridlington, North Humberside, YO16 4LZ Tel: (01262) 678800 Fax: (01262) 678830 *Sign manufrs*

Morley Stoves Co Ltd, Marsh Lane, Ware, Hertfordshire, SG12 9QB Tel: (01920) 468001 Fax: (01920) 463893 E-mail: info@morley-stoves.co.uk *Multi-fuel burning stoves retailers*

Morley Upholstery Works Ltd, Troutbeck, 84-86 Albany Street, London, NW1 4EJ Tel: (020) 7387 3846 Fax: (020) 7388 0651 E-mail: sales@morleyupholstery.co.uk *Upholstery manufrs*

Morley Waste Traders Ltd, Treefield Industrial Estate, Gelderd Road, Gildersome, Morley, Leeds, LS27 7JU Tel: 0113-252 6699 Fax: 0113-253 1091 E-mail: kay@morleywastetraders.fsnet.co.uk *Ferrous metal recycle services* Also at: Castleford, Dewsbury & Morley

Morleys, 2 Waterworks Road, Eastbourne, East Sussex, BN22 8LR Tel: (01323) 725793 Fax: (01323) 734193 *Removal & storage*

Morleys Leisurewear Centres Ltd, 25 Hereward Cross, Peterborough, PE1 1TE Tel: (01733) 562834 *Outdoor wear retailers*

▶ Morlings Ltd, House of Music, 149 London Road North, Lowestoft, Suffolk, NR32 1NG Tel: (01502) 565491 Fax: 01502 530223 E-mail: sales@morlingsmusic.co.uk *Retail of Musical instruments and all related equipment.*Retail of Domestic Appliances*

Mormet Alloys Ltd, Tamworth Road, Two Gates, Tamworth, Staffordshire, B77 1EA Tel: (01827) 285555 Fax: (01827) 286286 E-mail: sales@mormet.co.uk *Scrap metal merchants*

▶ Mormet Fabrications Ltd, Unit 9-10 Hale Trading Estate, Lower Church Lane, Tipton, West Midlands, DY4 7PQ Tel: 0121-522 2522 Fax: 0121-522 2551 *Specialist in high temperature alloy fabricators*

Morning Foods Ltd, North Western Mills, Crewe, CW2 6HP Tel: (01270) 213261 Fax: (01270) 500291 E-mail: sales@morningfoods.com *Oatmeal manufacturers & cereal distributors* Also at: London SE1

Morpheus, 6-7 The Courtyard, Eastern Road, Bracknell, Berkshire, RG12 2XB Tel: (01344) 458188 Fax: (01344) 458189 E-mail: info@morpheus.co.uk *Internet solutions*

Morplan Shop Fittings Mnfrs, 56 Great Titchfield Street, London, W1W 7DF Tel: (020) 7636 1887 Fax: (020) 7637 9597 E-mail: enquiries@morplan.co.uk *Fashion & retail trade suppliers*

Morplate Ltd, Hammerton Street, Burnley, Lancashire, BB11 1LE Tel: (01282) 428571 Fax: (01282) 413600 *Paint spraying & vacuum coating services*

▶ Morrell Homefinders, 97 Birchwood Way, Park Street, St. Albans, Hertfordshire, AL2 2SF Tel: (01727) 874622 Fax: (01727) 874611 E-mail: info@morrellhomefinders.co.uk *Morrell Homefinders Ltd is an independent company finding homes for private and corporate clients wishing to purchse or rent in Hertfordshire and North West London. *Services range from Full Home Search, Area Information & Tour, Agent Registration and Coordinated Conveyancing. Bespoke packages are also available.**

Morrell Products Ltd, Halesfield 5, Telford, Shropshire, TF7 4QJ Tel: (01952) 587306 Fax: (01952) 582456 E-mail: enquiries@morrellproducts.com *Automotive vehicle insulation, interior trim & board components*

Morrells Wood Finishers Ltd, 99 Mabgate Street, Leeds, LS9 7DR Tel: 0113-245 0371 Fax: (0845) 4501717 E-mail: leeds@morrells-woodfinishers.com *Wood finishers & polishing materials*

▶ Morricom Ltd, Fiboard House, 5 Oakleigh Gardens, London, N20 9AB Tel: (020) 8343 8663

Morris, Maes Y Clawdd Industrial Estate, Maesbury Road, Oswestry, Shropshire, SY10 8NN Tel: (01691) 670666 Fax: (01691) 670760 E-mail: info@morriscontractcleaning.co.uk *Contract cleaning services*

Allan Morris Transport Ltd, Factory Road, Sandycroft, Deeside, Flintshire, CH5 2QJ Tel: (01244) 533320 Fax: (01244) 533766 E-mail: enq@allanmorris.co.uk *Road hauliers*

Morris Bros Ltd, Phoenix Works, 215 Scotia Road, Stoke-on-Trent, ST6 4HB Tel: (01782) 834242 Fax: (01782) 575686 E-mail: sales@morrisbrothers.com *Pneumatic control systems distributors*

Morris Bufton & Co., 6 Gravel Hill, Ludlow, Shropshire, SY8 1QL Tel: (01584) 872244 Fax: (01584) 873910 *Agricultural & horticultural engineers*

▶ Morris Builders Ltd, Unit 6 Bondor Business Centre, London Road, Baldock, Hertfordshire, SG7 6HP Tel: (01462) 895540 Fax: (01462) 490081

D. & H Morris Group Ltd, Cumbernold House, Cumbernold, Glasgow, G67 3JG Tel: (01236) 868000 Fax: (01236) 868111 *Industrial electrical engineers*

Morris Engineering Design, Service, 36 Craighall Road, Edinburgh, EH6 4SA Tel: 0131-551 3333 Fax: 0131-551 3030 E-mail: mes@gamorris.co.uk *Consulting engineers*

F.A. Morris (Sheffield) Ltd, 83 Headford Street, Sheffield, S3 7WA Tel: 0114-276 7327 Fax: 0114-275 3862 E-mail: sales@famorris.co.uk *Precision engineers & abrasive dresser cutter manufrs*

▶ The Morris Furniture Group, 24 Rosyth Road, Glasgow, G5 0YD Tel: 0141-420 7700 Fax: 0141-300 7240 E-mail: enquiries@morrisfurniture.co.uk *Furniture manufrs*

Morris Gordon Engineering, Unit 1 New Mill End Farm, Chiltern Green Rd, Luton, LU1 3TS Tel: (01582) 460002 Fax: (01582) 460038 E-mail: sales@morrisgordon.co.uk *Manufacturers of railings, stainless steel bands, high tensile steel strappings & municipal street furniture*

H. Morris & Co. Ltd, 24 Rosyth Road, Glasgow, G5 0YD Tel: 0141-300 7200 Fax: 0141-300 7240 *Domestic, office & metal furniture manufrs*

J.T. Morris & Co., Downing Street, Smethwick, West Midlands, B66 2QG Tel: 0121-558 9388 Fax: 0121-558 2487 *Metal spinners & general dust controllers*

Morris & Laken Signs Ltd, 14 Ravenswood Industrial Estate, Shernhall Street, London, E17 9HQ Tel: (020) 8521 1910 Fax: (020) 8509 3803 *Sign manufrs*

▶ Morris Leslie, Moorlands Lane, Saltash, Cornwall, PL12 4HJ Tel: (01752) 843291 Fax: (01752) 840400

▶ Morris Leslie Plymouth Ltd, 53 Valley Road, Plymouth, PL7 1RF Tel: (01752) 341200 Fax: (01752) 330065

▶ Morris Leslie South-East Ltd, Greenbays Park, Carthouse Lane, Woking, Surrey, GU21 4YP Tel: (01276) 856642 Fax: (01276) 859014 *Plant hirers*

▶ Morris Lubricants, Castle Foregate, Shrewsbury, SY1 2EL Tel: (01743) 232200 Fax: (01743) 353584 E-mail: info@morris-lubricants.co.uk *Oil blenders & manufrs*

Morris Material Handling, E1 Premier Business Centre, Speedfields Park, Fareham, Hampshire, PO14 1TY Tel: (01329) 825603 Fax: (01329) 825624 *Crane installers*

Morris Material Handling, 3 Lambhill Quadrant, Glasgow, G41 1SB Tel: 0141-429 4347 Fax: 0141-429 4347 *Crane repairers*

Morris Material Handling Ltd, PO Box 7, Loughborough, Leicestershire, LE11 1RL Tel: (01509) 643200 Fax: (01509) 610666 E-mail: info@morriscranes.co.uk *Leading UK Manufacturer of cranes and hoists and other materials handling equipment with a nation-wide network of support centres providing spare-part, installation, maintenance and inspection aftersales service support back-up. Morris is also offers a Material handling consultancy and design service.*

Morris Material Handling, Lodge Way, Thetford, Norfolk, IP24 1HE Tel: (01842) 750252 Fax: (01842) 750909 *Crane maintenance & reconstruction services*

Morris Metal Products Ltd, Unit N6 Troon Way Business Centre, Humberstone Lane, Leicester, LE4 9HA Tel: 0116-246 1787 Fax: 0116-246 0196 E-mail: morrismetals@yahoo.co.uk *Steel fabricators, wire workers & prototypes manufrs*

Morris Nicholson Cartwright Ltd, 161-163 Ashley Road, Hale, Altrincham, Cheshire, WA15 9SD Tel: 0161-928 9489 Fax: 0161-928 6091 E-mail: mail@mnc-advertising.co.uk *Advertising & marketing agents*

Morris & Nolan, 115-120 Stafford Street, Walsall, WS2 8DX Tel: (01922) 637673 Fax: (01922) 637345 E-mail: info@morrisandnolan.co.uk *Horse riding wear manufrs*

Morris Packaging Ltd, 3a Telford Road, Ferndown Industrial Estate, Wimborne, Dorset, BH21 7QN Tel: (01202) 892623 Fax: (01202) 894903 E-mail: sales@packaging-uk.co.uk *Packaging materials manufrs*

Morris Plastics Comallo Ltd, Unit B Spring Bank Industrial Estate, Watson Mill Lane, Sowerby Bridge, West Yorkshire, HX6 3BW Tel: (01422) 831821 Fax: (01422) 834182 *Injection mouldings manufrs*

Morris Polythene Greenhouses, 53a Lenagh Road, Omagh, County Tyrone, BT79 7RG Tel: (028) 8164 8205 E-mail: sales@morrispolytunnels.co.uk *Polythene greenhouse manufrs*

Morris Printing Co. Ltd, 57-61 Pitt Street, Norwich, NR3 1DE Tel: (01603) 629796 Fax: (01603) 626836 E-mail: admin@morrisprint.co.uk *Printing services*

▶ R.J. Morris Services, 19 Tenby Way, Eynesbury, St. Neots, Cambridgeshire, PE19 2UR Tel: (01480) 213964 Fax: (01480) 390729 E-mail: info@rjms.co.uk *Database consultant services*

Raymond Morris Group Ltd, Invision House, Wilbury Way, Hitchin, Hertfordshire, SG4 0TW Tel: (020) 7729 1234 Fax: (020) 7251 0965 E-mail: infodesk@rmonline.com *Information consultants & registration agents*

Morris & Rosam Group Mouldings, The Sanderson Centre, Lees Lane, Gosport, Hampshire, PO12 3UL Tel: (023) 9252 5448 Fax: (023) 9251 3999 E-mail: w1lfs@yahoo.com *GRP moulders manufrs*

Morris Singer Ltd, Unit 10 Highfield Industrial Estate, Church Lane, Lasham, Alton, Hampshire, GU34 5SQ Tel: (01256) 381033 Fax: (01256) 381565 E-mail: info@morrissinger.co.uk *Casting (non-ferrous metal) manufrs*

▶ Morris Young Group, Hillyland Farm, 57-61 Crieff Road, Perth, PH1 2NU Tel: (01738) 625246 Fax: (01738) 629327

The Morrisby Organisation Ltd, Focus 31 North, Cleveland Road, Hemel Hempstead, Hertfordshire, HP2 7EY Tel: (01442) 215521 Fax: (01442) 240531 E-mail: info@morrisby.co.uk *Test publishers*

Morrisflex Ltd, London Road, Braunston, Daventry, Northamptonshire, NN11 7HX Tel: (01788) 891777 Fax: (01788) 891629 E-mail: sales@morrisflex.co.uk *Tungsten carbide rotary burr manufrs*

Morrish & Partners Ltd, 8 Parkway, Welwyn Garden City, Hertfordshire, AL8 6HG Tel: (01707) 336017 E-mail: eng@morrish.co.uk *Consulting engineers*

▶ Morrish S F & Sons, Telford Road, Salisbury, SP2 7BU Tel: (01722) 336764 Fax: (01722) 414165

Morrison Adhesive Tapes Ltd, PO Box 2279, Glasgow, G33 9AE Tel: 0141-779 5648 E-mail: morrisontapes@tiscali.co.uk *Self adhesive tapes*

Morrison Bowmore Distillers Ltd, Bowmore Distilleries, School Street, Bowmore, Isle of Islay, PA43 7JS Tel: (01496) 810441 Fax: (01496) 810757 E-mail: emailinfo@morrisonbowmore.com *Malt whisky distillers* Also at: Glasgow

▶ Morrison Building & Development Ltd, Atholl House, 49 Melville Street, Edinburgh, EH3 7HL Tel: 0131-226 4666

▶ Morrison Construction, Macadam Place, Dryburgh Industrial Estate, Dundee, DD2 3QR Tel: (01382) 833600 Fax: (01382) 833400

Morrison Construction Ltd, 37 Harbour Road, Longman Industrial Estate, Inverness, IV1 1UA Tel: (01463) 221016 Fax: (01463) 242245 *Building contractors*

▶ Morrison Construction Ltd, Singleton House Charter Court, Phoenix Way, Swansea Enterprise Park, Swansea, SA7 9DD Tel: (01792) 781450 Fax: (01792) 781435

▶ Morrison Construction Ltd, Shandwick House, Chapel St, Tain, Ross-Shire, IV19 1JF Tel: (01862) 892202

Morrison Glass Fibre, Rose Hill Works, Rose Hill, Denton, Manchester, M34 3ZA Tel: 0161-336 0632 Fax: 0161-335 9852 *Glass fibre & architectural glass fibre mouldings manufrs*

Morrison Hydraulics Ltd, 331-337 Derby Road, Bootle, Merseyside, L20 8LQ Tel: 0151-933 0044 Fax: 0151-944 1302 E-mail: chemicals@morrisonsgrp.co.uk *Ceramic fibre manufrs*

▶ Morrison & Macdonald Holdings Ltd, 63 Murray Street, Paisley, Renfrewshire, PA3 1QW Tel: 0141-889 8787 Fax: 0141-889 9760 E-mail: almacdonald@btconnect.com *Pipe & section bending services*

D. Morrison Machine Services, 104 Station Road, Portstewart, County Londonderry, BT55 7PU Tel: (028) 7083 5444 Fax: (028) 7083 5444 *Machinery servicing contractors*

Morrison Mud Engng Services, Sandford Lane, Everdene House, Wareham, Dorset, BH20 4DY Tel: (01929) 551245 Fax: (01929) 554245 E-mail: enquiries@morrisonmud.co.uk *Special products and techniques for civil engineering, tunnelling, drilling, mining, HDD, waste/spoil conditioning, and brownfield remediation muck stiffening.*

Morrison & Murray Engineering Ltd, Roxburgh Street, Galashiels, Selkirkshire, TD1 1PB Tel: (01896) 753226 Fax: (01896) 752570 *General engineers*

▶ Morrison Sporrans, Ruthvenfield Way, Inveralmond Industrial Estate, Perth, PH1 3UF Tel: (01738) 630103 Fax: (01738) 63105

Steven Morrison Associates (Bromley) Ltd, 51 Tweedy Road, Bromley, BR1 3NH Tel: (020) 8466 0880 Fax: (020) 8466 7100 E-mail: steven.morrison@virgin.net *Lift & escalator consultants*

Morrow Bros Ltd, 433 Walton Summit Centre, Preston, PR5 8AU Tel: 01772 311882 *Barrel, cask & keg reconditioners*

Morrow Transport, 7 Sanda Road, Newtownabbey, County Antrim, BT37 9UB Tel: (028) 9085 1867 Fax: (028) 9036 5061 *Road transport, haulage & freight services*

Morsafe Supplies, 192 Monkmoor Road, Shrewsbury, SY2 5BH Tel: (01743) 356319 Fax: (01743) 350875 *First aid supply services, health & safety equipment*

▶ Morse Brown, 517 Hagley Road, Smethwick, West Midlands, B66 4AX Tel: 0121-429 7770 E-mail: mail@morsebrowndesign.co.uk *Fresh and original graphic design from versatile, hard working designers. At home with the large corporate stuff and the small and niche. Both get the same personal service. We also seek to work in a way that minimizes our impact on the environment. Green clean design.*

Guy Morse Brown, Mill Lane Farmhouse, Mill Lane, Wombourne, Wolverhampton, WV5 0LE Tel: (01902) 893683 Fax: (01902) 893683 E-mail: mail@hatblocks.co.uk *Manufacturer of hat blocks*

Morse Systems Engineering, Unit 3, Wotton Road, Ashford, Kent, TN23 6LL Tel: (01233) 633800 Fax: (01233) 635500 E-mail: enquiries@morsesystems.co.uk *General engineers & engineering machinists*

Morse Welding Supplies Ltd, Watercombe Lane, Lynx West Trading Estate, Yeovil, Somerset, BA20 2SU Tel: (01935) 426390 Fax: (01935) 420451 E-mail: info@morsewelding.com *Welding engineering equipment sales*

Morses Club Ltd, 1 Watery Lane, St. Johns, Worcester, WR2 5UA Tel: (01905) 425051 Fax: (01905) 615443 *Mail order catalogue & financial consultants*

Morson Projects Ltd, 37 Liverpool Road, Irlam, Manchester, M44 6TB Tel: 0161-777 4000 Fax: 0161-777 4001 E-mail: enquiries@morson-projects.co.uk *Aeronautical designers*

Morson Projects Ltd, Unit 8, Furnace Lane, Moira, Swadlincote, Derbyshire, DE12 6AT Tel: (01283) 211711 Fax: (01283) 226868 E-mail: enquiries@mavitta.com *Engineering design consultants & special purpose machine manufrs*

Morspan Ltd, Woodside Industrial Estate, Usk, Gwent, NP15 1SS Tel: (01291) 672334 Fax: (01291) 673928 E-mail: richard@morspan.co.uk *Agricultural engineers*

▶ Mortgage Advice Co., 111 Union Street, Glasgow, G1 3TA Tel: 0141-204 5770 Fax: 0141-221 4055 E-mail: sales@mortgageadvicecompany.co.uk *United Kingdom Mortgage Broker Offering A Fresh Approach To Advice. No Broker Fee, Search And Apply Fully Online. Access To All UK Mortgage Products.*

▶ Mortgage Port Ltd, 6 St John's Hill, Shrewsbury, SY1 1JD Tel: (0870) 9509600 E-mail: oneport@shawsolutions.co.uk *One Port Ltd for client care and administration for independent financial advise brought to you through Andrew Mason & Company, Reece Norton & Company, AMA Insurance Services, Wealth Port Ltd, Mortgage Port Ltd, Online Conveyancing, Clear Financial Planning, Wills & Trusts, covering Shrewsbury, Shropshire, Mid-wales, Staffordshire, Cheshire and the West Midlands*

Mortgage Shop Ltd, King Georges Chambers, 1 St. James Square, Bacup, Lancashire, OL13 9AA Tel: (01706) 875746 Fax: (01706) 875122 E-mail: mortgageshopltd@btconnect.com *Independent financial advice & mortgage specialist*

▶ Mortgage Simplicity, Inglewood House, Inglewood, Alloa, Clackmannanshire, FK10 2HU Tel: (0845) 8381502 E-mail: info@mortgagesimplicity.co.uk *WE offer whole of market mortgage and insurance advice. We do not charge a broker fee and are open 7 days 9am to 8pm*

D.G. Mortimer & Co. Ltd, Hilton Road, Cobbs Wood Industrial Estate, Ashford, Kent, TN23 1EW Tel: (01233) 621601 Fax: (01233) 622169 E-mail: user@plasticomgroup.com *Plastics mould & tool manufrs*

Mortimer & Spake Engineering, Unit 7-8 Spitfire Quay, Hazel Road, Southampton, SO19 7GB Tel: (023) 8043 6643 Fax: (023) 8044 8800 *Precision engineers*

Mortimer Springs Ltd, Coleman Works, Villiers Road, London, NW2 5PU Tel: (020) 8459 1420 Fax: (020) 8451 7614 E-mail: sales@mortimersprings.com *Mortimer Springs Ltd, London has supplied wire and strip components from London to customers in the UK and abroad. Because we are BS EN ISO 9002 approved, we operate strict quality control, and can supply certification to suit your purpose - this enables us to supply Government departments and some of the largest companies in the country. *We use a large variety of ferrous and non ferrous materials, and together with excellent plating and heat treatment facilities, we can manufacture exactly what you specify. Mortimer Springs are large enough to provide all you need, and pride ourselves on being able to supply an individual service to all your requirements. * Compression Springs, Tension Springs, Torsion Springs, Wireforms, Multislide & Presswork, Split Rings, Dog Clips, Split Pins, Shim & Belleville Washers, Assemblies, Die Springs, Garter Springs, Clock Springs, Volute Springs and Stock of all types of wire and strip*

▶ Mortimers Transport, Unit A Chiltern Park Industrial Estate, Boscombe Road, Dunstable, Bedfordshire, LU5 4LT Tel: (01582) 471155 Fax: (01582) 471511

▶ Mortimers Yeovil Ltd, 2 Lynx Trading Estate, Yeovil, Somerset, BA20 2PJ Tel: (01935) 421342 Fax: (01935) 421342 *Bakery*

Mortimore Manufacturing Ltd, Burley Road, Cottesmore, Oakham, Leicestershire, LE15 7BN Tel: (01572) 813202 Fax: (01572) 813201 E-mail: mortimores@webleister.co.uk *Manufacturers of construction & landscape machinery*

Morton & Bone Services, PO Box 1, Gairloch, Ross-Shire, IV21 2AY Tel: (01445) 712322 Fax: (01445) 712310 E-mail: stopsurge@aol.com *Surge hydraulic arrester equipment & hydraulic accumulator manufrs*

Morton Contracts Ltd, The Dial House, Holly Bush Hill, Great Bentley, Colchester, CO7 8RN Tel: (01255) 820333 *Landscape gardening services*

Morton & Crowder Ltd, 14 Fortnum Close, Birmingham, B33 0JX Tel: 0121-783 7571 Fax: 0121-783 1327 E-mail: morcro@aol.com Principal Export Areas: Worldwide *Manufacturers of fasteners*

▶ Morton Fairview Electrical Services Ltd, 349 London Road, Mitcham, Surrey, CR4 4SA Tel: (020) 8646 3989 Fax: (020) 8648 1705

▶ Morton Garden Furniture, Kestrel Court, 37 Waterwells Drive, Waterwells Business Park, Quedgeley, Gloucester, GL2 2AT Tel: (01452) 371669 Fax: (0870) 4863818 E-mail: sales@mortonproducts.co.uk *Fine teak garden furniture*

Morton Industrial Plastics Ltd, Cook Lane, Heckmondwike, West Yorkshire, WF16 9JG Tel: (01924) 405550 Fax: (01924) 405770 E-mail: info@mipuk.com *Plastic fabricators & engineering services*

Morton Machine Co. Ltd, Atlantic Works, Newhouse Industrial Estate, Motherwell, Lanarkshire, ML1 5SW Tel: (01698) 732021 Fax: (01698) 732546 E-mail: info@morton-machines.co.uk *Industrial mixer manufrs*

Morton Medical Ltd, Unit 3 College Farm Buildings, Tetbury Road, Cirencester, Gloucestershire, GL7 6PY Tel: (01285) 655210 Fax: (0845) 8693116 E-mail: sales@mortonmedical.co.uk *Medical supplies*

R.H. Morton & Co. Ltd, 22 Crownpoint Road, Glasgow, G40 2BS Tel: 0141 5518136 *Catering equipment manufrs*

Morton Young & Borland Ltd, Stoneygate Road, Newmilns, Ayrshire, KA16 9AL Tel: (01560) 321210 Fax: (01560) 323153 E-mail: info@myb-ltd.com *Lace, madras & wide width manufrs*

▶ Morton's Ltd, Kenyons Lane, Lydiate, Liverpool, L31 0BP Tel: 0151-526 1046 Fax: 0151-520 1570

Mortons of Horncastle Ltd, Morton Way, Boston Road, Horncastle, Lincolnshire, LN9 6JR Tel: (01507) 523456 Fax: (01507) 527840 E-mail: admin@mortons.co.uk *Printers & publishers of newspapers & magazines*

▶ Morven Construction Ltd, The Hedges, Camlon, Falkirk, FK1 4DZ Tel: (01324) 636165

Morwood Electrical Services Ltd, 27a Ullswater Road, Urmston, Manchester, M41 8SY Tel: 0161-613 8280 Fax: (07092) 391474 *Electrical contractors*

Mos Computers Ltd, Queen Square, Saltford, Bristol, BS31 3EL Tel: (01225) 873117 Fax: (01225) 873776 E-mail: info@moscomputers.co.uk *Computer systems & software developers*

▶ Mosaic Co., Mosaic House, Phoenix Park, Eaton Socon, St. Neots, Cambridgeshire, PE19 8EP Tel: (01480) 474714 Fax: (01480) 474715 E-mail: sales@mosaiccompany.co.uk *Mosaic Company, Jasba, Provence, Toscana, Vitrogres, Ceramic Mosaic Tiles, Swimming pool tiles, Glass tiles, Mosaic specialists, Marble mosaics, Mosaic tile supplier, swimming pool mosaics, bathroom tiles, kitchen tiles, Ceramic tiles*

Mosaic Arts, 18 Buckland Cresent, London, NW3 5DX Tel: (020) 7722 1505 Fax: (020) 7722 9674 *Tiling & mosaic design products*

Mosaic Missions, 217a Forest Rd, Walthamstow, London, E17 6HE Tel: 020 85232444 Fax: 020 85232475 *Computer training*

▶ Mosaic Parties for Children, 404 Richmond Road, Twickenham, TW1 2EB Tel: 020 8977 4526 E-mail: sarahj.perkins1@virgin.net *Fun and creative for age 5+. We''ll come to your home/ venue and bring a wonderful array of colour and gold veined mosaic tiles. Each child makes a mosaic coaster, photo frame or mirror and everyone takes their completed item home.*

▶ Mosaic Print Management Ltd, Yealmpton, Plymouth, PL8 2NN Tel: (01752) 881508

▶ Mosaic Shaping Disability Services, Richard Iii Road, Leicester, LE3 5QT Tel: 0116-251 5565 Fax: 0116-251 9969 E-mail: administration@mosaic1898.co.uk *Voluntary organisation*

▶ Moschatel Transfer Printers, Unit 1, Vale Road Indust Estate, Spilsby, Lincolnshire, PE23 5HF Tel: (01790) 754775 E-mail: sales@moschatel.co.uk

Moscow Narodny Bank Ltd, 81 King William Street, London, EC4N 7BG Tel: (020) 7623 2066 Fax: (020) 7283 4840 *Banking services*

Mosdorfer C C L Systems Ltd, Unit B6, Market Overton Industrial Estate, Thistleton Road, Market Overton, Oakham, Leicestershire, LE15 7PP Tel: (01572) 768381 Fax: (01572) 767531 E-mail: office@mosdorferccl.co.uk *Overhead line fittings importer, distributor & manufrs*

Moseley Bros Tools Ltd, Unit 5b Vaughan Trading Estate, Sedgley Road East, Tipton, West Midlands, DY4 7UJ Tel: 0121-520 6703 Fax: 0121-520 4118 E-mail: netadmin@moseleybrothers.co.uk *Press tool*

Moseley Distributors Ltd, Rydenmains Road, Glenmavis, Airdrie, Lanarkshire, ML6 0PP Tel: (01236) 750501 Fax: (01236) 750503 *Coach distributors*

Moseley Rubber Co. Ltd, Hoyle Street, Mancunian Way, Manchester, M12 6HL Tel: 0161-273 3341 Fax: 0161-274 3743 E-mail: info@moseleysrubber.com *Paper industry roller covering manufrs*

Moserve Auto Engineers, 9 Avon Industrial Estate, Butlers Leap, Rugby, Warwickshire, CV21 3UY Tel: (01788) 561099 Fax: (01788) 337099 *Vehicle repair contractors*

Mosgrove, Alan Ltd, Tranker Lane, Shireoaks, Worksop, Nottinghamshire, S81 8AQ Tel: (01909) 473250 Fax: (01909) 478877 *Steel fabricators*

▶ Mosiac Corp Ltd, 1 & 2 Bentley Court, Finedon Road Industrial Estate, Wellingborough, Northamptonshire, NN8 4BQ Tel: (01933) 229190

▶ Mosketo, 1 Webster Street, Preston, PR2 1BY Tel: (07723) 042246 E-mail: enquiries@mosketo.net *Mosketo is a web design agency, offering a range of tailored solutions including web design, web content management and Internet marketing*

▶ MosleyDonaldson, Chimneys, Stretton on Fosse, Moreton-in-Marsh, Gloucestershire, GL56 9QU Tel: (01452) 547879 E-mail: enquiries@mosleydonaldson.co.uk *Based in Gloucestershire, we are a small friendly company of designer makers specialising in high quality handmade wooden furniture.*

Moss, 92-94 King Street, London, W6 0QW Tel: (020) 8748 3884 Fax: (020) 8741 2470 E-mail: info@mosstimber.co.uk *Timber importers, machinists & merchants*

Adrian Moss Associates, PO Box 473, Chichester, West Sussex, PO18 8BT Tel: (01243) 574500 Fax: (01243) 528923 E-mail: adrian@business-initiatives.com *Representative for computer software companies*

▶ Moss Bank Styles, 841 Moss Bank Way, Bolton, BL1 5SN Tel: (01204) 844496 Fax: (01204) 460088 *Moveable wall partition installation services*

▶ Moss Builders, 5 Central Depot, Forward Drive, Harrow, Middlesex, HA3 8NT Tel: (020) 8909 9936

▶ Moss Builders Ltd, 126-128 Uxbridge Road, London, W13 8QS Tel: (020) 8840 8877 Fax: (020) 8840 8899

Moss David Boat Builders, Wyre Road, Skippool Creek, Thornton-Cleveleys, Lancashire, FY5 5LF Tel: (01253) 893830 Fax: (01253) 893830 E-mail: mr.davidmoss@virgin.net *Wooden boats repair services & manufrs*

Moss Hydraulics, Mount Pleasant Farm, Icknield Street, Kings Norton, Birmingham, B38 0EH Tel: (01564) 822254 Fax: (01564) 822254 E-mail: robinmoss@blackgraves.freeserve.co.uk *Hose hydraulic flexible assemblies*

Moss Joinery, 96 Leckhampton Road, Cheltenham, Gloucestershire, GL53 0BP Tel: (01242) 222622 Fax: (01242) 260265 E-mail: moss.cheltenham@kier.co.uk *Construction*

Moss Lighting Ltd, Unit 2a Bordesley Street, Birmingham, B5 5PG Tel: 0121-643 0529 Fax: 0121-633 4576 *Lamp shade manufrs*

Moss Lodge Fish Farm & Water Garden Centre, Moss Road, Moss, Doncaster, South Yorkshire, DN6 0HF Tel: (01302) 700959 Fax: (01302) 707171 *Aquarium & pond suppliers*

▶ Moss Metal Finishing Ltd, Unit 9-14 Brow Mills, Brighouse Road, Hipperholme, Halifax, West Yorkshire, HX3 8EF Tel: (01422) 203527 Fax: (01422) 205857 E-mail: graham@moss-metal-finishing.co.uk *Metal finishing services*

Moss Office Equipment Ltd, Unit 14 Beauchamp Industrial Park, Watling Street, Wilnecote, Tamworth, Staffordshire, B77 5BZ Tel: (01827) 289155 Fax: (01827) 251847 *Office equipment & stationery retailers*

Peter Moss Ltd, Unit 36 Greenfield Business Park, Bagillt Road, Greenfield, Holywell, Clwyd, CH8 7HJ Tel: (01352) 714361 Fax: (01352) 711946 E-mail: petermoss.ltd@ei.dosnet.co.uk *Vehicle chemical cleaning product distributors*

▶ Moss Products Plastics Ltd, Isle of Wight Lane, Kensworth, Dunstable, Bedfordshire, LU6 2PP Tel: (01582) 873366 Fax: (01582) 873399 E-mail: sales@mossproducts.co.uk *Plastic products manufrs*

Moss Products Plastics Ltd, Isle of Wight Lane, Kensworth, Dunstable, Bedfordshire, LU6 2PP Tel: (01582) 873366 Fax: (01582) 873399 E-mail: sales@mossproducts.co.uk *Manufacturers of plastic disposable products*

Moss Projects Ltd, Victoria House, 28-32 Desborough Street, High Wycombe, Buckinghamshire, HP11 2NF Tel: (01494) 535238 Fax: (01494) 535248 E-mail: info@moss.ltd.uk *Office re-fitting & dry lining services*

Moss Switchgear Services Ltd, Ashwood House, Aragon Road, Blackbushe Business Park, Yateley, Hampshire, GU46 6GA Tel: (01252) 876767 Fax: (01252) 877313 E-mail: info@moss-switchgear.co.uk *Switchboard maintenance services*

Moss Tyre, Cranswick Industrial Estate, Beverley Road, Cranswick, Driffield, North Humberside, YO25 9QE Tel: (01377) 270790 Fax: (01377) 240042 *Tyre services*

Moss Vernon Electroplating Ltd, Churchfields Works, Churchfields Road, Brighouse, West Yorkshire, HD6 1DH Tel: (01484) 710153 Fax: (01484) 720329 *Metal finishing & polishing services*

Mosses & Mitchell Ltd, Unit 5, Bath Road Business Centre, Devizes, Wiltshire, SN10 1XA Tel: (01380) 722993 Fax: (01380) 728422 E-mail: sales@mosses-mitchel.com *Broadcast & studio equipment suppliers*

Mossley, Unit 89 Earls Road, Grangemouth, Stirlingshire, FK3 8XE Tel: (01324) 474555 Fax: (01324) 474555 E-mail: mossleyautos@aol.com

Mossley Hill Building Service Ltd, Bridge Road, Mossley Hill, Liverpool, L18 5EG Tel: 0151-280 2868 Fax: 0151-280 2868 E-mail: mhbsltd@yahoo.co.uk

▶ Mossspace Landscape Design, 36a Bird in Bush Road, Peckham, London, SE15 6RW Tel: (020) 7639 2475 E-mail: sue@mossspace.co.uk *creative landscape design service.*

Mossteel Ltd, Unit 22 Central Industrial Estate, Cable Street, Wolverhampton, WV2 2RJ Tel: (01902) 351832 Fax: (01902) 351231 *Steel sheet shearers & stockholders*

Moston Janitorial Supplies Ltd, 270 Lightbowne Road, Manchester, M40 5HQ Tel: 0161-688 8282 Fax: 0161-684 8791 E-mail: sales@mostonjanitorial.co.uk *Janitorial equipment distributors*

Mostyn Maritime Services Ltd, Mostyn Docks Mostyn, Mostyn, Holywell, Clwyd, CH8 9HE Tel: (01745) 560335 Fax: (01745) 560324 E-mail: portofmostyn@aol.com *Shipping organisation*

Motan Ltd, Unit 10 Blacklands Way, Abingdon Business Park, Abingdon, Oxfordshire, OX14 1RD Tel: (01235) 550011 Fax: (01235) 550033 E-mail: sales.ltd@motan.com *Distributors of materials handling equipment*

Motaquip Ltd, Torrington Avenue, Torrington Avenue, Tile Hill, Coventry, CV4 9UX Tel: (024) 7688 3000 Fax: (024) 7647 3235 E-mail: customer.services@motamail.net *All makes car parts brand*

Motech Control Ltd, Unit 14, Lloyds Court, Manor Royal, Crawley, West Sussex, RH10 9QX Tel: (01293) 440710 Fax: (01293) 440711 E-mail: sales@motech.co.uk *Electrical drive manufrs*

Motech Garages, Delph Industrial Estate, Delph Road, Brierley Hill, West Midlands, DY5 2UA Tel: (01384) 75599 Fax: (01384) 262474 *Motor vehicle engineering services*

Motex Systems Ltd, The Motex Centre, Winterstoke Road, Weston-super-Mare, Avon, BS23 3YW Tel: (01934) 421100 Fax: (01934) 421101 *Insurance & software suppliers*

Mother Hubbard's, Old Church, Craigour Road, Torphins, Banchory, Kincardineshire, AB31 4HE Tel: (01339) 882756 Fax: (01339) 882797 E-mail: sales@motherhubbardspine.com *Pine & oak furniture suppliers*

Mothercare plc, 156-160 High Street, Bromley, BR1 1HE Tel: (020) 8460 6730 *Baby & nursery equipment suppliers*

Mothercare plc, 5 Underhill Walk, Burton-on-Trent, Staffordshire, DE14 1DE Tel: (01283) 567472 *Baby wear retailers*

Mothercare plc, 16 High Street, Falkirk, FK1 1EX Tel: (01324) 629722 *Childrens clothing retail*

Mothercare plc, 123 Sauchiehall Street, Glasgow, G2 3DD Tel: 0141-332 7072 Fax: 0141-332 9485 *Baby equipment*

Mothercare plc, Z10-Z11 Shopping Centre, Brent Cross, London, NW4 3FD Tel: (020) 8202 5377 Fax: (020) 8202 5467 *Children's wear & equipment manufrs*

Mothercare plc, 168 Commercial Street, Newport, Gwent, NP20 1JN Tel: (01633) 259938 *Retail mothercare*

Mothercare plc, Unit 13 White Rose Centre, High Street, Rhyl, Clwyd, LL18 1EW Tel: (01745) 343524 *Children's equipment suppliers*

Mothercare plc, Stadium Way, Retail World, Parkgate, Rotherham, South Yorkshire, S60 1TG Tel: (01709) 780111 *Child ware retailers*

Mothercare plc, Unit 27 The Charles Darwin Centre, Shrewsbury, SY1 1BW Tel: (01743) 272191 *Baby & nursery retailers*

Mothercare plc, 6-8 Guildhall Shopping Centre, Market Square, Stafford, ST16 2BB Tel: (01785) 242603 *Baby clothes & baby equipment suppliers*

Mothercare P.L.C., Cherry Tree Road, Watford, WD24 6SH Tel: (01923) 241000 Fax: (01923) 241000 *Retailers*

Mothercare plc, 24-25 The Sovereign Centre, High Street, Weston-super-Mare, Avon, BS23 1HL Tel: (01934) 626977 *Mother & baby retailers*

Mothercare U.K Ltd, 71 St Johns Road, London, SW11 1QX Tel: (020) 7228 0391 E-mail: info@mothercare.com *Baby equipment suppliers*

MotherHemp Ltd, Spring Dale Farm, Rudstom, Diffield, East Riding of Yorkshire, YO25 4DJ Tel: (01262) 421100 Fax: (020) 7691 7475 E-mail: contact@motherhemp.com *Hemp health & food suppliers*

Motherwell Bridge (Holdings) Ltd, PO Box 4, Motherwell, Lanarkshire, ML1 3NP Tel: (01698) 266111 Fax: (01698) 269774 E-mail: info@mbgroup.com *Engineers & fabricators*

Motherwell Control Systems Ltd, 1 St Michaels Road, St. Helens, Merseyside, WA9 4WZ Tel: (01744) 815211 Fax: (01744) 814497 E-mail: sales@motherwellcs.com *Manufacturers of liquid level gauges, flame arresters, tank gauging systems & safety or relief valve*

Motherwell Fork Truck Services, 141 North Orchard Street, Motherwell, Lanarkshire, ML1 3JL Tel: (01698) 265667 Fax: (01698) 254088 E-mail: mftservices@btconnect.com *Fork truck repairs*

▶ Motif Magic Ltd, 1 Davis Road, Brooklands, Weybridge, Surrey, KT13 0XH Tel: (01932) 830800 Fax: (0870) 7052851 E-mail: linda@motifmagic.co.uk *Machine embroidery*

▶ Motion Engineering Ltd, 38 Sandy Way, Amington Industrial Estate, Tamworth, Staffordshire, B77 4DS Tel: (01827) 66047

Motion Industries UK Ltd, Unit 2 Bracken Trade Park, Duners Lane, Bury, Lancashire, BL9 9QP Tel: 0161-705 1237 Fax: 0161-705 1239 E-mail: enquires@bearingsuppliers.co.uk *Bearing & power transmissions service*

Motion Media Technology Ltd, Motion Media Technology Centre, Severn Bridge, Aust, Bristol, BS35 4BL Tel: (01454) 635400 Fax: (01454) 635401 *Video telephone equipment manufrs*

Motiv Business Gifts, 28 Moor Lane, Loughborough, Leicestershire, LE11 1BA Tel: (01509) 262272 Fax: (01509) 267276 *10signers & producers of promotional/premium products, advertising gifts, business incentives & souvenirs. Also advertising calendar & diary designers, producers & advertising/promotional pen producers, printers & designers.*

Motivair Compressors Ltd, 9 Mount Road Industrial Estate, Mount Road, Feltham, Middlesex, TW13 6AR Tel: (020) 8744 8833 Fax: (020) 8744 8822 E-mail: international@motivair.co.uk *Air compressor distributors*

Motivair Compressors Ltd, Chase Link, Lichfield Road, Brownhills, Walsall, WS8 6JZ Tel: (01543) 454454 Fax: (01543) 454334 E-mail: brownhills@motivair.co.uk *Compressor spare parts/wearing parts distributors or agents*

Motivair Compressors Ltd, Brittania Road, Waltham Cross, Hertfordshire, EN8 7NU Tel: (01992) 704300 Fax: (01992) 704170 E-mail: enquiries@leachlewis.co.uk *Air compressors & paint finishing equipment sales*

Motivated Engineering Techniques Ltd, 141 Roseville, Tongue End, Spalding, Lincolnshire, PE11 3JJ Tel: (01775) 670361 Fax: (01775) 670371 *Foundry equipment manufrs*

▶ Motivating Moves, 3 Cotswold Gardens, Downswood, Maidstone, Kent, ME15 8TB Tel: (07968) 947999 Fax: (01622) 863199 E-mail: enquires@motivatingmoves.co.uk *Business & sales consultancy*

Motivity, Unit 21 Brook Industrial Estate, Bullsbrook Road, Hayes, Middlesex, UB4 0JZ Tel: (020) 8561 5566 Fax: (020) 8561 4499 E-mail: sales@motivityuk.com *Packaging services*

Motokov UK Ltd, Bergen Way, North Lynn Industrial Estate, King's Lynn, Norfolk, PE30 2JG Tel: (01553) 817700 Fax: (01553) 691201 *Importer tyres & tractors*

Motoman Robotics UK Ltd, Unit 2 Johnson Park, Wildmere Road, Banbury, Oxfordshire, OX16 3JU Tel: (01295) 272755 Fax: (01295) 267127 E-mail: derekpasquire@motoman.co.uk *Manufacturers of robots*

Motor & Armature Rewinds Ltd, 242 London Road, Westcliff-on-Sea, Essex, SS0 7JG Tel: (01702) 330756 E-mail: dnagy69@hotmail.com *Electro, mechanical engineers*

Motor Body Care (Northwich) Ltd, Denton Drive, Northwich, Cheshire, CW9 7LU Tel: (01606) 331438 Fax: (01606) 331440 *Accident repair centre*

Motor Cycle Clothing Centre, 36 Norwich Road, Wymondham, Norfolk, NR18 0NS Tel: (01953) 606922 Fax: (01953) 606922 E-mail: enquiries@motorcycle-clothing.co.uk *Motorcycle clothing & accessory suppliers*

Motor Drive Seats, Ebury Street, Radcliffe, Manchester, M26 4BL Tel: 0161-724 5176 Fax: 0161-725 9265 E-mail: sales@motordrive.com *Rally seat manufrs*

Motor Mode, The Art Works, 53 Butchers Lane, Mereworth, Maidstone, Kent, ME18 5QA Tel: (01622) 817400 Fax: (01732) 868167 E-mail: office@motormode.com *Vehicle graphics & signwriters*

Motor Parts Direct Ltd, Unit 4 The Cobden Centre, Hawksworth, Didcot, Oxfordshire, OX11 7HL Tel: (01235) 817890 Fax: (01235) 813897 *Car parts & components merchants*

Motor Sport (Glass) Ltd, 11 Claymore, Tame Valley Industrial Estate, Wilnecote, Tamworth, Staffordshire, B77 5DQ Tel: (01827) 283688 Fax: (01827) 283689 E-mail: sales@heatedwindscreen.com *Heated fine wire windscreens manufrs*

Motor Technology Ltd, Motec House, Chadkirk Business Park, Stockport, Cheshire, SK6 3NE Tel: 0161-217 7100 Fax: 0161-217 7101 E-mail: sales@motec.co.uk Sales Contact: A.L. Fallows Principal Export Areas: Worldwide *Based in Stockport, just south of Manchester, we cover the whole of the UK, Ireland and World Wide. We are an independent supplier of servo drives & motors and associated equipment, including: AC and DC brushless servo motors, DC permanent magnet servo motors, precision planetary and worm gearboxes, metal bellows couplings and torque limiters, analogue and digital servo amplifiers, incremental and absolute encoders, as well as motion controllers for a wide range of applications. These include positioning, winding, synchronising, cam control, cut-to-length, flying-shear and speed /torque control. We also specialise in finding replacement parts and also repairs. Motor Technology has been providing excellent sales and technical service for over 20 years.*

Motor Trade Selection, Parkway House, Sheen Lane, London, SW14 8LS Tel: (020) 8392 1818 Fax: (020) 8876 4631 E-mail: recruit@mtselect.co.uk *Management recruitment consultants*

Motor Transport, Quadrant House, The Quadrant, Sutton, Surrey, SM2 5AS Tel: (020) 8652 3500 *Motor Transport is the weekly business newspaper of the UK distribution & logistics industry*

▶ Motor Vehicle Dismantlers Association Of Great Britain, 33 Market Street, Lichfield, Staffordshire, WS13 6LA Tel: (01543) 254254 Fax: (01543) 254274 E-mail: enquires@mvda.org.uk *MVDA - The UK Trade Association for Motor Vehicle Dismantlers, car salvage and automotive recycling industry*

▶ Motor Wheel Service (Distribution) Ltd, 50 Leestone Road, Sharston Industrial Area, Manchester, M22 4RF Tel: 0161-908 1023 Fax: 0161-908 1024 E-mail: julie@mwsdistribution.co.uk *Distribution of Commercial wheels, alloys, fitted units*

▶ Moto-Racing, 11 Pinewood Road, Matlock, Derbyshire, DE4 3HN Tel: (01629) 581552 Fax: (01629) 584394 E-mail: info@moto-racing.co.uk *Performance motorcycle parts retailers*

▶ Motorola Ltd, Viables Industrial Estate, Jays Close, Basingstoke, Hampshire, RG22 4PD Tel: (01256) 358211 Fax: (01256) 469838 E-mail: sales@mot.com *Mobile phone distributions*

Motorola Ltd, Redwood, Crockford Lane, Basingstoke, Hampshire, RG24 8WQ Tel: (01256) 790790 Fax: (01256) 817481 *Cellular telephone manufrs*

Motorola Ltd, Viables Industrial Estate, Jays Close, Basingstoke, Hampshire, RG22 4PD Tel: (01256) 358211 Fax: (01256) 469838 E-mail: sales@mot.com *Radio paging communication system*

Motorola Computer Group, 1 Oakwood Drive, Loughborough, Leicestershire, LE11 3NE Tel: (01509) 634444 Fax: (01509) 634333 E-mail: info@uk.europe.mcd.mct.com *Embedded computing platform manufrs*

Motorsport Events Ltd, Gripwood Farm, Jones Hill, Bradford-on-Avon, Wiltshire, BA15 2EF Tel: (0870) 7872116 Fax: (0870) 7872116 E-mail: ed@motorsport-events.com *Track days, driving days out, activity gifts, corporate driving days & driver training*

Motortech Marine Engineering Ltd, 4-5 The Slipway, Marina Keep, Port Solent, Portsmouth, PO6 4TR Tel: (023) 9220 1171 Fax: (023) 9220 1172 E-mail: enquiries@motortechmarine.co.uk *Marine engineering*

Motortune, 41 Carrhill Road, Mossley, Ashton-under-Lyne, Lancashire, OL5 0SE Tel: (01457) 832798 Fax: (01457) 831500 *Vehicle servicing & fuel injection engineers*

▶ Motoscope Ltd, 4 Rushton Road, Wilbarston, Market Harborough, Leicestershire, LE16 8QL Tel: (01536) 772236 Fax: (01536) 772306

Motovario Ltd, Rushock Trading Estate, Rushock, Droitwich, Worcestershire, WR9 0NR Tel: (01299) 250859 Fax: (01299) 251493 E-mail: sales@motovario.co.uk *Power transmission engineers*

Motronic Services, Peachley Court, Peachley Lane, Lower Broadheath, Worcester, WR2 6QR Tel: (01905) 640025 Fax: (01905) 640415 *Direct mail services*

Mott Macdonald Ltd, Prince House, 49-51 Prince Street, Bristol, BS1 4PS Tel: 0117-906 9500 Fax: 0117-922 1924 *Engineering consultants, structural*

Mott MacDonald, 43 Lambourne Cres, Cardiff Business Pk, Llanishen, Cardiff, CF14 5GG Tel: (029) 2075 5755 Fax: (029) 2075 5756 E-mail: cardiff@mottmac.com *Consulting engineers*

Mott Macdonald Ltd, St Anne House, 20-26 Wellesley Road, Croydon, CR9 2UL Tel: (020) 8774 2000 Fax: (020) 8681 5706 E-mail: marketing@mottmac.com *Consulting engineers or designers, mechanical engineering design services & project management consultants/contractors/engineers* Also at: Branches throughout the U.K.

Mott Macdonald, 1 Atlantic Quay, Broomielaw, Glasgow, G2 8GB Tel: 0141-222 4500 Fax: 0141-221 2048 E-mail: marketing@mottmac.com *Civil engineers*

Mott Macdonald Ltd, Capital House, 48-52 Andover Road, Winchester, Hampshire, SO23 7BH Tel: (01962) 893100 Fax: (01962) 863224 E-mail: marketing@mottmac.com *Civil engineering/public works contractors*

Mott Macdonald Group, Spring Bank House, 33 Stamford Street, Altrincham, Cheshire, WA14 1ES Tel: 0161-926 4000 Fax: 0161-926 4100 E-mail: manchester@mottmac.com *Control system manufrs*

Mott Macdonald UK Ltd, St Annes Wharf, 112 Quayside, Newcastle upon Tyne, NE1 3DX Tel: 0191-261 0866 Fax: 0191-261 1100 E-mail: marketing@mottmac.com *Engineers, multi-disciplinary*

Mott Macdonald (Wales) Ltd, 11 Wynnstay Rd, Colwyn Bay, Clwyd, LL29 8NB Tel: (01492) 534601 Fax: (01492) 533063 E-mail: colwyn.bay@mottmac.com *Consulting engineers*

Mottram Industrial Plastics, 99a North Street, Cannock, Staffordshire, WS11 0AZ Tel: (01543) 573735 Fax: (01543) 574925 E-mail: andy@mottramindustrialplastics.co.uk *Chemical storage, plastic & glass fibre tanks*

Mouchel Parkman plc, West Hall, Parvis Road, West Byfleet, Surrey, KT14 6EZ Tel: (01932) 337000 Fax: (01932) 340673 E-mail: info@mouchelparkman.com *Engineers & environmental management consultants* Also at: Branches throughout the U.K.

▶ Mouchel Parkman (South East) Ltd, 1st And 3rd Floor, Kingswood House, 47-51 Sidcup Hill, Sidcup, Kent, DA14 6HJ Tel: (020) 8308 0300

Moughton Engineering Services, Units 12-13, Faraday Road, Great Yarmouth, Norfolk, NR31 0NF Tel: (01493) 650195 Fax: (01493) 650199 *Precision engineers*

Mould Import Solutions Ltd, Units A, Crewe Close, Blidworth Industrial Park, Blidworth, Mansfield, Nottinghamshire, NG21 0TA Tel: (01623) 490070 Fax: (01623) 795687 *Plastic injection moulding*

Mould & Tool Masters, Unit 7 Borough Close, Paignton, Devon, TQ4 7EP Tel: (01803) 527664 Fax: (01803) 663425 *Plastics mould toolmakers*

Mouldcraft Joinery Manufacturers, 5 Bridge Street, Kilrea, Coleraine, County Londonderry, BT51 5RR Tel: (028) 2954 0099 Fax: (028) 2954 0889 *Architectural mould manufrs*

Moulded Acrylic Products, 4 Brook Farm, Horsham Road, Cowfold, Horsham, West Sussex, RH13 8AH Tel: (01403) 865220 Fax: (01403) 865224 E-mail: sales@mouldedacrylic.co.uk *Plastics embedment manufrs*

Mouldex Automation Ltd, 6, William Lee Buildings, Nottingham Science & Technology Park, University Boulevard, Nottingham, NG7 2RQ Tel: (0845) 0453136 Fax: (07930) 361652 E-mail: michael.pickles@mouldexautomation.com *Electrical insulation protection suppliers*

Moulding Bros & Merry Leicester Ltd, 11 Hilltop Road, Hamilton, Leicester, LE5 1TT Tel: 0116-276 5112 Fax: 0116-276 6596 *Shoe finishing tools manufrs*

Moulding Contracts Ltd, Block 3 St. Cuthberts House, Durham Way North, Aycliffe Industrial Park, Newton Aycliffe, County Durham, DL5 6DN Tel: (01325) 311422 Fax: (01325) 310725 E-mail: south@mouldingcontracts.com *Earth works, construction & civil engineers*

Mouldline Ltd, The Old Granary, Station Road, Eccles, Norwich, NR16 2JG Tel: (01953) 887544 Fax: (01953) 887072 E-mail: enquiries@mouldline.com *Plastics mould & toolmakers*

Mouldrite Toolmakers, Unit 6 Varney Industrial Estate Spon La Trading Estate, Varney A, West Bromwich, West Midlands, B70 6AE Tel: 0121-553 2199 Fax: 0121-553 2213 E-mail: mouldritetools@btconnect.com *Tool manufrs*

▶ Moulds Builders Ltd, Stoner Hill Road, Froxfield, Petersfield, Hampshire, GU32 1DY Tel: (01730) 264129 Fax: (01730) 260817

Mouldtype Foundry, Leyland Lane, Leyland, PR25 1XB Tel: (01772) 425026 Fax: (01772) 425001 E-mail: mtf@leyprint.co.uk *Printing sundries suppliers*

Moulton College Stud FM, Pitsford Road, Moulton, Northampton, NN3 7QL Tel: (01604) 643811 Fax: (01604) 491127 E-mail: mancentre@moulton.ac.uk *Training services*

Moulton & Cooper, 15 Shaw Lane Industrial Estate, Ogden Road, Doncaster, South Yorkshire, DN2 4SE Tel: (01302) 320831 Fax: (01302) 320831 *Spark erosion specialists*

Moulton Developments Ltd, Holt Road, Bradford-on-Avon, Wiltshire, BA15 1AH Tel: (01225) 865895 Fax: (01225) 864742 E-mail: mail@alexmoulton.co.uk *Bicycles manufrs*

Moulton Engineering Ltd, Swepstone Road, Heather, Coalville, Leicestershire, LE67 2RE Tel: (01530) 262504 Fax: (01530) 260399 *Agricultural engineering services*

▶ Moulton Johnson, 23a High Road, Byfleet, West Byfleet, Surrey, KT14 7QH Tel: (01932) 336733 Fax: (01932) 336615 E-mail: graham@mjresults.com

Mounsey Engineering Ltd, Unit 11 North Weylands Industrial Estate, Molesey Road, Walton-on-Thames, Surrey, KT12 3PL Tel: (01932) 888555 Fax: (01932) 225388 E-mail: mounseyengineering@tiscali.co.uk *Precision manufacturing engineers*

Mount Caravans Ltd, Kingswood, London Apprentice, St. Austell, Cornwall, PL26 7AR Tel: (01726) 874100 Fax: (01726) 67448 E-mail: sales@mountcaravans.co.uk *Caravan maintenance & repair*

Mount Hope, Viewfield Industrial Estate, Glenrothes, Fife, KY6 2RG Tel: (01592) 772612 Fax: (01592) 610360 E-mail: ian.stirling@stowewoodward.com *Industrial roll manufrs*

Keith Mount Liming Ltd, Rougham Industrial Estate, Rougham, Bury St. Edmunds, Suffolk, IP30 9ND Tel: (01359) 271033 Fax: (01359) 271151 E-mail: keith@mountliming.co.uk *Lime & fertilizer suppliers*

Mount Pleasant Steel Fabrications, Milton Street, Crook, County Durham, DL15 9JJ Tel: (01388) 763595 Fax: (01388) 768719 *Steel fabricators*

▶ Mount Pleasant Windows, 13 Bartleet Road, Redditch, Worcestershire, B98 0DQ Tel: (01527) 510400 Fax: (01527) 526700 *Window & door installation & manufrs*

Mount Sion Joinery, 17 Avon Street, Tunbridge Wells, Kent, TN1 2JG Tel: (01892) 547316 Fax: (01892) 547316 *Joiners*

Mount Tai Foods, 38 Eastdown Park, London, SE13 5HS Tel: (020) 8318 3818 Fax: (020) 8463 0302 E-mail: sales@mounttaifoods.co.uk *Chinese food manufrs*

Mount Trading Co. Ltd, Glan Yr Afon Industrial Estate, Llanbadarn Fawr, Aberystwyth, Dyfed, SY23 3JQ Tel: (01970) 611919 Fax: (01970) 627062 *Fence distributors*

▶ Mountain, Summit House, Northfield Road, Quarrington, Sleaford, Lincolnshire, NG34 8RT Tel: (0800) 0266936 Fax: (01529) 413857 E-mail: sales@greenmountains.co.uk *Skip Hire & Recycling in Peterborough, Lincoln, Grantham, Spalding, Bourne, Newark, Stamford, Sleaford - from 4 yard to 40 yard - households to large scale industrial contracts.*

Mountain Fever, 25 Brunswick Street, Stoke-on-Trent, ST1 1DR Tel: (01782) 266137 Fax: (01782) 285541 E-mail: sales@mountainfever.co.uk *Climbing & ski equipment suppliers*

▶ Mountain Leap LLP, 1st Floor, 25 Eccleston Square, London, SW1V 1NS Tel: (020) 7931 0621 Fax: (020) 7931 0613 E-mail: adam.honey@mountainleap.com *Mountain Leap organises corporate events in the Alps including client entertaining, teambuilding, motivational and incentives.*

Mountain Man Supplies, 133 South Street, Perth, PH2 8PA Tel: (01738) 632368 Fax: (01738) 580284 E-mail: enquiries@mountainsupplies.co.uk *Outdoor clothing suppliers*

▶ Mountain Roofing, 4 Micklemoss Drive, Mountain, Queensbury, Bradford, West Yorkshire, BD13 1NF Tel: 07941 693963 E-mail: David158@btinternet.com *General Roofing contractors:- Slating, Felting, Guttering, Facias+Sofits, Pointing and all types of general building work. No job too big or too small.*

▶ Mountain Skip Hire, The Recycling Centre, Whitley Way, Northfields Industrial Estate, Market Deeping, Peterborough, PE6 8AR Tel: (0800) 0263699 Fax: (0845) 0908112 E-mail: sales@greenmountains.co.uk *Skip hire*

Mountain Software, Withambrook Park Industrial Estate, Grantham, Lincolnshire, NG31 9ST Tel: (01476) 573718 Fax: (01476) 590563 E-mail: info@mountainsoftware.co.uk *Computer systems consultants*

Mountain Trail, The Lynch Building, 49 High Street, Holywood, County Down, BT18 9AB Tel: (028) 9042 8529 *Camping equipment suppliers*

Mountain View Ltd, 18 Soho Square, London, W1D 3QL Tel: (020) 7025 8013 Fax: (020) 7025 8113 E-mail: georgia@mountainview.co.uk *Brand marketing consultants*

Mountain Warehouse Ltd, The Great Western Desnr Village, Kemble Drive, Cheney Manor Industrial Estate, Swindon, SN2 2DZ Tel: (01793) 538273 Fax: (01793) 538273 *Outdoor clothing*

▶ Mountain Warehouse Ltd, 35a Stonegate, York, YO1 8AW Tel: (01904) 658458 Fax: (01904) 658458 *Outdoor equipment suppliers*

Mountains Of Boston, Marsh Farm, Wythes Lane, Fishtoft, Boston, Lincolnshire, PE21 0RG Tel: (01205) 351054 Fax: (01205) 366004 *Agricultural contractors*

Mountcity Investments Ltd, Wellington House, Bean Road, Bilston, West Midlands, WV14 9EE Tel: (01902) 887644 Fax: (01902) 887638 E-mail: mountcity@mountcity.com *Industrial estate proprietors*

Mountelm Ltd, 8 Junction Street, Carlisle, CA2 5XH Tel: (01228) 523136 Fax: (01228) 530550 E-mail: m.liddle@btconnect.com *Steel stockholders, metal recycling & demolition*

Mountelm Ltd, Cannon House, Rutland Road, Sheffield, S3 8DP Tel: 0114-275 3030 Fax: 0114-272 8864 E-mail: info@wellsrichardson.co.uk *Demolition contractors*

Mountfold, Roberts Farm, Mount Bures, Bures, Suffolk, CO8 5AZ Tel: 01787229955 *Lightening arresters surge capacitors*

Mountjopy Water Supplies, Parkhurst, Boyton, Launceston, Cornwall, PL15 8NS Tel: (01566) 785733 Fax: (01566) 785733 *Water pumps suppliers*

▶ Mountjoy, Quarr Business Centre, Whitcombe Road, Newport, Isle of Wight, PO30 1YS Tel: (01983) 550250 Fax: (01983) 550280 E-mail: sales@mountjoy.com *Building maintenance, refurbishment & new construction works in southern england*

▶ Mountjoy, Unit C 4 Mountbatten Business Park, Jackson Close, Portsmouth, PO6 1US Tel: (023) 9237 0137 Fax: (023) 9237 0138 *Mountjoy is a leading building maintenance and refurbishment service provider in Southern England*

▶ Mountjoy, Quarr House, Collingwood Road, West Moors, Wimborne, Dorset, BH21 6QF Tel: (01202) 895099 Fax: (01202) 895202 *Mountjoy is a leading building maintenance & refurbishment service provider in Southern England.*

Mountney Ltd, Vandyke Road, Leighton Buzzard, Beds, LU7 3HH Tel: (01525) 383131 Fax: (01525) 370443 *Roof rack distributors*

Mounts Bay Engineering Ltd, North Pier, Newlyn, Penzance, Cornwall, TR18 5JB Tel: (01736) 363095 Fax: (01736) 332010 *Marine engineers*

Mountstar Cable, Hobson Industrial Estate, Hobson, Newcastle upon Tyne, NE16 6EA Tel: (01207) 270731 Fax: (01207) 271004 E-mail: sales@mountstar.com *Cable recycling & re-processing, non-ferrous scrap metal merchants*

Mountstar Metal Corporation Ltd, Buckland Road, Pen Mill Trading Estate, Yeovil, Somerset, BA21 5HA Tel: (01935) 423061 Fax: (01935) 432069 E-mail: yeovil@mountstar.com *Non-ferrous scrap metal merchants*

Mountview Services Ltd, 41 Killyleagh Road, Saintfield, Ballynahinch, County Down, BT24 7EH Tel: (028) 9751 1111 Fax: (028) 9751 1700 *Industrial cleaning machines sales*

Mountwest Petroleum Engineering Ltd, Sir William Smith Road, Kirkton Industrial Estate, Arbroath, Angus, DD11 3RD Tel: (01241) 870611 Fax: (01241) 878669 E-mail: linda@mountwest-petrol.com *Drilling equipment maintenance services* Also at: Aberdeen

▶ Mountwest Services, 1 Barratt Trading Estate, Denmore Road, Bridge of Don, Aberdeen, AB23 8JW Tel: (01224) 222111 Fax: (01224) 222112 E-mail: sales@mountwestservices.com

Mourne Observer Ltd, Castlewellan Road, Newcastle, County Down, BT33 0QU Tel: (028) 4372 2667 Fax: (028) 4372 4566 E-mail: mobserver@btinternet.com *Newspaper printers & publishers*

Mouse Sails, Porthdafarch, Holyhead, Gwynedd, LL65 2LP Tel: (01407) 763636 Fax: (01407) 763049 *Sails manufrs*

The Mousepad, Stockwell Head, Hinckley, Leicestershire, LE10 1RE Tel: (01455) 233893 Fax: (0870) 0567193 E-mail: derick@themouse.co.uk *Computer maintenance & sales services*

Mouth & Foot Painting Artists, 9 Inverness Place, London, W2 3JG Tel: (020) 7229 4491 Fax: (020) 7229 7052 *Greeting cards & calendar manufrs*

Movac Group Ltd, 135 Ditton Walk, Cambridge, CB5 8QB Tel: (01223) 240568 Fax: (01223) 412459 *Vehicle & refinishing factors*

Movac Group Ltd, 11 Portman Road, Ipswich, IP1 2BP Tel: (01473) 213763 Fax: (0870) 8358601 E-mail: info@movac.com *Paint distributors or factors*

Movac Group Ltd, Unit 8 Brookside, Sumpters Way, Temple Farm Industrial Estate, Southend-on-Sea, SS2 5RR Tel: (01702) 602020 Fax: (01702) 602080 *Motor factors & paint distributors*

Movac Romford Ltd, 21a Bates Road, Romford, RM3 0JH Tel: (01708) 374227 Fax: (01708) 386877 E-mail: info@movac.com *Motor factors*

Movawall Systems Ltd, 63 Barwell Business Park, Leatherhead Road, Chessington, Surrey, KT9 2NY Tel: (020) 8391 8790 Fax: (020) 8391 8791 *Mobile partition suppliers*

▶ Move It Man, 1 Cranage Road, Crewe, CW2 8NJ Tel: (01270) 650888 E-mail: admin@the-move-it-man.com *House clearance/removal.*

Move Man SKG, 123 Abbey Lane, Leicester, LE4 5QX Tel: 0116-266 5353 *Disabled access & loading bay equipment suppliers*

Moveable Feasts, 60 Albany Road, Broughty Ferry, Dundee, DD5 1NW Tel: (01382) 480811 *Mobile caterers*

▶ Movement2, Unit 9, The Oak Business Centre 79-93, Ratcliffe Road, Sileby, Loughborough, Leicestershire, LE12 7PU Tel: (0870) 0170203 Fax: (0870) 7059953 E-mail: sales@movement2.co.uk *Supply, hoists, slings, stair lifts wheelchair access for disabled*

▶ Paul Edmund Moverley Ltd, Unit 1 Links Estate, Surrey Close, Granby Industrial Estate, Weymouth, Dorset, DT4 9TY Tel: (01305) 761192 Fax: (01305) 767108 E-mail: paul@pmpe.wanadoo.co.uk *Precision engineering*

▶ Company Moves, 39 Invincible Road, Farnborough, Hampshire, GU14 7QU Tel: (01252) 549381 Fax: (01252) 376413 E-mail: comoves7@aol.com *Commercial removal contractors*

Moving Home Co. Ltd, Serin House, Hindsley Place, London, SE23 2NF Tel: (020) 8699 6766 Fax: (020) 8699 5067 E-mail: services@movinghomecompany.com *Removal contractors*

Moving Methods Ltd, Brooks Lane, Middlewich, Cheshire, CW10 0JH Tel: (01606) 833262 Fax: (01606) 832304 Principal Export Areas: Worldwide *Conveyor accessory & system component manufrs*

Moving Sound & Security, 151-153 Burnley Road, Accrington, Lancashire, BB5 6DH Tel: (01254) 393331 Fax: 01254 398539 E-mail: sales@movingsound-security.co.uk *Car radio alarm fitters*

Mowbray & Son Ltd, North End Business Park, Station Road, Swineshead, Boston, Lincolnshire, PE20 3PW Tel: (01205) 820284 Fax: (01205) 820976 E-mail: mowbrayltd@tiscali.co.uk *Building contractors*

Mowden Controls Ltd, Mount View, Standard Way Industrial Estate, Northallerton, North Yorkshire, DL6 2YD Tel: (01609) 779535 Fax: (01609) 779539 E-mail: enquiries@mowden.co.uk *Electronics design & manufacture services*

Mower Services, Croft Road, Crowborough, East Sussex, TN6 1HA Tel: (01892) 662960 Fax: (01892) 664987 E-mail: mowerservices@btconnect.com *Mower services & equipment*

▶ Mowlem P.L.C., Askern Road, Carcroft, Doncaster, South Yorkshire, DN6 8DH Tel: (01302) 330491

▶ Mowlem P.L.C., Tilbury Docks, Tilbury, Essex, RM18 7EF Tel: (01375) 850840 Fax: (01375) 856954

Mowlem Building, Pendennis Court, Salmouth Business Park, Bickland Water Road, Falmouth, Cornwall, TR11 4SY Tel: (0870) 7774468 Fax: (0870) 7774469 E-mail: buildingcornwall@mowlem.com *Construction* Also at: Exeter & Plymouth

Mowlem Engineering Solutions, Bewley Court, Bylands Way, Belasis Hall Technology Park, Billingham, Cleveland, TS23 4EB Tel: (01642) 371313 Fax: (01642) 373101 *Engineers design & management services*

John Mowlem & Co. P.L.C., White Lion Court, Swan Street, Isleworth, Middlesex, TW7 6RN Tel: (020) 8568 9111 *Construction*

John Mowlem & Co. P.L.C., Port Causeway, Bromborough, Wirral, Merseyside, CH62 3PS Tel: 0151-482 3500 Fax: 0151-482 3585 *Building & civil engineering services*

▶ Mowlem Skill Base, Stone Place, Mayfield, Dalkeith, Midlothian, EH22 5PE Tel: 0131-663 3386

▶ Mowlem Utilities Services Ltd, 10 Woodhall Millbrae, Juniper Green, Midlothian, EH14 5BH Tel: 0131-453 6000

Mowlem Water Engineering, Port Causeway, Bromborough, Wirral, Merseyside, CH62 4TP Tel: 0151-334 4990 Fax: 0151-334 9403 *Engineering consultants* Also at: Billingham

Mowtec Elastomeric Components Ltd, Units 28 & 29, Sketchley Lane Industrial Estate, Burbage, Hinckley, Leicestershire, LE10 3EF Tel: (01455) 251324 Fax: (01455) 610760 E-mail: terry.eyre1@btinternet.com *Rubber mouldings manufrs*

Moxhams Ltd, 56-56a Portswood Road, Southampton, SO17 2FW Tel: (023) 8055 6644 Fax: (023) 8067 1667 E-mail: john@moxhams.co.uk *Audio visual equipment distributor, repair & install*

Moxon, Yew Tree Mills, Holmbridge, Holmfirth, HD9 2NN Tel: (01484) 691500 Fax: (01484) 691505 E-mail: sales@moxon.co.uk *Fine worsted & mohair cloth manufrs*

Moy Antique Pine, 12 The Square, Moy, Dungannon, County Tyrone, BT71 7SG Tel: (028) 8778 9909 Fax: (028) 8778 4895 *Pine retailers*

Moy Park Ltd, Screevagh, Lisnaskea, Enniskillen, County Fermanagh, BT92 0FA Tel: (028) 6772 1999 Fax: (028) 6772 2442 E-mail: fernefoods@btinternet.com *Food products manufrs*

Moyer Manufacturing Co. Ltd, Vansittart Estate, Duke Street, Windsor, Berkshire, SL4 1SG Tel: (01753) 830088 Fax: (01753) 818793 E-mail: moyer@tcom.co.uk Principal Export Areas: Asia Pacific, Africa & North America *Manufacturers of gaskets*

▶ Moyne UK Ltd, Building, 202d Elgin CR, London Heathrow Airport, Hounslow, TW6 2LS Tel: (020) 8759 1663 Fax: (020) 8759 1664 E-mail: admin@moyneuk.com

▶ MPBA Ltd, PO Box 190, Burgess Hill, West Sussex, RH15 8WN Tel: (0870) 0800667 Fax: (0870) 4325211 E-mail: info@mpba.co.uk *Computer software development & consultancy*

MPC, 3-4 Lawrence Way, Camberley, Surrey, GU15 3DL Tel: (01276) 21320 Fax: (01276) 21328 E-mail: sales@mpc4u.com *Printing services*

MPD, Bitham Brook House, Gibbs Close, Westbury, Wiltshire, BA13 3DT Tel: (01373) 827111 Fax: (01373) 827222 E-mail: sales@ukmpd.com *Velcro distributors supply display systems*

Mpe Electronics Ltd, Brambleside, Bellbrook Industrial Estate, Uckfield, East Sussex, TN22 1QQ Tel: (01825) 764822 Fax: (01825) 765850 E-mail: k.chamberlain@mpe-electronics.co.uk *Electronic assembly contractors*

▶ MPF, The Slough, Studley, Warwickshire, B80 7EN Tel: (01527) 853840 Fax: (01527) 853843 E-mail: lee@mpfltd.co.uk *Contract Packing*Print Finishing*Direct Mail*Transport*Storage*

▶ MPS Support Services Ltd, Units 7-8 Red Bridge House, Lower Bristol Road, Bath, BA2 3EW Tel: (01225) 402310 Fax: (01225) 316152 E-mail: info@mpssupportservices.com *Contract cleaning and manned guarding for shopping centres and related premises in England and Wales*

MPTC Elektrotechnik Ltd, Unit 9, Nether Friarton Ind Units, Friarton Rd, Perth, PH2 8DF Tel: 01738 643433 Fax: 01738 643678 *Electric motor distributors*

▶ MQM, Unit 5 Ashville Way, Whetstone, Leicester, LE8 6NU Tel: 0116-275 1564 Fax: 0116-275 3723 E-mail: andrew@mqmfabrications.co.uk *Steel fabricators*

▶ Mr.Amin, 3 Galen Place, London, WC1A 2JR Tel: (020) 7240 6774 Fax: (020) 7419 4729 E-mail: sales@microglobe.co.uk *Digital cameras lenses & accessories, also telescopes etc manufrs*

Mr Bagels Factory, 52-54 White Post Lane, London, E9 5EN Tel: (020) 8533 7553 Fax: (020) 8533 9633 *Food manufrs*

Mr Bounce, Y-Jays, London Rd, Flimwell, Wadhurst, E. Sussex, TN5 7PL Tel: (01892) 540324 Fax: (01580) 879707 *Bouncy castle hire*

▶ Mr Cable.co.uk, 79, Waldeck Street, Reading, RG1 2RF Tel: 07910 491212 E-mail: info@mrcable.co.uk *Installer of cables for Networks and telephones*

Mr Computer, 145 Victoria Street, St. Albans, Hertfordshire, AL1 3TA Tel: (01727) 834904 Fax: (01727) 834652 E-mail: ajones@mrcomputer-shop.co.uk *Computer & peripherals retail sales*

Mr Crisp Ltd, 1 Decoy Road, Worthing, West Sussex, BN14 8ND Tel: (01903) 877422 Fax: (01903) 877422 *Soft drinks & snack foods wholesalers*

MR Dental Supplies Ltd, 4 Manor Way, Woking, Surrey, GU22 9JX Tel: (01483) 773282 Fax: (01483) 740548 E-mail: mrdental@virgin.net *Dental & medical products manufrs*

▶ Mr D's Couriers Ltd, Gothic House, Barker Gate, Nottingham, NG1 1JU Tel: (0870) 7506396 Fax: (0870) 7506397 E-mail: mrdscouriers@hotmail.com *Telephone 08707 506396. We are able to give you a prompt response and are offering a service to take those urgent sameday (24 hours a day 7 days a week) deliveries nationwide from small packages up to 1500kg.*

▶ Mr Electric South London, 87 Sandy Lane South, Wallington, Surrey, SM6 9RF Tel: (020) 8773 1792 Fax: (020) 8773 2109 E-mail: southlondon@mail.mrelectric.com *Electrical contractors*

Mr Exhaust Supercentres, 18 London Road, Reigate, Surrey, RH2 9HY Tel: (01737) 243900 Fax: (01737) 224705 *Vehcile exhaust systems manufrs*

▶ Mr Fixit 4u Surbiton, 12 Perak Court, Elmbridge Avenue, Surbiton, Surrey, KT5 9EU Tel: (020) 8241 9893 Fax: (020) 8241 9893 E-mail: help.surbiton@mr-fixit-4u.com *Computer repairs & maintenance*

▶ Mr H Carpets, 1 Bevois Hill, Southampton, SO14 0SJ Tel: (0800) 8087654 Fax: (023) 8022 6182 E-mail: info@mrhcarpets.co.uk *Specialist Reseller of best quality Carpets, vinyl and wood flooring.*

▶ MR HOT TUBS LIMITED, UNIT 4 SHAW WOOD, BUSINESS PARK, LEGER WAY, Doncaster, South Yorkshire, DN2 5TB Tel: 01302 343988 E-mail: sales@mrhottubs.co.uk *SALES SERVICE AND MAINTENANCE OF SWIMMING POOLS SPAS HOT TUBS SAUNAS GAZEBOS CHEMICALS TO THE PUBLIC OR TRADE.*

▶ Mr McMichael, 37 Widnes Road, Widnes, Cheshire, WA8 6AZ Tel: 0151-424 3000 Fax: 0151-220 4020 *Firework manufrs*

Mr Overalls, Silfield Road, Wymondham, Norfolk, NR18 9AU Tel: (01953) 607050 Fax: (01953) 603148 E-mail: sales@mroveralls.uk *Protective clothing & footwear distribs*

▶ Mr Plant Hire plc, 120 Hertford Road, Enfield, Middlesex, EN3 5AX Tel: (020) 8351 3434 Fax: (020) 8351 3636 E-mail: info@mrplanthire.co.uk *Plant and tool hire suppliers in Enfield, covering home counties and greater london.*

Mr Plant Hire plc, 120 Hertford Road, Enfield, Middlesex, EN3 5AX Tel: (020) 8351 3434 Fax: (020) 8351 3636 E-mail: info@mrplanthire.co.uk *Plant hire & access equipment suppliers*

▶ Mr Pole, Unit 9B 38-40 Upper Clapton, London, E5 8BQ Tel: (020) 7923 4441 Fax: (020) 7254 7117 E-mail: feathersdeluxe@yahoo.com *Cushion manufacturers & feather dealers*

Mr Signs, 7a Austin Fields, King's Lynn, Norfolk, PE30 1PH Tel: (01553) 761100 Fax: (01553) 773535 *Sign manufrs*

Mr Tyre Ltd, Fairfield Industrial Estate, Louth, Lincolnshire, LN11 0YF Tel: (01507) 602484 Fax: (01507) 606404 *Motor vehicle tyres & exhausts batteries*

Mr Tyre Ltd, 1 Burton Street, Peterborough, PE1 5HA Tel: (01733) 560484 Fax: (01733) 342613 *Tyre & service centre distributors*

▶ Mr V Brown, Staunton Harold Hall, Melbourne Road, Staunton Harold, Ashby-de-la-Zouch, Leicestershire, LE65 1RT Tel: (0870) 4604758 E-mail: valton@valton.freeserve.co.uk *Registered Chartered Building Consultancy.*Full member of the Chartered Institute of Building and the Brtish Institute of Architectural Technologists.**Affordable Plans for Property extensions, conversions, etc...**Submissions for Building Regulation and Planning approval.**Project Management.**Professional, friendly service tailored to suit client requirements.*

Mr Wasp, King George V Drive North, Cardiff, CF14 4EJ Tel: (029) 2075 4796 *Pest control*

M-Real (U K) Ltd, Kings Chase, 107 King St, Maidenhead, Berkshire, SL6 1DP Tel: (01628) 411611 Fax: (01628) 411666 *Paper & board mill agents* Also at: Manchester

MRF Design & Fabrications Ltd, Unit 2, Jubilee Trading Centre, 130 Pershore Street, Birmingham, B5 6ND Tel: 0121-622 4447 *Sheet metalwork engineers or fabricators*

MRFS Group, 8 Canbury Business Park, Elm Crescent, Kingston upon Thames, Surrey, KT2 6HJ Tel: (020) 8547 4333 Fax: (020) 8547 4334 *Security systems installers*

▶ Mrgardenfurniture.Com, 7 Alder Mill, Sheepy Road, Atherstone, Warwickshire, CV9 3AH Tel: (01827) 722320 Fax: (01675) 481572 E-mail: sales@mygardenfurniture.com

▶ MRI Catering, 45 Bishops Way, Andover, Hampshire, SP10 3EH Tel: (01264) 339006 Fax: (01264) 363487 E-mail: kieran@mricatering.co.uk *Mobile catering service*

MRI Polytech P.L.C., Nab Works, Long Lane, Pott Shrigley, Macclesfield, Cheshire, SK10 5SD Tel: (01625) 575737 Fax: (01625) 575720 E-mail: karen@mri-polytech.com *Poly binders manufrs heavy duty marine fenders*

▶ MRN Screen Process Ltd, Unit 10 Priory Tec Park Saxon Way, Priory Park, Hessle, North Humberside, HU13 9PB Tel: (01482) 627717 Fax: (01482) 627718

MRP Alarms, The Forge Haggs Farm, Haggs Road, Follifoot, Harrogate, North Yorkshire, HG3 1EQ Tel: (01423) 873900 Fax: (01423) 872494 E-mail: sales@mrpalarms.com *Security alarms installations services*

mrs c bowen, 80 Quarrysprings, Harlow, Essex, CM20 3HS Tel: 07916 226171 Fax: 01279 869605 E-mail: hotelbooked@yahoo.co.uk *Room Only accommodation in one of our apartments, £40 per night per person in Harlow Close to Stansted Airport.tel 07916 226171*Our Taxis available on 07916 245161 Fare £30 to accommodation one way from Stansted Airport*

▶ Mrs Distribution Ltd, 41 Inchmuir Road, Whitehill Industrial Estate, Bathgate, West Lothian, EH48 2EP Tel: (01506) 634634 Fax: (01506) 631159 E-mail: mail@mrsdistribution.co.uk

▶ Mrs S Weddings, Unit 26B, Ramsey Industrial Estate, 8-10 Glasgow Road, Kirkintilloch, Glasgow, G66 1FH Tel: (0845) 1659565 E-mail: info@mrssweddings.com *Wedding planner*

MRW Engineering Ltd, Unit 23a Hoo Farm Industrial Estate, Worcester Road, Kidderminster, Worcestershire, DY11 7RA Tel: (01562) 745042 Fax: (01562) 746472 E-mail: sales@mrwe.co.uk *CNC precision engineering*

▶ MS Consultants, Barton Close, South Woodham Ferrers, Chelmsford, CM3 5UB Tel: (01245) 429111 Fax: (01245) 429111

▶ Ms Furniture Ltd, 123 Kettlebrook Road, Tamworth, Staffordshire, B77 1AG Tel: (01827) 313231 Fax: (01827) 314929 E-mail: info@msfurnituresolutions.co.uk *Kitchen suppliers & manufrs*

MS Pollard Ltd, St. Saviours Rd, Leicester, LE5 4HP Tel: 0116-276 7534 Fax: 0116-274 1547 E-mail: finn@mspollard.com *MS Pollard are the sole UK distributors for the extensive range of Mori Seiki CNC Machine tools. Supplying and supporting Lathes, Vertical and Horizontal Machining centres, Tsugami-Mori sliding head lathes, Roku-Roku micro Fine Vertical Machining Centres and Taiyo Koki Vertical Grinding Centres, MS Pollard are able to supply a machine tool for most metal cutting applications. Highly experience in supplying Total Manufacturing Solutions to all manufacturing industries, MS Pollard's Engineering support realise the full manufacturing disciplines required by manufacturing industries, with the use of Catia V5 CAD/CAM for handling customers data strengthens our ability to completely integrate a full turnkey engineering solution.*

▶ Ms Solicitors, 9 Marlborough Place, Brighton, BN1 1UB Tel: (01273) 609944 Fax: (01273) 609944 E-mail: info@ms-solicitors.co.uk

Msa Focus International Ltd, Ground Floor Suite, St Hilary Court Copthorne Way, Cardiff, CF5 6ES Tel: (029) 2067 1760 Fax: (029) 2059 9733 E-mail: marketing@msafocus.com *Multi media broadcast solutions*

MSCM, Unit 8 First Avenue, Marlow, Buckinghamshire, SL7 1YA Tel: (01628) 488361 Fax: (01628) 478760 E-mail: sales@mscmltd.co.uk *Valves, subsea*

MSD, Unit 1 Red Barnes Way, Darlington, County Durham, DL1 2RR Tel: (01325) 340034 Fax: (01325) 382599 E-mail: hire@msdcranes.com *Crane hire & steel erection*

▶ MSF, M S F House, Charlwood Road, Lowfield Heath, Crawley, West Sussex, RH11 0PT Tel: (01293) 543333 Fax: (01293) 597590 E-mail: sales@msf-fire.co.uk *SUPPLY AND SERVICE FIRE ALARMS ,EMERGENCY LIGHTING AND FIRE EXTINGUISHERS*

MSH Chemical Manufacturing Ltd, Unit 2 Oak Lane, Kingswinford, West Midlands, DY6 7JD Tel: (01384) 402991 Fax: (01384) 402989 *Chemical manufrs*

MSH Electronics Ltd, Unit 1B, Stone Lane Industrial Estate, Wimborne, Dorset, BH21 1HB Tel: (01202) 881733 Fax: (01202) 881366 E-mail: sales@mshuk.com *Located in Wimborne (nr Poole) Dorset MSH Electronics Ltd are Contract Electronics Manufacturers (CEM). We have provided high quality and competitive Sub-Contract Electronics Manufacturing of: Cable and Wire Assemblies, PCB Assemblies, Control Panels, Module Assembly, Electronic Assembly Prototyping and Electromechanical assembly services to the Electronics Industry for over 25 years, working with many leading companies throughout the UK. Our customers serve the Defence, Communications, Automotive, Security, Oil and Business sectors. Our mission is to help provide you with a competitive advantage in your served market by providing high quality manufacturing solutions at a competitive price and to become an integral part of your supply chain.*

Msi Marketing Research, Viscount House, River Lane, Saltney, Chester, CH4 8RH Tel: (0800) 1956756 Fax: (0800) 1956757 E-mail: enquiries@msi-marketingresearch.co.uk *Market research publications & marketing consultants*

▶ MSK, Main Road, Unstone, Dronfield, Derbyshire, S18 4AB Tel: (01246) 413755 Fax: (01246) 410178 *Specialist food ingredients suppliers*

MSK Fabrication, Unit 4 Orchard Park Industrial Estate, Sandiacre, Nottingham, NG10 5BP Tel: 0115-949 1500 Fax: 0115-949 1600 E-mail: info@mskfab.co.uk *Control panel cabinet manufrs*

▶ MSL Roofing & Cladding, 26 Wargrave Road, Newton-le-Willows, Merseyside, WA12 9QZ Tel: (01925) 223666 Fax: (01925) 226662 E-mail: info@msl-nw.co.uk *Installations of commercial roofing & cladding*

MSM Water Services, Landing Lane, Haxby, York, YO32 2NB Tel: (01904) 766878 Fax: (01904) 766878 *Water services*

MSR Electronics Ltd, Fernhill Court, Balsall Street, Balsall Common, Coventry, CV7 7FR Tel: (01676) 532468 Fax: (01676) 534247 E-mail: sales@msravionics.com *Industrial designers, design consultants electronic equipment*

MSS, Taffs Fall Road, Treforest Industrial Estate, Pontypridd, Mid Glamorgan, CF37 5TT Tel: (01443) 849200 Fax: (01443) 843377 E-mail: info@medsys.co.uk *Mattresses & cushions medical equipment suppliers*

▶ MT Distribution, 4a Carron Place, Edinburgh, EH6 7RE Tel: 0131-555 4500 Fax: 0131-555 4789 *Computer accessories suppliers*

MTB Environmental Ltd, Dominion House, Copse Lane, Hamble, Southampton, SO31 4QB Tel: (023) 8045 8050 Fax: (023) 8045 7356 E-mail: mtb@mtbenv.demon.co.uk *Tank cleaning & liquid waste disposal*

▶ MTC Insulation Solutions Ltd, Royston House, 267 Cranmore Boulevard Shirley, Shirley, Solihull, West Midlands, B90 4QT Tel: (0845) 2300082 Fax: (01564) 820083 E-mail: info@mtcltd.co.uk *Cold room installation,Food Factory,Design,refurbishment*

MTC Northwest Ltd, Gores Road, Knowsley Industrial Park, Liverpool, L33 7XS Tel: 0151-545 4750 Fax: 0151-545 4760 E-mail: sales@mtc-northwest.co.uk *Motor vehicle engineering services*

MTC Software Ltd, 7 Clarendon Place, Leamington Spa, Warwickshire, CV32 5QL Tel: (0870) 8031297 Fax: (0870) 8031298 E-mail: mtc@mtc-europe.co.uk *Develop & market software*

MTC Tees, 4 Forest Industrial Park, Forest Road, Ilford, Essex, IG6 3HL Tel: (020) 8501 0922 Fax: (020) 8559 8230 *T-shirt & sweatshirt manufrs*

M-Tec, 3 Craven Court, Canada Road, Byfleet, West Byfleet, Surrey, KT14 7JL Tel: (01932) 354100 Fax: (01932) 340200 E-mail: m.tec@lineone.net *Aerospace engineering services*

▶ M-Tech Engineering, 1 Third Avenue, Greasley Street, Nottingham, NG6 8ND Tel: 0115-979 4448 Fax: 0115-979 4449 E-mail: matt@mtechengineering.co.uk *Architectural metalwork, steel fabricators*

▶ M-Tek Computer Services, Units 25-26, Holman Road, Caradon Business Centre, Liskeard, Cornwall, PL14 3UT Tel: (07918) 664540 Fax: (01579) 348094 E-mail: sales@mtek.co.uk *PC maintenance services*

▶ MTEK Technical Services Ltd, 97 Charlton Road, Keynsham, Bristol, BS31 2JW Tel: 0117 330 6880 Fax: 0117 330 6142 E-mail: info@mtek-ts.co.uk

Mti Ltd, 8 Paramount Industrial Estate, Sandown Road, Watford, WD24 7XA Tel: (01923) 249844 Fax: (01923) 228951 E-mail: mti@dial.pipex.com *Dip bath brazing manufacturing services*

MTM Engineering Services, Redfern Indust Estate, Dawson Street, Hyde, Cheshire, SK14 1QZ Tel: 0161-367 7650 Fax: 0161-367 7650 E-mail: carolynoldham@hotmail.co.uk *Engineering & plastic injection moulding services*

MTM Shelly Ltd, Suite 304, 27 Colmore Row, Birmingham, B3 2EW Tel: (0870) 486 3755 Fax: (0870) 486 3944 E-mail: sales@mtmshelly.co.uk *Commercial cleaning, domestic cleaning, office cleaning & contract cleaning services,dust removal, graffiti, end of tenancy, national health service, station cleaning, residential cleaning, office cleaning, hospital cleaning, bin cleaning, canteen cleaning, domestic cleaning, office cleaners,*

▶ Mtool Ltd, Unit1 & 2 Derker Street, Oldham, OL1 4BE Tel: 0161-626 5556 Fax: 0161-626 3061 E-mail: pr@mtooluk.com *Toolmakers, prototype tools, precision engineer*

MTS, Greenside Way, Middleton, Manchester, M24 1SW Tel: 0161-345 4760 Fax: 0161-345 4766 E-mail: sales@mtsprecision.co.uk *Precision engineers*

▶ MTS International, Daisyfield Street, Darwen, Lancashire, BB3 0AT Tel: (01254) 707621 Fax: (08707) 661463 *Medical equipment manufrs*

▶ MTS Investments Ltd, 40, Princess Street, Manchester, M1 6DE Tel: 0161-234 0110 Fax: 0161-234 0001 E-mail: info@mtsinvestments.com *MTS Investments develop and sell custom properties and apartments in Bulgaria. MTS are specialist letting agents for properties in Bulgaria.*

▶ MTS Nationwide, Ablow Street, Wolverhampton, WV2 4ER Tel: (01902) 422479 Fax: (01902) 422481 E-mail: craig.colley@mtsbobcat.co.uk *Plant hire, mini excavators, parts service, plant operator training*

▶ MTS Occasions by Design, Inglenook House, 125 Mottram Old Road, Stalybridge, Cheshire, SK15 2SZ Tel: 01457 766088 E-mail: enquiries@mts-occasionsbydesign.co.uk *I specialise in party and wedding decoration providing fully coordinated accessories, flowers and balloons and hand made stationery for celebrations in the Cheshire, Derbyshire, Yorkshire, Lancashire areas. I can even decorate a venue with items you have alreday purchased.*

▶ MTW Architectural, Trinity Business Park, Turner Way, Wakefield, West Yorkshire, WF2 8EF Tel: (01924) 239100 Fax: (01924) 239600 E-mail: neville.taylor@mtwarchitectural.co.uk *Design, manufacture & install aluminium curtain walling*

▶ MTW Blasting, Morley Barn Farm, Kegworth Road, Gotham, Nottingham, NG11 0LG Tel: 07788 110197 E-mail: cars_r_me@msn.com *Restoration service*

Mubarak Food Co., 292 Leeds Road, Bradford, West Yorkshire, BD3 9QX Tel: (01274) 731754 Fax: (01274) 726161 *Bakery manufrs*

▶ Much More, Cumberland Avenue, Canterbury, Kent, CT1 1SL Tel: (01227) 455445 Fax: (01227) 379446 E-mail: enquires@muchmoreltd.com *Suppliers of Genuine & Remanufactured ink cartridges for all major brands printers, Blank computer media & Much More*

▶ Muck-trucks Scotland, PO Box 19570, Johnstone, Renfrewshire, PA9 1AD Tel: (01505) 702600 Fax: (01505) 703783 E-mail: sales@mucktrucksctland.com *Micro dumper suppliers*

Mudd Farm Equipment, Park View, Marthwaite, Sedbergh, Cumbria, LA10 5HS Tel: (01539) 620704 Fax: (01539) 621573 *Welding & fabrications*

Muddy Puddles Ltd, Hingston Farm, Bigbury, Kingsbridge, Devon, TQ7 4BE Tel: (0870) 4204950 Fax: (0870) 4204943 E-mail: help@muddypuddles.com *Childrens outdoor clothes*

▶ Muddy Trax Racing Ltd, The Gate House Cherry Tree Sawmills, Faygate Lane, Faygate, Horsham, West Sussex, RH12 4SJ Tel: (01293) 852600 E-mail: sales@muddytrax.co.uk *for all your quad biking needs including Sales, Service, Hire 6-66 , Traing, Clothing, Parts, Events, Racing, Stunts and display, Testing.*

G. Mudford & Sons Ltd, Aurillac Way, Hallcroft Road, Retford, Nottinghamshire, DN22 7PX Tel: (01777) 703489 Fax: (01777) 704743 E-mail: info@mudfordmarquees.co.uk *Tent, marquee hire & manufrs*

▶ Mudfords Sheffield Ltd, 400 Petre Street, Sheffield, S4 8LU Tel: 0114-243 3033 Fax: 0114-244 4536 E-mail: sales@mudfords.co.uk *Manufacturer vehicle side curtains & load lashing systems*

Mudie Bond Ltd, Newtown Trading Estate, Northway Lane, Tewkesbury, Gloucestershire, GL20 8JG Tel: (01684) 295090 Fax: (01684) 850616 E-mail: sales@mudie-bond.co.uk *Mercedes dealership*

Mueller Cooling Systems Ltd, Unit B Manor Farm, Main Street, Pinvin, Pershore, Worcestershire, WR10 2ES Tel: (01386) 561757 Fax: (01386) 561750 E-mail: phil.valentine@mueller-cooling.co.uk *Cooling & heating vessels suppliers*

Dr D. Mueller (UK) Ltd, Unit 7 Silver End Business Park, Brettell Lane, Brierley Hill, West Midlands, DY5 3LG Tel: (01384) 482806 Fax: (01384) 482808 E-mail: info.uk@mueller-ahlhorn.com *Electrical insulating materials manufrs*

Mueller Europe Ltd, Oxford Street, Bilston, West Midlands, WV14 7DS Tel: (01902) 499700 Fax: (01902) 405838 E-mail: sales@muellereurope.com *Tube manufrs*

The Mug Factory Ltd, 2 Wyndham Court, Clarion Close Enterprise Park, Swansea, SA6 8RB Tel: (01792) 776331 Fax: (01792) 781142 *Promotional or advertising gift manufrs*

▶ The Mug Man, Unit 2 Horsbeck Way, Horsford, Norwich, NR10 3SS Tel: (01603) 898538 Fax: (01603) 893486 E-mail: sales@themugman.co.uk *School fundraising services*

Company Information

Muggins Pottery Ltd, Burton Bandalls Farm, Burton Lane, Burton-on-the-Wolds, Loughborough, Leicestershire, LE12 5TE Tel: (01509) 266582 E-mail: info@muggins.com *Pottery sales & manufrs*

J. Muir Bookbinders Ltd, 64-68 Blackheath Road, London, SE10 8DA Tel: (020) 8692 7565 Fax: (020) 8692 2072 E-mail: jmuirbookbinders@yahoo.com *J. Muir & Co. (Bookbinders) Ltd are based in London offering bookbinding and print finishing to the trade and public. All styles from paperback books to hardback books. They offer P.U.R. binding, perfect binding, dove tail binding, thread sewing and short run case binding services.*

Muir Group Ltd, Muir House, Bellknowes Industrial Estate, Inverkeithing, Fife, KY11 1HF Tel: (01383) 416191 Fax: (01383) 410193 E-mail: muir@muir-group.co.uk *Building contractors*

Muir Matheson, Aberlan House, Blackburn Industrial Estate, Kinellar, Aberdeen, AB21 0RX Tel: (01224) 791222 Fax: (01224) 791555 E-mail: sales@muir-matheson.com *Meteorological systems manufrs, weather monitoring*

The Muir Maxwell Trust Ltd, 47 Esk Bank Road, Dalkeith, Midlothian, EH22 3BH Tel: 0131-454 0606 E-mail: info@muirmaxwelltrust.com *Charity service*

▶ Muir Morrison Ltd, 322 Broomloan Road, Glasgow, G51 2JQ Tel: 0141-440 1655 Fax: 0141-445 3911

Thomas Muir Haulage Ltd, Randolph Industrial Estate, Kirkcaldy, Fife, KY1 2TX Tel: (01592) 651076 Fax: (01592) 651138 *Haulage contractors & skip hire*

Thomas Muir (Metals) Ltd, Den Road, Kirkcaldy, Fife, KY1 2ER Tel: (01592) 202222 Fax: (01592) 642177 E-mail: muirmetals@aol.com *Metal processors*

▶ Muirfield Contracts Ltd, Souter Head Road, Altens Industrial Estate, Aberdeen, AB12 3LF Tel: (01224) 893300 Fax: (01224) 893301 E-mail: sales@muirfieldcontracts.co.uk

▶ Muirfield (Contracts) Ltd, North Tay Works, 48 Loons Road, Dundee, DD3 6AP Tel: (01382) 668288 Fax: (01382) 642776 E-mail: enquiries@muirfieldcontracts.co.uk

Andrew Muirhead & Son Ltd, Unit 10 Siberia Mill, Holgate Street, Briercliffe, Burnley, Lancashire, BB10 2HQ Tel: (01282) 424040 Fax: (01282) 420209 *Distribution of leather products*

Andrew Muirhead & Son Ltd, 273-289 Dunn Street, Glasgow, G40 3EA Tel: 0141-554 3724 Fax: 0141-554 4741 E-mail: info@muirhead.co.uk *Tanners of upholstery leather* Also at: Burnley

Muirhead Norcroft, East Portway, Andover, Hampshire, SP10 3LU Tel: (01264) 349600 Fax: (01264) 336444 E-mail: sales@muirheadaerospace.com *Brushless motor manufrs*

Muirhead Vactric Components Ltd, Oakfield Road, London, SE20 8EW Tel: (020) 8659 9090 Fax: (020) 8659 9906 E-mail: sales@muirheadaerospace.com *Electromechanical agents*

▶ Mukiwa Projects, 3 Augustus Road, London, SW19 6LL Tel: (020) 8788 6452 Fax: (020) 8788 6452 E-mail: info@mukiwaprojects.com *Project management & consulting*

▶ Mulalley & Co. Ltd, Teresa Gavin House, Southend Road, Woodford Green, Essex, IG8 8FA Tel: (020) 8551 9999 Fax: (020) 8550 7745

▶ The Mulberry Bush, Limberlost Farm, Swife Lane, nr. Broad Oak, Heathfield, East Sussex, TN21 8YA Tel: (01435) 882014 *A UK based online craft store ideal for card making, scrapbooks and weddings. Ideal for handmade gifts and crafts.*

Mulco Engineering Ltd, 9-10 St Machar Road, Aberdeen, AB24 2UU Tel: (01224) 481215 Fax: (01224) 486041 E-mail: info@mulco.co.uk *General engineers*

▶ Mulholland Contracts Ltd, Polbeth Industrial Estate, Polbeth, West Calder, West Lothian, EH55 8TJ Tel: (01506) 871376 Fax: (01506) 871156

▶ Mulholland Plant Hire Ltd, Polbeth Indust Estate, West Calder, West Lothian, EH55 8TJ Tel: (01506) 870297

Mulhouse Ltd, 36 Nobel Square, Burnt Mills Industrial Estate, Basildon, Essex, SS13 1LT Tel: (01268) 726222 Fax: (01268) 590424 E-mail: info@mulhouseltd.com *Lift cars & fire entrance manufrs*

C.A. Mulkern, 8 Springfield Road, Chesham, Buckinghamshire, HP5 1PW Tel: (01494) 783802 *Plumbing & heating engineers*

▶ Mullan Training, Amelia Street, Belfast, BT2 7GS Tel: (028) 9032 2228 Fax: (028) 9032 2229 E-mail: enquiries@mullantraining.com *We offer public & closed courses in a wide range of training courses - including Microsoft, Macromedia, Adobe, QuarkXpress, Crystal Reports, Business Objects, etc.**We also specialise in Report Writing & Database Development. Please see website www.mullantraining.com for shceudle and prices.*

Muller Dairy (UK) Ltd, Shrewsbury Road, Market Drayton, Shropshire, TF9 3SQ Tel: (01630) 692000 Fax: (01630) 692001 E-mail: consumers@muller.co.uk *Manufacturers of dairy produce*

Muller Holdings Ltd, Cleobury Mortimer, Kidderminster, Worcestershire, DY14 8DT Tel: (01299) 270271 Fax: (01299) 270877 E-mail: sales@muller-england.co.uk Principal Export Areas: Central Asia, Africa & North America *Precision turned part suppliers*

▶ Muller Martini Ltd, The Ridgeway, Iver, Buckinghamshire, SL0 9JQ Tel: (01753) 657700 Fax: (01753) 655658 E-mail: enquiries@mullermartini.co.uk *Manufacturers of printing trade finishing equipment*

Muller Redditch Ltd, Bartleet Road, Washford Industrial Estate, Redditch, Worcestershire, B98 0DG Tel: (01527) 526920 Fax: (01527) 502166 E-mail: sales@muller-redditch.co.uk Principal Export Areas: Worldwide *Precision engineers*

Martin Mulligan (UK) Ltd, Barcode House, Shaw Street, St. Helens, Merseyside, WA10 1EN Tel: (01744) 744200 Fax: (01744) 744216 E-mail: sales@martinmulligan.com *Barcode label printers suppliers & manufrs*

Neil Mullin & Sons Ltd, Mullans Quarry, 203 Altamuskin Road, Sixmilecross, Omagh, County Tyrone, BT79 9HX Tel: (028) 8075 8280 *Quarry*

Peter Mullins Cabinet Makers, 2 St. Marys Road, Hayling Island, Hampshire, PO11 9BY Tel: (023) 9246 7141 Fax: (023) 9246 9626 E-mail: p.mullins@btconnect.com *Cabinet maker*

Mulox Ltd, 2 High Carr Network Centre, Millennium Way, High Carr Business Park, Newcastle, Staffordshire, ST5 7XE Tel: (01782) 565659 Fax: (01782) 565252 E-mail: andrew.reardon@mulox.co.uk *Manufacturer of FIBCs*

Multequip Power Tools, 61 Willow Road, Bedford, MK42 0QU Tel: (01234) 340461 Fax: (01234) 340461 *Tool hire & machine repairs*

Multex Ltd, Caputhall Road, Deans Industrial Estate, Deans, Livingston, West Lothian, EH54 8AS Tel: (01506) 460661 Fax: (01506) 460816 *Test fixture manures*

Multex Chemicals, Multex House, Cannon Street, Hull, HU2 0AB Tel: (01482) 320432 Fax: (01482) 321777 E-mail: sales@multexchemicals.co.uk *Industrial cleaning products manufrs*

▶ Multi, Stanmore, Middlesex, HA7 3YR Tel: (0870) 0116220 Fax: (0870) 0116330 E-mail: mail@infantformula.co.uk *Infant formula baby milk powder manufrs*

▶ Multi Bore Structural Services Ltd, Unit 10 East Moors Business Park, East Moors Road, Cardiff, CF24 5JX Tel: (029) 2049 7373 Fax: (029) 2048 1370 E-mail: info@multibore.co.uk

Multi Clean Services Ltd, Lion Works, Paternoster Lane, Bradford, West Yorkshire, BD7 3LP Tel: (01274) 501666 Fax: (01274) 501777 E-mail: info@multiclean-services.com *Supply & repair new & re-furbished equipment*

Multi Engineering Components Co., E3 Seedbed Centre, Avenue Road, Nechells, Birmingham, B7 4NT Tel: 0121-359 6022 Fax: 0121-359 0137 E-mail: sales@multiengineering.co.uk *Plastics & fibre machining services*

Multi Fab Construction Ltd, Lower Field, Stretford, Leominster, Herefordshire, HR6 9DQ Tel: (01568) 720330 Fax: (01568) 720115 *Steel framed buildings construction & design cladding*

▶ Multi Fabricated Systems Ltd, Finchwood Farm, Copse Lane, Hayling Island, Hampshire, PO11 0QB Tel: (023) 9246 1211 Fax: (023) 9246 1800 E-mail: info@multifirescreens.com *Steel fire screens doors, windows & curtain walling*

Multi Fix Ltd, Normark House, 48 Mill Lane, Bradford, West Yorkshire, BD5 0HF Tel: (01274) 728065 Fax: (01274) 725213 *Power tool suppliers*

Multi Form Machine Tools Ltd, Aviation House, Aviation Way, Southend-on-Sea, SS2 6UN Tel: (0845) 0690290 Fax: (0845) 0690291 E-mail: info@fabricatorsworld.com *Precision engineers*

▶ Multi Madness, 1 Marsett Way, Whinmoor, Leeds, LS14 2DN Tel: 0113-216 4845 *Bouncy castle and Rodeo Bull hire for parties,weddings,events and shows*

Multi Marque Production Engineering Ltd, Unit 33 Monckton Road Industrial Estate, Wakefield, West Yorkshire, WF2 7AL Tel: (01924) 290231 Fax: (01924) 382241 E-mail: enquiry@multi-marque.co.uk *Construction equipment manufrs*

Multi Media Duplication Ltd, Suite 3 The White House, 7 Station Road, Hagley, Stourbridge, West Midlands, DY9 0NU Tel: (01562) 886808 Fax: (01562) 886808

Multi Media Medium Ltd, Bridge House, Glob Works Place, Bolton, BL2 1DG Tel: (01204) 387410 Fax: (01204) 369924 *Karaoke machine manufrs*

Multi Metal Stockholders, 7-19 Hulme Street, Salford, M5 4PY Tel: 0161-736 0918 Fax: 0161-745 7423 E-mail: sales@multimetals.fsnet.co.uk *Metal & plastics suppliers*

▶ Multi Metals Ltd, Belgrave Street, Bellshill Industrial Estate, Bellshill, Lanarkshire, ML4 3JA Tel: (01698) 841199 Fax: (01698) 841812 E-mail: sales@multimetals.com *Aluminium stockholders*

▶ Multi Network Solutions Ltd, Priory Gate House, 7 Priory Road, High Wycombe, Bucks, HP13 6SE Tel: 0870-746 1343 Fax: (01494) 793439

Multi Pneumatics, Motivair House, Crompton Court, Attwood Road, Burntwood, Staffordshire, WS7 3GG Tel: (0845) 0096161 Fax: (0845) 0096162 E-mail: enquiries@multi-pneumatics.co.uk *Hydraulics, pneumatics & compressed air industry suppliers*

Multi Process, Unit 8 Stroud Enterprise Centre, Lightpill, Stroud, Gloucestershire, GL5 3NL Tel: (01453) 750002 Fax: (01453) 758271 *Valve distributors/agents/stockholders. Also actuated, titanium, exotic materials, ball & butterfly valves. in addtion higher nickel alloy flanges/fittings, OEM (original end manufacturers & valve actuators*

Multi Resource Marketing Ltd, Barberton House, Farndon Road, Market Harborough, Leicestershire, LE16 9NR Tel: (01858) 410510 Fax: (01858) 434190 *Sales promotion handling*

▶ The Multi Room Co. Ltd, 4 Churchill House, Churchill Road, Cheltenham, Gloucestershire, GL53 7EG Tel: (01242) 539100 Fax: (01242) 539300 *Audio & visual entertainment distributors*

Multi Route Carriers, PO Box 287, Chertsey, Surrey, KT16 8LA Tel: (01932) 882882 Fax: (07005) 994213 E-mail: info@multiroutecargo.co.uk *Multi-Route Cargo are an independent freight forwarding company, providing air freight, sea freight, European road freight and Customs Clearance services.*

Multi Shades Ltd, Sandals Mill, Cliffe Avenue, Baildon, Shipley, West Yorkshire, BD17 6PB Tel: (01274) 580727 Fax: (01274) 531181 E-mail: sales@multishades.co.uk *Flooring industry, carpet patterns sample card manufrs*

Multi Sign Makers, 30 New John Street West, Birmingham, B19 3NB Tel: 0121-359 0707 Fax: 0121-359 6066 E-mail: sales@multisignmakers.co.uk *Screen process printers*

Multi Spray & Pneumatics Ltd, Unit 1 Hanley Business Park, Cooper Street, Hanley, Stoke-on-Trent, ST1 4DW Tel: (01782) 281376 Fax: (01782) 204426 E-mail: technical@multisprayandpneumatics.co.uk *Spray painting equipment distributors*

Multi Tech Contracts, Unit 6 Bowood Court, Calver Road, Winwick Quay, Warrington, WA2 8QZ Tel: (01925) 418333 Fax: (01925) 418800 E-mail: sales@mtcl.net *Design & project management designers*

Multi Tech Precision Engineering Wantage, 26 Charlton Road, Wantage, Oxfordshire, OX12 8HG Tel: (01235) 768922 *Precision engineers*

Multi Weldmesh Ltd, Heasandford Industrial Estate, Widow Hill Road, Burnley, Lancashire, BB10 2TJ Tel: (01282) 425300 Fax: (01282) 422204 *Wire mesh manufrs*

Multibasics Gas Service Engineers, 12 Thornton Road, Morecambe, Lancashire, LA4 5PE Tel: (01524) 415346 Fax: (01524) 412509 E-mail: sales@multibasics.com *Combination gas & heating services*

Multibelt Conveyor Belt Co., Unit 12 Kencot Way, Erith, Kent, DA18 4AB Tel: (020) 8310 9400 Fax: (020) 8310 2433 *Conveyor belt distributors*

▶ Multicare Electronics Ltd, Unit 5a Silver Royd Business Park, Silver Royd Hill, Leeds, LS12 4QQ Tel: 0113-279 1255 Fax: 0113-279 1255 E-mail: sales@multicare.org.uk *Repair service centre for faulty electronic equipment*

Multicell International Ltd, 6 Swannington Road, Broughton Astley, Leicester, LE9 6TU Tel: (01455) 283443 Fax: (01455) 284250 E-mail: help@multicell.co.uk *Battery suppliers*

▶ Multicoat North East Ltd, 3 Florence Street, Middlesbrough, Cleveland, TS2 1DR Tel: (01642) 213030 Fax: (01642) 213030 *Powder coating services*

Multicolor UK Ltd, The Drift, Nacton Road, Ipswich, IP3 9QP Tel: 01473 723443 Fax: (01473) 270671 E-mail: info@multicolor.co.uk *Colour cards*

Multicolour Developments, 67a Foxhill Road, Reading, RG1 5QR Tel: 0118-935 1676 Fax: 0118-935 2258 E-mail: printsplate@aol.com *Pad printers & printing services*

Multi-Contact (UK) Ltd, 3 Presley Way, Crownhill, Milton Keynes, MK8 0ES Tel: (01908) 265544 Fax: (01908) 262080 E-mail: uk@multi-contact.com *Connector distributors*

Multicore Ltd, 2 Dorset Street, London, W1U 4EE Tel: (020) 7935 4022 Fax: (020) 7935 2687 E-mail: multicore@ntlworld.com *Machinery & equipment suppliers*

▶ Multicreative Media, 261 Kingston Road, Epsom, Surrey, KT19 0BN Tel: (020) 8393 4200 E-mail: mail@multicreativemedia.co.uk *Welcome to the world of MULTIcreativeMEDIA, a dedicated company specialising in all aspects of multimedia and website design to suit the needs of all. We are a multimedia design company focusing on websites and multimedia content designed to your custom needs, located in Epsom, Surrey.*

Multidata Europe, Hunts Hill, Blunsdon, Swindon, SN26 7BN Tel: (01793) 706161 Fax: (01793) 706150 E-mail: nigel@multidata.co.uk *Modem & data communications manufrs*

Multifab Sheet Metal & Light Fabrication, Unit 31 Upper Mills, Cannal Side, Slaithwaite, Huddersfield, HD7 5HA Tel: (01484) 841222 Fax: (01484) 841333 *Shop fitting manufrs*

Multifabs Survival Ltd, Units 4-5, Balmoor Industrial Estate, Peterhead, Aberdeenshire, AB42 1QG Tel: (01779) 470848 Fax: (01779) 478099

Multi-Factor Europe Ltd, Harrison House, Rackery Lane, Llay, Wrexham, Clwyd, LL12 0PB Tel: (0845) 5314030 Fax: (01978) 855222 E-mail: mark.beeston@mfeuk.co.uk *Multi Factor Europe (MFE) specialises in the supply of high quality industrial filtration products. We can supply all areas of filtration, air conditioning, HVAC, hydraulic filtration, process filtration and Dust plants. We offer high quality filters from Mann Hummel, MP Filtri, Fileder filters, Camfil Farr to name but a few at competitive prices. MFE can offer full LEV surveys, dust plant servicing and full installation service along with the dust cartridges and bags, Goyen valves and spares required to keep your plant running. We have expanded our range of engineering consumables available online or via our dedicated sales engineers in Wrexham to include, Silverline tools, Fentex spill products, personal protection equipment and dosing systems to make MFE a true single source supplier. MFE is one of the leading aftermarket spare parts suppliers for the compressor service industry; we offer a full range of spares from original equipment suppliers and OEMS.*

Multiform Ltd, Skipton Road, Cross Hills, Keighley, West Yorkshire, BD20 7DS Tel: (01535) 636095 Fax: (01535) 635047 E-mail: enquiries@multiform.ltd.uk *Steel fabricators*

Multiform Machine Tool Ltd, Avaition House, Aviation Way, Southend Airport, Southend-on-Sea, SS2 6UN Tel: (0845) 0690290 Fax: (0845) 0690291 E-mail: info@mfmtl.co.uk *Sheet metalwork machinery merchants*

▶ Multiform Technology, Station Road, Hellingly,, Hailsham, East Sussex, BN27 4EU Tel: (01323) 848117 Fax: (01323) 441906 E-mail: sales@multiform-uk.com *Import & export lighting & sound*

▶ Multiglow Fires, Canterbury Road, St. Nicholas at Wade, Birchington, Kent, CT7 0PQ Tel: (01843) 847575 Fax: (01843) 848300 *Decorative burners*

Multi-Grind Services Ltd, Unit 10, Harefield Road Industrial Estate, Rickmansworth, Hertfordshire, WD3 1PQ Tel: (01923) 725230 Fax: (01923) 777915 E-mail: steve@multigrind.co.uk *CNC grinding & turning services specialists*

▶ Multiheat Ltd, 4 Cardinal House, 629 Stanningley Road, Leeds, LS13 4EP Tel: 0113-204 7555 Fax: 0113-204 7666

Multijet Hardening Ltd, 8 West Don Street, Sheffield, S6 3BH Tel: 0114-234 5592 Fax: 0114-231 4772 *Heat treatment & flame hardening services*

Multikwik Ltd, 37 High Street, Totton, Southampton, SO40 9HL Tel: (023) 8066 3777 Fax: (023) 8086 9996 E-mail: sales@multikwik.com *WC pan connectors*

Multilec Electrical Contractors, 11 Golf Links Avenue, Hindhead, Surrey, GU26 6PQ Tel: (01428) 607222 Fax: (01428) 607444 E-mail: multilec@ukonline.co.uk *Electrical contractors*

Multilift Fork Trucks, 4 Burma Road, Blidworth, Mansfield, Nottinghamshire, NG21 0RT Tel: (01623) 794094 Fax: (01623) 795095 E-mail: sales@mlift.co.uk *Sales, hire, service & repair of forklift trucks*

▶ Multilines Ltd, 1 255 Water Road, Wembley, Middlesex, HA0 1JW Tel: (020) 8997 7788 Fax: (020) 8997 9988 E-mail: sales@multilines.co.uk *Manufacturer of bedrooms & kitchens, shopfitters*

Multilingual Solutions Ltd, 27A Stonor Road, London, W14 8RZ Tel: (020) 7602 7555 Fax: (020) 7602 4190 *Languages software developers*

▶ Multilink Access Control Systems Ltd, 71 Hampermill Lane, Watford, WD19 4NT Tel: (01923) 224900 Fax: (01923) 224970 E-mail: info@multilinksecurity.co.uk *Security equipment suppliers & designers*

Multilink Edi Ltd, 118-120 Dominion Road, Multilink House, Worthing, West Sussex, BN14 8JP Tel: (01903) 821554 Fax: (01903) 235216 E-mail: sales@blueflag.co.uk *Software developers*

Multilink Resources Ltd, Suite 18, Vermont House, Bradley Lane, Standish, Wigan, Lancashire, WN6 0XF Tel: (01257) 427053 Fax: (01257) 427053 E-mail: enquire@multilink.co.uk *Manufacturers & suppliers of tube cleaning equipment*

Multimarine Composites Ltd, Foss Quarry, Mill Road, Millbrook, Torpoint, Cornwall, PL10 1EN Tel: (01752) 823513 Fax: (01752) 823179 E-mail: info@multimarine.co.uk *Boat builders*

▶ Multimedia Productions Ltd, Minster Chambers, Suite 1, 37 High St, Wimborne, Dorset, BH21 1HR Tel: (01202) 882059 Fax: (01202) 881091 E-mail: info@mmpuk.com *Independent UK video production, specialising in corporate promotion, TV advertising, sales tools for Distribution, broadcast equip for hire*

Multimetals (Scotland), Unit 1 Atlantic Way, Wednesbury, West Midlands, WS10 7WW Tel: 0121-505 2323 Fax: 0121-505 2324 E-mail: enquiries@multimetals.com *Steel stockholders*

Multi-Mix, Unit 2 Praed Road, Trafford Park, Trafford Park, Manchester, M17 1PQ Tel: (07958) 922361 Fax: 0161-776 0092 E-mail: multimix2005@hotmail.com *Concrete merchants*

▶ Multi-Mix UK Limited, 62 Arnold Road, Basford, Nottingham, NG6 0DZ Tel: 01159 858999 Fax: 01159 858999 E-mail: sales@multi-mix.co.uk **Our company has over 25 years of experience in the ink industry. We produce machinery specifically designed for litho, screen ink manufacturers and for the printing industry.* *We manufacture ink mixing machines and vacuum sealing machines which are specifically designed for the trade. * *We also sell general production equipment for the industry such as; industrial work benches, accurate scales and balances and dispensing nozzles. ***

▶ Multimodal Applied Systems Europe Ltd, 5 Hunters Walk, Canal Street, Chester, CH1 4EB Tel: (01244) 403294 Fax: (01244) 348471

Multipart Universal, 8 Stevenson Way, Sheffield, S9 3WZ Tel: 0114-261 1122 Fax: 0800 834500 E-mail: uksales@ucukltd.com Principal Export Areas: Asia Pacific, Central Asia, Middle East, Africa, Central/East Europe, West Europe & South America *Distributors & agents of commercial vehicle components & spare parts*

Multipix Imaging Ltd, 1 Tilmore Road, Petersfield, Hampshire, GU32 2HG Tel: (01730) 233332 Fax: (01730) 231062 E-mail: sales@multipix.com *Machine vision hardware & software components*

Multiple Fabric Co. Ltd, Vulcan Mills, William Street, Tong, Bradford, West Yorkshire, BD4 9QX Tel: (01274) 682323 Fax: (01274) 651341 E-mail: info@multiplefabric.co.uk *Manufacturers and suppliers of filter cloths, press cloths, centrifuge cloths and other filter media to a range of industries for solid/liquid and air filtration.*

Multiple Press Ltd, C Chiltern Trading Estate, Grovebury Road, Leighton Buzzard, Bedfordshire, LU7 4TU Tel: (01525) 380800 Fax: (01525) 380802 E-mail: sales@multiplepress.co.uk *Business form manufacturers.*

Multiple Winding Co. Ltd, Taylor Lane, Denton, Manchester, M34 3NR Tel: 0161-336 6125 Fax: 0161-335 9134 E-mail: chris@multiplewinding.co.uk *Wind electrical insulation yarns*

▶ Multiplex Construction, Elvin House, Stadium Way, Wembley, Middlesex, HA9 0DW Tel: (020) 8900 9111

Multiplex Security Communications Ltd, 32-34 Constitution Hill, Birmingham, B19 3JT Tel: 0121-236 6977 *Alarms & security systems monitoring service*

▶ multipointlocks.co.uk, 29 Westgate End, Wakefield, West Yorkshire, WF2 9RG Tel: (01924) 360444 E-mail: sales@multipointlocks.co.uk

Multipond Ltd, 20 St. Johns Road, Penn, High Wycombe, Buckinghamshire, HP10 8HW Tel: (01494) 816644 Fax: (01494) 816206 E-mail: multipond_uk@btconnect.com *Multi head linear weighing equipment distributors*

Multipower International Ltd, 8 Langney Green, Tattenhoe, Milton Keynes, MK4 3ES Tel: (01908) 522202 Fax: (0870) 7064855 E-mail: tech@multipower-int.com *Police & military batteries & chargers manufrs*

▶ Multiprint, Seafield Road, Kirkcaldy, Fife, KY1 1SR Tel: (01592) 204755 Fax: (01592) 203171

Multipulse Electronics Ltd, Unit 3 Goldsworth Park Trading Estate, Kestrel Way, Woking, Surrey, GU21 3BA Tel: (01483) 713600 Fax: (01483) 729851 E-mail: sales@multipulse.com *Telecommunication suppliers*

Multiquip Supplies Ltd, Unit 1, Glenmore Business Park, Bumpers Farm Industrial Estate, Chippenham, Wiltshire, SN14 6BB Tel: (01249) 654945 Fax: (01249) 654255 E-mail: sales@multiquip.uk.com *General engineers merchants*

Multi-Seal UK, 2B Randolph Road, Reading, RG1 8EB Tel: 0118-939 1980 Fax: 0118-939 1982 *Tyre sealant*

▶ Multisense Communications Ltd, Red Lion House, 600 London Road, High Wycombe, Buckinghamshire, HP11 1EX Tel: (01494) 461949 Fax: (01494) 536261 E-mail: sales@multisense.co.uk *Video conferencing systems*

Multiserv Group Ltd, Strawberry Lane, Willenhall, West Midlands, WV13 3RS Tel: (01902) 636381 Fax: (01902) 636186 E-mail: info@multiserv.com *Freight forwarding agents*

Multiserv UK Ltd, Wortley Road, Rotherham, South Yorkshire, S61 1LT Tel: (01709) 321000 Fax: (01709) 321003 *Provider of specialised outsourced services to the steel & metals industry*

▶ Multiserve Ltd, Bowden Hall, Bowden Lane, Marple, Stockport, Cheshire, SK6 6ND Tel: 0161-427 4270 Fax: 0161-427 8800 E-mail: sales@multiserveltd.com

▶ Multiserve Group, Aldwarke Works, Rotherham, South Yorkshire, S65 3SR Tel: (01709) 527743 Fax: (01709) 529458 *Steelworks contractors or designers*

Multisets Ltd, Suite 2B, Second Floor, Eastheath House, Eastheath Avenue, Wokingham, Berkshire, RG41 2PR Tel: 0118-936 7600 Fax: 0118-936 7601 E-mail: info@multisets.co.uk *Security printers & stationery manufrs* Also at: Windsor

Multishape Sheet Metal Work, 120 Camford Way, Luton, LU3 3AN Tel: (01582) 581133 Fax: (01582) 581158 E-mail: custserv@multishape.co.uk *Fine Limit Sheet Metalwork, ISO 9001, Laser Cutting, Punching Folding, Welding and Graining.*

Multisigns, Unit 6, Southern Avenue, Leominster, Herefordshire, HR6 0QF Tel: (01432) 353333 Fax: (01568) 612379 E-mail: multi_signs_uk@yahoo.com *Sign manufrs*

Multisigns, 31 Levellers Lane, Eynesbury, St. Neots, Cambridgeshire, PE19 2JL Tel: (01480) 471717 Fax: (01480) 471747 E-mail: sales@multisigns.co.uk *Sign suppliers, instillation & manufrs*

▶ Multisol Ltd, Sorby Road, Irlam, Manchester, M44 5BA Tel: 0161-775 1622 Fax: 0161-777 9783 E-mail: sales@multisol.co.uk *Independent & international chemical distributor*

Multispark Erosion Ltd, 145 Camford Way, Luton, LU3 3AN Tel: (01582) 502015 Fax: (01582) 507836 E-mail: sales@multispark.co.uk *Spark & wire erosion machining services*

Multispline Gear Cutters, Unit 66 Coleshill Industrial Estate, Station Road, Coleshill, Birmingham, B46 1JT Tel: (01675) 462253 Fax: (01675) 463485 E-mail: sales@multispline.co.uk *Gear grinding contractors*

Multi-Stroke Ltd, King Street, Old Hill, Cradley Heath, West Midlands, B64 6JJ Tel: (01384) 567481 Fax: (01384) 564382 *Twistlock & parking brake manufrs*

▶ Multitec Engineering Ltd, Darrion House, 37 Tudor Walk, Watford, WD24 7NY Tel: (01923) 213283 Fax: (01923) 213340 E-mail: Multiteceng@aol.com *Production & Development Engineers*

▶ Multi-Tech Systems (Europe) Inc, Alain Young, 11 Pilmuir Estate, Pilmuir Road, Newton Mearns, Glasgow, G77 6PS Tel: (07770) 574573 Fax: 0141-639 7164 *Label handling parts & machines*

Multitechnic Ltd, Coopies Lane, Morpeth, Northumberland, NE61 6JQ Tel: (01670) 512090 Fax: (01670) 503143 E-mail: sales@multitechnic.com *Photo chemical etchers*

Multitek Ltd, Lancaster Way, Earls Colne, Colchester, CO6 2NS Tel: (01787) 223228 Fax: (01787) 223607 E-mail: chris@multitek-ltd.com *Electronic transducer manufrs*

Mult-I-Tel, 27 Woodland Road, Melling, Liverpool, L31 1EB Tel: 0151-548 8122 E-mail: com_links@compuserve.com *Telecommunications equipment specialists*

Multitex G R P, Unit 5 Dolphin Industrial Estate, Salisbury, SP1 2NB Tel: (01722) 332139 Fax: (01722) 338458 E-mail: sales@multitex.co.uk *Glass fibre mouldings manufrs*

Multitone Electronics plc, Multitone House, Shortwood Copse Lane, Kempshott, Basingstoke, Hampshire, RG23 7NL Tel: (01256) 320292 Fax: (01256) 462643 E-mail: info@multitone.com *Telecommunication consultants*

Multitruck Components Ltd, 10 Clarke Road, Bletchley, Milton Keynes, MK1 1LG Tel: (01908) 644035 Fax: (01908) 379866 E-mail: multitruck@lineone.net *Truck components distributor* Also at: Welwyn Garden City

Multivac UK, Multivac House, Rivermead Drive, Swindon, SN5 7UY Tel: (01793) 425800 Fax: (01793) 616219 E-mail: sales@multivac.co.uk *Multivac UK Ltd based in Swindon are packaging machine manufacturers. Products include packaging machines for the food industry - thermoformers, tray sealers and chamber machines.*

Multiyork Furniture Ltd, 15 Piccadilly, York, YO1 9PB Tel: (01904) 674050 Fax: (01904) 674030 E-mail: york@multiyork.co.uk *Furniture manufrs*

Multy Abrasives Ltd, First Avenue, Deeside Industrial Park, Deeside, Clwyd, CH5 2NU Tel: (01244) 288261 Fax: (01244) 280305 E-mail: clare@multyabrasives.co.uk *Industrial cleaning materials suppliers & manufrs*

▶ Mulvey Building & Roofing Contractors Ltd, PO Box 2727, Glasgow, G61 2YB Tel: 0141-942 7788 Fax: 0141-942 7788

▶ Mumbles, 24 Newton Road, Mumbles, Swansea, SA3 4AX Tel: (01792) 369511 Fax: (01792) 369511E-mail: mumblescobbler@btinternet.com *Traditional shoe repairs, engraving, sports trophies & Key cutting*

Mumbles Pine Co., 42 The Grove, Mumbles, Swansea, SA2 0QR Tel: (01792) 472764 Fax: (01792) 360749 *Pine furniture suppliers*

Owen Mumford Holdings Ltd, Brook Hill, Woodstock, Woodstock, Oxfordshire, OX20 1TU Tel: (01993) 812021 Fax: (01993) 813466 E-mail: info@owenmumford.co.uk *Diabetic medical product manufrs*

Mumford & Wood Ltd, Tower Business Park, Kelvedon Road, Tiptree, Colchester, CO5 0LX Tel: (01621) 818155 Fax: (01621) 818175 E-mail: chrisw@mumfordwood.com *Timber sash windows, casements & doors*

Mundane Software Co., 78a Chapel Street, Thatcham, Berkshire, RG18 4QN Tel: (01635) 876387 Fax: (01635) 876388 E-mail: sales@mundanesoftware.co.uk *Project management software manufrs*

Munday C H Ltd, 8 St. Johns Road, Woking, Surrey, GU21 7SE Tel: (01483) 771588 Fax: (01483) 756627 E-mail: enquiries@chmunday.co.uk *Necktie manufrs*

Mundy & Side, Westwood Farm, Highcross Road, Southfleet, Gravesend, Kent, DA13 9PH Tel: (01474) 834455 Fax: (01474) 834457 E-mail: anyone@mundy-side.prestel.co.uk *Injection Mould toolmaker from design to production. Can produce any product for any industry in the UK*

Munich 72 Trophies, 6a Bombay Street, London, SE16 3UX Tel: (020) 7231 7095 Fax: (020) 7231 7095 E-mail: sales@munichtrophies.co.uk *Trophies & corporate awards manufrs*

Munitech Ltd, Hoo Marina Industrial Estate, Vicarage Lane, Hoo, Rochester, Kent, ME3 9LB Tel: (01634) 250771 Fax: (01634) 250388 E-mail: info@munitech.co.uk *Service vehicle wear parts*

▶ Munnelly Support Services Ltd, The Heights, 59-65 Lowlands Road, Harrow, Middlesex, HA1 3AW Tel: (020) 8515 0300 Fax: (020) 8861 5837

▶ Munro Builders Ltd, 45 Highfield Gardens, Westcliff-on-Sea, Essex, SS0 0SY Tel: (01702) 348319

▶ James Munro & Son Ltd, 8 Stanley Road, Edinburgh, EH6 4SJ Tel: 0131-552 2538 Fax: 0131-552 5767

Munro & Miller Fittings Ltd, 3 Westerton Road, East Mains Industrial Estate, Broxburn, West Lothian, EH52 5AU Tel: (01506) 853531 Fax: (01506) 856628 E-mail: sales@munro-miller.co.uk Principal Export Areas: Worldwide *Expansion joint, butt welding fitting manufrs*

Moira Munro Illustrations and Cartoons, Glasgow, G76 Tel: 0141-638 9851 E-mail: moira@moiramunro.com *Freelance illustrations, cartoons, leaflets, books, workshops, school*

▶ Munro W Rehab Ltd, Unit 8-10 Dunrobin Court, 14 North Avenue, Clydebank Business Park, Clydebank, Dunbartonshire, G81 2QP Tel: 0141-952 2323

William Munro Construction (Highland) Ltd, River Drive, Teaninich Industrial Estate, Alness, Ross-Shire, IV17 0PG Tel: (01349) 882373

Munters Ltd, Blackstone Road, Stukeley Meadows Industrial Estate, Huntingdon, Cambridgeshire, PE29 6EE Tel: (01480) 442327 Fax: (01480) 458333 E-mail: info@munters.co.uk *Property restoration, humidifier distributors & manufrs*

Muntons Agricultural Merchants, Needham Road, Stowmarket, Suffolk, IP14 2AG Tel: (01449) 618300 Fax: (01449) 677800 E-mail: grain@muntons.com Principal Export Areas: Worldwide *Malt flour processors*

Muraspec Ltd, 74-78 Wood Lane End, Hemel Hempstead, Hertfordshire, HP2 4RF Tel: (01442) 268890 Fax: (0870) 5329020 E-mail: customerservices@muraspec.com *Contract wall coverings distributors & manufrs* Also at: Altrincham, Birmingham, Bristol, Glasgow, Hemel Hempstead & Leeds

Muraspec, Tonbridge Road, East Peckham, Tonbridge, Kent, TN12 5JX Tel: (01622) 871384 Fax: (01622) 871011 E-mail: customerservices@muraspec.com *Wall covering manufrs*

Murata Electronics Ltd, Oak House, Ancells Road, Fleet, Hampshire, GU51 2QW Tel: (01252) 811666 Fax: (01252) 811777 E-mail: enquiry@murata.co.uk *Passive electronic component suppliers*

Muratec (UK) Ltd, Unit 23, Hewitts Industrial Estate, Elm Bridge Road, Cranleigh, Surrey, GU6 8LW Tel: (0870) 6086084 Fax: (0870) 2408725 *Photocopier manufrs*

Murch Bros (Engineers) Ltd, Bridge Works, Umberleigh, Devon, EX37 9AA Tel: (01769) 560369 Fax: (01769) 560759 *Agricultural engineers & machinery & garden machinery sales & service*

Murco, 40b Deacons Road, Kilsyth, Glasgow, G65 0BN Tel: (01236) 825297 Fax: (01236) 827697

▶ Murdoch Group Ltd, 23 Greenbank Industrial Estate, Ballyholland Road, Newry, County Down, BT34 2QN Tel: (028) 3025 0897 Fax: (028) 3025 1858

J. & M. Murdoch & Son Ltd, Crofthead Industrial Estate, Lochlibo Road, Neilston, Glasgow, G78 3NE Tel: 0141-580 6323 Fax: 0141-580 6323 E-mail: info@jmmurdoch.com *Skip contractors & haulage*

▶ Murdoch Mackenzie Construction Ltd, Coursington Road, Motherwell, Lanarkshire, ML1 1NR Tel: (01698) 265171 Fax: (01698) 276986

▶ Murdoch Smith & Co. Ltd, Crownest Loan, Stenhousemuir, Larbert, Stirlingshire, FK5 3BU Tel: (01324) 553167 Fax: (01324) 562194

Murex Welding Products Ltd, Hanover House, Queensgate, Britania Road, Waltham Cross, Hertfordshire, EN8 7TF Tel: (01992) 710000 Fax: (01992) 715803 E-mail: info@murexwelding.co.uk *Welding equipment & consumables manufrs*

Murley Agricultural Supplies Ltd, Crab Apple Way, Vale Park, Evesham, Worcestershire, WR11 1GP Tel: (01386) 765657 Fax: (01386) 765029 E-mail: sales@murley-agri.co.uk *Agricultural machinery suppliers*

▶ Murley Electrical Ltd, 5 Lyon Road, Romford, RM1 2BA Tel: (01708) 722544 Fax: (01708) 728884

Murmar-Phipps Ltd, PO Box 1, Northampton, NN4 8WN Tel: (01604) 763033 Fax: (01604) 23297 *Specialist fabric retailers & distributors*

Murphy Ltd, Ashley House, Ashley Road, London, N17 9LZ Tel: (020) 8885 3545 Fax: (020) 8801 1126 E-mail: emq@murphy-ltd-.uk *Cable contractors & civil engineers*

Frank W. Murphy Ltd, Swichgage House, Church Road, Laverstock, Salisbury, SP1 1QZ Tel: (01722) 410055 Fax: (01722) 410088 E-mail: sales@fwmurphy.co.uk *Manufacturers & suppliers of engine protection equipment*

▶ Murphy Jas (Falkirk) Ltd, 50 Dalderse Avenue, Falkirk, FK2 7EG Tel: (01324) 621866 Fax: (01324) 621877 E-mail: sales@jamesmurphy-falkirk.co.uk *Wire product manufrs*

Murphy Pipelines Ltd, Hiview House, Highgate Road, London, NW5 1TN Tel: (020) 7267 4366 Fax: (020) 7482 3107 E-mail: mail@murphygroup.co.uk *Pipeline & plant construction repair & maintenance*

Murphy & Son Ltd, Alpine Street, Nottingham, NG6 0HQ Tel: 0115-978 5494 Fax: 0115-924 4654 E-mail: info@murphyandson.co.uk *Brewers chemists* Also at: Nottingham

Murphy Telecommunications, 293 Salisbury Road, Totton, Southampton, SO40 3LZ Tel: (023) 8086 1479 Fax: (023) 8086 8483 E-mail: murtel@talktalk.net *Telecommunication contractors*

Murphys Saddlery, The Tack Shop, Hewish, Weston-super-Mare, Avon, BS24 6SG Tel: (01934) 833138 Fax: (01934) 832304 *Saddle shop*

Murrain Sports, 289 Walsall Road, Perry Barr, Birmingham, B42 1TY Tel: 0121-356 6090 Fax: 0121-344 3447 E-mail: sales@murrainsports.co.uk *Martial arts clothing specialists*

Murray, Castle Court, Bodmin Road, Coventry, CV2 5DB Tel: (024) 7658 7980 Fax: (024) 7658 7981 E-mail: jheadley@jheadley.co.uk *Workwear, corporate company uniforms, safety clothing, protective clothing & footwear, new lines, new prices, new stock - call us now for a quality service every time.*

▶ Murray Aquatics, 1 Houston Place, Glasgow, G5 8SG Tel: 0141-420 1020 Fax: 0141-420 1040 E-mail: sales@murrayaquatics.co.uk *Pet shops & garden centres*

▶ Murray & Burrell Ltd, Roxburgh Street, Galashiels, Selkirkshire, TD1 1PE Tel: (01896) 752364 Fax: (01896) 758189 E-mail: info@murrayandburrell.com

David Murray Horseboxes Ltd, 5 Hartford Industrial Estate, Suthers Street, Oldham, OL9 7TQ Tel: 0161-628 2649 Fax: 0161-628 2649 *Horsebox manufrs*

Murray Duguid Ltd, Mill of Cromlet, Oldmeldrum, Inverurie, Aberdeenshire, AB51 0BD Tel: (01651) 872535 Fax: (01651) 872933 *Grass seed merchants*

Murray Hogg Ltd, Sandy Lane, North Gosforth, North Gosforth, Newcastle Upon Tyne, NE3 5HE Tel: 0191-236 4211 Fax: 0191-236 3189 E-mail: sales@murrayhogg.co.uk *Haulage contractors & warehousing service providers*

Murray (International) Metals Ltd, Murray Works, Newbridge Industrial Estate, Newbridge, Midlothian, EH28 8PJ Tel: 0131-333 3333 Fax: 0131-333 4477 E-mail: mim_newbridge@murray-metals.co.uk Principal Export Areas: Worldwide *High yield quality steel stockists*

▶ Murray Lift Services Ltd, 130 Station Road, Sidcup, Kent, DA15 7AB Tel: (020) 8300 0614 Fax: (020) 181 7 181 E-mail: sales@murrayliftservices.com *Lift installation, planned preventative maintenance, lift repairs*

▶ Murray Mcgowan Ltd, Clock Mill Road, Gateshead, Tyne & Wear, NE8 2QX Tel: 0191-460 9696 Fax: 0191-460 9686

▶ Murray & Murray, 2-3 Boston Road, Glenrothes, Fife, KY6 2RE Tel: (01592) 774363 Fax: (01592) 774379 E-mail: kitchens@murrayandmurray.co.uk *Bespoke furniture*

Murray Power Tools & Abrasives, 14 Primrose Avenue Industrial Estate, Grangemouth, Stirlingshire, FK3 8YD Tel: (01324) 666185 Fax: (01324) 666184 E-mail: sales@murraypowertools.co.uk *Power tool services & retail*

Murray Services Ltd, Prospect Avenue, Seaton Delaval, Whitley Bay, Tyne & Wear, NE25 0DP Tel: 0191-237 3893 Fax: 0191-237 3801 E-mail: sales@murray-services.ltd.uk *Store shelving services*

Tony Murray Interiors Ltd, Rowden Works, Chaffinch Road, Beckenham, Kent, BR3 4NA Tel: (020) 8650 9331 Fax: (020) 8663 6576 *Joinery*

Murrelektronik Ltd, Albion Street, Pendlebury, Swinton, Manchester, M27 4FG Tel: 0161-728 3133 Fax: 0161-728 3130 E-mail: sales@murrelektronik.co.uk *Power supply system services*

▶ Murrell Asset Management, 13 Aberdour Road, Burntisland, Fife, KY3 0EL Tel: (01592) 872638 E-mail: robert@murrellassetmanagement.co.uk *Independent financial advisors*

Murtec Fire Protection Ltd, Unit 19-20 Oldgate, St Michaels Industrial Estate, Widnes, Cheshire, WA8 8TL Tel: 0151-423 2802 Fax: 0151-424 1441 E-mail: sales@murtec.co.uk *Fire protection engineers*

Murvi Motor Caravans Ltd, 4 East Way, Lee Mill Industrial Estate, Ivybridge, Devon, PL21 9GE Tel: (01752) 892200 Fax: (01752) 892202 E-mail: sales@murvi.co.uk *Motor caravan retailers & manufrs*

Muschamp Machine Services, 6-12 Whitebirk Road, Blackburn, BB1 3JD Tel: (01254) 263361 Fax: (01254) 697947 E-mail: info@muschamp.co.uk *Textile machine parts distributors*

Musgrave Generators Ltd, 1 Enderby Road Industrial Estate, Whetstone, Leicester, LE8 6HZ Tel: 0116-286 1534 Fax: 0116-286 1559 E-mail: info@musgrave-generators.com *Designers, manufacturers & installers of Diesel generating sets*

Musgrave Retail Partners, Waldrist Way, Erith, Kent, DA18 4AG Tel: (020) 8320 9200 Fax: (020) 8312 9126 *Food wholesalers*

▶ Musgrove Willows, Lakewall, Westonzoyland, Bridgwater, Somerset, TA7 0LP Tel: (01278) 691105 Fax: (01278) 699107 E-mail: info@musgrovewillows.co.uk *Garden arbours & wicker suppliers*

Mushroom Components, 28 College Street, Kempston, Bedford, MK42 8LU Tel: (01234) 363611 Fax: (01234) 326611 E-mail: pv@mushroom.co.uk *Semiconductors & electronic components distrbs*

▶ Mushroom Marketing Ltd, Melbury House, Oxford Road, Bournemouth, BH8 8ES Tel: (01202) 315538 Fax: (01202) 961351 E-mail: info@mushroommarketing.co.uk *Marketing & public relations services*

Mushtaq Sweet Centre, 143 Lozells Road, Birmingham, B19 2TP Tel: 0121-507 0732 Fax: 0121-258 2339 *Confectionary manufrs*

Mushtaq Sweet Centre, 102 Alum Rock Road, Birmingham, B8 1HU Tel: 0121-328 3837 Fax: 0121-258 2339 *Asian sweets retailer & manufr*

▶ Music 4, 41-42 Berners Street, London, W1T 3NB Tel: (020) 7016 2000 Fax: (020) 7016 2001 E-mail: office@music4.com *Audio production & music composers*

▶ Music Bugs, 4 Bowles Road, Abbey Meads, Swindon, SN25 4ZN Tel: (01793) 722072 E-mail: info@musicbugs.co.uk *Fun and friendly music classes for bouncing babies, toddlers and pre-schoolers. Classes run throughout Swindon, Wiltshire and surrounding areas. Very friendly groups, run by local mums. Come and have a free trial session first.*

The Music Corporation, 679 Christchurch Road, Bournemouth, BH7 6AE Tel: (01425) 470007 Fax: (01425) 480569 E-mail: sales@them.corporation.com *Musical equipment*

Music & Design Ltd, 12 Linnell Road, Redhill, RH1 4DH Tel: (01737) 768272 E-mail: chris.bayley@virgin.net *Musical instrument suppliers*

Music Education Supplies Ltd, Unit 1 Bentinck Workshops, Park Lane, Kirkby-in-Ashfield, NG17 9LE Tel: (0845) 0264703 Fax: (01623) 726871 E-mail: sales@mesdirect.com *Musical equipment suppliers*

Music Exchange (Manchester) Ltd, Claverton Road, Wythenshawe, Manchester, M23 9ZA Tel: 0161-946 1234 Fax: 0161-946 1195 E-mail: sales@music-exchange.co.uk *Music distributors*

▶ Music For London, 122 Wigmore Street, London, W1U 3RX Tel: (0845) 2262971 Fax: (0845) 2262972 E-mail: info@musicforlondon.co.uk *Live entertainment*

Music Works, 14 Stockport Road, Cheadle, Cheshire, SK8 2AA Tel: 0161-491 2932 Fax: 0161-428 3633 *Specialist Hi-fi mains cables manufrs*

Musical Images, 18 Monmouth Street, London, WC2H 9HB Tel: (020) 7497 1346 Fax: (020) 7497 9205 *Hi-fi, stereo & electronics retailers*

Musonic UK Ltd, Unit 13 Business Centre, Colne Way, Watford, WD24 7ND Tel: (020) 8950 5151 Fax: (020) 8950 5391 E-mail: sales@musonic.co.uk *Sound & vision suppliers & manufrs*

▶ Musselbrook Machine Maintenance Ltd, 136a Church Road, Croydon, CR0 1SE Tel: (020) 8686 2500 Fax: (020) 8649 9088 *Machinery repairs & maintenance*

Mussett Group Ltd, Beccles Industrial Estate, Loddon, Norwich, NR14 6JD Tel: (01508) 522500 Fax: (01508) 528769 E-mail: enquire@mussett.co.uk *Precision machining services*

Musson Wood Products Ltd, Common La Industrial Estate, Kenilworth, Warwickshire, CV8 2EL Tel: (01926) 859616 Fax: (01926) 850844 *Packing case & pallet manufrs*

▶ Must Av It, 28 Lattimore Road, Wheathampstead, Hertfordshire, AL4 8QE Tel: 0870 446 0146 Fax: 0870 762 6431 E-mail: info@webstract.co.uk

Mustang, Midland Road, Rotherham, South Yorkshire, S61 1SZ Tel: (01709) 559547 Fax: (01709) 556758 *Joiners*

Mustang Communications Ltd, Dunslow Road, Eastfield, Scarborough, North Yorkshire, YO11 3UT Tel: (01723) 582555 Fax: (01723) 581673 E-mail: kelly@mustang.co.uk *Sound system manufrs*

Mustard Research, Hop Studios, 2 Jamaica Road, London, SE1 2BX Tel: (020) 7231 4700 Fax: (020) 7231 1640 *Security consultants*

Mustard Seed, Boscawen Road, Perranporth, Cornwall, TR6 0EW Tel: (01872) 571421 *Health food & spice suppliers*

Mustdestroy.Com, Unit 1 Invicta Centre, Alfreds Way, Barking, Essex, IG11 0BA Tel: (020) 8591 7900 Fax: (020) 8591 7901 *Confidential waste destruction*

Musto Ltd, Christy Way, Laindon, Basildon, Essex, SS15 6TR Tel: (01268) 491555 Fax: (01268) 491440 E-mail: marketing@musto.co.uk *Waterproof f& sailing & country wear manufrs*

Muswell Manufacturing Co. Ltd, Unit D1 New Southgate Industrial Estate, Lower Park Road, London, N11 1QD Tel: (020) 8368 8738 Fax: (020) 8368 4726 E-mail: sales@muswell.co.uk Folding table manufrs

Mutad Engineering, Chartwell Road, Lancing, West Sussex, BN15 8TU Tel: (01903) 756006 Fax: (01903) 750423 Precision engineers

James Mutch Ltd, 105 King Street, Aberdeen, AB24 5SN Tel: (01224) 643452 Fax: (01224) 630763 E-mail: sales@jamesmutch.co.uk Cleaning equipment suppliers

Mutech Ltd, Unit 25, Waters Edge Business Park, Modwen Road, Salford, M5 3EZ Tel: 0161-872 0400 E-mail: sales@mutech.co.uk High technology designers & manufrs

▶ Mutek Ltd, Rashieburn, Fintray, Aberdeen, AB21 0YX Tel: (01651) 806455 Fax: (01651) 806696 E-mail: info@mutekrf.com Designers and manufacturers of high power RF amplifiers and low noise front end RF amplifiers including a range of very low noise and high dynamic range replacement front ends for existing radio equipment.

Mutleys Plant Service, Shepherds Forge, Sutton Road, West Langdon, Dover, Kent, CT15 5HN Tel: (01304) 853938 Fax: (01304) 853937 Plant & machinery repairers

▶ Muttley's, Promsfield, Craigbreck, North Kessock, Inverness, IV1 3XG Tel: (01463) 731743 E-mail: info@muttleys.com At Muttley"s we provide a friendly professional service for most pets large or small. We offer dog walking, pet transport and pet home visits We have extensive dog/pet handling experience and are fully insured so you can safely leave your best friend in our care.

▶ Muzikvoice Ltd, 32 Wareham House, Brompton Pool Road, Hall Green, Birmingham, B28 0SL Tel: 0121-474 5228 Music Promotion*Record Label*Media Services

▶ MVP Couriers, 64 Toms Town Lane, Studley, Warwickshire, B80 7QP Tel: (01527) 458716 E-mail: mickpegg@supanet.com UK Sameday and overnight deliveries. Technical service also available.

MVS, 1 The Croft, Flitwick, Bedford, MK45 1DL Tel: (01525) 718079 E-mail: mvs@ntlworld.com Digital satellite commercial installation & networking

▶ MW Electrical Services Ltd, Unit 2A, Kettlestring Lane, Clifton Moor, York, YO30 4XF Tel: (01904) 691166 Fax: (01904) 691199 E-mail: craig@mwelectric.demon.co.uk Electrical contractors

MW Scaffolding Ltd, Glan Yr Afon Industrial Estate, Llanbadarn Fawr, Aberystwyth, Dyfed, SY23 3JQ Tel: (01970) 624927 Fax: (01970) 624247 E-mail: sales@mwscaffolding.demon.co.uk Scaffolding contractors

▶ MWM Litho, Unit 17 Greenwich Centre Business Park, 53 Norman Road, London, SE10 9QF Tel: (020) 8858 8644 Fax: (020) 8858 8600

▶ MX-tech Ltd, 6 Wingfield Grove, Glossop, Derbyshire, SK13 8SW Tel: (01457) 865582 E-mail: enquiries@mx-tech.co.uk IT consultancy services

▶ My Computes, Unit 1, Central Buildings, Kingsway, Manchester, M19 1SP Tel: 0161-975 0220 Fax: 0161-975 0330

▶ My Credit Zoo, 1 Park Lane, Leeds, LS3 1EP Tel: 0113-242 4747 E-mail: james.dobson@eurodirect.co.uk Free service to find the best credit cards, loans

▶ My Home Bulgaria Ltd, 129 Wellington Road, London, london, E6 6EB Tel: (020) 8552 5920 Fax: (0870) 7622839 E-mail: zaur@pochta.ws Bulgarian property for sale with UK-Bulgaria based agency. Largest online catalogue of property in Bulgaria.

▶ My Marketing, Lion House, Bell Lane, Bellbrook Industrial Estate, Uckfield, East Sussex, TN22 1QL Tel: (01825) 766646 Fax: (01825) 768755 E-mail: begin@my-marketing.co.uk Telemarketing service & virtual sales

▶ My Modern Art, 81 Beveley Road, Oakengates, Telford, Shropshire, TF2 6SD Tel: (07740) 338778 E-mail: sales@mymodernart.co.uk We provide high quality canvas art to commercial buyers, as well as logo and website design. All of our work is bespoke & is designed to meet the exact requirements of our customers. We specialise in restaurant & retail art.

My Problems Solved, 39-43 Church Street, Cannock, Staffordshire, WS11 1DS Tel: (01543) 469499 Fax: (07000) 432985 ATM & computer cleaning services

Myatt & Degville Fabrications Ltd, Selborne Street, Walsall, WS1 2JN Tel: (01922) 648222 Fax: (01922) 613565 Security grille & fire escape manufrs

Myco Falcon, 8 Stanley Centre, Kelvin Way, Crawley, West Sussex, RH10 9SE Tel: (01293) 544533 Fax: (01293) 402737 E-mail: enquiries@rapidcare.com Medical surgical supplies distributors

Myco Systems Ltd, 17 Criss Grove, Chalfont St. Peter, Gerrards Cross, Buckinghamshire, SL9 9HG Tel: (01753) 893390 E-mail: enquiries@mycosystems.co.uk Computer consultancy

Mycol Engineering, 75 Tenter Road, Moulton Park Industrial Estate, Northampton, NN3 6AX Tel: (01604) 790389 Fax: (01604) 790389 Plastic mould & toolmakers

Myddelton & Major, The Estate Office, Quartermaster Road, West Wiltshire Trading Estate, Westbury, Wiltshire, BA13 4JT Tel: (01373) 822260 Fax: (01373) 823070 E-mail: wwte@myddeltonmajor.co.uk Managing agents for industrial property

▶ Alex Myers and Associates, Apartment 25, 9 Kean Street, London, WC2B 4AY Tel: (020) 7379 5124 Fax: (020) 7379 0269 E-mail: info@alexmyersassociates.co.uk Audio visual & programme producers

Myers & Bowman Ltd, Lillyhall West, Workington, Cumbria, CA14 4PE Tel: (01946) 832282 Fax: (01946) 832596 E-mail: info@myers-and-bowman.toyota.co.uk Toyota motor vehicle dealers & repairers

Myers John Associates, Park Street, Parkfield Business Centre, Stafford, ST17 4AL Tel: (01785) 224134 Fax: (01785) 246654 E-mail: jma@onetel.net.uk Exhibition stands, design & build panel systems sale & hire

Myers & Myers Imports Ltd, 35 Ringley Road, Whitefield, Manchester, M45 7LD Tel: 0161-798 9004 Fax: 0161-773 9700 Buyers & distributors of clothing

▶ Myersholm Construction Ltd, Station Yard, The Village, Strensall, York, YO32 5XD Tel: (01904) 490208 Fax: (01904) 491264

▶ myHotDesk, 27 John Player Building, Stirling Enterprise Park, Stirling, Stirling, FK7 7RP Tel: 01786 450022 E-mail: advice@www.myhotdesk.com My Hot Desk Stirling Scotland- Rent from myHotDesk for flexible computer, telephone, and Internet access - near Edinburgh, Glasgow, Falkirk and Perth

Mykon, 5 Stukeley Business Centre, Blackstone Road, Huntingdon, Cambridgeshire, PE2 96EF Tel: (01480) 415070 Fax: (01480) 450181 E-mail: sales@mykon-systems.com Architectural solutions for partitioning, flooring, screens and furniture, using composite materials such as aluminium sandwiched between skins of glass, glass fibre or polycarbonate.*

Mykro Hydraulics Distributors Ltd, Nortonthorpe Industrial Estate, Wakefield Road, Scissett, Huddersfield, HD8 9LA Tel: (01484) 865977 Fax: (01484) 865809 E-mail: mykrohydraulics@aol.co.uk Hydraulic equipment manufrs

Myland's Paints & Woodfinishes, 80 Norwood High Street, London, SE27 9NW Tel: (020) 8761 5197 Fax: (020) 8761 5700 E-mail: sales@mylands.co.uk French polish & wood & paint manufrs

▶ MyLife, PO Box 743, Bromley, BR2 7XX Tel: 07961 943896 E-mail: enquiries@mylives.co.uk We sell a range of condoms which are free from animal products and cruelty. They are of the highest UK and EU standards and are available at very cheap prices.

▶ My-Limo.Co.Uk, 140 Meadow Way, Norwich, NR6 6XU Tel: (0870) 2426958 Fax: (01603) 415077 E-mail: info@my-limo.co.uk my-limo.co.uk has earned an enviable reputation for the hire of limousines, based on our friendly and professional service ethic whilst ensuring our customers get maximum value for money.* *Our fleet of the latest imported American stretch limousines all come fully equipped with chilled drinks bar, mood & party lighting, DVD & CD and of course - opulent interiors! These remarkable vehicles offer style, luxury and promise a very memorable experience.**So whether you are looking to make a special entrance at your wedding, a stir at the nightclub, a relaxed airport transfer, a memorable anniversary dinner or just make an event truly unique - my.limo.co.uk can help you fulfill your dream.*

▶ Mylnefield Research Services Ltd, Invergowrie, Dundee, DD2 5DA Tel: (01382) 568568 Fax: (01382) 568501 Laboratory research services

▶ myNaturalife.com, 3 Horncastle Cottages, Plawhatch Lane, Sharpthorne, East Grinstead, West Sussex, RH19 4JH Tel: (020) 7990 7744 Fax: (020) 7990 7744 Natural health supplements and products, powerful anti-oxidants, liquid vitamins and minerals - made from organic ingredients with state-of-the-art biochemistry. GM free and not tested on animals.

Myona Ltd, Watery La Middleway, Bordesley, Birmingham, B9 4HE Tel: 0121-773 4333 Fax: 0121-773 4970 E-mail: sales@myona.co.uk Protective clothing & safety footwear retailers

Myra Plaster Mouldings, 24 Myra Road, Downpatrick, County Down, BT30 7JX Tel: (028) 4488 1676 Fax: (028) 4488 1676 Plaster moulding supplier & manufrs

▶ Myriad, 330 Dereham Road, Norwich, NR2 4DL Tel: (0800) 5875967 E-mail: uk-sales@myriad-uk.net High quality business gifts at the best possible price

Myriad, 10 Lawn Avenue, Peterborough, PE1 3RB Tel: (01733) 766617 Fax: (01733) 759727 E-mail: enquiries@myriadit.net Computer software

Myriad Audio Visual Sales Ltd, 106 Hampstead Road, London, NW1 2LS Tel: (020) 7380 0191 Fax: (020) 7388 9225 E-mail: info@myriad-av.co.uk Audio visual equipment sale & hire

Myriad Services Ltd, 111 Woods Lane, Derby, DE22 3UE Tel: (01332) 380763 Fax: (01332) 380763 Shell moulding casting manufrs

Myron Hunka Manufacturing Jewellers, 8a North Parade, Bradford, West Yorkshire, BD1 3HT Tel: (01274) 307634 Fax: (01274) 307634 Jewellery repairs, retail & manufrs

Mystic East Cushions, PO BOX 51568, London, LONDON, SE1 2JT Tel: 0845 612 1551 E-mail: mysticeastcushions@miscobjects.com We specialise in one off unique cushions using our own artwork and those of other designers that we collaborate with around the world. All artwork is transferred to our standard super soft twill cushions which have a special canvas area for printing. All covers are machine washable. These extra special "mini fabric works of art" really do add colour and life to any room in the home. Want to make a bold statement about your personality? well with these great home accessories by Mystic East cushions you will be able to achieve that dream.**We also do custom design...if you have a favourite piece of artwork, photography or painting that you would like to transfer to a large scatter cushion then do get in contact with us for further details.**We hold a large collection of unique designs. Please visit our website to take a look at some of the designs we have on offer.

Myston Services Ltd, Foxhanger House, Curtis Lane, Headley, Bordon, Hampshire, GU35 8PH Tel: (01428) 713174 Groundwork's & cable laying contractors

Mytchett Engineering Services, Sunnyhaven, Salisbury Terrace, Mytchett, Camberley, Surrey, GU16 6DB Tel: (01252) 511397 Fax: (01252) 377460 Heating & ventilation installers & pipeline fabricators

Myton Systems Ltd, 3 West End, Lund, Driffield, North Humberside, YO25 9TN Tel: (01377) 217364 Fax: (01377) 217364 E-mail: sales@mytonsystems.co.uk Quality management systems consultancy & auditing

MyVideoTalk, 2 Glebe Meadows, Chester, Cheshire, Mickle Trafford, Chester, CH2 4QX Tel: 01244 303253 Fax: 08700 513684 E-mail: post@videotalk4all.com The future for Online Marketing and Communication has arrived. Get in early. Representatives required - international business from home with great potential. Existing businesses - simple to use video e-mail/streaming to enhance communications and boost your marketing, brings economical video to all sizes of business.

MyVideoTalk, 163 Winchester Road, Highams Park, Waltham Forest, London, E4 9JN Tel: 020 85235278 E-mail: myvideotalk@uwclub.net Innovative communications.

MyWorkwear.co.uk, Unit 1-2, Kingsland Tradeing Estate, Telford, Shropshire, TF7 4QW Tel: (0870) 3503150 Fax: (01952) 585991 E-mail: orders@myworkwear.co.uk The UK's favourite online Workwear & Corporate Wear supplier. We also have a fully automated online embroidery service.

▶ N 2 N Ltd, Unit 26, Rosehill Business Centre, Normanton Road, Derby, DE23 6RH Tel: (01332) 200009 Fax: (01332) 292625

▶ N 4 Solutions Ltd, 1-4 Priory Court, Poulton, Cirencester, Gloucestershire, GL7 5JB Tel: (01285) 852200 Fax: (0870) 6085120 Financial software solution services

N A C D Ltd, 10 Avebury Court, Hemel Hempstead, Hertfordshire, HP2 7TA Tel: (01442) 211848 Fax: (01442) 212776 E-mail: sales@nacd.co.uk Electronic door entry system manufrs

N A Cullen & Co. Ltd, Hayhills Road, Silsden, Keighley, West Yorkshire, BD20 9NE Tel: (01535) 654968 Fax: (01535) 655590 E-mail: nacul@lineone.net Air conditioning design & install

▶ N A Curtain Walling Ltd, Unit 1 Westfield Industrial Estate, Horndean, Waterlooville, Hampshire, PO8 9JX Tel: (023) 9259 5757 Fax: (023) 9259 5757 E-mail: robbiew@nacurtainwalling.com Curtain walling & unitised glazing service

N A G Ltd, Wilkinson House Jordan Hill, Banbury Road, Oxford, OX2 8DR Tel: (01865) 311744 Fax: (01865) 310139 E-mail: info@nag.co.uk Computer software system consultants & services

▶ N A Hamilton Contractors Ltd, Hamilton House, West Road, Stanley, County Durham, DH9 7XA Tel: (01207) 233444 Fax: (01207) 238222

N A K Trading Co. Ltd, 153 Dukes Rd, Western Ave, Park Royal, London, W3 0SL Tel: (020) 8752 1815 Fax: (020) 8752 1878 Ladies fashion wholesalers

N A L Ltd, Kinloch Drive, Bolton, BL1 4LZ Tel: (01204) 496772 Fax: (01204) 845952 E-mail: sales@nal.ltd.uk Street furniture distributors

▶ N A L Plant Ltd, Farnsworth Farm, Welbeck Road, Bolsover, Chesterfield, Derbyshire, S44 6XF Tel: (01246) 241066 Fax: (01246) 241066

N A R Gorup Ltd, Unit 6, Quorn Way, Grafton Street Industrial Estate, Northampton, NN1 2PN Tel: (01604) 631666 Fax: (01604) 232673 E-mail: nargroup@btconnect.com Road spring radiators repairers & manufrs

N A Stordy Combustion Ltd, Heath Mill Road, Wombourne, Wolverhampton, WV5 8BD Tel: (01902) 891200 Fax: (01902) 895552 E-mail: sales@stordy.co.uk Combustion engineers services

▶ N B C Group Ltd, Crown Works, Orleton Lane, Wellington, Telford, Shropshire, TF1 2BG Tel: (01952) 222400 Fax: (01952) 641325 E-mail: enquiries.kell04@nbcgroup.co.uk Sales Contact: D. Edwards Ball Bearings, Roller, Imperial, Metric, Needle, Taper, Self Lube, Plummer Block, Thermoplastic, Bearings, Slewing Rings, Sprockets, Chain, Pulleys, Belts, Motors, Gearboxes, Seals, SKF, RHP, Timken, QCB, FSQ, TR, BRB, Robello, Renold, Fenner, Varvel, Neri, PTP.

N B Camber, Harley, Harley, Shrewsbury, SY5 6LN Tel: (01952) 510524 Fax: (01952) 510222 E-mail: sales@cambers.com Agricultural merchants

▶ N B Computer Maintenance Ltd, 50 Leys Road, Pattishall, Towcester, Northamptonshire, NN12 8JZ Tel: (01327) 831404 Fax: (01327) 830982 E-mail: sales@nbmaintenance.co.uk Computer maintenance consultants

N B Group It Consultancy, 34 Bedford Road, Gregans House, Hitchin, Hertfordshire, SG5 1HF Tel: (01462) 452452 E-mail: info@online-it.com Computer resellers

N B Information Ltd, 570 Lanark Road West, Balerno, Midlothian, EH14 7BN Tel: 0131-449 7922 E-mail: support@-info.co.uk Management consultants & software developers

N B Metals Ltd, Unit 10 Blenheim Court, Brownfields, Welwyn Garden City, Hertfordshire, AL7 1AD Tel: (01707) 324472 Fax: (01707) 324473 E-mail: info@nbmetals.co.uk Aluminium extrusion manufrs

N B S Solutions, Kelvin Way, Crawley, West Sussex, RH10 9WE Tel: (01293) 442797 Fax: (01293) 442798 E-mail: sales@nbs-solutions.co.uk Internet & e-commerce designers

N B Seed Processors Ltd, Willow Farm, Little Hale Fen, Sleaford, Lincolnshire, NG34 9BG Tel: (01529) 460021 Fax: (01529) 461740 Agricultural seed merchants

N B Services Olney Ltd, 8 Leyside, Bromham, Bedford, MK43 8NF Tel: (01234) 828900 Fax: (01234) 308972 Rotary vane vacuum pumps

N B Sign Services, 72 Winner Street, Paignton, Devon, TQ3 3BH Tel: (01803) 521160 Fax: (01803) 521135 Sign manufrs

N B Stairways Ltd, 2A Milton Road, London, E17 4SR Tel: (020) 8520 3566 Fax: (020) 8520 9673 E-mail: nicholsbros@btinternet.com Wood turners manufrs

N B Surveys Ltd, 182 Market Street, Aberdeen, AB11 5PQ Tel: (01224) 212324 Fax: (01224) 212306 E-mail: admin@nbsurveys.com 3D Laser Scanning*As-built Surveys*CAD Modelling*Land & Dimensional Surveys*

N Balfour & Sons, 12 Bilton Way, Luton, LU1 1UU Tel: (01582) 729621 Fax: (01582) 723334 E-mail: info@balfourhats.co.uk Hat manufrs

N & C Building Products Ltd, 41-51 Freshwater Road, Dagenham, Essex, RM8 1SP Tel: (020) 8586 4600 Fax: (020) 8586 4646 E-mail: head.office@nichollsandclarke.com Builders merchants

▶ N C D Electrical Ltd, 3 Grange Road, Batley, West Yorkshire, WF17 6LL Tel: (01924) 474765

N C Engineering Co. Ltd, 2 Killyrudden Road, Hamiltonsbawn, Armagh, BT61 9SF Tel: (028) 3887 1970 Fax: (028) 3887 0362 E-mail: nc.a.engineering@btinternet.com Agricultural & industrial machinery manufrs

N C Engineering Ltd, 1 Park Avenue, Bushey, WD23 2DA Tel: (01923) 691500 Fax: (01923) 691599 E-mail: sales@ncengineering.co.uk CNC machines, sale & service

N C Geary (Precision Engineering), 10 Mill Road, Christchurch, Dorset, BH23 2JY Tel: (01202) 483585 Fax: (01202) 471163 E-mail: nick@geary-engineering.co.uk Precision engineers

N C H Marketing Services Ltd, Earls Tree Industrial Estate, Corby, Northamptonshire, NN17 4DU Tel: (01536) 400123 Fax: (01536) 443319 E-mail: shagan@nchmarketing.co.uk Sales promotion handling, database services & coupon redemptions

N C Laser Cutting Services, Station Approach, Cark In Cartmel, Grange-over-Sands, Cumbria, LA11 7PT Tel: (01539) 558201 Fax: (01539) 558767 Laser cutting services

N C M P Ltd, 4 Falcon Way, Feltham, Middlesex, TW14 0XJ Tel: (020) 8751 0986 Fax: (020) 8751 5793 E-mail: ncmp-feltham@ncmp.co.uk Aluminium fabricators

N C O Europe, 3 The Green, Stratford Road, Shirley, Solihull, West Midlands, B90 4LA Tel: (020) 8565 4700 Fax: 0121-733 3154 Debt collection services Also at: Birmingham, Manchester & Edinburgh

N C R Ltd, Bakewell Road, Orton Southgate, Peterborough, PE2 6DP Tel: (01733) 363600 Fax: (01733) 363687 Paper till rolls & paper consumables manufrs

N C R UK Group Ltd, 206 Marylebone Road, London, NW1 6LY Tel: (020) 7723 7070 Fax: (020) 7725 8224 Computer makers Also at: Branches throughout the U.K.

N C S Inc, 49 Parc-y-Felin, Creigiau, Cardiff, CF15 9PB Tel: (029) 2089 1515 Fax: (029) 2089 1694 Electronic components

N C S Group P.L.C., Belville House, Ponteland, Newcastle Upon Tyne, NE20 9BF Tel: (01661) 803000 Fax: (01661) 860069 E-mail: marketing@ncs-plc.co.uk Computer system integration

N C Soft, 12 Nicholas Lane, London, EC4N 7BN Tel: (01252) 556000 Fax: (020) 7623 0442 E-mail: info@ncsoft.co.uk Financial systems developers

N C T Leather Ltd, Locher Works, Kilbarchan Road, Bridge of Weir, Renfrewshire, PA11 3RL Tel: (01505) 612182 Fax: (01505) 612123 E-mail: sales@nctleather.co.uk Tanners

N Code International Ltd, Innovation Technology Center, Advanced Manufacturing Park, Brunel Way, Catcliffe, Rotherham, South Yorkshire, S60 5WG Tel: 0114-254 1246 Fax: 0114-254 1245 E-mail: info@ncode.com Engineering software producers

N Coppard Groundworks, 13 Ghyll Road, Heathfield, East Sussex, TN21 0AQ Tel: (01892) 669163 Civil engineering

N D C Ltd, 72 Crooksbury Road, Farnham, Surrey, GU10 1QD Tel: (01252) 782666 Fax: (01252) 782666 Computer consultants

N D Jig & Gauge Co.Ltd, Bush Works, Leabrook Road, Wednesbury, West Midlands, WS10 7NB Tel: 0121-556 0824 Fax: 0121-556 8177 E-mail: sqplatewashers@aol.com Washers round or square (metallic), pressings, general presswork & nut manufrs

▶ N D S 8 Ltd, 11 Bankhead Broadway, Edinburgh, EH11 4DB Tel: (0845) 2260070 Fax: 0131-538 8202 E-mail: david.ashton@nds8.co.uk Network design & support

N D S L Ltd, Unit 2 Oakfield Industrial Estate, Eynsham, Witney, Oxfordshire, OX29 4TS Tel: (01865) 884288 Fax: (01865) 884289 E-mail: sales@ndsl.co.uk Battery monitoring equipment manufrs

▶ N D Solutions, 179 Pappert, Alexandria, Dunbartonshire, G83 9LG Tel: (01389) 602766 Metalworking services

N D T Consultants Ltd, Siskin Drive, Middlemarch Business Park, Coventry, CV3 4FJ Tel: (024) 7651 1151 Fax: (024) 7651 1696 E-mail: sales@ndt-consultants.co.uk Principal Export Areas: Middle East, West Europe & Central America Filter cartridges

N D T Electronics, 30 Royal Industrial Estate, Jarrow, Tyne & Wear, NE32 3HR Tel: 0191-428 0962 Fax: 0191-428 0904 E-mail: ian.armson@ndtelectronicservices.com Non-destructive testing & inspection equipment distributors

N D T Kenged, 5 Keith Street, Hamilton, Lanarkshire, ML3 7BL Tel: (01698) 285914 Fax: (01698) 891975 E-mail: ken@kenged.co.uk Principal Export Areas: Middle East, West Europe & North America Test equipment distributors

N Deal & Sons Ltd, 100 Hatton Garden, London, EC1N 8NX Tel: (020) 7430 1615 Fax: (020) 7404 4786 E-mail: info@nvogel.co.uk Jewellery manufrs

N E C Electronics, Cygnus House, Sunrise Parkway, Linford Wood, Milton Keynes, MK14 6NP Tel: (01908) 691133 Fax: (01908) 670290 E-mail: receptioneuk@ee.nec.de Electronic component distributors sales & marketing

N E C Europe Ltd, Unit G Stafford Park 12, Telford, Shropshire, TF3 3BJ Tel: (01952) 237000 Fax: (01952) 237006 E-mail: kevin.emlyn@uk.neceur.com *Technical centre*

N E C Grinding Services, 61b Shaw Heath, Stockport, Cheshire, SK3 8WH Tel: 0161-480 1899 Fax: 0161-480 1899 *Tool regrinding & manufrs*

▶ N E C Infrontia, 75 Swingbridge Road, Loughborough, Leicestershire, LE11 5JB Tel: (01509) 643100 Fax: (01509) 610206 E-mail: sales@necinfrontia.co.uk *Telecommunications*

▶ N E Cox Ltd, 190 Boldmere Road, Sutton Coldfield, West Midlands, B73 5UE Tel: 0121-355 8780 Fax: 0121-355 7436 E-mail: mail@necox.co.uk

▶ N E Fastenings Ltd, 175-179 Snowdon Road, Middlesbrough, Cleveland, TS2 1DB Tel: (01642) 244106 Fax: (01642) 244109 *Bolts & nut manufrs*

▶ N E L Technologies Ltd, 269b Queensway South, Team Valley Trading Estate, Gateshead, Tyne & Wear, NE11 0SD Tel: 0191-487 4181 Fax: 0191-264 0994 E-mail: sales@nel-ltd.co.uk

N E L UK Ltd, 75 Burton Road, Carlton, Nottingham, NG4 3FP Tel: 0115-940 1894 Fax: 0115-987 0878 E-mail: tony@nel-uk.co.uk *Coil winders & transformers*

N E M Co. Ltd, Stevenage Business Park, Wedgewood Way, Stevenage, Hertfordshire, SG1 4SX Tel: (01438) 346600 Fax: (01438) 346632 E-mail: sales@nemco.co.uk *Electronic designers & manufrs*

▶ N E M S Ltd, North Moor St, South Dock, Sunderland, SR1 2BQ Tel: 0191-514 5037 Fax: 0191 510 8108 E-mail: sales@nems.uk.com *With Headquarters in Sunderland Tyne and Wear NEMS Warehousing operates over 275000 sq ft of Bonded Warehousing in the North East of England, as well as operations in Hull, Liverpool, Singapore and China. Offering a full wet and dry bond service, NEMS also offers Personal storage facilities, Caravan and Vehicle storage, Document storage and retrieval and general warehousing. Situated close to the A1 and A19 trunk roads, and based in the Port of Sunderland, NEMS can handle loads quickly and efficiently by road, rail or sea.*

N E Plastics Ltd, 1 Ruxley Corner Industrial Estate, Edgington Way, Sidcup, Kent, DA14 5BL Tel: (020) 8308 9990 Fax: (020) 8308 9995 E-mail: sales@neplastics.co.uk *Plastic distributors*

▶ N E Print Ltd, Unit 5 Tile House Farm, Birds Green, Willingale, Ongar, Essex, CM5 0PN Tel: (01277) 899800 Fax: (01277) 899063 *Silk screen printers*

N F F O Services Ltd, Marsden Road, Grimsby, South Humberside, DN31 3SG Tel: (01472) 349009 Fax: (01472) 242486 E-mail: nffo@nffo.org.uk *Trade association*

N F F Precision Ltd, 4 Enterprise Way Aviation Park, Bournemouth Int Airp, Hurn, Christchurch, Dorset, BH23 6EW Tel: (01202) 583000 Fax: (01202) 583058 E-mail: sales@nff.uk.com *Precision engineers & fabricators*

N F I Ltd, 259 York Town Road, College Town, Sandhurst, Berkshire, GU47 0RT Tel: (01276) 600200 Fax: (01276) 600161 E-mail: info@nfi.uk.com Principal Export Areas: Worldwide *Distributors of fibre optic cables*

N F J Green Ltd, Moor Farm Road West, Airfield Industrial Estate, Ashbourne, Derbyshire, DE6 1HD Tel: (01335) 344801 Fax: (01335) 344801 *General engineers*

▶ N F M Solutions Ltd, 7 Standrigg Gardens, Brightons, Falkirk, FK2 0GJ Tel: (0870) 7776698 Fax: (0870) 7776398 E-mail: info@nfmsolutions.com *IT consultancy, web design & hosting*

N F R Racewear, 15 Water Street, Radcliffe, Manchester, M26 3DE Tel: 0161-723 4012 Fax: 0161-280 9949 E-mail: sales@nfrlivethedream.co.uk *Motor racing clothing manufrs*

N F S Fire Protection Ltd, Morton Street, Middleton, Manchester, M24 6AN Tel: 0161-643 9338 Fax: 0161-655 3878 *Fire protection equipment*

▶ N F T Distribution Ltd, 51 Eldon Way, Crick, Northampton, NN6 7SL Tel: (01788) 823921

▶ N Fairclough Builders Ltd, Bentley Road, Doncaster, South Yorkshire, DN5 9TG Tel: (01302) 783416 Fax: (01302) 783742

N Farrow, 18 Shingle Hill, Denham, Eye, Suffolk, IP21 5EU Tel: (01379) 870752 E-mail: technick1@btinternet.com *ELECTRONIC REPAIRS TO TV /VCR /DVD /RADIO /AUDIO SYSTEMS/MICROWAVE /VACUUM CLEANERS/DYSON /INSTALLATION & SET UP OF HOME ENTERTAINMENT SYSTEMS / FREEVIEW /TV RECEPTION AND AERIAL FAULT DIAGNOSIS. CALL OUTS TO RESIDENTIAL HOMES AND BUSINESS PREMISES /WORKSHOP FACILITIES. ALL MAKES OF APPLIANCES REPAIRED.*

▶ N Foster, 212 Cotswold Crescent, Billingham, Cleveland, TS23 2QJ Tel: (01642) 361932 Fax: (01642) 361932 E-mail: sales@nfosterelectrical.co.uk *Electrical contractors, commercial,domestic and industrial installations. Intruder and fire alarm systems.inspection and testing.*

▶ N G Bailey & Co. Ltd, Bairds Brae, Glasgow, G4 9SW Tel: 0141-332 8040 Fax: 0141-332 8272

▶ N G Bailey Ltd, Unit 8, Coulerdbank Industrial Estate, Lossiemouth, Morayshire, IV31 6NG Tel: (01343) 814807

N G C Consultancy Ltd, Unit 1A, The Mayfields, Southcrest, Redditch, Worcestershire, B98 7DU Tel: (01527) 404739 Fax: (01527) 404739 *Extrusion machine distributors & manufrs*

N G Joinery, Unit 2 The Stable Block Brewer Street Farm, Brewer Street, Brewer Street Farm Brewer Street, Redhill, RH1 4QP Tel: (01883) 744842 Fax: (01883) 744842 *Joinery services*

N G K Spark Plugs UK Ltd, Maylands Avenue, Hemel Hempstead, Hertfordshire, HP2 4SD Tel: (01442) 281000 Fax: (01442) 281001 E-mail: enquiries@ngk.co.uk *Motor component distributors*

N G Phillips, Lays Farm, Charlton Road, Keynsham, Bristol, BS31 2SE Tel: 0117-986 6172 Fax: 0117-986 6172 *Portable buildings manufrs*

N Gerstler Ltd, 4 Metro Trading Centre, Second Way, Wembley, Middlesex, HA9 0YJ Tel: (020) 8900 0200 Fax: (020) 8900 8558 *Lining & textile merchants*

N Gilks, Hailes Farm, Hailes, Cheltenham, Gloucestershire, GL54 5PB Tel: (01242) 604662 Fax: (01242) 604663 *Cabinet makers*

N Gosling, Occupation Lane, New Bolingbroke, Boston, Lincolnshire, PE22 7JZ Tel: (01205) 480691 Fax: (01205) 480691 *Fabrication engineering & garden furniture*

N H P Romsey Ltd, Tadburn Road, Romsey, Hampshire, SO51 5HS Tel: (01794) 523678 Fax: (01794) 515468 *Mechanical consultants*

▶ N H Picture Frames, 57 Brongwinau, Comins Coch, Aberystwyth, Dyfed, SY23 3BQ Tel: (01970) 615512 E-mail: kyleireland@hotmail.com *Picture framing*

▶ N. H. S. Edinburgh, Nine Mile Burn, Penicuik, Midlothian, EH26 9LT Tel: (01968) 679333 Fax: (01968) 679222

N H Weld Fab, 10 Ailwin Road, Bury St. Edmunds, Suffolk, IP32 7DS Tel: (01284) 724504 Fax: (01284) 766887 E-mail: nigel@nhweldfabltdc.o.uk *Decorative metal gates and railings. Metal furniture for the home and garden, including pond covers, weather vanes. Commissions and design service available. Free quotation. Domestic and industrial.*

N I C Ltd, Mariners Street, Goole, North Humberside, DN14 5BW Tel: (01405) 782600 Fax: (01405) 782612 E-mail: nic@damacgroup.co.uk *Cement manufrs & distributors*

N I C Components Europe, 14 Top Angel, Buckingham Industrial Estate, Buckingham, MK18 1TH Tel: (01280) 813737 Fax: (01280) 814737 E-mail: niesales@niccomp.com *Electronic components*

N I C Instruments Ltd, Gladstone Road, Folkestone, Kent, CT19 5NF Tel: (01303) 851022 Fax: (01303) 850155 E-mail: sales@nicltd.co.uk *Security services*

▶ N I Europe Ltd, 1 Beverley Road, Market Weighton, York, YO43 3JN Tel: (01430) 803355 Fax: (01430) 803356 E-mail: sales@networkinstallations.co.uk *Specialist provider of optical fibre data & voice solutions*

N I G, Crown House, 145 City Road, London, EC1V 1LP Tel: (020) 7656 6000 Fax: (020) 7251 0345 E-mail: marion.chan@nig-uk.com *Insurance company* Also at: Birmingham, Bristol, Leeds, Manchester & Peterborough

N I I B Group Ltd, 26-32 Central Avenue, Bangor, County Down, BT20 3AS Tel: (028) 9146 9415 Fax: (028) 9147 4455 E-mail: support@boiuk.co.uk *Credit & finance company*

N I I T Europe Ltd, Westfields, London Road, High Wycombe, Buckinghamshire, HP11 1HP Tel: (01494) 539333 Fax: (01494) 539444 *IT solutions*

N I S Holdings Ltd, Ackhurst Road, Chorley, Lancashire, PR7 1NH Tel: (01257) 265656 Fax: (01257) 275501 E-mail: info@nisltd.com *Engineering & design consultants*

N I S Holdings Ltd, Ackhurst Road, Chorley, Lancashire, PR7 1NH Tel: (01257) 265656 Fax: (01257) 275501 E-mail: tbromell@nisltd.com *Special purpose machinery design & general purpose specialists*

N I S Sign Group, Oakland Road, Leicester, LE2 6AN Tel: 0116-270 6228 Fax: 0116-270 3347 E-mail: info@signs-nis.co.uk *Sign making*

N J Aluminium, 223 Bowling Back Lane, Bradford, West Yorkshire, BD4 8SJ Tel: (01274) 733393 Fax: (01274) 732221 *Architectural aluminium fabricators*

▶ N J B Contractors, Eastlands Industrial Estate, King George Avenue, Leiston, Suffolk, IP16 4LL Tel: (01728) 830924 Fax: (01728) 833675

N J Bennett, Norbury, Weston under Penyard, Ross-on-Wye, Herefordshire, HR9 7PG Tel: (01989) 564284 Fax: (01989) 564284 *Fitted kitchens*

N & J Engineering Ltd, Vulcan Road, Solihull, West Midlands, B91 2JY Tel: 0121-704 0440 Fax: 0121-704 0550 E-mail: sales@dohertygroup.co.uk *Precision components stockers & distributors*

▶ N J Evans & Son, Jehu Road, Welshpool, Powys, SY21 7PE Tel: (01938) 552976 Fax: (01938) 552976

N J Froment & Co. Ltd, Cliffe Road, Easton on the Hill, Stamford, Lincolnshire, PE9 3NP Tel: (01780) 480033 Fax: (01780) 480044 E-mail: sales@froment.co.uk Principal Export Areas: Worldwide *Manufacturers of dynamometers, generator load frame*

▶ N J Grime, 32 Wentworth Drive, Euxton, Chorley, Lancashire, PR7 6FN Tel: (01257) 232602 Fax: (01257) 232602 E-mail: njgrimepurchaseservices@supanet.com *Purchasing & procurement service*

N J M Cleaning Ltd, 137 Essex Road, Romford, RM7 8BD Tel: (01708) 742127 E-mail: sales@njmcleaning.co.uk *Builders cleans, office, window vehicle cleaning*

N J M Sign & Display Ltd, 52 Bunting Road Industrial Estate, Northampton, NN1 3JY Tel: (01604) 250777 Fax: (01604) 250777 E-mail: njmsigns@aol.com *Sign manufrs*

N J M Trading, 32 Temple St, Wolverhampton, WV2 4AN Tel: 01902 429022 Fax: 01902 429052 *CCTV manufrs*

▶ N & J Mcfarlane Ltd, Dunvegan Road, Portree, Isle of Skye, IV51 9HD Tel: (01478) 613613 Fax: (01478) 613614

N J Meagor, Trelawder, St. Minver, Wadebridge, Cornwall, PL27 6RF Tel: (01208) 813235 Fax: (01208) 816392 E-mail: nickpoultry@aol.com *Incubator & poultry suppliers*

▶ N J Metals, Unit 2, Hawksworth Road, Horsforth, Leeds, LS18 4JP Tel: 0113-258 2611 Fax: 0113-274 8465 *Wrought ironworkers & display equipment*

N J Metals, R/O 10 Vesper Road, Leeds, LS5 3NX Tel: 0113-230 4818 *Wrought iron dealers*

N J R Installations Ltd, Chapel Street, Dudley, West Midlands, DY2 9PN Tel: (01384) 455555 Fax: (01384) 456177 *Heating & ventilating engineers*

N J Sewing, 2 Pretoria Place, Station Road, Brightons, Falkirk, FK2 0UF Tel: (01324) 711333 Fax: (01324) 711333 *Sewing machines retail & repairs*

N K Antcliffe, Brittania Works, Melton Road, Thurmaston, Leicester, LE4 8BD Tel: 0116-269 4743 *Woodwork machinery suppliers*

N K Coatings Ltd, 4 Michelin Road, Newtownabbey, County Antrim, BT36 4PT Tel: (028) 9083 3725 Fax: (028) 9083 7433 E-mail: mail@nkcoatings.com *Galvanising & powder coating services*

▶ N K Computer Supplies, Unit 5a Caxton Trading Estate, Printing House Lane, Hayes, Middlesex, UB3 1BE Tel: (020) 8813 6070 Fax: (020) 8574 3642 E-mail: sales@nkcomputersupplies.co.uk *Office & computer suppliers*

N K Computer Supplies, Unit 5a Caxton Trading Estate, Printing House Lane, Hayes, Middlesex, UB3 1BE Tel: (020) 8813 6070 Fax: (020) 8574 3642 E-mail: sales@nkcomputers.co.uk *Office supplies & stationery suppliers*

N K F Metal Services, Unit 5 East Thamesmead Business Park, Kencot Close, Erith, Kent, DA18 4AB Tel: (020) 8310 2199 Fax: (020) 8310 2204 E-mail: john.oshea60@virgin.net *Sheet metal workers suppliers & manufrs*

N K Fencing, 40 Trailcock Road, Carrickfergus, County Antrim, BT38 7NU Tel: (028) 9335 1172 Fax: (028) 9333 6433 E-mail: sales@nkfencing.com *Fencing contractors & fencing manufrs*

N K M Fire Protection Ltd, Broadford Oast, Goudhurst Road, Tonbridge, Kent, TN12 8ET Tel: (01892) 724242 Fax: (01892) 723242 *Installation of fire alarms & emergency lighting & servicing*

▶ N K Pollock International, 5 Prospect 3, Gemini CR, Dundee Technology Park, Dundee, DD2 1SW Tel: (01382) 568468 Fax: (01382) 561666

▶ N L R Precision Engineers Ltd, 71 Greystock Street, Sheffield, S4 7WA Tel: 0114-278 0060 Fax: 0114-278 0062

N L S Tools, Station Approach, Waltham Cross, Hertfordshire, EN8 7LZ Tel: (01992) 710888 Fax: (01992) 713938 E-mail: sales@nlstools.co.uk *Saws & woodworking tools manufrs*

N Long Printers, 8 Buckholt Business Centre, Buckholt Drive, Worcester, WR4 9ND Tel: (01905) 456140 Fax: (01905) 756903 *General printers*

▶ N M A Agencies Ltd, Birds Royd Lane, Brighouse, West Yorkshire, HD6 1LQ Tel: (01484) 400488 Fax: (01484) 711012

N M B Minebea UK Ltd, Doddington Road, Lincoln, LN6 3RA Tel: (01522) 500933 Fax: (01522) 500975 *Aerospace, rod end & spherical bearings manufrs*

N M B-Minebea (UK) Ltd, Suite 2.2, Doncastle House, Doncastle Road, Bracknell, Berkshire, RG12 8PE Tel: (01344) 426611 Fax: (01344) 485522 Principal Export Areas: Worldwide *Electric motor stockists & ball bearing manufrs*

▶ N M C Drainage Ltd, 140 Old Gartloch Road, Gartcosh, Glasgow, G69 8EH Tel: (01236) 870087 Fax: (01236) 870700

N M D Computer Consultants, 27 Friar Rd, Brighton, BN1 6NH Tel: (01273) 551060 Fax: (01273) 551060 E-mail: nick@mndconsulting.com *Computer consultants*

N M Design, The Foundry, Unit 5, Albert Street, Brigg, South Humberside, DN20 8HU Tel: (01652) 658559 Fax: (01652) 651758 E-mail: info@nmdesign.co.uk *Bespoke website, illustration, multimedia & design photographers*

N M Farley & Sons, Gaddon Spring Farm, Uffculme, Cullompton, Devon, EX15 3DL Tel: (01884) 840402 Fax: (01884) 840402 *Farming & agricultural contractors*

N & M Fibreglass (Holdings) Ltd, The Barns Unit 4, Hewell Lane Tardebigge, Tardebigge, Bromsgrove, Worcestershire, B60 1LP Tel: (01527) 870282 Fax: (01527) 576269 E-mail: nmfibreglass@aol.com *Fibreglass manufrs*

N M I Safety Systems Ltd, 17 Lake Business Centre, Tariff Road, London, N17 0YX Tel: (020) 8801 5339 Fax: (020) 8801 3491 E-mail: sales@nmisafty.com *Cargo securing equipment manufrs*

N M Rothschild & Sons Leasing Ltd, New Court Street, Swithins Lane, London, EC4P 4DU Tel: (020) 7280 5000 Fax: (020) 7929 1643 E-mail: infouk@rothschild.co.uk *Banking services* Also at: Cardiff & Manchester

N M Signs, Baltimore Road, Birmingham, B42 1DG Tel: 0121-357 9357 Fax: 0121-358 5600 E-mail: designssignsandgraphics@yahoo.co.uk *Sign manufrs*

N M Signs, Baltimore Road, Birmingham, B42 1DG Tel: 0121-357 9357 Fax: 0121-358 5600 *Sign manufrs*

▶ N Macdonald, Balliscate, Salen Road, Tobermory, Isle of Mull, PA75 6NS Tel: (01688) 302065 Fax: (01688) 302099

N N R Ltd, 94 Gervase Road, Edgware, Middlesex, HA8 0EP Tel: (020) 8906 1497 *Computer consultants*

N & N Signs, 353 Green Lanes, London, N4 1DZ Tel: (020) 8802 4929 Fax: (020) 8880 2591 *Sign makers*

N O'Dwyer & Partners, 15 Downshire Road, Newry, County Down, BT34 1EE Tel: (028) 3026 6915 Fax: (028) 3026 4810 E-mail: info@nicholasodwyer.co.uk *Civil engineers*

N P Aerospace Ltd, 473 Foleshill Road, Coventry, CV6 5AQ Tel: (024) 7663 8464 Fax: (024) 7668 7313 E-mail: info@np-aerospace.co.uk *Plastics moulding manufrs*

N P Automotive Coatings (Europe) Ltd, Brittania Trade Park, Radway Road, Swindon, SN3 4ND Tel: (01793) 823361 Fax: (01793) 823127 E-mail: janesandman@npae.co.uk *Automotive industry paint manufrs*

▶ N P M Ltd, Riverside Road, Pride Park, Derby, DE24 8HA Tel: (01332) 600020 Fax: (01332) 600313 *Printing*

N P S Shoes, South St, Wollaston, Wellingborough, Northamptonshire, NN29 7RY Tel: (01933) 664207 Fax: (01933) 664699 E-mail: npsshoes@eurotellbroadband.com *Boots & shoes*

N & P Thermo Plastic Moulders Acton Ltd, 69-73 Stirling Road, London, W3 8DJ Tel: (020) 8992 8258 Fax: (020) 8993 0860 *Precision toolmakers & injection moulding*

N & P Thermo Plastics Moulders (Whitton) Ltd, Silverdale Road, Hayes, Middlesex, UB3 1AQ Tel: (020) 8569 1300 Fax: (020) 8569 1480 *Injection moulders*

N Palmer, 131 Main Street, Horsley Woodhouse, Ilkeston, Derbyshire, DE7 6AX Tel: (01332) 780110 Fax: (01332) 780110 *Joinery manufrs*

▶ N R A Roofing & Flooring Services Ltd, Rock House, Belfield Street, Ilkeston, Derbyshire, DE7 8DU Tel: 0115-930 4019 Fax: 0115-944 1728

N R Automatics Ltd, Duckworth Mill, Skipton Road, Colne, Lancashire, BB8 0RH Tel: (01282) 868500 Fax: (01282) 869885 *Turned parts manufrs*

N R Burnett Ltd, West Carr Lane, Hull, HU7 0AW Tel: (01482) 838800 Fax: (01482) 822110 *Timber & wallboard merchants*

N R Components Ltd, Der Street, Todmorden, Lancashire, OL14 5QY Tel: (01706) 815821 Fax: (01706) 818505 E-mail: info@nrawnings.com *Awning manufrs*

N R Engineering, 5 Commercial Road, Reading, RG2 0QZ Tel: 0118-975 0303 Fax: 0118-975 3879 *Precision engineers*

▶ N R Evans & Son Ltd, Care Dawn Cardington, Meadow Lane, Cardington, Bedford, MK44 3SB Tel: (01234) 838153 Fax: (01234) 831674

N R G Group Ltd, 4 Rushmills, Northampton, NN4 7YB Tel: (01604) 732700 *Supply & service office equipment* Also at: Branches throughout the U.K.

N R G Kits, 18 Victoria Street, Queensbury, Bradford, West Yorkshire, BD13 1AR Tel: (01274) 816200 Fax: (01274) 816200 E-mail: nrgkitsfm@aol.com *Electronic kit manufrs*

N R G Management Ltd, 66 Chiltern Street, London, W1U 4AG Tel: (020) 7465 1000 Fax: (020) 7224 5740 Principal Export Areas: Worldwide *Photocopier & laser equipment manufrs*

▶ N R G Power Systems Ltd, 10 Westbourne Avenue, Worthing, West Sussex, BN14 8DF Tel: (01903) 200044 Fax: (01903) 200066 E-mail: nigel@nrgpowersystems.com *Power supplies*

N & R Manufacturing Ltd, Lawrence House Apollo, Lichfield Road Industrial Estate, Tamworth, Staffordshire, B79 7TA Tel: (01827) 57218 Fax: (01827) 60289 *Export case & pallet manufrs*

N & R Needham & Co. Ltd, Bridge Street Industrial Estate, Bridge Street, Clay Cross, Chesterfield, Derbyshire, S45 9NU Tel: (01246) 863171 Fax: (01246) 865411 *Precision engineers*

N R & P J Haywood, Battenhurst Road, Stonegate, Wadhurst, East Sussex, TN5 7DU Tel: (01580) 200571 Fax: (01580) 200920 *Farmers*

N R S Ltd, 14 Lysander Road, Bowerhill, Melksham, Wiltshire, SN12 6SP Tel: (01225) 709408 Fax: (01225) 708719 E-mail: info@n-rs.co.uk *Roofing & guttering manufrs*

N R Seal & Son, Main Street, Wick, Pershore, Worcestershire, WR10 3NU Tel: (01386) 555706 Fax: (01386) 555707 E-mail: nrsandson@tiscali.co.uk *Manufacturers of extruder barrels & screws*

N R T Packaging Supplies Ltd, Bampton Packaging Site, Lenton Lane, Nottingham, NG7 2NR Tel: 0115-957 8911 Fax: 0115-986 2984 E-mail: nrtsalesteam@bamptonpackaging.co.uk *Polythene tube & cover manufrs*

N Royston Ltd, Carham Road, Hoylake, Wirral, Merseyside, CH47 4FF Tel: 0151-632 4141 Fax: 0151-632 0569 E-mail: charleshumphreys@1stdental.co.uk *Dental laboratory*

▶ N S B Casements Ltd, 3 Steele Road, London, NW10 7AR Tel: (020) 8961 3090 Fax: (020) 8961 3050 E-mail: info@nsbcasements.co.uk *Steel windows manufrs*

N S D Ltd, South Park Road, Scunthorpe, South Humberside, DN17 2BY Tel: (01724) 810000 Fax: (01724) 819981 E-mail: sales@nsc.ltd.uk *Steel stockholders*

N S Enterprise Training, 22a Church Street, Dungannon, County Tyrone, BT71 6AB Tel: (028) 8772 9773 Fax: (028) 8772 4775 E-mail: sales@nsenterprise.co.uk *Computer & network integrator manufrs*

N S F Controls Ltd, Ingrow Bridge Works, Keighley, West Yorkshire, BD21 5EF Tel: (01535) 661144 Fax: (01535) 661474 E-mail: sales@nsfcontrols.co.uk Principal Export Areas: Worldwide *NSF Controls, situated in Keighley West Yorkshire is one of Europe's leading manufacturers of electro-mechanical components & assemblies, specialising in the supply of Actuation Products, including open frame solenoids, stepping solenoids, magnetically latched solenoids, rotary wafer switches code switches, encoders, lever switches, toggle switches & pushbutton switches. NSF through its Far Eastern partners provides logistic access to large volumes of the widest selection of electro-mechanical components available from a single source anywhere in Europe. Coupled with unbeatable levels of customer service & technical support, our in house facility builds on our expertise in product design & application engineering to deliver a streamlined operation dedicated to providing workable solutions to actuation challenges of every type & volume.*

N S H Turned Parts, Fordwater Trading Estate, Ford Road, Chertsey, Surrey, KT16 8HG Tel: (01932) 561761 Fax: (01932) 563178 *Automatic turned parts manufrs*

N S I Group Ltd, Whitacre Road Industrial Estate, Nuneaton, Warwickshire, CV11 6BY Tel: (024) 7637 5656 Fax: (024) 7664 1191 E-mail: sales@nsigroup.co.uk *Laser cutting services & in-house fabricators*

N S J Engineering, 231 Handsworth Road, Handsworth, Sheffield, S13 9BL Tel: 0114-243 1769 Fax: 0114-243 1408 E-mail: neil@nsjengineering.co.uk *General & precision engineers*

N S K Ltd, Northern Road, Newark, Nottinghamshire, NG24 2JF Tel: (01636) 705298 Fax: (01636) 605000 E-mail: info-uk@nsk.com Principal Export Areas: Africa *Ball & roller bearings, mechatronics products & automotive components manufrs*

N S K Bearings Europe Ltd, Davy Drive, North West Industrial Estate, Peterlee, County Durham, SR8 2PW Tel: 0191-518 0777 Fax: 0191-518 0303 *Bearings*

N S Lemos & Co. Ltd, St Clare House, 30-33 Minories, London, EC3N 1DD Tel: (020) 7481 8921 Fax: (020) 7481 4177 E-mail: nslemos@nslemos.com *Ship brokers*

▶ N & S OFFICE SOLUTIONS LTD, 25 PRINCES STREET, TUNBRIDGE WELLS, KENT, TN2 4SL Tel: 01892 514643 E-mail: nsoffice@btinternet.com *Virtual Assistant, Word Processing, Secretarial Services, Admin Assistance & Courier Services.*

N S Optimum Ltd, 7a Jenton Road, Leamington Spa, Warwickshire, CV31 1XS Tel: (01926) 880300 Fax: (01926) 886983 E-mail: sales@nsoptimum.co.uk *Computer distributors & manufrs*

N S P Building Services Ltd, 24 Nova Lane, Birstall, Batley, West Yorkshire, WF17 9LE Tel: (01924) 445648 Fax: (01924) 445648 *Building*

N & S Precision Components Ltd, 63F Milton Park, Abingdon, Oxfordshire, OX14 4RX Tel: (01235) 831563 Fax: (01235) 820253 E-mail: carolnixon@onetel.com *Precision engineers*

N S R Graphics, 56 Ashton Vale Road, Bristol, BS3 2HQ Tel: 0117-953 2352 Fax: 0117-953 2353 E-mail: nsr@nsr-eng.co.uk *Precision turned parts*

N S Reed Printing Supplies, 9 Dean Court, Great Western Business Park, Yate, Bristol, BS37 5NJ Tel: (01454) 323775 Fax: (01454) 326935 E-mail: nsreed.print@virgin.net *Lithographic & letterpress printers*

▶ N S T Direct Ltd, Premium House, Hambridge Road, Newbury, Berkshire, RG14 5SS Tel: (01635) 31177 Fax: (01635) 31184 E-mail: info@nstdirect.co.uk *Courier & transport worldwide*

N Schahid Ltd, Unit 3 Knoll Business Centre, Old Shoreham Road, Hove, East Sussex, BN3 7GS Tel: (01273) 424200 Fax: (01273) 424204 E-mail: nschahid@aol.com *Badge & uniform regalia manufrs*

N Schlumberger UK Ltd, Hillam Road, Bradford, West Yorkshire, BD2 1QN Tel: (01274) 394641 Fax: (01274) 370424 E-mail: n.schlumberber.uk@mail.com *Textile machinery agents & merchants*

N Small, 7 Flush Road, Newcastle, County Down, BT33 0QF Tel: (028) 4375 1312 *Livestock dealers*

N Smith & Co. Ltd, Leopold Works, 28 Hainge Road, Tividale, Oldbury, West Midlands, B69 2NZ Tel: 0121-557 1891 Fax: 0121-521 5700 E-mail: sales@nsmithbox.co.uk *Cardboard box, case & container manufrs*

N Stephenson & Son Kettering Ltd, 49 Grafton Street, Kettering, Northamptonshire, NN16 9DF Tel: (01536) 512625 Fax: (01536) 522869 E-mail: nstephenson@realemail.co.uk *Joinery & carpenter manufrs*

N Sys, Balgownie Road, Bridge of Don, Aberdeen, AB22 8GT Tel: (0845) 0559944 Fax: (0845) 0559945 *Sun accounts software & developers*

N T Burton, Oaklands, Loughborough Road, Rempstone, Loughborough, Leicestershire, LE12 6RQ Tel: (01509) 856150 Fax: (01509) 856444 *Agricultural contractors*

N T C Microcad, Morton Road, Darlington, County Durham, DL1 4PT Tel: (01325) 350220 Fax: (01325) 350767 *Computer aided design services*

▶ N T F S Ltd, 11 Northdown Arcade, Northdown Road, Cliftonville, Kent, CT9 2QB Tel: (01843) 294777 E-mail: david@ntfs.net

N T N Bearings UK Ltd, 11 Wellington Crescent, Fradley Park, Lichfield, Staffordshire, WS13 8RZ Tel: (01543) 445000 Fax: (01543) 445035 E-mail: jcd@ntn-europe.com *Manufacturers of ball, taper & roller bearings*

N T N Signs, Donegall Street, Belfast, BT1 2FJ Tel: (028) 9023 0703 Fax: (028) 9023 0703 *Engravers*

N T R Ltd, Unit 372a Thorp Arch Estate, Thorp Arch, Wetherby, West Yorkshire, LS23 7BJ Tel: (01937) 845112 Fax: (01937) 845467 E-mail: info@ntrltd.co.uk *Tool reclamation services*

N T S Aluminium Systems Ltd, Gainsford Drive, Halesowen, West Midlands, B62 8BQ Tel: 0121-501 3814 Fax: 0121-585 5492 *Aluminium shop front fitters & manufrs*

N T Security Ltd, Unit A Cambridge House, Waterside Court, Neptune Close, Medway City Estate, Rochester, Kent, ME2 4NZ Tel: (01634) 296869 Fax: (01634) 296992 E-mail: sales@ntsecurity.co.uk *Access control systems*

N T T Contracts Ltd, 307 Park Ho, 21 Park St, Croydon, CR0 1YE Tel: (020) 8405 8196 Fax: (020) 8681 5963 *Computer consultancy*

N T T Europe Ltd, Devon House, 58-60 St Katharines Way, London, E1W 1LB Tel: (020) 7977 1000 Fax: (020) 7977 1001 E-mail: info@ntt.co.uk *Telecommunications system manufrs*

N Taylor & Sons, 2 Hall Street, Cheadle, Cheshire, SK8 1PJ Tel: 0161-491 1824 Fax: 0161-491 1824 *Joinery manufrs*

N Thompson, Unit J & K Cardigan Workspace, Lennox Road, Leeds, LS4 2BL Tel: 0113-289 0819 *Motor vehicle components suppliers*

▶ N V C Construction Ltd, Bogenraith, Durris, Banchory, Kincardineshire, AB31 6DS Tel: (01330) 811788 Fax: (01330) 811780

N & V Motors, 13-14 Oakwood Industrial Park, Gatwick Road, Crawley, West Sussex, RH10 9AZ Tel: (01293) 547541 Fax: (01293) 611917 *Commercial vehicle repairers*

▶ N V Vamix, Martley Road, Lower Broadheath, Worcester, WR2 6RF Tel: (01905) 641616 Fax: (01905) 640905 E-mail: sales@vandemoortele.com *Manufacturers of frozen dough products*

N W C Business Forms Ltd, Unit 17-19, Greenfield Business Park, Holywell, Clwyd, CH8 7HW Tel: (01352) 712965 Fax: (01352) 713092 *Bespoke business printed form printers*

N W E Paints Ltd, 66-70 Ffordd Las, Rhyl, Clwyd, LL18 2EA Tel: (01745) 342342 Fax: (01745) 334746 E-mail: admin@nwepaints.co.uk *Protective paint distributors & decorators merchant*

N W F Agriculture Ltd, Wardle, Nantwich, Cheshire, CW5 6AQ Tel: (0800) 262397 Fax: (01829) 260061 E-mail: enquiries@nwfagriculture.co.uk *Agricultural merchants & ruminant feed manufrs* Also at: Leaton, Stoke-on-Trent & Whitchurch

N W F Country Store, Bert Smith Way, Adderley Road Industrial Estate, Market Drayton, Shropshire, TF9 3SN Tel: (01630) 655766 Fax: (01630) 658413 *Agricultural contractors*

N W F Swiftpak, 129 Church Road, Bason Bridge, Highbridge, Somerset, TA9 4RG Tel: (01278) 789200 Fax: (01278) 789100 E-mail: sales@narrowwidthfilms.cwc.net *Polythene packaging & stretch wrap film suppliers & manufrs*

N & W Global Vending, PO Box 25, Bilston, West Midlands, WV14 0LF Tel: 01902 355000 Fax: 01902 402272 E-mail: sales@nwglobalvending.co.uk *N & W Global Vending based in Bilston, West Midlands are an internationally acclaimed vending machine manufacturer. Areas of product expertise include hot and cold beverages, snack and food, can and bottle, hot beverage dispensers for the out-of-home and office coffee sectors.*

N W H, Downside Farm, Cobham Park Road, Downside, Cobham, Surrey, KT11 3NE Tel: (01932) 864767 Fax: (01932) 864767 *Precision engineers*

▶ N W Levers Ltd, Kingswinford Industrial Estate, Ham Lane, Kingswinford, West Midlands, DY6 7JH Tel: (01384) 400888

N W S Services Ltd, Mayswood Road, Wootton Wawen, Henley-in-Arden, West Midlands, B95 6AL Tel: (01564) 792546 *Vehicle hire, servicing & recovery*

▶ N Y C Jewellery, 333 Kilburn High Road, London, NW6 7QB Tel: (020) 7624 2900

N Y K Logistics, Common Road, Huthwaite, Sutton-in-Ashfield, Nottinghamshire, NG17 2JY Tel: (01623) 510510 Fax: (01623) 518612 E-mail: *Freight forwarders & transport services* Also at: Branches throughout the U.K.

▶ N2 Generation Ltd, 65 Hillary Drive, London, Isleworth, Middlesex, TW7 7EG Tel: (020) 8400 6981 Fax: (0870) 7622388 E-mail: sales@n2gen.com *Specialists in supplying Nitrogen Generation Solutions to Laboratories and Industry and Offshore. We operate in the UK and all international markets.*

▶ N2 Visual Communications Ltd, Unit 40 Oakwood Hill Industrial Estate, Oakwood Hill, Loughton, Essex, IG10 3TZ Tel: (020) 8508 8880 Fax: (020) 8508 2331 E-mail: sales@notaprint.com

▶ N-A Multigraphics, 55 Upper Seymour Street, Bradford, West Yorkshire, BD3 9LJ Tel: (01274) 394802 E-mail: namultigraphics@aol.com *Signs & banners manufrs*

NABIC, Delta Road, Parr, St. Helens, Merseyside, WA9 2ED Tel: (01744) 451616 Fax: (01744) 26791 E-mail: enquiries@deltafluidproducts.com *Safety & pressure relief valve manufrs*

▶ N-able Technologies Inc UK, 20 Garrick Street, London, WC2E 9BT Tel: (020) 7664 7821 Fax: (020) 7664 7878 E-mail: sales@n-able.com *Managed services*

Nabru Ltd, Unit 12, Sarum Complex, Salisbury Road, Uxbridge, Middlesex, UB8 2RZ Tel: (01895) 256868 Fax: (01895) 239214 E-mail: service@nabru.co.uk *Sofas self assembly, access difficult places in home, retail & manufrs*

▶ Nacco Materials Handling, Carn Industrial Area, Portadown, Craigavon, County Armagh, BT63 5YY Tel: (028) 3835 4499 Fax: (028) 3833 9977 *Forklift truck manufrs*

▶ Nacco Materials Handling Group Ltd, Flagship House, Reading Road North, Fleet, Hampshire, GU51 4WD Tel: (01252) 810264 Fax: (01922) 742469 E-mail: yaleinfo@nmhg.com

Nafeeze Knitwear, 37 Devonshire St South, Manchester, M13 9DA Tel: 0161-273 3178 Fax: 0161-273 6819 E-mail: info@knitwearemporium.com *Knitwear manufr*

Nagington Farming, Doley, Adbaston, Stafford, ST20 0RQ Tel: (01785) 280466 Fax: (01785) 280466 *Livestock farmers*

Nagra Bros, 149 Harrison Road, Leicester, LE4 6NP Tel: 0116-261 0511 Fax: 0116-261 1697 *Childrens leisurewear manufrs*

Nagra Fabrics, 42-46 Friday Street, Leicester, LE1 3BW Tel: 0116-251 3546 Fax: 0116-251 3546 *Fabric manufrs*

NAI Fuller Peiser, Whittington House, 19-30 Alfred Place, London, WC1E 7EA Tel: (0870) 7002233 Fax: (020) 7182 7388 *Chartered surveyors*

Nai Gooch Webster, 4 Albemarle Street, London, W1S 4BW Tel: (020) 7409 5100 Fax: (020) 7409 5199 *Chartered surveyors*

Naiad Plastics Ltd, 16 Thorgate Road, Wick, Littlehampton, West Sussex, BN17 7LU Tel: (01903) 724302 Fax: (01903) 730925 E-mail: naiad@naiadplastics.com *Injection moulders & plastics mouldings manufrs*

▶ Naiko UK Ltd, Spear Fir, Bardsey, Leeds, LS17 9EA Tel: (01937) 579888 Fax: (01937) 577518

▶ Nail It UK, 28 Stratford St North, Birmingham, B11 1BY Tel: 0121-245 0055 Fax: (0870) 3506561 *The specialist fixing distributor that offers a difference. Our product range is not often found in the majority of fixing companies catalogues and whenever they are you may be quoted several weeks for availability. At Nail It we have those products available for immediate despatch.*We carry, special application cartridge tool nails, scaffolding fixings, approved anchors for cracked concrete, new generation of electrical fixings and cavity fixings with a difference.*Also Midlands Mungo distributor.*

Nailfast, 3 Nobel Court, Nobel Road, West Gourdie Industrial Estate, Dundee, DD2 4UH Tel: (01382) 622993 Fax: (01382) 612993 E-mail: sale@nailfast.co.uk *Nailing & stapling equipment, building product distributors*

Nailsea Power Cleaning Ltd, Cherry Orchard Farm, Youngwood Lane, Nailsea, Bristol, BS48 4NP Tel: (01275) 810881 Fax: (01275) 810885 *Cleaning equipment manufrs*

▶ Nailsea Web Design, 23 Earlesfield, Nailsea, Bristol, BS48 4SG Tel: (01275) 857953

Nailsworth Services Ltd, Unit 5 Strensham Business Park, Strensham, Worcester, WR8 9JZ Tel: (01684) 274758 Fax: (01684) 274758 E-mail: helen@nailsworth.eclipse.co.uk *Hand railing & steel fabricators*

Nairb Controls, PO Box 1610, Salisbury, SP1 3XH Tel: (01722) 322922 Fax: (01722) 322922 *Heating, ventilation & air conditioning controls fabricators*

Naish Felts Ltd, Crow Lane, Wilton, Salisbury, SP2 0HD Tel: (01722) 743505 Fax: (01722) 744048 E-mail: sales@naishfelts.co.uk Sales Contact: D. Legatti *Naish Felts Ltd - Manufacturers of felt, including component, display, industrial usage, needleloom/needled, pressed, technical & washers. In addition self-adhesive die cut shape & plastic foam manufacturers, foam polyethylene & foam polyurethane converters*

▶ Naked Floors, 2 / 18 Stone Street, Brighton, BN1 2HB Tel: (01273) 208951 E-mail: enquiries@nakedfloors.com *Floor sanding, finishing & fitting services & flooring suppliers*

▶ Naked Knowledge, 138, Watling Street East, Towcester, Northants, NN12 6BT Tel: 0870-112 3000

Naked Orange, Fresh Produce Unit, Ballingry, Lochgelly, Fife, KY5 8LR Tel: (01592) 860490 E-mail: mwood869@btinternet.com *SUPPLY FRESH ORANGE JUICERS AND JUICING MACHINES AS WELL AS MOBILE AND STATIC JUICE BARS*

Nalco, 5 Riverside Business Park, Dogflud Way, Farnham, Surrey, GU9 7SS Tel: (01252) 735454 Fax: (01252) 734430 E-mail: enquiries@ondeo-nalco.com *Water hygiene chemical products*

Nalco, 20-22 Albion Way, Kelvin Industrial Estate, East Kilbride, Glasgow, G75 0YN Tel: (01355) 573900 Fax: (01355) 263660 *Water treatment chemical product manufrs*

Nalco Ltd, Weavergate Works, P O Box 11, Winnington Avenue, Northwich, Cheshire, CW8 4DX Tel: (01606) 74488 Fax: 01606 79557 Principal Export Areas: Worldwide *Water treatment chemical products*

Nalco, Pembroke Refinery, Pembroke, Dyfed, SA71 5SJ Tel: (01646) 641369 Fax: 01646 641369 *Specialist chemicals*

Nalco, Wilton International, Wilton, Redcar, Cleveland, TS10 4RG Tel: (01642) 430105 Fax: (01642) 459390 *Water treatment chemicals*

Nalco, Unit 5a Springside, Howard Road, Park Farm Industrial Estate, Redditch, Worcestershire, B98 7SE Tel: (01527) 453200 Fax: (01527) 520717 *Water industrial treatment service & manufrs*

Nalestar Ltd, Melton House, Melton Place, Leyland, Preston, PR25 4XU Tel: (01772) 431226 Fax: (01772) 622497 E-mail: sales@nalestar.co.uk *Uniform & fashion workwear manufrs*

Nalex Ltd, 4 Edgemead Close, Round Spinney Industrial Estate, Northampton, NN3 8RG Tel: (01604) 648133 Fax: (01604) 790435 E-mail: sales@nalex.co.uk *National distribution of fixings & fasteners*

▶ Nalli Ltd, 281 Kings Road, London, SW3 5EW Tel: (020) 7351 5292

▶ Namayasai LLP, Fair Hall, Southover High Street, Lewes, East Sussex, BN7 1HX Tel: (01273) 470667 Fax: (01273) 488816 E-mail: info@namayasai.co.uk *We are growers of pesticide-free Japanese vegetables and herbs for local doorstep delivery and direct to restaurants. All produce is picked on the day of delivery. Here in East Sussex, England, we are growing ashitaba, azuki bean, benibana, daikon, edamame, gobo, hourensou, kabocha, kabu, komatsuna, kyuuri, mitsuba, mizuna, myoga, naga-negi, nira, sansho, shiso, shungiku, soba, tatsoi, tonburi and udo.*

Namco Tooling Ltd, New Road, Studley, Warwickshire, B80 7LZ Tel: (01527) 853667 Fax: (01527) 852668 E-mail: sales@namco-tooling.com *Sole UK manufacturer of genuine Coventry Chasers, Dieheads, Namco dieheads. 1000's of standard/non-standard chasers in stock, with fast delivery on specials. UK's largest range of thread rolling dies to suit all current rolling heads & machines.*

▶ Namemark Ltd, PO Box 1792, Christchurch, Dorset, BH23 4YR Tel: (01425) 278070 Fax: (01425) 278070 *Labels And Tags Manufacturer*

Nameplate Services, The Iron Works, Union Street, Royton, Oldham, OL2 5JD Tel: 0161-620 4702 Fax: 0161-620 0503 E-mail: holt@nameplateservices.co.uk *Nameplate manufrs*

Nampak plc, Llantrisant Business Park, Llantrisant, Pontyclun, Mid Glamorgan, CF72 8LF Tel: (01443) 225520 Fax: (01443) 228970 E-mail: info@rpc-llantrisant.co.uk *Plastics bottles & containers manufrs*

Nampak Plastics, Unit 15, Number One Industrial Estate, Consett, County Durham, DH8 6SX Tel: (01207) 580402 Fax: (01207) 580265 *Blow moulders*

▶ Nampak Plastics Europe Ltd, Jenna Way Interchange Park, Newport Pagnell, Buckinghamshire, MK16 9PQ Tel: (01908) 611554 Fax: (01908) 614994 E-mail: jon.sweet@eu.nampak.com *Nampak Plastics Europe Ltd are a pan-european manufacturer of both standard & custom rigid plastic containers, using a wide range of polymers including HDPE, PP, & PET in mono & multi layer constructions. They have 14 sites across Western Europe focused on the following markets, food & drink, automotive, agrochemical, general chemicals & health & beauty*

Namrick Ltd, 124 Portland Road, Hove, East Sussex, BN3 5QL Tel: (01273) 736963 Fax: (01273) 726708 E-mail: sales@namrick.co.uk *Distributors of bolts & nuts, fasteners (industrial) & screws, machine. Also fastener, tooling merchants or agents*

Namron Aqua Products Ltd, Canklow Meadows Industrial Estate, West Bawtry Road, Rotherham, South Yorkshire, S60 2XL Tel: (01709) 371006 Fax: (01709) 367295 E-mail: namron@scubauk.com *Diving equipment & dry & wet-suit manufrs*

Namsbury Engineering Ltd, 56 Penistone Road, Sheffield, S6 3AE Tel: 0114-272 8111 Fax: 0114-270 1859 E-mail: enquiries@namsbury.demon.co.uk *Profile burning & steel fabricators*

Dr R.K. Nangia, West Point, 78 Queens Road, Maggs Ho, Bristol, BS8 1QX Tel: 0117-987 3995 Fax: 0117-987 3995 *Consulting aeronautical engineers*

Nangla Furniture, 1292-1296 Leeds Road, Bradford, West Yorkshire, BD3 8LF Tel: (01274) 664601 Fax: (01274) 664601 *Furniture cabinets manufrs*

▶ Nanny Tax, 28 Minchenden Crescent, London, N14 7EL Tel: 020 8882 6847 Fax: 020 8886 1624 E-mail: post@taxingnannies.co.uk *Taxing Nannies is a specialist nanny tax payroll service. The service includes opening a PAYE scheme, calculating tax and National Insurance, regular payslips, advising on Sick and Maternity Pay.*

▶ Nanny-Find Ltd Nanny Recruitment Agency, Bessemer Drive, Business & Technology Centre, Stevenage, Hertfordshire, SG1 2DX Tel: (0845) 6066162 E-mail: recruitment@nanny-find.co.uk *Recruitment of childcare professionals. Nanny-find Ltd recruits full-time and part-time Nannies, Mother''s Helpers, Home Support Workers, Nursery Assistants and Nursery Nurses in Hertfordshire and Essex.*

▶ Nanopoint UK, Unit 12, Stafford Park 12, Telford, Shropshire, TF3 3BJ Tel: (01952) 210355 Fax: (01952) 210355 *Computer hardware suppliers*

▶ Nano-Tek (UK) Technology Ltd, 19 Fore Lane Avenue, Sowerby Bridge, Halifax, West Yorkshire, HX6 1BQ Tel: (0870) 4285818 E-mail: enquiry@nano-tek.co.uk *Surface engineers*

Nantwich Veneers Ltd, Unit 3, Barony Employment Park, Beam Heath Way, Nantwich, Cheshire, CW5 6PQ Tel: (01270) 625361 Fax: (01270) 625597 E-mail: info@nantwichveneers.com *Veneer manufrs*

▶ Napa Products Ltd, North Main Street, Carronshore, Falkirk, FK2 8HT Tel: (01324) 573472 Fax: (01324) 573401 *Manufacturers of cleaning materials*

Napier Bros Engineers Ltd, 67 King Street, Rutherglen, Glasgow, G73 1JS Tel: 0141-647 6282 Fax: 0141-613 1611 *Mechanical & hydraulic engineers*

Napier Partnership Ltd, Birdham Road, Chichester, West Sussex, PO20 7DU Tel: (01243) 531123 Fax: (01243) 779070 E-mail: napier@napier.co.uk *Public relation services*

Napier Co (UK Division) Ltd, 3 Courtlands Rd, Eastbourne, E. Sussex, BN22 8SW Tel: (01323) 730196 Fax: (01323) 634206 *Fashion jewellery*

Napp Pharmaceutical Group Ltd, Science Park, Milton Road, Cambridge, CB4 0GW Tel: (01223) 424444 Fax: (01223) 424441 E-mail: vacancies@napp.co.uk *Pharmaceutical manufrs*

▶ NAPSYS Ltd, 6 Laurel Grove, Sidemoor, Bromsgrove, Worcestershire, B61 8LU Tel: (0870) 0638606 Fax: (0870) 0638607 E-mail: sales@napsys.co.uk *Well established IT Company in Worcestershire, Provides Web Design, Bespoke Web Application Development, Wi-Fi Wireless Networking, Domain Registration and Hosting, ADSL Connectivity and Web Maintenance - Nationwide Coverage.**

Narang Textiles, 121 City Road, Bradford, West Yorkshire, BD8 8JR Tel: (01274) 723157 Fax: (01274) 304334 E-mail: textiles@narang.co.uk *Importers, exporters & wholesale merchants of textiles & garments*

▶ David Narro Associates Ltd, 36 Argyle Place, Edinburgh, EH9 1JT Tel: 0131-229 5553 Fax: 0131-229 5090 E-mail: sales@davidnarro.co.uk

▶ Narrow Fabric Services Ltd, The Scotlands, London Road, Coalville, Leicestershire, LE67 3JJ Tel: (01530) 510141 Fax: (01530) 510137

Narrowcraft Ltd, Robeys Lane, Alvecote, Tamworth, Staffordshire, B78 1AS Tel: (01827) 898585 Fax: (01825) 897700 E-mail: sales@narrowboat.co.uk *Marina operators*

Narvida Ltd, Taxi Way, Hillend Industrial Park, Hillend, Dunfermline, Fife, KY11 9JT Tel: (01383) 823417 Fax: (01383) 823148 E-mail: info@narvida.co.uk *Stainless steel fabrication services*

Narvik Developments Ltd, Clay Lane, Oldbury, West Midlands, B69 4TH Tel: 0121-552 3429 Fax: 0121-552 6162 *Pattern manufacturers & vacuum forming tools*

Nasa Computers Ltd, 23 Stonefield Way, Ruislip, Middlesex, HA4 0YF Tel: (020) 8842 0931 Fax: (020) 8845 8577 *Software house*

Nasa Marine, Boulton Road, Stevenage, Hertfordshire, SG1 4QG Tel: (01438) 354033 Fax: (01438) 741498 E-mail: nasa.marine@aol.com *Marine electronics equipment manufrs*

Nasa Plant, Station Road, Four Ashes, Wolverhampton, WV10 7DB Tel: (01902) 791694 Fax: (01902) 790592 *Service plant machinery*

Nasco Ltd, Links Quarry, Newbiggin-by-the-Sea, Northumberland, NE64 6XQ Tel: (01670) 815849 Fax: (01670) 855297 *Sandstone products manufrs*

Nash & Co., 14 Bridge Street, Caversham, Reading, RG4 8AA Tel: 0118-947 2295 Fax: 0118-947 7010 E-mail: paulthejewel@aol.com *Engraving & signs manufactures also second hand fine jewellery*

Nash Conversions Ltd, Unit 5, Shaftesbury Court, Shaftesbury Road, Leyton, London, E10 7DA Tel: (020) 8539 2276 Fax: (020) 8558 3891 *Purpose made joinery service*

Nash Elmo UK Ltd, Road One, Winsford Industrial Estate, Winsford, Cheshire, CW7 3PL Tel: (01606) 542400 Fax: (01606) 542434 E-mail: sales@nasheng.com *Manufacturers of vacuum pumps, gas compressors & steam or air operated ejectors*

Nash Management, 7 The Chenies, Petts Wood, Orpington, Kent, BR6 0ED Tel: (01689) 820751 Fax: (01689) 875467 E-mail: nash@datel.ssworld.co.uk *Export merchants*

Nash Mechanical Seal Services Ltd, Nile Street, Bolton, BL3 6DW Tel: (01204) 388030 Fax: (01204) 361541 E-mail: enquiry@nashseal.com *Consultancy & specialist maintenance, repair & overhaul (MRO) company for high dependency mechanical seals, supplying to the UK & Europe. We supply, repair & improve the performance of high value, engineered mechanical seals utilised on critical rotating equipment, including pumps, agitators & high-speed turbo machinery.*

Nash Mynard Design Ltd, Dodford Mill, Dodford, Northampton, NN7 4SS Tel: (01327) 341643 Fax: (01327) 341801 *Consulting civil & structural engineers*

R.J. Nash Ltd, 74 Livery Street, Birmingham, B3 1RG Tel: (0121) 200 3900 Fax: (0121) 200 3906 E-mail: brookwelding@btinternet.com *Shot blasting services*

Sabih Nashat Contracts, Mosterley Farm, Cound, Shrewsbury, SY5 6BH Tel: (01694) 731731 Fax: (01694) 731739 E-mail: info@sabihnashat.com *Contract furnishing services*

Nashcourt Ltd, 9 Penuel Road, Pentyrch, Cardiff, CF15 9QJ Tel: (029) 2089 1201 E-mail: nashcourtltd@aol.com *Electronic instruments & instrumentation*

Nashil Automotive Engineers Ltd, 22 Burners Lane, Kiln Farm, Milton Keynes, MK11 3HB Tel: (01908) 307777 Fax: (01908) 307444 E-mail: arif@nashil-automotive.co.uk *Repair & servicing of motor vehicles*

Nash's Bakery, 63 Priory Road, Bicester, Oxfordshire, OX26 6BL Tel: (01869) 244647 Fax: (01869) 244844 E-mail: info@theoxfordbakery.com *Bakers*

Nason Foster Ltd, Moor Lane, Birmingham, B6 7HH Tel: 0121-356 5693 Fax: 0121-356 3818 E-mail: sales@nasonfoster.co.uk *Shop fitters & aluminium frontages*

▶ Nassau Industrial Doors Ltd, Dewsbury Road, Fenton Industrial Estate, Stoke-on-Trent, ST4 2TB Tel: (01782) 418700 *Industrial suppliers of doors*

Nasus Mechanical Handling Ltd, Unit 3 Monkmoor Trading Estate, Monkmoor Road, Shrewsbury, SY2 5TZ Tel: (01743) 355496 Fax: (01743) 235443 *Material handlers, forklift trucks & accessories suppliers*

▶ Nataris Ltd, 32 William Close, Southall, Middlesex, UB2 4UP Tel: (020) 8932 1612 Fax: E-mail: info.ks@nataris.com *We specialise in providing creative and strategic solutions web, multimedia and print. Our services include: web design and management, graphic design, branding, multimedia, online marketing, project management and copywriting.*

Natco Group, C/O Axsia Howmar Ltd, Albany Park Estate, Frimley Road, Camberley, Surrey, GU16 7QQ Tel: (01276) 681101 Fax: (01276) 681107 E-mail: ahl@axsia.com *Oil & gas processors*

Nater Leisurewear, Goodsmoor Road, Littleover, Derby, DE23 1NH Tel: (01332) 770554 Fax: (01332) 271201 E-mail: info@nater.co.uk *Protective clothing & leisurewear manufrs*

Natexis (Metals) Ltd, 47-53 Cannon Street, London, EC4M 5SH Tel: (020) 7648 4950 Fax: (020) 7248 5262 *Metal brokers*

Nathan Fabrics & Sundries Ltd, 31 Gildart Street, Liverpool, L3 8ET Tel: 0151-207 0777 Fax: 0151-298 1474 E-mail: sales@fabric-crafts.co.uk *Upholstery manufrs*

Nathan Software Ltd, 352 New Trows Road, Lesmahagow, Lanark, ML11 0JS Tel: (01555) 893548 Fax: (01555) 893589 *Computer software developer*

Nathan's Wastesavers Ltd, Unit 13 Winchester Avenue, Denny, Stirlingshire, FK6 6QE Tel: (01324) 826828 Fax: (01324) 826555 *Textile waste merchants & recovery contractors*

Nation Water Treatments Ltd, Unit 1 Shawlands Court, Newchapel Road, Lingfield, Surrey, RH7 6BL Tel: (01342) 833693 Fax: (01342) 833787 E-mail: nwt@nationwatertreatments.co.uk *Water treatment chemicals*

National Air Traffic Services, Atlantic House, Sherwood Road, Prestwick, Ayrshire, KA9 2NR Tel: (01292) 479800 Fax: (01292) 692733 *Air traffic control*

National Association Of Shopfitters, 411 Limpsfield Road, Warlingham, Surrey, CR6 9HA Tel: (01883) 624961 Fax: (01883) 626841 E-mail: nas@clara.net *Trade association*

National Bartender Magazine, PO Box 9667, Nottingham, NG10 9BZ Tel: 0115-925 5227 E-mail: sb@freebutler-gds.co.uk

National Bed Federation Ltd, Victoria House, Victoria Street, Taunton, Somerset, TA1 3FA Tel: (01823) 368008 Fax: (01823) 350526 E-mail: sales@bedfed.org.uk *Trade association*

National Britannia Ltd, Caerphilly Business Park, Caerphilly Business Park, Caerphilly, Mid Glamorgan, CF83 3GG Tel: (029) 2085 2852 Fax: (029) 2086 7738 E-mail: enquiries@natbrit.com *Occupational health consultants*

▶ National Brittania Group, 17 Brenkley Way, Blezard Business Park, Seaton Burn, Newcastle upon Tyne, NE13 6DS Tel: 0191-236 6061 Fax: 0191-236 6061

National Car Parks Ltd (N C P), 21 Bryanston Street, London, W1H 7AB Tel: (0870) 6067050 Fax: (020) 7491 3577 E-mail: marketing@ncp.co.uk *Car park owning/ managing company*

National Caravan Council Ltd, Catherine House, Victoria Road, Aldershot, Hampshire, GU11 1SS Tel: (01252) 318251 Fax: (01252) 322596 E-mail: info@nationalcaravan.co.uk *UK caravan industry trade association*

▶ National Carpet Group, Eclipse Centre, Buckley Road, Rochdale, Lancashire, OL12 9BH Tel: (01706) 714455 Fax: (01706) 714454 E-mail: info@nationalcarpets.co.uk *Warehouse & distribution services*

▶ National Carwash Systems, 2 Ravells Yard, Carr Lane, Hoylake, Wirral, Merseyside, CH47 4AZ Tel: 0151-633 2345 Fax: 0151-632 3750 E-mail: nationalcarwash@talktalk.net *Washing equipment suppliers*

▶ National Centre For Product Design & Development Research, Llandaff Campus, 200 Western Avenue, Cardiff, CF5 2YB Tel: (029) 2041 6725 Fax: (029) 2041 6973 E-mail: info-pdr@uwic.ac.uk *Product design & development centre*

The National Children's Wear Association Of Great Britain & Irela, 5 Portland Place, London, W1B 1PW Tel: (020) 7636 7788 Fax: (020) 7636 7515 E-mail: bita@dial.pipex.com *Trade association for interior textiles*

National Communications Group Ltd, Old Cider Works Lane, Abbotskerswell, Newton Abbot, Devon, TQ12 5GH Tel: (0870) 6084440 Fax: (0870) 5246642 E-mail: ops@nationalcommsgroup.co.uk *Vehicle telemetric systems*

▶ National Construction College Midlands, 83 Lifford Lane, Birmingham, B30 3JH Tel: 0121-459 8000 Fax: 0121-459 8830 E-mail: nationalconstruction.college@citb.co.uk *Construction training services*

▶ National Courier Network, Unit 1 2, Block 12, Nobel Road, West Gourdie Industrial Estate, Dundee, DD2 4UH Tel: (01382) 400900

▶ National Design Consultancy, Adam Ferguson House Eskmills Park, Station Road, Musselburgh, Midlothian, EH21 7PQ Tel: 0131-273 4343 Fax: 0131-273 4350

National Door Co., Pyramid House, 52 Guildford Road, Lightwater, Surrey, GU18 5SD Tel: (01276) 451555 Fax: (01276) 453666 E-mail: national4@beeb.net *Up & over garage door distribs*

National Electric & Engineering Co B'Ham Ltd, The Cape Industrial Estate, Cattell Road, Warwick, CV34 4JQ Tel: (01926) 492132 Fax: (01926) 494891 E-mail: enquiries@nationalelectric.co.uk *Electrical contractors*

▶ National Electric Exhibitions Ltd, National Agricultural Centre, First Street, Stoneleigh Park, Kenilworth, Warwickshire, CV8 2LZ Tel: (024) 7669 6601 Fax: (024) 7669 2151 E-mail: enquiries@nee.co.uk

The National Exhibition Centre Ltd, National Exhibition Centre, Birmingham, B40 1NT Tel: 0121-780 4141 Fax: 0121-767 3815 E-mail: nec-exhibitions@necgroup.co.uk *Exhibition centre with conference facilities*

National Federation Of Meat & Food Traders, 1 Belgrove, Tunbridge Wells, Kent, TN1 1YW Tel: (01892) 541412 Fax: (01892) 535462 E-mail: info@nfmft.co.uk *Trade organisation*

National Federation Of Retail Newsagents, Yeoman House, Sekforde Street, London, EC1R 0HF Tel: (020) 7253 4225 Fax: (020) 7250 0927 E-mail: info2@nfrn.org *Trade association*

National Federation of Roofing Contractors, 24 Weymouth Street, London, W1G 7LX Tel: (020) 7436 0387 Fax: (020) 7637 5215 E-mail: info@nfrc.co.uk *Roofing trade association*

National Grid Co. P.L.C., Littlebrook Manorway, Dartford, DA1 5PS Tel: (01322) 295160 Fax: (01322) 295040 E-mail: robin.greaves@ngc.co.uk *Electrical engineers (industrial) engineering services; oil waste recycling/disposal/recovery contractors/ merchants/processors or services; transformer engineers, installation/maintenance/repair services; oil management & filtration services; oil recovey companies/operators & oil filtration (industrial) equipment/systems manufrs*

▶ National Health & Safety Company Ltd, Suite 14 - 15 Axwel House, East Mains Industrial Estate, Broxburn, West Lothian, EH52 5AU Tel: 08700 611725 Fax: 0707 5023614 E-mail: admin@nhasco.com *Health & safety systems for SME"s full managed systems and abbreviated DIY assistance, YOU CHOOSE. Initial audit completed to ascertain what YOU require. Risk, COSHH, DDA, Asbestos assessments and audits. Accident investigation and legal assistance.*

▶ National Homebuyers, Stirling House, 1 20 Victoria Way, Burgess Hill, West Sussex, RH15 9NF Tel: (01444) 257111 Fax: (01444) 257333 E-mail: info@nationalhomebuyers.co.uk *Specialists in purchasing residential & commercial property*

National Industrial Fuel Efficiency Services Ltd, Nifes House, Sinderland Road, Altrincham, Cheshire, WA14 5HQ Tel: 0161-928 5791 Fax: 0161-926 8718 E-mail: hoffice@nifes.co.uk *Consulting engineers & designers*

National Institute Of Agricultural Botany, Folley Hill, Itchen Stoke, Alresford, Hampshire, SO24 9TF Tel: (01962) 779521 Fax: (01962) 779543 *Agricultural researchers*

National Labels, Unit 70, Hartlebury Trading Estate, Hartlebury, Kidderminster, Worcestershire, DY10 4JB Tel: (01299) 250981 Fax: (01299) 251386 E-mail: enquiries@labelsandtags.com *Label printers & overprinting service providers*

National Laser Toner Distribution, 30 Parsons Mead, Abingdon, Oxfordshire, OX14 1LS Tel: (01235) 525600 Fax: (01235) 520580 E-mail: julian@nationaltoners.com *Computer consumables*

National Magazine Co. Ltd, 72 Broadwick Street, London, W1F 9EP Tel: (020) 7439 5000 Fax: (020) 7437 6886 *Magazine publisher*

▶ National Mailshot, Northgate House, St. Peters Street, Colchester, CO1 1HT Tel: (01206) 574674 Fax: (01206) 764040 E-mail: sales@nationalmailshot.net *Direct mail marketing*

▶ National Microelectronics Institute, 1 Michaelson Square, Kirkton Campus, Livingston Village, Livingston, West Lothian, EH54 7DB Tel: (01506) 424890 Fax: (01506) 411711 *Paging company*

National Milk Records, Meaford Power Station, Meaford, Stone, Staffordshire, ST15 0UG Tel: (01782) 374057 Fax: (01782) 374059 *Transport milk samples collection*

National Mobile Windscreens, 36 Queens Road, Newbury, Berkshire, RG14 7NE Tel: (01635) 49494 Fax: (01635) 521661 E-mail: enquiries@nationalwindscreens.co.uk *Mobile windscreen replacements*

National Newspaper Mail Order Protection Scheme, 18a King Street, Maidenhead, Berkshire, SL6 1EF Tel: (01628) 641930 Fax: (01628) 637112 E-mail: enquiries@shops-uk.org.uk *Trade association*

National Oilwell (U K) Ltd, Unit 10, Kirkton Avenue, Dyce, Aberdeen, AB21 0BF Tel: (01224) 875071 Fax: (01224) 723034 *Manufacturers of tools*

▶ National Oilwell UK Ltd, 266 Auchmill Road, Bucksburn, Aberdeen, AB21 9NB Tel: (01224) 714499 Fax: (01224) 714599

National Oilwell (UK) Ltd, Badentoy Crescent, Badentoy Industrial Estate, Portlethen, Aberdeen, AB12 4YD Tel: (01224) 334960 *Drilling systems & equipment manufrs*

National Oilwell Varco, Holton Road, Holton Heath Trading Park, Poole, Dorset, BH16 6LT Tel: (01202) 631817 Fax: (01202) 631708 E-mail: pcesales@nov.com *Oilwell & multi-lateral completion equipment manufrs*

▶ National Pallet Services, Cummings Road, Tattersett Business Park, Tattersett Business & Leisure Park, Fakenham, Norfolk, NR21 7RG Tel: (01485) 529030 Fax: (01485) 529031

National Physical Laboratory, Hampton Road, Teddington, Middlesex, TW11 0LW Tel: (020) 8977 3222 Fax: (020) 8943 6458 E-mail: enquiry@npl.co.uk *National measurement institute*

National Polytunnels Ltd, 258 Station Road, Bamber Bridge, Preston, PR5 6EA Tel: (01772) 799200 Fax: (01772) 799250 E-mail: sales@nationalalpolytunnels.co.uk *Horticultural polythene greenhouse manufrs*

National Railway Supplies Ltd, Leeman Road, York, YO26 4ZD Tel: (01904) 522293 Fax: (01904) 522696 E-mail: commercial@natrail.com *Railway signaling & telecommunication equipment manufrs*

▶ National Road Planning, School Road, Bulkington, Bedworth, Warwickshire, CV12 9JB Tel: (024) 7664 0664 Fax: (024) 7664 0663

National Roofing, Imperial Buildings, Bridge Street, West End, Newport, Abercarn, Gwent, NP11 4SB Tel: (0800) 7834890 Fax: (01495) 248448 E-mail: sales@diyroofing.co.uk *Rubber Roofing Supplies lasting 40 years for professionals and DIY for flat roofs, gutters, balconies etc. Easy to fit ~ Apply primer, 2.5mm EPDM Self-Adhesive Rubber Sheeting and seal edges. Also 9m wide One-Piece EPDM.*

National Security Inspectorate, Orchard House, 2 Victoria Square, Droitwich, Worcestershire, WR9 8DS Tel: (01905) 773131 Fax: (01905) 773102 E-mail: admin@nsi.org.uk *Security inspectorate for manned guarding*

National Semi-Conductor (U K) Ltd, Milford House, Milford St, Swindon, SN1 1DW Tel: (01793) 614141 Fax: (01793) 427551 E-mail: elspethmurrin@nsc.com *Semi-conductor component manufrs*

National Semiconductor UK Ltd, Larkfield Industrial Estate, Greenock, Renfrewshire, PA16 0EQ Tel: (01475) 633733 Fax: (01475) 638515 *Semiconductors manufrs*

National Sign Co., Alleysbank Road, Rutherglen, Glasgow, G73 1LX Tel: 0141-647 4348 Fax: 0141-613 1309 E-mail: info@nationalsign.co.uk *Metal sign manufrs*

National Signshop, Courtney Street, Hull, HU8 7QF Tel: (01482) 225050 Fax: (01482) 323077 E-mail: info@nationalsignshop.co.uk *Engraving & sign manufrs*

National Sound Reproducers Ltd, Lower Priory Farm, Clamp Hill, Stanmore, Middlesex, HA7 3JJ Tel: (020) 8954 7677 Fax: (020) 8954 9329 *Audio equipment hirers*

National Stables, Badlesmere, Faversham, Kent, ME13 0JX Tel: (01233) 740933 Fax: (01233) 740950 *Stable manufrs*

National Starch & Chemical, James Street, Goole, North Humberside, DN14 5TG Tel: (01405) 762641 Fax: (01405) 760031 *Food manufrs*

National Starch & Chemical, Prestbury Court Greencourts Business Park, Styal Road, Manchester, M22 5LW Tel: 0161-435 3200 Fax: 0161-435 3351 *Speciality starch manufrs* Also at: Goole & Tilbury

National Tube Stockholders Ltd, Dalton Industrial Estate, Dalton, Thirsk, North Yorkshire, YO7 3HE Tel: (01845) 577440 Fax: (01845) 577165 E-mail: nts@nationaltube.co.uk *Steel tube stockholders*

National Tyre Service Ltd, Regent House, Heaton Lane, Stockport, Cheshire, SK4 1BS Tel: 0161-480 7461 Fax: 0161-475 3540 *Tyre battery exhaust distributors & retailers* Also at: Branches throughout Great Britain

National Windscreens Ltd, F Cottage Industrial Estate, Forstal Road, Aylesford, Kent, ME20 7AD Tel: (01622) 715696 Fax: (01622) 715738 *Windscreen replacements* Also at: Dartford

National Wool Textile Export Corporation, Lloyds Bank Chambers, 43-45 Hustlergate, Bradford, West Yorkshire, BD1 1PH Tel: (01274) 727877 Fax: (01274) 723124 E-mail: mailbox@bwtec.co.uk *Trade association*

Nationwide Access Ltd, 15 Midland Court, Central Park, Lutterworth, Leicestershire, LE17 4PN Tel: (01455) 558874 Fax: (01455) 550974 E-mail: sales@nationwideaccess.co.uk *Nationwide is one of the UK's leader in the rental of specialist powered access equipment. Our extensive range of modern self-propelled booms and scissor lifts, teamed with an expanding fleet of truck and trailer mounted platforms, located throughout our 50 depots, makes us perfectly placed to meet your needs and solve your access problems.*

Nationwide Air Systems Ltd, Bolney Grange Industrial Park, Bolney, Haywards Heath, West Sussex, RH17 5PB Tel: (01444) 230308 *Air handling unit suppliers*

Nationwide Alarm Call, 154 Wollaton Road, Beeston, Nottingham, NG9 2PH Tel: 0115-943 0981 Fax: 0115-922 2038 *Security alarm services*

▶ Nationwide Appliance Testing Co. Ltd, Westburn House, Prestwick Road, Monkton, Prestwick, Ayrshire, KA9 2PB Tel: (01292) 475555

Nationwide Autocentres Ltd, 10 Duncombe Street, Bletchley, Milton Keynes, MK2 2LY Tel: (01908) 270476 Fax: (01908) 642121 *Car repairs*

Nationwide Cables, Unit 34, Minworth Industrial Park, Forge Lane, Minworth, Sutton Coldfield, West Midlands, B76 1AH Tel: 0121-313 1001 Fax: 0121-351 4851 *Electric cable distributors*

Nationwide Coatings UK Ltd, 5 Canal Estate, Station Road, Langley, Slough, SL3 6EG Tel: (01753) 671612 Fax: (01753) 671613 E-mail: sales@nationwidecoatings.co.uk *Nationwide Coatings (UK) Ltd provide powder coating and stove enamelling services to industry. Based in Berkshire they operate two large box ovens suitable for jobs up to 7m long and 2.4m wide.*

Nationwide Crash Repair Centres Ltd, 11-13 York Street, Ayr, KA8 8AN Tel: (01292) 267142 Fax: (01292) 610307 *Motor body repairers* Also at: Dumfries, Falkirk & Glasgow

Nationwide Crash Repair Centres Ltd, Axe Road, Bridgwater, Somerset, TA6 5LN Tel: (01278) 422238 Fax: (01278) 427939 *Motor body repairers*

Nationwide Crash Repair Centres Ltd, Smeaton Road, West Gourdie Industrial Estate, Dundee, DD2 4UT Tel: (01382) 623133 Fax: (01382) 612962 *Vehicle accident repair centre*

Nationwide Crash Repair Centres Ltd, 171 Maxwell Road, Glasgow, G41 1TG Tel: 0141-429 5371 Fax: 0141-420 1084 *Vehicle damage repairs*

Nationwide Crash Repair Centres Ltd, Unit 1c Pentland Industrial Estate, Loanhead, Midlothian, EH20 9QH Tel: 0131-440 2323 Fax: 0131-440 4323 *Crash repairs*

Nationwide Express Parcels, Unit 4b Surrey Street, Glossop, Derbyshire, SK13 7AJ Tel: (01457) 860826 Fax: (01457) 855652 *UK express delivery services*

Nationwide Filter Co. Ltd, Unit 16 First Quarter, Blenheim Road, Epsom, Surrey, KT19 9QN Tel: (01372) 728548 Fax: (01372) 742831 *Air filter manufrs*

Nationwide Fire Protection Associates, Southcote Mill, Southcote Farm Lane, Reading, RG30 3DZ Tel: 0118-951 1799 Fax: 0118-951 1799 *Fire equipment sales*

▶ Nationwide Frame Services, Brookside Way, Huthwaite, Sutton-in-Ashfield, Nottinghamshire, NG17 2NL Tel: (01623) 551555 Fax: (01623) 552555

▶ Nationwide Healthcare Connections Ltd, Connections House, 105 Bellingdon Road, Chesham, Buckinghamshire, HP5 2HQ Tel: (01494) 773007 Fax: (01494) 773008 E-mail: sales@healthcare-connections.com *A 24 hour, 365 day nationwide service incorporating workplace drug testing and policy implementation, health assessments, vaccines, HAVS assessments and more. A network of 100+ nurses and 20 medical rooms throughout the country to provides services in the most convenient location.*

▶ Nationwide Instructor Training College, 441 Dudley Road, Wolverhampton, WV2 3AQ Tel: (0845) 1304035 Fax: (0845) 1304507 E-mail: info@drivinginstructorcollege.co.uk *Driving Instructor Training, Driving instructor courses, driving training aids and much more.*

Nationwide Machine Services Ltd, Westward House, Regent Road, Salford, M5 8LY Tel: 0161-872 4200 Fax: 0161-877 7610 *Amusement machine consultants*

Nationwide Maintenance Ltd, Nene House, Sopwith Way, Drayton Fields Industrial Estate, Daventry, Northamptonshire, NN11 8EA Tel: (01327) 311303 Fax: (01327) 300835 E-mail: accounts@nationmaint.co.uk *Electrical contractors & maintenance fitters*

Nationwide Print, Bucklers Lane, Holmbush, St. Austell, Cornwall, PL25 3JL Tel: (01726) 63638 Fax: (01726) 67831 E-mail: sales@nationwideprint.co.uk *Lithographic & letterpress printers*

Nationwide Retail Systems Ltd, Lamesley House, Durham Road, Birtley, Chester le Street, County Durham, DH3 1HU Tel: 0191-410 5167 Fax: 0191-410 3833 *Cash registers & epos systems supplier*

▶ Nationwide RPZ Valve Testing, Cedar Lodge, Priory Lane, Prestbury, Macclesfield, Cheshire, SK10 4AE Tel: (01625) 269168 *RPZ VALVE INSTALLATION AND TESTING, NATIONWIDE SERVICE, BACKFLOW PROTECTION to CLASS 4 WATER*

▶ Nationwide Safety Nets Ltd, Longdene House, Longdene Road, Haslemere, Surrey, GU27 2PH Tel: (0870) 345 0650 E-mail: info@nwsafetynets.com *Specialising in the installation of safety netting and steel decking (composite flooring). We provide competitive rates and our fully qualified staff can be on your site to work quickly and efficiently. We are based in Surrey but work nationwide.*

▶ Nationwide Security Blinds Ltd, Unit 4-5 Omega Centre, Sandford Lane, Wareham, Dorset, BH20 4DY Tel: (01929) 554901 Fax: (01929) 551023 E-mail: sales@nationwideltd.co.uk

▶ Nationwide Self Storage Ltd, 620 Western Avenue, London, W3 0TE Tel: (020) 8992 1700

Nationwide Signs Ltd, Derry Street, Wolverhampton, WV2 1EY Tel: (01902) 871116 Fax: (01902) 351195 E-mail: roadframes@aol.com *Sign frames for the construction/road maintenance industry*

▶ Nationwide Telesales Co., 56 John O'Gaunt Road, Kenilworth, Warwickshire, CV8 1DZ Tel: (01926) 511651 Fax: (01926) 511651 E-mail: chris.bradford@nationwidetelesales.co.uk *Specialists in outsourced tele-marketing projects & database cleaning*

Nationwide Trademarks, Somerset House, 40-49 Price Street, Birmingham, B4 6LZ Tel: 0121-678 9005 Fax: 0121-678 9001 E-mail: sales@anewbusiness.co.uk *National business name registry & protection*

▶ Nationwide Vehicles Direct Ltd, Dalriada Crescent, Motherwell, Lanarkshire, ML1 3XS Tel: 0141-587 8898 E-mail: joannecrawford03@yahoo.co.uk *Contract Hire & Car Leasing from Nationwide Vehicles Direct Ltd.*We are the UK''s leader in providing Contract Hire & Car Leasing. We guarantee to beat any genuine quote!.*

Nationwide Vulcanising Ltd, 100 Brownedge Road, Lostock Hall, Preston, PR5 5AD Tel: (01772) 698122 Fax: (01772) 335376 *Conveyor belts fitting & repairers*

Nationwide-ACR Ltd, 279-281 Leeds Road, Nelson, Lancashire, BB9 8EJ Tel: (0845) 6120611 Fax: (01282) 603016 E-mail: info@nationwide-acr.co.uk *Air conditioning & refrigeration services*

Native Systems Ltd, 22 St. Annes Grove, Knowle, Solihull, West Midlands, B93 9JB Tel: 0121-743 0875 E-mail: info@nativesystems.co.uk *Apple computer dealers*

▶ Natrahealth Health Foods, Unit 3-4 Jupiter Business Park, Airfield Industrial Estate, Hixon, Stafford, ST18 0PA Tel: (01889) 271333 Fax: (01889) 271355 *Supplies vitamins & supplements*

▶ Natta Country Homes, Rose Court, Mill Lane, Crondall, Farnham, Surrey, GU10 5RP Tel: (01252) 851158 Fax: (01252) 851150

Natural A C Ltd, 10 Ringwood Drive, Leigh-on-Sea, Essex, SS9 5HG Tel: (01702) 526154 Fax: (01702) 526154 E-mail: natural@aircond.freeserve.co.uk *Air conditioning manufrs*

Natural Active Materials Resources, 3A Magdalene Street, Glastonbury, Somerset, BA6 9EW Tel: (01458) 835970 Fax: (01458) 831361 *Cosmetics manufrs*

▶ Natural Alternative Products, PO BOX 3, Whitefield, M45 6WS Tel: 0161 7980671 E-mail: sales@natural-alternative-products.co.uk *15 seconds. No need for soap & water. Use at home or at school. Approved by the Vegetarian Society. Money reinvested by the Brazilian manufacturer to preserve the Amazon. Available in a choice of Rainforest or Natural fragrances in a convenient 59ml flip top bottle.*Emu oil (Australia)*Our free range emu oil is used in all Y-Not Natural products that specifically target people who may be prone to Arthritis, skin conditions such as eczema, dermatitis & psoriasis, haemorrhoids & general aches & pains.**

▶ Natural Blinds, PO Box 2082, Gloucester, GL3 3WX Tel: 0845 056 4415 Fax: 0845 056 4415 E-mail: info@naturalblinds.co.uk *Bathroom blinds,*

▶ Natural Care Products, Highcroft, 30 Old Lodge Lane, Purley, Surrey, CR8 4DF Tel: 020 86452552 E-mail: Andrew@natural-care-products.co.uk *Selling aloe vera products, nutritional supplements and vitamins online in the UK. Including products with glucosamine & chondroitin to help joint wear and tear, natural skin care and daily personal use goods*

Natural Cement Distribution, Unit 12 Redbrook Business Park, Wilthorpe Road, Barnsley, South Yorkshire, S75 1JN Tel: (01226) 299333 Fax: (01226) 299777 *Cement distribution*

▶ Natural Child, Lower Naunton Farm, Evesham Road, Winchcombe, Cheltenham, Gloucestershire, GL54 5BZ Tel: (01242) 620988 Fax: (01242) 620988 E-mail: info@naturalchild.co.uk *Natural Products for Mother & Baby - baby carriers and baby slings, washable nappies, natural toiletries, herbal & homeopathic remedies,supplements & natural medicines from natural child, UK*

Natural Choice, 13 Bridge Street, Darwen, Lancashire, BB3 2AA Tel: (01254) 773311 Fax: (01254) 773311 *Health food*

Natural Choice, 72 Westbourne Road, Huddersfield, HD1 4LE Tel: (01484) 513162 Fax: (01484) 687466 *Health food suppliers*

Natural Choice, 4 Market Place, Knaresborough, North Yorkshire, HG5 8AG Tel: (01423) 867705 *Health food retailers*

▶ Natural Comforts, Unit 10-11 Orde Wingate Way, Stockton-on-Tees, Cleveland, TS19 0GA Tel: (01642) 611172 Fax: (01642) 611173 E-mail: naturalcomfortsuk@btinternet.com *Cane furniture importers services*

Natural Europe Ltd, 70 Peveril Road, Beeston, Nottingham, NG9 2HU Tel: 0115-922 7284 Fax: 0115-922 7284 *Fleeting lines & rolling equipment agents*

Natural Feather UK Ltd, 31 Berkeley Road, London, N15 6HH Tel: (020) 8800 3355 Fax: (020) 8800 0101 *Cushion Makers For Upholstery & Interior Design Pillow and Duvet Manufacturer & Loose Feather/Down*

Natural Food Co., 37a Mansfield Road, Nottingham, NG1 3FB Tel: (01949) 876483 Fax: 0115-955 9914 E-mail: info@naturalfoodcompany.net *Health food suppliers*

▶ Natural Gardening, White House Farm, Talycoed, Monmouth, NP25 5HR Tel: (01600) 780488 Fax: (01600) 780489 E-mail: gerardthomas@naturalgardening.co.uk *Organic Gardening Products - Organic garden fertilisers. Thomas Fontaine Organic Garden Products are producers and suppliers of organic garden fertilisers for gardeners, farmers, allotments and growers.*

Natural Health Products Ltd, 1275 Stratford Road, Hall Green, Birmingham, B28 9AJ Tel: 0121-777 6000 Fax: 0121-777 6006 E-mail: mail@nhp.uk *Bedding & blankets retailer*

▶ Natural Interventions Ltd, Redwood House, Middleton Road, Eggleston, Barnard Castle, County Durham, DL12 0AQ Tel: (01833) 650022 Fax: (01833) 650033 E-mail: info@natural-interventions.co.uk *Trophy manufrs*

Natural Linens, 12 City Road, Littleport, Ely, Cambridgeshire, CB6 1NG Tel: (01353) 860849 Fax: (01353) 860849 E-mail: sales@natlin.force9.co.uk *Interior furnishings*

Natural Remedy Warehouse, 7 The Flaxmill Lane, Pinchbeck, Spalding, Lincolnshire, PE11 3YP Tel: (01775) 724994 Fax: (01775) 761104 E-mail: info@enzymepro.com *Health foods & remedies services*

▶ Natural Resource Group, 46A Manor Park, London, SE13 5RL Tel: (020) 8318 5344 E-mail: jim@naturalresourcegroup.co.uk *Solar energy & wind power, supply alternative energy products*

Natural Stone Co., Elm Cottage, Ockham Road North, Ockham, Woking, Surrey, GU23 6NW Tel: (01483) 211311 Fax: (01483) 211555 *Step manufrs*

▶ Natural Stone Features, 3B Kingston Industrial Estate, Ardgowan Street, Port Glasgow, Renfrewshire, PA14 5DG Tel: (01475) 744436

▶ Natural Stone Quarries Ltd, The Shore, Forth Bank Industrial Estate, Alloa, Clackmannanshire, FK10 1HA Tel: (01259) 721977 Fax: (01259) 723383 *Natural stone*

Natural Treasures Ltd, Unit 21a, Ben Nevis Industrial Estate, Fort William, Inverness-Shire, PH33 6PR Tel: (01397) 700770 Fax: (01397) 700770 *Gemstones & jewellery manufrs*

Naturally Health Foods, 5 Waterloo Court, Andover, Hampshire, SP10 1QJ Tel: (01264) 332375 Fax: (01264) 364084 E-mail: sales@naturallyhealthfoods.co.uk *Health food retails*

▶ Naturally Wood Ltd, 44 Forest Road, Loughton, Essex, IG10 1DX Tel: (020) 8508 2555 Fax: (020) 8508 6261 E-mail: info@naturallywood.net *Flooring fitters & suppliers*

▶ Naturalmotion Ltd, Innovation House, Mill Street, Oxford, OX2 0JX Tel: (01865) 250575 Fax: (01865) 250577 E-mail: sales@naturalmotion.com *Software developers*

Naturana Ltd, Eastern Avenue, Lichfield, Staffordshire, WS13 6RT Tel: (01543) 257333 Fax: (01543) 250230 E-mail: naturana.uk@btinternet.com *Brassiere & foundation garment manufrs* Also at: Tamworth

Nature Fare, 5 Towngate, Leyland, PR25 2EN Tel: (01772) 434693 *Health food product suppliers*

▶ Nature Nook, 14 Church Street, Ballymoney, County Antrim, BT53 6DL Tel: (028) 2766 4178 Fax: (028) 2766 4178 *Health shop*

Nature Publishing Group Ltd, Brunel Road, Houndmills, Basingstoke, Hampshire, RG21 6XS Tel: (01256) 329242 Fax: (01256) 479464 *Publishing*

Naturellr Consumer Products Ltd, 21 Mountjoy Road, Omagh, County Tyrone, BT79 7EQ Tel: (028) 8224 9396 Fax: (028) 8224 7793 E-mail: info@naturelle.ie *Medical dressings & hi-visibility clothing distributor*

Natures Aid Ltd, St. Georges Park, Kirkham, Preston, PR4 2DQ Tel: (01772) 686231 Fax: (01772) 671688 E-mail: sales@naturesaid.co.uk *Manufacture food, vitamins & supplements*

▶ Nature's Free Foods Ltd, 1400-1500 Blueprint, Dundas Spur, Portsmouth, PO3 5RW Tel: (023) 9265 5541 Fax: (023) 9265 5563 *Freshly prepared salads*

Nature's Own Ltd, Unit 8, Hanley Workshops, Hanley Road, Hanley Swan, Worcester, WR8 0DX Tel: (01684) 310022 Fax: (01684) 312022 E-mail: peter@well-being.co.uk *Vitamins & minerals distributors*

Natures Remedies, Bank Street, Warrington, WA1 2AR Tel: (01925) 444885 Fax: (01925) 654821 *Health food store*

Natures Way, 305 Upper Newtownards Road, Belfast, BT4 3JH Tel: (028) 9047 1333 Fax: (028) 9065 6694 *Health food retailers*

Natures Way, 1 North Road, Holsworthy, Devon, EX22 6EJ Tel: (01409) 254305 *Organic food suppliers*

Natures Way Foods Ltd, Park Farm, Chichester Road, Selsey, Chichester, West Sussex, PO20 9HP Tel: (01243) 603111 Fax: (01243) 605777 E-mail: natureswayfoods@nwfltd.co.uk *Salad processors*

▶ NatWeb, 345 Addiscombe Road, Croydon, CR0 7LG Tel: (020) 8407 0771 Fax: (020) 8407 0772 E-mail: robert.macleod@natweb.net *Web hosting for simple 'brochure' web sites, database driven web sites and e-commerce web sites are all catered for and backed up by a reliable infrastructure. All websites are hosted on multiple load-balanced servers. NatWeb also provide dedicated servers and colocation in the only data centre in Croydon.*

NatWest Stockbrokers Ltd, 55 Mansell Street, London, E1 8AN Tel: (0870) 6004080 Fax: (0870) 1288324 *Broker dealers*

Naughty Holdings Ltd, 5th Floor, 19-20 Berners Street, London, W1T 3LW Tel: (020) 7323 2222 Fax: (020) 7436 8835 E-mail: fashion@naughty.co.uk *Ladies fashions manufrs*

▶ Naughty Vend, Beltane, Moor Road, Langham, Colchester, CO4 5NR Tel: (01206) 271455 Fax: (01206) 273025 E-mail: mail@naughtyvend.co.uk *Vending franchise business suppliers*

▶ Nautical Antiques Center, 3a Hope Square, Weymouth, Dorset, DT4 8TR Tel: (01305) 777838 E-mail: info@nauticalantiques.org *Maritime Souvenirs & Collectables. Run by an ex seafarer, the company, which has been established over 12 years, has grown from a hobby to a small business. We supply maritime collectables, souvenirs & have over 00 different articles in stock, all to do with ships & the sea.*

Nauticalia Ltd, Ferry Lane, Shepperton, Middlesex, TW17 9LQ Tel: (01932) 244396 Fax: (01932) 241679 E-mail: sales@nauticalia.com *Marine leisure*

▶ Nauticality Nautical Gifts, Albrighton, Wolverhampton, WV7 3WL Tel: (01902) 373217 Fax: (01902) 375317 E-mail: nauticalitygift@aol.com *Gifts, corporate marketing*

▶ Nautronix Ltd, Howe Moss Avenue, Kirkhill Industrial Estate, Dyce, Aberdeen, AB21 0GP Tel: (01224) 775700 Fax: (01224) 775800 *Marine technology service*

▶ Navaho Ceramic Tiling, 7 Wroughton Business Park, Swindon Road, Wroughton, Swindon, SN4 9BH Tel: (01793) 815123 Fax: (01793) 815123 *Ceramic suppliers*

▶ Navayuga Europe Ltd, Progress Park, Ribocon Way, Chalton, Luton, LU4 9UU Tel: (01582) 585820 E-mail: info@navayuga.co.uk *Software developers*

▶ Navestock Metalworks, Horseman Side, Brentwood, Essex, CM14 5SU Tel: (07753) 565469 Fax: (01708) 703505 *Manufacture & install gates, railings & balustrade. Made to order.*

Navico UK Ltd, Premier Way, Abbey Park, Romsey, Hampshire, SO51 9DH Tel: (01794) 510010 Fax: (01794) 510006 E-mail: sales.uk@navico.com *Sonar & marine instrument equipment manufrs*

Navigate Ltd, Ducketts Wharf, 2 South Street, Bishop's Stortford, Hertfordshire, CM23 3AR Tel: (01279) 653249 Fax: (01279) 658129 E-mail: sales@navigate.ltd.uk *Navigate manufacture branded & promotional cool bags*

Navigator Systems Ltd, 3 Fullerton Road, Hartford, Northwich, Cheshire, CW8 1SR Tel: (01606) 782655 *Specialist software designers*

Navrish Ltd, Navrish Nivas, 17 Bishops Close, Mays Lane, Arkley, Barnet, Hertfordshire, EN5 2QH Tel: (020) 8440 0803 Fax: (020) 8441 6813 E-mail: sales@navrish.co.uk *Manufacturers of medical supplies (disposable) & scientific instrument*

Navtec North Europe Ltd, South Moore Lane, Havant, Hampshire, PO9 1JJ Tel: (023) 9248 5777 Fax: (023) 9248 5770 E-mail: navnor@navtec.net *Yacht & boat fittings* Also at: Warsash

Naxos Schoolwear, 369 High Road, London, N22 8JA Tel: (020) 8889 7950 Fax: (020) 8889 7950 *School uniform manufrs*

Nayler Chemicals Ltd, Unit 34b Kirkless Industrial Estate, Cale Lane, Aspull, Wigan, Lancashire, WN2 1HF Tel: (01942) 829955 Fax: (01942) 233400 E-mail: k.pover@naychem.freeserve.co.uk *Chemical manufrs*

▶ Nayler Group Ltd, Aero Mill, Kershaw Street, Church, Accrington, Lancashire, BB5 4JS Tel: (01254) 234247 Fax: (01254) 383996

Nayler Group Ltd, Aero Mill, Kershaw Street, Church, Accrington, Lancashire, BB5 4JS Tel: (01254) 234247 Fax: (01254) 383996 E-mail: info@naylorgroup.co.uk *General printers*

Chris Naylor (SOMA) Ltd, The Bungalow, 6 West Shevin Road, Merston, Ilkley, West Yorkshire, LS29 6BG Tel: (01943) 876513 Fax: (01943) 878814 E-mail: chrisnaylor@chrisnaylorsoma.demon.co.uk *Industrial brush suppliers*

Naylor Concrete Products Ltd, Clough Green, Cawthorne, Barnsley, South Yorkshire, S75 4AD Tel: (01226) 790591 Fax: (01226) 790531 E-mail: info@naylor.co.uk *Drain & sanitary pipe manufrs*

Naylor Concrete Products, Milner Way, Ossett, West Yorkshire, WF5 9JE Tel: (01924) 267286 Fax: (01924) 265674 E-mail: lintels@naylor.co.uk *Concrete lintel specialists*

Naylor Drainage, Cowley Street, Methil, Leven, Fife, KY8 3QQ Tel: (01592) 717900 Fax: (01592) 717906 *Plastic products*

Naylor Jennings Ltd, Green Lane Dye Works, Yeadon, Leeds, LS19 7XP Tel: 0113-250 2331 Fax: 0113-250 6698 E-mail: sales@naylorjennings.co.uk *Commissioned dyers & finishers of cotton fabrics*

John Naylor & Son, Redhall Road, Dudley, West Midlands, DY3 2NL Tel: (01384) 256346 Fax: (01384) 240486 *Meat pie manufrs*

Naylor Myers Ltd, Wakefield Road, Brighouse, West Yorkshire, HD6 1ZE Tel: (01484) 712531 Fax: (01484) 722365 *Builders, plumbers & timber merchants* Also at: Batley, Bradford, Denby Dale, Huddersfield, Silsden, Skipton & Thornton

Naylor & Walkden Ltd, Hatton Street, Adlington, Chorley, Lancashire, PR7 4HT Tel: (01257) 480222 Fax: (01257) 482696 E-mail: info@naylorwalkden.co.uk *Building contractors & joinery*

▶ Naylors Transport (Leyland) Ltd, Comet Road, Moss Side Industrial Estate, Leyland, PR26 7PF Tel: (01772) 424731 Fax: (01772) 621065

Naz Electric Ltd, 244 Melton Road, Leicester, LE4 7PG Tel: 0116-266 0940 Fax: 0116-266 0940 *Electrical contractors*

Nazeing Glassworks Ltd, Nazeing New Road, Broxbourne, Hertfordshire, EN10 6SU Tel: (01992) 464485 Fax: (01992) 450966 E-mail: admin@nazeing-glass.com Principal Export Areas: Worldwide *Manufacturers of glassware*

▶ NB Marine, Ainwee, Rahane, Helensburgh, Dunbartonshire, G84 0QW Tel: (020) 7870 6247 E-mail: mail@nbmairne.co.uk

NB Structures Ltd, Unit 1a Apex Works, Hackhurst Lane, Lower Dicker, Hailsham, East Sussex, BN27 4BW Tel: (01323) 848401 Fax: (01323) 848402 *Steel fabricators*

NBC Group, Heath Business Park, Runcorn, Cheshire, WA7 4QX Tel: 01928 513556 Fax: 01928 513557 E-mail: dave@nbcservices.co.uk *Decontamination showers and accessories, tactical shelters for multi-use*

▶ NBS Stone Products Ltd, Co Bam House, Pleasant Street, Stoke-on-Trent, ST6 3DL Tel: (01782) 838559 Fax: (01782) 838442

NBS Technologies Ltd, 7 Byfleet Technical Centre, Canada Road, West Byfleet, Surrey, KT14 7NB Tel: (01932) 351531 Fax: (01932) 351382 E-mail: sales@nbs.com *Identity card systems suppliers*

NCC Group, Oxford Road, Manchester, M1 7EF Tel: 0161-209 5200 Fax: 0161-209 5400 E-mail: response@nccgroup.co.uk *Technology assurance organisation*

▶ Nce Windows & Conservatories, Unit 10 Reginald Road Industrial Estate, Brindley Road, Reginald Road Industrial Estat, St. Helens, Merseyside, WA9 4HY Tel: (01744) 811111 Fax: (01744) 811111 *Double glazing & glazing products manufrs*

Nci, 2 Nelsons Lane, Hurst, Reading, RG10 0RR Tel: 0118-934 5316 Fax: 0118-934 2010 E-mail: info@nciservices.co.uk *Architectural welding fabricators & sheet metalwork engineers*

NCJ Media Ltd, Groat Market, Newcastle Upon Tyne, NE1 1ED Tel: 0191-232 7500 Fax: 0191-230 4144 *Newspaper publishers & printers*

▶ NClosure, Long Paddock, Peppershells Lane, Compton Dando, Bristol, BS39 4LL Tel: 01761 490374 Fax: 0871 6615701 E-mail: sales@nclosure.co.uk *Manufacturers of wooden & agricultural fencing*

NCMT Ltd, Ferry Works, Summer Road, Thames Ditton, Surrey, KT7 0QJ Tel: (020) 8398 4277 Fax: (020) 8398 3631 *Machine tool importers* Also at: Bury, Edinburgh & Leamington Spa

▶ NCR, 14 Whinhill, Dunfermline, Fife, KY11 4YZ Tel: (01383) 643000

NCS, Prizet Lodge, Helsington, Kendal, Cumbria, LA8 8AA Tel: (01539) 561666 Fax: (01539) 561999 *Air conditioning installation & repair services*

Ncube UK, 8 The Square, Stockley Park, Uxbridge, Middlesex, UB11 1FW Tel: (020) 8899 1706 Fax: (020) 8610 6869 *Video & media service*

NDE Power Transmissions Group, NDE Bldgs, Aldbourne Road, Coventry, CV1 4EQ Tel: (024) 7622 2272 Fax: (024) 7625 8499 E-mail: sales@ndeclarketransmissions.co.uk *Drive shaft & gear components manufrs*

▶ Ndesign Services Ltd, 74 Brighton Road, Newhaven, East Sussex, BN9 9NS Tel: (01273) 515081 Fax: (01273) 515168 E-mail: nathan@ndesignservices.co.uk *Professional building services consulting engineers with emphasis on low energy and sustainable design solutions.*

▶ NDF Associates, Chadwick House, Back Grange Avenue, Harrogate, North Yorkshire, HG1 2AN Tel: (01423) 529333 Fax: (01423) 529555 E-mail: enquiries@ndfassociates.co.uk *Personnel verification consultants*

Ndi Momentum Ltd, Stanley Court, Stanley Green Business Park, Wilmslow, Cheshire, SK9 3RL Tel: 0161-486 7878 Fax: 0161-486 7999 E-mail: info@momentum-uk.com *Purchases & marketing displays*

▶ NDK Search & Selection Ltd, Chadwick House, Warrington Road, Birchwood Park, Warrington, WA3 6AE Tel: (01925) 813888 Fax: (01925) 813999 E-mail: response@ndksearch.com *NDK Search and Selection Ltd is a International Executive Search Consultancy with a market presence in Western Europe and a client base of Corporate Blue-Chip clients.*

NDL Bends, Unit 3 Littleton Drive, Cannock, Staffordshire, WS12 4TR Tel: (01543) 579900 Fax: (01543) 577772 *Manufacturers of water meter bends*

▶ NDR Builders, Gainborough, Station Road, Tenterden, Kent, TN30 6HN Tel: (01580) 761222

▶ NDT Eagle, Kirkhill Place, Kirkhill Industrial Estate, Dyce, Aberdeen, AB21 0GU Tel: (01224) 722966 Fax: (01224) 773657 E-mail: sales@ndteagle.co.uk *Training services & inspections*

NDT Services Ltd, 5 Side Ley, Kegworth, Derby, DE74 2FJ Tel: (01509) 680088 Fax: (01509) 680080 E-mail: sales@ndtservices.co.uk *Non-destructive site, radiographic, ultrasonic inspection test service*

▶ Neaco Ltd, Norton Grove Industrial Estate, Norton, Malton, North Yorkshire, YO17 9HQ Tel: (01653) 695721 Fax: (01653) 600418 E-mail: alan.green@neaco.co.uk *Elderly & disabled showering product & accessory manufrs*

Neal Bros, Queens Buildings, Hastings Road, Leicester, LE5 0LJ Tel: 0116-274 0005 Fax: 0116-274 2028 E-mail: sales@nealbrothers.co.uk *Export packers & shippers*

▶ Lawrence Neal, 22 High Street, Stockton, Southam, Warwickshire, CV47 8JZ Tel: (01926) 811998 E-mail: sales@lawrencenealchairs.co.uk *Chair manufrs*

Neal Pestforce Ltd, Unit 3, Sutterton Enterprise Park, Sutterton, Boston, Lincolnshire, PE20 2JA Tel: (01205) 460446 Fax: (01205) 460886 E-mail: anninkirton@aol.com *Pest control services*

Nealbourne Ltd, PO Box 10, Keighley, West Yorkshire, BD21 4PP Tel: (01535) 667535 Fax: (01535) 609199 *Hernia support & surgical hosiery mail order services*

Neale Consulting Engineers Ltd, Highfield, Pilcot Hill, Dogmersfield, Hook, Hampshire, RG27 8SX Tel: (01252) 629199 Fax: (01252) 815625 E-mail: ncel@tribology.co.uk *Mechanical consultants & consulting engineer designers*

Neale Dataday Ltd, Charfleet Bindery, Canvey Island, Essex, SS8 0PA Tel: (0800) 0284536 Fax: (01268) 510636 E-mail: sales@nealedataday.co.uk *Diary publishers*

Neam Ltd, Hangar 7, Western Maintenance Area, Manchester Airport, Manchester, M90 5NE Tel: 0161-436 6666 Fax: 0161-493 9976 E-mail: sales@northernexec.com *Aircraft maintenance & charter*

▶ Nearly Construction Ltd, 19 Robertson Street, Glasgow, G78 1QW Tel: 0141-880 8720

continued

Neat Acoustics, 29b Harmire Enterprise Park, Barnard Castle, County Durham, DL12 8XT Tel: (01833) 631021 Fax: (01833) 630022 E-mail: bob@neat.co.uk *Hi-fi equipment manufrs*

▶ Neat Cards & Collectables, 5 Garbett Road, Winchester, Hampshire, SO23 0NY Tel: 01962 860816 E-mail: info@neatcards.biz *We offer a very wide range of Trading Cards from the 1980"s to Today. We offer competitive prices, and a friendly, efficient service for all your trading card needs. We specialise in Disney, Star Wars (1977 - Today), Coca Cola and Playboy Trading Cards. We offer a wide range of 1980"s - Today Movie and Television card sets and stickers, including Lord Of The Rings and many other cards from Marvel Comics to The Beatles and Elvis.*

Neat Concepts Ltd, F25 Hastingwood Trading Estate, 35 Harbet Road, London, N18 3HU Tel: (020) 8807 5805 Fax: (020) 8884 4963 E-mail: sales@neatform.com *Flexible mdf producer*

▶ Neat Crown Corwen Ltd, Station Yard Industrial Estate, Corwen, Clwyd, LL21 0EE Tel: (01490) 413121 Fax: (01490) 412177 *Contract packing*

Neat Ideas Ltd, Sandall Stones Road, Kirk Sandall Industrial Estate, Doncaster, South Yorkshire, DN3 1QU Tel: (01302) 890089 Fax: (01302) 886605 E-mail: sales@neat-ideas.com *Mail order office products supplier*

Neatawash Laundry, Boothen Green, Stoke-on-Trent, ST4 4BJ Tel: (01782) 413502 Fax: (01782) 747130 E-mail: service@neatawash.co.uk *Workwear industrial supply, laundry service*

Neate Militarian Antiques, PO Box 3794, Sudbury, Suffolk, CO10 9LX Tel: (01787) 248168 Fax: (01787) 248363 *Medal dealer suppliers*

Neath Coachbuilders Ltd, Cilfrew, Neath, West Glamorgan, SA10 8LF Tel: (01639) 643629 Fax: (01639) 646566 E-mail: enquiries@neathcoachbuilders.co.uk *Commercial vehicles*

Neath Guardian, 17 Queen Street, Neath, West Glamorgan, SA11 1DN Tel: (01639) 778888 Fax: (01639) 778884 E-mail: guardian@wme.co.uk *Newspapers*

Neath Valve & Engineering Co. Ltd, Tank Farm Road, Llandarcy, Neath, West Glamorgan, SA10 6EN Tel: (01792) 817418 Fax: (01792) 817418 *Valve recondition & general machining services*

Neaves Paving, School Lane, Smallburgh, Norwich, NR12 9NG Tel: (01692) 536378 *Concrete product manufrs*

Nebrak Ltd, 1 Ipplepen Business Park, Edgelands Lane, Ipplepen, Newton Abbot, Devon, TQ12 5UG Tel: (01803) 813900 Fax: (01803) 812300 E-mail: sales@nebrak.com *Exhibition design & construction manufacturers & suppliers*

▶ Nebula Audio, Unit 238 Ikon Estate, Droitwich Road, Hartlebury, Kidderminster, Worcestershire, DY10 4EU Tel: (01299) 253571 Fax: (01299) 250983 *Audio visual equipment suppliers & installers*

Nebula Computers, 73 Biggin Hall Cresent, Coventry, CV3 1HA Tel: (024) 7643 1211 Fax: (024) 7643 1711 E-mail: info@nebulacomputers.co.uk *Computer resellers*

Nec Europe Ltd, N E C House, 1 Victoria Road, London, W3 6BL Tel: (020) 8993 8111 Fax: (020) 8992 7161 *Computer & communication equipment*

necktiesonline.co.uk Ltd, Daymer, Ashmore Green Road, Ashmore Green, Thatcham, Berkshire, RG18 9ER Tel: (01635) 872499 E-mail: sales@necktiesonline.co.uk *Online retailer of polyester and silk neckties. Wholesale deals available for solid colour ties. Custom Made Tie service also available.*

Nectar, Artemis Court, St. Johns Road, Meadowfield Industrial Estate, Durham, DH7 8TZ Tel: 0191-378 1946 Fax: 0191-378 1469 E-mail: sales@nectar.uk.com *Computer manufrs*

▶ Necton Management Ltd, Oak Farm, North Pickenham Road, Necton, Swaffham, Norfolk, PE37 8DN Tel: (01760) 722183 Fax: (01760) 722342

▶ Nectorine Ltd, 36 Maes-Y-Sarn, Pentyrch, Cardiff, CF15 9QQ Tel: (029) 2089 1188 Fax: (029) 2089 1188 E-mail: service@nectarine.co.uk *Internet retailer*

Nederman Ltd, PO Box 503, Preston, PR5 8AF Tel: (01772) 334721 Fax: (01772) 315273 *Manufacturer of dust and fume extraction systems*

▶ Nedschroef Fasteners, Road Transport Workshop, 7000 Alec Issigonis Way, Oxford Business Park North, Oxford, OX4 2ZY Tel: (01865) 713030 Fax: (01865) 401274 *Automotive fasteners suppliers*

Nee Controls, 19b White Rose Way, Gateshead, Tyne & Wear, NE10 8YX Tel: 0191-415 9751 Fax: 0191-416 1603 E-mail: sales@nee-controls.com *Control systems & electronic motion control equipment*

▶ Needfull Things, 3 Woodlands Drive, Grantham, Lincolnshire, NG31 9DJ Tel: (01476) 569571 Fax: (01529) 455405 *Cleaning services*

▶ Needham, Florian House, 30 Wharfdale Road, Ipswich, IP1 4JP Tel: (01473) 220400 Fax: (01603) 891046

Needham Chalks Ltd, Ipswich Road, Needham Market, Ipswich, IP6 8EL Tel: (01449) 720227 Fax: (01449) 720520 E-mail: needhamchalks@btinternet.com *Chalk producers*

▶ Needham Electrical Ltd, Maitland Road, Lion Barn Industrial Estate, Needham Market, Ipswich, IP6 8NZ Tel: (01449) 722642 Fax: (01449) 722182 *Electrical contractors*

F.W. Needham Ltd, 84 Great Hampton Street, Birmingham, B18 6EP Tel: 0121-554 5453 Fax: 0121-554 9859 E-mail: fw-needham@btconnect.com *Watch, clock wholesalers & manufrs*

Roger Needham & Sons Ltd, Units 15-16 Salford Enterprise Centre, Guide Street, Salford, M50 1EW Tel: 0161-745 7277 Fax: 0161-745 7826 E-mail: franksnsl@aol.com *Industrial inks manufrs* Also at: Whitchurch

Roger Needham & Sons Ltd, Unit 2b, Civic Industrial Park, Waymills, Whitchurch, Shropshire, SY13 1TT Tel: (01948) 662629 Fax: (01948) 665045 E-mail: info@rnsl.co.uk *Industrial ink manufrs*

Needham Specialised Machines Ltd, Riverside Works, Storforth Lane, Chesterfield, Derbyshire, S40 2TU Tel: (01246) 238008 Fax: (01246) 277264 E-mail: sales@needhams.uk.com *Custom built machinery & flow meters manufrs*

▶ Needhams Removals, 302 Old Shoreham Road, Southwick, Brighton, BN42 4LN Tel: (01273) 889403 E-mail: info@needhams.co.uk *Needham's Removals Brighton have many years in the removals Industry, providing Stress free Removals in the Brighton, East Sussex and Worthing area, and offer a friendly, personal service that is unrivalled in our field. Don't delay, if you need it moved, call the best, call Needhams Removals Brighton !*

▶ Needhams Windows, Unit 1, Great Central Road, Loughborough, Leicestershire, LE11 1RW Tel: (01509) 264066 *Manufacture upvc products windows door & conservatories*

The Needle Co. Ltd, 27a Lubenham Hill, Market Harborough, Leicestershire, LE16 9DG Tel: (01858) 555500 Fax: (01858) 555588 E-mail: needles@btconnect.com *Rug & hand sewing needle distributors*

Needlespar Ltd, Harvey Crescent, 207 Warsash Road, Warsash, Southampton, SO31 9JE Tel: (01489) 573406 *Manufacturers of masts for sailing boats*

Needs Ltd, 13 Queensway, Enfield, Middlesex, EN3 4SG Tel: (020) 8804 2281 Fax: (020) 8364 7113 E-mail: sales@needsplastics.co.uk *Engineers in Plastics and Laminates*

Neesham Controls Ltd, Twerton Mill, Lower Bristol Road, Bath, BA2 1EW Tel: (01225) 402140 Fax: (01225) 448154 *Control panel & switchgear manufrs*

▶ Neesham Public Relations Ltd, The Gallery Ashlyns Hall, Chesham Road, Berkhamsted, Hertfordshire, HP4 2ST Tel: (01442) 879222 Fax: (01442) 879444 E-mail: allane@neesham.co.uk *Public relations consultancy*

Nefab Packaging UK Ltd, 151 Silbury Boulevard, Milton Keynes, MK9 1LH Tel: (01908) 424300 Fax: (01908) 424301 E-mail: helen.coffin@nefab.se *Nefab offers complete packaging solutions for the entire logistics flow of its customers. Through a system of products and services combined with Nefab´s global presence, the customer's total costs for logistics and product protection are reduced.*

▶ Nefco Ltd, Unit 8 Derwentdale Industrial Estate, Consett, County Durham, DH8 8PZ Tel: (01207) 593623 E-mail: info@nefco.co.uk *Fire extinguisher servicing,Fire protection equipmnet sales, Fire risk assessments, Staff training FREE consultations and surveys.*

Nefco Multi Metals Ltd, Unit 19 Maun Valley Industrial Estate, Junction Road, Sutton-in-Ashfield, Nottinghamshire, NG17 5GS Tel: (01623) 551313 Fax: (01623) 551195 E-mail: nefco@btconnect.com *Wide range of metals & plastics non-ferrous stockholders*

Negaplate, 5 Howard Road, London, E11 3PL Tel: (020) 8558 9050 Fax: (020) 8558 9050 E-mail: negaplate@btconnect.com *Lithographic printer manufrs*

Negus Ken Ltd, 90 Garfield Road, London, SW19 8SB Tel: (020) 8543 9266 Fax: (020) 8543 9100 E-mail: enquiries@kennegus.co.uk Purchasing Contact: R. McKinlay Sales Contact: G. Negus *Stone cleaning & restoration contractors.*

Nehl (UK) Ltd, Unit 2, Stafford Park 12, Telford, Shropshire, TF3 3BJ Tel: (01952) 292296 Fax: (01952) 290409 E-mail: enquiries@www.nehl(uk).com *Specialists in space saving furniture & upholstery*

Neida Blue 62 Ltd, Golden Hill Works, Coalwell Road, Freshwater, Isle Of Wight, PO40 9TD Tel: (01983) 758800 Fax: (01983) 758822 E-mail: simon.fisher@blue62.co.uk *Turned parts specialist manufrs*

Neida Products Engineering Ltd, Trentham Lakes South, Stoke-on-Trent, ST4 8GQ Tel: (01782) 643643 Fax: (01782) 644220 E-mail: sales@neida.co.uk *Precison turned parts manufrs*

Neil A Robertson Printers & Stationers, 7 Queen Street, Forfar, Angus, DD8 3AJ Tel: (01307) 464078 Fax: (01307) 468523 E-mail: neil.robertson17@btopenworld.com *Printers*

Neil Bath, Sedgemoor House, Othery, Bridgwater, Somerset, TA7 0QL Tel: 01823 698810 Fax: (01823) 698004 E-mail: neilbath@btinternet.com *Agricultural packaging services*Silage Repair Patch & Tape*Cow Tail Tape*Adhesive Tapes*

Neil Engineering, 28 Main Street, Glengarnock, Beith, Ayrshire, KA14 3AT Tel: (01505) 683608 Fax: (01505) 683608 *Automotive gear box repair services*

▶ Neil Grinnall, Galton Way, Hadzor, Droitwich, Worcestershire, WR9 7ER Tel: (01905) 827800 Fax: (01905) 827800 E-mail: enquiries@neilgrinnallhomes.co.uk

▶ Neil Hart Electrical Ltd, 33-35 Tryst Road, Stenhousemuir, Larbert, Stirlingshire, FK5 4QH Tel: (01324) 552799 Fax: (01324) 552819

▶ Neil Hipkiss Fine Art Studio, PO Box 781, Worcester, WR4 4BQ Tel: (01886) 888658 E-mail: neil.hipkiss@blueyonder.co.uk *fine art original oil paintings and limited edition prints - specialising in aviation and automotive - commissions accepted.*

R.K. Neil Ltd, The Old Sawmills, The Street, Kilmington, Warminster, Wiltshire, BA12 6RG Tel: (01985) 844112 Fax: (01985) 844113 E-mail: info@martinbrosltd.com *Road transport & haulage*

Neil S Bapty, Bayview, Low Askomil, Campbeltown, Argyll, PA28 6EP Tel: (01586) 552467 E-mail: nsbapty@btinternet.com *Provides, it & networking, design, implementation*

Neil Smith Export Services Ltd, 44 Hurricane Way, Norwich, NR6 6JB Tel: (01603) 409771 Fax: (01603) 788157 E-mail: sales@neilsmithexports.co.uk *Export packers*

Neil Smith Quality Home Improvements, 24 Hawthorn Hill, Trefechan, Merthyr Tydfil, Mid Glamorgan, CF48 2ES Tel: (01685) 723895 Fax: (01685) 723895 *Joinery*

Neil W Ingram, The Workshop, Church Street, Laurencekirk, Kincardineshire, AB30 1AP Tel: (01561) 378102 Fax: (01561) 378102 *Joinery manufrs*

▶ Neil Webster & Co. Ltd, 14 Finkle Street, Kendal, Cumbria, LA9 4AB Tel: (01539) 731518 Fax: (01539) 725602 E-mail: info@neilwebster.co.uk *Neil Webster & Co Accountants Kendal South Cumbria Furness North Lancashire Startups Bookkeeping Taxation*

▶ Neil Williams Haulage, Unit 13, Mayfield Industrial Estate, Dalkeith, Midlothian, EH22 4AD Tel: 0131-663 0048

B.C. Neill Air Conditioning Ltd, Brentwood Cronton Road, Prescot, Merseyside, L35 1SA Tel: 0151-423 3967 Fax: 0151-423 3978 E-mail: bcneill@tuscally.co.uk *Air conditioning systems installation & manufrs*

Neill & Brown Global Logistics Group Ltd, Overseas House, Livingstone Road, Hessle, North Humberside, HU13 0AW Tel: (01482) 644287 Fax: (01482) 644284 E-mail: whin@neillbrown.com *Freight forwarding, transport & shipping agents*

James Neill Holdings Ltd, Atlas Way, Atlas North, Sheffield, S4 7QQ Tel: 0114-281 4242 Fax: 0114-281 4201 E-mail: sales@neill-tools.co.uk *Holding company*

Neill King Partnership, 25 Garrard Close, Salford Priors, Evesham, Worcestershire, WR11 8XG Tel: (01789) 778462 Fax: (01789) 490486 E-mail: neil@neil-king.co.uk *Computer consultancy*

Neill Transport, 3 Walker Road, Irlam, Manchester, M44 6ZL Tel: 0161-288 3864 Fax: 0161-288 3864 E-mail: adrian@neill6562.fsbusiness.co.uk *sameday courier service covering uk & europe*

Neil's Steels Ltd, Westerman Complex, School Road, Hove, East Sussex, BN3 5HX Tel: (01273) 882323 Fax: (01273) 882323 E-mail: info@neilssteels.com *Steel work manufrs*

▶ Neilson Active Holidays, East Lockside, Brighton Marina Village, Brighton, BN2 5HA Tel: (0870) 3333346 Fax: (0870) 9099089 E-mail: sales@neilson.com *Neilson offer skiing, snowboarding and cross country skiing holidays in Europe, Scandinavia, Canada and USA with a wide range of travel options available.*

▶ Neilson Adam Ltd, Old Causeway, Kinross, KY13 8EZ Tel: (01577) 862673 Fax: (01577) 864401

Neilson Fjord Ltd, 51 Little Queen Street, Dartford, DA1 1TL Tel: (01322) 277322 Fax: (01322) 220630 *Joinery manufrs*

Neilson Hydraulics & Engineering Ltd, 22 Atlas Way, Sheffield, S4 7QQ Tel: (01709) 821002 Fax: 0114-244 0111 E-mail: sales@neilson-hydraulics.co.uk *Hydraulic power pack manufrs*

Neiman Packaging Ltd, Albion Road, New Mills, High Peak, Derbyshire, SK22 3EY Tel: (01663) 743924 Fax: (01663) 741078 E-mail: sales@roymere.co.uk *Plastic blow moulders*

Neisen Ltd, 8 West Newlands Industrial Park, St Ives Road, Somersham, Huntingdon, Cambridgeshire, PE28 3EB Tel: (01487) 840912 Fax: (01487) 843727 *Sub contract engineering & welding*

Nekem Bottle Suppliers, Trinity Street, Hull, HU3 1JR Tel: (01482) 223424 Fax: (01482) 228811 Principal Export Areas: Worldwide *Glass container & bottle distributors*

Nel Construction Ltd, Unit 1 Hodge Back Business Park, Reedyford Road, Nelson, Lancashire, BB9 8TF Tel: (01282) 612258 Fax: (01282) 616951 E-mail: sales@nel-construction.co.uk *Building contractors, design & build industrial*

Nelder & Southam, Mulberry Street, Stratford-upon-Avon, Warwickshire, CV37 6RS Tel: (01789) 267974 Fax: (01789) 267974 *Nelder & Southam offer many products including toughened & laminated glass & secondary glazing. Also picture frames & mirrors*

Nelipak Thermoforming, PO Box 28, Bristol, BS31 1XT Tel: 0117-986 7163 Fax: 0117-986 7197 *Thermoformed packaging*

▶ Nelson Associates, 186 Seacliff Road, Bangor, County Down, BT20 5HA Tel: (028) 9145 6109 Fax: (028) 9145 6109 E-mail: clivenelson@btinternet.com *Construction products*

Nelson Direct Mail Services, Unit 2, Quadrum Park Old Portsmouth Road, Peasmarsh, Guildford, Surrey, GU3 1LU Tel: (01483) 532737 Fax: (01483) 532837 E-mail: sales@nelsondirectmail.com *Direct mail services*

Nelson Hydraulics Ltd, Unit H1, Knockmore Industrial Estate, Lisburn, County Antrim, BT28 2AR Tel: (028) 9266 2781 Fax: (028) 9260 2952 E-mail: info@nelsonhydraulics.com *Hydraulic hose & fitting distributors*

▶ Nelson Joinery & Building, Glen Way, Brierfield, Nelson, Lancashire, BB9 5NH Tel: (01282) 615550 Fax: (01282) 619055

Nelson M Green & Sons Ltd, Rippingale Road, Kirkby Underwood, Bourne, Lincolnshire, PE10 0SH Tel: (01778) 440285 Fax: (01778) 440133 E-mail: mail@nelsongreen.com *Secondhand crawlers & spares suppliers*

Nelson Packaging, Waidshouse Mill, Townsley Street, Nelson, Lancashire, BB9 0RY Tel: (01282) 690215 Fax: (01282) 699976 *Polythene bag manufrs*

▶ The Nelson Press Ltd, Unit 9 Greatbridge Business Pa, Budds Lane, Romsey, Hampshire, SO51 0HA Tel: (01794) 515592

▶ Nelson The Removal Co., Irongrey Park, Irongray Road, Dumfries, DG2 0JE Tel: (01387) 722320 Fax: (01387) 722321 E-mail: info@nelsonremovals.co.uk *Domestic storage suppliers*

Nelson Roller & Rubber Co., Bankgate Mills, Bankgate, Slaithwaite, Huddersfield, HD7 5DL Tel: (01484) 845015 Fax: (01484) 842900 E-mail: info@nelco.co.uk *Rubber rollers & roller coverings*

Nelson Securities, View House, Rochester Way, Crowborough, East Sussex, TN6 2DR Tel: (01892) 652544 *Management consultants*

Nelson Sheetmetal Fabricators Ltd, Walton St Works, Walton St, Colne, Lancashire, BB8 0EW Tel: (01282) 866966 Fax: (01282) 866990 E-mail: nsc@fsmail.net *Sheet metalwork & welded fabricators*

Nelson Stanley Ltd, 217 Alder Road, Poole, Dorset, BH12 4AP Tel: (01202) 241020 Fax: (01202) 735204 *Scrap metal merchants*

Nelson Stokes Ltd, Highfield Industrial Estate, Camelford, Cornwall, PL32 9RA Tel: (01840) 213711 Fax: (01840) 213338 E-mail: enquiries@nelsonstokes.com *Hydraulic brake hose manufrs*

Nelson Stud Welding UK, Rabans Lane Industrial Area, 47-49 Edison Road, Aylesbury, Buckinghamshire, HP19 8TE Tel: (01296) 433500 Fax: (01296) 487930 E-mail: enquiries@nelson-europe.co.uk *Manufacturers of stud welding equipment & weld studs*

Nelson Textiles, 31 Elizabeth Street, Nelson, Lancashire, BB9 7YA Tel: (01282) 612234 Fax: (01282) 612234 E-mail: nelsontextiles@tiscali.co.uk *Textile merchants*

Nelson Thornes Ltd, Delta Place, 27 Bath Road, Cheltenham, Gloucestershire, GL53 7TH Tel: (01242) 267100 Fax: (01242) 221914 E-mail: sales@nelsonthornes.com *Publishers services*

Nelson Tool Co Stockport Ltd, Stringer Street, Stockport, Cheshire, SK1 2NZ Tel: 0161-480 6004 Fax: 0161-476 2325 E-mail: info@nelsontool.co.uk *Precision engineers & toolmakers*

Nelson Unit Ltd, Victoria Works, Lodge Lane, Dukinfield, Cheshire, SK16 5HY Tel: 0161-330 1007 Fax: 0161-343 1346 E-mail: info@nelsonunit.co.uk *Steel fabricators*

Nelsons Birstall Ltd, Perseverance Works, Gelderd Road, Batley, West Yorkshire, WF17 9PX Tel: (01924) 474981 Fax: (01924) 440871 E-mail: sales@nelsonseng.co.uk *Engineers & fabricators*

Nelsons For Cartons & Packaging Ltd, Auster Industrial Estate, Silverdale Drive, Thurmaston, Leicester, LE4 8NG Tel: 0116-264 1050 Fax: 0116-264 1051 *Corrugated packaging stockists & distribs*

Nelsons Labels MCR Ltd, Unit 3 Waterside, Trafford Park, Manchester, M17 1WD Tel: 0161-873 4500 Fax: 0161-873 4505 E-mail: sales@nelsons-labels.co.uk *Fabric label manufrs*

Nelsons Transport Keighley Ltd, Bocking Farm, Keighley, West Yorkshire, BD22 9BG Tel: (01535) 642097 Fax: (01535) 647015 E-mail: nelsonstransport@btinternet.com *Distribution storage & haulage contractors*

Nemac Fabrications Ltd, 5 Staition Road Industrial Estate, Station Road, Reddish, Stockport, Cheshire, SK5 6ND Tel: 0161-432 1030 Fax: 0161-443 2096 E-mail: neil@nemac.co.uk *Structural steelwork fabricators*

▶ Nemacom Computer Mnfrs, 6 Morgans Business Park, Bettys Lane, Norton Canes, Cannock, Staffordshire, WS11 9UU Tel: (01543) 495020 Fax: (01543) 495021 E-mail: sales@nemacom.co.uk *Computer displays & touch screen manufrs*

Nemco Metals International Ltd, 5 Pennard Close, Brackmills Indus Estate, Brackmills Industrial Estate, Northampton, NN4 7BE Tel: (01604) 666100 Fax: (01604) 768414 E-mail: sales@nemcometals.co.uk Principal Export Areas: Asia Pacific, Central/East Europe & West Europe *Brass, brass strip & non-ferrous metal distributors*

▶ Nemco Utilities Ltd, Hillside Business Park, 12 Kimpson Way, Bury St. Edmunds, Suffolk, IP32 7EA Tel: (01284) 724503 Fax: (01284) 724826

Nemesis Accessories Ltd, 16 Simmons Road, Henley On Thames, Henley-on-Thames, Oxfordshire, RG9 2ER Tel: (01491) 575550 Fax: (01491) 575550 E-mail: nemesis@cmcgowan.freeserve.co.uk *Costume & bridal jewellery*

▶ Nemesis Security & Training Ltd, Unit 15, Belmont Business Centre, East Hoathly, Lewes, East Sussex, BN8 6QL Tel: (0845) 3653768 E-mail: nemesissecurityltd@hotmail.com *Nemesis Security Ltd specialises in training companies and individuals in both Conflict Management and the SIA Door Supervisors Course.**We also provide well trained and highly qualified security staff and stewards for shows, events, and pubs/night clubs etc. **We are also able to cater for private parties, corporate functions and weddings etc**No job too big or too small for us to handle, please feel free to call us for advice or consultation etc*

Nemothon Computer Systems, Farleigh, East Grafton, Marlborough, Wiltshire, SN8 3DB Tel: (01672) 810901 Fax: (01672) 810883 *Computer consultants*

Nendle Acoustics Ltd, 153 High Street, Aldershot, Hampshire, GU11 1TT Tel: (01252) 344222 Fax: (01252) 333782 E-mail: info@nendle.co.uk *Noise & vibration designers*

Nene Catering Equipment, 19 Upper Priory Street, Grafton Street Industrial Estate, Northampton, NN1 2PT Tel: (01604) 621555 Fax: (01604) 621383 E-mail: sales@nenecateringequipment.co.uk *Commercial catering equipment suppliers*

Nene Engineering Peterborough Ltd, Wareley Road, Peterborough, PE2 9PF Tel: (01733) 553946 Fax: (01733) 894155 E-mail: info@neneengineering.co.uk *Steel fabrication*

Nene Mechanical Equipment, Nene House, Drayton Way, Drayton Fields Industrial Estate, Daventry, Northamptonshire, NN11 5EA Tel: (01327) 300456 Fax: (01327) 300737

continued

continuation
E-mail: sales@nene.co.uk *Materials handling equipment manufrs*

Nene Refrigeration, 12 Rotton Row, Raunds, Wellingborough, Northamptonshire, NN9 6HU Tel: (01933) 623441 Fax: (01933) 623441 *Refrigeration equipment*

Nene Storage Equipment Ltd, Nene House, Sopwith Way, Drayton Fields Indusrial Estate, Daventry, Northamptonshire, NN11 8EA Tel: (01327) 300456 Fax: (01327) 300737 E-mail: awbrooks@nene.co.uk *Hire of materials handling equipment & sales*

Nenplas, Airfield Industrial Estate, Ashbourne, Derbyshire, DE6 1HA Tel: (01335) 347300 Fax: (01335) 340271 E-mail: enquiries@nenplas.com Sales Contact: G. Kerr *Manufacturers of plastic extrusions and injection mouldings, who have an extensive range of standard and stocked products, as well as an in-house design facility for developing bespoke products.*

Neo Electronics Ltd, Compass House, Neville Street, Chadderton, Oldham, OL9 6LD Tel: 0161-633 2148 Fax: 0161-627 5324 E-mail: sales@neo.co.uk *Electronic contract manufacturing services*

Neo Interiors, The Old Dairy, Upper Thrift Street, Northampton, NN1 5HR Tel: (01604) 601981 Fax: (01604) 601989 E-mail: neointeriors@talk21.com *Suspended ceilings & partitions installers*

▶ Neobium Web Solutions, 18 Brackenwood, Orton Wistow, Peterborough, PE2 6YP Tel: 01733 371082 E-mail: info@neobium.co.uk *Web solutions*

Neogene Paints Ltd, 14 Caxton Way, Watford, WD18 8UJ Tel: (01923) 213737 Fax: (01923) 213617 E-mail: sales@neogenepaints.co.uk Principal Export Areas: Africa *Paint manufrs*

▶ Neoheat, Smallmead Gate, Pingemead Business Centre, Reading, RG30 3UR Tel: (0845) 1080361 Fax: (0845) 1081295 E-mail: infor@neoheat.com *Cables & under floor heating specialists*

The Neoknitting & Trim Ltd, Peter Pal House, Albion St, Leicester, LE2 5DE Tel: 0116-271 4923 Fax: 0116-271 4422 E-mail: sales@neotrims.com *Trimmings manufrs*

Neomet Ltd, 92 Cross Lane, Marple, Stockport, Cheshire, SK6 7PZ Tel: 0161-427 7741 Fax: 0161-449 0080 E-mail: fkirk@neomet.org *Honeycomb core for aircraft engines*

▶ Neon Effects, 70 Stanley Gardens, London, W3 7SZ Tel: (020) 8743 8801 Fax: (020) 8749 7347 *Sign contractors*

Neon & Sign Shop, 992-994 Argyle Street, Glasgow, G3 8LU Tel: 0141-248 9001 Fax: 0141-248 9002 *Sign manufrs*

Neon & Signmakers, Unit 1 Durham Yard, London, E2 6QF Tel: (020) 7729 5959 Fax: (020) 7772 9772 *Sign makers*

Neon Signs Northampton Ltd, 1 Colwyn Road, Northampton, NN1 3PZ Tel: (01604) 636341 Fax: (01604) 636341 *Manufacture neon signs*

Neonstream Ltd, 23 Woodcote, Maidenhead, Berkshire, SL6 4DU Tel: (01628) 622022 Fax: (01628) 785458 E-mail: rws@neonstream.net *Computer solutions packages*

Neophix Engineering Co. Ltd, Devonshire House, West Lane, Keighley, West Yorkshire, BD21 2LP Tel: (01535) 667382 Fax: (01535) 680825 E-mail: info@neophix.co.uk *Heavy duty hose clips, band, vee clamps & exhaust fitting manufrs*

Neosys Ltd, 14 Lomond Place, Erskine, Renfrewshire, PA8 6AP Tel: 0141-812 5937 Fax: 0141-812 5937 *Computer consultants*

▶ Neotex Services Ltd, 176 Hitchin Road, Arlesey, Bedfordshire, SG15 6SD Tel: (0870) 890 0086 Fax: 0870 033 9219 E-mail: info@neotex.co.uk *Manufactures environmentally friendly, non-acidic industrial cleaning solutions for specialist surface applications such as acrylics, vinyl, aluminium, uPVC, thermoplastics and painted enamel coatings. Bespoke cleaning products also developed for industry.*

Neoware Systems, Asmec Centre Eagle House, The Ring, Bracknell, Berkshire, RG12 1HB Tel: (01344) 382164 Fax: (01344) 303192 E-mail: info@neoware.com *Computer equipment supplier & manufrs*

▶ Neoworks Ltd, 2-3 North Mews, London, WC1N 2JP Tel: (020) 7025 0950 Fax: (020) 7637 9631 E-mail: sales@neoworks.com *Software developers*

Neppco Ltd, PO Box 88, Manchester, M60 1QD Tel: 0161-200 5706 Fax: 0161-200 5707 E-mail: sales@neppco.co.uk *Research, design & manufacturing for plastic industries*

Neptune Engineering Co., E Caxton Hill, Extension Road, Hertford, SG13 7LY Tel: (01992) 587889 Fax: (01992) 554478 E-mail: sales@neptune-eng.demon.co.uk *Precision engineers*

Neptune Fabrications Ltd, 5 Ibrox Industrial Estate, Carmichael Street, Glasgow, G51 2QU Tel: 0141-427 3773 Fax: 0141-427 3703 E-mail: nepfab@btconnect.co.uk *Sheet metalwork fabricators*

Neptune Glassfibre Mouldings, Old Ice Factory, Rolle Street, Barnstaple, Devon, EX31 1JP Tel: (01271) 374722 Fax: (01271) 371339 *Industrial glass fibre mould manufrs*

Neptune Glassfibre Mouldings, Old Ice Factory, Rolle Street, Barnstaple, Devon, EX31 1JP Tel: (01271) 374722 Fax: (01271) 371339 *Glass fibre products*

Neptune Plastic Fabrications, 22 Bull Green Road, Longwood, Huddersfield, HD3 4XW Tel: (01484) 656914 *Plastic fabricators*

Neptune Radar Ltd, Gardiners Farmhouse, Sandhurst Lane, Sandhurst, Gloucester, GL2 9NW Tel: (01452) 730479 Fax: (01452) 731315 E-mail: seawaves@enterprise.net *Electronic systems & softwaren agents*

▶ Nereus Alarms Ltd, 9 Britannia Road, Lower Parkstone, Poole, Dorset, BH14 8AZ Tel: (01202) 731886 Fax: (01202) 739060 E-mail: info@nereusalarms.co.uk *Gas alarm designers & manufrs*

Nero Signs Glass/Designs Ltd, 332-334 Brixton Road, London, SW9 7AA Tel: (020) 7737 8021 Fax: (020) 7733 8589 E-mail: sales@nerodesigns.co.uk *Glass decorating & embossing services*

Nersys, Stephenson Street, Newport, Gwent, NP19 4XJ Tel: (01633) 277673 Fax: (01633) 281787 E-mail: forename.surname@uk.nss.com *Sealed lead rechargeable battery manufrs*

Neschen UK Ltd, Emerald Way, Stone Business Park, Stone, Staffordshire, ST15 0SR Tel: (01785) 610110 Fax: (01785) 610111 E-mail: neschen@neschen.co.uk *Self-adhesive film distribs*

Nesco Weighing Ltd, 89-91 Lambert Street, Hull, HU5 2SH Tel: (01482) 346865 Fax: (01482) 445483 E-mail: info@nesco-weighing.co.uk *Industrial & marine weighing machine sales, services & manufrs*

▶ Neslo, Port Causeway, Wirral, Merseyside, CH62 4SY Tel: 0151-334 9326 Fax: 0151-334 0668 *Refurbishment services*

Nesor Equipment Co. Ltd, 166 Gilmore Road, London, SE13 5AE Tel: (020) 8852 8545 Fax: (020) 8852 1230 E-mail: nesor@supanet.com *Dental equipment retailers & installers*

▶ Ness Engineering Ltd, Sumburgh Airport, Virkie, Shetland, ZE3 9JP Tel: (01950) 460714 Fax: (01950) 460378

Nessco, Seymour House, The Street, Appledore, Ashford, Kent, TN26 2AF Tel: (01233) 758784 *Electronic equipment suppliers*

Nessco Services Ltd, Discovery House Arnhall Business, Park, Westhill, Aberdeenshire, AB32 6FG Tel: (01355) 266900 Fax: (01224) 428401 E-mail: sales@nessco.co.uk Principal Export Areas: Worldwide *Integrated telecommunication services*

The Nestbox Company Ltd, Bolton Farm Lyonshall, Lyonshall, Kington, Herefordshire, HR5 3JY Tel: (01544) 340657 Fax: (01544) 340672 E-mail: sales@nestbox.co.uk *Nest box manufrs*

Nestle Cereal Partners, Bridge Road East, Welwyn Garden City, Hertfordshire, AL7 1RR Tel: (01707) 824400 Fax: (01707) 824401 *Cereal manufrs*

Nestle Holdings UK plc, St George's House, Park Lane, Croydon, CR9 1NR Tel: (020) 8686 3333 Fax: (020) 8686 6072 *Nestle (UK) Ltd based in Croydon are well-known food producers covering ranges including chocolate and confectionery, pet foods, beverages, prepared foods, ice cream, baby foods and bottled water.*

Nestle Purina, Chilton Industrial Estate, Windham Road, Sudbury, Suffolk, CO10 2XD Tel: (01787) 886000 Fax: (01787) 886086 Principal Export Areas: Worldwide *Pet food manufrs*

Nestle Rowntree UK Ltd, Rowan Drive, Newcastle upon Tyne, NE3 3TR Tel: 0191-202 4200 Fax: 0191-202 4300 *Confectionary manufrs*

Nestle UK Ltd, Wheldon Road, Castleford, West Yorkshire, WF10 2JN Tel: (01422) 862100 Fax: (01422) 862101 *Confectionery services*

Nestle UK Ltd, Nestle Rowntree Division, Albion Mills, Halifax, West Yorkshire, HX3 9XT Tel: (01422) 862286 Fax: (01422) 862233 *Confectionary manufrs*

Nestle UK Ltd, Sarsons Works, Mills Hill Rd, Middleton, Manchester, M24 2ED Tel: 0161-653 4005 Fax: 01457 890164 *Vinegar manufrs*

Nestle Waters Pow Wow, Unit 7 Matrix Park, Talbot Road, Segensworth South, Fareham, Hampshire, PO15 5AP Tel: (01329) 849248 *Water cooler services*

Nestle Waters Pow Wow, Unit 6 Circle South, Wharside Way, Trafford, Manchester, M17 1NS Tel: (0845) 6013030 Fax: 0161-877 5258 *Pure bottled water manufrs*

▶ Nestle Waters Powwow, Units C-D, Guiness Circle, Guiness Road, Trafford Park, Manchester, M17 1EB Tel: 0161-772 8716 Fax: (01865) 405441 E-mail: contactus@uk.nestle-waters-powwow.com *Industrial water cooler manufrs*

Nestle Waters Powwow, St Georges Well, Long Hanborough, Witney, Oxfordshire, OX29 8BT Tel: (01993) 882802 Fax: (01993) 883872 *Mineral water suppliers*

Nestle Waters UK Ltd, Trinity Court, Church Street, Rickmansworth, Hertfordshire, WD3 1LD Tel: (01923) 897700 Fax: (01923) 897608 E-mail: enquiries@waters.nestle.com *Mineral water carbonated manufrs*

Nestles Water Powwow, Units D9-D10, Cross Green Industrial Estate, Leeds, LS9 0PF Tel: 0113-380 7050 Fax: 0113-380 7068 *Water coolers*

Nestor Healthcare Group P.L.C., The Colonnades, Beaconsfield Court, Beaconsfield Road, Hatfield, Hertfordshire, AL10 8HU Tel: (01707) 255635 Fax: (0845) 8501435 E-mail: info@nestorplc.co.uk *Holding companies & health care*

▶ Company Net Ltd, Research Park North, Riccarton, Edinburgh, EH14 4AP Tel: 0131-559 7500 Fax: 0131-559 7501 E-mail: info@company-net.com *Software development*

▶ Net Commerce Solutions Ltd, 6 Bramble Close, Harpenden, Hertfordshire, AL5 4AN Tel: (0870) 2467642 Fax: (0871) 4337349 E-mail: info@net-commerce-solutions.co.uk *Web design, search engine optimisation & internet promotion services*

Net Comp Ltd, 21 Shaftesbury Street South, Derby, DE23 8YH Tel: (01332) 290509 Fax: (01332) 384873 E-mail: sales@netcomp.ltd.uk *Components for data network distributors*

▶ Net Curtains Direct, 14 Alder Close, Dibden Purlieu, Southampton, SO45 5SJ Tel: (023) 8084 6946 *Net curtain manufrs*

▶ Net Experts, Pennyfoot Street, Nottingham, NG1 1GF Tel: 0115-985 2213 Fax: 0115-912 4546 E-mail: sales@netexperts.co.uk *IT support*

Net Formation Ltd, Godstone Green, Godstone, Surrey, RH9 8DZ Tel: (01883) 740000 Fax: (01883) 744465 E-mail: info@forfront.net *Bespoke software & website developers*

▶ Net Lynk, The Courtyard, Roman Way, Coleshill, Birmingham, B46 1HQ Tel: (01675) 466555 Fax: (01675) 466050

▶ Net Marketing, 6 Longhouse Grove, Henllys, Cwmbran, Gwent, NP44 6HQ Tel: (0845) 6440963 Fax: (0870) 7661806 E-mail: enquiries@nmuk.com *Web design, hosting & internet services*

▶ Net One Media Ltd, Newton Cap House, Bishop Auckland, County Durham, DL14 7SB Tel: (0870) 7668585 Fax: (0870) 7668595 E-mail: sales@365ink.co.uk *Online retailer of ink jet & toner cartridges*

Net Resources Ltd, 26a Palmerston Place, Edinburgh, EH12 5AL Tel: 0131-477 7127 Fax: 0131-477 7126 E-mail: info@netresources.co.uk *IT Training & website design*

▶ Net Sec (UK) Ltd, Austin Friars, London, EC2N 2HG Tel: (020) 7448 1400 Fax: (020) 7448 1401 *Computer systems security*

▶ Net Solutions London, 40 Sheen Lane, London, SW14 8LW Tel: 0208 2552483 Fax: 0208 2554022 E-mail: info@netsols.co.uk *Computer maintenance, consultants, wireless installation, broadband and internet sharing, computer and software sales*

▶ net:telecom, The Chase Business Centre, 39-41 Chase Side, Southgate, London, N14 5BP Tel: (0870) 8720202 Fax: (0871) 4742868 E-mail: henry.forde@nettelecom.uk.com *Telecommunications products, services, business telephone systems*

▶ Netahead, 10 Sunnybank, Epsom, Surrey, KT18 7DX Tel: 07950 335730 E-mail: info@netahead.co.uk *Netahead : high quality websites *for small & medium sized companies*

Netbuyer, 1 International House, St. Katharines Way, London, E1W 1UN Tel: (020) 7903 6807 Fax: (020) 7903 6000 E-mail: geoff.inns@cnet.com *Computer distributors*

Netco Ltd, 27 Quail Green, Wolverhampton, WV6 8DF Tel: (01902) 763879 Fax: (01902) 763879 E-mail: mail@netcotraceheating.com *Electrical trace heating systems*

Netcom Systems, 4 Beach Station Road, Felixstowe, Suffolk, IP11 2DR Tel: (01394) 271600 Fax: (01394) 271680 *Computer system builders & repairs*

▶ Netcomm Data Solutions Ltd, 93-95, Carshalton Grove, Sutton, Surrey, SM1 4NB Tel: (020) 8643 4908 Fax: (020) 8770 0831

Netcraft Ltd, Rockfield House, Charlcombe, Bath, BA1 9BQ Tel: (01225) 447500 Fax: (01225) 448600 E-mail: sales@netcraft.com *Internet services*

▶ Netfix Solutions Ltd, Heath House, West Drayton Road, Uxbridge, Middlesex, UB8 3LA Tel: (020) 8589 9966 Fax: (020) 8589 9955

▶ Nethervale Ltd, Gilburn Place, Shotts, Lanarkshire, ML7 5ES Tel: (01501) 822546

Netik Consulting Ltd, Sir John Lyon Ho, 5 High Timber St, London, EC4V 3LS Tel: (020) 7489 5899 Fax: (020) 7329 0829 *Computer consultancy*

▶ Netlog Technology, Pant Industrial Estate, Dowlais, Merthyr Tydfil, CF48 2SR Tel: (01685) 384654 Fax: (01685) 384674 E-mail: info@netlogtec.com *Netlogtec are a Networking and Linux Systems Integrator. We partner with best-of-breed manufacturers and are a Cisco SMB Select, 3Com Bronze Partner, ZEN Internet Partner and a member of the BECTA ICT Support Network. We provide design, installation and maintenance for converged networks and provision new technology deployments i.e. Wireless (Wi-Fi), IP Telephony, VoIP, Security & VPN, IP CCTV.*

Netlogic Consulting Ltd, Harlow, Essex, CM18 7NT Tel: (01279) 413355 Fax: (020) 8830 4173 E-mail: info@netlogicconsulting.com *Computer consultants*

▶ Netlon Ltd, New Wellington Street, Blackburn, BB2 4PJ Tel: (01254) 262431 Fax: (01254) 266867 E-mail: info@netlon.co.uk *A manufacture of extruded nets and meshes for use in the construction industry, horticulture and industrial filtration and various industrial protective applications*

Netmanage UK Ltd, Lyon Court, Walsworth Road, Hitchin, Hertfordshire, SG4 9SX Tel: (01462) 755050 Fax: (01462) 755055 *Software manufrs*

▶ Netmerchants, Unit 53 Ledcom Industrial Estate, Bank Road, Larne, County Antrim, BT40 3AW Tel: (028) 2827 7440 Fax: (028) 2826 7977 E-mail: info@netmerchants.co.uk *Retail & distribution of scale models*

The Netpoint Project Ltd, Hove, East Sussex, BN3 3RZ Tel: (01273) 778122 Fax: (07092) 385043 *Computer software development services*

▶ Netpresto Ltd, Wellington Street, Gateshead, Tyne & Wear, NE8 2AJ Tel: 0191-478 2233 Fax: 0191-477 7929 E-mail: sales@netpresto.co.uk *ISP providing business to business ads*

▶ Netron Wireless, 6 Wilmer Industrial Estate, Wilmer Place, London, N16 0LW Tel: (0870) 3509474 Fax: (020) 7249 3111 *Wireless net workers*

Netserv Ltd, 51a Station Road, Marston Green, Birmingham, B37 7AB Tel: 0121-770 3730 Fax: 0121-779 4131 E-mail: info@netservuk.com *Computer software developers*

Netshift Software Ltd, Kennet Side, Newbury, Berkshire, RG14 5PX Tel: (01635) 568800 Fax: (01635) 568850 E-mail: admin@netshift.com *Computer software developers*

▶ Netshop Ltd, Grays Place, Slough, SL2 5AF Tel: (01753) 691661 Fax: (01753) 691037 E-mail: sales@netshop.co.uk *Computer hardware, data communications & cable management product manufrs*

Netstal Ltd, Emerald Way, Stone Business Park, Stone, Staffordshire, ST15 0SR Tel: (01785) 815166 Fax: (01785) 815132 E-mail: email@netstal.co.uk *Injection moulding machine manufrs*

▶ Netstationers, 57 Water Lane, Wilmslow, Cheshire, SK9 5BQ Tel: (0800) 0833178 Fax: (0800) 0833179 E-mail: phil.hopkins@netstationers.co.uk

continued

General office supplies, stationery, bespoke printing, furniture

▶ Netsupport Ltd, Netsupport House, Towngate East, Market Deeping, Peterborough, PE6 8NE Tel: (01778) 382270 Fax: (01778) 382290 E-mail: s.craft@netsupportsoftware.com *PC remote control software & net support software manufrs*

Nettech Solutions, 20 Branch Road, Batley, West Yorkshire, WF17 5RY Tel: (01924) 524873 Fax: (01924) 501183 E-mail: nettech.solutions@ntlworld.com *Specialists in computer repairs, sales and upgrades. Also virus removal, networking, internet connections and more.*

▶ Nettfar Technology Ltd, Panda, Tweentown, Cheddar, Somerset, BS27 3JF Tel: 01934 743716 E-mail: mail@netttfar.co.uk *Computer Technology & Broadband Internet Supplies, we supply Hardware, Software, Networks, Help & Advise.**Somerset Region*

Nettlebank Monumental Masons Ltd, 26 Chapel Street, Cheadle, Stoke-on-Trent, ST10 1DY Tel: (01538) 750051 Fax: (01538) 750599 *Monumental masons & granite worktops manufrs*

Nettletons & Porters Ltd, Wakefield Road, Ossett, West Yorkshire, WF5 9JX Tel: (01924) 273047 Fax: (01924) 280584 E-mail: nettletons@freezone.co.uk *Fellmongers*

▶ Nettmedia Ltd, Unit 3, Red Cow Yard, Knutsford, Cheshire, WA16 6DG Tel: (01565) 652300 Fax: (01565) 654211 E-mail: info@nettmedia.co.uk *Fax Broadcasting, Fax Lists, Email Lists, Business Data, Email Broadcasting.*

Netwinner Ltd, 15 The Maltings, Longton, Preston, PR4 5ZS Tel: (01772) 616078 Fax: (01772) 616086 E-mail: sales@netwinner.co.uk Principal Export Areas: Worldwide *Computer software & internet services*

Network Appliance, Riley Court, Millburn Hill Road, Coventry, CV4 7HS Tel: (024) 7683 8838 Fax: (024) 7683 8801 E-mail: info@netapp.com *Computer storage services*

Network Appliance Ltd, Stockley Park, 1 Roundwood Avenue, Uxbridge, Middlesex, UB11 1EJ Tel: (020) 8756 6700 Fax: (020) 8756 6701 *Data storage specialist services*

Network Associates (Midlands) Ltd, Vincent House, Buntsford Park Road, Bromsgrove, Worcestershire, B60 3DX Tel: (01527) 576933 Fax: (0870) 706 2522 E-mail: enquiries@network-associates.co.uk *Computer software consultancy*

Network Business Communications, 57 London Road, Enfield, Middlesex, EN2 6DU Tel: (020) 8370 8370 Fax: (020) 8366 6844 *Telecommunications installers & distributors*

▶ Network & Cabling Solutions Ltd, Endeavour House, 259 Forstal Road, Aylesford, Kent, ME20 7AP Tel: (01622) 791001 Fax: (01622) 791001 E-mail: info@networkandcabling.co.uk *Network and Cabling Solutions (NCS) is a Kent-based company which specialises in the supply of ICT equipment and services to UK schools and colleges, including electrical and data network design and installation. As a Promethean Partner, NCS can supply and install the much acclaimed ACTIVboard along with any other customer specified Interactive Whiteboard. Some of our other products include both Voice and Video over IP, Network Security Camera's, Projector Security, the Techno Desk, and as a Hewlett Packard Partner we can advise you on the best way of managing your network. Not only are we an NICEIC approved contractor and a member of BICSI, but all our engineers are CRB checked (Criminal records Bureau), hold CCNSG health and safety passports, are first aid trained, and are fully qualified to conduct risk assessments.**As you can see we truly are the complete solution provider for all your networking needs.*

Network Car, Unit 6 The Willows, 80 Willow Walk, London, SE1 5SY Tel: (020) 7231 1122 Fax: (020) 7231 2082 *Car services*

▶ Network China Ltd, Suite 4 The Exchange, Spring, Lane, Colne, Colne, Lancashire, BB8 9BD Tel: (01282) 861001 Fax: (01282) 618115 E-mail: networkchina@btinternet.com *Network China Ltd is a specialist consultancy company assisting UK companies to capitalize on the low cost, high quality manufacturing available in the People's Republic of China. With offices in the UK, Hong Kong and China, and more than 50 years experience working in China, the team at Network China can assist in all areas of product design, development and manufacturing. Contact us today for a quotation.*

Network Connect Ltd, Egret Mill, 162 Old Street, Ashton-under-Lyne, Lancashire, OL6 7ST Tel: 0161-214 2000 Fax: 0161-214 2001 E-mail: sales@networkconnect.co.uk *Telecommunications installers*

▶ Network Conwy, Conwy Marina, Ellis Way, Conwy, Gwynedd, LL32 8GU Tel: (01492) 580001 Fax: (01492) 580004 E-mail: info@nybconwy.co.uk *Yachts & boats dealer*

Network Design International Ltd, 34 Mortimer Street, London, W1W 7JS Tel: (020) 7580 5151 Fax: (020) 7580 6242 E-mail: get.work@networkdesign.cc *Recruitment consultants*

Network Direct Ltd, PO Box 117, Guernsey, GY1 4ED Tel: (01481) 701400 Fax: (01481) 701456 E-mail: network@direct.guernsey.net *Insurance brokers & consultants*

Network Disaster Recovery Ltd, 220 Chester Street, Aston, Birmingham, B6 4AH Tel: 0121-380 2000 Fax: 0121-359 0534 E-mail: sales@ndr.co.uk *Computer breakdown supply services*

Network Engineering Technology Ltd, 6 Church Road, Swallowfield, Reading, RG7 1TH Tel: 0118-988 7014 Fax: 0118-988 7114 E-mail: sale@netec.co.uk *Installation & supply of computer cables*

Network Europe Group plc, 14 Capricorn Centre, Cranes Farm Road, Basildon, Essex, SS14 3JJ Tel: (0870) 3330321 Fax: (0870) 3330320 E-mail: sales@negplc.com Principal Export Areas: Worldwide *Telecommunication services*

▶ Network For Growth Ltd, 67 Shobnall Close, Burton On Trent, Burton-on-Trent, Staffordshire, DE14 2HX Tel: (01283) 546888 Fax: (0870) 7065342 E-mail: info@networkforgrowth.co.uk *Business Networking with the key focus on manufacturing engineering and distribution. Based near Derby, Network for Growth arranges a network of meetings and informal exhibitions to introduce industrial companies with the emphasis on increased sales and problem solving.*

▶ Network Instruments Ltd, 7 The Old Yard, Rectory Lane, Brasted, Westerham, Kent, TN16 1JP Tel: (01959) 569880 Fax: (01959) 569881E-mail: sales@networkinstruments.co.uk *Computer net workers*

Network Logic Ltd, 2 St Josephs Close, Droitwich, Worcestershire, WR9 0RY Tel: (01905) 795725 E-mail: network.logic@lineone.net *Computer & networking solutions supplier*

The Network Modelmakers, Arch 9, 67A St Marks Road, London, W11 1RE Tel: (020) 7243 1816 Fax: (020) 7243 1809 E-mail: mail@networkmodelmakers.com *Model makers.*

Network Perspectives Ltd, Elmbank Mill, The Charrier, Menstrie, Clackmannanshire, FK11 7BU Tel: (01259) 726636 Fax: (01259) 763388 E-mail: enquiries@net-spex.co.uk *Network consultancy*

▶ Network Plant Ltd, 76 Pretoria Road North, London, N18 1SP Tel: (020) 8803 3555 Fax: (020) 8803 3553 E-mail: info@networkplant.co.uk

Network Promotions, 5 Braehead Business Units, Braehead Road, Linlithgow, West Lothian, EH49 6EP Tel: (01506) 845797 Fax: (01506) 845149 *Club & company tie manufrs*

▶ Network Property Consulting & Construction, Network House, 119 Hagley Road, Birmingham, B16 8LB Tel: 0121-450 5020 Fax: 0121-450 5021 E-mail: osb@netrec.co.uk *recruitment amd engineering supply the construction industry and the built environment in the united kingdom*

Network Recruitment Partnership, 82 Abington Street, Northampton, NN1 2AP Tel: (01604) 234242 Fax: (01604) 232137 E-mail: northampton.network@pertemps.co.uk *Technical & accountancy recruitment*

Network Seafoods Ltd, Quarry Road, Newhaven, East Sussex, BN9 9DB Tel: (01273) 513884 Fax: (01273) 517884 E-mail: sales@networkseafoods.co.uk *Fish merchants*

▶ Network Secure Ltd, Unit 2, 5 High Street, Maidenhead, Berkshire, SL6 1JA Tel: (01628) 825665 Fax: (01628) 822613 E-mail: sales@netsecgroup.com *Network security*

Network Technologies & Associates Ltd, 38 High Street, Newmarket, Suffolk, CB8 8LB Tel: (01638) 668633 Fax: (01638) 561924 E-mail: info@networktechnologies.co.uk *Networking services*

Network Telex Ltd, Kingsland House, 514 Wimborne Road, Ferndown, Dorset, BH22 9NG Tel: (01202) 874156 Fax: (01202) 897827 E-mail: info.uk@telex-net.co.uk *Telex manufacturers & distributors*

Network Training, Mitre House, Tower Street, Taunton, Somerset, TA1 4BH Tel: (01823) 353354 Fax: (01823) 352202 E-mail: mail@network-training.ac.uk *Computer consultants services*

▶ Network17 UK Ltd, 111 Faraday Road, Wimbledon, London, SW19 8PA Tel: (020) 8540 2835 E-mail: dave@network17.co.uk *Web site services including web site design and construction, web site maintenance, web site promotion and Internet consultancy services.*

▶ The Networking Co, Riddell Road, West End, Lilliesleaf, Melrose, Roxburghshire, TD6 9JA Tel: (08456) 3 40844 Fax: (01835) 870380 *IT Services*

▶ Networks & Data Ltd, 2 Meadow Rise, Wadworth, Doncaster, South Yorkshire, DN11 9AP Tel: (01302) 854969 E-mail: dave@networksanddata.co.uk *Design and Technical Documentation Services to the electrical engineering and software industry*

▶ Networx Ltd, PO Box 8812, Lanark, ML11 9YQ Tel: (0870) 3501345 Fax: (0870) 3501346 *GPS, satellite & radar distribution*

Netx Voice & Data Installations, 76 Broad St, Ely, Cambs, CB7 4AH Tel: 01353 664242 Fax: 01353 776266 *Data cabling*

Netxtra Ltd, The Old Foundry, Hall Street, Long Melford, Sudbury, Suffolk, CO10 9JG Tel: (01787) 319393 Fax: (01787) 319394 E-mail: info@netxtra.net *Internet consultancy services & web developers*

Netzsch Nemo Pumps Ltd, Unit 3 Middlemore Business Park, Middlemore Lane West, Aldridge, Walsall, WS9 8BG Tel: (01922) 453433 Fax: (01922) 458404 E-mail: npl@netzsch.com *Progressing cavity pump manufacturers for such applications as food processing, chemical industry, petro-chemical and environmental.*

Netzsch-Instruments, Hayward Industrial Park, Vigo Place, Walsall, WS9 8UG Tel: (01922) 459006 Fax: (01922) 453320 E-mail: sales@netzsch-therma1.co.uk *Thermal analysis instruments*

Netzsch-Mastermix, 23 Lombard Street, Lichfield, Staffordshire, WS13 6DP Tel: (01543) 418938 Fax: (01543) 418926 E-mail: info@nmx.netzsch.com Principal Export Areas: Worldwide *Manufacturers of chemical plant & equipment*

Neuroscot Ltd, 8 Meadow Street, Falkirk, FK1 1RP Tel: 0131-453 3845 Fax: 0131-453 3838 E-mail: neuroscot@compuserve.com *Smart card reader distributors*

Neutra Rust International Ltd, 24-31 London Road, Newbury, Berkshire, RG14 1JX Tel: (01784) 455454 Fax: (01784) 450752 *Corrosion preventives manufrs*

Neutral Ltd, 167 Ardleigh Green Road, Hornchurch, Essex, RM11 2LF Tel: (01708) 701522 Fax: (01708) 701994 E-mail: info@neutral.co.uk *Computer systems & software services*

Neutrik (UK) Ltd, Westridge Business Park, Ryde, Isle Of Wight, PO33 1QT Tel: (01983) 811441 Fax: (01983) 811439 E-mail: sales@neutrik.co.uk *Audio test equipment & audio connectors suppliers*

Neva Consultants P.L.C., Neva House, Piltdown, Uckfield, East Sussex, TN22 3XL Tel: (0870) 4445725 Fax: (0870) 4445724 E-mail: sales@nevaplc.com *Fleet vehicle management & contract hire*

Neva Consultants Leeds, Unit 41, Unity Business Centre, 26 Roundhay Road, Leeds, LS7 1AB Tel: (0845) 2062277 Fax: (0845) 2072277 E-mail: howard.mostyn@nevaplc.co.uk *We are independent Contract Hire & Leasing Brokers, offering all makes of Cars & Vans to businesses and individuals. For over 15 years, Neva Consultants has developed relationships with major vehicle suppliers and Finance Companies, and our comprehensive knowledge of the marketplace enables us to offer consistently competitive prices. We offer free impartial advice, and free delivery and collection anywhere (UK mainland). Our priority is to give a professional and efficient personal service to all our clients. We are proud to be members of The British Vehicle Rental & Leasing Association and The Leeds Chamber Of Commerce. Let us quote you on any make of car or light commercial vehicle. **Please visit our website at www.business-contract-hire.co.uk for the full facts!**All our current Special Offers can be viewed at www.business-contract-hire.co.uk/ sdl.shtml**

▶ Never Compromise, 36 London Road, Pulborough, West Sussex, RH20 1AS Tel: (0845) 6449198 Fax: (0871) 2420836 E-mail: sales@never-compromise.com *Hotel Reservations, Travel, Events, Incentives, Business Services*

Neves Mobility Services, 25-35 Birkbeck Road, Sidcup, Kent, DA14 4DD Tel: (020) 8300 1000 Fax: (020) 8302 8941 *Disabled mobility services*

Nevesco Ltd, 3 Walton Road, Pattinson North, Washington, Tyne & Wear, NE38 8QA Tel: 0191-415 0037 Fax: 0191-415 3532 E-mail: nevescoltd@eol.com *Valve distributors*

Nevill Long, Chartwell Drive, Wigston, Leicestershire, LE18 2FL Tel: 0116-257 0670 Fax: 0116-257 0044 E-mail: sales@longnevill.co.uk *Interior building products & specialist distributors* Also at: Bristol, Dagenham, Leeds & Leicester

Nevill Long Interior Building Products, Centre House, Victory Way, Hounslow, TW5 9NS Tel: (020) 8573 9898 Fax: (020) 8813 5127 *Interior building products distributors*

Neville Fabrications, 1 Peet Street, Derby, DE22 3RF Tel: (01332) 294928 Fax: (01332) 294928 *Steel fabrication*

G.H. Neville Ltd, Unit 1, Travellers Lane, North Mymms, Hatfield, Hertfordshire, AL9 7HF Tel: (01707) 262 800 Fax: (01707) 263 888 E-mail: sales@emgeeonline.co.uk *Manufacturers of business cards, membership cards, labels etc which can be printed on your own office and home printer. Also EMGEE filing and stationery products.*

Neville & More Ltd, Oakhurst Business Park, Wilberforce Way, Southwater, Horsham, West Sussex, RH13 9RT Tel: (01403) 732290 Fax: (01403) 733507 E-mail: info@nevilleandmore.com *Glass & plastic bottle distributors*

Neville Roe Industries Ltd, Euro Works, Liverpool Street, Sheffield, S9 2PU Tel: 0114-243 0395 Fax: 0114-243 3310 E-mail: enquiries@nevroeind.com *Hard Chrome Plating and Cylindrical Grinding, Internal Grinding, Lumsden Segmental Surface Grinding, Horizontal Spindle Surface Grinding, Polishing, Planetary Bore Grinding, Hydraulic Cylinder or Ram Maintenance or Repair.Quality assured and ISO: 9001/ISO: 14001 registered, The Company undertakes both subcontract manufacturing and refurbishment work.*

Neville Tucker, Rotterdam Road, Hull, HU7 0XD Tel: (01482) 834900 Fax: (01482) 879852 E-mail: info@nevilletucker.co.uk *Heating engineers*

Nevis Centre, An Aird, Fort William, Inverness-Shire, PH33 6AN Tel: (01397) 700707 Fax: (01397) 700708 E-mail: info@theunderwatercentre.co.uk *Commercial diver training services*

▶ Nevis Heating & Vent Ltd, Unit 2a Caol Industrial Estate, Ardgour Road, Caol, Fort William, Inverness-Shire, PH33 7PH Tel: (01397) 705656 Fax: (01397) 701656

▶ Nevisprint, 3 Caol Industrial Estate, Ardgour Road, Caol, Fort William, Inverness-Shire, PH33 7PH Tel: (01397) 704083 Fax: (01397) 705890

▶ Nevista, 2nd Floor, 145-147 St John Street, London, EC1V 4PY Tel: 020 7754 5573 E-mail: phke@nevista.co.uk *At NeVista we have developed a unique business approach (NeVista Framework for Leadership) that enables Business leaders to get the view from the top and then quickly implement visionary value solutions. Consultancy for change management, increasing shareholder value and transforming the bottom line.*

▶ Nevron Eurotherm Insulation Services Ltd, Unit 16, Valley Road Business Park, Birkenhead, Merseyside, CH41 7EL Tel: 0151-652 6213 Fax: 0151-652 6213 E-mail: info@nevroninsulation.co.uk *Industrial insulation & heating services*

▶ New Age Systems P V C U Ltd, Units 38-40, Gelli Industrial Estate, Gelli, Pentre, Mid Glamorgan, CF41 7UW Tel: (01443) 431026 Fax: (01443) 422463 E-mail: sales@newagesystems.co.uk *PVCU windows doors & conservatories*

New Alliance Services Ltd, 403A Trelawny House, The Dock, Felixstowe, Suffolk, IP11 3EQ Tel: (01394) 676212 Fax: (01394) 676423 *Freight forwarders & customs clearance service providers*

New Angle Promotions, Temuka House, School Road, Foulden, Thetford, Norfolk, IP26 5AJ Tel: (01366) 328282 Fax: (01366) 328283 E-mail: mediagolf@aol.com *Golf promotions & clothing*

New Barn Farm, Whaddon Lane, Hilperton, Trowbridge, Wiltshire, BA14 7RN Tel: (01225) 777053 *Agricultural machinery repairs*

New Bath Hotel, New Bath Road, Matlock Bath, Matlock, Derbyshire, DE4 3PX Tel: (0870) 4008119 Fax: (01629) 580268 *Conference facilities & hotel*

The New Boat Co., Hanbury Wharf, Hanbury Road, Droitwich, Worcestershire, WR9 7DU Tel: (01905) 776646 Fax: (01905) 776750 *Boat builders & retailer*

New Brunswick Scientific UK Ltd, 17 Alban Park, Hatfield Road, St. Albans, Hertfordshire, AL4 0JJ Tel: (01727) 853855 Fax: (01727) 835666 E-mail: sales@nbsuk.co.uk *Scientific instrument manufrs*

New Burn Services, Bird House, Bishopswood Lane, Crossway Green, Stourport-on-Severn, Worcestershire, DY13 9SE Tel: (01299) 251200 Fax: (01299) 822831 *Heating engineers*

▶ New Car Discount.com Ltd, Unit 7A, Kayley Industrial Estate, Richmond Street, Ashton-under-Lyne, Lancashire, OL7 0AU Tel: (08703) 500144 Fax: (08703) 500244 E-mail: sales@new-car-discount.com *We are an online retailer of new UK cars. We sell most makes and models of cars and supply finance for these cars. We deliver in mainland UK to both business and private individuals. We supply single cars or large fleets and provide a tailored service for companies unsure whether to "opt out" of their company car schemes.*

New Century Air Conditioning & Refrigeration Ltd, 30 Station Road, Stoke Mandeville, Aylesbury, Buckinghamshire, HP22 5UL Tel: (01296) 614878 Fax: (01296) 613619 E-mail: sales@newcenturycooling.co.uk *Air conditioning & refrigeration service*

New Century Machinery Ltd, New Century House, Victoria Road, Dukinfield, Cheshire, SK16 4XS Tel: 0161-330 4242 Fax: 0161-343 1347 E-mail: hq@newcentury.co.uk *Machinery & machine tool merchants supplier*

New Century Systems Ltd, Ash Street, Bilston, West Midlands, WV14 8UP Tel: (01902) 405724 Fax: (01902) 353739 *Electrical contractors*

▶ New Century Technology International Ltd, NCT House, Wortley Road, Rotherham, South Yorkshire, S61 1LZ Tel: (0870) 7874833 Fax: (0870) 7874839 *Computer systems consultants*

New Cheshire Salt Works Ltd, Wincham Lane, Wincham, Northwich, Cheshire, CW9 6DD Tel: (01606) 42361 Fax: (01606) 48333 E-mail: general@ncsw.co.uk Principal Export Areas: Worldwide *Salt manufacturers including pharmaceutical & water softening manufrs*

New College, New College Drive, Swindon, SN3 1AH Tel: (01793) 436437 Fax: (01793) 436437 E-mail: admissions@newcollege.ac.uk *Education*

New Concept (Scotland) Ltd, 588 Glasgow Road, Clydebank, Dunbartonshire, G81 1NH Tel: 0141-952 7901 Fax: 0141-941 1006 E-mail: sales@newconcept-ltd.com *Catering equipment suppliers*

New Concept Upholsterer, 70 Thomas Street, Tamworth, Staffordshire, B77 3PR Tel: (01827) 51414 *Commerical interior refurbishers*

▶ New County Road Surfacing Ltd, Penshaw Way, Birtley, Chester Le Street, County Durham, DH3 2SA Tel: 0191-410 9061

New Covent Garden Soup Co. Ltd, Westwood Farm, Bretton Gate, Westwood, Peterborough, PE3 9UP Tel: (01733) 262601 Fax: (01733) 261201 *Natural soup producers & distributors*

New Crown Bakery Ltd, Callow Hill, Rock, Kidderminster, Worcestershire, DY14 9XD Tel: (01299) 266211 Fax: (01299) 266013 *Cake manufrs*

New Crystal Windows Ltd, 162 Winson Street, Winson Green, Birmingham, B18 4JW Tel: 0121-565 3244 Fax: 0121-565 3500 *Home & industrial window manufrs*

New Curtains Co. Ltd, 64 South Street, Epsom, Surrey, KT18 7PH Tel: (01372) 747970 *Installers & manufrs*

New Dimension Exhibitions Ltd, 1 Woodfield Road, Welwyn Garden City, Hertfordshire, AL7 1JQ Tel: (01707) 323244 Fax: (01707) 323366 E-mail: exhibit@newdimension.co.uk *Exhibition contractors & designers*

New Electrics Ltd, 90 Peasley Cross Lane, St. Helens, Merseyside, WA9 3BS Tel: (01744) 22244 Fax: (01744) 22264

New England Engineering Ltd, Sandy Lane Industrial Estate, Stourport-on-Severn, Worcestershire, DY13 9QB Tel: (01299) 827399 Fax: (01299) 827400 E-mail: machines@newengland.co.uk *Machine tool merchants*

▶ New England Shutter Co., 16 Jaggard Way, London, SW12 8SG Tel: (020) 8675 1099 Fax: (020) 8675 1099 E-mail: sales@tnesc.co.uk *Supply & install handcrafted, solid wood, interior shutters*

▶ New Equine Wear, Unit 3 Priory Industrial Estate, Tetbury, Gloucestershire, GL8 8HZ Tel: (01666) 501960 Fax: (01666) 501969 E-mail: sales@newequinewear.co.uk *Saddlery manufacturers & distributors*

New Era Oil UK, Bow Bridge Wharf, 1-9 High Street, London, E15 2RH Tel: (01279) 425757 Fax: (01279) 425758 *Lubricating oil distributors*

New Forest Binding Ltd, 1 25 Black Moor Road, Ebblake Industrial Estate, Verwood, Dorset, BH31 6BE Tel: (01202) 828877 Fax: (01202) 828844 E-mail: sales@newforestbinding.com *Print finishing services*

New Forest Estate Agents, New Forest Estate Agents, PO Box 5561, Ringwood, Hampshire, BH24 2ZS Tel: 08700 11 68 55 E-mail: info@NewForestEstateAgents.com *Prime New Forest property for sale from the leading New Forest property & estate agents*

▶ The New Forest Estate Agents, PO Box 5561, Ringwood, Hampshire, BH24 2ZS Tel: 08700 11 45 75 Fax: 08700 11 45 76 E-mail: info@NewForestEstateAgents.com *Prime*

continued

New Forest property for sale from the leading New Forest Estate Agents. Operating in Lymington, Beaulieu, Bucklers Hard, Brockenhurst, Lyndhurst, Ringwood, Sway, Burley and surrounding areas.

New Forest Fencing Ltd, Mill Lane, Nursling, Southampton, SO16 0YE Tel: (023) 8073 3442 Fax: (023) 8074 0181 *Fencing suppliers*

▶ New Forest Hire, 146 - 148 Commercial Road, Totton, Southampton, SO40 3AA Tel: (023) 8086 2410 Fax: (023) 8087 0882 E-mail: admin@newforesthire.co.uk *Full range of plant, tools & access equipment for hire & sale*

▶ New Forest Horse Boxes Ltd, Peartree Cottage, Arnewood Bridge Road, Sway, Lymington, Hampshire, SO41 6ER Tel: (01590) 682633 Fax: (01590) 683497 E-mail: sales@newforesthorseboxes.co.uk *Horse box manufrs*

New Forest Instrument Control Ltd, 84 Cobham Road, Ferndown Industrial Estate, Wimborne, Dorset, BH21 7RW Tel: (01202) 875308 Fax: (01202) 893462 E-mail: info@newforestinstruments.co.uk *NFI are an Overhaul, Refurbishment & Calibration company that service's products used to measure, indicate, record and control such variables as flow, temperature, pressure and level. Industries served are Petro-Chem & Marine. We specialise in the fast turn around of Control Valves. adding to this a vast array of spares and complete valves in stock. We provide a comprehensive 24 HOUR SERVICE for the fastest possible turn around of instrumentation, where availability of spares will allow. All work carried out is under the British standards of ISO 9001:2000. All gauge calibration and pressure testing is done to ISO 9001:2000.*

New Forest Precision Ltd, 3 Parkside, Ringwood, Hampshire, BH24 3SG Tel: (01425) 479007 Fax: (01425) 480231 E-mail: sales@n-f-p.co.uk *Precision sheet metalworkers*

▶ New Forest Printing, Riverside House, Brokenford Lane, Totton, Southampton, SO40 9DY Tel: (023) 8066 3484 Fax: (023) 8086 8549

▶ New Forest Tool Hire, 18 Gore Road, New Milton, Hampshire, BH25 6RX Tel: (01425) 621777 Fax: (01425) 618811 E-mail: sales@newforesthire.co.uk *Plant & tool hire*

▶ New Forest Woodburning Centre Ltd, The Old School House, Church Lane, Sway, Lymington, Hampshire, SO41 6AD Tel: (01590) 683585 Fax: (01590) 683587 E-mail: sales@woodburners.com *Fireplaces*

New Forset Pond Services, Station Road, Sway, Lymington, Hampshire, SO41 6AA Tel: (01590) 681339 Fax: (01590) 682302 *Butchers & sausage manufrs*

▶ New Generation Doors, Tattersall Way, Chelmsford, CM1 3UB Tel: (01245) 255519 Fax: (01245) 255525 *Door manufrs*

New Goswell Printing Co., Unit 4 100 The Highway, London, E1W 2BX Tel: (020) 7481 1775 Fax: (020) 7488 9130 *General commercial printers*

New Guard Coatings Ltd, Sandbeck Way, Wetherby, West Yorkshire, LS22 7DN Tel: (01937) 586311 Fax: (01937) 580041 E-mail: sales@newguard.co.uk *Industrial coating distributors*

New Haden Pumps Ltd, New Haden Works, Draycott Cross Road, Cheadle, Stoke-on-Trent, ST10 2NW Tel: (01538) 757900 Fax: (01538) 757999 E-mail: info@nhpumps.com *Pump distributor & manufacturer. Products include booster sets, GRP packaged pumping stations & submersible drainage & sewage pumps*

New Hampshire Ball Bearings (Europe), Suite 2.2, Doncastle House, Doncastle Road, Bracknell, Berkshire, RG12 8PE Tel: (01344) 308888 Fax: (01344) 485522 *Ball bearing manufacturers & distributors*

▶ New Health Network Ltd, The Leather Market, Weston Street, London, SE1 3ER Tel: (020) 7407 1618 *Computer maintenance services*

New Holland Sheet Metal Co. Ltd, Unit 30 Jubilee Trading Estate, Jubilee Road, Letchworth Garden City, Hertfordshire, SG6 1NE Tel: (01462) 674265 Fax: (01462) 480699 E-mail: newholland@btconnect.com *Sheet metalwork engineers*

▶ New Horizon Sailing, Troon Yacht Haven, Harbour Road, Troon, Ayrshire, KA10 6DJ Tel: (01844) 260854 Fax: (01844) 260854 E-mail: info@newhorizonsailing.com *Skippered charter in the West Coast of Scotland aboard a quality Oyster yacht from Tobermory or Troon.*Spectacular scenery, amazing wildlife and a warm welcome for individuals or groups, including beginners.*Something for everybody, from gentle sailing among the Scottish Islands to adventurous long distance passages.**

▶ New Horizons, Arthur House, Chorlton Street, Manchester, M1 3FH Tel: 0161-238 7000 Fax: 0161-238 7002 E-mail: louise.westall@nhmanchester.com *Technical and end-user IT Training provided throughout the UK or as web-based training.*

New Image Lighting, Crossfield Close, Manchester, M34 6LU Tel: 0161-336 4300 Fax: 0161-336 4300 E-mail: info@newimagelighting.co.uk *Provide laser shows using laser animation software*

▶ New Image Tattoo & Body Piercing Supplies, 66 Laughton Road, Dinnington, Sheffield, S25 2PS Tel: (01909) 560722 Fax: (0870) 7621361 E-mail: mark@tattookit.co.uk *New image provide quaility tattoo equipment to professional and begginers in the tattooing industry and sell most items needed including grips, tips, inks, needles, tattoo machine all with a good back up service 6 days a week.*

New Image Windows, Unit 1 Wood Street, Warsop, Mansfield, Nottinghamshire, NG20 0AX Tel: (01623) 842727 Fax: (01623) 842727 *Double glazing suppliers*

New Inn, 95 The Highway, New Inn, Pontypool, Gwent, NP4 0PN Tel: (01495) 762823 Fax: (01495) 769807 *Suppliers of paints & tools for body car shops*

▶ New Life Health, Rose Cottage, Ting Tang, Carharrack, Redruth, Cornwall, TR16 5SF Tel: (01209) 822207 Fax: (01209) 822207 E-mail: info@newlifehealth.co.uk *Health care product retailer*

New Line Promotions, 5 Wilbraham Road, Weaverham, Northwich, Cheshire, CW8 3JX Tel: (01606) 854600 Fax: (01606) 853527 *Embroidery printers*

▶ New Line Sales Recruitment Ltd, Clay House, 5 Horninglow Street, Burton-on-Trent, Staffordshire, DE14 1NG Tel: (01283) 500077 Fax: (08701) 163370 E-mail: sales@newlinesales.co.uk *New Line Sales Recruitment is a specialist in the recruitment of field based sales people. We operate on a nationwide basis and provide professional sales recruitment solutions to clients and candidates alike.**Our aim is to provide a personal and professional service. Giving clients and candidates one point of contact for all their sales recruitment. We are here to get you what you want and we strive to build long and lasting relationships with our clients.**"Providing professional sales recruitment solutions to candidates and clients alike."**The sales people we place are experienced in Field Sales within the following sectors:**+ Office Furniture*+ Contract Furniture*+ Commercial Interiors - Flooring, Lighting, Wall Coverings, Partitioning*+ Kitchens, Bedrooms and Bathrooms*+ Contract Hire*+ Motor Finance and other Fleet Related Products*+ HVAC*+ Heavy-side*+ Light-side*+ Business Products*+ Business Services*+ Telecommunications**

New Line Sheds Ltd, Padworth Saw Mills, Rag Hill, Aldermaston, Reading, RG7 4NU Tel: 0118-971 2245 Fax: 0118-942 6391 E-mail: sales@newlinesheds.co.uk *Sectional & portable building suppliers*

New Look Office Furniture, Chester Street, Saltney, Chester, CH4 8RD Tel: (01244) 682568 Fax: (01244) 671465 *Furniture distributors*

▶ New Look Sunblind Services, 310 Torquay Road, Paignton, Devon, TQ3 2DZ Tel: (01803) 323661 Fax: (01803) 698157 E-mail: richandjohn@newlook.wanadoo.co.uk *Manufacture & install internal & external blinds*

▶ New Look Windows, New Look House Shawclough Trading Estate, Shawclough Road, Rochdale, Lancashire, OL12 6ND Tel: (0800) 888333 Fax: (01706) 524929 E-mail: sales@newlookwindows.com *Upvc fabricators & installation service*

New Lyne Interiors, 1 Shrublands Drive, Lightwater, Surrey, GU18 5QS Tel: (01276) 474511 Fax: (01276) 474220 *Suspended ceilings & partition manufrs*

New Media Distribution (UK) Ltd, Unit 7, Sunderland Estate, Church Lane, Kings Langley, Hertfordshire, WD4 8JX Tel: (01923) 267267 Fax: (01923) 267266 E-mail: mark@panthercomputers.co.uk *Computer systems builder*

New Media Group P.L.C., Pinewood Studios, Pinewood Road, Iver, Buckinghamshire, SL0 0NH Tel: (01753) 655866 Fax: (01753) 655118 E-mail: info@newmediagroup.co.uk *Public relations consultants*

▶ New Meuro Design, 99 Bridge Road, Leicester, LE5 3LD Tel: 0116-276 8988 Fax: 0116-276 8988

New Mix Concrete, Stanningley Industrial Centre, Varley Street, Stanningley, Pudsey, West Yorkshire, LS28 7EL Tel: 0113-257 6738 Fax: 0161-832 0929 *Concrete suppliers*

New Mourne Trophies, 14 Margaret Street, Newry, County Down, BT34 1DF Tel: (028) 3026 9736 *Trophies, medals & rosette manufrs*

New Move, Tenmore House, Kennford Road, Marsh Barton Trading Estate, Exeter, EX2 8LY Tel: (01392) 491000 Fax: (01392) 491911

New Notations Computer Services Ltd, 7 Duncombe Hill, London, SE23 1QY Tel: (07968) 312032 Fax: (0870) 7604795 *Music engraving & computer sales*

New Paradigm Consultants Ltd, Walthams, Chart Road, Sutton Valence, Maidstone, Kent, ME17 3AW Tel: (01622) 844333 Fax: (01622) 844999 *Confectionery machinery engineers*

New Parking Solutions, Unit 81, Pembroke Centre, Cheney Manor Industrial Estate, Swindon, SN2 2PQ Tel: (01793) 700608 Fax: (01793) 700608 E-mail: sales@newparkingsolutions.co.uk *Specialist in Installation and Service of Security Systems. Products include Automatic Barriers, Gates, Bollards, Access Controls, Intercoms, CCTV & ANPR*

New Pig Ltd, Hogs Hill, Watt Place, Hamilton International Technology Park, Blantyre, Glasgow, G72 0AH Tel: (0800) 919900 Fax: (0800) 7315071 E-mail: pigpen@newpig.com *New Pig offers the world's largest selection of industrial absorbents for the clean-up of leaks & spills in the workplace. In addition we offer products for material handling, spill response, personal protection and plant safety.*

New Pro Foundries Ltd, Unit C, Horton Close, West Drayton, Middlesex, UB7 8EB Tel: (01895) 443194 Fax: (01895) 442968 E-mail: info@newpro.co.uk *Non-ferrous castings manufrs*

New Quay Developments Ltd, 68 Armagh Road, Tandragee, Craigavon, County Armagh, BT62 2HS Tel: (028) 3884 0444 Fax: (028) 3884 1811 E-mail: info@newquayconstruction.com *Industrial & commercial building contractors*

New River Industrial Communications Ltd, Nelson Court, Gladstone Road, Ware, Hertfordshire, SG12 0AG Tel: (01920) 468443 Fax: (01920) 460528 E-mail: info@newriver.co.uk *Press relations agency*

New Scientist, 147-151 Wardour St, London, W1F 8BN Tel: (020) 7611 1200 Fax: (020) 7331 2772 *New Scientist is the world's leading current affairs weekly, covering scientific & technological adv*

▶ New Span Design & Build, 103 Kingsway, Chandler's Ford, Eastleigh, Hampshire, SO53 1FD Tel: (023) 8026 9944 Fax: (023) 8026 9940 E-mail: info@newspan.co.uk *Designer & builders of garden centres*

New Splint Ltd, Unitech House, Units B1 B2, Bond Close, Kingsland Buisiness Park, Basingstoke, Hampshire, RG24 8PZ Tel: (01256) 365480 Fax: (01256) 365486 E-mail: sales.dept@newsplint.co.uk *Orthopaedic implants & related products*

New Star, Unit 1 Ucc Indust Estate, 219 Humberstone Lane, Leicester, LE4 9JT Tel: 0116-269 6937 Fax: 0116-269 6566 E-mail: enquiries@powdercoatings.gbr.fm *Powder coatings*

New Star Fashions Ltd, Arena House, Greenacres Road, Oldham, OL4 1HA Tel: 0161-628 2339 Fax: 0161-628 2337 E-mail: sales@newstarfashions.co.uk *Underwear importers & manufrs*

New Tech Finishing, Commercial Road, Walsall, WS2 7NQ Tel: (01922) 404604 Fax: (01922) 711083 E-mail: enquiries@ntfltd.co.uk *Decrement & wet paint finishes specialists* Also at: Wolverhampton

New Tonne Lifting Services Ltd, 16 Sankey Valley Industrial Estate, Junction Lane, Newton-le-Willows, Merseyside, WA12 8DN Tel: (01925) 224471 Fax: (01925) 223518 E-mail: sales@lifting-engineers.co.uk *Lifting gear hire & sales & inspection manufacture & repair*

New Town Printers Redditch Ltd, Brickyard Lane, Studley, Warwickshire, B80 7EE Tel: (01527) 850011 Fax: (01527) 850055 E-mail: info@newtownprinters.co.uk *Printed packaging manufrs*

New Ventures Products, Queens Yard, Long Wittenham Road, North Moreton, Didcot, Oxfordshire, OX11 9AX Tel: (0845) 4304030 Fax: (0845) 130 5833 E-mail: sales@newventureproducts.co.uk *Protecta-kote is a unique, advanced formula polyurethane anti-slip paint, incorporating rubber granules to give a totally flexible anti-slip (non-slip) finish that will not flake, chip or peel. With no mixing or blending required, it can be easily applied to almost any surface including metal, concrete, wood, fibreglass, plastic and rubber leaving an attractive textured anti-slip finish that is resistant to impacts.*

New Vision Associates Ltd, Vision Worksventnor Street, Bradford, West Yorkshire, BD3 9JP Tel: (01274) 728831 Fax: (01274) 308702 E-mail: sales@new-vision.co.uk *Sign manufrs*

▶ New Vision Print & Publishing Ltd, 101 Abercorn Industrial Estate, Abercorn Street, Paisley, Renfrewshire, PA3 4AT Tel: 0141-842 1010 Fax: 0141-887 7122 E-mail: enquiries@newvisionpublishing.co.uk

New Waste Concepts UK, Units 4-5 Topsham Business Units, Dart Business Park, Topsham, Exeter, EX3 0QH Tel: 01392 690167 Fax: 01392 877873 E-mail: kim.mullen@nwci.com *New Waste Concepts UK provides innovative solutions to meet specific needs of the environmental and landfill management industry. We provide a range of revolutionary landfill and remediation covers which can result in significant savings in money, time and landfill space.**All of our covers are made from recycled paper, a proprietary blend of polymers and are specifically engineered to perform as an Alternate Daily Cover (ADC) to the traditional soil cover method still commonly used. These non-toxic, non-hazardous and biodegradable covers are designed to control blowing litter while suppressing VOC"s, dust, odours and radon gas. **New Waste Concepts UK can improve the efficiency and effectiveness of your remediation projects and landfill sites which will ultimately, benefit your program and your environmental well being.**

New Wave Concepts, 59 St Andrews Street, St Andrews House, Cambridge, CB2 3BQ Tel: (0870) 6090911 E-mail: sales@new-wave-concepts.com *Computer software development*

▶ New Waves Cornwall Ltd, The Shell Factory, Long Rock, Penzance, Cornwall, TR20 8HX Tel: (01736) 365169 Fax: (01736) 368545 E-mail: keith@new-waves.co.uk *Wholesale sea shells and handicrafts to manufacturers and the gift trade.*

New Work Trust Co. Ltd, Station Road Workshops, Station Road, Kingswood, Bristol, BS15 4PJ Tel: 0117-957 5577 Fax: 0117-956 8776 E-mail: newworktrust@btconnect.com *Management consultants*

New World Electronics, Unit A Cuters Close Industrial Estate, Cuters Close, Leicester, LE19 2FZ Tel: 0116-284 8785 Fax: 0116-286 7797 E-mail: new.world@dial.pipex.com *Electronic component distributers*

New World Tech, 1776 Coventry Rd, Yardley, Birmingham, B26 1PB Tel: 0121-743 4570 Fax: 0121 7422171 *Computer reseller*

Newade Stainless Products Ltd, Jubilee Works, Jubilee Street North, Halifax, West Yorkshire, HX3 6QY Tel: (01422) 356658 Fax: (01422) 343793 E-mail: philwade@newade.co.uk *Steel fabricators*

Newal Print, Unit 21 Delph Road Industrial Estate, Delph Road, Brierley Hill, West Midlands, DY5 2UA Tel: (01384) 74469 Fax: (01384) 74995 *Printers & lithographic printer services*

Newark Alarm Systems, 2 Wetsyke Lane, Balderton, Newark, Nottinghamshire, NG24 3NY Tel: (01636) 674978 Fax: (01636) 640767 *Intruder alarms installers*

Newark Foundry Ltd, 142 Grange Road, Newark, Nottinghamshire, NG24 4PW Tel: (01636) 702909 *Cast iron castings & engineering agents*

▶ Newark Gas Appliances Ltd, 19 Portland Street, Newark, Nottinghamshire, NG24 4XF Tel: (01636) 676325 Fax: (01636) 611170

Newark Joiners Ltd, Newark Works, Castle Road, Port Glasgow, Renfrewshire, PA14 5NG Tel: (01475) 743555 Fax: (01475) 741269 *Ships furniture & fittings manufrs*

▶ Newark Learn Direct Business Centre, 31 Albert Street, Newark, Nottinghamshire, NG24 4BJ Tel: (01636) 611900 Fax: (01636) 611988 *Computer training agents*

▶ Newark Storage Co. Ltd, Bowbridge Road, Newark, Nottinghamshire, NG24 4EQ Tel: (01636) 680660

Newark Storage Co. Ltd, Bowbridge Road, Newark, Nottinghamshire, NG24 4EQ Tel: (01636) 680660 Fax: (01636) 673530 E-mail: sales@newark-steel.co.uk *Steel stockholders*

Newark Tools Ltd, Coppice Side Industrial Estate, Brownhills, Walsall, WS8 7EX Tel: (01543) 454600 *Injection mould toolmakers*

Newarke Designs Ltd, 502 Uppingham Rd, Leicester, LE5 2GG Tel: 0116-241 0170 Fax: 0116-241 0173 *IT consultants*

Newart, Mandervell Road, Oadby, Leicester, LE2 5LQ Tel: (0870) 7591650 Fax: (0870) 7591651 E-mail: sales@newartltd.com *Graded pattern & cutter manufrs* Also at: Leeds & Norwich

▶ Newarthill Engineers & Fabricators Ltd, 102-110 Carfin Road, Newarthill, Motherwell, Lanarkshire, ML1 5JZ Tel: (01698) 732684 Fax: (01698) 733177 *Engineers*

Neway Doors Ltd, Lionel Works, 89/91 Rolfe Street, Smethwick, West Midlands, B66 2AY Tel: 0121-558 6406 Fax: 0121-555 7140 E-mail: sales@priory-group.co.uk *Security shutters & grilles*

Neways Automatics Brecon, 25 Mill Street, Brecon, Powys, LD3 9BD Tel: (01874) 622849 Fax: (01874) 622849 *Gaming machine suppliers*

Newbar Engineers Ltd, 3 Pound Lane Industrial Estate, Maypole Fields, Halesowen, West Midlands, B63 2QB Tel: (01384) 639139 Fax: (01384) 411128 Principal Export Areas: Central/East Europe & West Europe *Plastic injection moulders*

Newbold & Davis Ltd, PO Box 282, Newcastle, Staffordshire, ST5 9HU Tel: (01782) 622305 Fax: (01782) 623043 E-mail: newbold-davis@nusyte.co.uk *Lens manufrs*

Newbourne Automobile Engineers, New Street, Luton, LU1 5DE Tel: (01582) 722522 Fax: (01582) 732800 E-mail: newbourne-arc@barclays.net *Vehicle mechanical repairers*

Newbow Hydraulic Equipment, Benacre Drive, Fazeley Street, Birmingham, B5 5RE Tel: 0121-772 6861 Fax: 0121-643 2637 E-mail: sales@newbow.co.uk *Manufacturers of hydraulic components & fittings*

Newbridge Steels Ltd, 14a High Street, Cowbridge, South Glamorgan, CF71 7AG Tel: (01446) 775517 Fax: (01446) 775355 E-mail: bronwennewbridge@yahoo.co.uk Principal Export Areas: West Europe *Steel stockholders*

Newbrook Engineering Ltd, Quakers Coppice, Crewe, CW1 6FA Tel: (01270) 584836 Fax: (01270) 584837 E-mail: cbherri@aol.com *Steel fabrication*

Newbrook Engineering Co. Ltd, Church Street, Donington, Spalding, Lincolnshire, PE11 4UA Tel: (01775) 820583 Fax: (01775) 820487 E-mail: newbrook.eng@virgin.net *Specialist gears & gear box manufrs*

Newburgh Engineering Co. Ltd, Newburgh Works, Bradwell, Hope Valley, Derbyshire, S33 9NT Tel: (01709) 724260 E-mail: sales@newburgh.co.uk *CNC engineering services*

Newburgh Management Services Ltd, 13 Cobbs Brow Lane, Newburgh, Wigan, Lancashire, WN8 7ND Tel: 0161-746 8582 Fax: (08700) 549489 E-mail: nmsl.ewj@btinternet.com *Interim management & consultancy company*

Newburgh Technologies Ltd, 2 Sandy Lane, Newburgh, Wigan, Lancashire, WN8 7TT Tel: (01257) 464200 Fax: (01257) 464200 *Computer software development & distribution*

Newburn Consulting plc, 1 Wood Street, Swindon, SN1 4AN Tel: (01793) 435000 Fax: (01793) 435001 E-mail: sales@newburn.co.uk *IT management consultants*

▶ Newburn Personnel Services, 5 Palmer Place, Kingseat, Dunfermline, Fife, KY12 0UQ Tel: (01383) 620239 Fax: (07968) 181610

Newbury Aeroplane Company Aircraft Repairs, Unit 2, Denford Manor, Lower Denford, Hungerford, Berkshire, RG17 0UN Tel: (01488) 682949 Fax: (01488) 682949 *Aircraft restoration*

Newbury Aquatics Centre, Wyevale Garden Centre, Bath Road, Thatcham, Berkshire, RG18 3AN Tel: (01635) 869900 Fax: (01635) 874774 *Supplying aquatic goods*

Newbury Electronic Services Ltd, 1 Berwick Courtyard, Berwick St. Leonard, Salisbury, SP3 5UA Tel: (01747) 820615 E-mail: sales@nes-ltd.com *Design & development of electronics & optics*

Newbury Fork Truck Centre Ltd, Unit 12 Bone Lane, Newbury, Berkshire, RG14 5SH Tel: (01635) 41635 Fax: (01635) 35388 *Fork lift truck distributors*

Newbury Heating, 1 Stainforth Road, Ilford, Essex, IG2 7EH Tel: (020) 8550 8175 *Central heating engineers*

▶ Newbury Self Store Ltd, A3 Cyril Vokins Road, Newbury, Berkshire, RG14 5XB Tel: (01635) 581811

Newbury Tools Ltd, 1 Hambridge Road, Newbury, Berkshire, RG14 5SS Tel: (01635) 30804 Fax: (01635) 529068 E-mail: sales@newburytools.com *Power, hand tool sales & hire*

Newby Automatics Ltd, Unit 1, Donachy Industrial Estate, Moor Lane, Witton, Birmingham, B6 7HH Tel: 0121-356 0322 Fax: 0121-356 9757 *Amusement machine distribs*

Newby & Son Ironfounders Ltd, Smiths Road, Wednesbury, West Midlands, WS10 0PB Tel: 0121-556 4451 Fax: 0121-505 3626 E-mail: sales@newbyfoundries.co.uk Principal Export Areas: Worldwide *Grey & ductile iron casting manufrs*

Newbyres Engineering, Unit 2, Sherwood Industrial Estate, Bonnyrigg, Midlothian, EH19 3LW Tel: 0131-653 6646 Fax: 0131-663 9046 E-mail: newbyres@aol.com *Aluminium fabrications & precision engineering services*

▶ newcar4me.com, Camelot House, Bredbury Park Way, Bredbury Park Industrial Estate, Bredbury, Stockport, Cheshire, SK6 2SN Tel: (0870) 9905583 Fax: (0870) 9905584 E-mail: alex.hamilton@newcar4me.com *Discounted new cars - all makes & models*

Newcastle & Gateshead Crane Hire, The Ferry House, Ryton Village, Ryton, Tyne & Wear, NE40 3QJ Tel: 0191-413 3763 Fax: 0191-413 5424 E-mail: nclcrane@aol.com *Crane hire supply & sales*

▶ Newcastle Mining Ltd, 12 Industrial Road, Hertburn Industrial Estate, District 11, Washington, Tyne & Wear, NE37 2SF Tel: (0191)-416 0077

Newcastle Tool & Gauge Ltd, Unit 250 Dukesway, Team Valley Trading Estate, Gateshead, Tyne & Wear, NE11 0PZ Tel: 0191-482 2455 Fax: 0191-491 0559 E-mail: admin@ntg-ltd.co.uk *Toolmakers*

▶ Newcel Paper Converters, 4 Milltown Industrial Estate, Greenan Road, Warrenpoint, Newry, County Down, BT34 3FN Tel: (028) 4175 3864 Fax: (028) 3026 0028

Newchurch Computer Systems, Causeway House, 13 The Causeway, Teddington, Middlesex, TW11 0JR Tel: (020) 8783 3300 Fax: (020) 8977 8198 E-mail: info@newchurch.co.uk *Management & information technology consultants*

Newco Wire Products Ltd, Unit 1, 257 Dalmarnock Road, Glasgow, G40 4LX Tel: 0141 5547732 *Wire product manufrs*

Newcom Computer Systems, 1a Sugarhouse Quay, Newry, County Down, BT35 6HZ Tel: (028) 3026 3149 Fax: (028) 3026 3149 *Computer hardware & software maintenance & repairers*

Newcom Precision Engineering Ltd, 1 Earith Business Park, Meadow Drove, Earith, Huntingdon, Cambridgeshire, PE28 3QF Tel: (01487) 840870 Fax: (01487) 740046 E-mail: info@newcom-engineering.co.uk *Precision engineers*

Newcom UK Ltd, 125 Poplar High Street, London, E14 0AE Tel: (020) 7517 1270 Fax: (020) 7517 1271 E-mail: newcom@newcomgroup.com *Translation & interpreting services*

▶ Newcomer Engineers' Merchants, Deeming Taylor Estate, Blackhorse Road, Exhall, Coventry, CV7 9FW Tel: (024) 7636 3535 Fax: (024) 7636 1777 E-mail: sales@newcomer.co.uk *Engineers*

Newcote Coachworks Ltd, Unit 4, Bessborough Works, Molesey Road, West Molesey, Surrey, KT8 2QS Tel: (020) 8979 0563 Fax: (020) 8941 7251 *Coach body accident repairers & maintenance*

Newcut Precision, Northern Mill Industrial Estate, Field Road, Ramsey, Huntingdon, Cambridgeshire, PE26 1JD Tel: (01487) 813131 Fax: (01487) 812400 *CNC turning & milling*

Newdawn & Sun Ltd, Springfield Business Park, Alcester, Warwickshire, B49 6EY Tel: (01789) 764444 Fax: (01789) 400164 E-mail: sales@newdawn-sun.co.uk *Manufacturers of conservatory roofing systems*

▶ Newdeal Skates, Auriol Drive, Greenford, Middlesex, UB6 0DU Tel: (020) 8515 5000 Fax: (020) 8422 0422

▶ Newdecade Productions, 16 Stevenage Road, Hitchin, Hertfordshire, SG4 9DL Tel: (01438) 369545 Fax: (01438) 369545 E-mail: paul@newdecade.co.uk

Newdev UK, 52-54 Snow Hill, Melton Mowbray, Leicestershire, LE13 1PH Tel: (01664) 569805 Fax: (01664) 481581 E-mail: newdevuk@aol.com *Printers & graphics services*

▶ Newel Plant Hire, 45 Colwyn Crescent, Rhos on Sea, Colwyn Bay, Clwyd, LL28 4RF Tel: (01492) 533612 Fax: (01492) 533612

Newelco (Ukside) Ltd, Church Street, Newport, Gwent, NP20 2TW Tel: (01633) 263021 Fax: (01633) 264413 E-mail: sales@newelco.co.uk Principal Export Areas: Worldwide *Special purpose furnace*

▶ Newell Plumbing Services Ltd, Lincoln Enterprise Park, Newark Road, Aubourn, Lincoln, LN5 9EJ Tel: (01522) 705522

Newey Ceilings Ltd, 1-4 South Uxbridge Street, Burton-on-Trent, Staffordshire, DE14 3LD Tel: (01283) 569696 Fax: (01283) 569699 *Suspended ceilings supply & install*

Newey & Eyre Ltd, Unit 15 17, Whittle Way, Crawley, West Sussex, RH10 9RW Tel: (01293) 517500 Fax: (01293) 561362 E-mail: neweyandeyre@hagemeyer.co.uk *Electrical goods distributors*

Newey & Eyre Ltd, 62 Manners View, Newport, Isle of Wight, PO30 5FA Tel: (01983) 523481 Fax: (01983) 520723 *Electrical goods distrbs*

Newfield Automation, Newfield House, Brook Lane, Astbury, Congleton, Cheshire, CW12 4TJ Tel: (01260) 282200 Fax: (01260) 282201 E-mail: team@newfieldautomation.com *System integrator & electronic repairs*

▶ Newfield Electrical, Unit A5 Coombswood Way, Halesowen, West Midlands, B62 8BH Tel: 0121-561 6060 Fax: 0121-561 6066

Newfield Engineering Co. Ltd, Hawksley Industrial Estate, Hawksley Street, Oldham, OL8 4PQ Tel: 0161-624 7222 Fax: 0161-652 1298 E-mail: sales@newfield-eng.u-net.com *Engineers machinists*

Newfield Fabrications Co. Ltd, Hall Lane, Elton, Sandbach, Cheshire, CW11 3TU Tel: (01270) 762331 Fax: (01270) 768003 E-mail: sales@newfield.co.uk *Laser cutting services, press brake facilities & steel fabricators*

▶ Newfield Jones Homes, Newfield House, 5 Fleet Street, Lytham St. Annes, Lancashire, FY8 2DQ Tel: (01253) 728760 Fax: (01253) 712204 E-mail: sales@newfieldjoneshomes.co.uk

Newfields Timber Yard Co. Ltd, 420 High Street, Stoke-on-Trent, ST6 5ES Tel: (01782) 834057 Fax: (01782) 839772 *Packing case & pallet manufrs*

Newfoil Ltd, Bradford Street, Farnworth, Bolton, BL4 9LS Tel: (01204) 861110 Fax: (01204) 862201 E-mail: info@newfoil.co.uk *Hot foil printing machine manufrs*

Newfoil Machines, Moorhey Street, Oldham, OL4 1JE Tel: 0161-620 5688 Fax: 0161-627 0551 E-mail: sales@newfoilmachines.co.uk *Label printing machine manufrs*

Newfold Ltd, Bridgewater Close, Reading, RG30 1NS Tel: 0118-957 3074 E-mail: sales@newfold.com *A complete manufacturing service under one roof - including design, metalwork, woodwork and all aspects of*

continued

continuation
finishing. Specialists in electronics industry and bespoke shop fitting equipment.. Our experienced team combined with top quality materials, ensures accuracy, flexibility and reliability at competitive prices.

Newform Distribution Ltd, Unit B4-5 Dudley Central Trading Estate, Shaw Road, Dudley, West Midlands, DY2 8QX Tel: (01384) 230666 Fax: (01384) 235666 E-mail: sales@newformdistribution.co.uk *Fastener distributors*

Newgate Clocks Ltd, 5 Maesbury Road Industrial Estate, Oswestry, Shropshire, SY10 8HA Tel: (01691) 679994 Fax: (01691) 679995 *World leading clock designer & manufacturer*

Newgate Gallery, 6a The Bank, Barnard Castle, County Durham, DL12 8PQ Tel: (01833) 695201 Fax: (01833) 695201 E-mail: sales@newgategallery.co.uk *Picture retailers & framing services*

Newgate (Newark) Ltd, Brunel Drive, Newark, Nottinghamshire, NG24 2DE Tel: (01636) 700172 Fax: (01636) 605400 E-mail: sales@newgate.uk.com Principal Export Areas: Worldwide *Electro-mechanic barriers & automatic gate systems manufrs*

Newgate Simms Ltd, PO Box 32, Chester, CH4 0BY Tel: (01244) 660771 Fax: (01244) 661220 E-mail: info@newgatesimms.co.uk *Distributors of speciality chemicals and products to the rubber and plastics industry, a distributor of synthetic greases and lubricants to industrial users, and as a spearate division operate as a contract filler and packer of a wide range of industrial and retail products.*

Newgate Stainless Ltd, Victoria Mills, Cleckheaton, West Yorkshire, BD19 5DR Tel: (01274) 852040 Fax: (01274) 852142 E-mail: newgatesales@btconnect.com *Stainless steel pipe & tube stockholders*

Newgate Systems, NTS House, Headley Road East, Woodley, Reading, RG5 4SZ Tel: 0118-927 7700 Fax: 0118-927 2143 *Systems designers*

Newgate Welding Supplies, Heritage Business Park, Heritage Way, Gosport, Hampshire, PO12 4BG Tel: (023) 9260 4555 Fax: (023) 9260 4554 E-mail: newgate@specfabs.co.uk *Welding equipment distributors*

▶ Newhall Janitorial Ltd, Holden Road, Cardiff, CF11 8BS Tel: (029) 2031 3313 Fax: (029) 2031 3314

Newham London Borough Of Inspection Development Service Education, Kirton Road, Credon Centre, London, E13 9BT Tel: (020) 8548 5034 Fax: (020) 8548 5068 *Information technology support*

▶ Newick Fencing, 31 Hamsland, Horsted Keynes, Haywards Heath, West Sussex, RH17 7DS Tel: (01825) 790990 E-mail: barry@newickfencing.com *Fencing services*

Newionaire, 10 Cofton Road, Marsh Barton Trading Estate, Marsh Barton Trading Estate, Exeter, EX2 8QW Tel: (01392) 829180 Fax: (01392) 410358 *Wholesale electrical goods distributors*

▶ Newland Corporate Communications, 34 Blackstone Court, Blaydon-on-Tyne, Tyne & Wear, NE21 4HH Tel: 0191-256 6000 Fax: 0191-256 6056 E-mail: hire@newlandcc.co.uk *Audio visual suppliers*

Newland Design Ltd, Lodge Quarry, Lancaster Road, Carnforth, Lancashire, LA5 9DW Tel: (01524) 733424 *Rotary atomiser manufrs*

Newland Engineering Co. Ltd, Captain Clarke Road, Hyde, Cheshire, SK14 4RF Tel: 0161-368 0326 Fax: 0161-367 8004 E-mail: info@newland-conveyors.com Principal Export Areas: Worldwide *Telescopic, industrial, portable mobile conveyers*

▶ Newland Homes Ltd, 8 Lansdown Place, Cheltenham, Gloucestershire, GL50 2HU Tel: (01242) 513600 Fax: (01242) 514700

▶ Newlife Cleaning Systems, Tyne View House, Templetown, South Shields, Tyne & Wear, NE33 5SH Tel: 0191-425 0231 Fax: 0191-425 0241 E-mail: admin@newlifecleaning.com *Professional Cleaning Company dealing with daily & industrial cleaning, specialist cleaning, emergency call-outs, stone & brickwork cleaning & decontamination, janitorial supplies*

Newlife Data Communications Ltd, Beacon House, 10 Forest Road, Loughborough, Leicestershire, LE11 3NP Tel: 01509 267231 Fax: 01509 211019 *Data communication resellers*

▶ Newline Products, 23 Royal Exchange Square, Glasgow, G1 3AJ Tel: 0141-248 4086 Fax: 0141-847 0530 E-mail: info@newlineproducts.co.uk *Promotional products distributors*

Newlins Access Ltd, Long Close Farm, Wimborne Road, Walford, Wimborne, Dorset, BH21 1NR Tel: (01202) 885300 Fax: (01202) 885400 E-mail: office@newlinaccess.co.uk Sales Contact: D. Solomon *Distributors of powered access platforms, also hiring, leasing & rental of contractors' plant & powered access platforms & operator training services*

Newlo International Ltd, Market Place, Chapel-en-le-Frith, High Peak, Derbyshire, SK23 0EN Tel: (01298) 812973 Fax: (01298) 813282 *Forgings & pipe fitters*

Newlove Ingravers & Signs Ltd, Unit 5 Hood Street, Hull, HU8 7AL Tel: (01482) 224670 Fax: (01482) 215610 E-mail: info@new-engravers.com *Industrial engravers*

Newly Weds Foods Europe Ltd, Owl Lane, Ossett, West Yorkshire, WF5 9AX Tel: (01924) 280444 Fax: (01924) 281042 *Food seasoning manufrs*

Newlyn Forge, 70 Bushey Hall Road, Bushey, WD23 2EQ Tel: (01923) 251660 Fax: (01923) 251660 *Blacksmiths & forge metal manufrs*

▶ Newmac Asphalt Services Ltd, Hunter Street, Paisley, Renfrewshire, PA1 1DN Tel: 0141-889 3174 Fax: 0141-889 3175

Newman Ltd, 219 Moseley Street, Birmingham, B5 6LE Tel: 0121-622 2884 Fax: 0121-622 1986 E-mail: singhsatnam@btconnect.com *Based in Birmingham, Nationwide coverage metal finishing, metal polishing, chrome plating, electroplating, powder coatings, epoxy powder coatings, Aluminium powder coatings. We are also offering on site powder coating and*

continued

refurbishment work to shopfronts and handrails e.t.c" Fast & efficient service.

Newman Business Solutions Ltd, Newman House, Farningham Road, Crowborough, East Sussex, TN6 2JR Tel: (01892) 664155 Fax: (01892) 669591 E-mail: enquiries@newmanbs.co.uk *Office machinery & stationary retailers & consultancy*

Newman Display Ltd, 23a Pakenham Street, London, WC1X 0LB Tel: (020) 7278 1400 Fax: (020) 7278 0996 E-mail: info@newman-displays.com *Sign manufrs*

F. Newman Ltd, 33 Linford St, London, SW8 4UP Tel: (020) 7720 1981 Fax: (020) 7622 0016 E-mail: fnewmans@aol.com *Print finishers & mailing house*

▶ Newman Joinery Ltd, 4 Sandy Lane North, Wallington, Surrey, SM6 8JX Tel: (020) 8647 7031 Fax: (020) 8669 9661

Newman Labelling Systems Ltd, Queens Road, Barnet, Hertfordshire, EN5 4DL Tel: (020) 8440 0044 Fax: (020) 8449 2890 E-mail: sales@newman.co.uk *Labelling machine manufacturer & retail*

▶ Newman Moore Ltd, 42b Northgate, Sleaford, Lincolnshire, NG34 7AF Tel: (01529) 302430 Fax: (01529) 414476 E-mail: enquiries@newmanmoore.co.uk

Peter Newman Flooring Ltd, Unit 27 Newtown Business Park, Albion Close, Parkstone, Poole, Dorset, BH12 3LL Tel: (01202) 747175 Fax: (01202) 723421 E-mail: info@peternewmanflooring.com *Floor coverings*

Newman Precision Engineering Ltd, 11-17 Steeple Street, Macclesfield, Cheshire, SK10 2QR Tel: (01625) 618627 Fax: (01625) 618627 E-mail: newmanprecision@aol.com *Precision engineers*

▶ Newman Scott Ltd, 1 Sadler Foster Way, Teesside Industrial Estate, Stockton-on-Tees, Cleveland, TS17 9JY Tel: (01642) 769696 Fax: (01642) 769669 E-mail: columbr@newmanscott.co.uk *Shop fitting services*

Newman Stallard Precision Engineers Ltd, 2 Westwood Court, Brunel Road, Totton, Southampton, SO40 3WX Tel: (023) 8086 4291 Fax: (023) 8042 8146 *The Company was founded in 1996, as a small precision engineering company aiming to provide a quality machining service to local businesses. Having since moved to larger premises we have adapted a plan of continuing investment in new CNC Milling, Turning, and Spark Erosion equipment to accommodate our increasing order book. We now employ five skilled personnel, and are continuing to expand our customer base and experience in this ever changing industry.*

Newman White Ltd, 36 Blind Lane, Southwick, Trowbridge, Wiltshire, BA14 9PJ Tel: (01225) 762337 *Export consultants*

Newman-Phoenix Drawn Tube Ltd, Phoenix Street, West Bromwich, West Midlands, B70 0AS Tel: 0121-543 5700 Fax: 0121-500 3030 *Steel tube & pipe manufrs*

Newmans Cheltenham Ltd, 180 Bath Road, Cheltenham, Gloucestershire, GL53 7NF Tel: (01242) 512361 Fax: (01242) 521666 *Corn merchants & horticultural sundriesmen*

Newmans Footwear Ltd, Garden Street, Blackburn, BB2 1TZ Tel: (01254) 56211 Fax: (01254) 680545 E-mail: newmans@nfw.co.uk *Footwear importers*

▶ Newmark Security Products Ltd, 8 Cromwell Business Centre, Howard Way, Interchange Park, Newport Pagnell, Buckinghamshire, MK16 9QS Tel: (01908) 283590 Fax: (01908) 283599

Y.M. Newmark, Duchess Street Industrial Estate, Duchess Street, Shaw, Oldham, OL2 7UT Tel: (01706) 291295 Fax: (01706) 291297 E-mail: info@newmarks.co.uk *Plastic floral gardening products*

Newmarket Insulation Contracts, Exchange House, Wash Road, Wickhambrook, Newmarket, Suffolk, CB8 8XQ Tel: (01440) 820612 Fax: (01440) 820628 E-mail: newmarktinscon@hotmail.com *Asbestos removal services*

Newmarket Paint Company Ltd, Unit 5 Studlands Business Centre, Newmarket, Suffolk, CB8 7EA Tel: (01638) 660262 Fax: (01638) 660262 *Paints & coatings manufrs*

Newmarket Racehorse Transport, Cricket Field Road, Newmarket, Suffolk, CB8 8BT Tel: (01638) 663155 Fax: (01638) 560894 *Racehorse transportation service*

Newmind Ltd, Yarburgh House, King Street, Yarburgh, Louth, Lincolnshire, LN11 0PN Tel: (01507) 363636 Fax: (01507) 363764 E-mail: sales@newmind.ltd.uk *Computer consultants*

Newmont Engineering Co. Ltd, 274 Worton Road, Isleworth, Middlesex, TW7 6EE Tel: (020) 8568 7718 Fax: (020) 8758 9442 *Precision engineers*

Newmor Group Ltd, Madoc Works, Henfaes Lane, Welshpool, Powys, SY21 7BE Tel: (01938) 552671 Fax: (01938) 554285 E-mail: enquiries@newmor.com *Vinyl wallcoverings manufrs*

Newnham Engineering, 6 Lancing Business Park, Marlborough Road, Lancing, West Sussex, BN15 8UF Tel: (01903) 851120 Fax: (01903) 761253 *Precision engineers*

Newnham Rubber Mills Ltd, Bullo Pill, Newnham, Gloucestershire, GL14 1ED Tel: (01594) 516233 Fax: (01594) 516608 E-mail: sales@lee-healey.fssnet.co.uk *Rubber manufrs*

Newnorth Print, College Street, Kempston, Bedford, MK42 8NA Tel: (01234) 341111 Fax: (01234) 271112 E-mail: newnorth@newnorth.co.uk *Colour printing services*

Newood Transmissions Ltd, 95 Prince Avenue, Southend-on-Sea, SS2 6RL Tel: (01702) 392525 Fax: (01702) 392525 E-mail: sales@newoodtransmissions.co.uk *Automatic & mains transmissions re-manufrs*

▶ Newport Building Services Ltd, Units 3-4 Victoria Court, Hurricane Way, Wickford, Essex, SS11 8YY Tel: (01268) 575550 Fax: (01268) 575551

Newport Commercial Refrigeration Ltd, 60 Commercial Road, Newport, Gwent, NP20 2PF Tel: (01633) 221100 Fax: (01633) 220810 E-mail: ntrltd@ntlworld.com *Retail refrigerators*

Newport Fabrications Ltd, Unit 22, Leeway Industrial Estate, Newport, Gwent, NP19 4SL Tel: (01633) 270666 Fax: (01633) 270068 E-mail: mark.nsl@virgin.net *Steel fabrication manufrs*

Newport Fish Co. Ltd, 200 Battery Road, Cookstown, County Tyrone, BT80 0HY Tel: (028) 8673 7326 Fax: (028) 8673 6132 *Fish suppliers*

▶ Newport Galvanisers Ltd, Whitehead Works, Mendalgief Road, Newport, Gwent, NP20 2NF Tel: (01633) 241100 Fax: (01633) 841352 E-mail: geoff.bulger@wedge-galv.co.uk *For quality at a competitive cost, Newport Galvanizers is the name for hot dip galvanizing in Wales. We offer unbeatable service, value for money, a fast turnaround - and access to back-up resources of one of Europe's premier metal-treating organisations, Wedge Group Galvanizing. Building on our already excellent reputation, we are investing in new technology, plant and facilities - all with on-going customer benefits and competitiveness in mind. Experienced experts provide a free advisory service about coating**requirements and steelwork design, so that you can make an informed choice about your individual needs.*

Newport Galvanisers Ltd., Llanwern Works, Newport, Gwent, NP19 4QX Tel: (01633) 277400 Fax: (01633) 277997 *Galvanizing services*

Newport & Gwent Chamber of Commerce & Industry, Unit 30, Enterprise Way, Newport, Gwent, NP20 2AQ Tel: (01633) 222664 Fax: (01633) 222301 E-mail: info@ngb2b.co.uk *Chamber of commerce*

▶ Newport Pagnell Construction Ltd, 55-57 Union Street, Newport Pagnell, Buckinghamshire, MK16 8ET Tel: (01908) 610899 Fax: (01908) 210494 E-mail: info@npcltd.co.uk

Newport Sewing Centre, Curlew Close, Queensway Meadows Industrial Estate, Newport, Gwent, NP19 4SY Tel: (01633) 284646 *Sewing machines & accessories*

The Newport Sign Company Ltd, 47 Dolphin Street, Newport, Gwent, NP20 2AT Tel: (01633) 263301 Fax: (01633) 676497 E-mail: bernie@aol.com *Signs services*

Newport Spark Erosion Services, 18-19 South Road, Harlow, Essex, CM20 2AR Tel: (01279) 415900 Fax: (01279) 454753 E-mail: sales@newport-eng.co.uk *Precision engineers*

▶ Newquay Hotels, Esplanade Road, Pentire, Newquay, Cornwall, TR7 1PS Tel: 01637 873333 Fax: 01637 851413 E-mail: info@newquay-hotels.co.uk *The Bay Hotel and the Esplanade Hotel together form the newquay-hotels website. Combined they have over 180 bedrooms and views over Fistral Beach.*

Newquay Radiators, Victoria Business Park, Roche, St. Austell, Cornwall, PL26 8JF Tel: (01726) 890922 Fax: (01726) 890974 *Car radiator manufrs*

▶ Newrap, 11 Castle Clough, Hapton, Burnley, Lancashire, BB12 7LN Tel: (01282) 777953 Fax: (01282) 778558 E-mail: info@newrap.co.uk *Manufacturers of Packaging Machinery and pallet wrapping machinery*

Newring Electronics Ltd, Unit 7-8 Justin Business Park, Sandford Lane, Wareham, Dorset, BH20 4DY Tel: (01929) 554790 Fax: (01929) 554789 E-mail: mail@newring.co.uk *Electronic assemblers*

Newrooss Impex Ltd, New Skopes House, 2 Cross Green Garth, Cross Green Industrial Estate, Leeds, LS9 0SF Tel: 0113-240 2211 Fax: 0113-248 9544 E-mail: sales@skopes.com *Menswear wholesalers*

Newry Golf Inn Ltd, Forkhill Road, Newry, County Down, BT35 8QY Tel: (028) 3026 3871 Fax: (028) 3026 3871 *Banqueting rooms*

Newry & Mourne Enterprise Agency, Win Business Park, Canal Quay, Newry, County Down, BT35 6PH Tel: (028) 3026 7011 Fax: (028) 3026 1316 E-mail: info@nmea.net *Enterprise agency & property management*

News International P.L.C., Virginia Street, London, E98 1XY Tel: (020) 7782 6000 Fax: (020) 7782 6097 *Publishers*

News (International) Ltd, 1 Pennington St, London, E98 1TT Tel: (020) 7481 4100 *Newspaper publishers*

News & Media Ltd, 233 Seven Sisters Road, London, N4 2DA Tel: (020) 7263 1417 Fax: (020) 7272 8934 E-mail: info@impact-magazines.com *Advertising & publishing services*

▶ News Transport, D Station Road, Ampthill, Bedford, MK45 2QY Tel: (01525) 404000 Fax: (01525) 404555 E-mail: info@newstransport.co.uk *Transportation*

News Vendors Equipment, Castle Trading Estate, Portchester, Fareham, Hampshire, PO16 9SF Tel: (023) 9222 1222 Fax: (023) 9222 1234 *Point of sale manufrs*

Newshield Enterprises Ltd, Unit 2h Northlands Business Park, Bognor Road, Warnham, Horsham, West Sussex, RH12 3SH Tel: (01306) 627087 Fax: (01306) 627119 E-mail: sales@newshield.co.uk *Exhibition, Display, Graphics, Signage, Large Format Printing, Signs, Estate Agent Display, Display Panel Hire, Stand Manufacture & Installation, Storage, Leaflet Holders, Vehicle Graphics, Graphic Design, Pop Up Display, Shopfitting, Window Display, Vinyl Lettering*

Newsigns Sign Writers, Unit 6a The Arches, Loveridge Road, London, NW6 2DS Tel: (020) 7328 9251 Fax: (020) 7624 7465 *Sign writers & sign contractors*

▶ Newsmate Stationery Mnfrs, Unit 1f Mullacott Cross Industrial Estate, Ilfracombe, Devon, EX34 8PL Tel: (01271) 867469 Fax: (01271) 879158 *Stationery suppliers*

Newsmith Stainless Ltd, Fountain Works, Child Lane, Liversedge, West Yorkshire, WF15 7PH Tel: (01924) 405988 Fax: (01924) 403304 E-mail: sales@newsmiths.co.uk *Industrial washing machines, mechnaical handling &*

continued

conveyor equipment for the food processing, pharmaceutical, laboratory & confectionery industries

Harold Newsome Ltd, Paragon Works, Elder Road, Leeds, LS13 4DJ Tel: 0113-257 0156 Fax: 0113-256 4095 E-mail: h.newsome@btconnect.com *Structural steel fabricators*

Newsome Holdings Ltd, Calderbank, Saddleworth Road, Elland, West Yorkshire, HX5 0RY Tel: (01422) 371711 Fax: (01422) 377372 E-mail: enquiries@newsome.ltd.uk *Refrigeration & air conditioning engineers*

J. Newsome (Tools) Ltd, Unit 1, Harleston Street, Sheffield, S4 7QB Tel: 0114-275 7002 Fax: 0114-279 7070E-mail: newsome@syol.com *Hand tool distributors*

Newson Boatbuilders Ltd, 3 Sea Lake Road, Lowestoft, Suffolk, NR32 3LQ Tel: (01502) 574902 Fax: (01502) 574902 E-mail: keith@newson.co.uk *Ship repairers & boat builders*

Newson Gale Ltd, Omega House, Private Road 8, Colwick, Nottingham, NG4 2JX Tel: 0115-940 7500 Fax: 0115-940 7501 E-mail: sales@newson-gale.co.uk *Safety for plant & process manufrs*

Newspaper Publishers Association Ltd, 34 Southwark Bridge Road, London, SE1 9EU Tel: (020) 7207 2200 Fax: (020) 7928 2067 *Trade association agents* Also at: Manchester

Newsquest Blackburn, High Street, Blackburn, BB1 1HT Tel: (01254) 678678 Fax: (01254) 682185 E-mail: let_editorial@lancashire.newsquest.co.uk *Newspaper publishers*

Newsquest Direct, 6 St Peters Court, Middleborough, Colchester, CO1 1WD Tel: (01206) 508250 Fax: (01206) 508266 E-mail: nqd@nqd.co.uk *Letterbox marketing services*

Newsquest Media Ltd, Reliance House, Long St, Dursley, Gloucestershire, GL11 4LF Tel: (01453) 544000 Fax: (01453) 540212 E-mail: reporters@dursleygazette.co.uk *Editing of newspapers*

Newsquest Printing Colchester, A Caxton Court, Newcomen Way, Severalls Industrial Park, Colchester, CO4 9TG Tel: (01206) 224600 Fax: (01206) 844335 E-mail: martyn_reed@essex-news.co.uk *Printers*

▶ Newstar Clothing Services, Newstar House, Salmon Street, Preston, PR1 4BQ Tel: (01772) 558862 Fax: (01772) 558879 E-mail: sales@newstarjeans.co.uk *Clothing manufrs*

Newstar Sectional Buildings, Ash Grove Beverley Road, Beverley Road, Hull, HU5 1LT Tel: (01482) 444256 Fax: (01482) 449885 *Sectional building manufrs*

Newstart Power Transmission, Unit 19 Tamworth Business Centre, Amber Cl, Tamworth, Staffs, B77 4RP Tel: (01827) 313737 Fax: (01827) 313838 *Bearings power transmission equipment distribs*

Newstyle Fabrications, Ifton Industrial Estate, St. Martins, Oswestry, Shropshire, SY11 3DA Tel: (01691) 773303 Fax: (01691) 773303 *Steel building manufrs*

Newtec Construction, 11 Cabot Rise, Portishead, Bristol, BS20 6NX Tel: (01275) 847863 Fax: (01275) 817818 *General builders*

Newtec Odense UK Ltd, 1 Park View, Arrow, Alcester, Warwickshire, B49 5PN Tel: (01789) 764590 Fax: (01789) 763836 E-mail: p.crouch@newtecuk.com *Weighing equipment import & service*

Newtech Lighting Ltd, Unit 27 Branbridges Industrial Estate, Branbridges Road, East Peckham, Tonbridge, Kent, TN12 5HF Tel: (0845) 6732203 Fax: (01622) 870090 E-mail: nigel@newtechltg.com *Lighting Manufacturers & Designers*

Newteq Engineering Ltd, 1 Waterside Industrial Estate, Ettingshall Road, Wolverhampton, WV2 2RQ Tel: (01902) 492622 Fax: (01902) 492379 E-mail: sales@newteq.co.uk *Precision production engineers & commercial vehicle spare part manufrs*

Newton Abbot Flooring, 129 Winner Street, Paignton, Devon, TQ3 3BP Tel: (01803) 525177 Fax: (01803) 520359 E-mail: classic.floors@virgin.net *Flooring contractors & carpets retailers*

▶ Newton Contracting Services, Faraday House, Wolfreton Drive, Anlaby, Hull, HU10 7BY Tel: (01482) 655565 Fax: (01482) 654924

Newton Controls Ltd, 26 Coltness Rd, Elburton, Plymouth, PL9 8HA Tel: (01752) 481528 Fax: (01752) 481972 *control systems manufrs*

Newton Derby Ltd, Belgrave Works, Town Street, Stanningley, Pudsey, West Yorkshire, LS28 6ES Tel: 0113-218 0717 Fax: 0113-257 2206 E-mail: sales@newtonderby.co.uk *Electrical engineering manufrs*

▶ Newton Ellis & Co, 29 Cheapside, Liverpool, L2 2DY Tel: 0151-236 1391 E-mail: info@newtonellis.co.uk *Camera and photographic equipment repairs. Second-hand classic and modern camera equipment for sale. New binoculars, telescopes, spotting-scopes, night vision optics, tripods & magnifiers for sale.*

▶ Newton Fabrications Ltd, 9 York Street, Ayr, KA8 8AN Tel: (01292) 269135 Fax: (01292) 610258 *Metalwork engineers & fabricators*

Newton Fabrications Ltd, 9 York Street, Ayr, KA8 8AN Tel: (01292) 269135 Fax: (01292) 610258 E-mail: davidcorson@newtonholdings.com *Secure door entry system*

Newton Forge, Stalbridge Lane, Sturminster Newton, Dorset, DT10 2JQ Tel: (01258) 472407 Fax: (01258) 471111 E-mail: mail@newtonforge.co.uk *Ornamental restoration blacksmiths*

Newton Friction Ltd, Unit A, 20 Mearns Street, Aberdeen, AB11 5AT Tel: (01224) 589336 Fax: (01224) 583389 E-mail: info@newtonfriction.co.uk *Brake & clutch lining distributors*

▶ Giffard Newton & Sons Ltd, 9 Power House, Highem Meed, Chesham, Buckinghamshire, HP5 2AH Tel: (01494) 782388 Fax: (01494) 775090 E-mail: mail@giffardnewton.com

continued

Company Information

continuation
Suppliers of industrial safety footwear & service footwear

Newton Information Technology Ltd, 1 Central Business Centre, Great Central Way, London, NW10 0UR Tel: (020) 8451 0027 Fax: (020) 8451 0029 E-mail: sales@newtonit.co.uk *Bespoke & turnkey computer systems manufrs*

Israel Newton & Sons Ltd, Summerley Works, Idle, Bradford, West Yorkshire, BD10 8TT Tel: (01274) 612059 Fax: (01274) 612059 *Steam boiler & locomotive boiler manufrs*

John Newton & Co. Ltd, 12 Verney Road, London, SE16 3DH Tel: (020) 7237 1217 Fax: (020) 7252 2769 E-mail: sales@newton-membranes.co.uk *Cavity drainage & damp proofing suppliers* Also at: London SE16

Newton Le Willows Blinds, Stall 55 Market Hall, The Galleries, Wigan, Lancashire, WN1 1PW Tel: (01942) 491494 Fax: (01942) 491494 *Blinds, canopies, curtains & canvas awnings retailers & manufrs*

Newton Newton, Bishop Tozers Chapel, Middlemarsh Road, Burgh le Marsh, Skegness, Lincolnshire, PE24 5AD Tel: (01754) 768401 Fax: (01754) 610612 E-mail: info@newtonnewtonflags.com *Manufacturers of superior quality flags & ceremonial banners*

Newton Pet & Garden Supplies, 1-2 Bridge House, Sherborne Road, Newton Abbot, Devon, TQ12 2QX Tel: (01626) 201219 Fax: (01626) 201219 *Aquatic suppliers*

▶ Newton Press, St Cuthberts Way, Aycliffe Industrial Estate, Aycliffe Industrial Park, Newton Aycliffe, County Durham, DL5 6DX Tel: (01325) 300212 Fax: (01325) 312893 E-mail: sales@newtonpress.co.uk

Newton Print, 27a Coleshill Road, Sutton Coldfield, West Midlands, B75 7AX Tel: 0121-378 3711 Fax: 0121-311 1779 E-mail: david.deere@virgin.net *Commercial printers & stationers*

Newton Propeller, Unit 26 Ddole Road Industrial Estate, Llandrindod Wells, Powys, LD1 6DF Tel: (01597) 824420 Fax: (01597) 824420 E-mail: sales@newtonpropeller.co.uk *Aircraft wooden propeller manufrs*

Newton Software Ltd, Hawthorn Dene, Gloucester Road, Tutshill, Chepstow, Gwent, NP16 7DB Tel: (01291) 627278 Fax: (01291) 627278 *Computer consultancy*

Newton Sports Ltd, Hill St Works, Hill Street, Hyde, Cheshire, SK14 5RL Tel: 0161-368 0707 Fax: 0161-368 4222 E-mail: sales@newtonsports.co.uk *Rugby sportswear manufrs*

▶ Newton Tesla (Electric Drives) Ltd, Unit G18 Warrington Business Park, Long Lane, Warrington, WA2 8TX Tel: (01925) 444773 Fax: (01925) 241477 E-mail: info@newton-tesla.com *Electronic drives speed controls design repair services distributors*

▶ Newton Transport & Storage, Wareing Road, Liverpool, L9 7AU Tel: 0151-524 0060

Newtons Of Bury, 151 The Rock, Bury, Lancashire, BL9 0ND Tel: 0161-764 1863 Fax: 0161-761 7129 E-mail: enquiries@tablecare.co.uk *Antique furniture & reproduction service providers*

Newtons4th Electronic Equipment Component, Loughborough Road, Mountsorrel, Loughborough, Leicestershire, LE12 7AT Tel: 0116-230 1066 Fax: 0116-230 1061 E-mail: sales@newtons4th.co.uk *Innovative products for the electronics industry manufrs*

Newtown Angling Centre, Newtown, Germoe, Penzance, Cornwall, TR20 9AQ Tel: (01736) 763721 *Fishing tackle suppliers*

▶ Newtown Construction (Scotland) Ltd, Unit 3, Acorn Business Centre, Arran Road, Perth, PH1 3DZ Tel: (01738) 446226

Newtown Engineering, Garleigh Road, Rothbury, Morpeth, Northumberland, NE65 7RG Tel: (01669) 620755 Fax: (01669) 620478 E-mail: enqs@newtownengineering.com *Agricultural & horticultural engineers*

Newtown Gate & Welding, Arundel Street, Newtown, Wigan, Lancashire, WN5 9BQ Tel: (01942) 238057 Fax: (01942) 238057 E-mail: newtowngatesandwelding@blueyonder.co.uk *Wrought work*

Newtown Pneumatic Services Ltd, Newtown Road, Worcester, WR5 1HA Tel: (01905) 29068 Fax: (01905) 24118 *Pneumatic fitting distributors*

Newtown Sideloaders Southern Ltd, 20 Windsor Avenue, Leighton Buzzard, Bedfordshire, LU7 1AP Tel: (01525) 378434 Fax: (01525) 378434 *Reconditioned fork lift trucks*

▶ Newtyne Computer Consultants, 6 Howe Street, Edinburgh, EH3 6TD Tel: 0131-225 6952 Fax: 0131-225 9324 E-mail: enquiry@newtyne.com *Newtyne provides a range of SAS Version 9 Training courses from their Edinburgh Education Centre. Newtyne Recruitment Services offer a personalized service to companies seeking SAS resource and candidates seeking new opportunities.*

Nex Craft Ltd, Gabriels Wharf, Castle Road, Maidstone, Kent, ME16 0LT Tel: (01622) 674971 Fax: (01732) 886769 *Boat building*

Nexans Logistics, Llewellyn House, Chesney Wold, Bleak Hall, Milton Keynes, MK6 1NE Tel: (01908) 250850 Fax: (01908) 250851 E-mail: info@nexans.co.uk *Cable support systems*

Nexcen Ltd, 16C Horse Street, Chipping Sodbury, Bristol, BS37 6DB Tel: (01454) 318686 Fax: 0171-433 4533 *Computer consultants*

▶ Nexday Handpiece Repairs, PO Box 334, Northampton, NN3 7XL Tel: (01604) 493308 Fax: (01604) 491139 E-mail: nexday@nexdayrepairs.co.uk *Repairers of dental drills*

Nexen Energy Services (International) Ltd, Mallard Court, Market Square, Staines, Middlesex, TW18 4RH Tel: (01784) 429500 Fax: (01784) 429550 *Oil & gas producers*

Nexillis Ltd, 1 Canada Square, Canary Wharf, London, E14 5DY Tel: (020) 7538 2533 Fax: (020) 7538 2534 E-mail: info@nexillis.com *Mobile networking & computer solutions*

▶ Nexnix Ltd, Landmark House, 75 Station Road, Horsham, West Sussex, RH13 5EX Tel: (01403) 756777 Fax: (01403) 756888 *Audio visual equipment sales & installations*

Nexpress Ltd, Unit 16, Gelders Hall Road, Shepshed, Loughborough, Leicestershire, LE12 9NH Tel: (01509) 501100 Fax: (01509) 601186 E-mail: sales@nexpress.co.uk *Remarketing of digital equipment*

▶ Nexprint Ltd, Units A, Oakfield Industrial Estate, Stanton Harcourt Road, Witney, Oxfordshire, OX29 4TH Tel: (01865) 883655

Nexsan Technologies, 33-35 Parker Industrial Estate, Mansfield Road, Derby, DE21 4SZ Tel: (01332) 291600 Fax: (01332) 291616 E-mail: info@nexsan.com *Computer consultants manufacturers & service providers*

Nexsoft, Lyth Business Centre, Crosthwaite, Kendal, Cumbria, LA8 8BP Tel: (01539) 568860 E-mail: sales@nexsoft.co.uk *Software designers*

▶ Nexsys Consultants, 22 Frys Lane, Yateley, Hampshire, GU46 7TJ Tel: (01252) 890633 *Computer systems consultants*

Next Control Systems Ltd, 6 Farnborough Business Centre, Eelmoor Road, Farnborough, Hampshire, GU14 7XA Tel: (01252) 406398 Fax: (01252) 406401 E-mail: jackie@nextcontrols.com *Control unit manufrs*

Next Day Computer Services, 32 Burnham Cl, Enfield, Middx, EN1 3RA Tel: 020 83665031 Fax: 020 83666323 *Computer hardware*

▶ Next Generation Computer Systems, 15 Tamworth Road, Amington, Tamworth, Staffordshire, B77 3BS Tel: (01827) 58100 Fax: (01827) 58100 E-mail: info@ngcstamworth.co.uk *Computer software services*

Next Step Developments, Glamafan Court, Port Talbot, West Glamorgan, SA13 2BN Tel: (01792) 323230 Fax: (01792) 323225 *Retail systems development*

Next Two, Colliery Road, Pinxton, Nottingham, NG16 6JF Tel: (01773) 864111 Fax: (01773) 582800 E-mail: sales@nexttwo.com *Loudspeakers manufacturers & distributors*

▶ Nextdesign, The Fence, Ring Fence, Woolaston, Lydney, Gloucestershire, GL15 6NX Tel: (07966) 171478 Fax: (07977) 017247 E-mail: enquiries@nextdesign.co.uk *Product design & development*

▶ Nextel Metals, 20 Woodlea Grove, Yeadon, Leeds, LS19 7YT Tel: (07946) 842491 Fax: 0113-250 4700 E-mail: nextelmetals@aol.com *I am looking for following surplus or secondary material* *1. Hot Rolled Sheets/Coils *2. Cold Rolled*3. CRGO*4. CRNGO*5. Sheet Cutting *6. Electro Galvanised*7. Galvanised Iron*8. Prepainted Sheets* *if you have any other type of ferrous scrap stock*

Nexus Ltd, 32 Carden Place, Aberdeen, AB10 1UP Tel: (01224) 620000 Fax: (01224) 620026

Nexus Alpha Ltd, 5a Old Town, London, SW4 0JT Tel: (020) 7622 6816 Fax: (020) 7622 6817 *Provide IT services to the transport industry*

Nexus Alpha Ltd, Unit 8 Beaufort Ho, Beaufort Court, Sir Thomas Longley Rd, Rochester, Kent, ME2 4FB Tel: (01634) 304226 Fax: (01634) 301315 *Computer & software developers*

▶ Nexus Carpet Ltd, 238, Coombe Lane, West Wimbledon, London, SW20 0QT Tel: (020) 8944 1491 E-mail: surveys@nexuscarpet.com *Carpet replacement specialists services*

Nexus Computer & Office Supplies, 64 Edward Road, Shaw, Oldham, OL2 7EY Tel: (01706) 846131 Fax: (01706) 846131 E-mail: peterradcliffefree@btopenworld.com *Office equipment suppliers*

▶ Nexus Data Solutions Ltd, Douglas House, 140 Hanham Road, Bristol, BS15 8NP Tel: (0845) 2263160 *Computer systems consultants*

Nexus Design & Print Ltd, 99-102 Preston Road, Brighton, BN1 6AF Tel: (01273) 702525 Fax: (01273) 887211 E-mail: sales@nexusdp.co.uk *Designers & printers*

Nexus G B Ltd, Rushdene, Dodsley Grove, Easebourne, Midhurst, West Sussex, GU29 9BE Tel: (01730) 816502 Fax: (01730) 817393 E-mail: johncbarrett@msn.com *Electronic component sales*

Nexus Graphic Systems Ltd, Apartment 11, Generator Hall, Electric Wharf, Coventry, CV1 4JL Tel: (024) 7622 3865 Fax: (024) 7622 3872 *Computer maintenance installers*

Nexus Open Systems Ltd, Vale House, Pynes Hill, Exeter, EX2 5AZ Tel: (01392) 205095 Fax: (01392) 205096 *Computer systems integration*

Nexus Precision Engineering Ltd, Badentoy Road, Badentoy Industrial Estate, Aberdeen, AB12 4YA Tel: (01224) 787300 *Sub-contract machining services*

▶ Nexus Precision Engineering, 1a Ligget Syke Place, East Mains Industrial Estate, Broxburn, West Lothian, EH52 5NA Tel: (01506) 855995 Fax: (01506) 854044 *Engineering services*

Ney Ltd, Middlemarch Business Park Coventry Trading Estate, Siskin Drive, Middlemarch Business Park, Coventry, CV3 4FJ Tel: (024) 7630 8100 Fax: (024) 7630 8102 E-mail: info@ney.co.uk *Woodworking machinery & material distributors*

▶ Neya Taste, 36 Hastings Road, Leicester, LE5 0HL Tel: 0116-276 7767 Fax: 0116-276 7767 *Suppliers & manufacturers of Asian sweets & savouries*

NFH Metal Co., 2b Selborne Road, London, N14 7DH Tel: (020) 8886 9667 *Dental supplies services*

N-Force Security Solutions, 95 Lambert Road, Grimsby, North East Lincolnshire, DN32 0NR Tel: (01472) 604609 E-mail: sales@n-force.co.uk *Sales & installation services for security equipment*

▶ NFT Distribution Ltd, 4 Riverside Industrial Estate, London Colney By Passage, London Colney, St. Albans, Hertfordshire, AL2 1AY Tel: (01727) 822771 Fax: (01727) 823309

NFU Mutual Ltd, Tiddington Road, Stratford-upon-Avon, Warwickshire, CV37 7BJ Tel: (01789) 204211 Fax: (01789) 298992 *Insurance company* Also at: Branches throughout the UK

▶ NG Office Solutions, 19 Regency Green, Colchester, CO3 4TD Tel: 01206 369 530 Fax: 01206 369 530 E-mail: enquiries@ngofficesolutions.com *Small, professional company offereing virtual office assistance. We cater for all office and admin needs, from basic word processing and faxing to Recruitment and Secretarial services. We offer a friendly and customer focused service with a guarantee of client confidentiality and a fast turn around.*

NGF, Unit 11, Allerton Bywater, Castleford, West Yorkshire, WF10 2DB Tel: (0845) 6444566 Fax: (0845) 6445123 E-mail: sales@ngfindustrialdoors.co.uk *Industrial, security & fire doors. Also roller shutter doors*

NGF Europe Ltd, Lea Green Road, St. Helens, Merseyside, WA9 4PR Tel: (01744) 853065 Fax: (01744) 816147 E-mail: sales@ngfeurope.com *Rubber coated glass fibre manufrs*

N-Grave Ltd, Legion Hall, Magdalen Road, Tilney St. Lawrence, King's Lynn, Norfolk, PE34 4RE Tel: (01945) 881133 Fax: (01945) 881144 E-mail: ngrave@btinternet.com *Engravers & Sign Makers*

▶ NHS 24, Beardmore Street, Clydebank, Dunbartonshire, G81 4HX Tel: (0845) 4242424

Nia Ltd, Unit 1 Churchill House, 114 Windmill Road, Brentford, Middlesex, TW8 9NB Tel: (020) 8847 5225 Fax: (020) 8560 1090 E-mail: peterchapman@niasteelworkltd.co.uk *Steel fabricators*

Niagara Falls Castings UK Ltd, Budbrooke Road, Warwick, CV34 5XH Tel: (01926) 496258 Fax: (01926) 496250 E-mail: sales@nf-castings.co.uk *Precious metal suppliers*

Niagara Lasalle UK, Victoria Steelworks, Bull Lane, Wednesbury, West Midlands, WS10 8RS Tel: 0121-506 7500 Fax: 0121-506 7501 E-mail: hotrolled@niag.com *Hot rolled section engineers*

Niagara Lasalle UK, Victoria Steelworks, Bull Lane, Wednesbury, West Midlands, WS10 8RS Tel: 0121-506 7500 Fax: 0121-506 7501 E-mail: hotrolled@niag.com *Major UK producer of hot rolled flats, narrow strip, squares, hexagons, rounds and special profiles. Carbon steel bar, carbon steel flats, carbon steel sections, Round steel bars, square steel bars, hot rolled and cold drawn steel bars, nickel alloy steel bars, steel alloy bars, bright steel bars, mild steel bars, black steel bars engineering steel bars. Worldwide distribution capabilities.*

Niagara Lasalle UK, Victoria Steelworks, Bull Lane, Wednesbury, West Midlands, WS10 8RS Tel: 0121-506 7500 Fax: 0121 506 7501 E-mail: hotrolled@niag.com *Niagara LaSalle (UK) produces a wide range of products, including hot rolled, cold finished, selenium stainless, cast iron, tool steel and tool room materials. Niagara LaSalle (UK) is known for its innovative processes and quality products which are simply second to none in the steel industry. Also see the details for - Midland Engineering Steel, Macreadys, GB Longmore, Wesson Bright Products and Niagara Hot Rolled Products.*

Niagra Lasalle, Planetary Road, Willenhall, West Midlands, WV13 3SW Tel: (01902) 307007 Fax: (01902) 864269 E-mail: brightbar@niag.com *Steel fabricators & draw bright steel*

Niagra Lasalle, Planetary Road, Willenhall, West Midlands, WV13 3SW Tel: (01902) 307007 Fax: (01902) 864269 E-mail: brightbar@niag.com Principal Export Areas: Worldwide *Bright drawn steel bars*

Niagri Engineering Ltd, Station Road, Lakenheath, Brandon, Suffolk, IP27 9AA Tel: (01842) 862500 Fax: (01842) 862501 E-mail: info@niagri.co.uk *Agricultural machinery design & manufacturing*

Niall Cars, 5 Fort Road, Wick, Littlehampton, West Sussex, BN17 7QU Tel: (01903) 722510 Fax: (01903) 722510 *Vehicle test & repairers*

▶ Niall Scaffolders Ltd, Hartwell Depot, Oxford Road, Hartwell, Aylesbury, Buckinghamshire, HP17 8QG Tel: (01296) 427171 Fax: (01296) 434427 E-mail: sales@niallscaffolders.com

Niarchos London Ltd, 41-43 Park Street, London, W1A 2JR Tel: (020) 7314 8400 Fax: (020) 7499 5481 *General agency*

▶ Niblock Builders Ltd, 135 Anerley Road, London, SE20 8AJ Tel: (020) 8778 3449 Fax: (020) 8659 0615

Nibra Sign Ltd, Ivy House Farm, Wolvershill Road, Banwell, Somerset, BS29 6LB Tel: (01934) 822772 Fax: (01934) 822517 E-mail: nibra.signs@btopenworld.com *Sign manufrs*

Ni-Cd Services, 4 Queens Park Road, Bournemouth, BH8 9BP Tel: (01202) 395404 Fax: (01202) 398393 E-mail: russellfrederick@mac.com *Special battery packs refurbishment & suppliers*

Nice Cti Systems UK Ltd, Tollbar Way, Hedge End, Southampton, SO30 2ZP Tel: (0870) 7224000 Fax: (0870) 7224500 E-mail: *Voice & sound recording equipment manufrs*

▶ NiceHR, 42 C Southcote Road, Bournemouth, BH1 3SR Tel: 01202 315437 E-mail: stephanie@nicehr.co.uk *HR Projects and Systems Implementation... Local Bournemouth, Dorset based company...*

Nicera European Works Ltd, Unit 5 Yeoman Industrial Park, Test Lane, Southampton, SO16 9JX Tel: (023) 8066 7908 Fax: (023) 8066 3758 E-mail: sales@nicera-uk.com *Manufacturer of pyrosensors*

Niche Kitchens, 28 Kay Street, Rossendale, Lancashire, BB4 7LS Tel: (01706) 217121 Fax: (01706) 212893 E-mail: info@nichekitchens.co.uk *Niche kitchens excel at delivering luxury kitchens,*

Niche Operable Systems Ltd, The Studio, Rear Of 18, Bath Street, Bolton, BL1 2DJ Tel: (01204) 381552 Fax: (01204) 381556 E-mail: enquiries@folding-partitions.co.uk *Movable partitioning suppliers*

▶ Niche Technologies Ltd, Ternion Court, 264-268 Upper Fourth Street, Milton Keynes, MK10 1DP Tel: 0870 7504471 Fax: 0870 1335371 E-mail: sales@niche-technologies.co.uk *If you manage appointments with your clients then the use of our Niche Appointments software will certainly benefit your business.**Avoid costly appointment booking mistakes and significantly reduce your "did not attend" rate by sending automatic text message reminders prior to your clients appointment.* *Niche Technologies specialise in providing professional appointment management software to health, hair and beauty businesses.*

Nichicon Europe Ltd, Riverside Way, Camberley, Surrey, GU15 3YL Tel: (01276) 405500 Fax: (01276) 686531 *Electronic components*

Nichol & Laidlow Ltd, Bridge End Industrial Estate, Hexham, Northumberland, NE46 4DQ Tel: (01434) 600111 Fax: (01434) 600979 *Bakery*

Nichol Transport Ltd, Brickyard Road, Aldridge, Walsall, WS9 8SR Tel: (01922) 458279 Fax: (01922) 458279 *Road transport/haulage/freight services*

▶ Nicholas Andrews Employment & Recruitment, 1 Whitehall Quay, Leeds, LS1 4HR Tel: 0113-245 6717 Fax: 0113-244 8242 E-mail: richardmhenley@aol.com *Accounting personnel recruitment agency*

James Nicholas International Removals, Units 12-13, Whitehill Industrial Park, Whitehill Lane, Wootton Bassett, Swindon, SN4 7DB Tel: (01793) 849315 Fax: (01793) 849317 *Removal contractors*

Nicholas Packaging Ltd, Ham Lane, Kingswinford, West Midlands, DY6 7JJ Tel: (01384) 400500 Fax: (01384) 270943 E-mail: sales@nicholaspackaging.com *Food packaging materials manufrs*

▶ Nicholas Pryke, 25 Hayfield Road, Oxford, OX2 6TX Tel: 07990 975261 Fax: 01865 510620 E-mail: angela.kennedy@xko.co.uk *Nicholas Pryke. Designer of interiors, contemporary furniture and architectural installations*

▶ Nicholas Rowell Haulage, Torr Quarry Industrial Estate, East Allington, Totnes, Devon, TQ9 7QQ Tel: (01548) 521333 Fax: (01548) 521292

Nicholas Soper & Co, 225 Citadel Road East, Plymouth, PL1 2NG Tel: (01752) 695748 Fax: (01752) 696740 *Gate joiner*

Nicholl Food Packaging Ltd, Bowdenhay Mill, Bowden Lane, Chapel-en-le-Frith, High Peak, Derbyshire, SK23 0JQ Tel: (01298) 812357 Fax: (01298) 815210 E-mail: sales@nichollfoodpackaging.co.uk *Aluminium food containers suppliers*

Nicholl Packaging Ltd, 4 Thackley Court, Thackley Old Road, Shipley, West Yorkshire, BD18 1BW Tel: (01274) 580563 Fax: (01274) 531675 E-mail: info@nichollpackaging.co.uk *Packaging merchants*

Nicholl & Wood Ltd, Netherton Works, Holmfield, Halifax, West Yorkshire, HX3 6ST Tel: (01422) 244484 Fax: (01422) 248777 E-mail: sales@niwood.co.uk *Shelving, foundry chaplets & studs*

Nicholls & Clarke Glass Ltd, Units 27 Gemini Business Park, Hornet Way, Beckton, London, E6 7FF Tel: (020) 7473 0999 Fax: (020) 7476 1017 *Glass & glazing materials suppliers*

Nicholls Colton & Partners Ltd, 7-11 Harding Street, Leicester, LE1 4DH Tel: 0116-253 6333 Fax: 0116-251 4709 E-mail: testing@nicholls-colton.co.uk *Consulting site investigation & construction materials testing*

Nicholls Commercials, 95a Mitcham Lane, London, SW16 6LY Tel: (020) 8677 0873 Fax: (020) 8769 0443 *Mechanical services*

▶ Nicholls Countryside Construction Ltd, Wyvern House, Station Road, Billingshurst, West Sussex, RH14 9SE Tel: (01403) 782009 Fax: (01403) 786659

Nicholls Fabrications Ltd, New Hold Industrial Estate, Garforth, Leeds, LS25 2LD Tel: 0113-232 0847 Fax: 0113-232 0718 *Sheet metal fabrication*

John Nicholls Trading Ltd, Overthorpe Road, Banbury, Oxfordshire, OX16 4TB Tel: (01295) 262294 Fax: (01295) 270895 *Builders & plumbers merchants*

Malcolm Nicholls Ltd, Waterloo Road, Bidford-on-Avon, Alcester, Warwickshire, B50 4JH Tel: (01789) 490382 Fax: (01789) 490130 E-mail: rp@mnl.co.uk *Rapid prototype engineers & model makers*

▶ Nicholls & Wilson Ltd, 44-45 Alston Drive, Bradwell Abbey, Milton Keynes, MK13 9HB Tel: (01908) 321123

Nichols plc, Laurel House 3 Woodlands Park, Ashton Road, Newton-le-Willows, Merseyside, WA12 0HH Tel: (01925) 222222 Fax: (01925) 222233 *Soft drink manufrs*

A. Nichols (Cowmills) Ltd, 8 London Road, Warmley, Bristol, BS30 5JF Tel: 0117-967 1447 *Animal feed & seed merchants*

Nichols & Nichols, Stour Wharf, 10 Stour Road, London, E3 2NT Tel: (020) 8986 3392 Fax: (020) 8986 3392 *Wood turnery manufrs*

▶ Nichols Secretarial Services, 18 St. Johns Road, Belton, Great Yarmouth, Norfolk, NR31 9NS Tel: (01493) 781899 E-mail: elizabeth@nicholssecretarialservices.co.uk *Secretarial services or agencies*

Nichols Sign Ltd, Units 1 & 14 Treeton Enterprise, Rother Crescent, Treeton, Rotherham, South Yorkshire, S60 5QY Tel: 0114-288 9998 Fax: 0114-288 9998 *Sign manufrs*

Nicholson & Bass Ltd, 3 Nicholson Drive, Newtownabbey, County Antrim, BT36 4FB Tel: (028) 9034 2433 Fax: (028) 9034 2066 E-mail: sales@nicholsonbass.com *General printing services*

Nicholson G Engineers Ltd, Blue House Lane, Washington, Tyne & Wear, NE37 2TD Tel: 0191-416 2041 Fax: 0191-415 5139 *Steel fabricators*

The Nicholson Group of Companies, Meridian Centre, King Street, Oldham, OL8 1EZ Tel: (08450) 540526 Fax: (08450) 540527 E-mail: enquiries@nicholson-group.co.uk Principal Export Areas: Central/East Europe, West Europe & Worldwide *Industrial conveyor system suppliers*

Nicholson House Coffee Shop, 14 St Georges Terrace, Millom, Cumbria, LA18 4DB Tel: (01229) 774534 *Health food merchants*

▶ Nicholson Jones Partnership Ltd, 20 St. Andrews Crescent, Cardiff, CF10 3DD Tel: (029) 2072 9500 Fax: (029) 2072 9501

▶ Nicholson Martin, 4 Thorley Hall Stables, Bishop's Stortford, Hertfordshire, CM23 4BE Tel: (0844) 4155508 Fax: (0844) 4155509 E-mail: gill@nicholsonmartin.co.uk *Recruitment Advertising Agency. Media booking with discounts. Small and bespoke. Many long standing clients. We welcome enquiries from small companies.*

Nicholson Plastics Ltd, 20b Lansdowne Road, Croydon, CR0 2BX Tel: (020) 8760 0930 Fax: (020) 8688 1811 *Glass fibre water containers* Also at: Kirkfield

Nicholson Plastics Ltd, Riverside Road, Kirkfieldbank, Lanark, ML11 9JS Tel: (01555) 664316 Fax: (01555) 663056 E-mail: sales@nicholsonplastics.co.uk *Glass fibre storage tank manufrs*

Nicholson Promotional Supplies, 198a Halfway Street, Sidcup, Kent, DA15 8DJ Tel: (020) 8308 1818 Fax: (020) 8309 5718 E-mail: jeff.nps@btinternet.com *Advertising gifts services*

Roy Nicholson, 101 Burringham Road, Scunthorpe, South Humberside, DN17 2DF Tel: (01724) 867213 Fax: (01724) 867213 *Joinery manufrs*

Roy Nicholson, 2 Henderson Avenue, Scunthorpe, South Humberside, DN15 7RL Tel: (01724) 856249 *Joinery manufacturer & PVC articles*

Nicholsons Sealing Technologies Ltd, Hamsterley, Newcastle upon Tyne, NE17 7SX Tel: (01207) 560505 Fax: (01207) 561004 E-mail: info@nicholsons.co.uk Principal Export Areas: Worldwide *Manufacturers of spital bound/ metal gaskets. In addition, metal seals*

▶ Nick Hodder, 74 St James's Street, London, E17 7PE Tel: (020) 8520 7082 Fax: (020) 8520 7082 *Bespoke furniture manufrs*

▶ Nick Owens, Broadwood, Holford, Bridgwater, Somerset, TA5 1DU Tel: (0845) 1235899 Fax: (0870) 0515953 *Computer software database*

▶ Nick Rees Designs Ltd, Unit 10 The Parkwood Centre, Aston Road, Waterlooville, Hampshire, PO7 7HT Tel: (023) 9225 3700 Fax: (023) 9225 6800

▶ NICK SMITH NEW YORK, Somerset House, 40-49 Price Street, Birmingham, B4 6LZ Tel: 0870 486 7021 Fax: 0870 4324196 E-mail: info@nsny.co.uk *NICK SMITH NEW YORK | Exclusive yet Inclusive.*

▶ Nick Sutcliffe, 74 High Ridge Park, Rothwell, Leeds, LS26 0NN Tel: (07717) 754441 E-mail: info@sutcliffevs.co.uk *Web design. Graphic design. Design packages. Web products and services.*

Nickel Blanks Co. Ltd, 6 Smithfield, Sheffield, S3 7AR Tel: 0114-272 5792 Fax: 0114-276 8519 E-mail: shefcutler@aol.com *Blank & table cutlery manufrs*

Nickel-Electro Ltd, Oldmixon Crescent, Weston-super-Mare, North Somerset, BS24 9BL Tel: (01934) 626691 Fax: (01934) 630300 E-mail: clifton@nickel-electro.co.uk *Laboratory equipment (technical) manufrs*

Nickell Crane Hire, 52 Church Road, Dover, Kent, CT17 9LR Tel: (01304) 211897 Fax: (01304) 211897 *Crane hire services*

Nickerson Europe Ltd, 24 Brunel Road, Earlstrees Industrial Estate, Corby, Northamptonshire, NN17 4JW Tel: (01933) 674144 Fax: (01536) 202196 E-mail: info@nickersoneurope.co.uk Principal Export Areas: Central/East Europe, West Europe, North America, Central America & South America *Plastics engineers*

▶ Nicki's, 33 Elmlea Drive, Olney, Buckinghamshire, MK46 5HU Tel: (01234) 714441 *Bouncy castle distributors*

H. Nickolls & Son (Milford) Ltd, The Green, Milford, Stafford, ST17 0UR Tel: (01785) 661221 Fax: (01785) 660122 E-mail: info@nickolls.co.uk *Road transport, haulage & freight services*

Nicks & Co Timber Ltd, Canada Wharf, Bristol Road, Gloucester, GL1 5TE Tel: (01452) 300159 Fax: (01452) 307682 *Timber importers & sawmillers* Also at: Hereford

Nicky's Fish, Slade House, 45 Overstone Road, Moulton, Northampton, NN3 7UU Tel: (01604) 644394 *Fish & aquarium equipment suppliers*

Niclec Services, 16 Gladstone Road, Orpington, Kent, BR6 7EA Tel: (01689) 858318 *Vehicle security installation*

Nico Ebergrip Ltd, The Runnings, Cheltenham, Gloucestershire, GL51 9NJ Tel: (01832) 735341 Fax: (01242) 222448 *Paper & film converter machinery manufrs*

Nicobond International Ltd, 26 Colquhoun Avenue, Hillington Industrial Estate, Glasgow, G52 4BN Tel: 0141-880 1200 Fax: 0141-880 1212 E-mail: nicobond.glasgow@nichollsandclarke.com *Ceramic flooring distributors*

Nicobond International Ltd, Cot Hill Trading Estate, Plymouth, PL7 1SR Tel: (01752) 339724 Fax: (01752) 342746 *Ceramic tile distributors*

Nicobond (South West) Ltd, 325-327 Penarth Road, Cardiff, CF11 7TT Tel: (029) 2039 0146 Fax: (029) 2022 4356 *Ceramics retailers*

▶ Nicol & Andrew, 170 Brand Street, Glasgow, G51 1DH Tel: 0141-419 9020 Fax: 0141-427 9974 E-mail: mspe@namspe.co.uk *Metal spraying services*

Nicol & Andrew plc, 2 Mossland Road, Hillington Industrial Estate, Glasgow, G52 4XZ Tel: 0141-882 4724 Fax: 0141-883 3350 E-mail: info@nicolandandrew.com *Hydraulic cylinder & ram reconditioning manufrs*

▶ C. Nicol & Son, Westside, Skene, Westhill, Aberdeenshire, AB32 6UJ Tel: (01224) 744473

M. Nicol & Co. Ltd, Unit 5, Slaidburn Crescent, Southport, Merseyside, PR9 9YF Tel: (01704) 509667 Fax: (01704) 509669 *Marquee hire & sail makers*

Nicol & Moon Ltd, 7 Wimbledon Stadium Business Centre, Riverside Road, London, SW17 0BA Tel: (020) 8879 6000 Fax: (020) 8879 6111 E-mail: info@nicolandmoon.ltd.uk *Poster producers, writers, screen digital printers*

Nicol Transmission Services, Coppice Trading Estate, Kidderminster, Worcestershire, DY11 7QY Tel: (01562) 752651 Fax: (01562) 823128 *Gear box manufrs*

Nicola & Mark Chadbourne, 69 Crowberry Drive, Harrogate, North Yorkshire, HG3 2UF Tel: (01423) 564237 *Healthcare products*

Nicoll Industries, 4 Steelfabs Industrial Estate, Victoria CR, Burton-on-Trent, Staffordshire, DE14 2QD Tel: (01283) 510570 Fax: (01283) 536188E-mail: enquiries@nicoll-industries.co.uk *Steel fabricators*

Nicoll & Jack Ltd, Locarno Works, Brown Street, Dundee, DD1 5EE Tel: (01382) 224398 Fax: (01382) 228591 *Lifting equipment repairers & distributors*

Nicolson Engineering Services Ltd, The Smiddy, Bowermadden, Wick, Caithness, KW1 4TT Tel: (01955) 641309 Fax: (01955) 641409 *Fabricating, machining, welding & boc agent*

Nicolson Hughes Sails (Sailmakers), Silverhills, Rosneath, Helensburgh, Dunbartonshire, G84 0RW Tel: (01436) 831356 Fax: (01436) 831356 E-mail: sailmaker@nh-sails.co.uk *Sail makers*

▶ Nicolson Maps, 3 Frazer Street, Largs, Ayrshire, KA30 9HP Tel: (01475) 689242 Fax: (01475) 689242 E-mail: enquiries@nicolsonmaps.com *Scotlands leading map publisher & distributor. All scales of Ordnance Survey maps available. Full range of street maps for Scotland. Extensive range of foreign maps in stock.*

▶ Nicolson Plant, Brae, Shetland, ZE2 9QG Tel: (01806) 522259

▶ Nicolsons, Terregles Street, Dumfries, DG2 9AT Tel: (01387) 269700 Fax: (01387) 257677

▶ Nicolson's Chartered Accountants, 49-50 Bayhead, Stornoway, Isle of Lewis, HS1 2DZ Tel: (01851) 700362 Fax: (01851) 700092 E-mail: sales@nicolsonmaps.com *Accountancy and taxation services delivered in a prompt and efficient manner by fully qualified accountants. Using technology to deliver the service faster and cheaper, and with our guaranteed timescale to complete your work.*

Nicom Ltd, Unit 9 Tamebridge Industrial Estate, Aldridge Road, Birmingham, B42 2TX Tel: 0121-356 1667 Fax: 0121-344 3336 *Print trade finishing & mailings*

Nicomatic UK Ltd, Unit 8 Campus 5 Third Avenue, Letchworth Garden City, Hertfordshire, SG6 2JF Tel: (01462) 677886 Fax: (01462) 480548 E-mail: sales@nicomatic.co.uk *Electronic components*

Nicro Print Services, Unit 13 Faraday Close, Washington, Tyne & Wear, NE38 8QJ Tel: 0191-417 8905 Fax: 0191-417 3496 E-mail: ray_foster@btconnect.co.uk *Lithographic printers*

Nidd Valley Saw Mills Ltd, Dacre Banks, Harrogate, North Yorkshire, HG3 4EA Tel: (01423) 780220 Fax: (01423) 780220 *Timber merchants & saw millers*

▶ Nield Engineering, 14 Great Central Way, Woodford Halse, Daventry, Northamptonshire, NN11 3PZ Tel: (01327) 263378 Fax: (01327) 263379 *Sheet metal working*

Nielson Chemicals Ltd, Rawdon Road, Moira, Swadlincote, Derbyshire, DE12 6DA Tel: (01283) 222277 Fax: (01283) 225731 E-mail: info@nielsenchemicals.com *Automobile cleaning chemical suppliers*

Nielson Chemicals Ltd, Rawdon Road, Moira, Swadlincote, Derbyshire, DE12 6DA Tel: (01283) 222277 Fax: (01283) 225731 E-mail: sales@arrowchem.com *Chemicals & aerosols products manufrs*

▶ Nieman Walters, 7 Bourne Court Southend Road, Woodford Green, Essex, IG8 8HD Tel: (020) 8550 3131 Fax: (020) 8550 6020 E-mail: howard@nwnaccounts.com *Chartered certified accountants*

Nifco UK Ltd, Yarm Road, Stockton-on-Tees, Cleveland, TS18 3RX Tel: (01642) 672299 Fax: (01642) 611004 E-mail: sales@nifcoeu.com Principal Export Areas: Worldwide *Plastic mouldings*

▶ Nifem Consultants Ltd, 5 Nelson Road, Portsmouth, Southsea, Hampshire, PO5 2AR Tel: (023) 9243 6353 E-mail: info@nifemconsult.com *NIFEM Consult provides full consultancy services for the water and geotechnical engineering sector. The areas covered include dams and reservoirs, water resources management, water treatment and distribution, pipeline leakage analysis, stormwater drainage analysis and design, flood mapping, computational hydraulics, river system modelling, flood forecasting, well hydraulics, sewerage, wastewater treatment system design, site investigation, soil data analysis and interpretation, analysis and design of retaining walls.***The services include among others data analysis, design, feasibility studies, asset management, project management and site supervision.**

Nifes Consulting Group Ltd, 8 Woodside Terrace, Glasgow, G3 7UY Tel: 0141-332 2453 Fax: 0141-333 0402 E-mail: glasgow@nifes.co.uk *Consultantancy*

Niftylift Ltd, Fingle Drive, Stonebridge, Milton Keynes, MK13 0ER Tel: (01908) 223456 Fax: (01908) 312733 E-mail: info@niftylift.com *Access platform manufrs*

▶ Nigel Beale, Woodlands, Forton, Chard, Somerset, TA20 4HB Tel: 01468 61824 Fax: 0870 770 9440 E-mail: nigel@thebeales.co.uk *Developing your company's marketing requirements is not always an easy task. So a little help from an experienced marketing professional may come as a welcome relief. *In many instances I help to co-ordinate campaigns and project manage marketing activities, although many of the key areas in which I am asked to assist cover:***

continued

**Copy writing*Design and production of corporate and sales literature*Web site development*Online and e-mail marketing *Search engine ranking*Advertising and promotions*New business support*Corporate identity and logo development*Strategy and planning* *It is always possible to develop and implement a plan that suits your needs in the most cost effective manner.*

Nigel Ferguson Fabricators, Old School Buildings, Cemetery Road, Aberbeeg, Abertillery, Gwent, NP13 2AX Tel: (01495) 212471 Fax: (01495) 320051 *Steel fabricators*

Nigel P Jacobs, 21 Roping Road, Yeovil, Somerset, BA21 4BD Tel: (01935) 476443 Fax: (01935) 476443 *Machine tool repairs*

▶ Nigel Raymond, 14 Old Bedford Road, Luton, LU2 7NZ Tel: (01582) 481263 Fax: (01582) 481519

Nigel Rice Ltd, Barmston Close, Swinemoor Lane, Beverley, North Humberside, HU17 0LS Tel: (01482) 862123 Fax: (01482) 872006 E-mail: info@nrice.co.uk *Road freight services*

▶ Nigel Tyas Hand Crafted Ironwork, Bullhouse Mill, Lee Lane, Millhouse Green, Sheffield, S36 9NN Tel: (01226) 761300 *Wrought ironworkers, blacksmith & metalworkers*

Nigel Wright Consultancy, 78 Grey Street, Newcastle upon Tyne, NE1 6AF Tel: 0191-222 0770 Fax: 0191-222 1786 E-mail: enquiries@nwc.co.uk *Recruitment & management consultants*

▶ Nightfreight (GB) Ltd, Tower House, Unitcc Capel Hendre Industrial Estate, Ammanford, Dyfed, SA18 3SJ Tel: (01269) 841241 Fax: (01269) 841251

▶ Nightfreight GB Ltd, Josselin Road, Burnt Mills Industrial Estate, Basildon, Essex, SS13 1PU Tel: (01268) 728484

Nightfreight GB Ltd, Europa House, 122 Conway Street, Birkenhead, Merseyside, CH41 6RY Tel: 0151-649 0123 Fax: 0151-649 0101 E-mail: itdepartment@nightfreight.co.uk *Road transport, haulage & freight services*

Nightfreight (GB) Ltd, Imberhorne Way, East Grinstead, West Sussex, RH19 1RL Tel: (01342) 316221 Fax: (01342) 316134 E-mail: info@nightfreight.co.uk *Transport services & express carriers*

▶ Nightfreight (GB) Ltd, Unit 5 3 Stars Industrial Estate, Ten Acre Lane, Egham, Surrey, TW20 8SJ Tel: (01784) 434435 Fax: (01784) 437157

Nightfreight GB Ltd., Doddington Road, Earls Barton, Northampton, NN6 0NW Tel: (01604) 812123 Fax: (01604) 812101 *Road transport, haulage & freight services*

▶ Nightfreight (GB) Ltd, Unit A3, Halesfield 5, Telford, Shropshire, TF7 4QJ Tel: (01952) 581558

Nightguard Security Systems Ltd, Unit 4, Handloom House, Rabone Lane, Smethwick, West Midlands, B66 5JH Tel: 0121-555 5523 Fax: 0121-555 6466 *Manufacturers of steel shutters*

Nighthood Security Ltd, 209 The Heights, Northolt, Middlesex, UB5 4BX Tel: (020) 8423 5677 Fax: (020) 8426 9009 *Security alarm installers*

▶ Nightingale Audio Systems, Unit 127 J C Albyn Complex, Burton Road, Sheffield, S3 8BZ Tel: 0114-270 1470 E-mail: sales@nightingale-audio.co.uk *PA hire*

▶ Nightingale Austen Designs, The Lodge, Guildford Road, Effingham, Leatherhead, Surrey, KT24 5PE Tel: (01372) 457815 Fax: (01372) 456804 E-mail: richard@naduk.com *Graphic & web design services*

Nightingale Care Beds, Unit 20 Abenbury Way, Wrexham Industrial Estate, Wrexham, Clwyd, LL13 9UZ Tel: (01978) 661699 Fax: (01978) 661705 *Medical equipment suppliers*

Nightingale Chancellors, 132 Sheen Road, Richmond, Surrey, TW9 1UR Tel: (020) 8940 4018 Fax: (020) 8332 1548 *Property managers*

▶ Nightingale Press Ltd, Newark Close, Royston, Hertfordshire, SG8 5HL Tel: (01763) 248393 Fax: (01763) 245825 E-mail: sales@nightingale-press.co.uk

▶ Nightingale Removal & Storage Ltd, Aisecome Way, Weston-super-Mare, Avon, BS22 8NA Tel: (01934) 625134 Fax: (01934) 629833

Nightspeed Ltd, 18 Stadium Way, Tilehurst, Reading, RG30 6BX Tel: 0118-942 2477

▶ Nightspeed Services Ltd, Delta Wharf Trading Estate, Tunnel Avenue, London, SE10 0QH Tel: (020) 8858 5282 Fax: (020) 8858 1861 E-mail: acceptabell@yahoo.co.uk

Niglon Ltd, Highlands Road, Shirley, Solihull, West Midlands, B90 4NP Tel: 0121-711 1990 Fax: 0121-711 1344 *Electrical connector distributors*

Nikad Electronics Ltd, Buchanan House, Malthouse Square, Princes Risborough, Buckinghamshire, HP27 9AQ Tel: (01844) 347350 Fax: (01844) 273888 E-mail: a.ward@nikad.com *Computer peripherals distributors*

Nikal Steels, Block 3 Unit 14 Grazebrook Industrial Park, Peartree Lane, Dudley, West Midlands, DY2 0XW Tel: (01384) 243717 Fax: (01384) 243718 E-mail: sales@nikalsteels.co.uk *Stainless steel flange manufrs*

▶ Nike Construction Ltd, Phoenix Business Park, John Nike Way, Bracknell, Berkshire, RG12 8TN Tel: (01344) 789300 Fax: (01344) 789301

Nike Consultants Ltd, Raynor House, 6 Raynor Road, Wolverhampton, WV10 9QY Tel: (01902) 566200 Fax: (01902) 566201 E-mail: sales@nike.co.uk *Computer resellers & distributors*

Nike UK Ltd, 1 Victory Way, Doxford International Business, Sunderland, SR3 3XF Tel: 0191-401 6453 Fax: 0191-401 2012 E-mail: enquiries@nike.com *Athletic footwear & equipment*

Nikita Clothing Co. Ltd, 1 Kamloops Cresent, Leicester, LE1 2HX Tel: 0116-262 3438 Fax: 0116-253 1939 E-mail: info@nikita.co.uk *Garment manufrs*

Nikken UK Ltd, 1 Deltic Avenue, Rooksley, Milton Keynes, MK13 8LD Tel: (01908) 202400 Fax: (0870) 4445445 E-mail: info@nikkenuk.com *Magnetic health equipment services*

Nikko Electronics Ltd, 358 Kingston Road, Epsom, Surrey, KT19 0DT Tel: (020) 8393 7774 Fax: (020) 8393 7395 E-mail: dalbani@nikko-electronics.co.uk *Electronic components distributors*

Nikomed Ltd, Stuart Court, Salisbury Road, Romsey, Hampshire, SO51 6DJ Tel: (01794) 525100 Fax: (01794) 525101 E-mail: sales@nikomed.co.uk *Surgical & medical equipment manufrs*

Nikon UK Ltd, Nikon House, 380 Richmond Road, Kingston upon Thames, Surrey, KT2 5PR Tel: (020) 8247 1718 Fax: (020) 8541 4584 *Photographic equipment distributors*

Nikwax Ltd, Unit B, Durgates Industrial Estate, Wadhurst, East Sussex, TN5 6DF Tel: (01892) 786400 Fax: (01892) 783748 E-mail: sales@nikwax.co.uk *Waterproofing product suppliers*

Nilfisk Northern Ireland Ltd, Unit 9, 48 Duncrue Street, Belfast, BT3 9AR Tel: (028) 9074 1444 Fax: (028) 9075 4555 E-mail: sales@nilfix.co.uk *Advance cleaning solutions*

Nilfisk-ALTO, Bowerbank Way, Penrith, Cumbria, CA11 9BQ Tel: (01768) 868995 Fax: (01768) 864713 E-mail: sales.uk@nilfisk-alto.com *High pressure industrial cleaning equipment suppliers*

▶ Nim (Ltd Engineering), Yardley House, 100 Chase Park Road, Yardley Hastings, Northampton, NN7 1HF Tel: (01604) 696120 Fax: (01604) 696122 E-mail: info@nimltdengineering.com *Smoking shelters & workplace smoking control products manufrs*

Stuart Niman Ltd, Units 1-3 Mushroom Street, Leeds, LS9 7NB Tel: 0113-246 7575 Fax: 0113-246 7669 E-mail: sales@stuartniman.co.uk *Wholesalers of children's clothes & baby wear*

Nimbus Laboratories Ltd, Lower Farm Road, Moulton Park Industrial Estate, Northampton, NN3 6XF Tel: (01604) 646411 Fax: (01604) 647375 E-mail: keith@nimbus-labs.co.uk *Contract soap & toiletry manufrs*

Nimbus Meters, 20 2a Ringwood Road, Eastbourne, East Sussex, BN22 8TA Tel: (01323) 639609 *Meter distributors*

Nimbus Products (Sheffield) Ltd, Julian Way, Tyler Street Industrial Estate, Sheffield, S9 1GD Tel: 0114-243 2362 Fax: 0114-243 5046 E-mail: sales@nimbusproducts.co.uk *Towing equipment distributors enamel cookware distributors*

Nimgrove Ltd, 8 Anglesey Business Park, Littleworth Road, Cannock, Staffordshire, WS12 1NR Tel: (01543) 426926 Fax: (01543) 426872 E-mail: sales@nimgrove.co.uk *Sheet metalwork engineers*

Nimlok Ltd, Nimlok House, 45 Booth Drive, Park Farm Industrial Estate, Wellingborough, Northamptonshire, NN8 6NL Tel: (01933) 409409 Fax: (01933) 409451 E-mail: info@nimlok.co.uk *Modular display system manufrs*

▶ Nimmo Industrial Buildings, 2 St. Anns Street, King's Lynn, Norfolk, PE30 1LT Tel: (01553) 775463 Fax: (01553) 775463 *Steel buildings manufrs*

Nimrod Fire Protection Ltd, Unit 1, Lower Soldridge Business Park, Soldridge Road, Medstead, Alton, Hampshire, GU34 5JF Tel: (01420) 561117 Fax: (01420) 561131 *Fire alarm & extinguisher installation services*

Nimrod Reflectives, Rushton Spencer, Macclesfield, Cheshire, SK11 0RN Tel: (01260) 226600 Fax: (01260) 226699 *Cycle equipment manufrs*

▶ Nimrod Transport, Kirktonlees, Castleton Road, Auchterarder, Perthshire, PH3 1JS Tel: (01764) 664400 Fax: (01764) 663371

▶ Nimulus Sound & Light, Ring Road, West Park, Leeds, LS16 6RA Tel: 0113-230 5222 E-mail: info@nimulus.co.uk *Lighting & sound production & hire*

Nine Hundred Communications, White Rose Way, Doncaster, South Yorkshire, DN4 5JH Tel: (01302) 368866 Fax: (01302) 340363 E-mail: sales@gbcomms.co.uk *Radio telephone contractors* Also at: Dunfermline & London

Nine Oaks, Craigfryn, Oakford, Llanarth, Dyfed, SA47 0RW Tel: (01545) 580482 *Trout & coarse fishery suppliers*

Ninefields Holdings Ltd, 1 & 2 Bruce Grove, Heron Trading Estate, Wickford, Essex, SS11 8DB Tel: (01268) 732148 Fax: (01268) 764394 E-mail: info@ninefields.co.uk *Injection mouldings plastic manufacturers & toolmakers*

▶ Nineplus Ltd, Unit 1b, Goonhavern Industrial Estate, Truro, Cornwall, TR4 9QL Tel: (01872) 572280 Fax: (01872) 572280

▶ Nineteen to the Dozen Ltd, Evesham House Business Centre, 48-52 Silver Street, Dursley, Gloucestershire, GL11 4ND Tel: (0845) 0701925 Fax: (0845) 0701926 E-mail: info@2gui4u.com *Marketing & website design services*

▶ NINS Trading (UK) Ltd, Unit 6, Penllwyn Gwent Industrial Estate, Saville Road, Ogmore V, Bridgend, Mid Glamorgan, CF32 7AX Tel: (01656) 842400 Fax: (01656) 842888 E-mail: ndjokic@nins.co.uk *Manufacturers of palisade fencing, brass*

Niphos Metal Finishing Co. Ltd, 25 Hope Street, Crewe, CW2 7DR Tel: (01270) 214081 Fax: (01270) 214089 *Electroplaters services*

Niplast Tanks, 187 Higher Hillgate, Stockport, Cheshire, SK1 3JG Tel: 0161-477 6777 Fax: 0161-429 8413 E-mail: contactus@niplast.com *Plastic tank designers*

Nippon Antenna Europe, Venture House, Bone Lane, Newbury, Berkshire, RG14 5SH Tel: (01635) 30001 Fax: (01635) 35406 E-mail: nae@nippon-antenna.co.uk *Car radio aerial distributors*

Nippon Distribution Ltd, 8c Reddicap Trading Estate, Sutton Coldfield, West Midlands, B75 7BU Tel: 0121-311 0313 Fax: 0121-311 0338 E-mail: nippondis@hotmail.com *Japanese starters & alternators distributors*

▶ Nippon Express UK Ltd, Unit 5110, Hunter Boulevard, Magna Park, Lutterworth, Leicestershire, LE17 4XN Tel: (01455) 205031 Fax: (01455) 558473

▶ Nippon Gohsei UK, Saltend, Hull, HU12 8DS Tel: (01482) 333320 Fax: (01482) 309332 *Chemical manufrs*

Nippon Kaiji Kyokai, Finsbury Circus House, 12-15 Finsbury Circus, London, EC2M 7EB Tel: (020) 7621 0963 Fax: (020) 7626 0383 E-mail: ln@classnk.or.jp *Registry of shipping*

▶ Nippon Oil (Europe), 15 Eldon Street, London, EC2M 7LD Tel: (020) 7309 6971 Fax: (020) 7309 6969 E-mail: info@eneos.co.uk *Oils & lubricants*

Nirmal Razai Mart & Co. Ltd, Carlisle Terrace, Bradford, West Yorkshire, BD8 8AT Tel: (01274) 775757 Fax: (01274) 771611 *Duvet manufrs*

Nisbets plc, Fourth Way, Bristol, BS11 8TB Tel: (0845) 1405555 Fax: (0845) 1435555 E-mail: sales@nisbets.co.uk *Catering equipment suppliers*

Nisha Wear Ltd, 215-216 Bradford Street, Deritend, Birmingham, B12 0RG Tel: 0121-773 6060 Fax: 0121-773 5573 *Banqueting suite*

Nissei Asb Ltd, 2 Milnyard Square, Bakewell Road, Orton Southgate, Peterborough, PE2 6GX Tel: (01733) 233544 Fax: (01733) 235647 E-mail: capsales@nisseiasb.co.uk *Plastics bottle moulding machinery*

▶ Nissen Packaging Ltd, Unit 31 Jubilee Trade Centre, Jubilee Road, Letchworth Garden City, Hertfordshire, SG6 1SP Tel: (01462) 676262 Fax: (01462) 481075 E-mail: info@nissenpackaging.co.uk *Packaging equipment manufrs*

▶ Nite International, Magnolia House, 19 Stour Road, Christchurch, Dorset, BH23 1PL Tel: 01202 487757 Fax: 01202 483836 E-mail: sales@niteproducts.com *Manufacturers & distributors of timepieces*

▶ Nite Life, 37 Huntly Street, Aberdeen, AB10 1TJ Tel: (01224) 561110 Fax: (01224) 561110 *Sexy clothes, shoes & exotic dancewear retail & wholesale*

Nitec Solutions, Unit 9 Technology Park, Belfast Road, Muckamore, Antrim, BT41 1QS Tel: (028) 9442 7000 Fax: (028) 9442 7030 E-mail: support@nitec.com *Computer support services*

Nitram Vacuum Heat Treatments Company Ltd, Pump Lane Industrial Estate, Silverdale Road, Hayes, Middlesex, UB3 3BN Tel: (020) 8573 5111 Fax: (020) 8756 1023 E-mail: enquiries@nitramvacuum.co.uk *Vacuum heat treatment specialists*

Nitronics Ltd, Nitronics House, The Maltings Centre, Station Road, Sawbridgeworth, Hertfordshire, CM21 9JX Tel: (01279) 307555 Fax: (01279) 307700 E-mail: sales@nitronics.co.uk *Electronic component distributors*

Nittan (UK) Ltd, Hipley Street, Woking, Surrey, GU22 9LQ Tel: (01483) 769555 Fax: (01483) 756686 E-mail: sales@nittan.co.uk *Smoke detectors, alarms services*

Nitto Kohki Europe Co. Ltd, Unit 21, Empire Centre, Imperial Way, Watford, WD24 4TS Tel: (01923) 239005 Fax: (01923) 248815 E-mail: nitto-uk@jais.co.uk *Pneumatic tool, quick release coupling, pumps & tool distributors*

Nitto UK Ltd, Unit2 Berkshire Business Centre, Berkshire Drive, Thatcham, Berkshire, RG19 4EW Tel: (01635) 872172 Fax: (01635) 872332 E-mail: nitto_uk@nittoeur.com *Industrial adhesive tape manufrs*

▶ Nivek Design Ltd, 7 Kingston Avenue, Shoeburyness, Southend-on-Sea, SS3 8TS Tel: (01702) 292400 E-mail: kevin@nivekdesign.com *Web design*

▶ Niven Milk Haulage, Lockerbie Creamery, Lockerbie, Dumfriesshire, DG11 1LW Tel: (01387) 811694 Fax: (01387) 811400

Niweld Fabrications Ltd, Unit 18 Two Gates Trading Estate, Watling Street, Two Gates, Tamworth, Staffordshire, B77 5AE Tel: (01827) 285189 Fax: (01827) 282264 *Fabricators & constructional engineers*

▶ Nixen Master Ltd, Cromwell House, 5 Cromwell Street, Hounslow, TW3 3LQ Tel: 0208 5696102 E-mail: office@nixenmaster.com *We are a London based company with many years experience of internet technologies, specializing in creating and managing web sites.*Our team is highly qualified and experienced with strong web building, search engine optimization and online marketing skills...*

Nixon Engineering Ltd, 7 Peterfield Road, Kingstown Industrial Estate, Carlisle, CA3 0EY Tel: (01228) 523956 Fax: (01228) 401919 E-mail: eddie@nixoneng ltd.freeserve.co.uk *General & precision engineers*

Nixon Industrial Diamonds Ltd, Albion Industrial Estate, Endermere Road, Coventry, CV6 5RR Tel: (024) 7668 6069 Fax: (024) 7663 7213 E-mail: sales@nixondiamonds.co.uk *Industrial diamond manufrs*

John Nixon Ltd, 99 Camburn Street, Glasgow, G32 6AX Tel: 0141-763 1213 Fax: 0141-763 2005 *Hire company*

Nixon Knowles, Longwall Avenue, Nottingham, NG2 1LP Tel: 0115-986 5252 Fax: 0115-986 2198 E-mail: sales@nixonknowles.co.uk *Joinery manufrs* Also at: Doncaster, Mansfield, Melbourne & Worksop

NJ Goulandris Ltd, Berkeley Square House, Berkeley Square, London, W1J 6BE Tel: (020) 7304 4900 Fax: (020) 7304 4802 E-mail: general@njgoulandris.com *Ship brokers*

▶ Njini, 1 Dome Buildings, The Square, Richmond, Surrey, TW9 1DT Tel: (020) 8334 8760 Fax: (020) 8334 8761 *Computer software developers*

NKC Computers Ltd, Unit 22 Ogmore Crescent, Bridgend, Mid Glamorgan, CF31 3TE Tel: (01656) 655009 Fax: (01656) 669025 *Computer system builders*

NKC Conveyors UK Ltd, Sunrise Parkway, Linford Wood, Milton Keynes, MK14 6LS Tel: (01908) 695611 Fax: (01908) 694632 *Conveyor manufrs*

NL Windows, 12 Pollard Street, Lofthouse, Wakefield, West Yorkshire, WF3 3HG Tel: (01924) 823314 Fax: (01924) 871766 *Window manufrs*

NLG Analytical Ltd, Grimshaw Lane, Bollington, Macclesfield, Cheshire, SK10 5JB Tel: (01625) 574633 Fax: (01625) 574699 E-mail: sales@nlg_analytical.co.uk *Scientific equipment services*

▶ NLP Solutions, Alsa Wood House, Stansted, Essex, CM24 8SU Tel: 01279 817976 E-mail: sian@nlpsolutions.com *Business, Career and Personal Development - Training, Coaching, Mentoring and Facilitation for organisations, teams and individuals.*

▶ NMP Electrics, PO Box 136, Leeds, LS27 0ZR Tel: 0113-204 9381 Fax: 0113-204 9381 E-mail: nmpelectrics@aol.com *Electrical contractors specialising in inspection & testing*

▶ NNZ Ltd, 37 Market Place, Long Eaton, Nottingham, NG10 1JL Tel: 0115-972 7021 Fax: 0115-946 1375 E-mail: info@nnzuk.co.uk *Retailers of packaging*

No 1 Garage Equipment Ltd, Canon Pyon Road, Hereford, HR4 7RB Tel: (01432) 272594 Fax: (01432) 343534 *Garage equipment*

▶ No 1 Scaffolding Services Ltd, Swinbourne Road, Burnt Mills Industrial Estate, Basildon, Essex, SS13 1EF Tel: (01268) 724793 Fax: (01268) 725606 E-mail: enquiries@no1scaffolding.co.uk

▶ No Cables Necessary, 3 Crown House, Andover Road, Ludgershall, Andover, Hants, SP11 9LZ Tel: (01264) 395426 Fax: (01264) 395426 E-mail: lee.patterson4@ntlworld.com *We distribute a range of GSM wireless door intercoms.Access control can be fitted without the necessity of long cable runs.*

No Climb Products, 163 Dixons Hill Road, North Mymms, Hatfield, Hertfordshire, AL9 7JE Tel: (01707) 282760 Fax: (01707) 282777 E-mail: info@noclimb.com *Fire detector system test equipment*

▶ No Limits, 28, Grenville Road, London, N19 4EH Tel: (020) 7263 0328

▶ No Plan B Ltd, PO Box 2157, Bristol, BS99 7JY Tel: 0117-907 8530 E-mail: info@noplanb.co.uk *We are HR Consultants that can give HR and Personnel Advice to companies across the South West and South Wales from our Bristol office. We can provide an HR manager from as little as half a day per month up to 3 days per week. Either for a one off project such as a Contract of Employment or redudancy to something more regular like on going HR support.*

▶ No Wires Networks, 4 Laxton Close, Luton, LU2 8SJ Tel: (0845) 0093781 Fax: (0870) 1162823 E-mail: info@nowiresnetworks.co.uk *No Wires Networks provide all of your information Technology requirements. From Wireless networks that save on the expense of traditional wiring to proactive management of your PC's and Servers. With Free Callout and tailored support plans at great hourly rates were here to help.*

John Noad (Ceilings) Ltd, Bardfield Centre, Braintree Road, Great Bardfield, Braintree, Essex, CM7 4SL Tel: (01371) 811112 Fax: (01371) 811124 E-mail: enquiries@jnoad.co.uk *Suspended ceiling & air conditioning design contractors*

Noahs Ark Aquatics, 28 Shannon Way, Canvey Island, Essex, SS8 0PD Tel: (01268) 514001 Fax: (01268) 693064 *Bavarian & aquatic pond manufrs*

H.F. Noakes (Ceilings) Ltd, 355 Railway Arches, Laburnum St, London, E2 8BB Tel: (020) 7739 9304 Fax: (020) 7739 3424 *Reproduction furniture*

Noakes T Partners Cold Stores, Goudhurst Road, Horsmonden, Tonbridge, Kent, TN12 8AY Tel: (01892) 722682 Fax: (01892) 723557 E-mail: admin@noakes-coldstores.co.uk *Warehousing, landlords*

Nobel Electronics Ltd, Tudor Cottages, Footscray High Street, Sidcup, Kent, DA14 5HN Tel: (020) 8309 0500 Fax: (020) 8302 7901 E-mail: nicknoakes.nobel@idnetfreemail.co.uk *Electronic Cable Assemblies or Harnesses, Data Cable Assemblies, Potentiometers, Power Resistors, Negative Temperature Coefficient (NTC) Thermistors, Positive Temperature Coefficient (PTC) Thermistors, Trimmers available from Nobel Electronics based in Sidcup, Kent. Click the links below to visit our website*

▶ Nobel Enterprises, P O Box 2, Stevenston, Ayrshire, KA20 3LN Tel: (01294) 487000 Fax: (01294) 487111

Nobel Fire Systems Ltd, Unit 6, Southgate Industrial Estate, Green Lane, Heywood, Lancashire, OL10 1ND Tel: (01706) 625777 Fax: (01706) 625325 E-mail: info@nobel-fire-systems.com *Nobel Fire Systems offers a comprehensive range of services, from risk-based analysis, consultation and design to distribution and installation, on a wide variety of economically viable, environmentally sound and well established fire suppression products. Specialist areas include but are not restricted to: Nobel K-Series range - Kitchen and Cooking Facility Protection. Land and Marine based solutions.*

Noberne Doors Ltd, Lupton Street, Leeds, LS10 2QP Tel: 0113-277 8577 Fax: 0113-277 2049 E-mail: nobernedoors@cs.com *Fire door manufrs*

Alexander Noble & Sons Ltd, Boatsbuilders, Girvan, Ayrshire, KA26 9HL Tel: (01465) 712223 Fax: (01465) 715089 E-mail: noble@boatbuilders.fsbusiness.co.uk *Boat builders*

Noble Computer Services, 9 Newton Road, Ipswich, IP3 8HE Tel: (01473) 424342 Fax: (01473) 424466 E-mail: info@noble-online.co.uk *Computer installation, network design & configuration*

Noble Denton Consultants Ltd, Noble House, 39 Tabernacle Street, London, EC2A 4AA Tel: (020) 7812 8700 Fax: (020) 7812 8701 E-mail: marketing@nobledenton.co.uk *Marine, offshore consultants & consulting engineers services*

Noble Drilling UK Ltd, Wellheads Road, Farburn Industrial Estate, Dyce, Aberdeen, AB21 7HG Tel: (01224) 401600 Fax: (01224) 771176 E-mail: mpope@noblecorp.com *Oilwell drilling contractors & engineers*

Noble Engineering Ltd, Greenhey Place, Skelmersdale, Lancashire, WN8 9SA Tel: (01695) 724764 Fax: (01695) 557573 E-mail: mail@nobleeng.co.uk *Conveyor systems/ mechanical handling & special purpose machinery*

Noble Fuels, Hutton Rudby, Skutterskelfe, Yarm, Cleveland, TS15 0JR Tel: (01642) 711401 Fax: (01642) 711547 E-mail: sales@noblefuels.sagehost.co.uk *Oil, fuel & lubricant distribs*

Noble Furs Regent Street Ltd, 3 New Burlington Place, London, W1S 2HR Tel: (020) 8734 6394 Fax: (020) 7734 6396 E-mail: enquiries@noblefurs.com *Furriers retail & manufrs*

Noble Gates Ltd, Ivy House Farm, Whiston, Penkridge, Stafford, ST19 5QH Tel: (01785) 714148 Fax: (01785) 714148 *Gates & railings manufrs*

▶ Noble Health & Safety Consultancy Ltd, Ermington Mill, Ermington, Ivybridge, Devon, PL21 9NT Tel: (0870) 8504439 Fax: (01548) 831464 E-mail: enquiries@noblegroup.uk.com *Asbestos surveying, training & health & safety*

Noble Heating (U K) Ltd, Unit 19-21, Small Heath Trading Estate, Armoury Road, Birmingham, B11 2RJ Tel: 0121-773 0114 Fax: 0121-766 6589 E-mail: info@noboheatinguk.com *Electric heaters*

Noble Integrated Systems, 211-213 Eaton Road, West Derby, Liverpool, L12 2AG Tel: 0151-228 8364 Fax: 0151-280 5145 *Security system installers*

Noble Masts, A Shed, Canons Road, Bristol, BS1 5UH Tel: 0117-929 7450 Fax: 0117-925 6033 *Wooden masts manufrs*

Noble Paul Photographic, Victoria Road, Unit 4, Burgess Hill, West Sussex, RH15 9LH Tel: (01444) 232367 E-mail: info@pnoblephoto.net *Commercial & industrial photographing services*

Noble Polythene Ltd, Unit 9-11, Prince Close, Andover, Hampshire, SP10 5LL Tel: (01264) 332459 Fax: (01264) 332874 *Polythene & packaging suppliers*

Robert Noble Ltd, March Street, Peebles, EH45 8ER Tel: (01721) 724311 Fax: (01721) 721893 E-mail: enquiries@robert-noble.co.uk *Woven apparel fabric manufrs*

Noble Russell Furniture Ltd, Station Road, Uppingham, Rutland, Leicestershire, LE15 9TX Tel: (01572) 821591 Fax: (01572) 823434 E-mail: sales@noblerussell.co.uk *Established in 1992, Noble Russell are design professionals specialising in the creation of contemporary furniture. They have grown the business to develop a highly skilled team in their workshop, enabling them to produce quality hand made commercial furniture. They are based in the picturesque village of Uppingham in Rutland, offering chairs, stools, seating, tables, bespoke seating, design consultancy and bespoke manufacturing.*

Nobles Amusements, 9 Union Terrace, Bury Old Road, Salford, M7 4ZH Tel: 0161-740 2367 Fax: 0161-720 7201 *Amusement arcade suppliers*

Nobles Engineering Solutions Ltd, 11 Mallard Close, Earls Barton, Northampton, NN6 0JF Tel: (01604) 810695 Fax: (01604) 812586 *Sheet metalwork dust extraction & ventilation engineers*

Noblestar Systems Ltd, Liberty House, 222 Regent Street, London, W1B 5TR Tel: (020) 7297 2038 Fax: (020) 7297 2142 E-mail: info@noblestar.co.uk *IT consultants*

Noblet Refrigeration, Unit 10 Kenyons Farm, Gough Lane, Bamber Bridge, Preston, PR5 6AQ Tel: (01772) 628828 Fax: (01772) 628417 E-mail: nobletref@btconnect.com *Refrigeration engineers*

Noconn Electrical Contacts Ltd, Unit 71, Storforth Lane Trading Estate, Chesterfield, Derbyshire, S41 0QZ Tel: (01246) 209556 Fax: (01246) 201440 E-mail: info@electricalcontacts.com *Electrical contact manufrs*

▶ Nodal Engineering Ltd, Riverside House, Riverside Drive, Aberdeen, AB11 7LH Tel: 01224 224360 Fax: 01224 224301 E-mail: info@nodalengineering.com *Electrical engineering, design & implementation services*

▶ Node Design, 43 Blaker Street, Brighton, BN2 0JJ Tel: (01273) 299119 Fax: (01273) 603162 E-mail: info@node.uk.com *Freelance & graphic designer*

▶ Noel's Taxi's, 60 The Haystack, Daventry, Northamptonshire, NN11 0NZ Tel: (01327) 871605 *Taxi service based in Daventry and is none smoking car and driver*

Nofotec Co. Ltd, 72-74 Westdale Lane, Carlton, Nottingham, NG4 3NF Tel: 0115-987 6696 Fax: 0115-940 0070 E-mail: info@nofotec.co.uk *Precision engineers*

Noico Ltd, Patrick House, Station Road, Hook, Hampshire, RG27 9HU Tel: (01256) 766207 Fax: (01256) 768413 E-mail: sales@noico.co.uk *Acoustic consultants/industrial noise control equipment manufrs*

Noirit Ltd, 17-18 Hatherton Street, Walsall, WS4 2LE Tel: (01922) 625471 Fax: (01922) 722339 E-mail: sales@noirit.com *Seat stick & fastenings manufrs*

Noise Insulation & Measurement Services, High Dardale House, Slaggyford, Brampton, Cumbria, CA8 7NW Tel: (01434) 381394 Fax: (01434) 382634 E-mail: noise@cwcom.net *Acoustic consultants & engineers*

Noise & Pulsation Control Ltd, 5 King Edwards Road, Ruislip, Middlesex, HA4 7AE Tel: (01895) 676215 Fax: (01895) 676215 E-mail: noiseandpulsationuk@btinternet.com *Noise control services*

Noise Seal Ltd, Unit 20 Digby Drive, Leicester Road Industrial Estate, Melton Mowbray, Leicestershire, LE13 0RQ Tel: (01664) 480678 Fax: (01664) 480678 E-mail: sales@noiseseal.com *Noise control vision panel & window manufrs*

Noise & Vibration Engineering Ltd, 1 Rothesay Avenue, London, SW20 8JU Tel: (020) 8542 9226 Fax: (020) 8540 8481 E-mail: enquiries@noise-vibration.co.uk *Noise & vibration consultancy services*

Nokell Fabrications Ltd, 18 Radway Industrial Estate, Radway Road, Shirley, Solihull, West Midlands, B90 4NR Tel: 0121-705 4771 Fax: 0121-711 3681 *Sheet metal fabricators*

Nokia (U K) Ltd, Summet Avenue, Farmborough, Farmborough, Farnborough, Hampshire, GU14 0NG Tel: (01252) 866000 Fax: (01252) 866001 *Cellular radio telephone equipment*

Nokia UK Ltd, Lancaster House, Lancaster Way, Ermine Business Park, Huntingdon, Cambridgeshire, PE29 6YJ Tel: (0870) 0555777 Fax: (01480) 435111 E-mail: firstname.surname@nokia.com *Telecommunication services*

Nolan Davis Contracting Ltd, Devas House, 7A Browning Avenue, Thornhil, Southampton, SO19 6PW Tel: (023) 8046 5000 Fax: (023) 8047 7620 E-mail: info@nd-contracting.co.uk *Building contractors*

▶ Nolan Electrical Services Ltd, 25 Palmerston Road, Melton Mowbray, Leicestershire, LE13 0SS Tel: (01664) 564223 E-mail: shaun.nolan6@btinternet.com

▶ Samantha Nolan, 18 Walton Road, Southampton, SO19 0JB Tel: (023) 8042 0916 *Crazy lenses and color contact lenses for fashion and cosmetic use, all lenses have been reduced in price, world-wide delivery.*

Nolene Ltd, Brunel Road, Newton Abbot, Devon, TQ12 4PB Tel: (01626) 333800 Fax: (01626) 368168 E-mail: info@nolene.co.uk *PVC welding folders & binders manufrs*

Nomad plc, Rockingham Road, Market Harborough, Leicestershire, LE16 7QE Tel: (01858) 464878 Fax: (01858) 410175 E-mail: nomadsolutions@aol.com *Manufacturers of bespoke cases & containers*

Nomad Travellers Store & Medical Centre, 3-4 Wellington Terrace, Turnpike Lane, London, N8 0PX Tel: (0845) 3104470 Fax: (020) 8889 9529 *Camping & health equipment manufrs*

Nomadic Display, The Nomadic House, 71 St Johns Road, Isleworth, Middlesex, TW7 6XQ Tel: 0121-333 4956 Fax: (020) 8326 5522 E-mail: hqsales@nomadicdisplay.co.uk *Portable & modular display systems manufrs*

Nomax Ltd, 22 Hyde Street, Winchester, Hampshire, SO23 7DR Tel: (01962) 840850 Fax: (01962) 841512 E-mail: quote@nomax.co.uk Principal Export Areas: Worldwide *Boiler tubes stockholders*

Nomeq Ltd, Unit 25-26 North St Industrial Estate, Droitwich, Worcestershire, WR9 8JB Tel: (01905) 795005 Fax: (01905) 796655 E-mail: info@nomeq.co.uk *Health care & rehabilitation equipment distributors*

Nomis Ltd, 146a Frimley Road, Camberley, Surrey, GU15 2QN Tel: (01276) 683449 Fax: (01276) 684799 E-mail: sales@nomislimited.com *Customer relationship management & sales performance specialists*

▶ Nomix Enviro Ltd, Portland Building, Portland Street, Staple Hill, Bristol, BS16 4PS Tel: 0117-957 4574 Fax: 0117-956 3461 E-mail: info@nomix.co.uk *Supplies weed killing & ant graffiti products*

Nomoco Ltd, 77 Shaftesbury Avenue, Roundhay, Leeds, LS8 1DR Tel: (0870) 7001925 Fax: (0870) 7002024 E-mail: contactus@warmco.co.uk *Heating & plumbing merchants*

▶ NoMoreBlockedGutters, 11 Victoria Ave, Scotforth, Lancaster, LA1 4SY Tel: 01524 849156 E-mail: nomoreblockedgutters@gmail.com *A system where 1 metre lengths of gutter brushes are inserted into an existing gutter to prevent blockages caused by the accumulation of leaves,twigs and other debris*

▶ Non Drip Plumbing & Heating, 2 Bosworth Way, March, Cambridgeshire, PE15 9BW Tel: (07952) 669008 E-mail: james@nondrip.co.uk *Corgi registered Gas Engineers*Institute of Plumbing & heating Engineering*For all types of Plumbing Heating & domestic natural gas work*

Non Entry Systems Ltd, Bruce Road, Fforestfach, Swansea, SA5 4HS Tel: (01792) 580455 Fax: (01792) 578610 E-mail: sales@nonentrysystems.com *Oil & nuclear waste handling equipment & oil systems design & manufrs*

Non Executive Directorship Exchange, Hurst House, City Road, Radnage, High Wycombe, Buckinghamshire, HP14 4DW Tel: (01494) 483728 E-mail: nedexchange@netscape.net *Non executive directors*

Non Ferrous Founders Ltd, Paudy Lane, Thrussington, Leicester, LE7 4TA Tel: (01509) 889483 Fax: (01509) 889484 E-mail: nfsleicester@aol.com *Casting manufrs*

Non Ferrous Stockholders Ltd, Dock Meadow Drive, Wolverhampton, WV4 6LE Tel: (01902) 353747 Fax: (01902) 491030 E-mail: info@non-ferrous.co.uk *Manufactures & Distributors of High Performance Strip/Sheet & Drawn Wire/Tube products.*Nickel, Nickel Alloy,Copper Nickel,Nickel Silver, Phos. Bronze, Stainless Steel, Aluminium*

Non Standard Socket Screw Ltd, Unit 2, Liddall Way, Horton Road, West Drayton, Middlesex, UB7 8PG Tel: (01895) 430003 Fax: (01895) 430004 E-mail: salestsa@aol.com *Engineers fasteners & socket screws*

Non Standard Socket Screws Ltd, 358-364 Farm Street, Birmingham, B19 2TZ Tel: 0121-515 0121 Fax: 0121-523 4440 E-mail: sales@nssocketscrews.com *Distributors & stockholders of bolts & nuts* Also at: London & Stockport

▶ Nonaghan Grinding Services, 1 Sandow Commercial Estate, Sandow Crescent, Hayes, Middlesex, UB3 4QH Tel: (020) 8589 9898 Fax: (020) 8589 9898 *Knife sharpening services*

Non-Corrosive Control Lines Ltd, 25 Blake House, Gunwharf Quays, Portsmouth, PO1 3TH Tel: (023) 9273 1178 Fax: (023) 9273 1196 E-mail: nccl@btconnect.com *Stainless & nickel chrome alloy tubes & compression fittings manufrs*

Nonpareil Taps & Dies Ltd, 15 Rookwood Way, Haverhill, Suffolk, CB9 8PB Tel: (01440) 703625 Fax: (01440) 712101 E-mail: info@nonpareiltapsanddies.co.uk *Tap & die manufrs*

▶ Nonslip Safety Products, 5-8 Chilford Court, Rayne Road, Braintree, Essex, CM7 2QS Tel: (01376) 333315 Fax: (01376) 551849 E-mail: info@nonslipsp.co.uk *Distribution non slip safety products*

Nor Chem Supplies, Loch Flemington, Inverness, IV2 7QR Tel: (01667) 462500 Fax: (01667) 462173 *Cleaning & hygiene suppliers & washroom services*

Nor Cote International Ltd, 7 Warrior Park, Eagle Close, Chandler's Ford, Eastleigh, Hampshire, SO53 4NF Tel: (023) 8027 0542 Fax: (023) 8027 0543 E-mail: sales@norcote.com *UV screen & flexo ink manufrs*

▶ Nor E X Hire Rail Ltd, Draycott Cross Road, Brookhouse Industrial Estate, Cheadle, Stoke-On-Trent, ST10 1PN Tel: (01538) 751777

Noral Ltd, Unit 1 The Oaks, Mill Farm Courtyard, Stratford Road, Beechampton, Milton Keynes, MK19 6DS Tel: (01908) 561818 Fax: (01908) 569785 E-mail: lighting@noral-gb.co.uk *Lighting manufrs*

Norba (UK) Ltd, 14-16 Thomas Road, Wooburn Industrial Park, Wooburn Green, High Wycombe, Buckinghamshire, HP10 0PE Tel: (01628) 535900 Fax: (01628) 530381 E-mail: sales@norbauk.com *Food ingredients suppliers*

Norbain SD Ltd, Eskdale Road, Winnersh, Wokingham, Berkshire, RG41 5TS Tel: 0118-944 0123 Fax: 0118-9440999 E-mail: james.smith@norbain.co.uk *Security systems distribs*

▶ Norbake Services Ltd, 8 Lady Ann Business Park, Lady Ann Road, Batley, West Yorkshire, WF17 0PS Tel: (01924) 442662 Fax: (01924) 420087 E-mail: sales@norbake.co.uk *Bakery equipment & catering suppliers*

Norbar Torque Tools Ltd, Beaumont Rd, Banbury, Oxfordshire, OX16 1XJ Tel: (01295) 753600 Fax: (01295) 753609 E-mail: sales@norbar.com Purchasing Contact: S. Chambers Sales Contact: P. Brodey Principal Export Areas: Worldwide *Norbar was the first company in the UK to manufacture torque wrenches and is now one of the largest in the World dedicated to the field of torque control. The product range includes torque wrenches, hand operated torque multipliers, pneumatic torque wrenches and a comprehensive range of torque testing and torque calibration equipment including torque transducers, torque sensors, rotary torque transducers and torque meters. Torque calibration services, accredited to local standards, are available from Norbar's companies in the UK (UKAS), USA, Australia and Singapore. Norbar are also expert in the field of ultrasonic bolt testing. Ultrasound is used to measure the change in length of the bolt during the tightening process and from this the induced tension in the bolt can be precisely calculated*

Norbeck Data Ltd, Lenten House, The Gravel, Trowbridge, Wiltshire, BA14 6QL Tel: (01225) 782865 Fax: (01225) 783284 *Computer services & data cabling manufrs*

Norbert Dentressangle, Billington Road, Leighton Buzzard, Bedfordshire, LU7 9HH Tel: (01525) 243900 Fax: (01525) 382066 *Road transport, haulage & freight services*

Norbord Ltd, Hill Village, Nadder Lane, South Molton, Devon, EX36 4HP Tel: (01769) 575350 Fax: (01769) 574848 Principal Export Areas: Worldwide *Chipboard & plywood manufrs*

Norbrook Exports Ltd, Camlough Road, Newry, County Down, BT35 6JP Tel: (028) 3026 4435 Fax: (028) 3025 1141 E-mail: enquiries@norbrook.co.uk *Pharmaceutical laboratory services*

Norbulk Shipping (UK) Ltd, 68 Glassford Street, Glasgow, G1 1UP Tel: 0141-552 3000 Fax: 0141-559 5250 E-mail: mail@norbulkshipping.com *Ship managers* Also at: London EC3

Norbury Fencing & Building Supplies Ltd, 28 Marshgate Drive, Hertford, SG13 7AJ Tel: (01992) 554327 Fax: (01992) 505978 E-mail: sales@norburyfencing.co.uk *Building materials merchants*

Norbury (Pallets) Ltd, Unit 28, Marshgate Drive, Hertford, SG13 7AJ Tel: (01992) 504236 Fax: (01992) 584978 E-mail: sales@norburypallets.com *Pallet, fencing & garden access manufrs*

Norcall Ltd, Victoria Chambers, 1 Victoria Road, Northampton, NN1 5EB Tel: (01604) 234333 Fax: (01604) 603866 *Mobile communications*

Norcliffe & Young, F Mill, Dean Clough Industrial Park, Halifax, West Yorkshire, HX3 5AJ Tel: (01422) 355830 *Joiners*

Norcontrol It Ltd, 12 High Street, Winterbourne, Bristol, BS36 1JN Tel: (01454) 774466 Fax: (01454) 774488 *Marine situation awareness systems manufrs*

Norcot Engineering Ltd, Richmond House, Hill Street, Ashton-under-Lyne, Lancashire, OL7 0PZ Tel: 0161-339 9361 Fax: 0161-343 3069 *Epoxy powder coating services*

Norcot Engineering Ltd, Unit 1, Windsor Road, Bedford, MK42 9SU Tel: (01234) 364324 Fax: (01234) 355915 E-mail: jade.operations@btconnect.com *Precision engineers*

Norcott Technologies Ltd, Brookfield House, Tarporley Road, Norcott Brook, Warrington, WA4 4EA Tel: (01925) 247600 Fax: (01925) 247610 E-mail: sales@norcott.co.uk *Electronic manufacturing services*

Norcraft Timber Products, Unit B9, Hamar Close, Tyne Tunnel Trading Estate, North Shields, Tyne & Wear, NE29 7XB Tel: 0191-200 8383 *Pine furniture producers & manufrs*

Norcrane Ltd, Unit E, Bedewell Industrial Park, Hebburn, Tyne & Wear, NE31 2XQ Tel: 0191-489 5066 Fax: 0191-483 9702 E-mail: norcrane@norcrane.co.uk *Overhead cranes & lifting equipment manufrs*

Norcroft Equestrian Development, 1 Norton Road, Loddon, Norwich, NR14 6JN Tel: (01508) 520743 Fax: (01508) 528879 *Equestrian buildings & fencing developments*

Nord Gear Ltd, 11 Barton Lane, Abingdon, Oxfordshire, OX14 3NB Tel: (01235) 534404 Fax: (01235) 534414 E-mail: info@nord.uk.com *Electric geared motors & inverters*

Nord Gear Ltd, Riverview House, Friarton Road, Perth, PH2 8DF Tel: (01738) 472023 Fax: (01738) 628855 E-mail: info@nord-uk.com *Transitions*

Nord Hydraulic Ltd, Unit Lkr3 L & M Business Park, Norman Road, Altrincham, Cheshire, WA14 4ES Tel: 0161-928 1199 Fax: 0161-941 5667 E-mail: david@nordhydraulic.co.uk *Valve manufrs*

▶ Nordal Fire Protection Services Ltd, Nordalmere House, 46 Midland Road, Raunds, Northamptonshire, NN9 6JF Tel: (01933) 625407 Fax: (01933) 626939E-mail: sales@nordal.co.uk *Supply fire safety equipment & training*

Norden Agricultural Contractors, Paper House Farm, Ashworth Road, Rochdale, Lancashire, OL11 5UP Tel: (01706) 642727 *Agricultural contractors*

Norden UK Ltd, Church Street, Baldock, Hertfordshire, SG7 5AF Tel: (01462) 895245 Fax: (01462) 895683 E-mail: enquiries@norden.co.uk *Tube filling machinery manufrs*

▶ Nordet Pins, PO Box 571, Solihull, West Midlands, B90 4WP Tel: 0121-247 5191 E-mail: mailroom@nordet.co.uk *Wholesale for pins & sell*

Nordic I D Ltd, Nordic House Clifford Mill, Clifford Road, Clifford Chambers, Stratford-upon-Avon, Warwickshire, CV37 8HW Tel: (01789) 294799 Fax: (01789) 294739 *Distribution of hand held scanners*

Nordic Marine Ltd, Unit 15 Prince Consort Industrial Estate, Hebburn, Tyne & Wear, NE31 1EH Tel: 0191-483 8370 Fax: 0191-483 2330 *General engineers*

Nordic Saunas Ltd, Unit 5, Fairview Industrial Estate, Holland Road, Oxted, Surrey, RH8 9BD Tel: (01883) 732400 Fax: (01883) 716970 E-mail: info@nordic.co.uk *Sauna, bathroom & steamroom equipment*

Nordiko Technical Services Ltd, Butterick Building, New Lane, Havant, Hampshire, PO9 2ND Tel: (023) 9248 8200 Fax: (023) 9248 8218 E-mail: enquiries@nordiko-tech.com *High vacuum equipment manufrs*

Nordis Industries, Cornhill Close, Lodge Farm Industrial Estate, Northampton, NN5 7UB Tel: (01604) 596910 Fax: 01604 758470 *Sign manufacturers, contractors & suppliers*

Nordot Engineering Services Ltd, Rosscliffe Road, Ellesmere Port, CH65 3AS Tel: 0151-355 4678 Fax: 0151-357 2450 *Pipework fabricators*

Nordsea Ltd, Captain Clarke Road, Hyde, Cheshire, SK14 4QG Tel: 0161-366 3010 Fax: 0161-366 3011 E-mail: nordsea@compuserve.com *Combustion equipment manufrs*

Nordson (UK) Ltd, Ashurst Drive, Cheadle Heath, Stockport, Cheshire, SK3 0RY Tel: 0161-495 4200 Fax: 0161-428 6716 *Powder & paint spraying manufrs*

Nordson UK Ltd, Wenman Road, Thame, Oxfordshire, OX9 3SW Tel: (01844) 264500 Fax: (01844) 215358 E-mail: salesoxf@uk.nordson.com *Adhesive application distributors*

Norec Ltd, Norec House, Fall Bank Industrial Estate, Dodworth, Barnsley, South Yorkshire, S75 3LS Tel: (01226) 730440 Fax: (01226) 730688 E-mail: sales@norec.ltd.uk *Project management consultants & management services*

Norex Forest Products, Walton Street, Walton on the Hill, Tadworth, Surrey, KT20 7RR Tel: (01737) 814567 Fax: (01737) 217524 E-mail: sales@norex.co.uk *Hardwood products distribution*

▶ Norfield Construction Ltd, Lower Farm House, Frankley Hill Lane, Birmingham, B32 4BE Tel: 0121-453 1202

Norfinish Engineering Ltd, Sleekburn Business Centre, West Sleekburn, Bedlington, Northumberland, NE22 7DD Tel: (01670) 855087 Fax: (01670) 855079 E-mail: info@norfinish.co.uk *Mass surface finishing/processes & equipment*

Norfolk Cabinet Makers Ltd, Park Farm Workshops, Beeston Lane, Beeston St. Andrew, Norwich, NR12 7BP Tel: (01603) 408904 Fax: (01603) 488718 E-mail: info@norfolkcabinetmakers.co.uk *Cabinet & wooden furniture manufrs*

Norfolk Chamber Of Commerce, 9 Norwich Business Park, Whiting Road, Norwich, NR4 6DJ Tel: (01603) 625977 Fax: (01603) 633032 E-mail: info@norfolkchamber.co.uk *Services to businesses* Also at: Great Yarmouth

▶ Norfolk Decking, 24 Parr Road, Norwich, NR3 2EF Tel: (01603) 469484 Fax: E-mail: pk.sayer@ntlworld.com *Timber decking design and construction.Paving Patios Fencing Turfing*

Norfolk Fasteners, Rash's Green, Dereham, Norfolk, NR19 1JG Tel: (01362) 696848 Fax: (01362) 695356 *Industrial fastener distributors*

Norfolk Feather Co. Ltd, Park Road, Diss, Norfolk, IP22 4AS Tel: (01379) 643187 Fax: (01379) 650413 E-mail: sales@norfolkfeathercompany.co.uk *Pillows, cushions & feather goods manufrs*

▶ Norfolk Frames Ltd, 26 Old Norwich Road, Marsham, Norwich, NR10 5PR Tel: (01263) 734469 Fax: (01263) 733058 E-mail: enquiries@norfolkframes.co.uk *Plastic windows*

Norfolk Greenhouses Ltd, Chiswick Avenue, Mildenhall, Bury St. Edmunds, Suffolk, IP28 7AZ Tel: (01638) 713418 Fax: (01638) 714715 E-mail: sales@norfolk-greenhouses.co.uk *Sheds & greenhouse manufrs*

Norfolk Gun Trading Co., 14 Greevegate, Hunstanton, Norfolk, PE36 6AA Tel: (01485) 533600 *Gunsmiths & outdoor clothing retailers*

Norfolk Heating Ltd, Prestige House, Salhouse Road, Norwich, NR7 9AR Tel: (01603) 429426 Fax: (01603) 424380 E-mail: nhlmech@aol.com *Heating engineers*

Norfolk Industries For The Blind, Oak Street, Norwich, NR3 3BP Tel: (01603) 667957 Fax: (01603) 624265 E-mail: sales@norfolk-industries.co.uk *Polyethylene coated wire goods*

Norfolk Lavender Ltd, Caley Mill, Lynn Road, Heacham, King's Lynn, Norfolk, PE31 7JE Tel: (01485) 570384 Fax: (01485) 571176 E-mail: admin@norfolk-lavender.co.uk *Fragrance distillers*

Norfolk Line, Transit 3, Westbank Road, Belfast, BT3 9JL Tel: (028) 9077 1122 Fax: (028) 9077 2645 E-mail: belfast@norfolkline.com *Road transport, haulage & freight services*

Norfolk Line Ltd, The Dock, Felixstowe, Suffolk, IP11 3UY Tel: (01394) 603614 Fax: (01394) 603608 E-mail: felixstowe@norfolkline.com *Road transport TIR*

▶ Norfolk Line, Middleton Avenue, Strutherhill Industrial Estate, Strutherhill Industrial Estate, Larkhall, Lanarkshire, ML9 2TL Tel: (01698) 552500 Fax: (01698) 552506

Norfolk Saw Services, Dog Lane, Horsford, Norwich, NR10 3DH Tel: (01603) 898695 Fax: (01603) 898695 E-mail: sales@norfolksawservices.co.uk *Saw & woodworking machinery services*

▶ Norfolk Scaffolding Service, Woodside, Fakenham Road, Morton on the Hill, Norwich, NR9 5SP Tel: (01603) 872183 Fax: (01603) 872293

▶ Norfolk Storage Equipment Ltd, 15 Maurice Gaymer Road, Attleborough, Norfolk, NR17 2QZ Tel: (01953) 458800 Fax: (01953) 458819 E-mail: sales@nsel.biz *Storage & mats handling systems & archive services*

Norfolk Textured Yarns Cromer Ltd, Holt Road, Cromer, Norfolk, NR27 9JW Tel: (01263) 513188 Fax: (01263) 515347 *Processors & merchandisers of synthetic fibres*

Norfolk Truck Enfield Ltd, Mollison Avenue, Enfield, Middlesex, EN3 7NE Tel: (020) 8804 1266 Fax: (020) 8443 2590 *Commercial vehicle dealers*

Norfolk & Waveney Enterprise Services, Queens Road, Great Yarmouth, Norfolk, NR30 3HT Tel: (01493) 850204 Fax: (01493) 330754 E-mail: enquiries@business-advice.co.uk *Enterprise agency*

Norfran Aluminium Ltd, West Chirton Trading Estate, North Shields, Tyne & Wear, NE29 7TY Tel: 0191-258 2611 Fax: 0191-257 1549 E-mail: jb@norfran.co.uk Principal Export Areas: Asia Pacific, Africa & North America *Diecastings, including pressure & aluminium alloy*

Norfran Products Ltd, Alveley Industrial Estate, Alveley, Bridgnorth, Shropshire, WV15 6HG Tel: (01746) 780919 Fax: (01746) 780297 E-mail: mail@norfran.com *Zinc & aluminium & alloy die casters manufrs*

▶ Norfrost Ltd, Unit 23 Industrial Estate, Evanton, Dingwall, Ross-Shire, IV16 9XJ Tel: (01349) 830037

Norgate Ltd, Unit 4b Newton Court, Wavertree Technology Park, Liverpool, L13 1EJ Tel: 0151-220 5556 Fax: 0151-254 1463 E-mail: sales@norgatetelecom.co.uk *Telecommunication equipment suppliers*

Norgine Ltd, New Road, Tiryberth, Hengoed, Mid Glamorgan, CF82 8SJ Tel: (01443) 812183 *Pharmaceutical manufrs*

Norgine Ltd, Chaplain House, Widewater Place, Moorhall Road, Uxbridge, Middlesex, UB9 6NS Tel: (01895) 826600 Fax: (01895) 825865 E-mail: enquiries@norgine.com *Pharmaceutical preparations manufrs* Also at: Hengoed

Norgren Ltd, Unit A3, Brookside Business Park, Greengate, Middleton, Manchester, M24 1GR Tel: 0161-655 7300 Fax: 0161-655 7373 E-mail: manchester@norgren.com *Pneumatic manufrs*

Norgren, Brookside Business Park, Greengate, Middleton, Manchester, M24 1GS Tel: (0800) 0560260 Fax: (0800) 0560261 E-mail: manchester@norgren.com *Norgren manufactures and distributes pneumatic components.* Also at: Lichfield (Head Office) & Manchester

Norhgate H R Ltd, Thorpe Park, Peterborough, PE3 6JY Tel: (01733) 555777 Fax: (01733) 312347 E-mail: enquiries@northgatehr.com *Human resources & payroll solutions services*

▶ Norian Mattress Manufacturers, Unit 4-6 Millfield, Chard, Somerset, TA20 2DA Tel: (01460) 239988

▶ Norish Ltd, P O Box 255, Dartford, DA1 9AL Tel: (0870) 7351318 Fax: (01322) 303470 E-mail: sales@norish.com *Head office and administration functions for the ambient and cold storage warehousing*

▶ Norish Plc, Block C, Walton Avenue, Felixstowe, Suffolk, IP11 3HH Tel: (01394) 675700 Fax: 01394 675440 E-mail: sales@norish.com *Third party food grade ambient warehousing providing a consolidation and picking service to importers, manufacturers, wholesalers, retailers and distributors*

▶ Norish Ltd, Station Lane, Shipton By Beningbrough, York, YO30 1BS Tel: (01904) 470523 Fax: (01904) 470580 E-mail: sales@norish.com *Third party food grade ambient warehousing providing a consolidation and picking service to importers, manufacturers, wholesalers, retailers and distributors*

▶ Norish Food Care, 1 Benfield Way, Braintree, Essex, CM7 3YS Tel: (01376) 347311 Fax: (01376) 550887 E-mail: sales@norish.com *Chilled & cold storage warehousing*

▶ Norish Food Care, Pedmore Road, Brierley Hill, West Midlands, DY5 1LJ Tel: (01384) 480858 Fax: (01384) 480425 E-mail: sales@norish.com *Chilled and frozen cold storage warehousing*

Norish Food Care Ltd, Northern Way, Bury St. Edmunds, Suffolk, IP32 6NL Tel: (01284) 763464 Fax: (01284) 768241 E-mail: enquiries@norish.com *Cold storage warehousing*

▶ Norish Food Care, Lympne Industrial Estate, Lympne, Hythe, Kent, CT21 4LR Tel: (01303) 233930 Fax: (01303) 233939 E-mail: sales@norish.com *Cold storage warehousing*

▶ Norish Food Care Ltd, Ash Road South, Wrexham Industrial Estate, Wrexham, Clwyd, LL13 9UG Tel: (01978) 660033 Fax: (01978) 660099 E-mail: sales@norish.com *Cold storage warehousing*

Norit UK Ltd, Clydesmill Place, Cambuslang Industrial Estate, Clydesmill Industrial Estate, Glasgow, G32 8RF Tel: 0141-641 8841 Fax: 0141-641 8411 E-mail: fisher.martin.nl@norit.com *Activated carbon manufrs*

Noritake (UK) Ltd, 26 Heathfield, Stacey Bushes, Milton Keynes, MK12 6HR Tel: (01908) 318446 Fax: (01908) 320932 E-mail: china@noritake.co.uk *Fine china earthenware tableware*

Norking Aluminium Ltd, Tickhill Road, Doncaster, South Yorkshire, DN4 8QG Tel: (01302) 855907 Fax: (01302) 310204 E-mail: sales@norking.com *Aluminium shop front windows & fittings manufrs*

Norland Burgess, 93-105 St. James Boulevard, Newcastle upon Tyne, NE1 4BW Tel: 0191-232 9722 Fax: 0191-232 9722 *Wholesale drapers*

▶ Norland Managed Services, Suite 3G, International House, Stanley Boulevard, Hamilton International Technology Park, Blantyre, Glasgow, G72 0BN Tel: (01698) 404720 Fax: (01698) 404721 *Property management*

Norland Managed Services Ltd, 454-460 Old Kent Road, London, SE1 5AG Tel: (020) 7231 8888 Fax: (020) 7231 7547 E-mail: reception@norlandmanagedservices.co.uk *Building services engineers*

▶ Norlaw, Unit 6 Blackwall Trading Estate, Lanrick Road, Poplar, London, London, E14 0JP Tel: 020 7093 3555 Fax: 020 7093 3777 E-mail: sales@norlaw.co.uk *Printing *Finishing including stiching, shrinkwrapping, kiss-cutting, die-cutting, folding, trimming, gluing, making-up, packing and much more*

Norlec Ltd, 2 Newton Court, Norwich Road, Dereham, Norfolk, NR20 3ES Tel: (01362) 696072 Fax: (01362) 696842 *Household electrical appliances spares & repairs*

Norlica Plastics Ltd, 26-29 Rutherford Close, Leigh-on-Sea, Essex, SS9 5LQ Tel: (01702) 522945 Fax: (01702) 520140 *Decorative laminate & kitchen worktop distributors*

▶ Norlite Medical Ltd, 21-23 Justice Mill Lane, Aberdeen, AB11 6EQ Tel: (01224) 573582 Fax: (01224) 572436 E-mail: bob@norlite.co.uk *Medical & physiotherapy equipment supply & service*

Normair Compressor Engineering Ltd, 8 Rippleside Commercial Estate, Barking, Essex, IG11 0RJ Tel: 020 89848893 *Compressor distributors & services*

Normalec Ltd, Kingsley House, 1 Kingsley Street, Leicester, LE2 6DY Tel: 0116-288 9922 Fax: 0116-288 8463 E-mail: sales@normalitefsnet.co.uk *Automotive bulb distributors*

Normalite Ltd, Kingsley Street, Leicester, LE2 6DY Tel: 0116-270 0893 Fax: 0116-270 1221 E-mail: sales@normalite.fsnet.co.uk *Exhibition display designers, producers & services*

Norman Ltd, 19 Commercial Buildings, St. Helier, Jersey, JE1 1BU Tel: (01534) 883388 Fax: (01534) 883334 E-mail: sales@normans.je *Timber & builders merchants*

Norman Bailey Engineers Ltd, Britannia Works, Britannia Street, Bingley, West Yorkshire, BD16 2NS Tel: (01274) 562194 Fax: (01274) 562121 E-mail: norman-bailey@lycos.co.uk *General engineers*

Norman Cull, 10 Morville Road, Dudley, West Midlands, DY2 9HR Tel: (01384) 255339 *Demolition & building contractors*

Norman Data Defense Systems UK Ltd, Exchange House, 494 Midsummer Boulevard, Milton Keynes, MK9 2EA Tel: (01908) 847410 Fax: (0871) 7176999 E-mail: info@normanuk.com *Computer consultants & anti virus vendors*

Norman Emerson, 118 Ardmore Road, Derryadd, Craigavon, County Armagh, BT66 6QP Tel: (028) 3834 0700 Fax: (028) 3834 0011 E-mail: sales@normanemerson.com *Sand & concrete suppliers*

Eric Norman, Mill Cottage, Newburgh, Coxwold, York, YO61 4AS Tel: (01347) 868255 *Agricultural engineers*

Norman F Ogg, West Kinwhirrie, Kirriemuir, Angus, DD8 4QA Tel: (01575) 540234 Fax: (01575) 540235 *Agricultural contractors & engineers*

Norman Global Logistics Ltd, 1 Griffin Centre, Staines Road, Feltham, Middlesex, TW14 0HS Tel: (020) 8893 2999 Fax: (020) 8893 1770 E-mail: pob@norman.co.uk *Logistics & forwarding services*

Norman Hay plc, Godiva Place, Coventry, CV1 5PN Tel: (024) 7622 9373 Fax: (024) 7622 4420 E-mail: info@normanhay.com *Metal finishers & specialist fabrication manufrs*

▶ Norman Industries, Snowdrop Lane, Haverfordwest, Dyfed, SA61 1JB Tel: (01437) 763650

J. Norman & Son, Riverside & Leigh Farm, Exton, Dulverton, Somerset, TA22 9LD Tel: (01643) 851385 Fax: (01643) 851385 *Agricultural contractors & farmers*

Norman Joinery Coventry Ltd, 207 Torrington Avenue, Coventry, CV4 9AP Tel: (024) 7647 4116 Fax: (024) 7646 0494 *Purpose made joinery*

Norman Lyons & Co Exports Ltd, 106 Cleveland Street, London, W1T 6NX Tel: (020) 7380 1515 Fax: (020) 7388 4526 *Textile fabric exporters & importers*

▶ Norman Offer (Transport) Ltd, Southern Road, Southampton, SO15 1HB Tel: (023) 8033 1515

Norman Pearn & Co. Ltd, Mill Pool Boatyard, Bridgend, Looe, Cornwall, PL13 2AE Tel: (01503) 262244 Fax: (01503) 262244 E-mail: sales@looeboats.co.uk *Boat builders*

Norman Pendred & Co. Ltd, Unit 4worsley Bridge Rdbroomsleigh Business Park, London, SE26 5BN Tel: (020) 8461 1155 Fax: (020) 8461 1166 E-mail: sales@pendred.com *Price ticketing systems manufrs*

Norman Printing Service, 32 Church Road, Ashford, Middlesex, TW15 2UY Tel: (01784) 253494 Fax: (01784) 257080 E-mail: normanprinting@btconnect.com *Lithographic, Letterpress and Digital Printers. Business Stationery, Letterheads and Business Cards.*

Norman Raw Farm Machinery, The Forge, Rudgate, Whixley, York, YO26 8AL Tel: (01423) 330391 Fax: (01423) 331422 *Agricultural machinery manufrs*

Norman Rew Decorations, 22 Sycamore Close, Wellington, Telford, Shropshire, TF1 3NH Tel: (01952) 255951 *Painting & decorating contractors*

Richard Norman Electrics Ltd, Clasford Farm Units 5-9, Aldershot Road, Guildford, Surrey, GU3 3HQ Tel: (01483) 233900 Fax: (01483) 236500 E-mail: sales@rne.co.uk *Exhibition electrical contractor service provider*

▶ Norman Spence, Thorp Arch, Wetherby, West Yorkshire, LS23 7RR Tel: 0870 7771110 Fax: 0870 7776665 E-mail: sales@normanspence.co.uk *Norman Spence is a leading specialist in the design and development of natural arthritis, sciatica, psoriasis, eczema and pain relief remedies fashioned using only the purest and most precious essential oils.*

Norman & Underwood Group Ltd, The Freeschool Building, 170 Scudamore Road, Leicester, LE3 1HP Tel: 0116-231 8000 Fax: 0116-231 8005 E-mail: info@nandu.co.uk *Glazing contractors*

Norman Walker, Anchor House, Reservoir Road, Hull, HU6 7QD Tel: (01482) 493982 Fax: (01482) 493983 E-mail: info@walkerair.co.uk *Distributors of compressed air equipment suppliers*

▶ Norman Wright Portsmouth Ltd, 5 Warren Avenue Industrial Estate, Warren Avenue, Southsea, Hampshire, PO4 8PY Tel: (023) 9273 6340 Fax: (023) 9273 0066

▶ Normanby Gateway, Lysaghts Way, Scunthorpe, South Humberside, DN15 9YG Tel: (01724) 275000 Fax: (01724) 275285 E-mail: info@climatechsafety.co.uk *Technical support services*

Charles Normandale, Warnford, Southampton, SO32 3LG Tel: (01730) 829300 Fax: (01730) 829608 *Blacksmith*

Normandy Air Compressors, Unit 1d Cranborne Industrial Estate, Cranborne Road, Potters Bar, Hertfordshire, EN6 3JN Tel: (01707) 662248 *Fastener distributors*

▶ Normandy Windows Ltd, 3 Crown Close, Crown Industrial Estate, Taunton, Somerset, TA2 8RX Tel: (01823) 256075 E-mail: info@normandy-windows.co.uk *Windows & conservatories installers*

Normans O E B, 30-32 Victoria Road, Scarborough, North Yorkshire, YO11 1SD Tel: (01723) 364307 Fax: (01723) 352775 E-mail: scarb@normansoffice.co.uk *Stationers*

Normanton Catering, Normanton Works, 2 Crompton Street, Shaw, Oldham, OL2 8AG Tel: (01706) 291783 Fax: (01706) 291783 E-mail: office@normantonltd.com *Rational service partners & catering equipment installation & repair*

Normec, PO Box 116, Leeds, LS13 9AP Tel: (0870) 7570078 Fax: (0870) 7570079 E-mail: normecleeds@aol.com *Spare parts and servicing department. Shrink film supplies. Reconditioned shrink wrapping machinery supplier. Sleeve sealers, "L" sealers and shrink tunnels. Manual semi or fully automatic systems. Offer machines for hire or rental.*

Normec (Manchester) Ltd, Westwood Industrial Estate, Arkwright Street, Oldham, OL9 9LZ Tel: 0161-627 2367 Fax: 0161-627 2378 E-mail: admin@normecmanchester.co.uk *Precision engineers*

Normid Plan Filing Systems, 476 London Road, High Wycombe, Buckinghamshire, HP11 1LP Tel: (01494) 474775 Fax: (01494) 474796 E-mail: sales@normid.co.uk *Plan filing equipment*

Nornova Knitwear Manufacturers, Muness, Uyeasound, Unst, Shetland, ZE2 9DL Tel: (01957) 755373 Fax: (01957) 755353 E-mail: nornovaknitwear@tiscali.co.uk *Knitwear manufrs*

Noroil Publications, PO Box 487, Kingston Upon Thames, Surrey, KT2 5WF Tel: (020) 8547 2411 Fax: (020) 8547 2157 E-mail: noroilcontacts@enterprise.net *Publishers of oil & gas reports*

▶ Norpower & Telecoms Ltd, Muir of Ord Industrial Estate, Great North Road, Muir of Ord, Ross-Shire, IV6 7UA Tel: (01463) 871010 Fax: (01463) 871022 *Electrical engineers*

Norprint Ltd, Horncastle Road, Boston, Lincolnshire, PE21 9HZ Tel: (01205) 365161 Fax: (01205) 364825 E-mail: norprint@norprint.co.uk *Labelling manufrs*

Nor-Rak Systems Ltd, Unit 103 Batley Enterprise Centre, 513 Bradford Rd, Batley, W. Yorkshire, WF17 8LL Tel: (0800) 0776169 Fax: (01924) 442777 E-mail: sales@nor-raksystems.co.uk *We are suppliers and installers of industrial and commercial racking and shelving systems, single and double skin steel partitioning, predecorated office partitioning, suspended ceilings, mezzanine floors and general warehouse equipment and consumables.*

Norris, Halas Industrial Estate, Forge Lane, Halesowen, West Midlands, B62 8EB Tel: 0121-585 6007 Fax: 0121-585 6007 *Precision engineers*

Norris Adams Fabrications, Unit 6, Upcott Avenue, Pottington Business Park, Barnstaple, Devon, EX31 1HN Tel: (01271) 322969 Fax: (01271) 322969 *Steel fabricators*

Norris Bedding Ltd, 86-88 Coldharbour Lane, London, SE5 9PU Tel: (020) 7274 5306 Fax: (020) 7274 5306 *Bed manufrs*

C. Norris (Spring Specialists) Ltd, Ladyhouse Spring Works, Newhey Road, Milnrow, Rochdale, Lancashire, OL16 4JD Tel: (01706) 642555 Fax: (01706) 648347 E-mail: andrewward@btconnect.com *Spring manufrs*

Norris & Sons, Home Farm, Palace Lane, Beaulieu, Brockenhurst, Hampshire, SO42 7YG Tel: (01590) 612673 Fax: (01590) 612978 *Agricultural retailers*

Norsat International Ltd, The Old School, School Lane, South Carlton, Lincoln, LN1 2RL Tel: (01522) 730800 Fax: (01522) 730927 E-mail: smullery@norsat.com *Telecommunication systems*

Norscot Cooling Services Ltd, 50 Flixton Road, Urmston, Manchester, M41 5AB Tel: 0161-747 0863 Fax: 0161-747 8883 E-mail: sales@norscot-cooling.co.uk *Condensers & water cooling systems suppliers*

Norscot Joinery Ltd, 20 Carsegate Road, Inverness, IV3 8EX Tel: (01463) 224040 Fax: (01463) 715755 E-mail: info@norscot.co.uk *Joinery*

▶ Norse Merchant Ferries, Victoria Terminal 2 West Bank Road, Belfast, BT3 9JN Tel: (028) 9077 9090 Fax: (028) 9077 5520

Norseman (Rainwear) Ltd, Viking Mill, Standish Street, Chorley, Lancs, PR7 3BB Tel: (01257) 262733 Fax: (01257) 261071 E-mail: general@norseman.fsbusiness.co.uk *Menswear & ladies rainwear manufrs*

Norsk Data Ltd, The Coach House, Turners Drive, Thatcham, Berkshire, RG19 4QB Tel: (01635) 35544 Fax: (01635) 865634 *Computer services & integration* Also at: Bradford, Cumbernauld, London, Tamworth & Warrington

Norson Services Ltd, Greenwell Place, East Tullos Industrial Estate, Aberdeen, AB12 3AY Tel: (01224) 895524 Fax: (01224) 879010 *Mechanical handling equipment* Also at: Aberdeen

Norsound, Unit 5, Regents Drive, Prudhoe, Northumberland, NE42 6PX Tel: 0 1661 831 311 Fax: 0 1661 830 099 E-mail: sales@norsound.co.uk Principal Export Areas: West Europe *We are specialists in all Seals and Gaskets, including: Acoustic Door Seals Smoke Seals Acoustic Seals Sound Proofing Noise Reduction Acoustic Solutions and applications Sound Damping Door Bottom Seals.*

Norstead, Metnor House, Mylord Crescent, Newcastle upon Tyne, NE12 5YD Tel: 0191-268 4000 Fax: 0191-268 6650 E-mail: engineering@norstead.co.uk *Electrical & mechanical contractors & services*

▶ Norstead Mechanical Engineers, 261 Springhill Parkway, Glasgow Business Park, Baillieston, Glasgow, G69 6GA Tel: 0141-781 2100 Fax: 0141-781 2101 E-mail: sales@norstead.co.uk *Mechanical engineers*

Norsys Ltd, Citadel House, Solvay Road, Northwich, Cheshire, CW8 4DP Tel: (01606) 784884 Fax: (01606) 784082 *Computer consultants*

Nortec Production Ltd, 11 Fourways, Atherstone, Warwickshire, CV9 1LG Tel: (01827) 717896 Fax: (01827) 717842 E-mail: robin.clements@nortec-prod.demon.co.uk *PCB assembly contractors*

Nortech Ltd, Unit 14 Terrace Factory, Bassington Industrial Estate, Cramlington, Northumberland, NE23 8AD Tel: (01670) 736811 Fax: (01670) 731252 E-mail: sales@nortechgaragedoors.co.uk *Garage door & gate automation specialists*

▶ Nortech Computers Ltd, 10 High Street, Portishead, Bristol, BS20 6EW Tel: (01275) 818699 Fax: (01275) 849316 *Build, service & repair computers*

▶ Nortech Design Ltd, 3 Alstonefield, Emerson Valley, Milton Keynes, MK4 2HA Tel: (01908) 330427 Fax: (0870) 7064019 E-mail: enquiries@nortechdesign.ltd.uk *Nortech Design is a small professional design company. Using Solid Edge (3D modelling software) Nortech can design and model for all stages for the project.*

Nortech Management Ltd, Tadcaster House, Kempton Road, Pershore, Worcestershire, WR10 2TA Tel: (0870) 0111992 Fax: (0870) 0111993 E-mail: info@nortechonline.co.uk *Fault finding equipment distributor & manufrs*

Nortech Services Ltd, Drypool Way, Hull, HU9 1NL Tel: (01482) 327791 Fax: (01482) 320550 E-mail: sales@nortech.co.uk Principal Export Areas: Worldwide *Distributors of engineers supplies, hydraulic equipment & power tools. Also industrial air conditioning equipment hire & do-it-yourself tool hire*

Nortek Educational Furniture & Equipment Ltd, Vale Works, Priesty Fields Industrial Estate, Congleton, Cheshire, CW12 4AQ Tel: (01260) 298321 Fax: (01260) 298169 E-mail: sales@nortekgroup.co.uk *Industrial & technical furniture manufrs*

Nortek Electronic Circuits Ltd, Bridge Mill, Royle Street, Congleton, Cheshire, CW12 1HR Tel: (01260) 276409 Fax: (01260) 299399 E-mail: mail@nortek.co.uk *Electrical contractors*

▶ Nortek Material Handling (M H E) Ltd, Vale Mill, Priesty Fields, Congleton, Cheshire, CW12 4AD Tel: (01260) 275105 *Furniture, furnishings & fittings*

Nortek Precision Sheet Steel Ltd, Priesty Fields, Congleton, Cheshire, CW12 4AQ Tel: (01260) 278839 Fax: (01260) 278201 *Precision sheet metalworkers*

Nortel Networks UK Ltd, Maidenhead Office Park, Westacott Way, Littlewick Green, Maidenhead, Berkshire, SL6 3QH Tel: (01628) 432000 Fax: (01628) 434318 E-mail: enquiries@nortelnetworks.com *Telecommunications equipment manufrs*

Nortel Networks UK Ltd, Maidenhead Office Park, Westacott Way, Littlewick Green, Maidenhead, Berkshire, SL6 3QH Tel: (01628) 432000 Fax: (01628) 432812 E-mail: enquiries@nortelnetworks.com Principal Export Areas: Worldwide *Telecommunication systems/equipment manufrs*

Nortest Scientific Apparatus, Unit 1 The Woodyard, Castle Ashby, Northampton, NN7 1LF Tel: (01604) 696192 Fax: (01604) 696198 E-mail: brian@nortest.co.uk *Materials testing instruments importer & distributor*

Nortex Ltd, 73 Arthur Street, Lakeside, Redditch, Worcestershire, B98 8JY Tel: (01527) 500742 Fax: (01527) 502999 E-mail: nortex.exhibitions@virgin.net *Exhibition designers & contractors*

North 4 Design, Unit 12, 2 Somerset Road, London, N17 9EJ Tel: (020) 8885 4404 Fax: (0870) 1308374 E-mail: websales@north4.co.uk *Architectural vision panels designers & manufrs*

North Account Book Manufacturing Co., 23 Oldfield Lane, Heckmondwike, West Yorkshire, WF16 0JE Tel: (01924) 402309 Fax: (01924) 412070 E-mail: sales@northaccountprinters.co.uk *Commercial printers & stationers*

▶ North American (UK) Ltd, Unit 1 Ashurst Drive, Lawnhurst Trading Estate, Cheadle Heath, Stockport, Cheshire, SK3 0SD Tel: 0161-491 5141

North Antrim Turkeys Ltd, 14 Seneirl Road, Castlecatt, Bushmills, County Antrim, BT57 8TS Tel: (028) 2074 1239 Fax: (028) 2074 1009 *Poultry processors*

▶ North Atlantic Fisheries College, Port Arthur, Scalloway, Shetland, ZE1 0UN Tel: (01595) 772000

North Atlantic Shipping Agency Ltd, Kingsway House, 103 Kingsway, London, WC2B 6QX Tel: (020) 7405 5554 Fax: (020) 7405 5125 *Shipping agents*

▶ North Avon Pumps Ltd, Copp Barn, Westerleigh Road, Westerleigh, Bristol, BS37 8HQ Tel: (01454) 315444 Fax: (01454) 327944 E-mail: sales@northavonpumps.co.uk *Supply & installation of flow systems & pumps & controls*

▶ North Ayrshire Commercials, 5 Irvine Road, Lugton, Kilmarnock, Ayrshire, KA3 4ED Tel: (01294) 850049 E-mail: enquiries@northayrshirecommercials.co.uk *North Ayrshire Commercials is a UK company that specialises in light commercial vehicle sales, van valeting and panel van wood lining. Established in 1996, the company has over years of commercial vehicle sales experience.**Specialising in professionally valeted one-owner vehicles, North Ayrshire Commercials can ensure that you get a quality vehicle that will give years of good service.**Centrally located in Ayrshire, the company has a wide range of commercial and private clients from Ayrshire, Glasgow, Kilmarnock and throughout the United Kingdom.*

North Belfast Spring Works, 2 Cosgrave Street, Belfast, BT15 2JN Tel: (028) 9035 1813 *Spring manufrs*

North Bristol Appliances, 42 Lockleaze Road, Bristol, BS7 9RT Tel: 0117-971 4964 *Domestic appliances repairs*

▶ The North British Distilliery Co. Ltd, Addiewell, West Calder, West Lothian, EH55 8NP Tel: (01506) 872666

▶ The North British Distilliery Co. Ltd, Addiewell, West Calder, West Lothian, EH55 8NP Tel: (01506) 872666

North British Tapes Ltd, Unit 5 Locomotion Way, Camperdown Industrial Estate, Newcastle upon Tyne, NE12 5US Tel: 0191-268 6272 Fax: 0191-268 7400 *Self-adhesive tape distributors*

North Cape Minerals Ltd, Pentagon House, Bucknall New Road, Stoke-on-Trent, ST1 2BA Tel: (01782) 208718 Fax: (01782) 286529 E-mail: alan.moseley@ncm.no *Mineral merchants*

North Catering Equipment Ltd, St. Georges Road Industrial Estate, Donnington, Telford, Shropshire, TF2 7QZ Tel: (01952) 616655 Fax: (01952) 417799 *Welding equipment sales & repair* Also at: Newtown (Powys)

▶ North Channel Energy Services, 5 Lambhill Quadrant, Kinning Park, Glasgow, G41 1SB Tel: 0141-429 4557

North Cheshire Labels, 16 Vernon Street, Hyde, Cheshire, SK14 1QH Tel: 0161-368 1345 Fax: 0161-351 7142 *Self-adhesive label manufrs*

North City Training, 275 Antrim Road, Belfast, BT15 2GZ Tel: (028) 9074 5408 Fax: (028) 9074 0329 *Business advisors*

▶ North Cornwall Glazing, Highfield Industrial Estate, Camelford, Cornwall, PL32 9RA Tel: (01840) 213593 Fax: (01840) 213313 *Upvc doors & conservatories*

North Dean Fabrications Ltd, Grove Street, Wakefield Road, Brighouse, West Yorkshire, HD6 1PL Tel: (01484) 710845 Fax: (01484) 722397 E-mail: mail@northdeanfabs.co.uk *Steel & plate fabricators*

North Devon Blinds Ltd, 131 East Reach, Taunton, Somerset, TA1 3HN Tel: (01823) 334665 Fax: (01823) 334665 *Blinds service & manufrs*

North Devon Electronics Ltd, Velator, Braunton, Devon, EX33 2DX Tel: (01271) 813553 Fax: (01271) 816171 E-mail: sales@nde.co.uk *Custom winders & transformer manufrs*

North Devon Hose & Hydraulics Ltd, Unit 20 Castle Park Road, Whiddon Valley Industrial Estate, Barnstaple, Devon, EX32 8PA Tel: (01271) 324443 Fax: (01271) 324568 E-mail: northdevon@hosehyd.fsnet.co.uk *Hydraulic & pneumatic hose assembly retailers*

North Devon Leisure, Unit 1 The Old Aerodrome, Chivenor, Barnstaple, Devon, EX31 4AY Tel: (01271) 817129 Fax: (01271) 813512 E-mail: northdevonleisure@btinternet.com *Leisure equipment rental services*

North Dingle Made Up Textiles, 4a Orwell Road, Liverpool, L4 1RQ Tel: 0151-944 1482 Fax: 0151-944 1482 *Industrial cover manufrs*

North Downs Instrument Co. Ltd, Ashleigh, Wrotham Road, Meopham, Gravesend, Kent, DA13 0QB Tel: (01474) 812406 Fax: (01474) 814265 E-mail: sales@mjwilsongroup.com *Industrial instrumentation*

North Downs International Ltd, Saxon Way, Wincanton Business Park, Wincanton, Somerset, BA9 9RT Tel: (01963) 828828 Fax: (01963) 828833 *Cheese packaging*

North East Chamber Of Commerce, Aykley Heads Business Centre, Aykley Heads, Durham, DH1 5TS Tel: 0191-386 1133 Fax: 0191-386 1144 E-mail: information@ne-cc.com *Chambers of commerce*

North East Communications, 76 High Street, Elgin, Morayshire, IV30 1BJ Tel: (01343) 551551 Fax: (01343) 540340 *Telecommunications & computer suppliers*

North East Contract Services Ltd, Howdon Terminal, Willington Quay, Wallsend, Tyne & Wear, NE28 6UL Tel: 0191-234 5511 Fax: 0191-234 0888 E-mail: newcastle@ofsprayltd.com *Ship repair services & contractors*

▶ North East Contracts Ltd, Knowes of Boysack, Arbroath, Angus, DD11 3SA Tel: (01241) 829000 Fax: (01241) 826000 E-mail: enquiries@northeastcontracts.co.uk *We are Roofing Specialists who have experience in all types of roofs and buildings. Our services include metal cladding, Dryseal fibreglass flat roofing system, slating, tiling, uPVC fascias etc.*

North East Foundry Supplies Ltd, Batts Works, Wolsingham, Bishop Auckland, County Durham, DL13 3BD Tel: (01388) 527299 Fax: (01388) 527593 *Foundry suppliers*

North East Lock & Key Co., 31 Harvey Close, Crowther, Washington, Tyne & Wear, NE38 0AB Tel: 0191-416 1843 Fax: 0191-415 0995 *Lock specialists & distributors*

North East One Ltd, 48 Leazes Park Road, Newcastle Upon Tyne, NE1 4PG Tel: 0191-261 5261 Fax: 0191-232 0637 E-mail: general@northeastone.co.uk *Market research agency*

▶ North East Outdoor, 27A Skinner Street, Whitby, North Yorkshire, YO21 3AH Tel: (01947) 600616 E-mail: sales@neoutdoor.co.uk *Climbing & outdoor equipment distributors*

North East Paper Co. Ltd, Benfield Road, Newcastle upon Tyne, NE6 4NT Tel: 0191-265 5000 Fax: 0191-224 0872 E-mail: sales@nep-uk.co.uk *Packaging wholesalers*

North East Profiling & Engineering Co. Ltd, Bellway Industrial Estate, Whitley Road, Longbenton, Newcastle upon Tyne, NE12 9SW Tel: 0191-266 4521 Fax: 0191-270 0983 E-mail: sales@northeastprofiling.com *Steel fabricators & profile burners*

North East Secure Electronics Ltd, North East Innovation Centre, Neilson Road, Gateshead, Tyne & Wear, NE10 0EW Tel: 0191-477 9235 Fax: 0191-478 3639 E-mail: g.ord@neic.co.uk *Automation equipment & designers*

North East Security Shutters, Ness House, Knox Lane, Scarborough, North Yorkshire, YO11 2BD Tel: (01723) 361644 Fax: (01723) 361644 E-mail: nessdoors@aol.com *Roller & security shutter manufrs*

▶ North East Site Coatings, 14 Elswick Way Industrial Estate, Newcastle Road, South Shields, Tyne & Wear, NE34 0LW Tel: 0191-454 4140 Fax: 0191-454 4140 E-mail: bobmckeith@blueyonder.co.uk *North East Site Coatings On Site and In Shop Structural Painters of Parapet, Posts, Rails, Anti Access Panels, P2 P4 P6, Gates and Railings, Lighting Columns, Bollards, Street Furniture etc.**We use Department of Transport and Railtrack approved Epoxy 2 Pack Coating Systems as well as Single Pack Paint.*

North East Slag Cement Ltd, 97 Godstone Road, Caterham, Surrey, CR3 6RE Tel: (01883) 331071 *Cement manufrs*

▶ North Eastern Electrical PLC, Irwell House, 40-42 Frederick Road, Salford, M6 6NY Tel: 0870 4215735 Fax: 0870 4215736 E-mail: nee@neeplc.co.uk *Electrical & Mechanical Contractors & Engineers*

North Eastern Iron Refining Co., Ironmasters Way, Stillington, Stockton-on-Tees, Cleveland, TS21 1LE Tel: (01740) 630212 Fax: (01740) 630555 E-mail: sales@metabrasive.com *Cast iron abrasive manufrs*

North Eastern Plant & Fixings, 120 Londesborough Sreet, Hull, HU3 1DR Tel: (01482) 226140 *Power tool hire & industrial workwear supplier*

North Eastern Slating & Building Co., 6 Balmoral Terrace, Aberdeen, AB10 6HH Tel: (01224) 211179 Fax: (01224) 211180 *Roofing & slating contractors*

North Engineering Works, Block 24 Kilspindie Road, Dunsinane Industrial Estate, Dundee, DD2 3QH Tel: (01382) 889693 Fax: (01382) 889808 E-mail: sales@northeng.co.uk *Press work & toolmaking services*

North Of England P & I, 100 Quayside, Newcastle upon Tyne, NE1 3DU Tel: 0191-232 5221 Fax: 0191-261 0540 E-mail: general@nepia.com *Marine insurance company*

North Gate P.L.C., Norflex House, Allington Way, Darlington, County Durham, DL1 4DY Tel: (01325) 467558 Fax: (01325) 381009 E-mail: info@northgateplc.com *Holding company*

North Gate Public Services, Sx3 House, Market Street, Bracknell, Berkshire, RG12 1QD Tel: (01344) 401111 Fax: (01344) 401100 *Software development*

North Hants Forklift Services Ltd, 2 Berry Court, Little London, Tadley, Hampshire, RG26 5AT Tel: 01256 850959 *Rental & sales of fork lift trucks*

North Hants Tyre & Remoulding, 2 Christy Estate, Ivy Road, Aldershot, Hampshire, GU12 4TX Tel: (01252) 318666 Fax: (01252) 318777 E-mail: sales@northhantstyres.com *Vintage & American tyres*

North Heath Motors Horsham, North Heath Industrial Estate, North Heath Lane, Horsham, West Sussex, RH12 5QE Tel: (01403) 255035 *MOT repairs & mechanical engineers*

North Herts Asphalt Ltd, Unit 15 The Cuttings, Station Approach, Hitchin, Hertfordshire, SG4 9UW Tel: (01462) 434877 Fax: (01462) 421539 *Mastic asphalt contractors*

North Hunts Welding & Engineering Co., America Farm Cottage, Oxney Road, Peterborough, PE1 5YR Tel: (01733) 222632 Fax: (01733) 222732 *Oil tank manufrs*

North Kent Chamber Of Commerce, Upper Rose Gallery, Bluewater, Greenhithe, Kent, DA9 9SP Tel: (01322) 381333 Fax: (01322) 381555 E-mail: enquiries@northkentchamber.org *Chamber of commerce*

North Kent Hydraulics, Unit 24 Castle View Business Centre, Gas House Road, Rochester, Kent, ME1 1PB Tel: (01634) 832211 Fax: (01634) 831981 *Hydraulic hose fitting manufrs*

North Kent Shot Blasting Co. Ltd, Grove Road, Northfleet, Gravesend, Kent, DA11 9AX Tel: (01474) 350030 Fax: (01474) 327329 E-mail: info@nksb.co.uk *Metal spraying contractors*

North Lands Creative Glass, Quatre Bras, Lybster, Caithness, KW3 6BN Tel: (01593) 721229 Fax: (01593) 721229 *Sculpture, painting & training courses*

▶ North Leicester Motor Cycles Ltd, 64 Whitehill Road, Ellistown, Coalville, Leicestershire, LE67 1EL Tel: (01530) 263381 Fax: (01530) 262960 E-mail: sales@motomorini.co.uk

North Light, Royal Victiora Pottery, West POrt Road, Birslum, Stoke-On-Trent, ST8 4AG Tel: (01782) 259403 Fax: (01782) 575195 *Animal resin figurines manufrs*

▶ North Lincs Engineering Ltd, College View Works, Manby Road, Grimoldby, Louth, Lincolnshire, LN11 8HE Tel: (01507) 328787 Fax: (01507) 329306 E-mail: mark@nle.demon.co.uk *North Lincs Engineering Ltd specialises in the Supply, Installation and Reconditioning of Industrial and Marine Diesel Engines and Generating Sets. We carry out a wide range of mechanical and electrical activities both overseas and in workshops equipped with heavy engineering machinery. We can also supply New or Reconditioned Spare Parts for most Diesel Engines and often source Spares or Replacement Parts for the associated Mechanical and Electrical Ancillary Equipment. Our team of Service Engineers can Repair, Service or Commission Land based or Marine Installations Worldwide. Our workshop facilities enable us to Overhaul, Refurbish and Load Test Diesel Engines and Generators up to 2MW in addition to Machining, Welding and Fuel Injection Repairs.*

North London Business, Heron House, Ferry Lane, London, N17 9NF Tel: (020) 8885 9200 Fax: (020) 8801 4274 E-mail: banddsales@btconnect.com *Timber importers & merchants*

North London Car Sounds Vhcle Security Systems, PO Box 302, Welwyn Garden City, Hertfordshire, AL8 7NQ Tel: (01707) 371681 E-mail: info@piranha-alarms.co.uk *Vehicle security & audio equipment retailers & installation services*

North London Ceramics Ltd, 585 High Road, Tottenham, London, N17 6SB Tel: (020) 8808 9216 Fax: (020) 8801 6159 *Dental laboratory*

North London Chamber Of Commerce Ltd, Enfield Business Centre, 201 Hertford Road, Enfield, Middlesex, EN3 5JH Tel: (020) 8443 4464 Fax: (020) 8443 3822 E-mail: nlcc@bl4london.com *Chamber of commerce*

North London & Herts Newspaper Ltd, 9-10 Riverside, Enfield, Middlesex, EN1 3SZ Tel: (020) 8367 2345 Fax: (020) 8366 4013 E-mail: newsenfield@trinitysight.co.uk *Newspaper publishers*

North London Plant Hire, 4-16 Shacklewell Lane, London, E8 2EZ Tel: (020) 7254 3328 Fax: (020) 7923 4129 E-mail: sales@nlph.co.uk *Contractors plant hire*

North Manchester Joinery, Hulme St, Bury, Lancashire, BL8 1AN Tel: 0161-705 2960 Fax: 0161-764 0552 *Builders & joiners*

North & Mid Wales Pest Control, 47 Minera Hall Road, Minera, Wrexham, Clwyd, LL11 3YF Tel: (01978) 753752 Fax: (01978) 753752 *Pest control services*

North Norfolk Joinery Ltd, Home Farm Ent, Hall Road, Cromer, Norfolk, NR27 9JG Tel: (01263) 515696 Fax: (01263) 515196 *Joinery manufacturers*

North Notts Sheet Metal Ltd, Unit 3 Welsh Croft Close, Kirkby-in-Ashfield, Nottingham, NG17 8EP Tel: (01623) 722123 Fax: (01623) 720562 *Sheet metalwork engineers*

North Notts Tool Makers Ltd, Unit 1 Fox Covert Way, Crown Farm Industrial Estate, Forest Town, Mansfield, Nottinghamshire, NG19 0FR Tel: (01623) 621188 Fax: (01623) 622662 E-mail: info@nntools.co.uk *Plastic injection mould tool manufrs*

North Offshore Ltd, Saltire House, Blackness Avenue, Altens Industrial Estate, Aberdeen, AB12 3PG Tel: (01224) 871906 Fax: (01224) 878828 E-mail: northoffshore@northgroup.co.uk *Fire resistant flooring & furniture manufrs*

North Quay Trading Ltd, Unit 47 Joseph Wilson Industrial, Estate Millstrood Road, Whitstable, Kent, CT5 3PS Tel: (01227) 771700 Fax: (01227) 773026 *Joinery manufrs*

North Safety Products, The Courtyard, Green Lane, Heywood, Lancashire, OL10 2EX Tel: (01706) 693800 Fax: (01706) 693801 E-mail: info@northsafety.co.uk *Industrial protective clothing manufrs*

North Sea Compactors, 7 Logman Centre, Greenbank Cresent, East Tullos Industrial Estate, Aberdeen, AB12 3BG Tel: (01224) 248455 Fax: (01224) 248454 E-mail: nscompac@netcomuk.co.uk *Offshore waste compactors*

North Sea Medical Centre Ltd, 3 Lowestoft Road, Gorleston, Great Yarmouth, Norfolk, NR31 6SG Tel: (01493) 414141 Fax: (01493) 441988 E-mail: occhealth@northseamedical.demon.co.uk *Occupational health consultants*

North Sea Roofing Co., 32 Arbroath Road, Dundee, DD4 6EP Tel: (01382) 453334 Fax: (01382) 458310 *Roofing contractors*

North Sea Ventilation Ltd, West Carr Lane, Hull, HU7 0BW Tel: (01482) 834050 Fax: (01482) 834060 E-mail: enquiries@nsv.co.uk *Air conditioning engineers & air handling equipment manufrs*

North Sea Winches Ltd, Dunslow Road, Eastfield, Scarborough, North Yorkshire, YO11 3UT Tel: (01723) 584080 Fax: (01723) 581605 E-mail: sales@nswinches.co.uk Principal Export Areas: Worldwide *North Sea Winches have specialised in the design and manufacture of winches, windlasses and capstans for over 30 years. Our modern technology is seen in applications for marine, industrial and civil engineering.*

▶ North Services, Doon Shagarry, Ose, Isle of Skye, IV56 8FH Tel: (01470) 572225 Fax: (01470) 572343

North Shields Grinding, The Old Maltings, Tanners Bank, North Shields, Tyne & Wear, NE30 1JH Tel: 0191-257 2342 Fax: 0191-258 5310 E-mail: nsgrinding@aol.com *Saw/blade sharpening & repairs services*

North Shropshire Conservative & Unionist Association, Sambrook Hall, Noble Street, Wem, Shrewsbury, SY4 5DT Tel: (01939) 235222 Fax: (01939) 232220 E-mail: sales@nsprint.co.uk *Printers & commercial stationers* Also at: Market Drayton

North & South Industries, Sidings Court, Doncaster, South Yorkshire, DN4 5NU Tel: (01302) 730037 Fax: (01302) 730073 Principal Export Areas: Worldwide *Ventilation distributors*

North & South Labels Ltd, Unit 1, 56A Bensham Grove, Thornton Heath, Surrey, CR7 8DA Tel: (020) 8653 4477 Fax: (020) 8653 5666 E-mail: sales@nslabels.co.uk *North & South Labels provide labelling solutions for all industries. Our comprehensive range of products include blank and pre printed labels and tags, numbered and bar coded labels, thermal ribbons and associated labelling consumables.*

▶ North Square, Hardwick, Wellingborough, Northamptonshire, NN9 5AL Tel: (01933) 401501 Fax: (01933) 402403 E-mail: info@north-square.com *North Square Interactive is an online consultancy that delivers cost effective, best practise website evaluation reports, usability testing, competitor analysis, accessibility audits, functionality testing, and more.*

North Stafford Hotel, Winton Square, Stoke-on-Trent, ST4 2AE Tel: (01782) 744477 Fax: (01782) 744580 E-mail: claire.portar@britanniahotels.co.uk *Hotel & conference centre*

North Staffs Aluminium Ltd, 530 Hartshill Road, Stoke-On-Trent, ST4 6AF Tel: (01782) 616578 Fax: (01782) 712904 *Scrap iron steel & metal merchants*

North Staffs Pipes Services, 23 High Street, Cheadle, Stoke-on-Trent, ST10 1AA Tel: (01538) 757177 Fax: (01538) 757177 *Pipework installers*

North Star Shipping Aberdeen Ltd, 207 Albert Quay, Aberdeen, AB11 5FS Tel: (01224) 592206 Fax: (01224) 584174 E-mail: callum.bruce@craig-group.com *Ship management & owners*

▶ North Star Signs, 6-7 Doncaster Road, Barnsley, South Yorkshire, S70 1TH Tel: (01226) 288228 Fax: (01226) 288228 E-mail: info@northstarsigns.co.uk *Sign manufrs*

▶ North Stone (NI) Ltd, Shinny Road, Macosquin, Coleraine, County Londonderry, BT51 4PS Tel: (028) 7032 1100 Fax: (028) 7035 7333

North Time & Data Ltd, Enterprise Crescent, Lisburn, County Antrim, BT28 2BP Tel: (028) 9260 4000 Fax: (028) 9260 5595 E-mail: sales@ntd.ltd.uk *Computer printer distributors*

North Wales Floorings Ltd, 117-119 Conway Road, Colwyn Bay, Clwyd, LL29 7LT Tel: (01492) 530448 Fax: (01492) 532800 *Flooring contractors*

▶ North Wales Joinery Ltd, Builder St, Llandudno, Gwynedd, LL30 1DR Tel: (01492) 870418

▶ North Wales Process Solutions, PO Box 226, Rhyl, Denbighshire, LL18 9AZ Tel: (0870) 0425071 Fax: (0870) 7627365 E-mail: contact@nwprocess-solutions.com *North Wales Process Solutions provides Civil Enforcemsnt Agents & Professional Investigators to members of the public, small to large businesses, local government and members of the legal profession. Our services include process serving, debt collections, tracing enquiries, repossession agents, employee vetting, pre-sue and means reports and dna testing. For more information please visit our website at www.nwprocess-solutions.com*

North Wales Trophies & Engravers, 34 Tan-Y-Bryn Road, Llandudno, Gwynedd, LL30 1UU Tel: (01492) 860363 *Trophy engravers & manufrs*

North Warwickshire & Hinkley College, The Bermuda Pk Innovation Ctr, St Davids Way, Bermuda Park Indust Est, Nuneaton, Warwickshire, CV10 7SD Tel: 024 76322928 Fax: 024 76322923 *Fork lift truck drivers training centre*

North West Aquatics, Webbs Garden Centre, Burneside Road, Kendal, Cumbria, LA9 4RT Tel: (01539) 720041 Fax: (01539) 727328 *Aquarium & pond supplies*

North West Business Link Ltd, Lee House, 90 Great Bridgewater Street, Manchester, M1 5JW Tel: 0161-236 4114 Fax: 0161-228 3043 E-mail: info@business-support-solutions.co.uk *Business information advisory services*

North West Cables Ltd, School Lane, Knowsley Business Park, Prescot, Merseyside, L34 9HD Tel: 0151-548 3888 Fax: 0151-549 1169 E-mail: sales@northwestcables.co.uk *Electric cable manufrs*

North West Caravan Breakers, Britannia Mill, Willow Street, Oldham, OL1 3QB Tel: 0161-652 7074 E-mail: flush2go@yahoo.co.uk *Caravan sales & hire & caravan accessories*

North West Compressed Air Co. Ltd, Unit 361 Leach Place, Walton Summit Centre, Bamber Bridge, Preston, PR5 8AS Tel: (01772) 311999 Fax: (01772) 312888 E-mail: sales@nwca.co.uk *Compressed air services*

North West Construction Services Ltd, Bleasby Street, Oldham, OL4 2AJ Tel: 0161 6261816 *Structural engineers*

North West Continuers Ltd, 20 Fylde Road Industrial Estate, Fylde Road, Preston, PR1 2TY Tel: (01772) 561144 Fax: (01772) 253392 E-mail: sales@nwestco.com *Computer consumable services*

North West Design Services, Chartwell, Hundred End Lane, Hundred End, Preston, PR4 6XL Tel: (01772) 814497 Fax: (01772) 815308 E-mail: nwds@btconnect.com *Press tool design services*

North West Drawing & Office Supplies, 19 Priory Lane, Penwortham, Preston, PR1 0AR Tel: (01772) 751481 Fax: (01772) 751946 E-mail: nwdrawing@ukonline.co.uk *Office suppliers*

North West Enamellers, Unit 14-15 Catheralls Industrial Estate, Brookhill Way, Buckley, Clwyd, CH7 3PS Tel: (01244) 549185 Fax: (01244) 544739 *Stove enamelling*

North West Engineering Group Ltd, Mill Lane, Halton, Lancaster, LA2 6NF Tel: (01524) 811224 Fax: (01524) 811288 E-mail: sales@luneside.co.uk *Precision machinists & engineers*

▶ North West Express, Mersey View Road, Widnes, Cheshire, WA8 8LL Tel: 0151-425 5555 Fax: 0151-425 4444

North West Fabrications Ltd, Station Works, Berry Street, Bootle, Merseyside, L20 8AT Tel: 0151-922 9518 Fax: 0151-933 6395 *General presswokers & engineers*

▶ North West Fencing, 55 Lacrosse Avenue, Oldham, OL8 4LU Tel: 0161-633 2426 *Fencing suppliers*

North West Fire Ltd, Ross Road, Ellesmere Port, CH65 3DB Tel: 0151-355 6822 Fax: (01978) 751646 *Fire protection equipment suppliers*

North West Fire Ltd, Glan Llyn Road, Bradley, Wrexham, Clwyd, LL11 4BB Tel: (01978) 720999 Fax: (01978) 751646 *Fire extinguisher engineers*

North West Fire Protection, 110 Pleasington Close, Blackburn, BB2 1TU Tel: (01254) 278555 Fax: (01254) 278666 *Fire extinguisher maintenance*

North West Forgings Ltd, Unit F2 Nasmyth Business Park, James Nasmyth Way, Eccles, Manchester, M30 0SN Tel: 0161-785 2785 Fax: 0161-785 2777 E-mail: sales@nationalforge.com Principal Export Areas: Worldwide *Manufacturers steel forgings*

North West Gases Ltd, Alma Street, St. Helens, Merseyside, WA9 3AR Tel: (01744) 753634 Fax: (01744) 24264 E-mail: sales@northwestgases.com *Industrial gas producers & suppliers*

North West Graphics, 195 St Helens Road, Bolton, BL3 3PY Tel: (01204) 657123 *Signs manufrs*

North West Inspex, Caddick Road, Knowsley Business Park, Prescot, Merseyside, L34 9HP Tel: 0151-548 9908 Fax: 0151-549 1182 E-mail: inspexuk@aol.com *Calibration inspection services & testing*

North West Office Services, Grove House, 27 Hawkin Street, Londonderry, BT48 6RE Tel: (028) 7126 1271 Fax: (028) 7126 5284 *Computer services* Also at: Coleraine & Strabane

▶ North West Packaging, 34 Kempton Park Fold, Southport, Merseyside, PR8 5PL Tel: (01704) 544733 Fax: (01704) 544733 E-mail: info@nwp.co.uk *Service, overhaul & maintenance of wrapping & packaging machinery*

North West Precision Forms Ltd, Unit 3a Ebenezer Street, Birkenhead, Merseyside, CH42 1NH Tel: 0151-643 8534 Fax: 0151-643 8539 E-mail: mail@northwestprec.demon.co.uk *Aircraft component manufrs*

▶ North West Propshafts, Regency Works, Regent Street, Coppull, Chorley, Lancashire, PR7 5AX Tel: (01257) 791681 Fax: (01257) 794232 E-mail: info@northwestpropshafts.com *Prop shaft manufacturers, repairers & suppliers*

North West Prototypes, The Little Mill, Palatine Street, Denton, Manchester, M34 3LY Tel: 0161-320 5529 Fax: 0161-335 0928 *3-dimensional displays & prototypes*

North West Radio Communications, 6 Low Hill, Liverpool, L6 1BS Tel: 0151-263 9993 Fax: 0151-263 9966 E-mail: sales@northwestradio.co.uk *Two way radio communication distributors.*

North West Roller Services Ltd, 1 Tudor Road, Manor Park, Runcorn, Cheshire, WA7 1TY Tel: (01928) 571711 Fax: (01928) 571775 E-mail: enquiries@nwrollers.co.uk *Printing roller manufrs*

▶ North West Seals & Profiles, 67 Stour Road, Tyldesley, Manchester, M29 7WB Tel: (01942) 731046 Fax: (01942) 745968 E-mail: sales@seals-profiles.co.uk *Manufacture, Repair and Design SEALS: (Piston/Shaft/Rod/ Wiper/Mechanical/Rotary Oil/Parker), Vari-Seals, O'Ring and Quad Seals. Pump/Ammonia Compressor/Shaft/Gland: Seals. Polymer Seals.*

North West Seating Ltd, 5 Tower Enterprise Park, Great George Street, Wigan, Lancashire, WN3 4DP Tel: (01942) 244074 Fax: (01942) 244074 E-mail: northwestseating@lineone.net *Seating manufrs*

North West Sunblinds, 19 Kilburn Close, Heald Green, Cheadle, Cheshire, SK8 3LP Tel: 0161-437 6808 Fax: 0161-437 6808 E-mail: nwblinds@aol.com *Blind & awning manufrs*

North West Supplies, Llwyn Onn Industrial Estate, Amlwch, Gwynedd, LL68 9BQ Tel: (01407) 832020 Fax: (01407) 832200 E-mail: support@northwestsupplies.co.uk *Military equipment supplies*

▶ North West Technologies Ltd, 15 Acacia Drive, Great Sutton, Ellesmere Port, CH66 2UT Tel: 0151-355 8075 E-mail: enquiries@nw-tech.co.uk *Engineering Science and Materials Consultancy.***

▶ North West Timber Products Ltd, Unit 11B, Newhaven Business Park, Barton Lane, Eccles, Manchester, M30 0HH Tel: 0161-7073797 Fax: 0161-7079717 E-mail: sales@nwtimberproducts.co.uk *Bespoke Joinery Manufacturer. Doors, Door Frames, Stairs, Windows, Screens, Machined Timber.*Hardwood, Softwood.*

North West Time Recording Co., 197 Bury Old Road, Prestwich, Manchester, M25 1JF Tel: 0161-798 8002 Fax: 0161-773 2441 E-mail: terry@nwtr.co.uk *Time recorder distributors*

North West Tippers Ltd, Rockfield Street, Blackburn, BB2 3RG Tel: (01254) 55441 Fax: (01254) 665015 E-mail: stephen@northwesttippers.co.uk *Specialist bodybuilders, fitting tippers & cranes services*

North West Wheels Ltd, Forward Works, Woolston, Warrington, WA1 4BA Tel: (01925) 816207 Fax: (01925) 825633 *Industrial wheel manufrs*

North West Window Blinds, 3 Abercorn Avenue, Portrush, County Antrim, BT56 8HW Tel: (028) 7082 3499 Fax: (028) 7082 3499 *Blind distributors*

North West Wiper Co., 6 Acorn Business Centre, Lees Road, Knowsley Industrial Park, Liverpool, L33 7SL Tel: 0151-546 4005 Fax: 0151-546 4005 *Cleaning cloth manufrs*

North Western Automarine, Largs Yacht Haven, Irvine Road, Largs, Ayrshire, KA30 8EZ Tel: (01475) 687139 Fax: (01475) 687139 *Marine engine distributors & repairers*

North Western Blanks Ltd, Grimshaw Lane, Middleton, Manchester, M24 2AA Tel: 0161-653 3500 Fax: 0161-655 3673 E-mail: sales@northwesternblanks.co.uk *Fishing rod manufrs*

North Western Insulations Ltd, Redwither Road, Wrexham Industrial Estate, Wrexham, Clwyd, LL13 9RD Tel: (01978) 661708 Fax: (01978) 661570 *Thermal insulation contractors & asbestos removal*

North Western Lead Co Hyde Ltd, Mill Street, Newton Moor Industrial Estate, Hyde, Cheshire, SK14 4LJ Tel: 0161-368 4491 Fax: 0161-366 5103 E-mail: sales@decraled.co.uk *Window lead manufrs*

North Wilts Office Supplies, Ford, Chippenham, Wiltshire, SN14 8RT Tel: (01225) 742569 Fax: (01249) 783207 E-mail: sales@nwos.co.uk *Office design refurbishment & builders*

North Yorkshire Artstone Ltd, Unit 12 Showfield Lane, Malton, North Yorkshire, YO17 6BT Tel: (01653) 697714 Fax: (01653) 692427 E-mail: artstone@ukonline.co.uk *Stone manufrs*

North Yorkshire Commercials Ltd, Dalton Airfield, Dalton, Thirsk, North Yorkshire, YO7 3HE Tel: (01845) 578123 Fax: (01845) 578144 *Vehicle repair services*

▶ North Yorkshire Construction Plant Ltd, P O Box 157, Middlesbrough, Cleveland, TS9 7JB Tel: (01642) 778444 *Specialist plant hire*Tracked Dumpers*Low Ground Pressure Plant*

▶ North Yorkshire County Contractors Ltd, Grimbald Park, Wetherby Road, Knaresborough, North Yorkshire, HG5 8LJ Tel: (01423) 865584 Fax: (01423) 861162

Northallerton Sign Co., The Units, Morton On Swale, Northallerton, N. Yorkshire, DL7 9RJ Tel: (01609) 777687 Fax: (01609) 777687 E-mail: sales@allertonsigns.co.uk *Industrial & commercial sign writers*

Northamber P.L.C., 23 Davis Road, Chessington, Surrey, KT9 1HS Tel: (020) 8296 7000 Fax: (020) 8296 7330 *Computer peripherals distributors*

Northampton Carton Service, 1 Orchard Cottage, Clifford Hill, Little Houghton, Northampton, NN7 1AL Tel: (01604) 899498 Fax: (01604) 899324 *Carton merchants*

Northampton Finishing Centre Ltd, Barn Way, Lodge Farm Industrial Estate, Northampton, NN5 7UW Tel: (01604) 580704 Fax: (01604) 757701 *Contract packaging services & distributors*

Northampton Footwear Distributors Ltd, Summerhouse Road, Moulton Park Industrial Estate, Northampton, NN3 6WD Tel: (01604) 790828 Fax: (01604) 790577 E-mail: footwear@n-f-d.fsnet.co.uk *Wholesale footwear*

Northampton Machinery Co., 7 Deer Park Road, Moulton Park Industrial Estate, Northampton, NN3 6RX Tel: (01604) 782220 Fax: (01604) 782230 E-mail: sales@mgshall.com *Table machinery manufrs*

Northampton Signs Ltd, Unit 5,, Stour Road,, Weedon Road Industrial Estate,, Northampton, NN5 5AA Tel: (01604) 758198 E-mail: sales@northamptonsigns.co.uk *Northampton Signs has been providing a manufacturing, installation and maintenance service for over 40 years to a diverse range of clients.**With a manufacturing facility in excess of 20,000 sq feet, over 40 staff and trained fitting teams, we are able to handle installation programs of over 200 sites in 3 months.**Current clients include Abbey, Arcadia Group, Ben & Jerrys, Travis Perkins & Phones 4u.**Working on a nationwide basis we supply our clients with first class production and project management. **If you have any questions or would like to arrange a meeting to discuss our services further please feel free to contact Martin Dilleigh at any time.*

Northamptonshire Chamber, Opus House, Anglia Way, Moulton Park Industrial Estate, Northampton, NN3 6JA Tel: (01604) 490490 Fax: (01604) 670362 E-mail: info@businesslinknorthants.org *Chamber of commerce*

▶ Northamptonshire Electrical Contracting Ltd, 81a Charles Street, Kettering, Northamptonshire, NN16 9RL Tel: (01536) 525700 Fax: (01536) 525701 E-mail: enquiries@nec-ltd.co.uk *Northamptonshire Electrical Contracting Ltd (NEC) is one of the UKs leading electrical and mechanical contractors delivering projects across the UK and Europe.*

Northane Chemicals Ltd, Sovereign House, The Bramhall Centre, Bramhall, Stockport, Cheshire, SK7 1AW Tel: 0161-439 3900 Fax: 0161-439 3992 E-mail: gtwiss@northane.com *Chemical agents & distributors*

Northants Computer Service, 67-69 Morley Street, Kettering, Northamptonshire, NN16 9LJ Tel: (01536) 522800 Fax: (01536) 414838 *Computer manufrs*

Company Information

Northants Debt Recovery Services, 31 Wellingborough Road, Earls Barton, Northampton, NN6 0JR Tel: (01604) 811254 Fax: (01604) 812566 E-mail: hunter.m@btconnect.com *Debt recovery services*

Northants Fire Ltd, 58a Ivy Road, Northampton, NN1 4QT Tel: (01604) 460026 Fax: (01604) 601900 E-mail: info@northhantsfire.co.uk *Fire extinguishers suppliers*

Northants Precision Grinding Ltd, 12 Tenter Road, Moulton Park Industrial Estate, Northampton, NN3 6PZ Tel: (01604) 648772 Fax: (01604) 642851 E-mail: sales@northantsgrinding.co.uk *Precision grinding engineers*

Northants Welding Supplies Ltd, 8-9 Vaux Road, Finedon Road Industrial Estate, Wellingborough, Northamptonshire, NN8 4TG Tel: (01933) 224614 Fax: (01933) 441045 *Welding equipment suppliers*

Northbourne Engineering Ltd, The Old Malt House, Easole Street, Nonington, Dover, Kent, CT15 4HF Tel: (01304) 842858 Fax: (01304) 842868 E-mail: northbourneeng@talk21.com *Metal fabricators*

Northcliffe Newspapers, 31-32 John Street, London, WC1N 2AT Tel: 0116-222 4060 Fax: (020) 7400 1518 *Newspaper publishers*

Northcot Brick Ltd, Blockley, Moreton-In-Marsh, Gloucestershire, GL56 9LH Tel: (01386) 700551 Fax: (01386) 700852 E-mail: info@northcotbrick.co.uk *Facing brick manufrs*

Northcott Electronics Ltd, 1 Marquis Business Centre, Royston Road, Baldock, Hertfordshire, SG7 6XL Tel: (01462) 490999 Fax: (01462) 490990 E-mail: info@northcott.co.uk *Electronic component distributors*

▶ Northcroft Ltd, Argall Works, Argall Avenue, London, E10 7QE Tel: (020) 8558 6919 Fax: (020) 8556 1097 E-mail: info@northcroft.uk.com *Furniture design & manufrs*

Northcroft, 1 Horse Guards Avenue, London, SW1A 2HU Tel: (020) 7839 7858 Fax: (020) 7930 2594 E-mail: surv@northcroft.co.uk *Quantity surveyors & construction consultants* Also at: Branches throughout the U.K.

Northdown Buildings & Supplies Ltd, Shipton Green, Etchenor, Chichester, West Sussex, PO20 7DA Tel: (01243) 513613 Fax: (01243) 671672 *Site accommodation, flatpack, sales & hire*

Northdown Packaging, 13c Quarry Wood Industrial Estate, Mills Road, Aylesford, Kent, ME20 7NA Tel: (01622) 710695 Fax: (01622) 790889 E-mail: sales@northdownpackaging.co.uk *Corrugated box manufrs*

Northdown Windows, 326 Northdown Road, Margate, Kent, CT9 3PW Tel: (01843) 232081 Fax: (01843) 224211 E-mail: info@northdown-windows.co.uk *Window manufrs*

Northeast Corrosion Engineers Ltd, Craigearn Business Park, Kintore, Inverurie, Aberdeenshire, AB51 0TH Tel: 01467 633593 *Corrosion prevention consultants*

Northend Ltd, Clyde Road, Sheffield, S8 0TZ Tel: 0114-250 0331 Fax: 0114-250 0676 E-mail: sales@northend.co.uk *Commercial printers*

Northend Construction, Maypole Crescent, Wallhouse Road, Erith, Kent, DA8 2JZ Tel: (01322) 333441 Fax: (01322) 333441 *Structural engineers*

Northern Access Ltd, Unit D Avondale Way, Wakefield, West Yorkshire, WF2 7QU Tel: (01924) 385869 Fax: (01924) 385868 E-mail: sales@northernaccess.co.uk *Access platforms sales & hire*

▶ Northern Ale Distributors, Holmcliffe Avenue, Bankfield Park, Huddersfield, HD4 7RN Tel: (01484) 302986 E-mail: sales@northernaledistributors.co.uk *Suppliers of real ales to the licensed trade*

Northern Arc Electric Welding Co Leicester Ltd, 161 Scudamore Road, Leicester, LE3 1UQ Tel: 0116-287 4949 Fax: 0116-287 5153 *Boiler & pressure vessel welders*

▶ Northern Automotive Systems Ltd, Gilwern Park Industrial Estate, T Y Mawr Road, Gilwern, Abergavenny, Gwent, NP7 0EB Tel: (01873) 832263 Fax: (01873) 832034 E-mail: info@norcorp.com *Metal & plastic nameplates, labels, panels, overlays & trim, screen printing, lithography, brushing, roller coating, stamping & forming processes, providing over 95 years of decorating, design & manufacturing experience*

Northern Blacking Ltd, 47 Catley Road, Sheffield, S9 5JF Tel: 0114-244 5333 Fax: 0114-261 8891 *Electroplating services*

Northern Box & Packaging Co. Ltd, Moss Bridge Mill, Blackburn Road, Darwen, Lancashire, BB3 0AJ Tel: (01254) 702375 Fax: (01254) 873709 *Cardboard box & container manufrs*

▶ Northern Brick Fabrications, Unit 7 Ascot Drive, Stockton-on-Tees, Cleveland, TS18 2QQ Tel: (01642) 602010 Fax: (01642) 672096 E-mail: brick-special@surffree.co.uk *Building equipment suppliers*

Northern Brick Specialists Ltd, Po Box 80, Corby, Northamptonshire, NN18 9ZA Tel: (01536) 460600 Fax: (01536) 460606 *Brick factors distributers*

Northern Cam Company Ltd, Unit 127 Whitehall Indust Estate, Whitehall Road, Leeds, LS12 5JB Tel: 0113-279 2733 Fax: 0113-279 4547 E-mail: info@northerncam.co.uk *CNC turning repetition work*

▶ Northern Carbide Specialists, Greenbank Business Park, Challenge Way, Blackburn, BB1 5QB Tel: (01254) 697171 Fax: (01254) 692800

Northern Cast Acrylics Ltd, 1 Aston Fields Road, Whitehouse Industrial Estate, Runcorn, Cheshire, WA7 3DL Tel: (01928) 790209 Fax: (01928) 790210 E-mail: nca@ncaltd.co.uk *Acrylic manufrs*

Northern Coil Services, Unit 6 Aston Court, Kingsland Grange, Woolston, Warrington, WA1 4SG Tel: (01925) 819642 Fax: (01925) 825865 E-mail: ncsdeakin@aol.com *Ferrite coil design & manufrs*

▶ Northern Combustion Systems Ltd, 64 Battye Street, Dewsbury, West Yorkshire, WF13 1NX Tel: (01924) 457300 Fax: (01924) 459487 E-mail: sales@ncsltd.co.uk *Combustion furnace manufrs*

Northern Communications Systems Ltd, Haigh Hall, Jebb Lane, Haigh, Barnsley, South Yorkshire, S75 4BT Tel: (01924) 830400 Fax: (01924) 830081 *Telecommunications dealer*

Northern Computer Markets, Tara House, Grains Road, Shaw, Oldham, OL2 8JB Tel: (01706) 299902 Fax: (01706) 840444 E-mail: sales@computermarkets.co.uk *Computer exhibitions*

Northern Connection Ltd, 23 Kelso Gardens, Newcastle upon Tyne, NE15 7DB Tel: 0191-274 5600 Fax: 0191-274 5625 *Computer consultants*

Northern Connectors Ltd, Abbotsfield Road, Reginald Road Industrial Estate, St. Helens, Merseyside, WA9 4HU Tel: (01744) 815001 Fax: (01744) 814040 E-mail: sales@northern-connectors.co.uk *Connectors & cables*

▶ Northern Construction Services (Engineering) Ltd, Silverburn Cresent, Bridge of Don Industrial Estate, Aberdeen, AB23 8EW Tel: (01224) 826012 Fax: (01224) 827292

Northern Containers Ltd, Haigh Park Road, Leeds, LS10 1RT Tel: 0113-270 8515 Fax: 0113-271 9687 E-mail: mailing@norcon.co.uk *Container repairers, sales & hire*

Northern Corrugated Cases Ltd, 16 Middlewich Road, Byley, Middlewich, Cheshire, CW10 9NX Tel: (01606) 836811 Fax: (01606) 836088 E-mail: sales@northcorr.co.uk *Box, carton & packaging materials manufrs*

▶ Northern Counties Insurance Broker, NCi House, Lowreys Lane, Low Fell, Gateshead, Tyne & Wear, NE9 5JB Tel: 0191 482 1219 Fax: 0191 420 0097 E-mail: contactus@northerncounties.com *Save Money on Your Business Insurance. Fast Online Insurance quotes available at www.northerncounties.com as well as all types of Commercial Insurance, Motor Trade Insurance, Nursery Insurance, Charity Insurance and Liability Insurance. Contact Northern Counties Insurance Brokers now and see how much you can save.*

▶ Northern County Forklift Ltd, 15 The Avenue, Rainford, St. Helens, Merseyside, WA11 8DR Tel: (01744) 883959 *Fork lift repairers*

Northern Creative Metal Arts, Lock Street, Dewsbury, West Yorkshire, WF12 9BZ Tel: (01924) 469944 Fax: (01924) 469944 *Wrought iron gate manufrs*

Northern Cullet Ltd, Pontefract Road, Barnsley, South Yorkshire, S71 1HJ Tel: (01226) 246541 Fax: (01226) 704529 E-mail: sales@northerncullet.co.uk *Glass recycling contractors*

Northern Dairy Supplies Ltd, Lea Road, Lea Town, Preston, PR4 0RA Tel: (01772) 720358 Fax: (01772) 726489 E-mail: admin@dairyhygiene.co.uk *Dairy hygiene chemicals & disinfectants manufrs*

Northern Data Machines, 35 The Square, Grantown-on-Spey, Morayshire, PH26 3HF Tel: (01479) 873777 Fax: (01479) 87377 E-mail: enquiries@northerndata.co.uk *Scales & weighing machines distributors*

Northern Design Electronics Ltd, 228 Bolton Road, Bradford, West Yorkshire, BD3 0QW Tel: (01274) 729533 Fax: (01274) 721074 E-mail: sales@ndmeter.co.uk *Power measurement instrument manufrs*

▶ Northern Developments, Oakvale House, Thomas Lane, Burgh Road Industrial Estate, Carlisle, CA2 7ND Tel: (01228) 533315 Fax: (01228) 592244

Northern Divers (Engineering) Ltd, Tower Street, Hull, HU9 1TU Tel: (01482) 227276 Fax: (01482) 215712 E-mail: contact@northerndivers.co.uk *Diving services down to 50 meters*

Northern Doors (UK) Ltd, Kingsforth Road, Thurcroft, Rotherham, South Yorkshire, S66 9HU Tel: (01709) 545999 Fax: (01709) 545341 E-mail: mail@northerndoors.co.uk *Industrial door & shutter manufrs*

Northern Electrical Connectors, Unit 8 Glover Centre, Egmont Street, Mossley, Ashton-Under-Lyne, Lancashire, OL5 9PY Tel: (01457) 837511 Fax: (01457) 835216 E-mail: martin@nec-ltd.net *Battery lead & cable accessories manufrs*

▶ Northern Electrical & Control Ltd, 120 Louis Pearlman Centre, Goulton Street, Hull, HU3 4DL Tel: (01482) 225300 Fax: (01482) 610375 E-mail: sales@necl.com

Northern Electrical Engineering Co. Ltd, 40 Earsham Street, Sheffield, S4 7LS Tel: 0114-275 7020 Fax: 0114-273 0476 E-mail: nengcoltd@tiscali.co.uk *Control panel manufrs*

▶ Northern Energy Services Ltd, 206 Askern Road, Bentley, Doncaster, South Yorkshire, DN5 0EU Tel: (01302) 820790 Fax: (01302) 873633

Northern Engineering Services, 16 Kew Gardens, Whitley Bay, Tyne & Wear, NE26 3LY Tel: 0191-253 4390 Fax: 0191-251 6674 E-mail: dshort@northeng.freeserve.co.uk *Energy utilisation consultants*

Northern Engineering Sheffield Ltd, Haigh Moor Drive, Dinnington, Sheffield, S25 2JY Tel: (01909) 560203 Fax: (01909) 560184 E-mail: sales@northerneng.co.uk *Technical sealing products manufrs*

▶ Northern Engineering & Welding Co. Ltd, Claggan Road, Fort William, Inverness-Shire, PH33 6PH Tel: (01397) 702588 Fax: (01397) 705091 E-mail: sales@newcolimited.co.uk *Metalworking & fabrication services*

Northern Engraving & Sign Co Ltd, John Spence Sands, Courtney St, Hull, HU8 7QF Tel: (01482) 328110 Fax: (01482) 323077 E-mail: enquiries@northernengraving.co.uk *General engravers & sign manufrs*

▶ Northern Environmental Services Ltd, 1 Burnfoot Workshops, Burnfoot Road, Hawick, Roxburghshire, TD9 8EL Tel: (01450) 370277 Fax: (01450) 371134 E-mail: inquires@nes.uk.com *Air vents*

Northern Executive Aviation Ltd, Hangar 7, Western Maintenance Area, Manchester Airport, Manchester, M90 5NE Tel: 0161-436 6666 Fax: 0161-436 3450 E-mail: info@northernexec.com *Air charter & maintenance*

Northern Fabrications, Albion Road, Bradford, West Yorkshire, BD10 9LT Tel: 01274 613874 *Stainless steel fabricators*

Northern Fabricators Ltd, Chanonry Industrial Estate, Elgin, Morayshire, IV30 6ND Tel: (01343) 546139 Fax: (01343) 549420 E-mail: enquiries@norfabs.co.uk *Stainless steel manufrs*

Northern Financial Solutions, 68 Bradford Road, Clayton, Bradford, West Yorkshire, BD14 6DN Tel: 01274 815999 Fax: 01274 883833 E-mail: enquiries@nfsonline.plus.com *FSA Directly Authorised Mortgage, Loan and General Insurance Brokers who source from the whole of market to get our clients the best deals available no matter what their credit history.***We specialise in: adverse mortgages, commercial mortgages, self-employed mortgages, fixed rate mortgages, discounted mortgages, capped mortgages, tracker mortgages, flexible mortgages, offset mortgages, secured loans, personal loans, commercial loans, life insurance, mortgage protection insurance, commercial insurance, pet insurance and travel insurance.***

Northern Fire & Safety Co, Lodge House, Morton Street, Middleton, Manchester, M24 6AN Tel: 0161-643 9338 Fax: 0161-655 3878 E-mail: info@fireandsafety.co.uk *Fire-fighting equipment manufrs*

Northern Flags Ltd, Unit 1 5 Matrix Court, Leeds, LS11 5WB Tel: 0113-205 5180 Fax: 0113-205 5181 E-mail: info@northernflags.com Principal Export Areas: Worldwide *Northern Flags are specialists in supplying bespoke fabric print solutions, offering expertise guidance through every stage of your display requirements. We are the UK office of Faber Pro-Motion, the largest fabric printer in Europe, & as a result, we have the expertise to provide solutions for any requirement. With our position as European number one, we have built up an established client base in a range of market segments from food & drink, retail through to house builders, FMCG & automotive. Clients include Heineken & Guinness, Paul Smith, Habitat & Adidas, NHBC & Lovell Group, Coca-Cola, Lotus, Mercedes Benz & Jaguar.**BANNERS-Internal banners external banners -PVC or Fabric banners.*FLAGS - Corporate flags, national flags & promotional flags.*FLAGPOLES - Fibreglass poles, aluminium poles, wall or ground mounted poles.*PARASOLS - Printed parasols, promotional parasols, smoking ban parasols.*FABRIC DISPLAYS - Fabric displays, banner displays, internal displays.*

Northern Fork Lifts, 22 Ballybrakes Road, Ballymoney, County Antrim, BT53 6LQ Tel: (028) 2766 3030 Fax: (028) 2766 9191 E-mail: sales@northernforklifts.com *Fork lift truck hire & repairers*

Northern Gaskets & Mouldings Ltd, Unit 1 Norquest Industrial Park, Birstall, Batley, West Yorkshire, WF17 9NE Tel: (01924) 422233 Fax: (01924) 422244 E-mail: sales@northerngaskets.com *Gasket manufrs*

▶ Northern Glass, 9-10 Hertburn Estate, Hertburn, Washington, Tyne & Wear, NE37 2SF Tel: 0191-416 0222 Fax: 0191-415 7139 E-mail: info@ew1-windows.co.uk

Northern Helicopter Products Ltd, Woodfield House, Woodfield Road, Broadheath, Altrincham, Cheshire, WA14 4ED Tel: 0161-928 5984 Fax: 0161-929 5984 *Rotor blades for model helicopter manufrs*

▶ Northern Heritage Developments Ltd, 19 Haw Grove, Hellifield, Skipton, North Yorkshire, BD23 4JA Tel: (01729) 851065

▶ Northern Highways Ltd, Charnock Road, Liverpool, L9 7ET Tel: 0151-521 8400 Fax: 0151-521 8500

▶ Northern Hi-Tec Industrial Graphics Ltd, Wasco House, Willow Lane, Lancaster, LA1 5NA Tel: (01524) 68655 Fax: (01524) 67544 E-mail: enquiry@nht.co.uk *Manufacturers of labels, decals, overlays, membrane switches*

Northern Hydraulics, 51 Gortgonis Road, Coalisland, Dungannon, County Tyrone, BT71 4QG Tel: (028) 8774 7444 Fax: (028) 8774 7544 E-mail: info@northernhydraulics.com *Hydraulic cylinder manufrs*

▶ Northern I T Consultancy, 5 Rishton Lane, Bolton, BL3 6QZ Tel: (0870) 7517444 Fax: 01204 456671 E-mail: Info@nitc.co.uk *One Stop Shop for IT Solutions*All your IT requirements from one company including:**Networking, website design & hosting, on-site support, hardware and software sales and support, ADSL & Broadband configuration and sales, BeSpoke software development. Everything at very competitive prices*

▶ Northern Illustrated Print, 141 Shakespeare Street, Southport, Merseyside, PR8 5AN Tel: (01704) 547222 Fax: (01704) 547333

Northern Industrial Roofing, Howley Lane, Warrington, WA1 2DN Tel: (01925) 244442 Fax: (01925) 244299 E-mail: david.gillam@northernindustrialroofing.co.uk *Northern Industrial Roofing cover every area of the UK, and can undertake contracts of any site. Below is a brief summary of just some of the roofing solutions we can offer to suit your needs, but should you have any further queries oon the services we offer please ring: 01925 244442, or e-mail us on: enquiries@northernindustrialroofing.co.uk. Commercial Services: Slating and Tiling Industrial Roofing and Cladding Flat and Felt Roofing Decking (for Flat Roofing) Waterproof Coatings Lead/Zinc/Copprt Roofing Guttering Single Ply Domestic Services New Flat Roofs Re-Roofing of Flat Roofs Repairs to Flat Roofs.*

Northern Ireland Chamber of Commerce & Industry, 22 Great Victoria Street, Belfast, BT2 7BJ Tel: (028) 9024 4113 Fax: (028) 9024 7024 E-mail: mail@northernirelandchamber.com *Chamber of commerce*

Northern Ireland Community Addiction Service, 219 Albertbridge Road, Belfast, BT5 4PU Tel: (028) 9073 1602 Fax: (028) 9046 0979 *Telecommunications*

Northern Ireland Plastics Ltd, 39 Shrigley Road, Killyleagh, Downpatrick, County Down, BT30 9SR Tel: (028) 4482 8753 Fax: (028) 4482 8809 E-mail: sales@nip-ltd.co.uk *Plastics manufacturers*

Northern Ireland Protective Clothing Co., 13 Balmoral Road, Belfast, BT12 6QA Tel: (028) 9068 1107 Fax: (028) 9066 2733 E-mail: sales@nipcco.co.uk *Protective clothing suppliers*

Northern Ireland Railways Co. Ltd, East Bridge, Belfast, BT1 3PR Tel: (028) 9089 9400 E-mail: feedback@translink.co.uk *Transport services*

▶ Northern Istallations Ltd, Lumbrook Mills, Westercroft Lane, Halifax, West Yorkshire, HX3 7TY Tel: (01422) 202777 Fax: (01422) 202888 E-mail: info@northerninstallations.co.uk *Installation & transport services*

Northern Jacks & Equipment Ltd, 4 Beverley Business Centre, St Nicholas Road, Beverley, North Humberside, HU17 0QT Tel: (01482) 882590 Fax: (01482) 867309 E-mail: info@scopeuk.fsnet.co.uk *Hydraulic engineers*

Northern Joinery, Daniel Street, Whitworth, Rochdale, Lancashire, OL12 8DA Tel: (01706) 852345 Fax: (01706) 853114 E-mail: northern-joinery@compuserve.com *Wooden staircase manufrs*

Northern Koi & Aquatics, 196 Manchester Road, Rixton, Warrington, WA3 6EA Tel: (01925) 812028 Fax: (01925) 823266 E-mail: enquiries@northernkoi.co.uk *Pets & aquatic services*

▶ Northern Light Stage & Technical Services Ltd, 39-41 Assembly Street, Edinburgh, EH6 7RG Tel: 0131-553 2383 Fax: 0131-553 3296 E-mail: info@northernlight.co.uk *Entertainment equipment supplier & installer*

Northern Machine Guard & Fabrications, Unit 14 Albert Mill, Albert Place, Lower Darwen, Darwen, Lancashire, BB3 0QE Tel: (01254) 662595 Fax: (01254) 662595 *Machine guards & steel fabricators*

Northern Machine Tools (Engineering) Ltd, P O Box Southbank 16, Middlesbrough, Cleveland, TS6 6LP Tel: (01642) 440551 Fax: (01642) 440141 E-mail: sales@nmt.onyxnet.co.uk *Machine tool merchants*

Northern Mens & Boyswear Ltd, 52 Lower Oxford Street, Castleford, West Yorkshire, WF10 4AF Tel: (01977) 556203 Fax: (01977) 556203 *Clothing manufrs*

Northern Minimix, Haverton Hill, Billingham, Cleveland, TS23 4EY Tel: (01642) 563243 Fax: (01642) 561509 *Concrete manufacturer & supplier*

Northern Minimix Ltd, New Building, Birch Road, Sheffield, S9 3XL Tel: 0114-244 6353 Fax: (01709) 790707 *Ready mixed concrete distributors*

Northern Molybdenum Ltd, Samson Close, Newcastle upon Tyne, NE12 6DZ Tel: 0191-268 9478 Fax: 0191-216 0004 *Molybdenum disulphide lubricants*

Northern Optical Manchester Co. Ltd, 1 Edwin Road, Manchester, M11 3NQ Tel: 0161-273 5222 Fax: 0161-274 3591 *Manufacturing opticians*

Northern Packaging Ltd, Selby Place, Stanley Industrial Estate, Skelmersdale, Lancashire, WN8 8EF Tel: (01695) 731445 Fax: (01695) 51865 E-mail: sales@northern-packaging.co.uk *Corrugated packaging for industry*

▶ Northern Packaging Distributors Ltd, 1 Angels Close, Aycliffe Industrial Park, Newton Aycliffe, County Durham, DL5 6BG Tel: (01325) 300133

Northern Plastics, Perseverance Works, Dewsbury Road, Elland, West Yorkshire, HX5 9AZ Tel: (01422) 311569 Fax: (01422) 376841 E-mail: rharrison@northernplastics.co.uk *Glass fibre, acid resisting & plastic tanks*

Northern Plastics 84 Ltd, Mount Street, Hyde, Cheshire, SK14 1NT Tel: 0161-368 2968 Fax: 0161-368 2183 E-mail: np84ltd@btconnect.com *Acrylic sign fabricators & manufrs*

Northern Platforms Ltd, 8 Hind Heath Road, Wheelock, Sandbach, Cheshire, CW11 3LG Tel: (01270) 761954 Fax: (01270) 761954 E-mail: jc.wood@npl.com *Sales, service & training access*

Northern Polytunnels Ltd, Mill Green, Waterside Road, Colne, Lancashire, BB8 0TA Tel: (01282) 873120 Fax: (01282) 871733 E-mail: info@npstructures.co.uk *Film clad structures*

▶ Northern Power Clean Ltd, 26 Whitworth Drive, Aycliffe Industrial Estate, Newton Aycliffe, County Durham, DL5 6SZ Tel: (01325) 318070 Fax: (01325) 301711 E-mail: npcltd@btconnect.com *Manufacturer & distributor of high pressure cleaning equipment*

▶ Northern Power Plant Ltd, 1 Burdon Main Row, North Shields, Tyne & Wear, NE29 6SU Tel: 0191-257 2670 Fax: 0191-296 1434 E-mail: powerplant@btconnect.com *Generators sales, services & spares*

Northern Products Ltd, Unit 20 Rassau Industrial Estate, Rassau, Ebbw Vale, Gwent, NP23 5SD Tel: (01495) 352577 Fax: (01495) 307545 *Plastic injection moulding engineers*

Northern Profiles, Elm Tree Street, Wakefield, West Yorkshire, WF1 5EQ Tel: (01924) 291655 Fax: (01924) 372010 *Steel profilers*

Northern Protection, Unit 38 The Brampton Centre, Brampton Road, Wath-upon-Dearne, Rotherham, South Yorkshire, S63 6BB Tel: (01709) 879333 Fax: (01709) 879443 E-mail: cm@nightforce.co.uk *Manned guarding to industry & commerce supplier*

Northern Pump Suppliers Ltd, Bowling Back Lane, Bradford, West Yorkshire, BD4 8SR Tel: (01274) 721314 Fax: (01274) 730223 E-mail: sales-bradford@northern-pumps.co.uk *Pump distributors & agents* Also at: Bradford

Northern Radiators Ltd, 3 Dolly Lane, Leeds, LS9 7TU Tel: 0113-243 5051 Fax: 0113-245 7486 E-mail: info@radiatorsonline.co.uk *Motor radiator manufrs* Also at: Bradford, Huddersfield & York

Northern Radio Sytems, 96-98 Constitution Street, Edinburgh, EH6 6AW Tel: 0131-467 7620 Fax: 0131-553 7760 *Radio equipment*

Northern Recruitment Group Ltd, Lloyds Court, 56 Grey Street, Newcastle upon Tyne, NE1 6AH Tel: 0191-232 1222 Fax: 0191-261 8466 E-mail: newcastle@nrgplc.com *Recruitment agents*

Northern Refrigeration, 17 Moray Street, Wick, Caithness, KW1 5QF Tel: (01955) 603240 Fax: (01955) 604785 E-mail: j1mer@btopenworld.com *Refrigeration contractors & air conditioning services*

Northern Refrigeration & Catering Equipment Ltd, Rotherside Road, Eckington, Sheffield, S21 4HL Tel: (01246) 434340 Fax: (01246) 434341 *Manufacture commercial catering equipment*

Northern Refrigeration & Catering Equipment Ltd, Rotherside Road, Eckington, Sheffield, S21 4HL Tel: (01246) 434340 Fax: (01246) 434341 *Catering equipment suppliers & manufrs*

▶ Northern Scaffold Co. Ltd, Derbyshire Yard, 21 Chesterfield Road, Sheffield, S8 0RL Tel: 0114-255 3100

Northern Services, 10 Albion Way, East Kilbride, Glasgow, G75 0YN Tel: (01355) 241333 Fax: (01355) 241555 E-mail: sales@northernservices.co.uk *Mailing equipment services*

▶ Northern Signcases Ltd, Unit 9d Kayley Industrial Estate, Richmond Street, Ashton-under-Lyne, Lancashire, OL7 0AU Tel: 0161-343 6600 Fax: 0161-343 6611 E-mail: sales@northern-signcases.co.uk *Light box manufrs*

▶ Northern Steeplejacks Edinburgh Ltd, 7 Newbattle Road, Newtongrange, Dalkeith, Midlothian, EH22 4RA Tel: 0131-654 2700 Fax: 0131-654 2600

Northern Storage Systems Ltd, 5 Liff Park, Liff, Dundee, DD2 5PH Tel: 01382 581475 *Storage systems sales & installation*

Northern Structures Ltd, Amble Industrial Estate, Amble, Morpeth, Northumberland, NE65 0PE Tel: (01665) 710746 Fax: (01665) 712738 E-mail: sales@northernstructures.co.uk *Agricultural & industrial buildings*

Northern Survey Service, 199 Marlborough Avenue, Princes Avenue, Hull, HU5 3LG Tel: (01482) 342240 Fax: (01482) 448905 *Market researchers*

Northern Switch Gear & Controls, 2 Lloyd Court, Dunston, Gateshead, Tyne & Wear, NE11 9EP Tel: 0191-461 1130 Fax: 0191-461 1140 E-mail: nthnswitch@aol.com *Switchboard manufrs*

Northern Tool & Gear Co. Ltd, John St West, Arbroath, Angus, DD11 1RT Tel: (01241) 872626 Fax: (01241) 870040 E-mail: general@ntgear.co.uk *Gear manufacturers & cutters*

Northern Tools & Accessories Ltd, PO Box 5, Newcastle upon Tyne, NE6 5XB Tel: 0191-265 2821 Fax: 0191-276 2668 E-mail: marketing@crossling.co.uk *Power & hand tool distributors*

Northern Track Ltd, Garnet Road, Leeds, LS11 5JD Tel: 0113-276 2300 *Earth moving & demolition equipment manufrs*

Northern Trimmings, 4 Dale House, Vickers Street, Manchester, M40 8EF Tel: 0161-205 6845 Fax: 0161-205 6845 *Button merchants*

Northern Trophies Engravers, 41 Union Street, Middlesbrough, Cleveland, TS1 4EA Tel: (01642) 247877 Fax: (01642) 247877 *Trophies, rosettes & medal engravers service*

Northern Visions, 23 Donegall Street, Belfast, BT1 2FF Tel: (028) 9024 5495 Fax: (028) 9032 6608 E-mail: info@northanvisions.org *Film manufrs*

Northey Technologies Ltd, Nortech House, Allens Lane, Poole, Dorset, BH16 5DG Tel: (01202) 668600 Fax: (01202) 668500 E-mail: info@northey.net *Compressors (oil free) & vacuum pumps manufrs*

▶ Northfield Aluminium Ltd, Northfield Road, Rotherham, South Yorkshire, S60 1RR Tel: (01709) 372502 Fax: (01709) 378996

Northfield Engineering, 41 Hedon Road, Hull, HU9 1LH Tel: (01482) 320888 Fax: (01482) 587271 E-mail: sales@northfieldeng.co.uk *Hydraulic engineers & cylinder ram manufrs*

Northgate Aluminium Systems, Park Road East, Calverton, Nottingham, NG14 6LL Tel: 0115-965 5655 Fax: 0115-965 2227 E-mail: info@dalesidegroup.com *Aluminium doors, windows & curtain walling manufrs*

▶ Northgate Estate Agents, 22 High Northgate, Darlington, County Durham, DL1 1UP Tel: (01325) 285360 Fax: (01325) 285365 E-mail: info@northgate-estates.co.uk *Buy, Sell, Let.*

Northgate Information Solutions Ltd, 6 Woodlands Workshops, Coedcae Lane, Pontyclun, Mid Glamorgan, CF72 9DW Tel: (01443) 228740 *IT consultants*

Northgate Information Solutions Ltd, Channel House, South Road, Midsomer Norton, Radstock, BA3 2EZ Tel: (01761) 411664 Fax: (01761) 411159 *Computer software consultants*

Northgate Information Solutions, Prolog House, Littlemoor, Eckington, Sheffield, S21 4EF Tel: (01246) 439400 Fax: (01246) 439401 E-mail: enquiries@northgate-is.com *HR providers & payroll software specialists services*

Northgate Solar Controls, Barnet, Hertfordshire, EN4 9EW Tel: (020) 8441 4545 Fax: (020) 8441 4888 *Solar control & safety film distributor*

▶ Northlight Images, 86 Harrow Road, Leicester, LE3 0JW Tel: 0116-291 9092 E-mail: sales@northlight-it.com *Commercial, fine art, event & pr photography services*

▶ Northlogic Ltd, Newton Business Park, Talbot Road, Hyde, Cheshire, SK14 4UQ Tel: 0161-366 1002 Fax: 0161-366 1080

Northolt Glass Co. Ltd, 151-159 Church Road, Northolt, Middlesex, UB5 5AG Tel: (020) 8841 6989 Fax: (020) 8842 1944 E-mail: n.glass@talk21.com *Glazing contractors*

Northorpe Joinery, Northorpe, Atwick Road, Hornsea, North Humberside, HU18 1EJ Tel: (01964) 534407 Fax: (01964) 534407 *Joiners*

Northover & Gilbert Removals, Gundry Lane, Bridport, Dorset, DT6 3RJ Tel: (01308) 423939 Fax: (01308) 423939 *Removal contractors*

Northpoint Ltd, Globe Lane, Dukinfield, Cheshire, SK16 4UY Tel: 0161-330 4551 Fax: 0161-339 7169 E-mail: sales@northpoint.ltd.uk *Industrial powder coating suppliers*

Alan Northrop Ltd, Enterprise Way Airedale Business Centre, Keighley Road, Skipton, North Yorkshire, BD23 2TZ Tel: (01756) 700555 Fax: (01756) 795505 E-mail: info@alan-northrop.co.uk *Textile accessories & label manufrs*

Northshore Composites Ltd, Brockhampton Road, Havant, Hampshire, PO9 1JU Tel: (023) 9247 1428 Fax: (023) 9245 2228 E-mail: info@northshore-composites.co.uk *Composite component manufrs*

Northsleep Ltd, 19-21 St Clair Street, Aberdeen, AB24 5TA Tel: (01224) 632334 Fax: (01224) 649282 *Divan & mattress manufrs*

▶ Northstar Marketing & Design, Northstar House, 5 Ferns Mead, Farnham, Surrey, GU9 7XP Tel: (01252) 734070 Fax: (01252) 734071 E-mail: info@northstarmarketing.co.uk *Northstar help you achieve your business objectives through the provision of intelligent, creative marketing services ie. advertising, corporate and sales literature, direct mail, new media, website production, merchandising and brand development.*

▶ Northstone Quarry & Asphalt Division, 50 Craigadoo Road, Ballymena, County Antrim, BT42 4RB Tel: (028) 2589 8151 *Quarry & asphalt division*

Northumbria Blow Moulding Ltd, Northumbria House Unit 7 North Tyne Industrial Estate, Whitley Road, Benton, Newcastle upon Tyne, NE12 9SZ Tel: 0191-215 0958 Fax: 0191-266 7790 E-mail: sales@northblowmould.co.uk *Blow moulding*

Northumbria Optical Coatings Ltd, Unit 10 Burford Way, Boldon Business Park, Boldon Colliery, Tyne & Wear, NE35 9PZ Tel: 0191-537 4888 Fax: 0191-537 4777 E-mail: sales@noc-ltd.com *Infrared filter & coating manufrs*

Northumbria Plant Hire, Great Lime Road, West Moor, Newcastle Upon Tyne, NE12 0RU Tel: 0191-268 7000 Fax: 0191-216 0838 *Contractors plant hire & dealers*

Northumbrian Packaging, Gear House, Saltmeadows Road, Gateshead, Tyne & Wear, NE8 3AH Tel: 0191-490 3372 Fax: 0191-490 3372 E-mail: northpackaging@fsbdial.co.uk *Suppliers of quality packaging materials nationwide. Specialists in plain packaging, printed packaging, paper bags, polythene bags, carrier bags, refuse sacks, gift bags, gift boxes, food containers, bubble wrap, plastic bags. We offer a quality delivery service across the UK*

▶ Northumbrian Soap Co., 89 Station Road, Ashington, Northumberland, NE63 8RS Tel: (01670) 858936

Northvale Korting Ltd, Uxbridge Road, Leicester, LE4 7ST Tel: 0116-266 5911 Fax: 0116-261 0050 E-mail: sales@northvalekorting.co.uk Principal Export Areas: Worldwide *Control valve & fluid jet equipment manufrs*

▶ Northwall Dover Ltd, Coombe Works, Coombe Road, Dover, Kent, CT17 0LQ Tel: (01304) 226154 Fax: (01304) 240085 *Contract upholstery hotels cruise ships marine & leisure*

▶ Northwards Ltd, Anderson Base, Gremista, Lerwick, Shetland, ZE1 0PX Tel: (01595) 692626 Fax: (01595) 694920

▶ Northwards Ltd, Garson, Stromness, Orkney, KW16 3JU Tel: (01856) 851083 Fax: (01856) 851081 E-mail: sales@northwardsltd.co.uk

Northway Fire Protection & Marine Services, Farset Enterprise Park, 638 Springfield Road, Belfast, BT12 7DY Tel: (028) 9024 1700 Fax: (028) 9024 1901 *Suppliers & maintenance of fire fighting equipment*

Northwest Aero Dynamic Models Ltd, 206 Longhurst Lane, Mellor, Stockport, Cheshire, SK6 5PN Tel: 0161-427 8474 Fax: 0161-427 7027 *Model wind tunnels & proto type manufrs*

Northwest Air Lines Inc, Oakfield Court, Consort Way, Horley, Surrey, RH6 7AF Tel: (01293) 778400 Fax: (01293) 824871 *Air line company* Also at: Glasgow & Manchester

▶ Northwest Couriers, 30 Whitfield Cross, Glossop, Derbyshire, SK13 8NW Tel: (07939) 540345 E-mail: gleatherbarrow@hotmail.com *Guaranteed same day, next day nationwide courier service*

Northwest Threading Services, 7 Suthers Street, Oldham, OL9 7TE Tel: 0161-628 5557 Fax: 0161-628 3339 *Thread cutting machine manufrs*

Northwich Industrial Roofing Ltd, 4 Bridge Street, Northwich, Cheshire, CW9 7NR Tel: (01606) 43884 Fax: (01606) 43884 *Industrial roofing & cladding specialists*

Northwood Computer Tutorial Centre Ltd, Paget, Flaunden Lane, Flaunden, Bovingdon, Hemel Hempstead, Hertfordshire, HP3 0PQ Tel: (01442) 831234 *Teaching services for children*

Northwood Engineering Birmingham Co. Ltd, 122 Emily Street, Birmingham, B12 0XJ Tel: 0121-440 6731 Fax: 0121-440 3549 E-mail: northwoodengltd@aol.com *CNC & secondary operation works suppliers*

Northwood Paper Sales Ltd, 4 Warner House, Harrovian Business Village, Harrow, Middlesex, HA1 3EX Tel: (020) 8423 0100 Fax: (020) 8423 8880 E-mail: nps@northwoodpaper.com *Industrial paper suppliers*

Northwood Spares & Accessories Ltd, 87 Newington Causeway, London, SE1 6DH Tel: (020) 7407 9681 Fax: (020) 7940 0820 E-mail: info@northwoods-ltd.com *Car parts & accessories suppliers*

Nortim Tools Ltd, 5 New Mills Industrial Estate, Libbys Drive, Stroud, Gloucestershire, GL5 1RN Tel: (01453) 759613 Fax: (01453) 753803 E-mail: sue@nortim.co.uk *Precision engineers*

▶ Nortique, 58 Thoroughfare, Halesworth, Suffolk, IP19 8AR Tel: (01986) 875656 E-mail: nortique@nortique.co.uk *Antique pine furniture dealers*

Norton, Works Road, Letchworth Garden City, Hertfordshire, SG6 1LP Tel: (01462) 676944 Fax: (01462) 677192 E-mail: nif-ltd@btconnect.com *Engineers' supplies & fastener distributors*

Norton Cast Products Ltd, Capital Steel Works, Tinsley Park Road, Sheffield, S9 5DL Tel: 0114-244 8722 Fax: 0114-242 5523 E-mail: info@nortoncast.com *Manufacturers of castings including stainless steel, cobalts alloys, steel duplex & austenitic*

Norton Castings, 18 Oaklands, Old Buckenham, Attleborough, Norfolk, NR17 1SA Tel: (01953) 860998 Fax: (01953) 860998 E-mail: enquiries@nortoncastings.co.uk *House signs*

Norton Fabrications, 46 Light Pipe Hall Road, Stockton-on-Tees, Cleveland, TS18 4AH Tel: (01642) 674944 Fax: (01642) 890522 *Iron structure fabricators*

Norton Hydraulics Ltd, Factory 2, Kenninghall Road, London, N18 2PD Tel: (020) 8807 4295 Fax: (020) 8807 9990 E-mail: info@norton-hydraulics.co.uk *Hose coupling factor suppliers* Also at: Braintree

Norton Hydraulics Midland Ltd, 43-45 Meriden Street, Birmingham, B5 5LS Tel: 0121-643 0184 Fax: 0121-631 3617 E-mail: sales@nortonhydraulics.com *Hydraulic systems solutions providers* Also at: Leicester

▶ Norton Industrial Doors Ltd, Unit 58 Birch Road East Industrial Estate, Birch Road East, Birmingham, B6 7DB Tel: 0121-327 7775 Fax: 0121-327 6512 E-mail: sales@nortonindustrialdoors.co.uk *Industrial door manufacturers, repairs & servicing*

Norton Joinery Ltd, Derwent Road, York Road Business Park, Malton, North Yorkshire, YO17 6NW Tel: (01653) 692377 Fax: (01653) 696565 E-mail: mail@nortonjoinery.co.uk *Joinery manufrs*

▶ Norton Logistics, Fengate Road, West Pinchbeck, Spalding, Lincolnshire, PE11 3NE Tel: (01775) 641000 E-mail: info@nortonholgate.com *Cherries suppliers*

Norton Newman Investments Ltd, 1-6 Clay Street, London, W1U 6DA Tel: (020) 7486 4889 Fax: (020) 8441 8337 E-mail: mnorton@focusnet.co.uk *Investment & development property company*

Norton Plastics, The Old Gasworks, Belfield Street, Ilkeston, Derbyshire, DE7 8DU Tel: 0115-944 1245 Fax: 0115-932 8975 E-mail: norton.plastics@vigin.net *Plastic injection moulders*

Norton Precision Ltd, Botley Road, Horton Heath, Eastleigh, Hampshire, SO50 7DN Tel: (023) 8069 3232 Fax: (023) 8060 1551 E-mail: norton.pre@btclick.com *Precision engineers*

Norton Precision Mouldings, Unit 11, Crow Arch Lane Industrial Estate, Crow Arch Lane, Ringwood, Hampshire, BH24 1PD Tel: (01425) 461866 Fax: (01425) 471965 E-mail: sales@nortonmouldings.com *Plastic injection moulders*

Norton Transport Ltd, Norton Street, Miles Platting, Manchester, M40 8HD Tel: 0161-205 4455 Fax: 0161-205 3208 *Transport & general haulage*

▶ Norton Waste Services, The Heath Business & Technical Park, Runcorn, Cheshire, WA7 4QX Tel: (01928) 511655 Fax: (01928) 511656 E-mail: enquires@mortongreen.com

Norton Waugh Managment Software, The Old School, School Lane, Weston-Under-Lizard, Shifnal, Shropshire, TF11 8SZ Tel: (01952) 850333 Fax: (01952) 850649 E-mail: sales@nortonwaugh.co.uk *Computer software house*

Norton Wells, 69 Bolton Road, Windsor, Berkshire, SL4 3JX Tel: (01753) 855336 Fax: (01753) 856727 E-mail: brett@nortonwells.com *Spare parts for pumps on ships distributors*

Nortonics Ltd, Watts Street, Chadderton, Oldham, OL9 9LQ Tel: 0161-626 5316 Fax: 0161-627 0929 *Electronic timers & controlling relays*

Nortonics Ltd, The Old Bakery, 265 Yorktown Road, Sandhurst, Berkshire, GU47 9BN Tel: (01276) 32777 Fax: (01276) 31977 *Electronic component distributors*

Nortool Services Ltd, 573 Stanningley Road, Leeds, LS13 4EL Tel: 0113-257 9333 Fax: 0113-257 9222 E-mail: sales@nortool.com *Power tool suppliers*

Norvall Print Finishing Ltd, 266 York Way, London, N7 9PQ Tel: (020) 7609 8585 Fax: (020) 7700 5644 E-mail: sales@norvall.com *Print finishers*

▶ Norville Optical Co. Ltd, 8 Grange Road, Houstoun Industrial Estate, Livingston, West Lothian, EH54 5DE Tel: (01506) 434261 Fax: (01506) 431851

▶ Norville Optical Co. Ltd, Chevychase Court, Seaham Grange Industrial Estate, Seaham, County Durham, SR7 0PR Tel: 0191-523 8023 Fax: 0191-523 8024 *Optical lenses manufrs*

Norville Optical Group Ltd, Magdala Road, Gloucester, GL1 4DG Tel: (01452) 528686 Fax: (01452) 411094 E-mail: sales@norville.co.uk *Optical manufrs* Also at: Branches throughout the U.K.

Norwell Oil & Gas Exploration, Norwell House, 78 Queens Road, Aberdeen, AB15 4YE Tel: (01224) 498400 Fax: (01224) 208300 E-mail: samantha@norwellengineering.com *Drilling project management*

Norwest Acoustic Contractors, 9 Kirkstone Court, Congleton, Cheshire, CW12 4JW Tel: (01260) 280430 Fax: (01260) 280430 E-mail: norwestacoustics@btinternet.com *Industrial noise control engineers*

Norwest Engineering Ltd, Low Stripes, The Stripes, Cumwhinton, Carlisle, CA4 0AW Tel: (01228) 560408 Fax: (01228) 561696 E-mail: norwest@btclick.com *Laser cutting & precision sheet metalwork*

▶ Norwest Holst Ltd, 6230 Bishops Court, Birmingham Business Court, Birmingham Business Park, Birmingham, B37 7YB Tel: 0121-788 7300 Fax: 0121-707 3438

▶ Norwest Holst Construction Ltd, Clair House, Sir Frank Whittle Road, Derby, DE21 4SS Tel: (01332) 387500 Fax: (01332) 384507

Norwest Holst Construction Ltd, Astral House, Imperial Way, Watford, WD24 4YX Tel: (01923) 233433 Fax: (01923) 256481 *Building & civil engineering contractors*

▶ Norwest Holst Services Ltd, Norwest House, Ditton Road, Widnes, Cheshire, WA8 0WE Tel: 0151-420 6520 Fax: 0151-423 3934

Norwest Trading Co, 6 Buxton Old Road, Disley, Stockport, Cheshire, SK12 2BB Tel: (01663) 764668 Fax: (01663) 764668 E-mail: dr@norwest-trading.co.uk *Suppliers of used construction machinery*

▶ Norwich Balloon Art, 16 Reepham Road, Norwich, NR6 5LH Tel: (01603) 789100 *Balloon decorators*

▶ Norwich Colour Print Ltd, 2-3 Drayton Industrial Estate, Taverham Road, Drayton, Norwich, NR8 6RL Tel: (01603) 868862 Fax: (01603) 861371

▶ Norwich Engine Centre Ltd, Vulcan Road South, Mile Cross Lane, Norwich, NR6 6AF Tel: (01603) 425701 Fax: (01603) 484046 *Engine restoration services*

Norwich Plastics Ltd, Mission Road, Rackheath, Norwich, NR13 6PL Tel: (01603) 720714 Fax: (01603) 721539 *Plastics injection moulders*

Norwich Sheet Metal Co. Ltd, 11 Hurricane Way, Norwich, NR6 6EZ Tel: (01603) 419490 Fax: (01603) 404590 E-mail: nsmetal@btconnect.com *General sheet metalworkers*

Norwich Sunblinds Ltd, 8 St. Benedicts Street, Norwich, NR2 4AG Tel: (01603) 615945 Fax: (01603) 630972 E-mail: sales@norwich-sunblinds.co.uk *Manufacturers & suppliers of sun blinds*

Norwich Union Ltd, 5 Donegall Square South, Belfast, BT1 5AN Tel: (028) 9032 2232 Fax: (028) 9023 8731 *Insurance company*

Norwich Union P.L.C., St. Helen's, 1 Undershaft, London, EC3P 3DQ Tel: (020) 7283 7500 *Insurance company*

Norwich Union Travel Leisure, 69 Park Lane, Croydon, CR9 1BG Tel: (020) 7283 8611 Fax: (020) 7662 4088 *Travel insurance services*

Norwin Electronics Ltd, Unit 6 Industrial Estate, Station Road, Gamlingay, Sandy, Bedfordshire, SG19 3HB Tel: (01767) 651485 Fax: (01767) 651623 E-mail: sales@norwin.co.uk *Electronic engineers*

▶ Norwood Homes, Millbrae, Findhorn, Forres, Morayshire, IV36 3YY Tel: (01309) 691200 Fax: (01309) 691454

Norwood Instruments Ltd, New Mill Road, Honley, Holmfirth, HD9 6QD Tel: (01484) 661318 Fax: (01484) 661319 E-mail: gpc@norwood.cc *Scientific & medical instrument & dental consumables specialists*

▶ Norwood Marine Ltd, 5 Wilson Street, Peterhead, Aberdeenshire, AB42 1UD Tel: 01779 490660

Norwood Supplies, 28 Foulds Close, Gillingham, Kent, ME8 0QF Tel: (01634) 362670 Fax: (01634) 370042 *Car valeting suppliers*

Noshe Engineering, Beech Farm, Coopers Green Lane, St. Albans, Hertfordshire, AL4 9HW Tel: (01727) 837146 Fax: (01727) 854144 E-mail: andrewauld@nosche.co.uk *Bottle handling equipment designers & manufrs*

Nostalgia Amusements, 22 Greenwood Close, Thames Ditton, Surrey, KT7 0BG Tel: (020) 8398 2141 Fax: (020) 8398 4343 E-mail: bdavey@globalnet.co.uk *Hire equipment for themed parties*

Nostalgic Pine & Beds, 1038-1040 Stockport Road, Manchester, M19 3WX Tel: 0161-248 4846 Fax: 0161-248 4846 E-mail: nostalgicpine@aol.com *Pine retailers*

▶ Not Just Pine, New Cut Lane, Woolston, Warrington, WA1 4AG Tel: (01925) 289079 *Pine furniture manufrs*

Note Dome Ltd, 34 Herald Way, Binley Industrial Estate, Coventry, CV3 2RQ Tel: (024) 7663 5193 Fax: (024) 7663 5509 E-mail: sales@notedome.co.uk Principal Export Areas: Asia Pacific, Central Asia, Middle East, Africa, Central/East Europe, West Europe & North America *Manufacturers of polyurethane chemicals*

▶ Note Machine, Humphries House, Elvicta Estates, Crickhowell, Powys, NP8 1DF Tel: (01873) 811634 Fax: (01873) 811552 *ATM machine services*

The Notebook Centre, 17 Oxford Street, London, W1D 2DJ Tel: (020) 7287 4247 *Laptops & accessories & laptop repairs*

Nothern Gas Installation, 7 Alder Road, Failsworth, Manchester, M35 0GH Tel: 0161-682 8323 Fax: 0161-682 0043 E-mail: info@northerngasinstallations.com *Medical, industrial gas & compressed air systems installers*

▶ Noticeable Nails, 21 Boundary Street, Leyland, PR25 4ST Tel: 01772 455634 E-mail: info@nails-in-preston.co.uk *Mobile Nail services to Preston, Leyland, Chorley and surrounding areas. Over 3 years experience.*Noticeable Nails offers Acrylic Nail Enhancements, Gel Nail Enhancements, Manicures, Pedicures, Gel Toes, Nail Art and Pamper Parties.*

Notifier Ltd, Charles Avenue, Burgess Hill, West Sussex, RH15 9UF Tel: (01444) 230300 Fax: (01444) 230888 E-mail: sales@notifierfiresystems.co.uk *NOTIFIER Fire Systems has pioneered the policy of developing sophisticated advance technology fire detection systems, starting with simple conventional products through to the large networked multi-panel intelligent systems.*

Nottage Forge, 4 Locks Lane, Nottage, Porthcawl, Mid Glamorgan, CF36 3HY Tel: (01656) 783180 *Iron work manufrs*

Nottingham Braid Co. Ltd, Gresham Road, Derby, DE24 8AW Tel: (01332) 331314 Fax: (01332) 292977 E-mail: enquiry@nottinghambraid.co.uk *Trimmings manufrs*

▶ The Nottingham Center for Cosmetic Surgery, 6 Oxford Street, Nottingham, NG1 5BH Tel: 0800 0281 329 E-mail: web@thenottinghamcenterforcosmeticsurgery.co.uk *The Nottingham Center for Cosmetic Surgery is well-known institution for cosmetic surgery of face,breast and tummy under highly qualified plastic surgeons. It also offers non-surgical treatment like Botulimum Toxin or Botox.*

Nottingham Design Studio, Queen Elizabeth Way, Ilkeston, Derbyshire, DE7 4NU Tel: 0115-944 1944 Fax: 0115-944 1944 *Cement manufrs*

Nottingham Electrical Transmissions, Northern Court, Nottingham, NG6 0BJ Tel: 0115-975 3655 Fax: 0115-977 0366 E-mail: info@net-eng.co.uk *Gear box & unit manufrs*

Nottingham Engineering Products, Unit 5E, The Midway, Nottingham, NG7 2TS Tel: (0115) 986 9555 Fax: (0115) 986 9666 E-mail: sales@nepltd.co.uk *Engineering products manufacturers & distributors*

Nottingham Engineering Services Ltd, Mount Street, New Basford, Nottingham, NG7 7HX Tel: 0115 9780080

Nottingham Gauge & Thermometer Co., Unit C, Thornfield Industrial Estate, Off Hooton Street, Carlton, Nottingham, NG3 2NJ Tel: 0115-950 7213 Fax: 0115-950 7227 *Pressure gauge & thermometer manufrs*

▶ Nottingham Girls Model Agency, 49 Penrhyn Cresent, Nottingham, NG9 5PA Tel: 0115 841 9685 E-mail: agency@nottinghamgirls.co.uk *UK Based model agency providing staff for various assignments nationwide including fashion, photographic and promotions*

Nottingham Industrial Cleaners Ltd, Elizabeth House, Wigman Road, Bilborough, Nottingham, NG8 3HY Tel: 0115-900 7300 Fax: 0115-900 7310 *Office cleaning contractors*

▶ Nottingham International Construction Equipment Ltd, 22 Hunt Close, Radcliffe-on-Trent, Nottingham, NG12 2EQ Tel: 0115-933 6008 Fax: 0115-933 6009 E-mail: sales@niceuk.co.uk *Supply construction*

▶ Nottingham Lace Finishing, 81A Arnold Road, Nottingham, NG6 0ED Tel: 0115-978 1979

Nottingham Laces & Trimmings, Turret E, Harrington Mills, Leopold Street, Long Eaton, Nottingham, NG10 4QE Tel: 0115-946 0766 Fax: 0115-946 0741 E-mail: sales@harrington-nlt.co.uk *Lace importers & merchants*

Nottingham Moulding Co., Daleside Road, Nottingham, NG2 3GG Tel: 0115-986 6839 Fax: 0115-986 3709 *Wholesale picture moulding manufacturers & wood finishers*

Nottingham Narrow Fabrics, Block A Harrington Mills, Leopold Street, Long Eaton, Nottingham, NG10 4QG Tel: 0115-946 8883 Fax: 0115-946 8652 Principal Export Areas: Africa *Fabric tape & industrial webbing manufrs*

Nottingham Office Equipment Co. Ltd, Castle Boulevard, Nottingham, NG7 1FN Tel: 0115-950 5117 Fax: 0115-950 4880 E-mail: noe@tinyworld.co.uk *Office furniture suppliers*

Nottingham Offshore Marine, 35 Carlton Hill, Carlton, Nottingham, NG4 1BG Tel: 0115-961 2336 E-mail: jon.dann@tesco.net *Water ski & outboard engine retail & inflatable boats retailers*

Nottingham Paper Bag Co. Ltd, Mundella Works, Mundella Road, Nottingham, NG2 2EQ Tel: 0115-986 1376 Fax: 0115-986 2018 E-mail: sales@thepaperman.net *Paper merchants*

Nottingham Platers Ltd, Southwark Street, Nottingham, NG6 0DB Tel: 0115-978 4637 Fax: 0115-978 9754 E-mail: martin@chrome-platers.com *Electroplating services*

Nottingham Sleeper Co. Ltd, Alpine Industrial Park, Jockey Lane, Elkesley, Retford, Nottinghamshire, DN22 8BN Tel: (01777) 838097 Fax: (01777) 838098 E-mail: enquiries@nottssleeper.co.uk *Associated components*

Nottingham Suspended Ceilings Ltd, Wright Street, Netherfield, Nottingham, NG4 2PG Tel: 0115-987 9880 Fax: 0115-940 0086 E-mail: info@nsceilings.co.uk *Suspended ceiling contractors*

Nottingham Transformers Co. Ltd, Unit 37 Little Tennis Street, Nottingham, NG2 4EL Tel: 0115-958 8340 Fax: 0115-958 8341 E-mail: tony_medri@hotmail.com *Transformer manufrs*

Nottingham Zinc Group Ltd, Byron Avenue, Lowmoor Business Park, Kirkby-in-Ashfield, Nottingham, NG17 7LA Tel: (01623) 752107 Fax: (01623) 721453 E-mail: clive@nottinghamzinc.co.uk *Electroplating services*

Nottinghamshire Chamber of Commerce & Industry, 309 Haydn Road, Nottingham, NG5 1DG Tel: 0115-962 4624 Fax: 0115-985 6612 E-mail: info@nottschamber.co.uk *Chamber of commerce & industry* Also at: Mansfield

Notts Contractors Ltd, Barton Yards, Abbotsham, Bideford, Devon, EX39 5AP Tel: (01237) 479440 Fax: (01237) 478800 *Asbestos Removal, Asbestos surveys, Electrical contractors,demolition & groundworks*

Notts Industries Ltd, Carley Works, Garsdale, Frome, Somerset, BA11 1PR Tel: (01373) 452231 Fax: (01373) 451139 *Sheet metal pressing services*

▶ no-url.co.uk, 15 South Point, Emerald Quay, Harbour Way, Shoreham-by-Sea, West Sussex, BN43 5JL Tel: 01273 461461 *A customiseable marketing service for small-to-medium businesses, with special expertise in internet marketing. We are heavyweight professionals but we can provide your first website (5 pages) for only £175 to include hosting & your domain name - with no compromise on quality! See our website at http://no-url.co.uk for more details.*

▶ Nouveau Ceramics, 223 Longbridge Lane, Birmingham, B31 4RE Tel: 0121-477 2038 Fax: 0121-475 4004

▶ NOV8 Ltd, Hartham Park, Corsham, Wiltshire, SN13 0RP Tel: (01249) 700009 E-mail: kellysearch@nov8.biz *Culture*For us, it's about people and processes. That means attending firstly to how people feel. And secondly to all those little processes - appraisal, communication, innovation, reward - that make an organisation what it is.**Change*We work with people in an organisation facing change, confronting problems, dealing with fear and really involving them in the process of change.**Process*The really smart approach to process reinvention is to build your own organisational capability in it. An ability to reinvent your organisation. An attitude of mind, as much as tools and techniques. **Experiential Training*People retain a tiny proportion of what they hear, a bit more of what they see and a very large percentage of what they do. So our training is not for the lazy or reticent. There's a lot of doing. **Coaching*Do you want to create some space?*In a safe and tranquil place?*You'll find it easier to confide*With experience by your side.*

Nova, 3 Partnership House, Withambrook Park Industrial Estate, Grantham, Lincolnshire, NG31 9ST Tel: (01476) 577635 Fax: (01476) 577635 E-mail: novawindows@hotmail.com *Double glazing window & conservatory manufrs*

▶ Nova Aluminium, 11 Lawfords Gate, Bristol, BS2 0DY Tel: 0117-955 6463 Fax: 0117-955 6472 E-mail: sales@nova-aluminium.com *Aluminium extrusions & fabricators*

Nova Automation, 75 Beardmore Way, Clydebank, Dunbartonshire, G81 4HT Tel: 0141-951 8121 Fax: 0141-951 8121 E-mail: info@novagates.co.uk *Supply & service automatic gates*

Nova Blinds, 28 Frances Street, Newtownards, County Down, BT23 7DN Tel: (028) 9181 8679 Fax: (028) 9181 8679 E-mail: sales@wonderfu1-blinds.co.uk *Blinds repairs & manufrs*

Nova Controls Ltd, Cheshire House, Murhall Street, Stoke-On-Trent, ST6 4BL Tel: (01782) 824866 Fax: (01782) 825474 *Control system engineers services*

▶ Nova Darkroom Equipment Ltd, Unit 1a, Harris Road, Wedgnock Industrial Estate, Warwick, CV34 5JU Tel: (01926) 403090 E-mail: sales@novadarkroom.com

Nova Display, Unit 1, Peckfield Business Park, Phoenix Avenue, Micklefield, Leeds, LS25 4DY Tel: 0113-385 0200 Fax: 0113-385 0201 E-mail: howard@novadisplay.co.uk *Shop fitters services*

Nova Electronic Developments Co Ltd, 49 Florence Road, Gedling, Nottingham, NG4 2QL Tel: 0115-910 9910 Fax: 0115-910 9900 E-mail: sales@novadev.co.uk *Electric cable assembly & harness manufacturers & process control wiring*

Nova Electronics Ltd, 18 Springclough Drive, Worsley, Manchester, M28 3HS Tel: 0161-702 8643 Fax: 0161-702 8643 E-mail: sales@nova-electronics.co.uk *Burglar alarm installers*

Nova Electronics, 700-702 Attercliffe Road, Sheffield, S9 3RP Tel: 0114-244 7257 Fax: 0114-261 7721 E-mail: info@nova-electronics.co.uk *Electronic component distributors*

Nova Engineering Co., 5 Stephenson Road, Bayton Road Industrial Estate, Exhall, Coventry, CV7 9EQ Tel: (024) 7636 1408 Fax: (024) 7664 4845 E-mail: enquiries@novaeng.co.uk *Special fastener manufrs*

Nova Garden Furniture Ltd, Graveney Road, Faversham, Kent, ME13 8UN Tel: (01795) 535511 Fax: (01795) 539215 E-mail: sales@novagardenfurniture.co.uk *Garden furniture manufrs*

Nova Interior Contracts, Millennium House, Centenary Place, Congleton, Cheshire, CW12 1EZ Tel: (01260) 273759 Fax: (01260) 297397 *Office interiors refurbishment*

Nova Metals Ltd, Unit 13 Worsley Business Park, Mosley Common Road, Worsley, Manchester, M28 1NL Tel: 0161-799 4108 Fax: 0161-703 7294 E-mail: ssles@novametals.co.uk *Nova Metals produces a wide range of perforated metal sheets in steel, stainless steel, galvanised steel, aluminium, copper, brass and many other materials. Also available are an exciting range of exclusive architectural metals including decorative ceilings and surfaces. Nova Metals Ltd supply perforated mild steel , perforated aluminium, perforated stainless steel, and offer a whole lot more, from additional metal products including wire cloth, expanded metal, Stainless Steel & Bronze grating, to the fabricating and finishing services that are often performed to turn these materials into solutions. *Whether it's 1 sheet or 100, standard size or cut-to-length, fabricated or finished, we are committed to providing the product you want, the way you want it, when you want it. To achieve this, we offer over 500 items, stock the most popular configuration, material type, and thickness in each, and despatch many items the same day. We can also custom-design your perforated patterns with large blank areas and any combination of hole shapes and sizes. Our technical assistance and a full range of forming, fabricating and finishing services are available.*

Nova Press Printing, 3 The Old Mill, 61 Reading Road, Pangbourne, Reading, RG8 7HY Tel: 0118-984 5370 Fax: 0118-984 5370 E-mail: trevor@novapress.freeserve.co.uk *General & wedding printing services*

Nova Trimmings Ltd, 15 Abbey Gate, Leicester, LE4 0AA Tel: 0116-253 1144 Fax: 0116-251 5631 E-mail: nova.trimmings@virgin.net *Trimmings & haberdashery merchants* Also at: Birmingham

Nova Weigh Ltd, Unit 30 Walkers Road, Moons Moat North Indust Estate, Redditch, Worcestershire, B98 9HE Tel: (01527) 67557 Fax: (01527) 60213 E-mail: sales@novaweigh.co.uk *Supplier of a complete solution in respect of mobile, static and*

continued

*dynamic weighing systems. *Mobile weighing equipment covering weighing pallet trucks and Fork Lift Truck weighing systems. *Vessel weighing and platform scales. *ATEX systems for hazardous areas. *Batch weighing and control systems. *Instrumentation with open connectivity. *Data capture and process automation. *Full on-site installation, commissioning, maintenance & calibration engineering service for all weighing applications.*

▶ Novacheck Ltd, 438 London Road, High Wycombe, Buckinghamshire, HP11 1LP Tel: (01494) 526553 Fax: (01494) 526553 E-mail: contactus@novacheck.com *telemarketing services.**Our services include:*-Appointment setting*- Lead generation*-Database building and Validation*- Seminar and Exhibition Invites*- Channel/Reseller/Partner expansion*- Market Research*

Novacroft Ltd, Harvest Barn Spring Hill, Harborough Road, Pitsford, Northampton, NN6 9AA Tel: (01604) 889500 Fax: (01604) 889508 E-mail: clivenotley@novacroft.com *Project managers & managing agents specialising in the energy & smartcard sectors. Typical energy projects include the management of energy efficiency schemes, including 'cash-backs' for energy supply companies & local authorities. The Company also manage incentive travel & other PTAs and are experts in both smart& dumb card issue & management.*

Novacrylics Engineering, Shrewley Farm, Hockley Road, Shrewley, Warwick, CV35 7AT Tel: (01926) 400404 Fax: (01926) 400840 *Plastic fabrication, product design & manufrs*

▶ Novaglaze, Queens Mill Road, Huddersfield, HD1 3PG Tel: (01484) 517010 Fax: (01484) 517050 E-mail: sales@novaglaze.co.uk *Glass benders & processes*

▶ Novapak Equipment Ltd, 2 The Old Bakery, Stevington, Bedford, MK43 7QH Tel: (01234) 823018 *Reconditioning filling machines suppliers*

Novaplace Ltd, Intercel House, Main St, Overseal, Swadlincote, Derbyshire, DE12 6LG Tel: (01283) 763666 Fax: (01283) 763666 E-mail: sales@europond.co.uk *Aquatic product manufrs*

Novar ED&S, The Arnold Centre, Paycocke Road, Basildon, Essex, SS14 3EA Tel: (01268) 563000 Fax: (01268) 563538 E-mail: mk_reception@nova.com *Circuit protection manufrs* Also at: Basildon & Southend

Novartis Consumer Health UK Ltd, Novartis Horsham Research Centre, Wimblehurst Road, Horsham, West Sussex, RH12 5AB Tel: (01403) 210211 Fax: (01403) 323919 *Pharmaceutical suppliers*

Novartis Consumer Health UK Ltd, Novartis Horsham Research Centre, Wimblehurst Road, Horsham, West Sussex, RH12 5AB Tel: (01403) 210211 Fax: (01403) 323919 *Pharmaceuticals & chemicals manufacturers & distributors*

Novartis Consumer Health UK Ltd, Novartis Horsham Research Centre, Wimblehurst Road, Horsham, West Sussex, RH12 5AB Tel: (01403) 210211 Fax: (01403) 323919 *Healthcare preparations & products manufrs*

Novartis Pharmaceuticals (UK) Ltd, Frimley Business Park, Frimley, Camberley, Surrey, GU16 7SR Tel: (01276) 691676 Fax: (01276) 692508 *Pharmaceuticals*

Novaseal Plastics Ltd, 4 Blackbrook Business Park, Blackbrook Road, Fareham, Hampshire, PO15 5DR Tel: (01329) 233500 Fax: (01329) 230012 E-mail: info@novaseal.co.uk *PVC building products distributors*

Novatech Measurements Ltd, 83 Castleham Road, St. Leonards-On-Sea, East Sussex, TN38 9NT Tel: (01424) 852744 Fax: (01424) 853002 E-mail: info@novatechloadcells.co.uk *Load cell manufrs*

Novation International Ltd, 5 Minister's Park, East Kilbride, Glasgow, G74 5BX Tel: (01355) 268437 Fax: (01355) 260915 E-mail: novation.int@virgin.net *Marketing company*

▶ Novel Planet, 148 Butchers Road, Canning Town, London, E16 1NF Tel: (0795) 7763662 *Lots of novels:Romance,thriller,Fiction,Horror, Bestseller,Children E.T.C to read day or night.Better still there is no arguing over who has to take it back to the library, delivery and return is free.*check www.novelplanet.co.uk for details. ITs free.*

Novela Portable Trolleys, 4 Mayfield Gardens, London, NW4 2QA Tel: (020) 8202 8747 Fax: (020) 8203 3243 E-mail: novelatrolleys@aol.com *Import & distribute all purpose trolleys*

Novelis U.K Ltd, Castle Works, Rogerstone, Newport, Gwent, NP10 9YD Tel: (01633) 202020 Fax: (01633) 202000 E-mail: bunworth@novelis.com *Rolled aluminium packaging & building services*

Novelis UK Ltd, Stourbridge Road, Bridgnorth, Shropshire, WV15 6AW Tel: (01746) 765757 Fax: (01746) 761860 *Aluminium foil & technical products manufrs*

November Express, 25 Portswood Road, Southampton, SO17 2ES Tel: (023) 8058 5050 Fax: (023) 8067 1137 E-mail: novemberexpress@btinternet.com *Rubber stamp manufrs, printers & bookbinders*

Novo Designs, Church Farm, Eyeworth, Sandy, Bedfordshire, SG19 2HH Tel: 01767 631117 *Engineering pattern makers*

▶ Novo Gaming UK Ltd, Tudor House, Coychurch Road, Bridgend, Mid Glamorgan, CF35 5NS Tel: (01656) 668881 Fax: (01656) 655255 *Suppliers & operators of gaming equipment*

Novo Nordisk Holding Ltd, Novo Nordisk House, Broadfield Park, Crawley, West Sussex, RH11 9RT Tel: (01293) 613555 Fax: (01293) 613535 E-mail: sales@novonordisk.co.uk *Pharmaceutical manufrs*

▶ Novograf Ltd, 10 Langlands Place, Kelvin South Business Park, East Kilbride, Glasgow, G75 0YF Tel: (01355) 900100 Fax: (01355) 900200

Novolla Systems, 18 Lavender Road, London, SW11 2UG Tel: (020) 7228 5830 Fax: (020) 7228 5830 *Software house*

Novopac (UK) Ltd, Fieldhead Broomers Corner, Shipley, Horsham, West Sussex, RH13 8PR Tel: (01403) 740003 Fax: (01403) 740071 E-mail: richard@novopac.co.uk *Packaging equipment, machine & systems & shrink wrap machine manufrs*

▶ Novotronix, Creative Industury Centre, Mammoth Drive, Wolverhampton Science Park, Wolverhampton, WV10 9TG Tel: (01902) 424277 *Computer software developers*

Novus Foods Ltd, Suite 31 Salford University Business Park, Leslie Hough Way, Salford, M6 6AJ Tel: 0161-736 8180 Fax: 0161-736 8190 E-mail: novusfoods@supanet.com *Food manufrs*

Novus Interactive Ltd, 48 Rose Hill, Rednal, Birmingham, B45 8RT Tel: 0121-457 8008 *Computer information systems, public use*

Novus Sealing, Hunsworth Lane, Cleckheaton, West Yorkshire, BD19 4EJ Tel: (01274) 852543 Fax: (01274) 862588 E-mail: mailbox@novussealing.com *Industrial seals & gasket manufrs*

▶ Now Accountancy, 14 Drake Walk, Brigantine Place, Cardiff, CF10 4AN Tel: (029) 2048 9966 Fax: (029) 2049 7722 E-mail: info@nowaccountancy.com *Recruitment Agency specialising in Accountancy at all levels bith temporary and permanent*

▶ Now Plastics, Salters Lane, Sedgefield, Stockton-on-Tees, Cleveland, TS21 3EE Tel: (01740) 625228 Fax: (01740) 625204 E-mail: sales@nowplastics.com *Packing distribution*

▶ Now Recruitment Ltd, 5 The Square, Broad Street, Birmingham, B15 1AS Tel: 0121-693 9408 E-mail: info@nowrecruitment.com *Now Recruitment is an industry award-winning market leader with a network of branches providing employment solutions to a wide range of industries, including;**Construction*Accountancy* Commercial*Education*Driving & Industrial*Mechanical & Electrical*

▶ Now Recruitment Ltd, 3 Chester Street, Newcastle upon Tyne, NE2 1AT Tel: 0191-209 1900 Fax: 0191-209 1911 *A Recruitment company specialising in Construction, Technical, Mechanical, Electrical.*

▶ Now Shoes UK Ltd, 232 Leicester Road, Markfield, Leicestershire, LE67 9RG Tel: (01530) 242727 Fax: (01530) 242475

▶ Nowak Art Metal Co. (Krupa), 14 Brook Street, Bury, Lancashire, BL9 6AH Tel: 0161-792 3890 Fax: 0161-764 8722 E-mail: chris@krupabros-son.freeserve.co.uk *Wrought ironworkers, aluminium extrusion, press tools*

▶ NP Residential Management, 85 Granville Avenue, Northborough, Peterborough, PE6 9DE Tel: (0870) 7574461 *PROPERTIES TO RENT , SHORT TERM & LONG TERM IN AND AROUND CAMBRIDGESHIRE , LINCOLNSHIRE ETC*

Npil Pharmaceuticals UK Ltd, Whalton Road, Morpeth, Northumberland, NE61 3YA Tel: (01670) 562400 Fax: (01670) 562401 *Pharmaceuticals*

▶ NPK UK Ltd, PO Box 375, Fleet, Hampshire, GU51 5ZQ Tel: (01276) 20011

NPS Media, Ayrton Buildings, Forty Foot Road, Middlesbrough, Cleveland, TS2 1HG Tel: (01642) 231231 Fax: (01642) 256565 E-mail: sales@npsmedia.com *Provides advertising & multi-media needs, cd & dvd duplication*

NRC Plant Ltd, Neagron House, Stanford Road, Orsett, Grays, Essex, RM16 3BX Tel: (01375) 361616 Fax: (01375) 361818 E-mail: sales@nrcplant.co.uk *Crane hire & sales services* Also at: Old Bury & Oldham

NRF (UK) Ltd, Lamport Drive, Heartlands Business Park, Daventry, Northamptonshire, NN11 5YH Tel: (01327) 300242 Fax: (01327) 300225 E-mail: sales@nrf.co.uk Purchasing Contact: P. Allinson Sales Contact: M. Knowles Principal Export Areas: Africa *Manufacturers of motor vehicle radiators & air conditioning equipment. In addition, air & oil coolers, automotive radiators & aluminium heat exchangers. Also emergency standby generating set manufrs*

NRG Fabrications Ltd, Harlestone Road, Northampton, NN5 6UJ Tel: (01604) 580022 Fax: (01604) 580033 *Steel fabricators suppliers & manufrs*

NRG PLANT HIRE, North Road Garage, Great North Road, Tuxford, NEWARK, NOTTS, NG22 0NE Tel: (01777) 871199 Fax: (01777) 871199 E-mail: sarahlhoward@fsmail.net *HIRE OF KOMATSU JCB MINI DIGGERS 360 EXCAVATORS (DRIVER IF REQUIRED!) DUMPERS VANS TIPPERS 7.5 LORRIES CHOICE OF PLANT TRAILERS AND ALL BUILDING EQUIPMENT MIXERS WHACKER PLATES ETC*

▶ NRK Electrochem, Unit 7, Enterprise Centre, St. Thomas Road, Launceston, Cornwall, PL15 8BU Tel: 01566 779896 E-mail: info@nrkelectrochem.co.uk *Suppliers of single and mixed metal oxide coated electrodes for a range of electrochemical processes. Also offering electrode refurbishment service.*

▶ NRM Partnership Ltd, Brunell House, Swanwick Lane, Broughton, Milton Keynes, MK10 9LB Tel: (01908) 663307 Fax: (01908) 663260 E-mail: kat@cdpartner.co.uk *Building services consulting engineers*

NS Engineering Solutions, Units 23/24, Snibston Drive, Coalville, Leicestershire, LE67 3NQ Tel: (01530) 835400 Fax: (01530) 510947 E-mail: sales@nsengineering.co.uk Purchasing Contact: D. Wheatley *From Drawing to Delivery, we are your engineering solution.**Expertise & Flexibility *NS Engineering Solutions provides both precision and general purpose machining, fabrication and finishing solutions. Over the years since we first started providing our services in 1986 we have built up an extensive knowledge of the crusher, brick and rail industries and have expanded to other areas such as health-care, mining and power generation. NS Engineering Solutions has a diverse experience to offer the marketplace including production, spares, repairs, refurbishment and pattern work. Working*

continued

continuation
together with NS Engineering Solutions you can expect quality, on-time delivery, full traceability and a manufacturing experience coupled with modern machinery and systems.

NSG Enviromental Ltd, Scientia House Matrix Park, Western Avenue, Buckshaw Village, Chorley, Lancashire, PR7 7NB Tel: (01772) 458818 Fax: (01772) 458819 E-mail: mailbox@nsgenvironmental.co.uk *Radioactive Waste Management and Decommissioning Consultants & Contractors*

NSI, Queensgate House, 14 Cookham Road, Maidenhead, Berkshire, SL6 8AJ Tel: (0870) 2050000 Fax: (01628) 773367 E-mail: nacoss@nsi.org.uk *Electronic security industry inspectorates*

NSIN, 394A Poulton Road, Wallasey, Merseyside, CH44 4BT Tel: 0151-638 5575 Fax: 0151-637 1588 *Alarm fitters*

NSK Steering Systems Europe Ltd, Silverstone Drive, Gallagher Business Park, Coventry, CV6 6PA Tel: (024) 7658 8588 Fax: (024) 7658 8599 E-mail: surman@nsk.com *Steering column manufrs*

NSL Engineering, 6 Selby Place, Skelmersdale, Lancashire, WN8 8EF Tel: (01695) 556355 *Freight container handling spreader manufrs*

▶ NSS - Northern Sales & Services Ltd., Saw Pit Industrial Estate, Tibshelf, Derbyshire, DE55 5NH Tel: 01773 875667 Fax: 01773 875668 E-mail: info@nss-ltd.com *NSS are suppliers of new trolleys and shelters for the retail industry, offering maintenance, fleet management and refurbishment to new standard, including zinc plating and lacquering. **NSS outdoor division specialises in shelters (smoking, bus, bicycle, trolley) and metalwork.*

NSS (Roofing & Cladding) Ltd, Access House, Aviation Park Flint Road, Saltney Ferry, Chester, CH4 0GZ Tel: (01244) 504900 Fax: (01245) 4501901 E-mail: enquiries@nssgroupplc.com *Industrial scaffolding*

▶ NT Communications, 1 The Avenue, Danbury, Chelmsford, CM3 4QN Tel: (01245) 221466 Fax: (01245) 225172 E-mail: sales@neiltrask.co.uk *Provider of telecom services to business. We are an accredited reseller of Mitel, Panasonic, BT and other quality brands. Services include installation, support and consultancy.*

Nt2 Ltd, Unit A Warwick House, Market Pl, Braintree, Essex, CM7 3HQ Tel: (0870) 2410997 Fax: (0870) 2411717 *Software resellers*

Nte Vacuum Technology Ltd, 190-192 Stanley Green Road, Poole, Dorset, BH15 3AH Tel: (01202) 677715 Fax: (01202) 677723 E-mail: sales@ntepoole.co.uk *Stainless steel high vacuum chambers & vessels fabricators*

N-Tire Systems Ltd, P O Box 215, Brentford, Middlesex, TW8 8RT Tel: (0845) 658 1505 Fax: (0845) 658 1505 E-mail: office@n-tiresystems.co.uk *Computer solutions company*

NTL, Cambridge Research Park, Ely Road, Waterbeach, Cambridge, CB25 9TF Tel: (01223) 724040 Fax: (01223) 567222 *Cable telephone & television company*

▶ NTS International Express Ltd, 3 Capel Close, Leacon Road, Ashford, Kent, TN23 4GY Tel: (01233) 637722 Fax: (01233) 637733 E-mail: ashford@nts-express.co.uk *Dedicated express transportation services to Europe. Vans, trucks to a dedicated aircraft.**We also operate a 24Hr and 48Hr service to all of Germany. Operating from our Ashford depot.*

Nu Direct, Knowle Fields Industrial Estate, Alcester Road, Inkberrow, Worcester, WR7 4HR Tel: (01386) 793339 Fax: (01386) 792030 E-mail: sales@jump4joy.co.uk *Builders of horse jumps*

Nu Fire & Security Ltd, Unit 8A, Kayley Industrial Estate, Richmond Street, Ashton-under-Lyne, Lancashire, OL7 0AU Tel: 0161-331 7430 Fax: (0845) 4022309 E-mail: sales@nufire.co.uk *Security systems installation services*

Nu Gauge, 38 Hoyland Road, Sheffield, S3 8AB Tel: 0114-275 4006 Fax: 0114-275 4006 E-mail: sales@nu-gauge.co.uk *Gauge manufrs*

Nu Homes Manufacturing Ltd, Claymore, Tame Valley Industrial Estate, Wilnecote, Tamworth, Staffordshire, B77 5DQ Tel: (01827) 284061 Fax: (01827) 260632 *UPVC window frame manufrs*

Nu Instruments Ltd, Unit 74 Clywedog Road South, Wrexham Industrial Estate, Wrexham, Clwyd, LL13 9XS Tel: (01978) 661304 Fax: (01978) 664301 E-mail: sales@nu-ins.com *Scientific instrument manufrs*

Nu Line Engineering Ltd, George Street, Lincoln, LN5 8LG Tel: (01522) 544379 Fax: (01522) 544379 E-mail: nuline.ellis@tiscali.co.uk *Engine reconditioning & parts suppliers*

Nu Lite, 22 Ayloffs Walk, Hornchurch, Essex, RM11 2RJ Tel: (01708) 442232 Fax: (01708) 451696 *Neon signs & nameplates manufrs*

▶ Nu Look Blinds, 13 Down Business Centre Down Business Park, 46 Belfast Road, Downpatrick, County Down, BT30 9UP Tel: (028) 4461 3509 Fax: (028) 4461 3509

Nu Mac Steel Ltd, Temple Hill Road, Newry, County Down, BT34 2LR Tel: (028) 3026 8332 Fax: (028) 3025 2828 E-mail: sales@numac.co.uk *Skip & compactors manufrs*

Nu Ropes, Coker Ropery, West Coker, Yeovil, Somerset, BA22 9BN Tel: (01935) 862327 Fax: (01935) 862274 E-mail: evanstherope1@supanet.co.uk *Ropes & cordage manufrs*

Nu Screw & Nut, 311 Neasden La North, London, NW10 0AG Tel: (020) 8452 8633 Fax: (020) 8452 2987 E-mail: sales@nu-screw.co.uk *Distributors/agents/stockholders of general/ standard nuts & bolts*

Nu Star Fabricators Ltd, 15 Baltic Lane, Glasgow, G40 4UB Tel: 0141-550 8823 Fax: 0141-550 8824 *Ventilation engineers*

Nu Swift International Ltd, PO Box 10, Elland, West Yorkshire, HX5 9DS Tel: (01422) 372852 Fax: (01422) 379569 E-mail: customer.service@nuswift.co.uk *Fire fighting equipment distributors*

Nu Tac Trade Labels Ltd, Bradford Street, Farnworth, Bolton, BL4 9LS Tel: (01204) 861436 Fax: (01204) 862923 E-mail: info@newfoil.co.uk *Self-adhesive label manufrs*

Nu Tech Engineering Services Ltd, Unit 7 & 14 Newtown Business Park, Albion Close, Poole, Dorset, BH12 3LL Tel: (01202) 724100 Fax: (01202) 724114 E-mail: sales@nutech-eng.com *The company was formed in 1984, and since that time, has established itself as one of the South's Leading sub-contract Engineering Companies, and one of the U.K.'s leading manufacturer of Industrial Levelling Feet. The company which has ISO 9002 accreditation is committed to maximising customer satisfaction through the supply of products that are safe and reliable in service and conform to the customer's quality, delivery and performance requirements*

Nu Tech Security, Station House, 1 Banstead Road, Banstead, Surrey, SM7 1PZ Tel: (01737) 551966 Fax: (01737) 379494 *Install alarms*

Nu Tools Machinery Sales, Rockingham Way, Redhouse Interchange, Adwick-le-Street, Doncaster, South Yorkshire, DN6 7FB Tel: (01302) 721791 Fax: (01302) 728317 E-mail: sales@nutool.co.uk *Machine tool merchants manufrs/suppliers/distributors*

▶ Nu Vision Associates, 5A Prospect Street, Caversham, Reading, RG4 8JB Tel: 0118-947 5500 Fax: 0118-947 5588

Nu Way Ltd, PO Box 1, Droitwich, Worcestershire, WR9 8NA Tel: (01905) 794331 Fax: (01905) 794017 E-mail: info@nu-way.co.uk *Industrial oil & dual fuel burner manufrs* Also at: Belfast & East Kilbride

Nu Weld Engineering Services Ltd, 36 Oxford Street, Birmingham, B5 5NR Tel: 0121-633 0909 Fax: 0121-633 3124 E-mail: enquiries@nu-weld.co.uk *Metal fabricators & civil engineering contractors*

Nuaire Group, Western Indust Estate, Caerphilly, Mid Glamorgan, CF83 1BQ Tel: (029) 2088 5911 Fax: (029) 2088 7033 E-mail: info@nuaire.co.uk *Ceiling, bifurcated & axial fans*

The Nuance Group UK Ltd, 84-98 Southampton Road, Eastleigh, Hampshire, SO50 5ZF Tel: (023) 8067 3000 Fax: (023) 8067 3199 *Retail at airports*

Nub Engineering Ltd, Newhouse Industrial Estate, Newhouse, Motherwell, Lanarkshire, ML1 5RX Tel: (01698) 833873 Fax: (01698) 734322 E-mail: sales@nubeng.com *Fabrication*

▶ Nu-Care Products Ltd, Unit 21, Broadmead Business Park, Broadmead Road, Stewartby, Bedford, MK43 9NX Tel: (01234) 766738 Fax: (01234) 766739 E-mail: sales@nu-careproducts.co.uk *Mail order medical goods*

Nuclear Industry Association, First Floor Whitehall House, 41 Whitehall, London, SW1A 2BY Tel: (020) 7766 6640 Fax: (020) 7839 4695 E-mail: info@niauk.org *Nuclear information services*

Nufast Ltd, 17 Hayward Industrial Estate, Vigo Place Aldridge, Walsall, WS9 8UG Tel: (01922) 740360 Fax: (01922) 453610 E-mail: sales@nufast.co.uk *Threaded fastener distributors*

Nuffield Hospitals Ltd, Nuffield House, 1-4 The Crescent, Surbiton, Surrey, KT6 4BN Tel: (020) 8390 1200 Fax: (020) 8399 6726 *Charitable hospital*

Nuffield Radiographic Inspection, Unit B13-14, 46 Holton Road, Holton Heath Trading Park, Poole, Dorset, BH16 6LT Tel: (01202) 632200 Fax: (01202) 632042 E-mail: sales@nuffieldinspection.co.uk *Non-destructive testing specialists*

Nuglas Ltd, Euro Business Park, New Road, Newhaven, East Sussex, BN9 0DQ Tel: (01273) 517426 Fax: (01273) 513733 E-mail: sales@nuglas.co.uk *Window, door & conservatory installers & manufrs*

Nu-Heat (UK) Ltd, Heathpark House, Devonshire Road, Heathpark Industrial Estate, Honiton, Devon, EX14 1SD Tel: (01404) 549770 Fax: (01404) 549771 E-mail: info@nu-heat.co.uk *Under floor heating suppliers*

Nukem Nuclear Ltd, Kelburn Court, Daten Park, Warrington, WA3 6TW Tel: (01925) 858200 Fax: (01925) 811866 E-mail: info@nukem.co.uk *Nuclear waste decontamination service*

Nukta Ltd, PO Box 31434, London, W4 4FQ Tel: (020) 8996 9043 Fax: (07092) 336473 E-mail: sales@nuktaltd.co.uk *Business information & management advisors*

Nu-Line Marketing Ltd, Access Business Centre, First Way, Wembley Stadium Industrial Estate, Wembley, Middlesex, HA9 0JD Tel: (020) 8900 8660 Fax: (020) 8900 0606 E-mail: sales@nu-line.com *Catering disposable packers*

NUM (UK) Ltd, Unit 3, Fairfield Court, Seven Stars Industrial Estate, Coventry, CV3 4LJ Tel: (0871) 7504020 Fax: (0871) 7504021 E-mail: solutions@schneider-num.co.uk *Principal Export Areas: Asia Pacific, Middle East & Africa Manufacturers of CNC & Motion control equipment for the Machine Tool and Special Machine market. Providers of complete control solutions hardware, software, commissioning panel build and linear actuators. A motion one stop shop.*

Numac Engineering Ltd, Gerrard Street, Stalybridge, Cheshire, SK15 2JY Tel: 0161-338 2125 Fax: 0161-304 9435 *Precision engineers*

Number 1 Systems, Oak Lane, Bredon, Tewkesbury, Gloucestershire, GL20 7LR Tel: (01684) 773662 Fax: (01684) 773664 E-mail: sales@numberone.com *Electronic CAD software suppliers*

Number One Sails, New Road, Middlestown, Wakefield, West Yorkshire, WF4 4NS Tel: (01924) 274073 Fax: (01924) 274073 *Sail manufrs*

Numerate Technology Ltd, 4 Ashley Gardens, Tunbridge Wells, Kent, TN4 8TY Tel: (01892) 545049 *Engineering analysis services*

Numis Security, Cheapside House, 138 Cheapside, London, EC2V 6LH Tel: (020) 7776 1500 Fax: (020) 7776 1550 *Investment banks*

Nuneaton Fine Finishers, Maguire Industrial Estate, Unit 3 Torrington Avenue, Coventry, CV4 9HN Tel: (024) 7642 2002 Fax: (024) 7647 1460 *Polishing Plating services Resoration Nickel chrome*

Nuneaton Precisions Ltd, Veasey Close, Attleborough Fields Industrial Estate, Nuneaton, Warwickshire, CV11 6RT Tel: (024) 7634 3116 Fax: (024) 7664 2355 E-mail: sales@nuneaton-precisions.com *Precision engineers*

Nuneaton Signs, 3 Kelsey Close, Attleborough Fields Industrial Estate, Nuneaton, Warwickshire, CV11 6RS Tel: (024) 7634 1922 Fax: (024) 7664 1305 E-mail: sales@nuneatonsigns.co.uk *Illuminated, metal & plastic signs*

Nuprint Trimmings Ltd, Unit 21 Springtown Industrial Estate, Springtown Road, Londonderry, BT48 0LY Tel: (028) 7128 2080 Fax: (028) 7126 0009 *Label manufrs*

Nu-Pro Surface Treatments, Eagle Works, London Road, Thrupp, Stroud, Gloucestershire, GL5 2BA Tel: (01453) 883344 Fax: (01453) 731597 E-mail: sales@nu-pro.com *Specialists in metal finishing processes*

A.C. Nurden Plant Hire Ltd, Park Road, Malmesbury, Wiltshire, SN16 0BX Tel: (01666) 823518 Fax: (01666) 824810 *Contractors plant machinery hire*

▶ Henry Nurdin Instrument Repairs, 51 Garth Owen, Newtown, Powys, SY16 1JL Tel: (07779) 755814 E-mail: info@guitar-repairs.co.uk *Repair musical instruments fret, machine head replacement*

Nuromed Ltd, Unit 17A, Makerfield Way, Ince, Wigan, Lancashire, WN2 2PR Tel: (01942) 238259 Fax: (01942) 498491 E-mail: info@nuromed.com *Neuro-muscular stimulator manufrs*

▶ Nurse Care Uniform Co. Ltd, Lime Street, Southampton, SO14 3DA Tel: (023) 8022 5335 Fax: (023) 8032 2169

▶ Nurse Electrical Ltd, Harts Hill Road, Thatcham, Berkshire, RG18 4NX Tel: (01635) 865065 Fax: (01635) 877681

▶ Nursery Needs, 15 Newton Road, Rushden, Northamptonshire, NN10 0PS Tel: (01933) 419898 *Baby care equipment suppliers*

Nursery Needs, 93 Church Lane, Marple, Stockport, Cheshire, SK6 7AW Tel: 0161-427 7707 Fax: 0161-427 2145 *Baby & nursery equipment suppliers*

Nursey & Son Ltd, 12 Upper Olland Street, Bungay, Suffolk, NR35 1BQ Tel: (01986) 892821 Fax: (01986) 892823 E-mail: sales@nurseyleather.co.uk *Leather & sheepskin clothing manufrs*

▶ Nursing & General Supplies, Ivyhouse Industrial Estate, Haywood Way, Hastings, East Sussex, TN35 4PL Tel: (01424) 444411 Fax: (01424) 435009 *Nursing & janitorial supplies*

▶ Nurul Mobile PC Repairs, 3 Mount Pleasant Road, Sheffield, S7 1BA Tel: 0114-255 1188 Fax: (0870) 7052705 *Computer service & repairers*

Nus Consulting Group, Regent House, Queensway, Redhill, RH1 1QT Tel: (01737) 781200 Fax: (01737) 766799 E-mail: service@nusconsulting.co.uk *Utilities cost consultancy*

Nusell Engineering Co, 484 Penistone Road, Sheffield, S6 2FU Tel: 0114-233 0244 Fax: 0114-232 6998 *Sub-contract engineers*

▶ Nusoft Distribution, High Road, Chigwell, Essex, IG7 5BJ Tel: (020) 8500 5885 Fax: (020) 8500 6065 *Computer consultants*

Nusteel Structures Ltd, Lympne Industrial Estate, Hythe, Kent, CT21 4LR Tel: (01303) 268112 Fax: (01303) 266098 E-mail: general@nusteelstructures.com *Structural engineers & fabricators*

Nu-Style Products Ltd, 25 Silverburn Crescent, Bridge Of Don Industrial Estate, Aberdeen, AB23 8EW Tel: (01224) 823000 Fax: (01224) 823111 E-mail: info@nu-styles.co.uk *Roofing & cladding materials suppliers*

Nutan Printers, 67-69 Harrison Road, Leicester, LE4 6BT Tel: 0116-266 9405 Fax: 0116-261 0251 E-mail: sales@nutan-printers.co.uk *Commercial printers*

Nutberry Ltd, Unit 12 Apex Park, Diplocks Way, Hailsham, East Sussex, BN27 3JU Tel: (01323) 442070 Fax: (01323) 442071 E-mail: nutberry@easynet.co.uk *Metal bellow manufacturers high temp gas springs*

Nutec Centre For Safety, Nutec Centre For Safety, Haverton Hill Industrial Estate, Billingham, Cleveland, TS23 1PZ Tel: (01642) 566656 Fax: (01642) 563224 E-mail: enquiries@nutecuk.com *Offshore safety training*

Nutec Holdings Ltd, Eastern Avenue, Lichfield, Staffordshire, WS13 7SE Tel: (01543) 306312 Fax: (01543) 306307 *Vitamin supplement animal nutrition manufrs*

▶ Nutford Engineering Ltd, 11 Hales Road, Leeds, LS12 4PL Tel: 0113-231 1478 Fax: 0113-231 1469

Nuthall Pump & Engineering Services, Queen Street, Langley Mill, Nottingham, NG16 4EJ Tel: (01773) 530630 Fax: (01773) 531532 *Valve reconditioning services*

▶ Nutrafx Ltd, P.O. Box 157, Sandbach, Cheshire, CW11 4WY Tel: 08707 607551 Fax: 01270 766439 E-mail: lee@nutrafx.com *European agent for Bionutra NutraFEM, the widely acclaimed alternative to conventional hormone replacement therapy (HRT).*

Nutrica Ltd, Newmarket Avenue, White Horse Business Park, Trowbridge, Wiltshire, BA14 0XQ Tel: (01225) 768381 Fax: (01225) 768847 *Clinical & infant nutrition information services*

Nutrimetics International UK Ltd, 3 Garamonde Drive, Wymbush, Milton Keynes, MK8 8DF Tel: (01908) 262020 Fax: (01908) 262021 E-mail: info@nutrimetics.co.uk *Cosmetic & skin care distributors*

Nutrition Point Ltd, 13 Taurus Park, Europa Boulevard, Westbrook, Warrington, WA5 7ZT Tel: (01925) 258000 Fax: (01925) 258001 *Health food suppliers*

▶ Nutronic Ltd, 36 Towerfield Road, Shoeburyness, Southend-On-Sea, SS3 9QT Tel: (0845) 1235626 Fax: (01702) 382812 *Computer accessory suppliers*

Nuts, Cowling Brow Industrial Estate, Cowling Brow, Chorley, Lancashire, PR6 0QG Tel: (01257) 264040 Fax: (01257) 273782 E-mail: sales@nutsofchorley.co.uk *Suppliers of industrial fasteners & fixings*

Nuts & Bolts, Unit 10, Longton Industrial Estate, Weston-super-Mare, Avon, BS23 3YB Tel: (01934) 416765 Fax: (01934) 418704 E-mail: enquires@nut-and-bolts.co.uk *Industrial fasteners distributors*

Nuts & Bolts (Cannock) Ltd, Unit 40 Rumer Hill Business Estate, Rumer Hill Rd, Cannock, Staffordshire, WS11 0ET Tel: (01543) 466100 Fax: (01543) 466699 E-mail: sales@nutsandbolts-staffs.co.uk *Nuts & Bolts (Cannock) Ltd was formed in 1994 and are currently located in Cannock, Staffordshire. They offer a wide range of fasteners to the industrial and commercial markets including specialist nuts, bolts, fixings & fasteners.*

Nutscene Ltd, Forfar, Angus, DD8 2NS Tel: (01307) 468589 Fax: (01307) 467051 E-mail: sales@nutscene.com *Manufacturers of horticultural twine & gardening giftware*

Nutshell Packaging, Telford Road, Salisbury, SP2 7PZ Tel: (01722) 321630 Fax: (01722) 341479 *Portion pack sugar manufrs*

Alan Nuttall Ltd, Hall Street, Dudley, West Midlands, DY2 7DQ Tel: (01384) 245100 Fax: (01384) 245102 *Refrigerator fittings & accessories services*

▶ Nuttall Construction Ltd, Chadwick Road, Eccles, Manchester, M30 0WP Tel: 0161-787 7380 Fax: 0161-787 8505

Edmund Nuttall Ltd, St James House, Knoll Road, Camberley, Surrey, GU15 3XW Tel: (01276) 63484 Fax: (01276) 66060 E-mail: headoffice@edmund-nuttall.co.uk *Edmund Nuttall Ltd is a major UK civil engineering contractor with an annual turnover of over £500 million. Founded in 1865 by James Nuttall, the company has earned a reputation for quality, value and delivery across many disciplines. Nuttall is part of the Royal BAM Group, a leading Dutch construction company with an annual turnover in excess of £5 billion. Nuttall offers the full range of civil engineering services from the traditional areas such as road and rail construction, maintenance, maritime engineering, tunnelling, water and sewerage systems through to innovative, highly specialised construction solutions requiring box jacking and limpet dam technology.* Also at: Strood

Nuttall Electrical Contractors, 15-17 Chatham Place, Liverpool, L7 3HD Tel: 0151-703 0212 Fax: 0151-707 2133 E-mail: glynnuttalllimited@btconnect.com

The Nuttall Group UK Ltd, Orchard House, Dodwells Road, Hinckley, Leicestershire, LE10 3BZ Tel: (01455) 638300 Fax: (01455) 638302 E-mail: fsc@nuttalls.co.uk *Fresh food display cabinets*

J. Nuttall & Co. Ltd, Buxton Road, Newtown, New Mills, High Peak, Derbyshire, SK22 3JT Tel: (01663) 746041 Fax: (01663) 749046 *Sportswear manufacturers*

R.H. Nuttall Ltd, Century Works, Great Brook Street, Nechells Green, Birmingham, B7 4EN Tel: 0121-359 2484 Fax: 0121-359 4439 E-mail: sales@rhnuttall.co.uk *R H Nuttall a non metallic washer, gasket, and seal manufacturer based in Birmingham. Washers include foam washers, sponge washers, plastic washers (i.e. polythene washers, ABS washers, nylon washers, polypropylene washers,HDPE washers, PTFE washers, PVC washers,acetal washers), non-asbestos washers (Klingersil washers, novus washers), cork washers, leather washers, vulcanised fibre washers, fibre washers, flexoid washers, oil jointing washers, rubber washers (ie EPDM washers, Nitrile washers, WRAS EPDM washers, neoprene washers, viton washers), felt washers, millboard washers, silicone washers, silicone sponge washers, silicone rubber washers, adhesive backed washers, kiss cut washers. Gaskets include silicone sponge gaskets, silicone rubber gaskets, silicone gaskets, viton gaskets, cork gaskets, Klingersil gaskets, Novus gaskets, rubber gaskets, felt gaskets, plastic gaskets, PTFE sheet, felt sheet, fibre strip, viton strip, felt strip, silicone sponge strip, silicone rubber strip.*

Nutter Aircrafts Ltd, New Works, Chadwick Street, Blackburn, BB2 4AA Tel: (01254) 505200 Fax: (01254) 505205 *CNC machinists*

▶ Nutty Bolt, 63 Old Lane, Openshaw, Manchester, M11 1DE Tel: (07760) 257132 E-mail: info@nuttybolt.com *nuts bolts metric fine hand tools dronco*

▶ Nverge Technologies Ltd, 81 Southfleet Road, Orpington, Kent, BR6 9SN Tel: 0168 9869319 Fax: 0168 9869319 E-mail: sam@nvergetechnologies.com *We are an IT training company providing trainings on Cisco, Checkpoint, Linux and Security. These courses can be conducted either on one-on-one or group basis. For corporates it can be done on-site or off-site.**Please visit www.nvergetechnologies.com for more details.*

Nviro Cleaning Services, Mountbatten Business Park, Jackson Close, Portsmouth, PO6 1US Tel: (023) 9237 0044 Fax: (023) 9237 0047 E-mail: sales@nviro.co.uk *One of the South's leading providers of cleaning services to Commercial, Industrial, Retail & Educational establishments throughout Hampshire, Isle of Wight, West Sussex & Surrey.*

▶ Ny Snacks & Confectionery, 14 Hemmons Road, Manchester, M12 5ST Tel: 0161-256 0080 Fax: 0161-256 0080 *Pop corn manufrs*

Nybble Information Systems, 86 Darwen Street, Blackburn, BB2 2AJ Tel: (01254) 296590 Fax: (0870) 3301200 E-mail: enquiries@nybble.co.uk *IT consultants*

Nycholwood Ltd, 17 Brindley Road, Hinckley, Leicestershire, LE10 3BY Tel: 01455 610300 *Distributor of fixings & fasteners*

Nycom Ltd, Julia Avenue, Huntington, York, YO32 9JR Tel: (01904) 653383 Fax: (01904) 653005 E-mail: info@nycom.co.uk *Computer services*

▶ Nyk Line Europe Ltd, Citypoint, 1 Ropemaker Street, London, EC2Y 9AW Tel: (020) 7090 2000 Fax: (020) 7090 2100

▶ NYK Logistics Ltd, 99 Baillieston Road, Glasgow, G32 0TF Tel: 0141-778 5481 Fax: 0141-778 3022

Nylacast Ltd, 200 Hastings Road, Leicester, LE5 0HL Tel: 0116-276 8558 Fax: 0116-274 1954 E-mail: sales@nylacast.com *Engineering plastics manufacturers & machinists*

Nylon & Alloys Ltd., 74 Half Acre Road, Hanwell, London, W7 3JJ Tel: (020) 8579 5166 Fax: (020) 8579 6986 E-mail: na@nylonalloys.co.uk Sales Contact: A. Mckay Principal Export Areas: Worldwide *Welcome to Nylon & Alloys Ltd, Global distributors of Nylon, Aluminium Alloy, Titanium Fasteners and accessories to industry. Our range covers a multitude of sizes, grades and specifications, Nylon 6 and 66, Aluminium 6060 and 7075 (high tensile) grades with different surface treatments, Titanium commercial grade 2 and grade 5 (6AL-4V) The use of aluminium and titanium parts is more commonplace and is being widely used in the following sectors;- aerospace, petrochemical, treatment and motorsport, where their superior resistance to chemicals, weight reduction and strength are required. We offer standard items ex stock, and are able to supply special parts to specification/Drawing. We operate a QMS system approved to ISO 9001 2000 and are approved suppliers for BAE systems, Rolls-Royce plc Aerospace group & G.E.C. Marconi Aerospace. Friendly efficient service from enquiry through to delivery!*

Nylon Hosiery, 44 Upper Bond Street, Hinckley, Leicestershire, LE10 1RJ Tel: (01455) 631413 Fax: (01455) 636345 E-mail: rob@nylonhosiery.co.uk *Hosiery wholesale & manufrs*

▶ Nymfoodmaniacs Ltd, 15 Harefield Road, Uxbridge, Middlesex, UB8 1PH Tel: 01895 234456 Fax: 01895 234456 E-mail: pat@nymfoodmaniacs.co.uk *Nymfoodmaniacs sources world class ingredients and delivers them to your home.*Our suppliers also supply some of the UKs Michelin starred restaurants, so you can be assured of the freshness and quality of your ingredients. All purchases are sourced and delivered on the same day, a further assurance that your goods will reach you in peak condition.*

Nynas Ltd, Wallis House, 76 North Street, Guildford, Surrey, GU1 4AW Tel: (01483) 506953 Fax: (01483) 506954 *Oil refiners*

Nynas UK Ab, East Camperdown Street, Dundee, DD1 3LG Tel: (01382) 462211 Fax: (01382) 456846 *Bitumen refinery* Also at: Eastham

Nypro (UK) Ltd, 70 Clywedog Road East, Wrexham Industrial Estate, Wrexham, Clwyd, LL13 9XE Tel: (01978) 661180 Fax: (01978) 729215 E-mail: anne.day@nypro.com *Plastic injection moulding manufrs*

Nywled Technology Ltd, Farmerie Road, Hundon, Sudbury, Suffolk, CO10 8HA Tel: (01440) 786611 Fax: (01440) 786800 E-mail: quote@forpcbs.com *Electronic components manufrs*

O A G Worldwide, Church Street, Dunstable, Bedfordshire, LU5 4HB Tel: (01582) 600111 Fax: (01582) 695140 E-mail: sales@oag.com *Publishers of directories & travel information services*

O B C Shipping Ltd, Osprey House, Richmond Road, Pembroke Dock, Dyfed, SA72 6TS Tel: (01646) 622220 Fax: (01646) 622221 E-mail: pembroke.agency@obcgroup.com *Ships agents & freight forwarders* Also at: Pembroke

O B Metals Co. Ltd, Watery Lane Industrial Estate, Watery Lane, Willenhall, West Midlands, WV13 3SU Tel: (01902) 608691 Fax: (01902) 603312 *Nickel scrap merchants*

O B S Computer Maintenance & Sales, 113 Beech Hill Ave, Wigan, Lancs, WN6 7RP Tel: (01257) 421278 E-mail: sales@obscomputers.com *Computer service & maintenance*

O C A S Ltd, PO Box 228, Maidenhead, Berkshire, SL6 6PQ Tel: (01628) 510260 Fax: (01628) 510261 E-mail: ocas@vossnet.co.uk *Protective clothing manufrs* Also at: Manchester

O C & C Strategy Consultants Ltd, 233 Shaftesbury Avenue, London, WC2H 8EE Tel: (020) 7010 8000 Fax: (020) 7010 8100 *Strategy consultants*

▶ O C G Cacao UK Ltd, 5 Manton Wood Business Park, Retford Road, Worksop, Nottinghamshire, S80 2RS Tel: (01909) 509905 Fax: (01909) 509906

O C Interiors Ltd, 8 Swanwick Business Park, Bridge Road, Swanwick, Southampton, SO31 7GB Tel: (01489) 565522 Fax: (01489) 565585 E-mail: mail@ocinteriors.ltd.uk *Contract soft furnishings*

O C Jewellery Manufacturers & Design, 5 Rufus Court Row, Chester, CH1 2JW Tel: (01244) 319244 Fax: (01244) 342723 *Jewellery repairers & manufrs*

O C M Business Systems Ltd, O C M House, St. Peters Road, Droitwich, Worcestershire, WR9 7BJ Tel: (01905) 795001 Fax: (01905) 794567 *Computer systems & software sales*

O C S Group, Servia Road, Leeds, LS7 1NJ Tel: 0113-246 1281 Fax: 0113-234 1682 E-mail: ecleaning@ocs.co.uk *Industrial cleaning services*

O C S Group Ltd, Trafford Bank House, 32 Brindley Road, Manchester, M16 9SA Tel: 0161-876 9151 Fax: 0161-876 2702 E-mail: enquiries@ocs.co.uk *Property support services*

O C S Group Uk, 78 Gatwick Road, Crawley, West Sussex, RH10 9YB Tel: (01293) 553121 Fax: (01293) 663385 E-mail: info@catering.ocs.co.uk *Property support services - cleaning & support, security, technical, transport, hygiene, catering & support*

O & D Williams, 8 Larkhill Lane, Clubmoor, Liverpool, L13 9BR Tel: 0151-226 5654 Fax: 0151-270 2549 *Wholesale ironmongers & retailers*

O E Electronics Ltd, 6 Four Brooks Business Park, Stanier Road, Calne, Wiltshire, SN11 9PP Tel: (01249) 817370 Fax: (01249) 817346 E-mail: sales@pentagon-electronics.co.uk *Electronic repair services*

O E Electronics Ltd, 6 Four Brooks Business Park, Stanier Road, Calne, Wiltshire, SN11 9PP Tel: (01249) 817370 Fax: (01249) 817346 E-mail: sapres@oeelectronics.com *Car radio repair services*

▶ O E M Group Ltd, London Business Innovation Centre, Innova Science Park, Mollison Avenue, Enfield, Middlesex, EN3 7XH Tel: (020) 8344 8777 Fax: (020) 8344 8778 E-mail: steve@secureseal.com *Market a range of security products (reusable seals)*

O.E.M Louvres & Lighting, Browsholme Street, Keighley, West Yorkshire, BD21 5JZ Tel: (01535) 607025 Fax: 01535 663522 *Commercial lighting manufrs*

▶ O E R Franchising, 5 High Street, Seaford, East Sussex, BN25 1PE Tel: (01323) 873555 *Computer software manufrs*

O E S Ltd, Unit S1 Didcot Enterprise Centre, Southmead Industrial Pk, Hawksworth, Didcot, Oxon, OX11 7PH Tel: (01235) 511922 Fax: (01235) 511822 *Engineering services*

O E S (London) Ltd, Chadwell Heath Lane, Romford, RM6 4NP Tel: (020) 8597 7641 Fax: (020) 8599 5083 E-mail: sales@oes-london.demon.co.uk *Office furniture suppliers*

O F Bell Injection Moulding, Unit 1 Castleside Industrial Estate, Consett, County Durham, DH8 8HG Tel: (01207) 504912 Fax: (01207) 509869 E-mail: sylvia@ofbell.co.uk *Injection moulders & toolmakers*

O G Davies & Sons, Maes Yr Hedydd, Meidrim, Carmarthen, Dyfed, SA33 5QY Tel: (01994) 231041 Fax: (01994) 231041 *Agricultural contractors*

O G M Ltd, Stanton Harcourt Road, Witney, Oxfordshire, OX29 4JB Tel: (01865) 880444 Fax: (01865) 883838 E-mail: sales@ogm.uk.com *Plastic injection moulding services*

O H Hewett Ltd, 21 Farncombe Street, Godalming, Surrey, GU7 3AY Tel: (01483) 426917 Fax: (01483) 424810 E-mail: enquiries@ohhewett.co.uk *Necktie or scarf manufrs*

O H S Ltd, 11-17 Campus Road, Listerhills Science Park, Bradford, West Yorkshire, BD7 1HR Tel: (01274) 735848 Fax: (01274) 392280 E-mail: info@ohs.co.uk *Asbestos management consultants, occupational health & safety consultn* Also at: Branches throughout the U.K.

O Hanlon & Farrell, Springhill Road, Carnbane Industrial Estate, Newry, County Down, BT35 6EF Tel: (028) 3026 9213 Fax: (028) 3026 5513 E-mail: ohanlon_farrell@btinternet.com *Power line equipment manufrs*

O I E Services Ltd, Centurion Court, North Esplanade West, Aberdeen, AB11 5QH Tel: (01224) 256400 Fax: (01224) 256444 E-mail: info@optima-energy.com *Oilfield operation services* Also at: Hull

▶ O I Manufacturing Ltd, Devilla Quarry, Alloa, Clackmannanshire, FK10 3QD Tel: (01259) 730621 Fax: (01259) 730340 E-mail: barry.chalmers@eu.o-i.com *Sand quarry*

O I Manufacturing Ltd, PO Box 6068, Harlow, Essex, CM20 2UG Tel: (01279) 422222 Fax: (01279) 773165 *Glass packaging manufrs* Also at: Alloa, Harlow & St. Helens

O I W (Steels) Ltd, 12 Benfleet Road, Benfleet, Essex, SS7 1QB Tel: (01702) 557373 Fax: (01702) 551762 E-mail: sales@oiwsteels.co.uk *Steel stockholders & fabricators, builders merchants & gun dealers*

▶ O Imaging Corporation Limited, 1A Tavern Quay Business Centre, Rope Street, London, SE16 7TX Tel: 0870 429 6575 Fax: 0207 231 2456 E-mail: sgrierson@oimaging.co.uk *OIC supply bespoke Document Management solutions, Scan To PDF software, Document Delivery solutions and Bureau Service, to industry, commerce and government. Solutions range from stand alone to fully integrated world wide.*

O J Electronics Trustee Ltd, Crusader House, Roman Way Crusader Park, Warminster, Wiltshire, BA12 8SJ Tel: (01985) 213003 Fax: (01985) 213310 *Electronic manufrs*

▶ O J M Recruitment, Gresham House, 7 Veryan, Fareham, Hampshire, PO14 1NN Tel: (0845) 8330875 Fax: (0845) 8330873 E-mail: info@ojmrecruitment.com *At OJM Recruitment we will always be a company focused on people.**Finding the right people for the right people is our business and whether you are an employer or a work seeker we are committed to your success.**We aim to create long lasting relationships with both employers and work seekers by fulfilling their recruitment and employment needs in an efficient and professional manner.**

O K I (Europe) Ltd, Central House, Balfour Road, Hounslow, TW3 1HY Tel: (020) 8219 2190 Fax: (020) 8219 2199 *Fax machine & printer manufrs*

▶ O K I UK Ltd, 3 Castlecary Road, Wardpark North, Cumbernauld, Glasgow, G68 0DA Tel: (01236) 502502 Fax: (01236) 502528 E-mail: sales@okieurope.co.uk

▶ O K I UK Ltd, 3 Castlecary Road, Wardpark North, Cumbernauld, Glasgow, G68 0DA Tel: (01236) 502502 Fax: (01236) 502528 E-mail: sales@okieurope.co.uk *Manufacture printers & fax machines*

O K International Europe Ltd, Shepherds Grove Industrial Estate, Stanton, Bury St. Edmunds, Suffolk, IP31 2AR Tel: (01359) 250705 Fax: (01359) 250165 E-mail: sales@okinteurope.co.uk *Packaging & packing equipment manufrs*

O Kahn Printers Ltd, 10 Timberwharf Road, London, N16 6DB Tel: (020) 8800 9941 Fax: (020) 8809 4896 E-mail: samkahn@freenet.co.uk *Printing & packaging manufrs*

O Kay Engineering Services Ltd, Valley Way, Market Harborough, Leicestershire, LE16 7PS Tel: (01858) 435500 Fax: (01858) 435511 E-mail: sales@okay.co.uk *Conveyor systems manufrs*

O L D Engineering Co. Ltd, Unit 1 Sketchley Meadows, Hinckley, Leicestershire, LE10 3EN Tel: (01455) 612521 Fax: (01455) 635790 E-mail: m.topp@oldengineering.co.uk *Engineering sub-contractors*

O M C Fluidpower Ltd, Unit N, Harlow House, Corby, Northamptonshire, NN17 5XH Tel: (01536) 260372 Fax: (01536) 264422 *Hydraulic hose manufacturers & assembly services*

O M C UK Ltd, Candela House, Cardrew Industrial Estate, Redruth, Cornwall, TR15 1SS Tel: (01209) 215424 Fax: (01209) 215197 E-mail: omc-sales@omc-uk.com Principal Export Areas: Worldwide *Optoelectronics*

O M F Partnership, Old Manor Farm, Spring Lane, Little Bourton, Banbury, Oxfordshire, OX17 1RB Tel: (01295) 758857 Fax: (01295) 758131 E-mail: oldmanorfarm@ukonline.co.uk *Agricultural contractors*

▶ O M S Ltd, Origination House, 15 Strawberry Street, Hull, HU9 1EN Tel: (01482) 224429

O M Safety Fencing Supplies, 14A Wesley Street, Rodley, Leeds, LS13 1JH Tel: 0113-236 2241 *Safety barriers*

O M V UK Ltd, 14 Ryder Street, London, SW1Y 6QB Tel: (020) 7333 1600 Fax: (020) 7333 1610 E-mail: info@omv.com *Oil & gas exploration & production*

O N C, Unit 220 Tedco Business Centre, Jarrow, Tyne & Wear, NE32 3DT Tel: 0191-422 0229 Fax: 0191-428 3365 E-mail: s.owens@onc-computers.co.uk *Computer maintenance services*

O O C L UK Ltd, Oocl House, Bridge Road, Levington, Ipswich, IP10 0NE Tel: (01473) 659000 Fax: (01473) 654200 *Shipping line & ship owners*

O P B Paper Sales Ltd, 26-28 Sidney Road, Stockwell, London, SW9 0TS Tel: (020) 7737 3131 Fax: (020) 7738 7052 E-mail: opb-paper@freenetname.co.uk *Paper merchants & exporters*

O P C UK, Falcon House, 12 Barns Street, Ayr, KA7 1XA Tel: (01292) 272403 Fax: 01292 270123 E-mail: sales@opcuk.co.uk *Printed circuit board manufrs*

O P Chocolate Ltd, High Street, Dowlais, Merthyr Tydfil, CF48 3TB Tel: (01685) 352560 Fax: (01685) 352599 E-mail: opchoc@cemoi.com *Biscuit manufrs*

O P G Precision Engineering Ltd, Station Road, Rowley Regis, West Midlands, B65 0LD Tel: 0121-559 4121 Fax: 0121-559 3661 E-mail: sales@opg-ltd.co.uk *Grinding specialists*

O P W Fuel Management Systems, Unit K2 Welland Industrial Estate, Valley Way, Market Harborough, Leicestershire, LE16 7PS Tel: (01858) 433365 Fax: (01858) 463452 E-mail: sales@opwfms.com *Petroleum forecourt equipment distributors*

O R T Forwarding Ltd, Unit 24 Bourne Road Industrial Park, Bourne Road, Dartford, DA1 4BZ Tel: (01322) 555486 Fax: (01322) 528528 E-mail: enquiries@ort.co.uk *Freight forwarding*

O Rings Ltd, Gravel Lane, Chichester, West Sussex, PO19 8PQ Tel: (01243) 787817 Fax: (01243) 530440 E-mail: sales@oringslimited.co.uk *Rubber products stockists. Also o-ring & gasket distributors or agents*

O S F Ltd, Unit 6 Station Road, Four Ashes Industrial Estate, Four Ashes, Wolverhampton, WV10 7DB Tel: (01902) 798080 Fax: (01902) 794750 E-mail: sales@jcshopfitters.co.uk *Steel handrail manufrs*

O S G Ship Management (UK) Ltd, Horsley House, Regent Centre, Gosforth, Newcastle Upon Tyne, NE3 3HW Tel: 0191-285 0621 Fax: 0191-284 5644 *Ship management & brokers*

O S L Group Ltd, Imperial Works, Sheffield Road, Tinsley, Sheffield, S9 2YL Tel: 0114-221 2500 Fax: 0114-221 2560 E-mail: sales@oslgroup.com *Sealing component distributors*

O S O Products Ltd, 5-7 Hanbury Street, Droitwich, Worcestershire, WR9 8PL Tel: (01905) 795300 Fax: (01905) 797707 *Salt manufacturers & packing*

O S S Electrical Controls Ltd, 36 Bar Gap Road, Oldham, OL1 3RL Tel: 0161-633 9692 Fax: 0161-627 2352 E-mail: rss-elect@tiscali.co.uk *Control systems & panels designers & manufrs*

O S S Group Ltd, Valley Road, Morley, Leeds, LS27 8ES Tel: (0870) 8702088 Fax: 0113-252 7009 E-mail: sales@ossgroupltd.com *Waste oil collectors*

▶ O S Solutions, 5 High West Street, Dorchester, Dorset, DT1 1UJ Tel: (01305) 751713 *Computer systems consultants*

O T C Direct Ltd, Direct House, East Street, Epsom, Surrey, KT17 1BH Tel: (01372) 740004 Fax: (01372) 721175 E-mail: info@otc-direct-ltd.com *Pharmaceuticals specialists*

O Toffolo & Son Ltd, 42 Temple Street, Hull, HU5 1AE Tel: (01482) 342674 Fax: (01482) 441344 E-mail: carl@toffolo.co.uk *Terrazzo flooring specialists* Also at: Grimsby

O V Garland & Sons Ltd, The Forge, Dark Lane, North Wootton, Shepton Mallet, Somerset, BA4 4AQ Tel: (01749) 890288 Fax: (01749) 890288 *Agricultural engineers*

▶ O X, Unit B, New Baltic Wharf, Evelyn Street, London, SE8 5RJ Tel: (020) 8469 3331

O Y Z Staker Ltd, Guild House, Reddicap Trading Estate, Sutton Coldfield, West Midlands, B75 7BU Tel: 0121-241 1050 Fax: 0121-311 1778 E-mail: sales@midlandlaw.co.uk *Law stationers & printers*

O&W, 5 Grange Court Road, Bristol, BS9 4DP Tel: 0117-962 1777 Fax: 0117-962 1166 *Flooring consultants & contractors*

Oadby Plastics Ltd, Elland Road, Leicester, LE3 1TU Tel: 0116-232 1010 Fax: 0116-287 3577 E-mail: sales@oadbyplastics.ltd.uk *Plastic machinists, plastic materials*

Oadby Wrought Iron, Chapel Street, Oadby, Leicester, LE2 5AD Tel: 0116-271 5040 *Fire escape staircase manufrs*

Oak Cad Training Ltd, 18 Cubitts Close, Digswell, Welwyn, Hertfordshire, AL6 0DZ Tel: (01438) 712258 Fax: (01438) 712258 E-mail: alan@oakcad.co.uk *Training engineering, CAD*

Oak Die Stamping & Engraving Co. Ltd, Tyburn Industrial Estate, Ashold Farm Road, Birmingham, B24 9QG Tel: 0121-382 4585 Fax: 0121-377 6359 E-mail: ordes-oak@btconnect.com *Lithographers & foil blockers*

Oak Engineering Ltd, Oak Street, Cradley Heath, West Midlands, B64 5JZ Tel: (01384) 569859 Fax: (01384) 410954 E-mail: oakhinges@woden.com *Hinges manufrs*

▶ Oak Floral Design, Manor Farm, Main Street, Shangton, Leicester, LE8 0PG Tel: (07754) 07122 *Florist specialising in wedding design, from Bridal Flowers to Table Designs in an around leicestershire.*

Oak Frame Carpentry Co. Ltd, Nupend Farm, Nupend, Stonehouse, Gloucestershire, GL10 3SU Tel: (01453) 825092 Fax: (01453) 828788 E-mail: oakframe@btconnect.com *Oak frame suppliers*

Oak Hill Embroidery, 86 Bromley Road, Beckenham, Kent, BR3 5NP Tel: (020) 8650 6897 Fax: (020) 8663 3842 *Embroidered logos*

Oak Industrial Supplies, Hamilton Road, Sutton-in-Ashfield, Nottinghamshire, NG17 5LN Tel: (01623) 442222 Fax: (01623) 441234 E-mail: sales@oakis.co.uk *Distributors of protective clothing & equipment*

Oak Leasing Ltd, 21 Moor Street, Chepstow, Gwent, NP16 5DB Tel: (01291) 625211 Fax: (01291) 625212 E-mail: sales@oaklease.co.uk *Sales Aid Leasing Company*

Oak Medical Services Ltd, Unit 5-6 Island Carr Industrial Estate, Island Carr Road, Brigg, South Humberside, DN20 8PD Tel: (01652) 657200 Fax: (01652) 657009 E-mail: sales@oakmedicalservices.co.uk *Medical equipment suppliers & manufrs*

▶ Oak Mobility Ltd, 14 Bustleholme Lane, West Bromwich, West Midlands, B71 3AP Tel: (01384) 362091 Fax: 0845 1110313 E-mail: customerservice@oakmobility.co.uk *Suppliers of Stairlifts. Straight Stairlifts, Curved Stairlifts,Platform Lifts, Through the floor lifts, Bath Lifts, Lifting Cushions, Mobility Products.*

Oak Telecom Ltd, 7 Albany Park, Cabot Lane, Poole, Dorset, BH17 7BX Tel: (01202) 607000 Fax: (01202) 607001 *Telephone logging & voice mail systems manufrs*

Oak Tree Forge, Oak Tree Yard, Upper Manor Road, Paignton, Devon, TQ3 2TP Tel: (01803) 550436 Fax: (01803) 529277 *Constructional engineers of ornamental metalwork*

Oak Tree Plastic & Engineering Ltd, Spon La South, West Bromwich, West Midlands, B70 6AZ Tel: 0121-500 5164 Fax: 0121-500 5164 *Injection moulders*

Oak Valley Fabrications, The Workshop, rear of 91 Chesterfield Road, North Wingfield, Chesterfield, Derbyshire, S42 5LF Tel: 0782 117 9985 *Manufacturers of Premium quality, bespoke conservatory roofs.*

▶ The Oak Window Co. Ltd, Unit 4, Manton Industrial Estate, Manton, Rutland, Oakham, Leicestershire, LE15 8SZ Tel: (01780) 460621 Fax: (0800) 5424300 *Oak window frame & door suppliers*

Oak Wood Furniture Manufacturers Ltd, Oakwood, Old Parish Road, Ynysybwl, Pontypridd, Mid Glamorgan, CF37 3EY Tel: (01443) 791701 Fax: (01443) 791821 *Furniture manufrs*

▶ Oak-Apple Frames, Widcombe Farm, Culmhead, Taunton, Somerset, TA3 7DX Tel: (01823) 421395 Fax: (01823) 421395 E-mail: enquiries@oakappleframes.co.uk *Oak frame building*

▶ Oakbank Services, Mosspark Cottages, Braswell, Dumfries, DG1 4PH Tel: (01387) 268160 Fax: (01387) 251898

Oakbray Ltd, Whieldon Industrial Estate, Whieldon Road, Stoke-on-Trent, ST4 4JP Tel: (01782) 744555 Fax: (01782) 414244 E-mail: sales@oakbray.co.uk *Distributors of hosing, ducting & castors*

Oakcad Ltd, 116 Whalley Drive, Bletchley, Milton Keynes, MK3 6HU Tel: (01908) 365781 Fax: (01908) 365811 E-mail: alan@oakcad.co.uk *Training engineering & CAD*

▶ Oakdale Contracts Ltd, Walkerville Industrial Park, Catterick Garrison, North Yorkshire, DL9 4SA Tel: (01748) 834184 Fax: (01748) 833033 E-mail: inquieres@oakdalecontracts.co.uk *Concrete products*

Oakdale Fencing Ltd, Bedworth Road, Bulkington, Bedworth, Warwickshire, CV12 9LG Tel: (024) 7664 0120 Fax: (024) 7664 0120 E-mail: enquiries@oakdalefencing.co.uk *Fencing contractors*

Oakes Brothers Ltd, Fareham Road, Wickham, Fareham, Hampshire, PO17 5DH Tel: (01329) 832345 Fax: (01329) 833944 *Agricultural & grasscare machinery sales parts*

Oakes Bros Ltd, Ridgeway Works, Stanmore Road, East Ilsley, Newbury, Berkshire, RG20 7LU Tel: (01635) 281222 Fax: (01635) 281200 *Agriculture & horticulture engineers*

Oakes Brothers, Cowdown Farm, Micheldever, Winchester, Hampshire, SO21 3DN Tel: (01962) 794100 Fax: (01962) 794118 *Agricultural & horticultural engineers* Also at: Hungerford & Wantage

▶ Oakfield Construction, Dunsil Road Moorgreen Industrial Park, Engine Lane, Newthorpe, Nottingham, NG16 3QU Tel: (01773) 534000 Fax: (01773) 534222 E-mail: office@oakfieldconstruction.co.uk

Oakfield Consultancy Partnership, 1 Farndon Hall, Church Lane, Farndon, Chester, CH3 6QF Tel: (01925) 491234 Fax: (01925) 480088 E-mail: enquiries@oakfieldconsultancy.com *Consultants*

Oakfield Direct, Oakfield Riding Stables, Stanifield Lane, Farington, Leyland, PR25 4UA Tel: (01772) 421999 Fax: (01772) 619694 E-mail: info@oakfield-direct.co.uk *Saddlery & riding wear suppliers*

Oakfield Instruments Ltd, Oakfield Industrial Estate, Eynsham, Witney, Oxfordshire, OX29 4AN Tel: (01865) 882532 Fax: (01865) 883970 E-mail: info@flexilog.net *Medical electronic patient monitoring equipment*

Oakfield Rubber Co., 480 Hawthorne Road, Bootle, Merseyside, L20 9PP Tel: 0151-933 6266 Fax: 0151-922 8743 *Property management & storage suppliers*

Oakham Engineering, Newtown, Evesham, Worcestershire, WR11 8RZ Tel: (01386) 446513 *Mild steel wire component manufrs*

▶ Oakham Lift Services, 4 Hainge Road, Tividale, Oldbury, West Midlands, B69 2NH Tel: 0121-522 0050 Fax: 0121-522 0059 E-mail: sales@oakhamliftservices.co.uk *Service lifts*

Oakham Sheet Metal Co. Ltd, Brickhouse Lane, Great Bridge, West Bromwich, West Midlands, B70 0DS Tel: 0121-557 9656 Fax: 0121-522 2186 *Sheet metalworkers*

Oakhanger Aquatics, Nursery Road, Oakhanger, Crewe, CW1 5UY Tel: (01270) 872467 Fax: (01270) 884260 *Aquatics company*

Oakhill Optical Laboratory Ltd, PO Box 3, Stourbridge, West Midlands, DY9 8DA Tel: (01384) 894035 Fax: (01384) 423701 *Optical manufrs*

Oakhurst Business Systems Ltd, 11 Randiddles Close, Hurstpierpoint, Hassocks, West Sussex, BN6 9BG Tel: (01273) 835617 Fax: (01273) 832485 *Software consultants*

Oakland Associates, Westmead House, 123 Westmead Road, Sutton, Surrey, SM1 4JH Tel: (020) 8395 7799 Fax: (020) 8395 7676 E-mail: info@oaklandassociates.co.uk *Established in 1993, Oakland Associates Ltd is an IT support company based in Sutton, Surrey. The company provides IT related services to all sizes of businesses, specialising in network design, implementation and support. Visit our website for more information**

Oakland Coachbuilders Ltd, Unit 3, KDO Business Centre, Little Witley, Worcester, WR6 6LR Tel: (01299) 896754 Fax: (01299) 896885 E-mail: oakland.horsebox@btconnect.com *Horse box repairs & manufrs*

Oakland Elevators Ltd, 6 Mandervell Road, Oadby, Leicester, LE2 5LL Tel: 0116-272 0800 Fax: 0116-272 0904 E-mail: sales@oakland-elevators.co.uk *Lift manufrs & services*

▶ Oakland Interiors Ltd, Unit 1, Butterwaite Business Park, Green Lane, Ecclesfield, Sheffield, S35 9ZY Tel: 0114-245 6820 Fax: 0114-245 6342

Oakland International, 3 The Chancery, Bramcote, Nottingham, NG9 3AJ Tel: 0115-967 7141 Fax: 0115-967 7653 E-mail: info@loadingbay.co.uk *Oakland will refurbish and remodel your loading bay to suit new double deck and air suspension trailers with custom designed dock shelters, and the EXCLUSIVE Nytrex range of indestructible SAFETY YELLOW dock dumper and truck products.*

▶ Oakland International Ltd, Seafield Lane, Beoley, Redditch, Worcestershire, B98 9DB Tel: (01527) 596222 Fax: (01527) 596232 E-mail: sales@oakland-international.com *Chilled storage & contract packaging services & ambient storage services*

Oakland Kitchens & Bedrooms Ltd, 14 Tile Cross Trading Estate, Tile Cross Road, Birmingham, B33 0NW Tel: 0121-779 5732 Fax: 0121-779 5732 *Kitchen & bedroom fitters, retail & manufrs*

▶ Oakland Leicester Ltd, 7-11 Welford Road, Blaby, Leicester, LE8 4FT Tel: 0116-277 2252 Fax: 0116-278 8445 *Bathroom installation & retailers*

Oakland Supplies, Stevenage Indoor Market, St.Georges Way, Stevenage, Hertfordshire, SG1 1HP Tel: (01438) 314263 Fax: (01438) 314263 *Roller, vertical & venetian blinds manufrs*

▶ Oaklands Joinery, Unit 2c Langham Street, Liverpool, L4 4DA Tel: 0151-207 4217 Fax: 0151-207 4217

▶ Oaklands Pressure Washers, 343 Eakring Road, Mansfield, Notts, NG18 3EL Tel: 01623 651118 Fax: 07875 795050 E-mail: sales@oaklandspressurewashers.co.uk *Oaklands Pressure Washers - Gerni Pressure Washers, Gerni Steam Cleaners, Gerni Power Washer, Industrial Wet Dry Vacuum Cleaners.*

Oaklands Signs, 70 Draycott, Cam, Dursley, Gloucestershire, GL11 5DH Tel: (01453) 542312 Fax: (01453) 543353 E-mail: jilldavis.oaklands@btinternet.com *Engravers & trophy suppliers*

Oaklea Direct, Oaklea Pk, Tunbridge La, Bramshott, Liphook, Hants, GU30 7RF Tel: (01428) 727790 Fax: (01428) 787427 *Software*

Oakleaf Building Service, 1 Millside Park, Crouch Lane, Winkfield, Windsor, Berkshire, SL4 4PX Tel: (01344) 891277 Fax: (01344) 891299 *General builders*

Oakleaf Cabinet Makers, 20 Fieldside, Crowle, Scunthorpe, South Humberside, DN17 4HL Tel: (01724) 711027 Fax: (01724) 710018 E-mail: enquiries@oakleafcabinetmakers.co.uk *Kitchens & bedroom designers & cabinet makers*

Oakleaf Consultancy Ltd, 2A Talbot Road, Northampton, NN1 4JB Tel: (01604) 633566 Fax: (01604) 601102 E-mail: sales@oakleafconsultancy.com *IT consultants*

Oakleaf Graphics, Portland House, Bolsover Business Park, Woodhouse Lane, Bolsover, Chesterfield, Derbyshire, S44 6BD Tel: (01246) 828228 E-mail: sales@oakleafgraphics.co.uk *Graphic design & exhibition materials suppliers*

Oakleaf Reproductions Ltd, Ling Bob Mill, Main St, Wilsden, Bradford, West Yorkshire, BD15 0JP Tel: (01535) 272878 Fax: (01535) 275748 E-mail: sales@oakleaf.co.uk *Reproduction oak beams & wall panels*

Oakleigh Cases Ltd, 10 The Summit Centre, Summit Road, Potters Bar, Hertfordshire, EN6 3JN Tel: (01707) 655011 Fax: (01707) 646447 E-mail: sales@oakleighcases.com *Manufacturers of cases, including flight, instrument & sample*

Oakley Arnold Ltd, Cockshot Lane, Broseley, Shropshire, TF12 5NE Tel: (01952) 882322 Fax: (01952) 882707 *Scrap iron & steel merchants*

Arthur Oakley Transport Ltd, Ramsden Road, Rotherwas Industrial Estate, Hereford, HR2 6LR Tel: (01432) 266662 Fax: (01432) 356660 E-mail: sales@vanoaksteels.co.uk *Warehousing, import & export of steel*

Oakley Bros, 93 Greenfield Road, Flitton, Bedford, MK45 5DR Tel: (01525) 717171 Fax: (01525) 717171 *Bacon wholesaler*

Oakley Coachbuilders, High Cross, Ware, Hertfordshire, SG11 1AD Tel: (01920) 466781 Fax: (01920) 467895 E-mail: sales@oakleyhorseboxes.co.uk *Motorised horse box builders*

Oakley Fuel Oils Ltd, Halesfield 19, Telford, Shropshire, TF7 4QT Tel: (01952) 684600 Fax: (01952) 684577 E-mail: enquiries@oakleysfueloils.co.uk *Fuel & oil distribs*

Oakley Furniture, Unit 16 Oakley Wood, Benson, Wallingford, Oxfordshire, OX10 6QG Tel: (01491) 825880 Fax: (01491) 825880 *Furniture distributors*

Oakley Soils & Concrete Engineering Ltd, Rede Hall, Chedburgh, Bury St. Edmunds, Suffolk, IP29 4UG Tel: (01284) 850555 Fax: (01284) 850345 *Site investigation, monitoring & environmental boreholes*

▶ Oakley Systems Ltd, 10 Vickers House, Priestley Road, Basingstoke, Hampshire, RG24 9NP Tel: 01256 840010 Fax: 01256 840021 *CCTV Design and Installation, *Access Control Systems Design and Installation, *Intruder Alarm System Design and Installation,*Maintenance of Electronic Security Systems*

Oakleys, 161-163 Northfield Road, Sheffield, S10 1QQ Tel: 0114-268 1723 Fax: 0114-268 1723 *Fishing tackle suppliers*

▶ Oakley's Ltd, Unit1 Leasowes Business Park, Cressage, Shrewsbury, SY5 6AF Tel: (01952) 511000 Fax: (01952) 511005 E-mail: sales@oakleysgroundcare.co.uk

Oakmace Exhibitions Ltd, Aimes Green Farm, Galley Hill, Waltham Abbey, Essex, EN9 2AU Tel: (01992) 893768 Fax: (01992) 893981 E-mail: display@oakmace.com *Contractors designers & builders of exhibition stands*

Oakmere Technical Services Ltd, Unit 9, Pool Bank Business Park, High St, Chester, CH3 8JH Tel: (01829) 742100 Fax: (01829) 742109 E-mail: sales@oakmerets.com *Creosote manufrs*

Oakpark Alarms, Hydra House, 26 North Street, Ashford, Kent, TN24 8JR Tel: (01233) 643851 *Burglar alarm suppliers, installation & servicing*

Oakpark Alarms, Bayard Place, Verwood Road, Three Legged Cross, Wimborne, Dorset, BH21 6RJ Tel: (01202) 827776 Fax: (01202) 827776 E-mail: oakpark@fsbdial.co.uk *Alarm installers*

▶ Oakpark Alarms Surrey & Hampshire, Oakpark House, 337 London Road, Camberley, Surrey, GU15 3HQ Tel: (01276) 24149 Fax: (01276) 709515

Oakridge Direct Ltd, Maerdy Industrial Estate, Rhymney, Tredegar, Gwent, NP22 5YD Tel: (01685) 844000 Fax: (01685) 844911 *Sofa manufrs*

Oaks CCTV Ltd, 6 St. Helens Way, Thetford, Norfolk, IP24 1HG Tel: (01842) 820627 Fax: (01842) 820624 *CCTV sales & installation service providers*

Oaktarget Ltd, 33 Kitchener Road, Leicester, LE5 4AU Tel: 0116-274 0304 Fax: 0116-276 7782 E-mail: sales@oaktarget.com Principal Export Areas: Central/East Europe & West Europe *Clothing suppliers*

Oaktree Interiors Ltd, Frederick House, 498 Reading Road, Winnersh, Wokingham, Berkshire, RG41 5EX Tel: 0118-979 6600 Fax: 0118-979 4044 E-mail: sales@oaktreeoffice.com *Oaktree Interiors offer a flexible approach to your business requirements and provide a quality, reliable service that ensures customer satisfaction.*We undertake all forms of Office refurbishment works, design, space planning, fit outs, partitioning, air conditioning, mechanical and electrical work, as well as dilapidation contracts.*

▶ Oakville, 3 Badcox, Frome, Somerset, BA11 3BQ Tel: (01373) 461438 Fax: (01373) 461438 E-mail: customerservices@oakvillecarecentre.co.uk *Daily Living Aids*

Oakway Mechanical Equipment, 42 Oliver Street, Northampton, NN2 7JJ Tel: (01604) 792255 *Materials handling equipment*

▶ Oakwell Consultants, Billing Arbours House, Heather Lane, Northampton, NN3 8EY Tel: (01604) 413888 Fax: (0870) 1304049 E-mail: sales@oakwell-consultants.fsnet.co.uk *Provide outplacement & pre retirement planning services*

▶ Oakwood Builders & Joinery Ltd, Oaklands, Old Icknield Way, Benson, Wallingford, Oxfordshire, OX10 6PW Tel: (01491) 836440 Fax: (01491) 826020

▶ Oakwood Cabinets Ltd, 6 Julian Road, Sheffield, S9 1FQ Tel: 0114-261 7600

Oakwood Computing Ltd, 1 Dornton Road, South Croydon, Surrey, CR2 7DR Tel: (020) 8686 7213 E-mail: enquiries@oakwoodcomputing.co.uk *Computer based trainers*

Oakwood Steel Fabrications, 260 Oakwood Lane, Leeds, LS8 3LE Tel: 0113-235 9853 Fax: 0113-235 9884 *Wrought iron manufrs*

Oakwood Technology Group, Ill Road, Cheadle Hulme, Cheadle, Cheshire, SK8 6GN Tel: 0161-488 4343 Fax: 0161-488 4086 E-mail: sales@oakwoodair.co.uk *Air conditioner & mechanical services*

Oakwood Traditional Furniture Ltd, Crewe Hill, Crewe Hill Lane, Farndon, Chester, CH3 6PD Tel: (01829) 270704 Fax: (01829) 271709 E-mail: enquiries@oakwoodfurniture.co.uk *Furniture manufrs*

▶ Oakwrights Country Buildings, The Lakes, Swainshill, Hereford, HR4 7PU Tel: (0845) 2309560 Fax: (01432) 357733

▶ Oasis, Unit 12 The Wenta Business Centre, Colne Way, Watford, WD24 7ND Tel: (01923) 201551 Fax: (01923) 201561 E-mail: sales@oasis-blinds.co.uk *Blinds & awning retailers*

Oasis Air Conditioning Ltd, 80 Bramhall Lane, Davenport, Stockport, Cheshire, SK2 6JG Tel: 0161-477 1003 Fax: 0161-477 3110 E-mail: sales@oasisairconditioning.com *Air conditioning installers*

Oasis Art & Craft Products Ltd, Goldthorn Road, Kidderminster, Worcestershire, DY11 7JD Tel: (01562) 744522 Fax: (01562) 823181 E-mail: sales@oasisart.co.uk *Engraving craft kits manufrs*

▶ Oasis Art & Graphics, 68 East Meadway, Birmingham, B33 0AP Tel: 0121-786 2988 Fax: 0121-789 7146 E-mail: accounts@oasisag.co.uk

▶ Oasis Blinds, 322 Rayleigh Road, Leigh-on-Sea, Essex, SS9 5PU Tel: (01702) 510300 Fax: (01702) 510300 *Window blinds suppliers*

▶ Oasis Blinds, 159 Rice Lane, Liverpool, L9 1AF Tel: 0151-523 1777 Fax: 0151-523 1777 *Blind manufrs*

Oasis Blinds & Flooring, Comberton Hill, Kidderminster, Worcestershire, DY10 1QH Tel: (01562) 515445 Fax: (01562) 864278 *Blind contractors & suppliers*

▶ Oasis Design Studio, 1 Culzean Glen, Larne, County Antrim, BT40 2HF Tel: (028) 2827 0668 Fax: (028) 2827 0668 E-mail: info@oasisdesignstudio.co.uk *Graphic Design and Print Broking Services*

Oasis Environmental Products, 4 Nova Croft, Coventry, CV5 7FJ Tel: (024) 7646 6540 Fax: (024) 7646 4764 *Air cleaners*

▶ Oasis Environments Ltd, 2 Douglas Road, Horfield, Bristol, BS7 0JD Tel: 0117-951 9567 Fax: 0117-935 4467 E-mail: mail@oasis-bristol.co.uk *Bristol based installers of epoxy resin floor, wall & roof coatings, and external resin bonded aggregate surfacing systems.*

Oasis Fibreglass Ltd, Froxton Whitstone, Holsworthy, Devon, EX22 6TP Tel: (01288) 341628 Fax: (01288) 341565 *Fibre glass repairs*

Oasis Interior Landscaping, Towers Yard Farm, Towers Road, Poynton, Stockport, Cheshire, SK12 1DE Tel: (01625) 859195 Fax: (01625) 859898 *Floral display contractors*

Oasis M V, Unit F Drapers Yard, Warrenwood Industrial Estate, Stapleford, Hertford, SG14 3NU Tel: (01992) 554733 *Spring water suppliers*

Oasis Metal Products, Wonastow Road, Monmouth, Gwent, NP25 5AH Tel: (01600) 715732 Fax: (01600) 714878 *Sheet metalwork engineers & fabricator services*

▶ Oaston Engineering Ltd, 7-8 Ptarmigan Place, Attleborough Fields Industrial Estate, Nuneaton, Warwickshire, CV11 6RX Tel: (024) 7664 2324 Fax: (024) 7635 4597

Oasys, Unit 1, Briar Close, Bramble Lane, Wye, Ashford, Kent, TN25 5HB Tel: (01233) 812050 Fax: (01233) 812082 E-mail: enquiries@o-a-sys.co.uk *Computerised accountancy consultants*

Oasys Technologies Ltd, Unit 37 Jubilee Road, Letchworth Garden City, Hertfordshire, SG6 1NE Tel: (01462) 480933 Fax: (01462) 480292 *Card system technology*

▶ Ob Hire, Unit C-D Woodside, Brewery Road, Hoddesdon, Hertfordshire, EN11 8HF Tel: (01992) 468460 Fax: 01992 468463 E-mail: sales@obhire.com *Hire company providing self drive diggers,dumpers and general contracting equipment to the London, Herts & Essex areas.*

▶ Oban Precision Instruments, 47 Combie Street, Oban, Argyll, PA34 4HS Tel: (01631) 564330 *Watch & clock repairers*

Obara UK, 1 Tomlinson Industrial Estate, Alfreton Road, Derby, DE21 4ED Tel: (01332) 297868 Fax: E-mail: sales@obara.co.uk *Welding & electric resistance equipment manufrs*

Obc Shipping Ltd, 2a Gateway Business Park, Beancross Road, Grangemouth, Stirlingshire, FK3 8WX Tel: (01324) 482811 Fax: (01324) 665197 E-mail: grangemouth.agency@obcgroup.com *Shipping agents*

Obc Shipping, O B C House, Sabatier Close, Thornaby, Stockton-on-Tees, Cleveland, TS17 6EW Tel: (01642) 637500 Fax: (01642) 637502 *Shipping agents*

Obducat Camscan Ltd, Camscan House, Pembroke Avenue, Waterbeach, Cambridge, CB25 9PY Tel: (01223) 861066 Fax: (01223) 861077 E-mail: info@camscan.com Principal Export Areas: Worldwide *Scanning microscopes manufrs*

Obek UK Ltd, Unit C8 Baird Court, Park Farm Industrial Estate, Wellingborough, Northamptonshire, NN8 6QJ Tel: (01933) 675457 Fax: (01933) 675665 E-mail: obekuk@btconnect.com *CNC precision engineering*

Oberlin Filter Ltd, 6 Thames Centre, Aycliffe Industrial Park, Newton Aycliffe, County Durham, DL5 6UJ Tel: 01325 317900 *Filter & filter media manufrs*

▶ Oberoi Bros Lighting Ltd, Humbleton Drive, Derby, DE22 4AU Tel: (01332) 341027 Fax: (01332) 293863 E-mail: sales@lightsuk.com *Lighting specialists*

▶ Oberthur Card Systems Ltd, Alexandre Way, Ashchurch Business Centre, Tewkesbury, Gloucestershire, GL20 8GA Tel: (01684) 290290 Fax: (01684) 290111 E-mail: s.west@oberthurcs.com *Smart cards manufrs*

Objective Services Ltd, 10 Kingfisher Walk, Ash, Aldershot, Hampshire, GU12 6RF Tel: (01252) 345399 Fax: (01252) 345598 E-mail: info@objectiveservices.com *Database design, management*

Oblique, Stamford Works, Gillett Street, London, N16 8JH Tel: (020) 7249 7363 Fax: (020) 7275 7495 *Furniture manufrs*

Oblique, Stamford Works, Gillett Street, London, N16 8JH Tel: (020) 7503 2100 Fax: (020) 7275 7495 *Furniture manufrs*

▶ Oblong Furniture Ltd, 80a York Street, Leeds, LS9 8AA Tel: 0113-242 6111 Fax: 0113-243 1858 E-mail: info@oblongfurniture.co.uk *Supply of contract furniture to the leisure & office markets*

O'Brian Manufacturing Ltd, Robian Way, Swadlincote, Derbyshire, DE11 9DH Tel: (01283) 217588 Fax: (01283) 215613 *Machine tool spare part suppliers & manufrs*

▶ O'Brien Commisioning, Bridge Street, Pendlebury, Swinton, Manchester, M27 4DU Tel: 0161-728 3444 Fax: 0161-728 3555 E-mail: job.commissioning@ukonline.co.uk *Laboratory equipment maintenance*

▶ O'Brien Construction Ltd, Park Lane, Thurso, Caithness, KW14 8JZ Tel: (01847) 893666 Fax: (01847) 893888

Obtain-Wise Ltd, Captiva House, 34 Heathfield, Stacey Bushes, Milton Keynes, MK12 6HR Tel: (01604) 758999 Fax: (01908) 310555 E-mail: info@obtainwise.com *Janitorial supply services*

Oc Mechanical Services, 4 Broadwater Road, Worthing, West Sussex, BN14 8AE Tel: (01903) 232147 Fax: 01903 232147 *Air conditioning contractors*

Occasions, 96 Liverpool Road, Cadishead, Manchester, M44 5AN Tel: 0161-775 7979 Fax: 0161-775 7979 *Balloon & card retailers*

▶ Occasions Buffets, 84 Somerset Avenue, Luton, LU2 0PN Tel: (01582) 612345

▶ Occasions Caterers Ltd, Unit 22 Bow Triangle Business, Centre Eleanor Street Bow, London, E3 4UR Tel: (020) 8980 2770 *Occasions - Event Spoecialists, Caterers, organisers, Asian wedding Catering & bespoke event management, indian weddings asian weddings, www.occasionservcies.com , www.occasionsgroup.com 0208 980 7776, 0207 702 7775*

Occasions Catering Hire, 12 Oak Industrial Park, Chelmsford Road, Dunmow, Essex, CM6 1XN Tel: (01371) 872183 Fax: (01371) 872838 E-mail: petersimpson@occasionscateringhire.co.uk *All our hire wear is the finest quality. We refuse to use seconds or inferior goods ensuring that your catering is presented to its full advantage. We can usually arrange collections or deliveries at a time to suit you and because of our modern communication methods, through free phone, landlines and e-mail we are on call virtually 24 hours a day, 7 days a week. Our emphasis on quality & service does not compromise our prices. We feel our pricing makes us very competitive. We do not impose a deposit or holding charge and orders can be cancelled without penalty or charge. Prices are fixed at the time of ordering, even if the event is several months away, allowing you to budget for that special event accurately. Full delivery service is available in Essex, Hertfordshire, London, Cambridge and Suffolk .*

Occo Coolers Telford Ltd, St. Georges Road Industrial Estate, Donnington, Telford, Shropshire, TF2 7QZ Tel: (01952) 616381 Fax: (05600) 753354 E-mail: sales@occocoolers.co.uk *Cooling equipment manufrs*

▶ Occupational Counselling Consultants, Curtis House, 34 Third Avenue, Hove, East Sussex, BN3 2PD Tel: (07887) 751728 Fax: (01273) 777404 E-mail: info@salesplusconsultants.co.uk *Sales Plus is a European marketing agency, providing high level business development solutions to Small, Medium and Enterprise organisations.*

▶ Ocean Air Distribution, Prospect Close, Lowmoor Business Park, Kirkby-in-Ashfield, Nottingham, NG17 7LF Tel: (01623) 727414 Fax: (01623) 727419 E-mail: info@oceanair.uk.com *Air conditioning distributors*

Ocean Air Marine Ltd, 119 Third Avenue, Batchmere, Chichester, West Sussex, PO20 7LB Tel: (01243) 606909 Fax: (01243) 608300 *Blind manufrs*

Ocean Fix International Ltd, Waterton Grange, Stoneywood, Bucksburn, Aberdeen, AB21 9HX Tel: (01224) 714100 Fax: (01224) 714170 E-mail: pps@oceanfix-international.co.uk *Oceanfix International Ltd provide a comprehensive land, hydrographic & geophysical survey consultancy service based on over 32 years experience working within the construction & energy sectors.*Manpower Services -Providing manpower services for survey project management, client representation & overall quality control in all areas of data acquisition, processing & interpretation covering many roles in the oil & gas industry. Great care is taken to match particular skills & experience with the requirements of each Client & Project.*Calibrations -Providing a reputable & consistent quality assurance service to the offshore survey industry who require navigation & survey equipment calibration to the highest standard. Calibrations have been made possible by establishing a network of baselines covering many of the major UK & International ports.*Dimensional Control -Dimensional Control & Quality Assurance related services, providing quality orientated but competitive service to clients.*

▶ Ocean Leisure, 11-14 Northumberland Avenue, London, WC2N 5AQ Tel: (020) 7930 5050 Fax: (020) 7930 3032 E-mail: info@oceanleisure.co.uk *Water sport equipment retail*

Ocean Mouldings, Unit 7, Parrett Way, Bridgwater, Somerset, TA6 5LB Tel: (01278) 424447 Fax: (01278) 424447 *Plastics manufacturers & rotational moulders*

▶ Ocean Power Delivery, 104 Commercial Street, Edinburgh, EH6 6NF Tel: 0131-554 8444 Fax: 0131-554 8544 E-mail: enquiries@oceanpd.com *Renewable energy service*

Ocean Print, 70 Wood End Green Road, Hayes, Middlesex, UB3 2SL Tel: (020) 8561 3344 Fax: (020) 8561 5488 E-mail: enquiries@oceanprint.co.uk *We produce brochures, newsletters, fliers, postcards, stationery, business cards, magazines, folders, labels, forms, greeting cards, calendars, product inserts, CD inlays, envelopes, multi-part pads and many other products. We also print small or large jobs to specification.*

Ocean Refit Ltd, The Barnyard, Stennack, St. Ives, Cornwall, TR26 1QR Tel: (01736) 799440 Fax: (01736) 799440 E-mail: oceanrefit@btopenworld.com *Shop fitters & manufrs*

Ocean Road, Unit 43, Kersey Road, Flushing, Falmouth, Cornwall, TR11 5TR Tel: (0845) 0034220 Fax: (0870) 9159418 E-mail: enquiries@oceanroad.co.uk *Marina Management Software & Systems, Harbour Management Software & Systems, Yacht Club Management Software & Systems, Dry Stack Management Software & Systems, Web design & website hosting solutions & packages*

Ocean Safety Ltd, Saxon Wharf, Lower York Street, Southampton, SO14 5QF Tel: (023) 8072 0800 Fax: (023) 8072 0801 *Marine safety equipment*

Ocean Technical Systems Ltd, Oceantech House, Station Approach, Cheam, Sutton, Surrey, SM2 7AU Tel: (020) 8643 2233 Fax: (020) 8643 6444 E-mail: ots@oceantechsys.com *Control systems & data acquisition systems manufrs*

Ocean View Hotel, Park Road, Shanklin, Isle of Wight, PO37 6BB Tel: (01983) 863262 Fax: (01983) 867139 *Hotel & conference facility services*

Ocean Wave Digital Ltd, 138 Shepherds Bush Rd, London, W6 7PB Tel: 020 76104321 Fax: 020 76104453 *Computer consultants*

▶ OceanC Ltd, Kitling Road, Knowsley Business Park, Prescot, Merseyside, L34 9JA Tel: 0151-546 2727 Fax: 0151-547 2603 E-mail: info@oceanc.co.uk *Seafood manufrs*

▶ Oceanearing Ltd, Greenwell Road, East Tullos, Aberdeen, AB12 3AX Tel: (01224) 292168

Oceaneering International Services Ltd, Pitmedden Road, Dyce, Aberdeen, AB21 0DP Tel: (01224) 770444 Fax: (01224) 771583 Principal Export Areas: Worldwide *Underwater contractor* Also at: Gorleston

Oceaneering International Services Ltd, Sledgegate Farm, Sledgegate Lane, Lea, Matlock, Derbyshire, DE4 5GL Tel: (01629) 534164 Fax: (01629) 534172 *Gas inspection*

Oceaneering Multiflex, Dundas Road, Rosyth, Dunfermline, Fife, KY11 2XS Tel: (01383) 643400 Fax: (01383) 643590 E-mail: enquiries@oceaneering.com *Sub sea, underwater electric & hydraulic cable manufrs*

▶ Oceanic Design, Highview, Little Staughton, Bedford, MK44 2BH Tel: (01234) 378171 E-mail: sales@oceanicdesign.com *Web development for business*

Oceanic Maritime Ltd, 32 The Mall, London, W5 3TJ Tel: (020) 8566 1100 Fax: (020) 8579 0443 E-mail: containers@oceanicmaritime.com *Ship brokers*

Oceanic (SW) Ltd, Pelagic House, Dunkeswell, Honiton, Devon, EX14 4RB Tel: (01404) 891819 Fax: (01404) 891909 *Scuba diving equipment distributors*

▶ Oceanside Business Machines, 18 Town Farm, Redruth, Cornwall, TR15 2XG Tel: (01209) 210697 Fax: (01209) 210697 E-mail: mark@oceansidebizmachines.co.uk *Office equipment supply service & repair*

▶ Ochil Carriers, Hill Street, Tillicoultry, Clackmannanshire, FK13 6HF Tel: (01259) 750080

▶ Ochil Timber Products Ltd, 5 Winchester Avenue, Denny, Stirlingshire, FK6 6QE Tel: (01324) 825503 Fax: (01324) 824333

Charles Ockwell & Co. Ltd, Alkerton Works, Cricklade, Swindon, SN6 6AE Tel: (01793) 750216 Fax: (01793) 752239 E-mail: ockwellsas@hotmail.com *Protective clothing*

Ocmis UK Ltd, Higher Burrow, Burrow Hill, Kingsbury Episcopi, Martock, Somerset, TA12 6BU Tel: (0870) 6005131 Fax: (0870) 6005132 E-mail: sales@ocmis.com *Irrigation company*

Oco Ltd, 15 Essex Road, Dartford, DA1 2AU Tel: (01322) 276614 Fax: (01322) 227790 E-mail: headoffice@ocoltd.co.uk *Heating & mechanical engineers*

▶ Oco Ltd, Unit 3-4 Sherwood Court, Thurston Road, London, SE13 7SD Tel: (01322) 276614 Fax: (01322) 227790 E-mail: john-moore@ocoltd.co.uk

▶ O'Connor Constructions Plant Co. Ltd, 9 Colletts Drive, Tewksbury Road, Cheltenham, Gloucestershire, GL51 8JQ Tel: (01242) 241100 E-mail: info@oconnorplant.co.uk

T.J. O'Connor, Unit 16, Derby Road Business Park, Derby Road, Burton-On-Trent, Staffordshire, DE14 1RW Tel: (01283) 515222

▶ O'Connor Utilities Ltd, Unit 10 Sandfold Lane, Manchester, M19 3BJ Tel: 0161-248 9922 Fax: 0161-248 9933

▶ OCS Denver, Dairy Courtyard, 152-154 Ewell Road, Surbiton, Surrey, KT6 6HE Tel: (020) 8399 4253 Fax: (020) 8390 6044 E-mail: contact@denver.co.uk

OCS Group UK Ltd, Northgate House, Northgate White Lund, Morecambe, Lancashire, LA3 3BJ Tel: (0800) 3283695 Fax: (0870) 4443938 E-mail: enquiries@cannonhygiene.com *Cleaning consumables & janitorial supplies services*

Octagon Security, 87 High Road, Ickenham, Uxbridge, Middlesex, UB10 8LH Tel: (01895) 624545 Fax: (01895) 624546 E-mail: sales@octogan.ltc.co.uk *Intruder alarms & CCTV installation*

▶ Octal Sys, Romney Court, 62 Parkfield Drive, Northolt, Middlesex, UB5 5NT Tel: (0797) 9205777 Fax: E-mail: info@octalsys.co.uk *Octal Sys is a professional software development company providing comprehensive set of value added custom application development and product development services in the area of client/server, web applications & e-commerce. We work by combining our customer's business knowledge and our technology expertise to work out high-quality solutions to our clients "on time in budget".*

Octaveward Ltd, Balle Street Mill, Balle Street, Darwen, Lancashire, BB3 2AZ Tel: (01254) 773300 Fax: (01254) 773950 E-mail: info@octaveward.com Principal Export Areas: Worldwide *Glass fibre moulding manufrs*

▶ Octavian Ltd, Eastlays Warehouse, Gastard, Corsham, Wiltshire, SN13 9PP Tel: (01225) 810735 Fax: (01225) 811369

Octavius Hunt Ltd, Dove Lane, Redfield, Bristol, BS5 9NQ Tel: 0117-955 5304 Fax: 0117-955 7875 E-mail: info@octavius-hunt.co.uk *Specialist smokes & matches manufrs*

Octec Ltd, Unit 12-13 The Western Centre, Western Road, Bracknell, Berkshire, RG12 1RW Tel: (01344) 465200 Fax: (01344) 465201 E-mail: sales@octec.co.uk *Image processing equipment distributors & manufrs*

▶ OCTG Procter, Peregrine Road, Westhill Business Park, Westhill, Aberdeen, AB32 6JL Tel: (01224) 748600 Fax: (01224) 746676

▶ Octo Product Development Ltd, Design Works, William Street, Felling, Gateshead, Tyne & Wear, NE10 0JP Tel: 0191-469 3888 Fax: 0191-469 1888 E-mail: danm@octodesign.co.uk *Product design & development consultancy, plastic product design*

▶ October Textiles Ltd, Unit C14 Hartley Workspace,, Hadyn Road, Sherwood,, Nottingham, NG5 1DG Tel: 0115-962 6636 Fax: 0115-962 6636 E-mail: fardad@october.co.uk *Print & textiles*

▶ Octopi Ltd, 36 Trigon Road, London, SW8 1NH Tel: (020) 7735 5201 E-mail: sales@octopi.co.uk *Innovative group of Architects and designers working in all sectors.*Octopi offers a full architectural service or bespoke design services tailored to your needs.*

Octopus, Unit 2/4, Heron Quay, London, E14 4JP Tel: (020) 7531 8400 Fax: (020) 7531 8627 E-mail: info@conran-octopus.co.uk *Book publishers*

▶ Octopus Electrical Ltd, Battlefield Enterprise Park, Battlefield Enterprise Park, Shrewsbury, SY1 3JE Tel: (01743) 446347 Fax: (01743) 445777

Octopus Insight, 5 Windsor Works, Windsor Street, Beeston, Nottingham, NG9 2BW Tel: 0115-917 2222 Fax: 0115-917 2211 E-mail: photography@octopusinsight.com *Photographers, commercial & industrial*

Octopus Instruments Ltd, 2 Sussex Street, Bedale, North Yorkshire, DL8 2AJ Tel: (01677) 424213 Fax: (01677) 424597 E-mail: peter@octopus-instruments.co.uk *Supplier of emission monitoring equipment & process control*

Octupus Publishing Group, Unit 2-4 Heron Quay, London, E14 4JB Tel: (020) 7531 8400 Fax: (020) 7531 8560 E-mail: info@octopus-publishing.co.uk *Book publishers*

Ocular Press Ltd, West Avenue, Wigston, Leicestershire, LE18 2FG Tel: 0116-257 1400 Fax: 0116-257 1042 *Printing computer & commercial manufrs*

▶ Odd Ltd, Oxford, OX7 6WZ Tel: (01993) 830674 Fax: (01993) 832474 E-mail: mail@oddlimited.com *Garden furniture retailers*

▶ Odds & Suds, 30 The Market, Tavistock, Devon, PL19 0AL Tel: (01822) 618111 *Cosmetic manufacturers & distributors*

Odds W J Ltd, Crown Quay Lane, Sittingbourne, Kent, ME10 3JB Tel: (01795) 470844 Fax: (01795) 420463 *Timber & builders merchants*

▶ Oddy Builders Ltd, Woodlands Factory, Stanks Lane South, Leeds, LS14 5LN Tel: 0113-264 3734 Fax: 0113-232 6672

Oddy Hydraulics Ltd, Tristran Centre, Brown Lane West, Leeds, LS12 6BF Tel: 0113-244 8787 Fax: 0113-244 9786 E-mail: sales@oddy-hyds.com *Hydraulic equipment distributors & manufrs*

Oddyssey Glass Ltd, High Level Way, Halifax, W. Yorkshire, HX1 4PR Tel: (01422) 359028 Fax: (01422) 347888 E-mail: info@oddysseyglass.co.uk *General Glass Merchants & Processors. Specialist Glazing Contractors offering bespoke & imaginative solutions to projects throughout the UK. Local Glaziers offering general glazing repairs to the local community, including windows & decorative glass work*

▶ Oden Services Ltd, Unit 17 Highcroft Industrial Estate, Enterprise Road, Waterlooville, Hampshire, PO8 0BT Tel: (023) 9259 9898 Fax: (023) 9259 9696 *Computer repair services*

Odescan Ltd, 37 Redhills Road, South Woodham Ferrers, Chelmsford, CM3 5UL Tel: (01245) 325135 Fax: (01245) 329035 *Bottling engineers*

▶ Odessa Offset Ltd, Oakfield Road Industrial Estate, Oakfield Road, London, SE20 8RA Tel: (020) 8778 7888 Fax: (020) 8776 6646 E-mail: sales@odessaoffset.com

Laurence Odie Knitwear Ltd, Hoswick Woollen Mill, Sandwick, Shetland, ZE2 9HR Tel: (01950) 431215 Fax: (01950) 431202 *Knitwear manufrs* Also at: Scalloway

Odin Engineering Ltd, Unit 4, Fullwood Close, Aldermans Green Industrial Estate, Coventry, CV2 2SS Tel: (024) 7660 2622 Fax: (024) 7660 2649 *Broaching machines & grinding services*

Odlings M C R Ltd, Rosscliffe Road, Junction 8 Business Centre, Ellesmere Port, CH65 3AS Tel: 0151-355 0261 Fax: 0151-356 4423 E-mail: sales@odlingsmcr.co.uk *Manufacturers shot blast degreasing equipment*

▶ O'Donnell Site Services Ltd, The Cabin - Walkley Works, Walkley Lane, Heckmondwike, West Yorkshire, WF16 0PH Tel: (01924) 409111 Fax: (01924) 409444

Odour Control Systems Ltd, Manor Lane, Hawarden, Deeside, Clwyd, CH5 3PP Tel: (01244) 536700 Fax: (01244) 535184 E-mail: mail@odourcontrolsystems.ltd.co.uk *Odour control systems manufrs*

▶ Odour Services, Unit 6 Pillaton Hall Farm, Pillaton, Penkridge, Stafford, ST19 5RZ Tel: (01785) 716979 Fax: (01785) 716797 *Odour Services Limited is an independent service provider specialising in the field of odour control for both the water industry and industrial applications.**Formed in January 2005 we offer 15 years of expertise in the water industry with 9 years specialising in odour control.**As a truly independent company we are able to advise, scope and specify the most appropriate solution for any given situation.**

Odyssey Systems Ltd, Lockheed Close, Preston Farm Industrial Estate, Stockton-on-Tees, Cleveland, TS18 3SE Tel: (01642) 661800 Fax: (01642) 661801 E-mail: sales@odyssey-systems.co.uk *Telecoms supplier*

Odyssey Technologies Ltd, Hurlands Close, Farnham, Surrey, GU9 9JE Tel: (01252) 721821 Fax: (01252) 721211 E-mail: sales@odessey.co.uk *Repair and replace damaged or faulty component parts for your PC, Computer, Laptop, Server, Laser Printer, Colour Laser Printer, CRT Monitor, Flat Screen. We offer a national service and have a collection and delivery network across the UK.*

Oecos Agricultural Services, 11 High Street, Kimpton, Hitchin, Hertfordshire, SG4 8RA Tel: (01438) 832481 Fax: (01438) 832157 E-mail: sales@oecos.co.uk *Insect controllers*

Oel Held UK Ltd, 16 Colomendy Industrial Estate, Rhyl Road, Denbigh, Clwyd, LL16 5TA Tel: (01745) 814777 Fax: (01745) 813222 E-mail: info@oelheldgroup.co.uk *Spark erosion dielectric fluid & grinding fluid services*

▶ Oem Fabrication Ltd, 47 Sandilands Street, Glasgow, G32 0HT Tel: 0141-764 2150

Oerlikon Balzers Coatings UK Ltd, Bradbourne Drive, Tilbrook, Milton Keynes, MK7 8AT Tel: (01908) 377277 Fax: (01908) 361361 E-mail: info.balzers.uk@oerlikon.com *PVD coatings suppliers*

▶ Off Plan Investments Ltd, 27 Atlantic House, Waterson Street, London, E2 8HH Tel: (0800) 0341622 Fax: 0800 0342622 E-mail: info@off-plan.co.uk *Off Plan Investments a property investment company that offers investors high returns on off plan property investing*

▶ Off The Wall, Unit 11b Monksbridge Trading Estate, Outgang Lane, Dinnington, Sheffield, S25 3QZ Tel: (01909) 569131 Fax: (01909) 551683 *Pine & furniture manufrs*

Offa Industries Ltd, Offa House Unit 3 Knighton Enterprise Park, Ludlow Road, Knighton, Powys, LD7 1HJ Tel: (01547) 529401 Fax: (01547) 529398 *General engineers*

Offerclass Ltd, 73-75 Shacklewell Lane, London, E8 2EB Tel: (020) 7923 2560 Fax: (020) 7923 2692 E-mail: katrina@offerclass.com *Leather, pvc & fabrics manufrs*

Office 21 Projects Ltd, Whitby Oliver, 31 Hospital Fields Road, Fulford Industrial Estate, Fulford Road, York, YO10 4FS Tel: (01904) 655106 E-mail: info@office21.co.uk *Supply and Installation of Office Hotel, Restaurant furniture. Office design, Layout and Project management*Also Furniture for Schools, Clubs and Institutions.**

Office Angels Ltd, 30-38 Hammersmith Broadway, London, W6 7AB Tel: (020) 8741 8080 Fax: (020) 8741 9212 *Recruitment consultants*

Office Angels Commercial Cleaning, 12 Armstrong Close, Halstead, Sevenoaks, Kent, TN14 7BS Tel: (0845) 1084241 E-mail: officeangelscleaning@googlemail.com *We offer office cleaning of the highest standard throughout London Postcode Area and Kent.*Call Danielle today to arrange a free survey.*

▶ Office Assist, 2a Cowper Road, Bedford, MK40 2AS Tel: (07771) 995545 E-mail: mail@office-assist.co.uk *Professional, reliable and cost effective Office Administration and Secretarial Services for individuals and businesses. Services include typing, word processing, brochures, business cards, documentation, document formatting and conversion.*

▶ Office Business & Services, 68 High Street, Witney, Oxfordshire, OX28 6HJ Tel: (01993) 200400 Fax: (01993) 200401 E-mail: info@obsl.co.uk *Let us provide you with a cost effective telephone answering service and admin back up for a cost effective price. Call NOW for a 2 week FREE Trial.*

▶ Office Care, Collate House, Victoria Way, Pride Park, Derby, DE24 8AN Tel: (01332) 332331 Fax: (01332) 200212 E-mail: sales@officecare.uk.com *Cleaning Contractor with very high retention of customers. If you value a high corporate image it has to be Office Care. Daily cleaning of offices, car showrooms, night clubs, factories etc. Service includes Carpet Cleaning, Window Cleaning and Kitchen deep cleaning with Steam technology.*

The Office Centre, 24 Queen Street, Gravesend, Kent, DA12 2EE Tel: (01474) 560271 Fax: (01474) 334484 *Office furniture distribs*

Office Depot UK, Guilbert House, Greenwich Way, Andover, Hampshire, SP10 4JZ Tel: (0870) 7556611 Fax: (0870) 4114735 E-mail: name@officedepot.com *Commercial & office stationers requisites distributors & agents*

▶ Office Design Resource, Bridge Street, Bungay, Suffolk, NR35 1HD Tel: (01986) 895254 E-mail: officedesign@eggconnect.net *Office Design Resource offer space planning solutions, supporting facility managers with specialist workplace design and project and move management services.**The practice was established in 1991 to offer professional consultancy, design solutions and support across a wide spectrum of businesses. **Office Design Resource can provide on-site support solutions, whether it is assisting client in-house CAD teams, or providing full CAD support with everything from measured surveys, design solutions, building use studies, space analysis and calculations.**For more, in-depth information, visit the website - www.officedesign-resource.co.uk*

Office Economy, Camden House, Bridge Road, Kingswood, Bristol, BS15 4FW Tel: 0117-915 9990 Fax: 0117-957 3591 *Office equipment suppliers*

▶ Office Electrics Ltd, 1 Calder Point, Monckton Road Industrial Estate, Wakefield, West Yorkshire, WF2 7AL Tel: (01924) 367255 Fax: (01924) 290652 E-mail: sales@office-electrics.co.uk *Cable Management Systems, Power Units, Prisms*

Office Electronics Centre UK Ltd, Electronics House Enterprise Court, Gapton Hall Road, Great Yarmouth, Norfolk, NR31 0ND Tel: (01493) 600500 Fax: (01493) 650398 E-mail: sales@oecuk.co.uk *Sales & hire of electronic equipment for offices*

Office Equipment Selection Ltd, Mylord CR, Camperdown Industrial Estate, Newcastle upon Tyne, NE12 5RF Tel: 0191-268 3333 Fax: 0191-268 0344 E-mail: sales@oesltd.co.uk *Office equipment & stationery*

Office Equipment Servicing, 3 Trinstead Way, Nottingham, NG5 5RZ Tel: (07860) 787882 Fax: 0115-913 9901 *Photocopying agents*

Office Equipment UK Ltd, Unit 3, Blowick Business Park, Crowland Street, Southport, Merseyside, PR9 7RU Tel: (01704) 539133 Fax: (01704) 539180 E-mail: oeukltd@btopenworld.com *Office machine agents*

Office Equipment Workshop, 2 Elm Lane, Tongham, Farnham, Surrey, GU10 1BX Tel: (01252) 316700 Fax: (01252) 316705 E-mail: offequipworkshop@btinternet.com *Commercial & office stationers*

▶ Office Express, The Businees Centre, Gas Street, Newtown, Powys, SY16 2AD Tel: (01686) 611422 Fax: (01686) 611433 E-mail: sales@officeexpressuk.com *Suppliers of office furniture*

▶ Office Force, 4 Market Hill, Huntingdon, Cambridgeshire, PE29 3NJ Tel: (01480) 444750 Fax: (01480) 444751 E-mail: temp20@officeforce.net *Officeforce are an independent recruitment agency dealing in the supply of temporary and permanent staff to the commercial sector.*our Key areas of supply include the following: Customer service, Administration, I.T, Accounts, Marketing, HR, Logistics, Engineering, Sales, Management.*We are flexible in our approach and aim to build long term working relationships in which all parties aspire to the same goals.*

Office Of Health Economics Ltd, 12 Whitehall, London, SW1A 2DY Tel: (020) 7930 9203 Fax: (020) 7747 1419 E-mail: enquiries@ohe.org *Medical statistics & consultancy service providers*

Office Innovations, 1-3 Factory Lane, Beeston, Beeston, Nottingham, NG9 4AA Tel: 0115-925 7898 Fax: 0115-925 7899 E-mail: salesandenquires@officeinnovations.co.uk *Office furniture suppliers*

Office Interiors, 1-2 Trevilson, St. Newlyn East, Newquay, Cornwall, TR8 5JF Tel: (01872) 510953 Fax: (01872) 510954 E-mail: sales@officeinteriors.co.uk *Data cabling & electronics*

▶ Office Landscapes Midlands Ltd, 39 Macdonald Street, Birmingham, B5 6TG Tel: 0121-622 6000 Fax: 0121-622 3155 E-mail: mail@officelandscapes.co.uk *Office Plants for Business. We supply Live and Artificial office plant displays, either on rental with maintenance or outright purchase. As well as interior landscaping we also supply exterior plants and do Grounds Maintenance. We are a large family business and have been established for 40 years. We offer a fast freindly and professional service. Please call us for a free no obligation quotation. We look forward to hearing from you. **

Office Outlet, 38-40 Hastings Road, Leicester, LE5 0HL Tel: 0116-274 3308 Fax: 0116-276 1254 E-mail: sales@theofficeoutlet.co.uk *Office stationery distributors*

Office Overload, Peelers End, May Lane, Pilley, Lymington, Hampshire, SO41 5QR Tel: (01590) 688476 Fax: (01590) 675133 E-mail: sue@officeoverload.com *Freelance secretary*

Office Plant Displays, 9 Gables Close, Chalfont St. Peter, Gerrards Cross, Buckinghamshire, SL9 0PR Tel: (01494) 872573 *Plant & floral displays*

Office Plus Ltd, 1 Industrial Estate, Thomas Road, London, E14 7BN Tel: (020) 7537 0340 Fax: (020) 7537 0348 E-mail: sales@officeplus.ltd.uk *Stationery & office equipment distributors commercial*

Office Principles, 472 Basingstoke Road, Reading, RG2 0QN Tel: 0118-986 9860 Fax: 0118-967 2283 *Commercial interior contractors*

▶ Office Seating Ltd, 19 Aston Road North, Birmingham, B6 4DS Tel: 0121-359 7217 Fax: 0121-359 7507

Office Services, 1 Isaacs Yard, Wrafton Road, Braunton, Devon, EX33 2BT Tel: (01271) 817429 Fax: (01271) 816655 *Office equipment maintenance & repairers*

Office Software Solutions Ltd, 52 Chart La, Reigate, Surrey, RH2 7DZ Tel: 01737 241000 Fax: 01737 241000 *Software solutions*

Office Solutions Organisation Ltd, Unit 4-5, Silver End Industrial Estate, Bretteley Hill, Brierley Hill, West Midlands, DY5 3LA Tel: (01384) 351080 Fax: (01384) 351090 E-mail: birmingham@osol.co.uk *Commercial stationery distribs*

▶ Office Star Group, Crucible Close, Mushet Industrial Park, Coleford, Gloucestershire, GL16 8RE Tel: (01594) 810081 Fax: (01594) 810111 E-mail: 4schools@officestar-group.com *We supply competitively priced educational and office products to schools, colleges, universities and pre-school nursery"s throughout the UK.*

Office Support Ltd, Old Farm House, Moreton-on-Lugg, Hereford, HR4 8DE Tel: (01432) 761884 Fax: (01432) 760866 E-mail: enquiries@office-support.co.uk *Sage solutions centre*

Office Way, 64 Derby Road, Long Eaton, Nottingham, NG10 4QP Tel: 0115-849 1777 Fax: 0115-946 9801 E-mail: theofficeway@aol.com *Office stationery & consumable suppliers*

Office Wise, 73 New Crane Street, Chester, CH1 4JE Tel: (01244) 317505 Fax: (01244) 343413 E-mail: office.wise@virgin.net *Office equipment suppliers*

▶ OfficeGiant, Unit 1, Empress Business Centre, Chester Road, Manchester, M16 9EB Tel: (0800) 7317931 Fax: 0161-877 7772 E-mail: sales@officegiant.co.uk *Office products supply company*

▶ Officepoint Fivestar, 326 Kensal Road, London, W10 5BZ Tel: (020) 8969 8348 Fax: (020) 8969 8349 E-mail: sales@officepointfivestar.com *Office supplies for online sale*

▶ Officeset Ltd, 450 Bath Road, London Heathrow Airport, Longford, West Drayton, Middlesex, UB7 0EB Tel: (0845) 3457035 Fax: (0845) 3457037 E-mail: info@officeset.co.uk *Office supplies, furniture, Interiors & print*

Offitec Ltd, 72 West Hill, London, SW15 2UJ Tel: (020) 8871 2525 Fax: (020) 8871 0243 *Stationers & office furniture*

Offizone Office Stationery Supplies, 1-15 Middle Hillgate, Stockport, Cheshire, SK1 3AY Tel: 0161-480 2010 Fax: 0161-480 4133 E-mail: sales@offizone.co.uk *Office furniture & stationery suppliers*

▶ Offley Timber Structures Ltd, Unit 3, Raleigh Hall Industrial Estate, Eccleshall, Stafford, ST21 6JL Tel: (01785) 851333 Fax: (01785) 851933 E-mail: sales@offleytimber.com *Wooden windows doors conservatories manufrs*

Offset Holdings Ltd, 188 Forstal Road, Aylesford, Kent, ME20 7DB Tel: (01622) 710759 Fax: (01622) 717486 *Carton & greeting cards manufrs*

Offset Marketing, 2 Speedwell Close, Chandler's Ford, Eastleigh, Hampshire, SO53 4BT Tel: (023) 8027 4444 Fax: (023) 8027 0112 *Promotional product, business incentive gift & souvenir producers*

▶ Offshoot Clothing Ltd, Offshoot House, 68 The Grove, Ilkley, West Yorkshire, LS29 9PA Tel: (01943) 817650 Fax: (01943) 817660 E-mail: info@offshoot.co.uk *Retail*

Offshore Design Engineering Ltd, 12 Princeton Mews, 167-169 London Road, Kingston upon Thames, Surrey, KT2 6PT Tel: (020) 8481 1190 Fax: (020) 8546 4346 E-mail: ode_london@ode-ltd.co.uk *Offshore consulting engineers*

Offshore Marine Contractors Ltd, Magellan House, James Watt Close, Gapton Hall Industrial Estate, Great Yarmouth, Norfolk, NR31 0NX Tel: (01493) 658489 Fax: (01493) 658490 E-mail: yarmouth@omcon.com *Ships brokers*

Offshore Powerboats Ltd, 1 Lymington Yacht Haven, Kings Saltern Road, Lymington, Hampshire, SO41 3QD Tel: (01590) 677955 Fax: (01590) 671890 E-mail: chris@offshorepowerboats.co.uk *Boat distributors*

▶ Offshore Select, 116 Weddington Road, Weddington, Nuneaton, Warwickshire, CV10 0AL Tel: (024) 7632 7582 E-mail: suedeandleather@hotmail.co.uk *Suede & leather retail*

Offshore Shipbrokers Holdings Ltd, 9 11 Folgate Street, London, E1 6BX Tel: (020) 7377 9774 Fax: (020) 7377 9775 E-mail: london@offshore-shipbrokers.co.uk *Towage & salvage services* Also at: Aberdeen

Offshore Stainless Supplies, Gorsey Lane, Great Wyrley, Walsall, WS6 6AL Tel: (01922) 414003 Fax: (01922) 414606 E-mail: chris@off-shore.stainless.co.uk *Stainless steel bar, billet stockholder & producer*

Offshore Steel Boats, The Boat Yard, Waterside Road, Barton-upon-Humber, South Humberside, DN18 5BD Tel: (01652) 635864 Fax: (01652) 635864 *Boat builders*

▶ Offshore Systems UK Ltd, Unit 11, Milton Business Centre Wick Drive, New Milton, Hampshire, BH25 6RH Tel: (01425) 610022 Fax: (01425) 614794 E-mail: sales@osukl.com *Marine instruments manufrs*

▶ OffSight IT Services Ltd, Unit 3, Cannock Chase Enterprise Centre, Hednesford, Cannock, Staffordshire, WS12 0QU Tel: (01543) 426142 E-mail: enquiries@offsight.co.uk *IT services*

Offstat Office Supplies Ltd, 2nd Floor, 41 Dace Road, London, E3 2NG Tel: (020) 8525 7707 Fax: (020) 8525 7708 E-mail: office-services@offstat.sagehost.co.uk *Supply & repair of office equipment*

Offtek Ltd, Claremont House Broad Lane, Tanworth-in-Arden, Solihull, West Midlands, B94 5DY Tel: (01564) 742064 Fax: (01564) 743087 E-mail: sales@offtek.co.uk *Computer memory specialists consultants*

▶ O'Gallachor Painting & Decorating, Suite 61 Falkirk House, 165 Maida Vale, London, W9 1QX Tel: (07879) 484286 E-mail: colm01@blueyonder.co.uk *Supply labour plant material to carry out interiors and exteriors decoration*

Ogborne K.R, West Cleave, Germansweek, Beaworthy, Devon, EX21 5AL Tel: (01837) 871339 *Agricultural contractors*

▶ Neil Ogden Associates, 63 Franklin Avenue, Tadley, Hampshire, RG26 4EZ Tel: 0118-981 9556 E-mail: neil@neilogdenassociates.co.uk *Website design & proof reading*

Ogden Transteel, Butler Way, Town Street, Stanningley, Pudsey, West Yorkshire, LS28 6EZ Tel: 0113-257 8221 Fax: 0113-236 2340 E-mail: ogdentransteel@aol.com Principal Export Areas: Worldwide *Stockholders of steel tube & steel plates*

▶ Ogham Jewellery, Abbey House, Princes Street, Edinburgh, EH2 2ER Tel: 0131-225 7275 Fax: 0131-225 7275 E-mail: info@oghamjewellery.com *Jewellery suppliers*

Ogier Electronics Ltd, Sandridge Park, Porters Wood, St. Albans, Hertfordshire, AL3 6PH Tel: (01727) 853521 Fax: (01727) 852186 *Security systems, broadband internet, wireless access services*

Ogihara Europe Ltd, Hortonwood Industrial Estate, Queensway, Telford, Shropshire, TF1 7LL Tel: (01952) 222111 Fax: (01952) 222050 E-mail: sales@ogihara.co.uk *Vehicle pressings manufrs*

Ogilby Construction Ltd, 16 Endowood Road, Chesterfield, Derbyshire, S40 3LX Tel: (01246) 566082 *Steel constructors*

Ogilvy Interactive Ltd, 10 Carbot Square, Canary Wharf, London, E14 4QB Tel: (020) 7345 3999 Fax: (020) 7345 3888 *Advertising agents*

Ogl Computer Services Group, Worcester Road, Stourport-on-Severn, Worcestershire, DY13 9AT Tel: (01299) 873873 Fax: (01299) 873700 E-mail: enquiries@ogl.co.uk *Computer systems suppliers*

Ogley Bros Ltd, Smithfield, Sheffield, S3 7AS Tel: 0114-276 8948 Fax: 0114-275 5105 E-mail: ogleybrothers@btconnect.com *Plumbing & engineering services*

▶ Ogp Nursery, Faraday House, Woodyard Lane, Foston, Derby, DE65 5DJ Tel: (01283) 585933 Fax: (01283) 585181 E-mail: sales@ogpuk.com *Suppliers of non contact measuring machines*

▶ Oh Bounce, 16 Gorse Cover Road, Severn Beach, Bristol, BS35 4NP Tel: (01454) 632440 *We hire various sizes of bouncy castles and ball ponds.*

Oh Sew Pretty, 11 Shore Road, Skelmorlie, Ayrshire, PA17 5EQ Tel: (01475) 520101 *Soft furnishing manufrs*

Oh Yeah, 100 Southchurch Road, Southend-on-Sea, SS1 2LX Tel: (01702) 469785 Fax: (01702) 469785 *Fashion boutique*

O'Hagans's Sausages, 71 Fishbourne Road West, Chichester, West Sussex, PO19 3JJ Tel: (01243) 532833 Fax: (01243) 576733 E-mail: ohagans@topsausages.com *Sausages sales*

O'Hara Property Investment Holding Co. Ltd, 101 Rowlands Avenue, Hatch End, Pinner, Middlesex, HA5 4AW Tel: (020) 8900 0694 Fax: (020) 8900 1540 *Road surfacing contractors*

O'Hare & McGovern Ltd, Carnbane House, Shepherds Way, Newry, County Down, BT35 6EE Tel: (028) 3026 4662 Fax: (028) 3026 2747 E-mail: carnbanehouse@ohareandmcgovern.com *Civil engineers & public works contractors*

O'Hare Steel, 115 Newry Road, Kilkeel, Newry, County Down, BT34 4ET Tel: (028) 3085 1452 Fax: (028) 3085 1637 *Steel engineers*

Ohaus UK Ltd, 64 Boston Road, Leicester, LE4 1AW Tel: 0116-234 5075 Fax: 0116-235 9256 *Ohaus corporation is a leading manufacturer of scales and balances for the laboratory, education, industrial and speciality markets worldwide.*

Ohm Electronics Ltd, 515 Pinner Road, Harrow, Middlesex, HA2 6EH Tel: (020) 8427 0545 Fax: (020) 8863 7930 E-mail: sales@ohmelectronics.co.uk *Computer systems manufrs*

Ohmega Ltd, Wick Industrial Estate, Gore Road, New Milton, Hampshire, BH25 6SJ Tel: (01425) 619709 Fax: (01425) 638905 E-mail: ohmega@ohmega.freeserve.co.uk *Electronics subcontractors services*

▶ Ohmega Testing Services Ltd, Suite 48, Stephyns Chambers, Hemel Hempstead, Hertfordshire, HP1 1DD Tel: (0845) 6003402 Fax: (01442) 245585 E-mail: pttooley@ohmegatesting.co.uk *Portable appliance testing & fixed installation inspection & testing*

Jeffrey Ohrenstein Ltd, 35 Brunel Road, East Acton, London, W3 7XR Tel: (020) 8740 1100 Fax: (020) 8749 9889 E-mail: jeffrey@jogroup.co.uk *Children's wear, ladies wear & knitwear retailers & suppliers*

Oikos Storage Ltd, Hole Haven Wharf, Canvey Island, Essex, SS8 0NR Tel: (01268) 682206 Fax: (01268) 510095 E-mail: info@oikos.co.uk *Oil storage contracters*

Oil Cleanse, Julius Caesar House, 66 High Street, Alton, Hampshire, GU34 1ET Tel: (01420) 542027 Fax: (01420) 542027 E-mail: malcolm.woods.oil@talk21.com *Oil filtration & management service*

Oil & Colour Chemists Association, Priory House, 967 Harrow Road, Wembley, Middlesex, HA0 2SF Tel: (020) 8908 1086 Fax: (020) 8908 1219 E-mail: gensec@occa.org.uk *Trade association*

Oil Control Ltd, Unit 7 Herald Business Park, Golden Acres Lane, Binley Industrial Estate, Coventry, CV3 2SY Tel: (024) 7663 5711 Fax: (024) 7663 5041 E-mail: sales@oilcontrol.co.uk *Hydraulic valve distributors*

Oil Dri UK Ltd, Bannisters Row, Wisbech, Cambridgeshire, PE13 3HZ Tel: (01945) 581244 Fax: (01945) 581250 E-mail: sales@oil-dri.co.uk *Oil absorbent manufrs*

Oil Equipment & Engineering Co. Ltd, Southgate Avenue, Mildenhall, Bury St. Edmunds, Suffolk, IP28 7AT Tel: (01638) 713586 Fax: (01638) 510762 *Oil burner manufrs*

Oil & Gas Systems Ltd, Gemini House, The Business Park, Ely, Cambridgeshire, CB7 4EA Tel: (01353) 666640 Fax: (01353) 666650 E-mail: mb@ogsl.com *Gas conditioning & metering*

Oil Inventions Ltd, Leamore Close, Walsall, WS2 7NJ Tel: (01922) 477904 Fax: (01922) 710108 E-mail: info@oilinventions.co.uk *Industrial cutting & oil blenders*

The Oil Lab, 2 Little Orchard Gardens, Wolseley Road, Rugeley, Staffordshire, WS15 2ES Tel: (07050) 257431 Fax: (01889) 583682 E-mail: info@theoillab.co.uk *Oil analysis & oil condition monitoring*

Oil Plus Ltd, Unit E Dominion House, Kennet Side, Newbury, Berkshire, RG14 5PX Tel: (01635) 30226 Fax: (01635) 49618 E-mail: m.bowyer@oilplus.co.uk Principal Export Areas: Worldwide *Oil & gas industry consultancy, training, engineering services*

Oil Pollution Environmental Control Ltd, 1 Nab Lane, Birstall, Batley, West Yorkshire, WF17 9NG Tel: (01924) 442701 Fax: (01924) 471925 E-mail: sales@opec.co.uk *Manufacture & supply pollution control equipment*

▶ Oil Salvage Ltd, Lyster Road, Bootle, Merseyside, L20 1AS Tel: 0151-933 4084 Fax: 0151-922 8488 E-mail: sales@oilsalvage.com *Oil waste recycling, disposal & recovery contractors*

Oil Services South West, Chimsworthy, Bratton Clovelly, Okehampton, Devon, EX20 4JE Tel: (01837) 871444 Fax: (01837) 871525 *Central heating engineers*

The Oil Shop, 2 Little Orchard Gardens, Wolseley Road, Rugeley, Staffordshire, WS15 2ES Tel: (07050) 184420 Fax: (01889) 583682 E-mail: theoilshop@another.com *Professional lubrication engineers*

Oil States Industries (U K) Ltd, Blackness Road, Aberdeen, AB12 3LH Tel: (01224) 290000 Fax: (01224) 290110 E-mail: sales@oilstates-uk.com *Manufacturers & designers of oilfield equipment*

Oil States MCS Ltd, Bouthwood Road, Sowerby Woods Industrial Estate, Barrow-in-Furness, Cumbria, LA14 4RD Tel: (01229) 825080 Fax: (01229) 839791 E-mail: owen-osmhotherly@osmcs-bat.co.uk *Pressure testing & swaging services*

Oil & Steel UK Ltd, Rotherfield House, 7 Fairmile, Henley-on-Thames, Oxfordshire, RG9 2JR Tel: (01491) 411022 Fax: (01491) 411554 E-mail: info@oilandsteel.co.uk *Access platforms*

Oilab Lubrication Ltd, 31 Sutherland Road, Wolverhampton, WV4 5AR Tel: (01902) 334106 Fax: (01902) 333010 E-mail: sales@oilab.co.uk *Oil analysis equipment*

OilanHeat (Maintenance) Ltd, 161 High Street, Aldershot, Hampshire, GU11 1TT Tel: (01252) 329789 Fax: (01252) 342804 E-mail: ac@lowbeck.com *Building services engineers*

▶ Oilcats, Clydesdale Bank Buildings, Little Square, Oldmeldrum, Aberdeen, AB51 0AY Tel: (01651) 873171 Fax: (01651) 873214 E-mail: sales@oilcats.co.uk *Stock inventory services*

▶ Oilco (Swindon) Ltd, Bagbury Green Farm, Bagbury Lane, Purton, Swindon, SN4 5LX Tel: (01793) 772437 Fax: (01793) 772437 E-mail: oilcosw.kemp@btconnect.com *Oil, chemical & cleaning products distributors*

▶ Oilfield Chemical Technology Ltd, Craigshaw Road, West Tullos Industrial Estate, Aberdeen, AB12 3AP Tel: (01224) 248113 Fax: (01224) 248289 E-mail: octlimited@octl.co.uk *Oil & gas industry laboratory & consultancy services*

Oilfield Maintenance Repairs Ltd, 4 Salmon Road, Great Yarmouth, Norfolk, NR30 3QS Tel: (01493) 859985 Fax: (01493) 853385 *Crane maintenance & repair services*

Oilfield Material Management Ltd, 34 Abbotswell Road, Aberdeen, AB12 3AB Tel: (01224) 891011 Fax: (01224) 891012 E-mail: sales@omm.net *Oilfield equipment rental*

Oilfield Production Support Group Ltd, Old Stoneywood Church, Bankhead Road, Bucksburn, Aberdeen, AB21 9HQ Tel: (01224) 712332 Fax: (01224) 712333 E-mail: sales@opsgrp.com *Personnel services*

Oilfield Publications, 15 The Homend, Ledbury, Herefordshire, HR8 1BN Tel: (01531) 634561 Fax: (01531) 634239 E-mail: sales@oilpubs.com *Publishers of oil & marine related maps*

Oilfield Testing Services, Viking Road, Great Yarmouth, Norfolk, NR31 0NU Tel: (01493) 440555 Fax: (01493) 440737 E-mail: ots@oilfieldtesting.com *Non-destructive test & inspection services*

▶ Oilgear European Holdings, 37 Burley Road, Leeds, LS3 1JT Tel: 0113-394 7300 Fax: 0113-394 7301 E-mail: enquiries@oilgear-towler.co.uk Principal Export Areas: Worldwide *Hydraulic equipment/systems manufacturers. Also hydraulic pumps & electronic control systems* Also at: Bedford

Oiline Ltd, Whitehall Road, Tipton, West Midlands, DY4 7JZ Tel: 0121-557 1475 Fax: 0121-522 2311 *Industrial oil products manufrs*

Oilite Bowman, 10 Isis Court, Wyndyke Furlong, Abingdon Business Park, Abingdon, Oxfordshire, OX14 1DZ Tel: (01235) 815816 Fax: (01235) 811234 E-mail: steve@bowman.co.uk *Bowman International Limited, was founded in 1972 as a design and marketing company covering the UK, to specialise in bearings and high precision components. In 1984, the manufacture of certain products commenced. As well as its own manufacture, the company holds exclusive agencies of other manufacturer's products, which complement Bowman's range. Bowman International Limited was first approved for ISO 9001: 1994 in 1999 and in 2003 was approved to the later approval BS EN ISO 9001: 2000 (Certificate No. 960929).*

▶ OIS P.L.C., O I S House, Minto Avenue, Altens Ind Est, Aberdeen, AB12 3JZ Tel: (01224) 238000

Ok G800, 43 Cannon Street, Preston, PR1 3NT Tel: (01772) 881800 Fax: (01772) 881800 *Electronic surveillance systems suppliers*

OK Solutions Ltd, Albion Ho, 113 Station Rd, Hampton, Middlesex, TW12 2AL Tel: 020 84011301 Fax: 020 84011302 *Software supplier*

O'Kane Bros Woodworking Ltd, 13 Hass Road, Dungiven, Londonderry, BT47 4QH Tel: (028) 7774 1705 Fax: (028) 7774 2343 E-mail: okanebros@aol.com *Joinery manufrs*

O'Kane Hatcheries Ltd, 117 Raceview Road, Ballymena, County Antrim, BT42 4HY Tel: (028) 2586 1445 Fax: (028) 2586 2179 E-mail: okaneh@hotmail.com *Poultry hatchery*

▶ O'Kane Irish Foods, 8-9 Quad Road, East Lane, Wembley, Middlesex, HA9 7NE Tel: (020) 8385 1771 Fax: (020) 8385 1991 E-mail: sales@okaneirishfoods.co.uk *Food wholesalers & distributors*

Okasan Medical Ltd, 6 Stake Lane, Farnborough, Hampshire, GU14 8NP Tel: (01483) 570052 Fax: (01252) 511911 E-mail: sales@okasanpesticides.co.uk *Pest control chemicals & equipment suppliers*

O'Keeffe Groundworks Ltd, The Brickfields, Oxhey Lane, Watford, WD19 5RF Tel: (01923) 818603 Fax: (01923) 242311 E-mail: sandra@okeeffegroundworks.com *Civil engineering contractors*

Oki Buyer, 31a St. Neots Road, Eaton Ford, St. Neots, Cambridgeshire, PE19 7BA Tel: 0845 5314237 Fax: (01480) 403909 E-mail: sales@okibuyer.co.uk *Printer suppliers*

Oki Systems UK Ltd, 550 Dundee Road, Slough, SL1 4LE Tel: (01753) 819819 Fax: (01753) 819899 E-mail: sales@okieurope.co.uk *Laser printers*

▶ Olat Ltd, James House, 22-24 Corsham Street, London, N1 6DR Tel: (020) 72518556 Fax: (020) 72533806

Old Barn Catering Hire Ltd The, The Old Barn, The Bridge, Lower Eashing, Godalming, Surrey, GU7 2QF *Catering equipment hire*

Old Barn Model Craftsmen, 9 Monks Avenue, Lancing, West Sussex, BN15 9DJ Tel: (01903) 525077 *Model railway manufrs*

Old Basing Saddlery, 69 The Street, Old Basing, Basingstoke, Hampshire, RG24 0BY Tel: (01256) 323510 Fax: (01256) 323510 *Saddle & riding wear distributors*

▶ Old Brierley, 13 Stourdale Road, Cradley Heath, West Midlands, B64 7BG Tel: (01384) 569752 Fax: (01384) 568147

Old Ford Ltd, 381 Old Ford Road, London, E3 2LU Tel: (020) 8981 7373 Fax: (020) 8981 2784 E-mail: catering@oldford.co.uk *Catering equipment suppliers*

Old Forge Woodturners, Rear of, 126 London Road, Boston, Lincolnshire, PE21 7HB Tel: (01205) 353283 Fax: (01205) 353283 *Cabinet makers & bespoke architectural joinery*

▶ Old Hall Bookshop, 32 Market Place, Brackley, Northamptonshire, NN13 7DP Tel: (01280) 704146 Fax: (01280) 705131 E-mail: admin@oldhallbooks.com *Book suppliers*

Old Harbour Dive Centre, 11 Nothe Parade, Weymouth, Dorset, DT4 8TX Tel: (01305) 760888 Fax: (01305) 766889 *Diving equipment retailers & dive charter & school*

Old Jordans Guest House & Conference Centre, Jordans Lane, Jordans, Beaconsfield, Buckinghamshire, HP9 2SW Tel: (01494) 874586 Fax: (01494) 875657 E-mail: reception@oldjordans.org.uk *Guest house & conference centre*

Old Manse Joinery, 32 Boveedy Road, Kilrea, Coleraine, County Londonderry, BT51 5XU Tel: (028) 2954 1453 Fax: (028) 2954 1453 *Joiners*

Old Mill Furniture, Balk, Thirsk, North Yorkshire, YO7 2AH Tel: (01845) 597227 E-mail: theoldmill@btinternet.com *Hand made furniture in solid hardwood suppliers*

Old Oak Engineering, Unit 11, Gilchrist Thomas Industrial Estate, Blaenavon, Pontypool, Gwent, NP4 9RL Tel: (01495) 791615 Fax: (01495) 790866 *General engineers & machinists*

Old Oak Joinery, 5-11 Westway, London, W12 0PT Tel: (020) 8749 6258 Fax: (020) 8749 1762 *Joinery contractors*

Old Park Engineering Services Ltd, Woods Lane, Cradley Heath, West Midlands, B64 7AN Tel: (01384) 412550 Fax: (01384) 410784 E-mail: oldpark@blueyonder.co.uk *Manufacturers of aerosol industrial*

Old Pine Flooring, Park Copse Cottage, Hamptworth, Salisbury, SP5 2DS Tel: (01794) 390434 Fax: (01794) 390434 *Old pine reclaimers*

Old Rocket plc, Imperial Way, Watford, WD24 4XX Tel: (01923) 651400 Fax: (01923) 240334 E-mail: sales@rocketmedical.com *Medical equipment manufrs*

Old Sarum Engineering, Hangar 3, Old Sarum Airfield, Old Sarum, Salisbury, SP4 6DZ Tel: (01722) 415618 Fax: (01722) 323702 E-mail: enquiries@oldsarumflying.co.uk *Aircraft maintenance*

Old School Furniture, 10 Headbrook, Kington, Herefordshire, HR5 3DZ Tel: (01544) 239000 *Wooden furniture manufrs*

Old School Pine, The Old School, Kilmuir Easter, Invergordon, Ross-Shire, IV18 0NE Tel: (01862) 842611 Fax: (01862) 842854 *Pine furniture manufrs*

▶ Old School Windscreens, The Old School Cafe, Longcross Road, Longcross, Chertsey, Surrey, KT16 0DP Tel: (01932) 873506 Fax: (01932) 872933 E-mail: enquiries@oldschoolwindscreens.co.uk *Windscreen & window fitters*

Old Time, Dairy Hall, 2a John Street, Newtownards, County Down, BT23 4LZ Tel: (028) 9181 7417 Fax: (028) 9181 7169 E-mail: amacrory@aol.com *Furniture wholesalers*

Old Toll House, 1 Droitwich Road, Worcester, WR3 7LG Tel: (01905) 20608 Fax: (01905) 20608 E-mail: merylaskew@aol.com *Gifts & craft ware suppliers*

▶ Old Town Paving, Newburgh Building, Warncliffe Industrial Estate, McLintock Way, Barnsley, S. Yorkshire, S70 6BF Tel: (01226) 208005 Fax: (01226) 208005

Oldacres & Co. Ltd, 62 Hatton Garden, London, EC1N 8LR Tel: (020) 7242 3242 Fax: (020) 7831 9095 E-mail: services@oldacres.co.uk *Reprographic & offset printers* Also at: London W1

Oldbury Aluminium Alloys Ltd, Amberway, Halesowen, West Midlands, B62 8AY Tel: 0121-504 3880 Fax: 0121-504 3889 E-mail: oaaltd@aol.com *Secondary aluminium & alloy ingots manufrs*

Oldbury Engineering Co. Ltd, Bridge Works, Balcombe Road, Horley, Surrey, RH6 9HT Tel: (01293) 820600 Fax: (01293) 822610 E-mail: oldburyaero@compuserve.com *Aircraft ground equipment*

Oldbury UK Ltd, Bulliol Buisiness Park, Wobaston Road, Wolverhampton, WV9 5EU Tel: (01902) 397216 Fax: (01902) 878265 E-mail: sales@oldburyuk.co.uk *Designers & manufacturers of trailers*

oldcolours.co.uk, 16 Waterside Industrial Estate, Wolverhampton, WV2 2RH Tel: (01902) 402040 E-mail: sales@oldcolours.co.uk *Supplier of replacement bathroom products*

Olde House Trading Post, Loundsley Green Road, Chesterfield, Derbyshire, S40 4RN Tel: (01246) 274321 Fax: (01246) 221853 *Hotel & conference facilities*

Oldeani Ltd, Unit 2a Hoffmanns Way, Chelmsford, CM1 1GU Tel: (01245) 262611 Fax: (01245) 262885 E-mail: sales@oldeani.com *Promotional goods suppliers*

▶ Oldfield Machine Tools Ltd, 10 Bridge Street, Cambuslang, Glasgow, G72 7ED Tel: 0141-641 0440 Fax: 0141-646 2181 E-mail: mail@oldfield.co.uk *Machine tool merchants*

Oldfield Solutions Ltd, Oldfield House, Damery Lane, Woodford, Berkeley, Gloucestershire, GL13 9JR Tel: (01454) 261122 Fax: (01454) 261253 *Pallet repairs, suppliers & couriers*

Oldfields Quality Foods, Twelvetrees CR, London, E3 3JH Tel: (020) 7536 8000 Fax: (020) 7538 8316 *Food production centre*

▶ Oldham Bros Scrap Merchants Dismantlers Demolition, Kirkby Bank Road, Clarence House, Knowsley Industrial Park, Liverpool, L33 7SY Tel: 0151-546 5233 Fax: 0151-546 1258 E-mail: demolition@oldhambros.co.uk *Based in the North West we are Merseyside's leading waste recycler, demolition contractor and skip provider. We provide skips for hire, handle all types of demolition and can deposit all recyclable products. We handle enquiries from all over Liverpool, Wirral, Merseyside, North West, North Wales etc. For all skip hire, demolition contractors etc. Please give us a call.*

Oldham Controls, Middleton Road, Royton, Oldham, OL2 5LL Tel: 0161-624 1912 Fax: 0161-624 1912 *Electronic manufrs*

Oldham Evening Chronicle, PO Box 47, Oldham, OL1 1EN Tel: 0161-633 2121 Fax: 0161-652 2111 E-mail: cpdadmin@oldham-chronicle.co.uk *General printers*

Oldham Lighting Ltd, 1 James Corbett Road, Salford, M50 1DE Tel: 0161-745 8087 Fax: 0161-743 0266 *Lighting manufrs*

Mark Oldham Services, Somersby Street, Grimsby, South Humberside, DN31 1TT Tel: (01472) 344691 Fax: (01472) 344691 *Steel fabricators*

Oldham Metropolitan Borough Trading Standards, North House, 130 Rochdale Road, Oldham, OL1 2JA Tel: 0161-911 4474 Fax: 0161-911 3481 E-mail: env.tradingstandard@oldham.gov.uk *Calibrating, weighting & testing services & law*

▶ Oldham Plant Hire & Sales Ltd, 50 Oldham Road, Royton, Oldham, OL2 5PF Tel: 0161-627 0427 Fax: 0161-633 6590 E-mail: sales@oldhamhirecentre.co.uk *Tool hire and sales to trade and DIY Calor gas sales Professional power tool repairs*Heater hire carpet cleaner hire*aluminium tower hire*

Oldham Seals Ltd, Jetpac Works Gravel Lane, Quarry Lane Industrial Estate, Chichester, West Sussex, PO19 8PG Tel: (01243) 782296 Fax: (01243) 781933 E-mail: sales@oldhamseals.co.uk *Rubber products manufrs*

▶ Oldridge Consultants Ltd, 89 Hoynors, Danbury, Chelmsford, CM3 4RL Tel: (01245) 225894 Fax: 01245 225610 E-mail: mail@oldridgeconsultants.co.uk *strategic business and IT systems consultancy to the financial services and 'not for profit' sectors*

▶ Olema Engineering, M J F Yard, Chiddingfold Road, Dunsfold, Godalming, Surrey, GU8 4PB Tel: (01483) 200700 Fax: (01483) 200700 *Metal fabricators*

Olenol Ltd, Olenol House, Plot 7 Greenfield Farm Industrial Estate, Congleton, Cheshire, CW12 4TR Tel: (01260) 298276 Fax: (01260) 298267 *Metalworking fluid manufrs*

Oleo International Ltd, Longford Road, Longford Road, Coventry, CV7 9ND Tel: (024) 7664 5555 Fax: (024) 7664 5777 E-mail: roy@oleo.co.uk *Hydraulic buffer manufrs*

▶ Oleo Solutions Ltd, Westminster Business Centre, 10 Great North Way, Neter Poppleton, York, YO26 ^RB Tel: (01904) 520106 Fax: (01904) 520105 E-mail: garry.turner@oleosolutions.com *Sole UK distributor of Cognis Oleochemicals, encompassing Fatty Acids, Fatty Alcohols, Glycerol, Triacetin, Ozone Acids (Azelaic Acid) Esters and Plastic and Rubber Additives*

Oleotec Ltd, Rossfield Road, Ellesmere Port, CH65 3BS Tel: 0151-357 1778 Fax: 0151-357 1857 E-mail: sales@oleotec.com Principal Export Areas: Africa *Manufacturers & producers of chemical, fatty acids, oleo chemical*

Olesen Agriculture Limited, 32 Papermakers, Overton, Basingstoke, Hampshire, RG25 3NS Tel: (01256) 771887 Fax: (01256) 771956 E-mail: sales@olesenagri.co.uk *Agricultural machinery services*

▶ Olimax Property Care Ltd, Olimax Property Care Limited,, Olimax House, 17 Donald Aldred Drive, Burley In Wharfedale, Ilkley, West Yorkshire, LS29 7SG Tel: 01943 865721 E-mail: info@olimax.net *Burley in Wharfedale based property maintenance company providing a range of services including a plumber, electrician, plasterer, joiner, locksmith, decorator, glazer, roofer and fire and flood restoration*

Olivand Metal Windows Ltd, 43a Chesley Gardens, London, E6 3LN Tel: (020) 8471 8111 Fax: (020) 8552 7015 *Metal window refurbishers*

▶ The Olive Branch, Unit 2, Sandbeck Lane, Wetherby, West Yorkshire, LS22 7TW Tel: (01937) 582797 Fax: (01937) 582797 E-mail: info@olive-branch.biz *Kitchen furniture manufrs*

▶ The Olive Oil Store, 1 Saffron Road, Chafford Hundred, Grays, Essex, RM16 6NA Tel: 01375 483863 E-mail: sales@oliveoilstore.co.uk *Retail and trade suppliers of Organic Extra Virgin Olive Oil, Organic Olives, Salad Dressings and Tapenades.*

Olive & Padgett Ltd, Station Lane, Heckmondwike, West Yorkshire, WF16 0NF Tel: (01924) 405661 *Precision engineers & hydraulic engineers*

▶ Olive Tree Coffee and Chocolate Shop, Greenfields, Lhanbryde, Elgin, Morayshire, IV30 8LN Tel: (07817 430635 E-mail: shop@olivetreeofelgin.co.uk *We are a family run coffee shop that specialises in handmade belgian chocolates, cakes, wedding services and outside catering. Our menus definitely have a chocolatey bias!*

Oliver Adams Ltd, 262 Hillmorton Road, Rugby, Warwickshire, CV22 5BW Tel: (01788) 541104 *Bakery product suppliers*

▶ Oliver Connell & Son Ltd, 35 Junction Road, London, W5 4XP Tel: (020) 8568 0001 Fax: (020) 8232 8151

▶ Oliver Control Systems Ltd, Units 4 - 6 Sun Valley Business Park, Winall Close, Winchester, Hants, SO23 0LB Tel: (01962) 859306 Fax: (01962) 859304 E-mail: sales@oliver-control.com *Manufacturer of industrial joysticks, control equipment, professional switches and kaypads.*

▶ Oliver Goldsmiths Sunglasses, 15 All Saints Road, London, W11 1HA Tel: (0845) 0533440 Fax: (0870) 7541899 E-mail: info@olivergoldsmith.com *Handmade sunglasses manufrs*

Oliver & Graimes Design Associates Ltd, 1-3 Ship Street, Shoreham-by-Sea, West Sussex, BN43 5DH Tel: (01273) 748884 Fax: (01273) 465398 E-mail: info@oandg.co.uk *Graphic design-direct mail services-web designers*

Oliver Overhead Doors Ltd, 8 Magdalen Close, Syresham, Brackley, Northamptonshire, NN13 5YF Tel: (01280) 850206 Fax: (01280) 850077 E-mail: sales@oliveroverhead.co.uk *Installation of industrial doors*

▶ Pat Oliver Designs, 7-8 Park Gate, Skelmanthorpe, Huddersfield, HD8 9BB Tel: (01484) 864263 E-mail: patoliver@bbmax.co.uk *Develop & manage interior design & visual styling projects*

Oliver Seeds Ltd, Unit 3 Saxilby Enterprise Park, Skellingthorpe Road, Saxilby, Lincoln, LN1 2LR Tel: (01522) 706500 Fax: (01522) 706509 E-mail: enquiries@oliver-seeds.co.uk *Seed suppliers*

▶ Oliver & Son Ltd, 11 Coinagehall Street, Helston, Cornwall, TR13 8ER Tel: (01326) 572082 Fax: (01326) 572515 E-mail: info@oliversofhelston.co.uk *Furniture shop*

Oliver Valves Ltd, Haig Road, Parkgate Industrial Estate, Knutsford, Cheshire, WA16 8DX Tel: (01565) 632636 Fax: (01565) 654089 E-mail: sales@valves.co.uk *Ball & needle valves assemblers*

Oliver Valves Ltd, Haig Road, Parkgate Industrial Estate, Knutsford, Cheshire, WA16 8DX Tel: (01565) 632636 Fax: (01565) 654089 E-mail: cornwell@valves.co.uk *Valves manufrs*

Olivers Fine Furniture, 26 Pillory Street, Nantwich, Cheshire, CW5 5BG Tel: (01270) 628830 Fax: (01270) 628830 *Pine suppliers*

▶ Olivers Transport Ltd, Hassington Road, Eccles, Kelso, Roxburghshire, TD5 7QS Tel: (01890) 840547

▶ Oliveti Constructin Ltd, 2a Peatling Road, Countesthorpe, Leicester, LE8 5RD Tel: 0116-277 7771 Fax: 0116-277 7776

Olivien Craft Centre, 126 Burton Road, Manchester, M20 1JQ Tel: 0161-434 5444 *Pizza suppliers*

Ollard Westcombe, Bridge Street, Downpatrick, County Down, BT30 6HD Tel: (028) 4461 7557 Fax: (028) 4461 3580 E-mail: office@dthomason.freeserve.com *Webbing & stable belt manufrs*

▶ Ollerton Ltd, Samlesbury Mill, Goosefoot Lane, Samlesbury Bottoms, Preston, PR5 0RN Tel: (01254) 852127

▶ Olli Construction Services, 21 Johnstone Road, London, E6 6JB Tel: (020) 8552 7122 Fax: (020) 8552 6263

▶ Ollitec, 6 Fairview Close, Tonbridge, Kent, TN9 2UU Tel: (07775) 792288 Fax: (0870) 7059500 E-mail: grahamsimmonds@vodafone.net *Computer services & repairs, cheap broadband & home telephone calls*

Olney Headwear Ltd, 106 Old Bedford Road, Luton, LU2 7PD Tel: (01582) 731512 Fax: (01582) 729066 E-mail: info@olney-headwear.co.uk *Hat manufrs*

Olney Precision Ltd, 5 Stilebrook Road, Olney, Buckinghamshire, MK46 5EA Tel: (01234) 712055 Fax: (01234) 241102 *Sub contract precision engineers*

Olscot, 40 Dryden Road, Loanhead, Midlothian, EH20 9LZ Tel: 0131-448 2257 Fax: 0131-440 1359 *Industrial cleaners* Also at: Glasgow

Olympia Conference Centre, Hammersmith Road, Kensington, London, W14 8UX Tel: (020) 7370 8532 Fax: (020) 7370 8144 E-mail: conferences@eco.co.uk *Exhibition centre services*

▶ Olympia Executive, Garland Court, Garland Road, East Grinstead, West Sussex, RH19 1DN Tel: 01342 331144 Fax: 01342 331138 E-mail: executive@olyexec.co.uk *Human Resources Consultancy, Management/Staff Training & Development, & Investors in People Consultancy*

▶ Olympia Fabrications Ltd, Unit 16 Showell Road Industrial Estate, Showell Road, Wolverhampton, WV10 9LU Tel: (01902) 717708 Fax: (01902) 717708

Olympia Furniture Ltd, Whitelands Road, Ashton-under-Lyne, Lancashire, OL6 6UX Tel: 0161-331 4000 Fax: 0161-331 4029 E-mail: sales@olympia-furniture.co.uk *Upholstered furniture manufrs*

Olympia Interiors Ltd, Canterbury Road, Chilham, Canterbury, Kent, CT4 8DZ Tel: (01227) 732100 Fax: (01227) 732199 *Joinery manufrs*

Olympia Testing Holdings Ltd, Oldbush Street, Off Level Street, Brierley Hill, West Midlands, DY5 1UB Tel: (01384) 573164 Fax: (01384) 265832 *Crane & lifting gear testing & inspection*

Olympia Triumph International Ltd, 5 Queens Road, Swanage, Dorset, BH19 2EQ Tel: (01929) 424326 Fax: (01929) 427403 E-mail: sales@olympia-triumph.co.uk Principal Export Areas: Worldwide *Our Company manufactures and supplies a full range of safety and rescue equipment to cover vessel entry, confined space entry, rescue from buildings, shafts, etc., access equipment, full body harnesses and safety lines. We also offer Risk Assessment Reports, full service and back-up for all our equipment. As part of our service we offer on-site training packages tailored to your particular requirements.*

Olympiad Signs Ltd, 7 Dorma Trading Park, Staffa Road, London, E10 7QX Tel: (020) 8539 3006 Fax: (020) 8556 1075 E-mail: sales@olympiadsigns.co.uk *Sign contractors & suppliers*

Olympian Fire Protection Ltd, Charwell House Ash Farm, Ash Lane, Hale, Altrincham, Cheshire, WA15 8PH Tel: 0161-903 9941 Fax: 0161-904 7514 *Fire alarm consultants & installers*

Olympic Airways, 11 Conduit Street, London, W1S 2LP Tel: (0870) 6060460 Fax: (020) 7629 9891 *Air line*

Olympic Blinds Ltd, Olympic House Bilton Court, Bilton Way, Luton, LU1 1LX Tel: (01582) 737878 Fax: (01582) 402182 E-mail: sales@olympicblindsltd.co.uk *Window blind manufrs*

▶ Olympic Cleaning, 100 Wood Road, Heybridge, Maldon, Essex, CM9 4AU Tel: (01621) 856476 Fax: (01621) 852582 E-mail: sales@olympiccleaning.com *Full janitorial stockists, machines & equipment*

Olympic Engineering, Unit F5 Charles House, Bridge Road, Southall, Middlesex, UB2 4BD Tel: (020) 8574 4406 Fax: (020) 8571 1556 E-mail: oloieng@aol.com *CNC machine engineers*

Olympic Express Ltd, Head Office, 90-91 Moseley Street, Birmingham, B12 0RT Tel: (08451) 255505 Fax: 0121-666 7541 *Express couriers*

▶ Olympic Glass Products, 3 Queenborough Business Park, Main Road, Queenborough, Kent, ME11 5DY Tel: (01795) 668333 Fax: (01795) 668777 *Glass manufrs*

Olympic Gymnasium Services, Greatworth Park, Welsh Lane, Greatworth, Banbury, Oxfordshire, OX17 2HB Tel: (01295) 760192 Fax: (01295) 768092 E-mail: sales@olympicgymnasium.com *Gymnastic equipment suppliers*

Olympic Kitchens & Bedrooms, Unit 1 Tulketh Industrial Estate, Manchester, M40 9LY Tel: 0161-205 0055 Fax: 0161-205 0101 *Furniture manufrs*

Olympic Mato Ltd, West Rose Works, St. Mewan, St. Austell, Cornwall, PL25 5SP Tel: (01726) 61141 Fax: (01726) 70211 *Manufacturers of conveyor belting*

Olympic Sign Services, Unit 5, Bradbauy Drive, Springwood Indutrial Estate, Braintree, Essex, CM7 2SD Tel: (01376) 551300 Fax: (01376) 328121 E-mail: sales@olypicsignservices.co.uk *Sign contractors*

Olympic Signs Ltd, Units 30-31 Colebrook Industrial Estate, Longfield Road, Tunbridge Wells, Kent, TN2 3DG Tel: (01892) 548444 Fax: (01892) 538444 E-mail: sales@olympicsigns.co.uk *Signwriting & sign manufrs*

Olympic Of Waterhouses Ltd, Manifold Works, Leek Road, Waterhouses, Stoke-on-Trent, ST10 3HN Tel: (01538) 308486 Fax: (01538) 308185 *Window manufacturers & installers*

Olympic Welding Ltd, Station Road, Acle, Norwich, NR13 3BZ Tel: (01493) 750496 Fax: (01493) 751968 *Metal marine fabricators product manufrs*

Olympus Automation, 4 A1 Parkway, Southgate Way, Orton Southgate, Peterborough, PE2 6YN Tel: (01733) 394700 Fax: (01733) 394901 E-mail: sales@olympus-automation.co.uk *Systems integration agents & process engineering*

Olympus Distribution Ltd, Olympus Drive, Great Bridge, Tipton, West Midlands, DY4 7HY Tel: 0121-522 5600 Fax: 0121-522 5601 E-mail: sales@olympusdistribution.com *Bathroom fittings, accessories & industrial fastener distributors*

▶ Olympus Labels Ltd, Richardshaw Road, Grangefield Industrial Estate, Pudsey, West Yorkshire, LS28 6QW Tel: 0113-236 3283 Fax: 0113-236 3284

Olympus N D T Ltd, 12 Nightingale Court, Nightingale Close, Rotherham, South Yorkshire, S60 2AB Tel: (01709) 836115 Fax: (01709) 835177 E-mail: info.uk@olympusndt.com *Non-destructive test equipment manufrs*

Olympus UK Ltd, 2-8 Honduras St, London, EC1Y 0TX Tel: (020) 7253 2772 Fax: (020) 7251 6330 E-mail: info@olympus.uk.com *Olympus is a market leader in the manufacture and supply of many optical based products. We provide excellence in areas such as digital & film photography, microscopy and medical diagnostics products. www.olympus.co.uk*

▶ Oma UK Ltd, Unit 3-4 Greenfield Farm Industrial Estate, Hopkins Lane, Congleton, Cheshire, CW12 4TR Tel: (01260) 278585 Fax: (01260) 278590 E-mail: omauk@aol.com *Braiding machinery & bobbin winders for the textile, wire & hose industries*

▶ Omagh Business Forum, 33 Market Street, Omagh, County Tyrone, BT78 1EE Tel: (028) 8225 9595 Fax: (028) 8225 9596 E-mail: info@omaghchamber.com *As the largest, independent business body in the Omagh District our Mission is:*** to continue to grow and develop our membership throughout Omagh and the surrounding district* to develop our range of membership services and ensure that these remain relevant to the needs of our members * to represent the interests of our members to all appropriate influencers at a local and strategic level and to play a key role in improving the business climate in which our members operate thus leading to improved performance in both home and export markets.****

▶ Omagh Computer Repair Centre, E Mountjoy Road, Omagh, County Tyrone, BT79 7AD Tel: (028) 8225 9564 Fax: (028) 8225 1687 E-mail: ocrc@btconnect.com *Computer repairers*

Omar Foods, 123 Upwell Street, Sheffield, S4 8AN Tel: 0114-261 0052 Fax: 0114-258 0491 *Food manufrs*

Omar Homes Ltd, London Road, Brandon, Suffolk, IP27 0NE Tel: (01842) 810673 Fax: (01842) 814328 E-mail: sales@omar.co.uk *Manufacturers park homes*

Omar Trading Co., West Street, Rochdale, Lancashire, OL16 2EN Tel: (01706) 344273 Fax: (01706) 715136 *Ladies & childrens clothing*

Omco UK Ltd, New St Mills, Carlisle Road, Pudsey, West Yorkshire, LS28 8LW Tel: 0113-257 3172 *Cast iron bottle moulds manufrs*

Omega Automotive Ltd, 4 Europa Way, Britannia Enterprise Park, Lichfield, Staffordshire, WS14 9TZ Tel: (01543) 490628 Fax: (01543) 493421 E-mail: info@omega-automotive.com *Manufacturers & traders of automotive components*

Omega Bakery Equipment Ltd, 53 Hillmorton Rd, Rugby, Warwickshire, CV22 5AE Tel: 01788 552590 *Bakery equipment suppliers & manufrs*

Omega City Lifts Ltd, 8 Bridge Gate Centre, Martinfield, Welwyn Garden City, Hertfordshire, AL7 1JG Tel: (01707) 334962 Fax: (01707) 376594 E-mail: sanjay@omegacitylifts.co.uk *Lift engineers & services* Also at: Leicester

▶ Omega Cleaning Contractors, 79 Dundrennan Road, Glasgow, G42 9SL Tel: 0141-636 6801 Fax: 0141-636 6801 E-mail: info@omegacleaningltd.co.uk *Floor cleaning, builders cleans, & industrial cleans*

Omega Computers, 685 Cranbrook Road, Ilford, Essex, IG2 6SY Tel: (020) 8550 9295 Fax: (020) 8550 0830 E-mail: sale@omegacomputer.uk *Supplier of computer hardware materials*

▶ Omega Data Services Ltd, Unit 45-46, Howe Moss Avenue, Dyce, Aberdeen, AB21 0GP Tel: (01224) 772763 Fax: (01224) 772783 E-mail: sales@omega-data.com

Omega Diagnostics Ltd, Omega House, Carsebridge Court, Whins Road, Alloa, Clackmannanshire, FK10 3LQ Tel: (01259) 763030 Fax: (01259) 723251 E-mail: odl@omegadiagnostics.co.uk *Diagnostic kit systems*

Omega Diagnostics Ltd, Hillfoots Business Village, Alva Industrial Estate, Alva, Clackmannanshire, FK12 5DQ Tel: (01259) 763030 Fax: (01259) 761853

Omega Drapes, Unit 17 Riverside Industrial Estate, Thames Road, Barking, Essex, IG11 0ND Tel: (020) 8591 4945 Fax: (020) 8591 4139 E-mail: sales@omegadrapes.fsnet.co.uk *Exhibition soft furnishing manufrs*

▶ Omega Electronic Equipment Europe Ltd, Emerald Way, Stone Business Park, Stone, Staffordshire, ST15 0SR Tel: (01785) 812100

Omega Enclosures, 1 Dellmount Avenue, Bangor, County Down, BT20 4TZ Tel: (028) 9147 2536 *Flight cases manufrs*

Omega Environmental Technologies UK Ltd, 47 Bowness Crescent, London, SW15 3QN Tel: (020) 8870 9911 Fax: (020) 8549 1256 E-mail: omegaeurope@hotmail.com *Air conditioning installers*

Omega Foundry Machinery Ltd, 8 Stapledon Road, Orton Southgate, Peterborough, PE2 6TB Tel: (01733) 232231 Fax: (01733) 237012 E-mail: sales@omegafoundrymachinery.com *Foundry equipment & plant manufrs*

Omega Group UK Ltd, Morley Way, Peterborough, PE2 7BW Tel: (01733) 702000 Fax: (01733) 234114 E-mail: personnel@theomegagroup.co.uk *PVCu window, door & conservatory manufrs*

Omega Interiors, The Cavendish Centre, Winnall Close, Winchester, Hampshire, SO23 0LB Tel: (01962) 843542 Fax: (01962) 843062 E-mail: tony@omega-online.co.uk *Interior refurbishment contractors*

Omega Laser Services, Wood End House, Cubley, Penistone, Sheffield, S36 9AW Tel: (01226) 767221 Fax: (01226) 766807 *Survey & laser equipment agents*

Omega Lighting Ltd, 48 Potters Lane, Kiln Farm, Milton Keynes, MK11 3HQ Tel: (01908) 260015 Fax: (01908) 260019 E-mail: sales@omegalighting.co.uk *Lighting retailer*

Omega Mechanical Services Ltd, 14 Sringtown Road, Springtown Industrial Estate, Londonderry, BT48 0LY Tel: (028) 7137 0219 Fax: (028) 7137 2102 E-mail: omegamechanical@btinternet.com *Mechanical services*

▶ Omega Mobile Locksmiths, 11 Wensleydale Avenue, Ilford, Essex, IG5 0NA Tel: (020) 8550 1155 Fax: (020) 8220 5810 E-mail: malcolm@omegamobilelocksmith.co.uk

Omega Pistons Ltd, Oak Barn Road, Halesowen, West Midlands, B62 9DW Tel: 0121-559 6778 Fax: 0121-559 6779 E-mail: info@omegapistons.com *Piston & piston ring makers*

Omega Print, Unit 8, Duns Lane, Leicester, LE3 5LX Tel: 0116-253 7388 Fax: 0116-253 7388 *Lithographic printing*

▶ Omega Projects, 67 Buckstone Avenue, Alwoodley, Leeds, LS17 5EZ Tel: 0845 686 0099 E-mail: info@omega-projects.com

Omega Red Group, 10 Brewster Square, Brucefield Industrial Estate, Livingston, West Lothian, EH54 9BJ Tel: (01506) 464620 Fax: (01506) 461382 E-mail: sales@omegaredgroup.com *Lightning protection installers*

▶ Omega Red Group Ltd, Dabell Avenue, Blenheim Industrial Estate, Bulwell, Nottingham, NG6 8WA Tel: 0115-877 6666 Fax: 0115-876 7766 E-mail: aimiga@redgroup.co.uk *Lightning protection suppliers & installers* Also at: Leicester, London SE25 & Manchester

Omega Red Group Ltd, 28 Kansas Avenue, Salford, M50 2GL Tel: 0161-877 9881 Fax: 0161-877 9882 *Lightning protection equipment*

Omega Redgroup Ltd, 4 Avonbank Industrial Estate, West Town Road, Bristol, BS11 9DE Tel: 0117-938 1112 Fax: 0117-938 1522 *Supply & install lightning protection equipment*

Omega Research Ltd, 32 Wissey Way, Ely, Cambridgeshire, CB6 2WW Tel: (01353) 612520 Fax: (01353) 612520 E-mail: sales@omega-research.co.uk *Electronic design consultants*

Omega Resistance Wire Ltd, Hadley Works, Cranborne Road, Potters Bar, Hertfordshire, EN6 3JL Tel: (01707) 620111 Fax: (01707) 649225 E-mail: sales@omega-wire.com *Omega Wire are manufacturers of Cupro-Nickel, Nickel Chrome Resistance Wires, Ribbon, Strip, Stranded Wires, Nickel Iron, Phosphor Bronze, Nickel Silver, Pure Nickel, Iron Chrome Aluminium Wires and Tapes. Omega Wire offers high quality finished products in Spring, Annealed, Oxidised and Special Temper supplied in Coil, precision wound on Spools, or Straight Lengths, as requested*

Omega Scientific, Fynamore, Reading Road, Wallingford, Oxfordshire, OX10 9DT Tel: (01491) 837736 Fax: (01491) 825454 *Publishing services*

Omega Signs Ltd, Newmarket Approach, Leeds, LS9 0RJ Tel: 0113-240 3000 Fax: 0113-249 2228 E-mail: sales@omega-signs.co.uk *Sign manufrs*

Omega Thermo Engineering Ltd, Unit 30, Globe Industrial Estate, Rectory Road, Grays, Essex, RM17 6ST Tel: (01375) 898400 Fax: (01375) 898420 *Heat exchanger panel manufrs*

▶ Omega Windows, Exchange Road, Lincoln, LN6 3JZ Tel: (01522) 685444 Fax: (01522) 521 898

Omega Wipers, 12 Fordrough, Yardley, Birmingham, B25 8DL Tel: 0121-771 2653 Fax: 0121-771 2652 E-mail: omegawipers@aol.com *Clothing recycling & wipers manufrs*

Omega World Travel Ltd, 11 York Road, London, SE1 7NX Tel: (020) 7922 0770 Fax: (020) 7922 0799 E-mail: sales@owt.net *Business travel agent*

Omegaslate UK Ltd, 2 Chirk Close, Kidderminster, Worcestershire, DY10 1YG Tel: (01562) 755824 Fax: (01562) 742979 E-mail: info@omegaslate.com *Wear resistance engineers*

Omex Environmental Ltd, Riverside Industrial Estate, King's Lynn, Norfolk, PE30 2HH Tel: (01553) 770092 Fax: (01553) 776547 E-mail: enquire@omex.com *Waste water effluent treatment*

Omex Medical Ltd, Unit T6, Rudford Industrial Estate, Ford Road, Ford, Arundel, West Sussex, BN18 0BF Tel: (01903) 783744 Fax: (01903) 734368 *Health care suppliers*

Omg UK Ltd, Ashton New Road, Clayton, Manchester, M11 4AT Tel: 0161-230 2540 Fax: 0161-230 2662 *Automotive catalyst manufrs*

Omicron Development Ltd, Station Road, Stalbridge, Sturminster Newton, Dorset, DT10 2RQ Tel: (01963) 363632 Fax: (01963) 363632 E-mail: neil@omicrondev.co.uk *Computer consultants*

Omicron Electronics UK Ltd, Unit 9, Marconi Gate, Staffordshire Technology Park, Stafford, ST18 0FZ Tel: (01785) 251000 Fax: (01785) 252000 E-mail: info@uk.omicron.at *Manufacturers of electrical test equipment*

▶ Omicron Parts & Services, 5 Grand Union Enterprise Park, Grand Union Way, Southall, Middlesex, UB2 4EX Tel: (020) 8574 0647 Fax: (020) 8890 3418 *Computer maintenance services*

Omicways Ltd, Bude Straton Business Park, Bude, Cornwall, EX23 8LY Tel: (01288) 353838 Fax: (01288) 354978 E-mail: office@containergroup.co.uk *Giftware distributors & importers*

Omiran Ltd, Units 1-2, James Carter Road, Mildenhall, Bury St. Edmunds, Suffolk, IP28 7DE Tel: (01638) 716748 Fax: (01638) 716779 E-mail: sales@omiran.co.uk *Electronic test equipment distributors*

Omni Whittington Insurance Services Ltd, Bridgeway House, 21 Whitfield Street, Gloucester, GL1 1NA Tel: (01452) 428000 Fax: (01452) 301387 E-mail: info@omniwhittington.co.uk *General insurance*

Omnibus Solutions Ltd, Hollinwood Business Centre, Albert Street, Oldham, OL8 3QL Tel: 0161-683 3100 Fax: 0161-683 3102 *Computer software*

Omnibus Systems Ltd, Main Street, Stanford on Soar, Loughborough, Leicestershire, LE12 5PY Tel: (0870) 5004300 Fax: (0870) 5040003 E-mail: sales@omnibus.co.uk *TV station automation services*

Omnichem Ltd, Mill Street East, Dewsbury, West Yorkshire, WF12 9BQ Tel: (01924) 461341 Fax: (01924) 458995 E-mail: info@nickersons.co.uk *Chemicals for industry*

Omnico Plastics Ltd, Unit 12 Mace Industrial Estate, Mace Lane, Ashford, Kent, TN24 8PE Tel: (01233) 646749 Fax: (01233) 663101 E-mail: sales@omnico.co.uk *Plumbing equipment & PVC building products*

Omnico Plastics Ltd, Farthing Road, Ipswich, IP1 5AP Tel: (01473) 461461 Fax: (01473) 240518 E-mail: sales@omnico.co.uk *Plastic supplies to the building industry*

Omnikote Ltd, Chamberlain Road, Aylesbury, Buckinghamshire, HP19 8DY Tel: (01296) 483266 Fax: (01296) 392285 E-mail: sales@omnikote.co.uk *Nylon coating, Polyester powder coating, wet and powder applied Epoxy coatings, PTFE coatings, plastic coating processors, stove enamelling and two-pack paints. Specialists in warm to the touch ("not cold to the touch") Nylon Coated handrails and balustrades to comply with "document M" and DDA regulations. Pre-treatments include gritblasting, phosphating, and zinc metal spraying. Comprehensive, versatile finishing service with five separate plants of differing sizes enabling fast turnaounds on one-offs and prototypes or long runs and high volumes.*

Omni-Pac UK Ltd, South Denes, Great Yarmouth, Norfolk, NR30 3QH Tel: (01493) 855381 Fax: (01493) 858464 Principal Export Areas: Worldwide *Pulp packaging materials services*

Omnipole UK Ltd, 281 Addiscombe Road, Croydon, CR0 7HZ Tel: (020) 8654 4188 Fax: (020) 8407 0439 *Reverse osmosis, water treatment, window cleaning systems & access equipment suppliers*

Omnisigns Ltd, Devereux Way, Boston Road Industrial Estate, Horncastle, Lincolnshire, LN9 6AU Tel: (01507) 522000 Fax: (01507) 523710 E-mail: sales@omnisigns.co.uk *General & saftey sign manufrs*

Omnistitch Sewing Machines & Accessories, 52b Stapleton Road, Bristol, BS5 0RA Tel: 0117-961 3722 Fax: 0117-961 3790 *Industrial sewing machine distributors*

Omonia Continental Patisserie, 129 High Cross Road, London, N17 9NU Tel: (020) 8801 1182 Fax: (020) 8801 1182 *Continental patisserie manufrs*

Omron Electronics Ltd, 1200 Parkway, Whiteley, Fareham, Hampshire, PO15 7AD Tel: (01489) 886772 Fax: (01489) 886762 *Computer software developers*

Omser Scotland Ltd, Fernicleugh, Gartocharn, Alexandria, Dunbartonshire, G83 8RT Tel: (01389) 830408 Fax: (01389) 830349 *Coin & cash handling equipment & paper shredders*

▶ Omsons International, Suite No 1 Olympic Way, Wembley, Middlesex, HA9 0NP Tel: (020) 8434 0567 Fax: (020) 8434 0569 E-mail: eurostar@thinkomsons.com *Manufacturer & exporters of stainless steel, houseswares & hand tools*

Omya UK Ltd, 17 Munie Road, Glenarm, Ballymena, County Antrim, BT44 0BG Tel: (028) 2884 1333 Fax: (028) 2884 1687 E-mail: marvethblack@omya.co.uk *Limestone quarrying & processing*

▶ Omya UK Ltd, Stephensons Way, Wyvern Business Park, Chaddesden, Derby, DE21 6LY Tel: (01332) 674000 Fax: (01332) 544700 E-mail: enquiries.uk@omya.com *Manufactures of chemicals*

▶ On Air Telecom Ltd, West Point, 501 Chester Road, Manchester, M16 9HU Tel: 0161-906 9060 Fax: 0161-906 9061 E-mail: sales@onairtelecom.com *As a market leading telecommunications company, On Air Telecom is committed to helping our customers reduce their overheads, increase their efficiencies and examine new ways of using telecoms to streamline their business. *We can provide: Mobile Phones, Remote Email, Vehicle tracking, Telematics, Fixed line & Data solutions. **

On Cue With Michael Lowcock, 12 Hatfield Lane, Armthorpe, Doncaster, South Yorkshire, DN3 3EX Tel: (01302) 832978 Fax: (01302) 832978 *Snooker table suppliers*

On The Dot Ltd, Ripley Road, Bradford, West Yorkshire, BD4 7EX Tel: (01274) 723626 Fax: (01274) 723626 *Road works*

On Line It Ltd, 34 Bedford Road, Hitchin, Hertfordshire, SG5 1HF Tel: (01462) 624624 Fax: (01462) 452452 *Computer var*

▶ On Line Learning, 510 Wilbraham Road, Manchester, M21 9AW Tel: 0161-860 6814 *Computer training agents*

On Line Support Computing Ltd, The Old Station Works, 119 Sandycomb Road, Richmond, Surrey, TW9 2EP Tel: (020) 8940 9484 Fax: (020) 8948 2114 *Computer installation services*

▶ On The River Film & Video Production, 2/1 5 McIntyre Place, Paisley, Renfrewshire, PA2 6EE Tel: 0141-889 2411 Fax: 0141-889 2411 E-mail: info@concepttoscreen.com *Creating innovative films and videos, from concept to screen. Offering a complete in-house service for drama, corporate, music, community, training and promotional films and videos.*

▶ On Screen Productions, 33 Bridge Street, Chepstow, Gwent, NP16 5GA Tel: (01291) 636300 Fax: (01291) 636301 *Audio equipment hire services*

On Site Services, 10 Beechwood Avenue, Sunbury-on-Thames, Middlesex, TW16 7QN Tel: (01932) 770906 E-mail: info@on-site-paving.co.uk *We are a landscaping construction company based in Surrey covering every aspect of brick work and ground work, including concreting and block paving, patios, paths and driveways, as well as site clearance and machine hire throughout Surrey and beyond. For over 18 years On Site Services has been proud to offer the very best ground work, brick work and site clearance service in Surrey. From paving, patios and driveways to machine hire, we provide professional, reliable and competitively priced work by highly skilled tradesmen. We serve a variety of domestic and commercial customers throughout Surrey and the surrounding areas, with the complete landscaping package.*

On Site Services Gravesend Ltd, 1 Wharf Road, Gravesend, Kent, DA12 2RU Tel: (01474) 321552 Fax: (01474) 357778 E-mail: enquiries@onsiteservicesgravesend.co.uk *Architectural metalworks & steel manufrs*

On Site Supplies, Stephenson Way, Crawley, West Sussex, RH10 1TN Tel: (01293) 744444 *Access (building) equipment and towers.*

On Site Welding Solutions Ltd, 6b Sweetmans Yard, Plough Lane, Hereford, HR4 0EE Tel: (01432) 276639 Fax: (01432) 276639 E-mail: andrew-skinner@tiscaly.co.uk *Steel fabricators*

▶ On Spring Industrial, 11 North Broadgate Lane, Horsforth, Leeds, LS18 5AF Tel: 0113-217 5417 Fax: 0113-258 3110 E-mail: info@onspring.biz *Window screws*

▶ On The Table Ltd, 28 South Street, Dorchester, Dorset, DT1 1BY Tel: (01305) 257258 Fax: (01305) 257258 E-mail: sales@onthetable.biz *Tableware retailers*

▶ On Time Packing Ltd, New Greenham Park, Greenham, Thatcham, Berkshire, RG19 6HN Tel: (01635) 523797

On Your Bike, 52-54 Tooley Street, London, SE1 2SZ Tel: (020) 7378 6669 Fax: (020) 7357 7600 E-mail: enquiries@onyourbike.net *Bicycle retailers*

▶ Oncology Imaging Systems, Kennett House The Office Village, River Way, Uckfield, East Sussex, TN22 1SL Tel: (01825) 744063 Fax: (01825) 749557 *Medical equipment manufrs*

Ondrives, Unit 15 Foxwood Industrial Park, Foxwood Road, Chesterfield, Derbyshire, S41 9RN Tel: (01246) 455500 Fax: (01246) 455522 *Mechanical drive component manufrs*

▶ One 58 Associates Ltd, Unit 1 Grove Street, Cheltenham, Gloucestershire, GL50 3LZ Tel: (01242) 241158 Fax: (01242) 241580

One Accessories, Pasture Lane, Gaddesby, Leicester, LE7 4XD Tel: (01664) 840846 Fax: (01664) 840946 E-mail: sales@wileysdesign.co.uk *Handbag designers*

One Call Claim Centre, Unit 1A, Spa Road Industrial Estate, New Holder Street, Bolton, BL1 4SS Tel: (01204) 523772 Fax: (01204) 388498 E-mail: boltoncarpets@zenlen.co.uk *Insurance claims*

▶ One Call Equipment Hire, Neptune Industrial Estate, Neptune Close, Medway City Estate, Rochester, Kent, ME2 4LT Tel: (01634) 723222 Fax: (01634) 723721

One Call Hire Ltd, The Paragon Centre, 32 Crown Road, Enfield, Middlesex, EN1 1TH Tel: (020) 8443 7100 Fax: (0870) 4047004 E-mail: sales@onecallhire.com *Plant & tool hire, used excavator & plant sales.*

One For Instrumentation Ltd, 17 Townsend Road, Congleton, Cheshire, CW12 3DL Tel: (01260) 290846 Fax: 01260 290846 E-mail: enquiries@oneforinst.com *Supplier of Pressure and Temperature Gauges along with Pressure Regulators and Process Controllers. We also supply all areas of instrumentation for overseas projects in all areas of the process industry.*

One North East, Stella House, Goldcrest Way, Newcastle upon Tyne, NE15 8NY Tel: (0870) 1601781 Fax: 0191-229 6201 E-mail: enquiries@onenortheast.co.uk *Regional development agency*

▶ One Off Engineering Ltd, Simpson Street, Hyde, Cheshire, SK14 1BJ Tel: 0161-366 7276 Fax: 0161-366 7276 E-mail: oneoffeng@fsmail.net *Small batch engineering product services*

One For One Ltd, 121-141 Westbourne Terrace, London, W2 6JR Tel: (020) 7706 2306 Fax: (020) 7258 3757 *Sales promotion & direct marketing*

▶ One Red Sky, Watcombe Manor Industrial Units, Ingham Lane, Watlington, Oxfordshire, OX49 5EB Tel: (01491) 614756 E-mail: customerservices@oneredsky.com *Contemporary furniture*

One Step Beyond Ltd, 9-11 Bedford Street, Norwich, NR2 1AR Tel: (08703) 500252 Fax: (01603) 617378 *Computer services & retail*

▶ The One Stop Print Group, 123 Spring Bank, Hull, HU3 1BH Tel: (01482) 324752 Fax: (01482) 606847 E-mail: info@theonestop.co.uk *Printing services*

▶ One Stop Print Shop Ltd, 2 Black Swan Walk, Leominster, Herefordshire, HR6 8HU Tel: (01568) 613888 Fax: (01568) 613402 E-mail: sales@theonestopprintshop.co.uk *Printing & stationery suppliers*

▶ One Stop Promotions, 38 Hayhill, Barrow upon Soar, Loughborough, Leicestershire, LE12 8LD Tel: (01509) 814380 Fax: (01509) 814929 E-mail: info@onestoppromotions.co.uk *Promotional materials suppliers*

▶ One Stop Safety Services Ltd, Po Box 124, Bolton, BL3 1LX Tel: 01204 597454 Fax: 01204 604364 E-mail: sales@onestopsafetyservices.co.uk *Health and Safety Consultancy Services.**Sales of Personal Protective Equipment*

▶ One Stop Security Services Ltd, Eighth Floor, Six Acre House, Town Square, Sale, Cheshire, M33 7WZ Tel: 0161-969 6262

▶ One to One Engravers Ltd, 3 Cirrus Park, Lower Farm Road, Moulton Park Industrial Estate, Northampton, NN3 6UR Tel: (01606) 644604 Fax: (01604) 644755 E-mail: info@otoel.com *Acid etching, engraving & sublimation*

▶ One To One Industrial Design, Middle Meadow, Middle Street, Ilmington, Shipston-on-Stour, Warwickshire, CV36 4LS Tel: (01608) 682101 Fax: (01608) 682099 E-mail: enquiry@121id.co.uk *Industrial Design Consultant*

One To One Productions, Glasshoughton Cultural Industries Centre, Redhill Avenue, Castleford, West Yorkshire, WF10 4QH Tel: (01977) 603431 Fax: (01977) 735000 E-mail: sales@one2one-connected.com *Video producers*

One Way Circuits, Station Road, Lenwade, Norwich, NR9 5LY Tel: (01603) 875100 Fax: (0870) 7517518 E-mail: sales@onewaypcb.com *Printed circuit manufactures & assembly*

One Whitehall Place, 1 Whitehall Place, London, SW1A 2HD Tel: (020) 7839 3344 Fax: (020) 7839 3366 *Conferences & function services*

▶ Onebighost, 106 Drumaney Road, Coagh, Cookstown, County Tyrone, BT80 0HN Tel: (07050) 382091 Fax: (028) 8673 5871 E-mail: admin@onebighost.com *Web design & hosting*

Onecall, 50 Avenue Road, Aston, Birmingham, B6 4DY Tel: (0800) 6524646 Fax: 0121-333 3996 *Barrier fencing, lifting & jacking equipment*

▶ Onecallpc.Com, 25-29 High Street, Leatherhead, Surrey, KT22 8AB Tel: (0870) 7770999 Fax: (01372) 377092 *Computer software manufrs*

▶ OneDay Couriers, Unit 629, Great Northern House, 275 Deansgate, Manchester, M3 4EL Tel: 0800 8818178 *OneDay Couriers the 24 Hours, Nationwide Delivery Company*

Oneida Plastic Fabrications Ltd, 8e Alder Road, North Shields, Tyne & Wear, NE29 8SD Tel: 0191-258 5750 Fax: 0191-259 6969 E-mail: sales@oneidaplastics.com Principal Export Areas: Worldwide *Water treatment plant equipment manufactures & plastic fabricators*

Oneida Silversmiths Ltd, Cheshire Oaks Outlet Village, Kinsey Road, Ellesmere Port, CH65 9LA Tel: 0151-356 1024 Fax: 0151-356 1024 *Tableware manufrs*

O'Neil Software, Unit 6 Joplin Court, Crownhill, Milton Keynes, MK8 0JP Tel: (01908) 635320 Fax: (01908) 635328 E-mail: sales@oneilsoft.com *Computer software consultants*

▶ O'Neill Bros, 18 Pennyburn Industrial Estate, Londonderry, BT48 0LU Tel: (028) 7126 2701 Fax: (028) 7126 3215 E-mail: dessie.roddy@oneillbros.com *Specialist joinery manufactures & building contractors*

O'Neill Cleaning Ltd, Unit 5 Mitchelston Drive, Mitchelston Industrial Estate, Kirkcaldy, Fife, KY1 3NF Tel: (01592) 655777 Fax: (01592) 655777 E-mail: sales@oneillcleaning.com *Industrial cleaning services*

O'Neill Floor Preparation & Shotblasting Contractors, 28 Cherry Avenue, Bury, Lancashire, BL9 7NA Tel: 0161-763 9349 E-mail: oneillfloorprep@hotmail.co.uk *Dust free shot-blasting of industrial floor surfaces*

O'Neill & Mcbride, 6 Derrynoyd Road, Draperstown, Magherafelt, County Londonderry, BT45 7AH Tel: (028) 7962 8255 Fax: (028) 7962 8878 *Livestock auctioneers*

O'Neill Management Ltd, 9 Albany Drive, Bishops Waltham, Southampton, SO32 1GE Tel: (0787) 9463824E-mail: sales@oneill-management.com *Management services*

Robert O'Neill, 1 Queen Street, Ayr, KA8 0DW Tel: (01292) 260888 Fax: (01292) 619726 *Agriculture supplier*

O'Neill Signs, Bankes Lane, Weston Point, Runcorn, Cheshire, WA7 4HQ Tel: (01928) 592393 Fax: (01928) 592393 E-mail: oneillsigns@zoom.co.uk *Sign manufrs*

▶ Oneprint International, 34 Flairs Avenue, Arbroath, Angus, DD11 5DY Tel: (01241) 872288 Fax: (01241) 872288 *Computer accessories suppliers*

▶ Ones & Zeros, 30 Dulverton Road, Leicester, LE3 0SA Tel: (0870) 7705592 Fax: (08707) 705593 E-mail: john@oneszeros.biz *Suppliers of business telephone systems and Computer Telephony Integration products. We can find the system that will suit your business. We also offer data networking and Voice over IP services.*

▶ OneSafety Ltd, 33 Wadham Road, Woodthorpe, Nottingham, NG5 4JB Tel: 0115-920 8007 E-mail: info@onesafety.co.uk *Onesafety Ltd is health and safety and food safety consultancy supporting business in compliance with safety UK legislation. This is achieved through the development of health and safety and food safety management systems, risk assessment, and one off or programmed audits. Full details of services can be found on our website*

▶ Onesat Telecommunications Equipment, 34 Meadow Lane, Earith, Huntingdon, Cambridgeshire, PE28 3QE Tel: (01487) 741133 Fax: (01487) 843785 E-mail: sales@one-sat.com

▶ OneStopContactLenses, P O Box 5029, London, W1A 7ET Tel: 0207 323 9704 Fax: 0207 636 0281 E-mail: enquiries@onestopcontactlenses.co.uk *London UK Best Online Contact Lens Supplier, Tel: 020 7323 9704, Cheapest or Lowest UK price guarantee. Same Day delivery to Zone 1 London for £5. Buy disposable contact lenses Acuvue, Focus, O2Optix, Frequency 55, Soflens 66 Toric etc. Reputable, Reliable & managed by optometrists*

▶ Oneuponedown Creative Solutions Ltd, 413a Chingford Road, London, E17 5AF Tel: (020) 8527 4440 Fax: (020) 8527 4527 E-mail: info@lupldown.com *Graphic design, website design, production and promotion.*

▶ Onevillage.com, St. Benets, Church Lane, Charlbury, Chipping Norton, Oxfordshire, OX7 3SQ Tel: (01608) 811811 *Made-up fabric, cushion covers, duvet covers & accessories*

▶ one-wear Disposable underwear, po box 48611, London, NW8 7WZ Tel: (020) 7722 0687 E-mail: ask@one-wear.co.uk *one-wear disposable underwear brings you: Ultra-light disposable underwear created for travel, which is individually wrapped. The product line includes disposable boxers, briefs, panties, knickers and thongs, which makes ideal travel clothing for both men and women.*One-Wear""s disposable underwear is great for any situation where washing underwear is either inconvenient or impossible. For example, One-Wear""s disposable underwear is great when travelling/ trekking or business trips. One-Wear""s disposable underwear means that you don""t have to carry around dirty underwear or pay expensive hotel laundry fees. Other people like to use the disposable underwear for hospital stays, so that they don""t have to give their dirty underwear to other people to wash. Some people use One-Wear""s disposable underwear after going to the gym, as a change of underwear after showering, as each piece of underwear is compact and individually wrapped.*

Onexe Products, Unit 7 Shutterton Industrial Estate, Dawlish, Devon, EX7 0NH Tel: (01626) 865568 Fax: (01626) 865568 *Plastic manufrs*

Ongropack UK, 46 Gray's Inn Road, London, WC1X 8LP Tel: (020) 7831 4225 Fax: (020) 7831 9578 E-mail: allen@ongropack.fsnet.co.uk *Raw plastics distribution*

▶ Onink Ltd, Unit G Meadowside Industrial Estate, Meadowside Street, Renfrew, PA4 8YE Tel: 0141-886 6732 Fax: 0141-886 6733 E-mail: enquiries@onink-ltd.com *Inks, general service coatings & car valeting chemicals*

▶ On-It Ltd, 32 Demesne Road, Wallington, Surrey, SM6 8PP Tel: (020) 8773 9900 *IT Support and Consultancy*

Onix Process Analysis, Ion Path, Road Three, Winsford Industrial Estate, Winsford, Cheshire, CW7 3GA Tel: (01606) 548704 Fax: (01606) 548711 E-mail: glewis@onixpa.com *Analysis equipment*

Online Awareness, Balmoral Court, 22 Balmoral Road, Stockport, Cheshire, SK4 4DJ Tel: 0161-432 3669 Fax: 0161-718 9462 E-mail: enquiries@online-awareness.com *A professional Search Engine Marketing company. **We can help you increase your sales,leads,members,traffic and visibility.**We offer a free Web review.**contact: enquiries@online-awareness.com.*

▶ The Online Courier, 17 Armada Drive, Teignmouth, Devon, TQ14 9NF Tel: (0845) 6447069 E-mail: info@theonlinecourier.co.uk *Our speciality is for small parcels, data, letters, packages. We have also come to customers rescue, with lost keys, passport left behind and even briefcases. There generally is nothing we can""t do being, a sheet of paper to a ships container.*We consider all types of work, so if there is some particular job you need doing, that is out of the ordinary, (person to person. Wait with then return) get in contact with our staff, as I am sure we will be able to accomodate you.*

▶ Online Design Media Ltd, Caversham House, 4 Gosbrook Road, Caversham, Reading, RG4 8BS Tel: 0118-947 6644 Fax: 0118-947 6690 E-mail: sales@online-design.co.uk *Website Design by UK Professional Website Designers & Developers. **Online Design Media is a UK Web Development and Website Design Company. We*

continued

Company Information

continuation
specialise in Web Development, Website Design, Extranet and Intranet Applications, Website Marketing, Search Engine Optimisation, Search Engine Submission and Website Hosting solutions. Our aim is to enable businesses to utilise Internet based technologies to grow. *

▶ Online Desks Ltd, 2nd Floor, Wightman Chambers, Princess Street, The Square, Shrewsbury, SY1 1LP Tel: (0871) 2180503 Fax: (0870) 7633476 E-mail: OfficeFurniture@onlinedesks.co.uk

The Online Electrical Wholesaler Com Ltd, 36 Imex Business Centre, Balme Road, Cleckheaton, West Yorkshire, BD19 4EZ Tel: (01274) 865985 Fax: (01274) 865963 E-mail: onlineelec@tiscali.co.uk electrical wholesalers selling " online"- also selling hydroponics equipment to trade and public

▶ Online Electrical Wholesalers, 9 Welling High Street, Welling, Kent, DA16 1TR Tel: (020) 8303 8461 Fax: (020) 8303 8681 E-mail: info@onlineelectrical.co.uk ELECTRICAL & LIGHTING WHOLESALERS

▶ Online Gravel, Online Gravel, Mickering Lane, Ormskirk, Lancashire, L39 6SR Tel: 01695 422144 E-mail: kellysearch@onlinegravel.co.uk Supplier of gravels

▶ OnLine Office Services, 15 Knocklands Court, Ballymoney, County Antrim, BT53 6LN Tel: (028) 2766 9566 Fax: (028) 2766 9566 E-mail: info@onlineofficeservices.co.uk Secretarial/admin/business support services from our own fully equipped offices. Some of the services offered are:*Word Processing / Mailshots*Credit Control /Invoicing*Databases / Administration*Technical Manuscripts.*We offer fax and email receipt and forwarding and can provide a confidential mailing address.*We can provide long-term regular office support or the expertise required for a specific project. A service that is available 24 hours a day, 7 days a week.*

▶ Online Secretarial Services, 31 Derwent Drive, Ferry Fryston, Castleford, West Yorkshire, WF10 3SX Tel: 0771 8320166 E-mail: onlinesecretarialservices@hotmail.co.uk Online secretarial services offer a variety of services for professional people and businesses including sole traders. Over the phone dictation, web design, invoicing, function co-ordinator, CV building. Visit us at www.onlinesecretarialservices.co.uk

▶ On-Line Shipping Ltd, Unit 3 Argonaut Park, Galleymead Road, Colnbrook, Slough, SL3 0EN Tel: (01753) 687702 Fax: (01753) 684404 E-mail: paul@onlineshippingltd.co.uk Worldwide Freight Forwarder*Import & Export by Air & Sea*

▶ Online48 Ltd, 27 Seymour Terrace, Seymour Street, Liverpool, L3 5PE Tel: 0151-703 1065 Fax: 0151-703 1064 E-mail: enquiries@online48.co.uk Unique branding & website design & graphic design agency

▶ Online-Edge Ltd, The Old Smithy, 59 Lanark Road, Crossford, Carluke, Lanarkshire, ML8 5RE Tel: (01555) 860113 E-mail: sales@online-edge.co.uk Computer security & support engineers

Online-Flooring.co.uk, Willoughby Coachworks, Coxes Farm Road, Billericay, Essex, CM11 2UB Tel: (01277) 633053 E-mail: sales@online-flooring.co.uk Wooden flooring supplier

Onlinetrophies, The Smiddy, Glass, Huntly, Aberdeenshire, AB54 4XR Tel: (0870) 7570640 Fax: (0870) 7570641 E-mail: info@onlinetrophies.co.uk Secure online trophy & awards shop

▶ Only French, 21 Church Street, Maiden Bradley, Warminster, Wiltshire, BA12 7HW Tel: 01985 844659 E-mail: pascale@onlyfrench.com

Only Natural, 48 Westfield Street, St. Helens, Merseyside, WA10 1QF Tel: (01744) 759797 Health products

▶ Onny Developments Ltd, 3 Corvedale Road, Craven Arms, Shropshire, SY7 9NE Tel: (01588) 672430 Fax: (01588) 672930 E-mail: sales@onnydevelop.co.uk

Ono Pharma UK Ltd, Marble Arch Tower, 55 Bryanston Street, London, W1H 7AA Tel: (020) 7258 5300 Fax: (020) 7606 5555 Pharmaceutical distributor

▶ Onset Management Ltd, Nelson House (HF), 58 Wimbledon Hill Road, London, SW19 7PA Tel: 07803 901631 E-mail: info@onsetmanagement.co.uk We are a strategic management consultancy assisting clients to leverage growth. We do this through understanding and evaluating our clients' capabilities, systems and processes and then finding ways of improving or extending them. This may mean looking at totally new markets and/or strategic alliances etc. We will help you to plan and implement your new strategy and, if necessary help you to raise the finance to execute it. Please get in touch for an informal discussion if growth is what you want for your business.

▶ Onsite Crane & Commercial Ltd, Shrublands Avenue, Berkhamsted, Hertfordshire, HP4 3JG Tel: (01442) 878886 Fax: (01442) 878886

▶ Onsite Training Services, 3 Burnside Industrial Centre Wellheads Road, Farburn Industrial Estate, Dyce, Aberdeen, AB21 7HG Tel: (01224) 729500 Fax: (01224) 729300

Onspec Oscillators Ltd, Unit 10, Alliance Close, Attleborough Fields Industrial Estate, Nuneaton, Warwickshire, CV11 6SD Tel: (024) 7664 2024 Fax: (024) 7664 2073 E-mail: sales@onspec.co.uk Principal Export Areas: Worldwide Crystal manufrs

▶ Ontap Home Water Filter Systems, Westfield Road, Berkhamsted, Hertfordshire, HP4 3PW Tel: (01442) 876583 E-mail: sales@ontapsystems.co.uk Ontap Water Filter Systems supply economic Home Water Filters that solve Taste and Odour, Upset Stomach and Hardness/Scale problems. Our WRAS approved systems are simple to install and there is no need to cut any pipes. Visit our website for more information: http:// www.ontapsystems.co.uk*

Ontex UK Ltd, 97 Macadam Road, Earlstrees Industrial Estate, Corby, Northamptonshire, NN17 4JN Tel: (01536) 269744 Fax: (01536) 400134 E-mail: ontex@ontex.co.uk Incontinence products & baby nappy suppliers

Ontime Systems Ltd, Unit 3 Bessemer Crescent, Aylesbury, Buckinghamshire, HP19 8TF Tel: 0800 975 0960 Fax: (01296) 395787 E-mail: ontime-sales@btconnect.com Suppliers of Staff Attendance Time Recording Machines, 'Clocking IN Clocks', Job Time Recording Clocks, Documentation Time Stamps, Night Watchman Patrol Clocks, Specialist Display Clock Systems with Master Clocks and Computer Networked Integrated Systems including Building Entrance, (plus car park), Access Control.**All systems supported by experienced service staff together with a full range of spare parts, Ancillary Equipment and Consumable Supplies.

▶ OnTrack Systems Ltd, 27 Sandyford Place, Glasgow, G3 7NG Tel: 0141-248 7999 Fax: 0141-248 7998 E-mail: info@ontracksystems.co.uk IT products & services

Onward Fabrications Ltd, Unit 65 Owen Road, Willenhall, West Midlands, WV13 2PZ Tel: 0121-526 5263 Fax: 0121-568 6138 E-mail: sales@onwardfabs.co.uk Steel fabricators & engineers

Onyx Ltd, Unit 10a Greenway, Bedwas House Industrial Estate, Bedwas, Caerphilly, Mid Glamorgan, CF83 8DW Tel: (029) 2088 5897 Fax: (029) 2086 0228 Industrial & tank cleaning Also at: Branches throughout the U K

Onyx Conversions, Mitchell Main Industrial Estate, Mitchell Road, Wombwell, Barnsley, South Yorkshire, S73 8HA Tel: (01226) 752121 Fax: (01226) 270084 Coach body builders

Onyx Environmental Group P.L.C., 154A Pentonville Road, London, N1 9PE Tel: (020) 7812 5000 Fax: (020) 7812 5001 Fuel waste recyclers Also at: Branches throughout the U.K.

Oocl UK Ltd, Furness House, Furness Quay, Salford, M50 3XZ Tel: 0161-872 4466 Fax: 0161-876 7318 Shipping

▶ Ooh It, 49 Westcroft Gardens, Morden, Surrey, SM4 4DJ Tel: (020) 8543 6769 Fax: (0870) 705 8270 E-mail: Info@oohit.com Computer Support Services. *IT ongoing maintenance and network development. Have your computer system tailored to your needs by our team of qualified engineers.* Even if you have your own IT department, we offer affordable support contracts to provide the extra expertise when you need it.

Oomers Ltd, 8 St. Andrew's Road, London, E17 6BD Tel: (020) 8527 8388 Fax: (020) 8527 8288 E-mail: sales@oomers.co.uk Bed linen & household supplies export & import

Ooops! Net, 4 K & B Estate, Holyrood Close, Poole, Dorset, BH17 7BP Tel: (01202) 695999 Fax: (01202) 696333 E-mail: mail@ooops.net Cosmetic vehicle repairs

▶ Op Care, Hills Road, Cambridge, CB2 2DA Tel: (01223) 243391 Fax: (01225) 416564 Medical & surgical supplies & prosthetics industry materials

Opal Food Processing Systems Ltd, Unit 20-21 Earith Business Park, Meadow Drove, Earith, Huntingdon, Cambridgeshire, PE28 3QF Tel: (01487) 740131 Conveyor systems manufrs

Opal Services, 24 Aldershot Road, Fleet, Hampshire, GU51 3NN Tel: (01252) 812607 Fax: (01252) 812625 Computer software & hardware

Opal Signs Ltd, Stirling Way, Borehamwood, Hertfordshire, WD6 2HP Tel: (020) 8236 0103 Fax: (020) 8953 7984 E-mail: sales@opalsigns.com Sign makers & engravers

Opalion Plastics, Unit 1 Ashville Trading Estate, Royston Road, Baldock, Hertfordshire, SG7 6NN Tel: (01462) 895600 Fax: (01462) 895800 E-mail: sales@opalion.co.uk Opalion Plastics Limited are manufacturers & suppliers of flexible packaging including Carrier Bags (Flexi Loop Handle, Patch Handle & Punch Handle), Mailing Envelopes, Refuse Sacks, UN Approved Clinical Waste Sacks & Printed Film on roll for packaging of fresh & frozen goods. **All these products can be printed up to colours.

▶ Opalion Plastics Ltd, 9-11 Palacecraig Street, Coatbridge, Lanarkshire, ML5 4RY Tel: (01236) 420550 Fax: (01236) 420808 E-mail: sales@oapalion.co.uk Packaging products suppliers

Opals (Mirror-Flex) Co. Ltd, Unit 3 B Seaden Court, Steveson Road, Gorse Lane Industrial Estate, Clacton-On-Sea, Essex, CO15 4XN Tel: (01255) 423927 Fax: (01255) 221117 E-mail: sales@mirrorflex.co.uk Glassr manufrs

▶ Opcare Ltd, Unit 3, Princeville Road Industrial Estate, Duncombe Street, Bradford, West Yorkshire, BD8 9AJ Tel: (01274) 481122 Fax: (01274) 481139 E-mail: info@opcare.co.uk Surgical equipment distributors

▶ Opcare Ltd, Windmill Road, Headington, Oxford, OX3 7DD Tel: (01865) 761310 Fax: (01865) 741703 Health care supply services

Opecsystem Ltd, 1 Beech Leys, Steeple Claydon, Buckingham, MK18 2RP Tel: (01296) 730110 Fax: (07070) 653124 E-mail: trevor@opecsystem.com Computer software designers

Opella Ltd, Twyford Road, Rotherwas Industrial Estate, Hereford, HR2 6JR Tel: (01432) 357331 Fax: (01432) 264014 E-mail: sales@opella.co.uk Plastic valve tap accessory manufrs Also at: Wednesbury

Open Answers Ltd, Masons House, 1-3 Valley Drive, London, NW9 9NG Tel: (020) 8204 8600 Fax: (020) 8905 0156 Computer consultants

Open Business Solutions, 1 Highlands Court, Cranmore Avenue, Shirley, Solihull, West Midlands, B90 4LE Tel: 0121-711 2015 Fax: 0121-711 2873 E-mail: sales@novar-solutions.co.uk Computer software

▶ Open Creation, Fermoy House, Shepley Road, Barnt Green, Birmingham, B45 8JN Tel: 0121 2882205 E-mail: mail@opencreation.co.uk Open Creation provides excellent website design at extremely competitive prices.

▶ Open Destinations Ltd, Unit 11 Estilo, 7 Wenlock Road, London, N1 7SL Tel: (020) 7553 9220 Fax: (0870) 1343397 E-mail: surrport@opendestinations.com Computer software developers

Open File, 17 Springett Avenue, Ringmer, Lewes, East Sussex, BN8 5HD Tel: (01273) 814409 Fax: (01273) 814409 Computer consultancy

Open Interiors Ltd, The Studio, Hillside House, 22 Coleshill Street, Sutton Coldfield, West Midlands, B72 1SH Tel: 0121 354 1089 Fax: 0121-311 1402 E-mail: info@open-interiors.co.uk Design & build

▶ Open Interiors, 22 Barrack Close, Sutton Coldfield, West Midlands, B75 7HB Tel: 0121-311 1400 Fax: 0121-311 1400 E-mail: info@open-interiors.co.uk Open Interiors provides full interior design packages. we can provide designs not only for private and domestic clients but also for commercial clients as well. We provide colour and design schemes, CAD planning and project management for all interiors. Withover years experience we specialise in domestic interiors, hotel, bar, pub and restaurant design. We also have experience in office/reception design and planning. If you require any further information please do not hesitate to contact us.

Open International Ltd, Buckholt Drive, Warndon, Worcester, WR4 9SR Tel: (01905) 754455 Fax: (01905) 754441 Financial systems services Also at: Dublin, Wigan & Woking

Open Link Software Ltd, Carolyn Ho, 22-26 Dingwall Rd, Croydon, CR0 9XS Tel: (020) 8681 7701 Fax: (020) 861 7702 Software house

Open Logistics Ltd, PO Box 147, Harrogate, North Yorkshire, HG2 8AH Tel: (01423) 569642 Business consultants & trainers

Open Seas, 7 Nuffield Way, Abingdon, Oxfordshire, OX14 1RJ Tel: (01235) 537391 Fax: (01235) 535168 E-mail: info@openseas.co.uk IT consultancy

▶ The Open Server Project, 370 Welcombe Avenue, Swindon, SN3 2PB Tel: (01793) 619595 Fax: (01793) 619595

▶ Open Sesame, 32 Botanic Avenue, Belfast, BT7 1JQ Tel: (028) 9032 4343 Health food distributors

Open Systems Professional Services Ltd, Oak View Lodge, Friezland Lane, Greenfield, Oldham, OL3 7EU Tel: (01457) 820667 Fax: (01457) 877388 IT consultants

Open Text, Mulberry Business Park, Fishponds Road, Wokingham, Berkshire, RG41 2GY Tel: 0118-978 2800 Fax: 0118-936 0606 E-mail: enquiries@hummingbird.com Software management supply

Open Text UK Ltd, Webster House, 22 Wycombe End, Beaconsfield, Buckinghamshire, HP9 1NB Tel: (01494) 679700 Fax: (01494) 679707 E-mail: info.uk@opentext.com Computer software developers

▶ Openchoice Food Ltd, 5 Colville Court, Winwick Quay, Warrington, WA2 8QT Tel: (01925) 244506

▶ Openda Ltd, PO Box 2774, Swindon, SN5 3NY Tel: (0870) 0411890 Fax: (0870) 0411899 E-mail: enquiries@openda.com Supply chain solutions

▶ Openfield Systems Ltd, South Knoll, Southstoke Lane, Southstoke, Bath, BA2 7DN Tel: (01225) 833622

▶ Openhouse Products, 125 Craven Street, Birkenhead, Merseyside, CH41 4BW Tel: 0151-650 2300 Fax: 0151-647 4048 E-mail: bruce@openhouseproducts.com Emergency supplies

▶ Openings Disability Access, 327 Holdenhurst Road, Bournemouth, BH8 8BT Tel: (01202) 309946 Fax: (01202) 727071 E-mail: doors@openings.co.uk Manufacturers of automated sliding & swing door products

▶ Openspace Solar Energy, Northern House, Moss Street East, Ashton-under-Lyne, Lancashire, OL6 7BX Tel: (0800) 0276200 E-mail: sales@openspaceuk.net Openspace Solar Energy provide you and your home with the very latest Solar Thermal Systems which are highly efficient and designed to absorb the infra-red rays of the sun"s daylight which is present throughout the year, not just summer.

▶ Opera Public Relations, 4 West End, Baslow, Bakewell, Derbyshire, DE45 1RG Tel: (0845) 0600650 Fax: 0870 0113457 E-mail: pr@operapr.com Public relations & communications consultancy, from media relations to launch events and corporate videos. A personal, professional service tailored to meet our clients" communications needs.

Operandi, 62 St. Peters Road, Croydon, CR0 1HJ Tel: (020) 3251 0251 Fax: (020) 3251 0252 Graphic design

Operational UK Ltd, 7 Berkeley Court, Manor Park, Runcorn, Cheshire, WA7 1TQ Tel: (01928) 579473 Fax: (01928) 579517 E-mail: sales@operational.co.uk Consultants

Opex, Exhibition Centre, Warwick Road, London, SW5 9TA Tel: (020) 7370 8145 Fax: (020) 7370 8084 E-mail: enquiries@opex.co.uk Contracting services for the exhibition business

Opex Corporation, Carrington Business Park, Carrington, Manchester, M31 4YR Tel: 0161-776 4033 Fax: 0161-776 2663 E-mail: opexhr@opex.com Sales Contact: R. Patterson Mail handling equipment manufrs

Ophardt Product UK Ltd, 18 Shaftesbury St South, Derby, DE23 8YH Tel: (01332) 297666 Fax: (01332) 343354 E-mail: sales@ophardt.com Disinfectant dispenser manufrs

Ophthalmic Technologies, Dominion Way, Worthing, West Sussex, BN14 8NW Tel: (01903) 212316 Fax: (01903) 212317 E-mail: charmain.otl@btconnect.com Optical manufrs

Opico Ltd, Cherry Holt Road, Bourne, Lincolnshire, PE10 9LA Tel: (01778) 421111 Fax: (01778) 425080 E-mail: ask@opico.co.uk Agricultural machinery distributors

Opinion Research Corporation International, 1 Islington High Street, London, N1 9AH Tel: (020) 7675 1000 Fax: (020) 7675 1900 E-mail: website@orc.co.uk Market research services

Opitec-Hobbyfix, 7 West Road, Southampton, SO19 9AH Tel: (023) 8068 2404 Fax: 023 80446991 Art materials distributor & manufrs

▶ Opm Ltd, 219a Westminster Industrial Estate, London, SE18 5TS Tel: (020) 8316 6080 Fax: (020) 8316 6079 E-mail: info@opmfurniture.co.uk Furniture manufrs

Oppenheimer Engineering Services, 20 Vanguard Way, Shoeburyness, Southend-on-Sea, SS3 9RA Tel: (0870) 8722752 Fax: (0870) 8722750 E-mail: oes@oppenheimers.co.uk Valve distributors & agents

Opperman Mastergear Ltd, Hambridge Lane, Newbury, Berkshire, RG14 5TS Tel: (01635) 811500 Fax: (01635) 811501 E-mail: sales@opperman-mastergear.co.uk Geared electric motor manufrs

OPPM Ltd, Eagle Road, Quarry Hill Industrial Estate, Ilkeston, Derbyshire, DE7 4RB Tel: 0115-944 1236 Fax: 0115-944 0660 E-mail: sales@oppm.co.uk Metal pressing, injection moulding & tool assemblers & manufrs

Oppo Consulting Ltd, 38 Stoke Fields, Guildford, Surrey, GU1 4LS Tel: (01483) 563502 Fax: (01483) 453773 E-mail: sales@oppo-consulting.co.uk Web design & development, marketing & internet consultancy

▶ Ops Partnership, 22 Walkern Road, Stevenage, Hertfordshire, SG1 3RD Tel: (01707) 328660 Fax: (01707) 328661 E-mail: info@theopspartnership.com Operations consultancy & supplier of racking & shelving

Opsec Marketing Ltd, 27 Little End Road, Eaton Socon, St. Neots, Cambridgeshire, PE19 8JH Tel: (01480) 470400 Fax: (01480) 470401 E-mail: sales@dg2k.co.uk Electronic support products manufrs

Opsec Security Group P.L.C., Braxted House, 2 Penman Way, Enderby, Leicester, LE19 1ST Tel: 0116-282 2000 Fax: 0116-282 2100 Holographic label suppliers

▶ Opt Complete Print Solutions Ltd, 58 Coulsdon Road, Coulsdon, Surrey, CR5 2LA Tel: (020) 8405 9386 Fax: (020) 8405 9386 E-mail: sales@optlimited.co.uk Print Management Consultancy. OPT can source all your print requirements from design to delivery. Experts in print production for over 25 years. Brochures, leaflets, stationery, advertising and marketing material.

Optare Group Ltd, Manston Lane, Leeds, LS15 8SU Tel: 0113-264 5182 Fax: 0113-260 6635 E-mail: chris.wise@optare.com Passenger carrying vehicle manufrs

Optelma Lighting Ltd, 14 Napier Court, Barton Lane, Abingdon, Oxfordshire, OX14 3YT Tel: (01235) 553769 Fax: (01235) 523005 E-mail: sales@optelma.co.uk Assembly & distribution of commercial lighting

Optex Europe Ltd, 32a Clivemont Road, Maidenhead, Berkshire, SL6 7BZ Tel: (01628) 631000 Fax: (01628) 636311 E-mail: sales@optex-europe.com Security access control systems

Opthalmedica Ltd, Old Bury Hill Garden, Milton Street, Westcott, Dorking, Surrey, RH4 3PX Tel: (01306) 875255 Fax: (01306) 875255 E-mail: maureen.wright@btconnect.com Ophthalmic instruments & equipment

Optibelt UK Ltd, 5 Bishops Court, Winwick Quay, Warrington, WA2 8QY Tel: (0870) 4288800 Fax: (01925) 573751 E-mail: optibelt@optibeltuk.co.uk Manufacturers of rubber, polyurethane & wedge belting

▶ Optic Kleer, 20 Datchet Close, Hemel Hempstead, Hertfordshire, HP2 7JX Tel: (01442) 407716 Fax: (01442) 407716 E-mail: optickleer_hemel@hotmail.com we operate a mobile windscreen repair business offering free repairs subject to insurance cover.we also repair just about anything that requires laminated glass.

▶ Optic Lighting Ltd, Unit 4 Gisburn Business Park, Gisburn Road, Gisburn, Clitheroe, Lancashire, BB7 4JP Tel: (01200) 415980 Fax: (01200) 445757 E-mail: info@opticlighting.co.uk Fibre optic lighting manufrs

Optical Activity Ltd, Industrial Estate, Bury Road, Ramsey, Huntingdon, Cambridgeshire, PE26 1NF Tel: (01487) 813913 Fax: (01487) 812789 E-mail: sales@opticalactivity.com Polarimeter manufrs

▶ Optical Fibres (UK) Ltd, Network House, 11-13 Chester Close, Morecambe, Lancashire, LA3 3RF Tel: (01524) 414480 Fax: (01524) 419327 E-mail: lance@opticalfibresuk.com OTDR testing & fusion splicing & installation of fibre optics

Optical Filters Ltd, The Business Centre, 14 Bertie Road, Thame, Oxfordshire, OX9 3XA Tel: (01844) 260377 Fax: (01844) 260355 E-mail: information@opticalfilters.co.uk EMC & contrast enhancement windows

Optical Instruments Balham Ltd, Unit 39 Neville Court, 23 Neville Road, Croydon, CR0 2DS Tel: (020) 8664 9799 Fax: (020) 8664 9771 E-mail: info@optil.co.uk Optical component manufrs

Optical Marketing Ltd, Unit 2, 28 Park Street, London, SE1 9EQ Tel: (020) 7378 1268 Fax: (020) 7378 8690 E-mail: omretail@aol.com Designers & builders of shops

Optical Measurement Systems Ltd, Unit 6 Munro Place, Bonnyton Industrial Estate, Kilmarnock, Ayrshire, KA1 2NP Tel: (01563) 543822 Fax: (01563) 542350 E-mail: jane.savery@btclick.com Liquid level control equipment manufrs

Optical Products Ltd, 74-75 Brunner Road, London, E17 7NW Tel: (020) 8520 4047 Fax: (020) 8520 6593 E-mail: sales@ultrasolar.com Plastic injection moulders

Optical Record Systems, Eagle Close, Chandler's Ford, Eastleigh, Hampshire, SO53 4NF Tel: (023) 8026 7755 Fax: (023) 8061 8861 E-mail: info@orsgroup.com ORS provides both large archive and business critical daily imaging solutions that meet business need and budget by offering the following services:**Scanning (black & white, colour) up to AO size, Forms and Invoice Data Capture (machine and handprint,

continued

continuation
*Microfilm and Digitisation up to AO size, Secure Document Storage, Confidential Document Destruction, Facilities Management /Mailroom, Hosted Services, Document Management Software, Enterprise Content Management Software, Systems and Storage to support the solution, Software/Hardware Maintenance & Consumables, Consultancy and Support. Barclays Bank, Office Depot, B & Q - preferred supplier***

Optical Services, 15 Barkestone Close, Emerson Valley, Milton Keynes, MK4 2AT Tel: (01908) 526100 Fax: *Calibration services*

▶ Optical Solutions, 10 William Street, Edinburgh, EH3 7NH Tel: 0131-226 4699

Opti-cal Survey & Laser Equipment, Orpheus House, Calleva Park, Aldermaston, Reading, RG7 8TA Tel: 0118-982 0500 Fax: 0118-982 0509 E-mail: jim@surveyequipment.com *Survey & laser equipment specialists*

Optical Technology Training Ltd, Carleton Business Park, Carleton New Road, Skipton, North Yorkshire, BD23 2AA Tel: (01756) 797155 Fax: (01756) 797112 Principal Export Areas: Worldwide *Optical projector & vision system manufrs*

Optical Test & Calibration Ltd, 21-23 Campus Road, Listerhills Science Park, Bradford, West Yorkshire, BD7 1HR Tel: (01274) 393857 Fax: (01274) 393336 E-mail: sales@otc.co.uk *OTC is an independent calibration and test house based in the city of Bradford in West Yorkshire. We aim to provide an unrivalled service in the field of optical test equipment calibration and service. Our current capabilities include calibration, service and repair of an extensive range of Fibre Optic, Optoelectronic, Electronic, Electrical, Photometric and Radiometric equipment. UKAS accredited and BSI registered.*

Optical Tools For Industry, Brickfield Lane, Denbigh Road, Ruthin, Clwyd, LL15 2TN Tel: (01824) 704991 Fax: (01824) 705075 E-mail: info@optical-tools.co.uk *Optical test equipment manufrs*

Optical Vision Ltd, Unit 3 Woolpit Business Park, Windmill Avenue, Woolpit, Bury St. Edmunds, Suffolk, IP30 9UP Tel: (01359) 244200 Fax: (01359) 244255 E-mail: info@opticalvision.co.uk *Scientific & optical products importers & distributors*

▶ Opticast (UK) Ltd, Pipers Road, Park Farm Industrial Estate, Redditch, Worcestershire, B98 0HU Tel: (01527) 528400 Fax: (01527) 528700 E-mail: opticastuk@bntconnect.com *Suppliers of aluminium investment castings*

Optichrome Group Ltd, Maybury Road, Woking, Surrey, GU21 5HX Tel: (01483) 740290 Fax: (01483) 732609 E-mail: sales@optichrome.com *Commercial colour & digital printing services*

Opticon Ltd, 960 Capability Green, Luton, LU1 3PE Tel: (01582) 635100 Fax: (01582) 635200 E-mail: sales@opticon.co.uk *Auto ID equipment manufrs*

Opticron Plastics, Unit 3 Sabre Court, Gillingham Business Park, Gillingham, Kent, ME8 0RW Tel: (01634) 366385 Fax: (01634) 366397 E-mail: info@opticron.co.uk *Mould Polishing,*Flat Lapping,*Contract Lapping,*Polishing*

Optics Asia (UK) Ltd, Unit 430, Thorp Arch Trading Estate, Thorp Arch, Wetherby, West Yorkshire, LS23 7BJ Tel: (01937) 849932 Fax: (01937) 849836 E-mail: opticsasiaukltd@aol.com *Optical components supplier & manufr*

Optiglass Ltd, 52-54 Fowler Road, Hainault, Ilford, Essex, IG6 3UT Tel: (020) 8500 1264 Fax: (020) 8500 1955 E-mail: info@optiglass.co.uk *Optical component, lens & spectrophotometer accessories manufrs*

Optilan, Common Lane Industrial Estate, Kenilworth, Warwickshire, CV8 2EL Tel: (01926) 864999 Fax: (01926) 851818 *Fibre optic systems for communications & CCTV installation & maintenance*

▶ Optim, Viewfield Industrial Estate, Glenrothes, Fife, KY6 2RS Tel: (01592) 778567 Fax: (01592) 778508 E-mail: enquiries@optim.co.uk

Optim Contract Services Ltd, The Hop Exchange, 24 Southwark Street, London, SE1 1TY Tel: (020) 7940 2727 Fax: (020) 7378 0580 E-mail: info@optimgroup.co.uk *Contract cleaning & security services*

The Optima Co. Ltd, Robell Way, Storrington, Pulborough, West Sussex, RH20 3DW Tel: (01903) 744111 Fax: (01903) 746440 E-mail: sales@picnic-products.co.uk *Picnic basket manufrs*

▶ Optima Consultancy Services Ltd, Business Innovation Centre, Binley, Coventry, CV3 2TX Tel: (024) 7643 0200 Fax: (024) 7643 0291 E-mail: info@optima-cs.co.uk *Optima Consultancy provides corporate consulting in Sales and Marketing strategy and implementation. Our team has extensive experience and is dedicated to working with quality organisations that have a desire to be even better.**Working with a range of clients from industry sectors including (but not limited to) Information Technology, Communications, Manufacturing, Telematics and Logistics, Optima Consultancy continues to drive results through the application of intelligent and proven process.**Initial consultation without charge*

Optima Health Ltd, 47-48 St. Mary Street, Cardiff, CF10 1AD Tel: (029) 2038 8422 Fax: (029) 2023 3010 E-mail: admin@optimah.com *Health supplement distributors & manufrs*

Optima Legal Services Ltd, Arndale House, Charles Street, Bradford, West Yorkshire, BD1 1UN Tel: (01274) 553150 Fax: (01274) 513718 *Debt recovery services*

▶ Optima Partnership, 1 Howarth Court, Vicarage Lane, Water Orton, Birmingham, B46 1RF Tel: (0870) 9041188 Fax: (0871) 4337050 E-mail: info@optimapartnership.co.uk *Specialists in raising money, more of it and faster than anyone else; providing finance in difficult circumstances; removing the dangers of personal guarantees; increasing your personal wealth.*

Optima Products Ltd, Mill Road, Radstock, BA3 5TX Tel: (01761) 433461 Fax: (01761) 433919 *Engineering services*

Optima Systems Ltd, Optima Court Mill Court, Spindle Way, Crawley, West Sussex, RH10 1TT Tel: (01293) 562700 Fax: (01293) 562699 E-mail: sales@optima-systems.co.uk *Computer consultants*

Optimage Ltd, 26 St Fillans Terrace, Edinburgh, EH10 5PJ Tel: 0131-447 8800 *Computer consultants*

Optimal Geomatics Ltd, 44-46 King Street, Knutsford, Cheshire, WA16 6DT Tel: (0870) 7876728 Fax: 0161-367 9328 *Overhead lines survey services*

Optimal Technologies Ltd, 3 Marquis Business Centre, Royston Road, Baldock, Hertfordshire, SG7 6XL Tel: (01462) 491616 Fax: (01462) 491600 E-mail: sales@opt-tec.com *Ultrasonic equipment manufrs*

Optimax, 36 Douglas Road, Halesowen, West Midlands, B62 9HX Tel: 0121-561 1122 Fax: 0121-559 0541 *Optical lenses manufrs*

Optimec Ltd, Unit B 3The Haysfield, Malvern, Worcestershire, WR14 1GF Tel: (01684) 892859 Fax: (01684) 893037 E-mail: enquiries@optimec.com *Instruments for contact lens inspection*

Optimech, 14 Country Mews, Yewtree Gardens, Beardwood, Blackburn, BB2 7FJ Tel: (07710) 718593 Fax: (01282) 447111 E-mail: optimech@aol.com *Machine alignment, installation & relocation engineers*

Optimised Power Controls Ltd, Whitelands Road, Ashton-under-Lyne, Lancashire, OL6 6UG Tel: 0161-330 3318 Fax: 0161-285 3737 *Powder coating services*

▶ Optimorph, Hookstead, Faversham Road, Boughton Aluph, Ashford, Kent, TN25 4PQ Tel: (01233) 334458 E-mail: info@optimorph.co.uk *Change management, performance coaching, lean manufacturing, optimisation, high performance teams*

Optimum Air Conditioning, 1c Lyon Way, Greenford, Middlesex, UB6 0BN Tel: (020) 8813 1144 Fax: (0870) 8503132 *Air conditioning agents*

▶ Optimum Conservatory Roof Systems, Halliwell Mill, Raglan Street, Bolton, BL1 8AG Tel: (01204) 555920 Fax: (01204) 385111 E-mail: sales@windowfitplus.co.uk

Optimum Developments, Optimum House, Demmings Road, Demmings Industrial Estate, Cheadle, Cheshire, SK8 2PQ Tel: 0161-491 6171 Fax: 0161-491 6345 E-mail: sales@optimumlab.co.ukl *Laboratory furniture manufrs*

Optimum Oils Ltd, PO Box 2865, Kenilworth, Warwickshire, CV8 1YE Tel: (01452) 814476 Fax: (01452) 814476 E-mail: optimumboarders@hotmail.com *Lubricant sales*

Optimum Precision Engineering Ltd, 5b Lancaster Way Business Park, Ely, Cambridgeshire, CB6 3NW Tel: (01353) 666114 Fax: (01353) 666749 E-mail: sales@optimumprecision.co.uk *Precision sub-contract engineers*

▶ Optimum Security Services, Unit 3, Manor Business Park, Witney Road, Finstock, Chipping Norton, Oxfordshire, OX7 3DG Tel: (0870) 3502171 Fax: (0870) 3502172 E-mail: info@optimum.me.uk *Optimum is one of the leading independent security consultancies in the UK and is included in the Home Office list of approved consultants. It has no commercial interest in any equipment manufacturer, supplier or installer. Optimum is therefore able to exercise true impartiality in its search for the best design and delivery of our services to meet your requirements.*

Optimum Storage Systems Ltd, Po Box 121, Elland, West Yorkshire, HX5 9AJ Tel: (01422) 379549 Fax: (01422) 377344 *Storage & racking distributors*

Optimum Storage Systems Ltd, Unit 14 Bowers Mill, Branch Road, Barkisland, Halifax, West Yorkshire, HX4 0AD Tel: (01422) 379549 Fax: (01422) 377334 E-mail: sales@optstore.co.uk *Shelving & storage distributors*

Optimum Time, PO Box 39, Peterborough, PE6 8BS Tel: (01733) 333324 Fax: (01733) 333324 E-mail: sales@optimumtime.co.uk *Digital sports watches*

▶ Optimum Training Flintshire Ltd, 14 Bryn Awelon, Buckley, Clwyd, CH7 2QA Tel: (01244) 545745 Fax: (01244) 545745 E-mail: optimumflintshire@btinternet.com *We provide a wide range of HSE/OFTED/PLA approved First Aid training as well as CIEH Health & Safety Courses*

▶ Optimus Business Practice, The Manzar Centre, Whitlenge Lane, Hartlebury, Kidderminster, Worcestershire, DY10 4HD Tel: (01299) 250745 Fax: (01299) 250240 E-mail: info@optimusbp.co.uk *As Sourcing and Negotiating specialists we help companies / purchasing professionals achieve economic, efficient and secure supplies of ALL PURCHASES: RAW MATERIALS, OVERHEADS and ANCILLARIES.*

Optimus Models, 115 Crosshall Road, Eaton Ford, St. Neots, Cambridgeshire, PE19 7AB Tel: (01480) 473831 Fax: (01480) 384098 *Prototype model makers*

Optimus Music, 35 Elm Road, London, SW14 7JL Tel: (020) 8878 6989 Fax: (020) 8878 2058 *Audio visual production services*

Optimus UK Ltd, 131 Warwick Road, Kenilworth, Warwickshire, CV8 1HY Tel: (01926) 852352 E-mail: info@optimus.co.uk *Computer software suppliers & system providers*

Optinet Ltd, 115-117 Barnards Green Road, Malvern, Worcestershire, WR14 3LT Tel: (01684) 893857 Fax: (01684) 893859 *Optician databases design*

Option Systems Ltd, Osl House, East Link, Leicester, LE19 1XU Tel: 0116-291 6666 Fax: 0116-291 6667 E-mail: sales@styleman.com *Computer systems & software developers*

Option Technology Europe Ltd, Carrs Industrial Estate, Haslingden, Rossendale, Lancashire, BB4 5HR Tel: (01706) 605000 Fax: (01706) 605010 E-mail: sales@option.co.uk *Printed circuit laminator mass manufrs*

Options Mail Order Software Ltd, Samuel House, Chinnor Road, Thame, Oxfordshire, OX9 3NU Tel: (01844) 211820 Fax: (01844) 212999 *Software distributors*

▶ Opti-Pharma UK, Lynwood House, 56 Lynwood Crescent, Pontefract, West Yorkshire, WF8 3QX Tel: (01977) 791302 Fax: (01977) 791302 E-mail: info@optipharmauk.co.uk *Laboratory Fume Cupboards, Laminar Flow units & Extract systems. Refurbished & bespoke systems our speciality. COSHH validation services.*

Optisoft Ltd, Whinchat Hall, Skipwith Road, Escrick, York, YO19 6EJ Tel: (01904) 727300 Fax: (01904) 727332E-mail: info@optisoft.co.uk *Opticians practice management software*

Optium Brasses, 7 Castle Street, Bampton, Tiverton, Devon, EX16 9NS Tel: (01398) 331515 Fax: (01398) 331164 E-mail: brass@obida.com *Brass fittings distributors*

▶ Optivision (Yorkshire) Ltd, 12 Leeds Road, Ossett, West Yorkshire, WF5 9QA Tel: (01924) 277727

Opto International Ltd, Bayley Street, Stalybridge, Cheshire, SK15 1QQ Tel: 0161-330 9136 Fax: 0161-343 7332 E-mail: enquiry@optoint.co.uk *Display equipment & interior furnishings manufrs*

Optometrics (UK) Ltd, Unit C6, Cross Green Garth, Leeds, LS9 0SF Tel: 0113-249 6973 Fax: 0113-235 0420 E-mail: optouk@aol.com *Optical component manufrs*

▶ Optosci Ltd, Engineering Application Centre, 141 St James Road, Glasgow, G4 0LT Tel: 0141-552 7020 Fax: 0141-552 3886

Optus Resin Technology Ltd, 22 Tarran Way North, Tarran Industrial Estate, Wirral, Merseyside, CH46 4UA Tel: 0151-604 0001 Fax: 0151-522 0733 E-mail: information@optus.co.uk *Manufacturers of floor & wall coatings (industrial & decorative)*

▶ Optyma Security Systems, 6 Harcourt Road, Bexleyheath, Kent, DA6 8AQ Tel: (020) 8304 8635 Fax: (020) 8304 4633

▶ Opulent Computers, 23 Larkhill Walk, Leeds, LS8 1RA Tel: (0845) 0705145 Fax: (08450) 705154 E-mail: jay@opulentcomputers.co.uk *Reseller of computer hardware, software and complete systems.*

Opus, Adams House, 14 Market Street, Hertford, SG14 1BD Tel: (01992) 513000 Fax: (01992) 513046 *Insurance brokers* Also at: London EC3

▶ Opus Airconditioning Ltd, Unit 52 Victoria Industrial Park, Victoria Road, Dartford, DA1 5AJ Tel: (01322) 225111 Fax: (01322) 291389

Opus Carpets Ltd, 106 North End Road, London, W14 9PP Tel: (020) 7385 3151 Fax: (020) 7386 8252 *Carpet retailers*

▶ Opus Fabrication, Unit 3, Phoenix Works, Windsor Road, Enfield, Redditch, Worcestershire, B97 6DJ Tel: (01527) 68533 Fax: (01527) 68534 E-mail: opus-fab@btconnect.com *Shop fitting manufrs*

Opus Personnel Ltd, 106 Baker Street, London, W1U 6TW Tel: (020) 7247 6111 Fax: (020) 7486 2111 E-mail: sales@opuscity.co.uk *Recruitment agency*

Opus Publicity Ltd, Electron Works, Willow Avenue, Denham, Uxbridge, Middlesex, UB9 4BG Tel: (01895) 234441 Fax: (01895) 271520 E-mail: stacey@opus-publicity.freeserve.co.uk *Screen process printers*

Opus Scientific Ltd, The Old Bakery, Church Street, Litlington, Royston, Hertfordshire, SG8 0RD Tel: (01763) 853948 Fax: (01763) 853949 *Scientific consultants*

Opus Screen Print Ltd, Unit 11-12, 865 Ringwood Road, Bournemouth, BH11 8LW Tel: (01202) 590202 Fax: (01202) 580280 E-mail: enq@opus99.co.uk *Screen printers*

Opus Signs Ltd, Rollins House, Mimram Road, Hertford, SG14 1NW Tel: (01992) 501355 Fax: (01992) 501398 E-mail: sales@opussigns.co.uk *Sign & display manufrs*

Orac Computer Services, 143 Tankerton Rd, Whitstable, Kent, CT5 2AW Tel: (01227) 280522 Fax: (01227) 280533 E-mail: dave@orac.co.uk *Computer reseller*

Oracle Computers, 932 Shettleston Road, Glasgow, G32 7XW Tel: 0141-778 2906 E-mail: sales@oraclecomputers.co.uk *Computer hardware & software suppliers*

Oracle Corporation UK Ltd, Southgate Centre Two, 321 Wilmslow Road, Heald Green, Cheadle, Cheshire, SK8 3PW Tel: 0161-499 1717 Fax: 0161-493 4966 *Computer consultants*

Oracle Corporation UK Ltd, Oracle Parkway, Reading, RG6 1RA Tel: 0118-924 0000 Fax: 0118-924 3000 E-mail: sales@uk.oracle.com *Computer software systems* Also at: Bristol, Dublin, Edinburgh & London EC3

▶ Oracle Security Systems Ltd, 19 Godric Square, Woodston Industrial Estate, peterborough, PE2 7JL Tel: 08700 801716 Fax: 01733 233323 E-mail: info@oraclesecurity.co.uk *Installers of Intruder alarm, door access and CCTV systems both domestic and commercial*

▶ Oracle Vision Ltd, 11 Penarth Terrace, Upton, Pontefract, West Yorkshire, WF9 1DZ Tel: (0870) 7587676 Fax: (0870) 7587944 E-mail: sales@oracle-vision.com *Suppliers of Commercial and Industrial CCTV, Access Control, RFID Tagging and Wireless Data Networks. Our Services include Consultancy, Installation, Service and Maintenance.*

Oracstar, Weddell Way, Brackmills, Northampton, NN4 7HS Tel: (01604) 702181 Fax: (01604) 701743 E-mail: orac@oracstar.co.uk *DIY products suppliers*

Oral Ceramics, Crown House, Wassage Way, Hampton Lovett, Droitwich, Worcestershire, WR9 0NX Tel: (01905) 778686 Fax: (01905) 774545 *Dental laboratory*

Oral Prosthetics, 121 Headstone Road, Harrow, Middlesex, HA1 1PG Tel: (020) 8863 6977 *Dental laboratory*

▶ Orange Advertising Ltd, 4-6 Dryden Street, London, WC2E 9NH Tel: (020) 7379 9937 Fax: (020) 7379 7679

Orange Business Services, 217 Bath Road, Slough, SL1 4AA Tel: (020) 8321 4300 Fax: (020) 8321 4040 *Integrated communication network management systems*

Orange Chemicals Ltd, 34 St.Thomas Street, Winchester, Hampshire, SO23 9HJ Tel: (01962) 842525 Fax: (01962) 841101 E-mail: brianorange@orangechem.co.uk *Chemical merchants*

Orange DJ Gear Ltd, 734 Oxford Road, Reading, RG30 1EH Tel: 0118-950 9969 Fax: 0118-950 7072 E-mail: sales@djgear.co.uk *Disco equipment*

Orange Instruments Ltd, Lower Farm Road, Moulton Park Industrial Estate, Northampton, NN3 6XF Tel: (01604) 790490 Fax: (01604) 790690 E-mail: alan@orangeinst.demon.co.uk *Electronic instrumentation manufrs*

The Orange Square Co. Ltd, 45 Vauxhall Bridge Road, London, SW1V 2TA Tel: (020) 7630 9400 Fax: (020) 7630 9500 *Perfume distributors*

Orange Tree Events Ltd, 4 Furnival Close, Virginia Water, Surrey, GU25 4HR Tel: (01344) 430091 E-mail: info@orange-tree-events.co.uk *Team building, event organisers, sailing days, track days, water based corporate events, hen weekends, team building Surrey*

Orangeburst, 5 Hollingbury Terrace, Brighton, BN1 7JE Tel: (01273) 558112 Fax: (01273) 561249 E-mail: info@lemonburst.net *Natural products mail order*

Oranvale Ltd, Central Chambers, 4 Market Place, Ramsbottom, Bury, Lancashire, BL0 9HT Tel: (01706) 827327 Fax: (01706) 821488 E-mail: oranvale@telpark.co.uk *Management consultants*

Orapi Ltd, 1 Rosse Street, Bradford, West Yorkshire, BD8 9AS Tel: (01274) 822000 Fax: (01274) 822002 E-mail: jo.greenwood@orapi.com *Adhesive manufacturers & distribs*

Orb 2000 Ltd, 30 Cannon St, London, EC4M 6YN Tel: (020) 7653 5700 Fax: (020) 7653 5701 *Computer consultants*

Orb Recruitment Ltd, PO Box 50, Manchester, M3 4EL Tel: 0161-244 5526 Fax: 0161-244 5526 E-mail: richard@premier-recruit.com *Permanent & Temporary Recruitment Specialists for the Hospitality & Catering industries. Covering London, Manchester, UK and Overseas.*

Orb Systems, 2 Nelson House, 46 Station Road, Chertsey, Surrey, KT16 8BE Tel: (01932) 569100 Fax: (01932) 569100 *Electronic contract manufrs*

Orbik Electronics Ltd, Orbik House, Northgate Way, Aldridge, Walsall, WS9 8TX Tel: (01922) 743515 Fax: (01922) 743173 E-mail: info@orbik.co.uk *Lighting control gear manufrs*

▶ Orbimatic UK, 7 The Manor Grove Centre, Vicarage Farm Road, Peterborough, PE1 5UH Tel: (01733) 555285 Fax: (01733) 555831 Sales Contact: Steve Purnell *Orbital welding equipment*

▶ Orbis Events, 20 Elmfield Close, Woodfalls, Salisbury, SP5 2BF Tel: (01725) 511963 E-mail: info@orbisevents.com *Golf Event Management COmpany*

▶ Orbis Property Protection plc, 7 Harmony Court, Loanbank Place, Glasgow, G51 3HN Tel: 0141-445 4338 Fax: 0141-445 1571

Orbis Property Protection, 106 Oxford Road, Uxbridge, Middlesex, UB8 1NA Tel: (01895) 465500 Fax: (01895) 465499 E-mail: pat.sullivan@ux.orbis-opp.com *Security & property services to local authorities*

Orbis Technologies Ltd, 5 Thorpe Close, Banbury, Oxfordshire, OX16 4SW Tel: (01295) 273179 Fax: (01295) 276394 E-mail: orbis@orbitech.demon.co.uk *Semi-conductor manufrs*

▶ Orbis Telecoms, 12 Ettrick Rd, Branksome Park, Poole, Dorset, BH13 6LG Tel: 0845 638 0451 Fax: 0870 750 4513 E-mail: sales@orbistelecom.com *Orbis Telecom provides an excellent range of business class internet services for large and small businesses. Clients can expect a highly professional technical and customer service team. Orbis Telecom provide high quality business class Voice Over IP. We have a professional team who can help you setup your account. We have some of the best prices in the UK. We can provide anything from a single SIP phone up to multi office PBX installations or wholesale gateway minutes. We can provide revenue on numbers such as 0870, 0871, 0845 and also excellent rates on DID numbers such as 0800, 0207, 0208.*

Orbit Import Export, Ferry Terminal, Ramsgate, Kent, CT11 9FT Tel: (01843) 588899 Fax: (01843) 850278 *Freight import & export*

Orbit Information Systems Ltd, 6 Jasmine Close, Manchester, M23 9EY Tel: 0161-945 3886 Fax: 0161 945 3886 *IT Services*

Orbit International P.L.C., Orbit House, 5 Dugdale Street, Birmingham, B18 4JA Tel: 0121-558 8444 Fax: 0121-565 0385 E-mail: sales@orbit-int.co.uk *Industrial workwear manufrs*

Orbit Maintainence UK Ltd, Studio 6 The Mews, 46 Church Rd, Barnes, London, SW13 0DQ Tel: (020) 8563 2086 Fax: (020) 8563 2838 *Air conditioning engineers/maintenanca contracts*

▶ Orbital Communications, 11 Fountain Parade, Mapplewell, Barnsley, South Yorkshire, S75 6FW Tel: (01226) 388157 Fax: (0845) 6444864 E-mail: info@orbitalcomms.com *Car & vehicle tracking system manufrs*

▶ Orbital Contractors Ltd, Gale Buildings, Gale Road, Knowsley Industrial Park, Liverpool, L33 7YB Tel: 0151-546 0830

▶ Orbital Design Ltd, 2 33 Palmerston Road, Bournemouth, BH1 4HN Tel: (01202) 304455 Fax: (01202) 304466 E-mail: justin@orbital.co.uk *Creative design agency*

Orbital Epos Systems Ltd, Canada House Business Centre, 272 Field End Road, Eastcote, Ruislip, Middlesex, HA4 9NA Tel: (020) 8582 0331 Fax: (020) 8582 0335 E-mail: sales@epossystems.co.uk *Computer & network specialists*

▶ Orbital Express, 2 Falcon Road, Dewsbury, West Yorkshire, WF12 9NH Tel: (01924) 439977 E-mail: svali@orbital-express.co.uk *Quality assured courier/Dedicated Same day Next Day from Documents to Freight *Throughout UK & Worldwide*

Orbital Fasteners, Olds Approach, Tolpits Lane, Watford, WD18 9XT Tel: (01923) 777777 Fax: (01923) 779169 E-mail: sales@orbitalfasteners.co.uk *Bolts, fixings & fasteners distributors*

Orbital Food Machinery, 2 Cavendish Road, Bury St. Edmunds, Suffolk, IP33 3TE Tel: (01284) 725255 Fax: (01284) 725335 *Food machinery suppliers*

Orbital Media Ltd, 40 Balcombe Street, London, NW1 6ND Tel: (020) 7723 9216 Fax: 020 77233412 *Media rights*

▶ Orbital Productions, 38 Burnfoot Road, Hawick, Roxburghshire, TD9 8EN Tel: (01450) 378212 E-mail: sg1@orbital-productions.com *Video and Audio Production*Training in Music Technology, Cubase, ProTools, SoundForge etc*Training in Digital Editing for Video, Final Cut Pro, DVD Studio Pro, Avid Xpress Pro**

▶ Orbital Solutions, Hall Road, Heybridge, Maldon, Essex, CM9 4LA Tel: (01621) 878480 Fax: (01621) 851213 *Computer software manufrs*

Orbital Specialist Contracting Services, Unit 22 Business Development Centre, Telford, Shropshire, TF3 3BA Tel: (01952) 290777 Fax: (01952) 293277 *Pipework engineers/ fabricators/installers*

Orbiter Food Machinery, Private Road 7, Colwick Industrial Estate, Nottingham, NG4 2JW Tel: 0115-940 0372 Fax: 0115-961 8741 E-mail: enquiries@orbiterfoodmachinery.co.uk *Food processing & pie making machines*

Orby Engineering Ltd, 26 Seagoe Industrial Estate, Portadown, County Armagh, BT63 5QD Tel: (028) 3833 9145 Fax: (028) 3835 0540 E-mail: orbyengineering@btconnect.com *Livestock feeding equipment manufrs*

▶ Orca Divers, 125 Manchester Road, Chorlton Cum Hardy, Manchester, M21 9PG Tel: 0161 7183118 E-mail: enquiries@orcadivers.com *PADI training courses from beginners to instructors for diving*

Orca Logic, 83 South Street, Dorking, Surrey, RH4 2JU Tel: (01306) 640700 Fax: (01306) 889721 E-mail: sales@orcalogic.co.uk *Computer hardware distributors*

▶ Orcadian Ltd, Hatston Industrial Estate, Kirkwall, Orkney, KW15 1DW Tel: (01856) 879000

Orchard Drawing Boards, Union Square, Wakefield, West Yorkshire, WF1 1TT Tel: (01924) 291333 Fax: (01924) 290909 *Office furniture retail & manufrs*

▶ Orchard Electronic, Unit 6 Apex Way, Hailsham, East Sussex, BN27 3WA Tel: (01323) 844422 Fax: (01323) 844422 E-mail: sales@orchardelectronic.co.uk *PCB assembly & design services*

Orchard Environmental Ltd, 6 Newford Close, Hemel Hempstead, Hertfordshire, HP2 4QZ Tel: (01442) 253610 Fax: (01442) 253610 E-mail: info@orchard-environmental.co.uk *Water treatment services*

Orchard Farm, Hurst Lane, Auckley, Doncaster, South Yorkshire, DN9 3NW Tel: (01302) 770206 *Agricultural merchants*

▶ Orchard Fire & Security Ltd, Eckington Business Park, Rotherside Road, Eckington, Sheffield, S21 4HL Tel: (01246) 432788 Fax: (01246) 432799 *Fire & security alarm manufrs*

Orchard Joinery, Brick Kiln Farm, Heathfield, Bletchingdon, Kidlington, Oxfordshire, OX5 3DT Tel: (01869) 350008 Fax: (01869) 351361 *Joiners*

Orchard Materials Ltd, 7 Brunel Way, Thornbury, Bristol, BS35 3UR Tel: (01454) 415222 Fax: (01454) 415333 E-mail: sales@orchardmaterials.com *Duplex metal & nickel alloy stockholders*

Orchard Networks, 1 Fieldways, The Drift, Chard, Somerset, TA20 4DN Tel: (01460) 68787 Fax: (01460) 63519 E-mail: admin@orchardnetworks.com *Computer systems & software developers*

Orchard Stationary, 6 High Street, Stanstead Abbotts, Ware, Hertfordshire, SG12 8AB Tel: (01920) 870900 Fax: (01920) 871860 E-mail: sales@orchardstationery.co.uk *Office equipment suppliers*

Orchard Stationery, 1 Parkway, Harlow Business Park, Harlow, Essex, CM19 5QF Tel: (01279) 635234 Fax: (01279) 454564 E-mail: sales@orchardstationary.co.uk *Office suppliers*

Orchard Street Furniture, 119 The Street, Crowmarsh Gifford, Wallingford, Oxfordshire, OX10 8EF Tel: (01491) 826100 Fax: (01491) 642126 E-mail: sales@orchardstreet.co.uk *Outdoor furniture manufrs*

Orchard Technologies Ltd, Unit F5 Market Overton Industrial Estate, Thistleton Road, Market Overton, Oakham, Leicestershire, LE15 7PP Tel: (01572) 768489 Fax: (01572) 768181 E-mail: richard@orchard56.freeserve.co.uk *Cable & wire crimping services*

Orchardcrown Ltd, 586 Blackpool Road, Ashton, Preston, PR2 1JA Tel: (01772) 728191 Fax: (01772) 727963 E-mail: sales@balloonshot.co.uk *Balloon & novelties wholesaler & manufrs*

Orchestra Bristol Ltd, 17-19 Emery Road, Bristol, BS4 5PF Tel: 0117-972 4400 Fax: 0117-972 4501 E-mail: sales@orchestra.co.uk *Marketing services*

Orchestra Wotton Group Ltd, Walk Mills, Kingswood, Wotton-under-Edge, Gloucestershire, GL12 8JT Tel: (01453) 845019 Fax: (01453) 845019 E-mail: enquiries@orchestrawotton.co.uk *Cheque printing, form producers & stationery manufrs*

▶ Orchid Bridals, Britannia Buildings, Coventry Road, Burbage, Hinckley, Leicestershire, LE10 2HL Tel: (01455) 230033 Fax: (01455) 230035 E-mail: sales@orchidbrides.com *Bridal wear manufrs*

▶ Orchid Business Computing Ltd, 7 Mallard Way, Pride Park, Derby, DE24 8GX Tel: (01332) 360099 Fax: (01332) 360509 E-mail: sales@orchiduk.com *Network solutions services*

▶ Orchid Indulgence Ltd, 5 Swann Lane, Cheadle Hulme, Cheadle, Cheshire, SK8 7HU Tel: 0161 221 2673 E-mail: enquiries@orchidindulgence.com *Stress Management Seminars*Work based massage*

Orchid Logistics Ltd, Unit C14, Holly Farm Business Park, Honiley, Kenilworth, Warwickshire, CV8 1NP Tel: (01926) 484088 Fax: (01926) 484478 *Freight container operator services*

Orchid Plastics Ltd, The Lime Store, Florence Road, Kelly Bray, Callington, Cornwall, PL17 8EQ Tel: (01579) 384239 Fax: (01579) 383934 *Plastic moulding manufrs*

Orchid Soft Furnishing, 86 High Street, Earls Colne, Colchester, CO6 2QX Tel: (01787) 223030 Fax: 01787 223030 *Contract furnishing*

Orchid Software Ltd, 63 Westgate Road, Newcastle Upon Tyne, NE1 1SG Tel: 0191-232 5750 E-mail: adrian@orchidsoft.com *Software developers*

Orchidwood Mushrooms Ltd, Hobbs Lane, Beckley, Rye, East Sussex, TN31 6TS Tel: (01797) 260411 Fax: (01797) 260603 E-mail: info@orchidwood.co.uk *Mushroom processor*

Ord Carmell & Kritzler, 219 Golders Green Road, London, NW11 9DD Tel: (020) 8455 0057 Fax: (020) 8458 5880 *Surveyors, building property*

Co Ordinated Engineering Ltd, 2 Cantelupe Mews, Cantelupe Road, East Grinstead, West Sussex, RH19 3BG Tel: (01342) 410130 Fax: (01342) 410125 E-mail: info@cecgroup.org.uk *Merchants or agents*

Co Ordinated Packaging Ltd, 3-4 Robert Way, Wickford, Essex, SS11 8DD Tel: (01268) 570551 Fax: (01268) 570611 *Contract packers*

Co Ordinated Surveys, The Old Stables, Garage Street, Llandudno, Gwynedd, LL30 1DW Tel: (01492) 870277 Fax: (01492) 877759 E-mail: sales@uksurveys.com *Land,quarry & hydrographic surveyors*

Co Ordination Technologies Ltd, 5 Green Court, Eaton Bishop, Hereford, HR2 9QD Tel: (01981) 251529 E-mail: sales@coordtec.globalnet.co.uk *Business software*

Co Ordit Building Services Ltd, Barn Lodge, Shuttleworth Lane, Cosby, Leicester, LE9 1RF Tel: (01455) 208200 Fax: (01455) 201881 E-mail: sales@co-ordit.com *Air conditioning installation*

▶ Ords Group, Progress House, Usworth Road Industrial Estate, Hartlepool, Cleveland, TS25 1PD Tel: (01429) 273456 Fax: (01429) 861948 E-mail: sales@ords.co.uk

Ore An Ltd, Unit 15-21 Branxholme Industrial Estate, Bradford Road, Brighouse, West Yorkshire, HD6 4EA Tel: (01484) 400818 Fax: (01484) 711115 *Manufacture And Supply Of Hair Care Products*

▶ Oregon-Canadian Europe, Greenbank Business Park, 2-3 Swan Lane, Hindley Green, Wigan, Lancashire, WN2 4EZ Tel: (01942) 525040 Fax: (01942) 524240 E-mail: dan@oregoncanadian.com *Timber products*

Orga, A1 Kingsway Business Park, Oldfield Road, Hampton, Middlesex, TW12 2HD Tel: (0870) 6092452 Fax: (020) 8941 6683 E-mail: sales@orga.nl *Explosion proof electrical equipment suppliers*

▶ Organic & Natural Enterprise Group, Woodwind, The Avenue, Rowledge, Farnham, Surrey, GU10 4BD Tel: (01252) 793452 E-mail: myorganics@tiscali.co.uk *Certified organic - chemical free -healthcare & cosmetics. Unparalleled product purity, company and support network. The BEST products from the BEST company in the market place.*www.myorganics.net*

▶ Organic Potato Growers Scotland Ltd, Dalcross Industrial Estate, Inverness, IV2 7XB Tel: (01667) 462923 Fax: (01667) 461065 E-mail: sales@organicpotatogrowers.co.uk

▶ Organic Towel Co., 108 Weston Street, London, SE1 3QB Tel: (0870) 0501261 Fax: (0870) 7622371 E-mail: contact@organictowel.co.uk *Organic cotton bath linen, natural toiletries & spa accessories*

Organically Coated Steels, Hoo Farm Industrial Estate, Worcester Road, Kidderminster, Worcestershire, DY11 7RA Tel: (01562) 821400 Fax: (01562) 865396 E-mail: ocs@asdmetalservices.co.uk *Steel stockholders*

▶ Organicarian, Brownhill Road, Chandler's Ford, Eastleigh, Hampshire, SO53 2EA Tel: (023) 8027 0521 Fax: (023) 8027 0521 E-mail: sales@organicarian.com *online sales of 100% natural organic skincare & bodycare products. Visit our website to view our products & then buy on-line.*

▶ The Organisation, 168 Edward Street, Brighton, BN2 0JB Tel: (01273) 891770 Fax: (01273) 891771 E-mail: admin@the-organisation.co.uk *Hire outdoor equipment*

Organisation Of Horse Box & Trailer Owners, Whitehill Farm, Hamstead Marshall, Newbury, Berkshire, RG20 0HP Tel: (01488) 657651 Fax: (01488) 657652 E-mail: sales@horsebox-rescue.co.uk *Horse box & trailer breakdown cover company*

Organisation Resources Counsellors Inc, 127-131 Sloane Street, London, SW1X 9QP Tel: (020) 7591 5600 Fax: (020) 7591 5605 E-mail: sales@orcinc.co.uk *Business strategy consultants*

Organised Computer Systems Ltd, East House, Newpound, Wisborough Green, Billingshurst, West Sussex, RH14 0AZ Tel: (01403) 700959 Fax: (01403) 700969 E-mail: sales@ocsl.co.uk *IT solutions providers*

Organon Laboratories Ltd, 23 Science Park, Milton Road, Cambridge, CB4 0FL Tel: (01223) 432700 Fax: (01223) 424368 E-mail: sales@organon.co.uk *Pharmaceutical researchers*

▶ Organza Events, 72 Clarence Road, London, E12 5BH Tel: (020) 8553 5523 Fax: 0208 553 5523 E-mail: info@organzaevents.com *Organza Events is a one stop shop events company, we own chocolate fountains available for hire. We also organise and produce corporate parties and events.*

Orgapack, 58 Heatherhouse Road, Irvine, Ayrshire, KA12 8HQ Tel: (01294) 311911 Fax: (01294) 311920 *Tensional strapping equipment & tension strapping manfrs*

Oriel Blinds, 9 Acorn Close, Rassau, Ebbw Vale, Gwent, NP23 5UP Tel: (01495) 350975 Fax: (01495) 350975 *Blind manufrs*

▶ Oriel Computers, Enkalon Indust Estate, Randalstown Road, Antrim, BT41 4LJ Tel: (028) 9446 0021 Fax: (028) 9446 4545 E-mail: orielcomputers@tiscali.co.uk *Computer suppliers*

▶ Oriel Studios, Orrell Mount, Bootle, Merseyside, L20 6NS Tel: 0151-922 2785 Fax: 0151-933 5410 *Digital printers*

Oriel Systems Ltd, Unit 1, Industry Park, Cricketts Lane, Chippenham, Wiltshire, SN15 3EQ Tel: (01249) 705070 Fax: (01249) 705071 E-mail: sales@orielsystems.com *Oriel Systems specialises in the provision of innovative, PC based, telemetry remote monitoring solutions including Vendor Managed Inventory systems, we design & write custom software; for scientific applications, instruments & interface drivers for intelligent computer controlled devices. Oriel Systems has developed a range of products for your telemetry needs. Including video telemetry unit capable of transmitting live video feeds of your remote sites, giving you the ability to control and monitor digital and analogue signals. Oriel has also developed an intelligent telemetry unit that can be programmed to manage & control a site without any user input based on the signals it picks up. VMI solutions are used by bulk material supply companies to monitor stocks of their product. *Our "AWAX" Telemetry software is used across a very broad range of industries, because of its power & flexibility, from Water & Utility, Pharmaceuticals, Automated warehouses, Oil and Gas.*

▶ Oriel Transport, Ferrard Road, Kirkcaldy, Fife, KY2 5SA Tel: (01592) 201810

Oriental Linen Hire, 5 Alexander Trading Estate, Castlefield Street, Stoke-on-Trent, ST4 7AQ Tel: (01782) 205417 *Laundry supplier*

Oriental Motor (UK) Ltd, Unit 5, Faraday Office Park, Rankine Road, Basingstoke, Hampshire, RG24 8AH Tel: (01256) 347090 Fax: (01256) 347099 E-mail: info@oriental-motor.co.uk Principal Export Areas: Africa *Electric motors, ac & dc manufrs*

▶ Oriental Rugs, 4 Upper Richmond Road, London, SW15 2SD Tel: (020) 8874 1000 E-mail: Info@Al-Nasir.com *Oriental Rugs of London. Dealer in Fine persian and Oriental Rugs - sales (trade and retail) consultation, restoration cleaning, valuation and appraisal*

▶ The Oriental Stone Co. Ltd, Ashfarm, Leysters, Leominster, Herefordshire, HR6 0HP Tel: (01568) 750550 Fax: (01568) 750586 E-mail: info@orientalstone.co.uk *Marble & granite fabricators*

▶ Oriflame Info.biz, 27 Blackthorn Avenue, Lenzie, Glasgow, G66 4DE Tel: (0845) 0090384 E-mail: oriflamebiz@hotmail.co.uk *Oriflame Natural Swedish Cosmetics provide quality skincare, cosmetics, foot care, baby care, Mens range, toiletries, girls cosmetics, perfume, jewelery and other gifts and accessories.*These are promoted by consultants in several ways ie via an online store and website or by showing brochures to friends and family or by distributing brochures door to door locally and also by organising parties/demonstrations.*To view the products or to become a consultant please visit my website or contact Christine Adair on 08450 090 384*

Oriflame (UK) Ltd, Kiln Farm, Tilers Road, Milton Keynes, MK11 3EH Tel: (01908) 261126 Fax: (01908) 267444 E-mail: salesuk/ireland@oriflame.co.uk *Cosmetic distributor*

Origin, 32-33 Watling Street, Canterbury, Kent, CT1 2AN Tel: (01227) 762380 Fax: (01227) 760726 *Financial advisers*

▶ Origin Financial Solutions, 3 Parkgate Croft, Mosborough, Sheffield, S20 5DX Tel: 0114-248 8844 Fax: (0871) 2423782 E-mail: seanlee@thinkpositive.co.uk *Truly Independent Financial and Mortgage advice. FREE initial consultation.*

▶ Origin Frames, Unit 9 Lincolns Park Business Centre, Lincoln Road, Cressex Business Park, High Wycombe, Buckinghamshire, HP12 3RD Tel: (0845) 4506662 Fax: (0845) 4506663 E-mail: info@originframes.co.uk *Manufacturers of aluminium folding sliding patio doors for the trade*

Origin Leisure, Summerhouse Business Park, Canal Way, Harefield, Uxbridge, Middlesex, UB9 6TH Tel: (01895) 823366 Fax: (01895) 824445 E-mail: info@origindfl.co.uk *Swimming pools designers & builders*

Origin One UK Ltd, Dukes Yard Shakespeare Industrial Estate, Acme Road, Watford, WD24 5AL Tel: (01923) 246116 Fax: (01923) 246113 E-mail: info@origin-1.co.uk *Graphic design*

Origin Precision Mouldings Ltd, 19 Colvilles Place, Kelvin Industrial Estate, East Kilbride, Glasgow, G75 0PZ Tel: (01355) 244554 Fax: (01355) 245054 E-mail: admin@originprecision.com *Plastic injection mouldings manufrs*

▶ Origin Storage, 1 The Rutherford Centre, Rutherford Road, Basingstoke, Hampshire, RG24 8PB Tel: (01256) 351500 Fax: (0870) 1670987 *Computer components*

Original Blues Clothing Co. Ltd, Enterprise House, 133 Blyth Road, Hayes, Middlesex, UB3 1DD Tel: (020) 8813 7766 Fax: (020) 8813 7811 E-mail: sales@original-blues.com *Denim indigo knitwear manufrs*

Original Business Systems Ltd, The Stables, The Vatch, Stroud, Gloucestershire, GL6 7LE Tel: (01453) 751515 Fax: (01453) 753525 E-mail: info@obs.co.uk *Software consultants*

The Original Cheddar Cheese Co., The Cliffs, Cheddar, Somerset, BS27 3QE Tel: (01934) 743113 Fax: (01934) 744449 *Wines, ciders & cheese manufrs*

Original Marketing, 4 Prospect Street, Bridlington, North Humberside, YO15 2AL Tel: (01262) 675916 Fax: (01262) 675916 E-mail: originalmarketing@ukonline.co.uk *Thermal printing marketing services*

Original Pretzel Co. Ltd, 8 Temple Farm Industrial Estate, Sutton Road, Southend-On-Sea, SS2 5RN Tel: (01702) 461116 Fax: (01702) 461544 *Food distributors*

Original Style Ltd, Falcon Road, Sowton Industrial Estate, Exeter, EX2 7LF Tel: (01392) 474011 Fax: (01392) 219932 E-mail: info@stovax.com *Manufacturers ceramic, glass, natural stone tiles*

▶ Original Video UK, Central Way, Cheltenham Trade Park, Cheltenham, Gloucestershire, GL51 8LX Tel: (01242) 526565 Fax: (01242) 526565 E-mail: contact@original-video.com *Manufacture dvd rental machines*

Orin Engineering (UK) Ltd, PO Box 50, Wokingham, Berkshire, RG41 4HZ Tel: 0118-978 4646 Fax: 0118-977 0886 E-mail: orin@orin.co.uk *Telecoms consultants*

▶ Oriole Constructors, 196 Fernbank Road, Ascot, Berkshire, SL5 8LA Tel: (01344) 885557

Orion, 11b Baird House, Newark Road South, Glenrothes, Fife, KY7 4NS Tel: (01592) 775050 Fax: (01592) 772515 E-mail: fife@orioneng.com *Employment agency*

▶ Orion, 6 Astley Way, Astley La Industrial Estate, Swillington, Leeds, LS26 8XT Tel: 0113-232 0555 Fax: 0113-232 0505 *Office furniture manufrs*

▶ Orion Air Conditioning & Refrigeration, 16 Barkers Piece, Marston Moretaine, Bedford, MK43 0LZ Tel: (07905) 967307 Fax: (01234) 765580 E-mail: info@orionair.co.uk *Air conditioning and refrigeration installation, service, sales uk wide.*

Orion Alloys, Unit 3f River Way, Harlow, Essex, CM20 2DP Tel: (01279) 434422 Fax: (01279) 420044 E-mail: sales@orionalloys.co.uk *Stainless steel stockists*

Orion Cleaning & Support Services, Unit 12 Parmiter Industrial Centre, Parmiter Street, London, E2 9HZ Tel: (020) 8880 7222 Fax: 0208 880 7080 *London and South East commercial contract cleaning specialists, including office cleaning, window cleaning, waste management, femenine hygiene and maintenance.Orion customises its cleaning specifications to suit each individual client's needs.Orion is London's premier Cleaning and Support Service Company.*

Orion Electric (UK) Ltd, Unit 3, Kenfig Industrial Estate, Margam, Port Talbot, West Glamorgan, SA13 2PE Tel: (01656) 742400 Fax: (01656) 744700 E-mail: oeu@relay.co.uk *Electrical manufrs*

Orion Engineering Services Ltd, 21 Albert Street, Aberdeen, AB25 1XX Tel: (01224) 632121 Fax: (01224) 640046 E-mail: abz@orioneng.co.uk *Employment agency*

Orion Industries Ltd, Syma House, Halifax Road, Cressex Business Park, High Wycombe, Buckinghamshire, HP12 3SN Tel: (01494) 453800 Fax: (01494) 442762 E-mail: terry@aquila-innovations.co.uk *Polyurethane & injection moulded products manufrs*

▶ Orion Insulations, Unit 5 Kingsmark Freeway, Oakenshaw, Bradford, West Yorkshire, BD12 7HW Tel: (01274) 711470 Fax: (01274) 711471 E-mail: bradford@oriontrent.co.uk *Distributors of building materials products*

Orion Link Ltd, Unit 2 Lodge Ford Trading Estate, Cradley Heath, West Midlands, B64 7RW Tel: (01384) 565448 Fax: (01384) 565147 E-mail: sales@orion-link.co.uk *Manufacturers of specialist coil slitting machines*

Orion Narrow Boats Ltd, Ashwood, Kingswinford, West Midlands, DY6 0AQ Tel: (01384) 401464 Fax: (01384) 401464 E-mail: info@narrowboatsearch.co.uk *Boat builders & sales*

Orion Paints Ltd, Unit 22 Manor Complex, Kirkby Bank Road, Knowsley Industrial Park, Liverpool, L33 7SY Tel: 0151-548 6756 Fax: 0151-549 1572 E-mail: sales@orionpaints.co.uk *Manufacture & distribute paint wholesales*

Orion Precision, 18 Orion Court, Cranes Farm Road, Basildon, Essex, SS14 3DB Tel: (01268) 282445 Fax: (01268) 282445 *Injection mould toolmakers*

▶ Orion Print Ltd, Merlin Way, Quarry Hill Industrial Estate, Ilkeston, Derbyshire, DE7 4RA Tel: 0115-930 7517 Fax: 0115-932 3353

▶ Orion Safety Belts, 4 Parsons Green Estate, Boulton Road, Stevenage, Hertfordshire, SG1 4QG Tel: (01438) 361999 Fax: (01438) 361999 E-mail: orionsafetybelts@freeuk.com *Seat belt manufrs*

Orion Security Systems, 39 Nursery Lane, Northampton, NN2 7QG Tel: (01604) 474016 Fax: (01604) 468846 *Domestic intruder alarm suppliers & installers*

Orion Technical Services Ltd, Springfield Street, Warrington, WA1 1BB Tel: (01925) 242020 Fax: (01925) 242040 E-mail: ots@orioneng.com *Professional & technical employment agency*

Orion Telecom Ltd, Mays Farm, Sharnal Street, High Halstow, Rochester, Kent, ME3 8QL Tel: (01634) 255550 Fax: (01634) 251777 E-mail: sales@orion-telecom.co.uk *Export telecom equipment*

▶ Orion Windows Ltd, Clifton Industrial Estate, Audax Road, York, YO30 4US Tel: (01904) 690881 Fax: (01904) 691504

Orions Fashions, 1 Castlefield Street, Stoke-on-Trent, ST4 7AQ Tel: (01782) 287779 Fax: (01782) 201850 *Ladies & children's clothing manufrs*

Orior By Design, Unit 12 Greenbank Industrial Estate, Rampart Road, Newry, County Down, BT34 2QU Tel: (028) 3026 2620 Fax: (028) 3026 3810 E-mail: oriorbydesign@btconnect.com *Design & manufacturer of furniture*

O'Riordan Bond Estate Agents, St. Edmunds House, St. Edmunds Road, Northampton, NN1 5DY Tel: (01604) 632805 Fax: (01604) 609306 *Estate agents & mortgage brokers*

Oris GB Systems, 108 Henderson Street, Bridge of Allan, Stirling, FK9 4HF Tel: (01786) 833162 Fax: (01786) 834230 E-mail: sales@gbsystems.co.uk *Legal business systems software consultants*

Orix Rentec Ltd, 9 Falcon Park Industrial Estate, Neasden Lane, London, NW10 1RZ Tel: (020) 8208 8600 Fax: (020) 8208 8601 E-mail: info@orixrentec.co.uk *Test equipment*

▶ Orkney Aggregates Ltd, Garrison Road, Hatston Industrial Estate, Kirkwall, Orkney, KW15 1RE Tel: (01856) 871187 Fax: (01856) 871188 E-mail: sales@orkagg.co.uk *Concrete distributors*

Orkney Boats Ltd, Unit 1 Ford La Business Park, Ford, Arundel, West Sussex, BN18 0UZ Tel: (01243) 551456 Fax: (01243) 551914 E-mail: enquiries@orkneyboatsltd.co.uk *Boat builders*

Orkney Herring Co. Ltd, Garson Industrial Estate, Stromness, Orkney, KW16 3JU Tel: (01856) 850514 Fax: (01856) 850568 E-mail: sales@orkneyherring.com *Salmon & herring products*

▶ Orkney Line Shipping, Sparrowhawk Road, Hatston Industrial Estate, Kirkwall, Orkney, KW15 1GE Tel: (01856) 873658 Fax: (01856) 873563

Orkot Composites, Dodds Close, Rotherham, South Yorkshire, S60 1BX Tel: (01709) 789800 Fax: (01709) 374819

▶ ORLIN Technologies Ltd, 50 Station Road, Ridgmont, Bedford, MK43 0UH Tel: (01525) 306100 Fax: (0871) 2477366 E-mail: sales@orlin.co.uk *Distributors for micro & nano positioning systems*

Ormac Coatings Ltd, Thorncliffe Works, Thorncliffe Park Estate, Chapeltown, Sheffield, S35 2PH Tel: 0114-246 1237 Fax: 0114-257 0151 E-mail: orrmac@aol.com *Shot blasting & grit blasting contractors*

Ormandy Rycroft, Duncombe Road, Bradford, West Yorkshire, BD8 9TB Tel: (01274) 490911 Fax: (01274) 498580 E-mail: sales@rycroft.com *Clarifier & heat exchanger manufrs*

A.K. Orme & Son, 114-122 Arundel Street, Sheffield, S1 4RE Tel: 0114-272 2409 Fax: 0114-272 2409 E-mail: ormerings@aol.com *Welded rings for grind wheels*

Ormerod Developments Rochdale Ltd, Ormerod House, Caldershaw Business Park, Rochdale, Lancashire, OL12 7LQ Tel: (01706) 646808 Fax: (01706) 640694 E-mail: sales@ormerods.com *Label manufrs*

Timothy Ormerod Ltd, Bryngwyn Manor, Wormelow, Hereford, HR2 8EH Tel: (01981) 540476 Fax: (01981) 540846 E-mail: matormerod@hotmail.com *Toolmakers*

▶ Ormiston Electrical Services, 586a Blackpool Road, Ashton-on-Ribble, Preston, PR2 1JA Tel: (01772) 722512 Fax: (01772) 722507

▶ Ormond Construction Ltd, 91b Mora Road, London, NW2 6TB Tel: (020) 8450 2244 Fax: (020) 8450 1148

Ormrod Electric Ltd, 173 Chiswick High Road, London, W4 2DR Tel: (020) 8994 0118 Fax: (020) 8994 6008 *Electrical supplies wholesalers*

Ormskirk Microwaves & Kitchen Appliances, Ormskirk Market Hall, Moorgate, Ormskirk, Lancashire, L39 4RT Tel: (01695) 570277 *Electrical goods retailers*

Ormskirk Oils Ltd, Hardacre Street, Ormskirk, Lancashire, L39 2XD Tel: (01695) 578120 Fax: (01695) 578126 E-mail: sales@ormskirk-oils.co.uk *Oil fuel distributors*

▶ Ormston Technology Ltd, 2 Dalrymple Street, Fraserburgh, Aberdeenshire, AB43 9BH Tel: (01346) 511411 Fax: (01346) 513112 E-mail: sales@ormtec.co.uk *Marine electronics*

Orna Met Co., 337 Leysdown Road, Leysdown-on-Sea, Sheerness, Kent, ME12 4AR Tel: (01795) 510630 *Work wear supplier*

Ornamental Iron Works & Forge, Unit2, Pinfold La Industrial Estate, Bridlington, North Humberside, YO16 6XS Tel: (01262) 401498 Fax: (01262) 401498 E-mail: ornamental-ironwork@bridlington.net *Blacksmiths*

Ornamental Metals, 7 West Mills, Mill Street, Kirkcaldy, Fife, KY1 1SD Tel: (01592) 206335 Fax: (01592) 641507 *Metal fabricators*

Orostream Applied Contracting Ltd, Park Road, Crowborough, East Sussex, TN6 2QT Tel: (01892) 665888 Fax: (01892) 663218 E-mail: oracl@aol.com *Building services engineers*

▶ O'Rourke Construction Ltd, 154-158 Sydenham Road, London, SE26 5JZ Tel: (020) 8659 6559 Fax: (020) 8778 7224 E-mail: info@orouke-uk.com

▶ Orphans Press Ltd, Arrow Close, Leominster Enterprise Park, Stoke Prior, Leominster, Herefordshire, HR6 0LX Tel: (01568) 612460 Fax: (01568) 613559 E-mail: info@orphanspress.co.uk

Orr & Boss & Partners Ltd, Landmark House, Station Road, Cheadle Hulme, Cheadle, Cheshire, SK8 7BS Tel: (0870) 3216501 Fax: (0870) 3216502 E-mail: orrboss@aol.com *Management consultants*

▶ Orr Simpson, Morsel House, Moss Hill Lane, York, YO26 9SY Tel: (01423) 339569 Fax: (01423) 330724 E-mail: info@orrsimpson.co.uk *Head hunting. Recruitment services. Consultancy.*

▶ Orrell Filtration Ltd, Caroline House, 2b High Street, Stalybridge, Cheshire, SK15 1SE Tel: 0161-303 2344 Fax: 0161-304 7573 *Filter manufrs*

Orridge & Co. Ltd, Astra Centre, Edinburgh Way, Harlow, Essex, CM20 2BN Tel: (01279) 620800 Fax: (01279) 620806 E-mail: info@orridge.net *Stocktakers & valuers*

Orsogril UK, 4 Pentland Road, Edinburgh, EH13 0JA Tel: 0131-441 1255 Fax: 0131-441 4161 E-mail: sales@orsogril.co.uk *Steel fencing, wall cladding & flooring suppliers*

Orteguil (UK) Ltd, PO Box 2, Stockport, Cheshire, SK12 2NN Tel: (01663) 762187 Fax: (01663) 766721 E-mail: info@orteguil.com *Woodwork machinery suppliers*

Ortho Dynamics Ltd, Ambassador Industrial Estate, 10 Airfield Road, Christchurch, Dorset, BH23 3TG Tel: (01202) 481153 Fax: (01202) 481150 E-mail: enquiries@orthodynamics.co.uk *Hip joint replacements manufrs*

Ortho Europe Ltd, Mill Lane, Alton, Hampshire, GU34 2PX Tel: (01420) 83294 Fax: (01420) 80068 E-mail: keithbell@ortho-europe.co.uk *Artificial limb manufrs* Also at: Branches throughout the U.K.

Orthoeurope Ltd, Orth House, Kimber Road, Abingdon, Oxfordshire, OX14 1SG Tel: (01235) 555001 Fax: (01235) 555004 E-mail: info@ortho-europe.com *Prosthetic & orthopaedic suppliers*

▶ Orthopaedic Innovation, Carwood Road, Sheffield, S4 7SD Tel: 0114-249 5222 Fax: 0114-249 5223 E-mail: sales@o-i.co.uk

Orthos Ltd, The Stables, Leigh Court Business Centre, Abbots Leigh, Bristol, BS8 3RA Tel: (01275) 376377 Fax: (01275) 376378 *Medical equipment manufrs*

Orthos (Engineering) Ltd, No 2, 2 The Point, Market Harborough, Leicestershire, LE16 7QU Tel: (01858) 464246 Fax: (01858) 434480 E-mail: sales@orthos.uk.com *Mixer distributors*

Orthos Projects Ltd, Fernie Road, Market Harborough, Leicestershire, LE16 7PH Tel: (01858) 462806 Fax: (01858) 464403 E-mail: sales@orthos.uk.com *Mechanical handling equipment designers*

▶ Ortiga Ltd, Vienna House, Birmingham International Park, Bickenhill Lane, Birmingham, B37 7GN Tel: 0121-767 1934 Fax: 0121-705 3486 E-mail: enquiries@ortiga.co.uk *Telecommunications & IT Consultancy. We make technology "work" for your business.*

Ortlinghaus (UK) Ltd, 19 Sugarbrook Rd, Aston Fields Industrial Estate, Bromsgrove, Worcestershire, B60 3DN Tel: (01527) 579123 Fax: (01527) 579077 E-mail: sales@ortlinghaus.co.uk Sales Contact: G. Wainwright *With over 30 years experience in the technology of controlled torque Ortlinghaus UK is able to offer an extensive range of industrial clutches and brakes to satisfy the demands of today industrial needs. With a wide range of products available including pneumatic, hydraulic, electromagnetic and mechanical we supply to a diverse range of industries. Design technology is a key word and Ortlinghaus are able to offer bespoke designs to suit all our customers' individual needs. To reduce the amount of down time we carry a very extensive range of all spares to suit our products including plates, springs linings, power packs, safety valves, couplings and much more. Covering the whole of the UK and Ireland Ortlinghaus prides itself on it's quick and efficient response time.*

H. Orton & Sons Ltd, 2 Oxford Street, Earl Shilton, Leicester, LE9 7BB Tel: (01455) 844373 Fax: (01455) 848849 E-mail: ortonshoes@aol.com *Mens fashion manufacturers footwear*

▶ Ortus Professional Search, 5a The Courtyard, 707 Warwick Road, Solihull, West Midlands, B91 3DA Tel: 0121 7127820 *Ortus Professional Search specialises in assisting law firms to increase their fee income through strategic acquisition of key individuals who can meet organisational objectives. We also help companies reduce legal spend by sourcing the legal skills needed to deal with relevant issues in-house. Our executive search methods and international networking also means that we can aid individuals in the planning of their careers.*

Orvec International Ltd, Malmo Road, Hull, HU7 0YF Tel: (01482) 879146 Fax: (01482) 625325 E-mail: service@orvec.com *Disposable clothing manufrs*

Orville Engineering, Unit 4 315 Summer Lane, Birmingham, B19 3RH Tel: 0121-359 7560 Fax: 0121-359 7560 *Press toolmakers*

Orvis Shop, Bridge House, High Street, Stockbridge, Hampshire, SO20 6HB Tel: (01264) 810017 Fax: (01264) 810504 E-mail: admin@orvis.co.uk *Fishing tackle suppliers*

Orwak Environmental Services, Orwak Ltd, 6 Bevan Way, Smethwick, West Midlands, B66 1BZ Tel: (0800) 1693534 Fax: (0121) 565 7427 *Compactors & balers*

▶ Orwin Electrical Ltd, Unit 7, Temple Normanton Business Park, Mansfield Road, Corbriggs, Chesterfield, Derbyshire, S41 0JS Tel: (01246) 202030

Orwin (North East) Ltd, 1-3 Brockwell Road, Crowther Industrial Estate, District 3, Washington, Tyne & Wear, NE38 0AF Tel: 0191-417 7092 Fax: 0191-416 7277 *Special purpose automated machinery design manufrs*

Orxiom Fabrics, 43 Nicholsons Centre, Maidenhead, Berkshire, SL6 1LL Tel: (01628) 620703 Fax: (01628) 773677 *Haberdashery shop*

Oryx X L Ltd, XL House, Woodburn Road, Blackburn, Aberdeen, AB21 0PS Tel: (01224) 798400 Fax: (01224) 798401 E-mail: admin@xlg.co.uk *Computer training & software services*

Osai UK Ltd, Mount House, Bond Avenue, Bletchley, Milton Keynes, MK1 1SF Tel: (01908) 642687 Fax: (01908) 642688 E-mail: sales@osai.co.uk *General motion con & drives specialists*

Osborn Electrical Services Ltd, 433 Park Road, Hockley, Birmingham, B18 5TE Tel: 0121-551 1184 Fax: 0121-523 7837 E-mail: mail@osbornelectricalservices.co.uk *Electrical contractors*

Osborn International Ltd, Dendix House, Lower Church Street, Chepstow, Gwent, NP16 5XT Tel: (01291) 634000 Fax: (01291) 634098 E-mail: uksales@osborn.co.uk Principal Export Areas: Africa *Industrial brush manufrs*

Osborn Steel Extrusions Ltd, Brighouse Road, Low Moor, Bradford, West Yorkshire, BD12 0QL Tel: (01274) 677331 Fax: (01274) 607858 E-mail: extrusion@osbornbujon.com *Steel extrusion manufrs*

▶ Osborne Business Enterprises Ltd, Selsey Road, Sidlesham, Chichester, West Sussex, PO20 7NE Tel: 01243 641974 *Fabrication company offering bespoke engineering solutions. Workshop furniture,general fabrication & structural fabrication, garden accessories. Services include Manual Milling, Turning, Punching and Pressing.*

continued

Osborne Cabinet Makers, 10 Mowbray Gardens, Dorking, Surrey, RH4 1LL Tel: (01306) 713007 Fax: (01306) 644999 *Custom made furniture specialists*

Osborne & Collins Ltd, 133a Hersham Road, Walton-on-Thames, Surrey, KT12 1RW Tel: (01932) 224751 Fax: (01932) 254592 E-mail: info@osborneandcollins.co.uk *Electrical engineers & contractors*

Osborne Engineering, Unit 19 Atley Way, North Nelson Industrial Estate, Cramlington, Northumberland, NE23 1WA Tel: (01670) 737077 Fax: (01670) 736127 E-mail: info@osborne-engineering.com *Specialized manufacturer of hydrodynamic bearings & seals*

Geoffrey Osborne Ltd, Osborne House, Stockbridge Road, Chichester, West Sussex, PO19 8LL Tel: (01243) 787811 Fax: (01243) 531231 E-mail: andrew.smith@osborne.co.uk *Building & civil engineering contractors*

▶ Osborne Mandolins, Star Gallery, Castle Ditch Lane, Lewes, East Sussex, BN7 1YJ Tel: (01273) 473883 E-mail: info@osborne.co.uk *Musical instrument repair & manufrs*

Osborne Motor Bodies, Roothers Industries, Debden Green, Debden Green, Saffron Walden, Essex, CB11 3LX Tel: (01371) 831313 Fax: (01371) 831194 E-mail: sales@osborne.ltd.uk *Commercial motor body builders*

Osbourne Refrigerators Ltd, Rose Green Road, Bognor Regis, West Sussex, PO21 3EG Tel: (01243) 267711 Fax: (01243) 265853 E-mail: sales@osborne-ref.co.uk *Manufacturer of refrigerators for licenced and retail trade*

▶ Osborne Sheen LLP, 73 Celandine Avenue,, Locks Heath, Southampton, SO31 6WZ Tel: 07740 901848 *Osborne Sheen: Southampton full service VAT consultant, HM Revenue & Customs rulings, VAT Registration, VAT returns, VAT help and advice, VAT compliance, health checks & audits, UK VAT reclaims*

Osborne Stationers Ltd, 27 Market Street, Wolverhampton, WV1 3AG Tel: (01902) 427071 Fax: (01902) 771070 *Office equipment supplies*

Tim Osborne, Kenegie Home Farm, Gulval, Penzance, Cornwall, TR20 8YN Tel: (01736) 362515 Fax: (01736) 362515 *Agricultural*

▶ Osbornes Removals & Storage Ltd, Remco House, Wharf Road, Sale, Cheshire, M33 2AF Tel: 0161-236 0358 Fax: 0161-969 9879

Oscar Engineering Ltd, Michaels Lane, West Yoke, Ash, Sevenoaks, Kent, TN15 7HT Tel: (01474) 873122 Fax: (01474) 879554 E-mail: mail@oscar-acoustics.co.uk *Acoustic guarding engineers, noise & reverberation control services*

Oscar Kilo Ltd, Broad Parkham, Parkham, Bideford, Devon, EX39 5PJ Tel: (01237) 451517 *Oscar Kilo provides mathematical modelling systems and consultancy and specialises in rare event detection. The Detect product*provides both a rule-based and statistical risk-engine which draws on the latest research in sensor-fusion, ROC analysis plus our own research and exploits the rarity of anomolies like fraud.*A feature of Detect are the tools for optimising alert thresholds and for manageing alert notification. It is used in credit-card fraud detection, invoicing fraud, telecoms fraud etc.**

▶ Oscillyte, PO Box 169, Saffron Walden, Essex, CB10 9AG Tel: (01799) 534688 E-mail: enquiries@oscillyte.com *Business consultancy & web design, maintenance support*

▶ Osco Ltd, Avant Business Centre, Third Avenue, Bletchley, Milton Keynes, MK1 1DR Tel: (01908) 376688 Fax: (01908) 379916 E-mail: sales@osco.uk.com *Thermal management components manufrs*

Osco Office Supplies Ltd, H E M House, Kirkstall Road, Leeds, LS4 2BT Tel: 0113-279 3511 Fax: 0113-231 0926 E-mail: sales@oscodirect.com *Office furnishers & stationers*

Oscott Air Ltd, Sherlock Street, Birmingham, B5 6LT Tel: 0121-622 2789 Fax: 0121-666 6012 E-mail: sales@oscottair.com *Compressed air & spray distributors* Also at: Coventry

Oscott Equipments Ltd, 25 Great Lister Street, Birmingham, B7 4LS Tel: 0121-333 3200 Fax: 0121-333 2991 *Motor car part & accessories distributors*

▶ Osem North UK Ltd, Unit 18 Lyon Road Industrial Estate, Kearsley, Bolton, BL4 8NB Tel: (01204) 574371 Fax: (01204) 862847

Oshea J Sons Ltd, Orchard Street, Salford, M6 6FL Tel: 0161-925 9800 Fax: 0161-925 9801 E-mail: info@josheagroup.com *Excavation & groundwork contractors*

Osh-gosh Ltd, 151 Bethnal Green Road, London, E2 7DG Tel: (020) 7729 3733 Fax: (020) 7613 0676 *Leather clothing manufrs*

▶ Osier Graphics Ltd, 3 The Orion Centre, Beddington Lane, Croydon, CR0 4YY Tel: (020) 8688 8444 Fax: (020) 8774 6803 *Reprographic services*

Osmonds, Bradeley Green, Tarporley Road, Whitchurch, Shropshire, SY13 4HD Tel: (01948) 668100 Fax: (01948) 668101 E-mail: info@osmonds.co.uk *Animal health care products manufrs*

▶ Osmonds Transport & Planning Ltd, Greenacres Farm, Old Hay, Brenchley, Tonbridge, Kent, TN12 7DG Tel: (01892) 834193 Fax: (01892) 837141 E-mail: sales@osmonds-transport.com

Osmor Products Ltd, Unit 12 Ditchling Common, Ditchling, Hassocks, West Sussex, BN6 8SG Tel: (01444) 236900 Fax: (01444) 230770 E-mail: sales@osmor.co.uk *Cable management systems manufrs*

Osmose Ltd, Timber Treatments Division, Fieldhouse Lane, Marlow, Buckinghamshire, SL7 1LS Tel: (01628) 486644 Fax: (01628) 476757 E-mail: info@protimsolignum.com Principal Export Areas: Worldwide *Wood preservation product manufrs*

Ospray Systems Ltd, 76-80 Sherlock Street, Birmingham, B5 6LT Tel: (0870) 770 7650 Fax: (0870) 770 7651 E-mail: info@eurospraygroup.com *Automotive, industrial, manual and automatic, wet electrostatic spray and powder coating equipment; Technical advice and problem solving; Spray booths, ovens consumables, chemicals; Water Treatment systems; Airless/air assisted systems; Compliant, conventional and HVLP spray guns.*

Osprey Ltd, Unit 6-7, Mynd Industrial Estate, Church Stretton, Shropshire, SY6 6EA Tel: (01694) 723478 Fax: (01694) 724096 E-mail: sales@bec-uk.com *Plastic moulders*

Osprey Co., Guards Road, Coldstream, Berwickshire, TD12 4EE Tel: (01890) 883127 Fax: (01890) 882138 E-mail: sales@signsbynature.co.uk *Sign manufrs*

Osprey Ltd, 12A Eden Way, Pages Industrial Park, Leighton Buzzard, Bedfordshire, LU7 4TZ Tel: (01525) 851505 Fax: (01525) 851501 E-mail: leighton@osprey-plastics.co.uk *Plastics mouldings manufrs*

Osprey Ltd, Dunslow Road, Scarborough, North Yorkshire, YO11 3GS Tel: (01723) 585333 Fax: (01723) 585226 E-mail: jeff@osprey-plastics.co.uk *Plastics & injection mouldings* Also at: Church Stretton & Leighton Buzzard

Osprey Corporation, Units 84-85, John Wilson Business Park, Chestfield, Whitstable, Kent, CT5 3QT Tel: (01227) 770979 Fax: (01227) 770949 E-mail: sales@ospreycorporation.com *Energy pollution & dust control*

▶ Osprey Irrigation, Unit 2 The Old Creamery, Aston Road, Hadnall, Shrewsbury, SY4 5BA Tel: (01939) 236677 Fax: (01939) 210766 *Suppliers & installers of irrigation systems*

Osprey Mott Macdonald, Welken House, 10-11 Charterhouse Square, London, EC1M 6EH Tel: (020) 7566 7900 Fax: (020) 7566 7911 E-mail: brenda.wiggins@ospreymottmac.com *Project management service*

Osprey Networks & Communications, Tower House, High Street, Aylesbury, Buckinghamshire, HP20 1SQ Tel: (01296) 745500 Fax: (01296) 745055 E-mail: sales@ospreynet.co.uk *System integration services*

Ostcliffe Electronics Ltd, Barrowfield Road, Hoyland, Barnsley, South Yorkshire, S74 9TH Tel: (01226) 749233 *Electronic control systems manufrs*

Oster Trading Ltd, 77 Lords Wood, Welwyn Garden City, Hertfordshire, AL7 2HG Tel: (01707) 695446 Fax: (01707) 882649 E-mail: info@ostertrading.com *Blinds & fabric supplier*

Ostomed Ltd, Summit House, Kellet Lane, Bamber Bridge, Preston, PR5 6AN Tel: (01772) 626688 Fax: (01772) 626699 *Surgical appliance distributors*

O'Sullivan Promotions, 18 Bankes Avenue, Orrell, Wigan, Lancashire, WN5 8HU Tel: (01942) 707071 Fax: (01942) 515000 *Promotions & corporate entertainment equipment suppliers*

Oswald Bailey Ltd, 106 Commercial Road, Bournemouth, BH2 5LR Tel: (01202) 552742 *Outdoor clothing equipment manufrs*

Oswald Bailey Ltd, 61 The Horsefair, Bristol, BS1 3JP Tel: 0117-929 3523 Fax: (01202) 397274 *Camping equipment retailers*

Oswald Bailey Ltd, 2 Saxon Square, Christchurch, Dorset, BH23 1QA Tel: (01202) 483043 *Camping & outdoor clothing*

Oswald Record Plant Sales (Midlands) Ltd, Whittington Way, Whittington Moor, Chesterfield, Derbyshire, S41 9AG Tel: (01246) 451057 Fax: (01246) 454078 E-mail: sales@oswaldrecord.co.uk Sales Contact: A.J. Record *Oswald Record leads the way in Air Tools and Light Construction Plant.*

Oswald Road Pine & Country Furniture, Oswald Road, Oswestry, Shropshire, SY11 1RE Tel: (01691) 670690 Fax: (01691) 670690 E-mail: sales@pinestores.co.uk *Pine & reproduction furniture retailers*

▶ Oswald Springs, 76 Arthur Street, Redditch, , Worcestershire, B98 8LJ Tel: (01527) 527777 Fax: (01527) 527785 E-mail: oswald@oswaldsprings.co.uk *Spring clips & presswork manufrs*

Oswestry Cabin Services, 34 Oaklands Road, Chirk Bank, Wrexham, Clwyd, LL14 5DP Tel: (01691) 772904 Fax: (01691) 772904 *Mobile toilets distributors*

Oswestry Industrial Buildings Ltd, Maesbury Road, Oswestry, Shropshire, SY10 8HA Tel: (01691) 661596 Fax: (01691) 661597 *Oswestry Industrial Building Ltd, based in Shropshire are Structural Steelwork engineers. We specialise in steel framed industrial buildings from design, fabrication to erection. We do refurbishment to new build for industrial units, factories, sports halls, retail units and agricultural steel buildings.*

Oswin & Johnson, Occupation Road, Stoney Stanton, Leicester, LE9 4JJ Tel: (01455) 271707 Fax: (01455) 271728 *Designers, manufacturers & installation & steel fabricators*

Ot Africa Line, Marc House, 13-14 Great St. Thomas Apostle, London, EC4V 2BB Tel: (020) 7332 6000 Fax: (020) 7332 6003 E-mail: enquiries@otal.com *Shipping services*

Otc, Lees Road, Oldham, OL4 1JP Tel: 0161-624 5360 Fax: 0161-627 0560 E-mail: info@otctraining.co.uk *Training for industry & commerce*

OTG Ltd, Maidstone Road, Platt, Sevenoaks, Kent, TN15 8JE Tel: (01732) 780780 Fax: (01732) 780835 E-mail: info@otg-ltd.com *Leading specialist in the design and manufacture of tools and tooling for solderless crimped connectors worldwide. OTG products and services include: -The Design, Manufacture, Assembly and Testing of high quality quick-change (Industry standard) mini-Applicators -Medium/heavy duty applicators, custom designed for larger size connectors -Tooling & spare parts for OTG Applicators and compatible tooling for OEM applicators*

Otherland Toys, Lee Valley Technopark, Ashley Road, London, N17 9LN Tel: (020) 8880 4919 E-mail: alex@otherlandtoys.co.uk *Online toy retailers*

▶ Othy Ltd, Ashville Trading Estate, The Runnings, Cheltenham, Gloucestershire, GL51 9PT Tel: (01242) 246250

Oticon Ltd, PO Box 20, Hamilton, Lanarkshire, ML3 7QE Tel: (01698) 283363 Fax: (01698) 284308 E-mail: info@oticon.co.uk *Hearing aids manufrs*

▶ Otis Ltd, 13 Bon Accord Square, Aberdeen, AB11 6DJ Tel: (01224) 590213 Fax: (01224) 584620 E-mail: sales@otis.com *Lift manufrs, installation & repairs of elevators & escalators*

▶ Otis Ltd, 8 Ulster Bank House, Shaftesbury Square, Belfast, BT2 7DL Tel: (028) 9032 4242 Fax: (028) 9024 8631 *Elevators, lifts & escalators repairs service*

▶ Otis Ltd, 1 Albion Street, Birmingham, B1 3AH Tel: 0121-236 0081 Fax: 0121-233 0558 E-mail: heather.meally@otis.com *Lift installation & maintenance*

▶ Otis Ltd, Unit 2 Blenheim Court Beaufort Office Park, Woodlands, Bradley Stoke, Bristol, BS32 4NE Tel: (01454) 452810 Fax: (0845) 6032400 *Manufacturer of lifts & escalators*

Otis Ltd, Unit 1e & H, Wavertree Technology Park, Wavertree Boulevard South, Liverpool, L7 9PF Tel: 0151-472 1500 Fax: 0151-472 1520 *Industrial elevator manufrs*

Otis Ltd, 187 Twyford Abbey Road, London, NW10 7DG Tel: (020) 8955 3000 Fax: (020) 8955 3001 *Elevator & escalator manufrs*

▶ Otis Ltd, Stuart House Eskmills, Station Road, Musselburgh, Midlothian, EH21 7PB Tel: 0131-665 3455 Fax: 0131-653 1450 *Manufacture insulation & service repair of elevators & escalators*

Otley Casing & By-Products Ltd, Millshaw, Beeston, Leeds, LS11 8DB Tel: 0113-271 0039 *Natural sausage casing manufrs*

Otodynamics Ltd, 36-38 Beaconsfield Road, Hatfield, Hertfordshire, AL10 8BB Tel: (01707) 267540 Fax: (01707) 262327 E-mail: enquiries@oae-ilo.co.uk *Hearing test equipment manufrs*

Ott Hydrometry, Criftin Enterprise Centre, Oxton Road, Epperstone, Nottingham, NG14 6AT Tel: 0115-965 6549 Fax: 0115-965 4726 E-mail: sales@ott-hydrometry.co.uk *Water industry instrument manufrs*

Ottaway Engineering Ltd, Renown Close, Chandlers Ford Industrial Estate, Chandler's Ford, Eastleigh, Hampshire, SO53 4HZ Tel: (023) 8026 9977 Fax: (023) 8027 0270 E-mail: info@otteng.co.uk *Precision engineers*

▶ Ottawood Steel Fabricators, D Cambridge Works, Cambridge Grove, Hove, East Sussex, BN3 3ED Tel: (01273) 772456 Fax: (01273) 773456 *Metal works*

Otter Controls Ltd, Hardwick Square South, Buxton, Derbyshire, SK17 6LA Tel: (01298) 762300 Fax: (01298) 72664 E-mail: sales@ottercontrols.com *Thermostat circuit breaker manufrs*

Brian Otterburn Agricultural Engineers, Danby House, High Street, Harome, York, YO62 5JE Tel: (01439) 770265 Fax: (01439) 770525 E-mail: ian@brianotterburn.force9.co.uk *Agricultural engineers*

Otterburn Mill Ltd, Otterburn, Newcastle Upon Tyne, NE19 1JT Tel: (01830) 520225 Fax: (01830) 520032 E-mail: enquiries@otterburnmill.co.uk *Woollen product distributors*

▶ Ottersports, Cedar House, Hunston, Bury St. Edmunds, Suffolk, IP31 3EP Tel: (01359) 244366 Fax: (01359) 244366 E-mail: info@ottersports.com *Canoe, kayak & dinghy kit manufacturers*

Ottimo Supplies Ltd, 7 Livingstone Mills, Howard Street, Batley, West Yorkshire, WF17 6JH Tel: (01924) 469665 Fax: (01924) 463328 E-mail: sales@ottimo-supplies.com Principal Export Areas: Worldwide *Cleaning chemical products & industrial cleaning materials*

▶ Ottley & Sons, Downham Road, Ramsden Heath, Billericay, Essex, CM11 1PZ Tel: (01268) 711347 Fax: (01268) 711867

Ottma Ltd, 30 Leicester Villas, Hove, East Sussex, BN3 5SQ Tel: (01273) 414586 Fax: 01273 414586 *Software consultancy*

Otto Junker (U K) Ltd, Kingsbury Road, Curdworth, Sutton Coldfield, West Midlands, B76 9EE Tel: (01675) 470551 Fax: (01675) 470645 E-mail: sales@otto-junker.co.uk Principal Export Areas: Worldwide *Furnace repair services*

Otto Lift (UK) Ltd, Lindon House, Lindon Road, Walsall, WS8 7BW Tel: (01543) 374777 Fax: (01543) 374141 *List manufrs*

Otto UK Ltd, Beacon House, Reg's Way, Bardon Hill, Coalville, Leicestershire, LE67 1GH Tel: (01530) 277900 Fax: (01530) 277911 E-mail: sales@otto.co.uk *Lifting equipment manufrs*

Otto UK Ltd, Beacon House, Reg's Way, Bardon Hill, Coalville, Leicestershire, LE67 1GH Tel: (01530) 277900 Fax: (01530) 277911 E-mail: sales@otto.co.uk *Plastic injection mouldings & materials handling*

Our-Info, 279 Garstang Road, Fulwood, Preston, PR2 9XH Tel: (01772) 719648 E-mail: david@joyner.co.uk *Software programmes*

Out & About, 18 Bower Road, Harrogate, North Yorkshire, HG1 5BW Tel: (01423) 561592 Fax: (01423) 560668 E-mail: sales@outandabout-online.co.uk *Camping & climbing equipment retailers*

Out & About, 2 Elcho Street Brae, Peebles, EH45 8HU Tel: (01721) 723590 Fax: (01721) 723590 *Camping equipment suppliers*

Out & About, 88 Brighton Road, Worthing, West Sussex, BN11 2EN Tel: (01903) 234915 Fax: (01903) 234915 E-mail: enquiries@outandabout-online.co.uk *Camping equipment suppliers*

Out Board Electronics, Barrington Road, Orwell, Royston, Hertfordshire, SG8 5QP Tel: (01223) 208183 Fax: (01223) 208190 *Equipment for the entertainment industry manufrs*

Out Of The Woods, Mill Lane, Halton, Lancaster, LA2 6ND Tel: (01524) 811968 *Cabinet & kitchen manufrs*

Outboard & Hydroplane Services Ltd, 12 Springfield Road, Aughton, Ormskirk, Lancashire, L39 6ST Tel: (01695) 422350 Fax: (01695) 424106 E-mail: frank.lynch1@btconnect.com *Marine sales & service*

Outdoor Choice, High Street, Glan Y Traeth, Barmouth, Gwynedd, LL42 1DS Tel: (01341) 280948 *Outdoor & camping suppliers*

Outdoor & Country Store, Stone Road, Blackbrook, Newcastle, Staffordshire, ST5 5EG Tel: (01782) 680068 Fax: (01782) 680068 E-mail: sales@outdoorandcountry.co.uk *Outdoor leisure & sports shop*

Outdoor Group Ltd, Mansard Close, Westgate Industrial Estate, Northampton, NN5 5DL Tel: (01604) 441111 Fax: (01604) 441164 E-mail: enquiries@blacks.co.uk *Retailer of outdoor clothing & equipment*

▶ The Outdoor Pursuits Co-operative, 22-24 Radford Street, Stone, Staffordshire, ST15 8DA Tel: (01785) 818500 *Retailer of outdoor leisure equipment*

Outdoor Scene, 40-44 Carrington Street, Nottingham, NG1 7GD Tel: 0115-950 4998 Fax: 0115-948 3305 E-mail: carrington@outdoorscene.co.uk *Outdoor clothing retail*

Outdoor & Sports Co. Ltd, Redfern House, Dawson Street, Hyde, Cheshire, SK14 1RD Tel: 0161-366 5020 Fax: 0161-366 9732 E-mail: info@ronhill.com *Sportswear distributors*

▶ Outdoor Training Ltd, 15 Grand Parade, Hayling Island, Hampshire, PO11 9JD Tel: (023) 9246 2147 E-mail: adrian@trainingoutdoors.co.uk *Powerboat Training*RIB Training*Yacht Training*Corporate Training*RYA Courses*

Outdoor World, Mersey Buildings, 304 Winwick Road, Warrington, WA2 8JG Tel: (01925) 634794 Fax: (01925) 232717 E-mail: info@outdoorworld.org *Outdoor gear retailers*

Outdoors, 40-44 St. Georges Walk, Croydon, CR0 1YJ Tel: (020) 8688 1730 Fax: (020) 8688 1730 *Camping & travel equipment retailers*

Outhill Boat Builders Ltd, Outhill Boats, Henley Road, Outhill, Studley, Warwickshire, B80 7DU Tel: (01527) 853798 Fax: (01527) 854510 E-mail: outhillsales@aol.com *Boat builders*

▶ Outlook It Ltd, Unit 14 Enterprise House, Dalziel Street, Motherwell, Lanarkshire, ML1 1PJ Tel: (01698) 264266 *It company*

Outlook Stockholders (Metals) Ltd, Woodcote Grove Farm, Meadow Hill, Coulsdon, Surrey, CR5 2QQ Tel: (020) 8668 9656 Fax: (020) 8668 5111 *Stockholders of aluminium & other metals*

▶ Outlook Windows Ltd, 4 Fisher Industrial Estate, Wiggenhall Road, Watford, WD18 0FN Tel: (01923) 252984 Fax: (01923) 238546

Outmere Direct Mail Ltd, 5-6 Wellington Road, London, SW19 8EX Tel: (020) 8947 7577 Fax: (020) 8944 9736 E-mail: info@outmere.co.uk *Direct mail and data processing services.*

Outokumpu Ltd, Stevenson Road, Sheffield, S9 3XG Tel: 0114-242 1124 Fax: 0114-242 2152 *Stainless steel rodding services*

Outokumpu Copper Metal Supplies Ltd, Mill Road, Sharnbrook, Bedford, MK44 1NP Tel: (01234) 781234 Fax: (01234) 781915 E-mail: andrew.smith@outokumpu.com *Distribution of copper tubes*

▶ Outokumpu Stainless Ltd, PO Box 161, Sheffield, S9 1TR Tel: 0114-244 3311 Fax: 0114-244 8280 *Stainless steel manufrs*

Output Ltd, 1 Amptronic Industrial Estate, Heath Mill Road, Wombourne, Wolverhampton, WV5 8AP Tel: (01902) 895107 Fax: (01902) 895113 E-mail: sales@outputdigital.com *Digital reprographic services*

Outram Research Ltd, Haining House, Taylors Lane, Bosham, Chichester, West Sussex, PO18 8QQ Tel: (01243) 573050 Fax: (01243) 574136 *Data logging system designers*

Outreach plc, Abbots Road, Middlefield Industrial Estate, Falkirk, FK2 9AR Tel: (01324) 889000 Fax: (01324) 888901 E-mail: cmarshall@outreachltd.co.uk *Hydraulic lifting and access systems specialists*

▶ Outright Cleaning, 52 Edderston Ridge, Peebles, EH45 9NA Tel: (01721) 729066 E-mail: neil@outrightcleaning.co.uk *Carpet and upholstery cleaning service providing a quality solution at an affordable price.*

▶ Outsource 2 Solutions, Talbot House, 204-226 Imperial Drive, Rayners Lane, Harrow, Middlesex, HA2 7HH Tel: (020) 8426 1088 Fax: (020) 8426 1145 E-mail: enos@outsource2solutions.co.uk *Recruitment*

Outsource Electronics, Unit 600 Nest Business Park, Martin Road, Havant, Hampshire, PO9 5TL Tel: (023) 9245 2222 Fax: (023) 9248 1922 E-mail: chrisc@outsourceelectronics.co.uk Principal Export Areas: Worldwide *Outsource Electronics in Havant, Hampshire, specialise in your outsourcing of small to medium batch surface mount and conventional Printed Circuit Boards, Cable Assemblies, Cable Forms, and Electro-mechanical assemblies and electronic assemblies, to a recognised Quality Assurance accreditation. Outsource Electronics offer a flexible service to your specification, including design, prototype, pre-production, procurement, manufacture, cost engineering, production engineering, test and logistics. Testing includes either in-circuit, functional, or software driven, fixtures being Customer supplied or designed and built in house. Outsource Electronics work as part of your team, integrating at any point within your production process, and providing a high-quality and cost-effective way to meet your production requirements. All production is undertaken at the 27,000 sq ft Havant based factory in Hampshire, close to motorway, rail and ferry links.*

Outsourced H R Solutions, 54 Clarendon Road, Watford, WD17 1DU Tel: (01923) 431675 Fax: (01923) 431875 E-mail: info@invosoftsolutions.com *Invosoft is a provider of custom software solutions that are Web/Extranet/Intranet based. Solutions are delivered rapidly and fully managed at fixed cost. Whether your aim is to improve operational efficiencies, cut costs, improve customer service,* *continued* *or any other goal we can help your business implement the right solution for you.*

▶ Outsourced Personnel Services Ltd, PO Box 251, Sunbury-on-Thames, Middlesex, TW16 5SH Tel: (01932) 786066 Fax: (01932) 772032 E-mail: sean@personnelmanagement.co.uk *We provide Human Resource (HR) services to a diverse range of SMEs without the resources or expertise to effectively manage their employment issues at a fraction of the cost of employing their own resources. **Services vary from support and advice on the management of complex employment issues, production of HR documents (contracts, policies, procedures, handbooks etc.) to provision of fully outsourced HR services managing all aspects of the HR function.**

▶ Outsourced Technical Support Limited, Technology House, 9a Princess Avenue, Aldwick, Bognor Regis, West Sussex, PO21 2QT Tel: (08452) 008247 E-mail: enquiries@ots247.co.uk?src=kellysearch *Outsourced Technical Support are your Outsourced IT Department. We provide small and medium-sized businesses with access to a wide range of skills and knowledge, from project management to development and technical support skills. Outsourced Technical Support provide IT Support throughout the South East of England.**Our team of engineers, developers and consultants can provide you with everything normally associated with running a large internal IT Department for a fraction of the cost.**

Ouzledale Foundry Co. Ltd, PO Box 4, Barnoldswick, Lancashire, BB18 6BN Tel: (01282) 813235 Fax: (01282) 816876 *Iron castings manufrs*

Ovako Ltd, Unit 2 Yorks Park, Blowers Green Road, Dudley, West Midlands, DY2 8UL Tel: (01384) 213940 E-mail: graham.butler@ovako.com *Alloy & black bar manufrs*

Oval 316 Ltd, 10 Cowley Road, Nuffield Industrial Estate, Poole, Dorset, BH17 0UJ Tel: (01202) 682830 Fax: (01202) 665572 E-mail: office@oval316.co.uk *Aluminium & stainless steel tank manufrs*

Oval Automation Ltd, Lake Lane, Barnham, Bognor Regis, West Sussex, PO22 0AD Tel: (01243) 555885 Fax: (01243) 554846 E-mail: paul@oval.org.uk *Electronic engineers designers & metal sheet work manufrs*

Oval Bodyshop, Broadway North, West Wilts Trading Estate, Westbury, Wiltshire, BA13 4JX Tel: (01373) 855866 Fax: (01373) 858103 *Motor body builders & repairers*

Ovalring Ltd, 60 Prince of Wales Lane, Birmingham, B14 4JY Tel: 0121-436 6060 Fax: 0121-436 6061 *Self-adhesive label manufrs*

Ovalway Hydraulics, 11 Cannon Park Way, Middlesbrough, Cleveland, TS1 5JU Tel: (01642) 247106 Fax: (01642) 241874 E-mail: ohe@ovalway.co.uk Sales Contact: B. Sharp *Manufacturers of hydraulic control systems, equipment & power packs. In addition, hydraulic engineers, installation or service.*

▶ Ovation Audio Visual Systems, Belgrave Business Centre, 45 Frederick Street, Edinburgh, EH2 1EP Tel: (0845) 6448851 Fax: 0131-666 2556 E-mail: sales@ovationaudiovisual.com

Ovation Systems Ltd, Springfield Barn, Milton Common, Thame, Oxfordshire, OX9 2JY Tel: (01844) 279638 Fax: (01844) 279071 E-mail: sales@ovation.co.uk *Video security equipment manufrs*

Ovec Systems Ltd, 5 Brown Street, Coatbridge, Lanarkshire, ML5 4AS Tel: (01236) 770699 Fax: (01236) 770898 E-mail: info@ovec.co.uk *Automatic leak detection*

▶ Ovedas, 53 Wray Lane, Reigate, Surrey, RH2 0HX Tel: (01737) 222980 Fax: (01737) 245478

▶ Oven Butler, 17 Sheffield Road, Anston, Sheffield, S25 5DT Tel: (01909) 564411 E-mail: paul.allen15@btinternet.com *Professional, independant domestic oven cleaning service for all ovens, hobs, microwaves & extractors servicing Worksop, Sheffield, Rotherham, Doncaster Retford areas. Low odour biodegradable products used. Swift service.*

▶ Oven Master, 12 Fuchsia Close, Priorslee, Telford, Shropshire, TF2 9PG Tel: (01952) 210067 Fax: (01952) 210067 E-mail: ovenmaster@tiscali.co.uk *Oven cleaning*

Ovenden Engineers, 2 Radnor Street, Folkestone, Kent, CT19 6AQ Tel: (01303) 254387 Fax: (01303) 254387 *Steel fabricators*

Overall Workwear, 3 Alexander Square, Clayton, Bradford, West Yorkshire, BD14 6QU Tel: (01274) 814649 Fax: (01274) 814649 *Work wear & protective equipment suppliers*

Overbury P.L.C., 77 Newman Street, London, W1T 3EW Tel: (020) 7307 9000 Fax: (020) 7307 9001 E-mail: info@overbury.co.uk *Office fitting out services*

Overdrive Auto Services, A 5 Dalton Street, Hull, HU8 8BB Tel: (01482) 222441 Fax: (01482) 222441 E-mail: paul@overdrive.karoo.co.uk *Engineers*

Overdrive Repair Services, 50 Rother Valley Way, Holbrook, Sheffield, S20 3RW Tel: 0114-248 2632 Fax: 0114-248 2786 E-mail: sales@overdrive-repairs.co.uk *Machinery reconditioning services*

Overhead Line Fittings (U.K.) Ltd, 12 Wood Lane, Norton Juxta Twycross, near Atherstone, Atherstone, Warwickshire, CV9 3QB Tel: (01827) 880210 Fax: (01827) 880811 E-mail: sales@overheadlinefittings.co.uk *Overhead line fittings manufrs*

▶ Overland Marketing Ltd, The Barn, Parsonage Farm Lane, Woodditton, Newmarket, Suffolk, CB8 9RZ Tel: (01638) 730700 Fax: (01638) 730200 *Equestrian equipment distributors*

▶ Overload Management Ltd, Kyloe Cottage, Berwick-upon-Tweed, TD15 2PE Tel: (01289) 381287 *It management services*

Overmatic Ltd, 13 Clifton Road, Coulsdon, Surrey, CR5 2DW Tel: (020) 8668 3076 Fax: (020) 8668 3076 *Electric curtains manufrs*

Overprint Packaging plc, 1 Thame Road Industrial Estate, Thame Road, Haddenham, Aylesbury, Buckinghamshire, HP17 8BY Tel: (01844) 292959 Fax: (01844) 292979 E-mail: info@overprint.co.uk *Marking coding manufrs*

Overprint Packaging Ltd, 12 Canal Way, Harefield, Uxbridge, Middlesex, UB9 6TH Tel: (01895) 824090 Fax: (01428) 654769 E-mail: enquiries@prestonprinters.com *Hot foil stamping, blocking machines & coding machinery manufrs*

Overprinting Machines UK Ltd, Speedprint House, Halifax Road, Cross Roads, Keighley, West Yorkshire, BD22 9DH Tel: (01535) 642528 Fax: (01535) 643958 E-mail: info@opmlabels.com *Self-adhesive label manufrs*

Overs Of Camberley Ltd, Springlakes Estate, Deadbrook Lane, Aldershot, Hampshire, GU12 4UH Tel: (01252) 714233 Fax: (01252) 345861 E-mail: internationalrelocation@overs.co.uk *Removals & storage specialists*

Overseal Natural Ingredients Ltd, Swains Park Indust Estate, Swadlincote, Derbyshire, DE12 6JS Tel: (01283) 224221 Fax: (01283) 222006 E-mail: colours@overseal.co.uk *Food colouring manufrs*

Overseas Medical Supplies UK Ltd, 14 Cumberland Avenue, London, NW10 7QL Tel: (020) 8965 9711 Fax: (020) 8965 6894 E-mail: oms@overseasmedical.com *Distributors medical equipment supplies*

Overton Cabinet Makers, 85 Milestone Road, Carterton, Oxfordshire, OX18 3RL Tel: (01993) 843376 E-mail: info@thecraftsman.co.uk *Antique furniture restorers & polishers, furniture manufactures*

▶ Overton UK Ltd, 14 Farrier Road, Lincoln, LN6 3RU Tel: (01522) 690011 Fax: (01522) 690033 E-mail: sales@overton-uk.co.uk *Manufacturers of vacuum litter collectors*

Ovid Technologies Ltd, 250 Waterloo Road, London, SE1 8RD Tel: (020) 7981 0600 Fax: (020) 7981 0601 E-mail: europe@ovid.com *Publishing & internet service providers*

Ovington Boats Ltd, Mariners Lane, North Shields, Tyne & Wear, NE30 4AT Tel: 0191-257 6011 Fax: 0191-257 8489 *Boat builders & repairers*

Owen Barry, 32 Orchard Road, Street, Somerset, BA16 0BT Tel: (01458) 442858 Fax: (01458) 447319 E-mail: info@owenbarry.com *Sheepskin products manufrs*

Owen Coyle Anodising, 144 Blyth Road, Hayes, Middlesex, UB3 1BY Tel: (020) 8573 0184 Fax: (020) 8848 1170 E-mail: sales@owencoyle-anodising.co.uk *Anodising services*

Daniel Owen Associates, Unit 3 The Schoolhouse, Second Avenue, Trafford Park, Manchester, M17 1DZ Tel: 0161-888 2332 Fax: 0161-877 8088 E-mail: info@danielowen.co.uk *Professional construction recruitment*

Daniel Owen Associates, Hadwyn House, Field Road, Reading, RG1 6AP Tel: 0118-957 1011 Fax: 0118-957 1011 E-mail: paul.wells@danielowen.co.uk *Professional construction recruitment*

Edward Owen Engineering, Unit 2, The Mazes, East Street, Braintree, Essex, CM7 3JJ Tel: (01376) 345631 Fax: (01376) 345631 *General engineers*

Owen Joinery, 1a Derwent Street, Llanelli, Dyfed, SA15 3ES Tel: (01554) 777700 *Joinery manufrs*

Owen Joinery, 50 Stepney Place, Llanelli, Dyfed, SA15 1SE Tel: (01554) 771111 Fax: (01554) 771111 *Joiners*

K.A. Owen, 3 St. John Street, Low Town, Bridgnorth, Shropshire, WV15 6AG Tel: (01746) 765476 Fax: (01746) 767344 *Buy & sell equipment for hotel trade*

Owen Mumford Holdings Ltd, Brook Hill, Woodstock, Woodstock, Oxfordshire, OX20 1TU Tel: (01993) 812021 Fax: (01993) 813466 E-mail: steve.miles@owenmumford.co.uk *Manufacturers of plastic injection mouldings* Also at: Chipping Norton & High Wycombe

Owen & Palmer Ltd, Unit 12 Llandygai Industrial Estate, Llandygai, Bangor, Gwynedd, LL57 4YH Tel: (01248) 353515 Fax: (01248) 353736 E-mail: sales@owenandpalmer.co.uk *Electronic industry test equipment contractors*

▶ Owen (Road Services) Ltd, Dafen Industrial Estate, Dafen, Llanelli, Dyfed, SA14 8QE Tel: (01554) 754465 Fax: (01554) 770725 *We offer Road Transport, Distribution, Warehousing, Storage and Logistics Solutions throughout the UK and Europe. We are also part of a Nationwide Palletised Distribution Network offering next day deliveries anywhere in the UK.*

Owen Sails Ltd, Tralee Bay, Benderloch, Oban, Argyll, PA37 1QR Tel: (01631) 720485 Fax: (01631) 720545 E-mail: info@owensails.com *Sail making repairers & winter valeting & rigging service*

Owen Skip Hire, Lingard Lane, Bredbury Park Industrial Estate, Bredbury, Stockport, Cheshire, SK6 2RN Tel: 0161-430 5650 Fax: 0161-430 5650 E-mail: owenskiphire@tiscalli.co.uk *Skip hire & waste disposal*

Owen Springs Ltd, Aldwarke Terrace, Parkgate, Rotherham, South Yorkshire, S62 6BX Tel: (01709) 710700 Fax: (01709) 710666 E-mail: sales@owensprings.co.uk Principal Export Areas: Central/East Europe & West Europe *Springs*

▶ Owens Aquatics, Roden Lane, Roden, Telford, Shropshire, TF6 6BP Tel: (01952) 770362 Fax: (01952) 770362 E-mail: tim@owensaquatics.co.uk *Aquarium & pond suppliers*

Owens Conveyor, Westgate House, Westgate, Aldridge, Walsall, WS9 8EX Tel: (01922) 452333 Fax: (01922) 458777 E-mail: msullivan@ocon.co.uk *Conveyor systems & flexible roller manufrs*

Owens Corning Veil UK Ltd, PO Box 30, Liversedge, West Yorkshire, WF15 8AA Tel: (01274) 863336 Fax: (01274) 862597 *Glass fibre tissue manufrs*

Peter Owens, Frigidaile Mill, Great Smeaton, Northallerton, North Yorkshire, DL6 2NF Tel: (01609) 881941 Fax: (01609) 881941 E-mail: peterowens@home.3b.co.uk *Agricultural feed & mineral buckets & blocks manufrs*

Owens Polyscience Ltd, 34 Chester Road, Macclesfield, Cheshire, SK11 8DG Tel: (01625) 610118 Fax: (01625) 423850 *Scientific accessories suppliers*

Owl Security Services Ltd, 30C Cowbridge Road, Pontyclun, Mid Glamorgan, CF72 9EE Tel: (01443) 238600 Fax: (01443) 238600 E-mail: enquiries@owlsecurity.co.uk *CCTV, Alarm & door entry installation*

Owl Security Systems, 4 Balmoral Road, Gidea Park, Romford, RM2 5XD Tel: (01708) 454043 Fax: (01708) 440886 E-mail: enquiries@owlsecuritysystems.co.uk *Burglar alarm installers*

Ownglen Environmental Consultants, 169 Horbury Road, Wakefield, West Yorkshire, WF2 8BG Tel: (01924) 368822 Fax: (01924) 368833 *Environmental engineering*

Owta Ltd, Stratton House, Over Stratton, South Petherton, Somerset, TA13 5LQ Tel: (01460) 249170 Fax: (01460) 242235 *Computer consultancy*

▶ OX28 Media, Suite 3 Waterloo House, 58/60 High Street, Witney, Oxfordshire, OX28 6RJ Tel: (01993) 775388 E-mail: info@ox28media.com *Digital CDROM/ DVD printing duplication/replication/ packaging.*Video conversions from mini DV to DVD.*

Oxborrow Engineering, Malting Forge, Malting Lane, Kirby-le-Soken, Frinton-on-Sea, Essex, CO13 0EH Tel: (01255) 850850 Fax: (01255) 852666 E-mail: sales@oxborrowengineering.co.uk *Engineering steel fabrications stockholding*

▶ Oxcart Ltd, Unit 5a Power Park, Station Approach, Banbury, Oxfordshire, OX16 5AB Tel: (01295) 709607 Fax: (01295) 709807

Oxford Applied Research Ltd, Unit 31 Crawley Mill Industrial Estate, Dry Lane, Crawley, Witney, Oxfordshire, OX29 9SP Tel: (01993) 773575 Fax: (01993) 702326 E-mail: sales@oaresearch.co.uk *Scientific instrument manufrs*

Oxford Bearings Ltd, 41 Wedgewood Road, Bicester, Oxfordshire, OX26 4UL Tel: (01869) 249292 Fax: (01869) 241443 *Bearing & fastener distributors, agents & stockholders*

Oxford Bearings Ltd, 6 Chiltern Business Centre, Garsington Road, Oxford, OX4 6NG Tel: (01865) 718355 Fax: (01865) 747570 E-mail: oxford@oxfordbearings.co.uk *Nut & bolt distributors*

▶ Oxford Beds, 1a Bridge Street, Witney, Oxfordshire, OX28 1BY Tel: (01993) 771066 Fax: (01993) 771066 *Beds retailers*

Oxford Chemicals Ltd, Zinc Works Road, Seaton Carew, Hartlepool, Cleveland, TS25 2DT Tel: (01429) 863222 Fax: (01429) 867567 E-mail: sales@oxfordchemicals.com *Manufacturer of high impact aroma chemicals for use in the flavour and fragrance industry. *Experts in sulphur chemistry and toll manufacture capabilities.*

Oxford Computer Consultants Ltd, 23-38 Hythe Bridge Street, Oxford, OX1 2ET Tel: (01865) 305200 Fax: (01865) 793124 E-mail: oxford@cc.co.uk *Bespoke software design and development by highly qualified and experienced programmers in a well established company. We believe in giving first class service and support to our customers and aim to exceed their expectations.*

Oxford Computers, 30 Bulan Road, Headington, Oxford, OX3 7HT Tel: (01865) 747968 Fax: (01865) 747968 E-mail: oxford.computers@virgin.net *Computer maintenance & repairers*

Oxford Cryosystems, 3 Blenhiem Office Park, Lower Road, Long Hanborough, Witney, Oxfordshire, OX29 8LN Tel: (01993) 883488 Fax: (01993) 883988 E-mail: info@oxfordcryosystems.co.uk *Scientific equipment manufrs*

Oxford Design Bureau, 2 Fyfield Close, Wantage, Oxfordshire, OX12 8HN Tel: (01235) 770180 Fax: (01235) 770147 E-mail: oxfordpcbdesign@aol.com *PCB design & manufacturing services*

Oxford Electrical Ltd, 6 Sutton Oak Drive, St. Helens, Merseyside, WA9 3PH Tel: (01744) 820800 Fax: (01744) 820825 E-mail: oxfordrewind@aol.com *Electric motor repairs & sales*

Oxford Electronics, 5 Kendall Cresent, Oxford, OX2 8NE Tel: (01865) 510131 Fax: (01865) 311911 E-mail: sales@oxford-electronics.co.uk *Telephone equipment installers*

Oxford Fashions, 143 Oxford Street, Glasgow, G5 9JE Tel: 0141-429 4291 Fax: 0141-429 4291 *Clothing & fabric manufrs*

Oxford House College, 30 Market Place, London, W1W 8AW Tel: (020) 7436 4872 Fax: (020) 7323 4582 E-mail: english@oxfordhouse.co.uk *English language school*

▶ Oxford Instruments Analytical Ltd, Halifax Road, High Wycombe, Buckinghamshire, HP12 3SE Tel: (01494) 442255 Fax: (01494) 524129 E-mail: analytical@oxinst.co.uk Principal Export Areas: Worldwide *Laboratory instruments, manufrs*

Oxford Instruments Plasma Technology Ltd, North End Road, Yatton, Bristol, BS49 4AP Tel: (01934) 837000 Fax: (01934) 837001 E-mail: plasma.technology@oxinst.co.uk *Vacuum plasma & iron beam equipment*

Oxford Instruments Superconductivity, Tubney Woods, Abingdon, Oxfordshire, OX13 5QX Tel: (01865) 393200 Fax: (01865) 393333 E-mail: nanoscience@oxinst.co.uk *Manufacturers of cryogenic equip & scientific instruments*

▶ Oxford Internet Marketing, 10 Manor Farm Close, Kingham, Chipping Norton, Oxfordshire, OX7 6YX Tel: (01608) 658803 Fax: (0870) 1275668 E-mail: stephen@oxfordinternetmarketing.co.uk *Software development company*

▶ Oxford Lasers Ltd, Moorbrook Park, Didcot, Oxfordshire, OX11 7HP Tel: (01235) 814433 Fax: (01235) 810060 E-mail: admin@oxfordlasers.com *Laser systems suppliers*

Oxford Leathercraft, Northfield Works Sharps Yard, Long Wittenham, Abingdon, Oxfordshire, OX14 4QW Tel: (01865) 407100 Fax: (01865) 417120 *Leather goods manufrs*

▶ Oxford Management College, Eynsham Hall, North Leigh, Witney, Oxfordshire, OX29 6PN Tel: (01865) 514106 Fax: (01993) 883986 E-mail: info@oxfordmanagementcollege.com *Oxford Management College (OxMC) is a private independent college that, in partnership with London University, offers a challenging and motivational MBA programme leading to a London University Masters in International Business (MBA) Degree.*

Oxford Network Support, 6 Colwell Drive, Abingdon, Oxfordshire, OX14 1AU Tel: (01235) 468530 Fax: (01235) 555581 E-mail: sales@oxfordnetworksupport.com Sales Contact: C. Budd *Total manufacturing solutions including CNC machining, welding, assembly, test & supply chain management.*

▶ Oxford Pipework Services Ltd, Burcot Farm, Burcot, Abingdon, Oxfordshire, OX14 3DL Tel: (01865) 407812 Fax: (01865) 408015

Oxford Positron Systems Ltd, 5 Landscape Close, Weston-on-the-Green, Bicester, Oxfordshire, OX25 3SX Tel: (01869) 343618 Fax: (01865) 343619 *Imaging equipment manufrs*

Oxford Precision Components, Unit 1-5 Osney Mead, Oxford, OX2 0ES Tel: (01865) 798338 Fax: (01865) 798555 *CNC engineering services & machinists*

The Oxford Princeton Program, 1 St Floor, 59 St Aldates, Oxford, OX1 1ST Tel: (01865) 254520 Fax: (01865) 254599 E-mail: info@oxfordprinceton.com *Management training*

Oxford Refrigeration & Air Conditioning Ltd, 78-81 Magdalen Road, Oxford, OX4 1RF Tel: (01865) 424424 Fax: (01865) 424425 E-mail: ian.law@oracoxford.co.uk *Air conditioning installers*

Oxford Scientific Plastics, Varsity Works, Wimblestraw Road, Berinsfield, Wallingford, Oxfordshire, OX10 7QX Tel: (01865) 343555 Fax: (01865) 343123 *Precision plastic extrusions*

Oxford Scientific Products 2001, 74 Shakespeare Road, Eynsham, Witney, Oxfordshire, OX29 4PY Tel: (01865) 883211 Fax: (01865) 882232 E-mail: r.morton@ph.ox.ac.uk *Supply of nuclear radiation monitoring equipment*

Oxford Semiconductor Ltd, 25 Milton Park, Milton, Abingdon, Oxfordshire, OX14 4SH Tel: (01235) 824900 Fax: (01235) 821141 E-mail: sales@oxsemi.com *Integrated circuit consultants*

Oxford Software Engineering Ltd, 9 Spinners Court, West End, Witney, Oxfordshire, OX28 1NH Tel: (01993) 700878 Fax: (01993) 774132 E-mail: enquiries@ocl.co.uk *Software engineering consultants*

▶ Oxford Strategic Ltd, The Maggalen Centre, Oxford Science Park, Oxford, OX4 4GA Tel: (01865) 784110 Fax: (01865) 748111 E-mail: info@oxfordstrategic.com *Defence & communications consultancy.*Sales Assistance to overseas companies developing markets in the UK. *NHS Support Provider*

Oxford Technical Solutions, 77 Heyford Park, Camp Road, Upper Heyford, Bicester, Oxfordshire, OX25 5HD Tel: (01869) 238015 Fax: (01869) 238016 *Vehicle navigation equipment manufrs*

▶ Oxford Vacuum Science Ltd, 39 Southern Street, Middle Barton, Chipping Norton, Oxfordshire, OX7 7BU Tel: (01869) 349161 Fax: (01869) 349157 E-mail: ovs@oxford-vacuum.com *High vacuum design, consultancy & training service*

Oxford Water Softeners, 6 Bertie Road, Cumnor, Oxford, OX2 9PS Tel: (01865) 862795 Fax: (01865) 862795 *Water softening services*

Oxford Welding, Unit 1 Wharf Farm Buildings, Eynsham Road, Cassington, Witney, Oxfordshire, OX29 4DB Tel: (01865) 884366 Fax: (01865) 884366 *Metal welders*

Oxkem Chemical Mnfrs, 117 Loverock Road, Reading, RG30 1DZ Tel: 0118-952 2929 Fax: 0118-952 2959 E-mail: sales@oxkem.com *Chemical production & supply*

Oxleaze Workshop, Nempnett Thrubwell, Blagdon, Bristol, BS40 7UZ Tel: (01761) 462927 *Furniture making*

Oxley Developments Co. Ltd, Priory Park, Ulverston, Cumbria, LA12 9QG Tel: (01229) 582621 Fax: (01229) 483263 E-mail: sales@oxleygroup.com *Electronic component manufrs*

Graham Oxley Tool Steels Ltd, 55-57 Bridge Street, Sheffield, S3 8NS Tel: 0114-272 0403 Fax: 0114-275 2489 *Steel & spring steel stockholders. Also manufacturer of hand tools*

Oxley Threads Ltd, Guide Mills, South Street, Ashton-under-Lyne, Lancashire, OL7 0PJ Tel: 0161-339 6400 Fax: 0161-343 1705 E-mail: information@oxley-threads.com *Sewing thread manufrs*

Oxleys Furniture Ltd, Lapstone Farn, Westington Hill, Chipping Campden, Gloucestershire, GL55 6UR Tel: (01386) 840466 Fax: (01386) 840455 *Aluminium garden furniture manufrs*

▶ Oxlocks, 9 Marlborough Place, Charlbury, Chipping Norton, Oxfordshire, OX7 3SH Tel: (01608) 811418 E-mail: john@oxlocks.co.uk *Locksmiths*

Oxlox Burglar Alarm Systems, 33 Field Avenue, Oxford, OX4 6PA Tel: (01865) 747445 Fax: (01865) 747445 *Burglar alarm system manufrs*

Oxman & Walker, 4 Old Taunton Road, Bridgwater, Somerset, TA6 3NY Tel: (01278) 451783 Fax: (01278) 451783 *Joinery manufrs*

▶ Oxneygreen Ceramic Supplies & Services, Onega House, 112 Main Road, Sidcup, Kent, DA14 6NE Tel: (020) 8302 4935

Oxoid Holdings Ltd, Wade Road, Kingsland Industrial Park, Basingstoke, Hampshire, RG24 8PW Tel: (01256) 841144 Fax: (01256) 463388 E-mail: oxoid@oxoid.com *Microbiology diagnostics*

▶ Oxon Joinery & Interiors, Oxon Business Park, Bicton Heath, Shrewsbury, SY3 5DD Tel: (01743) 341902 Fax: (01743) 241400

▶ Oxplas Ltd, 104 Wycombe Road, Princes Risborough, Buckinghamshire, HP27 0EY Tel: (01844) 342184 Fax: (020) 8181 6050 E-mail: info@oxplas.co.uk *Buys & sells used recycling machinery for the plastics industry*

▶ Oxted Colour Printers Ltd, 6 Beadles Lane, Old Oxted, Oxted, Surrey, RH8 9JJ Tel: (01883) 712351 Fax: (01883) 717019

Oxted Health Foods, 75 Station Road East, Oxted, Surrey, RH8 0AX Tel: (01883) 730060 Fax: (01883) 730060 *Health food distributors*

Oxton Signs & Printers, Enfield Terrace, Prenton, Merseyside, CH43 4UB Tel: 0151-670 1779 Fax: 0151-652 6642 *Sign makers*

Oxy-Dry UK Inc, Unit 2, Whitworth Road, Stevenage, Hertfordshire, SG1 4QS Tel: (01438) 728881 Fax: (01438) 728309 *Supplies equipment for printing industries*

Oxygen 8, 10 Mount Ephraim, Tunbridge Wells, Kent, TN4 8AS Tel: (01825) 762444 Fax: (01892) 527652 E-mail: info@oxygenonline.co.uk *IT consultants*

▶ Oxygen Insurance Brokers Ltd, 34 Lime Street, London, EC3M 7AJ Tel: (0870) 1142643 Fax: (08701) 142644 *Oxygen is an insurance intermediary providing both broking and agency services. Our culture is one of entrepreneurialism reinforced through a disciplined approach to both business process and technology, thereby delivering a superior service to clients.*

Oxylitre Ltd, Morton House, 43-45 Skerton Road, Manchester, M16 0WJ Tel: 0161-872 6322 Fax: 0161-848 7914 E-mail: sales@oxylitre.co.uk *Healthcare equipment & services*

Oyez Straker, 4 City Park Industrial Estate, Gelderd Road, Leeds, LS12 6DR Tel: 0113-203 2100 Fax: 0113-263 9011 E-mail: sales.pudsey@oyezstraker.co.uk *Manufacturing stationers & printers*

Oyez Straker Office Supplies Ltd, Guild House, Wesley Drive, Newcastle upon Tyne, NE12 9UP Tel: 0191-215 0844 Fax: 0191-266 8450 *Office furniture, machines & equipment*

Oyez Straker Office Supplies Ltd, 2 Didcot Road, Nuffield Industrial Estate, Poole, Dorset, BH17 0GD Tel: (01202) 681456 Fax: (01202) 665274 E-mail: david.hale@oyezstraker.co.uk *Legal stationers & printers*

▶ Oyezstraker Professional Print, Unit 4 Stafford Cross Business Park, Croydon, CR0 4TU Tel: (020) 8603 5180 Fax: (020) 8686 4402

Oyster Pools & Leisure Ltd, Raglan Garden Centre, Abergavenny Road, Raglan, Usk, Gwent, NP15 2BH Tel: (01291) 690614 Fax: (01291) 690951 E-mail: info@oysterpools.co.uk *Swimming pool & hot tubs manufrs*

Oyster Products Ltd, Unit 3 Stonestile Farm, Stone Stile Farm, Selling, Faversham, Kent, ME13 9SD Tel: (01227) 732345 Fax: (01227) 738850 E-mail: oysterproducts@hotmail.com Principal Export Areas: Africa *Fibreglass mouldings manufrs*

▶ Oyster Software, Alexander House, Fleming Way, Swindon, SN1 2NG Tel: (01793) 530111 Fax: (01793) 530333

Ozbox, Herald Way, Binley Industrial Estate, Binley Industrial Estate, Coventry, CV3 2RQ Tel: (024) 7656 1561 Fax: (024) 7656 1555 E-mail: tena.snell@ozbox.co.uk *Corrugated carton manufrs*

▶ Ozon LPG Installations Ltd, Unit 10 Miller Court Millbay Road, Millbay, Plymouth, PL1 3LQ Tel: (01752) 249915 Fax: (01752) 249915 E-mail: info@ozonlpg.com *Duel fuel vehicles auto gas conversions*

Ozone Fire Protection Ltd, Havyatt Manor, Havyatt, Glastonbury, Somerset, BA6 8LF Tel: (0800) 006900 *Fire protection engineers*

▶ Oztec, 1 Compass Terrace, Southwell Business Park, Portland, Dorset, DT5 2NP Tel: (01305) 823322 Fax: (01305) 823355 E-mail: enquiries@oztec.co.uk *Refurbishing plastics*

OZ-UK Innovations Ltd, Christmas Cottage, Hilgay Road, West Dereham, King's Lynn, Norfolk, PE33 9RN Tel: (01553) 619483 Fax: (01553) 828497 E-mail: peach@oz-uk.com *Have the Building you WANT! Individually Custom designed! Fair Dinkum Sheds now available in the UK. We only use Gliderol roller doors. 2year electrical components warranty, 6year Mechanical parts warranty & 10years Door finish warranty! It's PLASTISOL coated & its CORUS steel! Low Cost Prefabricated Design, Innate fire proof qualities of Steel, Quality "Corus" Steel (British Steel) Strength, Longevity, Atheistic appeal, Plastisol Coated unless stated, Fully Galvanised 'C' Section Frame, Easy Self Erection. The price you see is the price you pay! Our buildings are available in a variety of sizes/ designs: Single Garages, Double garages, Triple garages, actually as many as you require garages! Contact our main office in Kings Lynn today! Workshops Norfolk, Equestrian Barns, Stables, Storage units, Light Industrial units. Garages Norfolk, Steel buildings Norfolk, Workshops Norfolk, Barns Norfolk, Equestrian barns Norfolk, Storage Units Norfolk. Steel Buildings, Steel buildings Norfolk.*

P + B Gora Ltd, 119 Oak Road, West Bromwich, West Midlands, B70 8HP Tel: 0121-580 4984 Fax: 0121-525 8742 *Outwear manufrs*

P 15 Plastics Ltd, 161 Waterside Road, Hamilton, Leicester, LE5 1TL Tel: 0116-276 1495 Fax: 0116-246 0489 E-mail: info@p15plastics.co.uk *Injection moulders*

P A Brenchley & Sons, Clergy Farm Sutton Road, Four Gotes, Tydd, Wisbech, Cambridgeshire, PE13 5PH Tel: (01945) 420738 Fax: (01945) 420788 *Fabrication engineers*

P A Bristow & Co., Station Yard Industrial Estate, Station Road, Heckington, Sleaford, Lincolnshire, NG34 9JJ Tel: (01529) 460540 Fax: (01529) 461232 E-mail: carolenpeter@aol.com *Power tool & fixing suppliers*

P A Business Systems Ltd, 5-7 The Pathway, Bowlalley Lane, Hull, HU1 1XJ Tel: (01482) 328607 Fax: (01482) 218236 E-mail: headoffice@pa-business.co.uk *Computer reseller & development*

▶ P.A.C.E Training Consultants, 21 Babylon Lane, Anderton, Chorley, Lancashire, PR6 9NR Tel: (01257) 474467 E-mail: info@adventure21.co.uk *No Nonsence Corperate training, team building, corporate events, management incentive days.*

P A C International Ltd, 1 Park Gate Close, Bredbury Park Way, Bredbury, Stockport, Cheshire, SK6 2SZ Tel: 0161-494 1331 Fax: 0161-430 8658 E-mail: info@pac.co.uk *Security access control systems manufrs*

P A C Software Ltd, Worcester Road, Hanley Swan, Worcester, WR8 0EA Tel: (01684) 311226 Fax: (01684) 311227 E-mail: sales@pacsoftware.co.uk *Design software developers*

P A Computers, Highcross Road, Southfleet, Gravesend, Kent, DA13 9PH Tel: (01474) 833933 Fax: (01474) 834446 E-mail: mail@pacomputers.co.uk *Computer repairs*

P A D International, National Trading Estate, Bramhall Moor Lane, Hazel Grove, Stockport, Cheshire, SK7 5AA Tel: 0161-456 5660 Fax: 0161-456 5660 *Workwear manufrs*

P A Electrical Ltd, Childerditch Industrial Park, Childerditch Hall Drive, Little Warley, Brentwood, Essex, CM13 3XU Tel: (01277) 812881 Fax: (01277) 812661 E-mail: cpettit55@aol.com *Electrical installation manufrs*

▶ P & A Engineering, Crown Works, Parry Lane, Bradford, West Yorkshire, BD4 8TJ Tel: (01274) 744887 Fax: (01274) 733335 E-mail: info@panda-engineering.co.uk *Engineers*

▶ P A F Systems Ltd, Brunel Close, Park Farm Industrial Estate, Wellingborough, Northamptonshire, NN8 6QX Tel: (01933) 403555 Fax: (01933) 403888 E-mail: sales@pafsystem.com *Workstations for industry, motor sports & education*

P A G Computers, 5 Bell Close, Knebworth, Hertfordshire, SG3 6AJ Tel: (01438) 814650 Fax: (01438) 814111 E-mail: admin@pagcomputers.com *Computer consultants*

P A G Sheet Metal Ltd, 4 River Brent Business Park, Trumpers Way, London, W7 2QA Tel: (020) 8574 3577 Fax: (020) 8893 5370 E-mail: sales@pagsheetmetal.com *Sheetmetal fabrication*

P A Gay, Westmanton, Ashwater, Beaworthy, Devon, EX21 5HD Tel: (01409) 211245 Fax: (01409) 211483 *Farm*

▶ P A Grant Electrical Contractors Ltd, 62 London Road, Canterbury, Kent, CT2 8JZ Tel: (01227) 472580 Fax: (01227) 763217

P & A Group of Companies, Mold Industrial Estate, Wrexham Road, Mold, Flintshire, CH7 4HE Tel: (01352) 752555 Fax: (01352) 755200 E-mail: sales@p-a-group.com *Pallet, fencing & shed manufrs*

P A Hill Fasteners Ltd, 25 Sherwood Road, Bromsgrove, Worcestershire, B60 3DR Tel: (01527) 575838 Fax: (01527) 870419 E-mail: sales@pahillfasteners.co.uk *Bolt, nut, screw & nail distributors*

P A International Consulting Group Ltd, 123 Buckingham Palace Road, London, SW1W 9SR Tel: (020) 7730 9000 Fax: (020) 7333 5050 E-mail: info@paconsulting.com *Management selection consultants* Also at: Branches throughout the U.K.

P A L Adhesive Products Ltd, Old Park Industrial Estate, Old Park Road, Wednesbury, West Midlands, WS10 9LR Tel: 0121-556 6686 Fax: 0121-505 1487 E-mail: sales@paladhesives.co.uk *Adhesive tape manufrs*

▶ P A L S Labelling Ltd, Quebec Street, Oldham, OL9 6QJ Tel: 0161-620 0236 Fax: 0161-627 1003 E-mail: sales@palslabelling.com *Labelling machine manufrs*

▶ P A Laing, Windyridge, Bonchester Bridge, Hawick, Roxburghshire, TD9 8QY Tel: (01450) 860200 Fax: (01450) 860362

P & A Leat Engineering Ltd, First Avenue, Midsomer Norton, Radstock, BA3 4BS Tel: (01761) 416964 Fax: (01761) 417134 *Steel fabricators*

P A Loading Systems Ltd, 9 Kineton Road, Kenilworth, Warwickshire, CV8 2AW Tel: (01926) 851619 Fax: (01926) 850478 E-mail: davidparry@mash-b.co.uk *Electric vehicle manufrs*

P A Moston, 1 Holly House Estate, Middlewich Road, Cranage, Middlewich, Cheshire, CW10 9LT Tel: (01606) 737464 Fax: (01606) 738300 *Commercial & agricultural repairs*

P & A Newcombe, 1 Canal Terrace, Worksop, Nottinghamshire, S80 2DF Tel: (01909) 475664 *Saddlery manufrs*

P & A Packing (Northern) Ltd, Huntsman Drive, Irlam, Manchester, M44 5PA Tel: 0161-777 8199 Fax: 0161-777 8089 E-mail: papack@globalnet.co.uk *Packaging services*

▶ P & A Press, P & A House, Alma Road, Chesham, Buckinghamshire, HP5 3HB Tel: (01494) 773075 Fax: (01494) 775858

P A R Communications (Leeds) Ltd, Mile End Road, Colwick Industrial Estate, Colwick, Nottingham, NG4 2BU Tel: 0115-961 4744 Fax: 0115-940 0714 E-mail: parcom@btconnect.com *Screw jack manufrs*

P A R Harris, Cloneen, Hindon Lane, Tisbury, Salisbury, SP3 6PU Tel: (01747) 871991 Fax: (01747) 871991 *Safety & transport services*

P A R (Preston) Ltd, Club Street, Bamber Bridge, Preston, PR5 6FN Tel: (01772) 322114 Fax: (01772) 627524 *Plastics, insulation & rubber products manufrs*

P A S M A, PO Box 168, Leeds, LS11 9WW Tel: (0845) 2304041 Fax: (0845) 2304042 E-mail: pasma@portfolio-support.co.uk *Aluminium scaffolding manufrs*

Company Information

P A Seccombe & Son Ltd, Syon Lane, Isleworth, Middlesex, TW7 5PW Tel: (020) 8560 2246 Fax: (020) 8847 2849 E-mail: sales@seccombe.co.uk *SECCOMBE GROUP OF BUILDERS' MERCHANTS is a long established group of companies trading in the industry for over 75 years. Trading in all Building and Maintenance materials from BRICKS SAND CEMENT TIMBER and CONCRETE products to decorative Supplies like PAVING PATIOS DECKING KITCHENS and BATHROOMS. You will find competitive prices on all your purchases from our comprehensive range of all BUILDING MATERIALS and extensive range of TIMBER, through to a full range of PLUMBING and IRONMONGERY FITTINGS, backed by a first class service offered by trained staff. We have excellent display showrooms, and can supply fitted kitchens and bathrooms. Our depots trade six days per week.* Also at: Croydon & West Wickham

P & A Services Ltd, Pepper Road, Hazel Grove, Stockport, Cheshire, SK7 5BW Tel: 0161-483 8060 Fax: 0161-483 8066 E-mail: sales@paservice.co.uk *Supply & install catering industry equipment*

▶ P A Sewell Ltd, Linchmere Place, Crawley, West Sussex, RH11 0EX Tel: (01293) 523790 Fax: (01293) 553849

▶ P A Smith & Son, Martins Grove, Whitchurch, Ross-On-Wye, Herefordshire, HR9 6BJ Tel: (01600) 890448

▶ P & A Taxi Meters, 6 Foundation Units, Westfield Road, Slyfield Industrial Estate, Guildford, Surrey, GU1 1SF Tel: (01483) 535353 Fax: (01483) 450222 E-mail: don@novaxuk.com *Supplier to the taxi trade*

P A Turney, The Corner Unit, Gatehouse Way, Aylesbury, Buckinghamshire, HP19 8DB Tel: (01296) 398005 Fax: (01296) 433005 *Agricultural & horticultural engineers*

P A Turney Ltd, Middleton Stoney, Bicester, Oxfordshire, OX25 4AB Tel: (01869) 343333 Fax: (01869) 343540 *Agricultural engineers* Also at: Chipping Norton, Wellingborough & Weston-on-the-Green

P A Turney Ltd, Worcester Road Industrial Estate, Chipping Norton, Oxfordshire, OX7 5XW Tel: (01608) 642131 Fax: (01608) 644413 *Agricultural equipment sales & service to trade & retail*

P A Turney Ltd, Edmonds Close, Denington Industrial Estate, Wellingborough, Northamptonshire, NN8 2QY Tel: (01933) 443333 Fax: (01933) 443340 *Agricultural engineers*

P A V Electronics Ltd, Unit 7, Stirling Road Industrial Estate, Airdrie, Lanarkshire, ML6 7UD Tel: (01236) 764162 Fax: (01236) 747700 E-mail: rob@pavelectronics.co.uk *Control systems manufrs*

▶ P B A Express Ltd, 51 Bishop Road, Ammanford, Dyfed, SA18 3HA Tel: (01269) 596210 Fax: (01269) 592553 E-mail: enquiries@pbaexpress.co.uk *Specialists in dedicated vehicles, delivering urgent and 'just in time' goods throughout the whole of Europe. Whether you require transport for exhibition stands or a pallet of urgent parts we can help. Unlike many freight companies PBA Express willl not tranship your goods between vehicles. We provide a professional, reliable, courteous and efficient service at a competitive price.*

P B A Heat Treating Ltd, Unit 7-8, Bevan Industrial Estate, Brierley Hill, West Midlands, DY5 3TF Tel: (01384) 480331 Fax: (01384) 78381 E-mail: sales@pbaheattreatment.co.uk *Metal heat treatment services*

P B Abrasives Ltd, 4 Gilston Road, Saltash, Cornwall, PL12 6TW Tel: (01752) 846713 Fax: (01752) 848771 *Super abrasive tools manufrs*

P B Baumann Hand Tools, Wharf Street, Warwick, CV34 5LB Tel: (01926) 403469 Fax: (01926) 403777 E-mail: sales@waricksupplies.com *Hand tool distributors*

P B Beauty, Aintree Avenue, White Horse Business Park, Trowbridge, Wiltshire, BA14 0XB Tel: (01225) 768491 Fax: (01225) 716100 *Toiletry suppliers*

▶ P & B Builders (Scotland) Ltd, 3-5 Rhannan Road, Glasgow, G44 3AZ Tel: 0141-633 2148

P B Design & Developments Ltd, Unit 9-10, Hither Green, Clevedon, Avon, BS21 6XT Tel: (01275) 874411 Fax: (01275) 874428 E-mail: administrator@pbdesign.co.uk *Power supply (standby) manufrs*

P B Designs, The Courtyard, Milton Road, Aylesbury, Buckinghamshire, HP21 7LZ Tel: (01296) 433393 Fax: (01296) 433393 E-mail: all@pbdesigns.demon.co.uk *Injection mould designers*

P & B Electrical Company, 1a St Dunstans Road, London, SE25 6EU Tel: (020) 8771 6555 Fax: (020) 8771 9867 *Electric motor & pump repair services*

P & B Engineering, Factory Estate College Road, Unit 7, Perry Barr, Birmingham, B44 8BS Tel: 0121-356 5490 Fax: 0121-356 4295 *Press toolmakers & production toolmakers*

P & B Engineering Ltd, Bell Vue Works, Boundary St, Manchester, M12 5NG Tel: 0161-230 6363 Fax: 0161-230 6464 E-mail: mail@pbeng.co.uk *Protection relay & motor protection manufrs* Also at: Manchester

P B Engineering, Ysgyborwen Farm Bungalow, Llantrisant, Usk, Gwent, NP15 1LU Tel: (01291) 673274 Fax: (01291) 673274 *Agricultural engineers*

P B F Press Ltd, 12 Little Ridge, Welwyn Garden City, Hertfordshire, AL7 2BH Tel: (01707) 372185 Fax: (01707) 375580 E-mail: pbf-press@btconnect.com *Commercial printers services*

P & B Fabrications Ltd, Unit 5 Marston Moor Business Park, Tockwith, York, YO26 7QF Tel: (01423) 359016 Fax: (01423) 359084 *Steel fabricators*

P B Group Ltd, On The Common, Rochester, Kent, ME1 1PR Tel: (01634) 845592 Fax: (01634) 832421 E-mail: pb@pbgroup.co.uk *Design print & exhibition*

P B H Precision Engineering Co. Ltd, 112 Windmill Road, Sunbury-on-Thames, Middlesex, TW16 7HB Tel: (01932) 785211 Fax: (01932) 781180 E-mail: sales@pbhprecision.com *General engineering services*

P B I International Ltd, Unit 29-30, Roper Close, Canterbury, Kent, CT2 7EP Tel: (01227) 455800 Fax: (01227) 458838 E-mail: sales@ball-bearings.co.uk Sales Contact: Y. Zens *Distributors/agents/stockholders of bearings including miniature/instrument, stainless steel & stainless steel thin section. In addition, distributors/agents/stockholders of bearings, including thrust, stainless steel, plastic, miniature & thin section*

P B I Precision Engineers, Unit A, Bull Street Trading Estate, Bull Street, Brierley Hill, West Midlands, DY5 3RA Tel: (01384) 79006 Fax: (01384) 79006 *Sub-contract manufrs*

P B K Micron Ltd, Unit 6 Kingfield Industrial Estate, Coventry, CV1 4DW Tel: (024) 7622 0376 Fax: (024) 7660 7819 E-mail: sales@pbk-micron.co.uk *Production engineers*

P B M Building Services Ltd, 70 Whalebone Lane South, Dagenham, Essex, RM8 1BB Tel: (020) 8595 5566

P & B Metal Components Ltd, Tyler Way, Colewood Road, Whitstable, Kent, CT5 2RR Tel: (01227) 793456 Fax: (01227) 793597 *Electronic components distributors & manufacturers metal components*

▶ P B National Products Ltd, Unit 107 Marchington Industrial Estate, Stubby Lane, Marchington, Uttoxeter, Staffordshire, ST14 8LP Tel: (01283) 576860 Fax: (01283) 821180

P B O Ltd, Unit 18 Shepperton Business Park, Govett Avenue, Shepperton, Middlesex, TW17 8BA Tel: (01932) 232233 Fax: (01932) 243516 E-mail: paul@pbologistics.com *International shipping & forwarding agents*

P B Power, Unit 4-5, Ferrybridge Business Park, Knottingley, West Yorkshire, WF11 8NA Tel: (01977) 677664 Fax: (01977) 672009 E-mail: info@pbworld.com *Plant assessment engineers*

P & B Power Engineering, Belle Vue Works, Boundary St, Manchester, M12 5NG Tel: 0161-223 5151 Fax: 0161-230 6464 E-mail: sales@pbeng.co.uk *Industrial switchgear manufrs*

P B R (Abrasives) Ltd, The Quadrant, 99 Parkway Avenue, Sheffield, S9 4WG Tel: 0114-243 3700 Fax: 0114-243 3527 E-mail: sales@pbrabrasives.com *Abrasives wheel distributor*

P B R Abrasives (Wolverhampton) Ltd, 8-10 Wolverhampton Street, Willenhall, West Midlands, WV13 2NF Tel: (01902) 368624 Fax: (01902) 634635 E-mail: sales@pbrabrasives.com *Distributor of grinding wheels & abrasives*

▶ P B R Building Services Ltd, 3 Holland Hurst Road, Coatbridge, Lanarkshire, ML5 2EG Tel: (07786) 837746 Fax: (01236) 423857 E-mail: jamie@pbr.me.uk *Roughcasting & rendering specialists services*

P B S Ltd, Unit 13 Lowesmoor Wharf, Lowesmoor, Worcester, WR1 2RS Tel: (01905) 617655 Fax: (01905) 726539 E-mail: gummpowder@aol.com *Powder coating plant installation.*

P B S C Ltd, Bradley Junction Industrial Estate, Leeds Road, Huddersfield, HD2 1UR Tel: (01484) 354500 Fax: (01484) 354504 E-mail: info@pbsc.co.uk *Clean room door supplier*

P B S Computers, 72-74 Ashley Road, Poole, Dorset, BH14 9BN Tel: (01202) 668822 Fax: (01202) 772627 E-mail: info@pbscomputers.co *IT consultants*

P B Signs & Designs, 88 Walthew Lane, Platt Bridge, Wigan, Lancashire, WN2 5AL Tel: (01942) 866240 Fax: (01942) 866240 *Sign manufrs*

P & B Weir, Unit 10 Leafield Industrial Estate, Leafield Way, Corsham, Wiltshire, SN13 9SW Tel: (01225) 811449 Fax: (01225) 810909 E-mail: sales@pbweir.com *Educational & industrial instruments*

P Bastow, Silver Street, Reeth, Richmond, North Yorkshire, DL11 6SP Tel: (01748) 884555 Fax: (01748) 884181 *Cabinet manufrs*

P Best Timber Preservation & Joinery, 1 Cowpen Lane, Billingham, Cleveland, TS23 1LA Tel: (01642) 551182 Fax: (01642) 361641 *Joinery manufrs*

P Binnington, Botany Farm, East Lulworth, Wareham, Dorset, BH20 5QH Tel: (01929) 400224 Fax: (01929) 400744 E-mail: p.binnington@aol.co.uk *Mirrors & decorative glass suppliers*

▶ P Brady Contractors Ltd, 48 Churchfield Road, London, W3 6DL Tel: (020) 8992 9861 Fax: (020) 8992 5597

▶ P Branson & Co., Unit 14 Annwood Lodge, Arterial Road, Rayleigh, Essex, SS6 7UA Tel: (01268) 728220 Fax: (01268) 728221

P Brockwell, Pocklington Industrial Estate, Pocklington, York, YO42 1NP Tel: (01759) 304742 Fax: (01759) 304742 E-mail: enquiries@brockwellfabrications.co.uk *General fabrication and welding work, general engineering, security and wrought iron work.*

▶ P Bromley & Sons Ltd, British Queen Depot, Huddersfield Road, Low Moor, Bradford, West Yorkshire, BD12 0TQ Tel: (01274) 605442 Fax: (01274) 670175

P Burley & Son, Magna Mile, Ludford, Market Rasen, Lincolnshire, LN8 6AH Tel: (01507) 313620 Fax: (01507) 313620 *Steel fabrication & crane hire*

▶ P C, Langley Parade, Crawley, West Sussex, RH11 7RS Tel: (01293) 530823 Fax: (01293) 530823 *Computer software manufrs*

P C 2000, 1339 Dumbarton Road, Glasgow, G14 9UZ Tel: 0141-959 4877 Fax: 0141-576 0156 *Computer systems, networking & hardware design & sales*

P C B Security Systems, 60 Kingswood Cresent, Rayleigh, Essex, SS6 7BH Tel: (01268) 741006 Fax: (01268) 741006 *Installers of security alarm systems*

P C B UK, Ramsey Road, Sydenham Industrial Estate, Leamington Spa, Warwickshire, CV31 1PG Tel: (01926) 744414 Fax: (01926) 744411 E-mail: sales@pcbuk.com *Manufacturers*

▶ P C C Maintenance Ltd, 162 Oundle Road, Thrapston, Kettering, Northamptonshire, NN14 4PQ Tel: (0845) 1662916

P C Cash Control Systems, 176 Tynemouth Road, North Shields, Tyne & Wear, NE30 1EG Tel: 0191-257 3738 E-mail: sales@pccash.co.uk *EPOS systems dealers*

▶ P C Clinic Plus, 28 Lenton Boulevard, Nottingham, NG7 2ES Tel: (0800) 5191010 Fax: E-mail: help@pcclinicplus.co.uk *Computer Hardware & Software repairs and upgrades direct to your home or office.*

P C Computer Clinic, Clyde Street, Londonderry, BT48 7EJ Tel: (028) 7128 3355 Fax: (028) 7128 3356 E-mail: jerry@pccomputerclinic.com *Computer maintenance & repairers*

P C Computer Services, 16 South Avenue, Bognor Regis, West Sussex, PO21 3QS Tel: (01243) 820840 Fax: (01243) 842961 E-mail: sales@pc-computers.co.uk *Computer consultants*

P C Concepts, 9 Bolton Road, Worsley, Manchester, M28 3AX Tel: 0161-703 9025 Fax: 0161-703 9426 E-mail: sales@pc-concepts.co.uk *Computer manufacturer & retailer*

▶ P C Construction Ltd, Chorlton Lane, Chorlton-by-Backford, Chester, CH2 4DD Tel: (01244) 851875 Fax: (01244) 851874 E-mail: pcconstruction@btopenworld.com *Gabion, reinforced earth walls construction specialists*

P C Consultants, Enterprise Court, Ryde Business Park, Ryde, Isle of Wight, PO33 1BD Tel: (01983) 811711 Fax: (01934) 811801 E-mail: sales@pcconsultants.co.uk *Web design & integrated database services*

P C Consulting, 1 Yate Lane, Oxenhope, Keighley, West Yorkshire, BD22 9HL Tel: (01535) 645226 E-mail: info@pcconsulting.co.uk *PC consultancy services*

▶ P C Consumables, Headingley Lane, Leeds, LS6 1BL Tel: 0113-289 9555 *Computer peripheral & components retailer*

P C Cox Ltd, Turnpike Industrial Estate, Newbury, Berkshire, RG14 2LR Tel: (01635) 264500 Fax: (01635) 264555 E-mail: sales@pccox.co.uk *Sealant application equipment & adhesive manufrs*

P C D Products Ltd, Cleveland Road, Hemel Hempstead Industrial Estate, Hemel Hempstead, Hertfordshire, HP2 7EY Tel: (01442) 248565 Fax: (01442) 241033 E-mail: sales@pcdproducts.co.uk *Sheet metalwork engineers or fabricators*

P C E S Ltd, 20 Wulfrun Trading Estate, Stafford Road, Wolverhampton, WV10 6HH Tel: (01902) 713402 Fax: (01902) 714216 E-mail: sales@pces.uk.com *Pipeline construction equipment distributors & agents*

P C Engravers World Of Trophies, 29 Lower Addiscombe Road, Croydon, CR0 6PQ Tel: (020) 8680 1354 Fax: (020) 8686 8706 E-mail: pcengravers@btconnect.com *Nameplate & sports trophy engravers* Also at: Mitcham

P C Express, 13 Whitchurch Lane, Edgware, Middlesex, HA8 6JZ Tel: (020) 8951 3304 Fax: (020) 8951 3305 E-mail: support@pcexpress.co.uk *Hardware manufrs*

P C Food, Blackbird Road, Leicester, LE1 5DR Tel: 0116-251 9933 Fax: 0116-251 5510 E-mail: sales@pc-food.co.uk *Computer consumable services*

▶ P C Friend, Unit 2, Windsor Court, Morley, Leeds, LS27 9BG Tel: 0113-259 7595 Fax: 0113-275 1552 *Computer software consumable suppliers*

P C G Hydraulics Ltd, Dutton Road, Aldermans Green Industrial Estate, Coventry, CV2 2LE Tel: (024) 7661 8533 Fax: (024) 7661 5944 E-mail: sales@pcg-hydraulics.co.uk *Hydraulic test rigs, systems, pumps, actuators suppliers*

P C Graphics, Unit 1, Langley House, Middlegreen Trading Estate, Langley, Slough, SL3 6DF Tel: (01753) 571220 Fax: (01753) 692380 E-mail: sales@pcgraphics.co.uk *Graphic, web and printing designers.*

▶ P C Graphics (UK) Ltd, 1 Westminster Court, Hipley Street, Woking, Surrey, GU22 9LG Tel: (01483) 770691 Fax: (01483) 729281 E-mail: info@pcgraphics.uk.com *Cartographers*

P C H Supplies, 47 Washway Road, Sale, Cheshire, M33 7AB Tel: 0161-976 4136 Fax: 0161-439 9435 *Catering Equipment Distributors. Light Catering Equipment Supplies, Tableware and Kitchen Equipment.*

▶ P & C Hamilton, 16 Grangestone Industrial Estate, Ladywell Avenue, Girvan, Ayrshire, KA26 9PF Tel: (01465) 714742 Fax: (01465) 714842

P C Henderson Ltd, Durham Road, Bowburn, Durham, DH6 5NG Tel: 0191-377 0701 Fax: 0191-377 1309 E-mail: sales@pchenderson.com *Garage door manufrs*

▶ P C Homecall, The Chase, Kilburn, Belper, Derbyshire, DE56 0PL Tel: (0845) 8385204 E-mail: matt@pchomecall.org.uk *PC Homecall deal with PC Repairs/Maintenance, Networking Wired and Wireless, Data Recovery, Web Design, Web Hosting and much more! Go on give us try*

P C Howard Ltd, West Hay, Kings Cliffe, Peterborough, PE8 6XX Tel: (01780) 444444 Fax: (01780) 444744 *Freight forwarders & export packers* Also at: Corby

P C Hydraulics (Northern) Ltd, 6-8 Hillkirk Street, Beswick, Manchester, M11 3EZ Tel: 0161-273 1660 Fax: 0161-273 5002 E-mail: enquiries@pc-hydraulics.co.uk *Hydraulic engineers*

P C I, Duke Street, New Basford, Nottingham, NG7 7JN Tel: 0115-970 3451 Fax: 0115-978 1547 E-mail: info@pacificconcept.com *Garment decoration systems manufrs*

▶ P C I London, Unit G4, Harbour Yard, Chelsea Harbour, London, SW10 0XD Tel: (020) 7544 7500 Fax: (020) 7352 7906 E-mail: reception@pci-live.com *Corporate events*

P C Ideals, 89 Albert Road, Southsea, Hampshire, PO5 2SG Tel: (023) 9282 9239 Fax: (023) 9286 2111 E-mail: sales@pcideals.com *Hardware suppliers*

▶ P C Image, Unit 4-5, The Square, Vicarage Farm Road, Peterborough, PE1 5TS Tel: (01733) 349032 Fax: (01733) 352472 E-mail: sales@pcimage.co.uk *PC services*

P C Innovations, 3 Cardine Close, Sittingbourne, Kent, ME10 2HY Tel: (01795) 410264 Fax: (01795) 410283 E-mail: enquiries@pc-i.co.uk *IT consultancy*

P C L Machinery, 5 Elan Court, Norris Way, Rushden, Northants, NN10 6BP Tel: (01933) 410707 Fax: (01933) 410807 E-mail: sales@pclmachinery.co.uk Principal Export Areas: Africa *Packaging equipment and packaging machinery, metal detectors for packaging industry, metal detectors for food stuffs. PCL Machinery concentrate on the more specific areas of checkweighting and metal detection. PCL Machinery encompass all machine makes and have become a major supplier to other machinery dealers of quality used machinery. PCL Machinery are unique in that all equipment is specified to suit each particular application - just as it would be if the customer purchased new. All refurbished units are supplied in the UK with a full six months parts and labour warranty against faulty operation or workmanship. Overseas the warranty extends to parts only, except where specific dealer arrangements apply.*

P C Link Supplies Ltd, Ruxox House, Maulden Road, Flitwick, Bedford, MK45 5BN Tel: (01525) 717772 Fax: (01525) 717773 E-mail: sales@businesshomecomputers.com *Computer software suppliers*

P C M, Prenton Way, North Cheshire Trading Estate, Prenton, Merseyside, CH43 3DU Tel: 0151-609 0101 Fax: 0151-609 0200 *Lifting equipment suppliers*

P C M Engineering Services Ltd, Castleblair Works, Castle Blair Lane, Dunfermline, Fife, KY12 9DP Tel: (01383) 733334 Fax: (01383) 739496 *Air compressors & mechanical engineers*

P C M Group, Folgate Lane, Magdalen, King's Lynn, Norfolk, PE34 3DA Tel: (01553) 811588 Fax: (01553) 810342 *Bottling equipment suppliers*

P C M Group UK Ltd, Pilot Road, Corby, Northamptonshire, NN17 5YF Tel: (01536) 740200 Fax: (01536) 740201 E-mail: sales@pcmgroupuk.eu *Pump distributors & manufrs*

P C M Technologies, 45 Borthwick Road, London, E15 1UE Tel: (020) 8519 4497 Fax: (020) 8519 1429 E-mail: sales@pcmtec.co.uk *apple macintosh computer sales and support services*

P C M Tooling UK Ltd, 825 The Ridge, St. Leonards-on-Sea, East Sussex, TN37 7PX Tel: (01424) 753174 Fax: (01424) 753089 E-mail: ukpcmtlg@aol.com *Machine tool holder systems importers*

▶ P C Mcqueenie, Carpet Lane, Edinburgh, EH6 6SP Tel: 0131-468 7061 Fax: 0131-467 0099

P C Microfix Ltd, 149 Uxbridge Road, London, W7 3ST Tel: (020) 8579 7474 Fax: (020) 8579 1667 E-mail: microfix@aol.com *Computer maintenance services*

P C P Gratings Ltd, Enterprise Drive, Four Ashes, Wolverhampton, WV10 7DF Tel: (01902) 791792 Fax: (01902) 791795 E-mail: sales@pcp.dk *Flooring contractors*

▶ P C Packaging Ltd, P C House, Vulcan Road, Bilston, West Midlands, WV14 7HT Tel: (01902) 495200 Fax: (01902) 495275 *Cardboard manufrs*

P & C Pallets Ltd, Timber Yard, Llandowlais Street, Oakfield, Cwmbran, Gwent, NP44 7HD Tel: (01633) 870055 E-mail: michelle@pcpallets.co.uk *manufacturers of wooden pallets & cases,suppliers of reconditioned & export/heat treated pallets & timber(ISPM15)*

P C Part X Computers, 77 Bawtry Road, Bramley, Rotherham, South Yorkshire, S66 2TN Tel: (01709) 701200 Fax: (01709) 701200 E-mail: sales@pcpartx.com *Computer parts suppliers, builders & repairers*

▶ P C Plastics, Unit A1, Locking Farm Industrial Estate, Locking Moor Road, Weston-Super-Mare, Avon, BS24 8PJ Tel: (01934) 820678 Fax: (01934) 820678 *Plastic injection moulders*

P C Point Of Sale, Units 1-3 The Rutherford Centre, Rutherford Road, Basingstoke, Hants, RG24 8PB Tel: (01256) 356161 Fax: (01256) 356112 *EPOS distributors*

▶ P & C Precision Engineers Ltd, Unit 3c Heron Trading Estate, Whitefield Avenue, Luton, LU3 3BB Tel: (01582) 581735 Fax: (01582) 581735

P C S, 143 East Reach, Taunton, Somerset, TA1 3HN Tel: (01823) 354000 *Computer hardware engineers*

P C S Amlico Ltd, Wakefield Commercial Park, Bridge Road, Horbury, Wakefield, West Yorkshire, WF4 5NW Tel: (01924) 280130 Fax: (01924) 280018 E-mail: info@pcsamlico.co.uk *Manufacturer of disposable paper products*

P C S Cables & Connectors Ltd, 14-16 Kingfisher Park, Three Cross Road, West Moors, Wimborne, Dorset, BH21 6US Tel: (01202) 871924 Fax: (01202) 895661 E-mail: enquiries@pcscables.com *Cable colouring & marking services*

▶ P C S Personal Computer Systems Ltd, 531 Millbrook Road West, Regents Park, Southampton, SO15 0LN Tel: (023) 8078 0548 E-mail: info@pcs-on-line.co.uk *Computer software services*

P C S Powders Ltd, Unit 3, Waterloo Industrial Estate, Flanders Road, Hedge End, Southampton, SO30 2QT Tel: (01489) 790400 Fax: (01489) 785295 E-mail: info@pcspowders.co.uk *Powder coating manufrs*

▶ P C S Sandbach, Craigneigh, Ashley Heath, Market Drayton, Shropshire, TF9 4PS Tel: (01630) 673867

P C S Technical Services, 70 Church Road, Aston, Birmingham, B6 5TY Tel: 0121-326 0011 Fax: 0121-366 0022 E-mail: sales@pcs-technical.com *Established in 1996, PCS is an independent national field service organisation specialising in the managed support of print, plot, scan, storage, audio visual and medical services**Our aim is to provide a comprehensive service tailored to meet our customer"s requirements and our expertise in Managed IT Services guarantee that we deliver a robust and reliable service delivery function that is truly scalable yet flexible enough to accommodate bespoke support requirements**PCS has a highly skilled geographically focused mobile engineering workforce, nationwide logistics as well as a dedicated call centre which enables us to get the best out of our on-site support philosophy.*

P C Services, 4-5 Cottesbrooke Park, Heartlands Business Park, Daventry, Northamptonshire, NN11 8YL Tel: (01327) 312222 Fax: (01327) 301633 E-mail: email@pcservices.co.uk *Computer administration software*

▶ P C Solutions & Support, 25 Marriotts Way, Hemel Hempstead, Hertfordshire, HP3 9EN Tel: (01442) 219149 *Computer systems consultants*

▶ P C Sos 24 7, Europa House, Adlington Industrial Estate, Adlington, Macclesfield, Cheshire, SK10 4NL Tel: (0870) 2863767 E-mail: help@pcsos247.com *PC repair services*

▶ P C Speed, Wessex House, 2B8 Upper Market Street, Eastleigh, Hampshire, SO50 9FD Tel: (023) 8064 4912

▶ P C Stuff, 22 Albion Road, Bradford, West Yorkshire, BD10 9PY Tel: (01274) 616201 *Computer maintenance & repair services*

P C Supplies, 119 Cavendish Street, Barrow-in-Furness, Cumbria, LA14 1DJ Tel: (01229) 833595 Fax: (01229) 877677 E-mail: sales@pcsuppliesuk.co.uk *Computer suppliers*

P C Supplies, 4 The Metro Centre, Peterborough, PE2 7UH Tel: (01733) 370000 Fax: (01733) 235528 *Industrial fastener distributors*

▶ P C Support & Networking, Unit 14, Prospect Way, Selby, North Yorkshire, YO8 8BD Tel: (0800) 1613395 Fax: (0871) 6617934 *Support & networking*

P C T Group Ltd, 45 Regent Street, Rochdale, Lancashire, OL12 0HQ Tel: (01706) 649321 Fax: (01706) 657452 E-mail: matterson@pctgroup.co.uk *Welding engineers & lifting specialists*

P C T I Solutions Ltd, The Old Coach House, Button Park, Pontefract, West Yorkshire, WF8 4HT Tel: (01977) 690977 Fax: (01977) 690966 *Software manufrs*

P C Tech Service & Support, 216 Kingston Road, New Malden, Surrey, KT3 3RJ Tel: (020) 8605 1641 *Computer software services*

▶ P C Textiles, 1 Glasgow Road, Denny, Stirlingshire, FK6 5DN Tel: (01324) 826993 Fax: (01324) 826442 *Cleaning & polishing cloths manufrs*

P & C Tools Ltd, 80 Cato Street North, Birmingham, B7 5AN Tel: 0121-333 7772 Fax: 0121-333 7776 E-mail: pctoolsltd@yahoo.co.uk *Cutting tool manufrs*

P C Utilities, 36 Westbury Lane, Bristol, BS9 2PP Tel: 0117-962 6364 Fax: 0117-962 6365 E-mail: spencer@pcutilities.co.uk *IT business support & telephone support services*

▶ P C Worxs, 89 Foxberry Road, London, SE4 2SS Tel: (020) 8691 9215 *Computer services*

P Casey, 39 Carrycastle Road, Dungannon, County Tyrone, BT70 1PZ Tel: (028) 3754 8709 Fax: (028) 3754 8709 *Crane suppliers*

▶ P Challen Ltd, Norfolk Estate Saw Mill, London Road, Arundel, West Sussex, BN18 9AU Tel: (01903) 885000 Fax: (01903) 885050 E-mail: info@pchallen.co.uk *Granite & marble work surfaces*

▶ P Chester & Sons Bedford Ltd, 31 Howard Avenue, Bedford, MK40 4EE Tel: (0800) 0520535 Fax: (01234) 404088

P Copping Ltd, Harvey Road, Basildon, Essex, SS13 1EP Tel: (01268) 590105 Fax: (01268) 591265 E-mail: sales@pcopping.com *Laundry & dry cleaning requisites*

▶ P & D, Unit 1-3, Allcoach Road, Tansley, Matlock, Derbyshire, DE4 5ND Tel: (01629) 581150 Fax: (01629) 581105 E-mail: sales@pjm-services.co.uk

P D A Ltd, Woodfield, Holmfirth Road, New Mill, Holmfirth, HD9 7LX Tel: (01484) 685879 Fax: (01484) 682775 E-mail: pda.international@easynet.co.uk *Management consultants*

P D A, Manor House, Main Road, Wycombe, Melton Mowbray, Leicestershire, LE14 4QG Tel: 0116-230 1997 Fax: (01664) 444530 *Marketing consultants*

P D Brick Ltd, Smalldale, Buxton, Derbyshire, SK17 8EA Tel: (01298) 25396 *Brick manufr*

P D Bricks, Somerset Works, Merehead Quarry, East Cranmore, Shepton Mallet, Somerset, BA4 4SQ Tel: (01749) 881100 Fax: (01749) 880707 *Brick manufrs*

P D C Brush UK Ltd, Marshfield Bank Employment Park, Marshfield Bank, Crewe, CW2 8UY Tel: (01270) 259777 Fax: (01270) 259770 *Assemblers & distributors of brushes*

P & D Case Making, Unit 12 Ventura Place, Poole, Dorset, BH16 5SW Tel: (01202) 632181 Fax: (01202) 621041 *Packing case manufacturers & export packing services*

▶ P D Commercials, 5c Kingswood Douglas Estate, Kingswood, Bristol, BS15 8HJ Tel: 0117-960 8757 Fax: 0117-960 8758 *Commercial workshop & vehicle repairs*

P D Dixon, Pickering Fold Farm, Bezza Lane, Balderstone, Blackburn, BB2 7LQ Tel: (01772) 877289 Fax: (01772) 877479 E-mail: sales@phillipdixoncontractor.co.uk *Land drainage contractors*

▶ P D E Management, 1 Berry Street, Aberdeen, AB25 1HF Tel: (01224) 841317 Fax: (0870) 1674689

▶ P D F Fabricators, Unit 2, Plumpton House, Plumpton Road, Hoddesdon, Hertfordshire, EN11 0LB Tel: (01992) 446593 Fax: (01992) 446593

P & D Fasteners Ltd, Mapplewell BSNS Park, Blacker Road, Staincross, Barnsley, South Yorkshire, S75 6BP Tel: (01226) 388899 *Industrial fastener distributors & agents*

P D Gough Co. Ltd, Old Foundry, Common Lane, Watnall, Nottingham, NG16 1HD Tel: 0115-938 2241 Fax: 0115-945 9162 E-mail: info@pdgough.com *Stainless steel exhaust manufrs*

▶ P D Holden, 9 Woodman Avenue, Elland, West Yorkshire, HX5 0PE Tel: (01422) 310739

P D Hunt Ltd, Lynwood Grange, Winsor Road, Winsor, Southampton, SO40 2HE Tel: (023) 8081 4348 Fax: (023) 8081 2911 *Electrical contractors*

P & D Installation Services, 16 Badger Way, Prenton, Merseyside, CH43 3HQ Tel: 0151-608 0672 Fax: 0151-608 0672 *Ventilation engineers*

P D Labels, Unit 3, Elmcross Business Park, Bradford-On-Avon, Wiltshire, BA15 2AY Tel: (01225) 863627 Fax: (01225) 868152 *Manufacturers of self adhesive labels*

P D Levi & Son, Brine Pits Cottage, Wychbold, Droitwich, Worcestershire, WR9 0BY Tel: (01527) 861580 *Livestock haulage services*

P D Logistics, Cowpen Lane, Billingham, Cleveland, TS23 4DB Tel: (01642) 560456 Fax: (01642) 564061 E-mail: durhams@thpal.co.uk *Road transport & warehousing services*

P D M Office Supplies, 3 Parklands Parade, Bath Road, Hounslow, TW5 9AX Tel: (020) 8570 4488 Fax: (020) 8569 6050 *Drawing & general office suppliers*

P & D Manufacturing Ltd, Unit A11 Fiveways Industrial Estate, Westwells Road, Hawthorn, Corsham, Wiltshire, SN13 9RG Tel: (01225) 812900 Fax: (01225) 812600 E-mail: sales@pdmanufacturing.co.uk *Plastic injection mouldings manufrs*

P D Models, 2-3 Priory Wharf, Hertford, SG14 1RJ Tel: (01992) 553082 Fax: (01992) 550584 E-mail: jan@pdmodels.demon.co.uk *Engineering prototype manufrs*

P D Morgan, Wyndham Street, Ogmore Vale, Bridgend, Mid Glamorgan, CF32 7EU Tel: (01656) 849260 Fax: (01656) 849396 *Joiners*

P & D Northern Steels Ltd, Mosshey Street, Shaw, Oldham, OL2 8QL Tel: (01706) 848811 Fax: (01706) 841153 E-mail: sales@pdnorthern.co.uk *Steel & steel plate stockholders*

P D O'Rourke Ltd, 30 Grafton Street, Liverpool, L8 5SF Tel: 0151-709 1694 Fax: 0151-709 3293 E-mail: admin@pdorourke.co.uk *General engineering service*

P D P Associates Ltd, 23 Darlington Rd, Stockton-on-Tees, Cleveland, TS18 5BL Tel: (01642) 657010 *Computer consultants*

P & D Plant Hire Ltd, 5 Victory Way, Hounslow, TW5 9NN Tel: (020) 8573 5948 Fax: (020) 8573 2725

P & D Pneumatic Supplies, Unit 21 Lichfield Road Industrial Estate, Cavendish, Tamworth, Staffordshire, B79 7XH Tel: (01827) 310849 Fax: (01827) 310849 *Pneumatic supplies*

P & D Precision Engineering Ltd, 8 Crondal Road, Exhall, Coventry, CV7 9NH Tel: (024) 7636 8095 Fax: (024) 7664 4903 E-mail: sales@pandd.wireless.pipex.net *Precision engineers*

▶ P D Precision Grinding, Clarendon Road, Blackburn, BB1 9SS Tel: (01254) 663235 Fax: (01254) 695222 E-mail: pdperc@aol..com *Engineering services*

▶ P D Pumps Ltd, 8 Stuart Road, Bredbury, Stockport, Cheshire, SK6 2SR Tel: 0161-494 5522 Fax: 0161-406 8889 E-mail: sales@pdpumpsltd.co.uk *Distributors of pumps*

▶ P.D.Q.Logistics, 11 The Lizard, Wymondham, Norfolk, NR18 9BH Tel: (07944) 087289 E-mail: pdqlogistics@hotmail.co.uk *sameday/ nextday courier company based in norwich,fully insured with goods in transit insurance*

P D Q Packing, 4-6 Shaw Road, Dudley, West Midlands, DY2 8TP Tel: (01384) 242242 Fax: (01384) 242212 *Contract packers*

▶ P D Q Print Services, 93 Commercial Street, Dundee, DD1 2AF Tel: (0800) 0640794 Fax: (01382) 201776

P D Q Storage, St Vincent Works, Silverthorne Lane, Bristol, BS2 0QD Tel: 0117-971 6009 Fax: 0117-908 9909 *Express couriers & business storage*

P D R Engineering Ltd, 18-20 Uddens Trading Estate, Wimborne, Dorset, BH21 7LE Tel: (01202) 894015 Fax: (01202) 894021 *Precision & production engineers*

▶ P D S C N C Engineering Ltd, Unit 10 Riverside Business Centre, Cliffe Street, Nelson, Lancashire, BB9 7QR Tel: (01282) 619848 Fax: (01282) 611024

P D S Consultants, 82 London Road, Leicester, LE2 0QR Tel: 0116-254 4645 Fax: 0116-247 0092 E-mail: info@pds-consultants.co.uk *Computer consultants*

P D S Direct, Units 7 & 8, Church Lane Industrial Estate, West Bromwich, West Midlands, B71 1AR Tel: 0121-553 7555 Fax: 0121-553 5990 *Road transport, haulage & freight services*

▶ P D S Printers, 11 Kay Close, Plympton, Plymouth, PL7 4LU Tel: (01752) 343491 Fax: (01752) 343511 E-mail: sales@pdsprinters.co.uk

P D Stevens & Sons Ltd, Greenfields Lane, Market Drayton, Shropshire, TF9 3SL Tel: (01630) 652396 Fax: (01630) 652141 *Commercial vehicle body builders & accident repairers*

P D Supplies Ltd, Walker Road, Bardon Hill, Coalville, Leicestershire, LE67 1TU Tel: (01530) 813996 Fax: (01530) 839111 *Hydraulic hoses manufrs*

P D Systems, 20 West Craigs Crescent, Edinburgh, EH12 8NB Tel: 0131-339 4171 Fax: 0131-538 7713 E-mail: pdsystems@blueyonder.co.uk *Voice data network installations*

▶ P D Tattersall, Beevers Bridge, Sykehouse, Goole, North Humberside, DN14 9AB Tel: (01405) 862791 Fax: (01405) 862793

P D Tools Ltd, 4 Murrills Estate, Fareham, Hampshire, PO16 9RD Tel: (023) 9238 3635 Fax: (023) 9238 3652 E-mail: reception@pdtools.co.uk Principal Export Areas: Africa & North America *Lead castings & fabricators*

▶ P.Dee Cleaning Services, 1 Woodlea Gardens, Sauchie, Alloa, Clackmannanshire, FK10 3BD Tel: (01259) 218097 E-mail: peter_docherty@hotmail.co.uk *Domestic and commercial carpet and upholstery cleaning central scotland estd 1979*

P Dobbins Chester Ltd, British Railway Building, Saltney Ferry Road, Saltney Ferry, Chester, CH4 0BN Tel: (01244) 680095 Fax: (01244) 680095 *Scrap metal processors & merchants services*

▶ P E C Barr (Printers) Ltd, Barr Building, Carron Place, Edinburgh, EH6 7RE Tel: 0131-554 1736

P E C Furniture Ltd, Amble Industrial Estate, Amble, Morpeth, Northumberland, NE65 0PE Tel: (01665) 710593 Fax: (01665) 712735 E-mail: pecfurn@aol.com *Upholstery manufrs*

P E C Video Ltd, 65-66 Dean Street, London, W1D 4PL Tel: (020) 7437 4633 Fax: (020) 7025 1320 E-mail: sales@pec.co.uk *Film & video equipment distributors*

P E D Technologies Ltd, Brunel Close, Park Farm Industrial Estate, Wellingborough, Northamptonshire, NN8 6QX Tel: (01933) 403777 Fax: (01933) 403888 E-mail: sales@pafsystem.com *Infra-red heating manufrs*

P E Hines & Sons Ltd, Whitebridge Lane, Stone, Staffordshire, ST15 8LU Tel: (01785) 814921 Fax: (01785) 818808 E-mail: p.e.hines@iclwebkit.co.uk *Industrial minerals merchants & processors*

▶ P E I Delta Ltd, Furness Drive, Poulton Industrial Estate, Poulton-le-Fylde, Lancashire, FY6 8JS Tel: (01253) 894411 Fax: (01253) 894422

P E L Agencies Ltd, 7 Longbridge Industrial Park, Floating Bridge Road, Southampton, SO14 3FL Tel: (023) 8022 8934 Fax: (023) 8022 4389 E-mail: info@pelagencies.co.uk *Southampton based freight agent, conversant with all aspects of your Import & Export requirements*

P E M E, Rayfern House, Newark Road, Peterborough, PE1 5DE Tel: (0870) 8449393 Fax: (01753) 539156 E-mail: enquries@peme.co.uk *Electrical & mechanical installation & maintenance*

P E M Plant & Chemicals International Ltd, 6 Brindley Road, Clacton-on-Sea, Essex, CO15 4XL Tel: (01255) 426366 Fax: (01255) 426046 E-mail: rklueter@pemchemicals.co.uk *Chemicals for the printing industry*

P E M S Butler Ltd, The Red House, Axminster, Devon, EX13 5SE Tel: (01297) 631435 Fax: (01297) 631437 E-mail: sales@superquick.co.uk *Hobby kits & printed card suppliers*

P E M Sheetmetal Ltd, 3 Springfield Road Industrial Estate, Burnham-on-Crouch, Essex, CM0 8TE Tel: (01621) 783367 Fax: (01621) 785086 E-mail: sales@pemltd.co.uk *Sheetmetal manufacturing & design service*

▶ P E P Technologys Ltd, Acorn House, 2 Greenhill Crescent, Watford, WD18 8AH Tel: (01923) 212611 Fax: (01923) 238344 E-mail: pep@peptech.co.uk *IT Support & suppliers*

P E Sports, Portland Mill, Portland St South, Ashton-under-Lyne, Lancashire, OL6 7SX Tel: 0161-330 4075 Fax: 0161-304 7692 E-mail: pesports@btconnect.com *Sports ware & trophy manufrs*

P.E.T. Hire Centre Ltd, 68-70 Earle Street, Crewe, CW1 2AT Tel: (01270) 582222 Fax: (01270) 505938 *Plant tool hire services*

P E Thomas Precision Ltd, Glan Road, Porthcawl, Mid Glamorgan, CF36 5DF Tel: (01656) 783555 Fax: (01656) 783555 E-mail: p.e.thomas@talk21.com *Aircraft component manufrs*

P & F Amusements, 6 Springtown Road, Londonderry, BT48 0LY Tel: (028) 7130 9292 Fax: (028) 7137 7468 E-mail: sales@pandfamusements.com *Amusement machine suppliers*

P F C Group Ltd, Roman Way Business Centre, Berry Hill Industrial Estate, Droitwich, Worcestershire, WR9 9AJ Tel: (01905) 797000 Fax: (01905) 797274 E-mail: marketsales@pfcgroup.co.uk *Direct mail printing supplier* Also at: Thirsk

P F C Industries, 1 Livingstone Road, Sheffield, S9 3XX Tel: 0114-256 1508 Fax: 0114-256 1485 *General fabricated & stainless steel pressings*

P F Couriers Ltd, Unit 2, Lowfield Heath Industrial Estate, Crawley, West Sussex, RH11 0PQ Tel: (01293) 515661 Fax: (01293) 547045 E-mail: reception@pfcouriers.co.uk *National & international haulage courier services*

P F D S Ltd, 1st Floor 2 Stakes Hill Road, Waterlooville, Hampshire, PO7 7HY Tel: (023) 9225 6366 Fax: (023) 9225 6371 E-mail: sales@pfds.co.uk *Design & installation of fire alarms*

P F E International Ltd, P F E International House, Oakwood Hill Industrial Estate, Oakwood Hill, Loughton, Essex, IG10 3TZ Tel: (020) 8502 1011 Fax: (020) 8502 4187 E-mail: marketing@pfe.co.uk *Mail handling equipment manufrs*

▶ P & F Engineering, Unit C The Poplars, Beeston, Nottingham, NG9 2PD Tel: 0115 9220777

▶ P F I Property Maintanence, 1-3 Roland Court, Huntington, York, YO32 9PW Tel: (01904) 750255 Fax: (01904) 750616

P F K Ling Ltd, 55 Mendham Lane, Harleston, Norfolk, IP20 9DW Tel: (01379) 853213 Fax: (01379) 854373 E-mail: power@lings.com *Motor cycles, cars & power equipment & spare parts suppliers*

P F M Packaging Machinery Ltd, P F M House, 2 Pilgrim Way, Stanningley, Pudsey, West Yorkshire, LS28 6LU Tel: 0113-239 3401 Fax: 0113-239 3402 E-mail: pfm@pfm-ltd.co.uk *Packaging machinery manufrs*

P & F Machine Tools Co. Ltd, 1 Glentrool Mews, Bolton, BL1 5JH Tel: (01204) 840545 Fax: (01204) 841804 *Sheet metalworking machinery agent*

P F P Electrical Products Ltd, 22 Fortnum Close, Mackadown Lane, Kitts Green, Birmingham, B33 0LB Tel: 0121-783 7161 Fax: 0121-783 5717 E-mail: sales@pfp-elec.co.uk *Explosion protected equipment*

P F S (Helston) Ltd, Unit 9, Water-Ma-Trout Industrial Estate, Helston, Cornwall, TR13 0LW Tel: (01326) 565454 Fax: (01326) 565505 E-mail: sales@pfs-uk.co.uk Sales Contact: M. Bywater *Being an independent pump company, PFS (Helston) Ltd offers everything from water supply to sewage disposal. PFS (Helston) Ltd offers a supply only or supply and fit service covering domestic, Agricultural, Horticultural and Industrial applications*

▶ P F Whitehead Storage Ltd, 120 Beddington Lane, Croydon, CR9 4ND Tel: (020) 8665 0110 Fax: (020) 8665 0110 E-mail: info@pfwhitehead.com

P Fahey & Sons Holdings Ltd, 92 Chorlton Road, Stretford, Manchester, M15 4AL Tel: 0161-226 5959 Fax: 0161-227 9747 E-mail: removals@faheygroup.co.uk *Removal & storage contractors*

▶ P Ferguson Computers, PO BOX 29437, Glasgow, G67 9AX Tel: (07709) 264553 E-mail: pferguson22@hotmail.com *Computer maintenance & repair services*

P G A Rewinds, 58 Temperance Street, Manchester, M12 6DP Tel: 0161-273 4484 Fax: 0161-273 4484 *AC & DC motor rewinders*

P G Allder & Partners Ltd, 3a Peacock Alley, Leighton Buzzard, Bedfordshire, LU7 1HF Tel: (01525) 372664 Fax: (01525) 372996 E-mail: headoffice@alldersopticians.com *Opticians*

▶ P G Bones & Sons Ltd, Unit 25 Riverside Industrial Park, Rapier Street, Ipswich, IP2 8JX Tel: (01473) 602555 Fax: (01473) 602580

P G C Motors, Unit 1, High Street, Arlesey, Bedfordshire, SG15 6TB Tel: (01462) 834544 *Services & repairers*

P G & C Nottingham Ltd, Main Road, Tallington, Stamford, Lincolnshire, PE9 4RN Tel: (01778) 380666 Fax: (01778) 381707 E-mail: enquiries@pgcnottingham.co.uk *Cleaning products equipment distributors*

P G Carmichael, B Toynbee Road, Eastleigh, Hampshire, SO50 9DH Tel: (023) 8061 5900 Fax: (023) 8026 6480 *General steel fabricators*

P G Cleaning, Unit F15, Hastingwood Industrial Park, Wood Lane, Erdington, Birmingham, B24 9QR Tel: (0845) 2572031 E-mail: enquiries@pgcleaning.co.uk *Cleaning machines retail*

▶ P G Common Ltd, Bredbury Park Way, Bredbury Park Industrial Estate, Bredbury, Stockport, Cheshire, SK6 2SN Tel: 0161-430 8060

P G Components, 9 Knightsbridge Business Centre, Knightsbridge Green, Knightsbridge, Cheltenham, Gloucestershire, GL51 9TA Tel: (01242) 530930 Fax: (01242) 680260 E-mail: pgc@knightsbridge.fsbusiness.co.uk *Precision engineers*

▶ P & G Contractors Ltd, 1 Birch Street, Ashton-under-Lyne, Lancashire, OL7 0NX Tel: 0161-339 0831 Fax: 0161-285 3393

P & G Engineering Ltd, Unit 19 Bow Triangle Business Centre, Eleanor Street, London, E3 4NP Tel: (020) 8980 2387 Fax: (020) 8980 6680 *Fuel injection engineering services*

P G Gibbins & Son, 19 Forknell Avenue, Coventry, CV2 3EN Tel: (024) 7644 5229 Fax: (024) 7644 5229 *Butchers*

P G Joinery, Gas Works Yard, Oakenshaw, Bradford, West Yorkshire, BD12 7AR Tel: (01274) 672257 Fax: (01274) 602898 *Joinery*

P G Lawton, Caldene Business Park, Burnley Road, Mytholmroyd, Hebden Bridge, West Yorkshire, HX7 5QJ Tel: (01422) 883903 Fax: (01422) 884278 E-mail: pg.lawton@uk.sglcarbon.de *Specialty filter media for concrete manufrs*

P & G Processors Ltd, 26 Trojan Centre, Finedon Road Industrial Estate, Wellingborough, Northamptonshire, NN8 4ST Tel: (01933) 270967 Fax: (01933) 270967 E-mail: pgprocess@aol.com *Plastic fabricators*

P G Products Ltd, Folgate Road, North Walsham, Norfolk, NR28 0AJ Tel: (01692) 500390 Fax: (01692) 402863 E-mail: sales@pgproducts.com Principal Export Areas: Worldwide *Marine safety equipment manufrs*

P G Reeves & Sons, 129-133 Dogsthorpe Road, Peterborough, PE1 3AH Tel: (01733) 563887 Fax: (01733) 555582 *Industrial air compressor suppliers*

▶ P G S (Birmingham), Unit 5, Saltley Business Park, Dorset Road, Saltley, Birmingham, B8 1BG Tel: 0121-327 9292 *Road transport & haulage*

P G S Supplies Ltd, Worthing Road, Sheffield, S9 3JB Tel: 0114-276 5566 Fax: 0114-276 5265 E-mail: sales@pgs-supplies.co.uk *Manufacturers of tarpaulins*

▶ P G Services, 84 Tyron Way, Sidcup, Kent, DA14 6AZ Tel: 0208 3005738 Fax: 0208 3026330 E-mail: p.gservices@btinternet.com

P & G Stage Electrical Ltd, Studio House, North Stage, Broadway, Salford, M50 2UW Tel: 0161-877 4933 Fax: 0161-877 4944 E-mail: sales@pgstage.co.uk *Stage lighting & audio equipment manufrs*

P G Watson Brickwork Contractors, 104 The Causeway, Carshalton, Surrey, SM5 2NB Tel: (020) 8773 3476 Fax: (020) 8401 6340 E-mail: jdw1812@aol.com *Brickwork & paving contractors*

▶ P G Winch Repairs, Unit 14d Miller Business Park, Station Road, Liskeard, Cornwall, PL14 4DA Tel: (01579) 348146 Fax: (01579) 340613 E-mail: sales@winchrepairs.co.uk *Selling & repairing winches*

P Gillan & Sons, 1 Blezard Court, Enterprise Park, Blaydon-on-Tyne, Tyne & Wear, NE21 5NH Tel: 0191-499 0294 Fax: 0191-414 5353 *Steel fabricators & site erectors*

Company Information

▶ indicates data change since last edition

P Gray Ltd, PO Box 299, Croydon, CR9 6EQ Tel: (020) 8681 6637 Fax: (020) 8681 6630 E-mail: pgraylimited@aol.com *Paper makers agents*

P & H Co., Station Road, West Hallam, Ilkeston, Derbyshire, DE7 6HB Tel: 0115-932 0155 Fax: 0115-932 7177 E-mail: sales@phseakayaks.com *Canoe equipment*

P H Antell & Sons Ltd, Blandford Road, Shillingstone, Blandford Forum, Dorset, DT11 0SF Tel: (01258) 860233 Fax: (01258) 860266 *Commercial vehicle repairers*

P H B Industries Ltd, Fitzherbert Road, Farlington, Portsmouth, PO6 1SB Tel: (023) 9237 9696 Fax: (023) 9237 5822 *Jig & precision engineers & press tool manufrs*

P H B Textiles Ltd, PO Box 35586, London, NW4 1XG Tel: (07958) 492545 Fax: (020) 8203 5388 *Billiard cloth & suiting fabric manufrs*

P H C (UK) Ltd, Bassington Industrial Estate, Cramlington, Northumberland, NE23 8AE Tel: (01670) 707203 Fax: (01670) 707204 *Hydraulic cylinder & ram manufrs*

P & H Castings, Greenfield Road, Colne, Lancashire, BB8 9PD Tel: (01282) 871449 Fax: (01282) 859199 *Casting manufrs*

P H Chandler, Heybridge Farm, Uttoxeter Road, Tean, Stoke-on-Trent, ST10 4LN Tel: (01538) 722127 Fax: (01538) 723949 *Lime spreaders & agricultural contractors*

P H Chandler Leyland Ltd, 5 The Forward Industrial Estate, Talbot Road, Leyland, PR25 2ZJ Tel: (01772) 421651 Fax: (01772) 621493 E-mail: carolw@phchandler.co.uk *Contract furniture manufrs*

P & H Cleaning Co. Ltd, 72-74 Gipsy Hill, London, SE19 1PD Tel: (020) 8761 5324 Fax: (020) 8761 7306 E-mail: admin@pandhcleaning.co.uk *Office & window cleaning services*

P H D Automation Ltd, Hutchinson Street, Stockton-on-Tees, Cleveland, TS18 1RW Tel: (01642) 677770 Fax: (01642) 676330 E-mail: info@phdautomation.co.uk *Robots for plastic injection machinery*

▶ P H D Couriers, 158 Coneygree Road, Stanground, Peterborough, PE2 8LQ Tel: (01733) 560270 E-mail: phday68@yahoo.co.uk *Same day uk courier*Documents parcels*Loads upto 550kg**

P H D Import & Export Ltd, 1st Floor, 44-45 Great Hampston Street, Hockley, Birmingham, B18 6EL Tel: 0121-554 3722 Fax: 0121-554 8978 E-mail: sjhutti2000@yahoo.co.uk *Electrical wholesalers*

▶ P H D S Engineering Recruitment, 3 Silvan Court, Silvan Way, Southfields Business Park, Laindon, Basildon, Essex, SS15 6TU Tel: (01268) 455520 Fax: (01268) 455521 E-mail: info@phds.co.uk *Recruitment services*

▶ P & H Delivery Services Ltd, Unit 40 Goodwins Yard, Rougham Industrial Estate, Rougham, Bury St. Edmunds, Suffolk, IP30 9ND Tel: (01359) 272797 Fax: (01359) 271700 E-mail: sales@wedeliverit.net *Courier /Light haulage Collection and delivery service*

P H Electrical, 5 Crawshaw Avenue, Sheffield, S8 7DZ Tel: 0114-274 7823 *Electrical security system manufrs*

P & H Export Services Ltd, 212 Katherine Street, Ashton-under-Lyne, Lancashire, OL6 7AS Tel: 0161-343 8558 Fax: 0161-343 2492 E-mail: info@phexports.co.uk *Export administration systems*

P H Griffiths & Son, Birch Orchard, Bettws Newydd, Usk, Gwent, NP15 1JN Tel: (01873) 880336 *Agricultural engineering*

P H Hardwill Ltd, Hurst Works, Blackdown, Beaminster, Dorset, DT8 3LE Tel: (01460) 30661 Fax: (01460) 30173 *Structural engineers*

P H I Design Ltd, Miles Lane, High Street, Long Buckby, Northampton, NN6 7RJ Tel: (01327) 842323 Fax: (01327) 843554 *Plastic design & manufrs*

▶ P H Jones, Unit 18 The Bell Centre, Newton Road, Crawley, West Sussex, RH10 9FZ Tel: (01293) 518829 Fax: (01293) 534924

▶ P H Jones Ltd, Aqua House, Hampton Heath Industrial Estate, Hampton, Malpas, Cheshire, SY14 8LY Tel: (01948) 820244 Fax: (01948) 820484

P H M Plant Services Ltd, 117 Bath Road, Stroud, Gloucestershire, GL5 3JW Tel: (01453) 763532 Fax: (01453) 755083 *Power tools retailers*

P & H Machine Tool Co. Ltd, 9 Elm Croft, Little Paxton, St. Neots, Cambridgeshire, PE19 6QP Tel: (01480) 212973 Fax: (01480) 474848 E-mail: info@phmachinetools.com *New & used machine tool suppliers*

P & H Minepro Services Ltd, Seaman Way, Ince, Wigan, Lancashire, WN1 3DD Tel: (01942) 614400 Fax: (01942) 614419 E-mail: ph-min@phmining.com *Mining spare parts, sales & service*

P H Pallet Services, Broadway, Globe Lane Industrial Estate, Dukinfield, Cheshire, SK16 4UJ Tel: 0161-351 1333 Fax: 0161-366 9322 E-mail: sales@phpallets.com *Pallet maintenance/repair services & pallet (reconditioned) rebuilders* Also at: Ashton-under-Lyne

▶ P & H Plant Ltd, Burnbrae Drive, Linwood, Paisley, Renfrewshire, PA3 3BW Tel: (01505) 322252

P H S Group plc, Unit D Austin House, Austin Road, Ashford, Kent, TN23 6JR Tel: (01233) 623414 Fax: (01233) 645885 E-mail: wynnglenn@phs.co.uk *Hygiene equipment & products*

P H S Group Kleenair, Western Industrial Estate, Lon-Y-Llyn, Caerphilly, Mid Glamorgan, CF83 1XH Tel: (029) 2080 9111 Fax: (029) 2080 9091 E-mail: sales@phs.co.uk *Supplier of mats & matting*

P H S Group Kleenair, Western Industrial Estate, Lon-Y-Llyn, Caerphilly, Mid Glamorgan, CF83 1XH Tel: (029) 2080 9111 Fax: (029) 2086 3288 E-mail: sales@phs.co.uk *Air cleaning machine manufrs*

P H S Mat Services Ltd, Unit 5 Transport Avenue, Brentford, Middlesex, TW8 9HF Tel: (020) 8568 1005 Fax: (020) 8568 7425 *Floor protection service & product manufrs*

▶ P & H Services, 24b Northbrook Industrial Estate, Newmills Road, Coleraine, County Londonderry, BT52 2JB Tel: (028) 7035 2579 Fax: (028) 7035 1182

P H Services Ltd, 37 Limberline Spur, Portsmouth, PO3 5DX Tel: (023) 9269 3448 Fax: (023) 9263 9094 E-mail: huntphill@aol.com Sales Contact: P. Hunt *Air conditioning engineers, clean room installation & heat pump engineers*

P H Services Ltd, 37 Limberline Spur, Portsmouth, PO3 5DX Tel: (023) 9269 3448 Fax: (023) 9263 9094 E-mail: huntphill@aol.com *Air conditioning services*

P H Welding Services, Freehold Mill, Market Street, Shawforth, Rochdale, Lancashire, OL12 8HJ Tel: (01706) 854320 *Welding Services*

P Handley & Sons, The Smithy, Smithy Lane, Knighton, Market Drayton, Shropshire, TF9 4HP Tel: (01630) 647268 Fax: (01630) 647268 *Farriers*

P Harcombe Couriers, Bretby Business Park, Ashby Road, Bretby, Burton-on-Trent, Staffordshire, DE15 0YZ Tel: (01283) 219903 Fax: (01283) 219903 E-mail: paulhark@madasafish.com *sameday and express courier*

P Hartwell Timber, Timber Yard, Weston-Subedge, Chipping Campden, Gloucestershire, GL55 6QH Tel: (01386) 840373 Fax: (01386) 841370 E-mail: info@hartwellfencing.co.uk *Timber merchants*

▶ P Hayward & Son Ltd, Broomhouses Industrial Estate, Lockerbie, Dumfriesshire, DG11 2RF Tel: (01576) 203982

P Hird & Sons Ltd, English Street, Hull, HU3 2BT Tel: (01482) 227333 Fax: (01482) 587710 E-mail: sales@peter-hird.co.uk *Specialist lifting & factory machine moving; crane & aerial platform hire; access & material handling equipment sales & operator training providers*

P Hooper Designs, 1 Buckholt Business Centre, Buckholt Drive, Worcester, WR4 9ND Tel: (01905) 457858 Fax: (01905) 757477 E-mail: sales@phooperdesigns.co.uk *Fitted kitchen planners & manufrs*

P I A Software Ltd, 10 Brunel Close, Hedge End, Southampton, SO30 2TA Tel: (01489) 799364 Fax: (01489) 795191 E-mail: sales@pia.co.uk *Software development*

P I C Photos, 9 Park Lane, Harefield, Uxbridge, Middlesex, UB9 6BJ Tel: (01895) 822100 Fax: (01895) 822500 E-mail: scott_picphotos@yahoo.com *Photographers*

P & I Design Ltd, 2 Reed Street, Thornaby, Stockton-on-Tees, Cleveland, TS17 7AF Tel: (01642) 617444 Fax: (01642) 616447 E-mail: drr@pidesign.co.uk *Instrument engineering services*

P I Design International, 1-5 Colville Mews, London, W11 2AR Tel: (020) 7727 3226 Fax: (020) 7908 0809 E-mail: hello@piglobal.com *Packaging designers*

P I F Medical Supplies Ltd, Standard House, Prospect Place, Nottingham, NG7 1RX Tel: 0115-947 4531 Fax: 0115-941 7097 E-mail: sales@pif-medical.co.uk *Wholesale chemists*

▶ P I M S, Unit 12, Sovereign Way, Downham Market, Norfolk, PE38 9SW Tel: (01366) 385382 Fax: (01366) 387202 E-mail: steve.pims@virgin.net *Plastic manufrs*

▶ P I P S, Waterside House, Falmouth Road, Penryn, Cornwall, TR10 8BE Tel: (01326) 372500 Fax: (0871) 9898823 *Water treatment company*

P I Research, The Brookfield Motorsports Centre, Twentypence Road, Cottenham, Cambridge, CB4 8PS Tel: (01954) 253600 Fax: (01954) 253601 E-mail: sales@piresearch.co.uk *Racing car & rally vehicles services*

▶ P J A Electrics Ltd, Carlton House, Arrow Road North, Redditch, Worcestershire, B98 8NN Tel: (01527) 596592 Fax: (01527) 596599

▶ P J Allison Wirral Ltd, 4 May Road, Wirral, Merseyside, CH60 5RA Tel: 0151-342 7797 Fax: 0151-342 9244

▶ P & J Associates Ltd, Pulsar, Damask Green Road, Weston, Hitchin, Hertfordshire, SG4 7DA Tel: (01462) 790446 E-mail: info@pjassociates.co.uk *Business advisers with skills in IT Strategy, Finance, Marketing Communications.*One Director is An Accredited*Associate of IIB (Institute for Independent Business)*

P J B Systems Technology Ltd, Systems House, Blackbrook Business Park, Fareham, Hampshire, PO15 5DR Tel: (01329) 826156 Fax: (01329) 826111 E-mail: sales@pjbsystems.co.uk *Electronics & Mechanical Engineering design consultants*

P J Busby & Sons, 3 Main Road, Tadley, Hampshire, RG26 3NJ Tel: 0118-981 4710 Fax: 0118-981 4710 *Joinery manufrs*

P J Butler & Son Ltd, Parsonage St, Oldbury, West Midlands, B69 4PH Tel: 0121-552 1052 Fax: 0121-544 8618 *Road transport, haulage & freight services*

P J C, 22 The Drive, Orpington, Kent, BR6 9AP Tel: (07718) 267453 E-mail: studio@pjcdesign.co.uk *Product design*

▶ P J C Plant Services Ltd, 56 Sanvey Gate, Leicester, LE1 4BQ Tel: 0116-253 6177 Fax: 0116-251 6961

▶ P J Carey Contractors Ltd, Chesney Wold, Bleak Hall, Milton Keynes, MK6 1NJ Tel: (01908) 668383 Fax: (01908) 667596

▶ P & J Ceramics Ltd, 4 Salisbury House, Salisbury Road, Newton Abbot, Devon, TQ12 2DF Tel: (01626) 366866 Fax: (01626) 366833 *Bespoke ceramics cabinet knobs & giftware suppliers*

P J Colours Ltd, Excelsior Works, Castle Park, Flint, Clwyd, CH6 5NT Tel: (01352) 732157 Fax: (01352) 735530 E-mail: info@pjcolours.com *Chemicals, colours & iron oxides manufrs*

▶ P J D Engineering Ltd, 4 Henlow Industrial Estate, Henlow, Bedfordshire, SG16 6DS Tel: (01462) 815544 Fax: (01462) 816677 *Sheet metalworkers/fabrication/precision engineers.*

▶ P J D Heating, 623 Manchester Road, Wardley, Swinton, Manchester, M27 9QH Tel: 0161-793 9471 Fax: 0161-728 4300

P J D Instruments, Unit 15 Antrim Enterprise Centre, 50 Upper Greystone Road, Antrim, BT41 1JZ Tel: (028) 9442 5700 Fax: (028) 9446 5760 E-mail: pjdinstruments@aol.com *Instrument calibration suppliers*

P J Douglas Engineering Ltd, 2-4 Short Street, Uttoxeter, Staffordshire, ST14 7LH Tel: (01889) 568800 Fax: (01889) 568801 E-mail: peterdouglas@pjdltd.co.uk *Manufacturers & maintenance of industrial boilers*

▶ P J Doyle (Electrical) Ltd, 78 Cumnor Road, Oxford, OX1 5JP Tel: (01865) 327222

P J Drew Engravers Ltd, Lower Vicarage Road, Southampton, SO19 7RJ Tel: (023) 8044 6062 Fax: (023) 8042 2981 E-mail: sales@pjdrew.co.uk *Machine engravers & sign manufrs*

P & J Dust Extraction Ltd, Otterham Quay, Gillingham, Kent, ME8 8NA Tel: 01634 233933 Principal Export Areas: Worldwide *Manufacture installation of dust & fume extraction*

▶ P J Emmerson Ltd, 2 Bunting Road, Bury St. Edmunds, Suffolk, IP32 7BX Tel: (01284) 760751 Fax: (01284) 762368 *Printing services*

P J Engineering Products Ltd, Elswick Way Industrial Estate, Newcastle Road, South Shields, Tyne & Wear, NE34 0LW Tel: 0191-454 5553 Fax: 0191-455 0892 E-mail: sales@pjeng.co.uk *Special purpose machinery manufrs*

▶ P J G Creative Design Ltd, 11 Mayer Gardens, Shenley Lodge, Milton Keynes, MK5 7EN Tel: (01908) 231175 E-mail: info@pjgcreative.com *Technical documentation, health & safety & risk assessment consultants*

P J G Electrical Ltd, 14 Silver Street, Stony Stratford, Milton Keynes, MK11 1JR Tel: (01908) 561100 Fax: (01908) 561181 *Electrical contractors services*

P J Gerring, Home Farm, Buckland, Faringdon, Oxfordshire, SN7 8RG Tel: (01367) 870245 Fax: (01367) 870245 E-mail: peter.gerring@btconnect.com *Agricultural contractors*

▶ P J Grant & Sons Haulage Contractors, Forres Road, Nairn, IV12 5QD Tel: (01667) 452243 Fax: (01667) 454168

▶ P J Heaven, PO Box 164, Beverley, North Humberside, HU17 7AP Tel: (01482) 860777 Fax: (01482) 860777 E-mail: sales@pjheaven.co.uk *UK based online & mail order retailer of pyjamas, nightwear, sleepwear and t shirts. Cotton & cotton flannel. Sourced in the UK,Europe and USA using unique prints. Cosy, comfortable, quality product.*

P J Hifi, 3 Bridge Street, Guildford, Surrey, GU1 4RY Tel: (01483) 504801 Fax: (01483) 504801 E-mail: info@pjhifi.co.uk *Hi-fi sound equipment retailers*

▶ P & J Hunter, Unit 4a Charlesfield Industrial Estate, St. Boswells, Melrose, Roxburghshire, TD6 0HH Tel: (01835) 824751 Fax: (01835) 824752

▶ P & J Labels Ltd, 18 Wharfedale Road, Ipswich, IP1 4JP Tel: (01473) 747424 Fax: (01473) 747425 E-mail: pjlabels@btconnect.com *Label producers*

▶ P J M C Ltd, 4 Church End, Radford Semele, Leamington Spa, Warwickshire, CV31 1TA Tel: (01926) 312886 Fax: (01926) 435355 E-mail: info@pjmc.com *PJMC Marketing Communications is a successful UK-based PR company that provides a full range of public relations services.*

P J & M E Norris & Son, Units 7-8 The Old Creamery, Station Road, Wrenbury, Nantwich, Cheshire, CW5 8EX Tel: (01270) 780003 Fax: (01270) 780003 *Cabinet makers*

▶ P J M Transport, 1 St. Andrews Road, Salisbury, SP2 9NT Tel: (028) 6865 8231 Fax: (028) 6865 9192 E-mail: flyer43@tiscali.co.uk *Our business is small but Very Flexible.*

P J Mcgowan, Gethceln House, Dawley Road, Hayes, Middlesex, UB3 1EH Tel: (020) 8573 1571 Fax: (020) 8561 3750 *Sheet metalwork engineers*

P J Metals & Plastics, Unit 4 Park Street, Kidderminster, Worcestershire, DY11 6TN Tel: (01562) 824570 Fax: (01562) 865170 *Aluminium & plastic stockholders, engineers & fabricators*

▶ P J Milligan, 54 Wilson Place, East Kilbride, Glasgow, G74 4QD Tel: (01355) 260990 E-mail: craig.hamilton@pjmilligan.com *Fine furniture for every room in the home suppliers*

P J Mouldings Ltd, 423-424 Montrose Avenue, Slough, SL1 4TP Tel: (01753) 521002 *Plastics injection mouldings manufrs*

P J Osborne, 16 James Watt Close, Drayton Fields Industrial Estate, Daventry, Northamptonshire, NN11 8RJ Tel: (01327) 312664 Fax: (01327) 342400 *Adjustable & conveyor levelling feet manufrs*

▶ P.J.P Ltd, Paul Jackson Potatoes, Station Road, Firsby, Spilsby, Lincolnshire, PE23 5QS Tel: (01754) 830330 E-mail: sales@pjp.org.uk *Wholesale potato merchants*

P J P Services Ltd, PO Box 173, Rochester, Kent, ME2 4SY Tel: (01634) 724393 Fax: (01634) 724699 E-mail: sales@pjpservices.co.uk *Installation of safety line systems & safety eyebolts supplies*

P J Packaging Ltd, 20 High Street, Wem, Shrewsbury, SY4 5DL Tel: (01939) 235073 Fax: (01939) 235074 E-mail: sales@pjpackaging.ltd.uk *Cardboard box manufrs*

P & J Plastics, 7 Lower Cherwell Street, Banbury, Oxfordshire, OX16 5AY Tel: (01295) 269814 Fax: (01295) 275557 *Polycarbonate sheet manufrs*

P & J Powder Coatings, 17 Evanton Place, Thornliebank, Glasgow, G46 8JE Tel: 0141-620 1652 Fax: 0141-620 0928 *Powder coating refurbishment*

P J Rowley Paintors & Decorators, 18 Martin Drive, Willenhall, West Midlands, WV12 4QR Tel: (01902) 631510 Fax: (01902) 410948 E-mail: info@pjrowley.com *Painting & decorating contractors*

P J S Chemicals, 8 Station Estate, Station Road, Tadcaster, North Yorkshire, LS24 9SG Tel: (01937) 832928 Fax: (01937) 834852 E-mail: pjschemicals@aol.com *Printing industry chemical manufrs*

P J S Electrical, 11 Unity Avenue, Hessle, North Humberside, HU13 9NF Tel: (01482) 649123 Fax: (01482) 627281 E-mail: info@pjse.co.uk *Electrical alarms installation*

P J S Mechanical & Electrical Building Services, Barn House, Folly Farm, Basingstoke, Hampshire, RG25 2BS Tel: (01256) 397544 Fax: (01256) 398304 *Building services, commissioning services*

▶ P J Scaffolding, Fort Bridgewood, Maidstone Road, Rochester, Kent, ME1 3DQ Tel: (01634) 828829 Fax: (01634) 828971

P J Signs, 37 Priory Avenue, Taunton, Somerset, TA1 1XZ Tel: (01823) 283985 Fax: (01823) 321391 E-mail: sales@pjsigns.co.uk *Sign manufrs*

P & J Smith Agricultural, Brook Farm, Redisham, Beccles, Suffolk, NR34 8NF Tel: (01986) 781505 Fax: (01986) 781505 *Agricultural engineers*

P J Stainless Steel Products, 22 Skidmore Road, Coseley, Bilston, West Midlands, WV14 8SE Tel: (01902) 401053 Fax: (01902) 405548 *Catering equipment manufrs*

P J T Engineering, Unit 3 367 Bryn Road, Ashton-in-Makerfield, Wigan, Lancashire, WN4 8BS Tel: (01942) 712022 Fax: (01942) 712022 E-mail: sales@pjtengineering.gbr.cc *Steel fabricators*

P J Tooling, Hassall Road Industrial Estate, Skegness, Lincolnshire, PE25 3TB Tel: (01754) 767818 Fax: (01754) 767818 *Injection moulders & toolmakers*

P J Tooling Ltd, Millers Road, Warwick, CV34 5AN Tel: (01926) 492693 Fax: (01926) 410057 E-mail: pj.tooling@virgin.net *Cutting & form tool manufrs*

P & J UK Ltd, 1 Kenwood Road, Stockport, Cheshire, SK5 6PH Tel: 0161-443 1557 Fax: 0161-443 1821 E-mail: geoff.walters@pandj.net *Pattern book & card manufrs*

P J Valves Ltd, 8 Merchant Drive, Mead Lane, Hertford, SG13 7BH Tel: (01992) 587878 Fax: (01992) 550132 E-mail: scharles@pjvalves.co.uk *Valve distributors*

P & J W Meters, Unit 1, Salisbury House, Salisbury Road, Newton Abbot, Devon, TQ12 2DF Tel: (0800) 5875540 Fax: (0800) 216905 *Electrical meter manufrs*

P J Wade Site Engineering Ltd, 38 Tuffley CR, Gloucester, GL1 5NE Tel: (01452) 304228 Fax: (01452) 304359 *Site engineering*

P & J Webster Gate Manufacturers, 251 Wakefield Road, Dewsbury, West Yorkshire, WF12 8ET Tel: (01924) 452720 Fax: (01924) 452720 *Wooden gates & fencing manufrs*

P J Welding & Fabricating, Unit 12, Summerhill Industrial Estate, Goodman Street, Birmingham, B1 2SS Tel: 0121-236 8152 Fax: 0121-212 1705 *Welding & fabricating*

P J Williams Automatics Ltd, The Cedars, Off Lodge Road, Maldon, Essex, CM9 6SJ Tel: (01621) 828795 Fax: (01621) 828795 *Amusement machines*

P James Fabrications Ltd, Dock Meadow Drive, Lanesfield, Wolverhampton, WV4 6LE Tel: (01902) 408818 Fax: (01902) 408818 *Structural steelwork fabrications*

P Jeffrey & Sons, Rosebank, Hutton, Berwick-upon-Tweed, TD15 1TS Tel: (01289) 386398 *Vegetable growers*

▶ P Johnson Engineering, 16b Mimram Road, Hertford, SG14 1NN Tel: (01992) 552543 Fax: (01992) 552436 E-mail: pjengsvf@aol.com *Tool design services*

▶ P K A Co., Park Road, Sowerby Woods Industrial Estate, Barrow-in-Furness, Cumbria, LA14 4QR Tel: (01229) 870168 Fax: (01229) 870699 E-mail: sales@pka-company.co.uk *Suppliers of pipeline & ancillary equipment, pumps & valves*

P K A Promotions Ltd, 6 South Folds Road, Corby, Northamptonshire, NN18 9EU Tel: (01536) 461122 Fax: (01536) 744668 E-mail: sales@pkapromotions.com *Promotions & incentives services*

P K Commercial Tyres Ltd, 4 Forstal Road, Aylesford, Kent, ME20 7AU Tel: (01622) 717277 Fax: (01622) 717377 E-mail: info@commercialtyres.co.uk *Tyre distributors*

P K D Precision Sheet Metal Ltd, Unit 7 Furlong Industrial Estate, Dain Street, Stoke-on-Trent, ST6 3LN Tel: (01782) 824800 Fax: (01782) 811746 E-mail: sales@pkdsheetmetal.co.uk *Precision sheet metalwork*

P K Engineering West Bromwich Ltd, Unit 3 Kelvin Way, West Bromwich, West Midlands, B70 7TN Tel: 0121-500 5847 Fax: 0121-553 1622 E-mail: sales@pk-engineering.co.uk *Producing large & small hydraulic & pneumatic fittings*

▶ P K Enginerring, Windsor Avenue, Darton, Barnsley, South Yorkshire, S75 5LN Tel: (01226) 230411 E-mail: dimwits.daft1@blueyonder.co.uk *Family run company which give a high standard of precision and General Engineering*Hydraulics*Pneumatics*Fabrication* Electrical work*

P K Hardwood, Wotton Road, Brill, Aylesbury, Buckinghamshire, HP18 9UB Tel: (01844) 238282 Fax: (01844) 238016 *Hardwood importer*

P K K Storage Systems Ltd, Gibbons Lane, Brierley Hill, West Midlands, DY5 4RY Tel: (01384) 79555 Fax: (01384) 75588 E-mail: pkkcontracts@aol.com *Demountable, dry construction & steel partition contractors*

PKL Group (UK) Ltd, Stella Way, Bishops Cleeve, Cheltenham, Glos, GL52 7DQ Tel: (01242) 663000 Fax: (01242) 677819 E-mail: postbox@pkl.co.uk *PKL Foodservice; Portable Kitchens, catering equipment hire, military kitchens, kitchen facilities management, permanent kitchen facilities, event catering facilities. PKL Healthcare: fast-track healthcare buildings - operating theatres; diagnostic imaging, sterilisation, aseptic suites, laboratories, wards, treatment centres.*

P K Marine Freight Services Ltd, 1 Perimeter Road, Knowsley Industrial Park, Liverpool, L33 3AY Tel: 0151-547 3822 Fax: 0151-548 0884 E-mail: sales@pkmarine.co.uk *Export packers & freight forwarders*

P K N D Computer Services, 26 Parkfield Row, Leeds, LS11 7LT Tel: 0113-276 5758 Fax: 0871 5216882 E-mail: info@pknd.co.uk *PKND Computer Services offer a range of computer services, support and products to home and small business users in the Leeds and Yorkshire region*

P & K Services Ltd, Albert Street, Horwich, Bolton, BL6 7AP Tel: (01204) 667703 Fax: (01204) 667702 *Shutter manufrs*

▶ P & K Shutter Services Ltd, Canada House, Canada Street, Horwich, Bolton, BL6 7PB Tel: (01204) 667703 Fax: (01204) 667702 E-mail: pk_shutters@hotmail.com *Manufacturers of industrial doors, nationwide installation & delivery*

P Keable, 12 Avenue Clamart, Scunthorpe, South Humberside, DN15 8EQ Tel: (01724) 855989 Fax: (01724) 855989 *Workshop equipment suppliers*

▶ P Kent Ltd, 6 Howard Court, Nerston Industrial Estate, East Kilbride, Glasgow, G74 4QZ Tel: (01355) 230005 Fax: (01355) 230050 E-mail: sales@kentphk.co.uk

P L Control, 18 Holdsworth Road, Holmfield, Halifax, West Yorkshire, HX2 9TH Tel: (01422) 382052 Fax: (01422) 241956 *Control systems manufrs*

P L F International, Riverside House Iconfield Park, Freshfields Road, Parkeston, Harwich, Essex, CO12 4EN Tel: (01255) 552994 Fax: (01255) 552995 E-mail: sales@plfinternational.com *Powder filling machines manufrs*

▶ P L F (U K) Ltd, Unit 3 Vicarage Farm, 712 Main Road, Harwich, Essex, CO12 4LT Tel: (01255) 553822 E-mail: sales@plfuk.co.uk

P L G Distributors Ltd, 6 Francis Road, Yardley, Birmingham, B25 8HP Tel: 0121-766 1000 Fax: 0121-766 1002 *Wholesale cash & carry stationers suppliers to own branches* Also at: Branches throughout the U.K.

P L G Yorkshire Ltd, Sherman House, 5 Waterloo Way, Leeds, LS13 2EF Tel: 0113-236 1155 Fax: 0113-236 1156 E-mail: plgoffice@btconnect.com *Manufacturers of high quality embossing & hot foiling tools*

P L Grinding, Unit B8 Guy Motors Industrial Park, Park Lane, Wolverhampton, WV10 9QF Tel: (01902) 723597 Fax: (01902) 723597 E-mail: thegrindingway@blueyonder.co.uk *Precision grinding services*

P & L Industrial Equipment Ltd, Lind Street, Manchester, M40 7ES Tel: 0161-273 2626 Fax: 0161-274 3633 E-mail: sales@plcastors.co.uk *Castors and wheels industrial supplier distributor*

▶ P & L Meals, Oswin House, Oswin Avenue, Balby, Doncaster, South Yorkshire, DN4 0NR Tel: (01302) 850885 Fax: (01302) 850885 *Meals on wheels*

P L Moors, Hillside Farm, Willington, Tarporley, Cheshire, CW6 0LX Tel: (01829) 732222 Fax: (01829) 730794 *Crane hire*

P & L Networks Ltd, Solway Court, Crewe, CW1 6LD Tel: (01270) 259740 Fax: (01270) 259759 *Networks maintenance & support*

P L P Lift Trucks Ltd, 3 Monksbridge Business Park, Monksbridge Road, Dinnington, Sheffield, S25 3QS Tel: (01909) 564257 Fax: (01909) 567818 E-mail: plplifttrucks@msn.com *Fork lift dealers & hirers*

P L Plastics Machinery Ltd, Unit 6 Telmere Industrial Estate, Albert Road, Luton, LU1 3QF Tel: (01582) 429224 Fax: (01582) 459133 E-mail: info@pl-plasticsmachinery.co.uk *Plastics ancillary equipment suppliers*

P L S Associates Ltd, Brackendale, The Green, Palgrave, Diss, Norfolk, IP22 1AN Tel: (01379) 644500 Fax: (01379) 644038 E-mail: sales@webpressworld.co.uk *Design engineers*

▶ P & L Tapes Ltd, 39 The Airfield, Little Staughton, Bedford, MK44 2BN Tel: (01234) 376421 Fax: (01234) 376115 E-mail: nickckd1@aol.com *Packaging & self adhesive tapes specialists*

P L W Associates Ltd, 37 Elmers Green, Skelmersdale, Lancashire, WN8 6RZ Tel: (01695) 559990 Fax: (01695) 559990 E-mail: plwunderscoreass@msn.com *Computer systems & software developers*

▶ P Lipton & Sons Ltd, 7-11 Gourock Street, Glasgow, G5 9RY Tel: 0141-429 7341 Fax: 0141-418 0470

P M A Ltd, Grant Thornton House, 24-26 Rothesay Road, Luton, LU1 1QX Tel: (01582) 400184 Fax: (01582) 487740 *Telephone advisory redundancy services*

P M A Group, Unit 8, Waterside Road, Hamilton Industrial Park, Leicester, LE5 1TL Tel: 0116-246 1400 Fax: 0116-246 1659 E-mail: sales@pmagroup.co.uk *Automotive number plates & radiators* Also at: Bolton & Leeds

P & M Associates, 6 Brendan Close, Coleshill, Birmingham, B46 3EF Tel: (01675) 465566 Fax: (01675) 464440 E-mail: marketing@pmassoc.co.uk *Marketing consultants*

P M Associates, Lyjon House, Merseyton Road, Ellesmere Port, CH65 2AP Tel: 0151-357 2196 Fax: 0151-357 1120 *Computer systems building & maintenance agents*

▶ P M B Software Solutions, Suite 3B, Keswick Hall, Keswick, Norwich, NR4 6TJ Tel: (0800) 7813526 E-mail: info@pmbsoftwaretraining.co.uk *Offical sage business partners offering discounted software, training and support. Microsoft XP software training courses, either classroom based or held on companies premises*

P & M Blinds Ltd, 94 Vallentin Road, London, E17 3JH Tel: (020) 8521 0121 Fax: (020) 8509 0754 E-mail: enquiries@pandmblinds.com *Window blinds supplies & fitting services*

P M Bradley Fabrications Ltd, 8 Lodge Lane Industrial Estate, Lodge Lane, Tuxford, Newark, Nottinghamshire, NG22 0NL Tel: (01777) 871222 Fax: (01777) 871922 E-mail: info@pmbfabrications.co.uk *Steel fabricators*

P M C, Cedar House, 100 Station Avenue, Coventry, CV4 9HS Tel: (024) 7642 2777 Fax: (024) 7647 1111 *Retailers of movable wall systems*

P M C Polythene Ltd, Unit 35 Park Farm Industrial Estate, Ermine Street, Buntingford, Hertfordshire, SG9 9AZ Tel: (01763) 271300 Fax: (01763) 271338 *Polythene bag manufrs*

P & M Ceilings, 10 Eastdale Place, Altrincham, Cheshire, WA14 5LG Tel: 0161-928 3631 Fax: 0161-928 3631 *Suspended ceilings contractors*

▶ P M Clarke Ltd, Seven Brethren Bank, Sticklepath, Barnstaple, Devon, EX31 2AS Tel: (01271) 345151 Fax: (01271) 323103

P M Components Ltd, Unit 17D, Eurolink Industrial Centre, Upper Field Road, Sittingbourne, Kent, ME10 3UP Tel: (01795) 419450 Fax: (01795) 430835 E-mail: sales@pmcomponents.co.uk *Electronic valve distributors*

P M Consultants, 414 North Deeside Road, Cults, Aberdeen, AB15 9TD Tel: (01224) 868239 Fax: (01224) 869711 E-mail: billatpm@tiscali.co.uk *Marketing research management consultancy maintenance*

P M D Building Services Ltd, 32 Vilier Street, Sunderland, SR1 1EJ Tel: 0191-514 3444 Fax: 0191-514 3445

P M D Magnetics, Avenue Farm Industrial Estate, Birmingham Road, Stratford-upon-Avon, Warwickshire, CV37 0HR Tel: (01789) 268579 Fax: (01789) 414450 E-mail: sales@pmdmagnetics.co.uk *Physio, audio & cata media distributors*

P M D UK Ltd, Broad Lane, Coventry, CV5 7AY Tel: (024) 7646 6691 Fax: (024) 7647 3034 E-mail: sales@pmdgroup.co.uk *Electroplating chemical products manufrs*

P M D UK Ltd, Broad Lane, Coventry, CV5 7AY Tel: (024) 7646 6691 Fax: (024) 7647 3034 E-mail: sales@pmdgroup.co.uk *Chemical product manufrs*

P & M Dabner Ltd, Unit C2 Springhead Enterprise Park, Springhead Road, Northfleet, Gravesend, Kent, DA11 8HD Tel: (01474) 335678 Fax: (01474) 334678 E-mail: enquiries@etchedglass.co.uk *Double glazing, design & etching manufrs*

P & M Decorative Metal Work Ltd, Unit 1, Park Street, Oldbury, West Midlands, B69 4LQ Tel: 0121-544 8880 Fax: 0121-544 4617 E-mail: pmdeco@aol.com *Balustrades & fire escapes manufrs*

P M E Engraving & Screen Printing Ltd, 11 Robert Cort Industrial Estate, Britten Road, Reading, RG2 0AU Tel: 0118-986 4858 Fax: 0118-975 3415 E-mail: pms-sales@compuserve.com *Printing services*

P M E Sugar Craft, Chadwell Heath Lane, Romford, RM6 4NP Tel: (020) 8590 5959 Fax: (020) 8590 7373 E-mail: admin@cakedecoration.co.uk *Cake icing equipment manufrs*

P & M Embroidery, Glebe Road, Huntingdon, Cambridgeshire, PE29 7DR Tel: (01480) 411311 Fax: (01480) 412839 E-mail: sales@pmembroidery.co.uk *Promotional clothing suppliers & embroidery manufrs*

P M Fabrication, Unit F3 Doulton Trading Estate, Doulton Road, Rowley Regis, West Midlands, B65 8JQ Tel: (01384) 561498 Fax: (01384) 561498 *Sheet metalwork engineers*

▶ P M Fireplaces, 56 Ballygawley Road, Dungannon, County Tyrone, BT70 1TZ Tel: (028) 8772 5215 Fax: (028) 8772 2505 *Manufacture, retail stone products*

P & M Fixings, Franchise Street, Wednesbury, West Midlands, WS10 9RG Tel: 0121-526 5775 Fax: 0121-568 6108 E-mail: info@pmfixings.com *Industrial fasteners, partition components & screws*

P M G Technical Services Ltd, Unit 9, Walton Industrial Estate, Beacon Road, Stone, Staffordshire, ST15 0NN Tel: (01785) 818857 Fax: (01785) 816587 E-mail: info@pmgtech.co.uk *Design, supply, installation & commissioning of quality process plant for the chemical & water treatment, pharmaceutical & food industries. Our specialist process knowledge includes gas scrubbing, absorption systems, reation units, distillation processes & odour control*

P M H Coachbuilders Ltd, Longcroft House, Glasgow Road, Dennyloanhead, Bonnybridge, Stirlingshire, FK4 1QW Tel: (01324) 841702 Fax: (01324) 849458 *Coach builders & repairers*

P M H Precision Engineering Ltd, Unit 1, Such Close Works Road, Letchworth Garden City, Hertfordshire, SG6 1JF Tel: (01462) 682616 Fax: (01462) 682616 *Precision engineers*

▶ P M Harris Ltd, Coton-in-the-Clay, Ashbourne, Derbyshire, DE6 5GY Tel: (01283) 821222 Fax: (01283) 821211

P M Hill Engineering, 59 Rowsley Street, Leicester, LE5 5JP Tel: 0116-273 7132 *Precision engineers*

P M I Services, Glen Villa, Ashbrooke Range, Sunderland, SR2 9BP Tel: 0191-528 1469 Fax: 0191-511 0369 *Metal analysis service*

P & M Joinery, P & M Joinery Workshop At Bottom Of Drive, Rear Of 63 Lord Haddon Road, Ilkeston, Derbyshire, DE7 8AU Tel: 0115-930 1071 *Joinery manufrs*

P M L (Cold Store) Ltd, Brighton Road, Pease Pottage, Old Brighton Road South, Crawley, West Sussex, RH11 9NG Tel: (01293) 517260 Fax: (01293) 613970 *Cold storage services*

P M Large Screen Services, 170 Jockey Road, Sutton Coldfield, West Midlands, B73 5PN Tel: 0121-355 5099 Fax: 0121-355 6059 E-mail: pm_bigscreen@msn.com *Big television screen suppliers*

P & M Mouldings, 1 Brampton Sidings Industrial Estate, Hempstalls Lane, Newcastle, Staffordshire, ST5 0SR Tel: (01782) 713237 Fax: (01782) 713237 *Plastics moulding manufrs*

P M N Aviation Ltd, Unit B, Crawford Street, Rochdale, Lancashire, OL16 5NU Tel: (01706) 655134 Fax: (01706) 631561 E-mail: info@pegasusaviation.co.uk *Aviation support products manufrs*

P M P L Telford Ltd, Unit 25 Heath Hill Industrial Estate, Dawley, Telford, Shropshire, TF4 2RH Tel: (01952) 507978 Fax: (01952) 507978 E-mail: daviespmp@aol.com *CNC machining services*

P M P Micros, Rock Cottage, Hawber Lane, Silsden, Keighley, West Yorkshire, BD20 0LE Tel: (07967) 173739 Fax: (01535) 653006 E-mail: peter@pmp-micros.co.uk *Computer maintenance*

P & M (Packing) Ltd, Unit 11, Alstam Complex, Campbell Road, Eastleigh, Hampshire, SO50 5AD Tel: (023) 8049 0400 Fax: (023) 8049 0444 E-mail: naomi@pmpacking.com *Export packers*

P M Precision Engineering, Unit 2A, Bridge Works, Bridge Road, Camberley, Surrey, GU15 2QR Tel: (01276) 691285 Fax: (01276) 27193 E-mail: hillary@pmeng.co.uk *Precision engineers*

P M R Ceilings & Partitioning Ltd, Unit 3-4 Bridge Road Industrial Estate, Litherland, Liverpool, L21 6PH Tel: 0151-928 6668 Fax: 0151-920 2090 *Suspended ceiling suppliers*

P M R Electrical, Lodge Lane, Langham, Colchester, CO4 5ND Tel: (01206) 231894 Fax: (01206) 231895 E-mail: tony@pmrelec.fsnet.co.uk *Electrical contractors*

P M R Industrial Services, 13-21 Liverpool Road, Kidsgrove, Stoke-on-Trent, ST7 1EA Tel: (01782) 776325 Fax: (01782) 771912 *Industrial brush & replacement brush manufacturers. Also hydraulic equipment & systems maintenance & repair services*

P & M Regrinds, Unit 9, Brittania Industrial Park, High Wycombe, Buckinghamshire, HP12 3ES Tel: (01494) 437949 Fax: (01494) 471815 E-mail: pmtools@tiscali.co.uk *Tool & cutter grinding services*

P M S Developments, Netherwood Road, Rotherwas Industrial Estate, Hereford, HR2 6JU Tel: (01432) 265768 Fax: (01432) 263782 E-mail: sales@pmssystems.com Principal Export Areas: Worldwide *Electronic control systems*

P M S Diecasting, Unit 11 Braithwell Way, Hellaby, Rotherham, South Yorkshire, S66 8QY Tel: (01709) 701901 Fax: (01709) 700833 E-mail: gpanter@pmsdiecasting.co.uk *High pressure zinc diecasting & power coating*

P M S International Group plc, International House, Cricketers Way, Basildon, Essex, SS13 1ST Tel: (01268) 505050 Fax: (01268) 505000 E-mail: sales@pmsinternational.com *Toy manufrs*

P M S Micro Ltd, 3 Brown Avenue, Leeds, LS11 0DS Tel: 0113-277 3523 Fax: 0113-277 6867 E-mail: mail@pmsmicro.co.uk *Microbiological & chemical analysis service*

P M S Morley Ltd, 3 High Mill Business Park, Mill Street, Morley, Leeds, LS27 0WJ Tel: 0113-259 7557 Fax: 0113-259 7251 *Shop fitting & project management*

P & M Services (Rochdale) Ltd, Stoneswood Mill, Bacup Road, Todmorden, Lancashire, OL14 7HG Tel: (01706) 815212 Fax: (01706) 818636 E-mail: sales@p-m-services.co.uk *Printed circuit manufrs*

P & M Thornton, Blackheath Farm, Milton-under-Wychwood, Chipping Norton, Oxfordshire, OX7 6HX Tel: (01993) 823365 Fax: (01933) 823365 *Excavation & groundwork contractors*

P M Tools & Fasteners Ltd, 7 Phoenix Road Industrial Estate, Phoenix Road, Wolverhampton, WV11 3PX Tel: (01902) 727959 Fax: (01902) 738558 E-mail: info@pmtools.co.uk *General engineering tool suppliers*

▶ P M Transport Ltd, 189 Rose Lane, Liverpool, L18 5EA Tel: 0151-724 3190 Fax: 0151-724 3190

▶ P M Vending Ltd, Unit 25 Clearview Business Park, Loughborough Road, Quorn, Loughborough, Leicestershire, LE12 8DU Tel: (01509) 415333 Fax: (01509) 211650 E-mail: pmvending@btopenworld.com *Vending machine sales & lease*

P M W Gifts, Springfield House, Water Lane, Wilmslow, Cheshire, SK9 5BG Tel: (01625) 536036 Fax: (01625) 536320 E-mail: sales@pmwgifts.co.uk *In the past 20 years PMW gifts has grown to become a leading company in the supply of personalised business gifts and promotional merchandise to the business communities, sports and leisure industries within the U. K. Promotional items and business gifts are arguably the most cost effective vehicles for promoting your company. With thousands of promotional gifts we have something for every occasion and every marketing budget. Why PMW Gifts? Established over 20 years In house design and artwork Worldwide sourcing In house fulfilment Over 80% repeat orders Total reliability and understanding of our clients No order too big or too small Our aim is to answer our client's every requirement, whatever you are looking for, be it off the shelf items or made to order items, we will source it for you at the right price. Our buying experience is worldwide*

P M W Precision Engineering Ltd, 47-55 Alcester Street, Deritend, Birmingham, B12 0PY Tel: 0121-773 9105 Fax: 0121-773 9141 *Gear box & machine tool repair*

▶ P M Windows Ltd, Holme Street, Grimsby, South Humberside, DN32 9AD Tel: (01472) 251261 Fax: (01472) 251471 E-mail: sales@pmwindows.co.uk

P Mcquaid, Hill Street, Milford, Armagh, BT60 3PB Tel: (028) 3751 0057 *Joinery & window manufrs*

▶ P Maddison Haulage Ltd, Coldham Road, Coningsby, Lincoln, LN4 4SD Tel: (01526) 342597 Fax: (01526) 343064 E-mail: info@maddisonhaulage.demon.co.uk

P Messenger, 6 Twin Lakes Industrial Park, Bretherton Road, Croston, Leyland, PR26 9RF Tel: (01772) 600889 Fax: (01772) 600255 E-mail: sales@stoneandconcrete.co.uk *Concrete cast stone manufacturers & retailers*

▶ P Milton Ltd, 1a Mill Road, Mile End, Colchester, CO4 5LD Tel: (01206) 852774 Fax: (0870) 256526 E-mail: miltongroup@aol.com

P Monkhouse, Durham Road, Wolsingham, Bishop Auckland, County Durham, DL13 3JB Tel: (01388) 528814 Fax: (01388) 527213 E-mail: sales@monkhousehaulage.co.uk *Haulage contractors*

▶ P Moran Ltd, Smeaton, Dalkeith, Midlothian, EH22 2NN Tel: 0131-663 6246 Fax: 0131-663 9908

P & N Corporate Media Ltd, 9c Aven Industrial Park, Tickhill Road, Maltby, Rotherham, South Yorkshire, S66 7QR Tel: (01709) 818999 Fax: (01709) 769911 E-mail: studio@cncorpmedia.co.uk *Design and Print, Digital Print, Large format Print, Signs, Display, Banners, Exhibition Stands, Websites*

P N L Tools, 5 The Hawthorns, Hawthorns Lane, Staunton, Gloucester, GL19 3NY Tel: (01452) 840966 Fax: (01452) 840965 *Computer software engineers*

P N P Computers, 178 Bispham Road, Southport, Merseyside, PR9 7BP Tel: (01704) 233888 Fax: (01704) 233888 E-mail: sales@pnpshop.co.uk *Computer hardware suppliers*

P N R UK Ltd, 13 16 Sugarbrook Road, Bromsgrove, Worcestershire, B60 3DW Tel: (01527) 579066 Fax: (01527) 579067 E-mail: sales@pnr.co.uk *PNR has focused on an innovative approach to the industrial sector. Our production methods for spray nozzles & supporting equipment are second to none and a programme of continuous upgrading of production machinery & IT is a naturally evolving procedure. This mechanism operates along side a sophisticated testing laboratory offering the regular checking for day-to-day spray nozzle manufacturing. This also allows for specific testing required by our customers individual needs. . PLEASE QUOTE YOU FOUND US THROUGH KELLYSEARCH.*

P N Tools, Unit 33 34, Fourways, Carlyon Road Industrial Estate, Atherstone, Warwickshire, CV9 1LH Tel: (01827) 720013 Fax: (01827) 720039 *Cutting tool manufrs*

P N Ventilation, 65 Southend Road, Bungay, Suffolk, NR35 1DN Tel: (01986) 893706 Fax: (01986) 895050 *Dust extraction services*

▶ P O Ltd, 311 Spitfire Studios, 63-71 Colier Street, London, N1 9BE Tel: (020) 7837 2322 Fax: (020) 7837 2321 E-mail: paula@poltd.co.uk *UK & Eire London based fashion agency for wholesale of designer labels: Guess Kids & Baby, Guess Handbags & Mens Leather Goods, Dimensione Danza, Patty Shelabarger Kids, Pickwick Baby & Junior. For more information please go to www.poltd.co.uk*

P & O Aerosols, 2 Hale Industrial Estate, Lower Church Lane, Tipton, West Midlands, DY4 7PQ Tel: 0121-520 8883 Fax: 0121-520 8080 E-mail: sales@pxoaerosols.co.uk *Aerosol contract packers*

P & O Cruises Ltd, Castlewood House, 77 New Oxford Street, London, WC1A 1PP Tel: (0845) 3585585 Fax: (023) 8052 3720 *Cruise ship company*

The P & O Cruises Ltd, Richmond House, Terminus Terrace, Southampton, SO14 3PN Tel: (023) 8053 4200 Fax: (023) 8022 7920 *Cruise lines*

P & O Developments Ltd, 4 Carlton Gardens, Pall Mall, London, SW1Y 5AB Tel: (020) 7839 5611 Fax: (020) 7930 2098 *Property development*

P & O European Ferries Ltd, Copse Road, Fleetwood, Lancashire, FY7 6RP Tel: (01253) 615700 Fax: (01253) 615702 E-mail: info@poisfreight.com *Ferry service* Also at: Ardrossan, Leeds, Leighton Buzzard, Liverpool & Stoke-on-Trent

P & O Ferries, King George Dock, Hedon Road, Hull, HU9 5QA Tel: (01482) 795141 Fax: (01482) 708255 E-mail: sales@ponsf.com *Ferry service* Also at: Ipswich & Middlesbrough

▶ P & O Ferrymasters Ltd, Dock Street, Fleetwood, Lancashire, FY7 6HR Tel: (01253) 615800 Fax: (01253) 615801

▶ P & O Nedlloyd Ltd, Northfleet Hope House, Tilbury, Essex, RM18 7HX Tel: (01375) 812200

P & O Nedlloyd Global Logistics Ltd, Capital Gate, 320 New North Road, Ilford, Essex, IG6 3ES Tel: (020) 8918 6000 Fax: (020) 8918 6088 E-mail: centraladmin@mersk.com *Container services, road, rail & sea freight*

P O P Enterprises, 34 Southwark St, Nottingham, NG6 0DA Tel: 0115-913 0233 Fax: 0870 0520990 *Model shop*

▶ P O S Lighting Ltd, Unit 4 Thurmaston Court, Thurmaston, Leicester, LE4 8EB Tel: 0116-269 3500 Fax: 0116-269 3512 E-mail: poslightingltd@btopenworld.com *Lighting manufrs*

P O S Packaging Ltd, Cressex Business Park, 30A Wellington Road, High Wycombe, Buckinghamshire, HP12 3PR Tel: (01494) 473701 Fax: (01494) 473801 E-mail: unique.pkg@online.rednet.co.uk *Corrugated boxes, cartons & packaging*

P O S S Ltd, 36 Holly Pk, Huby, Leeds, LS17 0BT Tel: (01423) 734977 Fax: (01423) 734977 E-mail: mark@possltd.co.uk *Design & development engineering*

P & O Steam Navigation Co, Peninsular House, 79 Pall Mall, London, SW1Y 5EJ Tel: (020) 7930 4343 Fax: (020) 7930 8572 E-mail: groupinformation@pogroup.com *Freight forwarders*

P O'Neill Electrical Ltd, 27 Salisbury Road, Luton, LU1 5AP Tel: (01582) 456361 Fax: (01582) 728637 E-mail: jean@ponmail.co.uk *Industrial electrical contractors*

P & P Clothing, Old Mill La Industrial Estate, Mansfield Woodhouse, Mansfield, Nottinghamshire, NG19 9BG Tel: (01623) 422044 Fax: (01623) 424557 E-mail: sales@pandp.force9.co.uk *Manufacturer & supplier of protective workwear*

P P Composites Ltd, Unit 39c Vale Business Park, Llandow, Cowbridge, South Glamorgan, CF71 7PF Tel: (01446) 775885 Fax: (01446) 775822 E-mail: sales@ppcomposites.ltd.uk *Suppliers of inhibitors & castings*

▶ P & P Computer Centre, Contract House, Stafford Street, Stone, Staffordshire, ST15 8QW Tel: (01785) 812299 Fax: (01785) 812277

continued

P & P Drysdale, Darnoch Farm, Dunkeld, Perthshire, PH8 0JE Tel: (01350) 727467 Fax: (01350) 727467 E-mail: drysdale467@tiscali.co.uk *Agricultural services*

▶ P & P Duct Services Ltd, Zagale House, Kelpatrick Road, Slough, SL1 6BW Tel: (01628) 666616 Fax: (01628) 666604 *Ventilation systems maintenance*

P.P.E. Ltd, Horsecroft Rd, The Pinnacles, Harlow, Essex, CM19 5BH Tel: (01279) 412345 Fax: (01279) 419533 E-mail: sales@ppe.co.uk *One of Europe's leading designers and manufacturers of standard and bespoke Point of Sale (POS) displays and Merchandising equipment. PPE supply everything from an extensive range of standard display items including leaflet dispensers and menu holders, shelf management equipment, sign, print and poster holders to full in-store fixtures and bespoke displays. PPE provide a unique One-Stop shop facility. Everything from concept generation, visualising, prototyping and development, through to production, storage and installation. Manufacturing processes include:- injection moulding, vacuum forming, metalworking, laser cutting, powder coating, screen printing, large format digital printing*

P P Engineering, Charles Street, Kilnhurst, Mexborough, South Yorkshire, S64 5TG Tel: (01709) 578877 Fax: (01709) 578555 E-mail: ppengineering@talk21.com *Mobile crane hire*

P P Fashions, 45 Forest Road, Leicester, LE5 0DW Tel: 0116-253 9226 Fax: 0116-251 2948 *Leisurewear manufrs*

P P G Industries UK Ltd, Needham Road, Stowmarket, Suffolk, IP14 2AD Tel: (01449) 613161 Fax: (01449) 677161 *Car paint manufrs*

P P Injection Moulds & Moulding Ltd, Beversbrook Industrial Estate, Redman Road, Calne, Wiltshire, SN11 9PL Tel: (01249) 823100 Fax: (01249) 823103 E-mail: sales@ppmoulds.co.uk *Award winning injection moulds and mouldings* Also at: Chippenham

P & P Installation P.L.C., Unit 5 Empire Centre, Imperial Way, Watford, WD24 4YH Tel: (01923) 226357 Fax: (01923) 254434 *Computer, telephone & electrical insulations & fibre*

P & P Joinery, 157 Hornsey Park Road, London, N8 0JX Tel: (020) 8881 1111 Fax: (020) 8881 0027 *Cabinet*

P & P Joinery, Unit 19 Lord Nelson Industrial Estate, Commercial Road, Hanley, Stoke-On-Trent, ST1 3QE Tel: (01782) 273708 Fax: (01782) 273708 *Joinery*

P P L Graphex, 241a Selbourne Road, Luton, LU4 8NP Tel: (01582) 599529 Fax: (01582) 583366 E-mail: bgale@pplgraphex.com *Exhibition stand contractors*

P P Lift Chains Ltd, 14 Williams Road, Radford Semele, Leamington Spa, Warwickshire, CV31 1UR Tel: (01926) 313218 Fax: (01926) 313218 *Fork lift chains suppliers*

P P Machine Tools Ltd, 45 The Ridgeway, Rothley, Leicester, LE7 7LE Tel: 0116-230 3050 Fax: 0116-230 4430 E-mail: pp_cnc@yahoo.com *CNC engineers*

P & P Non Ferrous (Stockists) Ltd, 47B Premier Trading Estate, The Leys, Brierley Hill, West Midlands, DY5 3UP Tel: (01384) 482888 Fax: (01384) 482088 E-mail: sales@ppnonferrous.co.uk *Non-ferrous metal & phosphor bronze stockholders*

▶ P P P UK Ltd, Orchard House, Henwood, Ashford, Kent, TN24 8DH Tel: (01233) 665597 Fax: (01233) 665598 E-mail: hassansard@aol.com *Packaging material manufrs*

P P Plasma, New Factory, Vere Street, Salford, M50 2GQ Tel: 0161-736 9299 Fax: 0161-745 7915 *Stainless steel profilers*

P & P Print & Packing, F 7 Gore Road, Burnham, Slough, SL1 8AA Tel: (01628) 666249 Fax: (01628) 602471 E-mail: printandpacking@btconnect.com *Carrier bags, printing & packaging*

P P Profiles Ltd, Neills Road, Bold, St. Helens, Merseyside, WA9 4SY Tel: (01744) 818992 Fax: (01744) 820179 E-mail: sales@ppprofilesltd.co.uk *Profile cutting services*

P P Profiles (West Yorkshire) Ltd, Springfield Works, Stocks Lane, Batley, West Yorkshire, WF17 8PA Tel: (01924) 441381 Fax: (01924) 472681 E-mail: info@pp-profiles.co.uk *Steel profilers & grinders*

P P S Commercials Ltd, Cemetery Road, Radcliffe, Manchester, M26 4FT Tel: 0161-724 5022 Fax: 0161-723 5918 E-mail: enquiries@ppscommercials.co.uk *Commercial vehicle body builders*

P P S Construction Plant Sales Ltd, Tomlinson Road, Leyland, PR25 2DY Tel: (01772) 456392 Fax: (01772) 621368 E-mail: info@ppsplantsales.co.uk *Construction equipment sales & service*

▶ P P S Food Projects, 11 The Crescent, Plymouth, PL1 3AB Tel: (01752) 510173 Fax: (01752) 512489 E-mail: brianlr@ppsfoodprojects.co.uk *Project management and design services, specialists in food factory design, food process design, feasibility and concept to commissioning.*

P P S Glassfibre Ltd, Harlaw Way, Harlaw Road Industrial Estate, Inverurie, Aberdeenshire, AB51 4SG Tel: (01467) 621907 Fax: (01467) 620265 E-mail: ppsglassfibre@btconnect.com *Glass fibre tanks, cabinets & kiosks*

P P S Hydraulics & Pneumatics Ltd, Foxwood Close, Foxwood Industrial Park, Sheepbridge, Chesterfield, Derbyshire, S41 9RN Tel: (01246) 451509 Fax: (01246) 450831 E-mail: ppshydraulics@btconnect.com *Hose & tube fittings distributors*

▶ P P S Print Communication Ltd, 198 Deansgate, Manchester, M3 3NE Tel: 0161-832 4024 E-mail: sales@ppsprintcom.com

P P S Recovery Systems Ltd, 9 Metrocentre, Welbeck Way, Peterborough, PE2 7WH Tel: (01733) 390029 Fax: (01733) 390031 E-mail: enquiry@pps-ltd.com *Waste recycling or processing plant & equipment services*

P P Scene Ltd, 68 High Street, Chislehurst, Kent, BR7 5BL Tel: (020) 8467 0935 Fax: (020) 8467 7490 *Drawing equipment wholesaler*

P & P Seating, 429 Meadway, Birmingham, B33 0DZ Tel: 0121-784 9441 Fax: 0121-789 7061 E-mail: info@ppseat.co.uk *Motor cycle seat & luggage manufrs*

P & P Supplies Ltd, Units 9-11, Ely Distribution Centre, Heol Trelai, Ely, Cardiff, CF5 5NJ Tel: (029) 2059 7593 Fax: (029) 2059 1268 E-mail: info@pandpsupplies.co.uk *Sheet metalwork engineers or fabricators*

P P Systems, Unit 23, Enterprise Centre, Bryn Road, Bridgend, Mid Glamorgan, CF32 9BS Tel: (01656) 724859 Fax: (01656) 724859 *Metal fabricators*

P P Systems, Templandshaw, Sorn, Mauchline, Ayrshire, KA5 6NG Tel: (01290) 551543 Fax: (01290) 552165 *Computer systems supply & support services*

P & P Technology Ltd, 1 Kestrel Park, Finch Drive, Springwood Industrial Estate, Braintree, Essex, CM7 2SF Tel: (01376) 550525 Fax: (01376) 552389 E-mail: info@p-p-t.co.uk Principal Export Areas: Asia Pacific, Central/East Europe, West Europe & North America *P & P Technology is a specialist manufacturer of EMI/RFI screening and shielding products.**They produce an extensive range of shielded windows, attenuation vents, gaskets, contact finger strips, conductive foil tapes and conductive adhesives, fabricated from a wide range of materials. All their products can be completely customised for specific applications and requirements.*

P P V Electronics Ltd, Unit 1a, Bridge St Mills, Bridge St, Macclesfield, Cheshire, SK11 6QA Tel: (01625) 502062 Fax: (01625) 420507 E-mail: markhough@ppv-electronics.com *Electronics contractors*

▶ P Pritchard Sheet Metal Ltd, Unit 15 White Horse Business Park, Ware Road, Stanford in the Vale, Faringdon, Oxfordshire, SN7 8NY Tel: (01367) 710060 Fax: (01367) 710105

P & Q International plc, Wickham House, Station Road, Braughing, Ware, Hertfordshire, SG11 2PB Tel: (0845) 1300707 Fax: (0845) 1300727 E-mail: sales@pandq.com *Software developers time & attendance systems & data collection services*

P Quinton, 2 Northern Court, Nottingham, NG6 0BJ Tel: 0115-975 5837 Fax: 0115-975 5837 E-mail: paul@paul-quinton.freeserve.co.uk *Welding & fabrication engineers*

▶ P R Automation Ltd, Quality House, Fisher Street, Dudley Port, Tipton, West Midlands, DY4 8XE Tel: 0121-557 4311 Fax: 0121-557 4314 *P R Automation provide total control solutions for industry.*

▶ P R Cooper Footline Ltd, Sycamore Works, Melton Road, Tilton on the Hill, Leicester, LE7 9LG Tel: 0116-259 7263 Fax: 0116-259 7489

P R D Fasteners Ltd, Unit 10 Monmer Close Industrial Estate, Willenhall, West Midlands, WV13 1JR Tel: (01902) 636246 Fax: (01902) 605759 E-mail: sales@prdfasteners.co.uk *Bolt & nut manufrs*

P R D Holdings Ltd, Unit 13, Monmer Close, Willenhall, West Midlands, WV13 1JR Tel: (01902) 639360 Fax: (01902) 639365 E-mail: info@prdholdings.com *Manufacturers & suppliers of fasteners*

▶ P R Designs, Tong Lane Bus Centre, Tong Lane, Whitworth, Rochdale, Lancashire, OL12 8BE Tel: (01706) 854264 Fax: (01706) 854264 E-mail: prdesignssales@timewarpuk.net *Model makers, mimics, acrylics*

P R Designs, 13 Davenport Park Road, Davenport Park, Stockport, Cheshire, SK2 6JU Tel: 0161-483 2655 Fax: 0161-483 2655 E-mail: info@prdesigns.co.uk *Industrial, mechanical, product design & innovation services*

P & R Disposal Services, 117 Clydesdale Place, Leyland, PR26 7QS Tel: (01772) 454129 Fax: (01772) 622258 E-mail: sales@distillex.xo.uk *Solvent & chemical waste recovery & recycling services*

▶ P R Engineering Ltd, 6a Aizlewood Road, Sheffield, S8 0YX Tel: 0114-250 9077 E-mail: sales@laser-level.co.uk *Manufacturer & distributor of measuring instruments*

P & R Engineering Midlands Ltd, Cable Street, Wolverhampton, WV2 2HX Tel: (01902) 870637 Fax: (01902) 871569 *Fencing, railway, bridge parapet & balustrade manufrs*

P R Epoxy Systems Ltd, Unit D2 The Court, Kestrel Road, Trafford Park, Manchester, M17 1SF Tel: 0161-872 7618 Fax: 0161-876 4597 E-mail: prepoxy@aol.com *Epoxy resin based products*

P & R Finishing, 1 Site 2 North Bridge Road, Berkhamsted, Hertfordshire, HP4 1EH Tel: (01442) 873962 Fax: (01442) 873962 *Shot blasting & powder coating*

P R Firman Fork Trucks Ltd, Unit 8, Roudham Road, Harling Road, Norwich, NR16 2QN Tel: (01953) 717770 Fax: (01953) 717770 E-mail: info@firmanforktrucks.co.uk *Fork lift truck hire & sales services*

P & R Gearboxes, Woodside Service Station, Copthorne Road, Crawley, West Sussex, RH10 3PD Tel: (01293) 888141 *Gearbox service & repairers*

P R Gibson Refridgerated Container Sales, Little Tennis St South, Nottingham, NG2 4EU Tel: 0115-950 6298 Fax: 0115-950 6299 *Container sales*

P R Hollowayltd, 34 West Barnes Lane, Raynes Park, London, SW20 0BP Tel: (020) 8946 8872 Fax: (020) 8946 8872 *Precision engineers*

P R Hunter Plastics Ltd, 5 Pembroke Road, Stocklake Indus Estate, Aylesbury, Buckinghamshire, HP20 1DB Tel: (01296) 422423 Fax: (01296) 422423 E-mail: hunter_plastics@hotmail.com *Finished products in plastic welding*

▶ P & R Installations Co Ltd, 35-37 Waite Davies Road, London, SE12 0NE Tel: (020) 8851 2211 Fax: (020) 8851 6611

P R Kyte, Unit 2 Hamilton Road, Sutton-in-Ashfield, Nottinghamshire, NG17 5LD Tel: (01623) 556636 Fax: (01623) 556636 *General & precision engineers*

P & R Labpak Ltd, Unit 6, Ketterer Court, St. Helens, Merseyside, WA9 3AH Tel: 0870 0342055 Fax: 0870 0342056 E-mail: steve.morris@prlabs.co.uk *Supplier of laboratory chemicals, equipment, consumables & laboratory apparatus*

P & R Labpak Ltd, 6 Ketterer Court, St. Helens, Merseyside, WA9 3AH Tel: 0870 0342055 Fax: 0870 0342056 E-mail: sales@prlabs.co.uk *Laboratory supplies, chemicals, equipment, consumables and disposal services*

▶ P & R Materials, Clint Bank, Burnt Yates, Harrogate, North Yorkshire, HG3 3DW Tel: (01423) 770731 Fax: (01423) 771527

▶ P R Metals, 7 Maybrook Industrial Estate, Maybrook Road, Walsall, WS8 7DG Tel: (01543) 360157 Fax: (01543) 360167 E-mail: prmetals@btconnect.com *Stockholder and suppliers of bars,rods,sections and components in,Copper,Brass,Aluminium,Stainless steel,Bronze and plastic materials.*

P R Newswire Europe Ltd, 209-215 Blackfriars Road, London, SE1 8NL Tel: (020) 7490 8111 Fax: (020) 7490 1255 E-mail: info@prnewswire.co.uk *Public relations support services*

P R O Marketing Co. Ltd, Unit 10 Jubilee Trade Centre, Jubilee Road, Letchworth Garden City, Hertfordshire, SG6 1SP Tel: (01462) 677188 Fax: (01462) 685275 E-mail: sales@proengraving.com *Seal makers, engravers, heraldic & embossing machine manufrs*

P R P Optoelectronics Ltd, Woodburcote Way, Towcester, Northamptonshire, NN12 6TF Tel: (01327) 359135 Fax: (01327) 359602 E-mail: sales@prpopto.co.uk *Display (LED) panel, module & systems manufrs*

P R Pallet Services, Macdermott Road, Widnes, Cheshire, WA8 0PF Tel: 0151-495 1422 Fax: 0151-495 1123 *Pallet rebuilders & suppliers*

P & R Pallets & Cases, 2 Bridge Industrial Estate, Hot Lane, Stoke-on-Trent, ST6 2DL Tel: (01782) 822555 Fax: (01782) 822555 *Reconditioned pallet rebuilders*

P R Plus Ltd, 196 Barker Butts Lane, Coventry, CV6 1ER Tel: (024) 7659 0721 Fax: (024) 7659 0700 *Pr marketing services*

P R Portable Buildings, The Lawns, 52 West Street, Crewkerne, Somerset, TA18 8BA Tel: (01460) 72033 Fax: (01460) 72033 *Garden building designers*

P R R Computers, Duckworth Street, Blackburn, BB2 2JQ Tel: (01254) 664515 Fax: (01254) 664545 E-mail: sales@prrcomputers.co.uk *Computer network manufrs*

▶ P R S Building Contractors, Port Road, Palnackie, Castle Douglas, Kirkcudbrightshire, DG7 1PQ Tel: (01556) 600351 Fax: (01556) 600240

P R S Communications Ltd, 2 Birch Avenue, Harwich, Essex, CO12 4DB Tel: (01255) 240523 Fax: (01255) 240523 E-mail: sales@prscomms.com *Radio systems marine electronics retailers*

P R S Invistech, The Technology Centre, Easting Close, Worthing, West Sussex, BN14 8HQ Tel: (01903) 217337 Fax: (01903) 217713 E-mail: sales@prsl.co.uk Principal Export Areas: Worldwide *Printed circuit board problem solving*

▶ P R S Management Depot UK Ltd, Unit 15B, Wilden Industrial Estate, Stourport-On-Severn, Worcestershire, DY13 9JY Tel: (01299) 878282

▶ P R S Plumbing & Heating Services Ltd, Premier House, Popham, Micheldever, Winchester, Hampshire, SO21 3BJ Tel: (01256) 398881 Fax: (01256) 398889

P R Salmon, Red House Farm, Station Road, Onneley, Crewe, CW3 9QQ Tel: (01782) 750255 Fax: (01782) 750255 *Agricultural contractors*

▶ P & R Security Systems Ltd, 119 Lees Road, Oldham, OL4 1JW Tel: 0161-652 9984 Fax: 0161-620 8111 E-mail: sales@pandrsecurities.co.uk *CCTV installation & monitoring*

▶ P R Smith Engineering, Station Works, Lyndhurst Road, Ascot, Berkshire, SL5 9ED Tel: (01344) 874763 Fax: (01344) 875433 E-mail: topmut@themutznutz.com *Precision engineers*

▶ P R Stockinger (Transport) Ltd, 5 Furlong Road, Stoke Ferry, King's Lynn, Norfolk, PE33 9SU Tel: (01366) 500971

▶ P R Systems, 22 Leyshade Court, DUNDEE, DD4 8XN Tel: 01382 522467 Fax: 01382 522467 E-mail: sales@prsystems.net *Professional web design, hosting, domain name registration and search engine submissions. PC sales and service.*

P R Textiles, 31-32 Cliveland Street, Birmingham, B19 3SH Tel: 0121-359 2741 Fax: 0121-333 3600 *Casual clothing*

P R V Engineering Ltd, Pegasus House, Polo Grounds, New Inn, Pontypool, Gwent, NP4 0TW Tel: (01495) 769697 Fax: (01495) 769776 E-mail: enquiries@prv-engineering.co.uk *Drilling services, fabricators & erectors*

P Robinson, 10 London Road, Worcester, WR5 2DL Tel: (01905) 764077 *Electroplating services*

P S A Ltd, 52 The Downs, Altrincham, Cheshire, WA14 2QJ Tel: 0161-924 0011 Fax: 0161-924 0022 E-mail: sales@psafilms.co.uk *Cinema & television commercial producers*

P S A Batteries Ltd, Faraday House, 39 Thornton Road, Wimbledon, London, SW19 4NQ Tel: (0870) 873 2002 Fax: (020) 8944 6694 E-mail: jem@psaparts.co.uk *Computer batteries manufrs*

P S A Professionals Solutions, 67 Park Street, Thame, Oxfordshire, OX9 3HT Tel: (01844) 261750 Fax: (01840) 261751 E-mail: info@psaconnect.com *Computer re-sellers*

P S A Transport Ltd, 16 Devonshire Street, London, W1G 7AF Tel: (020) 7637 3271 Fax: (020) 7255 2229 E-mail: sales@psatransport.co.uk *Freight forwarders*

P S B Group Ltd, Williamson Street, Stoke-on-Trent, ST6 6AS Tel: (01782) 837644 Fax: (01782) 837378 E-mail: psb@psbgroup.co.uk *PVC curtains & industrial filters manufrs*

P S Construction Doncaster Ltd, Grange Farm, Mere Lane, Edenthorpe, Doncaster, South Yorkshire, DN3 2HS Tel: (01302) 300100 Fax: (01302) 300354 E-mail: sales@psconstruction.co.uk *Building & joinery contractors*

▶ P & S Construction (Swindon) Ltd, Unit 5, Kendrick Trading Estate, Galton Way, Swindon, SN2 2DU Tel: (01793) 534921

P S Consultants, Hockham Hill House, Spring Elms Lane, Little Baddom, Chelmsford, CM3 4SD Tel: (01245) 224065 Fax: (01245) 287057 E-mail: info@ps-consultants.co.uk *IT consultants*

P S D Contracts Ltd, 28 Essex Street, London, WC2R 3AT Tel: (020) 7970 9700 Fax: (020) 7936 3976 *Executive recruitment consultancy*

P S D Group plc, 7 Perrymount Road, Haywards Heath, West Sussex, RH16 3TN Tel: (01293) 802000 Fax: (01293) 802001 E-mail: finance@psdgroup.com *Recruitment consultants*

▶ P & S Electrical Contractors, 427 Minster Road, Minster on Sea, Sheerness, Kent, ME12 3NS Tel: (01795) 871945 Fax: (01795) 871945

P S Engineering, 2 London Road, West Kingsdown, Sevenoaks, Kent, TN15 6ET Tel: (01474) 853586 Fax: (01474) 853586 *Industrial cleaning machinery sales, supply & maintenance*

▶ P S G Networks, College Lane, Hatfield, Hertfordshire, AL10 9AB Tel: (0845) 2418777 Fax: (01707) 284274 E-mail: info@psgnetworks.com *Sell & install business telephone systems*

P S G Precision Tooling, 158 Hearsall Lane, Coventry, CV5 6HH Tel: (024) 7671 1388 Fax: (024) 7667 8617 *Machine tool manufrs*

P S Gill & Sons, 261-277 Rookery Road, Handsworth, Birmingham, B21 9PT Tel: 0121-554 7521 Fax: 0121-554 9033 E-mail: ssgill@psgill.com *Leisure wear manufacturers clothing manufrs*

P S I Global Ltd, Bowburn South Industrial Estate, Bowburn, Durham, DH6 5AD Tel: 0191-377 0550 Fax: 0191-377 0769 E-mail: sales@psiglobal.co.uk *Oil free & air filters specialists*

P S I (Resources) Ltd, Unit 3, Barlow Street, Walkden, Manchester, M28 3BQ Tel: 0161-703 8911 Fax: 0161-703 8995 E-mail: sales@p-s-i.co.uk *Heating & ventilation servicing & maintenance services*

P S L Access Control, 8 Curtis Road, Epsom, Surrey, KT19 0LG Tel: (020) 8337 0517 Fax: (020) 8390 6972 E-mail: paul@psiac.freeserve.co.uk

P S L Energy Services Ltd, Badentoy Avenue, Badentoy Industrial Estate, Portlethen, Aberdeen, AB12 4YB Tel: (01224) 783008 Fax: (01224) 783005 E-mail: sales@psles.com Principal Export Areas: Worldwide *Well services, pipeline process excavation services*

P S L (Weir) Ltd, Ashcroft Road, Knowlsley Industrial Estate North, Liverpool, L33 7TW Tel: 0151-547 2222 Fax: 0151-549 1060 E-mail: psllpool@hotmail.com *Architectural ironmongers*

P S Label, 102 Vernon Road, Leicester, LE2 8GB Tel: 0116-244 0576 Fax: 0116-244 0576 E-mail: pslabels@btconnect.com *Label printers services & manufrs*

▶ P S M Builders, Orchard, Birdham Road, Chichester, West Sussex, PO20 7EQ Tel: (01243) 774605

P S M International plc, Longacre, Willenhall, West Midlands, WV13 2JS Tel: (01902) 600000 Fax: (01902) 600073 E-mail: tlspsm@compuserve.com *Fasteners general, zinc, industrial & micron capsulation services*

P S Office Supplies Ltd, 40 Great Lister Street, Birmingham, B7 4LS Tel: 0121-333 5000 Fax: 0121-333 5001 E-mail: sales@psonline.co.uk *Business to business office suppliers*

P S P Dental Co. Ltd, 3-5 Dylan Road, Belvedere, Kent, DA17 5QS Tel: (020) 8311 7337 Fax: (020) 8310 0920 E-mail: sales@pspdental.com *Dental manufrs*

P S P Safety Products Ltd, 9 Aintree Road, Keytech 7 Business Park, Keytec 7 Business Park, Pershore, Worcestershire, WR10 2JN Tel: (01386) 552555 Fax: (01386) 552592 *Fire fighting equipment manufrs*

P S Power Tools, Unit G, Tinhay Industrial Estate, Tinhay, Lifton, Devon, PL16 0AH Tel: (01566) 784385 *Power tools sales & repair & hire*

P & S Promotions Sign & Print, 16 Hodgsons Court, Hodgsons Way, Wickford, Essex, SS11 8XR Tel: (01268) 572616 Fax: (01268) 572122 *Sign contractors*

P S R Industrial Ltd, 72 Snow Hill, Melton Mowbray, Leicestershire, LE13 1PH Tel: (01664) 565401 Fax: (01664) 560030 E-mail: sales@psr-industrial.co.uk *Thermoplastic product stockists & machinists*

▶ P S Ridgway Ltd, 5 Smeaton Road, West Gourdie Industrial Estate, Dundee, DD2 4UT Tel: (01382) 614500 Fax: (01382) 614522

P S S Agency, Warrington, WA4 4JU Tel: (01928) 711700 Fax: (01928) 711258 *Commercial recruitment agency*

P S T Construction, 3 Brooke Street, Sunderland, SR5 1BN Tel: 0191-510 9241 Fax: 0191-567 6311 *Construction steel fabrication specialists*

P & S Textiles Ltd, Hornby Street, Bury, Lancashire, BL9 5BL Tel: 0161-764 8617 Fax: 0161-763 7260 E-mail: info@pstextiles.co.uk *Industrial textiles*

P S Thurtle, Great Horton Road, Bradford, West Yorkshire, BD7 4DU Tel: (01274) 502754 *Wholesale pie manufrs*

P & S Tools, Spring La South, Malvern, Worcestershire, WR14 1AT Tel: (01684) 563632 Fax: (01684) 560825 E-mail: info@pstools.co.uk *Specialising in small quantity complex aerospace components (Rolls Royce Approved) and petro chemical parts. All types of toolmaking, i.e. plastic, blowmould etc.*

▶ P S Transport, 1 Enterprise Way, Ladysmith Road, Grimsby, South Humberside, DN32 9TW Tel: (01472) 359426 Fax: (01472) 347745 E-mail: sales@pstransport.co.uk

P S U Designs Ltd, 7 Bloomfield Park, Bloomfield Road, Tipton, West Midlands, DY4 9AP Tel: 0121-557 6499 Fax: 0121-557 6498 E-mail: sales@psudesigns.co.uk *Switch mode power supply manufrs*

P S U Electronics Ltd, Unit 8 Tweedale Court, Tweedale North Industrial Estate, Telford, Shropshire, TF7 4JZ Tel: (01952) 583637 Fax: (01952) 583637 *Design & manufacture custom power supplies*

▶ P S V Transport Systems Ltd, Unit 21 Impresa Park, Pindar Road, Hoddesdon, Hertfordshire, EN11 0DL Tel: (01992) 479950 Fax: (01992) 471676 E-mail: sales@psv-transport-systems.co.uk *Manufacturers of re-conditioned components to bus, coach industry*

▶ P S W Building Contractors Ltd, 163 A Donald Street, Cardiff, CF24 4TP Tel: (029) 2048 9648

P Smith, Rushton Spencer, Macclesfield, Cheshire, SK11 0RX Tel: (01782) 513294 Fax: (01782) 513294 *Agricultural contractors*

P Stratford Engineering, 4 Russell Gardens, Wickford, Essex, SS11 8QG Tel: (01268) 769844 Fax: (01268) 769844 *Fabrication engineers*

▶ P T Co., Greensleeves, Green Bottom, Wimborne, Dorset, BH21 2LW Tel: (01202) 639243 Fax: (01202) 639243 E-mail: sales@ptcompany.co.uk *Online suppliers of aftermarket parts and accessories for the Chysler PT Cruiser. Large stocks and goods are normally despatched within 24 hours.*

P T C (UK) Ltd, Inavation House, Harvest Crescent, Fleet, Hampshire, GU51 2QR Tel: (01252) 817000 Fax: (01252) 817000 *Computer software developers*

P T E Plant Co., Kelham St, Doncaster, South Yorkshire, DN1 3TA Tel: (01302) 321221 *Contractors' plant hire/generators/power tools*

P T F E Components Ltd, Unit 2 Northend Industrial Estate, Bury Mead Rd, Hitchin, Herts, SG5 1RT Tel: (01462) 434502 Fax: (01462) 434503 E-mail: ptfecomp@btconnect.com *Plastic machinists*

P T G Precision Engineers Ltd, Meadow Close, Langage Business Park, Plympton, Plymouth, PL7 5EX Tel: 0845 2130534 Fax: (01752) 345652 E-mail: sales@ptgltd.co.uk *Precision engineers*

P T G Work Holding, 7 Eclipse Office Park, High Street, Staple Hill, Bristol, BS16 5EL Tel: 0117-970 1101 Fax: 0117-970 1181 *Collect chuck manufrs*

P T M UK Ltd, Haigh Avenue, Stockport, Cheshire, SK4 1NZ Tel: 0161-477 6486 Fax: 0161-480 4624 E-mail: sales@ptmuk.co.uk *Industrial sealing products manufrs & distributors*

▶ P T Marine, Metalstock House, Vanguard Way, Shoeburyness, Southend-On-Sea, SS3 9RE Tel: (07973) 780930 Fax: (07814) 182901 E-mail: service@marine-eng.co.uk *Inboard & outboard specialists service & repair engineers*

P T Marine & General Fabrications, North Parade, Falmouth, Cornwall, TR11 2TD Tel: (01326) 311004 Fax: (01326) 311004 *Steel fabrications*

P T Phelan Ltd, 11 Manchester Street, Luton, LU1 2QB Tel: (01582) 725651 Fax: (01582) 700099 E-mail: sphelan@freenetname.co.uk *Retail & manufacturing jewellers*

P T R Associates Ltd, 21A Peach Street, Wokingham, Berkshire, RG40 1XJ Tel: 0118-979 4000 Fax: 0118-979 4035 E-mail: sales@ptr.co.uk *Training*

P T S Ltd, 2 Academy Street, Coatbridge, Lanarkshire, ML5 3AU Tel: (01236) 431277 Fax: (01236) 431052 E-mail: mailbox@pts.ltd.uk *Technical agents*

P T S - Total Quality Management, Verulam Road, Stafford, ST16 3EA Tel: (01785) 250706 Fax: (01785) 250906 *Weld testing services*

P T S UK Ltd, 10 Cliff Road, Ipswich, IP3 0AY Tel: (01473) 282600 Fax: (01473) 287521 E-mail: sales@ptsukltd.co.uk *Freight forwarders, Scandinavian trailer operators, warehousing & distribution*

▶ P T Saunders, Southleigh Farm, Southleigh Road, Havant, Hampshire, PO9 2NX Tel: (023) 9248 0878

▶ P & T Scaffolding Ltd, Bells Yew Green Business Centre, Bells Yew Green, Tunbridge Wells, Kent, TN3 9BL Tel: (01892) 750715 Fax: (01892) 750967

P T Services Co Ltd, Unit 2, Priory Ct, 71 St. Leonards Rd, Norwich, NR1 4JW Tel: (01603) 762233 Fax: (01603) 664098 *Computer services*

▶ P T Smith Builders Ltd, Unit 18 Fysh House Farm, Cuckoo Hill, Bures, Suffolk, CO8 5LD Tel: (01787) 227786 Fax: (01787) 227287

▶ P Telling, Lower Broad Oak, Elstead Road, Seale, Farnham, Surrey, GU10 1JA Tel: (01252) 781709 Fax: (01252) 783617 E-mail: sales@paultelling.co.uk

▶ P Trant Guernsey Ltd, Fairfield, Forest Road, St. Martin, Guernsey, GY4 6UG Tel: (01481) 240471 Fax: (01481) 230468

P Tuckwell Ltd, Ardleigh Hall, Dedham Road, Ardleigh, Colchester, CO7 7LG Tel: (01206) 231293 Fax: (01206) 231218 E-mail: ardleigh@tuckwell.co.uk *Agricultural engineering services & contractors*

P U Components Ltd, Shay Lane, Halifax, West Yorkshire, HX2 9AX Tel: (01422) 380786 Fax: (01422) 380702 E-mail: sales@pucomponents.co.uk *Polymer foam converters*

P U Electrical Wholesalers Ltd, 104 Soho Hill, Birmingham, B19 1AD Tel: 0121-554 1371 Fax: 0121-554 8190 E-mail: info@puelectrical.co.uk *Electrical supplies wholesalers*

P V F Installations & Services, Division Lane, Blackpool, FY4 5DZ Tel: (01253) 792408 Fax: (01253) 792408 *Air conditioning installators*

P V H Rubber & Plastic Linings & Manufacturing Ltd, Unit 16, Webnor Industrial Estate, Ettingshall Road, Wolverhampton, WV2 2LD Tel: (01902) 409186 Fax: (01902) 497265 E-mail: kdelveir@aol.com *Chemical plant engineers*

P V L Ltd, 9 Lexden Lodge Industrial Estate, Crowborough Hill, Crowborough, East Sussex, TN6 2NQ Tel: (01892) 664499 Fax: (01892) 663690 E-mail: info@pd1.co.uk *Distributors of pressure switches*

P V O'Neill Ltd, 32a Commercial Street, Shipley, West Yorkshire, BD18 3SP Tel: (01274) 584716 Fax: (01274) 596598 *Surgical appliances manufrs*

P V R Direct Ltd, 8 St. Stephens Business Centre, Poplar Road, Warmley, Bristol, BS30 5HT Tel: 0117-967 5115 Fax: 0117-935 2399 E-mail: vivrooker@aol.com *Engineering merchants*

P V S Engineers Ltd, 1-2 Murrills Estate, Fareham, Hampshire, PO16 9RD Tel: (023) 9237 9495 Fax: (023) 9238 8801 E-mail: rec@pvsengineers.co.uk *Precision machinists*

P Valli & Son, 14 Ministry Wharf, Wycombe Road, Saunderton, High Wycombe, Buckinghamshire, HP14 4HW Tel: (01494) 564558 E-mail: enquiries@pvalli.com *Precision engineers*

P W Adamson Ltd, Howe Moss Drive, Kirkhill Industrial Estate, Dyce, Aberdeen, AB21 0GL Tel: (01224) 724976 Fax: (01224) 724851 E-mail: support@pwadamson.co.uk *Refrigeration engineers*

P W Agriculture, 37 Cartlett, Haverfordwest, Dyfed, SA61 2LH Tel: (01437) 763553 Fax: (01437) 779095 *Agriculture merchants*

▶ P W Archer & Son Ltd, Springwell Lane, Northallerton, North Yorkshire, DL7 8QP Tel: (01609) 772466 Fax: (01609) 770111 E-mail: cranes@archers-removals.co.uk *Lorry mounted crane service, nationwide. Haulage and storage*

▶ P W Butler Ltd, 7 Grafton Place, Bilston, West Midlands, WV14 6LH Tel: (01902) 568623 Fax: (01902) 568623 E-mail: pb004l7138@blueyonder.co.uk *Automation engineering design & manufrs*

P W Cannon & Son Ltd, 36 Hythe Avenue, Bexleyheath, Kent, DA7 5NY Tel: (01322) 432247 Fax: (01322) 432248 *Brassware manufrs*

P W Crispin, 117-119 Marlborough Road, Romford, RM7 8AP Tel: (01708) 732880 Fax: (01708) 732880 *Architectural metalwork*

P W Defence Ltd, Wilne Mill, Draycott, Derby, DE72 3QJ Tel: (01332) 872475 Fax: (01332) 873046 *Pyrotechnic & explosives manufrs*

P.W. Forming Ltd, Highgrove Close, Willenhall, West Midlands, WV12 5SZ Tel: (01922) 401615 Fax: (01922) 409517 Principal Export Areas: Worldwide *Manufacturers of roll forming (cold rolled section) machines, tube bending machines, coil handling equipment, section rolling machine, sheet metalworking machinery & special purpose custom built machinery constructors.*

P W Greenhalgh & Co. Ltd, Newhey Bleach & Dye Works, Milnrow, Rochdale, Lancashire, OL16 3TH Tel: (01706) 847911 Fax: (01706) 881217 E-mail: sgreenhalgh@pwgreenhalgh.com *Bleachers, dyers, finishers & coaters manufrs*

P W Group Ltd, 2 Wedgwood Road, Bicester, Oxfordshire, OX26 4UL Tel: (01869) 253688 Fax: (01869) 240249 E-mail: sales@portablewelders.ltd.uk *Welding equipment for the car industries & general engineers*

P W Hall Ltd, Woodilee Industrial Estate, Lenzie, Kirkintilloch, Glasgow, G66 3UR Tel: 0141-776 2384 Fax: 0141-776 2382 E-mail: dir@pwhall.co.uk *Pigment dispersions*

P W Knight, Silverdale Park, Perranwell Station, Truro, Cornwall, TR3 7LW Tel: (01872) 862395 *Farriers manufrs*

P W M Environmental Group, Bassett Road, Halesowen, West Midlands, B63 2RE Tel: (01384) 564866 Fax: (01384) 560945 E-mail: info@pwmills.co.uk *Asbestos removal & encapsulation*

▶ P & W Maintenance Contracting Ltd, Redwither Business Centre, Redwither Business Park, Wrexham, Clwyd, LL13 9XR Tel: (01978) 660040 Fax: (01978) 667110 E-mail: info@p-wcontracting.co.uk

▶ P W Maintenance Services, 38 Richmond Avenue, Kettering, Northamptonshire, NN15 5JG Tel: (01536) 830070 Fax: (01536) 522564 E-mail: admin@pwmservices.com *Maintenance services & data communications*

P W Mobile Repairs, 40 Cornfields, Holbeach, Spalding, Lincolnshire, PE12 7QN Tel: (01406) 426630 Fax: (01406) 426909 *Tarpaulin maintenance & installers*

P W P Direct Mail Services Ltd, A 21 Broadwater Road, Welwyn Garden City, Hertfordshire, AL7 3BQ Tel: (01707) 882255 Fax: (01707) 883322 E-mail: pwp@dial.pipex.com

P W P Industrial, 84 Pilcroft Street, Bedford, MK42 9BP Tel: (01234) 345111 *Manufacturers of plasma cutting equipment. In addition, distributors & agents of plasma cutting consumables & plasma welding equipment*

▶ P W Reynolds Ltd, 50a Chatterton Road, Bromley, BR2 9QE Tel: (020) 8466 1001 Fax: (020) 8466 8555

P W S Ltd, 132 Fairway, Keyworth, Nottingham, NG12 5DL Tel: 0115-937 4723 Fax: 0115-937 6842 *Software suppliers for the textile industry*

P W S Ltd, Strawberry Lane, Willenhall, West Midlands, WV13 3SE Tel: (01902) 365200 Fax: (01902) 365201 *Steel stockholding*

P W S Ltd, Strawberry Lane, Willenhall, West Midlands, WV13 3SE Tel: (01902) 365200 Fax: (01902) 365201 *Metal fabricators*

P.W.S Metal Finishing, Coppen Road, Unit A, Dagenham, Essex, RM8 1HJ Tel: (020) 8595 9994 Fax: (020) 8592 3740 E-mail: mjratpws@aol.com *Stove enamellers & powder coating services*

P.W.S SYSTEMS, Unit 22D, Barking Industrial Park, RIPPLE ROAD, BARKING, ESSEX, IG11 0TJ Tel: (020) 8594 7574 E-mail: tws_office@yahoo.co.uk *Dealers in new & used shelving & racking*

P W T, Park Works, Lister Lane, Halifax, West Yorkshire, HX1 5JH Tel: (01422) 358361 Fax: (01422) 359379 *Power operated & special purpose chucks*

▶ P W Transport, Hercules Way, Bowerhill, Melksham, Wiltshire, SN12 6TS Tel: (01225) 704865 Fax: (01225) 702661

▶ P Warren, The Forge, Higher Mill Lane, Cullompton, Devon, EX15 1AG Tel: (07860) 285481 E-mail: sales@peterwarrenkitchens.co.uk

▶ P Wright & Co Plumbers Ltd, 46 Calder Road, Mirfield, West Yorkshire, WF14 8NR Tel: (01924) 492954 Fax: (01924) 491258

P X Manufacturing & Distribution Co. Ltd, Unit 1A, Lyon Way Industrial Estate, Lyon Way, Rockware Avenue, Greenford, Middlesex, UB6 0BN Tel: (020) 8575 0407 Fax: (020) 8578 2887 E-mail: sales@pxcables.com *Electric cable distributors*

P Y C Engineering Co., 2 Eastside Industrial Estate, Jackson Street, St. Helens, Merseyside, WA9 3AS Tel: (01744) 732931 Fax: (01744) 451058 E-mail: sales@pyc-engineering.co.uk *Precision engineers & light fabrication*

P Z Cussons International Ltd, Cussons House, Bird Hall Lane, Stockport, Cheshire, SK3 0XN Tel: 0161-491 8000 Fax: 0161-491 8191 *Soap & toiletries manufrs*

P&D, 2 Power Industrial Estate, Slade Green Road, Erith, Kent, DA8 2HU Tel: (01322) 346834 Fax: (01322) 336817 *Printed circuit manufrs*

P&I, Hillside Garage, Hill Corner Road, Chippenham, Wiltshire, SN15 1DP Tel: (01249) 652998 E-mail: diana@boatshop.fsnet.co.uk *Ships chandler & boat repairs*

P&O Property Accounts Ltd, 247 Tottenham Court Road, London, W1T 7HH Tel: (020) 7637 1400 Fax: (020) 7631 4280 *Property management*

▶ P&S Couriers (Croydon), 112 Hartscroft, Croydon, CR0 9LE Tel: 0800 5118348 E-mail: pscouriers@hotmail.com *Specialist Same Day courier service throughout the UK. Fast and Reliable with over 14 years experience. Dedicated vehicles for YOUR delivery. Accounts welcome.*

▶ PA Sound Hire.co.uk, 58 Newport Road, Countess Wear, Topsham, Exeter, EX2 7EE Tel: (01392) 875865 E-mail: andrew@pasoundhire.co.uk *Professional sound, lighting & audio visual equipment hire*

▶ Pab Coventry Ltd, Midland House Falkland Close, Charter Avenue Industrial Estate, Charter Avenue Industrial Esta, Coventry, CV4 8AU Tel: (024) 7669 4419 Fax: (024) 7646 7799 E-mail: info@pabconventry.co.uk *Prototype production & development for automotive & aerospace*

Pabco (UK) Ltd, Unit 2, Balnea Creekmoor Industrial Estate, Poole, Dorset, BH17 7EB Tel: (01202) 696365 Fax: (01202) 696365 *Metal finishers*

▶ Pacair, Unit 1, Eastman Way, Hemel Hempstead Industrial Estate, Hemel Hempstead, Hertfordshire, HP2 7DU Tel: (0870) 2405767 Fax: (01442) 251401 E-mail: sales@pacair.co.uk *Air conditioning equipment suppliers*

Pacc Engineering, 4b Tulnacross Road, Cookstown, County Tyrone, BT80 9NH Tel: (028) 8675 1796 *Structural steel*

Pacc Security Ltd, 90 Lots Road, London, SW10 0QD Tel: (020) 7376 3000 Fax: (020) 7376 3100 E-mail: security@paccsecurity.com *Installation of electronic security equipment*

Pace P.L.C., Victoria Road, Saltaire, Shipley, West Yorkshire, BD18 3LF Tel: (01274) 532000 Fax: (01274) 532010 *Pace plc is a leading technology developer for the global payTV industry. Pace's main focus is on creating intelligent and innovative products and services that benefit our customers and fuel the development of digital TV. Over the last 25 years, Pace has developed one of the world's most experienced specialist engineering teams and is now the partner of choice for leading payTV operators across the globe. Pace's international headquarters are in Saltaire, West Yorkshire, UK, with further offices in the USA, France, India and Hong Kong. For more information on Pace, please visit www.pace.com.*

▶ Pace Aerospace Bearings Ltd, Unit 18 Finns Business Park, Bowenhurst Lane, Crondall, Surrey, GU10 5HP Tel: (01252) 852525 Fax: (01252) 852555 E-mail: sales@pacebeaings.co.uk *Distribution company*

Pace Bearings Ltd, Unit 4 Dock Meadow Industrial Estate, Wolverhampton, WV4 6UD Tel: (01902) 409120 Fax: (01902) 409121 E-mail: pacebearings@freeserve.co.uk *Ball bearing & bearing distributors*

Pace Components Ltd, 38 Ballmoor, Buckingham Industrial Estate, Buckingham, MK18 1RQ Tel: (01280) 822733 Fax: (01280) 823839 E-mail: sales@pacecomponents.co.uk *Manufacturers of high frequency transformers & inductors*

Pace Computers, Greenways, Hudswell, Richmond, North Yorkshire, DL11 6BQ Tel: (01748) 850310 Fax: (01748) 850413 E-mail: pacecomputers@talk21.com *Computer repairs & sales*

Pace Cycles Ltd, Great Edstone, York, YO62 6PD Tel: (01751) 432929 Fax: (01751) 432691 E-mail: pace@pace-racing.co.uk *Mountain bike components manufrs*

Pace Europe Ltd, 10 Kelvin Drive, Knowlhill, Milton Keynes, MK5 8NH Tel: (01908) 277666 Fax: (01908) 277777 Principal Export Areas: Worldwide *Soldering & rework equipment manufrs*

Pace Group International Ltd, 171 Alcester Road, Birmingham, B13 8JR Tel: 0121-449 4492 Fax: 0121-449 9695 E-mail: ho@pace-gi.com *Architectural planning consultants*

▶ Pace Print & Design, 4 Buckholt Drive, Worcester, WR4 9ND Tel: (01905) 754554 Fax: (01905) 754543 E-mail: sales@paceprintanddesign.co.uk

Pace Timber Engineering Ltd, Bleak Hall, Milton Keynes, MK6 1LA Tel: (01908) 302880 Fax: (01908) 397881 E-mail: enquiries@pacete.com *Timber roof erectors*

Pacegrade Ltd, Unit 1 Providence Street, Stourbridge, West Midlands, DY9 8HL Tel: (01384) 892237 Fax: (01384) 895041 *Joinery contractors, suppliers & manufrs*

Pacegrove Ltd, Unit 13 Courtyard Workshops, Bath Street, Market Harborough, Leicestershire, LE16 9EW Tel: (01858) 431381 Fax: (01858) 432426 E-mail: winlab@pacegrove.co.uk *Pharmaceutical & chemical*

▶ Paceprint Printers, 4b Kenn Road, Clevedon, Avon, BS21 6EL Tel: (01275) 874238 Fax: (01275) 343733

Pacer Cats, 33 Hanworth Road, Sunbury-On-Thames, Middlesex, TW16 5DA Tel: (01932) 778090 Fax: (01932) 338080 *Ticketing services*

Pacer Components plc, Unit 4 Horseshoe Park, Pangbourne, Reading, RG8 7JW Tel: 0118-984 5280 Fax: 0118-984 5425 E-mail: pacer@pacer.co.uk *Electronic component distributors or agents*

▶ Pacer Leisure Vehicles Ltd, Unit 10 Bates Industrial Estate, Wycombe Road, Stokenchurch, High Wycombe, Buckinghamshire, HP14 3RQ Tel: (01494) 484664 Fax: (01494) 484424 E-mail: sales@pacerleisure.co.uk *Children & adult go-karts manufrs*

Pacer Systems Ltd, Gauntley Street, Nottingham, NG7 5HF Tel: 0115-988 7777 Fax: 0115-988 7788 E-mail: sales@pacersys.co.uk *Routing machine manufrs*

Pacer Technology Ltd, 196 Wilden Lane, Stourport-on-Severn, Worcestershire, DY13 9JR Tel: (01299) 825900 Fax: (01299) 827001 E-mail: sales@pacertechnology.com *Adhesive & sealent manufrs*

Pacet Manufacturing Ltd, Wyebridge, Cores End Road, Bourne End, Buckinghamshire, SL8 5HH Tel: (01628) 526754 Fax: (01628) 810080 E-mail: enquiries@pacet.co.uk *Motor accessories*

Pacific Brands (UK) Ltd, Unit 1 Stretton Green Distribution Park, Langford Way, Barleycastle Lane, Appleton, Warrington, WA4 4TQ Tel: (01925) 212212 Fax: (01925) 212222 *Sports & general footwear distribs*

Pacific Scientific, Howarth Road, Maidenhead, Berkshire, SL6 1AP Tel: (01628) 682200 Fax: (01628) 682250 E-mail: custadmin@pacscieurope.com *Quality service to aviation industry*

Pacific Sound & Light, 505 Bristol Road, Selly Oak, Birmingham, B29 6AU Tel: 0121-471 3110 Fax: 0121-471 3103 E-mail: enquiries@pacificsoundandlight.co.uk *Sound & lighting hire & repair services*

▶ Pacific Sports, Unit 4b, Exhibition House North View, Staple Hill, Bristol, BS16 4NY Tel: 0117-910 9876 Fax: 0117-910 9966 *Cycle suppliers*

Pack 2 Pack UK Ltd, Avonmouth Way, Avonmouth, Bristol, BS11 9HD Tel: 0117-982 3584 Fax: 0117-923 5396 E-mail: sales.avo@uk.pack2pack.com *Merchants, suppliers & reconditioners of drums*

Glen Pack Ltd, 36 Kelvinhaugh Street, Glasgow, G3 8PB Tel: 0141-221 5012 Fax: 0141-248 2555 E-mail: glenpackltd@tiscali.co.uk *Carton printing services & manufrs*

pack2pack UK Ltd, Clifton Bridge Works, Wood Street, Brighouse, West Yorkshire, HD6 1PW Tel: (01484) 714484 Fax: (01484) 711172 E-mail: alan.mcgougan@uk.pack2pack.com *Drum & tank reconditioners service*

Package Control (U.K.) Ltd, Unit 5 Bunas Business Park, Hollom Down Road, Lopcombe, Salisbury, SP5 1BP Tel: (01264) 782143 Fax: (0844) 8800384 E-mail: sales@package-control.co.uk *Load lashing & strapping systems distributors*

Packaging, Flemming Way, Crawley, West Sussex, RH10 9JY Tel: (01293) 611111 Fax: (01293) 550555 *Packaging material stockists & distributors*

Packaging Co., 195 Scudamore Road, Leicester, LE3 1UQ Tel: 0116-231 3444 Fax: 0116-231 3344 E-mail: sales@thepackagingcompany.co.uk *Suppliers of packaging materials and corrugated cartons*

Packaging Ltd, Dierden St Works, Dierden Street, Winsford, Cheshire, CW7 3DL Tel: (01606) 594149 Fax: (01606) 861390 *Contract filling & packaging services*

Packaging Aids Ltd, 1 Lords Way, Basildon, Essex, SS13 1TN Tel: (01268) 885858 Fax: (01268) 885860 E-mail: sales@packer-products.co.uk *Packaging machinery & materials*

Packaging Automation Ltd, 1 Montgomery Close, Parkgate Industrial Estate, Knutsford, Cheshire, WA16 8XW Tel: (01565) 755000 Fax: (01565) 751015 E-mail: sales@pal.co.uk *Heat sealing machinery manufrs*

Packaging Craftsman Ltd, Units 1a-1b, Park Mill Way, Clayton West, Huddersfield, HD8 9XJ Tel: (01484) 865680 Fax: (01484) 865681 E-mail: sales@packagingcraftsman.co.uk *Paper folding machinery reconditioners*

▶ Packaging Direct, Lock House, The Meads, Hertford, SG13 7BD Tel: (01992) 505056 Fax: (01992) 505777 *Printers of polythene carrier bags*

Packaging Engineers Automation Ltd, Unit 10 Sandown Estate, Sandown Road, Watford, WD24 7UB Tel: (01923) 237121 Fax: (01923) 236125 *Packaging machinery manufrs*

▶ Packaging First, Nash Hall, Chelmsford Road, High Ongar, Ongar, Essex, CM5 9NL Tel: (01277) 363656 Fax: (01277) 362277 *Packaging equipment manufrs*

▶ Packaging Images New World Ltd, 3 St. Editha's Court, Church Eaton, Stafford, ST20 0AT Tel: (01785) 824080 Fax: 01785 824889 E-mail: packagingimages@btopenworld.com *Carrier bags, polypropylene & polythene plain and printed bags with reseal tapes, hooks & hangers for retail, food, garden centres & diy store use.*

Packaging Industries Ltd, Beaumont Way, Aycliffe Industrial Pk, Newton Aycliffe, Co. Durham, DL5 6SN Tel: (01325) 313444 Fax: (01325) 300246 E-mail: sales@pi-box.co.uk *Looking for strong, secure transit protection for your products? Our wide range of plywood and timber packaging - including the unique No-Nail® and Easy-Klip plywood cases - has provided quality solutions for over fifty years.*

Packaging Products Ltd, Collyhurst Road, Manchester, M40 7RT Tel: 0161-205 4181 Fax: 0161-203 4678 E-mail: sales@packagingproducts.co.uk *Waterproof paper manufacturers & corrugated boxes*

▶ Packaging Services UK Ltd, Pen Court, Standard Way Industrial Estate, Northallerton, North Yorkshire, DL6 2XE Tel: (01609) 773850 Fax: (01609) 773850 E-mail: sales@packagingservicesukltd.com *Manufacturers machines*

Packaging Services Unette Ltd, Bank Hill Street, Mount Pleasant, Oldham, OL4 1HR Tel: 0161-621 0800 Fax: 0161-621 0801 E-mail: sales@unette.co.uk *Contract packaging services*

▶ Packaging Solutions Provider, 21 Pinewood Drive, Markfield Court, Markfield, Leicestershire, LE67 9RQ Tel: (01530) 243743 E-mail: bob.locke@packaginsolutionsprovider.co.uk *OVER 25 YEARS EXPERIENCE IN TAKING THE COST OUT OF THE SUPPLY CHAIN BY USE OF BARCODES, RFID, RE-USEABLE PACKAGING, OUTERCASE PRINTING AND BATCH TRACEABILITY.*

Packaging Supplies Ltd, Unit 2-3 Thorney Lane North, Iver, Buckinghamshire, SL0 9HF Tel: (01753) 653303 Fax: (01753) 655276 E-mail: sales@pack-supplies.co.uk *Packaging supplier*

Packaging Supplies, Unit 1, Hill Street, Kidderminster, Worcestershire, DY11 6TD Tel: (01562) 743621 Fax: (01562) 827433 E-mail: enquiries@printedcarrierbags.co.uk *Printed carrier bag & packaging manufrs*

Packaids Ltd, Ruscombe Park, Ruscombe Lane, Ruscombe, Reading, RG10 9LU Tel: 0118-934 3877 Fax: 0118-934 0273 E-mail: sales@packaids.co.uk *Print trade finishing specialists*

Packline Ltd, Unit 8-9 Newtown Business Park, Poole, Dorset, BH12 3LL Tel: 01202 724138 *Packline Limited has established itself as one of the U/K Leading manufactures of reel Lifting Equipment for the Food, Diary, Pharmaceutical, Chemical and Medical processing industries. The company's main product the Compac is a Mobile reel lifting machine designed to reduce injury to operating personnel, downtime and damage during transportation of stock from storage to processing machinery.*

Packman Furniture Ltd, 256-261 Paradise Row, London, E2 9LE Tel: (020) 7729 4268 Fax: (020) 7729 0169 *Furniture manufrs*

Jim Packman, Uplees Cottages, Uplees Road, Oare, Faversham, Kent, ME13 0QR Tel: (01795) 533741 *Fencing supplier*

▶ Pack-Online Ltd, Chestnut House Spetisbury, Blandford, Spetisbury, Blandford Forum, Dorset, DT11 9DF Tel: (01258) 450389 Fax: (01258) 459252 E-mail: boxoffice@pack-online.co.uk *Presentation & display cartons, box & lids, jewellery boxes, corrugated cases, printed, foil blocked, fittings.....everything to do with cardboard boxes!*

Packpost (International) Ltd, Griffin House, Griffin Lane, Aylesbury, Buckinghamshire, HP19 8BE Tel: (01296) 487493 Fax: (01296) 392369 E-mail: sales@packpost.co.uk *Mailing contractors*

▶ Packserve Ltd, Business Unit 1, Pitville Street, Darwen, Lancashire, BB3 1HJ Tel: (01254) 760123 Fax: (01254) 760155 E-mail: info@packserve.co.uk *Engineering outsource provider. Installation Maintenance Service*

▶ PACKWIN, 576 Bath Road, Hounslow, TW5 9UX Tel: (07968) 442616 E-mail: rajumarwaha@hotmail.com *Specialist household removals and light commercial haulage business.*Fully trained staff and fully equipped transport vehicle - we cater for all needs big or small alike.*Packing materials supplied*Nationwide coverage*West London based business.*

Pacojet (UK) Ltd, Unit 5, Maybrook Industrial Estate, Brownhills, Walsall, WS8 7DG Tel: (01543) 375311 *Distributors of ice machines*

▶ Pacs Com, Unit 6 Nursling Industrial Estate, Majestic Road, Nursling, Southampton, SO16 0YT Tel: (023) 8073 7557 Fax: (023) 8073 1600 E-mail: sales@pacscom.com *Scada, L/F Radio, Telemetry, Wireless Communications*

Pacscom Ltd, 6 Majestic Road, Nursling Industrial Estate, Southampton, SO16 0YT Tel: (023) 8073 7557 Fax: (023) 8073 1600 E-mail: sales@pacscom.com *Supervisory control & data acquisition systems manufrs*

▶ Pactiv Europe Ltd, 4 Young Square, Brucefield Industrial Estate, Livingston, West Lothian, EH54 9BX Tel: (01506) 462247 Fax: (01506) 415458 E-mail: sales@pactiv.com *Packaging products & services*

Pactiv Europe Ltd, 4 Young Square, Brucefield Industrial Estate, Livingston, West Lothian, EH54 9BX Tel: (01506) 462247 Fax: (01506) 415458 E-mail: sales@pactiv.com *Packaging products & services*

▶ Pactum Partium Ltd, 24 Nursery Gardens, Bedford, MK41 8DU Tel: (07890) 267779 E-mail: info@pactern-partium.com *Service -contract consultancy*

▶ Pacy & Wheatley Ltd, 113 Thorne Road, Doncaster, South Yorkshire, DN2 5BQ Tel: (01302) 760843 Fax: (01302) 342992

Paddington Motor Springs, Unit 46 Stadium Business Centre, North End Road, Wembley, Middlesex, HA9 0AT Tel: (020) 8795 3300 Fax: (020) 8795 5954 *Spring manufrs*

Paddington Steels Ltd, 6 Paddington Court, New Road, Kidderminster, Worcestershire, DY10 1AQ Tel: (01562) 827300 Fax: (01562) 827301 *Steel processors*

Paddock Fabrications Ltd, Fryers Road, Walsall, WS2 7LZ Tel: (01922) 470940 Fax: (01922) 476021 E-mail: sales@paddockfabrications.co.uk *Door & window locks manufrs*

▶ Paddock Gear Engineering Ltd, 2 Kingsbury Link, Trinity Road, Piccadilly, Tamworth, Staffordshire, B78 2EX Tel: (01827) 875566 Fax: (01827) 875880

Paddox Home Interiors, 282 Hillmorton Road, Rugby, Warwickshire, CV22 5BW Tel: (01788) 542461 Fax: (01788) 339239 *Soft furnishings services*

Padgett & Braham Ltd, 10 Shacklewell Road, London, N16 7TA Tel: (020) 7254 6362 Fax: (020) 7254 7175 E-mail: pandb@tinyworld.co.uk *Silverware manufrs*

Padgett & Braham Ltd, 10 Shacklewell Road, London, N16 7TA Tel: (020) 7254 6362 Fax: (020) 7254 7175 E-mail: p&b@tinyworld.co.uk *Manufacturing goldsmiths*

Padiham Glass Ltd, Glasstec Centre, Unit 10A Shuttleworth Mead Business Park, Padiham, Burnley, Lancashire, BB12 7NG Tel: (01282) 774124 Fax: (01282) 774951 E-mail: sales@padihamglass.co.uk *Glass merchants*

▶ Padma Textile Manufacturing, 2b Heath Hurst Road, London, NW3 2RX Tel: (020) 7794 9988 Fax: (020) 7794 5599 *Clothing manufrs*

Padmode Ltd, Unit 9 Denvers Yard, Ware, Hertfordshire, SG11 1AL Tel: (01279) 843035 *CNC engineering services, machinists & alternators*

Padtec Ltd, 14 Balmercut, Buckingham Industrial Estate, Buckingham, MK18 1SQ Tel: (01280) 822251 Fax: (01280) 822958 E-mail: sales@padtec.co.uk *Silicone printing pads, jigs & fixtures manufrs*

Paellastore.com, 32 Moray Close, Hinckley, Leicestershire, LE10 0UY Tel: (01455) 459585 E-mail: info@paellastore.com *Paella sets gas burners & pans*

Pag, 565 Kingston Road, London, SW20 8SA Tel: (020) 8543 3131 Fax: (020) 8540 4797 E-mail: email@paguk.com *Advanced battery systems manufrs*

▶ Pagazzi Lighting Ltd, Unit 4, Almondvale South Retail Park, Livingston, West Lothian, EH54 6XG Tel: (01506) 407610 Fax: (01506) 464907 E-mail: lighting@pagazzi.com *Lighting distributors*

Andrew Page Ltd, Apson House, Colton Mill, Bullerthorpe Lane, Leeds, LS15 9JL Tel: 0113-397 0200 Fax: 0113-397 0295 E-mail: accounts@andrewpage.com *Motor car accessories factors* Also at: Bradford, Bramley, Bury, Harrogate, Newcastle, Stockport, Wakefield & York

Brian Page Controls, 18 Pooley Green Road, Egham, Surrey, TW20 8AF Tel: (01784) 435850 Fax: (01784) 434278 E-mail: brianpagecontrols@hotmail.com *Suppliers of driving controls for disabled drivers*

Page Bros Norwich Ltd, Mile Cross Lane, Norwich, NR6 6SA Tel: (01603) 778800 Fax: (01603) 778801 E-mail: info@pagebros.co.uk *Book & journal typesetters & printers*

Page Castor Ltd, Blakemore Road, West Bromwich, West Midlands, B70 8JF Tel: 0121-553 1710 Fax: 0121-525 0631 *Castors for bedding & upholstery*

Page Hargrave, Manfield House, 1 Southampton Street, London, WC2R 0LR Tel: (020) 7240 6933 Fax: (020) 7379 0268 E-mail: london@pagehargrave.co.uk *Trade mark & patent agents*

Page Lacquer Co. Ltd, 3 Ferrier Industrial Estate, Ferrier Street, London, SW18 1SN Tel: (020) 8871 1235 Fax: (020) 8874 8167 E-mail: info@pagelacquer.co.uk *Custom made furniture manufrs*

Page Lithoprint Ltd, Enterprise House, Cranes Close, Basildon, Essex, SS14 3JB Tel: (01268) 464464 Fax: (01268) 464465 E-mail: sales@pagemediagroup.com *Printing advertising & design specialists*

Page The Packers, Old Station Road, Ventnor, Isle of Wight, PO38 1DX Tel: (01983) 852951 Fax: (01983) 855956 E-mail: info@page-packers.fsnet.co.uk *Removal contractors*

Page Plus, Old School Building, Outclough Road, Brindley Ford, Stoke-on-Trent, ST8 7QD Tel: (01782) 523263 Fax: (01782) 839284 E-mail: pete@pageplus.co.uk *Printers*

Page & Taylor Ltd, Watery Lane, Ashton-on-Ribble, Preston, PR2 2XH Tel: (01772) 726222 Fax: (01772) 727207 E-mail: sales@pageandtaylor.co.uk *Timber merchants*

Page & Wells, 52-54 Kings Street, Maidstone, Kent, ME14 1DB Tel: (01622) 756703 Fax: (01622) 671351 E-mail: sales@page-wells.co.uk *Commercial & professional property services*

Page White & Farrer, 54 Doughty Street, London, WC1N 2LS Tel: (020) 7831 7929 Fax: (020) 7831 8040 E-mail: sales@pagewhite.com *Trade mark & patent attorneys services.*

Pageantry Electronic Systems, Unit 7 55 Weir Road Industrial Estate, London, SW19 8UG Tel: (020) 8947 3100 Fax: (020) 8879 0068 E-mail: sales@pageantry.co.uk *Electronic equipment manufacturers & installers*

▶ Pagefast Ltd, 4-6 Lansil Way, Lancaster, LA1 3QY Tel: (01524) 841010

Pageforward Learning, PO Box 230, Diss, Norfolk, IP22 1TA Tel: (01379) 650927 Fax: (01379) 642555 E-mail: info@pageforward.co.uk *Providers of computer training courses*

▶ Pagefree Ltd, 11 Pennine Road, Glossop, Derbyshire, SK13 6NN Tel: (01457) 857006 Fax: (01457) 857006 E-mail: sales@pagefree.co.uk *Document management services*

Pageone Communications Ltd, 2 Brentside Executive Centre, Great West Road, Brentford, Middlesex, TW8 9DA Tel: (0870) 0555300 Fax: (020) 8914 5212 E-mail: customerservices@pageone.co.uk *Business paging systems*

Paget Ltd, 115 Penarth Road, Cardiff, CF11 6JU Tel: (029) 2022 2552 Fax: (029) 2037 8439 *Tools & fastener distributors*

Paget Computer Services, 32 Paget Lane, Enniskillen, County Fermanagh, BT74 7HT Tel: (028) 6632 8868 Fax: (028) 6632 8854 *Software sales*

Pagets Builders Merchants Ltd, 94 Broadfield Road, Sheffield, S8 0XL Tel: 0114-292 3000 Fax: 0114-250 9350 E-mail: info@c-paget.co.uk *Building material merchants*

Pago Ltd, 7 Crown Gate, Wyncolls Road, Severalls Industrial Park, Colchester, CO4 9HZ Tel: (01206) 755206 Fax: (01206) 755210 E-mail: sales@pago.co.uk *Labelling machine manufacturers & printers*

Paice Ventilation Ltd, 5 Vinegar Hill, Alconbury Weston, Huntingdon, Cambridgeshire, PE28 4JA Tel: (01480) 890778 *Holding company*

▶ Paige Hire Fleet Management, Phoenix House, River Gardens, Feltham, Middlesex, TW14 0RD Tel: 0208 8900334 Fax: 0208 8906992 E-mail: info@paigerental.com *We specialise in custom-built truck contract hire and short-term hire. Also, using our sister companies, we can recover large vehicles and repair and maintain trucks and trailers, including MOT"s and PMI checks*

Paige's Fishing Tackle, 36 Station Road, Hayling Island, Hampshire, PO11 0EQ Tel: (023) 9246 3500 *Fishing tackle retailers*

Paignton Engineering, 3 Alders Way, Baytor Industrial Estate, Paignton, Devon, TQ4 7QJ Tel: (01803) 551302 Fax: (01803) 551302 *Stainless steel & aluminium manufrs*

Paignton Glassworks Ltd, 16 Marldon Road, Paignton, Devon, TQ3 3QZ Tel: (01803) 558096 Fax: (01803) 522044 E-mail: enquiries@paigntonglass.co.uk *Glass merchants & double glazed unit manufrs*

Paine Manwaring Ltd, 7-11 Ardsheal Road, Worthing, West Sussex, BN14 7RW Tel: (01903) 237522 Fax: (01903) 236511 E-mail: enquires@painemanwearing.co.uk *Heating & plumbing engineers*

Pains Wessex Ltd, High Post, Salisbury, SP4 6AS Tel: (01722) 411611 Fax: (01722) 428798 E-mail: info@chemringcm.com *Distress signal & military counter measure manufrs*

▶ Paint Box Textiles, 16 Valley Road, Liversedge, West Yorkshire, WF15 6JY Tel: (01924) 235123 Fax: (01924) 235223 E-mail: sales@paintboxtextiles.co.uk *Small weight package dyers manufrs*

▶ Paint Plant Marketplace, Risby Business Park, Newmarket Road, Risby, Bury St. Edmunds, Suffolk, IP28 6RD Tel: (01638) 552020 Fax: (01638) 750454 E-mail: ppmarketplace@aol.com *Paint Plant Marketplace. All new and used paint plant and powder equipment exchange and relocation specialists. Pre-treatment, booths, ovens, conveyors, degreasers, guns, and more.*

▶ Paint Protection Systems, 10 Oak Rd, Withington, Manchester, M20 3DA Tel: (07949) 094708 Fax: 0161-448 9240 E-mail: tim@paintprotectionsystems.co.uk *Distributors of protection, masking, foam, tapes/ films, non-wovens, lambswool, wet wipes, fasteners (dual-lock), PPE overalls, microfibre cloths & paint sealants to the automotive, aerospace & marine industries. Heat shrink products & abrasives*

Paint Research Association, 14 Castle Mews, High Street, Hampton, Middlesex, TW12 2NP Tel: (020) 8487 0800 Fax: (020) 8487 0801 E-mail: coatings@pra.org.uk *Research association*

Paint & Timber Workshop, The Kennels The Oak Tree, Ellenbrook Lane, Hatfield, Hertfordshire, AL10 9NT Tel: (01707) 258727 Fax: (01707) 258727 E-mail: workshop@paintimber.fsnet.co.uk *Furniture manufrs*

Paint & Trim Company North Wales Ltd, Unit 1, Snow Nest Court, Tirllwyd Industrial Estate, Kinmel Bay, Rhyl, Conwy, LL18 5JA Tel: (0800) 0933277 Fax: 01745 369019 E-mail: info@paint-and-trim.com *We provide a service to repair alloy wheels, minor bodywork damage, bumpers, interior trim, paintwork & upholstery on your vehicle all from our secure workshop*

Painter Bros Ltd, Holmer Road, Hereford, HR4 9SW Tel: (01432) 374400 Fax: (01432) 374427 E-mail: enquiries@painterbrothers.com *Structural steelwork fabricators*

Painter & Peart, 15 Holmethorpe Avenue, Redhill, RH1 2NB Tel: (01737) 773777 Fax: (01737) 773932 E-mail: sales@thesuitcentre.co.uk *Menswear wholesalers*

Painter & Son Ltd, Pope Iron Road, Worcester, WR1 3HB Tel: (01905) 22787 Fax: (01905) 24181 *Aluminium sand foundry*

▶ painting@decorating, 35 Phoenix Road, Chatham, Kent, ME5 8SY Tel: (01634) 306379 E-mail: keithnegus@blueyonder.co.uk *Industrial painting*

Paisley Computer Exchange, 7 Wellmeadow St, Paisley, Renfrewshire, PA1 2WE Tel: 0141-889 9691 Fax: 01418896060 *Computer supplies*

Graeme Paisley Ltd, Herberts Farmhouse, Quay Lane, Hanley Castle, Worcester, WR8 0BS Tel: (01684) 594066 Fax: (01684) 594066 E-mail: graeme.paisley@btinternet.com *Packaging component manufrs*

▶ Paisley Textile Scotland Ltd, Unit 9-10, Abbey Mill Business Centre, Paisley, Renfrewshire, PA1 1TJ Tel: 0141-561 7196 Fax: 0141-561 7197 *Textile manufrs*

▶ PAJM Business Design Services, 1 Brecksfield Lane, Moorlands Road, Skelton, York, YO30 1YB Tel: 01904 471972 Fax: 01904 471972 E-mail: info@pajmyorkservices.co.uk *PAJM Business Design offers cost effective web & IT solutions for sole-traders and small to medium sized businesses.*

Pak Nylon Hosiery Co, 31 Broughton Street, Cheetham Hill, Manchester, M8 8LZ Tel: 0161 832 7371 Fax: 0161 839 5134 E-mail: C_M_Afzal_Khan@hotmail.co.uk *Fashion wholesalers*

Pak Wraps Ltd, Unit 16 Sefton Lane Industrial Estate, Liverpool, L31 8BX Tel: 0151-924 0767 Fax: 0151-924 6555 *Packaging consultants*

Pakex UK plc, 1 Prime Point, Bessemer Road, Welwyn Garden City, Hertfordshire, AL7 1FE Tel: (01707) 384858 Fax: (01707) 332838 E-mail: sales@pakexuk.com *Janitorial, polythene & adhesive tape suppliers*

Pakistan International Airlines, 1-15 King Street, London, W6 9HR Tel: (020) 8741 8066 Fax: (020) 8741 9376 E-mail: longrpk@piac.com.pk *Airline company*

Pakmark, Units 1-2 Benson Industrial Estate, Benson Rd, Birmingham, B18 5TS Tel: 0121-523 0665 Fax: 0121-523 5343 E-mail: pakmark@btconnect.com *Stencil plate; staples collated strip; marking device; stencil cutting/plate cutting services/engineers*

Pakprint Tapes Ltd, Woodlands, Dale Street, Longwood, Huddersfield, HD3 4TG Tel: (01484) 644884 Fax: (01484) 460094 E-mail: gat@pakprint.co.uk *Packaging machinery & printed & plain self adhesives*

Paksafe Crates & Packing Cases, 1 Tewin Court, Welwyn Garden City, Hertfordshire, AL7 1AU Tel: (01707) 391939 Fax: (01707) 390989 E-mail: jag.1@virgin.net *Export packers & packing case manufrs*

▶ Paktron Ltd, Unit 2D, Rink Road Industrial Estate, Ryde, Isle of Wight, PO33 2LT Tel: (01983) 611357 Fax: (01983) 563328 E-mail: contracting@paktron.co.uk

Paktronic Engineering Co. Ltd, Alma Park Road, Grantham, Lincolnshire, NG31 9SE Tel: (01476) 567623 Fax: (01476) 566503 E-mail: info@paktronic.co.uk *Manufacturers of control panels*

▶ Pal Technologies, 141 St. James Road, Glasgow, G4 0LT Tel: 0141-552 6085 Fax: 0141-552 6085 E-mail: sales@paltechnologies.com

Palace Cuisine, 4 West End Industrial Estate, West End, Witney, Oxfordshire, OX28 1UB Tel: (01993) 702942 Fax: (01993) 702942 E-mail: palacecuisine@btconnect.com *Baking & catering services*

Palace Furniture Ltd, Stour House, High Street, Wollaston, Stourbridge, West Midlands, DY8 4PF Tel: (01384) 377771 Fax: (01384) 377772 E-mail: info@palace-furniture.co.uk *Furniture manufrs*

Palace Lamp Co. Ltd, 4 Century Building, 117 Summers Road, Brunswick Business Park, Liverpool, L3 4BL Tel: 0151-709 4000 Fax: 0151-707 0074 E-mail: duncan@palacelamp.com *Wholesale electrical supplies*

Palace Perma Signs Ltd, Lowmoor Industrial Estate, Prospect Close, Kirkby-in-Ashfield, Nottingham, NG17 7LF Tel: (01623) 754899 Fax: (01623) 752341 *Powder coaters*

▶ Palace Tech Ltd, B14 Culpeper Close, Medway City Estate, Rochester, Kent, ME2 4HU Tel: (01634) 294200 Fax: (01634) 715432 E-mail: palt1994@aol.com *Air conditioning designers*

Paladon Systems Ltd, Ferro Fields, Brixworth Industrial Estate, Brixworth, Northampton, NN6 9UA Tel: (01604) 880700 Fax: (01604) 882424 E-mail: enquiries@paladon.co.uk *Valve automation centre*

Palagan Ltd, Tavistock Street, Dunstable, Bedfordshire, LU6 1NE Tel: (01582) 600234 Fax: (01582) 601636 E-mail: mail@palagan.co.uk *Polythene bag manufrs*

Palamine Ltd, Homefield Road, Haverhill, Suffolk, CB9 8QP Tel: (01440) 762616 Fax: (01440) 762573 E-mail: sales@palamine.co.uk *Specialist manufacturers of custom bespoke precision hydraulic presses up to 2000 tonnes for the bonding, composite & moulding industries*

Palatine Paints, Smallbrook Lane, Leigh, Lancashire, WN7 5PZ Tel: (01942) 884122 Fax: (01942) 887085 *Paint manufrs*

Palatine Precision Ltd, Airport Industrial Estate, 45 Laker Road, Rochester, Kent, ME1 3QX Tel: (01634) 684571 Fax: (01634) 200836 E-mail: sales@palatineprecision.co.uk *Precision edge welded bellows manufrs*

Palebeck Telecommunications Technology Ltd, 9 Little Portland Street, London, W1W 7JF Tel: (020) 7580 7226 Fax: (020) 7580 3115 E-mail: sales@pttl.co.uk *Telecommunications products & services*

▶ Palegallery Design, Moubray Grove, South Queensferry, West Lothian, EH30 9PE Tel: 0131-319 1403 E-mail: info@palegallery.com *Web & graphic design services*

Palgrave Brown, Unit C2-C5 16-17 Boston Industrial Centre, Norfolk Street, Boston, Lincolnshire, PE21 9HG Tel: (01205) 362468 Fax: (01205) 350892 E-mail: sales@palgravebrown.co.uk *Roof manufrs*

Palgrave Brown UK Ltd, St Andrews Road, Avonmouth, Bristol, BS11 9HT Tel: 0117-982 2375 Fax: 0117-982 9259 E-mail: info@palgravebrown.co.uk *Trussed rafter manufrs*

Palgrave Brown UK Ltd, Canterbury Industrial Park, Island Road, Hersden, Canterbury, Kent, CT3 4HQ Tel: (01227) 712322 Fax: (01227) 712852 *Roof truss manufrs*

Palgrave Brown UK Ltd, Pool Road Industrial Estate, Pool Road, Nuneaton, Warwickshire, CV10 9AE Tel: (024) 7634 4034 Fax: (024) 7634 5251 *Timber merchants*

Palick Ltd, The Mill, Silverdale Road, Newcastle, Staffordshire, ST5 2TA Tel: (01782) 661600 Fax: (01782) 630404 E-mail: sales@palick.co.uk *Pallet manufacturers & suppliers*

Palick (Wolverhampton) Ltd, Hilton Main Industrial Estate, Bognop Road, Essinton, Wolverhampton, WV11 2BE Tel: (01902) 727691 E-mail: sales@palick.co.uk *Pallet rebuilders or suppliers*

R.J. Palin & Co. (Strensall) Ltd, Strensall Camp, York, YO32 5SW Tel: (01904) 492000 *Joinery manufrs*

Palintest Ltd, Kingsway, Team Valley Trading Estate, Gateshead, Tyne & Wear, NE11 0NS Tel: 0191-491 0808 Fax: 0191-482 5372 E-mail: sales@palintest.com *Palintest is a world-leading manufacturer of water testing and environmental products for water quality, drinking water, and swimming pool testing.*Palintest leads the way in technology for the domestic, industrial and commercial water and soil management markets as well. We supply a wide*

continued

continuation
*range of photometer and comparator instruments, test kits and reagent systems for the detection of many elements.*Whatever your applications, Palintest instruments offer the most reliable methods available in portable meters using the latest technology.*

Pall Life Sciences, Walton Road, Farlinton, Portsmouth, PO6 1TD Tel: (023) 9230 2600 Fax: (023) 9230 2601 *Specialist filter manufrs*

Pallam Precast Ltd, 41 Lockfield Avenue, Enfield, Middlesex, EN3 7PY Tel: (020) 8805 6811 Fax: (020) 8804 9825 *Terrazzo product manufrs*

Pallard Contracts Ltd, 84 Court Lane, Cosham, Portsmouth, PO6 2LR Tel: (023) 9221 0075 Fax: (023) 9232 5716 E-mail: enquiries@pallard.co.uk *Roofing contractors flat roofing services*

▶ Pallas Athena Limited, PO Box 1, Chester, CH1 3SH Tel: 0151 472 3880 Fax: 0151 472 3881 E-mail: david.pye@pallas-athena.com *Pallas Athena specialise in Business Process Management. In addition to consultancy services we author, own and support Protos, business process modelling software, Protos Activate, business automation software and FLOWer, advanced workflow and case management software*

Pallas Connections Ltd, Unit 1 Field Farm Business Centre, Launton, Bicester, Oxfordshire, OX26 5EL Tel: (01869) 277053 Fax: (01869) 277058 E-mail: hornby@pallasconnections.co.uk *Electrical component cable harness distributors*

▶ Pallas Forwarding Ltd, Unit 1 Bewicke Main Birtley, Chester Le Street, Chester le Street, County Durham, DH3 1ST Tel: 0191-410 5620 Fax: 0191-492 1314

▶ Pallet Express Systems Ltd, Dalewood Road, Lymedale Business Park, Newcastle, Staffordshire, ST5 9QH Tel: (01782) 566628 Fax: (01782) 566390

Pallet Handling Ltd, Chiddingstone Causeway, Tonbridge, Kent, TN11 8JD Tel: (01892) 870655 Fax: (01892) 870746 *Storage equipment & pallet suppliers*

▶ Pallet Logistics Ltd, Fordoun Aerodrome, Fordoun, Laurencekirk, Kincardineshire, AB30 1JR Tel: (01561) 320896 Fax: (01561) 320545 E-mail: sales@palletlogistics.co.uk

Pallet Racking Co., Sandfield Mill, Saul, Gloucester, GL2 7JY Tel: (01452) 740000 Fax: (01452) 740440 *Storage equipment suppliers*

Pallet Truck Services, 11 Moorfield Road, Irlam, Manchester, M44 6JT Tel: 0161-775 1716 Fax: 0161-775 1716 *Pallet trucks services & repairers*

Pallet Truck Services, 3 Blackgates Court, Tingley, Wakefield, West Yorkshire, WF3 1TH Tel: 0113-252 7852 Fax: 0113-252 7852 *Forklift trucks suppliers*

Pallet Trucks Direct, 61 Greenways, Fleet, Hampshire, GU52 7XF Tel: 01252 617028 Fax: 01252 615096 E-mail: pallettrucksdirect@btopenworld.com *Pallet Trucks Direct are one of the leading suppliers of New & Used Materials Handling Equipment in the South of England. We can offer all types of equipment ranging from hand pallet trucks to large capacity forklift trucks. As one of the leading dealers of Logitrans UK Ltd and a sub dealer of Doosan Daewoo Forklift trucks we offer a full range of New reliable forklifts, stackers and powered pallet trucks at competitive prices and with a large selection of used machines consisting of various well known brands such as Linde, Hyster, Toyota, Nissan and Daewoo you can get a great deal. We offer short and long term rental options from 1 day up to 7 year contracts. Pallet Trucks Direct can offer full finance packages such as Lease Purchase, Contract Hire with or without maintenance.*

Palletforce Crates & Packing Cases, Waterton Industrial Estate, Bridgend, Mid Glamorgan, CF31 3WT Tel: (01656) 662600 Fax: (01656) 661190 E-mail: palletforce67@owens-logistics.com *General haulage*

Palletlink Crates & Packing Cases, Clare House, Pinewood Road, High Wycombe, Buckinghamshire, HP12 4DA Tel: (01494) 558282 Fax: (01494) 558383 E-mail: info@palletlink.co.uk *Pallet associations advisors*

Palletower (GB) Ltd, Pallet Centre Europe, Dane Road Industrial Estate, Sale, Cheshire, M33 7BH Tel: 0161-905 2233 Fax: 0161-972 0922 E-mail: info@palletower.com *Pallets, stillages & converters*

Pallets Unlimited, Barley Croft End, Furneux Pelham, Buntingford, Hertfordshire, SG9 0LL Tel: (01279) 777715 Fax: (01279) 777736 E-mail: janborltd@aol.com *Wood recycling, new, used pallet supplier & manufrs*

▶ Pallett Force, Quickbury Farm, Hatfield Heath Road, Sawbridgeworth, Hertfordshire, CM21 9HY Tel: (01279) 600377

Pallett Racking Systems Ltd, Fryer Works, Ann Street, Willenhall, West Midlands, WV13 1EN Tel: (01902) 606205 Fax: (01902) 606681 E-mail: pallettrackingsys@aol.com *Warehouse racking*

▶ Palm Graphic Services Ltd, Inigma Building, Bilton Road, Bletchley, Milton Keynes, MK1 1HW Tel: (01908) 270400 Fax: (01908) 270614

Palm Paper Ltd, The Former Courthouse, County Court Road, King's Lynn, Norfolk, PE30 5EJ Tel: (01553) 818570 Fax: (01553) 692397 E-mail: derek.harman@palmpaper.co.uk *Paper agents*

▶ Palm Pro Ltd, Unit 5 South John Street, Carlisle, CA2 5AJ Tel: (01228) 591911 Fax: (01228) 591241 E-mail: mail@palmprosigns.co.uk *Sign manufrs*

▶ Palm Signs Systems, 35a Greenfield Business Park, Bagillt Road, Greenfield, Holywell, Clwyd, CH8 7HJ Tel: (01352) 712222 Fax: (01352) 712255 E-mail: info@palmsigns.co.uk *Sign & graphic designers & manufrs*

▶ Palmac Contracting, 4 Adams Way, Springfield Business Park, Alcester, Warwickshire, B49 6PU Tel: (01789) 766022 Fax: (01789) 763662

Palmar Avard & Galloway Ltd, 2 Romney Place, Maidstone, Kent, ME15 6LE Tel: (01622) 691651 Fax: (01622) 678112 E-mail: insurance@pagib.co.uk *Specialist commercial insurance*

▶ Palmaris Services, Granitehill Road, Aberdeen, AB16 7AX Tel: (01224) 680220 Fax: (01224) 697802

▶ Palmaris Services, 27 Waverley Street, Northburn Road, Coatbridge, Lanarkshire, ML5 2HY Tel: (01236) 438040

▶ Palmer Consulting Ltd, Unit 45 Basepoint Business Centre, Metcalf Way, Crawley, West Sussex, RH11 7XX Tel: (01293) 817730 Fax: (01293) 817731 E-mail: enquiries@palmerconsulting.co.uk *Construction sales industry recruitment services*

Palmer Environmental Ltd, Ty Coch House, Llantarnam Industrial Park, Cwmbran, Gwent, NP44 3AW Tel: (01633) 489479 Fax: (01633) 877857 E-mail: information@palmer.co.uk *Leak detection equipment & services*

Palmer & Harvey Ltd, 11 Barnes Wallis Road, Fareham, Hampshire, PO15 5TT Tel: (01489) 555800 Fax: (01489) 555883 E-mail: enquiries@palmersgroup.co.uk *Distribution centre* Also at: Branches throughout the U.K.

Palmer & Harvey Mclane Holdings Ltd, 106 112 Davigdor Road, Hove, East Sussex, BN3 1RE Tel: (01273) 222100 Fax: (01273) 222101 *Wholesale tobacco & confectionery* Also at: Branches throughout the U.K.

John Palmer Brushes Ltd, Unit 5, Oakley Industrial Estate, Norwich Road, Besthorpe, Attleborough, Norfolk, NR17 2LB Tel: (01953) 455003 Fax: (01953) 455905 E-mail: johnpalmerbrushes@line1.net *Brush manufrs*

Palmer Pest Control Ltd, 33 Ross, Rowley Regis, West Midlands, B65 8DY Tel: 0121-561 5417 Fax: 0121-533 9462 E-mail: ppc.ltd@blueyonder.co.uk *Pest control services*

Palmer Pine & Design, Unit 6 Alexandra Road, Sudbury, Suffolk, CO10 6XH Tel: (01787) 379819 Fax: (01787) 882425 *Pine furniture manufrs*

R. Palmer, Keynsham, Bristol, BS18 3ST Tel: (01225) 443206 E-mail: info@goldn.co.uk *Gold and silver portable electroplating kits for plating antiques and jewelry etc. Free advice on starting your own related business opportunity. Chrome, copper and nickel also available.*

▶ Palmer Riley, 40 Westgate, Skelmersdale, Lancashire, WN8 8AZ Tel: (01695) 721555 Fax: (01695) 726555 E-mail: sales@pred.co.uk

▶ The Palmer & Rose Partnership, Maree House, 149 New Road, Booker, High Wycombe, Buckinghamshire, HP12 4RH Tel: (01494) 637499 Fax: (01494) 452630 E-mail: info@palmer-rose.co.uk *Advertising, Web & PR Agency*

Palmer Timber Ltd, 104 Station Road, Cradley Heath, West Midlands, B64 6PW Tel: 0121-559 5511 Fax: 0121-561 4562 E-mail: sales@palmertimber.com *Timber merchants & importers*

▶ Palmers Ltd, North Lane, Aldershot, Hampshire, GU12 4QN Tel: (0870) 0465188 Fax: (0870) 0465189 E-mail: aldershotenq@palmersgroup.co.uk

Palmers Agricultural Ltd, Redwall Farm, Redwall Lane, Linton, Maidstone, Kent, ME17 4AX Tel: (01622) 749819 Fax: (01622) 749829 E-mail: sales@johndeertractors.com *Agricultural machinery suppliers*

▶ Palmers Of Oakham, 9 Penn Street, Oakham, Leicestershire, LE15 6BB Tel: (01572) 722096 Fax: (01572) 724653

Palmhive Technical Textiles Ltd, NTG House, Willow Road, Nottingham, NG7 2TA Tel: 0115-970 7900 Fax: 0115-970 7999 E-mail: enquiries@palmhive.co.uk *Textile manufrs*

▶ Palo Alto Software Ltd, Crown House, 72 Hammersmith Road, London, W14 8TH Tel: (020) 7559 3500 Fax: (020) 7559 3401 *Computer software suppliers*

Paloma Systems Ltd, 2 Frederick Terrace, Frederick Place, Brighton, BN1 1AX Tel: (01273) 778688 Fax: (01273) 323927 E-mail: sales@paloma.co.uk *IT consultants*

Palway Ltd, 6 Macadam Close, Drayton Fields Industrial Estate, Daventry, Northamptonshire, NN11 8RX Tel: (01327) 876387 Fax: (01327) 872615 E-mail: sales@palway.com *Weigh & weighing systems manufrs*

▶ Palziv Insulation Materials, Unit 10 Droicon Industrial Estate, Portway Road, Rowley Regis, West Midlands, B65 9BY Tel: 0121-559 7676 Fax: 0121-559 9191 E-mail: palziv@btconnect.com *Closed sale polyethylene foam*

Pam Textiles Ltd, 24,Manor Road, Lymm, Cheshire, WA13 0AU Tel: (07771) 644363 E-mail: murphypamtex@aol.com *Textile merchants*

Pam Ties Ltd, Pam House, Milk Street, Tyldesley, Manchester, M29 8DQ Tel: (01942) 887920 Fax: (01942) 887921 E-mail: pamties@btconnect.com *Tie manufrs*

Pamarco Europe Ltd, New Cut Lane, Woolston, Warrington, WA1 4AQ Tel: (01925) 456789 Fax: (01925) 456778 E-mail: solutions@pamarco.co.uk *Suppliers to the print & packaging industry*

Pamarco Europe Ltd, New Cut Lane, Woolston, Warrington, WA1 4AQ Tel: (01925) 456789 Fax: (01925) 456778 E-mail: sales-roll@pamarco.co.uk Principal Export Areas: Worldwide *Flexography printing equipment suppliers*

Pamargan Products Ltd, Unit 47 Mochdre Industrial Estate, Mochdre, Newtown, Powys, SY16 4LE Tel: (01686) 625181 Fax: (01686) 627849 E-mail: info@pamargan.co.uk *Mechanical seal manufrs*

Pamela Neave, 18 St. Augustines Parade, Bristol, BS1 4UL Tel: 0117-921 1831 Fax: 0117-925 1019 E-mail: enquiries@pamela-neave.co.uk *Recruitment*

Pan Amusements, Austerlands Mill, Huddersfield Road, Austerlands, Oldham, OL4 3QB Tel: 0161-624 5578 Fax: 0161-627 5357 E-mail: info@panamusements.com *Amusement equipment manufrs*

Pan European Foods Ltd, Units 9-10, Brailwood Close, Bilsthorpe, Newark, Nottinghamshire, NG22 8UG Tel: (01623) 411488 Fax: (01623) 411420 *Juices manufrs*

▶ Pan Heat, 126 Allerton Road, Mossley Hill, Liverpool, L18 2DG Tel: 0151-733 2121 Fax: 0151-733 3131

Panacea Ltd, Winton House, Winton Square, Basingstoke, Hampshire, RG21 8EN Tel: (01256) 305050 Fax: (01256) 305030 *Information technology solutions & services*

Panacea Ltd, Unit 6 Murrell Green Business Pk, London Road, Hook, Hampshire, RG27 9GR Tel: (01256) 305050 Fax: (01256) 305006 E-mail: support@panacea.co.uk *Information technology consultants*

Panacea Services Ltd, 20 St Mary at Hill, London, EC3R 8EE Tel: (020) 7375 3757 Fax: (020) 7375 1525 E-mail: info@panacea-services.co.uk *IT solutions & computer systems services*

Panache Fibreglass Ltd, Unit 1c The Foundry, Market Street, Shipdham, Thetford, Norfolk, IP25 7LZ Tel: (01362) 821515 Fax: (01362) 821505 E-mail: sales@panache-fibreglass.freeserve.co.uk *Fibreglass doors supply & install*

Panache Fitted Furniture, Birches Bridge, Wolverhampton Road, Codsall, Wolverhampton, WV8 1PE Tel: (01902) 847910 Fax: (01902) 847902 *Kitchen, bedroom & bathroom installation & showroom*

▶ Panad Ltd, Unit 27, Brierley Business Centre, Mirion St, Crewe, CW1 2AZ Tel: (01270) 253533 Fax: (01270) 253544 E-mail: panad.limited@ntlworld.com *SITO registered Retail and Static & Patrol Basic Job Training parts 1 (Security) & 2 (Conflict Management and Communications Skills) Training Providers/Examiners in assocoation with Stoke-on-Trent College - Also Providers of Risk Assessment, Manual Handling, Fire & BA/ Confined Spaces training, also able to provide NVQ Qualifications/A1 candidate Mentoring support in a broad range of disciplines from Levels 1 through to 5.*

▶ PANAD Limited, Panad House, Alvaston Business Park, Middlewich Road, Nantwich, Cheshire, CW5 6PF Tel: (01270) 618520 Fax: (01270) 626613 E-mail: info@panadgroup.org *PANAD Ltd, provide Health & Safety Training, Equipment and Personnel to major blue chip companies throughout the UK.*

▶ Panaf Car Accessories, 174 Enterprise Court, Eastways, Witham, Essex, CM8 3YS Tel: (01376) 511550 Fax: (01376) 515131 E-mail: panaf@btclick.com *Motor vehicle spares stockists & exporters*

Panalpina World Transport Ltd, Great South West Road, Feltham, Middlesex, TW14 8NE Tel: (020) 8587 9000 Fax: (020) 8587 9200 *International freight forwarders* Also at: Branches throughout the U.K.

Panararmer Furniture, Bank House, Leasgill, Milnthorpe, Cumbria, LA7 7FG Tel: (01539) 563523 Fax: (01539) 563466 *Kitchen, bedroom & bathroom retail & installation*

Panasonic Air Conditioning, Panasonic House, Willoughby Road, Bracknell, Berkshire, RG12 8FP Tel: (01344) 853186 Fax: (01344) 853217 E-mail: nicky.dopson@panasonic.co.uk *Manufacturers of air conditioning equipment*

Panasonic Electric Works UK Ltd, Sunrise Parkway, Linford Wood, Milton Keynes, MK14 6LF Tel: (01908) 231555 Fax: (01908) 231599 E-mail: info-uk@eu.pewg.panasonic.com *Automation control components & systems suppliers*

Panasonic Mobile Communicationdevelopment Of Eu, Daytona Drive, Colthorpe, Thatcham, Berkshire, RG19 4ZD Tel: (01635) 871466 Fax: (01635) 871345 *Cellular radio telephone equipment*

Panda Cleaning Machines Ltd, 18 Thomas Flawn Road, Irthlingborough, Wellingborough, Northamptonshire, NN9 5PA Tel: (01933) 653545 Fax: (01933) 653545 *Cleaning machine repairs & sales*

▶ Panda Distribution, Unit 11, Windrush Millennium Centre, 70 Alexandra Road, Manchester, M16 7WD Tel: (0870) 7772971 Fax: (0870) 7772973 E-mail: kellyenquiries@pandadistribution.co.uk *Leaflet distribution*

▶ Panda Lifts Ltd, Brilanda Vineyard, Beer Ferrers, Yelverton, Devon, PL20 7JX Tel: (01822) 841178 Fax: (01822) 841178 E-mail: sevvice@euro-lifts.co.uk *Lifts*

Panda Model Wholesale, Unit 8A, Bramley Hedge Farm, Redhill Road, Cobham, Surrey, KT11 1EQ Tel: (01932) 865388 Fax: (01932) 865388 E-mail: sales@panda-models.demon.co.uk *Model fittings & material distributors*

▶ Panda Press Stone Ltd, 1 Newcastle Street, Stone, Staffordshire, ST15 8JU Tel: (01785) 815110

Pandaprint, 104 Park Road, Rosyth, Dunfermline, Fife, KY11 2JL Tel: (01383) 417847 Fax: (01383) 411863 *Printers*

Pandect Instrument Laboratories Ltd, Wellington Road, Cressex Business Park, High Wycombe, Buckinghamshire, HP12 3PX Tel: (01494) 526301 Fax: (01494) 464503 E-mail: enquiries@pandect.demon.co.uk *Aircraft instrumentation maintenance contractors*

Pandect Precision Components Ltd, Wellington Road, High Wycombe, Buckinghamshire, HP12 3PX Tel: (01494) 526303 Fax: (01494) 465557 E-mail: enquiries@pandect.demon.co.uk *Slip ring & component manufrs*

Pandelco Ltd, Canal Street, Burton-on-Trent, Staffordshire, DE14 3TB Tel: (01283) 542738 Fax: (01283) 511774 E-mail: sales@pandelco.co.uk *Control panel manufrs*

Pandet Ltd, 1 Premier Drum Works, Canal Street, Wigston, Leicestershire, LE18 4PL Tel: 0116-277 2372 Fax: 0116-277 2672 E-mail: sales@kuroma.com *Food processing machinery manufrs*

Pandora Glaze, 41-45 Lind Road, Sutton, Surrey, SM1 4PP Tel: (020) 8643 2132 Fax: (020) 8642 1133 *Double glazed unit replacements*

▶ Pandora Graphics, 150-160 Dumers Lane, Radcliffe, Manchester, M26 2GF Tel: 0161-766 1774 Fax: 0161-766 1774 E-mail: info@pandoragraphics.co.uk *Pandora Graphics is a company based in Manchester UK. Our state of the art studio houses a small team of designers who offer a very friendly and professional design service. Photography, web design, hot foil supplies, labels, brochures, stationary, adverts, exhibition*

▶ Pandora's Hat Boxes, Althorpe Lodge, Main Street, Althorpe, Scunthorpe, North Lincolnshire, DN17 3HJ Tel: (01724) 784493 E-mail: giuseppina@pandorashatboxes.co.uk *Individually designed fabric covered boxes & hat boxes*

Pandrol UK Ltd, Bonemill Lane, Worksop, Nottinghamshire, S81 7AX Tel: (01909) 476101 Fax: (01909) 500004 *Rail fastenings manufrs*

Panduit Europe Ltd, West World, Westgate, London, W5 1UD Tel: (020) 8601 7200 Fax: (020) 8601 7319 *Electric cable accessories*

Panel Print Industrial Screen Printers, 7-12 Morris Road, Poole, Dorset, BH17 0GG Tel: (01202) 686575 Fax: (01202) 675733 E-mail: panelprint@btconnect.com *Precision industrial screen printers suppliers*

Panel Projects, Portview Road, Avonmouth, Bristol, BS11 9LQ Tel: 0117-316 7020 Fax: 0117-316 7001 E-mail: sales@panelprojects.com *Composite panel manufrs*

▶ Panel Supplies, Harvey Road, Basildon, Essex, SS13 1ES Tel: (01268) 729100 Fax: (01268) 729700 E-mail: jonhaak@panelsupplies.co.uk *Supplier of all wooden panels*

Panel Systems Ltd, Unit 3-9 Welland Close, Sheffield, S3 9QY Tel: 0114-275 2881 Fax: 0114-276 8807 E-mail: mail@panelsystems.co.uk *Panel component fabricator & cnc machining services*

Panel Technology Ltd, Whittle Road, Hinckley, Leicestershire, LE10 3DW Tel: (01455) 631622 Fax: (01455) 615693 E-mail: enquiries@certec.co.uk *Metal pressings manufrs*

Panelbond Ltd, 1 King Edward Street, Grimsby, South Humberside, DN31 3JU Tel: (01472) 250130 Fax: (01472) 250784 E-mail: roybarber@panelbond.com *Insulated panel manufrs*

Panelec Ltd, 1 Hollies Trading Estate, Graiseley Row, Wolverhampton, WV2 4HE Tel: (01902) 712582 Fax: (01902) 712582 *Control panels manufrs*

Panelkraft Ltd, Unit 18a-20c Hixon Airfield Estate, New Road, Hixon, Stafford, ST18 0PF Tel: (01889) 270018 Fax: (01889) 270977 *Composite sandwich panel manufrs*

Panelkraft Kitchen Planners, Unit 16d Birkdale Close, Manners Industrial Estate, Ilkeston, Derbyshire, DE7 8YA Tel: 0115-944 0911 Fax: 0115-932 6119 *Kitchen unit manufrs*

Panelmate Handling Ltd, Staveley Grange, Kanaresborough, Staveley, Knaresborough, North Yorkshire, HG5 9LD Tel: (0845) 6653534 Fax: (0845) 6653533 E-mail: peter@panelmatehandling.com *Materials handling equipment manufacturers & specialising in sheet materials & panels. Makers of Panelmate trolleys Panel Grips, Stock Trolleys with custom builds and specialist beds available.*

Panels & Profiles, Tewkesbury Business Park, Severn Drive, Tewkesbury Business Park, Tewkesbury, Gloucestershire, GL20 8TX Tel: (01684) 856600 Fax: (01684) 856601 E-mail: sales@coruspanelsandprofiles.co.uk *Profiled metal cladding & roofing*

▶ Panelscreens, 18 Lower Road, Breachwood Green, Hitchin, Hertfordshire, SG4 8NS Tel: (01438) 833728 Fax: (01438) 833728 E-mail: paulfurse@panelscreens.co.uk *Office furniture & screening suppliers*

Panelslot Ltd, The Crossways, Nettleden, Hemel Hempstead, Hertfordshire, HP1 3DQ Tel: (01442) 878681 Fax: (01442) 878682

Paneltex Ltd, Kingston International Park, Somerden Road, Hull, HU9 5PE Tel: (01482) 787236 Fax: (01482) 787238 E-mail: sales@paneltex.co.uk *Cold store manufrs*

Panema Trailer Engineering Ltd, Chalk Lane, Snetterton, Norwich, NR16 2JZ Tel: (01953) 887622 Fax: (01953) 888515 E-mail: info@panematrailers.co.uk *Trailer maintenance & body builders services*

John Panes, Regal Garage, Hanley Road, Upton-upon-Severn, Worcester, WR8 0HU Tel: (01684) 592316 *Crane hire & petrol sales*

▶ Pang Properties Ltd, Bleets Farm Buildings, Feltham, Frome, Somerset, BA11 5NA Tel: (01373) 453177 Fax: (01373) 453178

Pang UK Ltd, Studlands Park Industrial Estate, Newmarket, Suffolk, CB8 7AU Tel: (01638) 663575 Fax: (01638) 662274 *Tyre repair materials supplied*

Pangborn UK Ltd, Riverside House Brymau Three Trading Estate, River Lane, Saltney, Chester, CH4 8RQ Tel: (01244) 659852 Fax: (01244) 659853 E-mail: sales@pangborn.co.uk *Shot blasting equipment manufrs*

Pangborn (UK) Ltd, Orgreave Drive, Sheffield, S13 9NR Tel: 0114-288 0786 Fax: 0114-288 0791 E-mail: panguk@aol.com *Foundry equipment & plant manufacturers. In addition blast cleaning & shot blasting equipment/ component/spare part manufrs*

▶ Panic Transport (Contracts) Ltd, Dunchurch Trading Estate, London Road, Dunchurch, Rugby, Warwickshire, CV23 9LN Tel: (01788) 815501

Panilet Tables, 17 Dragon Court, Crofts End Road, Bristol, BS5 7XX Tel: 0117-951 1858 Fax: 0117-951 1858 E-mail: info@panilettables.co.uk *Height adjustable tables & cutting presswork trays*

Panks Engineers, 8 Heigham Street, Norwich, NR2 4TE Tel: (01603) 620297 Fax: (01603) 762679 E-mail: sales@panks.co.uk *Pump distributors & engineers*
Panmer Plastics Ltd, 5 Delta Centre, Mount Pleasant, Wembley, Middlesex, HA0 1UX Tel: (020) 8903 7733 Fax: (020) 8903 3036 E-mail: info@panmer.com *CD packaging & flexible multimedia packaging manufrs*
Pannell Cabinet Makers, Maytham Works Maytham Farm, Hatters Hill, Rolvenden, Cranbrook, Kent, TN17 4QA Tel: (01797) 270927 *Cabinet maker*
Pannell Signs Ltd, Chelsea House, Chelsea Street, New Basford, Nottingham, NG7 7HN Tel: 0115-970 0371 Fax: 0115-942 2452 E-mail: sales@pannellsigns.co.uk *Sign makers*
Panoptic Solutions Ltd, 43 Temple Row, Birmingham, B2 5LS Tel: (0121) 2376057 Fax: (0121) 2376100 E-mail: info@panopt.co.uk *Turnaround & Change Management***
Panorama Antennas Ltd, 61 Frogmore, London, SW18 1HF Tel: (020) 8877 4444 Fax: (020) 8877 4477 E-mail: sales@panorama.co.uk *Antenna manufrs*
Panoramic Ltd, 534 London Road, North Cheam, Sutton, Surrey, SM3 9QE Tel: (020) 8641 4488 Fax: (020) 8641 5900 E-mail: sales@panoramic-products.co.uk *Window frame manufrs*
Panoramic Window & Door Centre, 2 Richmond Road, Mangotsfield, Bristol, BS16 9HB Tel: 0117-956 0321 Fax: 0117-956 0456 E-mail: info@panoramicwindows.co.uk *Windows, doors & conservatories installers*
▶ Panoramix Aviation Rentals Ltd, 30 Silver Hill Road, Sheffield, S11 9JG Tel: 0114 2621140 Fax: 0114 2621556 E-mail: sales@panoramixltd.freeserve.co.uk *Aircraft rental*
▶ Panos Furnishings, 101a-103 Whitelands Road, Ashton-under-Lyne, Lancashire, OL6 6UG Tel: 0161-368 0808 Fax: 0161-339 0006 *Blind manufrs*
▶ Panrix Computer, Unit 19, Sheepscar Street South, Leeds, LS7 1AD Tel: 0113-244 4958 Fax: 0113-244 4268 E-mail: gulberg@panrix.co.uk
Pansoft Ltd, 28 Landport Terrace, Portsmouth, PO1 2RG Tel: (023) 9285 1513 Fax: (023) 9285 1529 E-mail: sales@pansoft.co.uk *Computer software house*
Pantex Coatings (Yorkshire) Ltd, Unit 7 Stephenson Road, Inkersall Road Industrial Estate, Staveley, Chesterfield, Derbyshire, S43 3JN Tel: (01246) 475233 Fax: (01246) 475284 E-mail: enquiries@hayford.com *Trade coaters*
▶ Panther Building Systems Ltd, 5 Orchard Way, Antrim, BT41 2RU Tel: (028) 9446 8622 Fax: (028) 9446 7144 *Engineering*
▶ Panther Computing, 2 Lions Way, Sleaford, Lincolnshire, NG34 8GN Tel: (01529) 415566 Fax: (01529) 415588 *Computer systems, software & networks, sales, installation & contract support, system repairs, servicing & upgrades, website development & hosting*
Panther Design Services Ltd, Barleyfield, Hinckley, Leicestershire, LE10 1YE Tel: (01455) 890033 Fax: (01455) 890066 E-mail: sales@panther-designs.co.uk *Electronic consultants*
Panther Dryers, Hillside House, Intwood Road, Norwich, NR4 6TG Tel: (01603) 505509 E-mail: charlie@pantherd.freeserve.co.uk *Infra red dryer manufrs*
▶ Panther Express Ltd, Unit 9-10 The Three Sisters En, Antler Court, Ashton-in-Makerfield, Wigan, Lancashire, WN4 8DU Tel: (01942) 728400
Panther Platform Rentals, Derby Dell, Lasham, Alton, Hampshire, GU34 5RX Tel: (01256) 381515 Fax: (01256) 381505 E-mail: basingstoke@panther.uk.com *Plant hire services*
Panther UK Ltd, Panther House, 1 Panther Drive, London, NW10 0JP Tel: (020) 7887 7777 Fax: (020) 7887 7711 E-mail: products@pantheronline.co.uk Principal Export Areas: Worldwide *Electrical wholesaler*
Pantherella Ltd, Hallaton St, Leicester, LE2 8QY Tel: 0116-283 1111 Fax: 0116-283 0695 E-mail: mail@pantherella.co.uk *Hosiery manufrs*
Pantograph Precision Ltd, 15 Willow Road, Colnbrook, Slough, SL3 0BS Tel: (01753) 684343 Fax: (01753) 681363 E-mail: stuart@pantagraph.demon.co.uk *Plastic & rubber mould design & manufrs*
George Panton & Son Ltd, 34 Argyll Arcade, Glasgow, G2 8BE Tel: 0141-221 8579 Fax: 0141-204 4920 E-mail: georgepanton@sol.co.uk *Wholesale jewellers*
Panton (Sheet Metalworks) Ltd, 67 Swaisland Drive, Crayford Industrial Estate, Crayford, Dartford, DA1 4HS Tel: (01322) 554180 Fax: (01322) 555157 E-mail: enquiries@pantonsheetmetal.co.uk *Fine limit sheet metalwork & general fabrication*
▶ The Pantry, 105 High Street, Ilfracombe, Devon, EX34 9NH Tel: (01271) 862031 *Bakers*
Pantry Frans, 1A Key Street, Lostwithiel, Cornwall, PL22 0BS Tel: (01208) 872407 *Dairy & pastry retailers*
▶ Paolo's Ice Creams, Walls Ice Cream Depot, Unit 6A Cemetery Road Industrial Estate, Dawley Bank, Telford, Shropshire, TF4 2BS Tel: (01952) 505855 Fax: (01952) 505855 *Wholesale, retail ice cream*
Paper Bag Co., Units 8 & 9 Oakfield Business Centre, Northacre Industrial Estate, Stephenson Road, Westbury, Wiltshire, BA13 4WF Tel: 01373 825834 Fax: 01373 865984 E-mail: sales@paperbagco.co.uk *Manufacture and design of retail and promotional bags.*
Paper Collect, 83 Guildford Street, Chertsey, Surrey, KT16 9AS Tel: (0870) 3308627 Fax: (0870) 3308617 E-mail: admin@ip3.org *Professional institute for people paper industry*
Paper Converting Machine Co. Ltd, Southway Drive, Plymouth, PL6 6EL Tel: (01752) 735881 Fax: (01752) 733290 E-mail: pcmcuk@papcon.co.uk *Paper converting machine manufrs*
Paper Flow Ltd, Unit 5 & 6, 20 Bugsby Way, London, SE7 7SJ Tel: (020) 8331 2090 Fax: (020) 8331 2001 E-mail: sales@paperflowonline.com *Paper merchants stationery suppliers*
Paper Hygiene Services, Sandleas Way, Leeds, LS15 8AW Tel: 0113-232 6777 Fax: 0113-232 6730 *Chemical & paper retailers*
Paper Life Ltd, Unit 13 Ahed House, Sandbeds Trading Estate, Ossett, West Yorkshire, WF5 9ND Tel: (01924) 281666 Fax: (01924) 281444 E-mail: sales@paperlife.co.uk *Paper & print testing equipment distributors*
Paper Moon Productions, Wychwood House, Burchetts Green Lane, Burchetts Green, Maidenhead, Berkshire, SL6 3QW Tel: (01628) 829819 Fax: (01628) 825949 E-mail: info@paper-moon.co.uk *Television film & video producers*
Paper Pulp Solutions, Pulp Mill House, Banton Mill, Mill Road, Banton, Kilsyth, G65 0RD Tel: (0870) 770 8883 Fax: (0870) 770 8884 E-mail: sales@paperpulpsolutions.co.uk *Paper Pulp Solutions design and manufacture moulded pulp packaging products for electronics, DVD players, TV, Hi-Fi, speakers, glass bottles, hazardous chemicals, wine and spirits, mobile phones, protective corners for windows doors and furniture, horticultural products, mushroom trays, direct food contact trays, confectionary packaging any many more applications.*
Paper Shapers, 10 Premier Drum Works, Canal Street, Wigston, Leicestershire, LE18 4PL Tel: 0116-277 4433 Fax: 0116-277 4300 E-mail: cutters@papershapers.co.uk *Manufactures of bespoke die cutters for all die cutting equipment*
Paper Tigers, 77 Greenfield Road, London, E1 1EJ Tel: (020) 7377 0070 Fax: (01732) 362429 *Envelopes & calendar suppliers*
▶ Paper Trading Co. Ltd, 59a Alma Road, Clifton, Bristol, BS8 2DE Tel: (0870) 1662663 E-mail: sales@papertradingcompany.com
▶ Paper Trail Mill Ltd, Frogmore Mill, Fourdrinier Way, Hemel Hempstead, Hertfordshire, HP3 9RY Tel: (01442) 231234 Fax: (01442) 275749 E-mail: frogmoremill@thepapertrial.org.uk *Commercial paper mill & visitors attraction*
Paperchain Technology Ltd, Unit 9 Sandwell Business & Tec, Oldbury, W. Midlands, B68 8NA Tel: 0121-552 1144 Fax: 0121 552 1144 *Computer components*
▶ Paperchase Business Services, Warrington, WA4 6QQ Tel: (07939) 145015 Fax: (01925) 638440 *Book keeping & administration services*
▶ Paperfree Solutions Ltd, 1a High Street, Epsom, Surrey, KT19 8DA Tel: (01372) 727333 Fax: (01372) 727248 E-mail: sales@paperfreesolutions.net *Computer software*
Paperhat Imaging Ltd, 44a Curlew Street, London, SE1 2ND Tel: (020) 7089 0360 Fax: (020) 7407 5880 E-mail: tim@paperhat.co.uk *Print management, cost reduction*
Paperline Northwest, 38 Blundell Drive, Southport, Merseyside, PR8 4RE Tel: (01704) 567162 Fax: (01704) 567144 *Hygiene disposables suppliers*
▶ Paperpact Ltd, Gordon House, 6 Lissenden Gardens, London, NW5 1LX Tel: (020) 8838 9780 Fax: (020) 8838 9782
Papersticks Ltd, Govett Avenue, Shepperton, Middlesex, TW17 8AB Tel: (01932) 228491 Fax: (01932) 242828 E-mail: sales@papersticks.co.uk *Medical & confectionery stick manufrs*
▶ Paperstone, 67-69 Whitfield Street, London, W1T 4HF Tel: (020) 7462 7800 Fax: (020) 7462 7781 E-mail: jim@paperstone.co.uk *Office supplies & furniture*
▶ Papertex Ltd, PO Box 11, Skipton, North Yorkshire, BD23 9AF Tel: (01756) 649033 Fax: (0870) 8362330 E-mail: info@papertex.co.uk *Technical & sales consultancy*
Paperun Group Of Companies, 1 East Barnet Road, Barnet, Hertfordshire, EN4 8RR Tel: (020) 8447 4141 Fax: (020) 8447 4241 E-mail: paper4u@paperun.com *International paper merchants broker agents*
▶ Paperwork (UK) Ltd, Victoria Road, Skegness, Lincolnshire, PE25 3SN Tel: (01754) 613120
▶ Papi Transport (UK) Ltd, 69 Southend Road, Hockley, Essex, SS5 4PZ Tel: (01702) 205545
Papworth Furniture Ltd, Unit 4 Stirling Way, Papworth Everard, Cambridge, CB23 3GX Tel: (0845) 1308300 Fax: (01480) 830516 E-mail: sales@papworth-furniture.co.uk *Laboratory & school furniture manufrs*
▶ Par Building Services, 1404 Pershore Road, Stirchley, Birmingham, B30 2PH Tel: 0121-459 9714 Fax: 0121-459 6403
Par Metals Ltd, Unit 68 Birch Road East Industrial Estate, Birch Road East, Birmingham, B6 7DB Tel: 0121-327 2891 Fax: 0121-327 2765 *Scrap metal merchants*
Par Opti Projects Ltd, 67 Stirling Road, London, W3 8DJ Tel: (020) 8896 2588 Fax: (020) 8896 2599 E-mail: paropti@aol.com *Fibre optic light guide manufrs*
Par Pak Party Time Ltd, 12-14 Gloucester Street, Leamington Spa, Warwickshire, CV31 1EE Tel: (01926) 314699 Fax: (01926) 422122 E-mail: sales@partytimeballoons.co.uk *Party products*
Par Printing Press & Rubber Stamps, 9 Garton Street, Peterborough, PE1 4EL Tel: (01733) 562666 Fax: (01733) 567883 E-mail: parprinting@onetel.net *Printing & rubber stamp makers*
▶ Par Scaffolding Ltd, 74 Albion Road, Edinburgh, EH7 5QZ Tel: 0131- 656 9333 Fax: 0131- 656 9444 E-mail: par.scaffolding@virgin.net *Scaffolding contractor & hire & sales*
Parade Products Ltd, 656B Chester Road, Erdington, Birmingham, B23 5TE Tel: 0121-350 8031 Fax: 0121-350 8031 *Precision toolmakers manufrs*
Paradigm Audio Visual Ltd, Box End Road, Bromham, Bedford, MK43 8LT Tel: (01234) 843388 Fax: (01234) 854477 E-mail: info@rearpro.com *Audio & visual equipment*
▶ Paradigm Communications Systems Ltd, Station Road, Alton, Hampshire, GU34 2PZ Tel: (01420) 88199 Fax: (08709) 024001 *Solutions provider for broadband wireless*
Paradigm Geo-Physical UK Ltd, Mackenzie Buildings, 168 Skene Street, Aberdeen, AB10 1PE Tel: (01224) 649555 Fax: (01224) 649496 *Computer training company*
Paradigm Redshift Ltd, Lion Gate Barn, Petworth Road, Witley, Godalming, Surrey, GU8 5QW Tel: (01428) 684710 E-mail: enquiries@paradigm-redshift.com *Publishing services*
▶ Paradigm Web Solutions Ltd, Building 188 First Street, New Greenham Park, Newbury, Berkshire, RG19 6HW Tel: (01635) 277499 Fax: (01635) 277497 E-mail: info@parawebsol.co.uk *Professional internet website design*
▶ Paradise Associates, 24 Manor Crescent, Guildford, Surrey, GU2 9NF Tel: (0776) 6523151 E-mail: john@paradiseassociates.co.uk *Training & race & diversity consultants*
Paradise Computing Ltd, Albion House, Albion Place, Northampton, NN1 1UD Tel: (01604) 604575 Fax: (01604) 670375 E-mail: sales@paradisecomputing.co.uk *Network installation & training*
Paradise Pools GB Ltd, Paradise House, 2 Swans Ghyll, Priory Road, Forest Row, East Sussex, RH18 5PA Tel: (01342) 824715 E-mail: paradisepools@btinternet.com *Swimming pool installation & refurbishment*
▶ Paradise Windows, Unit 14 Block 15 Amber Business Centre, Greenhill Lane, Riddings, Alfreton, Derbyshire, DE55 4BR Tel: (01773) 606333 Fax: (01773) 606444 *Manufacturing windows*
Parafix, Spencer Road, Church Hill Industrial Estate, Lancing, West Sussex, BN15 8UA Tel: (01903) 750000 Fax: (01903) 767728 E-mail: sales@parafix.co.uk Principal Export Areas: Africa *Adhesive tape distributors or agents*
Paragon Ltd, Park Road, Castleford, West Yorkshire, WF10 4RR Tel: (01977) 669700 Fax: (01977) 603036 E-mail: sales@paragon-castleford.com *Business form manufrs*
Paragon Business Furniture, Sturmer Road, Haverhill, Suffolk, CB9 7UU Tel: (01440) 712160 Fax: (01440) 712157 E-mail: enquiries@paragon-businessfurn.com *Office furniture manufrs*
Paragon Business Solutions Ltd, 3 Greenock Road, London, W3 8DU Tel: (020) 8993 8995 Fax: (020) 8993 8999 E-mail: info@credit-scoring.co.uk *Computer systems & software developers*
Paragon By Heckmondwike, Farfield Park, Manvers, Rotherham, South Yorkshire, S63 5DB Tel: (01709) 763800 Fax: (0800) 7314521 *Carpet tile manufrs*
Paragon Circuits Ltd, 5 Wainman Road, Peterborough, PE2 7BU Tel: (01733) 234754 Fax: (01733) 238196 E-mail: info@paragoncircuits.co.uk *Printed circuit manufrs*
Paragon Cutting Forms, Unit 23 Blaydon Business Centre, Cowen Road, Blaydon-on-Tyne, Tyne & Wear, NE21 5TW Tel: 0191-487 9555 Fax: 0191-487 9666 E-mail: sales@paragoncfl.com *Cutting formes & print finishers*
▶ Paragon Design & Print, 10 Lawn Street, Paisley, Renfrewshire, PA1 1HB Tel: 0141-840 1122 Fax: 0141-887 7149 E-mail: sales@paragon-design.co.uk
Paragon Electronic Components plc, Wolseley Road, Kempston, Bedford, MK42 7UP Tel: (01234) 840101 Fax: (01234) 840707 E-mail: sales@paragon-plc.com *Specialised electronic component kitting services*
Paragon Electronics, 10 Market Place, Flat 1, Bideford, Devon, EX39 2DR Tel: (01237) 421324 Fax: (01237) 421016 E-mail: computers@paragon2.fsnet.co.uk *Computer manufrs*
▶ Paragon Europe Ltd, The Island, Wey Meadows, Weybridge, Surrey, KT13 8XY Tel: 0870 224 2644 E-mail: val@paragoneurope.com *One of the best live event production and management teams in the UK, providing highly qualified creative design and technical production for events in the UK and Worldwide. Paragon provides everything from venue sourcing to top celebrities, stage, set, lighting, theming and entertainment. We strive to deliver the most creative, impactful and cost effective event solutions for our clients.*
The Paragon Group Of Companies plc, St Catherine S Court, Herbert Road, Solihull, West Midlands, B91 3QE Tel: 0121-712 2505 Fax: 0121-712 2555 E-mail: marketing@paragon-group.co.uk *Consumer finances*
Paragon Group UK Ltd, Pallion Trading Estate, Sunderland, SR4 6ST Tel: 0191-514 0716 Fax: 0191-567 1842 E-mail: enquiries@paragonuk.com *Business form manufrs*
▶ Paragon Hi Tech Ltd, Unit 5/9, 1A Willan Road, Tottenham, London, N17 6NG Tel: (020) 8808 8084 Fax: (020) 8808 8084 E-mail: paragonhitech@tiscali.co.uk *Building and Property Maintenance.*Refurbishment*Plastering Decorating*Carpentry Plumbing*Roofing & Ceilings*Extensions Loft Conversions*
▶ Paragon Joinery Ltd, Skitts Manor Farm, Moor Lane, Marsh Green, Edenbridge, Kent, TN8 5RA Tel: (01732) 867580 Fax: (01732) 865809 E-mail: paul.hemple@paragonjoinery.com *Timber window and door manufacturer. Joinery*
▶ Paragon Materials Ltd, Maritime House, Southside 3, Chatham Docks, Chatham, Kent, ME4 4SR Tel: (01634) 890744 Fax: (01634) 890745 *Importers & distributors of cement*
Paragon Precision Products, 36 Camford Way, Luton, LU3 3AN Tel: (01582) 505005 Fax: (01582) 505010 E-mail: info@paragon-precision.co.uk *Precision turned parts*
Paragon Pressings, 3b Harpings Road, Hull, HU5 4JF Tel: (01482) 462822 Fax: (01482) 462833 *Sheet metal punching services*
▶ Paragon Professional Handyman, Unit 142, 22 Notting Hill Gate, London, W11 3JE Tel: 07835 478129 E-mail: freequote@paragonhandyman.co.uk *Handyman London Plumber, Bathroom Kitchen Fitter, fully insured, professional,managed and guaranteed service.*
▶ Paragon Quality Foods Ltd, Derbyshire Court, Armthorpe, Doncaster, South Yorkshire, DN3 3FD Tel: (01302) 834141 Fax: (01302) 836216
▶ Paragon Rapid Technologies Ltd, Block 11, Teesside International Airport, Darlington, County Durham, DL2 1PD Tel: 01325 333141 *Rapid prototype services*
Paragon Signs & Labels Ltd, Paragon House, Homefield Road, Haverhill, Suffolk, CB9 8QP Tel: (01440) 761405 Fax: (01440) 712147 E-mail: sales@paragon-signs.co.uk *General engravers & sign services*
Paragon Toolmaking & Precision Engineering Co. Ltd, 321 National Avenue, Hull, HU5 4JB Tel: (01482) 343439 Fax: (01482) 448623 E-mail: sales@paragon-tools.co.uk Principal Export Areas: Worldwide *Press tool manufacturers & wire erosion machining services*
Paraid Ltd, Unit 4 Bond Street, West Bromwich, West Midlands, B70 7DQ Tel: 0121-580 0111 Fax: 0121-580 0222 *Powder coating & wet spray painting*
▶ Parallel Blue Marine Corporate Sailing Events, Griffin Mill, London Road, Thrupp, Stroud, Gloucestershire, GL5 2AZ Tel: (01453) 887766 *Parallel Blue Marine designs, produces, manages and delivers outstanding corporate events and regattas worldwide . Call 01453 887766 now to organise your next corporate sailing regatta.*
Parallel Computer Systems, 14 Trent Road, Bulkington, Bedworth, Warwickshire, CV12 9QD Tel: (024) 7631 4447 E-mail: support@parasys.co.uk *Computer software developers*
Parallel House Ltd, 70 The Green, Christian Malford, Chippenham, Wiltshire, SN15 4BQ Tel: (0870) 0762538 Fax: (07002) 226262 *Firework stockiest*
Parallel Solutions Ltd, 62 Manor Lane, Sunbury-on-Thames, Middlesex, TW16 6JA Tel: (01932) 782759 Fax: (01932) 782759 E-mail: gerald.roberts@dial.pipex.com *Electronics consultants information technology consultants*
▶ Param Impex Ltd, 14 Cox Close, Kesgrave, Ipswich, IP5 2DW Tel: (01473) 636673 Fax: (0870) 1365111 E-mail: paramimpex@b2bquote.com *Param Impex Limited is a major Importer & Supplier of wide range of Garden & Home Decorative Products in UK. We also represent a pioneer Indian Manufacturer of Premium Quality Home & Garden Decorative Products. We are specialized primarily in Garden Animals ,Statues & Planters.**PIL brings you a wide range of exquisitely Decorative products that include*ANIMAL STATUES - Garden , Tableware ,Show ,Fountain Animals*HUMAN STATUES - Art ,Nude ,Religious ,Garden Statues*PLANTER - Crafted in Iron ,Brass & Aluminium ,Fibre Glass*FOUNTAINS , FIREPLACE , STREET LAMPS , WALL DECORATIONS ,CHRISTMAS ORNAMENTS , COLOURED FIGURES ,EXCLUSIVE WIRE BASKETS.. Many more *We offer you wide range under one roof at very reasonable terms of business. You would enjoy the advantages of Best Quality ,Timely Delivery ,Flexible Terms & Conditions & Best Price .*Should you have any enquiries ,please contact us on Phone 01473 636673 or email us to paramimpex@yahoo.co.uk.***
Paramaeth Agricultural Merchants, Unit 9 Penyrorsedd Industrial Estate, Llangefni, Gwynedd, LL77 7JD Tel: (01248) 724959 Fax: (01248) 724092 *Agricultural services*
Paramatta Tool & Gauge Co. Ltd, Worrall St, Salford, M5 4TH Tel: 0161-873 7655 *Toolmakers & precision engineers*
▶ Paramet Computer Systems, Northgate House, Plough Road, Great Bentley, Colchester, CO7 8LG Tel: (01206) 255300 E-mail: sales@paramet.cpm *Programmers*
▶ Paramo Ltd, Durgates Industrial Estate, Durgates, Wadhurst, East Sussex, TN5 6DF Tel: (01892) 786444 Fax: (01892) 784961
Paramo Tools Group Ltd, Bailey St, Sheffield, S1 3BS Tel: 0114-249 0880 Fax: 0114-249 0881 *Tool manufrs* Also at: Ecclesfield, Rotherham & Walsall
Paramode Ltd, Harbour Road, Lowestoft, Suffolk, NR32 3LZ Tel: (01502) 574213 Fax: (01502) 501503 E-mail: sales@paramode.co.uk *Engineering designers, consultants & project management*
Paramount 26 Ltd, Unit 5 B & 5 C, Thames Road, Barking, Essex, IG11 0JP Tel: 020 85327940 *Roller shutter manufrs*
Paramount Catering Disposables Ltd, 29 Byron Road, Wealdstone, Harrow, Middlesex, HA3 7SY Tel: (020) 8427 5617 *Disposable plates, cups & cutlery wholesalers*
Paramount Contracts Ltd, St. Margarets, Bromley Green Road, Ruckinge, Ashford, Kent, TN26 2EF Tel: (01233) 733399 Fax: (01233) 733608 *Baby respiration monitor manufrs*
Paramount Engineering Ltd, Unit 15 Pontcynon Industrial Estate, Abercynon, Mountain Ash, Mid Glamorgan, CF45 4EP Tel: (01443) 741897 Fax: (01443) 741897 E-mail: paramount@dial.pipex.com *Test fixture manufacturers to the electronics*
Paramount Co. Formations Ltd, 35 Firs Avenue, London, N11 3NE Tel: (020) 8883 6161 Fax: (020) 8883 1269 E-mail: pcfltd@aol.com *Company registration agents*
▶ Paramount Industries, Arowry House, Hanmer, Whitchurch, Shropshire, SY13 3EQ Tel: (01948) 830641 Fax: (01948) 830605 *Glass fibre manufrs*
▶ Paramount Learning Ltd, 478 Halifax Road, Bradford, West Yorkshire, BD6 2LH Tel: (01274) 600410 E-mail: info@paramountlearning.co.uk

Paramount Marine Hotel, 8 Crosbie Road, Troon, Ayrshire, KA10 6HE Tel: (01292) 314444 Fax: (01292) 316922 E-mail: marine@paramount-hotels.co.uk *Hotel, restaurant, conference & banqueting facilities*

Paramount Mould Co. Ltd, Abercromby Avenue, High Wycombe, Buckinghamshire, HP12 3AX Tel: (01494) 531516 Fax: (01494) 465483 E-mail: tech@paramount-group.net *Plastics mould toolmakers*

Paramount Office Interiors, Paramount House, Pascal Close, St. Mellons, Cardiff, CF3 0LW Tel: (029) 2083 9800 Fax: (029) 2083 9801 E-mail: sales@paramountinteriors.com *Office interior designers & fitters*

Paramount Plating Ltd, South Stour Avenue, Ashford, Kent, TN23 7RS Tel: (01233) 626748 Fax: (01233) 641787 E-mail: home.supplies@virgin.net *Electroplating services*

Paramount Powders UK Ltd, 4 Squirrels Trading Estate, Viveash Close, Hayes, Middlesex, UB3 4RZ Tel: (020) 8561 5588 Fax: (020) 8561 5599 E-mail: sales@paramountpowders.co.uk *Powder coating distributors & manufrs*

▶ Paramount Precision, Izons Indust Estate, Oldbury Road, West Bromwich, West Midlands, B70 9BS Tel: 0121-553 5553 Fax: 0121-532 0065 E-mail: allan@paramountprecision.fsnet.co.uk *Sub contract machine shop*

Paramount Precision Engineering Ltd, Unit D Wellington CR, New Malden, Surrey, KT3 3NE Tel: (020) 8949 7766 Fax: (020) 8949 0042 E-mail: paramount@technicalwebservices.com *Precision sheet metalworkers & machinists*

▶ Paramount Print Group, Caxton Park, Wright Street, Manchester, M16 9EW Tel: 0161-872 0444 Fax: 0161-872 0514

Paramount Printers Ltd, 199 Causewayside, Edinburgh, EH9 1PH Tel: 0131-667 4441 Fax: 0131-662 0659 E-mail: sales@ourprinters.com *Printers*

▶ Paramount Printing (Hanley) Ltd, Print House, 10 Woodhouse St, Stoke-on-Trent, ST4 1EH Tel: (01782) 413529

▶ Paramount Services Co., PO Box 4739, Reading, RG6 1XA Tel: (0870) 3214801 Fax: (0870) 3214802 E-mail: info@paramount-services.co.uk *Printed circuit board (PCB) & industrial electronics manufrs*

Paramount Steel Fence, Florida Close, Hot Lane Industrial Estate, Stoke-on-Trent, ST6 2DJ Tel: (01782) 833333 Fax: (01782) 832222 E-mail: steelfence@btinternet.com *Palisade fencing & railing manufrs*

Paramount Supplies, 12 Twizel Close, Fingel Drive, Stelnbridge, Milton Keynes, MK13 0TX Tel: (01908) 221141 Fax: (01908) 223212 E-mail: sales@phcleaningsupplies.co.uk *Industrial cleaning equipment suppliers*

Paramount Tools & Fasteners Ltd, Unit 7 Paramount Business Park, Nile Street, Burslem, Stoke-on-Trent, ST6 2BG Tel: (01782) 821444 Fax: (01782) 821777 E-mail: paramtoolandfast@aol.com *Tool & fastener distributors*

▶ Paramount Training Group, 24 High Street, Cheadle, Cheshire, SK8 1AL Tel: 0161-428 8002 *Computer training services*

Parasol Blinds, 134 Magdalen Street, Norwich, NR3 1JD Tel: (01603) 666008 Fax: (01603) 410333 *Sunblind & conservatory blind manufrs*

Paravizion Ltd, 16 Lyndhurst Road, Heswall, Wirral, Merseyside, CH61 0HB Tel: 0151-648 7223 E-mail: ajc@discframe.co.uk *Software developers*

Parbury Brothers Ltd, The Vicarage, Great Wolford, Shipston-On-Stour, Warwickshire, CV36 5NQ Tel: (07973) 696524 E-mail: sales@parbury.co.uk *Specialised stationery*

▶ Parc UK Ltd, Claremont House, 20 North Claremont Street, Glasgow, G3 7LE Tel: 0141-331 2383 Fax: 0141-331 2385

▶ Parcel Net, Unit 23 Mitcham Industrial Estate, Streatham Road, Mitcham, Surrey, CR4 2AP Tel: (020) 8646 6646 Fax: (020) 8648 5227

Parcelcarry.co.uk, 1 Lauderdale, Farnborough, Hampshire, GU14 0RR Tel: (01252) 642986 E-mail: info@parcelcarry.co.uk *Parcelcarry.co.uk a parcel delivery and collection service for the UK. Based in Farnborough, Hampshire, providing an economy parcel service for home and business customers. We provide a very competitive parcel service for eBay sellers, keeping the prices low and therefore attracting more bidders. Online bookings, accepting most major credit cards and PayPal and instant tracking of your parcels.*

Parcelflight.Co.Uk, 96 Manchester Road, Worsley, Manchester, M28 3FU Tel: 0161-975 7700 E-mail: parcelflight@ntlworld.com *UK AND INTERNATIONAL COURIER SERVICE*

Parceline Ltd, Roebuck Lane, Smethwick, West Midlands, B66 1BY Tel: (0845) 9505505 Fax: 0121-500 2646 E-mail: info@parceline.com *UK international express parcel services* Also at: Branches throughout the U.K.

▶ Parcelnet Logistics, Anchor House, Ingleby Road, Bradford, West Yorkshire, BD99 2XG Tel: (01274) 625625

R.C. Pardoe, Hill Farm, Putley, Ledbury, Herefordshire, HR8 2RF Tel: (01531) 670552 Fax: (01531) 670552 E-mail: robertpardoe@aol.com *Hay & straw merchants*

Pareco Fork Trucks Service Ltd, Unit 13 Park Road Industrial Estate, Park Road, Swanley, Kent, BR8 8AH Tel: (01322) 613222 Fax: (01322) 615028 E-mail: sales@pareco.co.uk *Fork lift truck servicing, hire, sales & repairs*

▶ Pareto Law plc, Barfield House, 24-28 Alderley Road, Wilmslow, Cheshire, SK9 1PL Tel: (01625) 255255 Fax: (01625) 255256 E-mail: graduate@paretolaw.co.uk *A UK recruitment company specialising in sourcing and training graduates for high profile sales jobs.*

Parexel International, The Quays, 101- 125 Oxford Road, Uxbridge, Middlesex, UB8 1LZ Tel: (01895) 238000 Fax: (01895) 238494 *Pharmaceutical distributors*

Parfix Equipment Company Ltd, Locksley House, Unit 4 Locksley Business Park, Belfast, BT6 9JD Tel: (028) 9070 6800 Fax: (028) 9070 6801 E-mail: dflood@parfixwholesaledirect.com *Builders merchants*

Parflo Ltd, Huxley Street, Broadheath, Altrincham, Cheshire, WA14 5EL Tel: 0161-928 3579 Fax: 0161-926 8140 *Workwear, footwear & welding accessories manufrs*

Par-Fox Products Ltd, High Street, Golborne, Warrington, WA3 3AN Tel: (01942) 726862 Fax: (01942) 722080 *Plastic products manufrs*

▶ Pargat & Co. Ltd, Birmingham Road, West Bromwich, West Midlands, B71 4JZ Tel: 0121-525 1218 Fax: 0121-525 4843 E-mail: ada@paragat.com *Manufacturing catering equipment*

Pargenta Electrical Co. Ltd, Unit 1 Prospect Row, Dudley, West Midlands, DY2 8SG Tel: (01384) 232380 Fax: (01384) 230620 E-mail: micheal.trinder@btinternet.com *Electrical contractors*

Parglas Ltd, Barton Manor, Bristol, BS2 0RP Tel: 0117-955 2325 Fax: 0117-941 1806 E-mail: parglas@btclick.com *Glass fibre mouldings manufrs*

Parguild Ltd, 41 Lordsmead, Cranfield, Bedford, MK43 0HP Tel: 01234 752299 Fax: 01234 752266 *Computer software, hardware & devel opers services*

Pari Medical Ltd, The Old Sorting Office, Rosemount Avenue, West Byfleet, Surrey, KT14 6LB Tel: (01932) 341122 Fax: (01932) 341134 E-mail: parimedical@compuserve.com *Respiratory equipment*

▶ Parish Chest Ltd, Credvill,, Quakers Road, Perranwell Station, Truro, Cornwall, TR3 7PJ Tel: (01872) 864807 Fax: (01872) 870719 E-mail: forefathers@btconnect.com *The premier online family history & genealogy*

▶ Parish Of East Ham Night Shelter, 292b Barking Road, London, E6 3BA Tel: (020) 8470 0011 Fax: (020) 8586 0185 E-mail: gordonowen1@yahoo.com *Help, support & referrals of Homeless People in Newham. See also: http://websites.uk-plc.net/St%5FBartholomews%5FChurch%5FEAST%5FHAM%5F169282/products/Homeless_in_Newham__What_is_available_and_where.htm*

Parity Computers Ltd, Port Causeway, Bromborough, Wirral, Merseyside, CH62 3PS Tel: 0151-343 0200 Fax: 0151-343 0300 *Computer systems & software development*

Parity Solutions Ltd, Wimbledon Bridge House, 1 Hartfield Road, London, SW19 3RU Tel: (020) 8543 5353 Fax: (020) 8545 6456 E-mail: marketing@parity.co.uk *Business IT services*

Parity Solutions Ltd, Wimbledon Bridge House, 1 Hartfield Road, London, SW19 3RU Tel: (020) 8543 5353 Fax: (020) 8545 6456 E-mail: sales@paritytraining.com *IT training services*

Park, 11 South Street, Havant, Hampshire, PO9 1BU Tel: (023) 9248 8500 Fax: (023) 9248 8501 E-mail: havent@parc-group.com *Recruitment of contract engineers & technicians*

Park Bakery, 45 Queens Road, Weybridge, Surrey, KT13 9UQ Tel: (01932) 847822 Fax: (01932) 849893 *Bakery products*

▶ Park Cake, Bakewell Works, Duckworth Street, Bolton, BL3 4DY Tel: (01204) 61226 Fax: (01204) 660666 *Bakery*

Park Cakes Bakeries Ltd, Ashton Road, Oldham, OL8 2ND Tel: 0161-633 1181 Fax: 0161-626 6199 *Baker wholesale manufrs*

Park Communications Ltd, Lea Mill, Eastway, London, E9 5NU Tel: (020) 8525 6200 Fax: (020) 8525 6201 E-mail: heath.mason@btinternet.com *Colour printers*

Park Computers, 100 Darwen Street, Blackburn, BB2 2AJ Tel: (01254) 696111 Fax: (01254) 696111 E-mail: sales@parkcomputers.co.uk *PC manufrs*

Park Crescent Conference Centre, 229 Great Portland Street, London, W1W 5PN Tel: (020) 7631 8306 Fax: (020) 7631 8307 E-mail: conference@ish.org.uk *Conference centre*

Park Cross Engineering, 33 Moss Lane, Worsley, Manchester, M28 3WD Tel: 0161-799 0660 Fax: 0161-703 8006 E-mail: mail@park-cross.co.uk *Roller makers & plasma hard facing repairers & manufrs*

Park, Davidson & Co., Ltd, 308 The White Studios, Templeton On The Green, Glasgow, G40 1DA Tel: 0141-556 3350 Fax: 0141-556 1212 E-mail: info@patdavidson.co.uk *Ladies fashion wholesalers*

▶ Park Decking Timber, Ercall Park, High Ercall, Telford, Shropshire, TF6 6AU Tel: (01952) 770779 Fax: (01952) 770121 *Timber products manufrs*

Park Display plc, 10 Telford Road, Bicester, Oxfordshire, OX26 4LD Tel: (01869) 245703 Fax: (01869) 249675 E-mail: sales@parkdisplay.co.uk *International exhibition contractors*

Park Electrical Services, Crown Trading Centre, Clayton Road, Hayes, Middlesex, UB3 1DU Tel: (020) 8813 5889 Fax: (020) 8813 5946 E-mail: info@pes-group.co.uk *Industrial switchgear distributors*

Park Engineering, Manor Farm, Manor Road, South Hinksey, Oxford, OX1 5AS Tel: (01865) 327050 Fax: (01865) 327050 *Paint stripping & steel fabricators*

Park Engineering Ltd, Kenwood Road, Stockport, Cheshire, SK5 6PH Tel: 0161-431 8140 Fax: 0161-431 8154 E-mail: sales@parkengineering.co.uk *Precision engineers & jig borers manufrs*

Park Engineering, 20 Surrey Close, Granby Industrial Estate, Weymouth, Dorset, DT4 9TY Tel: (01305) 778420 Fax: (01305) 771401 E-mail: parkengin@aol.com *CNC turning services*

Park Engineering Derby Ltd, 123b Nottingham Road, Derby, DE1 3QP Tel: (01332) 342342 Fax: (01332) 385361 *Steel fabricators*

Park Engineering Wolverhampton Co. Ltd, Portersfield Industrial Estate, Portersfield Road, Cradley Heath, West Midlands, B64 7BW Tel: (01384) 566263 Fax: (01384) 564700 E-mail: neil_roberts@btconnect.com *CNC turned parts manufrs*

Park Glass Supplies Ltd, 139 Kings Road, Kingston upon Thames, Surrey, KT2 5JE Tel: (020) 8546 8737 Fax: (020) 8546 4001 *Glazing contractors & glass suppliers*

Park Hotel, Dunnings Bridge Road, Bootle, Merseyside, L30 6YN Tel: 0151-525 7555 Fax: 0151-525 2481 *Hotel with conference & function facilities*

Park In Heathrow, Bath Road, West Drayton, Middlesex, UB7 0DU Tel: (020) 8759 6611 Fax: (020) 8759 3421 E-mail: sales@lemeridian.com *Conference facilities & hotels*

Park Interiors, 49 Purdeys Industrial Estate, Purdeys Way, Rochford, Essex, SS4 1ND Tel: (01702) 549424 Fax: (01702) 542199 E-mail: paul@parkinteriors.co.uk *Custom built furniture*

Park Lane Flanges & Fittings Ltd, Unit 12A Bluebird Industrial Estate, Park Lane, Wolverhampton, WV10 9QG Tel: (01902) 728400 Fax: (01902) 728600 E-mail: parklaneltd@hotmail.com *Flange & fittings manufrs*

Park Lane Groundworks Ltd, 54 Park Lane, Fen Drayton, Cambridge, CB24 4SW Tel: (01954) 232886 Fax: (01954) 232639 E-mail: enquiries@parklanegroundworks.co.uk *Groundwork contractors*

Park Leisure Ltd, Fairview Indust Park, Brisley Lane, Ruckinge, Ashford, Kent, TN26 2PW Tel: (01233) 733782 Fax: (01233) 733578 E-mail: info@parkleisure.com *Playground equipment*

▶ Park Logistics, Private Road No 4, Colwick Industrial Estate, Nottingham, NG4 2JT Tel: 0115-940 3332 Fax: 0115-940 2728 E-mail: sales@parklogistics.co.uk *Park Logistics based in Nottingham offer solutions to all your logistical needs from Warehousing and Transport to Supply Chain Management.*

Park Mill Extrusions Ltd, 2 Campden Street, Mossley, Ashton-under-Lyne, Lancashire, OL5 9BD Tel: (01457) 835339 Fax: (01457) 838591 E-mail: parkmill88@hotmail.com *Plastic extrusion manufrs*

Park Packaging Ltd, 2 Ashley Drive, Bothwell, Glasgow, G71 8BS Tel: (01698) 801943 Fax: (01698) 801925 E-mail: info@parkpackaging.co.uk *Packaging material & paper merchants*

Park Paints, Head Office, 493 Battersea Park Road, London, SW11 4LW Tel: (020) 7228 0547 Fax: (020) 7924 3927 *Decorators*

Park Pantry, Longstone Business Park, Great Longstone, Bakewell, Derbyshire, DE45 1TD Tel: (01629) 640264 Fax: (01629) 640264 E-mail: parkpantry@btinternet.com *Bakery*

Park Patterns, Overend Road, Corngreaves Trading Estate, Cradley Heath, West Midlands, B64 7DD Tel: (01384) 569962 Fax: (01384) 569962 *Pattern makers*

Park Recruitment Partnership, Webster House, Dudley Road, Tunbridge Wells, Kent, TN1 1LE Tel: (01892) 535351 Fax: (01892) 543020 E-mail: sales@partjobs.com *Sales & management recruitment*

Park Road Commercials, Manchester Road Garage, Blackrod, Bolton, BL6 5RU Tel: (01942) 811017 Fax: (01942) 811017 *Commercial vehicle sales*

Park Rose Ltd, Covert Court Lane, Bridlington, North Humberside, YO15 3QF Tel: (01262) 602823 Fax: (01262) 400202 E-mail: sales@parkrose.fsbusiness.co.uk *Ceramic lamp manufrs*

Park Row Garage Ltd, 61 Hoskins Street, London, SE10 9PB Tel: (020) 8305 0870 Fax: (020) 8305 0870 E-mail: sales@parkrowgarage.co.uk *Motor vehicle repair & restoration services*

Park Scientific Ltd, 24 Low Farm Place, Moulton Park Industrial Estate, Northampton, NN3 6HY Tel: (01604) 646495 Fax: (01604) 648241 E-mail: info@park.com *Laboratory chemical products manufrs*

Park Sheet Metal Co. Ltd, Bayton Road, Exhall, Coventry, CV7 9DJ Tel: (024) 7636 1606 Fax: (024) 7664 4078 E-mail: office@parksheetmetal.co.uk *Sheet metal workers*

Park Street Test Centre, Paynes Yard, Park Street Lane, Park Street, St. Albans, Hertfordshire, AL2 2NE Tel: (01727) 873814 Fax: (01727) 875449 E-mail: parkstreetguns@talk21.com *Gunsmiths*

Park Tonks Ltd, 48 North Road, Great Abington, Cambridge, CB21 6AS Tel: (01223) 891721 Fax: (01223) 893571 E-mail: mail@parktonks.co.uk *Nutritional ingredients importers & exporters*

Park Way Joinery Ltd, Nicholson Road, Ryde, Isle of Wight, PO33 1BE Tel: (01983) 567812 Fax: (01983) 611775 E-mail: parkwayjoinery@btconnect.com *Purpose made joinery manufacturer.*

Park Welding & Fabrication Co. Ltd, Slade Lane, Brighouse, West Yorkshire, HD6 3PP Tel: (01484) 716651 Fax: (01484) 723022 E-mail: sales@parkwelding.co.uk *Metal fabrication service & manufrs*

Park Wire Display Ltd, 63a Hawks Road, Kingston upon Thames, Surrey, KT1 3EF Tel: (020) 8546 8323 *Point of sale units*

▶ Parkburn Ltd, 26 Whistleberry Industrial Park, Hamilton, Lanarkshire, ML3 0ED Tel: (01698) 828957

Parkdale Press, 11-12 Tilley Road, Crowther, Washington, Tyne & Wear, NE38 0AE Tel: 0191-417 8927 Fax: 0191-419 2459 E-mail: parkdale.press@virgin.net *Printer manufrs*

Parke Electrical, 7 Gate Lane, Sutton Coldfield, West Midlands, B73 5TR Tel: 0121-357 3532 Fax: 0121-354 2491 E-mail: parke.electrical@btopenworld.com *DESIGN AND INSTALLATION OF ALL TYPES ELCTRICAL INSTALLATIONS*

S. Parke & Co. Ltd, Station Road, Stalbridge, Sturminster Newton, Dorset, DT10 2RZ Tel: (01963) 363377 Fax: (01963) 363640 E-mail: sales@wmhughes.co.uk *Manufacturers of piano strings*

Parker Air Conditioning Ltd, Gloucester House, Clarence Court, Rushmore Hill, Orpington, Kent, BR6 7LZ Tel: (01689) 858787 Fax: (01689) 858966 E-mail: parker.ac@btinternet.com *Air conditioning contractors*

Parker Ceilings & Partitions Ltd, Park Lane, Laughton, Lewes, East Sussex, BN8 6BP Tel: (01323) 811000 Fax: (01323) 811130 E-mail: parkerceiling@bt-click.com *Interior ceilings & partitions sub-contracted*

Parker Clay Pigeon Traps, Marshland Farm, Middle Drove, St. Johns Fen End, Wisbech, Cambridgeshire, PE14 8JP Tel: (01945) 430465 Fax: (01945) 430465 E-mail: sales@parkertraps.com *Clay pigeon trap manufrs*

▶ Parker & Collinson Ltd, 42 Church Street, Lenton, Nottingham, NG7 2FH Tel: 0115-942 0140 Fax: 0115-942 0917

▶ Parker Contract Cleaning, 141 Banbury Road, Kidlington, Oxfordshire, OX5 1AJ Tel: (01865) 376655 E-mail: benb40@hotmail.com

Parker Dayco, Belfont Trading Estate, Mucklow Hill, Halesowen, West Midlands, B62 8DR Tel: 0121-504 3400 Fax: 0121-550 4274 E-mail: sales@parker.com *Hydraulic connectors & adaptors*

Parker Diving Ltd, A P Valves Building, Water Ma Trout Industrial Estate, Nancegollan, Helston, Cornwall, TR13 0BN Tel: (01326) 561040 Fax: (01326) 573605 E-mail: sales@apvalves.com *Diving equipment manufrs*

Parker Finishing Ltd, The Basement, 31 Eyre St Hill, London, EC1R 5EW Tel: (020) 7713 5660 Fax: 0207 713 6366 *Electroplating*

Parker Foods Ltd, Cams Alders, Redlands Lane, Fareham, Hampshire, PO16 0QH Tel: (01329) 823777 Fax: (01329) 823888 *Liquid egg manufrs*

Parker Furniture, 5 The Crown Centre, Bond Street, Macclesfield, Cheshire, SK11 6QS Tel: (01625) 614396 Fax: (01625) 263632 E-mail: sales@parkerfurniture.co.uk *Kitchen & bedroom furniture manufrs*

▶ Parker Gees, 52 Station Road, Clacton-on-Sea, Essex, CO15 1SP Tel: (01255) 422240 Fax: (01255) 428943 E-mail: sales@parkergees.com *Estate agency, residential sales & property valuers*

Parker Graphics Ltd, Progress House, Erskine Road, London, E17 6RT Tel: (020) 8520 7182 Fax: (020) 8521 7846 *Printing down frame manufrs*

Parker Hannifin plc, Triton Works, Woods Lane, Cradley Heath, West Midlands, B64 7AS Tel: (01384) 566592 Fax: (01384) 567275 *Fluid connectors*

Parker Hannifin plc, 66 Wakefield Road, Ossett, West Yorkshire, WF5 9JS Tel: (01924) 282200 Fax: (01924) 282299 E-mail: Principal Export Areas: Worldwide *Denison Hydraulics is a powerful and respected international supplier of precision hydraulic products. Their products are renowned for quality and reliability in the most demanding applications.* Key factors behind Denison's growth and success are its commitment to supplying a full range of competitively priced products; maintaining its technical expertise through on-going research and training, providing the best level of customer support and service.* Denison Hydraulics is part of Parker Hannifin Ltd, and can offer complete support on any hydraulic application.* Also at: Burgess Hill

Parker Hannifin, Unit A30 Arena Business Centre, Holyrood Close, Poole, Dorset, BH17 7BA Tel: (01202) 606300 Fax: (01202) 606301 E-mail: sales.digiplan@parker.com *At its European locations, the Electromechanical Automation Europe (EME) Divison develops and manufactures components and systems that are used for state-of-the-art Motion Control automation.**Control and drive technology, Human Machine Interfaces and other user interface devices are part of the comprehensive product portfolio, as is a wide range of mechanical components for handling and precision applications.*

Parker Hannifin P.L.C., Arena Business Park, Holyrood Close, Poole, Dorset, BH17 7FJ Tel: (01202) 699000 Fax: (01202) 606301 E-mail: sales.digiplan@parker.com *Automation equipment manufrs*

Parker Hannifin plc, Tachbrook Park Drive, Warwick, CV34 6TU Tel: (01926) 833700 Fax: (01926) 889172 E-mail: epic@parker.com *Motion & control manufrs*

Parker Hannifin Dennison, Unit F1 Sheddingdean Business Centre, Marchants Way, Burgess Hill, West Sussex, RH15 8QY Tel: (01444) 238300 Fax: (01444) 246121 *Manufacturers of hydraulic control systems & hydraulic manifold*

Parker International Ltd, Globe Lane Industrial Estate, Globe Lane, Dukinfield, Cheshire, SK16 4RE Tel: 0161-330 7421 Fax: 0161-339 2653 E-mail: info@parkerinternational.co.uk *Storage services* Also at: London SE16 & Trafford Park

John Parker, The Market, Aberdare, Mid Glamorgan, CF44 7EB Tel: (01685) 875749 Fax: (01685) 875749 *Jewellery engraving & snooker equipment*

John Parker International Ltd, Little Owl Barn, Pedlinge, Hythe, Kent, CT21 4JJ Tel: (01303) 266621 Fax: (01303) 269400 *Horse transporters*

Parker Knoll Cabinets Ltd, London Road, Chipping Norton, Oxfordshire, OX7 5AX Tel: (0870) 7429904 Fax: (0870) 7429906 E-mail: retailsales@parkerknoll.co.uk *Dining room furniture manufrs*

Maurice Parker Ltd, Alfred House, Alfreton Road, Derby, DE21 4AF Tel: (01332) 363422 Fax: (01332) 293455 E-mail: sales@mauriceparker.co.uk *Bathrooms & ceramic tiles distributors*

Parker Mechanical Services, 15 Waverley Drive, Camberley, Surrey, GU15 2DJ Tel: (01276) 65407 Fax: (01276) 65408 *Air conditioning installers*

Parker Merchanting, Unit 1 Block E Larkfield Trading Estate, New Hythe Lane, Aylesford, Kent, ME20 6XQ Tel: (01622) 710863 Fax: (01622) 719222 *Suppliers of personal protective, road works & site equipment*

Parker Merchanting Ltd, Chester Street, Aston, Birmingham, B6 4AE Tel: 0121-503 4500 Fax: 0121-503 4501 E-mail: info.parker@hagemeyer.co.uk *Construction equipment suppliers*

Parker Merchanting Ltd, Cofton Road, Marsh Barton Trading Estate, Exeter, EX2 8QW Tel: (01392) 288900 Fax: (01392) 288901 E-mail: info.parker@hagemeyer.co.uk *Constuction equipment suppliers*

Parker Merchanting Ltd, 730 South Street, Glasgow, G14 0TR Tel: 0141-342 5600 Fax: 0141-342 5601 E-mail: info.parker@hagemeyer.co.uk *Construction equipment suppliers*

Parker Merchanting Ltd, Spitfire Close, Ermine Business Park, Huntingdon, Cambridgeshire, PE29 6YF Tel: (01480) 433335 Fax: (01480) 433409 *Supply goods to the construction industry*

Parker Merchanting Ltd, John O Gaunts Trading Estate, Leeds Road, Rothwell, Leeds, LS26 0DU Tel: 0113-282 2933 Fax: 0113-282 2620 E-mail: info.parker@hagemeyer.co.uk Principal Export Areas: Worldwide *Market leaders in the supply of personal protective equipment,* Also at: Branches throughout the U.K.

Parker Merchanting Ltd, Benfield Road, Newcastle upon Tyne, NE6 5XA Tel: 0191-265 8312 Fax: 0191-276 2509 E-mail: info.parker@hagemeyer.co.uk *Construction equipment suppliers*

Parker Merchanting Ltd, Units 19-20 White Lodge Business Park, Hall Road, Norwich, NR4 6DG Tel: (01603) 763778 Fax: (01603) 763776 E-mail: info.parker@hagemeyer.co.uk *Construction equipment supplier*

Parker Merchanting Ltd, 1-2 Longwall Avenue, Queens Drive Industrial Estate, Nottingham, NG2 1NA Tel: 0115-986 2121 Fax: 0115-986 2509 E-mail: info.parker@hagemeyer.co.uk *Construction equipment suppliers*

Parker Merchanting Ltd, 3 Cowley Business Centre, Watlington Road, Cowley, Oxford, OX4 6NH Tel: (01865) 785700 Fax: (01865) 785777 E-mail: info.parker@hagemeyer.co.uk *Construction equipment supplier*

Parker Merchanting Ltd, Unit 8-9 Seaway Parade Industrial Estate, Port Talbot, West Glamorgan, SA12 7BR Tel: (01639) 813878 Fax: (01639) 823079 E-mail: info.parker@hagemeyer.co.uk *Construction equipment suppliers*

Parker Merchanting Ltd, J Guild Trading Estate, Ribbleton Lane, Preston, PR1 5DP Tel: (01772) 796939 Fax: (01772) 793138 E-mail: info.parker@hagemeyer.co.uk *Construction equipment suppliers*

Parker Merchanting Ltd, Unit 38 South Hampshire Industrial Park, Totton, Southampton, SO40 3SA Tel: (023) 8066 1414 Fax: (023) 8066 1415 E-mail: info.parker@hagemeyer.co.uk *Construction equipment suppliers*

Parker Merchanting, Unit 3, 1 Glen Tye Road, Broadleys Industrial Estate, Stirling, FK7 7LH Tel: (01786) 463921 Fax: (01786) 450089 E-mail: stirling.parker@hagemeyer.co.uk *Supply personal protective equipment, road works & site equipment to the construction industry*

Parker Merchanting Ltd, 4 Horton Industrial Park, Horton Road, West Drayton, Middlesex, UB7 8JD Tel: (01895) 444040 Fax: (01895) 420036 E-mail: info.parker@hagemeyer.co.uk *Suppliers of personal protective equipment*

Parker Merchanting, 2 Page Lane, Widnes, Cheshire, WA8 0AF Tel: 0151-420 7787 Fax: 0151-495 1589 E-mail: info.parker@hagemeyer.co.uk *Personal protection equipment & site equipment suppliers*

Parker Merchanting, Ward Street, Ettingshall, Wolverhampton, WV2 2PJ Tel: (01902) 385066 Fax: (01902) 385060 E-mail: info.parker@hagemeyer.co.uk *Industrial safety equipment distributors*

Parker Merchanting, Unit 2 3, Orbital Centre Southend Road, Woodford Green, Essex, IG8 8HH Tel: (020) 8709 7600 Fax: (020) 8709 7636 E-mail: info.parker@hagemeyer.co.uk *Protective equipment, road works & site equipment*

▶ Parker Networks, 36 Rosemary Avenue, Felixstowe, Suffolk, IP11 9HX Tel: (01394) 276246 E-mail: info@parkernet.co.uk *Parker Networks ~ Independent IT Consultancy * *Parker Networks has almost 20 years experience in IT solutions design, specification and project management, a qualified Microsoft Professional, Prince 2 project manager, Mimesweeper Engineer.**Parker Networks aims to provide an end-to-end IT support system for the smaller business. **Being independent from all major manufacturers enables Parker Networks to give honest and impartial advice on anything from a single PC purchase and help with installation to designing and installing a corporate network for the small business.**Parker Networks who are based in Felixstowe, are aiming to bring the advantages of computer networking to the small business and home office, by installing and configuring either wired or wireless networks which in turn will enable the sharing of printers, Internet access, E-mail and documents. * *Regards Graham Parker*

Parker & Osborn Ltd, 342 Summer Lane, Birmingham, B19 3QL Tel: 0121-359 8222 Fax: 0121-359 8555 E-mail: parkosb@aol.com *Glass processors*

P.R. Parker, Lea Green Farm, Long La, Scorton, Preston, PR3 1DB Tel: (01524) 791397 Fax: (01524) 791397 *Agricultural consultants*

Parker Plant Ltd, PO Box 146, Leicester, LE4 6HD Tel: 0116-266 5999 Fax: 0116-261 0812 E-mail: sales@parkerplant.com *Asphalt plants, crushing & screening plants*

▶ Parker Plant Hire Ltd, East Moors Road, Cardiff, CF24 5EE Tel: (029) 2045 2255 Fax: (029) 2045 2205

Parker Plant Hire Ltd, Glyncoed Terrace, Halfway, Llanelli, Dyfed, SA15 1HQ Tel: (01554) 772431 Fax: (01554) 775457 E-mail: sales@parker-hire.co.uk *Commercial works contractors*

▶ Robert Parker Engravers, Unit 5 & 6, Dunsinane Industrial Estate, Dunsinane Avenue, Dundee, DD2 3QN Tel: (01382) 858666

▶ Parker Robinson Recruitment Ltd, The Imex Business Park, Shobnall Road, Burton-On-Trent, Staffordshire, DE14 2AU Tel: (01283) 543406 Fax: (01283) 519191 E-mail: owen@parkerrobinson.co.uk *Suppliers of clerical, industrial, driving & Catering Staff*

Parker Severn Builders Merchants Ltd, Lillington Road South, Bulwell, Nottingham, NG6 8NG Tel: 0115-927 7412 Fax: 0115-977 1382 *Builders & fencing merchants*

▶ Sophiee Parker, 12 Jupiter House, Calleva Park, Aldermaston, Reading, RG7 8NN Tel: (0800) 0015446 E-mail: sophiee.parker@gmail.com

T.W. Parker Ltd, 90-118 Green Lane, London, N13 5UP Tel: (020) 8888 3477 Fax: (020) 8888 2273 *Timber merchants & moulding manufrs*

Tom Parker Ltd, PO Box 36, Preston, PR1 1HY Tel: (01772) 251405 Fax: (01772) 827088 E-mail: sales@tom-parker.co.uk *Pneumatic & hydraulic component distributors*

V. & F. Parker Ltd, 51 Vyse Street, Hockley, Birmingham, B18 6HS Tel: 0121-554 3587 Fax: 0121-523 2232 *Jewellery distributors & manufrs*

▶ Parker Ward Ltd, 9 College Hill, Shrewsbury, SY1 1LZ Tel: (01743) 242499 Fax: (01743) 242566 E-mail: tim@parker-ward.com *We have developed a range of services to meet organisations marketing communications needs.**> Public Relations - working with the full range of media, from business and trade publications to local and national media.**> Advertising - we identify the best mix of media, print, broadcast or online - suited to your target market.* *> Brand Identity - from simple logo creation through to complete overhaul of your corporate identity.**> Print and design - all printed literature, ranging from several paged brochures to short newsletters and promotional flyers.* *> Copywriting - for all commercial and technical applications.* *> Event management - for product launches, press conferences, promotional events and hospitality.**> Exhibitions - from small portable pop-up displays through to bespoke international exhibition stands.**> Websites - including design, development, hosting, and on-going management with our "Virtual Webmaster" service.*

Parkerfarm Weighing Systems, Titan Works, Bridge Way, Broombank Road, Chesterfield, Derbyshire, S41 9QJ Tel: (01246) 456729 Fax: (01246) 260844 E-mail: sales@parkerfarm.com *Weighing equipment*

▶ Parker-Hannifin plc, Sheddingdean Business Centre, Marchants Way, Burgess Hill, West Sussex, RH15 8QY Tel: (01444) 238300 Fax: (01444) 246121 *Hydraulic equipment & systems*

▶ Parkersell L & E Services Ltd, Unit E4, North Caldeen Road, Coatbridge, Lanarkshire, ML5 4EF Tel: (01236) 440310

Parkersell Lighting, 4th Floor The Connect Centre, Kingstone Crescent, Portsmouth, PO2 8AD Tel: (023) 9262 3700 Fax: (023) 9262 3720 E-mail: enquiries@parkersell.com *Planned lighting & electrical equipment suppliers* Also at: Birmingham, Cardiff, Glasgow, London, Manchester, Newcastle & Plymouth

▶ Parkersell Lighting & Electrical Services Ltd, 40 Old Glamis Road, Dundee, DD3 8JQ Tel: (01382) 832451 Fax: (01382) 813365

▶ Parkersell Lighting & Electrical Services Ltd, 10 Blackchapel Road, Edinburgh, EH15 3QU Tel: 0131-657 1232 Fax: 0131-657 4999

▶ Parkersell Lighting & Electrical Services Ltd, Unit 6 Bridge Industries, Fareham, Hampshire, PO16 8SX Tel: (01329) 231235 Fax: (01329) 288119

▶ Parkersell Lighting & Electrical Services Ltd, 1439 Clock Tower Road, Isleworth, Middlesex, TW7 6DT Tel: (020) 8569 8595 Fax: (020) 8758 9923 *Lighting assembly services*

▶ Parkersell Lighting & Electrical Services Ltd, 17 Shield Drive, Wardley Industrial Estate, Worsley, Manchester, M28 2QB Tel: 0161-727 8205 Fax: 0161-727 7098

▶ Parkersell Lighting & Electrical Services Ltd, Unit 7 Hill La Industrial Estate, Markfield, Leicestershire, LE67 9PN Tel: (01530) 245360 Fax: (01530) 244586

▶ Parkersell (Lighting & Electrical) Services Ltd, 6 Moorview Court, Estover Close, Plymouth, PL6 7PL Tel: (01752) 733295 Fax: (01752) 695436

Parkersell Lighting & Electrical Services Ltd, Unit 24 Heads of The Valley Industrial Estate, Rhymney, Tredegar, Gwent, NP22 5RL Tel: (01685) 844678 Fax: (01685) 844504 *Lighting & electrical service*

Alan Parkes Designs Ltd, Unit 1, Birch Lane Business Park, Birch Lane, Walsall, WS9 0NF Tel: (01543) 682111 *Radiator cabinet manufrs*

Parkes & Billingham Ltd, Peartree Lane, Dudley, West Midlands, DY2 0QW Tel: (01384) 480660 Fax: (01384) 70271 E-mail: parkesandbillingham@office01.fsnet.co.uk *Steel stockholders & slitters*

Parkes Galvanizing Ltd, Marshgate Lane, London, E15 2NQ Tel: (020) 8555 9051 Fax: (020) 8519 8151 E-mail: parkes@wedge-galv.co.uk *Hot dip galvanizing specialists*

Parkes Machine Tools Ltd, Berkswell, Coventry, CV7 7WF Tel: (01676) 530053 Fax: (01676) 530030 E-mail: sales@parkesmachinetools.co.uk *Used power presses/rotary machinery merchant*

▶ Parkes Office & Event Solutions, The Priors, Bedworth, Warwickshire, CV12 9NZ Tel: (024) 7631 6995 Fax: (024) 7675 8822 E-mail: info@parkesoes.com *Business support services*

Parkes Print & Design, 41 Hitchin Street, Biggleswade, Bedfordshire, SG18 8BE Tel: (01767) 603930 Fax: (01767) 603936

Parkett Borse Ltd, 81 Bolton Street, Chorley, Lancashire, PR7 3AG Tel: (01257) 270148 Fax: (01257) 270147 E-mail: info@parkettborse.com *Suppliers & installers of all types of wood flooring*

▶ Parkfield Electronics, 4 Parkfield Avenue, Rose Green, Bognor Regis, West Sussex, PO21 3BW Tel: 01243 261990 Fax: 01243 261990 E-mail: info@parkfieldelectronics.co.uk *Pat testing service*

Parkfield Paper, 1-2 Faraday Close, Drayton Fields Industrial Esta, Daventry, Northamptonshire, NN11 8RD Tel: (0870) 8506661 Fax: (08708) 506662 E-mail: info@parkfieldpaper.co.uk *Suppliers of paper bags & packaging materials*

Parkgate Lettings, 8 Eton Street, Richmond, Surrey, TW9 1EE Tel: (020) 8940 2991 Fax: (020) 8332 2134 E-mail: sales@parkgate-lettings.co.uk *Letting agents & property management consultants*

Parkhead Farms, Maryculter, Aberdeen, AB12 5GL Tel: (01224) 733240 Fax: (01224) 733240 *Agricultural merchants, farmers & contractors*

▶ Parkhead Welding Co. Ltd, 201 Baltic Street, Dalmarnock, Glasgow, G40 3HA Tel: 0141-556 2739 E-mail: enquiries@parkheadwelding.com

Parkhouse Automatics, 34 Commercial Street, Maesteg, Mid Glamorgan, CF34 9DH Tel: (01656) 732403 Fax: (01656) 732478 *Juke boxes & fruit machine hire services*

Parkin International Engineering Services Ltd, Trinity Business Park, Wakefield, West Yorkshire, WF2 8EF Tel: (01924) 331700 Fax: (01924) 331733 E-mail: info@parkingroup.co.uk *Build & design company*

▶ Parking Protection Services Ltd, PO Box 489, Edgware, Middlesex, HA8 9ZR Tel: (0870) 3450310 E-mail: info@parkingprotectionservices.co.uk *Free parking enforcement services*

Parkins of Aylesbury Ltd, Unit 15, Park Street Industrial Estate, Aylesbury, Buckinghamshire, HP20 1EB Tel: (020) 8539 7559 Fax: (01296) 483018 E-mail: orders@postglow.co.uk *Foil blockers & printing services*

Parkins Industrial Supplies, Blundells Road, Tiverton, Devon, EX16 4DA Tel: (01884) 254444 Fax: (01884) 258142 *Industrial suppliers* Also at: Barnstaple, Clyst St. Mary, Plymouth & Taunton

Parkinson Plastics Ltd, Bankwood Lane, New Rossington, Doncaster, South Yorkshire, DN11 0PS Tel: (01302) 864959 Fax: (01302) 864954 *Plastic fabricators & plastic powder coating services*

▶ Parkinsons Electrical, 18 Lealand Way, Boston, Lincolnshire, PE21 7SW Tel: (01205) 367376 Fax: (01205) 310807

Parkinson-Spencer Refractories Ltd, Holmfield, Halifax, West Yorkshire, HX3 6SX Tel: (01422) 254472 Fax: (01422) 254473 E-mail: admin@parkinson-spencer.co.uk *Refractory brick manufrs*

Parkland Engineering Ltd, 72 Dykehead Street, Glasgow, G33 4AQ Tel: 0141-774 6200 Fax: 0141-774 0034 E-mail: glasgowsales@parkland-eng.co.uk *Flexible hose & fittings distributors*

Parkland Engineering, C Roebuck Road, Ilford, Essex, IG6 3TU Tel: (020) 8501 0211 Fax: (020) 8501 0211 *Precision engineers*

Parkland Machines Ltd, 6 Portland Street, Bury, Lancashire, BL9 6EY Tel: 0161-762 9737 Fax: 0161-762 9738 E-mail: sales@parkland-international.com *Slitting, winding & core cutting machines manufrs*

Parkland Products, Owley Farm, Acton Lane, Wittersham, Tenterden, Kent, TN30 7HL Tel: (01797) 270399 Fax: (01797) 270899 E-mail: mapipersonfarms@btconnect.com *Auto feeders*

▶ Parklands UK Ltd, 4 Burnet Close, Hemel Hempstead, Hertfordshire, HP3 9ES Tel: (01442) 400953 Fax: (01442) 400953 E-mail: info@parklands-uk.com *Landscape Maintenance Specialists to Residential Developments - Industrial Parks - Retail Parks - Leisure Parks. SAFEcontractor accredited. Fully insured.**

▶ Parklifeangels, 30 Coronation Road, Clenchwarton, King's Lynn, Norfolk, PE34 4BL Tel: (01553) 760806 E-mail: kimberleyhorsnell53@msn.com *Textiles manufrs*

▶ Parkol Marine Engineering Ltd, Eskside Wharf, Church St, Whitby, North Yorkshire, YO22 4AE Tel: (01947) 602669 E-mail: info@parkol.freeserve.co.uk

Parkside Cabinets & Interiors Ltd, The Old Goods Yard, West Wycombe Road, High Wycombe, Buckinghamshire, HP12 4AH Tel: (01494) 530301 Fax: (01494) 472440 E-mail: worktop@globalnet.co.uk *Kitchen manufrs*

Parkside Group Ltd, 5 Willow Business Centre, 17 Willow Lane, Mitcham, Surrey, CR4 4NX Tel: (020) 8685 9685 Fax: (020) 8646 5096 E-mail: sales@parksidegrp.co.uk *Architectural aluminium stockholders*

Parkside Packaging Ltd, Willenhall Lane, Binley, Coventry, CV3 2AS Tel: (024) 7645 5455 Fax: (024) 7645 6056 E-mail: sales@parkside-pkg.co.uk *With over 70,000 sq.ft. of warehousing and our own fleet of vehicles we can stock & supply all your packaging .... just in time!!! Products we supply include cartons, plain & printed, diecuts & fittings, heavy duty cases, c/w pallets. A comprehensive range of packaging materials from bubblewrap, postal bags and tapes to polythene bags and corrugated rolls. Inhouse gluing and assembly facilities for composite and specialist packs including both cardboard & foam. Distributors for Jiffy Products and Inca Pallets. Litho printed folding cartons, laminated cartons and rigid boxes. We also offer a full graphic and constructional design service. We cover all areas within a 50 mile radius of Coventry including Birmingham, Leicester, Northampton, Warwick, Leamington, Nuneaton,*

continued

Hinckley and Tamworth. Contact us now for a quote or more information

Parkside Steel (Stockholders) Ltd, Waterways Business Centre, Navigation Drive, Enfield, Middlesex, EN3 6JJ Tel: (01992) 703500 Fax: (01992) 719857 *Steel stockholders*

Parkside Warehousing & Transport Co. Ltd, Parkside House, Tomo Industrial Estate, Creeting Road, Stowmarket, Suffolk, IP14 5AY Tel: (01449) 676551 Fax: (01449) 672954 *Warehousing & transport facilities* Also at: Ipswich

▶ Parkstone Removals, Unit 23 Newtown Business Park, Albion Close, Poole, Dorset, BH12 3LL Tel: (01202) 733803 Fax: (01202) 732559

Parksville Plastics, Unit 27-29 Crown Trading Centre, Clayton Road, Hayes, Middlesex, UB3 1DU Tel: (020) 8848 4500 Fax: (020) 8573 9596 *Plastic injection moulders manufrs*

▶ Parkview Private Clinic, 2-4 Lord St West, Blackburn, BB2 1JX Tel: (01254) 59990 Fax: (01254) 59992 E-mail: parkclinics@blackburnmail.com *Park Clinics specialises in a range of non-surgical cosmetic treatments. We at park Clinics are dedicated to providing the highest quality service possible in discreet, comfortable surroundings. We provide the personal touch in a clinical world with friendly, approachable nurses and specialists. **We have the very latest equipment - our Nd:YAG laser will remove tattoos without the scarring previously associated with tattoo removal. Our Ellipse Flex IPL system is a medical grade system used only by clinics and hospitals. It is used to remove unwanted hair, thread veins, pigmentation marks and port wine stains. We offer Restylane, Perlane, Restylane Touch,*Hydrafill and Juvederm injections to soften fine lines and wrinkles and to reshape the lips and facial contours. In addition, we are the only clinic in the area to offer Restylane skin rejuvenation using Restylane Vital.*

Parkview Saddlery, 19 Market Street, Hemsworth, Pontefract, West Yorkshire, WF9 4JY Tel: (01226) 714640 Fax: (01226) 714964 E-mail: parkview.saddlery@btinternet.com *Saddlery & tack suppliers*

Parkway Coach Building, 7 Ballycreely Road, Comber, Newtownards, County Down, BT23 5PX Tel: (07713) 489506 Fax: (028) 9752 8918 *Commercial vehicle body builders*

Parkway Fine Foods, 44 High Street, Pinner, Middlesex, HA5 5PW Tel: (020) 8421 5452 Fax: (020) 8421 5452 E-mail: emporiodomani@aol.com *Food wholesalers*

Parkway Sheet Metal Works Ltd, Rawmarsh Road, Rotherham, South Yorkshire, S60 1RZ Tel: (01709) 374726 Fax: (01709) 829739 *Sheet metalwork fabricators & welding*

▶ Parkway Yorkshire Ltd, South Park Industrial Estate, Wentworth Road, Scunthorpe, South Humberside, DN17 2SY Tel: (01724) 863135 Fax: (01724) 858161

Parkwood Arts Ltd, Staple Ash Lane, Froxfield Green, Petersfield, Hampshire, GU32 1DJ Tel: (01730) 266151 Fax: (01730) 265866 E-mail: sales@parkwood-arts.co.uk *Parkwood is a specialist woodworking company providing a comprehensive in-house design and manufacturing service to supply customers with purpose built bespoke wooden cases fine quality wooden cabinets and storage cases. Parkwood also supplies a CNC Routing service in Alphacam, Cad/Cam designing drawing and programming. They are also able to offer other subcontract wood machining & assembly services. Parkwood are also able to offer precision-engineered wooden component and instrument cases and a range of Gauge Block Cases & cases for delicate electronic components.*

Parkyn Interiors, 2 Bilton Grove Avenue, Harrogate, North Yorkshire, HG1 4HJ Tel: (01423) 563628 *We are Bathroom Fitters in the Harrogate Wetherby Areas*

Parland Engineering Ltd, Unit 7, Cobblestone Court, Hoults Estate, Newcastle upon Tyne, NE6 1AB Tel: 0191-276 6660 *Engineers*

Parlec Engineers, E Syston Centre, Station Road, Kingswood, Bristol, BS15 4GQ Tel: 0117-967 4881 Fax: 0117-960 3800 E-mail: sales@parlec.com *Live & static tooling distributors manufrs*

▶ Parlett & Cordell, Creeches Lane, Walton, Street, Somerset, BA16 9RR Tel: (01458) 446820

Parlex Europe Ltd, Taylor Road, Newport, Isle of Wight, PO30 5LG Tel: (01983) 526535 Fax: (01983) 524964 E-mail: sales@uk.parlex.com *Flexible circuits - interconnectors*

Parlok UK Ltd, Cornwall Street, Parr Industrial Estate, St. Helens, Merseyside, WA9 1PT Tel: (01744) 639191 Fax: (01744) 612870 E-mail: sales@parlok.co.uk *Distributors for trailers, commercial vehicle components & spares*

Parmac Engineering Services Ltd, Cannon Street, Hull, HU2 0AB Tel: (01482) 227200 Fax: (01482) 211849 *Machine tool manufrs*

Parmac Engineers, Broad Street, Long Eaton, Nottingham, NG10 1JH Tel: 0115-972 7679 Fax: 0115-946 8483 *Tubular fabricators*

Arvin Parmar, 23 Queniborough Road, Leicester, LE4 6GW Tel: (07941) 360350 E-mail: agentarvin@hotmail.com *Mortgage & insurance consultant*

▶ Parmar Clothing, 9 Wanlip Street, Leicester, LE1 2JS Tel: 0116-251 5820 *Clothing manufrs*

▶ Parmar Udai & Co., 29 New Way Road, London, NW9 6PL Tel: (020) 8931 0504 E-mail: info@udaiparmar.co.uk *Udai parmar & Co - Accountant Affordable Prices Bookkeeping Audit Start-ups *Taxation Flexible Approach Changing Accountants*

Parmatic Esplen Ltd, Second Avenue, Flixborough Industrial Estate, Scunthorpe, South Humberside, DN15 8SD Tel: (01724) 281202 Fax: (01724) 858365 E-mail: info@parmaticfilter.co.uk *Oily water separating equipment*

Parmavex Services, 17 Perryhill Lane, Oldbury, West Midlands, B68 0AG Tel: 0121-422 9818 Fax: 0121-421 7114 E-mail: contact@parmavex.co.uk *Exporters of spare parts for UK & European construction equipment & diesel engines*

Parmelee Ltd, Middlemore Lane West, Aldridge, Walsall, WS9 8BH Tel: (01922) 457421 Fax: (01922) 473275 E-mail: sales@parmelee-safety.com *Sight spectacle manufrs*

P.J. Parmiter & Sons Ltd, Station Works, Tisbury, Salisbury, SP3 6QZ Tel: (01747) 870821 Fax: (01747) 871171 E-mail: mail@parmiter.co.uk *Agricultural implement manufrs*

Parmley Graham Ltd, Saltmeadows Road, Gateshead, Tyne & Wear, NE8 3BG Tel: 0191-477 4625 Fax: 0191-478 6801 E-mail: hq@parmley-graham.co.uk *Electrical control gear distributors* Also at: Branches throughout the U.K.

Parmley Graham Ltd, Unit 6 Pasadena Close Trading Estate, Hayes, Middlesex, UB3 3NQ Tel: (020) 8848 9667 Fax: (020) 8848 1968 E-mail: london@parmley-graham.co.uk *Factory automation distributors*

▶ Parmley Graham Ltd, 1 Westleigh Business Park, Winchester Avenue, Blaby, Leicester, LE8 4EZ Tel: 0116-277 3783 Fax: 0116-277 5696 E-mail: sales@parmley-graham.co.uk *Control & automation distributors*

Parnaby Cyclones International Ltd, Avenue One, Chilton, Ferryhill, County Durham, DL17 0SH Tel: (01388) 720849 Fax: (01388) 721415 E-mail: enquiries@parnaby.co.uk *Coal preparation plant manufrs*

Parnell Lang Ltd, Copplestone Mills, Copplestone, Crediton, Devon, EX17 5NF Tel: (01363) 84561 Fax: (01363) 84147 E-mail: sales@ernest-charles.com *Bird seed & grass seed manufrs*

▶ Parr Engineering, Unit 22-25 Lodge Farm Business Centre, Wolverton Road, Castlethorpe, Milton Keynes, MK19 7ES Tel: (01908) 510822 Fax: (01908) 510937 *Metal office furniture manufrs*

Joseph Parr (Middlesbrough) Ltd, Blue House Point Road, Portrack Lane Trading Estate, Stockton-On-Tees, Cleveland, TS18 2PJ Tel: (01642) 679381 Fax: (01642) 617222 E-mail: jparrboro@aol.com *Building materials merchants & timber merchants* Also at: Bootle, Edinburgh & Oldham

Parr Sewing Machines, 17 Lower Quest Hills Road, Malvern, Worcestershire, WR14 1RP Tel: (01684) 563106 Fax: (01684) 563106 *Sewing machine repairers*

Parris Wolfe Communications Ltd, Trade Tower, Coral Row, London, SW11 3UF Tel: (020) 7738 1111 Fax: (020) 7738 0111 *Portable cellular telephone agents*

J. Parrish & Son, Stanford Bury, Stanford Road, Shefford, Bedfordshire, SG17 5NS Tel: (01462) 814870 Fax: (01462) 814644 E-mail: info@jparrish.co.uk *Machinery installation & removal*

▶ Parrisianne Ltd, Brighton Road, Lower Kingswood, Kingswood, Tadworth, Surrey, KT20 6SY Tel: (01737) 830007 Fax: (01737) 830199 E-mail: info@parrisianne.com *Sales & technical support union dry-cleaning machines*

Parry & Blockwell Ltd, Magdelene Street, Haverfordwest, Dyfed, SA61 1JJ Tel: (01437) 763129 Fax: (01437) 766713 *Motor body builders*

Parry Bowen, Unit S Chasewater Industrial Estate, Burntwood Business Park, Burntwood, Staffordshire, WS7 3GQ Tel: (01543) 678000 Fax: (01543) 677237 *Curtain walling systems fabricators & subcontractors*

▶ Parry Scragg Ltd, 25-33 Dalrymple Street, Liverpool, L5 5HB Tel: 0151-207 5867 Fax: 0151-207 5868 E-mail: dprawcliffe@msn.com *Tripe, black pudding, savoury ducks & ox tongue processors*

John Parry-Jones Engineering, Unit 8A, Garth Works, Taffs Well, Cardiff, CF15 7YG Tel: (029) 2081 0089 Fax: (029) 2081 0089 *General engineers*

Parry's Signs, Link Industrial Estate, 8 Howsell Road, Malvern, Worcestershire, WR14 1TF Tel: (01684) 892998 Fax: (01684) 572754 E-mail: enquires@parryssigns.co.uk *Sign contractors & suppliers*

Pars Foods Ltd, 8-12 Glentanar Road, Glasgow, G22 7XS Tel: 0141-336 7755 Fax: 0141-336 5522 *Pastry product manufrs*

Pars Office Systems, 57 High Street, Tetsworth, Thame, Oxfordshire, OX9 7BS Tel: (01844) 280100 Fax: (01844) 281373 E-mail: anne@parsoffice.com *Furniture installation & manufrs*

▶ Pars Technology Ltd, 4 Newmarket Court, Kingston, Milton Keynes, MK10 0AQ Tel: (01908) 512000 Fax: (01908) 512038 E-mail: sales@pars.co.uk

Parsia International Ltd, Unit 4 Powergate Business Park, Volt Avenue, London, NW10 6PW Tel: (020) 8453 6580 Fax: (020) 8453 6590 E-mail: sales@parsia.co.uk *Photocopier parts distributors*

Parson & Crosland Ltd, PO Box 10, Middlesbrough, Cleveland, TS2 1HG Tel: (01642) 244161 Fax: (01642) 230487 E-mail: sales@parson-crosland.co.uk *Steel stockholders & processors*

Parsons Brinckerhoff, Quadrant Court, 45 Calthorpe Road, Edgbaston, Birmingham, B15 1TH Tel: 0121-452 7400 Fax: 0121-452 1799 *Consulting engineers*

Parsons Brinckerhoff, 29 Cathedral Road, Cardiff, CF11 9HA Tel: (029) 2082 7000 Fax: (029) 2082 7001 *Marine services*

Parsons Brinckerhoff, Crown House, River Way, Harlow, Essex, CM20 2DL Tel: (01279) 450900 Fax: (01279) 450898 *Consulting engineers*

Parsons Brinckerhoff Ltd, Amber Court, William Armstrong Drive, Newcastle Business Park, Newcastle upon Tyne, NE4 7YQ Tel: 0191-226 1234 Fax: 0191-226 2104 E-mail: pbpower@pbworld.com *Engineering consultants*

▶ Parsons Brinckerhoff, Calyx House, South Road, Taunton, Somerset, TA1 3DU Tel: (01823) 424400 Fax: (01823) 424401 E-mail: slocomben@pbworld.com *Consulting engineers*

Parsons Chain Co., Worcester Road, Stourport-On-Severn, Worcestershire, DY13 9AT Tel: (01299) 827700 Fax: (01299) 872659 E-mail: sales@parsonschain.co.uk *High quality chain manufrs*

Colin Parsons & Sons Ltd, Heywood Bridge, Mucklow Hill, Halesowen, West Midlands, B62 8DL Tel: 0121-550 7531 Fax: 0121-585 5341 *Road transport contractors & waste transfer station*

▶ Parsons Engineering UK, Private Road 3, Colwick Industrial Estate, Nottingham, NG4 2BD Tel: 0115-961 1888 Fax: 0115-961 1777 E-mail: mail@parsonenguk.plus.com *Mould fabrication services*

Parsons Son & Basley, 32 Queens Road, Brighton, BN1 3YE Tel: (01273) 326171 Fax: (01273) 821224 E-mail: property@parsons-son-basley.co.uk *Estate agents & surveyors*

▶ Part P electrical service, Arch 269 Cold Harbour Lane, London, SW9 8SE Tel: 0791 9802057 Fax: 0871 6618109 *Electrical installation testing and certification.*Wiring, re-wiring and up-grades*

Part Time Careers Ltd, 10 Golden Square, London, W1F 9JA Tel: (020) 7437 3103 Fax: (020) 7494 1154 E-mail: parttimecareers@btinternet.com *Employment agency & recruitment (manpower/labour) agencies/consultants/services*

Partco Autoparts Ltd, Redstone Caravan Park, Boston, Lincolnshire, PE21 8AL Tel: (01205) 365984 Fax: (01205) 352716 E-mail: ap.boston.m@unipart.co.uk *Car part sales & refinishing services*

Partco Autoparts Ltd, Unit 11 Gatwick Int Distribution Centre, Cobham Way, Crawley, West Sussex, RH10 9RX Tel: (01293) 524211 Fax: (01293) 518187 *Motor component distributors*

Partco Autoparts Ltd, Ellen Street, Hove, East Sussex, BN3 3LZ Tel: (01273) 779973 Fax: (01273) 326086 E-mail: ap.hove.m/ead/unipart@unipart.com *Motor factor distributors*

Partech Electronics Ltd, Charlestown Road, St. Austell, Cornwall, PL25 3NN Tel: (01726) 879800 Fax: (01726) 879801 E-mail: sales@partech.co.uk *Process control instrument manufrs*

Partex Engineering, 7a Hicks Road, Markyate, St. Albans, Hertfordshire, AL3 8LJ Tel: (01582) 840188 Fax: (01582) 840188 *CNC machining specialists*

Partex Service Ltd, Station Road, Pershore, Worcestershire, WR10 2DB Tel: (01386) 554838 Fax: (01386) 556895 E-mail: partexservice@aol.com *Excavator spare parts distributors*

Particle Measuring Systems Europe Ltd, Grovewood Road, Malvern, Worcestershire, WR14 1XZ Tel: (01684) 581000 Fax: (01684) 560337 E-mail: marketing@pmeasuring.co.uk *Supply particle counters*

▶ Parties Galore, Catriona Crescent, Arnold, Nottingham, NG5 8EN Tel: 0115-956 9143 E-mail: info@partiesgalore.co.uk *Parties Galore is a complete disco & karaoke company offering competitive national rates. With all the latest sounds, big screen and club effect lighting, we are sure to cater for all your requirements. Music genes of R "n" B, Pop, Garage, 70"s-00"s and even the good old Rock "n" Roll.*

Parties-Direct.Com, 45 Gatwick Road, Crawley, West Sussex, RH10 9RD Tel: (01293) 561560 Fax: (01293) 561577 E-mail: sales@parties-direct.com *At Parties-Direct we supply all you need to have a fantastic celebration, whether it's for children or adults, birthdays, anniversaries, or just an excuse to party! If you're fed up with not finding what you want within a theme of your choice, look no further - your search ends here. From Batman to My Little Pony and Rock 'n' Roll to 25th Wedding Anniversary, we can help with everything. Tableware, Banners, Helium & Latex Balloons, Confetti Cannons, Presents, Cards, Wrapping Paper, Pinatas, Loot Bags.........the list is endless and available! For all you arty types, our Craft Shop has an extensive range for both children and adults. Products include Candle Making Kits, Cards, Stamps & Inks, Embellishments, Peel-offs and much more. See for yourself - browse our on-line shop or visit our showroom which has plenty of free parking*

Partington & Co., Fawkham Road, Longfield, Kent, DA3 7QP Tel: (01474) 709299 Fax: (01474) 709295 E-mail: gailpart@aol.com *Hi-fi equipment sales & manufrs*

Partingtons Pies, 294 Manchester Road, Bolton, BL3 2QS Tel: (01204) 521488 *Pie manufrs*

Partitioning Plus Ltd, 342b Farnham Rd, Slough, SL2 1BT Tel: 01753 572373 Fax: 01753 694422 *Internal office refurbishment*

Partitions & Ceilings Ltd, 13 Gloucester Road, London, E11 2ED Tel: (020) 8989 9384 Fax: (020) 8989 2892 E-mail: part.ceilings@ntlworld.com *Dry lining & ceiling contractors*

Partminer UK Ltd, 14 High Street, Leatherhead, Surrey, KT22 8AN Tel: (01372) 379930 Fax: (01372) 384998 E-mail: uk@partminer.com *Electronic components suppliers*

Partnatech, Unit 6, 7 College Park Coldhams Lane, Cambridge, CB1 3HD Tel: (01223) 414419 Fax: (01223) 244177 E-mail: info@partnertech.co.uk *Contract electronic manufacturing*

Partners in Print, Venture Place, 45 Lord Street, Birmingham, B7 4DQ Tel: 0121-359 0202 Fax: 0121-359 5550 E-mail: mail@partnersinprint.co.uk *Printers & designers*

Partners In Training Ltd, 8 Marsden Park, York, YO30 4GX Tel: (01904) 691777 Fax: (01904) 691102 E-mail: info@pint.co.uk *Management training & development*

Partners In Water, Old Forge, Rochford, Tenbury Wells, Worcestershire, WR15 8SP Tel: (01584) 781782 Fax: (01584) 781783 *Industrial water treatment*

▶ Partners Press Ltd, Brunel Drive, Newark Industrial Estate, Newark, Nottinghamshire, NG24 2EG Tel: (01636) 702597

Partnertech Poole Ltd, Turnkey House, 31 Benson Road, Nuffield Industrial Estate, Poole, Dorset, BH17 0RY Tel: (01202) 674333 Fax: (01202) 678028 E-mail: info@hansatech.co.uk *Electronic contract manufacturing & assembly services*

A.J. Parton, Field House Farm, Slindon, Stafford, ST21 6LX Tel: (01782) 791305 Fax: (01782) 791305 *Agricultural contractor*

Parton Fibreglass Ltd, P F G House, Claymore, Tame Valley Industrial Estate, Tamworth, Staffordshire, B77 5DQ Tel: (01827) 261771 Fax: (01827) 261390 E-mail: sales@pfg-tanks.com *Glass fibre tank manufrs*

Partpulse Ltd, Aelred, Ballfield Road, Godalming, Surrey, GU7 2HE Tel: (01483) 419190 Fax: 01483418039 *Computer consultants*

▶ Partrac - Science for Sediment Management, 141 St. James Road, Glasgow, G4 0LT Tel: 0141-303 8255 E-mail: info@partrac.com *Environment consultants services*

Partridge Buildings, 2 Woodland Road, Broadclyst, Exeter, EX5 3LP Tel: (01392) 461771 Fax: (01392) 464352 *Designers & constructors*

Partridge Microdrilling Services, Priestley Way, Crawley, West Sussex, RH10 9NT Tel: (01293) 526525 Fax: (01293) 526525 E-mail: partridrill@aol.com *Subcontract precision small hole drilling of holes from 1.5mm down to 50 microns*

Partridge Plastics Worthing Ltd, G H Northbrook Trading Estate, Northbrook Road, Worthing, West Sussex, BN14 8PN Tel: (01903) 213178 Fax: (01903) 204684 E-mail: sales@partridgeplastics.com *Injection mouldings (plastic) manufrs*

Parts 4 Cars Ltd, 991 Wolverhampton Road, Oldbury, West Midlands, B69 4RJ Tel: 0121-544 4040 Fax: 0121-544 5558 E-mail: info@davidmanners.co.uk *Principal Export Areas: Worldwide Motor vehicle accessories wholesale distributors*

Parts Center, Unit C Tamar Road, Bristol, BS2 0TX Tel: 0117-972 1376 Fax: 0117-977 6399 E-mail: nrs-bristol@climatecentre.co.uk *Refrigeration equipment wholesalers*

Parts Center Commercial, Unit 14, Harp Road, Off Guinness Road, Trafford Park, Manchester, M17 1SR Tel: 0161-848 0546 Fax: 0161-872 0265 *Heating controls & boiler spares distributors*

Parts Centre Ltd, Unit 1A, New Market Business Park, Newmarket, Suffolk, CB8 7ER Tel: (01638) 668341 Fax: (01638) 660014 E-mail: leighnarracott@wolseley.co.uk *Heating spares*

Parts Centre, PO Box 48, Ripon, North Yorkshire, HG4 5NB Tel: (01765) 690690 *Heating & control spares distributors* Also at: Branches throughout the U.K.

Parts Export Ltd, Welham Street, Grantham, Lincolnshire, NG31 6QU Tel: (01476) 560161 Fax: (01476) 566723 E-mail: sales@partsexport.co.uk *Construction equipment exporters*

▶ Parts For Laptops.Com, 88 High Street, Colliers Wood, London, SW19 2BT Tel: (020) 8545 0222 *Computer accessories & consumable suppliers*

Partscale Ltd, 42 Hutton Close, Crowther, Washington, Tyne & Wear, NE38 0AH Tel: 0191-416 3440 Fax: 0191-416 2665 *Hand metal spinners manufrs*

Party Ark Ltd, 4 Winters Bridge Cottages, Portsmouth Road, Thames Ditton, Surrey, KT7 0TB Tel: (020) 8972 9041 *Party Ark sells stylish children"s party supplies, themes, games and accessories throughout the UK and Ireland.*

▶ Party Knights, 7 Stanford Road, Swindon, SN25 2AB Tel: (01793) 702880

▶ Party Pants, 25 Queen Street, Redcar, Cleveland, TS10 1AB Tel: (01642) 515144 Fax: (01642) 805020 E-mail: info@partypants.co.uk *Sale of fancy dress costumes & 60s, 70s clothing*

The Party People, 41 Croydon Road, Beckenham, Kent, BR3 4AB Tel: (020) 8658 1110 Fax: (020) 8658 1548 *Marquee hire*

▶ Party Poppers Balloons, 26 Church Street, Littleborough, Lancashire, OL15 9AA Tel: (01706) 374951 *Cards, gifts & balloon suppliers*

▶ Party Suppliers, Unit 6, Thistle Industrial Estate, Broxburn, West Lothian, EH52 5BB Tel: 01506 863982 E-mail: INFO@PARTYSUPPLIES.CO.UK

▶ Party Supplies, North Kelsey Road, Caistor, Market Rasen, Lincolnshire, LN7 6SF Tel: (01472) 851430 E-mail: info@partysupplies-for-u.co.uk *Party suppliers & toys*

Party Time Ltd, 37 Cartergate, Newark, Nottinghamshire, NG24 1UA Tel: (01636) 611669 Fax: (01636) 615669 E-mail: enquiries@zillionsofchuckles.com *Party entertainment supplier*

Party Time, 51 Bransholme Drive, York, YO30 4XN Tel: (01904) 691991 E-mail: yorkhire@tesco.net *Party balloons suppliers*

▶ Party Wizard, Unit 1c Allenbrooks Way, Wymondham, Norfolk, NR18 0NW Tel: (01953) 605556 E-mail: clive@partywizard.co.uk *On line party supplies & goods*

▶ Partyrama, 73 Garamonde Drive, Wymbush, Milton Keynes, MK8 8DD Tel: (0870) 0420173 Fax: (0870) 0420173 E-mail: admin@partyrama.co.uk *Suppliers party supplies*

▶ Partytime Jewellery, 8 Magnet Road, East Lane Business Park, Wembley, Middlesex, HA9 7RG Tel: 0116-286 6632 Fax: (020) 8904 8802

▶ Partytime Leisure Hire, 51 The Glen, Palacefields, Runcorn, Cheshire, WA7 2TB Tel: (01928) 710136 Fax: (01928) 710136 E-mail: partytimeleisure@tiscali.co.uk *Hire of bouncy castles, sumo suits & bouncy boxing etc*

PartyTimeKids, 2 Apollo Close, Oakhurst, Swindon, SN25 2JB Tel: 07719 570976 E-mail: info@partytimekids.co.uk *Children"s party entertainment, we come to your party and provide the materials and creativity to make it a party to remember. Themes include, princess, pirate, face painting, t-shirt painting, card making, halloween, easter, make-up and many more!*

Parvalux Electric Motors Ltd, 490-492 Wallisdown Road, Bournemouth, BH11 8PU Tel: (01202) 512575 Fax: (01202) 530885 E-mail: sales@parvalux.co.uk *Europe's premier small powered motor and geared motor unit manufacturer. From our range of 5000 stock motors, units can be supplied within 3-5 days. Contact us for more information and take a look at our new web site.*

Parweld Ltd, Alton Works, Long Bank, Bewdley, Worcestershire, DY12 2UJ Tel: (01299) 266800 Fax: (01299) 266900E-mail: info@parweld.co.uk *Welding torch manufrs*

▶ Parwin Heaters UK Ltd, 21 High Haden Road, Glatton, Huntingdon, Cambridgeshire, PE28 5RU Tel: (01487) 834630 Fax: (01487) 830407 E-mail: paul@metalspec.freeserve.co.uk *Manufacturers of green house heaters*

▶ Parwin Heaters UK Ltd, 21 High Haden Road, Glatton, Huntingdon, Cambridgeshire, PE28 5RU Tel: (01487) 834630 Fax: (01487) 830407 E-mail: paul@metalspec.freeserve.co.uk *Horticultural power heater manufrs*

▶ Pas (UK) Ltd, Willow Park Business Centre, 14 Upton Lane, Stoke Golding, Nuneaton, Warwickshire, CV13 6EU Tel: (01455) 213344

▶ Pascal Molliere Photography, 6 Egham Court, Grove Road, Surbiton, Surrey, KT6 4DW Tel: 020 8390 5890 E-mail: pascal@pascalphoto.co.uk *Photography - Portraits, actors headshots, theatre stills, film stills, weddings, portfolio, private commissions, web photography. Black & white, colour, digital or film. Online web album service and discounts available for students. Book now on 077 242948*

Pascal Roll Camber Grinding Ltd, 8 Showell Road, Wolverhampton, WV10 9LU Tel: (01902) 424445 Fax: (01902) 423636 *Precision grinding services*

Pascal Scientific Ltd, 10 Chesterfield Way, Hayes, Middlesex, UB3 3NW Tel: (020) 8848 1849 Fax: (020) 8848 8595 E-mail: admin@pascalscientific.co.uk *Environmental monitoring equipment*

▶ Pasco Spices & Herbs Ltd, Makerfield Way, Ince, Wigan, Lancashire, WN2 2PR Tel: (01942) 493220 Fax: (01942) 826523 E-mail: sales@pascal-spices.co.uk *Manufacturers of food products*

Pascoe Engineering Ltd, 127 Nitshill Road, Glasgow, G53 7TD Tel: 0141-880 6444 Fax: 0141-881 4832 E-mail: info@pascoelimited.com *Toolmakers & injection moulders*

Pascoe's Ltd, Kelleythorpe Industrial Estate, Kellythorpe, Driffield, East Yorkshire, YO25 9DJ Tel: (01377) 252571 Fax: (01377) 252576 E-mail: info@pascoes.co.uk *Manufacturers of animal feed*

Pashley Bicycles, Harrods, 87-135 Brompton Road, London, SW1X 7QN Tel: (020) 7730 1234 Fax: (020) 7581 0470 *Department store*

Pashley Holdings Ltd, Masons Road, Stratford-Upon-Avon, Warwickshire, CV37 9NL Tel: (01789) 292263 Fax: (01789) 414201 E-mail: enquiries@pashley.co.uk *Cycle manufacturers & designers* Also at: Tenbury Wells

▶ Pasquill Roof Trusses Ltd, Grays Road, Uddingston, Glasgow, G71 6ET Tel: (01698) 801560 Fax: (01698) 801570 E-mail: uddingston@pasquill.co.uk *Roof trusses specialists*

▶ Pasquill Roof Trusses Ltd, 3 Dalcross Industrial Estate, Inverness, IV2 7XB Tel: (01667) 462102 Fax: (01667) 462131 E-mail: inv@pasquill.co.uk *Design roof trusses*

Pass Fabrications Ltd, Trent Street, Sheffield, S9 3XU Tel: 0114-244 2276 Fax: 0114-244 2276 *Sheet metalwork engineers & fabricators*

Pass & Co. (St. Albans) Ltd, 37 Thornton Road, Little Heath, Potters Bar, Hertfordshire, EN6 1JJ Tel: (01727) 851172 Fax: (01707) 654327 *Timber preservation & damp proofing*

Passfield Data Systems Ltd, Passfield Business Centre, Lynchborough Road, Passfield, Liphook, Hampshire, GU30 7SB Tel: (01428) 751155 Fax: (01428) 751137 *Computer consultancy*

▶ Passion for Property Ltd, 66 Lower Bridge Street, Chester, CH1 1RU Tel: (01244) 350300 Fax: (01244) 350311 E-mail: info@passionforproperty.com *Estate agents*

▶ The Passion Store, 25 Sunart Way, Hawthorn Common, Nuneaton, Warwickshire, CV10 9TB Tel: 0800 6121069 Fax: 0800 6121068 E-mail: sales@thepassionstore.co.uk

▶ Passionet Ltd, 537 Norwood Road, Entrance 1 Chestnut Road, West Norwood, London, SE27 9DL Tel: 0845 330 9498 Fax: 020 8761 1469 E-mail: info@passionet.net *The UK's largest online black & urban bookseller, selling a 1,000s of titles within A-Z book categories. Passionet.net bring to you all the best sellers, newly released and classic titles that exist in the marketplace through our links in the UK, USA, Caribbean and Africa in order to always offer you a huge selection to pick and choose from. Gift certificates and Gift packages also available.*

Passive Systems Ltd, Unit 8, Caburn Enterprise Park The Broyle, Ringmer, Lewes, East Sussex, BN8 5NP Tel: (01273) 813505 Fax: (01273) 813259 *Alarm services*

Passmores Portable Buildings Ltd, Canal Road, Strood, Rochester, Kent, ME2 4DR Tel: (01634) 290033 Fax: (01634) 290084 E-mail: info@passmores.co.uk *Portable building manufrs*

▶ Pass-n-Bye, 16 Reid Street, Burnbank, Hamilton, Lanarkshire, ML3 0RQ Tel: (01698) 300951 E-mail: info@pass-n-bye.co.uk *Driving Lessons. *Driving Instructor Training.*Part 3 Diagrams*

Past & Present, Faxfleet Hall, Faxfleet, Goole, North Humberside, DN14 7YT Tel: (01430) 449090 *Pine furniture manufrs*

Company Information

Pasta Foods Ltd, Pasteur Road, Great Yarmouth, Norfolk, NR31 0DW Tel: (01493) 656071 Fax: (01493) 653346 E-mail: enquiries@pastafoods.com *Food manufrs*

Pastry World, Unit 2. 173-177 Green Lane Road, Leicester, LE5 4PD Tel: 0116-276 9911 *Puff pastry manufrs*

Pasuda Buildings Ltd, Highfield Lane, Sheffield, S13 9NA Tel: 0114-254 0188 Fax: 0114-254 0705 E-mail: sales@pasuda.co.uk *Portable building hire, leasing & rental*

Pat C G Wilson, Loanleven Farm, Almondbank, Perth, PH1 3NF Tel: (01738) 583370 Fax: (01738) 583546 *Agricultural engineers*

▶ Pat South Wales Ltd, Newport Enterprise Agency, Enterprise Way, Newport, Gwent, NP20 2AQ Tel: (01633) 263655 Fax: (01633) 263655 E-mail: a.johnson@patsouthwales.co.uk *Portable Appliance Testing - Nationwide from £1.19, Materials Handling Equipment, Storage Solutions, Health & Safety Training*

▶ PAT Testing Services Ltd, 148 Uxbridge Road, Ealing, London, W13 8SB Tel: (0800) 4585041 Fax: (020) 8840 1434 E-mail: sales@pattestingservices.com *PAT Testing electronic, fix wire & periodic testing specialists*

▶ Pat Tests R Us, 8 Broomfield, Silver End, Witham, Essex, CM8 3RL Tel: (01376) 585471 E-mail: pat.tests@virgin.net *portable appliance testing at a fixed price. we include most common repairs for free and only carry out pat testing.*

Pataks Foods Ltd, Kiribati Way, Leigh, Lancashire, WN7 5RS Tel: (01942) 267000 Fax: (01942) 267070 E-mail: info.dept@pataksfoods.co.uk *Frozen meal manufrs*

Patay Bucks Castings Ltd, The Ridgeway, Iver, Buckinghamshire, SL0 9HW Tel: (01753) 652126 Fax: (01753) 651330 *Die casting manufrs*

Patcham Joinery, 19-20 Melbourne Street, Brighton, BN2 3LH Tel: (01273) 690138 Fax: (01273) 690138 *Joinery manufrs*

Patchi Ltd, Unit 26, Cariocca Business Park Hellidon Close, Ardwick, Manchester, M12 4AH Tel: 0161-272 7207 Fax: 0161-272 7207 *Mediterranean pastry suppliers*

Patchwork Gallery, 17 Mead Close, Knutsford, Cheshire, WA16 0DU Tel: (01565) 632553 E-mail: sales@patchworkgallery.co.uk *Patch working & quilting supplies*

Patech Solutions Ltd, Tame House, Wellington Crescent, Fradley Park, Lichfield, Staffordshire, WS13 8RZ Tel: (01543) 444707 Fax: (01543) 444709 *Computer programming suppliers*

Patent Ferrule Co. Ltd, 2 Palmers Road, Redditch, Worcestershire, B98 0RF Tel: (01527) 528925 Fax: (01527) 510533 E-mail: sales@patentferrule.co.uk *Metal sawing services*

Patent Filtration Ltd, 10 Chartmoor Road, Leighton Buzzard, Bedfordshire, LU7 4WG Tel: 01525 384858 *Air filter manufrs*

Patera Engineering Ltd, Unit 2a Galveston Grove, Oldfields Business Park, Stoke-on-Trent, ST4 3ES Tel: (01782) 318822 Fax: (01782) 318822 E-mail: pateraeng@cs.com *Industrial conveyor systems manufrs*

Pat'Erns Network UK Ltd, Stephenson Road, Clacton-on-Sea, Essex, CO15 4XA Tel: (01255) 427654 Fax: (01255) 420535 *Timber & sheet material suppliers*

Charles Paterson Search & Selection, 31 Ranelagh Grove, London, SW1W 8PA Tel: (020) 7730 6555 Fax: (020) 7730 6555 E-mail: charles@charlespaterson.com *Management consultants*

▶ Paterson Healthcare Recruitment, 120 Churchill Road, Bicester, Oxon, OX26 4XD Tel: 01869 244610 Fax: 01869 360024 E-mail: training@paterson-healthcare.co.uk *Complete recruitment service for permanent, temporary, locum, medical, health, nursing, child and social care personnel in Oxford, Oxfordshire and Milton Keynes*

J. Paterson, Gaywood Farm, Hole La, Edenbridge, Kent, TN8 6SL Tel: (01732) 864673 Fax: (01732) 864673 *Metal work manufrs*

Paterson J Son Plumbers Ltd, 28 East London Street, Edinburgh, EH7 4BQ Tel: 0131-556 7563 Fax: 0131-557 9080 E-mail: sales@ppservices.co.uk *Heating engineers, plumbing services*

Paterson Timber Ltd, 140 Elliot Street, Glasgow, G3 8EX Tel: 0141-221 6445 Fax: 0141-221 1842 E-mail: info@paterson-timber.com *Timber importers*

▶ Patersons Of Greenoakhill Ltd, Greenoakhill Quarry, Uddingston, Glasgow, G71 7SN Tel: 0141-771 3939 Fax: 0141-773 4248

▶ Patersons Quarrying, Blackwood, Kirkmuirhill, Lanark, ML11 0JQ Tel: (01555) 894134

▶ Patey London Ltd, 1 9 Gowlett Road, London, SE15 4HX Tel: (020) 7635 0030 Fax: (020) 7732 9538 E-mail: sales@pateyhats.com

Path Group plc, 8 Dormer Road, Thame, Oxfordshire, OX9 3UD Tel: (01844) 219000 Fax: (01844) 219099 Principal Export Areas: Worldwide *Hi-fi & audio accessory suppliers*

Path Way, 6 Netherwood Road, London, W14 0BJ Tel: (020) 7603 3393 Fax: (020) 7603 4222 *Computer & tourism training*

Pathdale Systems Ltd, Unit L, Ringstones Indust Estate, Whaley Bridge, High Peak, Derbyshire, SK23 7RX Tel: (01663) 734462 Fax: (01663) 734462 E-mail: sales@pathdale.co.uk *Bespoke electronics & software manufrs*

▶ Pathfinder Technologies UK Ltd, Lancaster Street, Birmingham, B4 7AR Tel: 0121-333 7000 E-mail: sales@pftec.co.uk *Computer system consultants*

Pathfinder Trust, Unit 1, The Candar, Ilfracombe, Devon, EX34 9DS Tel: (01271) 866761 Fax: (01271) 866761 E-mail: info@path-finder.org.uk *Computer trainers*

Pathtrace P.L.C., 45 Boulton Road, Reading, RG2 0NH Tel: 0118-975 6084 Fax: 0118-975 6143 E-mail: enquiry@pathtrace.com *Software development services for the engineering industry*

Pathway Insentives Ltd, 47 Keats Way, Rushden, Northamptonshire, NN10 6EE Tel: (01933) 350244 Fax: (01933) 350255 E-mail: pathway@harryg.freeserve.co.uk *Business gifts & incentives suppliers*

Pathway Workshop, Dunnock Way, Blackbird Leys, Oxford, OX4 7EX Tel: (01865) 714111 Fax: (01865) 715111 *Garden furniture manufrs*

Patio Garden Centres, 100 Tooting Bec Road, London, SW17 8BG Tel: (020) 8672 2251 Fax: (020) 8682 2105 *Garden centre*

▶ Patio Heater Doctor Ltd, 159 Cavendish Street, Ipswich, IP3 8BG Tel: (01473) 735773 Fax: (01473) 738316 E-mail: Lisa.Bean@sierraleisure.co.uk *Maintenance, repair and servicing of all makes of Gas Patio Heaters.*

Patio Paving Centre, unit 7 Batch Indust Est, Rectory Way, Lympsham, Weston-super-Mare, Avon, BS24 0ES Tel: 01934 750010 Fax: 01934 750010 *Patio paving layers*

▶ Patioheaters4u.Com, Thor Industrial Estate, Swindon, SN3 5WZ Tel: (01793) 613900 E-mail: sales@patioheaters4u.com *Specialist patio heaters supplier*

Patman Portable Appliance Testing, 33 Fitzgeorge Avenue, London, W14 0SZ Tel: 020 7603 9214 Fax: 020 7603 5366 E-mail: tom@patman.info *PATMAN provide a professional portable appliance testing service for all types of organisations within a 20 mile radius of London. To ensure that your organisation complies with Health & Safety regulations just ask for PATMAN!*

▶ Patni Express, 127 Milton Avenue, London, E6 1BN Tel: (0870) 9504837 Fax: (0870) 9503897 E-mail: info@patniexpress.com *hundreds of sameday couriers nationwide that can arrange an immediate service at a moments notice.Whether you have business or personal delivery needs. Patni Express is available 24 hours a day 7 days a week. Patni Express is based within easy access to the M25 M11 motorways, A406 A12 A and central London Stansted and London City Airport.We pride ourselves on offering customers throuout United Kingdom cost effective courier solutions, whatever the destination. Would it be a letter to London, an urgent pallet to Manchester or a sample to Glasgow, we have the experience, network and flexibility to react to ANY of your courier requirements within your deadline. Patni Express will not only provide the solutions and the service trouble free, but will ensure you are given informed, impartial and accurate advise to guarantee you the best most proffesional same day courier service.Trained reliable professionals standing by 7 days a week 24 hours a day to assist y*

Patol Ltd, Rectory Road, Padworth Common, Reading, RG7 4JD Tel: 0118-970 1701 Fax: 0118-970 1458 E-mail: sales@patol.co.uk *Fire engineering & security systems*

Paton Brown Ltd, Calico House, Printwork Lane, Manchester, M19 3JP Tel: (0870) 4445501 Fax: (0870) 4445502 E-mail: info@patonbrown.co.uk *Direct mail house*

▶ Paton Electrical, Hydro Garage, Beechgrove, Moffat, Dumfriesshire, DG10 9RU Tel: (01683) 220025

Paton Hawksley Education Ltd, 59 Wellsway, Keynsham, Bristol, BS31 1PG Tel: 0117-986 2364 Fax: 0117-986 8285 *Diffraction grating manufrs & spectroscope manufrs.*

Stewart Paton, Croftnacreich North Kessock, Inverness, IV1 3ZE Tel: (01463) 731204 Fax: (01463) 731204 *Joinery manufrs*

▶ Patricia Taylor, Potter Row, Great Missenden, Buckinghamshire, HP16 9LT Tel: (01494) 868376 Fax: (01494) 868376 E-mail: patriciataylorphotography@yahoo.co.uk *Specialist children''s & family portrait photographer with rural studios. Also informal school photographs in colour or black & white*

Patrick Baxter Furniture, Girdwoodend Farm, Auchengray, Carnwath, Lanark, ML11 8LL Tel: (01501) 785460 Fax: (01501) 785450 *Furniture manufrs*

▶ Patrick Gillooly Ltd, Old Northfield Brickworks, Gray Street, Shotts, Lanarkshire, ML7 5EX Tel: (01501) 820150

John Patrick Engineering Ltd, Merlin Way, Quarry Hill Industrial Park, Ilkeston, Derbyshire, DE7 4RA Tel: 0115-944 0360 Fax: 0115-944 0373 E-mail: info@jpen.co.uk *Engineers & fabricators*

Patrick Pinker Ltd, Latteridge Lane, Iron Acton, Bristol, BS37 9TY Tel: (01454) 228416 Fax: (01454) 228617 E-mail: enquiries@patrickpinker.com *Suppliers of game rearing equipment, drinkers & feeders*

Patrick Stephenson, 47 Horringer Road, Bury St. Edmunds, Suffolk, IP33 2DQ Tel: (01284) 706090 Fax: (01284) 706090 E-mail: enquiries@patrickstephensonarchitects.co.uk *Offers a full range of architectural services throughout Suffolk and East Anglia. Including residential extensions and refurbishment, one-off houses.*

Patrol Jeanswear Ltd, Unit 4, Campbell St, Preston, PR1 5LX Tel: (01772) 653523 Fax: (01772) 655377 *Jeanswear*

Pat's Labels Ltd, 23 Newfield Road, Ash Vale, Aldershot, Hampshire, GU12 5LG Tel: (01252) 545534 Fax: (01252) 524577 *Sticky labels*

Patsystems UK Ltd, 22 Shand Street, London, SE1 2ES Tel: (020) 7940 0490 Fax: (020) 7940 0499 E-mail: info@patsystems.com *Professional automated trading systems*

▶ Pattemores Transport Crewkerne Ltd, Mosterton Road, Misterton, Crewkerne, Somerset, TA18 8NT Tel: (01460) 72046 Fax: (01460) 76435

▶ The Pattern Book Company Ltd, Book House, 39-41 Bull Close Lane, Halifax, West Yorkshire, HX1 2EF Tel: (01422) 353165 Fax: (01422) 380965 *Bespoke manufacturer of pattern books, swatches, waterfall hangers & all types of textile presentation, free advisory service, suppliers of components to in-house pattern rooms & design studios*

Pattern Equipment Co Ltd, 24 Mandervell Road, Oadby, Leicester, LE2 5LQ Tel: 0116-271 3254 Fax: 0116-271 3645 E-mail: sales@pattequip.demon.co.uk *Pattern manufrs*

Pattern Masters Ltd, 9 Norfolk Street, Peterborough, PE1 2NP Tel: (01733) 555171 Fax: (01733) 555191 E-mail: enquiries@patternmasters.co.uk *Textile pattern book manufrs*

Pattern Shop, 27 Offerton Industrial Estate, Hempshaw Lane, Stockport, Cheshire, SK2 5TH Tel: 0161-480 5670 Fax: 0161-480 4565 *Engineers pattern makers*

Patterns Ltd, Darley Abbey Mills, Darley Abbey, Derby, DE22 1DZ Tel: (01332) 342127 Fax: (01332) 298242 E-mail: enquiries@patternsderby.co.uk *Precision engineers & pattern makers*

Patterns & Dies Ltd, Bute Street, Stoke-on-Trent, ST4 3PW Tel: (01782) 343700 Fax: (01782) 343800 E-mail: sales@patterns-dies.co.uk *Engineers pattern makers*

Patterns & Moulds Ltd, Unit D2 Wymeswold Industrial Park, Wymeswold Road, Burton-on-the-Wolds, Loughborough, Leicestershire, LE12 5TY Tel: (01509) 881581 Fax: (01509) 881681 E-mail: info@patternsandmoulds.com *Pattern and mould makers for pre cast concrete and grp products.*Large scale 5 axis cnc machining of tooling for moulds and the marine industry*

Patterson, Unit 17 Baldock Industrial Estate, London Road, Baldock, Hertfordshire, SG7 6NG Tel: (01462) 893022 Fax: (01462) 490076 *Precision engineers*

Patterson Photographic, 51 Thorney Road, Emsworth, Hampshire, PO10 8BL Tel: (01243) 377167 *Photographic equipment repairers*

Patterson Pressings Ltd, Reliance Works, Newpound Common, Wisborough Green, Billingshurst, West Sussex, RH14 0AZ Tel: (01403) 700088 Fax: (01403) 700001 E-mail: r.patterson@patterson.uk.com *Press toolmaking & presswork manufrs*

Patterson & Rothwell Ltd, Mount Pleasant Street, Oldham, OL4 1HH Tel: 0161-621 5000 Fax: 0161-621 5001 E-mail: sales@patterson-rothwell.co.uk *Precision toolmakers & plastic injection moulders*

W.A. Patterson, Unit 34 Muckamore Industrial Estate, Muckamore, Antrim, BT41 4QE Tel: 028 94429090 *General engineers & specialist ring rolling services*

▶ Pattersons Tankers, Woodend House, Woodend Road, Lower Hopton, Mirfield, West Yorkshire, WF14 8QD Tel: (01924) 481850

Pattinson Roofing Co. Ltd, Oak Park East Road Industrial Estate, East Road, Sleaford, Lincolnshire, NG34 7EQ Tel: (01529) 302586 Fax: (01529) 305069 E-mail: brian@pattinsonroofing.co.uk *Roofing contractors*

Pattinson Scientific Services, Scott House, Penn Street, Newcastle upon Tyne, NE4 7BG Tel: 0191-226 1300 Fax: 0191-226 1266 E-mail: pattinsonscientic@btconnect.com *Agricultural chemistry consultants*

Pattison Brick & Cladding Merchants, 10 Batsford Close, Redditch, Worcestershire, B98 7TF Tel: (01527) 853163 Fax: (01527) 853163 E-mail: brickclad@suppanet.com *Brick merchants*

Pattison Eurotech Engineering Ltd, Western Industrial Estate, Caerleon, Newport, NP18 3NN Tel: (01633) 420133 Fax: (01633) 430181 E-mail: office@patteuro.com *Precision & general engineers*

T. Patton Ltd, 588 Lea Bridge Road, Leyton, London, E10 7DN Tel: (020) 8539 1599 Fax: (020) 8558 3578 E-mail: sales@tpatton.co.uk *Plumbing & heating merchants*

Pattonair Ltd, Kingsway Business Park, Forsyth Road, Sheerwater, Woking, Surrey, GU21 5SA Tel: (01483) 774600 Fax: (01483) 774619 E-mail: sales@pattonair.com *Aircraft components & inventory management systems*

Paul Antony, Station Road, Maldon, Essex, CM9 4LQ Tel: (01621) 850058 Fax: (01621) 840219 E-mail: paulantonymirrors@gmail.com

▶ Paul Brant Plumbing & Heating, 4 The Beaver Centre, Putney Road West, Leicester, LE2 7TD Tel: 0116-255 3520 Fax: 0116-255 6755

Paul Cartwright Branding, 53 Park Road, Ramsgate, Kent, CT11 9TL Tel: (0560) 2960506 Fax: 01843 591510 E-mail: info@paulcartwrightbranding.co.uk *Paul Cartwright Branding is a graphic design company based in Ramsgate, Kent. We have over sixteen years'' experience, with a particular focus on retail design and branding. From high street department stores to premium, niche retailers, we have worked on branding and packaging projects across mens/womens and childrens'' fashion, lingerie, homewares and health and beauty sectors. *Projects range from logo design to product and character branding, graphic marketing campaigns, toiletries and cosmetic branding to complete company rebranding including print and online identities.*Paul Cartwright Branding offers a complete design service from concept to final artwork.*Graphic design | Logo design | Stationery design | Packaging design | Product branding *Brochures | Flyers | Posters | Advertisments | Swing tickets | Product packaging*

▶ Paul Darroch FSHAA, 1 Wemyss Place, Edinburgh, EH3 6DH Tel: 0870 143 2273 E-mail: advice@darroch-hearing.co.uk *Hearing Aid Audiologist*

David Paul Construction, The Old Malthouse, Bridgnorth, Shropshire, WV15 5PJ Tel: (01746) 716310 Fax: (01746) 716581 *Construction & groundwork*

Paul & Deanfield, 47 South Molton Street, London, W1K 5RY Tel: (020) 7629 6324 Fax: (020) 7629 6324 *Furriers*

Paul Dentish, Unit E, Roe Cross Industrial Park, Mottram, Hyde, Cheshire, SK14 6NB Tel: (01457) 766304 Fax: (01457) 766305 *Mechanical services engineers*

Paul E Schweder Miller, 46-50 Tabernacle Street, London, EC2A 4SJ Tel: (020) 7490 5000 Fax: (020) 7250 0802 *Broker dealers*

Paul Earl Ltd, 1 Euro Business Park, New Road, Newhaven, East Sussex, BN9 0DQ Tel: (01273) 514356 Fax: (01273) 611036 E-mail: info@paulearl.co.uk *Electrical designers & contractors*

Paul Engineering Co. Ltd, Victoria Works, North Street, Coventry, CV2 3FW Tel: (024) 7645 8040 Fax: (024) 7644 9494 *Precision engineers, induction hardeners & manufrs*

▶ Paul Frampton, 3 Glendinning Avenue, Weymouth, Dorset, DT4 7QF Tel: (01305) 779052

Gary Paul Engineering, 4 Rosewood Park, St. James's Road, Blackburn, BB1 8ET Tel: (01254) 582263 Fax: (01254) 582263 *Gate & railing manufrs*

▶ Paul Gordon, 1 Wakeford Cottages, Selden Lane, Worthing, West Sussex, BN11 2LQ Tel: (01903) 211785 Fax: (01903) 211519 E-mail: info@paulgordon.net *Magic book suppliers*

▶ Paul Harness, 41 Pondfields Drive, Kippax, Leeds, LS25 7HJ Tel: 0113-286 0909 E-mail: sales@paulharness.freeserve.co.uk *Commercial & industrial photographer, with specialities in music, fashion, pr, event & other areas, covering the UK as well as Yorkshire*

▶ Paul Harrison Deliveries, 31 Pool Street, Southport, Merseyside, PR9 8HZ Tel: 07770 727490 Fax: 01704 505151 E-mail: Info@phdeliveries.co.uk *Nationwide Sameday delivery and collection service. document to 1500 kgs.*Competitive, reliable & fully insured including GIT(£20000)*Lwb unmarked dedicated modern Vehicle*

Paul Hett, 2-4 Market Street, Hyde, Cheshire, SK14 1AY Tel: 0161-368 9200 Fax: 0161-368 9200 *Trophy decorators*

▶ Paul Hunt Electrical Installations Ltd, 3 Cherry Street, Warwick, CV34 4LR Tel: (01926) 496664

Paul James Precision Sheet Metal Ltd, Unit B4 Sneyd Hill Industrial Estate, Stoke-on-Trent, ST6 2EB Tel: (01782) 812003 Fax: (01782) 812213 E-mail: pauljamessheetmetal@msn.com *Sheetmetal working to high precision/low tolerances in all materials*

▶ Paul John Construction Leicester Ltd, Telford Way, Stephenson Industrial Estate, Coalville, Leicestershire, LE67 3HE Tel: (01530) 513400 Fax: (01530) 513445

Paul K Sound & Vision, 16 Kings Lea, Adlington, Chorley, Lancashire, PR7 4EN Tel: (01257) 474233 Fax: (01257) 474233 *Sound, lighting & Cctv hire & installation*

▶ Paul Nixon, 7 Holkham Close, Rushmere St. Andrew, Ipswich, IP4 5DW Tel: (01473) 430707 Fax: (01473) 430707 E-mail: paulnixonphotography@ntlworld.com *Photography*

Paul Rhodes Precission Engineering, Walker Street, Scholes, Cleckheaton, West Yorkshire, BD19 6EQ Tel: (01274) 851225 Fax: (01274) 851270 *Precision engineers*

Paul Schoeller U K, Unit 2 70 Partridge Way, Cirencester, Gloucestershire, GL7 1BQ Tel: (01285) 657521 Fax: (01285) 657521 E-mail: sales@schoeller.co.uk *Photographic display products*

Paul Smith Foundation, Riverside Buildings, Riverside Way, Nottingham, NG2 1DP Tel: 0115-986 8877 Fax: 0115-986 2649 *Mens clothing manufrs*

Paul Snape Joinery Manufacturers, Harrison Street, Widnes, Cheshire, WA8 8TN Tel: 0151-423 6692 Fax: 0151-423 0812 *Joinery manufrs*

Paul Spencer Ltd, Consulate House, Sheffield Street, Stockport, Cheshire, SK4 1RU Tel: 0161-477 1688 Fax: 0161-480 4950 E-mail: sales@paulspencersigns.com *Sign manufrs*

Paul Strachan Consulting Ltd, 30 Turfbeg Drive, Forfar, Angus, DD8 3LH Tel: (01307) 460667 Fax: (0870) 420 3597 E-mail: info@strachanconsulting.co.uk *'Did you know energy costs, water charges and telecommunications expenses can make up as much as 25% of an organisation's operating budget? - Energy, Water, Fixed Line and Mobile Telecoms management is what we do best'*

Paul Stuart & Co., 9 Forge Industrial Estate, Greenacres Road, Oldham, OL4 1LE Tel: 0161-620 4129 Fax: 0161-628 4413 *Hydraulic hose & fitting distributors*

Paul Temple Associates Ltd, Laurel Cottage, 15a Hillside Road, Haslemere, Surrey, GU27 3RL Tel: (01428) 656150 Fax: (01428) 642676 E-mail: paul@paultempleassociates.com *We are specialist management consultants who enable clients to achieve performance improvement. We specialise in management development - Exec Coaching, Mgt. Training, Myers Briggs and NLP*

▶ Paul Thompson-Images, 5 Edgewood Drive, Bromborough, Wirral, Merseyside, CH62 6DP Tel: 0151-327 7260 E-mail: sales@paulthompson-images.com *We are a picture library offering high quality world-wide travel images as well as photographic prints and greeting cards of our local area, Liverpool and Wirral*

Paul Usher, 91 Luton Road, Harpenden, Hertfordshire, AL5 3BA Tel: (01582) 766449 Fax: (01582) 765619 E-mail: usherdesign@btinternet.com *Industrial designers*

Paula Rosa, Robell Way, Storrington, Pulborough, West Sussex, RH20 3DS Tel: (01903) 743322 Fax: (01903) 742140 E-mail: info@paularosa.com Principal Export Areas: Asia Pacific & Middle East *Kitchen furniture, unit & worktop manufrs*

▶ Paulcroft Ltd, 38 Norman Road, St. Leonards-on-Sea, East Sussex, TN38 0EJ Tel: (01424) 425796 Fax: (01424) 436412

Pauleys Ltd, Sondes Road, Willowbrook East Industrial Estate, Corby, Northamptonshire, NN17 5XP Tel: (01536) 207200 Fax: (01536) 207201 E-mail: sales@pauleys.co.uk *Pauleys are one of the UK's leading specialist fresh produce companies with 80 years' experience supplying caterers with their daily fresh fruit and vegetables. They stock over 500 lines of fresh*

continued

continuation
produce covering anything from salads, vegetables and fruit, as well as over 150 prepared products aimed at reducing time in the kitchen. They also offer a comprehensive range of dairy products such as cheese, butter and milk as well as dry condiments, such as extra virgin olive oil, cling film and tin foil. Bespoke products also offered to corporate clients.

▶ Pauli Frames, U14 Acton Business Centre, School Road, London, NW10 6TD Tel: (020) 8961 3023 Fax: (020) 8961 3023 E-mail: ricardo@pauliframes.com *Conservation picture frames, restore gilding pick up & deliver*

Pauls Knitwear Co. Ltd, Units 10-14 The Bridge Trading Estate, Bridge St North, Smethwick, West Midlands, B66 2BZ Tel: 0121-525 9595 Fax: 0121-558 7930 *Knitted trimmings & fabric manufrs*

Pauls Malt Ltd, Sidlaw, Burrelton, Blairgowrie, Perthshire, PH13 9PX Tel: 01821 650466 *Grain storage company*

▶ Pauls Malt Ltd, Glenesk Maltings, Kinnaber Road, Hillside, Montrose, Angus, DD10 9EP Tel: (01674) 830253 Fax: (01674) 830377

▶ Pauls Mini Bus, 14 Cross Walk, Bristol, BS14 0RX Tel: (01275) 542422 Fax: (01275) 831476 E-mail: info@paulsminibus.co.uk *16 seater, minibus, minicoach,*mini bus, mini coaches, Bristol based, nights out, holidays, day at the races, LET US DRIVE YOU THERE AND BACK, any place, any time.*

▶ Louis Paulsen, 24 Barwell Business Park, Leatherhead Road, Chessington, Surrey, KT9 2NY Tel: (020) 8397 4400 Fax: (020) 8397 4455 *Lighting manufrs*

Paun Computers, Unit 26 Vernon Mill, Mersey Street, Stockport, Cheshire, SK1 2HX Tel: 0161-429 8855 Fax: 0161-429 8877 *Computer systems*

Pav I T Services plc, King Business Centre, Reeds Lane, Sayers Common, Hassocks, West Sussex, BN6 9LS Tel: (01273) 834000 Fax: (01273) 834631 E-mail: info@pav.co.uk *Computer consultants*

Pave Automation Design & Development Ltd, Padholme Road East, Peterborough, PE1 5XL Tel: (01733) 342519 Fax: (01733) 563500 E-mail: pave@enterprise.net Principal Export Areas: Worldwide *Manufacturers of wire bending machinery*

▶ Pave Aways Ltd, Avenue Mill, Knockin, Oswestry, Shropshire, SY10 8HQ Tel: (01691) 682111 Fax: (01691) 682123

Pave The Way, Stonebridge Farm, Hundon Road, Kedington, Haverhill, Suffolk, CB9 7QT Tel: (01440) 710315 E-mail: sales@pave-the-way.com *Paving slabs manufrs*

Pavecost Manufacturing Ltd, Lilleshall Street, Newport, Gwent, NP19 0FB Tel: (01633) 263986 Fax: (01633) 266939 E-mail: dateelectronicsupp@tiscali.co.uk *Printed circuit assembly production services*

▶ Paveford Holdings Ltd, Units 3 & 4 East Park Industrial Estate, Purbrook Road, Wolverhampton, WV1 2EJ Tel: (01902) 871282 Fax: (01902) 457309

Paver Systems Ltd, Road Meetings Industrial Estate, Carluke, Lanarkshire, ML8 4QG Tel: (01555) 770555 Fax: (01555) 772868 *Concrete manufrs*

A.P. Pavers, Britania House, Goliath Road, Coalville, Leicestershire, LE67 3FT Tel: (01530) 510980 Fax: (01530) 516890 *Plant sales*

Pavilion Estates Ltd, 7 Somerby Road, Pickwell, Melton Mowbray, Leicestershire, LE14 2RA Tel: (01664) 454869 Fax: (01664) 454869 *Property developers*

▶ Pavilion Print Management Ltd, Old Run Road, Leeds, LS10 2AA Tel: 0113 201 6300 E-mail: enquiries@paviliongroup.co.uk *A leading print buying, print outsourcing and print management company. We specialise in Print Room management and printer and copier fleets*

▶ Pavillion Construction, 1 Kingston Workshops, Staverton, Totnes, Devon, TQ9 6AR Tel: (01803) 762729 Fax: (01803) 762284 E-mail: pavillion.construction@btinternet.com *Ground work contractors*

▶ Pavo Steel Specialists Ltd, Unit 10 Albyn Industrial Estate, Broxburn, West Lothian, EH52 6PQ Tel: (01506) 858802 Fax: (01506) 858803 *Structural steel fabricators*

Paw Flying Services Ltd, 8 Hall Lane, Harrogate, North Yorkshire, HG1 3DX Tel: (01423) 560294 Fax: (01423) 560294 *Aviation services*

▶ Pawling Systems, Block 1, Milton Road, Kirkintilloch, Glasgow, G66 1SY Tel: 0141-775 2219 Fax: 0141-775 2239 E-mail: douglas@pawlingsystems.com *Wall Protection, Corner Protection, Door Protection, Handrailing*

▶ Pawprintz, Barnsley BIC, Innovation Way, Barnsley, South Yorkshire, S75 1JL Tel: (01226) 249590 Fax: (01226) 731867 E-mail: info@pawprintz.co.uk *Website design & internet marketing*

PAWS4THOUGHT, 6 PARK COURT, Kidderminster, WORCESTERSHIRE, DY11 6TR Tel: 01562 510290 E-mail: elizabeth.watson63@tesco.net *PAWS4THOUGHT IS A PET & HOUSE SITTING SERVICE, WE ARE AN AFFORDABLE ALTERNATIVE TO KENNELS AND CATTERIES. WE ALSO PROVIDE A DOG AND CAT VISITING SERVICE, AND A DOG WALKING SERVICE. THE AREAS WE COVER ARE WORCESTERSHIRE, SHROPSHIRE & THE WEST MIDLANDS.*

Pawson & Son, 10 Marton Gill, Saltburn-by-the-Sea, Cleveland, TS12 1QU Tel: (01287) 622375 *Joinery manufrs*

▶ Pax Designs, 23 Abbey Close, Tatworth, Chard, Somerset, TA20 2LD Tel: (01460) 220402 E-mail: derek@pax-designs.co.uk *Electronic designers*

▶ Paxar Apparel Group Ltd, Private Road No 1, Colwick Industrial Estate, Nottingham, NG4 2JQ Tel: 0115-989 6500 Fax: 0115-989 6622 E-mail: info@paxar-emea.com *Labelling & identification solutions*

▶ Paxar EMEA HQ, Unit 3-4, Awberry Court, Hatters Lane, Watford, WD18 8PD Tel: 0115-989 6705 Fax: 0115-989 6766 E-mail: info@paxar-emea.com *Clothing labels to pricing guns & label printers to barcodes*

Paxman (Cases) Ltd, 252 Mawney Road, Romford, RM7 8DH Tel: (01708) 766363 Fax: (01708) 766363 *Musical instrument case makers*

Paxton Computers Ltd, 15 Kingsway, Bedford, MK42 9EZ Tel: (01234) 216666 Fax: (01234) 212705 E-mail: info@paxsoft.co.uk *Computer software*

Paxton Home Improvements, Goddards Yard, Thaxted Road, Saffron Walden, Essex, CB11 3AG Tel: (01799) 527542 Fax: (01799) 527541 E-mail: sales@paxtonsonline.com *Home improvements, glazing & glass processing*

Paxton Instruments, Trillium House, 32 New Street, St. Neots, Cambridgeshire, PE19 1AJ Tel: (01480) 356472 Fax: (01480) 356598 *Electronic test equipment distributors*

Paybacs Ltd, 2 Ashleigh Meadow, Tregondale, Liskeard, Cornwall, PL14 3RG Tel: (0845) 0670333 Fax: (01579) 349440 E-mail: info@paybacs.co.uk *Banking software*

Paycare, Paycare House, George Street, Wolverhampton, WV2 4DX Tel: (01902) 371000 Fax: (01902) 371030 E-mail: enquiries@paycare.org *Health care cash benefits insurance* Also at: Leicester & Stoke-on-Trent

▶ Paydirt Productions Ltd, 34 Headlands, Kettering, Northamptonshire, NN15 7HP Tel: (01536) 415347 Fax: (01536) 312535 E-mail: info@paydirtproductions.tv *Paydirt Productions is an approachable video production company.*From storyboard to master, we create everything in-house: 2D/3D animation/graphics, scripting, copy writing, editing, CD/DVD authoring, music composition and 48 track recording.*

▶ Payman Co UK Ltd, 3 Church Street, Frome, Somerset, BA11 1PW Tel: (01373) 453454 Fax: (01373) 461177 E-mail: info@payman.co.uk *Payroll management services, payroll bureau services*

Paymaster Systems Ltd, Moorlands, Oldfield Road, Bromley, BR1 2LE Tel: (020) 8467 6107 Fax: (020) 8467 6121 E-mail: paymaster@btclick.com *Computer systems & software developers*

▶ Payne Associates Ltd, R B R House, Hawksworth Road, Central Park, Telford, Shropshire, TF2 9TU Tel: (01952) 210300 Fax: (01952) 210301 E-mail: ian.payne@payne-associates.co.uk *Established in 1993, Payne Associates Limited is a client-driven, B2B recruitment/resourcing consultancy, specialising in senior and niche IS/IT appointments, and HR consultancy and support services, which include remote or on-site agency/resource management.**Our client base extends from the South Coast to Scotland and we enjoy Preferred Supplier status with an eclectic mix of public and private sector organisations. Our website at www.payne-associates.co.uk features a concise, bullet-pointed analysis of our services and some impressive client testimonials!**Payne Associates Limited is owned and managed by Ian M Payne FREC, who has specialised in executive IS/IT recruitment since 1980. He is a former senior manager and Director's PA with a Top 0 plc and renowned throughout the UK recruitment industry for his honesty, professionalism and ethical conduct.*

▶ Payne Bros East Anglia Ltd, Helhoughton Road, Hempton, Fakenham, Norfolk, NR21 7DY Tel: (01328) 864864 Fax: (01328) 856900 *Fertilizer manufrs*

Payne Bros UK Ltd, 20 Beatrice Street, Warrington, WA4 1DR Tel: (01925) 418180 Fax: (01925) 411717 E-mail: warrington.sales@paynebros.com *National distribution of bar, catering and hygiene equipment and consumables providing a "one stop" service to the licensed, restaurant and hospitality industries.*

Doug Payne Kinetics Ltd, 35 Billesley Lane, Moseley, Birmingham, B13 9QT Tel: 0121-449 1513 Fax: 0121-449 2613 *Safety consultants*

Payne & Gunter Ltd, Twickenham Stadium, Rugby Road, Twickenham, TW1 1DS Tel: (020) 8744 9997 Fax: (020) 8831 7990 E-mail: twickenhamexperience@rfu.com *Room hire & event organising, conference & banqueting services*

▶ Mark Payne, 53 South Coast Road, Peacehaven, East Sussex, BN10 8QW Tel: (01273) 583052 *Vokera boilers serviced and maintained, landlords gas safety inspections Worthing hove brighton eastbourne and hastings*

Payne Pallet Inverters Ltd, Dereham Road, Beeston, King's Lynn, Norfolk, PE32 2NQ Tel: (01328) 700138 Fax: (01328) 701879 E-mail: david@paynepalletinverters.co.uk *Pallet inverter manufrs*

Payne & Pool, 15c Deverill Road Trading Est, Deverill Rd, Sutton Veny, Warminster, Wilts, BA12 7BZ Tel: 01985 840912 *Service & repair agricultural machinery*

Payne & Son Engineers, 26 Bagthorpe Road, East Rudham, King's Lynn, Norfolk, PE31 8RA Tel: (01485) 528269 *Light steel fabrication manufrs*

▶ Payne's Heating & Plumbing Services, Oak Tree Barn, Lewes Road, Blackboys, Uckfield, East Sussex, TN22 5JL Tel: (01825) 891720 Fax: (01825) 891721 E-mail: keith@paynes-heating.co.uk *Suppliers & installers of oil tanks & plumbing & heating services*

▶ Payroll and Accounting (UK) Ltd, 15a High Street, Tunbridge Wells, Kent, TN1 1UT Tel: 01892 548930 Fax: 01892 542685 E-mail: info@pas-uk.com *PAS focuses on specialist outsourced Payroll and Accounting solutions. Our payroll bureau caters for companies with 1-500 employees we offer bookkeeping services for small businesses, and we also provide individual sage training.*We offer exceptional, reasonably priced services that allow confidentiality, flexibility and most importantly enable you to focus on your core business.*

PB Gelatins UK, Severn Road, Treforest Industrial Estate, Pontypridd, Mid Glamorgan, CF37 5SQ Tel: (01443) 849300 Fax: (01443) 844209 *Gelatin manufrs*

Pba Interiors, 119 Chiltern Drive, Surbiton, Surrey, KT5 8LS Tel: (020) 8390 6855 Fax: (020) 8399 0653 *Partitioning & suspended ceiling contractors*

PBL Packaging, 6 Maple Business Park, Walter Street, Birmingham, B7 5ET Tel: 0121-327 7757 Fax: 0121-328 3382 *Packaging material distributors*

PBM.DQS, Wellington Business Centre, Quebec Street, Elland, West Yorkshire, HX5 9AS Tel: (07967) 747030 E-mail: dlmaybank@pbm.co.uk *Suppliers of plastic products*

PBW Metal Products Ltd, Bridge End Mills, Tong Lane, Whitworth, Rochdale, Lancashire, OL12 8BG Tel: (01706) 854354 Fax: (01706) 854330 E-mail: sales@pbwmetal.com *Metal powders manufrs*

▶ PBXports (UK), Unit 15 Pennine Walk, Tunbridge Wells, Kent, TN2 3NN Tel: (01892) 529994 Fax: (0845) 1274904 E-mail: info@pbxports.co.uk *We specialise in the supply of telecommunications equipment, and currently export to many companies all over the world.**We are dealing with PBX systems such as Siemens, Avaya (Lucent), Mitel, Ericsson, Nortel, Alcatel,and many more. We supply complete systems, spare parts and telephone sets for all the above types of telephone system, and can also supply both brand new and refurbished equipment**We are also dealing with GSM and Data Transmission equipment from Ericsson, Nortel, Nokia, Juniper, Cisco, and many others**We are also always interested in finding reliable suppliers, for us to purchase new or second hand equipment from***A new area to our business is the supply of Solar Energy equipment including Solar Panels used in the leisure markets such as those for MotorHomes, Caravans, and Boats/Yachts***Visit our new On Line shop at www.pbxports-shop.co.uk*

▶ PC 2 U, Design Works, William Street, Gateshead, Tyne & Wear, NE10 0JP Tel: 0191-420 5345 Fax: 0191-420 5345 E-mail: sales@pc2u.co.uk

PC 2000, 7 Bridge Street, Dumbarton, G82 1NY Tel: (01389) 739290 Fax: (01389) 726885 E-mail: enquiries@pc2000.co.uk *Computer maintenance & business services*

▶ PC Angells, 11 Tuxford Close, Borehamwood, Hertfordshire, WD6 4LE Tel: (07941) 153532 E-mail: paul@pcangells.co.uk *For all your PC needs, rates just ·28ph. For a personal touch for your personal computer, at rates that won't distress.*

▶ PC Bits & Bytes, 7 Bath Street, Leek, Staffordshire, ST13 6JQ Tel: (01538) 385351 *Computer software providers*

PC Coaching, Innova Park, Kinetic CR, Enfield, Middlesex, EN3 7XH Tel: (020) 8350 4848 Fax: (0845) 6650744 E-mail: sales@pccoaching.com *Computer training*

▶ PC Cure, PO Box 332, Manchester, M16 0NB Tel: 0161-872 5297 Fax: 0870 2203165 E-mail: info@pccure.co.uk *Onsite PC & Mac repairs, support & installation in Manchester & Cheshire. We cater for domestic & business customers on a no fix no fee basis. Free & friendly advice, book an engineer appointment now.*

▶ PC Doctor, 26c London Road, Hertford Heath, Hertford, SG13 7PN Tel: (0870) 7771251 E-mail: enquiries@ukpcdoctor.co.uk *PC DOCTOR is a PC repair service based in Hertford that specialise in*providing a callout engineer to repair, service or upgrade your computer*in your home or office.The engineer will come to your home and repair*your computer at a time that suits you.*

▶ PC Emergency, 2 Sycamore Rise, Berkhamsted, Hertfordshire, HP4 2JZ Tel: (07746) 555729 E-mail: office@pcmrg.com *Computer software suppliers*

PC Express, 185 Washway Road, Sale, Cheshire, M33 4AH Tel: 0161-291 1044 Fax: 0161-291 1077 E-mail: info@pc-xp.com *Installations, maintenance & consumables networking*

▶ PC Flooring (Southern) Ltd, Lake House, Waltham Business Park, Brickyard Road, Swanmore, Southampton, SO32 2SA Tel: (01489) 894332 Fax: (01489) 891392 E-mail: pcf@pc-group.co.uk

▶ PC Friend, Printing Office Street, Doncaster, South Yorkshire, DN1 1TR Tel: (01302) 322486 E-mail: doncaster@pcfriend-online.com *Computer accessory suppliers*

PC Guru, 68 North Drive, Troon, Ayrshire, KA10 7DF Tel: (01292) 311688 E-mail: mark@pcguru-scotland.com *ICT Consultancy *Scotland*

PC Healthcare Ltd, 767 Wimborne Road, Bournemouth, BH9 2BA Tel: (01202) 525952 Fax: (01202) 526843 E-mail: sales@pchealthcare.co.uk *Computer manufacture & repairers*

▶ PC Help Centre, High St South, Dunstable, Bedfordshire, LU6 3HR Tel: (01582) 672606 Fax: (01582) 602508 E-mail: marketing@pchelpcentre.com *PC maintenance & repair service*

▶ PC Home Help, Hillfield, Ringland Circle, Newport, Gwent, NP19 9PL Tel: (01633) 673272 *Computer maintenance & repair services*

▶ PC Media Supplies LTD, Raleigh Road, Newton Abbot, Devon, TQ12 4HH Tel: 0845 4590038 E-mail: info@pcmediasupplies.co.uk *PC Media Supplies Ltd Supplys PC Components and Blank Recordable Media to the uk. Nationwide PC Repair is also available at a reasonable cost please visit the website for more information*

▶ PC Medic - Home PC Repair Service and Computer Sales, The Street, Gosfield, Halstead, Essex, CO9 1TP Tel: (01376) 321684 E-mail: info@pcmedicuk.net *PC Medic - Home PC Repair Service Upgrades and Sales - Computer repairs carried out in your own home or office - New computers custom built PC's - Networking, Wireless Networks*

▶ PC Medik, 66 Valley Gardens, Wallsend, Tyne & Wear, NE28 7HB Tel: (07960) 961593 E-mail: info@pcmedik.co.uk *Computer maintenance, service and repair. IT security specialists.*

▶ PC North, 79 Allhallowgate, Ripon, North Yorkshire, HG4 1LE Tel: (01765) 608400 Fax: (01765) 608400 *Computer repair services & suppliers*

▶ Pc Option Ltd, 19 Ragdale Road, Bulwell, Nottingham, NG6 8GP Tel: (0870) 3501560 Fax: 0115-877 8603E-mail: info@pcoption.co.uk *IT services*

▶ PC Paramedics, 36 Sefton Close, Stoke Poges, Slough, SL2 4LJ Tel: (01753) 645983 *Computer maintenance & repair*

PC Partnership Ltd, 15 Brookfield Road, Bury, Lancashire, BL9 5LA Tel: 0161-763 5976 Fax: 0161-763 7082 E-mail: pcpartnership@btconnect.com *Computer accounting systems*

▶ PC Parts, 28 Sandy Lane, Stockport, Cheshire, SK5 7NZ Tel: 0161-476 1199 Fax: 0161-477 0703 *Computer repair*

▶ PC Payless, 3 Farmfield Road, Bromley, BR1 4NE Tel: (020) 8480 1118

▶ PC Place, 198 High Street, Barnet, Hertfordshire, EN5 5SZ Tel: (020) 8447 5700 Fax: (020) 8447 5711 *Computer suppliers repairs & upgrades*

▶ PC Planet Ltd, Unit 7 Thomas Grant House, 20-28 Watling Street, Fenny Stratford, Milton Keynes, MK2 2BL Tel: (01908) 644500 Fax: (01908) 371148 E-mail: sales@pcplanet.co.uk *Computer components, networking products, systems & software suppliers*

PC Planet, 4 Gateford Road, Worksop, Nottinghamshire, S80 1EB Tel: (01909) 470044 Fax: (0870) 7052609 *Retail computer components*

▶ PC Pricebuster, 65 Devon Road, Wednesbury, West Midlands, WS10 0RT Tel: 0121-531 0065 E-mail: sales@pcpricebuster.co.uk *Supplier of pc accessories, web cams, printers*

PC Repair Centre Ltd, 22 Haydon Place, Guildford, Surrey, GU1 4LL Tel: (01483) 567817 Fax: (01483) 567817 E-mail: pcrepaircentre@yahoo.co.uk *Computer maintenance & repairers*

▶ PC Repair World, Ridyard Street, Little Hulton, Manchester, M38 9NF Tel: 0161-211 1715 E-mail: steven@pcrepairworld.co.uk *PC Repairs, Upgrades and Custom Built computers.*By a qualified Technician.*Hardware & Software*

▶ PC Response, 3 Heathlands Court, Wokingham, Berkshire, RG40 3AY Tel: 01344 761880 E-mail: help@pcresponse.net *We provide a friendly local computer support service for your home or small business, with a fast and professional response at a very affordable price.**With over years of relevant IT experience, we can confidently provide a quality range of services that include:** * Virus, Adware and Spyware removal* * Internet connections, whether dial-up or broadband* * Wireless network setup including correct encryption settings* * Configuration of additional security such as firewalls and Anti-Virus software* * Hard Disk Drive replacement* * CD/DVD drives and writers installed* * Hardware/Software upgrades and installations* * Advice and tuition**We are based in Wokingham, Berkshire, and can travel to local areas such as Reading, Bracknell, Ascot, Camberley.*

▶ PC Restore Ltd, 56 Glenarm Road, London, E5 0LZ Tel: (020) 8525 9795 *East London & Essex, onsite PC & laptop repairs. office networking, Data recovery, website & database developement. visit website to for all pricing.*

▶ PC Southwest Ltd, Unit 6 Bishops Court, Bishops Court Lane, Clyst St. Mary, Exeter, EX5 1DH Tel: (01392) 876600 E-mail: sales@pcsouthwest.co.uk *PC Southwest Ltd, are an IT solutions company who offer local businesses expert unbiased advice and solutions that meet all their IT requirements at a realistic price. These include PC and printer supply, repair and upgrade. Internet, email and Broadband solutions and Network Installation and solutions.*

▶ PC Specialist Ltd, Abbey Road, Huddersfield, HD8 8EL Tel: (0845) 2264036 Fax: (0845) 2264046 *Computer hardware suppliers & retailers*

▶ PC Systems, 19 Borthwick Close, Bransholme, Hull, HU7 5BE Tel: (01482) 827461 Fax: (01482) 827461 E-mail: info@pcsystems-ss.co.uk *All computer software, hardware, networking, cameras distributors*

PC Tech Ltd, 33 Cleveland Street, Normanby, Middlesbrough, Cleveland, TS6 0LT Tel: (01642) 460704 Fax: (01642) 461002 E-mail: sales@pctechcomputers.com *Computer upgrade & repairers*

▶ PC Tech Discount Computers, 55 Station Road, Redcar, Cleveland, TS10 1DT Tel: (01642) 481888 Fax: (01642) 461002 *Computer software services*

PC Tech International Ltd, 25 Loretto Gardens, Harrow, Middlesex, HA3 9LY Tel: (020) 8206 1505 Fax: (020) 8204 4579 *Computer systems & software*

▶ PC Tekit, 25 Churchill Terrace, Barry, South Glamorgan, CF63 2QX Tel: (01446) 405104 *Computer maintenance & repair services*

PC Werth, 45 Nightingale Lane, London, SW12 8SP Tel: (020) 8675 5151 Fax: (020) 8772 2701 E-mail: pcwerth@pcwerth.co.uk *Audiological equipment, hearing aids & noise measurement*

▶ PC Wizards, 97 Gordon Road, Gillingham, Kent, ME7 2NG Tel: (01634) 324188 E-mail: service@thepcwizards.net *PC repair installation services*

PC World, Tollgate West, Stanway, Colchester, CO3 8RG Tel: (0870) 2420444 Fax: (01206) 572969 E-mail: enquiries@pcworld.co.uk *Computer retailer*

continued

PC World, Leeds Road Retail Park, Leeds Road, Huddersfield, HD1 6PF Tel: (0870) 2420444 Fax: (01484) 437302 E-mail: customer.services@pcworld.co.uk *Computers & equipment services & retailers*

PC World, 1 Priory Retail Park, 131 High St Colliers Wood, London, SW19 2PP Tel: (0870) 2420444 Fax: 020 82541201 *Computer retail*

Pca Engineers Ltd, Homer House, Sibthorp Street, Lincoln, LN5 7SL Tel: (01522) 530106 Fax: (01522) 511703 E-mail: sales@pcaeng.co.uk *Computer software*

P-CAD, 3 Sycamore Road, Bournville, Birmingham, B30 2AA Tel: 0121-472 0235 E-mail: paul@bourniville51.freeserve.co.uk *Computer aided design engineers*

▶ Pcbee Computer Maintenance, 156 High Street, Broadstairs, Kent, CT10 1JB Tel: (01843) 604207 Fax: (01843) 604207

▶ PCC plc, Rivington House, 82 Great Eastern Street, London, EC2A 3JF Tel: 0207 749 7318 Fax: 0870 130 0261 E-mail: sales@pcc.plc.uk *Supplier of active pharmaceutical ingredients and excipients.*

▶ PCC Support Ltd, 162 Oundle Road, Thrapston, Kettering, Northamptonshire, NN14 4PQ Tel: (0845) 1662916 Fax: (0870) 7664154 E-mail: sales@pccsystems.co.uk *Computers & applications sellers*

▶ PCEazy Computer Systems, 172 Park Road, Bedworth, Warwickshire, CV12 8LA Tel: (0870) 3834821 E-mail: sales@pceazy.com

PCF Secure Document Systems, Oak House, Langstone Business Park, Langstone Park, Langstone, Newport, Monmouthshire, NP18 2LH Tel: (01633) 415570 Fax: (01633) 415599 E-mail: info@pcf.co.uk *'Headquartered in South Wales, covering the whole of the UK, PCF are the leading independent supplier of secure document systems including: cheque printing solutions, gift vouchers, id cards, barcode based stock control, visitor management software, online survey software, document archiving and accounts forms (invoices etc) laser printing with enveloping. Other security documents available include PIN letters, data mailers, pressure sealed pay forms, and security printed envelopes. '*

▶ PCL Health & Safety Consultants, Suite 401 Langham House, 302-308 Regent Street, London, W1B 3HH Tel: (07793) 815024 E-mail: emma@freesafetycheck.co.uk *Fully Certificated Training at Your premises £195/18 Delegates, courses include: Health and Safety, Manual Handling, DSE and DSE Risk Assessment and Fire Marshal/Fire Warden Training*

Pcme, Clearview Building, Edison Road, St. Ives, Cambridgeshire, PE27 3GH Tel: (01480) 468200 Fax: (01480) 463400 E-mail: sales@pcme.co.uk *Dust control & monitor systems manufrs*

PCMI Signs & Badges, Northern Road, Cosham, Portsmouth, PO6 3EP Tel: (023) 9232 2828 Fax: (023) 9232 2831 E-mail: sign.sales@portsmouthcc.gov.uk *Sign manufacture, installations, interchangeable signs, badges & engraving*

The PCMS Group plc, PCMS House, Torwood Close, Westwood Business Park, Coventry, CV4 8HX Tel: (024) 7669 4455 Fax: (024) 7642 1390 E-mail: mail@pcms-group.co.uk *Computer development & managed services*

Pc-Pos Ltd, Hamilton Close, Basingstoke, Hampshire, RG21 6YT Tel: (01256) 390700 Fax: (01256) 356112 E-mail: sales@pc-pos.co.uk *Over 10 years experience as a Manufacturer & distributor of EPOS hardware for Retail, hospitality & leisure markets. Also distributors of POS printers, scanners, Chip & PIN terminals, displays, keyboards, cash drawers & consumables - and offering additional service tailored to individual's requirements.*

▶ PCR Systems, 92 Langdale Road, Leyland, PR25 3AS Tel: 01772 457327 Fax: 01772 457280 E-mail: info@winfloor.com *Authors and distributors of Winfloor Precast Concrete Flooring Software Solutions for manufacturers of concrete T-beam, hollow-core slab and plate floors. Design, Drawing, Costing and Scheduling of all types od precast concrete floor.*

▶ PCS Ltd, 9-11 Wellington Street, Gateshead, Tyne & Wear, NE8 2AJ Tel: 0191-477 4779 Fax: 0191-477 7929 E-mail: sales@profcom.co.uk *IT & internet security, firewalls, smooth wall partner*

▶ PCS, Unit 60-62 Stephenson Way, Formby Business Park, Formby, Liverpool, L37 8EG Tel: (01704) 879204 Fax: (01704) 879204 E-mail: webdevelopment@pcsflooring.com *Flooring services*

PCS, Wakefield Road, Ossett, West Yorkshire, WF5 9AJ Tel: (01924) 281777 Fax: (01924) 266920 *Resellers of micro systems*

▶ PCS Computers, Unit 50 Elms Business Centre, Main Road, Great Haywood, Stafford, ST18 0ST Tel: (01889) 883091 E-mail: sales@staffordshirelaptopcentre.co.uk *New & refurbished laptop units from £99. spares & accessories, collect/return repair service available. Wireless internet specialists*

▶ PCS Food Group, 5 Bilston Key Industrial Estate, Oxford Street, Bilston, West Midlands, WV14 7DW Tel: (01902) 401230 Fax: (01902) 409906

▶ PCS Industries Ltd, Review House, 35 Websters Way, Rayleigh, Essex, SS6 8JQ Tel: (01268) 777395 Fax: (01268) 777574 E-mail: info@pcs-industries.co.uk *Machine vision systems manufrs*

▶ PCS Printing, PO Box 317, Cheltenham, Gloucestershire, GL51 9SN Tel: (0845) 0569463 E-mail: sales@pcsprinting.co.uk *Supply plastic card printing*

PCs R Us, Drumbrughas North, Lisnaskea, Enniskillen, County Fermanagh, BT92 0PE Tel: (028) 6772 3242 Fax: (028) 6772 3131 E-mail: zubbie75@hotmail.com *Computer services*

▶ PCT Porsche Specialists, Fast Lane Building, A45 Dunchurch Highway, Allesley, Coventry, CV5 9QA Tel: (0845) 6444993 E-mail: info@pctcars.co.uk *Independent servicing, repair, parts & accessory service for porsche*

PD Edenhall Ltd, Danygraig Works, Danygraig Road, Risca, Newport, Gwent, NP11 6DP Tel: (01633) 612671 Fax: (01633) 601280 E-mail: enquiries@pd-edenhall.co.uk *Manufacturers of concrete products*

PD Electronics Ltd, The Old Barn, Woods Lane, Potterspury, Towcester, Northamptonshire, NN12 7PT Tel: (01908) 543150 Fax: (01908) 543139 *Electric control systems manufrs*

▶ PD Limos, New Haugh Farm, Haugh Square, Newhey, Rochdale, Lancashire, OL16 3RG Tel: 01706 880666 Fax: 01706 880666 E-mail: info@pdlimos.co.uk *Cheap limousine hire throughout North West, Limo hire Rochdale Manchester Bury Stockport, We cater for Weddings, Stag Hen Nights, parties, special occasions.*

▶ Pda Electronics Ltd, 7 Bevan Hill, Chesham, Buckinghamshire, HP5 2QS Tel: (01494) 794949 Fax: (01494) 791820 E-mail: info@pdaelectronics.com

▶ PDL Computers, The Barracks, Hillesden, Buckingham, MK18 4DE Tel: (01280) 817743 E-mail: support@pdlcomputers.com *Computer support company for businesses & home users*

PDL Engineering Ltd, 5 Whittle Road, Ferndown Industrial Estate, Wimborne, Dorset, BH21 7RJ Tel: (01202) 871188 Fax: (01202) 892499 *Irrigation equipment manufacturer & dynamic balancing service*

PDM Neptec Ltd, 4-6 Alton Business Centre, Omega Park, Alton, Hampshire, GU34 2YU Tel: (01420) 85848 Fax: (01420) 84288 E-mail: sales@pdmneptec.com *Marine connector & cable assemblies suppliers & manufrs*

PDM Products, 104 Rushlake Road, Brighton, BN1 9AF Tel: (01273) 604691 Fax: (01273) 673238 E-mail: sales@pdmproducts.co.uk *Rubber stamp manufrs*

▶ PDP Design Ltd, 74a Pine Avenue, Gravesend, Kent, DA12 1QZ Tel: (01474) 743334 Fax: 01474 746558 E-mail: mail@pdpdesign.co.uk

▶ PDQ Couriers (York), Netherwindings, Haxby, York, YO32 3FB Tel: (01904) 760180 Fax: (01904) 760180 E-mail: pdqcouriers@fsmail.net *PDQ Couriers offer a range of services from very urgent same day work, to contract work for major road hauliers.Our impressive database of reputable hauliers is testimony to our professionalism and efficiency.All vehicles are fitted with sat nav to maximise efficiency and give you the best possible service.All loads are fully insured and credit facilities are available on request.*

PDQ Direct, Sureline House, Easting Close, Worthing, West Sussex, BN14 8HQ Tel: (01903) 282500 Fax: (01903) 282599 E-mail: sales@pdqdirect.co.uk *Stationery & office suppliers*

PDQ Engineering Ltd, Industrial Road, Hertburn, Washington, Tyne & Wear, NE37 2SA Tel: 0191-417 2343 Fax: 0191-416 5518 E-mail: john@pdqengineering.com *Precision engineers*

▶ PDTS Ltd, 10 Thorlby Road Culcheth, Warrington, WA3 4JU Tel: (07916) 105654 Fax: (01925) 762428 *Recruitment agency*

Pe Systems, Victoria Industrial Estate, Victoria Street, Leigh, Lancashire, WN7 5SE Tel: (01942) 260330 Fax: (01942) 261835 E-mail: sales@pe-systems.co.uk *Battery charger manufrs*

Peacehaven Angler, 135 South Coast Road, Peacehaven, East Sussex, BN10 8PA Tel: (01273) 586000 *Fishing tackle retail*

▶ Peach Data Services P.L.C., Lakeside, Festival Park, Stoke-on-Trent, ST1 5RY Tel: (01782) 267484 Fax: (01782) 267454 E-mail: john.burnett@peachdata.co.uk

Stephen Peachey Agricultural Engineering, Highwood Farm, Main Road, Rookley, Ventnor, Isle Of Wight, PO38 3NH Tel: (01983) 721333 Fax: (01983) 721588 *Agricultural spares & repairs suppliers*

Peachman Refrigeration Ltd, 2 Jupiter Road, Norwich, NR6 6SU Tel: (01603) 789574 Fax: (01603) 789574 E-mail: mail@peachman.co.uk *Refrigeration engineers*

Peacock & Binnington, Old Foundry, Brigg, South Humberside, DN20 8NR Tel: (01652) 600200 Fax: (01652) 657532 E-mail: sales@peacock.co.uk *Agricultural & garden machinery*

Peacock & Binnington, Old Foundry, Brigg, South Humberside, DN20 8NR Tel: (01652) 600200 Fax: (01652) 657532 E-mail: sales@peacock.co.uk *Agricultural machinery distributors* Also at: Corringham, Hatfield, Louth & Market Rasen

Peacock & Binnington, High Street, Corringham, Gainsborough, Lincolnshire, DN21 5QP Tel: (01427) 838696 Fax: (01427) 838411 *Agricultural engineers*

Peacock & Chandler Ltd, 134 Villiers Road, London, NW2 5PU Tel: (020) 8459 0519 Fax: (020) 8451 1049 E-mail: sales@peacockandchandler.com *Beds to specification*

Peacock Joinery, Ranswood Farm, 18 The Common, West Wratting, Cambridge, CB21 5LR Tel: (01223) 290275 Fax: (01223) 290370 *Cabinets suppliers*

Peacock Salt Ltd, North Harbour, North Harbour Street, Ayr, KA8 8AE Tel: (01292) 292000 Fax: (01292) 292001 E-mail: info@peacocksalt.co.uk Principal Export Areas: Worldwide *Salt merchants, road gritting materials & water softening services*

Peacock & Trelfa Ltd, Barfillan Drive, Glasgow, G52 1BQ Tel: 0141-882 5424 Fax: 0141-882 5424 E-mail: john.peacock@btinternet.com *Electroplating services*

Peacock's Medical Group Ltd, Benfield Business Park, Benfield Road, Newcastle upon Tyne, NE6 4NQ Tel: 0191-276 9600 Fax: 0191-276 9696 *Medical suppliers*

Peacock's Medical Group Ltd, Benfield Business Park, Benfield Road, Newcastle upon Tyne, NE6 4NQ Tel: 0191-276 9600 Fax: 0191-276 9696 *Surgical & medical equipment suppliers*

Peacocks Stores Ltd, Atlantic House, Tyndall Street, Cardiff, CF10 4PS Tel: (029) 2027 0000 Fax: (029) 2044 0400 *Departmental stores*

Peak Aquatics Ltd, Ashbourne Road Industrial Estate, Staden Lane, Buxton, Derbyshire, SK17 9SZ Tel: (01298) 24438 Fax: (01298) 27340E-mail: peak@aquatics99.freeserve.co.uk *Aquariums & aquatic products manufrs*

Peak Box Designs Ltd, Unit 1, Ensor Way, New Mills, High Peak, Derbyshire, SK22 4NQ Tel: (01663) 747889 Fax: (01663) 743979 *Solid board carton manufrs*

Peak Communications, Kirklees House, 22 West Park Street, Brighouse, West Yorkshire, HD6 1DU Tel: (01484) 714200 Fax: (01484) 723666 E-mail: sales@peakcom.co.uk *Commercial satellite communications equipment suppliers & manufrs*

▶ Peak Contracts Ltd, 7 Church Street, Hartshorne, Swadlincote, Derbyshire, DE11 7ER Tel: (08451) 566843 Fax: 08451 566843 E-mail: enquiries@peakcontracts.co.uk *General Engineering contractors, design, manufacture and instalation of both mechanical and electrical projects.*Project management to service contracts and maintenance, all from one company.*

Peak Development Ltd, 2 Flanders Industrial Park, Flanders Road, Hedge End, Southampton, SO30 2FZ Tel: (01489) 796979 Fax: (01489) 796798 E-mail: sales@peak-uk.com *Cards for consumer electronics*

Peak Document Solutions, Tapton Park Innovation Centre, Brimington Road, Chesterfield, Derbyshire, S41 0TZ Tel: (01246) 245490 Fax: (01246) 245491 *Designing & writing software*

▶ Peak Health Promotions, 39 Shurnhold, Melksham, Wiltshire, SN12 8DF Tel: (01225) 700997 E-mail: trainenq@peakhealth.firm.org.uk *COSHH assessment consultancy on site inspection & safety audit*

John Peak & Sons, Three Bells, Church Road, Frating, Colchester, CO7 7HE Tel: (01206) 250543 Fax: (01206) 250543 *Agricultural contractors*

▶ Peak Machine Tools, 19 Hallam Grange Crescent, Sheffield, S10 4BA Tel: 0114-230 7122 E-mail: rod@peakmachinetools.co.uk *Suppliers of filter paper*

Peak Pattern Co. Ltd, 31 Staniforth Road, Sheffield, S9 3HB Tel: 0114-244 1812 Fax: 0114-242 6685 *Engineer's pattern makers & steel founders manufrs*

▶ Peak Performance Upvc Installations, 1d Payne Street, Glasgow, G4 0LE Tel: 0141-353 1771 Fax: 0141-353 1996 *Installation specialists in UPVC*

Peak Plastics Ltd, Derwent Business Park, Heage Road, Ripley, Derbyshire, DE5 3GH Tel: (01773) 743152 Fax: (01773) 513478 E-mail: sales@peakplastics.co.uk *Plastic mouldings manufrs*

Peak Precision Engineering Ltd, Alexandra Works, St Annes Road, Manchester, M34 3DY Tel: 0161-303 4800 Fax: 0161-303 4801 *Precision engineers & toolmakers*

Peak Precision Tools Mansfield Ltd, 9 Anglia Way Industrial Estate, Anglia Way, Mansfield, Nottinghamshire, NG18 4LP Tel: (01623) 623993 Fax: (01623) 623993 *Precision toolmakers*

Peak Production Equipment Ltd, Peak House, Works Road, Letchworth Garden City, Hertfordshire, SG6 1GB Tel: (01462) 475605 Fax: (01462) 480294 E-mail: sales@thepeakgroup.com *Test equipment manufrs* Also at: Sunderland

Peak Refrigeration, Unit 3 Cedar Avenue, Talke, Stoke-on-Trent, ST7 1JZ Tel: (01782) 782829 Fax: (01782) 774244 *Refrigeration repairers*

▶ Peak Rock, Unit 30 Drca Business Centre, Charlotte Despard Avenue, London, SW11 5HD Tel: (020) 7498 8444 Fax: (020) 7498 8333 E-mail: sales@peakrock.com *Interior display systems, picture hanging & lighting, cable display systems, exhibition panels & lighting for hire or purchase*

Peak Scientific Instruments Ltd, Fountain Crescent, Inchinnan Business Park, Inchinnan, Renfrew, PA4 9RE Tel: 0141-812 8100 Fax: 0141-812 8200 E-mail: info@peakscientific.com *Gas generators*

Peak Sports Ltd, Unit 4, Ford Street, Brinksway, Stockport, Cheshire, SK3 0BT Tel: 0161-480 2502 Fax: 0161-480 1652 E-mail: sales@peaksports.co.uk *Cricket, lacrosse & hockey fives experts*

Peak Test Services, 152a Front Street, Chester le Street, County Durham, DH3 3AY Tel: 0191-387 1923 Fax: 0191-387 1994 E-mail: peak.test@thepeakgroup.com *Drill bit & test equipment manufrs*

▶ Peak Toolmakers Ltd, Smeckley Wood Close, Chesterfield Trading Estate, Chesterfield, Derbyshire, S41 9PZ Tel: (01246) 268588 Fax: (01246) 268599 E-mail: info@raprecision.com *Manufacturers of injection mould tools*

Peak Transmissions Ltd, Unit 8 Hardwick Court, Hardwick View Road, Holmewood, Chesterfield, Derbyshire, S42 5SA Tel: (01246) 856758 Fax: (01246) 856850 E-mail: sales@peakgroupltd.com *Industrial braking Systems, clutch & coupling, transmission supply*

PeakCooling Solutions Ltd, 9 Kellerr Close, Martland Mill Business Park, Wigan, Lancashire, WN5 0LP Tel: (01942) 223300 Fax: (01942) 218718 E-mail: enquries@peakcoolingsolutions.co.uk *Refrigeration service & sales*

Peake & Son Ltd, Welch Street, Stoke-on-Trent, ST4 4DF Tel: (01782) 847496 Fax: (01782) 847496 E-mail: chris@speakeandson.fsnet.co.uk *Painting & decorating contractors*

Peakmix Concrete, Peak Forest, Buxton, Derbyshire, SK17 8EW Tel: (01298) 23013 *Pre-mix concrete suppliers*

Pear Computing Systems Ltd, The Pentagon Centre, 44 Washington Street, Glasgow, G3 8AZ Tel: 0141-221 3115 Fax: (0870) 2411589 E-mail: enquiries@pearsystems.com *Software developers*

Pearce Construction, Great Western House, Old Station Road, Barnstaple, Devon, EX32 8GW Tel: (01271) 345261 Fax: (01271) 322164 E-mail: buildit@pearcebarnstaple.co.uk *Building contractors* Also at: Bristol

Pearce Display Ltd, Appleton Works, Holmfirth Road, Shepley, Huddersfield, HD8 8BB Tel: (01484) 605458 Fax: (01484) 606031 E-mail: info@pearcedisplays.co.uk *Jewellery display manufrs*

Pearce Engineering, Fishmore Road, Fishmore, Ludlow, Shropshire, SY8 3DP Tel: (01584) 876016 Fax: (01584) 876016 E-mail: sales@pearcecycles.co.uk *Car repair work shop*

Pearce Forecourt Signs Ltd, 456 Margate Road, Broadstairs, Kent, CT10 2PU Tel: (01843) 869585 Fax: (01843) 868340 *Signs manufrs*

H. & C. Pearce & Sons Ltd, Farndon Road, Market Harborough, Leicestershire, LE16 9NP Tel: (01858) 432704 Fax: (01858) 466026 E-mail: info@hcpearce.co.uk *Veterinary medicine & animal health requisites*

H. & C. Pearce & Sons Ltd, Aylesbury Road, Thame, Oxfordshire, OX9 3AS Tel: (01844) 212034 Fax: (01844) 261358 E-mail: info@hcpearce.co.uk *Agricultural requisites*

Pearce Joinery, Alderford Common, Swannington, Norwich, NR9 5NG Tel: (01603) 860856 Fax: (01603) 860856 *Joinery manufrs*

Pearce Pine, 3 The Old Dairy, Culverthorpe, Grantham, Lincolnshire, NG32 3NQ Tel: (01529) 455756 Fax: (01529) 455756 *Pine furniture manufrs*

▶ Pearce Real Kab Co., 24 New Houses, Pantygasseg, Pontypool, Torfaen, NP4 6UH Tel: (01495) 756511 Fax: (01495) 759911 E-mail: mikeyjpearce@hotmail.com *taxi & minibus hire*wheelchair access taxi's*

Pearce Recycling Co. Ltd, 4 Acrewood Way, St. Albans, Hertfordshire, AL4 0JY Tel: (01727) 861522 Fax: (01727) 846428 E-mail: sales@pearce-recycling.co.uk *Recycling services* Also at: Luton & Milton Keynes

Pearce Seeds, Rosedown Farm, Sandford Orcas, Sherborne, Dorset, DT9 4SX Tel: (01935) 811400 Fax: (01935) 816800 *Seed merchant*

Pearce Signs Central, 5 Ninian Park, Ninian Way, Wilnecote, Tamworth, Staffordshire, B77 5ES Tel: (01827) 281555 Fax: (01827) 287555 E-mail: central@pearcegroup.com *Sign manufacturers & installers* Also at: Branches throughout the U.K.

Pearl Assurance plc, The Pearl Centre, Peterborough Business Park, Lynch Wood, Peterborough, PE2 6FY Tel: (0870) 8970028 Fax: (01733) 475141 *Insurance company* Also at: Branches throughout the U.K.

Pearl Building Services, Atlas House, 9 Wheatlands, Farsley, Pudsey, West Yorkshire, LS28 5HH Tel: 0113-255 2877 Fax: 0113-255 2877 *Building contractors*

Pearl Carriers, 123 Aldersgate Street, London, EC1A 4JQ Tel: (020) 7253 3660 Fax: (020) 7608 2512 *Ship brokers*

Pearl Chemicals Ltd, The White House, Darlaston Park, Stone, Staffordshire, ST15 0ND Tel: (01785) 819747 Fax: (01785) 811567 E-mail: g.dee@pearlchem.co.uk *Chemical distributor, agent*

▶ Pearl & Coutts Ltd, 116 Clarence Road, London, E5 8JA Tel: (020) 7843 3788 Fax: (020) 7843 3799 E-mail: enquiries@pearl-coutts.co.uk *Commercial and residential property, offices, shops, flats and apartments to rent in London and surrounding areas. Pearl and Coutts specialises in letting property in the West End and City of London.*

Pearl Products, 2 Manor Trading Estate, Armstrong Road, Benfleet, Essex, SS7 4PW Tel: (01268) 756216 Fax: (01268) 565589 E-mail: info@pearlproducts.co.uk *Manufacturers & distributors automotive*

Pearl Technology Ltd, 34 Cecil Avenue, Barking, Essex, IG11 9TF Tel: (020) 8507 0507 E-mail: pearl@ukenet.com *Internet consultancy*

▶ Pearl UK Ltd, 11 Presley Way, Crownhill, Milton Keynes, MK8 0ES Tel: (01908) 260055 Fax: (01908) 262545 *Musical instruments suppliers*

Pearl Window Systems Ltd, 34 Great Bank Road, Westhoughton, Bolton, BL5 3XU Tel: (01942) 843586 Fax: (01942) 843587 E-mail: info@pearlwindows.co.uk *Window frame manufrs*

Pearlgreen Engineering Ltd, 300 Hawthorn Avenue, Hull, HU3 5LL Tel: (01482) 618441

Pearlpex Sales Ltd, Davis House, 29 Hatton Gardens, London, EC1N 8DA Tel: (020) 7242 3025 Fax: (020) 7405 4933 *Antique jewellery dealers*

▶ The Pearls Company, 1 Thomson Green, Deer Park, Livingston, West Lothian, EH54 8TA Tel: 01506 201327 Fax: 01506 210327 E-mail: info@thepearlscompany.co.uk *We are the UK and International wholesale office of our large Chinese pearl farm and factory. We cultivate, process and produce high quality fresh water loose pearls, pearl strands, finished classical pearl jewelleries including necklace, earrings, rings, bracelets, brooches, cufflinks, and fashion designed and bridal design pearl jewelleries. As we directly import to UK from China, our clients in European countries can benefit from easy logistics (no hassle of importing and taxation), fast delivery and low prices.*

Pearpoint Holdings Ltd, 47 Woolmer Trading Estate, Bordon, Hampshire, GU35 9QE Tel: (01420) 489901 Fax: (01420) 477597 *Camera control systems*

A.R. Pearson & Son, Hilltop Farm, Blankney, Lincoln, LN4 3BH Tel: 01526 378358 *Grain merchants*

Pearson Bros (Engravers) Ltd, Chapel Lane, Halifax, West Yorkshire, HX3 0QN Tel: (01422) 360674 Fax: (01422) 348678 E-mail: sales@pearsonbrothers.co.uk *Rapid*

continued

continuation
turnaround of stainless steel, aluminium and brass nameplates. Normally from order to your hand within four working days.

▶ Pearson & Brunlees Ltd, Colearine Works, Poynton Road, London, N17 9SN Tel: (020) 8808 5220 Fax: (020) 8801 3684

Pearson Eduction Ltd, Edinburgh Gate, Edinburgh Way, Harlow, Essex, CM20 2JE Tel: (01279) 623623 Fax: (01279) 431059 E-mail: sales@pearson.com *Educational publishers* Also at: Edinburgh

Pearson Engineering Services, Wincomblee Road, Newcastle Upon Tyne, NE6 3QS Tel: 0191 2340001 *Steel fabricators*

Pearson Hydraulics Ltd, 11 Cardinal Close, Lincoln, LN2 4SY Tel: (01522) 510777 Fax: (01522) 510508 E-mail: sales@pearson-hyds.co.uk *Hydraulic hose & fittings manufrs*

Pearson Knight, 65 Pitcairn Road, Smethwick, West Midlands, B67 5NE Tel: 0121-429 4396 Fax: 0121-420 1699 *Storage equipment & partitioning*

Pearson Matthews Ltd, 9 Princess Mews, Horace Road, Kingston upon Thames, Surrey, KT1 2SZ Tel: (020) 8547 0470 Fax: (020) 8547 0123 E-mail: design@pearsonmatthews.com *Product designers*

Pearson Panke Equipment Ltd, 1 3 Halegrove Gardens, Mill Hill, London, NW7 3LR Tel: (020) 8959 3232 Fax: (020) 8959 5613 E-mail: sales@pearsonpanke.co.uk *Metal forming machinery distributors*

▶ Pearson Print Ltd, 337 Manchester Road, Denton, Manchester, M34 3QN Tel: 0161-335 0055 Fax: 0161-335 0066

Pearson Production Systems Ltd, Stargate Industrial Estate, Ryton, Tyne & Wear, NE40 3EX Tel: 0191-413 8080 Fax: 0191-413 8822 *Hydraulic machine repair services*

Pearson Profilers, Skippers Lane, Skippers Lane Industrial Estate, Middlesbrough, Cleveland, TS6 6HA Tel: (01642) 466566 Fax: (01642) 466299 E-mail: sales@pearsonprofilers.co.uk *Profile cutting & stockholders*

Richard Pearson Ltd, Priory Road, Freiston, Boston, Lincolnshire, PE22 0JZ Tel: (01205) 760383 Fax: (01205) 761064 E-mail: info@richardpearson.com *Agricultural machinery manufrs* Also at: St. Saviour

Pearsons Bed & Linen Centre, 238 High Road, Loughton, Essex, IG10 1RB Tel: (020) 8502 3949 Fax: (020) 8502 3949 *Beds & linens retailers*

Pearsons Glass Ltd, 9-11 Maddrell Street, Liverpool, L3 7EH Tel: 0151-207 2874 Fax: 0151-207 2110 E-mail: info@pearsonsglass.co.uk *Glass & mirror merchants*

Pearsons Packages Ltd, Benington Road, Butterwick, Boston, Lincolnshire, PE22 0EX Tel: (01205) 760755 Fax: (01205) 761080 *Agricultural wooden box manufrs*

Pearsons Professional Services Ltd, Rushton House, Nantwich Road, Audley, Stoke-on-Trent, ST7 8DL Tel: (01782) 720753 Fax: (01782) 720798 E-mail: ppsltd@a-b.co.uk *Computer consultants & expert forensic witness services*

Pearton Tooling Ltd, Unit 8 Manor Way, Old Woking, Woking, Surrey, GU22 9JY Tel: (01483) 773648 Fax: (01483) 756639 E-mail: pearton@pearton.com *Plastic mould toolmakers*

Peartree Engine & Clutch Centre, 1 Peartree Farm, Welwyn Garden City, Hertfordshire, AL7 3UW Tel: (01707) 322026 Fax: (01707) 322026 *Welding specialists*

Peartree Pantry, Peartree Farm, Spring Lane, Hatfield Peverel, Chelmsford, CM3 2JW Tel: (01245) 381461 *Bakers*

Peavey Electronics Ltd, Great Folds Road, Oakley Hay Industrial Estate, Corby, Northamptonshire, NN18 9ET Tel: (01536) 461234 Fax: (01536) 747222 E-mail: info@peavey-eu.com *Musical instruments manufrs*

Pebble Business Services Ltd, 20 Bonville Road, Bristol, BS4 5QH Tel: 0117-971 5435 Fax: 0117-977 8863 E-mail: data@pebble.co.uk *Mailing services*

▶ Pebble Promotions, 303a Chester Road, Hartford, Northwich, Cheshire, CW8 1QL Tel: (01606) 75677 Fax: (01606) 75688 E-mail: sales@pebblepromotions.co.uk *Promotion gift house service*

Peboc Division of Eastman Co. (UK) Ltd, Industrial Estate, Llangefni, Gwynedd, LL77 7YQ Tel: (01248) 750724 Fax: (01248) 723890 *Organic fine chemicals manufrs*

Pec Forklifts Ltd, Bridge Farm, Besthorpe Road, North Scarle, Lincoln, LN6 9EZ Tel: (01522) 778894 Fax: (01522) 778895 E-mail: pecforklifts@aol.com *Forklift hire & service*

Peca Electronics, 1 Parnell Court, Andover, Hampshire, SP10 3LX Tel: (01264) 355975 Fax: (01264) 366536 E-mail: sales@peca-electronics.co.uk *CCTV equipment design services*

Pechiney UK Ltd, Pechiney House, The Grove, Slough, SL1 1QF Tel: (01753) 522800 Fax: (01753) 522014 E-mail: enquiries@pechiney.co.uk *Aluminum sheet sales*

G. & J. Peck Ltd, Lisle Lane, Ely, Cambridgeshire, CB7 4PU Tel: (01353) 664515 Fax: (01353) 666032 E-mail: judith@peck.co.uk *Agricultural & horticulture machinery dealers* Also at: Ramsey St. Mary's

G. & J. Peck Ltd, Elsoms Way, Pinchbeck, Spalding, Lincolnshire, PE11 3JG Tel: (01775) 724343 Fax: (01775) 722073 E-mail: ssales@peck.co.uk *Agricultural machinery dealers & engineers*

▶ Peckam Springs, 3 Waterside Road, Haslingden, Rossendale, Lancashire, BB4 5EN Tel: (01706) 230969 Fax: (01706) 223595 E-mail: info@peckamsprings.com *Mineral water suppliers*

Pecks Agri-Trac, Wardentree Park, Pinchbeck, Spalding, Lincolnshire, PE11 3ZN Tel: (01775) 712310 Fax: (01775) 722073 E-mail: sales@peck.co.uk *Tractor dealerships*

Peco Controls (Europe) Ltd, Kempton Road, Pershore, Worcestershire, WR10 2TA Tel: (01386) 556622 Fax: (01386) 552252 E-mail: office@peco-europe.com *Suppliers of inspection & ancillary systems for the food*

Peco Electrical Services, The Maltings, Roydon Road, Stanstead Abbotts, Ware, Hertfordshire, SG12 8HG Tel: (01920) 877548 Fax: (01920) 877936 E-mail: peter.coard@breathemail.net *Street lighting gear trays*

Peco Publications & Publicity Ltd, Beer, Seaton, Devon, EX12 3NA Tel: (01297) 20580 Fax: (01297) 20229 E-mail: sales.peco@btconnect.com *Consumer journals*

Peco Services Ltd, Unit 13 Stonefield Park Industrial Estate, Martins Lane, Chilbolton, Stockbridge, Hampshire, SO20 6BL Tel: (01264) 860888 Fax: (01264) 860564 E-mail: pecoservices@btopenworld.com *Manufacturers of specialized heating equipment*

Peco Signs, Unit 5, Arrow Road North, Lakeside, Redditch, Worcestershire, B98 8NT Tel: (01527) 595364 Fax: (01527) 595366 E-mail: info@pecostudios.com *Sign manufacturers & exhibition graphics*

Pectel Group, Pectel Court, Burnt Mills Road, Basildon, Essex, SS13 1DT Tel: (01268) 591222 Fax: (01268) 590998 E-mail: info@pectel-group.co.uk *Asbestos removal & construction*

▶ Pedarson Heating, Unit 16, Martlesham Creek Industrial Estate, Sandy Lane, Martlesham, Woodbridge, Suffolk, IP12 4SD Tel: (01394) 384077 Fax: (01394) 387177 E-mail: info@pedarson.com *Electric under floor heating systems distributors*

Pedder & Summers Ltd, 2a Ashton Road, Hartwell, Northampton, NN7 2HW Tel: (01604) 863881 Fax: (01604) 863755 E-mail: sales@pedderandsummers.co.uk *Office furnishers & furniture distributors*

Pedler Robin, Empire Buildings, 47-49 Church Street, Stoke-on-Trent, ST4 1DQ Tel: (01782) 749749 Fax: (01782) 747840 E-mail: sales@sgbworldservice.com *Building services engineers & electrical contractors*

Pedley Furniture International Ltd, Shire Hill, Saffron Walden, Essex, CB11 3AL Tel: (01799) 522461 Fax: (01799) 543403 E-mail: sales@pedley.com *Pedley Furniture International Ltd based in Saffron Walden, Essex are manufacturers of hotel bedroom furniture including beds, wardrobes, desks, tables and bedside cabinets.*

Pedoka Ltd, 4 The Old School, Church Street, Biggleswade, Bedfordshire, SG18 0JS Tel: (01767) 318318 Fax: (01767) 310960 E-mail: pedoka@pedoka.com *Electronic component importers*

Pedrette Engineering Ltd, Unit 1, Ashville Trading Estate, Bristol Road, Gloucester, GL2 5EU Tel: (01452) 410447 *Stainless steel fabricators & manufrs*

▶ Pedro's Yacht Refinishing, Quarry House, Galmpton, Brixham, Devon, TQ5 0EH Tel: (01803) 845475 Fax: (01803) 845475 E-mail: enquiries@pedrosyachtrefinishing.co.uk *the leading s/w yacht painter and repairer specialising in high quality topsides painting ,osmosis treatment,insurance repair work*and from a small repair to a total refit the only blakes and awlgrip approved centres in the area,all from friendly and helpful people who are mainly boatowners themselves.*

Peek Traffic Ltd, Hazelwood House, Lime Tree Way, Chineham, Basingstoke, Hampshire, RG24 8WZ Tel: (01256) 891800 Fax: (01256) 891870 E-mail: sales@peek-traffic.co.uk *Traffic consultancy services*

Peek Traffic Ltd, Centurion Way, Meridian Business Park, Leicester, LE19 1WH Tel: 0116-282 8500 Fax: 0116-282 8528 *Traffic lights vehicle detection equipment suppliers*

▶ Peel Electrical & Security Systems Ltd, 34 Henfield Close, Clayton le Moors, Accrington, Lancashire, BB5 5WP Tel: (01254) 398181 Fax: 01254 398181 E-mail: SALES@PEELSECURITY.CO.UK *ALARMS & ELECTRICAL INSTALLATIONS*

Peel Graphics, 104-106 Bridge Street, Heywood, Lancashire, OL10 1JG Tel: (01706) 621960 Fax: (01706) 625249 E-mail: sales@peelgraphics.co.uk *Manufacturers of signs*

John Peel & Son Ltd, Baildon Mills, Northgate, Baildon, Shipley, West Yorkshire, BD17 6JY Tel: (01274) 583276 Fax: (01274) 598533 E-mail: mail@peelflock.com *Decorative flock & fibre filler manufrs*

Peel Weld, Rosebank, Church Bank, Llandovery, Dyfed, SA20 0BA Tel: (01550) 720854 Fax: (01550) 720945 E-mail: info@peelweld.co.uk *Steel publication*

▶ Peeny Weeny Baby, PO Box 71, Shanklin, Isle of Wight, PO37 6ZW Tel: (01983) 863532 *Specialist premature baby clothes and products online store. Clothes, toys, gifts, dummies, comforters, and much much more.*

Peerdown Engineering Ltd, 24 Dunstall Hill Ind Estate, Gorsebrook Road, Wolverhampton, WV6 0PJ Tel: (01902) 773663 Fax: (01902) 773663 *Precision engineers*

Peerless Designs Ltd, Unit 9, Brunswick Industrial Estate, Brunswick Way, London, N11 1JL Tel: (020) 8362 8500 Fax: (020) 8362 8525 E-mail: enquiries@peerlessdesigns.com *Designers & manufacturers of shopfitting & shelving systems*

▶ Peerless Gas Controls Ltd, Unit 11 Maple Business Park, Walter Street, Aston, Birmingham, B7 5ET Tel: 0121-327 6777 Fax: 0121-327 4555 E-mail: info@peerlesscontrols.com *Gas control manufrs*

▶ Peerless Literature Services, 97 Spon Lane, West Bromwich, West Midlands, B70 6AQ Tel: 0121-553 2511 Fax: 0121-525 6440

Peerless Maintenance Services Ltd, Coppins Yard, Grove Green Lane, Weavering, Maidstone, Kent, ME14 5JW Tel: (01622) 631444 Fax: (01622) 631222 *Fire alarm services*

Peers Hardy (U K) Ltd, Tompion House, 25 Birmingham Road, West Bromwich, West Midlands, B70 6RR Tel: 0121-525 8577 Fax: 0121-500 5276 E-mail: nbaker@peershardy.co.uk *Clocks & watches importers & suppliers*

Peers Jackson Engineering Company Ltd, Timmis Road, Stourbridge, West Midlands, DY9 7BQ Tel: (01384) 422503 Fax: (01384) 422568 *Special fasteners*

Pegasus, Old Surrenden Farm, Bethersden, Ashford, Kent, TN26 3DF Tel: (01233) 820867 Fax: (01233) 820867 *Sheet metalworker fabricators*

Pegasus, 86-92 Stewarts Road, London, SW8 4UG Tel: (020) 7622 2222 Fax: (020) 7622 1616 E-mail: sales@pegasus-couriers.com *Air freight forwarders, storage & distribution services*

Pegasus, 86-92 Stewarts Road, London, SW8 4UG Tel: (020) 7622 2222 Fax: (020) 7622 1616 E-mail: sales@pegasus-couriers.com *International couriers*

Pegasus Fire Protection, 8 Southedge Close, Hipperholme, Halifax, West Yorkshire, HX3 8DW Tel: (01422) 206076 Fax: (01422) 206076 *Fire equipment retailers*

Pegasus Fork Truck Services Ltd, 3-4 Quarry Farm, Row of Ashes Lane, Redhill, Bristol, BS40 5TU Tel: (01934) 863781 Fax: (01934) 863782 *Fork lift truck sales & repairs*

Pegasus Group Public Ltd Company, Orion House, Orion Way, Kettering, Northamptonshire, NN15 6PE Tel: (01536) 495000 Fax: (01536) 495001 E-mail: sales@pegasus.co.uk Principal Export Areas: Asia Pacific, Central Asia, Middle East, Central/East Europe, West Europe, North America & South America *Buisness software services*

Pegasus International UK Ltd, The Academy, Belmont Street, Aberdeen, AB10 1LB Tel: (01224) 623300 Fax: (01224) 623301 E-mail: aberdeen@pegasus-international.com *Pipeline engineers & subsea consultants* Also at: Putney

▶ Pegasus Marine Surveys, 12 Rockfield Road, Tobermory, PA75 6PN Tel: (01688) 302112 Fax: (01688) 302112 E-mail: surveys@pegasusmarine.co.uk *Independant Marine Surveyor specialising in leisure and commercial small craft surveys and MCA Code of Practice examinations. A member of the International Institute of Marine Surveying.*

Pegasus National Ltd, Pegasus House, Battersea Road, Stockport, Cheshire, SK4 3EA Tel: 0161-432 0575 Fax: 0161-442 2388 E-mail: info@adocsystem.com *Stationery manufrs*

Pegasus Plastics UK Ltd, Unit 24 Eldon Way, Paddock Wood, Tonbridge, Kent, TN12 6BE Tel: (01892) 832326 Fax: (01892) 832328 E-mail: sales@pegasusplastics.co.uk *Plastic moulders & promotional gifts*

▶ Pegasus Power & Communications, Unit 2 Tollpark Road, Wardpark East, Cumbernauld, Glasgow, G68 0LW Tel: (01236) 452555

Pegasus Products (Leeds) Ltd, Rear of, 90 High Street, Yeadon, Leeds, LS19 7AA Tel: 0113-250 0303 Fax: 0113-261 1629 E-mail: info@pegasusproducts.co.uk *Safety equipment & garage equipment manufrs*

Pegasus Profiles Ltd, Stephenson Way, Thetford, Norfolk, IP24 3RJ Tel: (01842) 755711 Fax: (01842) 755711 E-mail: sales@pegpro.co.uk *Profile cutting & plough grinding supplier*

Pegasus Profiles Southern Ltd, Unit 12 Hopkinson Way, Telford Gate, Andover, Hampshire, SP10 3SF Tel: (01264) 358525 Fax: (01264) 366319 E-mail: info@pegpro.co.uk *Steel, cut plate, sheet & laser manufrs*

▶ Pegasus Retirement Homes Ltd, Head Office, 105-107 Bath Road, Cheltenham, Gloucestershire, GL53 7LE Tel: (01242) 576610 Fax: (01242) 222723

▶ Pegasus Systems Ltd, 127 Greenford Road, Harrow, Middlesex, HA1 3QN Tel: (020) 8423 1104 Fax: (020) 8423 9975 E-mail: pegasus@pegasus-systems.co.uk

▶ Peglar, Belmont Works, St. Catherines Avenue, Doncaster, South Yorkshire, DN4 8DF Tel: (0870) 1200285 Fax: (01302) 367661 *Plumbing & heating manufrs*

Peglar, Belmont Works, St. Catherines Avenue, Doncaster, South Yorkshire, DN4 8DF Tel: (0870) 1200285 Fax: (01302) 367661 E-mail: export@pegler.com *Plumbing & heating fittings manufrs*

Pegmount Ltd, Unit 1 Apex Centre, Lovell, Lichfield Road Industrial Estate, Tamworth, Staffordshire, B79 7TA Tel: (01827) 69804 Fax: (01827) 69929 E-mail: sales@phoenixmanufacturing.co.uk *CNC engineering services or machinists*

Pegrex, Unit 1e Pearsall Drive, Oldbury, West Midlands, B69 2RA Tel: 0121-511 1475 Fax: 0121-511 1474 E-mail: nstruman@aol.com *Pressworkers*

Pekay Tools, Wattville Road, Smethwick, West Midlands, B66 2NU Tel: 0121-558 8028 Fax: 0121-558 8028 *Precision grinders*

▶ Pektek Embroiderers, 9 Mill Hill Business Centre, 5 Mill Hill Road, Hinckley, Leicestershire, LE10 0AX Tel: (01455) 844712 Fax: (01455) 631653 E-mail: colin@pektek.co.uk *Embroidery services, promotional, corporate wear, sportswear*

Pektron Group Ltd, Alfreton Road, Derby, DE21 4AP Tel: (01332) 832424 Fax: (01332) 833270 E-mail: info@pektron.co.uk *Electronic equipment manufrs*

Pel Engineering Ltd, Ashforth Street, Nottingham, NG3 4BG Tel: 0115-958 3022 Fax: 0115-958 3022 *Lifting equipment engineers*

Pelham Leather Goods Ltd, Pelham Centre, 110 Centennial Avenue, Borehamwood, Hertfordshire, WD6 3SB Tel: (020) 8731 3500 Fax: (020) 8731 3501 E-mail: sales@pelhamgroup.co.uk *Leather goods distributors*

▶ Pelican Fine Foods, 6 St. Johns Lane, Bewdley, Worcestershire, DY12 2QZ Tel: (01299) 400598 Fax: (01299) 404090 E-mail: pelican@wasteoil.co.uk *Collection of waste cooking oil, suppliers of cooking oils and related products, distributors of "FuelMeister" biodiesel production systems and "Magic-Line" cooking oil management systems.*

Pelican Flooring, 178 Stoke Newington Road, London, N16 7UY Tel: (020) 7254 7955 Fax: (020) 7254 7955 *Carpet & flooring specialists*

Pelican Healthcare Ltd, Cardiff Business Park, Cardiff, CF14 5WF Tel: (029) 2074 7000 Fax: (029) 2074 7001 E-mail: mailroom@pelicanhealthcare.co.uk *Manufacturers of medical disposable products*

Pelican Software Ltd, 35D Newland Street, Eynsham, Witney, Oxfordshire, OX29 4LB Tel: (01865) 883644 Fax: (01865) 883365 E-mail: jobs@pelicansoftware.co.uk *Software manufrs*

▶ PELICAN Solutions Ltd, 5 Westbrook Court, Sharrow Vale Road, SHEFFIELD, S11 8YZ Tel: 0114 233 5200 *PELICAN Solutions is a Construction Management Consultancy, facilitating answers for your organisation........Temporary Management Staff, Business Development and Planning and IT.....Websites, Computer Systems, Networks and Hardware.*

▶ Pelican Trading UK Ltd, Galloway Lane, Pudsey, West Yorkshire, LS28 7UG Tel: 0113-257 2468 Fax: 0113-229 5834 *HOME TEXTILE PRODUCTS: - Towels, Bath Towels, Hand Towels, Face Towel, Bath Sheet, Tea Towel, Terry Towel, Flannel Cloth, Dish Cloths, Raschale Knitted Dish Cloth, Jackarde Towels, and Dobby Towels. Our range of Home Textiles can be customized in terms of quality, colour, size and logo. We are accredited to ISO 9002 and are approved by all major supermarkets of the UK and Europe. - - - - - - - - - - SPORTS PRODUCTS: - Handmade SOCCER Ball, FOOTBALL, MATCH Ball, TRAINING Ball, Baseballs, BEACH Volleyballs, Handballs, RUGBY ball, PROMOTIONAL balls, Medicine balls, Customized balls, SOCCER KIT, SHIN GUARD, Goalkeeper Gloves, Weight Lifting Gloves, Working Gloves, Cycle Gloves, Boxing Gloves, Track Suits and Sports wears. - - - - *Our manufacturing plants are equipped with highly innovative machinery, latest testing laboratory, qualified engineers and highly motivated and skilled workforce. Our quality management system is accredited to the ISO9001 and ISO9002.*

Pelicans Manufacturing Co. Ltd, B 5 Parr Road, Stanmore, Middlesex, HA7 1NP Tel: (020) 8952 4222 Fax: (020) 8951 3639 E-mail: sales@pelicans.co.uk *Business gift manufrs*

Pelikan Hardcopy Scotland Ltd, Markethill Road, Turriff, Aberdeenshire, AB53 4AW Tel: (01888) 564200 Fax: (01888) 562042 E-mail: sales@phi-psl.co.uk *Computer consumables suppliers & manufrs*

Pell Frischmann Group Ltd, 4 Manchester Square, London, W1A 1AU Tel: (020) 7486 3661 Fax: (020) 7487 4153 E-mail: pflondon@pellfrischmann.com *Structural engineers*

▶ Pellco Partitions, Church Lane, Challock, Ashford, Kent, TN25 4BU Tel: (01233) 740777 Fax: (01233) 740577 E-mail: info@pellco.co.uk *Sliding folding acoustic partitions - movable/ operable acoustic walls*

Pelle Ltd, 129 Bethnal Green Road, London, E2 7DG Tel: (020) 7729 7898 Fax: (020) 7729 7773 E-mail: pelleltd@aol.com *Leather clothing manufrs*

Pellfold Parthos Ltd, 1 The Quadrant, Howarth Road, Maidenhead, Berkshire, SL6 1AP Tel: (01628) 773353 Fax: (01628) 773363 E-mail: sales@pellfoldparthos.co.uk *Acoustic movable walls & folding partitions*

▶ Pelloby Engineering Ltd, Halesfield 19, Telford, Shropshire, TF7 4QT Tel: (01952) 586626 Fax: (01952) 587871 E-mail: sales@pelloby.com *Manufacturers of cranes & lifting equipment to suit all applications*

W.J. Pellow Ltd, 17 Regent Place, Birmingham, B1 3NL Tel: 0121-236 9121 Fax: 0121-236 7779 *Jewellery retailers & manufrs*

Pelma, 14 Corbet Drive, Adderley, Wollerton, Market Drayton, Shropshire, TF9 3LW Tel: (01630) 655611 E-mail: pelma@fsbdial.co.uk *Food consultant*

Pelmark Ltd, Barley Road, Flint Cross, Heydon, Royston, Hertfordshire, SG8 7PU Tel: (01763) 208020 Fax: (01763) 208021 E-mail: reception@pelmark.co.uk *Promotional leisurewear*

D. Pelosi & Son Ltd, 38 Nithsdale Road, Glasgow, G41 2AN Tel: 0141-423 5944 Fax: 0141-423 5945 E-mail: enquiries@pvend.com *Cigarette vending machine operators*

Pelsall Tool & Engineering Co.Ltd, Sheffield Mill, Mill Rd, Pelsall, Walsall, WS4 1BU Tel: 01922 682551 *Tool-making*

Pelstar Computing Ltd, Merlin House, 122-126 Kilburn High Road, London, NW6 4HY Tel: (020) 7624 6880 Fax: (020) 7328 9626 E-mail: info@pelstar.co.uk *Computer consultants*

▶ Pema Rules, Unit 15 Leyton Business Centre, Etloe Road, London, E10 7BT Tel: (020) 8988 4083 Fax: (020) 8556 8543 E-mail: sales@pemarules.com *Printing & packaging supply services*

Pemberton Building Supplies Ltd, Richmond Hill, Wigan, Lancashire, WN5 8AA Tel: (01942) 218222 Fax: (01942) 225205 *Builders & plumbers merchants*

Pemberton Dear Ltd, Parndon Mill, Parndon Mill Lane, Harlow, Essex, CM20 2HP Tel: (01279) 434868 Fax: (01279) 434875 E-mail: design@pemberton-dear.co.uk *Product design & developers consultancy, industrial design & engineering*

Pemberton Engineering, Unit 48 Planetary Industrial Estate, Planetary Road, Willenhall, West Midlands, WV13 3XB Tel: (01902) 863666 Fax: (01902) 863666 E-mail: pembertoneng@btconnect.com *Precision engineers & press tool manufrs*

Pemberton Leisure Homes Ltd, Woodhouse Lane, Wigan, Lancashire, WN6 7NF Tel: (01942) 321221 Fax: (01942) 234150 E-mail: info@pembertonlh.co.uk *Caravan holiday home manufrs*

Pemberton Technologies Ltd, 47 Knowl Piece, Wilbury Way, Hitchin, Hertfordshire, SG4 0TY Tel: (01462) 440003 Fax: (01462) 440550 E-mail: pemtech@clara.co.uk *Screen process printers*

Pembertons Sewing Machine Centre, 21-25 Friars Street, Stirling, FK8 1HA Tel: (01786) 462993 Fax: (01786) 461998 E-mail: sales@pembertons.org *Sewing machines sales & repair*

Pembridge Terracotta Ltd, East Street, Pembridge, Leominster, Herefordshire, HR6 9HB Tel: (01544) 388696 Fax: (01544) 388987 E-mail: info@gardenpots.co.uk *Flower pot suppliers*

► Pembroke Homes Ltd, Pembroke House, 3 Altrincham Road, Wilmslow, Cheshire, SK9 5ND Tel: (01625) 530330 Fax: (01625) 528221

Pembroke Packaging & Print Ltd, Victoria Hall, Nelson Street, Pennar, Pembroke Dock, Dyfed, SA72 6RU Tel: (01646) 684664 Fax: (01646) 622226 *Pembroke Packaging & Print Ltd are based in Pembroke covering the Dyfed area. Offering a range of flexible packaging including Paper, Sacks and Bags. Printed carrier bag Specialists, Protective Packaging for house removals, etc. Also Stock Catering consumables and Office Stationery Products*

► Pembrokeshire Classics (Motorcycles), Bromleigh, Reynalton, Kilgetty, Dyfed, SA68 0PH Tel: (01834) 891685 Fax: (01834) 891685 E-mail: mail@pembrokeshireclassics.com *Classic motorcycle stockists*

Pembrokeshire Video Productions, Thorne Cottage, Cresselly, Kilgetty, Dyfed, SA68 0TY Tel: (01646) 651555 Fax: (01646) 651555 E-mail: nickpudsey@pembrokeshirevideo.co.uk *Video production*

Pembs Steel Buildings Ltd, Y Llys, Gellifedi Road, Brynna, Pontyclun, Mid Glamorgan, CF72 9QG Tel: (07765) 905283 E-mail: sales@pembs-steelbuildings.co.uk *Supplies residential, agricultural & industrial steel buildings*

Pembury Fencing, Unit, Church Farm, Collier Street, Tonbridge, Kent, TN12 9RT Tel: (0870) 2423707 Fax: (0870) 2423708 E-mail: pemburyfencing@tiscali.co.uk *Fencing contractors*

► Pemsa UK Ltd, Leathley Road, Leeds, LS10 1BG Tel: 0113-277 5939 Fax: 0113 244 6555 E-mail: sales@pemsa.co.uk *Manufacturer and supplier of Wire Mesh and Perforated Cable Tray Systems.*

Pen Cutting Tools Ltd, Bold Street, Sheffield, S9 2LR Tel: 0114-243 0055 Fax: 0114-243 0066 E-mail: sales@pencuttingtools.co.uk *Tungsten carbide, steel cutting tools & special machine parts manufrs*

Pen Mobile Solutions, Court Farm, Moor Road, Banwell, Avon, BS29 6ET Tel: (01934) 823800 Fax: (01934) 820220 E-mail: sales@penmobile.co.uk *An established barcode & RFID company. Our expertises are in barcode hardware, repair & maintenance, software development, integration and solutions tailored to your specific business needs.*

► Pen Tools Ltd, Jubilee Building, Westfields Trading Estate, Hereford, HR4 9NS Tel: (01432) 273018 *Hand power tool retail*

Penarth Industrial Services Ltd, 8 Gripoly Mills, Sloper Road, Cardiff, CF11 8AA Tel: (029) 2064 1555 Fax: (029) 2064 1899 E-mail: info@pisltd.com *Pipe & steel fabricators*

Penatube Ltd, Boomes Trading Estate Dovers Corner, New Road, Rainham, Essex, RM13 8QT Tel: (01708) 555595 Fax: (01708) 526276 E-mail: SAQIB21@GMAIL.COM *Plastic mouldings manufrs*

Pencil House Ltd, 16 Brunel Road, Earlstrees Industrial Estate, Corby, Northamptonshire, NN17 4JW Tel: (01536) 400107 Fax: (01536) 265694 *Party goods distributors*

Penclawdd Forge, Station Square, Penclawdd, Swansea, SA4 3XT Tel: (01792) 850124 Fax: (01792) 416267 *Iron fabricators*

► Pencroft Ltd, Old Road, Clifton-on-Teme, Worcester, WR6 6DR Tel: (01886) 812822 Fax: (01886) 812833

► Pend Logistics, 62 St. Marys Road, Edmonton, London, N9 8NJ Tel: (07957) 728769 E-mail: sales@pendlog.com *Pend Logistics, The Same Day Courier Company.**We offer an efficent, friendly service to all our customers both Personal and Business. **Our rates are reasonable and all quotes are obligation free.* *Try us! you might be surprised!*

Pendax UK Ltd, 57 Sutton Park Avenue, Earley, Reading, RG6 1AZ Tel: 0118-966 8383 Fax: 0118-966 8895 E-mail: sales@pendax.co.uk *Presentation equipment manufacturers & suppliers*

► Pendelfin Studios Ltd, PO Box 431, Burnley, Lancashire, BB10 2HG Tel: (01282) 432301 Fax: (01282) 459464 *Gift & toy retailers*

Pendennis Shipyard (Composite) Ltd, Falmouth Docks, Falmouth, Cornwall, TR11 4NR Tel: (01326) 211344 Fax: (01326) 319253 E-mail: info@pendennis.com *Luxury yacht builders*

Pendle Business Micro, Riverside, Bridge Street, Colne, Lancashire, BB8 0DR Tel: (01282) 861511 Fax: (01282) 871560 E-mail: peter@pendlebusinessmicro.fsbusiness.co.uk *Computer programmers*

Pendle Doors Ltd, Plumbe Street, Burnley, Lancashire, BB11 3AG Tel: (01254) 870850 Fax: (01282) 703027 E-mail: info@pendledoors.co.uk *Doors manufrs*

Pendle Metal Craft, 7-9 Rookery Road, Barnoldswick, Lancashire, BB18 6YH Tel: (01282) 817333 Fax: (01282) 852751 *Metal fabricators*

Pendle Nu Tech, Old School House, School Lane, Laneshawbridge, Colne, Lancashire, BB8 7EQ Tel: (01282) 861111 Fax: (01282) 871113 *Fire extinguisher suppliers & services*

Pendle Refrigeration Services Ltd, Whithams Mill, Plumbe Street, Burnley, Lancashire, BB11 3AW Tel: (01282) 412352 Fax: (01282) 451807 E-mail: sales@pendle-refrig.co.uk *Refrigeration & air conditioning wholesaler & distributors*

Pendle Signs & Plastics Ltd, Kirby Road, Lomeshaye Industrial Estate, Nelson, Lancashire, BB9 6RS Tel: (01282) 601842 Fax: (01282) 617361 E-mail: sales@pendlesigns.co.uk *Sign makers & plastic engineers*

Pendle Textiles Wholesale Textile Merchant, Halifax Road, Briercliffe, Burnley, Lancashire, BB10 3QU Tel: (01282) 454375 Fax: (01282) 412750 E-mail: sales@pendle-textiles.co.uk *Textile merchants & wholesales*

► Pendleton Bathroom Design Ltd, 64 Longfileds Road, Thorpe St Andrew, Norwich, NR7 0NA Tel: 01603 435070 E-mail: sales@pendletonbathroomdesign.co.uk *Pendleton Bathroom Design offer a comprehensive bathroom installation service. This includes everthing from the initial design and supply of fittings, through to complete installation, all guaranteed for 24 months. Please look at our website for further information, thank you.*

Pendleton Consultants Ltd, Stuart House, The Back, Chepstow, Gwent, NP16 5HH Tel: (01291) 620290 Fax: (01291) 628030 E-mail: mlp@pendleton-consultants.co.uk *Executive consultancy work*

► Pendleton Events Ltd, Pendleton House 37 Horseshoe, Close Pound Hill, Crawley, West Sussex, RH10 7YS Tel: (07984) 510856 Fax: 0845 330 7263 E-mail: info@pendletonevents.co.uk *Pendleton Events seeks to create conferences and events that are acknowledged as excellent in all respects. Just as every event has its own distinctive character, Pendleton Events aims to ensure that everyone involved from hosts and sponsors to guests are left with equally distinctive memories.**Pendleton Events provides a range of service to both corporate and private clients. Whether you are looking to hold a national sales conference for hundreds of people or planning a birthday bash for ten, we can help make it an event to remember. Contact us today to discuss your corporate or private entertainment and hospitality requirements. Don"t forget we also offer a FREE venue finding service!!*

Pendragon Contracts Ltd, Sir Frank Whittle Road, Derby, DE21 4AZ Tel: (01332) 292777 Fax: (01332) 364270 E-mail: info@pendragon-contracts.co.uk *Car leasing agents*

► Pendragon Fireplaces, 12 Market Street, Stourbridge, West Midlands, DY8 1AD Tel: 01384 376441 Fax: 01384 376441 E-mail: pendragongifts@hotmail.com *Fireplaces & fireplace accessories suppliers*

Pendragon Fireworks & Pyrotechnics, 125 Newport Road, Cwmcarn/Cross Keys, Cross Keys, Newport, Gwent, NP11 7LZ Tel: (01633) 482626 E-mail: sales@pendragonfireworks.com *Firework displays*

► Pendragon Homes Ltd, Pendragon House, General Rees Square, Cwmbran, Gwent, NP44 1AJ Tel: (01633) 872406

Pendrich Hype Services Ltd, 78-82 Carnethie Street, Rosewell, Midlothian, EH24 9AW Tel: 0131-440 1991 Fax: 0131-448 2157 E-mail: enquiries@pendrich.com *Steeplejacks-height services*

Pendrigh Computer Services, 31-37 Church Street, Reigate, Surrey, RH2 0AD Tel: (01737) 221510 E-mail: info@pendrighcomputerservices.co.uk *Computer consultants*

► Penduke Models, 84 Robinhood Street, Gloucester, GL1 5PP Tel: (01452) 415511 E-mail: penduke@mystargaze.net *Model Railway Accessories and Trains.*

► Penec UK Ltd, Unit 11 Prime Enterprise Park, Prime Park Way, Derby, DE1 3QB Tel: (01332) 224141 Fax: (01332) 224140

Penfold Metalising Co. Ltd, Barnham Road, Barnham, Bognor Regis, West Sussex, PO22 0ES Tel: (01243) 552178 Fax: (01243) 554472 E-mail: info@penmet.co.uk *Grit blasting contractors*

Penfold Motors, 345 Lee High Road, London, SE12 8RU Tel: (020) 8355 8000 Fax: (020) 8355 8018 E-mail: sales@penfolds-vauxhall.co.uk *Motor sales, repairers & service*

Penfold Public Works (Sussex) Ltd, The Chalk Pit, Mile Oak Road, Portslade, Brighton, BN41 2RB Tel: (01273) 412224 Fax: (01273) 412563 E-mail: info@penfoldpublicworks.co.uk *Public buildings works & plant hire contractors*

Sally Penfold, Imasas, Middletown, Hailey, Witney, Oxfordshire, OX29 9UB Tel: (01993) 822922 Fax: (01993) 822922 *Soft furniture manufrs*

Penfold & Sons, Old Talbot House, High Street, Cuckfield, Haywards Heath, West Sussex, RH17 5JX Tel: (01444) 454164 Fax: (01444) 451120 *Saddlery*

Pengrave Engineering Ltd, Fairway, Off Delta Way, Bridgtown, Cannock, Staffordshire, WS11 0BE Tel: (01543) 577142 Fax: (01543) 577930 E-mail: pengrave@compuserve.com *To provide fully designed, manufactured, installed & commissioned paint finishing plant, either as main contractor or subcontract, including immersion & spay pre-treatment systems; ovens including dry-off, curing, infra-red & batch type; powder coating booths & recovery systems; water wash & dry filter spray booths; ductwork, air replacement systems, conveyors, effluent treatment & pain de-naturing systems. We also offer service/maintenance packages for all new or existing plant.*

Penguin Books Ltd, 80 Strand, London, WC2R 0RL Tel: (020) 7010 3000 Fax: (020) 7010 6060 E-mail: info@pearson.com *Book & magazine publishers*

Penhall Ltd, 9 Enterprise Court, Newton Close, Park Farm Industrial Estate, Wellingborough, Northamptonshire, NN8 6UW Tel: (01933) 678851 Fax: (01933) 674204 *Aluminium, alloy & zinc die casting manufrs*

► Penhill Quarry & Haulage Ltd, Launcells, Kilkhampton, Bude, Cornwall, EX23 9LQ Tel: (01288) 321489

Penhow Plant Hire Ltd, Langstone, Newport, Gwent, NP18 2HJ Tel: (01633) 415333 Fax: (01633) 415334 *Plant hire suppliers*

Penico Systems Ltd, Albion Works, Keighley Road, Bingley, West Yorkshire, BD16 2RD Tel: (01274) 511044 Fax: (01274) 510770 *Wire erosion & CNC machiners*

► Penicuik Home Improvements, Eastfield Industrial Estate, Penicuik, Midlothian, EH26 8HA Tel: (0845) 7515000 Fax: (01968) 664023

Penicuik Home Improvements, Eastfield Industrial Estate, Penicuik, Midlothian, EH26 8HA Tel: (0845) 7515000 Fax: (01968) 664023 *Windows, conservatories, roofline, doors suppliers*

► Peninsula Business Services Ltd, Delphian House, New Bailey Street, Salford, M3 5PB Tel: 0161-834 2773 Fax: 0161-833 9517 E-mail: enquiries@peninsula-uk.com *Leading UK & Ireland consultancy providing Employment Law and Health & Safety services, Employment Tribunal, H&S representation. Provides a pro-active approach to protect clients by; reducing areas where clients are vulnerable to litigation, offers coaching, documentation and 24/7 advice to keep clients secure and includes an indemnity to pay for the most robust legal defence plus some awards. Few companies guarantee their services like this!*

Peninsula Films, 9 Saxon Road, Cambridge, CB5 8HS Tel: (01223) 460459 E-mail: sales@peninsulafilms.com *Corporate video & new-media production service*

► Peninsula Plastics Ltd, Coronation Street, Stockport, Cheshire, SK5 7PG Tel: 0161-476 2025 Fax: 0161-476 2068

► Peninsula Solutions, Unit 10 Orchard Court, Heron Road, Sowton Industrial Estate, Exeter, EX2 7LL Tel: (01392) 444757 Fax: (01392) 444412 E-mail: sales@peninsula.co.uk

► Peninsula Windows Ltd, Star Crossroads, Star, Gaerwen, Gwynedd, LL60 6AL Tel: (01248) 715555 Fax: (01248) 713383 E-mail: sales@peninsulawindows.co.uk

► Peninsular Acoustics, 114 Shrewsbury Road, Prenton, Merseyside, CH43 8SP Tel: 0151-652 6270 Fax: 0151-652 6270 E-mail: noise@btconnect.com *Industrial noise control, vibration control consultants & designers*

Peninsular Nameplates, Peninsular House, Carr Lane, Hoylake, Wirral, Merseyside, CH47 4AY Tel: 0151-632 5814 Fax: 0151-632 1090 E-mail: info@peninsular-nameplates.co.uk *Nameplate, sign & label manufacturers including safety*

Penistone Hard Metals Ltd, Roman Ridge Road, Sheffield, S9 1FH Tel: 0114-243 2471 Fax: 0114-242 6570 E-mail: info@penistonehardmetals.co.uk *Hard facing contractors & wear plates*

Penistone Reinforcements Ltd, Stanley Mills, Talbot Road, Penistone, Sheffield, S36 9ED Tel: (01226) 762158 Fax: (01226) 766166 E-mail: chris@p-reinforcements.demon.co.uk *Wire manufrs*

Penketh's Ltd, Bassendale Road, Croft Business Park, Wirral, Merseyside, CH62 3QL Tel: 0151-334 4417 Fax: 0151-737 5001 E-mail: enquiries@penkeths.co.uk *Office product suppliers*

► Penkiln, Baldoon Stores, Wigtown, Newton Stewart, Wigtownshire, DG8 9AF Tel: (01988) 402414 Fax: (01988) 840300

Penleigh Irving Ltd, 25 Fairwood Road, Dilton Marsh, Westbury, Wiltshire, BA13 3SN Tel: (01373) 827649 Fax: (01373) 827077 E-mail: keratex.uk@btconnect.com *Equine hoof care product manufrs*

Penlon Ltd, 8 Salford Enterprise Centre, Guide Street, Salford, M50 1EW Tel: 0161-745 7952 Fax: 0161-745 7953 E-mail: east.healthcare@penlon.co.uk *Medical gas pipeline engineers*

Penman Engineering Ltd, Heathhall Industrial Estate, Heathhall, Dumfries, DG1 3NY Tel: (01387) 252784 Fax: (01387) 267332 E-mail: info@penman.co.uk *Safety cab & vehicle body manufrs*

James Penman Plant Hire, Glenleven Industrial Estate, Leslie, Glenrothes, Fife, KY6 3EU Tel: (01592) 654555 Fax: (01592) 620245 E-mail: penmanplant@yahoo.co.uk *Plant hire*

► Penman Plant Hire, Merchant Place, Mitchelston Industrial Estate, Kirkcaldy, Fife, KY1 3NJ Tel: (01592) 654555 Fax: (01592) 654554

Penmann Climatic Systems Ltd, Highfield, Pool Road, Pool in Wharfedale, Otley, West Yorkshire, LS21 1EG Tel: 0113-202 7300 Fax: 0113-202 7301 E-mail: office@penmann.co.uk *Air conditioning & refrigeration manufrs*

Penn Fishing Tackle Europe, Cartside Avenue, Inchinnan, Renfrew, PA4 9RX Tel: 0141-814 6565 Fax: 0141-814 6560 E-mail: sales@pennfishing.com *Fishing equipment distributor*

Penn Nyla Ltd, Acton Road, Long Eaton, Nottingham, NG10 1FX Tel: 0115-973 4441 Fax: 0115-946 1085 E-mail: sales@penn-nyla.com *Textile manufrs*

Penn Pharmaceuticals Services Ltd, Unit 23 & 24, Tafarnaubach Industrial Estate, Tafarnaubach, Tredegar, Gwent, NP22 3AA Tel: (01495) 711222 Fax: (01495) 711225 E-mail: penn@pennpharm.co.uk *Pharmaceutical products*

Penn Refractories Ltd, Dudley Road, Stourbridge, West Midlands, DY9 8EL Tel: (01384) 422192 Fax: (01384) 422195 *Refractories producers & manufrs*

Penn Studios, Penn Farm Studios, Harston Road, Haslingfield, Cambridge, CB23 1JZ Tel: (01487) 773282 *Penn studios provides quality rural office rental, work space and storage premises near Cambridge and Huntingdon*

► Penn Transport, Purbrook Road, Wolverhampton, WV1 2EJ Tel: (01902) 455601 Fax: (01902) 454381

Penna plc, Regent Arcade House, 19-25 Argyll Street, London, W1F 7TS Tel: (020) 7663 6633 Fax: (020) 7663 7321 E-mail: londonwest@e-penna.com *Outplacement*

► Penna Consulting, 7 Queens Gardens, Aberdeen, AB15 4YD Tel: (01224) 619205 Fax: (01224) 626227

Pennant Automotive & Industrial Supplies, University Farm, Wasthill Lane, Kings Norton, Birmingham, B38 9EP Tel: 0121-459 4276 Fax: 0121-451 2488 *Workshop consumable distributors*

Pennant International Group Ltd, Pennant Court, Staverton Technology Park, Old Gloucester Road, Staverton, Cheltenham, Gloucestershire, GL51 6TL Tel: (01452) 714914 Fax: (01452) 714920 E-mail: ptsl@pennantplc.co.uk *Audio visual simulator manufrs*

Pennant P B M Ltd, 8 Locarno Avenue, Luton, LU4 9EJ Tel: (01582) 576422 Fax: (01582) 581792 E-mail: pennant@email.com *Shop fitters*

Cecil Penney Ltd, Sheffield Road Garage, Penistone, Sheffield, S36 6HF Tel: (01226) 763102 Fax: (01226) 370346 *Motor vehicle repair, restoration & garage*

► Penney Electrical Ltd, Reynolds Road, Crawley, West Sussex, RH11 7HA Tel: (01293) 550800 Fax: (01293) 510700

Pennine Arts International Ltd, Long Lea Works, Halifax Road, Elland, West Yorkshire, HX5 0SH Tel: (01422) 378123 Fax: (01422) 370879 E-mail: sales@pennine-arts.co.uk *Exhibition contractors*

Pennine Components Ltd, PO Box 1, Todmorden, Lancashire, OL14 5BB Tel: (01706) 815737 Fax: (01706) 817628 E-mail: sales@penninecomponents.co.uk *Electrical components distributors product modifiers*

Pennine Drawing Office Services, Unit X1 2 Keighley Business Centre, South Street, Keighley, West Yorkshire, BD21 1AG Tel: (01535) 667422 Fax: (01535) 610130 E-mail: pennine@totalise.co.uk *Distributor of office equipment*

Pennine Drawing Office Supplies North East, 63g Lord Avenue, Thornaby, Stockton-on-Tees, Cleveland, TS17 9JX Tel: (01642) 763762 Fax: (01642) 763768 E-mail: sales@penninedrawing.co.uk *Drawing office equipment suppliers*

Pennine Electrical Rewinding Ltd, Clamark House, 63 Stalker Lees Road, Sheffield, S11 8NP Tel: 0114-266 3131 Fax: 0114-266 4944 E-mail: info@crystal-abrasives.com *Electric motor repairers & rewind services*

Pennine Environmental Services Ltd, Sherwood House, Thornhill Drive, Calverley, Pudsey, West Yorkshire, LS28 5QW Tel: 0113-239 3999 Fax: 0113-256 9175 E-mail: pennine@pennine-env.co.uk *Refrigeration & cooling engineers*

Pennine Fire Extinguisher Services, Pleasington Street, Blackburn, BB2 1UF Tel: (01254) 263378 Fax: (01254) 278898 E-mail: info@penninefire.co.uk *Fire equipment suppliers*

Pennine Forge, Peel Park Works, Peel Park View, Bradford, West Yorkshire, BD3 0JY Tel: (01274) 642248 Fax: (01274) 634132 *Industrial noise control specialists*

Pennine Labels Ltd, Unit 26 Clayton Street, Nelson, Lancashire, BB9 7PH Tel: (01282) 601602 Fax: (01282) 611566 E-mail: sales@penninelabels.co.uk *Textile labels manufrs*

Pennine Lubricants, Unit 35 Limestone Cottage Lane, Sheffield, S6 1NJ Tel: 0114-285 2987 Fax: 0114-285 2988 E-mail: sales@penninelubricants.co.uk *Lubricant manufrs*

Pennine Machine Tools Ltd, Brookwoods Industrial Estate, Burnwood Way, Holywell Green, Halifax, West Yorkshire, HX4 9BH Tel: (01422) 370109 Fax: (01422) 371338 E-mail: sales@pennine.co.uk *Machine tool manufacturers & industrial control systems*

Pennine Optical Group Ltd, Pennine House, Manchester Road, Stockport, Cheshire, SK4 1TX Tel: 0161-477 8964 Fax: 0161-477 6949 E-mail: pennine@pog.co.uk *Spectacle frame & optical accessories distribution*

Pennine Packaging Co Ltd, Dell Road, Rochdale, Lancashire, OL12 6BZ Tel: (01706) 655787 Fax: (01706) 860418 E-mail: penninepackaging@hotmail.com *Direct mail services*

Pennine Parcels Ltd, Listers Road, Shibden, Halifax, West Yorkshire, HX3 7XA Tel: (01422) 330215 Fax: (01422) 330187 E-mail: robert.rushworth@penparcels.co.uk *Distribution & warehousing services*

Pennine Pest Control, 54 Mear House, Sheffield Road, New Mill, Holmfirth, HD9 7HA Tel: (01484) 683010 *Pest control*

► Pennine Plant Services, Woodlands, Dale Street, Longwood, Huddersfield, HD3 4TG Tel: (01484) 647129 Fax: (01484) 647290

► Pennine Pneumatic Services, 5-7 Pellon New Road, Halifax, West Yorkshire, HX1 4UB Tel: (01422) 321772 Fax: (01422) 342430

► Pennine Print, Widow Hill Road, Heasandford Trading Estate, Burnley, Lancashire, BB10 2BE Tel: (01282) 453716 Fax: (01282) 707276

Pennine Printing Services Ltd, Commercial Mills, Oldham Road, Sowerby Bridge, West Yorkshire, HX6 4EH Tel: (01422) 825333 Fax: (01422) 825444 E-mail: pennineprinting@btconnect.com *General printing services*

Pennine Products, Marsh House, Market Place, Honley, Holmfirth, HD9 6NG Tel: (01484) 666303 Fax: (01484) 663260 E-mail: sales@pennineproducts.co.uk *Business gifts & promotions suppliers*

Pennine Projects Ltd, New Line Industrial Estate, Bacup, Lancashire, OL13 9RW Tel: (01706) 877555 Fax: (01706) 879754 E-mail: info@pennine-group.co.uk *Ground engineering company*

Pennine Radio Ltd, 82 Fitzwilliam Street, Huddersfield, HD1 5BE Tel: (01484) 538211 Fax: (01484) 542004 E-mail: info@pr1.co.uk *Transformers, electronics & sheet metal working*

► Pennine Seals, Unit 7-8, Ashley Industrial Estate Leeds Road, Huddersfield, HD2 1UR Tel: (01484) 480237 Fax: (01484) 420044 E-mail: toolsales@pennine-tools.co.uk *Distributor, stockist and manufacturer of hydraulic and pneumatic seals, gaskets, 0-rings and sealing systems*

Pennine Services, Bredbury Park Way, Bredbury Park Industrial Estate, Bredbury, Stockport, Cheshire, SK6 2SN Tel: 0161-406 7555 Fax: 0161-406 7555 *Mobile site accommodation manufrs*

Pennine Systems Ltd, Crossley Works, Stockfield Mount, Off Peel Street, Chadderton, Oldham, OL9 9LR Tel: 0161 678 2998 Fax: 0161 678 2997 E-mail: sales@penninesystems.co.uk *Manufacturers of Flue Pipe, Accessories, Chimney Products and Log Stores*

Pennine Tea & Coffee Limited, 6-8 Hall Street, Halifax, West Yorkshire, HX1 5AY Tel: (01422) 347734 Fax: (01422) 347734 E-mail: aespresso@aol.com *Pennine Tea & Coffee are based in West Yorkshire (United Kingdom). They are an independent wholesaler supplying hot beverage equipment and ingredients to cafe bars, hotels, tea and coffee shops, restaurants, public houses, offices and any other business that requires a quality coffee service. Products include espresso machines, coffee, tea and auxiliary items.*

Pennine Telecom Ltd, Pennine House, Salford Street, Bury, Lancashire, BL9 6YA Tel: 0161-763 3333 Fax: 0161-763 3332 E-mail: info@penninetelecom.com *Suppliers of mobile radio & telephone equipment*

Pennine Tools Ltd, PO Box B98, Huddersfield, HD2 1UR Tel: (01484) 519660 Fax: (01484) 420044 E-mail: toolsales@pennine-tools.co.uk *Engineering equipment & cutting tool specialists*

Pennine Trims, 5 Rosewood Business Park, St James's Road, Blackburn, BB1 8ET Tel: (01254) 582715 Fax: (01254) 663309 *Manufacture & wholesale of textile trimmings*

Pennine Way Hotel, Manchester Street, Oldham, OL8 1UZ Tel: 0161-624 0555 Fax: 0161-627 2031 E-mail: sales@pennineway hotel.co.uk *Conference facilities & hotel*

Pennine Yarn Dyeing Ltd, Bridge End Works, Saddleworth Road, Elland, West Yorkshire, HX5 0RY Tel: (01422) 372401 Fax: (01422) 373735 E-mail: info@pyd.com *Carpet dyers*

Penning Springs, Bolton Road North, Ramsbottom, Bury, Lancashire, BL0 0LY Tel: (01706) 824614 Fax: (01706) 821636 *Spring manufrs*

Jack Pennington Ltd, 3 Hird Street, Shipley, West Yorkshire, BD17 7ED Tel: (01274) 534444 Fax: (01274) 534433 E-mail: sales@pennington.co.uk *General engineering services*

▶ Pennington Lacey & Sons Ltd, 5-7 Park Road, Southampton, SO15 3AS Tel: (023) 8063 1555 Fax: (023) 8033 4017 E-mail: sales@penningtonlacey.co.uk *Double glazing manufrs*

Penny Corporations Ltd, Unit 15, Brookvale Trading Estate, Moor Lane, Witton, Birmingham, B6 7AE Tel: 0121-356 5523 Fax: 0121-356 3511 E-mail: info@euro-icecream.co.uk *Ice cream manufrs*

Penny & Giles Aerospace Ltd, 1 Airfield Road, Christchurch, Dorset, BH23 3TH Tel: (01202) 409409 Fax: (01202) 484846 E-mail: mike.carling@pennyandgiles.com *Penny and Giles Aerospace ltd. specialises in Avionics/ Aerospace products, Air Data Computers/ Modules, Quick Access Maintenance recorders, Solid State FDR,CVR and Combined Solid State Recorders, including Acquisition, Mass Storage Memory Modules, Ice and Snow detection and Ground Test Equipment All of these items have been supplied into both the commercial and the military market -place. To support these products P&G also developed an Air data Test set ,to support installation of Air data computers. Other product ranges include Ice and snow detection system for rotary aircraft, a selection of LVDT,RVDT ,solenoids and potentiometers. The companies expertise also includes level A software applications and a very quick development cycle for both hardware and software applications suited to the Aerospace industry. Penny and Giles Aerospace Ltd. is a wholly owned subsidiary of the Curtiss-Wright Corporation forming part of the "Controls Inc., as part of the "Integrated Sensing Division" along with Autronics*

Penny & Giles Controls Ltd, 15 Airfield Rd, Christchurch, Dorset, BH23 3TG Tel: (01202) 409409 Fax: (01202) 409475 E-mail: sales@pennyandgiles.com Purchasing Contact: L Stammas Sales Contact: C. Durling Principal Export Areas: Worldwide *Penny + Giles Controls Ltd is an established manufacturer of high quality transducers, position sensors, joystick controllers, audio faders, solenoid valves and associated signal conditioning electronics. We specialise in rapid delivery of standard products, but are also experts in the design of custom solutions for the large volume user. We work with the largest names in the industry. Our position sensors are the first choice by Formula One teams. Our linear and rotary transducers are selected by aircraft systems designers for their reliability and performance under critical conditions. Our studio faders are a benchmark in the audio and broadcasting industries. Our joystick controllers are the most rugged for Off-Highway vehicle use. We have over 50 years of knowledge and experience in solving customer's application problems by using the most appropriate technology, packaged to match your operating environment.*

Penny & Giles Controls Ltd, Unit 36 Nine Mile Point Industrial Estate, Cwmfelinfach, Ynysddu, Newport, Gwent, NP11 7HZ Tel: (01495) 202000 Fax: (01495) 202006 E-mail: sales@pennyandgiles.com *Sound recording & aerospace equipment*

Penny Hydraulics Ltd, Station Road, Clowne, Chesterfield, Derbyshire, S43 4AB Tel: (01246) 811475 Fax: (01246) 810403 E-mail: sales@pennyhydraulics.com *Hydraulic engineers*

▶ Penny Lane Builders, 88 Ash Grove, Wavertree, Liverpool, L15 1ET Tel: 0151-734 2171 Fax: 0151-733 9208 E-mail: office@pennylanebuilders.co.uk

Penny Lane Computers Ltd, 243 Dales Road, Ipswich, IP1 4JY Tel: (01473) 255955 Fax: (01473) 255900 E-mail: tech@pennylane.co.uk *Computer sales & services*

▶ Penny Pack Ltd, 22 Blackhurst Road, Lydiate, Liverpool, L31 4JW Tel: 0151-520 0880 Fax: 0151-520 0890 E-mail: info@pennypack.co.uk *Cost effective packaging solutions for the North West. Supplier of all types of packaging with a quick turnaround and unique solutions to your packaging problems.*

▶ Penny Print, Hills Court, Brittania Enterprise Park, Blaydon-on-Tyne, Tyne & Wear, NE21 5NH Tel: 0191-499 0808

Pennycress Computers, 5 St. James Street, Weston-super-Mare, Avon, BS23 1SS Tel: (01934) 644893 Fax: (01934) 644863 E-mail: pennycress@hotmail.com *Computers selling & repair*

Penrhos Marine, The Boat Yard, Aberdovey, Gwynedd, LL35 0RY Tel: (01654) 767478 *Boat builders*

Penridge Multi-Media Ltd, The Barn, Rashwood Meadow, Rashwood Hill, Rashwood, Droitwich, Worcestershire, WR9 0BJ Tel: (01527) 861911 Fax: (01527) 861899 E-mail: sales@penridge.com *Manufacturer & supplier of video tapes*

Penrith Survival Equipment, Sandale, Coupland Beck, Appleby-in-Westmorland, Cumbria, CA16 6LN Tel: (01768) 351666 Fax: (01768) 353666 E-mail: hg@survival.u-net.com *Survival equipment manufrs*

Penrose, 50 Church Street, Falmouth, Cornwall, TR11 3DS Tel: (01326) 312705 Fax: (01326) 312033 E-mail: robbie@penrosesales.freeserve.co.uk *Cover & sail makers*

Penrose Wood Industries Ltd, Whitesmith, Lewes, East Sussex, BN8 6JB Tel: (01825) 872828 Fax: (01825) 873059 *Sawmill manufrs*

Pens Unlimited, 1 Pottery Units, Forde Road, Newton Abbot, Devon, TQ12 4AD Tel: (01626) 334520 Fax: (01626) 334519 E-mail: pens.unltd@virgin.net *Printed promotional pens & souvenirs designers*

Penshaw Engineering Ltd, 23 Harvey Close, Crowther, Washington, Tyne & Wear, NE38 0AB Tel: 0191-416 5013 Fax: 0191-415 3949 *Precision engineers & toolmakers*

▶ Pensher-Skytech, Felling Works, William Street, Gateshead, Tyne & Wear, NE10 0JP Tel: 0191-438 0455 Fax: 0191-438 2328 E-mail: sales@pensher.co.uk *Pensher Skytech specialises in the manufacture and installation of a range of metal doors, screens, windows, curtain walling, and glazed structures. Specialist performance fenestration systems include fire, bomb blast, bullet and vandal resistance for both the on-shore and marine markets.*

Penspell Ltd, 1 Bradfield Road, Finedon Road Industrial Estate, Wellingborough, Northamptonshire, NN8 4HB Tel: (01933) 443605 Fax: (01933) 271489 E-mail: penspell@btclick.com *Plastic injection mouldings manufacturers. Also automotive industry plastic mouldings & plastic engineered products/components*

▶ Penstar Process & Technical Services Ltd, Penstar, Rhoshill, Cardigan, Dyfed, SA43 2TX Tel: (01239) 841458 Fax: (01239) 841307 E-mail: sales@penstar.co.uk *Water treatment company*

Pensteel Ltd, Unit 1, Horndon Industrial Park, West Horndon, Essex, CM13 3XL Tel: (01277) 810211 Fax: (01277) 811971 E-mail: sales@pensteel.co.uk *Liquid packaging service*

Penta Consulting, Chervil House, 28 Stafford Road, Wallington, Surrey, SM6 9BH Tel: (020) 8647 3999 Fax: (020) 8647 2777 *IT recruitment agents*

Penta Precision Engineering Ltd, Aspen House, Airport Service Road, Portsmouth, PO3 5RA Tel: (023) 9266 8334 Fax: (023) 9266 8335 E-mail: sales@pentaprecision.co.uk *Manufacturers of precision machined components & tooling in aluminium, plastic, stainless & tool steel, carbide & ceramic.*

▶ Pentacor plc, Capital House 4 Parkhouse Business Centre, Desborough Park Road, High Wycombe, Buckinghamshire, HP12 3DJ Tel: (01494) 898300 Fax: (01494) 898301 E-mail: info@pentacor.co.uk *Local Creative Design Company in High Wycombe, who are creative experts in Logo design, Direct mail, Concept, Corporate Identities, & all design other related services.*

Pentad Engineering, Unit 10, The Parkway Centre, Heneage Street, Birmingham, B7 4LY Tel: 0121-359 5190 Fax: 0121-359 4743 E-mail: sales@pentad.net *Bearing material manufrs*

Pentag Gears & Oilfield Equipment Ltd, 5 John Street, Sheffield, S2 4QR Tel: 0114-258 3473 Fax: 0114-258 4264 E-mail: meril@pentage-gears.com *Manufacturers of gears: precision, spur & worm*

Pentagon Alarms, 27 The Gables, Dinas Powys, South Glamorgan, CF64 4DN Tel: (07767) 202397 Fax: 029 20515521 *Security installations*

Pentagon Auto Tints, Freeth Street, Unit 14-15, Birmingham, B16 0QZ Tel: 0121-456 1516 Fax: 0121 456 2826 *Operating from Birmingham, Pentagon Auto-Tints is a lively company offering window tinting /auto electrics to clients throughout Birmingham. Formed in 2000 the company has years of experience in the Window Tinting business. Pentagon Auto-Tints complement the existing hue of automotive glass to produce a richer, more distinctive appearance, dramatically enhancing the look of any type of vehicle and adding value. *The Pentagon system of tinting is so professional that it is impossible to distinguish between Pentagon finish and the original glass.*

Pentagon Chemicals, Dock Road, Northside, Workington, Cumbria, CA14 1JJ Tel: (01900) 604371 Fax: (01900) 66943 E-mail: sales@pentagonchemicals.co.uk Principal Export Areas: Worldwide *Chemical suppliers*

▶ Pentagon Colourprint Ltd, Pentagon House, Park Road, St. Helens, Merseyside, WA11 9AZ Tel: (01744) 697500 Fax: (01744) 25115

▶ Pentagon Control Systems Ltd, Unit 2, Burton Close, Norwich, NR6 6AZ Tel: (01603) 404828 *Electrical control panel manufrs*

Pentagon Control Systems, The Old Vicarage, Whitlingham Lane, Trowse, Norwich, NR14 8TN Tel: (01603) 629909 Fax: (01603) 666379 E-mail: enquiries@pentagon-controls.co.uk *Control panels manufrs*

Pentagon Freight Services plc, Pentagon House, Unit 102 Crayfield Industrial Park, Orpington, Kent, BR5 3HP Tel: (01689) 877777 Fax: (01689) 878477 E-mail: operations@pfsheadoffice.co.uk *International freight forwarders*

Pentagon Instruments Ltd, Unit 4 Wayside, Commerce Way, Lancing, West Sussex, BN15 8SW Tel: (01903) 765225 Fax: (01903) 765547E-mail: sales@pentagoninstruments.com *Instrument & transducer manufrs*

Pentagon Press Ltd, Harriot Drive, Heathcote Industrial Estate, Warwick, CV34 6TJ Tel: (01926) 833481 Fax: (01926) 314017 *Commercial printers*

Pentagon-Europe Ltd, No11 Earlsfield, Holyport, Maidenhead, Berkshire, SL6 2LZ Tel: (01628) 627247 Fax: (01628) 624553 *Fume extraction equipment manufrs*

Pentagram Design Ltd, 11 Needham Road, London, W11 2RP Tel: (020) 7229 3477 Fax: (020) 7727 9932 E-mail: email@pentagram.co.uk *Graphic & product design*

▶ Pentalver Container Sales, West Bay Road, Western Docks, Southampton, SO15 0GN Tel: (023) 8070 6070 Fax: (023) 8070 6074 E-mail: soupentsal@pentalver.com *Container sales & storage*

Pentam Composites, 9 Martin Court, Bleneim Industrial Estate, Nottingham, NG6 8US Tel: 0115-979 4494 Fax: 0115-979 4495 *Glass fibre mouldings manufrs*

▶ Pentangle Engineering Services Ltd, Isaac Newton Way, Grantham, Lincolnshire, NG31 9RT Tel: (01476) 572354 Fax: (01476) 590356 E-mail: nigel.rivers@pentangle-eng.co.uk *Engineering welding equipment suppliers*

Pentax UK Ltd, Pentax House, Heron Drive, Slough, SL3 8PN Tel: (01753) 792792 Fax: (01753) 792794 E-mail: contactus@.pentax.co.uk *Optical & electronic products suppliers*

Pentech Moulding Co. Ltd, Pump Lane Industrial Estate, Silverdale Road, Hayes, Middlesex, UB3 3BN Tel: (020) 8569 3439 Fax: (020) 8569 1219 E-mail: rapidpartner@gmail.com *Plastic injection moulders & mould manufrs*

Pentex Sales Ltd, Hamilton House Broadfields, Bicester Road, Aylesbury, Buckinghamshire, HP19 3BG Tel: (01296) 318220 Fax: (01296) 339973 E-mail: sales@pentex.co.uk *Thermoforming & injection moulds, extrusion sheet & film, flat dies, dy offset printing machinery*

▶ Pentland Ferries Ltd, The Pier, St. Margarets Hope, Orkney, KW17 2SW Tel: (01856) 831226 Fax: (01856) 831614 E-mail: sales@pentlandferries.co.uk

▶ Pentland Precision Engineering, Unit 1-4 Pentland View, Pentland Industrial Estate, Loanhead, Midlothian, EH20 9QH Tel: 0131-448 2224

Pentland Security Scotland, 8 The Loan, Loanhead, Midlothian, EH20 9AF Tel: 0131-440 4466 Fax: 0131-440 4499 *Burglar alarm installation*

Pentland Systems, 8 Alderstone Business Park, Macmillan Road, Livingston, West Lothian, EH54 7DF Tel: (01506) 464666 Fax: (01506) 463030 E-mail: sales@pentlandsys.com *Bus boards*

▶ Pentland Tech, 8 Hardengreen Industrial Estate, Dalkeith, Midlothian, EH22 3NX Tel: 0131-561 9373 Fax: 0131-561 9374 *Fabrication sheet metalworkers*

Pentol Enviro UK Ltd, Belasis Business Centre, Coxwold Way, Belasis Hall Technology Park, Billingham, Cleveland, TS23 4EA Tel: (01642) 566086 Fax: (01642) 560087 E-mail: office.gb@pentol.co.uk *Flue gas conditioning chemicals*

Penton Service Centre Ltd, Penton Hook Marina, Mixnams Lane, Chertsey, Surrey, KT16 8QR Tel: (01932) 568772 Fax: (01932) 568967 E-mail: sales@pentonservicecentre.co.uk *Marine engineers*

Pentonville Rubber Products Ltd, 104-106 Pentonville Road, London, N1 9JB Tel: (020) 7837 4582 Fax: (020) 7278 7392 E-mail: enquiries@pentonvillerubber.co.uk *Foam rubber factors*

Pentos Office Furniture Ltd, Asher Lane, Pentrich, Ripley, Derbyshire, DE5 3RE Tel: (01773) 570700 Fax: (01773) 570160 E-mail: email@pentos-plc.co.uk *Workspace office furniture manufrs*

▶ Pentranic Group Ltd, 4 Michaelson Square, Kirkton Campus, Livingston, West Lothian, EH54 7DP Tel: (01506) 463330 Fax: (01506) 463320 E-mail: info@pentranic.com *Manufacturers suppliers of displays, touch screen monitors for gaming*

Pentre Overseas Holdings Ltd, Neills Road, Bold Industrial Park, Bold, St. Helens, Merseyside, WA9 4TJ Tel: (01744) 811820 Fax: (01744) 819994 E-mail: sales@pentre.co.uk *Engineering*

Pentre Reels Ltd, Unit 2 Moss Industrial Estate, Off St Helens Road, Leigh, Lancashire, WN7 3PF Tel: (01942) 607080 Fax: (01942) 261878 E-mail: sales@pentrereels.co.uk *Cable reel & drum manufrs*

Penygroes Concrete Products Ltd, Norton Road, Penygroes, Llanelli, Dyfed, SA14 7RU Tel: (01269) 842278 Fax: (01269) 845026 *Concrete blocks*

▶ Penzance Computer Centre, 76 Market Jew Street, Penzance, Cornwall, TR18 2LG Tel: (01736) 366999 Fax: (01736) 366999 E-mail: sales@pzcomputers.com *Retail computer services with backup repairs & maintenance section*

Penzance Dry Dock Ltd, Wharf Road, Penzance, Cornwall, TR18 4BW Tel: (01736) 363838 Fax: (01736) 351207 E-mail: admiral.1@btconnect.com *Dry dock facilities ship repairers*

People Agenda Ltd, 167 Watling St West, Towcester, Northamptonshire, NN12 6BX Tel: (01327) 354871 Fax: (01327) 358799 E-mail: sales@peopleagenda.com *Search selection assessment outplacement services*

▶ People and Performance Consulting, 400 Thames Valley Park Drive, Thames Valley Park, Reading, RG6 1PT Tel: 0118 9653440 Fax: 0118 9653441 E-mail: contact@papcl.com *People and Performance is an organisational development and people management consultancy, working on developing people processes, top team and management development, executive coaching, assessment, performance management, culture change and organisational improvement, 360 and other surveys.*

▶ The People Consultancy, 18 Clapgate Road, Bushey, WD23 3NF Tel: (020) 8950 2876 E-mail: rachel@peopleconsultancy.com *Recruitment services*

People Marketing, 4 Bowden Drive, Boulevard Industrial Park, Beeston, Nottingham, NG9 2JY Tel: 0115-922 3335 Fax: 0115-922 6560 E-mail: sales@peoplemarketing.co.uk *Recruitment consultancy*

People & Property Ltd, 18 Coulson Street, London, SW3 3NB Tel: (020) 7225 1313 Fax: (020) 7225 2765 E-mail: peopleandproperty@btinternet.com *Relocation for executive*

▶ People Tree Training, 117 Windingbrook Lane, Collingtree Park, Northampton, NN4 0XN Tel: (07712) 582957 E-mail: info@peopletreetraining.co.uk *Sally Foan is a personal development coach specialising in the field of communication. Group training and one to one coaching available in-house or at our quality venue in the midlands. Do you need to improve core skills for both business and life success? Sally can help improve assertiveness, presentation skills, interpersonal skills, customer care skills and much more. If you are rolling out an appraisal system you need your people to be able to deliver feedback in a way that addresses the issues but does not destroy motivation. Sally can help you and your colleagues to deliver effective feedback to any sort of colleague for positive results. For a full list of avaliable courses, client portfolio and delegate feedback please go to www.peopletreetraining.co.uk**

Pep Socks, 3 Clyde Street, Leicester, LE1 2BG Tel: 0116-251 1467 Fax: 0116-251 1467 *Socks manufrs*

Pepberry Ltd, Marwain House, Clarke Road, Bletchley, Milton Keynes, MK1 1LG Tel: (01908) 643022 Fax: (01908) 648132 *General commercial & small packaging printers services*

Pepcon Ltd, PO Box 272, Sunbury-on-Thames, Middlesex, TW16 6WB Tel: (01932) 788545 Fax: (01932) 788496 E-mail: sales@pepcon.org *Builders fixtures & fittings & construction chemicals*

▶ Pepe Garden Furniture, Unit 2b Honeybourne Airfield Trading Estate, Honeybourne, Evesham, Worcestershire, WR11 7QF Tel: (01386) 833211 Fax: (01386) 833269 E-mail: info@pepegarden.co.uk *Garden furniture retailers*

Pepe Jeans (London) Ltd, 99C Talbot Road, London, W11 2AT Tel: (020) 7313 3800 Fax: (020) 7313 3803 *Denim wear distributors*

▶ Pepi Plumbers, 7 Wellburn Street, Dundee, DD2 2RR Tel: (01382) 623222

▶ Peplertech Ltd, The Vicarage, Birtles Lane, Over Alderley, Macclesfield, Cheshire, SK10 4RX Tel: (01625) 861443 Fax: (01625) 861445 E-mail: info@peplertech.co.uk *Equipment software services to pcb industry*

Peplicity Ltd, 20a Meadow Lane, Loughborough, Leicestershire, LE11 1JY Tel: (01509) 217397 Fax: (01509) 217397 *Screen process printers*

Peplow Concrete Products, 1 Swinton Road, Mexborough, South Yorkshire, S64 9JB Tel: (01709) 570812 *Concrete product manufrs*

Pepper Kitchens, Station Road, Warboys, Huntingdon, Cambridgeshire, PE28 2TH Tel: (01487) 822882 Fax: (01487) 826001 E-mail: pepperkit@aol.com *Kitchen furniture manufrs*

Peppercorn 84, 11 Railway Street, Pocklington, York, YO42 2QR Tel: (01759) 303275 Fax: (01759) 303275 *Whole foods & health foods distributors & retailers*

Peppercorn Pine, 25 High Street, Headcorn, Ashford, Kent, TN27 9NH Tel: (01622) 891773 Fax: (01622) 891773 *Pine furniture sales*

Pepperl & Fuchs, 77 Ripponden Road, Oldham, OL1 4EL Tel: 0161-633 6431 Fax: 0161-624 6537 E-mail: sales@pepperl-fuchs.com *Products control & automation services*

Pepperl & Fuchs, 77 Ripponden Road, Oldham, OL1 4EL Tel: 0161-633 6431 Fax: 0161-624 6537 E-mail: sales@pepperl-fuchs.com *Manufacturer of electronic products* Also at: Fleet

Peppers Marquees Ltd, Crosshill, Snaith, Goole, North Humberside, DN14 9JT Tel: (01405) 860249 Fax: (01405) 862098 E-mail: info@peppersmarquees.co.uk *Contract marquee hire*

Pera, Pera Innovation Park, Melton Mowbray, Leicestershire, LE13 0PB Tel: (01664) 501501 Fax: (01664) 501264 E-mail: sales@pera.com *Consultancy & technology developers* Also at: Glasgow, London SW1, Oxford & Swindon

Peradon Ltd, 128 Richmond Row, Liverpool, L3 3BL Tel: 0151-298 1470 Fax: 0151-298 2988 E-mail: peradon@eaclare.co.uk Principal Export Areas: Worldwide *Snooker & billiard cue manufrs*

Perception Kayaks Ltd, Bellbrook Business Park, Uckfield, East Sussex, TN22 1QQ Tel: (01825) 765891 Fax: (01825) 763707 E-mail: info@perception.co.uk *Canoes, kayaks & water sports goods manufrs*

▶ Perceptions International Ltd, Unit 15 Dawkins Business Centre, Dawkins Road, Poole, Dorset, BH15 4JY Tel: (01202) 676282 Fax: (01202) 660103

Company Information

Perchcourt Ltd, Unit 6b Heath St Industrial Estate, Abberley Street, Smethwick, West Midlands, B66 2QZ Tel: 0121-555 6161 Fax: 0121-555 6176 E-mail: sales@perchcourt.co.uk *Stainless steel stockholders*

H.A. Percheron Ltd, 202 The Chambers, Chelsea Harbour, London, SW10 0XF Tel: (020) 7349 1590 Fax: (020) 7349 1595 E-mail: info@hapercheron.co.uk *Furnishing fabric importers*

Percival Aviation, Sapphire House, 15 Barnes Wallis Road, Fareham, Hampshire, PO15 5TT Tel: (01489) 564378 Fax: (01489) 569050 E-mail: info@percival-aviation.co.uk *Aerospace safety & interior products services*

Percival Engineering Ltd, Spring Valley Lane, Ardleigh, Colchester, CO7 7SB Tel: (01206) 230064 Fax: (01206) 231655 E-mail: sales@percivalengineering.co.uk *Earth moving equipment repairs*

Joseph Percival & Co., Shawcross Street, Stockport, Cheshire, SK1 3EZ Tel: 0161-480 3858 Fax: 0161-480 7394 *Steel fabricators & architectural metalworkers*

Percliff Plant Hire Ltd, Percliff Way, Philips Road, Blackburn, BB1 5PF Tel: (01254) 676600 Fax: (01254) 676630 E-mail: info@percliff.co.uk *Construction plant hire*

Percuil Boat Yard, Portscatho, Truro, Cornwall, TR2 5ES Tel: (01872) 580564 Fax: (01872) 580044 *Boat maintenance & repairs*

▶ Percy Ingles Bakery Ltd, The Pavilion, High Street, Waltham Cross, Hertfordshire, EN8 7BZ Tel: (01992) 767403 *Bakers*

Percy Lane Ltd, Lichfield Road, Tamworth, Staffordshire, B79 7TL Tel: (01827) 63821 Fax: (01827) 310159 E-mail: sales@percy-lane.co.uk *Aluminium window & door manufacturers for vehicles & portable buildings*

Perdaw Engineering Co. Ltd, 4 Liverpool Road, Cadishead, Manchester, M44 5AF Tel: 0161-775 4133 Fax: 0161-777 9634 E-mail: sales@perdaw.co.uk *Architectural ironworkers*

▶ Perdune Ltd, Hayward Road Indust Estate, Hayward Road, Staple Hill, Bristol, BS16 4NY Tel: 0117-957 4499 Fax: 0117-957 6955

▶ Peregrine International, 1 Berkeley Street, London, W1J 8DJ Tel: (0800) 0432211 E-mail: info@peregrine-international.com *Security consultant, bodyguard, surveillance, investigations & business intelligence services, operating locally, nationally & internationally*

Peregrine Systems Ltd, Peregrine House, 26-28 Paradise Road, Richmond, Surrey, TW9 1SE Tel: (020) 8332 9666 Fax: (020) 8939 1170 *Software infrastructure management company*

Perei Group Ltd, Sunbury House 4 Christy Estate, Ivy Road, Aldershot, Hampshire, GU12 4TX Tel: (01252) 350833 Fax: (01252) 350875 E-mail: enquiries@perei.co.uk *Motor vehicle lamps & lighting fitting manufrs*

Perfab Engineering Ltd, Unit 3 Northway Lane, Tewkesbury, Gloucestershire, GL20 8HA Tel: (01684) 298423 Fax: (01684) 850427 *Fabricators & engineers*

▶ Perfect Banqueting, PO BOX 2104, Leigh-on-Sea, Essex, SS9 3WW Tel: 01702 476360 E-mail: perfectbanqueting@uwclub.net *More than just caterers....*Family Celebrations.*Corporate Functions.*Business Lunches.*Dinner Dances.*Full Silver Service.*Buffets and Bereavements.*and also featuring "The Perfect Day", Wedding Receptions.*

Perfect Engineering, Harfreys Road, Great Yarmouth, Norfolk, NR31 0JL Tel: (01493) 657131 Fax: (01493) 441526 E-mail: info@lgperfect.com *MOT's & repair services*

▶ Perfect Example, Kendall, Roack Road, St. Minver, Wadebridge, Cornwall, PL27 6PN Tel: (01208) 869555 E-mail: info@perfectexample.co.uk *Domestic cleaning in North Cornwall. We offer the following quality services: Regular House Cleans, Spring Cleans, Full Holiday Home Services, Property Management Services, Spring/Builder/Tenant, Housekeeper Services, Property Security Checks and Linen & laundry Services. For a free consultation, please telephone 01208 869555*

Perfect Leather Sales Ltd, Carmel Works, Chapel Street, Porth, Mid Glamorgan, CF39 0PU Tel: (01443) 757150 Fax: (01443) 757150 E-mail: petervalek@petervalek.worldonline.co.uk *Watch straps manufacturer*

▶ Perfect Logistics Ltd, Churchill Road, Doncaster, South Yorkshire, DN1 2TH Tel: (01302) 363733 Fax: (01302) 730797

▶ Perfect Media, 15 Queen Square, Leeds, LS2 8AJ Tel: 08707 121999 Fax: 08707 121999 E-mail: info@perfectit.co.uk *perfect IT are a professional web design specialist with offices in Leeds, West Yorkshire and Bolton, Lancahire, England offering bespoke website design, e-commerce solutions, content management systems, web development, Flash, graphic design and Internet marketing services including email campaigns and search engine optimisation.*

Perfect Pipework Ltd, 49 Rabans Close, Rabans Lane Industrial Area, Aylesbury, Buckinghamshire, HP19 8RS Tel: (01296) 399330 Fax: (01296) 487029 E-mail: sales@perfectpipework.co.uk *Plumbing & heating engineers*

▶ Perfect Solutions Cosmetics & Toiletries, 2d Northlands Bus Park, Bognor Road, Warnham, Horsham, West Sussex, RH12 3SH Tel: (01306) 628484 Fax: (01306) 628485 E-mail: enquiries@perfectsolutions-ct.com

Perfecta Ltd, Ashmead Business Centre, Ashmead Road, Keynsham, Bristol, BS31 1SX Tel: 0117-986 8800 Fax: 0117-986 1687 E-mail: info@perfecta.ltd.uk *Herbs spices package, distributors & manufrs*

Perfecta Windows, Unit 11, Longton Trading Estate, Winterstoke Road, Weston-super-Mare, Avon, BS23 3YB Tel: (01934) 624632 Fax: (01934) 636631 *PVC frame window installers*

▶ perfectevents, No 18., Salford, M7 2FS Tel: 0161 792 0915 E-mail: lolaheavey@perfectevents.org.uk *Corporate catering and sandwich delivery service to businesses. Outside catering for children''s parties, coming of age parties and all other social events. African and Caribbean catering our speciality.*

Perfectio Print Finishers Ltd, Wright Street, Manchester, M16 9EW Tel: 0161-877 6238 Fax: 0161-872 0514 *Commercial print finishing services*

Perfection Electro Plating Ltd, Unit 2 Brunswick Industrial Centre, Hertford Street, Birmingham, B12 8NJ Tel: 0121-440 3173 Fax: 0121-440 2661 *Brass plating specialists*

Perfectools Plastics, Coombend, Radstock, BA3 3AS Tel: (01761) 432299 Fax: (01761) 435575 E-mail: sales@perfecttools.co.uk *Injection/plastic mould toolmakers & plastic mouldings manufrs*

Perfectos Printing Inks Co. Ltd, Perfectos Mills, Normanton Lane, Bottesford, Nottingham, NG13 0EL Tel: (01949) 842179 Fax: (01949) 843493 E-mail: info@perfectos.co.uk *Specialised printing inks*

Perforag Ltd, Unit 4, Greaves Way, Leighton Buzzard, Bedfordshire, LU7 4UB Tel: (01525) 376743 Fax: (01525) 850297 E-mail: sales@perforag.com *Photo-finishing material distributors*

▶ Performance Alloys.com, Randalstown Road, Enkalon Industrial Estate, Antrim, BT41 4LD Tel: (028) 9446 5151 E-mail: sales@performancealloys.com *Alloy wheels suppliers*

▶ Performance Analytics Ltd, 212 Piccadilly, London, W1J 9HG Tel: (0845) 0574155 Fax: (020) 7439 0262 E-mail: info@performanceanalytics.co.uk *We provide software & consultancy services*

▶ Performance Automotive, Unit 5 Bridgeway, St. Leonards-On-Sea, East Sussex, TN38 8AP Tel: 01424 200825 E-mail: performanceautomotive@hotmail.co.uk *At Performance Automotive we are here to do the day to day maintenance and servicing of your car, including MOT's, Brakes, welding etc, but our hearts lay with Racing, Tuning, and the engineering involved in building and preparing road /rally performance cars.**Performance Automotive currently prepare and maintain six cars for Rally Cross, Enduro Rally, and Road Rally.**So if you are in need of any of the services we list, just give us a call, and we will be happy to help from family cars to performance cars.*

Performance Composites Ltd, Unit 13a The Old Sawmills, Halves Lane, East Coker, Yeovil, Somerset, BA22 9JJ Tel: (01935) 864098 Fax: (01935) 863807 E-mail: sms@performance-composites.com *Carbon composite engineers*

Performance Computers North East Ltd, 10-11 Post House Wynd, Darlington, County Durham, DL3 7LU Tel: (01325) 267333 Fax: (01325) 489093 E-mail: sales@performancecomputers.co.uk *Computer retailers*

Performance Computers North East Ltd, 4 Zetland Street, Northallerton, North Yorkshire, DL6 1NA Tel: (01609) 772442 Fax: (0871) 2771281 E-mail: northallerton@performancecomputers.co.uk *Computer software suppliers*

▶ Performance Construction, Greenland Crescent, Cardiff, Cardiff, CF5 3HE Tel: 02920 218995 Fax: 02920 218995 *Fixing and Maintenance :**windows, doors, patio doors, curtain walls - aluminium/UPVC**beds and bedroom furniture fitted**kitchen and bathroom furniture fitted* All building works completed with minimum distruption*** Call Martin on: 07868 766543*

▶ Performance Dynamics (UK), 192 Hinckley Road, Leicester Forest East, Leicester, LE3 3LR Tel: (0844) 484 5431 *INTERNAL CONSULTANCY SKILLS COURSES: 2-day in-house Internal Consultancy Skills courses in London, Birmingham, Manchester, Bristol, Edinburgh, Glasgow and Newcastle. For specialists in HR, IT, OD, Project Management, Learning & Development, Business Improvement, Risk Management, QA, Internal Audit etc*

▶ Performance Electrical Ltd, 123 Radcliffe Road, Bury, Lancashire, BL9 9LD Tel: 0161-797 3476 Fax: 0161-764 2903 E-mail: sales@performanceelectrical.co.uk

Performance Feeders, Lavender House, Station Road, Hammerwich, Burntwood, Staffordshire, WS7 0JZ Tel: (01543) 454055 Fax: (01543) 454047 E-mail: enquiries@performancefeeders.co.uk *Vibratory bowl feeder equipment, vibratory feeder conveyor, elevator manufrs*

▶ Performance Improvement Associates, Peregrino House, 33, Crimchard, Chard, Somerset, TA20 1JT Tel: 01460 239020 Fax: 01460 239020 E-mail: enquiries@perfimp.com *Over 15 years'' experience, throughout the British Isles, focussing exclusively on aiding Human Resources/Training organisations & Consultants to identify, win & retain new clients. All programmes are designed - with the client - to match their precise needs, situation & budget.*

Performance Master Batches Ltd, Blaenant Industrial Estate, Blaenavon Road, Brynmawr, Ebbw Vale, Gwent, NP23 4BX Tel: (01495) 310583 Fax: (01495) 312158 E-mail: customer.service@pmb.co.uk *Colour & performance masterbatches manufrs*

Performance Master Batches Ltd, Blaenant Industrial Estate, Blaenavon Road, Brynmawr, Ebbw Vale, Gwent, NP23 4BX Tel: (01495) 310583 Fax: (01495) 312158 E-mail: customer.service@pmb.co.uk *Plastic coloured granules*

Performance Monitoring Systems Ltd, 52 Coventry Street, Southam, Warwickshire, CV47 0EP Tel: (01926) 814846 Fax: (01926) 815516 *Computer software designers*

▶ Performance Motorcare Products Ltd, 64 Elmbridge Road, Birmingham, B44 8AD Tel: 0121-694 5537 E-mail: info@performancemotorcare.com *Quality*

continued

car and motor care products including Meguiars, Mothers, Sonax, Chamois Leathers, Microfibre Cloths, Waxes, Polishes, Leather care, Hydra Flexi Blades - Buy Online.

▶ Performance Oils Ltd, 40 Broad Walk, Hounslow, TW5 9AQ Tel: (020) 8737 0649 Fax: (020) 8577 3974 E-mail: greenlynx@blueyonder.co.uk *Online retailers of performance oils for automotive industry*

▶ Performance Plastics, Brock House, Grigg Lane, Brockenhurst, Hampshire, SO42 7RE Tel: (01590) 622666 Fax: (01590) 622629 E-mail: info@performance-plastics.co.uk *Distributors of Engineering Thermoplastic Raw Materials*

Performance Products Ltd, Cleaver House, Sarus Court, Manor Park, Runcorn, Cheshire, WA7 1UL Tel: (01928) 579579 Fax: (0870) 7871700 *Car suppliers*

Performance Sailcraft (Europe) Ltd, Station Works, Station Road, Long Buckby, Northampton, NN6 7PF Tel: (01327) 841600 Fax: (01327) 841651 E-mail: info@lasersailing.com *Boat & dinghy builders*

Performance Sails, Victoria Loft, Hill Furze, Pershore, Worcestershire, WR10 2NB Tel: (01386) 861161 Fax: (01386) 861253 E-mail: performancesails@hotmail.com *Performance sail & tensile structures manufrs*

Performance Springs Ltd, Queensway Industrial Estate, Scafell Road, St Annes, Lytham St. Annes, Lancashire, FY8 3HE Tel: (01253) 716900 Fax: (01253) 716911 E-mail: sales@performance-springs.com *Spring, coil, valve & compression spring manufrs*

Perhome Ltd, 23 Old Court House, 24 Old Court Place, London, W8 4PD Tel: (020) 7938 4099 Fax: (020) 7938 2409 *Export service company*

Periam & Williamson Ltd, Norfolk Street, Boston, Lincolnshire, PE21 6PW Tel: (01205) 362281 Fax: (01205) 362281 E-mail: richard@p-wltd.totalserve.co.uk *Electrical contractors & engineers*

Pericom P.L.C., The Priory, Cosgrove, Milton Keynes, MK19 7JJ Tel: (01908) 265533 Fax: (01908) 265534 E-mail: sales@pericom.co.uk *IT services*

Pericom SW Ltd, 46b Sea King Road, Lynx Trading Estate, Yeovil, Somerset, BA20 2NZ Tel: (01935) 410377 Fax: (01935) 410755 E-mail: mail@lbts.co.uk Principal Export Areas: Central/East Europe *Computer services*

Perimeter Internal Protection, Office 32, The Valley, 67 Church Road, Newtownabbey, County Antrim, BT36 7LS Tel: (028) 9086 8413 Fax: (028) 9086 8718 E-mail: info@pipsecurity.com *Security systems*

Perimeter Security Solutions, Roeacre House, Fir Street, Heywood, Lancashire, OL10 1NW Tel: (0870) 8508739 Fax: (01706) 627767 *Alarm systems services & installers*

Period Flooring, Commerce House, 4 High Street, Nutfield, Redhill, RH1 4HQ Tel: (01737) 823053 Fax: (01737) 822862 E-mail: info@stairropes.co.uk *handmade stair ropes, bannister ropes, handrails etc... mail order or visit our showroom*

Period Oak Reproduction Ltd, Stonham Road, Mickfield, Stowmarket, Suffolk, IP14 5LS Tel: (01449) 711782 Fax: (01449) 711569 *Oak furniture reproduction company*

Peripheral Store, 2 Manorial Road, Sutton Coldfield, West Midlands, B75 5UD Tel: 0121-323 3633 Fax: 0121-323 3535 *Colour printers & supplies*

Peripheral Support Services Ltd, Unit 14 Enterprise Court, Rankine Road, Basingstoke, Hampshire, RG24 8GE Tel: (01256) 844685 Fax: (01256) 810082 E-mail: sales@pss-firequest.co.uk *Fire alarm manufrs*

▶ Peritus Training, Kingsland House, 512 Wimborne Road East, Ferndown, Dorset, BH22 9NG Tel: (01202) 871971 Fax: (01202) 871971

Peritys Greenhouses, Bona Lane, Leverington, Wisbech, Cambridgeshire, PE13 5JQ Tel: (01945) 410471 Fax: (01945) 410471 E-mail: sales@peritys.co.uk *Greenhouse manufrs*

Perkin Elmer, Sorbus House, Mulberry Business Park, Wokingham, Berkshire, RG41 2GY Tel: 0118-977 3003 Fax: 0118-977 3493 E-mail: sales@perkinelmer.com *Fibre optic equipment manufrs*

Perkinelmer Ltd, Chalfont Road, Seer Green, Beaconsfield, Buckinghamshire, HP9 2FX Tel: (01494) 874515 Fax: (01494) 679331 *Scientific instruments supplier*

Perkinelmer Ltd, Chalfont Road, Seer Green, Beaconsfield, Buckinghamshire, HP9 2FX Tel: (01494) 874515 Fax: (01494) 679331 E-mail: greenca@perkin-elmer.com *Analytical laboratory instrument manufrs*

Perkinelmer Ltd, Chalfont Road, Seer Green, Beaconsfield, Buckinghamshire, HP9 2FX Tel: (01494) 874515 Fax: (01494) 679331 E-mail: cc.uk@perkinelmer.com *Scientific & nucleonic instrument manufrs*

Perkins Ltd, Unit 17, Finnimore Trading Estate, Ottery St. Mary, Devon, EX11 1NR Tel: (01404) 812605 Fax: (01404) 815300 E-mail: fwp@fwperkins.prestel.co.uk *Agricultural suppliers*

Perkins Closure Ltd, Lion Gate Ct, Petworth Rd, Witley, Godalming, Surrey, GU8 5QW Tel: 01428 685577 Fax: 01428 684477 *Wine cork suppliers*

Perkins Contracts Ltd, Knights Court, South Chailey, Lewes, East Sussex, BN8 4QF Tel: (01273) 401401 Fax: (01273) 401400 E-mail: info@perkinscontracts.co.uk *Insulation & fire protection distributors*

Perkins Dyers & Cleaners Ltd, 6 Holly Bush Vale, Hampstead, London, NW3 6TX Tel: (020) 7794 4849 Fax: (020) 7433 1088 E-mail: perkinscleaners@aol.com *Dry cleaning & group property development*

Perkins Engine Co (Stafford) Ltd, Tixall Road, Stafford, ST16 3UB Tel: (01785) 215700 Fax: (01785) 215110 *Diesel engine manufrs*

Perkins Engines Co. Ltd, Perkins Powerpart Distribution Centre, Frank Perkins Way, Irlam, Manchester, M44 5PP Tel: 0161-776 5000 Fax: 0161-776 5100 *Diesel engine spare parts distributors*

Perkins Engines Co. Ltd, Frank Perkins Way, Eastfield, Peterborough, PE1 5NA Tel: (01733) 583000 Fax: (01733) 582240 E-mail: purdy_claire@perkins.com *Diesel engine & gas engine manufrs*

M. Perkins & Son Ltd, 2 Weyside Park, Newman Lane, Mill Lane, Alton, Hampshire, GU34 2YY Tel: (01420) 541171 Fax: (01420) 541173 E-mail: sales@mperkins.co.uk *Textile product manufrs*

▶ Perkins & Perry, Wheal Chance, Radnor Road, Redruth, Cornwall, TR16 5EQ Tel: (01209) 820983 Fax: (01209) 821869 E-mail: mail@perkinsandperry.co.uk *Manufacture timber products*

▶ Perkins R & Sons, 201 London Central Markets, London, EC1A 9LH Tel: (020) 7329 4612 Fax: (020) 7329 4192 E-mail: info@rperkins.co.uk *Air conditioning & refrigeration units suppliers & services*

Perkins & Stockwell, 12 Abbey Gate, Leicester, LE4 0AB Tel: 0116-251 6501 Fax: 0116-251 0697 *Curtain manufrs*

▶ Perlam Sheet Metal Work, Wandle Trading Estate, Mill Green Road, Mitcham, Surrey, CR4 4HZ Tel: (020) 8685 9276 Fax: (020) 8640 0551 E-mail: sales@perlamsheetmetal.co.uk *Sheet metal work manufrs*

Perle Systems Europe Ltd, Abbey House, Wellington Way, Brooklands Business Park, Weybridge, Surrey, KT13 0TT Tel: (01932) 268591 Fax: (01932) 268592 E-mail: mwebster@perle.com *Manufactures of serial network connectivity products*

Permabond Laminates Ltd, Gibbons Street, Nottingham, NG7 2SB Tel: 0115-978 7633 Fax: 0115-942 3380 E-mail: sales@permabondlaminates.co.uk *Laminate postforming fabricators, toilet cubicles, worktops, fire doors & reception counters*

Permacell Finesse Ltd, Western Road, Silver End, Witham, Essex, CM8 3QB Tel: (01376) 583241 Fax: (01376) 584227 E-mail: sales@pfl.co.uk *Plastic extrusion manufrs*

Permadeck Systems Ltd, Unit 12 Westside Industrial Estate, Jackson Street, St. Helens, Merseyside, WA9 3AT Tel: (01744) 751869 Fax: (01744) 22551 E-mail: enquiries@safteysurfacing.uk.com *Slip resistant & safety flooring manufrs*

Permadoor, Upton-Upon-Severn, Worcester, WR8 0RX Tel: (01684) 595200 Fax: (01684) 594283 E-mail: info@permadoor.co.uk *Upvc composite door manufrs*

Permafast Ltd, Derby Road, Clay Cross, Chesterfield, Derbyshire, S45 9AG Tel: (01246) 250150 Fax: (01246) 250085 E-mail: info@permafast.co.uk *Industrial fasteners distributors*

Permag Ltd, Block 1 Unit 2 Strutherhill Indust Estate, Larkhall, Lanarkshire, ML9 1LR Tel: (01698) 884823 Fax: (01698) 884823 E-mail: sales@permag.freeuk.com *Transformer cores*

▶ Permagard Car Washing Supplies, 1u-1v Unit Standard Industrial Estate, Factory Road, London, E16 2EJ Tel: (020) 7473 0099 Fax: (020) 7474 0771 E-mail: sales@permagard.info *Paint protection system manufrs*

▶ Permanent Coatings, 33 Normandy Way, Bodmin, Cornwall, PL31 1HA Tel: (01208) 264999 Fax: (01208) 264998 *Paints manufrs*

Permanite, Cawder Quarry, Matlock, Derbyshire, DE4 2JH Tel: (01629) 580680 Fax: (01629) 57099 E-mail: info@permanite-asphalt.co.uk *Mastic & asphalt manufrs* Also at: Salford

Permanoid Ltd, Hulme Hall Lane, Miles Platting, Manchester, M40 8HH Tel: 0161-205 6161 Fax: 0161-205 9325 E-mail: sales@permanoid.co.uk *Electric cable manufrs*

Permarock Products Ltd, Jubilee Drive, Loughborough, Leicestershire, LE11 5TW Tel: (01509) 262924 Fax: (01509) 230063 E-mail: sales@permarock.com *Manufacturers of concrete protection systems*

Permaseal Roofing, PO Box 2, Wellington, Somerset, TA21 0AW Tel: (01823) 662262 Fax: (01823) 662262 *Roofing contractors* Also at: Bristol & Exeter

Permastore Ltd, Airfield Industrial Park, Eye Airfield Industrial Estate, Eye, Suffolk, IP23 7HS Tel: (01379) 870723 Fax: (01379) 870530 E-mail: sales@permastore.co.uk *Sludge, slurry & silo tank manufrs*

Permat Machines Ltd, Station Road, Coleshill, Birmingham, B46 1JG Tel: (01675) 463351 Fax: (01675) 465816 E-mail: sales@permat.com *Permat Machines, a specialist supplier to the automotive industry of production machines and services. They are based in Birmingham and offer a wide range of products and services including honing, superfinishing, tape finishing machines, deep hole drilling machines, assembly and leak testing machines, tooling, diamond and stone supply plus excellent customer support.*

Perma-Tie, 20 South Street, Havant, Hampshire, PO9 1DA Tel: (023) 9266 8116 Fax: (023) 9245 5785 *Wall tie fittings suppliers*

Permatt Fork Lift Trucks, Unit 7c Mylord CR, Camperdown Industrial Estate, Newcastle upon Tyne, NE12 5UJ Tel: (0870) 1451450 Fax: (0870) 1451451 *Fork lift truck hire & sales*

Permess UK Ltd, Low Prudhoe Industrial Estate, Prudhoe, Northumberland, NE42 6HD Tel: (01661) 832774 Fax: (01661) 832633 E-mail: sales@tencate.co.uk *Textile manufrs*

Permoid Industries Ltd, Horndale Avenue, Aycliffe Industrial Estate, Aycliffe Industrial Park, Newton Aycliffe, County Durham, DL5 6DW Tel: (01325) 300767 Fax: (01325) 312186 *Light & non ferrous metal fabricators*

Pernic Forge, Unit B1 Porthmellon Industrial Estate, Porth Mellon, St. Mary's, Isles of Scilly, TR21 0JY Tel: (01720) 423353 Fax: (01720) 423353 *Steel fabricator & general engineers*

▶ Peron Plastics, Unit 10 Dunscar Industrial Estate, Blackburn Road, Egerton, Bolton, BL7 9PQ Tel: (01204) 597546 Fax: (01204) 596928 E-mail: sales@peronplastics.co.uk *We have been established since 1977 specialising in point of sale display casing/fabrications*

continued

continuation throughout the UK. All plastic acrylics can be cut to size. Full packages for museums, retail shops, estate agents, petrol station and many other commercial outlets available.

Peros Ltd, 8 Century Point, Halifax Road, Cressex Business Park, High Wycombe, Buckinghamshire, HP12 3SL Tel: (01494) 436426 Fax: (01494) 769545 E-mail: coffee@peros.co.uk *Peros is based in High Wycombe, Buckinghamshire, and is the UK's leading independent Fairtrade coffee supply and coffee machine company. Services range from marketing to ancillary products plus many more.*

▶ Perpetual Environmental, Cody Technology Park, Ively Road, Farnborough, Hampshire, GU14 0LX Tel: (01252) 395272 Fax: (01252) 395157 *Janitorial equipment suppliers*

Perpetual Photophonics, 10 Park End, London, NW3 2SE Tel: (020) 7435 9880 Fax: (020) 7435 9880 *Audio visual production*

Perrett & Kane Ltd, 2 Pumping Station House Chelvey Lane, West Town, Backwell, Bristol, BS48 4AJ Tel: (01275) 464404 Fax: (01275) 464404 E-mail: enquiries@perrettandkane.co.uk *Food machinery specialists*

Perrigo UK, William Nadin Way, Swadlincote, Derbyshire, DE11 0BB Tel: (01283) 228300 Fax: (01283) 228328 E-mail: info@perrigouk.com *Vitamin & supplement manufrs*

Perrite Plastic Compounds, 1 Kingsland Grange, Woolston, Warrington, WA1 4RA Tel: (01925) 810608 Fax: (01925) 840001 E-mail: sales@jgp-perrite.co.uk *Thermoplastic raw materials manufrs*

Perrott Engineering Group Ltd, Woodroyd, Lightcliffe, Halifax, West Yorkshire, HX3 8PS Tel: (01422) 202575 Fax: (01422) 202959 *Holding company*

Perry Castings, Bank Street, Wolverhampton, WV10 9DU Tel: (01902) 732910 Fax: (01902) 721046 *Aluminum & alloy manufrs*

Perry Clothes Ltd, 43 Carr Crofts, Leeds, LS12 3HB Tel: 0113-263 7841 Fax: 0113-231 1490 E-mail: lisa@perryclothes.co.uk *Schoolwear clothes manufrs*

Perry Ellis Europe Ltd, Crittall Road, Witham, Essex, CM8 3DJ Tel: (01376) 502345 Fax: (01376) 500733 E-mail: custserv@farah.co.uk *Menswear*

Graham Perry Steels Ltd, Units 1-3 Dock Meadow Drive Industrial Estate, Lanesfield Drive, Spring Road, Ettingshall, Wolverhampton, WV4 6LE Tel: (01902) 490450 Fax: (01902) 490217 E-mail: sales@grahamperrysteels.co.uk *Steel stockholders*

Perry & Co Hinges Ltd, Doulton Road, Cradley Heath, West Midlands, B64 5QW Tel: (01384) 414000 Fax: (01384) 411100 E-mail: aperry@hinges.co.uk *Hinge manufacturers plus builders ironwork & security products*

P.G. Perry, Summerfield House, Watling Street, Muckley Corner, Lichfield, Staffordshire, WS14 0BD Tel: (01543) 375695 *Bedroom furniture fittings*

Perry Pearson Engineering Co. Ltd, Unit 6 219 Torrington Avenue, Coventry, CV4 9HN Tel: 024 76460339 *Jig/fixture construction/boring/grinding engineers/custom builders. Also gauges, precision inspection/measurement. In addition. special purpose custom built machinery constructors & multi-spindle drilling machine manufrs*

▶ Perry Plating Jigs & Co. Ltd, 71a Lifford Lane, Birmingham, B30 3DY Tel: 0121 4591800

Perry Process Equipment Ltd, Station Road, Aycliffe Industrial Park, Newton Aycliffe, County Durham, DL5 6EQ Tel: (01325) 315111 Fax: (01325) 301496 E-mail: info@perryprocess.co.uk Purchasing Contact: P. Cook Sales Contact: A. Moat Principal Export Areas: Worldwide *Distributors or agents of chemical plants & equipment*

Perry Slingsby Systems Ltd, Ings Lane, Kirkbymoorside, York, YO62 6EZ Tel: (01751) 431751 Fax: (01751) 431388 E-mail: pssl@uk.perrymail.com *Underwater engineers*

Perry Street Tile Centre, 38 Perry Street, Dungannon, County Tyrone, BT71 6AJ Tel: (028) 8772 9316 Fax: (028) 8772 4939 *Tile merchants*

Tony Perry, Red Bull Basin, 17 Congleton Road South, Church Lawton, Stoke-on-Trent, ST7 3AJ Tel: (01782) 779033 *Boat repair & maintenance*

▶ Perrys, Unit 4 Mitchells Enterprise Centre, Bradberry Balk Lane, Wombwell, Barnsley, South Yorkshire, S73 8HR Tel: (01226) 755655 Fax: (01226) 751172

Perrys Portables, Goatsmoor Lane, Stock, Ingatestone, Essex, CM4 9RS Tel: (01277) 652036 Fax: (01277) 652036 *Shed manufrs*

Perrys Recycling, Rimpton Road, Marston Magna, Yeovil, Somerset, BA22 8DL Tel: (01935) 850111 Fax: (01935) 851555 E-mail: sam@perrys-recycling.co.uk *Security shredding & recyclers services* Also at: Barnstaple, Dorchester & Taunton

▶ Perryscope Productions, 3 Chapel Place, Arthur Street, Montgomery, Powys, SY15 6QZ Tel: (01686) 668114 Fax: (01686) 668537 E-mail: perrypro@globalnet.co.uk *Broadcasting services*

Pershore Leisure Centre, PO Box 2000, Pershore, Worcestershire, WR10 1QU Tel: (01386) 552346 Fax: (01386) 556559 E-mail: post@c2000.com *Computer supply, training, & web design*

Persimmon Consultants Ltd, Pine View, Forest Dale Road, Marlborough, Wiltshire, SN8 2AS Tel: (01672) 514500 E-mail: info@persim.com *Computer maintenance & repair*

Persimmon Homes Ltd, 10 Collingwood Road, Witham, Essex, CM8 2EA Tel: (01376) 518811 Fax: (01376) 514027 *Building contractors*

Persimmon Homes Developments Ltd, Persimmon House, Fulford, York, YO19 4FE Tel: (01904) 642199 Fax: (01904) 610014 *Property developers*

▶ Persimmon Homes East Yorkshire Ltd, Persimmon House, Morton Lane, Beverley, North Humberside, HU17 9DD Tel: (01482) 871885 Fax: (01482) 870080

Persimmon Homes South East Ltd, Persimmons House, Brooklands Business Park, Weybridge, Surrey, KT13 0YP Tel: (01932) 350555 Fax: (01932) 350022 *Construction of homes*

▶ Persimmon Homes South West Ltd, Mallard Road, Sowton Trading Estate, Sowton Industrial Estate, Exeter, EX2 7LD Tel: (01392) 252541 Fax: (01392) 430195

▶ Persimmon Homes West Yorkshire Ltd, 3 Hepton Court, York Road, Leeds, LS9 6PW Tel: 0113-240 9726 Fax: 0113-240 8967

▶ Persimmon Partnerships (Scotland) Ltd, Bothwell Road, Hamilton, Lanarkshire, ML3 0DW Tel: (01698) 457117

▶ Persona Creative Ltd, 5 King Edward Court, King Edward Street, Nottingham, NG1 1EW Tel: 0115-948 4454 Fax: 0115 8335456 E-mail: team@personacreative.com *A full service marketing communications agency using New Media, Marketing & P.R. to deliver effective integrated marketing campaigns.*

▶ Personal Comfort Ltd, 9 Woodside, Wimbledon, Woodside, London, SW19 7AR Tel: (020) 8404 1319 *Imports*

Personal Homefinders, 15 London Road, Southampton, SO15 2AE Tel: (023) 8063 5860 Fax: (023) 8063 5877 E-mail: post@personal-homefinders.com *Property management consultants*

▶ Personal Portraits, 41 Grantchester Street, Cambridge, CB3 9HZ Tel: (07989) 654499 E-mail: sales@annajeffries.co.uk *High quality pencil sketches & oil paintings suppliers*

Personal Touch, Stag House, Western Way, Exeter, EX1 2DE Tel: (01392) 410260 Fax: (01392) 421235 E-mail: sales@personaltouch-emb.co.uk *Personalised leisurewear embroidery & printers*

▶ Personal Touch, Unit 1 Moorgate, Ormskirk, Lancashire, L39 4RT Tel: (07966) 711459 Fax: 0151 2932008 E-mail: suedelane@blueyonder.co.uk *Helium & Party Balloons*Greetings Cards*Bespoke design of handmade cards*Handmade stationery*Wedding & Party Favours*

▶ Personal Touch Leicester, 111 Belvior Road, Coalville, Leicestershire, LE67 3PH Tel: 0871 750 4330 Fax: 0871 750 4327 E-mail: enquires@ptimortgages.co.uk

Personalised Coiffeur Products, 1 Kincath Avenue, Rutherglen, Glasgow, G73 4RP Tel: 0141-634 3935 Fax: 0141-570 3453 *Hair products*

Personalised Services, 18-20 Boundaries Road, Balham, London, SW12 8HU Tel: (020) 8675 3313 Fax: (020) 8675 7042 *Washroom hygiene services*

Personalized Sports Equipment, 4 Geralds Grove, Banstead, Surrey, SM7 1NE Tel: (01737) 210224 Fax: (01737) 360046 *Sports equipment printing*

Personna International UK Ltd, Unit 11 Ratcher Way, Forest Town, Mansfield, Nottinghamshire, NG19 0FS Tel: (01623) 638600 Fax: (01623) 638638 E-mail: sales@personna.co.uk *Cutting tools & machinery manufrs*

▶ Personnel Placements Employment Agency, 20 Oatmeal Row, Salisbury, SP1 1TH Tel: (01722) 334433 Fax: (01722) 413208 E-mail: sales@pp-online.co.uk *Employment agency*

Personnel Selection, 46 West Street, Brighton, BN1 2RA Tel: (01273) 205281 Fax: (01273) 204091 E-mail: brit@persel.co.uk *Employment agency*

Personnel Today, Quadrant House The Quadrant, Brighton Road, Sutton, Surrey, SM2 5AS Tel: (020) 8652 8008 Fax: (020) 8652 3279 E-mail: info@personneltodayjobs.com *Personnel Today is the HR profession's news magazine.*

▶ Personnel Vending Services Ltd, Unit 16 Tuffley Park, Lower Tuffley Lane, Gloucester, GL2 5DE Tel: (01452) 411689 Fax: (01452) 522932 E-mail: sales@personnelvending.co.uk *SUPPLIERS OF HOT AND COLD DRINK MACHINES, BEAN TO CUP, FOOD/SNACK AND WATER COOLERS*

Perspective Marketing, 18 Manor Way, Hail Weston, St. Neots, Cambridgeshire, PE19 5LG Tel: (01480) 477990 E-mail: research@perspective-marketing.co.uk *Market research services*

Perspective Scientific Ltd, 100 Baker Street, London, W1U 6WB Tel: (020) 7486 6837 Fax: (020) 7487 3023 E-mail: nick@perspective.co.uk *Radiation monitor distributors*

Perspective Signs Ltd, 21 Riverside Industrial Park, Rapier Street, Ipswich, IP2 8JX Tel: (01473) 681684 Fax: (01473) 601746 *Sign installers & manufrs*

Persuasion Public Relations, Suite 2 Cheviot House, Beaminster Way East, Newcastle upon Tyne, NE3 2ER Tel: 0191-214 0222 Fax: 0191-214 0240 E-mail: hq@persuasion-pr.com *Public relations company*

Persys Consulting Ltd, 77 Bradvue Crescent, Bradville, Milton Keynes, MK13 7AH Tel: (01908) 319555 Fax: (07092) 104535 *Management consultancy services*

Pert Building Services Ltd, 31 Bunbury Road, Northfield, Birmingham, B31 2DR Tel: 0121-411 2333 Fax: 0121-411 2600 E-mail: barrieroberts@pert-aircon.co.uk *Air conditioning engineers*

Pertemps plc, 13 Bennetts Hill, Birmingham, B2 5RS Tel: 0121-643 5000 Fax: 0121-230 9116 *Provide temporary & permanent staff*

Pertemps Group, Main Road, Meriden, Coventry, CV7 7LA Tel: (01676) 525598 Fax: (01676) 525259 *Recruitment agency*

Pertemps Partnership, 81-82 Darlington St, Wolverhampton, WV1 4JD Tel: (01902) 312345 Fax: (01902) 714357 E-mail: leannesharp@pertemps.co.uk *Employment agency*

Pertemps Recruitment Partnership Ltd, 16-18 Temple Street, Birmingham, B2 5BG Tel: 0121-233 2222 Fax: 0121-631 2278 E-mail: birmingham038@pertemps.co.uk *Employment agency*

Pertemps Recruitment Partnership Ltd, 22 High Street, Cardiff, CF10 1PY Tel: (029) 2022 0776 Fax: (029) 2023 9345 E-mail: cardiff@pertemps.co.uk *Employment agency*

Pertemps Recruitment Partnership Ltd, Butleigh Road, Glastonbury, Somerset, BA6 8AQ Tel: (01384) 455666 Fax: (01384) 239593 *Recruitment agency*

Pertemps Recruitment Partnership Ltd, 9-11 Bull Street, West Bromwich Ringway, West Bromwich, West Midlands, B70 6EU Tel: 0121-525 5151 Fax: 0121-553 3688 *Provide temporary & permanent staff*

▶ Perth Removals & Transport, The Warehouse, Inveralmond Road, Inveralmond Industrial Estate, Perth, PH1 3TW Tel: (01738) 633080 Fax: (01738) 643766 E-mail: sales@perthremovals.sagenet.co.uk

▶ Perthdown Ltd, Bootham Lane Industrial Estate, Bootham Lane, Dunscroft, Doncaster, South Yorkshire, DN7 4JU Tel: (01302) 351378 Fax: (01302) 849337

Perton Signs, 3 Roslin Road, London, W3 8DH Tel: (020) 8992 5775 Fax: (020) 8992 5885 E-mail: sales@pertonsigns.co.uk *Exhibition & conferences & event seminars sign suppliers*

Pertwee Holdings Ltd, Lodge Lane, Langham, Colchester, CO4 5NE Tel: (01206) 231000 Fax: (01206) 231132 E-mail: mail@pertwee.co.uk *Property investors, managers & developers* Also at: King's Lynn

Pervasic Ltd, 2 Queen Caroline Street, London, W6 9DX Tel: (020) 8741 8777 Fax: (020) 8323 8013 E-mail: sales@pervasic.com *Computer systems & software development for wireless application*

Perwill P.L.C., 13A Market Square, Alton, Hampshire, GU34 1UR Tel: (01420) 545000 Fax: (01420) 545001 E-mail: info@kewill.com *EDI & electronic commerce*

▶ Pescado Ltd, Wingham Business Centre, Goodnestone Road, Wingham, Canterbury, Kent, CT3 1AR Tel: (01227) 723130 Fax: (01227) 723149 E-mail: info@pescado.co.uk *Pescado provide web based survey solutions for HR surveys, Customer surveys or more complex data capture exercises.*

▶ Pesentation Display Ltd, Unit 3, Ayers Yard, Station Road, Wallingford, Oxfordshire, OX10 0JB Tel: (01491) 825588 Fax: (01491) 826106 E-mail: presentation@f2s.com *Design & manufacturer of display units*

▶ Pest Control Products UK, PO Box 50758, London, NW6 9AN Tel: 020 7993 4640 E-mail: neil@pestcontrolproducts.co.uk *Secure, online shop selling safe, DIY pest control solutions for eradicating or deterring rats, mice, flies, cockroaches, ants, bedbugs, fleas, moths, carpet beetles and all household pests from your business premises. Products include electronic repellers, electric fly killing machines, safe insecticides and traps.*

Pest Control Services, Church House, Kimbolton Road, Bolnhurst, Bedford, MK44 2ES Tel: (01234) 376271 *Pest control services*

Pest Destruction Services Ltd, 32 Colchester Road, West Bergholt, Colchester, CO6 3JG Tel: (01206) 242050 Fax: (01206) 242002 *Pest control services*

Pest Quest, Back Lane, Chellaston, Derby, DE73 6TP Tel: (01332) 704107 Fax: (01332) 704107 *Pest control services*

▶ Pest Shield Environmental Services, 17 Unit Factory Estate, Boulevard, Hull, HU3 4AY Tel: (01482) 581505 Fax: (01482) 580678 E-mail: sales@pestshield.co.uk

▶ Pest Solutions Ltd, 38, Colwood Place, Glasgow, G53 7YB Tel: 0141-880 8895

Pestarrest Control Service, 6 Alton Park, Beeford, Driffield, East Yorkshire, YO25 8BZ Tel: (01262) 488306 E-mail: peter.burnel@btopenworld.com *Pest control services*

Pestatak Ltd, Pean Hill Park, Whitstable, Kent, CT5 3BJ Tel: (01227) 768189 Fax: (01227) 787298 E-mail: sales@pestatak.co.uk *Pest controllers*

Pestcall, Spring Close, Eastbourne, East Sussex, BN20 9HD Tel: (01323) 500151 Fax: (01323) 500151 *Pest control*

▶ Pestcontrolpro .Co.Uk, 37 Lyndon Road, Bramham, Wetherby, West Yorkshire, LS23 6RH Tel: (07725) 317112 *Pest control services*

Pestfree D & D Services, 40 Spencer Drive, Llandough, Penarth, Vale of Glamorgan, CF64 2LR Tel: (029) 2031 6860 Fax: (07971) 115024 E-mail: pestfree@pestfreedd.co.uk *Domestic & Commercial pest control services. Cardiff and South Wales. Online purchases of EFK (Electronic Fly Killers), Air Freshners, hotel and washroom equipment.*

Pestline Environmental Services UK Ltd, 12 Sunderland Rd, Forest Hill, London, SE23 2PR Tel: (020) 8699 3663 Fax: (020) 8699 1879 *Pest control*

▶ Pestokill, Graveoak, East Lancs Road, Leigh, Lancashire, WN7 3SE Tel: (0870) 0660999 Fax: (01942) 607570 E-mail: sales@pestokill.co.uk *Pest control service company*

Pestokill, Graveoak, East Lancs Road, Leigh, Lancashire, WN7 3SE Tel: (0870) 0660999 Fax: (01942) 607570 E-mail: sales@pestokill.co.uk *Pest control services*

Pestproof Ltd, Mitre Street, Failsworth, Manchester, M35 9BY Tel: 0161-684 9451 Fax: 0161-947 0485 *Pest control services*

Pet Food Manufacturers Association Ltd, 20 Bedford Street, London, WC2E 9HP Tel: (020) 7379 9009 Fax: (020) 7379 8008 E-mail: sales@pfma.com *Trade association*

▶ pet2rest, Frizley House, 8 Radford Bank, Stafford, ST17 4PL Tel: 01785 211052 Fax: 01785 227649 E-mail: sales@pet2rest.com *The flat pack pet coffin company provides the bereaved pet owner the perfect way to lay their pet to rest in the private and familiar surroundings of their home and garden. 5 standard sizes of coffin are available on a next day delivery to all mainland UK postal addresses.*

Petal Postforming Ltd, Drumharvey, Irvinestown, Enniskillen, County Fermanagh, BT94 1ET Tel: (028) 6862 1766 Fax: (028) 6862 1004 E-mail: sales@petalgroup.com *Washroom equipment manufrs*

Petans Ltd, Bullocks Hill, Horsham St. Faith, Norwich, NR10 3HT Tel: (01603) 891255 Fax: (01603) 890827 E-mail: michael@petans.co.uk Principal Export Areas: Worldwide *Training offshore services or centres*

Petards Ltd, 8 Windmill Business Village, Brooklands Close, Sunbury-on-Thames, Middlesex, TW16 7DY Tel: (01932) 788288 Fax: (01932) 788322 E-mail: sales@petards.com *Mobile data*

Petch Waters, Little Ayton Lane, Great Ayton, Middlesbrough, Cleveland, TS9 6HY Tel: (01642) 724000 Fax: (01642) 723999 *Portable toilet suppliers & fencing*

▶ Petchcast, 25 Trent Street, Digbeth, Birmingham, B5 5NL Tel: 0121 643 3130 Fax: 0121 633 4283 E-mail: david@petchcast.co.uk *Die castings & zinc alloy, brass plated*

Petchem Engineering Services Ltd, 61 Ringsfield Road, Beccles, Suffolk, NR34 9PE Tel: (01502) 711330 Fax: (01502) 711081 E-mail: petchemengserv@aol.com *Oil & gas industry pipeline fittings*

▶ Pete Haslam Painters and Decorators, 74 Riverside, Lowmoor, Clitheroe, Lancashire, BB7 2NS Tel: (01200) 425595 E-mail: peter@thedecorator55.fsnet.co.uk *First class painters & decorators, established in 1979*all work carried out by qualified decorators*

▶ Pete & Johnny, Unit 28 Talina Centre, Bagleys Lane, London, SW6 2BW Tel: (020) 7348 7464 Fax: (020) 7384 2032 *Fresh fruit drink suppliers*

Peter Abbott, Unit 10 Keyford Court, Marston Trading Estate, Frome, Somerset, BA11 4BD Tel: (01373) 461261 Fax: (01373) 451513 E-mail: sales@peterabbott.co.uk *Bolts, nuts & industrial fasteners*

▶ Peter Baines Ltd, Woods Lane, Derby, DE22 3UD Tel: (01332) 362465 Fax: (01332) 291981 E-mail: enquiries@peterbainesltd.fsnet.co.uk

Peter Beyson Packaging Ltd, 2 Duchess Industrial Estate, Sievewright Street, Rutherglen, Glasgow, G73 1QS Tel: 0141-613 0001 Fax: 0141-613 1526 E-mail: sales@peterbrysonpackaging.com *Polythene packers*

Peter Black Europe Ltd, Lawkholme Lane, Keighley, West Yorkshire, BD21 3BB Tel: (01535) 661131 Fax: (01535) 609973 E-mail: pbh@peterblack.co.uk *Holding company*

Peter Brotherhood Holdings Ltd, Werrington Park Way, Peterborough, PE4 5HG Tel: (01733) 292200 Fax: (01733) 292300 E-mail: sales@peterbrotherhood.co.uk Purchasing Contact: K. Bouch Sales Contact: S. Canham Principal Export Areas: Worldwide *Peter Brotherhood specialises in the design and manufacture of steam turbines, gas compressors, packaged CHP systems and special purpose machinery and supports this with an aftermarket division. The company has considerable experience in supplying reliable and efficient steam turbines (1 MW - 40 MW) for a variety of applications including FPSO vessels, marine applications, power generation, waste to energy and renewable and sustainable energy applications. Peter Brotherhood specialise in the design and manufacture of API 618 reciprocating gas compressors as complete packages incorporating the prime mover, gas processing plant, instrumentation and controls. The company has experience in providing compressors for refineries, petrochemical plants, gas processing plants and offshore applications. The company designs and manufactures bespoke CHP systems through its business unit Aircogen CHP Solutions. The company has an extensive reference list and considerable operational experience providing CHP systems that can be configured to supply hot water, steam, chilled water or heated air.*

▶ Peter Clegg & Son Builders Ltd, 54 Henry Road, West Bridgford, Nottingham, NG2 7NB Tel: 0115-982 5666 Fax: 0115-982 5777

Peter Cook International, Aneal Business Centre, Cross Green Approach, Leeds, LS9 0SG Tel: 0113-235 1111 Fax: 0113-235 0034 E-mail: sales@petercookint.com *Manufacturers & distributors of furniture components*

▶ Peter Cooper Ltd, 14 Queensway, New Milton, Hampshire, BH25 5NN Tel: (01425) 621172 Fax: (01425) 638479

▶ Peter Cousins, 14 Dryden Court, Clinton Park, Tattershall, Lincoln, LN4 4PR Tel: 01526 345174 E-mail: portraitsrusltd@aol.com *Wedding, Christening and Commercial Photography covering Lincolnshire, visit our web site for details. Quality doesn"t have to be expensive!*

▶ Peter Cox Ltd, Unit 10, Avon Riverside Estate, Victoria Road, Avonmouth, Bristol, BS11 9DB Tel: 0117 938 7130 Fax: 0117 938 7137

Peter Cox Ltd, Unit 17, Engineer Park, Sandycroft, Deeside, Clwyd, CH5 2QB Tel: (01244) 538610 Fax: (01244) 534720

▶ Peter Cox, Unit 11d Station Approach, Team Valley Trading Estate, Gateshead, Tyne & Wear, NE11 0ZF Tel: 0191-487 2293 Fax: 0191-487 4804 E-mail: petercox.newcastle@ecolab.com *Damp proofing & timber treatment service*

▶ Peter Cox Ltd, St. Andrews House, 385 Hillington Road, Hillington Industrial Estate, Glasgow, G52 4BL Tel: 0141 810 9100 Fax: 0141 810 9111

▶ Peter Cox Ltd, 103 Sadler Road, Lincoln, LN6 3RS Tel: (01522) 500214 Fax: (01522) 688838

▶ Peter Cox Ltd, 209 Century Buildings, Summers Road, Brunswick Business Park, Liverpool, L3 4BL Tel: 0151 709 1090 Fax: 0151 708 5304

▶ Peter Cox Ltd, 62h Lord Avenue, Thornaby, Stockton-on-Tees, Cleveland, TS17 9JX Tel: (01642) 769983 Fax: (01642) 769421

Peter Cox Marketing Ltd, High Street, Wrestlingworth, Sandy, Bedfordshire, SG19 2EN Tel: (01767) 631733 Fax: (01767) 631722 E-mail: info@petercoxmarketing.co.uk *Food processing machinery sales services*

Peter D Stirling Ltd, Reema Road, Bellshill, Lanarkshire, ML4 1RR Tel: (01698) 749555 Fax: (01698) 740569 *Rail connected road haulage services*

Peter Devine, 94 Matilda Street, Sheffield, S1 4QF Tel: 0114-275 0479 Fax: 0114-275 0479 *General engravers*

Peter Evans Ltd, Wickwar Road, Chipping Sodbury, Bristol, BS37 6BQ Tel: (01278) 793339 Fax: (01278) 793251 E-mail: mail@peforktrucks.co.uk *Fork lift truck hire, service & repair*

Peter Evans Ltd, Wickwar Road, Chipping Sodbury, Bristol, BS37 6BQ Tel: (01278) 793339 Fax: (01278) 793251 E-mail: mail@peforktrucks.co.uk *Storage equipment & mezzanine flooring*

▶ Peter Field Transport Ltd, Unit 8, Heron Business Estate, Whitefield Avenue, Luton, LU3 3BB Tel: (01582) 595377

▶ Peter Fowler Electrical Ltd, 6 Westfield Road, Hatfield, Doncaster, South Yorkshire, DN7 6PZ Tel: (01302) 842760 Fax: (01302) 351588

Peter Fraenkel Maritime Ltd, 21-37 South Street, Dorking, Surrey, RH4 2JZ Tel: (01306) 879797 Fax: (01306) 879798 E-mail: contact@fraenkel.co.uk *Consulting engineers, marine* Also at: Edinburgh, Glasgow & Leicester

Peter Freebody & Co., Mill Lane, Hurley, Maidenhead, Berkshire, SL6 5ND Tel: (01628) 824382 Fax: (01628) 820238 E-mail: peterfreebody@btconnect.com *Boat builders services*

Peter Gillard & Co. Ltd, Alexandra Way, Ashchurch Business Centre, Tewkesbury, Gloucestershire, GL20 8NB Tel: (01684) 290243 Fax: (01684) 290330 E-mail: sales@gillard.co.uk *Plastic cutting machine manufrs*

▶ Peter Grant Associates Ltd, 18 Bakewell Road, Loughborough, Leicestershire, LE11 5QY Tel: (01509) 610580 Fax: (01509) 217346

Peter Greig & Co., Victoria Linen Works, 147-151 St Clair Street, Kirkcaldy, Fife, KY1 2BU Tel: (01592) 651901 Fax: (01592) 655596 E-mail: rosie@petergreig.co.uk *Textile canvass, fabric furnishing & linen fabric manufrs*

Peter Haddock Ltd, Pinfold Lane Industrial Estate, Bridlington, North Humberside, YO16 6BT Tel: (01262) 678121 Fax: (01262) 400043 E-mail: info@phpublishing.co.uk *Children's book publishers*

Peter Hare Ltd, The Cottage, Post Office Lane, Little Totham, Maldon, Essex, CM9 8JL Tel: (01621) 891591 *Transport & plant hire*

Peter Hope Metals Ltd, 2 Grange Road Business Park, Grange Road, Batley, West Yorkshire, WF17 6LL Tel: (01924) 440055 Fax: (01924) 442200 E-mail: peterhope.metalsltd@virgin.net *Steel stockholders & fabricators*

Peter Hunter Seeds, Keepers Cottage, Oulton Park, Oulton, Tarporley, Cheshire, CW6 9BL Tel: (01829) 760397 Fax: (01829) 760526 E-mail: peter.hunter.associates@farming.co.uk *Seed merchants & grassland consultants*

▶ Peter Hunts Bakery Foods, The Bakery, Unit 14 Lyon Road Industrial Estate, Kearsley, Bolton, BL4 8NB Tel: (01204) 793446 Fax: (01204) 794533

Peter James Packaging Co., Unit 35 Darbishire Street, Bolton, BL1 2TN Tel: (01204) 381469 Fax: (01204) 386514 *Polythene film & bag manufacturers also packaging materials distributors*

Peter Jones Ilg Ltd, Lower Monk Street, Abergavenny, Gwent, NP7 5NA Tel: (01873) 852742 Fax: (01873) 857573 E-mail: sales@peterjonesilg.co.uk *Leather cases, cash bags, radio cases & police equipment manufrs*

▶ Peter M Tutty Partnership, 37-39 Princes Avenue, Hull, HU5 3RZ Tel: (01482) 341458 Fax: (01482) 445691 E-mail: sales@tutty.co.uk *Office interior design & supply*

▶ Peter Mckerral & Co., Darlochan Yard, Campbeltown, Argyll, PA28 6NT Tel: (01586) 820258 Fax: (01586) 820488

Peter Marshall Ltd, Gelderd Road, Morley, Leeds, LS27 7LL Tel: 0113-307 6730 Fax: 0113-307 5968 *Steel staircase manufrs*

▶ Peter Martin Lighting Design Ltd, Unit 1 Lincoln Business Park, Lincoln Road, High Wycombe, Buckinghamshire, HP12 3RD Tel: (01494) 464363 Fax: (01494) 462413

Peter Moore, 18 College Gardens, London, SW17 7UG Tel: (020) 8767 2103 Fax: (020) 8767 2103 E-mail: peter@toastmasterlondon.com *Peter is a Member of the Independent Toastmasters Association, Freeman of The City Of London. Available for Your Special Day {London and Home Counties} He is the Final Touch to Any Occasion. A Toastmaster for over 25rys He has Officiated at Events, and Functions, Both in the UK and Overseas. Be it a Wedding Reception, Charity Ball, Civic Function, Masonic Ladies Festival, Royal Event, Corporate Function. Do Give Him a Telephone Call or Send a Email, He Looks Forward to Hearing From You*

Peter Nicholls, Braunston Marina Trade Centre, The Wharf, Braunston, Daventry, Northamptonshire, NN11 7JH Tel: (01788) 899109 Fax: (01788) 899109 E-mail: enquiry@steelboats.com *Boat builders & repairers*

▶ Peter Norris Haulage Ltd, Station Approach, St. Mary Cray, Orpington, Kent, BR5 2NB Tel: (01689) 832228 Fax: (01689) 896299

Peter Pine, 123 Outram Street, Sutton-in-Ashfield, Nottinghamshire, NG17 4BG Tel: (01623) 555744 *Pine furniture manufrs*

▶ Peter Ramsey & Sons Denholme Timber Ltd, Sawmills, Wellington Street, Laisterdyke, Bradford, West Yorkshire, BD4 8BW Tel: (01274) 656563 E-mail: info@ramsey-uk.com *Machinists and Importers Of Timber Components To Bed Manufacturers - Including; Bed Slats, Divan Base Components, Head Board Struts, Drawers, Frame Design, Contract Suppliers To Home Shopping Catalogues And DIY Stores.*

Peter Randle & Son Grinding, 9 The Washford Industrial Estate, Heming Road, Redditch, Worcestershire, B98 0DH Tel: (01527) 528891 Fax: (01527) 528891 *Precision grinding services*

▶ Peter Reid, 23-27 High Street, Buckie, Banffshire, AB56 1AL Tel: (01542) 832158 Fax: (01542) 835551

▶ Peter Robinson Electrical Ltd, 1 Broadfield Industrial Estate, Seymour Street, Heywood, Lancashire, OL10 3AJ Tel: (01706) 364046 Fax: (01706) 625916

Peter S Neale, Clays Road, Sling, Coleford, Gloucestershire, GL16 8LJ Tel: (01594) 837309 Fax: (01594) 835363 E-mail: sales@peter-s-neale.demon.co.uk *Architectural metalworkers & fabricators*

Peter S Toms & Co., Charlton Mead Lane, Hoddesdon, Hertfordshire, EN11 0DJ Tel: (01992) 464436 Fax: (01992) 448433 *French polishing contractors spray finishing*

Peter Saxon & Co., 362 Church Road, London, SW19 2QF Tel: (07956) 379622 Fax: (020) 8648 7829 E-mail: peter@petersaxton.co.uk *Accountant*

▶ Peter Scott Printers Ltd, Belshaw Court, Billington Road, Burnley, Lancashire, BB11 5UB Tel: (01282) 452221 Fax: (01282) 412353 E-mail: sales@psprintdirect.co.uk

▶ Peter Simpson & Sons, Long Chimney, 83 Thorpe Lane, Leeds, LS10 4EP Tel: 0113-277 8780 Fax: 0113-271 8997

▶ Peter Swales, Manchester Abattoir, Riverpark Road, Manchester, M40 2XP Tel: 0161-231 2041

Peter Taylor & Co., 8 Hanover Street, London, W1S 1PT Tel: (020) 7290 2662 Fax: (020) 7290 2686 *Surveyors & estate agents*

Peter Tipper Signs & Plates Ltd, 33 Purdeys Industrial Estate, Purdeys Way, Rochford, Essex, SS4 1ND Tel: (01702) 549830 Fax: (01702) 549831 E-mail: info@tipper-signs.co.uk *Sign makers*

Peter Tomas & Co., 50 Lancaster Street, Higham Ferrers, Rushden, Northamptonshire, NN10 8HY Tel: (01933) 359688 *Security Services*

Peter Walters (U K) Ltd, Brindley Road, Dodwells Bridge Industrial Estate, Hinckley, Leicestershire, LE10 3BY Tel: (01455) 631707 Fax: (01455) 611360 E-mail: pwuk@peter-wolters.com Principal Export Areas: Worldwide *Lapping machine manufrs*

▶ Peter Warr, 6 Newing Close, Littlebourne, Canterbury, Kent, CT3 1UX Tel: (07736) 060302 E-mail: peter.warr@btinternet.com *Hand engraved glass, sandblasting & acid etching manufrs*

Peter Whiting Chemicals Ltd, 8 Barb Mews, London, W6 7PA Tel: (020) 8741 4025 Fax: (020) 8741 1737 E-mail: sales@whiting-cemicals.co.uk *Chemical distributors*

Peter Wood & Co. Ltd, Riverside House, Weedon Street, Sheffield, S9 2FT Tel: 0114-244 0000 Fax: 0114-244 4646 *Gas leak searcher bar manufrs*

▶ Peterborough Appliances, 25 Candidus Court, Peterborough, PE4 5DB Tel: (01733) 755200 Fax: (0871) 6613572 E-mail: sales@i-ac.co.uk *Retail kitchen appliances, fridges, freezers, fridge freezers, cookers*

▶ Peterborough Cleaning Supplies Ltd, 60 Thistlemoor Road, Peterborough, PE1 3HP Tel: (0800) 9961772

Peterborough Continental Bakery, 34a Towler Street, Peterborough, PE1 2TX Tel: (01733) 567075 Fax: (01733) 567654 *Bakery supplies*

Peterborough Hose & Couplings Ltd, Cranesgate South, Whaplode St. Catherines, Spalding, Lincolnshire, PE12 6SN Tel: (01406) 540592 Fax: (01406) 540561 E-mail: sales@phccouplings.co.uk *Steel fabricators*

Peterborough Plating, 12 Maxwell Road, Peterborough, PE2 7HU Tel: (01733) 233250 Fax: (01733) 371411 E-mail: sales@peterboroughplating.co.uk *Specialists in technical precision anodising*

▶ Peterborough Pools Ltd, 3 Fenlake Business Centre, Fengate, Peterborough, PE1 5BQ Tel: (01733) 319222 Fax: (01733) 319111 E-mail: enquiries@peterboroughpools.co.uk *Design, supply & installation of swimming pools*

Peterborough Printing Services Ltd, Ainsley House, Fengate, Peterborough, PE1 5XG Tel: (01733) 349881 Fax: (01733) 310711 E-mail: info@pps-print.com *Commercial printers*

Peterborough Sheet Metal Ltd, Unit 12 Towermead Business Centre, High Street, Peterborough, PE2 9DY Tel: (01733) 344880 Fax: (01733) 898421 *Sheet metalwork engineers manufrs*

Peterborough Signs, 17-18 Leofric Square, Peterborough, PE1 5TU Tel: (01733) 555060 Fax: (01733) 344293 E-mail: info@peterbourgh-signs.co.uk *Signwriters & manufrs*

Peterborough Web, Oundle Road, Peterborough, PE2 9QH Tel: (01733) 342525 Fax: (01733) 896514 *Newspaper web off set printers*

Peterhead Box Co. Ltd, Balmoor Industrial Estate, Peterhead, Aberdeenshire, AB42 1QG Tel: (01779) 470676 Fax: (01779) 473952 *Polystyrene box manufrs*

Peterhead Ice Co., Model Jetty, Seagate, Peterhead, Aberdeenshire, AB42 1JP Tel: (01779) 478681 Fax: (01779) 470018 *Ice merchants*

▶ Peterhead Marine Electrics Ltd, 8 Bridge Street, Peterhead, Aberdeenshire, AB42 1DH Tel: (01779) 479461 Fax: (01779) 480106

▶ Peterhead Transport, Suite 1 Alexandra House, Port Henry Pier, Peterhead, Aberdeenshire, AB42 1ZY Tel: (01779) 477282 Fax: (01779) 476556

Peterlee Glass Co. Ltd, 28 Lister Road, North West Industrial Estate, Peterlee, County Durham, SR8 2RB Tel: 0191-586 4626 Fax: 0191-518 0459 E-mail: sales@peterleeglass.com *Glass processors*

Peter's, 41a The Mall, Burnley, Lancashire, BB11 1BA Tel: (01282) 839859 *Jewellers*

Peters plc, Chichester Marina, Chichester, West Sussex, PO20 7EJ Tel: (01243) 512831 Fax: (01243) 511382 E-mail: sales@petersplc.com *Yacht & boat sales & service*

Peters David Photography, Unit 14 Fordhouse Road Indust Estate, Bushbury, Wolverhampton, WV10 9XB Tel: (01902) 397739 Fax: (01902) 397001 E-mail: info@davidpeters.co.uk *Photography*

Peters Edition Ltd, 2-6 Bachers Street, London, N1 6DN Tel: (020) 7553 4000 Fax: (020) 7490 4921 E-mail: sales@uk.edition-peters.com *Music publishers* Also at: London W1

▶ Peters Food Service, Lincoln Road, Cressex Business Park, High Wycombe, Buckinghamshire, HP12 3RD Tel: (01494) 463925 Fax: (01494) 464278

John Peters Bed Centre, Guiseley Retail Park, Park Road, Guiseley, Leeds, LS20 8QH Tel: (01943) 879248 Fax: (01943) 879248 *Bed retailers*

▶ Peters & May Ltd, Prysmian House, Dew Lane, Eastleigh, Hampshire, SO50 9PX Tel: (023) 8048 0501 Fax: (01752) 775699 E-mail: enquiriesplh@petersandmay.com *Export services, shipping, storage*

Peters Removals, 14 Alun Cresent, Chester, CH4 8HN Tel: (01244) 682084 *Removal contractors*

Peters Roofing Contractors, 564 Davidson Road, Croydon, CR0 6DG Tel: (020) 8655 3598 Fax: (020) 8655 3598 E-mail: pete@petersroofing.co.uk *Zinc, copper, lead, slate & tiled roofing*

Trevor Peters Design, Unit 18 Portway Business Centre, Old Sarum, Salisbury, SP4 6QX Tel: (01722) 412227 Fax: (01722) 414179 E-mail: tpd@tpdesign.co.uk *Exhibition, advertising, graphic design & print*

Peter's Trophies, 10 West Street, Weston-super-Mare, Avon, BS23 1JT Tel: (01934) 620206 Fax: (01934) 620206 E-mail: monty19452003@yahoo.co.uk *Trophy engravers*

Petersen Stainless Rigging Ltd, Blaydon Business Centre, Cowen Road, Blaydon-on-Tyne, Tyne & Wear, NE21 5TW Tel: 0191-414 0156 Fax: 0191-499 0041 E-mail: admin@petersen-stainless.co.uk *Shackle manufrs*

Peterson Design Ltd, 27 Mendip Drive, Frome, Somerset, BA11 2HT Tel: (01373) 465507 Fax: (01373) 465507 E-mail: enquiries@peterson.eu.com *Automation equipment design & manufrs*

Peterson Electronics Ltd, Academy Street, Forfar, Angus, DD8 2HA Tel: (01307) 462591 Fax: (01307) 462591 *Electronic control apparatus manufrs*

Peterson Engineering Cleveland Ltd, Limerick Road, Redcar, Cleveland, TS10 5JU Tel: (01642) 472361 Fax: (01642) 488816 E-mail: info@peterson-engineering.co.uk *General & precision engineers*

Peterson Spring Europe Ltd, Unit 21, Trescott Road, Trafford Park, Redditch, Worcestershire, B98 7AH Tel: (01527) 585657 Fax: (01527) 588317 E-mail: sales@peterson.co.uk *Spring & presswork manufrs*

Peterson Spring (UK) Ltd, Reddings Lane, Tyseley, Birmingham, B11 3HA Tel: 0121-706 2236 Fax: 0121-708 1253 E-mail: enquiries@psprings.euroe.co.uk *Spring manufrs*

▶ Petes Bakehouse & Pantry Ltd, 59 Church Street, Bilston, West Midlands, WV14 0AX Tel: (01902) 650666 *Bakery*

Petra, 1 Moat Lane Crossing, Moat Lane, Caersws, Powys, SY17 5SE Tel: (01686) 688131 Fax: (01686) 688283 E-mail: sales@cardtables.co.uk *Furniture manufs*

Petra Style Ltd, 10a Gourley St, London, N15 5NG Tel: 020 88026665 Fax: 020 88021999 *Clothing manufrs*

Steve Petrek Signs, Unit 5 Ladford Trading Park, Seighford, Stafford, ST18 9QL Tel: (01785) 282497 Fax: (01785) 282497 *Sign writing services, vehicle livery*

Petrie Technologies Ltd, Common Bank Industrial Estate, Ackhurst Road, Chorley, Lancashire, PR7 1NH Tel: (01257) 241206 Fax: (01257) 267562 E-mail: sales@petrieltd.com *Industrial drying & defrosting equipment manufrs*

Petro Lube, 276 Chase Road, London, N14 6HA Tel: (020) 8886 8002 Fax: (020) 8886 7716 *Oil blenders & distributors*

Petrobrass Europe Ltd, 6th Floor, 35-38 Portman Square, London, W1H 6LR Tel: (020) 7535 1100 Fax: (020) 7467 5800 E-mail: petrobrass.europe@petrobrass.com *Oil traders*

Petro-Canada, Bowater House, 114 Knightsbridge, London, SW1X 7LD Tel: (020) 7225 7100 Fax: (020) 7584 6459 *Oil & gas exploration & production company* Also at: Aberdeen

Petrochem, Cedar Court, Guildford Road, Fetcham, Leatherhead, Surrey, KT22 9RX Tel: (01372) 360000 Fax: (01372) 380403 E-mail: msports@petrochemcarless.com *Petro chemicals*

Petrofer UK plc, Harcourt Business Park, Halesfield 17, Telford, Shropshire, TF7 4PW Tel: (01952) 580100 Fax: (01952) 580101 E-mail: sales@petrofer.co.uk *Industrial oils & chemicals*

Petrogramme Management Services (UK) Ltd, 32 Alexandra Road, Lowestoft, Suffolk, NR32 1PJ Tel: (01502) 500050 Fax: (01502) 516574 E-mail: vacancies@petrogramme.co.uk *Recruitment agency*

Petroil Pump & Tank Services, Common Platt, Lydiard Millicent, Purton, Swindon, SN5 5JZ Tel: (01793) 770494 Fax: (01793) 772517 E-mail: petroil.eng@btconnect.com *Petroleum engineers*

Petroleum Experts Ltd, Spectrum House, 2 Powderhall Road, Edinburgh, EH7 4GB Tel: 0131-474 7030 Fax: 0131-474 7031 E-mail: edinburgh@petex.com *Software developers*

▶ Petrology Ltd, Robert Clyde House, Erskine Ferry Road, Old Kilpatrick, Glasgow, G60 5EU Tel: (01389) 801700 Fax: (01389) 801702 E-mail: rose.pollock@petrology.com *Welding service*

Petro-Man Ltd, Sneyd Street, Stoke-on-Trent, ST6 2NP Tel: (01782) 200750 Fax: (01782) 200755 E-mail: peslenquiries@aol.com *Environmental equipment suppliers to oil industry*

Petron Amusements Ltd, Salisbury Road, Hoddesdon, Hertfordshire, EN11 0HU Tel: (01992) 473900 Fax: (01992) 573905 E-mail: sales@petronamusements.co.uk *Maintained Hire of the latest:- Fruit Machines-Fixed Odds Terminals Pool Tables / Club Machines Video Machines + Online Tournaments All over the South East Quality service for 35 years*

Petropipe International Ltd, Barnsmead, Stockland Bristol, Bridgwater, Somerset, TA5 2PY Tel: (01278) 652545 Fax: (01278) 652565 *Industrial pipeline equipment distributors*

Petrostock Control Systems Ltd, 78 Malone Road, Woodley, Reading, RG5 3NJ Tel: 0118-962 6041 Fax: 0118-969 5695 E-mail: sales@petrostock.demon.co.uk *Petroleum products suppliers*

Pets Choice Ltd, Gladstone Street, Blackburn, BB1 3ES Tel: (01254) 54545 Fax: (01254) 681446 E-mail: info@petschoice.co.uk *Pet food manufrs*

Petter Potter Ltd, Water Lane, Storrington, Pulborough, West Sussex, RH20 3EA Tel: (01903) 743397 Fax: (01903) 746248 *Shop fitting metalwork & screen printing machine manufrs*

The Pettifer Group Ltd, 50 Stratford Road, Shipston-On-Stour, Warwickshire, CV36 4BA Tel: (01608) 666600 Fax: (01608) 666611 E-mail: macpherson@pettifer.co.uk *Building contractors*

Pettigrews Of Kelso, Pinnaclehill Industrial Estate, Kelso, Roxburghshire, TD5 8DW Tel: (01573) 224234 Fax: (01573) 223717 E-mail: sales@pettigrews.com *Chutney & pickles manufrs*

Alfred Pettitt Ltd, Unit 6 Hillgate Business Centre, Swallow Street, Stockport, Cheshire, SK1 3AU Tel: 0161-476 4545 Fax: 0161-476 4505 *Lithographic & letter press printers*

Pettitt Joinery Co. Ltd, Royce Road, Peterborough, PE1 5YB Tel: (01733) 567742 Fax: (01733) 567742 *Joinery manufrs*

Peugeot Motor Co Plc, P O Box 25, Coventry, CV3 1BD Tel: (024) 7688 6000 Fax: (024) 7688 4001 *Car manufrs*

Peugeot Motor Co. P.L.C., Torrington Avenue, Tile Hill, Coventry, CV4 0UX Tel: (024) 7688 3000 Fax: (024) 7688 3551 *Car parts suppliers & distributors*

Peveril Decorators Ltd, Peveril House, Alfreton Road, Derby, DE21 4AG Tel: (01332) 344739 Fax: (01332) 368622 E-mail: sales@peverildecorators.co.uk *Painting & decorating contractors*

Peveril Interiors Ltd, Peveril House, Alfreton Road, Derby, DE21 4AG Tel: (01332) 344956 Fax: (01332) 380893 E-mail: peverilinteriors@peveril-house.co.uk *Ceiling & partition contractors*

Peveril Manufacturing Co Sportswear Ltd, 1 Campbell Street, Darvel, Ayrshire, KA17 0DL Tel: (01560) 321965 Fax: (01560) 322016 *Sportswear suppliers*

▶ Pevonia UK, Williamsport Way, Lion Barn Industrial Estate, Needham Market, Ipswich, IP6 8RW Tel: (0845) 2307270 Fax: (01449) 727001 E-mail: info@pevoniauk.com *Skincare distributor*

▶ Pewag Contiweiss Deutschland GmbH, 39 Beechwood Park Road, Solihull, West Midlands, B91 1ES Tel: 0121 2405527

▶ Pewter Art Online Giftware Specialist Ltd, 492 Chigwell Road, Woodford Green, Essex, IG8 8PA Tel: (07801) 533103 Fax: (020) 8504 4528 E-mail: sales@yourpewter.com *Sell gifts & provide engraving service*

▶ Pewter Charms, 12 Ponsford Road, Bristol, BS4 2UP Tel: 0117-300 5635 Fax: 0117 971 9927 E-mail: customer-service@pewtercharms.co.uk *Pewter charms and letter beads. Charms from 25p. Lead free and 3D*Excellent detail. Contact us if you can"t find what your lokking for.*

Pfaff-Silberblau Ltd, Prenton Way, North Cheshire Trading Estate, Prenton, Merseyside, CH43 3DU Tel: 0151-609 0099 Fax: 0151-609 0852 E-mail: anyone@pfaff-silberblau.co.uk Purchasing Contact: P. Kelly Sales Contact: P. Kelly *Lifting gear manufacturers including hoists (electric) & jacks (worm gear/screw operated)*

▶ PFAMetals.com, 2 Stone Circle Road, Northampton, NN3 8RF Tel: (01604) 671536 Fax: (01604) 670831 E-mail: sales@pfametals.com *Bar, Plate, Tube, Sheet, Welding Wire, many grades available*

Pfaudler Balfour, Riverside Road, Leven, Fife, KY8 4RW Tel: (01333) 423020 Fax: (01333) 427432 E-mail: sales@pfaudlerbalfour.co.uk *Glass lined reactor systems manufrs*

Pfe Orion Division, Draycott Business Park, Cam, Dursley, Gloucestershire, GL11 5DQ Tel: (01453) 890881 Fax: (01453) 890312 E-mail: mike.comer@orionmachinery.com *Paper handling machine manufrs*

Pfeifer Drako Ltd, Marshfield Bank, Crewe, CW2 8UY Tel: (01270) 587728 Fax: (01270) 587913 E-mail: admin@pfeiferdrako.co.uk *Steel wire ropes for elevators & cranes*

Pfiffner UK Ltd, 9 Manor Courtyard, Hughenden Avenue, High Wycombe, Buckinghamshire, HP13 5RE Tel: (01494) 510166 Fax: (01494) 510211 *Machine tools distributor*

Pfizer Ltd, Walton Oaks, Dorking Road, Tadworth, Surrey, KT20 7NS Tel: (01304) 616161 Fax: (01304) 656221 *Pharmaceutical manufrs*

Pfleiderer Industry, Oakfield House, Springwood Way, Tytherington Business Park, Macclesfield, Cheshire, SK10 2XA Tel: (01625) 660410 Fax: (01625) 617301 E-mail: info@pfleiderer.co.uk *Manufacturers of components for kitchen units*

PGI Group P.L.C., 81 Carter Lane, London, EC4V 5EP Tel: (020) 7236 6135 Fax: (020) 7248 1081 *Holding company*

▶ PG's Cherished Numbers, Weir Wood, Spring Hill Farm, Forest Row, East Sussex, RH18 5HT Tel: (01342) 824444 *Motor vehicle number plate manufrs*

PGS Engineering Ltd, Quayside Drive, Walsall, WS2 9LA Tel: (01922) 425555 Fax: (01922) 425556 *Steel fabricators*

▶ PH Cleaning Ltd, 5 Green Place, Links Road Flackwell Heath, High Wycombe, Buckinghamshire, HP10 9LW Tel: (01628) 530157 Fax: (01628) 530157 E-mail: info@phcleaning.co.uk *Office, upholstery cleaning & stain removal*

The PH Control Co. Ltd, The Old Byre, Farm Hall, Kinnerley, Oswestry, Shropshire, SY10 8EJ Tel: (01691) 682505 Fax: (01691) 682494 E-mail: phcontrolco@btinternet.com *Analytical instruments suppliers*

PH Industrial Ltd, 8 Wheldon Road, Widnes, Cheshire, WA8 8FW Tel: 0151-257 9696 Fax: 0151-257 8585 *Industrial safety equipment distributors*

▶ Pha Multimedia, The Studio, 6 Foxley Grove, Welwyn, Hertfordshire, AL6 0DW Tel: (01438) 840084 E-mail: peter.holt@pha.uk *DVD & video production*

Phantasia Ltd, 5 Fenlock Court, Blenheim Office Park, Long Hanborough, Witney, Oxfordshire, OX29 8RX Tel: (01993) 883700 Fax: (01993) 883750 E-mail: sales@phantasia.net *Computer consultants*

Pharaos Foods, 271 Upper Brook Street, Manchester, M13 0HR Tel: 0161-272 6340 Fax: 0161-272 6341 *Food processors*

Pharma Machines Ltd, 64 Windsor Avenue, London, SW19 2RJ Tel: (020) 8542 9966 Fax: (020) 8540 1600 E-mail: sales@pharma-machines.com *Pharmaceutical industry processing & packaging machinery*

▶ Pharmaceutical Development & Manufacturing Services (PDMS) Ltd, 22 Seagoe Industrial Estate, Craigavon, County Armagh, BT63 5QD Tel: (028) 3836 3363 Fax: (028) 3836 3300 E-mail: info@pdms-almac.com *PDMS provides a broad spectrum of outsourcing services to the international pharmaceutical and biotechnology sectors, ranging from formulation development to commercial-scale manufacture and packaging. Facilities are MHRA-licensed and FDA-approved.*Development services include: formulation development, process optimisation and stability studies.*Dosage forms include: tablets, capsules, powders, penicillins and cephalosporins.*Packaging into blisters, bottles, sachets and wallet cards.**

Pharmaceutical Machine Sales Ltd, Unit 1, 106 Downs Street, West Molesey, Surrey, KT8 2TA Tel: (020) 8941 2818 Fax: (020) 8941 8625 E-mail: pms@pmsuk.com *Pharmaceutical process & packaging machinery*

▶ Pharmalink Consulting, Vandervell House, Vanwall Business Park, Maidenhead, Berkshire, SL6 4UB Tel: 01628 509090 Fax: 01628 509125 E-mail: info@pharmalinkconsulting.com *Pharmaceutical regulatory affairs specialist*

Pharmaserve Ltd, Wynne Avenue, Clifton, Swinton, Manchester, M27 8FF Tel: 0161-794 7423 Fax: 0161-794 0328 E-mail: sales@pharmaserveltd.co.uk *Pharmaceutical & veterinary contract manufacturers & packers*

Pharmatube Ltd, Units 1-2, Shield Drive, Wardley Business Park, Manchester, M28 2QB Tel: 0161-794 7391 Fax: 0161-727 8318 E-mail: sales@pharmatube.com Principal Export Areas: Worldwide *Collapsible aluminium tubes manufrs*

Pharmeurope, 4 Rendezvous Street, Folkestone, Kent, CT20 1EX Tel: (01303) 246611 Fax: (01303) 246677 E-mail: pharmeurope@btconnect.com *Pharmaceutical distributor*

▶ Pharmitas, 38 Hackford Road, Wicklewood, Wymondham, Norfolk, NR18 9QJ Tel: (01953) 423000 Fax: (01953) 423002 E-mail: jon@pharmitas.co.uk *Consultancy to the pharmaceutical industry offering regulatory, technical and QP services. Reliable technical assistance - just when you need it.*

Pharon Powder Coatings Ltd, 4 Beech Road, Box Hill, Corsham, Wiltshire, SN13 8HF Tel: (01225) 743507 Fax: (01225) 744389 *Powder coatings manufrs*

Pharon S & R Ltd, 228 Lythalls Lane, Foleshill, Coventry, CV6 6GF Tel: (024) 7668 7235 Fax: (024) 7666 4397 E-mail: skelcher&rowe@pipemedia.co.uk *Tool & cutter grinding services*

Pharos Engineering Ltd, Unit 27 Chess Business Park, Moor Road, Chesham, Buckinghamshire, HP5 1SD Tel: (01494) 775611 Fax: (01494) 784003 *Deep drawn press manufrs*

Pharos Redco Ltd, 228 Lythalls Lane, Foleshill, Coventry, CV6 6GF Tel: (024) 7668 7235 Fax: (024) 7666 6355 E-mail: mwinstone@pharosengineering.co.uk *Thread, broaching, hydraulic clamping manufrs*

▶ pharos technology ltd, Ground Floor, Ashe Hill, Ashe, Basingstoke, Hampshire, RG25 3AE Tel: 01256 770566 E-mail: info@pharostechnology.co.uk *pharos provides marketing strategy, planning and implementation services, including image, branding, marketing programmes, marketing databases, website templates,and webhosting.*

Phasa Developments, International House, Horsecroft Road, Harlow, Essex, CM19 5SU Tel: (01279) 630200 Fax: (01279) 630222 E-mail: sales@phasa.co.uk *Manufacture of assembly machines*

▶ Phase 2, 1 Wheeler Grove, Wells, Somerset, BA5 2GB Tel: (01749) 674458 Fax: (01749) 671319 E-mail: info@phase2.org.uk *Website design & photography for business*

Phase 2 Computers Services, The Mansley Centre, 19 Timothys Bridge Road, Stratford-upon-Avon, Warwickshire, CV37 9NQ Tel: (01789) 295444 Fax: (01789) 298444 E-mail: sales@phase2.co.uk *Computer solution providers*

▶ Phase 4, 29 Regent Parade, Harrogate, North Yorkshire, HG1 5AZ Tel: (01423) 525277 Fax: (01423) 709922 *Computer maintenance & repair services*

Phase 8 Electronics & Alarms Ltd, 189 Headstone Lane, Harrow, Middlesex, HA2 6ND Tel: (020) 8863 8792 Fax: (020) 8861 0478 E-mail: phase8alarms@aol.com *Burglar installers*

Phase C R S Ltd, Beacon Lodge, Texas Street, Morley, Leeds, LS27 0HG Tel: 0113-238 0558 Fax: 0113-238 0484 E-mail: sales@phase.crs.co.uk *Computer repair specialists*

Phase Hire, 140a Kents Hill Road, Benfleet, Essex, SS7 5PH Tel: (01268) 792648 Fax: (01268) 792641 *Generator/generating set hire/leasing/ rental, installation services & maintenance/repair services. Also generating sets, diesel driven*

Phase Ii Firearms, 57 The Chase, Rayleigh, Essex, SS6 8QW Tel: (01268) 774606 Fax: (01702) 300201 E-mail: sales@stalkingscotland.com *Sells firearms*

▶ Phase One DJ Solutions, Station Road, Darlington, County Durham, DL3 6TA Tel: (01325) 480507 E-mail: mike@djanddiscostuff.com *Retail dj & disco suppliers*

Phase One Electronics, Orion Court, 2 Rodney Road, Southsea, Hampshire, PO4 8SZ Tel: (023) 9286 2394 Fax: (023) 9286 2396 E-mail: tonys@t1e.uk.com *Printed circuit assembly services*

Phasetech Ltd, Industry Park, Cricketts Lane, Chippenham, Wiltshire, SN15 3EQ Tel: (01249) 651436 Fax: (01249) 462356 E-mail: sales@phasetech.co.uk *Power factor correction engineers & distributors*

PHD, Bromley Road, Congleton, Cheshire, CW12 1PP Tel: (01260) 271243 *Disposable catering supplies*

▶ Pheby Colour Litho UK, Unit A3 Newton Industrial Estate, Eastern Avenue West, Romford, RM6 5SD Tel: (020) 8599 9842 Fax: (020) 8598 1966 E-mail: ajpheby@aol.com *Litho printing services*

Pheeco Horticulture Ltd, The Seed Bed Centre, Shadow Brook Lane, Hampton-In-Arden, Solihull, West Midlands, B92 0DL Tel: (0845) 4570800 Fax: (0870) 0601620 E-mail: info@pheeco.co.uk *Plant decor, floral display contractors & specialists services*

Phelps Bros, Sudmeadow Road, Gloucester, GL2 5HG Tel: (01452) 527133 Fax: (01452) 418513 E-mail: nick@phelpsbros.co.uk *Scrap iron & steel merchants*

▶ Phemisters Software, 64 Columbia Avenue, Livingston, West Lothian, EH54 6PR Tel: (01506) 413733 Fax: (08701) 322096 *Writing software tools manufrs*

Phenomenex Ltd, Melville House, Queens Avenue, Hurdsfield Industrial Estate, Macclesfield, Cheshire, SK10 2YF Tel: (01625) 501367 Fax: (01625) 501796 E-mail: info@phenomenex.com *Scientific instrument distributors*

▶ Pheonix Clothing, Unit E Lower Parliament Street, Nottingham, NG1 3BB Tel: 0115-959 9944 Fax: 0115-911 5345 E-mail: pheonixclothing@hotmail.com *Clothing manufrs*

▶ Pheonix Scaffolding, Unit H Smarden Business Estate, Smarden, Ashford, Kent, TN27 8QL Tel: (01233) 770373 Fax: (01233) 770776

Pheonix Systems, Phoenix House, 15-19 Norway Street, Portslade, Brighton, BN41 1GN Tel: (01273) 418874 Fax: (01273) 418363 E-mail: info@phoenix-sys.co.uk *Storage shelving & racking suppliers, commercial interiors fittings*

▶ Phew Design, Crowhill Farm, Ravensden Road, Wilden, Bedford, MK44 2QS Tel: (01234) 772261 Fax: (0845) 1259071 E-mail: info@phewdesign.com *Internet marketing company services*

▶ PHFS, Chance Hall Lane, Scholar Green, Stoke-on-Trent, ST7 3ST Tel: 01270 873072 E-mail: phfsbask2000@yahoo.co.uk *Clipper blade reconditioning for trade & public*

▶ PHG Services, 6 Hartshead Avenue, Stalybridge, Cheshire, SK15 1BY Tel: (07976) 325482 E-mail: phgservices@btconnect.com *Plumbing, heating & gas installers, services & repairers*

Phi@Falmouth Ltd, Bickland Industrial Park, Falmouth, Cornwall, TR11 4RY Tel: (01326) 373134 Fax: (01326) 377249 E-mail: info@phi-falmouth.co.uk *Magnetic recording head manufrs*

▶ Phil Jay, 12 Gower Rise, Gowerton, Swansea, SA4 3DZ Tel: (01792) 875523 Fax: (01792) 875523 E-mail: phil@philjaymagic.com *Phil Jay Close up magician available for all corporate and private events throughout the UK*

Phil Kool, Graynoth Place, Otham Street, Otham, Maidstone, Kent, ME15 8RL Tel: (01622) 862123 Fax: (01622) 862160 *Air conditioning units design & installation*

Phil Light Tractors, Tipplefield Farm, Brickworth Road, Whiteparish, Salisbury, SP5 2QG Tel: (01794) 884141 Fax: (01794) 884141 *Agricultural engineers*

Phil Morgan Contracting, Blue Barns, Church Stoke, Montgomery, Powys, SY15 6EN Tel: (01588) 620355 Fax: (01588) 620355 *Agricultural contractors*

Phil Partners Micro Help, 8 Bleak Hill Way, Mansfield, Nottinghamshire, NG18 5EZ Tel: (01623) 651444 Fax: (01623) 633661 E-mail: philj@microhelpuk.net *Computer consultants & software*

▶ Phil Rogerson Ltd, Tarnwater, A6 Road, Yealand Conyers, Carnforth, Lancashire, LA5 9RJ Tel: (01524) 736432 Fax: (01524) 734236

▶ Philantech Computer Systems, 207 Waterloo Road, London, SE1 8XD Tel: (020) 7401 9901 Fax: (020) 7401 9901 *Software suppliers*

Philbar & Co. Ltd, 254 Kilburn High Road, London, NW6 2BX Tel: (020) 7624 8681 Fax: (020) 7624 8683 *Hardware importers*

▶ Philiam Construction, The Quadrant, Manor Park CR, Edgware, Middlesex, HA8 7LU Tel: (020) 8905 7995 Fax: (020) 8905 6777

Philip Bennett Lithographic Printers Ltd, Avenue Farm Industrial Estate, Birmingham Road, Stratford-upon-Avon, Warwickshire, CV37 0HR Tel: (01789) 269256 Fax: (01789) 297023 *Lithographic printing services*

▶ Philip Chambers, 17 Brockenhurst Close, Woking, Surrey, GU21 4DS Tel: (01483) 765618 Fax: (01483) 765618 E-mail: philpchambers@philipchambers.f9.co.uk *Photographer, video*

Philip Cornes & Co. Ltd, Lanner Building, Clews Road, Redditch, Worcestershire, B98 7ST Tel: (01527) 555000 Fax: (01527) 547000 E-mail: philipcornes.sales@twmetals.co.uk *Nickel alloy & stainless steel stockholders*

Philip Holden, Harmire Enterprise Park, Barnard Castle, County Durham, DL12 8XT Tel: (01833) 637224 Fax: (01833) 690312 *Animal health care products*

Philip Lodge Ltd, Machine Works, New Mill Road, Brockholes, Holmfirth, HD9 7AE Tel: (01484) 661143 Fax: (01484) 661164 *Textile machinery engineers*

Philip Myers Press Holdings Ltd, 9 Clayton Road, Birchwood, Warrington, WA3 6PH Tel: (01925) 819021 Fax: (01925) 828147 E-mail: print@myerspress.com *Colour printers*

▶ Philip Shovlin Plant Hire Ltd, Brook Business Complex, Bennett St, West Gorton, Manchester, M12 5AU Tel: 0161-273 8900

Philip Sidford, Bridzor Farm, Wardour, Tisbury, Salisbury, SP3 6RN Tel: (01747) 870456 Fax: (01747) 871656 E-mail: pjs@sidford.com *Agricultural contractors*

▶ Philip Steatham Ltd, Planks Lane, Wombourne, Wolverhampton, WV5 8EB Tel: (01902) 324555 Fax: (01902) 324323 E-mail: enquires@steatham.co.uk *Computer printers*

Philip & Tacey Ltd, North Way, Andover, Hampshire, SP10 5BA Tel: (01264) 332171 Fax: (01264) 384808 E-mail: export@philipandtacey.co.uk *School stationers manufacturers & distributors*

Philip & Tacey Ltd, Riverside Road, Pottington Business Park, Barnstaple, Devon, EX31 1LR Tel: (01271) 340300 Fax: (01271) 345086 *Distribute teaching resources*

Philip Walker Engineering, 2 Thistleton Road, Market Overton, Oakham, Leicestershire, LE15 7PP Tel: (01572) 767444 Fax: (01572) 767571 E-mail: walkerengineers@aol.com *Precision engineers*

▶ Philip Whitfield Textiles Ltd, Remoor Mill, Buxton Road, New Mills, High Peak, Derbyshire, SK22 3JT Tel: (01663) 746220 Fax: (01663) 746158 E-mail: paul.butler@philipwhitfield.co.uk *Textile merchants*

Philip Wilson Ltd, 9 Blair Street, Edinburgh, EH1 1QR Tel: 0131-225 3040 Fax: 0131-225 3009 *Grain processor & distributor*

Philips, Cross Oak Lane, Redhill, RH1 5HA Tel: (01293) 815000 Fax: (01293) 815511 *Supplier of semiconductors*

Philips Business Communication, Philips House Cambridge Business Park, Cowley Road, Cambridge, CB4 0HB Tel: (01223) 468000 Fax: (01223) 468444 E-mail: sales@sopho.philips.co.uk *Telecommunications suppliers*

Philips Medical Systems, PO Box 263, Reigate, Surrey, RH2 0FY Tel: (01737) 230400 Fax: (01737) 230401 E-mail: claire.daynes@philips.com *Diagnostic imaging equipment* Also at: Gateshead, Leeds, Llantresant, Nottingham, Stirling, Tewkesbury & Warrington

Philips Speech Processing, 8 The Courtyards, Wyncolls Road, Severalls Industrial Park, Colchester, CO4 9PE Tel: (01206) 755755 Fax: (01206) 755888 E-mail: info@speech.philips.com *Dictating machine manufrs*

Phillard Pump Co., Unit B, Holmes Court, Horncastle, Lincolnshire, LN9 6AS Tel: (01507) 523281 Fax: (01507) 527437 *High pressure & cleaning pump manufrs*

Phillip Chapman Of Malton, York Road Industrial Estate, Malton, North Yorkshire, YO17 6YD Tel: (01653) 699030 *Stainless steel manufrs*

Phillip Trim, Frensham, Chamberlaynes, Bere Regis, Wareham, Dorset, BH20 7LS Tel: (01929) 472192 Fax: (01929) 472555 *Agricultural contractors*

Phillipa Enterprises Ltd, 33 West Drive, Ferring, Worthing, West Sussex, BN12 5QY Tel: (0781) 4548428 Fax: (01903) 242789 E-mail: bryanlp@totalise.co.uk *Security consultancy*

Phillips (1969) Ltd, Unit 3, Stambermill Industrial Estate, Lye, Stourbridge, West Midlands, DY9 7BJ Tel: (01384) 897324 Fax: (01384) 895435 E-mail: phillips@bradleeboilers.com *Glass fibre moulding materials manufrs*

▶ A.W. Phillips Ltd, Unit L OYO Business Unit, Hindmans Way, Dagenham, Essex, RM9 6LN Tel: (020) 8517 0902 Fax: (020) 8517 0832 E-mail: sales@awphillips.co.uk *Service, sales, installation on all industrial makes*

Berwyn Phillips, Unit 5 St James Street, Blue Bridge, Milton Keynes, MK13 0BW Tel: (01908) 221885 Fax: (01908) 221885 *Furniture manufrs*

Phillips Bros Farriers, Lillingstone House, Lillingstone Dayrell, Buckingham, MK18 5AG Tel: (01280) 860334 Fax: (01280) 860150 *Farrier*

Phillips & Carpenter, 23 Bentinck Street, London, W1U 2EZ Tel: (020) 7486 5333 Fax: (020) 7491 7084 *Recruitment consultants*

Phillips Digital Services, Unit 16 Jubilee Trade Centre, Jubilee Road, Letchworth Garden City, Hertfordshire, SG6 1SP Tel: (01462) 674733 Fax: (01462) 677223 E-mail: sales@phillipsdigital.co.uk *Digital services*

Phillips Duplicators Ltd, 149b Masons Hill, Bromley, BR2 9HW Tel: (020) 8460 2772 Fax: (020) 8460 2772 *Copying machines distributors*

Phillips Engineering, Bulmer Road Industrial Estate, Bulmer Road, Sudbury, Suffolk, CO10 7HJ Tel: (01787) 373549 Fax: (01787) 880276 *General engineers*

Phillips Haulage, 236 Queens Road, Sheffield, S2 4DL Tel: 0114-276 0281 Fax: 0114-270 1510 *Transport & haulage contractors*

Phillips & Leigh, 5 Pemberton Row, London, EC4A 3BA Tel: (020) 7822 8888 Fax: (020) 7822 8899 E-mail: mail@pandl.com *Patent attorneys*

Phillips Payne Products Ltd, Crabtree Farm, Church Street, Newnham, Daventry, Northamptonshire, NN11 3ET Tel: (01327) 879100 Fax: (01327) 871633 E-mail: mh@icm-cambs.co.uk *Chemical & janitorial distributors*

Phillips Products Dudley Ltd, Dawley Brook, Kingswinford, West Midlands, DY6 7AS Tel: (01384) 273592 Fax: (01384) 400036 *Steel tube stockholders*

Phillips & Sons, 110-111 Lewes Road, Brighton, BN2 3QB Tel: (01273) 682751 Fax: (01273) 677469 *Monumental consultants*

Steve Phillips Plumbing, Cockett Farm, Basford, Leek, Staffordshire, ST13 7ET Tel: (01538) 361110 *Plumbing services*

Phillips Welding, Sedgedale Cottage, Killingworth Village, Newcastle upon Tyne, NE12 6BL Tel: 0191-268 6741 Fax: 0191-268 6741 *Welding & fabrication contractors*

▶ Ian Phillips-McLaren Photographers, Orchard End, Watling Lane, Thaxted, Essex, CM6 2QY Tel: (07889) 861654 E-mail: ian@ianphillips-mclaren.com *Seventeen Years Of Photography *Food, Lifestyle, Interiors, People, product and Still life.*For major clients and magazines*

Phill's Model Shop, 41-42 Nile Street, North Shields, Tyne & Wear, NE29 0BB Tel: 0191-272 8443 Fax: 0191-272 8443 E-mail: sales@phillsmodels.com *Model shop*

Philmac (U K) Ltd, Diplocks Way, Hailsham, East Sussex, BN27 3JF Tel: (01323) 847323 Fax: (01323) 844775 E-mail: philmacorders@philmac.co.uk *Plastic pipe fittings manufrs*

Philman Engineering Ltd, Kingsnorth Works, Hoo, Rochester, Kent, ME3 9NZ Tel: (01634) 253968 Fax: (01634) 253968 *Bulk materials handling equipment manufrs*

Philpot Dairy Products Ltd, Philpot House, Station Road, Rayleigh, Essex, SS6 7HH Tel: (01268) 775522 Fax: (01268) 773848 E-mail: claud.bilbao@dairycrest.co.uk *Export dairy products*

Philpot Enterprises Ltd, West Town Farm, Farm Road, Taplow, Maidenhead, Berkshire, SL6 0PT Tel: (01628) 602003 Fax: (01628) 660905 E-mail: angus@philpot-group.co.uk *Archive storage services*

▶ Philpott & Cowlin Ltd, Unit 12 Liberty Industrial Park, South Liberty Lane, Bristol, BS3 2SU Tel: 0117-966 8431 Fax: 0117-966 0129 E-mail: philpottcowlin@pcweldmetals.co.uk *Welding distributors* Also at: Cardiff

Philrae Fabrications Ltd, 53 Circular Road, Storforth Lane Trading Estate, Chesterfield, Derbyshire, S41 0QR Tel: (01246) 279234 Fax: (01246) 234862 *Steel & welded fabrication manufacturers*

▶ Phil's Garden & Maintanance Services, 129 Canary Road, Stoke-on-Trent, ST2 0SS Tel: (01782) 342714 Fax: (01782) 342714 E-mail: phil_taylor100@msn.com *All aspects of garden work*

Phils (Wholesale) Ltd, 709 North Circular Road, London, NW2 7AX Tel: (020) 8830 8830 Fax: (020) 8830 8833 E-mail: mark@trimarkfsnet.co.uk *Afro & Caribbean cosmetics*

Philspace Ltd, 109-111 Bitterne Road West, Southampton, SO18 1AR Tel: (023) 8022 3333 Fax: (023) 8021 5100 E-mail: sales@rigfone.co.uk *Portable building hire*

▶ Philtech Installations Ltd, Bath Street, Walsall, WS1 3BZ Tel: (01922) 643805 Fax: (01922) 643845

Philton Fire & Security Ltd, 61 Lower Road, Harrow, Middlesex, HA2 0DE Tel: (020) 8864 7534 Fax: (020) 8864 8631 *Fire alarm installation & maintenance*

Philton Polythene Converters Ltd, Charfleets Road, Canvey Island, Essex, SS8 0PQ Tel: (01268) 696331 Fax: (01268) 510517 E-mail: sales@philton.co.uk Principal Export Areas: Worldwide *Container liner (plastic), pallet cover manufrs*

Phoceenne, Birtley House, Claremont Avenue, Woking, Surrey, GU22 7QB Tel: (01483) 742772 Fax: (01483) 742774 *Piping materials manufrs &stockists*

Phoebus Solutions Ltd, 2a Market Street, Heanor, Derbyshire, DE75 7NR Tel: (0870) 7270300 Fax: (08707) 270400 E-mail: sales@pheobus-solutions.com *Computer network system suppliers*

▶ Phoenix, 14 Pindar Road, Hoddesdon, Hertfordshire, EN11 0BZ Tel: (01992) 479444 Fax: (01992) 478878 *Medical or surgical supplies*

Phoenix Abrasive Wheel Co. Ltd, 71 Shepley Industrial Estate South, Audenshaw, Manchester, M34 5DW Tel: 0161-320 9580 Fax: 0161-335 9074 E-mail: phoenixabr@aol.com *Abrasive grinding wheel manufrs*

Phoenix Accessories Safety Ltd, Waterloo Mills, Waterloo Road, Pudsey, West Yorkshire, LS28 8DQ Tel: 0113-257 4475 Fax: 0113-255 0208 E-mail: phoenixsafety@lineone.com *Safety equipment distributor*

Phoenix Agronomy Ltd, The Stables, Featherbed Lane, Wighill Park, Tadcaster, North Yorkshire, LS24 8BN Tel: (01937) 832200 Fax: (01937) 834968 *Agricultural merchants*

Phoenix Air Conditioning Co. Ltd, Unit 2 Chichester Road, Romiley, Stockport, Cheshire, SK6 4BL Tel: 0161-430 7878 Fax: 0161-430 7979 E-mail: tony@crs-limited.co.uk *Air conditioning suppliers*

Phoenix Analytical, The Laboratory, 270 London Road, Wallington, Surrey, SM6 7DJ Tel: (020) 8647 0003 Fax: (020) 8647 0004 *Consulting & analytical chemists*

▶ Phoenix Beattie Ltd, Jubilee Industrial Estate, Ashington, Northumberland, NE63 8UB Tel: (01670) 520565 Fax: (01670) 520535 E-mail: sales@phoenixbeattie.co.uk *Hose*

continued

continuation
distributors or agents including couplings, high pressure & reels

Phoenix Blinds, 1 Wolseley Place, Edinburgh, EH8 7AD Tel: 0131-652 9963 Fax: 0131-661 6660 *Blind manufrs*

▶ Bobby Phoenix Construct Academy, Deadmans Hole Lane, Sheffield, S9 1QQ Tel: (01709) 836700 Fax: (01709) 836700 E-mail: bobby@cowercranetraining.co.uk *Telescopic handler suppliers*

Phoenix Brick Co. Ltd, The Accounting House, Pottery Lane East, Whittington Moor, Chesterfield, Derbyshire, S41 9BH Tel: (01246) 233223 Fax: (01246) 230777 E-mail: erichall@phoenixbrick.freeserve.co.uk *Brick manufacturers*

Phoenix Calico Ltd, Phoenix Works, 6 Huddersfield Road, Stalybridge, Cheshire, SK15 2QA Tel: 0161-304 7144 Fax: 0161-304 7244 *Textile merchants & converters*

Phoenix Casuals Ltd, Deltex, Flathouse Rd, Portsmouth, PO1 4QS Tel: 023 92877715 Fax: 023 92877715 *Clothing manufrs*

▶ Phoenix Ceramic Consultants Ltd, Unit 105 Wincolmlee, Hull, HU2 0PZ Tel: (01482) 217283 Fax: (01482) 217283

Phoenix Colour plc, 11 Knighton Fields Road West, Leicester, LE2 6LH Tel: 0116-283 5817 Fax: 0116-244 0061 E-mail: admin@phoenix-photo.co.uk *Lithographers & digital printers*

Phoenix Control Systems, Unit 14 Dewar Court, Astmoor Industrial Estate, Runcorn, Cheshire, WA7 1PT Tel: (01928) 590500 Fax: (01928) 590811 *Process control systems*

Phoenix Conveyors Ltd, Unit 6 Cobnash Industrial Estate, Kingsland, Leominster, Herefordshire, HR6 9RW Tel: (01568) 709144 Fax: (01568) 709145 *Mechanical handling engineers & conveyor manufrs*

Phoenix Corporation UK Ltd, Unit 5 North Weylands Industrial Estate, Molesey Road, Walton-on-Thames, Surrey, KT12 3PL Tel: (01932) 246236 Fax: (01932) 246236 *Powder coating & stove enamelling services*

Phoenix County Metal Ltd, Great Central Way Industrial Estate, Great Central Way, Woodford Halse, Daventry, Northamptonshire, NN11 3PZ Tel: (01327) 260581 Fax: (01327) 260191 *Toxic & precious metal services*

Phoenix Crankshafts Ltd, 37 The Business Village, Wexham Road, Slough, SL2 5EJ Tel: (01753) 821303 Fax: (01753) 692485 *Crankshaft manufrs*

Phoenix Datacom Group Ltd, Phoenix House, Smeaton Close, Aylesbury, Buckinghamshire, HP19 8UW Tel: (01296) 397711 Fax: (01296) 394431 E-mail: info@phoenixdata.com *Data communication systems*

Phoenix Dental Castings Ltd, Unit 1 The Alpha Centre, Osprey Road, Sowton Industrial Estate, Exeter, EX2 7LH Tel: (01392) 444456 Fax: (01392) 445725 E-mail: phoenix.dental@btinternet.com *Dental laboratories*

▶ Phoenix Design Print, 56 Wilbury Way, Hitchin, Hertfordshire, SG4 0TP Tel: (01462) 427500 Fax: (01462) 427501 E-mail: mark@pcsltd.org.uk *Graphic Design for, Logos, Corporate Identity, Leaflets, Brochures, Direct Mail, Advertising, Display, Point-Of-Sale, Exhibitions, Photography, Print Management*

▶ Phoenix Development & Construction Ltd, Manor Road, Horbury, Wakefield, West Yorkshire, WF4 6HH Tel: (01924) 260230

Phoenix Electrical Co. Ltd, Yeoman House, 63 Croydon Road, London, SE20 7TS Tel: (020) 8778 9666 Fax: (020) 8659 9386 E-mail: davidrosedon@pheonixelectrical.co.uk *Electrical contractors*

Phoenix Electronics Ltd, Phoenix House, Carluke, Lanarkshire, ML8 5UF Tel: (01555) 751566 Fax: (01555) 751562 E-mail: sales@phoenix1.co.uk *Electronic components*

Phoenix Engineering Co., Combe Street, Chard, Somerset, TA20 1JE Tel: (01460) 63531 Fax: (01460) 67388 E-mail: sales@phoenixeng.co.uk *Road surfacing plant manufrs*

Phoenix Engines Ltd, Phoenix House, Railway Lane, Dimminsdale, Willenhall, West Midlands, WV13 2BE Tel: (01902) 601676 Fax: (01902) 601474 E-mail: david.scriven@phoenixengines.co.uk *Engine reconditioners & manufrs*

Phoenix Engraving Ltd, 108 Alcester Road, Birmingham, B13 8EF Tel: 0121-449 3711 Fax: 0121-449 3712 E-mail: info@phoenixengraving.com *Engravers manufrs*

Phoenix Erection Co. Ltd, 7 The Grove, Walton-on-Thames, Surrey, KT12 2HP Tel: (01932) 243074 Fax: (01932) 240743 *Steel erectors & onsite fabrication welders*

Phoenix Fabrications Ltd, Unit 11 Meadow Drove, Earith, Huntingdon, Cambridgeshire, PE28 3QF Tel: (01487) 843888 Fax: (01487) 843905 *Steel fabricating specialists*

Phoenix Fencing Supplies, The Chalk Hole, Harbour Farm, Molash, Canterbury, Kent, CT4 8HN Tel: (01233) 740004 *Garden furniture manufrs*

▶ Phoenix Feng Shui, Climperwell Cottage, Climperwell, Brimpsfield, Gloucester, GL4 8LQ Tel: (01452) 863288 Fax: (0794) 1581202 E-mail: dee.ramage@phoenixfengshui.co.uk *Feng Shui Consultancy services based in the Cotswolds. Providing consultations nationwide. Residential & commercial work undertaken including Property search surveys of offices, warehouses, retail sector, hotels, spa"s, as well as new build and renovation project management for energetic design concepts tailor made to your companies individual'requirements.*

Phoenix Fire Alarms, Phoenix House, Gollburne Street, Keighley, West Yorkshire, BD21 1YR Tel: (01535) 600200 Fax: (01535) 600200 *Fire alarm manufrs*

Phoenix Fire Extinguishing Services, 32 Bullar Road, Southampton, SO18 1GS Tel: (023) 8055 8638 Fax: (023) 8034 9121 *Service & supply of fire extinguishers*

Phoenix Fire Protection Midlands Ltd, Mountfield House, High Street, Kingswinford, West Midlands, DY6 8AL Tel: (01384) 295529 Fax: (01384) 271391 E-mail: sales@phoenix-fire.co.uk *Fire alarm and sprinkler system contractors*

Phoenix Fire Services Ltd, Homes Court House, 29a Bridge Street, Kenilworth, Warwickshire, CV8 1BP Tel: (01926) 855991 Fax: (01926) 855338 E-mail: paul@phoenixfireservices.co.uk *Fire protection services*

Phoenix Fireworks Ltd, The Garth, Hill Park Farm, Wrotham Hill Road, Wrotham, Sevenoaks, Kent, TN15 7PX Tel: (0800) 781 1747 Fax: (01732) 823916 E-mail: info@phoenixfireworks.co.uk *Firework display organisors & firework suppliers*

▶ Phoenix Fitted Furniture, Industrial Estate, Old Church Road, East Hanningfield, Chelmsford, CM3 8AB Tel: (01245) 400920 Fax: (01245) 401057 *Door fittings & furnishings manufrs*

▶ Phoenix Fitted Furniture Ltd, Wilton Road, Humberston, Grimsby, South Humberside, DN36 4AW Tel: (01472) 811581 Fax: (01472) 811593 *Furniture manufrs*

Phoenix Fixings Ltd, 21 Park Road, Bingley, West Yorkshire, BD16 4BQ Tel: (01274) 779001 Fax: (01274) 771277 E-mail: info@phoenixfixings.co.uk *Construction industry suppliers*

Phoenix Floor Maintenance Equipment Ltd, Unit 7, Padgets Lane, South Moons Moat, Redditch, Worcestershire, B98 0RA Tel: (01527) 517161 Fax: (01527) 520765 E-mail: sales@jangro.co.uk *Cleaning material suppliers*

Phoenix Foods Ltd, Brakey Road, Weldon North Industrial Estate, Corby, Northamptonshire, NN17 5LU Tel: (01536) 200101 Fax: (01536) 202218 E-mail: sales@phoenixfoods.co.uk *Dry food manufrs*

Phoenix Grace Ltd, 8 Worset Lane, Hartlepool, Cleveland, TS26 0LJ Tel: (01429) 279814 Fax: (01429) 231255 *Computer supplies & printers*

Phoenix Hazmat, Unit 6 Dabble Duck Industrial Estate, Shildon, County Durham, DL4 2RA Tel: (01388) 779220 Fax: (01388) 779230 E-mail: info@phoenixhazmatltd.co.uk *Licensed Asbestos Removal and Licensed Hazardous Waste Carrier*

Phoenix Healthcare Distribution Ltd, Eddison Road, Hamshall Distribution Park, Coleshill, Birmingham, B46 1DA Tel: (01675) 436500 Fax: (01675) 436502 *Pharmaceutical wholesalers*

Phoenix Healthcare Distribution Ltd, South Elgin Street, Clydebank, Dunbartonshire, G81 1PL Tel: 0141-952 3261 Fax: 0141-951 1708 *Wholesale pharmaceutical distributors*

Phoenix Healthcare Distrubtions Ltd, Farrington Place, Rossendale Road, Burnley, Lancashire, BB11 5TZ Tel: (01282) 426363 Fax: (01282) 477630 E-mail: burnley@pheonixmedical.co.uk *Wholesale chemists*

Phoenix Home Improvement Services Ltd, 21 Sandmere Road, Leechmere Industrial Estate, Sunderland, SR2 9TP Tel: 0191-523 7006 Fax: 0191-523 8737 *Window & door manufrs*

Phoenix Hose & Couplings Ltd, Unit 1 Kencot Close, Waldrist Way, Yarnton Way, Thamesmead, Erith, Kent, DA18 4AB Tel: (020) 8311 7204 Fax: (020) 8310 0406 E-mail: phoenix999@btclick.com *Hydraulic engineers, installation or service*

Phoenix I T Group plc, Technology House, Hunsbury Hill Avenue, Northampton, NN4 8QS Tel: (01604) 769000 Fax: (01604) 706666 E-mail: sales@phoenixitservices.co.uk *I.T. services & resellers of compurter parts & hardware*

▶ Phoenix Industrial Packaging Ltd, Phoenix Way, Rushden, Northamptonshire, NN10 6ER Tel: (01933) 312553 Fax: (01933) 418418 *Design & supply of corrugated packaging solutions*

Phoenix Inspection Systems Ltd, 46 Melford Court, Hardwick Grange, Woolston, Warrington, WA1 4RZ Tel: (01925) 826000 Fax: (01925) 838788 E-mail: pryan@phoenixisl.co.uk Sales Contact: P. Ryan Principal Export Areas: Worldwide *Phoenix Inspection Systems design and manufacture manipulators/transducers and inspection systems for specialised inspections in the Nuclear Industry. An extensive range of NDT products and services is offered, including standard and special ultrasonic transducers for most applications, automatic and semi-automatic inspection systems and manipulators for weld, turbine and corrosion mapping; feasibility studies, project management and consultancy services. In addition PISL area of excellence include the supply of both manual and automatic equipment for examining turbine rotor shafts from the bore, Turbine rotor inspection manipulators for UT examination of exterior surfaces of rotors; End ring manipulators for in-situ inspections of all end rings and a wide range of pipe and plate scanners.*

▶ Phoenix Instrumentation Ltd, Ivel Road, Shefford, Bedfordshire, SG17 5JU Tel: (01462) 851747 Fax: (01462) 815382 E-mail: sales@phoenixinstrumentation.ltd.uk *Water quality instrumentation services*

Phoenix International Ltd, Unit 2 Coronation Business Centre, Hard Ings Road, Keighley, West Yorkshire, BD21 3ND Tel: (01535) 691756 Fax: (01535) 611900 *Builders hardware import & exporters*

Phoenix International, 7 Hendford Grove, Yeovil, Somerset, BA20 1UT Tel: (01935) 420721 Fax: (01935) 432598 E-mail: sales@phoenix-intl-ltd.com *Jewellery manufrs*

Phoenix International Freight Services, Trent Lane Indust Estate Unit 2, Sycamore Road, Castle Donnington, Derby, DE74 2LL Tel: (01332) 817350 Fax: (01332) 850530 *Air & sea freight forwarders*

Phoenix Ironworks Co. Ltd, Newall Street, Littleborough, Lancashire, OL15 9DL Tel: (01706) 378102 Fax: (01706) 379937 E-mail: sales@phoenix-ironworks.co.uk *Roll manufacturers & specialist engineers*

Phoenix Lifting Supplies Ltd, Unit 54 Bowen Industrial Estate, Aberbargoed, Bargoed, Mid Glamorgan, CF81 9EP Tel: (01443) 821577 Fax: (01443) 821503 *Lifting gear distributors & manufrs*

Phoenix Machinery Ltd, Riverside Studios, Mill Lane, Dronfield, Derbyshire, S18 2XL Tel: (01246) 290027 Fax: (01246) 290093 *New & used sheet metal & plateworking equipment. In addition, machine tools*

▶ Phoenix Marcom Ltd, Newton Hall, Newton, Cambridge, CB22 7ZE Tel: (01223) 873318 Fax: (01223) 874173 E-mail: paul.carter@phoenixmarcom.co.uk *Marketing communications*

Phoenix Marine Ltd, 2 Marrowbone Slip, Sutton Rd, Plymouth, PL4 0HX Tel: (01752) 267428 Fax: (01752) 267415 E-mail: info@phoenix316.com Principal Export Areas: Worldwide *Stainless steel & aluminium fabricators*

Phoenix Mecano Ltd, 6-7 Faraday Road, Aylesbury, Buckinghamshire, HP19 8TX Tel: (01296) 619100 Fax: (01296) 398866 E-mail: info@phoenix-mecano.ltd.uk *Manufactures of enclosures for electrical & electronic equipment*

Phoenix Metals, Firs Industrial Estate, Kidderminster, Worcestershire, DY11 7QN Tel: (01562) 822777 Fax: (01562) 822477 *Steel stockholders*

Phoenix Optics UK Ltd, Unit B The Grange, Colesden, Bedford, MK44 3DB Tel: (01234) 376120 Fax: (01234) 376122 E-mail: sales@phoenixoptics.co.uk *Fibre optics installers*

▶ Phoenix PCS, Unit 215 Tedco Business Centre, Viking Industrial Park, Jarrow, Tyne & Wear, NE32 3DT Tel: 0191-428 3338 Fax: 0191-428 3529 E-mail: sales@phoenix-pcs.co.uk *North East UK Based supplier of computer systems and components. We also stock a range of consumer electronics.*

Phoenix Phones, 2 Stanley Cottages, London Road, Hartley Wintney, Hook, Hampshire, RG27 8RT Tel: (01252) 845845 Fax: (01252) 845888 E-mail: admin@phoenix-phones.co.uk *Telecommunication services*

▶ Phoenix Pine, Unit 3-4 Ebor Business Park, Ure Bank Top, Ripon, North Yorkshire, HG4 1JD Tel: (01765) 602070 Fax: (01765) 608100 *Pine furniture manufrs*

▶ Phoenix Power, 323 Goring Road, Goring-by-Sea, Worthing, West Sussex, BN12 4NX Tel: (01903) 248999 Fax: (01903) 249555 E-mail: sales@phoenixpower.net

Phoenix Precision Ltd, Crompton Road, Southfield Industrial Estate, Glenrothes, Fife, KY6 2SF Tel: (01592) 772077 Fax: (01592) 773535 E-mail: sales@phoenixprecision.com *Precision sheet metalworkers*

Phoenix Pressings Ltd, Wakefield Road, Brighouse, West Yorkshire, HD6 1PE Tel: (01484) 712422 Fax: (01484) 716471 E-mail: sales@phoenixpressings.co.uk *General pressings manufrs*

Phoenix Publicity & Print Ltd, Unit 2, Lister Street, Dudley Hill, Bradford, West Yorkshire, BD4 9PQ Tel: (01274) 681642 Fax: (01274) 681692 E-mail: info@phoenixprinting.com *General printers*

▶ Phoenix Retail Service Ltd, Fryers Farm Office, Fryers Farm Lane, Lane End, High Wycombe, Buckinghamshire, HP14 3NP Tel: (01494) 880200 Fax: (01494) 881204 E-mail: sales@phoenixretail.com *Suppliers of refrigerated display cabinets*

Phoenix Safe Co. Ltd, Apex House, No. 1 Orrell Mount, Liverpool, L20 6NS Tel: 0151-944 6444 Fax: 0151-944 6445 E-mail: sales@phoenixsafe.co.uk *We are a world leader manufacturing a range of state of the art safes to suit all requirements, ranging from lockable key boxes right through to our top-of-the-range Millennium Duplex 4630 data protection safe series. Our comprehensive range of attractive yet tough hotel room safes are designed to compliment any guest bedroom, providing security and peace of mind for the guest. We also supply a wide range of back office protection against fire and theft, protecting cash, keys and your essential computer data and software on media such as CD-ROM and diskette.*

▶ Phoenix Safety Services, Unit 23 Prestwood Court, Leacroft Road, Birchwood, Warrington, WA3 6SB Tel: (01925) 880008 Fax: (01925) 880008 E-mail: enquiries@phoenixsafetyhire.co.uk *Safety equipment hire*

Phoenix Saxton Ltd, Thornton Industrial Trading Estate, Milford Haven, Dyfed, SA73 2RR Tel: (01646) 690588 Fax: (01646) 690570 *Safety, engineering & industrial suppliers*

▶ Phoenix Seating, Second Avenue, Pensnett Trading Estate, Kingswinford, West Midlands, DY6 7UZ Tel: (01384) 296622 Fax: (01384) 287831 *Seating suppliers & manufrs*

Phoenix Security Systems Ltd, 95 Park Road, Sale, Cheshire, M33 6JA Tel: 0161-976 6566 Fax: 0161-976 3869 *Intruder systems suppliers*

Phoenix Signs, 1 Paynes Place Farm, Cuckfield Road, Burgess Hill, West Sussex, RH15 8RG Tel: (01444) 254040 Fax: (01444) 258553 E-mail: alan_cooper@btconnect.com *Vehicle livery, digital printing & vinyl banners & tinting services*

Phoenix Signs Ltd, Unit 7, Continental Approach, Westwood Industrial Estate, Margate, Kent, CT9 4JG Tel: (01843) 228682 Fax: (01843) 227373 E-mail: vince@phoenixsignsuk.ltd.uk *Trade Manufacturers, Supplying built up stainless & ali letters*

Phoenix Signs, 49 North Bridge Street, Sunderland, SR5 1AH Tel: 0191-567 5021 Fax: 0191-567 5021 E-mail: phoenix.sings@virgin.net *Signs & engravings manufrs*

▶ Phoenix Site Services, Unit 4b Gateway Close, Parkgate, Rotherham, South Yorkshire, S62 6LJ Tel: (01709) 529951 Fax: (01709) 529549 E-mail: paul.phoenixservices@btopenworld.com *Specialist in cremation & incineration for all industries worldwide*

Phoenix Steel Services Ltd, Units 3-4, Charlotte Street, Dudley, West Midlands, DY1 1TD Tel: (01384) 458866 Fax: (01384) 455576 E-mail: sales@phoenixsteelservices.co.uk *Slit coil processors*

Phoenix Steels Co., Speedwell Road, Birmingham, B25 8EL Tel: 0121-707 0165 Fax: 0121-766 7767 E-mail: sales@phoenixsteels.com *Steel stockholders & shearers*

Phoenix Straps Ltd, 30 Springfield Gardens, Morganstown, Cardiff, CF15 8LQ Tel: (029) 2084 3677 Fax: (029) 2084 3677 E-mail: phoenixstraps@aol.com *Watch strap manufrs*

Phoenix Tavinor Engineering, Lichfield Road Industrial Estate, Apollo, Tamworth, Staffordshire, B79 7TA Tel: (01827) 58704 Fax: (01827) 311443 *Engineering*

▶ Phoenix Technology UK Ltd, 4 Stone Lodge Lane, Ipswich, IP2 9PA Tel: (0871) 4251236 E-mail: info@ptu.biz *Computer & network support & installation services*

Phoenix Tile Studio, Winkhill Mill, Swan Street, Stoke-on-Trent, ST4 7RH Tel: (01782) 745599 Fax: (01782) 745599 E-mail: office@phoenixtilestudio.fsbusiness.co.uk *Tile manufrs*

Phoenix Tooling Ltd, 2 Saracen Close, Gillingham Business Park, Gillingham, Kent, ME8 0QN Tel: (01634) 363168 Fax: (01634) 361103 E-mail: phoenixtooling@btconnect.com *Precision engineers*

Phoenix Tools, 1 Sandygate Business Park, Strap Lane, Kingsteignton, Newton Abbot, Devon, TQ12 3XF Tel: (01626) 332862 Fax: (01626) 331860 *Tool distributors*

▶ Phoenix Total Security, 297 Wood Lane, Dagenham, Essex, RM8 3NH Tel: (020) 8596 7920 Fax: (020) 8596 7921 E-mail: sales@phoenix-total-security.com *Installation of Burglar Alarms*

Phoenix Transworld Ltd, Wharf Way, Glen Parva, Leicester, LE2 9TF Tel: (0870) 7505022 Fax: (0870) 7505033 E-mail: sales@phoenixtransworld.com *Asphalt plant & associated equipment suppliers*

Phoenix Turned Parts, 4-5 Mica Close, Tamworth, Staffordshire, B77 4DR Tel: (01827) 59441 Fax: (01827) 54750 E-mail: mike.pegg@btbusinessconnect.co.uk *CNC engineering services or machinists*

Phoenix Ventilation & Engineering Ltd, Unit 6 Camphill Industrial Estate, Camphill Road, West Byfleet, Surrey, KT14 6EW Tel: (01932) 336125 Fax: (01932) 336132 E-mail: sales@phoenixventilation.co.uk *Air conditioning equipment hire & air conditioning engineers*

Phoenix Walking Stick Co. Ltd, Unit 6a-6c Nailsworth Mills, Avening Road, Nailsworth, Stroud, Gloucestershire, GL6 0BS Tel: (01453) 835816 Fax: (01453) 835819 E-mail: jf@sticks.org *Walking stick manufrs*

▶ Phoenix Whirlpools, Scott Lane, Morley, Leeds, LS27 0NQ Tel: 0113-201 2260 Fax: 0113-202 2268 *Whirlpools manufrs*

Phoenix (Wirral) Ltd, Unit 28-34, Thursby Road, Bromborough, Wirral, Merseyside, CH62 3PW Tel: 0151-334 9044 Fax: 0151-334 9045 E-mail: chris@phoenixchem.com *Pharmaceuticals & chemicals contractors services*

Phoenix-Saxton Ltd, Pomeroy Works, Clarence Road, Cardiff Bay, Cardiff, CF10 5FA Tel: (029) 2048 7848 Fax: (029) 2049 3493 E-mail: sales@phoenix-saxton.com Principal Export Areas: Worldwide *Abrasive product supplies distributors, agents, stockholders*

Phoenox Home Furnishings Ltd, Spring Grove Mills, Clayton West, Huddersfield, HD8 9HH Tel: (01484) 863227 Fax: (01484) 865352 E-mail: info@phoenox.co.uk *Carpet manufrs*

Phone Coach Ltd, Unit 21 Kent House, Old Bexley Business Park, Bexley, Kent, DA5 1LR Tel: (01322) 551170 Fax: (01322) 556680 E-mail: enquiries@phonecoach.com *Telephone training equipment suppliers*

The Phone & Fax Co., 35 Norwich Street, Fakenham, Norfolk, NR21 9AF Tel: (01328) 856566 Fax: (01328) 856506 E-mail: fakenham@digital-phone.co.uk *Mobile phones suppliers*

▶ Phone It Ict Helston, 17 Marconi Close, Helston, Cornwall, TR13 8PD Tel: (01326) 565335 Fax: (01326) 573541 E-mail: philipeade@btconnect.com *INSTALATION AND MAINTENANCE OF TELEPHONE PABX SYSTEMS AND DATA CABLEING NETWORKS.*

Phone-In, 34 Queensferry Street, Edinburgh, EH2 4QS Tel: 0131-220 4325 Fax: (0870) 1221438 E-mail: enquiries@phone-in.com *Telecom retail supplier*

Phoneline, 26 High Street, Long Eaton, Long Eaton, Nottingham, NG10 1LL Tel: 0115-946 5656 Fax: 0115-946 4188 E-mail: jgcomms@msn.com *Cellular radio telephone equipment distributor & retail*

Phonelink Installations Ltd, 94 Sterry Road, Gowerton, Swansea, SA4 3BW Tel: (01792) 875999 Fax: (01792) 875111 E-mail: sales@phonelink-inst.co.uk *Cable system installers*

▶ Phones 4U Ltd, Lower Level, White Rose Shopping Centre, Leeds, LS11 8LL Tel: 0113-270 3754 *Retail mobile phones*

▶ Phones-GB, 6 Hathaway Close, Balsall Common, Coventry, CV7 7EP Tel: 01676 530407 E-mail: stevemorris@uk2.net *Mobile Phones, all major networks including insurance and ringtones.*

▶ Phormium Ltd, Braehead Cottage, Finavon, Forfar, Angus, DD8 3PX Tel: (01307) 850715 Fax: (01307) 850756 E-mail: p.s.ingham@btinternet.com *Design & produce hand painted silk ties & waistcoats*

Photek Ltd, 26 Castleham Road, St. Leonards-On-Sea, East Sussex, TN38 9NS Tel: (01424) 850555 Fax: (01424) 850051 E-mail: sales@photek.co.uk *Opto-electronic component manufrs*

Photo Centre, Bridge Street, Berwick-upon-Tweed, TD15 1ES Tel: (01289) 306434 Fax: (01289) 303400 *Commercial & industrial photographers*

Photo Data, Photo Data House 12 Knowl Piece, Wilbury Way, Hitchin, Hertfordshire, SG4 0TY Tel: (01462) 452616 Fax: (01462) 422830 E-mail: sales@photodata.com *Printed circuit photography services*

▶ Photo Dreams, 101 Burford, Brookside, Telford, Shropshire, TF3 1LJ Tel: (01952) 279110 E-mail: ian@photodreams.co.uk *The Photography of Ian Mannering for Portraits, Fashion, Glamour and Commercial Photography.*A FREE to use Model Directory.*

▶ Photo Express, 7 Melville Terrace, Edinburgh, EH9 1ND Tel: 0131-667 2164 Fax: 0131-667 2164 E-mail: info@photo-express-edinburgh.co.uk *General practice photographers*

Photo Gen Ic Ltd, Unit 4 Parc Industrial Estate, Llanidloes, Powys, SY18 6RB Tel: (01686) 413292 Fax: (01686) 413425 E-mail: sales@photogenic.co.uk *Sintered filter manufrs*

Photo Imaging Council, Orbital House, 85-87 Croydon Road, Caterham, Surrey, CR3 6PD Tel: (01883) 334497 Fax: (01883) 334490 E-mail: pipa@admin.co.uk *Trade association*

Photo Me (International) plc, Church Road, Bookham, Leatherhead, Surrey, KT23 3EU Tel: (01372) 453399 Fax: (01372) 459064 E-mail: christianname.surname@photo-me.co.uk *Photo booth distributors*

Photo Mechanical Services Essex Ltd, Co-Ordinated Industrial Estate, Claydons Lane, Rayleigh, Essex, SS6 7UP Tel: (01268) 741486 Fax: (01268) 782538 E-mail: pcbs@photomechanical.co.uk *Printed circuit manufrs*

▶ Photo Models UK, 1 Burford, Brookside, Telford, Shropshire, TF3 1LJ Tel: (01952) 279110 E-mail: info@photomodelsuk.co.uk *The Model Directory, Model Showcase and Forum for UK based Models and Photographers.*

▶ Photo My Wedding, 16 Carnation Way, Red Lodge, Bury St. Edmunds, Suffolk, IP28 8TN Tel: (01638) 751889 *fantastic wedding photos service, professional wedding photographers, husband and wife team*Royal photographic society members and society of wedding and portrait photographers see our web site for details and prices. www.photomywedding.co.uk*

Photo Optix Ltd, 8 Oak Road, London, W5 3SS Tel: (020) 8840 7028 *Retail photography*

Photo Optix Ltd, 14 Clivemont Road, Maidenhead, Berkshire, SL6 7BU Tel: (01628) 778787 Fax: (01628) 776145 *Photographic retailers*

▶ Photo Restoring, 9 Coombe Road, Steyning, West Sussex, BN44 3LF Tel: (01903) 813184 E-mail: brian@restoring-photos.co.uk *Top quality restoration, repair and enhancement of your photos. Friendly & helpful service - take a look and then ask away*

Photo Shot Holding, 29-31 Saffron Hill, London, EC1N 8SW Tel: (020) 7421 6004 Fax: (020) 7421 6006 E-mail: colin@uppa.co.uk *Press & commercial photographic services*

▶ PhotoBloc, Leorific House, Binley Road, Coventry, CV3 1JN Tel: (024) 7667 1076 E-mail: submit@photobloc.com *A photo canvas printing service that's quick & easy. Send in your photo's, illustrations etc and we print the image onto canvas.*

Photocast Products Ltd, Unit 78 Venture Point West, Speke, Liverpool, L24 9PB Tel: 0151-486 2826 Fax: 0151-486 2826 E-mail: photocastproducts@btinternet.com *Sign manufrs*

Photochemical Reactors Ltd, Blounts Court Road, Sonning Common, Reading, RG4 9PA Tel: 0118-972 4906 Fax: 0118-972 2065 *Scientific apparatus*

Photocopier Maintenance Servicing, 3 Church Square, Nottingham, NG7 1SL Tel: 0115-941 4656 Fax: 0115-941 4471 *Photocopier maintenance, supplies & services*

▶ Photocopier Sales, 137 Kings Road, Kingston upon Thames, Surrey, KT2 5JE Tel: (020) 8547 1222 Fax: (020) 8547 3666 E-mail: info@kingsofficesupplies.com *Sales, Service & Consumables on most makes of office equipment, incl Canon & HP at some of the lowest, unbeatable prices in the UK.*

Photofabrication Services Ltd, 14 Cromwell Road, St Neots, St. Neots, Cambridgeshire, PE19 2HP Tel: (01480) 475831 Fax: (01480) 475801 E-mail: sales@photofab.co.uk Principal Export Areas: Asia Pacific, Africa, Central/East Europe, West Europe & North America *Chemical milling & photo etching metal trade services*

Photoflex Ltd, 36 Spindus Road, Liverpool, L24 1YA Tel: (07860) 836145 Fax: 0151-207 2783 E-mail: mail@photoflex.co.uk *Corporate photographers & video producers* Also at: Manchester

▶ Photografit Photo Restoration, The Lodge, Rainham, Essex, RM13 9YN Tel: 07910 725237 E-mail: info@photografit.co.uk *Photografit is a specialist photo restoration company based in London. All faded, creased and torn photos restored. We can also add or remove people from your photographs. Fast, professional service.*

Photography & Philosophy Ltd, 20 Camden Crescent, Bath, BA1 5HY Tel: (01225) 484446 Fax: (01225) 484446 E-mail: jacquimustard@photographyphilosophy.com *Fine photo gallery and library for office art, corporate art, interior design, architectural, publishing and advertising. Exquisite photos apply the timeless ideals of philosophy to our contemporary world. London. Platinum, selenium, lith, thiocarbamide and silver gelatin limited edition prints on handcrafted paper. R-type colour prints. Hasselblad. Medium format negative.*

▶ Photolatitude.com, 67 North Drive, TROON, Ayrshire, KA10 7DL Tel: 01292 318028 Fax: 01292 318037 E-mail: info@photolatitude.com *Online gallery displaying & selling stunning fine art photography*

Photomation Copier Services, 25 Kingshill Road, Dursley, Gloucestershire, GL11 4BJ Tel: (01453) 542652 Fax: (01453) 548580 E-mail: sales@photomation.co.uk *Photocopiers sales, service & suppliers*

Photomec (London) Ltd, Porters Wood, Valley Road Industrial Estate, St. Albans, Hertfordshire, AL3 6NU Tel: (01727) 850711 Fax: (01727) 843991 E-mail: photomec@photomec.co.uk *Film processing equipment manufrs*

Photon Beard Ltd, Unit K3, Cherrycourt Way, Stanbridge Road, Leighton Buzzard, Bedfordshire, LU7 4UH Tel: (01525) 850911 Fax: (01525) 850922 E-mail: info@photonbeard.com *Film & television lighting manufrs*

Photon Power Technology Ltd, PO BOX 306, Emsworth, Hampshire, PO10 7SU Tel: 01243 373551 Fax: 0845 8338923 E-mail: info@photonpower.co.uk *We specialise in the design and manufacture of standard and custom power solutions for both low and high voltage applications. With extensive experience in industrial, medical and communications products, we are confident that we will be able to meet your power supply needs.*Products Include:**Fanless ATX Power Supplies*Medical Power Supplies*X-Ray Generators*Laser Power Supplies*Photomultiplier Modules**For and extensive range of low voltage power supplies for medical and industrial applications, please go to www.mgpower.co.uk**

▶ Photonic Materials, Unit 6 Mallard Way, Strathclyde Business Park, Bellshill, Lanarkshire, ML4 3BF Tel: (01698) 573810 Fax: (01698) 573811

Photonic Solutions plc, A Gracemount Business Pavilion, Captains Road, Edinburgh, EH17 8QF Tel: 0131-664 8122 Fax: 0131-664 8144 E-mail: sales@psplc.com *Laser equipment sales & service*

▶ Photopia Photography, 4, Halifax Road,, Hove Edge, Brighouse, West Yorkshire, HD6 2EN Tel: 07795 313032 E-mail: becca@photopiaphotography.co.uk

▶ Photos On Things, 1 Witney Close, Uxbridge, Middlesex, UB10 8EL Tel: (01895) 635714 Fax: (01895) 635714 E-mail: sheenarosser@photosonthings.co.uk *Photographic services for gift items*

▶ Photoscreen, 1378 Ashton Old Road, Manchester, M11 1JU Tel: 0161-301 5348 *Sign & kicking plates suppliers*

Photosound Communications Ltd, Stansted Road, Birchanger, Bishop's Stortford, Hertfordshire, CM23 5PT Tel: (01279) 818400 Fax: (01279) 647746 *Conference organizers*

Photostatic Copiers Ltd, Unit 13-14 Village Court, Village Farm Industrial Estate, Pyle, Bridgend, Mid Glamorgan, CF33 6BX Tel: (01656) 743100 Fax: (01656) 744047 E-mail: sales@photostatic.co.uk *Photocopiers specialists suppliers*

Photostatic Copiers & Co., 3 Westmead Drive, Redhill, RH1 5DB Tel: (01293) 775061 Fax: (01293) 824696 E-mail: info@intastatic.co.uk *Photocopier repairs, sales & service*

Photostatic Copiers Anglia & Co., 39-41 West End Street, Norwich, NR2 4NA Tel: (01603) 613969 Fax: (01603) 667373 E-mail: sales@photostatic.com *Photocopier services & sales*

Photovisual, 315 London Road, Westcliff-On-Sea, Essex, SS0 7BX Tel: (01702) 348296 Fax: (01702) 346991 E-mail: photography@photo-visual.com *Commercial photographers*

▶ Photoworks Photographers, 309-315 Holdenhurst Road, Bournemouth, BH8 8BX Tel: (01202) 302393 Fax: (01202) 392691 E-mail: info@photoworks.co.uk *Photographic services, film E6 & slide processing, film scanning, scanning of fine art, large paintings, drawings & plans, black & white printing & processing, digital printing, digital printing onto canvas & fine art paper, slide writing, prints from prints, prints from transparencies & negatives*

Photronics UK Ltd, 1 Technology Drive, Bridgend, Mid Glamorgan, CF31 3LU Tel: (01656) 662171 Fax: (01656) 656183 E-mail: wales@photronics.com *Semi-conductor photomask manufrs*

▶ Photronics (UK) Ltd, Trafford Wharf Road, Manchester, M17 1PE Tel: 0161-930 4700 Fax: 0161-930 4801 *First process of the micro chip*

PHS Associates Ltd, 38 Ashworth Park, Knutsford, Cheshire, WA16 9DL Tel: (01565) 653330 E-mail: sales@p-h-s.co.uk *Manufacturing interim management*

▶ PHS Greenleaf, Western Industrial Estate, Lon-Y-Llyn, Caerphilly, Mid Glamorgan, CF83 1XH Tel: (029) 2085 1000 Fax: (029) 2080 9064 E-mail: enquiries@phs.co.uk *Interior landscaping specialist*

PHS Teacrate, PO Box 43, London, NW10 6RH Tel: (020) 8202 0000 Fax: (020) 8282 0022 E-mail: info@teacrate.com *Crate hire*

PHS Teacrate The Crate Rental Specialists, 151 Scrubs Lane, London, NW10 6RH Tel: (020) 8282 0000 Fax: (020) 8282 0022 E-mail: info@teacrate.com *Crate hire, leasing & rental*

Phull Knitwear Manufacturing Co., 146 Soho Road, Birmingham, B21 9LN Tel: 0121-554 1559 Fax: 0121-554 1559 *Knitwear manufrs*

Physical Acoustics Ltd, Norman Way, Over, Cambridge, CB24 5QE Tel: (01954) 231612 Fax: (01954) 231102 E-mail: info@pacuk.co.uk *Non-destructive test equipment & services*

▶ Physio In The City, Seymour Leisure Centre, Seymour Place, London, W1H 5TJ Tel: (020) 7724 8008 Fax: (020) 7724 7150 E-mail: info@physiointhecity.co.uk *Allied Health Private Practice. Physiotherapy, Podiatry, Chiropody, Sports Massage, Acupuncture,*

continued

Pilates, Shiatsu, Homeopathy. Insurance approved.

Phytec Technology Holding AG, 24 Leek Lane, Biddulph Moor, Stoke-on-Trent, ST8 7NE Tel: (01782) 514652 Fax: (01782) 514652 E-mail: info@phytec.co.uk *Hardware development of embedded systems*

Phyto Products Ltd, Park Works, Park Road, Mansfield Woodhouse, Mansfield, Nottinghamshire, NG19 8EF Tel: (01623) 644334 Fax: (01623) 657232 E-mail: info@phyto.co.uk *Herbal products manufrs*

Pi Ally Ltd, 24 Merton Road, Benfleet, Essex, SS7 5QJ Tel: (01268) 569190 Fax: (01268) 565517 E-mail: johnhall@pially.com *Helping Construction Organisations Improve Performance - technology, supply chain, process and people skills*

▶ Pi Computers, Unit 17 Rosebridge Court, Rosebridge Way, Ince, Wigan, Lancashire, WN1 3DP Tel: (01942) 244959 Fax: (01942) 244966 E-mail: picomp@f2s.com *Computers & peripherals, computer networks & broadband connections*

▶ Pi Consulting, St. Johns Innovation Centre, Cowley Road, Cambridge, CB4 0WS Tel: (01763) 838610 Fax: (01763) 838610 E-mail: sales@pican.co.uk *Business performance improvement*

▶ PI Consulting, Beech House, Melbourn Science Park, Cambridge Road, Melbourn, Royston, Hertfordshire, SG8 6HB Tel: (01763) 226242 E-mail: vincent.bryant@piconsulting.org.uk *Business consulting and advisory services*

▶ Pi Solicitors Specialists In Dental Negligence, Quinney View, Marshbrook, Church Stretton, Shropshire, SY6 6QE Tel: (01694) 781247 Fax: 01694 781387 E-mail: sales@personalinjuryplus.co.uk *The leading UK specialist solicitor dealing in dental negligence claims upon behalf of patients.*

Pi Tape Ltd, Dean Court, Upper Dean, Huntingdon, Cambridgeshire, PE28 0NL Tel: (01234) 708882 Fax: (01234) 708677 E-mail: sales@pitape.co.uk *Diameter measuring tapes distributors*

Pi Technology, Milton Hall, Ely Road, Milton, Cambridge, CB4 6WZ Tel: (01223) 441434 Fax: (01223) 203999 E-mail: enquiries@pitechnology.com *Pi Technology is a world leader in automotive electronic systems development, providing product development, engineering services, specialised test equipment, and consultancy. Pi Technology"s work covers a wide range of electronic modules for powertrain, infotainment, and alternative fuels applications. Pi Technology has considerable experience of development projects of all kinds, including systems engineering, advanced technology demonstrators, production designs, and fast-track projects where time-scales are tight and milestones important.*

Piab Ltd, PO Box 43, Loughborough, Leicestershire, LE12 8NY Tel: (01509) 814280 Fax: (01509) 814647 E-mail: sales@piab.co.uk *Suction equipment manufrs*

Pianoforte Supplies Ltd, Simplex Works, Ashton Road, Roade, Northampton, NN7 2LG Tel: (01604) 862441 Fax: (01604) 862427 E-mail: sales@psluk.co.uk *Automotive trim manufrs*

▶ Picador Engineering Co. Ltd, 103 Louth Road, Holton-le-Clay, Grimsby, South Humberside, DN36 5AD Tel: (01472) 824520 Fax: (01724) 280999 E-mail: picadoreng@aol.co.uk Principal Export Areas: Worldwide *Manufacturers of aluminium vee pulleys, handwheels & plummer blocks. In addition, polishing, buffing, grinding composition & compound material distributors or agents*

Piccadilly Hire Ltd, Unit 4-5 Thorncross Close, Manchester, M15 4LU Tel: 0161-835 1999 Fax: 0161-839 5322 E-mail: man@picc.co.uk *Audio visual equipment services*

Piccadilly Precision Engineering Co. Ltd, Units H4 & H5, Halesfield 19, Telford, Shropshire, TF7 4QT Tel: (01952) 582113 Fax: (01952) 583239 E-mail: sales@piccadillyprecision.co.uk *Precision gauging products manufrs*

▶ Piccadilly Secretarial Services, Piccadilly, Manchester, M1 2AQ Tel: 0161-228 1721 Fax: 0161-228 6542 *Paint Spray Safety the site for paint spraying safety equipment, visors, hoods and helmets.*All products featured comply with EN 1835 : 1999 LDH3.*CLASS 3 products - the most stringent requirement and the safest possible.*

Piccadily Hire, 100 Bagot Street, Birmingham, B4 7BA Tel: 0121-333 4300 Fax: 0121-333 4441 E-mail: erictaylor@picc.co.uk *Audio visual equipment hire*

▶ Piccolo, 28 Chester Street, Saltney, Chester, CH4 8BJ Tel: (01244) 677002

Piccolo Blinds, 51 Princes Road, Ellesmere Port, CH65 8AT Tel: 0151-355 6644 Fax: 0151-355 6644 *Blind manufrs*

▶ Piccolo Press, 90 Harbour Street, Nairn, IV12 4PG Tel: (01667) 454508 Fax: (01667) 454509

Pick Quick Service, 380 Meanwood Road, Leeds, LS7 2JF Tel: 0113-216 8811 Fax: 0113-216 8833 E-mail: sales@pickquick.co.uk *Concrete repair products distributors & manufrs*

Pickard Group, Fagley Lane, Eccleshill, Bradford, West Yorkshire, BD2 3NT Tel: (01274) 637307 Fax: (01274) 626146 E-mail: sales@pickard.co.uk *Natural stone producers & quarry owners*

J. Pickard & Co. (Burrington) Ltd, Burrington, Umberleigh, Devon, EX37 9JJ Tel: (01769) 520279 Fax: (01769) 520424 E-mail: graham@pickards.co.uk *Seed merchants*

Bryan Pickering, 30 The Street, Costessey, Norwich, NR8 5DB Tel: (01603) 742002 Fax: (01603) 743352 *Sausage manufrs*

Pickering Computer Exchange, Old Drill Hall Coopers Building, Southgate, Pickering, North Yorkshire, YO18 8BL Tel: (01751) 474777 Fax: (01751) 474777 E-mail: sales@pickeringcomputerexchange.com *Computer suppliers*

Pickering Electronics Ltd, Stephenson Road, Clacton-on-Sea, Essex, CO15 4NL Tel: (01255) 428141 Fax: (01255) 475058 E-mail: sales@pickeringrelay.com *Electronic component manufrs*

Frank Pickering & Co. Ltd, Beeley Wood Works, Claywheels Lane, Sheffield, S6 1ND Tel: 0114-231 8819 Fax: 0114-285 2564 *Forgings forged-rolled bar manufrs*

M. Pickering (Scarborough) Ltd, 66 Londesborough Road, Scarborough, North Yorkshire, YO12 5AF Tel: 01723 373852 *Steel & welding fabricators*

Pickering & Molloy Ltd, 86 Bank Street, Rossendale, Lancashire, BB4 8EG Tel: (01706) 213450 Fax: (01706) 216978

Pickerings Europe Ltd, 9 Glasgow Road, Baillieston, Glasgow, G69 6JT Tel: 0141-771 7575 Fax: 0141-771 8585 E-mail: info@pickerings.co.uk *Passenger lift manufrs*

Pickerings Europe Ltd, 31 Stanley Road, Worsley, Manchester, M28 3DT Tel: 0161-703 8028 Fax: 0161-703 8035 *Lift manufrs*

Pickerings Europe Ltd, PO Box 19, Stockton-on-Tees, Cleveland, TS20 2AD Tel: (01642) 607161 Fax: (01642) 677638 E-mail: sales@pickerings.co.uk *Lift manufrs* Also at: Birmingham, Bristol, Caterham, Glasgow, Hull, Leeds & Manchester

Pickerings Transport Services Ltd, 852 Melton Road, Thurmaston, Leicester, LE4 8BT Tel: 0116-269 6111 Fax: 0116-260 7436 *Commercial vehicle body builders*

Pickersgill Electroplaters Ltd, Pepper Road, Leeds, LS10 2PP Tel: 0113-271 4909 Fax: 0113-276 0546 E-mail: sales@pickersgills.co.uk *Powder coating, metal finishing services*

Pickersgill Electroplaters Ltd, Pepper Road, Leeds, LS10 2PP Tel: 0113-271 4909 Fax: 0113-276 0546 E-mail: paul@pkaye.co.uk *Metal finishers*

Scott Pickford Ltd, 4th Floor, Leon House, 233 High Street, Croydon, CR0 9XT Tel: (020) 8253 4000 Fax: (020) 8253 4001 *Oil exploration consultants*

▶ Pickfords Ltd, Minto Avenue, Altens Industrial Estate, Aberdeen, AB12 3JZ Tel: (01224) 871609 Fax: (01224) 899791 E-mail: sales@pickfords.co.uk

▶ Pickfords Ltd, 15 Banks Road, Darlington, County Durham, DL1 1YF Tel: 0191-497 3800 Fax: 0191-487 1350

▶ Pickfords Ltd, 62 West Harbour Road, Edinburgh, EH5 1PW Tel: 0131-552 4242 Fax: 0131-552 0362

Pickfords Ltd, 2a Brunel Way, Fareham, Hampshire, PO15 5TX Tel: (023) 9282 1325 Fax: (01489) 573128 *Removals & storage contractors*

▶ Pickfords Ltd, Great Western Road, Gloucester, GL1 3NJ Tel: (01242) 517393 Fax: (01452) 422420

▶ Pickfords Ltd, Olympic Business Park, Drybridge Road, Dundonald, Kilmarnock, Ayrshire, KA2 9BE Tel: (01292) 611613 Fax: 0141-336 5335

▶ Pickfords Ltd, Olympic Business Park, Drybridge Road, Dundonald, Kilmarnock, Ayrshire, KA2 9BE Tel: (01292) 611613 Fax: 0141-336 5335

Pickfords Ltd, 37C Munster Rd, London, SW6 4ES Tel: (020) 7736 2381 Fax: (020) 7731 6459 *Removals*

▶ Pickfords Ltd, Trafford Park Road, Trafford Park, Manchester, M17 1NJ Tel: 0161-873 2460 Fax: 0161-877 7483

▶ Pickfords Ltd, Pickfords House, Foxbridge Way, Normanton Industrial Estate, Normanton, West Yorkshire, WF6 1TN Tel: (01482) 878866 Fax: (01924) 899387

▶ Pickfords Ltd, Pickfords House, Foxbridge Way, Normanton Industrial Estate, Normanton, West Yorkshire, WF6 1TN Tel: (01482) 878866 Fax: (01924) 899387

▶ Pickfords Ltd, Hucknall Industrial Park, Watnall Road, Hucknall, Nottingham, NG15 7LN Tel: 0115-968 1321 Fax: 0115-968 1477

▶ Pickfords Ltd, 12 Canal CR, Perth, PH2 8HT Tel: (01738) 627201

▶ Pickfords Ltd, Boscombe Down Business Park, Mills Way, Amesbury, Salisbury, SP4 7RX Tel: (01202) 548355 Fax: (01202) 548366

▶ Pickfords Ltd, Phoenix Industrial Estate, Kerse Road, Stirling, FK7 7SG Tel: (01786) 475867 Fax: 0141-336 8891

▶ Pickfords Ltd, Unit 3 Treliske Industrial Estate, Treliske, Truro, Cornwall, TR1 3LP Tel: (01208) 76083 Fax: (01872) 270339 E-mail: enquiries5@pickfords.com

▶ Pickfords Business Moving, 2 Hurricane Park, Heartlands Parkway, Birmingham, B7 5PP Tel: (0845) 6121008

▶ Pickfords Business Moving, 3-9 Willow Lane, Mitcham, Surrey, CR4 4NA Tel: (0845) 6121008 Fax: (020) 8646 1973

▶ Pickfords Vanguard, 14-16 Lomond Street, Glasgow, G22 6JZ Tel: 0141-347 0177 Fax: 0141-336 7968

Pickhill Engineers Hipperholme Ltd, Broad Lea, Pickhill, Thirsk, North Yorkshire, YO7 4JU Tel: (01845) 567234 Fax: (01845) 567690 E-mail: sales@pickhill-engineers.co.uk *Welding transformer & generator manufrs*

Pickles Bros Slaters Ltd, 2 323 Burley Road, Leeds, LS4 2HY Tel: 0113-275 2620 Fax: 0113-275 2620 E-mail: sales@picklesbros.co.uk *Roofing contractors*

Bruce Pickles Engineering Ltd, 6 Maple Works, Maple Road, Redhill, RH1 5HE Tel: (01737) 770123 Fax: (01737) 778040 E-mail: paul@brucepickles.freeserve.co.uk *Rivet & brake relining machine & tool manufrs. Stockists and distributors of C.V & P.S.V brake shoes, brake linings and disc pads*

J. Pickles Healthcare, Beech Ho, 62 High St, Knaresborough, N. Yorkshire, HG5 0EA Tel: (01423) 867314 Fax: (01423) 869177 E-mail: enquiries@jpickleshealthcare.com *Licensed manufacturer of topical pharmaceuticals, toiletries & cosmetics, technical services, product development & analytical services*

Michael Pickles, Camp House Farm, Moor Road, Bramhope, Leeds, LS16 9HL Tel: 0113-284 2242 *Agricultural contractors*

▶ Pickles Printing Co. Ltd, Carlton Works, Savile Park Road, Halifax, West Yorkshire, HX1 2EN Tel: (01422) 353239 Fax: (01422) 353872 E-mail: sales@picklesprinters.co.uk

Pickup H Mechanical Electrical Services Ltd, Durham House, Lower Clark Street, Scarborough, North Yorkshire, YO12 7PW Tel: (01723) 369191 Fax: (01723) 362044 E-mail: pickup@hpickup.co.uk *Heating & electrical engineers*

▶ Pickup Pc's, 78 Crossley Road, St. Helens, Merseyside, WA10 3ND Tel: (01744) 26660 Fax: (01744) 26660

Pickwell & Arnold, Unit 10 Nanholme Mill, Shaw Wood Road, Todmorden, Lancashire, OL14 6DA Tel: (01706) 812411 Fax: (01706) 812411 *Boat builders*

Pico Technology Ltd, The Mill House, Cambridge Street, St. Neots, Cambridgeshire, PE19 1QB Tel: (01480) 396395 Fax: (01480) 396296 E-mail: vikki@picotech.com *Oscilloscopes & data acquisition system suppliers*

Picon Ltd, St. Christophers House, Holloway Hill, Godalming, Surrey, GU7 1QZ Tel: (01483) 412000 Fax: (01483) 412001 E-mail: info@picon.co.uk *Trade association & exhibition organisers & management services*

Picross Precision Engineering Co. Ltd, 16-18 Lister Road, Eastbourne, East Sussex, BN23 6PU Tel: (01323) 507322 Fax: (01323) 507581 E-mail: sales@picross-eng.com *Precision engineers & precision machining services*

▶ Picter & Berry, Tetbury Road, Sherston, Malmesbury, Wiltshire, SN16 0LU Tel: (01666) 841485 Fax: (01666) 841485

▶ Picton Press Ltd, Village Farm Indust Estate, Pyle, Bridgend, Mid Glamorgan, CF33 6RP Tel: (01656) 740411 Fax: (01656) 744183 E-mail: sales@pictonpressprinters.co.uk

Picton & Tree, The Bungalow, Edward Street, Milford Haven, Dyfed, SA73 2HY Tel: (01646) 692762 Fax: (01646) 692762

Picture Palace Films Ltd, 13 Egbert Street, London, NW1 8LJ Tel: (020) 7586 8763 Fax: (020) 7586 9048 E-mail: info@picturepalace.com *Film & television producers*

Picture Perfect Audio Visuals Ltd, AV House, Wallingford Road, Uxbridge, Middlesex, UB8 2RW Tel: (01895) 454 650 Fax: (01895) 454 657 E-mail: enquiries@ppav.co.uk *Supply all types of audio visual equipment including projection, plasma & computers for any event, big or small, supply all leading brands for sale of hire*

Picture Workshop, 45 Highgate Place, Highgate, Birmingham, B12 0DD Tel: 0121-440 2342 Fax: 0121-440 2844 E-mail: sales@pictureworkshop.co.uk *Advertising photographers*

▶ Picturesque, 1a Asquith Avenue,, Leeds, LS27 9QA Tel: 01132 535588 *Picturesque is a contemporary photography studio based in Leeds. We offer a service which is unrivalled by any other studio. Bringing photography and design together we create modern pieces of art to display in your home.*

▶ Pidcock & Beastall Ltd, 1 Flowery Leys Lane, Alfreton, Derbyshire, DE55 7HA Tel: (01773) 832358 Fax: (01773) 834866

Pidra Environments Ltd, 23 Avebury Avenue, Sherbourne Park Estate, Choppington, Northumberland, NE62 5HE Tel: 0191-267 7111 Fax: 0191-267 7222 E-mail: david@pidra.ltd.uk *Air conditioning, fire ventilation & smoke control systems specialists*

Pie Cuisine, 5 Wemyss Road, Dysart, Kirkcaldy, Fife, KY1 2XZ Tel: (01592) 650555 Fax: (01592) 655654 *Pie makers*

Pie Data U K Ltd, 4 Mill Court, Spindle Way, Crawley, West Sussex, RH10 1TT Tel: (01293) 510231 Fax: (01293) 510234 E-mail: sales@piedata.com *Medical equipment suppliers*

PIE International Ltd, The Exchange, Express Park, Bridgwater, Somerset, TA6 4RR Tel: (0870) 7877872 Fax: (0870) 7877873 E-mail: info@pieinternational.com *Environmental consultants providing services including environmental assessments, effluent and waste treatment, strategy development and regulation, environmental management and training as well as corporate environmental responsibiilty and communications.*

▶ Pied Ltd, 11 Malvern Terrace, Perth, PH1 1LY Tel: (01738) 587815 E-mail: lynne.fisher@linksputt.com *LinksPutt - The WORLDS' ONLY practice putting greens of their kind! No other indoor putting greens allow you the facility to practice contoured putts from 1 metre to 5 metres, whilst standing on the same slope as the putt itself!"*

▶ Pied Piper, 53 Woodstock Gardens, Blackpool, FY4 1JW Tel: (01253) 404445 Fax: (01253) 404445 E-mail: sales@the-piedpiper.com *Pest controllers*

▶ Pied Piper Enviromental Services, Eastern Avenue, Lichfield, Staffs, WS13 6RL Tel: (01543) 254111 Fax: (01543) 254111

▶ Pied Piper Promotions, 94 Dursley Road, Trowbridge, Wiltshire, BA14 0NS Tel: (01225) 764890 Fax: (01225) 764890 E-mail: sales@piedpiperpromtions.com *Fairs, Markets, CarBoot Sales, Merchandising.*

Pied Piper (UK) Ltd, Flat 22, Tempsford Ct, Sheepcote Rd, Harrow, Middlesex, HA1 2JJ Tel: 020 89061459 Fax: 0208 8646184 *Computer consumables distributors*

Pielle & Co. Ltd, Museum House, 25 Museum St, London, WC1A 1PL Tel: (020) 7323 1587 Fax: (020) 7631 0029 E-mail: team@pielleconsulting.com *Public relations management & consultancy services*

Pier Design, 1 Browning Road, Poole, Dorset, BH12 2JU Tel: (01202) 734400 E-mail: sales@pierdesign.co.uk *Modual exhibition stands, popup stands, graphics & portable displays*

▶ Pier House Ltd, Unit 3, Bourne Mill, Guildford Road, Farnham, Surrey, GU9 9PS Tel: (01252) 735000 Fax: (01252) 738110 E-mail: pam.hudson@pierhouse.co.uk *Marketing consultancy*

Pierce Engineering Services Ltd, Horton Close, West Drayton, Middlesex, UB7 8EB Tel: (01895) 447689 Fax: (01895) 447689 *Metal fabricators*

Pierce Management Services, Essex House Cromwell Park, Banbury Road, Chipping Norton, Oxfordshire, OX7 5SR Tel: (01608) 647100 Fax: (01608) 641881 *Maintenance and Estate Management Specialists*

Pierceton Engineering Ltd, 2 Macadam Place, South Newmoor Industrial Estate, Irvine, Ayrshire, KA11 4HP Tel: (01294) 214427 Fax: (01294) 214440 *Sheet metalworkers manufrs*

Piercy Adams Computer & Electronic Systems Ltd, Cochrane House, Church Road, Bookham, Leatherhead, Surrey, KT23 3JP Tel: (01372) 459577 Fax: (01372) 459343 *Computer & electronic consultants*

Pieri Interiors Ltd, New Road, Sheerness, Kent, ME12 1BW Tel: (01795) 580100 Fax: (01795) 580654 *Interior ceilings installers*

▶ Pierrepont Consulting Ltd, 21 Ivydene, Knaphill, Woking, Surrey, GU21 2TA Tel: 01483 836124 E-mail: garry@pierrepontconsulting.co.uk *IT Consultancy, specializing in Web Design, Web Maintenance, Capacity Planning, Performance Management, SAS Programming, and abstracting and proofreading.*

Piers-Roger (Electronics) Ltd, Knights Court, Magellan Close, Walworth Industrial Estate, Andover, Hampshire, SP10 5NT Tel: (01264) 400800 Fax: (01264) 400900 E-mail: sales@polycomp.co.uk *Electronic signs, LED displays, scoreboards*

▶ Pietra Tile Distribution Ltd, 28 Silver Street, Bradford-on-Avon, Wiltshire, BA15 1JY Tel: (01225) 867678 Fax: (01225) 867678 E-mail: jakelewis@pietrastone.co.uk *Wall tiles distributor*

▶ Piezoptic Ltd, Viking House Ellingham Industrial Centre, Ellingham Way, Ashford, Kent, TN23 6NF Tel: (01233) 641990 Fax: (01233) 645020

▶ The Pig Farmer Ltd, 5 Redvers Way, Moorhayes Park, Tiverton, Devon, EX16 6XL Tel: (01884) 256941 Fax: (07092) 203325 E-mail: design@thepigfarmer.co.uk *Web design services*

Piggins & Rix Ltd, Meridian Street, Montrose, Angus, DD10 8DS Tel: (01674) 672827 Fax: (01674) 676135 *Ships agents* Also at: Hull

Piggott Printers Ltd, H The Paddocks, 347 Cherry Hinton Road, Cambridge, CB1 8DH Tel: (01223) 404800 Fax: (01223) 404801 *Lithographic printing services*

▶ Piggott & Whitfield Ltd, Pishiobury House, Pishiobury Drive, Sawbridgeworth, Hertfordshire, CM21 0AF Tel: (01279) 600940 Fax: (01279) 600540

▶ Piggotts, 43 London Road, Stanford Rivers, Ongar, Essex, CM5 9PJ Tel: (01277) 363262 Fax: (01277) 365162 E-mail: sales@piggott.co.uk *Flags & banners, christmas tree retailers*

▶ Piggy's Childrens Footwear Ltd, 14 St. Marys Hill, Stamford, Lincolnshire, PE9 2DP Tel: (01780) 763758 Fax: (01780) 763758 E-mail: sales@piggys-shoes.co.uk *Children's footwear & clothing retailers*

▶ Pignone Engineering, Badentoy CR, Portlethen, Aberdeen, AB12 4YD Tel: (01224) 784400 Fax: (01224) 785130 *Metalworking & fabrication*

Pigott Shaft Drilling Ltd, PO Box 63, Preston, PR4 0BD Tel: (01772) 690076 Fax: (01772) 690840 E-mail: sales@psdmud.co.uk *Solid separation equipment*

F.J. Pike (Ramsgate) Ltd, 111-115 Hardres Street, Ramsgate, Kent, CT11 8QU Tel: (01843) 593438 Fax: (01843) 595639 E-mail: contact@fjpike.co.uk *Shop fitters*

▶ Pike W L & Son Ltd, Tarvonga, Hill Brow Road, Liss, Hampshire, GU33 7LH Tel: (01730) 892884 Fax: (01730) 895647

Pike Ward Ltd, Old Quay, Teignmouth, Devon, TQ14 8EU Tel: (01626) 772311 Fax: (01626) 770218 E-mail: agency@pikeward.co.uk *Ship brokers & shipping agents*

Pi-Kem Ltd, Yew Tree House, Tilley Wem, Wem, Shrewsbury, SY4 5HE Tel: (01939) 234801 Fax: (01939) 235394 E-mail: pikem.rouse@virgin.net *Advanced material sapphire & silicon suppliers*

Pilbeam Racing Designs Ltd, Graham Hill Way, Bourne, Lincolnshire, PE10 9PJ Tel: (01778) 424838 Fax: (01778) 393032 E-mail: info@pilbeamracing.co.uk *Racing car & suspension parts manufrs*

Pile Fabric Dyers Ltd, Woodhouse Mill, Greenbooth Road, Norden, Rochdale, Lancashire, OL12 7TD Tel: (01706) 523535 Fax: (01706) 659490 E-mail: admin@storyvelvets.co.uk *Textile dyers & finishers*

Pilgrim Cars (U K) Ltd, Unit 14 Mackley Industrial Estate, Henfield Road, Small Dole, Henfield, West Sussex, BN5 9XR Tel: (01273) 493860 Fax: (01273) 494889 E-mail: sales@pilgrimcars.com *Kit car manufrs*

Pilgrim International Ltd, Southlink Business Park Unit 10, Oldham, OL4 1DE Tel: 0161-785 7700 E-mail: info@pilgrim-international.co.uk *Hydraulic coupling bolt manufrs*

▶ Pilgrim Lube Services, 64 Greystoke Avenue, Austin Farm, Plymouth, PL6 8LG Tel: (01752) 708419 Fax: (01752) 708419 E-mail: sales@pilgrimlubeservices.co.uk *Distributors of lubrication Equipment,suppliers of industrial lubrication systems and equipment,suppliers of automatic lubrication equipment interlube systems ltd, AC,XGS,AX,GX,Meter units,Pdus,positive displacment units,dropsa, Tecalemit garage equipment,gear pumps, major radial,minor radial, garage equipment, garage lifting equipment, garage tools and equipment, garage lubrication equipment, garage hose reels, oil drainers,Kingnut*

Pilgrim Payne & Co. Ltd, Units 12-14 Wharfeside, Rosemont Road, Wembley, Middlesex, HA0 4PE Tel: (020) 8453 5350 Fax: (020) 8453 5604 E-mail: info@pilgrimpayne.co.uk *Specialist curtain & carpet cleaners*

▶ Pilgrim Technical Security Services, 65 Duke Street, Mayfair, London, W1M 6PP Tel: 0870 041 6457 Fax: 0871 236 1944 E-mail: ops@pilgrimtechnical.com *Technical Surveillance Countermeasures, Communications Security, Secure Satellite and other Communications, Encryption Equipment and other areas.*

Pilgrim Technology, 53 Carlton Road, Boston, Lincolnshire, PE21 8PA Tel: (01205) 363833 Fax: (01205) 363833 *Medical device distributors*

Pilkington Automotives, Triplex House, Eckersall Road, Birmingham, B38 8SR Tel: 0121-254 3000 Fax: 0121-254 3188 *Glass manufrs*

Pilkington Birmingham, Nechells Park Road, Birmingham, B7 5NQ Tel: 0121-326 5300 Fax: 0121-328 4277 E-mail: john.hawkins@pilkington.com *Glass merchants*

Pilkington Glass, Unit 10 12, Sherrington Way, Basingstoke, Hampshire, RG22 4DQ Tel: (01256) 469651 Fax: (01256) 464047 *Glass merchants*

Pilkington Group Ltd, Prescot Road, St. Helens, Merseyside, WA10 3TT Tel: (01744) 28882 Fax: (01744) 692660 *Glass distributors & manufrs*

Pilkington Plyglass, Cotes Park, Somercotes, Alfreton, Derbyshire, DE55 4PL Tel: (01773) 520000 Fax: (01773) 520052 *Glass processors*

Pilkington Plymouth, Plymbridge Road, Plymouth, PL6 7JS Tel: (01752) 761500 Fax: (01752) 761506 E-mail: sales@pilkington.com *Plate glass manufrs*

Pilkington Sealed Units, Churchbridge Indust Estate, Oldbury, West Midlands, B69 4FH Tel: 0121-541 1601 Fax: 0121-552 3748 E-mail: sealed.units@pilkington.com *Double glazed unit manufrs*

Pilkington UK Ltd, 1 Dunnswood Road, Wardpark South, Cumbernauld, Glasgow, G67 3EN Tel: (01236) 728298 Fax: (01236) 729876 E-mail: cumbernauld@pilkington.com *Sealed double glazed units manufrs*

Pilkington UK Ltd, Knowsthorpe Gate, Leeds, LS9 0NS Tel: 0113-235 0101 Fax: 0113-240 1434

Pilkington UK Ltd, Unit 26 Bermondsey Trading Estate, Rotherhithe New Road, London, SE16 3LE Tel: (020) 7252 0004 Fax: (020) 7237 1428 E-mail: glazing@pilkington.com *Glass merchants*

▶ Pilkington UK Ltd, 78 North Ormesby Road, Middlesbrough, Cleveland, TS4 2AG Tel: (01642) 242258 Fax: (01642) 232135 *Glass manufrs*

Pilkington UK Ltd, 2-6 Mallard Road, Victoria Business Park, Netherfield, Nottingham, NG4 2PE Tel: 0115-940 0980 Fax: 0115-961 7993 *Glass merchants*

Pilkington UK Ltd, 10-12 Alder Hills, Poole, Dorset, BH12 4AL Tel: (01202) 742700 Fax: (01202) 736155 *Glass processors*

Pilkington UK Ltd, Orgreave Drive, Sheffield, S13 9NR Tel: 0114-254 0444 Fax: 0114-254 0861 E-mail: joanne.marlow@pilkington.com *Double glazed unit manufrs*

Pilkingtons Ltd, Belgrave Court, Caxton Road, Fulwood, Preston, PR2 9PL Tel: (01772) 705566 Fax: (01772) 705599 E-mail: info@pilkingtonsltd.com *Shuttle & wood turnery manufrs*

Pilkington's Tiles Ltd, Blandford Road, Poole, Dorset, BH15 4AR Tel: (01202) 672741 Fax: (01202) 671866 *Ceramic tile manufrs*

Pilkingtons Tiles Group Plc, P O Box 4, Manchester, M27 8LP Tel: 0161-727 1000 Fax: 0161-727 1122 E-mail: info@pilkingtontiles.com *Ceramic wall, floor tile & terrazzo manufrs* Also at: Poole

Pillar Publications Ltd, 45 Woodland Grove, Weybridge, Surrey, KT13 9EQ Tel: (01932) 820282 Fax: (01932) 858035 E-mail: sales@pillardirect.demon.co.uk *List management & mailing house facilities*

▶ Pillar R C & Sons Ltd, 4 Anzac Street, Dartmouth, Devon, TQ6 9DL Tel: (01803) 832121 Fax: (01803) 834882 E-mail: sales@rcpillarandsonsltd.co.uk

Pillar Spin Galvanizing Ltd, Metaltreat House, Canal Road, Bradford, West Yorkshire, BD2 1AN Tel: (01274) 221500 Fax: (01274) 221520 E-mail: pillar.spin@wedge-galv.co.uk *Galvanizing services*

Pillar Wedge Ltd, Green Lane, Heywood, Lancashire, OL10 2DY Tel: (01706) 366191 Fax: (01706) 625939 E-mail: pillar-wedge@wedge-galv.co.uk *Hot dip galvanizing organisation, part of nation-wide Wedge Group*

Piller UK Ltd, 91 Chesterton Lane, Cirencester, Gloucestershire, GL7 1YE Tel: (01285) 657721 Fax: (01285) 654823 E-mail: ukmail@piller.com *Computer power supply systems*

Pillerhouse International Ltd, Rodney Way, Chelmsford, CM1 3BY Tel: (01245) 491333 Fax: (01245) 491331 E-mail: sales@pillarhouse.co.uk *Soldering production equipment systems manufrs*

▶ Pilot House, Globe Park, Broxburn, West Lothian, EH52 6EF Tel: (01506) 855727 E-mail: tim@pilothouse.co.uk *Providing businesses with practical, affordable Sales and Marketing planning and support to boost your profits and generate sustained growth.*

▶ Pilot Industries UK Ltd, Swinbourne Road, Burnt Mills Industrial Estate, Basildon, Essex, SS13 1EF Tel: (01268) 590570 Fax: (01268) 590580 *Production of engine parts*

Piltec Rubber & Plastic Ltd, Waterloo Park, Bidford-on-Avon, Alcester, Warwickshire, B50 4JG Tel: (01789) 778271 Fax: (01789) 772886 E-mail: sales@piltec.com *Rubber products & plastic extrusions*

Pilz Automation Technology, Willow House, Medlicott Close, Oakley Hay Business Park, Corby, Northamptonshire, NN18 9NF Tel: (01536) 460766 Fax: (01536) 460866 E-mail: sales@pilz.co.uk Purchasing Contact: S. Austin Sales Contact: M. Palmer Principal Export Areas: Worldwide *Suppliers of safety consulting, automation and safety control products*

Pimpernel (Holdings) Ltd, 26-32 Derwent Street, Consett, County Durham, DH8 8LY Tel: 01207 588402 Fax: (01207) 507873 E-mail: sales@pimpernelinternational.com *Place mats, coasters & accessories manufrs & supply*

Pims, 42-44 Stapledon Road, Orton Southgate, Peterborough, PE2 6TH Tel: (01733) 235523 Fax: (01733) 235522 *Direct mailing*

Pims Associates Ltd, 15-16 Basinghall Street, London, EC2V 5BR Tel: (020) 7776 2800 Fax: (020) 7776 2828 E-mail: info@pimsconsulting.com *Management consultants*

Pims Group, Unit 1 106 Hawley Lane, Farnborough, Hampshire, GU14 8JE Tel: (01252) 513891 Fax: (01252) 516404 E-mail: sales@pimsgroup.co.uk *Pump installation, maintenance & servicing*

Pin Croft Dyeing & Printing Co. Ltd, Adlington Works, Market Street, Adlington, Chorley, Lancashire, PR7 4HJ Tel: (01257) 480202 Fax: (01257) 480898 *Commissioned dyers & printers on textiles*

The Pinball Heaven, 302B Liverpool Road, Southport, Merseyside, PR8 4PW Tel: (0870) 7465704 Fax: (0870) 7465705 E-mail: sales@pinballheaven.co.uk *Pinball machine sales, also parts, Novus plastic polish, Millwax, new Stern Pinballs and more!*

▶ Pinball Pleasure, High Road, Chadwell Heath, Romford, RM6 6AU Tel: (020) 8599 6121 E-mail: sales@pinballmachines.co.uk *Repair pinball machines*

Pinco Industries Ltd, 38 Hunters Way, Uckfield, East Sussex, TN22 2BB Tel: (01825) 762387 E-mail: sales@pinco.co.uk *Exporters of lubricants*

Pindar Set Ltd, Newlands House, Caxton Way, Scarborough, North Yorkshire, YO11 3YT Tel: (01723) 502000 Fax: (01723) 502002 E-mail: enquiries@pindarset.com *Directory typesellers*

Pinder P.L.C., Unit 481 Walton Summit Centre, Bamber Bridge, Preston, PR5 8AR Tel: (01772) 620999 Fax: (01772) 620888 E-mail: k.ashley@pinder.com *Printers service*

Pinder Bros Ltd, Sheaf Plate Works, Arundel Street, Sheffield, S1 1DJ Tel: 0114-275 2277 Fax: 0114-272 6718 E-mail: sales@pinder.co.uk *Pewter & silverware manufrs*

J.L. Pinder & Son Ltd, 138 Hanbury Road, 8-11 The Old Basin, Stoke Prior, Bromsgrove, Worcestershire, B60 4JZ Tel: (01527) 876438 Fax: (01527) 576435 E-mail: sales@jlpindersandsons.co.uk *Steel boat builders*

Pinder Versatool Ltd, Padholme Road East, Peterborough, PE1 5XL Tel: (01733) 552727 Fax: (01733) 552717 E-mail: malcolm.bayes@pinder-versatool.co.uk *Cabinets suppliers*

William Pinder & Sons Ltd, 4 Harling Road, Sharston Industrial Estate, Manchester, M22 4UZ Tel: 0161-998 1729 Fax: 0161-946 0734 E-mail: info@pinderblades.com Principal Export Areas: Asia Pacific, Central Asia, Middle East, Africa, Central/East Europe & West Europe *Manufacturers of blades for printing equipment*

▶ Pinders Dewsbury Ltd, 241 Bradford Road, Batley, West Yorkshire, WF17 6JQ Tel: (01924) 437123 Fax: (01924) 437124 E-mail: info@pindersign.co.uk *Sign contractors*

Pine & Bed Centre, 63-65 Pasture Road, Goole, North Humberside, DN14 6BP Tel: (01405) 720444 Fax: (01405) 720444 *Pine funiture manufrs*

Pine Direct, 46 John St, Aberdeen, AB25 1LL Tel: (01224) 626404 *Pine manufrs*

Pine Emporium, Piccotts End, Hemel Hempstead, Hertfordshire, HP1 3BA Tel: (01442) 244644 Fax: (01442) 246181 *Pine suppliers*

Pine Factory, 2 Ford Farm, Braintree Road, Dunmow, Essex, CM6 1HU Tel: (01371) 872292 E-mail: sales@pine-factorydunmow.co.uk *Pine & oak furniture retailer & manufrs*

Pine Factory, Nortonthorpe Mill, Wakefield Road, Scissett, Huddersfield, HD8 9JL Tel: (01484) 865042 Fax: (01484) 866289 E-mail: sales@the-pinefactory.co.uk *Furniture retailers*

The Pine Factory (Truro) Ltd, Unit 2 Visicks Yard, Perranarworthal, Truro, Cornwall, TR3 7NR Tel: (01872) 862696 Fax: (01872) 870394 *Furniture makers*

Frank Pine Ltd, Crown Mill, 1 Crown Street, Salford, M3 7DH Tel: 0161-834 0456 Fax: 0161-832 0385 E-mail: fpinetex@aol.com *Manufacturers of waterproof canvas*

▶ Pine Nation Ltd, 3 Arrow Industrial Estate, Straight Road, Willenhall, West Midlands, WV12 5AE Tel: (01922) 711177 Fax: (01922) 711177 E-mail: pinenation@btconnect.com *Furniture manufrs*

Pine Place, 1 The Old Foundry, Victoria Road, Kington, Herefordshire, HR5 3DA Tel: (01544) 231766 *Pine manufrs*

Pine Plus, 1 G E C Industrial Estate, Beanacre Road, Melksham, Wiltshire, SN12 8RP Tel: (01225) 707777 *Pine furniture retailers*

Pine Products Ltd, 1 Hope Carr Way, Leigh, Lancashire, WN7 3DE Tel: (01942) 604999 Fax: (01942) 260734 E-mail: info@pine-products.net *Wood recyclers & pallet manufrs*

Pine Range, Pottery Hill, Ewenny, Bridgend, Mid Glamorgan, CF35 5AP Tel: (01656) 665468 *Furniture retailers*

Pine Stable, 78 Carroway Head, Canwell, Sutton Coldfield, West Midlands, B75 5RZ Tel: 0121-308 0231 Fax: 0121-308 1100 E-mail: aagadar@aol.com *Wooden furniture & turnings manufrs*

Pine Store, 2 9a Burnett Road, Inverness, IV1 1TF Tel: (01463) 716718 Fax: (01463) 716718 *Pine furniture finisher & manufrs*

Pine Studio, 11-11a Friars Street, Sudbury, Suffolk, CO10 2AA Tel: (01787) 379624 Fax: (01787) 370982 E-mail: info@pine-studio.co.uk *Pine furniture manufrs*

The Pine Table Co. Ltd, Unit 2, Sleaford Road Industrial Estate, Bracebridge Heath, Lincoln, LN4 2ND Tel: (01522) 511220 Fax: (01522) 511225 *Pine furniture manufrs*

▶ Pine Telecom, 75 Pinders Road, Hastings, East Sussex, TN35 5HE Tel: (0845) 3701067 E-mail: sales@pine-telecom.co.uk *Provide telephone extensions for home & business*

Pine Time Trading, 96 London Road, Bexhill-on-Sea, East Sussex, TN39 3LE Tel: (01424) 213002 Fax: (01424) 213002 E-mail: enquiries@pinetimetrading.com *Pine manufrs*

Pine Trading Co., 94-96 The Horsefair, Bristol, BS1 3JS Tel: 0117-929 9186 Fax: 0117-925 4099 E-mail: sales@pinetrading.co.uk *Pine & oak furniture manufrs*

Pine Trading Co., 77 Queens Way, Southampton, SO14 3HJ Tel: (023) 8033 7339 Fax: (023) 8033 7303 *Pine, oak & beech furniture distribution*

▶ Pine Tree, 69 Bruntcliffe Road, Morley, Leeds, LS27 0LQ Tel: 0113-252 0808 Fax: 0113-252 0808 E-mail: sales@thepinetreemorley.co.uk *Pine furniture sales*

Pine Warehouse Ltd, 21 Osborne Street, Hull, HU1 2NL Tel: (01482) 224583 Fax: (01482) 224583 E-mail: pwarehousehull@hotmail.com *Furniture manufrs*

Pine Warehouse, Unit 4 Portrack Retail Park, Holme House Road, Stockton-on-Tees, Cleveland, TS18 1BT Tel: (01642) 670222 Fax: (01642) 670444 *Pine furniture suppliers*

Pine Workshop, 150 Shore Road, Greenisland, Carrickfergus, County Antrim, BT38 8TT Tel: (028) 9036 4754 *Pine furniture manufrs*

Pine Workshop, Manor Barn, Browns Lane, Keyworth, Nottingham, NG12 5BL Tel: 0115-937 7227 Fax: 0115-937 7227 *Pine furniture manufrs*

Pine Workshop, 1a Northmill, North Mill Road, Bledlow, Princes Risborough, Buckinghamshire, HP27 9PU Tel: (01844) 342400 Fax: (01844) 342400 *Kitchen furniture manufrs*

Pine World, 64 Union Road, Camelon, Falkirk, FK1 4PF Tel: (01324) 624467 Fax: (01324) 626217 E-mail: sales@pineworld.co.uk *Pine furniture suppliers*

Pine World, 14 Riverside Walk, Thetford, Norfolk, IP24 2BG Tel: (01842) 766060 *Pine furniture manufrs*

The Pine Xchange, Melbourne Airfield, Seaton Ross, York, YO42 4NF Tel: (01759) 318833 Fax: (01759) 318822 *Country pine furniture*

▶ Pineapple Joe's Ltd, Unit 4b Bessingby Industrial Estate, Bridlington, North Humberside, YO16 4SJ Tel: (01262) 672733 Fax: (01262) 676225 E-mail: sales@pineapplejoes.com *Corporate work wear, embroidery & promotional items manufrs*

▶ Pinebank Design, 30 Pine Bank, Hindhead, Surrey, GU26 6SS Tel: 020 88168613 E-mail: contact@pinebankdesign.com *For a helping hand presenting yourself to a whole world of potential customers...Pinebank Design is your one-stop-shop for Website Design, Photography, Decorative Art, Illustration and Graphic Design.*

The Pinery, 233 Oakbrook Road, Sheffield, S11 7EB Tel: 0114-230 2635 Fax: 0114-230 2635 E-mail: mail@pinery.co.uk *Furniture retailer & manufrs*

▶ Pinetime, Rutland Village, Ashwell Road, Oakham, Leicestershire, LE15 7QN Tel: 01572 756285 Fax: 01572 756983

▶ Pinetree Workshop, 57A Southfield Road, Hinckley, Leicestershire, LE10 1UB Tel: (01455) 613298 Fax: (01455) 613298 *Furniture manufrs*

Pinetum Ltd, Roman Way Crusader Park, Warminster, Wiltshire, BA12 8SJ Tel: (01985) 224540 Fax: (01985) 211158 E-mail: sales@pinetum.co.uk *Pine & oak furniture manufrs*

Pinewood Drapilux UK Ltd, Albert Street, Leek, Staffordshire, ST13 8AH Tel: (01538) 399153 Fax: (01538) 373235 E-mail: sales@pinewood-fabrics.com *Pinewood drapilux UK Ltd offer a vast choice of flame retardant fabrics is offered at sensible prices making them an excellent choice for any contract situation. Trevira CS fabrics are especially suitable for the Healthcare & Hotel markets where safety and durability are paramount. The whole of this range is completely reversible - making it perfect for cubicle curtains. Trevira CS Bioactive fabrics are woven in antimicrobial fibres with permanent bioactive properties that prevent bacteria multiplying and meet the highest hygiene requirements - a must for any healthcare environment. An innovation in textiles is drapilux air® - a revolutionary finish - which when applied to our Trevira CS range filters out smells and harmful particles - leaving cleaner fresher air! All are flame retardant to meet BS5867 part 2 type C - and EN 13773.*

Pinewood Electronics Ltd, Riverside Business Park, Stoney Common Road, Stansted, Essex, CM24 8ND Tel: (01279) 816666 Fax: (01279) 816161 E-mail: info@pinewood.gb.com *Electronic component distributors*

Pinewood Furniture, 15 Kilmandil Road, Dunloy, Ballymena, County Antrim, BT44 9BH Tel: (028) 2763 8653 Fax: (028) 2763 8653 E-mail: info@pine-furniture.co.uk *Pine furniture retailers & manufrs*

Pinewood Joiners, Unit 3-4, Pickwick Industrial Estate Tintern Road, St. Helen Auckland, Bishop Auckland, County Durham, DL14 9EL Tel: (01388) 450749 Fax: (01388) 450749 *Cabinet manufrs*

Pinewood Structures Ltd, 3 Station Road, Gamlingay, Sandy, Bedfordshire, SG19 3HB Tel: (01767) 651218 Fax: (01767) 651928 E-mail: enquiries@pinewood-structures.co.uk *Timber frame house & roof manufrs*

The Pinewood Studio, The Lays Farm, Charlton Road, Keynsham, Bristol, BS31 2SE Tel: 0117-986 3950 *Furniture*

Pinewood Studios Ltd, Godley Road, Halifax, West Yorkshire, HX3 6AH Tel: (01422) 369666 Fax: (01422) 320227 *Pine & oak furniture services*

Pineworld, Timworth Green, Timworth, Bury St. Edmunds, Suffolk, IP31 1HS Tel: (01284) 728621 Fax: (01284) 728191 E-mail: sales@pineworlduk.com *Pine furniture manufr*

Pinfold Fabrications, Pinfold Road, Bourne, Lincolnshire, PE10 9HT Tel: (01778) 421554 Fax: (01778) 393456 *Roof flashing fabricators & manufrs*

▶ Ping Executive Search, PO Box 841, St. Albans, Hertfordshire, AL3 6BG Tel: (01727) 840850 E-mail: info@pingexecsearch.co.uk *A boutique head hunter specialising in placing high-calibre candidates within the Cards and e-payments marketplace.*

Pingly Boris Ltd, 113 Hardwick Road, Streetly, Sutton Coldfield, West Midlands, B74 3DW Tel: 0121-353 3840 Fax: 0121-353 3840 E-mail: sales@pinglyboris.com *Pipe support distributors*

▶ Pink Cow, Unit 5 Bracknell Beeches, Bracknell Old La West, Bracknell, Berkshire, RG12 7BW Tel: (01344) 867007 Fax: (01344) 860217 E-mail: enquiries@pinkcowselect.com *Educational supplies*

Pink & Jones, Britannia House, Riley Road, Telford Way Industrial Estate, Kettering, Northamptonshire, NN16 8NN Tel: (01604) 714448 Fax: (01604) 410584 E-mail: removals@pinkandjones.co.uk *Removals storage & shipping* Also at: Corby & Northampton

▶ Pink Pigeon Ltd, 34-35 Berwick Street, London, W1F 8RP Tel: (020) 7439 3266 Fax: (020) 7439 3277 E-mail: info@pinkpigeon.net *Authoring house, covering every aspect of dvd production*

Pink Telecommunications, 15 The Broadway, Woodford Green, Essex, IG8 0HL Tel: (020) 8506 6464 Fax: (020) 8506 6400 *Telecommunication systems sales*

Pink Wedding Days, The Business Centre, Edward Street, Redditch, Worcestershire, B97 6HA Tel: (01527) 596913 Fax: (01527) 66332 E-mail: info@pinkweddingdays.co.uk *Online wedding directory*

Pinkerton Consulting & Investigations Ltd, 102 College Road, Harrow, Middlesex, HA1 1ES Tel: (020) 8424 8884 Fax: (020) 8424 9744 E-mail: sales@pinkerton-europe.com *Detective agencies, corporate & private investigation services*

▶ Pinkerton Forklift Training, Bryn Hyfred, Garth Farm, Llangwstenin, Llandudno Junction, Conwy, LL31 9JF Tel: (01492) 540521 Fax: (01492) 540521 E-mail: wendy.brown10@virgin.net *Forklift Training*Full courses*Refresher courses*RTIB Registered*

▶ Pinkroccade Group, Old Greenock Road, Inchinnan, Renfrew, PA4 9LH Tel: 0141-814 1000 Fax: 0141-814 1151 *Computer maintenance & repair services*

▶ Pinktoast, 88 High Street, Street, Newmarket, Suffolk, CB8 8JX Tel: 01763 221833 E-mail: info@pinktoast.com *Your on-line wedding organiser*Pinktoast offers you and your partner the complete guide to a stress free wedding planning and organisation to help create the perfect day.*

Pinmill Products, Units 5H-5K, Baker House, Manor Way Industrial Estate, Curzon Drive, Grays, Essex, RM17 6BG Tel: (01375) 392944 Fax: (01375) 379127 E-mail: pinmill@btinternet.com *Plumbing products*

Pinnacal Aluminium Ltd, East Moons House, Oxleasow Road, East Moons Moat, Redditch, Worcestershire, B98 0RE Tel: (01527) 830424 Fax: (01527) 830425 E-mail: sales@pinnacal.co.uk *Aluminium tube supplier*

▶ Pinnacle Academy of Martial Arts, Sir Charles Lucas School, Acacia Avenue, Colchester, CO4 3JL Tel: 01206 323343 E-mail: enquiries@pinnacleacademy.co.uk *Pinnacle was setup to provide the highest quality martial arts instruction in the Colchester & Lawford /Manningtree Area. *We perform a range of disciplines from Korean Karate to Son^Chin, Kickboxing to Self-Defence. *We teach all age groups ranging from 4 years and above. All our instructors are fully qualified, insured and police checked with the CRB. *Pinnacle is affiliated with EKKA which is one of the most successful associations at competition level. The senior coach for Karate is 4th Dan Black Belt Milo Hodge who is an England International team member, the current Commonwealth Champion.*Kickboxing is taught by Liam Cullen who is quite active on the fighting circuit. *Son^Chin is quite a secretive but highly effective martial. It incorporates the strengths and principles of several key martial arts ranging from karate, street fighting, weapons and jujitsu. *Pinnacle''s Little Dragons programme offers more than martial arts education alone for children aged 4-7 years.*

▶ Pinnacle Business Solutions Ltd, Unit 10a, Balmakeith Industrial Estate, Nairn, IV12 5QW Tel: (01667) 458450 Fax: (0870) 0746644 E-mail: pinnacle@pinsol.com *Information technology applications & services*

Pinnacle C N C Ltd, 5 Kirby Road, Nelson, Lancashire, BB9 6RS Tel: 01282 695222 *Precision CNC engineers*

▶ Pinnacle Cleaning, 41 Bramble Court, Ferndown, Bournemouth, BH22 0HL Tel: 0870 345 5757 E-mail: webenquiries@pinnacle-cleaning.co.uk *Specialist Domestic & Commercial Cleaning services with 15 years experience - Reliable cleaning contractor, Proven track-record, Many Testimonials, High Quality Finish. Full House & Carpet Cleaning, Office cleaning, Contract cleaning, Builder''s cleans/Sparkle cleans/ Courtesy cleans. Fully-trained Fire and Flood Restoration specialists. COSHH safety datasheets, Risk Assessments, stringent Health & Safety policy. Operating throughout Dorset, Hampshire, London & the South of England.*

▶ Pinnacle Commercial Solutions Ltd, Unit 6, Canal Lane, Tunstall, Stoke-on-Trent, ST6 4PA Tel: (01782) 834800 Fax: (01782) 822033 E-mail: enquiries@pinnaclecommercialsolutions.com *Commercial Relocations/Office Moves, IT Data Centre Relocations, PC Roll Out, Move Management/Project Management, Moves/Adds/ Changes, IT/Furniture Disposal, All Office moves catered for*

Pinnacle Computer Systems Ltd, BRE Complex, Bucknalls Lane, Watford, WD25 9XX Tel: (01923) 686000 Fax: (01923) 686001 E-mail: sales@pinnaclecomputers.co.uk *Service management software & mobile data solutions*

Pinnacle Ductwork Manufacturers Ltd, Unit 8 Seagull Lane, Emsworth, Hampshire, PO10 7QH Tel: (01243) 377214 Fax: (01243) 376448 E-mail: pinnacleductwork@aol.com *Sheet metalworkers & ducting contractors*

▶ Pinnacle Heating Services Ltd, 1 Trinity Place Park Street, Aston, Birmingham, B6 5SH Tel: 0121-328 7800 Fax: 0121-773 3004

Pinnacle Images Ltd, 69-85 Tabernacle Street, London, EC2A 4BD Tel: (020) 7253 0383 Fax: (020) 7253 2159 E-mail: studio@pinnacleimages.co.uk *Reprographic printing services*

Pinnacle Insulation Ltd, Sandgate Industrial Estate, Hartlepool, Cleveland, TS25 1TZ Tel: (01429) 233828 Fax: (01429) 861047 E-mail: mark@pinnacle-aic.com *Thermal insulation contractors*

Pinnacle International Freight Ltd, C Mortimer Road, Narborough, Leicester, LE19 2GA Tel: 0116-286 6566 Fax: 0116-286 7928 E-mail: lecmail@pif.co.uk *Freight forwarding agents*

Pinnacle Partition Systems Ltd, 6 Cawley Hatch, Harlow, Essex, CM19 5AN Tel: (01279) 641317 Fax: (01279) 641329 E-mail: sales@pinnacle-partitions.co.uk *Partition & ceiling installers*

Pinnacle Power Equipment Ltd, 235 Berwick Avenue, Slough, SL1 4QT Tel: (01753) 576655 *Vacuum cleaner importers & distributors*

Pinnacle Precision Engineers Ltd, 22 Cogan Street, Glasgow, G43 1AP Tel: 0141-649 6638 Fax: 0141-649 6638 *Precision engineers*

▶ Pinnacle Print & Packaging Ltd, J Tyburn Industrial Estate, Ashold Farm Road, Birmingham, B24 9QG Tel: 0121-694 8800 Fax: 0121-694 8822 E-mail: sales@pinnaclepp.co.uk *Distributors of business printers*

▶ Pinnacle Services, 22 Carnoustie, Bolton, BL3 4TF Tel: (01204) 61043 E-mail: info@oneroof.co.uk *Specialist in: Slating & Tiling plus flag roofs. Lead Flashings, Chimneys, Fascias & Soffits, Storm damage, insurance work, Velux windows and converting flat roofs into pitch roofs.*

Pinnacle Software, Heather Court, 6 Maidstone Road, Sidcup, Kent, DA14 5HH Tel: (01322) 665652 E-mail: info@pinnacle-software.co.uk *Computer systems & software suppliers*

Pinnacle Structures, Unit 7 Westwood Industrial Estate, Ewyas Harold, Hereford, HR2 0EL Tel: (01981) 241414 Fax: (01981) 241195 E-mail: mail@pinnaclestructures.co.uk *Industrial building manufrs*

▶ Pinnacle Telecommunications, 142N, St. Clair Street, Kirkcaldy, Fife, KY1 2BZ Tel: (01592) 654176 Fax: (01592) 654176

Pinnacle Tooling Ltd, Aston Hill, Lewknor, Watlington, Oxfordshire, OX49 5SG Tel: (01844) 354999 Fax: (01844) 354888 E-mail: sales@pin-tooling.co.uk *Tooling equipment, injection mould toolmakers repair services*

Pinnacle Web Design, PO Box 233, Hitchin, Herts, SG4 9WW Tel: 0208-144 0081 Fax: E-mail: info@pinnaclewebdesign.co.uk *Providing professional, affordable web site design and maintenance to small and medium sized businesses, primarily in the Hertfordshire, Bedfordshire, Buckinghamshire and Cambridgeshire area.**Graphic and logo design, multi-media and search engine optimisation/ submission services are also available*

Pinnees Clothing Co., 85 Liscard Road, Wallasey, Merseyside, CH44 9AE Tel: 0151-638 1073 Fax: 0151-638 1073 E-mail: sales@pinnees.com *Uniform & work wear manufrs*

Pinnegar & Barnes Patio Slabs, The Wharf, Bugbrooke, Northampton, NN7 3QB Tel: (01604) 830291 Fax: (01604) 830496 *Concrete producers*

Pinner Metal Window Services, 102-104 Church Road, Teddington, Middlesex, TW11 8PY Tel: (020) 8943 2335 Fax: (020) 8943 3151 *Replacement window servicing*

Pinnstrip Steel Services Ltd, Portway Road, Wednesbury, West Midlands, WS10 7DZ Tel: 0121-556 4493 Fax: 0121-556 6526 E-mail: sales@pinnstrip.co.uk *Hot rolled Steel strip manufacturers, cold rolled steel strip manufrs*

Pino International Ltd, 287-291 Talbot Road, Stretford, Manchester, M32 0YA Tel: 0161-291 1111 Fax: 0161-291 1122 E-mail: donald@pino.co.uk *Computer hardware distributors*

Pinpoint Badges & Promotions Ltd, Alma Road, Sidcup, Kent, DA14 4EA Tel: (020) 8302 8008 Fax: (020) 8302 4008 E-mail: sales@pinpointbadges.com *Specialists in top quality metal pin badges, keyrings, printed lanyards, wristbands, flexible PVC keyrings & magnets & machine embroidered badges*

▶ Pinpointworld, 24 Orton Enterprise Centre, Bakewell Road, Orton Southgate, Peterborough, PE2 6XU Tel: (01733) 233550 Fax: (01733) 233650 E-mail: contact@pinpointworld.com *Email Marketing*

▶ Pinsent Masons, 18-22 Melville Street, Edinburgh, EH3 7NS Tel: 0131-225 0000 Fax: 0131-225 0099 E-mail: enquiries@pinsentmasons.com *UK based full service law firm and trade mark attorneys with offices in Birmingham, Bristol, Edinburgh, Glasgow, Leeds, London, Manchester, Brussels, Hong Kong and Shanghai offering services in the areas of construction, major projects, energy and utilities, employment, litigation, outsourcing and technology, corporate finance, mergers and acquisitions, intellectual property, insurance and pensions, property and tax.*

Pinsent Masons LLP, 1 Park Row, Leeds, LS1 5AB Tel: 0113-244 5000 Fax: 0113-244 8000 E-mail: enquiries@pinsentmasons.com *Full service law firm and trade mark attorneys with*

continued

offices in Birmingham, Bristol, Edinburgh, Glasgow, Leeds, London, Manchester, Brussels, Hong Kong and Shanghai offering services in the areas of construction, major projects, energy and utilities, employment, litigation, outsourcing and technology, corporate finance, mergers and acquisitions, intellectual property, insurance and pensions, property and tax.

Pinsent Masons LLP, Woodbridge House, 30 Aylesbury Street, London, EC1R 0ER Tel: (020) 7490 4000 Fax: (020) 7490 2545 E-mail: enquiries@pinsentmasons.com *Law firm for construction, major projects, energy & utilities, employment, litigation, outsourcing & technology, corporate finance, mergers & acquisitions, intellectual property, insurance & pensions, property & tax with an integrated trade mark attorney practice*

Pinson, 44a-44b Pinson Road, Willenhall, West Midlands, WV13 2PR Tel: (01902) 606302 Fax: (01902) 609327 *Padlock manufrs*

Pinstripe Clothing Co. Ltd, 49-51 Dale Street, Manchester, M1 2HF Tel: 0161-236 5640 Fax: 0161-236 8863 *Fashion casual manufrs*

Pinstructure Ltd, Unit 50, Enfield Industrial Estate, Redditch, Worcestershire, B97 6DE Tel: (01527) 67999 Fax: (01527) 66557 E-mail: sales@pinstructure.com *We manufacture and distribute Unthreaded Fasteners and associated products in all regular materials (Mild Steel, Stainless Steel, Phosphor bronze, Spring Steel, Silver Steel). These include: Extractable Dowel pins, Dowel pins DIN6325/ISO2338B/ DIN7, Cotter pins, Retaining pins, Linch/Pipe pins DIN11023, Taper pins, Spring pins, Coiled Spring pins, Ball pins, Bowed washers DIN137, Waved washers DIN137, Button clips, Cable ties, Circlips, Clevis pins, Collars, Conical washers DIN6796, Serrated/Toothed washers, Disc springs DIN2093, Drop nose pins, Groove pins DIN1471/DIN1472/DIN1473/DIN1474/ ISO8743/ISO8742/ISO8746, Hose Clamps DIN3017, Pierced Hose Clips, Tridon Quick release clips, Self clamping clips, Mini clips, Double wire clips, Heavy Duty Mikalor clips, P clips DIN3016, Double & Single Ear clips, Banding, Engineers keys, Push on fixings, Rings, Serrated Safety washers, Shims, Support washers, Thru locking pins, Tool clips, Drive pins, Grease nipples, Fibre & Copper washers.*

Pintorex Ltd, Unit 16 The Royal London Estate, 33 West Road, London, N17 0XL Tel: (020) 8808 0882 Fax: (020) 8801 9846 E-mail: pintorex@pintorex.co.uk *Import & export merchants*

Pioneer Ltd, Birley Street, Blackburn, BB1 5DN Tel: (01254) 678642 Fax: (01254) 678645 *Meat products manufrs*

Pioneer Associates Ltd, Ibex Barn, Ferro Fields, Brixworth, Northampton, NN6 9UA Tel: (01604) 882362 Fax: (01604) 882362 E-mail: sales@pioneer-associates-ltd.co.uk *Plastic mould & toolmakers*

Pioneer Blinds, 265 Bury Old Road, Prestwich, Manchester, M25 1JA Tel: 0161-773 4447 Fax: 0161-773 4447 *Blinds manufrs*

Pioneer Concrete UK Ltd, Horton Road, Gloucester, GL1 3QA Tel: (01452) 303685 Fax: (01452) 303505 *Concrete manufacturer*

Pioneer Concrete (uk), Dunham Ho, Cross St, Sale, Cheshire, M33 7HH Tel: 0161-969 0702 Fax: 0161-969 6240 *Concrete products manufacturer*

Pioneer Finishers, Pioneer Business Park, Princess Road, Ramsgate, Kent, CT11 7RX Tel: (01843) 596615 Fax: (01843) 580933 E-mail: pioneer.paul@talk21.com *Powder coating & stove enamellers*

Pioneer Food Service, PO Box 30, Carlisle, CA1 2RR Tel: (01228) 523474 Fax: (01228) 512906 E-mail: sales@pioneerfoodservice.co.uk *Specialist butchers suppliers*

Pioneer Marking Devices, Amy House, Askew Road West, Gateshead, Tyne & Wear, NE8 2PD Tel: 0191-477 8444 Fax: (08451) 668197 E-mail: pioneer@marking.wonadoo.co.uk *Rubber stamp manufrs*

▶ Pioneer Mechanical Services Ltd, 4 Four Ashes Enterprise Centre, Four Ashes, Wolverhampton, WV10 7BY Tel: (01902) 791715 Fax: (01902) 791778 E-mail: info@pioneerchemicalservices.co.uk *Industrial & commercial heating & ventilation engineers*

Pioneer Oil Tools Ltd, Sir William Smith Road, Kirkton Industrial Estate, Arbroath, Angus, DD11 3RD Tel: (01241) 877776 Fax: (01241) 871037 E-mail: sales@pioneeroiltools.com *Down-hole fishing tool designers & manufrs*

Pioneer Packaging Ltd, Unit 16, Dunsinan Industrial Estate, Dunsinan Avenue, Dundee, DD2 3QT Tel: (01382) 833233 Fax: (01382) 832256 E-mail: sales@pioneerpackaging.co.uk *Suppliers of packaging materials*

Pioneer Print Ltd, 8 Raven Road, London, E18 1HB Tel: (020) 8505 1552 Fax: (020) 8505 9982 E-mail: sales@pioneerprint.co.uk *Lithographic printers*

Pioneer Pump Ltd, Corner Farm Industrial Estate, Woolpit Road, Rattlesden, Bury St. Edmunds, Suffolk, IP30 0RZ Tel: (01449) 736777 *Pump manufrs*

Pioneer Technology (U K) Ltd, Pioneer House, Whitwood Common Lane, Castleford, West Yorkshire, WF10 5PE Tel: (01977) 551830 Fax: (01977) 512430 Principal Export Areas: Worldwide *Audio visual home in car entertainment suppliers*

▶ Pioneer Trading Co., Warners Farm, Main Road, Great Waltham, Chelmsford, CM3 1BN Tel: (01245) 362727 Fax: (01245) 362421 *Window manufrs*

Pioneer Weston, Smithfold Lane, Worsley, Manchester, M28 0GP Tel: 0161-703 2000 Fax: 0161-703 2025 E-mail: info@pwi-ltd.com *Oil & mechanical seal manufrs*

Pionер Fristads (UK) Ltd, 7 Wensum Mount Business Centre, Low Road, Hellesdon, Norwich, NR6 5AQ Tel: (01603) 786160 Fax: (01603) 414540 E-mail: enquiries@fristads-co.com Principal Export Areas: Worldwide *Work wear manufrs*

▶ PiP Graphics Ltd, 9 First Close, West Molesey, Surrey, KT8 1PL Tel: (020) 8979 4898 Fax: (020) 8979 4898 E-mail: info@quickchilli.com *Suppliers of graphic solutions*

Pip Recording, Mendip View, Binhay Road, Yatton, Bristol, BS49 4HA Tel: (01934) 830301 Fax: (01934) 830302 E-mail: piprecording@aol.com *Recording & sound production studios, audio cassette & cd duplications*

Pipaway Engineering Ltd, Milton Road, Drayton, Abingdon, Oxfordshire, OX14 4EZ Tel: (01235) 531272 Fax: (01235) 523833 *Engineers*

Pipcar Ltd, Unit 4b Valley Industries, Hadlow Road, Hadlow, Tonbridge, Kent, TN11 0AH Tel: (01732) 851807 Fax: (01732) 850255 E-mail: admin@pipcar.co.uk *Special heat transfer component manufrs*

Pipe Center, Unit 8B Cosgrove Way, Luton, LU1 1XL Tel: (01582) 404162 Fax: (01582) 459170 *Tubes valves & fittings distributors*

Pipe Centre, 18-22 Pages Walk, London, SE1 4SB Tel: (020) 7237 4421 Fax: (020) 7231 3223 E-mail: br.bermondey@wolseley.co.uk *Building & plumbing equipment manufrs*

Pipe Centre Plus, Unit 8, Spring Road Industrial Estate, Ettingshall, Wolverhampton, WV4 6JZ Tel: (01902) 409341 Fax: E-mail: p15.wolverhampton@wolsely.com *Plastics pipes & fittings distributors* Also at: Highbridge

Pipe Centre Plus, Unit 8, Spring Road Industrial Estate, Ettingshall, Wolverhampton, WV4 6JZ Tel: (01902) 409341 Fax: (01902) 353817 E-mail: p15.wolverhampton@wolseley.co.uk *Plastic stockholders*

Pipe Coil Technology, Hadrian Road, Wallsend, Tyne & Wear, NE28 6HF Tel: 0191-295 9910 Fax: 0191-295 9911 *Pipe coil machinery manufrs*

Pipe Equipment Specialists Ltd, 66a Dukesway, Teesside Industrial Estate, Stockton-on-Tees, Cleveland, TS17 9LT Tel: (01642) 769789 Fax: (01642) 769456 E-mail: info@pipe-equipment.co.uk *Pipework installation accessories manufrs*

Pipe Fabrication Equipment Services, Unit 4, Townley Business Park, Hanson Street, Middleton, Manchester, M24 2UF Tel: 0161-653 7459 Fax: 0161-654 7286 *Thread cutting machine merchants*

▶ Pipe Flow (Worthing) Ltd, 14 Third Avenue, Worthing, West Sussex, BN14 9NZ Tel: 01903 236714 E-mail: pipeflow@aol.com *PLumbing, Heating, Property mainmtenance, Refurbishments, doemstic & Commercial. Specializing to property management agents*

John Pipe Ltd, Mayflower Close, Chandler's Ford, Eastleigh, Hampshire, SO53 4AR Tel: (023) 8036 0100 Fax: (023) 8027 3080 E-mail: sales@johnpipe.co.uk *Export & defence packers forwarding agents*

Pipe Line Centre, 33 Hawkins Lane, Burton-on-Trent, Staffordshire, DE14 1PT Tel: (01283) 567334 Fax: (01283) 510207 E-mail: enquiries@pipelinecenter.co.uk *Engineers*

Pipe Line Centre, Unit D3 Premier Business Centre, Speedfields Park, Fareham, Hampshire, PO14 1TY Tel: (01329) 237215 Fax: (01329) 823641 E-mail: k73.fareham@wolseley.co.uk *Industrial fittings distributors*

Pipe Supports Ltd, Salwarpe Road, Droitwich, Worcestershire, WR9 9BH Tel: (01905) 795500 Fax: (01905) 794126 E-mail: sales@pipesupports.com *Pipe support systems to power generation & petrochemical industries*

▶ Pipe Systems Ltd, Pipe Systems House, 57a Park Terrace East, Horsham, West Sussex, RH13 5DJ Tel: (01403) 263888 Fax: (01403) 263399

Pipe & Tube Group Ltd, Armstrong Road, Basingstoke, Hampshire, RG24 8NU Tel: (01256) 811121 Fax: (01256) 842310 E-mail: info@pipeandtubegroup.co.uk *Steel tube stockholders*

▶ Pipeclear Ltd, Cliff Mount, Whins Lane, Simonstone, Burnley, Lancashire, BB12 7QU Tel: (01282) 776454 Fax: (01282) 779829 E-mail: stephenatpipeclear@btinternet.com *Civil engineering pipe work supplies*

▶ Pipedream Design, Durham House, Durham House Street, London, WC2N 6HG Tel: (0870) 8032293 E-mail: andy@pipedreamdesign.co.uk *Pipedream offer a full web design service at competitive prices to all areas of business*

Pipefreezing & Hot Tapping Ltd, The Premises, 209 Hackney Road, London, E2 8JL Tel: (020) 7739 0680 Fax: (020) 7739 0690 E-mail: sales@pipefreeze.co.uk *Whilst PHL was incorporate in 1996, our technicians have been involved in the industry for 30 years, and have probably the most experienced and highly trained staff in this field. We operate nationally with new, purpose built specialist equipment. We carry out Site surveys, Method statements, Feasibility studies and Risk assessments without cost or obligation. Our company is finally tuned to respond when you need the service and for it to be carried out in a manner that instills confidence to our clients. -Providing the most practical, efficient and cost effective solution for every project. -Offering flexibility without compromise -Keeping pipe streams flowing -Avoiding shut downs -Providing the best solution with the minimum amount of disruption at the most affordable price -Removing the 'hassle factor' from busy engineers and contract managers.*

Pipehawk plc, Systems House, Mill Lane, Alton, Hampshire, GU34 2QG Tel: (01420) 590990 Fax: (01420) 590920 E-mail: sales@pipehawk.com *Ground probing radar manufrs*

Pipeline Center Plastics Ltd, Braidhurst Industrial Estate, Motherwell, Lanarkshire, ML1 3SN Tel: (01698) 261414 Fax: (01698) 275424 *Drainage & gutter distributors*

Pipeline Centre, Unit 303a Dean Road, Bristol, BS11 8AT Tel: 0117-982 4828 Fax: 0117-982 4832 *Pipe & tube stockholders*

Pipeline Centre, 118a Newmarket Road, Bury St. Edmunds, Suffolk, IP33 3TG Tel: (01284) 753046 Fax: (01284) 750042 *Plumbing systems & tube fittings distributors*

Pipeline Centre, Unit 3 Dominion Way Industrial Estate, Cardiff, CF24 1RF Tel: (029) 2048 0046 Fax: (029) 2049 6517 *Pipe merchant*

Pipeline Centre, Millmarsh Lane, Enfield, Middlesex, EN3 7QG Tel: (020) 8805 9588 Fax: (020) 8805 2297 *Plastic pipeline products distributors*

Pipeline Centre, Kelvin Estate, Long Drive, Greenford, Middlesex, UB6 8PG Tel: (020) 8578 2300 Fax: (020) 8575 3556 E-mail: greenford-pipe@ncenters.co.uk *Tube fittings distributors*

Pipeline Centre Ltd, Leads Road, Hull, HU7 0BY Tel: (01482) 838880 Fax: (01482) 878827 E-mail: sales@piplinecenter.co.uk *Steel tube valve fittings distributors* Also at: York

Pipeline Centre, Ingram Road, Leeds, LS11 9BB Tel: 0113-242 8280 Fax: 0113-242 8283 E-mail: sales@pipeline.com *Plastic pipes & pipework stockists* Also at: Branches throughout the U.K.

Pipeline Centre, 17 Mowlem Trading Estate, Leeside Road, London, N17 0QJ Tel: (020) 8808 6633 Fax: (020) 8801 0632 *Heating & ventilating equipment distributors*

Pipeline Centre, Helmet Street, Manchester, M1 2NT Tel: 0161-276 0200 Fax: 0161-276 0201 *Pipeline equipment merchants*

Pipeline Centre, 2 Hartburn Close, Crow Lane Industrial Estate, Northampton, NN3 9UE Tel: (01604) 410888 Fax: (01604) 410777 E-mail: bv.northhampton@wolsley.co.uk *Pipe fittings mechanical industrial product distribution*

Pipeline Centre, 4 Deacon Trading Centre, Knight Road, Rochester, Kent, ME2 2AU Tel: (01634) 290469 Fax: (01634) 290128 *Valves & tube fittings distributors*

Pipeline Centre, Shails Lane, Trowbridge, Wiltshire, BA14 8LQ Tel: (01225) 762331 Fax: (01225) 777370 E-mail: sales@pipeline.centre.co.uk Principal Export Areas: Worldwide *Tube fittings valves & steel stockists* Also at: Branches throughout the U.K.

Pipeline & Electrical Supplies, 75 Reddal Hill Road, Cradley Heath, West Midlands, B64 5JT Tel: (01384) 566381 Fax: (01384) 410781 E-mail: paulacton@btconnect.com *Heating parts stockists*

Pipeline Equipment Supply, Unit 8 Meadow Lane Industrial Park, Ellesmere Port, CH65 4TY Tel: 0151-357 1524 Fax: 0151-357 1958 E-mail: pesnwltd@aol.com *Valves & actuators*

Pipeline Induction Heat Ltd, Farrington Road, Burnley, Lancashire, BB11 5SW Tel: (01282) 415323 Fax: (01282) 415326 E-mail: sales@pih.co.uk *Induction heat treatment services*

Pipeline Industries Guild, 14-15 Belgrave Square, London, SW1X 8PS Tel: (020) 7235 7938 Fax: (020) 7235 0074 E-mail: hqsec@pipeguild.co.uk *Guild association*

Pipeline Maintenance Ltd, Unit 12 Merlin Park, Fred Dannatt Road, Mildenhall, Bury St. Edmunds, Suffolk, IP28 7RD Tel: (01638) 711955 Fax: (01638) 711953 *Cathodic protection system manufrs*

Pipeline & Metal Coatings Ltd, Atlantic Shed South Dock, Alexandra Docks, Newport, Gwent, NP20 2NQ Tel: (01633) 256031 Fax: (01633) 840285 *Anticorrosion engineering*

Pipeline Products Ltd, Units 15-16 Five C Business Centre, Concorde Drive, Clevedon, Avon, BS21 6UH Tel: (01275) 873103 Fax: (01275) 873801 E-mail: info@pipelineproducts.ltd.uk *Tube fittings & valve manufrs*

Pipeline Seal & Insulator Co. Ltd, Unit 1A, Colmworth Business Park, St. Neots, Cambridgeshire, PE19 8YH Tel: (01480) 404661 Fax: (01480) 404662 E-mail: sales@pipelineseal.co.uk *Insulating gasket manufrs*

Pipeline Services Ltd, 21 Princes Drive Industrial Estate, Coventry Road, Kenilworth, Warwickshire, CV8 2FD Tel: (01926) 511316 Fax: (01926) 512744 E-mail: sales@pipeserve.co.uk *Pipeline contractors & fabricators*

▶ Pipeline Technology Ltd, 6 Albany Business Centre, Wickham Road, Fareham, Hampshire, PO17 5BD Tel: (01329) 234888 Fax: (01329) 231717 E-mail: sales@pipetech.co.uk *Water & gas industry suppliers*

▶ Pipemaster Mechanical Services Ltd, 489 Hartshill Road, Stoke-On-Trent, ST4 6AA Tel: (01782) 710881

▶ Pipemedia Ltd, Unit 1 Warren Park Way, Enderby, Leicester, LE19 4SA Tel: (0871) 5757575 Fax: (0871) 4250008 E-mail: sales@pipemedia.com *Pipemedia offer a range of Business Telecommunications Services including Broadband ADSL, SDSL, subscription dialup access, server hosting and co-location and secure e-commerce services.*

Pipemore, 3 Crompton Road, Glenrothes, Fife, KY6 2SF Tel: (01592) 630633 Fax: (01592) 630623 E-mail: sales@pipemorescotland.co.uk *Pneumatics, pipes & fittings distributors*

Piper Boats Ltd, Unit 2a, 6 Prospect Way Knypersley, Stoke-on-Trent, ST8 7PL Tel: (01782) 510610 Fax: (01782) 512332 *Boat builders & repairers*

Piper Communications, 4 Severn Road, Chilton, Didcot, Oxfordshire, OX11 0PW Tel: (01235) 834328 Fax: (01235) 834328 *Radio communication equipment distributors*

Piper Developments Ltd, Townsend House, Townsend Way, Birmingham, B1 2RT Tel: 0121-242 1194 Fax: 0121-242 1194 *Machine tool engineers*

Piper Fabrication & Fencing Supplies Ltd, 214 Northwood Road, Harefield, Uxbridge, Middlesex, UB9 6PT Tel: (01895) 824372 Fax: (01895) 824372 *Fencing suppliers & manufrs*

Piper Media Products, Unit G Bastre Enterprise Park, Newtown, Powys, SY16 1DZ Tel: (01686) 610640 Fax: (01686) 610660 *DVD & video cases distributors*

Piper Test & Measurement Ltd, The Barn, Bilsington, Ashford, Kent, TN25 7JT Tel: (01233) 720130 Fax: (01233) 720140 E-mail: piper@piper-ltd.co.uk *Engineer testing equipment & services*

Piper Toughened Glass Ltd, 29-43 Sydney Road, Watford, WD18 7PZ Tel: (01923) 224047 Fax: (01923) 222741 E-mail: sales@piperglass.co.uk *Toughened glass manufrs*

Pipers Cave, 138 Dungannon Road, Cookstown, County Tyrone, BT80 9BD Tel: (028) 8676 3615 Fax: (028) 8676 2983 *Bag pipe manufrs*

Pipestoppers Ltd, Stukeley Meadow, Gwscwm Road, Burry Port, Dyfed, SA16 0BU Tel: (01554) 836836 Fax: (01554) 836837 E-mail: pipestoppers@huntingdonfusion.com *The Company was established in 1975 and now has 30 years of trading history and experience. *HFT has become a brand name that is synonymous with being the first for weld purge. *You can be confident that HFT offer a solution for all your purging needs: Whatever your looking for, if it's: Bladders or Stoppers, oxygen sniffers or oxygen monitors, water soluble dams or inflatable dams, trailing shields, glove boxes or welding tents, bungs or stoppers, electrode force calibration or pressure gauges, non thoriated tungstens or environmentally friendly tungstens, ceramic tiles or glass fibre support tape.... Whatever your weld purge needs HFT's product range is the professionals choice...*

Pipework Engineering Services Ltd, 124 Emily Street, Birmingham, B12 0XJ Tel: 0121-440 5995 Fax: 0121-440 3246 E-mail: thehamoffice@pipeworkengineering.co.uk *Pipework fabricators*

Pipework Fabrication Services Ltd, Western Industrial Estate, Caerleon, Newport, NP18 3NN Tel: (01633) 430099 Fax: (01633) 430099 *Pipework fabricators*

Pipework & Mechanical Contracts Ltd, Ty Verlon Industrial Estate, Cardiff Road, Barry, South Glamorgan, CF63 2BE Tel: (01446) 748611 Fax: (01446) 746906 *Mechanical engineers, engineering contractors & pipework fabricators*

Pipework Utilities Ltd, Newcastle Road, Smallwood, Sandbach, Cheshire, CW11 2TZ Tel: (01477) 500344 Fax: (01477) 500755 E-mail: sales@pipeworkutilities.co.uk *Pipe work fabricators*

▶ Pipeworks Plumbing Ltd, 8 Carlton Close, Woodley, Reading, RG5 4JS Tel: 0118-901 4513 Fax: 0118-9014513 E-mail: info@pipeworksuk.com *Plumbing services for the Berkshire area, heating maintenance, installation, power flushing, bathroom & kitchen installation, water softeners etc.*

Pipex Ltd, Pipex House Lowman Way, Tiverton Business Park, Tiverton, Devon, EX16 6SR Tel: (01884) 243564 Fax: (01884) 253285 *Supplying design & build corrosion*

Pipex Internet Ltd, Unit 1 Pipex House, Medway Technology Park, Rutherford Close, Stevenage, Hertfordshire, SG1 2EF Tel: (08706) 004454 Fax: (01438) 311100 E-mail: sales@dial.pipex.com *Internet service providers*

Pipextra Stainless Ltd, 2b Red Rose Court, Sunnyhurst Road, Blackburn, BB2 1PS Tel: (01254) 672999 Fax: (01254) 676784 E-mail: sales@stainlesscutpipe.co.uk *Stainless steel pipe cutting service*

Pipistrel Retail Software Ltd, 23 Woodbridge Road, Guildford, Surrey, GU1 1DY Tel: (01483) 440099 Fax: (0870) 1164400 E-mail: support@pipistrel.com *Software developers*

Piplers Chandlers, The Quay, Poole, Dorset, BH15 1HF Tel: (01202) 673056 Fax: (01202) 683065 E-mail: sales@piplers.co.uk *Yacht chandlers* Also at: Lilliput

Pippas Blinds, 84 Mill Road, Cambridge, CB1 2AS Tel: (01223) 364001 Fax: (01733) 703334 E-mail: sales@pippasblinds.co.uk *Blind retailers*

Pique Precision Engineering Ltd, Packet Boat Lane, Cowley, Uxbridge, Middlesex, UB8 2JR Tel: (01895) 443373 Fax: (01895) 431137 E-mail: pique_eng@compuserve.com *Precision engineering services*

▶ Pira Health & Safety Services Ltd, 50 The Terrace, Torquay, TQ1 1DD Tel: (01803) 295510 Fax: 01803 295512 E-mail: info@pira-uk.net *PIRA Health and Safety Services Limited was formed in 1998, to provide professional health and safety services to businesses throughout the South West of England...**With over 30 years experience in the service, leisure, manufacturing and construction industries PIRA are fully qualified to undertake consultancy services for all sizes of business...**PIRA can assist in all aspects of health and safety, however, its most popular task is to create specific health and safety policy manuals for clients. The provision of a good quality health and safety manual is the foundation of a sound Health and Safety Management Systems...**We would be pleased to offer advice in all aspects of health and safety management, whatever the size of your business. **PIRA also have an extensive range of training programmes, which you can access and book on-line.. We hold courses at a variety of venues. If this does not suit your needs then we can come to your workplace.... ***

Pira International, Cleeve Road, Leatherhead, Surrey, KT22 7RU Tel: (01372) 802000 Fax: (01372) 802238 E-mail: membership@pira-international.co.uk *Research company packaging*

Piranha Corporation, 35 Olivine Close, Walderslade Woods, Chatham, Kent, ME5 9NQ Tel: (01634) 869889 Fax: (01634) 869889 *Internet website designers & business services*

▶ Pirbright Electrical Contractors Ltd, Toad Hall, Vapery Lane, Pirbright, Woking, Surrey, GU24 0QD Tel: (01483) 474888 Fax: (01483) 489141

▶ Pirelli Cables Ltd, Carr Lane, Prescot, Merseyside, L34 1PD Tel: 0151-430 4300 Fax: 0151-430 4390 E-mail: neil.bootman@pirelli.com *Copper wire & strip manufrs*

▶ Pirelli Cables & Components, Hall Lane, Prescot, Merseyside, L34 5UR Tel: 0151-430 3655 Fax: 0151-430 3636 E-mail: energysales@pirelli.com *Cable & components manufrs*

▶ Pirelli Construction Co. Ltd, Robslee Drive, Giffnock, Glasgow, G46 7QX Tel: 0141-638 1151

Pirholite Plastics, 2 Crowhurst Hop Farm, Bullen Lane, East Peckham, Tonbridge, Kent, TN12 5LP Tel: (01622) 872657 Fax: (01622) 872679 *Plastic mould polishers services*

F.J. Pirie & Co. Ltd, Unit 2 Palmermount Works, Bypass Road, Dundonald, Kilmarnock, Ayrshire, KA2 9BL Tel: (01563) 850325 Fax: (01563) 851081 *Agricultural engineers*

▶ Pirie & Hunter, 12 College Bounds, Aberdeen, AB24 3DU Tel: (01224) 483137 Fax: (01224) 277321

Simon Thomas Pirie, Slepe Farm Workshop, Dorchester Road, Lytchett Minster, Poole, Dorset, BH16 6HT Tel: (01202) 625725 Fax: (01202) 625725 E-mail: sales@simonthomaspirie.co.uk *Furniture manufrs*

Pirongs Ltd, 10 Silverhills Road, Decoy Industrial Estate, Newton Abbot, Devon, TQ12 5NA Tel: (01626) 352655 Fax: (01626) 336574 E-mail: mail@pirongs.co.uk *Educational year diary publishers*

Piroto Labelling Ltd, 9 Pond Wood Close, Moulton Park Industrial Estate, Northampton, NN3 6RT Tel: (01604) 646600 Fax: (01604) 492090 E-mail: info@piroto-labelling.com *Label manufrs*

Pirtek, 2 Oxford Court, Oxford Street, Birmingham, B5 5NF Tel: 0121-633 0101 Fax: 0121-633 0043 E-mail: info@pirtekbirmingham.co.uk *Hose assembly distributor & agent*

Pirtek, Unit 35 Seymour Street, Millers Bridge Industrial Estate, Bootle, Merseyside, L20 1EE Tel: 0151-933 9000 Fax: 0151-933 5333 E-mail: info@pirtekuk.com *Mobile hydraulics & pneumatics company manufrs*

Pirtek, St. Andrews Road, Avonmouth, Bristol, BS11 9HQ Tel: 0117-982 0056 Fax: 0117-982 4361 E-mail: info@pirtekbristol.co.uk *On site hydraulic hose services*

Pirtek, 5 Stockwell Centre, Stephenson Way, Crawley, West Sussex, RH10 1TN Tel: (01293) 571707 Fax: (01293) 571711 E-mail: pirtekcrawley@fsbdial.co.uk *Hydraulic hose repair, supply & manufrs*

Pirtek, 10 Tuffley Trading Estate, Pearce Way, Gloucester, GL2 5YD Tel: (01452) 308010 Fax: (01452) 307447 E-mail: gloucester@pirtekcentre.co.uk *Mobile hose replacement service*

Pirtek, Moorfield Road, Guildford, Surrey, GU1 1RB Tel: (01483) 454546 Fax: (01483) 454549 E-mail: claire@pirtekportsmouth.co.uk *Pipes & fittings, flexible manufrs*

Pirtek, Unit 35, Acton Park Industrial Estate, The Vale, Acton, London, W3 7QE Tel: (020) 8749 8444 Fax: (020) 8749 8333 E-mail: info@pirtek.co.uk *Hose manufacturers & distributors*

Pirtek, 6 Westbrook Trading Estate, Westbrook Road, Trafford Park, Manchester, M17 1AY Tel: 0161-877 0000 Fax: 0161-877 8899 E-mail: pirtek-manchester@supanet.com *Mobile hydraulics systems manufrs*

Pirtek, Unit 11 Liongate Enterprise Park, Morden Road, Mitcham, Surrey, CR4 4NY Tel: (020) 8640 6565 Fax: (020) 8640 2252 E-mail: pirtek.mitcham@zen.co.uk *Supply & fitting of hydraulic hoses*

Pirtek, 337 Ranglet Road, Walton Summit Centre, Bamber Bridge, Preston, PR5 8AR Tel: (01772) 620111 Fax: (01772) 629996 E-mail: preston@pirtekcentre.co.uk *Hydraulics supply & manufrs*

Pirtek, 5 Bergland Park, Maritime Close, Medway City Estate, Rochester, Kent, ME2 4AD Tel: (01634) 297080 Fax: (01634) 297087 E-mail: zen24815@zen.co.uk *Hydraulic hose suppliers*

Pirtek, 3 Alert House, Dannemora Drive, Sheffield, S9 5DF Tel: 0114-249 3666 Fax: 0114-249 3667 E-mail: sheffield@pirtekcentre.co.uk *Hydraulic hose & fittings suppliers*

Pirtek, Unit 8 Westmill Street, Stoke-on-Trent, ST1 3EL Tel: (01782) 206206 Fax: (01782) 206306 E-mail: stoke@pirtekcentre.co.uk *Hydraulic industrial hose & assembly manufrs*

Pirtek (Nottingham) Ltd, Unit 4 Trentview Court, Moreland Street, Nottingham, NG2 3FX Tel: 0115-985 0081 Fax: 0115-985 0132 E-mail: info@pirteknottingham.co.uk *Hydraulic hose suppliers*

Pisani plc, Unit 12 Transport Avenue, Brentford, Middlesex, TW8 9HF Tel: (020) 8568 5001 Fax: (020) 8847 3406 E-mail: sales@pisani.co.uk *Marble & granite wholesalers*

Pisces, Westwood Studios, Marshfield Bank, Crewe, CW2 8UY Tel: (01270) 216211 Fax: (01270) 586150 E-mail: info@pisces-art.co.uk *Educational suppliers*

▶ Pisces Accounts, Doe House Farm, Bradfield, Sheffield, S6 6LE Tel: 0114 2851384 E-mail: alanoakes@piscesaccounts.co.uk *Accountancy Services for the Small Business, Self Employed and Freelance. VAT Returns and Self Assessment at Competitive Prices. Postal Service Available For Clients .Website Design from Templates. Professional Service.*

Pisces Computers, Moor Street, Chepstow, Gwent, NP16 5DE Tel: (01291) 625100 Fax: (01291) 621068 E-mail: piscescomputers@aol.com *Computer shop*

▶ Pisces Conservation Ltd, Irc House, The Square, Pennington, Lymington, Hampshire, SO41 8GN Tel: (01590) 676622 Fax: (01590) 675599 E-mail: sales@pisces-conservation.com *Pisces is an environmental consultancy specialising in the aquatic and marine environment. We have special expertise in the effects of power generation on the environment. As well as EIA work, we also develop and market a wide range of software products for ecological research and teaching.*

Pisces Engineering Services, 12 Loch Laxford, East Kilbride, Glasgow, G74 2DL Tel: (01355) 243220 Fax: (01355) 243220 E-mail: pisces@compuserve.com *Computer software engineers*

Pisces Plastics Ltd, 5-6 Old Racecourse Road, Liverpool, L31 8AW Tel: 0151-531 1175 Fax: 0151-531 1175 *Security plastics*

Pisys Ltd, Campus 1, Balgownie Road, Bridge of Don, Aberdeen, AB22 8GT Tel: (01224) 332014 Fax: (01224) 332055E-mail: info@pisysltd.co.uk *Pisys specialise in the creation & delivery of specialist software products & consultancy services to a worldwide client base.*

▶ Pitch Perfect (UK) Ltd., Communications House, 26 York Street, London, W1U 6PZ Tel: 0845 351 0615 E-mail: info@pitchperfect.biz *Pitch Perfect (UK) Ltd. specialises in the provision of Sales Recruitment solutions.*

Pitchdesign Ltd, Zion Works, Zion Street, Colne, Lancashire, BB8 0SP Tel: (01282) 869998 Fax: (01282) 860131 *Joiner manufrs*

Pitchford Steelstock, Pedmore Road, Brierley Hill, West Midlands, DY5 1TH Tel: (01384) 489030 Fax: (01384) 480209 *Steel stockholders*

Pitchmastic P M B Ltd, Royds Works, Attercliffe Road, Sheffield, S4 7WZ Tel: 0114-270 0100 Fax: 0114-276 8782 E-mail: info@pitchmasticpmb.co.uk *Building contractors & waterproofing services*

▶ PITHON Limited, Ground Floor, 74 Markland Avenue, Uckfield, East Sussex, TN22 2DG Tel: 01825 767669 E-mail: info@pithon.co.uk *PITHON Limited is a training and consultancy organisation working with clients mainly across Europe and also in many other parts of the World. The Directors and Managing Consultants are Paul Hazell and Ian Girdler.*

Pitkerro Ltd, Emmock Road, Tealing, Dundee, DD3 0PZ Tel: (01382) 816272 Fax: (01382) 811512 E-mail: wallace.wiseman@pitkerro.co.uk *Plumbing & heating installation*

Pitkin & Ruddock Ltd, Unit 6 Moorpark Indust Estate, Bury St. Edmunds, Suffolk, IP32 7AJ Tel: (01284) 767579 Fax: (01284) 760784 *Refrigeration & air conditioning engineers service*

Pitkin Unichrome, Dene Road, Healey House, Andover, Hampshire, SP10 2AA Tel: (01264) 409200 Fax: (01264) 334110 E-mail: sales@tempus-publishing.com *Books, publishing*

Pitlochry Of Scotland, 2a Bell Street, St. Andrews, Fife, KY16 9UX Tel: (01334) 472113 *Knitwear & textiles manufrs*

Pitman Joinery Works, Limington, Yeovil, Somerset, BA22 8EG Tel: (01935) 840431 Fax: (01935) 841100 *Joiners*

▶ Pitman Training, Bishops Stortford, Suite 3, 15 Market Square, Bishop's Stortford, Hertfordshire, CM23 3UT Tel: (01279) 466200 Fax: (01279) 466220 E-mail: bishopsstortford@pitman-training.net *Computer training*

Pitman Training Centre Ltd, Portsmouth House, Portsmouth Road, Guildford, Surrey, GU2 4BL Tel: (01483) 572855 Fax: (01483) 300859 E-mail: guildford@pitman-training.net *Trade & vocational training services*

Pitman Training Centre Ltd, Ferrari House, 258 Field End Road, Ruislip, Middlesex, HA4 9UU Tel: (020) 8868 0111 Fax: (020) 8868 1001 E-mail: harrowanduxbridge@pitman-training.net *Training consultants*

Pitney Bowes Office Direct, London Road, London, SE1 6LF Tel: (020) 7200 5408 Fax: (020) 7200 5432 E-mail: hassan.dayem@pb.com *Digital franking machine manufrs*

Pitney Press, 50 Main Road, Middlezoy, Bridgwater, Somerset, TA7 0NN Tel: (01823) 698181 Fax: (01823) 698605 *Boxes manufrs*

Pitt & Dickson Ltd, 140 Bridgeman Street, Walsall, WS2 9NW Tel: (01922) 623048 Fax: (01922) 620261 E-mail: pitt.dickson@virgin.net *Engineers*

Pittards P.L.C., Sherborne Road, Yeovil, Somerset, BA21 5BA Tel: (01935) 474321 Fax: (01935) 427145 E-mail: pittardsenquire@pittards.com *Manufacturer of leather*

Pitter Bros Ltd, Botley Road Garage, Botley Road, West End, Southampton, SO30 3HA Tel: (023) 8047 2385 Fax: (023) 8046 4291 E-mail: traffic@pitterbrothers.idps.co.uk *Road transport, haulage & freight services*

▶ Pittmans Accounting Services, Parhema, Lees Court Road, Sheldwich, Faversham, Kent, ME13 0LY Tel: 01795 531085 Fax: 01795 531085 E-mail: info@pittmansage.co.uk *Sage training*

▶ Pitts Presentation Products Ltd, Hill Top Lane, Whittle-le-Woods, Chorley, Lancashire, PR6 7QR Tel: (01257) 220247 Fax: (01257) 220246 E-mail: info@pittspresentation.co.uk *Manufacturers of a range of presentation products*

Pitts Wilson Electrical Ltd, Cutler House, Wakefield Road, Bradford, West Yorkshire, BD4 7LU Tel: (01274) 771100 Fax: (01274) 771188 E-mail: enquiries@pwe-elec.com *Electrical installation engineers*

▶ Pittsburgh Corning UK Ltd, 63 Milford Road, Reading, RG1 8LG Tel: 0118-950 0655 Fax: 0118-950 9019 E-mail: sales@foamglass.co.uk *Cellular glass insulation product fabricators & manufrs*

▶ Piv Drive, Posiva Works 8 Skipping Dale Industrial Estate, Exmoor Avenue, Scunthorpe, South Humberside, DN15 8NJ Tel: (01724) 281868 Fax: (01724) 282808 *Industrial gear box sales & repairs*

▶ Pivotal Holdings Ltd, 143 New Bond Street, London, W1S 2TP Tel: (020) 7493 5550 Fax: (020) 7493 5559 E-mail: enquiries@pivotalwoodflooring.com *Pivotal Holdings is a London based volume importer and wholesale distributor of wood flooring. We supply trade buyers in the UK and the Turks and Caicos Islands.**We offer competitive prices while maintaining high standards of quality through our partnership with the only European owned wood flooring factory in China.*

Pix Electrical Co. Ltd, Unit 6, Muslin Street, Salford, M5 4NF Tel: (0161) 925 9829 Fax: (0161) 737 9438 E-mail: phillip.hall@pixelectrical.co.uk *Switchgear & control panel manufrs*

Pix Europe Ltd, Unit 24 Farthing Road Industrial Estate, Sproughton, Ipswich, IP1 5AP Tel: (01473) 744612 Fax: (01473) 744613 E-mail: info@pixeuro.com *Power transmission companies*

Pixel Fountain, Bowden Hall, Bowden Lane, Marple, Stockport, Cheshire, SK6 6NE Tel: 0161-427 8684 Fax: 0161-427 8691 E-mail: pfinfo@pixelfountain.co.uk *Internet & multimedia*

Pixel Image Ltd, 100 Constitution Street, Edinburgh, EH6 6AW Tel: 0131-555 3003 Fax: 0131-555 5927 E-mail: ssmith@pixelimage.co.uk *3D visualisation services*

Pixel Management, 125 Dove House Lane, Solihull, West Midlands, B91 2EL Tel: 0121-688 8990 E-mail: sales@pml.co.uk *Independent software vendor*

▶ Pixel Perfect, The White House, Copse Road, Haslemere, Surrey, GU27 3QQ Tel: (01428) 643500 E-mail: sales@pixelperfect.co.uk *3D CGI design & animation service*

Pixel Visual Communications Ltd, Shieling House, 30 Invincible Road Industrial Estate, Farnborough, Hampshire, GU14 7QU Tel: (01252) 375750 Fax: (01252) 521155 E-mail: info@pixelvisual.com *We offer creative and cost effective photographic solutions for all your business needs, from a simple packshot photograph to a full studio room set or location shoot. We cover Surrey, Hampshire, Berkshire, West Sussex and London.*

▶ Pixelate Imaging, 8 Flitcroft Street, London, WC2H 8DL Tel: (020) 7240 9808 Fax: (020) 7240 9188 E-mail: studio@pixelate.biz

▶ Pixeleyes Photography, 3rd floor, 21 perseverance works, 38 kingsland road, London, London, E2 8DA Tel: 020 7739 7239 Fax: 020 7739 7377 E-mail: studio@pixeleyesphotography.co.uk *We specialise in digital product, packshot, and advertising photography for web and print useage.*We shoot jewellery, cosmetics, clothing, food and drink, people, interiors and exteriors.*You get quality imaging at realistic prices*

Pixie Developments Ltd, 2 New Mills Industrial Estate, Post Office Road, Inkpen, Hungerford, Berkshire, RG17 9PU Tel: (01488) 669184 Fax: (01488) 669185 E-mail: pixiedev.ltd@ukonline.co.uk Principal Export Areas: Africa *Pixie Developments Ltd is a manufacturing unit for extruded thermoplastic products using extrusion machinery designed, built & developed by our own engineering company, the company undertakes the design, development & production of profile, pipes, tubes, strip etc, we use a wide variety of thermoplastics in our production, acrylics, polycarbonate, PVC, UPVC, PP, polystyrene GP, high impact polystyrene, we supply to the construction, aerospace, medical, automotive, sports, leisure, caravan & fashion industries, we are always pleased to offer advice on product, design, materials & tooling*

▶ Pizza Two Four (Manufacturing) Ltd, Radfords Field, Industrial Estate, Maesbury Road, Oswestry, Shropshire, SY10 8HA Tel: (01691) 657664

▶ Pizzeria (Swindon), 25 Manchester Road, Swindon, SN1 2AB Tel: (01252) 315956

PJ Sealants Ltd, Barton House, 36 Ashby Road, Kegworth, Derby, DE74 2DH Tel: (01509) 670333 Fax: (01509) 670456 E-mail: pjsealants@aol.com *Sealant application contractors*

PJH Engineering Ltd, Unit 15e Bergen Way, Sutton Fields Industrial Estate, Hull, HU7 0YQ Tel: (01482) 370375 Fax: (01482) 370385 Principal Export Areas: Worldwide *Manufacturers of conveyor systems*

▶ PJM Advertising Ltd, 9 Rempstone Barns, Rempstone, Corfe Castle, Wareham, Dorset, BH20 5JH Tel: (01929) 481520 Fax: (01929) 481519 E-mail: office@pjmsouth.co.uk *Advertising & marketing agency*

PJP Plant Hire, Mill Street, Radcliffe, Manchester, M26 1AJ Tel: 0845 5314214 Fax: 0161-959 1111 E-mail: hire@pjpuk.com *PJP Plant Hire are the North's premier self drive hire company supplying house builders, major utility, building and civil engineering companies. Our modern fleet comprises, excavators, backhoe loaders, tracked dumpers, wheeled dumpers, tractor winches, telescopic handlers, rough terrain forklifts, rollers, hydraulic breakers, trailers, bunded bowsers, winch tractors plus a lot more. Our fleet is supported by a dedicated team using state of the art tracking systems as well as our own in house paint facilities and engineering workshops. Contact us today and see why many companies have PJP as their preferred supplier.*

PJP Precision Engineering Ltd, 5 Berkshire Business Centre, Berkshire Drive, Thatcham, Berkshire, RG19 4EW Tel: (01635) 872792 Fax: (01635) 864390 E-mail: pjpm@msn.com *Precision engineers*

▶ PJP Southern Ltd, Unit 2 Wellington Park, Hedge End, Southampton, SO30 2QU Tel: (01489) 790545 Fax: (01489) 790492

PJ's Workwear, 42 The Tything, Worcester, WR1 1JT Tel: (01905) 22051 Fax: (01905) 617476 *Embroidery & work wear manufrs*

▶ PK Hydraulics Ltd, River House, South Esplanade East, Aberdeen, AB11 9PB Tel: (01224) 249600 Fax: (01224) 870701 E-mail: kevin@pkhydraulics.co.uk *Hydraulics & pneumatic equipment suppliers*

▶ Plabeasy, PO Box 4160, Cardiff, CF14 3ZY Tel: (0777) 9850236 Fax: E-mail: info@plabeasy.com *Studying alone for the PLAB test can be a daunting experience for many doctors.**PLABEASY provides hundreds of questions designed to PLAB exam standards.**PLABEASY Courses will teach you how to tackle and pass the PLAB test.**

Plad Timber & Damp Proofing Specialists Ltd, 168 Birmingham Road, Shenstone Wood End, Lichfield, Staffordshire, WS14 0NX Tel: 0121-308 4241 Fax: 0121-323 3683 *Damp proofing & timber preservation services*

Plain Tree Furniture, Main Street, Kirkby Malzeard, Ripon, North Yorkshire, HG4 3SD Tel: (01765) 658955 *Furniture manufrs*

▶ Plaistere & Hanger Cartons, Pilot Road, Corby, Northamptonshire, NN17 5YH Tel: (01536) 443896 Fax: (01536) 443894 E-mail: pnh60@btconnect.com *Recycling services*

▶ Plan 2 Ltd, The Old Chapel, 8 High Street, Blakesley, Towcester, Northamptonshire, NN12 8RE Tel: (01327) 861101 Fax: (01327) 860944 E-mail: adrian@plan2.ltd.uk *If you need a new house, extension or alterations to your commercial premises we can give you what you need for a price you can afford. We take pride in not charging the earth whilst providing a quality of service and product second to none. If you want to build, let us cut the "red tape"*

▶ Plan 4 Print Ltd, Goshawk Road, Quarry Hill Industrial Estate, Ilkeston, Derbyshire, DE7 4RG Tel: 0115-930 5393 E-mail: sales@plan4print.co.uk

▶ Plan Engineers, 1 Ashton Grange Industrial Estate, Bryn Road, Ashton-in-Makerfield, Wigan, Lancashire, WN4 8BX Tel: (01942) 271299 Fax: (01942) 721756 *Steel pallets manufrs*

Plan It, 13 Palacecraig Street, Coatbridge, Lanarkshire, ML5 4SB Tel: (01236) 421082 Fax: (01236) 424311 E-mail: peryslick@gmail.com *Precision subcontract engineers*

Plan It Business Systems, 41 Blackburn Street, Radcliffe, Manchester, M26 1NR Tel: 0161-723 0999 Fax: 0161-723 3888 E-mail: info@planitbs.co.uk *Business to business IT*

▶ Plan It Contracts Ltd, 37 Colquhoun Avenue, Glasgow, G52 4PL Tel: 0141-883 8741 Fax: 0141-882 7071

Plan Personnel, Stonemead House, 95 London Road, Croydon, CR0 2RF Tel: (020) 8681 0846 Fax: (020) 8253 5993 E-mail: speto@planpersonnel.co.uk *Employment agency commercial domiciliary care drivers.* Also at: Branches throughout the U.K.

Plan Plastics Ltd, 40 The Warren, Chartridge, Chesham, Buckinghamshire, HP5 2RY Tel: (01494) 772577 Fax: (01494) 772577 *Ultrasonic welding engineers, services & subcontractors*

Planahome Ltd, 105 High St, Golborne, Warrington, WA3 3BU Tel: (01942) 728059 Fax: (01942) 271643 E-mail: sales@planahome.co.uk *Fitting bedrooms & bathrooms & kitchens manufrs*

Plancraft Marine Ltd, 4 Little Shellwood Farm, Clayhill Road, Leigh, Reigate, Surrey, RH2 8PA Tel: (01306) 611100 Fax: (01306) 611101 E-mail: sales@plancraft.co.uk *Boat builders*

Plandent, Summit House, Cranborne Road, Potters Bar, Hertfordshire, EN6 3EE Tel: (01707) 822400 Fax: (01707) 649901 *Dental equipment wholesalers*

Planer plc, 110 Windmill Road, Sunbury-on-Thames, Middlesex, TW16 7HD Tel: (01932) 755000 Fax: (01932) 755001 E-mail: sales@planer.co.uk *Temperature & measurement equipment for electronic & industrial applications*

Planet, 23 Albert Drive, Burgess Hill, West Sussex, RH15 9TN Tel: (01444) 247933 Fax: (01444) 248799 E-mail: enquiries@planetpartitoning.co.uk *Internal partition manufacturers & contractors*

▶ Planet Carp, Alfreton Road, Nottingham, NG7 3PE Tel: 0115-942 4941 Fax: 0115-978 4158 E-mail: sales@carpfishingonline.com *Fishing tackle suppliers*

▶ Planet Computer Systems Ltd, 35 Kaims Court, Livingston Village, Livingston, West Lothian, EH54 7DB Tel: (01506) 414552

▶ Planet Dance, PO Box 233, Leeds, LS16 0AQ Tel: (0870) 1453995 Fax: 0113-226 9295 E-mail: info@planetdancedirect.co.uk *Retailers of designer dancewear*

Planet Engineering, Unit 1, Southampton Road, Petersfinger, Salisbury, SP5 3DB Tel: (01722) 410010 Fax: (01722) 410010 *Custom motor cycle manufrs*

Planet Gears Ltd, 2 Maguire Industrial Estate, Coventry, CV4 9HN Tel: 024 76474213 *Gear & gear coupling manufrs*

Planet Kids, 8 Actons Walk, Wood Street, Wigan, Lancashire, WN3 4HN Tel: (01942) 403910 Fax: (01942) 231188 E-mail: sales@planetkids.org.uk *Designer clothing & nursery store*

▶ Planet Leisure UK, The LnS Building, Unit 4, Crockford Lane, Chineham, Basingstoke, Hampshire, RG24 8NA Tel: (01256) 841950 Fax: (01256) 818255 E-mail: sales@planetleisureuk.co.uk *Suppliers of Commercial Leisure Furniture & Accessories, including Parasols, large Umbrellas, Awnings, Banners and much more...*

Planet Merchandising Products Ltd, Unit 219b, Aldington Road, London, SE18 5TS Tel: (020) 8855 9594 Fax: (020) 8316 2745 E-mail: sales@planetmerchandising.co.uk *Shop fitting manufacturers & steel fabricators*

Planet Micro, Unit 1 Beresford Street, Failsworth, Manchester, M35 0HD Tel: (08707) 453555 Fax: (08707) 454555 E-mail: sales@planetmicro.co.uk *Computer hardware consultants*

Planet Organic Ltd, 42 Westbourne Grove, London, W2 5SH Tel: (020) 7221 7171 Fax: (020) 7221 1923 *Organic food retailers*

▶ Planet Partitions, Cavalier Court, 14 Bristol Road, Bumpers Farm, Chippenham, Wiltshire, SN14 6LH Tel: (01249) 448920 Fax: (01249) 446942 *Supplying & installing*

Planet Pine, 57 Framfield Road, Uckfield, East Sussex, TN22 5AJ Tel: (01825) 766048 *Pine furniture retailers & manufrs*

▶ Planet Platform Western Ltd, Peel House, Peel Road, Skelmersdale, Lancashire, WN8 9PT Tel: (01695) 559980 Fax: (01695) 559960 *Access equipment manufrs*

Planet Platforms Ltd, 146 Wakefield Road, Ossett, West Yorkshire, WF5 9AR Tel: (01924) 263377 Fax: (01924) 267090 E-mail: enquiries@planetplatforms.co.uk *Access equipment manufrs*

Planet Processing Ltd, 24 Fairfax Road, Heathfield Industrial Estate, Newton Abbot, Devon, TQ12 6UD Tel: (01626) 832229 Fax: (01626) 835559 E-mail: sales@planetprocessing.com

Planet Welding Supplies Ltd, Unit 4 Artesian Close, London, NW10 8RW Tel: (020) 8451 5553 Fax: (020) 8451 1079 E-mail: info@planetwelding.fsnet.co.uk *Welding supplies & distributors*

▶ PlanetStream Streaming Media, Unit 25 Stockwood Business Park, Stockwood, Redditch, Worcestershire, B96 6SX Tel: (01386) 792972 Fax: (0870) 4793791 E-mail: info@planetstream.net *On demand online steaming service*

Planit EOD Ltd, The Old Granary, Radwinter Road, Saffron Walden, ESSEX, CB10 2ET Tel: (0870) 7663210 Fax: (0870) 7663230 E-mail: sales@planiteod.com *PLANIT EOD Limited is the UK's premier supplier of Unexploded Ordnance (UXO) Clearance and Disposal Services. *PLANIT EOD conducts; Historical Desktop Studies (HDS) to assess the likely UXO contamination on a site; Non-intrusive UXO site investigation, down to a maximum depth of 10.8 metres; Intrusive UXO site investigation; clearance and disposal of UXO found on site.**If you have any questions about UXO contamination on a site, our previous clients and projects, please contact us and we will assist you as best we can.*

Planit International Ltd, 1 Trinity Road, Eureka Science Park, Ashford, Kent, TN25 4AB Tel: (01233) 635566 Fax: (01233) 627855 E-mail: sales@planit.com *Computer aided design systems*

Planit Systems, 21B Coda Centre, Munster Road, London, SW6 6AW Tel: (020) 7381 8494 Fax: (020) 7381 8817 E-mail: info@planitsystems.co.uk *IT company*

Planline International Ltd, 3 Boddington Road, Byfield, Daventry, Northamptonshire, NN11 6UP Tel: (01327) 264406 Fax: (01327) 264406 E-mail: sales@planlineinternational.com *Manufacturer & suppliers of plan filing*

Planmaster Systems Ltd, York House, Wycombe End, Beaconsfield, Buckinghamshire, HP9 1XA Tel: (01494) 672184 Fax: (01494) 670218 E-mail: sales@planmaster.co.uk *Computer software developers services*

▶ Plann Architects Ltd, Studio 1 Welland Indust Estate, Valley Way, Market Harborough, Leicestershire, LE16 7PS Tel: (01858) 466946 Fax: (01858) 466879 E-mail: mcl@plann-architects.co.uk *Architects dealing with design of houses, traditional contemporary & oak, offices & public buildings*

Planned Access Maintenance, 11 Hague Park Coppice, South Kirkby, Pontefract, West Yorkshire, WF9 3SU Tel: (01977) 649719 Fax: (01977) 649719 E-mail: plannedam@aol.com *Hydraulic platforms manufrs*

Planned Maintenance Engineers Ltd, Unit 2, Site 5B, Ocean Way, Cardiff, CF24 5HF Tel: (029) 2022 0602 Fax: (029) 2089 5598 E-mail: info@pme.co.uk *Air Conditioning & heating maintenance*

Planned Maintenance (Pennine) Ltd, Vine Grove Works, Commerce St, Haslingden, Rossendale, Lancashire, BB4 5JT Tel: (01706) 227865 Fax: (01706) 836111 E-mail: info@pmp-ltd.co.uk *Contractors confined spaces specialists*

Planned Packaging Ltd, 20 High Street, Great Budworth, Northwich, Cheshire, CW9 6HF Tel: (01606) 891432 Fax: (01606) 891466 E-mail: plannedpackagingltd@btinternet.com *Packaging materials*

Planned Publicity, 241a Selbourne Road, Luton, LU4 8NP Tel: (01582) 599529 Fax: (01582) 583366 E-mail: briangale@pplgraphics.co.uk *Exhibition artwork designers & builders*

Planned Storage Systems Ltd, Castle House, Victoria St, Englefield Green, Egham, Surrey, TW20 0QL Tel: (01784) 471471 Fax: (01784) 471343 E-mail: sales@planned-storage.co.uk *Partitioning contractors*

Planned Storage Systems Ltd, Murdock Road, Dorcan, Swindon, SN3 5HY Tel: (01793) 694071 Fax: (01793) 610516 E-mail: mail@hi-lo.co.uk *pallet racking & heavy duty shelving manufacturers*

Planners Services & Sundries Ltd, 8-9 Brandon Road, London, N7 9AA Tel: (020) 7609 8321 Fax: (020) 7700 2010 *Floor covering distributors*

Planning & Development, The Highland Council, Glenurquhart Road, Inverness, IV3 5NX Tel: (01463) 702250 Fax: (01463) 702298 E-mail: planning@highland.gov.uk *Planning & developers*

▶ Planning Precision, Planning Precision, Twitten End, North Street, Storrington, West Sussex, RH20 4PB Tel: 01903 742976 E-mail: william@planning-precision.co.uk *Design and Planning for Precision Engineering.*Providing detailed shop-floor drawings, encompassing 3D views, Stage drawings, Fixture and Special Tooling Design.**Component Planning/Machine Tool Routing, encompassing operation instruction sheets, customised to suit your equipment.*

Plansee Metals Ltd, 3 Lidstone Court, Uxbridge Road, George Green, Slough, SL3 6AG Tel: (01753) 576959 Fax: (01753) 577591 *Metal & plastic container distributors*

A Plant P.L.C., Daleside Road, Nottingham, NG2 4DJ Tel: 0115-958 0085 Fax: 0115-948 3348 E-mail: garyhorton@aplant.com *Tool hire*

Plant & Automation Ltd, Lord North St, Miles Platting, Manchester, M40 8HT Tel: 0161-205 5756 Fax: 0161-205 0503 *Pipe & tube bending specialists*

Plant Care, The Nurseries Bath Road, Swineford, Bitton, Bristol, BS30 6LN Tel: 0117-932 5080 Fax: 0117-932 1339 *Interior landscaping services*

Plant Displays Plus, 38 Park Road, Ashford, Middlesex, TW15 1EY Tel: (01784) 888000 Fax: (01784) 888001 E-mail: sales@plantdisplaysplus.com *Plant & floral designers*

Plant Equipment Ltd, Clover Nook Road, Cotes Park Industrial Estate, Somercotes, Alfreton, Derbyshire, DE55 4RF Tel: (01773) 836060 Fax: (01773) 520630 E-mail: info@plantequip.co.uk *Plant equipment*

▶ Plant Glazing Ltd, Ruthvenfield Place, Inveralmond Industrial Estate, Perth, PH1 3XU Tel: (01738) 626421 *Plant machinery glazers*

Plant Hire Ltd, Unit 3, Aquarius Business Park, Priestley Way, London, NW2 7AN Tel: (020) 8208 3838 Fax: (020) 8450 3716 *Contractors plant hire*

▶ Plant i, Bryn y gog, Machynlleth, Powys, SY20 8HN Tel: 01654 703295 E-mail: sam@plant-i.net *Securitry and Telemetry solutions designed and installed for the plant and fleet market.*Full remote monitoring from 90p per day.*

Plant Installations (Coventry) Ltd, Crondal Road, Exhall, Coventry, CV7 9NH Tel: (024) 7636 0421 Fax: (024) 7664 4303 E-mail: sales@plantinstallations.co.uk *Machinery removal contractors*

Plant Life, 9 Woodland Way, Morden, Surrey, SM4 4DS Tel: (020) 8286 9461 Fax: (020) 8542 4456 E-mail: sales@plantlife.me.uk *Plant services*

Plant Life Controls Ltd, Unit 1c Causeway Park, Central Road, Warrington, WA4 6RF Tel: (01925) 234788 Fax: (01925) 234781 E-mail: enquiries@plc1.co.uk *Mechanical engineers*

Plant Mart Ltd, 7 Langhedge Lane Industrial Estate, Langhedge Lane, London, N18 2TQ Tel: (020) 8366 7375 Fax: (020) 8803 0814 E-mail: sales@aircon4u.co.uk *Air conditioning distributors*

▶ Plant Parts International Ltd, 10 High Street, Pensnett, Kingswinford, West Midlands, DY6 8XD Tel: (01384) 408950 Fax: (01384) 404600 E-mail: sales@dig-dog.com *Power head services*

Plant Plan, Lyon Close, Wigston, Leicestershire, LE18 2BJ Tel: 0116-281 1933 Fax: 0116-288 6973 *Interior design contractors*

Plant & Planters, Bow Wharf, 221 Grove Road, London, E3 5SN Tel: (0845) 6123663 Fax: (020) 8981 9568 E-mail: sales@tropical-plants.co.uk *Plant displays*

Plant Welding & Engineering Ltd, Private Road 7, Colwick Industrial Estate, Nottingham, NG4 2AB Tel: 0115-987 0702 Fax: 0115-940 0375 *Welded fabrications*

Plant Zone Ltd, Silver House Ireland Industrial Estate, Adelphi Way, Staveley, Chesterfield, Derbyshire, S43 3LJ Tel: (01246) 472727 Fax: (01246) 472727 E-mail: michael@plantzone.co.uk *Horticultural & plant display contractors*

Plantation Rug Co. Ltd, Steanard Lane, Mirfield, West Yorkshire, WF14 8EZ Tel: (01924) 493200 Fax: (01924) 493600 E-mail: sales@plantationrug.co.uk *Rug manufacturers & importers*

Plantech Ltd, 160 Queen Victoria Street, London, EC4V 4BF Tel: (020) 7202 8100 Fax: (020) 7928 8060 E-mail: sales@plantechltd.co.uk *Computer software sales*

Planters Clayton Ltd, Unit 6, Rivington House, Horwich Business Park, Chorley New Road, Horwich, Bolton, BL6 5UE Tel: (01204) 690003 Fax: (01204) 690170 E-mail: office@plantersclayton.com *Planters Clayton based in Bolton, Lancashire are designers and manufacturers of hydraulic balers and baling presses for synthetic and natural rubber, aluminium and steel cans, UBCs, aluminium trim, ferrous, non ferrous alloys, copper wire and swarf, cotton and tobacco. Hydraulic and pneumatic drum and can crushers.*

Plantforce Ltd, The Hatchery, Hawthorn, Crick, Caldicot, Gwent, NP26 5UT Tel: (01291) 431111 Fax: (01291) 424803 *Excavator bucket & attachments manufrs*

Plantlife Ltd, The Barn, Old Gardens, Blackhorse Road, Woking, Surrey, GU22 0QT Tel: (01483) 799980 Fax: (01483) 799988 E-mail: info@plantlife-ltd.co.uk *Interior landscapes & plants for offices*

Plant-Mec Ireland, 39 Drumconwell Road, Armagh, BT60 2AT Tel: (028) 3751 1717 Fax: (028) 3751 8448 E-mail: info@plantmecireland.com *Industrial & plant suppliers*

Plantrite, Woodside Nursery, Long Wittenham, Abingdon, Oxfordshire, OX14 4PT Tel: (01865) 407337 Fax: (0870) 6094684 *Floral display contractors*

Plantronics Ltd, Interface Business Park, Binknoll Lane, Wootton Bassett, Swindon, SN4 8QQ Tel: (01793) 842200 Fax: (01793) 848853 *Communication systems manufrs*

▶ Plants With Pots Ltd, 26 Ipswich Gardens, Grantham, Lincolnshire, NG31 8SE Tel: (01476) 565634 Fax: (01476) 565634 E-mail: mj@plantswithpots.com *We supply quality interior and exterior planting to the commercial sector throughout the midlands. We carry out on-going maintenance contracts to the interior planting and also supply a full exterior grounds maintenance service.*

Plantscape, The Dower House, Decker Hill, Shifnal, Shropshire, TF11 8QL Tel: (01952) 462582 *Floral & plant displays contractors*

Plantz Floral & Plant Displays, S The Enterprise Centre, Hastings Road, Bromley, BR2 8NA Tel: (020) 8249 0709 *Commercial landscapers*

▶ Planwell Roofing Supplies Ltd, The Roofing Centre, March Road East, Buckie, Banffshire, AB56 4BY Tel: (01542) 832170 Fax: (01542) 832182 E-mail: sales@planwell.co.uk

Planworld Computers Ltd, 1 Farnham Road, Guildford, Surrey, GU2 4RG Tel: (01483) 549888 Fax: (01483) 549100 E-mail: kellysearch@planworld.co.uk *Not a hardware supplier but a SME company based in Guildford providing strategic Consultancy, Custom Development & Outsourcing Inshore solutions to clients in both the financial & commercial world who are looking to maintain or advance from their current market position. We see ourselves as your partner in the transformation & implementation of your requirements into a successful solution. Our experience, skills & knowledge enables us to quickly understand your aims & aspirations, translating them using tried & tested methodologies & structures into workable solutions acceptable to in-house procedures, concepts & practices*

Plas Equestrian, Plas Y Mista Farm, Rhydargaeau Road, Rhydargaeau, Carmarthen, Dyfed, SA32 7JJ Tel: (01267) 253251 Fax: (01267) 253251 E-mail: sales@plasequestrian.co.uk *Saddlers & riding wear manufrs*

Plas Heat, 33 Cramlington Road, Birmingham, B42 2EE Tel: 0121-357 5077 Fax: 0121-358 1377 E-mail: plasheat@yahoo.co.uk *Industrial heating elements distributor & manufrs*

Plas Tech Windows Ltd, Unit 1-2 Silverwood, Snow Hill, Crawley Down, Crawley, West Sussex, RH10 3EN Tel: (01342) 717714 Fax: (01342) 717715 *Double glazing installers*

▶ Plas Tech Windows, Whitegate House, White Lund Industrial Estate, Morecambe, Lancashire, LA3 3BS Tel: (01524) 849170 Fax: (01524) 846929 *Doors & windows*

▶ Plas Tek, Delamare Road, Cheshunt, Waltham Cross, Hertfordshire, EN8 9SB Tel: (01992) 781800 Fax: (01992) 781811 E-mail: info@plas-tek.co.uk *Packaging equipment manufrs*

Plasart Ltd, Chilton Industrial Estate, Windham Road, Sudbury, Suffolk, CO10 2XD Tel: (01787) 375641 Fax: (01787) 311041 *PVC loose leaf binder manufrs*

Plasbrun Plastics Engineering Ltd, Unit C, Brookfield Drive, Cannock, Staffordshire, WS11 0JR Tel: (01543) 462802 Fax: (01543) 462806 E-mail: plasbrunplastics@yahoo.co.uk *Plastics fabricators*

Plascolour Ltd, Unit 1 Sherrington Way, Basingstoke, Hampshire, RG22 4DQ Tel: (01256) 470303 Fax: (01256) 817207 E-mail: plascolour@compuserve.com *Plastic raw material suppliers & processors*

Plascore (UK), PO Box 2, Cheltenham, Gloucestershire, GL54 5YR Tel: (0871) 918 1525 Fax: (0871) 918 1525 E-mail: info@coretexgroup.co.uk *Manufacturers of energy absorbtion elements, honeycomb core (structural), NXT Speaker Panels, Clean Room Wall Systems*

Plascut Stainless, Coleford Road, Darnall, Sheffield, S9 5PJ Tel: 0114-251 9535 Fax: 0114-251 9536 E-mail: sheffield.zi2@centers.co.uk *Stainless steel profile suppliers*

Plas-Dent Co. Ltd, Middlemore Road, Smethwick, West Midlands, B66 2DQ Tel: 0121-558 3601 Fax: 0121-555 5567 E-mail: richard@plas-dent.co.uk *Dental suppliers*

Plasian Products, Alkincote Street, Unit 5, Keighley, West Yorkshire, BD21 5JT Tel: (01535) 681975 Fax: (01535) 611471 *Industrial hand wheels manufrs*

Plaskett Protective Equipment, 10 Robert Street, Scunthorpe, South Humberside, DN15 6LU Tel: (01724) 871750 Fax: (01724) 874941 *Industrial equipment services & military clothing, camping equipment*

Plaslant Ltd, Unit 154-156 Block 17, Newhouse Industrial Estate, Newhouse, Motherwell, Lanarkshire, ML1 5RX Tel: (01698) 732009 Fax: (01698) 732106 E-mail: plaslant@aol.com *Plastics injection mould makers*

▶ Plaslyne, Unit D Stafford Park 7, Telford, Shropshire, TF3 3BQ Tel: (01952) 292511 Fax: (01952) 292025 *Plastic product suppliers*

Plasma Biotal Ltd, 1 Meverill Road, Tideswell, Buxton, Derbyshire, SK17 8PY Tel: (01298) 872348 Fax: (01298) 873708 E-mail: general@plasma-group.co.uk *Manufacturers of hydroxylapatite & coatings*

Plasma Coatings Ltd, 3 Meverill Road, Tideswell, Buxton, Derbyshire, SK17 8PY Tel: (01298) 873700 Fax: (01298) 873708 E-mail: info@plasma-group.co.uk *Metal & plasma spraying contractors*

Plasma & Thermal Coating Ltd, Unit 20 Maesglas Industrial Estate, Newport, Gwent, NP20 2NN Tel: (01633) 245600 Fax: (01633) 245601 E-mail: sales@plasmacoat.co.uk *Plasma & Thermal Coatings Ltd offers: full production coating services, coating development, application engineering and technology transfer. Specialist technologies include....HVOF, Plasma, Arc, and combustion spray coating processes.....Accreditation: BS EN ISO 9002:1994, and ISO 14001: 1996, RR 9000:SABRe.*

Plasman Laminate Products Ltd, Plasman Industrial Centre, Marquis Street, Manchester, M19 3JH Tel: 0161-224 0330 Fax: 0161-224 9961 E-mail: info@plasman.co.uk *Laminate & worktop distributors*

Plasmech Packaging Ltd, Unit 27 Cam Centre, Wilbury Way, Hitchin, Hertfordshire, SG4 0TW Tel: (01462) 432525 Fax: (01462) 432124 E-mail: derek@plasmechpackaging.co.uk *Polyethylene & polythene packaging & refuse sacks manufrs*

Plasmold Plastics Ltd, 8-11 Oak Industrial Park, Chelmsford Road, Dunmow, Essex, CM6 1XN Tel: (01371) 876445 Fax: (01371) 876874 E-mail: lee@plasmoldplastics.co.uk *Plastic injection moulders*

Plasmold Precision, Knightsbridge Gardens, Romford, RM7 9AD Tel: (01371) 876445 Fax: (01708) 732691 E-mail: lee@plasmoldplastics.co.uk *Plastic injection moulders & toolmakers*

Plasmon Data Systems, Whiting Way, Melbourn, Royston, Hertfordshire, SG8 6EN Tel: (01763) 261516 Fax: (01763) 264444 E-mail: sales@plasmon.co.uk *Data storage solution producers*

Plasmor Ltd, Womersley Road, Knottingley, West Yorkshire, WF11 0DN Tel: (01977) 673221 Fax: (01977) 607071 E-mail: sales@plasmor.co.uk *Concrete building block manufrs* Also at: Aycliffe, Biggleswade, London E1 & Widnes

▶ Plasmor Halton Ltd, Tanhouse Lane, Widnes, Cheshire, WA8 0SQ Tel: 0151-423 1161 Fax: 0151-495 1015

Plasmotec, F Lincoln Park, Ward Road, Buckingham Road Industrial Estate, Brackley, Northamptonshire, NN13 7LE Tel: (01280) 701335 Fax: (01280) 701341 E-mail: sales@plasmotec.co.uk *Plastics injection mouldings manufrs*

Plaspertex Paint Co. Ltd, 71 Mereside, Soham, Ely, Cambridgeshire, CB7 5EE Tel: (01353) 720796 Fax: (01353) 624327 E-mail: mail@plaspertex.co.uk *Paint manufrs*

Plasplant Ltd, Unit 4 Oakhanger Farm, Oakhanger, Bordon, Hampshire, GU35 9JA Tel: (01420) 473013 Fax: (01420) 475152 E-mail: sales@plasplant.com Purchasing Contact: K. Simpson Sales Contact: B. Simpson Principal Export Areas: Asia Pacific & Middle East *Plastic extrusions.*

Plasson UK Ltd, Plasson House, 27 Albert Drive, Burgess Hill, West Sussex, RH15 9TW Tel: (01444) 244446 Fax: (01444) 258683 E-mail: sales@plasson.co.uk *Plastic water fittings distributors*

Plastal Commercial Ltd, Alders Way, Paignton, Devon, TQ4 7QE Tel: (01803) 697111 Fax: (01803) 559619 *Window frame maintenance & repair*

Plastec Engineering Developments, 14 Bennerley Avenue, Ilkeston, Derbyshire, DE7 8PF Tel: 0115-932 4422 Fax: 0115-932 4422 *Plastic engineering*

Plastech, 4 Ricebridge Works, Brighton Road, Bolney, Haywards Heath, West Sussex, RH17 5NA Tel: (01444) 881960 Fax: (01444) 881244 *Injection moulders*

Plastech Group Ltd, Flemington Road, Glenrothes, Fife, KY7 5PZ Tel: (01592) 752212 Fax: (01592) 610315 E-mail: sales@plastechgroup.com *Plastic injection mouldings manufrs*

Plastech Precision Moulders, 31 Ivatt Way, Peterborough, PE3 7PH Tel: (01733) 266116 Fax: (01733) 266134 E-mail: sales@plastech-mld.freeserve.co.uk *Injection mouldings manufrs*

Plastech Print Ltd, Debdale Lane, Keyworth, Nottingham, NG12 5HN Tel: 0115-937 4041 Fax: 0115-937 3426 E-mail: sales@plastechprint.co.uk *Plastic badge & plastic printing services key fob manufrs*

Plastengrave Ltd, Unit 29 77-87 Trafalgar Business Centre, River Road, Barking, Essex, IG11 0JU Tel: (020) 8591 2595 Fax: (020) 8594 0459 E-mail: sales@plastengrave.co.uk *Sign installers & manufrs*

Plaster Elegance, Suite 1 Watling Chambers, 214 Watling Street, Bridgtown, Cannock, Staffordshire, WS11 0BD Tel: (01543) 466362 Fax: (01543) 466362 *Ornate plaster manufrs*

▶ Plaster Products, 319 Pleck Road, Walsall, WS2 9HA Tel: (01922) 633774

Plastestrip Profiles Ltd, Trenance Mill, St. Austell, Cornwall, PL25 5LZ Tel: (01726) 74771 Fax: (01726) 69238 E-mail: sales@plaspro.force9.co.uk *Stockists of plastic or aluminium extrusions for cladding and construction. Full range of fixings and adhesives.*

Plastic Art Company, Unit 7 Glover Way, Leeds, LS11 5JP Tel: 0113-271 7744 Fax: 0113-271 9590 *Print finishers*

Plastic Art Co., Unit 6f Hewlett House, 5 Havelock Terrace, London, SW8 4AS Tel: (020) 7627 1976 Fax: (020) 7498 2369 E-mail: london@plastic-art.co.uk *Print laminating in capsulators* Also at: Leeds & Manchester

Plastic Associates Ltd, Unit 1 North Street Trading Estate, Brierley Hill, West Midlands, DY5 3QF Tel: (01384) 480470 Fax: (01384) 480470 *Injection & plastic mouldings manufrs*

Plastic Bottle Supplies Ltd, 6 Boundary Industrial Estate, Stafford Road, Wolverhampton, WV10 7EL Tel: (01902) 397397 Fax: (01902) 397666 E-mail: sales@plasticbottlesupplies.co.uk *We offer a quality efficient and reliable service. We have a vast range of plastic bottles, plastic containers & plastic closures for all trades & purposes. We offer both our Standard range of products and Custom moulding facilities. Our range includes Detergent bottles, Household chemical Containers. Lubricating oil containers, Chemical containers, Confectionery & food containers, Toiletries bottles & containers. Health & beauty bottles & containers. D.I.Y. containers, Plastic Intermediate bulk containers (IBC), Plastic dispensing bottles, HDPE bottles, LDPE bottles, PP bottles, PVC bottles, and much more. Plastic Bottle Supplies Ltd adding power to your organisation.*

Plastic Card Design Services Ltd, 15 Bramshill Ave, Kettering, Northamptonshire, NN16 9FL Tel: (01536) 410557 Fax: (01536) 510509 E-mail: info@plasticcardsuk.com *Plastic Card Design Services have established itself as a reliable and efficient supplier of Plastic Card Printers and Plastic Cards. We have supplied Plastic Card Printers and Plastic Cards for producing Photo ID Cards, Membership Cards, Training Certification Cards, Event & Conference Badges, Swipe Cards and many many more *Operating from our Northamptonshire location, we cover the United Kingdom and can supply into Europe and Worldwide.*We are Resellers of the popular Zebra Card Printer Products and have recently introduced the Fargo Card Printer range. As well as supplying the Zebra and Fargo Card Printer units we also supply from stock a full range of ribbons, blank cards and cleaning materials.* Pre-printed cards can be produced by digital or litho processes and then thermally printed and encoded by our Bureau Service. Lanyards, Card Holders, Clips etc can be supplied for applications where the card has to be visible. For further information,*

Plastic Card Imaging Ltd, 2 Rose Villa, Bressingham Road, Roydon, Diss, Norfolk, IP22 5XW Tel: (01379) 688344 *Identification cards equipment distributors*

The Plastic Card Shop, Kemps Place, Selborne Road, Greatham, Liss, Hampshire, GU33 6HG Tel: (0845) 6448171 Fax: (0845) 2260814 E-mail: sales@theplasticcardshop.co.uk *PVC plastic card manufrs*

Plastic Coatings, Pontymister Industrial Estate, Risca, Newport, Gwent, NP11 6NP Tel: (0845) 6120333 Fax: (01633) 612320 E-mail: enquiries@plastic-coatings.com *Plastic Coatings Ltd can supply all your coating requirements, from electrostatic * dip powder coatings, PTFE & electropaint from our 3 factories - Midlands, South Wales, SE England*

Plastic Data Card Ltd, Unit 1lg Dajen Business Park, Second Avenue, Chatham, Kent, ME4 5AU Tel: (01634) 811455 Fax: (01634) 831080 E-mail: sales@plasticdatacard.co.uk *Plastic cards manufrs*

▶ Plastic Design Solutions Ltd, 80 Church Road, Stockton-on-Tees, Cleveland, TS18 1TW Tel: (01642) 671711 Fax: (01642) 671762 E-mail: admin@plastic-design-solutions. freeserve.co.uk *Product Design, Manufacturing and Engineering Consultants. FEA and Mould Filling (Flow). Light machining,manufacture.*

Plastic Development Techniques Ltd, Lyon Way, St. Albans, Hertfordshire, AL4 0LB Tel: (01727) 866317 Fax: (01727) 847060 *Plastic injection moulding manufrs*

Plastic Development Techniques Ltd, Unit 4, Block 2 Wednesbury Trading Estate, Darlaston Road, Wednesbury, West Midlands, WS10 7JN Tel: 0121-556 9966 Fax: 0121-556 0208 E-mail: charles@pdt-ltd.freeserve.co.uk *Disposable plastic tableware & plastic mouldings manufrs*

▶ Plastic Enclosures Ltd, Unit 24, Broughton Grounds, Broughton, Milton Keynes, Newport Pagnell, MK16 0HZ Tel: (01908) 676560 Fax: (01908) 200148 E-mail: info@evatron.com *Plastic & metal enclosures for the electrical & electronic markets*

Plastic Engineering Ltd, Juno Drive, Leamington Spa, Warwickshire, CV31 3TA Tel: (01926) 334248 Fax: (01926) 461720 E-mail: plastic@pels.co.uk *Injection mouldings, plastic & thermo plastic mouldings manufrs*

Plastic Fabrications Ltd, Unit 12 Newstead Industrial Park, Hazelford Way, Newstead Village, Nottingham, NG15 0DQ Tel: (01623) 720400 Fax: (01623) 720800 E-mail: fabrications@btconnect.com *Manufacturers of machine guards*

Plastic Fabrications (1991), Unit 10, Bickford Road, Aston, Birmingham, B6 7EE Tel: (0121) 327 1013 Fax: (0121) 326 6139 *Fume extraction plant manufrs*

Plastic Facilities, Fen End, Stotfold, Hitchin, Hertfordshire, SG5 4BA Tel: (01462) 832832 Fax: (01462) 832830 E-mail: sales@plasticfacilities.co.uk *Based on the Bedfordshire Hertfordshire border, covering the whole of > the UK, we supply plastic fabrications to many industries such as > Chemical, Food, Printed circuit board, Electroplating, Water > purification and many more, these fabrications include Holding Tanks, > Catchment Trays, Feed Hoppers, Machine Guarding and Fume Extraction > systems in a wide range of industrial plastics. A bespoke machining > service is also available. Being established since 1972 we have a > level of expertise that is unsurpassed.*

Plastic Formers Ltd, Unit 1, King Street, Stockport Road, Denton, Manchester, M34 6PF Tel: 0161-320 7200 Fax: 0161-335 0109 E-mail: enquiries@plasticformers.co.uk *Plastic fabricators & stockists*

▶ The Plastic Handrail Co. Ltd, Unit 6 Bessemer Park, 250 Milkwood Road, London, SE24 0HG Tel: (020) 7924 9444 Fax: (020) 7737 6377 *Supply & fitting a quality plastic handrail*

Plastic Machining Services, Halesfield 23, Telford, Shropshire, TF7 4NY Tel: (01952) 680369 Fax: (01952) 680371 E-mail: info@p-m-s.co.uk *CNC engineering services & plastic machinists*

Plastic Merchant Ltd, 10 Church Street, Brighton, BN1 1US Tel: (01273) 329958 Fax: (01273) 329958 *Plastic materials stockists & distributors*

Plastic & Metal Engravings, 9 Benson Road, Poole, Dorset, BH17 0GB Tel: (01202) 677393 Fax: (01202) 681455 E-mail: sales@plasticandmetalengraving.co.uk *Machine engravers of plastic & metals to the industry*

Plastic Metal & Profiles Ltd, Unit 99 14 North Tyne Industrial Estate, Whitley Road, Benton, Newcastle upon Tyne, NE12 9SZ Tel: 0191-266 5050 Fax: 0191-266 5724 E-mail: sales@pmpnameplates.co.uk *Machine engraved printed nameplates manufrs*

▶ Plastic Mouldings Ltd, 4 Ailsa Road, Irvine Industrial Estate, Irvine, Ayrshire, KA12 8LP Tel: (01294) 278091 Fax: (01294) 311655 E-mail: info@plasticmouldings.com *Latex dipped mouldings & plastic vacuum formed products manufacturers. Also manufacturers of rubber bellows, neoprene rubber, plastic dip mouldings, plastic rotational mouldings & rubber dipped products*

Plastic Moulds Designs Kingston Ltd, Drake Road, Mitcham, Surrey, CR4 4HQ Tel: (020) 8640 0064 Fax: (020) 8640 0371 E-mail: terry.behing@pmdltd.com *Plastic injection mouldings manufrs*

The Plastic Mountain UK Ltd, Oakwood BSNS Park, Stephenson Road West, Clacton-on-Sea, Essex, CO15 4TL Tel: (01255) 221534 Fax: (01255) 476817 E-mail: info@mantair.com *Septic tank manufrs*

Plastic Parts Centre, Unit 2 St. Lukes Business Estate, St. Luke'S Place, Glasgow, G5 0TS Tel: 0141-420 3806 Fax: 0141-420 3806 E-mail: scotlandsales@plastic-parts.co.uk *Warehouse distribution of plastics*

Plastic Parts Centre, Unit 4, Harelaw Industrial Estate, Annfield Plain, Stanley, County Durham, DH9 8HN Tel: (01207) 290599 Fax: (01207) 299718 E-mail: newcastlesales@plastic-parts.co.uk Purchasing Contact: Clive Scott *Manufacturers & distributors of pipe caps, flange protection, general protection parts, finishing components, hardware, castors, fasteners & fixings, electrical cable fixings, packaging /security parts & masking protection. In addition we also supply custom moulding within our manufacturing facitlity.*

Plastic Parts Centre, Unit 12 Old Forge Trading Estate, Dudley Road, Stourbridge, West Midlands, DY9 8EL Tel: (01384) 424248 Fax: (01384) 424348 E-mail: sales@mossplastics.co.uk *Plastic moulding distributors*

Plastic Parts Centre, New Road, Ridgewood, Uckfield, East Sussex, TN22 5SX Tel: (0845) 7585070 Fax: (01825) 762621 E-mail: sales@plastic-parts.co.uk *Manufacturers & distributors of plastic*

Plastic Parts Direct Ltd, Thorpe Way, Banbury, Oxfordshire, OX16 4SP Tel: (01295) 269333 Fax: (01295) 273276 E-mail: info@apmonline.co.uk Principal Export Areas: Worldwide *Plastic mouldings manufrs*

Plastic Pipe Manufacturers Society, 89 Cornwall Street, Birmingham, B3 3BY Tel: 0121-236 1866 Fax: 0121-200 1389 E-mail: sales@wenhammajor.co.uk *Trade association*

Plastic Products International Ltd, 8-11 Capital Place, Harlow, Essex, CM19 5AS Tel: (01279) 445041 Fax: (08704) 601340 E-mail: sales@plastics-products.net *Plastic mouldings manufrs*

Plastic Promotions, Unit 1 Carn Industrial Area, Portadown, Craigavon, County Armagh, BT63 5YY Tel: (028) 3835 6600 Fax: (028) 3835 6601 E-mail: gilbert@plasticpromotion.co.uk *Plastic welding equipment manufrs*

Plastic Rework Solutions Ltd, Unit 9a Castle Mill Works, birmingham New Road, Dudley, West Midlands, DY1 4DA Tel: (01384) 211169 E-mail: prs01384@btconnect.com *plastic /metal work rework company, for all rework solutions.*

Plastic Sensor Technology Ltd, 1 Vicarage Lane, The Bourne, Farnham, Surrey, GU9 8HN Tel: (01252) 724110 Fax: (01252) 716110 E-mail: pingpoint@btinternet.com *Acoustic transducers*

Plastic Sheet Services, Unit 4, 270 Lakey La, Birmingham, B28 8RA Tel: 0121-777 0322 Fax: 0121-777 8987 E-mail: hewston@aol.com *Plastic sheet stockholders/suppliers, fabricators & manufacturers*

Plastic Shims & Gaskets Co. Ltd, 49-53 Glengall Road, Peckham, London, SE15 6NF Tel: (020) 7740 9705 Fax: (020) 7635 9791 E-mail: sales@psggroup.co.uk Principal Export Areas: Worldwide *Gasket, insulator component & shim manufrs*

Plastic Tanks & Fabrications Ltd, Unit 5, Stone Lane Industrial Estate, Wimborne, Dorset, BH21 1HD Tel: (01202) 888133 Fax: (01202) 886288 E-mail: ptf@avnet.co.uk *Liquid storage tanks*

Plastic Technology Service Ltd, Flamstone Street, Bishopstone, Salisbury, SP5 4BZ Tel: (01722) 781088 Fax: (01722) 781071 E-mail: info@ptsuk.com *Plastics distributors*

Plastic Treatments Ltd, Cleggs Lane Mill, Seddon Street, Little Hulton, Manchester, M38 9RN Tel: 0161-799 1039 Fax: 0161-703 8671 *Plastics coating services*

▶ Plastic Village Ltd, Unit A, 126 Rickmansworth Road, Watford, WD18 7AA Tel: (01923) 244577

▶ Plastic Welded Containers Ltd, The Cottage, Alcester Road, Spernal Ash, Studley, Warwickshire, B80 7PD Tel: (01527) 598848 Fax: (01527) 598848 *Plastic Fabricators*

Plastica Ltd, Perimeter House, Napier Road, St. Leonards-On-Sea, East Sussex, TN38 9NY Tel: (01424) 857857 Fax: (01424) 857858 E-mail: info@plastica.ltd.uk *Swimming pool equipment manufrs*

Plasticable Ltd, Unit 3 Riverwey Industrial Park, Newton Lane, Alton, Hants, GU34 2QL Tel: (01420) 80911 Fax: (01420) 80922 E-mail: sales@plasticable.co.uk Sales Contact: B. Cotter *Plastic coating, insulating & extrusion services*

▶ Plasticlad Double Glazing Installers, 20 Bracken Close, Huntington, York, YO32 9NZ Tel: (01904) 763907 Fax: (01904) 763907 E-mail: plasticlad@btinternet.com *Fitting Fascias,Guttering Cladding, Car Ports, Door Canopies, E.P.D.M flat roofing, Fitted Kitchens and Double Glazing.*

Plastico Ltd, 100 Morden Road, Mitcham, Surrey, CR4 4DA Tel: (020) 8646 0456 Fax: (020) 8646 0500 E-mail: sales@plastico.co.uk *Plastico is a specialist in the design, development and manufacture of catering accessories for the foodservice and retail markets. The company was founded in 1947 and was originally set up as an importer. It then entered the manufacturing arena in the late 60s, with injection moulded products.* Today Plastico combines a mix of manufacturing and manufacturing alliances to meet the needs of a diverse range of customers. Through this experience and knowledge Plastico is able to offer a varied range of products and services including disposable cutlery, tumblers, accessories and catering workwear.*

▶ Plasticom Ltd, Hilton Road, Cobbs Wood Industrial Estate, Ashford, Kent, TN23 1EW Tel: (01233) 621604 Fax: (01233) 622169 E-mail: enquiries@plasticomgroup.com *Injection mould toolmakers*

Plasticon, 7 Dunlop Way, Queensway Industrial Estate, Scunthorpe, South Humberside, DN16 3RN Tel: (01724) 855036 Fax: (01724) 872526 E-mail: sales@plasticon.co.uk *Engineers in re-enforced plastics* Also at: Beverley

Plasticon (U K) Ltd, Grovehill Industrial Estate, Beverley, North Humberside, HU17 0JT Tel: (01482) 862194 Fax: (01482) 871398 E-mail: sales@plasticon.co.uk *Manufacturers of glassfibre reinforced plastic*

Plasticotta, Union Road, Bolton, BL2 2HL Tel: (01204) 381991 Fax: (01204) 528863 *PVC coated fabric suppliers*

Plasticraft Ltd, Godiva Place, Coventry, CV1 5PN Tel: (024) 7625 3099 Fax: (024) 7655 1402 E-mail: sales@plasticraft.co.uk *Plastic fabricators & tank manufrs*

Plastics & Engineering Co., Unit 8-9 Merretts Mill, Bath Road, Woodchester, Stroud, Gloucestershire, GL5 5EX Tel: (01453) 836206 Fax: (01453) 836245 E-mail: sales@plastics-machining.com *Plastics engineering plastics machining & prototype design*

continued

Plastics For Games Ltd, Riverside View, Wickham Market, Woodbridge, Suffolk, IP13 0TA Tel: (01728) 745300 Fax: (01728) 745309 E-mail: sales@plasticsforgames.co.uk *Manufacturers of dice & game components*

Plastics Manchester Ltd, Plasman Industrial Centre, Peter Moss Way, Manchester, M19 3PX Tel: 0161-257 2929 Fax: 0161-257 3203 E-mail: info@thompson-plastics-group.co.uk *Manufacturers of caravan fittings & plastic vacuum formed products*

Plastics Software Ltd, Unit 1, Farmcroft, Farnham Lane, Haslemere, Surrey, GU27 1HD Tel: (01428) 656595 Fax: (01428) 656595 E-mail: sales@plasware.co.uk *Software house for plastics industry*

Plastics Solutions Ltd, 25 St. Martins Road, Upton, Poole, Dorset, BH16 5NQ Tel: (01202) 623598 Fax: (01202) 623598 E-mail: alan@plastics-solutions.com *Plastics consultants & manufacturers agents*

Plastics Stockholder Ltd, Unit 4 Cullwick Street, Wolverhampton, WV1 2UL Tel: (01902) 404145 Fax: (01902) 404858 E-mail: sales@plasticsstockholder.co.uk *Conservatory roofs*

Plastics & Veneers Sales Ltd, Stronghold House, 43 Fourth Street, Kirkdale, Liverpool, L20 8NL Tel: 0151-944 7150 Fax: 0151-944 7157 E-mail: sales@plasticsandveneers.co.uk *Veneered panel manufrs*

Plastics W Graham Ltd, 114 Cowgate, Dundee, DD1 2JU Tel: (01382) 223734 Fax: (01382) 201799 E-mail: sales@pwgsigns.com *Safety signs, general engravers & fabricators*

Plasticum UK Ltd, 2 Bramble Way, Clover Nook Industrial Park, Somercotes, Alfreton, Derbyshire, DE55 4RH Tel: (01773) 833866 Fax: (01773) 520085 *Plastic cap manufrs*

▶ Plastidip UK, Unit 1, Harvesting Lane, East Meon, Petersfield, Hampshire, GU32 1QR Tel: (01730) 823823 Fax: (01730) 823321 E-mail: info@plastidip.co.uk *Import & retail*

Plastiflex UK Ltd, Ripley Close, Normanton Industrial Estate, Normanton, West Yorkshire, WF6 1TB Tel: (01924) 783600 Fax: (01924) 896715 E-mail: info@plastiflex.co.uk Purchasing Contact: A. Blair Sales Contact: D. Carter Principal Export Areas: Worldwide *Manufacturers of flexible tubing (including plastic) & conduits*

Plastigauge, Unit 2, Gaugemaster Way, Ford, Arundel, West Sussex, BN18 0RX Tel: (01903) 882822 Fax: (01903) 884962 E-mail: sales@plastigauge.co.uk Purchasing Contact: L. Harwood Sales Contact: Sarah Harwood Principal Export Areas: Asia Pacific, Central Asia, Africa, Central/East Europe, West Europe & North America *Manufacturers of bearing measurement gauges, precision inspection/measurement & gauges, automotive bearing*

Plastimo Ltd, Hamilton Business Park, Botley Road, Hedgend, Southampton, SO30 2HE Tel: (01489) 778850 Fax: (0870) 7511950 E-mail: sales@plastimo.co.uk *Marine equipment distributor*

Plastisigns, Oak Tre Farm, Escrick Road, Wheldrake, York, YO19 6BQ Tel: (01904) 449970 Fax: (01904) 449970 E-mail: plastisigns@supanet.com *Sign & display specialists*

Plastmo Profiles Ltd, Lower Farm Road, Moulton Park Industrial Estate, Northampton, NN3 6XF Tel: (01604) 790780 Fax: (01604) 790110 E-mail: info@plastmo.co.uk *Window systems manufrs*

Plastohm Technical Parts UK Ltd, Unit 4 Sunrise Enterprise Park, Ferryboat Lane, Sunderland, SR5 3RX Tel: 0191-549 4531 Fax: 0191-549 2891 *Plastic injection moulders*

Plastohm UK Ltd, Unit 2 Pacemanor Centre, Bellbrook Industrial Estate, Uckfield, East Sussex, TN22 1YA Tel: (01825) 768812 Fax: (01825) 768780 E-mail: jsaleuk@plastohm.com *Plastic container distributors*

Plastok Associates Ltd, 79 Market Street, Birkenhead, Merseyside, CH41 6AN Tel: 0151-666 2056 Fax: 0151-650 0073 E-mail: sales@plastok.co.uk *Manufacturers of filter leaves*

Plastotype Ltd, Crustable Close, Mushep Industrial Park, Coleford, Gloucestershire, GL16 8RE Tel: (01594) 837474 Fax: (01594) 837312 E-mail: info@plastotype.com *Stereotype printing plate services*

Plastribution Ltd, Glenbervie Business Centre, Glenbervie Business Park, Larbert, Stirlingshire, FK5 4RB Tel: (01324) 682105 Fax: (01324) 682106 E-mail: sales@plastribution.co.uk *Plastics raw materials distributor*

Plastube Ltd, The Old Foundry, Leech Street, Stalybridge, Cheshire, SK15 1SD Tel: 0161-338 5505 Fax: 0161-338 5502 E-mail: admin@plastube.co.uk *Cable gland manufrs*

▶ Plasurf Engineering, Park Farm, Feckenham Road, Hanbury, Bromsgrove, Worcestershire, B60 4DH Tel: (01527) 821038 Fax: (01527) 821038 E-mail: vic@plasurf.co.uk *Specialised welding & metal spray services*

▶ Plasvent Constructions, 22 Clausen Way, Pennington, Lymington, Hampshire, SO41 8BJ Tel: (01590) 678959 Fax: (01590) 688654

▶ Plasware, Plasware House, Westmoreland Road, Kingsbury, London, NW9 9RN Tel: (020) 8621 2611 E-mail: info@plaswareuk.com *Disposable catering & food packaging products*

Plates A Plenty, 78 Glebe Road, Minchinhampton, Stroud, Gloucestershire, GL6 9LQ Tel: (01453) 882051 Fax: (01453) 882051 *Catering equipment hirers*

Platform, Lift House, Gloucester Road, Almondsbury, Bristol, BS32 4HY Tel: (01454) 270705 Fax: (01454) 312497 E-mail: info@platformcompany.co.uk *Access platform hire*

▶ The Platform Co., Knowsley Industrial Estate Nor, Kirkby, Liverpool, L33 7SA Tel: 0151-549 2223

▶ Platform Co. Ltd, Don Pedro Avenue, Normanton Industrial Estate, Normanton, West Yorkshire, WF6 1TD Tel: (01924) 893250 Fax: (01924) 898855 E-mail: sales@platformcompany.co.uk *Powered access machinery rental & sales*

▶ Platform44, Sparkhouse Studios, Rope Walk, Lincoln, LN6 7DQ Tel: (01522) 837241 Fax: (01522) 837201 E-mail: projects@platform44.com *Platform44 Design Consultancy**Services include:*Product Design, *Point of Sale Design,*Packaging Design,*Furniture Design, *3D Visualisation and Animation, **Add value, identity and distinctiveness to your projects *Re enforce your identity *Build and establish your brand *Exploit design to access new markets *Develop new product opportunities *Visualise your project quickly at a competitive price *Win new clients and gain more business**

Plating Company Ltd, The, Curriers Cl, Canley, Coventry, CV4 8AW Tel: (024) 7647 0545 Fax: (024) 7669 4120 E-mail: crplating@btconnect.com *Zinc plating specialists*

▶ Platinum A V Ltd, Ground Floor, 131 Reading Road, Henley-on-Thames, Oxfordshire, RG9 1DJ Tel: (01491) 575100 Fax: (0870) 9506590 E-mail: info@avlamps.co.uk *Projector lamps & bulbs suppliers*

▶ Platinum Accident Repair Centre, Cheltenham Street, Bath, BA2 3EX Tel: (01225) 448590 Fax: (01225) 443098 *Car accident repairs*

▶ Platinum Chauffeurs, 42 Church Street, Needingworth, St. Ives, Cambridgeshire, PE27 4TB Tel: (01480) 463777 E-mail: info@platinumdrive.co.uk *Executive chauffeur and Private hire service, Airport transfers, corporate meetings, Conference, exhibitions, Special letter/parcel Service,Wedding Support Service.Vehicle transportation. All your transport needs catered for.*

Platinum Computer Consultants Ltd, Woodfield Way, Redhill, RH1 2DP Tel: (01737) 789555 E-mail: sales@platinumcc.co.uk *Computer consultants*

▶ Platinum Construction, 31 Cavern Road, Torquay, TQ1 1NS Tel: (01803) 405332 *Paving company, Groundworks*

Platinum Engineering & Fabrications Ltd, National Avenue Ind Estate, Hull, HU5 4HF Tel: 01482 446123 *Storage tank & sheet metal work manufrs*

▶ Platinum Motor Group, 16-17 The Causeway, Chippenham, Wiltshire, SN15 3DA Tel: (01249) 654321 Fax: (01249) 462683 E-mail: platinum.chippenham.sales@net.vauxhall.co.uk *Car dealers & garage services*

▶ Platinum Nissan, Meridian Motor Park, North Bradley, Trowbridge, Wiltshire, BA14 0BJ Tel: (01225) 759510 Fax: (01225) 759501 E-mail: d17115man@uk.nissan.biz *Car dealers & garage services, parts*

▶ Platinum Nissan Box, St Martins Garage, Bath Road, Box, Corsham, Wiltshire, SN13 8AE Tel: (01225) 744444 Fax: (01225) 744477 E-mail: sales@platinumnissan.co.uk *Car dealers & Garage services*

▶ Platinum Permanent Recruitment, 1 Emperor Way, Exeter Business Park, Exeter, EX1 3QS Tel: (01392) 314053 Fax: (01392) 314224 E-mail: rayseo@gmail.com

▶ Platinum Print Ltd, Park House, Hookstone Park, Harrogate, North Yorkshire, HG2 7DB Tel: (01423) 881158 Fax: (01423) 886072 E-mail: sales@platinumprint.com *Printers*

▶ Platinum Renault, Meridian Business Park, North Bradley, Trowbridge, Wiltshire, BA14 0BJ Tel: (01225) 759525 Fax: (01225) 759526

▶ Platinum Renault Bath, Lower Bristol Road, Bath, BA2 3DN Tel: (01225) 485410 Fax: (01225) 338653 *Car dealers & Garage services*

▶ Platinum Renault Chippenham, London Road, Chippenham, Wiltshire, SN15 3BB Tel: (01249) 651131 Fax: (01249) 658813 *Car dealers & Garage services*

▶ Platinum Scaffolding, 28 Barnet Lane, Barnet, Hertfordshire, EN5 2DN Tel: (020) 8447 0957 E-mail: platinumscaffolding@yahoo.co.uk *Scaffolding services*

▶ Platinum Skoda, Lower Bristol Road, Bath, BA2 3DR Tel: (01225) 324910 Fax: (01225) 324919 E-mail: enquiries@platinumskoda.co.uk *Car dealers & Garage services**

▶ Platinum Toyota, Meridian Motor Park, North Bradley, Trowbridge, Wiltshire, BA14 0BJ Tel: (01225) 759560 Fax: (01225) 759551 *Car dealers & garage services*

▶ Platinum Toyota Bath, Lower Bristol Road, Bath, BA2 3DN Tel: (01225) 486200 Fax: (01225) 420815 E-mail: im-pb@platinum.toyota.co.uk *Car dealers & Garage services*

▶ Platinum Vauxhall, 8 Meridian Business Park, North Bradley, Trowbridge, Wiltshire, BA14 0BJ Tel: (01225) 759585 Fax: (01225) 759576 *Car dealers, garage services & vehicle repairs*

▶ Platinum Vauxhall Frome, Manor Road, Marston Trading Estate, Warminster, Wiltshire, BA12 6HR Tel: (01373) 463351 Fax: (01373) 462001 E-mail: platinum.frome.sales@net.vauxhall.co.uk *Car dealers, Garage services & Car body repairs*

Platonoff & Harris, Suite 206 Mill Studio Business Centre, Crane Mead, Ware, Hertfordshire, SG12 9PY Tel: (01920) 444255 Fax: (01920) 487673 E-mail: tony.ph@shopfitters.net *Joinery manufrs* Also at: Ware

Platt Haworth & Co. Ltd, Fourways House, 18 Tariff Street, Manchester, M1 2FN Tel: 0161-236 0764 Fax: 0161-236 7543 E-mail: sales@platthaworth.com *Cotton goods manufrs*

Platt & Hill Ltd, Belgrave Mill, Fitton Hill Road, Oldham, OL8 2LZ Tel: 0161-621 4400 Fax: 0161-621 4408 E-mail: sales@phfillings.co.uk *Foam & fibre filling manufrs*

Platt Office Equipment Ltd, 65 Minchenden Crescent, London, N14 7EP Tel: (020) 8886 9632 Fax: (020) 8886 2142 E-mail: melvyn@plattoffice.co.uk *Office furniture retailers & typewriters*

Platt UK, Macart House, Farnham Road, Bradford, West Yorkshire, BD7 3JG Tel: (01274) 525903 Fax: (01274) 524033 E-mail: eddif@platt.co.uk *Textile machinery manufrs*

▶ Platterpuss Karaoke, 107 Station Road, Hayes, Middlesex, UB3 4BX Tel: (020) 8569 1090 Fax: (020) 8569 1036 E-mail: sales@platterpuss.com *The place for all things karaoke, including players, discs, starter packs or karaoke systems for home*

▶ Platts & Nisbett Ltd, Woodfold Works, Sheffield, S3 9PE Tel: 0114-275 0387 Fax: 0114-279 8434

Plaut International Ltd, Heron Mews House, 1A Balfour Road, Ilford, Essex, IG1 4HP Tel: (020) 8553 3471 Fax: (020) 8478 1876 E-mail: panels@plautint.co.uk *Timber import merchants & agents*

Plaxton, Ryton Road, North Anston, Sheffield, S25 4DL Tel: (01909) 551166 Fax: (01909) 567994 *Coaches parts*

Play & Leisure Ltd, Unit 6-8 Catheralls Industrial Estate, Brookhill Way, Buckley, Clwyd, CH7 3PS Tel: (01244) 546797 Fax: (01244) 549732 E-mail: sales@playandleisure.org.uk *Children's playground manufrs*

Play Rite plc, Wellington Mills, Liversedge, West Yorkshire, WF15 7XA Tel: (01924) 412488 Fax: (01924) 412337 E-mail: info@play-rite.co.uk *Synthetic sports surface manufrs*

Play Services, 2 Wright Road, Ipswich, IP3 9JG Tel: (01473) 270820 *Playground equipment distributors*

Playdale Playgrounds Ltd, Haverthwaite, Ulverston, Cumbria, LA12 8AE Tel: (015395) 31561 Fax: (01539) 531539 E-mail: enquiries@playdale.co.uk *Playground equipment manufrs*

Playden Tools Ltd, Factory 5-6 The Elms, Church Road, Harold Wood, Romford, RM3 0JR Tel: (01708) 343874 Fax: (01708) 376531 *Mould toolmakers*

Player Appeal Automatics, Summerfield, Division Lane, Blackpool, FY4 5DZ Tel: (01253) 693055 E-mail: coinop@btinternet.com *Amusement machine hire & suppliers*

Player N, Caravan, Tanhouse Farm, Redstocks, Melksham, Wiltshire, SN12 6RF Tel: (01380) 828867 Fax: (01380) 828961 *Agricultural engineer & security vehicle suppliers*

Playford Packaging, Ash Road, Wrexham, Clwyd, LL13 9JT Tel: (01978) 661043 Fax: (01978) 661273 *Corrugated box manufrs*

Playfords Ltd, Unit B1 Brookfields Centre, 20 Pents Road, Cambridge, CB24 8PS Tel: (01954) 251966 Fax: (01638) 661206 E-mail: office@playfords.co.uk *Electrical contractors*

Playground Services, Newton Mews, Hungerford, Berkshire, RG17 0HN Tel: (01488) 683797 Fax: (01488) 685053 E-mail: info@playground-services.co.uk *Childrens playground equipment installer & seller*

Playgrounds Scotland Ltd, 2 Stewarton Road, Fenwick, Kilmarnock, Ayrshire, KA3 4AA Tel: (01560) 600744 Fax: (01560) 600755 *Children's playground contractors*

Playle Engineering Co., Home Farm Works, Birch Park, Birch, Colchester, CO2 0LS Tel: (01206) 330315 Fax: (01206) 330138 E-mail: sales@playleengineering.com *General engineers*

Playline Design Ltd, 72a Gestridge Road, Kingsteignton, Newton Abbot, Devon, TQ12 3HH Tel: (01626) 363262 Fax: (01626) 200302 E-mail: playline.design@lineone.net *Playground equipment manufrs*

▶ Playmocounce, 5A Burntwood Lane, Caterham, Surrey, CR3 5UN Tel: (01883) 346294 E-mail: playmobounce@hotmail.co.uk *Bouncy castle hire*

Playpoint Playground Equipment, 5 Woodside Walk, Strathaven, Lanarkshire, ML10 6HL Tel: (01357) 520929 Fax: (01357) 529239 *Nursery & educational equipment supplier*

Playquest Adventure Ltd, Main Road, Ffynnongroyw, Holywell, Clwyd, CH8 9SW Tel: (01745) 561117 E-mail: sales@playquest.co.uk *Children's adventure playground manufrs*

Playquip Leisure, Hayfarm Industrial Estate, Cockaynes Lane, Alresford, Colchester, CO7 8BZ Tel: (01206) 825869 Fax: (01206) 827968 E-mail: sales@playquipleisure.co.uk *Playground equipment manufrs*

Playsafe, 7 Churchfields Rd, Folkingham, Sleaford, Lincs, NG34 0TR Tel: 01529 497513 Fax: 01529 497513 *Safety servicing*

Playsafe Monitoring, 14 The Maltings Industrial Estate, Brassmill Lane, Bath, BA1 3JL Tel: (01225) 311323 Fax: (01225) 445217 E-mail: sales@playsafemonitoring.com *Computer systems electronic data loggers*

Playsafe Playgrounds Ltd, The Carthouse, Goldrings Farm, Elsted, Midhurst, West Sussex, GU29 0JS Tel: (01730) 815472 Fax: (01730) 815872 E-mail: sales@playsafeplaygrounds.co.uk *Playground equipment manufrs*

Playscape Playground Equipment, The Street, Surlingham, Norwich, NR14 7AJ Tel: (01508) 538016 Fax: (01508) 538610 E-mail: sales@playscape-playground-equipment.co.uk *Children's playground equipment manufrs*

Playscene, Watering Farm, Creeting St. Mary, Ipswich, IP6 8ND Tel: (01449) 721729 Fax: (01449) 722477 *Supply landscapers*

Playtex Ltd, Unit D Park Indust Estate, Gareloch Road, Port Glasgow, Renfrewshire, PA14 5XH Tel: (01475) 741631 Fax: (01475) 743119 E-mail: enquiries@playtex.co.uk *Foundation garment manufrs* Also at: Woking

▶ Playtime Nanny Agency, Burley, Bagshot Road, Knaphill, Woking, Surrey, GU21 2SG Tel: (01483) 488511 E-mail: sales@playtimenannies.co.uk *Playtime Nanny Agency est 1990 based in Woking surrey childcare recruitment specialist Nannies available and required Guildford, Weybridge, Cobham, Woking, Godalming, Camberely,all staff personally interviewed mothers helps babysitters surreys top Agency CRB checks carried out on all applicants*

▶ Playtop Ltd, Brunel House, Jessop Way, Newark, Nottinghamshire, NG24 2ER Tel: (01636) 614180 Fax: (01636) 610222 E-mail: sales@playtop.com *Children's safety surfacing*

▶ Playways, Maiden Green, Upottery, Honiton, Devon, EX14 9QT Tel: (01404) 861379 Fax: (01404) 861379 E-mail: enquiries@playways.co.uk *Wooden children's playhouse manufrs*

Playwrite Group plc, 25-27 Curtain Road, London, EC2A 3PN Tel: (020) 7247 6611 Fax: (020) 7247 5450 E-mail: sales@playwritegroup.com *Stationers, toys & christmas decorations distribution*

PLCS Ltd, Wartell Bank, Kingswinford, West Midlands, DY6 7QJ Tel: (01384) 298000 Fax: (01384) 400845 E-mail: sales@pressleakage.com Principal Export Areas: Worldwide *Gas sealing material manufrs*

Plean Precast Ltd, President Kennedy Drive, Plean, Stirling, FK7 8AX Tel: (01786) 812221 Fax: (01786) 815369 E-mail: mail@plean-precast.co.uk *Recast concrete manufrs*

Pleatward Engineering Ltd, Rawfolds Industrial Estate, Bradford Road, Rawfolds, Cleckheaton, West Yorkshire, BD19 5LT Tel: (01274) 874771 Fax: (01274) 851180 E-mail: sales@pleatward.co.uk *Steel & pipe work fabricators*

Pleatwise Packaging Sussex Ltd, 27 Albert Drive, Burgess Hill, West Sussex, RH15 9TN Tel: (01444) 870654 Fax: (01444) 244171 *Manufacturers of packaging materials*

Pledge Office Chairs Ltd, Millstream Works, Mill Road, Leighton Buzzard, Bedfordshire, LU7 1BA Tel: (01525) 376181 Fax: (01525) 382392 E-mail: sales@pledgechairs.co.uk *Office seating manufrs*

Plenty Filters, Plenty House, Hambridge Road, Newbury, Berkshire, RG14 5TR Tel: +44 (0) 1635 42363 Fax: +44 (0) 1635 49758 E-mail: filters@plenty.co.uk *Filters*

Plexus Cotton, 2 Ivy Street, Birkenhead, Merseyside, CH41 5EF Tel: 0151-650 8888 Fax: 0151-650 8889 E-mail: mail@plexus-cotton.com *Raw cotton merchants*

PLG Agronomy, Bishops Tawton, Barnstaple, Devon, EX32 0EA Tel: (01271) 831003 Fax: (01271) 830826 *Agronomic agriculture*

Plinth 2000 Ltd, Wetheringsett Manor, Wetheringsett, Stowmarket, Suffolk, IP14 5PP Tel: (01449) 767887 Fax: (01449) 766122 E-mail: sales@plinth2000.com *Plinths & chiropody chair manufrs*

▶ Plough Engineering Services Ltd, 3 Boardman Industrial Estate, Boardman Road, Swadlincote, Derbyshire, DE11 9DL Tel: (01283) 215815 Fax: (01283) 550247 E-mail: sales@plougheng.co.uk *Plate heat exchanger supply, servicing, design & testing*

▶ Ploughcroft Building Services, Unit 4 Bull Fold Garage, Owler Ings Road, Brighouse, West Yorkshire, HD6 1EJ Tel: (0800) 0344100 Fax: (01484) 723355

Plowden & Thompson Ltd, Dial Glass Work, Stourbridge, West Midlands, DY8 4YN Tel: (01384) 393398 Fax: (01384) 376638 E-mail: sales@plowden-thompson.com Principal Export Areas: Worldwide *Glassware manufrs*

Plowman Craven & Associates, 141 Lower Luton Road, Harpenden, Hertfordshire, AL5 5EQ Tel: (01582) 765566 Fax: (01582) 765370 E-mail: sbarnes@plowmancraven.co.uk *Land surveyors*

PLP Commercial Printers, 7 Mowlem Street, London, E2 9HE Tel: (020) 8983 3439 Fax: (020) 8981 3655 E-mail: sales@plpcommercial.co.uk *Printers*

G.W.J. Pluess Ltd, Trevoutter, Poundstock, Bude, Cornwall, EX23 0DH Tel: (01288) 361368 Fax: (01288) 361361 *Agriculture machinery & equestrian services*

▶ Plugtest Ltd, 9 Mill Lane, Alwalton, Peterborough, PE7 3UZ Tel: (0870) 0630200 Fax: (0870) 0630201 E-mail: sales@plugtest.co.uk *Nationwide portable appliance testing service*

Plum Technology, 21-23 Wordsworth Avenue, Sinfin, Derby, DE24 9HQ Tel: (01332) 272210 Fax: (01332) 272203 E-mail: sales@plum.co.uk *Computer maintenance*

▶ Plumb Center Ltd, 1 Pennybridge Industrial Estate, Ballymena, County Antrim, BT42 3HB Tel: (028) 2564 1222 Fax: (028) 2564 1777

Plumb Center, Station Approach, Coulsdon, Surrey, CR5 2YB Tel: (020) 8668 4121 Fax: (020) 8660 8795 E-mail: bk.colcon@woloseley.co.uk *Builder materials suppliers* Also at: Branches throughout the U.K.

Plumb Center Ltd, 2 Dukeminster Estate, Dunstable, Bedfordshire, LU5 4HU Tel: (01582) 666811 Fax: (01582) 664303 *Plumbers merchants*

Plumb Center Ltd, 2 Clarks Industrial Estate, Newtown Road, Hove, East Sussex, BN3 7BA Tel: (01273) 324352 Fax: (01273) 208482 *Builders merchants*

Plumbase Ltd, 123-129 Portland Road, Hove, East Sussex, BN3 5QW Tel: (01273) 746161 Fax: (01273) 424065 E-mail: john.bolton@btinternet.com *Plumbers merchants* Also at: Bognor Regis

Plumbase Ltd, 123-129 Portland Road, Hove, East Sussex, BN3 5QW Tel: (01273) 746161 Fax: (01273) 737677 E-mail: admin.marketing@plumbase.com *Plumbing & heating materials suppliers & retailers*

Plumbase Ltd, 542 Millbrook Road West, Southampton, SO15 0LN Tel: (023) 8077 4499 Fax: (023) 8077 3388 *Plumbers merchants* Also at: Lymington

▶ Plumbcity Bathroom Equipment, 4-5 Bunting Road, Bury St. Edmunds, Suffolk, IP32 7BX Tel: (01284) 763355 Fax: (01284) 763335 *Bathroom fittings or accessories suppliers*

Plumbing & Heating Services, 194 Winchester Road, London, E4 9JP Tel: (020) 8523 2222 Fax: (020) 8527 6776 E-mail: phs@chris14.fsnet.co.uk *Plumbing & heating services*

▶ Plumbing & Heating Services Ltd, Elphinstone Road, Tranent, East Lothian, EH33 2LG Tel: (01875) 610621 Fax: (01875) 613505 E-mail: mail@phs.org.uk

▶ PlumbSearch UK Ltd, 219 Abbey Road, Basingstoke, Hampshire, RG24 9EG Tel: 0800 6120731 Fax: 01256 471488 E-mail: info@plumbsearch.eu.com *We aim to solve any plumbing challenge, from a simple leak, to the most complex repairs or installation work. PlumbSearch provides a full range plumbing and drainage services at competitive prices.*

▶ Plummer Electrical Engineering, Shanklin, Plough Road, Great Bentley, Colchester, CO7 8LG Tel: (01206) 250158 Fax: (01206) 251169

Plumridge & Peters Ltd, Unit 5, Gillmans Industrial Estate, Natts Lane, Billingshurst, West Sussex, RH14 9EY Tel: (01403) 783762 Fax: (01403) 784288 E-mail: plumridge@ndirect.co.uk *Screen printers & mould engravers*

Plunkett Tiling Ltd, Dukes Way, Low Prudhoe Industrial Estate, Prudhoe, Northumberland, NE42 6PQ Tel: (01661) 836960 Fax: (01661) 836847 E-mail: personnel@plunketttiling.co.uk *Tiling contractors*

Plus Components, Harlequin Business Park, Kenny Hill, Bury St. Edmunds, Suffolk, IP28 8DS Tel: (01353) 675555 Fax: (01353) 675555 E-mail: info@pco.co.uk *Computer software & developers*

Plus Facades Ltd, Unit 9, Woking Business Park, Woking, Surrey, GU21 5TY Tel: (01483) 757511 Fax: (01483) 757522 E-mail: pluswall@pluswall.com *Specialists in the design manufacture and installation of curtain walling and associated works. Being a design led company, we have developed a wide range of Pluswall products which includes panellised, unitised and structural glazing together with fully integrated stone, terracotta and photovoltaic systems, concealed automatic vents, fire rated facades and atria roof glazing.*

▶ Plus in Boots Ltd, 150 Magna Road, Poole, Dorset, BH11 9NB Tel: 01202 581566 *Are you fed up with never finding wide fitting fashionable boots and shoes that fit? Well we were too, which is why we have set up this company, to provide wide calf boots, wide fitting boots and wide fitting shoes. Listening to our customers needs, we have developed our own PlusinBoots calf fitting boots in 6 calf sizes along with a collection of brands that follow fashion trends, but do not compromise on comfort - fashion that fits*

Plus Online Stores Ltd, Natson Mill, Bow, Crediton, Devon, EX17 6JE Tel: (01363) 82923 Fax: (01363) 82931 E-mail: ch@base10.ws *Computer services writers & sales*

▶ Plus Organisation Ltd, Plymouth Industrial Services, Clittaford Road, Plymouth, PL6 6DF Tel: (01752) 306630 Fax: (01752) 696225 E-mail: plus@pluss.org.uk *Retail disabled & elderly person aids, mobility*

▶ Plus Windows & Doors Ltd, Units 16 & 18 Moor Park Industrial Centre, Tolpits Lane, Watford, WD18 9SP Tel: (01923) 225855 Fax: (01923) 256106 E-mail: sales@apluswindows.co.uk *Supplier to the trade of aluminium, timber and PVCu windows, doors and conservatories.*

Pluscrab Ltd, 30 St Phillips Avenue, Wolverhampton, WV3 7DU Tel: (01902) 340529 *Software consultants*

Plym Ironworks, Rear of 186 Exeter Street, Off Alma Street, Plymouth, PL4 0NQ Tel: (01752) 226316 *Steel fabricators*

Plymol Tubes Ltd, 6 Ravells Yard, Carr Lane, Hoylake, Wirral, Merseyside, CH47 4AZ Tel: 0151-632 1354 Fax: 0151-632 4912 E-mail: sales@flagstaffs.co.uk *Welding & structural engineers*

Plymouth Agencies Ltd, Oakfield Press, Elliott Road, Plymouth, PL4 0SG Tel: (01752) 262323 Fax: (01752) 228764 E-mail: sales@plymouthagencies.co.uk *Packaging service & paper suppliers*

Plymouth Boat Cruises Ltd, Millbrook, Torpoint, Cornwall, PL10 1DA Tel: (01752) 822797 Fax: (01752) 408590 E-mail: soundcruising@btinternet.com *Pleasure boat services*

Plymouth Chamber Of Commerce, 22 Lockyer Street, Plymouth, PL1 2QW Tel: (01752) 220471 Fax: (01752) 600333 E-mail: chamber@plymouth-chamber.co.uk *Chamber of commerce*

Plymouth Citybus Ltd, Milehouse, Milehouse Road, Plymouth, PL3 4AA Tel: (01752) 264207 Fax: (01752) 567209 E-mail: hq@plymouthbus.co.uk *Transport consultants*

▶ Plymouth Ink Jets, Unit 87 & 95, 68 Market Stalls, Plymouth, PL1 1PR Tel: (01752) 222527 Fax: (01752) 606868 *Computer accessory & consumable suppliers*

Plymouth Joinery, Warlow Street, Merthyr Tydfil, Mid Glamorgan, CF47 0YW Tel: (01685) 371328 *Joinery manufrs*

Plymouth Metal Fabrications, 13 Porsham Close, Roborough, Plymouth, PL6 7DB Tel: (01752) 788883 Fax: (01752) 788228 *Fire escape manufrs*

Plymouth Packaging Services Ltd, Baird House, Darklake Close, Estover, Plymouth, PL6 7TJ Tel: (01752) 696330 Fax: (01752) 695589 *Contract packaging specialists*

Plymouth Packaging Services Ltd, Baird House, Darklake Close, Estover, Plymouth, PL6 7TJ Tel: (01752) 696330 Fax: (01752) 695589 *Packaging services*

▶ Plymouth Piano Centre, 77a Upland Drive, Plymouth, PL6 6BE Tel: (01752) 669428 Fax: (01752) 709400 E-mail: enquiries@plymouthpianocentre.co.uk

Plymouth Rubber Hose & Hydraulics, Drill Hall, Rocky Hill, Tavistock, Devon, PL19 0DZ Tel: (01822) 616061 Fax: (01822) 617755 E-mail: sales@hoseandhydraulicsgroup.co.uk *Flexible hose & tubing suppliers*

Plymouth Trophyman, 75 Hyde Park Road, Plymouth, PL3 4JN Tel: (01752) 226787 *Trophies medals & rosettes*

Plympton Tack, 11 Underwood Rd, Plymouth, PL7 1SY Tel: 01752 343384 *Tack wholesaler*

Plysolene Ltd, Unit 21 Star Road Trading Estate, Star Road, Partridge Green, Horsham, West Sussex, RH13 8RA Tel: (01403) 713555 Fax: (01403) 713666 E-mail: info@wattsgroup.co.uk Principal Export Areas: Middle East, Central/East Europe, West Europe & North America *Manufacturer and worldwide supplier of the Plyload range of high performance, polymeric damp-proof courses including Plyload GR, the radon and methane resistant version. Complete damp proof waterproofing service available. Also manufacture and supply worldwide Plysolene PIB, the polyisobutylene sheet for waterproofing insulation ; butyl sheet for expansion joints and Insulgard twinwall polycarbonate glazing sheet for greenhouses and coldframes.*

▶ PMC Independent, 160 Old Road, Heage, Derbyshire, DE56 2BN Tel: (01773) 856700 Fax: (01773) 850182 E-mail: enquiries@pmcindependent.co.uk *Waste management & recycling solutions*

▶ PMC Safety Netting Ltd, Unit 3, Appian Way, Europa Business Park, Grimsby, Lincolnshire, DN31 2UT Tel: (01472) 267733 Fax: (01472) 350921 E-mail: pmc.safetynetting@ntlworld.com *Safety netting, edge protection, tower design & tested decking suppliers*

PMC Systems, Whitehill Industrial Estate, Whitehill Lane, Wootton Bassett, Swindon, SN4 7DB Tel: (01793) 848817 Fax: (01793) 848846 E-mail: pmccards@aol.com *Plastic card printing services*

▶ PM-CS Ltd, 28 Ballantyne Way, Lowton, Warrington, WA3 2LS Tel: 0870 7487103 Fax: 0870 7487103 E-mail: admin@pm-cs.com *PM-CS Ltd works with organisations such as the National Heath Service (NHS) and City Learning Centres. Our experience lies in software development, networking, communications and project management, so we have the skills, ability and professionalism *to produce solutions for all business sizes, from small businesses to corporate clients and our strengths are our experience and our flexibility. We understand that our customers' businesses are unique, and that changing their business practices to fit pre-packaged software *simply does not work. We therefore offer a range of solutions that can be shaped to fit around our clients needs. We help them effectively manage valuable human and physical resources at a glance. This increases efficiency, helping to remove double bookings, low utilisation and stacks of paper*

PMF, N Quarry Road, Newhaven, East Sussex, BN9 9DG Tel: (01273) 517333 Fax: (01273) 517222 E-mail: sales@pmfdesigns.co.uk *Metal fabrications & sheet metalwork specialists*

▶ PMF Fortuna Ltd, 5 Allens Road, Ramsden Heath, Billericay, Essex, CM11 1JA Tel: (01268) 710037

▶ Pmis Consulting Ltd, The Magdalen Centre, 1 Robert Robinson Avenue, Oxford, OX4 4GA Tel: (01865) 784040 Fax: (01865) 784042 *Founded in 1993, PMIS provides project management consulting and training*

▶ PMJ Consultants, 77, Melford Road, Stowmarket, Suffolk, IP14 2PR Tel: 01449 673883 E-mail: peterjones@pmjconsultants.com *Consultants for plastics & plastic users*

PML Programme Management Ltd, Unit 34, Threadneedle Street, London, EC2R 8AY Tel: (020) 7256 2216 Fax: (020) 7510 0061 E-mail: kim_newman@pmlgroup.com *Management consultancy services*

PMP Construction, 3 Devesky Road, Sixmilecross, Omagh, County Tyrone, BT79 9BU Tel: (028) 8076 1074 Fax: (028) 8076 0604

PMR Fixers Ltd, Mayfield Road, Ashbourne, Derbyshire, DE6 2BJ Tel: (01335) 347629 Fax: (01335) 344051 *Specialists in metal deck floor fixing & stud welding*

▶ PMR Ventilation Ltd, 14 Park Lane Business Centre, Park Lane, Nottingham, NG6 0DW Tel: 0115-977 1759 Fax: 0115-977 1757 E-mail: pmrventilation@tiscali.co.uk *Ventilation installers*

▶ PNC Print & Design, Unit Stirling Industrial Centre, Stirling Way, Borehamwood, Hertfordshire, WD6 2BT Tel: (020) 8953 6116 Fax: (020) 8207 0430 E-mail: info@pnc-print.co.uk *Print & design solutions*

PNC Telecom Services Ltd, Cavallino House, Corsley Heath, Corsley, Warminster, Wiltshire, BA12 7PL Tel: (07000) 707070 Fax: (07000) 707071 *Telecommunication services*

▶ PNComms (UK) Ltd, 96 Wilsthorpe Road, Breaston, Derby, DE72 3AG Tel: (07977) 178771 E-mail: info@pncomms.com *Specialist engineering services*

▶ Pneu Air, 6 Saxon Business Park, Hanbury Road, Stoke Prior, Bromsgrove, Worcestershire, B60 4AD Tel: (01527) 559561 Fax: (01527) 559562 *Tyre inflation products manufrs*

Pneu Fix, 255 Kingston Road, Willerby, Hull, HU10 6PG Tel: (01482) 651019 Fax: (01482) 651019 *Pneumatic equipment retailer*

Pneumatic Components Ltd, Holbrook Rise, Holbrook Industrial Estate, Sheffield, S20 3GE Tel: 0114-248 2712 Fax: 0114-247 8342 E-mail: info@pclairtechnology.com *UK manufacturer of Air Line Products and Tyre Inflation Equipment*

Pneumatic & Electrical Systems, Automation Works, 656 Leeds Road, Deighton, Huddersfield, HD2 1UB Tel: (01484) 533527 Fax: (01484) 512058 E-mail: enquiries@pesystems.co.uk *Process controller & control instrumentation manufrs*

Pneumatic Engineering & Distribution Ltd, Unit D1 Springhead Enterprise Park, Springhead Road, Northfleet, Gravesend, Kent, DA11 8HH Tel: (01474) 536836 Fax: (01474) 536830

continued

E-mail: SALES@PNEUMATICENGINEERING.COM *DISTRIBUTORS OF PNEUMATIC ENGINEERING.DESIGN & BUILDING OF CONTROL SYSTEMS.PANELS & CYLINDERS ETC*

Pneumatic Equipment Services, C2 Jubilee Road, Newtownards, County Down, BT23 4YH Tel: (028) 9182 8833 Fax: (028) 9182 8844 E-mail: matik@nireland.com *Pneumatic controls & air compressor manufrs*

Pneumatic & Hydraulic Couplings Ltd, Atlas Way, Sheffield, S4 7QQ Tel: 0114-244 2704 Fax: 0114-244 2705 E-mail: sales@phcltd.net *Pneumatic & hydraulic coupling resellers*

Pneumatic Lines Ltd, Brunel House, 1 Archers Court, Huntingdon, Cambridgeshire, PE29 6XG Tel: (01480) 432104 Fax: (01480) 414534 *Vehicle chemical distributor*

▶ Pneumatic Solutions International Ltd, Unit 8, Stratfield Park, Elettra Avenue, Waterlooville, Hampshire, PO7 7XN Tel: (023) 9223 3611 Fax: (023) 9225 2112 E-mail: sales@pneusol.co.uk *Pneumatic Valves & Components*

Pneumatic Systems Ltd, Unit 32 Poplar Industrial Estate, Witton, Birmingham, B6 7AD Tel: 0121-344 3800 Fax: 0121 344 3866 E-mail: pneumaticsys@aol.com *Special Purpose Machines, Control Panels and Pneumatic Engineering*

▶ Pneumatic Systems Ltd, Unit 32 Poplar Industrial Estate, Witton, Birmingham, B6 7AD Tel: 0121-344 3800 Fax: 0121-344 3866 E-mail: pneumaticsys@aol.com *Pneumatic components import & distribute*

Pneumatic Tool Services Ltd, Worthing Road, West Grinstead, Horsham, West Sussex, RH13 8LG Tel: (01403) 865609 Fax: (01403) 864198 E-mail: sales@pneumatictoolservices.co.uk *Industrial & construction tools suppliers*

▶ Pneumatic Tools & Compressors Ltd, Acton Road, Long Eaton, Nottingham, NG10 1FU Tel: 0115-973 4099 Fax: 0115-946 3030 E-mail: info@pneumatictools.sagehost.co.uk *Retail & service of air compressors & tools*

Pneutek (International) Ltd, Unit 1, Sovereign Way, Trafalgar Industrial Estate, Downham Market, Norfolk, PE38 9SW Tel: (01366) 388866 E-mail: airfasteners@thesmallbusinessclinique.com *Steel fastening systems distributors*

Pneutrol Ireland Ltd, 5 Caulside Drive, Antrim, BT41 2DU Tel: (028) 9448 1800 Fax: (028) 9448 1801 E-mail: info@pneutrol.com *Suppliers of control panels for the concrete industry*

PNJ Monitors, 41 Brookfield, Bayston Hill, Shrewsbury, SY3 0LR Tel: (01743) 872935 Fax: (01743) 872935 *Computer monitor repairs & screens*

Pobs Precision Tools Mould Toolmkrs, 44 Bickford Road, Birmingham, B6 7EE Tel: 0121-327 5736 Fax: 0121-328 5261 E-mail: pobs.tools@btconnect.com *Plastics mould toolmakers*

▶ Pochin P.L.C., Birniehill, Whitburn Road, Bathgate, West Lothian, EH48 2HR Tel: (01606) 833333

Pochin Contractors Ltd, Brooks Lane, Middlewich, Cheshire, CW10 0JQ Tel: (01606) 833333 Fax: (01606) 833331 E-mail: sales@pochins.plc.uk *Building contractors & plant hire*

Robert Pochin Ltd, 11 St Georges Way, Leicester, LE1 1SH Tel: 0116-251 5051 Fax: 0116-253 8829 E-mail: sales.enquiries@robertpochin.co.uk *Plumbers & ironmongers merchants*

Robert Pochin Ltd, Manor House Road, Long Eaton, Nottingham, NG10 1LR Tel: 0115-973 5155 Fax: 0115-946 1247 E-mail: sales.enquiries@robertpochin.co.uk *Plumbers & heating merchants, architectural & builders hardware*

▶ Pocket Bike Imports, 1 Looseleigh Park, Plymouth, PL6 5JL Tel: 01752 360066 Fax: 01752 360066 *We supply Chinese commodity vehicles including Seascooters and Minimotos to the public and the trade at wholesale prices. By overseeing the whole import process, from purchase in China to point of sale in the UK, we can eliminate middleman and keep overheads to a minimum. This adds up to great products at great prices! *For current Mini Motos, Mini Dirt Bike and Seascooter offers please visit our website. www.pocketbikeimports.co.uk**

Pocklington Steel Structures, Heron House, Carnaby Industrial Estate, Lancaster Road, Carnaby, Bridlington, North Humberside, YO15 3QY Tel: (01262) 402400 Fax: (01262) 402401 *Steel fabricators*

Pocklingtons Bakery Ltd, Sunnyhome, Main Road, Withern, Alford, Lincolnshire, LN13 0LD Tel: (01507) 450222 Fax: (01507) 450781 *Bakery products production*

Poclain Hydraulics Ltd, Nene Valley Business Park, Oundle, Peterborough, PE8 4HN Tel: (01832) 273773 Fax: (01832) 274990 E-mail: info@poclain-hydraulics.com *Hydraulic equipment manufrs*

Poddymeter Ltd, Unit 2 Park Works, Borough Road, Kingston Upon Thames, Surrey, KT2 6BD Tel: (020) 8546 9311 Fax: (020) 8547 2325 E-mail: poddy.ltd@virgin.net *Pressure gauge & flow meter manufrs*

Podmores Builders, Haydock Street, Warrington, WA2 7UW Tel: (01925) 582850 Fax: (01925) 582859 E-mail: admin@podmores.com

Poerlink Electronic Ltd, Powerlink House, Ivy Arch Road, Worthing, West Sussex, BN14 8BX Tel: (01903) 209550 Fax: (01903) 215526 E-mail: admin@powerlinkelectronics.co.uk *Thyristor controller manufrs*

Poeton Cardiff Ltd, Penarth Road, Cardiff, CF11 8UL Tel: (029) 2038 8182 Fax: (029) 2038 8185 E-mail: cardiff@poeton.co.uk *Electroplating, anodising & spray painting*

Poeton Industries Ltd, Eastern Avenue, Gloucester, GL4 3DN Tel: (01452) 300500 Fax: (01452) 500400 E-mail: sales@poeton.co.uk *Electroplaters services* Also at: Cardiff & Southampton

Poetstyle Ltd, 1 Bayford Street Industrial Units, Bayford Street, London, E8 3SE Tel: (020) 8533 0915 Fax: (020) 8985 2953 E-mail: sofachairs@aol.com *Upholstery manufacturers & contract furnishers*

▶ Pogo Entertainment Ltd, 787 Southchurch Road, Southend-on-Sea, SS1 2PP Tel: (0870) 7662446 Fax: (01702) 384043 E-mail: info@pogoboxes.com *Manufacturer record studio*

Pogson Joinery, Unit 19 Heath House Mill, Heath House Lane, Golcar, Huddersfield, HD7 4JW Tel: (01484) 654059 Fax: (01484) 654059 *Joinery manufrs*

▶ Poindexters Ltd, 103 Newgate Street, Bishop Auckland, County Durham, DL14 7EW Tel: (01388) 604004 Fax: (01388) 604004 E-mail: poindexters@dsl.pipex.com *Computer suppliers*

▶ Point Digital, 18 Union Street, Hereford, HR1 2BT Tel: (01432) 276335 Fax: (01432) 276335 *Computer hardware suppliers*

Point Eight Ltd, Unit 14 Blackbrook Valley Industrial Estate, Narrowboat Way, Dudley, West Midlands, DY2 0EZ Tel: (01384) 238282 Fax: (01384) 455746 E-mail: sales@point8.co.uk *Library & educational furniture manufrs*

Point Of Purchase Display, Finchley Avenue, Mildenhall, Bury St. Edmunds, Suffolk, IP28 7BG Tel: (01638) 515708 Fax: (01638) 712836

Point Source Ltd, Mitchell Point, Ensign Way, Hamble, Southampton, SO31 4RF Tel: (023) 8074 4500 Fax: (023) 8074 4501 E-mail: sales@point-source.com *Laser & fibre optic systems manufrs*

Point To Point Couriers Ltd, Unit 11 Mitre Bridge Industrial Park, Mitre Way, London, W10 6AU Tel: (020) 8960 2222 Fax: (020) 8960 0956 *Courier services*

Point To Point Couriers Ltd, Eve Road, Woking, Surrey, GU21 5JS Tel: (01483) 723511 Fax: (01483) 750427 *Courier & parcel delivery services* Also at: Cambridge, Crawley, Farnborough, Guildford, Harlow, Leatherhead, London, Reading & Staines

▶ Pointblank Media, PO Box 1949, Salisbury, SP4 8ZN Tel: (01980) 594949 E-mail: info@pointblankmedia.net - *Corporate PowerPoint Presentations*- Video Production*- Video Conversions*- Sales and Training Videos*- Web Design and Web Hosting*- Web Marketing*- Microsoft Office Training*- Business Stationery*

Pointer Design & Manufacture Ltd, Chartwell Drive, Wigston, Leicester, LE18 2FL Tel: 0116-212 0000 Fax: 0116-212 6427 E-mail: sales@pointerdesign.co.uk *Pointer designs sales*

Pointer Pet Foods Ltd, Chesterton Road, Eastwood Trading Estate, Rotherham, South Yorkshire, S65 1SX Tel: (01709) 820569 Fax: (01709) 837415 E-mail: office@pointerpetfoods.co.uk *Animal feed binders manufrs*

Pointer Print, 24 The Green, Hasland, Chesterfield, Derbyshire, S41 0LJ Tel: (01246) 231970 Fax: (01246) 277298 E-mail: pointerprint@vipnet.co.uk *Label printers*

Pointfore, Old Priory Road, Easton-in-Gordano, Bristol, BS20 0PB Tel: (01275) 374212 Fax: (01275) 374212 *Racket sports equipment distributors*

Pointing Saddlery, Blathwayt Stables, Lansdown, Bath, BA1 9BT Tel: (01225) 462136 Fax: (01225) 483983 E-mail: info@pointings-saddlery.co.uk *Saddlers, riding wear & outdoor clothes*

▶ Points Of Sale, 95-97 Rectory Road, Duckmanton, Chesterfield, Derbyshire, S44 5EE Tel: (01246) 823982 Fax: (01246) 241192 *Sign makers*

Poitdell Ltd, Slaney Place, Headcorn Road, Staplehurst, Tonbridge, Kent, TN12 0DT Tel: (01580) 891020 Fax: (01580) 890132 *Security services*

▶ Poker Shop, Unit 2, Fletchers Square, Southend-on-Sea, SS2 5RN Tel: (0870) 8712007 Fax: (0870) 8736007 E-mail: srush@poker-shop.co.uk *Gaming tables for poker, blackjack, roulette & poker chips sales*

▶ Poker Store Ltd, 10 Rutland Avenue, Southend On Sea, Southend-on-Sea, SS1 2XH Tel: (01702) 615413 E-mail: katy@poker-store.co.uk

▶ Polacap, Unit 4, Shaw Lane Industrial Estate, Shaw Lane, Stoke Prior, Bromsgrove, Worcestershire, B60 4DT Tel: (01527) 874410 Fax: (01527) 874411 *Transport refrigeration*

Polar Air Ltd, Huntingdon House, 278-290 Huntingdon Street, Nottingham, NG1 3LY Tel: 0115-955 0055 Fax: 0115-955 7037 *Air conditioning designers*

▶ Polar Bear, 5 Faygate Business Centre, Faygate Lane, Faygate, Horsham, West Sussex, RH12 4DN Tel: (01293) 852258 Fax: (01293) 852244 *Air conditioning services*

Polar Car Air Conditioning, 178 Bury New Road, Whitefield, Manchester, M45 6QF Tel: 0161-798 4884 Fax: 0161-796 7673 *Air conditioning repairs*

Polar Ford Barnsley, 223 Dodworth Road, Barnsley, South Yorkshire, S70 6PA Tel: (01226) 732732 Fax: (01226) 732867 E-mail: ford@barnsley.polar-motor.co.uk *Retail automotive ford main agent*

Polar Ford York, Jockey Lane, Huntington, York, YO32 9GY Tel: (01904) 625371 Fax: (01904) 622238 E-mail: ford@york.polar-motor.co.uk *New & used commercial vehicles sales*

Polar Instruments Ltd, Garenne Park, St. Sampson, Guernsey, GY2 4AF Tel: (01481) 253081 Fax: (01481) 252476 E-mail: mail@polarinstruments.com *Supplier of controlled impedance test systems*

Polar Paper, 1 East Barnet Road, Barnet, Hertfordshire, EN4 8RR Tel: (020) 8447 4240 Fax: (020) 8447 4241 E-mail: paper4u@polarint.com *Paper merchants (export & import)*

Polar Print Group Ltd, Venturi House, 9-17 Tuxford Road, Hamilton Industrial Park, Leicester, LE4 9WE Tel: 0116-274 4700 Fax: 0116-274 4799 *Fine colour printing & publishing*

Polar Pumps Ltd, Brunel Industrial Estate, Harworth, Doncaster, South Yorkshire, DN11 8QA Tel: (01302) 751253 Fax: (01302) 751254 *Refrigerant handling equipment manufrs*

Polar Seal Tapes & Conversions, Guildford Road Industrial Estate, Guildford Road, Farnham, Surrey, GU9 9PZ Tel: (01252) 726000 Fax: (01252) 728125 Sales Contact: J. Rich *Distributors of adhesive tape including double sided, medical applications & masking. Also adhesive & self-adhesive tape converters*

Polar Systems Ltd, Austin Fields, King's Lynn, Norfolk, PE30 1PH Tel: (01553) 691472 Fax: (01553) 691473 E-mail: sales@polar-systems.co.uk *Specialist processing equipment*

Polarcold Refrigeration Ltd, 2 The Parade, Tattenham Way, Burgh Heath, Tadworth, Surrey, KT20 5NG Tel: 01737 373367 Fax: 01737 373387 E-mail: info@polarcold.co.uk *commercial refrigeration and air conditioning sales and service. Ice Machines, Chillers, Freezers, Bottle Coolers, Display Equipment, Authorised Foster Dealers, Leasing Facilities.*

Polarcool Refrigeration Ltd, Unit K1 Beckingham Business Park, Tolleshunt Major, Maldon, Essex, CM9 8LZ Tel: (01621) 868584 Fax: (01621) 868989 E-mail: sales@polarcool.co.uk *Refrigeration engineers & electrical contractors*

▶ Polaris Apparel Ltd, Business Park, Station Road, Bolsover, Chesterfield, Derbyshire, S44 6BH Tel: (01246) 240218 Fax: (01246) 241560 *Cycle apparel*

▶ Polaris Training & Development Systems, Awford House, 43-45 Rectory Grove, Leigh-on-Sea, Essex, SS9 2HA Tel: (01702) 474499 Fax: (01702) 474018 E-mail: systems@gedgilligan.co.uk *Business Management Systems, Consultancy and Training. ISO9001 Quality Management Standard, ISO14001 Environmental Management Standard, Integrated Mnagement Systems, TQM,Supervisor and Manager skills, tools and technique coaching. Internal auditing, technical writing.*

Polaroid, 800 Capability Green, Luton, LU1 3BA Tel: (01582) 409800 Fax: (01582) 409801 *Instant cameras & films manufrs*

▶ Polaroid UK Ltd, Vale of Leven Industrial Estate, Dumbarton, G82 3PW Tel: (01389) 712000 Fax: (01389) 755101

Polaroid UK Ltd, Vale of Leven Industrial Estate, Dumbarton, G82 3PW Tel: (01389) 712000 Fax: (01389) 755101 *Photographic equipment manufrs*

Polaron Cortina Ltd, 26 Greenhill Cresent, Watford Business Park, Watford, WD18 8XG Tel: (01923) 495495 Fax: (01923) 228796 E-mail: sales@polaron.co.uk *Tilt switches manufrs*

Polartech Ltd, Nash Road, Trafford Park, Manchester, M17 1SX Tel: 0161-876 5673 Fax: 0161-872 1922 E-mail: marketing@polartech.co.uk *Metalworking fluids & chemicals*

▶ Polarwall, Unit 3 Old Mill Industrial Estate, Stoke Canon, Exeter, EX5 4RJ Tel: (01392) 841777 Fax: (01392) 841936 E-mail: info@polarwall.co.uk *Supplying the latest generation of insulating concrete formwork*

▶ polat socks, Flat 39, Langbourne Mansions, Langbourne Avenue, Highgate, London, N6 6PT Tel: (020) 8348 9995 Fax: (020) 8349 9995 E-mail: tarik@polat.wanadoo.co.uk *we are a socks importer company in london.we are supplying wholesaler and market traders.we do free delivery for nationwide.for information about our products and prices,please contact us.*

Poldark Cabinet Makers, Woodbine Cottage, Gerrards Cross Road, Stoke Poges, Slough, SL2 4EL Tel: (01753) 662920 Fax: (01753) 662920 *Furniture & joinery manufrs*

Pole Star Space Applications, Whiteleys Centre, 301-303 Queensway, London, W2 4YN Tel: (020) 7313 7400 Fax: (020) 7313 7401 *Global tracking services*

▶ Poles4curtains, 4 Manywells Industrial Centre, Cullingworth, Bradford, West Yorkshire, BD13 5DX Tel: (01535) 273355 Fax: (01535) 273344 E-mail: info@poles4curtains.co.uk *Poles for curtains manufrs*

Polestar Chromoworks Ltd, Wigman Road, Nottingham, NG8 3JA Tel: 0115-900 8300 Fax: 0115-900 8320 *Colour printers & lithographic printing*

▶ Polestar Cooling Ltd, Ford Airfield, Ford Airfield Industrial Estate, Ford, Arundel, West Sussex, BN18 0HY Tel: (01903) 724200 Fax: (01903) 725169 E-mail: info@polestarcooling.com *Refrigeration services*

Polestar Digital Labels Ltd, 501 Dewsbury Road, Leeds, LS11 5LL Tel: 0113-201 6600 Fax: 0113-276 2552 E-mail: leeds.direct@polestar-group.com *Direct mail printers* Also at: Dunstable

Polestar Greaves Ltd, Cayton Low Road, Eastfield, Scarborough, North Yorkshire, YO11 3BX Tel: (01723) 588200 Fax: (01723) 581387 *Printers & binders*

Polestar Jowetts, Evanston Avenue, Kirkstall Road, Leeds, LS4 2HR Tel: (0113) 279 5041 Fax: (0113) 231 0193 *Carton printers*

Polestar Varnicoat Ltd, Terrace Road, Pinvin, Pershore, Worcestershire, WR10 2DN Tel: (01386) 552181 Fax: (01386) 556554 *Gravure printers*

▶ Polestar Wheatons Ltd, Hennock Road, Marsh Barton, Exeter, EX2 8RP Tel: (01392) 420222 Fax: (01392) 420300 E-mail: exeter.reception@polestar-group.com

Polesworth Jig & Tool, 49 High Street, Polesworth, Tamworth, Staffordshire, B78 1DX Tel: (01827) 893812 Fax: (01827) 893812 *Jig & tool manufrs*

Polesworth Patterns, Mount Farm, Warton Lane, Grendon, Atherstone, Warwickshire, CV9 3DT Tel: (01827) 895198 Fax: (01827) 895198 *Joinery manufrs*

Polgain Ltd, 1 Crown Score, Lowestoft, Suffolk, NR32 1JH Tel: (01502) 539803 Fax: (01502) 539804 E-mail: info@polgain.co.uk *POLGAIN LIMITED are manufactures of Cams, Camshafts, Gangmasters and Precision Engineers for OEM customers as well as the after-market, engine developers, motorsport and re-conditioners.*

Polham Controls Ltd, Block E Bath Road Business Park, Bath Road, Bridgwater, Somerset, TA6 4SZ Tel: (01278) 433433 Fax: (01278) 436999 E-mail: polham.controls@btinternet.com *Electronic control & distribution equipment*

Poli Chrome Engineers Moulds Ltd, Adswood Road, Stockport, Cheshire, SK3 8HR Tel: 0161-477 7370 Fax: 0161-477 1020 E-mail: ianlusby1@hotmail.com *Hard chrome plating, electroplating & electrochemical plating services*

▶ Police Aviation News, 7 Windmill Close, Honey Lane, Waltham Abbey, Essex, EN9 3BQ Tel: 01992 714162 E-mail: bryn.elliott@btopenworld.com *Air sea rescue equipment suppliers*

Police Review Publishing Co. Ltd, 180 Wardour Street, London, W1F 8FY Tel: (020) 8700 3700 Fax: (020) 7287 4765 *Magazine & book publishers*

Poligrat (UK) Ltd, 2 Holder Road, Aldershot, Hampshire, GU12 4RH Tel: (01252) 336337 Fax: (01252) 322791 E-mail: info@poligratuk.co.uk *General metal deburring subcontract services, electropolishing plant & equipment & stainless steel pickling paste manufacturers. Electropolishing & stainless steel finishing/polishing pickling/ cleaning services and on site services.*

Polimoon Ltd, Babbage Road, Engineer Park, Sandycroft, Deeside, Clwyd, CH5 2QD Tel: (01244) 537555 Fax: (01244) 526645 E-mail: sales@polimoon.com *Plastic container & crate manufrs*

▶ Polineri Europa UK Ltd, Bo'Ness Road, Grangemouth, Stirlingshire, FK3 9XE Tel: (01324) 692200 Fax: (01324) 473915 *Rubber products*

Polish Inc, 4 Justin Business Park, Sandford Lane, Wareham, Dorset, BH20 4DY Tel: (01929) 554037 Fax: (01929) 555262 *Metal finishing services*

Polish Craft Ltd, 68g Sapcote Trading Centre, Wyrley Road, Birmingham, B6 7BN Tel: 0121-322 2344 Fax: 0121-322 2344 *Plastic mould polishing specialists & hard chrome plating*

▶ Polished Stone, Moulton Park Business Centre, Redhouse Road, Moulton Park Industrial Estate, Northampton, NN3 6AQ Tel: (01604) 648668 Fax: (01604) 648388 E-mail: sales@polishedstone.com *Granite Worktops: Cheap Granite worktops. Granite worktops for you kitchen. Pre-cut Granite stone will speed the fitting. Granite worktops to fit your budget.*

Arthur Pollard Ltd, Unit 38 Churchill Way, Fleckney, Leicester, LE8 8UD Tel: 0116-240 3728 E-mail: arthur.pollard@virgin.net *Boiler plant heating engineers*

Pollard Boxes, Feldspar Close, Enderby, Leicester, LE19 4SD Tel: 0116-275 2666 Fax: 0116-275 2888 E-mail: info@pollardboxes.co.uk *Presentation box makers*

▶ Pollard Electrical Ltd, 39 Warwick Drive, Beverley, North Humberside, HU17 9TB Tel: (01482) 679434 E-mail: abarker@pollard-electrical.co.uk *Electrical contractors*

Gregory Pollard Ltd, Regent Road, Countesthorpe, Leicester, LE8 5RF Tel: 0116-277 9789 Fax: 0116-278 4395 E-mail: info@magicfit.co.uk *School hosiery & tights manufrs*

▶ Syd Pollard Commercial Interiors, 98 Marlowe Road, Worthing, West Sussex, BN14 8EZ Tel: (01903) 533483 Fax: (01903) 533483 E-mail: info@partitions.org.uk *Specialists in Fitting Out and Refurbishing Commercial Premisis Including the Supply of Partitions, Suspended Ceilings and Associated Electrical Works Flooring etc,*

Pollards Engineering, Mundy Street, Ilkeston, Derbyshire, DE7 8EU Tel: 0115-932 4787 Fax: 0115-930 3559 E-mail: info@pollardengineering.com *Precision engineers & fabricators*

Pollards Fyrespan, Units 3-5 Haslemere Business Centre, Lincoln Way, Enfield, Middlesex, EN1 1AY Tel: (020) 8443 5511 Fax: (020) 8443 3804 E-mail: info@pollardsfyrespan.co.uk *Architectural metalworkers manufrs*

Pollards Woodworking Machines Of Switzerland Ltd, 49 Aylesbury Street, Bletchley, Milton Keynes, MK2 2BQ Tel: (01908) 644877 Fax: (01908) 271552 E-mail: sales@pollards.co.uk *Cleaning supplies*

▶ Pollen Palace, 39 Snowsfields, London, SE1 3SU Tel: (0800) 0437901 Fax: (020) 7378 1058 E-mail: enquiries@pollenpalace.com *Pollen Palace Prides itself on designing Amazing Flowers for**Discerning Individual*Weddings - Our Forte*Flower For Events - Private & Corporate*High Impact Reception & Restaurant Arrangments*Exotic Plants *Gift Items**

Pollen Recording Studios, 97 Main Street, Bishop Wilton, York, YO42 1SP Tel: (01759) 368223 E-mail: enquiries@pollenstudio.co.uk *Multimedia & web site designers, video production*

▶ Pollington Storage Ltd, 32-34 Moxon Way, Sherburn-In-Elmet, Leeds, LS25 6NZ Tel: (01757) 702235

Alexander Pollock Ltd, Hospital Road, Haddington, East Lothian, EH41 3PD Tel: (01620) 823344 Fax: (01620) 824252 E-mail: jstewart@alexander-pollock.co.uk *Engraving services*

Pollock & Cochrane Ltd, Thrushcraig Works, Rowan Street, Paisley, Renfrewshire, PA2 6RT Tel: 0141-889 2009 Fax: 0141-840 2114 *Dyers & finishers of piece goods*

Pollock Express Ltd, 42-52 Nelson Street, London, E1 2DQ Tel: (020) 7790 3266 Fax: (020) 7265 8498 E-mail: express@pollock.co.uk *Road transport, haulage & freight services*

James Pollock & Son, 53-61 Castle Street, Ballymoney, County Antrim, BT53 6JZ Tel: (028) 2766 3333 Fax: (028) 2766 5951 *Horticultural wholesalers*

▶ Pollock (Scotrans) Ltd, Unit 1-6 Royal Elizabeth Yard, Kirkliston, West Lothian, EH29 9EN Tel: 0131-319 2200 Fax: 0131-319 2233

▶ Pollock Scotrans Ltd, Olivebank, Newhailes Road, Musselburgh, Midlothian, EH21 6SW Tel: 0131-665 2375 Fax: 0131-653 6200

Pollution Control UK Ltd, Mounsey Road, Bamber Bridge, Preston, PR5 6LS Tel: (01772) 620066 Fax: (01772) 628996 E-mail: sales@pollution-control.co.uk *Effluent treatment plant manufrs*

▶ Polly Products, Home Farm Barn, Winkburn, Newark, Nottinghamshire, NG22 8PQ Tel: (01636) 636135 Fax: (01636) 636643 E-mail: sales@pollyproducts.co.uk *Suppliers of equestrian goods in the distinctive polly products style*

Pollyaim Ltd, 9 Churchill Court, 58 Station Road, North Harrow, Harrow, Middlesex, HA2 7SA Tel: (020) 8863 0457 Fax: (020) 8863 0459 E-mail: sales@pollyaim.com *Corrosion protection specialists*

PollyLingua, Po Box 195, Tunbridge Wells, Kent, TN2 5YA Tel: (01892) 544600 Fax: (07092) 019583 E-mail: email@pollylingua.com *Language translation & interpreter service*

Polmeric Mouldings Ltd, 1 Spon Lane Trading Estate, Varney Avenue, West Bromwich, West Midlands, B70 6AE Tel: 0121-525 7887 Fax: 0121-500 6495 E-mail: fred.green@polmeric.co.uk *Plastics injection moulders*

Polstore Storage Systems Ltd, PO Box 408, Dorking, Surrey, RH5 5YF Tel: (0870) 8504012 Fax: (0870) 8504013 E-mail: info@polstore.co.uk *Distributors & manufacturers high density storage systems & mobile units*

Poltec Ltd, 1 Old Stafford Road, Slade Heath, Wolverhampton, WV10 7PH Tel: (01902) 790238 E-mail: sales@poltec.co.uk *High Quality Veterinary equipment, direct from our Uk Factory.*

Poly Advisory Services Ltd, 2 Hollygate Industrial Park, Hollygate Lane, Cotgrave, Nottingham, NG12 3JW Tel: 0115-989 4167 Fax: 0115-989 9215 E-mail: sales@polyadvisory.com *Swimming pool restorers*

Poly Fasteners Ltd, 11-12 Rabans Close, Rabans Lane Industrial Area, Aylesbury, Buckinghamshire, HP19 8TP Tel: (01296) 333500 Fax: (01296) 333509 E-mail: sales@polyfasteners.co.uk *Manufacturer & distributor of blind rivet nuts associated tooling*

Poly Hi Solidur (U K) Ltd, Halifax Road, Todmorden, Lancashire, OL14 5QQ Tel: (01706) 811000 Fax: (01706) 817571 E-mail: sales@polyhisolidur.co.uk *High density & UHMW-PE polyethylene semi-finished/finished components manufrs. QuickSilver tipper truck liners*

Poly Plastics Co., 19 Port Hope Road, Birmingham, B11 1JS Tel: 0121-771 1194 Fax: 0121-753 0244 *Polythene film carrier manufrs*

▶ Poly Postal Packaging, Unit 2 Carlton Grove, Ermine Estate, Lincoln, LN2 2EA Tel: 07986 373236 Fax: 07075 020627 E-mail: enquiries@polypostalpackaging.co.uk *Manufacturer""'s and Converters of Polythene Bags, Mailing Envelopes, Mailing Bags, Post Bags, Postal bags, Mail Bags, Bags Self Seal, Sacks, Carrier Bags, Retail Bags, Packaging, Display Bags, Cash Bags, Security Bags, Tamper Proof Bags, Mailtough Bags, Courier Bags, Despatch Bags, Greetings Card Bags, PP Bags, OPP Bags, Gripseal, Self Seal, Plain or Printed*

Poly Print, 59 High St, London, E17 7AD Tel: (020) 8521 4408 Fax: (020) 8521 4568 E-mail: polyprint@carrierbag.freeserve.co.uk *Polythene & paper bag distribs*

Polyaire Ltd, 17 Enterprise Court, Newton Close, Park Farm Industrial Estate, Wellingborough, Northamptonshire, NN8 6UW Tel: (01933) 402666 Fax: (01933) 402777 E-mail: sales@polyaireuk.demon.co.uk *Air conditioning products*

Polyan Covers, 5 Bainbridge Wharf, Farnhill, Keighley, West Yorkshire, BD20 9BX Tel: (01535) 631212 Fax: (01535) 631313 *Manufacturers of packaging products*

Polybeam Ltd, Polybeam House, Isleport Business Park, Highbridge, Somerset, TA9 4JU Tel: (01278) 780807 Fax: (01278) 780907 *Bathroom products manufrs*

Polybond Ltd, Unit 6 William Street, Northam, Southampton, SO14 5QH Tel: (023) 8022 3266 Fax: (0870) 0527587 E-mail: tom@polybond.co.uk *Paint & adhesive manufrs*

▶ Polybox (Stornoway) Ltd, Marybank, Isle of Lewis, HS2 0DB Tel: (01851) 704079 Fax: (01851) 704706

Polybron Plastics Ltd, Unit 4c Loughborough Motorway Trading Estate, Gelders Hall Road, Shepshed, Loughborough, Leicestershire, LE12 9NH Tel: (01509) 507123 Fax: (01509) 507594 E-mail: sales@polybron.co.uk *Plastic sheet stockists*

Polybuild Ltd, Upper Chancton Farm, London Road, Washington, Pulborough, West Sussex, RH20 3DH Tel: (01903) 892333 Fax: (01903) 892777 E-mail: sales@polybuild.com *Horticultural & agricultural tunnels & greenhouse manufrs*

Polycam, 24 Petersfield Road, Duxford, Cambridge, CB2 4SF Tel: (01223) 835195 Fax: (01223) 510153 E-mail: andrew.huckstep@ntlworld.com *Plastic raw material suppliers*

Polycast Ltd, Clocktower Buildings, Shore Road, Warsash, Southampton, SO31 9GQ Tel: (01489) 885560 Fax: (01489) 885608 E-mail: sales@polycast.ltd.uk Purchasing Contact: Glenn Harris Sales Contact: Glenn Harris Principal Export Areas: North America *Manufacturer of investment castings, aluminium, alloy & stainless steel castings Investment casting is a method of making small, simple or intricately shaped parts to a relatively high degree of accuracy and with a smooth surface,Aluminium alloys are melted in bale-out furnaces, whilst all other alloys are melted in high-frequency induction furnaces. The metal is poured into a hot shell, enabling the material to flow into thin wall sections giving fine furnace detail. Polycast Ltd. is a member of British Investment Casting Trade Association and the Castings Development Centre.*

Polyclear (Southampton) Ltd, First Avenue, Millbrook Trading Estate, Southampton, SO15 0LG Tel: (023) 8070 1158 Fax: (023) 8077 1044 E-mail: 20robby@polyclear.co.uk *Polythene film extruders printers converters*

▶ Polycol Ltd, Stephanie Works, Bayley Street, Stalybridge, Cheshire, SK15 1PY Tel: 0161-338 4400 Fax: 0161-338 3377

Polycones Bolt Boxes Ltd, 9 Ashfold Avenue, Findon Valley, Worthing, West Sussex, BN14 0AP Tel: (01903) 526538 Fax: (01903) 526538 *Polystyrene bolt boxes manufrs*

▶ Polycool Ltd, Church Lane, Kinwarton, Alcester, Warwickshire, B49 6HB Tel: (01789) 766880 Fax: (01789) 764162E-mail: pol@polycool.co.uk *Conservatories, solar inserts retain solar heat suppliers*

Polycrown Ltd, Unit 3 Smiths Forge, North End Road, Yatton, Bristol, BS49 4AU Tel: (01934) 876349 Fax: (01934) 835406 E-mail: sales@polycrown.com *Resin coated emblem & logo manufrs*

Polydiam Instant Rubber Stamp Co., 70-72 Markfield Road, London, N15 4QF Tel: (020) 8493 1060 Fax: (020) 8885 5711 E-mail: sales@rubberstamp.co.uk *Instant rubber stamps manufrs*

Polydraft Ltd, The Tracings, 3-5 Dunston Road, London, E8 4EH Tel: (020) 7923 1130 Fax: (020) 7249 6818 E-mail: info@polydraft.co.uk *Reprographic materials suppliers*

▶ Polydron UK Ltd, Old RAF Hangar, Kemble, Cirencester, Gloucestershire, GL7 6BQ Tel: (01285) 770055 Fax: (01285) 770171 E-mail: headoffice@polydron.com *Educational toy manufrs*

▶ Polyester Converters Ltd, 49-53 Glengall Road, Peckham, London, SE15 6NF Tel: (020) 7740 9740 Fax: (020) 7277 5654 E-mail: sales@psggroup.co.uk Principal Export Areas: Worldwide *Supplier of paper, board & tissue products*

Polyfab & Formings Ltd, Hindley Green Business Park Leigh Road, Hindley, Wigan, Lancashire, WN2 3LL Tel: (01942) 523617 Fax: (01942) 523533 E-mail: sales@polyfab.co.uk *Plastic vacuum formed products*

Polyfashion Ltd, 34 Parliament Street, Small Heath, Birmingham, B10 0QJ Tel: 0121-772 7754 Fax: 0121-766 6744 E-mail: info@polyfashion.co.uk *Shirt manufrs*

Polyfibre UK, 18 Wainwright St, Aston, Birmingham, B6 5TJ Tel: 0121-327 2360 Fax: 0121-327 3089 E-mail: polyfibre@allcomm.co.uk *Glass fibre moulding material agents*

Polyfield Services Ltd, College Lane, Hatfield, Hertfordshire, AL10 9AB Tel: (01707) 281080 Fax: (01707) 281083 E-mail: sales@polyfield.co.uk *Consultancy and training in quality, health & safety, information security, human resources and environmental management systems. Operate Q-Share® management scheme.*

▶ Polyfilters (UK) Ltd, PO Box 18, Mirfield, West Yorkshire, WF14 0NL Tel: (01924) 496584 Fax: (01924) 496249 E-mail: info@polyfilters.com *Vacuum belt filters & energy saving devices manufrs*

Polyflor Ltd, P O Box 3965, Manchester, M45 7NR Tel: 0161-767 1111 Fax: 0161-767 1100 E-mail: info@polyflor.com *Pvc flooring manufrs*

Polyfoam Foam Products, 380c Ringwood Road, Poole, Dorset, BH12 3LT Tel: (01202) 736353 Fax: (01202) 736023 E-mail: peterthompson@polyfoam.sagehost.co.uk *Foam products, polyurethane, polyethylene. Suppliers to: upholsterers, marine, engineering & many other trades for: cushions, mattresses, packaging, linings, case inserts, specialist design, small bath orders catered for. Cut to any shape or size. No minimum order. Regular deliveries.*

Polyformes Ltd, Cherrycourt Way, Leighton Buzzard, Bedfordshire, LU7 4UH Tel: (01525) 852444 Fax: (01525) 850484 E-mail: sales@polyformes.co.uk *Foam (plastic) converters & foam (polyethylene) converter manufacturers. Also closed loop packaging & foam packaging*

Polygonum, 2 Wellington Business Park, Dukes Ride, Crowthorne, Berkshire, RG45 6LS Tel: (01344) 774664 Fax: (01344) 778886 E-mail: sales@polygonum.com *Advertising & promotional gifts*

▶ Polygraphic Ltd, Raebarn House, Hulbert Road, Waterlooville, Hampshire, PO7 7JT Tel: (023) 9223 1888 Fax: (023) 9223 1999 E-mail: sales@inteqniq.com *Logistic support & technical documentation*

Polygraphica Equipment Ltd, 1 Benton Office Park, Horbury, Wakefield, West Yorkshire, WF4 5RA Tel: (01924) 200444 Fax: (01924) 363714 E-mail: sales@polygraphica.com *Providers to the flexographic, gravure, sheetfed offset printing, packaging & converting industries. Professional consultancy services, covering the supply of quality printing machinery & ancillary equipment. We also have a portfolio of new machinery from several international companies for whom Polygraphica act as sole distributors in the U.K. & various overseas countries, all based around the flexographic, gravure, label, offset & corrugated industries*

Polyhedron Software Ltd, Linden House, 93 High Street, Witney, Oxfordshire, OX29 7RH Tel: (01865) 300579 Fax: (01865) 300232 E-mail: wwwsales@polyhedron.com *Software developers*

Polymaps, 41 Truro Rd, St. Austell, Cornwall, PL25 5JE Tel: (01726) 66666 Fax: (01726) 64797 *Map framing & encapsulating services*

Polymark (G B) Ltd, Unit 14, Sopwith Way, Drayton Field Industrial Estate, Daventry, Northamptonshire, NN11 8PB Tel: (01327) 308600 Fax: (01327) 308611 E-mail: polymark.sales@polymark.co.uk Principal Export Areas: Worldwide *Overhead conveyor systems manufrs*

Polymark (G B) Ltd, Unit 14, Sopwith Way, Drayton Field Industrial Estate, Daventry, Northamptonshire, NN11 8PB Tel: (01327) 308600 Fax: (01327) 308610 *Laundry marking equipment manufrs*

Polymark International P.L.C., Polymark House, Abbeydale Road, Wembley, Middlesex, HA0 1LQ Tel: (020) 8991 0011 Fax: (020) 8998 8080 E-mail: sales@technographics.co.uk *Heath field transfers*

Polymathic Trucks Ltd, Coolie House, Unit 2 Anders, Lichfield Road Industrial Estate, Tamworth, Staffordshire, B79 7TA Tel: (01827) 63441 Fax: (01827) 310765 E-mail: sales@coolie.co.uk *Materials handling engineers*

▶ Polymax, School of Electrical & Mechanical Engineers, Budds Lane, Bordon, Hampshire, GU35 0JE Tel: (01420) 474123 Fax: (01420) 487816 E-mail: contactus@polymax.co.uk *Anti vibration, rubber matting, flooring rubber etc manufrs*

Polymer Holdings Ltd, 1 Windmill Lane, Denton, Manchester, M34 3RN Tel: 0161-320 7710 Fax: 0161-320 9940 E-mail: sales@rubberengineering.co.uk *Plastic rotational mouldings manufrs*

Polymer Holdings Ltd, Spurryhillock Industrial Estate, Broomhill Road, Stonehaven, Kincardineshire, AB39 2NH Tel: (01569) 766226 Fax: (01569) 766419 E-mail: sales@tubetec.co.uk *Rubber mouldings manufrs*

▶ Polymer Laboratories Ltd, Essex Road, Church Stretton, Shropshire, SY6 6AX Tel: (01694) 723581 Fax: (01694) 722171 E-mail: sales@polymerlabs.com Principal Export Areas: Worldwide *Polymer Laboratories is a high technology manufacturing company focused on advanced polymer analysis & polymeric particles in the fields of chromatography, clinical diagnostics & medicinal/combinatorial chemistry**

▶ Polymer Recruitment Services, 71 Warstones Gardens, Wolverhampton, WV4 4PE Tel: (01902) 344631 Fax: (01902) 344631 E-mail: mike_bunce@consultant.com *Recruitment agency for the plastics & rubber industries*

Polymer Systems Technology Ltd, 6 Vernon Building, Westbourne Street, High Wycombe, Buckinghamshire, HP11 2PX Tel: (01494) 446610 Fax: (01494) 528611 E-mail: sales@silicone-polymers.co.uk *Silicone solutions providers*

Polymeric Labels Ltd, 12 Greenacres Road, Oldham, OL4 1HA Tel: 0161-678 9005 Fax: 0161-627 1378 E-mail: sales@polymeric.co.uk *Rubber branding products & rubber labels manufrs*

▶ Polymers 1st, D5 West Bridgewater Street, Leigh, Lancashire, WN7 4HB Tel: (01942) 670007 Fax: (01942) 873422

▶ Polymorit Ltd, Unit B1 Little Heath Industrial Estate, Old Church Road, Coventry, CV6 7NB Tel: (024) 7670 5522 Fax: (024) 7670 5533 E-mail: sales@polymorit.com *Manufacturers of aids for the disabled*

▶ PolyOil Ltd, Unit A2, Wellheads Crescent, Wellheads Industrial Estate, Dyce, Aberdeen, AB21 7GA Tel: (01224) 799950 Fax: (01224) 799951 E-mail: info@polyoil.com *Suppliers of engineering polymer downhole tools to oil & gas industry*

Polyone Acrol, Unit G 3, Newton Business Park, Talbot Road, Hyde, Cheshire, SK14 4UQ Tel: 0161-367 8773 Fax: 0161-367 8281 *PVC coated fabrics services & manufrs*

PolyONE Corporation UK Ltd, Langley Road South, Salford, M6 6SN Tel: 0161-737 1717 Fax: 0161-737 3611 *Compounders & suppliers of plastic raw*

Polyone Formulators UK Ltd, Everite Road, Ditton, Widnes, Cheshire, WA8 8PT Tel: 0151-424 1341 Fax: 0151-495 1853 *PVC plastisol manufrs*

Polypack Polythene Co., 4 Heath St Industrial Estate, Abberley Street, Smethwick, West Midlands, B66 2QZ Tel: 0121-558 9977 Fax: 0121-555 6077 E-mail: info@polypackuk.com *Polythene extruders & converters*

Polypal Ltd, Polypal House, Monckton Road Industrial Estate, Wakefield, West Yorkshire, WF2 7AL Tel: (01924) 200015 Fax: (01924) 201160 E-mail: enquiry@polypal.co.uk *Supply, delivery & install designed storage*

▶ Polyphil Ltd, 50 Hurst Lane, Rawtenstall, Rossendale, Lancashire, BB4 7RE Tel: (01706) 229122 Fax: (01706) 211464 E-mail: polyphil@tiscali.co.uk *Polyurethane, rubber & plastic technology*

Polypipe Bathroom & Kitchen Products Ltd, Edlington Lane, Warmsworth, Doncaster, South Yorkshire, DN4 9LS Tel: (01302) 310666 Fax: (01302) 856421 *Sanitary ware die casters/manufrs*

Polypipe Civils Ltd, Boston Road Industrial Estate, Holmes Way, Horncastle, Lincolnshire, LN9 6JW Tel: (01507) 527373 Fax: (01507) 525099 *Plastic pipes manufrs*

Polypipe Civils Ltd, Bishop Meadow Road, Loughborough, Leicestershire, LE11 5RE Tel: (01509) 615100 Fax: (01609) 610215 E-mail: sales@polypipecivils.co.uk *Plastic land drainage pipe manufrs*

Polyplas Extrusions Ltd, Unit 1 Wilden Industrial Estate, Wilden Lane, Stourport-on-Severn, Worcestershire, DY13 9JY Tel: (0845) 5314086 Fax: (01299) 827016 E-mail: info@polyplas.co.uk Principal Export Areas: West Europe *Manufacturers of profiles offering local service nationally from Worcestershire. General purpose plastic extruders serving all industries offering design and development service to value engineer profile shapes. Tooling designed and developed in-house. All products made to order. Rigid, flexible and dual hardness profiles; specialists in co-extrusion (rigid and flexible). Materials used include uPVC /PP /LDPE /HDPE /PC /PETg / ABS /HIPS /SBC /PPE /WC-PVC (rigids) and PVC /PVC Nitrile /TPE /TPV /TEEE (flexibles). ISO 9001 certified. Over 50 years' experience. Friendly, family-run, business with the emphasis on service*

PolyPlus Packaging Ltd, Unit 1 Headley Park Ten, Headley Road East, Woodley, Reading, RG5 4SW Tel: 0845 4941732 Fax: 0118-944 8141 E-mail: sales@polypluspackaging.co.uk *Polyplus are specialist manufacturers of polythene packaging based in Reading producing pink static control, mail, anti corrosion, deep freeze, medical, food grade, and chemical waste bags and packaging*

Polyportables Ltd, Brickbarns Farm, Evesham Road, Egdon, Worcester, WR7 4QR Tel: (01905) 345840 Fax: (01905) 345849 *Portable sanitation manufrs*

Polypostals, Unit 21, Sea Vixen Industrial Estate, Wilverley Road, Christchurch, Dorset, BH23 3RU Tel: (01202) 479932 Fax: (01202) 488118 *Direct mail services*

Polypress Ltd, 20 Bridgeland Street, Bideford, Devon, EX39 2QE Tel: (01237) 472272 Fax: (01237) 421414 *Printers & commercial stationers*

Polyprint Mailing Films Ltd, Mackintosh Road, Rackheath Industrial Estate, Rackheath, Norwich, NR13 6LJ Tel: (01603) 721807 Fax: (01603) 721813 E-mail: jneville@polyprint.co.uk *Printers of polythene for mailing*

Polyprint Plastics (Nottingham) Ltd, Nicholas House, 385 Nottingham Road, New Basford, Nottingham, NG7 7FE Tel: 0115-970 4475 Fax: 0115-942 2531 E-mail: info@poly-print.com *Screen printing & digital*

Polyroof Products Ltd, Castle Park Industrial Estate, Evans Street, Flint, Clwyd, CH6 5XA Tel: (01352) 735135 Fax: (01352) 735182 E-mail: info@polyroof.co.uk *Flat roofing services*

Polysafe Level Crossing Systems Ltd, Unit26 King St Industrial Estate, Langtoft, Peterborough, PE6 9NF Tel: (01778) 560555 Fax: (01778) 560773 E-mail: sales@polysafe.co.uk *Rail (special purpose) equipment manufrs*

Polyscot Polystyrene, 4 Craigluscar Road, Dunfermline, Fife, KY12 9JA Tel: (01383) 732296 Fax: (01383) 620365 E-mail: eps@polyscot.co.uk *Polystyrene packaging products converters*

Polysec Cold Rooms Ltd, Blackpole Trading Estate West, Hindlip Lane, Blackpole, Worcester, WR3 8TJ Tel: (01905) 458551 Fax: (01905) 754137 E-mail: mail@polysec.co.uk *Polyurethane panels for coldrooms*

▶ Polyshapes Ltd, Unit 3, Sidings Business Park, Freightliner Road, Hull, HU3 4XA Tel: (01482) 211955 Fax: (01482) 215656 E-mail: sales@polyshapes.co.uk *Suppliers of structured & solid polycarbonate sheets*

Polysigns Signs & Nameplates, 121-123 Newfoundland Road, Bristol, BS2 9LU Tel: 0117-954 0888 Fax: 0117-935 0213 E-mail: polysigns@aol.com *Sign manufrs*

Polysius Ltd, The Brackens, London Road, Ascot, Berkshire, SL5 8BE Tel: (01344) 884161 Fax: (01344) 886438 E-mail: sue.caveren@thyssenkrupp.com *Cement & mineral processing plant*

Polysleeve Products Ltd, Groby Lodge Farm, Groby, Leicester, LE6 0GN Tel: (01530) 249719 Fax: (01530) 249729 *Cable installation equipment*

Polystar Plastics Ltd, Peel House, Peel Street, Southampton, SO14 5QT Tel: (023) 8023 2153 Fax: (023) 8023 2157 E-mail: sales@polystar.co.uk *Extruders & converters high quality polythene bags*

Polystrop Ltd, Bridge Road, Kingswood, Bristol, BS15 4FW Tel: 0117-970 1196 Fax: 0117-970 1205 *Lifting & webbing sling manufrs*

Polytec Holden Ltd, Porthouse Industrial Estate, Bromyard, Herefordshire, HR7 4NS Tel: (01885) 485153 Fax: (01885) 483057 E-mail: gareth.anderson@polytec-holden.com *Motor vehicle plastics moulders*

Polytec Personnel Ltd, Orwell House, Cowley Road, Cambridge, CB4 0PP Tel: (01223) 423267 Fax: (01223) 420268 E-mail: recruit@ppluk.net *Technical recruitment agency*

Polytec Plastic Products, Ormrod Street, Bury, Lancashire, BL9 7HF Tel: 0161-705 1901 Fax: 0161-705 1935 E-mail: dmworsley@polytecpf.fsnet.co.uk *Thermoplastic fabricators*

Polytech Plastic Products, Bullock Street, West Bromwich, West Midlands, B70 7HE Tel: 0121-525 7777 Fax: 0121-525 6777 E-mail: riaarnumber2@aol.com *Plastics injection mouldings manufrs*

Polytek Chemical Mnfrs, 7 Beech Court, Doune, Perthshire, FK16 6HT Tel: (01786) 841541 Fax: (01786) 841537 *Janitorial suppliers*

Polytek UK Ltd, Water Lane, Exeter, EX2 8BZ Tel: (01392) 204116 Fax: (01392) 204114 E-mail: ghb@polytekuk.com *Water sewage tank manufrs*

▶ Polythene Envelope Co., 6 Delta Close, Norwich, NR6 6BQ Tel: (01603) 409999 Fax: (01603) 485584 E-mail: sales@polytheneenvelopecompany.co.uk *Manufacturers of polythene envelopes*

Polytypos Ltd, Radstock, BA3 3WD Tel: (01761) 411018 Fax: (01761) 411551 E-mail: karenn@polytypos.com *Print broker*

Polyurethane Progress Ltd, Church Street, Wakefield, West Yorkshire, WF1 5QY Tel: (01924) 387310 Fax: (01924) 382951 E-mail: enquiries@polyurethane-progress.co.uk *Hydraulic & pneumatic seals, moulded components industrial polyurethane manufrs*

▶ Polzeath Linen Services, Unit 9b Pityme Industrial Estate, St. Minver, Wadebridge, Cornwall, PL27 6NS Tel: (01208) 869700 E-mail: marion@polzeathlinenservices.com *Commercial laundry & linen hire services*

▶ Pom Print, Station Road, Mintlaw, Peterhead, Aberdeenshire, AB42 5EE Tel: (01771) 623000 Fax: (01771) 623300 E-mail: info@pomprint.co.uk *Suppliers of embroidery & printed products*

Pometon Ltd, 5, Queensway Link Industrial Estate, Telford, Shropshire, TF3 3DN Tel: (01952) 299777 Fax: (01952) 299008 E-mail: sales@pometon.demon.co.uk *Abrasive metallic & shot blasting materials distrbutors*

Pompadour Ltd, Chequers Road, West Meadows Industrial Estate, Derby, DE21 6EN Tel: (01332) 342228 Fax: (01332) 342228 *Hair & beauty suppliers*

Pompadour Laboratories Ltd, Mount Street, New Basford, Nottingham, NG7 7HF Tel: 0115-978 1383 Fax: 0115-978 4598 *Hairdressers & beauty sundries supplier* Also at: Derby, Lincoln & Mansfield

Pond Liners Direct Ltd, 8 Millbrook Business Park, Hoe Lane, Nazeing, Waltham Abbey, Essex, EN9 2RJ Tel: (01992) 890901 Fax: (01992) 893393 E-mail: info@e-pond.co.uk *We have been a supplier of BUTYL rubber technology for water containment and water-proofing since 1974. We also support trade and retail sales for ponds, direct from our factory outlet.*

Pond Plants, Birley Moor Garden Centre, 27 Moor Valley, Mosborough, Sheffield, S20 5BB Tel: 0114-251 3536 Fax: 0114-251 3336 *Aquarium centre*

Pond & Sharman Ltd, Browells Lane, Feltham, Middlesex, TW13 7EQ Tel: (020) 8890 8222 Fax: (020) 8751 0179 E-mail: pond@cogg.co.uk *Motor repairs*

Pondakoi Aquatics, Sussex Country Gardens, Mark Cross, Crowborough, East Sussex, TN6 3PJ Tel: (01892) 853388 Fax: (01892) 853388 *Live fish retailers*

Ponden Mill Ltd, 23 College Walk, Keighley, West Yorkshire, BD21 3QA Tel: (01535) 610984 *Linen & curtain manufrs*

Ponden Mill Ltd, 13 Westgate, Wakefield, West Yorkshire, WF1 1JZ Tel: (01924) 377777 *Soft furnishings & bedding suppliers*

Pongees Ltd, 28-30 Hoxton Square, London, N1 6NN Tel: (020) 7739 9130 Fax: (020) 7739 9132 E-mail: sales@pongees.co.uk *Silk merchants*

▶ Pontardawe Refergation, Unit A, Lon Hir, Alltwen, Pontardawe, Swansea, SA8 3DE Tel: (01792) 869515 Fax: (01792) 869522 *Refrigeration services*

Pontiac Coil Europe Ltd, PO Box 246, Nottingham, NG2 1NQ Tel: 0115-986 1126 Fax: 0115-986 0563 E-mail: info@pontiaccoil.co.uk *Transformer manufrs*

Pontrilas Timber & Builders Merchants Ltd, The Saw Mills, Pontrilas, Hereford, HR2 0BE Tel: (01981) 240444 Fax: (01981) 240748 E-mail: sales@pontrilastimber.co.uk *Timber import merchants*

The Pool Co. Ltd, 50 Torwood Street, Torquay, TQ1 1DT Tel: (01803) 291900 Fax: (01803) 290399 E-mail: info@the-pool-co.com *Swimming pool dealership*

▶ Pool Construction Standfield Ltd, Poplar Farm, Dean Road, West Tytherley, Salisbury, SP5 1NR Tel: (01794) 341909 Fax: (01794) 341795

Pool Filtration Ltd, 76 Stafford Road, Wallington, Surrey, SM6 9AY Tel: (020) 8669 0657 Fax: (020) 8773 0647 E-mail: poolfiltrationltd@tiscali.co.uk *Swimming pool equipment suppliers*

Herbert Pool Ltd, 95 Fleet Road, Fleet, Hampshire, GU51 3PJ Tel: (01252) 620444 Fax: (01252) 622292 *Mechanical handling equipment manufrs*

▶ Pool Meadow House, Pool Meadow Close, Off Warwick Road, Solihull, West Midlands, B91 3HS Tel: 01604 591577 E-mail: enquiries@johnshepherd.com *Exclusive development of new apartments and houses in Solihull, West Midlands by Tripod Crest Homes*

Pool N Spa Services Ltd, Falcon Road, Sowton Industrial Estate, Exeter, EX2 7LJ Tel: (01392) 446910 Fax: (01392) 446912 E-mail: poolnspaservicesltd@btconnect.com *Swimming pool equipment suppliers*

▶ The Pool Shop, 60 The Grove, Christchurch, Dorset, BH23 2HB Tel: (01202) 480232 Fax: (01202) 480222 E-mail: sales@pool-shop.co.uk *Leading internet suppliers of swimming pool products & accessories*

Pool Vac Ltd, 229 London Road, Camberley, Surrey, GU15 3EY Tel: (01276) 25252 Fax: (01276) 21796 E-mail: poolvac@web-hq.com *Swimming pool contractors*

Poole Computers Ltd, 865 Ringwood Road, Bournemouth, BH11 8LL Tel: (01202) 591548 Fax: (01202) 590944 E-mail: pcl@lds.co.uk *Technical staff recruitment agency*

George Poole Metal Processors, Clough Street, Hanley, Stoke-On-Trent, ST1 4AS Tel: (01782) 265377 Fax: (01782) 263226 E-mail: georgepoolescrap@aol.com *Scrap iron, steel merchants & haulage services*

Poole Grinders Ltd, 81 Sterte Avenue West, Poole, Dorset, BH15 2AL Tel: (01202) 675650 Fax: (01202) 666388 *Centreless & cylindrical grinding*

Poole Instrument Calibration Ltd, 6 Cabot Business Village, Holyrood Close, Poole, Dorset, BH17 7BA Tel: (01202) 658333 Fax: (01202) 659966 E-mail: sales@pooleinstruments.com *Calibration services*

Poole Lighting Ltd, Cabot Lane, Poole, Dorset, BH17 7BY Tel: (01202) 690945 Fax: (01202) 600166 E-mail: vanessa.saxby@poolelighting.com *Domestic lighting manufrs*

The Poole Pottery, 48 Wyatts Lane, Corfe Mullen, Wimborne, Dorset, BH21 3SQ Tel: (01202) 600838 E-mail: chris@mrpottery.co.uk *A replacement service for discontinued tableware and collectables from Poole Pottery, Hornsea Pottery, Denby Pottery, Royal Doulton and most other manufacturers.*

Poole Process Equipment Ltd, 43-49 Nuffield Road, Nuffield Industrial Estate, Poole, Dorset, BH17 0RA Tel: (01202) 674683 Fax: (01202) 665265 E-mail: postmaster@poole-process.co.uk *Heat exchanger manufrs*

Poole & Son Scoops Ltd, Unit 15 Delta House, Adderley Street, Birmingham, B9 4ED Tel: 0121-753 0912 Fax: 0121-753 0912 *Weighing machine parts manufrs*

Poole Technical Plating Services Ltd, Unit 32-33 Dawkins Business Centre, Dawkins Road, Poole, Dorset, BH15 4JY Tel: (01202) 673640 Fax: (01202) 682414 E-mail: sales@ptpuk.com *Electroplating services*

continued

▶ indicates data change since last edition

Poole Waite & Co. Ltd, 3 Clerkenwell Road, London, EC1M 5PE Tel: (020) 7253 8117 Fax: (020) 7490 0579 E-mail: sales@poolewaite.co.uk *Architectural ironmongers*

Poolec Automotive Products Ltd, Fourth Way, Bristol, BS11 8DL Tel: 0117-982 9109 Fax: 0117-982 7690 E-mail: poolec.bristol@btconnect.com *Auto-electrical suppliers*

PooleIT Ltd, 1st Floor Unit 3A Parkside, Ringwood, Hampshire, BH24 3SG Tel: (01425) 1308099 Fax: (01425) 483294 E-mail: sales@pooleit.com *Based In Poole covering the South Coast, PooleIT Ltd are an IT consultancy specializing in Small to Medium size business requirements for reliable computer system infrastructures. We provide a flexible & friendly service. Please contact us for help & advise for your company's IT requirements.*

Poolpump Ltd, 2 Beaulieu Road, Christchurch, Dorset, BH23 2EA Tel: (01202) 499392 Fax: (01202) 473662 *Pump manufrs*

Pools & Gardens Ltd, Walk Mills Farm, Wychbold, Droitwich, Worcestershire, WR9 0DH Tel: (01527) 861597 Fax: (01527) 861881 *Swimming pool distributors*

▶ Poolsafe Fencing Supplies, 96A Devonshire Road, Chorley, Lancashire, PR7 2DJ Tel: (0798) 0936847 E-mail: poolsafefencing@lancsmail.com *Sales and installation of swimming pool security fences and solar pool heating systems throughout the UK, France, Spain and Portugal.*

Poolserve Leisurebuild Ltd, 39 Windsor Road, Chobham, Woking, Surrey, GU24 8LD Tel: (01276) 856677 Fax: (01276) 856061 E-mail: mail@poolserveleisurebuild.co.uk *Swimming pool contractors & maintenance*

Pope Bros Building Contractors Swindon Ltd, 13 Cricklade Street, Swindon, SN1 3EZ Tel: (01793) 522113 Fax: (01793) 522517 *Building contractors*

Pope Group of Companies, Vernon Place, Northern Court, Nottingham, NG6 0DE Tel: 0115-976 0732 Fax: 0115-927 5169 E-mail: pope-group@lineone.net *Textile engineers*

Pope & Meads Ltd, Star Street, Ware, Hertfordshire, SG12 7AN Tel: (01920) 462366 Fax: (01920) 462332 *Precision engineers manufrs*

Pope & Parr, 118-120 Talbot Street, Nottingham, NG1 5HH Tel: 0115-947 3015 Fax: 0115-950 3194 *Double glazing, stained glass & glaziers services*

Poplar Products (Leeds) Ltd, Ramshead Approach, Seacroft, Leeds, LS14 1LR Tel: 0113-273 2288 Fax: 0113-273 4744 E-mail: mail@poplarseating.co.uk *Contract furniture manufrs*

Popper & Carter, Billets Farm, Great Wigborough, Colchester, CO5 7RW Tel: (01206) 738222 Fax: (01206) 734535 E-mail: nigel@popperandcarter.co.uk *Steel fabricators*

Poppetwear Ltd, Old Co-Operative Building, Newstead Road, Annesley, Nottingham, NG15 0AX Tel: (01623) 751586 Fax: (01623) 751591 *Leisure clothing manufrs*

▶ Poppleton & Appleby, 32 High Street, Manchester, M4 1QD Tel: 0161-834 7025 Fax: 0161-833 1548 E-mail: enquires@pandamanchester.co.uk *insolvency practitioners practitioner specialists insolvent trade creditor independent Company Individual Arrangements Administrative Receiverships Creditors Members Voluntary Liquidation CVA Bankruptcies Administration Orders Creditor Representation Financial Restructuring Corporate Recovery Credit management company searches credit status accounts bankruptcies fraudulent trading enterprise act 2003 corporate insolvency law company rescue debts court order administrator asset realisation floating charge agricultural break up sale county court judgement disqualification compulsory investor compensation licensed insolvency practitionerpetition proxy receiver receivership secured secure security statutory demand trustee winding up banks*

Popplewells Coach Works Ltd, High Road, Thornwood, Epping, Essex, CM16 6LP Tel: (01992) 574040 Fax: (01992) 576653 *Motor body repairers*

Poppy, 91 Allerton Road, Shrewsbury, SY1 4QW Tel: (01743) 369800 *Office & domestic cleaning services*

▶ Poppy Signs, Unit 5 Traceys Industrial Estate, Wigan Road, Leyland, PR25 5UA Tel: (07949) 026542 E-mail: info@poppysigns.co.uk *Sign service design manufacture supply & installation*

Porcelanosa Yorkshire Ltd, Unit 15 Shaw Lane Industrial E, Ogden Rd, Doncaster, South Yorkshire, DN2 4SQ Tel: (01302) 341029 Fax: (01302) 739273 *Ceramic tiles & bathroom suite distribs*

Pork Farm Bowyers, 55 Stallard Street, Trowbridge, Wiltshire, BA14 8HH Tel: (01225) 777367 Fax: (01225) 777367 E-mail: mike.godley@pork-farms.co.uk *Meat pie manufrs*

Pork Farms Bowyers, Longmead, Shaftesbury, Dorset, SP7 8PL Tel: (01747) 851511 Fax: (01747) 853401 *Meat (processed & cooked) products manufrs*

Pork Farms Bowyers Ltd, Dartmouth Rd, Smethwick, W. Midlands, B66 1AS Tel: 0121-558 6672 Fax: 0121-555 6310 *Pork pie distributors*

Porky Pine, West Street, Coggeshall, Colchester, CO6 1NT Tel: (01376) 563323 Fax: (01376) 563323 E-mail: info@pinefurnitureessex.com *Pine furniture retailers oak*

▶ Porosol Ltd, Tennis House, 249-251 Belper Road, Stanley Common, Ilkeston, Derbyshire, DE7 6FY Tel: 0115-930 7977 Fax: 0115-944 2147 E-mail: t.shaw@porosol.fsnet.co.uk *Cards, decorations & wedding decorations manufrs*

Port Agric Ltd, Unit 5 Hailsham Industrial Park, Diplocks Way, Hailsham, East Sussex, BN27 3JF Tel: (01323) 841207 Fax: (01323) 844942 E-mail: sales@portagric.co.uk *Manufacturers of agricultural equipment*

▶ Port Designs, 128 High Street, Burbage, Marlborough, Wiltshire, SN8 3AB Tel: (01672) 810366 Fax: (01672) 810803 E-mail: info@portdesigns.co.uk *For the past 12 years PORT has designed, developed and manufactured a range of laptop accessories that are all ergonomically-designed to benefit laptop users and the laptops themselves, increasing productivity and reducing injury to the user. The products fall into two areas, A range of fun, frisky and functional cases and bags for technology and Ergonomic products to enhance user safety and Laptop performance. The PORT laptop bags have been designed to provide the highest standards of user comfort and laptop safety. Amongst their products is the Ergo Station, a docking station for your laptop.*

Port of London Authority, Barkers Hall, 7 Harp Lane, London, EC3R 6LB Tel: (020) 7743 7900 Fax: (020) 7743 7998 E-mail: marketing@portoflondon.co.uk *General cargo ports*

Port PCS Ltd, Port Elphinstone Post Office, Elphinstone Road, Port Elphinstone, Inverurie, Aberdeenshire, AB51 3UR Tel: (01467) 629935 *Computer maintenance*

▶ Port Strategy, The Old Mill, Lower Quay, Fareham, Hampshire, PO16 0RA Tel: 01329 825335 Fax: 01329 825330 E-mail: info@portstrategy.com *Port Strategy magazine meets the information needs of government strategists, port executives, marine terminal operators and key port users, with informed reporting and opinions on the key changes and opportunities that lie ahead in the global port industry.*

Port Of Sunderland, Quayside House Wylam Wharf, Low Street, Sunderland, SR1 2BU Tel: 0191-553 2146 Fax: 0191-553 2145 E-mail: sales@portofsunderland.org.uk *Port services including import & export*

Port Of Workington, Prince of Wales Dock, Workington, Cumbria, CA14 2JH Tel: (01900) 602301 Fax: (01900) 604696 E-mail: workington.port@cumbriacc.gov.uk *Port authority*

Porta Tool Fixings Ltd, Units 6-8, Brunel Road, Leigh-on-Sea, Essex, SS9 5JL Tel: (01702) 510080 Fax: (01702) 510030 E-mail: portatools@btconnect.com *Fixings distributors*

▶ Portable Air Conditioning Solutions Ltd, 1 Mill Way, Bushey, WD23 2AF Tel: (0845) 1658071 *Air conditioning*

▶ Portable Air Conditioning Solutions Ltd, 1 Longfield Cottages, Killicks, Cranleigh, Surrey, GU6 7BB Tel: (0845) 1658071

▶ Portable Air Conditioning Solutions Ltd, 43 Richings Way, Iver, Buckinghamshire, SL0 9DB Tel: (0845) 1658071

▶ Portable Air Conditioning Solutions Ltd, 10 Barley Mow Passage, London, W4 4PH Tel: (0845) 1658071

▶ Portable Air Conditioning Solutions Ltd, 10 Warwick Road, West Drayton, Middlesex, UB7 9BZ Tel: (0845) 1658071

Portable Appliance Safety Services Ltd, 1 Hunters Buildings, Bowesfield Lane, Stockton-on-Tees, Cleveland, TS18 3QZ Tel: (01642) 603039 Fax: (0870) 1431869 E-mail: info@pat-services.co.uk *Specialists in electronic & electrical test equipment, calibration, portable appliance testing, training & equipment sales*

Portable Conveniences, Weavers Weft, Engine Brow, Tockholes, Darwen, Lancashire, BB3 0ND Tel: (01254) 200181 Fax: (01254) 777787 E-mail: sales@portableconveniences.com *Portable toilet hire*

Portable Conveyors Ltd, Bowling Green Lane, Albrighton, Wolverhampton, WV7 3HB Tel: (01902) 373735 Fax: (01902) 374755 E-mail: enquiries@portable-conveyors.co.uk *Conveyor hire & sales*

▶ Portable Offices Hire Ltd, Woodyard Lane, Foston, Derby, DE65 5DJ Tel: (01283) 585822 Fax: (01283) 585833 E-mail: derby@portableoffice.co.uk *Portable building hirers*

Portable Refrigeration Co. Ltd, St Georges House, Gaddesby Lane, Rearsby, Leicester, LE7 4YH Tel: (01483) 233133 Fax: (01483) 233135 E-mail: admin@portablerefrigeration.co.uk *Refrigeration equipment hire*

Portables Direct Ltd, Unit 5 Westmoreland House Cumberland Park, Scrubs Lane, London, NW10 6RE Tel: (020) 8968 1222 Fax: (020) 8968 1777 E-mail: sales@portables.co.uk *Computer retailers*

Portakabin Ltd, 19-21 Glasgow Road, Newbridge, Midlothian, EH28 8SY Tel: 0131-335 3114 Fax: 0131-335 3110 *Portacabin hire*

Portal Contracting Ltd, Unit 1 Yeldon Court, Finedon Road Industrial Estate, Wellingborough, Northamptonshire, NN8 4SS Tel: (01933) 270970 Fax: (01933) 270760 *Building contractors*

Portal Telecommunications Equipment, Sapphire House, Roundtree Way, Norwich, NR7 8SQ Tel: (01603) 785300 Fax: (01603) 785303 *Telecommunications distributors*

▶ PORTALP Automatic Doors, Unit 16, Invincible Road Industrial Estate, Farnborough, Hampshire, GU14 7QU Tel: 0845 603 1137 Fax: 0845 450 6356 E-mail: sales@metro-doors.com *Nationwide installation, service and maintenance of all automatic doors from Britain""s leading entrance specialist.*

Portals, Overton Mill, Overton, Basingstoke, Hampshire, RG25 3JG Tel: (01256) 770770 Fax: (01256) 770937 E-mail: sales.portals@delarue.co.uk *Bank-note paper makers*

Portaprompt Ltd, Spearmast Industrial Park, Lane End Road, High Wycombe, Buckinghamshire, HP12 4JQ Tel: (01494) 450414 Fax: (01494) 437591 E-mail: helen@portaprompt.co.uk *Hire & sale of television & conference products*

Portaramp, Roudham Road, Harling Road, Norwich, NR16 2QN Tel: (01953) 714599 Fax: (01842) 714598 E-mail: sales@portaramps.co.uk *Disabled & handicapped ramp manufrs*

Portasilo Ltd, New Lane, Huntington, York, YO32 9PR Tel: (01904) 624872 Fax: (01904) 611760 E-mail: bulk@portasilo.co.uk Principal Export Areas: Asia Pacific, Africa, Central/East Europe, West Europe & North America *Bulk materials handling systems suppliers*

Portch Trimmings Ltd, 2 Ireton Avenue, Leicester, LE4 9EW Tel: (0116) 276 6537 Fax: (0116) 246 0778 *Belt & shoe components*

Portchester Engineering, 19 Windmill Grove, Fareham, Hampshire, PO16 9HP Tel: (023) 9237 4771 Fax: (023) 9221 9253 E-mail: sales@portchesterengineering.co.uk *Precision engineers*

Portcullis Computer Security Ltd, Grange Barn, Pikes End, Pinner, Middlesex, HA5 2EX Tel: (020) 8868 0098 Fax: (020) 8868 0017 *Anti-virus software*

Portec Rail Products (UK) Ltd, Vauxhall Industrial Estate, Wrexham, Clwyd, LL14 6UY Tel: 01978 820820 *Railway products distributors*

Portech Systems, The Green House, Gibb Street, Birmingham, B9 4AA Tel: 0121-224 7299 Fax: 0121-624 0550 E-mail: info@portech.co.uk *Software developers*

Portek Ltd, Blease Farm, Old Hutton, Kendal, Cumbria, LA8 0LU Tel: (01539) 722628 Fax: (01539) 741282 E-mail: sales@portek.co.uk *Agricultural wholesalers*

▶ Porteous Fabrication, 1 Baronscourt Road, Willowbrae, Edinburgh, EH8 7ET Tel: 0131 6610907 *Stainless steel sheet metal work & fabricators*

Portequip Ltd, Penninghame Home Farm, Penninghame, Newton Stewart, Wigtownshire, DG8 6RD Tel: (01671) 402775 Fax: (01671) 403791

Porter Agriculture, Gowers Farm, Tumblers Green, Braintree, Essex, CM77 8AZ Tel: (07831) 447102 Fax: (01376) 334375 E-mail: mike@porterag.co.uk *Agricultural brokers*

▶ Andrew Porter Ltd, Huyton Road, Adlington, Chorley, Lancashire, PR7 4EZ Tel: (01257) 482398 Fax: (01257) 484324

Porter Bros Ltd, King's Dock Mill, Tabley Street, Liverpool, L1 8JH Tel: 0151-709 5155 Fax: 0151-709 6637 E-mail: sales@flagsbyporters.co.uk *Flag & banner manufrs*

C. Porter Ltd, Britannia Road, Waltham Cross, Hertfordshire, EN8 7PE Tel: (01992) 713565 Fax: (01992) 712980 *Quarry operators, ballast merchants & waste management*

Porter Environmental Supplies Ltd, 18 Montpelier Avenue, Bexley, Kent, DA5 3AL Tel: (020) 8298 1919 Fax: (020) 8298 7737 *Filter bag & cage manufrs*

Porter & Haylett Ltd, Viaduct Works, Wroxham, Norwich, NR12 8RX Tel: (01603) 782472 Fax: (01603) 783089 E-mail: sales@connoisseurafloat.com *Boat builders & hirers*

Porter & Laker, Dissegna House, Weston Avenue, West Thurrock, Grays, Essex, RM20 3ZP Tel: (01708) 689400 Fax: (01708) 689401 *Freight forwarders*

Porter Packaging Co. Ltd, Hardwick Grange, Woolston, Warrington, WA1 4RT Tel: (01925) 822828 Fax: (01925) 837593 *Packaging material manufrs*

Porter Precision Products Ltd, Masons Road, Stratford-upon-Avon, Warwickshire, CV37 9NF Tel: (01789) 292409 Fax: (01789) 292241 *Press tool punch manufrs*

Steve Porter Transport Ltd, Dallimore House Somerton Industrial Park, Newport Road, Cowes, Isle of Wight, PO31 8PB Tel: (01983) 291732 Fax: (01983) 299746 E-mail: freight@steveportertransport.com *Road transport, haulage & freight services*

Porters, George Cayley Drive, Clifton Moore, York, YO30 4XE Tel: (01904) 690023 Fax: (01904) 692045 *Timber & wallboard merchants*

Porters Of Woking, 5 North Road, Woking, Surrey, GU21 5DS Tel: (01483) 765432 Fax: (01483) 756432 E-mail: sales@portersremovals.co.uk *Removal & storage contractors*

Portex Concrete Products, Limekiln Farm Buildings, Easton Lane, Portland, Dorset, DT5 1BW Tel: (01305) 820064 Fax: (01305) 820064 *Concrete products manufrs*

Port-Formance, 59 Canberra Square, Warrington, WA2 0DY Tel: (01925) 724278 Fax: (01925) 724278 E-mail: steveposo@ntlworld.com *High performance engine tuning specialists*

Porthcawl Angling Centre, 10 Dock Street, Porthcawl, Mid Glamorgan, CF36 3BL Tel: (01656) 772404 Fax: (01656) 772404 *Fishing tackle retailers*

Porthmadog Concrete Ltd, Glan Byl, Criccieth, Gwynedd, LL52 0RD Tel: (01766) 530644 Fax: (01766) 530407 E-mail: robert@porthmadog.co.uk *Concrete manufrs*

Porthmadog Skip Hire, Penamser Industrial Estate, Porthmadog, Gwynedd, LL49 9NZ Tel: (07979) 506624 Fax: (01766) 515217 E-mail: welshskips@supanet.com *Industrial gases & skip hire services*

▶ Porthmeor Hotel, Godrevy Terrace, St. Ives, Cornwall, TR26 1JA Tel: (01736) 740260 E-mail: sales@porthmeor.com

Portico Products, Lath Lane, Smethwick, West Midlands, B66 1EA Tel: 0121-553 7222 Fax: 0121-553 3577 E-mail: sales@porticoproducts.com *Components of roller shutters*

Portix, Belvedere, Basing View, Basingstoke, Hampshire, RG21 4HG Tel: (0870) 4607710 Fax: (01256) 396501 *Machine computer solution services*

Portland Aquaria, 22 Portland Street, Chatham, Kent, ME4 5LS Tel: (01634) 841145 *Aquaria supplies*

Portland Chimneys, 4 Portland Avenue, The Industrial Estate, Irvine, Ayrshire, KA12 8JD Tel: (01294) 274813 Fax: (01294) 312008 *Chimney manufrs*

Portland Commercial Bodies Ltd, Unit 2 Portland Street, Birmingham, B6 5RX Tel: 0121-327 2713 Fax: 0121-328 0302 E-mail: portlandbodies@btconnect.com *Commercial vehicle body builders*

Portland Engineering Co. Ltd, Wide Street, Portland, Dorset, DT5 2JP Tel: (01305) 821273 Fax: (01305) 821499 E-mail: office@portlandengineering.com *Brake disc design & manufrs*

Portland Janitorial Products Ltd, 14 York Street, Ayr, KA8 8AN Tel: (01292) 288388 Fax: (01292) 288189 E-mail: sales@portland-janitorial.co.uk *Janitorial supplies*

▶ Portland Optical Laboratories Ltd, 7 New Street, Bridgtown, Cannock, Staffordshire, WS11 0DD Tel: (01543) 579442 Fax: (01543) 579055

Portland Pressings Ltd, Moor Lane, Birmingham, B6 7HH Tel: 0121-356 8187 Fax: 0121-344 3039 *Presswork manufrs*

▶ Portland Print, Telford Way, Telford Way Industrial Estate, Kettering, Northamptonshire, NN16 8UN Tel: (01536) 511555 Fax: (01536) 310136

▶ Portland Stock Taking & Inventories, PO Box 7526, Newark, Nottinghamshire, NG22 9ZR Tel: (01623) 836000 Fax: 01623 862502 E-mail: audit@portlandhq.co.uk *Stocktaking, stock auditing and valuation services to the licensed, catering and retail trades*

Portland Thistle Hotel, 3-5 Portland Street, Manchester, M1 6DP Tel: 0161-228 3400 Fax: 0161-228 6347 E-mail: manchester@thistle.co.uk *Hotels*

Portlantis Ltd, Queenscot House, Sandhurst Road, Wokingham, Berkshire, RG40 3LS Tel: 0118-977 4529 E-mail: info@portlantis.com *Supplier of high quality work wear*

▶ Portlock Software, Vickers House Vickers Business Centre, Priestley Road, Basingstoke, Hampshire, RG24 9NP Tel: (01256) 392990 Fax: (01256) 473010 E-mail: sales@portlock.com *IT software*

Portman Doors Ltd, Unit 3 Bradshaw Works, Printers Lane, Bolton, BL2 3DW Tel: (01204) 699521 Fax: (01204) 669094 E-mail: info@portmandoors.co.uk *Roller shutters, garage doors, security shutters & screens manufrs*

Portman Electronics Ltd, 159 Commercial Road, Newport, Gwent, NP20 2PJ Tel: (01633) 841007 Fax: (01633) 222951 *Telecommunication systems distribution*

Portman Hill & Co. Ltd, P.O. Box 10, Middlesbrough, Cleveland, TS2 1HH Tel: (01642) 218538 Fax: (01642) 245775 E-mail: exports@parson-crosland.demon.co.uk *Export agents*

Portmeirion Enterprises Ltd, London Road, Stoke-on-Trent, ST4 7QQ Tel: (01782) 744721 Fax: (01782) 744061 E-mail: nhuxley@portmeirion.co.uk *Pottery*

▶ Portmeirion Potteries, 473 King Street, Stoke-on-Trent, ST3 1EU Tel: (01782) 326661 Fax: (01782) 326664

Portmere Rubber Ltd, Victoria Street, Northam, Southampton, SO14 5QZ Tel: (023) 8022 3628 Fax: (023) 8022 3250 Purchasing Contact: J. Baker Sales Contact: P. Howard Principal Export Areas: Asia Pacific, Central Asia, Middle East, Africa, Central/East Europe & West Europe *Manufacturers & suppliers of rubber sheeting, extrusions, strip & gaskets, mouldings, hand built custom hose clips & couplings, rubber hoses, plant & equipment, PVC hose & ducting & technical assistance*

Portobello Engineering Ltd, Milton Works, Bowden Lane, Chapel-en-le-Frith, High Peak, Derbyshire, SK23 0QG Tel: (01298) 812309 Fax: (01298) 812336 E-mail: hal@portobelloltd.co.uk *Pipework & air conditioning*

Portobello Fabrications Ltd, Coleford Road, Sheffield, S9 5PE Tel: (0870) 4284406 Fax: 0114-244 2261 E-mail: sales@portobello-fab.co.uk *Portobello Fabrications Ltd was established in 1933 and is a subsidiary of Compass (Holdings) Limited, a UK based group of engineering companies. The company specialises in the mechanical design and fabrication of process plant and equipment to meet stringent pressure systems requirements. The markets serviced include all the bulk process industries, including Petrochemicals, Water, Fine Chemicals, Pharmaceuticals, Food, Power generation and Nuclear industries. The company has established a reputation for quality products at competitive price levels and is accredited to ISO9001 (LRQA) and authorised by ASME for the supply of 'U' stamped equipment. The necessary organisational requirements to comply with European Pressure Equipment Directive have been addressed and virtually all equipment manufactured is CE marked.*

Portobello Press Ltd, 69-71 Scrubs Lane, London, NW10 6QU Tel: (020) 8960 6796 Fax: (020) 8960 2708 E-mail: sales@portobellopress.co.uk *Printers*

▶ Portobello Printers Ltd, 9 Morris Road, Newtongrange, Dalkeith, Midlothian, EH22 4ST Tel: 0131-663 1292

Portobello Wholefoods, 266 Portobello Road, London, W10 5TY Tel: (020) 8968 9133 Fax: (020) 8560 1840 *Health food retailers*

▶ Portofino Studio Collection Ltd, Gore Road, New Milton, Hampshire, BH25 6SH Tel: (01425) 611722 Fax: (01425) 611218

Portola Packaging Ltd, 3 Carriage Drive, Doncaster, South Yorkshire, DN4 5NT Tel: (01302) 552400 Fax: (01302) 365541 *Plastic milk & juice closure manufrs*

▶ Portrack Severnsides Ltd, Grange BSNS Centre, The Grange Business Centre, Belasis Avenue, Billingham, Cleveland, TS23 1LG Tel: (01642) 554063 Fax: (01642) 554063 E-mail: phandling@aol.com

▶ Portreath Bakery Ltd, 3 The Square, Portreath, Redruth, Cornwall, TR16 4LA Tel: (01209) 842612

▶ Ports Decor Limited, 46 Passingham Avenue, Billericay, Essex, CM11 2TD Tel: (01277) 657558 Fax: (01277) 657548 E-mail: enquiries@portsdecorltd.co.uk *Ports Décor Ltd are a Decorating Contractor with over 20 years experience. *Our services include, Interior & Exterior Decorating, Paper hanging & coving, Specialised finishing's, Maintenance*New Builds,Insurance work**

Portsdown Office Ltd, 1 Warrior Business Centre, Fitzherbert Road, Portsmouth, PO6 1TX Tel: (023) 9232 4611 Fax: (023) 9221 0164 E-mail: sales@portsdown.co.uk *Office furniture distribs*

▶ Portsea Harbour Company Ltd, South Street, Gosport, Hampshire, PO12 1ZZ Tel: (023) 9252 4551

Portsmouth Aviation Ltd, Airport Service Road, Portsmouth, PO3 5PF Tel: (023) 9266 2251 Fax: (023) 9267 3690 E-mail: info@portav.co.uk *Electroplating services*

Portsmouth Gun Centre, 295 London Road, Portsmouth, PO2 9HF Tel: (023) 9266 0574 Fax: (023) 9264 4666 *Gun makers, dealers & agents/gunsmiths*

H. Portsmouth & Son, 1033-1043 London Road, Leigh-On-Sea, Essex, SS9 3JY Tel: (01702) 478255 Fax: (01702) 473640 E-mail: print@hportsmouth.freeserve.co.uk *Printers & commercial stationers*

Portsmouth Handling Services Ltd, Britney Centre, Wharf Road, Portsmouth, PO2 8RU Tel: (023) 9287 0087 Fax: (023) 9287 0104 E-mail: trevorphs@tiscali.co.uk *Freight container handling services*

Portsmouth Marriott Hotel, North Harbour, Portsmouth, PO6 4SH Tel: (023) 9238 3151 Fax: (023) 9238 8701 *Hotel & conference facility providers*

Portsmouth & South East Hampshire Chamber of Commerce & Industry, Regional Business Centre, Harts Farm Way, Havant, Hampshire, PO9 1HR Tel: (023) 9244 9449 Fax: (023) 9244 9444 E-mail: sehants@chamber.org.uk *Training exporting & business support services*

▶ Portsmouth Surgical Equipment Ltd, 38 New Lane, Havant, Hampshire, PO9 2NF Tel: (023) 9249 9922 Fax: (023) 9249 8899 *Hospital equipment*

Portsmouth Water P.L.C., 8 West Street, Havant, Hampshire, PO9 1LG Tel: (023) 9249 9888 Fax: (023) 9245 3632 *Water utility company*

Portus & Rhodes (Fabrications) Ltd, 77 St Mary S Road, Garston, Liverpool, L19 2NN Tel: 0151-427 6885 *Sheet metal & steel fabrication*

Portview Fitout Ltd, 46 Florenceville Avenue, Belfast, BT7 3GZ Tel: (028) 9064 4765 Fax: (028) 9064 1330 E-mail: info@portview.co.uk *Building & shopfitting contractors.*

Portway Dental Laboratory, 203-205 (rear of) Avonmouth Road, Avonmouth, Bristol, BS11 9EG Tel: (0117) 982 2813 *Dental laboratory*

▶ Portway Plumbing Ltd, Castlegate Business Park, Salisbury, SP4 6QX Tel: (01722) 329268 Fax: (01722) 328257

Portway Tool & Gauge Ltd, 27 Dudley Road, Lye, Stourbridge, West Midlands, DY9 8EX Tel: (01384) 892458 Fax: (01384) 424371 E-mail: info@portwaytoolgauge.co.uk *Designers & manufacturers of tools & gauges*

Portways, Sedgley Road East, Tipton, West Midlands, DY4 7UY Tel: 0121-557 7641 Fax: 0121-522 2012 E-mail: sales@vitafibres.com *Synthetic fillings for soft furnishings manufrs*

Portwest Clothing Ltd, Fields End Business Park, Thurnscoe, Rotherham, South Yorkshire, S63 0JF Tel: (01709) 894575 Fax: (01709) 880830 E-mail: orders@portwest.com *Clothing suppliers*

Porvair plc, 50 Bergen Way, North Lynn Industrial Estate, King's Lynn, Norfolk, PE30 2JG Tel: (01553) 765500 Fax: (01553) 765599 E-mail: lclare@porvair.com *Multinational Group specialising in the development of material technologies- specialist filtration & porous materials; waterproof breathable membranes used in leather, textile & printing applications; unique ceramic mould materials & machinery; microplate filtration products; high performance metals & handling materials; fuel cell & fuel reformation materials*

Porvair Sciences Ltd, 6 Shepperton Business Park, Govett Avenue, Shepperton, Middlesex, TW17 8BA Tel: (01932) 224539 Fax: (01932) 254393 E-mail: int.sales@porvair.com *Laboratory plastic ware manufrs*

Porvair Technology Ltd, Clywedog Road South, Wrexham Industrial Estate, Wrexham, Clwyd, LL13 9XS Tel: (01978) 661144 Fax: (01978) 664554 E-mail: enquiries@porvairfiltration.com Principal Export Areas: Worldwide *Industrial filter elements*

Pos, 1 Horbury Bridge Mills, Bridge Road, Horbury, Wakefield, West Yorkshire, WF4 5RW Tel: (01924) 276666 Fax: (01924) 276777

▶ POS Consumables, Unit 7 Louis Pearlman Centre, Goulton Street, Hull, HU3 4DL Tel: (0870) 1632885 Fax: (01482) 606885 E-mail: sales@pos-consumables.co.uk *Retailers of consumables*

Pos Direct Ltd, 99 Boston Road, Leicester, LE4 1AW Tel: 0116-234 4400 Fax: 0116-235 8947 E-mail: sales@pos-direct.co.uk *POS Direct Ltd are an established company specialising in Fulfilment (Order Processing and Pick & Pack), Distribution (via Royal Mail, Courier, Haulier, Own Fleet) and Warehousing (Storage & Stock Management) of Multi-Channel Product Lines, Consumer Goods, Point of Sale/Point of Purchase Materials, Display & Promotional Items, Sales Literature and Print throughout the UK, Europe and Worldwide. We undertake these services for many blue chip companies ranging from one-off single item projects to ongoing multiple product line operations utilising our Ecommerce solution. This includes System Integration, Order Downloads, Tailored Database Management, Online Track & Trace and real time 24/7 Online Ordering & Bespoke Reporting. We have a consistent and proven track record with high profile brands, retailers and publishers and our objective is to provide Premium Service with complete Visibility, Outstanding Value for Money and Innovation in delivering the best solution for you.*

Poseidon Maritime (UK) Ltd, 480 Union Street, Aberdeen, AB10 1TS Tel: (01224) 561133 Fax: (01224) 561144 E-mail: info@poseidonuk.com *Marine, engineering & safety consultants*

Poselco Lighting, 1 Bristol Road, Greenford, Middlesex, UB6 8UW Tel: (020) 8813 0101 Fax: (020) 8813 0099 E-mail: sales@poselco.com *Lighting supply, design, conversions & repair*

Posford Haskoning, Eastchester House, Harlands Road, Haywards Heath, West Sussex, RH16 1PG Tel: (01444) 458551 Fax: (01444) 440665 E-mail: sales@royalhaskoing.com *Consulting engineers*

▶ Posh Eyes, Westbury House, 52 French Laurence Way, Chalgrove, Oxford, OX44 7YF Tel: 01865 400384 E-mail: message@posheyes.co.uk *UK"s Leading Online Retailer of Designer Glasses and Branded Contact Lenses at Discounts of up to 70% off High St. prices.*

▶ The Posh Pud & Sandwich Co., 76 Garden Road, Dunstable, Beds, LU6 3JD Tel: (01582) 673334 Fax: (01582) 673334 E-mail: enquiries@poshpuds.co.uk *Delivered sandwiches,savouries and desserts for breakfast and lunchtime business meetings within a 20 mile radius of Dunstable.Key towns included for free delivery are Hemel Hempstead,Leighton Buzzard and Luton.*

Posh Wosh - Mobile Car Valeting Ashford Kent, Unit 19, Dunnock Road, Kennington, Ashford, Kent, TN25 4QJ Tel: (07811) 547041 Fax: (01233) 630537 E-mail: posh_wosh2003@hotmail.com *Car & commercial vehicle valeting*

Posiflex, 46-48 Wilbury Way, Hitchin, Hertfordshire, SG4 0UD Tel: (01462) 443131 Fax: (01462) 443128 E-mail: info@posiflex.co.uk *Pipe fittings & couplings manufrs*

Posiflex International Ltd, Saddleworth Business Centre, Huddersfield Road, Delph, Oldham, OL3 5DF Tel: (01457) 877720 Fax: (01457) 877730 *Epos hardware suppliers*

Posit Design, The Granary, Station Road, Sandford, Winscombe, Avon, BS25 5RA Tel: (01934) 823931 Fax: (01934) 823958 *Point of sale design consultants*

Positek Ltd, L6 The Link, Andoversford Industrial Estate, Cheltenham, Gloucestershire, GL54 4LB Tel: 01242 820027 Fax: 01242 820615 E-mail: mark@positek.com *Electronic sensors manufrs*

Posi-Thread (UK) Ltd, 4-5 Bridgewater Road, Hertburn Industrial Estate, District 11, Washington, Tyne & Wear, NE37 2SG Tel: 0191-417 8178 Fax: 0191-415 3120 E-mail: info@posithread.co.uk *Threading & grooving insert manufrs*

▶ Positive Associates Ltd, PO Box 354, Dorking, Surrey, RH5 6FU Tel: (01306) 731482 Fax: (01306) 731534 E-mail: sales@positive-associates.com *Industrial chemicals & raw material suppliers*

▶ Positive Business Partners Ltd, 6 Sussex Mews, The Pantiles, Tunbridge Wells, Kent, TN2 5QJ Tel: (01892) 616262 Fax: (01892) 513118 E-mail: info@positive-business.com *Results driven business growth consultancy with unique guaranteed results programme through client partnership development programme*

▶ Positive Clothing London Ltd, 20 Wells Mews, London, W1T 3HQ Tel: (020) 7299 3500 Fax: (020) 7299 3518 *Wholesalers of womens clothing*

Positive Computer Systems, New Forest Enterprise Centre, Chapel Lane, Totton, Southampton, SO40 9LA Tel: (023) 8057 7733 Fax: (023) 8057 7755 E-mail: sales@positive-computers.co.uk *Computer consultants*

▶ Positive Electrical Installations Ltd, Unit 1 Central Trading Estate, Stallings Lane, Kingswinford, West Midlands, DY6 7LJ Tel: (01384) 405320 Fax: (01384) 405321

▶ Positive Focus Ltd, Unit 12 C Shepperton Business Park, Govett Avenue, Shepperton, Middlesex, TW17 8BA Tel: (01458) 250603 Fax: (01458) 250604 E-mail: sales@positivefocus.co.uk *Computer software distributors*

▶ Positive Health & Safety Ltd, 218 Gazette Buildings, 168 Corporation Street, Birmingham, B4 6TF Tel: 0121-212 2020 E-mail: info@positivehands.co.uk *OFFERING THE ONE STOP SOLUTION TO ALL YOUR HEALTH AND SAFETY REQUIREMENTS*

Positive Metering Systems, Suite 5, The Cloisters, Broyle Place Farm, Laughton Road, Ringmer, East Sussex, BN8 5SD Tel: (01273) 815990 Fax: (01273) 815999 E-mail: projects@positivesystems.co.uk *Chemical injection systems supplier & designer*

▶ Positive Pixels Photography, Stoneleigh, Bulford Road, Durrington, Salisbury, SP4 8DH Tel: (01980) 653138 E-mail: positive_pixels@tiscali.co.uk *Professional photography and bespoke photographic training. Correspondence tutoring. NVQ Assessment.*

Positive Solutions Ltd, Solutions House, School Lane, Brinscall, Chorley, Lancashire, PR6 8QP Tel: (01254) 833300 Fax: (01254) 833333 *Epos systems suppliers*

▶ Positivexperience Ltd, The Old Vicarage, Market Place, Castle Donington, Derby, DE74 2JB Tel: (01332) 856393 Fax: (01332) 810769 E-mail: gordon.beck@positivexperience.co.uk *In depth human resources skills & solutions for business*

Poskitt Painters Ltd, Empire Works, Holywell Lane, Castleford, West Yorkshire, WF10 3HJ Tel: (01977) 553089 Fax: (01977) 555765 E-mail: plastics@hotmail.com *Wood pallets & packing case manufrs*

Possilpark Shotblasting Co. Ltd, 73 Dunn Street, Glasgow, G40 3PE Tel: 0141-556 6221 Fax: 0141-551 0714 E-mail: admin@possilparks.co.uk *Metal finishing & blast cleaning services*

Possum Controls Ltd, 8 Stocklake Park Industrial Estate, Farmborough Close, Aylesbury, Buckinghamshire, HP20 1DQ Tel: (01296) 481591 Fax: (01296) 394349 E-mail: info@possum.co.uk *Handicapped person aid designers*

Post Anchor Co., Halesfield 21, Telford, Shropshire, TF7 4PA Tel: 0121-522 4585 *Fencing products*

Post & Column Company Ltd, Unit 1, Road Four, Winsford, Cheshire, CW7 2NU Tel: (01606) 550502 Fax: (01606) 550857 E-mail: info@postandcolumn.co.uk *Manufacturers and suppliers of sign posts, lighting columns and fixings in a variety of finishes including, plastic coated, galvanised and full highways agency approved paint finishes.*

▶ The Post Factory, 7Th Floor Newcombe House, 45 Nottinghill Gate, London, W11 3LQ Tel: (020) 7229 6015 Fax: (020) 7727 8509 E-mail: info@postfactory.co.uk *Television post erection service*

▶ Post Safe, Unit B3 Thanet Reach BSNS Park, Millennium Way, Broadstairs, Kent, CT10 2LA Tel: (01843) 860212 Fax: (01843) 864393 E-mail: sales@postsafe.co.uk *Manufacturer of peel & seal polythene envelopes & sacks*

Post Safe Ltd, 158 Broadway, Knaphill, Woking, Surrey, GU21 2RL Tel: (01483) 486618 Fax: (01483) 489267 *Envelopes manufrs*

▶ Posters4u, Westhill Business Centre, Arnhall Business Park, Westhill, Aberdeenshire, AB32 6UF Tel: (01224) 742598 E-mail: posters4u@yahoo.co.uk *Personalised labels for whisky, champagne etc*

Postfield Structure Solutions Ltd, Old Barn Lane, Kenley, Surrey, CR8 5AT Tel: (020) 8668 8241 Fax: (020) 8660 1693 E-mail: info@postfieldcables.com *Telecom & datacom cable manufrs*

▶ Postfield Systems, 53 Ullswater Crescent, Coulsdon, Surrey, CR5 2HR Tel: (020) 8645 9760 Fax: (020) 8655 6070 E-mail: sales@postfield.co.uk *Installation & maintenance of customer information displays*

Postglow Printers, 139 Francis Road, London, E10 6NT Tel: (020) 8539 7559 Fax: (020) 8556 1970 E-mail: sales@frankel.co.uk *Printers & stationers manufrs*

Posthouse Cardiff City, Castle Street, Cardiff, CF10 1XD Tel: (0870) 4008140 Fax: (029) 2037 1495 *Hotel with conference facilities*

▶ Postpots Ltd, 108 Titan House, Cardiff Bay Business Centre, Cardiff, CF24 5BS Tel: (02920) 472002 Fax: (02920) 472003

Postroom Suppliers Ltd, Unit D3, Lomer Farm Industrial Estate, Wrotham Road, Meopham, Gravesend, Kent, DA13 0AN Tel: (01474) 815850 Fax: (01474) 815860 E-mail: sales@europeanpostalsystems.co.uk *Mailing franking machines suppliers*

▶ Pot Of Gold, Akroyd Mill, 4 Akroyd Place, Halifax, West Yorkshire, HX1 1YH Tel: (01422) 380704 Fax: (01422) 380706 *Cosmetics suppliers*

Pot Ready Processing, Lisnaskea, Enniskillen, County Fermanagh, BT92 0AW Tel: (028) 6772 3272 Fax: (028) 6772 3272 *Vegetable food processors*

▶ Potato Academy Ltd, The Old Barn, Ferringham Lane, Ferring, Worthing, West Sussex, BN12 5LL Tel: (01903) 500368 E-mail: contact@potatoacademy.co.uk

Potato Man Ltd, Mellor Street, Rochdale, Lancashire, OL11 1PF Tel: (01706) 644384 Fax: (01706) 639926 E-mail: enquiries@ronchalker.co.uk *Wholesale potato & fruit merchants*

Potbury & Sons Ltd, 17-31 High Street, Sidmouth, Devon, EX10 8LN Tel: (01395) 515555 Fax: (01395) 512608 E-mail: potbury@aol.com *Removal contractors furniture stores*

Potclays Ltd, Brick Kiln Lane, Stoke-on-Trent, ST4 7BP Tel: (01782) 219816 Fax: (01782) 286506 E-mail: sales@potclays.co.uk *Ceramic clay, glazes, kilns, materials supplier & manufrs*

Poten & Partners UK Ltd, 20 Balderton Street, London, W1K 6TL Tel: (020) 7493 7272 Fax: (020) 7629 7078 E-mail: info@poten.com *Gas brokers energy researchers*

Poth Hille & Co. Ltd, 37 High Street, London, E15 2QD Tel: (020) 8534 7091 Fax: (020) 8534 2291 E-mail: enquiries@poth-hille.co.uk *Wax refiners & manufrs*

Pott Shrigley Joinery Ltd, Moorside Engine House The Old Brickworks, Bakestonedale Road, Pott Shrigley, Macclesfield, Cheshire, SK10 5RX Tel: (01625) 575590 Fax: (01625) 572446

The Potted Plant Co., 72 Austrey Road, Warton, Tamworth, Staffordshire, B79 0HQ Tel: (01827) 330032 *Interior landscaping*

Potter Cowan & Co Belfast Ltd, Phoenix House, 20 Duncrue Cresent, Belfast, BT3 9BW Tel: (028) 9037 0050 Fax: (028) 9077 7333 E-mail: pottercowan@btconnect.com *Kitchen installers & distributors*

G. Potter, The Forge, Village Road, Bonchurch, Ventnor, Isle Of Wight, PO38 1RG Tel: (01983) 855233 *Blacksmiths*

George Potter & Co. (Musical Instruments) Ltd, 26-28 Grosvenor Road, Aldershot, Hampshire, GU11 3DP Tel: (01252) 323226 Fax: (01252) 342921 E-mail: pottersdrums@aol.com *Musical instrument sale & repairers*

Potter Group Ltd, Cutnall Green, Rushock, Droitwich, Worcestershire, WR9 0NS Tel: (01299) 851441 Fax: (01299) 851390 E-mail: droitwich@pottergroup.co.uk *Logistic services*

▶ Potter Group Ltd, Rail Freight Terminal, Woodward Road, Knowsley Industrial Park, Liverpool, L33 7UY Tel: 0151-290 0671 Fax: 0151-289 1310 E-mail: knowsley@pottergroup.co.uk *Shared user warehousing & distribution incorporating rail freight*

Potter Group Ltd, Barlby Road, Selby, North Yorkshire, YO8 5DZ Tel: (01757) 702303 Fax: (01757) 210834 E-mail: selby@pottergroup.co.uk *3rd party logistics storage & distribution*

H. Potter Engineering Ltd, Fisher Street, Low Walker, Newcastle Upon Tyne, NE6 4LT Tel: 0191-295 4420 Fax: 0191-295 4482 *Hose & fittings manufrs*

Richard Potter, Millstone Lane, Nantwich, Cheshire, CW5 5PN Tel: (01270) 625791 Fax: (01270) 610483 E-mail: richardpotter@fortimber.demon.co.uk *Timber merchants & DIY suppliers*

Potter & Soar Ltd, Beaumont Road, Banbury, Oxfordshire, OX16 1SD Tel: (01295) 253344 Fax: (01295) 272132 E-mail: potter.soar@btinternet.com *Manufacturers of wire mesh*

Potter & Upton, 4 St Martins Industrial Estate, Tat Bank Road, Oldbury, West Midlands, B69 4NP Tel: 0121-544 8400 Fax: 0121-544 4050 *Wood & metal pattern makers*

Potteries Demolition Co. Ltd, Brocksford Street, Stoke-on-Trent, ST4 3EZ Tel: (01782) 313234 Fax: (01782) 598371 *Demolition contractors & heavy haulage*

Potteries Die Co. Ltd, 136 Knypersley Road, Stoke-On-Trent, ST6 8JD Tel: (01782) 534348 Fax: (01782) 535297 E-mail: nick@potteriesdie.co.uk *Specialist toolmakers*

Potteries Powder Coating, 9 Hyde Park Trading Estate, City Road, Stoke-on-Trent, ST4 1DS Tel: (01782) 749292 Fax: (01782) 749393 *Powder coating*

Potteries Specialist Auctions, 271 Waterloo Road, Stoke-on-Trent, ST6 3HR Tel: (01782) 286622 Fax: (01782) 213777 E-mail: potteriesltd@aol.com *Ball bearing distributors & agents*

Potteries Towers, Unit 10 Norton Industrial Estate, Bellerton Lane, Stoke-on-Trent, ST6 8ED Tel: (01782) 537263 Fax: (01782) 537213 *Steel scaffold manufrs*

Potters, 1 Botanic Court, Martland Park, Orrell, Wigan, Lancashire, WN5 0JZ Tel: (01942) 219960 Fax: (01942) 219966 E-mail: info@pottersherbals.co.uk *Health food products manufrs*

Potters Ballotini Ne Ltd, Darlington Road, West Auckland, Bishop Auckland, County Durham, DL14 9PR Tel: (01388) 830800 Fax: (01388) 830819 *Manufacturers of glass beads*

Potters Bar Denture Centre, 13 The Service Road, Potters Bar, Hertfordshire, EN6 1QA Tel: (01707) 660303 E-mail: philtucker40@skynow.net *Dental technicians*

Potters Bar Health Foods, 21 The Broadway, Darkes Lane, Potters Bar, Hertfordshire, EN6 2HX Tel: (01707) 652255 Fax: (01707) 652255 *Health care consultants & retailers*

▶ Potters Europe, Ask House, 2 Northgate Avenue, Bury St. Edmunds, Suffolk, IP32 6BB Tel: (01284) 715400 Fax: (01284) 715401 E-mail: info.potters@dial.pipex.com *Glass micro sphere manufrs* Also at: West Auckland

▶ The Potters Friend, 6 Rawle Close, Cheadle, Stoke-On-Trent, ST10 1UX Tel: (01538) 751200 E-mail: thepottersfriend@aol.com *Ceramic consultancy*

Potters Herbal Supplies Ltd, Leyland Mill Lane, Wigan, Lancashire, WN1 2SB Tel: (01942) 405100 Fax: (01942) 820255 E-mail: info@pottersherbals.co.uk *Health food products manufrs*

Potters (London) Ltd, Rollesby Road, Hardwick Industrial Estate, King's Lynn, Norfolk, PE30 4HP Tel: (01553) 774271 Fax: (01553) 692312 E-mail: sales@pottersuk.com *Boxes for the jewellery trade*

Potters Packaging, Govan Road, Fenton Industrial Estate, Stoke-On-Trent, ST4 2RS Tel: (01782) 848888 Fax: (01782) 848900 *Carton manufrs*

▶ Potters Pork Products Ltd, Unit 3 Newfield Close, Walsall, WS2 7PB Tel: (01922) 624001 Fax: (01922) 614540

Potters Potclais Group, Pelsall Road, Walsall, WS8 7DL Tel: (01543) 377015 Fax: (01543) 372301 *Ceramic suppliers*

Potterton Commercial, Brooks House, Coventry Road, Warwick, CV34 4LL Tel: (0870) 6001991 Fax: (01926) 405305 *Domestic heaters commercial heaters*

Pottery & Porcelain Restoration, 3 Whessoe Road, Darlington, County Durham, DL3 0QP Tel: (01325) 460319 Fax: (01325) 460319 *Pottery & porcelain restoration services*

Potterycrafts Ltd, Winton House, Winton Approach, Croxley Green, Rickmansworth, Hertfordshire, WD3 3TL Tel: (01923) 800006 Fax: (01923) 245544 *Ceramic materials suppliers*

Potterycrafts Ltd, Campbell Road, Stoke-on-Trent, ST4 4ET Tel: (01782) 745000 Fax: (01782) 746000 E-mail: sales@potterycraft.co.uk *Ceramic & pottery equipment & materials*

Potton Windows Ltd, Shannon Place, Potton, Sandy, Bedfordshire, SG19 2SP Tel: (01767) 260626 Fax: (01767) 262048 E-mail: sales@pottonwindows.co.uk *PVCU window frames installers & manufrs*

Jonathan Potts Ltd, Estate Road 1, South Humberside Industrial Estate, Grimsby, South Humberside, DN31 2TB Tel: (01472) 355946 Fax: (01472) 267843 *Scrap metal merchants*

Trevor Potts Plant Hire, Hellaby Lane, Hellaby, Rotherham, South Yorkshire, S66 8HN Tel: (01709) 700200 Fax: (01709) 701875 E-mail: trevor@pottsplanthire.fsnet.co.uk *Contractors plant hire*

Potts & Ward Woodcocks Ltd, Lion House, Crowhurst Road, Brighton, BN1 8AF Tel: (01273) 557211 Fax: (01273) 557093 *Floor covering wholesalers*

William Potts & Sons Ltd, 112 Alfreton Road, Derby, DE21 4AU Tel: (01332) 345569 Fax: (01332) 290642 E-mail: sales@pottsofleeds.com *Tower clock manufrs*

Poulten & Graf Ltd, 1 Alfreds Way Industrial Estate, Alfreds Way, Barking, Essex, IG11 0AS Tel: (020) 8594 4256 Fax: (020) 8594 8419 E-mail: volacjpl@aol.com *Scientific glassware manufrs*

Poulten Selfe & Lee Ltd, Russell House, Burnham Business Park, Burnham-On-Crouch, Essex, CM0 8TE Tel: (01621) 787100 Fax: (01621) 787175 E-mail: info@rheotek.com Principal Export Areas: Worldwide *Petroleum testing equipment manufrs*

Ann Poulter, 2a Worksop Road, Swallownest, Sheffield, S26 4WD Tel: 0114-287 6707 Fax: 0114-287 6707 *Curtain manufrs*

continued

Poulton Remedial Services Ltd, 86-88 Church Street, Old Town, Eastbourne, East Sussex, BN21 1QJ Tel: (01424) 422122 Fax: (01323) 734596 E-mail: enquiries@structuralrepairs.com *Remedial service contractors*

Poultry Air Ltd, Unit 11 The Stables, Stonham Aspal, Stowmarket, Suffolk, IP14 6AU Tel: (01473) 890040 Fax: (01473) 890040 *Plastic ventilation poultry products*

Poultry First Ltd, The Manor House, Greenways Manor Estate, Woodhall Spa, Lincolnshire, LN10 6PY Tel: (01526) 352471 Fax: (01526) 352022 *Poultry producers*

Pound Hill Security Ltd, 8 Balliol Close, Crawley, West Sussex, RH10 3TE Tel: (01293) 883821 Fax: (01293) 883821 E-mail: poundshillsecurity@freenet.co.uk *Alarm installers*

Pound International Ltd, 109 Baker Street, London, W1U 6RP Tel: (020) 7935 3735 Fax: (020) 7224 3734 E-mail: pound@dial.pipex.com *OTC pharmaceutical product manufrs*

▶ PoundSpinner Ltd, 194 Soho Road, Birmingham, B21 9LR Tel: 0121 5519000 Fax: 0121 5540533 E-mail: www.poundspinner@hotmail.com *Our Main line of products and services are based on £1 products, this ranges from hardware, homeware, gadgets, stationary, toys etc. But we are also providers of various products met to our clients needs, If a particular product is required we will find it for the best price and deliver directly to your door step.(Try-US)*

Pourshins plc, The Lodge, Harmondsworth Lane, West Drayton, Middlesex, UB7 0AB Tel: (020) 8917 5777 Fax: (020) 8917 5791 E-mail: info@pourshins.com *Food distributors*

Pow Ltd, Conitor House, Denbury Road, Newton Abbot, Devon, TQ12 6AD Tel: (01626) 361490 Fax: (01626) 333359 E-mail: sales@powplastics.co.uk *GRP tanks, clinical waste units & portable kiosk manufrs*

Pow Sport & Leisure Co., PO Box 28, London, W4 4WT Tel: (0870) 3503650 Fax: (0870) 3503651 E-mail: info@pow-sport.co.uk *Suppliers to sport & leisure facilities*

Powa Pak Cleaners Ltd, Bletchley, Market Drayton, Shropshire, TF9 3RZ Tel: (01630) 638276 Fax: (01630) 638548 E-mail: sales@powapak.co.uk *Building restoration services*

Powair Automation Ltd, Powair House, Nest Road, Gateshead, Tyne & Wear, NE10 0ER Tel: 0191-469 5211 Fax: 0191-469 1858 E-mail: automation@powair.com *Press shop equipment manufrs*

Powda Paint Finishing Plant Ltd, p.o. box 60, Dudley, West Midlands, DY3 1TP Tel: (01902) 677033 Fax: (01902) 678319 E-mail: info@pfpltd.co.uk *Metal finishing Systems*

Powdat Enamellers Ltd, Sanders Road, Finedon Road Industrial Estate, Wellingborough, Northamptonshire, NN8 4NL Tel: (01933) 445920 Fax: (01933) 445924 *Powder coating specialist services*

Powder Coatings Ltd, 215 Tyburn Road, Birmingham, B24 8NB Tel: 0121-250 2145 Fax: 0121-250 2154 E-mail: roger@abbeyland.co.uk *Finishing services to the trade, powder coaters*

Powder Link, 47 Meyrick Drive, Newbury, Berkshire, RG14 6SY Tel: (01635) 30457 Fax: (01635) 31310 E-mail: sales@powderlink.co.uk *Powder paint services*

Powder & Liquid Products Ltd, Factory 37, No 1 Industrial Estate, Consett, County Durham, DH8 6TW Tel: (01207) 591217 Fax: (01207) 592119 E-mail: sales@plp.co.uk *Laundry detergent & household cleaners manufrs*

▶ Powder Process Technology Ltd, Unit 18 Tardebigge Court, Hewell Lane, Redditch, Worcestershire, B97 6QJ Tel: (01527) 540404 *Materials handling engineers*

Powder Systems Ltd, Estuary Business Park, Speke, Liverpool, L24 8RG Tel: 0151-448 7700 Fax: 0151-448 7702 E-mail: sales@p-s-l.com Principal Export Areas: Asia Pacific, Central Asia, Africa, North America & South America *Pharmaceutical producers*

▶ The Powdertech Group, 108 Churchill Road, Bicester, Oxfordshire, OX26 4XD Tel: (01869) 320600 Fax: (01869) 246330 E-mail: lisa.r@powdertech.co.uk *The Powdertech group are specialists in high quality powder coatings and unique finishes. The Group comprises four independent businesses, including Powdertech Bicester, Corby, ESP and Spectrum. Each business, which is underpinned by the main corporate organisation, focuses on different market sectors offering expert knowledge, specialist skills and a very personal service.*

▶ Powel Automation Ltd, Commerce Way, Lancing Industrial Estate, Lancing, West Sussex, BN15 8TA Tel: (01903) 762700 Fax: (01903) 763652 E-mail: sales@powel.co.uk *Roof tile machine manufrs*

Powelectrics Ltd, 46 Kepler, Tamworth, Staffordshire, B79 7XE Tel: (01827) 310666 Fax: (01827) 310999 E-mail: sales@powelectrics.co.uk *Manufacturers, ultrasonic sensing equipment & (automated inspection)*

Powell & Associates, Bilbrook Cottage, 36 Dukes Wood Avenue, Gerrards Cross, Buckinghamshire, SL9 7JT Tel: (01753) 893162 Fax: (01753) 893162 E-mail: david.powell@powell-assoc.com *IT consultants services*

▶ Powell Demolition, 91 Eastham Village Road, Eastham, Wirral, Merseyside, CH62 0AW Tel: 0151-327 5700 Fax: 0151-327 7153

Powell Electrical Ltd, 53 Churchfield Street, Dudley, West Midlands, DY2 8QN Tel: (01384) 259911 Fax: (01384) 211446 E-mail: john@powellelectrical.co.uk *Electrical contractors*

Powell Gee & Co Ltd, PO Box 15, Wednesbury, West Midlands, WS10 0UF Tel: 0121-556 6729 Fax: 0121-556 6729 E-mail: sales@powellgee.co.uk *Fastener manufacturers & distributors*

Powell & Harber, Brickfields Road, Worcester, WR4 9WN Tel: (01905) 731717 Fax: (01905) 724787 E-mail: info@powell-harber.co.uk *Plastic injection moulders & toolmakers*

Harry Powell, 1 Hill Road, Clevedon, Avon, BS21 7LN Tel: (01275) 875907 Fax: (01275) 349237 E-mail: sales@harrypowell.com *Kitchen, bathroom & bedroom showroom retailers*

Powell Mcneil Machinery Co. Ltd, Newcombe Drive, Hawkesworth Trading Estate, Swindon, SN2 1DZ Tel: (01793) 533675 Fax: (01793) 616171 E-mail: powellmcneil@compuserve.com *Sheet metal machinery distributors*

Powell Manufacturing Co. (Coventry) Ltd, Cromwell Street, Coventry, CV6 5EX Tel: (024) 7668 5131 Fax: (024) 7663 7886 *Precision engineers & press tool manufrs*

Powell Marketing Ltd, P M House Cromer Industrial Estate, Hilton Fold Lane, Middleton, Manchester, M24 2LE Tel: 0161-653 7770 Fax: 0161-655 3795 E-mail: enquiries@powellmarketing.co.uk *Screen printers & display material manufrs*

▶ Powell Packaging Ltd, Birkdale Road, Scunthorpe, South Humberside, DN17 2AU Tel: (01724) 853625 Fax: (01724) 280159 E-mail: powellpackaging@btconnect.com *Card board box manufrs*

Powell's Automatics, 8 Marine Gardens, Whitley Bay, Tyne & Wear, NE26 1EQ Tel: 0191-253 1985 Fax: 0191-251 1493 *Amusement machine distributors & manufrs*

Powells Of Coolham Ltd, The Mill, Coolham, Horsham, West Sussex, RH13 8GR Tel: (01403) 741226 Fax: (01403) 741784 *Horse feed suppliers & animal feed supplements*

Powells Forest & Gardens, Cap View, Llangua, Abergavenny, Gwent, NP7 8HD Tel: (01981) 240403 Fax: (01981) 240403 *Garden tools suppliers*

Powell's of Sherborne, Middlemarsh, Sherborne, Dorset, DT9 5QW Tel: (01300) 345255 Fax: (01300) 345367 E-mail: pow@connect-2.co.uk *Pallet & crate manufrs*

▶ Power 4 Gamers Ltd, PO Box 6227, Bishop's Stortford, Hertfordshire, CM23 3DF Tel: (01279) 504475 Fax: (01279) 504475 E-mail: nick.levens@power4gamers.co.uk *Suppliers of top-notch PC Games and Hardware for the hard core gaming community.Power4Gamers are geared to supply top-notch PC Games and Hardware with the performance needed to get the most out of "em!!!*

Power Adhesives Ltd, 1 Lords Way, Basildon, Essex, SS13 1TN Tel: (01268) 885800 Fax: (01268) 885810 E-mail: sales@poweradhesives.com *Adhesive manufrs*

Power Assemblies Ltd, Cooper Street, Wolverhampton, WV2 2JL Tel: (01902) 456767 Fax: (01902) 456761 *Petrol engine part manufrs*

Power Blast International, 9 Colhook Industrial Park, Petworth, West Sussex, GU28 9LP Tel: (01428) 707895 Fax: (01428) 707894 E-mail: sales@powerblast.co.uk Principal Export Areas: Middle East *Shot blasting equipment manufrs*

Power Capacitors Ltd, 30 Redfern Road, Birmingham, B11 2BH Tel: 0121-708 2811 Fax: 0121-765 4054 E-mail: sales@powercapacitors.co.uk *Capacitor, power factor correction & phase converter equipment manufrs*

Power Clean Services, 3 Regent Business Centre, Pump Lane, Hayes, Middlesex, UB3 3NP Tel: (020) 8573 9893 Fax: (020) 8573 7765 *Cleaning equipment distributors*

▶ Power & Control Solutions KTD, 21-22 Anniesland Industrial Estate, Glasgow, G13 1EU Tel: 0141-950 2288 Fax: 0141-950 2299

Power & Distribution Transformers Ltd, Westland Works, Westland Square, Leeds, LS11 5SS Tel: 0113-271 7588 Fax: 0113-277 5124 E-mail: sales@wilsonpowersolutions.co.uk Principal Export Areas: Worldwide *Manufacturer of electrical power transformers*

Power Drive Drum Co. Ltd, Unit M1 Cherrycourt Way, Leighton Buzzard, Bedfordshire, LU7 4UH Tel: (01525) 370292 Fax: (01525) 852126 E-mail: info@mypowerdrive.com *Studio lighting fittings & equipment*

Power Electronic Measurement Ltd, 164 Lower Regent Street, Beeston, Nottingham, NG9 2DJ Tel: 0115-925 4212 Fax: 0115-967 7685 E-mail: info@pemuk.com *Electrical current measuring equipment manufrs*

Power Electronics & Controls Ltd, 1 Kingsthorne Park, Henson Way, Telford Way Industrial Estate, Kettering, Northamptonshire, NN16 8PX Tel: (01536) 310070 Fax: (01536) 525466 E-mail: sales@powerelectronics.co.uk *Automatic welding equipment manufrs*

Power Equipment Design & Supplies Ltd, Lyndhurst Cottage, Seymour Road, Bath, BA1 6DZ Tel: (01225) 463721 Fax: (0845) 2804920 E-mail: info@pedsltd.co.uk *Electrical suppliers*

Power Equipment Services Ltd, Oldington Trading Estate, Kidderminster, Worcestershire, DY11 7QP Tel: (01562) 742400 Fax: (01562) 865826 *Garden machinery & repair distributors*

Power Factor Systems Ltd, 23 Lyndon Road, North Luffenham, Oakham, Leicestershire, LE15 8JZ Tel: (01780) 721783 Fax: (01780) 721783 E-mail: pfsystems@tiscali.co.uk *Power factor correction equipment*

G. John Power Ltd, Hayseech Road, Halesowen, West Midlands, B63 3PF Tel: 0121-550 3112 Fax: 0121-585 5147 E-mail: sales@gjohnpower.co.uk *Cold drawn & inter annealed steel wire*

Power Health Products Ltd, Air Field Estate, Pocklington, York, YO42 1NR Tel: (01759) 302734 Fax: (01759) 304286 E-mail: jenny.baillie@power-health.co.uk *Health food products manufrs*

▶ Power Installations Ltd, Southglade Business Park, Hucknall Road, Nottingham, NG5 9RA Tel: 0115-927 0483

Power Jacks Ltd, South Harbour Road, Fraserburgh, Aberdeenshire, AB43 9BZ Tel: (01346) 513131 Fax: (01346) 516827 E-mail: sales@powerjacks.co.uk *The Power Jacks Group is an engineering group focused on providing customers with the best solution for precision linear actuation, power transmission and mechanical jacking. The group brings together Power Jacks, Neeter Drive, Precision Actuation Systems, Youngs Lifting, Duff-Norton and Fortune Engineering Ltd. Power Jacks Group is the UKs largest manufacturer of screw jacks, linear actuators and spiral bevel gearboxes. Our product ranges include screw jacks, electric linear actuators, mechanical jacks, bevel gearboxes, planetary roller screws, reduction gearboxes, winches and rotary unions. The products can be supplied in single or multiple arrangements with materials and enclosures to suit each application. This provides a vast array of motion solutions for a wide variety of industries including paper, glass, plastics, rubber, oil, gas, food processing, water, textiles, nuclear, aluminium, steel, chemicals, automotive, rail, aerospace, medical, communications and leisure.*

Power Lift Plant, The Garage, Panfield Lane, Braintree, Essex, CM7 5RN Tel: (01376) 331812 Fax: (01376) 341742 *Construction equipment hire services*

Power Lifting Services Limited, Linen Hall, 162-168 Regent Street, London, W1B 5TG Tel: 0207 0383881 Fax: 0207 0383845 E-mail: powerlifting@btinternet.com *Supply of contract lifting services,plant movements, traffic management,hoist hire and trailer mounted crane hire and sales covering the United kingdom.*

Power Line, Power House, Station Road, Shipley, West Yorkshire, BD18 2JL Tel: (01274) 582721 Fax: (01274) 581495 E-mail: injection@power-line.co.uk *Diesel fuel injection engineering services*

▶ Power Lines Pipes & Cables Ltd, Roadmeetings, Carluke, Lanarkshire, ML8 4QE Tel: (01555) 772572 Fax: (01555) 772976 E-mail: info@plpc.co.uk

Power Magnetics Ltd, Pace House, 15 Little Balmer, Buckingham Industrial Estate, Buckingham, MK18 1TF Tel: (01280) 817243 Fax: (01280) 823167 E-mail: sales@powermagnetics.co.uk *Electrical components distributors*

Power Metal Supplies, 2-4 Winton Square, Basingstoke, Hampshire, RG21 8EN Tel: (01256) 811821 Fax: (01256) 811824 E-mail: powermetal@ukonline.co.uk *Specialist metals, steel tubes, alloy & pipeline fittings manufrs*

Power One, 24 Upper High Street, Worthing, West Sussex, BN11 1DL Tel: (01903) 823323 Fax: (01903) 823324 E-mail: sales@powerone.com *Power supplies, & DC/AC connectors*

Power Packing Export Services Ltd, Pinhoe Trading Estate, Venny Bridge, Exeter, EX4 8JN Tel: (01392) 468088 Fax: (01392) 467987 E-mail: mail@powerpacking.co.uk *Freight forwarders & export packers*

Power Panels Electrical Systems Ltd, Landywood Green, Cheslyn Hay, Walsall, WS6 7AL Tel: (01922) 419109 Fax: (01922) 418181 E-mail: sales@power-panels.co.uk *Electrical engineers manufrs*

▶ Power Partners Development, 4 Blackthorn Close, Biddisham, Axbridge, Somerset, BS26 2RN Tel: 01934 750364 *ILM Business Performance Coaching and Training. Accredited NVQ programmes for Personal and Corporate Development*

Power Pipes Pendle, Maud Street Works, Maud Street, Barrowford, Nelson, Lancashire, BB9 8NX Tel: (01282) 601896 Fax: (01282) 697034 E-mail: sales@powerpipes.co.uk *Machine assembly & hose distributors*

Power Place The, 48a Kingsway, Stoke-on-Trent, ST4 1JH Tel: (01782) 744789 Fax: (01782) 744789 *Electrical repairs*

Power Plant Gears Ltd, Unit 1, Eagle Works, Greets Green Road, West Bromwich, West Midlands, B70 9EJ Tel: (01484) 465500 Fax: 0121-520 0951 *Gear manufacturers & cutters & reconditioned services*

Power Plant Hire Ltd, Power House, Whitehall Road, Halesowen, West Midlands, B63 3JS Tel: 0121-585 4200 Fax: 0121-585 4232 E-mail: birmingham@powerplanthire.co.uk *Contractors plant hire* Also at: Accrington, Bolton, Pontypool & Wychbold

Power Plant Hire Glasgow Ltd, 25 Robert Street, Glasgow, G51 3HB Tel: 0141-445 4437 Fax: 0141-425 1764 E-mail: paul@powerplanthire.demon.co.uk *Tool & plant hirers*

Power Plant UK Ltd, Shalowstones, Baldersby, Thirsk, North Yorkshire, YO7 4PP Tel: (01765) 640641 Fax: (01765) 640222 *Retailers of heavy plant recycling equipment*

Power Porter, Hill View Industrial Estate, Eastwood End, Wimblington, March, Cambridgeshire, PE15 0PU Tel: (01354) 741133 Fax: (01354) 741833 E-mail: sales@easybarrow.co.uk *Wheelbarrow manufrs*

Power Precision & Fabrication Ltd, Greenhill Works, Delaware Road, Gunnislake, Cornwall, PL18 9AS Tel: (01822) 832608 Fax: (01822) 834796 *Precision engineers*

Power Press Repairs Ltd, 69 Kings Road, Tyseley, Birmingham, B11 2AX Tel: 0121-772 1698 Fax: 0121-772 5323 E-mail: sales@powerpressrepairs.co.uk *Power press repair specialists*

Power Products International Ltd, Commerce Way, Edenbridge, Kent, TN8 6ED Tel: (01732) 866424 Fax: (01732) 866399 E-mail: sales@ppi-uk.com *Rectifier equipment, rectifier assemblies, power semiconductors, fuses, solid-state-relays, heatsinks, MOVs, capacitors, film power resistors**

Power Promotions, Prospect House, West Craven Drive, Earby, Barnoldswick, Lancashire, BB18 6JZ Tel: (01282) 841000 Fax: (01282) 841010 E-mail: powerpromotions@compuserve.com *Hairdressing equipment distributors*

Power Quality Products Ltd, 51 Steatite Way, Stourport On Severn, Stourport-on-Severn, Worcestershire, DY13 8PQ Tel: (01299) 879593 Fax: (01299) 825879 E-mail: info@powerqualityproducts.co.uk *Suppliers of power factor correction equipment*

Power Quip Ltd, Greenbank Road, Liskeard, Cornwall, PL14 3DP Tel: (01579) 345307 Fax: (01579) 345307 *Portable power tool services*

Power Rewind Ltd, 1 Conder Way, Colchester, CO2 8JN Tel: (01206) 791316 Fax: (01206) 792689 *Portable power tool distributors*

Power Rod & Crann Ltd, 237 Clarkston Road, Glasgow, G44 3DS Tel: 0141-637 4452

▶ Power Seal Europe, Gwilliam Killands Complex, Broadway, Biddington, Bridgwater, Somerset, TA7 9JN Tel: (01278) 722095 E-mail: powersealeurope@btinternet.com *Gasket manufrs*

Power Solutions Ltd, 7 Copnor, Woolton Hill, Newbury, Berkshire, RG20 9UP Tel: (01635) 255570 Fax: (01635) 255560 E-mail: powersol@eclipse.co.uk *UPS & generators*

Power Sonic Europe Ltd, 3 Buckingham Square, Hurricane Way, Wickford, Essex, SS11 8YQ Tel: (01268) 560686 Fax: (01268) 560902 E-mail: info@power-sonic.co.uk *Rechargeable battery manufrs*

Power Steering Services, Units 1-2, Grinnall Business Centre, Sandy Lane Industrial Estate, Stourport-On-Severn, Worcestershire, DY13 9QB Tel: (01299) 879281 Fax: (01299) 879345 E-mail: enquiries@powersteeringservices.co.uk *Power steering manufrs*

Power Steering Specialists, Unit 1-2 Brocklebank Industrial Estate, Brocklebank Road, London, SE7 7SX Tel: (020) 8858 0168 Fax: (020) 8858 7595 E-mail: sales@powersteering.co.uk *Power steering refurbishment*

Power System Components Ltd, Hawthorne House, Main Street, York, YO61 1RS Tel: (01347) 838154 Fax: (01347) 838154 *Generator control protection product manufrs*

Power System Services Ltd, Foxwood Close, Sheepbridge Industrial Estate, Chesterfield, Derbyshire, S41 9RB Tel: (01246) 268800 Fax: (01246) 268811 E-mail: info@powersystemsservices.co.uk *Air cushion conveyor systems manufrs*

Power Systems Warehouse Ltd, Powerguard House, Grimsby Road, Louth, Lincolnshire, LN11 0SX Tel: (01507) 600688 Fax: (01507) 600621 E-mail: sales@powerguard.co.uk *Based at Louth in Lincolnshire, covering the whole of the UK, Power Systems Warehouse Ltd is an innovative electronics company committed to supplying the best and most economical solutions to our customer's power problems. We are a leading specialist supplier of excellent value Power Protection Systems including Uninterruptible Power Systems site survey and installation, UPS commissioning, UPS maintenance and UPS repair. We manufacture and supply bespoke Inverters, Battery Chargers, Generator Inverters and are one of the largest specialist designers and manufactures of OEM Central Battery Emergency Lighting Units for the UK market. We specialise in Off-grid Diesel Generators and Stand-by Diesel Generator Systems. Our eco-friendly, innovative Generator Inverter System saves up to 70% of Generator fuel by automating generator run-time, storing surplus power to batteries and converting energy to mains quality AC. We are the UK Distributor for Vision VRLA Batteries.*

▶ Power Tool Hire Ltd, 504-506 Portswood Road, Southampton, SO17 3SP Tel: (023) 8031 5316 Fax: (023) 8031 5888 E-mail: glen@powertoolhiresales.uk.com *Power tool distributors*

Power Tool Rentals Ltd, Halifax Road, Hipperholme, Halifax, West Yorkshire, HX3 8ER Tel: (01422) 205616 Fax: (01422) 206282 E-mail: enquiries@powertoolrentals.co.uk *Tool & small plant hire services*

Power Tool Services, 2 Earl Road, Rackheath, Norwich, NR13 6NT Tel: (01603) 722077 Fax: (01603) 722866 *Power tools & hardware supply & repair*

Power Tool Supplies Ltd, 379 Kingsway, Hove, East Sussex, BN3 4QD Tel: (01273) 420111 Fax: (01273) 422313 *Power tool hire & nuts & bolt distributor*

Power Tool Warehouse, 309 Rochdale Road, Royton, Oldham, OL2 5SN Tel: 0161-624 9190 *Power tools*

Power Tools Plus, 131 Gloucester Road, Bishopston, Bristol, BS7 8AX Tel: 0117-949 9700 Fax: 0117-914 7758 *Power tools distributors*

▶ Power Tools Plus Ltd, 360-362 Carlton Hill, Carlton, Nottingham, NG4 1JB Tel: 0115-940 4414 Fax: 0115-940 1114 *Power tool & accessory distributors*

Power Tools Services (Wolverhampton) Ltd, Holland House, 126 High Street, Princes End, Tipton, West Midlands, DY4 9JA Tel: 0121-557 8690 Fax: 0121-557 5009 *Industrial power tool distributors*

Power Torque Engineering Ltd, 27 Herald Way, Binley Industrial Estate, Coventry, CV3 2RQ Tel: (024) 7663 5757 Fax: (024) 7663 5878 E-mail: sales@powertorque.co.uk *Diesel & petrol engine component suppliers*

▶ Power Train Projects, Trinity House, Coventry Road, Hinckley, Leicestershire, LE10 0NB Tel: (01455) 622229 Fax: (01455) 622370 E-mail: sales@ptp-ltd.co.uk *High performance engines & upgrades*

Power Transmission Equipment Ltd, Unit 12 Spires Business Units, Mugiemoss Road, Bucksburn, Aberdeen, AB21 9NY Tel: (01224) 680022 Fax: (01224) 680033 *Trading power equipment*

Power Utilities Ltd, Queen Street, Premier Business Park, Walsall, WS2 9QE Tel: (01922) 720561 Fax: (01922) 720461 E-mail: filters@power-utilities.com *Industrial filters manufrs* Also at: Aberdeen

▶ Power Wise Systems UK, Sheling House, Invincible Road Industrial Estate, Farnborough, Hampshire, GU14 7QU Tel: (01252) 661160 Fax: (01252) 693453 E-mail: darren.pws@tiscali.co.uk *Electrical Contractors (Domestic, Commercial and Industrial)*Fire Protection Engineers*Mechanical Engineers**

Company Information

Power X Hire Ltd, 113 Penarth Road, Cardiff, CF11 6JT Tel: (029) 2066 5454 *Power tools hire*

Powerail Ltd, High Road, Finchley, London, N12 8PT Tel: (020) 8446 0350 Fax: (020) 8446 7054 *Materials handling systems*

Powerbond Adhesives Ltd, 253 Scotia Road, Stoke-on-Trent, ST6 6AB Tel: (01782) 823874 Fax: (01782) 837038 E-mail: info@preo.co.uk *Industrial adhesive products manufrs & distributer*

Powerclimber UK Ltd, Unit 27 Cromer Industrial Estate, Middleton, Manchester, M24 2LT Tel: 0161-654 0999 Fax: 0161-653 0555 *Access equipment hirer*

Powerco (International) Ltd, 1 Strawberry Vale, Twickenham, TW1 4RY Tel: (0208) 831 6634 Fax: (0208) 891 6435 E-mail: radin.powerco@virgin.net *Motor generator set manufrs*

Powercom Trading Ltd, 5 Uxbridge Road, Slough, SL1 1SN Tel: (01753) 553838 Fax: (01753) 553828 *Mobile phones wholesalers*

Powercut Ltd, Unit 15, Paragon Way, Bayton Road Industrial Estate, Coventry, CV7 9QS Tel: (024) 7664 4224 Fax: (024) 7664 4220 E-mail: sales@calibration-services.co.uk *Instrument & calibration repairers & manufrs*

▶ Powerday plc, Crossan House, 28-31 Hythe Road, London, NW10 6RS Tel: (020) 8960 4646 Fax: (020) 8960 3110

▶ Powerdeck Ltd, Unit 4, Blackhill Industrial Estate, Black Hill, Stratford-upon-Avon, Warwickshire, CV37 0PH Tel: (01789) 730444 Fax: (01789) 730888 E-mail: sales@powerdeck.co.uk *Raised storage platform manufrs*

Powerdial Telecommunications Equipment, The Studio, East Batterlaw Farm, Hawthorn, Seaham, County Durham, SR7 8RP Tel: 0191-527 5000 Fax: 0191-527 0036 *Telecommunication contractors*

Powerdoor & Gate Ltd, High Bar Lane, Thakeham, Pulborough, West Sussex, RH20 3EH Tel: (01798) 815700 Fax: (01798) 815900 E-mail: sales@powerdoor.co.uk *Automation for gates manufrs*

Powerdrive Diesel Fuel Injection Specialists, Unit 7, Dundas Spur, Portsmouth, PO3 5NX Tel: (023) 9265 0404 Fax: (023) 9265 5158 *Diesel fuel injection & electrical engineers*

▶ Powered Access Ltd, Block 3, Unit 3B Central Avenue, Blantyre Industrial Estate, Blantyre, Glasgow, G72 0UZ Tel: (01698) 820300 Fax: (01698) 829988 E-mail: info@poweredaccessuk.com *Access equipment manufrs*

Powered Access, Drury Way, London, NW10 0JH Tel: (020) 8830 3333 Fax: (08702) 415949 E-mail: phillomax@poweredaccess.com *PASS (Powered Access Sales & Service) are the UK's leading independent powered access company. Specialising in providing complete access solutions, including new and used sales, rental, LOLER inspections, service/maintenance, operator training and consultancy.*

Powered Access Services Ltd, Middleton Depot Lochlibo Road, Beith, Ayrshire, KA15 1HZ Tel: (01505) 850150

Powerfactor Ltd, 8 Pear Tree Farm, Townsend, Marsh Gibbon, Bicester, Oxfordshire, OX27 0EY Tel: (01869) 278585 Fax: (01869) 278989 E-mail: sales@powerfactor.co.uk *Power supply distributors*

▶ Powerflo Rentals P.L.C., Unit 1D, Blackness Road, Altens Industrial Estate, Aberdeen, AB12 3LH Tel: (01224) 891234

Powergen plc, Westwood Way, Westwood Business Park, Coventry, CV4 8LG Tel: (024) 7642 4000 Fax: (024) 7642 5432 E-mail: domestic@powergen.co.uk *Supply gas,electricity & telephone to home & business*

Powergen plc, Colliers Way, Nottingham, NG8 6AL Tel: (0870) 4191539 Fax: 0115-995 6738 E-mail: sales@eme.co.uk *Supply gas, electricity and telephone to homes and businesses Tel: Customer Service 0800 363363*

Powergen plc, Kingsnorth & Grain Power Stations, Hoo, Rochester, Kent, ME3 9NQ Tel: (01634) 250088 Fax: (01634) 872130 *Energy Suppliers*

Powerglide Billiards & Snooker Ltd, 119-121 Stanstead Road, Forest Hill, London, SE23 1HJ Tel: (020) 8291 3344 Fax: (020) 8699 4008 E-mail: assist@unicorngroup.com *Billiard & snooker equipment & accessories manufrs*

Powergraphic Displays Ltd, 6 Blenheim Road, Cressex Business Park, High Wycombe, Buckinghamshire, HP12 3RS Tel: (01494) 450936 Fax: (01494) 461975 E-mail: edwardbutler@powergraphicdisplays.com *Powergraphics design and manufacture an extensive range of moving and illuminated displays, multigraphic back-lit rollavisions, rotagraphics, and exciting range of lightboxes, including 19.8mm wafer thin edgeslim lightboxes compatible with the new Edgeslim Display System*

Powerguards Ramping Systems, Bennetts Mead, Southgate Road, Wincanton, Somerset, BA9 9EB Tel: (01963) 31206 Fax: (01963) 31904 E-mail: powerguardsinc@beeb.net *Machine guards & for wheelchair ramps manufrs*

▶ PowerHeat Ltd, Sheinton, Cressage, Shrewsbury, SY5 6DN Tel: (01952) 510648 Fax: (01952) 510381 E-mail: info@powerheat.co.uk *Combined heat power solutions providers*

▶ Powerhouse Retail Ltd, Unit 11 Powerhouse Fitness Business Division, 12 Whitehall Street, Glasgow, G3 8BN Tel: 0141-221 3885

Powerlase Ltd, Imperial House Link 10, Napier Way, Crawley, West Sussex, RH10 9RA Tel: (01293) 456222 Fax: (01293) 456233 E-mail: sales@powerlase.com *Manufacturers of high powered, solid state, diode pumped YAG lasers*

Powerlec Products Ltd, Clapgate Farm Woodford Lane, Wombourne, Wolverhampton, WV5 8DS Tel: (01902) 897846 Fax: (01902) 897846 *Printed circuit assemblies*

Power-Lifts Ltd, Marlborough House, 18 Marlborough Road, Woodthorpe, Nottingham, NG5 4FG Tel: 0115-926 9996 Fax: 0115-966 1173 E-mail: info@powerlift.co.uk *Power-Lift is a competitive, world class designer and*

continued

manufacturer of standard and custom built electro- hydraulic scissor lift tables. We are a major supplier into the automotive, distributive, manufacturing, nuclear, off-shore and aerospace industries. Most of our wide range can also be provided in stainless steel or hot dip galvanised, or in any combination. We pride ourselves on producing 'engineered' products with high quality bearings, cylinders and power-packs. Our lifts are tested before despatch. We are the manufacturer of choice to clients requiring heavy duty equipment operating in a 24 hour a day environment where reliability is essential. We offer a wide range of basic and specialist features including turn tables, roller track, tilting devices, handrails, bridging plates and loading flaps, castors or wheels. Power-Lift also distribute a wide range of ancillary material handling equipment including pallet trucks, stackers, small mobile lift tables and work positioners.

Powerlight Engineering Co., 29 Alwinton Avenue, Stockport, Cheshire, SK4 3PU Tel: 0161-432 3195 *Electrical engineers & inspection services*

Powermann Ltd, 16 Commercial Road, Poole, Dorset, BH14 0JW Tel: (01202) 722111 Fax: (01202) 722888 E-mail: sales@powermann.co.uk *High voltage electrical contractors, electrical engineers services*

Powermaster, Springfield Mills, Spa Street, Ossett, West Yorkshire, WF5 0HW Tel: (01924) 272696 Fax: (01924) 272711 E-mail: info@power-master.co.uk *Electronic devises for energy saving on pumps fans and industrial electric motors.*Energy saving for swimming pools, leisure centres, hotels, factories, injection moulding machines*

Powerminster Ltd, 20 Don Road, Sheffield, S9 2UB Tel: 0114-282 0220 Fax: 0114-282 0221 E-mail: info@powerminster.co.uk *Mechanical, electrical engineers & contractors*

Powernail Fasteners & Fixing Devices, Lancaster Fields, Crewe, CW1 6FF Tel: (01270) 588839 Fax: (01270) 500669 E-mail: enquiries@powernail.co.uk *Collated nail & staple distributors & manufrs*

Powernetics International Ltd, Jason Works, Clarence Street, Loughborough, Leicestershire, LE11 1DX Tel: (01509) 214153 Fax: (01509) 262460 E-mail: sales@powernetics.co.uk *Power supply equipment manufrs*

Powernets UK Ltd, 32 Eastlands, Stafford, ST17 9BB Tel: (01785) 242235 Fax: (01785) 612261 E-mail: gbr@powernets.com *Power equipment consultants & suppliers*

▶ PowerPerfector P.L.C., 1-10 Praed Street, London, W2 1QY Tel: (0845) 6014723 Fax: (08700) 569259 E-mail: martin@powerperfector.com *Energy saving technology services*

Powerplace Ltd, The Firs, Newton-By-Frodsham, Frodsham, WA6 6TE Tel: (01928) 787127 Fax: (01928) 788448 E-mail: powerplace@fsbdial.co.uk *Building products distributors & manufrs*

Powerplan, Brockholes Way, Claughton On Brock, Preston, PR3 0PZ Tel: (01995) 640844 Fax: (01995) 640798 E-mail: enquiries@powerplan.co.uk *Cable management systems manufrs*

Powerplant Stamford Ltd, Wackerley Works, Bourne Road, Essendine, Stamford, Lincolnshire, PE9 4LT Tel: (01780) 766017 Fax: (01780) 750910 E-mail: sales@powerplantstamford.co.uk *Generating set hire & manufrs*

Powerplus Electric Motors, 5 Clydesmuir Industrial Estate, Clydesmuir Road, Cardiff, CF24 2QS Tel: (029) 2046 1602 Fax: (029) 2048 4820 E-mail: sales@powerpluselectricmotors.co.uk *Importers & distributors of electric motors*

Powerpoint Stores Ltd, 9 The Parade, Donnington, Telford, Shropshire, TF2 8EB Tel: (01952) 604051 Fax: (01952) 606604 *Laundry equipment sales & repairs services*

Powerrun Ltd, Prospect Works, South Street, Keighley, West Yorkshire, BD21 1DB Tel: (01535) 667614 Fax: (01535) 667616 E-mail: powerrun@powerrun.co.uk *Pipe work vessel fabricators & mechanical installation*

▶ Powersafe Communications Ltd, Tangiers, Haverfordwest, Dyfed, SA62 4BU Tel: (01437) 779977 Fax: (01437) 779639 E-mail: enquiries@powersafe.co.uk *Closed circuit television equipment manufrs*

Powersafe Security Systems, Temple Court, Cathedral Road, Cardiff, CF11 9HA Tel: (029) 2066 8880 Fax: (01437) 779639 E-mail: enquiries@powersafe.co.uk *Security systems designers, suppliers & maintenance*

Powerscreen International Distribution Ltd, Coalisland Road, Dungannon, County Tyrone, BT71 4DR Tel: (028) 8774 0701 Fax: (028) 8774 7231 E-mail: sales@powerscreen.co.uk *Material handling manufrs* Also at: Leicester, Pontyprith & Warrington

Powerscribe Internet Solutions, 28 Kineton Road, Wellesbourne, Warwick, CV35 9LQ Tel: (01789) 471541 Fax: (01789) 881105 E-mail: enquiries@powerscribe.com *Search engine optimisation*

Powersem Ltd, Dawill, Lower Road, Little Hallingbury, Bishop's Stortford, Hertfordshire, CM22 7RA Tel: (01279) 726911 Fax: (01279) 600589 E-mail: pb@pbentley.com *Semi-conductor rectifier stack & components*

Powersoft Computer Services, 4 Pelham Court, Pelham Place, Crawley, West Sussex, RH11 9SH Tel: (01293) 562730 Fax: (01293) 522006 E-mail: support@powersoft-services.co.uk *Software house & consultancy*

▶ Powersoft Systems Ltd, 3 Finchley Close, Troedyrhiw, Merthyr Tydfil, Mid Glamorgan, CF48 4HR Tel: (01443) 693326 Fax: (01443) 693326

Power-Sprays Ltd, Avonmouth Way, Bristol, BS11 9YA Tel: 0117-982 0067 Fax: 0117-982 0060 *Mixing, pumping & spraying equipment manufrs*

▶ Powerstream Electrical & Building Services Ltd, Burbank Street, Hartlepool, Cleveland, TS24 7JW Tel: (01429) 277053 Fax: (01429) 865473 E-mail: sales@powerstream-ebs.com

Powersystems UK Ltd, Badminton Road Trading Estate, Badminton Road, Yate, Bristol, BS37 5GG Tel: (01454) 318000 Fax: (01454) 318111 E-mail: sales@powersystemsuk.co.uk *Cable laying & jointing contractors*

Powertec, Spa Lane, Linthwaite, Huddersfield, HD7 5QB Tel: (01484) 842293 Fax: (01484) 842293 *Commercial body builders services*

▶ Powertech, Unit 5, 35 Catley Road, Sheffield, S9 5JF Tel: 0114-244 2404 Fax: 0114-244 2404 *Fork lift truck hire sales & repair services*

Powertech Systems & Consultancy Ltd, 35 Maiden La Centre, Lower Earley, Reading, RG6 3HD Tel: 0118-935 0000 Fax: 0118-935 0001 E-mail: sales@powertech.co.uk *Software consultants services*

▶ Powertherm Access Services Ltd, Lunn Lane, Beal, Goole, North Humberside, DN14 0SE Tel: (01977) 670111 Fax: (01977) 670444

Powertherm Contracts Insulation Ltd, C Crown Works, Rotherham Road, Beighton, Sheffield, S20 1AH Tel: 0114-288 9119 Fax: 0114-288 9882 E-mail: powertherm@aol.com *Asbestos removal & stripping contractors*

Powertrain Products Ltd, Stringes Close, Willenhall, West Midlands, WV13 1LE Tel: (01902) 366000 Fax: (01902) 366504 *Remanufacture of transmissions for CV plant & PSV*

Powertran Hydraulic Equipment, 13 Comber Road, Newtownards, County Down, BT23 4QP Tel: (028) 9181 3427 Fax: (028) 9182 6516 *Hydraulic hose & coupling assemblies*

Powertronic Drive Systems Ltd, Treetops House, Gillotts Lane, Henley-On-Thames, Oxfordshire, RG9 1PT Tel: (01491) 579118 Fax: (01491) 412211 E-mail: sales@powertronic.co.uk *Explosion, flame & splash proof electric motors*

Powertruck Services, 18 Main Rd, Springside, Irvine, Ayrshire, KA11 3AN Tel: 01294 211745 Fax: 01294 211745 *Fork lift trucks, sacks & service*

Powervac Ltd, 111 Lightburn Road, Cambuslang, Glasgow, G72 8XN Tel: 0141-641 6611 Fax: 0141-641 9988 *Conveyor system suppliers & manufrs*

▶ Powerview Consulting Services, 44 Rectory Avenue, Corfe Mullen, Wimborne, Dorset, BH21 3EZ Tel: (01202) 699977 Fax: (01202) 699977 E-mail: business.growth@powerview-services.com *If you have a master goal... if you won''t rest until you''ve climbed to the very top of your particular market to gain competitive advantage and volume market share... if you want to be known as THE company in your field - THE company at the tip of your customers'' tongues - yet you are stuck at a sales volume plateau you can''t rise above... or your market has become wary and slowed... or you''re in the process of expanding and want to make absolutely sure you succeed at a high level, then I''m interested in your potential. Call or email me and tell me a little more about your business and why you think you and I may be suited to work together.*

Powerwall Systems Ltd, 4 Netherton Road, Wishaw, Lanarkshire, ML2 0EQ Tel: (01698) 373305 Fax: (01698) 374503 E-mail: sales@powerwall.co.uk *Manufacturer of polymer renders*

Powerwave (UK) Ltd, Enterprise Drive, Station Road, Four Ashes, Wolverhampton, WV10 7DF Tel: (01902) 798204 Fax: (01902) 798205 *Microwave ceramics for telecommunications industry*

Powerwise Consultant Engineering, Unit 4 Randswood Farm, The Common, West Wratting, Cambridge, CB21 5LR Tel: (01223) 291250 Fax: (01223) 291260 E-mail: powerwise@powerwise.co.uk *Electronic engineers*

Powles Hunt International, Stirling Road Industrial Estate, Airdrie, Lanarkshire, ML6 7UJ Tel: (01236) 626306 Fax: (01236) 626301 E-mail: sales@powleshunt.co.uk *Detergent manufrs*

Powlett & Loach, 20 Western Road, Stratford-upon-Avon, Warwickshire, CV37 0AH Tel: (01789) 269879 Fax: (01789) 299892 E-mail: powlett@aol.com *Metal spinners & spinning manufrs*

Powlift Handling Systems Ltd, 3a Blackberry Lane, Halesowen, West Midlands, B63 4NX Tel: 0121-550 4750 Fax: 0121-585 5226 E-mail: sales@powlift.co.uk *Manufacture lifting equipment*

Powlson The Printers, Erw Wen Road, Colwyn Bay, Clwyd, LL29 7SD Tel: (01492) 532156 Fax: (01492) 532707 E-mail: sales@powlsons.co.uk *General commercial printers*

William Pownall & Sons Ltd, Ensor Mill, Queensway, Rochdale, Lancashire, OL11 2NU Tel: (01706) 716000 Fax: (01706) 649002

Powrmatic Ltd, Hort Bridge, Ilminster, Somerset, TA19 9PS Tel: (01460) 53535 Fax: (01460) 52341 E-mail: info@powrmatic.co.uk *Powrmatic Limited is one of Europe''''s foremost manufacturer of commercial and industrial heating equipment and a leading specialist in natural, powered and smoke ventilation.**Architectural products include Brise Soleil, louvre and acoustic louvre.**

Powrwheel Ltd, 8 Queensway, New Milton, Hampshire, BH25 5NN Tel: (01425) 623123 Fax: (01425) 623111 E-mail: info@powrwheel.com *Electromechanical equipment manufrs*

▶ Powwow Face Painting, 76 Delves Crescent, Walsall, WS5 4LT Tel: (01922) 440261 Fax: 01922 440261 E-mail: powwowfp@btopenworld.com *Face & body art, temporary tattoos & balloon modelling services*

Powys Instrument & Engineering Services Ltd, 3 Subway Road, Barry, South Glamorgan, CF63 4QT Tel: (01446) 737785 Fax: (01446) 742616 *Instrument & electrical engineering & contracting*

Powys Windows, 1 Enterprise Works, Trawsffordd Road, Ystradgynlais, Swansea, SA9 1BS Tel: (01639) 849243 Fax: (01639) 849243 *Window frame fabricators*

J.F. Poynter Ltd, Unit 23 More House Farm Business Centre, Ditchling Road, Wivelsfield, Haywards Heath, West Sussex, RH17 7RE Tel: (01444) 471491 Fax: (01444) 471777 E-mail: sales@maximlamps.co.uk *Electric lamp & accessory wholesalers*

Poynton Valves Ltd, 81a Coppice Road, Poynton, Stockport, Cheshire, SK12 1SL Tel: (01625) 871014 Fax: (01625) 879814 E-mail: sales@poyntonvalves.com *Valves & actuator distributors, agents & stockholders*

Poyry Forest Industry Consulting Ltd, 2 Station Way, Sutton, Surrey, SM3 8SW Tel: (020) 8770 2144 Fax: (020) 8770 2115 *Forest product consultants*

▶ PP Construction, Deepwater Yard, Part Lane, Swallowfield, Reading, RG7 1TB Tel: 0118-988 7211 Fax: 0118-988 7266

The PP Group, Dukesway, Teeside Industrial Estate, Thornaby, Stockton-On-Tees, Cleveland, TS17 9LT Tel: (01642) 765566 Fax: (01642) 760692 E-mail: sales@ppgroup.co.uk *Advertising gift designers*

▶ PPC, 39 High Street, Rowhedge, Colchester, CO5 7ET Tel: (01206) 729393 *Paint metals*

PPG Aerospace, Darlington Road, Shildon, County Durham, DL4 2QP Tel: (01388) 772541 Fax: (01388) 774373 *Aerospace coatings & sealants*

▶ PPL Marine Products, Tufthane Building, Falkland Close, Coventry, CV4 8AU Tel: 02476 464509 Fax: 02476 694313 E-mail: sales@ppl-marine.com *Marine products suppliers*

PPL Therapeutics plc, High Street, Roslin, Midlothian, EH25 9PP Tel: 0131-440 4777 Fax: 0131-440 4888 E-mail: info@ppl-therapeutics.com *Therapeutic pharmaceutical proteins production*

▶ PR Machinery Services Ltd, Unit 14 Hindley Business Centre, Hindley, Wigan, Lancashire, WN2 3PA Tel: 01942 526999 *Repair, Refurbishment & re-engineering of production machinery. Slitting machines supplied & repaired. Food machinery engineers and suppliers.*

▶ The PR Shop, 70 Priory Road, Kenilworth, Warwickshire, CV8 1LQ Tel: 01676 534319 E-mail: kelly@pr-shop.co.uk *PR & media relations consultants, news releases, publicity.*

Praba UK Ltd, 300-310 High Road, Ilford, Essex, IG1 1QW Tel: (020) 8478 0606 Fax: (020) 8478 3766 *Banqueting suite for hire*

Pracctice Ltd, 216 Straight Mile Road, Rotherwas, Hereford, HR2 6JP Tel: (01432) 372100 Fax: (01432) 372111 *Computer software developers*

▶ Practical Bid Solutions, Genesys Court, Denton Drive, Northwich, Cheshire, CW9 7LU Tel: (01606) 353870 Fax: (0870) 4215142 E-mail: chriswhyatt@pbsl.co.uk *Bid process design & implementation, plus bid resources*

▶ Practical Car & Van Rental, Unit 6 Willow Road, Trent Lane Indust Estate, Derby, DE74 2NP Tel: (01332) 812151 Fax: (01332) 853530 E-mail: andrewsherwood1@hotmail.com

Practical Compounds Ltd, West Side, Tyne Dock, South Shields, Tyne & Wear, NE34 9PL Tel: 0191-456 9191 Fax: 0191-454 5523 E-mail: practical.comp@btinternet.com *Industrial paints manufrs*

▶ Practical Control Ltd, 448 Brightside Lane, Sheffield, S9 2SP Tel: 0114-256 1888 Fax: 0114-261 7052 E-mail: sales@practicalcontrol.co.uk *Software design*

Practical Designs, South Road, Harlow, Essex, CM20 2AS Tel: (01279) 432509 Fax: (01279) 431971 E-mail: sales@practical-design.co.uk *Product designers*

▶ Practical Metrology, 6a Station Parade, South Street, Lancing, West Sussex, BN15 8AA Tel: (01903) 525000 Fax: (01903) 525001 *Measuring equipment manufrs*

Practical Services Southern, PO Box 112, Orpington, Kent, BR6 7HB Tel: (01689) 850233 Fax: (01689) 857876 E-mail: info@pss-couriers.com *Courier services*

▶ Practical Solutions International Ltd, Spencers Wood, Reading, RG7 1YF Tel: 0118-988 8033 Fax: 0118-988 8033 *Food technology consultants*

Practical Upholsterers Ltd, 35a Pound Farm Road, Chichester, West Sussex, PO19 7PU Tel: (01243) 786090 Fax: (01243) 786090 *Upholsterers & carpet planners*

▶ Practically Picasso, 48 Holly Bush Lane, Sevenoaks, Kent, TN13 3TL Tel: (01732) 464004 *Manufacturer of ceramics*

Practice Engine Group Ltd, The Stables, Byford, Hereford, HR4 7JU Tel: (01981) 590410 Fax: (01981) 590411 E-mail: sales@praceng.com *Accountancy software house*

Practice Nurse, Quadrant House, The Quadrant, Sutton, Surrey, SM2 5AS Tel: (020) 8652 3500 Fax: 020 8652845 *Publishing company*

Practiceworks Ltd, Elopak House, Rutherford Close, Stevenage, Hertfordshire, SG1 2PR Tel: (01438) 245000 Fax: (01438) 245001 *Computer software for dental industry*

Practicon Ltd, Chapel Lane, Rode Heath, Stoke-on-Trent, ST7 3SD Tel: (01270) 876211 Fax: (01270) 878887 E-mail: sales.systems@practicon.co.uk Principal Export Areas: Africa *Process control manufrs*

Practivewear, 47-49 Park Royal Road, London, NW10 7LQ Tel: (020) 8963 0888 Fax: (020) 8963 0343 *T-shirt printing services*

▶ Prangle & Carey Ltd, Bath Road, Chippenham, Wiltshire, SN14 0AB Tel: (01249) 653705 Fax: (01249) 447438

Pratt Burnerd International, Park Works, Lister Lane, Halifax, West Yorkshire, HX1 5JH Tel: (01422) 366371 Fax: (01422) 359379 E-mail: sales@chucksuk.co.uk *Chuck manufrs*

▶ Pratts Furniture, 9 Regent Street, Leeds, LS2 7QN Tel: 0113-234 8000 Fax: 0113-234 4404 E-mail: sales@cpratts.co.uk *Furnishings*

Praxair Surface Technologies Ltd, Westfield Road, Kineton Road Industrial Estate, Southam, Warwickshire, CV47 0JH Tel: (01926) 812348 Fax: (01926) 817775 *Resistant coatings* Also at: Swindon

Praxair Surface Technologies Ltd, 2 Oldmixon CR, Weston-super-Mare, Avon, BS24 9AX Tel: (01934) 411300 Fax: (01934) 411301 E-mail: sales@praxair.com *Surface coating company*

Praxis Farm Ltd, Hoe Lane, Flansham, Bognor Regis, West Sussex, PO22 8NN Tel: (01243) 587354 Fax: (01243) 587353 *Furniture manufrs*

▶ Praxis42 Ltd, Toppesfield Hal, Hadleigh, Ipswich, IP7 5DN Tel: (0870) 4464201 Fax: (0870) 1674459 E-mail: sales@praxis42.com *Occupational Health, Safety & Environmental management - Outsourced. With broad range of e-Learning solutions to support these core disciplines.*

Praybourne Ltd, Unit 11, Dunlop Road, Hunt End Industrial Estate, Redditch, Worcestershire, B97 5XP Tel: (0870) 2420004 Fax: (01527) 543752 E-mail: inquiries@praybourne.co.uk *Computer accessory & fire products manufrs*

Prayon Speciality Products Ltd, River Lodge, West Common, Harpenden, Hertfordshire, AL5 2JD Tel: (01582) 765228 Fax: (01582) 769989 E-mail: info@prayon.co.uk *Chemical manufrs* Also at: Bradford, Goole, Immingham & Rugby

Pre Fab Southern Ltd, 10 Alphage Road, Gosport, Hampshire, PO12 4DU Tel: (023) 9251 0200 Fax: (023) 9251 0300 E-mail: admin@pre-fab.co.uk *Sheet metalworkers & fabricators*

Pre Mac International Ltd, Unit 5 Morewood Close, Sevenoaks, Kent, TN13 2HU Tel: (01732) 460333 Fax: (01732) 460222 E-mail: office@pre-mac.com *Water purifier manufactures & distributors*

Pre-Applied Technologies Ltd, Unit 66 The Washford Industrial Estate, Redditch, Worcestershire, B98 0EA Tel: (01527) 523484 Fax: (01527) 517883 E-mail: info@threadlocking.co.uk *Thread locking products, thread coating services*

Prebon Marshall Yamane Ltd, 155 Bishopsgate, London, EC2N 3DA Tel: (020) 7200 7000 Fax: (020) 7200 7177 *Brokers & dealers*

Precedent Industrial Products UK Ltd, PO Box 2668, Poole, Dorset, BH17 0RT Tel: (01202) 673339 Fax: (01202) 673339 E-mail: sales@galvtech.com *Galvanizing repair material distributors*

Preci Spark Ltd, School Street, Syston, Leicester, LE7 1HN Tel: 0116-260 7911 Fax: 0116-260 9461 E-mail: andrerussell@preci-spark.uk.com *Aerospace engineers*

Precia-Molen UK, Unit 30 Walkers Road, Moons Moat North Industrial Es, Redditch, Worcestershire, B98 9HE Tel: (01527) 590320 Fax: (01527) 590301 E-mail: sales@preciamolen.co.uk *Weighing systems manufrs*

Precimatic Ltd, 2 Balthane Industrial Estate, Balthane, Ballasalla, Isle of Man, IM9 2AQ Tel: (01624) 823030 Fax: (01624) 824600 *Sub contract machining service*

▶ Precious Years, 84 Aylesbury Street, Milton Keynes, MK2 2BA Tel: 01908 644000 Fax: 01908 644000 E-mail: neil@preciousyears.co.uk *Precious years caters for all kind of occasions from birth of a baby, christening, birthday, wedding, anniversary, retirement to corporate and personalised gifts.*

Precisa, Unit 4 Vermont Place, Tongwell, Pennyland, Milton Keynes, MK15 8JA Tel: (01908) 211175 Fax: (01908) 211909 E-mail: sales@precisa.co.uk *Laboratory balances*

Precise Electro Plating Works Ltd, Pitt Road, Southampton, SO15 3FQ Tel: (023) 8022 8014 Fax: (023) 8022 8114 *Electroplating services*

Precise Engineering Ltd, Cowley Road, Blyth, Northumberland, NE24 5TF Tel: (01670) 363606 Fax: (01670) 352792 *Sub-contract engineering services*

▶ Precise Engineering, Penrhiwfer Road, Tonypandy, Mid Glamorgan, CF40 1RL Tel: (01443) 435341 Fax: (01443) 423666

Precise Fastenings & Supplies Ltd, Ivanhoe Road, Finchampstead, Wokingham, Berkshire, RG40 4QQ Tel: 0118-932 8832 Fax: 0118-932 8519 E-mail: precisefastenings@fixings.fsworld.co.uk *General fastener distributors*

▶ Precise Solutions, Cote House, Wetheral, Carlisle, CA4 8HZ Tel: (01228) 562234 Fax: (01228) 501912 E-mail: derekjohnston@precise-solutions.co.uk *Precision farming products, farm management & GPS*

Precision 2000 Ltd, Princesway, Team Valley Trading Estate, Gateshead, Tyne & Wear, NE11 0TU Tel: 0191-420 0057 Fax: 0191-423 0100 E-mail: sales@precision2000.co.uk Purchasing Contact: R Scarr Sales Contact: S Burgess *Precision 2000 are Precision Engineers and Precision Machinists giving high quality with value for money. Specialising in CNC Milling, CNC Turning, Conventional Milling, Conventional Turning, Grinding, Wire Erosion and Spark Erosion. Small to medium batches produced as well as one offs - particularly complex geometric components. Full assemblies and kits of parts, prototype projects and complete Toolmaking. Working with many different types of materials from plastics to exotic metals. Approved to ISO9001:2000 Precision 2000 work with Aerospace and Defence, Oil and Gas, Power and Energy, Medical, Consumer Products and other industries. Company Policy of continuous investment in people and equipment is targeted to maximise productivity, quality and value for money for the customer.*

Precision 82, 2 Ebley Industrial Park, Westward Road, Ebley, Stroud, Gloucestershire, GL5 4SP Tel: (01453) 752481 Fax: (01453) 767910 E-mail: info@precision82.co.uk *Precision 82 Ltd based in Stroud, Gloucestershire, specialises in precision turned components.*

Precision Aerospace Component Engineering Ltd, Blackwell Drive, Braintree, Essex, CM7 2QJ Tel: (01376) 340000 Fax: (01376) 552210 E-mail: sales@pace-ltd.co.uk *Aerospace fastener manufrs*

Precision Alarms, Pauls Court, 12b Meppel Avenue, Canvey Island, Essex, SS8 9RZ Tel: (01268) 696787 Fax: (01268) 696922 E-mail: sales@precisionalarms.co.uk *Vehicle security installation & distribution*

Precision Antennas Ltd, Masons Road, Stratford-upon-Avon, Warwickshire, CV37 9NU Tel: (01789) 266131 Fax: (01789) 298497 E-mail: sales@precision-antennas.co.uk *Antennas, satellite dish & tower manufrs*

Precision Applications Ltd, Unit 19 Lodge Hill Industrial Estate, Station Road, Westbury sub Mendip, Wells, Somerset, BA5 1EY Tel: (01749) 870525 Fax: (01749) 870525 E-mail: sales@precisionapplications.co.uk *Magnetic recording head manufrs*

Precision Balance Services, 3 Atlas Court, Coalville, Leicestershire, LE67 3FL Tel: (01530) 834650 Fax: (01530) 834650 E-mail: sales@precisionbalance.co.uk *Weighing equipment suppliers*

Precision Blinds Ltd, 3 Sinclair Street, Halkirk, Caithness, KW12 6XP Tel: (01847) 831896 Fax: (01847) 831896 *Blinds manufrs*

Precision Cableforms & Terminations, Thetford Road, Ingham, Bury St. Edmunds, Suffolk, IP31 1NR Tel: (01284) 729514 Fax: (01284) 729515 E-mail: mark_pctltd@hotmail.com *Cable assembly, harness cutting & stripping*

Precision CAE, 6 Catholic Road, Brynmawr, Ebbw Vale, Gwent, NP23 4EF Tel: (01495) 313216 Fax: (0871) 661 5891 E-mail: abarnes@precisioncae.com *Mechanical/ Electromechanical design services, design for hostile environments, jig & tool design, 2D to 3D solid model conversion, design of electronic enclosures, photorealistic images of designs, CAD and PDM pre & post implementation guidance.*

Precision Carbide Tools Ltd, Unit 23, Stafford Park12, Telford, Shropshire, TF3 3BJ Tel: (01952) 205850 Fax: (01952) 293561 E-mail: sales@precision-carbide.com *Tungsten carbide & high speed steel tool manufrs*

Precision Cast Components, Uskway, Newport, Gwent, NP20 2JY Tel: (01633) 214565 Fax: (01633) 216204 E-mail: info@precision-cast.co.uk *Polyurethane plastics, moulders & phonetic services*

Precision Chains Ltd, Clee Road, Dudley, West Midlands, DY2 0YG Tel: (01384) 455455 Fax: (01384) 230751 E-mail: mark.kyte@precision-chains.co.uk Principal Export Areas: Worldwide *Conveyor chain & sprocket manufrs*

▶ Precision Cleaning Technology, C Paynetts Business Park, Cranbrook Road, Goudhurst, Cranbrook, Kent, TN17 1DY Tel: (01580) 212661 Fax: (01580) 212038 E-mail: cleanlite2000@aol.com *Commercial Lighting Louvre Cleaning company, utilising the latest in ultrasonic cleaning techniques to restore your lighting levels. Various services available please see our website.*

▶ Precision Colour Printing Ltd, Halesfield 1, Telford, Shropshire, TF7 4QQ Tel: (01952) 585585 Fax: (01952) 583925

Precision Component Blasting, Unit13 Fazeley Industrial Estate, Fazeley Street, Birmingham, B5 5RS Tel: 0121-643 1478 Fax: 0121-643 1478 *Shot blasting contractors*

Precision Component Manufacturing, 8 Holme Mills, West Slaithwaite Road, Huddersfield, HD7 6LS Tel: (01484) 846965 Fax: (01484) 846965 E-mail: precisioncomponent@daisybroadband.co.uk *Precision engineers*

Precision Components & Equipment Ltd, Railway Street, Heywood, Lancashire, OL10 1LX Tel: (01706) 621421 Fax: (01706) 621319 E-mail: mike-pce@johnbradleygroup.co.uk *Electronic & instrument case manufrs*

▶ Precision Construction Ltd, 44 Telford Road, Cumbernauld, Glasgow, G67 2AX Tel: (01236) 782600

Precision Cut Rubber Co. Ltd, Leafield Industrial Estate, Leafield Way, Corsham, Wiltshire, SN13 9RU Tel: (01225) 816300 Fax: (01225) 816327 E-mail: sales@pcrltd.co.uk *Manufacturers of rubber moldings, gaskets & foam*

Precision Dipping Marketing Ltd, Stover Trading Estate, Millbrook Road, Yate, Bristol, BS37 5PB Tel: (01454) 318004 Fax: (01454) 319961 E-mail: sales@precisiondippings.co.uk *Rubber dipped products manufrs*

Precision Disc Castings Ltd, 16 Mannings Heath Road, Poole, Dorset, BH12 4NJ Tel: (01202) 715050 Fax: (01202) 715068 E-mail: shumps@pdcastings.co.uk *Brake discs & drums manufrs*

Precision Electronics Assemblies Wingham, School Lane, Wingham, Canterbury, Kent, CT3 1BD Tel: (01227) 720360 Fax: (01227) 720360 *Electronic assemblies*

Precision Engine Services (Inverness), Units 1-4, 48 Seafield Road, Inverness, IV1 1SG Tel: (01463) 235537 Fax: (01463) 712684 *Diesel fuel injection engineering services* Also at: Aberdeen

▶ Precision Engineering Components Ltd, Bentalls, Basildon, Essex, SS14 3BS Tel: (01268) 271144 Fax: (01268) 273222 *Precision engineering*

Precision Engineering Plastics Ltd, Unit 4b Triumph Trading Estate, Tariff Road, London, N17 0EB Tel: (020) 8801 4226 Fax: (020) 8808 7421 E-mail: sales@pep-ltd.co.uk Principal Export Areas: Central/East Europe & West Europe *Molding manufrs*

Precision Engineering Products Ltd, Bellingham Grove, Sneyd Green, Stoke-on-Trent, ST1 6LF Tel: (01782) 202053 Fax: (01782) 285667 E-mail: tsteventon@aol.com *Printed circuit manufrs*

Precision Engineers Pontefract Ltd, South Baileygate, Pontefract, West Yorkshire, WF8 2JL Tel: (01977) 702439 Fax: (01977) 600284 *Special purpose custom built machinery suppliers*

Precision Fabrications Ltd, Units 8-9 Sea Vixen Industrial Estate, 3 Wilverley Road, Christchurch, Dorset, BH23 3RU Tel: (01202) 474406 Fax: (01202) 473821 E-mail: enquiries@precisionfabricationsltd.co.uk *Sheet metalwork & small fabricators*

Precision Formes Ltd, 13 Glegg Street, Liverpool, L3 7DX Tel: 0151-207 2446 Fax: 0151-298 1539 E-mail: info@pfl3.co.uk *Print finishers & cutter manufrs*

Precision General Engravers, Unit 10 Mowat Industrial Estate, Sandown Road, Watford, WD24 7UY Tel: (01923) 233826 Fax: (01923) 817124 E-mail: pngengravers@yahoo.co.uk *General engravers services*

▶ Precision Identification Ltd, Redwood CR, East Kilbride, Glasgow, G74 5PA Tel: (01355) 840021 Fax: (01355) 230875

▶ Precision International Ltd, Chiltern House, 114 Severalls Avenue, Chesham, Buckinghamshire, HP5 3EL Tel: (01494) 782467 Fax: (01494) 785340 *Engineers*

▶ Precision Joinery Ltd, 1l Kingswood Douglas Estate, Kingswood, Bristol, BS15 8HJ Tel: 0117-961 2010 Fax: 0117-961 2087 *Joinery & furniture*

Precision Labelling Systems Ltd, Plows Way, Leeming Bar, Northallerton, North Yorkshire, DL7 9UL Tel: 01677 423533 *Self-adhesive labeling systems & labels equipment suppliers*

Precision Labelling Systems (Print) Ltd, Bridge Mill, Gauxholme Fold, Todmorden, Lancashire, OL14 7PW Tel: (01706) 815094 Fax: (01706) 816411 E-mail: production@precision-labelling.com *Self adhesive labels manufrs*

Precision Lapping Ltd, Unit 16 Marino Way, Finchampstead, Wokingham, Berkshire, RG40 4RF Tel: 0118-973 5989 Fax: 0118-973 7241 E-mail: paullap@aol.com Principal Export Areas: Worldwide *Lapping services*

Precision Laser Processing Ltd, Butlers Leap, Rugby, Warwickshire, CV21 3RQ Tel: (01788) 546004 Fax: (01788) 546005 E-mail: sales@prelaspro.co.uk *Precision laser cutting services*

▶ Precision Lift Services Ltd, Unit 10 Upminster Trading Park, Warley Street, Upminster, Essex, RM14 3PJ Tel: (01708) 250800 Fax: (01708) 250400 E-mail: info@precisionlifts.co.uk *Lift engineering services*

▶ Precision Louvre Co. Ltd, Swinbourne Road, Burnt Mills Industrial Estate, Basildon, Essex, SS13 1EH Tel: (01268) 729554 Fax: (01268) 729563 E-mail: sales@precision-louvre.co.uk *Commercial florescent & multi purpose lighting manufrs*

Precision Machining Engineers (Harrow) Ltd, Brember Road, Harrow, Middlesex, HA2 8UN Tel: (020) 8590 5959 Fax: (020) 8422 5077 E-mail: info@cakedecoration.co.uk *Injection mouldings manufrs*

Precision Magnetics Ltd, Mangham Road, Barbot Hall Industrial Estate, Rotherham, South Yorkshire, S61 4RJ Tel: (01709) 829783 Fax: (01709) 371506 E-mail: sales@precisionmagnetics.co.uk Sales Contact: G. Erskine *Magnetic design, prototype and manufacturing solutions from simple holding magnets through complex, high specification magnetic systems for aerospace, medical, oil and gas and industrial applications*

Precision Mechanical Services, 48 Elliott Road, Love Lane Industrial Estate, Cirencester, Gloucestershire, GL7 1YS Tel: (01285) 655300 Fax: (01285) 641490 E-mail: sales@pms-partners.co.uk *Machine & toolmaker sub contractors, precision engineers*

Precision Metal Products, Lady Indust Estate Albion Street, Southwick, Brighton, BN42 4EG Tel: (01273) 592886 Fax: (01273) 592711 E-mail: info@precisionmetalproducts.co.uk *Sheet metalworkers*

Precision Micro, Vantage Way, Erdington, Birmingham, B24 9GZ Tel: 0121-380 0100 Fax: 0121-359 3313 E-mail: sales@precisionmicro.com Principal Export Areas: Africa *It's no secret that innovative component design, rapid prototyping and high volume component production have given Precision Micro a world-class reputation. Clear leaders in our field and the largest independent manufacturing operation of its kind in Europe, we're continually investing on behalf of our global customer base. We pride ourselves on finding better ways to do things: successfully taking on projects that others consider too complex or technically demanding. And we continue to develop a wide range of precision manufacturing processes, combining them with a refreshingly inventive approach to production. Precision Micro offers a unique range of manufacturing technologies including Photo Etching, Wire EDM, Electroforming, Forming, Finishing and Micro Machining, used individually or in combination, to the ultimate benefit of customers.*

Precision Motion (Cofil) Ltd, Unit 63, Roman Way, Longridge Road, Ribbleton, Preston, PR2 5BE Tel: (01772) 653366 Fax: (01772) 653163 E-mail: pmcofil@btconnect.com *Manufacturers of cams, assembly machines & conveyor indexing systems*

▶ Precision Navigation Ltd, 12 Court Farm, Stutton Road, Brantham, Manningtree, Essex, CO11 1PW Tel: (01473) 327813 Fax: (01473) 326859 *Electrical marine equipment suppliers*

Precision Pest Management Solution Ltd, 267 Iveson Drive, Leeds, LS16 6LP Tel: 0113-226 6800 E-mail: enquiries@precisionpest.co.uk *Pest control services*

Precision Pipe Supports, Unit 40/41, Alma Works, Freds Place, Sticker Lane, Dudley Hill, Bradford, West Yorkshire, BD4 8RL Tel: (01274) 680744 Fax: (01274) 680042 E-mail: sales@autoliftuk.com *Pipe support products manufrs*

Precision Pipework Ltd, Horn Hill, Lowestoft, Suffolk, NR33 0PX Tel: (01502) 500646 Fax: (01502) 566957 E-mail: sales@pumps4all.com *Distributor of pumps & pumping equipment*

Precision Plus, 6 Fiery Hillock, Fortrose, Ross-Shire, IV10 8SE Tel: (01381) 620480 Fax: (01381) 621534 *Computer consultants*

Precision Polymer Engineering Ltd, Greenbank Road, Blackburn, BB1 3EA Tel: (01254) 295400 Fax: (01254) 680182 E-mail: sales@prepol.com Principal Export Areas: Worldwide *Precision Polymer Engineering (PPE) offers a range of high performance elastomer seals for critical sealing applications in the food & dairy, pharmaceutical, chemical processing, oil & gas, marine diesel engines & power generation, aerospace, defence and semiconductor industries.**PPE moulds O-rings and custom shaped components from many types of rubber including silicone, FKM, HNBR, Nitrile, EPDM, and Perlast Perfluoroelastomer (FFKM). Many of these meet various international approvals and conformance requirements (eg. FDA, USP Class VI, 3A, NES337, Explosive Decompression, etc)**PPE offers the highest level of service and responsiveness with some of the shortest manufacturing lead-times in the industry. Independent testing and analysis, technical design and consultancy service also available.*

Precision Polymers & Reclaim Ltd, Bath Road Trading Estate, Lightpill, Stroud, Gloucestershire, GL5 3QF Tel: (01453) 753717 Fax: (01453) 753717 *Plastic reprocessors*

Precision Polyurathnne & Rubber, 7-8 East Bank Road, Felnex Industrial Estate, Newport, Gwent, NP19 4PP Tel: (01633) 279704 Fax: (01633) 278653 *Polythene & rubber manufs*

Precision Powertrain UK Ltd, Catto Drive, Peterhead, Aberdeenshire, AB42 1RL Tel: (01779) 473161 Fax: (01779) 477424 *Gear & gearbox manufrs*

Precision Printing Plates Ltd, Philips Park Road, Beswick, Manchester, M11 3FU Tel: 0161-274 4010 Fax: 0161-274 3542 E-mail: sales@ppp-digital.co.uk *Packaging designers*

▶ Precision Productions Ltd, 14 Cow Lane, Wareham, Dorset, BH20 4RD Tel: (01929) 551062 Fax: (0870) 7058657 E-mail: enquiries@precisionproductions.net *IT consultancy. Software design & development.*Website & web-based applications. Impartial security, data protection, IT support & advice. Institution of Analysts & Programmers - link - http://www.iap.org.uk/ Services/Consult/display.php?RegId=188&*

Precision Products, 2a Penner Road, Havant, Hampshire, PO9 1QH Tel: (023) 9248 1848 Fax: (023) 9245 5024 E-mail: salesppp@aol.com *Manufacturers of airshafts, airbags & mandrels*

▶ Precision Products (Cumberland) Ltd, Highmill, Alston, Cumbria, CA9 3HT Tel: (01434) 381228 Fax: (01434) 381038 E-mail: sales@shawprocess.co.uk *Precision steel casting manufrs.*

Precision Profiles, Southway Drive, Bristol, BS30 5LW Tel: 0117-960 9922 Fax: 0117-960 9944 E-mail: info@precisionprofiles.co.uk *Engineers supplies & stockholders*

Precision Relays Ltd, 3 Seafield Road, Inverness, IV1 1SG Tel: (01463) 233929 Fax: (01463) 712514 E-mail: sales@precisionrelays.co.uk Principal Export Areas: Worldwide *Precision relay manufrs*

Precision Repetition Ltd, 87 Leamore Lane, Walsall, WS2 7BU Tel: (01922) 473335 *Repetition turned part manufrs*

▶ Precision Safety Footware, St. Ivel Way, Bristol, BS30 8TY Tel: 0117-961 2400 Fax: 0117-961 2470 E-mail: sales@precisionsafety.co.uk *Safety footwear manufrs*

Precision Sawing Services Ltd, Union Road, Oldbury, West Midlands, B69 3EX Tel: 0121-544 9233 Fax: 0121-544 8846 E-mail: pssl2@aol.com *Metal sawing engineers*

Precision Services Of Redditch, 59 Padgets Lane, Redditch, Worcestershire, B98 0RD Tel: (01527) 528000 Fax: (01527) 517174 *CNC engineering*

Precision Sheets Products Ltd, 60 Victoria Road, Burgess Hill, West Sussex, RH15 9LR Tel: (01444) 247010 Fax: (01444) 233335 *Sheet metalwork fabricators*

Precision Stainless Fasteners, Unit 5 Bilston Industrial Estate, Oxford Street, Bilston, West Midlands, WV14 7EG Tel: (01902) 408222 Fax: (01902) 409222 E-mail: apexbilston@btinternet.com *Stainless steel fasteners, bolts & nuts distributors*

Precision Stiching, 7 Beck Street, Nottingham, NG1 1EQ Tel: 0115-955 7373 Fax: 0115-956 2230 E-mail: precisionstiching@yahoo.co.uk *Textiles manufrs*

Precision Supply Co., 5 Block 3, Thornliebank Industrial Estate, Thornliebank, Glasgow, G46 8TU Tel: 0141-638 9060 Fax: 0141-638 9848 E-mail: sales@scottishtools.co.uk *Precision engineers engineering components suppliers*

Precision Technologies International Ltd, 22 Mariner, Tamworth, Staffordshire, B79 7UL Tel: (01827) 54371 Fax: (01827) 310406 E-mail: sales@ptiltd.co.uk Principal Export Areas: Worldwide *Precision toolmakers*

Precision Tool & Engineering Co., Pountney Street, Wolverhampton, WV2 4HX Tel: (01902) 459752 Fax: (01902) 458928 E-mail: mail@precisiontool.co.uk *Manufacturer of spare parts for diecasting machines*

Precision Toolmakers & Engineers Rugby Ltd, 19 Somers Road, Rugby, Warwickshire, CV22 7DG Tel: (01788) 543661 Fax: (01788) 565742 E-mail: precisiontmrugby@aol.com *Sub-contract engineers services*

▶ Precision Tools, 40 Kingfisher Court, Hambridge Road, Newbury, Berkshire, RG14 5SJ Tel: (01635) 31977 Fax: (01635) 528865 E-mail: sales@precisiontoolsnewbury.co.uk *Importer and distributor of presion tools and cutting tools for the UK engineering industry.*

Precision Units Dorset Ltd, 2a Gloucester Road, Poole, Dorset, BH12 2AP Tel: (01202) 741664 Fax: (01202) 716473 E-mail: enquiries@precisionunits.co.uk *Machine engravers & plastics engineers*

Precision Valve UK, Precision House, Bakewell Road, Lynch Wood, Peterborough, PE2 6XU Tel: (01733) 238181 Fax: (01733) 238553 *Aerosol valve manufrs*

Precision Varionics Ltd, 307 The Commercial Centre, Picket Piece, Andover, Hampshire, SP11 6RU Tel: (01264) 334522 Fax: (01264) 334422 E-mail: sales@varionics.co.uk *Potentiometer & resolve manufrs*

Precision Vending Machines Ltd, Unit 2, Avonside Industrial Estate, Feeder Road, St. Philips, Bristol, BS2 0UB Tel: 0117-972 3232 Fax: 0117-972 3887 *Vending machines manufrs*

Precision Windings Ltd, Unit J, Durban Road, South Bersted, Bognor Regis, West Sussex, PO22 9QT Tel: (01243) 823311 Fax: (01243) 823318 E-mail: sales@precisionwindings.co.uk *Manufacturers of a range of quality laminated & ferrite transformers*

Preco Broadcast Systems Ltd, Unit 3 Four Seasons Crescent, Sutton, Surrey, SM3 9QR Tel: (020) 8644 4447 Fax: (020) 8644 0474 E-mail: sales@preco.co.uk *Sound broadcasting equipment distributors*

Preco Industries International Inc, St. James House, Castle Street, Canterbury, Kent, CT1 2QD Tel: (01227) 473900 Fax: (01227) 473901 *Cutting machinery manufrs*

Preconomy, Orchard Way, Sutton-in-Ashfield, Nottinghamshire, NG17 1JU Tel: (01623) 492100 Fax: (01623) 514057 E-mail: sales@preconomy.com *High pressure diecasting die makers*

▶ Predator Exhaust System, 84 Tewin Road, Welwyn Garden City, Hertfordshire, AL7 1BD Tel: (01707) 334050 Fax: (01707) 339009 E-mail: sales@predatormotersport.co.uk *Exhaust system manufrs*

Predator Rugby Equipment, Higher Wampford, Kings Nympton, Umberleigh, Devon, EX37 9TG Tel: (0800) 0183706 Fax: (01769) 574219 E-mail: sales@predator.co.uk *Rugby training equipment distributors & manufrs*

Predominant Engs Ltd, Park Mill Industrial Estate, Manchester Road, Mossley, Ashton-under-Lyne, Lancashire, OL5 9BQ Tel: (01457) 832050 Fax: (01457) 835263 *Subcontract engineers*

K. Preece Engineering, The Mill, Argyle Street, Glascote, Tamworth, Staffordshire, B77 3EG Tel: 01827 53391 Fax: (01827) 53391 *Broaching services & precision engineers*

Prefab Steel Co. Ltd, 114 Brighton Road, Shoreham-by-Sea, West Sussex, BN43 6RH Tel: (01273) 597733 Fax: (01273) 597774 E-mail: prefabsteel@btinternet.com *Steel fabricators, structural steelwork engineers & welding services*

▶ Preferred Office Environments, Oriel Chambers, 14 Water Street, Liverpool, L2 8TD Tel: 0161-976 6400 Fax: 0161-975 4399 E-mail: solutions@preferredoffices.co.uk *Specialists in office design, fit-out and refurbishment*

Preferred Tubes Ltd, Bird Hall Lane, Stockport, Cheshire, SK3 0SZ Tel: 0161-428 5355 Fax: 0161-428 7555 *Steel tube stockholders*

Preform Insulations Ltd, Unit 29 & 30 Enterprise Works, 13 & 14 Bergen Way, North Lynn Industrial Estate, King's Lynn, Norfolk, PE30 2JG Tel: (01553) 776382 Fax: (01603) 881254 E-mail: sales@preforminsulations.co.uk *Insulation (thermal industrial) contractors/ engineering services*

Preformed Line Products GB Ltd, East Portway, Andover, Hampshire, SP10 3LH Tel: (01264) 366234 Fax: (01264) 356714 E-mail: sales@preformed.com Principal Export Areas: Worldwide *Overhead transmission fittings*

Preformtools Ltd, First Avenue, Bletchley, Milton Keynes, MK1 1DY Tel: (01908) 370788 Fax: (01908) 362802 E-mail: sales@preformtools.co.uk *Machine tool re-builders & toolmakers*

Pregem Computing Ltd, 9 Oriel Business Park, Omega Park, Alton, Hampshire, GU34 2YT Tel: (01420) 544514 Fax: (01420) 544599 E-mail: sales@pregem.com *Software developers*

Preline Ltd, Rutherford Square, Brucefield Industrial Estate, Livingston, West Lothian, EH54 9BU Tel: (01506) 412297 Fax: (01506) 416536 E-mail: sales@preline.co.uk *Abrasive products distributors*

▶ Prelite Plenums Ltd, Chainbridge Road, Blaydon-on-Tyne, Tyne & Wear, NE21 5ST Tel: 0191-414 3331 Fax: 0191-414 3331 *Cable ductwork manufrs*

Prelude Fabrications Ltd, 129 Mereside, Soham, Ely, Cambridgeshire, CB7 5EG Tel: (01353) 722402 Fax: (01353) 624608 *Industrial conveyor systems manufacturers & steel fabricators*

Prelude Technology Investment Holdings Ltd, Sycamore Studios, New Road Over, Cambridge, CB24 5PJ Tel: (01954) 288090 Fax: (01954) 288099 E-mail: prelude@prelude-ventures.com *Independent venture capital fund manager*

Prem Fill Ltd, Chambers Road, Hoyland, Barnsley, South Yorkshire, S74 0EZ Tel: (01226) 741944 Fax: (01226) 351005 E-mail: office@prem-fill.freeserve.co.uk *Contract bottling services*

Premaberg Manufacturing Ltd, 22-24 High St, Halstead, Essex, CO9 2AP Tel: (01787) 475651 Fax: (01787) 475046 E-mail: sales@premaberg.com *Air filtration equipment manufrs*

Premax Engineering Ltd, 56 Porchester Street, Birmingham, B19 2LA Tel: 0121-359 5380 Fax: 0121-333 3097 E-mail: info@premax.co.uk Principal Export Areas: North America & South America *Machinists, precision machining services*

Premdor Crosby Ltd, Huddersfield Road, Darton, Barnsley, South Yorkshire, S75 5JS Tel: (01226) 383434 Fax: (01226) 388808 E-mail: ukmarketing@premdor.com *Door & windows manufrs*

▶ Premedian.com, Ivy House, Main Street, Leyburn, North Yorkshire, DL8 4EX Tel: 01969 625674 E-mail: ttalbot@premedian.com *Very low cost Remote Colour Production Services for Reprographics & Digital Print **Premedian.com operating from 3 Continents provides a unique service in the provision of offshore reprographics for the graphic arts industry offering consultancy, automated and managed prepress facilities. Whether you want us to manage the process in your country, or you want to work directly with an offshore partner we are here to help.*

continued

*Premedian will provide your company with the link to high-quality low cost labour resources that will, in some cases save you up to 40% against current costs.**Do you wish for: **Significantly lower costs? **Very high-quality product?**FREE software tools for you and your clients to help improve efficiencies?**Increased speed-to-market? *A wider range of prepress services without increasing your overhead or hardware spend?***

Premi-air Systems, Newbattle Road, Dalkeith, Midlothian, EH22 3LL Tel: 0131-654 1565 Fax: 0131-654 1565 *Ventilation engineers*

▶ Premier, 24 Brunel Way, Fareham, Hampshire, PO15 5SD Tel: (01489) 565577 Fax: (01489) 565588 E-mail: sales@psap.co.uk *Freight forwarders of yachts & powerboats distributors*

▶ Premier, The Commercial Centre, 2 Commercial Brow, Hyde, Cheshire, SK14 2JW Tel: 0161-351 1212 Fax: 0161-351 1001 E-mail: sales@premierelectricalsupplies.com *Premier Services deliver a complete accredited energy efficiency service to thousands of homes and businesses throughout the UK.*

Premier Alloys, Newbridge Industrial Estate, Newbridge, Midlothian, EH28 8PJ Tel: 0131-333 4140 Fax: 0131-333 4727 E-mail: premier_alloys@mih.co.uk *Steel bar stockholders*

Premier Amusements, 205 Station Road, Shirebrook, Mansfield, Nottinghamshire, NG20 8AF Tel: (01623) 747094 Fax: (01623) 747094 *Amusement machine suppliers*

Premier Automatics Ltd, 42 West Church Street, Buckie, Banffshire, AB56 1HL Tel: (01542) 832777 *Games machines & pool table supplier*

Premier Badges, Unit 8 Little Hyde Farm, Ingatestone, Essex, CM4 0DU Tel: (01277) 355078 Fax: (01277) 355092 E-mail: sales@premierbadges.co.uk Principal Export Areas: Worldwide *Supply badges*

▶ Premier Barcode Systems, 27 Bromhurst Way, Warwick, CV34 6NS Tel: (01926) 499139 *Computer software developers*

Premier Bartleet Ltd, Mountbatten House Fairacres Industrial Estate, Dedworth Road, Windsor, Berkshire, SL4 4LE Tel: (01753) 754850 Fax: (01753) 754851 E-mail: info@prembar.com *Suppliers of confectionery equipment*

Premier Bathrooms Ltd, Hewell Road, Redditch, Worcestershire, B97 6BW Tel: (01527) 67711 Fax: (01527) 594227 E-mail: info@premier-bathrooms.com *Bathroom equipment manufrs*

Premier Bearing Co. Ltd, Chaucer Street, Northampton, NN2 7HB Tel: (01604) 718107 Fax: (01604) 720654 E-mail: sales@premierbearing.co.uk *Bearings, power transmission & fluid power stockists*

Premier Bearings & Transmissions Ltd, Unit 2b Mariner, Lichfield Road Industrial Estate, Tamworth, Staffordshire, B79 7UL Tel: (01827) 60686 Fax: (01827) 60637 E-mail: sales@premierbearings.co.uk *Nationwide Distributors and stock holders of vast ranges of bearings, belts, pulleys, chains, sprockets, motors, gearboxes, hydraulics, seals, lubricants, conveyor belts and rollers etc. Seventeen years experience within the industry enabling comprehensive knowledge of products ensuring best advice is confidently offered. LAUNCH of Condition Monitoring Product!!!*

▶ Premier Beds, 268a Bradford Road, Batley, West Yorkshire, WF17 6HD Tel: (01924) 420683 Fax: (01924) 445563 *Furnishings*

Premier Blinds & Awnings Ltd, 107 The Street, Fetcham, Leatherhead, Surrey, KT22 9RD Tel: (01372) 377112 Fax: (01372) 360824 E-mail: jane@blindsawnings.com *Blinds & awnings manufacture & sales*

Premier Blinds Wales Ltd, 1 Tyle Teg, Heol Ty Gwyn Industrial Estate, Maesteg, Mid Glamorgan, CF34 0BQ Tel: (01656) 734800 Fax: (01656) 735582 *Window blind manufrs*

Premier Bodies Ltd, Llay Hall Industrial Estate, Mold Road, Cefn Y Bedd, Wrexham, Clwyd, LL12 9YG Tel: (01978) 762224 Fax: (01978) 762693 *Plasma cutting & grinding services*

Premier Bodyshops Ltd, 15 Bilton Way, Luton, LU1 1UU Tel: (01582) 424100 Fax: (01582) 483615 E-mail: info@premierbodyshops.co.uk *Motor accident body repair centre that specialises in the repair of executive marque vehicles such as Porsche, Jaguar & Lexus. Also an authorised seller of Zymöl Estate waxes & glazes*

Premier Calibration Ltd, Unit 3l Lake Enterprise Park, Sandall Stones Road, Kirk Sandall Industrial Estate, Doncaster, South Yorkshire, DN3 1QR Tel: (01302) 888448 Fax: (01302) 881197 E-mail: premcal@btconnect.com *Mechanical equipment & pressure calibration services*

▶ Premier Car Systems Ltd, Units 18-19, The Stacey Bushes Trading Centre, Erica Road, Stacey Bushes, Milton Keynes, MK12 6HS Tel: (01908) 220337 *Vehicle alarm systems installers*

Premier Cars Ltd, Ffordd Maelgwyn, Tremarl Industrial Estate, Llandudno Junction, Gwynedd, LL31 9PL Tel: (01492) 582999 Fax: (01492) 582599 E-mail: mail@premiercars.bmw-net.co.uk *BMW & mini dealers*

Premier Cash Registers, 20 Orchy Gardens, Clarkston, Glasgow, G76 8ND Tel: 0141-633 1440 Fax: 0141-577 0058 *Cash registers distributors*

Premier Cleaning Solutions Ltd, 6 Carrock Road, Croft Business Park, Bromborough, Wirral, Merseyside, CH62 3RA Tel: 0151-201 6767 Fax: 0151-201 6767 E-mail: phil_morris@tinyworld.co.uk *Cleaning supply distributors*

Premier Coatings Ltd, Marley Farm, Headcorn Road, Smarden, Ashford, Kent, TN27 8PJ Tel: (01233) 770663 Fax: (01233) 770633 E-mail: premiercoating@aol.com *Anti-corrosion tape manufrs*

Premier Coatings & Converters, West Portway, Andover, Hampshire, SP10 3LF Tel: (01264) 358633 Fax: (01264) 334701 E-mail: sales@pcc-ltd.com *Adhesive application & coating services*

Premier Colloid Mills, Building A302 Vickers Drive, Brooklands Industrial Park, Weybridge, Surrey, KT13 0YU Tel: (01932) 355366 Fax: (01932) 352660 E-mail: sales@bptskerman.com Principal Export Areas: Worldwide *Chemical plant & mixing machine manufrs*

▶ Premier Computer Training Services, Unit 144, Enkalon Industrial Estate, Randalstown Road, Antrim, BT41 4LD Tel: (028) 9446 9442 Fax: (028) 4468 9256

▶ Premier Concrete, Meadow Drove Farm, Meadow Drove, Bourne, Lincolnshire, PE10 0AL Tel: (0845) 6008113 Fax: (01778) 420374 *Concrete manufrs*

Premier Control Technologies Ltd, 1 Highland Close, St. Helens Way, Thetford, Norfolk, IP24 1HG Tel: (01842) 753456 Fax: (01842) 752424 E-mail: sales@pctflow.com *Flow meter distributors & manufrs*

Premier Controls Ltd, 48 Marlow Road, Stokenchurch, High Wycombe, Buckinghamshire, HP14 3QJ Tel: (01494) 485758 Fax: (01494) 485696 *Control systems manufrs*

▶ Premier Decking, 73 Leighton Street, Wishaw, Lanarkshire, ML2 8BQ Tel: (01698) 376965 Fax: (01698) 376965

Premier Decorations, Braintree Road, Ruislip, Middlesex, HA4 0EJ Tel: (020) 8624 5555 Fax: (020) 8624 5678 E-mail: sales@premierdec.com *Import merchants & christmas decorations*

Premier Diamond Products, Chislet Close, Lakesview International Business Park, Hersden, Canterbury, Kent, CT3 4LB Tel: (01227) 711555 Fax: (01227) 710540 *Diamond cutting equipment distribs & manufrs*

▶ Premier Display Ltd, 1 Mill Lane Industrial Estate, The Mill Lane, Glenfield, Leicester, LE3 8DX Tel: 0116-231 3335 Fax: 0116-232 0015 E-mail: sales@premdisp.co.uk

▶ Premier Drapers, 28 Linden Street, Leicester, LE5 5EE Tel: 0116-249 0043 Fax: 0116-249 0070

Premier E D A Solutions, 1st Floor, Millers House, Roydon Road, Stanstead, Ware, Hertfordshire, SG12 8HN Tel: (01920) 876250 Fax: (01920) 872615 E-mail: sales@eda.co.uk *Electronic design software & pcb training services*

▶ Premier Electrical (N I) Ltd, 87 Dromore Road, Ballynahinch, County Down, BT24 8HT Tel: (028) 9756 4046

Premier Engineering Co. Ltd, 59a Virginia Street, Southport, Merseyside, PR8 6SJ Tel: (01704) 535955 Fax: (01704) 535955 *General engineers machinists*

Premier Fabrications, St 1, 54-76 Bissell Street, Birmingham, B5 7HP Tel: 0121-693 9059 Fax: 0121-693 9058 *Balustrade, fire escape, railing, gate, grill installers & manufrs*

Premier Fabrications, Unit 1, Tainton Park Gelderd Road, Leeds, LS12 6HD Tel: 0113-244 2356 Fax: 0113-244 2356 *Wrought iron gate manufrs*

Premier Fencing (Yorkshire) Ltd, Unit 4, Strafford Industrial Park, Gilroyd Lane, Dodworth, Barnsley, South Yorkshire, S75 3EJ Tel: (01226) 285333

Premier Fire Protection Northumberland Ltd, 5 Farm Court, Druridge Bay, Morpeth, Northumberland, NE61 5EG Tel: (01670) 862088 Fax: (01670) 862088 E-mail: tony_pfp@msn.com *As a company we provide and efficient and high quality service by using a small workforce of well-trained and experienced applicators.*

Premier Fixings, Clarence Street, Aberdeen, AB11 5BH Tel: (01224) 585810 Fax: (01224) 575710 *Fixtures & fastenings suppliers*

Premier Flexible Packaging Ltd, 14 Aber Road, Flint, Clwyd, CH6 5EX Tel: (01352) 733365 Fax: (01352) 733152 E-mail: info@premierflexible.co.uk *Polythene bag & sack manufrs*

Premier Foods, Batchelors Factory, Claylands Avenue, Worksop, Nottinghamshire, S81 7AY Tel: (01909) 475522 Fax: (01909) 530381 *Food manufrs*

Premier Fuel Systems Ltd, Trent Lane Industrial Estate, Castle Donnington, Derby, DE74 2NP Tel: (01332) 850515 Fax: (01332) 850749 E-mail: info@premier-fuel-systems.com *Fuel tank manufrs*

Premier Fuels & Lubricants, Unit 1 Little Row, Fenton Industrial Estate, Stoke-on-Trent, ST4 2SQ Tel: (01782) 410389 Fax: (01782) 410684 *Lubricant suppliers*

Premier Gaskets, Unit 16 Bell Farm Industrial Park, Nuthampstead, Royston, Hertfordshire, SG8 8ND Tel: (01763) 848849 Fax: (01763) 848848 *Gasket manufrs*

Premier Gate Automation, 21 Buckwins Square, Burnt Mills Industrial Estate, Burnt Mills Industrial Estate, Basildon, Essex, SS13 1BJ Tel: (01268) 590560 Fax: (0845) 8386932 E-mail: info@premiergate.co.uk *Automated Gate Installers, Manufacturers of Gates & Railings.**We also supply & install Intercom Systems, Barriers and a wide range of other products & services.*

Premier Gifts, Crimple Court, Hornbeam Square North, Harrogate, North Yorkshire, HG2 8PB Tel: (01423) 815611 Fax: (01423) 815612 E-mail: sales@premier-gifts.co.uk *Corporate & promotional gift suppliers*

Premier Glass Co., 3a Railway Arches, Brady Street, London, E1 5DT Tel: (020) 7247 9908 Fax: 020 72479908 *Bedroom furniture manufacturer*

Premier Guillotine Systems Ltd, Fairweather Green Works, Rear of 900 Thornton Road, Bradford, West Yorkshire, BD8 0JG Tel: (01274) 499832 Fax: (01274) 547818 *Printers engineers*

Premier Gunite Ltd, Heritage House, Worplesdon Road, Guildford, Surrey, GU2 9XN Tel: (01483) 235988 Fax: (01483) 233483 *Shot crete suppliers*

Premier Hair & Beauty Supplies, 28 Martello Drive, Hythe, Kent, CT21 6PH Tel: (01303) 238383 Fax: (01303) 238950 *Hair & beauty products suppliers*

Premier Hazard Ltd, Moorfield Estate, Yeadon, Leeds, LS19 7BN Tel: 0113-239 1111 Fax: 0113-239 1131 *Emergency vehicle warning equipment*

Premier Health Products, Wolfe Road, Coventry, CV4 9UP Tel: (024) 7642 2050 Fax: (024) 7647 3577 E-mail: sales@premier-health.co.uk *Vitamin distributors*

Premier Hydraulics & Pneumatics, Unit 4, Cliffton Business Park, Preston New Road, Clifton, Preston, PR4 0XQ Tel: (01772) 253455 Fax: (01772) 204155 *Hydraulics & pneumatics*

▶ Premier Impressions Ltd, Unit 10 & 11 West E Plan Estate, New Road, Newhaven, East Sussex, BN9 0EX Tel: (01273) 512512 Fax: (01273) 517518 E-mail: sales@premierimpressions.co.uk

Premier Industrial Painting, Unit 10C Newbattle, Abbey College Annexe, Dalkeith, Midlothian, EH22 3LJ Tel: 0131-660 9699 Fax: 0131-660 6841 *Powder coating services*

Premier Interlink, Catfoss Airfield, Brandesburton, Driffield, North Humberside, YO25 8EJ Tel: (0800) 3160888 Fax: (01964) 545001 E-mail: sales@waco.co.uk *Sale & hire of modular relocatable accommodation*

Premier International Foods, Lynn Road, Wisbech, Cambridgeshire, PE13 3DG Tel: (01945) 585161 Fax: (01945) 464968 *Food processors*

Premier Lab Serve Ltd, Gethceln House, Dawley Road, Hayes, Middlesex, UB3 1EH Tel: (020) 8581 4055 Fax: (020) 8581 4056 E-mail: info@premierlabserve.co.uk *Laboratory equipment & fume extraction engineers*

▶ Premier Labelling Solutions Ltd, Blacknest House, Blacknest Industrial Estate, Blacknest, Alton, Hampshire, GU34 4PX Tel: (0845) 2266973 Fax: (0845) 2266974 E-mail: sales@premierlabelling.co.uk *Labelling manufrs*

Premier Labels, 29 Gloucester St, Cirencester, Gloucestershire, GL7 2DJ Tel: (01285) 656255 Fax: 01285 656255 *Self adhesive tape manufrs*

Premier Labels, 100 Dalsholm Road, Glasgow, G20 0TF Tel: 0141-945 4443 Fax: 0141-945 4449 E-mail: info@premier-labels.co.uk *Printers*

Premier Labels & Name Plates, Harrow Lane, Farncombe Street, Godalming, Surrey, GU7 3LD Tel: (01483) 423424 *Adhesive labels manufrs*

Premier Lifts, Arundel Business Centre, 49 Station Road, Harold Wood, Romford, RM3 0BS Tel: (01708) 373332 Fax: (01708) 373766 *Lift specialists services*

▶ Premier Limousines, 1 Briarwood Gardens, Sunnyside, Rotherham, South Yorkshire, S66 3XR Tel: (0800) 4584966 Fax: (01709) 533735 E-mail: info@premier-limousines.co.uk *Limo hire chauffeur driven. Only quality American stretched limousines used for all occasions. Travel in comfort and style in our luxury limousines. Covering Leeds, Harrogate, Nottingham, Sheffield, Rotherham, Doncaster and surrounding areas.*

Premier Logistics International, 6 Ballard Business Park, Cuxton Road, Rochester, Kent, ME2 2NY Tel: (01634) 304403 Fax: (01634) 403408 E-mail: sales@premier-logistics.com *Quality solutions for your office and leisure furniture requirements. Stylish products for all budgets from home offices to the largest business projects*

Premier Mailing, Park House, 15-19 Greenhill CR, Watford, WD18 8PH Tel: (01923) 676319 Fax: (01923) 674333 E-mail: sales@premiermailing.co.uk *Direct mail services*

Premier Managed Payphones Ltd, Unit 10 Alexandra Way, Ashchurch, Tewkesbury, Gloucestershire, GL20 8NB Tel: (01684) 298974 Fax: (01684) 290616 *Telephone (payphone) equipment retailers*

▶ Premier Management, 18 Balmoral CR, Oswestry, Shropshire, SY11 2XG Tel: (01691) 653505 E-mail: carl.palmer@premierconsultancy.com

Premier Manufacturing Joiners, 4 Canal Yard, Shieldhill Road, Glen Village, Falkirk, FK1 2BE Tel: (01324) 638802 Fax: (01324) 638802 *Joiners & manufrs*

Premier Marble Ltd, 3 Dewing Road, Rackheath Industrial Estate, Rackheath, Norwich, NR13 6PS Tel: (01603) 721995 Fax: (01603) 721948 E-mail: premarble@aol.com *Granite, marble & stone craftsmen*

Premier Marinas Ltd, Western Concourse, Brighton Marina Village, Brighton, BN2 5UP Tel: (01273) 819919 Fax: (01273) 675082 E-mail: brighton@premiermarinas.com *Provider of berths & boatyard services*

▶ Premier Moving Services, 4f Morses Lane, Brightlingsea, Colchester, CO7 0SF Tel: (01206) 306644 Fax: (01206) 306688

Premier Networks UK, Garsett House, St. Andrews Hall Plain, Norwich, NR3 1AU Tel: (01603) 305659 E-mail: info@premiernetworks.co.uk *Premier Networks UK Ltd in Norwich provide contracted IT support, Configuration and installation for your IT infrastructure. Making sure your company's IT systems are maintained at the highest level, ensuring total and complete IT security.*

Premier Office Automation, 137 Middle Road, Shoreham-By-Sea, West Sussex, BN43 6LL Tel: (01273) 455571 Fax: (01273) 455573 *Office equipment maintenance & repair specialist services*

▶ Premier Oil Fuel Services Ltd, Kirkton Avenue, Dyce, Aberdeen, AB21 0BF Tel: (01224) 724900 Fax: (01224) 770191

Premier Oil & Gas Services Ltd, 23 Lower Belgrave Street, London, SW1W 0NR Tel: (020) 7730 1111 Fax: (020) 7730 4696 E-mail: premier@premier-oil.com *Oil & gas exploration*

Premier Optical Services Ltd, 104 Oxford Road, Clacton-on-Sea, Essex, CO15 3TH Tel: (01255) 424999 Fax: (01255) 426646 E-mail: enquires@premieropticals.co.uk *Manufacturing opticians*

Premier Paper Ltd, Premier House, Faringdon Avenue, Harold Hill, Romford, RM3 8SP Tel: (01708) 330330 Fax: (01708) 330325 *Paper & board distributors*

Premier Pattern Leicester Co. Ltd, 79 Coleman Road, Leicester, LE5 4LE Tel: 0116-276 6094 Fax: 0116-276 5371 *Timber mould pattern makers*

▶ Premier Paving, Higher Polscoe Farm, Lostwithiel, Cornwall, PL22 0HR Tel: (01208) 871010 Fax: (01208) 871010 E-mail: sales@premierpaving.co.uk *Paving & driveway services*

Premier Percussion Ltd, Blaby Road, Wigston, Leicestershire, LE18 4DF Tel: 0116-277 3121 Fax: 0116-277 6627 E-mail: info@premier-percussion.com *Percussion instruments*

Premier Pest Control Ltd, 2 Hawksbrook Lane, Beckenham, Kent, BR3 3SR Tel: (020) 8663 1911 Fax: (020) 8658 1711 E-mail: premierpestcontrol@hotmail.com *Pest control services*

Premier Pipeline Supplies Ltd, Chatham Street, Halifax, West Yorkshire, HX1 5BU Tel: (01422) 322002 Fax: (01422) 348817 E-mail: info@premierpipeline.co.uk *Valve & pipeline stockholders & distributors & agents*

Premier Plant Engineering, Hud Hey Road, Haslingden, Rossendale, Lancashire, BB4 5JH Tel: (01706) 222181 Fax: (01706) 222133 E-mail: info@premierplantengineering.co.uk *General engineers*

Premier Plastics Ltd, Unit 43 St. Helens Court, St. Helens Way, Thetford, Norfolk, IP24 1HG Tel: (01842) 750461 Fax: (01842) 754743 E-mail: enquiries@premierplastics.org.uk *Plastic fabrications, repairs & welding engineering*

Premier Plating Ltd, Lancaster Road, Cressex Business Park, High Wycombe, Buckinghamshire, HP12 3PY Tel: (01494) 533650 Fax: (01494) 473726 E-mail: gregmurray@premier-plating.co.uk *Electroplaters & metal finishers*

Premier Plating Jigs Ltd, 16 New Bartholomew Street, Birmingham, B5 5QS Tel: 0121-643 0727 Fax: 0121-633 3392 *Plating jig manufacturers & light engineers*

Premier Plating Works Walthamstow Ltd, 90 Shernhall Street, London, E17 9HP Tel: (020) 8520 5361 Fax: (020) 8520 5375 E-mail: sales@premierplatingworks.co.uk *Premier Platings Works Ltd, established in 1934 and based in North East London, provide electroplating and metal finishing services to the electronics, engineering, architectural and manufacturing sectors across the South of England.*

Premier Pool Services, 25A The Street, Charlwood, Horley, Surrey, RH6 0BY Tel: (01293) 863841 Fax: (01293) 863841 *Swimming pool maintenance services*

Premier Power Products Ltd, 1 Dampier Mews Edward Close, Hounstone Business Park, Houndstone Business Park, Yeovil, Somerset, BA22 8RU Tel: (01935) 432412 Fax: (01935) 433557 *Bearing & conveyor distributors* Also at: Exeter

▶ Premier Precast, Unit 11 Kelliebank, Alloa, Clackmannanshire, FK10 1NT Tel: (01259) 219966 Fax: (01259) 219988 *Fabric*

Premier Print & Design Services Ltd, Unit 33 Park Farm Industrial Estate, Ermine Street, Buntingford, Hertfordshire, SG9 9AZ Tel: (01763) 272461 Fax: (01763) 272955 *Lithographic printers & graphic design*

▶ Premier Print Services UK Ltd, 8 Henshaw Road, Bristol, BS15 1QF Tel: 0117-330 2050 Fax: 0117-330 2051 E-mail: premierprint@blueyonder.co.uk *Printers & Designers of Quality Business Stationery, from Letterheads, Business Cards, Business Forms to Full colour Brochures & Folders. We have also been known to supply printed Mugs and even Balloons!*

Premier Promotional Services, 38 Bearton Road, Hitchin, Hertfordshire, SG5 1UE Tel: (01462) 442288 Fax: (01462) 458883 E-mail: sales@premierpromotional.co.uk *Promotional item manufrs*

▶ Premier Properties (Fife) Ltd, Unit 22 Elgin Street Industrial Estate, Dickson Street, Dunfermline, Fife, KY12 7SL Tel: (01383) 625250

Premier Propshaft Co Ltd, 24-26 Atherstone Road, Hartshill, Nuneaton, Warwickshire, CV10 0SP Tel: (024) 7639 3806 Fax: (024) 7639 3452 *Propshaft repairers & manufrs*

Premier Pure water, Unit 8 Spires Business Centre, Mugiemoss Road, Aberdeen, AB21 9NY Tel: (01224) 680866 Fax: (01224) 680876 E-mail: stacey@premierpure.com *Water cooler hire*

Premier Radiator Cabinets, 3 Aintree Road, Bootle, Merseyside, L20 9DL Tel: 0151-933 0070 Fax: 0151-284 3274 E-mail: sales@premiercabinets.fsnet.co.uk *Joiners*

Premier Rainwear, 46 Stanley Street, Manchester, M8 8SH Tel: 0161-834 9481

▶ Premier Recruitment International Ltd, PO Box 250, London, W1T 6DU Tel: (020) 7631 0050 Fax: 0870 288 4990 E-mail: info@premier-recruit.com *Permanent & Temporary Recruitment Specialists for the Hospitality & Catering industries. Covering London, Manchester, UK and Overseas.*

Premier Reprographics, Marblemand House, 25 Yarm Road, Stockton-on-Tees, Cleveland, TS18 3NJ Tel: (01642) 806680 Fax: (01642) 806680 *Office equipment repairs & sales*

Premier Rewinds, 566-568 Attercliffe Road, Sheffield, S9 3QP Tel: 0114-261 9104 Fax: 0114-244 9111 *Motor rewind & repair services*

Premier Sacks & Packaging Ltd, Dean Farm, King St Woodford, Woodford, Stockport, Cheshire, SK7 1RL Tel: (01625) 521971 Fax: (01625) 521972 E-mail: info@premiersacks.co.uk *Paper sacks & packaging manufrs*

▶ Premier Scaffolding, Coalpit Lane, Rugeley, Staffordshire, WS15 1EW Tel: (01889) 586152 Fax: (01889) 570274

Premier Schoolwear, 688-690 Becontree Avenue, Dagenham, Essex, RM8 3HD Tel: (020) 8592 0141 Fax: (020) 8984 0953 *Clothing distributors*

Premier Seating International Ltd, Parkside Mill, Walter Street, Blackburn, BB1 1TL Tel: (01254) 673400 Fax: (01254) 665571 E-mail: sales@premierseating.co.uk *Office furniture distribs*

Premier Security Services Ltd, 42 Second Avenue, Stafford, ST16 1PR Tel: (01785) 225951 Fax: (01785) 225951 E-mail: sales@premiersecurityservices.co.uk *Cctv installers*

▶ Premier Service & Installation, Premier House, Unit 6, Station Terrace, Station Road,, Kegworth, Derbyshire, DE74 2GE Tel: 01509 670600 Fax: 01509 673275 E-mail: info@premservices.co.uk *We specialise in the installation and servicing of Whirlpools, Airspas, Steam enclosures, Hot tubs and Saunas. We have a team of experienced engineers and installers who travel all over the country.*

Premier Sheds & Fencing, Streatham Common, Station Approach, London, SW16 5NR Tel: (020) 8677 0459 Fax: (020) 8677 3778 E-mail: premiershedsresponse@btconnect.com *Shed & fence builders & fitters*

Premier Sheet Metal & Engineering Co. Ltd, 4 Premier Building, Brockhampton Road, Havant, Hampshire, PO9 1JU Tel: (023) 9247 2633 Fax: (023) 9249 8210 E-mail: sales@premiersheetmetal.co.uk *Sheet metalworkers*

▶ Premier Shredding Ltd, Unit 3J, North Road, Marchwood Industrial Park, Marchwood, Southampton, SO40 4BL Tel: (023) 8086 8888 Fax: (023) 8086 7475 E-mail: sales@premiershredding.co.uk *We cater for all areas of confidential waste from documentation to cd"s, tapes & uniforms, collection & destruction service on a scheduled basis or as & when required.*

▶ Premier Signs, 3 Hedgend Industrial Estate, Shuart Lane, St. Nicholas at Wade, Birchington, Kent, CT7 0NB Tel: (01843) 843895 Fax: (01843) 843895 *Sign manufacturers & installation*

Premier Signs, 5 Somers Road, Rugby, Warwickshire, CV22 7DB Tel: (01788) 565361 Fax: (01788) 569165 *Sign manufrs*

Premier Software Solutions, Premier House, Hollys Court, Hollys Park Road, Cannock, Staffordshire, WS11 1DB Tel: (01543) 466580 Fax: (01543) 466579 E-mail: sales@chasebs.com *Leisure management software suppliers*

Premier Solutions, Unit 122 City Business Park, Somerset Place, Plymouth, PL3 4BB Tel: (01752) 605222 Fax: (01752) 605255 E-mail: barabara@premier-solutions.co.uk *Bar coding & label printers*

Premier Solutions (Nottingham) Ltd, Ascot Industrial Estate, Sandiacre, Nottingham, NG10 5DL Tel: 0115-939 4122 Fax: 0115-949 0453 E-mail: info@premier-solutions.biz *Disco & public address system manufrs*

Premier Source Ltd, Cott Abbey, Winstone, Cirencester, Gloucestershire, GL7 7JT Tel: (01285) 821599 Fax: (01285) 821444 E-mail: ralph@premiresourceorg.org *Computer hardware suppliers*

Premier Sport & Fitness, 7-11 Darlington Street, Wigan, Lancashire, WN1 1DL Tel: (01942) 495695 Fax: (01942) 495695 E-mail: enquiries@fitness-equipment.uk.com *Fitness equipment retailers*

Premier Stampings Ltd, Station Street, Cradley Heath, West Midlands, B64 6AJ Tel: (01384) 353100 Fax: (01384) 353101 *Drop forging manufrs*

Premier Supply Co., Perram Works, Merrow Lane, Guildford, Surrey, GU4 7BN Tel: (01483) 534346 Fax: (01483) 303992 E-mail: countylr@aol.com *Vehicle parts & accessories wholesales* Also at: Nuneaton

Premier Systems Ltd, Fritham, Lyndhurst, Hampshire, SO43 7HH Tel: (023) 8081 1100 *Document management system suppliers*

Premier Systems Technology Ltd, Newton Silk Mill, Holyoak Street, Manchester, M40 1HA Tel: 0161-682 2100 Fax: 0161-682 2090 E-mail: sales@premier-tech.com *Computer software developers*

Premier Tape Converters Ltd, Unit 2, 24-26 Boulton Road, Stevenage, Hertfordshire, SG1 4QX Tel: (01732) 521122 Fax: (01438) 759555 *Manufacturers of identification & safety pipeline tape*

Premier Telecom, 1 Dungannon Park, Moy Road, Dungannon, County Tyrone, BT71 6BT Tel: (028) 8775 2986 Fax: (028) 8775 2986 *Telecommunications installations*

Premier Telecommunications Ltd, The Old Chapel, Main Street, Branston, Burton-on-Trent, Staffordshire, DE14 3EY Tel: (01283) 568301 Fax: (01283) 568352 *Telecommunication systems supply & install*

Premier Textiles Ltd, 61 Bloom Street, Manchester, M1 3LY Tel: 0161-236 2212 Fax: 0161-236 9786 E-mail: info@premier-textiles.com *Loom state fabric merchants*

Premier Textiles Ltd, Green Lane Industrial Estate, Green Lane, Stockport, Cheshire, SK4 2JR Tel: 0161-429 5770 Fax: 0161-429 5777 E-mail: sales@premier-textiles.com *Textile supply cotton goods, grey yarn cloth manufrs*

Premier Tool Hire Ltd, Premier House, 34 Arthur Road, Yardley, Birmingham, B25 8HA Tel: 0121-771 4777 Fax: 0121-771 1187 *Industrial tool hire, sales & repair services*

▶ Premier Traffic Management Ltd, Unit 13 Tudhoe Industrial Estate, Spennymoor, County Durham, DL16 6TL Tel: (01388) 815661 Fax: (01388) 420993

Premier Transline Group, Catwick Lane, Brandesburton, Driffield, North Humberside, YO25 8RW Tel: (01964) 542131 Fax: (01964) 543572 *Modular & Relocatable Accommodation Sales & Hire.*

Premier Trophies, 42-44 Outram Street, Sutton-in-Ashfield, Nottinghamshire, NG17 4FS Tel: (01623) 512849 Fax: (01623) 480443 *Trophy manufrs*

Premier Voice & Data, Motokov House, North Lynn Indust Estate, North Lynn Industrial Estate, King's Lynn, Norfolk, PE30 2JG Tel: (01553) 779950 Fax: (01553) 779950 E-mail: info@premiervoiceanddata.co.uk *Telecommunication systems installation*

▶ Premier Voile Co Ltd, Cound, Shrewsbury, SY5 6BH Tel: (01694) 731 747 E-mail: sales@premiervoile.com *Premier Voile Co Ltd. The UKs leading stockist and bespoke manufacturer of voiles and sheers. From Trevira Cs coloured theatrical drapes, display materials & stage drapes to Hotel flame retardant voile, organzas and designer sheers for retail. On line order system!*

Premier Waste Management Ltd, Prospect House, Aykley Heads, Durham, DH1 5TS Tel: 0191-384 4000 Fax: 0191-384 5869 *Waste management services*

Premier Watch Co. Ltd, 107 The Street, Capel St. Mary, Ipswich, IP9 2EH Tel: (01473) 312123 *Clocks & watches wholesale & manufrs*

▶ Premier Watercoolers Ltd, 17 Ash, Kembrey Park, Swindon, SN2 8UN Tel: (0800) 1955740 *Water cooler manufrs*

Premier Welding Services (North) Ltd, 8 Atlas Way, Atlas North Industrial Estate, Sheffield, S4 7QQ Tel: 0114-243 0555 Fax: 0114-243 0777 E-mail: premierwelding@btconnect.com *Welding supplies distributors*

Premier Workwear Ltd, 24 Friern Watch Avenue, London, N12 9NT Tel: (020) 8445 5115 Fax: (020) 8445 4567 E-mail: info-uk@chefwork.com *Uniforms & staff wear retailers*

Premier World Trading Ltd, Raintex House, Smethwick, West Midlands, B66 2AA Tel: 0121-555 6479 Fax: 0121-555 6532 E-mail: sales@pwtltd.co.uk *Wholesalers & manufacturers of clothing*

Premiere Castings Ltd, The Old Foundry, Green Street, Oldham, OL8 1TA Tel: 0161-620 6605 Fax: 0161-678 6552 E-mail: premier.castings@btconnect.com *Iron & non-ferrous casting manufrs*

Premiere Eurocom Ltd, The Courtyard, 9 Waterside Drive, Langley, Slough, SL3 6EZ Tel: (01753) 543712 Fax: (01753) 583536 E-mail: admin@premeuro.com *Mobile phone service & repair centre*

Premiere People, 55 Royal Avenue, Belfast, BT1 1FX Tel: (028) 9023 5777 Fax: (028) 9033 2792 E-mail: belfast@premiere-agency.com *Employment agency*

Premiere Products, Bouncers Lane, Cheltenham, Gloucestershire, GL52 5JD Tel: (01242) 537150 Fax: (01242) 528445 E-mail: premiere@premiereproducts.co.uk *Manufacturer and retailer of quality Cleaning Chemicals, Janitorial Equipment & Industrial Vacuum, Rotary, Carpet Cleaner and Scrubber Drier Machines*

Premier-Ware Ltd, Vander House, Starn Hill Close, Ecclesfield, Sheffield, S35 9TG Tel: 0114-257 2700 Fax: 0114-257 1364 E-mail: sales@premier-ware.co.uk *Manufacturing silversmiths.*

▶ Premierwheel Refurbishment, 1 Harvil Farm, Harvil Road, Harefield, Uxbridge, Middlesex, UB10 8AJ Tel: (01895) 259100 *Alloy wheels refurbishing service*

Premium Bermad UK Ltd, Newbury Crash Repair Centre, Arnhem Road, Newbury, Berkshire, RG14 5RU Tel: (01635) 528717 Fax: (01635) 528642 E-mail: chris.elliott@2bermad.co.uk *Pressure control valves manufrs*

▶ Premium Catering Consultants, 166 Green Lane, Shepperton, Middlesex, TW17 8DZ Tel: (01932) 220168 Fax: (01932) 220168 E-mail: lunch@premiumcatering.com *The specialist corporate caterer that delivers to your office*

▶ Premium Collections, PO Box 448, Altrincham, Cheshire, WA14 1PJ Tel: 0161-929 6200 Fax: 0161-929 3956 E-mail: premiumcollect@aol.com *Debt collection, credit management, absconder tracing, asset tracing, vehicle repossessions.*

Premium Fire Protection Ltd, 68 Edwin Street, Daybrook, Nottingham, NG5 6AY Tel: 0115-926 7736 Fax: 0115-919 0111 *Fire extinguisher suppliers*

▶ Premium Incentives Ltd, 5 Harbour House, Harbour Way, Shoreham-by-Sea, West Sussex, BN43 5HZ Tel: (01273) 452244 Fax: (01273) 452265 E-mail: info@premium-incentives-uk.com *Promotional merchandising for companies daring to be different*

Premium Oil Co., Brunel Way, Minehead, Somerset, TA24 5BY Tel: (01643) 706951 Fax: (01643) 706956 E-mail: sales@oilco.co.uk *Cooking oil supply & waste collection*

Premium Pest Control, 56 Oldfield Road, London, NW10 9UE Tel: (020) 8451 7426 Fax: (020) 8451 1044 *Pest controllers*

Premium Power Units Ltd, Block 10, Unit 4, Beardmore Way, Clydebank, Dunbartonshire, G81 4HT Tel: 0141-952 4344 Fax: 0141-952 6350 E-mail: sales@premiumpowerunits.co.uk *Electric motors & gears repair services & distributors*

▶ Premium Source Ltd, 30 Whiteladies Road, Bristol, BS8 2LG Tel: 0117-949 0088 Fax: 0117-949 0088

Premmit Associates Ltd, 33 Eccleston Square, London, SW1V 1PB Tel: (020) 7834 7253 Fax: (020) 7834 3544 E-mail: info@premmit.com *Aerospace & defence staff services*

▶ Prendy Scaffolding Ltd, Daventry Works, 17 Daventry Avenue, London, E17 9AQ Tel: (020) 8520 8556 Fax: (020) 8521 6330

Prentice Logistics Ltd, 14 Clifton Road, Cambridge, CB1 7EA Tel: (01223) 213131 Fax: (01223) 240021 E-mail: mail@prenticeofcambridge.com *Specialist laboratory removal & storage*

▶ Prentice Roofing, 2 Front Road, Lisburn, County Antrim, BT27 5JZ Tel: (028) 9082 7187 Fax: (028) 9082 7167 E-mail: info@prenticeroofing.co.uk *Supply and fixing service for all natural slate, clay tile and concrete tile products also lead flashing and lead roofing to commercial and private clients.** *By operating independently from manufacturers we are able to offer wider and more varied solutions to roofing requirements, including concrete tiles, natural slate, clay tiles, fibre-cement slates, *reconstituted slates as well as lead flashing, lead roofing*

Prentis Engineering, Prentis Quay, Sittingbourne, Kent, ME10 2QD Tel: 01795 477128 *Structural steelworkers*

Prep Tec Systems Ltd, Fern Hill Business Centre, Todd Street, Bury, Lancashire, BL9 5BJ Tel: 0161-761 5214 Fax: 0161-764 1914 E-mail: info@prep-tec.co.uk *Stainless steel fabricators*

Prepair Ltd, 11 Flowers Industrial Estate, Latimer Road, Luton, LU1 3XA Tel: (01582) 455000 Fax: (01582) 416000 E-mail: prepair@easynet.co.uk *Battery & thyristor charger manufrs*

▶ Preparation Group, Deacon Road, Lincoln, LN2 4JB Tel: (0870) 2243606 Fax: (0870) 2243607 E-mail: sales@ppcgroup.co.uk *One of the largest suppliers of surface preparation services in the UK. Worldwide contracting services providing experienced operatives and equipment.**Our range of equipment includes shotblasters, planers, multi stripping machines, grinders, dust extraction, handtools and the original creatangle mixers.*

Prepcraft, 11 Hunsdon, Welwyn Garden City, Hertfordshire, AL7 2PN Tel: (07775) 928822 Fax: (01707) 371413 E-mail: enquiries@prepcraft.co.uk *Shot blasting contractors*

Prescience Communications Ltd, Haymarket House, 8 Clifton Terrace, Edinburgh, EH12 5DR Tel: 0131-313 3599 Fax: 0131-346 1294 *Consultancy, training, events management specialists*

Prescient Engineering Ltd, 25 Mereside, Soham, Ely, Cambridgeshire, CB7 5EE Tel: (01353) 720787 Fax: (01353) 723356 E-mail: contact@prescientengineeringltd.co.uk *Multislide tools & production*

Prescot Door & Window Centre, Squires House, Cyprus Street, Prescot, Merseyside, L34 5RY Tel: 0151-430 9601 Fax: 0151-426 2212 *Window frame suppliers*

Prescott Graphics Services, Unit 17M, Westside Ind Est, St. Helens, Merseyside, WA9 3AT Tel: (0800) 9546172 E-mail: enquiries@precottgraphics.co.uk

Prescott Powell Ltd, 466 Moseley Road, Birmingham, B12 9AN Tel: 0121-446 4411 Fax: 0121-446 4681 E-mail: liam.duggan@prescottpowell.co.uk *Supplier to automotive industry, supplying presswork, tube manipulation & pressed & tubular robotic welded auto structures & exhaust components*

Prescription Footwear Associates Ltd, P F A House, Lake Lane, Barnham, Bognor Regis, West Sussex, PO22 0JB Tel: (01243) 554407 Fax: (01243) 554407 E-mail: sales@pfa.sageweb.co.uk *Manufactures of orthotic appliances & bespoke footwear*

Present (UK) Ltd, Unit 11, Northbrook Close, Gregorys Mill Street, Worcester, WR3 8BP Tel: (01905) 28999 Fax: (01905) 723392 *Video & audio equipment hire* Also at: Coventry

Presentation For Business, L1-L2 Unit Kent Kraft Industrial Estate, Lower Road, Northfleet, Gravesend, Kent, DA11 9SR Tel: (01322) 386717 Fax: (01322) 385506 E-mail: info@p4b.co.uk *Sales presenter designers*

Presentation Cases (Birmingham) Ltd, 51 Vyse Street, Hockley, Birmingham, B18 6HS Tel: (01453) 842181 Fax: 0121-523 2232 E-mail: ardenvfp@yahoo.com *Case manufrs*

Presentation Products Ltd, Dundee Road, Arbroath, Angus, DD11 2PT Tel: (01241) 878441 Fax: (01241) 875560 E-mail: ppm@giftpacks.co.uk *Manufacturers of presentation packaging*

▶ Presentation Services Ltd, Unit 3, Mitre Bridge Industrial Estate, Mitre Way, London, W10 6AU Tel: (020) 8964 1440 Fax: (020) 8964 2449 E-mail: phill.dale@pslevents.com *Audio visual sales & hire*

▶ Presentation Services, Cranborne Industrial Estate, Cranborne Road, Potters Bar, Hertfordshire, EN6 3JN Tel: (01707) 655131 Fax: (01707) 648131 E-mail: info@presservgroup.com *Audio, lighting, video & data projection*

▶ PresentsToGo Christening & Birthday Gifts Co., Sunnywood Drive, Haywards Heath, West Sussex, RH16 4PE Tel: 01444 415096 E-mail: jw@presentstogo.co.uk *Great gift ideas for that 18 birthday or 21 birthday, with gift for weddings, anniversary, christmas, golf, corporate, baby, child, christening or something just that little original or unusual you""ll find it here on the Presentstogo website.*

Presight Marketing Consultants, 4 Addison Avenue, London, W11 4QR Tel: (020) 7603 6553 Fax: (020) 7602 8089 E-mail: presight@presight.co.uk *Marketing consultants*

Presletta Graphics, 66 Kitchener Road, High Wycombe, Buckinghamshire, HP11 2SN Tel: (01494) 526285 Fax: E-mail: roy@presletta.com *Screen printers dry transfers vinyl stickers & labels manufrs*

Presman Bullion Ltd, 56 Hatton Garden, London, EC1N 8HP Tel: (020) 7404 0903 Fax: (020) 7405 8053 *Precious metal recovery contractors*

Presreg Valve, 18 Bakewell Road, Loughborough, Leicestershire, LE11 5QY Tel: (01509) 264242 Fax: (01509) 263308 *Valves & regulators manufrs*

▶ The Press, 38-42 Garman Road, London, N17 0UL Tel: (020) 8365 1595 Fax: (020) 8365 1481

▶ Press Ltd, Cross Road, Annesley, Nottingham, NG15 0AL Tel: (01623) 723444 Fax: (01623) 720784

Press Co., Kiln Lane, Swindon, SN2 2NP Tel: (01793) 716316 Fax: (01793) 511345 E-mail: sales@presco-uk.com *Print finishing & presentation products*

▶ Press & Banks Ltd, The Street, Framfield, Uckfield, East Sussex, TN22 5NN Tel: (01825) 890255 Fax: (01825) 890102

Press Computer Systems Ltd, Castle Street, Wolverhampton, WV1 3AD Tel: (01902) 374757 Fax: (01902) 373622 E-mail: postmaster@presscomputers.com *Computer services & software developers*

▶ Press Contact, 15 Old Mill Close, Eynsford, Dartford, DA4 0BN Tel: 01322 866293 E-mail: info@presscontact.co.uk *Public Relations, PR marketing, press release distribution and branding solutions for businesses and projects in Kent and the South East. Book your place in the media spotlight!*

Press Control Systems, Unit 6 Tinsley Street, Tipton, West Midlands, DY4 7LH Tel: 0121-557 0001 Fax: 0121-557 0002 *Press control systems manufrs*

Press Fab Ltd, 10 Bayton Way, Exhall, Coventry, CV7 9ER Tel: (024) 7636 2509 *Sheet metalwork engineers or fabricators*

Press & Fab Ltd, Unit 1 Boathouse Lane, Stockton-on-Tees, Cleveland, TS18 3AW Tel: (01642) 616114 Fax: (01642) 605598 *Steel fabrication services*

▶ Press & Go, 1 Stockgill Close, West Bridgford, Nottingham, NG2 6SA Tel: 0115-981 5153 Fax: 0115-981 5153 E-mail: t.summerson@ntlworld.com *Professional ironing service equipped with commercial ironing tables and pressing equipment , providing a quality service with free collection and delivery , home or office. 24/48 service available , clean room enviroment , trained staff , strict quality control , laundry service available.*

Press Labels, Main Road, Sibsey, Boston, Lincolnshire, PE22 0RR Tel: (01205) 750095 Fax: (01205) 750008 *Label manufrs*

Press Metal Products Ltd, 5 Abberley Industrial Centre, Abberley Street, Smethwick, West Midlands, B66 2QL Tel: 0121-555 6061 Fax: 0121-555 6058 E-mail: sales@pressed-metal.com *Manufacture pressed metal*

Press & Shear Machinery Ltd, 12/14 Ninian Park Ninian Way, Wilnecote, Tamworth, Staffordshire, B77 5ES Tel: (01827) 250000 Fax: (01827) 250022 E-mail: sales@pressandshear.com *Metalworking machinery manufrs*

Press Start Ltd, 9 Wragg Drive, Newmarket, Suffolk, CB8 7SD Tel: (01638) 608046 Fax: (01638) 603203 E-mail: sales@pressstart.co.uk *Computer services*

Pressac Communications Ltd, Glaisdale Dr West, Nottingham, NG8 4GY Tel: 0115-936 5200 Fax: 0115-936 5252 E-mail: sales@presscom.co.uk *Holding companies or groups*

Pressbrake Tools, Breeza Works, Bocking, Cross Roads, Keighley, West Yorkshire, BD22 9AP Tel: (01535) 647169 Fax: (01535) 647013 E-mail: pressbrake@legend.co.uk *Press brakes engineers*

▶ PressCare UK Ltd, PO Box 3426, Walsall, WS3 4ZY Tel: (0845) 2267617 Fax: (0845) 2267627 E-mail: enquiries@presscare.co.uk *Distributor for seyi presses in the european union*

Pressco Components Ltd, Selborne Street, Walsall, WS1 2JN Tel: (01922) 620202 Fax: (01922) 726101 E-mail: press-sales@presco.co.uk *Scaffolding fittings & metal pressing parts*

Presscraft Components Ltd, 3 Woodburn Road, Smethwick, West Midlands, B66 2PU Tel: 0121-558 1888 Fax: 0121-555 5498 E-mail: info@presscraft-limited.co.uk *Motor parts & metal pressing manufrs*

▶ Presscut Components, Station Road, Bagworth, Coalville, Leicestershire, LE67 1BH Tel: (01530) 230220 Fax: (01530) 230218 E-mail: sales@presscutcomponents.co.uk *Car parts, sheets & metal works manufrs*

Pressdram Ltd, 6 Carlisle Street, London, W1D 3BN Tel: (020) 7437 4017 Fax: (020) 7437 0705 E-mail: strobes@private-eye.co.uk *Publishers*

Pressed Flights Ltd, 6 Ferrand Lodge, Todmorden Road, Littleborough, Lancashire, OL15 9EG Tel: (01706) 372551 Fax: (01706) 377598 E-mail: sales@pressedflights.co.uk *Screw conveyor manufrs*

▶ Pressed Steel Products, 11 All Saints Industrial Estate, Bishop Auckland, Shildon, County Durham, DL4 2RD Tel: (01388) 770490 Fax: (01388) 778068 E-mail: sales@pspuk.com *Steel fabricators*

Pressed For Time Ltd, 1 Johnston Road, Woodford Green, Essex, IG8 0XA Tel: (020) 8559 2015 Fax: (020) 8505 9581 E-mail: andrew@pft.uk.com *Graphic & web design & print services*

Pressential, 222 Godstone Road, Whyteleafe, Surrey, CR3 0EE Tel: (01883) 623329 Fax: (01883) 625506 *Public relations services*

Pressex Engineers, Express Technical Centre, Kingsway, Team Valley Trading Estate, Gateshead, Tyne & Wear, NE11 0JL Tel: 0191-497 3430 Fax: 0191-497 3431 E-mail: pressex@responsive-engioneering.com *Pressex combines expertise and experience with technology to offer an unrivalled service for the production of pressing, formed components, light fabrications and assemblies. The pressing business is fully supported with a well equipped tool room and machining facility for the manufacture, machining and repair of tools. In addition to this Pressex has a commercial welding facility and is part of the Responsive Engineering group of companies*

Pressfab Products Pressworkers, 9 Lion Industrial Estate, Clinton Road, Leominster, Herefordshire, HR6 0RJ Tel: (01568) 613693 Fax: (01568) 613501 *General pressworkers*

Pressmain (Pressurisation) Co. Ltd, Opal Works, Denhill Road Industrial Estate, Moss Side, Manchester, M15 5NR Tel: 0161-226 4727 Fax: 0161-226 5848 E-mail: sales@pressmain.com *Pressurisation & booster unit manufrs*

Pressmech Sewing Machines, 3 Walton New Road, Bruntingthorpe, Lutterworth, Leicestershire, LE17 5RD Tel: 0116-247 8071 Fax: (01455) 251320 E-mail: pressmech@aol.com *Sewing machine & heat transfer presses manufrs*

Presspart Manufacturing Ltd, Phillips Road, Blackburn, BB1 5RF Tel: (01254) 582233 Fax: (01254) 584100 E-mail: sales@presspart.com *Deep drawn metal pressings*

Presspeed Precision Tools Ltd, Hartlepool Workshops, Hartlepool, Cleveland, TS25 1PD Tel: (01429) 269739 *Plastic mould toolmakers*

Pressplan Travel Ltd, 17 Verulam Road, St. Albans, Hertfordshire, AL3 4DA Tel: (01727) 833291 Fax: (01727) 867435 E-mail: info@pressplantravel.com *Business travel agent & specialist trade fairs*

Pressrite Engineering Ltd, 24 Ogmore Crescent, Bridgend Industrial Estate, Bridgend, Mid Glamorgan, CF31 3TE Tel: (01656) 657067 Fax: (01656) 645857 *Light steel pressings & assemblers services*

Pressure Cast Products Ltd, Fairacres Industrial Estate, Dedworth Road, Windsor, Berkshire, SL4 4LE Tel: (01753) 868969 Fax: (01753) 840475 E-mail: info@pressurecast.co.uk *Pressure die castings suppliers*

Pressure Coolers Ltd, 11-17 Powerscroft Road, Sidcup, Kent, DA14 5NH Tel: (020) 8300 8080 Fax: (020) 8309 0912 E-mail: office@pressurecoolers.co.uk *Pressure Coolers Limited was established in 1963 and is the Sole Distributor and Service Centre for OASIS water coolers and drinking fountains as seen in many prestigious locations worldwide. *Pressure Coolers has been operating for longer than most of its competitors and has dealt with a very wide range of customers across all sectors of industry and commerce as well as almost every part of the public sector. *We cover the whole of the UK and are able to install and maintain water coolers anywhere in the country.*

Pressure Design Hydraulics Ltd, Goldthorpe Industrial Estate, Goldthorpe, Rotherham, S. Yorkshire, S63 9BL Tel: (01709) 897121 Fax: (01709) 895305 E-mail: sales@pressuredesign.co.uk Purchasing Contact: M. Penty Sales Contact: A. Grundy Principal Export Areas: Worldwide *Manufacturers of hydraulic equipment including presses. Also distributors, agents & repair services of hydraulic presses*

Pressure Flex, 111 Great Barr Street, Birmingham, B9 4BB Tel: 0121-766 8228 Fax: 0121-766 7818 E-mail: sales@wakefind.co.uk *Manufacturers of hoses including high pressure & hydraulic*

Pressure & Flow Ltd, Victoria House, 50 Albert Street, Rugby, Warwickshire, CV21 2RH Tel: (01788) 560426 Fax: (01788) 561228 E-mail: uk@sensortechnics.com *Solenoid valves & pressure sensors*

Pressure Gauges Ltd, Park Street, Oldbury, West Midlands, B69 4LE Tel: 0121-544 4408 Fax: 0121-544 7332 E-mail: enquiries@pressure-gauges-ltd.com Principal Export Areas: Central/East Europe & West Europe *Pressure gauges manufrs*

Pressure Systems International Ltd, 124 Victoria Road, Farnborough, Hampshire, GU14 7PW Tel: (01252) 510000 Fax: (01252) 510099 E-mail: sales@pressure-systems.com *Jet engines pressure scanner manufrs*

Pressure Tech Ltd, Unit 6, Graphite Way, Hadfield, Glossop, Derbyshire, SK13 1QG Tel: (01457) 899307 Fax: (01457) 899308 E-mail: steve@pressure-tech.com *Pressure regulator manufrs*

Pressure Welding Machines Ltd, Belmont Farm Business Centre, Snoad Hill, Bethersden, Ashford, Kent, TN26 3DY Tel: (01233) 820817 Fax: (01233) 820591 E-mail: sales@pwmltd.co.uk *Welding equipment manufrs*

Pressurefast Ltd, Forge Road, Machynlleth, Powys, SY20 8EG Tel: (01654) 702865 Fax: (01654) 703450 E-mail: info@pressurefast.com *Construction plant repair kit manufrs*

Presswheel Ltd, 180 Ilderton Road, London, SE15 1NT Tel: (020) 7635 8686 Fax: (020) 7635 0414 E-mail: info@presswheel.co.uk *Lithographic printers*

Prestech Exhibition Services, Unit 14 Belgrave Industrial Estate, Belgrave Road, Southampton, SO17 3EA Tel: (023) 8055 0557 Fax: (023) 8055 2452 E-mail: prestech@prestech.co.uk *Exhibition stand contractors*

Prestige Air Engineers Ltd, Kinnesswood, Withybush Road, Haverfordwest, Dyfed, SA62 4BN Tel: (01437) 766126 Fax: (01437) 765151 E-mail: p.air@btconnect.com *Aircraft inspection & repair services*

Prestige Audio, 12 High Street, Rickmansworth, Hertfordshire, WD3 1ER Tel: (01923) 711113 Fax: (01923) 776606 *Home cinema, car audio & security services*

▶ Prestige Bedrooms, 99 Blackshaw Lane, Royton, Oldham, OL2 6NT Tel: (01706) 845691

Prestige Blinds & Interiors, Wharf Road, Newport, Gwent, NP19 8ET Tel: (01633) 263103 Fax: (01633) 243613 *Blind manufrs*

Prestige Building Services (SE), 27 Lennard Road, Dunton Green, Sevenoaks, Kent, TN13 2UX Tel: (01732) 458936 Fax: (07092) 375881 E-mail: sales@prestigebuilding.com *General building & property maintenance, extensions, conversions specialists*

▶ Prestige Car Valeting, 8 The Oaks, West Byfleet, Surrey, KT14 6RL Tel: (07811) 111999 Fax: (01932) 402124 E-mail: prestigecarvaleting@yahoo.co.uk *Car valeting services*

Prestige Coatings Ltd, 10 Enderby Road Industrial Estate, Whetstone, Leicester, LE8 6HZ Tel: 0116-275 0007 Fax: 0116-275 1692 E-mail: sales@prestigecoatings.co.uk *Plastic finishers*

▶ Prestige Computer Services, 3-4 Park Road, Malmesbury, Wiltshire, SN16 0BX Tel: (01666) 825620 Fax: (01666) 826686 E-mail: service@pcs-uk.net *PC maintenance & services & data recovery*

Prestige Conservatory Blinds, Unit 20 Birchbrook Industrial Park, Lynn Lane, Shenstone, Lichfield, Staffordshire, WS14 0DJ Tel: (01543) 483780 Fax: (01543) 483784 *Conservatory roof & side blind manufacturer & installer*

Prestige Engineering, 27 Thornleigh Trading Estate, Dudley, West Midlands, DY2 8UB Tel: (01384) 234488 Fax: (01384) 238884 E-mail: prestigeengineering@btconnect.com *General presswork*

Prestige Enterprises, PO Box 1160, Newtownabbey, County Antrim, BT36 5YP Tel: 0845 230 3818 Fax: 0845 230 3819 E-mail: sales@prestigeenterprises.com *Huge Range of Business Gifts, Promotional Product and Promotional Clothing*

Prestige Fire Protection, 14 Malvern Road, Southampton, SO16 6QA Tel: (023) 8077 3231 Fax: (023) 8052 8393 E-mail: prestige@rfwebb..co.uk *Alarm systems services*

Prestige Glazing Services Ltd, Unit 2 Shuttleworth Court, Shuttleworth Road, Elm Farm Industrial Estate, Bedford, MK41 0EN Tel: (01234) 346454 Fax: (01234) 219063 E-mail: prestigeglazing@btconnect.com *UPVC & aluminium windows & doors*

▶ Prestige Imports & Logistics Ltd, Porterfield House 157 Harton Lane, South Shields, Tyne & Wear, NE34 0PW Tel: 0191 4200585 Fax: 0191 4200585 E-mail: enqurіes@pil-ltd.com *We are international import /export agents. We source goods from all over Asia and send them direct to you. We guarantee we will not be beaten on price. Please check our website for a full list of services.*

Prestige Industrial (Pullman International), India Mill, Clarendon Road, Skew Bridge, Blackburn, BB1 9SY Tel: (01254) 53333 Fax: (01254) 690484 E-mail: sales@prestigeindustrial.co.uk *Prestige Industrial Ltd has been operating from its factory in Blackburn, U.K. since 1956. Occupying a 100,000 sq.ft. site, housing its manufacturing and coating facilities. As the leading manufacturer of quality bakeware products and coatings, Prestige supplies to the industrial plant bakeries and food processing industries throughout the UK and overseas. Through our craft bakery division (Pullman International), we supply a standard range of ex-stock bakeware products and willow display baskets*

Prestige Marble Co., Armoury Works, Armoury Way, London, SW18 1EZ Tel: (020) 8874 7100 Fax: (020) 8870 0025 E-mail: prestigemarble@aol.com

▶ Prestige Network Solutions, Baynard House, 135 Queen Victoria Street, London, EC4V 4AA Tel: (020) 7601 0000 Fax: (020) 7495 5177 E-mail: sales@prestige.networks.com *Computer maintenance & service*

▶ Prestige Number Plates & Signs Ltd, 283 Duke Street, Glasgow, G31 1HX Tel: 0141-550 1323 Fax: 0141-550 1324 *Number plate components*

Prestige Pumps Ltd, 327 Wakefield Road, Wrenthorpe, Wakefield, West Yorkshire, WF2 0LX Tel: 0845 4940719 Fax: (01924) 379953 E-mail: sales@prestigepumps.co.uk *Prestige Pumps Ltd are specialist pump distributors, offering excellent service levels with excellent cost savings to the customer. We have over 40 years experience in the supply, installation and repair of pumps. Our service includes comprehensive on site surveys, pump selection, pump installations and repairs. Our expertise will allow us to supply any pumping equipment from a flooded cellar to chemical and process pumps to standards such as ANSI and API 610. *Should you have any pumping requirements or require a site visit please do not hesitate to contact us.*

▶ Prestige Recruitment Services Ltd, 39 Deansgate, Manchester, M3 2BA Tel: 0161-835 3999 Fax: 0161 835 3777 E-mail: callcentre@prestigeltd.co.uk *Providing recruitment solutions for senior professionals within the call and contact centre environment from Directors to Team Leaders.*

▶ Prestige Recruitment Services Ltd, Saddlers Court, 650 Warwick Road, Solihull, West Midlands, B91 3DX Tel: 0121-244 4484 Fax: 0121-244 4494 *Recruitment services*

▶ Prestige Shop Fitting Installations, 79 Carron Place, East Kilbride, Glasgow, G75 0YL Tel: (01355) 244540 Fax: (01355) 235080 E-mail: lindadesign@prestigeinstalations.net *Refrigerated cabinet supply services*

Prestige Signs, 33 Daryl Road, Wirral, Merseyside, CH60 5RD Tel: 0151-342 6372 Fax: 0151-342 6372 *Sign manufrs*

▶ Prestige Windows Ltd, Vicar Street, Dudley, West Midlands, DY2 8RG Tel: (01384) 456744

▶ Prestigue Civil Engineering Westbury Ltd, Duncote, Towcester, Northamptonshire, NN12 8AL Tel: (01327) 358653 Fax: (01327) 358753 E-mail: info@prestigecivil.co.uk

Prestision Engineers, 15-16 St Andrews Industrial Estate, Sydney Road, Birmingham, B9 4QB Tel: 0121-772 4414 Fax: 0121-771 0472 E-mail: geoff@prestision.co.uk *Presswork & precision machining*

Presto Engineering, Unit 11 Lakeside Industrial Estate, Stanton Harcourt, Witney, Oxfordshire, OX29 5SL Tel: (01865) 883508 Fax: (01865) 881228 *Machinists*

Presto Fencing, Unit 1b, The Old Forge, Main Rd, Huntley, Gloucester, GL19 3DZ Tel: 01452 831 466 Fax: 01452 831 516 *Fencing manufrs*

Presto International Ltd, Penistone Road, Sheffield, S6 2FN Tel: 0114-234 9361 Fax: 0114-234 7446 E-mail: kevin.blackwell@presto-tools.com *Cutting tools manufrs*

Prestolite Electric, 12-16 Bristol Road, Greenford, Middlesex, UB6 8UP Tel: (020) 8231 1000 Fax: (020) 8575 9575 E-mail: sales@prestolite.co.uk *Heavy duty motors manufrs*

Prestolite Electric Ltd, Larden Road, Acton, London, W3 7SX Tel: (020) 8735 4500 Fax: (020) 8735 4777 *Starter motors & alternators manufrs*

Preston City Council, Premier House, Church Street, Preston, PR1 3BQ Tel: (01772) 563957 Fax: (01772) 558524 *Regeneration division for city council*

▶ Preston Components Ltd, 19 Watt Road, Hillington Industrial Estate, Glasgow, G52 4RY Tel: 0141-882 1766 Fax: 0141-882 6363 *Engineering*

Preston Electrical Ltd, Dalton Airfield Indutrial Estate, Dalton, Thirsk, North Yorkshire, YO7 3HE Tel: (01845) 577753 Fax: (01845) 578182 E-mail: enquiries@prestonelectrical.co.uk *Electrical contractors*

Frank Preston (Textiles), Newhaven Business Park, Barton Lane, Eccles, Manchester, M30 0TH Tel: 0161-786 1080 Fax: 0161-786 1144 *Textile merchant converters*

Preston Hall BMW, Concorde House, Concorde Way, Preston Farm Industrial Estate, Stockton-on-Tees, Cleveland, TS18 3RB Tel: (01642) 618618 Fax: (01642) 608613 E-mail: info@prestonhallbmw.co.uk *Vehicle management services*

Preston Industrial Plastics, Aqueduct Street, Preston, PR1 7JQ Tel: (01772) 555224 Fax: (01772) 259473 E-mail: sales@prestonindustrialplastics.co.uk *Plastics tube pipe fittings distributors* Also at: Motherwell

Preston Joinery, Walton Avenue, North Shields, Tyne & Wear, NE29 9NQ Tel: 0191-257 0776 Fax: 0191-257 2002 *Joinery, windows & doorframes manufrs*

▶ Keith Preston Joinery Co. Ltd, 20 Brest Road, Plymouth, PL6 5XP Tel: (01752) 781700 Fax: (01752) 777423 E-mail: sales@keithprestonjoinery.co.uk *Joinery manufacture*

Preston Refrigeration Ltd, Units 3-4 Chantry Industrial Estate, Kingsbury Road, Curdworth, Sutton Coldfield, West Midlands, B76 9EE Tel: (01675) 470899 Fax: (01675) 470838 *Compressor service & repairers*

Richard Preston & Son Ltd, Potto, Northallerton, North Yorkshire, DL6 3HX Tel: (01642) 700243 Fax: (01642) 700081 E-mail: pofpotto@aol.com *Road transport, haulage & freight services*

Preston & Thomas Ltd, Woodville Engineering Works, Heron Road, Rumney, Cardiff, CF3 3JE Tel: (029) 2079 3331 Fax: (029) 2077 9195 E-mail: info@prestonandthomas.co.uk *Fish frying range makers* Also at: Bristol, Glasgow, Lincoln & London

Prestons (Cash & Carry) Ltd, 110 Oldham Road, Manchester, M4 6AG Tel: 0161-236 9258 Fax: 0161-236 7760 *Hardware & fancy goods wholesalers* Also at: Leeds & Stoke

▶ Prestwood Interiors, 24 Orchard Lane, Prestwood, Great Missenden, Buckinghamshire, HP16 0NN Tel: (0800) 1694615 Fax: (01494) 890607 E-mail: asheri1234@aol.com *Specialists in all aspects of uphulstery including re-upholstery &bespoke furniture*

Pretech Engineering, Barrett Court, Cardiff Road, Reading, RG1 8ED Tel: 0118-957 3123 Fax: 0118-957 3123 E-mail: info@pretech.co.uk *CNC engineering services, precision machined parts*

▶ Pretty Chairs, 32 St. Matthews Close, Renishaw, Sheffield, S21 3WT Tel: (01246) 430883 E-mail: sales@prettychairs.co.uk *Affordable chair covers for weddings and formal events covering Sheffield, Barnsley, Doncaster, Rotherham.*

Pretty Ponies Ltd, Unit 9 The Sidings, Whalley, Clitheroe, Lancashire, BB7 9SE Tel: (01254) 822044 Fax: (01254) 822034 E-mail: sales@prettyponies.co.uk *Equestrian show wear manufacturers & sellers*

T. Pretty Engineers, Unit 1 Homestead Farm, Queniborough, Leicester, LE7 3FP Tel: 0116-260 6362 Fax: 0116-260 6362 *Welding engineers*

Preview, Unit 4 Babbage Ho, Dukes Meadow, Millboard Rd, Bourne End, Bucks, SL8 5XF Tel: (01628) 819200 Fax: (01628) 810314 *Software computers*

Preview Productions Ltd, The Old Dairy Manor Farm, Hermitage, Thatcham, Berkshire, RG18 9SD Tel: (01635) 202972 Fax: (01635) 202973 *Conference & video production*

PRF Composite Materials, 3 Upton Road, Poole, Dorset, BH17 7AA Tel: (01202) 680022 Fax: (01202) 680077 E-mail: mail@prfcomposites.com *Reinforced plastic distributors*

▶ PRG Europe, 201 Coventry Road, Small Heath, Birmingham, B10 0RA Tel: 0121-766 6400 Fax: 0121-766 6150 E-mail: birminghaminfo@prgeurope.com *We are the leading provider of performance lighting equipment with an unrivalled reputation for quality and innovation, providing lighting services for all types of live shows, corporate events, sporting events, concert tours etc.*

PRG Trailers & Towing Equipment, The Old Wood Yard, Lightwood Green Avenue, Audlem, Crewe, CW3 0EN Tel: (01270) 812402 Fax: (01270) 811293 E-mail: info@prgtrailers.co.uk *Trailer manufrs*

▶ Priam Software Ltd, The Old Telephone Exchange, 32-42 Albert Street, Rugby, Warwickshire, CV21 2SA Tel: (01788) 558000 Fax: (01788) 558001 E-mail: andrewk@priamsoftware.com *ERP CRM software for e-commerce, mail order, retailers & suppliers*

Pricast-Thermasill Ltd, Otley Road, Charlestown, Shipley, W. Yorkshire, BD17 7HU Tel: (01274) 590522 Fax: (01274) 532264 *Block Paving Contractors*

Price Bros, 1 Ross Road, Abergavenny, Gwent, NP7 5LT Tel: (01873) 853827 Fax: (01873) 853827 *Electric welders & blacksmiths*

Price Bros (Ascot) Ltd, Unit 1 Peter James Business Centre, Pump Lane, Hayes, Middlesex, UB3 3NT Tel: (020) 8569 2251 Fax: (020) 8569 2458 E-mail: info@pricebrothersascot.co.uk *Flooring & building contractors*

Price & Buckland Ltd, Benneworth Close, Hucknall, Nottingham, NG15 6EL Tel: 0115-964 0827 Fax: 0115-964 0769 E-mail: sales@price-buckland.co.uk *Knitwear manufrs*

David Price Woodworking Machinery Ltd, 21 Cae Garw, Thornhill, Cardiff, CF14 9DX Tel: (029) 2061 6977 Fax: (029) 2061 6977 E-mail: info@dpmachines.co.uk *Woodworking tools & machinery specialists*

Price Direct Ltd, 505A Norwood Road, London, SE27 9DL Tel: (020) 8761 7612 Fax: (020) 8761 7514 E-mail: info@pricedirect.com *Telephone marketing & data preparation*

Price Glass Ltd, 414-414a Bath Road, Slough, SL1 6JA Tel: (01628) 664466 Fax: (01753) 733121 E-mail: sales@priceglass.co.uk *Glass merchants, suppliers of mirrors, replacement*

continued

continuation
windows & doors, shower screens, double glazed sealed units, fire glass

Price Guarding Systems, Waterside Estate, Cradley Road, Dudley, West Midlands, DY2 9RG Tel: 0121-525 4973 Fax: (01384) 241039 *Machine guard installers & manufrs*

J. Price (Bath) Ltd, Quarry Hill, Box, Corsham, Wiltshire, SN13 8LH Tel: (01225) 742141 Fax: (01225) 743237 E-mail: derek@price30.fsbusiness.co.uk *Rubber anti-vibration mounts & custom mouldings manufrs*

Jim Price Machinery Ltd, Farmore Mills, Shrewsbury Road, Craven Arms, Shropshire, SY7 9QG Tel: (01588) 673746 Fax: (01588) 672956 *Agricultural sales & engineers*

Price John & Sons Ltd, Brook Street, Bilston, West Midlands, WV14 0NW Tel: (01902) 353441 Fax: (01902) 404728 E-mail: sales@john-price.co.uk *Lithographic printers*

▶ Neil Price Ltd, Bouthwood Road, Sowerby Woods Industrial Estate, Barrow-in-Furness, Cumbria, LA14 4RD Tel: (01229) 839966 Fax: (01229) 814310 E-mail: office.neilprice@tiscali.co.uk *Builder*

Price & Oliver Ltd, 254 Lozells Road, Birmingham, B19 1NR Tel: 0121-554 8491 Fax: 0121-554 8989 *Builders merchants & architectural ironmongers*

Price Systems Ltd, Meridian Office Park, Osborn Way, Hook, Hampshire, RG27 9HY Tel: (01256) 760012 Fax: (01256) 762122 E-mail: sales@pricesystems.com *Provide cost forecasting software services*

Price Technical Ltd, 27 Melbourne Terrace, Clevedon, Avon, BS21 6HQ Tel: (01275) 879811 Fax: (01275) 873052 E-mail: sales@pricetec.co.uk *Air ventilation equipment suppliers*

Price & Weston, Orchard St, Worcester, WR5 3DY Tel: (01905) 360463 Fax: (01905) 763040 E-mail: enquiries@price-weston.co.uk *Precision engineers & toolmakers*

Pricebusters, Unit 5b Petergreen Way, Furness Business Park, Barrow-in-Furness, Cumbria, LA14 2PE Tel: (01229) 432720 Fax: (01229) 432720 *Office equipment suppliers*

Priceless Computing, 45 Commerce Street, Glasgow, G5 8AD Tel: 0141-420 3735 Fax: 0141-429 1914 E-mail: sales@pless.co.uk *Computer manufrs*

▶ Priceless Print, Cross Park House, Low Green, Rawdon, Leeds, LS19 6HB Tel: 0113-239 1333 Fax: 0113-239 1444 E-mail: info@pricelessprint.co.uk *Print company*

Pricewaterhousecoopers, 1 Enbankment Place, London, WC2N 6RH Tel: (020) 7583 5000 Fax: (020) 7822 4652 E-mail: info@pcwglobal.com *Accountants*

Prickett's Wood Products, 73 Bredgar Rd, London, N19 5BS Tel: (020) 7272 3931 Fax: (020) 7272 3931 *Wood turnery manufrs*

Priday Sydney & Snewin Ltd, Oak Wharf, Timberwharf Road, London, N16 6DB Tel: (020) 8800 5661 Fax: (020) 8809 5521 E-mail: sales@pridays.sagehost.co.uk *Hardwood importers & merchants*

▶ Pride Collections Ltd, Unit 10, Leeds Industrial Estate, Wigan, Lancashire, WN3 4DW Tel: (01942) 829900

▶ Pride Computer Solutions, 21 Lynmouth Drive, Ilkeston, Derbyshire, DE7 9HN Tel: 0115-944 2410 Fax: (0870) 7063172 E-mail: info@pridecs.co.uk *IT excellence in computer consultancy, remote support and maintenance contracts in the East and West Midlands*

▶ Pride Mobility Scooters, 3 Longmore Road, Reading, RG2 8QG Tel: 0118-987 2695 E-mail: jim@pridemobility-scooters.com *DISCOUNT MOBILITY SCOOTER SALES ELECTRIC DISABILITY SCOOTERS*

▶ Pride North Sea (UK) Ltd, Torridon House, 73-75 Regent Quay, Aberdeen, AB11 5AR Tel: (01224) 587878

Pride Oil plc, Crown Road, Enfield, Middlesex, EN1 1DZ Tel: (020) 8345 8100 Fax: (020) 8804 9977 E-mail: info@pride-oils.co.uk *Edible oil & fruit juice distributor*

Priest Engineering Co Poole Ltd, Holton Heath Trading Park, Poole, Dorset, BH16 6LE Tel: (01202) 631663 Fax: (01202) 632573 E-mail: sales@priest-engineering.co.uk *CNC sheet metal fabricators manufrs*

Priestley Precision Engineering, 16 Leaside, Aycliffe Industrial Estate, Aycliffe Industrial Park, Newton Aycliffe, County Durham, DL5 6HX Tel: (01325) 316200 Fax: (01325) 310510 *Engine reconditioners & rebuilders*

Priestleys of Gloucester Ltd, Unit 41 Morlandlands Trading Estate, Bristol Road, Gloucester, GL1 5RZ Tel: (01452) 522281 Fax: (01452) 300702 E-mail: sales@preistgloucs.com *Point of sale display producers*

Priheath Ltd, Unit 7 Shire Hill, Saffron Walden, Essex, CB11 3AQ Tel: (01799) 525982 Fax: (01799) 521686 E-mail: priheath@cambridgerapid.co.uk *Electro-mechanical PCB assemblers service*

▶ Prima, 60 West Hendon Broadway, London, NW9 7AE Tel: (020) 8201 5857 Fax: (020) 8202 8282 *Stone worktops*

▶ Prima Air Conditioning & Refrigeration Ltd, 44 London Road, Cowplain, Waterlooville, Hampshire, PO8 8EN Tel: (023) 9226 8882

▶ Prima Board, 4-5 The Circuit Babbage Road, Engineer Park, Sandycroft, Deeside, Clwyd, CH5 2QD Tel: (01244) 535421 Fax: (01244) 538963 E-mail: sales@primaconverters.co.uk *Cardboard tubes manufacturers & distributors*

Prima Catering Supplies, 2 Whitworth Industrial Estate, Tilton Road, Birmingham, B9 4PP Tel: 0121-771 3116 Fax: 0121-772 2616 E-mail: primacatering@hotmail.com *Catering disposables & equipment*

Prima Coffee Service Ltd, Tewkesbury Business Park, Tewkesbury, Gloucestershire, GL20 8PF Tel: (01684) 854410 Fax: 01684 854410 E-mail: prima.coffee@btinternet.com *Coffee machine, sales & suppliers*

Prima Corporate Wear Ltd, 5 Greenwich View Place, London, E14 9NN Tel: (020) 7515 8877 Fax: (020) 7515 0077 E-mail: sales@primawear.com *Uniform clothing manufrs*

▶ Prima Distribution Services Ltd, Strudwick House, 92-94 Church Road, Mitcham, Surrey, CR4 3TD Tel: (020) 8640 8486

Prima Electronic Services Ltd, 4 Harding Way, St. Ives, Cambridgeshire, PE27 3WR Tel: (01480) 498338 Fax: (01480) 495172 E-mail: sales@primagroup.co.uk *Electronic contract manufacturing*

Prima Engineering, Stonewall Industrial Estate, Stonewall Place, Newcastle, Staffordshire, ST5 6NR Tel: (01782) 711900 Fax: (01782) 711909 *Engineers precision*

Prima Flow, Stargate Business Park, Cuckoo Road, Nechells, Birmingham, B7 5SE Tel: 0121-327 1234 Fax: (0121) 3274046 E-mail: info@muellerprimaflow.com *Wholesale plumbers & suppliers*

Prima Foam, Caxton Road, Elm Farm Industrial Estate, Bedford, MK41 0ZW Tel: (01234) 213121 Fax: (01234) 340119 *Foam converters*

▶ Prima Foods, Wheal Rose Bakery, Wheal Rose, Scorrier, Redruth, Cornwall, TR16 5BX Tel: (01209) 820321 Fax: (01209) 820402 E-mail: enquiries@primabakeries.co.uk *Wholesale bakers*

Prima Industrie UK Ltd, Unit 1 Phoenix Park, Bayton Road Industrial Estate, Coventry, CV7 9QN Tel: (024) 7664 5588 Fax: (024) 7664 5115 E-mail: info@primauk.com *Laser systems/ equipment manufrs*

Prima International, Abeles Way, Holly Lane Industrial Estate, Atherstone, Warwickshire, CV9 2QZ Tel: (01827) 715479 Fax: (01827) 715479 *Exhibition contractors*

▶ Prima Lasers, 121 Boundary Road, Wooburn Green, Buckinghamshire, HP10 0DJ Tel: (07841) 414839 E-mail: mail@primalasers.co.uk *2D & 3D laser cutting & welding machines manufrs*

Prima Plastics & Associates Ltd, London Road, Bagshot, Surrey, GU19 5HZ Tel: (01276) 453849 Fax: (01276) 453849 E-mail: sales@primaplastics.co.uk *Glass fibre & plastic products*

▶ Prima Print & Design, Henry Close, Battlefield Enterprise Park, Shrewsbury, SY1 3TJ Tel: (01743) 450938 Fax: (01743) 450930 E-mail: mail@primaprint.co.uk *High quality printing services*

Prima Products, 72 Leicester Road, Manchester, M7 4AR Tel: 0161-708 9090 Fax: 0161-792 0098 E-mail: prima@leisurego.co.uk *Food & toy manufrs*

▶ Prima Recycling, 7 D2 Trading Estate, Castle Road, Sittingbourne, Kent, ME10 3RH Tel: (01795) 439307 Fax: (01795) 437344 E-mail: webhouse@primapaper.co.uk *Paper recycling & reconstruction services*

Prima Solutions Ltd, Loughborough Technology Park, Ashby Road, Loughborough, Leicestershire, LE11 3NG Tel: (01509) 232200 Fax: (01509) 262323 *Computer solutions for clothing & footwear*

Prima Tapes & Labels Ltd, Prima House, Faraday Way, Orpington, Kent, BR5 3QW Tel: (01689) 816111 Fax: (01689) 816010 E-mail: sales@prima-tapes.com *Self-adhesive tape printers*

Primac, 6 New Mills, Post Office Road, Inkpen, Hungerford, Berkshire, RG17 9PU Tel: (01488) 668008 Fax: (01488) 668883 E-mail: primac@flowdatasystems.co.uk *Security barrier manufrs*

Primaflex Ltd, Arcadia Business Centre, Miller Lane, Clydebank, Dunbartonshire, G81 1UJ Tel: 0141-951 4188 Fax: 0141-952 2001 *Flexible hose manufrs*

Primagraphics Ltd, New Cambridge House, Bassingbourn Road, Litlington, Royston, Hertfordshire, SG8 0SS Tel: (01763) 852222 Fax: (01763) 853324 E-mail: cambridge_support@curtisswright.co.uk *Video hardware manufrs*

Primal Foods Ltd, Unit 8, The Nelson Centre, Portfield Road, Portsmouth, PO3 5SF Tel: (023) 9262 0020 Fax: (023) 92620021 E-mail: info@primalfoods.co.uk *Manufacturing soup & sauces*

Primarc Ltd, 816 Leigh Road, Slough, SL1 4BD Tel: (01753) 558001 Fax: (01753) 811678 E-mail: uv@primarc.com *Manufacturers of high quality medium pressure ultraviolet (UV) curing lamps, metal halide lamps and electrodeless microwave-powered bulbs, suitable for all known drying systems. Primarc UV curing lamps are designed and manufactured as direct replacement lamps or to meet the specific needs of original equipment manufacturers world-wide. Primarc's extensive range of uv curing lamps are used internationally for the drying of inks, coatings and varnishes, in addition to a wide variety of industrial applications. Primarc has pioneered UV curing technology since 1970 and is recognised as a world leader in the field. All lamps are manufactured to exacting standards within the scope of Primarc's ISO 9001: 2000 registration.*

Primarc Engineering Ltd, Unit 4 Esslemont Industrial Estate, Ellon, Aberdeenshire, AB41 8PA Tel: (01358) 724543 Fax: (01358) 724550 *Engineers*

Primarc Marketing, Unit 8 Wycombe Road, Wembley, Middlesex, HA0 1RH Tel: (020) 8900 8535 Fax: (020) 8900 2232 E-mail: sales@primarc.co.uk Principal Export Areas: Asia Pacific, Central Asia & Africa *Distributors of light fittings*

Primary Asset Recruitment, 13 Kingsway House, Kingsway, Gateshd, Gateshead, Tyne & Wear, NE11 0HW Tel: 0191-492 6170 Fax: 0191-206 4001 E-mail: mark.inger@primaryassetrecruitment.co.uk *Specialists in Permanent and Contract recruitment within Manufacturing and Engineering and IT in the North East of England*

Primary Designs Ltd, Unit 4 International House, Station Yard, Thame, Oxfordshire, OX9 3UH Tel: (01844) 216057 Fax: (01844) 216058 E-mail: patbarrett@primarydesigns.co.uk *We have been producing world-class motor sport*

continued

exhausts since 1998. With this success we are now offering limited edition performance upgrade kits for Ford, Subaru and Mitsubishi cars. We're looking to develop exhausts for a range of performance cars. We have a reputation for building high quality exhausts using the best components available. If your car is on our list and you're interested in an upgrade, please contact us. We also specialise in pipe bending, tube bending, pipe manipulation and bending. Based in Thame Oxfordshire, Covering Oxfordshire Bekshire, Home counties, Thames Valley and Southern UK.

Primary Fasteners Ltd, PO Box 571, Solihull, West Midlands, B90 4TA Tel: 0121 2475191 Fax: 0121 5357094 E-mail: mailroom@prifast.co.uk *quick release pins, pip pins, drop nose pins, detent pins, rivets, inserts, speed rivets & tooling*

Primary Fluid Power, Caddick Road, Knowsley Business Park, Prescot, Merseyside, L34 9HP Tel: 0151-632 9500 Fax: 0151-548 9896 E-mail: *Hydraulic & pneumatic equipment system distributors*

Primary Industries UK Ltd, 1 Warwick Row, London, SW1E 5ER Tel: (020) 7347 1500 Fax: (020) 7347 1501 E-mail: info@primaryuk.co.uk *Steel import & export merchants*

▶ Primary Plumbing Supplies, Unit 28 Hawthorn Road Industrial Estate, Eastbourne, East Sussex, BN23 6QA Tel: (01323) 734714 Fax: (01323) 649193 E-mail: eastbourne@diycity.com *Plumbing services*

▶ Primary Plus UK Ltd, PO Box 11232, Birmingham, B32 2XP Tel: 0121-241 9818 Fax: 0121-241 9818 E-mail: johncave@blueyonder.co.uk *Primary Plus is a supplier to both the UK and International school furniture market place and represents several leading British manufacturers in Europe and the Middle East*

▶ Primary Print, Glynteg House, Station Terrace, Ely, Cardiff, CF5 4AA Tel: (029) 2057 3925 Fax: (029) 2057 3929 E-mail: sales@primaryprint.co.uk

Primary Storage Ltd, Units D7-D9, Hortonwood 7, Telford, Shropshire, TF1 7YY Tel: (01952) 602600 Fax: (01952) 670063 E-mail: sales@primaryuk.com *Computer peripheral dealers*

▶ Primary Tuition, 40 Gilderdale Close, Birchwood, Warrington, WA3 6TH Tel: (01925) 821995 E-mail: mary@cottam.freeserve.co.uk *Private Tutor, Lady tutor, primary, key stage one, two, 11+, entrance exams. Numeracy, Literacy, Maths, English, North Cheshire, Manchester, Warrington.*

Primasil Silicones Ltd, Kington Rd, Weobley, Hereford, HR4 8QU Tel: (01544) 312600 Fax: (01544) 312601 E-mail: sales@primasil.com *Primasil Silicones are the largest independent silicone compounder & manufacturer in the UK and have been trading for over 30 years. An independent company, Primasil is ISO9001:2000 certified and is an expert in the formulation and mixing of silicone rubber compounds and in the processing of silicone using moulding and extrusion techniques. In addition, a state of the art cleanroom allows liquid silicone mouldings and platinum extrusions to be produced which are certified to ISO13485:2003 standards and supplied under the 'Medisil' brand. Primasil also supplies organic rubber mouldings which can be made in the UK or at our Primasil s.r.o. production facility in the Czech Republic. The personnel at Primasil are comfortable dealing with products at all stages of development from initial conception through to volume production. This flexibility coupled with the most experienced silicone personnel in the country are the reasons why Primasil are the UK market leaders in silicone*

Primat Recruitment, Haughton Road, Darlington, County Durham, DL1 2ED Tel: (01325) 376200 Fax: (01325) 358111 *Technical personnel recruitment agency Also at: Aberdeen, Glasgow, Kingswinford, London EC1 & Southampton*

▶ Primatec Edm Ltd, 6 Walkers Lane Lambourn, Hungerford, Berkshire, RG17 8YE Tel: (01488) 72766 Fax: (0870) 4602625 E-mail: m.schmitt@primatec-edm.de *Supplier of EDM wire erosion and spark erosion consumables*

▶ Primavera Aromatherapy Ltd, Manor House, Manor Road, Frome, Somerset, BA11 4BN Tel: (01373) 467103 Fax: (01373) 451532 E-mail: mail@primavera.co.uk *Natural skin care manufrs*

Primco Ltd, Grimshaw Lane, Middleton, Manchester, M24 2AE Tel: 0161-653 4876 Fax: 0161-655 3673 E-mail: sales@northwesternblanks.co.uk *Pre-impregnated materials manufrs*

Prime Computer Systems Ltd, 2 Medlar Close, Bredgar, Sittingbourne, Kent, ME9 8EL Tel: (01622) 884641 Fax: (01622) 884322 *Computer systems & software developers*

Prime Document Ltd, Unit 3, Park Seventeen, Moss Lane, Whitefield, Manchester, M45 8FJ Tel: 0161-766 5544 Fax: 0161-766 5599 E-mail: sthompson@primedoc.co.uk *Expert in data processing, laser printing & mailing*

Prime Garden Buildings, 1a Vale Drive, Worthing, West Sussex, BN14 0DD Tel: (01903) 873125 Fax: (01903) 873125 *Garden sheds supplier & installers*

▶ Prime Linens, 13 High Street, Dartford, DA1 1DT Tel: (01322) 274985 Fax: (01322) 274985 *Bed linen manufrs*

Prime Partitioning Systems Ltd, 7 Windmill Business Park, Windmill Road, Kenn, Clevedon, Avon, BS21 6SR Tel: (01275) 343646 Fax: (01275) 343898 E-mail: info@prime-partitioning.co.uk *Partition contractors*

▶ Prime Plastic Mouldings Ltd, 8 Heron Industrial Estate, Basingstoke Road, Spencers Wood, Reading, RG7 1PJ Tel: 0118-988 7525 Fax: 0118-988 7526 E-mail: sales@primeplas.com *Plastic injection moulders*

Prime Polymers & Compounders, Fernbank Mill, Fernbank Avenue, Barnoldswick, Lancashire, BB18 5UX Tel: (0870) 7707617 Fax: (0870) 7707612 *Plastic compound manufrs*

Prime Recruitment Ltd, 37 Locks Heath Centre, Centre Way, Locks Heath, Southampton, SO31 6DX Tel: (01489) 559090 Fax: (01489) 559995 E-mail: enquiries@prime-recruitment.co.uk *Permanent & contract staff recruitment consultancy services*

Prime Solutions UK Ltd, Brindley Place, Birmingham, B1 2JB Tel: 0121-698 8516 Fax: 0121-698 8600 E-mail: info@primesolutionsuk.com *Prime Solutions specialises in fitting out and refurbishment work in the commercial, retail and public property sector.**Our clients are those users and investors in property with budgets from one hundred thousand pounds up to five million pounds with which to fit out or upgrade existing properties.**

Prime Systems, Brickbarn House, Knowle Lane, Cranleigh, Surrey, GU6 8JL Tel: (01483) 276442 E-mail: sales@primecouk.com *Business equipment suppliers*

Prime Time Innovations, 22 Austin Way, Royal Oak Industrial Estate, Daventry, Northamptonshire, NN11 8QY Tel: (01327) 300761 Fax: (01327) 878743 *Window industry consumables distributors*

▶ Prime Web Solutions Ltd, Prime House, 32 Anyards Road, Cobham, Surrey, KT11 2LA Tel: (01932) 584488 Fax: (01932) 584466 E-mail: info@primews.com *Web design company specialising development of website solutions*

Prime50plus, PO Box 5050, Huddersfield, HD1 4WB Tel: (0845) 4562201 E-mail: paul.kern@prime50plus.co.uk *Prime50plus is a recruitment agency which specialises in "Putting Experience to Work " by matching the skills and experience of mature workers with the needs of employers*

▶ Primebuild Ltd, 5 Davieland Court, Broomloan Place, Glasgow, G51 2JR Tel: 0141-425 1902

Primemix, Nether Compton, Sherborne, Dorset, DT9 4PZ Tel: (01935) 389069 Fax: (01935) 815699 E-mail: howard@primix.demon.co.uk *Water treatments, dosing equipment distributors*

▶ Primepac Solutions Ltd, Unit 36, Rassau Industrial Estate, Rassau, Ebbw Vale, Gwent, NP23 5SD Tel: (01495) 309367 Fax: 01495 309367 E-mail: sales@primepacsolutions.co.uk *Contract packing of powders, liquids, tablets and capsules into sachets, bottles, strips and blisters. Specialists in the personal care, home care and health care markets*

Primetals Ltd, 282 Cutler Heights Lane, Bradford, West Yorkshire, BD4 9HU Tel: (01274) 654250 Fax: (01274) 651205 E-mail: sales@primetals.co.uk *Steel stockholders*

Primeware Ceramics Ltd, 1 Devonshire Gardens, Chiswick, London, W4 3TW Tel: (020) 8995 1119 Fax: (020) 8995 0903 E-mail: primeware.ceramics@virgin.net *Primeware Ceramics Ltd based in London provide food containers, china and earthenware dishes. Products include ceramic dishes, ceramic hot tiles, glass hot tiles and electric glass hot tops.*

Primex Plastics Ltd, Beaumont Way, Aycliffe Industrial Park, Newton Aycliffe, County Durham, DL5 6SN Tel: (01325) 315768 Fax: (01325) 308875 E-mail: info@primexuk.co.uk *Plastic manufrs*

Primo plc, Cumberland House, 24-28 Baxter Avenue, Southend-on-Sea, SS2 6HZ Tel: (01702) 225400 Fax: (01702) 225409 E-mail: enquiries@primoplc.com *Independent insurance brokers*

Primo Computers, 20 Fern Road, Godalming, Surrey, GU7 3EW Tel: (01483) 860777 E-mail: info@primocomputers.co.uk *Computer systems & software services*

▶ Primo Films, 3 Selbourne Cl, New Haw, Addlestone, Surrey, KT15 3RG Tel: (01932) 354316 E-mail: info@primofilms.com *Wedding & events videos*

Primo Play Ltd, Thornhill Road, Dewsbury, West Yorkshire, WF12 9QQ Tel: (01924) 466684 Fax: (01924) 468614 E-mail: sales@primoplay.co.uk *Sports equipment manufrs*

▶ Primo Teamwear, Factory Street, Bradford, West Yorkshire, BD4 9NW Tel: (01274) 682682 Fax: (01274) 652265 *Sports clothing manufrs*

Primopost Ltd, 1 Staden Park, Staden Lane, Buxton, Derbyshire, SK17 9RZ Tel: (01298) 79113 Fax: (01298) 70435 *Polypropylene film converters*

Primstone Electronics, 27a Whitehorse Street, Baldock, Hertfordshire, SG7 6QF Tel: (01462) 490594 Fax: (01462) 490595 E-mail: primstone@aol.com *Electronic assembly production*

Prince Electronics, 7 Leyden Street, London, E1 7LE Tel: (020) 7377 8871 Fax: (020) 7247 7986 E-mail: ali.budhwani@btconnect.com *Clocks & watches wholesalers*

Prince Manufacturing Co., Pool Street, Wolverhampton, WV2 4HN Tel: (01902) 714895 Fax: (01902) 714895 *Clothing manufrs*

Prince Petroleum Ltd, 139 Abbey Lane, Leicester, LE4 5QZ Tel: 0116-266 1828 Fax: 0116-261 0727 E-mail: lynn@prince-petroleum.co.uk *Petroleum oil sales*

Prince Rupert Hotel, Butcher Row, Shrewsbury, SY1 1UQ Tel: (01743) 499955 Fax: (01743) 357306 E-mail: post@prince-rupert-hotel.co.uk *Hotel & conference facilities*

▶ Princebuild Ltd, 18-19 Quarry Park Close, Moulton Park Industrial Estate, Northampton, NN3 6QB Tel: (01604) 645576 Fax: (01604) 643886

▶ Princebuild Ltd, 82-84 High Street, Gosberton, Spalding, Lincolnshire, PE11 4NA Tel: (01775) 841880 Fax: (01775) 841881

Princes, 45-75 Bogmoor Road, Glasgow, G51 4TJ Tel: 0141-440 2585 Fax: 0141-445 3053 *Soft drink manufrs*

Princes Foods International Trading Group, Royal Liver Building, Pier Head, Liverpool, L3 1NX Tel: 0151-236 9282 Fax: 0151-236 1057 *Food suppliers*

Princes Gate Springwater Ltd, New House Farm, Princes Gate, Ludchurch, Narberth, Dyfed, SA67 8JD Tel: (01834) 831225 Fax: (01834) 831305 E-mail: sales@princesgatespringwater.com *Bottling spring water manufrs*

Princes Soft Drinks, West Yorkshire Industrial Estate, Toftshaw Lane, Bradford, West Yorkshire, BD4 6SX Tel: (01274) 651777 Fax: (01274) 651088 E-mail: info@princes.co.uk *Soft drink manufrs*

Princes Soft Drinks Division, Lord North Street, Manchester, M40 2HJ Tel: 0161-202 1044 Fax: 0161-205 7741 *Fruit juice manufrs*

▶ The Princes Trust, Ashfield Avenue, Mansfield, Nottinghamshire, NG18 2AE Tel: (01623) 404520 Fax: (01623) 404502 E-mail: sales@solar-digital.co.uk *Computer software developers*

Princess Fitted Bedroom & Kitchen Furniture, 40 Whalebone Lane South, Dagenham, Essex, RM8 1BB Tel: (020) 8593 3884 *Furniture manufrs*

Princess Hats Ltd, 28 Reginald Street, Luton, LU2 7QZ Tel: (01582) 400488 *Ladies hat manufrs*

Princess International Sales & Service Ltd, Billing Wharf, Cogenhoe, Northampton, NN7 1NH Tel: (01604) 890559 Fax: (01604) 891202 E-mail: sales@princess.co.uk *Boat distributors & agents*

▶ Princess Stores, Latteridge House, Latteridge Green, Bristol, BS37 9TS Tel: 0870 1995481 E-mail: sales@princessstores.co.uk *Princess Stores supply ballgowns, eveningwear, prom dresses and other ladieswear to the independant retail industry. We specialise in superbly beaded, sequinned and embroidered gowns of the highest quality. We trade internet only which enables us save you money by keeping overheads down. Trade only please.*

Princess Yachts International plc, Newport Street, Plymouth, PL1 3QG Tel: (01752) 203888 Fax: (01752) 203777 E-mail: info@princess-yachts.com *Boat motor & power manufrs*

Princeton Consulting Ltd, 43-51 Windsor Road, Slough, SL1 2EE Tel: (01753) 217700 Fax: (01753) 217701 *IT consultants*

Princia Shipping Ltd, Unit C1a Purfleet Industrial Park, London Road, Aveley, South Ockendon, Essex, RM15 4YA Tel: (01708) 860848 Fax: (01708) 867765 E-mail: princia@princia.fsnet.co.uk *Freight forwarders*

Principal Appointments, 58 Leazes Park Road, Newcastle upon Tyne, NE1 4PG Tel: 0191-232 6660 Fax: 0870-990 1849 E-mail: newcastle@princeappoint.co.uk *Employment agency*

▶ Principal Cooling, Old Eglish Road, Dungannon, County Tyrone, BT71 7PG Tel: (028) 8775 0111 Fax: (028) 8775 0222

Principal Corporation Ltd, Principal House, Parsonage Business Park, Horsham, West Sussex, RH12 4AL Tel: (01403) 258486 Fax: (01403) 210131 E-mail: solutions@principalcorp.co.uk *Office solutions*

Principal Hygine System, Unit B4 Hilton Trading Estate, Hilton Road, Lanesfield, Wolverhampton, WV4 6DW Tel: (01902) 404550 Fax: (01902) 353455 E-mail: sales@principalhygiene.com *Washroom Service provider on a national basis, sanitary disposal, air fresheners, hand dryers, roller towels plus a full range of paper products.*

▶ Principal Image, Cherry Tree Lane, Rostherne, Altrincham, Cheshire, WA14 3RZ Tel: (01565) 830213 Fax: (01565) 830214 E-mail: info@principalimage.com *Design consultancy offering marketing, brochure design*

Principal Security Systems Ltd, 180 Bridge Road, Sarisbury Green, Southampton, SO31 7EH Tel: (01489) 886677 Fax: (01489) 886699 E-mail: sales@setonsecurities..co.uk *Finance brokers*

▶ Principal Technical Services Ltd, Durham House, 39 Dale Road, Buxton, Derbyshire, SK17 6NJ Tel: 01298 767414 E-mail: enquiries@principalts.co.uk *We are a small company that specialise in tendering support, estimating and quantity surveying services within the construction industry. We also offer other services tailored to the industry such as CAD drawings, new and paper to PC amongst other things. All our services are highlighted on our website, please feel free to have a look and contact us should you require any further help or assistance.*

Principally Pine, 47-49 Ferensway, Hull, HU2 8NA Tel: (01482) 588099 Fax: (01482) 609587 *Pine furniture manufrs*

▶ Principle Management Ltd, Britannia House, 29 Station Road, Kettering, Northamptonshire, NN15 7HJ Tel: (01536) 515855 Fax: (01536) 414000 E-mail: principle@principletechnology.com *Computer software specialists*

The Principle Nameplate Company Ltd, Unit 19 St. Michaels Trading Estate, Bridport, Dorset, DT6 3RR Tel: (01308) 459900 Fax: (01308) 459911 E-mail: sales@platesandplaques.com *Nameplates, labels & plaques*

James Pringle, 130 Buchanan Street, Glasgow, G1 2JR Tel: 0141-221 3434 *Heritage industry*

Pringle of Scotland Ltd, 141-142 Sloane Street, London, SW1X 9AY Tel: (020) 7259 1660 *Knitwear manufacturers, wholesalers & licensers* Also at: Hawick

▶ Prins Packaging Solutions, Unit 140 Hartlebury Trading Estate, Hartlebury, Kidderminster, Worcestershire, DY10 4JB Tel: (01299) 251400 Fax: (01299) 251800 E-mail: sales@prinsuk.com *Specialists automated weighing, filling & packaging*

Prinsen UK Ltd, Mayfair House, 11 Lurke Street, Bedford, MK40 3HZ Tel: (01234) 345066 Fax: (01234) 355640 *Dry products manufrs*

Print 2000 Ltd, 54 Finnieston Square, Glasgow, G3 8ET Tel: 0141-204 2400 Fax: 0141-204 2401

Print A Gift, 237 High Street, Acton, London, W3 9BY Tel: (020) 8993 4820 Fax: (020) 8993 2164 E-mail: info@pagl.co.uk Principal Export Areas: Central/East Europe & West Europe *T-Shirt*

▶ Print By Design, 7-9 Imperial Square, Cheltenham, Gloucestershire, GL50 1QB Tel: (01242) 216123 *Printers*

Print Consultants Ltd, Waterside Business Park, Waterside, Hadfield, Glossop, Derbyshire, SK13 1BE Tel: (01457) 860582 Fax: (01457) 856700 E-mail: sales@printconsultants.co.uk *Printing services*

▶ The Print & Design Centre Ltd, 5 Queen Anne's Court, Oxford Road East, Windsor, Berkshire, SL4 1DG Tel: (01753) 621444 Fax: (01753) 621444 E-mail: sales@pdc-windsor.co.uk *For all your printing, graphic design and Direct Mail needs. Call for a quote now!*

Print Express, 4 Sunnyside Terrace, London, NW9 5DL Tel: (020) 8200 0600 Fax: (020) 8200 6866 E-mail: printexpress@btclick.com Purchasing Contact: Moradian Sales Contact: Moradian *Printers, digital & printers, general/ commercial/jobbing/all types. Also exhibition display designers/producers/services*

The Print Factory Ltd, South Portway Close, Round Spinney, Northampton, NN3 8RH Tel: (01604) 790079 Fax: (01604) 492515 E-mail: info@theprintfactory.co.uk *Printing services*

Print Factory, Bell Lane, Bellbrook Industrial Estate, Uckfield, East Sussex, TN22 1QL Tel: (01825) 764707 Fax: (01825) 764253 *Lithographic printers*

Print Finishers Ltd, 35 Greenwich Church St, London, SE10 9BJ Tel: (020) 8858 5224 Fax: (020) 8265 6289 *Showcard mounting/hand finishing services*

Print Guard Ltd, Unit 2, Parsonage Street, Oldbury, West Midlands, B69 4PH Tel: 0121-552 5707 Fax: 0121-552 5506 E-mail: sales@printguard.co.uk *Safety guards*

▶ Print House, 54 Notting Hill Gate, London, W11 3HT Tel: (020) 7229 1171 Fax: (020) 7727 2498 E-mail: info@printhousenottinghil1.com

▶ Print Impressions Ltd, 230 Dansom Lane North, Hull, HU8 7RS Tel: (01482) 323889

▶ Print Innovative Technology Ltd, Camilla Court, The Street, Nacton, Ipswich, IP10 0EU Tel: (01473) 655141 Fax: (01473) 655148 E-mail: neil@print-it.tv *Print innovative technology service*

▶ Print It Ltd, Unit 11, St. Thomas Street Business Centre, St. Thomas Street, Newcastle Upon Tyne, NE1 4LE Tel: (0800) 0640770 Fax: 0191-233 0725 E-mail: steven@printitlimited.com *Print design & copying services*

Print One Ltd, Mayfield House, Tockholes Road, Darwen, Lancashire, BB3 1LL Tel: (01254) 776735 Fax: (01254) 775802 E-mail: mail@print1uk.com *Suppliers of thermal transfer ribbon*

Print Partnership, Unit 11 Pacific Business Park, Pacific Road, Cardiff, CF24 5HJ Tel: (029) 2047 4010 Fax: (029) 2047 4011 E-mail: repro@printpartnership.co.uk *Printing*

▶ Print People, 170-204 Elliot Street, Glasgow, G3 8EX Tel: 0141-248 7240 Fax: 0141-248 7771

Print Permanising Ltd, Graphic House, Telford Way, Severalls Business Park, Colchester, CO4 9QF Tel: (01206) 845655 Fax: (01206) 845246 E-mail: paulc@hythe-uk.com *Plastic printing services* Also at: Glasgow

▶ Print Plus, 126 Widemarsh Street, Hereford, HR4 9HN Tel: (01432) 272025 Fax: (01432) 353962

▶ Print Run Ltd, 28 Fulton Road, Olympic Way, Wembley, Middlesex, HA9 0TF Tel: (020) 8900 2480 Fax: (020) 8900 1455 E-mail: sales@printrun.co.uk *Printing services*

▶ Print Save Ltd, 7 Hawthorn Vale, Chapel Allerton, Leeds, LS7 4PJ Tel: 0113-293 9776 *Print broker & management*

Print Save of Preston, 9 Winckley Street, Preston, PR1 2AA Tel: (01772) 888878 Fax: (01772) 888879 E-mail: office@printsave.co.uk *Printers*

▶ Print Search Ltd, Westinghouse Road, Trafford Park, Manchester, M17 1PJ Tel: 0161-872 8921 Fax: 0161-848 7323 E-mail: sales@princesearchpromotionalproducts. co.uk *Promotional gifts & print & labelling services*

▶ Print Services UK Ltd, Print House, 66 Hartlebury Trading Estate, Hartlebury, Kidderminster, Worcestershire, DY10 4JB Tel: (01299) 250001 E-mail: visiboard@hotmail.com *The manufacture and distribution of a range of high quality illustrated bedroom furniture.**Although there is a large selection of designs to choose from it is now possible to do one off units using specific graphics of the end users choice .***

▶ Print Solutions, 89 St. Clair Street, Kirkcaldy, Fife, KY1 2NW Tel: (01592) 653451 Fax: (01592) 650214

Print & Stationery Management Co. Ltd, 114 Jacob Street, Bristol, BS2 0HU Tel: 0117-926 2459 Fax: 0117-925 1357 E-mail: sales@prism-ltd.co.uk *General printers & stationers & office furniture suppliers*

Print Systems Ltd, 11 Merse Road, Moons Moat North Industrial Estate, Redditch, Worcestershire, B98 9HL Tel: (01527) 64555 Fax: (01527) 62100 E-mail: info@print-systems.co.uk *Suppliers of business forms*

Print Systems (Midlands) Ltd, Steel House, 37 Church Street, Oldbury, West Midlands, B69 3AG Tel: 0121-541 1376 Fax: 0121-541 2292 E-mail: sales@printsystemsmidlands.co.uk *Business forms & computer stationery*

▶ Print Tech Ltd, 3 Power Park, Station Approach, Banbury, Oxfordshire, OX16 5AB Tel: (01295) 262202 Fax: (01295) 271722

▶ Print Wright Ltd, 6 Boss Hall Road, Ipswich, IP1 5BN Tel: (01473) 240897 Fax: (01473) 241307

Print4biz, PO Box 256, Bristol, BS16 5WW Tel: 0117-907 1907 Fax: 0117-907 1907 E-mail: enquiries@print4biz.org.uk *Printing, copying and binding - printing prices online. MS Publisher, PowerPoint, Excel and Word printing a speciality.*

Printafoil Ltd, 5 Mitcham Industrial Estate, Streatham Road, Mitcham, Surrey, CR4 2AP Tel: (020) 8640 3074 Fax: (020) 8640 2136 E-mail: info@blockfoil.com *Printing trade finishing services*

▶ Printank Ltd, 8 Bay Street, Leicester, LE1 3BX Tel: 0116-251 9797 Fax: 0116-251 9393

Printaply Printers' Services, Highfield Lane, Sheffield, S13 9NA Tel: 0114-269 3322 Fax: (0845) 0850077 E-mail: printaply@yahoo.co.uk *Printing trade finishing equipment distributors*

▶ Printcartridge Direct.Com Ltd, Heinzel Park, Aber Park Aber Road, Flint, Clwyd, CH6 5EX Tel: (01352) 735100 Fax: 01352 735500 E-mail: office@printcartridgedirect.com *Huge Savings on Printer Cartridges For All Makes of Printer. 0% Quality Guaranteed. Same Day Despatch. Uk Site.*

▶ Print-Craft, Mortimer-Reid House, 2 Herald Way, Binley Industrial Estate, Coventry, CV3 2NY Tel: (024) 7656 0920 Fax: (024) 7656 0930

Printcut Boxfast Ltd, 144 Charles Henry Street, Birmingham, B12 0SD Tel: 0121-622 4353 Fax: 0121-622 1254 E-mail: sales@pcbf.co.uk *Cardboard packaging designers*

Printec Ltd, 8 Petworth Industrial Estate, Petworth, West Sussex, GU28 9NR Tel: (01798) 343488 Fax: (01798) 344487 E-mail: sales@printec.co.uk *Printed circuit board manufrs*

▶ Printec Consultants, 19-20 Berners Street, London, W1T 3LW Tel: (020) 7636 6264

Printec (UK) Ltd, Unit 5, Deanfield Court, Link 59 Business Park, Clitheroe, Lancashire, BB7 1QS Tel: (01200) 425500 Fax: (01200) 425511 E-mail: info@printec.uk.com *Printec offers a Pad (Tampo) printing, Screen Printing and Rotary Printing service onto 3D products.**We are UK agents for TTN Pad Printing Machines, Marabu inks, Toyobo Printing Plates and manufacture our own range of Silpads for Pad Printing.**The experience gained from our hands-on product printing services allows us to give the highest level of technical support in all aspects of Pad Printing.**Printec's customers benefit from our Service and Quality.*

Printech Circuit Laboratories Ltd, 31-35 Haltwhistle Road, South Woodham Ferrers, Chelmsford, CM3 5ZA Tel: (01245) 323244 Fax: (01245) 329472 E-mail: sales@pcll.co.uk Principal Export Areas: Africa & North America *Specialised printed circuit boards*

Printed Circuit Design, 5 Holbrook Close, Great Waldingfield, Sudbury, Suffolk, CO10 0XX Tel: (01787) 310990 E-mail: d.holdaway@virgin.net *PCB design*

▶ Printed Wiring Technologies Ltd, 7-8 Alders Court, Watchmead, Welwyn Garden City, Hertfordshire, AL7 1LT Tel: (01707) 338871 Fax: (01707) 372622 E-mail: sales@pwtpcbs.com *Printed circuit boards.*

▶ The Printed Word Ltd, Newhouse Farm Business Centre, Old Crawley Road, Faygate, Horsham, West Sussex, RH12 4RU Tel: (01293) 851053 Fax: (01293) 851900 E-mail: info@printedword.co.uk

Printel, 43 Cross Road, Croydon, CR0 6TE Tel: (020) 8681 2262 Fax: (020) 8688 5883 E-mail: printel@btinernet.com *Office suppliers & printers*

Printer Connections Ltd, Unit 445 Oakshop Place, Walton Summit Industrial Estate, Bamber Bridge, Preston, PR5 8AT Tel: (01772) 314880 Fax: (01772) 314900 E-mail: sales@printerconnections.co.uk *Computer consumable services*

Printer Rescue, PO Box 198, Manchester, M32 0ZQ Tel: (0845) 3451498 E-mail: john.regan@printerrescue.co.uk *Printer sales & repairs*

▶ Printerbase, Victoria House, Victoria Street, Millbrook, Stalybridge, Cheshire, SK15 3HY Tel: 0161-304 7594 Fax: 0161-304 7598 E-mail: info@printerbase.co.uk *Reseller of mono & colour laser printers*

▶ Printerinks.com, 335 Rayners Lane, Pinner, Middlesex, HA5 5EN Tel: 0208 845 0661 Fax: 0208 845 3659 E-mail: info@printerinks.com *Internet retailer specialising in printer consumables (ink cartridges, laser toner, paper and media, inkjet refill kits). Selling original, compatible and remanufactured cartridges. Extensive range of printer cartridges at guaranteed low prices. Fast and free UK delivery. Same day dispatch on most orders. Free and easy returns procedure. 0% satisfaction guaranteed. Price Promise. Secure online shopping. Excellent Customer Service and Support. Ink cartridge recycling service.*

▶ Inc Printers, Rawmec Industrial Park, Plumpton Road, Hoddesdon, Hertfordshire, EN11 0EE Tel: (01992) 801970 Fax: (01992) 801985

Printers Partners Supplies Ltd, Unit 720 Tudor Estate, Abbey Road, London, NW10 7UN Tel: (020) 8951 9500 Fax: (020) 8963 1940 E-mail: sales@rotaprint.com *Offset press service & spares*

▶ Print-Eze Ltd, 349 Darnick Street, Kent House, Glasgow, G21 4AX Tel: 0141-558 7829 Fax: 0141-558 9100

▶ Printfine Ltd, Unit 14-18 King Edward Industrial Estate, Gibraltar Row, Liverpool, L3 7HJ Tel: 0151-242 0000 Fax: 0151-242 0001 E-mail: sales@printfine.co.uk

Printform Direct Ltd, 8 Longbridge, Willesborough, Ashford, Kent, TN24 0TA Tel: (01233) 639898 Fax: (01233) 636866 E-mail: sales@printform.co.uk *Printing & stationary*

▶ Printhouse Corporation Ltd, St Leonards Road, London, NW10 6ST Tel: (020) 8963 0123 Fax: (0871) 7171103 E-mail: sales@printhouse.co.uk *Printing services*

Printhouse Group, 8 Albert Drive, Burgess Hill, West Sussex, RH15 9TN Tel: (01444) 871776 Fax: (01444) 871731 E-mail: info@printhousegroup.com *Screen and large format digital printing on virtually any material including Perspex. glass, PVC, Foamex, Dibond metal panels/signage. From self-adhesive stickers to construction site signs and exhibition printing.*

▶ Printinc, Sutton Business Centre, Restmor Way, Wallington, Surrey, SM6 7AH Tel: 020 8255 2110 Fax: 020 8255 2115 E-mail: printinc2@btconnect.com *Printing Services - Photocopying and Colour Copying from disk or hard copy - design*

Printing Com (Orpington), 98 High Street, Farnborough, Orpington, Kent, BR6 7BA Tel: (01689) 870380 Fax: 01689 823590 E-mail: orpington@printing.com *Full colour print service for over 2700 fixed price products combined with in house Graphic Design if required.*

▶ Printing.Com@RasLtd, Lakeland House, 10 Boughton, Chester, CH3 5AG Tel: (01244) 343333 Fax: (01244) 346120 E-mail: sales@rasgroup.co.uk

Printing & Graphic Machinery Ltd, Millboard Road, Bourne End, Buckinghamshire, SL8 5XE Tel: (01628) 527372 Fax: (01628) 524466 E-mail: sales@pgm.co.uk *Printing machine sales*

▶ Printing Place, Hanbury Road, Chelmsford, CM1 3AE Tel: (01245) 251001 Fax: (01245) 267393

Printing Press, 21 Clare Place, Plymouth, PL4 0JW Tel: (01752) 250580 Fax: (01752) 223855 E-mail: theprintingpress@btconnect.com *Printing services*

Printing Press Services Ltd, Sellers Street, Preston, PR1 5EU Tel: (01772) 797050 Fax: (01772) 705761 E-mail: sales@ppsi.co.uk *Printing press manufrs*

Printing & Scanning Solutions Ltd, Carradale, Kirby Road, Woking, Surrey, GU21 4RJ Tel: 01483 852581 E-mail: sales@pass-barcodes.co.uk *PASS are suppliers of linear & 2D bar code scanners, RF Tags, Batch & RF Data collection hardware & software, thermal printers, labels tags, ribbons & bar code software. Applications include goods in goods out, warehouse product tracking, stock control, pallet labelling, print & apply, document tracking, garment tracking (for example, dry cleaning).*

Printline Ltd, Unit 12, Grosvenor Way, London, E5 9ND Tel: (020) 8806 9090 Fax: (020) 8806 9434 E-mail: sales@printline.co.uk *Commercial printers*

Printmarketing, 3 Doals Gate, Bacup, Lancashire, OL13 8JN Tel: (0845) 2578077 Fax: (0871) 7898077 E-mail: sales@printmarketing.co.uk *UK Supplier of Scratchcards, Charity Cards, Direct Mail and Colour Print.*

▶ Printon Plastics & Assemblies Ltd, Unit 4 Attwood Business Centre, Attwood Street, Lye, Stourbridge, West Midlands, DY9 8RY Tel: (01384) 77007 Fax: (01384) 77747 E-mail: info@printonplastics.co.uk *Sub contract printing service*

Printorama, 104 Lechmere Avenue, Woodford Green, Essex, IG8 8QG Tel: (0845) 1668828 Fax: (020) 8551 5448 E-mail: sales@printorama.com *Printing & Graphic Design services at sensible rates. Best quality production. Rates starting from £35 for 250 full colour Business cards.*

Print-Pac Services, Unit 3 Grampound Road Industrial Estate, Grampound Road, Truro, Cornwall, TR2 4TB Tel: (01726) 883336 Fax: (01726) 883382 *Printers*

Printpack Ltd, Bridge Hall Mills, Bridge Hall Lane, Bury, Lancashire, BL9 7PA Tel: 0161-764 5441 Fax: 0161-705 1624 E-mail: bbleasdale@printpack.com *Flexible packaging materials manufrs* Also at: Saffron Walden & St. Helens

Printpak Ltd, Lacey House, Holly Road, Hampton Hill, Hampton, Middlesex, TW12 1QQ Tel: (020) 8941 0952 Fax: (020) 8979 9367 E-mail: sales@printpak.com *Management information systems*

Printselect Ltd, 46 Watts Grove, London, E3 3RE Tel: (020) 7538 3448 Fax: (020) 7538 0222 E-mail: printselect.uk@virgin.net *Colour printers*

Printus Ltd, 359 Garratt Lane, London, SW18 4DY Tel: (020) 8870 8157 Fax: (020) 8874 2236 E-mail: wandsworth@printus.co.uk *Lithographic printers & stationers*

▶ Printwells Ltd, 1-4 Chapman Way, Tunbridge Wells, Kent, TN2 3EF Tel: (01892) 542788 Fax: (01892) 618787 E-mail: sales@printwells.com *High quality litho & digital printers, colour presses repro, finishing*

Printwise Haverhill Ltd, Homefield Road, Haverhill, Suffolk, CB9 8QP Tel: (01440) 707049 Fax: (01440) 704141 E-mail: gary@printwisegroup.com *Lithographic printers & designers*

Prion Associates, Branscombe, Chart Road, Sutton Valence, Maidstone, Kent, ME17 3AW Tel: (01622) 844595 Fax: (01622) 844595 E-mail: aq02@dial.pipex.com *IT consultancy*

Prior Diesel Ltd, Gapton Hall Road, Great Yarmouth, Norfolk, NR31 0NL Tel: (01493) 441383 Fax: (01493) 441796 E-mail: info@priordiesel.com *Diesel engineers & ship repair specialists*

George Prior Engineering Ltd, ABC Wharf, Southgates Road, Great Yarmouth, Norfolk, NR30 3LQ Tel: (01493) 852311 Fax: (01493) 330074 *Ship repairers & marine engineering services*

Prior Scientific Instruments Ltd, Unit 3-4 Fielding Industrial Estate, Wilbraham Road, Fulbourn, Cambridge, CB21 5ET Tel: (01223) 881711 Fax: (01223) 881710 E-mail: sales@prior.com *Manufacturers & distributors of microscope*

Priorclave Ltd, 129-131 Nathan Way, Woolwich, London, SE28 0AB Tel: (020) 8316 6620 Fax: (020) 8855 0616 E-mail: sales@priorclave.co.uk *Manufacturers of Laboratory Autoclaves for sterilising and other low-pressure uses in Universities and the food and drink, health and pharmaceutical industries. Priorclave autoclaves are fully manufactured in the UK and meet all current European Pressure Equipment Directive and other required safety and electrical standards. A full range of auxiliary services is also available including on site servicing, a range of maintenance and support contracts, calibration and performance testing and qualification. Priorclave is accredited by*

continued

continuation
UKAS as a calibration laboratory for the purpose of calibration and testing of laboratory thermal equipment. Priorclave low-pressure autoclaves can also be used to accelerate thermal processes in the plastics and construction industries and these are complimented by a range of climatic cabinets for testing electronics and packaging and for other industrial applications.

▶ Priority Branding Ltd, Quality House, Spring Lane, Willenhall, West Midlands, WV12 4HL Tel: (01902) 607111 Fax: (01902) 633043

Priority Industrial Supplies, Unit 15, Prince Of Wales Industrial Estate, Abercarn, Newport, Gwent, NP11 5AR Tel: (01495) 244940 Fax: (01495) 243469 E-mail: sales@priorityind.co.uk *Fastener distributors*

Priority Metals & Fasteners Ltd, 17 Murrills Estate, Fareham, Hampshire, PO16 9RD Tel: (023) 9220 0300 Fax: (023) 9220 0302 E-mail: sales@prioritymetals.co.uk *Fastener distributors & metal stockholders*

Priority Services Ltd, The Lodge, Castle Bromwich Hall, Birmingham, B36 9DE Tel: (0121) 748 8710 Fax: (0121) 748 8711 E-mail: enquiries@priorityservices.co.uk *Advertising & marketing PR consultants*

Priority Technical Services Ltd, Suite 7 Thorn Office Centre, Thorn Business Park, Rotherwas, Hereford, HR2 6JT Tel: (01432) 271080 Fax: (01432) 271137 *Priority Technical Services Ltd. has been based at Thorn Business Park, Holme Lacy Road, Hereford, since 1999. We have facilities for CNC tube manipulation, fabrication, sheet metal forming (including stainless steel), metal finishing including vibratory rumbling /barraling and phosphating, and a specialized machining area. This is backed up by an AutoCAD and co ordinate measuring machine facility. A trade powder coating facility is also available to supply the customer a complete engineering solution. **Types of production from one off to full batch productions are available. **We are able to supply components, sub-assemblies and complete assemblies to all sectors of industry including automotive, medical, refrigeration, plestic industry and air conditioning.***

Priors, 90 Western Road, Hove, East Sussex, BN3 1GG Tel: (01273) 772385 Fax: (01273) 747866 E-mail: management@wmprior.co.uk *Estate agents & chartered surveyors*

▶ Priory, 38 Old Priory Road, Bournemouth, BH6 3AQ Tel: (07766) 900820 E-mail: davidquinn@prioryrefrigeration.com *Refrigeration & air conditioning*

Priory Engineering Co Christchurch Ltd, 60 Purewell, Christchurch, Dorset, BH23 1ES Tel: (01202) 486538 Fax: (01202) 473740 E-mail: enquire@prioryengineering.co.uk *Engineers*

Priory Fitted Furniture, Sporehams Lane, Danbury, Chelmsford, CM3 4AJ Tel: (01245) 227330 Fax: (01245) 227331 *Furniture manufrs*

▶ Priory Furniture, The Old Red House Farm, Stratton-on-the-Fosse, Radstock, BA3 4QE Tel: (01761) 419849 Fax: (01761) 419849 E-mail: patlepper@tesco.net *Designers & builders of individual kitchens*

Priory Glass Centre, Dormston Trading Estate, Burton Road, Dudley, West Midlands, DY1 2UF Tel: (01902) 665999 Fax: (01902) 663300 *Glazing specialists*

The Priory Group Ltd, Lionel Works, 89-91 Rolfe Street, Smethwick, West Midlands, B66 2AY Tel: 0121-558 6406 Fax: 0121-555 7140 *Shutters, security grilles & automatic door manufrs*

Priory Hardwoods, Unit 57 Bowers Mill, Branch Road, Barkisland, Halifax, West Yorkshire, HX4 0AD Tel: (01422) 311700 Fax: (01422) 311118 E-mail: info@prioryhardwoods.com *Specialist importers & distributors of solid & engineered timber flooring. Products suited to High Street, restaurant, residential & apartment installations. Sports hall floors also available to DIN cert. Offering a wide range of timber flooring including solid wood flooring, wood block flooring, Versailles Pannels, Distressed flooring. Bespoke finishes available Engineered flooring guaranteed for use over underfloor heating, We supply a wide range of species in engineered and solid flooring including:- Hard Rock Maple Solid & engineered flooring, Wenge Solid, wood blocks & engineered hardwood flooring, Jatoba. Solid & engineered flooring, Sucupira Solid Flooring, Cumaru Solid wood flooring & decking, Ipe Solid wood flooring & decking, Teak solid wood blocks, flooring & decking, American Black Walnut in engineered and solid wood flooring, Baked or Smoked Oak available in wide long boards. Bespoke Hand tufted rugs & Wilton stair runners available to complement your installation.*

▶ Priory Paving (North East) Ltd, 1 Havelock Street, South Shields, Tyne & Wear, NE33 5DZ Tel: 0191-454 3111 Fax: 0191-454 5500 E-mail: sales@priorypaving.com *Domestic insulation & paving suppliers*

Priory Plant Ltd, Norman House, Wattons Lane, Southam, Warwickshire, CV47 0HX Tel: (01926) 812343 Fax: (01926) 813942 E-mail: vicky.t@prioryplant.co.uk *Contractors plant hire*

Priory Press, Unit 18 Apex Business Centre, Boscombe Road, Dunstable, Bedfordshire, LU5 4SB Tel: (01582) 699851 Fax: (01582) 667493 E-mail: info@priorypress.co.uk *Printers*

Priory Products, Townfoot Industrial Estate, Brampton, Cumbria, CA8 1TB Tel: (01697) 72944 Fax: (01697) 741017 E-mail: priory.products@btconnect.com *Jewellers findings manufrs*

Priory Steels Ltd, Cable Street, Wolverhampton, WV2 2HX Tel: (01902) 351001 Fax: (01902) 871345 E-mail: info@priorysteel.fsnet.co.uk *Steel stockholders*

Priory Woodfield Engineering Ltd, Millbrook Works, Lower Horseley Field, Wolverhampton, WV1 3DZ Tel: (01902) 351530 Fax: (01902) 351290 E-mail: sales@priorywoodfield.com *Flange & pipeline flange manufrs*

▶ Prism Data Cabinets, 34 Greenhill CR, Watford, WD18 8JA Tel: (01923) 698230 Fax: (01923) 211190 *Computer cabinets manufrs*

Prism Data Management Ltd, Colombia House, 1 Apollo Rise, Farnborough, Hampshire, GU14 0GT Tel: (01252) 556900 Fax: (01252) 556911 *Data management services*

Prism Digital Colour Ltd, 4 Moreton Park Industrial Estate, Moreton Road South, Luton, LU2 0TL Tel: (01582) 456144 Fax: (01582) 453396 E-mail: sales@prismdigital.co.uk *Digital print*

Prism Electronics Ltd, Burrel Road, St. Ives, Cambridgeshire, PE27 3NF Tel: (01480) 462225 Fax: (01480) 494047 E-mail: sales@prism-electronics.com *Contract electronic manufrs*

Prism Europe Ltd, Abbey Gate One, 8 Whitewell Road, Colchester, CO2 7DE Tel: (01206) 761300 Fax: (01206) 719900 E-mail: sales@prism-uk.com *Production monitoring systems suppliers*

Prisma Colour Ltd, Hole House Mill, Marple Road, Chisworth, Glossop, Derbyshire, SK13 5DH Tel: (01457) 856505 Fax: (01457) 856505 E-mail: sales@prismacolour.com *Master batch compound manufrs*

Prisma Products, 37 Parkside, Nottingham, NG8 2NQ Tel: 0115-925 4506 Fax: 0115-925 9327 *Supplier of parts to suppliers for sectional buildings*

Prismo Road Surfacing Material Mnfrs, 5 Drumhead Road, Chorley North Industrial Park, Chorley, Lancashire, PR6 7BX Tel: (01257) 225100 Fax: (01257) 224605 *Specialist road surfacing manufrs*

Prismo Signs & Systems Ltd, 9 Totman Crescent, Rayleigh, Essex, SS6 7UY Tel: (01268) 745353 Fax: (01268) 745194 *Road sign manufrs*

Pristine Alloy Wheel Refurbishers Ltd, Newport Road, Woburn Sands, Milton Keynes, MK17 8UD Tel: (01908) 282628 Fax: (01908) 281093 E-mail: sales@pristinealloywheels.co.uk *Alloy wheel refurbishment*

▶ Pristine Ceilings, Unit 10 Phoenix Workshops, Station Road, Mochdre, Colwyn Bay, Clwyd, LL28 5EF Tel: (01492) 544777 Fax: (01492) 544094 E-mail: robert.pierce@btconnect.com *Restoration of suspended ceilings*

▶ Pristine Cleaning, 4 Woodside Grove, Bristol, BS10 7RF Tel: 0117-950 1772 E-mail: pristine@marketable.co.uk

Pristine Computers & Computing Ltd, 45 High Street, Charing, Ashford, Kent, TN27 0HU Tel: (01233) 713660 Fax: (01233) 713727 E-mail: peter@pristineuk.com *Computer distributors*

▶ Pristine Engineering, Babcock Transformer Site, Oxford Street, Bilston, West Midlands, WV14 7DP Tel: (01902) 401799 Fax: (01902) 401809

▶ Pritchard Newport Accountants, Unit, Wingbury Courtyard Business Village, Wingrave, Aylesbury, Buckinghamshire, HP22 4LW Tel: (01296) 688022 E-mail: admin@pritchardnewport.co.uk *Accountants specialising in small to medium businesses, operating in the Beds, Bucks and Herts area.*

Pritchard Patent Product Co. Ltd, Underleys, Beer, Seaton, Devon, EX12 3NA Tel: (01297) 21542 Fax: (01297) 20229 *Model railways, track age suppliers & manufrs*

Pritchard Plastics Ltd, Kings Hill Industrial Estate, Kings Hill, Bude, Cornwall, EX23 8QN Tel: (01288) 353211 Fax: (01288) 355686 E-mail: sales@pritchard-plastics.co.uk *Manufacturers of plastic mouldings*

Pritchard Ropes & Canvas Solutions Ltd, Freehold Street, Loughborough, Leicestershire, LE11 1AN Tel: (01509) 212400 Fax: (01509) 219375 *PVC canvas rope, sunblind manufrs*

Pritchard Tyrite, Crockford Lane, Chineham, Basingstoke, Hampshire, RG24 8NA Tel: (01256) 400600 Fax: (01256) 400622 E-mail: martin@calhoun.co.uk *Cargo securing equipment manufrs*

Pritchards Saddlery, Newbridge Road, Llantrisant, Pontyclun, Mid Glamorgan, CF72 8EX Tel: (01443) 224370 Fax: (01443) 224370 *Saddlery suppliers*

Pritchitt Foods Ltd, Kingfisher House, 21-23 Elmfield Road, Bromley, BR1 1LT Tel: (020) 8290 7020 Fax: (020) 8290 7030 E-mail: sales@pritchitts.com *As one of Europe's leading food manufacturers, we deliver specialist, value-added products to the global foodservice and bakery markets. We produce a wide range of high quality extended life and long life dairy and dairy related products especially developed for the caterer*

Pritex Ltd, Station Mills, Wellington, Somerset, TA21 8NN Tel: (01823) 664271 Fax: (01823) 660023 E-mail: enquiries@pritex.co.uk *Manufacturers of foam & fibre products*

Pritt & Co. Ltd, 23 Pembridge Square, London, W2 4DR Tel: (020) 7221 0909 Fax: (020) 7727 4837 E-mail: sales@pritt.co.uk *Metals, chemicals & project machining*

Prittlewell Interiors, Rear of, 275 Victoria Avenue, Southend-on-Sea, SS2 6NE Tel: (01702) 330865 Fax: (01702) 392034 *Furniture manufrs*

▶ Private Hire, Laurel House, 2 Chapel Road, Langham, Colchester, CO4 5NZ Tel: 01206 271255 Fax: 01206 272277 E-mail: info@privatecarhire.co.uk *Car and chauffeur hire, airport transfers, corporate hire, business courier services, one to eight seater*

▶ Private Investors, 21 Dapps Hill, Keynsham, Bristol, BS31 1ES Tel: 0117-986 6880 E-mail: strategy@nildram.co.uk *Direct access to the largest Business Angel network in Europe, our strength is in raising capital between £0,000 and £2 million. We have no preferences on sector or stage, since our investor contacts have a very wide range of interests.*

▶ The Private Plate Co., PO Box 77, Swansea, SA7 9YR Tel: (01639) 888833 Fax: (01639) 888844 E-mail: sales@myownplate.co.uk *Private number plates suppliers*

▶ The Private Tutor, Cherry Tree House, 23 Elwin Road, Tiptree, Colchester, CO5 0HL Tel: (01621) 813066 Fax: (01621) 813066 E-mail: info@theprivatetutor.co.uk *Computer software applications*

Private View, 7 Windham Road, Sudbury, Suffolk, CO10 2XD Tel: (01787) 377199 Fax: (01787) 881979 E-mail: enquiries@privateviewuk.com *Bespoke picture & mirror frame services*

▶ PrivatePropertyMarket.com, Station Road, Roydon, King's Lynn, Norfolk, PE32 1AW Tel: (01485) 600810 E-mail: info@privatepropertymarket.com *Commission free property marketing company allowing our customers to save thousands of pounds in fees when selling a property*

Prize Coin Equipment, Central Avenue, Gretna, Dumfriesshire, DG16 5AQ Tel: (01461) 338320 Fax: (01461) 338688 *Game machines hire*

Prizma Graphics, Broadfields Court Broadfields Retail Park, Bicester Road, Aylesbury, Buckinghamshire, HP19 8BU Tel: (01296) 393700 Fax: (01296) 393794 E-mail: sales@prizmagraphics.co.uk *Drawing office equipment suppliers*

Pro Cubed UK Ltd, 10 Hunters Walk, Canal Street, Chester, CH1 4EB Tel: (01244) 355295 Fax: (01244) 341488 E-mail: 20support@pro-cubed.co.uk *Specialist software maintenance*

▶ Pro Dive, 247 Hinckley Road, NUNEATON, Warwickshire, CV11 6LL Tel: 0870 199 3099 Fax: 0709 280 8864 E-mail: emea@prodive.com.au *The worlds largest scuba training company, with centre"s all over the world*

▶ Pro Dive Europe, 268-270 Hillmorton Road, The Paddox, Rugby, Warwickshire, CV22 3BW Tel: (024) 7674 6397 Fax: (07092) 808864 E-mail: info@prodive.co.uk *The worlds largest Diving provider. Book dive holidays around the world online*

▶ Pro Drive IT Ltd, Headley House, Parklands-Queens Elizabeth Park, Railton Road, Guildford, Surrey, GU2 9JX Tel: (01483) 236000 Fax: (01483) 236111 E-mail: sales@prodriveit.co.uk *Computer networking & communication services*

Pro Ex Group Ltd, Hamilton House, Rackery Lane, Llay, Wrexham, Clwyd, LL12 0PB Tel: (01978) 855622 Fax: (01978) 855151 E-mail: enquiries@pro-ex.co.uk *Event marketing services, hire of mobile exhibition units*

Pro Face UK Ltd, Orchard Court Binley Business Park, Harry Weston Road, Coventry, CV3 2TQ Tel: (024) 7644 0088 Fax: (024) 7644 0099 E-mail: sales@profaceuk.com Principal Export Areas: Central Asia, Africa, Central/East Europe & West Europe *Industrial computers distributors*

Pro Found Electronics Ltd, The Forge, 31a The Broadway, Thatcham, Berkshire, RG19 3HX Tel: (01635) 872986 Fax: (01635) 872986 *Electronic equipment manufs*

Pro Hair Supplies, 320 Lymington Road, Highcliffe, Christchurch, Dorset, BH23 5EY Tel: (01425) 276074 Fax: (01425) 276074 *Retailers of professional hair products*

Pro Image Ltd, 20 Briddon Street, Manchester, M3 1LS Tel: 0161-839 2845 Fax: 0161-839 5830 E-mail: kuldipproimage@aol.com *Sports clothing & footwear*

▶ Pro Inovate, 46 The Lawns, Stevenage, Hertfordshire, SG2 9RT Tel: (01438) 221324 *Vacuum cleaners & systems*

Pro It Ltd, 24 Saffron Close, Chineham, Basingstoke, Hampshire, RG24 8XQ Tel: (01256) 358303 Fax: (01256) 358015 *Computer services*

Pro Kill Environmental Services, 174 Kirkway, Middleton, Manchester, M24 1LN Tel: (0800) 0289715 Fax: 0161-643 5062 *Pest controllers*

Pro Laminates, The Billet, Parsonage Lane, Sawbridgeworth, Hertfordshire, CM21 0ND Tel: (01279) 721035 Fax: (01279) 721048 E-mail: sales@pro-laminates.com *Fibre glass manufrs*

Pro Logic Computers, 6-8 Doncaster Road, South Elmsall, Pontefract, West Yorkshire, WF9 2HZ Tel: (01977) 649100 Fax: (01977) 651411 E-mail: paul@pro-logic.co.uk *Computer sales & business maintenance services*

▶ Pro Metal Manufacturing Ltd, 3b Maitland Road, Lion Barn Industrial Estate, Needham Market, Ipswich, IP6 8NZ Tel: (01449) 723082 Fax: (01449) 723080

▶ Pro Motion Hire, Unit 181, Hercules Road, London, SE1 7LD Tel: (020) 7735 9988 Fax: (020) 7735 6656 E-mail: info@promotionhire.co.uk *Broadcasting equipment hire*

Pro Mould Plastics, School Lane, Pendock, Gloucester, GL19 3PR Tel: (01684) 833048 Fax: (01684) 833049 *Plastic moulding manufrs*

Pro Net Uk Ltd, Bloomhill Road, Moorends, Doncaster, South Yorkshire, DN8 4SP Tel: (01405) 817557 Fax: (01405) 741277 *Safety netting manufrs*

Pro Pest Services, 12 Northumberland Road, Linford, Stanford-le-Hope, Essex, SS17 0PT Tel: (01375) 642619 Fax: (01375) 642619 *Pest control services*

Pro Plate Metal Finishing Co., 17 Manor Trading Estate, Armstrong Road, Benfleet, Essex, SS7 4PW Tel: (01268) 752037 Fax: (01268) 755862 *Electroplating service*

▶ Pro Putt Limited, 1 The Hawthorns, Aylesford, KENT, ME20 7LJ Tel: 07752539887 E-mail: info@proputt.org.uk *Pro Putt golf putting aid.*

Pro Services Audio, 7 Pumbro, Stonesfield, Witney, Oxfordshire, OX29 8QF Tel: (01993) 891765 Fax: (01993) 891009 E-mail: psa@ggilbaud.deman.co.uk *Recording studios*

▶ Pro Shine Valeting Services, 2 Metcalf Close, Sweet Briar Road Industrial Es, Norwich, NR3 2BP Tel: (01603) 487879 E-mail: info@pro-shine.co.uk *The premier auto valeters for Norwich and the surrounding areas.*

▶ Pro Source I T Ltd, Unit 1, Princess Mews Horace Road, Kingston upon Thames, Surrey, KT1 2SZ Tel: (020) 8541 0333 Fax: (020) 8549 1333 *Computer hardware suppliers*

▶ Pro Speed Exhausts, Rear of, 113 City Road, Cardiff, CF24 3BN Tel: (029) 2046 1444 Fax: (029) 2046 1444 *Exhaust systems manufrs*

Pro Sport International, 122a Wilford Grove, Nottingham, NG2 2DU Tel: 0115-986 9000 Fax: 0115-986 8000 E-mail: mail@prosportinternational.co.uk *Sportswear manufrs*

Pro Star, PO Box 20, Wakefield, West Yorkshire, WF2 7AY Tel: (01924) 291441 Fax: (01924) 364411 E-mail: info@prostar.co.uk *Sportswear manufrs*

Pro Tec, 120 Old Coach Road, Templepatrick, Ballyclare, County Antrim, BT39 0HA Tel: (028) 9443 3693 Fax: (028) 9443 3551 *Powder coating services*

Pro Tec Alarms Ltd, 91 Swansea Road, Pontlliw, Swansea, SA4 9EF Tel: (01792) 894995 Fax: (01792) 894995 *Security systems supplier*

Pro Tech GB Ltd, 44 Sandown Avenue, Dagenham, Essex, RM10 8XD Tel: (020) 8593 3417 Fax: (020) 8593 3800 E-mail: info@protechgb.co.uk *Speciality Products and Equipment Suppliers to the Sugar Industry. Predominately to the Cane Sugar Industry worldwide; generally speaking covering the area plus and minus 35 degrees Latitude around the Equator*

Pro Tect Security, 91 Albion Street, Birmingham, B1 3AA Tel: 0121-248 5522 Fax: 0121-248 5523 *Security services & man guarding*

Pro Tek Engineering Ltd, Unit 1, Waterloo Park, Alcester, Warwickshire, B50 4JG Tel: (01789) 490490 *Precision Engineers*

Pro Test Panels Ltd, Unit 38 Padgets Lane, South Moons Moat, Redditch, Worcestershire, B98 0RD Tel: (01527) 514404 Fax: (05601) 149560 E-mail: sales@testpanels.com *Test material manufacturer & distribs*

Pro Wash, 47 Milton Hill, Weston-super-Mare, Avon, BS22 9RE Tel: (01934) 418177 Fax: (01934) 643580 E-mail: prowash@btconnect.com *Dishwasher part suppliers*

▶ Pro Weld Installations, 13 A Bradley Hall Trading Estate, Bradley Lane, Standish, Wigan, Lancashire, WN6 0XQ Tel: (0870) 8744446 Fax: (0870) 7654341 *Proweld Installations, based in the heart of lancashire offer a full range of Welding Services.*

Proact International Ltd, 9a Vale Street, Denbigh, Clwyd, LL16 3AD Tel: (01745) 813586 Fax: (01745) 815096 *Software house services*

Proactis Group Ltd, Holtby Manor, Stamford Bridge Road, Dunnington, York, YO19 5LL Tel: (01904) 481999 Fax: (01904) 481666 *Computer software developers*

Proactive Computing Ltd, 28 Telford Close, High Shincliffe, Durham, DH1 2YJ Tel: 0191-386 7605 Fax: 0191-386 7605 E-mail: proactivecomputing@ic24.net *Computer consultants*

▶ Proactive Recruitment Solutions Ltd, Jewellery Business Centre, 95 Spencer Street, Birmingham, B18 6DA Tel: 0121-523 1006 Fax: 0121-523 1016 E-mail: enquiries@proactiverecruitment.co.uk *Recruitment services*

Pro-Active Signs, 5 New Mill, Post Office Road, Inkpen, Hungerford, Berkshire, RG17 9PU Tel: (01488) 669152 Fax: (01488) 669267 E-mail: sales@pro-activesigns.co.uk *Sign suppliers*

▶ Probadge, The Courtyard, 27 High Street, Winslow, Buckingham, MK18 3HE Tel: (01296) 712387 Fax: (01296) 715281 E-mail: sales@probadge.com *Engraved name badges with screen printed company logos*

Probe Oil Tools Ltd, Edison Way, Great Yarmouth, Norfolk, NR31 0NG Tel: (01493) 655471 Fax: (01493) 652746 E-mail: sales@probe-oil-tools.co.uk *Oilwell drilling equipment manufrs*

Probe Technical Recruitment, 6 Emmanuel Court, Sutton Coldfield, West Midlands, B72 1TJ Tel: 0121-321 4311 Fax: 0121-321 4312 E-mail: recruitment@probe-uk.com *Recruitment agency & consultants*

▶ Problem Solved, 29 Sheep House, Farnham, Surrey, GU9 8LR Tel: (01252) 727214 Fax: (01252) 727214 E-mail: problemsolved@whsmiths.co.uk *Pest control services*

Proband Ltd, 37-55 Camden Street, Birmingham, B1 3BP Tel: (0800) 262629 E-mail: tony.sheen@proband.co.uk *Computer hardware & software distrib*

▶ Probst North West Ltd, 26 Whitelegge Street, Bury, Lancashire, BL8 1SW Tel: 0161-272 0111 Fax: 0161-705 2525 *Mechanical handling equipment suppliers*

Probus Electronics Ltd, Findon, Southill Lane, Pinner, Middlesex, HA5 2EQ Tel: (020) 8866 7272 Fax: (020) 8866 2999 E-mail: sales@probus.freeserve.co.uk *Electronical parts distributors*

Probus Housewares, Unit 19 Empire Industrial Park, Aldridge, Walsall, WS9 8UQ Tel: (01922) 743586 Fax: (01922) 452484 E-mail: sales@probusmayfair.co.uk *Kitchen tools & kitchen textiles*

Probyns Office Stationery Supplies, 25 Tyrrel Street, Bradford, West Yorkshire, BD1 1RU Tel: (01274) 721717 Fax: (01274) 732349 E-mail: probyns@probyns.co.uk *Commercial stationery distributors*

Pro-Byte Computers Ltd, 163 Cleethorpe Road, Grimsby, South Humberside, DN31 3AX Tel: (01472) 235500 Fax: (01472) 235501 E-mail: sales@pro-byte.co.uk *Computer builders, networking, hardware & web pages*

Procal Ltd, Communications House, Woodfield Lane, Ashtead, Surrey, KT21 2BT Tel: (01372) 271313 Fax: (01372) 270100 E-mail: enquiries@procal.co.uk *Calibration services*

Procal Analytics Ltd, 5 Maxwell Road, Peterborough, PE2 7HU Tel: (01733) 232495 Fax: (01733) 235255 E-mail: post@procalanalytics.com *Process control & gas analysers*

Procameras, PO Box 461, Wolverhampton, WV10 7YX Tel: (01902) 791511 Fax: (01902) 791585 E-mail: david@davidcole.fsnet.co.uk *Photographic studio background products & digital lighting services*

Procare, PO Box 110, Bridgwater, Somerset, TA6 7NG Tel: (01278) 428600 *Suppliers of cleansing wipes for industrial, commercial & nursing use*

Procare GB Ltd, 1 Burcott Road, Purley, Surrey, CR8 4AD Tel: (020) 8763 8444 Fax: (020) 8668 8399 *Installation & repairers*

Procast Components Ltd, Unit 3 Cadwell Lane, Hitchin, Hertfordshire, SG4 0SA Tel: (01462) 441442 Fax: (01462) 436265 E-mail: procast@btclick.com *Aluminium & bronze casting manufrs*

Proceeds U.L.P. (UK) Ltd, Unit A, Stakehill Industrial Estate, Middleton, Manchester, M24 2SJ Tel: 0161-654 2500 Fax: 0161-655 4433 *Foam product*

Procella, 10 Ashby Road, Coalville, Leicestershire, LE67 3LA Tel: (01530) 810112 Fax: (01530) 510721 E-mail: enquiries@procella.co.uk *Welcome to Procella Scuba Diving, Wetsuit & WaterSport Equipment, the Online Store for adults & Junior Wetsuits, Scuba Diving Boots,WaterSport Gloves, Scuba Diving Hoods, Scuba Diving Masks, Snorkels, Fins & Flipers, Knives, Diving Equipment Bags and other Swimming, Snorkelling and Scuba Diving Products.*

▶ Process Automation, 17 South Lodge Court, Chesterfield, Derbyshire, S40 3QG Tel: (01246) 568868 E-mail: process.automation@fsmail.net *Printers*

Process Control Co, Griffin Lane, Aylesbury, Buckinghamshire, HP19 8BF Tel: (01296) 484877 Fax: (01296) 393122 *Static control services*

Process Control Equipment, 45 Dukesway, Teesside Industrial Estate, Stockton-on-Tees, Cleveland, TS17 9LT Tel: (01642) 768250 *Valves & stainless steel tube distributors*

Process Control Panels Ltd, Unit 13 Dunstall Hill Industrial Estate, Gorsebrook Road, Wolverhampton, WV6 0PJ Tel: (01902) 329990 Fax: (01902) 310743 *Control panels to specification*

Process Control Services UK Ltd, The Savoy, 4 Hall Bank, Buxton, Derbyshire, SK17 6EW Tel: (01298) 79969 Fax: (01298) 71151 *Industrial electrical site work*

Process Control Systems, 17 Stourfield Road, Bournemouth, BH5 2AR Tel: (01202) 428251 Fax: (01202) 424964 E-mail: processcontrol.systems@ntlworld.com *Instrumentation engineers*

Process Control Systems Ltd, St. Chads Church, Fisher Street, Brindley Ford, Stoke-On-Trent, ST8 7QJ Tel: (01782) 517601 Fax: (01782) 516921 *Control panel manufrs*

Process Cooling Solutions, 916 Castle La East, Bournemouth, BH7 6SN Tel: (01202) 434328 Fax: (01202) 434329 E-mail: office@ptcltd.co.uk *Process cooling systems engineers installation services*

Process Equipment International, 2 Como Place, Newcastle, Staffordshire, ST5 2QN Tel: (01782) 618101 Fax: (01782) 612616 E-mail: dougtee@tiscali.co.uk *Process equipment distributor*

Process Equipment Parts (UK) Ltd, Kershaw House, 449 Great West Road, Hounslow, TW5 0BU Tel: (020) 8754 3999 Fax: (020) 8754 3990 E-mail: mail@process-equipment.co.uk *Service for operators of oil & gas & processing plants*

Process Heating Services, 12 Noddington Avenue, Lichfield, Staffordshire, WS14 9NQ Tel: (01543) 432661 Fax: (01543) 432782 E-mail: sales@processheatingservices.com *Manufacturers of industrial electric heaters*

▶ Process Installations Ltd, Riverside Industrial Estate, Bridge Road, Littlehampton, West Sussex, BN17 5DF Tel: (01903) 730900 Fax: (01903) 730234 E-mail: peterb@pumpeng.co.uk *Installation of process plant, fluid handling & industrial pipe work services*

Process & Instrumentation Valves Ltd, Stewart House, Stewart Road, Falkirk, FK2 7AS Tel: (01324) 630030 Fax: (01324) 629112 E-mail: sales@piv-online.com *Valves distributors*

▶ Process Instruments UK Ltd, Process House, Dominion Court, Billington Road, Burnley, Lancashire, BB11 5UB Tel: (0870) 8502707 Fax: (01282) 422 268 E-mail: info@processinstruments.net *Charge analysers & consistency monitors manufrs*

Process Intelligence Ltd, Ebrington, Chipping Campden, Gloucestershire, GL55 6NL Tel: (01386) 593084 Fax: (01386) 593132 *IT consultants*

Process Line Ltd, Suite 15, Kirkfield Commercial Centre, Leeds, LS19 7LX Tel: 0113-239 7112 Fax: 0113-239 7113 E-mail: enquiries@processline.com *Process engineers*

Process Link Ltd, Tilemans Lane, Shipston-on-Stour, Warwickshire, CV36 4QZ Tel: (01608) 662878 Fax: (01608) 662968 E-mail: info@processlink.co.uk *Manufacture powder handling equipment*

Process Machinery Ltd, 30 Knowl Piece, Wilbury Way, Hitchin, Hertfordshire, SG4 0TY Tel: (01462) 421966 Fax: (01462) 422043 E-mail: sales@processmachinery.co.uk *Plastics machinery distributors*

Process Management International Ltd, Barclays Venture Centre Sir William Lyons Road, University of W, Coventry, CV4 7EZ Tel: (024) 7641 9089 Fax: (024) 7641 9480 E-mail: sales@pmi.co.uk *Management consultants*

Process Manufacturing Ltd, Well Spring Close, Atherstone, Warwickshire, CV9 1LQ Tel: (0121) 553 7772 Fax: (0121) 553 4746 E-mail: enquies@surfacedynamics.co.uk *Chemical process engineers*

Process Measurement & Analysis Ltd, Brockmill House, Carr Lane, Huddersfield, HD7 5BG Tel: 0151-649 8477 Fax: (01484) 843689 E-mail: sales@processmeasurement.uk.com *Process & measuring instrumentation distributors*

Process Pipe Work Services, North Lonsdale Road, Ulverston, Cumbria, LA12 9DL Tel: (01229) 583954 Fax: (01229) 581531 E-mail: admin@pps-ulv.co.uk *Sheet metalworkers*

Process Plastics, Process House, Norwich Street, Rochdale, Lancashire, OL11 1LJ Tel: (01706) 753623 Fax: (01706) 753624 E-mail: sales@processplastics.co.uk *Plastic injection moulding*

▶ Process Plus, Sybrig House, Ridge Way, Hillend, Dunfermline, Fife, KY11 9JN Tel: (01383) 825343 Fax: (01383) 824393 E-mail: sales@processplus.co.uk *Process engineers services, instrumental dist flow, analytical level*

Process Supplies London Ltd, 13-25 Mount Pleasant, London, WC1X 0AR Tel: (020) 7837 2179 Fax: (020) 7837 8551 E-mail: sales@process-supplies.co.uk *Photographic material wholesalers*

Process Technology Associates Ltd, 8 Waverton Business Park, Saighton Lane, Waverton, Chester, CH3 7PD Tel: (01244) 332441 Fax: (01244) 332325 E-mail: mail@processtech.co.uk *Water treatment chemical manufrs*

Process Valve Supplies Ltd, 2 Ringtail Industrial Estate, Tollgate Road, Burscough, Ormskirk, Lancashire, L40 8RT Tel: (01704) 894403 Fax: (01704) 897046 E-mail: sales@processvalve.co.uk *Ancillary product suppliers*

Processed Light Alloys Ltd, 2 Astra Centre, Royle Barn Road, Rochdale, Lancashire, OL11 3DT Tel: (01706) 345551 *Zinc platers & electroplaters*

Processheat Ltd, Chain Caul Road, Ashton On Ribble, Preston, PR2 2PD Tel: (01772) 722412 Fax: (01772) 722325 *Electrical heating equipment & system installers*

▶ Prochef, Gaerwen Industrial Estate, Gaerwen, Gwynedd, LL60 6HR Tel: (0845) 3700366 Fax: (01248) 422025 E-mail: sales@prochef.co.uk *Design to manufacture of ovens, hobs & range cookers*

Prochem Services Ltd, Mill Street, Congleton, Cheshire, CW12 2AD Tel: (01260) 299770 Fax: (01260) 299880 E-mail: info@prochem-services.com *Specialist valve manufrs*

Proclad International Forging Ltd, Nettlehill Road, Houstoun Industrial Estate, Livingston, West Lothian, EH54 5DL Tel: (01506) 607500 Fax: (01506) 607501 E-mail: info@proclad-int.com *Pipe & tube fittings manufrs*

Proclean Alloy Wheel Refurbishment, 61-63 Houghton Street, Prescot, Merseyside, L34 5RS Tel: 0151-292 5525 Fax: 0151-426 1885 *Refurbishers of alloy wheels & metal polishers services*

Proclean Tectonics Ltd, 19 Bourton Road, Solihull, West Midlands, B92 8AY Tel: 0121-707 8090 Fax: 0121-707 2896 *Environment cleaning & maintenance services*

▶ Pro-Cleanse North, 105 Dale Street, Milnrow, Rochdale, Lancashire, OL16 3NW Tel: (01706) 759696 Fax: (0870) 1304019 E-mail: mail@pro-cleanse.co.uk *Building cleaning & pressure washing*

Procom Ltd, Unit I3, Springhead Enterprise Park, Springhead Road, Northfleet, Gravesend, Kent, DA11 8HL Tel: (01474) 322244 Fax: (01474) 322135 E-mail: info@procom-pescot.co.uk *Radio communication sales & maintenance*

▶ Pro-Com Computer Services London Ltd, 53 St. Helier Avenue, Morden, Surrey, SM4 6HY Tel: (020) 8287 2772 Fax: (020) 8395 3565 E-mail: sales@procomcomputers.co.uk *Computers sales & service centre*

▶ Procom Services Ltd, 29 Broadmead, Tunbridge Wells, Kent, TN2 5RN Tel: (01892) 525387 E-mail: procom29@aol.com *Control system design, lighting*

Pro-Comm Audio Visual Consultants, Woodilee Road Unit 9, Lenzie, Kirkintilloch, Glasgow, G66 3UU Tel: 0141-776 2094 Fax: 0141-775 3419 E-mail: sales@procomm.ic24.net *Audio-visual conference & events services*

Procon Engineering Ltd, Vestry Estate, Vestry Road, Sevenoaks, Kent, TN14 5EL Tel: (01732) 781300 Fax: (01732) 781311 E-mail: sales@procon-eng.com *Scales & weighing equipme*

Procon Industrial Automation Ltd, Unit 5 Arclid Industrial Estate, Hemmingshaw Lane, Arclid, Sandbach, Cheshire, CW11 4SY Tel: (01270) 759708 Fax: (01270) 766350 E-mail: rn@proconuk.freeserve.co.uk *Industrial automation equipment*

Procon Systems, 7 St. Johns Close, Aberford, Leeds, LS25 3BP Tel: 0113-393 5085 Fax: 0113-393 5087 *Computer software writers*

Proconics Ltd, 43 Hipper St South, Chesterfield, Derbyshire, S40 1SS Tel: (01246) 221210 Fax: (01246) 563923 E-mail: petel@cathelco.co.uk *Electronic equipment manufrs*

▶ Procorr Packaging, Uppingham Road, Skeffington, Leicester, LE7 9YE Tel: 0116-259 9302 *Cardboard boxes manufrs*

Proco-STS Ltd, Unit 3, Castle Road, Chelston Business Park, Wellington, Somerset, TA21 9JQ Tel: (01823) 663535 Fax: (01823) 663373 E-mail: info@proco-sts.com *Manufacturing packaging*

Procter Bros Ltd, Ninelands Lane, Leeds, LS25 2BY Tel: 0113-287 6282 Fax: 0113-242 2649 E-mail: info@procter-brothers.co.uk *Procter Fencing Systems offers a nationwide service to survey, design, manufacture and erect a comprehensive range of Fencing Systems. This includes Mesh Panel, Palisade, Chain Link, Welded Mesh, Standard and Ornamental Railings, Procter also provides Hinged, Tracked or Cantilevered Sliding Gates and access controls, barriers, turnstiles etc compatible with each fencing system for a comprehensive perimeter protection package. Procter is an ISO9000 acredited supplier* Also at: Bedwas

Procter & Chester (Measurements) Ltd, Dalehouse Lane, Kenilworth, Warwickshire, CV8 2UE Tel: (01926) 864444 Fax: (01926) 864888 E-mail: info@pcm-uk.com *Load cells build & supply services*

Procter & Gamble Product Supply UK Ltd, Avenue Road, Seaton Delaval, Whitley Bay, Tyne & Wear, NE25 0QJ Tel: 0191-255 6000 Fax: 0191-237 7208 Principal Export Areas: Worldwide *Toiletry manufrs*

Procters Cheeses Ltd, The Cheese Warehouse, Saunders Raike, Chipping, Preston, PR3 2QR Tel: (01995) 61626 Fax: (01995) 61077 E-mail: sales@procterscheeses.co.uk *Cheese suppliers & distributors*

Procters Sausage Mnfrs, 12 The Walk, Ipswich, IP1 1EE Tel: (01473) 281191 E-mail: sales@procters-sausages.co.uk *Sausage manufrs*

Procter's Speciality Sausages, 17 Maidenhall Green, Ipswich, IP2 8PJ Tel: (01473) 683158 Fax: (01473) 683158 E-mail: sales@proctersspecialitysausages.co.uk *Sausage manufrs*

▶ James Proctor Ltd, PO Box 19, Burnley, Lancashire, BB11 1NN Tel: (01282) 453816 Fax: (01282) 416178 E-mail: sales@jamesproctor.com *Combustion equipment for solid fuel fired industrial boilers*

Proctor Process Plant Ltd, Taylor Holme House, Baldwin Street, Bacup, Lancashire, OL13 0LT Tel: (01706) 874444 Fax: (01706) 879686 E-mail: info@ppp-ltd.co.uk *Process heat burner manufrs*

▶ Victoria Proctor, 47 Lorne Street, Liverpool, L7 0JP Tel: 0151-228 6667 E-mail: unbrokendesigns@aol.com *Unique custom made fashion corsets from the theatrical to the sophisticated. Affordable and one of a kind.*

Procurement International Ltd, Falcon House, 30 Ivanhoe Road, Hogwood Industrial Estate, Finchampstead, Wokingham, Berkshire, RG40 4QQ Tel: 0118-973 4422 Fax: 0118-973 0808 E-mail: info@procurement.ltd.uk Principal Export Areas: Central/East Europe, West Europe & North America *Cameras, binoculars & audio product manufrs*

Procut Ltd, Unit 51 Youngs Industrial Estate, Paices Hill, Aldermaston, Reading, RG7 4PW Tel: 0118-981 7109 Fax: 0118-981 2832 *Profile cutting & plough grinding services*

Procyon Ltd, 44 Oxford Street, Wellingborough, Northamptonshire, NN8 4JH Tel: (01933) 278787 Fax: (01933) 278789 E-mail: julia@procyon.ltd.uk *Audio visual hire & internet website designers*

▶ ProdAuto Ltd, Creative Industries, Science Park, Wolverhampton, WV10 9TG Tel: 01902 420877 Fax: (01902) 716312 E-mail: info@prodauto.co.uk *Manufacturers of automation & special purpose equipment for production processes*

Prodec Contracting, Hallsford Bridge Industrial Estate, Stondon Road, Ongar, Essex, CM5 9RB Tel: (01708) 864774 Fax: (01277) 362225

Prodec Precision Manufacturing Co. Ltd, Armstrong Buildings, Kilton Terrace, Worksop, Nottinghamshire, S80 2DQ Tel: (01909) 474093 Fax: (01909) 500363 *Tin box tooling machinists*

▶ Prodo Ltd, Littleton Old Hall, Little Heath Road, Littleton, Chester, CH3 &DW Tel: 0870 7562828 Fax: 0870 7562838 E-mail: sales@prodo.com *Website and print design and marketing consultants in Chester.*

Prodrive Holdings Ltd, Acorn Way, Banbury, Oxfordshire, OX16 3ER Tel: (01295) 273355 Fax: (01295) 271188 E-mail: enquiries@prodrive.com *Automotive, motor sport industry & design engineers services*

Product Assurance Ltd, 10 Castle Street, Buckingham, MK18 1EQ Tel: (01280) 817346 Fax: (01280) 817932 *Food products manufrs*

▶ Product Development Corporation, Westminster Place, York Business Park, Nether Poppleton, York, YO26 6RW Tel: (01904) 606300 Fax: (01904) 606311 E-mail: sales@teampdc.co.uk

Product Express Ltd, Hartley Business Centre, 272-284 Monkmoor Road, Shrewsbury, SY2 5ST Tel: (01743) 359459 Fax: (01743) 359123 E-mail: sales@productexpress.co.uk *Cane goods & furniture merchants*

Pro-Duct (Fife) Ltd, 3 Church Wynd, Kingskettle, Cupar, Fife, KY15 7PS Tel: (01337) 831862 Fax: (01337) 831832 *Ventilations consultants*

Product Group, Unit 40a Colbourne CR, Nelson Park, Cramlington, Northumberland, NE23 1WB Tel: (01670) 730784 Fax: (01670) 734915 E-mail: product@theproductgroup.co.uk *Industrial product design consultancy*

Product Partners Ltd, Church Street, Biggleswade, Bedfordshire, SG18 0JS Tel: (01767) 600456 Fax: (01767) 600155 E-mail: sales@productpartners.co.uk *Industrial product design consultants*

▶ Product Plus International Ltd, Southbank Business Centre, Ponton Road, London, SW8 5BL Tel: (020) 7393 0033 Fax: (020) 7393 0080 E-mail: sales@product-plus.co.uk *With 20 years in the premium sourcing business, PPI have supplied promotional merchandise to many of the world's largest blue chip companies. Specialists in design, sourcing, project management and international logistics, PPI provide the creative solution to your promotional merchandise needs, on budget and on time.*

Product Release Europe Ltd, Cusson Road, Knowsley Industrial Park, Liverpool, L33 7BY Tel: 0151-549 1491 Fax: 0151-548 4035 *Approved corrosion resistant release coatings services*

Product Stream Ltd, 65 Oxford Street, Hull, HU2 0QP Tel: (01482) 327755 Fax: (01482) 327766 E-mail: info@productstream.co.uk *Product design & development from concept to launch*

Product Support Electronics Ltd, Unit 1/2, Letts Road, Far Cotton, Northampton, NN4 8HQ Tel: (01604) 764520 Fax: (01604) 706834 E-mail: ppse@aol.com *Manufacturers of printed circuit boards.*

Product Technology Partners Ltd, Barrington Road, Orwell, Royston, Cambridgeshire, SG8 5QP Tel: (01223) 208791 Fax: (01223) 208795 E-mail: frontdesk@ptpart.co.uk *Contact us for scientific & engineering software, machine control systems, automation, instrumentation and test & measurement equipment. Windows or Linux. PC-based - embedded - PLC - HMI - SCADA - Data acquisition & analysis - Vision inspection systems. Systems integration and software development. PalmOS & Pocket PC. USB driver development. LabVIEW & LabWindows /CVI.*

Production & Development Services Ltd, 1-2 Marshlands Road, Portsmouth, PO6 1ST Tel: 023 92215288 *Sheet metalwork engineers, fabricators & powder coaters*

Production Engineering Components Ltd, 104 College Street, Kempston, Bedford, MK42 8LU Tel: (01234) 346587 Fax: (01234) 325385 E-mail: jane@pec.uk.com *Tube manipulators & turned parts*

Production Glassfibre, Myregormie Place, Mitchelston Industrial Estate, Kirkcaldy, Fife, KY1 3NA Tel: (01592) 650444 Fax: (01592) 652444 E-mail: sales@productionglassfibre.co.uk *Custom moulders & glass fibre mouldings manufrs. Also a producer of Glassfibre Shuttering.*

The Production House, Old Customs House Studios, 1 West Harbour Road, Edinburgh, EH5 1PH Tel: 0131-551 1301 Fax: 0131-551 2473 E-mail: productionhouse1@aol.com *Photography graphic design, exhibition design installation & manufrs*

▶ Production Lines Northern Ltd, 14 Pleasant Row, Queensbury, Bradford, West Yorkshire, BD13 2BW Tel: (01274) 812035 E-mail: philip@productionlines.co.uk *Manufacturers agent*

Production Lubricants Ltd, Progress Industrial Estate, Station Road, Rogiet, Caldicot, Monmouthshire, NP26 3UE Tel: (01291) 426900 Fax: (01291) 426940 E-mail: enquiries@severnfuels.co.uk *Lubricating & fuel oil distributors*

Production Pneumatics, 10 Townsend Close, Bristol, BS14 8TS Tel: (01275) 835204 Fax: (01275) 835204 E-mail: sales@productionpneumatics.co.uk *Pneumatic control systems manufrs*

Production Presswork & Tooling Ltd, Unit 12 Enterprise Court, Rankin Road, Basingstoke, Hampshire, RG24 8GE Tel: (01256) 816836 Fax: (01256) 812970 *Various metals pressing manufacturers*

Production & Tooling Systems Essex, Unit 2 Europa Park, Croft Way, Witham, Essex, CM8 2FN Tel: (01376) 533150 Fax: (01376) 520932 *Precision Engineering Sub Contractors.*

Productivity Europe Ltd, Bedford Heights, Manton Lane, Bedford, MK41 7PH Tel: (01234) 215867 Fax: (01234) 218656 E-mail: prodeuro@atlas.co.uk *Productivity Europe is a leading provider of Lean Manufacturing Training and World Class Manufacturing Techniques. Our work builds on our relationships with some of the developers of world class manufacturing in Japan, combined with many years experience in UK manufacturing. Our knowledge of world class manufacturing encompasses kaizen, total quality, lean manufacturing training and total productive maintenance. Whether you simply want to train a small group or want to develop a more extensive Total Productive Maintenance or Lean Manufacturing Training initiative, Productivity Europe can provide implementation support tailored to your needs.*

Productivity Solutions Ltd, PO Box 2133, Stoke-on-Trent, ST3 4WP Tel: (01782) 855739 Fax: (01782) 855739 E-mail: headoffice@psleurope.com *Consultancy support, contract resource, recruitment, training or software solutions. Also distributors, installers & trainers for EASEworks, the state-of-the-art standards development & management software tool & producers of SmartTime handheld Time Study & RAS software package.*

Productivity Solutions Ltd, PO Box 3272, Stourbridge, West Midlands, DY8 2ZA Tel: (01562) 720630 Fax: (01562) 720630 E-mail: info@psleurope.com *Business consultancy*

Products Plan Ltd, 67 Europa Business Park, Bird Hall Lane, Stockport, Cheshire, SK3 0XA Tel: 0161-428 9966 Fax: 0161-428 9977 *Construction company*

Products To Europe Ltd, The Office On The Green, Wraysbury, Staines, Middlesex, TW19 5NA Tel: (01784) 488400 Fax: (01784) 488401 *Manufacturers representatives*

Produktion Teknik, The Rickyard, Eashing Lane, Godalming, Surrey, GU7 2QA Tel: (01483) 429490 Fax: (01483) 429094 E-mail: sales@syscoav.co.uk *Audio visual equipment hire*

Produmax Ltd, The Tannery, Station Road, Otley, West Yorkshire, LS21 3HX Tel: (01943) 461713 Fax: (01943) 850228 E-mail: mail@produmax.co.uk *Precision engineers*

Produsit Ltd, Precision Works, 69-70 Moland Street, Birmingham, B4 7EY Tel: 0121-359 5571 Fax: 0121-359 5572 E-mail: produsit@msn.com *Press tools, jigs & fixture contractors*

▶ Pro-Elec Ltd, 6 Willesborough Industrial Par, Willesborough, Ashford, Kent, TN24 0TD Tel: (01233) 611280

▶ Proem It Recruitment, Mere House, 61a King Street, Knutsford, Cheshire, WA16 6DX Tel: (01565) 624010 Fax: (01565) 624011 E-mail: cv@proem-it.com *It sales, pre-sales, project management & operations specialists*

Profab Fabrications, Unit 3, 10 Coldside Road, Dundee, DD3 8DF Tel: (01382) 832711 *Metal fabricators*

Profab Fabrications, Triton Works, Stringes Lane, Willenhall, West Midlands, WV13 1LD Tel: (01902) 633253 Fax: (01902) 633253 *Structural steel manufrs*

Profast Holdings Ltd, 26-30 Rydalmere Street, Belfast, BT12 6GF Tel: (028) 9024 3215 Fax: (028) 9033 3301 E-mail: sales@profast.co.uk *Architectural hardware distributors*

Profec Holdings Ltd, 10 Betts Avenue, Martlesham Heath, Ipswich, IP5 3RH Tel: (01473) 611422 Fax: (01473) 611919 E-mail: sales@profec.com *Telecommunication wound components*

Professional Accounting Systems Ltd, 52 High House Drive, Lickey, Birmingham, B45 8ET Tel: 0121-445 2200 Fax: 0121-447 8586 *Software accounting systems developers*

Professional Audio Visual Cambridge Ltd, Ares Yard, Chapel Street, Steeple Bumpstead, Haverhill, Suffolk, CB9 7DQ Tel: (01440) 731831 Fax: (01440) 731931 E-mail: hires@proav2000.com *Audio visual equipment suppliers*

▶ Professional Automation Support Services Ltd, Brierley Business Centre, Mirion Street, Crewe, CW1 2AZ Tel: (01270) 211111 Fax: (01270) 258282 *Automation equipment training & support services*

▶ Professional Barrier Systems Ltd, 16 Stapledon Road, Orton Southgate, Peterborough, PE2 6TD Tel: (01733) 361511

▶ Professional Beauty Systems, Unit 3 Newmains Avenue, Inchinnan, Renfrew, PA4 9RR Tel: 0141-812 5000 Fax: 0141-812 1919 *Cosmetic manufrs*

▶ Professional Bridal Make-up, 29 Burnell Gate, Beaulieu Park, Chelmsford, CM1 6ED Tel: 01245 462200 E-mail: info@professionalbridalmakeup.co.uk *As a professional skin care and make-up consultant I offer bridal make-up application on your wedding day at your home or wedding venue in Essex. Includes free luxury hand treatment. Free consultation and trial available.*

Professional Choice, 3 Wood Street, Corby, Northamptonshire, NN17 1PT Tel: (01536) 407300 Fax: (01536) 407353 *Hair & beauty products suppliers*

Professional Computer Group Ltd, Merley House, Merley House Lane, Wimborne, Dorset, BH21 3AA Tel: (01202) 857000 Fax: (01202) 857007 E-mail: enquiries@pcgl.co.uk *IT sales & services*

Professional Cycle Manufacturing Ltd, Forge Lane, Cradley Heath, West Midlands, B64 5AL Tel: (01384) 568521 Fax: (01384) 634494 E-mail: enquires@pcmgroup.co.uk *Cycle manufrs*

▶ Professional Design Consultancy Ltd, Pinnocks Avenue, Gravesend, Kent, DA11 7QD Tel: (01474) 745772 Fax: (01474) 745772 E-mail: pdcltd@blueyonder.co.uk *CAD outsourcing, cad design building services & plantroom designers*

Professional Equipment, Mill Farm, 42 Main St, Repton, Derby, DE65 6EZ Tel: (01283) 704432 Fax: (01283) 704432 E-mail: bob@profequip.fsnet.co *Engineering designers*

Professional Framing Co. Ltd, St. Georges Road, Redditch, Worcestershire, B98 8EF Tel: (01527) 63039 Fax: (01527) 597323 *Picture frame manufrs*

Professional Hairdressing Agencies Ltd, 76 Botley Road, Park Gate, Southampton, SO31 1BA Tel: (01489) 589553 Fax: (01489) 581441 E-mail: phaltd@fsbdial.co.uk *Hairdressing product suppliers*

Professional Hairdressing Distributors, 4 Haithwaite, Two Mile Ash, Milton Keynes, MK8 8LJ Tel: 01908 265168 Fax: 01908 265168 *Hairdressing products*

Professional Images, 12 Swindon Road, Highworth, Swindon, SN6 7SL Tel: (01793) 766379 Fax: (01793) 763335 E-mail: info@professional-images.com *Location publicity photographs services*

▶ Professional IT Logistics Ltd, Unit 5, Station Approach, Wendover, Buckinghamshire, HP22 6BN Tel: (0870) 3802999 Fax: (0870) 3802998 E-mail: support@professionalit.com *Software & networking services*

▶ Professional Management Resources Ltd, P O Box 23, Wadhurst, East Sussex, TN5 6XL Tel: (01892) 784226 Fax: 01892 784228 E-mail: info@pmr-worldjobs.co.uk *Recruitment Agency specialising in the provision of professional engineering manpower,ie.EPC, design, management, field, safety, contracts and support staff for oil, gas, petrochemical, civil construction, power, utilities, telecommunications industries for overseas projects in North Africa, Middle East, Asia, Europe and UK.*

Professional Mobile Valet Service, 31 Brimbleworth Lane, St. Georges, Weston-super-Mare, Avon, BS22 7XS Tel: (07811) 158953 E-mail: professionalmobilevaletservice@hotmail.co.uk *Car valet services to the south west area*

Professional Packaging Services Ltd, 1 The Barn, Hawksworth Lane, Guiseley, Leeds, LS20 8HD Tel: (01943) 882400 Fax: (01943) 878191 E-mail: sales@p-p-s-ltd.com *Packaging designers & consultants*

Professional Polishing Services Ltd, 18b Parkhouse Industrial Estate, Middlemore Road, Smethwick, West Midlands, B66 2DR Tel: 0121-555 6569 Fax: 0121-555 6613 E-mail: sales@professionalpolishing.co.uk *Stainless steel polishing services*

Professional Protection Systems Ltd, Protection House, Sherbourne Drive, Tilbrook, Milton Keynes, MK7 8HX Tel: (01908) 272240 Fax: (01908) 371605 *Decontamination equipment, units, chemical, gas resistant clothing & emergency shower unit manufrs*

Professional Retail Systems, Bridgewater Close, Hapton, Burnley, Lancashire, BB11 5TT Tel: (01282) 425566 Fax: (01282) 423831 E-mail: gt.prs-epos@btconnect.com *Cash register maintenance, repairs & sales*

▶ Professional Slitting Services, 6 Stourdale Road, Cradley Heath, West Midlands, B64 7BG Tel: (01384) 633322 Fax: (01384) 633323 E-mail: sales@reddifast.co.uk *Steel processors*

Professional Solutions Ltd, 109 Friern Park, London, N12 9LH Tel: (020) 8492 0550 *Cosmetics supply*

Professional Sound Consultancy, Unit 16 Spring Rise, Falconer Road, Haverhill, Suffolk, CB9 7XU Tel: (01440) 714006 Fax: (01440) 714007 E-mail: info@profsoundconsult.com *Life safety systems equipment & maintenance provider, voice alarm*

Professional Test Systems, Summer Court, Manafon, Welshpool, Powys, SY21 8BJ Tel: (01686) 650160 Fax: (01686) 650170 E-mail: sales@proftest.com *Water testing products*

▶ Professional Van and Light Truck Magazine, Golden Hill, Leyland, PR25 3NN Tel: (01772) 433303 Fax: (01772) 433772 E-mail: info@campbelluk.com *Direct mail specialists*

Professional Welding Services Ltd, 80-82 Cobham Road, Ferndown Industrial Estate, Wimborne, Dorset, BH21 7RW Tel: (01202) 895080 Fax: (01202) 861463 E-mail: sales@prowelding.co.uk *Aerospace engineering & welding services*

▶ Professor Paradox, 42 St. James Street, St. James, South Petherton, Somerset, TA13 5BN Tel: 01460 242549 E-mail: mike@wisefool.co.uk *Entertainment: Hilarious shows for children and families at parties and events*

▶ Professor Reg E Mental, 64 Wrangleden Road, Maidstone, Kent, ME15 9LJ Tel: (01622) 674643 E-mail: info@regemental.co.uk *Children's and Family Entertainer suitable for all private and corporate functions*

Proficio Cleaning Services, 52 Crossgates, Bellshill, Lanarkshire, ML4 2EE Tel: (01698) 740840 Fax: (01698) 740008 E-mail: sales@proficio.co.uk *Cleaning contractors, industrial*

▶ Proficio Solutions Ltd, 2 Cleaver Cottages Appleshaw, Andover, Hampshire, SP11 9AD Tel: (01264) 772047 Fax: (01264) 772047 E-mail: info@proficiosolutions.co.uk *We supply the services of Part Time Finance Directors, Non-executive Directors and Mentors. Contact us for a free no obligation meeting to see how we can help your business Accomplish, Advance and Progress*

Profile, Tingewick Mill, Church Lane, Tingewick, Buckingham, MK18 4RB Tel: (01280) 847494 Fax: (01280) 847495 E-mail: info@profile.co.uk *Software consultants*

Profile Ltd, Sir Frank Whittle Road, Derby, DE21 4XE Tel: 01332 366900 Fax: (01332) 369613 E-mail: mail@profileuk.com *Flat glass production*

Profile 2000 Ltd, Units 1-3 Carey Street, Kettering, Northamptonshire, NN16 0JL Tel: (01536) 522004 Fax: (01536) 416468 *Lighting manufrs*

Profile 2000 Plus, 16 Swadford Street, Skipton, North Yorkshire, BD23 1RD Tel: (01756) 796622 Fax: 01756 709525 *Upgrading Networking Computers & Retail*

▶ Profile 7000 Ltd, Station St West Business Park, Coventry, CV6 5BP Tel: 024 76683366

Profile Automation, Unit 6 Crayfields Industrial Park, Main Road, St. Pauls Cray, Orpington, Kent, BR5 3HP Tel: (01689) 878004 Fax: (01689) 821190 E-mail: info@profile-automation.com *Electronic equipment manufrs*

▶ Profile Design, 10 West Pallant, Chichester, West Sussex, PO19 1TF Tel: (01243) 537444 Fax: (01243) 537440 E-mail: sales@profiledesign.net *Graphic design including website design*

Profile Die Ltd, Unit 32 Knightsbridge Business Centre, Knightsbridge, Cheltenham, Gloucestershire, GL51 9TA Tel: (01242) 680735 Fax: (01242) 680880 E-mail: profiledie.ltd@btinternet.com *Tool manufrs*

▶ Profile Engineering, 10 Lower Clark St Industrial Estate, Scarborough, North Yorkshire, YO12 7PP Tel: (01723) 350111 Fax: (01723) 350222 *Engineering*

▶ Profile Events, Whiskett Hill, Barkisland, Halifax, West Yorkshire, HX4 0BN Tel: (01422) 371385 Fax: (01422) 371385 E-mail: sales@profileevents.co.uk *Manufacturers of the power turn off road buggy*

Profile & Fabrication Services, P O Box 1002, Yateley, Hampshire, GU46 6ZA Tel: (01252) 875739 Fax: (01252) 664124 *Profile cutting services*

Profile Gauge & Tool Co. Ltd, Mangham Way, Rotherham, South Yorkshire, S61 4RL Tel: (01709) 377184 Fax: (01709) 820281 *Precision engineers*

Profile Lighting Services Ltd, 7-8 Links Business Centre, Raynham Road, Bishop's Stortford, Hertfordshire, CM23 5NZ Tel: (01279) 757595 Fax: (01279) 755599 E-mail: mailbox@profile-lighting.co.uk *Industrial & commercial lighting fittings*

Profile Marketing Services, Profile House, 2 Hartfield Close, Kents Hill, Milton Keynes, MK7 6HN Tel: (01908) 605099 Fax: (01908) 672499 E-mail: services@profilemarketing.co.uk *Marketing & public relations services*

Profile Photography, 27 Palmerston Boulevard, Leicester, LE2 3YS Tel: 0116-288 3506 *Commercial photographers*

Profile Seating Ltd, Unit 11A, Fills Road, Willow Farm BusinessPark, Castle Donington, Derby, DE74 2US Tel: (01332) 817888 Fax: (01332) 817899 E-mail: mail@profileuk.com *Seat repairers*

Profile Security Services, 2 Brittens Court, Clifton Reynes, Olney, Buckinghamshire, MK46 5LG Tel: (01234) 240500 Fax: (01234) 240460 *Security guard suppliers*

Profile Techniques Ltd, Unit 12-14 Watery La Industrial Estate, Watery Lane, Willenhall, West Midlands, WV13 3SU Tel: (01902) 609545 Fax: (01902) 632319 E-mail: info@profiletechniques.co.uk *Plastic extrusion manufrs*

Profins Ltd, Burdon Drive, North West Industrial Estate, Peterlee, County Durham, SR8 2JH Tel: 0191-586 7669 Fax: 0191-586 0777 E-mail: info@profins.com *Heat exchange tubing manufrs*

▶ Profit Growth Unlimited, 21 Ruskin Close, Rugby, Warwickshire, CV22 5RU Tel: (01788) 812050 E-mail: sales@ruskininfo.co.uk *Software for efficient business'*

Profit Manufacturing Ltd, Unit 36 Albion Mills, Albion Road, Bradford, West Yorkshire, BD10 9TF Tel: (01274) 610590 Fax: (01274) 610541 E-mail: sales@pro-fit-int.com *Shoulder pad, waistband & interlining manufrs*

The Profit Partnership Ltd, White Gates, Oldway, Upton St. Leonards, Gloucester, GL4 8AF Tel: (01452) 372540 Fax: (01452) 372540 *Independent cost & management consultants*

▶ Proflex Hose Ltd, Unit 2 Cowling Business Park, Canalside, Chorley, Lancashire, PR6 0QL Tel: (01257) 220010 Fax: (01257) 220060 E-mail: sales@proflexhose.co.uk *Stainless steel hose manufrs*

Proform Aluminium Bending Ltd, Unit 1 Boundry Court, Gilbert Way, Burma Road, Blidworth, Mansfield, Nottinghamshire, NG21 0RT Tel: (01623) 491926 Fax: (01623) 491927 E-mail: proformalu@btconnect.com Purchasing Contact: R. Cunningham Sales Contact: S Harris *At Ansec Aluminium Forms Ltd, we have vast experience in curving architectural aluminium, stainless steel, shopfronts, thermally broken material and firescreen sections. We can offer quality, reliability, quick turnaround times, and competitive prices on of full range of aluminium bending, aluminium forming, stainless steel, draw bending, angles and channels, firescreen sections, thermally broken material, architectural aluminium, stainless steel, aluminium forming and bending and shopfronts*

Profusion plc, Aviation Way, Southend Airport, Southend-on-Sea, SS2 6UN Tel: (01702) 543500 Fax: (01702) 543700 E-mail: sales@profusionplc.com *Semi-conductor component distributors*

Progenitive Filtration Ltd, Hampson Street, Horwich, Bolton, BL6 7JH Tel: (01204) 478210 Fax: (01204) 478211 E-mail: sales@pflfiltermedia.com *Environmental consultants*

Program Products (Services) Ltd, Enterprise House, Station Approach, West Byfleet, Surrey, KT14 6NJ Tel: (01932) 345566 Fax: (01932) 336333 E-mail: info@program-products.co.uk *Software suppliers*

Programme Products UK Ltd, Newcourt Farm, Huntington Lane, Huntington, Hereford, HR4 7RA Tel: (01432) 354133 Fax: (01432) 270111 E-mail: sales@programmeproducts.co.uk *Kitchen manufrs*

Programmed Communications, Unit 9 Bluebird House, Povey Cross Road, Horley, Surrey, RH6 0AF Tel: (01293) 822033 Fax: (01293) 821958 *Public address systems distributor*

Programmed Environmental Maintenance Ltd, 135 Sandy Lane, Middlestown, Wakefield, West Yorkshire, WF4 4PR Tel: (01924) 270821 Fax: (01924) 264672 E-mail: inquiries@pem-ltd.co.uk *Building cleaning contractors*

▶ Programmed Logic Services, 59a Peach Street, Wokingham, Berkshire, RG40 1XP Tel: 0118-977 5855 Fax: 0118-979 2120 E-mail: microchips@btconnect.com *Electronic component distributors & agents*

Programming Research Ltd, 9-11 Queens Road, Walton-on-Thames, Surrey, KT12 5LU Tel: (01932) 888080 Fax: (01932) 888081 E-mail: web@prqa.co.uk *Software development tools & process improvement consultants*

▶ Progredi E-Business, 1 Whitelaw Cottages, Duns, Berwickshire, TD11 3LX Tel: (01890) 870306 E-mail: info@progredi.co.uk *Specialists in web development projects*

Progress Cleaning Services White Plume Ltd, 19 Middle Street, Southampton, SO14 6GH Tel: (023) 8022 5181 Fax: (023) 8063 0622 E-mail: sales@progresscleaningservices.co.uk *Factory, window & industrial cleaners*

▶ Progress Fire & Security Ltd, 54 Ashfield Road, Sale, Cheshire, M33 7DT Tel: 0161-976 4802 Fax: 0161-905 3948

Progress N C, Unit 14 Progress Business Park, Orders Lane, Kirkham, Preston, PR4 2TZ Tel: (01772) 687879 Fax: (01772) 687879 *CNC engineers*

Progress Panels, Stoke Mill, Mill Road, Sharnbrook, Bedford, MK44 1NP Tel: (01234) 781007 *Car body repairs*

Progress Partnership, 4 Garden Street, Hebden Bridge, West Yorkshire, HX7 8AQ Tel: (01422) 845245 Fax: (01422) 843964 *Consultancy of mobile computing*

Progress Shaving Brush Ltd, 24 Spring Valley Industrial Estate, Douglas, Isle of Man, IM2 2QR Tel: (01624) 676030 Fax: (01624) 662056 E-mail: enquiries@progress-vulfix.com *Shaving & wire brush manufrs*

Progressive Control Systems, 3 Pear Tree Grove, Shirley, Solihull, West Midlands, B90 1LL Tel: 0121-608 4091 Fax: 0121-604 0426 E-mail: sales@progressivecontrol.com *Heating & ventilation control system services*

Progressive Educational Tools Ltd, 139 Warwick Road, Kenilworth, Warwickshire, CV8 1HY Tel: (01926) 863360 Fax: (01926) 863360 E-mail: ssexton@petlanguages.co.uk *Educational software manufr*

Progressive Engineers Ltd, Groby Road, Audenshaw, Manchester, M34 5HT Tel: 0161-371 0444 Fax: 0161-371 0444 E-mail: info@progressive-eng.com *Valve manufrs*

Progressive Floor Surfaces Ltd, Unit 10 Westward House, Glebeland Road, Camberley, Surrey, GU15 3DB Tel: (01276) 681111 Fax: (01276) 66166 *Flooring contractors*

Progressive Optical Co. Ltd, 165 North Street, Barking, Essex, IG11 8LA Tel: (020) 8594 0160 Fax: (020) 8594 0139 E-mail: jgreen@btconnect.com *Manufacturing opticians & retail opticians*

▶ Progressive Print Services, Firs Industrial Estate, Kidderminster, Worcestershire, DY11 7QN Tel: (01562) 747356 Fax: (01562) 747357 E-mail: sales@progressive-print.co.uk *Commercial printers & suppliers of all aspects of print, litho, digital & flexor*

▶ Progressive Print Solutions Ltd, 6 Leodis Court, Leeds, LS11 5JJ Tel: 0113-244 2220 Fax: 0113-244 6011

Progressive Safety Footwear & Clothing Ltd, 101 Worthing Road, Sheffield, S9 3JN Tel: 0114-273 8349 Fax: 0114-275 2452E-mail: info@psf.co.uk *Distribution of safety footwear & protective work wear* Also at: Kidderminster

Progressive Supplies Paper Ltd, 18 Crawford Place, London, W1H 5AY Tel: (020) 7563 7330 Fax: (020) 7706 3058 E-mail: sales@progressivesupplies.com *Wholesale packaging merchants*

Progressive Tooling Systems Ltd, Newark Road, Eastern Industry, Peterborough, PE1 5UA Tel: (01733) 313400 Fax: (01733) 348052 E-mail: progt@progtool.co.uk *Plastics vacuum form toolmakers*

Progressive Woodworking Co. Ltd, West End Saw Mills, Broadbottom, Hyde, Cheshire, SK14 6BG Tel: (01457) 762102 Fax: (01457) 766080 *Joinery manufrs*

▶ ProInception, MSEC Zochonis Building, University of Manchester, Oxford Road, Manchester, M13 9PL Tel: 0161-275 1895 Fax: 0161-275 1919 E-mail: info@proinception.com *ProInception**ProInception provide an innovative and practical mechanical engineering design and product development service. The focus is on creative problem solving supported by sound engineering principles and a strong understanding of business constraints.**General Computer Aided Design (CAD) services and onsite Pro/Engineer training are also offered with expertise in both Pro/Engineer and also AutoCAD.**In summary, capabilities include:*·Concept design, visualisation and evaluation*·Product development*·Mechanical engineering design*·Computer Aided Design (speciality in Pro/Engineer and AutoCAD) with data output ready for Computer Numerical Control (CNC) machining and rapid prototyping.*·Completion of engineering drawings and large format plotting**A portfolio of past designs and further information can be found at www.ProInception.com*

▶ ProInnovate Ltd - Supplying Beam Central Vacuums, Business and Technology Centre, Bessemer Drive, Stevenage, Hertfordshire, SG1 2DX Tel: 01438 791049 E-mail: info@pro-innovate.com *Supply, installation and maintenance of Beam Central Vacuum systems.*

Projax Tools (1989) Ltd, Arthur St, Redditch, Worcestershire, B98 8DZ Tel: 01527 523734 *Tube manipulation tools manufrs*

▶ Project 17, Unit 9 Rossett Business Park, Rodley Lane, Leeds, LS13 1BQ Tel: 0113-255 7070 Fax: 0113-255 7070 E-mail: admin@project17.net *Joiners*

Project Building & Joinery Services, Burlais Works, Approach Road, Manselton, Swansea, SA5 8NL Tel: (01792) 649875 Fax: (01792) 465124 E-mail: sales@projectjoinery.co.uk *Joinery manufrs*

Project Central Ltd, 163 Turnpike Link, Croydon, CR0 5NW Tel: (020) 8688 8002 Fax: (07079) 013173 E-mail: sales@projectcentral.co.uk *Computer software*

Project Coin Machine Ltd, 682-684 London Road, Thornton Heath, Surrey, CR7 7HU Tel: (020) 8664 3400 Fax: (020) 8664 3449 *Fruit machine manufrs*

Project Co-Ordination Ltd, 34 Lower Addiscombe Road, Croydon, CR0 6AA Tel: (020) 8686 6844 Fax: (020) 8686 6815 E-mail: projectco@aol.com *Building services support documentation*

Project Design Services Ltd, 19 Station Square, Lowestoft, Suffolk, NR32 1BA Tel: (01502) 564892 Fax: (01502) 531658 E-mail: sales@projectdesign.co.uk *Technical personnel recruitment & engineering designers*

▶ Project Desk2Web, 5 Ashburn Avenue, Waterside, Londonderry, BT47 5QE Tel: (020) 8123 6355 E-mail: allannospam@desk2web.co.uk *Project Desk2Web offer personal and business off-site automated backup services, spam control, data encryption and a range of web based security tools.*

Project Electronics Ltd, Project House, Slade Green Road, Erith, Kent, DA8 2HX Tel: (01322) 350700 Fax: (01322) 351100 E-mail: mail@project-uk.com *Electronic consultants or designers*

Project Engineering Services, 26 The Hoskers, Westhoughton, Bolton, BL5 2DW Tel: (01942) 817445 Fax: (01942) 817445 E-mail: project@engservice.freeserve.co.uk *Project engineering/management*

▶ Project Finance International, Aldgate House, 33 Aldgate High Street, London, EC3N 1DL Tel: 020 73697454 Fax: 020 73697333 E-mail: marketing@tfn.com *Project Finance International is the leading source of intelligence surrounding the global Project Finance industry-giving you pipeline information, global coverage, sector analysis, historical data and deal analysis.*

▶ Project Heating Co. Ltd, 4 Norman Court, Budlake Road, Marsh Barton Trading Estate, Exeter, EX2 8PY Tel: (01392) 215790 Fax: (01392) 431528 E-mail: sales@projectheating.co.uk

Project Management & Design Solutions Ltd, 16 Hosefield Avenue, Aberdeen, AB15 5NN Tel: (07762) 595588 E-mail: robert.summers@pmd-ltd.co.uk *Management of training & development for company staff competency*

Project Management & Procurement Services, Old Billingham Business Centre, 1 Chapel Road, Billingham, Cleveland, TS23 1EN Tel: (01642) 353400 Fax: (01642) 353401 E-mail: ericbphelps@pmps.co.uk *Quantity surveyors*

Project Management Services, The Brow, Lothersdale, Keighley, West Yorkshire, BD20 8EQ Tel: (01535) 633802 E-mail: peter@pmservice.co.uk *Special purpose machinery*

▶ Project Management Software Centre, 6 Whinmoor Way, Silkstone, Barnsley, South Yorkshire, S75 4JE Tel: (01226) 792222 Fax: (01226) 792945

continued

Company Information

continuation
E-mail: kelly@pmscsolutions.co.uk *PMSC are specialists in construction project planning and management Windows software, with over 25,000 UK users. Project Commander is a high performance, quality system, that is easy to use, but with a low cost entry of £375 (plus VAT) for a stand-alone licence or a network licence that allows all workstations to access on a one concurrent licence. PMSC provide training and support nationwide and in Ireland. Project Commander is fully compatible with Microsoft Project, allowing users to open a MPP file and to save a MPX file - which can be read by MS Project. The Training department also provide training in MS Project.*

Project Metals Ltd, A P House, Neap House Road, Gunness, Scunthorpe, South Humberside, DN15 8TY Tel: (01724) 780100 Fax: (01724) 780101 E-mail: administrator@projectmetals.com *Project metals suppliers*

Project Monitor Ltd, 30 Gritstone Road, Matlock, Derbyshire, DE4 3GB Tel: (01629) 581384 Fax: (01629) 584972 E-mail: pdsl@dile.pipex.com *European & public sector funding & management consultants*

Project People Ltd, Whitefriars, Lewins Mead, Bristol, BS1 2NT Tel: 0117-908 7000 Fax: 0117-925 4676 E-mail: sales@handsets.com *IT & engineering mobile telecoms recruitment agency service*

Project Plastics Ltd, 9 Grange Way Business Park, Grange Way, Colchester, CO2 8HF Tel: (01206) 868696 Fax: (01206) 793737 E-mail: project.plastics@btinternet.com *Plastic fabricators*

▶ Project Scaffolding, 36 Grange Road, Houstoun Industrial Estate, Livingston, West Lothian, EH54 5DE Tel: (01506) 441144 Fax: (01506) 440044

Project Skills Solutions Ltd, 19 - 21 Kents Hill Road, Benfleet, Essex, SS7 5PN Tel: 0845 1307411 Fax: 01268 754520 E-mail: info@projss.co.uk *Training courses NRSWA, Cat and Genny training, Confined spaces training, IPAF training, PASMA training, working at height training, Manual handling training, Prince 2 project management training, Telecommunications training, first aid training, abrasive wheels training, CPCS training, Fire fighting training, RSAWA training, Project management services, electrical installation, Fibre optic installation and testing,OTDR testing,Ex forces recruitment, Temporary data cabling personnel, contract personnel, Project manager recruitment, security cleared personnel.*

▶ Project Spontaneous Ltd, 6 Westminster Road Urmston, Manchester, M41 0RR Tel: 0161-718 0395 E-mail: info@projectspontaneous.com *Project Spontaneous - Media Solutions and Services designed for you. Web Design, Graphic Design, Video/DVD/CD ROM Production, Advert design/Advertising solutions and modelling agent.*

Project Systems Support Ltd, Chatelaine, Gazing Lane, West Wellow, Romsey, Hampshire, SO51 6BS Tel: (01794) 322755 Fax: (01794) 323964 E-mail: robert_toogood@projectsystemssupport.co.uk *Management consultants services*

Projected Image, Havers Road, Norwich, NR3 2DU Tel: (01603) 481100 Fax: (01603) 481105 E-mail: info@projected.co.uk *Data projectors rent & hire*

Projected Image Products Ltd, Unit 8, Ynyschir Industrial Estate, Ynyschir, Porth, Mid Glamorgan, CF39 0HU Tel: (01443) 682196 Fax: (01443) 686840 E-mail: paul@projectimage.freeserve.co.uk *Embroidery manufrs*

▶ Projected Image Uk, 3 Mill Studios, 3 Mill Lane, London, E3 3DU Tel: 0208 2153331 Fax: 0208 2153472 E-mail: gobo@projectedimage.uk.com *In-house gobo manufacturing for custom and catalogue designs from metal to full colour glass. The fastest tunraround at very competitive prices.*

▶ Projection Advertising Ltd, 231 The Vale, London, W3 7QS Tel: (020) 8735 1390 E-mail: info@projectionadvertising.co.uk *Advertising lighting design*

Projection Lighting Ltd, Fourth Aveune, The Village, Trafford Park, Manchester, M17 1DB Tel: 0161-872 6868 Fax: 0161-872 6869 E-mail: pll@projectionlighting.co.uk *Lighting manufrs*

▶ Projector Hire, 36 Parrock Avenue, Gravesend, Kent, DA12 1QQ Tel: 0798 454 3625 *Projector hire for all areas in North; West Kent cheap rates Email :projector_hire @uk2.net or call 0798 454 3625 Our 'No-Worries-Install' service will organise it all for you. Quick efficient Drop down-Setup-Pickup Service. Weekend and single evening hire availabe. Full Training and Instructions provided. Provide advice/help with your presentation or graphics /logos. Special discounts for charities and community events. Great for Weddings, Conferences, Partys, Film Nights. Scene setter for bands, events and exhibitions. Delivery /Pickup tailored to your event.*

Projects Advertising & Marketing Ltd, Unit B5 Southways Park, London Road, Lowfield Heath, Crawley, West Sussex, RH10 9TQ Tel: (01293) 446949 Fax: (01293) 455071 E-mail: sales@projectsadv.co.uk *Marketing*

Projects Department Ltd, 26 Woodlands Road, Camberley, Surrey, GU15 3NA Tel: (01276) 681423 Fax: (01276) 537170 E-mail: info@projectsdepartment.com *Specialist suppliers in television lighting systems*

▶ The Projects Group plc, Windsor House, Lodge Place, Sutton, Surrey, SM1 4AU Tel: (020) 8722 8340 Fax: 020 8770 9555 E-mail: Susan.el-zarif@theprojectsgroup.co.uk *Headquartered in Surrey, The Projects Group plc (TPG) is in its 22nd year of delivering dedicated project and programme management training, education, and consultancy to individuals and organisations across the world. The company has always been managed exclusively by project managers, giving a uniquely focused and relevant perspective in the field.*

▶ Projects (SW) Ltd, 3 Huntersway, Culmstock, Cullompton, Devon, EX15 3HJ Tel: (01884) 841621 Fax: (01884) 841621 E-mail: info@projects-sw.co.uk

Projects XL Ltd, Glenville House, Spring Gardens, Romford, RM7 9LD Tel: (01708) 751919 Fax: (01708) 725294 E-mail: info@projectsxl.com *Printers & screen printers & stationers*

Projectworld Ltd, Morvern Works, Church Street, Briton Ferry, Neath, West Glamorgan, SA11 2JP Tel: (01639) 812332 Fax: (01639) 812496 E-mail: info@projectworld.co.uk *Cleaning equipment manufrs*

Projen plc, Winnington Avenue, Northwich, Cheshire, CW8 4EE Tel: (01606) 871111 Fax: (01606) 871133 E-mail: mailbox@projen.co.uk *Chemical & pharmaceutical plant contractors & designers*

▶ Projex Design, Van Alloys Industrial Estate, Busgrove Lane, Stoke Row, Henley-on-Thames, Oxfordshire, RG9 5QW Tel: (01491) 682757 Fax: (01491) 681778 E-mail: andy@projexdesign.co.uk *Design mechanical products*

Projexe Engineering, 7 Merriott House, Hennock Road, Marsh Barton Trading Estate, Exeter, EX2 8NJ Tel: (01392) 258441 Fax: (01392) 498441 *Welding & mechanical engineers*

Prolec Ltd, Unit 5, Link 35, Nuffield Industrial Estate, Poole, Dorset, BH17 0GB Tel: (01202) 681190 Fax: (01202) 677909 E-mail: sales@prolec.co.uk *Electronic safety systems*

Prolec Automation Services, A5 Arkwright Suite Coppull Enterprise Centre, Mill Lane, Coppull, Chorley, Lancashire, PR7 5BW Tel: (01257) 470460 Fax: (01257) 470469 E-mail: smprolec@tiscali.co.uk *Electrical panels installers & manufrs*

▶ Prolibris Limited, 72 Wallwood Road, London, E11 1AL Tel: 020 8558 8602 E-mail: info@prolibris.co.uk *Professional writing services, especially technical writing and online document development.*

▶ Prolific Marketing Ltd, 5th Floor, International House, 223 Regent Street, London, W1B 2QD Tel: 020 7544 1010 Fax: 020 7544 1090 E-mail: enquiries@prolificmarketing.co.uk

Proline Ltd, 530 Commercial Road, London, E1 0HY Tel: (020) 7702 1983 Fax: (020) 7791 2288 *CCTV security*

▶ Proline Engineering Ltd, Mill Street, Farnworth, Bolton, BL4 7BH Tel: (01204) 868620 Fax: (01204) 868621

Prolink Radio Systems Ltd, Saxon Business Park, Bromsgrove, Worcestershire, B60 4AD Tel: (01527) 577788 Fax: (01527) 577757 E-mail: service@prolink-radio.com *Radio communications hire & service*

Prolinx Ltd, View Farm Barn, Windmill Hill, Great Milton, Oxford, OX44 7NW Tel: (01844) 279199 Fax: (01844) 279144 E-mail: contact@prolinx.co.uk *Computer consultant services*

▶ Pro-Lite Technology LLP, The Cranfield Innovation Centre, University Way, Cranfield, Bedford, MK43 0BT Tel: (01234) 436110 Fax: (01234) 436111 E-mail: sales@pro-lite.uk.com *Lasers & photonics products distributors*

Prolog Systems Ltd, Century House, Station Way, Sutton, Surrey, SM3 8SW Tel: (020) 8715 1555 Fax: (020) 8715 1556 E-mail: sales@prologsystems.com *Computer software service management*

Prologic Computer Consultants Ltd, Redwood House, Rectory Lane, Berkhamsted, Hertfordshire, HP4 2DH Tel: (01442) 876277 Fax: (01442) 877245 E-mail: info@prologic.net *Computer software suppliers*

Prologic Systems Ltd, 65 Fortess Rd, London, NW5 1AG Tel: (020) 7485 3225 Fax: (020) 7209 0399 *Computer consultants*

Prom Chem Ltd, 89 High Street, Caterham, Surrey, CR3 5UH Tel: (01883) 341444 Fax: (01883) 341666 E-mail: promchem@prom.co.uk *Fine & speciality chemicals distributors & manufrs*

Prom UK, 23 Ash Close, Walters Ash, High Wycombe, Buckinghamshire, HP14 4TR Tel: (01494) 562253 *Press brake tooling & cnc*

Promac Precision Engineering Ltd, 49 Ivatt Way, Peterborough, PE3 7PN Tel: (01733) 333000 Fax: (01733) 333001 E-mail: management@promac.fsnet.co.uk *Jig, fixture & tool manufrs*

▶ Promac Process Design Ltd, 109 Norwood Grove, Beverley, North Humberside, HU17 9JP Tel: (01482) 860049 E-mail: promac_design@yahoo.co.uk *Design & projecting service*

▶ Promaintenance, 254 Walsall Road, Cannock, Staffordshire, WS11 0JL Tel: (01543) 469098

Promanex Ltd, The Stables Hurley Hall Barns Industrial Estate, Atherstone L, Hurley, Atherstone, Warwickshire, CV9 2HT Tel: (01827) 874567 Fax: (01827) 871030 E-mail: enquiries@promanex.co.uk *The Promanex Group comprises: Promanex Ltd, Thermal Energy Construction Ltd, Jefco Services Ltd. Contracts range from facilities management to specialised construction projects. The group supplies the full range of industrial support services utilising our 'in house' expertise, proven management processes & strategic alliance partners in the realisation of client added value*

▶ Promarco Ltd, Saltwells Road, Dudley, West Midlands, DY2 9PE Tel: (01384) 565646 Fax: (01384) 351000

Promark, Beeches, Park Wall Lane, Lower Basildon, Reading, RG8 9PE Tel: (01491) 671539 Fax: (01491) 671832 E-mail: sales@promarkgifts.co.uk *Business promotional items*

Promark Systems Ltd, 9 Clydach Road, Enfield, Middlesex, EN1 3SL Tel: (020) 8363 0467 Fax: (020) 8364 4300 *Computer consultants*

Promart Manufacturing Ltd, Caddick Road, Knowsley Industrial Park South, Knowsley Business Park, Prescot, Merseyside, L34 9HP Tel: 0151-547 4666 Fax: 0151-546 6152 E-mail: sales@promart.co.uk *Stainless steel manufrs*

▶ Promasol, 63 Harwood Lane, Great Harwood, Blackburn, BB6 7TB Tel: (01254) 885500 Fax: (01254) 885500 E-mail: info@promasol.co.uk *Promasol is a provider of Project Management Services and Management Consultancy Services*

Promat U.K Ltd, Wellingborough, Northamptonshire, NN8 6XS Tel: (01933) 271476 Fax: (01933) 276790 *Steel fire doors*

Promedics Ltd, Moorgate Street, Blackburn, BB2 4PB Tel: (01254) 619000 Fax: (01254) 619001 E-mail: sales@promedics.co.uk *Agent medical supplies service*

Promens, Unit 1, The Trident Centre, Armstrong Road, Basingstoke, Hampshire, RG24 8NU Tel: (01256) 844700 Fax: (01256) 844988 E-mail: jeremy.wilson@promens.com *Packaging material distribs*

Promentum Technologies Ltd, 3 Cobden Road, London, SE25 5NZ Tel: (020) 8656 8666 Fax: (020) 8656 8606 E-mail: technologies@promentum.co.uk *Computer consultants*

Promet Technology Ltd, 31 Chase Road, London, NW10 6PU Tel: (020) 8965 0500 Fax: (020) 8965 3030 *Steel fabricators*

ProMinent Fluid Controls (UK) Ltd, Resolution Road, Ashby-de-la-Zouch, Leicestershire, LE65 1DW Tel: (01530) 560555 Fax: (01530) 560777 E-mail: sales@prominent.co.uk *ProMinent Fluid Controls (UK) Ltd based in Ashby-de-la-Zouch, Leicestershire are manufacturers & suppliers of all water treatment equipment. Including cholorination plant, metering pumps, chemical dosing pumps & water treatment monitoring equipment*

Promo Branding Ltd, New Southgate Industrial Estate, Lower Park Road, London, N11 1QD Tel: (020) 8361 8820 Fax: (020) 8361 8821 E-mail: sales@promobranding.co.uk *Personalised match books, boxes & promotional items*

▶ Promo CDR, 30b Downleaze, Stoke Bishop, Bristol, BS9 1LY Tel: 0117-968 2865 E-mail: info@promocdr.co.uk *Short-run cd & dvd duplication & printing services*

Promocan, Plaistow Road, Loxwood, Billingshurst, West Sussex, RH14 0TS Tel: (01403) 753453 Fax: 0845 6120655 E-mail: tmursell@promocan.co.uk *Specialists in promotional packing into tins. From the standard 'baked bean' can we offer a range of sizes with a variety of closures: Ring pull ends; plain ends, requiring a can opener & slotted ends*

Promocorp Ltd, Unit 98 Springvale Industrial Estate, Cwmbran, Gwent, NP44 5BH Tel: (01633) 861291 Fax: (01633) 876543 E-mail: promocorp@oeugroup.co.uk *Office suppliers*

Promopack Ltd, Heanor Gate Road, Heanor, Derbyshire, DE75 7RG Tel: (01773) 533600 Fax: (01773) 710963 *Flexographic repro, design and platemakers*

▶ PromoRail, 128 Buckingham Palace Road, Victoria, London, SW1W 9SA Tel: 0207 8384000 E-mail: stephen.jenkins@maidenoutdoor.co.uk *"PromoRail sells face-to-face promotional advertising sites on 300 of the country's busiest railway concourses. Whether you wish to exhibit a brand, demonstrate a product, undertake product sampling, or leafleting, or sign up new customers; using a PromoRail exhibition or distribution site or venue, could be the perfect solution."*

▶ Promoseeds UK, White Hart Hill, Guestling, Hastings, East Sussex, TN35 4LP Tel: (01424) 813572 Fax: (01424) 814631 E-mail: tony@promoseeds.co.uk *Newspaper promotions*

▶ Promotional, 38 Beacon Close, Stone, Aylesbury, Buckinghamshire, HP17 8YH Tel: (01296) 747401 Fax: (01296) 747401 E-mail: sales@beaconpm.co.uk *Promotional merchandise*

▶ Promotional Business Ltd, 95 Welham Road, London, SW16 6QH Tel: (020) 8677 3738 *Supply vast range of promotional and business gifts. Including Mouse mats, mugs and computer related items.*

▶ Promotional Candy Co., 9 Burton Road, Blackpool, FY4 4NW Tel: (01253) 698298 Fax: (01253) 698600 E-mail: sales@promotionalcandy.com *Confectionery manufrs*

Promotional Ceramics Ltd, Spedding Road, Fenton Industrial Estate, Stoke-on-Trent, ST4 2SU Tel: (01782) 279957 Fax: (01782) 264080 E-mail: accounts@promotionalceramics.co.uk *Ceramic promotional product designers*

▶ Promotional Displays & Sign Co., Canterbury Mill, Canterbury Road, Nottingham, NG8 1PQ Tel: 0115-985 4222 Fax: 0115-985 4333 E-mail: promotional@lineone.net *Sign company*

Promotional Fabrics Ltd, The Maltings, School Lane, Amersham, Buckinghamshire, HP7 0ES Tel: (01494) 724172 Fax: (01494) 725283 E-mail: enquiries@amershamfabrics.com *Promotional textile manufrs*

Promotional Forming & Finishing, Moorend House, Highfield Road, Idle, Bradford, West Yorkshire, BD10 8QH Tel: (01274) 620205 Fax: (01274) 620209 E-mail: sales@pff.uk.com *Vacuum forming*

▶ The Promotional Gift Superstore, 79 Villa Road, Stanway, Colchester, CO3 0RN Tel: (0845) 3701022 Fax: (0845) 3701033 E-mail: sales@promogift-superstore.com *Promotional gift house*

▶ Promotional Identity, 35 Muscovy Road, Kennington, Ashford, Kent, TN25 4QN Tel: (01233) 651651 Fax: (01233) 650707 E-mail: info@promotionalid.co.uk *Embroidered, printed clothing, promotional gifts mugs, pens, bags manufrs*

▶ Promotional Keyrings, 28 Coulter Close, Cuffley, Hertfordshire, EN6 4RR Tel: (07005) 981697 E-mail: enquiries@promotionalkeyrings.co.uk *Cheap Blank Keyrings and acrylic fridge magnets also coasters. Available in the Uk at Trade Prices*

Promotional Logistics Ltd, Prolog House, Sudbury, Suffolk, CO10 2XG Tel: (01787) 370272 Fax: (01787) 379935 E-mail: bdm@prolog.uk.com *Promotional handling services*

Promotional Products Specialities Scotland Ltd, 537 Sauchiehall Street, Glasgow, G3 7PQ Tel: 0141-221 2420 Fax: 0141-221 9249 E-mail: sales@beaumontpps.com *Advertising gift producers*

▶ Pro-Moulds (Midlands) Ltd, Burma Road, Mansfield, Nottinghamshire, NG21 0RT Tel: (01623) 491313 Fax: (01623) 491314 E-mail: mark@pro-moulds.com *Plastic mould engineers*

Prompt Maintenance Services, 358 Edgware Road, London, W2 1EB Tel: (020) 7724 7234 Fax: (020) 7224 9854 E-mail: contracts@caesarceramics.co.uk *Ceramics tiles services*

Prompt Profiles Ltd, Liberator House, Bidwell Road, Norwich, NR13 6PT Tel: (01603) 720090 Fax: (01603) 720202 *Manufacturers of ductwork & ducting*

Prompt Technical Services, 12 Pool Road, West Molesey, Surrey, KT8 2HE Tel: (020) 8941 6896 Fax: (020) 8941 2799 E-mail: theopet@golbalnet.co.uk *IT support*

Promtek Ltd, Fisher Street, Brindley Ford, Stoke-on-Trent, ST8 7QJ Tel: (01782) 375600 Fax: (01782) 375605 E-mail: sales@promtek.com *Weighing system manufrs*

▶ Prontaprint Ltd, 85 New Elvet, Durham, DH1 3AQ Tel: 0191-384 3220 Fax: 0191-386 8044

▶ Prontaprint Ltd, Unit 5, Tuffley Park Lower Tuffley Lane, Gloucester, GL2 5DE Tel: (01452) 522411 Fax: (01452) 522411 E-mail: sales@gloucester.prontaprint.com

▶ Prontaprint Ltd, 367 High Street, Lincoln, LN5 7RN Tel: (01522) 530501 Fax: (01522) 538911

▶ Prontaprint Ltd, 1 Creed Lane, London, EC4V 5BR Tel: (020) 7236 7365 Fax: (020) 7248 4048

Prontaprint Ltd, 129 Crawford Street, London, W1U 6BH Tel: (020) 7486 7578 Fax: (020) 7486 0942 E-mail: enquiries@prontaprint-london.com *Printers*

▶ Prontaprint Ltd, 25 Collingwood Street, Newcastle upon Tyne, NE1 1JE Tel: 0191-232 5500 Fax: 0191-261 4158 E-mail: mailbox@newcastle.dial.prontaprint.co.uk

Prontaprint Ltd, Artemis, Odyssey Business Park West End Road, Ruislip, Middlesex, HA4 6QE Tel: (0800) 343334 Fax: (01895) 872141 E-mail: info@prontaprint.com *Quick print & designers* Also at: Branches throughout the U.K.

▶ Prontaprint Ltd, 652-654 Warwick Road, Solihull, West Midlands, B91 3DX Tel: 0121-705 9988 Fax: 0121-711 1309 E-mail: sales@solihull.prontaprint.com

▶ Prontaprint Ltd, 281 High Street, Uxbridge, Middlesex, UB8 1LQ Tel: (01895) 271939 Fax: (01895) 231551

Pronto Joinery Ltd, Dog Lane, Horsford, Norwich, NR10 3DH Tel: (01603) 890239 Fax: (01603) 891677 *Joinery manufrs*

▶ Proof Safe, Unit 17 Sealand Farm Workshops, Sealand Road, Sealand, Chester, CH1 6BS Tel: (01244) 881722 Fax: (01244) 880732 E-mail: djwalker@proofsafe.co.uk *Shop fitters*

Proofings Technology Ltd, Hare Hill Road, Littleborough, Lancashire, OL15 9HE Tel: (01706) 372314 Fax: (01706) 370473 E-mail: *Coated fabric processors*

Proops Brothers Ltd, Victoria Works, Saddington Road, Leicester, LE8 8AW Tel: 0116-240 3400 Fax: 0116-240 3300 *Modellers & jewellers tool suppliers*

Proops Manufacturing Ltd, Shaftesbury House, 46-47 New Street, Burton-On-Trent, Staffordshire, DE14 3QW Tel: (01283) 533280 Fax: (01283) 533280 E-mail: cjroe@lonw.fsnet.co.uk *Small DIY products*

A.M. Proos & Sons Ltd, Spring Vale Road, Darwen, Lancashire, BB3 2ES Tel: (01254) 777777 Fax: (01254) 706666 E-mail: info@proos.co.uk *Roofing material* Also at: Birmingham, Bradford, Glasgow, Hull, Manchester, Newcastle, Scunthorpe, Sheffiel d & Stoke

▶ Prop Logistics, 3 Faraday Court, Park Farm Industrial Estate, Wellingborough, Northamptonshire, NN8 6XY Tel: (01933) 401641 Fax: (01933) 402474

The Prop Shop, Unit 5 The Stable Yard, Alscot Pk, Atherstone on Stour, Stratford-upon-Avon, Warwickshire, CV37 8BL Tel: (01789) 450905 Fax: (01789) 450905 *Model boat propeller manufrs*

▶ Pro-Pac Contract Packaging Ltd, 30 Springwell Road, Leeds, LS12 1AW Tel: (0870) 4322567 Fax: (0870) 4322568 *Contract packing company*

Propack Automation Machinery Ltd, Unit 8 Binns Close, Coventry, CV4 9TB Tel: (024) 7647 0074 Fax: (024) 7647 1190 E-mail: sales@propack.co.uk *Packaging machinery agents*

▶ Propack Film, Unit 88 Leyland Trading Estate, Irthlingborough Road, Wellingborough, Northamptonshire, NN8 1RA Tel: (01933) 275111

Propak, Tything Road West, Kinwarton, Alcester, Warwickshire, B49 6EP Tel: (01789) 765111 Fax: (01789) 765720 E-mail: sales@propakbox.com *UK based cardboard box manufacturers, specialising in die cut packaging and point of sale units in corrugated and solid board. Full colour gloss printed or plain.*

Propak Sheet Metal Ltd, Unit C-D Gunnels Wood Park, Gunnels Wood Road, Stevenage, Hertfordshire, SG1 2BH Tel: (01438) 728885 Fax: (01438) 740298 E-mail: bruce@propak.co.uk *Sheet metalworkers*

Propath Software Ltd, Manor House, 23 Robin Lane, Pudsey, West Yorkshire, LS28 7BR Tel: 0113-255 4115 Fax: 0113-255 4690 E-mail: sales@propath.com *Computer software developers*

Propbrook Ltd, 389 Lichfield Road, Birmingham, B6 7SS Tel: 0121-327 7909 Fax: 0121-327 7423 *Lift & elevator engineering services*

Proper Mixed Concrete Ltd, Wood Lane, Ellesmere, Shropshire, SY12 0HY Tel: (01691) 626262 Fax: (01691) 626263 E-mail: enquiries@tggroup.co.uk *Builders merchants & fuel distributors* Also at: Oswestry, Tattenhall, Welshpool & Whitchurch

▶ Propert Preservation & Building, Unit 2 Farset Enterprise Park, 638 Springfield Road, Belfast, BT12 7DY Tel: (028) 9031 0522 Fax: (028) 9023 8799

Properteam Ltd, 15 Boulthurst Way, Oxted, Surrey, RH8 0HT Tel: (01883) 382888 E-mail: sales@properteam.co.uk *Property Investments & development consultants*

▶ The Property Coach, 33 Sandwich House, Sandwich Street, London, London, WC1H 9PR Tel: 020 7388 0242 E-mail: brian@property-coach.co.uk *The Property Coach offers advice on home staging and affordable interior design. Expert opinions, articles and ideas on how to make the most of your home and property.*

▶ Property Etc Limited, Lombard House, 12/17 Upper Bridge Street, Canterbury, Kent, CT1 2NF Tel: 01227 766389 E-mail: enquiries@property-etc.com *The company provides a range of services to individual owners,private landlords, Registered Social Landlords,Schools,Care Homes and Charities. These services include, but are not restricted to; planned and prevetative maintenance,capital works programmes, repairs, building projects, project management.*

▶ Property Maintenance Direct, 80 Loughborough Road, Thringstone, Coalville, Leicestershire, LE67 8LP Tel: (0845) 4589871 Fax: (01530) 459513 E-mail: enquiries@propertymaintenancedirect.co.uk *Maintain property*

▶ Property Network Services Ltd., 29 Woodlands Crescent, Johnstone, Renfrewshire, PA5 0AZ Tel: 01505 320281 *Specialist design wallcoverings that resemble slate, stone or brick. The panels are lightweight and canbe fitted onto any flat surface. Ideal for kitchens, bathrooms, hotels, restaurants, etc.*

▶ Property Protection, 80 Johnstone Avenue, Hillington Industrial Estate, Glasgow, G52 4NZ Tel: 0141-585 6710

Property Protection Services, Unit 5E Caldeshaw Centre, Ings Lane, Rochdale, Lancashire, OL12 7LQ Tel: (01706) 718000 Fax: (01706) 718888 *Roller shutter manufrs*

▶ Property Protection Systems, Old Tithe Barn, Witcombe, Martock, Somerset, TA12 6AJ Tel: (01935) 825892 Fax: (01935) 825892 E-mail: sales@property-protection-systems.co.uk *Closed circuit television equipment suppliers*

▶ Property Repair Ltd, 52 Montrose Terrace, Edinburgh, EH7 5DL Tel: 0131-478 3391 Fax: 0131 4777553 E-mail: info@propertyrepairltd.co.uk *www.propertyrepairltd.co.uk **electricians, joiners, plasterers, plumbers, painters, decorators, tilers, floor layers, window fitters, artexers, cornice fitters, etc**At Property Repair Ltd we have contracts with domestic and commercial clients and are also employed by major insurance companies to repair their clients homes from fire, flood & smoke damage.*Contact us for a FREE consultation or impartial advice*

,Property Repair Ltd, 52 Montrose Terrace, Edinburgh, EH7 5DL Tel: 0131-478 3391 E-mail: info@www.propertyrepairltd.co.uk *www.propertyrepairltd.co.uk **electricians, joiners, plasterers, plumbers, painters, decorators, tilers, floor layers, window fitters, artexers, cornice fitters, etc**At Property Repair Ltd we have contracts with domestic and commercial clients and are also employed by major insurance companies to repair their clients homes from fire, flood & smoke damage.*Contact us for a FREE consultation or impartial advice*

▶ Property Sale By Owner, 2 Windmill Hill Drive, Bletchley, Milton Keynes, MK3 7SD Tel: 01908 371494 Fax: 01908 371494 E-mail: davidf.mills@virgin.net *UK Property For Sale By Owner makes selling a home on your own easy.* *Your home''s selling price is determined by you, not a real estate agent who takes a fee for selling your home **You sell direct to the buyer.* **Your home will be seen by people searching the internet for property in the UK for sale giving you far more exposure to a much larger number of potential buyers. **Remember: the best person to sell your house is you, you know the area and you know your house better than anyone else, so it makes sense to sell it and save on the estate agents fees*

▶ Property4Spain.com, 326 Ashley Down Road, Ashley Down, Bristol, BS7 9BQ Tel: 0117-942 9245 E-mail: info@property4spain.com *Property for sale in Spain including property in Costa Blanca, property in Costa Calida, property in Costa Almeria and property in Costa del Sol.*

▶ PropertyChart.co.uk, PO Box 2657, Reading, RG1 5WQ Tel: 0845 8385927 Fax: 0845 8385928 E-mail: info@propertychart.co.uk *Estate agents, letting agents, property developers and overseas agents use PropertyChart to advertise their properties -- new homes, houses, apartments and flats -- for sale, to buy and to rent in UK and overseas.** **

▶ propertyinindia.co.uk, 214, Chigwell Road, London, London, E18 1HA Tel: 020 85069798 Fax: 020 85069798 E-mail: prop@propertyinindia.co.uk *Exclusive Services for NRI's (Non Resident Indians, for all your requirement of purchasing, managing or maintaining property in Delhi (NCR), Bombay, Calcutta and Punjab. 100% reliable services from India and UK based multimillion dollar worth real estate promoters. Get peace of mind like never before.*

▶ Propertystorm, The Coach House, Edstone, Wootton Wawen, Henley-in-Arden, West Midlands, B95 6DD Tel: (07971) 095664 E-mail: propertystorm@btinternet.com *Online estate agency without the fee. List property for sale, to let or for auction. World premier of our unique online auction facility. Buyers can contact vendors direct. For sale board delivered direct. Once sale agreed, solicitors take over so why pay comission to the middle man?*

▶ Propex Concrete Systems, No. 9, Royal Court, Basil Close, Chesterfield, Derbyshire, S41 7SL Tel: 0845 5314078 Fax: (01246) 564201 E-mail: trevor.atkinson@propexinc.co.uk *We are the world leader in supplying fibers for secondary concrete reinforcment to the construction market. Our synthetic fibers, steel fibers and highly engineered fiber blends are designed to provide superior concrete crack control over the entire life span of the concrete. Our portfolio of concrete fibre reinforcement products includes some of the most widely used brands, including fibermesh, novomesh, novocon, enduro and fibercast*

Propex Heating UK Ltd, Unit 5 Second Avenue, Millbrook, Southampton, SO15 0LP Tel: (023) 8052 8555 Fax: (023) 8052 8800 *Heating equipment manufrs*

▶ Prophecy, 85-103, Queens Road, Reading, RG1 4DA Tel: 0118-958 9955 Fax: 0118-958 9977

▶ Propipe Ltd, Park View West Industrial Estate, Hartlepool, Cleveland, TS25 1UD Tel: (01429) 890190 Fax: (01429) 890198

Proportion Display Ltd, Galatix House, 9 Dallington Street, London, EC1V 0LN Tel: (020) 7251 6943 Fax: (020) 7250 1798 E-mail: mail@proportionlondon.com *Tailors dummy manufrs*

▶ Proposal Masters, 7 Accommodtion Road, London, NW11 8ED Tel: 020 8209 3900 E-mail: kelly@proposalmasters.co.uk *Proposal Masters advises on development of sales strategy, implementation of sales processes and management systems. We provide focused training for all skills from basic sales to advanced negotiation.*

▶ Proprove Ltd, 2 New Road Langtoft, Peterborough, PE6 9LE Tel: (01778) 345990 Fax: (01778) 345990 E-mail: jim.yates@lycos.co.uk *Improvement Consultants*

▶ PROPS, Calais Gate, Cormont Road, Camberwell, London, SE5 9RQ Tel: (020) 7735 6940 E-mail: contact@designprops.co.uk *PROPS/! works to produce and promote the work of young designers from across the UK and around the world. We produce innovative, affordable and high quality design-led products. *We also offer advice to young designers on a wide range of matters, including development, project financing and manufacturing.*

Proptech Ltd, Unit 80-81, Hartlebury Trading Estate, Hartlebury, Kidderminster, Worcestershire, DY10 4JB Tel: (01299) 251247 Fax: (01299) 251240 E-mail: proptech@btinternet.com *Propshaft manufrs*

Proquest Informnation & Learning Ltd, The Quorum, Barnwell Road, Cambridge, CB5 8SW Tel: (01223) 215512 Fax: (01223) 215513 E-mail: mail@proquest.co.uk Principal Export Areas: Worldwide *Electronic learning*

Proquip Direct Ltd, Unit 1b Park Road Works, 125 Park Road, Beckenham, Kent, BR3 1QJ Tel: (020) 8639 0377 Fax: (020) 8639 0379 E-mail: sales@proquipdirect.com *Retail engineering*

Proquis Ltd, Building 1050 Cornforth Drive, Sittingbourne Research Centre, Sittingbourne, Kent, ME9 8PX Tel: (01795) 479001 Fax: (01795) 479009 E-mail: mark.fowler@proquis.com *Software developers*

Pro-Rol Ltd, 44 Yardley Road, Olney, Buckinghamshire, MK46 5ED Tel: (01234) 240177 Fax: (01234) 240188 E-mail: sales@projectorlisting.co.uk *Lifting gear manufrs*

▶ Proroute Ltd, PO Box 1092, Bristol, BS48 1YL Tel: (01934) 835629 E-mail: sales@proroute.co.uk *Refurbished Cisco Hardware Specialist.*network design, on-site technical services, hardware resale.**

Prosaw Ltd, Telford Way, Kettering, Northamptonshire, NN16 8UN Tel: (01536) 410999 Fax: (01536) 410080 E-mail: sales@prosaw.co.uk *Prosaw - Suppliers of quality sawing machines with comprehensive service and support.*

▶ Proscene Software, 198 Northfield Road, Sheffield, S10 1QU Tel: 0114-267 9679 Fax: 0114-268 7331 E-mail: proscene.software@proscenesoftware.com *Software developers*

▶ Prosceneium Ltd, Sladen Wood Mill, Todmorden Road, Littleborough, Lancashire, OL15 9EW Tel: (01706) 377226 Fax: (01706) 371953

Proscot Public Relations Consultants, Carpet Lane, Edinburgh, EH6 6SP Tel: 0131-468 7067 Fax: 0131-468 7056 E-mail: mail@proscot-pr.co.uk *Public relations consultants*

Proseal, 18 Terrace Row, Billington, Clitheroe, Lancashire, BB7 9NX Tel: (01254) 822699 Fax: (01254) 822699 *Adhesive & sealant fabricators*

Proseal Adhesives & Sealants, 4 Nuttall Avenue, Great Harwood, Blackburn, BB6 7ER Tel: (01254) 888646 Fax: (01254) 888646 *Mastic pointing*

Proseal UK Ltd, Adlington Road Business Park, Bollington, Macclesfield, Cheshire, SK10 5HG Tel: (01625) 856600 Fax: (01625) 856611 E-mail: info@prosealuk.com *Heat sealing, including rotary, machine manfurs*

Proserv (North Sea) Ltd, Riverside Business Centre, North Esplanade West, Aberdeen, AB11 5RJ Tel: (01224) 210067 Fax: (01224) 582616 E-mail: info@proservns.co.uk *Oil & gas sampling*

▶ Proserve UK Ltd, 7 Waterside Trading Estate, Mill Lane, Leigh, Lancashire, WN7 2BG Tel: (01942) 260062 Fax: (01942) 261212 E-mail: sales@mainbuild.co.uk

▶ Pro-Shine Valeting, 2 Myers Way, Charlton, Banbury, Oxfordshire, OX17 3DY Tel: (07944) 035810 E-mail: enquiries@Pro-ShineValeting.com *Pro-Shine Valeting is a professional, fully mobile valeting company offering a top quality service to commercial and private clients in North Oxfordshire, South Warwickshire, North Buckinghamshire and South Northamptonshire.*

Prosig Ltd, 44a High Street, Fareham, Hampshire, PO16 7BQ Tel: (01329) 239925 Fax: (01329) 239159 E-mail: info@prosig.com *Scientific & vibration monitoring*

Prosign, Unit 13 Hoddesdon Industrial Centre, Pindar Road, Hoddesdon, Hertfordshire, EN11 0DD Tel: (01992) 461145 Fax: (01992) 461143 *Sign manufrs*

Prosoft Systems Ltd, Marchwood House 934 St Albans, Road Watford, Watford, WD25 9NN Tel: (01923) 680223 Fax: (01923) 680683 E-mail: sales@prosoftonline.co.uk *Computer hardware sales*

Prosol UK, 18-24 Gleadless Road, Sheffield, S2 3AB Tel: 0114-255 7700 Fax: 0114-255 7171 *Garage equipment suppliers*

▶ ProSolutions Ltd, 3 Sunningdale Court, Crowstone Road, Westcliff-on-Sea, Essex, SS0 8LJ Tel: (0845) 4566854 Fax: (0870) 4608025 E-mail: enquiries@prosolutionsltd.com *Professional bookkeeping, tax advice, company secretarial services and accountancy for companies, sole traders and individuals. ProSolutions Ltd cover Essex, Kent and London. Free initial consultancy.*

Prosource Europe Ltd, The Timbers, Horsemans Green, Whitchurch, Shropshire, SY13 3DY Tel: (07834) 387979 Fax: (0870) 1128449 E-mail: info@pro-source.co.uk *Complete business sourcing solution*

▶ Prosource It UK Ltd, Hilldowntree Business Centre, Banchory Devenick, Aberdeen, AB12 5YL Tel: (01224) 877782

Prospect Pictures Ltd, Wansworth Plain, London, SW18 1ET Tel: (020) 7636 1234 Fax: (020) 8877 0234 E-mail: info@prospect-uk.com *Media group tv studios & new visual media*

Prospect Plant Display, Botanic House, 4 Aston Mount, Leeds, LS13 2BY Tel: 0113-255 7533 Fax: (0870) 2432270 *Interior landscapers*

Prospect Presentations, 7 St Johns Close, Rugeley, Staffordshire, WS15 2TG Tel: (01889) 579713 Fax: (0870) 7622664 E-mail: info@prospectpresentations.co.uk *Business presentations producers*

▶ Prospect Research, Gwydir Street, Cambridge, CB1 2LG Tel: (0870) 4604501 Fax: (0870) 1377425 E-mail: chris.walthew@prospectresearch.co.uk *Telemarketing company specialising in sales*

Prospect Swetenhams, Field House, 72 Oldfield Road, Hampton, Middlesex, TW12 2HQ Tel: (020) 8481 8730 Fax: (020) 8783 1940 E-mail: sales@prospectshop.co.uk Principal Export Areas: Worldwide *Book, magazine publishers & direct marketing services*

Prospect Training Organisations Ltd, Kingston House, Myton Street, Hull, HU1 2PS Tel: (01482) 606242 Fax: (01482) 609941 E-mail: info@prospect-training.co.uk *Youth, adult & private sector training*

▶ Prospects 4 Business Ltd, PO Box 6619, Derby, DE21 5AB Tel: (01332) 832518 Fax: (0870) 432518 E-mail: sales@prospects4business.co.uk *Telemarketing, sales lead generation & database cleaning services*

▶ Prospects Business Training Ltd, Prospects House, 10 Fairfax Drive, Westcliff-on-Sea, Essex, SS0 9AR Tel: (01702) 214100 Fax: (01702) 390488 E-mail: jane_trent@prospectscollege.co.uk *Training Provider of all aspects of training*

Prosper Engineering, Minto Drive, Altens Industrial Estate, Aberdeen, AB12 3LW Tel: (01224) 877776 Fax: (01224) 890666 *Manufacturers of studbolts, specialist machining, plating & coating*

Prosper Engineering Ltd, 3 Arkwright Way, North Newmoor Industrial Estate, Irvine, Ayrshire, KA11 4JU Tel: (01294) 224422 Fax: (01294) 215003 E-mail: sales@prosper-engineering.com *Fasteners manufrs* Also at: Stockport

▶ Prosser Bros Contractors Ltd, Sunningdale, Worcester Road, Upton Warren, Bromsgrove, Worcestershire, B61 7EU Tel: (01527) 831476 Fax: (01527) 831643

C.L. Prosser & Co. Ltd, 7 Parkfield Road, Stockton-On-Tees, Cleveland, TS18 3DJ Tel: (01642) 676043 Fax: (01642) 617418 E-mail: lenabain@freeserve.co.uk *Scrap metal merchants* Also at: Middlesbrough

▶ Pro-Stage Europe Ltd, The Stables, Watersplash Farm Ford Bridge Roa, Sunbury-on-Thames, Middlesex, TW16 6AU Tel: (01932) 779399 Fax: (01932) 779399 E-mail: info@prostageeurope.com *Set design & build services*

▶ pro-stitch.co.uk, 4th floor, constellation mill, hardman st, radcliffe, manchester, M26 4GY Tel: 0161 767 9494 Fax: 0161 737 7258 E-mail: lhcassidy@aol.com *sewing machine pressing equipment cutting machines and related attachments importers, repair rental sales service*

Prosys Computing Ltd, Titan House Cardiff Bay Business Centre, Titan Road, Cardiff, CF24 5EJ Tel: (029) 2049 4757 Fax: (029) 2049 4737 E-mail: sales@prosyscom.co.uk *Computer consultancy*

Protaform Components Ltd, Orchard Works, 76 Arthur Street, Redditch, Worcestershire, B98 8LJ Tel: (01527) 517500 Fax: (01527) 502373 E-mail: sales@protaform.com *Manufacturers of pressings, wire shapes prototype engineering production*

ProTag Retail Security, Units 2-3, Short Way, The Industrial Estate, Thornbury, Bristol, BS35 3UT Tel: (01454) 418500 Fax: (01454) 413708 E-mail: martin@touchpanels.co.uk *Alarm & security & security anti-theft devices installation*

Protak GB Ltd, Protak House, E1 Telford Road, Bicester, Oxfordshire, OX26 4LD Tel: (01869) 369997 Fax: (01869) 369994 E-mail: sales@protak.co.uk *Hot melts & adhesive manufrs*

Protape Audio Equipment, 59-61 Goldney Road, London, W9 2AR Tel: (020) 7616 5500 Fax: (020) 7616 5501 *Media distributors*

Protean Software Ltd, 101 Lockhurst Lane, Coventry, CV6 5SF Tel: (024) 7666 6612 Fax: (024) 7670 3566 E-mail: enquiries@proteansoftware.co.uk *Software house*

Protec, 52 Liscard Road, Wallasey, Merseyside, CH44 9AF Tel: 0151-639 1390 Fax: 0151-639 1390 *Protective clothing manufrs*

▶ Pro-Tec BS Ltd, 67-69, George Street, London, W1U 8LT Tel: 020 8830 5545 Fax: 020 8830 5545 E-mail: enquiries@pro-tecbsltd.co.uk *We are Heating and Plumbing company who specailise in Quality installations*

Protec The Cap Company Ltd, Princes Park Princesway, Team Valley Trading Estate, Gateshead, Tyne & Wear, NE11 0NF Tel: 0191-442 4242 Fax: 0191-442 4222 E-mail: sales@protecplastics.com *Plastic protective products manufrs*

Protec Fire Detection Export Ltd, Protec House, Churchill Way, Nelson, Lancashire, BB9 6RT Tel: (01282) 717171 Fax: (01282) 717273 E-mail: sales@protec.co.uk *Fire alarm & emergency lighting manufrs* Also at: Barking

Protec Manchester Ltd, 2 Rainard Street, Hyde, Cheshire, SK14 2HW Tel: (0870) 3333081 Fax: (0870) 3333061 E-mail: sales@protecdirect.co.uk *Protective clothing distribs* Also at: Birmingham

Protec Metal Work Ltd, 7 H T H Complex, Blackwater Way, Aldershot, Hampshire, GU12 4DN Tel: (01252) 310443 Fax: (01252) 341787 E-mail: protecmetal@btconnect.com *Sheet metalwork precision fine limit fabricators*

Pro-Tec Mouldings Ltd, Unit 22 Chadkirk Industrial Estate, Vale Road, Romiley, Stockport, Cheshire, SK6 3LE Tel: 0161-427 4944 Fax: 0161-427 8373 *Injection mould design, prototyping & tooling*

Protec Powder Coatings, Unit 3 Winsford Industrial Estate, Winsford Industrial Estate, Winsford, Cheshire, CW7 3PQ Tel: (01606) 593199 *Plastic coating services*

▶ Protec UK, The Underwater Studio, Archers Field, Burnt Mills Industrial Estate, Basildon, Essex, SS13 1DL Tel: 0845 8802253 Fax: 0845 8802254 E-mail: support@protecuk.com

Protech Ltd, 4 Nuffield Road, St. Ives, Cambridgeshire, PE27 3LX Tel: (01325) 310520 Fax: (01480) 300670 E-mail: sales@pro-tech-ltd.co.uk *Mobile phone & audio equipment suppliers*

Protech Electronic Services Ltd, 3 The Ringway Centre, Eddison Road, Basingstoke, Hampshire, RG21 6YH Tel: (01256) 818007 Fax: (01256) 819901 E-mail: bob@protech.freeuk.com *Sub-contract electronics manufacture with BGA & X-ray facility*

Protech Fabrications Ltd, Rushden Road, Milton Ernest, Bedford, MK44 1RU Tel: (01234) 826233 Fax: (01234) 822762 E-mail: info@protech-food-systems.co.uk *Stainless steel equipment manufrs*

▶ Pro-Tech Offshore, 10 Howe Moss Drive, Kirkhill Industrial Estate, Dyce, Aberdeen, AB21 0GL Tel: (01224) 729888 Fax: (0870) 1313377

Pro-Tech Precision Ltd, Station Road West, Ash Vale, Aldershot, Hampshire, GU12 5QD Tel: (01252) 516242 Fax: (01252) 524025 E-mail: sales@pro-techprecision.com *Precision fine limit sheet metalwork*

Protech Systems Northern Ltd, Woodside House, Woodside Lane, Sheffield, S3 9PB Tel: 0114-272 2705 Fax: 0114-272 2706 *Security fencing, gates & allied products manufrs*

Protechnic Ltd, Unit 109 Central Park, Petherton Road, Bristol, BS14 9BZ Tel: (01275) 833779 Fax: (01275) 835560 E-mail: sales@protechnic.com Principal Export Areas: Africa *Manufacturers of cases including flight & instrument. Also transit container manufrs*

Protechnical Services, 28 Rose Bushes, Epsom, Surrey, KT17 3NX Tel: (01737) 361135 Fax: (01737) 361135 E-mail: info@protechnical.co.uk *Commission air conditioning & water treatment services*

Protechnol Precision Engineers, Unit 4, Christie Place, Bognor Regis, West Sussex, PO22 9RT Tel: (01243) 842233 Fax: (01243) 842233 *Rapid proto-typing*

Protect Doors Ltd, Suite 13 Vickers Business Centre, Priestley Road, Basingstoke, Hampshire, RG24 9RA Tel: (01256) 814000 Fax: (01256) 814443 *Commercial industrial material suppliers*

Protect Enamel Ltd, G K Davies Industrial Estate, Hayes Lane, Stourbridge, West Midlands, DY9 8QX Tel: (01384) 898844 Fax: (01384) 424483 E-mail: sales@protecenamel.co.uk *Vitreous enamelling services*

▶ Protect Fire Equipment, 3a The Pound, Coate, Devizes, Wiltshire, SN10 3LG Tel: (01380) 860022 Fax: (01380) 860022 E-mail: mail@protect-fire.co.uk *Suppliers of quality AMEREX and FIREPOWER range of fire extinguishers.**We also service and refill most makes of extinguisher.**We cater for the Domestic - Commercial - Industrial market.**

▶ Protect My Work Ltd, 1st Floor, 16 Church Street, Ampthill, Bedford, MK45 2EH Tel: (01525) 406609 E-mail: support@protectmywork.com

▶ Protect Pest Control, 83 Southern Road, Eastbourne, East Sussex, BN22 9LS Tel: (01323) 500797

Protect Security Systems, Merrills Head Farm, Long Causeway, Cliviger, Burnley, Lancashire, BB10 4RR Tel: (01282) 425544 Fax: (01282) 420938 *Intruder alarms*

Protectall Lock & Safe Co. Ltd, 445b Stratford Road, Sparkhill, Birmingham, B11 4LB Tel: 0121-773 1609 Fax: 0121-773 8401 E-mail: sales@protectall-security.co.uk *Security services*

Protectavan Commercial Vehicle Bodybuilders, Orsett Fruit Farm, Orsett Road, Orsett, Grays, Essex, RM16 3BH Tel: (01375) 891646 Fax: (01375) 891646 *Interior van lining furnishers*

Protectis Ltd, 12a Hazel Street, Bulwell, Nottingham, NG6 8EA Tel: 0115-975 8820 Fax: 0115-975 8821 E-mail: info@protectis.co.uk *Protectis, serves the UK from bases in Nottingham and Bristol*

continued

continuation
providing a specialist contractor service in lightning protection and electrical earthing systems embracing: - Design of lightning protection systems Supply of lightning protection equipment and materials Installation of lightning protection systems Test and inspection of lightning protection systems Maintenance of lightning protection systems Design of lightning surge protection systems Supply of lightning surge protection equipment Installation of lightning surge protection systems Inspection of lightning surge protection systems Design of electrical earthing systems Installation of electrical earthing systems Test and inspection of electrical earthing systems Maintenance of electrical earthing systems Protectis design supply and install Faraday Cage based lightning protection systems to BS 6651 and BSEN 62305 Protectis design supply and install Early Streamer Emission [ESE] based lightning protection systems to NFC 17 102 Protectis design supply and install electrical earthing installations to BS7354; BS7430; BS7671; ENA 41/24 & S34.

Protective Clothing Co. Ltd, 8-14 Orsman Road, London, N1 5QJ Tel: (020) 7729 0405 Fax: (020) 7729 0405 *Protective clothing & workwear manufrs* Also at: Smethwick

Protective Finishing Group, 33 Crossgate Road, Park Farm Industrial Estate, Redditch, Worcestershire, B98 7SN Tel: (01527) 524126 Fax: (01527) 510361 E-mail: sales@profingroup.co.uk *The industrial metal coaters for all types of ferrous, zinc, aluminium and combination materials including die castings. 6hrs+ turnaround in application of wide range of high quality corrosion resistant finishes; programmable build cathodic electrophoretic paint, electropaint, ecoat, polyester powdercoat, epoxy powder coat, full range of gloss levels, RAL & BS colours available together with JCB and Caterpillar, metallics and textured powdercoat, pre-treatment phosphate and degreasing facilities, dip-spin centrifugal painting to include zinc rich flake hexavalent chrome free Zintek, PTFE, Xylan, colour coding, enamels, lacquers, stains & oils.*

Protective Packaging Ltd, Dane Road Industrial Estate, Sale, Cheshire, M33 7BH Tel: 0161-976 2006 Fax: 0161-976 3330 E-mail: info@protpack.com *Manufacturers of Barrier Foil bags and liners to provide total climatic protection for any product which may deteriorate due to moisture/oxygen ingress. Bags and liners are tailor-made to suit individual requirements.*

Protective Rubber Coatings Ltd, Paynes Shipyard, Coronation Road, Ashton Gate, Bristol, BS3 1RP Tel: 0117-966 1155 Fax: 0117-966 1158 E-mail: sales@bmspc.co.uk *Rubber coating & applicators manufrs*

Protective Tapes, Vale Park, Hamil Road, Stoke-on-Trent, ST6 1AW Tel: (01782) 833560 Fax: (01782) 833550 E-mail: sales@protective-tapes.co.uk *Protective tape distributors*

Protective Textured Coatings UK Ltd, Unit 16 Haywards Industrial Park, Orton Way, Birmingham, B35 7BT Tel: 0121-749 5088 Fax: 0121-693 7688 *Protective coating manufrs*

Protector Alarms UK Ltd, 20-22 Gipsy Hill, London, SE19 1NL Tel: (020) 8761 3771 Fax: (020) 8670 9441 E-mail: sales@protectoralarms.com *Fire alarm system manufrs*

ProtecX Medical Ltd, Units 1-2, Theobald Business Centre, Knowl Piece, Wilbury Way, Hitchin, Hertfordshire, SG4 0TY Tel: (01462) 440715 Fax: (01462) 440449 E-mail: enquiries@protecx.co.uk *Medical radiation protection*

Protega Coatings Ltd, Kelvin Way, West Bromwich, West Midlands, B70 7JZ Tel: 0121-525 5665 Fax: 0121-553 2787 E-mail: info@tikkurila.co.uk *Industrial paint manufrs*

Protek Ltd, Phoenix House, Phoenix Road, Hawks Green, Cannock, Staffordshire, WS11 7LR Tel: (01543) 467575 Fax: (01543) 462370 E-mail: sales@protekuk.co.uk *Manufacturers of high quality, innovative, well priced circuit protection equipment, including consumer units, mbc's. rcd's, rcbd's, 3 phase distribution boards in mcb's and mccb's, rotary switches in both metal & ip65 insulated, fuse switches in metal*

Protek Fencing Ltd, Coney Park, Harrogate Road, Yeadon, Leeds, LS19 7XS Tel: 0113-250 0995 Fax: 0113-250 1899 E-mail: contact@protek-fencing.co.uk *Safety barriers & security fencing*

▶ Protek security, 89 Circular Road, Denton, Manchester, M34 6NQ Tel: 0161-292 0662 E-mail: steventurnbull@msn.com

Protek Services Ltd, Unit 3, Whittall Industrial Estate, Argyle Way, Stevenage, Hertfordshire, SG1 2AD Tel: (01438) 750111 Fax: (01438) 311767 *Photocopier sales & repairs fax printers*

Protel Communications Ltd, Raleigh House, 9a The Wellsway, Keynsham, Bristol, BS31 1HF Tel: 0117-986 4486 Fax: 0117-986 5144 E-mail: info@protelcomms.co.uk *Business telecommunications*

▶ Protetch Printed Circuit Mnfrs, Unit 5 Galalaw Business Park, Hawick, Roxburghshire, TD9 8PZ Tel: (01450) 379728 Fax: (01450) 379728 *Printed circuit board manufrs*

Proteus Developments, West Lynne, 16 The Crescent, Northwich, Cheshire, CW9 8AD Tel: (01606) 350614 Fax: (01606) 350614 *Design consultants*

Proteus Equipment Ltd, P O Box 33, Bury St. Edmunds, Suffolk, IP33 2RS Tel: (01284) 753954 Fax: (01284) 701369 E-mail: enquiries@proteusequipment.com *Specialist construction equipment*

Proteus Fittings Ltd, Unit 6 Stonegravels Lane, Chesterfield, Derbyshire, S41 7LF Tel: (01246) 211303 Fax: (01246) 209700 E-mail: info@proteusfittings.co.uk Principal Export Areas: Worldwide *Tube fitting distributors*

▶ Proteus Switchgear, Pipers Road, Park Farm Industrial Estate, Redditch, Worcestershire, B98 0HU Tel: (01527) 517117 Fax: (01527) 526873

Proteus Switchgear, Stafford Park 12, Telford, Shropshire, TF3 3BJ Tel: (01952) 292001 Fax: (01952) 292837 *Electrical switchgear manufrs*

▶ Protherics plc, 5 Ludgate Hill, London, EC4M 7AA Tel: (020) 7246 9950 *Pharmaceutical manufrs*

Protherics P.L.C., The Heath Business & Technical Park, Runcorn, Cheshire, WA7 4QX Tel: (01928) 518000 Fax: (01928) 518002 E-mail: information@protherics.com *Manufacturers & distributors of pharmaceuticals*

Protherics UK Ltd, Blaenwaun, Ffostrasol, Llandysul, Dyfed, SA44 5JT Tel: (01239) 851122 Fax: (01239) 858800 *Biopharmaceutical products & accessories manufrs*

Protherm Controls, 21 Main Road, Ratcliffe Culey, Atherstone, Warwickshire, CV9 3NY Tel: (01827) 711039 Fax: (01827) 711041 E-mail: vince@pro-therm.co.uk *Electronic temperature, humidity & level controls specialists*

Protherm Engineering Shenstone Ltd, Unit 33 Birchbrook Industrial Estate, Lynn Lane, Lichfield, Staffordshire, WS14 0DJ Tel: (01543) 481143 Fax: (01543) 480330 E-mail: prothermeng@aol.com *Galvanising engineers & furnace manufrs*

Protim Services Ltd, Cockersdale Works, Whitehall Road, Drighlington, Bradford, West Yorkshire, BD11 1NQ Tel: 0113-285 2173 Fax: 0113-285 2243 E-mail: leeds@protim-services.co.uk *Damp proofing specialists*

Protimeter plc, Meter House, Fieldhouse Lane, Marlow, Buckinghamshire, SL7 1LW Tel: (01628) 472722 Fax: (01628) 474312 E-mail: sales@protometer.com *Moisture measuring equipment manufrs*

Proto Associates, 26 Fox Lane, Hilltop, Bromsgrove, Worcestershire, B61 7NL Tel: (01527) 831567 Fax: (01527) 831567 E-mail: aturchyn@globalnet.co.uk *Noise control & thermal insulation engineers*

Proto Precision Engineering, Unit 28 Heath Hill Industrial Estate, Dawley, Telford, Shropshire, TF4 2RH Tel: (01952) 506227 Fax: (01952) 506227 *Tools, jigs & metalwork engineers*

▶ Protocol 4 Business, 3 Bishops Road, Whitchurch, Cardiff, CF14 1LT Tel: (029) 2069 1111 Fax: (029) 2069 1001 E-mail: info@protocol4business.co.uk *Specialist consultants in Employment Law /Human Resources, Health & Safety, Quality and Data Protection.*

Protocol Control Systems Ltd, 2 Knighton Enterprise Park, Ludlow Road, Knighton, Powys, LD7 1HJ Tel: (01547) 529238 Fax: (01547) 529090 E-mail: info@protocolcontrolsystems.co.uk *Electrical control panel manufrs*

▶ Protocol Data Services Ltd, Wyndburgh, Lincoln Crescent, Wrockwardine Wood, Telford, Shropshire, TF2 6LU Tel: (01952) 412312 Fax: (0871) 2640312 E-mail: support@pdsnet.co.uk *IT consultants*

Protocol Engineering, Unit 17 Tanfield Lea Industrial Estate South, Tanfield Lea, Stanley, County Durham, DH9 9XB Tel: (01207) 290052 Fax: (01207) 290142 E-mail: protocol_engineering@yahoo.co.uk *Precision engineers*

Protocol Skills, Aldford House, Lloyd Drive, Ellesmere Port, CH65 9HQ Tel: 0151-373 7700 Fax: 0151-373 7701 *Training Provision*

Protocon Engineering Ltd, Stock Road, Southend-On-Sea, SS2 5QF Tel: (01702) 612312 Fax: (01702) 461717 E-mail: protocon@btconnect.com *Precision engineers*

Protoleague Fabrics, Union Mill, Vernon Street, Bolton, BL1 2PT Tel: (01204) 528900 Fax: (01204) 528250 E-mail: sales@protoleague.co.uk *Textile merchants & converters*

Protolink, 6 Zone B Chelmsford Road Industrial Estate, Chelmsford Road, Dunmow, Essex, CM6 1HD Tel: (01371) 875726 Fax: (01371) 876381 E-mail: sales@protolink.co.uk *Power supply systems manufrs*

Protolog Sound Ltd, 49 Beech Road, Alresford, Hampshire, SO24 9JS Tel: (01962) 734545 Fax: (01962) 733849 *Stage producers*

Protomould Ltd, Unit B2 Springhead Enterprise Park, Springhead Road, Northfleet, Gravesend, Kent, DA11 8HB Tel: (01474) 353525 Fax: (01474) 353526 E-mail: sales@protomould.co.uk *Plastic injection molding services*

The Proton Group Ltd, Ripley Drive, Normanton Industrial Estate, Normanton, West Yorkshire, WF6 1QT Tel: (01924) 892834 Fax: (01924) 220213 E-mail: mail@proton-group.co.uk *Chemical manufrs*

▶ Proton Storm, 22 Market Place, Wetherby, West Yorkshire, LS22 6NE Tel: (01937) 586888 Fax: (01937) 588709 *Web designers*

▶ Proton Supplies, Unit 18 Allshots Enterprises, Woodhouse Lane, Kelvedon, Colchester, CO5 9DF Tel: (01376) 584000 Fax: (01376) 583444 E-mail: sales@apcsolutionsuk.com *Packaging materials & products*

Proton Water Services Ltd, Knaptoft Hall Farm, Knaptoft, Lutterworth, Leicestershire, LE17 6PA Tel: 0116-279 9030 Fax: 0116-279 9082 E-mail: info@protonwater.com *Water treatment consultants services*

▶ Protosheet Engineering Ltd, 73 Swaisland Drive, Crayford, Dartford, DA1 4HY Tel: (01322) 550545 Fax: (01322) 555719 E-mail: sales@protosheet.co.uk *Sheet metal fabricators*

Prototype Pressing Ltd, Unit 12C, Shefford Industrial Park, Shefford, Bedfordshire, SG17 5DZ Tel: (01462) 816978 Fax: (01462) 817242 E-mail: pashby@ashfen.demon.co.uk *Prototype consultants & engineers*

ProTouch Cleaning, 61A Midmoor Road, Balham, London, SW12 0ES Tel: 0207 8010378 E-mail: info@protouchcleaning.co.uk *Pro Touch Cleaning is a complete professional cleaning service provider in London. We pride ourselves on our Quality, Honesty and Value for Money. We have built our reputation on our excellent quality of Service and superior customer service. We provide 21st Century cleaning service which encompasses a team who are orientated, environmentally focused and multi skilled.*

Pro-Treat (Timber & Damp Co) Ltd, Premier House, Holmes Road, Sowerby Bridge, West Yorkshire, HX6 3LD Tel: (01422) 834096 Fax: (01422) 839898 *Damp proofing services*

▶ Protronix Ltd, Unit 13 14, Wren Court, Strathclyde Business Park, Bellshill, Lanarkshire, ML4 3NQ Tel: (01698) 741007 Fax: (01698) 846363 E-mail: sales@protronix-uk.com

Protronix Industrial Services, 3-15 Cross Street, Luton, LU2 0DP Tel: (01582) 418490 Fax: (01582) 486588 E-mail: sales@protronix.co.uk *Data acquisition systems*

Protuning UK Ltd, 1 Meadow Rise, Lea, Gainsborough, Lincolnshire, DN21 5HE Tel: (01427) 610092 Fax: (01427) 811807 E-mail: enquiries@protune.org *Processing control instrumentation engineers*

Protura, Unit 33 Loughborough Technology Centre, Epinal Way, Loughborough, Leics, LE11 3GE Tel: (01509) 269018 Fax: (01509) 269022 E-mail: sales@protura.co.uk *Encoder interface equipment designer supplier & manufr*

Protus Electronics Ltd, Bosworth, Sulhamstead Road, Ufton Nervet, Reading, RG7 4DH Tel: 0118-973 0255 Fax: 0118-973 0070 E-mail: pandmhoward@aol.ccom.com *Computer & peripheral cabling manufrs*

Proudman Oceanographic Laboratory, Bidston Observatory, Bidston Hill, Prenton, Merseyside, CH43 7RA Tel: 0151-653 8633 Fax: 0151-653 6269 E-mail: sales@pol.ac.uk *Oceanographic research*

Provan Maintenance Ltd, 29 Winchester Avenue, Denny, Stirlingshire, FK6 6QE Tel: (01324) 826600 Fax: (01324) 822101 E-mail: provanmain@winning.sol.co.uk *Chemical merchants*

Provel Ltd, 46-48 Saville Street, Bolton, BL2 1BY Tel: (01204) 381911 Fax: (01204) 381891 E-mail: martyn@provel.fsbusiness.co.uk *Cosmetic vessels & cosmetic processing machinery*

Proven Engineering Products Ltd, Wardhead Park, Stewarton, Kilmarnock, Ayrshire, KA3 5LH Tel: (01560) 485570 E-mail: info@provenenergy.com *Energy system manufrs*

Provender Bakers' Shops, 103 Dartmouth Road, London, SE23 3HT Tel: (020) 8699 4046 *Organic bakers & whole foods*

▶ Proveya Ltd, Abbey Mill, Station Road, Bishops Waltham, Southampton, SO32 1DH Tel: (01489) 899103 Fax: (01489) 895542 E-mail: sandy@proveya.co.uk

▶ Providence Farm Trail, Castle-an-Dinas, St. Columb, Cornwall, TR9 6JB Tel: (01637) 889143 E-mail: dawn.smitheram@itwest.co.uk *A warm welcome awaits you at Providence Farm. A family run working farm attraction in Cornwall. Explore the fabulous farm trail, drink in the breathtakings views across the rural Cornish countryside. A popular attraction for birdwatching and astronomy enthusiasts.**

Provident Financial Management Services, Colonnade, Sunbridge Road, Bradford, West Yorkshire, BD1 2LQ Tel: (01274) 304044 Fax: (01274) 727300 E-mail: info@provident.co.uk *Personal credit & motor insurance*

Provimi Ltd, Maple Mill, Dalton Airfield, Dalton, Thirsk, North Yorkshire, YO7 3HE Tel: (01845) 577866 Fax: (01845) 578100 *Specialist feeds for young animals*

Provincial Engineers Colne Ltd, 2 Waterside Industrial Estate, Mill Green, Colne, Lancashire, BB8 0TA Tel: (01282) 863893 Fax: (01282) 868704 *Precision engineers*

Provincial Motor Factors, William Street, Sunderland, SR1 1TW Tel: 0191-565 8141 Fax: 0191-565 9296 E-mail: sales@provincialtyres.co.uk *Motor accessory factors distributors* Also at: Gateshead

Provincial Planters Ltd, Chalcraft Nurseries, Shirehall Road, Dartford, DA2 7SE Tel: (01322) 292644 *Plant display contractors*

Provincial Printing & Publishing Co. Ltd, Sanatorium Road, Cardiff, CF11 8DG Tel: (029) 2022 8729 Fax: (029) 2037 3494 E-mail: sales@printppp.co.uk *General printers*

Provincial Safety Services Ltd, Portway Road, Oldbury, West Midlands, B69 2BP Tel: 0121-544 5208 Fax: 0121-552 9075 E-mail: provincialsafety@btconnect.com *Industrial safety equipment & clothing*

Provincial Windows Ltd, Unit 3c Birches Industrial Estate, East Grinstead, West Sussex, RH19 1XZ Tel: (01342) 313767 Fax: (01342) 311407 *Installation of doors, windows & conservatories*

Proweight Ltd, 131 Beech Avenue, New Basford, Nottingham, NG7 7LS Tel: 0115-970 3778 Fax: 0115-979 0142 E-mail: roulstone@btconnect.com *Weighing machine manufrs*

Proweld Quality Vessels Ltd, Units 22-23, Lion Court, Daneshill, Basingstoke, Hampshire, RG24 8QU Tel: (01256) 814184 Fax: (01256) 814164 E-mail: simon@proweld.uk.com *Pipework fabricators, pressure vessel manufacturers & skid package units*

▶ Prowse & Hargood Ltd, Unit 3, Jessop Close, Clacton-on-Sea, Essex, CO15 4LY Tel: (0870) 2467740 Fax: (0870) 2467780 E-mail: info@prowseandhargood.com *Makers of pure cotton shirts, silk ties*

PRP, Unit 7 Tarsmill Court, Rotherwas Industrial Estate, Hereford, HR2 6JZ Tel: (01432) 357686 Fax: (01432) 352702 E-mail: info@prp.co.uk Principal Export Areas: Worldwide *Plastic mouldings rubber, metal bonded products & rubber mouldings*

PRTM Ltd, Kirkhill House, Broom Road East, Newton Mearns, Glasgow, G77 5LL Tel: 0141-616 2616 Fax: 0141-616 2555 E-mail: info@prtm.com *Management consultants*

▶ Pruce Newman Pipework, 5 Riverside House, Lower Southend Road, Wickford, Essex, SS11 8BB Tel: (01268) 739470 Fax: (01268) 764183 E-mail: mail@prucenewman.co.uk *Fabricators & metal workers*

▶ Pruce Newman Pipework Ltd, Ayton Road, Wymondham, Norfolk, NR18 0QJ Tel: (01953) 605123 Fax: (01953) 601115 E-mail: info@prucenewman.co.uk *Industrial Pipework and Structural Steelwork Contractors specialising in Fabrication and Installation of stainless and carbon steel pipework and associated services to the engineering construction industry with high regard to safety, quality and value in terms of experience, knowledge, relationships and cost. The company has a divisional structure that can offer diverse services e.g. Process Pipework & Mechanical Services, Heating & Ventilating, Utility Pipework Services, Skilled Labour Supply (for term maintenance & shutdowns etc), Project Management, Technical Services and CDM support etc.* Pipework specifications include Carbon & Stainless Steel (1/2" to 72"), UPVC, ABS, Polypropylene (PP), Polyethylene, PTFE, PVDF Lined MS, Glass, Copper & Galvanised Mild Steel etc. Jointing methods include high quality welding techniques to BS15614-1/EN287/288-3/ASME IX codes, screwed/threaded.*

Prudential, Laurence Pountney Hill, London, EC4R 0HH Tel: (020) 7220 7588 Fax: (020) 7548 3725 *Assurance company* Also at: Branches throughout the U.K.

Prudential Printers, Unit 71 Birch Road East Industrial Estate, Birch Road East, Birmingham, B6 7DA Tel: 0121-328 1454 Fax: 0121-327 7073 E-mail: prudential_printers@yahoo.co.uk *Commercial & colour printers*

Prudential-Bache International Ltd, 1-3 Strand, Trafalgar Sq, London, WC2N 5HE Tel: (020) 7439 4191 Fax: (020) 7437 9110 *Broker dealers*

▶ PRW Group Ltd, D Second Avenue, Westfield Industrial Estate, Midsomer Norton, Radstock, BA3 4BH Tel: (01761) 416885 Fax: (01761) 419381 E-mail: business@trwgroup.co.uk *Maintenance of electrical & security*

Pryce Bateman & Son, Prince William Avenue, Sandycroft, Deeside, Clwyd, CH5 2QZ Tel: (01352) 753056 Fax: (01244) 533775 E-mail: pbateman@callnetuk.com *Coal merchants*

Prym Fashion UK, Whitecroft, Lydney, Gloucestershire, GL15 4QG Tel: (01594) 562631 Fax: (01594) 564663 E-mail: sales@prymfashion.co.uk *Garment fastener manufrs*

Prym Whitecroft (UK) Ltd, Whitecroft, Lydney, Gloucestershire, GL15 4QG Tel: (01594) 562631 Fax: (01594) 563662 E-mail: sales@whitecroft.co.uk *Manufacturers of stationery*

Pryor Marking Technology Ltd, Egerton Street, Sheffield, S1 4JX Tel: 0114-276 6044 Fax: 0114-276 6890 E-mail: enquiries@pryormarking.com Principal Export Areas: Worldwide *Industrial permanent part marking equipment manufrs*

Pryorsign, Unit 3a, Denby Way, Hellaby, Rotherham, South Yorkshire, S66 8HR Tel: (01709) 700408 Fax: (01709) 532745 E-mail: david.fordham@pryorsign.com *Sign contractors, interpretation signs, vandal resistant signs, name plates, all glass fibre signs, atm surrounds, dda compliant signage, shopfront fascia signs, display boards, control panels, projecting signs, a boards**

Prysm Electrics Ltd, Daniels Way, Watnall Road, Hucknall, Nottingham, NG15 7LL Tel: 0115-968 1111 Fax: 0115-968 1110 E-mail: sales@prysm.co.uk *Engravers*

▶ P's & Q's Ltd, Devonshire House, Devon Street, Liverpool, L3 8HA Tel: 0151-207 1777

▶ Ps2 Digital Imaging, 1 Sarus Court, Manor Park, Runcorn, Cheshire, WA7 1UL Tel: (01928) 597888 Fax: (01928) 597886 E-mail: sales@ps2-digital.com

PSK, 42 Benington Road, Aston, Stevenage, Hertfordshire, SG2 7DY Tel: (01438) 880922 Fax: (01438) 880923 E-mail: kim.aston@btinternet.com *Shops, schools & office cleaning services*

PSL Ltd, 135 Bridgeman Street, Bolton, BL3 6BS Tel: (01204) 366555 Fax: (01204) 368020 *Tool & plant hire services* Also at: Liverpool & Preston

▶ PSL Couriers, Briarfield Gardens, Bradford, West Yorkshire, BD18 2BE Tel: (07890) 194132 E-mail: pslcouriers@yahoo.co.uk *Personal couriers worldwide for companies and the public too.*

PSL Freight Ltd, Quayside Park Indust Estate, Bates Road, Maldon (Essex), Maldon, Essex, CM9 4RS Tel: (01621) 854451 Fax: (01621) 854452 E-mail: sales@pslgroup.net *Exporters, importers & freight forwarders* Also at: Dover, Heston, Hinckley, Manchester & Portsmouth

▶ PSM Plant & Tool Hire Centres Ltd, 253-255 Blackfen Road, Sidcup, Kent, DA15 8PR Tel: (020) 8850 5658 Fax: (020) 8859 6553 E-mail: psmplant@supanet.com *Tool hire, ladders, steps saw drill grinder lawnmower cultivator*

▶ PSS Recruitment, Derwent Business Centre, Derby, DE1 2BU Tel: (01332) 363608 Fax: (01332) 363618 E-mail: info@pss-jobs.com *Professional recruiters for temporary, contract and permanent positions in Derbyshire. Roles include Office-based staff - Admin, Reception, Secretaries, HR, Accounts, Sales and Reception. Also skilled IT, Technical and Engineering personnel*

PSW Packaging Ltd, 1 Creslands, Oldmixon CR, Weston-super-Mare, Avon, BS24 9AX Tel: (01934) 418183 Fax: (01934) 626953 E-mail: pswpackagingltd@fsbdial.co.uk *Designers & manufacturers of cartons*

PSW Paper & Print Ltd, 16 Alcester Road, Studley, Warwickshire, B80 7NL Tel: (01527) 853136 Fax: (01527) 854879 E-mail: sales@psw.co.uk *Art & graphics materials retailers*

▶ Psychological Media 3-D, Milward Road, Hastings, East Sussex, TN34 3RT Tel: (01424) 715445 E-mail: marie@psymedia3d.com *3D graphic artists for modelling, visualisation & CG environments*

Psychometric Research & Development Ltd, Brewmaster House, The Maltings, St. Albans, Hertfordshire, AL1 3HT Tel: (01727) 841455 Fax: (01727) 847846 E-mail: steve@prd.co.uk *Custom made ability tests*

▶ Psychotherapy & Hypnosis Training Academy, 19 Burlington Gardens, London, W3 6BA Tel: (020) 8993 3803 E-mail: info@phta.co.uk *Phta courses, therapeutic & practical skills to set up a practise*

▶ Psymetrix Ltd, Sanderson House, 35 Water Street, Edinburgh, EH6 6SU Tel: 0131-625 1050

Psytech Ltd, Suite 11, 216-218 Main Road, Biggin Hill, Westerham, Kent, TN16 3BD Tel: (01959) 541415 Fax: (01959) 541096 E-mail: admin@psytech.demon.co.uk Principal Export Areas: Worldwide *Computer consultancy services*

PT Wire & Spark Erosion, Short Acre Street, Walsall, WS2 8HW Tel: (01922) 633708 Fax: (01922) 643072 *Wire erosion machining services*

▶ PTC Alliance UK, Gander Lane, Barlborough, Chesterfield, Derbyshire, S43 4PZ Tel: (01246) 573437 Fax: (01246) 573431 E-mail: darren.hunt@ptcalliance.com *Steel tube manufrs*

▶ PTC Communication, 62 Pensby Road, Heswall, Wirral, Merseyside, CH60 7RE Tel: 0151-342 6288 Fax: 0151-342 6289 E-mail: sales@ptc-security.co.uk

PTC Systems Ltd, 3 Priors, London Road, Bishop's Stortford, Hertfordshire, CM23 5ED Tel: (01279) 755855 Fax: (01279) 755923 *Telecommunications*

Pti Neepsend Engineering Ltd, Unit 13a Limestone Cottage Lane, Sheffield, S6 1NJ Tel: 0114-233 5580 Fax: 0114-233 5590 E-mail: sales@ptiuk.com *Distributors for industrial power transmission*

Pti Technologies UK Ltd, Orgreave Lane, Handsworth, Sheffield, S13 9NZ Tel: 0114-269 3999 Fax: 0114-269 1409 E-mail: filters@ptitechnologies.co.uk *Filter manufrs*

PTS Plumbing Trade Supplies Ltd, 2 Sabre Close, Quedgeley, Gloucester, GL2 4NZ Tel: (01452) 726100 Fax: (01452) 724474 E-mail: sales@bssgroup.com *Heating equipment distributors* Also at: Bristol, Cardiff, Chester, Exeter & Swansea

PTS Plumbing Trade Supplies Ltd, Buccaneer Way, Magna Park, Lutterworth, Leicestershire, LE17 4YZ Tel: (01455) 551210 Fax: (01455) 550772 E-mail: magnareception@bssgroup.com *Plumbing & heating supplies distributors*

PTS Plumbing Trade Supplies Ltd, 24 Boleness Road, Wisbech, Cambridgeshire, PE13 2RB Tel: (01945) 589990 Fax: (01945) 474827 *Plumbers trade suppliers*

Pub Dressing Co., 57 Lisanally La, Armagh, BT61 7HE Tel: (028) 3752 8899 Fax: (028) 3752 6358 *Public health interiors*

▶ The Pub Sign Co., 61 Church Meadow, Barton Mills, Bury St. Edmunds, Suffolk, IP28 6AR Tel: (01638) 713647 E-mail: thepubsigncompany@fsmail.net *Suppliers of digital art work*

Public Address Systems Ltd, Unit 5 Leestone Road Sharston, Sharston Industrial Area, Manchester, M22 4RN Tel: 0161-611 7171 Fax: 0161-611 7170 E-mail: sales@pad.co.uk *Loudspeaker systems manufrs*

Public Service Investigations Ltd, 5 Hunsterson Road, Hatherton, Nantwich, Cheshire, CW5 7RA Tel: 01270 842655 Fax: 01270 842427 E-mail: info@psi-ltd.com *A leading corporate investigation and security advisory company using a network of over 400 retired police investigators and specialists across the UK*

Publicity & Display Ltd, Corium House, Douglas Drive, Godalming, Surrey, GU7 1HJ Tel: (01483) 428326 Fax: (01483) 424566 E-mail: print@p-and-d.com *Screen printers & printing services*

▶ Publicity Printing Co., 986 Pollokshaws Road, Glasgow, G41 2HA Tel: 0141-649 2711 Fax: 0141-649 6087

▶ Publicode Ltd, 4 Fulton Court, Boundary Lane, Manchester, M15 6NW Tel: (0800) 1693228 E-mail: info@publicode.com *Qualified & experienced engineers provide services to computer users*

The Publishing Software Co., 6 Trevithick Close, Stourport-on-Severn, Worcestershire, DY13 8AN Tel: (0870) 0101780 Fax: (0870) 0101783 E-mail: laurence@p-s-c.co.uk *Computer systems & software development*

Pucella U K, Unit 4a St. Theodores Way, Brynmenyn Industrial Estate, Brynmenyn, Bridgend, CF32 9TZ Tel: (01656) 724848 Fax: (01656) 724838 E-mail: anielp@aol.com *Assemblers of PC's*

▶ Puckator Ltd, Lowman Works, East Tap House, East Taphouse, Liskeard, Cornwall, PL14 4NQ Tel: (01579) 321550 Fax: (01579) 321520 E-mail: kundenservice@puckator.de *Great value wholesale gifts of all kinds*

Pudelko Corrugated Cases Ltd, Unit 20 Goldicote Business Park, Banbury Road, Goldicote, Stratford-upon-Avon, Warwickshire, CV37 7NB Tel: (01789) 740973 Fax: (01789) 740395 E-mail: pudelkoccl@aol.com *Manufacturers of plain or printed corrugated packaging. Die-cut trays, die-cut or regular boxes, layer pads, dividers and fittings in any style or size. Facility to stock hold and j.i.t. delivery service.*

▶ Pudsey Diamond Engineering Ltd, Macadam Way, Andover, Hampshire, SP10 3LF Tel: 01264 336677 *Street lighting equipment manufrs*

Pudsey Mould Company Ltd, Albert Mills St Vincent Road, Pudsey, West Yorkshire, LS28 9EW Tel: 0113-257 4742 *Mould equipment suppliers*

Pudsey Plant Hire Ltd, Carlisle Drive, Pudsey, West Yorkshire, LS28 8QS Tel: 0113-257 6116 Fax: 0113-236 1360 E-mail: mail@pudseyplanthire.co.uk *Contractors plant hire & skip hire*

Pudsey Test & Inspection Ltd, Battye Street, Laisterdyke, Bradford, West Yorkshire, BD4 8AG Tel: (01274) 656736 Fax: (01274) 656797 E-mail: darrylatpti@aol.com *Non-destructive ultrasonic testing specialists*

Puerto Real Estate, 327 Birmingham Road, Sutton Coldfield, West Midlands, B72 1DL Tel: 0121-386 2000 Fax: 0121-350 5000 *Spanish property estate agents*

Puffer Parts Ltd, Hall Terrace, Riddlesden, Keighley, West Yorkshire, BD21 4HB Tel: (01535) 605703 Fax: (01535) 606229 E-mail: sales@pufferparts.co.uk *Chandlery sales & boat parts*

▶ Puffin Balloons, McGregor's Way, Turnoaks Business Park, Chesterfield, Derbyshire, S40 2WB Tel: 01246 205163 Fax: 01246 270566 E-mail: sales@puffinballoons.com *Printed balloon manufrs*

▶ Puffins Childcare Centre, 13 Mont Le Grand, Exeter, EX1 2PD Tel: (01392) 496017 Fax: (01392) 439903 E-mail: info@puffinschildcare.com *Training & development of early years care & education professionals*

Pugh Bros, Frondeg Farm, Rhostyllen, Wrexham, Clwyd, LL14 4NB Tel: 01978 759719 *Agricultural contractors*

Chas B. Pugh (Walsall) Ltd, Heath Road, Darlaston, Wednesbury, West Midlands, WS10 8LU Tel: 0121-568 7568 Fax: 0121-568 8666 E-mail: pughmail@supanet.com *Scrap & demolition contractors*

Pugh Computers Ltd, Denver House, Llanon, Dyfed, SY23 5LP Tel: (01974) 200200 Fax: (01974) 202628 E-mail: sales@pugh.co.uk *Computer software services*

Pugh Davies & Co. Ltd, 1 Tabley Mews, Stamford Street, Altrincham, Cheshire, WA14 1DA Tel: (0161) 929 1110 Fax: (0161) 228 2520 E-mail: info@pughdavies.co.uk *Property owning company*

Pugh Engineering Co., Unit 20 Poplar Drive, Witton, Birmingham, B6 7AD Tel: 0121-344 3240 Fax: 0121-344 3240 *Jigs, fixtures, press tools & presswork*

Gareth Pugh Steel Framed Buildings, Agrimont Depot, Station Yard, Abermule, Montgomery, Powys, SY15 6NH Tel: (01686) 630500 Fax: (01686) 630441 E-mail: enquiry@garethpugh.co.uk *Fabricators and Erectors of Agricultural, Industrial, Equestrian and Commercial Steel Framed Buildings. Also, Steel Stockholder, Cladding Specialists, bespoke Structural Steel Fabrication, with a Retail Outlet selling all of your building materials, plus Welding Equipment, Power Tools, PPE and Industrial Fixings, Fasteners and Bolts*

Pugh & Sanders Ltd, Unit 1 Moseley Business Park, Moseley Street, Burton-on-Trent, Staffordshire, DE14 1DW Tel: (01283) 510824 Fax: (01283) 511403 E-mail: pughsanders@aol.com *Fastener distributors*

Pugh & Sanders Ltd, Woods Lane, Derby, DE22 3UD Tel: (01332) 206770 Fax: (01332) 206771 *Industrial fastener suppliers*

Puglisi Pasta (UK) Ltd, 1 Glendale Drive, London, SW19 7BG Tel: (020) 8947 7036 Fax: (020) 8946 7987 E-mail: info@puglisi.co.uk *Dry pasta & products distributors & importers*

Puissance Computer Associates, 1 Bushey Coopers Cottage, Pond Hall Road, Hadleigh, Ipswich, IP7 5PS Tel: (01473) 822002 Fax: (01473) 829665 E-mail: sales@puissance.co.uk *Computer cabling designers & installation services*

Puk Holdings Ltd, F Timothy'S Bridge, Stratford-upon-Avon, Warwickshire, CV37 9PR Tel: (01789) 206800 Fax: (01789) 206801 E-mail: puk@pukservices.co.uk *Concrete & asphalt construction*

Pukka Pies Ltd, The Halfcroft, Syston, Leicester, LE7 1LD Tel: 0116-260 9755 Fax: 0116-264 0092 E-mail: info@pukka-pies.co.uk *Pies & pastry manufrs*

▶ Pukka Signs - PVC Banners- T-shirt Printing, 305 London Road, Westcliff-on-sea, Essex, SS0 7BX Tel: (01702) 300088 Fax: (01702) 300408 E-mail: sales@pukka.uk.com *PVC, digital printed pvc, vinyl pvc banners & t-shirt printers*

Pulling, Sweetlands Way, Gosberton, Spalding, Lincolnshire, PE11 4HH Tel: (01775) 841070 Fax: (01775) 840167 E-mail: info@andypullingengineering.co.uk *Fabrication & machinery manufrs*

Pullmaflex (U K) Ltd, Heol Las, Ammanford, Dyfed, SA18 3ED Tel: (01269) 592300 Fax: (01269) 593262 E-mail: info@pullmaflex.com *Car seat component manufrs*

Pullman Doors, Chelsea House, Heysham Road, Liverpool, Bootle, L30 6UZ Tel: 0151-525 6022 Fax: 0151- 525 6022 *Door manufrs*

Pullman Fleet Services, Rotherham Road, Maltby, Rotherham, South Yorkshire, S66 8EL Tel: (01709) 810230 Fax: (01709) 790174 E-mail: richard.austwick@pullmanfleet.co.uk *Commercial vehicle maintenance*

Pullman Fleet Services, Timber Works, Whiteball, Wellington, Somerset, TA21 0LY Tel: (01823) 672909 Fax: (01823) 672978 *Commercial HGV maintenance*

Pullman Instruments (UK) Ltd, Chatsworth House, Chatsworth Terrace, Harrogate, North Yorkshire, HG1 5HT Tel: (01423) 720360 Fax: (01423) 720361 E-mail: info@pullman.co.uk Principal Export Areas: Worldwide *Test instrument repairers & suppliers*

Abram Pulman & Sons Ltd, Walton Street, Sowerby Bridge, West Yorkshire, HX6 1AN Tel: (01422) 833993 Fax: (01422) 834100 E-mail: sales@pulmans.co.uk *Steel stockholders & processors*

Pulp & Paper Machinery Ltd, Holman House, Station Road, Staplehurst, Tonbridge, Kent, TN12 0QQ Tel: (01580) 893200 Fax: (01580) 893229 E-mail: sales@pandpmachinery.com *Paper & pulp machinery agents*

Pulsar Developments Ltd, Spracklen House, Dukes Place, Marlow, Buckinghamshire, SL7 2QH Tel: (01628) 473555 Fax: (01628) 474325 E-mail: sales@pulsardevelopments.com *Manufacturer of battery chargers*

▶ Pulsar Electrical Services Ltd, Great Maplestead, Halstead, Essex, CO9 2QT Tel: (01787) 462684 Fax: (01787) 461265

Pulsar Light Of Cambridge, 3 Coldhams Business Park, Norman Way, Cambridge, CB1 3LH Tel: (01223) 403500 Fax: (01223) 403501 E-mail: sales@pulsarlight.com *Lighting control systems*

▶ Pulsar Management Services Ltd, 9 Concorde Road, Norwich, NR6 6BH Tel: (01603) 787676

Pulsar Process Measurement Ltd, Oak House, Bromyard Road, Worcester, WR2 5HP Tel: (0870) 6039112 Fax: (0870) 6039114 E-mail: info@pulsar-pm.com *Process measurement equipment manufrs*

Pulsar Systems Ltd, Brynmeurig, Penrhyncoch, Aberystwyth, Dyfed, SY23 3EY Tel: (01970) 820520 Fax: (01970) 820529 *Computer systems & software developers*

Pulsation Dampers At Pulseguard Ltd, Unit 1, Greg Street Industrial Centre, Greg Street, Reddish, Stockport, Cheshire, SK5 7BS Tel: 0161-480 9625 Fax: 0161-480 9627 E-mail: sales@pulsation-dampers.co.uk Principal Export Areas: Worldwide *Manufacturers of pulsation dampers & hydraulic*

The Pulse, Mafeking Pl, Burnbank St, Campbeltown, Argyll, PA28 6JD Tel: 01586 552411 Fax: 01586 552411 *Health products*

▶ Pulse Computer Services Ltd, 10 Orchard Road, Basingstoke, Hampshire, RG22 6NU Tel: (01256) 422395 E-mail: pcsl@ntlworld.com *Computer support & services*

▶ Pulse Corporation Ltd, New Century House, Cordwallis Street, Maidenhead, Berkshire, SL6 7BE Tel: (01628) 777726 E-mail: sales@pulsecorp.co.uk *Website design*

Pulse Home Products Ltd, Vine Mill, Middleton Road, Royton, Oldham, OL2 5LN Tel: 0161-652 1211 Fax: 0161-626 0391 E-mail: info@pulse-uk.co.uk *Kitchen appliance manufrs*

Pulse Installations Ltd, 292 Worton Road, Isleworth, Middlesex, TW7 6EL Tel: (020) 8560 4040 Fax: (020) 8568 0133 E-mail: enquiries@pulse-inst.co.uk *Installation of cabling systems*

Pulse Media Ltd, 32-42 Station Road, Heaton Mersey, Stockport, Cheshire, SK4 3QT Tel: 0161-432 2225 Fax: 0161-442 9096 *Litho flexo plate manufacturers & originators*

Pulse Power & Measurement Ltd, 65 Shrivenham Hundred Business Park, Watchfield, Swindon, SN6 8TY Tel: (01793) 784389 Fax: (01793) 784391 E-mail: sales@ppm.co.uk *EMC test & measurement equipment manufacturers & distributors*

Pulse Power Process Equipment Ltd, 43 Bishops Walk, Forthampton, Gloucester, GL19 4QF Tel: (01684) 290029 Fax: (01684) 290222 E-mail: info@pulse-piv.co.uk *Pneumatic vibrator manufrs*

Pulse Telecoms, 106 Katherine Road, London, E6 1EN Tel: (020) 8586 0220 Fax: 0208 5860220 *Sell cheap international telephone calls*

▶ Pulse-Pr, 257 Bridgend Road, Maesteg, Mid Glamorgan, CF34 0NN Tel: (01656) 730343 Fax: (01656) 738566 E-mail: rhys@pulse-pr.co.uk *Publishing services*

John Pulsford Associates Ltd, 4 Sphere Industrial Estate, Campfield Road, St. Albans, Hertfordshire, AL1 5HT Tel: (01727) 840800 Fax: (01727) 840083 E-mail: info@jpa-furniture.com *Office furniture installation services*

Pulsonic Technologies Ltd, Riverside House North Dean Business Park, Stainland Road, Greetland, Halifax, West Yorkshire, HX4 8LR Tel: (01422) 363462 Fax: (0870) 9224026 E-mail: sales@pulsonictechnologies.com *Ultrasonic level & flow measurement systems*

▶ The Pulteney Distillery Co., Huddart Street, Wick, Caithness, KW1 5BA Tel: (01955) 602371 *Whiskey distilling*

Pultrex Ltd, Century House, North Station Road, Colchester, CO1 1PD Tel: (01206) 369555 Fax: (01206) 576554 E-mail: sales@pultrex.com *Manufacturers of filament winding, pullwinding & pultrusion machines as well as Gel test equipment & mat slitting machines for the composites industry*

Puma Computer Systems Ltd, 29 Waterloo Road, Wolverhampton, WV1 4DJ Tel: (01902) 714500 Fax: (01902) 710630 E-mail: info@pumacomputersystems.co.uk *Software developers*

Puma Products Ltd, Unit 6 Viscount Court, Andover, Hampshire, SP10 5NW Tel: (01264) 333305 Fax: (01264) 333310 E-mail: sales@pumaproducts.co.uk *Ventication equipment and air conditioning related products manufrs*

Puma UK Trustees Ltd, Challenge Court, Barnett Wood Lane, Leatherhead, Surrey, KT22 7LW Tel: (01372) 360255 Fax: (01372) 362081 *Sports goods manufrs* Also at: Branches throughout the U.K.

Pumex (UK) Ltd, Hall Road, Aylesford, Maidstone, Kent, ME20 7QZ Tel: (01622) 882022 Fax: (01622) 882441 E-mail: info@pumex.co.uk Principal Export Areas: Worldwide *Importers & distributors of industrial minerals*

Pump Action Ltd, 19 Hutchison Road, Edinburgh, EH14 1RA Tel: 0131-444 0888 Fax: 0131-444 2888 E-mail: enquiries@pumpactionltd.co.uk *Design, supply & installation of various tubes of pumps & equipment*

Pump International Ltd, Trevool, Praze, Camborne, Cornwall, TR14 0PJ Tel: (01209) 831937 Fax: (01209) 831939 E-mail: sales@pumpinternational.com *Pressure testing, hand pumps, aluminum casting & pump manufrs*

Pump Partners, Unit 50 Coney Green Business Centre, Wingfield View, Clay Cross, Chesterfield, Derbyshire, S45 9JW Tel: (01246) 250197 Fax: (01246) 250241 E-mail: admin@thepumppartners.co.uk *Pumps, industrial process*

Pump Service Engineering Ltd, Unit 16 Charlestown Industrial Estate, Robinson Street, Ashton-under-Lyne, Lancashire, OL6 8NS Tel: 0161-330 3875 Fax: 0161-330 5024 E-mail: pumpservice@talk21.com *Pump repairs, service & sales*

▶ Pump Supply & Repair Group, Armstrong Hall, Wharton Rd, Winsford, Cheshire, CW7 3AD Tel: 0161-794 8038 Fax: 0161-794 8052 E-mail: salesc@pumpgroup.co.uk *Distributors & agents of pumps, including barrel, centrifugal, chemical, air operated double diaphragm & water*

Pump Technical Sales Ltd, Unit 2b Beco Works, Kent House Lane, Beckenham, Kent, BR3 1LA Tel: (020) 8778 4271 Fax: (020) 8659 3576 E-mail: sales@pts-jung.co.uk *Submersible pumps suppliers*

Pump Technology Ltd, Unit 56 Youngs Industrial Estate, Paices Hill, Aldermaston, Reading, RG7 4PW Tel: 0118-982 1555 Fax: 0118-982 1666 E-mail: sales@pump-technology.co.uk *Waste water distributors*

▶ Pumpac Pump Mnfrs, Unit 16 Pentood Industrial Estate, Cardigan, Dyfed, SA43 3AG Tel: (01239) 621308 Fax: (01239) 614942 E-mail: sales@pumpac.co.uk *Manufacturer of packaged cold water pressure booster pumps*

Pumpernickel, 7 The Arcade, Bedford, MK40 1NS Tel: (01234) 348179 Fax: (01234) 219982 *Health food shop*

Pumpkin Balloon Company, 12 Swadford Street, Skipton, North Yorkshire, BD23 1RD Tel: (01756) 701505 Fax: (01756) 701522 E-mail: info@pumpkinballoons.co.uk *Tea rooms, card & gifts retailer*

Pumps & Ancilliaries, Churwell Vale, Shaw Cross Business Park, Dewsbury, West Yorkshire, WF12 7RD Tel: (01924) 468683 Fax: (01924) 469247 *Gear unit manufrs*

Pumps & Equipment Warwick Ltd, 6 Collins Road, Heathcote Industrial Estate, Warwick, CV34 6TF Tel: (01926) 451744 Fax: (01926) 451284 E-mail: sales@pumps-equip.co.uk *Manufacturers of pumps*

Pumps4U Ltd, Vortex Suite, Bradford, West Yorkshire, BD9 6SJ Tel: (07771) 741416 Fax: (01274) 821958 E-mail: sales@pumps4u.co.uk *Liquid handling consultancy, pump, valve, pipe fittings suppliers. Emergency lighting manufrs & engineers*

Pumptronics Europe Ltd, Folgate Road, North Walsham, Norfolk, NR28 0AJ Tel: (01692) 500640 Fax: (01692) 406710 E-mail: sales@pumptronics.co.uk *Petrol pump manufrs*

Punch Bowl, 214 Porchester Road, Nottingham, NG3 6HG Tel: 0115-958 9961 Fax: 0115-958 9962 *Public house*

Punch Sales Ltd, Lower Farm Road, Moulton Park Industrial Estate, Northampton, NN3 6XF Tel: (01604) 646426 Fax: (01604) 495245 E-mail: info@punchindustries.com *Shoe care product distribs*

Punchline Engineering Ltd, 9 Horton Road, West Drayton, Middlesex, UB7 8JL Tel: (01895) 420626 Fax: (01895) 443938 *Shop fitting equipment manufrs*

Punctual Precision Tooling, Unit 15 Blatchford Road, Horsham, West Sussex, RH13 5QR Tel: (01403) 269005 Fax: (01403) 252869 E-mail: sales@punctual-precision-tooling.co.uk *Mould manufrs*

▶ Punctum, Unit 57, Enterprise Way, Newport, Gwent, NP20 2AQ Tel: (01633) 843237 E-mail: enquiries@punctumphotographic.co.uk *Photographic services & designs*

Pundit Drapery, 73-78 John Street Market, Bradford, West Yorkshire, BD1 3SS Tel: (01274) 739264 *Textile*

▶ Punsh Graphics Ltd, Chestnut House, Northminster Business Park, Northfield Lane, Upper Poppleton, York, YO26 6QR Tel: (01904) 520555 Fax: (01904) 789974 E-mail: infogb@xeikon.com *Printing machine manufrs*

Puposet Ltd, 121 Blackburn Road, Haslingden, Rossendale, Lancashire, BB4 5HL Tel: (01706) 229260 Fax: (01706) 213645 E-mail: popuset@tim-jackson.co.uk *Industrial electronics designers*

▶ Pur Natural Skincare, Unit 4 Hubert Johns Buildings, Pant Industrial Estate, Dowlais, Merthyr Tydfil, CF48 2SR Tel: (029) 2055 2691 E-mail: simonfford@btinternet.com *Oraganic Skincare preparations making exclusive use of nature's purest organic cleansers, most vibrant moisturisers, and most potent renewal extracts.*

Purac Biochem UK Ltd, 50-54 St. Pauls Square, Birmingham, B3 1QS Tel: 0121-236 1828 Fax: 0121-236 1401 E-mail: puk@purac.com *Lactic acid manufrs*

Puraflow Ltd, 44a St James Street, Burnley, Lancashire, BB11 1NQ Tel: (01282) 831094 Fax: (01282) 455938 *Clean air systems*

Puratos Ltd, Buckingham Industrial Estate, Buckingham, MK18 1XT Tel: (01280) 822860 Fax: (01280) 822857 E-mail: info_uk@puratos.com *Bakers ingredients & prepared material producers*

Purbeck Angling, 28 South Street, Wareham, Dorset, BH20 4LU Tel: (01929) 550770 Fax: (01929) 550770 *Fishing tackle retailers*

Purbeck Glass & Glazing Ltd, Unit 11 Albany Park, Cabot Lane, Poole, Dorset, BH17 7BX Tel: (01202) 659559 Fax: (01202) 659560 *Windows, doors & conservatories manufrs*

Purbeck Pets & Equestrian, 8 West Street, Wareham, Dorset, BH20 4JU Tel: (01929) 552568 Fax: (01929) 554904 *Saddlery & riding wear retailers*

Purbeck Pottery Ltd, 11 Allens Lane, Poole, Dorset, BH16 5DA Tel: (01202) 621162 Fax: (01202) 625129 E-mail: sales@purbeckpottery.com *Pottery manufrs*

Purbeck Wholefoods, 37 North Street, Wareham, Dorset, BH20 4AD Tel: (01929) 552332 *Health food suppliers*

Purbrook Ltd, 22-26 Stannary Street, London, SE11 4AA Tel: (020) 7735 9142 Fax: (020) 7793 0609 E-mail: info@purbrooks.co.uk *Printers & designers*

▶ Purchasing Assistance Ltd, The Spinney 2 Park Road, Norton, Malton, North Yorkshire, YO17 9EA Tel: (01653) 696226 Fax: 01653 696226 E-mail: info@purchasing-assistance.co.uk *Purchasing and Management Consultancy. Assisting all businesses with cost reductions,*

continued

Company Information

continuation
sourcing, outsourcing, supplier management,and improving procedures to create greater profit.

James Purdey & Sons Ltd, 57 South Audley Street, London, W1K 2ED Tel: (020) 7499 1801 Fax: (020) 7355 3297 E-mail: sales@james-purdey.co.uk Principal Export Areas: Worldwide *Gun makers, dealers & agents (also accessories) & gunsmiths*

Purdie Floors Ltd, 351 Stratford Road, Shirley, Solihull, West Midlands, B90 3BW Tel: 0121-744 4471 Fax: 0121-744 4471 E-mail: info@purdiefloors.co.uk *Flooring contractors*

A.J. Purdy & Co. Ltd, 30 Stort Mill, River Way, Harlow, Essex, CM20 2SN Tel: (01279) 414556 Fax: (01279) 450931 E-mail: info@ajpurdy.co.uk Principal Export Areas: Worldwide *Photographic sales*

▶ Purdy Fabrication & Welding, Hunter House Industrial Estate, Hartlepool, Cleveland, TS25 2BE Tel: (01429) 278488 Fax: (01429) 236411 *Fabrications & welding services*

Purdy Gates, 1 Wards Farm, Greenmore, Woodcote, Reading, RG8 0RB Tel: (01491) 681181 Fax: (01491) 682933 *Purdy Gates are metal fabricators specialising in Architectural Metalwork covering Berkshire, Buckinghamshire, Oxfordshire, Surrey, London and the South East. We have a proven & trusted track record in looking after projects of any size and have a reputation for quality and craftmanship.All our work is custom made and includes wrought iron gates and railings for the domestic and commercial properties including automation, balustrades, balconies, hand rails, staircases, spiral staircases, security grills, structural steelwork for buildings, access ramps, we will always try to help no matter how large or small the project is.*

Purdy Graphic Systems, 37 Kings Road, Berkhamsted, Hertfordshire, HP4 3BJ Tel: (01442) 865112 Fax: (01442) 865113 E-mail: purdygs@globalnet.co.uk *Technical consultants*

Pure Air Ventilation Ltd, 9b 25 Osiers Road, London, SW18 1NL Tel: (020) 8874 2885 Fax: (020) 8877 1739 *Ducting contractors*

▶ Pure & Applied Conservation Framing, 169 Bermondsey Street, London, SE1 3UW Tel: (020) 7234 0123 Fax: (020) 7234 0123 E-mail: pureandapplied@lineone.net *Conservation framing & antique printing service*

▶ Pure Essence, 6a Woodend Mills, South Hill, Springhead, Oldham, OL4 5DR Tel: 0161-633 9988 E-mail: info@pureessence.co.uk *manufacturers/distributors of handmade natural soaps & cosmetics.mail-order/online. gifts ,bath bombs,body butters ,bath bags etc. special offers*

Pure Fabrications Plastics, 16 Bridge Street, Pilsley, Chesterfield, Derbyshire, S45 8HE Tel: (01773) 874206 Fax: (01773) 591699 *Plastic fabricators*

▶ Pure Genius Events Ltd, 15 Perrymead, Luton, LU2 8UF Tel: (01582) 457263 Fax: 01582 488108 E-mail: info@puregeniusevents.co.uk *Party and event organisers with a difference. We are available 24 hours a day 7 days a week to ensure your special occassion goes ahead with no hitch. We can assist or co-ordinate all occassions from hen and stag nights/weekends, weddings, engagement, all types of parties including childrens, anniversaries, birthdays, christenings, dinners, christmas. We offer a free consultation and very competitive rates thereafter. For more information call us on the number provided or visit our website at www.puregeniusevents.co.uk*

The Pure Group, 10 Mead Court, Cooper Road, Thornbury, Bristol, BS35 3UW Tel: (01454) 411888 Fax: (01454) 411117 E-mail: puregroup@puregroup.co.uk *Specialist water treatment systems suppliers*

▶ Pure Hire & Sales, 167 Hampton Road, London, E4 8NS Tel: (020) 8524 5115 Fax: (020) 8523 8751 E-mail: sales@purehire.co.uk *Tool & plant hire, survey & laser equipment*

Pure Malt Products Ltd, Victoria Bridge, Haddington, East Lothian, EH41 4BD Tel: (01620) 824696 Fax: (01620) 822018 E-mail: enquiries@puremalt.com *Malt extract & malt flour processors*

Pure Minerals, Heath & Reach, Leighton Buzzard, Bedfordshire, LU7 0AT Tel: (07816) 775100 *Natural loose mineral makeup - now available in the UK*

Pureclad, 9 Rake Top Avenue, Higham, Burnley, Lancashire, BB12 9BB Tel: (07710) 934133 Fax: (01282) 773712 *Pure clad*

▶ Purely Paintworks, 4 Collec Depot, Billington Road, Leighton Buzzard, Bedfordshire, LU7 9HH Tel: (01525) 371122

▶ Purely Plasma, Bluewater, Greenhithe, Kent, DA9 9SJ Tel: (01322) 427409 E-mail: sales@purelyplasma.com

Purely Scottish Ltd, Woollands, Cockburnspath, Berwickshire, TD13 5XW Tel: (01368) 860600 Fax: (01368) 861960 E-mail: sales@purelyscottish.com *Mineral water bottler & distributors*

Purely Websites, St Giles House, 38 York Road, Northampton, NN1 5QJ Tel: 01604 601456 Fax: 01604 601456 E-mail: info@shopzoneservices.com *Internet services provider including website design, e-commerce, online marketing, multimedia, web space, domain names, consultancy.*

Pureprint Group Ltd, Brambleside, Bellbrook Industrial Estate, Uckfield, East Sussex, TN22 1PL Tel: (01825) 768611 Fax: (01825) 768042 E-mail: print@beaconpress.co.uk *Printers*

Puretone plc, Unit 9-10 Henley Business Park, Trident Close, Medway City Estate, Rochester, Kent, ME2 4FR Tel: (01634) 719427 Fax: (01634) 719450 E-mail: sales@puretone.net *Hearing aid & equipment manufrs*

Purewell Fish Farming Equipment, Units 13-14 Wicormarine, Cranleigh Road, Portchester, Fareham, Hampshire, PO16 9DR Tel: (01329) 829100 Fax: (01329) 829100 *Fish farm equipment manufacturers & boat builders*

Purewell Timber, Unit 4 Lea Green Farm, Christchurch Road, Downton, Lymington, Hampshire, SO41 0LA Tel: (01590) 644477 Fax: (01590) 644477 E-mail: stephan@youworldtimber.com *Garden building suppliers*

Purfleet Commercials Ltd, 520 London Road, Grays, Essex, RM20 3BE Tel: (01708) 863931 Fax: (01708) 868226 E-mail: tmason@harris-group.co.uk *Haulage repairers*

Purico Ltd, Environment House, 6 Union Road, Nottingham, NG3 1FH Tel: 0115-901 3000 Fax: 0115-901 3100 E-mail: sales@purico.co.uk *Holding company*

Purification Products Ltd, Reliance Works, Saltaire Road, Shipley, West Yorkshire, BD18 3HL Tel: (01274) 530155 Fax: (01274) 580453 E-mail: sales@purification.co.uk Principal Export Areas: Worldwide *Manufacturers of activated carbon textiles*

Purified Air Ltd, Lyon House, Lyon Road, Romford, RM1 2BG Tel: (01708) 755414 Fax: (01708) 721488 E-mail: sales@purifiedair.co.uk *Installers of air conditioning equipment with approved supplier status for all leading brand names.*

Puriflo Ltd, 44 Holton Road, Holton Heath Trading Park, Poole, Dorset, BH16 6LT Tel: (01202) 625656 Fax: (01202) 621002 E-mail: sales@rhe-puriflo.co.uk Principal Export Areas: Worldwide *Effluent & water treatment plant services*

Purite Ltd, Bandet Way, Thame Industrial Estate, Thame, Oxfordshire, OX9 3SJ Tel: (01844) 217141 *Water purification system manufrs*

A.J. Purkiss Ltd, Horseshoe Farm, London Road, Latton, Harlow, Essex, CM17 9LH Tel: (01279) 422632 *Road transport, haulage & freight services*

Purley Plastics, 41 Haviland Road, Ferndown Industrial Estate, Wimborne, Dorset, BH21 7RY Tel: (01202) 892255 Fax: (01202) 892255 *Precision injection moulders & pad printing*

Purolator Products Automotive, Glenco Ho, Drake Ave, Staines, Middx, TW18 2AW Tel: (01784) 493555 *Pump manufrs*

Purolite International Ltd, Unit D, Llantrisant, Rct Walescf, Pontyclun, Mid Glamorgan, CF72 8LF Tel: (01443) 229334 Fax: (01443) 231113 E-mail: sales@purolite.com *Water treatment services*

▶ Purple Business Solutions, Sidney Avenue, Hesketh Bank, Preston, PR4 6PD Tel: (01772) 816060

▶ Purple Creature, 6 Rosemount Square, Aberdeen, AB25 2UB Tel: (01224) 643673 E-mail: info@purplecreature.co.uk *Typing /C.V.s /Small business assistance /Desk-top Publishing /Graphic Design /Administration*

▶ Purple Eye Design, 100 Brook Street, Macclesfield, Cheshire, SK11 7AW Tel: (0845) 4660132 Fax: (01625) 617595 E-mail: sales@plasticbanners.com *Suppliers of full colour digitally printed pvc & mesh banners, finished with hems & eyelets*

Purple Frog Media, 19 Westbourne Gardens, Hove, East Sussex, BN3 5PL Tel: (01273) 735475 Fax: (01273) 775787 E-mail: julie@purplefrogmedia.com *Script writers*

▶ Purple Lattice Solutions Ltd, Ealing House, 33 Hanger Lane, London, W5 3HJ Tel: (020) 8566 7772 Fax: (020) 8566 7772 E-mail: sales@purplelattice.com *Computer system consultants*

▶ Purple Patch Promotions, 3 Gowers Close, Kesgrave, Ipswich, IP5 2XE Tel: (01473) 333388 Fax: (01473) 333388 E-mail: sales@purplepatch.org *Sports & promotional trophy services*

▶ Purple Path, 28 Livermore Court, Grove Park, Liverpool, L8 0TL Tel: 0151-734 3530 E-mail: freddy@purplepath.co.uk *We offer highly competitive rates with a first class individual service.*We will photograph your home inside and out.*Write a full description.*Erect a For Sale Sign and advertise your home until sold for a set fee of £800.*No sale No fee*

▶ Purple Plum HR, Denewood, Pitt Court, North Nibley, Dursley, Gloucestershire, GL11 6EB Tel: (0845) 4666123 Fax: (0870) 7628212 E-mail: info@purpleplumHR.co.uk *Purple plum HR exists to help businesses that don''t employ a dedicated in-house professional Human Resources expert. We provide practical support for people managers.**We resolve your people management issues professionally and effectively leaving you to run your business. Our range of flexible services include: HR advice line, employment policies and documents and on-site support with individual cases and projects.**All services are provided by experienced and qualified members of the CIPD.******

Purple Prodjects, 9 Holtspur Close, Beaconsfield, Buckinghamshire, HP9 1DP Tel: (01494) 680855 Fax: (01494) 671670 *Building contractor*

Purple Trailers, 39-41 High Street, Clay Cross, Chesterfield, Derbyshire, S45 9DX Tel: (0870) 7878687 *Trailer Hire & Sales Parts & Accessories Towbar Fitting*

▶ Purple Triangle Ltd, 3 Hawk Close, Nuneaton, Warwickshire, CV11 6TG Tel: (024) 7632 0788 *Consultants of computer systems*

▶ PurpleWeb, Bedford Heights, Brickhill Drive, Bedford, MK41 7PH Tel: 01234 272570 Fax: 01234 272545 E-mail: chris@purplewebit.com *Specialist IT Recruitment and CV Vetting*

▶ Purpose Driven Solutions, Shenleybury Cottages, Shenleybury, Shenley, Radlett, Hertfordshire, WD7 9DJ Tel: (0845) 4581619 Fax: (0871) 5227288 E-mail: andrew.philips@pds-limited.com *Project Management, Cost Consulting and Quantity Surveying Consultancy Services*

Purpose Electrical Controls Ltd, 7 Salisbury Place Industrial Estate, Rosebery Street, Wolverhampton, WV3 0BD Tel: (01902) 712909 Fax: (01902) 712909 *Control panel manufrs*

Purpose Engineering Ltd, Manthorpe House, Brittain Drive, Ripley, Derbyshire, DE5 3ND Tel: (01773) 514200 Fax: (01773) 514315 E-mail: dennis.taylor@manthorpe.co.uk *Precision engineers*

▶ Purpose Made Joinery, 1 Bear Court, Basingstoke, Hampshire, RG24 8QT Tel: (01256) 818888 Fax: (01256) 818888 *Joiners*

Purpose Powder Coatings Ltd, 18 Manor Grove, London, SE15 1SX Tel: (020) 7639 2511 Fax: (020) 7277 5942 E-mail: sales@purposepowdercoatings.com *Powder coating services*

Purser Plant Ltd, Nyes Wharf, Frensham Street, London, SE15 6TH Tel: (020) 7639 1344 Fax: (020) 7639 2155 *Contractors plant merchants*

Purvers International Ltd, Gateway House, Fareham Road, Gosport, Hampshire, PO13 0FW Tel: (01329) 238111 Fax: (01329) 825888 E-mail: mail@purvers.co.uk *Commercial Moving, Relocation & Storage, Document Storage, Record Management, Shredding, Case & Crate Making, Export Packing, Shipping, Air Freight, Asset Management and Packaging Supplies.*

Purvin & Gertz Inc, Stratton House, Stratton Street, London, W1J 8LA Tel: (020) 7499 0115 Fax: (020) 7499 1985 E-mail: prwiley@purvingertz.com *Chemical engineers*

Purvis Marquee Hire, East Mains Holdings, Ingliston, Newbridge, Midlothian, EH28 8NB Tel: 0131-335 3685 Fax: 0131-335 0294 E-mail: sales@purvis-maquees.co.uk *Marquee hire & manufrs* Also at: Winsford

Push The Envelope Ltd, Unit 21/21a Merrett's Mills, Industrial Estate, Woodchester, Stroud, Gloucestershire, GL5 5EX Tel: (01453) 836200 Fax: (01453) 836 201 E-mail: info@pushtheenvelope.co.uk *Direct mail services*

▶ Put Your Family First, 5 Hastings Close, Ysbytty Fields, Abergavenny, Monmouthshire, NP7 9JD Tel: (01873) 851046 Fax: (01873) 851046 E-mail: barrie@putyourfamilyfirst.biz *Risk free home-based business. Not mlm. No stocking or inventory. Earn extra money without quitting your job. Guranteed.*

Putney Blinds, 4 Thornsett Road, London, SW18 4EN Tel: (020) 8874 6001 Fax: (020) 8874 6229 E-mail: sales@putneyblinds.co.uk *Sunblind installation & manufrs*

Putney Glass & Glazing, Arch 5 Deodar Road, London, SW15 2NP Tel: (020) 8870 0380 Fax: (020) 8874 6668 *Glass merchants*

Putzmeister Ltd, Carrwood Road, Chesterfield Trading Estate, Chesterfield, Derbyshire, S41 9QB Tel: (01246) 264200 Fax: (01246) 260077 E-mail: info@putzmeister.co.uk *Putzmeister Ltd offer sales and service of new and used mobile concrete pumps, placing booms, stationary pumps and line pumps. Putzmeister also supply new and used screed, mortar, plaster and render pumps for all scopes of application, as well as our Dynajet range of high pressure water cleaners.**Industrial pumps for sewage, biomass, general sludge, flyash, drill cuttings, tunneling waste and many other applications are also offered alongside silo systems for receiving and storing sludges. We also offer sprayed concrete and shotcrete pumps and other tunneling equipment such as grout injection systems.*

PW Signs, 21 Southgate, Pontefract, West Yorkshire, WF8 1LN Tel: (01977) 701701 Fax: (01977) 701701 E-mail: pwsigns@btconnect.com *Sign manufrs*

PWB Industrial Heating Services Ltd, Unit 14 Dawkins Road, Poole, Dorset, BH15 4JY Tel: (01202) 682500 Fax: (01202) 682565 E-mail: enquiries@pwbltd.co.uk *Industrial Heating & Air Conditioning.*Hire and Sales of Access Equipment.*

Pwe Coatings, 9 Nobel Square, Burnt Mills Industrial Estate, Basildon, Essex, SS13 1LS Tel: (01268) 729983 Fax: (01268) 727955 *Metal spraying & coating services*

▶ PWS, Ethel Street Studios, 78 Ethel Street, Hove, East Sussex, BN3 3LL Tel: (0845) 6585818 E-mail: stewart.h@pws-uk.com *Design services, brand development, advertising & marketing support*

Pye Bibby Agriculture, Lansil Way, Canton Road, Lancaster, LA1 3QY Tel: (01524) 597200 Fax: (01524) 597219 *Agricultural feed merchants* Also at: Millness

Clifford Pye Ltd, Lomond, Holt Road, Cawston, Norwich, NR10 4HS Tel: (01603) 871213 Fax: (01603) 871713 E-mail: cyeltdcawston@farming.co.uk *Agricultural haulage & farmers*

Pye London Ltd, Units 6-7, Hookers Road, London, E17 6DP Tel: (020) 8531 3334 Fax: (020) 8531 3336 E-mail: pye-london@btconnect.com *Lift & mechanical engineers*

Pygmalion Ltd, Latham House, 16 Minories, London, EC3N 1AX Tel: (020) 7680 9499 Fax: (020) 7480 7606 E-mail: training@pygmalion.com *IT trainers*

▶ Pym & Wildsmith, Bramshall Industrial Estate, Bramshall, Uttoxeter, Staffordshire, ST14 8TD Tel: (01889) 565653 Fax: (01889) 567064 E-mail: enquiries@pymandwildsmith.co.uk *Shot blasting paint spraying, powder coating & metal spraying*

Pyments Of Campden Ltd, Old Station Yard, Station Road, Chipping Campden, Gloucestershire, GL55 6LB Tel: (01386) 840233 Fax: (01386) 841057 E-mail: pymentsjoinery@btconnect.com *Joiners & ecclesiastical woodworkers*

▶ pyramads.com, 7 Meriden Avenue, Garforth, Leeds, LS25 1HX Tel: 0113-287 7885 E-mail: info@pyramads.com *Online advertising*

Pyramid Ltd, Turner House, 9-10 Mill Lane, Alton, Hampshire, GU34 2QG Tel: (01420) 593300 Fax: (01420) 593311 E-mail: sales@pyramid-ltd.co.uk *Computer distributors*

▶ Pyramid Computers, Langley Road, Burscough Industrial Estate, Ormskirk, Lancashire, L40 8JR Tel: (01704) 894857 Fax: (01704) 897814 E-mail: sales@pyramid-computers.co.uk *PCs, networking*

▶ Pyramid Construction UK Ltd, Unit 14 Fairway Industrial Centre, Golf Course Lane, Bristol, BS34 7QS Tel: 0117-969 2222 Fax: 0117-969 2299

Pyramid Consultancy, Murlain House, Union Street, Chester, CH1 1QP Tel: (01244) 357277 Fax: (01244) 357278 E-mail: sales@pyramidconsultancy.co.uk *Computer consultants*

Pyramid Contracts Ltd, 94 Walsall Road, West Bromwich, West Midlands, B71 3HN Tel: 0121-588 8411 Fax: 0121-588 7942 *Suspended ceilings & partitions*

Pyramid Displays, Unit 1, Navigation Road, Diglis Trading Estate, Worcester, WR5 3DE Tel: (01905) 358488 Fax: (01905) 358473 *Exhibition stand contractors*

Pyramid Engineering & Manufacturing Co. Ltd, 8 Palace Road, East Molesey, Surrey, KT8 9DL Tel: (020) 8979 4814 Fax: (020) 8979 4814 *Stencil cutting machine manufacturers & stencilling accessories*

Pyramid Engineering Services Co. Ltd, 4 Orchard Business Centre, Kangley Bridge Road, London, SE26 5AQ Tel: (020) 8776 5545 Fax: (020) 8768 7650 E-mail: enquiries@pyramideng.com *Welding equipment manufrs*

Pyramid Fire Protection Ltd, 132 Rutland Road, Sheffield, S3 9PP Tel: 0114-272 8921 Fax: 0114-272 7631 E-mail: sales@pyramid-fire.co.uk *Fire protection systems specialists*

▶ Pyramid Logistics, St. Albans Road Industrial Estate, Stafford, ST16 3DR Tel: (01785) 255227 Fax: (01785) 255446 E-mail: sales@pyramidlogistics.co.uk *Freight services*

Pyramid Plastics Ltd, Unit 22 Corringham Road Industrial Estate, Corringham Road, Gainsborough, Lincolnshire, DN21 1QB Tel: (01427) 810473 Fax: (01427) 612204 E-mail: david@pyramid-plastics.co.uk *Manufacture & marketing of plastic customizing bodywork accessories*

Pyramid Precision Engineering, Unit 25 Lythalls La Industrial Estate, Lythalls Lane, Coventry, CV6 6FL Tel: (024) 7666 3447 Fax: (024) 7666 3447 *Precision engineers*

▶ Pyramid Press Print & Design, 1 Ellesmere Business Park, Nottingham, NG5 1DX Tel: 0115-962 6262 Fax: 0115-969 3394 E-mail: sales@pyramidpress.co.uk *Printers offering fast, high quality print & design on demand*

Pyramid Production Services, 10 Stonehouse Street, Plymouth, PL1 3PE Tel: (01752) 257770 Fax: (01752) 261770 E-mail: info@pyramid-presentations.co.uk *Audio-visual equipment suppliers*

Pyramid Products Ltd, Unit 1 Victoria Street, Mansfield, Nottinghamshire, NG18 5RR Tel: (01623) 421277 Fax: (01623) 421288 E-mail: sales@pyramid-products.co.uk *Importer of caravan, camping & outdoor accessories*

▶ Pyramid Surveillance & Security, 6-8 Bread Street, Edinburgh, EH3 9AF Tel: 0131-229 7010 Fax: 0131-229 7074

Pyramid Tool & Die Co., Unit A, Leopold Street, Pemberton, Wigan, Lancashire, WN5 8DH Tel: (01942) 227938 Fax: (01942) 211179 E-mail: enquiries@pyramid-tool.co.uk *Injection, blow mould toolmakers & precision engineers services*

▶ Pyramid Training (UK) Ltd, Beechwood House, 34 Beechwood Avenue, Bradford, West Yorkshire, BD6 3AF Tel: (01274) 677776 E-mail: info@pyramid2000.fsnet.co.uk *Pyramid Training is a young and vibrant national management training company based in Yorkshire, specialising in tailored training solutions covering behavioural management, interpersonal skills, customer service, health and safety, and fire safety training.**

Pyramid Valley Computers, Heapriding Mill, Ford Street, Stockport, Cheshire, SK3 0BT Tel: 0161-477 3880 Fax: 0161-480 8741 E-mail: sales@pyramidvalley.co.uk *Computer maintenance & repair services*

Pyramid Visuals, Pyramid House, 105-109 Oyster Lane, Byfleet, Surrey, KT14 7JR Tel: (01932) 338899 Fax: (01932) 338888 E-mail: info@pyramidvisuals.co.uk *A complete solution for all your vehicle branding and signage needs from vehicle wrapping, van sign writing, fleet livery, car graphics, promotion branding, vehicle media, lorries, buses, taxi wraps, PVC banners, exhibitions displays, building wraps, mobile advertising, boat graphics, signs, large format printing billboards, Backdrops, Pop ups, full colour banners, window displays, event signage, bus promotions, point of sale, large banners, wall murals, taxi advertising, stickers, truck side advertising, vinyl graphics, corporate branding, sign writing, scaffolding mesh, illuminated signs, and digital printing. Full in-house production and nationwide fitting service all with a full Avery warranty.*

▶ Pyramid Windows (Upvc) Ltd, Block 1, Chapelhall Industrial Estate, Chapelhall, Airdrie, Lanarkshire, ML6 8QH Tel: (01236) 765071 Fax: (01236) 747400 *Plastic product specialists*

▶ Pyramide UK Trading Ltd, Suite 306, Parkway House, Sheen Lane, East Sheen, London, SW14 8LS Tel: (020) 8392 1123 Fax: (0870) 7628545 E-mail: sales@towelradiator.co.uk *Towel radiator & heated towel rail supplies*

Pyramif UK Ltd, Unit 1, Alexandra Way, Ashchurch Industrial Estate, Tewkesbury, Gloucestershire, GL20 8NB Tel: (01684) 298040 Fax: (01684) 293114 E-mail: sales@pyramifuk.com *Domestic sink distributors & manufrs*

▶ Pyranha Solutions Ltd, 4 Monkswell Drive, Bolton le Sands, Carnforth, Lancashire, LA5 8JZ Tel: (07808) 054533 E-mail: andrew@pyranha.co.uk *Payroll bureau, bookkeeping services, computer systems*

Pyricon Ltd, PO Box 4641, London, SE11 4XE Tel: (020) 7735 8777 *Passive fire protection systems manufrs*

Pyricon Membrane Systems, PO Box 4641, London, SE11 Tel: (020) 7735 8777 Fax: (020) 7735 8778 *Geo-textiles & geo-grids manufrs*

Pyro Glass Ltd, Unit 12 Roman Way, Longridge Road, Ribbleton, Preston, PR2 5BB Tel: (01772) 651265 Fax: (01772) 654912 E-mail: sales@pyroglass.com *Pyroglass have over 40 years experience in the design, production and marketing of specialist high*

continued

continuation
temperature sealing and insulating materials. Our products cover a wide range of applications and can be found in many Domestic and Industrial Heating Appliances including Boilers, Multi Fuel Stoves, Furnaces, Ovens, Cookers and Fires. Pyroglass products can also be found in Oil Refineries, Steel Plants and Thermal Acoustic applications. Our products include Fibreglass Webbing, Tapes, Yarn, Lagging, Ladder Tapes, Tadpole Seals, O Rings, Rope Seals, Square Braids, Sleevings, Gaskets and Stainless Steel Reinforced Seals. Pyroglass has a well established and satisfied customer base both in the UK and Export Markets. We can offer textile engineered solutions, made to order and designed to work.

▶ Pyroartistry, PO Box 3, Broughton-in-Furness, Cumbria, LA20 6GB Tel: (01229) 716700 Fax: (01229) 716700 E-mail: sales@pyroartistry.co.uk *Professionally fired firework displays for all occasions, in the North West and everywhere else!*

Pyroban Ltd, Endeavour Works, Dolphin Road, Shoreham-By-Sea, West Sussex, BN43 6QG Tel: (01273) 463311 Fax: (01273) 465313 E-mail: customerservice@pyroban.com *Manufacturers of diesel engine safety equipment*

Pyrol Frozen Foods Ltd, Warehouse Unit, Park Street, Nuneaton, Warwickshire, CV11 4NS Tel: (024) 7664 2255 Fax: (024) 7637 5755 E-mail: sales@pyrol.com *Frozen food processors & manufrs*

Pyrometer Systems Ltd, 20 Broadhurst Street, Stockport, Cheshire, SK3 8JH Tel: 0161-476 4994 Fax: 0161-476 2656 E-mail: sales@pyrometer.co.uk *Instrumentation engineers*

Pyrometrics Ltd, Unit 1a Westthorpe Business Park, Killamarsh, Sheffield, S21 1TZ Tel: 0114-251 1201 Fax: 0114-248 4453 E-mail: mail@pyrometrics.co.uk *Industrial temperature measuring equipment manufrs*

Pyronix Security Equipment Ltd, Pyronix House, Braithwell Way, Hellaby, Rotherham, South Yorkshire, S66 8QY Tel: (01709) 700100 Fax: (01709) 701042 E-mail: sales@pyronix.co.uk *Burglar alarm manufrs*

Pyropress Engineering Co. Ltd, Bell Close, Newnham Industrial Estate, Plympton, Plymouth, PL7 4JH Tel: (01752) 339866 Fax: (01752) 336681 E-mail: pyromail@pyropress.com Sales Contact: P.C. Springate Principal Export Areas: Worldwide *Automatic control systems, components, instrument panel & switch manufrs*

Pyrotec Fire Detection Ltd, 8 Caburn Enterprise Park, The Broyle, Ringmer, Lewes, East Sussex, BN8 5NP Tel: (01273) 813505 Fax: (01273) 813259 E-mail: sales@pyrotec.co.uk *Fire alarm maintenance service*

▶ Pyrotec Services Ltd, The Old Forge, Main Road, Fyfield, Abingdon, Oxfordshire, OX13 5LN Tel: (01865) 390190 Fax: (01865) 390088 E-mail: mail@pyrotec-systems.co.uk

Pyrotek Engineering Materials Ltd, Garamonde Drive, Wymbush, Milton Keynes, MK8 8LN Tel: (01908) 561155 Fax: (01908) 560473 E-mail: petwin@pyrotek-inc.com *Manufacturers of high temperature materials*

Pythagoras Communications Ltd, Clivemont Road, Maidenhead, Berkshire, SL6 7BZ Tel: (01628) 590700 Fax: (01628) 590717 *Computer software services*

▶ Q A P.L.C., Ashurst Manor, Church Lane, Ascot, Berkshire, SL5 7DD Tel: (01344) 876471 Fax: (0870) 4001841 *Computer training services*

Q A Bolting Systems, 41 Harding Avenue, Rawmarsh, Rotherham, South Yorkshire, S62 7ED Tel: (01709) 524680 Fax: (01709) 527887 *Thread fastener suppliers*

Q A Calibration Systems Ltd, Cressett Lane, Brierley Hill, West Midlands, DY5 3XT Tel: (01384) 70062 Fax: (01384) 261377 E-mail: qacs2000@aol.com *Calibration test equipment suppliers*

▶ Q A Equipment Ltd, Hutton Place, Grasslot, Maryport, Cumbria, CA15 8ED Tel: (01900) 812777 Fax: (0870) 7598333 E-mail: sales@qaequipment.co.uk *Source, supply & design services for lab, research & test equipment*

Q A Ironbridge Ltd, Lightmoor, Telford, Shropshire, TF4 3QN Tel: (01952) 432071 Fax: (01952) 432322 *Kitchen, bedroom & bathroom furniture manufrs*

Q A Weldtech Ltd, 1a Bowes Road, Middlesbrough, Cleveland, TS2 1LU Tel: (01642) 222831 Fax: (01642) 242003 E-mail: quality@qaweldtech.co.uk *Pipework fabricators*

Q B Furniture & Wooden Components, 85 Marlacoo Road, Richhill, Armagh, BT60 1JN Tel: (028) 3887 1788 Fax: (028) 3887 9939 E-mail: sales@qbfurniture.co.uk *Fitted kitchens & kitchen component manufrs*

Q B M Precision, Church Road, Stockton-on-Tees, Cleveland, TS18 2LY Tel: (01642) 673491 Fax: (01642) 677258 E-mail: info@qbmprecision.co.uk *Precision engineers manufrs*

Q B Print Ltd, 7 Parham Drive, Eastleigh, Hampshire, SO50 4NU Tel: (023) 8061 1833 Fax: (023) 8061 0828 E-mail: john@qbprint.co.uk *Screen & label printers*

Q C Cartons Ltd, Unit 1, 1 Sargon Way, Great Grimsby Business Park, Grimsby, South Humberside, DN37 9PH Tel: (01472) 268525 Fax: (01472) 268526 *Printing cartons*

Q C Plus Ltd, PO Box 229, Romsey, Hampshire, SO51 0GJ Tel: (01794) 341218 Fax: *Q C Plus is a specialist industrial and materials science test and inspection equipment manufacturer and supplier. We offer impressive options of microscopes from Olympus and Lieca with the very best in imaging systems. We have supplied Mitutoyo hardness testing equipment for 15 years often with our own automatic control and measurement systems.*

Q C Supplies Ltd, The Forum, Callendar Park, Falkirk, FK1 1XR Tel: (01324) 630022 Fax: (01324) 630055 *Computer suppliers*

Q Controls, Waterton House, Stoneywood, Bucksburn, Aberdeen, AB21 9HX Tel: (01224) 715464 Fax: (01224) 716079 E-mail: sales@jbpipeline.co.uk *Valve & actuator distributors & agents*

Q D Plastics Glasgow Ltd, Elm Road, Broadmeadow Industrial Estate, Dumbarton, G82 2RH Tel: (01389) 762377 Fax: (01389) 734438 E-mail: sales@qdplastics.co.uk *Plastic fabricators*

▶ Q E Paving, Unit 45, Tumulus Way, Llandow Trading Estate, Cowbridge, South Glamorgan, CF71 7PB Tel: (01446) 794793

Q Glazing Ltd, 83-89 Western Road, Wood Green, London, N22 6US Tel: (020) 8888 7733 Fax: (020) 8888 7744 E-mail: mail@qglazing.com *Aluminium fabricators & double glazing manufrs*

Q H Auto Electrics, Lichfield Road, Brownhills, Walsall, WS8 6LH Tel: (01543) 377281 Fax: (01543) 361062 *Auto-electrical re-manufacturers* Also at: Nuneaton

Q I S O F T Ltd, 3 Station Brow, Leyland, PR25 3NZ Tel: (01772) 641133 Fax: (01772) 641155 E-mail: admin@qisoft.com *Software development*

▶ Q Lawns, Corkway Drove, Hockwold, Thetford, Norfolk, IP26 4JR Tel: (01842) 828266 Fax: (01842) 827911 E-mail: sales@qlawns.co.uk *Turf growers & suppliers*

▶ Q Lawns In The Midlands, 41 Grafton Lane, Bidford-on-Avon, Alcester, Warwickshire, B50 4DX Tel: (01789) 772626 Fax: (01789) 772963 E-mail: davidpfisher@btconnect.com *Cultivated turf, dedicated haulier, all garden work*

▶ Q M J Publishing Ltd, 7 Regent Street, Nottingham, NG1 5BS Tel: 0115-941 1315 Fax: 0115-948 4035 E-mail: qm@quarrymanagment.com *Magazine publishers, concrete industry*

Q M J Publishing Ltd, 7 Regent Street, Nottingham, NG1 5BS Tel: 0115-941 1315 Fax: 0115-948 4035 E-mail: sales@qmj.co.uk *Publishers*

Q M Systems Ltd, 4 Manor Park Estate, Wyndham Street, Aldershot, Hampshire, GU12 4NZ Tel: (01252) 336612 Fax: (01252) 343018 E-mail: sales@qm-systems.com *Bespoke test solutions*

Q Mac, 13 Bencroft, Cheshunt, Waltham Cross, Hertfordshire, EN7 6BE Tel: (020) 8804 6666 Fax: (020) 8804 1313 E-mail: qmac@btinternet.com *Hygiene & catering consultants*

Q Mac Engineering, 161 Ballymaguire Road, Stewartstown, Dungannon, County Tyrone, BT71 5NN Tel: (028) 8673 7312 *Agricultural engineers*

▶ Q Motorsport Systems, 29 Stalham Road, Industrial Estate, Hoveton, Norwich, NR12 8DG Tel: (01603) 784408 Fax: (01603) 784409

Q P D Fabrications Ltd, Unit 2, Shelley Road, Preston, PR2 2DB Tel: (01772) 258992 Fax: (01772) 884371 *Steel fabricators*

Q P Share LLP, 8 Park Drive, Eldwick, Bingley, West Yorkshire, BD16 3DF Tel: (01274) 551007 Fax: (01274) 552932 *Software designers*

Q Par Angus Ltd, Barons Cross Laboratories, Barons Cross Road, Barons Cross, Leominster, Herefordshire, HR6 8RS Tel: (01568) 612138 Fax: (01568) 616373 E-mail: sales@q-par.com *Microwave component manufrs*

Q Plant Hire Ltd, Stampstone Street, Oldham, OL1 3PW Tel: 0161-620 2115 Fax: 0161-652 8342 E-mail: jamesquinnplanthire@jqph.co.uk *Plant hire*

▶ Q R 8 Design, Arundel Street, Sheffield, S1 2NS Tel: 0114-221 1818 Fax: (0870) 1338957 E-mail: jerry@lampson.co.uk *Design consultancy*

▶ Q R 8 Design, Arundel Street, Sheffield, S1 2NS Tel: 0114-221 1818 Fax: (0870) 1338957 E-mail: enquiries@miswebdesign.com *Web design, internet marketing & usability testing specialists*

Q R S Stamps, 71 Wordsworth Road, Small Heath, Birmingham, B10 0ED Tel: 0121-772 4165 Fax: 0121-766 6341 E-mail: print.man@virgin.net *Rubber stamp printers & manufrs*

▶ Q R T I (Scotland) Ltd, 156 Reid Street, Glasgow, G40 4PH Tel: 0141-551 8228 Fax: 0141-554 8474

Q R Tools Ltd, 251-253 Hanworth Road, Hounslow, TW3 3UF Tel: (020) 8570 5135 Fax: (020) 8572 6833 *Power tool distributors retail*

Q S Freelance Ltd, 12 Albert Road, Finedon, Wellingborough, Northamptonshire, NN9 5JE Tel: (01933) 682676 E-mail: colin@qsfreelance.co.uk *QS Freelance offers the services of an experienced in house Quality /Health & Safety Manager, but as and when you need one, at very economic rates.*

Q S S Aquarium & Koi Centre, 339 Wakefield Road, Bradford, West Yorkshire, BD4 7NJ Tel: (01274) 728361 Fax: (01274) 720718 E-mail: sales@qssaquarium.co.uk *Aquatic suppliers*

▶ Q S Supplies, 72 Forest Road, Leicester, LE5 0DG Tel: 0116-251 0051 Fax: 0116-251 1611 E-mail: info@qssupplies.co.uk *Bathrooms, showers, electrical, hardware wholesalers*

▶ Q Software Global Ltd, Ranmore Manor, Ranmore Common, Dorking, Surrey, RH5 6SX Tel: (01483) 280400 Fax: (01483) 280401 E-mail: info@qsoftware.com *Security software manufrs*

Q Sports, 99a High Street, Staple Hill, Bristol, BS16 5HF Tel: 0117-957 5599 Fax: 0117-956 3331 *Sports equipment manufrs*

▶ Q T F, 58A Drumarkin Road, Rathfriland, Newry, County Down, BT34 5ND Tel: (028) 4063 2494 Fax: (028) 4063 2495 E-mail: info@qtfhomes.co.uk *Timber framed manufrs*

Q V S Fruits, 106 Firle Road, Eastbourne, East Sussex, BN22 8ES Tel: (01323) 737323 Fax: (01323) 737313 *Fruit & vegetable wholesalers*

▶ Q X Components Ltd, 69 Higher Road, Urmston, Manchester, M41 9AP Tel: 0161-746 7676 Fax: 0161-746 7670 E-mail: sales@qxcomponents.co.uk *Manufacture, coils, starter motors, alternators*

Q\Dos Networks Ltd, Ropers, Manor Lane, Stutton, Ipswich, IP9 2TB Tel: (01473) 326300 Fax: (01473) 238544 E-mail: sales@qdos.co.uk *Voice & data communications, installation & supply*

▶ Q1 Leisure Ltd, Ruxley Manor, Maidstone Road, Sidcup, Kent, DA14 5BQ Tel: (020) 8309 0600 Fax: (020) 8300 7759 *Swimming pool equipment & installation*

Q2 Systems Ltd, Mill Studio Business Centre, Crane Mead, Ware, Hertfordshire, SG12 9PY Tel: (01920) 444285 Fax: (01920) 468686 E-mail: q2@q2systems.co.uk *Software development*

Q8 Fuel Care, Estuary Road, King's Lynn, Norfolk, PE30 2HH Tel: (01553) 614800 Fax: (01553) 614835 E-mail: enquiries@q8fuelcare.co.uk *Lubricant distribs*

Q8 Fuel Care, Estuary Road, King's Lynn, Norfolk, PE30 2HH Tel: (01553) 614800 Fax: (01553) 614835 E-mail: enquiries@q8fuelcare.co.uk *Fuel distributors*

Q8 Fuels Care, 10 Midurst Road, Fernhurst, Haslemere, Surrey, GU27 3EE Tel: (01428) 652218 Fax: (01428) 652250 *Fuel oil & lubricant distributors*

QA, QA House, Delta Office Business Park, Welton Road, Swindon, SN5 7WZ Tel: (08709) 060090 Fax: (01793) 696007 E-mail: responsecentre@qa.com *Consulting & training*

Qa Liftrucks Ltd, 111 Pritchett Street, Aston Birmingham, Birmingham, B6 4ES Tel: 0121-333 3597 Fax: 0121-359 6291 E-mail: sales@qaliftrucks.com *Suppliers of new & used forklifts & materials handling equipment*

Qa Scotland Ltd, 32 South Gyle Cresent, Edinburgh, EH12 9EB Tel: 0131-317 7600 Fax: 0131-317 7606 *Training consultants*

QAIQ Ltd, 55-65 Uxbridge Road, Slough, SL1 1SG Tel: (01753) 534421 Fax: (01753) 898305 E-mail: info@qa-iq.com *Computer training centre*

Qantas Airways Ltd, Qantas House, 395-403 King Street, London, W6 9NJ Tel: (020) 8846 0466 Fax: (020) 8746 3317 *Air line*

Qaotek Northern Ltd, Unit 431 Thorp Arch Trading Estate, Thorp Arch, Wetherby, West Yorkshire, LS23 7BJ Tel: (01937) 849491 Fax: (01937) 849492 E-mail: wsales@findit-solutions.com *Electronic repair services*

Qasco UK Ltd, 43d Brecknock Road, London, N7 0BT Tel: (020) 7267 3079 Fax: (020) 7267 4212 E-mail: sales@qasco.co.uk *Scissors, badges & emblems manufrs*

▶ Qbike Ltd, 18 Conglass Drive, Inverurie, Aberdeenshire, AB51 4LB Tel: (07815) 746035 E-mail: info@qbike.biz *One to one professional rider training from Driving Standards Agency CBT, Part 2 and DAS to Institute of Advanced Motorcyling standard. Based in Inverurie.*

QC Lighting Systems, 83 Mercia Avenue, Charlton, Andover, Hampshire, SP10 4EJ Tel: (01264) 332892 Fax: (01264) 332892 E-mail: sales@qclightingsystems.co.uk *Visual colour assessment lighting booths & hanging luminaires manufrs*

QC Packaging Films Ltd, Technology House, Heage Road Industrial Estate, Ripley, Derbyshire, DE5 3GH Tel: (01773) 740300 Fax: (01773) 740301 E-mail: info@qcpackagingfilms.com *Packaging films manufrs* Also at: Derby

▶ QC-online.co.uk, Longridge, School Lane, Eakring, Newark, Nottinghamshire, NG22 0DE Tel: (08700) 949808 E-mail: sales@qc-online.co.uk *Q.C. are Importers, Wholesales & Retailers of the Highest Quality Polishing /Cleaning Cloths and Hand Wipers. We have a cloth for every job and to fit every price. The highest quality service and products are are the result of 30 years of hard work. We look forward to helping you.*

QCS International Ltd, 13 The Wynd, Cumbernauld, Glasgow, G67 2ST Tel: (01236) 734447 Fax: (01236) 725070 E-mail: sales@qcsi.co.uk *QCS International provide training, consultancy and outsourced management services throughout Scotland and the UK for a range of management systems to ensure our clients effectively manage all aspects of Quality, Environment and Health & Safety.*Our expertise includes ISO 9001, ISO 14001, OHSAS 18001, ISO 485 and ISO/TS 16949.*

QD Ltd, 93 Great Titchfield Street, London, W1W 6RP Tel: (020) 7462 1700 Fax: (020) 7636 0652 *Design & advertising consultants*

Q-Deck, The Woodyard, Epping Road, Epping, Essex, CM16 6TT Tel: (01992) 561103 E-mail: sales@hoppings.co.uk *Manufacturers of quality softwood timber decking & accessories*

▶ QDS, 2 Glebelands Road, Sale, Cheshire, M33 6LB Tel: 0161-962 6600 Fax: 0161-962 8800

▶ Qed Freight, Unit 7, Little Row, Fenton Industrial Estate, Stoke-on-Trent, ST4 2SQ Tel: (01782) 414981 Fax: (01782) 414981 E-mail: qedfreight@btconnect.com *UK & European freight collection & delivery services*

Qed Industrial Controls plc, Premier House, Randalls Road, Leatherhead, Surrey, KT22 7LB Tel: (01372) 378666 Fax: (01372) 379667 E-mail: sales@qedindustrial.co.uk *Specialist electric equipment suppliers*

▶ Qed Waste Management Solutions, 30 Occupation Road, Wentworth, Rotherham, South Yorkshire, S62 7UF Tel: (01226) 742857 Fax: (01226) 742857 E-mail: info@qedwms.co.uk *Waste management & recycling solution equipment services*

Qes Ltd, Niall House, 24-26 Boulton Road, Stevenage, Hertfordshire, SG1 4QX Tel: (01438) 749849 Fax: (01438) 318420 E-mail: sales@qesltd.co.uk *Power supplies, custom built & plug-in, low voltage. Also power supply systems/unit maintenance/repair services*

QFS Technologies Ltd, Unit 10-11 Chelmsley Wood Industrial Estate, Waterloo Avenue, Birmingham, B37 6QQ Tel: 0121-770 1200 Fax: 0121-770 1232 *Prototype sheet metalworkers*

▶ Qikker Solutions Ltd, 17 Marble Street, Lowry House, Manchester, M2 3AW Tel: (0870) 7876611 Fax: (0870) 7876612 E-mail: sales@qikker.com *Computer software manufrs*

Qinetiq, Cody Technology Park, Ively Road, Farnborough, Hampshire, GU14 0LX Tel: 08700 100942 Fax: (01252) 393399 E-mail: contactus@qinetiq.com *QinetiQ, the global defence and security experts, delivering value from science and technology.*

▶ Qing Cables Ltd, Malmesbury Road, Kingsditch Trading Estate, Cheltenham, Gloucestershire, GL51 9PL Tel: (01242) 224141 Fax: (01242) 224134 E-mail: enquire@qingcables.co.uk *Communications & data cable specialists*

QK Honeycomb Products Ltd, Creeting Road, Stowmarket, Suffolk, IP14 5AS Tel: (01449) 612145 Fax: (01449) 677604 E-mail: sales@qkhoneycomb.co.uk *Lightweight honeycomb coreboards manufrs* Also at: Brigg

▶ Q-matic Ltd, 7 Gurnells Road, Seer Green, Beaconsfield, Buckinghamshire, HP9 2XJ Tel: (01494) 678060 Fax: (01494) 671110 E-mail: info@qmatic.co.uk *Suppliers & Insallers of:-*Garage Doors,remote controlled operators, Sun Awnings, Domestic Continental shutters, grills and gates.*

Q-Max (Electronics) Ltd, Bilton Road, Bletchley, Milton Keynes, MK1 1HW Tel: (01908) 368006 Fax: (01908) 270483 *Hole cutting tool manufrs*

Qmec Ltd, Quarry Road, Bolsover, Chesterfield, Derbyshire, S44 6NT Tel: (01246) 822228 Fax: (01246) 827907 *Corporate clothing manufrs*

QMH Ltd, Queens Court, 9-17 Eastern Road, Romford, RM1 3NG Tel: (01708) 730522 Fax: (01708) 762691 E-mail: headoffice.reception@qmh-hotels.com *Hotels & conference centres*

QMP, Timmis Road, Stourbridge, West Midlands, DY9 7BQ Tel: (01384) 899800 Fax: (01384) 899801 E-mail: qmp@qmp.uk.com *Manufacturers of Industrial furniture including workbenches, cupboards, lockers & smoking shelters.*

Qmusic Ltd, 23a Airport Industrial Estate, Newcastle upon Tyne, NE3 2EF Tel: 0191-286 2039 Fax: 0191-286 0177 E-mail: info@qmusic.co.uk *Entertainment, music, supplier & retail music group outlet.*

▶ QMX Laboratories Ltd, 4 Bolford Street, Thaxted, Dunmow, Essex, CM6 2PY Tel: (01371) 831611 Fax: (01371) 831622 E-mail: sales@qmxlabs.com *Laboratory equipment distribution*

QPQ, Exchange House, Elsthorpe Road, Stainfield, Bourne, Lincolnshire, PE10 0RS Tel: (01778) 570879 E-mail: sales@qpq.co.uk *Computer protection systems manufrs*

QRS Ltd, Malthouse Road, Tipton, West Midlands, DY4 9AE Tel: 0121-557 3601 Fax: 0121-520 1233 *Doors: industrial; insulating curtain; automatic; to customer specification. Also doors (automatic/electronically operated) & industrial contractors/installation/maintenance.services. In addition, shutters including rolling maintenance/repair/service*

▶ QRS Precision Engineering, Unit 4 Hartlepool Workshops, Usworth Road, Hartlepool, Cleveland, TS25 1PD Tel: (01429) 891300 Fax: (01429) 295933 E-mail: qrsengineering@aol.com *Precision engineers milling, turning, grinding*

▶ QS Discount Outlets, ENA MILL, Flapper fold lane, Atherton, M46 0HB Tel: 01942 879349 E-mail: sales@dsdiscount.com *Qs discount sell brand named products at massively reduced prices. They accept all major credit and debit cards along with paypal and Nochex.All items retail at half price or better. See for yourself.**

▶ QSI Europe, Unit 4, Commerce Way, Leighton Buzzard, Bedfordshire, LU7 4RW Tel: 01525 373800 Fax: 01525 374468 E-mail: gp@cirris.co.uk *Operator Interface Terminals -HMIs/MMIs*Rugged Touch Screen Computers*Graphic User Interface Terminals*Touch Screen Interface Terminals*Data Entry Terminals/ Character-Alphanumeric*Customisable*

▶ QSserv Ltd, 5 Joan Avenue, Greasby, Wirral, Merseyside, CH49 2PD Tel: (07747) 533644 Fax: (0871) 2424992 E-mail: i.lee@tiscali.co.uk *Quantity surveyors*

Qstar Precision Ltd, 2 Shortsands Yard, Cambridge Street, St. Neots, Cambridgeshire, PE19 1PQ Tel: (01480) 210915 Fax: (01480) 210927 E-mail: info@qstarprecision.co.uk *Component manufrs*

Qtech Mta Ltd, 34 Alcester Road, Hollywood, Birmingham, B47 5NB Tel: 0121-430 8848 Fax: 0121-430 8848 E-mail: qtechmtaltd@aol.com *Constructors & manufacturers of special custom built machinery*

Qtrax Ltd, 14 Valeside, Hertford, SG14 2AR Tel: (01992) 551484 *Audio visual equipment supplier*

Q-Tron Ltd, The Ross Wing, Redhill Court, Doncaster, South Yorkshire, DN11 9ED Tel: (01302) 311066 Fax: (01302) 311774 E-mail: q-tron@btconnect.com *Software & database writers*

Quad Bike Tours, Keepers Cottage, Inverlair, Fersit, Roy Bridge, Inverness-Shire, PH31 4AR Tel: (01397) 732371 E-mail: info@quadbiketours.co.uk *Quad Bike Tours offer guided off road quad bike trecks, off road driving experiences and clay pigieon shhoting in the Highlands Of Scotland. We can cater for groups, individuals and corporate events.*

The Quad Centre, 12 Hillcrest Way, Buckingham Industrial Park, Buckingham, MK18 1HJ Tel: (01280) 817350 Fax: (01280) 817351 E-mail: info@thequadcentre.com Principal Export Areas: Worldwide *Importing & exporting all terrain vehicles*

Quad Electroacoustics Ltd, I A G House, Sovereign Court, Huntingdon, Cambridgeshire, PE29 6XU Tel: (0845) 4580011 Fax: (01480) 431767 E-mail: info@quad-hifi.co.uk *High fidelity equipment manufrs*

Quad Vision Ltd, Unit C17, Arena Business Systems, 9 Nimrod Way, Ferndown, Dorset, BH21 7SH Tel: (01202) 862325 Fax: (01202) 862326 E-mail: sales@quadvision.co.uk Purchasing Contact: R. Hughes Sales Contact: H Smythe Principal Export Areas: Central/East Europe & West Europe *Computer multi screen graphic accelerators*

Company Information

Quadgraphics Printers, 22 Hambridge Road, Newbury, Berkshire, RG14 5SE Tel: (01635) 44442 Fax: (01635) 581044 E-mail: zak@quadgraphics.co.uk *General printers*

Quadmost Engineering Ltd, Mallibee, Pett Road, Pett, Hastings, East Sussex, TN35 4HE Tel: (01424) 814244 Fax: (01424) 814522 E-mail: bob@quadmost.fsnet.co.uk *General engineers*

Quadnet Ltd, Power House Cromwell Industrial Estate, Staffa Road, London, E10 7QZ Tel: (020) 8988 7710 Fax: (020) 8988 7719 E-mail: enquiries@quadnet.co.uk *IT consultants & suppliers of computers*

Quadplas Ltd, Mulberry Trading Estate, Foundry Lane, Horsham, West Sussex, RH13 5PX Tel: (01403) 241533 Fax: (01403) 268234 E-mail: steve.botting@quadplas.co.uk *We provide standards of excellence, efficiency and service in thermoplastic and glass fibre engineering. We operate in industrial and architectural environments providing:*Installation services.*Ductwork, design and manufacture.*Manufacture of storage and process equipment.*General fabrication in GRP.*General fabrication in all thermoplastics.*Cut thermoplastic sheet and tube in all materials and sizes.*Technical advice and design facilities.*Turn-key project capabilities*We have experienced industry professionals, supplying all needs from small custom built items to complete turn key projects. From conception through in house design to development, manufacture, installation and long term maintenance.*We provide our customers with the continuing service of competitive high quality products to recognised industry standards. We work in conjunction with complimentary industries to provide a variety of technologies ensuring you receive the best plastic and glass fibre service available.*

Quadrachem Ltd, Kingfisher House Forest Row Business Park, Station Road, Forest Row, East Sussex, RH18 5DW Tel: (01342) 820820 Fax: (01342) 820825 E-mail: sales@qclscientific.com *Laboratory supply services*

Quadralene Ltd, Bateman Street, Derby, DE23 8JL Tel: (01332) 292500 Fax: (01332) 295941 E-mail: info@quadralene.co.uk *Quadralene are manufacturers and suppliers of high quality cleaning chemicals and fluids into ten product sectors. These include technical, laboratory glassware, precision engineering and ultrasonic detergents, food and hygiene, vehicle cleaning, floorcare, handcare, janitorial and engineering. In addition we maufacture high quality leather cleaners and nourishers.*

▶ Quadrant, 83 Bridge Road East, Welwyn Garden City, Hertfordshire, AL7 1LA Tel: (01707) 361800 Fax: (01707) 361801 E-mail: contact@qplas.com *Plastic materials manufrs*

Quadrant Building Services Ltd, 143 Red Lion Road, Surbiton, Surrey, KT6 7RQ Tel: (020) 8397 8811 Fax: (020) 8974 2798 *Plastering contractors*

▶ Quadrant Consultants Ltd, 35 Endell Street, Covert Garden, London, WC2H 9BA Tel: (020) 7240 7200 Fax: 0207 240 7201 E-mail: huw.watkins@qcl.co.uk *Quadrant is a leading, London based consultancy*offering strategic advice, solutions and resourcing*to major private and public sector organisations.**We work closely with client teams and at speed to deliver market*breakthroughs and revenue growth through a sustained customer focused approach*

Quadrant Displays Ltd, 14 Woodham Road, Barry Dock, Barry, South Glamorgan, CF63 4JE Tel: (01446) 747142 Fax: (01446) 749696 *Exhibition stand contractors*

▶ Quadrant Modular Ltd, Unit 3d Priory Park, Mills Road, Aylesford, Kent, ME20 7PP Tel: (01622) 719090 Fax: (01622) 719191 *Carpet manufrs*

Quadrant Offset Ltd, Riverside House, Dicker Mill, Hertford, SG13 7AE Tel: (01992) 587373 Fax: (01992) 500216 E-mail: quadsale@quadrantoffset.co.uk *Creative lithographic printers, graphic design & mailing services*

Quadrant Research & Development Ltd, 3a Attenborough Lane, Beeston, Nottingham, NG9 5JN Tel: 0115-925 2521 Fax: 0115-943 1561 E-mail: sales@quadrantcctv.com *Suppliers/installers of CCTV/video systems*

Quadrant Systems Ltd, Victoria Gardens, Burgess Hill, West Sussex, RH15 9NB Tel: (01444) 246226 Fax: (01444) 870172 E-mail: pmasters@quadrant-systems.co.uk *Flight simulator training, updates & relocation*

Quadraproof Ltd, 12 Orwell Furlong, Cambridge, CB4 0WY Tel: (01223) 420202 Fax: (01223) 424729 E-mail: info@quadraproof.co.uk *Proof printers & general printers*

▶ Quadrille Services Ltd, 18 Riverside Way, Dewsbury, West Yorkshire, WF13 3LG Tel: (01924) 491633 Fax: (01924) 499073 *Maufactures aluminium fabrication*

▶ Quadroprint Ltd, Unit 11 Hamlet Industrial Centre, White Post Lane, London, E9 5EN Tel: (020) 8986 4818 Fax: (020) 8533 4171

▶ Quadsport Ltd, Burnbrae 17a Main Street, Blackridge, Bathgate, West Lothian, EH48 3SA Tel: (01501) 750100 Fax: (01501) 750101 E-mail: sales@quadsportuk.com *UK based importer & supplier quad bikes, motocross bikes*

▶ Quadstone Ltd, 16 Chester Street, Edinburgh, EH3 7RA Tel: 0131-220 4491 Fax: 0131-220 4492 E-mail: sales@quadstone.com

Quadtech UK Ltd, Maxted Road, Hemel Hempstead, Hertfordshire, HP2 7ED Tel: (01442) 236655 Fax: (01442) 232302 *Register control equipment*

Quadwall (Heavy Duty Corrugated) Ltd, Unit B5 (1 & 2) Moss Industrial Estate, St. Helens Road, Leigh, Lancashire, WN7 3PT Tel: (01942) 674012 Fax: (01942) 260167 E-mail: sales@quadwall.co.uk *Quadwall offer the largest range of board & composite packaging material in the UK. We specialise in the manufacture of quality heavy duty transit packs. As an ISO 9002 registered company, high levels*

continued

of quality and customer satisfaction are guaranteed. From lightweight double wall cases to Quadwall bins taking 1800kg we have the solution to any packaging problem with tailor made boxes to suit. Our range of products and services include heavy duty corrugated cardboard boxes or cases or containers, heavy duty corrugated cardboard cases, heavy duty corrugated fibreboard cases, industrial heavy duty containers, Intermediate bulk containers (IBC), triple walled corrugates cases, double walled corrugated cases, die cut boxes, glued, stitched etc. Please feel free to view our website or give us a call. We handle inquiries from all over the UK, North West, Merseyside, Lancashire, Manchester, North Wales etc.

▶ Quad-X, 37 Carnearney Road, Ahoghill, Ballymena, County Antrim, BT42 2PJ Tel: (028) 2587 2800 Fax: (028) 2587 8744 E-mail: info@quad-x.com *ATV accessories online catalogue*

Quainton Cottage Furniture, Brixton Buildings, Station Road, Quainton, Aylesbury, Buckinghamshire, HP22 4BX Tel: (01296) 655726 Fax: (0870) 516601 E-mail: jeff@qcf.uk.com *Furniture & joinery manufrs*

Quaker Lubricant Distributors, Unit 6 Brunel Way, Stroudwater Business Park, Stonehouse, Gloucestershire, GL10 3SX Tel: (01453) 820800 Fax: (01453) 820820 E-mail: cindy_basile@quakerchem.com *Lubricant distributors*

▶ Quaker Oats Ltd, Uthrogle Mills, Cupar, Fife, KY15 4PD Tel: (01334) 652961

Qualcot Profiling Machines Ltd, Oak Road, West Chirton North Industrial Estate, North Shields, Tyne & Wear, NE29 8SD Tel: 0191-257 5205 Fax: 0191-257 4961 E-mail: k.edmundson@qualcut.com *Cutting machine building*

Qualicut Engineering Ltd, Wharf Street, Chadderton, Oldham, OL9 7PF Tel: 0161-633 1633 Fax: 0161-633 1660 E-mail: info@qualicut.co.uk *General, precision & cnc engineers*

▶ Qualipack (U K), 50 Kinnersley, Severn Stoke, Worcester, WR8 9JR Tel: (01905) 371226 Fax: (01905) 371529 E-mail: sales@qualipack.co.uk *Automatic weighing & packaging machinery suppliers*

Qualitair Engineering Services Ltd, Francis Court, High Ditch Road, Fen Ditton, Cambridge, CB5 8TE Tel: (01223) 295111 Fax: (01223) 295112 E-mail: info@swynfordpaddocks.com *Aeronautical designing & engineering services*

Qualitank Services Ltd, Harrison Street, Widnes, Cheshire, WA8 8TN Tel: 0151-495 1116 Fax: 0151-424 6842 E-mail: sales@qualitank.co.uk *Tank stockholders, distributors, hire & leasing including waste/chemicals, stainless steel, fuel storage, chemical storage & acid resisting. Also containers & tankers for hire/leasing rental*

▶ Qualitape Ltd, 1 Sarah Court, Piperell Way, Haverhill, Suffolk, CB9 8PA Tel: (01440) 710747 Fax: (01440) 763526 E-mail: sales@qualitape.co.uk *Qualitape is a mature and successful company which prides itself on its philosophy of forming working partnerships with both suppliers and customers. We guarantee high quality products backed with a professional service and competitive prices*

▶ Qualitas Ltd, Suite 9, Coach House Cloisters, Hitchin Street, Baldock, Hertfordshire, SG7 6AE Tel: (01462) 491155 Fax: (01462) 896611 E-mail: enquiries@qualitaslimited.com *Data centre design & infrastructure services*

Qualitech Print Ltd, Bramhall Moor Industrial Park, Pepper Road, Stockport, Cheshire, SK7 5BW Tel: 0161-456 6866 Fax: 0161-487 1588 E-mail: sales@qualitech.co.uk *Printing & repro house*

Qualitetch Components Ltd, Century Way, March, Cambridgeshire, PE15 8QW Tel: (01354) 658787 Fax: (01354) 650385 E-mail: sales@qualitetch.co.uk Principal Export Areas: Central Asia, West Europe & North America *Chemical milling (metal), metal bending/forming & toolmakers/toolmaking services. Also shield/shielding (radio frequency interference) RFI/EMI manufrs*

Qualitext Business Services Ltd, 1 Howard Road, Reigate, Surrey, RH2 7JE Tel: (01737) 242999 Fax: (01737) 248117 E-mail: hialje@qualitext.freeserve.co.uk *Office services*

Qualitrol Hathaway Instruments Division, Brewery Road, Hoddesdon, Hertfordshire, EN11 8HF Tel: (01992) 463502 Fax: (01992) 463507 E-mail: sales@hathaway-systems.com Principal Export Areas: Worldwide *Cable fault locator manufrs*

Qualiturn Products Ltd, 18 Merchant Drive, Mead Lane, Hertford, SG13 7AY Tel: (01992) 584499 Fax: (01992) 551726 E-mail: kssales@qualiturn.co.uk *Manufacturers of turned & precision turned parts*

▶ Quality Advantage Limited, 15B Addington Close, Windsor, Berkshire, SL4 4BP Tel: 01753 857883 E-mail: terry.rose@qualityadvantage.co.uk *Quality Advantage Limited offers professional quality management services and support, tailored to your business needs*

Quality Air Conditioning Ltd, 4 Orlando Court, Vicarage Lane, Walton on the Naze, Essex, CO14 8PA Tel: (01255) 672777 Fax: (01255) 676777 E-mail: shaun@qualityac.co.uk *Air conditioning designers*

Quality Amusements Ltd, St Augustines Business Park, Estuary Close, Whitstable, Kent, CT5 2QJ Tel: (01227) 793300 Fax: (01227) 793399 E-mail: antony@qualityamusements.co.uk *Fruit machine supplier*

Quality Assessments (Sheffield) Ltd, 4 Rudyard Court, Rudyard Road, Sheffield, S6 2LD Tel: 0114-234 3343 Fax: 0114-234 3343 *Failure investigators*

Quality Assurance Advisors Ltd, 68 Ferryhill Road, Aberdeen, AB11 6RR Tel: (01224) 588885 Fax: (01224) 588885 E-mail: qaa@dial.pipex.com *Quality assurance consultants*

▶ Quality Business Promotions, 11 Arundel Close, Dronfield Woodhouse, Dronfield, Derbyshire, S18 8QS Tel: (01246) 414250 E-mail: enquiries@qbpromotions.co.uk *Web design hosting & promoting services*

Quality & Business Standards Alliance, Ground Floor, 462 Holdenhurst Road, Bournemouth, BH8 9AF Tel: (01202) 386741 Fax: (01202) 392760 E-mail: info@qbsa.org *Membership organisation providing free manuals*

Quality Castings Slough Ltd, Northern Way, Bury St. Edmunds, Suffolk, IP32 6NW Tel: (01284) 755941 Fax: (01284) 761770 E-mail: sales@qualitycastings.co.uk *Aluminium alloy sand & gravity die casting specialists*

Quality Clothing Industry, Threadsneedel House, 27 Copdale Road, Leicester, LE5 4FG Tel: 0116-273 0194 Fax: 0116-273 0199 E-mail: sales@quality-clothing.co.uk *Ladies & childrens clothing manufrs*

Quality Coatings Ltd, Russell Street, Chadderton, Oldham, OL9 9LD Tel: 0161-620 0008 Fax: 0161-627 2746 *Powder coating, shotblasting & beadblasting*

Quality Coin, Hill Cottage, Redmain, Cockermouth, Cumbria, CA13 0PZ Tel: (01900) 823393 Fax: (01900) 823391 *Amusement machine hire & service*

Quality Communications (S E), 5 Ribston Gardens, Paddock Wood, Tonbridge, Kent, TN12 6BA Tel: (01892) 835925 Fax: (01892) 832504 E-mail: sales@qualycom.co.uk *Telecommunications*

▶ Quality Component Engineering Ltd, Unit 19 Wolseley Close, Plymouth, PL2 3BY Tel: (01752) 609111 Fax: (01752) 551012 E-mail: tony-russell@btconnect.com *Manufacture machine components using latest cnc technology*

Quality Control Laboratory Ltd, 13a Newbury Road, London, E4 9JH Tel: (020) 8523 3003 Fax: (020) 8523 3003 E-mail: sales@qc2000.freeserve.co.uk *Scientific equipment manufrs*

Quality Control Metrology Services Ltd, Unit 10 Holly Park Industrial Estate, Spitfire Road, Birmingham, B24 9PB Tel: 0121-377 8989 Fax: 0121-377 8976 E-mail: qcms@qcms.fsnet.co.uk *Calibration services*

Quality Control Technology, 8 Gainsborough Close, Long Eaton, Nottingham, NG10 1PX Tel: 0115-946 9111 Fax: 0115-946 9222 E-mail: sales@q-c-t.demon.co.uk *CMM specialists services*

Quality Conveyors Ltd, 10 Elland Lane, Elland, West Yorkshire, HX5 9DU Tel: (01422) 377166 Fax: (01422) 377238 *Acoustic suspended ceilings specialists*

Quality Conveyors Ltd, 10 Elland Lane, Elland, West Yorkshire, HX5 9DU Tel: (01422) 377166 Fax: (01422) 377238 E-mail: qconveyor@aol.com *Suppliers of conveyors & fabrications to the food industry*

Quality Copies Ltd, 26 Durley Road, London, N16 5JS Tel: (020) 8809 3312 *Photocopier*

▶ Quality Dun Services, 14 The Wynd, Dalgety Bay, Dunfermline, Fife, KY11 9SH Tel: 01383 823837 E-mail: enquiries@qualitydunservices.co.uk *Help with the implementation of ISO 9001:2000 is provided to small companies of 3 - 60 employees. A range of options is available to suit resources and/or budget.*

Quality Electro Depositors Ltd, Shield House, Gatehouse Close, Gatehouse Industrial Area, Aylesbury, Buckinghamshire, HP19 8DE Tel: (01296) 426214 Fax: (01296) 487787 E-mail: wise.wise.owls@aol.com *Electroplating & finishing services*

Quality Engineered Products, Unit 9/10, Ditchling Common, Ditchling, Hassocks, West Sussex, BN6 8SG Tel: (01444) 247906 Fax: (01444) 243720 E-mail: msaville@qep.uk.com *Light machining services*

Quality Extraction Designs Ltd, 52 Sandiway Bank, Thornhill, Dewsbury, West Yorkshire, WF12 0SD Tel: (01924) 430802 Fax: (01924) 430892 E-mail: daviddenise@qedltd.fsnet.co.uk *Design & installation of dust & fume extraction equipment*

▶ Quality Eye, First Base, 239a Uxbridge Road, London, London, W12 9DL Tel: 0870 300 0931 Fax: 0870 486 5956 E-mail: info@qualityeye.com *Quality Eye provides an efficient focus group/mystery shopping service.*

Quality Fabrics, 52 Leabourne Road, London, N16 6TA Tel: (020) 8826 5040 Fax: (05601) 162220 E-mail: qualityfabrics@btconnect.com *Quality Fabrics based in London are suppliers of table linens including cloths, napkins and slips.*

Quality Films Ltd, Hoks Green Business Park, Martindale, Cannock, Staffordshire, WS11 7XL Tel: (01543) 577814 Fax: (01543) 577807 E-mail: sales@quality-films.co.uk *Manufacturers of pallet stretch films*

▶ Quality Financial Software Ltd, 3ND Floor, George Street House, George Street, Macclesfield, Cheshire, SK11 6HU Tel: (01625) 443210 Fax: (01625) 443219 E-mail: info@qfsl.co.uk *Computer consultancy & software developers*

Quality Foam Products, 70-72 Sussex St, Norwich, NR3 3DE Tel: (01603) 622730 Fax: (01603) 622730 *Foam & upholstery trimming suppliers*

Quality Foods, 3 Ferry Court, Broadway, Bath, BA2 4JA Tel: (01225) 336800 *Health & vegetarian wholesalers*

Quality Foods Ltd, Hammerton Street, Bradford, West Yorkshire, BD3 9RD Tel: (01274) 393328 Fax: (01274) 730194 *Aluminium foil manufrs*

Quality Forms Ltd, 13-21 Church Street, Grimsby, South Humberside, DN32 7SR Tel: (01472) 241583 Fax: (01472) 358660 *Packaging industry cutting tool manufrs*

▶ Quality Freight Services, Unit 5 Peel House, 2 Taunton Street, Shipley, West Yorkshire, BD18 3NA Tel: (01274) 580992 Fax: (01274) 580992 E-mail: dan@qualityfreight.co.uk *Freight forwarding service*

Quality Freight (UK) Ltd, 1st Floor Port Office, Manisty Wharf, Ellesmere Port, CH65 1AF Tel: 0151-355 6006 Fax: 0151-355 3273 E-mail: info@quality-freight.co.uk *Ship brokers & ships agents* Also at: Branches throughout the U.K.

▶ Quality Gas Services Ltd, 10-12 Eldon Street, Greenock, Renfrewshire, PA16 7UE Tel: (01475) 720865 Fax: (01475) 784681

Quality Glass Stoke On Trent Ltd, Leek New Road, Stoke-on-Trent, ST6 2JY Tel: (01782) 289700 Fax: (01782) 262656 E-mail: enquiries@qualityglass.co.uk *Architectural designers*

Quality Gunslips Ltd, Sarnau, Llanymynech, Powys, SY22 6QJ Tel: (01938) 590204 Fax: (01938) 590411 E-mail: sales@gunslips.co.uk *Leather goods manufrs*

Quality Heat Treatments Ltd, Chesterton Way, Eastwood Trading Estate, Rotherham, South Yorkshire, S65 1ST Tel: (01709) 379188 Fax: (01709) 829849 E-mail: j.mcconaghy@qhtltd.com *Metal heat treatment services*

Quality Hotel, Bell Common, High Road, Epping, Essex, CM16 4DG Tel: (0870) 3509027 Fax: (01992) 560402 *Hotel with conference facilities*

Quality Hydraulic Power Ltd, Unit 5 Chelford Close, Sealand Industrial Estate, Chester, CH1 4NE Tel: (01244) 393500 Fax: (01244) 393501 E-mail: sales@qhp.co.uk *Accumulators services*

▶ Quality Improvements UK Ltd, 26 Queensway Business Centre, Dunlop Way, Queensway Industrial Estate, Scunthorpe, South Humberside, DN16 3RN Tel: (01724) 855125 Fax: (01724) 855749 E-mail: info@quality-improvements.co.uk *Quality Improvements (UK) Ltd offer bespoke cost-effective solutions to small and medium enterprises (SME's) who need:**ISO9001:2000 Quality Management Systems *ISO14001 Environmental Management Systems *OHSAS18001 Health & Safety Management Systems *Integrated Management Systems *Internal & Supplier Audits *Improvement project management using lean, six-sigma and continuous improvement methodologies *An outsourced Quality Manager/Management Representative *Quality Systems Training *Continuing support to develop management systems and accreditations as the business grows *All certifications are through UKAS approved accreditation bodies**We are extremely proud of our 0% first time accreditation rate for our clients.**Please contact our direct number Tel: 01724 862825*

Quality Industries Ltd, Unit C 18 Stafford Park, Telford, Shropshire, TF3 3BN Tel: (01952) 292166 Fax: (01952) 292167 E-mail: sales@qivansystems.co.uk *High technology sheet metalwork & fabrication*

Quality Instrument Services, Unit 7, Walkers Road, Moons Moat North, Redditch, Worcestershire, B98 9HE Tel: (01527) 596704 Fax: (01527) 596705 *Instrumentation services*

▶ Quality Interior Components, Radclive Road, Gawcott, Buckingham, MK18 4JB Tel: (01280) 818950 Fax: (01280) 818955 E-mail: sales@qictrims.co.uk *Manufacturer of aluminium materials*

Quality Lenses Ltd, 89A King Street, Southport, Merseyside, PR8 1LQ Tel: (01704) 534108 Fax: (01704) 544132 *Manufacturing opticians*

▶ Quality Lubricant Supplies, Avalon, New Park Road, Kingsteignton, Newton Abbot, Devon, TQ12 3JJ Tel: (01626) 368262 E-mail: qlsdevon@hotmail.co.uk *Lubricants manufacturer for agriculture, automotive, commercial & industrial*

Quality Management Services, 279 Hagley Road, Pedmore, Stourbridge, West Midlands, DY9 0RJ Tel: (01562) 882677 Fax: (01562) 882677 *Quality assurance consultants*

▶ Quality Management Solutions (UK) Ltd, Iveson, Ampney St Peter, Cirencester, Gloucestershire, GL7 5SH Tel: 01285 850705 E-mail: qms-uk@tiscali.co.uk *Professional Consultancy given for all aspects of Quality, Environmental and health and safety*

▶ Quality Matters Ltd, PO Box 5479, Maldon, Essex, CM9 8GG Tel: (01621) 868767 Fax: (01621) 868728 E-mail: sales@quality-matters.com *Management consultants in quality*

Quality Measurement Systems Ltd, 55 Manor Road, East Preston, Littlehampton, West Sussex, BN16 1QA Tel: (01903) 850040 Fax: (01903) 786837 *Microprocessor systems manufrs*

Quality Metal Fabrication, Unit 2 Meadow View Industrial Estate, Ruckinge, Ashford, Kent, TN26 2NR Tel: (01233) 733544 Fax: (01233) 733544 *Sheet metal fabricators*

Quality Monitoring Instruments Ltd, 5 Hampstead West, 224 Iverson Road, London, NW6 2HL Tel: (020) 7328 3121 Fax: (020) 7328 5888 E-mail: qmi@oilmist.com *Industrial instrument manufrs*

Quality Mouldings, 3 Culverin Square, Limberline Road, Hilsea, Portsmouth, PO3 5BU Tel: (023) 9267 9704 Fax: (023) 9267 8531 *Glass fibre mouldings manufrs*

Quality Packing, 16-18 Ogmore Crescent, Bridgend Industrial Estate, Bridgend, Mid Glamorgan, CF31 3TE Tel: (01656) 669888 Fax: (01656) 656284 E-mail: qualitypacking@btinternet.com *Contract packers*

▶ Quality PC's, 26 Henderson Road, Norwich, NR4 7JW Tel: (01603) 506050 Fax: (01603) 453100 E-mail: sales@qualitypc.co.uk *New high quality PC's, repairs, tuition, installation. Virus, spyware, adware, malware removal, PC tidy and service.*

Quality Pipe Supports, 1 Dyffryn Industrial Estate, Pool Road, Newtown, Powys, SY16 3BD Tel: (01686) 629898 Fax: (01686) 629797 E-mail: q.p.s@btinternet.com *Pipework support systems manufrs*

Quality Plastics Supplies Ltd, Unit C 2 Endeavour Way, London, SW19 8UH Tel: (020) 8946 8388 Fax: (020) 8947 8909 E-mail: sales@qualityplastics.co.uk *Video cassette & dvd case manufrs*

Quality Plated Plastics, Shady Lane, Birmingham, B44 9ER Tel: 0121-366 7500 Fax: 0121-366 6436 *Plastic electroplating services*

▶ Quality Precision Electronics Ltd, 15 Faraday Road, Glenrothes, Fife, KY6 2RU Tel: (01592) 771455 Fax: (01592) 772944 E-mail: admin@qpe.co.uk

Quality Precision Electronics Ltd, 15 Faraday Road, Glenrothes, Fife, KY6 2RU Tel: (01592) 771455 Fax: (01592) 772944 E-mail: admin@qpe.co.uk *Electronic contract manufacturing services*

Quality Precision Mouldings Ltd, 70 Whitecraigs Road, Glenrothes, Fife, KY6 2RX Tel: (01592) 772314 Fax: (01592) 773426 E-mail: gplqpm@aol.com *Plastic injection moulding manufrs*

▶ Quality Products General Engineering Ltd, The Green, Old Sodbury, Bristol, BS37 6LY Tel: (01454) 325022 Fax: (01454) 315464 E-mail: info@sheetmetal.qualityproducts.co.uk *Welding & fabrication services*

Quality Scheme for Ready Mixed Concrete, 1 Mount Miews, High Street, Hampton, Middlesex, TW12 2SH Tel: (020) 8941 0273 Fax: (020) 8979 4558 E-mail: qsrmc@qsrmc.co.uk *Certifying authority*

Quality Services, Unit 35 Mountney Bridge Business Park, Westham, Pevensey, East Sussex, BN24 5NJ Tel: (01323) 767344 Fax: (01323) 460440 E-mail: qualityservices@jangro.net *Janitorial retail*

Quality Signs & Engraving, Victoria Buildings, Stringes Lane, Willenhall, West Midlands, WV13 1LN Tel: (01902) 604844 Fax: (01902) 604844 E-mail: qualitysigns@tinyworld.co.uk *Sign manufrs*

Quality Surface Coatings Ltd, Hackworth Industrial Park, Shildon, County Durham, DL4 1HE Tel: 01388 776197 *Powder coaters*

Quality System Services, C Sheffield Technology Park, 60 Shirland Lane, Sheffield, S9 3SP Tel: 0114-261 8899 Fax: 0114-261 8878 E-mail: qss@sci-tech.org.uk *Quality assurance training & consultants*

Quality Test & Measurement Services, 25 Chapelmere Close, Sandbach, Cheshire, CW11 1TB Tel: (01270) 767974 Fax: (01270) 766478 E-mail: martin@bissnet.co.uk *Instrument & gauge measuring equipment supplier*

Quality Tool & Engineering Ltd, Maesyllan, Llanidloes, Powys, SY18 6DF Tel: (01686) 412679 Fax: (01686) 413554 E-mail: qualitytools@btconnect.com *Presswork manufacturers & powder painters*

Quality Tool & Engineering Ltd, Station Road, Rowley Regis, West Midlands, B65 0JU Tel: 0121-561 1299 Fax: 0121-561 1299 *Press tools manufrs*

▶ Quality Tooling North East Ltd, 5 Back Norfolk Street, Sunderland, SR1 1EA Tel: 0191-514 5153 Fax: 0191-510 8485 E-mail: sales@quality-tooling.co.uk *Engineers tooling merchant*

▶ Quality Welding Equipment Ltd, Unit C11 Rosehill Industrial Estate, Rosehill Road, Stoke Heath, Market Drayton, Shropshire, TF9 2JU Tel: (01630) 638905 Fax: (01630) 638605 E-mail: sales@qweltd.com *Sales, service & repair for welding & cutting equipment*

Qualsoft Computer Consultants, 53 The Springs, Middleham, Leyburn, North Yorkshire, DL8 4RB Tel: (01969) 624575 Fax: (01969) 624637 E-mail: sales@qualsoft.com *Computer consultants*

Qualter Hall & Co. Ltd, Johnson Street, Barnsley, South Yorkshire, S75 2BY Tel: (01226) 205761 Fax: (01226) 286269 E-mail: admin@qualterhall.co.uk Principal Export Areas: Worldwide *Engineers*

Qualvis Litho Ltd, 854 Melton Road, Thurmaston, Leicester, LE4 8BT Tel: 0116-260 2220 Fax: 0116-260 1066 E-mail: jason@qualvis.co.uk *Printed carton manufrs*

Quansboro Plastics Ltd, Melford Road, Acton, Sudbury, Suffolk, CO10 0BB Tel: (01787) 377207 Fax: (01787) 311515 E-mail: quansboro@supanet.com *Plastic injection moulding manufrs*

Quante Telecommunications Ltd, Snailwell Business Pk, Fordham Rd, Snailwell, Newmarket, Suffolk, CB8 7NY Tel: (01638) 721333 Fax: (01638) 721233 E-mail: service@quante.co.uk *Sheet metalwork fabricators*

▶ Quantech Solutions, Howe Farm, Malton, North Yorkshire, YO17 6RG Tel: (01653) 694490 Fax: (01653) 694490 E-mail: sam.hoste@quantechsolutions.co.uk *Business and technical services to food, agriculture and bioscience industries*

Quantel Ltd, 31 Turnpike Road, Newbury, Berkshire, RG14 2NX Tel: (01635) 48222 Fax: (01635) 815815 E-mail: quantel@quantel.com Principal Export Areas: Worldwide *Graphic editing effects & server systems*

Quantitech Ltd, 3 Old Wolverton Road, Old Wolverton, Milton Keynes, MK12 5NP Tel: (01908) 227722 Fax: (01908) 227733 E-mail: quant@quantitech.co.uk *Gas detection equipment distributors*

Quantock Ceilings Southerrr Ltd, Unit 27 Hamp Industrial Estate, Old Taunton Road, Bridgwater, Somerset, TA6 3NT Tel: (01278) 446611 Fax: (01278) 446612 E-mail: sales@quantockceilings.co.uk *Suspended ceiling & fire protection installation*

Quantock Electric Co. Ltd, 70-72 St John Street, Bridgwater, Somerset, TA6 5HY Tel: (01278) 422530 Fax: (01278) 445843 *Electrical contractors*

Quantock Plastics Ltd, Unit 2 Roughmoor, Williton Industrial Estate, Taunton, Somerset, TA4 4RF Tel: (01984) 632090 Fax: (01984) 632129 E-mail: qp@quantockplastics.fsnet.co.uk *Plastic injection mouldings manufrs*

Quantran Systems Ltd, Unit 6 Garnett Close, Watford, WD24 7GN Tel: (01923) 252512 E-mail: sales@quantran.com *Control panel manufrs*

▶ Quants Ltd, 15 The Oval, Doncaster, South Yorkshire, DN4 5LJ Tel: (01302) 537551 Fax: (01302) 537551 E-mail: quantsltd@btconnect.com *Quantity surveying & commercial management services*

Quantum, Unit 5, Herbert Walker Avenue, Southampton, SO15 1HJ Tel: (023) 8033 3372 Fax: (023) 8033 3372

Quantum Air Technology, Unit 1 Victoria Way, Rawtenstall, Rossendale, Lancashire, BB4 7NY Tel: (01706) 835135 Fax: (01706) 836100 E-mail: graham@quantumairtech.com *Clean air & containment services*

Quantum Clothing, North Street, Huthwaite, Sutton-in-Ashfield, Nottinghamshire, NG17 2PE Tel: (01623) 447200 Fax: (01623) 447201 E-mail: K.Orward@quantumclothing.com *Clothing manufrs*

▶ Quantum Cooling Technology, Botany Way, Purfleet, Essex, RM19 1TB Tel: (01708) 890081 Fax: (01708) 863850 *Suppliers to the catering & brewery industry*

Quantum Data Solutions Ltd, 3-5 Marischal Street, Peterhead, Aberdeenshire, AB42 1BS Tel: (01779) 490426 Fax: (01779) 480074 E-mail: purchasing@qds.uk.net *Computer suppliers*

▶ Quantum Eds, Cefn Gwrgan Road, Margam, Port Talbot, West Glamorgan, SA13 2EZ Tel: (01639) 864646 Fax: (01639) 864676 E-mail: info@quantumeds.co.uk *Software & hardware for computers & design electronics*

Quantum Heat Treatment & Brazing Ltd, 43 Barton Road, Bletchley, Milton Keynes, MK2 3DE Tel: (01908) 642242 Fax: (01908) 368629 E-mail: quantumheat@hotmail.com *Heat treatment & brazing services*

Quantum Industries Ltd, D Frenbury Estate, Drayton High Road, Norwich, NR6 5DP Tel: (01603) 789000 Fax: (01603) 405476 E-mail: enquiries@selbix.co.uk *Retail furniture manufrs*

Quantum Laser Engineering Ltd, Unit 13, Albion Industrial Estate, Endemere Road, Coventry, CV6 5PY Tel: (024) 7666 3222 Fax: (024) 7666 3444 E-mail: matrixlaserslts@btconnect.com *Laser equipment manufrs*

Quantum Manufacturing Ltd, 1 Heathcote Way, Heathcote Industrial Estate, Warwick, CV34 6TE Tel: (01926) 885564 Fax: (01926) 450387 E-mail: info@quantumprecisiontoolmakers.co.uk *Special purpose machines & press tools manufrs*

Quantum Mouldings Ltd, Emville Street, Stourbridge, West Midlands, DY8 3TD Tel: (01384) 834422 Fax: (01384) 443743 E-mail: sales@quantummouldings.co.uk *Custom molding services*

Quantum Peripheral Products Ltd, Quantum House 3 Bracknell Beeches, Old Bracknell La West, Bracknell, Berkshire, RG12 7BW Tel: (01344) 353500 Fax: (01344) 353510 *Disk drive & hard drive manufacturers & distributors*

Quantum Precision Engineering Ltd, 5-11 Tower Street, Birmingham, B19 3UY Tel: 0121-333 4734 Fax: 0121-333 6394 E-mail: info@quantumprecision.co.uk *Precision turned part manufrs*

Quantum Print & Packaging Ltd, Ashmore Lake Business Park, Spring Lane, Willenhall, West Midlands, WV12 4HN Tel: (01902) 367100 Fax: (01902) 367200 E-mail: sales@quantumppkg.co.uk *Printers & card board box manufrs*

Quantum Print Services Ltd, 1b Bardsley Road, Earlstrees Industrial Estate, Corby, Northamptonshire, NN17 4AR Tel: (01536) 408392 Fax: (01536) 408492 E-mail: sales@quantum-print.co.uk *Printers & designers*

Quantum Production, Unit 25 Wornal Park, Menmarsh Road, Worminghall, Aylesbury, Buckinghamshire, HP18 9PH Tel: (01844) 339993 Fax: (01844) 339996 E-mail: info@quantumproduction.co.uk *Oxygen monitoring*

Quantum Profile Systems, Salmon Fields, Royton, Oldham, OL2 6JG Tel: 0161-627 4222 Fax: 0161-627 4333 E-mail: sales@quantum-ps.co.uk *PVC cavity closure services* Also at: Birmingham

Quantum Racing Services Ltd, Unit 9 Station Approach Industrial Estate, Pulborough, West Sussex, RH20 1AQ Tel: (01798) 875199 Fax: (01798) 875899 E-mail: quantum.racing@argonet.co.uk *Automotive racing damper manufrs*

Quantum System Management Ltd, 67 Tweedy Road, Bromley, BR1 3NH Tel: (020) 8460 2747 Fax: (020) 8313 3468 *Design & write computer software*

▶ Quantum (UK) Ltd, Unit 5 Station Court, Station Approach, Borough Green, Sevenoaks, Kent, TN15 8AD Tel: (01732) 781133

Quara Sportswear, The Old Smithy, Bethel, Caernarfon, Gwynedd, LL55 1UW Tel: (01248) 671114 Fax: (01248) 671049 *Clothing manufrs*

Quarmby Promotions, Britannia Road, Milnsbridge, Huddersfield, HD3 4QE Tel: (01484) 653011 Fax: (01884) 460008 *Drip mats manufrs*

Quarrier Ward Ltd, PO Box 8104, Birmingham, B15 3JY Tel: 0121-454 2818 Fax: 0121-454 2818 *Manuf Silversmiths*

▶ Quarry Fix, 6b Orritor Street, Cookstown, County Tyrone, BT80 8BE Tel: (028) 8676 6177 Fax: (028) 8676 6177 E-mail: info@quarryfix.co.uk *Manufacturing of concrete*

▶ Quarry Plant Installations, 56 Boston Road, Leicester, LE4 1AA Tel: 0116-235 0323 Fax: 0116-235 1323 *Steel fabrication*

Quarry Plant & Roadsprays (Q P R), Ivy Mill, Longton Road, Stone, Staffordshire, ST15 8TB Tel: (01785) 812706 Fax: (01785) 811747 E-mail: nsirrigation@aol.com *Sand washing plant manufrs*

The Quarry Shop, 27 Maengwyn, Machynlleth, Powys, SY20 8EB Tel: (01654) 702339 Fax: (01654) 702624 E-mail: amanda.green@cat.org.uk *Health food suppliers*

▶ The Quarry Stonehouse, Caswell's Yard, 215 Aylesbury Road, Wendover, Buckinghamshire, HP22 6BA Tel: (01296) 622750 Fax: (01296) 622750 E-mail: bert.roberts@thequarry.co.uk *Supplier of Sandstone, Quartzite, Slate, Marble, Granite, Limestone, Travertine, Mosaics & Pebbles. Nationwide delivery or collect. Showroom open 6 days/week.*

Quarrymead Ltd, 6 Foxes Pde, Sewardstone Rd, Waltham Abbey, Essex, EN9 1PH Tel: (01992) 712233 Fax: (01992) 650933 *Computer services*

Quartermasters Protective Equipment, 248 City Road, Cardiff, CF24 3JJ Tel: (029) 2049 1059 *Work wear & protective clothing*

▶ Quartet Computer Services, Astridge Park, Gyfelia, Wrexham, Clwyd, LL13 0YH Tel: (01978) 820343 E-mail: info@quartetcs.co.uk *Software development & it consultancy services*

Quartic Engineering Ltd, Priory Road, Rochester, Kent, ME2 2EG Tel: (01634) 722522 Fax: (01634) 714150 E-mail: stewart@quarticeng.co.uk *General mechanical engineers*

▶ Quartile Management Consulting Ltd, 10 Melville Crescent, Edinburgh, EH3 7LU Tel: 0131-666 1237 Fax: (07092) 313096

Quartslab Marketing Ltd, PO Box 19, Erith, Kent, DA8 1LH Tel: (01322) 330830 Fax: (01322) 334904 E-mail: sales@quartslab.com *Quartz crystal manufrs & distributors*

Quartz Electrical & Mechanical Services Ltd, 2 Brighouse Business Village, Riverside Park, Middlesbrough, Cleveland, TS2 1RT Tel: (01642) 244411 Fax: (01642) 244499

Quartz Plant UK Ltd, 5 Thomas Avenue, Radcliffe-On-Trent, Nottingham, NG12 2HT Tel: 0115-933 4947 Fax: 0115-933 4947 E-mail: brassandpower@ntlworld.com *Construction plant or equipment distributors, agents & suppliers*

Quartz Scientific Computing Ltd, Dukes Yard, Acme Road, Watford, WD24 5AL Tel: (01923) 213983 Fax: (01923) 247732 E-mail: mail@quartz-scientific.co.uk *Chemical analysts & consultants for building industry*

Quartzlock UK Ltd, Gothic, Plymouth Road, Totnes, Devon, TQ9 5LH Tel: (01803) 862062 Fax: (01803) 867962 E-mail: quartzlock@quartzlock.com *Time & frequency standard manufrs*

▶ Quasar Electronics Ltd, PO Box 6935, Bishop's Stortford, Hertfordshire, CM23 4WP Tel: (0870) 2461826 Fax: (0870) 4601045 E-mail: sales@quasarelectronics.com *Electronic kits manufrs*

Quasartronics Ltd, 3 Watt House Dudley Innovation Centre, Second Avenue, Pensnett Trading Estate, Kingswinford, West Midlands, DY6 7YD Tel: (01384) 401132 Fax: (01384) 400754 E-mail: sales@quasartronics.com *Electronic instruments*

Quassia Electronics Ltd, Bearwalden Business Park, Wendens Ambo, Saffron Walden, Essex, CB11 4JX Tel: (01799) 541174 Fax: (01799) 541937 E-mail: info@quassiaelectronics.co.uk *Multi-layer circuit board manufrs*

Quasson Ltd, Quasson House, Rennie Gate, Andover, Hampshire, SP10 3TU Tel: (01264) 332132 Fax: (01264) 334470 E-mail: sales@quasson.co.uk *Electronic manufacturing service to the broadcast*

Quatchem Chemicals Ltd, 1 Victoria Trading Estate, Drury Lane, Chadderton, Oldham, OL9 7PJ Tel: 0161-947 0177 Fax: 0161-947 0180 E-mail: sales@quatchem.co.uk *Disinfectant manufrs*

Quatroserve Steel Fabricators, Bay 11 Central Works, Peartree Lane, Dudley, West Midlands, DY2 0QU Tel: (01384) 480326 Fax: (01384) 74119 E-mail: sales@quatroserve.co.uk *Screen manufrs*

▶ Quattro, Victoria Road, London, NW10 6NG Tel: (020) 8838 5959 Fax: (020) 8838 2741

Quay 4 Fabrications Ltd, Shed 4 Middle Dry Dock, Grangemouth, Stirlingshire, FK3 8UF Tel: (01324) 486688 Fax: (01342) 483322 E-mail: info@quay4steel.co.uk *Steel fabrication*

Quay Education, Lutomer House Business Centre, 100 Prestons Road, London, E14 9SB Tel: (020) 7537 3399 Fax: (020) 7531 6793 E-mail: education@tslgroup.uk.com *Education recruitment services*

Quay I T Computers, 7-9 Ticklemore Street, Totnes, Devon, TQ9 5EJ Tel: (01803) 868009 Fax: (01803) 863092 E-mail: sales@quayitcomputers.com *Computer distributor*

Quay Outdoor Activity Centre, 23 Victoria Parade, Torquay, TQ1 2BD Tel: (01803) 292080 Fax: (01803) 214635 *Outdoor equipment*

Quay Sails Poole Ltd, 20 Lagland Street, Poole, Dorset, BH15 1QG Tel: (01202) 681128 Fax: (01202) 668270 E-mail: info@quaysails.com *Sail & covers manufrs*

▶ Quayfront Communications Ltd, 408 South Western House, Canute Road, Southampton, SO14 3AL Tel: (023) 8023 3140 E-mail: info@quayfront.fsnet.co.uk *Marketing & public relations*

Quayle Munro Ltd, 8 Charlotte Square, Edinburgh, EH2 4DR Tel: 0131-226 4421 Fax: 0131-225 3391 *Merchant bank*

▶ Quayline Boats Ltd, Unit 9 Silk Mead, Hare Street, Buntingford, Hertfordshire, SG9 0DX Tel: (01763) 848700 Fax: (01763) 848700 *Boat manufrs*

▶ Quaylink Transport, 1 Richmond Road, Manchester, M14 6YW Tel: 0161-873 8500 Fax: 0161-873 8500 E-mail: lisacquaylink@tiscali.co.uk *Mechanical services*

Quayshels Co. 677 Ltd, Top Floor, 5 Princes Road, Shepton Mallet, Somerset, BA4 5HL Tel: (01749) 330677 Fax: (01749) 330177 *Computer consumables distribution, sales & marketing*

▶ Quayside Bakery, Unit 19-20 Agecroft Enterprise Park, Shearer Way, Swinton, Manchester, M27 8WA Tel: 0161-737 3456 Fax: 0161-736 1966 E-mail: info@quaysidebakery.co.uk

Quayside Joinery Ltd, 24 Ullswater Close, Kitty Brewster Industrial Estate, Blyth, Northumberland, NE24 4RG Tel: (01670) 540111 Fax: (01670) 360479 *Joinery manufrs*

Quayside Marine Ltd, Mill Lane, Lymington, Hampshire, SO41 9AZ Tel: (01590) 679582 Fax: (01590) 679582 E-mail: quaysidemarine@btconnect.com *Boat builder & repairers*

▶ Quayside Marine, 56 Grange Road, Torquay, TQ1 1LF Tel: (01803) 293370 E-mail: sales@quaysidemarine.co.uk *Quayside Marine Brokerage offer a comprehensive brokerage service: Listing, Advertising and Contacting potential purchasers to ensure that we are focussed on successfully marketing your boat. **If we can assist you, please call or email, if we can"t help, we probably know someone who can. * *We also offer the following*SERVICES; *Antifouling *Engineering *Deliveries and Tuition *** **

▶ Quayside Precision Engineering, Unit 14-15 Vancouver Wharf, Hazel Road, Southampton, SO19 7BN Tel: (023) 8043 9700 Fax: (023) 8043 9701 *Stainless steel, titanium, aluminium plastic & marine specialists*

▶ Quaytech Ltd, 1 Wesley Yard, Newquay, Cornwall, TR7 1LB Tel: (01637) 876737 E-mail: sales@quaytech.com *Computer services repairs, networking, websites, email*

Quazar International, Unit 1c Deacon Trading Estate, Forstal Road, Aylesford, Kent, ME20 7SP Tel: (01622) 792222 Fax: (01622) 790099 E-mail: sales@quazarinternational.co.uk *Manufacturers of corporate badges, reflective products*

Qube Global Software, Pyrford Road, West Byfleet, Surrey, KT14 6LD Tel: (01932) 334700 Fax: (01932) 355654 E-mail: sales@fdsltd.co.uk *Computer software distribs*

Qubic Print Ltd, Sovereign Way, Chester West Employment Park, Chester, CH1 4QU Tel: (01244) 390222 Fax: (01244) 390211 *Qubic Print Direct supplies print related products, many of which can be personalised with company details, to over 30,000 businesses throughout the UK. Our broad product range is sold through five catalogues each tailored to a distinct market.*

Qubie Systems Ltd, 25 Streatham Common South, London, SW16 3BX Tel: 0208 764 8878 Fax: 0208 6798543 *Computer manufr*

Qubix International Ltd, Highclere House, 5 High Street, Knaphill, Woking, Surrey, GU21 2PG Tel: (01483) 480222 Fax: (01483) 473050 E-mail: sales@qubixinternational.com *Computer consultants*

Qudos Computer Software Ltd, Ashmead House, 3 The Common, Siddington, Cirencester, Gloucestershire, GL7 6EY Tel: (01285) 656812 *Computer software*

Que Packaging, 14 Chapel Street, Bradford, West Yorkshire, BD1 5DL Tel: (01274) 728498 Fax: (01274) 728498 E-mail: sales@quepackaging.com *Packaging materials distributors*

Quebecor World UK Holdings plc, 15 Saxon Way East, Oakley Hay Industrial Park, Corby, Northamptonshire, NN18 9EX Tel: (01536) 747474 Fax: (01536) 746042 E-mail: kspencer@quebecorworldplc.com *Printers*

Queen Anne Tableware Ltd, Holyhead Road, Wednesbury, West Midlands, WS10 7PD Tel: 0121-556 1471 Fax: 0121-556 4966 E-mail: queen.anne@btconnect.com *Silver plated giftware manufrs*

Queen Eleanor Ltd, Rutland Street, Kettering, Northamptonshire, NN16 8PW Tel: (01536) 522798 Fax: (01536) 410967 E-mail: info@queeneleanor.co.uk *Career & workwear manufrs*

Queen Elizabeth's Foundation, Bradmere House, Kingston Road, Leatherhead, Surrey, KT22 7NA Tel: (01372) 389940 Fax: (01372) 361386 E-mail: bradhouse@bradhouse.demon.co.uk *Designer & producers of premium promotional products*

▶ Queensbury Contractors, Plot 2 Units 1-3, Victoria Avenue Industrial Estate, Swanage, Dorset, BH19 1AU Tel: (01929) 424601

▶ Queensbury Shelters Ltd, Fitzherbert Road, Portsmouth, PO6 1SE Tel: (023) 9221 0052 Fax: (023) 9221 0059 *Bus shelters manufrs*

▶ Queensferry Metals Ltd, Port Edgar Marina, Port Edgar, South Queensferry, West Lothian, EH30 9SQ Tel: 0131-331 1791 Fax: 0131-331 4603

Queensfield Precision Engineering, Unit 4, Beeding Close, Southern Cross Trading Estate, Bognor Regis, West Sussex, PO22 9TS Tel: (01243) 868254 Fax: (01243) 829609 E-mail: post@queensfield.co.uk *Injection mould toolmakers*

▶ Queenstreet Furnishings, Church Road, Alphington, Exeter, EX2 8SW Tel: (01392) 433292 Fax: (01392) 411558 E-mail: sales@queenstreet-furnishings.co.uk *Furniture, bed & carpets suppliers*

Queensway 2k Ltd, 8 Cumberland Business Park, Cumberland Avenue, London, NW10 7RT Tel: (020) 8965 1676 Fax: (020) 8961 9235 E-mail: m.nelms@btconnect.com *Printers*

Queensway Engineering Scunthorpe Ltd, 3a Banbury Road, Scunthorpe, South Humberside, DN16 1UL Tel: (01724) 851219 Fax: (01724) 849814 *General engineers & machinists*

▶ Queenswood Home & Garden Products, Unit 4, Southern Avenue, Leominster, Herefordshire, HR6 0QF Tel: (01568) 611281 Fax: (01568) 614143 E-mail: sales@queenswood.co.uk

▶ Edward Quelch, 30 Bakers Lane, Lingfield, Surrey, RH7 6HD Tel: (01342) 834516 E-mail: enquiries@edwardquelch.co.uk *Commercial artist services*

Quelch Engineering Ltd, Threaf House, Wallingford Road, Uxbridge, Middlesex, UB8 2RW Tel: (01895) 233225 Fax: (01895) 811047 E-mail: doug@quelcheng.co.uk *CNC engineering services*

Quelfire Ltd, PO Box 35, Altrincham, Cheshire, WA14 5QA Tel: 0161-928 7308 Fax: 0161-924 1340 *Fire protection coatings*

Quenched & Tempered Steels Ltd, 60 Green Road, Leeds, LS6 4JP Tel: 0113-225 0400 Fax: 0113-228 6333 E-mail: sales@qandtsteels.fsnet.co.uk *Steel stockholders*

continued

Queniborough Aluminium Services Ltd, 1489 Melton Road, Queniborough, Leicester, LE7 3FP Tel: 0116-260 6005 Fax: 0116-260 3005 E-mail: tonybeall@btconnect.com *Aluminium fabricators*

Quentor Ltd, 10 Fitzmaurice Court, Rackheath, Norwich, NR13 6PY Tel: (01603) 721604 Fax: (01603) 721992 E-mail: sales@quentor.com Sales Contact: J. Pond Principal Export Areas: Worldwide *Quentor Limited, the world's leading manufacturer of custom lightweight flight cases (sometimes referred to as transit cases or transportation cases) for storage, operation and display. We can supply any case format from our ground breaking "Q-Case" building system, working with 10mm (3/8"),15mm (5/8") or 25mm (1") thickness panels in weight-saving Aluminium Honeycomb, Plastic Honeycomb or traditional Plywood materials. Our Vast range of options includes briefcases, instrument cases and rack products through to air-freightable workspace known as Air Cargo Shacks or Track Shacks. Choose from our vast standard range or select a custom specification to suit your exact needs. We can also supply or custom modify a broad range of case products (moulded or aluminium) and accessories manufactured by others.*

Quentrall Engineering Co. Ltd, 597 High Road, London, N12 0DY Tel: (020) 8445 0751 Fax: (020) 8446 9639 *Air conditioning services*

▶ Quenvhas, 253 Dysart Road, Grantham, Lincolnshire, NG31 7LP Tel: (01476) 409929 E-mail: enquire@quenvas.co.uk *Quality Environmental Health & Safety Business Services. Risk Assessments Gap Analysis, Noise Assessments, HAV Assessments, Ergonomic Assessment, DSE Assessments, Health Monitoring, Legionnaires Management, Asbestos Management and many more services. QMS, EMS and OHAS preparation and maintenance.*

▶ Quercus Rex Ltd, The Workshop, Crocker Hill Farm, Trotton, Petersfield, Hampshire, GU31 5EL Tel: (01730) 814814 Fax: (01730) 814814

Quest Ltd, Victoria House, Accrington Road, Burnley, Lancashire, BB11 5EF Tel: (01282) 838000 Fax: (01282) 452121 E-mail: sales@questelectrical.co.uk *Electrical wholesalers & control panel manufrs*

Of Quest Ltd, Irton House, Tower Estate, Warpsgrove Lane, Chalgrove, Oxford, OX44 7TH Tel: (01865) 891444 Fax: (01865) 893722 E-mail: customerservice@ofquest.co.uk *Office furniture manufrs*

Quest 4 Alloys Ltd, Alloys House, Dale Street, Bilston, West Midlands, WV14 7JY Tel: (01902) 409316 Fax: (01902) 409304 E-mail: info@quest4alloys.co.uk *Stainless steel stockholders*

Quest Computing, Queen St Chambers, 68 Queen Street, Sheffield, S1 1WR Tel: 0114-275 0006 Fax: 0114-276 1312 E-mail: general@questcomputing.co.uk *Computer consultants*

Quest Engineering, Coates Yard, Nottingham Road, Loughborough, Leicestershire, LE11 1EU Tel: (01509) 610474 Fax: (01509) 610474 *Precision & general engineers*

Quest Explosive Disposal Ltd, Hethfelton Hollow East Stoke, Wareham, Dorset, BH20 6HJ Tel: (01929) 405029 Fax: (01929) 405472 *Diving & marine services*

Quest Machining & Engineering Ltd, Units 5-9 Hewitt Business Pk, Winstanley Rd, Billinge, Wigan, Lancs, WN5 7XB Tel: (01695) 627555 Fax: (01695) 627666 E-mail: vickihunterq@aol.com *Stainless steel sheet metalworkers*

Quest Software, Ascot House, Westacott Way, Littlewick Green, Maidenhead, Berkshire, SL6 3QQ Tel: (01628) 518000 Fax: (01628) 822815 *Computer systems & software sales & supply*

Quester Capital Management Ltd, 29 Queen Annes Gate, London, SW1H 9BU Tel: (020) 7222 5472 Fax: (020) 7222 5250 E-mail: sales@quester.co.uk *Venture capital finance company*

▶ Queue Solutions Ltd, 5 Ellie Close, Stanford-le-Hope, Essex, SS17 0GZ Tel: (01375) 671349 E-mail: stevenf@queuesolutions.co.uk *Website design development*

Quibell & Son Holdings Ltd, Stepney Lane, Hull, HU5 1LJ Tel: (01482) 342177 Fax: (01482) 440296 E-mail: info@quibell.co.uk *Building masonry civil engineers services*

Quick Circuits Ltd, 1 Loverock Road, Reading, RG30 1DZ Tel: 0118-950 8921 Fax: 0118-956 8237 E-mail: sales@quick-circuits.com *Printed circuit board manufrs*

▶ Quick Copy, 334 Woodstock Road, Belfast, BT6 9DP Tel: (028) 9045 4511 Fax: (028) 9073 2180 *Photocopying services*

Quick Corp London Branch, 110 Middlesex Street, London, E1 7HY Tel: (020) 7377 2222 Fax: (020) 7377 2201 *Finance & information vendor*

▶ Quick Drill Ltd, 92 Castle Terrace, Winchburgh, Broxburn, West Lothian, EH52 6RH Tel: (01506) 891048 Fax: (01506) 891607 *Drilling contractors*

Quick Edge Engineering, Grosvenor Works, Windmill Lane, Denton, Manchester, M34 3LA Tel: 0161-335 0331 Fax: 0161-335 0332 E-mail: keith@quickedge.co.uk *Sub-contract machining*

Quick Fit, Unit 5 The Sidings, Leeds Road, Shipley, West Yorkshire, BD18 1BN Tel: (01274) 595127 Fax: (01274) 531271 E-mail: quickfit@btinternet.com *Supply & manufacturers scaffold towers, ladders & access equipment*

▶ Quick Gold Ltd, 52 Standard Road, London, NW10 6EU Tel: (020) 8965 1441 Fax: (020) 8965 2696 *Marble & granite suppliers*

Quick Hydraulics Ltd, North Tyne Industrial Estate, Benton, Newcastle upon Tyne, NE12 9SZ Tel: 0191-270 1160 Fax: 0191-270 1143 E-mail: quick@quick-hydraulics.com *Hydraulic equipment, systems distri butors & agents*

Quick Print Photographic Services Ltd, The Studios, Chartham Rd, South Norwood, London, SE25 4HW Tel: (020) 8654 7068 Fax: (020) 8655 3640 *Photographic prints mailing house*

▶ Quick Print UK Ltd, 1 Prince William Road, Loughborough, Leicestershire, LE11 5GU Tel: (01509) 236987 Fax: (01509) 239173 E-mail: info@quickprint.freeserve.co.uk

▶ Quick Response, 101 Commercial Road, London, E1 1RD Tel: (020) 7247 5555 Fax: (020) 7247 9477 E-mail: cs@quickcleaning.co.uk *Cleaning company*

Quick Sign, Unit 2 Evercreech Way, Walrow, Highbridge, Somerset, TA9 4AR Tel: (01278) 787268 Fax: (01278) 784611 E-mail: sales@quick-sign.co.uk *Sign manufrs*

Quick Stitch, Bromson Hill Court, Ashorne, Warwick, CV35 9AD Tel: (01926) 651286 Fax: (01926) 651286 E-mail: stuwartjys@aol.com *Horse rugs wash & repair services & personalised embroidery*

▶ Quick Thermal Transfer Ltd, 32 Cricketers Close, Ashington, Pulborough, West Sussex, RH20 3JQ Tel: (01903) 893308 E-mail: sales@qtt.info *Label printers services*

Quick Tools Ltd, Fitzherbert Road, Portsmouth, PO6 1RY Tel: (023) 9237 5718 Fax: (023) 9232 5203 E-mail: sales@quicktoolsltd.co.uk *CNC precision engineering for marine, aero, composite, filtration industries manufrs*

Quick Tripper Transport, 63 Wyrley Road, Birmingham, B6 7BT Tel: 0121-327 0925 Fax: 0121-327 1136 *General light haulers services*

Quick Wood UK, Station Road, Braughing, Ware, Hertfordshire, SG11 2PB Tel: (01920) 822922 Fax: (01920) 822909 *Woodworking machinery suppliers*

Quickcase Boxes, 2 Brimscombe Mills Estate, London Road, Brimscombe, Stroud, Gloucestershire, GL5 2SA Tel: (01453) 884572 Fax: (01453) 885552 *Cardboard boxes & fitments manufrs*

▶ Quickchill, 7 Church Street, Highbridge, Somerset, TA9 3AE Tel: (01278) 780948 Fax: (01278) 780948 E-mail: info@quickchill.co.uk *Water cooler manufrs*

Quickdrive Data Systems Ltd, 292-308 Southbury Road, Enfield, Middlesex, EN1 1TS Tel: (020) 8443 4260 Fax: (020) 8350 4029 *Computer system & software development*

Quickes Traditional Ltd, Home Farm, Newton St. Cyres, Exeter, EX5 5AY Tel: (01392) 851222 Fax: (01392) 851382 E-mail: sales@quickes.co.uk *Traditional farmhouse cheesemakers*

Quickfix, Arch 13 Bridgewater, Goswell Road, Windsor Castle, Windsor, Berkshire, SL4 1QY Tel: (01753) 840508 Fax: (01753) 831189 E-mail: fixings@quickfix.demon.co.uk *Fixings & fastenings suppliers for construction trade*

Quickfix Midlands, Unit B1, The Haysfield Business Centre, Malvern, Worcestershire, WR14 1GF Tel: (01684) 560700 Fax: (01684) 560020 E-mail: sales@quick-fix.demon.co.uk *Industrial fastener & suspended calling distributors*

▶ Quickfreight Services Ltd, Rednal Industrial Estate, Rednal, West Felton, Oswestry, Shropshire, SY11 4HS Tel: (01691) 610431 Fax: (01691) 610664

Quickhire, Pemway House, Carr Lane, Hoylake, Wirral, Merseyside, CH47 4AZ Tel: 0151-632 6945 Fax: 0151-632 6946 *Catering equipment & sundries hire services*

Quickil Pest Control Services, Unit 4 Roebuck Road Trading Estate 15-17 Roebuck Road, Hainault, Ilford, Essex, IG6 3TU Tel: (020) 8500 4999 Fax: (020) 8500 9440 E-mail: jconstantino@quickil.co.uk *Pest & vermin controllers*

Quicklift Ltd, 636 Birmingham Road, Lydiate Ash, Bromsgrove, Worcestershire, B61 0QB Tel: 0121-457 8995 Fax: 0121-457 8935 *Fork lift truck sales & service*

Quicklogic Electronic Equipment Component, 1a London Street, Chertsey, Surrey, KT16 8AP Tel: (01932) 579011 Fax: (01932) 570121 E-mail: eusupport@quicklogic.com *ESP devices*

▶ Quickmach Engineering Ltd, G Station Street Business Park, Station Street, Cinderford, Gloucestershire, GL14 2LG Tel: (01594) 829111 Fax: (01594) 829333

Quickmove Of Whiltshire Ltd, Harris Road, Portemarsh Trading Estate, Calne, Wiltshire, SN11 9PT Tel: (01249) 813430

Quickpack UK Ltd, 14 Linnell Way, Telford Way Industrial Estate, Kettering, Northamptonshire, NN16 8PS Tel: (01536) 510910 Fax: (01536) 410568 E-mail: quickpackuk@quickpack.com *Shrink wrap machine distributors*

Quickpak-UK Ltd, Office 2 Imex Business Centre, Oxleasow Road, Redditch, Worcestershire, B98 0RE Tel: (0845) 838 5979 Fax: (01527) 830 568 E-mail: sales@quickpak-uk.com *World importer, export contract packers*

▶ Quickpat, 12 St Bevans Road, Halifax, HX3 0RT Tel: (07050) 259465 Fax: (07050) 259475 E-mail: admin@quickpat.co.uk *QUICKPAT "A no frills Nationwide Portable Appliance Testing Company."We offer P.A.T. Testing Solution"s through our vast"Network of Electrical Testers."All trained to the highest standards of Electrical Safety."Working to guidelines as set in:"Health and Safety at Work etc. Act 1974""The Electricity at Work Regulations 1989""Provision and Use of Work Equipment Regulations 1998 (Particularly Section 6)"""NEW SERVICE ADDED AUGUST 2005"We can now offer service"s to the Drinks Dispence Industry. "*

Quickplumb, 13 Rockhall Rd, Cricklewood, London, NW2 6DT Tel: (020) 8438 0214 Fax: (020) 8438 9292 *Plumbing heating, drainage & 24 hour call out service*

Quickprint, 13 Marsh Parade, Newcastle, Staffordshire, ST5 1BT Tel: (01782) 625512 Fax: (01782) 717302 *General & commercial printers*

Quickset Chemical Flooring Ltd, 30 Runcorn Road, Birmingham, B12 8RQ Tel: 0121-440 0737 Fax: 0121-440 2255 E-mail: sales@uk-quickset.com Principal Export Areas: Africa *Manufacturers floor treatment products, floor screeds, coatings*

Quicksharp Services, Signal Hill Farm, Lenborough Road, Gawcott, Buckingham, MK18 4JG Tel: (01280) 822062 Fax: (08707) 778463 *Sliding door fittings & band saw manufrs*

Quicksharp Services, 20 Old Mill Road, Kings Langley, Hertfordshire, WD4 8QT Tel: (01923) 262054 Fax: (01923) 261150 *Fasteners supplier*

Quickshift UK Ltd, Gatwick Buisness Centre, Unit 10 Kennel Lane, Hookwood, Horley, Surrey, RH6 0AH Tel: (01293) 541215 Fax: (01293) 539067 E-mail: info@quickshift-couriers.com *National & international couriers*

Quicksign Signs & Nameplates, 7 Hightown Industrial Estate, Crow Arch Lane, Ringwood, Hampshire, BH24 1ND Tel: (01425) 470445 Fax: (01425) 476289 E-mail: steve@quicksign.co.uk *Sign makers & engravers*

▶ Quicksilver Ltd, 5 Centre Park, Marston Moor Business Park, Tockwith, York, YO26 7QF Tel: (01423) 359899 Fax: (01423) 359084 E-mail: info@profiling.co.uk *Laser cutting & sheet metal workers*

Quicksilver Refiners Ltd, 225a Finchley Road, London, NW3 6LP Tel: (020) 7431 0330 Fax: (020) 7435 6572 *Mercury manufrs*

Quickstitch Embroiderers, Willows Lane, Accrington, Lancashire, BB5 0SS Tel: (01254) 394538 Fax: (01254) 875335 *Commission embroiderers*

▶ Quigley & Booth Ltd, Cleggs Lane Mill, Seddon Street, Little Hulton, Manchester, M38 9RN Tel: 0161 7905695

Quigleys Bakery, 31-33 Grangeway, Runcorn, Cheshire, WA7 5LY Tel: (01928) 568244 *Bakery & confectionery supplies*

▶ Quik Snaps, 23 Shaftesbury Square, Belfast, BT2 7DB Tel: (028) 9023 0365 Fax: (028) 9023 0365 E-mail: sales@quiksnaps.co.uk *Photographic digital processing*

Quiligotti Terrazzo Ltd, PO Box 4, Manchester, M27 8LP Tel: 0161-727 1189 Fax: 0161-793 1173 E-mail: sales@pilkingtons.com *Tile manufrs*

Quill and Caplin Ltd, 12 Ogle Street, London, W1W 6HU Tel: (020) 7637 7213 Fax: (01582) 483462 E-mail: sales@quillcaplin.co.uk *Manufacturer of ladies' special occasion hats* Also at: Luton

Quill Exhausts, Unit 18, Golborne Enterprise Park, Kidglove Road, Golborne, Warrington, WA3 3DP Tel: (01942) 721744 E-mail: info@11outof10.com

Quill International, Quill International Group Ltd, Castle Lane, Melbourne, Derby, DE73 8JB Tel: (01332) 863292 Fax: (01332) 863292 E-mail: sales@quillinternational.com *Dustless blasting services & detergent manufrs*

▶ Quill Press, 20 Villiers Road, Mansfield, Nottinghamshire, NG18 3AG Tel: (01623) 641941 Fax: (01623) 656525 E-mail: thequillpress@btconnect.com *Hot foil printing equipment & polymer plate making systems manufrs*

▶ Quill Productions, Manor Farm, Pulham, Dorchester, Dorset, DT2 7EE Tel: (01258) 818239 Fax: (01258) 817261 E-mail: sales@quillprod.co.uk *Poultry equipment*

Quilver Business Services Ltd, Unit 13c Riverside Park, Station Road, Wimborne, Dorset, BH21 1QU Tel: (01962) 777631 Fax: (01962) 777565 E-mail: enquiries@quilver.co.uk *Photocopier & printer suppliers*

Quincey Mason Practices Ltd, 6a Highfield Road, Edgbaston, Birmingham, B15 3ED Tel: 0121-456 1110 Fax: 0121-452 1444 E-mail: mail@qmp.co.uk *Chartered surveyors*

▶ Quinessence Aromatherapy, 2 Forest Court, Linden Way, Coalville, Leicestershire, LE67 3JY Tel: (01530) 838358 Fax: (01530) 814171 E-mail: sales@quinessence.com *Aromatherapy retail services*

▶ Quinn Interiors Ltd, Number 4, Moorhey Street, Oldham, OL4 1JD Tel: 0161-785 3150 E-mail: sales@quinninteriors.co.uk *Shop fitters*

Quinn Radiators, Spinning Jenny Way, Leigh, Lancashire, WN7 4PE Tel: (01942) 261291 Fax: (01942) 261801 *Radiator manufrs*

W.J. Quinn Cutting Tools Ltd, 9 Wainwright Street, Aston, Birmingham, B6 5TH Tel: 0121-328 4640 E-mail: sales@quinntoolsgroup.co.uk *Complete cutting & grinding services*

Richard Quinnell Ltd, Rowhurst Forge, Oxshott Road, Leatherhead, Surrey, KT22 0EN Tel: (01372) 375148 Fax: (01372) 386516 E-mail: rjquinnell@aol.com *Wrought ironworkers*

Quinn's The Printers, 181 Donegall Street, Belfast, BT1 2FJ Tel: (028) 9032 3552 Fax: (028) 9031 9166 E-mail: desgin@quinnstheprinters.com *Memorial stationers & commercial printers*

Quinsee Swan Ltd, 6 Thames Industrial Estate, High Street South, Dunstable, Bedfordshire, LU6 3HL Tel: (01582) 471162 Fax: (01582) 609830 E-mail: sales@quinseeswan.co.uk *Electrical control panel designers & manufrs*

Quinshield Ltd, Unit 27-28, Capel Hendre Industrial Estate, Ammanford, Dyfed, SA18 3SJ Tel: (01269) 832220 Fax: (01269) 832221 E-mail: info@quinshield.com *GRP industrial housings manufrs*

▶ Quintdown Printers, Trevena House, 11 Trevena Terrace, Newquay, Cornwall, TR7 1LJ Tel: (01637) 875242 Fax: (01637) 875165 E-mail: sales@quintdown.co.uk

▶ Quintec Associates Ltd, Merlin House Gifford Court, Fox Den Road, Stoke Gifford, Bristol, BS34 8TT Tel: 0117-979 2888 Fax: 0117-979 2666

Quintech Computer Systems Ltd, Ashton Road, Beckford, Tewkesbury, Gloucestershire, GL20 7AU Tel: (01386) 883800 Fax: (01386) 883801 E-mail: info@quintech.co.uk *Computer hardware & software services*

▶ Quintessential Music, 72 Southview Rd, London, N8 7LS Tel: 020 8340 9870 E-mail: carmen@quintessentialmusic.com *Quintessential Music provides stylish live music for events, parties and weddings. Our ensembles are especially tailored for each event ensuring that the performance looks and sounds perfect.*

Quintet Publishing Ltd, 6 Blundell Street, London, N7 9BH Tel: (020) 7700 6700 Fax: (020) 7700 4191 E-mail: quarto@quarto.com *Book & magazine publishers*

▶ Quintiles, Almondvale Business Park, Almondvale Way, Livingston, West Lothian, EH54 6GA Tel: (01506) 818000 Fax: (01506) 818200 E-mail: sales@quintiles.co.uk *Drugs, crude or botanical or medicinal*

Quinto Crane Hire, The Drift, Nacton Road, Ipswich, IP3 9QR Tel: (01473) 712041 Fax: (01473) 720386 *Machinery removal & crane hire*

Quinto Crane & Plant Ltd, Drakes Lane, Boreham, Chelmsford, CM3 3BE Tel: (01245) 360531 Fax: (01245) 362427 *Machinery removal & plant hire*

Quinto Crane & Plant Ltd, Admiralty Road, Great Yarmouth, Norfolk, NR30 3DY Tel: (01493) 331800 Fax: (01603) 407269 *Machinery removal contractors & crane hirers*

Quinto Crane & Plant Ltd, Wisbech Road, King's Lynn, Norfolk, PE30 5JL Tel: (01553) 764383 Fax: (01553) 768716 *Crane hire*

Quinto Crane & Plant Ltd, Markfield Road, Groby, Leicester, LE6 0FT Tel: (01530) 244181 Fax: (01530) 244808 *Telescopic crane & hoist hire*

Quinto Crane & Plant Ltd, Anson Road, Norwich Airport, Norwich, NR6 6EH Tel: (01603) 410881 Fax: (01603) 404565 E-mail: cranehire@quinto.co.uk *Plant, crane & access equipment hire* Also at: Chelmsford, Great Yarmouth, Ipswich, King's Lynn, Leicester, Peterborough & Ware

Quinto Crane & Plant Ltd, Royce Road, Peterborough, PE1 5YB Tel: (01733) 560338 Fax: (01733) 890829 E-mail: adrian@quinto.co.uk *Crane hire services*

Quinton Crane Electronics Ltd, Carnival Way, Castle Donington, Derby, DE74 2HP Tel: (01332) 810955 Fax: (01332) 810475 E-mail: info@systekcontrols.com *Industrial control equipment manufacturers & electronic & pcb assembly*

Quinton Hazell Automotive Ltd, Conway Road, Colwyn Bay, Clwyd, LL28 5BS Tel: (01492) 544201 Fax: (01492) 542202 *Automotive component manufrs*

Quirepace Ltd, Cleveland Place, Cleveland Road, Gosport, Hampshire, PO12 2JG Tel: (023) 9251 1008 Fax: (023) 9251 3244 E-mail: info@quirepace.co.uk *Pneumatic tube carrier systems*

▶ Quires Ltd, Unit 14, CR Bates Industrial Estate, Wycombe Road, Stokenchurch, Buckinghamshire, HP14 3PD Tel: (01494) 485229 Fax: (01494) 485293 E-mail: sales@quires.co.uk *Stationary, office equipment suppliers*

Quiss Technology P.L.C., Unit 2 Tudor Estate, Abbey Road, London, NW10 7UW Tel: (020) 8961 9535 Fax: (020) 8961 9536 E-mail: contracts@quiss.co.uk *Computer services & consultants*

Quiswood Ltd, 3 Brackenley Court, Brackenley Lane, Embsay, Skipton, North Yorkshire, BD23 6PX Tel: (01756) 799737 *Marketing services*

C. Quitman Ltd, Ullswater Crescent, Coulsdon, Surrey, CR5 2HR Tel: (020) 8668 5295 Fax: (020) 8660 2589 E-mail: sales@cquitman.co.uk *Lighting accessory importer & distributors*

Quitmann Furniture, Unit 1, Avonmouth Way West, Bristol, BS11 9EX Tel: 0117-982 2004 Fax: 0117-982 2009 E-mail: info@quitmannfurniture.co.uk *Kitchen & dining room furniture manufrs*

Quma Systems Ltd, 7 Fraydene, Emsworth, Hampshire, PO10 8HU Tel: (01243) 373746 Fax: (01243) 379730 E-mail: quma.systems@btinternet.com *Adhesive application equipment manufrs*

Quoditch Engineering Ltd, Sycamore House, Ashwater, Beaworthy, Devon, EX21 5EF Tel: (01409) 211516 *Agricultural engineers*

▶ Quorum Ltd, 32 Canning Street, Edinburgh, EH3 8EG Tel: 0131-272 2717 Fax: 0131-272 2817

Quorum Business Systems Ltd, Unit 36 Watford Metro Centre, Dwight Road, Watford, WD18 9YA Tel: (01923) 231536 Fax: (01923) 221971 E-mail: mail@quorum-business.co.uk *Computer services provider*

▶ Quorum Technologies, Unit 15A, Euro Business Park, New Road, Newhaven, East Sussex, BN9 0DQ Tel: (01273) 510535

Quotecheckers, 55a Catherine St, St. Albans, Herts, AL3 5BN Tel: (07957) 951079 Fax: (07957) 234561 E-mail: sales@quotecheckers.co.uk *Check builders quotes*

Quovadx, Ambassador House, Maxted Road, Hemel Hempstead Industrial Estate, Hemel Hempstead, Hertfordshire, HP2 7DX Tel: (01442) 231081 Fax: (01442) 235775 *Software manufrs*

Qurius UK Ltd, Waterfall Business Park, Bury, Lancashire, BL9 7BR Tel: 0161-705 6000 Fax: 0161-705 6001 E-mail: mike.dickson@cedilla.co.uk *Financial software systems*

R A Atkins, Hunts Hill House, Hunts Hill, Normandy, Guildford, Surrey, GU3 2AH Tel: (01483) 811146 Fax: (01483) 811243 *Engineers' tools distributors*

R A & B A Linfield, Unit 22 Huffwood Trading Estate, Billingshurst, West Sussex, RH14 9UR Tel: (01403) 783784 Fax: (01403) 783486 E-mail: linfield-eng@btconnect.com *Precision engineers*

▶ R A B Electrical Services Ltd, 6 Catheralls Industrial Estate, Brookhill Way, Buckley, Clwyd, CH7 3PS Tel: (01244) 544545 Fax: (01244) 543410

R A B Enterprises, Rexon Meadows, Broadwoodwidger, Lifton, Devon, PL16 0JJ Tel: (01566) 784841 Fax: (01566) 784673 E-mail: sales@r-a-b.com *Tennis rackets manufrs*

R A Beaver Ltd, Sheepbridge Works, Dunston Road, Chesterfield, Derbyshire, S41 9QD Tel: (01246) 261110 Fax: (01246) 261098 E-mail: office@rabeaver.com *Heating & air conditioning service providers*

▶ R & A Builders, Laburnum House, Haymoor Green Road, Wybunbury, Nantwich, Cheshire, CW5 7HG Tel: (01270) 569817 Fax: (01270) 560527

▶ R A C E (Engineering) Services Ltd, 4 Mulberry Court, Bourne Industrial Park, Crayford, Dartford, DA1 4BF Tel: (01322) 429140 Fax: (01322) 429144

R A Chilton, Unit 5 Tarvin Sands, Barrow Lane, Tarvin, Chester, CH3 8JF Tel: (01829) 740992 Fax: (01829) 740629 E-mail: rob@chilton.u.net.com *Electro-formed products*

R & A Components, Thompson Street, Padiham, Burnley, Lancashire, BB12 7BG Tel: (01282) 774397 *Plastic moulders*

R A D Precision Die & Tool, Johnson House, Bilston Industrial Estate, Oxford Street, Bilston, West Midlands, WV14 7EG Tel: (01902) 494647 Fax: (01902) 604366 E-mail: andywalker@kespar.co.uk *Plastic & pressure tool manufrs*

R A D Products Ltd, 19 Dodwells Bridge Industrial Estate, Jacknell Road, Hinckley, Leicestershire, LE10 3BS Tel: (01455) 891122 Fax: (01455) 891133 E-mail: sales@radproducts.co.uk *Reinforcement & ground engineering products distributors*

▶ R A D Warehousing, 73 Station Road, Kennett, Newmarket, Suffolk, CB8 7QF Tel: (01638) 750949

R A Driair Ltd, 9 Maguire Industrial Estate, Torrington Avenue, Coventry, CV4 9HN Tel: (024) 7646 6061 Fax: (024) 7669 4516 E-mail: sales@driair.co.uk Principal Export Areas: Worldwide *Compressed gas dryer manufrs*

R A E Models, Unit 15, 113 Fordwater Road, Chertsey, Surrey, KT16 8HB Tel: (01932) 563600 Fax: (01932) 564778 E-mail: raemodels@supernet.com *Model making*

R & A Engineering, 15 Stocklake Industrial Estate, Pembroke Road, Aylesbury, Buckinghamshire, HP20 1DB Tel: (01296) 425057 Fax: (01296) 481085 E-mail: sales@randaeng.co.uk *Precision production engineers*

R & A F Engineers, Unit 5b Britannia Park Industrial Estate, North Road, Stoke-on-Trent, ST6 2PZ Tel: (01782) 201212 Fax: (01782) 201212 *Steel fabricators*

R A G, The Malthouse, Old Bexley Heath Business Park, 19 Bourne Road, Bexley, Kent, DA5 1LR Tel: (0800) 0431416 Fax: (0870) 850 1417 E-mail: info@ragcomms.com *R A G (Remote Analysis Generation) based in Kent provides data loggers, temperature sensors, temperature controls and temperature monitoring software.*

R & A Grantham, Keynor Lane, Sidlesham, Chichester, West Sussex, PO20 7NL Tel: (01243) 641678 Fax: (01243) 641808 *Fish merchants*

R A Green (Mechanical Servises) Ltd, Southdown, Western Road, Crowborough, East Sussex, TN6 3EW Tel: (01892) 652177 Fax: (01892) 667225 E-mail: ragreen@btinternet.com *Heating & ventilation engineers*

R A H Advertising Ltd, 320 Palatine Road, Northenden, Manchester, M22 4HF Tel: 0161-902 0555 Fax: 0161-902 0777 E-mail: info@rahadvertising.com *Commercial printers*

▶ R A Haulage Co. Ltd, 5 Princes Road, London, N18 3PR Tel: (020) 8803 7374 Fax: (020) 8807 7031

▶ R & A Home Services, 139 Huyton House Road, Liverpool, L36 2PF Tel: 0151-289 4217 Fax: 0151-480 2688 E-mail: enquiries@rahomeservices.co.uk *Residential /Commercial Window Cleaners & General Cleaners*

R A Howarth Engineering Ltd, Earl Road, Rackheath Industrial Estate, Rackheath, Norwich, NR13 6NT Tel: (01603) 721155 Fax: (01603) 721648 *Precision engineering & gear cutting*

R A Hulland Group Ltd, 239 High St, Cymmer, Porth, Mid Glamorgan, CF39 9AD Tel: (01443) 684844 Fax: (01443) 684847 E-mail: ray@rahullandgroup.co.uk *Property investment development & management services*

R A Irwin & Co. Ltd, Bannside Industrial Estate, Goban Street, Portadown, Craigavon, County Armagh, BT63 5AG Tel: (028) 3833 6215 Fax: (028) 3835 0310 E-mail: info@ra-irwin.co.uk *Textile manufrs*

R A K Fasteners Ltd, R A K Fasteners Ltd Unit 18 Pinfold Industrial Estate, Field Close, Bloxwich, Walsall, WS3 3JS Tel: (01922) 408508 Fax: (01922) 402037 *Stud & stud bolt & fastener (industrial) manufrs*

R A L Ltd, 449 Bethnal Green Road, London, E2 9QH Tel: (020) 7739 5149 Fax: (020) 7739 7856 E-mail: sales@ralphswimer.co.uk *Trimmings & textile merchants*

R A L Ltd, 368 Silbury Boulevard, Milton Keynes, MK9 2AF Tel: (01908) 696100 Fax: (01908) 393865 *Amusement arcade machinery distributors & agents*

R A Labone & Co. Ltd, Lower Middleton Street, Ilkeston, Derbyshire, DE7 5TN Tel: 0115-930 1339 Fax: 0115-944 8801 E-mail: reception@ralabone.co.uk *Precision engineers* Also at: Consett & Newhouse

R A Lewis, Galltyllan Farm, Penegoes, Machynlleth, Powys, SY20 8DF Tel: (01654) 702083 *Agricultural contractors*

R A Lubricants, Perseverance Mills, Lockwood Scar, Huddersfield, HD4 6BW Tel: (01484) 512836 Fax: (01484) 420793 *Lubricant distributor*

R A M Ltd, Unit B3 Guy Motors Industrial Park, Park Lane, Wolverhampton, WV10 9QF Tel: (01902) 863506 Fax: (01902) 728402 E-mail: r.a.m.ltd@eur-is.co.uk *Distribution of consumable's*

R A M Computers, 260d Gospel Lane, Birmingham, B27 7AH Tel: 0121-707 3353 Fax: 0121-706 1413 E-mail: sales@ramcomputers.co.uk *Computer services, distributors & manufrs*

R A & M D Butler, Murrays Service Station, Ashford Hill, Thatcham, Berkshire, RG19 8BQ Tel: 0118-981 3646 Fax: 0118-981 9139 E-mail: info@butlersgarage.co.uk *Garden machinery, chainsaws, lawnmowers, ride-on mowers*

R A M Mobile Electronics, 1 Therm Road, Hull, HU8 7BF Tel: (01482) 589522 Fax: (01482) 589546 E-mail: enquiries@rammobile.com *Car stereo suppliers & installers*

▶ R A M Perimeter Protection Ltd, 179 Higher Hillgate, Stockport, Cheshire, SK1 3JG Tel: 0161-477 4001 Fax: 0161-477 1007 E-mail: ramperimeterprotection@btconnect.com *Security products provider*

R A Mcmullen, 3a Ballyvannon Road, Ballinderry Upper, Lisburn, County Antrim, BT28 2LD Tel: (028) 9442 3133 Fax: (028) 9445 2830 *Agricultural engineers*

R A Newman & Sons, Indemnifying Farm, Chastleton, Moreton-in-Marsh, Gloucestershire, GL56 0SP Tel: (01608) 674288 Fax: (01608) 674573 *Agricultural contractors & landfill services*

▶ R & A Office Environments, Marshall Stevens Way, Trafford Park, Manchester, M17 1PP Tel: 0161-877 5666 Fax: 0161-877 6550 E-mail: richard.clarke@randaoffice.co.uk *Office furniture dealers*

R A Owen & Sons, Minavon, Llandinam, Powys, SY17 5DG Tel: (01686) 688271 Fax: (01686) 688057 E-mail: info@raowenandsons.co.uk *Coal & agricultural equipment suppliers*

R A P Conveyors Ltd, Conveyors House, Newcastle, Staffordshire, ST5 7LU Tel: (01782) 566440 Fax: (01782) 566385 E-mail: suegater@btconnect.com *Rubber belting suppliers & site services*

▶ R A P Industries Ltd (Sheet Metal), Welbeck Way, Peterborough, PE2 7WH Tel: (01733) 394941 Fax: (01733) 391825 *Manufacturers of office furniture*

R A P Marketing, 24 The Business Village, Wexham Road, Slough, SL2 5HF Tel: (01753) 554160 Fax: (01753) 518532 E-mail: awrap@aol.com *Anniversary label production services*

R A Peatey & Sons Ltd, Green Lane, Yeadon, Leeds, LS19 7BY Tel: 0113-250 1046 Fax: 0113-250 7364 *Metal finishers & powder coaters suppliers*

R A Poole, 5 Kingston Business Centre, Fullers Way South, Chessington, Surrey, KT9 1DQ Tel: (020) 8391 9140 Fax: (020) 8391 9150 E-mail: sales@rapoole.com *Fastener & bolt & nut manufrs*

R A Roberts, Llawr Y Pant Hall, Selattyn, Oswestry, Shropshire, SY10 7HX Tel: (01691) 653913 *Agricultural contractors*

R A Robinson & Son, Unit 7 Turnpike Industrial Estate, Newbury, Berkshire, RG14 2LR Tel: (01635) 41045 Fax: (01635) 41045 *Sausage & burger manufrs*

▶ R A Rousell & Son, The Poplars, Latcham, Wedmore, Somerset, BS28 4SA Tel: (01934) 712518 Fax: (01934) 713755

▶ R A S Crockett & Partners, 69-71 Scott Street, Dundee, DD2 2BA Tel: (01382) 669892 Fax: (01382) 669892

▶ R & A Sheet Metal, 30-31 Sedling Road, Wear Industrial Estate, Washington, Tyne & Wear, NE38 9BZ Tel: (07801) 768398 Fax: 0191-419 2700 E-mail: randasheetmetal@aol.com *Manufacture & supply of quality sheet metal work*

R & A Software Systems Ltd, Bank Chambers, 244 Fulwood Road, Sheffield, S10 3BB Tel: 0114-267 9669 Fax: 0114-267 9670 E-mail: info@rasoft.co.uk *Software developers*

R & A Stevens, 2 Church Terrace, Bures, Suffolk, CO8 5ED Tel: (01787) 227291 Fax: (01787) 228252 E-mail: stevens.ra@virgin.net *Hot melt gluing systems suppliers*

R A Watts Ltd, 36-38 Woodcote Road, Wallington, Surrey, SM6 0NN Tel: (020) 8647 1074 Fax: (020) 8773 3595 E-mail: sales@rawatts.fsbusiness.co.uk *Chemical merchants*

▶ R A Wheeler, The Hollies, North Road, Middleham, Leyburn, North Yorkshire, DL8 4PJ Tel: (01969) 622144 Fax: (01969) 622144 E-mail: sales@raw-construction.com

R A Young, 582 Clarkston Road, Glasgow, G44 3SQ Tel: 0141-632 5950 *Industrial protective clothing*

R Allen Tonbridge Ltd, 18 Lyons Cresent, Tonbridge, Kent, TN9 1EX Tel: (01732) 353499 *Motor engineering services*

▶ R Austin, 35 Searle Way, Eight Ash Green, Colchester, CO6 3QS Tel: (01206) 572217 Fax: (01206) 572217 *Fitted kitchens, bedrooms, bathrooms. Extensions, conservatories. All carpentry work*

R B Allfree & Co Ltd, Unit 2a Turnoaks Lane, Chesterfield, Derbyshire, S40 2HA Tel: (01246) 554050 Fax: (01246) 554060 E-mail: info@rballfree.freeserve.co.uk *Civil engineering contractors*

R B Associates, 65 Sea Mills Lane, Stoke Bishop, Bristol, BS9 1DR Tel: 0117-968 1374 Fax: 0117-968 1374 Fax: rbass@avnet.co.uk *Anti-vibration mounting suppliers & stockists*

R & B Autos, Hackhurst Lane, Lower Dicker, Hailsham, East Sussex, BN27 4BW Tel: (01323) 845487 *Car spraying & repairers services*

R B B Refractory Engineers Ltd, 291 Watling Street, Dartford, DA2 6EP Tel: (01322) 394850 Fax: (01322) 394860 E-mail: enquiries@rbbrefractory.co.uk *Refractory installers*

R B C Captial Markets, 71 Queen Victoria Street, London, EC4V 4AY Tel: (020) 7489 1133 Fax: (020) 7248 3940 *Broker dealers*

R B Cranes Ltd, Thrumpton Lane, Retford, Nottinghamshire, DN22 7AN Tel: (01777) 700039 Fax: (01777) 713192 E-mail: info@jnd.co.uk Principal Export Areas: Worldwide *Crane & excavator manufrs*

R B D Builders Norfolk Ltd, 32 Southgates Road, Great Yarmouth, Norfolk, NR30 3LL Tel: (01493) 855891 Fax: (01493) 331615 *Windows*

▶ R & B Electrical Skipton Ltd, 3-5 Bowers Wharf, Skipton, North Yorkshire, BD23 2PD Tel: (01756) 793039 Fax: (01756) 793945

▶ R B Electronics, Unit 16 Jubilee Enterprise Centre, 15 Jubilee Close, Weymouth, Dorset, DT4 7BS Tel: (01305) 750555 Fax: (01305) 750555

R B Emerson, 8a Temple Farm Industrial Estate, Coopers Way, Temple Farm Industrial Estate, Southend-on-Sea, SS2 5TE Tel: (01702) 461999 Fax: (01702) 462001 E-mail: sales@emersons.uk.com *Electrical contractors, computer & building interiors*

R B Engineering Services, Unit 43 College Street, Kempston, Bedford, MK42 8LU Tel: (01234) 211263 Fax: (01234) 328835 *Engineering lifting gear & cranes*

R B F Fibreglass Ltd, Far Lane, Normanton on Soar, Loughborough, Leicestershire, LE12 5HA Tel: (01509) 646560 Fax: (01509) 646669 E-mail: rbffibreglass@aol.co.uk *Fibre glass moulding services*

R & B Fabrications, 4 Vulcan Road, Solihull, West Midlands, B91 2JY Tel: 0121-711 3279 Fax: 0121-711 3279 *Ventilation ductwork fabricators*

R B G, Norfolk House, Pitmedden Road, Dyce, Aberdeen, AB21 0DP Tel: (01224) 215100 Fax: (01224) 723406 E-mail: john.walker@rigblast.com *Industrial chemical cleaning & decontamination service*

R B I Recovery Services, Geddings Road, Hoddesdon, Hertfordshire, EN11 0NW Tel: (01992) 445566 Fax: (01992) 441785 *Computer breakdown & breakdown recovery*

R & B Industrial Ltd, 41 Charlton Road, Andover, Hampshire, SP10 3JH Tel: (01264) 351844 Fax: (01264) 354191 E-mail: info@rbindustrial.co.uk *Dust collection, bag & cartridge filter manufacturers & suppliers*

R B Industrial Finishers, Unit 4 Kents Avenue, Hemel Hempstead, Hertfordshire, HP3 9XH Tel: (01442) 244343 Fax: (01442) 235127 *Stove enamelling & powder coating services*

R & B Instruments Ltd, Unit 3A Farnley Low Mills, Bangor Terrace, Leeds, LS12 5PS Tel: 0113-279 1066 Fax: 0113-231 9655 E-mail: sales@rbinstruments.com *Manufacturers of laser refractometers, used by anaesthetic vaporiser manufacturers.*

R B James, Ashdown Farm, Badsey Road, Evesham, Worcestershire, WR11 7PA Tel: (01386) 41585 Fax: (01386) 41541 *Tipper lorry hire*

R B Labels Ltd, 37 Grove Road, Ilkley, West Yorkshire, LS29 9PF Tel: (01943) 468302 Fax: (01943) 850406 E-mail: sales@tradelabels.co.uk *Self-adhesive label specialists*

R B Lewis & Co., Wherley Rough Garage, Lower Heath, Prees, Whitchurch, Shropshire, SY13 2BH Tel: (01948) 840886 Fax: (01948) 840109 *Fork lift truck distributors*

R B Lyttle, 60 Station Road, Garvagh, Coleraine, County Londonderry, BT51 5LA Tel: (028) 2955 8264 Fax: (028) 2955 7043 *Potato equipment manufacturing*

R B M Agricultural Ltd, Waterloo Works, Jameson Bridge Street, Market Rasen, Lincolnshire, LN8 3EW Tel: (01673) 844079 Fax: (01673) 844632 E-mail: steveplewesrbm@btconnect.com *Agricultural machinery dealers & repairers*

R B M Wound Components, The Sanderson Centre, Lees Lane, Gosport, Hampshire, PO12 3UL Tel: (023) 9252 0777 Fax: (023) 9252 4777 E-mail: ron@rbmwoundcomps.co.uk *Transformer manufrs*

R B Medical, 2 Alton Road Industrial Estate, Ross-on-Wye, Herefordshire, HR9 5ND Tel: (01989) 563958 Fax: (01989) 768267 E-mail: a.ross@rimbros.co.uk *Scientific instrument manufrs*

R B Mentor Services, 152 West Regent Street, Glasgow, G2 2RQ Tel: 0141-248 1212 Fax: 0141-248 3324 *Banking*

R B Montague & Sons, Edmont, Preston-on-Wye, Hereford, HR2 9JT Tel: (01981) 500310 Fax: (01981) 500310 *Agricultural contractors*

R B Mouldings Ltd, 3 Kings Haven, Kings Road, Charfleets Industrial Estate, Canvey Island, Essex, SS8 0QW Tel: (01268) 690626 Fax: (01268) 510106 E-mail: roger@rbmouldings.fsbuisness.co.uk *Plastics injection moulding manufrs*

▶ R B Networks, Copthorne Common, Copthorne, Crawley, West Sussex, RH10 3LG Tel: (01342) 715396 E-mail: sales@e-delta.net

R B Plant Construction Ltd, The Square, Lenham, Maidstone, Kent, ME17 2PG Tel: (01622) 858387 Fax: (01622) 858920 E-mail: mail@rb-plant.co.uk *Pharmaceutical consultants*

R B Polishes Ltd, 579 London Road, Isleworth, Middlesex, TW7 4EJ Tel: (020) 8560 6348 Fax: (020) 8568 1253 *Floor polish manufrs*

▶ R B Precision Moulding, Unit F9 Anchor Brook Industrial Park, Aldridge, Walsall, WS9 8BZ Tel: (01922) 745030 Fax: (01922) 745039 E-mail: rbmoualding@aol.com *Plastic product manufrs*

▶ R B Print, 45-55 Bowlers Croft, Basildon, Essex, SS14 3EB Tel: (01268) 530053 Fax: (01268) 534453

R B Punching Services Ltd, College Road, Aston Clinton, Aylesbury, Buckinghamshire, HP22 5EZ Tel: (01296) 630262 Fax: (01296) 630485 E-mail: rbpunch@globalnet.co.uk *Precision sheet metal services*

R B Ross Steel Fabrications Ltd, Moss-Side, Dyce, Aberdeen, AB21 7AS Tel: (01224) 770577 Fax: (01224) 772079 E-mail: info@rbross.co.uk *Seal fabrication plant location services*

R B S Engineering Storage & Fabrications Ltd, Protection Works Martin Street, Rear of 934 Bradford Road, Birstall, Batley, West Yorkshire, WF17 9PJ Tel: (01924) 440021 Fax: (01924) 443674 E-mail: info@rbs.co.uk *Engineering storage & fabrications*

R B S Office Supplies, Tollgate Business Centre, Tollgate Drive, Tollgate Industrial Estate, Stafford, ST16 3HS Tel: (01785) 254859 Fax: (01785) 220400 E-mail: sales@rbsofficesupplies.co.uk *Office equipment distributors*

▶ R B S Scaffolding Ltd, The Grove, Upper Northam Drive, Hedge End, Southampton, SO30 4BG Tel: (023) 8047 1119 Fax: (023) 8047 2828

R B Stainless, Unit 6 West Stockwith Park, Stockwith Road, Misterton, Doncaster, South Yorkshire, DN10 4ES Tel: (01427) 891988 Fax: (01427) 891988 *Stainless steel fabricators*

R & B Switchgear Services Ltd, The Courtyard, Green Lane, Heywood, Lancashire, OL10 2EX Tel: (01706) 369933 Fax: (01706) 364564 *Switchgear servicing*

R & B Trophies, 16 St Nicholas Street, Weymouth, Dorset, DT4 8AA Tel: (01305) 776826 Fax: (01305) 776826 E-mail: rbtrophys@tiscali.co.uk *Trophies & medals distributors*

R B Wholesale Ltd, The Broadway, Mansfield, Nottinghamshire, NG18 2RL Tel: (01623) 623247 Fax: (01623) 629311 E-mail: sales@rbwholesale.co.uk *Janitorial glassware distributors*

▶ R B Wilson Electrical Ltd, 14 Pittodrie Street, Aberdeen, AB24 5QL Tel: (01224) 630187 Fax: (01224) 640393

R B Woodworking, Gidding Road, Hamerton, Huntingdon, Cambridgeshire, PE28 5QU Tel: (01832) 293384 Fax: (01832) 293384 *Joinery services*

R Barker & Sons Transport Ltd, School House Farm, Tollgate Road, Burscough, Ormskirk, Lancashire, L40 8LD Tel: (01704) 893303 Fax: (01704) 893878 E-mail: barkertransport@btconnect.com *Road transport, haulage & freight services*

R Barker Tarring Ltd, 32 South Street, Tarring, Worthing, West Sussex, BN14 7LN Tel: (01903) 233680 Fax: (01903) 824690 E-mail: rbarkerltd@mail.com *Electrical retailing, repair & hire*

R Baron Ltd, Peel Hall Street Works, Preston, PR1 6PU Tel: (01772) 795115 Fax: (01772) 204562

R Beal & Co. Ltd, Newtown Industrial Estate, Birtley, Chester le Street, County Durham, DH3 2QW Tel: 0191-492 0123 Fax: 0191-492 0567 E-mail: sales@bealandco.com *Steel fabricators*

R Bedford & Sons Cooked Meats, Cunliffe Road, Blackburn, BB1 5SU Tel: (01254) 52553 Fax: (01254) 583701 *Frozen food processors/ products manufrs*

▶ R Bell, 14 Birch Close, North Walsham, Norfolk, NR28 0UD Tel: (01692) 409080 Fax: (0800) 7832212 E-mail: contact@rbellplatformhire.co.uk *specialists in tracked access platform hire.**All of east anglia covered*

R Bennett & Sons, Fal Valley Tannery, Grampound, Truro, Cornwall, TR2 4RX Tel: (01726) 882417 *Slaughter house service*

R Bickley & Co., 13 Redcar Road, Romford, RM3 9PT Tel: (01708) 348557 *Pest control services*

R Biller & Co., 22-36 Charles Street, Rochester, Kent, ME2 2BL Tel: (01634) 290666 Fax: (01634) 296700 *General motor factors*

R. Billson & Sons Ltd, 431 Thurmaston Boulevard, Off Claymill Road, Leicester, LE4 9LA Tel: 0116-276 2555 Fax: 0116-276 9234 *Rope & twine merchants/canvas goods manufrs*

R Bishop, Hill Grove Farm, Crawley Dry Lane, Minster Lovell, Witney, Oxfordshire, OX29 0NA Tel: (01993) 779009 Fax: (01993) 779009 *Joinery manufrs*

▶ R Blight Builders Ltd, Morton Works, Clovelly Road, Bideford, Devon, EX39 3QU Tel: (01237) 476927 Fax: (01237) 425407 E-mail: info@blightsbuilders.com

▶ R Brewer Construction Ltd, Bathurst House, Smythen St, Exeter, EX1 1BN Tel: (01392) 494424 E-mail: sales@rbrewer.co.uk

▶ R Brewer Construction Ltd, 87 Alexandra Road, St. Austell, Cornwall, PL25 4QW Tel: (01726) 69354

R Brumwell & Co., Compton House, Walnut Tree Close, Guildford, Surrey, GU1 4TX Tel: (01483) 302276 Fax: (01483) 302292 E-mail: brumwell@btinternet.com *Marine cargo surveyors*

R C Beresford Ltd, 48 St. Georges Street, Birmingham, B19 3QU Tel: 0121-236 8455 Fax: 0121-236 8493 *Metal spinning & engineering*

R C Billington Farmer, Stubbins Farm, Preston, PR3 0PL Tel: (01995) 640467 Fax: (01995) 640073 *Agricultural engineering*

R C Boreham & Co., Woodfield Farm, Pleshey, Chelmsford, CM3 1HU Tel: (01245) 231320 Fax: (01245) 231435 E-mail: sales@rcboreham.co.uk *Agricultural & horticultural parts, sales, hire*

R & C Church Ltd, Anglian House, Sutton Road, Great Yarmouth, Norfolk, NR30 3NB Tel: (01493) 858715 Fax: (01493) 859786 E-mail: ron@church-precision.co.uk *Precision engineers*

R C Coppin Ltd, Unit 2 Park Drive, Braintree, Essex, CM7 1AP Tel: (01376) 550009 Fax: (01376) 551436 E-mail: sales@rccoppinltd.co.uk *R.C.Coppin Ltd is a family orientated business specialising in all areas of the Marble-Granite-Stone trade with four generations of stonemasons. Whilst celebrating four generations of trading its with this accumulated knowledge that the practices adopted from classic to modern are as strong as the product portfolio. The modern day accepts that modern technology can monitor the quality and durability of all materials during the manufacturing process however there is no substitute for an experienced eye. R.C.Coppin Ltd is a highly respected company built from reputation, recommendation and professionalism, producing only the best as only the best is available.*

R C Cutting & Co. Ltd, 10-12 Arcadia Avenue, London, N3 2JU Tel: (020) 8371 0001 Fax: (020) 8371 0003 E-mail: info@rccutting.co.uk *Lightning conductor engineers*

R C Design Ceramics, Unit 3 Chelson Street, Stoke-on-Trent, ST3 1PT Tel: (01782) 334886 Fax: (01782) 334886 *Ceramic transfer designs*

▶ R & C Electrical Engineers Ltd, Cheshire House, Murhall Street, Stoke-on-Trent, ST6 4BL Tel: (01782) 824660 Fax: (01782) 825474

continued

Company Information

R C F Bolt & Nut Co. Ltd, Park Lane East, Tipton, West Midlands, DY4 8RF Tel: 0121-522 2353 Fax: 0121-522 2304 E-mail: rcf@dial.pipex.com *Bolts, nuts & agricultural machinery spare parts*

R & C Glen Scotland Ltd, Glen House, 29 Orleans Avenue, Glasgow, G14 9NF Tel: 0141-959 9988 Fax: 0141-959 9666 E-mail: sales@rcglen.co.uk *Suppliers of Marine Rubber & ELASTOPAL Fenders, complete fender systems, UHMW-PE fenders, Pneumatic Fenders with tyres/net cage, Cast iron Bollards 5 - 200 tonne, Mooring Rings, anchors and chains for ships and moorings from 6mm up to 152mm dia in all marine grades Studlink or openlink chains*

▶ R C H Group, 93-95 Pall Mall, Leigh-on-Sea, Essex, SS9 1RF Tel: (01702) 714959 Fax: (01702) 710005

R C H Quality & Design, The Glen, Trevor Road, Llangollen, Clwyd, LL20 7UH Tel: (01978) 860706 E-mail: roberrt.hicks@btclick.com *Management consultants*

R C H Signs, Unit 18 Marian Mawr Industrial Estate, Dolgellau, Gwynedd, LL40 1UU Tel: (01341) 423577 Fax: (01341) 422646 E-mail: sales@rchsigns.com *Sign manufrs*

R & C Imports Ltd, Orient House, 15 Newton St, Hyde, Cheshire, SK14 4RY Tel: 0161-366 8888 Fax: 0161-366 0000 E-mail: info@randcliving.co.uk *Ornamental giftware importers*

R C Kennedy Ltd, 1 North Street, Manchester, M8 8RE Tel: 0161-832 6182 Fax: 0161-834 3053 *Furnishing fabrics & curtain manufrs*

▶ R C L Air Conditioning, Unit 10 Birch Business Park, Progress Drive, Cannock, Staffordshire, WS11 0BF Tel: (01543) 462422 Fax: (01543) 468777 *Service & maintenance of all air conditioning systems*

▶ R & C Landscapes, 82 Groveside Close, Carshalton, Surrey, SM5 2ET Tel: (020) 8773 8296 E-mail: robertgibbs364@hotmail.com *Driveway & paving contractors, turf, fencing & patios*

▶ R C M Joinery, Unit 15 Four Crosses Creamery, Four Crosses, Llanymynech, Powys, SY22 6RH Tel: (01691) 830851

R C M Products, 19 Burners Lane, Kiln Farm, Milton Keynes, MK11 3HA Tel: (01908) 263131 Fax: (01908) 265454 E-mail: sales@rcmproducts.co.uk *Grille manufrs*

R C Marble & Sons Ltd, 158a Ovenden Road, Halifax, West Yorkshire, HX3 5QG Tel: (01422) 345990 E-mail: sales@rcmarble.co.uk *Sign manufrs*

R & C Motor Co. Ltd, White Hart Road, Slough, SL1 2SF Tel: (01753) 529454 Fax: (01753) 517021 *Restoration services*

R C Murray, 17 Woodland Gardens, North Wootton, King's Lynn, Norfolk, PE30 3PX Tel: (01553) 631770 Fax: (01553) 631770 E-mail: rcmkl@freeuk.com *Civil & structural engineers* Also at: Kings Lynn

R C P Consultants Ltd, Richards House, 81 Broadway, Didcot, Oxfordshire, OX11 8AJ Tel: (01235) 510116 Fax: (01235) 515302 E-mail: sales@acp.co.uk *Specialist software solutions*

R C Perry & Co. Ltd, Unit 4 Worthington Way, Wigan, Lancashire, WN3 6XE Tel: (01942) 494012 Fax: (01942) 494021 E-mail: inquiries@rcperry.co.uk *Label manufrs*

R & C Plant Services Ltd, 187 Old Heath Road, Colchester, CO2 8AT Tel: (01206) 793525 Fax: (01206) 792332 *Plant sales & repairs*

▶ R & C Poole, 7 Lyric Court, Rax Lane, Bridport, Dorset, DT6 3JS Tel: (01308) 427422 Fax: (01308) 421696

R C R Aviation Ltd, Andover, Hampshire, SP10 5XZ Tel: (01264) 359352 Fax: (01264) 359351 E-mail: sales@rcr-aviation.com *Helicopter suppliers*

R C S Filling Machines Ltd, Unit 1 Brand Street, Nottingham, NG2 3GW Tel: 0115-985 1717 Fax: 0115-985 1948 E-mail: sales@rcsfilling.com *Bespoke manufacturers of filling and decanting machinery*

R C S Hose & Hydraulics Ltd, Crucible Road, Corby, Northamptonshire, NN17 5TS Tel: 0800 3893132 *Hydraulic equipment & systems distributor*

▶ R C S UK Ltd, Brunel Road, Wakefield 41 Industrial Estate, Wakefield, West Yorkshire, WF2 0XG Tel: (01924) 870888 Fax: (01924) 871888

R C Snelling Investments Ltd, Blofield Corner, Blofield, Norwich, NR13 4SQ Tel: (01603) 712202 Fax: (01603) 716052 E-mail: sales@snellingtv.co.uk *TV, audio rental, service & repair & sales*

R C Stiven & Co., Unit 31 Faraday Street, Dryburgh Industrial Estate, Dundee, DD2 3QQ Tel: (01382) 833322 Fax: (01382) 889133 E-mail: aws@rcstiven.sol.co.uk *Paint merchants*

R C T Manufacturing Services, Leona Trading Estate, Nimmings Road, Halesowen, West Midlands, B62 9JQ Tel: 0121-561 5492 Fax: 0121-561 2444 E-mail: rctmanufacturing@btconnect.com *Welders & fabricators*

R C Thanet Ltd, 20 Albion Road, Broadstairs, Kent, CT10 2UP Tel: (01843) 862288 *Steel fabricators*

▶ R C Tucker Ltd, 2 Kimberley, Stathern Lane, Harby, Melton Mowbray, Leicestershire, LE14 4DA Tel: (01949) 860203 Fax: (01949) 861094

▶ R & C Williams Ltd, Salford Bridge Wharf, Tyburn Road, Birmingham, B24 8NP Tel: 0121-326 9696 Fax: 0121-328 3171

▶ R.C_ Annie Ltd, 34 Pullman Place, Eltham, London, SE9 9EG Tel: (07811) 390313 Fax: (0802) 3782880 E-mail: ruth@arty-annie.com *Specialists in the entertainment industry*

R Cadisch & Sons, Unit 1, 879 High Road, London, N12 8QA Tel: (020) 8492 0444 Fax: (020) 8492 0333 E-mail: info@cadisch.com Principal Export Areas: Worldwide *Filtration & separation manufrs*

R Campbell, 6 Oaklands Park, Hatherleigh Road, Okehampton, Devon, EX20 1LN Tel: (01837) 52540 Fax: (01837) 52540 *Ground works contractors*

R Carslaw, Chelsea Reach, 79-89 Lots Road, London, SW10 0RN Tel: (020) 7376 4440 Fax: (020) 7351 3258 E-mail: sales@robertcarslaw.com *Interior & office designers*

R Carter, Hale Manor Farm, Hale Common, Newport, Isle of Wight, PO30 3AR Tel: (01983) 867312 Fax: (01983) 868200 *Ready mix concrete suppliers*

R Chander, Alfred Street North, Nottingham, NG3 1AE Tel: 0115-950 2631 Fax: 0115-950 4668 E-mail: ashwansee@aol.com *Lace & textile wholesalers & importers*

R Charnock, 1 Adswood Industrial Estate, Adswood Road, Stockport, Cheshire, SK3 8LF Tel: 0161-477 3082 Fax: 0161-480 9854 E-mail: sales@rickcharnockcomponents.co.uk *Motor car component factors*

▶ R Collard Ltd, Fleet Road, Hartley Wintney, Hook, Hampshire, RG27 8ED Tel: (01252) 844688 Fax: (01252) 844668

R Collett & Sons Transport Ltd, Albert Road, Halifax, West Yorkshire, HX2 0DF Tel: (01422) 255233 Fax: (01422) 255244 E-mail: sales@collett.co.uk *Heavy haulage specialists* Also at: Keighley

R Couch, Bodwen Farm, Bodwen, Bodmin, Cornwall, PL30 4QU Tel: (01208) 72507 Fax: (01208) 851264 *Agricultural engineers*

▶ R Cox Haulage Ltd, Trent Street, Sheffield, S9 3XU Tel: 0114-244 2115 Fax: 0114-244 8275

▶ R Cundle, 12 Whinbrook Crescent, Leeds, LS17 5PN Tel: 0113-288 8390 Fax: 0113-288 8390 *Suit manufrs*

▶ R D A, 33 Hazle Close, Ledbury, Herefordshire, HR8 2XX Tel: (01531) 630002 Fax: (0870) 4605824 E-mail: info@rdauk.co.uk *RDA offers new and unique levels of professional service for the retail interiors and point of purchase industry. "We work with brands, retailers and agencies providing you with the services to design and manufacture retail display equipment."To find out more about the way we work please contact info@rdauk.co.uk"*

R D A Organic, 118 Putney Bridge Road, London, SW15 2NQ Tel: (020) 8875 9740 Fax: (020) 8875 0370 E-mail: info@rdaorganic.com *Fruit juice suppliers*

R & D Aggregates Ltd, 12 Lisle Avenue, Kidderminster, Worcestershire, DY11 7DL Tel: (01562) 745683 Fax: (01562) 820861 E-mail: info@unitstolet.net *Property leasing*

▶ R D Anderson Haulage Ltd, 64 Longstone Road, Edinburgh, EH14 2BA Tel: 0131-443 5981 Fax: 0131-443 9438 E-mail: sales@rdanderson.co.uk

R D Aviation Ltd, Oxford Airport, Kidlington, Oxfordshire, OX5 1QX Tel: (01865) 841441 Fax: (01865) 842495 E-mail: sales@afeonline.com *Aircraft & gliding equipment distributors*

R D B Services, The Forge, Ockendon Road, North Ockendon, Upminster, Essex, RM14 3PS Tel: (01708) 852319 Fax: (01708) 851610 *Agricultural engineers*

R D Barrett Small Tools, Brow Mills Industrial Estate, Brighouse Road, Hipperholme, Halifax, West Yorkshire, HX3 8DD Tel: (01422) 205828 Fax: (01422) 202358 E-mail: j.n.rushby@supanet.com Principal Export Areas: Worldwide *Machine tool merchants*

R D Bennett Farming Contractors, Hollyhedge Farm, Hollyhedge Lane, Higher Walton, Warrington, WA4 5QP Tel: (01925) 262342 Fax: (01925) 268703 *Farmer*

R D Brett Electrical Contractors Ltd, Lower Nursery, Sunningdale, Ascot, Berkshire, SL5 0PA Tel: (01344) 620444 Fax: (01344) 624873 E-mail: enquiries@rdbrett.co.uk *Electrical contractors*

R D Campbell & Co. Ltd, Unit 14 Mill Farm Business Park, Millfield Road, Hounslow, TW4 5PY Tel: (020) 8898 6611 Fax: (020) 8898 6622 *Food flavouring & perfume based compounds*

R D Castings Ltd, Leyton Avenue, Mildenhall, Bury St. Edmunds, Suffolk, IP28 7BL Tel: (01638) 717944 Fax: (01638) 716590 *Die casting manufrs*

R & D Ceilings (South West) Ltd, 232 Wells Road, Bristol, BS4 2PJ Tel: 0117-977 0222 Fax: 0117-977 0313 E-mail: info@randdcellings.co.uk *Suspended ceiling*

R D Computer Systems, 39 Ballyroney Rd, Rathfriland, Newry, Co. Down, BT34 5NQ Tel: (028) 4063 1626 Fax: (028) 4063 1636 *Computer software consultants*

▶ R D Downie, 133 Shore Street, Fraserburgh, Aberdeenshire, AB43 9BP Tel: (01346) 518855 Fax: (01346) 515776

▶ R D Engineering, 1130 Melton Road, Syston, Leicester, LE7 2HA Tel: 0116-260 7567 *Plastic injection moulding*

R & D Engineering, Springfield Industrial Estate, Failsworth, Manchester, M35 0GA Tel: 0161-682 6068 Fax: 0161-682 6068 *Steel fabricators & site maintenance services*

R & D Engineering Ltd, 4 Robin Hood Works, Robin Hood Road, Knaphill, Woking, Surrey, GU21 2LX Tel: (01483) 488545 Fax: (01483) 488058 *Precision engineers*

R D Equipment, 9 Bownham Mead, Rodborough Common, Stroud, Gloucestershire, GL5 5DZ Tel: (01453) 872623 E-mail: rdequipment@tesco.net *Suppliers of used air compressors*

R D F Beaufort Ltd, Kingsway, Dunmurry, Belfast, BT17 9AF Tel: (028) 9030 1531 Fax: (028) 9062 1765 E-mail: sales@rfdbeaufort.com *Aviation life saving equipment* Also at: Belfast

R D F Consulting Ltd, 15 Queen Square, Brighton, BN1 3FD Tel: (01273) 200100 Fax: (01273) 205005 E-mail: sales@rdfgroup.com *IT consultants*

▶ R D F Consulting, Fairways Business Park, 5 Deer Park Road, Livingston, West Lothian, EH54 8AF Tel: (01506) 836200 Fax: (01506) 444222 E-mail: sales@rdf-consulting.co.uk

R D F Eurobars, 55 Second Drove, Peterborough, PE1 5XA Tel: (01733) 555263 Fax: (01733) 555913 E-mail: sales@eurobars.co.uk *Vehicle towing brackets & accessory manufrs*

R & D Fabrications, Units 65-67 Boughton Industrial Estate, New Ollerton, Newark, Nottinghamshire, NG22 9LD Tel: (01623) 862473 Fax: (01623) 862866 E-mail: sheila@randdfabs.fsnet.co.uk *Steel boat builders & fabricators*

R & D Fastenings Systems Ltd, 135 High St, Newton-le-Willows, Merseyside, WA12 9SQ Tel: (01925) 224442 Fax: (01925) 222711 E-mail: david.cunningham@f9.co.uk *Industrial fastener distribs*

▶ R D G Ltd, In-Spec House, Wellheads Drive, Dyce, Aberdeen, AB21 7GQ Tel: (01224) 845100 Fax: (01224) 845290 *Offshore company*

R D H Components Ltd, Nelson Lane, Warwick, CV34 5JB Tel: (01926) 409330 Fax: (01926) 409331 *Vehicle component manufrs*

R & D Hope, 9 Caulside, Canonbie, Dumfriesshire, DG14 0RT Tel: (01387) 371297 *Agricultural contractors*

R D Industries Ltd, Estover Road, Plymouth, PL6 7PS Tel: (01752) 844148 *Stationery manufrs*

R D J, Unit 1 A, Cranmer Road, West Meadows Industrial Estate, Derby, DE21 6JL Tel: (01332) 345472 Fax: (01332) 293509 Principal Export Areas: Worldwide *Industrial & quarrying electrical contractors & engineers*

▶ R D J Builders (Rochdale) Ltd, 18A Bridge Street, Milnrow, Rochdale, Lancashire, OL16 3ND Tel: (01706) 632243

R D Jukes & Co. Ltd, Walsingham Works, 1 Walsingham Street, Walsall, WS1 2JZ Tel: (01922) 624222 Fax: (01922) 630587 E-mail: info@rdjukes.co.uk *Electrical engineers & contractors*

▶ R D K Construction Ltd, 52a Hamilton St, Saltcoats, Ayrshire, KA21 5DS Tel: (01294) 468365

▶ R D Kearton & Sons Ltd, Museum View, Boldron, Barnard Castle, County Durham, DL12 9RQ Tel: (01833) 631229 Fax: (01833) 631866

R D M Distribution, Santareen Road, Unit 3, Tharston, Norwich, NR15 2NZ Tel: (01508) 530115

▶ R D Machine Tools, Unit 1-3 Minerva Lane, Wolverhampton, WV1 3LU Tel: (01902) 870701 Fax: (01902) 870071 *Machine tools manufrs*

R D Musgrave & Sons, Edder Acres Farm, Shotton Colliery, Durham, DH6 2QB Tel: 0191-526 2965 *Farming agricultural contractors*

R D P Group Ltd, Grove Street, Heath Town, Wolverhampton, WV10 0PY Tel: (01902) 457512 Fax: (01902) 452000 E-mail: sales@rdpelectronics.com *Manufacturers of sensors, transducers & measuring instrumentation*

R D P Howden Ltd, Southam, Warwickshire, CV47 0ZD Tel: (01926) 813141 Fax: (01926) 810007 E-mail: info@rdphowden.co.uk *Testing machine materials*

R D Piper Recruitment, 1 Riverside House, Lower Southend Road, Wickford, Essex, SS11 8BB Tel: (01268) 561020 Fax: (01268) 571483 E-mail: enquiries@rdpiper.co.uk *Personnel recruitment agency*

R D Precision, Unit 1e Pentre Industrial Estate, Chester Road, Pentre, Deeside, Clwyd, CH5 2DQ Tel: (01244) 520559 Fax: (01244) 531992 E-mail: enquiries@rdprecision.co.uk *Precision engineers*

R D Precision Ltd, Golden Hill Park, Freshwater, Isle Of Wight, PO40 9UJ Tel: (01983) 754811 Fax: (01983) 754186 E-mail: info@rdprecisions.co.uk Principal Export Areas: Worldwide *Aerospace engineering services*

▶ R & D Property Maintenance, 46 Oakthorpe Gardens, Tividale, Oldbury, West Midlands, B69 2LF Tel: 0121-601 3979 E-mail: Davenscribe@blueyonder.co.uk *All aspects of property maintenance domestic and commercial undertaken.*

R D R Bearings, 20 Ravenhill Road, Belfast, BT6 8EA Tel: (028) 9073 2321 Fax: (028) 9073 1889 E-mail: rdr@nbcgroup.co.uk *Bearing suppliers*

R D Robins Upholsterers Ltd, The Mews, 39b Church Hill Road, London, E17 9RX Tel: (020) 7704 8182 Fax: (020) 8520 5226 E-mail: rdrobinsuphole@aol.com *Upholsterer & re-upholsterers*

▶ R D S, 5 Rigby Close, Heathcote Industrial Estate, Warwick, CV34 6TH Tel: (01926) 435255 Fax: (01926) 336594 E-mail: sales@rdstransport.co.uk *Catering & refrigeration engineers*

R D S Cartons Ltd, 3 Schoolfield Road, Grays, Essex, RM20 3HR Tel: (01708) 861355 Fax: (01708) 863913 E-mail: rdscartons@btconnect.com *Carton printers & manufrs*

R D S South-West Ltd, 162 Chemical Road, West Wiltshire Trading Estate, Westbury, Wiltshire, BA13 4JN Tel: (01373) 864415 Fax: (01373) 825415 *Sell & service electronic monitoring*

R D S Technology Ltd, Cirencester Road, Minchinhampton, Stroud, Gloucestershire, GL6 9BH Tel: (01453) 733300 Fax: (01453) 733311 E-mail: info@rdstec.com *Agricultural electronics manufrs*

R & D Signs Ltd, 37 Lichfield Road, Birmingham, B6 5RW Tel: 0121-327 3041 Fax: 0121-326 6983 E-mail: info@rdsigns.co.uk *Sign Manufacturers*

▶ R D T Precision Engineers Ltd, 3 Colvilles Road, Kelvin Industrial Estate, East Kilbride, Glasgow, G75 0RS Tel: (01355) 248072 Fax: (01355) 264380 E-mail: info@rdtprecision.com *Metal work engineers*

R D Techniques, 3 Mounts Road, Wednesbury, West Midlands, WS10 0BU Tel: 0121-502 0570 Fax: 0121-505 3238 E-mail: rd.techniques@cableinet.co.uk *Precision engineers & toolmakers*

R & D Tool & Engineering Ltd, Hamilton Road, Sutton-in-Ashfield, Nottinghamshire, NG17 5LD Tel: (01623) 556287 Fax: (01623) 552240 E-mail: sales@rdtool.co.uk *Plastics mould toolmakers*

R & D Trophy Supplies, Unit 1 Phoenix Park, Coldred Road, Maidstone, Kent, ME15 9XN Tel: (01622) 753884 Fax: (01622) 688443 E-mail: sales@rdtrophy.co.uk *Sports trophy wholesalers & manufrs*

R D W Advertising Ltd, Urlay Nook Road, Eaglescliffe, Stockton-On-Tees, Cleveland, TS16 0LA Tel: (01642) 790047 Fax: (01642) 781589 E-mail: info@rdw-advertising.co.uk *Advertising agents*

R D W Glass, 139 Meadowpark Street, Glasgow, G31 2SY Tel: 0141-556 3312 Fax: 0141-556 3468 E-mail: info@rdwglass.co.uk *Decorative glass & stained glass manufrs*

▶ R D Williams & Sons (Haulage) Ltd, Wayside, Thrapston Road, Easton, Huntingdon, Cambridgeshire, PE28 0UA Tel: (01480) 891494 Fax: (01480) 890181

R Davidson & Sons Ltd, South Park, Lochfoot, Dumfries, DG2 8NH Tel: (01387) 730308 Fax: (01387) 730777 *Livestock haulage*

▶ R Donnan, Commerce Road, Stranraer, Wigtownshire, DG9 7DD Tel: (01776) 706283 Fax: (01776) 706283

R Durtnell & Sons Ltd, Rectory Lane, Brasted, Westerham, Kent, TN16 1JR Tel: (01959) 564105 Fax: (01959) 564756 E-mail: rds@durtnell.co.uk *Architectural contractors*

R E Ashworth & Co. Ltd, 123 Mansfield Road, Daybrook, Nottingham, NG5 6HT Tel: 0115-967 0022 Fax: 0115-920 6875 E-mail: wendy@mirabeluk.com *Net & voile curtains manufrs*

R E Bowers & Freeman Ltd, 15 Saffron Road, Wigston, Leicestershire, LE18 4TG Tel: 0116-278 5311 Fax: 0116-277 9544 E-mail: info@bowersfreeman.co.uk *Diesinkers & engravers*

R E Building Services, Aspen House, Minster Drive, Minster on Sea, Sheerness, Kent, ME12 2ND Tel: (01795) 874479 *Building management systems manufrs*

▶ R E C Ltd, Osprey House, 217-227 Broadway, Salford, M50 2UE Tel: 0161-868 1300 Fax: 0161-868 1301 E-mail: paulf@recltd.co.uk *Resource & environmental consulting services*

R E Cross & Co. Ltd, Joule Road, Basingstoke, Hampshire, RG21 6XH Tel: (01256) 465878 Fax: (01256) 817743 E-mail: sales@recross.co.uk *Precision engineers*

R.E.D. Computing Ltd, 179 Malden Road, New Malden, Surrey, KT3 6AA Tel: (020) 8336 1513 Fax: (020) 8942 9385 E-mail: sales@redcomputing.com *Software developers*

R E D S Services, 5 Spires Business Units, Mugiemoss Road, Bucksburn, Aberdeen, AB21 9NY Tel: (01224) 693284 Fax: (01224) 699687 *Chemical equipment engineers*

R E Dickie Ltd, Parkinson Lane, Halifax, West Yorkshire, HX1 3UB Tel: (01422) 341516 Fax: (01422) 357891 E-mail: wool@dickie.co.uk *Wool merchants*

R & E Engineers, Rock Channel, Rye, East Sussex, TN31 7HJ Tel: (01797) 223757 Fax: (01797) 222819 *Light steel manufrs*

▶ R E Field Services Ltd, Unit 3, Fieldhouse Way, Industrial Estate, Petre Street, Sheffield, S4 7SF Tel: 0114-256 0425 Fax: 0114-242 5545 E-mail: sales@refieldservices.com *HV motor & generator overhaul, maintenance, service & testing*

R E Fielding Trucking Ltd, Iconfield Park, Freshfields Road, Parkeston, Harwich, Essex, CO12 4EN Tel: (01255) 504848 Fax: (01255) 508754 *Road transport, haulage & freight services*

R E Gore Building Services Ltd, Unit 1c Skillion Business Park, Thames Road, Barking, Essex, IG11 0JP Tel: (020) 8594 3700 Fax: (020) 8594 3704 E-mail: sales@regore.com *Building services engineers*

R E Green, Gubberford House, Gubberford Lane, Garstang, Preston, PR3 1PS Tel: (01995) 605318 E-mail: rigreen@talk21.com *Building contractors*

R E H Kennedy Ltd, Whitehouse Road, Ipswich, IP1 5LT Tel: (01473) 240044 Fax: (01473) 240098 E-mail: sales@rehkennedy.co.uk *Reproduction furniture manufrs*

R E Knight Ltd, Fishers Way, Belvedere, Kent, DA17 6BS Tel: (020) 8310 8900 Fax: (020) 8311 4530 E-mail: enquiries@reknight.co.uk *Plastic mould & tool makers*

R E Knowles Ltd, Buxton Road, Furness Vale, High Peak, Derbyshire, SK23 7PJ Tel: (01663) 744127 Fax: (01663) 741562 *Fireclay goods manufrs*

R E L Contracts, Springfield, Brumstead Road, Stalham, Norwich, NR12 9DE Tel: (01692) 582238 *Industrial cleaning services*

R E L Freight Ltd, 346 Garratt Lane, London, SW18 4ES Tel: (020) 8874 2435 Fax: (020) 8874 7344 *Freight forwarders*

R E L Interexpo, 4 West House, West Avenue, Wigston, Leicestershire, LE18 2FB Tel: 0116-288 6622 Fax: 0116-281 3983 E-mail: info@interexpo.co.uk *Exhibition stand contractors*

R E Lay Construction Ltd, 146 West Street, Dunstable, Bedfordshire, LU6 1NX Tel: (01582) 608571 Fax: (01582) 472092 E-mail: admin@r-e-lay.co.uk *Underpinning & building contractors*

R E M Engineering Ltd, Unit 16, Crown Business Centre, Failsworth, Manchester, M35 9BW Tel: 0161-682 8833 Fax: 0161-682 8700 E-mail: david@remengineering.co.uk *Factory removal relocation, machinery removal contractors, machinery engineers erecting, installing & plant installation, erection, dismantling engineers. Moving of machinery and heavy equipment. Can handle all the associated electrical work and freight forwarding or logistics. Electrical Engineers.*

R E Martin Manchester Ltd, Unit 8-9-Spring Road Industrial Estate, Lanesfield Drive, Wolverhampton, WV4 6UA Tel: (01902) 496342 Fax: (01902) 404760 E-mail: info@remartin.com *Painters & decorators*

R E Olds & Co., 9 Ashmead Business Centre, Ashmead Road, Keynsham, Bristol, BS31 1SX Tel: 0117-986 0268 Fax: 0117-986 9594 E-mail: info@reolds.co.uk *Joinery contractors*

R E Ormerod & Sons Ltd, Union Mill, Bacup Road, Rossendale, Lancashire, BB4 7JN Tel: (01706) 215391 Fax: (01706) 210368 *Wedding & dance shoe manufrs*

R E Page Engineering Co. Ltd, Winterstoke Road, Weston-super-Mare, Avon, BS23 3YS Tel: (01934) 628547 Fax: (01934) 643265 *Mechanical engineers*

R & E Parry & Sons Agricultural Contractors, Fron Farm, Llangoed, Beaumaris, Gwynedd, LL58 8PA Tel: (01248) 490032 *Agricultural contractors*

▶ R E Pearce Properties Ltd, South Western Business Park, Sherborne, Dorset, DT9 3PS Tel: (01935) 816204 Fax: (01935) 816104

R E Rose, 4 Oakwood Business Park, Stephenson Road West, Clacton-on-Sea, Essex, CO15 4TL Tel: (01255) 428928 Fax: (01255) 434937 *Stainless steel fabricators*

▶ R E Rowlands Ltd, Station Yard, Station Road, Hungerford, Berkshire, RG17 0DY Tel: (01488) 682130

R E S Ltd, Station Road, Queensferry, Deeside, Clwyd, CH5 2TB Tel: (01244) 831134 Fax: (01244) 822453 E-mail: sales@res-engineering.co.uk *Steel engineers manufrs*

R E S Services Ltd, Unit 16 Ilford Trading Estate, Paycocke Road, Basildon, Essex, SS14 3DR Tel: (01268) 531153 Fax: (01268) 525227 E-mail: janeryan@resservices.co.uk *Building services*

R E Thorns & Co., 22 Exchange Street, Norwich, NR2 1AT Tel: (01603) 622891 Fax: (01603) 622952 E-mail: mail@thornsdiy.com *Ironmongers tool merchants home & garden wholesale*

R E V Gomm Ltd, 31 Commercial St, Birmingham, B1 1RJ Tel: 0121-643 7427 Fax: 0121-633 3394 E-mail: gomms@shawmunstergroup.co.uk *Badge manufrs*

R E Woods Cabinet Makers, Mountain Ash, Dereham Road, Thuxton, Norwich, NR9 4QH Tel: (01362) 850460 Fax: (01362) 858360 E-mail: rewoods@cabinetmaker76.freeserve.co.uk *Cabinet manufrs*

▶ R E Wright (Bradford) Ltd, Cragg Works, Pannal Street, Great Horton, Bradford, West Yorkshire, BD7 4HG Tel: (01274) 502765

▶ R & E Yachting Ltd, 2 Pretoria Villas Main Road, Colden Common, Winchester, Hampshire, SO21 1RR Tel: (01962) 712545 E-mail: info@reyachtcharter.co.uk *Bareboat and skippered yacht charter in the Solent. Extensively outfitted Gosport based sun odyssey 40.3.*

R Ekin, Claylands Avenue, Worksop, Nottinghamshire, S81 7BE Tel: (01909) 472638 Fax: (01909) 472638 *Manufacturers of fire escape staircases*

▶ R Elliott & Co. Ltd, Alchorne Place, Portsmouth, PO3 5QL Tel: (023) 9262 7700 Fax: (023) 9266 9991 *Printers & sign manufrs*

▶ R Elliott & Sons Ltd, Sandford Farm, Newhouse, Motherwell, Lanarkshire, ML1 5SX Tel: (01698) 870222

R Elliott & Sons Ltd, 21 Bridge Street, Uttoxeter, Staffordshire, ST14 8AR Tel: (01889) 565241 Fax: (01889) 563203 *Distributors of pallets*

R F Brookes, Magna Road, Wigston, Leicestershire, LE18 4ZA Tel: 0116-258 1000 Fax: 0116-258 1001 E-mail: sales@rfbrookes.co.uk *Food manufrs*

▶ R & F Campbell (Inverness) Ltd, 3 Walker Road, Inverness, IV1 1TD Tel: (01463) 231726

R F Clarke Ltd, 31 Windmill Road, Saintfield, Ballynahinch, County Down, BT24 7DX Tel: (028) 9751 2920 Fax: (028) 9751 2929 E-mail: sales@rfclarke.com Principal Export Areas: Central/East Europe & West Europe *Conveyor & power transmission belting manufrs*

R F Design Ltd, 27 Weelsby Way, Hessle, North Humberside, HU13 0JN Tel: (01482) 629270 Fax: (01482) 629270 E-mail: martyn@rfdesign.karoo.co.uk *RF & EMC design & development services, experts in low power radio, RF CO2 laser amplifiers & EMC testing /development*

R F Electronics Controls Ltd, 8 Nazeing New Road, Broxbourne, Hertfordshire, EN10 6SU Tel: (01992) 460046 Fax: (01992) 442299 E-mail: sales@rfeltd.com *Electronic control systems manufrs*

R F Giddings & Co. Ltd, 28 Sharlands Road, Fareham, Hampshire, PO14 1RD Tel: (01329) 234670 Fax: (01329) 234670 *Fencing materials distributors*

R F I B Group Ltd, Staple Hall, Stone House Court, 87-90 Houndsditch, London, EC3A 7NP Tel: (020) 7621 1263 Fax: (020) 7623 6175 *Insurance & reinsurance brokers*

R F I Seals & Gaskets Ltd, Unit 2, Saltash Business Park, Moorlands Trading Estate, Forge Lane, Saltash, Cornwall, PL12 6LX Tel: 01752 841051 Fax: 01752 847559 E-mail: sales@rfiseals.co.uk *RFI gasket manufrs*

R F I Shielding Ltd, Warner Drive, Springwood Industrial Estate, Braintree, Essex, CM7 2YW Tel: 01342 315044 Fax: (01376) 346442 Sales Contact: S. Spinks Principal Export Areas: Worldwide *Electromagnetic interference shielding materials,shield/shielding (radio frequency interferece) (RFI/EMI) & gaskets EM/RF manufrs*

R F Insight Ltd, 47 Percival Road, Rugby, Warwickshire, CV22 5JU Tel: (01788) 541790 Fax: (01788) 541790 E-mail: sales@vvlp.co.uk *Electronic engineers*

R & F Insulations Ltd, Unit 7 Bardwells Yard, Latchingdon Road, Cold Norton, Chelmsford, CM3 6JG Tel: (01621) 828222 Fax: (01621) 828933 E-mail: sales@randf-insulation.co.uk *Asbestos removals*

R F M Workwear Ltd, 36 Glenburn Road, College Milton North, East Kilbride, Glasgow, G74 5BA Tel: (01355) 238161 Fax: (01355) 263682 E-mail: sales@corstonsinclair.com *Workwear overall manufrs*

R F Martin Haulage Ltd, 26 Mark Avenue, Horncastle, Lincolnshire, LN9 5BD Tel: (01507) 523212 Fax: (01507) 522623 *Road transport, haulage & freight services*

▶ R & F Mechanical Services Ltd, 13 Seymour Street, Ballymoney, County Antrim, BT53 6JR Tel: (028) 2766 2627 Fax: (028) 2766 4056

▶ R F Peachey & Sons Ltd, Orchard Place, London, N17 8BH Tel: (020) 8808 2461 Fax: (020) 8365 0437

R F R Precision Engineering Ltd, Unit 16 Lythalls Lane Industrial Estate, Lythalls Lane, Coventry, CV6 6FJ Tel: (024) 7668 9427 Fax: (024) 7668 9427 *Precision engineer services*

R F Roberts, Selattyn, Oswestry, Shropshire, SY10 7DY Tel: (01691) 659716 Fax: (01691) 650129 *Hay & straw merchants*

R F S UK Ltd, 9 Haddenham Business Park, Thame Road, Haddenham, Aylesbury, Buckinghamshire, HP17 8LJ Tel: (01844) 294900 Fax: (01844) 294944 E-mail: sales@rfsworld.com *Distributors of connectors*

R F Shielding Ltd, Unit 16, Rising Sun Industrial Estate, Blaina, Abertillery, Gwent, NP13 3JW Tel: (01495) 292999 Fax: (01495) 292550 E-mail: info@rfshielding.co.uk *Robotic spraying services*

R F Solutions Ltd, Unit 21, Cliffe Industrial Estate, South Street, Lewes, East Sussex, BN8 6JL Tel: (01273) 898000 Fax: (01273) 480661 E-mail: sales@rfsolutions.co.uk *Radio frequency electrical module distributors & manufrs*

R F T Tooling Ltd, 2 Brickfields Industrial Estate, Finway Road, Hemel Hempstead, Hertfordshire, HP2 7QA Tel: (01442) 252566 Fax: (01442) 252532 E-mail: enquires@rft-tooling.com *Injection moulding manufrs*

R.F. Technology Ltd, Unit 15d Compton Pl, Surrey Ave, Camberley, Surrey, GU15 3DX Tel: (01276) 686889 Fax: (01276) 686244 *Radio communications systems consultants*

R & F Trimmings, 185 Earlham Grove, Forest Gate, London, E7 9AP Tel: (020) 8221 1515 Fax: (020) 8221 1414 E-mail: randftrimms@aol.com *Leather belt manufrs*

R Fawcett & Sons, Woodhall Park, Woodhall, Askrigg, Leyburn, North Yorkshire, DL8 3LB Tel: (01969) 663255 Fax: (01969) 663114 *Welding manufrs*

R Foster Screenprint Ltd, 184 Uxbridge Road, London, W7 3TB Tel: (020) 8567 2272 Fax: (020) 8567 2485 E-mail: sales@rfoster.co.uk *Screen printers*

▶ R & G, Lucas Green Nurseries, Lucas Green Road, West End, Woking, Surrey, GU24 9LY Tel: (01483) 474041 Fax: (01483) 476371 E-mail: enquiries@freshherbsolutions.com *Herbs & spices suppliers*

▶ R G A UK Ltd, R G A Centre, Holwell, Burford, Oxfordshire, OX18 4LD Tel: (01993) 822303 Fax: (01993) 822501 E-mail: info@venuemarketingservices.co.uk *Contact data of uk event organisers. Direct marketing, mailshots & call centre services for conference & meeting venues targeting UK corporate event buyers.*

R G Abercrombie, Caledonian Road, Alloa, Clackmannanshire, FK10 1NB Tel: (01259) 222500 Fax: (01259) 222528 E-mail: info@diageo.com *Copper fabricators, distillation plant (industrial) manufacturers, engineers, general engineering & stainless steel fabricators*

R G Attachments, 86 Belper Street, Leicester, LE4 6EA Tel: 0116-261 1038 Fax: 0116-261 2403 E-mail: info@rga.co.uk *Industrial sewing machines manufrs*

R G Automatics, 7 Spa Road, Hockley, Essex, SS5 4AZ Tel: (01702) 205251 *Automatic transmission repairers*

R G B Products, Unit 2 Gilmans Industrial Estate, Billingshurst, West Sussex, RH14 9EZ Tel: (01403) 783670 Fax: (01403) 783670 *Joinery & settee frame manufrs*

R G Bell & Sons, The Wath, Caldbeck, Wigton, Cumbria, CA7 8EY Tel: (01697) 478204 *Agricultural contractors services*

R G Bennett & Co. Ltd, 60 Colvey Road, Dartford, DA1 1UH Tel: (01322) 224258 Fax: (01322) 289660 E-mail: sales@rgbennett.co.uk *Kitchenware wholesalers*

▶ R G C General Builders, 35 Kingfisher Court, Newbury, Berkshire, RG14 5SJ Tel: (01635) 523321 Fax: (01635) 523679

R G C Transmission Services Ltd, Unit 26 Westend Estate, Bruntcliffe Road, Morley, Leeds, LS27 0LJ Tel: 0113-252 3520 *Gear box services*

R G Cables & Crimps, Unit 10 Fleckney Industrial Estate, Churchill Way, Fleckney, Leicester, LE8 8UD Tel: 0116-240 4500 Fax: 0116-240 4501 *Cable assemblies*

R G Carey, Mill Lane, Hooe, Battle, East Sussex, TN33 9HS Tel: (01424) 892051 Fax: (01424) 892051 *Wheel manufrs*

R G Carter Building Ltd, Riverside Industrial Estate, Marsh Lane, Boston, Lincolnshire, PE21 7PJ Tel: (01205) 365557 Fax: (01205) 365515

▶ R G Carter (Cambridge) Ltd, Horizon Park, Barton Road, Comberton, Cambridge, CB3 7BN Tel: (01223) 265300

R G Carter Colchester Ltd, 5 Grange Way, Colchester, CO2 8HF Tel: (01206) 794455 Fax: (01206) 790872 E-mail: mail@rgcarter-colchester.co.uk *Building contractors*

▶ R G Carter Ipswich Limited, 48 St. Nicholas Street, Ipswich, IP1 1TP Tel: 01473 233655 Fax: 01473 211097 E-mail: mail@rgcarter-ipswich.co.uk *Building contractors*

R G Chapman, 53 Gainsborough Street, Sudbury, Suffolk, CO10 2ET Tel: (01787) 312850 E-mail: info@rgchapman.co.uk *Jewellery manufrs*

R G Clark & Sons, Hemnall Street, Epping, Essex, CM16 4LW Tel: (01992) 572081 *Agricultural engineers*

R G Collins Ltd, 43 Melton Street, Kettering, Northamptonshire, NN16 9DT Tel: (07753) 627331 Fax: (01536) 514127 *Master upholsterers*

R & G Construction (Manchester) Ltd, Phoenix Buildings, Heywood Road, Prestwich, Manchester, M25 1FN Tel: 0161-773 7867 Fax: 0161-773 8617 *Construction company*

R G D Engineering Co. Ltd, Stonecross Industrial Estate, Downham Market, Norfolk, PE38 0AD Tel: (01366) 382962 Fax: (01366) 384938 E-mail: rgdengineering@btconnect.com *Sub-contract & precision engineers*

R G E Engineering Co. Ltd, Bridge Works, The Avenue, Godmanchester, Huntingdon, Cambridgeshire, PE29 2AF Tel: (01480) 450771 Fax: (01480) 411359 E-mail: sales@rgegroup.com *Plastic injection moulding services*

R G Engineering, 3 Stoney Court, Hotchkiss Way, Binley, Coventry, CV3 2RL Tel: (024) 7644 0508 Fax: (024) 7663 6680 E-mail: r.g.eng@dial.pipex.com *Manufacturers & constructors of special purpose custom built machinery*

R G Engineering, 54 Dunster Street, Northampton, NN1 3JY Tel: (01604) 639673 Fax: (01604) 639673 E-mail: rgengineering@btopenworld.com *Toolmakers & trade injection moulders manufrs*

R G Ergonomics Ltd, 7 Princewood Road, Earlstrees Industrial Estate, Corby, Northamptonshire, NN17 4AP Tel: (01536) 263691 Fax: (01536) 274988 E-mail: enquires@rgergonomics.co.uk *Railway carriage seats manufrs*

R G Foster Textile Machinery Ltd, Burnham Way, Queens Bridge Road, Nottingham, NG2 1NB Tel: 0115-988 2222 Fax: 0115-985 1881 E-mail: sales@foster-tm.co.uk *Textile finishing machinery manufrs*

R G G Malmos, 52 Hainge Road, Tividale, Oldbury, West Midlands, B69 2PD Tel: 0121-522 2140 Fax: 0121-520 1773 *General engineers*

R G H Rubber & Plastics Ltd, Acorn House, Oak Industrial Park, Chelmsford Road, Great Dunmow, Dunmow, Essex, CM6 1XN Tel: (01371) 875941 Fax: (01371) 873804 E-mail: sales@rghrubber.co.uk *As one of the leading self adhesive tape and foam converters in the U.K., *RGH specialise in producing tailor-made solutions to individual customers needs. **RGH"s product range includes Self Adhesive Foams, Double Sided Tapes, Magnetic Products, Hangtabs, Solid and Expanded Rubber as well as Transparent Tapes, Cork, Felts and anti rattle materials. **All of our high performance products are manufactured using a management system register to TS16949 and BS EN ISO9000 quality standards*

▶ R G H Solutions, 20, Mount Crescent, South Normanton, Derbyshire, DE55 3NS Tel: 0777 1737364 E-mail: rghsolutions@ntlworld.com *Simple, low cost solutions for home computing*

R G & I M Heaman, Remberton Farm, Cullompton, Devon, EX15 1LY Tel: (07768) 651417 *Farming contractor*

▶ R G I S Inventory Specialists, Imperial House, Holly Walk, Leamington Spa, Warwickshire, CV32 4YB Tel: (01926) 888882 Fax: (01926) 888883 E-mail: sales@rgis.com *The worlds largest stock taking company. RGIS can deliver a variety of services for virtually anything that requires physical counting or measurement, with services ranging from physical audits and cycle counts to more diverse activities such as merchandising, price verification, stock replenishment etc*

▶ R & G Industrial Sewing Machines, 6 Mossfield Road, Swinton, Manchester, M27 6EN Tel: 0161-793 4555 Fax: 0161-793 4224 *Sewing machine distributors*

R G Jones, 16 Endeavour Way, London, SW19 8UH Tel: (020) 8971 3100 Fax: (020) 8971 3101 E-mail: enquiries@rgjones.co.uk *Sound engineers*

R G K (UK) Ltd, Champfleurie House, Linlithgow, West Lothian, EH49 6NB Tel: (01506) 847999 Fax: (01506) 847174 E-mail: sales@rgk.co.uk

▶ R G L Contract Services, Burnfoot Yard, Old Carlisle Road, Moffat, Dumfriesshire, DG10 9QN Tel: (01683) 220122 Fax: (01683) 220644

▶ R G L Contracts, North Tay Works, Balfield Road, Dundee, DD3 6AG Tel: (01382) 641842 Fax: (01382) 642169 *Welders fabricators*

R G L Security, 21 Denbigh Grove, Burnley, Lancashire, BB12 6AX Tel: (01282) 416051 E-mail: sales@rglsecurity.co.uk *Security & alarms*

R & G Lawrie, Old Philpstoun, Linlithgow, West Lothian, EH49 7RY Tel: (01506) 834205 Fax: (01506) 834205 *Agricultural engineers*

R G Linton, 83 Edenbane Road, Garvagh, Coleraine, County Londonderry, BT51 5NA Tel: (028) 2955 8489 *Agricultural contractors*

▶ R G & M F Sadler Electrical Ltd, 60 East Road, Oundle, Peterborough, PE8 4BZ Tel: (01832) 273677 Fax: (01832) 273677

R G M Music Ltd, 24 Nelson Street, Kilmarnock, Ayrshire, KA1 1BA Tel: (01563) 537711 Fax: (01563) 530209 *Music equipment retailers*

▶ R G Macdonald, 21 Francis Street, Wick, Caithness, KW1 5PZ Tel: (01955) 602516 Fax: (01955) 604358 *Bakery products*

R & G Marine & Industrial Services, Units 1a-2a Brickmakers Industrial Estate, Castle Road, Sittingbourne, Kent, ME10 3RL Tel: (01795) 470430 Fax: (01795) 429722 E-mail: sales@randgmarine.co.uk *Lifting gear manufrs*

R & G Metal Products, 172-174 Colne Road, Twickenham, TW2 6RE Tel: (020) 8893 3300 *Sheet metal workers*

R G Obern Ltd, Overdale, Wells Road, Chilcompton, Radstock, BA3 4EY Tel: (01761) 232723 Fax: (01761) 233287 *Joinery manufrs*

R G P Design Innovation, 62 Cause End Road, Wootton, Bedford, MK43 9DE Tel: (01234) 767143 Fax: (01234) 767143 E-mail: rgpdesign@talk21.com *Design consultant*

R & G Precision Engineering Ltd, 106 Washbrook Road, Rushden, Northamptonshire, NN10 6UL Tel: (01933) 411662 Fax: (01933) 411663 E-mail: sales@rgprecisionltd.co.uk *Precision engineers*

R G Printing Co, 27c-27d Unit, Vale Business Park, Llandow, Cowbridge, South Glamorgan, CF71 7PF Tel: (01446) 771393 Fax: (01446) 771681 *Printing & designers services*

R G R Fabrications & Welding Services Ltd, Pensnett Trading Estate, Kingswinford, West Midlands, DY6 7PP Tel: (01384) 401055 Fax: (01384) 400068 E-mail: sales@rgrltd.com *Coded pipework fabricators*

R G S Electro Pneumatics Ltd, West End Business Park, Oswaldtwistle, Accrington, Lancashire, BB5 4WZ Tel: (01254) 872277 Fax: (01254) 390133 E-mail: sales@rgs-e-p.co.uk *Pneumatic control manufrs*

R G S Labels, Units 7 & 8, Roman Way Small Business Park, London Road, Godmanchester, Huntingdon, Cambridgeshire, PE29 2LN Tel: (01480) 456556 Fax: (01480) 456578 E-mail: sales@rgslabels.co.uk *RGS are the label suppliers of Pre-printed labels, Self Adhesive labels, Thermal Transfer labels, Thermal Transfer ribbons, Printers & Software, Support Contracts and more. We have been label suppliers for 8 years and have been providing label and packaging solutions for all sectors of business in the UK, producing work exactly to our clients specifications, from concept through to production & shipment from our premises in Cambridgeshire, UK . We are professional label suppliers that are experienced in meeting and exceeding our customers' expectations through a clear understanding of our customers' challenges, a close client dialogue and a focus on building labelling solutions that respond to real requirements. You are welcome to contact us today for a free sample label suppliers pack and a quotation on: 01480 456556 or email sales@rgslabels.co.uk*

R G Scales, 92 Southwark Bridge Road, London, SE1 0EX Tel: (020) 7928 9738 Fax: (0845) 3459182 E-mail: info@document-centre.co.uk *Document presentation & hard cover binder manufrs*

R G Services, PO Box 1864, Radstock, BA3 3ZA Tel: (01761) 435858 Fax: (01761) 435858 E-mail: sales@rgservices.co.uk *Sign manufrs*

▶ R & G Services Ltd, Hillhouse International Site, Fleetwood Road North, Thornton-Cleveleys, Lancashire, FY5 4QD Tel: (01253) 864033 Fax: (01253) 828603 E-mail: cleanup@ukonline.co.uk *Commercial & industrial cleaning.*

R G Software, Stocktons Courtyard, Overbury, Tewkesbury, Gloucestershire, GL20 7NT Tel: (01242) 233255 Fax: (01386) 725109 E-mail: sales@rgsoftware.co.uk Principal Export Areas: Central/East Europe & West Europe *Software developers*

R G Spiller Ltd, Millfield Close, Chard, Somerset, TA20 2DJ Tel: (01460) 62881 Fax: (01460) 65781 *Building contractors*

R G Stokes & Son, Bellwood, Shobdon, Leominster, Herefordshire, HR6 9NJ Tel: (01568) 708642 Fax: (01568) 708642 *Agricultural contractors*

R G T Ltd, Chapel Road, Smallfield, Horley, Surrey, RH6 9NW Tel: (01342) 844411 Fax: (0870) 7771333 E-mail: sales@rgt.co.uk *Telecommunications systems*

R G Technofinish Ltd, Unit 5, Bilton Road, Hitchin, Hertfordshire, SG4 0SB Tel: (01462) 434002 Fax: (01462) 452556 E-mail: technofinish.ltd@virgin.net *Electroplaters & metal finishers*

R & G Theatre Services, 19-21 Foxes Bridge Road, Forest Vale Industrial Estate, Cinderford, Gloucestershire, GL14 2PQ Tel: (01594) 823197 Fax: (01594) 826045 E-mail: sales@lampo.co.uk *Stage lighting engineers*

R G Watts, Norville Steam Bakery, The Causeway, Mark, Highbridge, Somerset, TA9 4PX Tel: (01278) 788154 *Bakery & confectionery suppliers*

R G Wilbrey Consultants Ltd, Aspen House, Great Brickkiln Street, Wolverhampton, WV3 0PT Tel: (01902) 420920 Fax: (01902) 426981 E-mail: wilbrey@compuserve.com *Safety consultants*

R G Wylie & Co. Ltd, Vanguard Way, Shoeburyness, Southend-on-Sea, SS3 9QY Tel: (01702) 296751 Fax: (01702) 297560 E-mail: rg.wylie@dtconect.com Principal Export Areas: Middle East, Africa, Central/East Europe & West Europe *Belting & pulley manufrs*

▶ R Gilmour & Son Ltd, 501 Crow Road, Glasgow, G11 7DN Tel: 0141-959 1961 Fax: 0141-569 1961

R Gledhill Ltd, Pingle Mill, Pingle Lane, Delph, Oldham, OL3 5EX Tel: (01457) 874651 Fax: (01457) 872428 E-mail: general@rgledhill.co.uk *Woollen yarn spinners*

R Glover Ascroft Ltd, Ace Works, 157 Ordnance Road, Enfield, Middlesex, EN3 6AW Tel: (01992) 717272 Fax: (01992) 714040 E-mail: enquiries@r-glover-ascroft.com *Gloves plastic & rubber, protective clothing manufrs*

R Gorton & Associates Electronics Ltd, 308-310 Slade Lane, Manchester, M19 2BY Tel: 0161-224 5650 Fax: 0161-257 2761 E-mail: gortonelectronics@btinternet.com *Manufacturers of control systems & electronic equipment*

▶ R & H Ltd, Unit18 Equity Trading Centre, Hobley Drive, Swindon, SN3 4NS Tel: (01793) 616891

R H Adams Forest Hill Ltd, Hindsleys Place, London, SE23 2NQ Tel: (020) 8699 4803 Fax: (020) 8699 8493 *Heating engineers*

R H Associates, 79 Cherry Grove, Sketty, Swansea, SA2 8AX Tel: (01792) 410500 Fax: (01792) 410506 E-mail: tracey@jackland.demon.co.uk *Computer consultants*

R H B, Unit 115B The Big Peg, 120 Vyse Street, Hockley, Birmingham, B18 6NB Tel: 0121-236 5310 Fax: 0121-236 5310 *Jewellery manufrs*

R H Bruce Co Ltd, 4 The Idas, Pontefract Road, Leeds, LS10 1SP Tel: 0113-271 5533 Fax: 0113-271 8833 *Wholesale ironmongers*

Company Information

R H Bunner & Son Ltd, Arthur Street, Montgomery, Powys, SY15 6RA Tel: (01686) 668308 Fax: (01686) 668564 E-mail: sales@rhbunner.co.uk *Hardware & agricultural merchants*

R H Buxton Ltd, Fell Bank, Birtley, Chester le Street, County Durham, DH3 2SP Tel: 0191-410 6111 Fax: 0191-410 6655 E-mail: buxtonsne@beeb.net *High pressure water jetting*

R H C Consultancy, 202 Raedwald Drive, Bury St. Edmunds, Suffolk, IP32 7DW Tel: (01284) 717184 Fax: (01284) 717184 E-mail: rhcroft@btconnect.com *Sales consultancy, storage equipment, distribution & tooling*

▶ R H Cambridge Storage Ltd, Argoed Farm, Kinnerley, Oswestry, Shropshire, SY10 8DH Tel: (01691) 682361 Fax: (01691) 682513

R H Colvill Associates, Pointers South, Pointers Road, Cobham, Surrey, KT11 1PQ Tel: (01932) 860950 Fax: (01932) 860950 *Computer graphics consultants & trainers*

R & H Electric Ltd, Unit 2, Rose Green Road, Fishponds Trading Estate, Fishponds, Bristol, BS5 7XE Tel: 0117-952 1261 Fax: 0117-952 0590 E-mail: dangerfield-moir@rhelectric.co.uk *Wholesale electrical supplies*

▶ R H Electrical, 1a Stone Lane, Kinver, Stourbridge, West Midlands, DY7 6EQ Tel: (07836) 299206 Fax: (01384) 877874

R H Export Packers Ltd, Lenton Freight Terminal, Lenton Lane, Nottingham, NG7 2NR Tel: 0115-943 8034 Fax: 0115-943 8045 E-mail: sales@rhep.co.uk *Export packers & case makers*

▶ R H F Boiler Service Ltd, 71 73 Enville Street, Stourbridge, West Midlands, DY8 1XW Tel: (01384) 393694 Fax: (01384) 393744

R H F Fans Ltd, 2 Ferrous Way, Irlam, Manchester, M44 5FS Tel: 0161-776 6400 Fax: 0161-775 6566 E-mail: sales@rhf-fans.co.uk *RHF Fans Ltd was established in 1980. We set out to create a range of industrial fan products that would achieve specified duties efficiently, be structurally well engineered & be produced in the most cost effective way. We have continually raised the standard & quality of our fan products, become more competitive & provide the highest levels of sales & service to meet the ever increasing demands of our customers*

R H Fibreboard Containers Ltd, 18 Knights Road, Chelston Business Park, Wellington, Somerset, TA21 9JH Tel: (01823) 663918 Fax: (01823) 665560 E-mail: enquiries@r-h-f.co.uk *Corrugated board & packaging materials suppliers & manufrs*

R H Foster Ltd, 16 Essex Road, Basingstoke, Hampshire, RG21 7TD Tel: (01256) 465414 Fax: (01256) 841216 *Industrial electrical contractors*

R H G Stone Engineering, 121 Main Street, Walton, Street, Somerset, BA16 9QL Tel: (01458) 442167 Fax: (01458) 447252 E-mail: info@rhgstone.co.uk *Precision & sub-contract engineers*

R H Group, Building 110, East Midlands Airport, Castle Donington, Derby, DE74 2SA Tel: (01332) 811348 Fax: (01332) 811938 E-mail: penny.rowe@rhfreight.co.uk *Air freight forwarders* Also at: Birmingham Airport & Heathrow (London)

R H Group, Lenton Lane, Nottingham, NG7 2NR Tel: 0115-943 8000 Fax: 0115-943 8045 *International road hauliers & warehousing contractors*

▶ R H Hammond Ltd, Unit 7, Northbrook Industrial Estate, Vincent Avenue, Southampton, SO16 6PB Tel: (023) 8077 2442

R H I Refractories UK Ltd, PO Box 3, Clydebank, Dunbartonshire, G81 1RW Tel: 0141-952 1990 Fax: 0141-435 7445 Principal Export Areas: Worldwide *Ceramic tube manufacturers for continuous casting of steel*

R H I Refractories UK Ltd, International House, Brunel Drive, Newark, Nottinghamshire, NG24 2EG Tel: (01636) 704494 Fax: (01636) 704495 E-mail: rhi.uk@rhi-ag.com *Refractory merchants*

R H Insulation Services Ltd, Unit 14, Wingate Road, Gosport, Hampshire, PO12 4DR Tel: (023) 9250 1141 Fax: (023) 9251 1409 *Asbestos removal services & insulation*

R H K Davidson, 35 Bushmills Road, Coleraine, County Londonderry, BT52 2BP Tel: (028) 7034 2281 Fax: (020) 7035 7097 E-mail: rhkdavidson@btopenworld.com *Electrical contractors*

R H Leather, 36 Goulston Street, London, E1 7TP Tel: (020) 7247 5181 *Leathergoods manufacturers*

R H Ling, 82 Forest Road, Frome, Somerset, BA11 2TQ Tel: (01373) 467592 Fax: (01373) 467592 *Earth thermal blocks*

R H Loveys, Lower Hare Farm, Whitestone, Exeter, EX4 2HW Tel: (01392) 811368 *Pallets engineers*

R H M Technology Ltd, Lord Rank Centre, Lincoln Road, High Wycombe, Buckinghamshire, HP12 3QR Tel: (01494) 526191 Fax: (01494) 428080 E-mail: enquiries@rhmtech.co.uk *Microbiological & food technology analysts & consultants*

▶ R H Marine Ltd, 27 York Place, Aberdeen, AB11 5DH Tel: (01224) 580319

R H Matthews & Sons, The Firs, Hempstead Road, Holt, Norfolk, NR25 6DQ Tel: (01263) 712239 Fax: (01263) 712239 *Agricultural engineers*

R H Mawdsley Ltd, 39 Gorsey Lane, Mawdesley, Ormskirk, Lancashire, L40 3TE Tel: (01704) 822204 Fax: (01704) 822204 *Groundwork contractors*

R H Mawson Engineers Ltd, Avenue D Thorp Arch Trading Estate, Thorp Arch, Wetherby, West Yorkshire, LS23 7BJ Tel: (01937) 845333 Fax: (01937) 843768 *Fabricating engineers*

R H Miller Agricultural Ltd, 64-66 Old Town, Peebles, EH45 8JE Tel: (01721) 720711 Fax: (01721) 729968 *Agricultural merchants*

R H P Marine, Shepards Wharf, Medina Road, Cowes, Isle of Wight, PO31 7HT Tel: (01983) 290421 Fax: (01983) 290114 E-mail: rhpmarine@aol.com *Marine & electronic engineers*

R H Positive, 42 Invincible Road, Farnborough, Hampshire, GU14 7QU Tel: (01252) 377836 Fax: (01252) 375737 E-mail: ralphheppell@rhpositive.fsnet.co.uk *Sign manufacturers & designers*

R H Products & The Sleep Doctor, 87-89 Shaw Street, St. Helens, Merseyside, WA10 1EN Tel: (01744) 733622 Fax: (01744) 733623 E-mail: roger9000h@hotmail.com *Plastic lap trays & clothes peg manufrs*

R H Smith Worthing Ltd, Southdownview Way, Worthing, West Sussex, BN14 8NL Tel: (01903) 238316 E-mail: rhsmith1956@tiscali.co.uk *Chemical damp proofing & timber treatment*

R H Steel, Church Farm, Hamerton, Huntingdon, Cambridgeshire, PE28 5QX Tel: (01832) 293501 Fax: 01832 293670 *Farming contractors*

R H Stevens Tankers Ltd, Gunco Lane, Off Byrons Lane, Macclesfield, Cheshire, SK11 7JL Tel: (01625) 613939 Fax: (01625) 616829 E-mail: enquiries@rhstevens.co.uk *Road transport, haulage & freight services*

R H Stone & Son, 30 College Hill Road, Harrow, Middlesex, HA3 7HE Tel: (020) 8954 1835 Fax: (020) 895 6739 *Joinery manufrs*

R & H Testing Services Ltd, Cannel Road, Burntwood Business Park, Burntwood, Staffordshire, WS7 3FU Tel: (01543) 677400 Fax: (01543) 677477 E-mail: sales@randhtesting.com *Calibration services, test equipment, inspection certification engineers & test equipment, materials*

R & H Tomlinson Ltd, The Recycling Centre, Hackworth Industrial Park, Shildon, County Durham, DL4 1HF Tel: (01388) 778222 Fax: (01388) 778333 E-mail: nicktomlinson007@aol.com *Waste disposal & scrap metal merchants*

R H W Spooner Glass Merchants Ltd, 203 Gillingham Road, Gillingham, Kent, ME7 4EX Tel: (01634) 851848 Fax: (01634) 575105 E-mail: sales@spooners.sagehost.co.uk *Window repairs*

▶ R H White Ltd, 33 Burleigh Road, Enfield, Middlesex, EN1 1NY Tel: (020) 8367 4964 Fax: (020) 8364 4015

R H Wilkins Ltd, 31-35 Kirby Street, London, EC1N 8TE Tel: (020) 7405 5187 Fax: (020) 7831 2805 E-mail: sales@rhwilkins.co.uk *Engraving services*

R H Wilson, 8 Derryhollagh Lane, Randalstown, Antrim, BT41 3HT Tel: (028) 7965 0614 *Tractors repairs*

R Hamilton & Co. Ltd, Quarryfield Industrial Estate, Mere, Warminster, Wiltshire, BA12 6LA Tel: (01747) 860088 Fax: (01747) 861032 E-mail: info@hamilton-litestat.com *Electrical accessories manufrs*

R Hardaker & Co. Ltd, Ashley House, Ashley Lane, Shipley, West Yorkshire, BD17 7DB Tel: (01274) 589166 Fax: (01274) 531511 E-mail: mail@hardakers.com *Textile merchant converters*

R Harris Systems Ltd, 89 University Street, Belfast, BT7 1HP Tel: (028) 9032 6802 Fax: (028) 9032 5269 E-mail: pframe@harrissystems.co.uk *Book-keeping & stock taking services*

▶ R Harrison & Sons, Carr End, Glaisdale, Whitby, North Yorkshire, YO21 2QH Tel: (01947) 897249 Fax: (01947) 897007

R Hatton, 3 Drapers Way, Stevenage, Hertfordshire, SG1 3DT Tel: (01438) 350933 Fax: (01438) 740297 E-mail: mail@richardhatton.co.uk *Structural & civil engineering consultants*

▶ R Hayman & Son Ltd, 11a Blackbrook Business Park, Blackbrook Road, Fareham, Hampshire, PO15 5DR Tel: (01329) 221207 Fax: (01329) 245480

R Hind, Durranhill Trading Estate, Carlisle, CA1 3NQ Tel: (01228) 523647 Fax: (01228) 512712 *Vehicle body builders & repairers*

R Howard Ltd, Croft Bank, Skegness, Lincolnshire, PE24 4AW Tel: (01754) 880226 Fax: (01754) 881263 *Print, packaging, carton manufacturers & commercial printers*

▶ R I Building Services, 30 Tyock Industrial Estate, Elgin, Morayshire, IV31 1XY Tel: (01343) 548062

R I C S, Surveyor Court, Westwood Business Park, Westwood Way, Coventry, CV4 8JE Tel: (024) 7669 4757 Fax: (020) 7334 3800 E-mail: contact@rics.org *Professional body*

▶ R I E Consultancy, Eastway Road, Wigston, Leicestershire, LE18 1NJ Tel: 0116-281 2274

R & I Electrical Services, 278 Philip Lane, London, N15 4AD Tel: (020) 8801 5771 Fax: (020) 8365 1800 *Electrical contractors*

R I N C Engineering, 22 Singer Road, Kelvin Industrial Estate, East Kilbride, Glasgow, G75 0XS Tel: (01355) 248610 Fax: (01355) 248610 E-mail: rinc@wwwmail.co.uk *Sheet metalwork engineers & fabricators*

R I T C Cambridge Ltd, 23 Signet Court, Swann Road, Cambridge, CB5 8LA Tel: (01223) 503190 Fax: (01223) 506293 *Internet service agents*

▶ R J Aynsley, Unit 10 Sawmills Industrial Estate, South Road, Alnwick, Northumberland, NE66 2QW Tel: (01665) 602803 Fax: (01665) 510990

R J B Engineering Ltd, Unit 5 Oak Industrial Park, Chelmsford Road, Dunmow, Essex, CM6 1XN Tel: (01371) 876377 Fax: (01371) 876378 E-mail: rbrown7571@aol.com *CNC engineering services*

R J B Engineering, Westminster Industrial Estate, Station Road, North Hykeham, Lincoln, LN6 3QY Tel: (01522) 690491 Fax: (01522) 697543 E-mail: info@sje-engineering.co.uk *Export & turbine maintenance service*

R J Barrington Ltd, 3 Barrington Buildings, Clinton Road, Leominster, Herefordshire, HR6 0RJ Tel: (01568) 612101 Fax: (01568) 612501 E-mail: mary@rjbarringtonltd.co.uk *Sheet metalwork engineers*

▶ R.J. BUILDING SERVICES, 34 HIGH STREET, OAKFIELD, RYDE, ISLE OF WIGHT, PO33 1EL Tel: 01983 811196 E-mail: rjbuildingservices@ukbuilder.com _R.J. BUILDING SERVICES: BUILDING CONTRACTORS. *EXTENSIONS,BRICKWORK,RENOVATIONS, CONVERSIONS,DRIVEWAYS,PROPERTY MAINTENANCE.*FULLY INSURED BUILDERS*FOR ALL YOUR GENERAL BUILDING REQUIREMENTS AT A COMPETATIVE PRICE._

▶ R J C Electrical Ltd, 34-36 Offerton Industrial Esta, Hempshaw Lane, Stockport, Cheshire, SK2 5TJ Tel: 0161-477 2244

▶ R & J C Fish, 31 North Street, Peterhead, Aberdeenshire, AB42 1JS Tel: (01779) 480590 Fax: (01779) 480590 *Fish merchant*

▶ R J C Projects Engineering Ltd, Unit 1 & 2 Federal Estate, Newton Road, Higham Ferrers, Rushden, Northamptonshire, NN10 8HW Tel: (01933) 418999 Fax: (01933) 418998

▶ R J Cadman Construction Ltd, Sixth Avenue, Flixborough, Scunthorpe, South Humberside, DN15 8SH Tel: (01724) 270033 Fax: (01724) 271160

R J Canning Ltd, Highbank House, Pear Tree Lane, Newbury, Berkshire, RG14 2LU Tel: (01635) 33606 Fax: (01635) 33607 E-mail: highbanks@supanet.com *Ground working services*

R J Cannon Ltd, Maldon Road, Tiptree, Colchester, CO5 0PH Tel: (01621) 815396 Fax: (01621) 817939 E-mail: rjcannon@btclick.com *Plant & crane hire*

▶ R J Caraco, Unit 12 Globe Court, Bentinck Road, West Drayton, Middlesex, UB7 7RQ Tel: (01895) 447509 Fax: (01895) 447611 E-mail: sales@dixontools.com *Tool Manufrs*

R J Clark, Unit 7 Enterprise Trading Est, Pedmore Road, Brierley Hill, West Midlands, DY5 1TX Tel: (01384) 480290 Fax: (01384) 481961 *Hot brass stamping dies*

R J Coleman Plumbing & Heating, Glebe Road, Scunthorpe, South Humberside, DN15 6AF Tel: (01724) 851111 Fax: (01724) 852111 E-mail: sales@rjc.co.uk *Contractors of refrigeration*

R & J Computer Services, Unit 17, Bingham Park Farm, Potten End Hill, Water End, Hemel Hempstead, Hertfordshire, HP1 3BN Tel: (01442) 231943 Fax: (01442) 255207 E-mail: sales@max-technology.co.uk *Computer services*

R J D Fabrications Ltd, Hellaby Industrial Estate, Hellaby Lane, Rotherham, South Yorkshire, S66 8HN Tel: (01709) 531951 Fax: (01709) 700252 E-mail: sales@rjd-eng.com *Steel fabricators*

▶ R J Dance Contractors Ltd, 310 Brighton Road, Sutton, Surrey, SM2 5SU Tel: (020) 8288 1840 Fax: (020) 8288 1841

R & J Dickinson Brighouse Ltd, 11 Owlers Ings Road, Brighouse, West Yorkshire, HD6 1EJ Tel: (01484) 400049 *General engineers*

R J Donaghy & Sons, 71b Lissan Road, Cookstown, County Tyrone, BT80 8QX Tel: (028) 8676 3202 Fax: (028) 8676 2835 *Concrete & brick suppliers*

▶ R J Edwards, Unit 15 Ashcroft Road, Knowsley Industrial Park, Liverpool, L33 7TW Tel: 0151-545 1060 Fax: 0151-545 1061 *Steel workers*

R J Edwards, Unit 15 Ashcroft Road, Knowsley Industrial Park, Liverpool, L33 7TW Tel: 0151-545 1060 Fax: 0151-545 1061 *Building industry engineers*

▶ R J Engineering Ltd, 19 Enterprise Way, Jubilee Business Park, Derby, DE21 4BB Tel: (01332) 367611 Fax: (01332) 291635 *Precision engineering*

R & J Engineering, Gate House Cam Centre, Wilbury Way, Hitchin, Hertfordshire, SG4 0TW Tel: (01462) 620444 Fax: (01462) 620777 *Portable temperature indicator manufrs*

R J Engineering, Derby Works, Liverpool Road South, Burscough, Ormskirk, Lancashire, L40 7SU Tel: (01704) 897771 Fax: (01704) 897772 E-mail: r.j.engineering@amserve.net *Corrugated fastener manufrs*

R.J. EXPRESS FREIGHT., 69 NORTHFIELD DRIVE, WOODSETTS, WORKSOP, NOTTINGHAMSHIRE, S81 8QF Tel: 0800 043 3255 Fax: 01909 561475 E-mail: sales@rjexpressfreight.co.uk *Professional Haulage company with over 20years experience. No job to small.We guantee your deliveries are delivered on the day/or time specified by our customers or we give a full refund of that specific consignment.*

R J Faulkes, Unit C3 Guy Motors Industrial Park, Park Lane, Wolverhampton, WV10 9QF Tel: (01902) 306662 Fax: (01902) 306662 *Electroplating plant & equipment manufrs*

▶ R J Foods Ltd, 1-5 7 Airfield Road, Christchurch, Dorset, BH23 3TQ Tel: (01202) 481471 Fax: (01202) 481471

R & J Garroway Ltd, 6 The Docks, Grangemouth, Stirlingshire, FK3 8UB Tel: (01324) 665455 Fax: (01324) 474754 *Chemical manufrs*

R J H Engineering, Eagle Road, Quarry Hill Industrial Estate, Ilkeston, Derbyshire, DE7 4RB Tel: 0115-944 5202 Fax: 0115-944 5202 *Engineering manufrs*

R J H Plastics Ltd, 86 Plume Street, Birmingham, B6 7RT Tel: 0121-327 0297 Fax: 0121-327 2297 *Manufacturers of polyethylene, polythene bags, sacks & carriers*

R & J Harnesses Ltd, Unit 6-7 The Courtyard Deeside Enterprise Centre, Rowleys Drive, Shotton, Deeside, Clwyd, CH5 1PP Tel: (01244) 812282 Fax: (01244) 818100 *Cable assemblers*

R & J Hill Engineering Ltd, Parker Drive Business Centre, 47 Parker Drive, Leicester, LE4 0JP Tel: 0116-236 6888 Fax: 0116-236 8777 E-mail: sales@hillsport.com *Sports equipment manufrs*

R & J Industrial Supplies, Clay Flatts Trading Estate, Workington, Cumbria, CA14 2TQ Tel: (01900) 605411 Fax: (01900) 605415 *Hydraulic hose fitting distributors*

R J J Freight Ltd, R J J House, Haven Exchange South, Felixstowe, Suffolk, IP11 2QE Tel: (01394) 695560 Fax: (01394) 673031 E-mail: sales@rjjfreight.co.uk *Freight forwarding & warehousing services*

R J Joinery, 67-69 Oxford Street, Rugby, Warwickshire, CV21 3NE Tel: (01788) 565634 Fax: (01788) 565634 *Joiners*

▶ R J K Decorating /Handyman Services, 4 Springfield Road, Blakelaw, Newcastle upon Tyne, NE5 3QQ Tel: (07950) 155928 E-mail: minifill@hotmail.com _DECORATING ,PAINTING ,PAPERHANGING TIME SERVED DECORATORS. BASIC ELECTRICAL, JOINERY, PLUMBING.*SMALL JOBS ARE OUR GAME PER HOUR RATES AND FREE ESTIMATES_

R J Kingston Engineering Ltd, Timothys Bridge Road, Stratford-upon-Avon, Warwickshire, CV37 9NQ Tel: (01789) 205008 Fax: (01789) 415645 *Steel fabricators*

▶ R J Lewis Ltd, 90 Cobham Road, Ferndown Industrial Estate, Wimborne, Dorset, BH21 7RE Tel: (01202) 893739 E-mail: info@rjlewis.com *Engineering design & build, specialists in plastics*

▶ R J Lift & Testing Services Ltd, Suite 210. Astra House, Arklow Road, London, SE14 6EB Tel: (020) 8691 5920 Fax: (020) 8691 5921 E-mail: mail@rjliftandtestingservices.co.uk *Lift repairs, testing, & maintenance services*

▶ R J M Windows, 32-34 Bridge Street, St. Blazey, Par, Cornwall, PL24 2NS Tel: (01726) 816922 Fax: (01726) 816722 E-mail: info@rjmwindows.com *Manufactures of upvc*

▶ R J Mckelvey Building & Civil Engineering Contractors, 17 Carrickdartans Road, Castlederg, County Tyrone, BT81 7NQ Tel: (028) 8167 0586 Fax: (028) 8167 9449

▶ R J Mcleod Contractors Ltd, Atlantean House, Fodderty Way, Dingwall Business Park, Dingwall, Ross-Shire, IV15 9XB Tel: (01349) 860000 Fax: (01349) 860005

▶ R J Mcleod Contractors Ltd, 2411 London Road, Glasgow, G32 8XT Tel: 0141-764 2411

▶ R & J Malone, 113-115 Slateford Road, Edinburgh, EH11 1QY Tel: 0131-337 7621

R & J Maritime Ltd, 89 Durnford Street, Plymouth, PL1 3QW Tel: (01752) 671586 Fax: (01752) 265744 E-mail: rjmedler@supanet.com *Naval architects & naval engineering services*

▶ R & J Mesh, 2 The Wallows Industrial Estate, Fens Pool Avenue, Brierley Hill, West Midlands, DY5 1QA Tel: (01384) 70488 Fax: (01384) 265663 E-mail: sales@rjmesh.co.uk *Wire gauze, mesh & cloth distributors*

▶ R & J Milne Ltd, Norwood Ardmiddle, Turriff, Aberdeenshire, AB53 4HJ Tel: (01888) 562945 Fax: (01888) 563670

R J Mobility Ltd, Boxtree Mills, Wheatley, Halifax, West Yorkshire, HX3 5AE Tel: (01422) 358888 Fax: (01422) 355924 E-mail: sales@rjmobility.com *Invalid chair manufrs*

R J Noble, 2 Stainsacre La Industrial Estate, Fairfield Way, Whitby, North Yorkshire, YO22 4PU Tel: (01947) 820413 Fax: (01947) 820413 *Shellfish merchants & curers*

R J P Royal Cleaning Contractors, 5 Ermine Street, Buntingford, Hertfordshire, SG9 9AZ Tel: (01763) 272912 *Office cleaning contractors*

R J Parry Ltd, The Owl Complex, Manor Road, Sealand, Deeside, Clwyd, CH5 2SB Tel: (01244) 821600 Fax: (01244) 823181 E-mail: sales@parryjoinery.co.uk *Joinery manufrs*

R & J Partington, Failsworth Mill, Ashton Road West, Failsworth, Manchester, M35 0FR Tel: 0161-934 4040 Fax: 0161-683 4280 E-mail: partington@fabric.co.uk *Textile merchants*

R & J Paving, The Yard, Stone Lane, Lydiard Millicent, Swindon, SN5 3LD Tel: (01793) 770071 *Suppliers of sand, gravel, aggregates, rockery stone, bottled gas, for the trade and DIY market. Wet cast concrete products. For all your landscaping needs.*

R J Phillips & Sons Removers & Storage, Harlescott Lane, Shrewsbury, SY1 3AH Tel: (01743) 442230 Fax: (01743) 446739 E-mail: wayt@tdg.co.uk *Temperature controlled storage*

▶ R J Pickford Electrical Ltd, Newbourne House, Bedford Grove, Nottingham, NG6 9DE Tel: 0115-976 4445 Fax: 0115-976 4440

R & J Pine, Harmers Yard, Hall La, Walton on the Naze, Essex, CO14 8HW Tel: (01255) 673124 Fax: (01255) 673124 *Pine furniture*

R J Plastics, 83-84 Buckingham Street, Birmingham, B19 3HU Tel: 0121-233 1077 Fax: 0121-236 6355 Principal Export Areas: Asia Pacific, Central Asia & Africa *Manufacturers of fume extraction plant & equipment*

▶ R J Poots & Co, 22 Bridge Street, Dromore, County Down, BT25 1AN Tel: (028) 9269 2349 E-mail: enquiries@rjpoots.co.uk *Services including wedding car hire.*

▶ R J Priestley & Son, Station Road, Langworth, Langworth, Lincoln, LN3 5BD Tel: (01522) 752519 Fax: (01522) 750850 E-mail: rjp@vodavp.com

R J Pryce & Co. Ltd, Trinity Road, Lowestoft, Suffolk, NR32 1XJ Tel: (01502) 574141 Fax: (01502) 501213 E-mail: sales@rjpryce.co.uk *Industrial & builders merchants*

R J & R J Scaffolding, 22 Chambers Drive, Apse Heath, Sandown, Isle Of Wight, PO36 0LR Tel: (01983) 864674 Fax: (01983) 401092 E-mail: anne-kevin@hotmail.com *Scaffolding*

R J Rudd & Co., Westwood Farm, Highcross Road, Southfleet, Gravesend, Kent, DA13 9PH Tel: (01474) 833899 Fax: (01474) 833799 *Fork lift servicing & repairers*

R J S Electrical Contractors, Park House, Suckley, Worcester, WR6 5DJ Tel: (01886) 884000 Fax: (01886) 884777 *Electrical contractors*

▶ R J S Heating Plumbing & Mechanical Services Ltd, 26 Chipstead Station Parade, Chipstead, Coulsdon, Surrey, CR5 3TF Tel: (01737) 550110 Fax: (01737) 556770

R J S Kennedy, 46 Drumfad Road, Millisle, Newtownards, County Down, BT22 2JA Tel: (028) 9186 2000 Fax: (028) 9186 2077 *Car parts manufrs*

R J Sharples, Riverside Sawmill, Fishwick Bottoms, Preston, PR2 5AU Tel: (01772) 556019 Fax: (01772) 250708 E-mail: info@rjsharples.co.uk *Timber merchant & slate merchants*

R J Smith Ltd, 41-42 Tenby St North, Birmingham, B1 3EG Tel: 0121-233 2160 Fax: 0121-233 9630 E-mail: sales@rjs-ltd.com *Corporate jewellery manufrs*

continued

continued

R J Stoddart & Co., 96 Orbiston Street, Motherwell, Lanarkshire, ML1 1PX Tel: (01698) 263333 Fax: (01698) 263333 *Engineers pattern makers*

▶ R J Stokes & Co. Ltd, Little London Road, Heeley, Sheffield, S8 0UH Tel: 0114-258 9595 Fax: 0114-250 9836 E-mail: sales@rjstokes.co.uk *Paint manufrs*

R J Supplies, Wellington House, 65 Wellington Street, Stapleford, Nottingham, NG9 7BE Tel: 0115-939 3933 *Medical disposal equipment distributors*

R J T Conveyors (International) Ltd, Unit 20 Beven Industrial Estate, Beven Road, Brierley Hill, West Midlands, DY5 3TF Tel: (01384) 864458 Fax: (01384) 827777 E-mail: sales@rjtconveyors.com *Overhead conveyor chain & chain conveyor systems services*

R J T Excavations Ltd, Oxnam Road Indust, Oxnam Road Industrial Estate, Jedburgh, Roxburghshire, TD8 6LS Tel: (01835) 862367 Fax: (01835) 863025 *Plant hire*

R J T Furnaces Ltd, Unit 10 Holland Park, Bentley Road South, Wednesbury, West Midlands, WS10 8LN Tel: 0121-568 6474 Fax: 0121-568 6269 *Furnace engineers*

R & J Turner Engineering, Purfleet Industrial Park, London Road, Aveley, South Ockendon, Essex, RM15 4YA Tel: (01708) 865043 Fax: (01708) 869403 E-mail: roger@rjturner.com *Precision engineers*

R J Vickers & Son Ltd, 152 Soho Hill, Birmingham, B19 1AF Tel: 0121-523 6235 Fax: 0121-523 9397 E-mail: vickers.metform@virgin.net *Specialists in pressings*

R J W Ltd, Unit A5, Watery Lane, Sevenoaks, Kent, TN15 6PW Tel: 01732 763122 *Precision & production engineers & supplier of charpy izod prep equipment*

R J W Sheet Metal Ltd, 40 Cobham Road, Ferndown Industrial Estate, Wimborne, Dorset, BH21 7NP Tel: (01202) 875852 Fax: (01202) 893953 E-mail: enquiries@rjwsheetmetal.com *Sheet metalworkers*

▶ R J Watkinson & Partners, 12 High Street, Lyndhurst, Hampshire, SO43 7BD Tel: (023) 8028 3794 Fax: (023) 8028 3655 E-mail: rjwptrs@rjwatkinsons.co.uk *Civil & structural consulting engineers*

R & J Watson Gardening Landscape, 6 Charter Road, Slough, SL1 5JE Tel: (07730) 434118 *Landscape garden design & maintenance company covering Berkshire, Surrey & Buckinghamshire*

R J Wey & Sons, South Street, Crewkerne, Somerset, TA18 8DA Tel: (01460) 72873 Fax: (01460) 72873 *Portable building sales & manufrs*

R J White, Unit F10 Briarsford, Perry Road, Witham, Essex, CM8 3UY Tel: (01376) 500524 *Grinding services*

▶ R J Wilson Electricians Ltd, A17 Washway Road, Fleet, Holbeach, Spalding, Lincolnshire, PE12 8LT Tel: (01406) 423331 Fax: (01406) 425533

▶ R J Winnicott Ltd, 11 The Green, Rowland's Castle, Hampshire, PO9 6BW Tel: (023) 9241 2741 Fax: (023) 9241 2212 E-mail: mail@winnicott.co.uk

R Jardine, Watchhill, Carlisle Road, Annan, Dumfriesshire, DG12 6QR Tel: (01461) 205319 Fax: (01461) 201457 E-mail: rjardine.annan@btopenworld.com *Joinery & roofing contractors*

R JS, 134 High Street, Sheerness, Kent, ME12 1UB Tel: (01795) 660134 Fax: (01795) 427348 *Protective, leisure & outsize clothing retailers*

R K Atkinson Ltd, Main Street, Garton-on-the-Wolds, Driffield, North Humberside, YO25 3EU Tel: (01377) 254090 Fax: (01377) 255700 E-mail: richard@rk-atkinson.co.uk *Propeller repairers & reconditioners*

▶ R K Bell Ltd, Dunwear Depot, Dunwear, Bridgwater, Somerset, TA7 0AA Tel: (01278) 424883 Fax: 01278 425944 E-mail: jerome@rkbell.com

R K Burt & Co. Ltd, 57 Union Street, London, SE1 1SG Tel: (020) 7407 6474 Fax: (020) 7403 3672 E-mail: sales@rkburt.co.uk *Fine art paper merchants*

R K Clothing Manufacturers Ltd, 300-306 Park Road, Hockley, Birmingham, B18 5HE Tel: 0121-551 1379 Fax: 0121-551 1379 *Jackets & promotional wear*

R K Components, 5b Eley Estate, Angel Road, London, N18 3BH Tel: (020) 8884 1366 Fax: (020) 8884 3881 E-mail: info@rkcomponents.com *Precision turned parts manufrs*

R K D Computers Liverpool, 6 Glenluce Road, Liverpool, L19 9BX Tel: 0151-281 0860 Fax: 0151-427 3022 *Computer consultants*

R K Davies, 8 Spinnaker Road, Hempsted Lane, Hempsted, Gloucester, GL2 5FD Tel: (01452) 410555 Fax: (01452) 310452 *Precision turned parts manufrs*

▶ R K Eggleton, Curridge, Thatcham, Berkshire, RG18 9DR Tel: (01635) 202604

▶ R K Electrical Bradford Ltd, Britannia Buildings, Reservoir Road, Halifax, West Yorkshire, HX2 0ET Tel: (01422) 364035 Fax: (01422) 348573

▶ R K Engineering, 40 Fourways, Atherstone, Warwickshire, CV9 1LG Tel: (01827) 715041 Fax: (01827) 718135

R K Furniture Ltd, The Airfield, Tholthorpe, York, YO61 1ST Tel: (01347) 838182 Fax: (01347) 838330 E-mail: enquiries@rkfurniture.co.uk *Furniture manufrs*

▶ R K & J Jones, Southery Road, Seltwell, Thetford, Norfolk, IP26 4EH Tel: (01842) 828101

R K J Precision Engineering Ltd, Park Hall Workshop, Tonypandy, Mid Glamorgan, CF40 2BQ Tel: (01443) 434967 *Injection mouldings toolmakers*

R K L Ltd, Roland Road, Stockport, Cheshire, SK5 6TJ Tel: 0161-477 9192 Fax: 0161-480 3852 *Biscuit machinery refurbishers*

R K Leighton, 2 Partridge Court, Price Street, Birmingham, B4 6JZ Tel: 0121-359 0514 Fax: 0121-333 3130 E-mail: sales@rk-leighton.co.uk *Car & motor cycle upholstery repairs*

R K M Display, 50 Chewton Way, Walkford, Christchurch, Dorset, BH23 5LS Tel: (01425) 274295 Fax: (01425) 274295 *Function decorators*

R K M Joinery, Unit 6, Lochty Industrial Estate, Almondbank, Perth, PH1 3NP Tel: (01738) 582060 Fax: (01738) 582060 *Joinery manufrs*

R & K Metal Components, Unit 37 Claro Court Business Centre, Claro Road, Harrogate, North Yorkshire, HG1 4BA Tel: (01423) 523139 Fax: (01423) 523139 *Precision engineers*

▶ R K Plant & Transport Ltd, Moorclose, Trewithey Farm, North Hill, Launceston, Cornwall, PL15 7NH Tel: (01566) 782995 Fax: (01566) 782765

R K R Engineering, Northpoint, Enterprise Close, Medway City Estate, Rochester, Kent, ME2 4LY Tel: (01634) 723565 Fax: (01634) 712912 *Precision engineers*

R K R Security Ltd, 6 Bilton Road, Erith, Kent, DA8 2AN Tel: (01322) 334881 *Security product manufrs*

R K Refrigeration Ltd, 2-4 South Croston Street, Manchester, M16 7WP Tel: 0161-232 9163 Fax: 0161-232 7277 E-mail: rkrefrigeration@talk21.com *Refrigeration equipment suppliers & manufrs*

R K Ross & Co. Ltd, Unit 1 George Leigh Street, Manchester, M4 6BD Tel: 0161-205 1822 Fax: 0161-203 4609 *Cotton & synthetic textiles*

R K S Maintenance, 650 Woodborough Road, Nottingham, NG3 5FS Tel: 0115-960 2284 Fax: 0115-960 2285 E-mail: rksltd@btopenworld.com *Property maintenance services*

R K Shipman Ltd, 1 Barnfield Crescent, Exeter, EX1 1QY Tel: (01392) 278491 Fax: (01392) 425793 E-mail: sales@rkshipman.co.uk *Insurance brokers & financial advisers* Also at: Exmouth

R K Styles Ltd, Unit 2 Alma Street, Smethwick, West Midlands, B66 2RL Tel: 0121-565 3630 Fax: 0121-565 1004 E-mail: sales@rkstyles.co.uk *Workwear clothing manufrs*

R K Trucks Centre Ltd, Edgar Road, Comber Road, Carryduff, Belfast, BT8 8NB Tel: (028) 9081 3600 Fax: (028) 9081 4115 E-mail: donna@rktrucks.com *Commercial vehicles*

R K W Associates, 22 Bishops Mead, Laverstock, Salisbury, SP1 1RU Tel: (01722) 502600 Fax: (01722) 337344 *RKW Associates was formed in 1985. On-site facilities include design office, stores and a workshop. Our charging structures can be based either on an hourly rate or a fixed price*

R Kirkland Blyth Ltd, 62-66 Bridge Street, Blyth, Northumberland, NE24 2AP Tel: (01670) 352196 Fax: (01670) 360238 *Heating engineers*

▶ R L Davies, 25 Raven Road, Walsall, WS5 3PZ Tel: (01922) 645443 Fax: (01922) 645443

▶ R L Electronics, 16 Gurney Close, Bradford, West Yorkshire, BD5 9QR Tel: (01274) 229753 Fax: (01274) 229753 E-mail: rlad@rland.fsnet.co.uk *PCB assembly & test for leaded components*

▶ R L Engineering Services Ltd, Polmadie Works, Jessie Street, Glasgow, G42 0PZ Tel: 0141-423 2367 Fax: 0141-422 2156

R & L Enterprises Ltd, Swinnow View, Leeds, LS13 4NA Tel: 0113-257 4208 Fax: 0113-256 0876 E-mail: subcon@rexaloy.co.uk *Laboratory apparatus manufacturers & subcontract engineers*

R L Insulations, 4 Sentinel Works, Northgate Avenue, Bury St. Edmunds, Suffolk, IP32 6AZ Tel: (01284) 760937 Fax: (01284) 755031 E-mail: info@rlinsulation.fsnet.co.uk *Asbestos Removal*

R L M Accountancy Services, 14A The Green, Milford, Stafford, ST17 0UR Tel: (01785) 665094 Fax: (01785) 665094 *Book keeping, tax returns & SAGE support*

R L M Packaging Ltd, Dairycoates Industrial Estate, Wiltshire Road, Hull, HU4 6PA Tel: (01482) 505585 Fax: (01482) 568115 E-mail: info@rlm-packaging.co.uk *Tin box & drum manufrs*

▶ R L Property Maintenance Service, 4 Babylon View, Oxford Road, Pen Mill Trading Estate, Yeovil, Somerset, BA21 5HR Tel: (01935) 414204 Fax: (01935) 475925

▶ R L R Engineers Ltd, 456 Warrington Road, Rainhill, Prescot, Merseyside, L35 9JE Tel: 0151-426 0245 Fax: 0151-426 8288 E-mail: admin@rlrengineers.co.uk *Precision engineering company, established for over 35 years specialising in production of CNC turned / milled parts on multi-axis fixed head and sliding head CNC turning centres.*

R L S Associates, 68 Crabtree Lane, Bromsgrove, Worcestershire, B61 8NZ Tel: (01527) 875144 Fax: (01527) 575912 *Risk management, health & safety consultants*

R L Services, 1 Bryn Road, Loughor, Swansea, SA4 6PG Tel: (01792) 897594 Fax: (01792) 416505 E-mail: ritchieslaundry@hotmail.com *Dry cleaning & laundry services*

R & L Slaughter Ltd, Unit 11 Saxon House Upminster Trading Park, Warley Street, Upminster, Essex, RM14 3PJ Tel: (01708) 228409 Fax: (01708) 228728 E-mail: info@slaughter.co.uk *Laboratory equipment & chemicals suppliers*

R L Smith & Sons Ltd, Herriot Bank Farm, Whitsome, Duns, Berwickshire, TD11 3NB Tel: (01890) 870241 Fax: (01890) 870369 E-mail: sales@rlsmithandsons.co.uk *Agricultural contractors & equipment hire*

R & L Superfix, 1 Mead Park Industrial Estate, Mead Road, Cheltenham, Gloucestershire, GL53 7EF Tel: (01242) 224664 Fax: (01242) 222977 *Power tools & fixings distributors*

R L Trim, 9 Acreman Street, Cerne Abbas, Dorchester, Dorset, DT2 7LD Tel: (01300) 341209 Fax: (01300) 341815 *Wood component marquee manufrs*

R Lancaster & Son, 21 Bryning Lane, Wrea Green, Preston, PR4 2WJ Tel: (01772) 684222 *Agricultural contractors*

▶ R Levitt Ltd, 37 Low Street, Sherburn In Elmet, Leeds, LS25 6BB Tel: (01977) 682264

▶ R Lindsay & Co. Ltd, Hayfield Place, Hayfield Industrial Estate, Kirkcaldy, Fife, KY2 5DH Tel: (01592) 260154 Fax: (01592) 641813 E-mail: sales@rlindsay.com

R Lunn Engineering, 2 Vincent Mill, Vincent Street, Macclesfield, Cheshire, SK11 6UJ Tel: (01625) 611682 Fax: (01625) 611682 *Manufacturer of tools & tool making services*

R M P.L.C., New Mill House, 183 Milton Park, Abingdon, Oxfordshire, OX14 4SE Tel: (01235) 826000 Fax: (01235) 826999 E-mail: salesdesk@rm.com *Microcomputer manufacturers & educational software*

▶ R & M A Stewart Ltd, 349A Wandsworth Road, London, SW8 2JH Tel: (020) 7720 7810

R M Addy & Sons, 127 Station Road, Deeping St. James, Peterborough, PE6 8RQ Tel: (01778) 343314 Fax: 01778 343314 *Hay & straw suppliers*

R M B Contractors Ltd, Ripley Road, Ambergate, Belper, Derbyshire, DE56 2EP Tel: (01773) 853151 Fax: (01773) 857306 *Civil engineering contractors*

▶ R M B Engineering Services Ltd, Union Street, West Bromwich, West Midlands, B70 6BP Tel: 0121-500 1940 Fax: 0121-500 1941 E-mail: sales@rmbgroup.co.uk *Repair, industrial gearboxes, fabricators*

R M B Engineering Services Ltd, Union Street, West Bromwich, West Midlands, B70 6BP Tel: 0121-500 1940 Fax: 0121-500 1941 E-mail: sales@rmbderitend.co.uk Principal Export Areas: Worldwide *Gearbox distributors*

R M B Engineering Services Ltd, Union Street, West Bromwich, West Midlands, B70 6BP Tel: 0121-500 1940 Fax: 0121-500 1941 E-mail: sales@rmbgroup.co.uk *Steel fabricators*

R M B Engineering Services Ltd, Union Street, West Bromwich, West Midlands, B70 6BP Tel: 0121-500 1940 Fax: 0121-500 1941 E-mail: sales@rmbgroup.co.uk *Gear box & unit suppliers*

R M B Engineering Services Ltd, Union Street, West Bromwich, West Midlands, B70 6BP Tel: 0121-500 1940 Fax: 0121-500 1941 E-mail: sales@rmbgroup.co.uk *Deburring equipment manufrs*

▶ R M B Maintenance Services Ltd, 1 Alcester Road, Birmingham, B13 8AR Tel: 0121-449 5777 Fax: 0121-449 4945

R & M Bearings Ltd, Unit 13 Manhattan Works, Dundonald Street, Dundee, DD3 7PY Tel: (01382) 455400 Fax: (01382) 454645 E-mail: sales@rmbearings.co.uk *Power transmission equipment & bearing suppliers*

R M C Ltd, St. Omers Road, Dunston, Gateshead, Tyne & Wear, NE11 9EJ Tel: 0191-460 5085 Fax: 0191-460 0908 *Concrete products*

R M C Concrete Products Ltd, Dale Road, Dove Holes, Buxton, Derbyshire, SK17 8BG Tel: (01298) 22324 Fax: (01298) 815221 *Brick, block & decorative paving*

R M C Group, Crown House, Evreux Way, Rugby, Warwickshire, CV21 2DT Tel: (01788) 542111 Fax: (01788) 540166 E-mail: enquiries@rugbycement.co.uk *Building materials manufrs*

R M C Materials Ltd, Tannochside Park, Uddingston, Glasgow, G71 5PH Tel: (01698) 811100 Fax: (01698) 816068 *Quarry operators aggregates & concrete suppliers*

▶ R M C Mechanical Services, 3 Landport Road, Wolverhampton, WV2 2QJ Tel: (01902) 451541 Fax: (01902) 871534

R M C Mortars Ltd, Weeford Quarry, London Rd, Canwell, Sutton Coldfield, W. Midlands, B75 5SZ Tel: 01543 481044 Fax: 01543 481380 *Ready mixed mortar*

R M C Ready Mixed Concrete (Scotland) Ltd, Blackcastle Quarry, Nairn, IV12 5NX Tel: (01667) 452536 Fax: (01667) 452429 *Concrete suppliers & consultants*

R M C Readymix Midlands, Wolverhampton Road, Oldbury, West Midlands, B69 4RJ Tel: (0870) 7762762 Fax: 0121-544 7970 *Ready mixed concrete suppliers* Also at: Branches throughout the West Midlands

R M C Roadstone Ltd, Roadstone, Huggate, York, YO42 1YR Tel: (01377) 288117 Fax: (01377) 288461 *Tarmac manufrs*

▶ R M C Russell, Cowieslinn Crossing, Peebles, EH45 8QZ Tel: (01721) 730251 Fax: (01721) 730379

R M C South West Ltd, Moorlands Trading Estate, Saltash, Cornwall, PL12 6LX Tel: (01752) 481011 Fax: (01752) 848862 *Concrete manufrs*

R M C Western Ltd, Warmwell Quarry, Moreton Road, Warmwell, Dorchester, Dorset, DT2 8HU Tel: (01305) 852253 *Concrete mixing*

R M Canopies, 5 3 Lower Balloo Road, Groomsport, Bangor, County Down, BT19 6LU Tel: (028) 9188 4463 Fax: (028) 9188 4463 *Kitchen furniture manufrs*

▶ R M D Office Solutions, 1 Montrose Terrace, Old Wrexham Road, Gresford, Wrexham, Clwyd, LL12 8UN Tel: (01978) 853721 Fax: (01978) 856470 E-mail: enquiries@officesols.co.uk *Providers of outsourced administration solutions & office furniture*

R M D (U K) Ltd, Thornham Works, Oozewood Road, Royton, Oldham, OL2 5SQ Tel: 0161-620 4418 *Point of sale merchandising units*

▶ R & M Developments, Clifton Street, Miles Platting, Manchester, M40 8HF Tel: 0161-202 3030 Fax: 0161-202 2120

R M Display Systems Ltd, 44 Murrell Green Business Park, Hook, Hampshire, RG27 9GR Tel: (01256) 740211 Fax: (01256) 740201 E-mail: info@rmdisplay.co.uk *Hire & sell modular exhibition stands, Print and production of graphics, Banners, Pop-ups, Leaflet racks and plinths*

R & M Distribution Ltd, 1 Mitchelson Drive, Mitchelston Industrial Estate, Mitchelston Industrial Estate, Kirkcaldy, Fife, KY1 3NF Tel: (01592) 655565 Fax: (01592) 655542 E-mail: enquiries@rmdist.com *Industrial fastener distributors & electrical wholesalers*

R M Electrical, 340a Thornton Road, Bradford, West Yorkshire, BD8 8LD Tel: (01274) 549252 Fax: (01274) 549253 E-mail: admin@rmelectrical.co.uk *Control panel manufrs*

R M Engineering, Unit D Colchester Road, Maldon, Essex, CM9 4NL Tel: (01621) 842845 Fax: (01621) 842845 *Precision machining custom made components*

R & M Enterprise Windows Ltd, Unit 2 Thames House, Middlegreen Trading Estate, Langley, Slough, SL3 6DF Tel: (01753) 526334 Fax: (01753) 517694 E-mail: info@randmwindows.fsnet.co.uk *Aluminium & upvc window manufrs*

R M F Engineering Ltd, Rotherham Road, Dinnington, Sheffield, S25 3RF Tel: (01909) 567683 Fax: (01909) 562725 E-mail: sales@rmf-engineering.co.uk *Corrosion resistant process plant manufrs*

R M F Ventilation Ltd, Stoneholme Business Centre, 42 High Street, Bury, Lancashire, BL8 3AN Tel: 0161-761 6099 Fax: 0161-764 1699 E-mail: rmf.ventilation@btinternet.com *Ventilation & air conditioning design engineers*

▶ R M Fabrications, Ringwood Road, Three Legged Cross, Wimborne, Dorset, BH21 6QZ Tel: (01202) 828240 Fax: (01202) 828250 *Steel fabricators*

R M G Fabrications Ltd, 32a Heming Road, Redditch, Worcestershire, B98 0DH Tel: (01527) 525442 Fax: (01527) 527642 *Welded steel fabrication & engineering*

R M Gearings, Milber Down, Coffinswell, Newton Abbot, Devon, TQ12 4SE Tel: (01803) 872651 Fax: (01392) 257057 *Fresh meat wholesalers*

R M George & Son, 6 Firs Road, Firsdown, Salisbury, SP5 1SF Tel: (01980) 862267 *Excavation, groundwork & agricultural contractors*

R M Gillingham & Son Ltd, 44 East Street, Bridport, Dorset, DT6 3LJ Tel: (01308) 423777 Fax: (01308) 458791 E-mail: info@gillinghams-insurance.co.uk *Insurance brokers & financial advisers*

R M H Refinishing, 2 Rutland Court, Manners Avenue, Manners Industrial Estate, Ilkeston, Derbyshire, DE7 8EF Tel: 0115-944 1528 Fax: 0115-944 1526 *Paint spraying contractors*

R M J Alloys Ltd, 48 Bayton Road, Exhall, Coventry, CV7 9EJ Tel: (024) 7636 7508 Fax: (024) 7636 0280 E-mail: sales@rmjalloys.co.uk *Aluminium castings & spiral staircases*

▶ R M J Engineering Ltd, Lion Works, Station Road, Whittlesford, Cambridge, CB2 4NL Tel: (01223) 839900

R M J M Ltd, 83 Paul Street, London, EC2A 4UT Tel: (020) 7549 8900 Fax: (020) 7250 3131 E-mail: london@rmjm.com *Architects, engineers & planners*

R M J Mouldings, 4B Centurion Park, Kendel Road, Shrewsbury, SY1 4EH Tel: (01743) 450470 Fax: (01743) 351584 *Glass fibre mouldings & tank manufrs*

R M K Supplies, 9 Carterweys, Dunstable, Bedfordshire, LU5 4RB Tel: (01582) 699137 Fax: (01582) 814055 *Janitorial supplies*

R M Mallen C N C Machinery Ltd, 15 Hainge Road, Tividale, Oldbury, West Midlands, B69 2NR Tel: 0121-557 3141 Fax: 0121-557 3814 *Precision machinists*

R & M Microwave Ovens, 8 The Cloisters, Fareham, Hampshire, PO15 5PU Tel: (01329) 844517 Fax: (01329) 843522 *Domestic & commercial suppliers*

R M Mogridge, Henbury Farm, East Orchard, Shaftesbury, Dorset, SP7 0LG Tel: (01747) 811718 Fax: (01747) 812113 *Civil engineers*

▶ R M P Products Ltd, Unit 26 G W S Trading Estate, Leabrook Road, Wednesbury, West Midlands, WS10 7NB Tel: 0121-505 3066 Fax: 0121-505 3077 E-mail: rmpproducts@btconnect.com *Steel profiling*

R M Pugh & Co. Ltd, 35 Hylton Street, Birmingham, B18 6HJ Tel: 0121-554 4283 Fax: 0121-523 8709 *Jewellery pad manufrs*

R M R Engineering Ltd, 90-92 Tontine Street, Folkestone, Kent, CT20 1JW Tel: (01303) 253166 Fax: (01303) 220380 E-mail: sales@rmrengineering.co.uk *Sheet metalworkers & fabrication services*

R M R Materials Testing Co. Ltd, Deepdale Lane, Dudley, West Midlands, DY3 2AF Tel: (01384) 234515 Fax: (01384) 235511 E-mail: rmrmaterialstestingco@callnetuk.com *Test engineering services*

R M Recycling, 9 Twyford Business Centre, London Road, Bishop's Stortford, Hertfordshire, CM23 3YT Tel: (01279) 654366 Fax: (01279) 654366 *Non-ferrous scrap merchants*

R M Reinforcements Ltd, 3-5 Church Street, Brierley Hill, West Midlands, DY5 3PT Tel: (01384) 262601 Fax: (01384) 262605 E-mail: rmreinforcements@aol.com *Reinforcing (concrete etc) steel reinforcement manufrs*

R M Rotary Services Ltd, New Lane, Havant, Hampshire, PO9 2LT Tel: (023) 9249 2360 Fax: (023) 9249 2544 E-mail: info@rmrotary.co.uk *Printing machine equipment distributors*

R M S, Unit 6 Hopton Court, Hopton Industrial Estate, Devizes, Wiltshire, SN10 2EU Tel: (01380) 729292 Fax: (01380) 729140 *Refrigeration engineers*

R M S Commercial, 48A Osborne Road, Newcastle Upon Tyne, NE2 2AL Tel: 0191-212 0000 Fax: 0191-281 9074 E-mail: info@ellisonrms.co.uk *Business transfer agents*

R M S Engineering Prestwick Ltd, 5 Glenburn Industrial Estate, Shawfarm Road, Prestwick, Ayrshire, KA9 2NS Tel: (01292) 671160 Fax: (01292) 671404 E-mail: info@rmsstainlesssteelexhausts.com *Exhaust system & pipework manufrs*

▶ R M S International Ltd, 66 Pendlebury Road, Swinton, Manchester, M27 4GY Tel: 0161-727 8182 Fax: 0161-727 8191 E-mail: jmcdermott@rmsint.com *Distributors of student/childrens stationary*

Company Information

▶ indicates data change since last edition

R M S Vibration Test Laboratory, 26 Coder Road, Ludlow Business Park, Ludlow, Shropshire, SY8 1XE Tel: (01584) 861395 Fax: (01584) 861395 E-mail: rms.vibes@avignon.enta.net *Vibration consultants*

R & M Signmakers, 2 Whitehill Lane, Gravesend, Kent, DA12 5LY Tel: (01474) 568358 Fax: (01474) 568358 *Sign makers, contractors & signwriters*

R M Supplies Inverkeithing Ltd, Cruickness Road, Ferryhills Road, Inverkeithing, Fife, KY11 1HL Tel: (01383) 418901 Fax: (01383) 418198 *Scarp metal merchants*

R & M Sutcliffe, Clifton Warehouse, Lower Clifton Street, Sowerby Bridge, West Yorkshire, HX6 2BY Tel: (01422) 831038 Fax: (01422) 839841 E-mail: pml@bbn.co.uk *Engineers merchants*

R M T-Gabro Ltd, Hilton Road, Cobbs Wood Industrial Estate, Ashford, Kent, TN23 1EW Tel: (01233) 628976 Fax: (01233) 631888 E-mail: sales@mjallen.co.uk *Metal folding machines, guillotine, section rolling machine manufrs*

R & M Tools, 105 Frederick Street, Walsall, WS2 9NJ Tel: (01922) 627276 Fax: (01922) 721780 *Press toolmakers*

R M Upholstery, Rear of, 107 Evesham Road, Redditch, Worcestershire, B97 4JX Tel: (01527) 544490 *Re-upholstery services*

R M W Witney Ltd, Unit 10br Bromag Industrial Estate, Burford Road, Minster Lovell, Witney, Oxfordshire, OX29 0SR Tel: (01993) 702505 Fax: (01993) 774103 E-mail: sales@rmwwitneyltd.co.uk *CNC precision engineers*

R M Walkden & Co. Ltd, 14 Pensioners Court The Charterhouse, Charterhouse Square, London, EC1M 6AU Tel: (020) 7253 6677 Fax: (020) 7253 2154 *Financial & taxation*

R M Welch & Son Ltd, Fountainbrae, Monifieth, Dundee, DD5 4DU Tel: (01382) 532139 Fax: (01382) 535138 E-mail: bruce@welchseeds.co.uk *Agricultural seed merchants*

▶ R & M Wheildon Ltd, 10 Stonegate, Burton Road, Lower Bentham, Lancaster, LA2 7DY Tel: (01524) 262330 Fax: (01524) 262330

R Mcateer, 7 Tullaghmore Road, Coalisland, Dungannon, County Tyrone, BT71 4PN Tel: (028) 8774 0504 Fax: (028) 8774 0504 *Tractors & farm machinery services & repairs*

R Mccann, 405 Oxhill Road, Birmingham, B21 8JT Tel: 0121-554 3232 Fax: 0121-554 3232 *Monumental memorial masons*

R Mcmahon Engineering Ltd, Unit 5 Oldends Industrial Estate, Oldends, Stonehouse, Gloucestershire, GL10 3RQ Tel: (01453) 828666 Fax: (01453) 828360 E-mail: howard@mcmahon-engineering.com *Production engineers*

R Mansell (Developments) Ltd, Roman House, 13/27 Grant Road, Croydon, CR9 6BU Tel: (020) 8654 8191 Fax: (020) 8655 1286 E-mail: mailbox@mansell.plc.uk *Building contractors & maintenance specialists*

R Martin, School House, Darlton Road, Dunham-on-Trent, Newark, Nottinghamshire, NG22 0UJ Tel: (01777) 228259 Fax: (01777) 228259 *Manufacturing & retail of shotguns*

R Mason Chemicals Ltd, Hare Law Industrial Estate, Stanley, County Durham, DH9 8UL Tel: (01207) 237373 Fax: (01207) 237373 E-mail: masonchem@cs.com *Pharmaceutical manufrs*

▶ R Miller (Blacksmiths & Welders) Ltd, Barton Hall Works, Overtown Road, Waterloo, Wishaw, Lanarkshire, ML2 8EW Tel: (01698) 373770

R Moss Fork Lifts, White House, Staithes Road, Preston, Hull, HU12 8TH Tel: (01482) 896524 Fax: (01482) 896524 *Fork lift truck repairers & refurbishments*

▶ R Moulding & Co Salisbury Ltd, Ryeville, Warminster Road, South Newton, Salisbury, SP2 0QW Tel: (01722) 742228 Fax: (01722) 744502

R N B Industrial Door Service Ltd, 6 Davenport Centre, Renwick Road, Barking, Essex, IG11 0SH Tel: (020) 8595 1242 Fax: (020) 8595 3849 *Industrial door manufrs*

▶ R & N Cessford, Whanland Farm, Farnell, Brechin, Angus, DD9 6UF Tel: (01674) 674253 Fax: (01674) 820225

R N Contract Blinds, 57 Dyott Avenue, Whittington, Lichfield, Staffordshire, WS14 9NF Tel: (01543) 433433 Fax: (01543) 304047 *Vertical blind installers*

R N D Clothing Manufacturers Ltd, 998 Foleshill Road, Coventry, CV6 6EN Tel: (024) 7663 8989 Fax: (024) 7666 6214 E-mail: rdhami@rndclothing.co.uk *Corporate & work wear manufrs*

R N D O Services Ltd, Colchester Road, Coggeshall, Colchester, CO6 1RR Tel: (01376) 563636 Fax: (01376) 563635 *Stainless steel manufrs*

R N Electronics Ltd, Arnolds Farm Lane, Mountnessing, Brentwood, Essex, CM13 1UT Tel: (01277) 352219 Fax: (01277) 352968 E-mail: sales@rnelectronics.com *EMC testing services*

R N Garments, Vulcan House, 8 Vulcan Road, Leicester, LE5 3EF Tel: 0116-262 0105 *Children & ladies clothing manufrs*

R N Peace & Co., 103 High Street, Witney, Oxfordshire, OX28 6HZ Tel: (01993) 702434 Fax: (01993) 702434 E-mail: mrrbpeace@aol.com *General household linen merchants*

R N Shields Ltd, 109 Leicester Road, New Packington, Ashby-de-la-Zouch, Leicestershire, LE65 1TR Tel: (01530) 412786 Fax: (01530) 415465 E-mail: rnshieldsltd@aol.com *Joinery manufrs*

▶ R N Thomson, West Sanquhar Road, Ayr, KA8 9HP Tel: (01292) 265533

▶ R Neck & Son Ltd, The Yard, St. Peters Road, Warley, Brentwood, Essex, CM14 5JF Tel: (01277) 232265 Fax: (01277) 261200

R O B A Metals Ltd, Kinwarton Farm Road, Kinwarton, Alcester, Warwickshire, B49 6EH Tel: (01789) 763232 Fax: (01789) 400660 E-mail: info@robametals.co.uk *Metal merchants aluminium processors*

R O C C Computers Ltd, Stanford Gate, South Road, Brighton, BN1 6SB Tel: (01273) 274700 Fax: (01273) 274707 E-mail: marketing@rocc.co.uk *Software solutions*

R O C Engineering, 13 Melton Road, Queniborough, Leicester, LE7 3FP Tel: 0116-269 6801 Fax: 0116-269 6807 E-mail: rocengi@btconnect.com *Sub-contract engineers*

R O Donaghey Ltd, 8 Oldington Trading Estate, Kidderminster, Worcestershire, DY11 7QP Tel: (01562) 820351 Fax: (01562) 829825 E-mail: r.o.donagheyltd@tinyworld.co.uk *Builders & civil engineers*

R O M Ltd, Wheaton Road, Witham, Essex, CM8 3BU Tel: (01376) 533200 Fax: (01376) 533227 E-mail: sales@rom.co.uk *Tunnelling support & lining systems manufrs*

▶ R & O Textiles, Unit 1 Frederick Street, Walsall, WS2 9NJ Tel: (01922) 613183 Fax: (01922) 613183

R O Williams & Son, Dyers Lane, Iron Acton, Bristol, BS37 9XT Tel: (01454) 228663 Fax: (01454) 228663 *Agricultural contractors*

R Open & Son Ltd, Unit 15 Oakwood Hill, Oakwood Hill Inustrial Estate, Loughton, Essex, IG10 3TZ Tel: (020) 8989 5741 Fax: (020) 8508 2115 E-mail: ropenremovals@aol.co.uk *Household, office & storage & removal contractors services*

R Ovenden & Son, 29 Oxford Road, Littlemore, Oxford, OX4 4PF Tel: (01865) 779357 Fax: (01865) 779357 *Wrought iron gates manufrs*

R P A International Ltd, P.O. Box 441, Tonbridge, Kent, TN9 9DZ Tel: (0845) 8803222 E-mail: info@rpainternational.co.uk *Precision, CNC engineers & gunsmiths*

R P A Motorcycle Powder Coating, 4 Queen Victoria Street, Bristol, BS2 0QR Tel: 0117-954 1002 Fax: 0117-941 2870 *Powder coating specialists & manufrs*

R P Business Forms Ltd, Unit 17 Fallings Park Industrial Estate, Park Lane, Wolverhampton, WV10 9QB Tel: (01902) 723500 Fax: (01902) 723116 E-mail: rpbusinessforms@btinternet.com *Business form printing services*

R P C Cleaning Services Ltd, 201 Acton Lane, London, W4 5DA Tel: (020) 8994 4778 Fax: (020) 8994 4178 *Office cleaning contractors*

R P C Container, Plenmeller Works, Haltwhistle, Northumberland, NE49 0HN Tel: (01434) 320526 Fax: (01434) 320136 *Plastics bottles & container manufrs*

RPC Containers Ltd, 4 Sallow Road, Weldon North Industrial Estate, Corby, Northamptonshire, NN17 5JX Tel: (01536) 263488 Fax: (01536) 272910 E-mail: sales@rpc-corby.co.uk *Multi-layer blow moulding & thermoforming of plastic containers for the food and catering industries.*

R P C Containers Ltd, Fourth Avenue, Colchester Road, Halstead, Essex, CO9 2SY Tel: (01787) 473224 Fax: (01787) 474151 E-mail: sales@rpc-halstead.co.uk *Plastic dispenser, cap & closure manufrs*

▶ R P C Tedeco-Gizeh UK Ltd, Kenfig Industrial Estate, Margam, Port Talbot, West Glamorgan, SA13 2PG Tel: (01656) 746655 Fax: (01656) 743074 E-mail: sales@rpc-tedeco-gizeh.com *Recyclable plastic packaging products. Specialists in disposable packaging for the catering industry.*

▶ R P C Wildlife Environmental Services, 74 High Street, Wouldham, Rochester, Kent, ME1 3UP Tel: (0800) 8498042 E-mail: mail@rpcwildlife.co.uk *Pest & vermin control*

R P Davidson Cheese Factors, 31 Market Hall, Chesterfield, Derbyshire, S40 1AR Tel: (01246) 201203 Fax: (01246) 201203 *Dairy produce merchants*

▶ R P E Mechanical Engineers Ltd, Unit 7 Off Low Mills Lane, Ravensthorpe Industrial Estate, Dewsbury, West Yorkshire, WF13 3LN Tel: (01924) 494549 Fax: (01924) 480874 *Engineering services*

▶ R P Fabrications Ltd, Unit 1, New Mill End Farm, Chiltern Green Road, Luton, LU1 3TS Tel: (01582) 713660 Fax: (01582) 460038

R P G Associates Ltd, 35 St. Georges Road, Cheltenham, Gloucestershire, GL50 3DU Tel: (01242) 252444 Fax: (01242) 252888 *Advertising agency services*

R P H Engineering, 83 Cobham Road, Ferndown Industrial Estate, Wimborne, Dorset, BH21 7QD Tel: (01202) 870999 Fax: (01202) 870888 E-mail: enquiries@rphmanufacturing.co.uk *Precision component manufrs*

R P Hardware Ltd, 6 Parkside Industrial Estate, Hickman Avenue, Wolverhampton, WV1 2EN Tel: (01902) 351161 Fax: (01902) 871434 E-mail: sales@rp-hardware.co.uk *Cabinet fittings & door furniture distributors*

R P Hill, Kidmore Lane, Waterlooville, Hampshire, PO7 6JY Tel: (023) 9263 2644 *Agricultural contractors services*

▶ R P Installations & Co., 30 The Glebe, Blackwater, Camberley, Surrey, GU17 9BB Tel: (01276) 31142 Fax: (01276) 508459 E-mail: rpiuk@hotmail.com *Mechanical installation engineers*

R P Joinery, Unit 3, 2 Beresford Road, Whitstable, Kent, CT5 1JP Tel: (01227) 281820 Fax: (01227) 281830 *Joiners*

R P L, Brittannic House, 5-7 St Marys Gate, Derby, DE1 3JA Tel: (01332) 349255 Fax: (01332) 294688 *Railway refurbishers*

R P L (1983) Ltd, Unit 39, Nortonthorpe Industrial Park, Wakefield Road, Scissett, Huddersfield, HD8 9FB Tel: (01484) 868283 Fax: (01484) 868258 E-mail: info@rplltd.co.uk *Dust extraction manufrs*

▶ R P L Concrete Products, The Homestead, Doncaster Road, Whitley, Goole, North Humberside, DN14 0JW Tel: (01977) 662064 Fax: (01977) 663669 E-mail: enquiries@rflandscapeproducts.co.uk

R.P.L.Photography, Liverpool, L1 1EB Tel: (07947) 543764 E-mail: r.p.l.photography@mac.com *I AM A LOCAL MERSEYSIDE UK PHOTOGRAPHER, THAT HAS JUST LEFT UNIVERSITY AND I AM OFFERING MY PHOTOGRAPHIC SERVICES FOR HIRE, I CAN PRODUCE BEAUTIFUL MODELLING PORTFOLIO'S, FOR MY CLIENTS AT AFFORDABLE PRICES PLEASE CHECK OUT MY SITE WWW.RPLPHOTOGRAPHY.COM*

R P L Productions Ltd, Northcote Road, Birmingham, B33 9BE Tel: 0121-624 5000 Fax: 0121-784 5400 E-mail: info@rplproductions.co.uk *Repetition turned parts manufrs*

R P Lampshades, 3 Lyttleton Road, Pershore, Worcestershire, WR10 2DF Tel: (01386) 555212 Fax: (01386) 555212 *Lamp shade manufrs*

R P M 2000 Ltd, Millfields Road, Wolverhampton, WV4 6JE Tel: (01902) 490615 Fax: (01902) 490241 *Recycling plant maintenance*

R P M Fasteners Ltd, Ashland St, Wolverhampton, WV3 0BN Tel: (01902) 421252 Fax: (01902) 715585 E-mail: sales@rolevet.com *Manufacturers special industrial fasteners*

R P M Model Making, 3 Station Approach, Wendover, Aylesbury, Buckinghamshire, HP22 6BN Tel: (01296) 622625 Fax: (01296) 625755 E-mail: enquiries@rpm.modelmakers.co.uk *Model makers manufrs*

R & P Macdonald, South Esplanade East, Aberdeen, AB11 9PB Tel: (01224) 879402 Fax: (01224) 896958 *Fish merchants*

▶ R P Metal Co. Ltd, Toutley Industrial Estate, Toutley Road, Wokingham, Berkshire, RG41 1QN Tel: 0118-978 8006 Fax: 0118-977 6388 E-mail: rpmetalwork@btconnect.com *Sheet metal workers & engineers*

R P Panels Ltd, Pindar Road, Hoddesdon, Hertfordshire, EN11 0BZ Tel: (01992) 444221 Fax: (01992) 466656 *Panel product importers & distributor*

R P Printing Services, 136 High Street, Hanham, Bristol, BS15 3HF Tel: 0117-960 4400 Fax: 0117-960 4400 *General printers*

R P R Linings Ltd, Doctors Lane, Henley-in-Arden, West Midlands, B95 5AW Tel: (01564) 792940 Fax: (01564) 794795 E-mail: rpr_linnings@talk21.com *Suspended ceiling partitions contracting services*

R P R Power Tools, 15 Charterfield Drive, Cannock, Staffordshire, WS12 3XH Tel: (01543) 275862 Fax: (01543) 275862 *Power tool repairs*

R P S Construction, Kingston Lodge Jekylls Gate, Holbeach Fen, Holbeach, Spalding, Lincolnshire, PE12 8QS Tel: (01406) 424406 Fax: (01406) 426260 E-mail: rps@rpsconstruction.co.uk *Building contractors to the food industry*

R P S Consultants Ltd, Executive Freight Building, Kirkhill Drive, Kirkhill Industrial Estate, Aberdeen, AB21 0EU Tel: (01224) 773734 Fax: (01224) 724220 E-mail: rpsad@rpsplc.co.uk *Geological & environmental consultants*

R P S Engineering & Safety, Dalton House, 105 Dalton Avenue, Birchwood, Warrington, WA3 6YF Tel: (01925) 831000 Fax: (01925) 831231 E-mail: rpswa@rpsgroup.com *Nuclear health & safety consultants* Also at: Alton

R P S Flooring Ltd, Old Mill Lane Industrial Estate, Mansfield Woodhouse, Mansfield, Nottinghamshire, NG19 9BG Tel: (01623) 624198 Fax: (01623) 620931 *Floor covering wholesalers*

R P S Industrial Flooring Contractors Ltd, Woodhouse, Packhorse Lane, Headley Heath, Birmingham, B38 0DN Tel: (01564) 824900 Fax: (01564) 823447 *Industrial flooring contractors & waterproofing*

R P S Laboratories Ltd, Unit 12 Waters Edge Business Park, Modwen Road, Salford, M5 3EZ Tel: 0161-872 2443 Fax: 0161-877 3959 E-mail: rpsma@rpsplc.co.uk *RPS Labs specialise in the analysis of workplace and ambient atmospheric pollutants, stack emissions, biological samples, asbestos containing materials and Face Fit Testing. Please contact us to discuss your analytical or fit testing requirements.*

R P S Trading Ltd, Unit 2, S D H Industrial Estate, Asquith Bottom Mill, Sowerby Bridge, Halifax, West Yorkshire, HX6 3BT Tel: (01422) 839303 Fax: (01422) 836800 *Furniture wholesalers*

R P Shaw Fabrications, Rendova Farm, Powey Lane, Mollington, Chester, CH1 6LH Tel: (01244) 881043 Fax: (01244) 881023 *Welding & fabrication*

R P T Computer Installations Ltd, 41 Anson Grove, Fareham, Hampshire, PO16 8JQ Tel: (023) 9234 8819 *Design & installation of computer networks*

R P Textiles, Castley Lane, Castley, Otley, West Yorkshire, LS21 2PY Tel: (01423) 734682 Fax: (01423) 734687 E-mail: ronpattex72@tiscali.co.uk *Textile yarn merchants & agent*

R P Towing, Unit 1d Abercromby Avenue, High Wycombe, Buckinghamshire, HP12 3BW Tel: (01494) 528233 Fax: (01494) 638802 E-mail: rp.towing@ntlworld.com *Tow bar fitting & trailer services*

▶ R P Tyson Ltd, 1 Mitcham Road, Blackpool, FY4 4QN Tel: (01253) 696800 Fax: (01253) 696801

R P Whitehead Ltd, Gelderd Road, Leeds, LS12 6NB Tel: 0113-263 0613 Fax: 0113-263 0602 *Flexible packaging specialists*

R Page Concrete Buildings Ltd, 951-953 High Road, Romford, RM6 4HB Tel: (020) 8590 3701 Fax: (020) 8590 1791 *Concrete building manufrs*

R Palfrey & Sons, Engineering Works, Sandford, Crediton, Devon, EX17 4PN Tel: (01363) 84494 Fax: (01363) 85219 *Agricultural engineers*

▶ R Park & Sons Ltd, Unit 1 Aldwych Court, 586A Blackpool Road, Ashton-On-Ribble, Preston, PR2 1JA Tel: (01772) 720007

R Petrie & Sons Ltd, Lornshill Farm, Alloa, Clackmannanshire, FK10 2EP Tel: (01259) 725848

R Q Consultancy, The Gables, Pankridge Drive, Prestwood, Great Missenden, Buckinghamshire, HP16 9BZ Tel: (01494) 862406 Fax: (01494) 862382 E-mail: info@trqc.co.uk *IT management*

R & R Catering Hire Ltd, 9 Coln Park, Andoversford Industrial Estate, Andoversford, Cheltenham, Gloucestershire, GL54 4HJ Tel: (01242) 820100 Fax: (01242) 820050 E-mail: enquiries@rrhire.co.uk *Hire of best quality china, cutlery, glassware & linen ware*

R & R Ceilings And Partitions, Searchwood, Bishops Down Park Rd, Tunbridge Wells, Kent, TN4 8XU Tel: 01892 544889 Fax: 01892540242 *Install ceilings partitions*

R & R Country, Hull Road, Hemingbrough, Selby, North Yorkshire, YO8 6QJ Tel: (01757) 638555 Fax: (01757) 630770 E-mail: randrcountry@btconnect.com *Equestrian, country suppliers & pet food*

R & R Development, Llewellyns Quay, The Docks, Port Talbot, West Glamorgan, SA13 1SD Tel: (01639) 870330 Fax: (01639) 890317 *Plant & machinery maintenance/repair*

R & R Engineering Ltd, Oak Road, Wrexham Industrial Estate, Wrexham, Clwyd, LL13 9RG Tel: (01978) 661523 Fax: (01978) 661227 E-mail: sales@rrengineeringltd.com Principal Export Areas: Worldwide *Steel fabricators*

R & R Flexo Ltd, Concorde Road, Norwich, NR6 6BW Tel: (01603) 485707 Fax: (01603) 408363 E-mail: andy@mailingfilms.co.uk *Flexographic printing services*

R & R Formings Ltd, Unit 5 Riparian Way, Cross Hills, Keighley, West Yorkshire, BD20 7BW Tel: (01535) 614010 Fax: (01535) 614019 E-mail: richard@rrfoodbox.co.uk *Vacuum forming services*

R & R Industries Ltd, Witney Road, Standlake, Witney, Oxfordshire, OX29 7PR Tel: (01865) 300093 Fax: (01865) 300096 *Repair, refurbish & recycle damaged plastics*

R & R Joiners, Sthe Workshops, Lades Road, St. Austell, Cornwall, PL25 4HA Tel: (01726) 61891 Fax: (01726) 61891 *Joinery manufacturer*

▶ R & R Joinery, Surrey House, 103 London Road, Staines, Middlesex, TW18 4HN Tel: (01784) 465308 Fax: (01784) 450124 E-mail: rr-joinery-staines@supernet.com *Architectural joinery services to industry*

▶ R & R Lift Co. Ltd, 71a High Road, London, E18 2QP Tel: (020) 8518 8937 Fax: (020) 8518 8938

R & R Models, Unit 13, Radway Industrial Estate, Shirley, Solihull, West Midlands, B90 4NR Tel: 0121-709 0343 *Metal casting & giftware*

▶ R R Pullen, Frying Pan Farm, Melksham Lane, Broughton Gifford, Melksham, Wiltshire, SN12 8LL Tel: (01225) 702343 Fax: (01225) 793652 E-mail: rpbp@dsl.pipex.com *Make & Mend anyting Machanical.*Turning. Milling. Tig Welding.*Steam Plant & Parts.*

▶ R & R Scaffolding Services Ltd, Podder Lane, Nottingham, NG3 5RL Tel: 0115-967 0047 Fax: 0115-967 3130

R & R Security Services, 171 South Ealing Road, London, W5 4QP Tel: (020) 8560 3413 Fax: (020) 8560 3413 E-mail: info@randrsecurity.com *Lock fitting specialist services*

R & R Sheet Metal Fabrications Ltd, R & R House, North Bridge Road, Berkhamsted, Hertfordshire, HP4 1EH Tel: (01442) 876969 Fax: (01442) 877979 *Sheet metalwork fabricators*

R & R Shepherd, 227 Pilling Lane, Preesall, Poulton-le-Fylde, Lancashire, FY6 0HH Tel: (01253) 811101 *Agricultural contractors*

R & R Systems Ltd, 390 Bolton Road, Aspull, Wigan, Lancashire, WN2 1PR Tel: (01942) 833402 Fax: (01942) 833107 E-mail: info@rarsys.co.uk *Software writers*

▶ R & R Trading Ltd, 76 Hollywood Lane, Wainscott, Rochester, Kent, ME3 8AR Tel: (01634) 714140 Fax: (01634) 712777

R R Transport Ltd, Stanley Way, Cardrew, Redruth, Cornwall, TR15 1SP Tel: (01209) 310816 Fax: (01209) 210141 E-mail: contact@rrtransport.com *Road transport, haulage, freight & warehousing services*

▶ R R Walls Ltd, Electric Parade, Seven Kings Road, Ilford, Essex, IG3 8BY Tel: (020) 8597 1126 Fax: (020) 8598 1707

▶ R & R Web Design, 90 Barnard Road, Chelmsford, CM2 8SR Tel: 01245 472959 E-mail: info@randrwebdesign.co.uk *Website design or creation services*

R Reid & Son Ltd, Tipperty Industrial Centre, Tipperty, Ellon, Aberdeenshire, AB41 8LZ Tel: (01358) 722229 Fax: (01358) 721880 E-mail: r.reid@bosinternet.com *Welding & steelwork fabrication*

R Riddles Bros, 35 Castlewarren Road, Dunamanagh, Strabane, County Tyrone, BT82 0PJ Tel: (028) 7139 8242 Fax: (028) 7139 8529 *Agricultural sand & gravel contractors*

R Roberts & Son, 260 Conway Road, Mochdre, Colwyn Bay, Clwyd, LL28 5DS Tel: (01492) 546917 Fax: (01492) 543600 *Building contractors*

▶ R Rollo & Sons, 51 High Street, Cockenzie, Prestonpans, East Lothian, EH32 0DG Tel: (01875) 811335 Fax: (01875) 814437

R Russell, 45 Townsend Road, Chesham, Buckinghamshire, HP5 2AA Tel: (01494) 782837 Fax: (01494) 791598 E-mail: info@r-russellbrush.co.uk *Manufacturers of general brushes*

R S A Security Inc, R S A House, Western Road, Bracknell, Berkshire, RG12 1RT Tel: (01344) 781000 Fax: (01344) 781010 *Electronic data security supplier & manufrs*

R S Audio & Alarms, 86-88 College Road, Perry Barr, Birmingham, B44 8DA Tel: 0121-603 1938 Fax: 0121-331 4404 E-mail: info@rsaudio.co.uk *Car alarm suppliers*

R S B Services, 16a Verney Rd, London, SE16 3DH Tel: (020) 7277 5161 Fax: (020) 7277 5115 *Cardboard box manufrs*

R S Brookhouse Ltd, Waterloo Industrial Estate, Waterloo Road, Bidford-on-Avon, Alcester, Warwickshire, B50 4JH Tel: (01789) 772485 Fax: (01789) 490129 E-mail: brookhouse.eng@btinternet.com *Rental of specialist pipeline equipment suppliers*

▶ R S C Ltd, Unit 1a Horndon Business Park, West Horndon, Brentwood, Essex, CM13 3XL Tel: 01277 810111

R S C Partnership Ltd, 1A Belmont Road, Wallington, Surrey, SM6 8TE Tel: (020) 8773 2299 E-mail: mail@rscpartnership.com *Computer systems & software developers*

R S C Spares Ltd, B 4 CWM Road, Swansea, SA1 2AY Tel: (01792) 654639 Fax: (01792) 654658 E-mail: sales@rsc-spares.co.uk *Refrigerator distribution & sales*

continued

▶ indicates data change since last edition

R S Castle Joinery, 1a Tower Street, Hertford, SG14 3HD Tel: (01992) 584410 Fax: (01992) 584410 *Joinery specialist manufrs*

R S Clare & Co. Ltd, 8 Stanhope Street, Liverpool, L8 5RQ Tel: 0151-709 2902 Fax: 0151-709 0518 E-mail: sales@rsclare.com *Industrial grease manufrs*

R S Concrete Products, 20 Balunasollus Road, Cookstown, County Tyrone, BT80 9TQ Tel: (028) 8675 1378 Fax: (028) 8675 1378 *Concrete manufrs*

R S Covers, 57 Strand Road, Bootle, Merseyside, L20 4BG Tel: 0151-933 9059 Fax: 0151-923 2490 *Banners & industrial cover manufrs*

▶ R S Cranes, Asrc Bussiness Centre, 2 Cassel Court, Haverton Hill Road, Billingham, Cleveland, TS23 1RB Tel: (01642) 674250 Fax: (01642) 673368 *Crane hire specialists*

R S Curving Services, Unit 8 Abbey Ct, Wallingford Rd, Leicester, LE4 5RD Tel: 0116-266 6803 Fax: 0166 266 6803 *Radiator covers*

▶ R S D Supplies & Services Ltd, 2 Norton Centre, Poynernook Road, Aberdeen, AB11 5RW Tel: (01224) 213213 *Welding material & protective clothing suppliers*

R S Dawe Motor Body Repair Centre, Norfolk Road, Gravesend, Kent, DA12 2PS Tel: (01474) 365840 Fax: (01474) 350900 *Motor body repair centre*

▶ R S Deacon, 74 Station Road, Teynham, Sittingbourne, Kent, ME9 9SN Tel: (01795) 520963 Fax: (01795) 520716 E-mail: rsdeconltd@hotmail.com *Groundwork & civil engineers*

▶ R S E Associates Ltd, Seascape, Main Road, Trevone, Padstow, Cornwall, PL28 8QX Tel: (01841) 520915 Fax: (01841) 520833 *Dust & fume extraction equipment design & manufacture*

R S Express, Earlesfield Lane, Grantham, Lincolnshire, NG31 7NT Tel: (01476) 570601 Fax: (01476) 750268 E-mail: info@rsexpress.co.uk *Sameday courier*UK parcel services*Logistics*Storage*Pick and Pack*

▶ R S Eyre & Co. Ltd, Unit A9, Prospect Street, Erskine Industrial Estate, Liverpool, L6 1AP Tel: 0151-264 0752 Fax: 0151-263 9367 E-mail: eyrecraft@hotmail.co.uk *Lithographic jobbing printers*

R S Farmah & Sons, 111 Hubert Road, Birmingham, B29 6ET Tel: 0121-472 6672 Fax: 0121-472 8017 E-mail: peter@rsfarmah.freeserve.co.uk *Embroiders suppliers*

R & S Fencing, 31 Kingsland Close, Portsmouth, PO6 4AL Tel: (023) 9221 0365 *Fencing*

R & S Fork Trucks, 6 Ardmore Road, South Ockendon, Essex, RM15 5TH Tel: (01708) 851444 Fax: (01708) 557076 E-mail: randsforklifts@aveley.fsnet.co.uk *Forklift truck distributors & maintenance*

▶ R & S Furnishings, 2 Winster Park, Corporation Road, Ilkeston, Derbyshire, DE7 4BN Tel: 0115-932 5361 Fax: 0115-932 5362 *Bed manufrs*

R & S Greeting Cards Ltd, 157 Fallsbrook Road, London, SW16 6DY Tel: (020) 8677 5212 Fax: (020) 8664 7108 *Greeting cards suppliers* Also at: Wembley

R S H Services Ltd, Southedge Works, Hipperholme, Halifax, West Yorkshire, HX3 8EF Tel: (01422) 202840 Fax: (01422) 206070 E-mail: rshservices@tiscali.co.uk *Seat frame manufrs*

R & S Installations, 54 Lowestoft Road, Carlton Colville, Lowestoft, Suffolk, NR33 8JB Tel: (01502) 572144 Fax: (01502) 572144 E-mail: sales@rsinstallations.co.uk *Electronics gates, barrier & camera installation*

R S J Process Machinery Ltd, Phoenix House, Tame Street, Stalybridge, Cheshire, SK15 1SY Tel: 0161-338 7288 Fax: 0161-338 3574 E-mail: aquafil@btconnect.com *Plastic, rubber & chemical machinery suppliers*

R S J Security Systems, 1 Sterry Drive, Epsom, Surrey, KT19 0TG Tel: (020) 8393 6269 Fax: (020) 8393 6304 E-mail: email@rsjsecurity.co.uk *Security systems*

R S J Steels Lincoln Ltd, 97 Sadler Road, Lincoln, LN6 3RS Tel: (01522) 500400 Fax: (01522) 500401 E-mail: sales@rsj-steels.co.uk *Steel stockholders*

R S Joinery, 7-8 Chieveley Parade, Mayplace Road East, Bexleyheath, Kent, DA7 6EB Tel: (01322) 555922 Fax: (01322) 521995 *Joinery product manufrs*

R S L South West Ltd, Unit 15 Millfield Industrial Estate, Chard, Somerset, TA20 2BB Tel: (01460) 67373 Fax: (01460) 61669 E-mail: sales@rslsouthwest.com *Steel fabricators*

R S L Steeper Ltd, Disability Centre Queen Marys, Hospital, Roehampto, London, SW15 5PL Tel: (01634) 297010 Fax: (020) 8788 0137 E-mail: sales@rehab.co.uk *Rehabilitation services*

R & S Laser Cutting & Fabrications Ltd, R & S House, Clement Street, Birmingham, B1 2SW Tel: 0121-237 5646 Fax: 0121-236 9339 E-mail: sales@rs-laser-cutting.co.uk *Laser cutting & profile cutting services*

R S Leisurewear, House of Rs, 26 Smith Dorien Road, Leicester, LE5 4BF Tel: 0116-274 0234 Fax: 0116-246 1259 E-mail: rsgroup@webleicester.co.uk *Leisurewear manufrs*

R S Lloyd Midlands, Unit 33 Dawley Trading Estate, Stallings Lane, Kingswinford, West Midlands, DY6 7AP Tel: (01384) 401030 Fax: (01384) 401023 *Steel trading & stockholding*

R S M Beare Stoke Canon, Coads Green, Launceston, Cornwall, PL15 7LY Tel: (01566) 782100 Fax: (01566) 782012 *Agricultural engineers*

R S M Castings Ltd, 7 North Portway Close, Round Spinney Industrial Estate, Northampton, NN3 8RQ Tel: (01604) 671333 Fax: (01604) 491012 E-mail: enquiries@rsm-castings.co.uk *Shell moulded castings manufrs*

R S M Engineering Tamworth Ltd, Unit 14 Two Gates Industrial Estate, Watling Street, Two Gates, Tamworth, Staffordshire, B77 5AE Tel: (01827) 250816 Fax: (01827) 287898 *Stainless steel fabricators*

R S M Industries Ltd, School Lane, Exhall, Coventry, CV7 9NN Tel: (024) 7636 2082 Fax: (024) 7655 3715 E-mail: admin@rsmindustries.co.uk *Metal pressings to 600 tons manufrs*

R S M J Computers Ltd, 11 Lammas Way, Ampthill, Bedford, MK45 2TR Tel: (01525) 841800 Fax: (01525) 841800 *Computer consultants*

R S M Refko Installations Ltd, 8 Capstan Centre, Thurrock Park Way, Tilbury, Essex, RM18 7HH Tel: (01375) 855500 Fax: (01375) 855533 *Fire protection & sprinkler systems*

▶ R S Merriman Ltd, Cairston Road, Stromness, Orkney, KW16 3JS Tel: (01856) 850105 Fax: (01856) 850632

R S Micro, 129 Brookfield Place, Walton Summit Centre, Bamber Bridge, Preston, PR5 8BF Tel: (01772) 628000 Fax: (01772) 628888 E-mail: rs_micro@compuserve.com *Press brake manufrs*

▶ R & S Midland, 16 Primrose Meadow, Cannock, Staffordshire, WS11 7FN Tel: (01543) 274383 E-mail: richard.smith077@ntlworld.com

R & S Mobility, 120 Courtney Street, Hull, HU8 7QF Tel: (01482) 320289 Fax: (01482) 320289 E-mail: rsmobility@hotmail.com *Disability accessories & car conversion services*

R S Paskin & Co. Ltd, Mount Pleasant, Brierley Hill, West Midlands, DY5 2YR Tel: (01384) 78081 Fax: (01384) 76480 E-mail: sales@rspaskin.co.uk *Engineers merchants,Distributors of Hand Tools,Fasteners & Protective clothing.*

▶ R S Piper Ltd, 2 St. Johns Court Foster Road, Ashford Business Park, Sevington, Ashford, Kent, TN24 0SJ Tel: (01233) 500200 Fax: (01233) 500300 E-mail: sales@pipercams.co.uk

R S Plumbing & Heating Engineers, Oaklands, Smithwood Lodge, Cranleigh, Surrey, GU6 8QY Tel: (01483) 276494 Fax: (01483) 548949

R S Precision, Unit 30 Hercules Way, Bowerhill, Melksham, Wiltshire, SN12 6TS Tel: (01225) 702738 Fax: (01225) 702583 *Tool manufacturers general engineering precision engineering*

R S Precision Engineering, Units 6-7 Parker Industrial Centre, Watling Street, Dartford, DA2 6EP Tel: (01322) 284111 Fax: (01322) 284338 E-mail: sales@rsprec.com *Precision engineers*

▶ R & S Property Services, Unit 2, 14 Barr's Road, Taplow, Maidenhead, Berkshire, SL6 0LE Tel: (01628) 661666 E-mail: rnsa1@hotmail.com *All aspects of Property Maintenance including first class kitchen & bathrooms installations, conservatories and all aspects of building*

R S R Ltd, The Avenue Industrial Park, Croescadarn Close, Cardiff, CF23 8HE Tel: (029) 2073 2076 Fax: (029) 2073 2704 *Medical diagnostics distributors & manufrs*

R S Richardson Belting Co. Ltd, Crown Works, Staincliffe Road, Dewsbury, West Yorkshire, WF13 4SB Tel: (01924) 468191 Fax: (01924) 458065 E-mail: mail@diepress-richardson.co.uk Principal Export Areas: Worldwide *Manufacturers of suction, food industry & conveyor belting. Also belting (transmission) distributors*

▶ R.S Skips Ltd, 25, Darnley Road, Gravesend, Kent, DA11 0RZ Tel: 01474 362862 Fax: 01474 362862 E-mail: info@rsskips.co.uk *R.S Skips Ltd is a fully licensed, family run skip hire firm that specialises in the hire of 4 yard to 14 yard skip containers. We provide services to both domestic and commercial users, on road permits can easily be arranged for all customers and new commercial user accounts are also welcome. **We currently operate in the followings areas: Gravesend, Dartford, Bexley, Bexleyheath, Erith, Medway, Grain and Allhallows. **

R & S Steel Services Ltd, Haywood Industrial Complex, Hereford, HR4 0LT Tel: (01432) 830140 Fax: (01432) 830807 *Steel fabrication manufrs*

▶ R S Sykes & Co. Ltd, 2 Warlingham Court Farm, Tithepit Shaw Lane, Warlingham, Surrey, CR6 9AT Tel: (01883) 626757 Fax: (01883) 622618 E-mail: sales@rssykes.co.uk

R S Systems, 79 Blaney Road, Altnamachin, Newry, County Down, BT35 0EA Tel: (028) 3087 8602 Fax: (028) 3087 8141 *Computer repairers*

R S T Precision Engineering Ltd, Unit 31 South Hampshire Industrial Park, Totton, Southampton, SO40 3SA Tel: (023) 8066 3663 Fax: (023) 8066 3461 E-mail: rst.prec.eng@virgin.net *Precision engineers*

R S T Spark Erosion Ltd, 7 Firbank Court, Leighton Buzzard, Bedfordshire, LU7 4YJ Tel: 01525 850797 *Spark erosion machining services*

R S Taylor & Co UK Ltd, 18 Merchant Drive, Mead Lane, Hertford, SG13 7AY Tel: (01992) 551881 Fax: (01992) 500177 *Sheet metalwork fabricators, vehicle cab manufacturers, lasercutting*

R S Tooling Ltd, 368 Brook Lane, Sarisbury Green, Southampton, SO31 7DP Tel: (01489) 584956 Fax: (01489) 584965 *Precision engineering*

R S Tools Ltd, Unit 8, Brunswick Road, Birmingham, B12 8NP Tel: 0121-440 4484 Fax: 0121-440 4484 E-mail: r.s.tools@btconnect.com *Tool makers*

R & S Whiting, Oak Lodge, North Walsham Road, Norwich, NR6 7JG Tel: (01603) 425832 Fax: (01603) 787900 *Horizontal boring services*

R & S Wire Ltd, Grove Street, Kirklees Steel Works, Brighouse, West Yorkshire, HD6 1PL Tel: (01484) 715120 Fax: (01484) 711882 *Steel wire manufrs*

▶ R S Workshop Equipment, Unit 28 Barnwell Manor Estate, Barnwell, Peterborough, PE8 5PL Tel: (01832) 741007 Fax: (01832) 741008 E-mail: sales@rsworkshopequipment.co.uk *Motorcycle workshop equipment manufrs*

R Sanderson & Sons Ltd, Cannon Street, Hull, HU2 0AB Tel: (01482) 226286 Fax: (01482) 327220 E-mail: info@robert-sanderson.co.uk *Stainless steel fabricators*

R Savage Plant Hire Co. Ltd, 222 St Margarets Road, Ward End, Birmingham, B8 2BG Tel: 0121-328 1100 Fax: 0121-327 3548 E-mail: enquiries@savageplanthire.co.uk *Contractors' plant hire*

R Simeon, Dalts Farm House, Daltes Lane, St. Osyth, Clacton-on-Sea, Essex, CO16 8SA Tel: (01255) 821874 Fax: (01255) 821874 E-mail: robsimeon@aol.com *Farm contractors*

R Simon Dryers Ltd, Private Road No 3 Colwick Industrial Estate, Colwick Industrial Estate, Nottingham, NG4 2BD Tel: 0115-961 6276 Fax: 0115-961 6351 E-mail: sales@simon-dryers.co.uk *Calcining equipment & flaking machine manufrs*

▶ R Sorley Electrical Services, 5 Pollock Walk, Dunfermline, Fife, KY12 9DA Tel: (01383) 736933 Fax: (01383) 736933

R Spivey & Son Ltd, 54 Upper Station Road, Batley, West Yorkshire, WF17 5TA Tel: (01924) 473372 Fax: (01924) 442921 E-mail: david@spiveydrums.co.uk Principal Export Areas: Worldwide *Re-conditioners & suppliers of reconditioned plastic & steel drums*

R Stahl Ltd, Unit 43 Stahl House Elmdon Trading Estate, Bickenhill Lane, Birmingham, B37 7HE Tel: 0121-767 6400 Fax: 0121-767 6480 E-mail: info@rstahl.co.uk *Crane manufrs*

R Steel & Co., 28 Sinclair Street, Helensburgh, Dunbartonshire, G84 8SU Tel: (01436) 675444 Fax: (01436) 675004 E-mail: info@rbsteel.co.uk

▶ R Steel & Co., 28 Sinclair Street, Helensburgh, Dunbartonshire, G84 8SU Tel: (01436) 675444 Fax: (01436) 675004 E-mail: info@rbsteel.co.uk

R Strachan, Harbour Road, Fraserburgh, Aberdeenshire, AB43 9BN Tel: (01346) 510800 Fax: (01346) 511801 *Metal fabricators*

▶ R Swain, Priory Road, Rochester, Kent, ME2 2BD Tel: (01634) 733333 Fax: (01634) 733344

▶ R Swain & Sons, 41 Wynne Avenue, Swinton, Manchester, M27 8FT Tel: 0161-794 4226 Fax: 0161-794 9582

▶ R T A Associates Ltd, Albury House, Church Way, Sparsholt, Wantage, Oxfordshire, OX12 9PY Tel: (01235) 751287 Fax: (01235) 751594

R T A Joinery Ltd, 5 Birling Road, Tunbridge Wells, Kent, TN2 5LX Tel: (01892) 543897 Fax: (01892) 545345 E-mail: rtajoinery@btconnect.com *Joining services*

R T Bearings Ltd., Units 19 & 20, Bevan Industrial Estate, Brockmoor, Brierley Hill, West Midlands, DY5 3TF Tel: (01384) 868458 Fax: (01384) 865458 E-mail: sales@rtbearings.co.uk *Conveyor bearing manufrs*

R T C Agricultural Ltd, Newton Hollows, Frodsham, WA6 6HY Tel: (01928) 740493 Fax: (01928) 740593 E-mail: sales@rtc-agricultural.co.uk *Agricultural engineers*

R.T.C Engineering, 39 Kiltyclogher Road, Cookstown, County Tyrone, BT80 9BZ Tel: (028) 8676 5218 Fax: (01687) 65218 E-mail: sales@rtcubolts.com *Fastener tooling manufrs*

R T C Safety Surfaces, Beech House, Smallshaw Lane, Burnley, Lancashire, BB11 5SQ Tel: (01282) 414131 Fax: (01282) 414133 E-mail: sales@rtcsafety.co.uk *Playground safety surfaces suppliers*

R T D Products, Unit 10-11 A K Business Park, Russell Road, Southport, Merseyside, PR9 7SA Tel: (01704) 507696 Fax: (01704) 507055 E-mail: rnice@rtd-products.co.uk *Resistance thermometer manufrs*

R T Display Systems Ltd, 10 Lyon Road, South Wimbledon, London, SW19 2RL Tel: (020) 8545 2945 Fax: (020) 8545 2955 E-mail: sales@octanorm.co.uk *Shop fitting, exhibition & display systems*

R T E Electronics, 568 Burnley Road, Rossendale, Lancashire, BB4 8AJ Tel: (01706) 227234 Fax: (01706) 227531 E-mail: brain@rtepower.co.uk *Telecommunication equipment power supply systems*

R T E Fabrications Ltd, Lomax Street, Darwen, Lancashire, BB3 0DR Tel: (01254) 873002 Fax: (01254) 704919 E-mail: sales@rtefabs.co.uk *UPVC fabricators*

R T H Sales, Queen St, Houghton Regis, Dunstable, Beds, LU5 5BT Tel: 01582 867222 Fax: 01582 585758 *Diamond tools dealer*

R T Harris & Son Electrical Contractors Ltd, Shotover Kilns, Shotover Hill, Headington, Oxford, OX3 8ST Tel: (01865) 742300 Fax: (01865) 741405 E-mail: office@rtharris.co.uk *Electrical contractors, designers & installers*

R T I (UK) Ltd, Unit 6 Swan Wharf, Waterloo Road, Uxbridge, Middlesex, UB8 2RA Tel: (01895) 252191 Fax: (01895) 274692 E-mail: email@rtiuk.co.uk *Broadcast film & video equipment distributors*

R & T Industrial Engravers, 26 The Tanneries, Brockhampton Lane, Havant, Hampshire, PO9 1JB Tel: (023) 9245 4751 Fax: (023) 9247 2709 E-mail: rt.engraving@tinyworld.co.uk *Engravers*

R T L Enterprises, Windrush, Tormarton Road, Marshfield, Chippenham, Wiltshire, SN14 8NN Tel: (01225) 891899 Fax: (01225) 891890 *Beverage dispenser manufrs*

R T Little Brickwork Ltd, Orchard House, Commercial Road, Southampton, SO15 1GG Tel: (023) 8022 6262 Fax: (023) 8022 6266

R T M Ltd, 1-4 Morris Close, Park Farm North, Wellingborough, Northamptonshire, NN8 6XF Tel: (01933) 673066 Fax: (01933) 678933 E-mail: sales@rtm-uk.com *Supply & install telecommunication support structures*

▶ R T McEwan Ltd, Myreside Farm, Arbroath, Angus, DD11 5RL Tel: (01241) 830261

R T Refrigaration & Air Conditioning, 1a Rowan Trade Park, Neville Road, Bradford, West Yorkshire, BD4 8TQ Tel: (01274) 737248 Fax: (01274) 309767 *Air conditioning refrigeration distributors*

R T S, Northbank Industrial Park, Irlam, Manchester, M44 5AY Tel: 0161-777 2000 Fax: 0161-777 2095 E-mail: sales@rts-group.co.uk *Multi-disciplined engineering & automation*

R T S Computers, 13 New Street, Louth, Lincolnshire, LN11 9PT Tel: (01507) 606600 Fax: (01507) 606600 E-mail: rtscomputers@freebie.net *Computer system & software sellers*

R T S Engineering (Somerset) Ltd, Unit 6, Sedgemount Industrial Park, Bristol Road, Bridgwater, Somerset, TA6 4AR Tel: (01278) 457294 Fax: (01278) 453772 *Heating & ventilation engineers*

R T S Gate Automation, 224 Spen Lane, Gomersal, Cleckheaton, West Yorkshire, BD19 4PJ Tel: (01274) 852006 Fax: (01274) 871074 E-mail: info@rtsautomaticgates.co.uk *Automatic gates manufrs*

R & T Shipping Co Ltd, 2nd Floor, Holegate House, Holegate Court, Western Road, Romford, RM1 3JS Tel: (0870) 7745612 Fax: (0870) 7745602 *Freight forwarders*

▶ R T Stamp & Son Ltd, Skellingthorpe Road, Saxilby, Lincoln, LN1 2LR Tel: (01522) 702111 Fax: (01522) 704089

▶ R Taylor & Sons, Tieglum Road, Milton Industrial Estate, Lesmahagow, Lanark, ML11 0JN Tel: (01555) 890155 Fax: (01555) 890166

R Tek Ltd, Unit 1 Triangle Business Park, Pentrebach, Merthyr Tydfil, Mid Glamorgan, CF48 4TQ Tel: (01685) 373159 Fax: (01685) 373204 E-mail: maindesk@r-tek.co.uk *Motor vehicle trimming manufrs*

R Thompson & Co., 12 Manderston Street, Edinburgh, EH6 8LY Tel: 0131-554 6501 *Blacksmiths & welders*

R Thompson & Son, Parsons Lane, Alford, Lincolnshire, LN13 9HR Tel: (01507) 462292 Fax: (01507) 466576 *Repair & restore windmills & water mills*

▶ R Thomson Electrical Contractors Ltd, West Quay Road, Winwick Quay, Warrington, WA2 8TL Tel: (01925) 636773

R Thorne & Sons, Mannington Sawmills, Holt Road, Three Legged Cross, Wimborne, Dorset, BH21 6SE Tel: (01202) 822204 Fax: (01202) 824410 E-mail: robertthorne@fsbdial.co.uk *English timber merchants*

R Tincknell & Son Ltd, Brinsea Road, Congresbury, Bristol, BS49 5JG Tel: (01934) 832318 Fax: (01934) 834569 E-mail: sales.congresbury@tincknellag.com *Agricultural engineers Also at: Cannington, Clanfield, Devizes, Tetbury & Wells*

R Tindall Fabricators Ltd, Ward Street, Chadderton, Oldham, OL9 9EX Tel: 0161-624 3961 Fax: 0161-627 2978 E-mail: john@tindall-fabricators.co.uk *Pipework fabricators & installation & erection contractors*

R Todd, Ramshaw, Bishop Auckland, County Durham, DL14 0PE Tel: (01388) 833117 *Agricultural contractors*

▶ R U 21, 1b Mallard Court, Mallard Way, Crewe, CW1 6ZQ Tel: (01270) 254445 E-mail: info@ru21sales.co.uk *Healthcare preparation services*

R U D Chains Ltd, Units 10-14, John Wilson Business Park, Thanet Way, Whitstable, Kent, CT5 3QT Tel: (01227) 276611 Fax: (01227) 276586 E-mail: sales@rud.co.uk Sales Contact: A. Chandler *The RUD brand is synonymous with high-quality steel chains for lifting, pulling and transport as well as for tyre protection, snow and off road chains. Over 500 patents both at home and abroad document RUD's innovative approach*

R U Safe Ltd, Aizlewoods Mill, Nursery Street, Sheffield, S3 8GG Tel: 0114-282 3498 Fax: 0114-282 3302 E-mail: rusafe@it-installations.co.uk *Electrical testing of portable appliances & fixed wiring*

R V J Engineering, Cannock Chase Enterprise Centre, Hednesford, Cannock, Staffordshire, WS12 0QU Tel: (01543) 425264 Fax: (01543) 512451 E-mail: rvj.com@virgin.net *Tool & cutter grinding cutter resharpening*

R V L Ltd, Sion Street, Radcliffe, Manchester, M26 3SB Tel: 0161-723 5039 Fax: 0161-724 9078 E-mail: rvl.ltd@ukgateway.net *Lighting manufrs*

R V L (Northern) Ltd, Victoria Works, Raglan Street, Bradford, West Yorkshire, BD3 8NL Tel: (01274) 668223 Fax: (01274) 668021 *Refrigerated van conversions*

▶ R V Rugg Ltd, Station Lane, Featherstone, Pontefract, West Yorkshire, WF7 5BA Tel: (01977) 791944 Fax: (01977) 707468 *Wire formed shaped component manufrs*

R V W Pugh Ltd, Mellington, Church Stoke, Montgomery, Powys, SY15 6TQ Tel: (01588) 620545 Fax: (01588) 620515 E-mail: rvwpugh@farmersweekly.net *Dealers, services & repairers of agricultural machinery*

▶ R W A Ltd, R W A House 66 Cardiff Road, Glan-Y-Llyn, Taffs Well, Cardiff, CF15 7QE Tel: (029) 2081 5050 Fax: (029) 2081 5051 E-mail: enquiries@rwa-net.co.uk *Travel & finance software developers*

R W Almond & Co. Ltd, Heysham Road, Bootle, Merseyside, L30 6UA Tel: 0151-521 5454 Fax: 0151-525 0115 E-mail: sales@rwalmond.co.uk *Building materials suppliers & plant hire*

R W Almond & Co., R W Almond & Co Stephenson Way, Formby Business Park, Formby, Liverpool, L37 8EG Tel: (01704) 878651 Fax: (01704) 833821 E-mail: enquiries@rwalmond.co.uk *Builders merchants*

R W Bennett & Son, 7 Paget Cottages, Munden Road, Dane End, Ware, Hertfordshire, SG12 0NL Tel: (01920) 438781 *Ground work contractors*

R W Boyles Transport Ltd, Shires Road, Buckingham Road Industrial Estate, Brackley, Northamptonshire, NN13 7EZ Tel: (01280) 702690 Fax: (01280) 701619 E-mail: ron@boyles.fslife.co.uk *Haulage contractors & vehicle repairs*

R W Burt & Co Ltd, 47 Swindon Road, Cheltenham, Gloucestershire, GL50 4AH Tel: (01242) 525051 Fax: (01242) 525051 *Panel beaters & car sprayers*

R W Crawford Agricultural Machinery Ltd, 42-44 Cutlers Road, South Woodham Ferrers, Chelmsford, CM3 5XJ Tel: (01245) 322733 Fax: (01245) 322241

continued

Company Information

continuation
E-mail: sales@rwcrawford.co.uk *Agricultural machine sales & repairs*

R W Cresswell Ltd, Unit 2 79-81 Cheapside, Deritend, Birmingham, B12 0QH Tel: 0121-772 4565 *Turned components manufrs*

▶ R W Curle Ltd, Wadd Lane, Snape, Saxmundham, Suffolk, IP17 1QN Tel: (01728) 688444 Fax: (01728) 688931

R W Cushway & Co. Ltd, 180 Brooker Road, Waltham Abbey, Essex, EN9 1HT Tel: (01992) 713749 Fax: (01992) 788367
E-mail: info@cushways.co.uk *Resistance welding components manufrs*

R W D Coin Amusements, Race View, Factory Road, Enniskillen, County Fermanagh, BT74 6DT Tel: (028) 6632 5423 Fax: (028) 6632 8765 *Amusement machine suppliers*

R W Davis & Son Ltd, Junction Dry Dock, Canal Bank, Saul, Gloucester, GL2 7LA Tel: (01452) 740233 Fax: (01452) 741307
E-mail: sales@rwdavis.co.uk *Boat builders & marine engineers*

R W E npower, Birchfield House, Joseph Street, Oldbury, West Midlands, B69 2AQ Tel: 0121 544 2988 Fax: 0121 541 2404 *Gas & electricity suppliers*

R W E Solutions (UK) Ltd, 29 Bressenden Place, London, Greater London, SW1E 5DD Tel: 020 78287995 *Multi utility providers*

▶ R W Electrics, 16 Castle Douglas Road, Dumfries, DG2 7NX Tel: (01387) 250099 Fax: (01387) 250099

R W Evans Transport Ltd, Hilton Bank, Shifnal, Shropshire, TF11 8RH Tel: (01952) 691666 Fax: (01952) 691466 *Commercial vehicle distributors*

R W F Huxter, Filford Farm, Filford, Bridport, Dorset, DT6 5JW Tel: (01308) 488651 *Agricultural contractors*

R W G Engineering Ltd, Unit 5, Portlands Centre, Sutton Road, St. Helens, Merseyside, WA9 3DR Tel: (01744) 454225 Fax: (01744) 454226 *Metal spraying & general engineering specialists*

R.W Gear Ltd, Stargate Industrial Estate, Bailey House, Ryton, Tyne & Wear, NE40 3DG Tel: 0191-413 2244 Fax: 0191-413 1133
E-mail: rwryton@rwtransmissions.com *Gear & gear box manufrs*

▶ R W Greeff, Neilson Road, Gateshead, Tyne & Wear, NE10 0EW Tel: 0191-490 0110 Fax: 0191-490 0261 *Distributor industrial goods*

R W Greeff, Tame Park, Vanguard, Wilnecote, Tamworth, Staffordshire, B77 5DY Tel: (01827) 255200 Fax: (01827) 255255
E-mail: rwgreeff@univareurope.com *Industrial consumables specialists services*

R W Gregory & Partners, Cathedral Buildings, Dean Street, Newcastle upon Tyne, NE1 1PJ Tel: 0191-232 6306 Fax: 0191-232 5359
E-mail: newcastle@rwgregory.co.uk *Consulting engineers* Also at: Branches throughout the U.K.

▶ R & W Griffiths Ltd, 37 Ashton Road, Leeds, LS8 5JQ Tel: 0113-235 0020

R W H Stock Solutions Ltd, Station Lane, Offord Cluny, St. Neots, Cambridgeshire, PE19 5ZA Tel: (01480) 813800 Fax: (01480) 813813
E-mail: sales@rwh-enterprises.com *Job buyers & wholesalers*

R W H Supplies, 15 The Rodings, Upminster, Essex, RM14 1RL Tel: (01708) 780629 Fax: (01708) 780629 *Janitorial clothing*

R W Joinery Stockport Ltd, Unit 26 Vernon Mill, Mersey Street, Stockport, Cheshire, SK1 2HX Tel: 0161-480 8722 Fax: 0161-474 7646
E-mail: info@rwjoinery.co.uk *Joinery manufrs*

R W Knight & Son, Castle Farm, Marshfield, Chippenham, Wiltshire, SN14 8HU Tel: (01225) 891469 Fax: (01225) 892369
E-mail: enquires@knight-stoves.co.uk *Stove distributors*

▶ R W L Civil Engineering, 138 Nethergate, Dundee, DD1 4ED Tel: (01382) 204679

R W M C Engineering Ltd, Harrow Wood Farm & Caravan Park, Poplar Lane, Bransgore, Christchurch, Dorset, BH23 8JE Tel: (01425) 674450 Fax: (01425) 674450 *General engineers/ Shop fitters*

R W M Data Management Ltd, R W M House, 1-2 Boundry Road, Harfreys Industrial Estate, Great Yarmouth, Norfolk, NR31 0LY Tel: (0870) 2406053 Fax: (01493) 667657
E-mail: info@rwm.co.uk *An Established Scanning Bureau*Providing a High Quality Service*at a cost effective price since 1994. Based in Norfolk, RWM offer a complete document scanning and archival service, performing OCR and indexing to the customers requirements to enable the data to be searched and documents to be located rapidly.**

R.W.M. Mandrian Ltd, PO Box 517, Reading, RG30 6WF Tel: 0118-972 4455 Fax: 0118-972 4477 *Welding manufrs*

▶ R W M Training, 3 Dunnet Place, Thurso, Caithness, KW14 8JE Tel: (01847) 894934 Fax: (07876) 844044
E-mail: info@rwm-training.co.uk *Training for Fork lift Trucks, Telescopic Handlers, M.E.W.P.S, Abrasive wheels, etc, etc.*All training complies with recommendations as set out in the Approved Code of Practice for each field.*Also consultancy service for factory/production environments.*Time and Motion, machinery requirments, etc, etc.*

R W M Wolverhampton Ltd, 34 Commercial Road, Wolverhampton, WV1 3RD Tel: (01902) 871272 *Welding equipment repairers & manufrs*

R W Marsh Ltd, Station Road, Brigg, South Humberside, DN20 8HX Tel: (01652) 651810 Fax: (01652) 650822
E-mail: c.rothery@rwmarsh.co.uk *Agricultural engineers*

R W Marsh Ltd, The Forge, Markham Moor, Retford, Nottinghamshire, DN22 0QU Tel: (01777) 838888 Fax: (01777) 838000 *Agricultural engineers*

R W Marsh, London Road, Sleaford, Lincolnshire, NG34 8NX Tel: (01529) 303093 Fax: (01529) 413363 E-mail: sales@rwmarsh.com *Agricultural engineers*

R W Marsh & Sons, The Village, Little Hallingbury, Bishop's Stortford, Hertfordshire, CM22 7PX Tel: (01279) 723193 Fax: (01279) 726948 *Civil engineers & ground work services*

R W Oliver, 38 Alma Street, Eccles, Manchester, M30 0EX Tel: 0161-789 8474 *Invention consultants*

R W P Joinery, 1 Sandcliff Road, Erith, Kent, DA8 1NY Tel: (01322) 430537 Fax: (01322) 430537 E-mail: info@rwp-joinery.co.uk *Bespoke joiners*

▶ R W P Scaffolding & Safety Netting Services, 1 Pelton Walk, Monsall, Manchester, M40 8QY Tel: 0161-277 9704 Fax: 0161-205 5981
E-mail: rwpscaffolding@aol.com *SUPPLYING AND INSTALLING SAFETY NETTING AND EDGE PROTECTION COVERING MOST OF THE UK.*SCAFFOLDING ALSO AVAILABLE.*

R W Pierce & Co. Ltd, 17 Dargan CR, Belfast, BT3 9HJ Tel: (028) 9037 1010 Fax: (028) 9037 2501 *Security & general printers & digital print*

R W Plastics (UK) Ltd, 16 Manor Park, 35 Willis Way, Fleet Industrial Estate, Poole, Dorset, BH15 3SZ Tel: (01202) 673373 Fax: (01202) 632018 *Hot foil stamping, blocking & printing*

R W S Group, Tavistock House, Tavistock Square, London, WC1H 9LG Tel: (020) 7554 5400 Fax: (020) 7554 5454
E-mail: sales@rws-group.com *Patent & technical information searchers*

R W Simon Ltd, Hatchmoor Industrial Estate, Torrington, Devon, EX38 7HP Tel: (01805) 623721 Fax: (01805) 624578
E-mail: info@rwsimon.co.uk *Acoustic ventilators & grill services*

▶ R W Simpson Transport Ltd, 263 Oilmills Road, Ramsey Mereside, Ramsey, Huntingdon, Cambridgeshire, PE26 2TT Tel: (01733) 844235 Fax: (01733) 844651

▶ R W Simpson Transport Ltd, Hydra Park, Nether Lane, Ecclesfield, Sheffield, S35 9ZX Tel: 0114-232 9100 Fax: 0114-232 9111

R W Taylor Joinery, 9b Catton Road, Arnold, Nottingham, NG5 7JD Tel: 0115-920 1656 Fax: 0115-967 3063 *Joinery manufrs*

R W Unwin & Co. Ltd, 10 Prospect Place, Welwyn, Hertfordshire, AL6 9EW Tel: (01438) 716441 Fax: (01438) 716067
E-mail: sales@rwunwin.co.uk *Pharmaceutical import distribution agents*

R W Vesey Ltd, 734 Melton Road, Thurmaston, Leicester, LE4 8BD Tel: 0116-269 6241 Fax: 0116-269 6243
E-mail: info@vesey-airflow.com *Air pollution control consultants*

R W Wilson Ltd, 166 Findon Road, Worthing, West Sussex, BN14 0EL Tel: (01903) 264979 Fax: (01903) 264979
E-mail: mikejupp@btconnect.com *Electric motor rewind specialist services*

R W Woodmachines Ltd, 25-27 Murdock Road, Bicester, Oxfordshire, OX26 4PP Tel: (01869) 244943 Fax: (01869) 253498
E-mail: sales@rw-machines.co.uk *Woodworking machinery distributors*

▶ R Walker, 41 The Pastures, Lower Bullingham, Hereford, HR2 6EU Tel: (01432) 341636
E-mail: enquires@rwalker-plans.co.uk *Architects, planning application consultancy,*

R Walker & Sons Preston Ltd, 103 Market St West, Preston, PR1 2HB Tel: (01772) 254176 Fax: (01772) 202246 *PVCU window installation, joinery & building contractors services*

R Welsh & Son, 28 Castle Street, Duns, Berwickshire, TD11 3DP Tel: (01361) 883466 Fax: (01361) 883466 *Gunsmiths*

▶ R Whatmore Ltd, Brook Street, Oswaldtwistle, Accrington, Lancashire, BB5 3JH Tel: (01254) 233214 Fax: (01254) 385747

R Whitehead Concrete Ltd, Gin Close Way, near Afwsworth, Giltbrook, Nottingham, NG16 2HH Tel: 0115-930 3104 Fax: 0115-944 1935 *Concrete products & cast stone products*

R Whitehouse & Son, 16d Halfpenny Green Airport, Bobbington, Stourbridge, West Midlands, DY7 5DY Tel: (01384) 221304 Fax: (01384) 221533
E-mail: colin.whitehouse3@btinternet.com *Gear box, unit (reconditioned) manufacturers or suppliers*

▶ R Williamson Ltd, 118 Duke Street, Glasgow, G4 0XW Tel: 0141-552 3654

R Withers Holdings Ltd, Beddington Farm Road, Croydon, CR0 4XB Tel: (020) 8684 7557 Fax: (020) 8689 2101
E-mail: enq@withers-group.co.uk *Construction, piling & underpinning*

R Woodhead & J Fisher, Unit 2 Oak St Trading Estate, Oak Street, Quarry Bank, Brierley Hill, West Midlands, DY5 2JQ Tel: (01384) 261189 Fax: (01384) 261189 *Engineers' pattern makers*

R Worsdall & Co., 17-19 Reform Street, Hull, HU2 8EF Tel: (01482) 320383 Fax: (01482) 320383 *Wire balloon manufrs*

R Wright & Son Marine Engineers Ltd, Church Broughton Road, Foston, Derby, DE65 5PW Tel: (01283) 812177 Fax: (01283) 812052 *Food processing plant manufrs*

R X Laboratories, Unit 12, Ryeland Farm Industrial Estate, Wellington, Somerset, TA21 9PZ Tel: (01823) 660429 Fax: (01823) 660429
E-mail: sales@rxlabs.com *Foot support manufrs*

R Y B Marine Sales Ltd, Maidenhead Road, Windsor, Berkshire, SL4 5HT Tel: (01753) 851717 Fax: (01753) 868172
E-mail: sales@ryb.co.uk *Boat sales*

R Y Thomson & Son, 15 Ash Street, Dundee, DD1 5AR Tel: (01382) 221460 Fax: (01382) 907005 E-mail: rythomson@btconnect.com *Sheet metalworkers, fencing contractors & blacksmiths*

R Yates, 231 Scotia Road, Stoke-on-Trent, ST6 4EZ Tel: (01782) 837579 Fax: (01782) 835646 *General engineers*

▶ R Young & Son Printers Ltd, 360 Brighton Road, South Croydon, Surrey, CR2 6AL Tel: (020) 8680 2242 Fax: (020) 8681 0873
E-mail: info@youngprint.com *Full service commercial print shop, printing, prepress & bindery*

R Z Construction Ltd, Pembroke Centre, 3 Cheney Manor Estate, Swindon, SN2 2PQ Tel: (01793) 614441 Fax: (01793) 420251 *Civil groundwork engineers*

R&C, Unit 16 Earlsdon Business Centre, Warwick Street, Coventry, CV5 6ET Tel: (024) 7671 3313 Fax: (024) 7667 8905 *Insurance consultants*

▶ R&P, 64 Greenhead Road, Dumbarton, G82 2PN Tel: (01389) 765367 Fax: (01389) 765368

R&R, 79 Mortimers Lane, Fair Oak, Eastleigh, Hampshire, SO50 7BT Tel: (023) 8069 2476 Fax: (023) 8069 2720 *Civil engineers*

R2 B2, Wyse Hill House, Finchampstead, Wokingham, Berkshire, RG40 4JR Tel: 0118-973 7171 Fax: 0118-973 7172
E-mail: r2b2@r2b2.co.uk *IT consultants*

▶ R2R Rollers Ltd, Unit 1C Victoria Court, Colliers Way, Clayton West, Huddersfield, HD8 9TR Tel: (0845) 6017658 Fax: (0845) 6017659
E-mail: a.hives@r2rrollers.co.uk *Rubber roller manufrs*

▶ RA Mitchell Painting & Decorating, The Mayflower, Harriets Corner, Pilgrims Lane, Whitstable, Kent, CT5 3BL Tel: 01227 274317
E-mail: info@ramitchell.co.uk

Raaco GB Ltd, Wenrisc House Meadow Court, High Street, Witney, Oxfordshire, OX28 6ER Tel: (01993) 776333 Fax: (01993) 776444
E-mail: sales@raaco.com *Storage systems manufrs*

▶ Raal Supply Ltd, Pinfold Lane, Bottesford, Nottingham, NG13 0AR Tel: (01949) 844045 Fax: (01949) 844131 *Crane design*

▶ Ra'Alloy Trading Company Ltd, Hortonwood 10, Telford, Shropshire, TF1 7ES Tel: (01952) 677877 Fax: (01952) 677883
E-mail: sales@raalloy.com *Manufacturers of aluminium disabled access ramps.*

Rab Down Equipment, 32 Edward Street, Sheffield, S3 7GB Tel: 0114-275 7544 Fax: 0114-278 0584
E-mail: sales@rab.uk.com *Down clothing & sleeping bag manufrs*

Rab Personnel Management Services, 18 Dolphin Close, London, SE28 8PY Tel: (020) 8311 1261 Fax: (020) 8311 1261
E-mail: sales@rabpms.co.uk *Personnel & human resource management consultancy*

Rabbit Computers Ltd, Ashfield Avenue, Bushey, WD23 4HJ Tel: (020) 8420 5902 Fax: (020) 8420 5901
E-mail: sales@rabbit-computers.ltd.uk *Computer systems*

Rabbitt Recycling, 27-29 New Street, Charfield, Wotton-under-Edge, Gloucestershire, GL12 8ES Tel: (01453) 844343 Fax: (01453) 521330
E-mail: info@rabbittrecycling.co.uk *Waste management services*

Rabbitt Recycling, 27-29 New Street, Charfield, Wotton-under-Edge, Gloucestershire, GL12 8ES Tel: (01453) 844343 Fax: (01453) 521330
E-mail: info@rabbittrecycling.co.uk *Consultancy and facility management services for recycling of dry waste materials from medium to large companies. Operates nationwide.*

Rabco Fittings Ltd, Unit 15 Palmers Road, East Moons Moat, Redditch, Worcestershire, B98 0RF Tel: (01527) 510733 Fax: (01527) 510735 E-mail: admin@rabco-fittings.com *Copper heating & plumbing fitters*

Rabo Merchants Ltd, 267 Bearwood Road, Smethwick, West Midlands, B66 4NA Tel: (01386) 700193 Fax: 0121-429 4993
E-mail: reception@rabo.co.uk *Export merchants & agents*

▶ Rabrook Design, 225 Orphanage Road, Birmingham, B24 0BD Tel: 0121-382 8111 Fax: 0121-382 8111 *Materials handling equipment suppliers*

Rabtherm International Ltd, Unit 11, Empire Close, Aldridge, Walsall, WS9 8XZ Tel: (01922) 743273 Fax: (01922) 743119
E-mail: bgas@rabtherm.co.uk *Distributors & agents of air conditioning & refrigeration*

Rac Signs, Rac Ho, 1 Forest Rd, Feltham, Middx, TW13 7RR Tel: (0845) 6010000 Fax: (0845) 2082502 *Sign consultants*

J.T. Raca International Ltd, 92-100 Earl Street, Northampton, NN1 3AX Tel: (01604) 230808 Fax: (01604) 620866 E-mail: info@jtraca.com *Textile manufacturers & international transport*

Racal Acoustics, Waverley Industrial Park, Hailsham Drive, Harrow, Middlesex, HA1 4TR Tel: (020) 8515 6200 Fax: (020) 8427 0350
E-mail: email@racalacoustic.com *Telecommunication equipment manufrs*

Racal Antennas Ltd, First Avenue, Southampton, SO15 0LJ Tel: (023) 8070 5705 Fax: (023) 8070 1122 E-mail: sales@raycalantennas.com *Radio communications equipment distributors*

Raccoon Signs & Display Ltd, 9 Warsop Trading Estate, Hever Road, Edenbridge, Kent, TN8 5LD Tel: (01732) 864966 Fax: (01732) 867612
E-mail: enquiries@raccoon.co.uk *Marketing & safety construction sign manufrs*

Race, 10 Manchester Road, Wilmslow, Cheshire, SK9 1BG Tel: (01625) 521100
E-mail: design@race-international.com *Marketing solutions*

Race Engine Components, Kingswood Farm, Kingswood, Albrighton, Wolverhampton, WV7 3AQ Tel: (01902) 373770 Fax: (01902) 373772 E-mail: jivey10194@aol.com *Valves guides for racing cars & bikes*

Race Products, Unit 1 Parkview, Gallamore Lane Industrial Estate, Market Rasen, Lincolnshire, LN8 3HZ Tel: (01673) 842704 Fax: (01673) 842470 E-mail: raceproducts@aol.com *Motorcycle racing bodywork*

Racecourse Information Systems Ltd, Chapland Cottage, Lanark, ML11 7RH Tel: (01555) 663285 Fax: (01555) 663285 *Electronic sign manufrs*

▶ Racemettle Ltd, Caldicott Drive, Heapham Road Industrial Estate, Gainsborough, Lincolnshire, DN21 1FJ Tel: (01427) 679784 Fax: (01427) 810593 E-mail: steve@racemettleltd.co.uk *Lightweight alternators & high torque starter motors distributors*

Raceparts (UK) Ltd, Unit 3, Rockfort Industrial Estate, Hithercroft Road, Wallingford, Oxfordshire, OX10 9DA Tel: (01491) 822000 Fax: (01491) 822009
E-mail: sales@raceparts.co.uk *Racing car engineering services suppliers*

▶ Rachel Ellen Design, 313 Hucknall Road, Nottingham, NG5 1FJ Tel: 0115-962 2862 Fax: 0115-969 2724
E-mail: rachel@rachelellen.fsworld.co.uk *Greeting card designers*

Rachel's Bakery, Unit B2 South Point, Foreshore Road, Cardiff, CF10 4SP Tel: (029) 2045 6596 *Bakery suppliers*

Racing Developments, 48-50 Tanners Drive, Blakelands, Milton Keynes, MK14 5BW Tel: (01908) 210775
E-mail: info@racingdevelopments.com *Race preparation, sports car servicing rolling road*

Rack, 25 Burrowfield, Welwyn Garden City, Hertfordshire, AL7 4SS Tel: (01707) 394847 Fax: (01707) 391523
E-mail: sales@rackstorage.co.uk *Storage system suppliers*

Rack International UK Ltd, Pant Industrial Estate, Dowlais, Merthyr Tydfil, CF48 2SR Tel: (01685) 383133 Fax: (01685) 383836
E-mail: sales@cavesystems.co.uk *Steel rack & storage manufrs*

Rack Stor Ltd, Suite 14 South West Centre, Archer Rd, Sheffield, S8 0JR Tel: 0114-296 0066 Fax: 0114-296 0055
E-mail: contactus@rackstor.co.uk *Specialist cantilever racking manufacturers operating throughout the UK, providing long load storage solutions to the industry*

Rack Systems (Engineering) Ltd, Kirkby Mills Industrial Estate, Kirkby Mills, Kirkbymoorside, York, YO62 6QR Tel: (01751) 432647
E-mail: info@racksystems.co.uk *Office furniture manufrs*

▶ Rackham Engineering, Hellesdon Park Industrial Estate Road, Norwich, NR6 5DR Tel: (01603) 485038 Fax: (01603) 787106
E-mail: sale@rackhamengineering.co.uk *Sheet metalwork engineers or fabricators*

Rackham Housefloors Ltd, Broadmoor Road, Cinderford, Gloucestershire, GL14 2YE Tel: (01594) 826602 Fax: (01594) 826502 *Concrete floor beams*

Rackhams, Deben Mills, Wickham Market, Woodbridge, Suffolk, IP13 0RG Tel: (01728) 746207 Fax: (01728) 747772 *Animal feed & solid fuel merchants*

▶ Rackinabag, 15 Ambridge Close, Northampton, NN4 9RW Tel: (01604) 768598 Fax: (01604) 767645 E-mail: sales@rackinabag.co.uk *Roof rack suppliers*

Rackline Systems Storage Ltd, Oaktree Lane, Talke Pits, Stoke-on-Trent, ST7 1RX Tel: (01782) 777666 Fax: (01782) 777444
E-mail: sales@rackline.co.uk *Office storage solutions manufrs*

Rack-N-Stak Ltd, Aston Way, Moss Side, Leyland, PR26 7UX Tel: (01772) 644300 *Fork lift trucks*

▶ Racks Industries Ltd, Unit 8 Castlefields Trad Estate, Bradford, Bingley, West Yorkshire, BD16 2AF Tel: (01274) 551170 Fax: (01274) 560594
E-mail: enquiries@racks-industries.co.uk *Manufacturers of cantilever racking & storage systems*

Raco Air Conditioning, Addison Industrial Estate, Blaydon-on-Tyne, Tyne & Wear, NE21 4TE Tel: 0191-440 4400 Fax: 0191-440 4401 *Air conditioning maintenance & sales*

Raco Laser Supplies, 6 Elm Way, Hackleton, Northampton, NN7 2BT Tel: (0845) 3273431 Fax: (01604) 870970 *Laser printer consumable distributors*

Rad Machinery Ltd, 3 Queens Road, Walsall, WS5 3NF Tel: (01922) 725602 Fax: (01922) 725503 E-mail: sales@radmachinery.co.uk *Machinery manufrs*

Radagh Glass Ltd, Monk Bretton, Barnsley, South Yorkshire, S71 2QG Tel: (01226) 710211 Fax: (01226) 716808 E-mail: *Glass bottle manufrs*

Radamec Control Systems Ltd, Euro House, Abex Road, Newbury, Berkshire, RG14 5EY Tel: (01635) 40528 Fax: (01635) 47453
E-mail: sales@radamec-controls.co.uk *Marine & environmental engineers*

Radan, Limpley Mill, Limpley Stoke, Bath, BA2 7FJ Tel: (0844) 8001248 Fax: (01225) 721333
E-mail: sales@uk.radan.com *Computer aided design manufrs*

Radar Signs, 143 Beehive Lane, Ilford, Essex, IG4 5DR Tel: (020) 8551 0216 Fax: (020) 8551 1458 E-mail: radarsigns@btclick.com *Sign manufrs*

▶ Radargirl, 197 St Helens Avenue, Swansea, SA1 4NE Tel: (0800) 1698000 Fax: (01792) 481364 E-mail: sales@radargirl.com *Radar detector specialists*

Radcliffe Building Supplies Ltd, Lord Street, Radcliffe, Manchester, M26 3BA Tel: 0161-724 6363 Fax: 0161-725 9128 *Builders merchants*

▶ Radcliffe Contractors, Queens Square, Leeds Road, Huddersfield, HD2 1XN Tel: (01484) 420212 Fax: (01484) 540891

Radcliffe Machinery Ltd, Radcliffe Machinery Limited, Binn Brow Binns Lane, Holmfirth, HD9 3BJ Tel: (01484) 687811 Fax: (01484) 687769 E-mail: tim@radcliffemachinery.com *Polythene bag converting machinery manufrs*

Thomas Radcliffe Ltd, Unit 21, White Hoe, Old Castletown Road, Douglas, Isle Of Man, IM2 1QD Tel: (01624) 626767 Fax: (01624) 677337 E-mail: thomasradcliffe@mcb.net *Paper & packaging merchants suppliers*

▶ Radclyffe & Culross & Sproston, 6-7 Glebe Road, London, E8 4BD Tel: (020) 7254 6293 Fax: (020) 7923 3862

Radco Services Ltd, Little Limekilns, Middle Lypiatt, Stroud, Gloucestershire, GL6 7LR Tel: (01453) 883746 Fax: (01453) 884211 *Air pollution control equipment suppliers & manufrs*

Radcom Radio Telephone Services Ltd, Belvoir Way, Fairfield Industrial Estate, Louth, Lincolnshire, LN11 0HP Tel: (01507) 604055 Fax: (01507) 600489
E-mail: radcomlimited@louthssbusiness.co.uk *Radio communicator suppliers*

Radcot Armoured Components Ltd, Park Road, Faringdon, Oxfordshire, SN7 7BP Tel: (01367) 240970 Fax: (01367) 242641 *Wear plate engineers*

Rademaker, Suite 105 Standish Centre, Cross Street, Standish, Wigan, Lancashire, WN6 0HQ Tel: (01257) 421120 Fax: (01257) 422339
E-mail: sales@rademaker.co.uk *Industrial food equipment manufrs*

Radflex Contract Services Ltd, Unit 35 Wilks Avenue, Questor, Dartford, DA1 1JS Tel: (01322) 276363 Fax: (01322) 270606 E-mail: expjoint@radflex.co.uk *Joints, coatings* Also at: Chester-le-Street

Radford Customer Guidance & Checkouts Division, Sherbourne Drive, Tilbrook, Milton Keynes, MK7 8BA Tel: (01908) 366688 Fax: (01908) 368811 E-mail: sales@radford.co.uk *Retail equipment manufrs*

Radford Ezy-Net, Charford House, Machinefarm, Hill Furze, Pershore, Worcestershire, WR10 2NE Tel: (01386) 861029 Fax: (01386) 861029 E-mail: enquiries@radfordezynet.co.uk *Sports ground equipment distributors*

Radford Press Ltd, Miller House, 30 Wilmot Road, London, E10 5LU Tel: (020) 8558 4814 Fax: (020) 8558 0345 E-mail: sales@radfordpress.co.uk *Lithographic, continuous & digital printers, in-house design studio,*

Radiall Ltd, Ground Floor, 6 The Ground Union Office Park, Packet Boat Lane, Uxbridge, Middlesex, UB8 2GH Tel: (01895) 425000 Fax: (01895) 425010 E-mail: info@radiall.com *Connectors, coaxial, rectangular, fibre optic & circular multi-pin manufrs*

Radiant Blinds Ltd, 101 Ewell Road, Surbiton, Surrey, KT6 6AH Tel: (020) 8390 8755 Fax: (020) 8390 2005 E-mail: info@radiantblinds.co.uk *Family run business with over 100 years' experience. Quality products manufactured to individual requirements. Awnings and canopies - electric/ manual Choice of fabrics Signwriting/logos on awnings if required Alfresco restaurant screens Interior blinds including woodslat, roller, pleated, venetian, vertical, roman. Plantation wooden shutters Members of the BBSA (British Blind and Shutter Association) Large Umbrellas Heaters*

The Radiator Cover Co., Lincoln Avenue, Sandiacre, Nottingham, NG10 5GZ Tel: 0115-939 9125 Fax: 0115-939 9125 E-mail: theradiatorcovercompany@gmail.com

Radio 88, 88 Longbridge Road, Barking, Essex, IG11 8SF Tel: (020) 8594 9979 Fax: (020) 8591 6642 *Communications system builders*

▶ Radio Accessories Direct Ltd, Unit 45 Elderpark Workspace, 100 Elderpark Street, Glasgow, G51 3TR Tel: 0141-445 8828 Fax: 0141-445 8814

Radio Active, 24 Silverdale Ave, Westcliff-on-Sea, Essex, SS0 9BA Tel: 01702 348975 Fax: 01702 348975 *Audio visual fitting*

▶ Radio Communications Online Ltd, 168 Long Meadow, Aylesbury, Buckinghamshire, HP21 7EB Tel: (0845) 8682226 E-mail: sales@radiocommunicationsonline.com *Radio communications suppliers*

Radio Coms Systems Ltd, 170a Oval Road, Croydon, CR0 6BN Tel: (020) 8680 1585 Fax: (020) 8686 9433 E-mail: info@radiocoms.co.uk *Cellular radio telephone equipment distribs*

Radio Data Logger Co. Ltd, 75 Silver Street, Newport Pagnell, Buckinghamshire, MK16 0EQ Tel: (01908) 618932 Fax: (01908) 618932 E-mail: enq@radiolog.co.uk *Data loggin equipment manufrs*

▶ Radio Europe Ltd, 17-21 Hastings Street, Luton, LU1 5BE Tel: (01582) 481114 Fax: (01582) 481115 E-mail: sales@red-radio.co.uk *Radio & communications*

Radio Links Communications Ltd, Eaton House, Great North Road, Eaton Socon, St. Neots, Cambridgeshire, PE19 8EG Tel: (01480) 217220 Fax: (01480) 406667 E-mail: info@radio-links.co.uk *Radio Links Communications Ltd: HIRE, SALES, SERVICE OF TWO WAY RADIO COMMUNICATIONS. Dealers for Motorola, Entel, HYT, Icom, Kenwood. Established since 1972 as the first independent radio company in the U.K. to hire professional radio communications. The company rapidly evolved into radio system SALES and SERVICE. Radio systems are designed to individual requirements and can include VOIP and Health and Safety features such as Man-down, Lone Worker, Panic Button and GPS. Visit our website for full details on products, services and customer testimonials. Onsite Communications Ltd is a group company of Radio Links formed to deal with the demand for hire of a management package of communications for major sporting events, providing wide coverage of radio communications, public address, media interview/recording facilities, on site engineering back-up and much more. Sales and service of public address and audio products is also supplied to the private, commercial and retail sectors.*

▶ Radio Products UK Ltd, The Granary, Sutton Lane, Langley, Bucks, Slough, SL3 8AR Tel: (01753) 582030 *RPUK markets & distributes a range of accessories for two way radios*

Radio Service, Unit 129 Brookfield Place, Walton Summit Industrial Estate, Bamber Bridge, Preston, PR5 8BF Tel: (01772) 628000 Fax: (01772) 628888 E-mail: ians@rstechnology.co.uk *2-way radio communication system contractors*

Radiocoms Systems Ltd, 170a Oval Road, Croydon, ,Hounslow, Hounslow, TW6 2BG Tel: (0870) 4604600 Fax: (020) 8759 1411 *Cellular equipment manufrs*

Radiodetection Ltd, Western Drive, Bristol, BS14 0AF Tel: 0117-988 6232 Fax: (01275) 550004 E-mail: sales@radiodetection.com *Water leakage detection/control services*

Radiographic Accessories Ltd, Durham Lane Industrial Park, Guisley Way, Stockton-On-Tees, Cleveland, TS16 0RS Tel: (01642) 790580 Fax: (01642) 790420 E-mail: jack@radac.demon.co.uk *Industrial x-ray accessory manufrs*

Radiometer Ltd, Manor Court, Manor Royal, Crawley, West Sussex, RH10 9FY Tel: (01293) 517599 Fax: (01293) 531597 E-mail: sales@radiometer.co.uk *Blood gas analyser manufrs*

Radiometrix, 231 Kenton Lane, Harrow, Middlesex, HA3 8RP Tel: (020) 8909 9595 Fax: (020) 8909 2233 E-mail: info@radiometrix.co.uk *Design & marketing of low power radio data links*

▶ Radioscan.co.uk, Southwell Court, Broad Oak, Hereford, HR2 8RA Tel: 01600 750333 E-mail: contact@radioscan.co.uk *Retailers in handheld radio scanners & related accessories*

Radioscape Ltd, 2 Albany Terrace, London, NW1 4DS Tel: (020) 7224 1586 Fax: (020) 7224 1595 E-mail: info@radioscape.com *Software design*

Radio-Tech Ltd, Radio House, The Old Brewery, Lindsey Street, Epping, Essex, CM16 6RD Tel: (01992) 576107 Fax: (01992) 561994 E-mail: sales@radtec.demon.co.uk *Systems & equipment manufrs*

Radiotronic, Advance Park Rhonymedre, Wrexham, Clwyd, LL14 3YR Tel: (01978) 823900 Fax: (01978) 822913 E-mail: sales@aslgroup.uk.com *Distributors of capacitors, impact extrusion & metal labels*

Radisson Edwardian Mayfair, Stratton Street, London, W1A 2AN Tel: (020) 7629 7777 Fax: (020) 7629 1459 E-mail: mayfair@radisson.com *Hotel & conference facilities*

Radius Refrigeration Ltd, 19 Wilshaw Street, London, SE14 6TN Tel: (020) 8694 2786 Fax: (020) 8694 2786 *Refrigeration sales & repairs*

Radius Reinforcements Ltd, 1 Villa Place, Clackmannan, FK10 4HZ Tel: (01259) 215129 Fax: (01259) 215129 E-mail: radiusrebar1@freeuk.com *Reinforced steel suppliers*

Radius Services, Unit 23-24, Resolution Way, London, SE8 4NT Tel: (020) 8692 0257 Fax: (020) 8694 2786 *Commercial refrigeration units supply & repair*

Radius Shipping Ltd, 886 Old Kent Road, London, SE15 1NQ Tel: (020) 7639 2048 Fax: (020) 7639 7313 E-mail: office@radius.uk.net *Freight forwarding agents*

Radius Solutions Ltd, Manor House, High Street, Dronfield, Derbyshire, S18 1PY Tel: (01246) 290331 Fax: (01246) 412401 E-mail: infouk@radiussolutions.co.uk *Management information systems consultants*

▶ Radix Systems Ltd, Unit D3-D4 The Premier Centre, Premier Way, Romsey, Hampshire, SO51 9DG Tel: (01794) 830240 Fax: (01794) 830143 E-mail: info@radixsystems.co.uk *Electronic sorting equipment manufrs*

Radlett Valve & Engineering Co. Ltd, 38 Watling Street, Radlett, Hertfordshire, WD7 7NN Tel: (01923) 852131 Fax: (01923) 854484 E-mail: sales@radlettvalve.co.uk *Valve brokers & suppliers*

radley fabrications, 16 St Michaels Drive, Roxwell, Chelmsford, CM1 4NU Tel: 01245 248983 Fax: 01245 248983 E-mail: jennick@mcgregor247.fsnet.co.uk *specialising in staircases balustrades railings gates balconies grills etc*

R.B. Radley & Co. Ltd, Shirehill, Saffron Walden, Essex, CB11 3AZ Tel: (01799) 513320 Fax: (01799) 513283 E-mail: sales@radleys.co.uk *Laboratory supplies & scientific glassware manufrs*

Radleys Discovery Technologies Ltd, Shire Hill Industrial Estate, Shire Hill, Saffron Walden, Essex, CB11 3AZ Tel: (01799) 525381 Fax: (01799) 528066 E-mail: enquiries@sgatech.co.uk *Hermetic fills manufrs*

Radleys Glassworkers, Shire Hill, Saffron Walden, Essex, CB11 3AZ Tel: (01799) 513320 Fax: (01799) 513283 E-mail: sales@radleys.co.uk *Scientific glassblowing*

Radmore Agencies Ltd, Perry House, Torton, Kidderminster, Worcestershire, DY10 4HY Tel: (01299) 250621 Fax: (01299) 251444 *Housewares importers & Technology Products*

Radphone Ltd, Unit 1 Caughey Street, Hull, HU2 8TH Tel: (01482) 228725 Fax: (01482) 324717 *Radio communications*

Radshape Sheet Metal Ltd, Shefford Road, Birmingham, B6 4PL Tel: 0121-242 3323 Fax: 0121-242 3385 E-mail: info@radshape.co.uk *Sheet metal fabricators manufrs*

Radun Controls Ltd, Unit 42 Aberaman Industrial Estate, Aberaman, Aberdare, Mid Glamorgan, CF44 6UZ Tel: (01685) 887600 Fax: (01685) 887601 E-mail: general@radun.com *Instrument & control test equipment manufrs*

Radway Control Systems, Business & Technology Centre, Radway Grn, Crewe, CW2 5PR Tel: (01270) 886176 Fax: (01270) 886275 E-mail: pjtomkinson@radway.co.uk *Control panel manufrs*

Radway Door & Windows Ltd, Radway House, Oxneasow Road, East Moons Moat, Redditch, Worcestershire, B98 0RE Tel: (01527) 503700 Fax: (01527) 503701 E-mail: info@radways.co.uk *UPVC window & door manufrs*

RADYNE, Molly Millars Lane, Wokingham, Berks, RG41 2PX Tel: 0118-978 3333 Fax: 0118-977 1729 E-mail: sales@radyne.co.uk Purchasing Contact: J. Beacham Sales Contact: M. Lee *Furnaces, billet heating; furnaces, induction; induction heat treatment equipment manufacturers; induction heating equipment manufacturers; induction heating (brazing/ soldering) equipment manufacturers; power supply (induction heating) systems/unit manufacturers & furnaces, induction. Induction wire heating & induction pipe heating & coating.*

▶ RAE Computing Ltd, Unit 8, Pennine Industrial Estate, Hangingroyd Lane, Hebden Bridge, West Yorkshire, HX7 7BZ Tel: (0845) 0048435 E-mail: info@raecomputing.com *Network installation*

Douglas Rae, 55 Regent Street, Greenock, Renfrewshire, PA15 4NP Tel: (01475) 723469 Fax: (01475) 723469 *Glazing contractor*

Rae Electrical Services, 116a Blackstock Road, London, N4 2DR Tel: (020) 7226 2962 Fax: (020) 7359 3354 E-mail: raeelectrical@aol.com *Electrical & ceiling contractors*

▶ Rae Marion Chandler, 3 Sudbourne Avenue, Clacton-on-Sea, Essex, CO16 7EN Tel: (01255) 426448 E-mail: sunnyside1946@onetel.com *Essentials Care Service*Friendly, professional care suit suit the individual need of all age grkoups in their own home.**Complementary Healthcare products being sold at trade prices, for a more natural way to positive health. High quality vitamins, minerals, herbs, nutritional supplements & essentials oils.*In assoc. with Goldshield Group Plc.)*

Raeburn Brick Ltd, East Avenue, Blantyre, Glasgow, G72 0JB Tel: (01698) 828888 Fax: (01698) 824039 *Bricks making & haulage services*

Raedek Electronics, Unit 12 Avenue Fields Industrial Estate, Avenue Farm, Stratford-upon-Avon, Warwickshire, CV37 0HT Tel: (01789) 209294 Fax: (01789) 295757 E-mail: sales@raedek.com *General electronic tubes & valves distribs*

Raegurn Group Ltd, Ruby House, Ruby Place, Aberdeen, AB10 1QZ Tel: (01224) 625050 Fax: (01224) 626840 E-mail: heather.milne@raeburn.com *One of Aberdeen's leading recruitment agencies with over 28 years experience. Raeburn Group Limited specialises in a wide range of markets which include the provision of engineering, technical, offshore, accountancy, HR, IT, nurse & healthcare personnel. Local, national & international opportunities available. REC & IIP accredited.*

Rael Brook (Group) Ltd, Grosvenor Street, Ashden Underline, Ashton-Under-Lyne, Lancashire, OL7 0JY Tel: 0161-344 5618 Fax: 0161-308 5060 E-mail: admin@raelbrookshirts.com *Shirt manufrs*

Rael Securities, 139 Rickerscote Road, Stafford, ST17 4HE Tel: (01785) 227632

Raffenday Ltd, 11 Fleming Close, Park Farm Industrial Estate, Wellingborough, Northamptonshire, NN8 6UF Tel: (01933) 673333 Fax: (01933) 675555 E-mail: sales@raffenday.com *Connector distributors*

Rafferty Hospitality Products Ltd, Unit 1 Shepherds Drive, Carnbane Industrial Estate, Newry, County Down, BT35 6JQ Tel: (028) 3025 2205 Fax: (028) 3025 2206 E-mail: sales@raffertyhospitality.com *Printers.*

Raffles Of Portsmouth, 1 Mitchell Way, Portsmouth, PO3 5PY Tel: (023) 9265 3000 Fax: (023) 9265 1770 *Bakery supplies distributor*

Raffray Ltd, La Rue Sinnatt, La Rue Des Pres Trading Estate, St. Saviour, Jersey, JE2 7QT Tel: (07797) 721087 Fax: (01534) 769489 E-mail: michael@raffray.co.uk *General engineers*

Rafi (GB) Ltd, Unit 1 Perrywood Business Park, Honeycrock Lane, Salfords, Redhill, RH1 5DZ Tel: (01737) 778660 Fax: (01737) 778722 E-mail: sales@rafi.co.uk *Control panels & custom designed keyboard manufrs*

Raflatac Ltd, Wareham Road, Eastfield, Scarborough, North Yorkshire, YO11 3DX Tel: (01723) 583661 Fax: (01723) 584896 E-mail: raflatac@raflatac.com *Paper converters* Also at: Stevenage

Rafseal Ltd, Millers Avenue, Brynmenyn Industrial Estate, Brynmenyn, Bridgend, Mid Glamorgan, CF32 9TD Tel: (01656) 725118 Fax: (01656) 724520 E-mail: rafseal@btclick.com *Suppliers of gaskets, strips, washers & other fabrications in a wide range of materials*

▶ Raft Marketing Ltd, Hesketh House, Water Lane, Wilmslow, Cheshire, SK9 5BQ Tel: (01625) 547900 Fax: (01625) 540678 E-mail: phil.storton@theraft.co.uk *Marketing services*

Ragamuffin, Armadale, Ardvasar, Isle of Skye, IV45 8RS Tel: (01471) 844217 Fax: (01471) 844225 *Knitwear & textile distributors & manufrs*

Ragdoll Ltd, Timothys Bridge Road, Stratford-upon-Avon, Warwickshire, CV37 9NQ Tel: (01789) 404100 Fax: (01789) 404136 E-mail: info@ragdoll.co.uk *Television production company*

Rahman Company, 9 Rampart Street, London, E1 2LA Tel: (020) 7790 0608 Fax: (020) 7790 8140 *Accountants*

Rahmans Ltd, 10-14 Hollybush Gardens, London, E2 9QP Tel: (020) 7739 7790 Fax: (020) 7739 0562 E-mail: enquiries@rahmans.co.uk *Leather garments manufrs*

Rai Computing Services Ltd, 20 Cawnpore Rd, Coventry, CV6 4EN Tel: 024 76666610 *Computer software writers*

▶ Rai Group, 298 Soho Road, Handsworth, Birmingham, B21 9LX Tel: 0121-554 4100 Fax: 0121-551 4100

▶ Rai Lea Fabrications Ltd, Units 8-9 Woods Farm, Britwell Salome, Watlington, Oxfordshire, OX49 5HD Tel: (01491) 613300 Fax: (01491) 613300

▶ Raigmore Electronic Services, Ettrick Riverside, Dunsdale Road, Selkirk, TD7 5EB Tel: (01750) 505041

▶ Rail Ability Ltd, Unit B Tilcon Avenue, Stafford, ST18 0YJ Tel: (01785) 214747 Fax: (01785) 214717 E-mail: mail@railability.co.uk

Rail Business Intelligence, Quadrant Ho, The Quadrant, Brighton Rd, Sutton, Surrey, SM2 5AS Tel: (020) 8652 3500 *A fortnightly newsletter charting the twists & turns of Britain's privatised rail network*

Rail Order, Unit 2, Anglia Way, Mansfield, Nottinghamshire, NG18 4LP Tel: 01623 627208 Fax: 01623 633914 E-mail: sales@rail-order.co.uk *Supplier of Traction Consumables, and Janitorial supplies to the UK Rail Industry. Stock over 4000 products (see online catalogue) Approved distributor of Huber + Suhner Traction Cable.*

Railex Systems Ltd, Station Road, Lawford, Manningtree, Essex, CO11 1DZ Tel: (08706) 006664 Fax: (01206) 391465 E-mail: info@railex.co.uk *Office filing systems manufrs*

Railex Systems Ltd, Crossens Way, Marine Drive, Southport, Merseyside, PR9 9LY Tel: (01704) 226866 Fax: (01704) 225814 E-mail: info@railex.co.uk *Filing systems manufrs*

Railko Ltd, Boundary Rd, Loudwater, High Wycombe, Bucks, HP10 9QU Tel: (01628) 524901 Fax: (01628) 810761 E-mail: info@railko.co.uk *Market leaders in plastic bearing technology and have been designing, developing and manufacturing thermoplastic and thermosetting plastic bearings for the marine, rail, automotive and general engineering markets worldwide for nearly 50 years.*

Railstore Ltd, Childerditch Lane, West Horndon, Brentwood, Essex, CM13 3ED Tel: (01277) 814600 Fax: (01277) 814609 E-mail: sales@railstore.co.uk *Warehousing storage & haulers*

Railtec Engineering Ltd, Wakefield Road, Dearne Works, Scissett, Huddersfield, HD8 9HS Tel: (01484) 862001 Fax: (01484) 864793 E-mail: john@railtec.co.uk *Concrete placing skips manufrs*

Railton Products Ltd, Unit 11 Ladbrook Park, Millers Road, Warwick, CV34 5AE Tel: (01926) 496351 Fax: (01926) 410574 E-mail: info@railtonproducts.co.uk *Manufacturers of tapping attachments*

▶ Railway Electrical Services Ltd, St.Bartholomews Church, Hallam Fields Road, Ilkeston, Derbyshire, DE7 4AZ Tel: 0115-944 4608 Fax: 0115-944 4988

Railway Industry Association, 22 Headfort Place, London, SW1X 7RY Tel: (020) 7201 0777 Fax: (020) 7235 5777 E-mail: ria@riagb.org.uk *Trade association*

Railway Mine & Plantation Equipment Ltd, 4 Grosvenor Place, London, SW1X 7DG Tel: (020) 7201 3399 Fax: (020) 7201 3311 *Mine railway equipment distributors or agents; mining plant & equipment distributors or agents & railway material contractors or suppliers*

Railway Sleeper.com, Kilgraney, Owthorpe Road, Cotgrave, Nottingham, NG12 3PU Tel: 0115-989 0445 Fax: 0115-989 3366 E-mail: enquiries@kilgraney.com *Landscaping material sales*

Railweight, Hurstfield Industrial Estate, Hurst Street, Stockport, Cheshire, SK5 7BB Tel: 0161-431 5155 Fax: 0161-443 1356 E-mail: sales@railweight.co.uk *Railway vehicle weighing systems manufrs*

Rain Or Shine, Ashfield House, Common Platt, Purton, Swindon, SN5 5JZ Tel: (01793) 541134 Fax: (01793) 541134 *Hardwood garden furniture manufrs*

Rainbow Bag UK Ltd, 3A Bess Park Road, Trenant Industrial Estate, Wadebridge, Cornwall, PL27 6HB Tel: (01208) 812442 Fax: (01208) 816181 E-mail: sales@rainbowbags.co.uk *Packing distributors*

Rainbow Blinds, 64 Hamilton Road, Rutherglen, Glasgow, G73 3DQ Tel: 0141-613 1347 E-mail: col.stan@ntlworld.com *Blind manufrs*

Rainbow Colour, 2 High St, Steventon, Abingdon, Oxfordshire, OX13 6RS Tel: (01235) 200700 Fax: (01235) 200707 E-mail: rainbow.colour@tiscali.co.uk *Rainbow Colour are high quality printers based near Oxford, offering a wide range of printed products from banners, posters and exhibitions prints to vehicle signs and lettering, wraps, netting tags, labels and booklets. We cover areas in Oxfordshire, Abingdon and Didcot.*We also design from basics, to produce imaginative printed stationery and leaflets.*Great deals available for print up to exhibition posters and banners - please ask for details.*Please click on a service below for more information, or call 0800 458 3778 to discuss your requirements:*

Rainbow Crafts Fife, Crosshill Centre, Main Street, Crosshill, Lochgelly, Fife, KY5 8BJ Tel: (01592) 860444 Fax: (01592) 861527 *Educational equipment manufrs*

Rainbow Engineering Services, Unit 17 Shaftesbury Industrial Centre, Icknield Way, Letchworth Garden City, Hertfordshire, SG6 1RR Tel: (01462) 480442 Fax: (01462) 480449 E-mail: sales@rainbow-dukane.com *Ultrasonic plastic welding services*

▶ Rainbow Enterprises, 4 Old Court Road, Nurston, Barry, South Glamorgan, CF62 3BH Tel: (01446) 719112 Fax: (01446) 711978 *Ceramics suppliers*

Rainbow Equipment Ltd, 5 Great Groves, Goffs Oak, Waltham Cross, Hertfordshire, EN7 6SX Tel: (01707) 879876 Fax: (01707) 879876 *Snooker table sale & hire*

▶ Rainbow Florist Supplies, Unit 2e Herald Industrial Estate, Hedge End, Southampton, SO30 2JW Tel: (01489) 787955 Fax: (01489) 790322 E-mail: sales@rainbowfloristsupplies.co.uk *Wholesale suppliers & distributors to the retail & freelance florists*

▶ Rainbow Glass Studios, 172 Stoke Newington Church Street, London, N16 0JL Tel: (020) 7249 0276 Fax: E-mail: richard@rainbowglassstudios.co.uk *Contemporary Fused Glass and Traditional Stained Glass made to requirements for any architectural, ecclesiastic or domestic setting. We design, make and install glass to customer specification at competative rates.*

▶ Rainbow Glass Studios, 82 Berelands Road, Prestwick, Ayrshire, KA9 1ER Tel: (01292) 474279 Fax: (01292) 471426 E-mail: info@rainbowglass.biz *Design, manufacture & install ecclesiastical, stained glass*

▶ Rainbow Graphics, 14 Hilton Avenue, Scunthorpe, South Humberside, DN15 8BD Tel: (01724) 282455 Fax: (01724) 343823 E-mail: rainbowgraphics@ntlworld.com *Sign makers & fitters*

Rainbow Group, 15-17 Stanley Street, Manchester, M8 8SH Tel: 0161-834 8435 Fax: 0161-834 8435 *Baby goods & foam converters*

▶ Rainbow Mini Gym Ltd, 152 Pitmore Road, Eastleigh, Hampshire, SO50 4LT Tel: (023) 8036 4956 E-mail: enquiries@rainbowminigym.co.uk *Activity classes, bouncy castle hire, party hosting*

▶ Rainbow Playsystems, Ham Lane, Orton Waterville, Peterborough, PE2 5UU Tel: (01733) 391222 Fax: (01733) 391223 E-mail: peterborough@rainbowplaysystems.co.uk *Playground equipment retailers*

▶ indicates data change since last edition

Rainbow Pools, The Tannery, Queen Street, Gomshall, Guildford, Surrey, GU5 9LY Tel: (0870) 4050567 Fax: (0870) 4050568 E-mail: info@rainbowgroup.com *Swimming pool design & construction*

▶ Rainbow Services Ltd, 369 Wellingborough Road, Northampton, NN1 4EU Tel: (01604) 627227 Fax: (01604) 627337

Rainbow Spray Services, 5 Berrite Works, Ironbridge Road, West Drayton, Middlesex, UB7 8HY Tel: (01895) 430852 Fax: (01895) 430853 *Stove enameling & powder coating manufrs*

▶ Rainbow Wholesale, 141 West Nile Street, Glasgow, G1 2RN Tel: 0141-333 6599

▶ Rainbows Bouncy Castle Hire, 58 Cornish Road, Chipping Norton, Oxfordshire, OX7 5LB Tel: (01608) 645995 *Bouncy castle hire services*

Raindirk Audio Ltd, 15 Thieves Bridge Road, Watlington, King's Lynn, Norfolk, PE33 0HL Tel: (01553) 810096 E-mail: cyril@raindirk.com Principal Export Areas: Worldwide *Sound recording equipment manufrs*

Raine and Shine, Haywood Way, Ivyhouse Industrial Estate, Hastings, East Sussex, TN35 4PL Tel: (01424) 444411 *Janitorial suppliers*

▶ Rainer Schneider & Ayres, 3 Hereford Close, Buxton, Derbyshire, SK17 9PH Tel: (01298) 79903 Fax: (01298) 72124 E-mail: rsa_bxt@btconnect.com *Transformer components & thermal protectors manufrs*

▶ Rainer Schneider Ayres, 17 Shirlock Road, London, NW3 2HR Tel: (020) 7267 0812 Fax: (020) 7284 0672 E-mail: rsa_bxt@btinternet.com *Transformer core, magnet & bobbin (transformer) manufrs*

Raine's Refrigeration Equipment, Stewner Park Farm, Marton, Ulverston, Cumbria, LA12 0NR Tel: (01229) 463871 Fax: (01229) 465056 *Refrigerator repair services*

▶ Rainey Engineering Solutions, Enterprise Crescent, Lisburn, County Antrim, BT28 2BP Tel: (028) 9266 9233 Fax: (028) 9266 9239 *Engineering services*

▶ John Rainey & Co., Wattstown Indust Estate, Newbridge Road, Coleraine, County Londonderry, BT52 2LB Tel: (028) 7035 7774

Rainford Models Ltd, Bingswood Industrial Estate, Whaley Bridge, High Peak, Derbyshire, SK23 7LY Tel: (01663) 719119 Fax: (01663) 719109 E-mail: sales@rainfordmodels.co.uk *Prototype model making & pattern making*

▶ William Rainfords Concrete, Watery Lane, St. Helens, Merseyside, WA9 3SN Tel: (01744) 750206 Fax: (01744) 25895 *Concrete blocks*

Rainham Healthy Living Centre, 103-107 High Street, Rainham, Gillingham, Kent, ME8 8AA Tel: (01634) 337706 *Metal products*

Rainham Steel Co. Ltd, Kathryn House, Manor Way, Rainham, Essex, RM13 8RE Tel: (01708) 522311 Fax: (01708) 559024 E-mail: info@rainhamsteel.co.uk *Steel stockholders*

Rainham Welding Works Ltd, 152 New Road, Rainham, Essex, RM13 8RS Tel: (01708) 554107 Fax: (01708) 554107 *Welding specialists*

Rainharvesting Systems Ltd, Cheltenham Road, Bisley, Stroud, Gloucestershire, GL6 7BX Tel: (01452) 772000 Fax: (01452) 770115 E-mail: sales@rainharvesting.co.uk *Rainwater harvesting systems*

Raining Data, Mitford House, Benhall, Saxmundham, Suffolk, IP17 1JS Tel: (01728) 603011 Fax: (01728) 604154 *Computer software producer*

Rainmec Systems Ltd, Roxley, Moor Lane, Copmanthorpe, York, YO23 3TJ Tel: (01653) 628535 Fax: (01653) 628535 E-mail: info@rainmec.co.uk *Irrigation equipment manufrs*

Rainsford & Lynes Ltd, Diadem Works, Kings Road, Tyseley, Birmingham, B11 2AJ Tel: 0121-706 6301 Fax: 0121-707 0995 E-mail: sales@rainsford-lynes.co.uk *Manufacturers of hot brass stampings, machined and un-machined. Subcontract assemblies.*

Rainworth Fencing Manufacturers, Helmsley Road, Rainworth, Mansfield, Nottinghamshire, NG21 0DG Tel: (01623) 795066 Fax: (01623) 797543 E-mail: sales@rainworthfencing.com *Fencing manufactures*

▶ Rair International Ltd, 2 Brougham Street, Leicester, LE1 2BA Tel: 0116-253 3078 Fax: 0116-253 3078

▶ Rais A Cabin Transport Ltd, 112 Beddington Lane, Croydon, CR0 4TD Tel: (020) 8665 0051 Fax: (020) 8665 0054

Raised Floor Systems, Peak House, Works Road, Letchworth Garden City, Hertfordshire, SG6 1GB Tel: (01582) 734161 Fax: (01582) 400946 E-mail: sales@raisedfloorsystems.co.uk Principal Export Areas: Worldwide *Raised access flooring systems*

▶ Raiseprint Plc, Units E 1-E 2, Royd Way, Keighley, West Yorkshire, BD21 3LG Tel: (01535) 681452 E-mail: sales@raiseprint.com

Raithby Lawrence & Co. Ltd, 18 Slater Street, Leicester, LE3 5AS Tel: 0116-251 0961 Fax: 0116-253 2581 E-mail: sales@rlprint.com *Quality colour printing & packaging services*

Raitt Orr & Associates, 16-18 Victoria Chambers, Strutton Ground, London, SW1P 2HP Tel: (020) 7222 5479 Fax: (020) 7222 5480 E-mail: info@raittorr.co.uk *Public relations consultants*

Raja Frozen Foods, Doris Road, Bordesley Green, Birmingham, B9 4SJ Tel: 0121-771 0039 Fax: 0121-771 0030 *Frozen ethnic food processors*

Rajan Trading International Ltd, Rajan House, 61 Great Ducie Street, Manchester, M3 1RR Tel: 0161-834 2147 Fax: 0161-835 2435 E-mail: sales@rajan-group.co.uk *Fashionwear & knitwear, importers & exporters*

Rajapack, Unit 1, Marston Gate, Bridgemont, Bedford, MK43 0YL Tel: (0800) 5424428 Fax: (0800) 5424429 E-mail: sales@rajapack.co.uk *Mail order catalogue suppliers*

Rakem Ltd, Wellington Street, Bury, Lancashire, BL8 2BD Tel: 0161-762 0044 Fax: 0161-762 0033 E-mail: info@rakem.co.uk *Pigment & filler manufrs*

Rakeplan Engineering Co. Ltd, Unit F2 Hilton Trading Estate, Hilton Road, Lanesfield, Wolverhampton, WV4 6DW Tel: (01902) 408010 Fax: (01902) 408484 *General machining engineers*

Raker Freight, 100 Ellingham Industrial Centre, Ellingham Way, Ashford, Kent, TN23 6LZ Tel: (01233) 651660 Fax: (01233) 651661 E-mail: info@rakerfreight.co.uk *Freight agents*

Rako Products Ltd, Brunel Way, Stonehouse, Gloucestershire, GL10 3SX Tel: (01453) 829900 Fax: (01453) 829928 E-mail: sales@rako-products.co.uk *Portable conveyor systems, ventilators & fans*

Ralawise Ltd, Cornbrook Park Road, Manchester, M15 4EE Tel: 0161-872 8112 Fax: 0161-872 2554 E-mail: sales@ralawise.com *Distributors of unprocessed leisurewear*

Raldon Precision Engineering Ltd, 9 Morcom Road, Birmingham, B11 2JE Tel: 0121-707 5757 Fax: 0121-706 7290 E-mail: sales@raldonengineering.com *Manufacturers of precision turned parts. CNC machining centres, precision grinding, precision. Subcontract precision engineering, prototype engineering. UK wide customers accepted.*

Ralegh Ltd, Aries House, Manby Park, Manby, Louth, Lincolnshire, LN11 8UT Tel: (01507) 327040 Fax: (01507) 327039 E-mail: diesolutions@ralegh.co.uk *Dye cutting*

Raleigh Adhesive Coatings, Unit 1c Raleigh Hall Industrial Estate, Eccleshall, Stafford, ST21 6JL Tel: (01785) 852824 Fax: (01785) 851358 *Adhesive application & coating services*

Raleigh UK Ltd, Triumph Road, Nottingham, NG7 2DD Tel: 0115-942 0202 Fax: 0115-942 0214 *Cycle manufrs*

Raleigh Workshop Ltd, 1a Saltoun Road, London, SW2 1EN Tel: (020) 7733 8110 Fax: (020) 7733 8778 *Furniture manufrs*

Ralin Group Ltd, Brierley Lane, Bilston, West Midlands, WV14 8TU Tel: (01902) 491954 Fax: (01902) 357299 E-mail: sales@ralingroup.co.uk *Non-standard bolt & nut manufrs*

Rallin (Glasgow) Ltd, 81 James Street, Glasgow, G40 1DB Tel: 0141-554 8248 Fax: 0141-554 1266 E-mail: admin@rallin.com *Amusement machine suppliers*

Rallock Door Systems Ltd, 30 Hardhill Road, Bathgate, West Lothian, EH48 2BW Tel: (01506) 634134 Fax: (01506) 650333 *Automatic door service & repair services*

Ralloy Engineering Ltd, The Industrial Estate, York Road, Sheriff Hutton, York, YO60 6RZ Tel: (01347) 878987 Fax: (01347) 878997 *Aluminium fabrication*

▶ Ralls Builders Ltd, Unit 3 Parklands Business Park, Forest Road, Waterlooville, Hampshire, PO7 6XP Tel: (023) 9225 3250 Fax: (023) 9225 3496 E-mail: paul.kelly@ralls-group.com

Rally Industrial Services Ltd, Beacon Works, Bilston Street, Dudley, West Midlands, DY3 1JE Tel: (01902) 884341 Fax: (01902) 880333 *Electrical Engineers*

Ralph Coidan Ltd, 2 Boltby Way, Eaglescliffe, Stockton-on-Tees, Cleveland, TS16 0RH Tel: (01642) 790100 Fax: (01642) 790488 E-mail: sales@coidan.co.uk Purchasing Contact: K Lynch Sales Contact: B. Boulby Principal Export Areas: Worldwide *Manufacturers of graphite & carbon components, graphite electrodes, furnace parts, heat exchangers & process plant*

▶ Ralph D J Owen, Old Badland, New Radnor, Presteigne, Powys, LD8 2TG Tel: (01544) 350304 Fax: (01544) 350304 E-mail: james@ralphscider.fsnet.co.uk *Cider & perry producers*

Ralph Martindale & Co. Ltd, Strawberry Lane, Willenhall, West Midlands, WV13 3RS Tel: (01902) 826826 Fax: (01902) 826827 E-mail: crocodile@ralphmartindale.co.uk *Agricultural edge toolmakers*

Ralph Plastics, Unit 12b Macmerry Industrial Estate, Tranent, East Lothian, EH33 1RD Tel: (01875) 615247 Fax: (01875) 615247 E-mail: trishralph@aol.com *Glass fibre moulders & fabricators*

▶ Ralphs Health Foods, 73 St. James Street, Newport, Isle of Wight, PO30 1LQ Tel: (01983) 522353 Fax: (01983) 522353 *Health food retailers*

Ralspeed Ltd, Hurstwood Court, Mercer Way Shadsworth BSNS Park, Shadsworth Business Park, Blackburn, BB1 2QU Tel: (01254) 582345 Fax: (01254) 668414 E-mail: sales@ralspeed.com *Injection distributors & manufrs*

Ram Computer Systems Ltd, 2 Chandos Place, Bletchley, Milton Keynes, MK2 2SQ Tel: (01908) 371086 Fax: (01908) 643961 E-mail: enquiries@ramcom.co.uk *HP centre of excellence*

Ram Gasket Solutions Ltd, Unit 14, Cardrew Indust Estate, Redruth, Cornwall, TR15 1SS Tel: (01209) 314700 Fax: (01209) 314900 E-mail: mailbox@ramgasket.co.uk *Gasket & seal manufrs*

Ram Machining Ltd, Providence Street, Stourbridge, West Midlands, DY9 8HS Tel: (01384) 424144 Fax: (01384) 892396 *Subcontract machinists*

Ram Mobile Electronics Ltd, 63a Westgate End, Wakefield, West Yorkshire, WF2 9RL Tel: (01924) 201884 Fax: (01924) 332440 *Car security & radio services*

Ram Peripherals, 14 Lombard Road, Merton, London, SW19 3TZ Tel: (020) 8543 9696 Fax: (020) 8543 3419 E-mail: sales@ram-peripherals.co.uk *Software duplication systems*

▶ Ram Plant, 5 Markham Road, Bournemouth, BH9 1HY Tel: (0800) 1952043 Fax: (01202) 539527 *Plant hirers*

Ram Power Ltd, 16 Greenhill Crescent, Watford, WD18 8SE Tel: (01923) 231661 Fax: (01923) 246856 E-mail: rmpwr@aol.com *Hydraulic engineers/hydraulic power pack manufrs*

Ram Reman Ltd, Gundrymoor Trading Estate, Collingwood Road, West Moors, Wimborne, Dorset, BH21 6QJ Tel: (01202) 861888 Fax: (01202) 861668 *Hydraulic equipment manufrs*

▶ Ram Scaffolding, 2 Grays Terrace, Taunton, Somerset, TA1 3HE Tel: (01823) 283692 Fax: (01823) 333395

Ram Services, 240-244 Lowerhouse Lane, Burnley, Lancashire, BB12 6NG Tel: (01282) 452211 Fax: (01282) 452244 E-mail: sales@ramservices.co.uk *Diamond drilling & floor sawing, specialist demolition, fixing design*

Ram Signs, 4 Brighton Road, Lower Kingswood, Tadworth, Surrey, KT20 6SY Tel: (01737) 833444 Fax: (01737) 833432 E-mail: rsgsales@aol.com *Sign manufrs*

Ramac Engineering, 142 Old Shoreham Road, Hove, East Sussex, BN3 7BD Tel: (01273) 622394 Fax: (01273) 202009 E-mail: nfo@whippendell-marine.co.uk *Electrical engineers. Manufacturers of control panels, systems. Also switchgear (industrial) & (marine)*

Ramada Jarvis, Grange Park Lane, Willerby, Hull, HU10 6EA Tel: (01482) 656488 Fax: (01482) 655848 *Hotel & conference facilities*

Ramada York, Shipton Road, Skelton, York, YO30 1XW Tel: (01904) 670222 Fax: (01904) 670311 *Hotel & conference facilities*

▶ Ramar Electronics Services Ltd, Masons Road, Stratford-upon-Avon, Warwickshire, CV37 9NF Tel: (01789) 204879 Fax: (01789) 299727 E-mail: info@ramarpcb.co.uk *Printed circuit board manufrs*

Ramcke Concrete Products, Penyrheol Farm, Five Roads, Llanelli, Dyfed, SA15 5AJ Tel: (01269) 860505 Fax: (01269) 860505 *Concrete patio product manufrs*

Ramco Tubular Services Ltd, Badentoy Road Badentoy Park, Badentoy Industrial Estate, Portlethen, Aberdeen, AB12 4YA Tel: (01224) 782278 Fax: (01224) 783001 E-mail: info@ramco-plc.com *Oilfield tubular services*

Ramesys E Business Services Ltd, Glaisdale Dr East, Nottingham, NG8 4GU Tel: 0115-971 2000 Fax: 0115-971 4600 E-mail: enq@ramesys.com *IT consultants*

▶ Ramfoam Ltd, 84 Birmingham Road, Dudley, West Midlands, DY1 4RF Tel: (01384) 453160 Fax: (01384) 254955

Ramic Engineering Co. Ltd, 96 Upper Wickham Lane, Welling, Kent, DA16 3HQ Tel: (020) 8855 7122 Fax: (020) 8854 8801 E-mail: ramengco@btconnect.com *General engineers*

Ramp Industries Ltd, 22 Garrett Road, Lynx Trading Estate, Yeovil, Somerset, BA20 2TJ Tel: (01935) 427290 Fax: (01935) 420753 E-mail: mail@ramp.co.uk *Precision engineers*

Ramport Scaffolding Co. Ltd, Martins Yard, 82a Endwell Road, London, SE4 2PD Tel: (020) 7732 4646 Fax: (020) 7732 0321 E-mail: scaffolding@ramport.co.uk *Scaffolding contractors*

Ramsay Of Carluke Ltd, 22 Mount Stewart Street, Carluke, Lanarkshire, ML8 5ED Tel: (01555) 772277 Fax: (01555) 750686 E-mail: sales@ramsayofcarluke.co.uk *Bacon & ham curers & merchants*

▶ Ramsay Electrical Co., 40 Ashley Terrace, Edinburgh, EH11 1RY Tel: 0131-346 7494

Ramsay Fabrications, Baden-Powell Road, Kirkton Industrial Estate, Arbroath, Angus, DD11 3LS Tel: (01241) 870314 Fax: (01241) 870314 *Fabrication & welding contractors*

Ramsay Precision Engineers Coventry Ltd, Unit 3 Burnsall Road Industrial Estate, Coventry, CV5 6BU Tel: (024) 7667 4220 Fax: (024) 7667 0721 E-mail: info@ramsay-precision.co.uk *Sub-contract precision engineers*

Ramsay & Primrose Ltd, 18 Lynedoch Street, Glasgow, G3 6EY Tel: 0141-332 4015 Fax: 0141-333 9197 E-mail: rndpltd@btconnect.com *Consulting engineers & designers*

Ramsay Rubber Ltd, Units 5 & 6, Speed Road, Barnfield Industrial Estate, Tipton, West Midlands, DY4 9DX Tel: (01384) 453160 Fax: (01384) 254955 E-mail: sales@ramson.com *Rubber & sponge products manufrs*

Ramsay Services Ltd, Unit C Bamburgh Court, Team Valley Trading Estate, Gateshead, Tyne & Wear, NE11 0TX Tel: 0191-422 4200 Fax: 0191-422 4222 *O-ring & seal manufrs*

Ramsay Soil Injection Ltd, Units 2 & 3 Moorlands Trading Estate, Moor Lane, Metheringham, Lincoln, LN4 3HX Tel: (01526) 328663 Fax: (01526) 323529 E-mail: ramsay.soil@btclick.com *Agricultural engineering services*

▶ Ramsay & Sons Forfar Ltd, 61 West High Street, Forfar, Angus, DD8 1BG Tel: (01307) 462255 Fax: (01307) 466956 *Ladder manufrs*

Ramsay Systems, Bratton House, Dogpole, Shrewsbury, SY1 1ES Tel: (01743) 232278 E-mail: charlie@ramseysystems.co.uk *Software consultants*

▶ Ramsdale Windows, Maxwell Road, Middlesbrough, Cleveland, TS3 8TE Tel: (01642) 227026 Fax: (01642) 227027 *Windows manufrs*

Ramsden Bros Huddersfield Ltd, Crosland Moor Mills, Blackmoorfoot Road, Huddersfield, HD4 5AH Tel: (01484) 421042 Fax: (01484) 559236 *Woollen & worsted manufrs*

Ramsden & Whale Ltd, Harrold Street, Tipton, West Midlands, DY4 0JF Tel: 0121-557 3656 Fax: 0121-522 3144 *Oil drum recondition services, disposers & manufrs*

Ramsell-Naber Ltd, Vigo Place, Aldridge, Walsall, WS9 8YB Tel: (01922) 455521 Fax: (01922) 455277 E-mail: info@ramsell-naber.co.uk *Leading suppliers in furnaces*

Ramsey Glass & Window Co (Chipwel), A Highlode Industrial Estate, Stocking Fen Road, Ramsey, Huntingdon, Cambridgeshire, PE26 2RB Tel: (01487) 813007 Fax: (01487) 710364 E-mail: salesramseyglass@hotmail.com *Upvc window & door fabricators*

Ramsey Steamship Co. Ltd, 8 Auckland Terrace, Parliament Street, Ramsey, Isle of Man, IM8 1AF Tel: (01624) 816202 Fax: (01624) 816206 E-mail: tony@ramsey-steamship.com *Ship owners, brokers & marine engineer*

Ramsgate Trophies, 111 King Street, Ramsgate, Kent, CT11 8PH Tel: (01843) 593872 Fax: (01843) 593872 *Trophies suppliers*

Rana Textiles Ltd, 914-918 Stratford Road, Sparkhill, Birmingham, B11 4BT Tel: 0121-777 3986 Fax: 0121-247 2255 *Casual clothing distributors*

Ranbaxy UK Ltd, 3Rd Floor CP House, 97/107 Uxbridge Road, Ealing, London, W5 5TL Tel: (020) 8280 1600 Fax: (020) 8280 1617 *Pharmaceuticals manufrs*

Ranburn Ltd, Tunnel Avenue, London, SE10 0PT Tel: (020) 8858 2293 Fax: (020) 8293 4373 *Diesel & auto electrical engineers*

Rand Equipment Europe Ltd, Unit 8 Commonwealth Close, Leigh, Lancashire, WN7 3BD Tel: (01942) 606062 Fax: (01942) 606087 *Garage equipment automotive*

Rand Markings Ltd, 39-40 Brunel Road, St. Leonards-on-Sea, East Sussex, TN38 9RT Tel: (01424) 854646 Fax: (01424) 854645 E-mail: info@randmarkings.co.uk *Nameplate & badge manufrs*

Rand Worldwide, Unit 3 Interchange 25 Business Park, Bostock Lane, Sandiacre, Nottingham, NG10 5QG Tel: 0115-921 0000 Fax: 0115-921 0001 *Supply computer software & hardware*

Randal Home Bakery, 58 Main Street, Randalstown, Antrim, BT41 3BB Tel: (028) 9447 9944 *Bakery & confectionary suppliers*

Randall & Daniels (Electrical) Ltd, Abbey Industrial Estate, Neath Abbey, Neath, West Glamorgan, SA10 7DR Tel: (01792) 813231 Fax: (01792) 321816 E-mail: sales@rd-electrical.com *Electrical & instrument contractors*

▶ Randall & Hodgkinson, The Old Stables, Queens Square, Kirkby Lonsdale, Carnforth, Lancashire, LA6 2AZ Tel: (01524) 271136 Fax: (01524) 271136 *Electrical contractors & control panel specialists*

▶ Randall Plant Ltd, 6 110 River Road, Barking, Essex, IG11 0DS Tel: (020) 8709 1870 Fax: (020) 8507 7002

Randall Ribbons, 12 Frederick Street, Luton, LU2 7QS Tel: (01582) 721301 Fax: (01582) 720060 E-mail: sales@randallribbons.com *Hat trimmings, ribbon & thread merchants*

Randall Storage Systems Ltd, 5 Beaucroft Road, Wimborne, Dorset, BH21 2QW Tel: (01202) 848059 Fax: (01202) 848059 *Storage distributors*

Randalls, 304-312 Selbourne Road, Luton, LU4 8NX Tel: (01582) 496911 Fax: (01582) 494144 E-mail: sales@randallsluton.co.uk *Safety equipment retailers*

Randalls Fabrications Ltd, Randall Fabrication, Hoyle Mill Road, Kinsley, Pontefract, West Yorkshire, WF9 5JB Tel: (01977) 615132 Fax: (01977) 610059 E-mail: sales@randallsfabrications.co.uk *Waste disposal, skip & scrap container manufrs*

Randalls (Groundworks) Ltd, Monmouth House, Northgate, Park Road, Abergavenny, Gwent, NP7 5TT Tel: (01873) 851656 Fax: (01873) 851667 *Groundwork contractors*

▶ J. Randalls of Dunstable, 38 Downs Road, Dunstable, Bedfordshire, LU5 4DD Tel: (07967) 247788 E-mail: jim.randall@btinternet.com *Unique kitchen & bathroom designers*

Randalls Profiles Ltd, Cranford Street, Smethwick, West Midlands, B66 2SB Tel: 0121-558 0144 Fax: 0121-558 7426 E-mail: gary.bailey@randals-profiles.co.uk *Profile cutting*

Randell NFM Ltd, 3 Maurice Gaymer Road, Attleborough, Norfolk, NR17 2QZ Tel: (01953) 452468 Fax: (01953) 453229 E-mail: enquiries@randallnfm.co.uk *Agricultural machinery equipment*

Randle Signs, 29 Blackdown Avenue, Chesterfield, Derbyshire, S40 4QQ Tel: (01246) 205905 Fax: (01246) 205905 *Manufacturers of signs*

▶ Randle Thomas, 2 Wendron St, Helston, Cornwall, TR13 8PP Tel: (01326) 572951 Fax: 01326 563122 E-mail: rt@randlethomas.co.uk *A modern legal practice working with a dedicated team of legal and support staff.*

Randolph Coachworks Ltd, Evenwood, Bishop Auckland, County Durham, DL14 9QU Tel: (01388) 832560 Fax: (01388) 834504 *Commercial vehicle body builders*

Randolph Hotel, Beaumont Street, Oxford, OX1 2LN Tel: (0870) 4008200 Fax: (01865) 791678 E-mail: info@macdonald-hotels.co.uk *Hotels*

Random House UK Ltd, 20 Vauxhall Bridge Road, London, SW1V 2SA Tel: (020) 7840 8400 Fax: (020) 7233 8791 *Publishers*

Randstad Ltd, Unit 37 Crow Hall Road, Nelson Park East, Cramlington, Northumberland, NE23 1WH Tel: (01670) 735575 Fax: (01670) 590739 E-mail: enquiries@ranstadltd.co.uk *Motor component distributors*

Ranelagh Co. Ltd, 8 Kent Close, Granby Industrial Estate, Weymouth, Dorset, DT4 9TF Tel: (01305) 777602 Fax: (0870) 7061481 *Precision engineers*

▶ Ranell Ltd, Unit 7a Beckingham Business Park, Tolleshunt Major, Maldon, Essex, CM9 8LZ Tel: (01621) 869048 Fax: (01621) 868978 E-mail: info@ranell.com

Ranford Doors, Unit 6 Sterling Industrial Estate, Rainham Road South, Dagenham, Essex, RM10 8TX Tel: (0800) 037 9133 Fax: (020) 8984 0378 E-mail: sales@lbsgroup.co.uk *Manufacturers & Installers of Security products including, manually & electrically operated Doors & Roller shutters, Fire shutters, Insulated & industrial Doors, Roller Grilles, PVC Curtains, Gates, Barriers, automatic doors and locks, & Steel Hinged Doorsets. ISO 9001 registered, we offer a 24hr Repair Service*

Range Storage & Material Handling Equipment Ltd, Parry Lane, Bradford, West Yorkshire, BD4 8TJ Tel: (01274) 736363 Fax: (01274) 743322 E-mail: range.storage@lineone.net *Steel pallet manufrs*

Rangemaster, Meadow Lane, Long Eaton, Nottingham, NG10 2AT Tel: 0115-946 4000 Fax: 0115-946 0374 E-mail: sales@rangemaster.co.uk *Manufacturers of kitchen sinks, hobs & cookers*

Rangemaster Leisure, Clarence Street, Leamington Spa, Warwickshire, CV31 2AD Tel: (01926) 427027 Fax: (01926) 450526 E-mail: consumers@leisurecp.co.uk *Gas appliance manufrs*

Rangemile (Air Commuter) Ltd, Coventry Airport, Coventry, CV8 3AZ Tel: (024) 7630 4452 Fax: (024) 7663 9031 E-mail: rangemile@air-commuter.co.uk *Business aircraft charter*

Ranger Caradoc Hydraulics Ltd, The Gables, Worcester Road, Great Witley, Worcester, WR6 6HR Tel: (01299) 896953 Fax: (01299) 896963 E-mail: sales@rangercaradoc.com *Manufacturers of hydraulic cylinders*

▶ Ranger Distribution, Copse Road, Fleetwood, Lancashire, FY7 7NY Tel: (01253) 878888 Fax: (01253) 878999 E-mail: enquires@rangeruk.co.uk *Bathrooms, baths, toilets, showers, whirlpools, cabinets, furniture, towel rails, radiator*

Ranger Fixings Ltd, 8 Central Business Park, Southcote Road, Bournemouth, BH1 3SJ Tel: (01202) 297125 Fax: (01202) 294087 E-mail: ranger.fixings@tiscali.co.uk *Fixings & fastener distributors*

Ranger Instrument Co. Ltd, Rutherford Road, Basingstoke, Hampshire, RG24 8PG Tel: (01256) 464911 Fax: (01256) 464366 E-mail: ranger@bayham.demon.co.uk *Oil & heat meter manufrs*

Ranger Labels, Unit 2, Reach Road Industrial Estate, Burwell, Cambridge, CB25 0GH Tel: (01638) 743506 Fax: (01638) 743507 *Printed & plain label manufrs*

Rangetek Catering Equipment, Unit 1a Crabtree Close, Gravesend Road, Wrotham, Sevenoaks, Kent, TN15 7JL Tel: (01732) 822477 Fax: (01732) 822477 E-mail: sales@rangetek.co.uk *Service & repair fish frying equipment*

▶ Ranier Technology Ltd, Greenhouse Farm, Newmarket Road, Teversham, Cambridge, CB5 8AA Tel: (01223) 505045 Fax: (01223) 505046 E-mail: ranier.technology@ranier.co.uk *Medical equipment suppliers*

The Rank Co. Ltd, Isaacs Place, Port Talbot, West Glamorgan, SA12 6NP Tel: (01639) 882540 Fax: (01639) 892483 *Catering equipment manufrs*

Rank.Com, 6 Connaught Place, London, W2 2ET Tel: (020) 7766 1111 Fax: (020) 7262 9886 E-mail: enquiries@rank.com *Holding company*

Rank Engineering, Unit 4b Barton Hill Trading Estate, Herapath Street, Bristol, BS5 9RD Tel: 0117-955 1298 Fax: 0117-955 6528 *Production & general engineers*

Rank Fabrications Ltd, Finnington Industrial Estate, Feniscowles, Blackburn, BB2 5JD Tel: 01254 202315 *Steel fabricators*

▶ Rank Hovis Ltd, Scottstoun Mill, Partick Bridge Street, Glasgow, G11 6PH Tel: (0870) 7281111 Fax: 0141-303 5550 *Cereal food products*

▶ Rank Hovis Ltd, Canklow Road, Rotherham, South Yorkshire, S60 2JG Tel: (01709) 726800 Fax: (01709) 360513

Rankin Brothers & Sons, Unit 3c Drakes Farm, Drakes Drive, Long Crendon, Aylesbury, Buckinghamshire, HP18 9BA Tel: (01844) 203100 Fax: (01844) 203101 E-mail: sales@rankincork.co.uk *Cork & closures manufrs*

Rankinco Ltd, 4 Blades Close, Leatherhead, Surrey, KT22 7JY Tel: (01372) 276390 Fax: (01372) 276390 E-mail: ian_rankin@compuserve.com *Machinery merchants*

Rankins Glass Company Ltd, 24-34 Pearson Street, London, E2 8JD Tel: (020) 7729 4200 Fax: (020) 7729 7135 E-mail: sales@rankinsglass.co.uk *Glass processors & glaziers*

Ranks Enterprises, Ranks House, Unit B4 Neptune Road, Harrow, Middlesex, HA1 4HX Tel: (020) 8863 9993 Fax: (020) 8424 8887 E-mail: sales@ranksent.com *Specialist corporate clothing manufacturing, covering shirts, t-shirts, sweatshirts, polo/rugby shirts, fleeces, skinny's, trousers, aprons, tabards, football shirts, childrenswear, and babywear. Offering Next day service . All ex-stocks. Free quotations. Competitive prices.*

Ranmor Computing Ltd, Lake Meadows Office Village, 14 Woodbrook Cresent, Billericay, Essex, CM12 0EQ Tel: (01277) 635500 Fax: (01277) 631777 E-mail: info@ranmor.com *General purpose computer resellers*

Rannoch Knitwear, 17 Avenue Street, Stewarton, Kilmarnock, Ayrshire, KA3 5AP Tel: (01560) 485454 Fax: 01560 485454 *Knitwear manufrs*

William Ransom & Son P.L.C., Alexander House, 40a Wilbury Way, Hitchin, Hertfordshire, SG4 0AP Tel: (01462) 437615 Fax: (01462) 420528 E-mail: info@williamransom.com *Pharmaceutical manufrs*

Ransome Group Services Ltd, Unit 5-6 Clopton Commercial Park, Clopton, Woodbridge, Suffolk, IP13 6QT Tel: (01473) 737731 Fax: (01473) 737398 E-mail: info@ransomeengineering.co.uk *Refrigeration, tail lift, bodywork & mobility engineers*

Ransome Sporting Goods, Wood Street, Middlesbrough, Cleveland, TS1 1JP Tel: (01642) 224444 Fax: (01642) 226000 *Sporting distributors*

▶ Rantec Automotive Europe Ltd, 58 Stoke Poges Lane, Slough, SL1 3PD Tel: (01753) 527276 E-mail: info@classic-automotive.com *Manufacturer of brake, engine, steering and suspension components and finished goods for the classic car and aftermarket industries. The company has offices in Europe and North America.*

Ranyard Signs Ltd, Brigg Road, Caistor, Market Rasen, Lincolnshire, LN7 6RX Tel: (01472) 852528 Fax: (01472) 851516 E-mail: sales@ranyard-signs.co.uk *Sign manufrs*

Rap, Clowes Street, Hollinwood, Oldham, OL9 7LY Tel: 0161-947 3700 Fax: 0161-947 3729 E-mail: enquiries@rapspiderweb.com *Colour printers*

Rapco Electronics Ltd, 10 Joule Road, Basingstoke, Hampshire, RG21 6XF Tel: (01256) 325454 Fax: (01256) 322695 E-mail: info@rapco.co.uk *Time code systems manufrs*

Raphael Creative Design, Raphael Court, Upper St. John Street, Lichfield, Staffordshire, WS14 9DX Tel: (01543) 261220 Fax: (01543) 261221 E-mail: info@raphaeldesign.co.uk *Marketing & design*

▶ Rapid Ltd, 8 Portway Road Industrial Estate, Oldbury, West Midlands, B69 2PP Tel: 0121 5440767

Rapid Climate Control Ltd, 423 Becontree Avenue, Dagenham, Essex, RM8 3UH Tel: 0121-543 6211 Fax: (020) 8590 8303 E-mail: info@rapidclimatecontrol.com *Portable air conditioning, hire & sales*

Rapid Colour Services Ltd, D 2 Moss Industrial Estate, Leigh, Lancashire, WN7 3PT Tel: (01942) 675932 Fax: (01942) 602229 E-mail: sales@rapidcolour.co.uk *Colour & additive masterbatch manufrs*

▶ Rapid Electronic Repairs, Unit 6, The progress centre, Charlton place, Ardwick green, Manchester, M12 6HS Tel: (0870) 1657296 Fax: (0870) 1657296 E-mail: steve@rapid-electronic-repairs.co.uk *Northwest based company-providing support to engineers and companies who face problems with electronic based equipment. Back to base repairs and on-site services covering electronics problems with minimal manufacturers information or support. Also supporting service companies who maybe working with equipment that incorporates electronics and are looking for outside assistance to augment their own services or teams.*

Rapid Engraving Horley Ltd, Bayhorne Lane, Balcombe Road, Horley, Surrey, RH6 9ES Tel: (01293) 820688 Fax: (01293) 820655 E-mail: rapidengraving@hotmail.com *Screen printers & engravers*

Rapid Envelopes, Potters Bar, Herts, EN6 4SP Tel: (01707) 878783 *Envelopes/Printers*

Rapid Fabrications Ltd, Unit 1 Belgrave Mill, Fitton Hill Road, Oldham, OL8 2LZ Tel: 0161-628 6776 Fax: 0161-628 6776 E-mail: rapfab@btconnect.com *Steel fabricators*

Rapid Grinding Services Ltd, 3 Bilston Key Industrial Estate, Oxford Street, Bilston, West Midlands, WV14 7DW Tel: (01902) 354040 Fax: (01902) 354055 *Cutting tool specialists*

▶ Rapid Group, Unit 18 Avon Trading Park, Reid Street, Christchurch, Dorset, BH23 2BT Tel: (01202) 703040 Fax: (01202) 470212 E-mail: sales@rapidgroup.net *Computer maintenance & repair services*

▶ Rapid ICT, PO BOX 460, Harrogate, North Yorkshire, HG2 0WP Tel: (07092) 160826 *RAPID ICT Web Site Design.*

Rapid Industrial Fasteners Ltd, 9 Gun Barrel Industrial Centre, Hayseech, Cradley Heath, West Midlands, B64 7JZ Tel: 0121-501 3903 Fax: 0121-585 5163 E-mail: sales@rapidfast.co.uk *Bolt, nut & fastener distributors*

Rapid International Ltd, 96 Mullavilly Road, Tandragee, Craigavon, County Armagh, BT62 2LX Tel: (028) 3884 0671 Fax: (028) 3884 0880 E-mail: info@rapidinternational.com *Concrete batching plant manufrs*

▶ Rapid Metal Developments Ltd, 4-7 Marsh Road, Wembley, Middlesex, HA0 1ES Tel: (020) 8998 1727

Rapid Packaging Supplies Ltd, 26 Bayton Road, Exhall, Coventry, CV7 9EJ Tel: (024) 7636 0800 Fax: (024) 7664 4322 E-mail: sales@rapidpackaging.co.uk Sales Contact: J. Williams *One of the UK's leading distributors of Wooden pallets, reconditioned pallets, pallets to specification, wooden crates, corrugated cases, cardboard boxes, cases or containers, wooden stillages, wooden boxes, pallet maintenance or repair, contact us now for a fast friendly service*

Rapid Print, 3 Portland Close, Townsend Industrial Estate, Houghton Regis, Dunstable, Bedfordshire, LU5 5AW Tel: (01582) 609108 Fax: (01582) 696137 *Lithographic printers*

Rapid Prototyping Systems Ltd, Bowden Hall, Bowden Lane, Marple, Stockport, Cheshire, SK6 6ND Tel: 0161-426 0465 Fax: 0161-426 0467 E-mail: sales@rpsys.co.uk *Software house*

Rapid Radio Communications, Unit 5 The Acorn Centre, Roebuck Road, Hainault, Ilford, Essex, IG6 3TU Tel: (020) 8500 9999 Fax: (020) 8500 8124 E-mail: mail@rapidradio.com *Radio communications equipment suppliers*

Rapid Co. Services Ltd, 209A Station Lane, Hornchurch, Essex, RM12 6LL Tel: (01708) 478690 Fax: (01708) 478680 *Company registration agents*

Rapid Tool Rec Ltd, Unit 2 Armoury Road Trading, Estate Armoury Road, Small Heath, Birmingham, B11 2RG Tel: 0121-771 1555 Fax: 0121-706 2479 E-mail: sales@rapidtool-rec.co.uk *Engineer tools manufrs*

▶ Rapid Weldings & Industrial Supplies Ltd, Unit 1 C, Hamilton Road, Portchester Park, Portsmouth, PO6 4QE Tel: (023) 9221 4214 Fax: (023) 9220 1505 E-mail: sales@rapidwelding.co.uk *Welding product suppliers, services & hire*

▶ Rapide Reprographics, St. James House, Pendleton Way, Salford, M6 5FW Tel: 0161-743 0302 Fax: 0161-743 0305 E-mail: sales@rapide-repro.co.uk *Data archiving, data &media storage*

Rapide Security Surveillance Ltd, 878-880 Alum Rock Road, Birmingham, B8 2TY Tel: 0121-327 3939 Fax: 0121-327 1088 *CCTV & intruder alarm installation services*

Rapide Tankers, The Airfield, Full Sutton, York, YO41 1HS Tel: (01759) 372224 Fax: (01759) 372231 *Fabrication welders*

Rapideze Ltd, 2 Barnsdale, Great Easton, Market Harborough, Leicestershire, LE16 8SG Tel: (01536) 770282 Fax: (01327) 830725 *Industrial chemical manufrs*

▶ Rapidflame Ltd, Brian Royd Mills, Saddleworth Road, Greetland, Halifax, West Yorkshire, HX4 8NF Tel: (01422) 311232 Fax: (01422) 311248 E-mail: sales@rapidflame.com *Gas burners & flame treatment systems manufacturers*

Rapidgrid Ltd, Progress Industrial Estate, Station Road, Rogiet, Caldicot, Gwent, NP26 3UE Tel: (01291) 424576 Fax: (01291) 424320 *Groundwork contractors*

▶ Rapidline Ltd, Unit 1, 1000 North Circular Road, London, NW2 7JP Tel: 0808 101 6 101 Fax: 020 8830 8379E-mail: info@doorsteptotheworld.com *Sameday, Overnight and International Couriers. Express and Economy speed for all your delivery needs. No account required.*

Rapidocolor UK Ltd, Unit 15 Waverley Industrial Estate, Hailsham Drive, Harrow, Middlesex, HA1 4TR Tel: (020) 8863 6404 Fax: (020) 8863 1434 E-mail: sales@rapidocolor.co.uk *Full colour & paper plastic printers*

Rapidos Ltd, Unit 11 Steyning Way, Hounslow, TW4 6DL Tel: (020) 8570 9393 Fax: (020) 8577 3450 E-mail: printroom@repropoint.com *Drawing office supplies & reprographics*

Rapidpaint Birmingham Ltd, 197-199 Bradford Street, Birmingham, B12 0JD Tel: 0121-693 4020 Fax: 0121-693 5665 *Paint, varnishes & lacquers distributors*

Rapidvan Distribution, 15 Murrayfield Terrace, Bannockburn, Stirling, FK7 8NG Tel: (07795) 621490 *Contract Distribution services carried out in Stirling and Edinburgh.Express shuttle service daily a.m. from Edinburgh to all of Central Scotland.*Express Courier services covering Scotlands Central Belt*

Rapier Precision Sheet Metal Ltd, 1 Princes Works, Princes Road, Teddington, Middlesex, TW11 0RW Tel: (020) 8943 4788 Fax: (020) 8977 1686 E-mail: info@rapierprecision.co.uk *Sheet metalwork engineers*

Rapier Public Relations, 33 Brookfield Road, Churchdown, Gloucester, GL3 2PG Tel: (01452) 536810 Fax: (01452) 536810 E-mail: ray@rapier-pr.co.uk *Public relations & marketing consultancy*

Rapiergroup, Rapier House, Crane Mead, Ware, Hertfordshire, SG12 9PW Tel: (0870) 9007782 Fax: (0870) 9007783 E-mail: info@rapiergroup.com *Business, project & conference management*

Rapierstar, Star Business Park, Buxton Road, Bosley, Macclesfield, Cheshire, SK11 0PS Tel: 0870 300 3313 Fax: 0870 300 3314 E-mail: sih@rapierstar.com *Screws & fixing suppliers*

Rapitypes Ltd, Rockey Studios, Abbey Meadows, Leicester, LE4 5DF Tel: 0116-253 6591 Fax: 0116-253 9827 E-mail: info@rapitypes.com *Rapid prototyping engineers*

Rapp Ecosse UK Ltd, Station Brae, Ellon, Aberdeenshire, AB41 9DY Tel: (01358) 720717 Fax: (01358) 720173 E-mail: info@rappecosse.co.uk *Hydraulic engineers*

Rappa Fencing Ltd, Steepleton Hill, Stockbridge, Hampshire, SO20 6JE Tel: (01264) 810665 Fax: (01264) 810079 E-mail: sales@rappa.co.uk *Electric fencing manufrs*

Rappell Switchgear Ltd, Moston Road, Sandbach, Cheshire, CW11 3HL Tel: (01270) 761135 Fax: (01270) 762997 E-mail: sales@rappell.co.uk *Low voltage electrical switchgear manufrs*

M.A. Rapport & Co. Ltd, Ivor House, Bridge Street, Cardiff, CF10 2TH Tel: (029) 2037 3737 Fax: (029) 2022 0121 E-mail: info@rapportlondon.com *Clock importers & manufrs*

Rapport Presentations, The Wheel House, Raypark Road, Maidenhead, Berkshire, SL6 8QU Tel: (01628) 770474 *Conference production*

Rapport Software Ltd, 33 Clerkenwell Cl, London, EC1R 0AU Tel: (020) 7713 9233 Fax: (020) 7490 5785 *Computer software consultancy*

Rapra Technology, Shawbury, Shrewsbury, SY4 4NR Tel: (01939) 250383 Fax: (01939) 251118 E-mail: info@rapra.net Principal Export Areas: Middle East, Africa, Central/East Europe, West Europe, North America & South America *Plastic & rubber consultants*

▶ Rapunzel's Hair Shop Ltd, 429 Smithdown Road, Wavertree, Liverpool, L15 3JJ Tel: 0151-733 4333 Fax: 0151-733 4303 *supplier of human and synthetic hair and related products. supply to trade and public.*

Rare It Ltd, Unit 35 Meridian House, Road One, Winsford Industrial Estate, Winsford, Cheshire, CW7 3QG Tel: (01606) 860607 Fax: (01606) 860608 E-mail: info@rareit.com *Software & IT trainers*

Rasburn Fence Suppliers, 699 Crankwood Road, Leigh, Lancashire, WN7 4PP Tel: (01942) 605604 Fax: (01942) 861188 *Fencing manufrs*

Rascahan Engineering Ltd, 51 Ballykelly Road, Limavady, County Londonderry, BT49 9DS Tel: (028) 7772 2618 Fax: (028) 7772 2197 *Precision engineers*

Rascal Confectionery Ltd, Samal House, Loxford Road, Barking, Essex, IG11 8PU Tel: (020) 8594 1122 Fax: (020) 8594 3645 E-mail: sales@rascal-chocolate.com *Confectionery manufrs*

Raschig UK Ltd, Trafford Road, Salford, M5 4QD Tel: 0161-877 3933 Fax: 0161-877 3944 E-mail: raschig.uk_ltd@virgin.net *Plastics raw materials manufrs*

▶ Rase Steels, Gallamore La Industrial Estate, Gallamore Lane, Market Rasen, Lincolnshire, LN8 3HA Tel: (01673) 843973 Fax: (01673) 844117 E-mail: mail@rasesteels.co.uk *Cladding materials suppliers*

▶ Rashbel Marketing Ltd, 24-28 Hatton Wall, London, EC1N 8JH Tel: (020) 7831 5646 Fax: (020) 7831 5647 E-mail: order@rashbel.com *Jewellery services*

▶ Arshad Rashid, 145 West Street, Banbury, Oxfordshire, OX16 3HE Tel: (0871) 2006250 Fax: (0871) 2006251 E-mail: enquiries@yourhomefurniture.co.uk *UK's leading stockists of household furniture*

▶ Rasmi Electronics Ltd, Unit 14a Tanfield Industrial Estate, Tanfield Lea, Stanley, County Durham, DH9 9UU Tel: (01207) 232159 Fax: (01207) 231934 E-mail: sales@rasmi.com *Manufacture lighting & filters*

Rafmi Electronics, Morrison Road, Stanley, County Durham, DH9 7RX Tel: (01207) 291300 Fax: (01207) 291304 E-mail: accounts@rasmi.com *Transformer manufrs*

Mark Rastin IT Help, Support & Training, Croft House, Cymdda, Bridgend, Mid Glamorgan, CF32 9SL Tel: (01656) 729971 E-mail: mark@rastin.net *CRM professional training it & sage act*

Rastrick Engineering Ltd, 7 Martin Street, Brighouse, West Yorkshire, HD6 1DA Tel: (01484) 715748 Fax: (01484) 720639 *Hospital equipment manufrs*

Ratae Engineers Ltd, Green Lane Works, George Street, Manchester, M30 0RG Tel: 0116-253 1721 Fax: 0161-787 7508 E-mail: sales@rataeengineers.com *Hexagon nut manufrs*

Ratan Sports Ltd, 23 Claremont Road, Wolverhampton, WV3 0EA Tel: (01902) 339833 Fax: (01902) 339833 *Sports goods distributors*

Ratatak Pest & Vermin Control, Osbourne House, 5 Massingham Road, Grimston, King's Lynn, Norfolk, PE32 1BD Tel: (01485) 600368 *Rat control*

D.A. Ratchford, 6 Chester Hall Lane, Basildon, Essex, SS14 3BG Tel: (01245) 322720 Fax: (01268) 534828 *Brazing/soldering special purpose machinery*

Ratcliff Care Ltd, Unit 19, Saddleback Road, Westgate Industrial Estate, Northampton, NN5 5HL Tel: (01604) 591359 *Commercial vehicle modifications* Also at: Bristol, London, Manchester, Stoke-on-Trent & Enfield (H.O.)

▶ Ratcliff & Roper Ltd, Kilton Road, Worksop, Nottinghamshire, S80 2EE Tel: (01909) 500444 Fax: (01909) 500614 E-mail: sales@ratcliffandroper.co.uk

Ratcliff Tail Lifts Ltd, Bessemer Road, Welwyn Garden City, Hertfordshire, AL7 1ET Tel: (01707) 325571 Fax: (01707) 327752 E-mail: info@ratcliffpalfinger.co.uk *Mechanical handling equipment* Also at: Leeds

P. & R. Ratcliffe Ltd, Stanley Mill, Shackleton Street, Burnley, Lancashire, BB10 3BH Tel: (01282) 421026 Fax: (01282) 412321 E-mail: underlays@tiscaly.co.uk *Carpet felt manufrs*

Ratcliffe Service Tools, Wilmore Lane, Byrkley, Rangemore, Burton-on-Trent, Staffordshire, DE13 9RD Tel: (01283) 711400 Fax: (01283) 711900 *Specialised tool manufrs*

Ratcliffe & Son, Westport Iron Works, Foundry Road, Malmesbury, Wiltshire, SN16 0AW Tel: (01666) 823222 Fax: (01666) 823222 *Agricultural & horticultural engineers*

Rathbone Brothers plc, 159 New Bond Street, London, W1S 2UD Tel: (020) 7399 0000 Fax: (020) 7399 0011 E-mail: marketing@rathbones.com *Banking & investment*

Rathbone Neilson Cobbold Ltd, Port of Liverpool Building, Pier Head, Liverpool, L3 1NW Tel: 0151-236 9224 Fax: 0151-243 7001 E-mail: marketing@rathbones.com *Broke dealers*

▶ Rathbone Printflo Ltd, Caroline Street, Stoke-on-Trent, ST3 1DB Tel: (01782) 320022 Fax: (01782) 594056 E-mail: sales@tslimited.com *Ceramic transfer manufrs*

Rathbones, Durranhill Trading Estate, Brunel Way, Carlisle, CA1 3NH Tel: (01228) 527541 Fax: (01228) 515195 E-mail: bakery@robertsonsltd.freeserve.co.uk *Bakers wholesale manufacturing*

Rather Brothers, 26 Knowsley St, Manchester, M8 8HQ Tel: 0161-832 7361 Fax: 0161 8327361 *Household goods manufrs*

The Rather Nice Co. Ltd, Quill House, 91 High Street, Markyate, St. Albans, Hertfordshire, AL3 8JG Tel: (01582) 842107 Fax: (01582) 842113 *Stationary manufrs*

Rathfriland Farmers Co-Operative Society Ltd, Bog Road, Rathfriland, Newry, County Down, BT34 5DT Tel: (028) 4063 8493 Fax: (028) 4063 1539 *Agricultural merchants*

▶ Rating Room Ltd, 5 Swanston Village, Edinburgh, EH10 7DT Tel: 0131-313 1884 *Online marketing specialists offering SearchEngine Optimisation, Pay Per Click advertising and conversion improvement.*

Rationel Windows (U K) Ltd, 7 Avonbury Business Park, Howes Lane, Bicester, Oxfordshire, OX26 2UA Tel: (01869) 248181 Fax: (01869) 249693 E-mail: sales@rationel.com *Window frames manufrs*

Ratpak Engineering Ltd, Moor Lane, Thorpe-on-the-Hill, Lincoln, LN6 9BW Tel: (01522) 686070 Fax: (01522) 691112 E-mail: sales@ratpak.co.uk *Pest control equipment*

Ratsey & Lapthorn Ltd, 37 Medina Road, Cowes, Isle of Wight, PO31 7BX Tel: (01983) 294051 Fax: (01983) 294053 E-mail: ratseysails@ratsey.com *Sail manufrs*

Raught Ltd, 117 The Drive, Ilford, Essex, IG1 3JE Tel: (020) 8554 9921 Fax: (020) 8554 8337 E-mail: raughtltd@aol.com *Pharmaceutical chemicals suppliers & manufrs*

Raupack Ltd, 131 High Street, Old Woking, Woking, Surrey, GU22 9LD Tel: (01483) 736800 Fax: (01483) 736810 *Packaging equipment merchants*

Rautomead Ltd, Nobel Road, West Gourdie Industrial Estate, Dundee, DD2 4UH Tel: (01382) 622341 Fax: (01382) 622941 E-mail: sales@rautomead.com *Continuous casting machine manufrs*

Raven Electronic Services Ltd, Unit 13, Little End Road, Eaton Socon, St. Neots, Cambridgeshire, PE19 8JH Tel: (01480) 407744 Fax: (01480) 470382 E-mail: dave@ravenelectronics.co.uk *Electronic assemblies to specification*

Company Information

Raven Engineering Developments, Raven Engineering Developments, 291 Watling Street, DARTFORD, DA2 6EP Tel: (01322) 421290 Fax: 0870 8900064 *Hire & sales of air conditioning & dust extraction*

Raven Equipment Ltd, 4 Ford Farm Industrial Unit, Braintree Road, Dunmow, Essex, CM6 1HU Tel: (01371) 875576 Fax: (01371) 876760 *Measuring instrument manufrs*

Raven Insulation Supply Co., 39 Church Street, Weybridge, Surrey, KT13 8DG Tel: (01932) 856731 Fax: (01932) 855685 *Industrial insulation distributors*

Raven Manufacturing Ltd, Metcalf Drive, Altham Industrial Estate, Accrington, Lancashire, BB5 5TU Tel: (01282) 770000 Fax: (01282) 770022 E-mail: sales@raven.co.uk Principal Export Areas: Africa & North America *Pressings, including automotive industry, general & electronic components*

▶ Raven Supplies Ltd, A Great Bank Road, Westhoughton, Bolton, BL5 3XU Tel: (01942) 850500 Fax: (01942) 850511

Raven Systems, Gear House, Saltmeadows Road, Gateshead, Tyne & Wear, NE8 3AH Tel: 0191-478 6262 Fax: 0191-478 6363 E-mail: info@raven-systems.co.uk *Computer services*

▶ Raven Web, 14 Endsleigh Close, South Croydon, Surrey, CR2 8RT Tel: (020) 8651 2322 E-mail: johnjanowskibsc@hotmail.com *Offering high quality web design at an affordable price*

Ravencourt Ltd, Drift Road, Stamford, Lincolnshire, PE9 1UZ Tel: (01780) 489100 Fax: (01780) 489099 E-mail: sales@ravencourt.com *Science suppliers equipment for education*

Ravendell Foods, Blowick Business Park, Crowland Street, Southport, Merseyside, PR9 7SJ Tel: (01704) 539181 Fax: (01704) 539247 E-mail: sales@ravendellfoods.co.uk *Sauce & rib manufrs*

Ravenfield Designs Ltd, Russell Street, Heywood, Lancashire, OL10 1NX Tel: (01706) 369307 Fax: (01706) 360472 E-mail: post@ravenfield.com *Viscometer & rheometer manufrs*

Ravenheat Manufacturing Ltd, Chartists Way, Morley, Leeds, LS27 9ET Tel: 0113-252 7007 Fax: 0113-238 0229 *Domestic boiler manufrs*

Ravenhill Farm Services, Beech Business Park, Tillington Road, Hereford, HR4 9QJ Tel: (01432) 352333 Fax: (01432) 278042 E-mail: hereford.sales@ravenhill.co.uk *Agricultural engineers*

Ravensbourn Plastics, Unit 6 7 Studio Two Waterside Court, Third Avenue, Burton-on-Trent, Staffordshire, DE14 2WQ Tel: (01283) 500525 Fax: (01283) 500535 E-mail: sales@ravensbourn.co.uk *Plastic injection mouldings manufrs*

Ravensbourne Heating, Unit 4, 102 Tindal St, Moseley, Birmingham, B12 9QL Tel: 0121 4499633 Fax: 0121 4499633 *Central heating designers & suppliers*

Ravensby Glass Co. Ltd, Fowler Road, West Pitkerro Industrial Estate, Broughtyferry, Dundee, DD5 3RU Tel: (01382) 480842 Fax: (01382) 480323 *Glass merchants & sealed unit manufrs*

Ravenscroft Cameras, 61 Grimsby Road, Cleethorpes, South Humberside, DN35 7AF Tel: (01472) 342007 Fax: (01472) 250504 E-mail: ravenscroftcameras@btinternet.com *Camera specialists*

▶ Ravenstock MSG Ltd, Chittening Industrial Estate, Chittening, Bristol, BS11 0YB Tel: 0117-938 0110 Fax: 0117-938 0220 E-mail: webenquiries@ravenstockmsg.com *Portable cabins, storage containers, modular buildings, hire & sale*

▶ Ravenstock MSG Ltd, Barras Lane, Dalston, Carlisle, CA5 7ND Tel: (01228) 711911 Fax: (01228) 711737 E-mail: webenquiries@ravenstockmsg.com *Portable cabins, storage containers, modular buildings, hire & sale*

▶ Ravenstock MSG Ltd, 3 Hornock Road, Coatbridge, Lanarkshire, ML5 2QA Tel: (01236) 449060 Fax: (01236) 710593 E-mail: info@mobilestorage.com *Portable cabins, storage containers, modular buildings, hire & sale*

▶ Ravenstock MSG Ltd, Albion Parade, Gravesend, Kent, DA12 2RN Tel: (01474) 534665 Fax: (01474) 534668 E-mail: webenquiries@ravenstockmsg.com *Portable cabins, storage containers, modular buildings, hire & sale*

Ravenstock MSG Ltd, Philadelphia Complex, Philadelphia, Houghton le Spring, Tyne & Wear, DH4 4TG Tel: 0191-584 1992 Fax: 0191-584 9191 E-mail: webenquiries@ravenstockmsg.com *Portable cabins, storage containers, modular buildings hire & sale*

▶ Ravenstock MSG Ltd, Herald Avenue, Truimph Trading Park, Speke Hall Road, Liverpool, L24 9GG Tel: 0151-448 1338 Fax: 0151-448 1929 E-mail: webenquiries@ravenstockmsg.com *Portable cabins, storage containers, modular buildings, hire & sale*

Ravette Publishing Ltd, Star Road, Partridge Green, Horsham, West Sussex, RH13 8RA Tel: (01403) 711443 Fax: (01403) 711554 E-mail: ravettepub@aol.com *Book publishers*

Raw Chemical Distribution, Morton Peto Road, Harfreys Industrial Estate, Great Yarmouth, Norfolk, NR31 0LT Tel: (01493) 443223 Fax: (01493) 443177 E-mail: sales@rawchem.co.uk *Chemical suppliers*

G.K. Raw & Co. Ltd, Claro Way, Claro Road, Harrogate, North Yorkshire, HG1 4DE Tel: (01423) 501241 Fax: (01423) 530865 *Building & joinery contractors*

R.D. Rawcliffe Ltd, Highfield House, Royds Lane, Leeds, LS12 6DU Tel: 0113-263 1535 Fax: 0113-289 0955 *Fitted furniture retail services*

▶ Rawdata IT, 101-103 Corbiehall, Bo'ness, West Lothian, EH51 0AU Tel: (01506) 517037 Fax: (01506) 517038

▶ Rawhide Ltd, Carnaby Industrial Estate, Lancaster Road, Carnaby, Bridlington, North Humberside, YO15 3QY Tel: (01262) 400278 Fax: (01262) 401960 E-mail: enquiries@rawhidesaccesories.com *Distributor & wholesaler of fashion accessories*

▶ Rawhide Corsets, Unit 209 The Custard Factory, Gibb Street, Birmingham, B9 4AA Tel: 0121-608 1220 E-mail: sales@rawhidecorsets.co.uk *Specialist ladies corsets suppliers*

Rawle Gammon & Baker Holdings Ltd, Gammon House, Riverside Road, Pottington Business Park, Barnstaple, Devon, EX31 1LX Tel: (01271) 375501 Fax: (01271) 329982 E-mail: barnstable@rgbltd.co.uk *Builders & plumbers merchants* Also at: Bideford & Exeter

John Rawle Automotives, Unit 4, The Millwalk, Birmingham, B31 4HX Tel: 0121-478 2064 Fax: 0121-478 2064 *Gear boxes*

Rawley Event Toilets, Harvey Road, Basildon, Essex, SS13 1RP Tel: (01268) 722311 Fax: (01268) 722313 E-mail: enq@rawley.co.uk *Event toilets hire, single, hot wash, disabled, baby-change & luxury*

Rawley Hirespace, Burnt Mills Industrial Estate, Harvey Road, Basildon, Essex, SS13 1RP Tel: (01268) 722300 Fax: (01268) 722313 E-mail: enq@rawley.co.uk *Portable toilet & site accommodation hire for construction sites*

Rawlings & Son (Bristol) Ltd, Cecil Road, Kingswood, Bristol, BS15 8NA Tel: 0117-960 4141 Fax: 0117-960 3989 E-mail: enq@rawlings-bristol.co.uk *Bottle merchants*

Rawlplug Ltd, Skibo Drive, Thornliebank Industrial Estate, Thornliebank, Glasgow, G46 8JR Tel: 0141-638 7961 Fax: 0141-273 2333 E-mail: info@rawlplug.co.uk Principal Export Areas: Worldwide *Structural & construction fixing manufrs*

Rawmec Eec, Rawmec Industrial Park, Plumpton Road, Hoddesdon, Hertfordshire, EN11 0EE Tel: (01992) 471796 Fax: (01992) 471797 E-mail: rawmec@btconnect.com *Plastics & rubber machinery distribs*

Raworth Moss & Cook, 36 Sydenham Road, Croydon, CR0 2EF Tel: (020) 8688 8318 Fax: (020) 8760 0055 E-mail: rmc@raworth.co.uk *Patent & trade marks attorneys - patents, designs & trade marks throughout the world**

Rawral Engineering, The Roost, Three Gates Rd, Fawkham, Longfield, Kent, DA3 8NZ Tel: 01474 704238 Fax: 01474 704238 *Agricultural tool manufrs*

Rawson Automation Ltd, 42 Muskham Street, Nottingham, NG2 2HB Tel: 0115-986 2077 Fax: 0115-986 2077 *Automated equipment builders*

Rawson Carpets Ltd, Castlebank Mills, Portobello Road, Wakefield, West Yorkshire, WF1 5PS Tel: (01924) 382860 Fax: (01924) 290334 E-mail: sales@rawsoncarpets.co.uk *Fibre bonded carpet manufrs*

▶ Raxel Storage Systems Ltd, Southern Barn Farm, The Heath, Leadenham, Lincoln, LN5 0QG Tel: (01400) 275000 Fax: (01400) 275110 E-mail: sales@raxel.co.uk

A.F.G. Ray & Sons, The Old Coal Yard, Worcester Road, Kidderminster, Worcestershire, DY11 1HN Tel: (01562) 755585 Fax: (01562) 825218 *Builders & plumbers merchants* Also at: Stourport-on-Severn

Ray Bros, 9-13 Pleasant Hill Street, Liverpool, L8 5SY Tel: 0151-709 2271 Fax: 0151-709 7763 *Cleaning & hygiene supplies*

▶ Ray Cotton Interiors Ltd, Unit 4 620 Bristol Road South, Northfield, Birmingham, B31 2JR Tel: 0121-478 1488 Fax: 0121-475 3344

Ray & Company Hairdressers Sundries Men Ltd, Green Street, Darlington, County Durham, DL1 1HL Tel: (01325) 288840 Fax: (01325) 284620 *Hairdressing wholesale suppliers* Also at: Gateshead & Middlesbrough

J.W. Ray & Co. Liverpool Ltd, Unit 87 North Mersey Business Centre, Woodward Road, Knowsley Industrial Park, Liverpool, L33 7UY Tel: 0151-546 2534 Fax: 0151-549 1645 *Marine & industrial instrument suppliers*

Ray Larrington Hydraulics Brothertoft Ltd, North Forty Foot Bank, Brothertoft, Boston, Lincolnshire, PE20 3SU Tel: (01205) 280304 Fax: (01205) 280230 *Hydraulic equipment repairs*

Ray Lowe Ltd, Rohais Road, St. Peter Port, Guernsey, GY1 1YP Tel: (01481) 722618 Fax: (01481) 711903 *Decorators merchant*

Ray Oil Tool Co. Ltd, Unit 48 Howe Moss Avenue, Dyce, Aberdeen, AB21 0GP Tel: (01224) 773313 Fax: (01224) 773304 E-mail: sales@rayoiltool.co.uk *Cementing products & solid casing centralisers*

Ray Pillinger, Aldred Close, Norwood Industrial Estate, Killamarsh, Sheffield, S21 2JH Tel: 0114-248 3739 Fax: 0114-248 8081 *Stainless steel buyers & processors*

Ray Ran Test Equipment Ltd, Kelsey Close, Attleborough Fields Ind Estate, Nuneaton, Warwickshire, CV11 6RS Tel: (024) 7634 2002 Fax: (024) 7664 1670 E-mail: polytest@ray-ran.com *Plastic testing equipment suppliers & manufrs*

Ray Smith Group plc, Fengate, Peterborough, PE1 5XG Tel: (01733) 563936 Fax: (01733) 377090 *Tail lifts & demountable systems manufrs*

Ray Ward Gunsmith (London) Ltd, 12 Cadogan Place, Knightsbridge, London, SW1X 9PU Tel: (020) 7235 2550 Fax: (020) 7259 6359 E-mail: john@raywardgunsmith.co.uk *Gunsmiths*

Ray Weld, Dayton Drive, Darent Industrial Park, Erith, Kent, DA8 2LE Tel: (01322) 334499 *Specialist welders & engineers*

Ray Wilson & Co., The Myrtles, Pious Drove, Upwell, Wisbech, Cambridgeshire, PE14 9AN Tel: (01945) 772352 Fax: (01945) 772375 *Agricultural merchants*

Raybestos G B F Ltd, Unit 1 Preserve Works, Jubilee Way, Thackley Old Rd, Shipley, W. Yorkshire, BD18 1QB Tel: (01274) 597332 Fax: (01274) 597357 E-mail: info@raybestosgbf.freeserve.co.uk *Friction materials & clutches*

▶ Raybloc Ltd, 32 Bilston Lane, Willenhall, West Midlands, WV13 2QD Tel: (01902) 633383 Fax: (01902) 609453 E-mail: raybloc@btconnect.com *Manufacturers & installers of x-ray protective product*

▶ Raybrook Sheet Metal Works Ltd, 9 Towerfield Close, Shoeburyness, Southend-on-Sea, SS3 9QP Tel: (01702) 293208 Fax: (01702) 297628 E-mail: info@raybrook.com *General metal fabrications services*

Rayburn Plastics Ltd, Whitehouse Street, Walsall, WS2 8HR Tel: (01922) 625572 Fax: (01922) 723333 E-mail: sales@rayburn.co.uk *Plastics machinists & fabricators*

Rayburn Sound Services, 138 Gooch Street, Birmingham, B5 7HF Tel: 0121-622 6066 Fax: 0121-622 6065 E-mail: sales@4dj.co.uk *Sound equipment distributors*

Raycell Ltd, Unit 2 Sherwood Works, Brighton Road, Handcross, Haywards Heath, West Sussex, RH17 6BZ Tel: (01444) 400999 Fax: (01444) 400883 E-mail: raycell@mistral.co.uk *Gold, chrome & silver electroplating*

Rayco, 199 King Street, Hoyland, Barnsley, South Yorkshire, S74 9LJ Tel: (01226) 744594 Fax: (01226) 744594 E-mail: info@rayco-chemicals.co.uk *Photographic chemical products*

Wylie Systems, Drury Lane, St. Leonards-on-Sea, East Sussex, TN38 9XS Tel: (01424) 421235 Fax: (01424) 433760 E-mail: wylie@raycowylie.com *Safe load indicator manufrs*

Raydon Associates Ltd, Hadleigh Farm, Raydon, Ipswich, IP7 5PZ Tel: (01473) 652679 Fax: (01473) 652679 E-mail: hfhraydon@btinternet.com

Raydon Sheet Metal Co. Ltd, Birch Walk, Fraser Road, Erith, Kent, DA8 1QX Tel: (01322) 431535 Fax: (01322) 433637 *Stainless steel sheet metalwork*

Rayflex Ltd, Unit 6-9, 35 River Road, Barking, Essex, IG11 0DA Tel: (020) 8591 9418 Fax: (020) 8591 9419 E-mail: info@rayflexltd.co.uk *Manufacturers of shoulder pads*

Rayflex Rubber Ltd, 11b Palatine Industrial Estate, Causeway Avenue, Warrington, WA4 6QQ Tel: (01925) 638753 Fax: (01925) 416621 E-mail: sales@rayflexrubber.co.uk *Rubber mouldings manufrs*

Rayhome Manufacturers, Walshaw Road, Bury, Lancashire, BL8 1PY Tel: 0161-761 1132 Fax: 0161-764 6015 E-mail: sales@rayshim.co.uk *Stainless steel shim manufrs*

Rayitson Communications, 17 Balfour Business Centre, Balfour Road, Southall, Middlesex, UB2 5BD Tel: (020) 8574 4340 Fax: (020) 8574 4289 *Security alarm installers*

▶ Rayleigh Coldstore Ltd, Stadium Trading Estate, Stadium Way, Benfleet, Essex, SS7 3NZ Tel: (01268) 741131 Fax: (01268) 745030 E-mail: admin@rayleighcoldstore.co.uk

Rayleigh Engineering Ltd, 19 Nobel Square, Burnt Mills Industrial Estate, Basildon, Essex, SS13 1LP Tel: (01268) 728380 Fax: (01268) 728205 E-mail: rayleigh.engineer@btconnect.com *Engineering designers*

Rayleigh Galvanizers Ltd, 6 Rawreth Industrial Estate, Rawreth Lane, Rayleigh, Essex, SS6 9RL Tel: (01268) 784456 Fax: (01268) 784456 *Hot dip galvanizing*

▶ Rayleigh Instruments Ltd, Raytel House, 19 Brook Road, Rayleigh, Essex, SS6 7XH Tel: (01268) 749300 Fax: (01268) 749309 E-mail: sales@rayleigh.co.uk *Sales & manufacture of a wide range of electrical instrumentation, measuring relays, safety relays & associated products*

Rayleigh Steel, Unit 7 Westfield Close Rawreth Industrial Estate, Rawreth Lane, Rayleigh, Essex, SS6 9RL Tel: (01268) 783600 Fax: (01268) 783620 *Steel stockholders*

Raymac Signs Ltd, Prospect Works, Showfield Lane, Malton, North Yorkshire, YO17 6BT Tel: (01653) 600015 Fax: (01653) 691600 E-mail: sales@raymac.co.uk *Sign & lighting manufrs*

Raymarine Ltd, Quaypoint, North Harper Road, Portsmouth, PO6 3TD Tel: (023) 9269 3611 Fax: (023) 9269 4642 E-mail: info@raymarine.com *Marine electronics manufrs*

C. Rayment (Precision Engineering) Ltd, Addison Road, Chilton Industrial Estate, Sudbury, Suffolk, CO10 2YW Tel: (01787) 372697 Fax: (01787) 881448 E-mail: sales@c-rayment.demon.co.uk *CNC engineering services*

Rayment Holland, 1-3 Wealdstone Road, Sutton, Surrey, SM3 9QN Tel: (020) 8641 7272 Fax: (020) 8644 4779 E-mail: mail@frewerbrothers.co.uk *Specialist printers to the trade*

▶ Rayment & Hull, Bedlam Court Lane, Minster, Ramsgate, Kent, CT12 4HQ Tel: (01843) 822619 Fax: (01843) 821635 E-mail: r.h2004@btinternet.com *Design and manufacture of bespoke Silvewrware and Jewellery. Platinum and Diamond specialist.*

▶ Raymond Brown Building Ltd, 160 Christchurch Road, Ringwood, Hampshire, BH24 3AR Tel: (01425) 472241 Fax: (01425) 480625

Raymond Cullen & Sons, 6 Rock Road, Lisburn, County Antrim, BT28 3TF Tel: (028) 9264 8783 Fax: (028) 9264 8331 E-mail: raymondcullensons@btinternet.com *Portable building installers*

▶ Raymond Mcleod Farms Ltd, Longham Hall, Longham, Dereham, Norfolk, NR19 2RJ Tel: (01362) 687240 Fax: 0870 7626195 E-mail: mcleod@mcleodfarms.co.uk *TIMBER, GRAVEL, MACHINERY and FARMING*

Raymond Miller Butchers Ltd, Strathspey Industrial Estate, Grantown On Spey, Grantown-on-Spey, Morayshire, PH26 3NB Tel: (01479) 872520 Fax: (01479) 872892 *Meat wholesalers*

Raymond Travel, 192 High Street, Dorking, Surrey, RH4 1QR Tel: (01306) 743780 Fax: (01306) 743764 E-mail: info@raymondtravel.co.uk *Buyers & sellers of used processing & packaging machinery*

▶ Raymond's, 11 Comiston Road, Edinburgh, EH10 6AA Tel: 0131-447 3177 Fax: 0131-452 9855

Rayne Precision Engineering Ltd, Unit 5 Far Lane Industrial Estat, Froghall Road, Ipstones, Stoke-on-Trent, ST10 2NA Tel: (01538) 266100 Fax: (01538) 266800 E-mail: rayne_precision@yahoo.co.uk *Specialists in precision CNC engineering*

Rayner & Co. Ltd, 4 Bull Lane, Edmonton, London, N18 1TQ Tel: (020) 8807 3080 Fax: (020) 8807 9205 E-mail: info@rayner.co.uk *Food flavour manufrs*

Rayner & Eve Ltd, Unit 5 37-39 Western Road, Mitcham, Surrey, CR4 3ED Tel: (020) 8646 2770 Fax: (020) 8646 3151 *Dental laboratory*

Rayner Firefighting Equipment Ltd, 71 Harehills Road, Leeds, LS8 5HS Tel: (0845) 3000440 Fax: 0113-293 0493 *Fire fighting equipment, service & sales*

Rayner J C B Ltd, 3 Tamdown Way, Braintree, Essex, CM7 2QL Tel: 01376 550246 Fax: 01376 556150 *Construction plant service sales & parts*

Rayners Bakery Ltd, 12a Deer Park Road, London, SW19 3UQ Tel: (020) 8543 6695 Fax: (020) 8545 0736 E-mail: rayners@raynersgroup.fsnet.co.uk *Bakers*

Rayners Buildings Ltd, Meadrow, Godalming, Surrey, GU7 3HR Tel: (01483) 416242 Fax: (01483) 419378 *Garden building manufrs*

▶ Raynesway Construction Services Ltd, Reema Road, Bellshill, Lanarkshire, ML4 1RT Tel: (01698) 503503 Fax: (01698) 503556

▶ Raynesway Construction (Southern) Ltd, 260 Aztec West, Almondsbury, Bristol, BS32 4SY Tel: (01454) 617620

Raynesway Interiors, 5 227 Derby Road, Chaddesden, Derby, DE21 6SY Tel: (01332) 280585 Fax: (01332) 280585 *Blinds, & cane distributor & manufrs*

Raynesway Pine Company Ltd, 227 Derby Road, Spondon, Derby, DE21 7LW Tel: (01332) 820211 *Pine furniture manufrs*

Raynor Industrial, The Poplars, Foxwood Lane, Woodborough, Nottingham, NG14 6ED Tel: 0115-965 5424 Fax: 0115-965 6481 *Cleaning equipment manufrs*

Rayovac Europe Ltd, Watermans House, Watermans Court, Kingsbury Crescent, The Causeway, Staines, Middlesex, TW18 3BA Tel: (01784) 411411 Fax: (01784) 411412 *Batteries manufrs*

Ray-Play, 15 Victoria Rd, Bexleyheath, Kent, DA6 7LT Tel: 020 83034751 *Children's amusements*

Rayridge Conveyors Ltd, Willenhall Trading Estate, Midacre, Willenhall, West Midlands, WV13 2JW Tel: (01902) 603763 Fax: (01902) 605081 E-mail: mail@ercongroup.com *Industrial conveyor systems manufrs*

Raysigns Ltd, 11-13 Tower Hamlets Road, Dover, Kent, CT17 0BJ Tel: (01304) 214506 Fax: (01304) 202915 E-mail: andrew@raysigns.fsnet.co.uk *Sign manufrs*

Rayson Engineering, 4 Albion Business Park, Spring Road, Smethwick, West Midlands, B66 1LY Tel: 0121-580 1498 Fax: 0121-580 1498 *Pressed tools, jigs & fixtures*

Raysun Machine Tools, 6 Prospect Park, Valley Drive, Rugby, Warwickshire, CV21 1TF Tel: (01788) 541777 Fax: (01788) 541577 E-mail: raysun@tinyonline.co.uk *Consulting engineers & designers*

Raytec Presswork Plastics, Lobro Tools, Premier Business Park, Walsall, WS2 9XP Tel: (01922) 640440 Fax: (01922) 611117 E-mail: sales@raytec-diecastingandplastics.com *Fabricators & moulders*

Raytech International, Coldnose Road, Rotherwas Industrial Estate, Hereford, HR2 6JL Tel: (01432) 340833 Fax: (01432) 340844 E-mail: sales@raytech.uk.com *RTC branded range manufrs*

▶ Raytel Controlgear Supplies Ltd, Raytel House, 19 Brook Road, Rayleigh, Essex, SS6 7XH Tel: (01268) 740290 Fax: (01268) 740299 E-mail: action@raytelcontrolgear.co.uk *Suppliers of industrial control gear components*

▶ Raytel Security Systems Ltd, 3 Block 5 Oakbank Industrial Estate, Garscube Road, Glasgow, G20 7LU Tel: 0141-332 4232 Fax: 0141-332 6952 E-mail: sales@raytelsecurity.co.uk *Security access control systems suppliers*

▶ Raytel Security Systems Ltd, 19 Brook Road, Rayleigh, Essex, SS6 7XH Tel: (01268) 749311 Fax: (01268) 745001 E-mail: info@raytelsecurity.co.uk *Manufacturers & suppliers of access control & door entry systems*

Raytheon E-Systems Ltd, The Pinnacles, Elizabeth Way, Harlow, Essex, CM19 5BB Tel: (01279) 426862 Fax: (01279) 410413 *Radar navigation equipment manufrs*

Raytheon Systems Ltd, Fullerton Road, Queensway Industrial Estate, Glenrothes, Fife, KY7 5PY Tel: (01592) 754311 Fax: (01592) 759775 E-mail: carol.fleming@raytheon.co.uk *MOD product manufrs*

Raytheon UK Ltd, Harman House, George Street, London, Uxbridge, Middlesex, UB8 1QQ Tel: (020) 7569 5500 Fax: (020) 7569 5599 E-mail: corporatecommunications@raytheon.co.uk *Electronic navigational equipment*

Rayvac Electrics, East Thurrock Road, Grays, Essex, RM17 6SP Tel: (01375) 371253 Fax: (01375) 381381 E-mail: rayvac@btopenworld.com *Domestic appliance service centre*

Rayvac Refrigeration Services, East Thurrock Road, Grays, Essex, RM17 6SP Tel: (01375) 390113 Fax: (01375) 381381 E-mail: keithneall@btopenworld.com *Air conditioning engineers*

Raywill Engineering Ltd, 87b Whitby Road, Slough, SL1 3DR Tel: (01753) 533552 Fax: (01753) 534464 E-mail: r_welch@btconnect.com *General engineers*

Razorback Vehicles Corporation Ltd, Regus Building, Central Boulevard, Shirley, Solihull, West Midlands, B90 8AG Tel: (01564) 711051 Fax: (01564) 711451

continued

▶ indicates data change since last edition

continuation
E-mail: sales@razorback-vehicles.com *Car manufrs*

Razzamatazz, 166 West Street, Fareham, Hampshire, PO16 0EH Tel: (01329) 822051 Fax: (01329) 313232 E-mail: info@razzzmatazzfancydress.co.uk *Fancy dress hire shop*

▶ RB Document Solutions Ltd, 85 Frankland Close Weston, Bath, BA1 4EL Tel: (01225) 336058 E-mail: enquiries@rbdsl.com *A complete Document Management service including consultancy, installation and training. High quality document imaging and management solutions including a Scanning Service Bureau. Laserfiche Value Added Reseller.*

RB Maintenance Services Ltd, Unit 28 Penley Industrial Estate, Penley, Wrexham, Clwyd, LL13 0LQ Tel: (01948) 830595 Fax: (01948) 830672 E-mail: rbms@ic24.net *Seal manufrs*

▶ RB Transport Co. Ltd, Unit 14 Oldbury Road, West Bromwich, West Midlands, B70 9DE Tel: 0121-553 3674 Fax: 0121-553 7743

▶ RCC Data Systems Ltd, 30 Torquay Road, Kingskerswell, Devon, TQ12 5EZ Tel: (0845) 0048411 E-mail: info@rccds.co.uk *IT support services for small businesses*

RC-Catering-solutions.co.uk, 12 Blackthorn mews, Chippenham, Wiltshire, SN15 3PG Tel: (01249) 652099 E-mail: info@rc-catering-solutions.co.uk *Caterer, Private Chef hire, event catering, Consultancy, Catering Recruitment*

RCD Projects Ltd, 62 Portman Road, Reading, RG30 1EA Tel: 0118-950 2021 Fax: 0118-950 2036 E-mail: sales@rcdprojects.co.uk *Office refurbishment services*

RCJ Metal Finishers Ltd, 3 Pindar Road, Hoddesdon, Hertfordshire, EN11 0BZ Tel: (01992) 467931 Fax: (01992) 471547 E-mail: john@rcjmf.co.uk *Electroplaters & polishers*

RCJ Precision, Llay Hall Industrial Estate, Mold Road, Cefn-y-Bedd, Wrexham, Clwyd, LL12 9YG Tel: (01978) 761060 Fax: (01978) 762337 E-mail: rcjprec@dialstart.net *Precision engineers manufrs*

RCL Sales, 55 Throgmorton Road, Yateley, Hampshire, GU46 6FA Tel: (01252) 890047 Fax: (01252) 861220 *Packaging manufrs*

▶ RD Financial Recruitment, St.Stephens House, Arthur Road, Windsor, Berkshire, SL4 1Ry Tel: 01753 621902 Fax: 01753 621901 E-mail: paul@rdfr.co.uk *RD Financial Recruitment, based in Windsor, Berkshire, is a privately owned consultancy managed by qualified accountants with extensive senior level financial experience including the recruitment of large accounting teams.**Our previous experience, as both recruiters and candidates, provides us with an excellent insight to the recruitment needs of clients and the career ambitions of our candidates.**Handling permanent and temporary assignments, we can assist with the recruitment of accounting staff at all levels of qualification. Our clients range from SME's to some of the world's largest organisations.*

Rda, Unit 1 Plot 7 River Way Industrial Estate, Newport, Isle of Wight, PO30 5UX Tel: (01983) 821189 Fax: (01983) 821149 E-mail: sales@rda-eng.com *Refrigerant handling equipment manufrs*

▶ RDA Building Solutions, 16 Enterprise Close, Warsash, Southampton, SO31 9BD Tel: 01489 572295 Fax: 01489 557634 E-mail: buildingsolutions@uk2,net *I provide freelance Quantity Surveying, Building Estimating & Property Maintenance Management services from my base on the south coast - please look up my web site for more details.*

RDB Belting Ltd, Perseverance Mill, Church Lane, Mow Cop, Stoke-on-Trent, ST7 4LS Tel: (01782) 511014 Fax: (01782) 523220 *Conveyor & transmission belt manufrs & suppliers*

RDL Distribution Ltd, Shireoaks, Worksop, Nottinghamshire, S81 8NW Tel: (01909) 537700 Fax: (01909) 537753 *Haulage contractor*

RDMG Aerospace, Boardman Road, Swadlincote, Derbyshire, DE11 9EN Tel: (01283) 550960 Fax: (01283) 550961 E-mail: administration@tecalemitaero.co.uk *Precision engineers*

Re Bar Engineering Design Ltd, 68a Reddicap Hill, Sutton Coldfield, West Midlands, B75 7BG Tel: 0121-378 3777 Fax: 0121-378 0214 E-mail: rebardesignltdsc@aol.com *Reinforced concrete engineers* Also at: Leamington Spa

▶ Re Cartridge, 59 Queens Road, Leicester, LE2 1TT Tel: 0116-270 5505 E-mail: recartridge@hotmail.co.uk *Computer services*

Re Nu Electrical Service, Murdock Road, Manton Industrial Estate, Bedford, MK41 7PE Tel: (01234) 261933 Fax: (01234) 269120 E-mail: sales@renu-electrical.com *Electric motor rewinding & repairs*

Re Trem & Co. Ltd, Old Bawtry Road, Finningley, Doncaster, South Yorkshire, DN9 3BX Tel: (01302) 770203 Fax: (01302) 770868 E-mail: sales@enginesandgenerators.com Principal Export Areas: Worldwide *Merchants or agents for diesel engine components/spare parts, also distributors of generators/generating sets, marine engineering equipment & generating sets, diesel driven. In addition diesel engine (reconditioned) rebuilders or suppliers*

▶ Re:Word Ltd, Ginsborough House, 33 Throgmorton Street, London, EC2N 2BR Tel: (020) 7397 3315 E-mail: info@rewordweb.com *Specialists in legal & financial translation services*

▶ Rea Distribution Ltd, 30 Main Street, Ballyclare, County Antrim, BT39 9AA Tel: (028) 9334 2320 Fax: (028) 9335 2699

Rea Metal Windows Ltd, 126-136 Green Lane, Stoneycroft, Liverpool, L13 7ED Tel: 0151-228 6373 Fax: 0151-254 1828 E-mail: all@reametal.co.uk *Metal window manufrs*

Reabrook Ltd, Rawdon Road, Moira, Swadlincote, Derbyshire, DE12 6DA Tel: (01283) 221044 Fax: (01283) 225731 E-mail: sales@greenhill.co.uk *Chemical manufrs*

▶ Reaburn Developments, The Square, Blackness, Linlithgow, West Lothian, EH49 7NG Tel: (01506) 834833

▶ Reach & Clean, 18 Veronica Gardens, Streatham Vale, London, SW16 5JS Tel: (0870) 1993533 Fax: (0709) 2809786 E-mail: info@reachandclean.co.uk *Reach and Clean System:*Window cleaning equipment and reverse osmosis systems to clean windows with the pure water fed poles.*

▶ Reach New Media Ltd, Clayton House, Tummock Road, Ballymoney, County Antrim, BT53 8NR Tel: (028) 2766 7987 Fax: (028) 2544 6130 E-mail: info@reach-newmedia.com *Reach new media provide professional web design*

Reach2Mobile Ltd, Keswick House, 26 Myrtle Avenue, Ruislip, Middlesex, HA4 8RZ Tel: 08707 665232 E-mail: infok@reach2mobile.co.uk *Text messaging is the most effective means to reach people immediately, wherever they are and capture their immediate reaction to your offer. Using our unique software application MOJIO Messenger you can now provide your customers with a fun, convenient and lo-cost way to interact with your business and help them act the moment they receive your offer.*

▶ Reach-Wash, 67 Clarendon Gardens, Dartford, DA2 6EY Tel: (01322) 273779 Fax: (01322) 273482 E-mail: enquires@reach-wash.co.uk *Ladderless Window Cleaning up to the 6th floor.*

▶ React Building Services, Unit E3, Park Lane, Birmingham, B35 6LJ Tel: 0121-748 3666 *Air conditioning designers*

React Computer Partnership, 38 Manor Farm Road, St. Neots, Cambridgeshire, PE19 1PW Tel: (01480) 356145 Fax: (01473) 630707 *Computer consultancy*

React Computer Partnership, Unit 5, Old Maltings Approach, Woodbridge, Suffolk, IP12 1EF Tel: (01394) 387337 Fax: (01394) 610554 E-mail: enquiries@reactcp.co.uk *Computer consultants*

▶ React Transport Services Ltd, 24 West Shore Road, Edinburgh, EH5 1QD Tel: 0131-551 5531 Fax: 0131-551 5528

▶ Reactfast, Unit 1 Jubilee Trade Centre, 130 Pershore Street, Birmingham, B5 6ND Tel: 0800 195 1269 E-mail: enquiries@reactfast.co.uk *Reactfast provide 24 hour emergency repair and maintenance services across the UK. Services include emergency plumbers, locksmiths, central heating and boiler repair, glazing, drainage, carpentry and electrics.*

▶ Reaction International Ltd, PO Box 617, Southampton, SO16 4RP Tel: (023) 8023 1111 Fax: (023) 8023 1111 E-mail: sales@hovpod.com *Hovercraft manufrs*

▶ Reactive Solutions, 6 Lakeside Business Park, Pinfold Road, Thurmaston, Leicester, LE4 8AT Tel: 0116-260 3930 Fax: 0116-260 3931 E-mail: dean@reactive-solutions.com *Pos assembly & contract packing services*

▶ Read Construction Ltd, Station Road, Trevor, Llangollen, Clwyd, LL20 7TT Tel: (01978) 824288

Read Cosine Ltd, Unit 1 Leanne Business Centre, Sandford Lane, Wareham, Dorset, BH20 4DY Tel: (01929) 550727 Fax: (01929) 550357 E-mail: sales@readcosine.com *Importers & distributors of keyboards*

Read Foundry Ltd, Meeting Lane, Brierley Hill, West Midlands, DY5 3LB Tel: (01384) 79399 Fax: (01384) 79399 *Casting (non-ferrous metal) manufrs*

George Read, Wilderness Quarry, Mitcheldean, Gloucestershire, GL17 0DF Tel: (01452) 830530 Fax: (01452) 830530 *Quarry & waste transport*

J.J. & J. Read (Sewing Machines) Ltd, 336 Shirley Road, Southampton, SO15 3HJ Tel: (023) 8077 1398 Fax: (023) 8077 1398 *Sewing machine distributors*

▶ Read Maurice Residential, 48 Andover Road, Cheltenham, Gloucestershire, GL50 2TL Tel: (01242) 241122 Fax: (01242) 243377 E-mail: post@readmorris.co.uk *Residential Estate Agents located in Cheltenham, selling flats, apartments and quality town houses.*

Read Precision Engineering Ltd, 10 William Street, Northampton, NN1 3EW Tel: (01604) 601372 Fax: (01604) 601373 E-mail: sales@readengineering.co.uk *Stainless steel & CNC turned components manufrs*

▶ Read Riggs, St. Clare House, 30-33 Minories, London, EC3N 1DD Tel: (020) 7265 2060 Fax: (020) 7265 2066 *Computer software development*

Read Scientific Ltd, 32 Brancaster Way, Swaffham, Norfolk, PE37 7RY Tel: (01760) 724546 Fax: (01760) 724340 E-mail: bill.read@ntlworld.com *Supply & service of meteorological instruments*

Read & Sutcliffe Ltd, St. Johns Road, Boston, Lincolnshire, PE21 6HG Tel: (01205) 310444 Fax: (01205) 310500 E-mail: info@rsboston.com *Road Haulage & Warehousing*

Read T, 30 Elmtree Road, Basildon, Essex, SS16 4TN Tel: (01268) 456160 *Trophy suppliers & engravers*

Read Well Services Ltd, Viking House, 1 Claymore Avenue, Bridge of Don, Aberdeen, AB23 8GW Tel: (01224) 336600 Fax: (01224) 336611 E-mail: sales@readgroupuk.com *Seismic survey & corrosion monitoring services*

Reade Signs Ltd, 4 Holder Road, Aldershot, Hampshire, GU12 4RH Tel: (01252) 333535 Fax: (01252) 333535 E-mail: sales@readesigns.com *Sign contractors, suppliers & installers manufrs*

▶ Reader Storage Ltd, Catwick La Industrial Estate, Brandesburton, Driffield, North Humberside, YO25 8RY Tel: (01964) 542242 Fax: (01964) 543387 E-mail: keith@readerhaulage.co.uk *National road transport services*

Reader's Digest Association Ltd, 11 Westferry Circus, London, E14 4HE Tel: (020) 7715 8000 Fax: (020) 7715 8181 E-mail: info@readersdigest.co.uk *Book & magazine publishers*

Reading Carpentry Services Ltd, 1a Eaton Place, Reading, RG1 7LP Tel: 0118-950 0971 Fax: 0118-950 0971 *Carpentry & joinery*

Chris Reading Associates, 6 Charfield Close, Winchester, Hampshire, SO22 4PZ Tel: (07802) 618656 Fax: (01962) 861496 E-mail: consult@cvrassociates.freeserve.co.uk *Building services consulting engineers & acoustics*

Reading Chronicle, 50-56 Portman Road, Reading, RG30 1BA Tel: 0118-950 3030 Fax: 0118-939 1619 E-mail: sales@readingchronicle.co.uk *Newspaper publishers*

Reading Extinguisher Services, 139b Caversham Road, Reading, RG1 8AU Tel: (0800) 7310727 Fax: 0118-959 1167 E-mail: sales@extinguishers.co.uk *Fire equipment sales & services*

Reading Filter Services, Richmond Road, Caversham, Reading, RG4 7PR Tel: 0118-947 6895 Fax: 0118-946 3310 E-mail: stan@readingfilters.fsworld.co.uk *Filter commercial vehicle distributors*

▶ Reading Maintenance Co., 621 Oxford Road, Reading, RG30 1HP Tel: 0118-950 7450

Reading Marine Co. Ltd, Aldermaston Wharf, Wharf Side, Padworth, Reading, RG7 4JS Tel: 0118-971 3666 Fax: 0118-971 4271 E-mail: sales@readingmarine.com *Boat builders & hirers*

Readman Steel Ltd, Cochranes Wharf, Cargo Fleet, Middlesbrough, Cleveland, TS3 6AW Tel: (01642) 242641 Fax: (01642) 241912 E-mail: mail@wgrsteels.co.uk *Steel section tubes & plates stockholders*

Reads Construction Ltd, 6 Speedwell Way, Harleston Industrial Estate, Harleston, Norfolk, IP20 9EH Tel: (01379) 853063 Fax: (01379) 853676 E-mail: readsconstruction@harleston.fsbusiness.co.uk *Structural steelwork engineers*

▶ Reads light haulage & courier service 24/7, 92 Church Lane, Brinsley, Nottingham, NG16 5AB Tel: (07925) 17653 E-mail: david.read67@virgin.net *courier service 24/7 uk/eu,sameday,overnight.*fully insured.transit 350,lwb.*upto 3standard pallets or max 1500kgs*

Reads Removal, Westwood Farm, Westwood, Peterborough, PE3 9UW Tel: (01733) 334411 Fax: (01733) 334320 E-mail: sales@readsremovals.co.uk *Furniture removal & storage contractors*

▶ Readscroft Ltd, 33-35 Prince Albert Street, Birmingham, B9 5AG Tel: 0121-772 5664 Fax: 0121-771 0085

Readwell Signs Ltd, 357 Hedon Road, Hull, HU9 1RA Tel: (01482) 227233 Fax: (01482) 219823 E-mail: sales@readwell.co.uk *Sign manufrs*

Ready Heat UK Ltd, Unit B5 Bulwell Business Centre, Sellers Wood Drive, Bulwell, Nottingham, NG6 8GN Tel: 0115-975 4500 Fax: 0115-975 4500 *Hot water system suppliers*

Ready Mix (NI) Ltd, RMC House, Upper Dunmurry Lane, Belfast, BT17 0AJ Tel: (028) 9061 6611 Fax: (028) 9061 9969 *Quarry manufrs* Also at: Branches throughout the U.K.

Ready Mixed Concrete Ltd, Quarry, Llanelwedd, Builth Wells, Powys, LD2 3UB Tel: (01982) 553421 Fax: (01982) 552402 *Producers of ready mixed concrete*

Ready Mixed Concrete Ltd, Larne Road, Carrickfergus, County Antrim, BT38 7NN Tel: (028) 9335 1087 *Concrete distributors & manufrs*

Ready Mixed Concrete Ltd, 64 Killough Road, Downpatrick, County Down, BT30 8BL Tel: (028) 4461 2688 *Ready mix concrete manufrs*

Ready Mixed Concrete Ltd, Fairfield Way, Stainsacre Industrial Estate, Stainsacre, Whitby, North Yorkshire, YO22 4NT Tel: (01947) 604363 Fax: (01947) 821698 *Concrete & mortar ready mixed product suppliers*

Ready Mixed Concrete Eastern Ltd, Woodhall Road, Tattershall Thorpe, Lincoln, LN4 4JT Tel: (01526) 342187 *Mixed concrete manufrs*

Ready Mixed Concrete Huddersfield Ltd, Sheffield Road, Penistone, Sheffield, S36 6HJ Tel: (01226) 762476 Fax: (01226) 760920 *Mix concrete suppliers*

Ready Mixed Concrete (London) Ltd, Randells Roadlkings Cross, London, N1 0DJ Tel: (020) 7607 8881 *Concrete producers & distributors*

Ready Mixed Concrete Midlands Ltd, Slack Lane, Heanor, Derbyshire, DE75 7GX Tel: 0115-922 5225 Fax: 01159-22827 *Ready mixed concrete suppliers*

Ready Mixed Concrete North West Ltd, Barden Lane, Reedley, Burnley, Lancashire, BB12 0RZ Tel: (01282) 428545 Fax: (01772) 769826 E-mail: info@rmc.co.uk *Concrete manufrs*

Ready Mixed Concrete Northern Ltd, Charlestown Road, Halifax, West Yorkshire, HX3 9XQ Tel: (01422) 320277 *Ready mix concrete suppliers*

Ready Mixed Concrete Northern Ltd, Black Quarry, Moor Road, Leyburn, North Yorkshire, DL8 5LA Tel: (01969) 623014 Fax: (01969) 624340 *Concrete Ready Mixed Distributors*

Ready Mixed Concrete Northern Ltd, 2 Showfield Lane, Malton, North Yorkshire, YO17 6BT Tel: (01653) 693565 Fax: (01653) 697787 *Ready made concrete manufrs*

Ready Mixed Concrete (Northern) Ltd, Wiltons Yard, Jarrow Road, South Shields, Tyne & Wear, NE34 9PL Tel: 0191-455 3381 *Concrete plant*

Ready Mixed Concrete Scotland Ltd, Hawbank Road, East Kilbride, Glasgow, G74 5HB Tel: (01355) 236611 Fax: (01355) 264345 *Ready mixed concrete & mortar producers*

Ready Mixed Concrete South West Ltd, Kilmington Quarry, Kilmington, Axminster, Devon, EX13 7RU Tel: (01297) 32684 Fax: (01297) 631235 *Ready mixed concrete manufacturers & distributors*

Ready Mixed Concrete South West Ltd, Venn Quarries, Landkey, Barnstaple, Devon, EX32 0NU Tel: (01271) 830385 Fax: (01271) 830214 *Concrete production*

Ready Mixed Concrete South West Ltd, The Old Railway Sidings, Bridgerule, Holsworthy, Devon, EX22 7EB Tel: (01288) 381292 Fax: (01208) 74327 *Concrete & mortar ready mixed suppliers*

Ready Mixed Concrete South West Ltd, 10 Concrete Works, Trewoon, St. Austell, Cornwall, PL25 5SL Tel: (01726) 74201 Fax: (01726) 73027 *Concrete & mortar ready mixed*

Ready Mixed Concrete South West Ltd, Priorswood Road, Taunton, Somerset, TA2 8DF Tel: (01823) 282331 Fax: (01823) 327928 *Ready mixed concrete*

Ready Mixed Concrete (Transite) Ltd, The Willows, Barnet Road, London Colney, St. Albans, Hertfordshire, AL2 1BD Tel: (01727) 822331 Fax: (01727) 826606 E-mail: readymix.homecounties@rmc.co.uk *Ready mixed concrete & mortar*

Ready Mixed Concrete Ulster Ltd, Quarry Road, Banbridge, County Down, BT32 3TW Tel: (028) 4066 2758 Fax: (028) 9061 9969 *Concrete manufrs*

Ready Mixed Concrete Ulster Ltd, 2 Hillview Avenue, Londonderry, BT47 2NU Tel: (028) 7131 1274 *Concrete & mortar manufrs*

Ready Mixed Concrete (West Midlands) Ltd, Brick Kiln Lane, Stoke-On-Trent, ST4 7BN Tel: (01782) 202227 Fax: (01782) 267008 *Concrete suppliers*

Ready Mixed Concrete Western Ltd, RMC House, 82-87 Feeder Road, Bristol, BS2 0UE Tel: 0117-977 9534 Fax: 0117-971 7534 *Concrete manufrs*

▶ Ready Mixed Concrete Western Ltd, Bristol Road, Gloucester, GL2 5DH Tel: (01452) 528463 Fax: (01452) 307862 *Concrete ready mix*

Ready Mixed Concrete (Western) Ltd, C/O Bromfield Sand & Gravel, Bromfield, Ludlow, Shropshire, SY8 2JR Tel: (01584) 856253 Fax: (01584) 856261 *Concrete distributors & manufrs*

Ready Mixed Concrete Western Ltd, Cleveland Farm, Ashton Keynes, Swindon, SN6 6QP Tel: (01285) 860301 Fax: 0117-937 2789 *Ready mixed concrete manufrs*

Ready Mixed Home Counties, New Building, Hardwick Gravel Pits, Hardwick, Witney, Oxfordshire, OX29 7QF Tel: (01865) 300155 Fax: (01865) 300427 *Construction services & concrete manufacturers*

Ready Power Engineering Ltd, Station Road, Kings Langley, Hertfordshire, WD4 8LF Tel: (01923) 264593 Fax: (01923) 269350 *Operated & self drive plant hire providers*

Ready Roll Ltd, Unit 14, Harris Business Park, Hambury Road, Stoke Piror, Bromsgrove, Worcestershire, B60 4AA Tel: (01527) 881993 Fax: (01527) 881994 *Engineers*

Ready Use Concrete Co. Ltd, 17a Trench Road, Londonderry, BT47 3UB Tel: (028) 7134 1367 *Pre mixed concrete manufrs*

Ready Use Concrete Co. Ltd, 140 Mallusk Road, Newtownabbey, County Antrim, BT36 4QN Tel: (028) 9034 2291 *Ready mixed concrete manufrs*

▶ Ready Use Concrete Co. Ltd, Ballybarnes Road, Newtownards, County Down, BT23 4UE Tel: (028) 9181 4676 *Ready mix concrete specialists*

Readyblock, 20 Ballypalady Road, Doagh, Ballyclare, County Antrim, BT39 0QY Tel: (028) 9335 2259 Fax: (028) 9335 2223 *Block manufrs*

Readyblock, 45 Craighulliar Road, Portrush, County Antrim, BT56 8NN Tel: (028) 7082 3374 Fax: (028) 7082 2682 *Manufacture blocks & bricks*

Readycrest Ltd, PO Box 75, Chatham, Kent, ME5 9DL Tel: (01634) 304060 Fax: (01634) 304070 E-mail: info@readycrest.co.uk *Computer system consultants*

Readyfix, Lodge Street, Preston, PR1 8XE Tel: (01772) 250060 Fax: (01772) 250075 *Fastener, bolt & nut distributors*

Readymix Concrete, Hermitage Lane, Mansfield, Nottinghamshire, NG18 5HB Tel: (01623) 622174 *Concrete product manufrs*

Readymix Huddersfield Ltd, Red Doles Lane, Leeds Road, Huddersfield, HD2 1YD Tel: (01484) 535311 Fax: (01484) 558255 E-mail: sales@readymix-huddersfield.co.uk *Builders merchants*

Readymix London & South East Ltd, 15 Townmead Road, London, SW6 2QL Tel: (020) 7384 4900 Fax: (020) 7371 0039 *Ready mixed concrete & mortar* Also at: Branches throughout the U.K.

Readyplus Ltd, 2 Rochdale Road, Manchester, M4 4JR Tel: 0161-832 2240 Fax: 0161-832 7236 *Knitwear manufrs*

▶ Readypower Engineering Ltd, Readypower House, Molly Millars Bridge, Wokingham, Berkshire, RG41 2WY Tel: 01189 774901 Fax: 01189 774902 E-mail: info@readypower.co.uk *Since 1992 Readypower has offered operated or self drive plant for both the rail and construction industries. We have an extensive range of both road rail and construction machines with tracked & wheeled excavators, forward tipping dumpers, dumptrucks, access platforms, bulldozers (available with and without both GPS and standard lazers) and hiab lorries complemented with a range of hydraulic attachments and loose lifting tackle. Road rail plant is now approved to run on London Underground infrastructure. Our Head Office is based in Wokingham, Berkshire with depots nationwide located in Derby, Hertfordshire, Southampton and Manchester. We can supply operators with CPCS cards and where required for rail work, PTS cards, CPCS Road Rail cards and London Underground certified operators. Accredited to ISO 14001 and ISO 9001:2000 with documented Safety, Quality and Environmental management systems we aim to deliver a professional and reliable service whatever your plant needs.*

Real 60 Minute Money, 6A Bell Flats, 280-286 High Road, Willesden, London, NW10 2EX Tel: (0870) 896 4064 Fax: (0870) 762 3512 E-mail: info@real60minutemoney.co.uk *You can secure a better financial future today!*You can join one of the fastest growing & most established and ethical in-home business programs. Learn how to earn up to £500-£2,0/ month part time around your existing schedule. Create the option to develop a full time career income of up to £5,000 or more per month. Find out how to join a Real, Honest, Ethical Home*

continued

continuation
*Based Business and take a quick tour NOW.*Thanks to my proven step-by-step system, you can start part time and make the internet work for you. My turnkey program is so simple that even if you are an Internet beginner, you can be successful. Join the hundreds of other successful people with my proven system. *Success is possible for anyone with our program.*

▶ Real Access Platforms, Acorn Centre, 51 High Street, Grimethorpe, Barnsley, South Yorkshire, S72 7LR Tel: (01226) 781666 Fax: (01226) 781333

Real Cheese Shop, 62 Barnes High Street, London, SW13 9LF Tel: (020) 8878 6676 *Cheese shop*

▶ Real Clothing Co. Ltd, Unit 19 Lockwood Industrial Park, Mill Mead Road, London, N17 9QP Tel: (020) 8885 9500 Fax: (020) 8365 1926

The Real Deli At Seaford, 15 Broad Street, Seaford, East Sussex, BN25 1LS Tel: (01323) 895380 Fax: (01323) 895380 *Deli*

Real Kleen, Units 12-13 Harmill Industrial Estate, Grovebury Road, Leighton Buzzard, Bedfordshire, LU7 4FF Tel: (01525) 370795 Fax: (01525) 852267 *Industrial cleaning chemicals & equipment suppliers*

▶ Real Mckay Ltd, March Road East, Buckie, Banffshire, AB56 4BY Tel: (01542) 833949 Fax: (01542) 833953

Real Mackay Water Bottling Co., Penyffin, Nantgaredig, Carmarthen, Dyfed, SA32 7LJ Tel: (01267) 290655 Fax: (01267) 290960 *Bottled water distributors*

▶ Real Oasis, 19 Station Road, Weaverham, Northwich, Cheshire, CW8 3PY Tel: (01606) 851740 E-mail: enquiries@realoasis.com *Real Oasis are an award-winning garden design and build company who also offer a range of landscaping services, garden lighting, water features, conservatories, stables through to planting plans and all the back up information needed to maintain a successful garden. In addition we also provide a pre buy land evaluation service.*

▶ Real Smart Hypnosis, Nova Lodge, Kenilworth Road, Leamington Spa, Warwickshire, CV32 6JJ Tel: (01926) 332935 E-mail: paulhastings@mac.com *Hypnosis, hypnotherapy, NLP & Hunar in Warwickshire*

Real Solutions Ltd, Alexander House, Atlantic Street, Altrincham, Cheshire, WA14 5EW Tel: 0161-926 2600 Fax: 0161-996 1778 E-mail: enquiries@realsolutionsuk.com *Computer consultants*

Real Time Associates Ltd, Canning Ho, 59 Canning Rd, Croydon, CR0 6QF Tel: (020) 8656 7333 *Computer software systems*

Real Time Consultants International Ltd, 118-120 Warwick Street, Leamington Spa, Warwickshire, CV32 4QY Tel: (01926) 313133 Fax: (01926) 422165 E-mail: contract@rtc.co.uk *Recruitment consultants*

Real Time Micro Systems Ltd, 2 Grange Park, London, W5 3PL Tel: 020 88409038 Fax: 020 88409038 *Software development*

Real Time Systems Ltd, 78 Cannon St, London, EC4P 4LN Tel: (020) 7861 0700 Fax: (020) 7861 0899 E-mail: sales@rtsgroup.net *Computerised trading services*

▶ Real Time World Ltd, 152 West Market Gate, Dundee, DD1 1NJ Tel: (01382) 202821 Fax: (01382) 228188 *Software developers*

Real Water, 29 Albion Street, Kenilworth, Warwickshire, CV8 2FX Tel: (01926) 851100 Fax: (01926) 511893 E-mail: sales@realwater.co.uk *Water purification system manufrs*

Real Wooden Window Co., Unit 7-8 Alms Close, Stukeley Meadows Industrial Estate, Huntingdon, Cambridgeshire, PE29 6DY Tel: (01480) 356463 E-mail: info@realwoodenwindows.co.uk *Real wooden windows & door manufrs*

Real World, Unit 10 Broughton Manor Business Park, Broughton, Newport Pagnell, Buckinghamshire, MK16 0HF Tel: (01908) 676812 Fax: (01908) 698463 E-mail: sales@realworldsolutions.co.uk *Computer consultants*

Realia, Godmersham Park, Godmersham, Canterbury, Kent, CT4 7DT Tel: (01227) 731210 Fax: (01227) 731209 E-mail: paul.williamson@realia-marketing.com *PR & marketing providers*

Realistic Digital Graphics, Stafford Studios, 129a Stafford Road, Wallington, Surrey, SM6 9BN Tel: (020) 8669 4900 Fax: (020) 8773 0129 E-mail: info@realistic-digital.com *Large format exhibition graphics for displays*

Reality Consulting Ltd, 4 Waverley Court, Brinsea Road, Congresbury, Bristol, BS49 5JG Tel: (0870) 6070116 *IT consultants*

▶ Reality Logic Ltd, 28 Harsfold Road, Rustington, Littlehampton, West Sussex, BN16 2QE Tel: (01903) 775352 Fax: (0870) 4589021 E-mail: jeremy.aston@realitylogic.com *Plasma tv sales, supply, rent & install learning technology*

Really Useful Group Ltd, 22 Tower Street, London, WC2H 9TW Tel: (020) 7240 0880 Fax: (020) 7240 1204 *Theatre*

▶ Really Useful Research, 9 Balmoral Grange, Prestwich, Manchester, M25 0GZ Tel: 0161-720 9924 Fax: 0161-740 0561 E-mail: sales@forensic-marketing.com *Marketing research & consultancy*

▶ Realstone Ltd, Barclay Curle Complex, 739 South Street, Glasgow, G14 0BX Tel: 0141-954 1161 Fax: 0141-958 1261 *Manufactures natural stone products*

▶ Realsys Technology, 24 Velsheda Road, Shirley, Solihull, West Midlands, B90 2JN Tel: 0121-244 2936 Fax: (0871) 2422788 E-mail: sales@realis8ion.com *Business Computer Projects, Technology, Support services . Serving the local Business community with quality Computer systems, services and Products at LOW prices.*

Realtime Business Services, The Birches, 82 Church Street, Pinchbeck, Spalding, Lincolnshire, PE11 3YA Tel: (01775) 769731 Fax: (01775) 711582

continued

E-mail: allan@realtime-bs.com *Computer consultants*

Realtime Online, Blackstone Road, Huntingdon, Cambs, PE29 6EF Tel: (01480) 435881 Fax: (01480) 411120 E-mail: sales@realtimeltd.co.uk *Distribution of Computer Components to the trade. Authorised partners of Corsair, Sapphire (ATI), Seagate, Relisys, Abit, BTC, AOpen, Waterchill & Vapochill*

Reardon Engineering Co., Unit 6 9, 35 River Road, Barking, Essex, IG11 0DA Tel: (01708) 748253 Fax: (020) 8594 7398 *General engineers*

Reason Technology Ltd, Elmbank Mill, The Charrier, Menstrie, Clackmannanshire, FK11 7BU Tel: (01259) 763444 Fax: (01259) 763388 E-mail: info@reason-technology.com *IT consultants*

▶ Reavey & Son, Unit 21 Mitchell Point, Ensign Way, Hamble, Southampton, SO31 4RF Tel: (023) 8045 4560 Fax: (023) 8045 4561

▶ Rebate Ltd, Rebate House, Stourport Road, Kidderminster, Worcestershire, DY11 7BD Tel: (01562) 740065 *Bespoke hardwood timber conservatories & garden rooms*

▶ Rebecca Rayner, Glebe Farm, Kings Ripton, Huntingdon, Cambridgeshire, PE28 2NL Tel: 01487 773282 *We are organic farmers and producers of highest quality organic bread mixes, speciality organic flours and gluten-free products. Fresh flour is stoneground milled and bagged on our farm or by local windmills.*

▶ Rebekka Cairns, 5 Temple Square, Temple Street, Liverpool, L2 5RH Tel: 0151 255 2300 Fax: 0151 255 2301 E-mail: rebekka.cairns@mitchellcharlesworth.co.uk *Bredth of our services -*Companies, Partnerships, Individuals, Trusts, Charities and Guarantee companies**General client services include:*Audit & accounting*Personal tax planning*Corporate tax advice*Internal audit*Business start-up advice*Business development advice and business health checks*Grant and fundraising assistance*Payroll service**Specialist services include:*Pension & investment advice*Business assurance (internal audit)*Corporate recovery and insolvency*Corporate finance*Forensic*Services specific to solicitors*Services specific to the medical professions*Services specific to charities*Services specific to RSL"s /Housing Associations**

Reboc Engineering Corp Ltd, 66 Sunbeam Road, Park Royal, London, NW10 6JQ Tel: (020) 8453 0284 Fax: (020) 8453 0288 *General engineers*

▶ Reboot Computer Services, 106 Walcot Street, Bath, BA1 5BG Tel: (01225) 447227 Fax: (01225) 471166

Rebore Service Sutton Ltd, 34 Lind Road, Sutton, Surrey, SM1 4PL Tel: (020) 8642 3419 Fax: (020) 8642 6119 *Motor engineers recondition*

Rebourn Ltd, 14 The Green, Chipping Norton, Oxfordshire, OX7 5NH Tel: (01608) 642020 Fax: (01608) 642031 *Computer consumable suppliers*

Rebus Badges & Regalia Ltd, Clayfields, Bodenham, Hereford, HR1 3LG Tel: (01568) 797401 Fax: (01568) 797402 E-mail: sales@e-badges.co.uk *Badge, medal & regalia manufrs*

Rebus Control Systems Ltd, 156 Burton Road, Lincoln, LN1 3LS Tel: (01522) 882200 Fax: (01522) 882211 E-mail: sales@rebuscontrol.co.uk *Control systems manufrs*

▶ Recadnet, Minerva Road, London, NW10 6HJ Tel: (0870) 2240656 E-mail: admin@recadnet.com *recAdnet specialise in the search & selection of permanent staff only. covering Greater london and the UK. our clients are SME and Corporate Blue chip.We recruit all disciplines for manufacturing, hospitality and catering, accountancy, aviation, telecoms.*

Recearch & Enterprise Office, University of Hull, Cottingham Road, Hull, HU6 7RX Tel: (01482) 465139 Fax: (01482) 466852 E-mail: k.j.butler@admin.hull.ac.uk *Industrial engineers*

▶ Receptor Ltd, Elizabeth House, 73 High Street, Syston, Leicester, LE7 1GQ Tel: 0116-260 2500 Fax: 0116-260 5656 E-mail: graham@firefirefire.co.uk *Fire protection services*

Receptor Technologies Ltd, The Barn, Crofts Lane, Adderbury, Banbury, Oxfordshire, OX17 3NB Tel: (01295) 812600 Fax: (01295) 812700 E-mail: sales@receptortechnologies.co.uk *Distribute laboratory testing equipment*

Rechner UK Ltd, Unit 6, The Old Mill, Reading Road, Pangbourne, Reading, RG8 7HY Tel: 0118-976 6450 Fax: 0118-976 6451 E-mail: info@rechner-sensors.co.uk *Sensor distributor*

Reckitt Benckiser, Delta 1200, Welton Road, Delta Business Park, Swindon, SN5 7XZ Tel: (01793) 427200 Fax: (01793) 511572 *Consumer product manufrs*

Reckitt Benckiser Healthcare, Dansom Lane, Hull, HU8 7DS Tel: (01482) 326151 Fax: (01482) 582532 *Pharmaceuticals manufrs*

▶ Reckon LLP, 20 Theobalds Road, London, WC1X 8PF Tel: (020) 7841 5850 Fax: (020) 7841 5850 E-mail: feedback@reckon.co.uk *London-based consultancy firm specialising in regulation and competition economics*

▶ Reco Handling Ltd, Brighton Road, Stockport, Cheshire, SK4 2BQ Tel: 0161-431 5010 Fax: 0161-431 5020 E-mail: sales@reco-handling.com *Material handling , roll cages*

▶ Recognition Express, Heytor House, Long Road East, Dedham, Colchester, CO7 6BH Tel: (01206) 321270 Fax: (08702) 851464 E-mail: sales@re-anglia.co.uk *Suppliers of enamel badges, corporate gifts and promotional product.*Manufacturing name badges including magnetic. Photo ID cards. Printed and engraved plaques and awards. Door and desk nameplates. Braille and tactile signs. Internal signs. Key fobs. . **

Recognition Express, Venture Business Park, Grimsby, South Humberside, DN31 2UW Tel: (01472) 362900 Fax: (01472) 267647 E-mail: mailbox@recog-grimsby.co.uk *Manufacturing name badges including magnetic. Photo ID cards. Printed and engraved plaques and awards. Door and desk nameplates. Braille and tactile signs. Internal signs. Key fobs. Suppliers of enamel badges, corporate gifts and promotional products.*

Recognition Express, Grosvenor House First West Business Centre, Linnell Way, Telford Way Industrial Estate, Kettering, Northamptonshire, NN16 8PS Tel: (01536) 527800 Fax: (01536) 412022

Recognition Express, St. Michaels House, Parkgate Drive, Lancaster, LA1 3FN Tel: (01524) 846555 Fax: (01524) 843693 E-mail: sales@re-lancaster.co.uk *Badges manufrs*

Recognition Express, 10-16 Victoria Parade, Urmston, Manchester, M41 9RE Tel: 0161-748 1716 Fax: 0161-755 3650 E-mail: sales@re-manchester.co.uk *Badge, signs & promotional items manufrs*

Recognition Express, Gregory Court, Rothbury, Morpeth, Northumberland, NE65 7PJ Tel: (01669) 621018 Fax: (01669) 620508 *Badge & sign service manufrs*

▶ Recognition Express, Unit 2b Boundary Business Park, Wheatley Road, Garsington, Oxford, OX44 9EJ Tel: (0844) 8004265 Fax: 01865 368080 E-mail: sales@re-oxford.co.uk *We can put a name,logo or message on virtually anything. So whether you are looking for 1 million button badges or just one polo shirt we can help you. We provide Business Gifts, Promotional Products, Corporate Clothing, Large Format Posters, Name Badges, Plaques & Awards, Braille & Tactile Signage. So to make your logo work harder come to the people who provide unique solutions in promoting your image*

Recoil Ltd, 162-164 Ravenscroft Road, Beckenham, Kent, BR3 4TW Tel: (020) 8659 6977 Fax: (020) 8659 2973 E-mail: info@recoilltd.com *Coil winders, transformer manufrs*

Recoil Springs International Ltd, Anchor Lane, Abbess Roding, Ongar, Essex, CM5 0JR Tel: (01279) 876020 Fax: (01279) 876747 *Spring manufrs*

Recon Services, Unit 3 Barratt Industrial Park, St. Oswalds Road, Gloucester, GL1 2SH Tel: (01452) 415116 Fax: (01452) 415124 E-mail: reconservi@aol.com *Tea bag contract packers*

Reco-Prop UK Ltd, Unit 4 New Town Trading Estate, Chase Street, Luton, LU1 3QZ Tel: (01582) 412110 Fax: (01582) 480432 E-mail: info@reco-prop.com *Supplier of universal joint and constant velocity (CV) joint couplings. Manufacture and modification of standard and bespoke propshafts and driveshafts. Repairs and balancing services.*

Record Dimensions Co., Kelvedon House, Hall Lane, Knutsford, Cheshire, WA16 7AE Tel: (01565) 873300 Fax: (01565) 873000 E-mail: sales@rdco.co.uk *Manufacturers of aluminium containers, cases & flight cases & padded bag packaging*

Record Electrical Associates Ltd, Unit C1, Longford Industrial Trading Estate, Thomas Street, Stretford, Manchester, M32 0JT Tel: (0845) 5314117 Fax: (0845) 2571054 E-mail: info@reauk.com *Formed in 1911, Record Electrical has become a specialist supplier of Analogue Moving Coil and Moving Iron indicators with the "RECORD" and "CIRSCALE" trademark's known worldwide as a symbol of quality and accuracy. All our indicators are manufactured and calibrated in our Stretford factory to a quality system certified to BS EN ISO 9001:2000. Some special indicators have been certified for use in hazardous area applications holding ATEX certification for both intrinsically safe and Type nl areas suitable for field mounting, having IP66 rating, and panel mounting with IP54 rating. State of the art technology is used in our latest instruments for innovative solutions to difficult applications, one example is the Speedometers being supplied to the new breed of trains indicates not only the actual speed of the train but also sends a duplicate signal to the "On Train Monitor"*

▶ Record Packaging Systems Ltd, Unit 41 Stretford Motorway Estate, Stretford, Manchester, M32 0ZH Tel: 0161-864 3971 Fax: 0161-864 1390 E-mail: sales@recordpackaging.com *Record packaging service*

Record Playground Equipment Ltd, Waterfront Complex, Shipyard Industrial Estate, Selby, North Yorkshire, YO8 8AP Tel: (01757) 703620 Fax: (01757) 705158 E-mail: sales@recordplaygrounds.co.uk *Playground equipment manufrs*

Record U.K. Ltd, Smith Avenue, Garrion Business Park, Wishaw, Lanarkshire, ML2 0RY Tel: (01698) 376411 Fax: (01698) 376422 E-mail: patrick.montague@recorduk.co.uk Sales Contact: S. Chapman *Manufacture automatic doors, Install automatic doors, developers in automatic doors ,Specialising in automatic doors, Disability Discrimination act, DDA Compliant, D,D,A Act, Shopfronts, Glass Shopfronts, Aluminium shopfronts, Roller shutters, Automatic door openers, Toughened glass assembly's Aluminium windows , Aluminium screens, Automation of doors, Glass entrances, Glass and Aluminium entrances, P,F,I projects.*

Recordacall Telecommunications Equipment, Recall House, 44 Main Road, Denholme, Bradford, West Yorkshire, BD13 4BL Tel: (01274) 832575 Fax: (01274) 834593 *Telecommunication systems & equipment manufrs*

▶ Recording Studio Design, Pages Industrial Park, Eden Way, Leighton Buzzard, Bedfordshire, LU7 4TZ Tel: (01525) 217111 Fax: (01525) 378466 E-mail: enquiries@studiomaster.com *Pro audio equipment*

Recording Systems Ltd, 111 Upper Bristol Road, Weston-super-Mare, Avon, BS22 8DN Tel: (01934) 616162 E-mail: sales@recordingsystems.co.uk *Instrumentation distributors*

Recordpass Ltd, 4 Glencoe Business Park, Warne Road, Weston-super-Mare, Avon, BS23 3TS Tel: (01934) 629220 E-mail: warn.joinery@virgin.net *Timber shop fitters*

Recover Debt Solutions Ltd, 24 Winckley Square, Preston, PR1 3JJ Tel: (0870) 8532090 Fax: (0870) 8532091 E-mail: enquiries@recoveryourdebts.com *True No Win-No Fee Fast Track Business Debt Collection - Let Recover bring rapid relief to your business debts. Our legal process will be insured against the costs of failing to recover your debts.*

▶ RecruitEU Ltd, PO Box 43574, London, UK, SW15 1XA Tel: 0207 8708824 Fax: 0870 7051298 E-mail: nigelholmes@recruiteu.com *RecruitEU Ltd was launched in 2005 by the founders of the popular on-line recruitment facility www.workhaven.com to meet the needs of UK corporate clients wishing to recruit employees in volume from the new Eastern European accession states (Latvia, Lithuania, Estonia, Slovakia, Slovenia, Hungary, Czech Republic, Poland). RecruitEU operates through a network of Eastern European partner agents to provide local knowledge and recruitment expertise whilst ensuring consistency of approach and adherence to UK professional standards.*

Recruitment Initiative, St. Albans House, Portland Street, Leamington Spa, Warwickshire, CV32 5EZ Tel: (01926) 424111 Fax: (01926) 424142 E-mail: sales@therecruitmentinitiative.com *Employment agency*

▶ Recruitment Training (Edinburgh) Ltd, 32 & 34 Heriot Hill Terrace, Edinburgh, EH7 4DY Tel: 0131-558 9209 Fax: 0131-558 9187 E-mail: info@rtl-training.com *Recruitment training*

Rectella International Ltd, Queensway House, Queensway, Clitheroe, Lancashire, BB7 1AU Tel: (01200) 442299 Fax: (01200) 452015 E-mail: sales@flexr.co.uk *Instant bbq's & charcoal*

Recticel Carobel, Norham Road, North Shields, Tyne & Wear, NE29 7UX Tel: 0191-296 1010 Fax: 0191-296 3321 E-mail: carobel@compuserve.com *Foam converters*

Recticel Corby, 83-84 Manton Road, Earlstrees Industrial Estate, Corby, Northamptonshire, NN17 4JL Tel: (01536) 402345 Fax: (01536) 400524 E-mail: enquiries@recticel.co.uk *Manufacturers of foam, plastic converters*

▶ Recticel Gwalia, Unit 19 Rassau Industrial Estate, Rassau, Ebbw Vale, Gwent, NP23 5SD Tel: (01495) 356555 Fax: (01495) 356556

Recticel Insulation, Mitchell Hay Mills, College Road, Rochdale, Lancashire, OL12 6AE Tel: (01706) 715500 Fax: (01706) 715511 *Thermal insulation material manufrs*

Recticel Manufacturing, 1 Bluebell Close, Clover Nook Industrial Park, Somercotes, Alfreton, Derbyshire, DE55 4RD Tel: (01773) 835721 Fax: (01773) 835563 E-mail: uk@rect.com *Foam manufrs*

Recticel Midlands, Unit 3, Azalea Close, Clover Nook Industrial Park, Alfreton, Derbyshire, DE55 4QX Tel: (01773) 520242 Fax: (01773) 520513 E-mail: recticel@midlands.co.uk *Polyurethane foam converters & manufrs*

Recticel Pendle, Dale Mill, Hallam Road, Nelson, Lancashire, BB9 8AN Tel: (01282) 697528 Fax: (01282) 694766 *Foam products manufrs*

▶ Rectifier Technologies (UK) Limited, Unit A8, Sturmer End Industrial Estate, Sturmer Road, Haverhill, Suffolk, CB9 7UU Tel: (01440) 706777 Fax: (01440) 762810 E-mail: sales@duvine.co.uk *Designers & manufacturers of switch-mode and thyristor DC power supplies, rectifiers, battery chargers and batteries.*Applications include, telecoms, rail, road, utilities, military, aviation, offshore, control panels, industrial and renewable.*

Rectory Tool Company Ltd, 7 Port Hope Road, Camp Hill, Birmingham, B11 1JS Tel: 0121-773 9135 Fax: 0121-773 9342 E-mail: dianne@ctr.uk.com *Cold heading tool manufrs*

Rectro Ltd, 237 Bexley Road, Erith, Kent, DA8 3EX Tel: (01322) 340372 Fax: (01322) 335657 *Cycle wholesalers & spares*

▶ Rectron Computer Consumables, 5-6 Northfield Drive, Northfield, Milton Keynes, MK15 0DQ Tel: (01908) 235600 Fax: (01908) 235620 *Computer accessories suppliers*

Recuperator Ltd, 1437 Pershore Road, Stirchley, Birmingham, B30 2JL Tel: 0121-433 3677 Fax: 0121-433 3601 E-mail: sales@recuperator.co.uk *Heat recovery systems*

▶ Recyber Direct, The Old Town Hall, St. Andrews Street, Droitwich, Worcs, WR9 8DY Tel: (01905) 779993 Fax: (01905) 773080

▶ Recycle Force Ltd, 23 Symonds Way, Mawsley, Kettering, Northamptonshire, NN14 1GW Tel: (01536) 790007 Fax: (01536) 799132 E-mail: sales@recycleforce.co.uk *Recycling services*

▶ Recycle Print & Design Ltd, Swains Industrial Estate, Ashingdon Road, Rochford, Essex, SS4 1RG Tel: (01702) 531313 Fax: (01702) 531414

▶ Recycles Africa, Walnut Cottage, Brockhampton Lane, Swindon Village, Cheltenham, Gloucestershire, GL51 9RS Tel: (01242) 572161 Fax: (01242) 530774 E-mail: tony@recyclesafrica.com *Recycles Africa imports and distributes art from Southern Africa. Products are made from recycled metals and mine spoil.*

▶ Recycling In Action Ltd, Capital Valley Industrial Estate, Rhymney, Tredegar, Gwent, NP22 5PT Tel: (0870) 2404356 Fax: (0870) 2404357 E-mail: info@recycleinginactoin.com *Plastics recyclers*

Recycling World Magazines, Hilltop, Church Rd, Webheath, Redditch, Worcs, B97 5PQ Tel: (01527) 404550 Fax: (01527) 404644 E-mail: recycling@tecweb.com *Publishers*

▶ Recyclo, Prince William Avenue, Sandycroft, Deeside, Clwyd, CH5 2QZ Tel: (01244) 521800 Fax: (0845) 4515332 E-mail: enquiries@recyclowastemanagement.co.uk *Recycle commercial & industrial waste service*

▶ Red Plc, Unit1a, Canalside Industrial Estate, Woodbine St East, Rochdale, Lancashire, OL16 5LB Tel: (01706) 525623 Fax: (01706) 860590 E-mail: info@red-plc.co.uk *Designers & manufacturers of rail seating rail interior product*

Red Alce, Spithurst, Barcombe, Lewes, East Sussex, BN8 5ED Tel: (01273) 400780 Fax: (01273) 400744 E-mail: redalce@ukbuilder.com *Structural steelwork engineers*

Red Ant Innovations Ltd, 3-4 Southernhay West, Exeter, EX1 1JG Tel: (01392) 274707 Fax: (01392) 421475 E-mail: sales@redant.uk.com *Sage dealers*

▶ Red Apple, 2 Wrawby Road, Brigg, South Humberside, DN20 8DL Tel: (01652) 653704 Fax: (01652) 657777 E-mail: Sales@redapplecleaning.co.uk

▶ Red Apple Dental, Kangley Bridge Road, London, SE26 5AQ Tel: (0800) 3288080 Fax: (0800) 3288181 E-mail: red-apple@dial.pipex.com *Dental supplies, equipment, products, tools, cement, gloves*

Red Bank Manufacturing Co. Ltd, Atherstone Road, Measham, Swadlincote, Derbyshire, DE12 7EL Tel: (01530) 270333 Fax: (01530) 270542 E-mail: info@redbank-manufacturing.co.uk *Flue lining & air brick manufrs*

Red Bay Boats Ltd, Coast Road, Cushendall, Ballymena, County Antrim, BT44 0QW Tel: (028) 2177 1331 Fax: (028) 2177 1474 E-mail: info@redbayboats.com *Boat builders*

Red Box Supplies, Unit 19d, Bergen Way, Hull, HU7 0YQ Tel: (01482) 321713 Fax: (01482) 321714 E-mail: sales@redboxsupplies.co.uk *Conveyor belting manufrs*

▶ The Red Carpet, 21 Morris Court, Waltham Abbey, Essex, EN9 3DX Tel: 01992 619469 E-mail: theredcarpet@hotmail.co.uk *CARPET AND UPHOLSTERY CLEANING THROUGHOUT ESSEX AND HERTFORDSHIRE*

▶ RED Control Systems Otley Ltd, Wharfebank House, Wharfebank Business Centre, Ilkley Road, Otley, West Yorkshire, LS21 3JP Tel: (01943) 851000 Fax: (08714) 259742 E-mail: enquiries@redcontrolsystems.com *Supply and commission intelligent building control systems*Specialist BACnet building automation systems providor. *BACnet integration specialist*Automated logic WebCtrl partner*

The Red Corner Document Solutions Ltd, 7200 The Quorum, Oxford Business Park North, Oxford, OX4 2JZ Tel: (01865) 481488 Fax: (01865) 882164 *Digital outputs & solutions suppliers & service agents*

▶ Red Create, 145-157 St. John Street, London, EC1V 4PY Tel: (020) 7060 5004 Fax: 0871 4330485 E-mail: Info@redcreate.com *Personal website Hosting and Design service including domain registration and SSL*

▶ Red Design & Build, Unit 6, Parkfield Industrial Estate, London, SW11 5BA Tel: (020) 7622 7000 Fax: (0870) 4601277 E-mail: nick@reddesignandbuild.com *Established building and interior design business specialising in refurbishment work in central London.*

Red Devil, Unit 2e Beehive Lane Works, Beehive Lane, Chelmsford, CM2 9TE Tel: (01255) 553555 Fax: (01255) 553555 E-mail: sales@reddevilmachines.co.uk *Printers & printing machinery manufrs*

▶ Red Devil Storage Ltd, 14 - 16 Kempson Close, Gatehouse Industrial Estate, Aylesbury, Buckinghamshire, HP19 8UQ Tel: (01296) 381818 Fax: (01296) 381919 E-mail: kempsonclose@reddevilstorage.co.uk *Red Devil Storage specialise in offering professional and personal service for all your storage requirements. For both private and commercial customers. We are open 7 days a week giving you complete flexibility.*

▶ Red Devil Storage, Units 1 - 2, The Wynne Jones Centre, Tring Road, Aylesbury, Buckinghamshire, HP21 7RL Tel: (01296) 397215 Fax: (01296) 397216 E-mail: tringroad@reddevilstorage.co.uk *Red Devil Storage offers professional and personal solutions to all your storage requirements. We are open 7 days a week and cater for both private and commercial customers.*

▶ Red Devil Storage Ltd, 381 Kennington Road, London, SE11 4PT Tel: (0800) 0561773 Fax: (020) 7480 8120 E-mail: enquiries@reddevilstorage.co.uk *Red Devil Storage offer a professional and personal service for all your storage requirements for both private individuals and companies alike. We are open 7 days a week giving you total flexibility.*

▶ Red Dog Photography, 31 Cheadle Road, Uttoxeter, Staffordshire, ST14 7BX Tel: (01889) 569232 E-mail: duncan@reddogphoto.co.uk *Commercial photography*

Red Dot Ltd, 98 White Hart Lane, London, N22 5SG Tel: (020) 8888 2354 Fax: (020) 8881 0497 E-mail: sales@reddotracing.co.uk *Brake distributors*

Red Dot Ltd, Unit 4, Blueprint Commercial Centre, Imperial Way, Watford, WD24 4JD Tel: (01970) 3002354 *Performance brakes* Also at: Bradford

▶ Red Eagle, 38 Bouverie Square, Folkestone, Kent, CT20 1BA Tel: (01303) 851133 Fax: (01303) 851134 E-mail: jobs@red-eagle.co.uk *Recruitment agency temporary & permanent opportunities*

Red Forge Ltd, 5 Palmers Road, Redditch, Worcestershire, B98 0RF Tel: (01527) 526112 Fax: (01527) 523862 E-mail: sales@redforge.co.uk *Electric cab heaters & vehicle weighing equipment manufrs*

▶ Red Frog Design, 24 Loxley Way, Brough, North Humberside, HU15 1GB Tel: (07813) 649556 E-mail: alex@theredfrog.com

Red Funnel Group Ltd, 12 Bugle Street, Southampton, SO14 2JY Tel: (0870) 4448889 Fax: (0870) 4448897 E-mail: post@redfunnel.co.uk *Ferry operators & freight distributors*

▶ Red Galleon Ltd, Beech House Docking Road, Sedgeford, Hunstanton, Norfolk, PE36 5LR Tel: (01485) 579363 Fax: (01485) 579396 E-mail: info@redgalleon.com *Established September 2000. A division of ee-scape.net ltd we have over twenty five years experience in the IT Industry. We stand behind all the products we supply, many of which we use to ensure the efficient running of our own business. We know our products and we understand the challenges of introducing them into your business. Our products will deliver needed solutions to increase productivity of your business and home office. ***

Red Hot Plants, 3 Evesham Close, Mossgate Park, Heysham, Morecambe, Lancashire, LA3 2FL Tel: (01524) 851017 E-mail: mail@redhotplants.co.uk *Suppliers of high quality artificial plants and trees for hotels and restaurants. Also a large range of artificial outdoor topiary trees for dressing doorways and entrance halls.*

Red House Consultancy, 10 Badger Lane, Blackshaw Head, Hebden Bridge, West Yorkshire, HX7 7JX Tel: (01422) 846846 Fax: (01422) 846846 E-mail: simon@red-house-consultancy.co.uk *Technical authors & writers consultancy*

▶ Red House Distribution, 57 Highcliff Drive, Leigh-on-Sea, Essex, SS9 1DQ Tel: 07775 795304 E-mail: redhousedistribution@hotmail.com *Quality and reliable door to door leaflet distribution.*

Red Interior Solutions Ltd, St. Johns Industrial Estate, Lees, Oldham, OL4 3DZ Tel: 0161-633 4740 Fax: 0161-633 4740 E-mail: redint@aol.com *Shop fitting & joinery manufrs & interior refurbishment*

Red Joinery Ltd, Aquaduct Wharf, Hurst Lane, Bollington, Macclesfield, Cheshire, SK10 5LP Tel: (01625) 572128 *Specialist joinery manufacturers & timber yard*

▶ Red Kestrel Consulting, 17 Constance Avenue, Trentham, Stoke-on-Trent, ST4 8TE Tel: (01782) 643438 E-mail: info@redkestrel.co.uk *Provides IT security consultancy and software development services including: computer/ network security, firewalls, PKI, bespoke development (C#, .NET, C, Python).**

Red Leaver Signs, 80 Dalling Road, London, W6 0JA Tel: (020) 8741 4306 Fax: (020) 8741 4307 *Sign manufrs*

Red Ledge Ltd, Red Ledge Business Centre, 289-291 Huddersfield Road, Thongsbridge, Holmfirth, HD9 3UA Tel: (01484) 686769 Fax: (01484) 687879 E-mail: sales@redledge.co.uk *Bar Code Systems - Software Developers*

Red Lion 49 Ltd, 25 Springhill Road, Begbroke, Kidlington, Oxfordshire, OX5 1RU Tel: (01865) 842300 Fax: (01865) 842118 E-mail: sales@solid-state-logic.com *Automated mixing console manufrs*

Red Machine, Black Barn, Cornwells Farm, Sheephurst Lane, Marden, Kent, TN12 9NS Tel: (01622) 832010 Fax: (01622) 832177 E-mail: contact@redmachine.co.uk *Media producers*

Red Mill Snack Foods Ltd, Globe Street, Wednesbury, West Midlands, WS10 0NN Tel: 0121-505 1500 Fax: 0121-505 2424 E-mail: info@redmill.co.uk *Snack food manufrs*

▶ Red Paw Solutions Ltd, 5a/1 Starbank Road, Edinburgh, EH5 3BW Tel: (07745) 428130

The Red Pelican Coffee Company Ltd, Little Horwood Road, Great Horwood, Milton Keynes, MK17 0NZ Tel: (01296) 713280 Fax: (01296) 714961 *Import vending machine ingredients*

Red Rhino Crushers, Unit 3 Triangle Business Park, Quilters Way, Stoke Mandeville, Aylesbury, Buckinghamshire, HP22 5BL Tel: (0870) 6064949 Fax: (0870) 6063939 E-mail: info@redrhinocrushers.net *Crushing machines*

Red River Technologies Ltd, 16 Marshall Street, Nottingham, NG5 4AF Tel: 0115-969 1008 E-mail: info@red-river.co.uk *Information technology consultants*

▶ Red Rock Controls, 36 Sunnyside Lane, Balsall Common, Coventry, CV7 7FY Tel: (07968) 217494 E-mail: roger@redrockcontrols.co.uk *Software development for machine tools & automation*

Red Rose Construction, Charter Street, Accrington, Lancashire, BB5 0SG Tel: (01254) 239300 Fax: (01254) 239300

Red Rose Cookware Ltd, Unit 7-9 11-15 Francis Avenue, Bournemouth, BH11 8NX Tel: (01202) 575900 Fax: (01202) 582120 *Cookware manufacturers & distributors*

Red Rose Distribution, Parliament Street, Burnley, Lancashire, BB11 3JT Tel: (01282) 724600 Fax: (01282) 724644 *Laminated plastics distributors*

Red Rose Iron Work, The Old Press House, Irwell Vale Road, Rossendale, Lancashire, BB4 6LF Tel: (01706) 830506 Fax: (01706) 830506 *Wrought ironsmiths*

Red Rose Mouldings, Unit 9 Fountain Mill, Carluke Street, Blackburn, BB1 3JR Tel: (01254) 693329 Fax: (01254) 278134 *Injection Moulders*

Red Rose Packaging Ltd, Newby Road Industrial Estate, Newby Road, Hazel Grove, Stockport, Cheshire, SK7 5DA Tel: 0161-483 4433 Fax: 0161-487 2161 E-mail: redrose.packaging@virgin.net *Corrugated carton manufrs*

Red Rose Products Ltd, Albion Works, Silver Street, Oldham, OL1 1HX Tel: 0161-624 5261 Fax: 0161-627 0946 *Producers of disposable stitched products*

▶ Red Seal, Technium Business Park, Kings Road, Swansea, SA1 8PH Tel: (01792) 295004 Fax: (01792) 485577 E-mail: studio@red-seal.com *Creative consultants*

Red Shark Technologies, Unit 12a, North Road Industrial Estate, Berwick-upon-Tweed, TD15 1UN Tel: (01289) 303303 Fax: (01289) 302333 E-mail: sales@bigredshark.net *Ink Jet cartridge manufrs*

Red Signs, Unit 14 105 Hopewell Business Centre, Hopewell Drive, Chatham, Kent, ME5 7DX Tel: (01634) 309434 Fax: (01634) 309436 E-mail: info@redsigns.co.uk *Sign manufrs*

▶ The Red Word, 15 Heath Drive, Binfield Heath, Henley-on-Thames, Oxfordshire, RG9 4LX Tel: 0118-947 1181 E-mail: info@theredword.co.uk *Press releases, brochures, direct mail, adverts and optimised web copy to get your business really noticed.*

Redapt Engineering Co. Ltd, Darlaston Central TRDG Estate, Salisbury Street, Wednesbury, West Midlands, WS10 8BQ Tel: 0121-526 7058 *Thread conversion products manufrs*

▶ Redarch Associates Ltd, Unit 1 42 Feering Hill, Feering, Colchester, CO5 9NH Tel: (01376) 573767 Fax: (01376) 573900 E-mail: enquiry@redarch.co.uk *Redarch provides Clients with support and advice in 'Plain English' in line with the way they work helping them to define and achieve their strategic goals.*

Redashe Ltd, Unit 8 The Brook Trading Estate, Deadbrook Lane, Aldershot, Hampshire, GU12 4XB Tel: (01252) 785010 Fax: (01252) 329328 E-mail: info@redashe.co.uk *Supplier of workshop equipment to the industrial & automotive markets*

▶ Redbark, Badger House, Desborough, Kettering, Northamptonshire, NN14 2NS Tel: 01604 648773 Fax: 0871 242 5181 E-mail: redbark@tiscali.co.uk *Simple Video Emailing*FACT 30 billion emails sent every day, FACT video email will replace standard text emailing*Brilliant for business promotion or family*

Redbay Projects Ltd, 15 Dalton Court, Astmoor Industrial Estate, Runcorn, Cheshire, WA7 1PU Tel: (01928) 581782 Fax: (01928) 580619 E-mail: redbayprojects@aol.com *Mechanical & electrical services*

▶ Redblack Software Ltd, Kings House, 12 King Street, York, YO1 9WP Tel: (01904) 622888 Fax: (01904) 654888 E-mail: enquiries@redblacksoftware.co.uk *Computer software development*

Redbooks, Bridewell House, Bridewell Lane, Tenterden, Kent, TN30 6EP Tel: (01580) 764225 Fax: (01580) 763720 E-mail: sales@estate-publications.co.uk *Map publishers*

Redbourn Engineering Ltd, Chiswick Avenue, Mildenhall, Bury St. Edmunds, Suffolk, IP28 7AY Tel: (01638) 713484 Fax: (01638) 713809 E-mail: sales@redbourn.com *Pressings designers & manufrs*

Redbourn International Forwarding Ltd, 43A Adelaide Street, Luton, LU1 5BD Tel: (01582) 425611 Fax: (01582) 405705 E-mail: office@redbourninternational.co.uk *International freight forwarders*

▶ Redbows Ltd, 24 Bryntirion Drive, Prestatyn, Clwyd, LL19 9NU Tel: (01745) 852520 Fax: (0845) 8386369 E-mail: sales@redbows.co.uk *Promotional gifts & product suppliers*

▶ Redbox Consulting Ltd, 49 Clarendon Road, Watford, WD17 1HZ Tel: (0870) 4455660 Fax: (0870) 4455661 E-mail: info@redbox-group.com *Telecom consultants*

Redbox Fire Control, 7 South View Road, Southampton, SO15 5JD Tel: (023) 8077 6131 Fax: (023) 8077 6131 E-mail: enquiries@redboxfire.co.uk *Fire protection equipment manufrs*

Redbreast Industrial Equipment Ltd, 1 Stavely Way, Brixworth, Northampton, NN6 9EU Tel: (01604) 882088 Fax: (01604) 882015 E-mail: sales@redbreastrobin.co.uk *Industrial engines, pumps & generators importers*

▶ Redbrook Conservatories Ltd, Floor 3, 53 Hamilton Square, Birkenhead, Merseyside, CH41 5AS Tel: (0800) 1613034 E-mail: enquiries@redbrookconservatories.com *Conservatory manufrs*

▶ Redcar Plumbing & Heating, The Innovation Centre, Vienna Court, Kirkleatham Business Park, Redcar, Cleveland, TS10 5SH Tel: (01642) 777800 Fax: (01642) 777850

Redcliffe Catering Ltd, Westbourne Road, Edgbaston, Birmingham, B15 3TR Tel: 0121-456 2244 Fax: 0121-450 4620 E-mail: sales@redcliffe.com *Banqueting & conference centre*

Redcliffe Catering Ltd, 100 Icknield Port Road, Edgbaston, Birmingham, B16 0AA Tel: 0121-456 4545 Fax: 0121-454 9118 E-mail: cc.conferences@redcliffe.com *Catering & conference services*

▶ Redcliffe Computers Ltd, 1st Floor Unity Court, 431 Meanwood Road, Leeds, LS7 2LD Tel: 0113-246 0777 Fax: 0113-245 0944 E-mail: info@redcliffe-computers.co.uk *Computer software developers*

Redcliffe Imaging Ltd, 21 Dragon Court, Crofts End Road, Bristol, BS5 7XX Tel: 0117-952 0105 Fax: 0117-951 8911 E-mail: info@redcliffe.co.uk *Exhibition stands, banners stands, pop-up displays*

Redcliffe Joinery, 82 Ballymena Road, Cullybackey, Ballymena, County Antrim, BT43 5QS Tel: (028) 2588 0972 Fax: (028) 2588 1443 *Joiners*

Redcliffe Magtronics, 19 Clothier Road, Brislington, Bristol, BS4 5PS Tel: 0117-972 9400 Fax: 0117-972 3013 E-mail: enquiries@redcliffe.biz Principal Export Areas: Asia Pacific & North America *Electronics design & manufacturer*

Redco Ltd, Airedale House Sapphire Way, Rhombus Business Park, Norwich, NR6 6NN Tel: (01603) 400920 Fax: (01603) 418716 E-mail: rhredco@aol.com *Plastic stockholders & precision engineers service*

▶ Redco Recruitment Group Limited, Redco House, 165 Lea Road, Pennfields, Wolverhampton, WV3 0LQ Tel: 0845 111 0735 Fax: 0845 111 0736 E-mail: info@redcorecruitment.com *Specialist recruitment consultants for the Freight Forwarding, Finance and Banking, Sales and Marketing, Technology and Call Centres sectors.*

Reddick Forge, Crawley Down Road, Felbridge, East Grinstead, West Sussex, RH19 2PS Tel: (01342) 302055 Fax: (01342) 302055 E-mail: sales@reddickforge.co.uk *Wrought ironworker specialists*

Reddie & Grose, 16 Theobalds Road, London, WC1X 8PL Tel: (020) 7242 0901 Fax: (020) 7242 3290 E-mail: enquiries@reddie.co.uk *Patent & trade mark attourneys*

Reddiplex Group Logistics, Unit 33 The Furlong, Berry Hill Industrial Estate, Droitwich, Worcestershire, WR9 9BG Tel: (01905) 774400 Fax: (01905) 791866 E-mail: reddiplex@reddiplex.com Principal Export Areas: Worldwide *Plastic & rubber extrusion services*

Reddish Electroplating, Mersey Street, Stockport, Cheshire, SK1 2HX Tel: 0161-480 7890 Fax: 0161-480 4383 E-mail: rep-sales@btconnect.com *Chrome hard plating & grinding services*

▶ Reddish Vale Installations, Albion House, Under Lane, Chadderton, Oldham, OL9 7PP Tel: 0161-688 6444 Fax: 0161-688 6448 E-mail: info@reddishvale.co.uk *Reddish Vale Insulations Ltd is a mature, established ARCA accredited asbestos removal company situated in the north of England with over twenty years experience. During this time we have built a strong reputation providing a service for our customers that is of the highest technical standards combined with an attention to safety, quality and cost-effectiveness that is second to none. Compliance to all regulations is very carefully managed and monitored and all of our operatives are fully certified in all aspects of asbestos removal. We have a policy of continual training in line with health and safety requirements to ensure that the highest standards are maintained. Reddish Vale Insulations is qualified to undertake asbestos surveys to The Health and Safety Executive"s standard MDH0.**

Redditch Electro Plating Co. Ltd, Arrow Road North, Redditch, Worcestershire, B98 8NT Tel: (01527) 63858 Fax: (01527) 591504 *Electroplating services*

Redditch Fire Protection, Bliss Gate House, Edgioake Lane, Astwood Bank, Redditch, Worcestershire, B96 6BG Tel: (01527) 893336 Fax: (01527) 893336 E-mail: brogers@redditchfire.co.uk *Fire protection engineers*

Redditch Joinery (Holdings) Ltd, 21a Weights Farm, Weights Lane, Redditch, Worcestershire, B97 6RG Tel: (01527) 66111 Fax: (01527) 68180 *Cabinet makers & joinery manufrs*

Redditch Lasercutting Ltd, 9 Broad Ground Road, Redditch, Worcestershire, B98 8YP Tel: (01527) 510474 Fax: (01527) 510432 Principal Export Areas: Central/East Europe & West Europe *Specialists in laser & water jet cutting, offering 2D, 3D & tube cutting.*

▶ Redditch Lift Truck Training Services, 19 Goodrich Close, Redditch, Worcestershire, B98 0NE Tel: 01527 502632 Fax: 01527 502632 E-mail: Info@rltts.freeserve.co.uk

The Redditch Partitions & Storage Co. Ltd, Unit 1 Old Forge Business Centre, Little Forge Road, Park Farm North, Redditch, Worcestershire, B98 7SF Tel: (01527) 517055 Fax: (01527) 517025 E-mail: info@redditch-partitions.co.uk *Suspended ceiling, mezzanine floors, platforms & partitioning manufrs*

Redditch Plastic Products, Pipers Road, Park Farm Industrial Estate, Redditch, Worcestershire, B98 0HU Tel: (01527) 528024 Fax: (01527) 520236 E-mail: sales@rpp.uk.com *Manufacture of electrical accessories*

Redditch Production Machining, 47 Padgets Lane, Redditch, Worcestershire, B98 0RD Tel: (01527) 500568 Fax: (01527) 510976 *Turned parts sub contractors*

Redditek Systems Ltd, Unit 53 South Moons Moat Industrial Estate, Padgets Lane, Redditch, Worcestershire, B98 0RD Tel: (01527) 501687 Fax: (01527) 510320 E-mail: sales@redditek.co.uk *Metal cabinets, lockers & work benches manufrs*

Reddiwire Ltd, 9 Dunlop Road, Hunt End, Redditch, Worcestershire, B97 5XP Tel: (01527) 550202 Fax: (01527) 546856 E-mail: reddiwire@dial.pipex.com *Wire & strip stockholders*

Dr Reddy's Laboratories UK Ltd, Riverview Road, Beverley, North Humberside, HU17 0LD Tel: (01482) 860228 Fax: (01482) 872042 *Pharmaceutical manufrs*

▶ Redefining Financial Solutions Ltd, 9 Hardwicke Gardens, Amersham, Buckinghamshire, HP6 6AH Tel: (01494) 431739 E-mail: info@redefiningfinancialsolutions.com *Business Management and Training Consultants, offering the following range of services:**Business Guidance and Counselling;**Business Decision Making Support;**Strategic Planning and Commercial Insight;**Finance Training and Development;**Business Processes and Systems Re-engineering.*

Redfab Ltd, 656 Portslade Road, London, SW8 3DH Tel: (020) 7622 2221 Fax: (020) 7622 2221 E-mail: redfablimited@hotmail.com *Engineering, design & fabrication*

Redfern & Birchall, 6 Fernhill Street, Bury, Lancashire, BL9 5BG Tel: 0161-764 4929 Fax: 0161-764 4929 *Sheet metalwork & air conditioning*

▶ Redfern Building Services Ltd, Construction House, North Bondgate, Bishop Auckland, County Durham, DL14 7PG Tel: (01388) 661113 Fax: (01388) 607571

Redfern Engineering, Unit 7 Durban Road, Bognor Regis, West Sussex, PO22 9QT Tel: (01243) 864191 Fax: (01243) 862514 *Precision engineering services*

Company Information

G.F. Redfern & Co., 7 Staple Inn, Holborn, London, WC1V 7QF Tel: (020) 7242 7680 Fax: (020) 7831 7957 *Patent & trade mark attorneys*

Redfern Stevens Ltd, 40 Brickfield Road, Birmingham, B25 8HE Tel: 0121-766 6464 Fax: 0121-766 6651 E-mail: info@redfernstevens.co.uk *Stampings & pressings manufrs*

Redfern Transports Ltd, Mount Street Mill, Mount Street, Bradford, West Yorkshire, BD3 9RJ Tel: (01274) 392721 Fax: (01274) 370851 E-mail: sales@redferntransports.co.uk *Freight & air freight forwarders*

▶ Redferns Furniture, 2 Glover Centre, Egmont Street, Mossley, Ashton-under-Lyne, Lancashire, OL5 9PY Tel: (01457) 839282 Fax: (01457) 839282 *Furniture manufrs*

Redford Cairns Ltd, PO Box 17252, London, SE19 3ZN Tel: (020) 8653 6365 Fax: (020) 8653 1001 E-mail: rrcl@redfordcairns.com *Recruitment consultancy*

Redfyre Cookers, Osprey Road, Sowton Industrial Estate, Exeter, EX2 7JG Tel: (01392) 444070 Fax: (01392) 444804 E-mail: redfyre@gazco.com *Make handcrafted cookers & stainless steel outdoor barbeques*

Redgate Holdings Ltd, Redgate Lane, West Gorton, Manchester, M12 4RY Tel: 0161-273 5575 Fax: 0161-274 4113 E-mail: redgateholdings@hotmail.co.uk *State-of-the-art waste transfer station & world's first online skip hire service. We recycle over 70% of all waste collected and aim to give the best customer service in our industry*

Redgold Fashions Ltd, 219-221 Bow Road, London, E3 2SJ Tel: (020) 8980 9745 Fax: (020) 8980 4979 *Clothing*

Redgold Hydraulic & Engineering Services, 5 Bradley Hall Trading Estate, Bradley Lane, Standish, Wigan, Lancashire, WN6 0XQ Tel: (01257) 425917 Fax: (01257) 425927 E-mail: francistaylor@redgoldhydraulics.co.uk *Hydraulic engineers & cylinder repairers*

Redgoldfish Jobs, Cornelius House, Whitehouse Court, Cannock, Staffordshire, WS11 3DA Tel: (01543) 468800 Fax: (01543) 468900 E-mail: info@redgoldfish.co.uk *Job Search facilities, online recruitment & Career services.*

Redhall Engineering Services Ltd, Bydales Lane, Winestead, Hull, HU12 0NW Tel: (01964) 631338 Fax: (01964) 631689 *Steel fabricators & shot blasters*

Redhill Bearings Ltd, The White House, Brighton Road, Handcross, Haywards Heath, West Sussex, RH17 6BZ Tel: (01444) 400900 Fax: (01444) 400753 E-mail: redhillbearings@aol.com *Bearing stockists*

Redhill Manufacturing Ltd, Unit 6, Padgets Lane, South Moons Moat Industrial Estate, Redditch, Worcestershire, B98 0RA Tel: (01527) 529002 Fax: (01527) 523950 E-mail: sales@redhillmanufacturing.co.uk *Manufacturers of office, warehouse & industrial use products*

Redhill Marine Ltd, Ratcliffe On Soar, Nottingham, NG11 0EB Tel: (01509) 672770 *Marina boat moorings*

▶ Redhouse Forge, 86 Copenhagen Place, London, E14 7DE Tel: 020 7987 8664 Fax: 020 7987 8664 E-mail: mail@redhouseonline.com *Furniture Designer Makers and Architectural Ironworkers. We specialise in the fabrication and finishing of sheet material (copper, brass, stainless steel), Wrought Iron and Hardwood Carpentry.*Our website shows some of the regular furniture we make but not really the architectural or interiors work.*Please feel free to contact us.*

Redhouse Lane Communications, 14-15 Bedford Square, London, WC1B 3JA Tel: (020) 7462 2600 Fax: (020) 7462 2601 E-mail: sales@redhouselane.com *Copywriting & design agency service*

Redhurst Hotel, 77 Eastwoodmains Road, Giffnock, Glasgow, G46 6QE Tel: 0141-638 6465 Fax: 0141-620 0419 E-mail: redhurst@line1.net *Hotel with conference facilities*

Redi Fire Ltd, 15 Evesham Road, Redditch, Worcestershire, B97 4JU Tel: (01527) 542369 *Fire Fighting Equipment*

Redileads Anglesey Ltd, Industrial Estate Road, Llangefni, Gwynedd, LL77 7JA Tel: (01248) 750280 Fax: (01248) 722031 E-mail: enquiries@redileads.co.uk Principal Export Areas: Africa *Manufacturers of electronic cable assembly harness*

Redirack Ltd, Wharf Road, Kilnhurst, Mexborough, South Yorkshire, S64 5SU Tel: (01709) 584711 Fax: (01709) 589821 E-mail: sales@redirack.co.uk *Manufacturers of racking, storage equipment & mezzanine floors*

Rediset Business Forms Ltd, Factory Road, Upton Industrial Estate, Poole, Dorset, BH16 5SJ Tel: (01202) 622679 Fax: (01202) 623375 *Computer & business stationery printers services*

▶ RedKite IT Solutions Ltd, 127 Stonegate, Hunmanby, Filey, North Yorkshire, YO14 0PU Tel: (01723) 890890 Fax: (07812) 356040 E-mail: enquiries@redkiteit.com *IT solutions with expert consultancy, sales & support*

Redkyte Computers, 142 Flixton Road, Urmston, Manchester, M41 5BG Tel: 0161-749 7861 E-mail: sales@redkyte.com *Computer maintenance, repairs & retail*

Redlaw Shearing (Lye) Ltd, The White House, Pearson Street, Lye, Stourbridge, West Midlands, DY9 8BB Tel: (01384) 422398 Fax: (01384) 422398 *Manufacturers of electrical laminations*

Redlaw Shearing (Lye) Ltd, The White House, Pearson Street, Stourbridge, West Midlands, DY9 8BB Tel: (01384) 422398 Fax: (01384) 422398 *Transformer lamination manufrs*

Redleaf Vehicle Leasing, 28-29 Westhampnett Road, Chichester, West Sussex, PO19 7HH Tel: (08457) 669988 Fax: (01243) 780750 *All types of vehicle finance arranged for both businesses and individuals. Any make of car and light commercial can be supplied.*Why not ask for a Quote?*

Redler Ltd, Dudbridge Works, Dudbridge, Stroud, Gloucestershire, GL5 3EY Tel: (01453) 763611 Fax: (01453) 763582 E-mail: sales@redler.com Principal Export Areas: Worldwide *Redler is renowned for quality in materials handling equipment for coal, ash and biomass. European headquarters of stock equipment company who are the leading manufacturer of coal feed systems and innovative environmental control technologies.*

Redlin Print Ltd, 33 Hanbury Road, Chelmsford, CM1 3AE Tel: 01245 280555 E-mail: sales@redlin.co.uk *General & commercial printers & colour digital & black & white printers*

Redline C N C, Units 4-5, 15 Balcombe Road, Horley, Surrey, RH6 7JR Tel: (01293) 820090 Fax: (01293) 820091 E-mail: sales@redline-cnc.co.uk *Manufactures of precision machined components produced on CNC Lathes and Machining Centres. *Quality Management Systems Approved to BS EN ISO 9001:2000*

▶ Redline Group P.L.C., Brandon House 30, 23-25 Brandon Street, Hamilton, Lanarkshire, ML3 6DA Tel: (01698) 527120 Fax: (01698) 527105 E-mail: info@redlineplc.com *Recruitment*

Redlynch Leisure Installations Ltd, PO Box 1181, Chippenham, Wiltshire, SN15 3ZD Tel: (01249) 444537 Fax: (01249) 655002 *Construction of children play areas*

Red-M Services Ltd, Graylands, Langhurstwood Road, Horsham, West Sussex, RH12 4QD Tel: (01403) 211100 Fax: (01403) 248597 *Wireless network services*

Redman Controls & Electronics Ltd, Brick Kiln Industrial Estate, Malders Lane, Maidenhead, Berkshire, SL6 6NQ Tel: (01628) 630514 Fax: (01628) 625254 E-mail: sales@redmancontrols.com *Electronic control welding equipment suppliers & manufrs*

Redman Sheet Metal Ltd, Unit 13 Isis Trading Estate, Swindon, SN1 2PG Tel: (01793) 692781 Fax: (01793) 491688 E-mail: jim@redman-sheet-metal.co.uk *Sheet metalwork engineers, subcontract sheetmetal*

Wylie Redman (Moulds) Ltd, 17 Watt Road, Glasgow, G52 4RZ Tel: 0141 8835284 *Plastic mould makers, tool makers*

Redmayne Engineering Ltd, Romsey Indust Estate, Greatbridge Road, Romsey, Hampshire, SO51 0HR Tel: (01794) 830832 Fax: (01794) 830123 *Precision engineers*

Redmill Fabrication Ltd, 19 Inchmuir Road, Whitehill Industrial Estate, Bathgate, West Lothian, EH48 2EP Tel: (01506) 634333 Fax: (01506) 634999 *General & installation engineers*

Redmill Snack Foods Ltd, Great Bank Road, Wingates Industrial Estate, Westhoughton, Bolton, BL5 3XU Tel: (01942) 815543 Fax: (01942) 810614 E-mail: enquiries@redmill.co.uk *Food product manufrs*

Redmire Stables & Buildings Ltd, Five Oaks Sawmill, Five Oaks, Billingshurst, West Sussex, RH14 9BD Tel: (01403) 785508 Fax: (01403) 785333 E-mail: enquiries@redmire.co.uk *Timber buildings manufrs*

Rednal Industries Ltd, Mile Oak Industrial Estate, Maesbury Road, Oswestry, Shropshire, SY10 8GA Tel: (01691) 659601 Fax: (01691) 655021 E-mail: sales@rednall.co.uk *Pressure vessels, air receivers & separators manufrs*

Rednal Polishing & Spraying Co. Ltd, Station Works, 17-19 Station Road, Northfield, Birmingham, B31 3TE Tel: 0121-475 4826 Fax: 0121-475 2712 *Metal fabricators & paint sprayers*

▶ ReDox Electronic Archiving Ltd, The Old Farmhouse, Pillerton Hersey, Warwick, CV35 0QJ Tel: 01789 740811 Fax: 01789 740811 E-mail: rw@papersave.co.uk *Electronic archival of commercial documents. High speed scanning, sorting, and saving. Provision of consultancy about, and supply of various storage media options. Optical disk, network served, or online access.*

Redport Net Ltd, Broadgauge Business Park, Bishops Lydeard, Taunton, Somerset, TA4 3RU Tel: (01823) 431885 Fax: (01823) 431886 E-mail: sales@ptwinchester.co.uk *Angling & billiard table net manufrs*

Redpost Electronic Products Ltd, The Old Pumping Station, Toft Road, Bourn, Cambridge, CB23 2TT Tel: (01954) 718001 Fax: (01954) 718002 *Electronic brewer equipment manufrs*

▶ Redprairie, Beacon House, Ibstone Road, Stokenchurch, High Wycombe, Buckinghamshire, HP14 3AQ Tel: (01494) 486500 Fax: (01494) 485465 E-mail: sales@online-internet.co.uk *IT systems & software installation & maintenance services*

Redreef Ltd, 8 Vale Road, Bromley, BR1 2AL Tel: (020) 8467 3445 Fax: (020) 8467 4108 E-mail: redreef@compuserve.com *Export merchants*

Redrock Forestry, Felin Hen Farm, Felin Hen Road, Bangor, Gwynedd, LL57 4BB Tel: (01248) 364362 Fax: (01248) 364232 *Forestry consultants*

Redrow Homes, Redrow House, St David's Park, Ewloe, Deeside, Clwyd, CH5 3RX Tel: (01244) 520044 Fax: (01244) 520580 E-mail: heather@redrow.demon.co.uk *Building contractors*

▶ Redrow Homes (Midlands) Ltd, 2 Kinsel Green, Wilnecote, Tamworth, Staffordshire, B77 5PB Tel: (01827) 260600 Fax: (01827) 262454

▶ Redrow Homes Scotland Ltd, 3 Central Park Avenue, Central Park, Larbert, Stirlingshire, FK5 4RX Tel: (01324) 555536 Fax: (01324) 574890

▶ Redrow Homes West Midlands Ltd, Steelpark Road, Halesowen, West Midlands, B62 8HD Tel: 0121-504 0280 Fax: 0121-504 0281

▶ Redshark, Zetland House, Paul Street, London, EC2A 4LF Tel: (020) 7729 0030 Fax: (020) 7739 4918 E-mail: info@redshark.tv *Video editing post production services*

Redstone Computers UK Ltd, Suit 3 Stone House Business Centre, Market Street, Chipping Norton, Oxfordshire, OX7 5NA Tel: (0870) 0119433 Fax: (01608) 811359 E-mail: emac@sagesolutions.co.uk *Computer dealer & accountancy software suppliers*

Redstor Ltd, 1 London Road, Reading, RG1 5BJ Tel: 0118 9011969 Fax: 0118-377 6501 E-mail: sales@redstor.com *Computer data storage & equipment services*

Redtitan Ltd, 5 Regius Court, Penn, High Wycombe, Buckinghamshire, HP10 8RL Tel: (0870) 8705432 Fax: (0870) 8704560 E-mail: sales@redtitan.com *Computer software for laser printers*

▶ Redtrap Ltd, 6 Heron Way, Chippenham, Wiltshire, SN14 0XE Tel: (01793) 480133 E-mail: info@redtrap.com *Computer software developers*

▶ Reduce My Bills, 11 New River Green, Exning, Newmarket, Suffolk, CB8 7HS Tel: (0845) 3312673 E-mail: info@reducemybills.co.uk *Provider of the UK"s cheapest Gas and Electricity, Broadband Internet, Line Rental and Mobile Phones.*

▶ Redvers Consulting Ltd, Channelsea House, Canning Road, Stratford, London, E15 3ND Tel: (020) 8503 1211 E-mail: info@redversconsulting.co.uk *Computer & software services*

Redverse, Unit 3, Benbow Business Park Harlescott Lane, Shrewsbury, SY1 3FA Tel: (01743) 466668 Fax: (01743) 466669 E-mail: info@redverse.com *Lithographic printers*

Redview Computers, 17A North End, Longhoston, Alnwick, Northumberland, NE66 3AG Tel: (01665) 572027 E-mail: tom@redview.co.uk *Computer dealers & advisers*

Redweb Ltd, Quay House, 7 The Quay, Poole, Dorset, BH15 1HA Tel: (01202) 779944 Fax: (01202) 773643 E-mail: stuart@redweb.co.uk *Web designers*

▶ Redwells Joinery Ltd, 1 Crompton Road, Glenrothes, Fife, KY6 2SF Tel: (01592) 772010 Fax: (01592) 630093 *Joinery manufrs*

Redwood Energy Ltd, 68a High St, Ware, Herts, SG12 9DA Tel: (08700) 777999 Fax: (01920) 460071 E-mail: phil-coles@redwoodenergy.co.uk *Energy consultants.*

Redwood Joinery Ltd, 26a Vicarage Road, Woolavington, Bridgwater, Somerset, TA7 8DX Tel: (01278) 685010 Fax: (01278) 685011 E-mail: jimtrowbridge@btconnect.com *Joinery manufrs*

▶ Redwood Kitchens, 81 Tamar Way, Wokingham, Berkshire, RG41 3UB Tel: 0118-977 2233 Fax: (0845) 2265658 E-mail: sales@redwoodkitchens.co.uk *Design, supply & installation of domestic kitchens*

▶ Redwood Partnership, Maritime House, Basin Road North, Portslade, Brighton, BN41 1WR Tel: (01273) 414515 Fax: 08716 618938 E-mail: consult@redwoodpartnership.co.uk *Transport and highway design consulting engineers providing highway advice to developers, councils and general public*

Redwood Photographic, 7 Brunel Court, Brunel Way, Severalls Industrial Park, Colchester, CO4 9XW Tel: (01206) 751241 Fax: (01206) 855134 E-mail: info@redwoodphoto.com *Colour & black & white photographic processors*

Redwood Strip Curtains Ltd, Unit 21 Southfield Road Trading Estate, Southfield Road, Nailsea, Bristol, BS48 1JE Tel: (01275) 810289 Fax: (01275) 810290 E-mail: sales@redwoodstripcurtains.co.uk *PVC strip curtains manufrs*

Redwood Systems Ltd, Headway Business Park, Denby Dale Road, Wakefield, West Yorkshire, WF2 7AZ Tel: (01924) 880760 Fax: (01924) 880759 *Software services*

Redworth Products Ltd, Church Farm Barns, Church Farm Lane, Marsworth, Tring, Hertfordshire, HP23 4ND Tel: (01296) 662882 Fax: (01296) 660880 E-mail: redworth-products@lineone.net *Office equipment distributors & manufrs*

▶ Ree Distribution Ltd, Unit 1, Summerlands Industrial Estate, Endmoor, Kendal, Cumbria, LA8 0ED Tel: (01539) 561222

Ree Distribution, Unit N Main Line Industrial Estate, Crooklands Road, Ackenthwaite, Milnthorpe, Cumbria, LA7 7LR Tel: (01539) 565477 Fax: (01539) 565466 *Bread product distributor*

Ree Even Hire, 186-188 Portland Road, Hove, East Sussex, BN3 5QN Tel: (01273) 778222 Fax: (01273) 778223 E-mail: sales@ree-even.co.uk *Small tool hire & work wear*

Reebitex Fabrics Ltd, Rope Walk, Ilkeston, Derbyshire, DE7 5HX Tel: 0115-930 9619 Fax: 0115-930 8769 E-mail: sales@reebitex.com *Curtain fabric suppliers*

A M F Reece (UK), Clayton Wood Close, West Park Ring Road, Leeds, LS16 6QE Tel: 0113-275 9131 Fax: 0113-275 4116 E-mail: amfreece@amfreece.co.uk *Automatic sewing & buttonhole machine manufrs*

Brian Reece Scientific Ltd, 12 West Mills, Newbury, Berkshire, RG14 5HG Tel: (01635) 32827 Fax: (01635) 34542 E-mail: brian@brsl.co.uk *Brian Reece Scientific Ltd (or BRSL) specialise in the supply of equipment and systems incorporating video and digital imaging technology for applications in science and industry. Products include digital cameras, video cameras, compact video cameras, progressive scan cameras, remote head cameras, digital imaging systems, digital printers, forensic document examination equipment, forgery detection equipment, frame grabbers, image analysers, image processing equipment, non-contact inspection equipment, non-contact measurement equipment, LCD monitors, video monitors, video printers, digital printers, lenses, video microscopes, camera mounts, video inspection systems, video overlay generators, video processors, digital video processors, machine inspection systems etc. BRSL can provide a total solution to most imaging problems - please contact us to discuss your requirements.*

▶ Reed Boardall Transport, Bar Lane, Boroughbridge, York, YO51 9NN Tel: (01423) 321301 E-mail: sales@reedboardall.com

Reed Business Information, Windsor Court, East Grinstead Ho, Wood St, East Grinstead, West Sussex, RH19 1XA Tel: (01342) 326972 Fax: (01342) 335612 E-mail: information@reedinfo.co.uk *Directory publisher & business information & services provider*

Reed Business Information Ltd, Quadrant House, The Quadrant, Sutton, Surrey, SM2 5AS Tel: (020) 8652 3500 E-mail: webmaster@rbi.co.uk *Directory publishers*

Reed Business Information Ltd, Quadrant House, The Quadrant, Sutton, Surrey, SM2 5AS Tel: (020) 8652 3674 Fax: (020) 8652 8986

Reed Computing Personnel, 37 King Street, 2Nd Floor, Manchester, M2 7AT Tel: 0161-830 1691 Fax: 0161-830 1691 E-mail: northwest.computing@reed.co.uk *Recruitment agency*

Reed Connections Ltd, 120 Coombe Lane, London, SW20 0BA Tel: (020) 8399 5221 Fax: (020) 8274 4391 *Employment agency* Also at: Branches throughout the U.K.

Reed Elsevier Group plc, Second Floor, Grand Buildings, London, WC2N 5JR Tel: (020) 7930 7077 Fax: (020) 7166 5799 E-mail: strand.reception@reedelsevier.com *Publishing & information*

Reed Employment Ltd, 31 Wheeler Gate, Nottingham, NG1 2NA Tel: 0115-947 6301 Fax: 0115-947 6135 E-mail: nottingham.employment@reed.co.uk *Employment services*

Reed Employment Ltd, 24 Victoria Road, Surbiton, Surrey, KT6 4LD Tel: (020) 8399 5367 Fax: (020) 8390 8051 *Recruitment agency*

Reed Employment Ltd, 68 High Street, Watford, WD17 2BS Tel: (01923) 471104 Fax: (01923) 471101 E-mail: watford.employment@reed.co.uk *Specialists in administration accountancy recruitment*

Reed Exhibition's Ltd, Oriel House, 26 The Quadrant, Richmond, Surrey, TW9 1DL Tel: (020) 8910 7910 Fax: (020) 8940 2171 E-mail: rxinfo@reedexpo.co.uk *Exhibition organisers* Also at: Solihull

Reed Fabrications, Station Road, North Hykeham, Lincoln, LN6 3QY Tel: (01522) 693974 Fax: (01522) 501731 *Sheet metalwork*

Reed Harris, 27 Carnwath Road, London, SW6 3HR Tel: (020) 7736 7511 Fax: (020) 7736 2988 E-mail: enquiries@reed-harris.co.uk *Ceramic & stone tiles retailers*

Reed Hycalog, 6 Abbotswell Road, Aberdeen, AB12 3AF Tel: (01224) 877688 Fax: (01224) 898651 *Oil drill bit manufrs* Also at: Great Yarmouth

J.M. Reed & Co. Ltd, Kingsbury Episcopi, Martock, Somerset, TA12 6BD Tel: (01935) 822505 Fax: (01935) 823971 E-mail: dms@southcombe.com *Fashion clothing manufrs*

Reed Microsonix, 7a Station Road, Hednesford, Cannock, Staffordshire, WS12 4DH Tel: (01543) 426174 Fax: 01543 277211 *Computer services*

Peter Reed Textiles Ltd, 2 Gisburn Road, Bolton By Bowland, Clitheroe, Lancashire, BB7 4NP Tel: (01282) 692416 Fax: (01200) 447708 E-mail: mreed@peterreedtextiles.com *Domestic textile manufrs*

Robin Reed Ltd, Oldbury One, Brades Road, Oldbury, West Midlands, B69 1XX Tel: 0121-552 1001 Fax: 0121-544 5009 E-mail: crackers@robinreed.com *Christmas cracker manufrs*

Reed & Seymour Ltd, Cressex Industrial Estate, Lancaster Road, High Wycombe, Buckinghamshire, HP12 3NN Tel: (01494) 474964 Fax: (01494) 474964 *Turned parts manufrs*

Reed Smith, Park House, Station Square, Coventry, CV1 2FL Tel: (024) 7629 3020 Fax: (024) 7629 3031 E-mail: coventry-email@warner-cranston.com *Lawyers* Also at: London SE1 & Manchester

Reed & Sons Ltd, Brittleware Farm Buildings, Norwood Hill Road, Charlwood, Horley, Surrey, RH6 0EB Tel: (01293) 863333 Fax: (01293) 863334 E-mail: reedandsonsltd@yahoo.com *Builders & decorators*

Reed Technology Ltd, 33 Wine Street, Bristol, BS1 2BQ Tel: 0117-914 7340 Fax: 0117-914 7338 *Recruitment agency*

Reed Technology, East Wing Offices South Quay Plaza, 185 Marsh Wall, London, E14 9SH Tel: (020) 7001 2880 Fax: (020) 7001 2899 E-mail: london.computing@reed.co.uk *Recruitment agency*

Reed Technology Group, Dominion House, Woodbridge Road, Guildford, Surrey, GU1 4PU Tel: (01483) 569061 Fax: (01483) 301151 E-mail: southeast.computing@reed.co.uk *Recruitment agency*

Reed Of Trowbridge Ltd, Canal Road Industrial Estate, Trowbridge, Wiltshire, BA14 8RL Tel: (01225) 752525 Fax: (01225) 751089 *Motor vehicle repairers & car sales* Also at: Torbay

Reedbut Ltd, Bond Avenue, Bletchley, Milton Keynes, MK1 1JJ Tel: (01908) 630200 Fax: (01908) 630210 E-mail: sales@reedbut.com *Cardboard & corrugated box manufrs*

Reeder Lock & Safe Co. Ltd, 587 Barking Road, London, E13 9EZ Tel: (020) 7476 5450 Fax: (020) 7476 4155 *Locksmiths*

Reedprint, Vale Road, Windsor, Berkshire, SL4 5JL Tel: (01753) 869691 Fax: (01753) 830480 E-mail: sales@reedprint.co.uk *General printers* Also at: Bracknell

Reeds, Mount Pleasant Yard, White Street, Market Lavington, Devizes, Wiltshire, SN10 4DP Tel: (01380) 816516 Fax: (01380) 816457 *Heavy plant machinery hire & repair*

Reeds Of Cambridge, 70 Water Street, Cambridge, CB4 1PA Tel: (01223) 425348 Fax: (01223) 566717 E-mail: reedsofcambridge@dsl.tipex.com *Boating, clothing, heart rate monitors & canoeing suppliers*

▶ Reeds Plant Ltd, New Tyne Iron House, Highrow, Newcastle Upon Tyne, NE15 8SE Tel: 0191-264 0404 Fax: (01912) 641889

continued

▶ Reeds Transport, 86 Welley Road, Wraysbury, Staines, Middlesex, TW19 5EP Tel: (01784) 483235 Fax: (01784) 483569

▶ Reef Inc, P.O.Box 185, Manchester, M41 6XG Tel: 0870 211 9888 *We supply DJ Equipment, Keyboards, Clubwear M&F, Music Production Hardware, Studio Software and Monitors, Vinyl, Club merchandise and more! If you are into music, get into us!*

Reef Engineering, Unit 2 Mayfair Industrial Estate, Maldon Road, Lachingdon, Chelmsford, CM3 6LF Tel: (01621) 744689 Fax: (01621) 744285 E-mail: reefengineering@btconnect.com *Soldering machine & special purpose machine manufrs*

Reefworld Aquarium & Pond Supplies, 219 Fir Tree Road, Epsom, Surrey, KT17 3LB Tel: (01737) 370777 Fax: (01737) 212777 E-mail: sales@reefworld.co.uk *Aquatic supplies*

Reekie Engineering Ltd, Baden Powell Road, Kirkton Industrial Estate, Arbroath, Angus, DD11 3LS Tel: (01241) 871997 Fax: (01241) 877419 *Holding company*

Reekie Lothian, Haddington Road, Tranent, East Lothian, EH33 1DZ Tel: (01875) 615355 Fax: (01875) 615012 *Agricultural plant repairs*

Reekie Machine (Sales) Ltd, South Street, Inchinnan Industrial Estate, Inchinnan, Renfrew, PA4 9RL Tel: 0141-812 0411 Fax: 0141-812 0137 E-mail: info@reekiemachining.co.uk *Metal machining engineers & general manufrs*

Reekie Steeltec Ltd, Baden Powell Road, Kirkton Industrial Estate, Arbroath, Angus, DD11 3LS Tel: (01241) 873841 Fax: (01241) 877419 E-mail: colin.cromar@reekiesteeltec.com *Laser cutting & industrial painting services*

Reekie (Stirling), 19 Kerse Road, Stirling, FK7 7SY Tel: (01786) 445577 Fax: (01786) 447138 *Agriculture machinery services*

Reel Control, Woodlands, Draycott-in-the-Clay, Ashbourne, Derbyshire, DE6 5GZ Tel: (01283) 821128 Fax: (01283) 821228 E-mail: enquiries@reelcontrol.com *Leisure machine consultants*

▶ Reel Form Ltd, Riverside Road, Pride Park, Derby, DE24 8HY Tel: (01332) 200222 Fax: (01332) 200805

Reel Furniture, 37 St. Stephens Square, Norwich, NR1 3SS Tel: (01603) 629356 E-mail: info@reelfurniture.co.uk *Environmentally friendly wooden furniture manufrs*

Reel Service Ltd, 55-56 Nasmyth Road, Glenrothes, Fife, KY6 2SD Tel: (01592) 773208 Fax: (01592) 774696 E-mail: gchristison@reelserviceltd.com *Electronic supplies services*

Reel Thing, 17 Royal Opera Arcade, London, SW1Y 4UY Tel: (020) 7976 1830 Fax: (020) 7976 1850 *Antique fishing tackle*

▶ Reelfix Ltd, Unit 4, Norton Industrial Estate, Lower Norton Lane, Kewstoke, Weston-super-Mare, Avon, BS22 9YR Tel: (01934) 425222 Fax: (01934) 425028 E-mail: mk@reelfix.co.uk *Manufacturer of tie wire reel for steel fixing*

Reeling Systems Ltd, Unit A3 Pegasus Court, Ardglen Road, Whitchurch, Hampshire, RG28 7BP Tel: (01256) 896517 Fax: (01256) 895624 *MOD hosiery designers & manufrs*

Reelprint Register Sets Ltd, Spring Road Industrial Estate, 13 Lanesfield Drive, Wolverhampton, WV4 6UA Tel: (01902) 405177 Fax: (01902) 405178 E-mail: reelprint@lineone.net *Continuous stationery manufrs*

Reels & Deals, 61b St. Thomas Street, Weymouth, Dorset, DT4 8EQ Tel: (01305) 787848 Fax: (01305) 787783 *Fishing tackle suppliers*

Reelstock Ltd, Old Wharf Industrial Estate, Old Wharf Road, Grantham, Lincolnshire, NG31 7AA Tel: (01476) 567979 Fax: (01476) 565542 E-mail: sales@reelstock.freeserve.co.uk *Paper merchants & agents & paper converters*

Re-engineering Maintenance Conversion Ltd, 30 Christchurch Rd, Bournemouth, BH1 3PD Tel: 01202 438344 Fax: 01202 438388 *Software house*

Rees David Fencing Construction, The Grove, Clarbeston Road, Dyfed, SA63 4SP Tel: (01437) 731308 Fax: (01437) 731551 E-mail: davidreesfencing@lineone.net *Fencing contractors*

Rees Engineering Services Ltd, 401-403 Rayleigh Road, Benfleet, Essex, SS7 3ST Tel: (01268) 778274 Fax: (01268) 745204 E-mail: reception@reesteel.com *Steel fabrications, heavy steel*

Rees Flooring Ltd, Unit 12 Sovereign Park, Cleveland Way, Hemel Hempstead Industrial Estate, Hemel Hempstead, Hertfordshire, HP2 7DA Tel: (01442) 283250 Fax: (01442) 283263 *Carpet & flooring contractors*

George Rees, North Street, Caerwys, Mold, Clwyd, CH7 5AW Tel: (01352) 720111 *Agricultural merchants*

Rees Pipeline Services Ltd, Clare House, Coppermill Lane, Harefield, Middlesex, UB9 6HZ Tel: (01895) 823711 Fax: (01895) 825263 E-mail: dave.fitzgerald@clancygroup.co.uk *Civil engineers & pipeline rehabilitation*

Rees Productions Ltd, Unit 14 Cygnus Business Centre, Dalmeyer Road, London, NW10 2XA Tel: (020) 8459 1886 Fax: (020) 8459 8126 E-mail: info@reesproductions.co.uk *Scarf importers & fashion accessories*

Rees Switchgear Ltd, 157 Clarence Avenue, Northampton, NN2 6NY Tel: (01604) 597860 Fax: (01604) 597861 E-mail: janwimpress@rf-plc.com *Control panel & switchgear manufrs*

▶ W.D. Rees Steeplejacks And Lightning Protection Ltd, Dominion Way Industrial Estate, Cardiff, CF24 1RF Tel: (029) 2047 2110 Fax: (029) 2047 2112 *Lightning conductors & installers*

Reeset Electronics, 19 Ray Lea Road, Maidenhead, Berkshire, SL6 8QP Tel: (01628) 628146 Fax: (01628) 628146 E-mail: ed@reeset.com *Electronic design & development services*

▶ ReetPetite, The Cottage, Ragnall Lane, Walkley Wood, Nailsworth, Gloucestershire, GL6 0RX Tel: 01453 833996 E-mail: reet@reetpetite.biz *Makers & suppliers of 40"s dancewear & embroiderers*

Reeve Metal Finishing Co. Ltd, 40 Anne Road, Smethwick, West Midlands, B66 2NZ Tel: 0121-558 0692 Fax: 0121-558 4708 E-mail: cw@reevemetalfinishing.co.uk *Large, long established metal finishing company specializing in Chrome plating, Chrome plating on aluminium. Vat zinc plating barrel zinc plating, full range of passivations. Etch anodising, bright anodising, colour anodising, multicolour anodising. fade effect anodising alochrome 1200, bright tin plating vat and barrel, dull tin plating vat and barrel. Also nickel plating services, anodizers or anodizing processors or services, anodizing aluminium, chromium plating services and metal finishing or polishing*

Reeve Photography, Rectory Farm, 1 Brewery Road, Pampisford, Cambridge, CB22 3EN Tel: (01223) 832200 Fax: (01223) 832242 E-mail: pix@reevephotography.co.uk *Commercial & industrial photographers*

Reeves 2000, Appleby Hill, Austrey, Atherstone, Warwickshire, CV9 3ER Tel: (01827) 830894 Fax: (01827) 830631 E-mail: sales@ajreeves.com *Model castings & materials manufrs*

Reeves Calendar, Knowling Mead, Tenby, Dyfed, SA70 8ED Tel: (01834) 842652 Fax: (01834) 842337 E-mail: info@reeve-calendars.com *Calendar designers & producers*

Reeves Engineering Ltd, 15 Swinbourne Drive, Springwood Industrial Estate, Braintree, Essex, CM7 2YP Tel: (01376) 322613 Fax: (01376) 551522 *Sheet metalworkers*

Reeves Green Partners Ltd, Station Road, Lichfield, Staffordshire, WS13 6HX Tel: (01543) 250505 Fax: (01543) 255522 E-mail: marketing@reeves-green.co.uk *Advertising agency & public relations consultants*

Reeves Lund, The Courtyard, 55 Charterhouse Street, London, EC1M 6HA Tel: (020) 7739 8888 Fax: (020) 7490 4488 E-mail: sales@reeveslund.com *Telecommunication equipment distributors*

Peter G. Reeves & Co. Ltd, Haden Works, Haden Street, Birmingham, B12 9HN Tel: 0121-440 4225 Fax: 0121-446 4252 *Commercial vehicle body builders*

Reeves Pine, 213 High Street, Chatham, Kent, ME4 4BG Tel: (01634) 401043 *Pine furniture & kitchens wholesalers & retailers*

Reevite Ltd, 16 Murdock Road, Bicester, Oxfordshire, OX26 4PP Tel: (01869) 252520 Fax: (01869) 241394 E-mail: info@reevite.co.uk *Manufacturers of rubber or substitute grommets*

▶ Reevu Ltd, Parsons House, Parsons Road, Washington, Tyne & Wear, NE37 1EZ Tel: 0191-418 7755 Fax: 0191-418 7799 E-mail: enquires@reevu.com *Sports equipment manufrs*

Refer Scientific, Hareburn House, Bridge of Don, Aberdeen, AB23 8BT Tel: (01224) 825394 Fax: (01224) 706324 E-mail: info@referscientific.co.uk *Laboratory supply services*

▶ Reffold Electrical, 7 Hessle Road, Hull, HU3 2AA Tel: (01482) 320638 Fax: (01482) 586233

▶ Refill Express, 6 New Union Street, Coventry, CV1 2HN Tel: (024) 7663 3333 Fax: (024) 7663 2331 E-mail: sales@refillexpress.co.uk *Trade warehouse for computer consumables*

▶ Refina Ltd, Unit 7 Upton Industrial Estate, Factory Road, Poole, Dorset, BH16 5SL Tel: (01202) 632270 Fax: (01202) 632432 E-mail: sales@refina.co.uk *REFINA supply one of the largest ranges of professional quality, specialist application tools including mixing, surface preparation, diamond drilling, flooring and spray equipment. Hand tools are also stocked in depth for the refurbishment, wet and trowel trades. We carry some of the largest stocks of specialist power tools and accessories in the UK. Many of those difficult to find tools are available off the shelf. Because of our large stock holding, we aim to despatch 90% of orders within 24 hours to customers across the UK. We also run a 48 hour collect and repair service*

▶ Refinecatch Ltd, Broad Street, Bungay, Suffolk, NR35 1EF Tel: (01986) 895888 Fax: (01986) 895695

Refkit Ltd, 25 Nash Avenue, Wolverhampton, WV6 7SS Tel: (01902) 746329 E-mail: sales@refkit.co.uk *Mail order services*

Reflec plc, Road One, Winsford Industrial Estate, Winsford, Cheshire, CW7 3QQ Tel: (01606) 593911 Fax: (01606) 559535 E-mail: info@reflec.co.uk *Powder processing services*

▶ Reflectalux-Sheriton Fitted Bedrooms, Avondale Way, Avondale Industrial Estate, Pontrhydyrun, Cwmbran, Gwent, NP44 1TS Tel: (01633) 860555 Fax: (01633) 484579 *Manufacturer & retail of office & kitchen materials*

Reflecting Roadstuds Ltd, 1 Mill Lane, Halifax, West Yorkshire, HX3 6TR Tel: (01422) 360208 Fax: (01422) 349075 *Reflecting road stud distributors*

Reflection Art Furniture, Tresparrett, Camelford, Cornwall, PL32 9ST Tel: (01840) 261212 Fax: (01840) 261212 E-mail: cornishfunky@aol.com *Custom made one-off wood sculptures specialists*

▶ Reflections Bathroom & Tile Centres, Old Laundry Trading Estate, Bridport, Dorset, DT6 3BD Tel: (01308) 428555

▶ Reflections Mirrors Ltd, 128b Station Road, Sidcup, Kent, DA15 7AB Tel: (020) 8302 3004 Fax: (020) 8302 3003 E-mail: sales@reflections-mirrors.com

▶ Reflective Ceilings, 6 Moorhead Road, Horsham, West Sussex, RH12 4ND Tel: (07961) 863678 Fax: (01403) 270337 E-mail: james@reflective-ceilings.co.uk *installation of extenzo stretch ceilings in homes, shops & swimming pools*

Reflective Safety, 1 King George Court, Renfrew, PA4 0AU Tel: 0141-886 5674 Fax: 0141-886 5674 E-mail: kn@rspp.co.uk *Manufacturers & suppliers of reflective cycle safety & promotional products*

Reflex Communications, Arden Hall, 66 Brooklands Road, Sale, Cheshire, M33 3SJ Tel: 0161-973 4007 Fax: 0161-973 2150 *Conference production services*

Reflex Computer Recruitment Ltd, Regent House 1-3 Queensway, Redhill, RH1 1QT Tel: (01737) 778282 Fax: (01737) 778950 E-mail: reflexgroup@reflexgroup.co.uk *IT recruitment agency*

Reflex Design, 10 Pelham Street, Oadby, Leicester, LE2 4DJ Tel: 0116-272 1239 Fax: (0870) 0111611 E-mail: sales@reflexdesign.uk.com *Sign manufrs & vehicle graphics*

▶ Reflex Furniture, Backridge Farm, Twitter Lane, Waddington, Clitheroe, Lancashire, BB7 3LQ Tel: (01200) 429695 Fax: 01200 429695 E-mail: info@reflexfurniture.co.uk *Reflex Furniture is a company that designs and makes hand crafted bespoke furniture. Through a team of dedicated designers and craftsmen, we offer a distinctive service that guarantees to turn your vision into reality. Our creative talents have been recognised by many international companies and our global register of discernable clients continues to grow. Our company's vision is attention to detail; we believe this quality creates beautifully crafted fine furniture, which present and future generations will enjoy*

▶ Reflex International Ltd, 1 Butchers Road, London, E16 1PH Tel: (020) 7511 4541 Fax: (020) 7474 6861 E-mail: ian@reflexinternational.com *Screen printers & embroiderers*

Reflex Nutrition Ltd, 77A Rutland Road, Hove, East Sussex, BN3 5FE Tel: (01273) 297295 Fax: (01273) 297357 *Health food manufrs*

Reflex Print & Design Ltd, Unit 4 Kiln Hill Industrial Estate, Slaithwaite, Huddersfield, HD7 5JS Tel: (01484) 846950 Fax: (01484) 847644 *General printers & design services*

Reflex Safety Systems Ltd, Inertia House, Lowther Road, Stanmore, Middlesex, HA7 1EP Tel: (020) 8204 0200 Fax: (020) 8204 1100 E-mail: enq@reflexsafety.co.uk *Seatbelts & safety equipment supply & manufrs*

Reflex Studio Ltd, Reflex House, Bells Yew Green, Tunbridge Wells, Kent, TN3 9BQ Tel: (01892) 752888 Fax: (01892) 752889 E-mail: sales@reflex-print.co.uk *Litho & screen printers to pvc*

▶ Reflexol Conservatory Blinds Northwest, 1 Cuba Industrial Estate, Bolton Road North, Ramsbottom, Bury, Lancashire, BL0 0NE Tel: (01706) 825511 Fax: (01706) 825522 E-mail: info@reflexol.com *Manufacture, supply and installation of high quality 20mm Pleated conservatory blinds to both Trade and retail sectors. Approved suppliers of all types of blinds products to Commercial,Industrial, Local Authority,Licensed trade and Health Trust contracting.*

▶ Reflexol Conservatory Blinds Northwest, 1 Cuba Industrial Estate, Bolton Road North, Ramsbottom, Bury, Lancashire, BL0 0NE Tel: (01706) 825511 Fax: (01706) 825522 E-mail: info@reflexol.com *Blind manufrs*

Reflex-Rol, Ryeford Hall, Ryeford, Ross-on-Wye, Herefordshire, HR9 7PU Tel: (01989) 750704 Fax: (01989) 750768 E-mail: reflexrol@btinternet.com *Insulating solar control systems & sunblinds*

▶ Reform Technologies, Unit 5, Building 2, 2 Sandwich Industrial Estate, Sandwich, Kent, CT13 9LY Tel: (01304) 611875 Fax: (0870) 2203346 *Suppliers of IT hardware*

Reform & Weld, Building A, Gobowen, Oswestry, Shropshire, SY10 7JZ Tel: (01691) 650479 Fax: (01691) 650461 *Agricultural trailer & skip manufrs*

▶ ReformIS, 18 Christchurch Hill, London, NW3 1LG Tel: (020) 7152 9638 Fax: (020) 7152 9639 *IT consultancy &, programme management*

Refractory Installation Services, 27 Park Lane, Rothwell, Leeds, LS10 3BA Tel: 0113-282 2258 E-mail: paul.harvey@ris-leeds.co.uk *Refractory lining installations*

▶ Refreshed Media Ltd, Homelife House Business Centre, Bournemouth, BH8 8EZ Tel: (01202) 242200 Fax: 08701 315094 E-mail: sarah@refreshedmedia.com *Web design & development*

▶ Refreshed Media Ltd, Aardvark House, 24 Poole Hill, Bournemouth, BH2 5PS Tel: (0845) 7337374 Fax: (0845) 2008360 E-mail: kellysearch@refreshedmedia.com *Online web services*

▶ The Refreshing Water Co. Ltd, 113A Leyland Trading Estate, Wellingborough, Northamptonshire, NN8 1RT Tel: (01933) 443820 Fax: (01933) 225559

▶ RefreshU, 1 Scotts Close, Downtown Business Centre, Salisbury, SP5 3HU Tel: 0800 389 3461 Fax: (01725) 513135 E-mail: vending@refreshu.com *Distributors & operatives for coffee vending machines, snack vending machines, food vending machines, can & bottle vending machines, water vending maachines, cold drink vending machines, used vending machines, free vending machines, vending machine repair, service, sales, rental & parts. Nationwide outlets*

Refrigerated Storage Systems Ltd, Avon Valley Busines Park, Pixash Lane, Keynsham, Bristol, BS31 1TS Tel: 0117-986 9333 Fax: 0117-986 8978 E-mail: enquiries@refrigerationdesign.co.uk *Refrigeration contractors*

▶ Refrigerated Transport, 57, Wellington Street, Aberdeen, AB11 5BX Tel: (01224) 210549 Fax: (01224) 210325

Refrigerated Transport Information Society, 140 Newmarket Road, Cambridge, CB5 8HE Tel: (01223) 461352 Fax: (01223) 461522 E-mail: crt@crtech.demon.co.uk *Refrigerated transport & storage information services*

Refrigeration Aberdeen Ltd, Hillview Road, East Tullos Industrial Estate, Aberdeen, AB12 3HB Tel: (01224) 873115 Fax: (01224) 899919 *Refrigeration installation engineers/equipment manufrs*

Refrigeration & Air Conditioning Services, 25 Highfield Road, London, N21 3HD Tel: (020) 8360 0701 Fax: (020) 8360 4345 *Refrigeration equipment*

Refrigeration Engineering Ltd, 120 Victoria Road, Scarborough, North Yorkshire, YO11 1SW Tel: (01723) 375711 Fax: (01723) 375712 *Refrigeration engineers*

Refrigeration & Engineering Services Ltd, Humber Street, Grimsby, South Humberside, DN31 3HL Tel: (01472) 352201 Fax: (01472) 250842 *Refrigeration engineers*

▶ Refrigeration & Heat Pump Services Ltd, Unit 7a Canalside Industrial Park, Kinoulton Road, Cropwell Bishop, Nottingham, NG12 3BE Tel: 0115-989 9985 Fax: 0115-989 1730

▶ Refrigeration Lindum Ltd, King Edward St, Grimsby, South Humberside, DN31 3JP Tel: (01472) 351491 Fax: (01472) 240630 E-mail: lindenref@aol.com *Refrigeration & air conditioning repairers*

Refrigeration Mitton Ltd, Polar House, East Norfolk Street, Carlisle, CA2 5JL Tel: (01228) 522481 Fax: (01228) 514897 *Refrigeration & air conditioning specialists*

Refrigeration Norwest (Llandudno) Ltd, Tremarl Industrial Estate, Llandudno Junction, Gwynedd, LL31 9PN Tel: (01492) 581358 Fax: (01492) 593171 *Commercial & domestic refrigeration*

Refrigeration On The Wolds, Albion Street, Driffield, North Humberside, YO25 6PZ Tel: (01377) 252518 *Refrigeration engineers*

▶ Refrigeration Parts Wholesale Ltd, Unit 2 Vine Street, Aston, Birmingham, B6 5TS Tel: 0121-328 8388 Fax: 0121-327 7266 *Refrigeration wholesale*

▶ Refrigeration Parts Wholesale Ltd, Delta House, Fairway, Cannock, Staffordshire, WS11 0DJ Tel: (01543) 437010

Refrigeration Parts Wholesale Ltd, Delta House, Fairway, Cannock, Staffordshire, WS11 0DJ Tel: (01543) 437010 Fax: (01543) 437029 E-mail: sales@rpw.co.uk *Distributors & agents of refrigeration equipment*

Refrigeration Sales & Rentals Ltd, 129 Dorchester Road, Upton, Poole, Dorset, BH16 5NW Tel: (01202) 624007 Fax: (01202) 249186 E-mail: j.forsyth@virgin.net *Refrigeration & air conditioning suppliers & repairers*

Refrigeration Service (Ruislip) Ltd, 288 West End Road, Ruislip, Middlesex, HA4 6LS Tel: (01895) 622286 Fax: (01895) 622259 *Refrigeration service engineers*

Refrigeration Services, 6 Fort Street, Ayr, KA7 1HU Tel: (01292) 264098 Fax: (01292) 261191 E-mail: refridgerationservices@lycos.co.uk *Refrigeration sales & services*

Refrigeration Services, 9 Wynford Road, Bournemouth, BH9 3ND Tel: (01202) 512188 *Installation of commercial refrigeration*

Refrigeration Spares Ltd, 31 Harrow Road, London, E11 3PT Tel: (020) 8555 1321 Fax: (020) 8519 8219 *Refrigerator component distributors* Also at: Coventry, Exeter, Glasgow & Manchester

Refrigeration Spares (Manchester) Ltd, Milltown Street, Radcliffe, Manchester, M26 1WN Tel: 0161-723 4426 Fax: 0161-725 9169 *Commercial & industrial freezers spares*

▶ Refrigeration Support Ltd, Burtonhead Road, St. Helens, Merseyside, WA9 5DS Tel: (01744) 736002 Fax: (01744) 736164

Refrigeration Yorkshire Ltd, Woodhouse Street, Hull, HU9 1RJ Tel: (01482) 587333 Fax: (01482) 589593 E-mail: ryorks1@aol.com Principal Export Areas: Worldwide *Air conditioning unit distribs*

Reg Morris (Brierley Hill) Ltd, Canal Street, Brierley Hill, West Midlands, DY5 1JJ Tel: (01384) 78187 Fax: (01384) 75361 *Secondary ingot manufrs*

Rega Research Ltd, 119 Park Street, Westcliff-On-Sea, Essex, SS0 7PD Tel: (01702) 333071 Fax: (01702) 432427 E-mail: service@rega.co.uk Principal Export Areas: Central/East Europe *Audio/Hi-fi equipment systems manufr*

▶ Regal Aluminium, Unit 29 Snugborough Trading Estate, Union Mills, Isle of Man, IM4 4LH Tel: (01624) 620254 Fax: (01624) 661976 E-mail: enquiries@regalaluminium.co.uk

Regal Beauty Supplies, 22 Rigg Approach, London, E10 7QN Tel: (020) 8539 5112 Fax: (0870) 2000664 E-mail: sales@regalbeauty.co.uk *Cosmetics supply, sales & distributors*

Regal Construction, La Grande Route De St. Laurent, St. Lawrence, Jersey, JE3 1NN Tel: (01534) 865333 Fax: (01534) 861431 E-mail: regal-con@jerseymail.co.uk *Builders & civil engineers*

Regal Credit Consultants Ltd, Regal House, 18 High Street, Bagshot, Surrey, GU19 5AA Tel: (01276) 470500 Fax: (01276) 470503 E-mail: sales@regalcredit.co.uk *Credit control consultants, debt collection & tracing agency*

Regal Dyeing & Finishing Co. Nottingham, The Poplars, Wollaton Road, Beeston, Nottingham, NG9 2PD Tel: 0115-925 4416 Fax: 0115-925 4416 E-mail: johncharles@tiscali.co.uk *Textile trade dyers & finishers*

Regal Engineering, Church Lane, Kelbrook, Barnoldswick, Lancashire, BB18 6UJ Tel: (01282) 844224 Fax: (01282) 841030 E-mail: regal.eng@btconnect.com *Fabrication engineers*

Regal Engineering Co. Ltd, Speedwell House, West Quay Road, Southampton, SO15 1GY Tel: (023) 8036 6407 Fax: (023) 8036 6301 E-mail: engineering@bsa-regal.co.uk *General machining*

Regal Engines, Unit B, 16 Juliet Way, Aveley, South Ockendon, Essex, RM15 4YD Tel: (01708) 868805 Fax: (01708) 868885 E-mail: info@engine-reconditioners.co.uk *Diesel, marine & industrial engine reconditioning*

Regal Engravers, Polsole Bridge Works, Hamlin Lane, Exeter, EX1 2RY Tel: (01392) 278790 Fax: (01392) 278790 E-mail: regalengravers@yahoo.com *Flexographic plate manufrs*

▶ Regal Environmental Systems Ltd, Regal House, Upham Street, Upham, Southampton, SO32 1JA Tel: (01489) 860966 Fax: (01489) 860977 E-mail: sales@regalenviron.co.uk *Environmental systems, heating & ventilation*

Regal Fans Ltd, Ventris House, Lakes Road, Braintree, Essex, CM7 3SS Tel: (01376) 342914 Fax: (01376) 348208 E-mail: tim@regalfans.co.uk *Laboratory furniture manufrs*

▶ Regal Fire Ltd, Alfreton Road, Sutton-in-Ashfield, Nottinghamshire, NG17 1JB Tel: (01623) 510068 Fax: (01623) 510068 *Fire extinguisher supply and maintenece,service, Risk Assessments, Fire*

continued

Company Information

continuation
Safety Awareness training, Signs, escape route products, ,Chesterfield, Ashfield Mnasfield,Derbyshire, Nottinghamshire areas covered.

Regal House International Ltd, 1102 High Road, London, N20 0QX Tel: (020) 8446 7448 Fax: (020) 8446 7448 E-mail: regalds@btinternet.com *Giftware importers & consultants*

Regal Joinery, 5 Tudor House, Moseley Road, Bilston, West Midlands, WV14 6JD Tel: (01902) 631322 Fax: (01902) 631322 *Joinery manufrs*

▶ Regal Litho Ltd, 352 Selbourne Road, Luton, LU4 8NU Tel: (01582) 493332

▶ Regal Logistics Ltd, 7 The Gateway Centre, Coronation Road, Cressex Business Park, High Wycombe, Buckinghamshire, HP12 3SU Tel: (01494) 531100 Fax: (01494) 519123

Regal Paints Ltd, Meadow Lane Indust Estate, Meadow Lane, Alfreton, Derbyshire, DE55 7EZ Tel: (01773) 830700 Fax: (01773) 832652 E-mail: regalpaintslimited@tiscali.co.uk *Floor & sports marking paint services*

Regal Signs & Graphics, 2 Restmor Way, Wallington, Surrey, SM6 7AH Tel: (020) 8835 2332 Fax: (020) 8835 2326 E-mail: sales@regalsigns.co.uk *Sign manufrs*

Regal Sterling Blinds, 16 Thirlmere, Great Ashby, Stevenage, Hertfordshire, SG1 6AH Tel: (01438) 238650 E-mail: gary@regalsterling.com *Suppliers & fitters of blinds*

Regal Tanks, Ellough Park, Benacre Road, Beccles, Suffolk, NR34 7XD Tel: (01502) 710100 Fax: (01502) 710103 E-mail: info@regaltanks.co.uk Sales Contact: D. Alger *REGAL TANKS is an independent United Kingdom business, based in East Anglia, who specialise in the supply, hire and purchase of new and used tanks and silos. With over 35 years experience, we can offer an efficient and reliable service. **As a leading supplier, we can offer storage tanks and silos suitable for virtually any liquid or powder, ranging in capacity from 250 gallons (1,135 litres) to 44,000 gallons (200,000 litres). **Regal Tanks are in a position to cater for all your storage requirements. Should you require new, used, hire or ancillaries, use our quick search facility or call on 01502 710100.*

Regal Windows & Conservatories, 4 Callenders, Paddington Drive, Swindon, SN5 7YW Tel: (0800) 616200 Fax: (01793) 886778 E-mail: regalwindows@tinyworld.co.uk *Double glazing installer*

Regalspire Ltd, Ormonde Street, Stoke-on-Trent, ST4 3RR Tel: (01782) 335988 Fax: (01782) 598138 *Steel fabricators*

Regam Electric Ltd, Macaulay Street, Leeds, LS9 7SW Tel: 0113-245 0946 Fax: 0113-244 9397 *Electrical wholesaler, repairer & retailer*

Regan Consulting Practice Ltd, Choni Cottage, Manor Road, South Wingfield, Alfreton, Derbyshire, DE55 7NH Tel: (01773) 521528 Fax: (01773) 830688 E-mail: helpdesk@reganconsulting.co.uk *Organisation development consultants*

▶ Dennis Regan, Suites 2 & 4, Beauford House, Serpentine Road, Cleckheaton, West Yorkshire, BD19 3HU Tel: (01274) 850940 Fax: (01274) 850940 E-mail: sales@therapyexpressltd.co.uk *Sport related services, natural products, health food & dietary*

Pat Regan Mobile Welding, 7 Copland Close, Broomfield, Chelmsford, CM1 7DT Tel: (01245) 440951 Fax: (01245) 440951 *Welding contractors*

▶ Regarder Limited, 0-6-2 Omnia One, 125 Queen Street, Sheffield, S1 2DG Tel: 0114 279 2828 Fax: 0114 279 2829 E-mail: regarder1@aol.com *We are a Print, design and promotions company. We print all stationary products such as business cards, letter heads, leaflets/flyers. And also promotional merchandise such as T-shirts, Mugs, Mounce mats, and much more. All our designs are produced in house. For all your printing needs please give us a call!*

Regatta Ltd, Risol House Mercury Park, Mercury Way, Urmston, Manchester, M41 7RR Tel: 0161-749 1313 Fax: 0161-749 1210 E-mail: sales@regatta.com *Work leisure clothing & footwear*

Regatta Great Outdoors Factory Outlet, Freeport Village, Anchorage Road, Fleetwood, Lancashire, FY7 6AE Tel: (01253) 777705 Fax: (01253) 777705 E-mail: enquiries@regatta.co.uk *Outdoor equipment retail*

Regency Banqueting Suite, 113 Bruce Grove, London, N17 6UR Tel: (020) 8885 2490 Fax: (020) 8885 1739 E-mail: enquiries@regencybanqueting.com *Conference & banqueting suites for hire*

Regency Blinds, 92 Wansbeck Gardens, Hartlepool, Cleveland, TS26 9JH Tel: (01429) 860057 Fax: 0191-387 5967 *Blind manufrs*

Regency Building Services Ltd, 33 Station Road, Ingrebourne, Romford, RM3 0DQ Tel: (01708) 341114 Fax: (08707) 770664 E-mail: info@rbsmail.co.uk *Air conditioning systems instillation & building maintenance services*

Regency Computers, 67 Whitchurch Road, Shrewsbury, SY1 4EE Tel: (01743) 461829 Fax: (01743) 460880 E-mail: sales@regencycomputers.com *Computer resellers, sales, repairs & networking*

▶ Regency Design & Print Ltd, Unit G2 Lambs Business Park, Tilburstow Hill Road, South Godstone, Godstone, Surrey, RH9 8LJ Tel: (01342) 892172 Fax: (01342) 892315 *Screen printing*

▶ Regency Factors plc, 2 Regency Chambers, Jubilee Way, Bury, Lancashire, BL9 0JW Tel: 0161-761 4017 Fax: 0161-761 4018 E-mail: info@regencyfactors.com *Financial advisers*

Regency Forwarding Ltd, Unit 6 Moorfield Road Estate, Yeadon, Leeds, LS19 7BN Tel: 0113-250 7714 Fax: 0113-250 8391 E-mail: sales@regencyforwarding.com *Freight forwarders*

Regency Glass, Hope Carr Industrial Estate, Butt St, Leigh, Lancashire, WN7 3XA Tel: (01942) 262162 Fax: (01942) 261555 E-mail: dean@regencyglass.co.uk *Glazing specialists*

Regency Gold Ltd, Unit 4 Minafon Yard, Betws Yn Rhos, Abergele, Clwyd, LL22 8AW Tel: (01492) 680440 Fax: (01492) 680633 E-mail: support@regencygold.co.uk *Furniture polish manufrs*

Regency Hair Supplies, Common BNK Indust Estate, Ackhurst Road, Chorley, Lancashire, PR7 1NH Tel: (01257) 263943 Fax: (01257) 263943 *Hairdressing accessories suppliers*

Regency International Safety Group Ltd, Allenby Street, Scunthorpe, South Humberside, DN15 6EL Tel: (01724) 277933 Fax: (01724) 277933 E-mail: regencyintgrp@aol.com *Environmental safety equipment suppliers*

Regency Marquees Ltd, Bilsington Road, Willow Court, Ruckinge, Ashford, Kent, TN26 2PB Tel: (01233) 732130 Fax: (01233) 733757 E-mail: info@regencymarquees.co.uk *Marquees hire*

Regency Mouldings Worcester Ltd, Hylton Road, Worcester, WR2 5JS Tel: (01905) 424909 Fax: (01905) 748310 E-mail: timco@btclick.com *Injection moulders & tool makers*

Regency Mowbray Co. Ltd, Hixon Industrial Estate, Hixon, Stafford, ST18 0PY Tel: (01889) 270554 Fax: (01889) 270927 E-mail: sales@regencymowbray.co.uk *Food flavouring, colouring & fruit preparations manufrs*

▶ Regency Preservation, Conbar House, Mead Lane, Hertford, SG13 7AP Tel: (01992) 509201 Fax: (01992) 552277 E-mail: enquiries@regencypreservation.co.uk *Damp & timber infestation restoration*

Regency Press, 2a Kent Street, Belfast, BT1 2JA Tel: (028) 9032 1724 Fax: (028) 9033 2280 *Printers & stationers*

▶ Regency Press Ltd, 88 Moseley Street, Birmingham, B12 0RT Tel: 0121-622 4536 Fax: 0121-622 3307

Regency Products, 101-107 Broughton Lane, Sheffield, S9 2DE Tel: 0114-244 1205 *Wrought iron manufrs*

Regency Refrigeration, 5 Medina Way, Kidsgrove, Stoke-on-Trent, ST7 4TJ Tel: (01782) 773103 *Refrigeration services*

Regency Signs, 5 Knowle Farm Bus Centre, Wadhurst Road, Frant, Tunbridge Wells, Kent, TN3 9EJ Tel: (01892) 510738 Fax: (01892) 515352 E-mail: sales@regencysigns.co.uk *Sign makers*

Regency Stairs & Joinery Contractors Ltd, 13 Delling Bond Street, Greenock, Renfrewshire, PA15 4RN Tel: (01475) 722900 Fax: (01475) 787931 E-mail: enq@regencyjoinery.fsnet.co.uk *Joiners*

Regency Swimming Pools, Regency House, 88A Great Brickkiln Street, Graisley, Wolverhampton, WV3 0PU Tel: (01902) 427709 Fax: (01902) 422632 E-mail: info@jwgswimming.co.uk *Swimming pool construction equipment supply*

▶ Regency Windows (North East) Ltd, 2-3 Charles Street, Bonners Field Industrial Estate, Sunderland, SR6 0AN Tel: 0191-510 9050 E-mail: enquiries@regencywindows.com

Regenersis Ltd, 1 James Wort Avenue, Westwood Park, Glenrothes, Fife, KY7 4UA Tel: (01592) 774704 Fax: (01592) 774150 E-mail: margaret.lessels@crc-group.com *Computer peripheral repair services*

Regent Belt Co. Ltd, Leo House The Business Centre, Ross Road, Weedon Road Industrial Estate, Northampton, NN5 5AX Tel: (01604) 684700 Fax: (01604) 684719 E-mail: sales@regentbelt.co.uk *Leather belts & other leather goods manufrs*

Regent Dental Laboratories Ltd, 4 Bassett Road, Leighton Buzzard, Bedfordshire, LU7 1AR Tel: (01525) 374646 Fax: (01525) 374887 E-mail: enquiries@regentdental.com *Dental laboratory*

▶ Regent Distributors Ltd, 3 Regent Road, Handsworth, Birmingham, B21 8AB Tel: 0121-554 7107 Fax: 0121-682 3958 E-mail: info@regentskincare.com *Suppliers of skin care products for industry, protection & cleansing*

Regent Distributors Ltd, 3 Regent Road, Handsworth, Birmingham, B21 8AB Tel: 0121-554 7107 Fax: 0121-682 3958 E-mail: info@regent-uk.com *National cleaning/ hygiene product suppliers*

▶ Regent Garden Collection Ltd, Unit 16 Bordon Trading Estate, Old Station Way, Bordon, Hampshire, GU35 9HH Tel: (01420) 478888 Fax: (01420) 478999 *Garden furniture wholesalers*

Regent Hose & Hydraulics Ltd, Unit 16-18, Rabans Close, Rabans Lane Industrial Area, Aylesbury, Buckinghamshire, HP19 8RS Tel: (01296) 420171 Fax: (01296) 392306 E-mail: info@regenthose.co.uk *Industrial & hydraulic hose manufrs* Also at: Milton Keynes & Witney

Regent Hose & Hydraulics Ltd, 128-130 Tanners Drive, Blakelands, Milton Keynes, MK14 5BP Tel: (01908) 612602 Fax: (01908) 211009 E-mail: info.mk@regenthose.co.uk *Hydraulic & pneumatic equipment stockists*

Regent House Manufacturing, Harveys Warehouse, Newport Road, Gnosall, Stafford, ST20 0BL Tel: (01785) 823544 Fax: (01785) 822953 E-mail: sales@regentbespokecabinets.co.uk *Cabinet makers*

Regent Kemicals Ltd, 20 Jubilee Drive, Glenfield, Leicester, LE3 8LJ Tel: 0116-233 6430 Fax: 0116-233 6429 *Release agent distributors & manufrs*

Regent Lock Co. Ltd, Bath Road Industrial Estate, Chippenham, Wiltshire, SN14 0AB Tel: (01249) 650416 Fax: (01249) 443014 *Garage door locking handle manufrs*

Regent Print Ltd, 30 Albert Street, Huddersfield, HD1 3PU Tel: (01484) 530789 Fax: (01484) 542533 E-mail: sales@regentprint.co.uk *Commercial business forms & printing*

Regent Publicity Ltd, 8 Milnthorpe Road, Hove, East Sussex, BN3 5HT Tel: (01273) 820300 Fax: (01273) 820144 E-mail: southern.sales@regentpublicity.co.uk *Promotional business gifts*

Regent Rentals, 1-1a Margaret Street, Coalville, Leicestershire, LE67 3LY Tel: (01530) 836611 Fax: (01530) 836611 *Video, tv, radio & mobile phone*

Regent Reprographics Ltd, Regent House, 38 Hawkes Drive, Heathcote Industrial Estate, Warwick, CV34 6LX Tel: (01926) 450960 Fax: (01926) 450316 E-mail: info@regentdigital.co.uk *Photocopying machine rental*

Regent Seafoods Ltd, 388 (Rear Of) Yorktown Road, College Town, Sandhurst, Berkshire, GU47 0PU Tel: (01276) 32622 Fax: (01276) 35509 *Meat & fish*

Regent Systems Ltd, Unit D11c, Dower House Farm, Blackboys, Uckfield, East Sussex, TN22 5HJ Tel: (01435) 864424 Fax: (01435) 868102 *Wall tie treatment services*

▶ Regents Chartered Accountants, Grosvenor Gardens House, 35-37 Grosvenor Gardens, London, SW1W 0BS Tel: (020) 7828 5440 E-mail: info@euroaccountants.uk.com *At Euro Accountants, we have one key objective - to provide you with the broadest range of personal and corporate business services to the highest professional standards. *Welcome to A fresh approach to AccountingReceive our E-Newsletter*Enter your name and email address below:*Name: *Email: *Subscribe Unsubscribe We offer an efficient, reliable, professional and discreet service at competitive rates to businesses large and small. **We take pride in the quality of service we provide and, indeed, our existing clientele has, for the most part, been obtained through recommendations.***

Reggiani Ltd, 7-8 Warwick Road, Borehamwood, Hertfordshire, WD6 1US Tel: (020) 8953 0855 Fax: (020) 8236 3099 E-mail: reggiani@reggiani.net *Light fitting manufrs*

▶ Regie (UK) Ltd, Bearley, Stratford-Upon-Avon, Warwickshire, CV37 0TY Tel: (0870) 8810167 Fax: (0870) 8810168 *Computer software developers*

Region Services Ltd, Unit 3 Fullwood Close, Aldermans Green Industrial Estate, Coventry, CV2 2SS Tel: (024) 7661 8189 Fax: (024) 7662 2246 E-mail: info@rslkiosks.co.uk *It manufrs*

Regional Freight Services Ltd, Airport Business Centre, Regional House, Norwich, NR6 6BS Tel: (01603) 414125 Fax: (01603) 402542 E-mail: rfs@regfrt.co.uk *Freight forwarding agents* Also at: Bristol, Great Yarmouth & Heathrow

Regional Webs, & Lanb Plot, Chetnole, Sherborne, Dorset, DT9 6PQ Tel: (0870) 7461290 Fax: (0870) 7461291 *Internet consultancy*

▶ Regionport Ltd, 3 Chowns Mill Business Park, Station Road, Irthlingborough, Wellingborough, Northamptonshire, NN9 5QQ Tel: (01933) 651656 Fax: (01933) 650046

Regis Machinery Sales Ltd, 9b Arun Business Park, Bognor Regis, West Sussex, PO22 9SX Tel: (01243) 825661 Fax: (01243) 829364 E-mail: sales@regismachinery.co.uk *Machinery sales*

Regis Plastic Signs, Providence Street, Stourbridge, West Midlands, DY9 8HN Tel: (01384) 892366 Fax: (01384) 892367 *Sign makers*

Regis Plastic Signs, Providence Street, Stourbridge, West Midlands, DY9 8HN Tel: (01384) 892366 Fax: (01384) 892367 *Fire extinguisher suppliers*

Regis Reproduction Ltd, Unit 2 Station Road, Rowley Regis, Rowley Regis, West Midlands, B65 0JY Tel: 0121-561 5674 Fax: 0121-561 5680 Principal Export Areas: Worldwide *Furniture component manufrs*

Reglaze Windows Ltd, 49-51 Collingdon Street, Luton, LU1 1RT Tel: (01582) 730847 Fax: (01582) 417615 *Aluminium, pvc window & commercial door manufrs*

▶ Regon Ltd, Unit 21B, Avenue 2, Station Lane Industrial Estate, Witney, Oxfordshire, OX28 4YG Tel: (01993) 771441 Fax: (01993) 774105 E-mail: sales@regon.co.uk *Brass castings*

Re-Graphics, Unit 10 Freshways House, 16 Eastman Road, London, W3 7YG Tel: (020) 8743 3529 Fax: (020) 8743 3629 *Sign & exhibition graphics*

Regulators Europa Ltd, Port Lane, Colchester, CO1 2NX Tel: (01206) 799556 Fax: (01206) 792685 Principal Export Areas: Worldwide *Engine speed & control systems manufrs*

Regus (Central London), 1 Northumberland Avenue, London, WC2N 5BW Tel: (020) 7872 5500 Fax: (020) 7872 5611 E-mail: karl.newman@regus.com *Office letting agency*

▶ Rehabilitation Services Ltd, Unit 51 Riverside Estate, Sir Thomas Longley Road, Medway City Estate, Rochester, Kent, ME2 4DP Tel: (01634) 297010 Fax: (01634) 297011 *Manufacture prosthesis, medical & surgical supplies*

Rehau Ltd, Hill Court, Walford, Ross-on-Wye, Herefordshire, HR9 5QN Tel: (01989) 762600 Fax: (01989) 762601 E-mail: enquiries@rehau.com *Plastic extrusion manufrs*

▶ Reheat International Ltd, Caker Stream Road, Alton, Hampshire, GU34 2QF Tel: (01420) 80633 Fax: (01420) 80644 E-mail: sales@reheat.co.uk *Repairers of gallier equipment services*

Reichenbacher-Hamuel, Unit 2 The Moorlands, Lee Lane, Millhouse Green, Sheffield, S36 9NN Tel: (01226) 761799 Fax: (01226) 761589 E-mail: denise@r.co.uk *Woodwork machinery manufrs*

Alex Reid Ltd, 128-130 Beddington Lane, Croydon, CR0 4YZ Tel: (020) 8684 7667 Fax: (020) 8683 4335 E-mail: sales@alexreid.co.uk *Dry cleaning & laundry suppliers*

Andrew Reid & Partners, 36-37 Furnival Street, London, EC4A 1JQ Tel: (020) 7430 1611 Fax: (020) 7404 0553 E-mail: general@andrewreid.co.uk *Consulting engineers*

Reid & Bate, Unit E1, Warrington Business Park, Long Lane, Warrington, WA2 8TX Tel: 01925 596133 Fax: (0871) 247 5001 E-mail: enquiries@reid-bate.co.uk *Electrical & lift specialists services*

Reid Bros Glasgow, Unit 64 Elderpark Workspace, 100 Elderpark Street, Glasgow, G51 3TR Tel: 0141-425 1060 Fax: 0141-440 2257 E-mail: scottishsales@thorneandderrick.co.uk *Strapping systems distributors*

▶ Reid Business Services Ltd, 333A Prince Regent Lane, Victoria Docks, London, E16 3JL Tel: (020) 7511 3745 Fax: (01234) 381112 E-mail: dr.reid@reidbusinessservices.co.uk *ELECTRICAL AND HOME AUTOMATION SYSTEMS DESIGN AND INSTALLATION.*

▶ Reid Cooper Partnership, 78 Carlton Place, Glasgow, G5 9TH Tel: 0141-429 4656 Fax: 0141-429 1494

Reid Electrical & Computer Services, Elmsbrook, Lovacott, Newton Tracey, Barnstaple, Devon, EX31 3PU Tel: (01271) 858546 E-mail: info@reidelectrical.fsnet.co.uk *Electrical contractors*

Reid F Contractor, Crewe Park Road, Glenavy, Crumlin, County Antrim, BT29 4NJ Tel: (028) 9442 2486 *Hedge cutting & groundwork services*

Reid Fishing Tackle & Sports, 33 Hope Street, Crook, County Durham, DL15 9HU Tel: (01388) 763867 Fax: (01388) 763867 *Fishing equipment distributor*

▶ Reid Freight Services Ltd, Cinderhill Industrial Estate, Stoke-on-Trent, ST3 5LB Tel: (01782) 599581 Fax: (01782) 593323

The Reid Gear Co., Napier Street, Linwood, Paisley, Renfrewshire, PA3 3AN Tel: (01505) 321591 Fax: (01505) 321645 E-mail: info@reidgear.com Principal Export Areas: Worldwide *Gear box manufrs*

▶ Ian Reid Removals, Hagdale Industrial Estate, Baltasound, Unst, Shetland, ZE2 9DS Tel: (01957) 711410

James Reid & Son, 10 Bon Accord Square, Aberdeen, AB11 6DJ Tel: (01224) 588309 Fax: (01224) 584598 E-mail: aberdeen@jamesreidandson.co.uk *Sheriff officers & messengers-at-arms*

Reid Lifting Ltd, 3 Bulwark Business Park, Bulwark Road, Bulwark, Chepstow, Gwent, NP16 5JG Tel: (01291) 620796 Fax: (01291) 626490 E-mail: enquiries@reidlifting.com *Lightweight portable lifting equipment*

Reid Printers, 79-109 Glasgow Road, Blantyre, Glasgow, G72 0LY Tel: (01698) 826000 Fax: (01698) 824944 E-mail: sales@reid-print-group.co.uk *Colour & commercial printers*

▶ Reid Transport Co. Ltd, Cassillis Garage, Cassillis, Maybole, Ayrshire, KA19 8DN Tel: (01292) 442324

▶ Reid Williamson Print Ltd, 26 Civic Street, Glasgow, G4 9RH Tel: 0141-332 1143

Reid Wire Ltd, 162 Glenpark Street, Glasgow, G31 1PG Tel: 0141-554 7081 Fax: 0141-556 4483 E-mail: sales@reidwire.com *Industrial wire goods manufrs*

Reid's, 1 51 Seafield Road, Inverness, IV1 1SG Tel: (01463) 717722 Fax: (01463) 717766 E-mail: admin@reidnutsandbolts-uk.com *Bolt, nut & fastener distributors*

▶ Reids Food Service, 38 James Street, Dalry, Ayrshire, KA24 5ET Tel: (01294) 833001 Fax: (01294) 833032

Reif & Son Ltd, 8 Blue Chip Business Park, Atlantic Street, Broadheath, Altrincham, Cheshire, WA14 5DD Tel: 0161-927 9192 Fax: 0161-927 9193 E-mail: reif@btconnect.com *Timber & veneer merchants*

Reilloc Chain Ltd, Stourport Road, Kidderminster, Worcestershire, DY11 7BQ Tel: (01562) 820717 Fax: (01562) 820377 *Mining chain manufrs*

▶ Reilly Civil Engineers, 21 Watt Road, Hillington Industrial Estate, Glasgow, G52 4RY Tel: 0141-882 9791

John Reilly Civil Engineering Ltd, 103 Desborough Road, Eastleigh, Hampshire, SO50 5NT Tel: (023) 8062 9900 Fax: (023) 8061 3571 E-mail: info@johnreilly.co.uk *Civil engineering & groundworks*

Reilly & Warnock, 2 Pokelly Place, Stewarton, Kilmarnock, Ayrshire, KA3 5PF Tel: (01560) 484279 *Painting & decorating contractors*

Reilor Ltd, Astra Business Centre, Roman Way, Preston, PR2 5AP Tel: (01772) 793793 Fax: (01772) 797877 E-mail: sales@reilor.com *Door furniture manufacturers & pet products*

Reiner Fixing Devices, Church Lane, North Ockendon, Upminster, Essex, RM14 3QH Tel: (01708) 856601 Fax: (01708) 852293 E-mail: sales@reinerfixings.co.uk *Insulation fixing manufrs*

Reinforcements Peterborough, 1 Fenlake Business Centre, Fengate, Peterborough, PE1 5BQ Tel: (01733) 558321 Fax: (01733) 555260 *Concrete steel reinforcing products*

▶ Reiss Electrical Contractors, 5 Odeon Parade, Holloway Road, London, N7 6LS Tel: (020) 7272 5988

Reisser Ltd, Pepper Road, Hazel Grove, Stockport, Cheshire, SK7 5BW Tel: 0161-483 5557 Fax: 0161-483 4631 E-mail: reisser@dial.pipex.com *Fastener distribs*

Reitech Communications, 1 Castle Street, Dover, Kent, CT16 1QH Tel: (07831) 407346 Fax: (01304) 214078 E-mail: info@reitech.co.uk *Data cabling design, installation & support*

Reiver Boat, Rescue Station House, South Moor, Stanley, County Durham, DH9 6AA Tel: (01207) 283040 Fax: (01207) 283040 *Boat building, engine maintenance & repairs*

Reject Pot Shop, 56 Chalk Farm Road, London, NW1 8AN Tel: (020) 7485 2326 Fax: (020) 7485 2326 E-mail: sales@rejectpotshop.co.uk *China & glass retailers*

▶ Rekar Ltd, Sandy Cross, Heathfield, East Sussex, TN21 8QR Tel: (01435) 860100 Fax: (01435) 869718 *IT services & software developers*

Rekord Sales Great Britain Ltd, Manor Road, Mancetter, Atherstone, Warwickshire, CV9 1RJ Tel: (01827) 712424 Fax: (01827) 715133 E-mail: sales@rekord.com *Agricultural implement manufacturers, distributors & importers*

▶ Related Life Sciences Ltd, 9 Hazelwood Drive, Barlborough, Chesterfield, Derbyshire, S43 4WR Tel: (07739) 708557 Fax: (01246) 813281 E-mail: info@rlsciences.com Suppliers of contamination prevention and infection control equipment and consumables to the Life Sciences Industries

Relational Consultants Ltd, 38 Northgate Street, Bury St. Edmunds, Suffolk, IP33 1HY Tel: (01284) 765723 E-mail: info@relcon.co.uk Computer consultancy

▶ Relaxation Zone Ltd, 5 Roundwood Lane, Harpenden, Hertfordshire, AL5 3BW Tel: (0845) 0563550 E-mail: info@relaxationzone.co.uk There are plenty of pressures around us that may cause us stress; including: - work pressures, home pressures, financial worries, noise and pollution, bereavement....and much more. Different people deal with these pressures in different ways. Sometimes just taking a little time out to relax can help put everything into perspective, helping you to cope better with the pressures of modern day life.

Relay Engineering Services, 1a Dicker Mill, Hertford, SG13 7AA Tel: (01992) 586234 Fax: (01992) 582894 E-mail: info@relayeng.com Electrical test equipment suppliers

Relcom Communications, Unit 1, Oliver Business Park, Oliver Road, London, NW10 7JB Tel: (020) 8965 2333 Fax: (020) 8965 2323 E-mail: info@relcom.co.uk Radio communication system hire & retailers

Reldale Ltd, 60 Dunster Street, Northampton, NN1 3JY Tel: (01604) 632438 Fax: (01604) 632438 E-mail: enquiries@reldaleltd.co.uk Printing circuit designers & precision engineers

Relga Ltd, 31 Mexborough Road, Bolton Woods, Bradford, West Yorkshire, BD2 1BL Tel: (01274) 591677 Fax: (01274) 591677 Knitwear & textile services

▶ Reliability Plus, 5 High Street, South Woodchester, Stroud, Gloucestershire, GL5 5EL Tel: 01453 878540 Fax: 01453 878595 E-mail: bob.page@environmental.org.uk Technical consultancy & training

Reliable Fire Sprinkler Ltd, Unit A2 Epsom Business Park, Kiln Lane, Epsom, Surrey, KT17 1JF Tel: (01372) 728899 Fax: (01372) 724461 E-mail: rfsl@reliablesprinkler.com Automatic sprinkler manufrs

▶ Reliable Property Maintenance, 43-45 Windsor Drive, Orpington, Kent, BR6 6EY Tel: (01689) 855647 Fax: (01689) 858809

▶ Reliable Removals, Unit 14 Globe Industrial Estate, Rectory Road, Grays, Essex, RM17 6ST Tel: (0800) 0931660 Fax: (01375) 399994

Reliable Spring & Manufacturing Co. Ltd, Unit 4a Princes End Industrial Estate, Nicholls Road, Tipton, West Midlands, DY4 9LG Tel: 0121-557 4999 Fax: 0121-557 6959 E-mail: sales@reliablespring.co.uk Spring manufacturers; springs, coil; springs, compression; springs, flat; springs, torsion & wire formed/shaped component/product manufrs

Reliable Stamping, 38 New John St West, Birmingham, B19 3NB Tel: 0121-359 6918 Fax: 0121-333 4691 E-mail: sales@reliable-stamping.co.uk Principal Export Areas: Africa Medal distributors & manufrs

Reliable Techniques Ltd, Unit 59 Parkhouse Industrial Estate West, Brick Kiln Lane, Newcastle, Staffordshire, ST5 7AS Tel: (01782) 565002 Fax: (01782) 565001 E-mail: optics@reliabletechniques.fsnet.co.uk Supplier of optical accessories

Reliagraphics Engineering, 11 Bilton Road, Erith, Kent, DA8 2AN Tel: (01322) 342375 Fax: (01322) 338916 E-mail: enquires@reliagraphicsengineering.co.uk Stainless steel specialists

Reliamatics, Units 1&2 Rear of 36, Palace Avenue, Paignton, Devon, TQ3 3HB Tel: (01803) 551944 Fax: (01803) 551944 Gaming machine suppliers

Reliance Barker Davies, Cheapside, Bridgend Industrial Estate, Bridgend, Mid Glamorgan, CF31 3UN Tel: (01656) 656381 Fax: (01656) 663869 E-mail: info@reliancebarkerdavies.com Wire rope attachment manufrs

▶ Reliance Converting Ltd, Salters Lane, Sedgefield, Stockton-on-Tees, Cleveland, TS21 3EE Tel: (01740) 621415 Fax: (01740) 621424 E-mail: sales@relianceconverting.co.uk Food packaging materials

Reliance Engineering, Unit 5 Knowle Industrial Estate, Knowle, Braunton, Devon, EX33 2NA Tel: (01271) 817642 Fax: (01271) 816594 E-mail: ggre240208@aol.com General engineers

Reliance Engineering, Giles Lane, Landford, Salisbury, SP5 2BG Tel: (01794) 322904 Fax: (01794) 323620 Steel fabricators

Reliance Engineering & Fabrication Ltd, Retford, Nottinghamshire, DN22 1WS Tel: (07771) 634203 E-mail: gbrumpton@aol.com General engineering fabrications

Reliance Fashions, Duncrue Cresent, Belfast, BT3 9BW Tel: (028) 9077 6848 Fax: (028) 9077 6848 Clothing wholesalers

Reliance Garage Ltd, Turnlee Road, Glossop, Derbyshire, SK13 6PW Tel: (01457) 853222 Motor vehicle repair services

Reliance Marine, Marine Centre, South Parade, West Kirby, Wirral, Merseyside, CH48 0QG Tel: 0151-625 5219 Fax: 0151-625 6779 E-mail: sales@reliance.com Yacht Chandler*Compasses*Cookers*Deck*Depth* Direction*Distance*Drysuits*Echo*Engine* Epoxies*Eye*Fairleads*Fibreglass*Fiddle*Fillers* Fish*Finders*Fittings*Fixings*Flags*Fouling*Full* Furling*GPS*Genoa*Gloves*Gudgeons* Handheld*Handles*Hatches*Hooks*Indicators* Inshore*Jackets *Kayaks*Keelband*Kicking*Knives*Leads* Levers*Lifebuoys*Logs*Lubricants*Mainsheet* Mast*Navigation*Navtex*Nuts*Oil*Outboard* Paint*Pins*Pintles*Plates*Plotters*Plugs*Pumps* Radar*Radios*Ratchet*Rigging*Rings*Rivets* Rope*Rowlocks*Rudder*Sail*Sanitation*Screws* Sealants*Shackles*Shear*Slides*Slip*Sounder* Spark*Speed*Spinnaker*Spring*Stanchion*Stay* Steering*Storage*Strap*Studs*Switches*Swivel* Tails*Tell*Tenders*Thermal*Thimbles*Tiller*Toe* Tools*Tops*Tracks*Trapeze*Trousers*VHF*

continued

Radios*Varnish*Watches*Waterproof*Weather* Weather*Wetsuits*Winch*Wind*Wing*Wire

Reliance Precision Mechatronics LLP, Rowley Mills, Penistone Road, Lepton, Huddersfield, HD8 0LE Tel: (01484) 601000 Fax: (01484) 601001 E-mail: sales@reliance.co.uk Precision motion control components & mechatronic assemblies

Reliance Scrap Metal Merchants Ltd, 78-86 Nuffield Road, Nuffield Industrial Estate, Poole, Dorset, BH17 0RS Tel: (01202) 673539 Fax: (01202) 669509 Scrap metal merchants & contractors

Reliance Security Group plc, Boundary House, Cricketfield Road, Uxbridge, Middlesex, UB8 1QG Tel: (01895) 205000 Fax: (01895) 205100 E-mail: info@reliancesecurity.co.uk Security consultants

Reliance Security Services Ltd, London Street, 2-4 Old Pye Street, London, SW1P 2LE Tel: (020) 7222 6044 Fax: (020) 7222 9415 E-mail: info@reliancesecurity.co.uk Security services

Reliance Security Services Ltd, Surety House Kingsway Industrial Estate, Kingsway, Luton, LU1 1LP Tel: (01582) 452278 Fax: (01582) 720505 E-mail: info@reliancesecurity.co.uk Security guard services

Reliance Veneer Co. Ltd, Timberwharf Road, London, N16 6DE Tel: (020) 8802 2361 Fax: (020) 8802 2368 E-mail: veneer@reliance99.freeserve.co.uk Veneer manufrs

Reliance Water Controls Ltd, Worcester Road, Evesham, Worcestershire, WR11 4RA Tel: (01386) 47148 Fax: (01386) 47028 E-mail: sales@rwc.co.uk Flow control valves

Reliant, Argyle Business Centre, 39 North Howard Street, Belfast, BT13 2AP Tel: (028) 9031 5193 Fax: (028) 9031 5130 Industrial doors fitters & manufrs

Reliant Design Development Co. Ltd, 60 Woolmer Way, Bordon, Hampshire, GU35 9QF Tel: (01420) 478321 Fax: (01420) 489322 E-mail: sales@rdd.co.uk Aircraft test equipment & ground support equipment service providers

Reliant High-Tec Ltd, Surety House, 70 Barweel Business Park, Leather Head Road, Chessington, Surrey, KT9 2NY Tel: (020) 8391 2200 Fax: (01689) 890738 E-mail: sales@relitech.co.uk Supply & install electronic security systems

Reliant Machinery Ltd, 17 Asheridge Road, Chesham, Buckinghamshire, HP5 2PY Tel: (01494) 792299 Fax: (01494) 791317 Principal Export Areas: Worldwide Textile machinery & laminating manufrs

▶ Reliant Marking Tools Co. UK, Unit 2, Benson Industrial Estate, Benson Road, Birmingham, B18 5TS Tel: 0121-523 6565 E-mail: webmaster@reliantmarkingtools.co.uk Reliant Marking Tools Co: manufacturers of stencils, marking tool, engraving tools, embossing tools and stamping tools. We are using latest CAD/CAM/CNC technology for roll marking, steel types, marking stamps, marking punches, blocks and die sinking.

Reliant Parts World Ltd, Unit C, Orbital Way, Cannock, Staffordshire, WS11 8XW Tel: (01543) 431941 Fax: (01543) 431966 E-mail: info@reliant-motors.co.uk Piaggio & Legier car importers

Reliant Printers Ltd, Journeymans Way, Temple Farm Industrial Estate, Southend-on-Sea, SS2 5TF Tel: (01702) 618161 Fax: (01702) 444880 E-mail: sales@kestrel-printing.co.uk General printers

Relief 4 Debt, 72 London Road, St. Albans, Hertfordshire, AL1 1NS Tel: (01727) 869966 Fax: (01727) 869149 E-mail: enquiries@relief4debt.co.uk Debt collection.

Relion Broma Ltd, Avenue Industrial Estate, Gallows Corner, Romford, RM3 0BY Tel: (01708) 341177 Fax: (01708) 384999 Stove enamellers/ powder coaters

Rella Ltd, Unit 2 Silver Indust Est, Reform Row, London, N17 9SZ Tel: 020 88855517 Fax: 020 88852037 Ladies garments manufrs

Rellumit Filters Ltd, PO Box 69, Princes Risborough, Buckinghamshire, HP27 9RW Tel: (01844) 273213 Fax: (01844) 273235 Industrial filter manufrs

Relmfield Builders Ltd, Hammond Road, Elm Farm Industrial Estate, Bedford, MK41 0RJ Tel: (01234) 218101 Fax: (01234) 357892 E-mail: sonia@relmfield.co.uk Building contractors

▶ Relocate Cambridge, Manor Farm House, 68 Town Street, Newton, Cambridge, CB2 5PE Tel: (01223) 871394 Fax: (01223) 871394 E-mail: info@relocatecambridge.co.uk An independent relocation company specialising in residential property search and acquisition for rental or purchase within Cambridge UK. Relocate Cambridge"s extensive knowledge of the Cambridge property market and friendly professional approach ensures they will find you the location which suits you best and will make your move a positive experience.

▶ Relocate South West, 12 Aish Park, Shebbear, Beaworthy, Devon, EX21 5QL Tel: (01409) 281546 Fax: (01409) 281991 E-mail: enquiries@relocatesouthwest.co.uk Property search specialist for The South West of England. We provide a professional, friendly and cost effective way to find a home in Devon or Cornwall.

Relocation Information Services, 4 Oxted Chambers, 185 Station Road East, Oxted, Surrey, RH8 0QE Tel: (01883) 732000 Fax: (01883) 732222 E-mail: info@ris-move.co.uk Relocation consultants

▶ Relocation Relocation, 35A Ludgate, Alloa, Clackmannanshire, FK10 1DS Tel: (01259) 212478 Fax: (01259) 212478 E-mail: lisa@relocationrelocation.net Property find service

▶ Rely Consulting Ltd, 76 Valley Drive, Brighton, BN1 5FD Tel: (01273) 822082 Fax: (0870) 1383454 E-mail: darren.trussell@relycon.com Operational, business & management consultancy services

Relyon Ltd, Station Mills, Wellington, Somerset, TA21 8NN Tel: (01823) 667501 Fax: (01823) 666079 E-mail: enquries@reylon.co.uk Bed manufrs

Relyon Heating Engineering Ltd, Bridge Works, Midland Road, Luton, LU2 0BL Tel: (01582) 730806 Fax: (01582) 481499 E-mail: admin@relyonheating.co.uk Heating installation engineers

Rem, Great Western House, Westover Trading Estate, Langport, Somerset, TA10 9YU Tel: (01458) 254700 Fax: (01458) 254701 Educational software suppliers

Rem, 5 Stockton End, Sandy, Bedfordshire, SG19 1RY Tel: (01767) 691592 Fax: (01767) 691599 E-mail: mmorse@remchem.co.uk Metal finishing process chemicals

Rem Electronic Equipment, Arkle House, Mill Lane, Birch, Colchester, CO2 0NG Tel: (01206) 331657 Fax: (01206) 331657 Capital equipment suppliers

Rem Systems Ltd, Unit 24 26, Sabre Close, Quedgeley, Gloucester, GL2 4NZ Tel: (01452) 314100 Fax: (01452) 314101 E-mail: sales@remsystems.co.uk Quick change tooling

Rema Tip Top UK, Mill Lane, Coppull, Chorley, Lancashire, PR7 5AW Tel: (01257) 793487 Fax: (01257) 793930 E-mail: kath.greenhalgh@tip-top.co.uk Rubber linings & lining systems

Remal Thermal Cycling Ltd, 4 Pinfold Place, Skelmersdale, Lancashire, WN8 9PQ Tel: (01695) 720462 Fax: (01695) 50414 E-mail: sales@remal-thorid.com Metal finishers

Remane Bros Ltd, 63-66 Hatton Garden, London, EC1N 8RF Tel: (020) 7405 6794 Fax: (020) 7831 6289 E-mail: remanegems@aol.com Imitation & real jewellery

Remark Telecommunications, Unit 3 The Manor Grove Centre, Vicarage Farm Road, Peterborough, PE1 5UH Tel: (01733) 551255 Fax: (01733) 551755 E-mail: sales@remarktelecomm.com Telephone systems & maintenance services

Rembrand Ltd, 51 Angel Road, Norwich, NR3 3HR Tel: (01603) 788477 Fax: (01603) 788466 Office supplies & services providers

▶ Rembrand Timber Ltd, Shielhill Wood, Tealing, Dundee, DD4 0PW Tel: (01382) 323200 Fax: (01382) 382520

Rembrand Timber Ltd, Bonnington Road Lane, Edinburgh, EH6 5BJ Tel: 0131-553 5351 Fax: 0131-554 2332 E-mail: leith@rembrand-timber.co.uk Timber merchants

Rembrandt Engravers, Northgate, White Lund Industrial Estate, Morecambe, Lancashire, LA3 3BE Tel: (01524) 63236 Fax: (01524) 39874 Photogravure cylinders manufrs

Remchem Ltd, Unit K Harlow House, Shelton Road, Willowbrook East Industrial Estate, Corby, Northamptonshire, NN17 5XH Tel: (01536) 205562 Fax: (01536) 401608 E-mail: sales@remchem.co.uk Building exterior cleaning contractors

▶ Remco Safety Ltd, Unit 1 Haxter Close, Belliver Industrial Estate, Roborough, Plymouth, PL6 7DD Tel: (01752) 786452 Fax: (01752) 767198 E-mail: remglo@aol.com Manufacture of protective clothing

Remco Signs Ltd, Mundy Street, Ilkeston, Derbyshire, DE7 8DH Tel: 0115-930 7769 Fax: 0115-932 7714 E-mail: sales@remcosigns.com Sign contractors & lighting manufrs

▶ Remik Engineering Ltd, 61 Nasmyth Road, Glenrothes, Fife, KY6 2SD Tel: (01592) 631260 Fax: (01592) 631262 Sheet metalwork engineers & fabricators

▶ Reminis Ltd, Gledrid Industrial Park, Gledrid, Chirk, Wrexham, LL14 5DG Tel: (01691) 778899 Fax: (01691) 773552 E-mail: sales@reminis.co.uk Retail furniture

Remmers UK Ltd, Remmers House, 14 Victoria Way, Burgess Hill, West Sussex, RH15 9NF Tel: (01444) 244144 Fax: (01444) 243500 E-mail: sales@remmers.co.uk Industrial roof & flooring systems & restoration & waterproofing

Remondis UK Ltd, A Scot La Industrial Estate, Scot Lane, Blackrod, Bolton, BL6 5SL Tel: (01942) 831362 Fax: (01942) 833051 E-mail: sales@remondisuk.co.uk Hazardous Waste collection, disposal, recycling and treatment. Farm Waste collection, Agriculture Waste collection, Plastic recycling, Electronic Waste (WEEE) recycling, Print waste, Photographic waste, Silver recovery, Photo-waste management

Remote Control Ltd, Unit 40 Trent Valley Trading Estate, Station Road, Rugeley, Staffordshire, WS15 2HQ Tel: (01889) 577676 Fax: (01889) 577676 E-mail: lesgarbett@remotecontrol.co.uk Acuators manufrs

▶ Remote Data Services Ltd, Blair Atholl, Pitlochry, Perthshire, PH18 5TL Tel: (01796) 473560 Fax: (01796) 473639 E-mail: info@rdserv.com I.T. Products and services. Cabling soltions for all medias, satellite broadband, mobile broadband, electronic identification, CCTV and electrical repairs.

Remote Marine Systems, Derwent Road, York Road Business Park, Malton, North Yorkshire, YO17 6YB Tel: (01653) 690001 Fax: (01653) 690002 E-mail: sales@rmsltd.com Principal Export Areas: Worldwide Manufacturers of electric connectors sub sea & underwater

▶ Remote New Media, 17 Lower Down, Lydbury North, Shropshire, SY7 8BB Tel: (01588) 680480 E-mail: info@remote.uk.com Database driven websites management services

Remote Technologies, West Greenbank, Hickmans la, Haywards Heath, W. Sussex, RH16 2DR Tel: (01273) 813869 Business consultants

▶ Remotecontrolgolf.com, Fairfax, Paignton, Devon, TQ4 5LH Tel: (01803) 402668 High specification remote control golf trolleys for sale. Free Uk mainland delivery

▶ Remous Ltd, Wyvern Buildings, North Street, Milborne Port, Sherborne, Dorset, DT9 5EP Tel: (01963) 250920 Fax: (01963) 251054

▶ Removal Services Scotland, 11 Granton Square, Edinburgh, EH5 1HX Tel: 0131-551 4272 Fax: 0131-551 5949

▶ Remploy Ltd, Stone Court, Siskin Drive, Middlemarch Business Park, Coventry, CV3 4FJ Tel: (024) 7651 5800 Fax: (024) 7651 5860 E-mail: info@remploy.co.uk Electronic contract manufacturing services

Remploy Ltd, 13-6 South Gyle CR, Edinburgh, EH12 9EB Tel: 0131-334 2266 Fax: 0131-334 3167 Electronic contract manufacturing services

▶ Remploy Ltd, Bede Trading Estate, Jarrow, Tyne & Wear, NE32 3EG Tel: 0191-489 7528 Fax: 0191-483 3087

▶ Remploy Ltd, Unit 1, Banbeth Industrial Estate, Leven, Fife, KY8 5HD Tel: (01333) 429607 Marine products

Remploy Ltd, Nathan Way, London, SE28 0BD Tel: (020) 8855 5050 Fax: (020) 8316 6923

Remploy Ltd, 63a Effra Road, London, SW2 1BZ Tel: (020) 7274 6681 Fax: (020) 7274 0715 Cable & wiring

Remploy Ltd, Botany Avenue, Mansfield, Nottinghamshire, NG18 5NG Tel: (01623) 629137 Fax: (01623) 420814 Packaging & assembly agents

Remploy Ltd, Croespenmaen Industrial Estate, Kendon, Crumlin, Newport, Gwent, NP11 3AG Tel: (01495) 246505 Fax: (01495) 248334 E-mail: john.lundie@remploy.co.uk Packaging manufrs

▶ Remploy Ltd, Unit C9, Treforest Industrial Estate, Pontypridd, Mid Glamorgan, CF37 5UD Tel: (01443) 843417 Fax: (01443) 846099

Remploy Ltd, 14 Alder Hills, Poole, Dorset, BH12 4AS Tel: (01202) 743445 Fax: (01202) 715337 E-mail: marine@remploy.co.uk Textile merchants

Remploy Ltd, Gordon Banks Drive, Trentham Lakes North, Stoke-on-Trent, ST4 4TJ Tel: (01782) 658438 Fax: (01782) 643492 Packaging material & equipment manufrs

▶ Remploy Ltd, Excelsior Park, Netherhall Road, Netherton Industrial Estate, Wishaw, Lanarkshire, ML2 0JG Tel: (01698) 354800 Fax: (01698) 354801

Remploy Ltd, Railway Road, Wrexham, Clwyd, LL11 2DN Tel: (01978) 291465 Fax: (01978) 290017 E-mail: gerrard.newrick@remploy.co.uk Wooden furniture manufrs

Remploy Furniture Group, Cwmgarw Road, Upper Brynamman, Ammanford, Dyfed, SA18 1DG Tel: (01269) 822141 Fax: (01269) 826188 E-mail: anna.davies@remploy.co.uk Furniture manufrs

Remploy Furniture Group Ltd, 15-16 Fall Bank Industrial Estate, Dodworth, Barnsley, South Yorkshire, S75 3LS Tel: (01226) 284064 Fax: (01226) 720131 Furniture manufrs

Remploy Furniture Group Ltd, Bank Top, Blackburn, BB2 1TH Tel: (01254) 52271 Fax: (01254) 618419 E-mail: blackburn@remploy.co.uk Metal office furniture manufrs

Remploy Furniture Group, Baglan Energy Park, Central Avenue, Baglan, Port Talbot, West Glamorgan, SA12 7AX Tel: (01639) 824637 Fax: (01639) 424685 E-mail: furniture@remploy.co.uk Office storage furniture manufrs

Remploy Manufacturing Services, 79 Torrington Avenue, Coventry, CV4 9AQ Tel: (024) 7646 2715 Fax: (024) 7642 7064 E-mail: graham.howard-spink@remploy.co.uk Electronic contract manufacturing services

▶ Remploy Packaging, Broadstone Road, Stockport, Cheshire, SK5 7AT Tel: 0161-431 3604 Fax: 0161-442 9909 Packaging services

Remploy Recycle Ltd, Cymmer Road, Porth, Mid Glamorgan, CF39 9BW Tel: (01443) 497200 Fax: (01443) 497228 E-mail: mike.clarke@remploy.co.uk Electronic contract manufacturing services

Remtech Computer Security Ltd, PO Box 60, Epsom, Surrey, KT17 2YT Tel: (020) 8786 8788 Fax: (020) 8786 8788 E-mail: sales@remtech.uk.com Computer room designers

Ren Tools Ltd, 247 Great Lister Street, Birmingham, B7 4BS Tel: 0121-359 7231 Fax: 0121-359 7502 E-mail: sales@rentals.co.uk Cutting tool manufrs

Renaddress Ltd, Target House, Lea Road, Waltham Abbey, Essex, EN9 1AE Tel: (01992) 712592 Fax: (01992) 760902 E-mail: reg@target-sys.co.uk Addressing machine distributors service

Renair Antennae Ltd, 11-15 Chase Road, London, NW10 6PT Tel: (020) 8965 3001 Fax: (020) 8965 5773 E-mail: sales@renair.co.uk Aerial & antenna designers & manufrs

▶ Renaissance, 1 Emperor Way, Exeter Business Park, Exeter Business Park, Exeter, EX1 3QS Tel: (01803) 404047 Fax: (01803) 404048 E-mail: enquiries@debt-recovery-services.com Commission only debt collection. National. Members of The Credit Services Association.Consumer and Commercial debt.

Renaissance, 1 Emperor Way, Exeter Business Park, Exeter Business Park, Exeter, EX1 3QS Tel: (01803) 404047 Fax: 01392 434047 E-mail: enquiries@commercial-investigation.com Nationwide Investigation Services with over 150 investigators providing a fast and effective service throughout England,Wales and Scotland. Surveillance; Fraud Investigation; Stock loss and shrinkage ; Tracing; Undercover operations. Process Services; Company searches.

Renaissance Corporate (Barnet) Ltd, Unit 1 Stroud Wood Business Centre, Frogmore, St. Albans, Herts, AL2 2NN Tel: (01727) 875500 Fax: (01727) 874808 E-mail: sales@rencorp.co.uk Computer system & software development

Renaissance Henna, PO Box 45882, London, London, E11 3WW Tel: 0208 530 1130 Fax: 0208 5301130 E-mail: info@renaissancehenna.com WE SPECIALISE IN PROVIDING HIGH QUALITY HERBAL NATURAL HAIR CARE PRODUCTS. WE SUPPLY PURE AND FRESH 100% PURE CHEMICAL FREE HENNA,INDIGO, AND CASSIA OBOVATA FOR HAIR; WE ALSO SUPPLY OTHER NATURAL HAIR CARE PRODUCTS.

Company Information

▶ Renaissance Language Services, 51 Auckland Road, Tunbridge Wells, Kent, TN1 2HX Tel: 01892 538932 Fax: 01892 538932 E-mail: info@renaissance-training.co.uk *Independent, local (Tunbridge Wells, Kent) organisation which provides individual and small group tuition in English as a foreign language, French, Italian and English at KS2 and 3.*

Renaissance Period Mouldings, 262 Handsworth Road, Sheffield, S13 9BS Tel: 0114-244 6622 Fax: 0114-261 0472 *Period fireplace mouldings manufrs*

▶ Renaissance Regeneration Ltd, 33 St. Andrews Street North, Bury St. Edmunds, Suffolk, IP33 1SZ Tel: (01284) 765563 Fax: (01284) 777445 E-mail: magnus.willatts@renreg.co.uk *National Environmental Search and Report Provision, environmental consultancy, Solicitor due diligence services, property transfer coordination all additonal Environmental services.*

Renaissance Sales & Distribution Ltd, Pennywell Industrial Estate, Sunderland, SR4 9EN Tel: 0191-534 6061 Fax: 0191-534 3626 E-mail: info@armour-plastics.com *Plastic vacuum forming toolmakers, & bath manufrs*

Renatex Ltd, Nam House, 58 Spencer Street, Birmingham, B18 6DS Tel: 0121-233 9999 Fax: 0121-236 9295 E-mail: sales@renatex.com *Battery distributors*

Renault, 1 Crofton Road, Orpington, Kent, BR6 8AB Tel: (01689) 897897 Fax: (01689) 877188 *Renault car sales & technical*

Renault Printing Co. Ltd, 54 Factory Estate, College Road, Perry Barr, Birmingham, B44 8BS Tel: 0121-356 0331 Fax: 0121-356 0153 E-mail: sales@renaultprint.co.uk *Colour printers services*

Renault UK Ltd, Rivers Office Park, Denham Way, Maple Cross, Rickmansworth, Hertfordshire, WD3 9YS Tel: (01923) 895000 Fax: (01923) 895101 E-mail: enquiries@renault.co.uk *Motor car manufrs* Also at: Branches throughout the U.K.

Renbow International Ltd, 60 Church Road, Leyton, London, E10 5JP Tel: (0870) 3665410 Fax: (0870) 3665411 E-mail: sales@renbow.co.uk *Hair cosmetic manufrs*

Renco, Bath Road Trading Estate, Lightpill, Stroud, Gloucestershire, GL5 3QF Tel: (01453) 752154 Fax: (01453) 752155 E-mail: sales@renco-netting.co.uk *Electric fencing manufrs*

Renco Engineering Machine Services, Unit 14 Deeleys Trading Estate, Leamore Lane, Walsall, WS2 7BY Tel: (01922) 476868 Fax: (01922) 476878 *Machinists & general engineers*

Rencol Tolerance Rings, Second Way, Bristol, BS11 8DF Tel: 0117-938 1700 Fax: 0117-915 7982 E-mail: sales@rencol.co.uk *Design & manufacture of tolerance rings*

▶ Rencraft Ltd, Unit 9 Chart Farm, Seal, Sevenoaks, Kent, TN15 0ES Tel: (01732) 762682 Fax: (01732) 762535 *Kitchen manufrs*

▶ Rendall Builders, 8 Grainshore Drive, Hatston, Kirkwall, Orkney, KW15 1FL Tel: (01856) 878338 Fax: (01856) 878338

▶ Rendezvous (Lincoln) Ltd, Unit 4 Lydon Business Park, Farrier Road, Lincoln, LN6 3RU Tel: (01522) 500000 Fax: (01522) 500000 *Hair & beauty suppliers*

Rendrive Haulage Ltd, Church Manor Way, Erith, Kent, DA8 1DE Tel: (01322) 442206 Fax: (01322) 463232 *Road transport, haulage & freight services*

Renegade Engineering Co. Ltd, Unit F Penfold Works, Imperial Way, Watford, WD24 4YY Tel: (01923) 230788 Fax: (01923) 219496 *General engineering services*

Renegade Products, Unit 2-3 Clearways Industrial Estate, London Road, West Kingsdown, Sevenoaks, Kent, TN15 6ES Tel: (01474) 852255 Fax: (01474) 852999 *Exhaust manufrs*

Renelec Ltd, Brownstone House, New Park Street, Devizes, Wiltshire, SN10 1DS Tel: (01380) 726363 Fax: (01380) 729255 E-mail: postmaster@renelec.co.uk *Electrical, plumbing heating & groundwork contractors*

▶ Renewable Devices Energy Solutions, Bush Estate, Penicuik, Midlothian, EH26 0PH Tel: 0131-535 3403 Fax: 0131-535 3303 E-mail: info@renewabledevices.com *Wind turbine systems design services*

Renfor Four Colour, Paper Mill End Industrial Estate, Birmingham, B44 8NH Tel: 0121-356 9555 Fax: 0121-356 3555 E-mail: info@renfor.co.uk *Printing services*

Renforce Ltd, 26A Collegiate Crescent, Sheffield, S10 2BH Tel: 0114-266 7521 Fax: 0114-268 4331 *Reinforcing (concrete etc) steel reinforcement manufrs*

Renfrew Group, 33 Rutland St, Leicester, LE1 1RE Tel: 0116-253 1961 Fax: 0116-253 9827 E-mail: info@renfrew.com *Award-winning Renfrew Group is a multidisciplinary design and development organisation with specialisms across the entire spectrum of commercial activity in consumer, industrial, medical, and automotive fields. With every assignment, this innovative group unlocks the minds of the consumer to deliver products with robust intellectual property and high market appeal. For more than twenty years Renfrew Group has worked with clients from fresh start-ups to large multinationals providing them with specialist teams in product design, design engineering, engineering analysis, prototyping and production data. The consultancy is based in the heart of the UK and has extensive facilities including 2 automotive studios and large general prototyping workshops*

Renfrew Motor Engineers, Unit 2 Brown Street, Renfrew, PA4 8HW Tel: 0141-886 6667 Fax: 0141-561 1019 *Car repairs & mot*

W.G. Renfrew, Unit1, Shanks Industrial Park, Blackbyres Road, Barrhead, Glasgow, G78 1EB Tel: 0141-881 1481 Fax: 0141-880 8085 *Blacksmiths*

▶ Renfrewshire Electronics, Block 15, Dubbs Road, Port Glasgow, Renfrewshire, PA14 5UG Tel: (01475) 794350 Fax: (01475) 744787 E-mail: sales@renfrew-elec.co.uk

Renham & Wade Ltd, Units 1-6 Gas Lane Industrial Estate, Gas La, Middleton In Teesdale, Barnard Castle, County Durham, DL12 0TN Tel: 01833 640050 Fax: 01833 640995 E-mail: enquiries@renhamandwade.co.uk *Clean room plastic injection*

Renishaw plc, Heriot-Watt Research Park, Riccarton, Currie, Midlothian, EH14 4AP Tel: 0131-451 1616 Fax: 0131-451 1717

Renishaw Plc, New Mills, Wotton-under-Edge, Gloucestershire, GL12 8JR Tel: (01453) 524126 Fax: (01453) 524201 E-mail: uk@renishaw.com Principal Export Areas: Worldwide *Encoders, rotary & linear. Also manufacturers of measuring equipment*

Renlim Labels, 1065 Thornton Road, Bradford, West Yorkshire, BD8 0PA Tel: (01274) 882222 Fax: (01274) 884449E-mail: renlim@netserv.net *Self-adhesive label manufrs*

Renlon Holdings Ltd, Richardson House, Boundary Business Court, Mitcham, Surrey, CR4 3TD Tel: (020) 8687 4000 Fax: (020) 8687 4040 E-mail: survey@renlon.com *Damp proofing services*

▶ Rennie & Hodge Ltd, 47 Middlesex Street, Glasgow, G41 1EE Tel: 0141-429 6431 Fax: 0141-429 6427

Ian Rennie Precast, Alfred Street, Montrose, Angus, DD10 8HW Tel: (01674) 672792 Fax: (01674) 672792 E-mail: sales@rennierecast.co.uk *Concrete manufrs*

J.C. Rennie, Milladen, Mintlaw, Peterhead, Aberdeenshire, AB42 8LA Tel: (01779) 871400 Fax: (01779) 478989 *Fabrics wool & spinning suppliers*

Rennie & Kirkwood Ltd, 95 Morrison Street, Glasgow, G5 8BE Tel: 0141-429 2810 Fax: 0141-420 3728 E-mail: mail@rkglasgow.fsnet.co.uk *Consulting, structural & civil engineers* Also at: Dumfries & Hawick

Rennie Tool Co. Ltd, 227 Upper Brook Street, Manchester, M13 0HB Tel: 0161-273 3901 Fax: 0161-273 3348 E-mail: rennietool@btconnect.com *Lathe cutting tool manufrs*

Renntec, 69 Woolsbridge Industrial Estate, Three Legged Cross, Wimborne, Dorset, BH21 6SP Tel: (01202) 826722 Fax: (01202) 826747 E-mail: info@renntec.com *Motor cycle accessories manufrs*

Rennyco Ltd, West Tree Building, Whessoe Road, Darlington, County Durham, DL3 0QT Tel: (01325) 480502 Fax: (01325) 384278 E-mail: sales@rennycoltd.com *Steel fabricators security & industrial fencing*

Renoco Engineering Ltd, Unit 36, Station Lane Industrial Estate, Old Whittington, Chesterfield, Derbyshire, S41 9QX Tel: (01246) 454725 Fax: (01246) 454599 E-mail: renocoeng@aol.com *Mechanical & structural engineers*

Renoir Jewels Ltd, Pegasus Works, Roebuck Road, Hainault Business Park, Ilford, Essex, IG6 3UF Tel: (020) 8500 2301 Fax: (020) 8501 2301 E-mail: enquiries@renoirjewels.co.uk *Jewellery manufrs*

Renold Gears, Station Road, Milnrow, Rochdale, Lancashire, OL16 3LS Tel: (01706) 751000 Fax: (01706) 751001 *Hydraulics & variators*

Renold Gears, Station Road, Milnrow, Rochdale, Lancashire, OL16 3LS Tel: (01706) 751000 Fax: (01706) 751001 E-mail: gears.sales@renold.com *Manufactacturer of gearboxes , both helical and worm , specialised wormgear and helical production , subsidiary of Renold PLC.*

Renold High Tech Couplings, 112 Parkinson Lane, Halifax, West Yorkshire, HX1 3QH Tel: (01422) 255000 Fax: (01422) 320273 E-mail: sales@hitec.renold.com *Couplings manufrs*

Renolit UK Ltd, Renolit House, Hamond Road, Bedford, MK41 0UD Tel: (01234) 272999 Fax: (01234) 357313 E-mail: info@renolit.co.uk *Distributors of pvc windows & furniture foils*

▶ Renotex Ltd, Pollard Street, Lofthouse, Wakefield, West Yorkshire, WF3 3HG Tel: (01924) 820003 Fax: (01924) 829529 E-mail: sales@renotex.co.uk *Sales & export of coating systems*

Renovate Contracts Ltd, 91 Park Road, Earl Shilton, Leicester, LE9 7ZY Tel: 01455 851900 Fax: 01455 851900 E-mail: duncan@renovatecontracts.wanadoo.co.uk *We are Professional Wood Flooring Contractors working in the Contract Flooring sector throughout the UK. Our Flooring Services include Floor Sanding /Court Marking /Floor Marking /Repairs to all types of existing Wood Flooring /Timber Flooring /Hardwood Flooring / Granwood and Gransprung Flooring . We are Junckers Approved Maintenance Contractors and are recommended School Flooring Contractors by many Local Authorities. Our Floor Sanding , Staining and Sealing is of an extremely high standard as are the new Wood Floors which we install Nationwide. Wherever possible , we will Scrub and Reseal an existing Wooden Floor rather than Sanding as this preserves the life of the floor . We are a totally dependable and reputable company , and we have a pro-active attitude towards Health and Safety and the Environment. Our Company Ethos is the belief that our customers satisfaction should be of paramount importance to us , and is the reason why most of our Customers become our Clients*

▶ Renovation Seating Service, 96 Stone Cross La North, Lowton, Warrington, WA3 2SG Tel: (07766) 727811 Fax: (01942) 723033 E-mail: renovation.seating@fsmail.net *repair and renovate existing cinema and theatre chairs no quantity too great or too small, service contracts undertaken*

▶ Renovations Radiators Kitchens Bathrooms Shop, 286 High Street, Batheaston, Bath, BA1 7RA Tel: (01225) 852236 Fax: (01225) 852425 E-mail: sales@radiatorfinder.com *Selling a huge selection of radiators both modern & trad*with delivery to your door.*Extensive knowledge & know how willingly given just telephone//*

Renown Elec Co., 111 Bishops Road, London, SW6 7AU Tel: (020) 7731 1970 *Electrical contractors*

Renown Engineering Ltd, South Cramlington Industrial Estate, Cramlington, Northumberland, NE23 7RH Tel: 0191-250 0113 Fax: 0191-250 1980 E-mail: sales@renown-engineering.co.uk *General engineers & defence contractors*

Renown Welding, Unit 12 Diplocks Way, Hailsham, East Sussex, BN27 3JF Tel: (01323) 847742 Fax: (01323) 440471 *Steel fabricators & metalworkers*

▶ Renrod Ltd, Union House, Union Street, Trowbridge, Wiltshire, BA14 8RY Tel: (01225) 756100 Fax: (01225) 756149 E-mail: enquiries@renrodmg.co.uk *Motor Group*

▶ Renrod Financial Solutions, 36 Victoria Road, Warminster, Wiltshire, BA12 8HF Tel: (0800) 3281188 Fax: (01985) 211857 E-mail: sales@platinumfinancialsolutions.co.uk

Renshaw Scott Ltd, Crown Street, Liverpool, L8 7RF Tel: 0151-706 8200 Fax: 0151-706 8201 E-mail: info@renshawscott.co.uk *Marzipan & sugar paste manufrs*

▶ Renson Fabrications, Fairfax House, Bircholt Road, Maidstone, Kent, ME15 9SF Tel: (01622) 685658 Fax: (01622) 688762 E-mail: info@rensonuk.net *Manufacturers of window ventilators, louvres & grilles*

▶ Renson Products Ltd, Stainland Road, Greetland, Halifax, West Yorkshire, HX4 8LR Tel: (01422) 344222 Fax: (01422) 344766

Rent A Merc, 87 Dargan Road, Belfast, BT3 9JU Tel: (028) 9077 9755 Fax: (028) 9077 4374 E-mail: sales@rentamerc.co.uk *Rent-A-Merc Commercial Vehicle Hire - Northern Ireland"s leading supplier of commercial vehicles for rent. We use only quality Mercedes-Benz truck and vans for self drive and contract hire. Servicing and used sales are also available from our sites in Belfast, Mallusk and Campsie.*

▶ Rent A Merc, 87 Dargan Road, Belfast, BT3 9JU Tel: (028) 9077 9755 Fax: (028) 9077 4374 E-mail: sales@rentamerc.co.uk *Provide quality vehicles for self drive or contract hire*

Rent A Plant Ltd, 245 Cathedral Road, Cardiff, CF11 9PP Tel: (029) 2089 2825 Fax: (029) 2023 3044 *Floral display contractors*

Rent A Pump Services, Mold Road, Alltami, Mold, Clwyd, CH7 6LG Tel: (01244) 544962 Fax: (01244) 548557 E-mail: info@rentapump.co.uk *Pump hire, sale & repair services*

Rent A Ramp Ltd, Unit 37 Station Lane Industrial Estate, Station Lane, Old Whittington, Chesterfield, Derbyshire, S41 9QX Tel: (01246) 260602 Fax: (01246) 260493 E-mail: sales@rentaramp.com *Manufacturers & rental of ramps*

▶ Rent A Tent Marquees, 7 Nobles Close, Grove, Wantage, Oxfordshire, OX12 0NR Tel: (01235) 760026 E-mail: info@rentatentmarquees.co.uk *Providing marquee hire to Oxfordshire and surrounding Counties. Stunning marquees for any event at competitive prices. Weddings, Corporate, Garden Party. Any event covered.*Marquee hire in Oxfordshire, look no further.**

Rentacom Ltd, Hart Hill Farm, Hart Hill, Charing, Ashford, Kent, TN27 0HP Tel: (01233) 713555 Fax: (01233) 713511 *Cabin hire & sales*

Rent-A-Crane Ltd, 25 Rock Road, Solihull, West Midlands, B92 7LB Tel: 0121-706 7340 *Crane hire*

Rentajet Ltd, Paultons Park, Ower, Romsey, Hampshire, SO51 6AL Tel: (023) 8081 2921 Fax: (023) 8081 4016 E-mail: sales@rentajet.co.uk *Hydrodemolition/ hydro demolition contractors. Water jetting services, UHP ultra high pressure water jet cutting Abrasive jet cutting, blast cleaning. Dust free abrasive blasting services. Abrasive blasting painting services. High pressure pump hire, water jetting equipment hire. Vacuum blasting services. Surface preparation. Industrial water jetting services, Heat exchanger cleaning, tube cleaning. Condenser tube cleaning. Bundle blasting services and blasting services.*

Rental Options Ltd, Hillfoot House, Beenham Hill, Beenham, Reading, RG7 5LS Tel: 0118-971 2864 Fax: 0118-971 2820 E-mail: sales@rentaloptions.co.uk *Computer equipment rental services*

Rentequip Check Out Services, 8 Popple Way, Stevenage, Hertfordshire, SG1 3TG Tel: (01438) 359852 Fax: (01438) 361910 *Hire & repair till machines*

▶ Rentinbulgeria.com Ltd, 30 Wood Edge Close, Bolton, BL3 2PD Tel: 01204 709439 E-mail: sales@rentinbulgeria.com *Rent, Rental, Rentals, Bulgaria, Bulgarian, holiday, holidays, ski chalet, villa, apartment, Villas, Apartments, Houses, Skiing Chalets, property, properties, advertise, advertising, inland, city, beach, Resorts, countryside., forests, mountains, lakes, rivers, fishing, health spas, balneoligical centres, flights, car hire, travel insurance, swimming, skiing, riding, climbing, hunting, fishing, nature, sunny beaches, healing spas, monasteries, churches, towns, villages, beautiful, safe, blue flag standard, history, roman, cuisine, wines, shopping, kebapcheta, tarator, Shopska, Black sea, Sofia, Plovdiv, Burgas, Varna Bansko, Pamporovo, Borovets, Aleko, Golden Sands, Albena, Riviera, Sunny Beach,*

Rentmeister Distribution (N I), Unit 29 Cido Business Complex, Charles Street, Lurgan, Craigavon, County Armagh, BT66 6HG Tel: (028) 3834 6736 Fax: (028) 3834 6738 E-mail: sales@rentmeister.co.uk *Computer distributors*

Rentokil Ltd, Rentokil House, 4 London Road, Baldock, Hertfordshire, SG7 6ND Tel: (01462) 894422 Fax: (01462) 490174 *Pest control services*

Rentokil, 4 Singer Road, East Kilbride, Glasgow, G75 0UL Tel: (01355) 239140 Fax: (01355) 264172 *Pest control & hygiene services*

Rentokil, Chartists Way, Leeds, LS27 9EG Tel: 0113-252 6633 Fax: 0113-218 9087 *Pest control*

Rentokil, Hart Street, Maidstone, Kent, ME16 8RH Tel: (01622) 679821 Fax: (01622) 661206 *Pest controllers*

Rentokil Facilities Maintenance Ltd, Thames House, 27 Elmcroft Road, Orpington, Kent, BR6 0HZ Tel: (01689) 876511 Fax: (01689) 828898 E-mail: rentokfm@netcomuk.co.uk *Property maintenance*

Rentokil Initial plc, Unit 2-3 Wendle Court, 131-137 Wandsworth Road, London, SW8 2LH Tel: (020) 7498 5978 Fax: (020) 7501 0042 *Pest control*

Rentokil Pest Control, 43-45 Duncrue Cresent, Belfast, BT3 9BW Tel: (028) 9037 0631 Fax: (028) 9037 0492 E-mail: fcarville@rentokilpestcontrol.co.uk *Pest control & healthcare suppliers*

Rentokil Pest Control, St. Agnes Gardens, Ryton, Tyne & Wear, NE40 4LH Tel: (0800) 389 2319 Fax: 0191-413 3409 *Pest control services*

Rentokil Tropical Plants, Pipehouse Nursery, Pipehouse, Freshford, Bath, BA2 7UJ Tel: (01225) 722655 Fax: (01225) 722725 *Tropical plants*

Rentokil Tropical Plants, York Road, Leeds, LS15 4NF Tel: 0113-265 0050 Fax: 0113-265 0788 E-mail: enquiries@rentokil-tps.co.uk *Tropical plants distributors*

Rentokil Tropical Plants, Middlemore Lane, Walsall, WS9 8SP Tel: (01922) 745970 Fax: (01922) 745972 *Tropical plants supply & display*

Rentokil Tropical Plants, Acorn Nursery, Barrow Lane, Cheshunt, Waltham Cross, Hertfordshire, EN7 5LL Tel: (01992) 627333 Fax: (01992) 643568 *Tropical plant retailers*

Rentrifone Ltd, Premier House, 309 Ballards Lane, London, N12 8NE Tel: (020) 8455 3304 Fax: (020) 8609 0627 E-mail: rentrifone@hotmail.co.uk *Door intercom, CCTV, TV-fm & satellite installation*

▶ Renvac Scaffolding Ltd, Front Street, Bebside, Blyth, Northumberland, NE24 4HP Tel: (01670) 821385 Fax: (01670) 825640

Renwick Bros Ltd, 16 Brougham Street, Penrith, Cumbria, CA11 9DW Tel: (01768) 864913 Fax: (01768) 864913 E-mail: peter.renwick@btconnect.com *Joinery contractors*

Reny Martan, Carley Drive, Westfield, Sheffield, S20 8NQ Tel: 0114-251 1598 Fax: 0114-251 1599 E-mail: admin@renymartan.co.uk *Knitwear manufrs*

Renz UK Ltd, Hill End Farm, Hill End, Hatfield, Hertfordshire, AL9 5PQ Tel: (01707) 270001 Fax: (01707) 271769 E-mail: sales@renz.co.uk *Binding & laminating systems*

Renzland Forge Ltd, 83A London Road, Copford, Colchester, CO6 1LG Tel: (01206) 210212 Fax: (01206) 211290 *Architectural & industrial metalworkers*

Reo UK Ltd, Unit 8-9 Long Lane Industrial Estate, Long Lane, Craven Arms, Shropshire, SY7 8DU Tel: (01588) 673411 Fax: (01588) 672718 E-mail: sales@reo.co.uk *Transformer & resistor manufrs*

Reon Computing, 3 Aghanloo Industrial Estate, Aghanloo Road, Limavady, County Londonderry, BT49 0HE Tel: (028) 7776 7273 E-mail: reon@btinternet.com *Computer systems & software developers*

Rep Air Services, Unit 23 Monarch Way, Loughborough, Leicestershire, LE11 5XG Tel: (01509) 213452 Fax: (01509) 212102 E-mail: sales@rep-air.co.uk *Air compressors & tool distributors*

▶ Rep Engineering & Manufacturing, Unit 11 Rippleside Commercial Estate, Ripple Road, Barking, Essex, IG11 0RJ Tel: (020) 8526 7711 Fax: (020) 8526 7722 *Eyeletting machine manufrs*

▶ Repair Protection & Maintenance Ltd, Roall Lane, Kellington, Goole, North Humberside, DN14 0NY Tel: (01977) 663111 Fax: (01977) 663222

Repaircraft plc, The Common, Cranleigh, Surrey, GU6 8LU Tel: (01483) 273536 Fax: (01483) 278078 E-mail: hq@repaircraft.co.uk *Aircraft component distributors or agents*

Repairs & Rewinds, 7 Walsall Street, Wednesbury, West Midlands, WS10 9BZ Tel: 0121-556 0806 Fax: 0121-556 0806 *Electric motor repair, rewind services & electric motor stockists*

Repeat Marketing, 2 Moor Knoll Drive, E Ardsley, Wakefield, West Yorkshire, WF3 2DR Tel: (01924) 871730 Fax: (01924) 823381 *Computer consultants*

Repfab Engineering Ltd, Unit 6 Whiteleather Square, Billingborough, Sleaford, Lincolnshire, NG34 0QP Tel: (01529) 240600 Fax: (01529) 240647 *Sheet metalwork engineers*

Replacement Door Co. Ltd, 24 Millfield, Livingston, West Lothian, EH54 7AR Tel: 01506 411434 *Domestic doors*

▶ Replacement Kitchen Door Co., 1 Hollow Cottages, London Road, Purfleet, Essex, RM19 1QP Tel: (01708) 865386 Fax: (01708) 890595 E-mail: sales@replacementkitchendoor.co.uk

Replacement & Maintenance Supplies Ltd, Dunsford Road, Meadow La Industrial Estate, Alfreton, Derbyshire, DE55 7RH Tel: (01773) 520181 Fax: (01773) 836370 *Bearing & transmission suppliers*

Replin Fabrics, March Street Mills, March Street, Peebles, EH45 8ER Tel: (01721) 724310 Fax: (01721) 721893 E-mail: enquiries@replin-fabrics.co.uk *Upholstery fabric weavers*

▶ Repolishing.Co.Uk, Connors Yard, Crowborough Hill, Crowborough, East Sussex, TN6 2DA Tel: (01892) 668001 Fax: (01892) 861301 E-mail: gavin.mason@repolishing.co.uk *French furnishing*

▶ Repose Manufacturing Ltd, High Street, Great Cheverell, Devizes, Wiltshire, SN10 5XZ Tel: (01380) 813367 Fax: (01380) 813356 E-mail: sales@marineperformancesolutions.com *Marine products manufrs*

▶ Repossessed House Sales, 31 Weavers House, Mannheim Quay, Swansea, SA1 1RU Tel: (01792) 529 575 E-mail: repossessed-house-sales@fsmail.net *Online database of repossessed houses for sale in UK. Updated daily.Service for investors and landlords.*

REP-RAM Hydraulic Services, Unit 6 Prospect Court, Nunn Close, County Estate, Sutton-In-Ashfield, Nottinghamshire, NG17 2HW Tel: (01623) 557471 *Hydraulic ram repairers*

Repro Factory Ltd, Faber House, Main Yard, 94 Wallis Road, London, E9 5LN Tel: (020) 8985 2278 Fax: (020) 8533 0755 E-mail: mail@reprofactory.com *Lithographic plate makers*

▶ Reprodux Printers Ltd, Unit 7, Barrs Court Trading Estate, Station Approach, Hereford, HR1 1BB Tel: (01432) 269341 E-mail: enquiries@reprodux.co.uk

▶ Reprographic Warehouse London Ltd, Unit 14 West Block Westminster Business Square, Durham Street, London, SE11 5JH Tel: (020) 7582 9000 Fax: (020) 7582 2266 E-mail: sales@reproforlondon.co.uk *Digital print reprographics & photocopying services*

Reprographics NI Ltd, Unit A2, 4 Westbank Drive, Belfast, BT3 9LA Tel: (028) 9037 0057 Fax: (028) 9037 0069 E-mail: reprographic@btconnect.com *Reprographics & printers*

Repropoint Ltd, 332 London Road, Portsmouth, PO2 9JY Tel: (023) 9266 9941 Fax: (023) 9269 6514 E-mail: info@repropoint.com *Reprographics & office suppliers*

Resad Polymers Ltd, 53 Royce Close, West Portway Industrial Estate, Andover, Hampshire, SP10 3TS Tel: (01264) 334633 Fax: (01264) 332639 E-mail: sales@resad.co.uk *Raw materials for adhesives manufrs*

Resco Products UK Ltd, Newbold Works, Worthington Lane, Newbold Coleorton, Coalville, Leicestershire, LE67 8PJ Tel: (01530) 222694 Fax: (01530) 223086 E-mail: rescoukltd@aol.com *Monolithic refractory castable manufrs*

Rescroft Ltd, 20 Oxleasow Road, Redditch, Worcestershire, B98 0RE Tel: (01527) 521300 Fax: (01527) 521301 E-mail: enquiries@rescroft.com *Motor vehicle seat manufrs*

Rescue Building & Plumbing Ltd, 126 Yardley Road, Acocks Green, Birmingham, B27 6LR Tel: 0121-708 1333 Fax: 0121-708 1933 E-mail: a1_rescue@hotmail.com *Building contractors*

▶ Rescue From Technology, 17 Linley Court, Thicket Road, Sutton, Surrey, SM1 4QA Tel: 0870 3831519 Fax: 07092 309964 E-mail: enquiries@rescuefrom.com *Computers user intructions manufrs*

Rescue IT Ltd, 6 Braham Street, London, E1 8EE Tel: (0870) 6090999 Fax: (07092) 102103 E-mail: info@rescueit.co.uk *Computer disaster recovery specialists & online backup of systems & data*

Rescue & Medical Equipment, Field House, Blackrock, Clydach, Abergavenny, Gwent, NP7 0LW Tel: (01873) 830031 Fax: (01873) 831748 E-mail: sales@rescueandmedical.com *Rescue medical equipment*

Resdev Ltd, Puma Floor House, Ainley Industrial Estate, Elland, West Yorkshire, HX5 9JP Tel: (01422) 379131 Fax: (01422) 370943 E-mail: info@resdev.co.uk Purchasing Contact: D. Greenwood Sales Contact: M.D. Spindley Principal Export Areas: Asia Pacific, Africa, Central/East Europe, West Europe & North America *Industrial flooring systems, epoxy resin flooring, polyurethane flooring. From simple floor seals to heavy duty flooring systems - epoxy and polyurethane formulations for optimum choice of finish, Resdev's name is the undisputed hallmark of flooring excellence.*

Resdev Ni Ltd, 4 22 Duncrue Road, Belfast, BT3 9BP Tel: (028) 9077 6882 Fax: (028) 9077 8492 E-mail: info@resindevelopment.com *Epoxy & polyurethane resins*

Research Associates, 282 Latimer Road, London, W10 6QW Tel: (020) 7854 9000 Fax: (020) 7854 9090 E-mail: paulhawkes@investigationservices.co.uk *Investigators*

Research Associates, 282 Latimer Road, London, W10 6QW Tel: (020) 7854 9000 Fax: (020) 7854 9090E-mail: private@investigationservices.co.uk *Private investigators*

Research Associates UK Ltd, 99 Oulton Road, Stone, Staffordshire, ST15 8DX Tel: (01785) 813164 Fax: (01785) 813268 E-mail: sales@research-associates.co.uk *Industrial market research*

Research Equipment London Ltd, 72 Wellington Road, Twickenham, TW2 5NX Tel: (020) 8977 5529 Fax: (020) 8943 2219 E-mail: info@research-equipment.com *Scientific apparatus & viscometer manufrs*

The Research House Ltd, 124 Wigmore St, London, W1U 3RY Tel: (020) 7935 4979 Fax: (020) 7224 2494 E-mail: researchhouse@btinternet.com *Market research services*

Research Instruments Ltd, Kernick Road, Penryn, Cornwall, TR10 9DQ Tel: (01326) 372753 Fax: (01326) 378783 E-mail: sales@research-instruments.com *Medical instruments manufrs*

Research International Group Ltd, 6-7 Grosvenor Place, London, SW1X 7SH Tel: (020) 7656 5500 Fax: (020) 7235 0202 E-mail: riuk@research-int.com *International market research services*

Research & Marketing Ltd, Trefor House, Galdames Place, Cardiff, CF24 5RE Tel: (029) 2043 5800 Fax: (029) 2048 3540 E-mail: info@rmltd.net *Marketing services agency*

Research Micro Systems Ltd, Radclyffe House, 66-68 Hagley Road, Birmingham, B16 8PF Tel: 0121-410 5860 *Business machine wholesalers*

▶ Research247.com, 23 Riverford Close, Harpenden, Hertfordshire, AL5 4LX Tel: (01582) 469699 E-mail: info@research247.com *Specialist employment website dedicated to the Market Research Industry, free to employees and employers alike.*

Resilient Tile & Flooring Co. (Ealing) Ltd, 2 Replingham Rd, London, SW18 5LS Tel: (020) 8874 6655 Fax: (020) 8874 6656 *Flooring & floor tiling contractors*

Resin Express Ltd, 11 Valley Business Centre, Gordon Road, High Wycombe, Buckinghamshire, HP13 6EQ Tel: (01494) 459881 Fax: (01494) 795334 E-mail: sales@resinexpress.com *Plastics raw materials distribs*

▶ Resin Surfaces Ltd, Lowick Close, Newby Industrial Estate, Hazel Grove, Stockport, Cheshire, SK7 5ED Tel: 0161-483 1232 Fax: 0161-483 2565 E-mail: andrew.hawkins@resinsurfaces.co.uk *RSL is a leading manufacturer of high performance resin based industrial floor and wall finishes, which are frequently specified and applied worldwide. RSL wide range of floor and wall finishes are designed to meet all industrial health and safety requirements, including the following specialist environments:- Industrial .. Food .. Aviation .. Automotive .. Hospital / Healthcare .. Wall Finishes***

Resin Technical Systems, 6 Alphage Road, Gosport, Hampshire, PO12 4DU Tel: (023) 9258 5899 Fax: (023) 9251 0306 E-mail: sales@resintek.co.uk *Encapsulation services to the electronics industry sub contract potting, sub contract encapsulation, cartridge filling and resin distributors.*

Resinbond Ltd, 2A Bugle Industrial Estate, Rosevear Road, Bugle, St. Austell, Cornwall, PL26 8PJ Tel: (01726) 851497 *Resin supplies*

Resinfab & Associates, 6 Imex Business Park, Kings Road, Tyseley, Birmingham, B11 2AL Tel: 0121-706 1848 Fax: 0121-706 1848 E-mail: tech@resinfab.co.uk *Consultants, designers, specifiers & inspectors of corrosion resistant plant & equipment*

Resistalloy International Ltd, 36 Wheatacre Road, Stocksbridge, Sheffield, S36 2GB Tel: 0114-288 3872 *Suppliers of high temprature electrical resistant alloys*

▶ Resistance Wires Ltd, 110 Carnegie Road, Hillington Industrial Estate, Glasgow, G52 4JZ Tel: 0141-891 8881 Fax: 0141-891 8549 E-mail: sales@resistancewires.co.uk *Wire products suppliers*

Resistek Ltd, 46 Holton Road, Holton Heath Trading Park, Poole, Dorset, BH16 6LT Tel: (01202) 625605 Fax: (01202) 632438 E-mail: sales@resistek.co.uk *Aluminium sign manufrs*

Resisystems Ltd, Systems House, 18 Exeter Drive, Darlington, County Durham, DL1 2SE Tel: (0870) 1628971 Fax: (01325) 749141 E-mail: sales@resisystems.co.uk *Computer software suppliers*

Resmar Ltd, Adec House, Fitzherbert Road, Portsmouth, PO6 1RU Tel: (023) 9221 5700 Fax: (023) 9237 6744 E-mail: sales@resmar.co.uk *Breathing apparatus, maintenance, repair & service*

Resmar Ltd, 39 Dean Street, Winsford, Cheshire, CW7 1HG Tel: (01606) 863399 Fax: (01606) 558200 E-mail: wyn@resmar.co.uk *Breathing apparatus distributors*

▶ Resolution Imaging, Unit 15 16, Salvesen Way, Brighton Street Industrial Estate, Hull, HU3 4UQ Tel: (01482) 212589 Fax: (01482) 211721

▶ Resolution (UK) Ltd, 2 Rose Hill Arch Mews, Rose Hill, Dorking, Surrey, RH4 2ER Tel: (01306) 640004 Fax: (01306) 640004 E-mail: director@resolutionuk.com *Geophysical Consultants: Geophysical Research & Development, Seismic Data Processing & Analysis, Vertical Seismic Profiling (VSP), In-mine Seismic Processing (MSP).*

▶ Resolution UK Performance Products, The Business Centre Oaklands Office Park, Hooton Road, Hooton, Ellesmere Port, CH66 7NZ Tel: 0151-326 2521 Fax: 0151-326 2541

Resound Ltd, Parkway House, Haddenham Business Park, Thame Road, Haddenham, Aylesbury, Buckinghamshire, HP17 8LJ Tel: (01844) 292346 Fax: (01844) 292860 E-mail: mail@resound.co.uk *Radio communications equipment supply service hire & installation*

▶ Resource Centre For Innovation & Design, Claremont Road, Newcastle upon Tyne, NE1 7RU Tel: 0191-222 5897 Fax: 0191-222 5833 E-mail: bf.dixon@ncl.ac.uk *Engineering design centre*

Resource Engineering Projects, Waterlinks House, Richard Street, Birmingham, B7 4AA Tel: 0121-678 7880 Fax: 0121-678 7899 E-mail: technical@topmode.co.uk *Software development services*

▶ Resource Environmental Services Ltd, Sabre House, Bath Road, Midgham, Reading, RG7 5UU Tel: 0118-971 5900 Fax: 0118-971 5920 *Maintenance of air conditioning*

Resource Group, 105 West George Street, Glasgow, G2 1PE Tel: 0141-226 1220 Fax: 0141-248 6782 E-mail: sales@trgrecruitment.net *Recruitment for technical, secretarial, call centre & legal*

Resource Management Associates Ltd, 4 Western Road, Romford, RM1 3JT Tel: (01708) 735888 Fax: (01708) 735999 E-mail: charleskeep@rma-uk.org *Mergers & acquisition consultants*

Resource Management Systems, Mexborough Business Centre, College Road, Mexborough, South Yorkshire, S64 9JP Tel: (01709) 578300 Fax: (01709) 578010E-mail: sales@rmsuk.co.uk *Software consultants*

▶ Resource N D T, 5 Sideley, Kegworth, Derby, DE74 2FJ Tel: (01509) 673084

Resources Computer Support Ltd, Norwich Road, Attleborough, Norfolk, NR17 2JX Tel: (01953) 457977 Fax: (01953) 457978 *Computer consultancy*

Respirex, F Kingsfield Business Centre, Philanthropic Road, Redhill, RH1 4DP Tel: (01737) 778600 Fax: (01737) 779441 E-mail: sales@respirex.co.uk Principal Export Areas: Worldwide *Protective clothing chemical respiratory manufrs*

Respironics (UK) Ltd, Unit 8, Cityfields Business Park, City Fields Way, Tangmere, Chichester, West Sussex, PO20 2FT Tel: (0800) 1300840 Fax: (0800) 1300846 E-mail: info@respironics.com *Respiratory products suppliers*

▶ Response, Media House, Hobson Industrial Estate, Hobson, Newcastle upon Tyne, NE16 6EA Tel: (01207) 272761 Fax: (01207) 272784

▶ Response 2000 Ltd, 792 Green Lanes, Winchmore Hill, London, N21 2SH Tel: (020) 8360 0202 Fax: (0870) 2006567 E-mail: info@response2000.com *Maintenance service*

Response Conveyor Belting Services, 41 Holly Court, St. Modwen Road, Plymouth, PL6 8LG Tel: (01752) 267111 Fax: (01752) 662110 E-mail: response.conveyors@btinternet.com *Conveyer belt manufrs*

▶ Response Furniture Systems Ltd, 52 Tanners Drive, Blakelands, Milton Keynes, MK14 5BW Tel: (01908) 216466 Fax: (01908) 216467 E-mail: sales@responsefurnituresystems.co.uk

Response It Services, 31 Prospect Place, Epsom, Surrey, KT17 1WW Tel: (0870) 2642062 E-mail: simon@response-it.co.uk *IT outsourcing company, server & network support*

▶ Response Safety Netting Ltd, RSN Units, Purbrook Raod, Wolverhampton, WV1 2EJ Tel: (01902) 451812 Fax: (01902) 871297

▶ Response Technical Services Ltd, Pool House, Bancroft Road, Reigate, Surrey, RH2 7RP Tel: (01737) 244408 Fax: (01737) 242472 E-mail: noel.reilly@responsets.co.uk *Document scanner hardware sell & service providers*

▶ Responsive Engineering Group, Kingsway South, Team Valley, Gateshead, Tyne & Wear, NE11 0SH Tel: 0191-497 3400 Fax: 0191-497 3401E-mail: sales@responsive-engineering.com *Engineering services*

Ressoft Soft Ltd, Wesley Chmbers, Queens Road, Aldershot, Hampshire, GU11 3JD Tel: (01252) 337377 Fax: (01252) 338111 *Software packages developers*

Restall Bros Ltd, Colliery Road, West Bromwich, West Midlands, B71 4JT Tel: 0121-500 1300 Fax: 0121-500 1301 E-mail: contact@restallgroup.co.uk *Vehicle seating manufacture & designers* Also at: West Bromwich

Restall Brown & Clennell Ltd, 21 North Street, Lewes, East Sussex, BN7 2PE Tel: (01273) 473612 Fax: 01273 477783 E-mail: sales@rbc-furniture.co.uk *Furniture manufrs*

▶ Restalls Finance Brokers, Earl Road, Mold, Clwyd, CH7 1AX Tel: (01352) 700033 Fax: (01352) 759236E-mail: sales@restalls.com *personal and corporate lending on all assets. cars/hgv/agricultural/industrial/it equipment. all levels of credit catered for including credit repair for both personal and business. hp leasing mortgages etc*

▶ Restaurant Supplies Ltd, 10 Kishorn Court, Glenrothes, Fife, KY7 6ES Tel: (01592) 749149 Fax: (01592) 749149 E-mail: sales@restaurantsuppliesltd.com *Wholesaler & restaurant suppliers*

▶ Re-Stone, Windermere Drive, Goole, East Yorkshire, DN14 6JW Tel: (01405) 720281 Fax: (01405) 761883 E-mail: info@re-stone.co.uk *The on-site service providing repairs to stone and cast stone products. We repair cracks, chips, fading and any other damage using our exclusive RE-STONE materials. We colour match to existing stonework to ensure complete customer satisfaction.*

▶ Restoraphoto.com, The Old Magistrates Court, 1 Cross Lane, Melbourn, Royston, Hertfordshire, SG8 6AG Tel: (01763) 260625 E-mail: les@restoraphoto.com *Professional UK based photograph restoration service staffed by qualified photographers.*

▶ Restoration & Renovation Scotland Ltd, South Street, Milnathort, Kinross, KY13 9XB Tel: (01577) 862919 Fax: (01577) 861409

Restore Ltd, Redhill Distribution Centre, Salbrook Road, Redhill, RH1 5DY Tel: (01293) 446270 Fax: (01293) 446276 E-mail: john.minton@restore.co.uk *Managed archive storage & retrieval*

Result Technology Ltd, President Drive, Rooksley, Milton Keynes, MK13 8PP Tel: (01296) 641944 Fax: (01908) 201148 *Software applications engineers*

The Results Corporation Ltd, Pendragon House, 170 Merton High Street, London, SW19 1AY Tel: (0870) 2201748 Fax: (020) 8241 3333 E-mail: gds@gordonsknight.co.uk *Accounts*

Resurgem Engineering Co. Ltd, Bury Manor, High Street, Wick, Bristol, BS30 5SH Tel: 0117-937 2987 Fax: 0117-937 3516 E-mail: sales@resurgem.co.uk *Engineering stainless steel*

▶ Retail Answers, Surrey House, 196 Barnett Wood Lane, Ashtead, Surrey, KT21 2LW Tel: 01372 272800 E-mail: info@retailanswers.co.uk *Systems consultancy, project management & software development*

▶ Retail Asset Management Ltd, Unit 3, 223-225 High St, Epping, Essex, CM16 4BL Tel: (01992) 561101 Fax: (01992) 561050 E-mail: retailasset@aol.com *Cash registers & EPOS equipment*

Retail Assist Ltd, 3 Westleigh Park, Scirroco Close, Northampton, NN3 6AP Tel: (01604) 647002 Fax: (01604) 644625 *Computer software services*

Retail Business Solutions Ltd, 24-26 Vincent Avenue, Crownhill, Milton Keynes, MK8 0AB Tel: (01908) 226226 Fax: (01908) 225533 *Computer consultants & software suppliers*

▶ Retail Cleaning Co., Unit E 1 Kestrel Road Trafford Park, Kestrel Road, Manchester, M17 1SF Tel: (0845) 6440901 Fax: (0845) 6440902 E-mail: info@retailcleaning.co.uk *Industrial & commercial building cleaning service*

Retail Display Ltd, 6 Clarendon Drive, Wymbush, Milton Keynes, MK8 8DA Tel: (01908) 262822 Fax: (01908) 564604 E-mail: sales@retaildisplay.co.uk *Shop fittings manufacturers*

Retail Display Centre Ltd, 42 Kirkfield View, Livingston Village, Livingston, West Lothian, EH54 7BP Tel: (01506) 462228 Fax: (01506) 857730 E-mail: retaildisplaycentre@hotmail.com *Shop fitting suppliers*

Retail Display Solutions, St. Andrew House, St. Andrews Trading Estate, Bridport, Dorset, DT6 3EX Tel: (01308) 459950 Fax: (01308) 424410 E-mail: sales@retaildisplaysolutions.co.uk *Retail display manufacturers & sheet metalwork services*

▶ Retail Doctor, PO Box 49, Downham Market, Norfolk, PE38 9QP Tel: (0870) 2409905 Fax: (0870) 2409905 E-mail: greg@theretaildoctor.co.uk = *Real solutions to operational issues carried out to help you maximise sales *= New business start up ' 'a one stop shop' We aim to Reduce Costs immediately- let us show you *= Business name registration, VAT registration and trademark searches *= Build and (re)design profit & loss accounts for new and existing businesses *= Build and design business plans for start ups expansions and/or funding *= Build and design budgets and forecasts for all your staffing levels**

▶ Retail Engineering Design Ltd, Unit 2, Pioneer Park, Clough Road, Hull, HU6 7HW Tel: (01482) 333803 Fax: (01482) 333809 E-mail: info@redltd.karoo.co.uk *Acrylic point of sale fabricators & manufrs*

Retail Equipment Ltd, 21-22 Chilton Industrial Estate, Addison Road, Sudbury, Suffolk, CO10 2YW Tel: (01787) 372488 Fax: (01787) 311941 *Shop equipment manufrs*

Retail Equipment Sales & Services Ltd, 12 Everite Road Industrial Estate, Westgate, Widnes, Cheshire, WA8 8RA Tel: 0151-420 2147 Fax: 0151-420 2147 E-mail: sales@retailequipment.co.uk *Retail equipment & janitorial suppliers*

▶ Retail Furniture Ltd, Unit E, Halesfield 13, Telford, Shropshire, TF7 4PL Tel: (01952) 587277 Fax: (01952) 201269 *Shop fittings manufrs*

Retail Human Resources, 12 Bristol Gardens, London, W9 2JG Tel: (020) 7432 8888 Fax: (020) 7289 1968 E-mail: enquiries@rhr.co.uk *Recruitment consultants*

▶ Retail Java Ltd, 6 Bluecoats Avenue, Hertford, SG14 1PB Tel: (01992) 538074 *Retail-J develops core retail applications implemented by partner integrators. Our strategy is to continue to enhance these products while developing our application development expertise and resources. By remaining focussed on products and technologies we keep abreast of the latest developments and produce generic applications that satisfy a wide range of retail sectors. Retail-J software is distributed in the UK, Europe and North America through a network of specialised dealers. For more information about Retail-J visit www.retail-j.com.'*

▶ Retail Plastics Plus, Unit 2 Cranleigh Gardens Industrial Estate, Southall, Middlesex, UB1 2BZ Tel: (020) 8574 9005 Fax: (020) 8574 9007 *Plastic product manufrs*

Retail System Services Ltd, Reave Cottage, Long Stratton, Norwich, NR15 2RP Tel: (07771) 724450 Fax: (0870) 70599471 *Computer software services & repairs*

▶ Retail Technology, Armstrong House 3rd Floor, 38 Market Square, Uxbridge, Middlesex, UB8 1TG Tel: (01895) 421111 Fax: (01895) 431252 E-mail: info@retailtechnology.co.uk *Monthly magazine covering IT & Telecom issues for IT Managers in medium to large retailers. Covering EPoS, Supply chain, In-store technology, Hospitality systems and marketing systems.*

Retainagroup Ltd., 134-136 Buckingham Palace Road, London, SW1W 9SA Tel: (020) 7823 6868 Fax: (020) 7823 6864 E-mail: general.sales@retainagroup.co.uk *Security marking system manufrs*

Retec Europe Ltd, Campus 5, Third Avenue, Letchworth Garden City, Hertfordshire, SG6 2JF Tel: (01462) 482944 Fax: (01462) 484255 E-mail: sales@retec-europe.com *Retail technology*

▶ Re-TekDIRECT, 1 Langlands Place, Kelvin South Business Park, East Kilbride, G75 0YF Tel: (01355) 271101 Fax: (01355) 271100 E-mail: web@retekdirect.co.uk *Re-TekDIRECT is part of a global group of companies supplying computer hardware and consumer goods to trade and retail customers. We stock new retail, OEM and quality refurbished products.*

Retell, 53 Thames Street, Sunbury-on-Thames, Middlesex, TW16 5QH Tel: (01932) 779755 Fax: (01932) 780383 E-mail: sales@retell.co.uk *Telephone conversation recorder manufrs*

Retellin Ltd, 78 Rainham Road, Rainham, Essex, RM13 7RL Tel: (01708) 553310 *Computer hardware supplier*

Retford Angling Centre, Northfield Way, Retford, Nottinghamshire, DN22 7LR Tel: (01777) 706168 Fax: (01777) 709779 *Angling supplies distributors*

Retford Pine, Beehive Street, Retford, Nottinghamshire, DN22 6JE Tel: (01777) 869669 Fax: (01777) 700701 E-mail: sales@squeakfree.co.uk *Pine bed & bedroom furniture manufrs*

Retford Saddlery Services, Bramble House, London Road, Retford, Nottinghamshire, DN22 7JG Tel: (01777) 701707 Fax: (01777) 701707 *Saddlery retailers*

Retford Wall Coverings, 1c Birkdale Road, Scunthorpe, South Humberside, DN17 2AU Tel: (01724) 281154 Fax: (01724) 875151 E-mail: admin@retwall.co.uk *Paintable wallpaper manufrs*

▶ Retiarius Internet Design, 8 Princes Road, Buxton, Derbyshire, SK17 7LB Tel: 01298 23389 E-mail: webmaster@retiarius.com *Website designers*

Retif, 33-37 Admiral Street, Glasgow, G41 1HP Tel: 0141-429 0537 Fax: 0141-420 1036 *Shop fittings distributors*

▶ Retina Productions Ltd, 6 Mount Pleasant Crescent, London, N4 4HP Tel: (020) 7272 4448 Fax: (020) 7272 5756 E-mail: nisrine@retina-productions.co.uk *Corporate video & audio production company*

Retone Ltd, Retone House, 60 Sherborne St, Manchester, M8 8LR Tel: 0161-839 0500 Fax: 0161-839 0600 E-mail: info@retone.co.uk *Manufacturers & suppliers of laser printer toner cartridges*

Retrac Productions Ltd, 3-5 Bramble Road, Techno Trading Estate, Swindon, SN2 8HB Tel: (01793) 524616 Fax: (01793) 511899 E-mail: andycarter@retrac-group.com *Engineers' pattern makers*

The Retreat, 61 Coronation Road, Crosby, Liverpool, L23 5RE Tel: 0151-931 1991 Fax: 0151-931 1991

Retreat Boatyard Topsham Ltd, Retreat Drive, Topsham, Exeter, EX3 0LS Tel: (01392) 874720 Fax: (01392) 876182 E-mail: sales@retreatboatyard.co.uk *Boat repairers & boatyard services*

Retriever Software, 47 St. Georges Terrace, Jesmond, Newcastle upon Tyne, NE2 2SX Tel: 0191-212 1029 Fax: (07092) 281285 *Computer software services*

Retriever Technology Ltd, PO Box 3, Tenbury Wells, Worcestershire, WR15 8YX Tel: (01584) 781444 Fax: (01584) 781403 E-mail: support@reetec.co.uk *Computer software developers*

▶ Retro Spectives, The Minories, Rother Street, Stratford-upon-Avon, Warwickshire, CV37 6NF Tel: (01789) 297706 E-mail: sales@retrospectives.co.uk *Art gallery*

Retrofit Alarmacar, 652 Chester Road, Sutton Coldfield, West Midlands, B73 5JR Tel: 0121-382 8933 Fax: 0121-682 7720 E-mail: sales@retrofit.co.uk *Vehicle security services*

▶ Retrofit Controls Ltd, 15 Moorlands, Wickersley, Rotherham, South Yorkshire, S66 1AS Tel: (01709) 739791 Fax: (01709) 730918 E-mail: info@retrofitcontrols.co.uk *Suppliers of temperature control equipment. Stockists of Eurotherm thyristors, controllers, programmers and Chessell data recorders. Service exchange units available from stock. Calibration and repair services available.*

▶ Retrolutions Ltd, 85 Lincoln Road, Stevenage, Herts, SG1 4PL Tel: 01438 743346 E-mail: richard.thatcher@retrolutions.com *Offering IT services. Renting Computers, Software Design, Website Design, Office Relocations, EPOS Solutions, Onsite/Remote Desktop Support, Backup Consultation, Database Design, Network Installation, Data Recovery, Buy/Sell IT Equipment.*

▶ Retrospecs.co.uk, 20 George Street, St. Albans, Hertfordshire, AL3 4ES Tel: (01727) 761048 E-mail: admin@retrospecs.co.uk *Vintage Eyewaer Store,selling glasses and sunglasses from the 50"s, 60"s 70"s and 80"s*

▶ RE-Tshirt, Unit 11, Keyford Court, Marston Trading Estate, Frome, Somerset, BA11 4BD Tel: (01373) 455389 Fax: (01373) 455389 E-mail: sales@re-tshirt.com *Screen printers of t-shirts polo shirts & work wear*

▶ Rettendon Trucks & Bodies, Tile Works Lane, Rettendon Common, Chelmsford, CM3 8HB Tel: (01245) 400465

▶ Return On Investment Ltd, 7 Pepper Street, Nantwich, Cheshire, CW5 5AB Tel: (01270) 610400 Fax: (01270) 628135 E-mail: diane.hawkins@roiltd.co.uk *We offer a marketing service aimed at generating interest/ leads/appointments, etc. on behalf of your company. We are a mature based company having real conversations with senior decision makers - not a call-centre environment.*We also offer customer service/after sales calls.*If we can offer you a better service than your current provider or are in need of generating more business, then give us a call!*

Reuse Collections Ltd, 49 Lidgate CR, South Kirkby, Pontefract, West Yorkshire, WF9 3NR Tel: (01977) 608020 Fax: (01977) 644021 E-mail: info@berrymans-uk.co.uk *Glass recyclers*

Revampsuites, 17 Bonny Brow Street, Middleton, Manchester, M24 4RJ Tel: 0161-654 4262 E-mail: revampsuites@aol.com *Furniture re-covering & upholstery*

Revelation Shirts Ltd, 3 Bewsey Street, Warrington, WA2 7JF Tel: (01925) 634372 Fax: (01925) 418438 E-mail: infomation@revelationshirts.co.uk *Blouse & shirt manufrs*

E. Revell & Sons Ltd, Unit 1C Joesph Wilson Industrial Estate, Mill Strood Road, Whitstable, Kent, CT5 3PS Tel: (01227) 277020 Fax: (01227) 770839 *Cardboard & paper tube manufrs*

Revells Warehousing & Transport, Eastlands Industrial Estate, Leiston, Suffolk, IP16 4LL Tel: (01728) 830849 Fax: (01728) 830849 E-mail: revellsremovals@aol.com *Furniture removal contractors*

Revenger Boat Co Ltd, Forward Buildings, 46 Windsor Road, Slough, SL1 2EU Tel: (01753) 525496 Fax: (01489) 572419 *Boat builders*

▶ Reverse Billed SMS, Canford Chambers, Lower Ground Floor, 22 St. Peters Road, Bournemouth, BH1 2LE Tel: (0870) 7504906 Fax: (0870) 7061094 E-mail: Alan@palmmedia.co.uk *Reverse Billed SMS Services. SMS Revenue Services. Cheap Bulk SMS Sending. Ringtones. Picture Messaging. MMS. General TXT and SMS Services.*

▶ Reverv Marketing & Communications, 57 Enterprise Centre, Bryn Road, Aberkenfig, Bridgend, Mid Glamorgan, CF32 9BS Tel: (0870) 2424661 Fax: (0870) 2424663 E-mail: enquiries@reverbmarketing.co.uk *Have you ever wanted a 'bolt on' marketing department? One that's there when you need it? Well, Reverb can help! Whatever the size of your business, from SME to multinational, you can benefit from a creative professional service that can be integrated into your team. Reverb*

continued

can provide all the elements of the marketing mix. From a top-level marketing strategy and consultancy, proactive press and public relations activity, innovative promotional programmes through to day-to-day marketing support. Reverb is positioned to fulfil your requirements with a blend of commercial experience, realism and creative strategies.

Review Consultancy, Beechcroft, 138 London Road, Waterlooville, Hampshire, PO7 5ST Tel: (023) 9223 2647 Fax: (023) 9223 2647 E-mail: info@reviewconsultancy.co.uk

Reviseopen Ltd, 65 Sunfield Lane, Diggle, Oldham, OL3 5PT Tel: (01457) 875525 Fax: (01457) 875525 E-mail: admin@reviseopen.com *IT consultants*

Revital, 154 High Street, Hounslow, TW3 1LR Tel: (020) 8570 4560 Fax: (020) 8572 0310 *Health food sales*

Revival Technologies, Unit 2 Pooley Lane, Tamworth, Staffordshire, B78 1JA Tel: (01827) 330888 Fax: (01827) 898496 E-mail: revivaltechnologies@hotmail.co.uk *Computer hardware suppliers*

Revlon International Corporation, Highgate Studio, Highgate Road, London, NW5 1TL Tel: (020) 7284 8700 Fax: (020) 7428 5625 *Cosmetic manufrs* Also at: Maesteg

Revol Ltd, Samson Close, Newcastle upon Tyne, NE12 6DZ Tel: 0191-268 4555 Fax: 0191-216 0004 E-mail: sales@revol.co.uk *Lubricant manufrs*

Revolution Entertainment Systems Ltd, Showell Road, Wolverhampton, WV10 9NL Tel: (01902) 713000 Fax: (01902) 711555 *Coin operated equipment manufrs*

▶ Revolution Ink, 1b Market Place, Holt, Norfolk, NR25 6BE Tel: (01263) 711102 Fax: (01263) 578314 *Computer accessories suppliers*

▶ Revolution Power Ltd, Office 1-1st Floor-Block B, Technology Court, Bradbury Road, Newton Aycliffe, County Durham, DL5 6DA Tel: (01325) 320910 E-mail: info@revolutionpower.co.uk *Install & supply, air source heat pumps & wind turbines*

▶ Revolutionary Pod Modules (UK) Ltd, Unit 3, Central Park, Cornwall Street, Hull, HU8 8AF Tel: (01482) 871717 Fax: (01482) 867727 E-mail: info@pod-modules.co.uk *Manufacturer & supply prefabricated steel frame pods*

Revolver Films, 10 Lambton Place, London, W11 2SH Tel: (020) 7243 4300 Fax: (020) 7243 4302 E-mail: info@revolvergroup.com *Film distributors*

Revvo Castor Co., Somerford Road, Christchurch, Dorset, BH23 3PZ Tel: (01202) 484211 Fax: (01202) 477896 E-mail: sales@revvo.co.uk *Castor manufrs*

Reward Manufacturing Company Ltd, Sackville Mills, Sackville Street, Skipton, North Yorkshire, BD23 2PR Tel: (01756) 797755 Fax: (01756) 796644 E-mail: info@rewardtrolleys.com *Reward Trolleys are one of the UK's favourites names amongst schools, hotels, hospitals and dozens of other types of institutions who require trolleys for a myriad of purposes. Whether you want to move food, clothing, books or widgets, there's a Reward trolley to fit both your needs and your budgets. But it's not just trolleys where Reward excels. In this catalogue you will find all of our most popular trolley products alongside some new additions to our range. We now offer a whole range of products from Tensator barriers and menu displays to cocktail bars and food dispensers*

Rewinds & J. Windsor & Sons (Engineers) Ltd, 81 Regent Road, Liverpool, L5 9SY Tel: 0151-207 2074 Fax: 0151-298 1442 E-mail: accounts@rjweng.com *Electric motor repair services* Also at: Wallasey

Rewood Shipping Ltd, 149-151 High Road, Chadwell Heath, Romford, RM6 6BJ Tel: (020) 8597 3382 Fax: (020) 8478 0310 E-mail: mervyn@rewood.co.uk *Freight forwarders*

Rex Bousfield Ltd, Fairview Industrial Estate, Holland Road, Oxted, Surrey, RH8 9BD Tel: (01883) 717033 Fax: (01883) 717890 E-mail: john.medcraft@bousfield.com *Specialist panel fabricators*

Rex Campbell Properties Ltd, Phoenix Works, Steeley Lane, Chorley, Lancashire, PR6 0RJ Tel: (01257) 266521 Fax: (01257) 241362 E-mail: kim@rex-campbell.co.uk *Electrical & mechanical engineers*

Rex Caunt, 6 Kings Court, Kingsfield Road, Barwell, Leicester, LE9 8NZ Tel: (01455) 846963 Fax: (01455) 846963 E-mail: rex@rexcauntracing.com *Develop self generating ignition systems for motorcycles*

Rex Crystal Fixings, Commercial St, Wakefield, West Yorkshire, WF1 5RN Tel: (01924) 374099 Fax: (01924) 370045 E-mail: sales@rexcrystal.co.uk *Fixings & fastenings distributors*

Rex Electrical Wholesale, 231 London Road, Staines, Middlesex, TW18 4HR Tel: (01784) 463366 Fax: (01784) 449781 *Electrical wholesalers* Also at: Basingstoke, Chandlers Ford, Guildford, Hounslow & Southampton

Rex H Perkins Ltd, Hucknall Aerodrome, Watnall Rd, Hucknall, Nottingham, NG15 6EQ Tel: 0115-963 5712 Fax: 0115-963 0129 E-mail: sales@rhperkins.co.uk *Yarn merchants & agents*

Rex Howard Drapes Ltd, Eastman Road, London, W3 7QS Tel: (020) 8740 5881 Fax: (020) 8740 5994 E-mail: rexdrapes@yahoo.com *Theatre curtain hirers & manufrs*

Rex Leisure (Scotland) Ltd, 105 Bothwell Road, Hamilton, Lanarkshire, ML3 0DW Tel: (01698) 283283 Fax: (01698) 201290 E-mail: info@rexleisure.co.uk *Gaming machines distributor*

Rex Software Ltd, Chesil House, Arrow Close, Eastleigh, Hampshire, SO50 4SY Tel: (023) 8062 9429 Fax: (0870) 0548257 *Software house*

Rexel Electrical Wholesalers, 2 Sidney Robinson Business Park, Ascot Drive, Derby, DE24 8EH Tel: (01332) 755918 Fax: (01332) 757673 *Electrical wholesalers*

Rexel Senate Electrical Wholesalers Ltd, Senate House, 6-16 Southgate Road, Potters Bar, Hertfordshire, EN6 5DS Tel: (01707) 640000 Fax: (01707) 640111 *Electrical wholesaler*

▶ Rexodan International, PO Box 24, Widnes, Cheshire, WA8 0RB Tel: 0151-422 1100 Fax: 0151-422 1111 E-mail: export@rexodan.com *Laundry chemical suppliers & manufrs*

Reycol Heating Co. Ltd, 15 Park Place, Newdigate Road, Harefield, Uxbridge, Middlesex, UB9 6EJ Tel: (01923) 720900 Fax: (01895) 824699 *Building services heating ventilation contractors*

Reycol S V C Ltd, Unit 6 Lagley Wharfe, Kings Langley, Watford, WD18 9EQ Tel: (01923) 262522 E-mail: reycolsvc@aol.com *Industrial air conditioning & handling manufrs*

Reymar Ltd, 9 Reynolds Close, London, NW11 7EA Tel: (020) 8905 5261 Fax: (020) 8905 5263 *Distributors of soplaril packaging*

Reynards UK Ltd, Greengate, Middleton, Manchester, M24 1RU Tel: 0161-653 7700 Fax: 0161-655 3891 E-mail: swood@reynards.com *Distributors of bakery & catering disposables* Also at: Aberdeen, Birmingham, Glasgow, London NW10 & Solihull

Reynolds & Associates, Mendota, Stonehouse Lane, Cookham, Maidenhead, Berkshire, SL6 9TP Tel: (01628) 471680 Fax: (01628) 471680 E-mail: br@reynoldsconsult.co.uk *Management & business consultancy*

Reynolds & Bennett Contracts, 4 Kilbegs Road, Antrim, BT41 4NN Tel: (028) 9446 4385 Fax: (028) 9446 8664 E-mail: info@reynoldsandbennett.co.uk *Building contractors*

Reynolds Blinds, 254 High Street, Erdington, Birmingham, B23 6SN Tel: 0121-373 7017 Fax: 0121-373 7059 E-mail: sales@reynoldsblinds.co.uk *Window blind specialists*

Reynolds Blinds, 118 London Road, Headington, Oxford, OX3 9AX Tel: (01865) 764731 Fax: (01865) 742243 *Window blind manufrs*

Reynolds Blinds, 17 Fleet Street, Swindon, SN1 1RQ Tel: (01793) 526617 Fax: (01793) 526823 *Blinds manufrs*

Reynolds Boughton (Devon) Ltd, Winkleigh Airfield, Winkleigh, Devon, EX19 8DR Tel: (01837) 83555 Fax: (01837) 83768 E-mail: sales@boughton.co.uk *Fire engine & ejection trailers manufrs* Also at: Amersham

Reynolds Cycle Technology (2000) Ltd, Redfern Road, Tyseley, Birmingham, B11 2BS Tel: 0121-706 5151 Fax: 0121-707 0081 *Cycle tube manufrs*

▶ Reynolds Embroidery & Sewing, 3 Bin Avenue, Cairnie, Huntly, Aberdeenshire, AB54 4TZ Tel: (07867) 957739 *made to order curtains and bedding,cushion covers, also we can embroider any name or design on to anything you want and we can also digitalize photos then add it to what ever you require for more info contact me for details*

Gerry Reynolds Saddlery, Unit 3,, Victoria Way, Studlands Industrial Estate, Newmarket, Suffolk, CB8 7SH Tel: (01638) 668837 Fax: (01638) 665890 E-mail: gr.saddlery@btconnect.com *Make horses saddles*

Reynolds Industrial & Cleaning Services Ltd, Unit 21 Capstan Centre, Thurrock Park Way, Tilbury, Essex, RM18 7HH Tel: (01375) 856555 Fax: (01375) 856956 E-mail: reynoldsno1@aol.com *Tank & factory cleaning services*

John Reynolds & Sons Ltd, Units 5-6 Church Lane Industrial Estate, West Bromwich, West Midlands, B71 1AR Tel: 0121-553 2754 Fax: 0121-500 5460 E-mail: sales@johnreynolds.co.uk *Cut nail & drive screw manufrs*

Reynolds & Kent Ltd, Unit 5 Wessex Business Centre, Meadow Lane, Westbury, Wiltshire, BA13 3EG Tel: (01373) 864767 Fax: (01373) 858697 E-mail: rnkglobes@aol.com *Glove manufrs*

Reynolds Software Services, 37 Ratby Close, Lower Earley, Reading, RG6 4ER Tel: 0118-986 4579 Fax: 0118-986 2838 E-mail: rss@reynoldssoftwareservices.co.uk *Computer consultancy*

Reynolds Sports, 12-13 Crofton Close, Lincoln, LN3 4NT Tel: (01522) 513333 Fax: (01522) 530383 *Sports clothing manufrs*

Reynolds Trading Ltd, 364 Cleveland Street, Birkenhead, Merseyside, CH41 8EG Tel: 0151-670 1213 Fax: 0151-670 0064 *Timber merchants*

▶ Reynolds Transport Hereford Ltd, 26 Romney Huts, Chapel Road, Rotherwas Industrial Estate, Hereford, HR2 6LD Tel: (01432) 279289

Reynopoly, Polythene Place, Newark Road, Peterborough, PE1 5YD Tel: (01733) 891322 Fax: (01733) 891452 E-mail: sales@reynopoly.freeserve.co.uk *Polythene converters & general packaging supplies*

Reyton Metals Ltd, 1 Malvern View Business Park, Stella Way, Cheltenham, Gloucestershire, GL52 7DQ Tel: (01242) 631000 Fax: (01242) 631110 *Aluminium stockholders & copper tube manufrs*

Rezet & Son, 491 Hornsey Road, London, N19 3QL Tel: (020) 7272 2788 Fax: (01763) 262459 *Food manufrs*

Reznor UK Ltd, Park Farm Road, Park Farm Industrial Estate, Folkestone, Kent, CT19 5DR Tel: (01303) 259141 Fax: (01303) 850002 E-mail: marketing@reznor.co.uk *Manufacturers of air heaters (gas fired) & heating equipment*

RF & Noise Components Ltd, 10 Crouchmans Yd, Poynters Lane, Shoeburyness, Southend-on-Sea, SS3 9TS Tel: (01702) 535298 Fax: (01702) 535299 E-mail: sales@rfandnoisecomponents.co.uk *Supplier of high performance microwave & rf components*

▶ RFA Design & Prototyping, 6 Willaim Lee Buildings, Science & Technology Park, University Boulevard, Nottingham, NG7 2RQ Tel: 0115-967 3107 Fax: 0115-925 6147 E-mail: richard.fletcher@rfadesign.co.uk *RFA Design is a Nottingham based company which is*

continued

primarily involved with 3D CAD modelling and rapid prototyping. From conceptual design through to design for manufacture, 2D to 3D conversions and a wide range of conceptual and functional prototypes.

▶ RFB Engineering, Unit 9, London Road Business Park, Retford, Nottinghamshire, DN22 6HG Tel: (01777) 860000 Fax: (01777) 860000 *Fencing manufrs*

RFI Global Services Ltd, Ewhurst Park, Ramsdell, Tadley, Hampshire, RG26 5RQ Tel: (01256) 851193 Fax: (01256) 312001 E-mail: sales@rfi-global.com *Testing facilities*

Rfid, Wolseley Road, Kempston, Bedford, MK42 7UP Tel: (01234) 840102 Fax: (01234) 840707 E-mail: info@rfid.co.uk *Radio frequency identification products*

▶ RFID+ Practical RFID consultancy, 70 Dalnabay, Silverglades, Aviemore, Inverness-Shire, PH22 1RG Tel: (0870) 7487078 Fax: (07092) 197823 E-mail: enquiries@plasticate.com *RFID Practical solutions. From idea to implementation and testing. RFID+ can plan an RFID solution for any company, tiny or huge. From automotive to logistics.*

RGB Associates, 20 Newling Way, Worthing, West Sussex, BN13 3DG Tel: (01903) 694904 Fax: (01903) 260899 E-mail: sales@rgb.uk.com *Electronic design and support*

▶ RGB Solutions Ltd, Bonnington Mill, 72 Newhaven Road, Edinburgh, EH6 5QG Tel: 0131-554 8888 Fax: 0131-555 1032 E-mail: info@rgbsolutions.co.uk *RGB Solutions is an Edinburgh based company providing Apple Macintosh Sales, Service and Support to businesses throughout Scotland.*

Rgit Montrose Ltd, Blackness Avenue, Altens Industrial Estate, Aberdeen, AB12 3PG Tel: (01224) 899707 Fax: (01224) 873221 E-mail: aberdeen@rgitmontrose.co.uk *Technical & industrial training services*

▶ RGS Plant Hire, 28 Whitley Spring Road, Ossett, West Yorkshire, WF5 0QA Tel: (07968) 722984 E-mail: rgsplanthire@fsmail.net *1.5t mini diggers for self drive hire. Flexible delivery times, Delivery & collection free within 25 mile radius. Free tank of fuel. easy to use machine, complete with three bucket sizes. £85 for one day, £150 for two days/weekend. £220 for 7 days.*

RGS Signs & Screenprinting, Reval Green, Oathlaw, Forfar, Angus, DD8 3PT Tel: (01307) 850260 Fax: (01307) 850260 E-mail: sales@revalgreen.com *Screen printing & sign manufrs*

RH Freight Services Ltd, The Atlantic Terminal, Liverpool Intermodal Freeport Terminal, Bootle, Merseyside, L20 1HA Tel: 0151-944 4455 Fax: 0151-944 4433 *Transport services*

RH Industrial Electronics, Unit 11d Dabble Duck Industrial Estate, Shildon, County Durham, DL4 2RA Tel: (01388) 777823 Fax: (01388) 775902 E-mail: rhie@comp42.freeserve.co.uk *Instrumentation & control specialists*

RH Rentals, Lenton Lane, Nottingham, NG7 2NR Tel: 0115-943 8030 Fax: 0115-943 8045 E-mail: daniel.stevenson@rh-freight.co.uk *Commercial vehicle trailer rentals*

▶ RH Stevens Tankers Ltd, Bentley Moor Lane, Adwick-Le-St, Doncaster, South Yorkshire, DN6 7BD Tel: (01302) 337337

▶ RH2 Renewable Energy, 2nd Floor, 145-157 St. John Street, LONDON, EC1V 4PY Tel: 0870 446 7424 E-mail: info@rh-2.co.uk *RH2 Renewable Energy is a consultancy dedicated to providing Clean Sustainable Energy solutions and Enhancing Waste Management. SERVICES Include: Anaerobic Digestion , Hydro Power , Solar Power (PV & Thermal), Wind Power , Biodiesel , Bioenergy , Biomass , Energy Audit , Energy Feasibility Studies , Energy from Waste , Gasification , Heat Pumps , Project Management , Wood Combustion , Integrated Solutions. Alternative Energy.*

Rhayader Farm Supplies, Commerce Ho, West St, Rhayader, Powys, LD6 5AF Tel: 01597 810336 *Feed supplies distributor*

Rhead, Meir Road, Stoke-on-Trent, ST3 7JD Tel: (01782) 599770 Fax: (01782) 599771 E-mail: peter.stephenson@normanrhead.co.uk *Cast stone specialist manufrs*

Rhead Buildbase Ltd, Meir Road, Normacot, Stoke-On-Trent, ST3 7JD Tel: (01782) 599550 Fax: (01782) 599551 E-mail: stokeontrent@buildbase.co.uk *Buildbase is one of the UK's fastest growing builders merchants. All of our branches are long established companies which have been serving local trades people for many years, with knowledge and experience to match. We believe strongly in understanding the needs of trades professional and our business has been developed specifically to meet those demands. Massive stocks, top quality products, competitive pricing, reliable delivery, specialist staff and exceptional customer service*

▶ Rhedin Ltd, 73 Milford Road, Reading, RG1 8LG Tel: 0118-950 9541 Fax: 0118-957 2616

Rhenus Hauser Ltd, Bowden House, Luckyn Lane, Basildon, Essex, SS14 3AX Tel: (01268) 592180 Fax: (01268) 592181 E-mail: london@uk.rhenus.com *Freight forwarders*

Rheon UK, PO Box 25630, London, Greater London, N17 6AZ Tel: 020 83520021 *Bakery equipment supplier & manufrs*

▶ Rhewum GB, 3 The Point Business Park, Market Harborough, Leicestershire, LE16 7QU Tel: (01858) 468088 Fax: (01858) 433934 E-mail: info@rhewum.de *Materials handling equipment, supply screening machines & feeders*

▶ Rhi Refractories UK Ltd, Hillview Road, Bonnybridge, Stirlingshire, FK4 2EH Tel: (01324) 819400 Fax: (01324) 814218

▶ RHI Refractories UK, PO Box 3, Clydebank, Dunbartonshire, G81 1RW Tel: 0141-952 1990 E-mail: firstname.secondname@rhi-ag.com *Steel manufrs*

Rhino Construction Services Ltd, Thanamar, Chester Road, Llong, Mold, Flintshire, CH7 4JP Tel: (01244) 543441 Fax: (01244) 543441 E-mail: rhinoconstruction@fsmail.net *Suppliers of new & used concrete batch plant*

▶ Rhino Linings UK, Barnstaple, Devon, EX31 2WQ Tel: (0870) 2074466 E-mail: info@rhinoliningsuk.co.uk *Protective coating provider applicator & distributor*

▶ Rhino Security, 25 Willow Farm Way, Broomfield, Herne Bay, Kent, CT6 7PF Tel: (0870) 7491950 Fax: (0870) 0056833 E-mail: sale@rhinosecurityltd.co.uk *Security*

Rhinocad Ltd, 23 Avon Road, Kenilworth, Warwickshire, CV8 1DH Tel: (0845) 6037223 E-mail: info@rhinocad.co.uk *Computer software retailers & training services*

Rhinopac Ltd, Tri-Star House, Unit 4, The Arena, Mollison Avenue, Enfield, Middlesex, EN3 7NL Tel: (020) 8443 9100 Fax: (020) 8443 9118 E-mail: sales@rhinopac.com Principal Export Areas: North America *Professional kitchen packaging systems including vacuum packaging & food sampling*

RHM Ltd, Prospect Works, Spa Street, Cobridge, Stoke-On-Trent, ST6 2LN Tel: (01782) 286711 Fax: (01782) 264352 E-mail: jphillips@centura.co.uk *Producers & distributors of table cookers*

RHM Brands, Booth Lane, Middlewich, Cheshire, CW10 0HD Tel: (01606) 834747 Fax: (01606) 737590 *Food manufrs*

Rhoda Precision Tooling Ltd, Unit 2 Lansdown Industrial Estate, Cheltenham, Gloucestershire, GL51 8PL Tel: (01242) 233791 Fax: (01242) 226236 E-mail: rhodaprecision@btinternet.com *Jig, fixtures, tools & moulds manufrs*

▶ Rhodar Ltd, Unit 51 Canal Bridge Enterprise Centre, Meadow Lane, Ellesmere Port, CH65 4EH Tel: 0151-355 3334 Fax: 0151-355 0919 E-mail: info@rhodar.co.uk *Asbestos removal services*

Rhodar Ltd, Subway Street, Hull, HU3 4EL Tel: (01482) 212723 Fax: (01482) 327309

Rhodar Ltd, Beza Road, Leeds, LS10 2BR Tel: 0113-270 0775 Fax: 0113-270 4124 E-mail: info@rhodar.co.uk *Asbestos removal services*

Rhodes, Delta Road, Parr, St. Helens, Merseyside, WA9 2ED Tel: (01744) 451616 Fax: (01744) 26791 E-mail: enquiries@deltafluidproducts.com *Sight glass manufrs*

Rhodes Barrellings, Unit 4, Victoria Avenue, Borrowash, Derby, DE72 3HE Tel: (07718) 160144 Fax: (01332) 666090 E-mail: rhodesbarrelling@aol.com *Sub-contract debarring & finishing services*

Rhodes Electrical, 77 St. Marys Road, Garston, Liverpool, L19 2NN Tel: 0151-427 6885 Fax: 0151-494 1535 E-mail: rhodeselectrical@onetel.com *Electrical engineers*

Rhodes Engineering Group Ltd, High Street Mills, High Street, Heckmondwike, West Yorkshire, WF16 0DL Tel: (01924) 410740 Fax: (01924) 410164 E-mail: tranter@rhodesengineering.co.uk *General engineers, specializing in access products for the water industry.*

Rhodes Group Ltd, The Coach House, The Rectory, Swathwich Lane, Wingerworth, Chesterfield, Derbyshire, S42 6QW Tel: (01246) 208229 Fax: (01246) 260486 *Machine installation*

Joseph Rhodes Ltd, Bell Vue, Elm Tree Street, Wakefield, West Yorkshire, WF1 5EQ Tel: (01924) 371161 Fax: (01924) 370928 E-mail: sales@joseph-rhodes.co.uk *Sheet metalworking machinery*

Keith Rhodes Machinery Installations Ltd, Ashmore House, Lower Tuffley Lane, Gloucester, GL2 5DP Tel: (01452) 303037 Fax: (01452) 311166 E-mail: keithrhodes@lineone.net *Industrial removals, factory relocations*

Rhodes & Kimberley, Bell Place, Blakenhall, Wolverhampton, WV2 4LY Tel: (01902) 458085 Fax: (01902) 458085 *Engineers' pattern makers*

Rhodes Nicholson Ltd, Emerald Ironworks, Emerald Street, Huddersfield, HD1 6BY Tel: (01484) 537383 Fax: (01484) 542931 E-mail: gerry@rhodes-nicholson.co.uk *Iron castings & pattern makers*

Rhodi plc, 1 Fishwick Park, Mercer Street, Preston, PR1 4LZ Tel: (01772) 562288 Fax: (01772) 562277 E-mail: fp@rhodiplc.co.uk *Clothing distributors*

Rhodia Organique Fine Ltd, St. Andrews Road, Avonmouth, Bristol, BS11 9YF Tel: 0117-948 4242 Fax: 0117-948 4256 E-mail: mike.inscew@rhodia.co.uk *Chemical manufrs*

Rhodia Pharma Solutions, Three Trees Road, Newbie, Annan, Dumfriesshire, DG12 5QH Tel: (01461) 203661

Rhodia Pharma Solutions, Dudley Lane, Dudley, Cramlington, Northumberland, NE23 7QG Tel: 0191-250 0471 Fax: 0191-250 1514 E-mail: john.lindley@eu.rhodia.com Principal Export Areas: Worldwide *Pharmaceutical active ingredient manufacturer plus contract manufacturer & development service to the pharmaceutical industry including research & development, small scale manufacture & clinical trials. Supply plus commercial manufacture. Accustomed to carrying out complex multistage organic syntheses coupled with powerful chiral technologies; such as "Sharpless" asymmetric dihydroxylation, Jacobson chiral epoxidation & kinetic resolution. Access to the innovative technologies of Shasun itself further enhances the Shasun Pharma Solutions services to our customers.*

Rhodia Sealants Ltd, 4 Pomeroy Drive, Oadby, Leicester, LE2 5NE Tel: 0116-206 3400 Fax: 0116-206 3460 E-mail: rhodia.sealants@eu.rohodia.com *Silicone sealants*

Rhodia UK Ltd, Oak House, Reeds Crescent, Watford, WD24 4QP Tel: (01923) 485868 Fax: (01923) 211580 E-mail: info@rhodia.com *Chemicals manufrs*

Rhombus Systems Ltd, Sumpter House, 8 Station Road, Histon, Cambridge, CB4 9LQ Tel: (01223) 568240 Fax: (01223) 566909 E-mail: sales@rhombus.co.uk *Machine monitoring software manufrs*

Rhondda Ready Mix Concrete, 1 Sunnybank, Williamstown, Tonypandy, Mid Glamorgan, CF40 1PE Tel: (01443) 440044 *Ready mix concrete*

Rhone Joinery Ltd, Mold Road Industrial Estate, Gwersyllt, Wrexham, Clwyd, LL11 4SB Tel: (01978) 262488 Fax: (01978) 262488 E-mail: enquiries@rhonejoinery.co.uk *Joinery manufrs*

Rhophase Microwaves Ltd, Earlstrees Court, Earlstrees Industrial Estate, Corby, Northamptonshire, NN17 4RH Tel: (01536) 263440 Fax: (01536) 260764 E-mail: sales@rhophase.co.uk Principal Export Areas: Worldwide *A respected British company, established in1985, supplying Rf and microwave coaxial assemblies. Offering quality products and excellent technical and commercial support services*

Rhopoint Components Ltd, Fairview Industrial Estate, Holland Road, Oxted, Surrey, RH8 9AX Tel: (01883) 717988 Fax: (01883) 712938 E-mail: components@rhopoint.co.uk *Precision electronic components suppliers*

Rhopoint Instrumentation, 12 Beeching Road, Bexhill-on-Sea, East Sussex, TN39 3LG Tel: (01424) 730600 Fax: (01424) 730600 E-mail: enquiries@rhopointinstruments.com *Gloss Meters (standard):*Measures the reflective qualities of manufactured surfaces.*Single Angle (20º/45º/60º/75º and 85º). *Dual Angle (20º/60º). *Triple Angle (20º/60º/85º). * *Gloss Meter (curved). *To measure the gloss of convex and concave surfaces, they can also be used to measure flat surfaces and areas which are too small to measure with standard glossmeters***

Rhos Designs Ltd, 3 Heol Aur, Dafen Industrial Estate, Dafen, Llanelli, Dyfed, SA14 8QN Tel: (01554) 749366 Fax: (01554) 749377 E-mail: rhos@compuserve.com *Design engineers*

Rhoswell Plant, The Yard, Walton East, Clarbeston Road, Dyfed, SA63 4SU Tel: (01437) 731528 *Agricultural contractors*

RHP Marine, Shepards Wharf, Medina Road, Cowes, Isle of Wight, PO31 7HT Tel: (01983) 200036 Fax: (01983) 299114 *Marine engineers*

RH-TS Cad Services, Rosemead House, 10 Leyton Cross Road, Wilmington, Dartford, DA2 7AP Tel: 01322 225014 Fax: (07075) 209713 E-mail: enquiries@rh-ts.co.uk *S Consultants & Contractors involved in the UK Building services construction sectors. complete delivery & collection service.*Conversion of designs or mark-ups to electronic CAD drawings *""As installed"" & record drawings *3D Drawings & visualization *24 hour printing & distribution of your drawing issues in all major formats. *Secure data file storage with full back-up. *A comprehensive scanning & plotting service *Encapsulation & framing of drawings for maintenance or O&M requirements**

Rhubarb, 25 Dunholme Avenue, Loughborough, Leicestershire, LE11 4SG Tel: (01509) 558830 Fax: E-mail: sara@rhubarbmedia.com *Website design for Leicester & Loughborough by professional web page designers. UK Internet e-business solutions including website design, redesign, corporate identity, database, e-commerce, and Search engine optimisation.*

Rhw Computers, 22 Cow Wynd, Falkirk, FK1 1PU Tel: 01324 635761 *Computer repair & retailers*

▶ Rhyal Engineering Ltd, Unit 8 Thornton Industrial Trading Estate, Milford Haven, Dyfed, SA73 2RX Tel: (01646) 699191 Fax: (01646) 699192

Rhyme Systems Ltd, Stapeley House, London Road, Stapeley, Nantwich, Cheshire, CW5 7JW Tel: (01270) 626023 Fax: (01270) 625948 *Financial software suppliers*

▶ Rhys Davies Freight Logistics Scotland Ltd, Murraysgate Industrial Estate, Whitburn, Bathgate, West Lothian, EH47 0LE Tel: (01501) 743772 Fax: (01501) 742232

Rhys Davies & Sons Ltd, Moy Road Industrial Estate, Taffs Well, Cardiff, CF15 7QR Tel: (029) 2081 0587 Fax: (029) 2081 0717 E-mail: sales@rhysdavies.co.uk *RHYS DAVIES FREIGHT LOGISTICS was founded in 1952 by Rhys Davies, the father of the present Chairman, Gwyn Davies. In the last decade, the Company has grown from a single base in South Wales into a National company with nine depots throughout the UK. *It offers a comprehensive nationwide pallet distribution service, as well as specialising in "Total Logistics Solutions" to customers with more demanding warehousing and distribution requirements, with an annual turnover in excess of £32m. *The fleet, in excess of 150 vehicles, ranges from vans to rigids through to a substantial fleet of articulated vehicles, with some 150 curtain-sided and double deck trailers. *The Company's premises in Cardiff, provides warehousing in excess of 160,000 square feet and, together with our own operating centres in Andover, Birmingham, Cwmbran, Haydock, London, Scotland, Wakefield, and the newly opened site at Rainham, form a national network of warehousing in excess of 500,000 square feet.*

▶ Rhys Davies & Sons Ltd, Old Parkbury Lane, Colney Street, St. Albans, Hertfordshire, AL2 2EB Tel: (01923) 853666 Fax: (01923) 853611

▶ Rhys International, Unit 41 42 Halliwell Industrial Estate, Rossini Street, Bolton, BL1 8DL Tel: (01204) 848430 Fax: (01294) 848431 E-mail: info@rhysinternational.co.uk *Suppliers and brokers of laboratory equipment, medical equipment and waste management services including waste disposal, chemical disposal, site clearances, relocatons and industrial and laboratory removals*

▶ Riach Independent Financial Advisers, 239 Ashby High Street, Scunthorpe, South Humberside, DN16 2SQ Tel: (01724) 276000 Fax: (01724) 276021 E-mail: sales@riachifa.com *Riach Telecom has developed a new approach to communications using the latest technology whilst keeping the the end product simple and easy to use.*Our partners are leading worldwide players in the provision of SMS services and telephone services. The client list includes some of the world's leading portals, national broadcasters,*

continued

*national and regional publishers, international carriers and network operators. **From Freephone numbers, premium numbers to the latest in SMS Services, we are able to satisfy most of you business' communication needs**

Riada Signs, Unit 4d Ballybrakes Industrial Estate, Ballybrakes Road, Ballymoney, County Antrim, BT53 6LW Tel: (028) 2766 2845 Fax: (028) 2766 2228 E-mail: enquiries@riadasigns.co.uk *Sign makers*

▶ Rialto Homes P.L.C., Winterthur Way, Basingstoke, Hampshire, RG21 6SZ Tel: (01256) 474740

▶ Riaz Knitwear U.K. Ltd, 8 Dolphin Street, Ardwick Manchester, Manchester, M12 6BG Tel: 0161-273 2321 Fax: 0161-273 2358 *Knitwear manufrs*

Ribble Fuel Oils, Churchill Way, Trafford Park, Manchester, M17 1BS Tel: (0800) 5423835 Fax: (01772) 620094 E-mail: paul@ribblefueloils.co.uk *TOTAL Authorised Fuel Distributor for Lancashire & Cheshire Regions.Bulk & Barrel deliveries of Diesel,Gas Oil, Kerosene, Paraffin, DERV, Petrol, ADBLUE solutions supplied in cans,barrels,IBCs & bulk,AdBlue equipment, Lubricants, Fuel Tanks*

▶ Ribble Fuel Oils, Unit 281 Carrfield Place, Walton Summit Centre, Bamber Bridge, Preston, PR5 8AN Tel: (01772) 337367 Fax: (01772) 620094 E-mail: info@ribblefueloils.co.uk *Fuel company*

Ribble Packaging Ltd, Greengate Street, Oldham, OL4 1DF Tel: 0161-284 9000 Fax: 0161-627 5049 E-mail: ribble@ribble-pack.co.uk *Corrugated container manufrs*

Ribbons Ltd, Cae Mawr Industrial Estate, Treorchy, Mid Glamorgan, CF42 6EJ Tel: (01443) 432473 Fax: (01443) 437413 *Industrial webbing manufrs*

Ribchester Janitorial Supplies, Barnard Terrace, Bradford, West Yorkshire, BD4 7DU Tel: (01274) 305290 Fax: (01274) 395786 E-mail: ribchester@btinternet.com *Janitorial suppliers*

Ribdeal Ltd, 15 Walton Park La, Walton-on-Thames, Surrey, KT12 3HF Tel: (01932) 246337 Fax: (01932) 225678 *Butchers catering & retail*

Riber Engineering Ltd, Brindley Way, Speedwell Industrial Estate, Staveley, Chesterfield, Derbyshire, S43 3JF Tel: (01246) 471244 Fax: (01246) 471233 E-mail: ribereng@aol.com *General fabricators*

▶ Ribtec, Collingwood Road, Dartmouth, Devon, TQ6 9JY Tel: (01803) 832060 Fax: (01803) 839090 E-mail: sales@ribi.co.uk *Boats sales*

Ric Woods, Unit 6-7 The Capri Centre, Oakfield Road, Stockport, Cheshire, SK3 8SG Tel: 0161-483 4810 Fax: 0161-483 6817 E-mail: sales@ricwood.com *Vehicle repairs & export*

Ricardo Consulting Engineers Ltd, Bridge Works, Old Shoreham Road, Shoreham-by-Sea, West Sussex, BN43 5FG Tel: (01273) 455611 Fax: (01273) 464124 *Consulting engineers*

Ricardo Tarragon Ltd, Ground Floor Block 5, The Westbrook Centre, Milton Road, Cambridge, CB4 1YG Tel: (01223) 323336 Fax: (01223) 323337 E-mail: sales@tarragon-et.co.uk *Software consultants*

Ricardo UK Ltd, Midlands Technical Centre, Southam Road, Leamington Spa, Warwickshire, CV31 1FQ Tel: (01926) 319319 Fax: (01926) 319300 *Automotive designers*

D.L. Ricci Ltd, Station Road, Furness Vale, High Peak, Derbyshire, SK23 7QA Tel: (01663) 746600 Fax: (01663) 746611 E-mail: rpurcell@globalnet.co.uk *Suppliers & rental of portable machining equipment*

▶ Rice Associates, Sherwood House, 104 High Street, Crowthorne, Berkshire, RG45 7AX Tel: 01344 761415 E-mail: admin@rice-associates.co.uk *Chartered Accountants offering accountancy, taxation and business consultancy services to owner managed and family owned businesses, Charities and Pension Funds.*

C. Rice Engineering, Units 1,2 & 3 Brookfield Works, Christie Street, Stockport, Cheshire, SK1 4LR Tel: 0161-477 0380 Fax: 0161-480 7387 E-mail: info@criceeng.com *Production & precision machinist services*

Joseph Rice & Son Ltd, 26 Hempsted Lane, Gloucester, GL2 5JF Tel: (01452) 527473 Fax: (01452) 300456 E-mail: info@joseph-rice.co.uk *Road transport, haulage & freight services*

▶ Rich Complements, Barker Business Park, Melmerby Green Lane, Melmerby, Ripon, North Yorkshire, HG4 5NB Tel: (01765) 640077 Fax: (01765) 640077 E-mail: info@richcomplements.co.uk *Manufacturer of sandwich fillings & salads, chilled food distributor*

N. & G. Rich, 2 Coval Gardens, London, SW14 7DG Tel: (020) 8878 2976 Fax: (020) 8392 8653 *Essential oil suppliers*

Rich Wood Joinery, Unit 40, Gaerwen Indust Estate, Gaerwen, Gwynedd, LL60 6HR Tel: (01248) 421596 Fax: (01248) 421596 *Joinery manufrs*

Richaprint Ltd, Priory Road, Freiston, Boston, Lincolnshire, PE22 0JZ Tel: (01205) 760774 Fax: (01205) 761084 E-mail: roger.young@richprint.co.uk *Printers*

Richard A Fores Ltd, Dagmar Road, Southall, Middlesex, UB2 5NX Tel: (020) 8574 5287 Fax: (020) 8574 3105 E-mail: r.a.fores@btinternet.com *Precision engineers*

▶ Richard Baty & Sons, Gibbhill Sawmill, Kirkcudbright, DG6 4TJ Tel: (01557) 330568

Richard Cullinan Joinery Ltd, 8 Ferrier Industrial Estate, Ferrier Street, London, SW18 1SW Tel: (020) 8871 0029 Fax: (020) 8871 0020 E-mail: richard@rcjoinery.co.uk *Joiners*

Richard Haworth & Co. Ltd, Kearsley Mill, Stoneclough, Radcliffe, Manchester, M26 1RH Tel: (01204) 708508 Fax: (01204) 705772 E-mail: info@richardhaworth.co.uk *Bed & table linen distribs*

▶ Richard Henderson Ltd, Lancaster Road, Bishopbriggs, Glasgow, G64 2HU Tel: 0141-762 4645 Fax: 0141-762 4122

Richard Hill Pumps Ltd, Brooke Road, Ridlington, Oakham, Leicestershire, LE15 9AJ Tel: (01572) 823385 Fax: (01572) 821660 *Single-multi stage centrifugal pump manufrs*

Howard Richard Sales Ltd, 10 Holkham Road, Orton Southgate, Peterborough, PE2 6TE Tel: (01733) 237779 Fax: (01733) 230027 E-mail: sales@hrsales.co.uk *Aluminium shelving manufrs*

▶ Richard Hutchinson & Co., 9 College Street, Nottingham, NG1 5AQ Tel: 0115-959 9700 Fax: 0115-959 9234 E-mail: enquiries@richard-hutchinson.co.uk *Richard Hutchinson & Co is one of the few law practices in the East Midlands dealing exclusively with employment law matters.The firm advises on a wide range of employment issues but specialises in representing clients in Employment Tribunals and offering tailor-made training days.*

Richard Ingram Land Drainage, 10 Church Lane, Gaddesby, Leicester, LE7 4WE Tel: (01664) 840480 Fax: (01664) 840480 *Agricultural contractors*

Richard J Reading, Westwood Cottage, Trolliloes, Hailsham, East Sussex, BN27 4QR Tel: (01435) 830249 Fax: (01435) 830249 *Cabinet makers*

Richard Kell, Blyth Valley Venture Workshops, Plessey Road, Blyth, Northumberland, NE24 4BN Tel: (01670) 363626 Fax: (01670) 363626 *Tool & instrument maker*

▶ Richard Murray Plant Hire, 26 Brierie Gardens, Crosslee, Johnstone, Renfrewshire, PA6 7BZ Tel: (01505) 615733 Fax: (01505) 610201

Richard Parry, Yockleton, Shrewsbury, SY5 9QQ Tel: (01743) 821333 Fax: (01743) 873604 *Commercial vehicle bodybuilders*

▶ Richard Perkins & Associates, The Barn, 2 Gunton Church Lane, Lowestoft, Suffolk, NR32 4LE Tel: (01502) 514738 Fax: (01502) 568674 E-mail: sales@richard-perkins.co.uk *Commercial Property Consultants*

▶ Richard Preston & Son Ltd, Howard Road, Eaton Socon, St. Neots, Cambridgeshire, PE19 8ET Tel: (01480) 213200 Fax: (01480) 405671

Richard Read Ltd, Monmouth Road, Longhope, Gloucestershire, GL17 0QG Tel: (01452) 830456 Fax: (01452) 831422 E-mail: sales@richardreadtransport.co.uk *Road transport, haulage & freight services*

Richard T Porter Transport Services Ltd, Hylton Road, Worcester, WR2 5JS Tel: (01905) 748384 Fax: (01905) 748385 *Road transport, haulage & freight services*

Richard Thraves Joinery Ltd, Mill Lane Workshops, Mill Lane, Scarborough, North Yorkshire, YO12 4ED Tel: (01723) 375708 *Joiners*

▶ Richard Ward Oxford Ltd, High Street, Islip, Kidlington, Oxfordshire, OX5 2RX Tel: (01865) 379244 Fax: (01865) 379246

Richard Watkins, 142 Lower Marsh, London, SE1 7AE Tel: (020) 7593 0088 Fax: (020) 7593 0080 E-mail: engineers@rwalondon.co.uk *Consulting structural engineers*

Richard Wilkinson & Co., Devonshire Yard, Pitt Street, Keighley, West Yorkshire, BD21 4PF Tel: (01535) 602512 Fax: (01535) 602713 E-mail: sales@wilktool.co.uk *Engineers' pattern makers*

Richard Williams, 7 28 Plantation Road, Amersham, Buckinghamshire, HP6 6HL Tel: (01494) 729026 Fax: (01494) 721169 E-mail: r@richardwilliamsfurniture.com *Furniture design manufrs*

Richard Williams Joinery, The Elms, Bratton Road, Bratton, Telford, Shropshire, TF5 0BT Tel: (01952) 242514 Fax: (01952) 242514 *Joinery manufrs*

▶ Richard-Allan Medical Industries (UK) Ltd, 95 Bromsgrove Raod, Redditch, Worcestershire, B97 4RL Tel: (01527) 460302 Fax: (01527) 460303 E-mail: m.penver@blueyonder.co.uk *Medical wire products & suture eyed needles manufrs*

A.R. Richards Ltd, Cobscott Farm, Norton In Hales, Market Drayton, Shropshire, TF9 3TW Tel: (01630) 653757 *Agricultural contractors*

Richards Bros, Noyadd, Cilmery, Builth Wells, Powys, LD2 3NT Tel: (01982) 552308 *Agricultural contractors*

Richards Brothers, Cardrew Industrial Estate, Redruth, Cornwall, TR15 1SS Tel: (01209) 212234 Fax: (01209) 219464 *Petrol & diesel fuel injection specialist services*

▶ Richards Construction Ltd, 98 Cardiff Road, Llandaff, Cardiff, CF5 2DT Tel: (029) 2055 3440 Fax: (029) 2057 8219

Dave Richards, 73 Church Road, Newport, Gwent, NP19 7EH Tel: (01633) 254910 *Fishing tackle*

David Richards Engineering Ltd, Unit 7B, Herald Industrial Estate, Hedge End, Southampton, SO30 2JW Tel: (01489) 790900 Fax: (01489) 790333 E-mail: drengineering@aol.com *Ultra hard cutting tool manufrs*

Gordon Richards Tools (Birmingham), Unit 28, Roman Way, Coles Hill, Birmingham, B46 1HQ Tel: 0121-328 5454 Fax: 0121-322 2148 *Engineers supplies distributors*

Richards & Hewitt Sales Ltd, Dorset Way, Byfleet, West Byfleet, Surrey, KT14 7LB Tel: (01932) 346025 Fax: (01932) 348517 *Merchants of chain link & steel fencing manufrs*

J. H. Richards & Co. Ltd, Saltley Road, Birmingham, B7 4TD Tel: 0121-359 2257 Fax: 0121-359 7340 E-mail: andrew@jhrichards.co.uk *Based in Birmingham, we are an independent supplier of white metal bearings, and indeed most types of plain bearings. We repair, often on an emergency basis, rewhitemetal and manufacture all types of whitemetal bearings including journal bearings, thrust bearings, combined journal and thrust bearings, main bearings, big end bearings, diesel bearings, thrust pads, journal pads, tilting pad journal bearings, tilting pad thrust bearings, turbine bearings, alternator bearings, generator bearings, motor bearings, gearbox bearings, fan bearings, pump bearings, compressor bearings, crusher bearings, indeed bearings for any application involving rotating equipment. We also manufacture and sell a variety of whitemetal alloys.*

Richards James Weldon, 5-6 The Mews, Hatherley Road, Sidcup, Kent, DA14 4BH Tel: (020) 8300 7878 Fax: (020) 8300 9709 *Trimmings merchants & tie linings*

▶ Richards Liftruck Services, 66 Wantage, Telford, Shropshire, TF7 5PB Tel: (07971) 626858 E-mail: richardnash1@blueyonder.co.uk *Sale, services, hire & repair forklifts & other material handling equipment*

Richards & Co. (Mansfield) Ltd, Matlock Mill, Sheepbridge Lane, Mansfield, Nottinghamshire, NG18 5DJ Tel: (01623) 621527 Fax: (01623) 622250 *Building contractors*

Richard & Osborne Ltd, Goss Moor, Fraddon, St. Columb, Cornwall, TR9 6EU Tel: (01726) 860308 Fax: (01726) 861135 *Road transport contractors*

Richards & Philips Ltd, Century House, Vickers Business Centre, Priestley Road, Basingstoke, Hampshire, RG24 9RA Tel: 01256 358651 Fax: 01256 333369 E-mail: sales@richards-philips.co.uk *Business, promotional & incentive gift suppliers*

Richards & Shaw (Trim) Ltd, 57 Cradley Road, Cradley Heath, West Midlands, B64 7BP Tel: (01384) 633800 Fax: (01384) 410791 E-mail: slynch@richards-shaw.co.uk *Manufacturers of quality seating for all types of passenger carrying vehicles*

Richardson & Co. Ltd, Smithfold Lane, Worsley, Manchester, M28 0GP Tel: 0161-702 7002 *Manufacturers of trucks, trolleys & warehouse handling equipment*

Richardson, Courville House, 1 Ellerbeck Court, Stokesley, Middlesbrough, Cleveland, TS9 5PT Tel: (01642) 714791 Fax: (01642) 714387 E-mail: enquiries@pcrichardson.co.uk Principal Export Areas: Africa, Central/East Europe & West Europe *Civil engineering & nuclear decommissioning services*

Alexander Jon Richardson & Associates, Severals House, Church Lane, Doddington, March, Cambridgeshire, PE15 0TA Tel: 01354 740076 *Alexander Jon Richardson & Associates, based in March, Cambridgeshire, provides catering consultancy services.*

▶ Bernie Richardson, Unit 2 Abbey Manor Industrial Estate, Yeovil, Somerset, BA21 3AR Tel: (01935) 413317 *Grit blasting & powder coaters*

Bob Richardson Tools & Fasteners Ltd, Pedmore Road, Dudley, West Midlands, DY2 0RL Tel: (01384) 482789 Fax: (01384) 481888 E-mail: sales@toolstoday.co.uk *Tool & fastener distributors*

Richardson Bros, 39 Leg Street, Oswestry, Shropshire, SY11 2NN Tel: (01691) 656980 Fax: (01691) 656980 *Kitchen & bathroom manufrs*

Richardson Cardy, 44a-48 Railway Street, Lisburn, County Antrim, BT28 1XP Tel: (028) 9267 8884 Fax: (028) 9266 3509 *Luxury kitchen & bedroom manufrs*

Richardson Carpenter, Manor Farm, Cliddesden, Basingstoke, Hampshire, RG25 2JB Tel: (01256) 353700 Fax: (01256) 358100 *Marketing & advertising consultants*

Richardson Developments Ltd, 100 Dudley Road East, Oldbury, West Midlands, B69 3DY Tel: 0121-544 8000 Fax: 0121-552 9838 *Property development company*

Richardson Electronics, Inspring House, Searby Road, Lincoln, LN2 4DT Tel: (01522) 542631 Fax: (01522) 545453 E-mail: info@rell.com *RF components, CCTV & medical equipment distributors*

Richardson Ford, Westgate, Driffield, North Humberside, YO25 6SY Tel: (01377) 255294 Fax: (01377) 252887 E-mail: info@richardson-ford.co.uk *Main ford dealer* Also at: Bridlington

▶ Richardson Printing Ltd, Colville Road Works, Oulton Broad, Lowestoft, Suffolk, NR33 9QS Tel: (01502) 516991 Fax: (01502) 517588

▶ Richardson Projects, 585 Oldham Road, Rochdale, Lancashire, OL16 4SU Tel: (01706) 527505 Fax: (01706) 516400 E-mail: sales@richardsonprojects.co.uk *Building contractor & housebuilder*

▶ Richardson Removal & Storage Contractors Ltd, Vickers Close, Preston Farm Industrial Estate, Stockton-on-Tees, Cleveland, TS18 3TD Tel: (01642) 673207 Fax: (01642) 671080

▶ Richardson & Starling Northern Ltd, 3 Block 1 Maxwelltown Industrial Estate, Glasgow Road, Dumfries, DG2 0NW Tel: (01387) 269681 Fax: (01387) 264667 *Wood preservation*

Richardsons Boatbuilders, Island Harbour Marina, Mill Lane, Binfield, Newport, Isle of Wight, PO30 2LA Tel: (01983) 821095 Fax: (01983) 522372 E-mail: info@richardsonsyacht.co.uk *Boat builders & repair*

Richardsons Commercials Oldham Ltd, Glen Trading Estate, Wellyhole Street, Oldham, OL4 3BF Tel: 0161-652 4241 Fax: 0161-628 4070 *Commercial vehicle bodybuilders & repairers*

Richardsons Of Leicester, 112a Milligan Road, Leicester, LE2 8FB Tel: 0116-283 8604 Fax: 0116-283 7109 E-mail: sales@richardsonsofleicester.co.uk *Laboratory equipment suppliers*

Richardsons Nyewood Ltd, Station Yard, Nyewood, Petersfield, Hampshire, GU31 5HX Tel: (01730) 821771 Fax: (01730) 821834 E-mail: office@r-nl.co.uk *Building & restoration contractors*

Richbrook International Ltd, 18 York Road, London, SW19 8TP Tel: (020) 8543 7111 Fax: (020) 8543 9111 E-mail: sales@richbrook.co.uk *Car accessories manufrs*

Len Riches & Son, Tricity Works, Hatherleigh, Okehampton, Devon, EX20 3LR Tel: (01837) 810480 *Steel fabricators*

▶ Richfield Control Systems Ltd, 2 Aspley Close, Four Ashes Industrial Estate, Four Ashes, Wolverhampton, WV10 7DE Tel: (01902) 798411 Fax: (01902) 798412

Richfield Graphics Ltd, Unit 4b Paddock Road Industrial Estate, Paddock Road, Caversham, Reading, RG4 5BY Tel: 0118-946 2225 Fax: 0118-946 2618 E-mail: sales@richfieldgraphics.co.uk *Graphic designers & general printers*

Richfield Springs, 73 Other Road, Redditch, Worcestershire, B98 8DP Tel: (01527) 595882 Fax: (01527) 595883 *Coil spring manufrs*

Richkeen Chemicals Ltd, 33 Chapmans Cresent, Chesham, Buckinghamshire, HP5 2QT Tel: (01494) 786669 Fax: (01494) 786503 E-mail: richkeenc@aol.com *Drilling fluid additives distributors*

▶ Richley Dental Studio, 1 Nimmings Road, Halesowen, West Midlands, B62 9JQ Tel: 0121-561 4444 Fax: 0121-561 4563

▶ Richmack Building Services, 14 Nettlehill Road, Uphall Station, Livingston, West Lothian, EH54 5PP Tel: (01506) 505010 Fax: (01506) 505007

Richman Ring Ltd, Eurolink Way, Sittingbourne, Kent, ME10 3HH Tel: (01795) 427365 Fax: (01795) 428804 E-mail: info@richman-rwg.com *Removal contractors*

Richman's Removals (Swindon) Ltd, Transfer Bridge Industrial Estate, County Road, Swindon, SN1 2EL Tel: (01793) 526621 Fax: (01793) 542795 E-mail: enquiries@richmansswindon.co.uk *Removal & storage contractors*

Richmond & Brown Joinery Services, Florence Street, Middlesbrough, Cleveland, TS2 1DR Tel: (01642) 246959 Fax: (01642) 246959 *Joinery manufrs*

▶ Richmond Building Products, The Barn, White Horse Lane, Witham, Essex, CM8 2BU Tel: (01376) 510002 *Roofing materials manufrs*

▶ Richmond Electronic Services Ltd, 42 Hurricane Way, Norwich Airport Industrial, Estate Norfolk, Norwich, NR6 6JB Tel: (020) 7942 0700 Fax: (020) 7942 0701 *Electrical test equipment*

Richmond Electronics & Engineering International Ltd, Armtec Estate, North Lopham, Diss, Norfolk, IP22 2LR Tel: (01379) 686800 Fax: (01379) 688519 E-mail: info@richmondeei.co.uk *Electronic engineers & engineering services*

Richmond Film Services, The Old School, Park Lane, Richmond, Surrey, TW9 2RA Tel: (020) 8940 6077 Fax: (020) 8948 8326 *Recording equipment hire services*

Richmond Fire Engineers, 30 Firby Road, Gallowfields Trading Estate, Richmond, North Yorkshire, DL10 4ST Tel: (01748) 825612 Fax: (01748) 825935 E-mail: sprinklers@richmondfire.co.uk *Fire protection engineers*

▶ Richmond Homes Scotland Ltd, Pitreavie Court Pitreavie Business Park, Queensferry Road, Dunfermline, Fife, KY11 8UU Tel: (01383) 622127 E-mail: sales@richmondhomes.co.uk

▶ Richmond House Clearance, 5 Grena Gardens, Richmond, Surrey, TW9 1XP Tel: 0208 9407920 E-mail: info@bluekatzhosting.co.uk

Richmond Industries UK Ltd, C11 Acre Business Park, Acre Road, Reading, RG2 0SA Tel: 0118-931 0396 *Sensor manufrs*

Richmond Measurement Services, Po Box 44, Derby, DE24 8ZT Tel: (01332) 364354 Fax: (01332) 362737 *Instrumentation services*

Richmond Precision Services, Lancaster Road, Bowerhill, Melksham, Wiltshire, SN12 6SS Tel: (01225) 706840 Fax: (01225) 700841 E-mail: richard.hand@richmondprecision.co.uk *Precision CNC Engineers*

Richmond Reproduction (Manufacturing) Ltd, Balloo Industrial Estate, 40 Balloo Avenue, Bangor, County Down, BT19 7QT Tel: (028) 9127 0930 Fax: 028) 9127 0711 E-mail: enquires@richmond.ltd.uk *Contract furniture manufrs*

Richmond Towers Ltd, 26 Fitzroy Square, London, W1T 6BT Tel: (020) 7388 7421 Fax: (020) 7388 7761 E-mail: mail@richmondtowers.com *Public relations services*

▶ Richmonds Bathrooms, 21 Berridale Avenue, Cathcart, Glasgow, G44 3AF Tel: 0141 571 7261 E-mail: steve@richmondsbathrooms.co.uk

Richmonds Of London Ltd, 66 Weir Road, London, SW19 8UG Tel: (020) 8879 3500 Fax: (020) 8879 3563 E-mail: sales@richmondsoflondon.co.uk *Engineers suppliers plumbers merchants*

Richwood Bedrooms, Unit 13 Bacon House Farm, Warren Road, Little Horwood, Milton Keynes, MK17 0PS Tel: (01908) 507907 Fax: (01908) 507976 E-mail: keith@richwoodbedrooms.co.uk *Design & installation of fitted bedrooms*

Richwood Furniture, Unit 3 Mill Lane, Billinghay, Lincoln, LN4 4ES Tel: (01526) 861440 Fax: (01526) 861440 *Cabinet making services*

Rickerby Ltd, Currock Road, Carlisle, CA2 4AU Tel: (01228) 527521 Fax: (01228) 533008 E-mail: martyn.henderson@rickerby.net *Agricultural engineers* Also at: Alenwick, Cockermouth, Dumfries, Hexum & Penrith

Rickerby Ltd, Brunswick Road, Penrith, Cumbria, CA11 7JP Tel: (01768) 863718 Fax: (01768) 899117 E-mail: sales@rickerby.net *Agricultural engineers*

Rickerby Agricultural Machinery, Elmsfield Park, Holme, Carnforth, Lancashire, LA6 1RJ Tel: (01539) 563416 Fax: (01539) 563248 E-mail: rob.bell@rickerby.net *Agricultural machinery & equipment manufrs*

David Ricketts & Son, Court Newydd, St. Brides Major, Bridgend, M. Glam, CF32 0TG Tel: (01656) 880373 *Sell hand machinery & repairs*

Ricketts Radiators Ltd, 4 Viking Way, Winch Wen Industrial Estate, Winch Wen, Swansea, SA1 7DA Tel: (01792) 796504 Fax: (01792) 428338 *Motor radiator reconditioners*

▶ Rickman Decorators Ltd, Charterhouse, 11 Marine Drive, Barton on Sea, New Milton, Hampshire, BH25 7EG Tel: (01425) 618883 Fax: (01425) 618883 E-mail: office@paint4you.co.uk *Rickman Ltd.established 25 years, commercial and residential, interior, exterior decorators and property improvement specialists, serving Dorset and Hampshire.*

Rickmar, Westminster Road Industrial Estate, Station Road, North Hykeham, Lincoln, LN6 3QY Tel: (01522) 691441 Fax: (01522) 694056 E-mail: sales@rickmarplantsales.co.uk *Contractors plant sales*

Ricochet Signs & Designs, B3 Browings Farm Workshops, Blackboys, Uckfield, East Sussex, TN22 5HG Tel: (01825) 890088 Fax: (01825) 890088 E-mail: info@ricochetsigns.co.uk *Signs & designs*

Ricoh UK Ltd, 1 Plane Tree Crescent, Feltham, Middlesex, TW13 7HG Tel: (020) 8261 4000 Fax: (020) 8261 4004 E-mail: info@ricoh.co.uk *Manufacturers of photocopying, fax mail & laser printing machines*

Ricor Ltd, Arrow Works, Birmingham Road, Studley, Warwickshire, B80 7AS Tel: (01527) 857757 Fax: (01527) 857224 E-mail: ricorjrobinson@aol.com *Automotive engineers*

Rics Royal Institute Chartered Surveyors, 12 Great George Street, London, SW1P 3AE Tel: (020) 7222 7000 Fax: (020) 7334 3811 E-mail: contactrics@rics.org *Professional governing body for chartered surveyors*

Rictor Engineering Ltd, Derby Street, Denton, Manchester, M34 3SD Tel: 0161-320 8842 Fax: 0161-335 0973 *Sheet metal engineers & fabricators*

▶ Ridat Co., Unit E1, Neath Vale Supplier Park, Resolven, Neath, West Glamorgan, SA11 4SR Tel: (0845) 0506525 Fax: (0845) 0506526 E-mail: info@ridat.com *Machinery thermoformed components & engineering services*

▶ Ridd Wood Partnership Ltd, Market House, 19-21 Market Place, Wokingham, Berkshire, RG40 1AP Tel: 0118-978 7930 Fax: 0118-977 4689

John Riddel & Son Ltd, 1A Dagger Road, Lisburn, County Antrim, BT28 2TJ Tel: (028) 9262 0810 Fax: (028) 9262 0811 E-mail: sales@riddel.co.uk *Wholesale hardware distributors*

E.T. Riddiough Sales Ltd, Lodge Mill, Barden Lane, Burnley, Lancashire, BB12 0DY Tel: (01282) 434678 Fax: (01282) 412524 E-mail: etriddiough@onetel.net.uk *Caravan accessory wholesalers*

Riddle & Simmons, 4 Sanders Close, Finedon Road Industrial Estate, Wellingborough, Northamptonshire, NN8 4HQ Tel: (01933) 276567 Fax: (01604) 406545 *Sectional builders* Also at: Northampton

▶ Ride Low Ltd, 27-29 Church Street, Manchester, M4 1PE Tel: 0161-834 5788 E-mail: george@ridelow.co.uk

Ride On Motor Cycles, 19-21 Nithsdale Street, Glasgow, G41 2PZ Tel: 0141-424 0404 Fax: 0141-423 4685 E-mail: sales@ride-on-motorcycles.co.uk *Motorcycle dealers*

▶ Ride Solutions, 33 Illingworth Way, Foxton, Cambridge, CB2 6RY Tel: (01223) 701012 Fax: (01223) 709184 E-mail: sales@ride-solutions.com *Van & truck rubber suspension consultant & sales*

Rideout Engineering Ltd, 197 South Liberty Lane, Bristol, BS3 2TN Tel: 0117-953 8900 Fax: 0117-953 8800 *Engineers' machinists & orbital welding services*

Rider Hunt International, 9 Carden Place, Aberdeen, AB10 1UR Tel: (01224) 650222 Fax: (01224) 631289 E-mail: elizabeth.robertson@rhi-group.com *Engineering project management services* Also at: London

▶ RideRight UK, 47 Leafields, Houghton Regis, Dunstable, Bedfordshire, LU5 5LT Tel: (07932) 746662 E-mail: info@riderightuk.co.uk *Advanced Motorcycle Training. **Training provided by Police Motorcycle and Police Trained Instructors. We pride ourselves on our expertise in the field of motorcycle advanced riding, our instructors have years of experience to offer you, we offer all types of training for all current advanced motorcycle tests.**However, if its just a few hours in the saddle you need to refresh your current skill level, we can help too. We are with out doubt the best value for money in the UK today, give us a call or drop us an email, you will not regret it. **

▶ Riders, Longlands Lane, Brodsworth, Doncaster, South Yorkshire, DN5 7XB Tel: (01302) 722255 Fax: (01302) 722255 E-mail: info@riders-equestrian.co.uk *Equestrian equipment distributors*

Riders Jaguar, 53 Dracaena Avenue, Falmouth, Cornwall, TR11 2EL Tel: (01326) 212222 Fax: (01326) 212006 *Motor vehicle repair services & sales*

Riders Landrover, Threemilestone Industrial Estate, Threemilestone, Truro, Cornwall, TR4 9LD Tel: (01872) 263377 Fax: (01872) 261606 E-mail: sales@riders-landrover.co.uk *Land rover motor trader franchise & sales*

Ridge Interiors Ltd, Contract House, 19a Watford Heath, Watford, WD19 4EU Tel: (01923) 240976 Fax: (01923) 212654 *Commercial building contractors*

Ridge Tools, Arden Press Way, Pixmore Avenue, Letchworth Garden City, Hertfordshire, SG6 1LH Tel: (01462) 485335 Fax: (01462) 485315 E-mail: sales.uk@ridgid.com *Drain cleaning & plumbing tools manufrs*

Ridgedeck Road Markings Ltd, Station Road, East Preston, Littlehampton, West Sussex, BN16 3AA Tel: (01903) 782465 Fax: (01903) 859671 *Thermoplastic road markings & road studs*

Ridgemond Training, Caxton Way, Stevenage, Hertfordshire, SG1 2DF Tel: (01438) 842200 Fax: (01438) 842250 E-mail: c.collins@ridgemond.freeserve.co.uk *Training specialists*

Ridgeons Ltd, Trinity Hall Industrial Estate, Nuffield Road, Cambridge, CB4 1TS Tel: (01223) 466000 Fax: (01223) 466079 *Builders merchants*

Ridgeons Ltd, Ashdon Road Commercial Centre, Saffron Walden, Essex, CB10 2NQ Tel: (01799) 583000 Fax: (01799) 583039 E-mail: steven.sutton@ridgeons.co.uk *Builders merchants*

Ridgeons Ltd, Alexandra Road, Sudbury, Suffolk, CO10 2XH Tel: (01787) 881777 Fax: (01787) 881186 E-mail: sudburysales@ridgerns.net *Timber & builders merchants* Also at: Diss & Lowestoft

▶ Ridgeway Architectural Glazing Ltd, 6 Onslow Mills, Trout Road, West Drayton, Middlesex, UB7 7RR Tel: (01895) 449666 Fax: (01895) 447666

Ridgeway Components Ltd, Unit 5, Prosperity Way, Middlewich, Cheshire, CW10 0GD Tel: (01606) 841010 Fax: (01606) 841011 E-mail: sales@ridgeway-components.co.uk *Electronic component distributors*

Ridgeway Co Extrusion Technology Ltd, Unit 22 W & G Industrial Estate, Faringdon Road, East Challow, Wantage, Oxfordshire, OX12 9TF Tel: (01235) 760435 Fax: (01235) 763021 *Precision engineers*

Ridgeway Plant Co. Ltd, Airport Road West, Belfast, BT3 9AD Tel: (028) 9045 4599 Fax: (028) 9045 4596 E-mail: info@ridgeway-online.com *Niche products & tools for hire or sale & training*

Ridgeway Plastics (Iver) Ltd, Unit 7B Waldeck House, Waldeck Road, Maidenhead, Berkshire, SL6 8BR Tel: (01628) 636621 Fax: (01628) 636621 *Plastics vacuum forming fabricators & manufrs*

▶ Ridgewell Fitted Furniture, 1 Melton Road, Queniborough, Leicester, LE7 3FP Tel: 0116-269 6615 Fax: 0116-269 6615 *Built in furniture manufrs*

Ridgewood Roofing Contracts Ltd, Oakfield House, 31 Main Street, Glasgow, G74 4JU Tel: (01355) 236336 Fax: (01355) 573150 *Roofing contractors*

▶ Ridgway Machines Ltd, Bridge Works Leicester Road, Anstey, Leicester, LE7 7AT Tel: 0116-235 3055 Fax: 0116-235 3057 E-mail: sales@ridgwayeng.com *Taping machine manufrs*

Ridings Construction Co. Ltd, The Ropewalk, Hallfield Road, York, YO31 7XG Tel: (01904) 625269 Fax: (01904) 642280 E-mail: info@ridingsconstruction.co.uk *Civil engineers*

▶ Ridings Food Brokers Ltd, Unit 7 8 & 9, Linthwaite Business Centre, Manchester Road, Huddersfield, HD7 5QS Tel: (01484) 841920

Ridley Sawmill, Ansty, Salisbury, SP3 5QD Tel: (01747) 870351 Fax: (01747) 870351 *Sawmill services*

Riello Ltd, Ermine Centre, Hurricane Close, Ermine Business Park, Huntingdon, Cambridgeshire, PE29 6WX Tel: (01480) 432144 Fax: (01480) 432191 E-mail: sales@rielloburners.co.uk *Domestic & commercial multi fuel burners*

Riello Ups Ltd, Unit 51 & 66, Clywedog Road North, Wrexham Industrial Estate, Wrexham, Clwyd, LL13 9XN Tel: (01978) 729297 Fax: (01978) 729290 E-mail: sales@riello-ups.co.uk *Uninterruptible power supply & standby power protection services*

Rieter Automotive Great Britain Ltd, Keller House, Hereward Rise, Halesowen, West Midlands, B62 8AN Tel: 0121-504 4500 Fax: 0121-504 4521 E-mail: steve.nash@rieterauto.com *Automotive insulated panels*

Rieter-Scragg Ltd, Heather Close, Lyme Green Business Park, Macclesfield, Cheshire, SK11 0LR Tel: (01625) 506300 Fax: (01625) 506301 E-mail: sales@rieterscragg.com *Research & development for textile industry*

▶ Rig Engineering Sas, 621 George Street, Aberdeen, AB25 3YE Tel: (01224) 627200 Fax: (01224) 647308 E-mail: info@rigengineering.com *Rig engineering*

Rig Lift UK Ltd, Richmer Road, Erith, Kent, DA8 2HN Tel: (01322) 341166 Fax: (01322) 341165 *Mobile cranes*

Rigal Chemical & Process Plant Ltd, Gravelhill Lane, Whitley, Goole, North Humberside, DN14 0JJ Tel: (01977) 661095 Fax: (01977) 662165 E-mail: sales@rigal-luton.co.uk *Mixers & storage tank wholesalers & manufrs*

Rigby Taylor Paints Ltd, Crown Lane, Horwich, Bolton, BL6 5HP Tel: (01204) 677776 Fax: (01204) 677785 E-mail: sales@rigbytaylor.com *Sports turf suppliers & weed control services*

Rigby Wireworks & Co. (1982) Ltd, Cross Smithfields, Sheffield, S3 7AU Tel: 0114-272 4615 Fax: 0114-276 6840 *Wire mesh stockists & fabricators*

Rigfone Electrics Ltd, 109-111 Bitterne Road West, Southampton, SO18 1AR Tel: (023) 8021 5100 Fax: (023) 8021 5101 E-mail: sales@rigfone.co.uk *We are a progressive, energetic electrical contracting & maintenance service company whose policy is to keep abreast of the latest trends in electronic peripherals & the electrical contracting world. We couple this with the employment of technicians/ electricians only of a high standard, who are encouraged & given every opportunity to maintain & improve their efficiency by attending refresher & update courses on all matters relevant to their employment & the works undertaken by the company. The company - which was founded in 1963 - currently employs 40 members of staff & maintains a personal, efficient & high quality service backed by good supervision*

▶ Rigg Construction Southern Ltd, 21 Market Place, Melksham, Wiltshire, SN12 6ES Tel: (01225) 705668 Fax: (01225) 790069

Frank Rigg Ltd, 489 Edenfield Road, Rochdale, Lancashire, OL11 5XR Tel: (01706) 644509 Fax: (01706) 643910 *Maintenance & production engineers*

J. Rigg, 43 Bolton Road, Bury, Lancashire, BL8 2AB Tel: 0161-763 9903 Fax: 0161-763 9903 E-mail: jrsigns@aol.com *Sign manufrs*

▶ Riggott & Co. Ltd, Station Lodge, Lodge Lane, Tuxford, Newark, Nottinghamshire, NG22 0NL Tel: (01777) 872525 Fax: (01777) 872626 E-mail: info@riggott.co.uk *Line marking specialists, general road line markings, car park markings, specialist floor markings, floor graphics, road stud installation, car park & grounds maintenance*

Right Management Consultants, Augustine House, 6A Austin Friars, London, EC2N 2HA Tel: (020) 7448 8750 Fax: (020) 7588 2114 E-mail: rightaugustine@right.com *Career management consultants*

▶ The Right Service, Bradford Road, Birmingham, B36 9AA Tel: 0121-246 8490 Fax: 0121-246 8490 E-mail: questions@therightservice.com *Multi Media designers & tailor made web site creations of all descriptions, UK based, we will listen to you!*

Right Track Ltd, 15 34 Union Road, Macclesfield, Cheshire, SK11 7BN Tel: (01625) 618581 Fax: (01625) 616586 E-mail: right@tract1534.freeserve.co.uk *Printed circuit board manufrs*

▶ Right Units Ltd, Imperial Way, Watford, WD24 4YH Tel: (01923) 224477 Fax: (01923) 211119 E-mail: info@rightunits.com *Aluminium door & window manufrs*

Righton Ltd, Unit 7-10 Beeches Trading Estate, Waverley Road, Yate, Bristol, BS37 5FF Tel: (01454) 318601 Fax: (01454) 273392 E-mail: bristol@righton.co.uk *Bespoke aluminium extrusions, copper alloys, pipe, tube fittings supply*

Righton Ltd, Unit 13b Anniesland Industrial Estate, Glasgow, G13 1EU Tel: 0141-954 8962 Fax: 0141-959 3467 E-mail: info@righton.co.uk *Righton Limited, the UK's leading independent stockholder of metals and plastics supply brass, copper, aluminium, stainless steel & high performance copper alloys, in rod, bar, tube, sheet, plate and extrusion as well as aluminium composite material and semi finished plastics. Our plastics range includes acrylic, polycarbonate, foam PVC, PET-G and engineering plastics. We specialise in the supply of bespoke aluminium extrusions, high performance copper alloys, stainless steel pipe, tube fittings and flanges, aluminium composite sheet and materials for the marine industry. Cut-to-size and processing facilities are available at our eight Service Centres in Birmingham, Bristol, Glasgow, Leeds, Manchester, High Wycombe, Plymouth & Portsmouth. Our expertise in materials sourcing, market & product information, stock management and technical support ensures an unrivalled level of service for all our customers.* Also at: Birmingham, Glasgow & Welwyn Garden City

Righton Ltd, Units 5-6, The Nelson Centre, Portsmouth, PO3 5SE Tel: (023) 9262 3070 Fax: (023) 9267 7502 E-mail: portsmouthsales@righton.co.uk *Righton Limited, the UK's leading independent stockholder of metals and plastics supply brass, copper, aluminium, stainless steel & high performance copper alloys, in rod, bar, tube, sheet, plate and extrusion as well as aluminium composite material and semi finished plastics. Our plastics range includes acrylic, polycarbonate, foam PVC, PET-G and engineering plastics. We specialise in the supply of bespoke aluminium extrusions, high performance copper alloys, stainless steel pipe, tube fittings and flanges, aluminium composite sheet and materials for the marine industry. Cut-to-size and processing facilities are available at our eight Service Centres in Birmingham, Bristol, Glasgow, Leeds, Manchester, High Wycombe, Plymouth & Portsmouth. Our expertise in materials sourcing, market & product information, stock management and technical support ensures an unrivalled level of service for all our customers.*

Rightway Environmental Spraying & Pest Control, Noir View, Sexburga Drive, Minster on Sea, Sheerness, Kent, ME12 2LB Tel: (01795) 873119 Fax: (01795) 873119 *Pest control services*

Rightweld Welding Equipment, Unit 6 Ebbsfleet Industrial Estate, Northfleet, Gravesend, Kent, DA11 9DZ Tel: (01474) 320575 Fax: (01474) 536768 *Welding & cutting equipment*

Rigid Containers Ltd, Stoke Albany Road, Desborough, Kettering, Northamptonshire, NN14 2SR Tel: (01536) 760266 Fax: (01536) 762714 *Corrugated container manufrs* Also at: Crudwell & Selby

Rigid Paper Ltd, Denison Road, Selby, North Yorkshire, YO8 8DB Tel: (01757) 705151 Fax: (01757) 210009 E-mail: paper@rigid.co.uk *Paper makers*

Rigidal Systems Ltd, Unit 62 Blackpole Trading Estate West, Worcester, WR3 8ZJ Tel: (01905) 750500 Fax: (01905) 750555 E-mail: info@rigidal.co.uk *Aluminium & steel roof & wall cladding manufrs*

Rigiflex Extrusions Ltd, Ibex Barn Ferro Fields, Brixworth Indust Estate, Brixworth, Northampton, NN6 9UA Tel: (01604) 880217 Fax: (01604) 880129 E-mail: sales@rigiflexextrusions.co.uk *Plastics extrusion manufrs*

Rigman Offshore (UK) Ltd, Wellheads Centre, 5A Wellheads Crescent, Wellheads Industrial Estate, Aberdeen, AB21 7GA Tel: (01224) 725532 Fax: (01224) 724047 E-mail: admin@rigman.ifb.co.uk *Recruitment agency*

Rigserv Ltd, Unit 9 Wellheads Crescent, Wellheads Industrial Estate, Aberdeen, AB21 7GA Tel: (01224) 724212 Fax: (01224) 724282 E-mail: information@rigserv.com *Drilling instruments manufrs*

▶ Rika Telephone Equipment, 170-172 Honeypot Lane, Stanmore, Middlesex, HA7 1EE Tel: (020) 8204 5400 Fax: (020) 8206 1815 E-mail: ameed@rika.co.uk *Small business support*

Riker Ltd, Unit 12 Boat House Meadow, Salisbury, SP2 7LD Tel: (01722) 333153 Fax: (01722) 333139 *Power electronics*

▶ Rikz International, Kierbeck Business Complex, North Woolwich Road, London, E16 2BG Tel: (020) 7474 7526 Fax: (020) 7474 7526

Riley Engineering Ltd, Ellifoot Lane, Burstwick, Hull, HU12 9EF Tel: (01964) 670993 Fax: (01964) 670532 E-mail: enquiries@rileyengineering.co.uk *Structural fabricators*

Riley Industries Ltd, 152 Wellhead Lane, Birmingham, B42 2SY Tel: 0121-356 2020 Fax: 0121-356 1117 E-mail: sales@rileyindustries.co.uk *Merchant supplying the finishing industry*

▶ Jon Riley Furniture, Moores Farmhouse, Corse Lawn, Gloucester, GL19 4LY Tel: (01452) 781074 E-mail: enquiries@jon-riley.co.uk *Handcrafted kitchens & furniture manufrs*

Riley (Lifting Equipment) Ltd, Britannia House, Greenfield Rd, Colne, Lancashire, BB8 9PD Tel: (01282) 867177 Fax: (01282) 863698 E-mail: sales@superclamp.co.uk *Lifting gear manufrs*

Riley Metal Works Ltd, 23 Yorkshire Road, London, E14 7LR Tel: (020) 7790 3597 *Sheet metalwork engineers*

Riley Product Handling Ltd, Unit 2b, Meteor Business Park Mansfield Ro, Derby, DE21 4ST Tel: (01332) 866000 Fax: (01332) 866127 E-mail: paolo.graziani@rileyproducthandling.com *Manufacturers of conveyor systems vibratory & materials handling equipment. Global suppliers to blue chip food processing industry.*

Rileys Crane Hire, Grove House, Cloford, Frome, Somerset, BA11 4PH Tel: (01373) 836366 *Crane hire services*

Rillatech Ltd, Callywhite Lane, Dronfield, Derbyshire, S18 2XP Tel: (01246) 291488 Fax: (01246) 291227 *Food packaging materials manufrs*

▶ Rilmac Fabrication Ltd, Crofton Drive, Allenby Road Industrial Estate, Lincoln, LN3 4NJ Tel: (01522) 531711 Fax: (01522) 510291 E-mail: enquiries@rilmac.co.uk *Metal engineers*

▶ Rilmac Insulation Ltd, Crofton Drive, Allenby Road Industruial Estate, Lincoln, LN3 4NJ Tel: (01522) 531711 Fax: (01522) 510291 E-mail: enquiries@rilmac.co.uk *Thermal insulation manufrs*

▶ Rilmac Scaffold Scunthorpe Ltd, Brigg Road, Scunthorpe, South Humberside, DN16 1AX Tel: (01724) 845888 Fax: (01724) 876005 E-mail: enquiries@rilmac.co.uk *Scaffolding*

▶ Rilmac Scaffolding Ltd, Crofton Drive, Lincoln, LN3 4NJ Tel: (01522) 531711 Fax: (01522) 781444 E-mail: enquiries@rilmac.co.uk *Holdings*

▶ Rilmac Scaffolding Ltd, Crofton Drive, Allenby Road Industrial Estate, Lincoln, LN3 4NJ Tel: 01522 531711 Fax: 01522 510291 E-mail: enquiries@rilmac.co.uk *Scaffolding contractors*

▶ Rilmac Scaffolding Ltd, Brigg Road, Scunthorpe, North Lincolnshire, DN16 1AX Tel: (01724) 845888 Fax: (01724) 876005 E-mail: enquiries@rilmac.co.uk *Scaffolding*

Rim Plastics Technology Ltd, 1 Wollaston Way, Burnt Mills Industrial Estate, Basildon, Essex, SS13 1DJ Tel: (01268) 729679 Fax: (01268) 729031 E-mail: sales@rimplas.co.uk *Injection mould toolmakers*

Rimco Services, 20 Orchard Road, Malton, North Yorkshire, YO17 7BH Tel: (01653) 600707 Fax: (01653) 600707 E-mail: sales@rimco.co.uk *Polypropylene slatted flooring manufrs*

Rimer-Alco Ltd, Cardiff Bay Business Centre, Titan Road, Cardiff, CF24 5EJ Tel: (029) 2049 9969 Fax: (029) 2049 2223 E-mail: rimer@rimeralco.co.uk *Oxygen concentrators & gas driers manufrs*

Rimex Metals, Aden Road, Ponders End, Enfield, Middlesex, EN3 7SU Tel: (020) 8804 0633 Fax: (020) 8804 7275 E-mail: sales@rimexmetals.com Principal Export Areas: Worldwide *Sheet metal patterning services*

Rimington Solutions Ltd, The Vine, St David Street, Presteigne, Powys, LD8 2BP Tel: (01544) 260098 Fax: (0870) 7053329 E-mail: enquiries@rimington.co.uk *Computer consultants*

Rimington-Vian, 1 Emtres Mews, Camblewell, London, SE5 9BT Tel: (020) 7733 4441 Fax: (020) 7733 4441 E-mail: post@rimingtonvian.co.uk *Glassware designer & manufrs*

Rimparts, 249 Gladstone Road, Barry, Vale of Glamorgan, CF63 1NJ Tel: (01446) 732849 Fax: (01446) 732849 *Plastic component development & manufacture of bowls*

Rimstock plc, Church Lane, West Bromwich, West Midlands, B71 1BY Tel: 0121-525 2525 Fax: 0121-553 1083 *Manufacturers of aluminium wheels*

▶ Rimtex Ltd, 8-9 Lawson Street, North Shields, Tyne & Wear, NE29 6TF Tel: 0191-257 6400 Fax: 0191-259 5006 E-mail: scottmack@btconnect.com *Clothing manufrs*

Ring Containers Ltd, 1 Southern Cross, London Road, Swanley, Kent, BR8 8DE Tel: (01322) 615302 Fax: (01322) 614931 *Container manufrs*

Ring Group Ltd, Nina Works, Gelderd Road, Leeds, LS12 6NB Tel: 0113-276 7676 Fax: 0113-263 0475 E-mail: enquiries@ring.ltd.uk *Light fitting distributors*

Ring Group Ltd, Nina Works, Gelderd Road, Leeds, LS12 6NB Tel: 0113-276 7676 Fax: 0113-263 0475 E-mail: enquiries@ring.ltd.uk *Domestic lighting suppliers & manufrs*

Ring Mounts Ltd, 88-90 Hatton Garden, London, EC1N 8PN Tel: (020) 7405 9366 Fax: (020) 7430 0139 E-mail: info@ringmounts.co.uk *Manufacturing jewellers*

Ringdale UK Ltd, 26 Victoria Way, Burgess Hill, West Sussex, RH15 9NF Tel: (01444) 871349 Fax: (01444) 870228 E-mail: sales@ringdale.com *Computer peripheral equipment distributors & agents*

▶ Ringland Construction Ltd, 3a High Street, Dronfield, Derbyshire, S18 1PX Tel: (01246) 290260 Fax: (01246) 290760

Ringlink Scotland Ltd, New Elgin Road, Elgin, Morayshire, IV30 6BE Tel: (01343) 550123 Fax: (01343) 551665 *Agriculture co-operative & machinery contractors*

Ringlink Scotland Ltd, 10 High Street, Laurencekirk, Kincardineshire, AB30 1AE Tel: (01561) 378231 Fax: (01561) 378231 *Agricultural engineers*

▶ Ringprop plc, Haslar Road, Gosport, Hampshire, PO12 2AU Tel: (023) 9233 5788 Fax: (023) 9233 5787 E-mail: info@ringprop.com *Marine Propeller Manufacture*

▶ Ringready Ltd, 353-355 Old Durham Road, Gateshead, Tyne & Wear, NE9 5LA Tel: 0191-490 1494

Ringtag International, 50 Whitehall Street, Rochdale, Lancashire, OL12 0LN Tel: (01706) 354854 Fax: (01706) 712181 E-mail: ring_tag@onetel.com *Clothing & textile manufrs*

Ringtel Electronics (UK) Ltd, Ringtel House, Lakeview, Llantarnam Industrial Park, Cwmbran, Gwent, NP44 3HP Tel: (01633) 489550 Fax: (01633) 489570 E-mail: sales@ringtel.com *Telecommunication components*

Ringway Blinds, PO Box 72, Cheadle, Cheshire, SK8 3DA Tel: 0161-437 4419 *Blind suppliers*

▶ Ringway Highway Services, St. Michaels Close, Aylesford, Kent, ME20 7TZ Tel: (01622) 882274 Fax: (01622) 790987

▶ Ringway Highway Services, Stanton House, Stanton Way, Huntingdon, Cambridgeshire, PE29 6PY Tel: (01480) 434365 Fax: (01480) 433282

▶ Ringway Signs Ltd, Twenty Twenty Industrial Estate, St. Laurence Avenue, Allington, Maidstone, Kent, ME16 0LL Tel: (01622) 693476 Fax: (01622) 685992

Ringway Signs Ltd, Winterstoke Road, Weston-super-Mare, Avon, BS24 9BQ Tel: (01934) 421400 Fax: (01934) 421401 E-mail: signs@ringway.co.uk *Road marking signs*

Ringwood Company Builders, Unit 22 Brookvale Trading Estate, Moor Lane, Birmingham, B6 7AQ Tel: 0121-356 0157 Fax: 0121-344 4867 *Plumbing & electrical installations*

Ringwood Glass, 14 Lions Wood, St. Leonards, Ringwood, Hampshire, BH24 2LU Tel: (01425) 478445 Fax: (01425) 478484 *Glazing contractors, window & conservatory installation*

▶ Ringwood Hydraulics Ltd, 78 Cobham Road, Ferndown Industrial Estate, Wimborne, Dorset, BH21 7RW Tel: (01202) 890401 Fax: (01202) 897713 *Hydraulic cylinder/ram manufacturers, hydraulics repair specialists & on-site hydraulic engineers*

Ringwood Machinery Spares, 16 College Road, Ringwood, Hampshire, BH24 1NX Tel: (01425) 479459 *Machinery parts distributor*

▶ Ringwood Pest Control, 86 Hightown Gardens, Ringwood, Hampshire, BH24 3EJ Tel: (01425) 474111

Ringwood Precision, 2 Millstream Trading Estate, Christchurch Road, Ringwood, Hampshire, BH24 3SA Tel: (01425) 476296 Fax: (01425) 476296 E-mail: ukroy@freenetname.co.uk *Precision engineers, material stock holding steel & plastic*

Rio Tinto P.L.C., 6 St. Jamess Square, London, SW1Y 4LD Tel: (020) 7930 2399 Fax: (020) 7930 3249 E-mail: sales@riotinto.co.uk *Mining company*

Rion Ltd, Rion House, Lowton Way, Hellaby Business Park, Rotherham, South Yorkshire, S66 8RY Tel: (01709) 703703 Fax: (01709) 700880 E-mail: rionltd1@aol.com *Pvc-u joinery manufrs*

Ripca (UK) Ltd, First Fl, Unit 5 Capricorn Centre, Craines Farm Road, Basildon, Essex, SS14 3JJ Tel: (01268) 293020 Fax: (01268) 571852 *Cable distributors*

Ripco Sales, Bulldozer House, New Road, Sheerness, Kent, ME12 1AU Tel: (01795) 660666 Fax: (01795) 661559 E-mail: info@atecoaccess.com *Working platforms, aerial access, articulated vehicle mounted services*

▶ Ripe, Science & Technology Centre Earley Gate, Whiteknights Road, Reading, RG6 6BZ Tel: 0118-935 7316 Fax: 0118-926 7917 E-mail: sales@ripe.org.uk *Graphic design*

Ripley Engineering Ltd, Rankine Road, Basingstoke, Hampshire, RG24 8PP Tel: (01256) 473940 Fax: (01256) 479991 E-mail: services@ripley-eng.co.uk *Precision engineers services*

Ripley Transformers Ltd, Suite 11, Waterside Centre, North Street, Lewes, East Sussex, BN7 2PE Tel: (01273) 475385 Fax: (01273) 477811 E-mail: sales@grandchain.co.uk *Transformer designers & manufrs*

Ripling Engineering Ltd, Globe Mills, Lower Globe Street, Bradford, West Yorkshire, BD8 8JW Tel: (01274) 726727 Fax: (01274) 307772 E-mail: ripling@riplingeng.com *General engineers*

Ripmax Ltd, Ripmax Corner, Green Street, Enfield, Middlesex, EN3 7SJ Tel: (020) 8282 7500 Fax: (020) 8282 7501 E-mail: mail@ripmax.com *Battery assemblies & manufrs*

Ripon Farm Service Ltd, Station Road, Ottringham, Hull, HU12 0BJ Tel: (01964) 622351 Fax: (01964) 624078 E-mail: ottsales@r-f-s.com *Agricultural engineers* Also at: Ripon & Tadcaster

Ripon Farm Services, Dallamires Lane, Ripon, North Yorkshire, HG4 1TT Tel: (01765) 692255 Fax: (01765) 606475 E-mail: sales@riponlandrover.co.uk *Vehicle & agricultural machinery dealers*

Ripon Select Foods Ltd, Dallamires Way North, Ripon, North Yorkshire, HG4 1TL Tel: (01765) 601711 Fax: (01765) 607481 E-mail: ingredients@rsf.co.uk *Sausage, rusk, breadcrumb & batter manufrs*

Rippin Ltd, Unit 38 Thistle Industrial Estate, Church Street, Cowdenbeath, Fife, KY4 8LP Tel: (01383) 518610 Fax: (01383) 513099 *Steel fabricators*

Rippin's Books, 77 Coleman Road, Leicester, LE5 4LE Tel: 0116-246 0044 Fax: 0116-246 0404 *Publish hand made books*

Ripple Group Ltd, Greenacres Road, Oldham, OL4 2AB Tel: 0161-624 8201 Fax: 0161-624 4205 E-mail: info@ripple.co.uk *In-store merchandising equipment & point of purchase*

Ripple Irrigation Ltd, Bow Cottage, Bow Lane, Ripple, Tewkesbury, Gloucestershire, GL20 6EW Tel: (01684) 299371 Fax: (01684) 299371 *Irrigation equipment contractors & manufrs*

▶ Rippleside Metal Works Ltd, Thames Road, Grays, Essex, RM17 6JP Tel: (01375) 383741 Fax: (01375) 391514 *Sheet metal & steel work*

Rippon Cheese Stores, 26 Upper Tachbrook Street, London, SW1V 1SW Tel: (020) 7931 0668 Fax: (020) 7828 2368 *Cheese retailers & wholesale*

▶ Rippon Cutting Tools, Hollingworth Road, Bredbury, Stockport, Cheshire, SK6 2AZ Tel: 0161-430 3660 Fax: 0161-430 3661 E-mail: info@rippontools.co.uk *Press tool punches & cutting tools manufrs*

Rippon Farm Services, Dalesgate Works, Skipton Road, Cross Hills, Keighley, West Yorkshire, BD20 7BX Tel: (01535) 632661 Fax: (01535) 633752 E-mail: sales@r-f-s.com *Agricultural engineers*

▶ Rippon Homes Ltd, Leeming Lane South, Mansfield Woodhouse, Mansfield, Nottinghamshire, NG19 9AQ Tel: (01623) 659000 Fax: (01623) 420807 E-mail: info@ripponhomes.co.uk

Ripponden Carriers Ltd, Oldham Road, Ripponden, Sowerby Bridge, West Yorkshire, HX6 4ED Tel: (01422) 822266 Fax: (01422) 823882 E-mail: info@rippondencarriers.co.uk *Distributors services*

▶ RIS Products Ltd, Prospect Place, Welwyn, Hertfordshire, AL6 9EW Tel: (01438) 840135 Fax: (01438) 716067 E-mail: sales@risproducts.co.uk *Provide people & their pets with all-natural products*

Risborough Agricultural Services Ltd, Woodway, Princes Risborough, Buckinghamshire, HP27 0NN Tel: (01844) 275275 Fax: (01844) 274264 E-mail: sales@risag.com *Agricultural engineers*

▶ Risbridger Engineering Services, 25 Trowers Way, Redhill, RH1 2LH Tel: (0845) 6442323 Fax: (0845) 6442453 E-mail: info@risbridger.com

Risby Air Conditioning Co. Ltd, Princes Road, Bourne End, Buckinghamshire, SL8 5HZ Tel: (01628) 850123 Fax: (01628) 850122 E-mail: info@risby.co.uk *Air conditioning engineers*

Riscr Group, Commerce House, Whitbrook Way, Stakehill Distribution Park, Middleton, Manchester, M24 2SS Tel: 0161-655 5555 Fax: 0161-655 5599 E-mail: sales@riscrgroup.co.uk *Alarm equip distributors & manufrs*

▶ Rise Advanced Cable Systems, Conway House, Tenterfields, Thornhill Road, Dewsbury, West Yorkshire, WF12 9QW Tel: 01924 464343 Fax: 01924 438388 E-mail: sales@rise-uk.com *Rise specialise in prefabricated wiring, connection and control systems for lighting, designed to save time and money on-site*

▶ Rise & Recline Ltd, Leopold Street, Long Eaton, Nottingham, NG10 4QD Tel: 0115-913 3572 Fax: 0115-913 3570 E-mail: info@riseandrecline.co.uk *Furniture for the mobility market distributors*

▶ Rise & Shine, Willow Road, Potton, Sandy, Bedfordshire, SG19 2PP Tel: (01767) 262629 Fax: (01767) 262756 *Beds distributors & manufrs*

Riseborough Refrigeration Service Ltd, 164 Glenroy Street, Roath, Cardiff, CF24 3LA Tel: (029) 2049 6007 Fax: (029) 2049 2409 *Refrigeration services*

Risewood Ltd, 68 Birchwood Road, Lichfield, Staffordshire, WS14 9UW Tel: (01543) 417550 Fax: (01543) 264212 *Road transport, haulage & freight services*

Rishton Welding Co. Ltd, Heys Lane, Great Harwood, Blackburn, BB6 7UA Tel: (01254) 886361 Fax: (01254) 888530 E-mail: mrpilling@btconnect.com *Structural steel engineers*

▶ Risk Assessment & Training, Fire House, 205 West Lake Avenue, Hampton Vale, Peterborough, PE7 8LN Tel: (01733) 247172 Fax: (01733) 247172 E-mail: angliafiresafety@btinternet.com *FIRE RISK ASSESSMENTS, FIRE EXTINGUISHER TRAINING & FIRE WARDEN /MARSHAL COURSES. FIRE RISK ASSESSMENTS carried out. CAMBRIDGE, EAST ANGLIA and UK wide service . All staff ex fire service professionals,30years experience. Qualified Fire Risk assessors. Reasonably priced quotations.*

Risk Factor Solutions Ltd, Units B-C Kemps Farm, London Road, Balcombe, Haywards Heath, West Sussex, RH17 6JH Tel: (01444) 819460 Fax: (01444) 819461 E-mail: info@riskfactor-solutions.com *Computer consultancy*

▶ Risk Management Support, 11 The Street, Chirton, Devizes, Wiltshire, SN10 3QS Tel: (01380) 848170 Fax: (01380) 840152 *Risk management consultancy services*

▶ Riskend Aggregates Ltd, 1 Garrell Avenue, Kilsyth, Glasgow, G65 9PZ Tel: (01236) 823015 Fax: (01236) 823256 E-mail: enquiries@riskend.co.uk *Riskend is a privately owned company established in 1967. The company currently operates two dock facilities on the River Clyde shipping in cargos of quality sands and aggregates, predominantely granite from glensanda quarry. Distribution is then provided to a wide range of customers . Both recycling activities and sand & aggregate sales have grown steadily over recent years and Riskend continues to maintain growth while providing service and quality products to new and existing customers. ***

Riskend Quarry Ltd, 6 Garrell Road, Kilsyth, Glasgow, G65 9JY Tel: (01236) 821486 Fax: (01236) 823256 E-mail: riskendquarry@supanet.com *Quarry operators & ready mix concrete suppliers*

▶ Risktec Solutions, Riverside House, Riverside Drive, Aberdeen, AB11 7LH Tel: (01224) 224454 Fax: (01224) 224455 E-mail: mark.taylor@risktec.co.uk *Independent and specialist safety and risk management consulting company. We assist Clients in major hazard industries and commercial sectors to manage safety and business risk*

Rispond Marine, 6 Craft Village, Balnakeil, Durness, Lairg, Sutherland, IV27 4PT Tel: (01971) 511722 Fax: (01971) 511722 E-mail: rispond@aol.com *Boat builders & repairers*

Ristes Motor Co. Ltd, Gamble Street, Nottingham, NG7 4EY Tel: 0115-978 5834 Fax: 0115-942 4351 E-mail: info@ristes.zee-web.co.uk *Vintage car restoration services & manufrs*

Ristretto, Banbridge Enterprise Centre, Scarva Road, Banbridge, County Down, BT32 3QD Tel: (028) 4062 3242 E-mail: mark@ristrettocoffee.com *Freshly roasted speciality coffee, machines and accessories*

Risuda Fabrications Ltd, Hare Street, Hopwood Lane, Halifax, West Yorkshire, HX1 4DJ Tel: (01422) 369782 Fax: (01422) 348251 *Sheet metalwork & stainless steel fabricators*

Ritchey, Fearby Road, Masham, Ripon, North Yorkshire, HG4 4ES Tel: (01765) 689541 Fax: (01765) 689851 E-mail: info@ritchey.co.uk *Moulded plastics products*

▶ Ritchie Electrical, 52 Betty Cocker Grove, Sudbury, Suffolk, CO10 2PL Tel: (01787) 371494 Fax: (01787) 371494 E-mail: ritchiegang@aol.com *Electrical contractor*

Ritchie Hart, 18 Cyprus Avenue, Belfast, BT5 5NT Tel: (028) 9065 4594 Fax: (028) 9065 6196 E-mail: ritchie.hart@charity.vfree.com *Lift engineers*

Ritchie Stoke, 315 Hartshill Road, Stoke-on-Trent, ST4 7NR Tel: (01782) 633733 Fax: (01782) 714864 E-mail: sales@ritchies-ltd.com *Catering equipment & hotel ware suppliers*

Ritchie (UK) Ltd, Hurlford Road, Riccarton, Kilmarnock, Ayrshire, KA1 4LA Tel: (01563) 528711 Fax: (01563) 524468 E-mail: sales@ritchie.vir.co.uk *Printers* Also at: Edinburgh & Glasgow

▶ Ritchies Bakery, 1 Falconer Place, Inverurie, Aberdeenshire, AB51 4RN Tel: (01467) 620573

▶ Rite Systems, 43 The Stripe, Stokesley, Middlesbrough, Cleveland, TS9 5PX Tel: (01642) 713140 E-mail: jgreen@ritesystems.com

Ritec Automation, 3 Broad Street, Cannock, Staffordshire, WS11 0DA Tel: (01543) 577331 Fax: (01543) 502816 E-mail: ritec@ukonline.co.uk *Process control & instrumentation manufrs*

Ritec International Ltd, 15 Royal London Estate, West Road, London, N17 0XL Tel: (020) 8885 5155 Fax: (020) 8885 5072 E-mail: admin@ritec.co.uk *Glass coating manufrs*

Ritetrack, Harrowby Business Centre, Harrowby Place, Cardiff, CF10 5GB Tel: (029) 2049 9877 Fax: (029) 2046 2462 *Suppliers of curtain tracks*

▶ Ritetrak Engineering Wales Ltd, Gilfach Farm, Cwmbach, Whitland, Dyfed, SA34 0DN Tel: (01994) 448666 Fax: (01994) 448687

Riteweld Engineering Ltd, Beaumont Road, Banbury, Oxfordshire, OX16 1RH Tel: 01295 250995 Fax: 01295 273505 E-mail: doug@riteweld.fsnet.co.uk *Riteweld Engineering Banbury, Oxfordshire, UK Welding and fabrication specialists. Based in Banbury Oxfordshire providing Fire Escapes, Staircases, structural steelwork, Architectural Metalwork, Hand Rails, Balustrades and all your Engineering needs.*

Ritherdon & Co. Ltd, Lorne Street, Darwen, Lancashire, BB3 1QW Tel: (01254) 819100 Fax: (01254) 819101 E-mail: info@ritherdon.co.uk *Sheet metalwork & metal finishing*

Ritrama UK Ltd, Lynwell Road, Lyntown Trading Estate, Eccles, Manchester, M30 9QG Tel: 0161-786 1700 Fax: 0161-786 1701 E-mail: info@ritrama.co.uk *Ritrama, an international group of companies dedicated to the world-wide manufacture of specialty and commodity self-adhesive materials.*

Ritter Courivaud Ltd, Unit 4 Westlinks, Alperton Lane, Wembley, Middlesex, HA0 1ER Tel: (020) 8991 4350 Fax: (020) 8991 4383 E-mail: sales@rittercourivaud.co.uk *Fine food distributors*

Ritz Software Ltd, 139 High Street, Farnborough, Orpington, Kent, BR6 7AZ Tel: (01689) 860444 Fax: (01689) 856234 E-mail: sales@ritzaccounts.co.uk *Write software for accounts & sales*

Riva Consulting Ltd, Chedeham House, Cot Lane, Chichester, West Sussex, PO18 8ST Tel: (01243) 575955 Fax: (01243) 575966 E-mail: sales@riva-consulting.com *Computer consultants services*

▶ Riva Financial Systems, Old Chapple, Main Road, Union Mills, Isle of Man, IM4 4AD Tel: (01624) 853712 Fax: (01624) 853712 E-mail: sales@revafs.com *Computer software developers*

▶ Rival, 116 West Street, Faversham, Kent, ME13 7JB Tel: (01795) 590473 E-mail: sales@rivaldancewear.co.uk *Dancewear and schoolwear retailers with online shopping facility specialising in gymnastics,ballet,tap,latin, ballroom and irish dancing selling shoes from Arabesque,Antonio Pacelli,Supadance and Roch Valley.*We also supply many schools with schoolwear from Banner,Rowlinson and Zeco.*

Rivendale Systems Ltd, The Old Bakery, North End, Newbury, Berkshire, RG20 0AY Tel: (01635) 254464 Fax: (01635) 255359 E-mail: enquiries@rivendale.co.uk *Computer software development services*

▶ Rivendell UK Ltd, Unit 21 Bonville Business Centre, Bonville Road, Bristol, BS4 5QR Tel: 0117-977 2550 Fax: 0117-977 2530

Charles River Laboratories, Tranent, East Lothian, EH33 2NE Tel: (01875) 614545 Fax: (01875) 614555 *Contract research organisation consumer products*

Charles River UK Ltd, Manston Road, Margate, Kent, CT9 4LT Tel: (01843) 823388 Fax: (01843) 823497 E-mail: enquiries@uk.criver.com *Bio medical research produce systems*

▶ River Communications, 9 The Terrace, Woodford Green, Essex, IG8 0XS Tel: (020) 8504 4009 Fax: (020) 8504 4454 E-mail: info@river-communications.com *Public relations, marketing & event management travel & lifestyle services*

River Island Clothing Co. Ltd, Chelsea House, Westgate, London, W5 1DR Tel: (020) 8991 4500 *Clothing manufrs*

River Plate Shipping & Trading Agency Ltd, Ingersol House, 9 Kingsway, London, WC2B 6XF Tel: (020) 7836 1155 Fax: (020) 7836 9922 *Shipping agents & exporters*

River Road Foundry Ltd, Weavers House, 10 New Road, Mistley, Manningtree, Essex, CO11 2AG Tel: (08700) 001118 Fax: (08700) 001540 E-mail: fq34@dial.pipex.com *Ferrous & non-ferrous founders*

River Stone Clothing, 44 River St, Birmingham, B5 5SA Tel: 0121-766 8921 *Clothing manufr*

River Street Glassworks, Bridgeman Street, Bolton, BL3 6BS Tel: (01204) 454444 Fax: (01204) 454445 *Glass merchants & glazing contractors*

River Tees Engineering & Welding Ltd, Slipways, Normanby Wharf, Middlesbrough, Cleveland, TS3 8AT Tel: (01642) 226226 Fax: (01642) 245544 E-mail: river-tees@the-slipways.fsnet.co.uk *Heavy & marine engineers*

Riverdale Hall Hotel, Bellingham, Hexham, Northumberland, NE48 2JT Tel: (01434) 220254 Fax: (01434) 220457 E-mail: reservations@riverdalehallhotel.co.uk *Hotel*

Riverdale Mahoney Ltd, Unit 3 Dicker Mill, Hertford, SG13 7AE Tel: (01992) 583988 Fax: (01992) 583988 E-mail: riverdalema@btinternet.com *Sheet metalwork engineers*

Riverdele Paper plc, Earlsway, Team Valley Trading Estate, Gateshead, Tyne & Wear, NE11 0RQ Tel: 0191-482 4271 Fax: 0191-482 4214 E-mail: info@riverdalepaper.co.uk *Security shredding services*

Riverfarm Smokery Shop, Wilbraham Road, Bottisham, Cambridge, CB25 9BU Tel: (01223) 812577 Fax: (01223) 812319 *Food smokery*

▶ Riverford Home Delivery, 20 Deepdene Road, London, SE5 8EG Tel: (020) 7738 5076 Fax: (020) 7738 5076 *Riverford Home Delivery are a organic veg box scheme, including many organic extras. Delivery is free to customers homes in the Bromley & Croydon area.*

▶ Riverhall Systems, Warnford Court, 29 Throgmorton Street, London, EC2N 2AT Tel: (0870) 3210034 E-mail: andrew@riverhall.co.uk *Bespoke software development & consultancy*

Riverlea Construction Equipment, Millfield, Whitland, Dyfed, SA34 0QQ Tel: (01994) 240965 Fax: (01994) 240285 E-mail: paul.a@riverlea.co.uk *Dealer for new & used construction machinery*

Riverlea Tractors Ltd, Riverlea, Crymych, Dyfed, SA41 3QX Tel: (01239) 831733 Fax: (01239) 831668 E-mail: sales@riverlea.co.uk *Agricultural machinery & equipment*

Riverlea Tractors Ltd, Millfield, Whitland, Dyfed, SA34 0QQ Tel: (01994) 240644 Fax: (01994) 240747 E-mail: sales@riverlea.co.uk *Agricultural machinery sales*

Rivermeade Signs Ltd, Rowley Industrial Park, Roslin Road, London, W3 8BH Tel: (020) 8896 6900 Fax: (020) 8752 1691 E-mail: info@rivermeade.com *Signs manufrs*

Rivermeade Signs Ltd, Rowley Industrial Park, Roslin Road, London, W3 8BH Tel: (020) 8896 6900 Fax: (020) 8752 1691 E-mail: info@rivermeade.com *Designers & installers of custom made signs*

Rivers Engineering Co Winchester Ltd, Moorside Road, Winchester, Hampshire, SO23 7RX Tel: (01962) 865065 Fax: (01962) 840829 E-mail: riveng1@aol.com *Precision engineers*

Riverscape Ltd, Business & Innovation Centre, Wearfield, Sunderland Enterprise Park, Sunderland, SR5 2TA Tel: 0191-516 6456 Fax: 0191-516 6457 E-mail: info@riverscape.co.uk *IT consultants*

Riverside Aquaria, 27 Linden Avenue, Stirling, FK7 7PQ Tel: (01786) 473450 Fax: (01786) 470843 *Aquarium suppliers*

Riverside At Branston, Riverside Drive, Branston, Burton-on-Trent, Staffordshire, DE14 3EP Tel: (01283) 511234 Fax: (01283) 511441 E-mail: riverside.branston@oldenglishinns.co.uk *Hotel with conference facilities*

Riverside Automation Ltd, 103 Carlisle St East, Sheffield, S4 8DQ Tel: 0114-270 1997 Fax: 0114-270 1998 E-mail: kcowley@zoom.co.uk *Control panels & systems manufrs*

Riverside Automation Ltd, 61 Wostenholm Road, Sheffield, S7 1LE Tel: 0114-255 5500 Fax: 0114-255 5505 E-mail: sales@riverauto.co.uk *Process control & automation engineers*

Riverside Balloons Ltd, 1 Whirlowdale Crescent, Millhouses Sheffield, Sheffield, S7 2NA Tel: 0114-262 1860 Fax: 0114-225 7446 *Childrens rides operators*

Riverside Blinds, 284 Park Road, Toxteth, Liverpool, L8 4UE Tel: 0151-283 5600 Fax: 0151-283 0998 *Vertical blind manufrs*

Riverside Engineering Services Ltd, Prince Charles Wharf, Stannergate Road, Dundee, DD1 3NA Tel: (01382) 450099 Fax: (01382) 450088 E-mail: enquiries@resl.co.uk *Steel & pipework fabricators*

Riverside Financial Management, Cutter House, Woodrolfe Road, Tollesbury, Maldon, Essex, CM9 8SE Tel: (01621) 860700 Fax: (01621) 860400 E-mail: info@riverside-financial.co.uk *Independent financial advisors*

Riverside Group, Tondu Road, Bridgend, Mid Glamorgan, CF31 4JA Tel: (01656) 656541 Fax: (01656) 662077 E-mail: emma@riverequip.co.uk *Air conditioning installators*

Riverside Hardware & Engineers Supplies, North Road, Bridgend Industrial Estate, Bridgend, Mid Glamorgan, CF31 3TP Tel: (01656) 662449 Fax: (01656) 768375 *Engineers supplies*

Riverside Joinery Co. Ltd, Barker Street, Norwich, NR2 4TN Tel: (01603) 624858 Fax: (01603) 614924 *Bespoke joinery services*

Riverside Motors Selby Ltd, Maltings Yard, Ousegate, Selby, North Yorkshire, YO8 8BL Tel: (01757) 704999 Fax: (01757) 704999 *Car body repairs & refinishers*

Riverside Office Supplies, 1 Apex Centre, Clywedog Road South, Wrexham Industrial Estate, Wrexham, Clwyd, LL13 9XS Tel: (01978) 660066 Fax: (01978) 661767 *Office furniture suppliers*

▶ Riverside Packaging Printers Ltd, Roughmoor, Williton Industrial Estate, Taunton, Somerset, TA4 4RF Tel: (01984) 631757 Fax: (01984) 635910 E-mail: sales@rppl.co.uk *Flexible products packaging & waxed paper*

Riverside Pine, 3 Pingle Farm, Seine Lane, Enderby, Leicester, LE19 4PD Tel: 0116-284 1737 *Pine retail & manufrs*

Riverside Precision Products Ltd, Riverside Industrial Estate, Bridge Road, Littlehampton, West Sussex, BN17 5DF Tel: (01903) 732570 Fax: (01903) 732778 E-mail: enquiries@riverside-precision.co.uk *Precision engineers*

▶ Riverside Press Ltd, 14-15 Riverside Industrial Park, Rapier Street, Ipswich, IP2 8JX Tel: (01473) 687679 Fax: (01473) 687690

Riverside Printing Co., 90 Wallis Road, London, E9 5LN Tel: (020) 8986 5123 Fax: (020) 8986 4776 *Lithographic printers*

Riverside Screen Print Ltd, 59-61 Blundell Street, Liverpool, L1 0AJ Tel: 0151-709 0421 Fax: 0151-708 7257 *Screen printers & printing services*

Riverside Smoked Foods Ltd, Frizington Industrial Estate, Frizington, Cumbria, CA26 3QY Tel: (01946) 817000 Fax: (01946) 818939 E-mail: sales@riverside-smoked-foods.co.uk *Smoked foods producers*

▶ Riverside Studios, Four Horse Shoes Yard, Milnsbridge, Huddersfield, HD3 4NE Tel: (01484) 642131 E-mail: contact@riversidestudios.info *Recording & Rehearsal Studios**1200 FT2 24 Track digital recording studio,seperate live room, drum & vocal booths. Experienced engineers.**Custom built rehearsal studios.*All inc- digital mixers, huge P.A"s, mic"s, lighting rigs, stages,sofa"s.*Snacks & refreshments, equipment spares shop, huge individual lockers, quality full backline, ground floor, private carpark*

Riverstone Management Ltd, 66 Mark Lane, London, EC3R 7HS Tel: (020) 7977 1600 Fax: (020) 7977 1610 *Underwriters* Also at: Brighton

Riverstone Spinning Ltd, Ravensthorpe Mill, Huddersfield Road, Ravensthorpe, Dewsbury, West Yorkshire, WF13 3NA Tel: (01924) 462182 Fax: (01924) 461626 *Carpet yarn spinners & dyers*

Rivertrace Engineering Ltd, P Kingsfield Business Centre, Philanthropic Road, Redhill, RH1 4DP Tel: (0870) 7702721 Fax: (0870) 7702722 E-mail: info@rivertrace.com Principal Export Areas: Worldwide *Oil-in-water monitoring instrument manufrs*

Riverway Building & Signage Ltd, Riverway, Trowbridge, Wiltshire, BA14 8LL Tel: (01225) 760131 Fax: (01225) 777207 E-mail: mail@riverwaywilts.co.uk *Signwriters*

▶ Rivet Software, 16 Lynton Road, New Malden, Surrey, KT3 5EE Tel: 020 7043 8603 E-mail: bill.seddon@rivetsoftware.com *We represent Rivet Software in Europe. Rivet are the authors of Dragon Tag, the XBRL enabler, which is an easy to use Microsoft Office(R)-based solution that takes the complexity out of converting financial statements to industry standard XBRL documents.*

Rivetnut Technology Systems Ltd, 5 Bridgegate Business Park, Gatehouse Way, Gatehouse Industrial Area, Aylesbury, Buckinghamshire, HP19 8XN Tel: (01296) 330331 Fax: (01296) 331018 E-mail: sales@rivetnut.com *Rivet, nut & fastener solutions*

Rivfast Ltd, Unit 23 Bordesley Trading Estate, Bordesley Green Road, Birmingham, B8 1BZ Tel: 0121-359 4500 Fax: 0121-359 4501 E-mail: mark@rivfast.co.uk *Eyelet & rivet distributors or agents. Also riveting machine & rivet manufrs*

Riviera Blinds, The Maisonette, 58 St. Albans Road, Lytham St. Annes, Lancashire, FY8 1XD Tel: (01253) 726843 Fax: (01253) 726843 E-mail: info@blindsandawnings.co.uk *Blind distributors & manufrs*

Riviera Signs Ltd, 2 104 Barton Road, Torquay, TQ2 7NY Tel: (01803) 324303 Fax: (01803) 314105 E-mail: sales@rivierasigns.co.uk *Lettering & sign services*

Rixon Matthews Appleyard Ltd, Exchange Court, Lowgate, Hull, HU1 1XW Tel: (01482) 327605 Fax: (01482) 217184 E-mail: sales@rixon-insurance.co.uk *Insurance brokers & independent finacial advisers*

Rixonway Kitchens Ltd, Churwell Vale, Shaw Cross Business Park, Dewsbury, West Yorkshire, WF12 7RD Tel: (01924) 431300 Fax: (01924) 431301 E-mail: sales@rixonway.co.uk *Kitchen manufrs*

Rixonway Kitchens Ltd, Churwell Vale, Shaw Cross Business Park, Dewsbury, West Yorkshire, WF12 7RD Tel: (01924) 431300 Fax: (01924) 431301 E-mail: sales@rixonway.co.uk *Kitchen units manufrs*

Rizla UK Ltd, Severn Road, Treforest Industrial Estate, Pontypridd, Mid Glamorgan, CF37 5SP Tel: (01443) 841641 Fax: (01443) 841138 *Cigarette paper manufrs*

▶ RJ Haulage, 15 Kingscote Road, Croydon, CR0 7DP Tel: 079 32156627 E-mail: roger@rjhaulage.co.uk *South London"s friendliest removal and delivery service. We can help with anything from a home relocation to a single item removal. Call 07932156627 for a competitive quote.*

RJH Morrisflex Holdings Ltd, Artillery Street, Heckmondwike, West Yorkshire, WF16 0NR Tel: (01924) 402490 Fax: (01924) 404635 E-mail: sales@rjheng.co.uk *Grinding & polishing machine makers*

RJM Sports Ltd, 54 Cow Wynd, Falkirk, FK1 1PU Tel: (01324) 873804 Fax: (01324) 873804 E-mail: sales@rjmsports.co.uk *Supplier of all types of sports *equipment*

RJN Chemicals Ltd, 6 The Ridgeway, Iver, Buckinghamshire, SL0 9HX Tel: (01753) 655076 Fax: (01753) 652983 E-mail: info@rjnchemicals.com *Concentrated cleaning products suppliers*

▶ RJS Ascot Ltd, 8 Beechwood Close, Ascot, Berkshire, SL5 8QJ Tel: (01344) 890442 Fax: (01344) 883685 E-mail: rjsascot@aol.com *Electrical & mechanical engineers & contractors*

▶ RJT Consultancy, 6 The Oaks, Kitlings Lane, Stafford, ST17 0LE Tel: (01785) 660000 Fax: (01785) 660000 *Agricultural consultants*

RK Print Coat Instruments Ltd, Abington Road, Litlington, Royston, Hertfordshire, SG8 0QZ Tel: (01763) 852187 Fax: (01763) 852502 E-mail: sales@rkprint.com *Sell & manufacture laboratory test equipment*

Rka Services Ltd, Unit 25, Stevenage Enterprise Centre Orc, Stevenage, Hertfordshire, SG1 3HH Tel: (01438) 361888 *Window control systems installers*

RLH Developments, 3 Coombe Avenue, Croydon, CR0 5SD Tel: (020) 8681 8811 Fax: (020) 8666 0147 E-mail: info@rlhdevelopments.co.uk *Damp proofing & timber treatment*

▶ RM Alderton Designs Ltd, 5 Temple Bar Business Park, Strettington, Chichester, West Sussex, PO18 0TU Tel: (0870) 754 2665 Fax: (0870) 622 0445 E-mail: sales@rmalderton.com *Product & tool design consultancy*

▶ R-M C Power Recovery Ltd, Unit 6, Stamford Business Park, Ryhall Road, Stamford, Lincolnshire, PE9 1XT Tel: (01780) 762555 Fax: (01780) 762599 *Manufacture of performance enhancing cleaning chemicals*

RM Hydraulics, Station Street, Leek, Staffordshire, ST13 8BP Tel: (01538) 399980 Fax: (01538) 388869 *Hydraulic engineering specialists*

▶ RM Security, 42 Waldeck Road, Dartford, DA1 1UA Tel: (01322) 281274 E-mail: info@rmsecurity.co.uk *CCTV, access control & door entry specialists*

▶ RMA UK, 23 Westcroft Square, Stamford Brook, London, W6 0TD Tel: (0871) 2262207 Fax: (0871) 2262208 E-mail: imkisa@routemasterassociates.com *The aim is to provide clients with a single, comprehensive source of specialist knowledge, methodologies and experience supported through cost effective and manageable services and solutions to enable the effective deployment of management, people, computerised, manual or hybrid solutions to meet specific objectives*

RMB Hydroseeding, Lower Wick Farm, Lower Wick, Dursley, Gloucestershire, GL11 6DD Tel: (01453) 511365 Fax: (01453) 511364 E-mail: info@hydroseeding.co.uk *RMB Hydroseeding specialists in hydroseeding/ Hydraseeding have over 35 years experience in the industry. Our services include Hydraulic Mulch Seeding, Erosion Control, Landscapes, Land Restoration, Land Stabilisation, Seeding, Hessian Blankets, Wild Flower Seeding, Direct Tree Seeding, Hydraulic Seeding, Grass, aquaseeders & commercial landscaping. RMB Hydroseeding operates throughout the United Kingdom and Ireland from bases in Gloucestershire, South Wales and West Yorkshire. RMB Hydroseeding are an established landscaping firm offering a complete landscaping service covering all aspects of construction and maintenance. Contracts previously undertaken range from land reclamation to road, railway and major civil engineering projects. Our belief in commitment to quality in all aspects of our work has resulted in the rapid growth of our client and contract portfolio and has lead to the completion of many hydroseeding projects.*

RMC, Twechar, Kilsyth, Glasgow, G65 9TW Tel: (01236) 822461 Fax: (01236) 825249 E-mail: admin@rmc.co.uk *Precast concrete blocks*

RMC Aggregates Eastern Ltd, Dowding Road, Lincoln, LN3 4PN Tel: (01522) 540721 Fax: (01522) 576438 *Road surfacing contractors*

RMC Concrete Products UK Ltd, Shap, Penrith, Cumbria, CA10 3QQ Tel: (01931) 716444 Fax: (01931) 716617 *Concrete*

RMC Readymix East Anglia, R M C House, Whitehall Road, Colchester, CO2 8HD Tel: (01206) 862222 Fax: (01206) 860768 E-mail: enqiries.readymix.eastanglia@rmc.co.uk *Ready mixed concrete & mortar*

RMC Readymix Eastern, Lock Keepers Cottage, Langford Lane, Kidlington, Oxfordshire, OX5 1HT Tel: (01865) 372424 Fax: (01865) 842303 *Concrete suppliers*

RMC Readymix Southwest Ltd, Haye Quarry, Stag Lane, Plymouth, PL9 8AX Tel: (01208) 74321 *Concrete manufrs*

RMC Readymix Western, Hawkesworth Trading Estate, Swindon, SN2 1EF Tel: (01793) 525190 Fax: (01793) 692562 *Ready mixed concrete manufrs*

▶ RMC Services Ltd, Cornerways House, School Lane, Ringwood, Hampshire, BH24 1LG Tel: (01425) 654467 *Construction services*

RMC South East Ltd, Aylesford Sand Pit, Rochester Road, Aylesford, Kent, ME20 7DX Tel: (01622) 716904 Fax: (01622) 882462 *Building suppliers*

RMC South East, Gravel Pit, Snails Lane, Blashford, Ringwood, Hampshire, BH24 3PG Tel: (01425) 478396 Fax: (01425) 478396 *Ready mixed concrete distributors*

▶ RMD Contracts, 4 Outram Road, Dukinfield, Cheshire, SK16 4XE Tel: 0161-339 9910 Fax: 0161-343 2015 E-mail: info@rmdcontracts.com

▶ Rmig Ltd, 1-2 Adlington Court, Risley Road, Birchwood, Warrington, WA3 6PL Tel: (01925) 839600 Fax: (01925) 826326 E-mail: info.uk@rmig.com Purchasing Contact: H. McLay Sales Contact: K.A. Johnson *RMIG is the largest perforator in the world. We offer a wide range of perforation patterns in a wide range of materials and we also offer related products.*

RMJM Scotland Ltd, 10 Bells Brae, Dean Village, Edinburgh, EH4 3BJ Tel: 0131-225 2532 Fax: 0131-226 5117 E-mail: info@rmjm.com *Architects & civil engineers*

▶ RMK Portable Appliance Testing Ltd, 51 Kings Drive, Hassocks, West Sussex, BN6 8DY Tel: (01444) 870885 Fax: (01444) 230999 E-mail: sales@rmk-pat.co.uk *Portable electrical appliance testing*

RMM Distribution Ltd, 5 Greets Green Road Industrial Estate, Greets Green Road, West Bromwich, West Midlands, B70 9EW Tel: 0121-520 5938 Fax: 0121-557 3089

continued

continuation
E-mail: sales@wb-fast.demon.co.uk *Janitorial disposable product distributor*

RMR Control & Automation, 2 Denington Court, Denington Industrial Estate, Wellingborough, Northamptonshire, NN8 2QR Tel: (01933) 441110 Fax: (01933) 441130 E-mail: sales@rmr.co.uk *General engineers*

▶ RMS Technical Services, 8 Sandwick Close, Fulwood, Preston, PR2 9RZ Tel: 01772 721310 E-mail: info@rmstechnical.co.uk *RMS Technical Services is a consultancy specialising in BRC Accreditation, the Auditing and Designing of Technical Systems and HACCP"s for the Food and Beverage Industries**We can provide*Technical advice on quality systems*BRC Accreditation, Training, Design and Auditing*Basic Food Hygiene Training and Examination*HACCP Design, Development, Analisys, Training and Auditing*

▶ Rmuk Ltd, 100 Morgan Close, Willenhall, West Midlands, WV12 4LH Tel: (01902) 602333 Fax: (01902) 602335 *Garment manufrs*

▶ RMXdirect Ltd, Unit , George Business Park, Cemetery Road, Southport, Merseyside, PR8 5EF Tel: (020) 7870 7179 E-mail: paul@rmxdirect.co.uk *Online UK shop for Rimax products.*

RNG Agdrive Ltd, Unit 5-6 Linton Trading Estate, Worcester Road, Bromyard, Herefordshire, HR7 4QT Tel: (01885) 483662 Fax: (01885) 482080 E-mail: rng@eur-ist.co.uk *Agricultural components suppliers*

Ro Dor Ltd, Stevens Drove, Houghton, Stockbridge, Hampshire, SO20 6LP Tel: (01794) 388080 Fax: (01794) 388090 E-mail: info@ro-dor.co.uk *Roller shutter door manufrs*

Ro Co Engineering Services, Unit 8 Sinclair Court, Great Yarmouth, Norfolk, NR31 0NH Tel: (01493) 602744 Fax: (01493) 658450 *Structural fabricators*

Roach Bros Ltd, Havelock Street, Hull, HU3 4JH Tel: (01482) 324838 Fax: (01482) 219050 E-mail: roachbrosltd@yhoo.co.uk *Fish curers*

▶ Roach Bros Ltd, 129 Woodcote Road, Wallington, Surrey, SM6 0QD Tel: (020) 8647 1740 Fax: (020) 8669 8149

▶ Roach Foods, West Side, Newport Industrial Estate, Launceston, Cornwall, PL15 8EX Tel: (01566) 773326

Roach Manufacturing Ltd, Off Whitemoor Lane, Ower, Romsey, Hampshire, SO51 6AJ Tel: (023) 8081 4287 Fax: (023) 8081 3970 *Vintage & classic car body manufrs*

Roach Pumps Ltd, Rotten Row Farm, Hambleden, Henley-on-Thames, Oxfordshire, RG9 6NB Tel: (01491) 410716 Fax: (01491) 410718 E-mail: roachpumps@aol.com *Hand pump sales & distributors*

Roaches 4 Tackle, Bridge Hill, Stainforth, Doncaster, South Yorkshire, DN7 5JE Tel: (01302) 844688 *Fishing tackle retailers*

Roaches International Ltd, Upperhulme, Leek, Staffordshire, ST13 8TY Tel: (01538) 300425 Fax: (01538) 300364 E-mail: info@roaches.co.uk *Textile laboratory machines manufrs*

▶ Road Cases, Unit 15b Clarence Works, Effingham Road, Sheffield, S4 7YS Tel: 0114-272 8666 Fax: 0114-272 8666 E-mail: ian@road-cases.com *Flyt case manufrs*

Road Cool Refrigeration Ltd, Unit 17-18 Sandybridge Lane Industrial Estate, Shafton, Barnsley, South Yorkshire, S72 8PH Tel: (01226) 781999 Fax: (01226) 781888 E-mail: sales@roadcoolrefrigeration.co.uk *Transport refrigeration engineers*

Road Equipment Ltd, 32-34 Feltham Road, Ashford, Middlesex, TW15 1DL Tel: (01784) 256565 Fax: (01784) 240398 E-mail: roadequipment@aol.com *Plant hire contractors*

Road Radio Ltd, 41 Station Road, Burgess Hill, West Sussex, RH15 9DE Tel: (01444) 242107 Fax: (01444) 871040 *Car audio, security & alarms*

Road Recruitment, Trioka House 2, East Union Street, Rugby, Warwickshire, CV22 6AJ Tel: (01788) 572841 Fax: (01788) 578609 E-mail: sales@rdrecruit.com *Contract engineers*

Road Research, Research House Norwich Road, Eastgate, Cawston, Norwich, NR10 4HA Tel: (01603) 872331 Fax: (01603) 879010 E-mail: info@looking.co.uk *IT consultants*

Road & Sea Express Ltd, Unit 9 Holmes Chapel Business Park, Manor Lane, Holmes Chapel, Crewe, CW4 8AF Tel: (01477) 536536 Fax: (01477) 536537 E-mail: sales@roadseaexpress.co.uk *Road transport, haulage & freight services*

Road Tankers Northern Ltd, Platts Common Industrial Estate, Barrowfield Road, Hoyland, Barnsley, South Yorkshire, S74 9TH Tel: (01226) 350650 Fax: (01226) 360528 E-mail: suzanne@rtnltd.co.uk *Road tanker manufrs*

▶ Road Traffic Signs, West Coppice Road, Brownhills, Walsall, WS8 7HB Tel: (01543) 377280 Fax: (01543) 373079 E-mail: sullivan.holdings@tiscali.co.uk *Road traffic signs manufrs*

Roadcare Ltd, Roadcare House, New Works Road, Low Moor, Bradford, West Yorkshire, BD12 0RU Tel: (01274) 606770 Fax: (01274) 602802 *Holding company & road marking contractor*

Roadcraft (Crane & Plant Hire) Ltd, 8-18 Strand Road, Bootle, Merseyside, L20 1AN Tel: (0151) 922 4567 Fax: (0151) 922 2396 *Crane hire services* Also at: Liverpool, Stoke-on-Trent & Warrington

▶ Roade IT Training, 23 Abbotts Way, Roade, Northampton, NN7 2LY Tel: (07709) 336819 *IT training services*

Roadferry Ltd, 65 Dargan Road, Belfast, BT3 9JU Tel: (028) 9051 3513 Fax: (028) 9051 3514 E-mail: customer.services@roadferry.co.uk *Road transport, haulage & freight service providers*

Roadferry Ltd, Carr Lane, Leyland, Leyland, PR25 3RD Tel: (01772) 455338 Fax: (01772) 422311 *Logistics provider* Also at: Branches throughout the U.K.

▶ Roadform Civil Engineering Co. Ltd, Roadform House, Milber Trading Estate, Newton Abbot, Devon, TQ12 4SG Tel: (01626) 331564 E-mail: sales@roadform.co.uk

Roadliner International Ltd, Unit 7, Graham Industrial Estate, Belfast, BT3 9LP Tel: (028) 9037 1701 Fax: (028) 9037 1901 E-mail: sales@roadliner.com *Road transport, haulage & freight services*

Roadlink International Ltd, Strawberry Lane, Willenhall, West Midlands, WV13 3RL Tel: (01902) 606210 Fax: (01902) 606604 E-mail: j.darwin@roadlink-international.co.uk *Commercial vehicle components*

Roadmix Ltd, Ballyvesey Road, Newtownabbey, County Antrim, BT36 4SY Tel: (028) 9034 2189 Fax: (028) 9084 8198 *Ready mixed concrete manufrs*

▶ Roadtech Cutting Services, 11 Mount Road, Burntwood, Staffordshire, WS7 0AJ Tel: (01543) 466810 Fax: (01543) 676309

Roadways, Barton Dock Road, Urmston, Manchester, M41 7BQ Tel: 0161-911 5300 Fax: 0161-911 5239 *Freight consolidation services*

Roadways & Car Parks Ltd, 174 Twickenham Road, Isleworth, Middlesex, TW7 7DW Tel: (020) 8560 7211 Fax: (020) 8560 1894 E-mail: reg.havard@roadways.demon.co.uk *Civil engineering contractors services*

Roadways Container Logistics, Box Lane, Renwick Road, Barking, Essex, IG11 0SQ Tel: (020) 8700 4932 Fax: (020) 8700 2163 E-mail: rcl@roadways.co.uk *Cargo handling & customs clearance agents*

Roadways Container Logistics Ltd, Gartsherrie Road, Coatbridge, Lanarkshire, ML5 2DS Tel: (01236) 504700 Fax: (01236) 504730 *Inland container depot & haulage*

Roadways Container Logistics, Valley Farm Way, Leeds, LS10 1SE Tel: 0113-296 8400 Fax: 0113-296 8322 *Freight consolidation services*

Roadwheel Tyre & Exhaust Ltd, 468 London Road, Portsmouth, PO2 9RN Tel: (023) 9269 4741 Fax: (023) 9266 1923 *Car servicing, tyre, exhaust & battery retailers*

▶ Roalco Building Services, 219 Holton Road, Barry, South Glamorgan, CF63 4HR Tel: (01446) 722241 Fax: (01446) 721774

Rob Installations Ltd, 25 Chesterford Green, Basildon, Essex, SS14 3PR Tel: (01268) 522471 Fax: (01268) 286657 *Remote control window installers*

Jack Rob Motors Ltd, East Lane Business Park, 2 Bell Lane, Wembley, Middlesex, HA9 7RB Tel: (020) 8908 5577 Fax: (020) 8904 8515 E-mail: jackrob@motormenu.co.uk *Vehicle body repairers & servicing*

Rob Rowe Livestock Haulage, St. Teath, Bodmin, Cornwall, PL30 3LJ Tel: (01208) 850730 *General hauliers*

▶ Rob Roy Wooden Toys, 81 College Street, Long Eaton, Nottingham, NG10 4NN Tel: 0115-973 3943 E-mail: robroytoy@yahoo.co.uk *Sale & manufacture of quality wooden toys*

Robal Ltd, Station Road, Greenfield, Holywell, Clwyd, CH8 7EL Tel: (01352) 713052 Fax: (01352) 713502 *Steel fabricators*

Roballo Engineering Co. Ltd, 2 Mill Hill, North West Industrial Estate, Peterlee, County Durham, SR8 2HR Tel: (0191) 518 5600 Fax: 0191-586 9096 E-mail: info@roballo.co.uk *Slewing ring, non-standard bearing manufrs*

Roband Electronics plc, Charlwood Works, Lowfield Heath Road, Charlwood, Horley, Surrey, RH6 0BU Tel: (01293) 843000 Fax: (01293) 843001 E-mail: postmaster@roband.co.uk *Power supplies for aircraft manufrs*

Robank Engineering Ltd, Meridian Centre, King Street, Oldham, OL8 1EZ Tel: 0161-633 9126 Fax: 0161-633 9136 E-mail: robank@globalnet.co.uk *Drying, industrial & stoving oven manufrs*

Robant Services Ltd, Unit 24 Mersey Street, Stockport, Cheshire, SK1 2HX Tel: 0161-429 8728 Fax: 0161-474 7630 E-mail: sales@robant.co.uk *Printing & rubber roller specialists*

▶ Robatech UK Ltd, The Street, Broughton Gifford, Melksham, Wiltshire, SN12 8PH Tel: (01225) 783456 Fax: (01225) 783400 E-mail: sales@robatech.co.uk *Packaging equipment*

Robatech UK Ltd, The Street, Broughton Gifford, Melksham, Wiltshire, SN12 8PH Tel: (01225) 783456 Fax: (01225) 783400 E-mail: sales@robatech.co.uk *Distributors of adhesive applications*

▶ Robb Fordyce, Greenburn Tornaveen, Torphins, Banchory, Kincardineshire, AB31 4LL Tel: (01339) 883832 E-mail: john@robb-fordyce.co.uk *Interim Management and Organisational Development Consultancy.**Comprehensive suite of self-assessment business diagnostics including EFQM, Knowledge Management, Collaborative/ Team Based Working, Health and Safety, Quality, and Stress in the workplace.*

Wm. & A.M. Robb Ltd, 84 Cheapside Street, Glasgow, G3 8BE Tel: 0141-221 4631 Fax: 0141-221 2377 E-mail: sales@wmrobb.co.uk *Button & trimmings merchants*

▶ ROBBERS DOG ANIMATION, 3rd FLOOR, 168 VICTORIA STREET, BELGRAVIA, LONDON, SW1E 5LB Tel: 0207 630 6549 Fax: 0207 630 6549 E-mail: kevin@robbersdog.com *High quality 2D animation using computer and traditional drawn techniques.*

Robbins & Chapman, 24 Hill Road, Middleton, King's Lynn, Norfolk, PE32 1RN Tel: (01553) 774619 Fax: (01553) 774619 *Heating engineers, plumbers & electricians*

Robbins Timber, 8-18 Brookgate, Bristol, BS3 2UN Tel: 0117-963 3136 Fax: 0117-963 7927 E-mail: sales@robbins.co.uk *Timber merchants*

Robby Tanks Ltd, Cruwys Morchard, Tiverton, Devon, EX16 8LY Tel: (01363) 866310 Fax: (01363) 866310 *Glass fibre custom mouldings manufrs*

Robell Control Systems Ltd, 56 Cato Street, Nechells, Birmingham, B7 4TS Tel: 0121-333 4306 Fax: 0121-333 4811 *HVAC control panels & systems*

Robelle Consulting Ltd, 91 Cumberland Road, London, E13 8LH Tel: (020) 7473 2558 Fax: (020) 7473 2558 E-mail: robelle_oldfield@msn.com *Software distributors*

Roben Equipment, PO Box 4021, Milton Keynes, MK14 5YD Tel: (01908) 217306 Fax: (01908) 617775 *Distribution of construction & agricultural equipment*

Robert Ballantine & Son, East End, Star, Glenrothes, Fife, KY7 6LQ Tel: (01592) 758542 Fax: (01592) 610707 *Fencing contractors & manufrs*

Robert Bell, Derby House, 60 Derby Road, Kirkdale, Liverpool, L20 8EA Tel: 0151-922 5186 Fax: 0151-922 3468 *Joinery manufrs*

Robert Bellairs Ltd, The Old Saddlery, Main Street, Woodnewton, Peterborough, PE8 5EB Tel: (01780) 470450 Fax: (01780) 470130 *Grain merchants*

Robert Bion & Co., 14 Portman Road, Reading, RG30 1LZ Tel: 0118-959 2700 Fax: 0118-959 2701 E-mail: sales@bion.co.uk Purchasing Contact: Barbara Wardman Sales Contact: N. Elliot Principal Export Areas: Worldwide *Manufacturers or services of perforated metal products & perforated plastic products*

Robert Birkbeck & Son Ltd, Thurcroft Industrial Estate, New Orchard Road, Thurcroft, Rotherham, South Yorkshire, S66 9HY Tel: (01709) 546459 Fax: (01709) 546780 E-mail: robertbirkbeckandson@hotmail.com *Timber merchants & pallet manufrs*

Robert Brydon & Sons, 12 Drumlanrig Square, Hawick, Roxburghshire, TD9 0AS Tel: (01450) 370462 Fax: (01450) 372431 *Joiners service*

Robert Caerwen Evans, 10 Friars Avenue, Oswestry, Shropshire, SY11 2JJ Tel: (01691) 661611 Fax: (01691) 661611 *Agricultural contractors*

▶ Robert Cambell & Associates, Overseas Investment Property Dept, Greenhills, Winsham, Braunton, Devon, EX33 2LX Tel: 0870 241 2139 E-mail: enquires@totalplanet.co.uk *overeas investment dept. property amnagement*

Robert Charles Engineering Ltd, Ashley CR, Southampton, SO19 9NA Tel: (023) 8044 0144 Fax: (023) 8068 5825 E-mail: uksales@robertcharlestools.com *Countersink & counterbore manufrs*

Robert Claire & Co. Ltd, Unit 5-6 Discovery Business Park, St James's Road, London, SE16 4RA Tel: (020) 7231 9000 Fax: (020) 7231 5657 *Freight forwarders*

Robert Collins Electrical Ltd, 30 Wood End Gardens, Northolt, Middlesex, UB5 4QJ Tel: (020) 8864 6939 Fax: (020) 8423 3177 E-mail: johnwhittle7@aol.com *Electrical contractors*

Robert Cresser, 40 Victoria Street, Edinburgh, EH1 2JW Tel: 0131-225 2181 Fax: 0131-225 2181 *Brush specialist retailers*

▶ Robert Darvall Ltd, 4 Acre Road, Reading, RG2 0SX Tel: 0118-986 4422 Fax: 0118-975 1358

Robert Deards Ltd, Deards Corner, North Circular Road, London, N12 0SH Tel: (020) 8368 5562 Fax: (020) 8368 0002 *Property investment company*

Robert Duncan Ltd, Green Lane, Gateshead, Tyne & Wear, NE10 0JS Tel: 0191-469 8743 Fax: 0191-469 8903 E-mail: enquiries@robertduncan.co.uk *Hard, softwood & sheet material importers*

▶ Robert Dunlop Bros, Hillhead Farm, Auchengray, Carnwath, Lanark, ML11 8LN Tel: (01501) 785200

▶ Robert Dunn Plant Hire Ltd, 28 Towerhill Avenue, Kilmarnock, Ayrshire, KA3 2TS Tel: (07710) 769087

▶ Robert Dyas Holdings Ltd, 2 Old Basing Mall, Basingstoke, Hampshire, RG21 7AW Tel: (01256) 329153

Robert Flannigan Engineering, 1 Flemington Industrial Park, Craigneuk Street, Motherwell, Lanarkshire, ML1 2NT Tel: (01698) 309307 Fax: (01698) 309312 E-mail: rfeconveyors@aol.com *Engineering services-conveyors*

▶ Robert G Evans & Associates, 17 Crymlyn Parc, Neath, West Glamorgan, SA10 6DG Tel: (01792) 814956 Fax: (01792) 814956 E-mail: rgevans@associates0.demon.co.uk

Robert Gibbs Contracting Co. Ltd, Bridge Works, Rye Park Industrial Estate, Hoddesdon, Hertfordshire, EN11 0EW Tel: (01992) 441585 Fax: (01992) 463932 E-mail: sales@gibbsscrap.co.uk *Scrap metal merchants*

Robert Greig, The Mariners Hall, Irwell Lane, Runcorn, Cheshire, WA7 1RP Tel: (01928) 572638 Fax: (01928) 572638 E-mail: mike@robertgreig.co.uk *Industrial textiles, tarpaulins, fitted covers, PVC banners manufrs*

▶ Robert H Leach T/A Whitaker, Eurocam Technology Park, Chase Way, Bradford, West Yorkshire, BD5 8HW Tel: (01274) 391460

Robert Half International, 1st Floor, 2 Thames Avenue, Windsor, Berkshire, SL4 1QP Tel: (01753) 835900 Fax: (01753) 835901 E-mail: windsor@roberthalf.co.uk *Employment agency finance & accounting services*

Robert Hill & Co. Ltd, 62 Strathblane Road, Milngavie, Glasgow, G62 8DJ Tel: 0141-956 2245 Fax: 0141-955 1011 *Electrical engineering*

Robert Horne, Huntsman House, Woodside Road, Eastleigh, Hampshire, SO50 4ET Tel: (023) 8061 8811 Fax: (023) 8061 0005 *Paper merchants or agents*

Robert Horne Co. Ltd, 3 Nicholson Drive, Newtownabbey, County Antrim, BT36 4FB Tel: (028) 9034 2742 Fax: (028) 9034 2413 E-mail: rh.northern.ireland@roberthorne.co.uk *Paper merchants or agents*

Robert Horne Group plc, Unit 5a Ty-Nant Court, Morganstown, Cardiff, CF15 8LW Tel: (029) 2081 5555 Fax: (029) 2081 5500 E-mail: sales@roberthorne.co.uk *Paper merchants or agents*

Robert Horne Group plc, 1 Deerdykes Court South, Cumbernauld, Glasgow, G68 9HW Tel: (01236) 617777 Fax: (01236) 735463 E-mail: rh.scotland@roberthorne.co.uk *Paper merchants or agents*

Robert Horne Group plc, Orleans House, Edmund Street, Liverpool, L3 9NG Tel: 0151-236 4411 Fax: 0151-255 0359 E-mail: total.support@roberthorne.co.uk *Paper merchants or agents*

Robert Horne Group plc, Huntsman House, B2 Evelyn Street, London, SE8 5DL Tel: (020) 7231 9634 Fax: (020) 7231 5641 *Paper merchants or agents*

Robert Horne Group Plc, Huntsman House, Mansion Close, Moulton Park, Northampton, NN3 6LA Tel: (01604) 495333 Fax: (01604) 673495 E-mail: terry.cattle@roberthorne.co.uk *Supply materials to sign maker*

Robert Horne Group plc, Horse Fair House, St Faiths Lane, Norwich, NR1 1NE Tel: (01603) 610386 Fax: (01603) 633381 E-mail: rh.norwich@roberthorne.co.uk *Paper merchants or agents*

Robert Horne Group plc, Huntsman House, The Midway, Nottingham, NG7 2TS Tel: 0115-986 9161 Fax: 0115-986 1384 E-mail: sales@roberthorne.co.uk *Paper merchants or agents*

Robert Hough (Fibres) Ltd, 50-52 Thomas Road, London, E14 7BJ Tel: (07976) 558234 Fax: (020) 7537 2838 E-mail: enquiries@robert-hough.u-net.com *Waste paper processors & confidential shredding*

▶ Robert Irving Photography, 36 Parkway, Dorking, Surrey, RH4 1EU Tel: (01306) 879853 E-mail: info@robirvingphotography.com *Rob Irving is a professional photographer operating from a studio in Dorking, Surrey, producing high quality digital and film prints for advertising, portraits, promotional images and all commercial photographic applications.*

▶ Robert J Dutton, 2 Springfield Road, Shepshed, Loughborough, Leicestershire, LE12 7EE Tel: (01509) 502402 Fax: (01509) 600327 *Plumbing & heating*

Robert J V Kelso, Oughterard Road, Dungannon, County Tyrone, BT70 3HT Tel: (028) 8775 8686 E-mail: moreeholsteans@hotmail.com *Agricultural merchants*

Robert Lee, Lea Road, Waltham Abbey, Essex, EN9 1AS Tel: (01992) 703200 Fax: (0800) 3765556 *Plumbers brass foundry wholesalers* Also at: Swindon, Tamworth & Thetford

Robert Lickley Ltd, Dudley, West Midlands, DY1 2RL Tel: (01902) 880123 Fax: (01902) 880019 E-mail: admin@robertlickley.co.uk *Refractory manufrs*

▶ Robert Loudon Builders Ltd, Unit 1 Burnfield Avenue, Thornliebank, Glasgow, G46 7TL Tel: 0141-637 7777 Fax: 0141-637 7755 E-mail: enquiries@robertloudon.co.uk *Industrial & Commercial Construction, building on our experiance since 19*

Robert Lyon & Co, 39-40 Longbridge Road, Barking, Essex, IG11 8TS Tel: (020) 8591 5600 Fax: (020) 8591 2785 E-mail: rlyonlondon@compuserve.com *Marine surveyors & consulting engineers* Also at: Immingham & Manchester

Robert Mcalpine Ltd, Eaton Court, Maylands Avenue, Hemel Hempstead Industrial Estate, Hemel Hempstead, Hertfordshire, HP2 7TR Tel: (01442) 233444 Fax: (01442) 230024 E-mail: sales@sir-robert-mcalpine.com *Construction*

Robert Mcbride Group Ltd, Park Road, Barrow-in-Furness, Cumbria, LA14 4BN Tel: (01229) 814000 Fax: (01229) 836518 *Washing tablet manufrs*

▶ Robert Mccarroll Ltd, 8 Crowhill Road, Bishopbriggs, Glasgow, G64 1QR Tel: 0141-772 1884 Fax: 0141-772 7172

Robert Mackie & Co. Ltd, Holm Mill, Stewarton, Kilmarnock, Ayrshire, KA3 5HT Tel: (01560) 482124 Fax: (01560) 485213 E-mail: mackies@dial.pipex.com *Knitwear, headwear, gloves & scarf manufrs*

Robert Malatier, Cigna House, 8 Lime Street, London, EC3M 7AH Tel: (020) 7623 4524 Fax: (020) 7623 3648 E-mail: people@robert-malatier-ltd.com *Underwriters*

Robert Martins (Printers) Ltd, Pindar Road, Hoddesdon, Hertfordshire, EN11 0DP Tel: (01992) 440676 Fax: (01992) 446840 E-mail: sales@robertmartins.co.uk *General printers manufrs*

▶ Robert Mason, 29 Provost Wynd, Cupar, Fife, KY15 5HE Tel: (01334) 655092 Fax: (01334) 655660

▶ Robert Norman Associates Ltd, Unit 20, Red House Farm, Marlborough Road, Saxtead, Woodbridge, Suffolk, IP13 9RD Tel: (01728) 685040

Robert P D Frost & Co. Ltd, 45 Burrowfield, Welwyn Garden City, Hertfordshire, AL7 4SS Tel: (01707) 331188 Fax: (01707) 393714 E-mail: sales@rpdfrost.co.uk *Injection moulding prototype plastic manufrs*

Robert Prettie Co., Colwick Business Park, Private Road 2, Colwick Industrial Estate, Nottingham, NG4 2JR Tel: 0115-940 2222 Fax: 0115-940 2232 E-mail: r.prettie@robert-prettie.co.uk *Plumbing contractors*

Robert Price Timber & Roofing merchants, Forest Road, Taffs Well, Cardiff, CF15 7YE Tel: (029) 2081 1681 Fax: (029) 2081 3605 *Timber & Plywood merchants & importers*

Robert S Maynard Ltd, P O Box 8, Wilmslow, Cheshire, SK9 5ER Tel: (01625) 524055 Fax: (01625) 524584 E-mail: robert.s.maynard.ltd@dial.pipex.com *Textile machinery agents & importers. Consultants to the Textile Industry*

Robert Samuel & Co. Ltd, 7 Court Parade, Wembley, Middlesex, HA0 3JA Tel: (020) 8904 1144 Fax: (020) 8904 6349 *Engineering tool merchants*

Company Information

Robert Scott & Sons, Oakview Mills, Manchester Road, Greenfield, Oldham, OL3 7HG Tel: (01457) 873931 Fax: (01457) 819490 E-mail: admin@robert-scott.co.uk *Industrial & domestic textiles manufrs*

Robert Smith Steels Ltd, Cathcart Quay, Cathcart Street, Birkenhead, Merseyside, CH41 3HZ Tel: 0151-647 4221 Fax: 0151-647 4839 E-mail: sales@robertsmithsteel.co.uk *Steel plate specialists* Also at: Liverpool

Robert Stewart, 52 Victoria Road, Dunoon, Argyll, PA23 7AE Tel: (01369) 702202 Fax: (01369) 704182 *Electrical contractor*

Robert Stuart plc, 10-11 Edinburgh Wa, Harlow, Essex, CM20 2DH Tel: (01279) 442931 Fax: (01279) 626063 E-mail: sales@robertstuart.plc.uk *Electroplating services*

Robert Walker Haulage Ltd, Hall Lane, Woodley, Stockport, Cheshire, SK6 1PR Tel: 0161-430 2618 Fax: 0161-430 3154 E-mail: john@rwalkers.co.uk *Forklift truck transport*

Robert Walters Ltd, 55 Strand, London, WC2N 5WR Tel: (020) 7379 3333 Fax: (020) 7509 8714 E-mail: contact@robertwalters.com *Recruitment consultants*

▶ Robert Whitaker Ltd, Southview, Oxford Road, Long Compton, Shipston-on-Stour, Warwickshire, CV36 5LD Tel: (01608) 684982 E-mail: robwhitaker@onetel.com *Shop fitters*

▶ Robert Wiseman Dairies Ltd, Minto Avenue, Altens Industrial Estate, Aberdeen, AB12 3JZ Tel: (01224) 890444 Fax: (01224) 894844 *Milk*

▶ Robert Wiseman Dairies Ltd, 12 Brunthill Road, Kingstown Industrial Estate, Carlisle, CA3 0EH Tel: (01228) 511006 Fax: (01228) 511008 *Diary*

Robertet Ltd, Kings Road, Haslemere, Surrey, GU27 2QU Tel: (01428) 644236 Fax: (01428) 656230 E-mail: robertetuk@aol.com *Perfume producers*

Roberto Group, Limestone Road, Nantyglo, Ebbw Vale, Gwent, NP23 4ND Tel: (01495) 310798 Fax: (01495) 313320 E-mail: keri.davis@robertogroup.co.uk *Tie manufrs*

Roberts & Co., Art Cedar Farm Galleries, Mawdesley, Ormskirk, Lancashire, L40 3SY Tel: (01704) 822433 Fax: (01704) 822005 E-mail: sales@e-coffee.co.uk *Coffee roasters*

Alan Roberts (Engravers) Ltd, 39A-43A Knight Street, Liverpool, L1 9DT Tel: 0151-709 3404 Fax: 0151-707 8081 E-mail: mail@alanrobertsengravers.co.uk *Engravers & sign contractors, suppliers & installers*

▶ Bryn Roberts Workshops Ltd, Abbey Road North, Wrexham Industrial Estate, Wrexham, Clwyd, LL13 9RX Tel: (01978) 661828 Fax: (01978) 661553 E-mail: b.robertsryn@btconnect.com *Purpose made joinery man*

Roberts & Burling Roofing Supplies Ltd, 120 Beddington Lane, Croydon, CR0 4YZ Tel: (020) 8689 0481 Fax: (020) 8689 3063 E-mail: bmcroydon@robertsandburling.co.uk *Roofing materials distributors*

▶ Roberts (C G T) Ltd, Lunn Lane, Beal, Goole, North Humberside, DN14 0SE Tel: (01977) 670082

Roberts & Chick (Timber Lines) Ltd, 95 St James Mill Road, St James Business Park, Northampton, NN5 5JP Tel: (01604) 753223 Fax: (01604) 586100 E-mail: sales@roberts-chick.co.uk *Upholstery manufrs*

Roberts Contract Furniture Ltd, 1-2 Badby Park, Heartlands Business Park, Daventry, Northamptonshire, NN11 8YT Tel: (01327) 311446 Fax: (01327) 300867 E-mail: chris@robertscontracts.com *Furniture finishers*

▶ Roberts Country Fayre, Bersham Enterprise Centre, Colliery Road, Rhostyllen, Wrexham, Clwyd, LL14 4EG Tel: (01978) 264444 Fax: (01978) 354303 E-mail: robertscountryfayre@virgin.net *Food manufrs*

Roberts Engineering, Bergen Way, Hull, HU7 0YQ Tel: (01482) 838240 Fax: (01482) 830697 E-mail: admin@robertsengineering.co.uk *Steelwork fabricators*

Roberts Forge Lift Ltd, 1 C Park Road Industrial Estate, Consett, County Durham, DH8 5PY Tel: (01207) 590163 Fax: (01207) 591600 E-mail: david@robertsforge.co.uk *Lifting gear distributors*

Herbert Roberts Ltd, Royd Works, Royd Lane, Keighley, West Yorkshire, BD20 6BN Tel: (01535) 602266 Fax: (01535) 611252 *Wool dyers & finishers manufrs*

J.M. Roberts, Ragley View, Allimore Lane, Alcester, Warwickshire, B49 5PR Tel: (01789) 762920 Fax: (01789) 762920 *Agricultural contractors*

Roberts Keith Ready Mixed Concrete, 98 Wernoleu Road, Ammanford, Dyfed, SA18 2JL Tel: (01269) 593452 *Ready mix concrete*

▶ Roberts & Lyons, 59 A Wymeswold Industrial Estate, Wymeswold Lane, Burton On The Wolds, Loughborough, Leicestershire, LE12 5TY Tel: (01509) 881207 Fax: (01509) 880668 E-mail: sales@robertsandlyons.co.uk *Industrial & commercial fencing contractors*

Roberts Of Port Dinorwic Ltd, Griffiths Crossing Industrial Estate, Griffiths Crossing, Caernarfon, Gwynedd, LL55 1TS Tel: (01286) 676111 Fax: (01286) 677669 E-mail: sales@innkeepers-selection.com *Ready meals*

Roberts Radio Ltd, PO Box 130, Mexborough, South Yorkshire, S64 8AJ Tel: (01709) 571722 Fax: (01709) 571255 E-mail: info@robertsradio.co.uk *Audio equipment*

Richard Roberts Fashion Ltd, 59 Clarke Road, Northampton, NN1 4PL Tel: (01604) 627126 Fax: (01604) 259831 *Ladies light clothing manufrs*

Stanley Roberts Ltd, Townsend, Montacute, Somerset, TA15 6XH Tel: (01935) 822645 Fax: (01935) 822645 *Agents for gloves*

Roberts Steels Ltd, Unit 2, Bay 3 Sovereign Works, Deepdale Lane, Dudley, West Midlands, DY3 2AF Tel: (01384) 259549 Fax: (01384) 456851 E-mail: sales@robertssteelsgroup.co.uk

continued

Principal Export Areas: Africa *Steel coil stockholders*

Roberts Welding Ltd, Readmans Industrial Estate, Station Road, East Tilbury, Tilbury, Essex, RM18 8QR Tel: (01375) 857736 Fax: (01375) 851280 *Steel fabricators*

William Roberts & Co. Ltd, Water Street, Menai Bridge, Gwynedd, LL59 5DE Tel: (01248) 712596 Fax: (01248) 717303 E-mail: dolgellau@williamroberts.co.uk *Timber & builders' merchants* Also at: Dolgellau

Roberts-Gordon, Oxford Street, Bilston, West Midlands, WV14 7EG Tel: (01902) 494425 Fax: (01902) 403200 E-mail: uksales@rg-inc.com *Heating equipment & fittings manufrs*

James Robertshaw & Sons (1954) Ltd, Albion Works, Lark Hill, Farnworth, Bolton, BL4 9LB Tel: (01204) 574764 Fax: (01204) 705424 E-mail: sales@jamesrobertshaw.co.uk *Blind & awning manufacturers including vertical louvre blinds & exterior sunblinds*

Roberts,Mart & Co.Limited, Aire Valley House, Thornes Farm Way, Leeds, LS9 0AN Tel: 0113-202 6500 Fax: 0113-202 6550 E-mail: info@roberts-mart.co.uk *Manufacturers of flexible packaging*

Robertson, Unit 5 Hardengreen Industrial Estate, Dalkeith, Midlothian, EH22 3NX Tel: 0131-663 6666 Fax: 0131-663 6664 *Meat products manufrs*

▶ A. Robertson & Son, 6 Argyle Street, Rothesay, Isle Of Bute, PA20 0AT Tel: (01700) 503575 Fax: (01700) 503834 E-mail: service@robertsonsfurniture.co.uk *Complete house furnishers*

▶ Robertson Acom Ltd, 52 Kilnside Road, Paisley, Renfrewshire, PA1 1RN Tel: 0141-887 7878 Fax: 0141-887 5677 E-mail: sales@robertsonacom.fsbusiness.co.uk

Alex Robertson, 63 High Street, Edzell, Brechin, Angus, DD9 7TA Tel: (01356) 648285 *Bakers*

▶ Allan Robertson & Son, 1 Angus Road, Scone, Perth, PH2 6QU Tel: (01738) 551424 Fax: (01738) 553935

Robertson & Armitage Ltd, 10 Limekiln Road, Ayr, KA8 8DG Tel: (01292) 282733 Fax: (01292) 287932 *Hydraulic fittings distributors*

C.S. Robertson (Packaging) Ltd, 4 Young Place, Kelvin Industrial Estate, East Kilbride, Glasgow, G75 0TD Tel: (01355) 244656 Fax: (01355) 265163 E-mail: csrobertsonpkg@btinternet.com *Packaging material distributors*

▶ Colin Robertson, Charlesfield, St Boswells, Melrose, Roxburghshire, TD6 0HH Tel: (01835) 822480 *Timber products*

Robertson Crop Services Ltd, Scotsburn Road, Kildary, Invergordon, Ross-Shire, IV18 0NJ Tel: (01862) 842552 Fax: (01862) 842700 *Agricultural chemical distributors*

Robertson Engineering, Chandlers Farm, Bollington Lane, Nether Alderley, Macclesfield, Cheshire, SK10 4TB Tel: (01625) 860007 Fax: (01625) 890007 *Pipework fabricators & general engineers. Also tube manipulation/bending services or fabricators*

Robertson Fabrications, 88 Middlesex Street, Glasgow, G41 1EE Tel: 0141-429 0139 Fax: 0141-429 6688 E-mail: robsab@talk21.com *Steel fabricators*

Robertson Failsworth Ltd, Mersey Road North, Failsworth, Manchester, M35 9FF Tel: 0161-681 2469 Fax: 0161-688 0389 *General engineers*

Robertson Geologging Ltd, York Road, Deganwy, Conwy, Gwynedd, LL31 9PX Tel: (01492) 582323 Fax: (01492) 582322 E-mail: sales@geologging.com *Geophysical equipment manufrs*

Robertson Group Construction Ltd, Whitemyres Avenue, Aberdeen, AB16 6NB Tel: (01224) 695498 Fax: (01224) 662264 *Building contractors & developers*

Robertson Refrigeration, Upper Gartally, Drumnadrochit, Inverness, IV63 6XS Tel: (01456) 450536 Fax: (01456) 450680 E-mail: rob.refrig@btopenworld.com *Manufacturers of refrigeration units*

▶ Robertson Residential, 10 Perimeter Road, Elgin, Morayshire, IV30 6AE Tel: (01343) 550000 Fax: (01343) 550100

Robertson Roofing Ltd, 21d Station Road, Knowle, Solihull, West Midlands, B93 0HL Tel: (01564) 776278 Fax: (01564) 779607 E-mail: enquiries@robertsonroofing.com *Industrial roofing contractors* Also at: Bristol, East Grinstead, Manchester & Wakefield

Robertson Timber Kit Ltd, 10 Perimeter Road, Elgin, Morayshire, IV30 6AE Tel: (01343) 549786 Fax: (01343) 552546 E-mail: sales@timberkit.co.uk *Timber homes*

Robertsons, 2 West Port, Arbroath, Angus, DD11 1RE Tel: (01241) 872541 *Newsagents*

Robertsons Home Bakery, 32 Colebrooke Road, Fivemiletown, County Tyrone, BT75 0QG Tel: (028) 8952 1077 Fax: (028) 8952 1077 *Bakery suppliers*

Robertsons Of Milnathort Ltd, New Road, Milnathort, Kinross, KY13 9XT Tel: (01577) 863342 Fax: (01577) 863342 E-mail: willie@electricfencingonline.co.uk *Agricultural retailers*

Robertsons Of Tain Ltd, Williamson Street, Wick, Caithness, KW1 5EU Tel: (01955) 602296 Fax: (01955) 603401 E-mail: sales@robertsonsoftain.co.uk *Agricultural engineers*

Robertsons Of Woodbridge Boat Builders Ltd, Lime Kiln Quay, Woodbridge, Suffolk, IP12 1BD Tel: (01394) 382305 Fax: (01394) 388788 E-mail: mike@robertsons-boatyard.co.uk *Boat building & repairers*

Robeslee Concrete Co. Ltd, 15 Hope Street, Glasgow, G2 6AB Tel: 0141-248 4841 Fax: 0141-248 4659 E-mail: sales@robeslee.co.uk *Concrete manufrs*

▶ Robin Engineering Services Ltd, Unit 12 203 Grindley Lane, Blythe Bridge, Stoke-on-Trent, ST11 9JS Tel: (01782) 392989 Fax: (01782) 398798 E-mail: robinengineering@aol.com *Materials handling & processing equipment manufrs*

▶ Robin Hawkins Engineering Ltd, 44 Holton Road, Holton Heath Trading Park, Poole, Dorset, BH16 6LT Tel: (01202) 621000 Fax: (01202) 621002 *Metalworking & fabrication services*

Robin Hood Clothing Ltd, 9 Riverside Business Park, Lyon Road, London, SW19 2RL Tel: (020) 8544 9977 Fax: (020) 8544 9979 E-mail: ssk@dircon.co.uk *Clothing manufrs*

Robin Hood Golf Centre, 200 Robin Hood Lane, Birmingham, B28 0LG Tel: 0121-778 5557 Fax: 0121-777 7544 E-mail: promo@golfcentre.com *We provide a comprehensive service to support organisers of golfing events throughout the country. The most successful companies use personalised golf balls & accessories to get their brand noticed. We offer a wide choice of products from golf balls to umbrellas, golf luggage - all personalised.*

Robin Hood Metals Ltd, Robin Hood Place, Church Gresley, Swadlincote, Derbyshire, DE11 9NL Tel: (01283) 217540 *Metal merchants & processors*

Robin Hume Associates Ltd, Unit 13 Hardwicke Industrial Estate, Shrewsbury, SY4 4AS Tel: (01939) 210417 Fax: (01939) 210890 E-mail: info@irrigationconsultants.co.uk *Golf course irrigation consultants*

Robin Instruments Ltd, PO Box 541, Bagshot, Surrey, GU19 5XB Tel: (01276) 451365 Fax: (01276) 474103 E-mail: sales@robin-instruments.co.uk *Based in Bagshot, Surrey and working in the industry for over 20 years. Suppliers of water and environmental monitoring equipment, including online process analysers and basic test kits.*

Robin Martin, 2a Lough Road, Ballinderry Upper, Lisburn, County Antrim, BT28 2PJ Tel: (028) 9264 8616 Fax: (028) 9264 8881 *Fork lift trucks services*

Robin Packaging Ltd, Unit 3c Quarryfield Industrial Estate, Mere, Warminster, Wiltshire, BA12 6LA Tel: (01747) 861500 Fax: (01747) 861600 E-mail: sales@printedcarriers.com *Packaging products distributors*

▶ Robin Ramps, The Courtyard, Durham Way North, Aycliffe Industrial Park, Newton Aycliffe, County Durham, DL5 6HP Tel: (01325) 304070 Fax: (01325) 304088 E-mail: info@robinproducts.com *Quality portable wheelchair & scooter ramps suppliers & manufrs*

Robin Sharp Agricultural Engineers, The Dean, Alresford, Hampshire, SO24 9BH Tel: (01962) 734400 Fax: (01962) 734873 E-mail: robinsharp25@tiscali.co.uk *Agricultural engineers*

A. Robins & Sons Ltd, Unit 9 Spring Lakes Industrial Estate, Deadbrooke Lane, Aldershot, Hampshire, GU12 4UH Tel: (0800) 243433 Fax: (01252) 345861 E-mail: sales@overs.co.uk *Removal & storage contractors*

▶ Robins Air Team, Unit 22, Llanelli Workshops, Trostre Industrial Park, Llanelli, Dyfed, SA14 9UU Tel: (0800) 0131440 Fax: (01554) 746569 E-mail: robin@robinsairteam.co.uk *Air compressor service engineers*

Robins Cabinet Makers, Lodge Farm Bungalow, Kineton, Warwick, CV35 0JH Tel: (01926) 640151 Fax: (01926) 640151 *Cabinet manufrs*

Robins Metal Polishers Ltd, Unit 4, Fleming Way, Cressex Business Park, High Wycombe, Buckinghamshire, HP12 3TS Tel: (01494) 536446 *Metal finishing & polishing services*

Robins Refrigeration Ltd, Units 18A & B, Chapman Way, Tunbridge Wells, Kent, TN2 3EF Tel: (01892) 537291 Fax: (01892) 549794 E-mail: sue@robinsrefrigeration.co.uk *Commercial refrigeration & air conditioning, sales, service, repairs & maintenance contracts, leasing available*

Robins Timber Co., Canalside Industrial Estate, Wedgebury Way, Brierley Hill, West Midlands, DY5 3JZ Tel: (01384) 78857 Fax: (01384) 485582 *Timber merchants*

Robinson & Co., Norton Road, Norton, Malton, North Yorkshire, YO17 9RU Tel: (01653) 697442 Fax: (01653) 696555 E-mail: robinsonsequestrian@hotmail.co.uk *Saddle manufrs*

▶ Robinson, Sandy Leas Lane, Elton, Stockton-on-Tees, Cleveland, TS21 1BT Tel: (01642) 588806 Fax: (01642) 588499

A. & M. Robinson Ltd, 1008 Pollokshaws Road, Glasgow, G41 2HQ Tel: 0141-632 0959 Fax: 0141-632 1384 E-mail: enquiries@robinsonsbeds.co.uk *Bed manufrs*

Robinson Architects, Merchants Quay, Ashley Lane, Shipley, West Yorkshire, BD17 7DB Tel: (01274) 532500 Fax: (01274) 534000 E-mail: rce@robinsongroup.co.uk *Consulting structural & civil engineers* Also at: Leeds

Robinson & Birdsell, Audby House, Audby Lane, Wetherby, West Yorkshire, LS22 7FD Tel: (01937) 548800 Fax: (01937) 548801 E-mail: r-b@robinson-birdsell.co.uk *Industrial dismantling contractors*

Robinson Bros, 86 Cumber Road, Claudy, Londonderry, BT47 4JA Tel: (028) 7133 8300 Fax: (028) 7133 7007 E-mail: garthrobinson@btconnect.com *Concrete block manufrs*

Robinson Brothers Ltd, Phoenix Street, West Bromwich, West Midlands, B70 0AH Tel: 0121-553 2451 Fax: 0121-500 5183 E-mail: sales@robinsonbrothers.ltd.uk *Chemical & pharmaceutical intermediates manufrs*

Robinson Buildbase Ltd, Green Street, Burton-On-Trent, Staffordshire, DE14 3RX Tel: (01283) 565021 Fax: (01283) 569240 E-mail: burton@buildbase.co.uk *Buildbase is one of the UK's fastest growing builders merchants. All of our branches are long established companies which have been serving local trades people for many years, with knowledge and experience to match. We believe strongly in understanding the needs of trades professional and our business has been developed specifically to meet those demands. Massive stocks, top quality products, competitive pricing, reliable delivery, specialist staff and exceptional customer service*

Charles Robinson (Cutting Tools) Ltd, Unit C1, Castle Park Industrial Estate, Bower Street, Oldham, OL1 3LN Tel: 0161-628 5550 Fax: 0161-628 5599 E-mail: sales@c-robinson.co.uk *Manufacturers of cutters*

Robinson College Enterprises Ltd, Grange Road, Cambridge, CB3 9AN Tel: (01223) 339100 Fax: (01223) 351794 *Conference centre*

Robinson Construction, Wincanton Close, Derby, DE24 8NJ Tel: (01332) 574711 Fax: (01332) 861401 E-mail: sales@robinsons.com *Building steel frame constructors or fabricators*

▶ Robinson & Dinidson, Oakwell Road, Castle Douglas, Kirkcudbrightshire, DG7 1JT Tel: (01556) 503585

F. Robinson & Co., 26 Hopgrove Lane South, York, YO32 9TG Tel: (01904) 426496 Fax: (01904) 431748 *Saddlery retailers*

Robinson Fork Trucks, Brookside Works, Wigton, Cumbria, CA7 9AW Tel: (01697) 342328 Fax: (01697) 345055 *Fork lift service contractors*

Robinson Gay Cabinet Makers Ltd, Shieldhall, Wallington, Morpeth, Northumberland, NE61 4AQ Tel: (01830) 540387 Fax: (01830) 540490 *Cabinet manufrs*

Robinson Geoffrey Ltd, Macklin Avenue, Cowpen Lane Industrial Estate, Billingham, Cleveland, TS23 4ET Tel: (01642) 370500 Fax: (01642) 370600 E-mail: enquiry@geoffreyrobinson.ltd.uk *Heating & ventilation engineers*

Robinson & Gronnow Ltd, 3 Mackenzie Industrial Estate, Bird Hall Lane, Stockport, Cheshire, SK3 0SB Tel: 0161-428 1199 Fax: 0161-428 0635 E-mail: info@robinson-gronnow.co.uk *Laboratory furniture manufrs*

Gus Robinson Developments Ltd, Stranton House, West View Road, Hartlepool, Cleveland, TS24 0BW Tel: (01429) 234221 Fax: (01429) 869822 E-mail: gus.hartlepool@gusrobinson.com *General business contractors*

▶ Robinson Haulage, 1 The Ridgeway Business Park, The Ridgeway, Blunham, Bedford, MK44 3DE Tel: (01767) 641244 Fax: (01767) 641255

Robinson Healthcare Ltd, Lawn Road, Carlton In Lindrick, Carlton-in-Lindrick, Worksop, Nottinghamshire, S81 9LB Tel: (01909) 735001 Fax: (01909) 731103 E-mail: enquiry@robinsoncare.com *Manufacturers & distributors health care products*

▶ I. Robinson, 75 Cumber Road, Claudy, Londonderry, BT47 4JA Tel: (028) 7133 8250 Fax: (028) 7133 7170 *Manufacture bricks & blocks, supply sand & gravel*

▶ Robinson Instrument Machinery, Unit 2, 24 Battle Road, Heathfield Industrial Estate, Newton Abbot, Devon, TQ12 6XU Tel: (01626) 836789 Fax: (01626) 836790 E-mail: ron@robinsoninst.co.uk *Sub-contract engineers*

▶ Robinson International Removals, Unit 1 Hamilton Close, Basingstoke, Hampshire, RG21 6YT Tel: (01256) 859410 E-mail: oxford@robinsons-intl.com

James Robinson Ltd, PO Box B3, Huddersfield, HD1 6BU Tel: (01484) 320500 Fax: (01484) 320300 E-mail: sales@james-robinson.ltd.uk *Speciality chemical manufrs*

L. Robinson & Co., London Chambers, Mill Road, Gillingham, Kent, ME7 1HJ Tel: (01634) 851182 Fax: (01634) 280101 E-mail: sales@jubileeclips.co.uk Principal Export Areas: Worldwide *Manufacturers of hose clips*

Robinson & Liddell Ltd, Redburn Road, Newcastle upon Tyne, NE5 1NB Tel: 0191-286 2049 Fax: 0191-214 0564 E-mail: sales@rlfurniture.co.uk *Tubular steel furniture manufrs*

M. Robinson Inc Ltd, 20 Victoria Terrace, Newbridge, Newport, Gwent, NP11 4ET Tel: (01495) 244593 Fax: (01495) 244593 E-mail: mrsewingmachines@aol.com *Sewing machine manufrs*

Robinson & Mornin Bookbinders Ltd, Belfast Industrial Complex, Louden St, Belfast, BT13 2EZ Tel: (028) 9024 0942 Fax: (028) 9033 0687 E-mail: trevor@rmbookbinders.com *Bookbinders*

Robinson & Neal Ltd, 129 Sefton Street, Toxteth, Liverpool, L8 5SN Tel: 0151-709 9481 Fax: 0151-707 1377 *Decorators merchants* Also at: Bangor, Birkenhead, Chester & Warrington

▶ Neil Robinson, Goyt Mill, Upper Hibbert Lane, Marple, Stockport, Cheshire, SK6 7HX Tel: 0161-449 5444 Fax: 0161-449 5444 *Domestic furniture designers & manufrs*

Robinson Pattern Equipment Ltd, Rabone Lane, Smethwick, West Midlands, B66 3JH Tel: 0121-558 4576 Fax: 0121-555 5295 E-mail: sales@robpatequip.demon.co.uk *Engineers pattern & mould manufrs*

Robinson Plastic, Lowmoor Road, Kirkby-in-Ashfield, Nottingham, NG17 7JU Tel: (01623) 752869 Fax: (01623) 751726 E-mail: plas@r1pp.co.uk *Packaged food, beverage & confectionary plastics injection mould manufrs*

▶ Robinson Reed Layton, Peat House, Newham Road, Truro, Cornwall, TR1 2DP Tel: (01872) 276116 Fax: (01872) 222172 E-mail: info@rrl-truro.co.uk

Robinson & Sawdon Ltd, Alexandra House, English Street, Hull, HU3 2DJ Tel: (01482) 325577 Fax: (01482) 219341 *Building contractors*

Robinson Seabrook Ltd, 16 Moat Way, Barwell, Leicester, LE9 8EY Tel: (01455) 846151 Fax: (01455) 846383 E-mail: rwells1047@aol.com *Automotive electrical accessories*

Robinson Timber & Building Supplies, Dansom Lane North, Hull, HU8 7RS Tel: (01482) 320081 Fax: (01482) 586741 *Timber & builders' merchant*

Robinson Video Productions, Pine Cottage Studio, New Road, St. Hilary, Penzance, Cornwall, TR20 9EA Tel: (01736) 763603 Fax: (01736) 763603 E-mail: robvidff@aol.com *Video productions*

▶ indicates data change since last edition

Robinson Willey Ltd, Mill Lane, Old Swan, Liverpool, L13 4AJ Tel: 0151-228 9111 Fax: 0151-228 6661 E-mail: info@robinson-willey.com *Gas & electric heating appliance manufrs*

Robinson Wire Cloth Ltd, 1 Rebecca Street, Stoke-On-Trent, ST4 1AG Tel: (01782) 412521 Fax: (01782) 412766 E-mail: info@wirecloth.uk.com *Robinson Wire Cloth Ltd are a supplier of all types of filter meshes and materials. Our extensive in-house facilities enable us to manufacture woven mesh screens to suit all types of screening equipment. As one of the few Sieve Manufacturers in the world today, our products are supplied globally and to a wide range of industries.*Our range of products include wire mesh, woven wire mesh, stainless steel woven wire mesh, filters, perforated sheets, fly sceen mesh etc. We carry out all mesh repairs and replacements and handle enquiries from all over the UK and the Globe. Please feel free to view our website or give us a call.*

▶ Robinson Wood Products Ltd, The Racks, Collin, Dumfries, DG1 4PU Tel: (01387) 750205 Fax: (01387) 750129 *Manufacturers of doors trusses*

Robinsons, Charlton House East Service Road, Raynesway, Spondon, Derby, DE21 7BF Tel: (01332) 679898 Fax: (01332) 671717 E-mail: tony@wsrobinson.com *Confectionery equipment manufrs*

Robinsons, Braybrooke Road, Great Oxendon, Market Harborough, Leicestershire, LE16 8LU Tel: (01858) 461900 Fax: (01858) 465646 *Steam cleaners & industrial cleaning equipment*

Robinsons Country Leisure Ltd, 71-77 Warrington Road, Ashton-In-Makerfield, Wigan, Lancashire, WN4 9PJ Tel: (01942) 712555 Fax: (0870) 1123644 *Saddlery & riding gear retailers*

▶ Robinsons Foundry Ltd, Broad Oak Road, Canterbury, Kent, CT2 7QG Tel: (01227) 378400 Fax: (01227) 454726 E-mail: sales@robinsonsfoundry.co.uk *Motor cycle dealer*

Robinsons International Removals Ltd, Nuffield Way, Abingdon, Oxfordshire, OX14 1TN Tel: (01235) 552266 Fax: (01235) 553573 E-mail: oxford@robinsons-intl.com *Removal & storage contractors*

▶ Robinsons International Removals, 5 Aquarius Business Park, Priestley Way, London, NW2 7AJ Tel: (020) 8208 8480 Fax: (020) 8208 8488

▶ Robinsons International Removals Ltd, Park Seventeen, Moss Lane, Whitefield, Manchester, M45 8FJ Tel: 0161-766 8414 Fax: 0161-767 9057 E-mail: manchester@robinsons-intl.com *Storage manufrs*

Robinsons International Removals Ltd, Bartleet Road, Redditch, Worcestershire, B98 0DG Tel: (01527) 830850 Fax: (01527) 526812 E-mail: redditch@robinsons-intl.com *Removers, storers & shippers* Also at: Abingdon, Basingstoke, Bristol, Bicester, London NW2, Manchester, Oxford & Southampton

▶ Robinsons International Removals Ltd, Oakley Road, Southampton, SO16 4LL Tel: (023) 8051 5111

▶ Robinsons Internation Removals, Nuffield Way, Abingdon, Oxfordshire, OX14 1TN Tel: (01235) 552255 Fax: (01235) 552292 E-mail: oxford@robinsons-intl.com

Robinsons Scotland Ltd, Broomhouses 2 Industrial Estate, Old Glasgow Road, Lockerbie, Dumfriesshire, DG11 2SD Tel: (01576) 205905 Fax: (01576) 204466 E-mail: sales@rbscotland.com *Robinsons the building people. A site featuring quality steel framed kit buildings supplied to the UK industrial and agricultural market. We specialise in agricultural building erection, agricultural buildings, agricultural buildings, steel construction, agricultural buildings, steel framed, building composite frame, steel or concrete, building composite frame, steel or concrete, building renovation, steel framed, building steel frame constructors or fabricators, buildings, modular, steel frame, permanent, buildings, modular, steel frame, relocatable, buildings, steel frame, office, civil engineering, steel frame buildings, cladding systems, steel framed with composite panels, industrial frames, steel, portal frames, steel, prefabricated steel frame buildings, and recladding, steel framed buildings.*

▶ Robinsons Of Wigan Ltd, Kilshaw Street, Wigan, Lancashire, WN5 8EB Tel: (01942) 214511 Fax: (01942) 223935

▶ Robinsons Wire Products, Unit 4 Reliance Enterprise Park, Manchester, M40 3AL Tel: 0161-681 6810 Fax: 0161-681 6853 *Wire mesh products manufrs*

▶ Robison & Davidson, Dalserf House, Linnet Way, Strathclyde Business Park, Bellshill, Lanarkshire, ML4 3RA Tel: (01698) 747000 Fax: (01698) 845459

Robison & Davidson Ltd, St. Catherine's, 35-39 Annan Road, Dumfries, DG1 3AF Tel: (01387) 267423 Fax: (01387) 264200 E-mail: mail@robisongroup.co.uk *Building contractors & developers*

▶ Robochef Freelance Catering Services, 40 Hamill drive, Kilsyth, Glasgow, G65 0EQ Tel: (0785) 4400849 E-mail: mark@robochef.co.uk *Freelance Hospitality Staff recruitment help centre Submition site where Post profiles Cvs for all Hospitality members *specialise in Chefs*

▶ Robop, Peregrine House, Haddington Road, Tranent, East Lothian, EH33 1HW Tel: (01875) 619991 Fax: (01875) 619992 *Pest controllers*

Robor Cartons Ltd, Chartwell Road, Lancing, West Sussex, BN15 8TX Tel: (01903) 750428 Fax: (01903) 766151 E-mail: sales@robor.co.uk *Printed folding carton manufrs*

▶ Robot Units UK, Woodford Park Industrial Estate, Leslie Road, Woodford Park Industrial Estat, Winsford, Cheshire, CW7 2RB Tel: (01606) 869690 Fax: (01606) 869692 E-mail: info.uk1@robotunits.com *Building systems manufrs*

Robotas Ltd, Broadlands House, Foxendown Lane, Gravesend, Kent, DA13 0AE Tel: (01474) 815815 Fax: (0870) 0056914 E-mail: sales@robotas.co.uk *Manufacturers of production equipment*

▶ Robotic Gripping Solutions, 6 Clyde Road, Manchester, M20 2WH Tel: 0161-446 2079 E-mail: sales@roboticgrippingsolutions.co.uk *RGS, based in Manchester in the north west of England specialise in the research, design, manufacture, testing and commissioning of intelligent and advanced robotic gripping and manipulation solutions. RGS provide versatile, reliable and robust solutions in the manipulation, grasping and robot tooling fields*

▶ Robotic Handling, Crossfield Close, Denton, Manchester, M34 6LU Tel: 0161 336 4300 Fax: 0161 336 4300 E-mail: info@robotichandling.co.uk *Custom Gripper Designs for Robotic Applications, with much experience with leading robot manufacturers and large UK automotive businesses. Automation products for production and assembly lines and load /unload machine applications.*

Robotica Ltd, 17-19 Park Terrace Lane, Glasgow, G3 6BQ Tel: 0141-353 2261 Fax: 0141-353 2614

Robotica Ltd, 17-19 Park Terrace Lane, Glasgow, G3 6BQ Tel: 0141-353 2261 Fax: 0141-353 2614 *Product designers*

Robotics-technology.com, 54 Haymarket, London, SW1Y 4RP Tel: (020) 7590 9933 Fax: (020) 7590 9944 E-mail: info@robotics-technology.com *Robotics-technology.com allows buyers & specifiers to source the right products & services amongst the leading manufacturers of robotics technologies*

Robric Engineering Co., Baldock Road, Stotfold, Hitchin, Hertfordshire, SG5 4NZ Tel: (01462) 732143 Fax: (01462) 735273 *Sheet metalworkers*

Robrook Press Ltd, Queens Road, Morley, Leeds, LS27 0PF Tel: 0113-253 5753 Fax: 0113-238 0231 E-mail: paul@robrook.com *Commercial printers*

Robseal Kits Ltd, 3 Nimrod Industrial Estate, Nimrod Way, Reading, RG2 0EB Tel: 0118-975 4888 Fax: 0118-975 4854 *Roofing material suppliers*

Robseal Roofing Ltd, Unit 3 Nimrod Way, Elgar Road South, Reading, RG2 0EB Tel: 0118-975 4800 Fax: 0118-975 4854 E-mail: mail@robseal.co.uk *Roofing contractors*

Robson & Francis Ltd, Unit 2 Hardess Street Industrial Estate, London, SE24 0HN Tel: (020) 7733 2353 E-mail: info@rewinds.co.uk *Winders & electric motor rewind manufrs*

▶ Robson Handling Technology Ltd, Coleford Road, Darnall, Sheffield, S9 5PA Tel: 0114-244 4221 Fax: 0114-243 3066 E-mail: info@robson.co.uk Principal Export Areas: Asia Pacific, Central Asia, Middle East, Africa, Central/East Europe, West Europe & North America *Wholesalers*

Robson & Moss Ltd, Ings Road, Batley, West Yorkshire, WF17 8LT Tel: (01924) 477745 Fax: (01924) 470053 *Light engineering services*

N.A. Robson Ltd, Robson Way, Highfurlong, Blackpool, FY3 7PP Tel: (01253) 393406 Fax: (01253) 300160 E-mail: sales@robson.uk.com *Abrasive blast cleaning equipment distributor*

Robson Print Ltd, Haugh La Industrial Estate, Hexham, Northumberland, NE46 3PU Tel: (01434) 602975 Fax: (01434) 608146 E-mail: dave.robsonprint@btinternet.com *Printers*

Robsons Glass, 101 Church Road, Formby, Liverpool, L37 3ND Tel: (01704) 875855 Fax: (01704) 875855 *Glazing contractors*

▶ Robstock Ltd, Unit 9-10, Rope Walk, Ilkeston, Derbyshire, DE7 5HX Tel: 0115-930 3308 Fax: 0115-932 4726 E-mail: sales@robstock.co.uk *Warehouse labels, barcodes & location systems manufrs*

Robush Ltd, Bridge Farm, Ash Road, Lower Hacheston, Woodbridge, Suffolk, IP13 0AA Tel: (01728) 748336 Fax: (01728) 748332 E-mail: sales@robush.co.uk Principal Export Areas: Worldwide *Anti-vibration bearings mountings manufrs*

Florence Roby, Caddick Road, Knowsley Business Park, Prescot, Merseyside, L34 9HP Tel: 0151-548 2228 Fax: 0151-549 2011 E-mail: froby@uniformcollection.com *Uniform designers & manufrs*

Robydome Ltd, Woodhall Business Park, Sudbury, Suffolk, CO10 1WH Tel: (01787) 310163 Fax: (01787) 880631 E-mail: peter@robydome.co.uk *Custom electronic system manufrs*

▶ ROC, 9 Kingsholm Close, Binley, Coventry, CV3 2UQ Tel: (0798) 4975146 Fax: (02476 274457 E-mail: chess@scalise.fsnet.co.uk *Plastering & rendering*

Roc Fencing Ltd, Firs Indust Estate, Kidderminster, Worcestershire, DY11 7QN Tel: (01562) 69440 Fax: (01562) 823718 E-mail: sales@rocfencing.co.uk *Timber panel fabricators & concrete products*

Roc Furniture Ltd, Austin Way, Birmingham, B42 1DF Tel: 0121-358 2436 Fax: 0121-358 6016 E-mail: sales@roc-office.co.uk *Office furniture suppliers*

▶ ROC Relocations Limited, Arion House, Fairview Industrial Park, Marsh Way, Rainham, Essex, RM13 8UH Tel: 01708 634400 Fax: 01708 634499 E-mail: info@rocuk.com *ROC Relocations Limited have been providing a professional service for over 30 years. We can offer you the complete relocation package: Commercial Relocations, Crate Hire, Commercial and Domestic Storage - a one-stop solution to all your relocation needs.*

Roc Wales Ltd, Plas Yn Bonwm House, Holyhead Road, Corwen, Clwyd, LL21 9EG Tel: (01490) 413440 Fax: (01490) 413452 E-mail: panelsys@aol.com *Thin brick cladding systems & steel floor systems manufrs*

Rocal Insulating Panels, Atherton Way, Brigg, South Humberside, DN20 8AR Tel: (01652) 659259 Fax: (01652) 650983 E-mail: sales@rocal.co.uk *Door panel manufrs*

Rocbore Ltd, 6 Salcombe Road, Alfreton, Derbyshire, DE55 7RG Tel: (01773) 521391 Fax: (01773) 521377 *Drilling equipment suppliers*

Roce Management, 27 Park Avenue, Wraysbury, Staines, Middlesex, TW19 5EU Tel: (01784) 489090 Fax: (01784) 489099 E-mail: info@roce.co.uk *Property developers commercial & residential*

Rocep Pressure Packs Ltd, Rocep Drive, Renfrew, PA4 8XY Tel: 0141-885 2222 Fax: 0141-886 7464 E-mail: info@rocep.com *Coatings application equipment suppliers*

Rocfast, Unit 20, Worton Hall Industrial Estate, Worton Road, Isleworth, Middlesex, TW7 6ER Tel: (020) 8568 1616 Fax: (020) 8568 5656 E-mail: Info@rocfast.co.uk *Distributors or agents of blind rivets & riveting tools*

Roch Valley Manufacturing Ltd, 157 Glodwick Road, Oldham, OL4 1AR Tel: 0161-633 2536 Fax: 0161-627 5652 *Aerobic equipment manufrs*

Rochamp Ltd, 5 Shaftesbury Industrial Estate, The Runnings, Cheltenham, Gloucestershire, GL51 9NH Tel: (01242) 525385 Fax: (01242) 227546 E-mail: sales@rochamp.com *Table lamp manufrs*

Rochdale Automatics, 6 Fairview Close, Rochdale, Lancashire, OL12 7SR Tel: (01706) 658929 Fax: 01706 658929 *Fruit & amusement machines*

Rochdale Borough Chamber, Old Post Office, The Esplanade, Rochdale, Lancashire, OL16 1AE Tel: (01706) 644664 Fax: (01706) 713211 *Business, education & training services*

Rochdale Equipment Centre Ltd, Howard Street, Rochdale, Lancashire, OL12 0LU Tel: (01706) 656092 Fax: (01706) 641825 E-mail: sales@officefurniture-online.co.uk *Pallet racking & shelving distributors*

Rochdale Fire Sprinklers Ltd, Unit 13, Rochdale Industrial Centre, Albion Road, Rochdale, Lancashire, OL11 4HQ Tel: (01706) 527177 Fax: (01706) 527179 E-mail: rochdalefire@btconnect.com *Fire protection engineers*

Rochdale Metal Spinning Co., 6 Bury Road, Rochdale, Lancashire, OL11 4AU Tel: (01706) 365309 Fax: (01706) 367077 E-mail: rochspin@ukonline.co.uk *General sheet metalworkers*

Rochdale Metal Units Ltd, Victoria Road, Adamroyd Mills, Todmorden, Lancashire, OL14 5LN Tel: (01706) 813071 Fax: (01706) 814916 E-mail: rmunits@btconnect.com *Sheet metal pressings manufrs*

Rochdale Power Tools & Equipment, Unit 1 Primrose Street, Rochdale, Lancashire, OL12 6AW Tel: (01706) 642466 Fax: (01706) 860022 *Industrial power tools suppliers & repairers*

▶ Anne Roche, Robertson Street, Barrhead, Glasgow, G78 1QW Tel: 0141-880 7789 *Soft furnishing manufrs*

Roche Diagnostics Ltd, Charles Avenue, Burgess Hill, West Sussex, RH15 9RY Tel: (01273) 480444 Fax: (0808) 1008060 E-mail: lewes.info-uk@roche.com *Sales promotion consultants*

Roche Engineering, Spodden Mill, Station Road, Whitworth, Rochdale, Lancashire, OL12 8LJ Tel: (01706) 853385 Fax: (01706) 853385 E-mail: alan@rocheengineering.fsnet.co.uk *Commercial security fence fabricators*

Roche Vitamins UK Ltd, Drakemyre, Dalry, Ayrshire, KA24 5JJ Tel: (01294) 832345 Fax: (01294) 832700 E-mail: *Vitamin C manufrs*

▶ Rochem Technical Services Europe Ltd, Unit 11 Sun Valley Business Park, Winnall Close, Winchester, Hampshire, SO23 0LB Tel: (01962) 890089 Fax: (01962) 890090

Rochester Corporation, 2nd Floor Taylor Building, 62-64 Bromham Road, Bedford, MK40 2QG Tel: (01234) 327013 Fax: (01234) 327062 E-mail: djharris@rochester-cables.com *Oilfield & oceanographic cable sales*

Rochester Partnership Ltd, 7 St Helens Place, London, EC3A 6AU Tel: (020) 7256 9000 Fax: (020) 7256 9111 *Executive selection agents*

Rochester Sails, 1 Old Cottages, Backfields, Rochester, Kent, ME1 1UH Tel: (01634) 407557 Fax: (01634) 407557 *Sail manufrs*

Anthony Rochford, 58 Walsingham Road, Wallasey, Merseyside, CH44 9DY Tel: 0151-691 1095 Fax: 0151-691 1095 *Steel fabricators*

Rochford Sports Knitwear, Summerleigh, Quaperlake Street, Bruton, Somerset, BA10 0HG Tel: (01749) 813240 Fax: (01749) 813240 *Cricket equipment manufrs*

Rochling Materials Ltd, Waterwells Drive, Waterwells Business Park, Quedgeley, Gloucester, GL2 2AA Tel: (01452) 727900 Fax: (01452) 728056 E-mail: sales@roechling.co.uk *Manufacturers of insulating materials (electrical)*

Rocialle Medical Ltd, Dales Manor Business Park, Grove Road, Sawston, Cambridge, CB22 3TJ Tel: (01223) 495700 Fax: (01223) 495701 E-mail: info@rocialle.com *Medical product suppliers & manufrs*

▶ Rock A Buy Baby, 1 Shopping Hall, 36 Sylvania Way South, Clydebank, Dunbartonshire, G81 1EA Tel: 0141-952 4506 Fax: 0141-952 4506

Rock Asphalte, Latymer House, 2 Ravenscourt Road, London, W6 0UX Tel: (020) 8748 7881 Fax: (020) 8748 7225 E-mail: enquiries@rockasphalte.com *Mastic asphalt & flat roofing contractors* Also at: Bedford

Rock Building Ltd, Rok Centre, Wellington House, Falcon Court, Preston Farm Industrial Estate, Stockton-on-Tees, Cleveland, TS18 3TS Tel: (01642) 616616 Fax: (01642) 679526 *Building & civil engineers*

Rock Chemicals Ltd, 90 Priestley Street, Warrington, WA5 1ST Tel: (01925) 636191 Fax: (01925) 632499 E-mail: sales@rockoil.co.uk *Lubricating oil & grease manufrs*

Rock City, Hawthorne Avenue, Hull, HU3 5JX Tel: (01482) 223030 Fax: (01482) 223030 E-mail: info@rockcity.co.uk *Indoor climbing wall & instructors*

▶ Rock Computer Corp, 1 Collins Road, Heathcote Industrial Estate, Warwick, CV34 6TF Tel: (0870) 2203600 Fax: (0870) 9909091 E-mail: sales@rockdirect.com *Laptop manufrs*

Rock Drill Services, 11A Main Street, Hothan, York, YO43 4UF Tel: (01430) 424814 Fax: (01430) 424991 E-mail: rockdrill@btclick.com *Dust collection equipment manufrs*

▶ Rock Electronics, 113 Glasgow Road, Dumbarton, G82 1RG Tel: (01389) 841473 Fax: (01389) 730300 E-mail: rockelectronics@fsbdial.co.uk *Supply electronics, electrical & musical goods hard-to-get products*

The Rock Factory, The Rock Factory, Back of Keswick Road, Blackpool, FY1 5PB Tel: (01253) 296554 Fax: (01253) 292745 *Confectionary manufrs*

Rock Forge, Whitebrook, Llanvaches, Newport, Gwent, NP20 6PN Tel: (01633) 400747 *Blacksmith*

Rock Foundry, Lakeside, Duncote, Towcester, Northamptonshire, NN12 8AL Tel: (01327) 351561 Fax: (01327) 353344 E-mail: rockfoundry@aol.com *Aluminium castings manufrs*

▶ Rock & Go, Unit 16 Millbuck Way, Sandbach, Cheshire, CW11 3HT Tel: (01270) 759949 Fax: (01270) 759939 E-mail: info@rockandgo.co.uk

Rock Oil Co. Ltd, 90 Priestley Street, Warrington, WA5 1ST Tel: (01925) 636191 Fax: (01925) 632499 E-mail: sales@rockoil.co.uk *Lubricants manufrs*

Rock Revelations Ltd, 19A High Street, Broughton, Kettering, Northamptonshire, NN14 1NF Tel: (0845) 3510415 Fax: (0845) 3510419 E-mail: info@rock-revelations.co.uk *Granite kitchens & tiles manufrs*

▶ Rock Solutions Ltd, 4 Meverill Road, Tideswell, Buxton, Derbyshire, SK17 8PY Tel: (01298) 872368 Fax: (01298) 872868

▶ Rock Special Projects, 131 Craighall Road, Glasgow, G4 9TN Tel: 0141-341 5055 Fax: 0141-341 5051

Rock & Tapping Ltd, 10 Wedgwood Road, Bicester, Oxfordshire, OX26 4UL Tel: (01869) 240404 Fax: (01869) 245500 E-mail: sales@stackltd.com *Automotive instrumentation manufrs.*

Rock Welding Supplies Ltd, Princes Dr Industrial Estate, Coventry Road, Kenilworth, Warwickshire, CV8 2FD Tel: (01926) 851430 Fax: (01926) 851562 *Welding consumables & equipment distributor*

▶ Rock'A'Bye Baby, Cotsford Lane, Peterlee, County Durham, SR8 4JJ Tel: 0191-569 1771 *Baby equipment retailers*

▶ Rockabyebabies, 201 Holton Road, Barry, South Glamorgan, CF63 4HR Tel: 01446 741185 Fax: 01446 741185 *Baby clothes & accessory manufrs*

Rockall Recruitment, Unit 1 Cleeve House, Lambourne Crescent, Llanishen, Cardiff, CF14 5GP Tel: (029) 2074 7748 Fax: (029) 2074 7874 *Construction recruitment*

▶ Rocket Box, 2 Nelson Place East, Bath, BA1 5DA Tel: (01225) 463911 Fax: (01722) 716901

▶ Rocket Creative Solutions, 70 Stanley Gardens, London, W3 7SZ Tel: (020) 8740 5225 Fax: (020) 8740 7450 *Set designers*

Rocket Mailing Ltd, 13 Lea Road, Waltham Abbey, Essex, EN9 1AS Tel: (01992) 788881 Fax: (01992) 788882 E-mail: sales@rocketmailing.co.uk *Direct mail services*

Rocket Science, Trident Bus Centre, 3 Startforth Road, Riverside Park Industrial Estate, Middlesbrough, Cleveland, TS2 1PJ Tel: (01642) 808888 Fax: (01642) 249049 E-mail: enquiries@rocketscience-crm.co.uk *Customer related marketing*

The Rockfield Partnership Ltd, Rockfield House Flagg Lane, Flagg, Buxton, Derbyshire, SK17 9QS Tel: (01298) 85202 Fax: (01298) 85758 E-mail: mf@etrp.co.uk *Business consultancy*

▶ Rockfield Software Ltd, Ethos Building, Kings Road, St. Thomas, Swansea, SA1 8AS Tel: (01792) 455577 Fax: (01792) 455648 E-mail: sales@rockfield.co.uk *Finite element software*

Rockford Group Ltd, Rockford House, Renalsham, Woodbridge, Suffolk, IP12 2GJ Tel: (01394) 420800 Fax: (01394) 420820 E-mail: sales@rockford.co.uk *Cable assembly & harness manufrs*

Rockgreen Ltd, 128 Whitechapel Road, London, E1 1JE Tel: (020) 7377 9552 Fax: (020) 7375 0549 E-mail: rockgreenltd@btinternet.com *Mens & childrenswear wholesalers*

Rockhill Engineering, Eastern Avenue Industrial Estate, Eastern Avenue, Dunstable, Bedfordshire, LU5 4JY Tel: (01582) 690022 Fax: (01582) 608040 *Precision engineers*

Rockhill Mailing Services Ltd, Unit 3 Brooks Road, Shepherd Industrial Estate, Lewes, East Sussex, BN7 2BY Tel: (01273) 479065 Fax: (01273) 479057 *Direct mail services*

▶ Rockingham Display & Cabinet Makers Ltd, Highfields Farm Enterprise Centre, Huncote Road, Stoney Stanton, Leicester, LE9 4DJ Tel: (01455) 273912 Fax: (01455) 271106

▶ Rockingham Manufacturing, M Harlow House, Shelton Road, Willowbrook East Industrial Estate, Corby, Northamptonshire, NN17 5XH Tel: (01536) 266953 Fax: (01226) 400493

▶ Rockoco Contemparary Slate Design, Middle Hill, Freystrop, Haverfordwest, Dyfed, SA62 4LD Tel: (01437) 764034 Fax: (01437) 764034 *Giftware suppliers*

▶ Rockpools (UK) Ltd, Unit 10, Post Horn Close, Forest Row, East Sussex, RH18 5DE Tel: (01342) 824092 Fax: (01342) 824833 E-mail: dcmrockpools@aol.com *Swimming pool manufrs*

Company Information

▶ indicates data change since last edition

Rockport Software Ltd, 551 Fairlie Road, Slough, SL1 4PY Tel: (01753) 577201 Fax: (01753) 577202 E-mail: info@rockportsoft.com *Software consultancy*

Rockrome, 156 Sandy Road, Liverpool, L21 1AQ Tel: 0151-928 0080 Fax: 0151-928 8388 *Hard chrome plastering services*

▶ Rocks, Studio 701 702 The Big Peg 120 The Big Peg, Vyse Street, Hockley, Birmingham, B18 6NF Tel: 0121-245 0500 Fax: 0121-245 0400 E-mail: rocksgb@yahoo.co.uk *Jewellery manufrs*

Rocktops Ltd, Matts Hill Farm, Matts Hill Road, Hartlip, Sittingbourne, Kent, ME9 7UY Tel: (01634) 264606 Fax: (01322) 349251 *Rocktops, formally known as Pantiles Marble and Granites, is a natural stone manufacturing company and has been established for 25 years. We have begun to develop an excellent reputation across the Kent area, based on our commitment to quality, value and customer satisfaction. We have recently relocated to Matts Hill Lane and cover all aspects of stone tiles and worktops including granite tiles, marble tiles, natural stone tiles, granite worktops, marble worktops, natural stone worktops, granite masonry, marble masonry and natural stone masonry.*

Rockways Aquarium & Pond Supplies, Unit 23-25 Crosby Sarek Works, Station Road, Sible Hedingham, Halstead, Essex, CO9 3QA Tel: (01787) 461616 Fax: (01787) 463020 *Garden waterfalls manufrs*

Rockwell Hitec Ltd, 6 Alpha Business Park, Travellers Close, North Mymms, Hatfield, Hertfordshire, AL9 7NT Tel: (01707) 269086 Fax: (01707) 269099 E-mail: rockwell@rockwellhitec.co.uk *Photographic laboratory equipment manufrs*

Rockwell Signs, 341 Southmead Road, Westbury-on-Trym, Bristol, BS10 5LW Tel: 0117-950 4506 Fax: 0117-950 4506 *Sign makers*

Rockwood Electronic Materials, Amber Business Centre, Greenhill Industrial Estate, Riddings, Alfreton, Derbyshire, DE55 4DA Tel: (01773) 844200 Fax: (01773) 844244 *Semi conductor industry supplies*

Rockwood Engineering, Ty-Rhiw Estate, Taffs Well, Cardiff, CF15 7YP Tel: (029) 2081 0011 Fax: (029) 2081 3361 E-mail: rockwoodeng@lineone.net *Precision engineers*

Rockwool Rockpanel B V, Pencoed, Bridgend, Mid Glamorgan, CF35 6NY Tel: (01656) 862621 Fax: (01656) 862302 E-mail: info@rockwool.co.uk *Manufacturers of insulation products & insulating materials*

▶ Rocky Tops, Unit 12c4, Anniesland Business Park, Glasgow, G13 1EU Tel: 0141-954 2455 Fax: 0141-954 2455 E-mail: kkirchmann@rockytops.co.uk *Design, manufacture & install worktops & vanities*

Ro-Clean Desmi Ltd, Unit 24 Shamrock Quay, William Street, Southampton, SO14 5QL Tel: (02380) 829751 Fax: (02380) 339190 E-mail: uk.ro-clean@desmi.com Principal Export Areas: Worldwide *Pollution control equipment manufrs*

Roco Truck Bodies Ltd, Roscoe House, Brighouse Road, Bradford, West Yorkshire, BD12 0QF Tel: (01274) 606056 Fax: (01274) 690057 E-mail: info@rocotruckbodies.co.uk *Commercial vehicle bodybuilders*

Rocom Ltd, Thorp Arch Trading Estate, Thorp Arch, Wetherby, West Yorkshire, LS23 7RR Tel: (01937) 847777 Fax: (01937) 847788 E-mail: sales@rocon.co.uk *The Rocom Group is one of the leading telephone distribution companies in the UK. Established for over 25 years Rocom offers next day delivery on any product in stock. We supply, install and maintain business telephone systems through our Technical Services Team.*

Rocon Foam Products Ltd, 14 Shrub Hill, Worcester, WR4 9EL Tel: (01905) 26616 Fax: (01905) 612319 E-mail: sales@roconfoam.co.uk *Foam converters & foam supplies*

Rocon Plastics Ltd, Unit 9e Dukesway, Prudhoe, Northumberland, NE42 6PQ Tel: (01661) 836938 Fax: (01661) 836939 E-mail: harry@rocon.demon.co.uk *Thermoplastics injection moulding manufrs*

Rocs Computer Services Ltd, 3rd Floor, 35 William Road, London, NW1 3ER Tel: (020) 7383 4447 Fax: (020) 7383 5831 E-mail: sales@rocs.co.uk *Software house*

Rod Brown Engineering Ltd, Western Villa 58 The Dean, Alresford, Hampshire, SO24 9BD Tel: (01962) 735220 Fax: (01962) 735239 E-mail: sales@rodbrowneng.co.uk *Manufacturers of motor vehicle handling/ manouvering machines. In addition paint spraying systems install ation & plant installation/ erection/dismantling engineers*

▶ Rod L Fryatt, 10 Amberley Court, Lowestoft, Suffolk, NR32 4RL Tel: (01502) 560869 *Clock & barometer repair services*

▶ Rod Page Woodturning, 11 Southmead Crescent, Crewkerne, Somerset, TA18 8DH Tel: (01460) 271426 Fax: E-mail: rod@rodpage-woodturner.co.uk *Design, make finely finished wooden bowls, vases, lamps & boxes*

▶ Rod Rest, 149 York Street, Heywood, Lancashire, OL10 4NX Tel: (01706) 622340 Fax: (01706) 622340 *Fishing tackle retailers*

Rod Rite Engeering Ltd, Unit 15 Horsehay Works, Horsehay Estate, Telford, Shropshire, TF4 3PY Tel: (01952) 630055 Fax: (01952) 505289 *General engineers*

Rodbers Of Richmond Ltd, The Old Cinema, 2 Queens Road, Richmond, North Yorkshire, DL10 4DN Tel: (01748) 822491 Fax: (01748) 826497 *Building materials merchants supplies*

Rodcraft UK Ltd, 138 Oyster Lane, Byfleet, West Byfleet, Surrey, KT14 7JQ Tel: (01932) 341020 Fax: (01932) 354954 *Pneumatic tool suppliers & services*

▶ Rodd Industrial Design, Chart House, Sandy Lane, Lyndhurst, Hampshire, SO43 7DN Tel: (023) 8028 2456 Fax: (023) 8028 3183 E-mail: sales@rodd.uk.com *Product design & development consultancy*

Rodell Chimneys Ltd, Ffrwdgrech Industrial Estate, Brecon, Powys, LD3 8LA Tel: (01874) 623723 Fax: (01874) 623725 E-mail: sales@rodell-chimneys.co.uk *Steeplejack services, steel chimney contractors & industrial chimneys*

Rodell Mechanical Services Ltd, Unit 14 Gardener Industrial Estate, Kent House Lane, Beckenham, Kent, BR3 1LF Tel: (020) 8778 2324 Fax: (020) 8676 9901 E-mail: rodellmsldt@hotmail.com *Steel & pipe work fabricators*

▶ Rodenstock (UK) Midland Division Ltd, Bridge Business Park, Bridge Park Road, Thurmaston, Leicester, LE4 8BL Tel: 0116-269 4060 *Lenses for glasses*

Rodent Service East Anglia Ltd, 24 Cooke Road, Lowestoft, Suffolk, NR33 7NA Tel: (01502) 517292 Fax: (01502) 538682 E-mail: enquiries@rodentservice.co.uk *Pest control services*

The Rodeo Bulll Co., PO Box 312, Harrogate, North Yorkshire, HG1 4QE Tel: (01423) 541867 Fax: (01423) 541999 *Amusement rides manufrs*

Roder UK Ltd, Unit 16 Earith Business Park, Meadow Drove, Earith, Huntingdon, Cambridgeshire, PE28 3QF Tel: (01487) 840840 Fax: (01487) 840843 E-mail: sales@roderuk.com *Marquee & tent manufacturers & designers*

▶ Roderick Macaskill Contractor, Ardhasaig, Isle of Harris, HS3 3AJ Tel: (01859) 502066

Rodette International Ltd, 19 Sturges Road, Ashford, Kent, TN24 8NE Tel: (01233) 611660 Fax: (01233) 011722 E-mail: sales@orbaorginals.com *Researchers*

▶ Rodgers Development Ltd, 33a Anthonys Road, Kilkeel, Newry, County Down, BT34 4PN Tel: (028) 4176 3146 Fax: (028) 4176 3146

Rodgers Paul Joinery, Unit 13, Ellerbeck Way, Middlesbrough, Cleveland, TS9 5JZ Tel: (01642) 714417 Fax: (01642) 714417 *Joinery, carpentry & upvc windows services*

Rodgers Wostenholm Ltd, 25-31 Allen Street, Sheffield, S3 7AW Tel: 0114-276 6123 Fax: 0114-273 8465 E-mail: sales@eggintongroup.co.uk *Pocket knife manufrs*

Roditi International Corp Ltd, Carrington House, 130 Regent Street, London, W1B 5SE Tel: (020) 7439 6142 Fax: (020) 7434 0896 E-mail: sales@roditi.com *Import & export merchants*

Rodmatic Precision Engineering Co. Ltd, Battle Farm Trading Estate, 30 Portman Road, Reading, RG30 1PD Tel: 0118-959 6969 Fax: 0118-939 3060 E-mail: sales@rodmatic.co.uk *Turned parts manufrs*

Rodo Ltd, Lumb Lane, Droylsden, Manchester, M43 7BU Tel: 0161-371 6400 Fax: 0161-371 6401 E-mail: sales@rodo.co.uk *Brush & safety clothing manufrs*

Rodol Ltd, Richmond Row, Liverpool, L3 3BP Tel: 0151-207 3161 Fax: 0151-207 3727 *Water treatment specialists*

Rods Oils Ltd, Two Gates Trading Estate, Tamworth, Staffordshire, B77 5AE Tel: (01827) 283211 Fax: (01827) 288906 E-mail: sales@rods-oils.co.uk *Oil blenders*

▶ Rods & Reels, King Street, Builth Wells, Powys, LD2 3DP Tel: (01982) 551706 Fax: (01982) 551706 *Fishing tackle suppliers*

▶ Rods & Reels, 6 Chapel Street, Barwell, Leicester, LE9 8DD Tel: 01455 842450 Fax: 01455 842451 E-mail: fishingebay@yahoo.co.uk *Fishing tackle suppliers*

Rodway & Taylor Birmingham Ltd, 85 Buckingham Street, Birmingham, B19 3HU Tel: 0121-236 4027 Fax: 0121-233 2972 E-mail: paul.rodway@virgin.net *Metal finishing plant*

Rodwell Engineering Group Ltd, 199-209 Hornchurch Road, Hornchurch, Essex, RM12 4TJ Tel: (01708) 448877 Fax: (01708) 700007 *Precision engineers & machinists*

Rodwell H T B, Bentalls, Basildon, Essex, SS14 3SD Tel: (01268) 286646 Fax: (01268) 287799 E-mail: sales@rodwell-autoclave.com Principal Export Areas: Worldwide *Auto sheet feeders & stackers* Also at: Hornchurch

Rodwell H T B, Bentalls, Basildon, Essex, SS14 3SD Tel: (01268) 286646 Fax: (01268) 287799 E-mail: sales@rodwell-autoclave.com *Air conditioning systems suppliers*

Rodwell Powell Ltd, Chester Hall Lane, Basildon, Essex, SS14 3DQ Tel: (01268) 286641 Fax: (01268) 286644 E-mail: info@rodwell-powell.com *Aircraft part & engineers manufrs*

Rodwell Regalia, 2 Shires Road, Trimmingham House, Buckingham Road Industrial Estate, Brackley, Northamptonshire, NN13 7EZ Tel: (01280) 701180 Fax: (01280) 704799 *Masonic regalia manufrs*

Roe, Salop Street, Bolton, BL2 1DZ Tel: (01204) 523188 Fax: (01204) 523178 E-mail: p_roe@btconnect.com *Plastic mouldings manufrs*

Roe Bros & Co. Ltd, 1 Fenlake Bus Centre, Fengate, Peterborough, PE1 5BQ Tel: (01733) 558321 Fax: (01733) 555260 E-mail: roegroup@btconnect.com *Reinforced bar fabricators*

▶ Roe Dry Lining, 295 Drumsurn Road, Limavady, County Londonderry, BT49 0PX Tel: (028) 7776 3274 Fax: (028) 7776 7187 *Ceiling erectors*

Roe Engineering Fleet Ltd, 10 Kings Road, Fleet, Hampshire, GU51 3AD Tel: (01252) 613404 Fax: (01252) 612733 E-mail: g.s.roe@btinternet.com *Engine reconditioning suppliers*

Jack Roe (CS) Ltd, Poplar House, Peterstow, Ross-On-Wye, Herefordshire, HR9 6JR Tel: (01989) 567474 Fax: (01989) 762206 E-mail: sales@jack-roe.co.uk *Cinema suppliers*

M.D. Roe, Whitford Drive, Shirley, Solihull, West Midlands, B90 4YG Tel: 0121-246 3465 Fax: 0121-246 3466 *Bolt & nut distributors*

Roebuck & Clarke Galvanising Ltd, Charles Work, Meadow Bank Road, Rotherham, South Yorkshire, S61 2NF Tel: (01709) 560888 Fax: (01709) 554277 E-mail: enquiries@roebuckandclarke.co.uk *Hot dip galvanisers & spinners*

▶ Roebuck & Holmes Ltd, 1-6 Farnley Mill, Farnley Road, Farnley Tyas, Huddersfield, HD4 6UN Tel: (01484) 665553 Fax: (01484) 664828 E-mail: admin@roebuckandholmes.co.uk *Joinery & office furniture*

Roemac Services Ltd, M90 Lathalmond, Dunfermline, Fife, KY12 0SJ Tel: (01383) 625553 Fax: (01383) 625554 E-mail: sales@roemac.co.uk *Mechanical engineers*

Roetan Holdings Ltd, Roetan House, Thorns Road, Brierley Hill, West Midlands, DY5 2PF Tel: (01384) 424227 Fax: (01384) 424906 *Holding company*

Roevin Management Services Ltd, 40-44 Rothesay Road, Luton, LU1 1QZ Tel: (01582) 727216 Fax: (01582) 732188 E-mail: luton@roevin.co.uk *Contract recruitment agency*

Roffey Park Institute, Forest Road, Colgate, Horsham, West Sussex, RH12 4TD Tel: (01293) 851644 Fax: (01293) 851565 E-mail: sales@roffeypark.com *Management trainers*

Rofin Baasel UK Ltd, 3 Brunel Close, Drayton Fields Industrial Estate, Daventry, Northamptonshire, NN11 8RB Tel: (0870) 9901020 Fax: (0870) 9901030 E-mail: sales@rofin-baasel.co.uk *Manufacturer of industrial lasers & laser systems*

Rofin Sinar UK Ltd, York Way, Willerby, Hull, HU10 6HD Tel: (01482) 650088 Fax: (01482) 650022 E-mail: info@rofin-uk.com Principal Export Areas: Worldwide *ROFIN is one of the world's leading designers and manufacturers of industrial lasers. The company has more that 20,000 laser units installed worldwide and serves more than 3000 customers in a wide variety of applications and industry sectors. Rofin-Sinar UK Ltd. supply RF excited, sealed CO2 lasers for cutting, drilling, welding, marking, engraving, heat treating and other applications, on many different types of material including glass, ceramic, plastic, cardboard, metal and wood. Our laser marking and coding solutions can also print barcodes, logos, graphics, date and time, product description information and much more onto most substrates. For more information on lasers for industrial applications or details of your local representative please visit our web site - co2 laser, co2 lasers, industrial laser, high power laser, sealed co2 lasers, laser marking, laser welding, laser welding, laser engraving, laser video, laser safety, laser cutting, laser information.* Also at: Daventry

Rofor Precision Engineering, 35 Dorchester Avenue, Bletchley, Milton Keynes, MK3 6PQ Tel: (01908) 375225 Fax: (01908) 646560 *Precision engineers*

Roften Galvanising Ltd, North Road, Ellesmere Port, CH65 1AB Tel: 0151-355 4257 Fax: 0151-355 0753 E-mail: creditacc_roften@yahoo.co.uk *Galvanizing & shot blasting services, access cover manufrs*

Rogan Heating Services, 4 Reach Road Industrial Estate, Reach Road, Burwell, Cambridge, CB5 0AH Tel: (01638) 743500 Fax: (01638) 743843 E-mail: roganhs@globalnet.co.uk *Commercial & industrial heating engineers*

Rogar Products Ltd, 9-12 Tewin Court, Welwyn Garden City, Hertfordshire, AL7 1AU Tel: (01707) 371251 Fax: (01707) 334838 E-mail: sales@rogar.co.uk *Corrugated cardboard case manufrs*

Rogate Paper Supplies, Bowness Avenue, Sompting, Lancing, West Sussex, BN15 9TP Tel: (01903) 755208 Fax: (01903) 751898 E-mail: sales@rogatepaper.co.uk *Wholesale stationers*

▶ Roger Askew, 14 Winterborne Road, Abingdon, Oxfordshire, OX14 1AJ Tel: (07971) 404571 E-mail: roger@rogeraskewphotography.co.uk *Roger Askew is a talented and experienced photographer based in Oxford.**I can produce fresh and positive images for your organisation.**I use the latest digital equipment too, so if you like what you see, please call me for a friendly chat to discuss*

Roger Baughan, Wayland Farm, Wharf Road, Fenny Compton, Southam, Warwickshire, CV47 2XD Tel: (01295) 770647 Fax: (01295) 770647 *Cabinet makers*

Roger Bayliss Transmissions, 5 Cradley Heath Factory Centre, Woods Lane, Cradley Heath, West Midlands, B64 7AB Tel: (01384) 564844 Fax: (01384) 636014 *Transmission repairers*

▶ Roger Bullivant Ltd, Cooperage Way, Alloa, Clackmannanshire, FK10 3LP Tel: (01259) 272050 Fax: (01259) 272051 *Pilling company*

▶ Roger Bullivant Ltd, Unit 160 Hayward Drive, Dartford Trade Park, Dartford, DA1 1JH Tel: (01322) 286565 Fax: (01322) 286566

▶ Roger Bullivant Ltd, Cleadon Lane, East Boldon, Tyne & Wear, NE36 0AJ Tel: 0191-537 2542 Fax: 0191-536 0404

▶ Roger Bullivant Ltd, Water Lane, Pontefract, West Yorkshire, WF8 2JX Tel: (01977) 791100 Fax: (01977) 704180

Roger E Smith, Barflies, Broadford Bridge, Billingshurst, West Sussex, RH14 9EB Tel: (01798) 813695 Fax: (01798) 813695 *Furniture manufrs*

Roger Eaves & Son Ltd, 13 London Street, Fleetwood, Lancashire, FY7 6JQ Tel: (01253) 874216 Fax: (01253) 773635 E-mail: rogereaves@btconnect.com *Building contractors*

Roger Hickman Paint & Wallcovering Ltd, Unit 32 The Wallows Industrial Estate, Fens Pool Avenue, Brierley Hill, West Midlands, DY5 1QA Tel: (01384) 75629 Fax: (01384) 483347 *Decorators merchant*

Roger Lascelles Clocks Ltd, Unit 11 Wimbledon Stadium Business Centre, Riverside Road, London, SW17 0BA Tel: (020) 8879 6011 Fax: (020) 8879 1818 E-mail: info@rogerlascelles.com *Clock manufrs*

Roger Sorrell, Shipton Gorge, Bridport, Dorset, DT6 4NJ Tel: (01308) 897861 Fax: (01308) 897861 *Agricultural contractors*

▶ Rogeroger, 24 Clonbrock Road, London, N16 8RR Tel: (020) 7254 7706 Fax: (020) 7254 7706 E-mail: info@rogeroger.co.uk *Furniture designer-makers*

Rogers Blinds & Awnings Ltd, Unit 6 Castle Buildings, Gilston Road, Saltash, Cornwall, PL12 6TW Tel: (01752) 840616 Fax: (01752) 840571 E-mail: rogersblinds@supanet.com *Window blind suppliers & manufrs*

Rogers Ceramics, Unit 3 Metcalf Way, Crawley, West Sussex, RH11 7SU Tel: (01293) 612057 Fax: (01293) 612047 E-mail: info@rogers-ceramics.com *Ceramic tiles wholesalers & retailer*

▶ Rogers Construction, 20 Berachah Road, Torquay, TQ1 3AX Tel: (01803) 200079 Fax: (01803) 291890

Rogers Duncan Engineering Ltd, 396 Hillington Road, Hillington Industrial Estate, Glasgow, G52 4BL Tel: 0141-882 6211 Fax: 0141-882 5818 E-mail: info@duncanrogers.com *Diesel & compressed air engineers*

E.M. Rogers (Transport) Ltd, Rye Hill Close, Lodge Farm Industrial Estate, Northampton, NN5 7UA Tel: (01604) 755511 Fax: (01604) 756417 *Road transport, haulage & freight services*

F.J. Rogers Engravers, 10 Tacket Street, Ipswich, IP4 1AY Tel: (01473) 251836 *Engravers of precious & non precious metals, glass & laminated plastic*

G. Rogers & Co., Springfield Road, London, N11 1RP Tel: (020) 8368 2426 *Purpose built joinery manufrs*

Rogers Industrial Equipment Ltd, 97 Castle Road, Mumbles, Swansea, SA3 5TA Tel: (01792) 361018 Fax: (01792) 361019 E-mail: barry@rogersboilers.fsnet.co.uk *Steam boiling engineers*

Roger's Machine Tools, Unit 21 Two Gates Trading Estate, Watling Street, Two Gates, Tamworth, Staffordshire, B77 5AE Tel: (01827) 283247 Fax: (01827) 262049 E-mail: rmtools@btopenworld.com *Gears testing chart recorders*

Michael Rogers, 2 Friars Lane, Richmond, Surrey, TW9 1NL Tel: (020) 8332 7788 Fax: (020) 8332 7799 E-mail: niall.christian@michaelrogers.co.uk *Chartered surveyors & commercial property consultants*

Roger's Tackle, Pilot House Wharf, Swansea, SA1 1UN Tel: (01792) 469999 Fax: (01792) 469999 *Fishing equipment*

Rogers & Taylor Agricultural & Equestrian Supplies, Blaenddol, Bow Street, Dyfed, SY24 5BH Tel: (01970) 828680 Fax: (01970) 828680 E-mail: rogersandtaylor@equestrianet.co.uk *Agricultural merchants*

Rogerson Yarns Ltd, Heathside, 1 Clifton Road, Halifax, West Yorkshire, HX3 0BT Tel: (01422) 364088 Fax: (01422) 348709 E-mail: jonathan@rogersonyarnsltd.co.uk *Single & double yarn agent*

▶ Rogue Designs, 75 Wytham View, Eynsham, Witney, Oxfordshire, OX29 4LY Tel: (01865) 881852 E-mail: sales@rogue-designs.co.uk *Contemporary interior design services*

Rohde & Schwarz UK Ltd, Ansells Bus Park, Fleet, Hampshire, GU51 2UZ Tel: (01252) 811377 Fax: (01252) 811447 E-mail: sales@rsuk.rohde-shwartz.com *Test, measurement & instrument systems*

RÖHM (Great Britain) Ltd, 12 Ashway Centre, Elm Crescent, Kingston Upon Thames, Surrey, KT2 6HH Tel: (020) 8549 6647 Fax: (020) 8541 1783 E-mail: sales@rohmgb.co.uk *Dial caliper gauge suppliers*

Rohm & Haas UK Ltd, Tyneside Works, Jarrow, Tyne & Wear, NE32 3DJ Tel: 0191-489 8181 Fax: 0191-489 8520 *Chemical manufrs*

Rojac Patterns Ltd, Automotive Components Park, Hallens Drive, Wednesbury, West Midlands, WS10 7DD Tel: 0121-556 0909 Fax: 0121-556 4343 E-mail: sales@rojac.com *Mould toolmakers*

Rojak Tool & Die Co. Ltd, Falkland Close, Coventry, CV4 8AU Tel: (024) 7646 7969 Fax: (024) 7669 4458 E-mail: rojak@ukf.net *CNC engineering services or machinists*

Rojay World Freight Ltd, 3 Eastern Road, Aldershot, Hampshire, GU12 4TD Tel: (01252) 354200 Fax: (01252) 354210 *Freight forwarding & packaging services*

Rok P.L.C., Rok Centre, Castle House, Woodingdean Business Park, Brighton, BN2 6NA Tel: (01273) 391193 Fax: (01273) 391194 E-mail: rok@rokgroup.com

Rok plc, Rok Centre, Guardian Road Exeter Business, Exeter Business Park, Exeter, EX1 3PD Tel: (01392) 354000 Fax: (01392) 354031 *Building contractors*

▶ Rok, Stanley Harrison House, Norton Road, Malton, North Yorkshire, YO17 7PD Tel: (01392) 354000 Fax: (01653) 691111

▶ Rok Ltd, Suite B Hinksley Court, West Way, Oxford, OX2 9JU Tel: (01865) 305950 Fax: (01865) 724450

Rok Property Solutions, 68 Macrae Road, Pill, Bristol, BS20 0DD Tel: (01275) 378800 Fax: (01275) 376369 E-mail: wilkinsonandcoventry@rokgroup.com *Building & maintenance contractors*

Rokbuild, PO Box 4444, Yeovil, Somerset, BA20 2XX Tel: (01935) 424444 Fax: (01935) 420006 E-mail: rok@rokgroup.com *Building contractors*

▶ Roke Manor Research, Roke Manor, Old Salisbury Lane, Romsey, Hampshire, SO51 0ZN Tel: (01794) 833000 Fax: (01794) 833433 E-mail: info@roke.co.uk *Contract R&D for communications & sensors*

Roker Hotel, Roker Terrace, Sunderland, SR6 9ND Tel: 0191-567 1786 Fax: 0191-510 0289 E-mail: info@rokerhotel.co.uk *Hotel services*

▶ Rokk Media Ltd, 2 Wesley Way, Exeter, EX2 8FY Tel: 01392 424300 E-mail: info@rokkmedia.co.uk *Rokk Media Ltd is offers unprecedented new media experience at very affordable rates. **Rokk Media is renowned for the highest quality customer care, striving relentlessly to ensure complete satisfaction at all times. Our extensive client list includes:*

continued

continuation
*"*T-Mobile UK / *Francis Clark Accountants / *South West Communications / Group / *Exeter Chiefs Rugby Club / *Exeter University / *Exeter City Council / *Exeter E-Friendly / *Exeter International Airport / *Devon Air Ambulance / *The Donkey Sanctuary / *Broadband 4 Devon / *Michele Knight / *Beechy Colclough / *e33 UK / *EDC / *Gard & Co / *Beale and Cole / *South West Rugby Academy / *Gold Ladder / *Broadband For Devon / *Wired West / *Certus Technology / *Lets Go Travel / *St Loyes Foundation..." *Whatever the requirement, Rokk Media can provide one of the strongest web design and development skill portfolios in the region.*

Rokonet UK Ltd, Commerce Way, Whitbrook Way, Middleton, Manchester, M24 2SS Tel: (01527) 576765 Fax: 0161-655 5501 E-mail: sales@riscogroup.co.uk *Security products*

Rok's Manufacturing Jewelers Ltd, 103 Hatton Garden, London, EC1N 8LY Tel: (020) 7405 4599 Fax: (020) 7831 3708 E-mail: sales@roks.co.uk *Jewellery manufrs*

Rol Lite Blinds Ltd, St Pauls Trading Estate, Demesne Drive, Stalybridge, Cheshire, SK15 2QF Tel: 0161-338 2681 Fax: 0161-338 4193 E-mail: rol-lite@ben.co.uk *Window blind manufrs*

Rol Trac Automatic Doors Ltd, Unit 1 Brookfield Works, Quebec Street, Elland, West Yorkshire, HX5 9AP Tel: (01422) 375000 Fax: (01422) 379076 E-mail: sales@roltrac.com *One of the world leaders in bespoke industrial door systems solutions*

Rola Cylinder Manufacturers Ltd, Porritt Street, Bury, Lancashire, BL9 6HJ Tel: 0161-761 3913 Fax: 0161-762 9281 *Printing roller manufrs*

Rolamat Ltd, Unit 5 Bunas Park, Hollom Down Road, Lopcombe, Salisbury, SP5 1BP Tel: (01264) 782143 Fax: (01264) 782580 E-mail: info@rolamat.co.uk *Industrial conveyor systems manufrs*

▶ Roland Amey, Unit B, Copley Hill Farm, Cambridge Road, Babraham, Cambridge, CB2 4AF Tel: (01223) 835725

Roland Plastics Ltd, High Street, Wickham Market, Woodbridge, Suffolk, IP13 0RF Tel: (01728) 747777 Fax: (01728) 748222 E-mail: ben@rolandplastics.com *Plastics moulding contractors*

▶ Roland Signs & Graphics Ltd, 30 Northfield Road, Reading, RG1 8AH Tel: 0118-939 1350 Fax: 0118-939 1350 E-mail: rolandsign@ntlworld.com *Manufacture, supply print services, vehicle graphics, banners*

Roland Tilts UK Ltd, Unit 1 Usher Street, Bradford, West Yorkshire, BD4 7DS Tel: (01274) 391645 Fax: (01274) 305156 *Vehicle tilt repairers & manufacturers, side curtains & spray suppression*

Roland UK Ltd, Atlantic House, Atlantic Close, Swansea Enterprise Park, Swansea, SA7 9FJ Tel: (01792) 702701 Fax: (01792) 600520 E-mail: sales@roland.co.uk *Musical instrument wholesalers*

▶ Roland Young Ltd, Hadleigh Buildings, Bangor Road, Conwy, Gwynedd, LL32 8DN Tel: (01492) 582666

Rolcar Electrical Co. Ltd, Prospect Barn, Prospect Farm, Wedgenock, Warwick, CV35 7PX Tel: (01926) 493331 Fax: (01926) 493113 E-mail: info@rolcarelectrical.co.uk *Electrical contractors*

Rolec, 14a Tickford Street, Newport Pagnell, Buckinghamshire, MK16 9AB Tel: (01908) 210679 Fax: (01908) 210678 E-mail: sales@rolec.co.uk

▶ Role'N'Play Model Shops, 174 Stafford Street, Wolverhampton, WV1 1NA Tel: (01902) 310027 E-mail: info@role-n-play.co.uk *Games retail store*

Roles & Associates Ltd, 3 Pucks Corner, Lower Hampton Road, Sunbury-on-Thames, Middlesex, TW16 5PR Tel: (020) 8783 0777 Fax: (020) 8783 0088 E-mail: roles@easynet.co.uk *Publishers technical reference books*

Rolex Watch Ltd, 19 St. James's Square, London, SW1Y 4JE Tel: (020) 7024 7300 Fax: (020) 7024 7317 *Watch importers* Also at: Bexley

Rolfe Industries, 14 High Street, Steyning, West Sussex, BN44 3GG Tel: (01903) 810600 Fax: (01903) 810611 E-mail: support@ri.uk.com *Choke & transformer distributors*

Rolfe Joinery Co., Holme Road, Stow Bridge, King's Lynn, Norfolk, PE34 3PW Tel: (01366) 382403 Fax: (01366) 388061 *Joinery manufrs*

Rolfe & Nolan Systems Ltd, Lowndes House, 1-9 City Road, London, EC1Y 1AE Tel: (020) 7374 4841 Fax: (020) 7374 0732 *Computer software services*

Rolinx Plastics Co. Ltd, Ledson Road, Wythenshawe, Manchester, M23 9WP Tel: 0161-610 6400 Fax: 0161-610 6474 E-mail: enquiries@rolinx.co.uk *Plastics mouldings manufrs*

Roll Ezy, Warrington Lane, Agden, Lymm, Cheshire, WA13 0SW Tel: (01925) 759554 Fax: (01925) 759588 E-mail: sales@rollezy.com *Conveyor system components manufrs*

Roll Form Technology Ltd, Unit 19 Spring Road Industrial Estate, Lanesfield Drive, Wolverhampton, WV4 6UB Tel: (01902) 491972 Fax: (01902) 491432 E-mail: marina@rollformtech.com *Special purpose & custom built machinery constructors & manufrs*

Rolla Ltd, Atlas Mill Road, Brighouse, West Yorkshire, HD6 1ES Tel: (01484) 710226 Fax: (01484) 718608 E-mail: sales@rolla.co.uk *Type tested integrated enclosure busbar systems*

Rollalong Hire, Unit 8 Fordwater Trading Estate, Ford Road, Chertsey, Surrey, KT16 8HG Tel: (0870) 7525929 Fax: (0870) 7525939 *Portable building hirers*

Rollalong Hire Ltd, Phoenix Industrial Estate, Inchinnan Road, Paisley, Renfrewshire, PA3 2RP Tel: 0141-887 4124 Fax: 0141-889 0077 *Sectional & portable buildings contractors*

James Rollason, 63 High Street, Wellington, Telford, Shropshire, TF1 1JT Tel: (01952) 244934 Fax: (01952) 257531 *Scrap metal recyclers*

Rolla-V / UKB, Falcon House, Bradley Road, Stourbridge, West Midlands, DY8 1UZ Tel: (01384) 378028 Fax: (01384) 378105 *Press brake tooling manufrs*

Rolled Alloys Ltd, Walker Industrial Park, Guide, Blackburn, BB1 2QE Tel: (01254) 582999 Fax: (01254) 582666 E-mail: sales@rolledalloys.co.uk *Steel, nickel alloy & aluminium stockholders*

Rollem Fabrications Ltd, The Common, Ecclesfield, Sheffield, S35 9WN Tel: 0114 2468119 *Stove enamellers & spray painters*

Rollem Patent Products Ltd, The Common, Ecclesfield, Sheffield, S35 9WN Tel: 0114-246 8981 Fax: 0114-246 5487 E-mail: sales@rollem.co.uk Principal Export Areas: Worldwide *Numbering & perforating machine manufrs*

▶ Roller Doors Direct Ltd, 6 Omaha Road, Bodmin, Cornwall, PL31 1ES Tel: (01208) 264888 E-mail: info@rollerdoorsdirect.co.uk *Garage door online retailer*

Rollers' Inks & Marking Ltd, PO Box 69, Hull, HU2 8HS Tel: (01482) 218172 Fax: (01482) 214999 E-mail: info@markcbrown.co.uk *Rubber stamp manufrs*

Rollform Sections Ltd, PO Box 92, Smethwick, West Midlands, B66 2PA Tel: 0121-555 1310 Fax: 0121-555 1311 E-mail: sales.rs@hadleygroup.co.uk *Cold rolled steel section manufrs*

Rollin Stock Hair & Beauty Supplies Ltd, 139 London Road, Benfleet, Essex, SS7 5UH Tel: (01268) 793300 Fax: (01268) 795689 E-mail: rollinstock@btopenworld.com *Hair beauty wholesalers*

▶ Rolling Productions Ltd, Winsford House, 189. Finchampstead Road, Wokingham, Berkshire, RG40 3HE Tel: 0118-9782463 E-mail: enquiries@rollingproductions.com *Event organisers*

Rolling Transport Systems Ltd, Unit 21 Old Yarn Mills, Westbury, Sherborne, Dorset, DT9 3RQ Tel: (01935) 814390 Fax: (01935) 815720 *Providers of cargo handling solutions*

J. Rollings & Son Ltd, 15-21 Cannock Street, Leicester, LE4 9HR Tel: 0116-276 0275 Fax: 0116-246 0554 *Builders merchants*

Rollins, 1 Parkway, Harlow Business Park, Harlow, Essex, CM19 5QF Tel: (01279) 401570 Fax: (01279) 401581 E-mail: sales@rollins.co.uk *Tool importers & distributors*

Rollmark Dieletlit Ltd, 22 Howlett Way, Thetford, Norfolk, IP24 1HZ Tel: (01842) 754984 Fax: (01842) 761018 E-mail: roll.mark@btopenworld.com *Lithographic printers*

Rollo Engineering Ltd, St Andrews Works, Bonnybridge, Stirlingshire, FK4 2EJ Tel: (01324) 812469 Fax: (01324) 814040 E-mail: mail@rolloeng.co.uk *Machine tool merchants & manufrs*

Rollo UK Ltd, Womersley Road, Grimsby, South Humberside, DN31 3SH Tel: (01472) 358989 Fax: (01472) 241141 E-mail: b.merrison@rollouk.com *Marine engineers & ship repairers* Also at: Bristol, Cumbernauld, Leeds & Rochester

Rollo UK Ltd, 2 Balm Road Industrial Estate, Beza Street, Leeds, LS10 2BG Tel: 0113-272 0444 Fax: 0113-272 0499 E-mail: info@rollouk.com *Generating set service & distributors*

Rollo UK Ltd, 2 Rochester Airport Industrial Estate, Laker Road, Rochester, Kent, ME1 3QX Tel: (01634) 669100 Fax: (01634) 669101 *Diesel power generation service & sales*

Roll-Rite Forklift Services Ltd, Unit 4, Golden Hillock Industrial Estate, 400 Golden Hillock Road, Sparkbrook, Birmingham, B11 2QG Tel: 0121-693 6301 Fax: 0121-693 6302 *Forklift truck hire services*

Rollrite Manufacturing (Sales) Ltd, 20 Regent Parade, Birmingham, B1 3NS Tel: (0121) 236 1643 Fax: (0121) 212 1550 *Castor & ball manufrs*

Rolls Refrigeration Ltd, 37 Hylton Drive, Cheadle Hulme, Cheadle, Cheshire, SK8 7DH Tel: 0161-486 0828 Fax: 0161-488 4033 *Refrigeration services*

Rolls Royce Plc, PO Box 3, Barnoldswick, Lancashire, BB18 5RU Tel: (01282) 818008 Fax: (01282) 818090 *Machinists components manufrs*

Rolls Royce, PO Box 1, Bedford, MK41 7PZ Tel: (01234) 272000 Fax: (01234) 353934 *Marine engine manufrs*

Rolls Royce Plc, P O Box 3, Bristol, BS34 7QE Tel: 0117-979 1234 Fax: 0117-979 7575 *Military & civil aircraft engines manufrs*

Rolls Royce Ltd, Ansty, Coventry, CV7 9JR Tel: (024) 7662 4000 Fax: (024) 7662 4666 E-mail: sales@sourcerer-online.com *Gas & marine turbine manufrs*

Rolls Royce, Nucleus, London Science & Business Park, Brunel Way, Dartford, DA1 5GA Tel: (01322) 312028 Fax: (01322) 312054 *Marine propulsion manufrs*

Rolls Royce plc, Taxi Way, Hillend Industrial Park, Hillend, Dunfermline, Fife, KY11 9JT Tel: (01383) 823188 Fax: (01383) 824038 E-mail: post.master@vickersmarine.com *Motion control equipment manufrs*

Rolls Royce plc, Building 316, Viscount Way, London Heathrow Airport, Hounslow, TW6 2RQ Tel: (020) 8897 6534 Fax: (020) 8897 0328 *Aircraft engines distributors*

Rolls Royce plc, Watnall Road, Hucknall, Nottingham, NG15 6EU Tel: 0115-963 3111 Fax: 0115-964 2345 *Sheet metalwork engineers*

Rolls Royce Marine Electrical Systems Ltd, Northarbour Road, Portsmouth, PO6 3TL Tel: (023) 9231 0000 Fax: (023) 9231 0001 *Electronic control equipment manufrs*

Rolls Royce Marine Power plc, PO Box 2000, Derby, DE21 7XX Tel: (01332) 248167 *Car manufrs*

Rolls Royce Power Engineering P.L.C., Atlantic Park, Dunnings Bridge Road, Bootle, Merseyside, L30 4UZ Tel: 0151-524 6555 Fax: 0151-524 6557 E-mail: m.morgan@ces.com *Gas turbine & gas compressor maintenance & manufrs*

Rolls Royce Primary Components HPV Ltd, Sinfin Lane, Derby, DE24 9GJ Tel: (01332) 271111 Fax: (01332) 271234 E-mail: sales@rollsroyce.com *Pressure vessel manufrs*

Rolls Wood Group Repair & Overhauls Ltd, Wellheads CR, Wellheads Industrial Estate, Aberdeen, AB21 7GA Tel: (01224) 797000 Fax: (01224) 771552 E-mail: reception@rwgroup.co.uk *Maintenance & repair services*

Rolls-Royce P.L.C., PO Box 31, Derby, DE24 8BJ Tel: (01332) 240642 Fax: (01332) 240604 *Magnesium, aluminium & alloy casting manufrs*

Rolls-Royce P.L.C., PO Box 31, Derby, DE24 8BJ Tel: (01332) 247018 Fax: (01332) 246970 *Investment castings equipment manufrs*

Rolls-Royce P.L.C., PO Box 31, Derby, DE24 8BJ Tel: (01332) 349077 Fax: (01332) 291118 *Aircraft composite moulding systems*

Rolls-Royce Aircraft Management Ltd, PO Box 31, Derby, DE24 8BJ Tel: (01332) 242424 Fax: (01332) 249936 *Manufacturing technology*

▶ Rollstore, Chatsworth Avenue, Long Eaton, Nottingham, NG10 2FL Tel: 0115-946 3524 E-mail: sales@rollstore.co.uk *,000 + Refurbished Rollcages/Rollcontainers in stock.*New Rollcages supplied.*Sale or Rental.**

Rollstud Ltd, 5 Denmore Industrial Estate, Denmore Road, Denmore Industrial Estate, Aberdeen, AB23 8JW Tel: (01224) 425300 Fax: (01224) 425333 Principal Export Areas: Worldwide *Stud-bolt & industrial fastener manufrs* Also at: Hartlepool

Rolpex Ltd, Marple, Stockport, Cheshire, SK6 6EF Tel: 0161-449 7707 Fax: 0161-449 7707 E-mail: rolpexuk@aol.com *Roll handling track systems*

▶ Rom Ltd, Murraysgate Industrial Estate, Whitburn, Bathgate, West Lothian, EH47 0LE Tel: (01501) 740661 E-mail: sales@rom.co.uk *Specialists supplier of reinforcement solutions*

Rom, Unit 3 4 Blaydon Industrial Park, Chainbridge Road, Blaydon-on-Tyne, Tyne & Wear, NE21 5AB Tel: 0191-414 9600 Fax: 0191-414 9650 E-mail: daniel_hall@rom.co.uk *Reinforcing steel & accessory manufrs*

Rom Ltd, Mill Street, Risca, Newport, Gwent, NP11 6LF Tel: (01633) 612751 Fax: (01633) 619841 E-mail: sales@rom.co.uk *Reinforcing steel & accessory manufrs*

Rom Ltd, 710 Brightside Lane, Sheffield, S9 2BR Tel: 0114-231 7900 Fax: 0114-231 7095 E-mail: sales@rom.co.uk *Steel fencing agents*

Rom Group Ltd, Eastern Avenue, Trent Valley, Lichfield, Staffordshire, WS13 6RN Tel: (01543) 414111 Fax: (01543) 421605 E-mail: sales@rom.co.uk Principal Export Areas: Worldwide *Manufacturers of reinforcing accessories* Also at: Cannock, Hyde, London, Newcastle, Risca, Sheffield, Whitburn & Witham

Rom Group Ltd, Eastern Avenue, Trent Valley, Lichfield, Staffordshire, WS13 6RN Tel: (01543) 414111 Fax: (01543) 421605 *Reinforced steel bar suppliers*

▶ Rom Joinery Ltd, 143 North Street, Romford, RM1 1ED Tel: (01708) 727512 Fax: (01708) 733089 *Building & construction specialists*

Rom Metals Ltd, Wonastow Road Industrial Estate, Monmouth, Gwent, NP25 5AH Tel: (01600) 712312 Fax: (01600) 712312 *Sheet metalwork fabricators*

Roma International P.L.C., Lady Lane Industrial Estate, Hadleigh, Ipswich, IP7 6BQ Tel: (01473) 823279 Fax: (01473) 827773 E-mail: sales@roma.co.uk Principal Export Areas: Worldwide *Manufacturers of bottle caps, closures & glass containers*

Roma Leather Collection Ltd, High Street, Naseby, Northampton, NN6 6DD Tel: (01604) 740181 Fax: (01604) 740867 E-mail: info@romaleather.com *Leather belt manufrs*

▶ Roma Marble Ltd, 3 Munro Drive, Cline Road, London, N11 2LZ Tel: (020) 8361 7818 Fax: (020) 8361 7819 E-mail: sales@romamarble.co.uk

Romaco Holdings UK Ltd, Lake View Court, Ermine Business Park, Huntingdon, Cambridgeshire, PE29 6WD Tel: (01480) 435050 Fax: (01480) 414220 E-mail: uk@romaco.com *Pharmaceutical suppliers*

Roman Blinds Ltd, Roman House, Wood Street, Macclesfield, Cheshire, SK11 6JQ Tel: (01625) 669779 Fax: (01625) 614698 E-mail: sales@romanblinds.com *Interiors manufrs*

Roman Glass Hereford Ltd, 6 Berrington Street, Hereford, HR4 0BJ Tel: (01432) 272764 Fax: (01432) 358511 E-mail: hereford@romanglass.co.uk *Glass merchants & glaziers*

Roman Mosaic Contracts Ltd, Bloomfield Road, Tipton, West Midlands, DY4 9ES Tel: 0121-557 2267 Fax: 0121-557 0975 E-mail: sales@romanmosaiccontracts.co.uk *Terrazzo specialists*

Roman Originals plc, 29 Inkerman Street, Birmingham, B7 4SB Tel: 0121-380 1900 Fax: 0121-380 1912 E-mail: enquires@romanoriginal.co.uk *Ladies dress manufrs*

Roman Timber Builders Merchants, 1 Roman Road, London, E6 3RX Tel: (020) 7476 8016 Fax: (020) 7473 3486 E-mail: romantimber@talk21.com *Timber merchants*

Roman Windows & Doors Ltd, Unit 3 Fir Ralph Trade Centre, Hopton Industrial Estate, London Road, Devizes, Wiltshire, SN10 2FD Tel: (01380) 729000 Fax: (01380) 729038 E-mail: romanwindows@romanglass.co.uk *Window & door distributors*

▶ Romanian Properties Ltd, 6 Hearne Court, Chalfont St. Giles, Buckinghamshire, HP8 4PW Tel: (07879) 604710 *We provide properties in Romania with the highest returns on investment using the best qualified real estate agents and fully insuring the sale and management of the properties*

Romantica Of Devon Ltd, 37 West St, Witheridge, Tiverton, Devon, EX16 8AA Tel: (01884) 860728 Fax: (01884) 860458 E-mail: enquiries@romanticaofdevon.co.uk *Wedding dress manufrs*

▶ Romaqua Bathroom Equipment, Unit 7-8 Craigmore Mill Industrial Estate, Craigmore Road, Bessbrook, Newry, County Down, BT35 6JR Tel: (028) 3026 2299 Fax: (0845) 1301743 *Bathroom fitting suppliers*

Romar Cash Registers, 140 Portway, London, E15 3QW Tel: (020) 8472 4157 Fax: (020) 8552 5748 E-mail: info@romar.co.uk *Cash register & EPOS system distributors*

Romar Packaging Ltd, New Market Lane, Leeds, LS9 0SH Tel: 0113-249 4543 Fax: 0113-249 1803 E-mail: info@romar-packaging.co.uk *Manufacturers of polyethylene*

Romar Process Engineering Ltd, 12 Faraday Road, Leigh-on-Sea, Essex, SS9 5JU Tel: (01702) 523351 Fax: (01702) 421402 E-mail: info@romar.uk.net *Process engineers, steel, pipework fabrication & installation*

Romarsh Ltd, Clarke Avenue, Portemarsh Industrial Estate, Calne, Wiltshire, SN11 9BS Tel: (01249) 812624 Fax: (01249) 816134 E-mail: sales@romarsh.co.uk *Transformer manufrs*

▶ Romart Tooling Ltd, 3 Tudor Industrial Estate, Wharfdale Road, Birmingham, B11 2DG Tel: 0121-707 7715 Fax: 0121-707 7811 *Engineering*

Rombus Computers Ltd, Fairney House Wesley Drive, Benton Square Industrial Estate, Newcastle upon Tyne, NE12 9UP Tel: 0191-259 9756 Fax: (0870) 7021112 E-mail: action@rombus.com *Computer software development & resale*

Rombyte Ltd, Unit 6-7 Kingfisher Court, Newbury, Berkshire, RG14 5SJ Tel: (01635) 528006 Fax: (01635) 528115 E-mail: sales@rombyte.co.uk *Electronic component distributors*

Romec, 3 Gorgie Park Road, Edinburgh, EH14 1UA Tel: 0131-452 7900 Fax: 0131-452 7955 *Security installation & engineering works*

Romec Security Services, 3 Gorgie Park Road, Edinburgh, EH14 1UA Tel: 0131-452 7974 Fax: 0131-452 7922 *Security systems installation & maintenance*

Romech Spiral Systems Ltd, Carnaby Industrial Estate, Lancaster Road, Carnaby, Bridlington, North Humberside, YO15 3QY Tel: (01262) 601128 Fax: (01262) 671905 E-mail: sales@romech.co.uk *Conveyor systems manufrs*

Romeike Ltd, Chess House, 34 Germain St, Chesham, Buckinghamshire, HP5 1SJ Tel: (0800) 289543 Fax: (020) 8882 6716 E-mail: info@romeike.com *Press cutting agency*

Romeo Trading Company Ltd, Romeo House, 160 Bridport Road, London, N18 1SY Tel: (020) 8803 0066 Fax: (020) 8803 0008 E-mail: admin@romeotrading.com *Casual wear distributors or agents*

Romer UK, Unit 16 Village Farm, Preston, Cirencester, Gloucestershire, GL7 5PR Tel: (01285) 885465 Fax: (01285) 885465 E-mail: info@romeruk.com *Portable 3D measuring arms, CMM software retrofits, CMM service & calibration. Second hand CMM's and subcontract inspection services.*

Romero UK Ltd, Sheraton House, Castle Park, Cambridge, CB3 0AX Tel: 01223 370088 Fax: 01223 370040 E-mail: ph@romero.uk.com *Design, manufacture and installation of laboratory furniture and fume cupboards.*Our service includes the preparation of 3D CAD drawings, costings and co-ordination with other sub-contractors. We are also able to provide a total fit out including building works.*

Romford Blinds & Shutters Ltd, Danes Road, Romford, RM7 0HL Tel: (01708) 754754 Fax: (01708) 733128 *Window blinds & shutters manufrs*

▶ Romford Chilled Transportation Ltd, Botany Way, Purfleet, Essex, RM19 1SR Tel: (01708) 864223 E-mail: sales@ytgroup.com

Romford Electrical Services Ltd, 608 Romford Road, London, E12 5AF Tel: (020) 8478 6065 Fax: (020) 8478 1686 *Electric motor maintenance*

▶ Romford Joinery, 10 Danes Road, Romford, RM7 0HL Tel: (01708) 720728 Fax: (01708) 720728 *Manufacture windows & door*

Romford Models, 1b Bridge Close, Romford, RM7 0AU Tel: (01708) 743390 Fax: (01708) 743390 *Model & precision engineers*

Romford Securities Ltd, 34 Victoria Road, Romford, RM1 2JH Tel: (01708) 727383 Fax: (01708) 727307 E-mail: romford.security@btconect.com *Safe installation services*

Romil Ltd, The Source, Convent Drive, Waterbeach, Cambridge, CB5 9QT Tel: (01223) 863873 Fax: (01223) 862700 E-mail: sales@romil.com *Chemical manufrs*

Romiley Glass & Windows Ltd, Green Lane, Romiley, Stockport, Cheshire, SK6 3JN Tel: 0161-494 0864 Fax: 0161-406 6290 *Joinery manufrs*

▶ Romiley Joinery Ltd, Green Lane, Romiley, Stockport, Cheshire, SK6 3JG Tel: 0161-494 0864 Fax: 0161-406 6290 *Joinery factory*

Rominar UK Ltd, 106 Columbia Road, London, E2 7RG Tel: (020) 7739 8567 Fax: (020) 7729 7099 E-mail: rominarukltd@aol.com *Stone cleaners & restorers*

Rommco (UK) Ltd, Road Care House, New Works Road, Lowmoor, Bradford, West Yorkshire, BD12 0RU Tel: (01274) 606770 Fax: (01274) 602802 *Manufacturer of road marking thermoplastics*

George Romney Ltd, Mintsfeet Road North, Kendal, Cumbria, LA9 6NA Tel: (01539) 720155 Fax: (01539) 720155 E-mail: sales@kendal.mintcake.co.uk *Manufacturer of confectionery*

Romo (Engineering) Ltd, Unit 12B, Waterfall Lane Trading Estate, Waterfall Lane, Cradley Heath, West Midlands, B64 6PU Tel: 0121-559 5966 Fax: 0121-559 5952 E-mail: press@romo.co.uk Principal Export Areas: Central/East Europe & West Europe *Press & design engineers*

Company Information

▶ Romold Plastic Products, Grangemouth Road, Bo'Ness, West Lothian, EH51 0PU Tel: (01506) 829623 Fax: (01506) 828639 *Manufacturers storage & containment products for oils & chemicals*

Romoprint, 140 Springhill Road, Wednesfield, Wolverhampton, WV11 3AQ Tel: (01902) 730862 *Printers*

Romotex Ltd, 22 London Road, Hazel Grove, Stockport, Cheshire, SK7 4AH Tel: 0161-419 9999 Fax: 0161-483 0101 *Electronic equipment manufrs*

Romsey Fire Protection Co., 3-4 Eastwood Court, Broadwater Road, Romsey, Hampshire, SO51 8JJ Tel: (01794) 514700 Fax: (01794) 524321 E-mail: enquire@romseyfire.co.uk *Fire extinguisher suppliers*

Romstor Ltd, Unit 22,, West Station Ind. Estate, Spital Road,, Maldon, Essex, CM9 6TS Tel: 01621 855600 Fax: 01621 875919 E-mail: sales@romstor.co.uk *Shelving, Racking, Mezzanines, Partitioning, Workshop - Storage & Materials Handling Equipment.*

Romus Sportswear, Dixies, High Street, Ashwell, Hertfordshire, SG7 5NT Tel: (01462) 742101 Fax: (01462) 742088 E-mail: johnrbonnett@aol.com *Sports clothing distributors*

▶ Ron Cowie Ltd, 9 Laurel Braes, Danestone, Aberdeen, Aberdeen, AB22 8XY Tel: (01224) 826696 E-mail: ron.cowie@homecall.co.uk *Hose fittings & pressure connections*

▶ Ron Smith & Co., 11 Copdale Road, Leicester, LE5 4FG Tel: 0116-273 6880 Fax: 0116-273 5088 *Distributors of personal protective equipment*

Ronacrete Ltd, Ronac House, Selinas Lane, Dagenham, Essex, RM8 1QH Tel: (020) 8593 7621 Fax: (020) 8595 6969 E-mail: sosen@ronacrete.co.uk *Civil engineering & building materials manufrs*

Ronaldsway Shoe Co. Ltd, Ballasalla, Isle Of Man, IM9 2RS Tel: (01624) 823011 Fax: (01624) 822441 *Shoe manufrs*

Ronan Engineering Ltd, Factory 1-2 Tilley Road, Crowther, Washington, Tyne & Wear, NE38 0AE Tel: 0191-416 1689 Fax: 0191-416 5856 E-mail: sales@ronan.com *Alarm & monitoring system manufrs*

Ronco Engineering Ltd, 3a-3b Unit Alderman Wood Road, Tanfield Lea Industrial Estate South, Tanfield Lea, Stanley, County Durham, DH9 9XF Tel: (01207) 284848 Fax: (01207) 290306 E-mail: enquires@ronco-engineering.co.uk *Precision engineers*

▶ Ronco Precision Engineering Ltd, Unit 19 Pilot Industrial Estate, Manchester Road, Bolton, BL3 2ND Tel: (01204) 397405 Fax: (01204) 364167 E-mail: ronco.ltd@torp21.com *Precision engineering*

Roncol Services Ltd, Plas Celyn, Bangor Road, Penmaenmawr, Gwynedd, LL34 6LD Tel: (01492) 623787 Fax: (01492) 622086 E-mail: sales@roncol.co.uk *Fuel installers*

Rondar Signs Ltd, 2 Outram Road, Dukinfield, Cheshire, SK16 4XE Tel: 0161-339 0194 Fax: 0161-339 1370 E-mail: info@rondar.co.uk *Signmakers & signwriters*

Rondec Screen Process, Lisle Lane, Ely, Cambridgeshire, CB7 4AS Tel: (01353) 645631 Fax: (01353) 667998 E-mail: sales@rondec.com *Silk screen process, inks & chemical distributors*

▶ Ronden Builders Ltd, Crawlaw Road Garage, Crawlaw Road, Peterlee, County Durham, SR8 3LR Tel: 0191-527 0764 Fax: 0191-527 1281

Ronin Group, 637 Forest Road, London, E17 4NE Tel: (020) 8531 4001 Fax: (020) 8531 2223 *Computer consultants*

Ronis-Dom Ltd, Moor Street South, Blakenhall, Wolverhampton, WV2 3JJ Tel: (01902) 715440 Fax: (01902) 715145 *Door & security lock manufrs*

Rontec Ltd, 11 Beckbridge Road, Normanton Industrial Estate, Normanton, West Yorkshire, WF6 1TE Tel: (01924) 898209 Fax: (01924) 899854 E-mail: sales@rontec.co.uk *Process control systems & software*

Joe Roocroft & Sons Ltd, Aston Way, Moss Side Development Park, Leyland, PR26 7UX Tel: (01772) 642810 Fax: (01772) 455714 E-mail: davidr@jroocroft.co.uk *Crash barrier installers*

▶ Roof Profiles Ltd, 7 Kyle Road, Irvine Industrial Estate, Irvine, Ayrshire, KA12 8JF Tel: (01294) 274488 Fax: (01294) 271199 E-mail: sales@roofprofiles.com *Roof trusses*

▶ The Roof Truss Company Ltd, Moycroft Industrial Estate, Elgin, Morayshire, IV30 1XZ Tel: (01343) 547474 Fax: (01343) 547990 E-mail: enquires@rtcs.co.uk *Timber products*

Roofdec Ltd, Braithwell Way, Hellaby, Rotherham, South Yorkshire, S66 8QY Tel: (01709) 546421 Fax: (01709) 701409 *Roofing & sheeting contractors*

Roofing Construction Services Ltd, 122 High Street, Lye, Stourbridge, West Midlands, DY9 8NF Tel: (01384) 423586 Fax: (01384) 894079 *Roofing contractors & suppliers*

▶ Roofing Contracts & Building Ltd, A 121a Shirley Road, Southampton, SO15 3FF Tel: (023) 8063 3030 Fax: (023) 8063 3998 E-mail: sales@roofingcladdingbuilding.com *Industrial roofing & cladding*

▶ Roofing Insulation Services, Hilldale House, 9 Hilldale Avenue, Blackley, Manchester, M9 6PQ Tel: (0800) 7318314 E-mail: info@sprayfoaminsulation.co.uk *Roofing insulation services (polyurethane spray-foam)*

▶ Roofing Solutions, 1 The Shipyard, Upper Brents, Faversham, Kent, ME13 7DZ Tel: (01795) 597998 Fax: (01795) 591811 E-mail: roofsolutions@btinternet.com *Suppliers of Reflective multi-layer Foil insulation systems, reflective breathable membranes, Alububble foil Insulation at wholesale prices.*

Roofproof Ltd, The Reach, Remenham, Henley-on-Thames, Oxfordshire, RG9 3DD Tel: (01491) 572966 Fax: (01491) 572967 E-mail: sales@roofproof.co.uk *Roof waterproofing contractors*

▶ RoofracksUK, Unit 12, Fountain Mill, Carluke Street, Blackburn, BB1 3JR Tel: (01254) 263558 Fax: (01254) 54776 E-mail: sales@roofracksuk.com *Manufacture & supply commercial vehicle roof racks*

Roofrite (East Anglia) Ltd, The Street, Sheering, Bishop's Stortford, Hertfordshire, CM22 7LY Tel: (01279) 734515 Fax: (01279) 734568 *Roofing contractors & suppliers*

Rooftech, RoofTech House, Four Seasons Crescent, Kimpton Road, Sutton, Surrey, SM3 9QR Tel: (020) 8641 7077 Fax: (020) 8641 7006 E-mail: mail@rooftech.info *RoofTech are an Industrial and Commercial Refurbishment Contractor that specialise in all aspects of roofing and cladding. Established in 1988 RoofTech combine a wealth of experience together with the all the latest in innovative ideas and solutions to offer a service that prides itself on high levels of communication and minimal disruption which is vitally important in the refurbishment sector. RoofTech's range of services include: Composite panel roof sheeting and cladding; Single Ply Membranes, Flat to Pitch conversions, Oversheeting of existing roofs, Rooflight replacement, High performance felt system, Elastomeric liquid coatings, gutter renewals and liners and all forms of roof safety systems.*

Rooftherm, Dane Mill, Broadhurst Lane, Congleton, Cheshire, CW12 1LA Tel: (01260) 285823 Fax: (01260) 295426 E-mail: info@rooftherm.co.uk *Polyurethane spray foam roof insulation is quick to install, insulates, sound proofs and stabilises your roof with negligible loading. Spray foam seals and prevents wind blown rain and debris from entering the loft. Guaranteed for 25 years.*

D. & P. Rooke, Coldharbour Cottage, Winchbottom Lane, High Wycombe, Buckinghamshire, HP10 9QG Tel: (01494) 526065 E-mail: info@luxury-toilets.com *Portable toilet hire*

Rooksby Roofing Ltd, Rooksby House, Lindway Lane, Brackenfield, Alfreton, Derbyshire, DE55 6DA Tel: (0844) 5762529 Fax: (0844) 5760149 E-mail: reception@rooksbyroofing.co.uk *Industrial roofing contractors*

Rooksmoor Timber Co. Ltd, Vatch Lane, Eastcombe, Stroud, Gloucestershire, GL6 7DY Tel: (01453) 882240 Fax: (01453) 731112 E-mail: enquiries@rooksmoor.com *Manufacturers in hardwood*

Rooley Consultants, Greenways, Church Lane, Stoke Poges, Slough, SL2 4PB Tel: (01753) 648040 Fax: (01753) 648048 E-mail: richard@rooley.com *Consulting engineers*

▶ The Room, 18 Molesworth Road, Cookstown, County Tyrone, BT80 8NR Tel: (028) 8675 8170 *Building contractors wood cabins, home offices*

▶ Room Rates, 85 Cavendish Drive, Northampton, NN3 3HL Tel: 0870 1439055

Roomer Products Ltd, Unit 111 Thorp Arch Trading Estate, Thorp Arch, Wetherby, West Yorkshire, LS23 7BJ Tel: (01937) 842002 Fax: (01937) 845174 *Light manufrs*

Roomfoss Ltd, Larch Road, Saddlebow, King's Lynn, Norfolk, PE34 3HP Tel: (01553) 771413 Fax: (01553) 691184 E-mail: sales@roomfoss.co.uk *Control systems manufrs*

Rooms, 98 Drumcroon Road, Blackhill, Coleraine, County Londonderry, BT51 4ER Tel: (028) 7086 8689 E-mail: wcollins@btconnect.com *Furniture manufrs*

Joe Rooney Floors & Ceilings Ltd, 2 Duncan Street, Gateshead, Tyne & Wear, NE8 3PU Tel: 0191-477 0045 Fax: 0191-477 8879 *Flooring & ceiling contractors*

Rooneys Scrap Merchants Ltd, South Shore Road, Gateshead, Tyne & Wear, NE8 3AE Tel: 0191-478 7833 Fax: 0191-478 7833 E-mail: rooneys@btconnect.com *Scrap metal dealers*

▶ Roope Robert Opticians Ltd, 20 George Street, St. Albans, Hertfordshire, AL3 4ES Tel: (01727) 857798 E-mail: robert@roope.co.uk *Ophthalmic & dispensing opticians, providing a full eye care service*

▶ The Rooster Ltd, 37 Sandelswood End, Beaconsfield, Buckinghamshire, HP9 2AA Tel: (01494) 672966 E-mail: adevillard@therooster.co.uk *The Rooster is a multi-discipline marketing & advertising agency that helps clients stand out from the crowd and connect with their target market. *We handle all aspects of marketing including:*- Branding*- Naming*- Advertising*- PR*- Corporate ID*- Design*- Direct marketing*- Email marketing*- Websites***

▶ Root 3 Automation, Beacon Park, Gorleston, Great Yarmouth, Norfolk, NR31 7RA Tel: (0845) 4301100 Fax: (01493) 446526 *Fire alarm maintenance*

Root Computers Ltd, Templars Way Industrial Estate, Marlborough Road, Wootton Bassett, Swindon, SN4 7SR Tel: (01793) 850880 Fax: (01793) 850960 E-mail: sales@rootcomputers.co.uk *Computer brokers*

William Root Ltd, White Rose Mill, Holdsworth Road, Halifax, West Yorkshire, HX3 6SN Tel: (01422) 246161 Fax: (01422) 246331 E-mail: info@cashmere-fibre.co.uk *Textile specialists*

▶ Roots Landscaping, 83 Cecil Road, Dronfield, Derbyshire, S18 2GX Tel: (01246) 290786 E-mail: info@roots-landscaping.com *Landscaping for all your garden requirements. Decking, Fencing, Patios, Brick & Stonework, Water features,Turfing, Block paving, paths & drives. Garden maintenance, garden makeovers. Free no obligation quotes and consultation.*

Rope Access Specialists Ltd, Newtate, Florence Court Demesne, Enniskillen, County Fermanagh, BT92 1DB Tel: (028) 6634 8443 Fax: (028) 6634 8081 *Rope access training & consultancy service*

▶ Rope Assemblies Ltd, Aurillac Way, Retford, Nottinghamshire, DN22 7PX Tel: (01777) 700714 Fax: (01777) 860719 E-mail: siobhan@ropeasseblies.co.uk *Wire rope assemblies manufrs*

Rope Services Tipton Ltd, St Georges Works, Bradleys Lane, Tipton, West Midlands, DY4 9EZ Tel: 0121-557 7521 Fax: 0121-557 8921 *Wire rope splicing specialists*

Rope & Tackle Solent Ltd, Marchwood Industrial Estate, Normandy Way, Marchwood, Southampton, SO40 4PB Tel: (023) 8066 5470 Fax: (023) 8066 5471 *Wire rope wholesalers*

Rope Technical Site Services, Rands Lane, Armthorpe, Doncaster, South Yorkshire, DN3 3DY Tel: (01302) 831987 Fax: (01302) 832559 E-mail: info@ropetech.co.uk Principal Export Areas: Worldwide *Non destructive testing consultants*

Roper Construction Ltd, 164-168 Powis Street, London, SE18 6NL Tel: (020) 8854 6622

Roper Electronic Engineering Ltd, Unit 22 Industrial Estate, Station Road, Ditton Priors, Bridgnorth, Shropshire, WV16 6SS Tel: (01746) 712670 Fax: (01746) 712746 E-mail: sales@roperelectronics.co.uk *Control systems, generator maintenance, repair*

M.A. Roper & Sons, Paer Tree Cottage, Town Road, Fleggburgh, Great Yarmouth, Norfolk, NR29 3AB Tel: (01493) 368176 Fax: (01493) 369807 *Agricultural contractors*

Ropesafe, P.O. Box 115, West Wickham, Kent, BR4 9YZ Tel: 07730 677936 E-mail: ropesafe@totalise.co.uk *Industrial rope access specialists to the window cleaning industry*

Ropetech International Ltd, The Old School, Brynrefail, Caernarfon, Gwynedd, LL55 3NB Tel: 01286 685471 Fax: 01286 685473 E-mail: info@ropetech.com *Rope access services and IRATA personnel supply contractor. Services include all forms of difficult access works, surveys, structural inspections, specialist historical building conservation, petro-chemical plant maintenance, rigging and instalations, safety bolt instalation, corrosion surveys, paint programs, turbine maintenance, confined space access.*

Ropetek Ltd, Unit 2 Caerphilly Business Park, Caerphilly, Mid Glamorgan, CF83 3ED Tel: (029) 2086 2688 Fax: (029) 2086 2767 *Lifting equipment & wire rope services, made to specification*

Roplan Ltd, 2 Enterprise Court, Rarking Rd, Daneshill West, Newbury, Berkshire, RG20 4SW Tel: (01635) 299091 Fax: (01635) 298505 E-mail: enquiries@roplan.com *Roplan manufacture Mechanical seals for the 'Original Equipment Manufacturing' sector of industry. Roplan have production plants and offices in Sweden and the UK, and are quality assured to ISO9001. We currently supply some of the largest hygienic pump manufactures in the UK and Europe, many you will know. We also produce seals for specialist machine manufacturers. We can supply standard products and bespoke designs; this is supplemented by a full seal refurbishment service.*

Roplex Engineering Ltd, Roplex House, Church Road, Shedfield, Southampton, SO32 2HW Tel: (01329) 835772 Fax: (01329) 834480 *Vapour recovery services distributors*

Rosch Engineering, Units 1 2, Calibre Indust Park, Four Ashes, Wolverhampton, WV10 7DZ Tel: (01902) 798100 Fax: (01902) 798844 E-mail: info@rosch.co.uk Purchasing Contact: M. Evans Sales Contact: R. Smith *We stock & supply all typkes of standard bolts, nuts, screws & washer, & have expanded our range to include plastic, nylong & rubber products. We also specialise in pre-pack fixings & can accommodate any packing requests*

▶ Jon Roscoe Outsourcing & Sub-Contract Specialist, 61, Bellevue Gardens, Shrewsbury, SY3 7JH Tel: (01743) 244829 Fax: (01743) 244829 E-mail: jonroscoeuk@aol.com *Outsourcing & sub-contracting services*

Pauline Roscoe & Associates Ltd, 183 Town Lane, Whittle-le-Woods, Chorley, Lancashire, PR6 8AG Tel: (01257) 260157 Fax: (01257) 260157 E-mail: pr@pauline-roscoe.co.uk *Heritage & environmental management consultants*

Roscope Ltd, Telford Way, Telford Way Industrial Estate, Kettering, Northamptonshire, NN16 8UN Tel: (01536) 415644 Fax: (01536) 316929 E-mail: roscope.sales@btconnect.com *Laser profilers, metal fabricators & laser cutting services*

A. Rose (Newark) Ltd, 17 Cross Street, Newark, Nottinghamshire, NG24 1PP Tel: (01636) 703581 Fax: (01636) 640363 *Road transport, haulage & freight services*

Rose Auto Supplies, Merlin Centre, County Oak Way, Crawley, West Sussex, RH11 7XA Tel: (01293) 536769 Fax: (01293) 553666 E-mail: roseautos@gogglemail.com *Fastener distributors*

▶ Rose Builders Ltd, Unit 3 Station Road, Mistley, Manningtree, Essex, CO11 1AA Tel: (01206) 392613 Fax: (01206) 392680 E-mail: info@rosebuilders.co.uk

Rose Colchester Ltd, Clough Road, Severalls Industrial Park, Colchester, CO4 9QT Tel: (01206) 844500 Fax: (01206) 845872 E-mail: sales@rosecalendars.co.uk *Advertising calendar publishers*

Rose Computing Systems, Pyle Enterprise Centre 18 Village Farm Road, Village Farm Industrial Estate, Pyle, Bridgend, Mid Glamorgan, CF33 6BL Tel: (01656) 744529 E-mail: info@rosecomputing.net *Software design and development.*

Rose Corrosion Services Ltd, 1 The Galloway Centre, Hambridge Lane, Newbury, Berkshire, RG14 5TL Tel: (01635) 552225 Fax: (01635) 568690 E-mail: rcsl@rosecorrosionservices.co.uk *Chemical injection equipment manufacturers, corrosion control/monitoring systems manufacturers, water treatment corrosion monitoring equipment manufacturers, cathodic protection systems manufacturers & test equipment, materials*

Dave Rose, 65 Horseshoe Lane, Kirton, Boston, Lincolnshire, PE20 1LW Tel: (01205) 722167 Fax: (01205) 723615 *Agricultural engineers*

Rose Forgrove, 101 Lilac Grove, Beeston, Nottingham, NG9 1PF Tel: 0115-967 8787 Fax: 0115-967 8707 E-mail: sales@rose-forgrove.co.uk *Flow wrapping machinery manufrs*

Rose Hill Polymers Ltd, Rose Hill Mill, Beech Road, Sowerby Bridge, West Yorkshire, HX6 2JT Tel: (01422) 839456 Fax: (01422) 835786 E-mail: sales@rosehill-polymers.ltd.uk *Polyurethane & industrial adhesives, sports surfaces manufrs*

Rose Hill Polymers Ltd, Rose Hill Mill, Beech Road, Sowerby Bridge, West Yorkshire, HX6 2JT Tel: (01422) 839456 Fax: (01422) 835786 E-mail: sales@rosehill-polymers.ltd.uk *Polyurethane & industrial adhesives. Also sports surface (binder) manufrs*

Rose & Krieger, Phoenix Mecano House, 6-7 Faraday Road, Rabans Lane Industrial Estate, Aylesbury, Buckinghamshire, HP19 8TX Tel: (01296) 398865 Fax: (01296) 398866 E-mail: rkgb@phoenix-mecano.ltd.uk *Framing (metal) systems & tubular jointing systems manufrs*

Rose Marie Fashions Ltd, Unit 5 First Floor, Sangra Building, Leicester, LE4 5AF Tel: 0116-262 8844 *Ladies knitwear manufrs*

Nigel Rose & Partners, 6 Langley Street, London, WC2H 9JT Tel: (020) 7836 9527 Fax: (020) 7379 0892 E-mail: london@nigelrose.com *Quantity surveyors & cost consultants*

Rose Partnership, 12 Copthall Avenue, London, EC2R 7DH Tel: (020) 7466 6000 Fax: (020) 7466 6058 *Executive search consultants*

Rose Plant Hire (Whittlesey) Ltd, Low Cross House, Padholme Road East, Peterborough, PE1 5XL Tel: (01733) 557575 Fax: (01733) 890005 E-mail: jon@roseplanthire.co.uk *Plant Hire & Earthmoving Contractors*

Rose Tissue Converter, Sefton Street, Oldham, OL9 7LT Tel: 0161-682 4447 Fax: 0161-682 7774 E-mail: enquires@rosetissues.co.uk *Toilet roll & kitchen towel manufrs*

▶ Rose UK, Unit 13 Vision Business Park, Firth Way, Nottingham, NG6 8GF Tel: 0115-927 9542 Fax: 0115-976 1986 E-mail: rose@roseuksecurityservices.co.uk *Manned guarding services*

▶ Rose Wood Packaging Scotland, 9-15 Napier Place, Wardpark North, Cumbernauld, Glasgow, G68 0LL Tel: (01236) 782500 E-mail: enquires@rosewoodpackaging.co.uk *Packaging manufrs*

▶ Rosebery Group Ltd, Hastings House, 79-83 Station Road, Ellesmere Port, CH65 4BN Tel: 0151-357 1066 Fax: 0151-357 2066 E-mail: general@rosebery.co.uk

Rosebud Preserves Ltd, Rosebud Farm, Healey, Ripon, North Yorkshire, HG4 4LH Tel: (01765) 689174 Fax: (01765) 689174 E-mail: elspath@rosebud.fsworld.co.uk *Jam manufrs*

Rosedale Aquatics, 81 Home Farm Crescent, Whitnash, Leamington Spa, Warwickshire, CV31 2QY Tel: (01926) 332493 Fax: (01926) 332493 E-mail: info@rosedaleaquatics.co.uk *Established in 1968 Rosedale Aquatics offers you the customer expert advice and quality Aquatic products. From fresh water tropical to marine and ponds. Don't go anywhere else until You have visited us. Just off the M40 with out of town parking. Make a day out and visit Leamington's great shopping and parks.*

Rosedale Building Systems Ltd, 234 Shay Lane, Holmfield, Halifax, West Yorkshire, HX2 9AD Tel: (01422) 244303 Fax: (01422) 247877 E-mail: r.b.s.ltd@btconnect.com *Portable building distributors*

▶ Rosedene Construction Ltd, Tripes Farm Yard Chelsfield Lane, Orpington, Kent, BR6 7RS Tel: (01689) 835807 Fax: (01689) 835807 E-mail: joan.rosedene@btopenworld.com *Plant hire, earth moving, landfill, courses, reservoir, lakes construction*

▶ Rosefame Properties, West Cottage, Church Street, Ticehurst, Wadhurst, East Sussex, TN5 7DL Tel: (01580) 201319 Fax: (01580) 201604 E-mail: info@rosefame.co.uk *Properties for sale in France, Spain and Italy.*

▶ Roselands Heating Ltd, 340 Seaside, Eastbourne, East Sussex, BN22 7RJ Tel: (01323) 639455 Fax: (01323) 649912

Roseline Group, Unit 10 Cadzow Industrial Estate, Old Waters Road, Hamilton, Lanarkshire, ML3 7QU Tel: (01698) 459390 Fax: (01698) 459567 *Soft furnishing manufacturers*

Rosemarie Tayler Ltd, The Chase, Purdis Farm Lane, Ipswich, IP3 8UF Tel: (01473) 272041 Fax: (01473) 272041 *Children's knitwear manufrs*

Rosemont Pharmaceuticals Ltd, Braithwaite St, York Dale Industrial Estate, Leeds, LS11 9XE Tel: 0113-244 1400 Fax: 0113-245 3567 E-mail: desk@rosepharma.com *Pharmaceutical manufrs*

Rosenberger Micro-Coax Ltd, 2 Mercury House, Calleva Park, Aldermaston, RG7 8PN Tel: 0118-981 0023 Fax: 0118-981 6180 E-mail: sales@rmcoax.com *Manufacturers & distributors of a comprehensive range of semi rigid & flexible coaxial cables, coaxial connectors, coaxial cable assembles, coaxial adapters, calibration kits, coaxial test cables & fibre optic cables & connectors*

Rosendale Gearboxes, Railway Arch 879, Rosendale Road, London, SE24 9EH Tel: (020) 8671 5074 *Gearbox manufrs*

Rosendale Motor Engineering Ltd, 4A-4C Tyrrell Road, East Dulwich, London, SE22 9NA Tel: (020) 8693 9511 Fax: (020) 8299 0968 E-mail: info@rosendale-motors.co.uk *Accident repair centre*

Rosenvinge & Co. Ltd, Suite 20 Albion House, Sidney Street, North Shields, Tyne & Wear, NE29 0DW Tel: 0191-258 0030 Fax: 0191-296 0520 *Ship brokers* Also at: Blythe, Grangemouth, Seaham & Sunderland

Rosenwheel Ltd, 181 Cambuslang Road, Rutherglen, Glasgow, G73 1PX Tel: 0141-643 1986 Fax: 0141-643 2177 *Joinery manufrs*

Roses Venetian Blind Centre, 14 Highlands, Littleborough, Lancashire, OL15 0DS Tel: 0161-624 8596 Fax: 0161-622 1480 E-mail: info@rosesblinds.co.uk *Window blind suppliers*

▶ Roseview Windows, Yardley Road Industrial Estate, Olney, Buckinghamshire, MK46 5EA Tel: (01234) 712657 Fax: (01234) 712823 E-mail: info@roseview.co.uk *Windows & doors locks manufrs*

Roseville Taxis, Stanier Street, Newcastle, Staffordshire, ST5 2SY Tel: (01782) 631234 Fax: (01782) 634800 *Mini cab & parcel delivery services*

Rosewell Engineers, Stockwitch Lodge, Bridgehampton, Yeovil, Somerset, BA22 8HN Tel: (01935) 840838 Fax: (01935) 840552 *Agricultural engineers*

Rosewood Joinery, Unit D The Paddocks, 347 Cherry Hinton Road, Cambridge, CB1 8DH Tel: (01223) 508777 Fax: (01223) 508777 *Joinery manufrs*

Rosewood Joinery, Unit 4 Hope & Aldridge Business Centre, Weddington Rd, Nuneaton, Warwickshire, CV10 0HF Tel: (024) 7638 3555 Fax: (024) 7638 3555 *Joinery manufacturers & contractors*

Rosewood Maufacturing Co. Ltd, Bede Trading Estate, Jarrow, Tyne & Wear, NE32 3EN Tel: 0191-428 1214 Fax: 0191-428 1021 E-mail: sales@rosewoodpackaging.co.uk *Packaging material suppliers*

Rosewood Pet Products Ltd, 45 Coalport Road, Broseley, Shropshire, TF12 5AN Tel: (01952) 883408 Fax: (01952) 884359 E-mail: sales@rosewoodpet.com *Pet products distributors*

▶ Rosewood Warehousing & Distribution, Unit /12 Seddon Place, Stanley Industrial Estate, Skelmersdale, Lancashire, WN8 8EB Tel: 01695 555580 Fax: 01695 724253 E-mail: parratt_andy@Btconnect.Com *Warehousing & distribution logistic solutions road haulage*

Rosh Engineering Ltd, Newtown Indust Estate, Chester le Street, County Durham, DH3 2QN Tel: 0191-410 6300 Fax: 0191-410 6319 E-mail: info@rosh.co.uk *Power Transformer and high voltage equipment repair, refurbishment, enhancement, supply & installation and commissioning.****

Roshview International Ltd, 3-11 Stean Street, London, E8 4ED Tel: (020) 7254 4836 Fax: (020) 7249 9886 *Freight forwarding agents export & import*

Roskel Contracts Ltd, Suite 1a Old Bank House, 50 St Johns Close, Knowle, Solihull, West Midlands, B93 0JU Tel: (01564) 732292 Fax: (01564) 732296 E-mail: sales@roskel.co.uk *Internal partitions manufrs*

Roskell Contracts Ltd, 102 Lower Guildford Road, Knaphill, Woking, Surrey, GU21 2EW Tel: (01483) 489905 Fax: (01483) 489925 *Suspended ceiling contractor*

Roskill Information Services, 27a Leopold Road, London, SW19 7BB Tel: (020) 8944 0066 Fax: (020) 8947 9568 E-mail: info@roskill.co.uk *Metal & mineral market consultants*

▶ Rosler UK, Unity Grove, Knowsley Business Park, Prescot, Merseyside, L34 9GT Tel: 0151-482 0444 Fax: 0151-482 4400 *Specialists in surface finishing & shot blasting systems*

Rospen Industries Ltd, Oldends Lane Industrial Estate, Oldends Lane, Stonehouse, Gloucestershire, GL10 3RQ Tel: (01453) 825212 Fax: (01453) 828279 E-mail: enquiries@rospen.com *Weighing & metering services*

▶ Ross, 3 Wellington Street, Millom, Cumbria, LA18 4DF Tel: (01229) 772551 Fax: (01229) 772510

▶ Ross A D T Ltd, 30 Byron St, Dundee, DD3 6QX Tel: (01382) 825050

B. Ross, 1B Windermere Avenue, London, SW19 3EP Tel: (020) 8540 9333 Fax: (020) 8543 3869 *Sign making & engraving*

Ross & Bonnyman Ltd, Roberts Street, Forfar, Angus, DD8 3DG Tel: (01307) 469366 Fax: (01307) 461567 *Taillifts & shutter door manufrs*

▶ Ross Care Centres Ltd, 3 Royal London Industrial Estate, Old Lane, Leeds, LS11 8AG Tel: 0113-277 7007 Fax: 0113-277 7040 *NHS contractors*

Ross Care Centres, Units 2-3 & 11, Westfield Road, Wallasey, Merseyside, CH44 7HX Tel: 0151-653 6000 Fax: 0151-653 8543 *Electric & invalid chair distributors*

Ross & Catherall Ltd, Forge Lane, Killamarsh, Sheffield, S21 1BA Tel: 0114-248 6404 Fax: 0114-247 5999 E-mail: rosscatherall@doncasters.com *Ferro-alloy producers*

Ross Ceramics Ltd, Derby Road, Denby, Ripley, Derbyshire, DE5 8NA Tel: (01773) 570800 Fax: (01773) 570152 E-mail: sales@rossceramics.co.uk *Manufacturers of pre-formed ceramic cores*

▶ Ross Chemicals & Storage Co. Ltd, Grange Dock, Grangemouth, Stirlingshire, FK3 8UD Tel: (01324) 474774 Fax: (01324) 485476

Ross & Cromarty Enterprise, 69-71 High Street, Invergordon, Ross-Shire, IV18 0AA Tel: (01349) 853666 Fax: (01349) 853833 E-mail: sales@race.co.uk *Local enterprise*

David Ross Fabrications Ltd, Unit 1E, Peckleton Lane Business Estate, Peckleton, Leicester, LE9 7RN Tel: (01455) 823721 Fax: (01455) 828339 E-mail: metalwork@davidrossfabrications.co.uk *Sheet metal fabricators*

▶ Ross Deeptech Initiatives Ltd, Broomhill Road, Stonehaven, Kincardineshire, AB39 2NH Tel: (01569) 767888 Fax: (01569) 766990 E-mail: admin@rossdeeptech.co.uk

Ross Electrical, Cloverhill Road, Bridge of Don, Aberdeen, AB23 8FE Tel: (01224) 222700 Fax: (01224) 823008 *Electrical distributors*

Ross Fabrics, Manor Mill Lane, Leeds, LS11 8LQ Tel: 0113-385 2200 Fax: 0113-277 8855 E-mail: sales@rossfabrics.co.uk *Upholsterers warehousemen*

Ross Farm Machinery Ltd, Usk Road, Raglan, Usk, Gwent, NP15 2HJ Tel: (01291) 690205 Fax: (01291) 690177 E-mail: ragland@rossfarm.co.uk *Agricultural machinery manufrs*

Ross Feed Ltd, Industrial Estate West, 2 Wonastow Road, Monmouth, Gwent, NP25 5AH Tel: (01600) 715448 Fax: (01600) 712480 *Animal feed distributors*

▶ Ross Fire Protection Ltd, 29 Deerdykes View, Cumbernauld, Glasgow, G68 9HN Tel: (01236) 738502 Fax: (01236) 727977

Ross Heat Exchangers Ltd, Units 6 & 7, Dryden Glen, Loanhead, Midlothian, EH20 9NA Tel: 0131-440 0066 Fax: 0131-440 4188 E-mail: sales@ross-heatexchangers.co.uk *Heat exchanger repairs & re-tubing service providers*

Ross Hillman Ltd, Station Road, Westbury, Wiltshire, BA13 3JP Tel: (01373) 822447 Fax: (01373) 824492 *Quarry stone supply merchants*

J.W.H. Ross & Co., 10 Annfield Place, Glasgow, G31 2XN Tel: 0141-554 2166 Fax: 0141-554 7639 E-mail: info@jwhross.co.uk *Consulting mining engineers*

Ross Lab plc, Ross Lab House, Fence Avenue Industrial Estate, Macclesfield, Cheshire, SK10 1LT Tel: (01625) 610077 Fax: (01625) 619877 E-mail: sales@rosslab.com *Medical & diagnostic products*

Malcolm Ross & Sons Ltd, PO Box 4, Alderley Edge, Cheshire, SK9 7PR Tel: (01625) 583853 Fax: (01625) 586340 E-mail: sales@malcolmross.co.uk *Merchants & agents of yarn, including cotton, jute & man-made fibre*

Ross Manufacturers, Altbarn Industrial Estate Lordswood Industrial Estate, Revenge Road, Chatham, Kent, ME5 8UD Tel: (01634) 684808 Fax: (01634) 684831 E-mail: rossarch@btconnect.com *Ross Architectural Manufacturers have a highly skilled workforce with vast experience in the manufacture of electro-mechanical products. This enables us to offer the widest range of products from large production runs to one off custom made specials. Our engineers"" experience and knowledge enable us to manufacture the most effective product possible and work to detailed drawings and specifications supplied by customers*

▶ Ross Off Shore, Unit 12b, Peterseat Drive, Altens Industrial Estate, Aberdeen, AB12 3HT Tel: (01224) 877774 Fax: (01224) 876066 *Heat exchanger suppliers*

▶ Ross Shire Journal, Dochcarty Road, Dingwall, Ross-Shire, IV15 9UD Tel: (01349) 863436 Fax: (01349) 863456

Ross Storage Equipment Co., 2 Abbotsford, Bishopbriggs, Glasgow, G64 1ED Tel: 0141-772 2453 Fax: 0141-772 2453 *Storage equipment*

Thomas Ross Ltd, St Marks Road, Binfield, Bracknell, Berkshire, RG42 4TR Tel: (01344) 862686 Fax: (01344) 862575 E-mail: sales@thomasross.co.uk *Fine art publishers*

Ross Tooling International, West Ings Lane, Knottingley, West Yorkshire, WF11 9BJ Tel: (01977) 672622 Fax: (01977) 670733 *Iron casting/aluminium bronze manufrs* Also at: Batley

Ross UK Ltd, Cakemore Road, Rowley Regis, West Midlands, B65 0QW Tel: 0121-559 4900 Fax: 0121-559 5309 E-mail: sales@rossuk.co.uk *Pneumatic equipment & systems distributors*

▶ Ross Wright Ltd, Unit 31 Northfield Way, Aycliffe Industrial Park, Newton Aycliffe, County Durham, DL5 6UF Tel: (01325) 320767 Fax: (01325) 320498

Rossal A/C Ltd, Systems House, 47 Palace Road, Bromley, BR1 3JU Tel: (020) 8466 0088 Fax: (020) 8466 1697 E-mail: rossalltd@aol.com *Air conditioning services*

Rossco Ltd, Croft Court, Grammar School Walk, Hitchin, Hertfordshire, SG5 1JD Tel: (01462) 431413 Fax: (01462) 431423 *PA sound equipment hire*

Rossendale Fork Trucks Ltd, 18 Thirlmere Avenue, Haslingden, Rossendale, Lancashire, BB4 6LU Tel: 01706 228583 *Fork lift trucks*

Rossendale Forme & Knife Co. Ltd, 245 Burnley Road East, Rossendale, Lancashire, BB4 9HU Tel: (01706) 213165 Fax: (01706) 831319 E-mail: info@rossforme.co.uk *Cutting forms & die manufacturer for printing*

Rossendale Group, Roman Way, South Hykeham, Lincoln, LN6 9UH Tel: (01522) 693423 Fax: (01522) 693988 *Lifting & safety equipment supplier*

Rossendale Packaging Services Ltd, Unit 24a Victoria Industrial Centre, Victoria Street, Accrington, Lancashire, BB5 0PH Tel: (01254) 382030 Fax: (01254) 382030 *Vacuum forming & blister packaging*

Rossendale Plastics, Station Road, Haslingden, Rossendale, Lancashire, BB4 5HX Tel: (01706) 214652 Fax: (01706) 830829 E-mail: info@rossendaleplastics.co.uk *Plastic fabricators & sign manufrs*

Rossendale Wipers, 19 Waingate Close, Rossendale, Lancashire, BB4 7SQ Tel: (01706) 221922 Fax: (01706) 221922 *Cleaning cloth distributors & manufrs*

▶ Rosser Morris, The White House, Hockliffe Street, Leighton Buzzard, Bedfordshire, LU7 1HD Tel: (01525) 217904 Fax: 0845 2805050 E-mail: enquiries@rossermorris.co.uk *Drawing plans and specifications prepared for Planning and Building Regulations permission.*Domestic & Commercial*New build, extensions & alterations*Barn conversions*Loft conversions*Structural calculations*Full land surveys*RICS qualified & fully insured*Qualified & experienced staff**

Rosser & Russell Building Services Ltd, Orbit House, 1-6 Ritz Parade, London, W5 3RD Tel: (020) 8982 2222 Fax: (020) 8982 2331 *Building service engineers*

Rossi Gearmotors Ltd, Unit 8-9 Phoenix Park, Bayton Road Industrial Estate, Coventry, CV7 9QN Tel: (024) 7664 4646 Fax: (024) 7664 4535 E-mail: sales@rossigears.com *Geared motors & gear manufrs*

Rossi Southend On Sea Ltd, 31 Lucy Road, Southend-on-Sea, SS1 2AU Tel: (01702) 467532 Fax: (01702) 391432 *Ice cream manufrs*

Rossi Sports & Leisurewear, 24 Blackhills Road, Peterlee, County Durham, SR8 4DW Tel: 0191-518 2228 Fax: 0191-518 2228 *Manufacturers of football strips, bowls clothing, embroidery & printing*

Rosskerr Plant & Tools Ltd, Coombe Works, Coombe Road, London, NW10 0EB Tel: (020) 8450 6606 Fax: (020) 8450 7372 *Plant & tool suppliers*

▶ Rosslyn Garden Craft, North Cottage, Rosebank, Roslin, Midlothian, EH25 9PU Tel: 0131-445 7698 E-mail: rosslyngardencraft@hotmail.com *landscape gardeners*garden and conservatory furniture*supplier*if it is in the gaden we supply it*

Rosslyn Research Ltd, 112 Boundary Road, St Johns Wood, London, NW8 0RH Tel: (020) 7328 8823 Fax: (020) 7624 1242 E-mail: admin@rosslyn-research.co.uk *Market research services*

▶ R. Rosssa & Son Ltd, 53 Stonebridge Street, Leicester, LE5 3PB Tel: 0116-276 7778 Fax: 0116-276 1424 *Ice cream & yoghurt manufrs*

▶ Ross-Shire Engineering Ltd, The Industrial Estate, Muir Of Ord, Ross-Shire, IV6 7UA Tel: (01463) 870049 E-mail: info@ross-ing.com *Engineering*

Rosswood Studios Ltd, 114 Wendover Road, Stoke Mandeville, Aylesbury, Buckinghamshire, HP22 5TE Tel: (01296) 612009 E-mail: marianne@rosswood.co.uk *Animation services*

Rosta Engineering Ltd, Resource House, 144 Castle Street, Stockport, Cheshire, SK3 9JH Tel: 0161-429 5300 Fax: 0161-429 5322 E-mail: mail@rosta.com *Recruitment agency*

Rosti Scotland Ltd, Baird Avenue, Strutherhill Industrial Estate, Larkhall, Lanarkshire, ML9 2PJ Tel: (01698) 888186 Fax: (01698) 888389 *Injection moulding*

Roston Castings, Mill Lane, Ellastone, Ashbourne, Derbyshire, DE6 2HF Tel: (01335) 324368 Fax: (01335) 324544 E-mail: sales@rostoncastings.co.uk Principal Export Areas: Worldwide *Aluminium founders/aluminium foundry manufacturers. In addition manufacturers of diecastings including aluminium alloy & gravity. Also aluminium/alloy casting manufrs*

▶ Rostrum Sportswear Ltd, Princes Street, Lochmaben, Lockerbie, Dumfriesshire, DG11 1PQ Tel: (01387) 811315 Fax: (01387) 811990 E-mail: info@rostrumsportswear.co.uk *Sportswear retailers*

Roswell It Services Ltd, James Watt Centre Scottish Enterprise Technology Park, James, East Kilbride, Glasgow, G75 0QD Tel: (01355) 265588 Fax: (01355) 265975 E-mail: sales@roswell-it.co.uk *Computer maintenance & support services*

Rota Engineering Ltd, Wellington Street, Bury, Lancashire, BL8 2BD Tel: 0161-764 0424 Fax: 0161-762 9729 E-mail: sales@rota-eng.com Principal Export Areas: Worldwide *Rotary actuators & BASEEFA rated connectors*

Rotable Repairs Group Ltd, Unit 1/4, Britannia Business Park, Comet Way, Southend-on-Sea, SS2 6GE Tel: (01702) 529888 Fax: (01702) 523580 E-mail: info@rotablerepairs.com *Aircraft wheels, brakes, freight systems & landing gear repairers*

Rotabroach, Imperial Works, Sheffield Road, Tinsley, Sheffield, S9 2YL Tel: 0114-221 2510 Fax: 0114-221 2563 E-mail: info@rotabroach.co.uk *Magnetic drill stands & magnetic drilling machines manufrs*

Rotadata Ltd, Bateman Street, Derby, DE23 8JQ Tel: (01332) 348008 Fax: (01332) 331023 E-mail: sales@rotadata.com *Turbo machinery instrumentation & telecommunications*

Rotadex Systems Ltd, Sytems House, Central Business Park, Mackadown Lane, Birmingham, B33 0JL Tel: 0121-783 7411 Fax: 0121-783 1876 E-mail: cathi.croton@rotadex.co.uk *Card index & filing systems manufacturers*

Rotadyne UK Ltd, Saxon House, Henson Way, Telford Way Industrial Estate, Kettering, Northamptonshire, NN16 8PX Tel: (01536) 414421 Fax: (01536) 411091 E-mail: pevans@rotadyne.com Principal Export Areas: Middle East, Central/East Europe, West Europe & North America *Manufacturers of rollers* Also at: Birmingham

Rotaflow Ltd, Unit 16 Peterley Business Centre, 472 Hackney Road, London, E2 9EQ Tel: (020) 7739 7072 Fax: (020) 7729 9179 E-mail: rotaflow@mwfree.co.uk *General printers*

Rotaflow F V Ltd, Rotec House, Bingswood Trading Estate, Whaley Bridge, High Peak, Derbyshire, SK23 7LY Tel: (01663) 735003 Fax: (01663) 735006 E-mail: sales@rotaflow.com *Rotaflow is a Worldwide manufacturer of swivel joints, rotary joints & articulated swivel loading arms. The Rotaflow swivel joint is a robust & durable pipe fitting. We specialise in swivel joints & flexible couplings for all pipework applications. Technical brochures available on our website.*

Rotaglade Ltd, 85 Park Road, Hale, Altrincham, Cheshire, WA15 9LQ Tel: 0161-980 3102 Fax: 0161-980 3102 *Storage equipment & racking installers*

Rotair Systems Ltd, 23 Whitestones, Basingstoke, Hampshire, RG22 4QX Tel: (0870) 0626027 Fax: (01256) 321519 E-mail: info@rotairsystems.co.uk *Air film solutions for moving heavy loads services*

Rotajet Systems, Richard Alan House, Shaw Cross Business Park, Dewsbury, West Yorkshire, WF12 7RD Tel: (01924) 468769 Fax: (01924) 485376 E-mail: info@rotajet.co.uk Principal Export Areas: Worldwide *Manufacturers of cleaning machines, industrial & special purpose*

Rotalink Ltd, Cropmead, Crewkerne, Somerset, TA18 7HQ Tel: (01460) 72000 Fax: (01460) 74278 E-mail: info@rotalink.com Principal Export Areas: Worldwide *Electric motors including AC, minature & stepper/stepping. Also manufacturers of electric geared motors, electrical/electromagnetic relays & timers*

Rotaloc Europe, 8 Wyvern Buildings, Grove Trading Estate, Dorchester, Dorset, DT1 1ST Tel: (01305) 257800 Fax: (01305) 259420 E-mail: sales@rotaloc.co.uk *Veck Fasteners manufacture and distribute high quality, low cost bonding fasteners and adhesives for use in assemblies throughout manufacturing.*

Rotamag, 41 Capley Road, Darnall, Sheffield, S9 5JF Tel: 0114-291 1020 Fax: 0114-261 8186 E-mail: sales@bryar.co.uk *Magnetic drilling systems manufrs*

Rotamec Ltd, 4 Winchester Farm, Draycott Road, Cheddar, Somerset, BS27 3RP Tel: (01934) 743165 Fax: (01934) 743168 E-mail: sales@rotamec.co.uk *Electric motor repairs & transmission specialists*

Rotamic Engineering Ltd, Marsh Road, Lords Meadow Industrial Estate, Crediton, Devon, EX17 1EU Tel: (01363) 774473 Fax: (01363) 773371 *Precision engineers*

Rotary Bearing & Transmission Co. Ltd, Unit 11 Forty 8 North 48, Duncrue Street, Belfast, BT3 9BJ Tel: (028) 9074 9377 Fax: (028) 9035 2949 E-mail: sales@rotarybearings-ni.com *Bearing & power transmission distributors*

Rotary Building Services, 53 Huntly Street, Aberdeen, AB10 1TH Tel: (01224) 633211 Fax: (01224) 633899 *Building contractors*

▶ Rotary Engineering Reading Ltd, Unit A8 Grovelands Avenue Workshops, Winnersh, Wokingham, Berkshire, RG41 5LB Tel: 0118-979 2200 Fax: 0118-979 2211

Rotary Equipment Services Ltd, Unit 5-6 Castle Way, Severn Bridge Industrial Estate, Portskewett, Caldicot, Gwent, NP26 5YG Tel: (01291) 420670 Fax: (01291) 430165 E-mail: sales@reslimited.com *Pump repair and Maintenance and repair of all rotating equipment. Also, condition monitoring & laser alignment services. Project Asset Management, Pump Station Refurbishment, Pump Management Programmes, Life Cycle Cost Analysis. National Service Centres at Caldicot, Loughborough and Chester. 66 Service Centres in Europe. Wholly owned subsidiary of KSB Ltd the Global Pump and Valve Manufacturer. Quality Assessment ISO 9001:2000, ISO 14001:2004 AND OHSAS 18001:1999. UVDB ACHILLES. Verify Utility Suppliers.* Also at: Bristol, Exeter, London W7, Manchester & Southampton

Rotary Equipment Services Ltd, Unit 2, Expressway Business Park, Station Road, Queensferry, Deeside, Clwyd, CH5 2TF Tel: (01244) 822402 Fax: (01244) 823960 E-mail: jeff.sheen@reslimited.com *Pump maintenance & repair*

Rotary Motion, Unit A5, Grovelands Avenue Ind Estate, Winnersh, Wokingham, Berkshire, RG41 5LB Tel: 0118-989 0000 Fax: (0118) 989 0484 E-mail: rotmot@aol.com *Bearing transmission engineers*

Rotary North West Ltd, Rotary House, Chantry Court, Chester West Employment Park, Chester, CH1 4QN Tel: (01244) 382233 Fax: (01244) 382458 *Mechanical & electrical engineering contractors*

Rotary Power Ltd, St. Peters, Newcastle upon Tyne, NE6 1BS Tel: 0191-276 4444 Fax: 0191-276 4462 E-mail: rotary.power@bel.co.uk Principal Export Areas: Worldwide *Hydraulic motors & underwater hydraulic equipment manufrs*

▶ Rotary Printers Ltd, Mitton Street, Stourport-on-Severn, Worcestershire, DY13 9AA Tel: (01299) 823839 Fax: (01299) 826991 E-mail: sales@rotaryprinters.co.uk

Rotary Products Ltd, Box Bush, Upper Redbrook, Monmouth, Gwent, NP25 4LU Tel: (01600) 715723 Fax: (01600) 716215 *Design engineers & mould manufrs*

▶ Rotary Scotland Ltd, 72 Kirk Road, Bathgate, West Lothian, EH48 1EH Tel: (01506) 633877 Fax: (01506) 634740

Rotary Southern Ltd, Rotary House, Breakspear Road, Ruislip, Middlesex, HA4 7ST Tel: (01895) 674264 Fax: (01895) 630673 E-mail: info@rotarysouthern.co.uk *Electrical & mechanical contractors*

Rotary Watches, Adia House 84-86 Regent Street, London, W1B 5RR Tel: (020) 7434 5500 Fax: (020) 7434 5548 E-mail: time@rotarywatches.com *Rotary watch distributors & manufacturers. Also electronic watches*

Rotary Yorkshire Ltd, 5 Buslingthorpe Green, Leeds, LS7 2HG Tel: 0113-262 0911 Fax: 0113-262 6342 E-mail: enquiries@rotary-yorkshire.co.uk *Electrical & mechanical contractors*

▶ Rotaset Documentation, Enterprise Road, Mablethorpe, Lincolnshire, LN12 1NB Tel: (01507) 472473 Fax: (01507) 473128 E-mail: sales@rotaset.co.uk

▶ Rotating Machinery Services, 126 Fletcher Road, Stoke-on-Trent, ST4 4AJ Tel: (01782) 747580 Fax: (01782) 749647

Rotational Mouldings Ltd, Knowles Industrial Estate, Buxton Road, Furness Vale, High Peak, Derbyshire, SK23 7PH Tel: (01663) 742897 Fax: (01663) 747584 E-mail: sales@rotationalmouldings.co.uk Principal Export Areas: Africa *Plastic rotational mouldings manufrs*

Rotatools UK Ltd, Brookfield Drive, Liverpool, L9 7EG Tel: 0151-525 8611 Fax: 0151-525 4868 E-mail: richard_dearn@hotmail.com *Boiler cleaning equipment manufrs*

Rotatrim, 8 Caxton Park, Caxton Road, Elm Farm Industrial Estate, Bedford, MK41 0TY Tel: (01234) 224545 Fax: (01234) 224540 E-mail: sales@rotatrim.co.uk *Guillotine (paper/board cutting), cutter (rotary) & paper trimmer manufrs*

Company Information

Rotech Ltd, Units 10 11 & 18, Blackworth Industrial Park, Highworth, Swindon, SN6 7NA Tel: (01793) 764700 Fax: (01793) 764554 E-mail: enquiries@rotechkeg.com *Machinery manufrs*

Rotech Machines Ltd, Bridge Road East, Welwyn Garden City, Hertfordshire, AL7 1JU Tel: (01707) 393700 Fax: (01707) 392800 *Rotech are one of the UK's leading suppliers of both online and off line printing equipment and the associated consumables such as foil, ribbon and type. **Our coding equipment centres on the three core technologies of Hot Foil, Thermal Transfer and Thermal Ink Jet that can print a wide variety of information onto a huge range of materials. **

Rotech Systems, Unit 53 Canal Bridge Enterprise Centre, Meadow Lane, Ellesmere Port, CH65 4EH Tel: 0151-356 2322 Fax: 0151-356 2437 *Heavy duty shaft encoders manufrs*

Rotex Europe Ltd, Whitehouse Vale, Aston La North, Runcorn, Cheshire, WA7 3FA Tel: (01928) 706100 Fax: (0870) 7529920 *Screeners, feeders*

Rothband & Co. Ltd, 4-6 Knowsley Road, Haslingden, Rossendale, Lancashire, BB4 4RX Tel: (01706) 830086 Fax: (01706) 830324 E-mail: sales@rothband.co.uk *Xray accessories, physiotherapy & massage couch distributors*

Rothbury Computers, Townfoot, Rothbury, Morpeth, Northumberland, NE65 7SL Tel: (01669) 620070 E-mail: johnrayner@rothburycomputers.com *Computer services*

Rothbury Home Bakery Ltd, Coquet View, Rothbury, Morpeth, Northumberland, NE65 7RZ Tel: (01669) 621273 Fax: (0870) 4581779 E-mail: sales@rothburybakery.com *Bread & pie product manufrs*

▶ Rothco Ltd, Brook House Church Road, Charsfield, Woodbridge, Suffolk, IP13 7QB Tel: (01473) 737759 Fax: 07050 664249 E-mail: rothco@msn.com *I am a consultant offering a wide range of I.T. services principally, but not exclusively across the Sage range of accounting software. Services include training, system review, project management, system design and bespoke programming.* Established in 1995, I have a wide range of clients across the South East of England from Manufacturing companies to Distribution and Warehousing services to companies working in the Leisure Industry.* A registered Sage Developer, I can offer a full systems analysis and bespoke programming service in the Sage Retrieve 4GL and Visual Basic languages. I can also offer bespoke solutions based on the full Microsoft Office suite. I provide training in all of the above software. * I can provide a range of reference sites, if required, who can provide an independent assessment of my capabilities.* Member of the Institution of Analysts and Programmers*

Rothenberger UK Ltd, 2 Kingsthorne Park, Henson Way, Telford Way Industrial Estate, Kettering, Northamptonshire, NN16 8PX Tel: (01536) 310300 Fax: (01536) 310600 E-mail: info@rothenberger.co.uk *Pipe tool & machine manufrs*

Rother Cartage South East Ltd, Unit 1 The Woodlands Centre, A22 Whitesmith, Lewes, East Sussex, BN8 6JB Tel: (01825) 873308 Fax: (01825) 873291 *Road transport, haulage & freight services*

Rothera & Brereton, Fairfield House, 186 Armley Road, Leeds, LS12 2QH Tel: 0113-387 4850 Fax: 0113-387 4820 *Paper merchants* Also at: Nottingham & Sheffield

▶ Rotherham CNC Ltd, Unit 30 Orgreave Close, Sheffield, S13 9NP Tel: 0114-269 9800 Fax: 0114-269 9800 *Precision engineering*

Rotherham Commercial Hydraulics Ltd, The Chain Works, Masbrough Street, Rotherham, South Yorkshire, S60 1ER Tel: (01709) 375515 Fax: (01709) 376247 E-mail: propshaft@aol.com *Propshaft repairs & manufrs*

Rotherham EAL Service, Eastwood Youth Centre, Cranworth Road, Rotherham, South Yorkshire, S65 1LN Tel: (01709) 828608 Fax: (01709) 828608 *Educational suppliers*

Rotherham Industrial Plastic Co. Ltd, Clifton Terrace, Rotherham, South Yorkshire, S65 2AG Tel: (01709) 372008 Fax: (01709) 820243 E-mail: steve@rip-co.co.uk *Plastic fabricators*

▶ Rotherham Investment and Development Office, Reresbey House, Bowbridge Close, Rotherham, South Yorkshire, S60 1YR Tel: (01709) 372099 Fax: (01709) 837953 E-mail: info@rido.org.uk

Rotherham Joinery Ltd, Coke Lane, Rotherham, South Yorkshire, S60 2JS Tel: (01709) 369676 Fax: (01709) 369676 *Joinery manufrs*

▶ Rotherham Logistics, Goods Station West, Russell Road, Kilnhurst, Mexborough, South Yorkshire, S64 5SH Tel: (01709) 571430 Fax: (01709) 571339

Rotherham Presition Engineering, Unit 2, Gateway Place, Parkgate, Rotherham, South Yorkshire, S62 6LL Tel: (01709) 526177 Fax: (01709) 710717 *Hydraulic engineers*

Rotherham Reboring & Leisureways, Masbrough Street, Rotherham, South Yorkshire, S60 1HW Tel: (01709) 834103 Fax: (01709) 834136 *Reconditioned engineer suppliers*

▶ Rotherham Reiki, 6 Rowan Rise, Maltby, Rotherham, South Yorkshire, S66 8BZ Tel: (01709) 817008 E-mail: rotherhamreiki@tiscali.co.uk *Complementary therapist*

Rotherham Sand & Gravel Co. Ltd, Scrooby Top Quarry, Scrooby Top, Doncaster, South Yorkshire, DN10 6AY Tel: (01777) 818203 Fax: (01777) 816040 *Sand & gravel producers*

Rotherham Stainless & Nickel Alloys Ltd, Northfield Road, Rotherham, South Yorkshire, S60 1RR Tel: (01709) 828055 Fax: (01709) 829716 *Stainless duplex steel stockists & manufrs*

Rotherham Waste Oils, Quarry Oil Depot, Kilnhurst Road, Kilnhurst, Mexborough, South Yorkshire, S64 5TL Tel: (01709) 527131 Fax: (01709) 719729 E-mail: sales@rwoil.co.uk *Oil storage & tank cleaning services*

Rothersthorpe Binders Ltd, Rothersthorpe Avenue, Rothersthorpe Avenue Industrial Estate, Northampton, NN4 8JH Tel: (01604) 762228 Fax: (01604) 768253 *Bookbinders*

Rothley Ltd, Macrome Road, Wolverhampton, WV6 9HG Tel: (01902) 756461 Fax: (01902) 745554 E-mail: sales@rothley.com *Steel tube manufrs*

H. Rothwell, 1 Simmonds Way, Brierfield, Nelson, Lancashire, BB9 5SS Tel: (01282) 601861 Fax: (01282) 605345 E-mail: nelson@rothwells.co.uk *Industrial supplies*

▶ Rothwell Robinson Ltd, Holyoake Road, Worsley, Manchester, M28 3DL Tel: 0161-790 9388 Fax: 0161-703 8863

Rothwell & Thomas, 7 Knowsley Street, Manchester, M8 8QN Tel: 0161-832 9100 Fax: 0161-839 4963 E-mail: tomrat@globalnet.co.uk *Furniture manufrs*

Roto Frank Ltd, Swift Point, Rugby, Warwickshire, CV21 1QH Tel: (01788) 558600 Fax: (01788) 558605 E-mail: uk_sales@roto-frank.com *Door & window hardware sales & distribution*

Rotolok Bulk Systems Ltd, 38 Woodham Lane, New Haw, Addlestone, Surrey, KT15 3NA Tel: (01932) 854756 Fax: (01932) 859427 E-mail: sales@blotch.co.uk *Manufacturers of handling equipment systems & couplings*

Rotometrics International Ltd, Walsall Business Park, Walsall Road, Aldridge, Walsall, WS9 0SW Tel: (01922) 610000 Fax: (01922) 610100 *Paper dye manufrs*

Roton Compressors Services Ltd, Roton House, Ellen Street, Oldham, OL9 6QR Tel: 0161-620 5107 Fax: 0161-627 1351 E-mail: roton@btconnect.com *Compressor distributors*

Roton Precision Engineering Ltd, The Old Ambulance, Stansfield Road, Todmorden, Lancashire, OL14 5DL Tel: (01706) 813399 Fax: (01706) 813399 *Precision & milling engineers*

Rotor Motion Midland Ltd, 3 Mandervell Road, Oadby, Leicester, LE2 5LQ Tel: 0116-271 0666 Fax: 0116-271 0333 E-mail: sales@plastic-and-rubber-engineer.ltd.uk *Food processing equipment manufrs*

Rotorspan Ltd, The Heliport, Hampton Lovett, Droitwich, Worcestershire, WR9 0LW Tel: (01905) 774831 Fax: (01905) 794657 E-mail: rotorspan@tesco.net *Helicopter maintenance & sales*

Rotosound Manufacturing Ltd, Unit 3B, Morewood Close, Sevenoaks, Kent, TN13 2HU Tel: (01732) 450838 Fax: (01732) 458994 E-mail: jason@rotosound.com Principal Export Areas: Worldwide *Music strings manufacturers & distributors*

Rotostock (Sales) Ltd, Porte Marsh Road, Calne, Wiltshire, SN11 8BW Tel: (01249) 822222 Fax: (01249) 822300 E-mail: sales@rotostock.co.uk *Thread cutting machines manufrs*

Rotrex Winches, Gryphon Works, Wimsey Way, Alfreton Trading Estate, Alfreton, Derbyshire, DE55 4LS Tel: (01773) 603997 Fax: (01773) 540566 E-mail: sales@rotrexwinches.co.uk *Marine & utility winches*

Rotronic Distribution Services, Unit 1a Crompton Fields, Crompton Way, Crawley, West Sussex, RH10 9EE Tel: (01293) 565556 Fax: (01293) 843710 E-mail: sales@rotronic.co.uk *Computer accessory distributors*

▶ Rouge Interiors Ltd, 19 Hoblands, Haywards Heath, West Sussex, RH16 3SB Tel: (01444) 415695 Fax: (01444) 416823 E-mail: info@rougeinteriors.co.uk *OFFICE FURNITURE, EDUCATIONAL FURNITURE, CAFE/RESTAURANT/BAR FURNITURE. INTERIOR DESIGN, SPACE PLANNING/CAD. INSTALLATION, REFURBISHMENT.*

▶ Rougham Hall Nurseries, Ipswich Road, Rougham, Bury St. Edmunds, Suffolk, IP30 9LZ Tel: (01359) 270577 Fax: (01359) 271149 E-mail: sales@roughamhallnurseries.co.uk *grower of hardy perennials to retail and trade customers wholesale enquiries welcome*

Roughton & Partners International Ltd, 321 Millbrook Road West, Southampton, SO15 0HW Tel: (023) 8070 5533 Fax: (023) 8070 1060 E-mail: hq@roughton.com *Consulting engineers, architects & surveyors*

▶ Roughtor Training, Roughtor House, 6 Sportsmans, Camelford, Cornwall, PL32 9QU Tel: 01840 211242 E-mail: Ashtonda1@aol.com *Provider of training courses, both open and in-house, in Quality Management,ISO 9001 and Internal Auditing at locations across the south west region.*

Roughway Converters Ltd, Roughway Mill, Dunks Green, Tonbridge, Kent, TN11 9SG Tel: (01732) 810811 Fax: (01732) 810838 E-mail: roughway@btconnect.com *Packaging merchants & board sheeting services*

Roulston Engineering, Flinders House, Stokenham, Kingsbridge, Devon, TQ7 2TB Tel: (01548) 580230 Fax: (01548) 580231 E-mail: rob.wiltshire@roulstoneng.co.uk *Marine, industrial pumps & centrifuges retailers*

D. & W. Round Scrap Metal Merchants Ltd, Triton Works, Woods Lane, Cradley Heath, West Midlands, B64 7AE Tel: (01384) 562720 Fax: (01384) 565922 *Scrap metal merchants & processors*

Round Green Engineering Ltd, 199 Camford Way, Luton, LU3 3AN Tel: (01582) 503808 Fax: (01582) 503898 E-mail: barrie@roundgreen.com *Metal fabricators*

Round House, 1 Meyrick Road, Bournemouth, BH1 2PR Tel: (01202) 553262 Fax: (01202) 557698 *Hotel with conference facilities*

Round House Ltd, 57 Pinbush Road, Lowestoft, Suffolk, NR33 7NL Tel: (01502) 515220 Fax: (01502) 500954 E-mail: sales@roundhouse.biz *Sheet metalworkers & general fabrications*

Round Oak Rail Terminal Ltd, Round Oak Terminal, Pedmore Road, Brierley Hill, West Midlands, DY5 1LJ Tel: (01384) 263109 Fax: (01384) 265428 *Warehouse & distribution services*

Round Tyres, 4 Grey Friars, Grantham, Lincolnshire, NG31 6PG Tel: (01476) 573273 Fax: (01476) 573273 *Tyres & exhaust fitters & services*

Roundabout Bookbinders Ltd, Vincent Lane, Dorking, Surrey, RH4 3HG Tel: (01306) 885336 Fax: (01306) 742604 *Trade bookbinders*

Roundbrand TWS, Cow House Lane, Armthorpe, Doncaster, South Yorkshire, DN3 3ED Tel: (01302) 833029 Fax: (01302) 832198 E-mail: enquiries@roundbrand.co.uk *PVCu products*

Roundcroft Metal Finishing, Unit 1 Roundcroft, Willenhall, West Midlands, WV13 2PN Tel: (01902) 606962 Fax: (01902) 606962 *Electro painting services*

Roundel Design UK Ltd, Flishinghurst Orchards, Chalk Lane, Cranbrook, Kent, TN17 2QA Tel: (01580) 712666 Fax: (01580) 713564 E-mail: sales@roundeldesign.co.uk *Kitchen & bedroom units installers & manufrs*

Roundford Ltd, The Old Co-Op, Croft Lane, Adderbury, Banbury, Oxfordshire, OX17 3NB Tel: (01295) 810137 Fax: (01295) 812056 E-mail: rdfd@walford-and-round.co.uk *Optical manufrs*

▶ Roundhere, Unit 2b Mansfield Business Park, Lymington Bottom Road, Medstead, Alton, Hampshire, GU34 5PZ Tel: (01420) 560036 Fax: (0871) 7336040 E-mail: sales@roundhere.uk.com *Roundhere Ltd is a supplier of contemporary furniture andlighting for offices, bars, restaurants, schools, universities, hotels and conference centres.**The manufacturers we represent include Vitra, Fritz Hansen, Lammhults, Knoll Studio, Alias, Tacchini, Gubi, Artifort and Flos. **The areas we cover are London, Surrey, Sussex, Kent, Hampshire, Berkshire and Dorset.*

Roundhill Computer Systems Ltd, Orchard Ho, Ogbourne St George, Marlborough, Wilts, SN8 1SU Tel: (01672) 841535 Fax: (01672) 841525 *Software house*

Roundhouse Software Ltd, The Cavendish Centre, Winnall Close, Winchester, Hampshire, SO23 0LB Tel: (01962) 877649 Fax: (01962) 834085 E-mail: sales@roundhouse-sw.com *Software development*

▶ Roundtrip Solutions Ltd, 15 Freuchie Mill, Freuchie, Cupar, Fife, KY15 7JL Tel: (01337) 858826 E-mail: sales@roundtripsolutions.com *Computer software development*

Roundwood Engineering Works, 15 Carrigs Road, Newcastle, County Down, BT33 0JZ Tel: (028) 4372 3550 Fax: (028) 4372 6636 *Engineers*

N. Rourke & Son (Engineering) Ltd, 4-6 Barkan Way, Swinton, Manchester, M27 8SF Tel: 0161-793 5171 Fax: 0161-794 4760 E-mail: nrourkeson@hotmail.com *Steel fabricators*

Rousant Sherwood Ltd, Van Alloys Indust Estate, Busgrove Lane, Stoke Row, Henley-on-Thames, Oxfordshire, RG9 5QW Tel: (01491) 680767 Fax: (01491) 682290 E-mail: rousant@msn.com *Precision engineers*

▶ Rouse Concrete, Gilbey Road, Grimsby, South Humberside, DN31 2RL Tel: (01472) 351987 Fax: (01472) 362202 *Concrete ready mix*

Rousselet Robatel UK Ltd, Parkside House, 17 East Parade, Harrogate, North Yorkshire, HG1 5LF Tel: (01423) 530093 Fax: (01423) 530120 E-mail: sales@rousselet.robatel.co.uk *Centrifuge manufrs*

▶ Route One Highways Ltd, Suite 3, 14 Rishworth Street, Wakefield, West Yorkshire, WF1 3BY Tel: (01924) 381970 Fax: (01924) 381971 E-mail: gary@routeonehighways.co.uk *Installers of:*Anti-skid Surfacing*Coloured Surfacing*Decorative Surfacing*Joint Sealing*Joint Repairs*Concrete Repairs*Bridge Joints*Surface Preparation*

Routec Ltd, Unit 7 Greys Green Business Centre, Rotherfield Greys, Henley-On-Thames, Oxfordshire, RG9 4QG Tel: (01491) 628989 Fax: (01491) 628989 *CNC routing repetition services*

Routeco, Unit 8, Spitfire Close, Coventry Business Park, Coventry, CV5 6UR Tel: (024) 7667 6513 Fax: (024) 7667 8490 E-mail: coventry@routeco.co.uk *Electronic component distrbutor*

Routeco plc, Davy Avenue, Knowlhill, Milton Keynes, MK5 8HJ Tel: (01908) 666777 Fax: (01908) 666738 *Electric & electronic contractors*

▶ The Routing & Packaging Company Ltd, Unit 1 Walk Mill Green Road, Colne, Lancashire, BB8 8AL Tel: (01282) 864629 Fax: (01282) 864661 E-mail: nigel@trppackaging.co.uk *Bespoke packaging services*

▶ Mike Routledge (Books), 22 Letchworth Crescent, Beeston, Nottingham, NG9 5LL Tel: 0115-922 3726 Fax: (0870) 1221950 E-mail: mikeroutledge@gmail.com *To promote books written and published by Mike Routledge*

Rovacabin, Powke Lane, Cradley Heath, West Midlands, B64 5PZ Tel: 0121-561 4003 Fax: 0121-561 4811 *Cabin manufrs*

Rovacabin, Williams Shipping Yard, Andes Road, Nursling, Southampton, SO16 0YZ Tel: (023) 8074 1345 Fax: (023) 8074 0108 E-mail: drice@sgb.co.uk *Portable accommodation suppliers*

Rovema Packaging Machines, The Coach House The Firs, High Street, Whitchurch, Aylesbury, Buckinghamshire, HP22 4SJ Tel: (01296) 642060 Fax: (01296) 641550 E-mail: sales@rovema.co.uk *Packaging equipment, machines & systems manufrs*

▶ Rover's Flooring Ltd, 2 Woodside Industrial Park, Works Road, Letchworth Garden City, Hertfordshire, SG6 1LA Tel: (01462) 486586 Fax: (01462) 486584 E-mail: info@rovers.nl *Solid hardwood flooring importers & distributors*

▶ Rovert Equipment Co. Ltd, Rovert House, Water Tower Road, Clayhill Light Industrial Park, Neston, CH64 3US Tel: 0151-336 2122 Fax: 0151-336 8997 E-mail: david@rovert.co.uk *Paper handling, binding machines, mailroom equipment suppliers*

Rovic Engineering, 36 Dawkins Road, Poole, Dorset, BH15 4JD Tel: (01202) 683446 Fax: (01202) 684824 E-mail: rovic@roviceng.co.uk *Special purpose machinery manufrs*

▶ Rovtech Ltd, Rovtech House Cothal View Kirkton Avenue, Pitmedden Industrial Estate, Dyce, Aberdeen, AB21 0BA Tel: (01224) 775527 Fax: (01224) 775547 *Under water surveys*

▶ Rovtech Systems Ltd, 7 The Old Brewery, Shore Street, Barrow-in-Furness, Cumbria, LA14 2UB Tel: (01229) 822121 Fax: (01229) 870208 E-mail: info@rovtechsystems.co.uk *ROV's & underwater video systems manufrs*

Rowan Associates, 77 Albert Road, Gourock, Renfrewshire, PA19 1NJ Tel: (01475) 631200 Fax: (01475) 638971 E-mail: enquiries@rowanassociates.co.uk *Computer consultants*

Rowan Dartington Ltd, Colston Tower, Colston Street, Bristol, BS1 4RD Tel: 0117-933 0000 Fax: 0117-933 0009 *International security dealers & stock brokers*

Rowan Engineering, Garland Works, Desborough Avenue, High Wycombe, Buckinghamshire, HP11 2RN Tel: (01494) 531213 Fax: (01494) 465226 E-mail: enquiries@drjeng.fsnet.co.uk *Sheet metalwork engineers*

Rowan Glen Dairy Products Ltd, Palnure, Palnure, Newton Stewart, Wigtownshire, DG8 7AX Tel: (01671) 403633 Fax: (01671) 402444 E-mail: enquiries@rowan-glen.co.uk *Dairy product manufrs*

Rowan Steels Ltd, 2 Park Street Works, Park Street, Kidderminster, Worcestershire, DY11 6TN Tel: (01562) 67476 Fax: (01562) 515412 E-mail: sales@rowansteels.co.uk *Steel & sheet steel stockholders*

Rowandale Cabinet Makers, Speedwell Mill, Millers Green, Wirksworth, Matlock, Derbyshire, DE4 4BL Tel: (01629) 824041 Fax: (01629) 824041 *Cabinet makers*

Rowbotham Decorative Flooring Ltd, 35 Bakewell Road, Loughborough, Leicestershire, LE11 5QY Tel: (01509) 263330 Fax: (01509) 237424 E-mail: enquiries@rdflooring.demon.co.uk *Flooring contractors*

Rowe Building Services Ltd, Unit 22 Challenge Centre, Sharps Close, Portsmouth, PO3 5RJ Tel: (023) 9265 2142 Fax: (023) 9265 2143

▶ Rowe Group of Companies, Cardrew Industrial Estate, Cardrew Business Park, Redruth, Cornwall, TR15 1SP Tel: (01209) 310800 Fax: (01209) 210140 E-mail: enquiries@rowegroup.co.uk *Property investment & administration, joinery manufacturing,*

Joslin Rowe Associates Ltd, Bell Court House, 11 Blomfield Street, London, EC2M 7AY Tel: (020) 7786 8055 Fax: (020) 7786 6451 E-mail: london@joslinrowe.com *Financial recruitment consultants*

Ralph Rowe Jeweller Ltd, Unit 4, 10 Eastcliffe Road, Par, Cornwall, PL24 2AH Tel: (01726) 813018 *Jewellery manufrs*

S.P. Rowe, Rosabil, Buller Road, Crediton, Devon, EX17 2AX Tel: (01363) 774380 Fax: (01363) 774380 *Building contractor & joinery specialist*

Roweaver Developments, Prospect House, Ainsdale Drive, Shrewsbury, SY1 3TL Tel: (01743) 445880 Fax: (01743) 441697 E-mail: sales@roweaver.co.uk *Specialist installers of aluminium & upvc eave systems*

Rowecon Systems Ltd, Treeton Centre, Rother Cresent, Treeton, Rotherham, South Yorkshire, S60 5QY Tel: 0114-254 0660 Fax: 0114-254 0661 E-mail: sales@rowecon.co.uk *Electronic weighing equipment suppliers & manufrs*

Rowecord Holdings Ltd, Neptune Works, Usk Way, Newport, Gwent, NP20 2SS Tel: (01633) 256433 Fax: (01792) 467308 E-mail: enquiries@rowecord.com *Steelwork fabricators* Also at: Swansea

▶ Rowelec Ltd, Unit 2b Granada Trading Estate, Demuth Way, Oldbury, West Midlands, B69 4LH Tel: 0121-544 1117 Fax: 0121-544 2228 E-mail: rowelec@ic24.net *For all commercial, industrial & domestic electrical works*

Rowen Structures Ltd, Fulwood Road South, Sutton-in-Ashfield, Nottinghamshire, NG17 2JW Tel: (01623) 558558 Fax: (01623) 558866 E-mail: sales@rowenstructures.co.uk *Structural engineering specialists*

Rowenta (UK) Ltd, 1A Langley Business Centre, Station Road, Slough, SL3 8PH Tel: (01753) 796400 Fax: (01753) 796499 *Domestic electric appliance distributors* Also at: Northampton

Rowham Steel Products Ltd, Lyons Road, Trafford Park, Manchester, M17 1RF Tel: 0161-786 3700 Fax: 0161-786 3707 E-mail: sales@rowhamsteel.co.uk *Steel stockholders & shearers*

Rowland Reinforcement Ltd, Goods Yard, Knollys Road, London, SW16 2JP Tel: (020) 8677 5228 Fax: (020) 8664 6473 *Reinforcing steel manufrs*

Rowland Sandwith Ltd, 32 Canford Bottom, Wimborne, Dorset, BH21 2HD Tel: (01202) 882323 Fax: (01202) 842815 E-mail: hancocks@rowland-sandwith.co.uk *Crayon manufacturers*

Rowland Tysoe Ltd, 80 High Street, Cranleigh, Surrey, GU6 8AH Tel: (01483) 272060 Fax: (01483) 278076 *Heating & plumbing materials merchants*

Rowland Way Ltd, Unit 2 Southmoor Lane, Havant, Hampshire, PO9 1JW Tel: (023) 9245 3879 Fax: (023) 9245 5593 E-mail: rowlandway@aol.com *Stove enamellers & powder coaters*

William Rowland Ltd, 7-23 Meadow Street, Sheffield, S3 7BL Tel: 0114-276 9421 Fax: 0114-275 9429 E-mail: e-mail@william-rowland.co.uk *Non ferrous metals stockists & distributors*

Rowlands & Naylor, Unit 2 Aerial Business Park, Lambourn Woodlands, Hungerford, Berkshire, RG17 7RZ Tel: (01488) 72229 Fax: (01488) 73048 E-mail: rowlands@rowlandsandnaylor.co.uk *Welding and metal fabrication. Batch production of steel components. Structural steel work, site work, stairways, fire escapes*

Rowlands Plant Services Ltd, Alchorne Place, Portsmouth, PO3 5QS Tel: (023) 9266 1143 Fax: (023) 9264 1656 E-mail: rowlandsplant@btconnect.com *Contractors plant hire*

Rowlescourt Engineering Ltd, 15 Clover Nook Road, Cotes Park Industrial Estate, Somercotes, Alfreton, Derbyshire, DE55 4RF Tel: (01773) 831115 Fax: (01773) 835925 E-mail: ruth.berry@rowlescourt.co.uk *Railway engineers, fabricators & machinists*

Charles Rowley & Co. Ltd, 22 Athole Street, Birmingham, B12 0DA Tel: 0121-440 7711 Fax: 0121-440 4837 E-mail: sales@charlesrowley.co.uk *Drapery hardware suppliers & manufrs*

▶ Rowley Engineering Co. Ltd, Tollgate Industrial Estate, Stafford, ST16 3HS Tel: (01785) 223831 Fax: (01785) 222764E-mail: sales@roweng.com *Wrought iron engineering services*

Rowley Gallery Ltd, 115 Kensington Church Street, London, W8 7LN Tel: (020) 7727 6495 Fax: (020) 7229 5561 *Picture frame makers*

Rowley & Hall Ventilation Ltd, 4 Canal Lane, Tunstall, Stoke-on-Trent, ST6 4NZ Tel: (01782) 837592 Fax: (01782) 833810 *Heating & ventilating engineers*

Rowley Plastics Co., Lower Road, Ledbury, Herefordshire, HR8 2DH Tel: (01531) 633700 Fax: (01531) 635973 *Plastics stockists & machinists*

T.& F. Rowley, 22 Lamb Ho, Elmington Estate, London, SE5 7JF Tel: 020 77015404 *Billiard & snooker table repairs*

Rowlinson Holdings Ltd, London House, London Road South, Stockport, Cheshire, SK12 1YP Tel: (01625) 877177 Fax: (01625) 879995 E-mail: enquiries.@rowcon.co.uk *General building contractors*

Rowlinson Knitwear Ltd, Woodbank Mills, Turncroft Lane, Stockport, Cheshire, SK1 4AR Tel: 0161-477 7791 Fax: 0161-480 2083 E-mail: info@rowlinson-knitwear.com *Knitwear & sweatshirt manufrs*

Rowlinson Packaging Ltd, Unit 1 Green Lane, Wardle, Nantwich, Cheshire, CW5 6BN Tel: (01829) 260571 Fax: (01829) 260718 E-mail: packaging@rowlinson.co.uk *Wooden box & case manufrs*

Rowlson Industrial Sewing Engineers Ltd, Westbury Road, Nottingham, NG5 1EJ Tel: 0115-979 1333 Fax: 0115-979 1444 E-mail: sales@rowlson.com *Sewing machine & attachments manufrs*

Rowpak Containers Ltd, Arrow Trading Estate, Corporation Road, Manchester, M34 5LR Tel: 0161-320 0026 Fax: 0161-335 0537 E-mail: john.lowe@rowpak.co.uk *Corrugated cardboard manufrs*

Rowsell Sails, 24 Camperdown Terrace, Exmouth, Devon, EX8 1EH Tel: (01395) 263911 Fax: (01395) 263911 *Boat builders & repairers*

Rowthorn Signs, 19 Milton Road, Portsmouth, PO3 6AN Tel: (023) 9273 7210 Fax: (023) 9229 3955 E-mail: rowthorn@btopenworld.com *Sign contractors*

The Rowton Group, Unit 14B, Hartlebury Trading Estate, Hartlebury, Kidderminster, Worcestershire, DY10 4JB Tel: (01299) 250107 Fax: (01299) 251141 E-mail: sales@rowtongroup.com *Engraved crystal glassware & gifts supply*

Rowton Hall Hotel, Rowton Lane, Rowton, Chester, CH3 6AD Tel: (01244) 336110 Fax: (01244) 335464 E-mail: sales@rowtonhallhotel.co.uk *Hotel & leisure club*

Roxar Ltd, Heritage Gate, Sandy Lane West, Littlemore, Oxford, OX4 6LB Tel: (01865) 712828 Fax: (01865) 712829 *Computer software systems consultants*

Roxburghe Hand Knits, 4 Dakers Place, Hawick, Roxburghshire, TD9 9JE Tel: (01450) 376689 Fax: (01450) 379571 E-mail: roxhandknits@aol.com *Knitwear manufrs*

Roxill Engineering & Hydraulics Co. Ltd, 12 Railway Terrace, Nechells, Birmingham, B7 5NG Tel: 0121-328 2189 Fax: 0121-327 7469 *Toolmakers/toolmaking services*

▶ Roxwell Ltd, 10-12 Stirling Road, London, E17 6BT Tel: (020) 8531 7778 Fax: (020) 8531 7761

Roxy Angling Supplies, 171 Queens Road, Ashton-under-Lyne, Lancashire, OL6 8EW Tel: 0161-339 1799 Fax: 0161-830 0162 *Fishing tackle suppliers*

Roy Beech Contractors Ltd, North Street, Stoke-on-Trent, ST4 7DJ Tel: (01782) 847925 Fax: (01782) 848863

▶ Roy Broad & Sons, High Lanes, High Lane, Manaccan, Helston, Cornwall, TR12 6HT Tel: (01326) 231403 Fax: (01326) 231101

▶ Roy C Smith Ltd, Manchester Road, Marsden, Huddersfield, HD7 6ND Tel: (01484) 844405 Fax: (01484) 845338

Roy Dickson Wilson, Alrewas House, Main Street, Alrewas, Burton-on-Trent, Staffordshire, DE13 7ED Tel: (01283) 792255 Fax: (01283) 792041 Principal Export Areas: Africa *Merchants & agents of tanning materials & water treatment*

▶ Roy Dixon Associates, Unit 4, Westerham Trade Centre, The Flyers Way, Westerham, Kent, TN16 1DE Tel: (01959) 561010 Fax: (01959) 563777

▶ Roy Dyke Electrical Contractors, 44 Poole Crescent, Bilston, West Midlands, WV14 8SU Tel: (01902) 492459 Fax: (01902) 493036

Roy E Wheeler, Holly House, High Street, Moorsholm, Saltburn-by-the-Sea, Cleveland, TS12 3JH Tel: (01287) 660625 Fax: (01287) 660625 E-mail: roycatwheeler@telco4u.net *Waste equipment suppliers & consultants*

▶ Roy Elliott Haulage Contractors, Green Lane, Chickerell, Weymouth, Dorset, DT3 4AL Tel: (01305) 785838

Roy Fabrications Ltd, 2 Chancel Way Industrial Estate, Birmingham, B6 7AU Tel: 0121 3444082 *Forklift truck attachment*

▶ Roy Francis Plant Hire Ltd, The Old Saw Mills, Bath Road, Sells Green, Melksham, Wiltshire, SN12 6RW Tel: (01380) 828988 *Roy Francis (Plant Hire) Ltd has been established since 1977, and supplies a large range of excavators, diggers, loading shovels, power tools, and work wear for sale and hire. We also are the sole UK supplier of the amazing new Hammer-Knife Mower. See our video of this machine on our website.*

▶ Roy Homes Ltd, 8 Lotland Street, Inverness, IV1 1PA Tel: (01463) 713838 Fax: (01463) 713161

Roy John Design, 117 Christchurch Road, Ringwood, Hampshire, BH24 3AQ Tel: (01425) 477644 Fax: (01425) 480254 E-mail: enquiries@royjohndesign.co.uk *We are specialists in the design, construction and installation of exhibition stands, conference sets and displays across the UK & overseas. We have a range to suit your budget, custom build, modular, pop-ups and portable systems.*

Rob Roy Homes (Crieff) Ltd, Dalchonzie, Comrie, Crieff, Perthshire, PH6 2LB Tel: (01764) 670425 Fax: (01764) 670419 E-mail: mail@robroyhomes.co.uk *Timber frame*

▶ Roy Sampson, Ings Road, Batley, West Yorkshire, WF17 8LT Tel: (01924) 478474 Fax: (01924) 441339

Royal Air Maroc, 205 Regent Street, London, W1B 4HB Tel: (020) 7439 4361 Fax: (020) 7734 6183 E-mail: ramlondon@btinternet.com *Airline company*

Royal Auping, 35 Baker Street, London, W1U 8EN Tel: (020) 7486 7154 Fax: (020) 7486 7143 E-mail: sh@misuraemme.co.uk *Beds and bedding*

▶ The Royal Bank of Scotland, P O Box 17, Edinburgh, EH3 6UY Tel: 0131-556 8555

Royal Bank Of Scotland, 135 Bishopsgate, London, EC2M 3UR Tel: (020) 7085 0000 Fax: (020) 7375 5050 E-mail: enquiries@rbsmarkets.com *Corporate & investment bankers*

Royal Brierley Crystal Ltd, Tipton Road, Dudley, West Midlands, DY1 4SQ Tel: 0121-530 5607 Fax: (01384) 457302 E-mail: brierleyshop@dartington.co.uk *Crystal glassware manufrs*

Royal British Legion Industries, Royal British Legion Village, Hall Road, Aylesford, Kent, ME20 7NL Tel: (01622) 795900 Fax: (01622) 882195 E-mail: enquries@rbli.co.uk *Road sign manufrs*

▶ Royal Brush UK Ltd, Unit K2 Peartree Industrial Park Crackley Way, Peartree Lane, Dudley, West Midlands, DY2 0UW Tel: (01384) 258188 Fax: (01384) 258770 E-mail: uk@royalbrush.com *Manufacturers of artist materials*

▶ Royal College Of Psychiatrists, 12 Queen Street, Edinburgh, EH2 1JE Tel: 0131-220 2910 Fax: 0131-220 2915

Royal Doulton, Sir Henry Doulton House, Forge Lane Etruria, Stoke-on-Trent, ST1 5NN Tel: (01782) 404040 Fax: (01782) 404000 E-mail: sales@royal-doulton.com *Chinaware manufrs*

Royal Haskoning, Rightwell House, Bretton Centrel, Bretton, Peterborough, PE3 8DW Tel: (01733) 336157 Fax: (01733) 262243 E-mail: info@peterborough.royalhaskoning.com *Engineering consultancy*

Royal Horticultural Halls & Conference Centre, 80 Vincent Square, London, SW1P 2PE Tel: (020) 7828 4125 Fax: (020) 7834 2072 E-mail: horthalls@rhs.org.uk *Conference centre & exhibition venue*

▶ Royal Infirmary of Edinburgh, 51 Little France Crescent, Edinburgh, EH16 4SA Tel: 0131-242 6871 *Hospital*

Royal Institution Of Great Britain, 21 Albemarle Street, London, W1S 4BS Tel: (020) 7409 2992 Fax: (020) 7629 3569 E-mail: info@ri.ac.uk *Scientific research*

Royal Jordanian Airlines, 32 Brook Street, London, W1K 5DL Tel: (020) 7878 6444 Fax: (020) 7629 4069 *Airline services*

Royal London Management Services Ltd, Refuge House, Alderley Road, Wilmslow, Cheshire, SK9 1PF Tel: (01625) 605040 Fax: (01625) 605401 E-mail: postmaster@royal-london.co.uk *Insurance services*

Royal London Management Services Ltd, Refuge House, Alderley Road, Wilmslow, Cheshire, SK9 1PF Tel: (01625) 605040 Fax: (01625) 605401 E-mail: postmaster@royal-london.co.uk *Insurance company* Also at: Branches throughout the U.K.

▶ Royal Mail, Bridge of Don Delivery Office, Cloverhill Road, Bridge of Don, Aberdeen, AB23 8AA Tel: (01224) 704168

▶ Royal Mail, Arbroath Delivery Office, 10 Hill Street, Arbroath, Angus, DD11 1AA Tel: (01241) 871060

▶ Royal Mail, Eyemouth Delivery Office, Upper Houndlaw, Eyemouth, Berwickshire, TD14 5BP Tel: (01890) 750267

▶ Royal Mail, 4 Ogilvys Close, Kirriemuir, Forfar, Angus, DD8 4AA Tel: (01575) 573950

▶ Royal Mail, 20 Turner Road, St Rollox Business & Retail Park, St. Rollox Business & Retail Park, Glasgow, G21 1AA Tel: 0141-557 4841

▶ Royal Mail, Delivery Office, 21 Muirend Avenue, Glasgow, G44 3DZ Tel: 0141-637 1346

▶ Royal Mail, Aldholm, Lochmaddy, Isle Of North Uist, HS6 5AA Tel: (01876) 500330

▶ Royal Mail, Leven Delivery Office, Banbeath Industrial Estate, Kennoway Road, Leven, Fife, KY8 5XY Tel: (01333) 423764

▶ Royal Mail, Motherwell Sorting & Delivery, 214-218 Muir Street, Motherwell, Lanarkshire, ML1 1AA Tel: (01698) 264397

▶ Royal Mail, Portree Delivery Office, Dunvegan Road, Portree, Isle of Skye, IV51 9AA Tel: (01478) 612799

▶ Royal Mail Group Ltd, Annan Post Office, Station Road, Annan, Dumfriesshire, DG12 6TS Tel: (01461) 202758

▶ Royal Mail Group Ltd, 22 Clerk Street, Brechin, Angus, DD9 6AA Tel: (01356) 625465

▶ Royal Mail Group Ltd, Letter Delivery Offices, Russell Road, Edinburgh, EH11 2DJ Tel: 0131-470 6801

▶ Royal Mail Group Ltd, 26 Queen Elizabeth Avenue, Hillington Industrial Estate, Glasgow, G52 4TT Tel: 0141-882 1307

▶ Royal Mail Group Ltd, Uddingston Delivery Office, 7 Church Street, Uddingston, Glasgow, G71 7LP Tel: (01698) 816542

▶ Royal Mail Group Ltd, Clarkston Delivery Office, Rowallan Lane, Clarkston, Glasgow, G76 7BE Tel: 0141-638 1527

▶ Royal Mail Group Ltd, Brodick Delivery Office, Mayish Road, Brodick, Isle of Arran, KA27 8AA Tel: (01770) 302507

▶ Royal Mail Group Ltd, Main Street, Lairg, Sutherland, IV27 4DB Tel: (01549) 402025

Royal Mail Group Ltd, 148 Old Street, London, EC1V 9HQ Tel: (020) 7250 2888 Fax: (020) 7250 2030 *Mail Delivery Services*

▶ Royal Mail Group Ltd, Nairn Delivery Office, Cawdor Street, Nairn, IV12 4QU Tel: (01667) 452154

▶ Royal Mail Group Ltd, Selkirk Sorting Office, 30 Market Place, Selkirk, TD7 4BP Tel: (01750) 21266

▶ Royal Mail Group Ltd, Stornoway Delivery Office, Sandwick Road, Stornoway, Isle of Lewis, HS1 2AA Tel: (01851) 702166 Fax: (01851) 706583

Royal Mail Group Ltd, 12 Church Street, Troon, Ayrshire, KA10 6AU Tel: (01292) 314437

Royal Mail Northern Ireland, Royal Mail House, 20 Donegall Quay, Belfast, BT1 1AA Tel: (0845) 7740740 Fax: (028) 9089 2305 *Royal mail-distribution of text & packages*

Royal National Pension Fund for Nurses, Frizzell House, County Gate, Bournemouth, BH1 2NF Tel: (01202) 292333 *Life insurance & pensions*

Royal Oak Furniture Co., Moor Lane, Grassington, Skipton, North Yorkshire, BD23 5BD Tel: (01756) 753378 Fax: (01756) 752865 E-mail: sales@royaloakfurniture.com *Furniture manufrs*

Royal Printers Stationers & Office Furniture Co., 111a Sheen Lane, London, SW14 8AE Tel: (020) 8408 2000 Fax: (020) 8330 1221 *Drawing office equipment distributors*

Royal Security, Warrington Street, Lees, Oldham, OL4 5AE Tel: 0161-620 2303 Fax: 0161-665 3550 *Security services*

Royal Selangor Pewter UK Ltd, 2 Eastbury Road, London, E6 6LP Tel: (020) 7474 5511 Fax: (020) 7474 5522 E-mail: sales@royalselangor.com *Prestige pewter giftware manufrs*

Royal Signs, 167 Culford Road, London, N1 4DT Tel: (020) 7254 6969 Fax: (020) 7249 0880 *Sign manufrs*

Royal Society For The Prevention Of Accidents Ltd, 353 Bristol Road, Edgbaston, Birmingham, B5 7ST Tel: 0121-248 2000 Fax: 0121-248 2001 E-mail: help@rospa.com *Training in industrial safety health & safety consultancy auditing*

Royal Society for Public Health, 3rd Floor Market Towers, 1 Nine Elms Lane, London, SW8 5NQ Tel: (020) 3177 1600 Fax: (020) 3177 1601 E-mail: info@rsph.org.uk *The Royal Institute of Public Health is a leading independent body with an international reputation dedicated to the promotion, practice and protection of the highest standards of public health.*

▶ Royal Springs, Unit 1 Goulbourne Street, Keighley, West Yorkshire, BD21 1JR Tel: (01535) 667990 Fax: (01535) 603700 *Natural mineral bottlers*

Royal Stafford, Royal Overhouse Pottery, Overhouse Street, Stoke-On-Trent, ST6 4EE Tel: (01782) 577244 Fax: (01782) 817336 E-mail: enquiries@royalstafford.co.uk *Fine earthenware tableware*

Royal Steel Ball Products, 6 Egerton Square, Knutsford, Cheshire, WA16 6EY Tel: (01565) 653881 Fax: (01565) 653870 E-mail: pmather@onetel.net.uk *Steel balls for grinding*

Royal Strathclyde Blindcraft Industries, 6 Candleriggs, Glasgow, G1 1LD Tel: 0141-553 2005 Fax: 0141-553 2060 *Furniture retailers*

Royal Strathclyde Blindcraft Industries Beds Mattresses Office Re, 12 Edgefauld Avenue, Glasgow, G21 4BB Tel: 0141-287 0800 Fax: 0141-287 0880 *Bedding, furniture, kitchen & office furniture manufrs* Also at: Aberdeen, Dundee, Edinburgh & Inverness

Royal & Sun Alliance Insurance P.L.C., Leadenhall Court, 1 Leadenhall St, London, EC3V 1PP Tel: (020) 7283 9000 Fax: (020) 7337 5200 E-mail: piumail@uk.royalsun.com *Insurance companies & commercial property insurance*

Royal & Sun Alliance Insurance Group P.L.C., Level 1, City Exchange, New Hall Place, Old Hall Street, Liverpool, L69 3EN Tel: (01422) 357211 Fax: (01422) 325911 *Insurance brokers*

Royal & Sun Alliance Insurance Group P.L.C., 1 Bartholomew La, London, EC2N 2AB Tel: (0845) 0772772 Fax: (01403) 232111

▶ Royal Surrey County Hospital, Egerton Road, Guildford, Surrey, GU2 7XX Tel: (01483) 464054 Fax: (01483) 406899

Royal Worcester, Royal Porcelain Works, Severn Street, Worcester, WR1 2NE Tel: (01905) 746000 Fax: (01905) 23601 E-mail: general@royal-worcester.co.uk *Bone chinaware manufrs*

Royal Yachting Association, Ensign Way, Hamble, Southampton, SO31 4RF Tel: (0845) 3450400 Fax: (0845) 3450329 E-mail: admin@rya.org.uk *Sports governing body*

▶ Royale Cuisine, Mill Mead Industrial Centre, Mill Mead Road, London, N17 9QU Tel: (020) 8808 3316 *Suppliers of cosher food products & caterers*

▶ Royale Motor Factors, Tel: (07885) 768133 E-mail: mail@motor-factors.com *Workshop supplies & consumables*

Royce Butterfield & Wilkey, Barbican Citygate, 1-3 Dufferin Street, London, EC1Y 8NA Tel: (020) 7374 0788 Fax: (020) 7638 1966 E-mail: michael.wilkey@virgin.net *Architects, arbitration & adjudication services*

Royce Development, Stowick, Evesham Road, Broadway, Worcestershire, WR12 7HU Tel: (01386) 830858 Fax: (01386) 830858 *Computer consultants*

Roycott Ltd, Royston Road, Byfleet, West Byfleet, Surrey, KT14 7NY Tel: (01932) 343515 Fax: (01932) 351285 E-mail: info@charlesausten.com *Wire goods & shelving manufrs*

Royde & Tucker Ltd, Unit 15-16 The High Cross Centre, Fountayne Road, London, N15 4QN Tel: (020) 8801 7717 Fax: (020) 8801 5747 E-mail: sales@ratman.co.uk *Builder's ironmongery manufrs*

Royden Engineering Ltd, Sandwash Close, Rainford Industrial Estate, Rainford, St. Helens, Merseyside, WA11 8LS Tel: (01744) 883636 Fax: (01744) 885730 E-mail: sbennett@royden.co.uk *Structural steelwork engineers*

continued

Royden Granulation, Fishwicks Industrial Estate, Baxters Lane, St. Helens, Merseyside, WA9 3NA Tel: (01744) 851941 Fax: (01744) 820324 E-mail: jd@roydon.com *Plastic granulating & reprocessing services*

Roydon Hamlet Water Garden Centre, Tylers Road, Roydon, Harlow, Essex, CM19 5LJ Tel: (01279) 792235 Fax: (01279) 792803 *Aquarium & pond suppliers*

Roydon Packaging Ltd, 16-19 Harolds Road, Harlow, Essex, CM19 5BJ Tel: (01279) 442772 Fax: (01279) 422727 E-mail: sales@roydonpkg.co.uk *Corrugated case manufrs*

▶ Roye Peters Motor Engineers, 1A Drygate Street, Larkhall, Lanarkshire, ML9 2AJ Tel: 01698 884037 E-mail: roye@royesgarage.co.uk

Royfreight Ltd, 2 Queen Annes Place, Enfield, Middlesex, EN1 2PX Tel: (020) 8360 3060 Fax: (020) 8360 0440 E-mail: enquires@royfrieght.co.uk *Shipping & forwarding agents*

Royhire Plant & Machinery Hire, 231b Southend Road, Stanford-le-Hope, Essex, SS17 7AB Tel: (01375) 678225 Fax: (01375) 678225 *Plant hire, leasing & rental services*

Royle Design Associates, 12 Old Street, London, EC1V 9BE Tel: (020) 7253 7108 Fax: (020) 7608 2074 E-mail: rda@royle-design.co.uk *Design consultants*

Royle & Gemmell, Booth House, Suthers Street, Oldham, OL9 7TQ Tel: 0161-628 9292 Fax: 0161-628 9292 *Sign writers & manufrs*

Royle Jackson Ltd, 1 Granville Street, Southampton, SO14 5FQ Tel: (023) 8033 1288 Fax: (023) 8033 9022 *Marine & industrial electrical engineers*

Roys Signs, 15 Hoobrook Industrial Estate, Worcester Road, Kidderminster, Worcestershire, DY10 1HY Tel: (01562) 829299 Fax: (01562) 829299 *Signs general*

▶ Roys Wroxham Ltd, B9 Pinetrees Road, Norwich, NR7 9BB Tel: (01603) 700954 Fax: (01603) 702670

▶ Royston Estate Agents, 118-120 Glenthorne Road, London, W6 0LP Tel: (020) 8563 7100 Fax: (020) 8563 7045 E-mail: kellysearch.com@roystonw6.co.uk *Royston Estate Agents - 75 years successful agency experience**A decade specialising within the ever changing and exciting Hammersmith, Shepherds Bush and Brackenbury Village market makes Roystons well qualified in their claim to be the area's most experienced team.**Their imaginative and 'value added' approach to marketing property has resulted in some spectacular property prices being obtained locally over recent years.**

Royston Fan Co. Ltd, Lumen Road, Royston, Hertfordshire, SG8 7AF Tel: (01763) 241400 Fax: (01763) 245654 E-mail: alan@roystonfan.co.uk *Manufacturers of blowers & fans including centrifugal & customer specification. Also fan (industrial) maintenance/ repair services and balancing (dynamic) services*

Royston Labels Ltd, 18 Orchard Road, Royston, Hertfordshire, SG8 5HD Tel: (01763) 212020 Fax: (01763) 248004 E-mail: info@roystonlabels.co.uk *Self-adhesive labels manufrs*

Royston Lead Ltd, Pogmoor Works, Stocks Lane, Barnsley, South Yorkshire, S75 2DS Tel: (01226) 770110 Fax: (01226) 730359 E-mail: info@roystonlead.co.uk Principal Export Areas: Worldwide *Lead sheet, lead anode & lead extrusion manufrs*

Royton Steel Stock Ltd, Caldershaw Centre, Ings Lane, Rochdale, Lancashire, OL12 7LQ Tel: (01706) 715555 Fax: (01706) 715443 *Steel stockholders*

RP Metal Ltd, The Coach House, 32 The Crescent, Belmont, Sutton, Surrey, SM2 6BS Tel: (020) 8642 8899 Fax: (020) 8661 9993 E-mail: info@rpmetal.co.uk *Heating & ventilation equipment installation services*

Rpa, Unit 3 Adams Close, Heanor, Derbyshire, DE75 7SW Tel: (01773) 764509 Fax: (01773) 764509 *Steel & aluminium fabricators*

RPC Containers Ltd, Haslingden Road, Blackburn, BB1 2PX Tel: (01254) 682298 Fax: (01254) 583752 E-mail: sales@rpc-blackburn.co.uk *Plastic packaging manufrs*

RPC Containers Ltd, St. Vincents Trading Estate, Feeder Road, Bristol, BS2 0UY Tel: 0117-977 9511 Fax: 0117-972 3602 *Plastic packaging manufacturers. Collation trays, hinged bakery & patisserie packaging, sandwich packs, trays for foods.*

▶ RPC Containers Ltd, Holme Lacy Road, Rotherwas, Hereford, HR2 6LB Tel: (01432) 291200 Fax: (01432) 291201 *Catering equipment, packaging suppliers*

RPC Containers Ltd, Gallamore Lane, Market Rasen, Lincolnshire, LN8 3HZ Tel: (01673) 840200 Fax: (01673) 840240 E-mail: sales@rpc-marketrasen.co.uk *Plastic container, bottle & jar manufacturers. Specialists in pharmaceutical packaging.*

▶ RPC Containers Ltd, Kilburn Road, Oakham, Leicestershire, LE15 6QL Tel: (01572) 723771 Fax: (01572) 756829 E-mail: sales@rpc-oakham.co.uk *Injection moulding of containers for paint services*

RPC Containers Ltd, Grove Street, Raunds, Wellingborough, Northamptonshire, NN9 6ED Tel: (01933) 623311 Fax: (01933) 622126 E-mail: sales@rpc-raunds.co.uk *Rigid plastic packaging manufacturers for the food, chemical and household product industries.*

▶ RPD Mouldings, 1c Market Street, Shipdham, Thetford, Norfolk, IP25 7LY Tel: (01362) 821211 Fax: (01362) 821211 E-mail: relement@aol.com *Glass fibre plastic moulders*

RPD Precision Drawings, Unit 7 North Lynn Industrial Estate, King's Lynn, Norfolk, PE30 2HZ Tel: (01553) 774765 Fax: (01553) 764816 E-mail: rpd@mywebpage.net *Glass screens & optical projectors charts manufrs*

▶ RPJ Document Management Ltd, Unit F2 Harlow Seedbed Centre, Coldharbour Road, Pinnacles East, Harlow, Essex, CM19 5AF Tel: (01279) 450600 Fax: (01279) 411400 E-mail: rpj.dm@btconnect.com *Document management systems & supplies*

▶ RPS Ltd, Wilton Centre, Wilton, Redcar, Cleveland, TS10 4RF Tel: 01642 465556 Fax: 01642 465929 E-mail: info@rpsltd.com *Recovery and return of reusable transport packaging including pallets, boxes and tops. repair and supply of new units.*

RPS Consulting Engineers, Elmwood House, 74 Boucher Road, Belfast, BT12 6RZ Tel: (028) 9066 7914 Fax: (028) 9066 8286 E-mail: belfast@rpsgroup.com *Consulting engineers*

RPS Energy Ltd, Goldsworth House, Denton Way, Woking, Surrey, GU21 3LG Tel: (01483) 746500 Fax: (01483) 746505E-mail: info@rpsgroup.com *Oil exploration consultants*

RPS Health, Safety and Environment, 185 Park Street, London, SE1 9DY Tel: (020) 7928 0999 Fax: (020) 7928 0708 E-mail: rpslo@rpsgroup.com *Environmental consultancy*

▶ RPS Water Services, Unit 22 Five C Business Centre, Concorde Drive, Clevedon, Avon, BS21 6UH Tel: (01275) 876687 Fax: (01275) 876421 E-mail: rpscl@rpsplc.co.uk *Waste water support services*

▶ RQS Engineering Solutions Ltd, 110 Main Street, Lennoxtown, Glasgow, G66 7DA Tel: (01360) 310554 E-mail: alanjlawson@btinternet.com *Service and maintenance of fume extraction equipment. i.e. fume cupboards, L.E.V"s and associated plant and equipment including dedicated air make-up/air input systems*

RRP Rotational Mould Makers, Unit 5 Sanders Lodge Industrial Estate, Rushden, Northamptonshire, NN10 6BQ Tel: (01933) 413493 Fax: (01933) 413931 E-mail: sales@rrp.uk.com *Rotational mould makers*

RS Agribusiness Ltd, Balstone Farm, Ibworth, Tadley, Hampshire, RG26 5TJ Tel: (01256) 850777 Fax: (01256) 850930 E-mail: info@rmhmixers.co.uk *Diet feeders manufrs*

RS Components (Watford), Unit 2A, Colonial Way, Watford, WD24 4WP Tel: (01923) 219696 Fax: (01923) 211177 E-mail: watford.tradecounter@rs-components.com *Adhesive tapes, electrical or electronics industry*

R's Electrics, 815 High Road, London, N17 8ER Tel: (0870) 7746333 Fax: (020) 8808 4955 E-mail: sales@rs-electrics.co.uk *Car radio & security systems suppliers*

▶ RS (UK) Computer Services Ltd, 71 Leonard Street, London, EC2A 4QS Tel: 020 70339003 Fax: 020 70339004

▶ RS Villas, Caxton House, Caxton Avenue, Blackpool, FY2 9AP Tel: (01253) 591169 E-mail: info@rsvillas.com *If you plan to rent or buy a villa in Florida or stay in a vacation rental home near Disney, Orlando, then we have a beautiful selection of 3-7 bedroom villas for you to choose from in all areas from Kissimmee to the West of Disney.*

▶ Rs100, 56 Park Road, Glasgow, G4 9JF Tel: (08707) 661650 *Disco equipment & lighting retailers*

▶ Rsa Direct, Boundary House, Boston Road, London, W7 2QE Tel: (020) 8434 3680 Fax: (020) 8434 3449 E-mail: richard.gibson@rsadirect.com *Fed up with poor results from your mailing lists? Contact an expert. **RSA Direct is a new kind of list company offering strategic data selection advice, data management and sales and direct marketing consulting Our services are focussed on delivering value for our clients. We provide imaginative data sourcing and a really proactive list management service. Our experience covers consumer and business to business direct marketing in international and domestic markets as well as privacy and compliance. We are independent and unbiased.*

▶ RSC Services, 74 Wrexham Avenue, Walsall, WS2 0DQ Tel: (07855) 302995 E-mail: richard@rstowe.wanadoo.co.uk *Manufacturers of fish and chip shop frying ranges. Complete shop fitting service with wide range of experience in all aspects of stainless steel fabrication for the catering industry*

▶ RSD Systems Ltd, 20 Lower Bere Wood, Waterlooville, Hampshire, PO7 7NQ Tel: (023) 9226 9627 Fax: (023) 9226 9627 E-mail: rsdsystems@btinternet.com *Suspended ceilings & partitioning contractors*

RSD Technology Ltd, Kingsway Business Centre, Kingsway, Fforestfach, Swansea, SA5 4DL Tel: (01792) 585859 Fax: (01792) 580651 E-mail: admin@rsd.uk.com *Employment agency & employment business* Also at: Crewe

▶ RS-Events Ltd, 72 Overcliff Road, Lewisham, London, SE13 7UA Tel: (020) 8473 5529 E-mail: info@rs-events.co.uk *RS Events are part of a cluster of Event Management Companies who have the experience needed to organise your event, wedding, birthday or function. RS Events also offer the best to Corporate clients in Entertainment, Team Building, Staff Development and Motivation. The whole event or just one feature can be co-ordinated by RS Events. London based with clients nationwide. Be bold, be brave, be different!!*

RSF Commercial Services Ltd, Unit 24 Walkers Road, Moons Moat North Industrial Estate, Redditch, Worcestershire, B98 9HE Tel: (01527) 598777 Fax: (01527) 598538 E-mail: office@rsfonline.co.uk *Provide packing & forwarding agents services*

RSG, 6 Arunside Industrial Estate, Fort Road, Arunside Industrial Estate, Littlehampton, West Sussex, BN17 7QU Tel: (01903) 715550 Fax: (01903) 715550 *Mechanical repairers*

▶ RSH, Unit 2a Chipchase Court, Seaham Grange Industrial Estate, Seaham, County Durham, SR7 0PP Tel: 0191-523 8989 Fax: 0191-523 8890 E-mail: rshseaham@aol.com *Hygiene equipment suppliers*

RSK E N S R Ltd, 16 Frogmore Road Industrial Estate, Frogmore Road, Hemel Hempstead, Hertfordshire, HP3 9RW Tel: (01442) 437500 Fax: (01442) 437550 E-mail: info@rsk.co.uk *Environmental consultants & testing services*

RSL Steeper Ltd, Cavendish Road, Manchester, M20 1LB Tel: 0161-434 4167 Fax: 0161-448 9446 *Artificial limb manufrs*

▶ RSM2000 Ltd, Wrest Park, Silsoe, Bedford, MK45 4HS Tel: (01525) 862555 Fax: (01525) 862500 E-mail: enquiries@rsm2000.com *Direct debit bureau & facilities management services*

RSR Fasteners Ltd, 2 Pasadena Close, Hayes, Middlesex, UB3 3NQ Tel: (020) 8756 1818 Fax: (020) 8756 1819 E-mail: sales@rsrfasteners.co.uk *Fasteners, nuts & bolts sales & distribution*

RSS Edge Shoes, 184 Wellington Road, Bilston, West Midlands, WV14 6BE Tel: (01902) 353007 Fax: (01902) 353823 E-mail: sales@edgeshoes.com *Ladies shoe import wholesalers*

RSS Group, Unit 32A/32B Village Farm Industrial Estate, Pyle, Bridgend, Mid Glamorgan, CF33 6BL Tel: (01656) 740074 Fax: (01656) 747057 E-mail: steve@rssgroup.co.uk Principal Export Areas: Worldwide *Rope and Sling Specialists are an independently owned company based at Pyle in South Wales, specialising in the manufacture, supply, hire, testing and repair of all types of Lifting Equipment .Equipment 1. 1000 tonne 'Talurit' Hydraulic Press Capacity 1mm - 54mm dia Wire Rope Comprehensive range of die-sets including taper, steel and straight ferrule terminations. 2. 150 Tonne 'Talurit' Mini-Press Capacity 1mm - 24mm dia Wire Rope. 3. 'Talurit' Hand Press Portable on-site rigging. Services 1. Hand Splicing - for Wire & Fibre Ropes up to 75mm dia. 2. White Metal/Resin Socketing - for Wire Rope. (Both the above services are available on-site.) 3. Flat Braided Wire Rope Slings recommended for lifting steel coil, bundles of tubes, reinforcing bar and timber. Stock 1. Steel Wire Rope from 1mm - 54mm dia including General Engineering, Rotation - resistant and compacted constructions, Galvanised and Stainless Steel finishes available. We also hire ropes.*

RSS International Ltd, Carr Mills, Bradford Road, Birstall, Batley, West Yorkshire, WF17 9JY Tel: (01924) 443553 Fax: (01924) 443320 *Gasket manufrs*

▶ RSVP Design, Mirren Court Three, 123 Renfrew Road, Paisley, Renfrewshire, PA3 4EA Tel: (0560) 0493245 Fax: 0141-887 3613 E-mail: graham@rsvpdesign.co.uk *Design & sale of training activities & programmes*

Rsy Air Conditioning Ltd, Refrigeration House, Potter Hill, Rotherham, South Yorkshire, S61 4NU Tel: (01709) 553355 Fax: (01709) 740814 E-mail: info@rsyaircon.co.uk *Air conditioning installation services*

▶ RT Media Ltd, Allen House, 2a East Borough, Wimborne, Dorset, BH21 1PF Tel: (01202) 888192 Fax: (01202) 888192 E-mail: info@rtmedia.com *Brand & logo design, web design & strategic planning*

Rta Wine Rack Co. Ltd, Station Road, Great Ryburgh, Fakenham, Norfolk, NR21 0DX Tel: (01328) 829666 Fax: (01328) 829667 E-mail: rtawr@globalnet.co.uk *Specialist wine rack manufrs*

RTC International, 13-15 Osyth Close, Brackmills Industrial Estate, Northampton, NN4 7DY Tel: (01604) 541000 Fax: (01604) 541020 *Retail hardware & maintenance*

Rte UK Ltd, 101a Hall Farm Road, Benfleet, Essex, SS7 5JW Tel: (01268) 569393 Fax: (01268) 751753 E-mail: rte-uk@lineone.net *Timber roof truss suppliers*

R-Tek Ltd, Stephenson Road, Washington, Tyne & Wear, NE37 3HR Tel: 0191-415 7000 Fax: 0191-415 7070 *Car accessories manufrs*

RTF, Little Brixham, Ashford Road, Bethersden, Ashford, Kent, TN26 3AX Tel: (01233) 820718 Fax: (01233) 820718 *Model aircraft kit manufrs*

Rti Conveyors, Common Road, Eton Wick, Windsor, Berkshire, SL4 6QY Tel: (01753) 855888 Fax: (01753) 855800 E-mail: rtiservices@btinternet.com *Conveyor belt engineers*

RTL Couriers Ltd, 2. Astlethorpe Two Mile Ash, Two Mile Ash, Milton Keynes, MK8 8EN Tel: (01908) 568016 Fax: (08707) 620334 *RTL Couriers provides delivery services by van or motorbike. *This can be same day express delivery, next day /next day timed delivery, or contract work.* ***

RTN, Ironside Way, Hingham, Norwich, NR9 4LF Tel: (01953) 851411 Fax: (01953) 851239 E-mail: g.muff@rtn-racing.co.uk *racing technology norfolk Limited provides a speciality motorsport, low volume, design, engineering and manufacturing service. racing technology norfolk Limited prides itself as being a centre of excellence for Carbon Fibre Reinforced Plastics (CFRP) design, engineering, manufacturing and prototyping.*

RTR Handelsgesellschaft, 8 Kingsway House, Kingsway, Team Valley Trading Estate, Gateshead, Tyne & Wear, NE11 0HW Tel: 0191-491 1292 Fax: 0191-491 1246 E-mail: sales@rtr.co.uk *Alloy steel & boiler tube stockholders*

Ruardean Garden Pottery, West End, Ruardean, Gloucestershire, GL17 9TP Tel: (01594) 543577 Fax: (01594) 544536 *Garden pottery manufacturers & suppliers*

Ruark Acoustics Ltd, 59 Tailors Court, Southend-on-Sea, SS2 5TH Tel: (01702) 601410 Fax: (01702) 601414 E-mail: info@ruark.co.uk *Loudspeaker system*

▶ Rubax Lifts Ltd, Prospect House, Foots Cray High Street, Sidcup, Kent, DA14 5HN Tel: (020) 8302 8800 Fax: (020) 8302 6644 E-mail: sales@rubax.co.uk *Lift engineers*

Rubb Buildings Ltd, Dukesway, Team Valley Trading Estate, Gateshead, Tyne & Wear, NE11 0QE Tel: 0191-482 2211 Fax: 0191-482 2516 E-mail: info@rubb.co.uk *Portable building manufrs*

Rubbarite Ltd, 23-27 Boundary Street, Liverpool, L5 9ZQ Tel: 0151-298 1038 Fax: 0151-298 1910 E-mail: rubbarite@btconnect.com *Rubber products manufrs*

Rubber Components Stalybridge Ltd, Millwood Mill, Wakefield Road, Stalybridge, Cheshire, SK15 1AB Tel: 0161-338 2435 Fax: 0161-338 2435 *Rubber moulders*

Rubber Consultants, Brickendonbury, Brickendon, Hertford, SG13 8NL Tel: (01992) 554657 Fax: (01992) 504248 E-mail: info@tarrc.co.uk *Rubber research centre*

▶ Rubber Dragon Limited, 19 Juno Way, Swindon, SN5 9ZD Tel: (07879) 637159 *Website design, internet services, site renewal, management, maintenance & promotion services, client focused, aesthetic & clear budget internet design using flash, html, javascript, java, perl, actionscript & php, please visit our extensive online portfolio*

Rubber Duck Home Improvements, 361 Holburn Street, Aberdeen, AB10 7FQ Tel: (01224) 212397 *Kitchens & bathroom suites manufrs*

Rubber Engineering Services, 4 Gorton Cresent, Windmill Lane Industrial Estate, Denton, Manchester, M34 3RB Tel: 0161-320 9900 Fax: 0161-320 9940 E-mail: sales@rubberengineering.co.uk *High precision rubber moulding services*

▶ Rubber Extrusions & Seal Ltd, Lancashire House, 251 Higginshaw Lane, Royton, Oldham, OL2 6HW Tel: 0161-622 0020 Fax: 0161-622 0010 E-mail: gculley251@aol.com *We are manufacturers of industrial seals, silicone extrusions, draught excluders, draughtproofing, weatherstripping, brush seals, brush strip, strip brush, door seals, rubber extrusions, plastic extrusions, EPDM extrusions, rubber mouldings, gaskets, washers, neoprene, silicone tubing**

▶ The Rubber Flooring Co., Unit 12-13, Phoenix Way, Smallshaw Industrial Estate, Burnley, Lancashire, BB11 5SX Tel: (01282) 411014 Fax: (01282) 411015 E-mail: mail@therubberflooringcompany.co.uk *Industrial, domestic rubber flooring manufrs*

▶ Rubber Flooring Online, Chy Rudden, Mill Lane, Grampound, Truro, Cornwall, TR2 4RU Tel: (01726) 883783

Rubber & Plastic Profiles Co., Unit 1, 35 Boldmere Road, Sutton Coldfield, West Midlands, B73 5UY Tel: 0121-354 6356 Fax: 0121-355 7290 E-mail: info@rubberandplasticprofiles.co.uk *Rubber & plastic product manufrs*

▶ Rubber & Plastics, Vincent Street, Balsall Heath, Birmingham, B12 9SG Tel: 0121-246 2000 Fax: 0121-246 2001 E-mail: lorayne@rubberproducts.co.uk *We are major suppliers of all of Industrial Rubber Products. We supply:- Sheeting, Ribbed Matting, BS921 Electrical Switchboard Matting, Equestrian Matting, Flooring Products, Playground Safety Matting, Foam, Sponge, Gaskets, Extrusions, Rubber Mouldings & Fabrications**

Rubber Products Leeds Ltd, Ingram Road, Leeds, LS11 9RQ Tel: 0113-243 4358 Fax: 0113-245 4945 *Foam merchants*

Rubber Stamp Of Northampton, 10 Freehold Street, Northampton, NN2 6EW Tel: (01604) 720663 Fax: (01604) 720663 E-mail: sales@rubberstamp.uk.com *Rubber stamp manufrs*

Rubberatkins Ltd, Hareness Road, Altens Industrial Estate, Aberdeen, AB12 3LE Tel: (01224) 248341 Fax: (01224) 248342 E-mail: sales@rubberatkins.com *Rubber moulding manufrs*

Rubberlast (Britain) Ltd, Unit 2 Gelderd Trading Estate, Brown Lane West, Leeds, LS12 6BD Tel: 0113-245 5234 Fax: 0113-244 8293 E-mail: sales@rubberlast.com *Rubber factors & distributers*

Rubbernek Fittings Ltd, Hall Lane, Walsall Wood, Walsall, WS9 9AP Tel: (01543) 453533 Fax: (01543) 453531 E-mail: mjones@rubbernek.co.uk *Manufacturers of hydraulic fittings, couplings & adaptors*

▶ Rubbershield EPDM Flat Roofing Material Suppliers, 529 Leeds Road, Bradford, West Yorkshire, BD10 8PA Tel: 0845 838 5312 Fax: 01274 617045 E-mail: info@rubbershield.co.uk *EPDM flat roofing materials supplier to cover flat roofs with flat roof membranes replacing flat roof felts. EPDM flat roof system is now the premier flat roofing product to seal against water ingress.*

▶ Rubberstamp-World, 3 Millennium Heights, Lune Street, Lancaster, LA1 2AT Tel: (01524) 848833 Fax: (01524) 848833 E-mail: enquiries@rubberstamp-world.co.uk *Arts & grafts*

Rubbertec International Ltd, Maydown Industrial Estate, Londonderry, BT47 6UQ Tel: (028) 7186 0005 Fax: (028) 7186 1411 E-mail: info@rubbertecinternational.com *Rubber moulding manufrs*

Rubell Print Ltd, The Hollies, College Lane, Bunbury, Tarporley, Cheshire, CW6 9PQ Tel: (01829) 260420 Fax: (01829) 260426 E-mail: info@rubell.org *Commercial printers*

Rubert & Co. Ltd, Acru Works, Demmings Road, Cheadle, Cheshire, SK8 2PG Tel: 0161-428 5855 Fax: 0161-428 1146 E-mail: info@rubert.co.uk *Surface roughness gauge manufrs*

Rubicon Ltd, Unit 11 Rockingham Business Park, Rockingham Row, Birdwell, Barnsley, South Yorkshire, S70 5TW Tel: (01226) 351515 Fax: (01226) 351535 E-mail: mail@rubiconsteel.co.uk *Steel/steel plate stockholders*

▶ Rubicon Corporation Ltd, 35 Great St. Helen's, London, EC3A 6HB Tel: (0870) 8507100 Fax: (020) 7618 6888 *Innovative services & solutions to the financial services industry*

▶ Rubicon Workflow Solutions, Pump Lathurley Farm Business Unitsgrazeley, Grazeley, Reading, RG7 1LL Tel: 0118-988 8780 Fax: 0118-988 8782 E-mail: sales@rubicon-solutions.co.uk *Fishing tackle suppliers*

Rubislaw Studio, 94a Hamilton Place, Aberdeen, AB15 5BA Tel: (01224) 624460 *Photographers*

Rubitex Protective Clothing, 52 Lord Street, Manchester, M3 1HN Tel: 0161-834 3340 Fax: 0161-834 3326 E-mail: info@rubitex.co.uk Principal Export Areas: Worldwide *School wear, medical & catering work wear wholesale suppliers*

▶ Rubus Consultants Ltd, Llanvair Discoed, Chepstow, Monmouthshire, NP16 6LY Tel: (01633) 400 051 E-mail: andrew.miller@rubus-consultants.co.uk *The company has extensive knowledge of people management & development in the hotel & leisure industry, financial services sector, retail manufacturing industry, civil engineering, telecommunications & the avionics sector as well as world wide experience of organisational development & strategy*

Ruby Fashions, 333-335 High Street North, London, E12 6PQ Tel: (020) 8472 7387 Fax: (020) 8472 7387 *Textile retailers*

Ruck Engineering, Kellaw Road, Darlington, County Durham, DL1 4YA Tel: (01325) 286081 Fax: (01325) 480722 E-mail: sales@ruckengineering.com *Cleaning products & equipment suppliers*

▶ Bobb Rudd Leisure, Blencathra Business Centre, Threlkeld, Keswick, Cumbria, CA12 4TR Tel: (01768) 779761

Rudd Engineering Ltd, 18 Sebergham Grove, London, NW7 2AU Tel: (020) 8959 8181 *Central heating & plumbing services*

Rudd Joinery, Treowen Road, Pembroke Dock, Dyfed, SA72 6NY Tel: (01646) 685712 Fax: (0871) 7334946 E-mail: ray@ruddjoinery.com *Joinery services*

Lindsay Ruddock Ltd, 34 Orchard Avenue, Castle Donington, Derby, DE74 2JZ Tel: (07785) 932272 E-mail: lindsayruddock@ntlworld.com *Electronic consultants*

Ruddy Joinery Ltd, Enterprise Way, Flitwick, Bedford, MK45 5BS Tel: (01525) 716603 Fax: (01525) 718595 E-mail: enquiries@ruddy.co.uk *Specialist joinery service*

▶ Rude Goose Ltd, Balfron, Balfron, Glasgow, G63 0LF Tel: (01360) 551205 E-mail: zoe@rudegoose.com *Rude Goose specialise in creation and development of brand image across all media. Web services we offer include static brochure sites, ecommerce and content managed sites. Graphic design projects include brochures, stationery and signage.*

Rudolf Chemicals Ltd, Keys Road, Nixs Hill Industrial Estate, Alfreton, Derbyshire, DE55 7FQ Tel: (01773) 832703 Fax: (01773) 520092 E-mail: rudolf@rudolfchemicals.freeserve.co.uk *Chemical manufrs*

Rudolph Carne & Co Ltd, 416-418 London Road, Isleworth, Middlesex, TW7 5AE Tel: (020) 8560 1182 Fax: (020) 8568 6882 E-mail: info@carne.co.uk *Machine tool merchants*

▶ Rudridge Ltd, The Coxbridge Pit, Alton Road, Farnham, Surrey, GU10 5EH Tel: (01252) 711911 Fax: (01252) 718623

▶ Ruf, Willowbath Mill, Water Lane, Wirksworth, Matlock, Derbyshire, DE4 4AA Tel: (01629) 826888 Fax: (01335) 347317

▶ RUF NECK, 463 Lichfield Road, Birmingham, B6 7SS Tel: 08456 446876 E-mail: raj@ruf-neck.com *Ruf Neck Limited is a buying and sourcing agency based in Birmingham with its branch office in Karachi, Pakistan. Ruf Neck deals in all Types of Fabrics, Textile Products including Fabric, Textile Made UPS, Yarn, Knitted & Woven Garments, Men's and Women's Undergarments, Leather Goods, Ruf Neck clothing brand, Home Textiles, Towels & Terry Products, Foodstuffs etc. As regards to Locus Standings - Ruf Neck has good standings with Pakistani - UK, USA, EU, South East Asian, UAE suppliers and buyers of textile and garment industry worldwide.*

Rufflette Ltd, Sharston Road, Sharston Industrial Area, Manchester, M22 4TH Tel: 0161-998 1811 Fax: 0161-945 1123 E-mail: sales@rufflette.com *Curtain tape manufrs*

Rufford Studios Ltd, 3 Monks Dairy, Isle Brewers, Taunton, Somerset, TA3 6QL Tel: (01460) 281878 *Sign makers*

Ruffs, 62 Shore Road, Warsash, Southampton, SO31 9FT Tel: (01489) 578867 Fax: (01489) 581104 E-mail: mail@ruffs.co.uk *Jewellery designers & manufrs*

Rug Doctor Ltd, 29 Decoy Road, Worthing, West Sussex, BN14 8ND Tel: (01903) 235558 Fax: (01903) 209671 E-mail: enquiries@rugdoctor.com *Carpet cleaning equipment manufrs*

▶ The Rug Seller Ltd, Unit 19 The Bridgewater Centre, Off Robson Ave, Trafford Park, Manchester, M41 7TE Tel: 0161 7469545 E-mail: sales@therugseller.co.uk *Online rug sellers*

Rugby Clothing Co. Ltd, 101 Old Westgate, Dewsbury, West Yorkshire, WF13 1NB Tel: (01924) 460130 Fax: (01924) 457960 E-mail: enquiries@rugby-clothing.co.uk *Sports clothing manufrs*

Rugby Electronics, 57 Somers Road, Rugby, Warwickshire, CV22 7DG Tel: (01788) 572492 Fax: (01788) 540005 E-mail: sales@rugbyelectronics.com Purchasing Contact: M.H. Hoskin Sales Contact: M.H. Hoskin *Manufacturers of electronic equipment (industrial), counter (electronic) & encoders. In addition control systems, electronic; electronic engineers/engineering services; electronic consultants & electronic equipment (custom built) consultants/designers*

Rugby Estates plc, 14 Garrick Street, London, WC2E 9SB Tel: (020) 7632 2200 Fax: (020) 7632 2222 E-mail: assets@rugbyestates.plc.uk *Property investors*

Rugby Glass Centre, 17 Somers Road, Rugby, Warwickshire, CV22 7DG Tel: (01788) 543756 Fax: (01788) 540078 *Glass merchants*

Rugby Livestock, 1 High Street, Whittlebury, Towcester, Northamptonshire, NN12 8XH Tel: (01327) 858858 Fax: (01327) 858858 *Livestock breeders & dealers*

Rugby Locksmiths Ltd, 3 St. Matthews Street, Rugby, Warwickshire, CV21 3BY Tel: (01455) 554999 Fax: (01788) 544222 E-mail: info@thekeyshop.co.uk *24 HOUR AND EMERGENCY LOCKSMITH CALLOUT SERVICE 07791 800 450.House,vehicle,office or commercial premises,full key cutting service,full retail locksmith shop stocking locks keys & safes etc*

Rugby Plastics Ltd, 11 Lanchester Way, Royal Oak Industrial Estate, Daventry, Northamptonshire, NN11 8PH Tel: (01327) 702668 Fax: (01327) 300468 E-mail: sales@rugbyplastics.com *Injection moulding manufrs*

▶ Rugby Suites & Beds, 104 Railway Terrace, Rugby, Warwickshire, CV21 3HE Tel: 01788 577335 Fax: 01788 577335 *Bed & 3 piece suite retailers*

▶ Rugby Tackle, 155a Bilton Road, Rugby, Warwickshire, CV22 7DS Tel: (01788) 544913 Fax: (01788) 570645 E-mail: sales@rugbytackle.co.uk *Tackle fishing supplies*

Rugby Windows Mant Ltd, Rugby House, Hinckley Road, Sapcote, Leicester, LE9 4FU Tel: (01455) 274747 Fax: (01455) 274686 *Window manufrs*

Rugeley Aluminium Products Ltd, 5a Knighton Road, Sutton Coldfield, West Midlands, B74 4NY Tel: 0121-353 0006 Fax: 0121-353 5586 E-mail: teakandco@aol.com *Aluminium alloy & ingot traders*

▶ Rugeley Training Centre, 16 Upper Brook Street, Rugeley, Staffordshire, WS15 2DN Tel: (01889) 579579 Fax: 01889 579579 *Computer training agents*

Rugged Systems Ltd, 1 Compton Place, Surrey Avenue, Camberley, Surrey, GU15 3DX Tel: (01276) 686707 Fax: (01276) 684329 E-mail: jjy@rugged-systems.com *Computer distributors service*

Ruggerbug Leisure Island Embroidery, Unit 39 Dyffryn Business Park, Ystrad Mynach, Hengoed, Mid Glamorgan, CF82 7RJ Tel: (01443) 862067 Fax: (01443) 862067 E-mail: contact@ruggerbug.com *Rugby jersey manufrs*

▶ Rugs @ Rugs UK, 93 Highgate, Kendal, Cumbria, LA9 4EN Tel: (0808) 1089657 E-mail: mark_battista@hotmail.com *Rugs suppliers*

Ruislip Carpets, 22 Long Drive, Ruislip, Middlesex, HA4 0HG Tel: (020) 8845 7603 Fax: (020) 8845 7603 *Carpet manufrs*

Ruislip Tractor Hire, 71 Lea Cresent, Ruislip, Middlesex, HA4 6PW Tel: (01895) 673326 *Plant machinery repairs*

Ruislip Tyre Service, 75 Park Way, Ruislip, Middlesex, HA4 8NS Tel: (01895) 632652 Fax: (01895) 678971 *Motor tyre distributors*

Rullion Engineering Personnel Ltd, PO Box 124, Altrincham, Cheshire, WA14 4RJ Tel: 0161-926 1717 Fax: 0161-926 1727 E-mail: engineering@rullion.co.uk *Recruitment consultants*

Rumenco Ltd, Derby Road, Stretton, Burton-on-Trent, Staffordshire, DE13 0DW Tel: (01283) 511211 Fax: (01283) 546152 E-mail: sales@rumenco.co.uk *Manufacturer of animal feed supplement*

Rumsey & Sons, Market House, Market Road, Richmond, Surrey, TW9 4LZ Tel: (020) 8892 1896 Fax: (020) 8876 9969 E-mail: removals@rumseyandson.com *Removal & storage specialists*

▶ Rumseys Chocolaterie, 26 High Street, Wendover, Aylesbury, Buckinghamshire, HP22 6EA Tel: (01296) 625060 Fax: (01296) 625060 E-mail: sales@rumseys.co.uk *Confectionery suppliers*

Runcent Joinery, 50 North Cross Road, London, SE22 9EU Tel: (020) 8299 2421 Fax: (020) 8299 4119 E-mail: info@runcent.com *Joinery manufrs*

▶ Runcorn Express Deliveries, 17 Victoria Road, Runcorn, Cheshire, WA7 5BN Tel: 01928 830280 E-mail: enquiries@runcornexpresscourires.co.uk *The company is a small Runcorn based concern providing a fast personal service for customers.*Available 24 hours a day 7 days a week.*The couriers that collects your parcel delivers your parcel.*The service provided covers all the UK on a sameday or next day delivery as overheads are minimal.*

Rundle Brownswood Ltd, Leigh Court, Pill Road, Abbots Leigh, Bristol, BS8 3RA Tel: (01275) 374994 Fax: (01275) 374681 E-mail: info@rundlebrownswood.com *Management consultants - international service search & selection*

Runflat International Ltd, Gawne Lane, Cradley Heath, West Midlands, B64 5QY Tel: (01384) 414845 Fax: (01384) 414848 E-mail: info@runflatinternational.com *Tyre inserts for safety & security on wheels*

Runfold Medical Ltd, Passfield Mill, Mill Lane, Passfield, Liphook, Hampshire, GU30 7QU Tel: (01428) 751999 Fax: (01428) 751990 E-mail: mail@runfoldmedical.com *Suppliers & manufacturers of medical or surgical goods, plastic*

Runners, Signal Hill, Lenborough Road, Gawcott, Buckingham, MK18 4BU Tel: (01280) 822288 *Sliding door fittings & running gear manufacturers distributors*

Runrig International Ltd, Fairview House, 27 Sun Street, Biggleswade, Bedfordshire, SG18 0BP Tel: (01767) 601102 Fax: (01767) 312106 E-mail: runrigintltd@btinternet.com *Manufacturers of earth boring & drilling equipment*

▶ Runtime Revolution Ltd, 15-19 York Place, Edinburgh, EH1 3EB Tel: (0870) 7471165 Fax: (0845) 4588487 *Computer services*

Rup Ltd, Unit 16 Netherton Business Centre, Kemnay, Inverurie, Aberdeenshire, AB51 5LX Tel: (01467) 642950 E-mail: ruplt d@rup.co.uk *Computer consultants*

▶ Rupee Design Ltd, 12a Sutherland Avenue, Maida Vale, London, W9 2HQ Tel: (020) 7289 3201 E-mail: rupeedesign@yahoo.co.uk *We provide all structural engineering services on domestic construction, structural and condition surveys, drainage design, commercial buildings and residential buildings.*

Rural Development Service, Southgate Street, Bury St. Edmunds, Suffolk, IP33 2BD Tel: (01284) 750102 Fax: (01284) 753658 *Conservation consultants*

Rural Development Services Ltd, 54 Church Road, Gracehill, Ballymena, County Antrim, BT42 2NL Tel: (028) 2565 1283 Fax: (028) 2563 0103 E-mail: sales@farmrelief.co.uk *Farm services*

▶ Rural Energy Ltd, Main Street, Owston, Oakham, Leicestershire, LE15 8DH Tel: (01664) 454989 Fax: (01664) 454230 E-mail: info@ruralenergy.co.uk *Renewable energy & heating system suppliers*

The Rural Media Company, Sullivan House, 72-80 Widemarsh Street, Hereford, HR4 9HG Tel: (01432) 344039 Fax: (01432) 270539 E-mail: info@ruralmedia.co.uk *Media & film production*

Rural Pine Crafts, Wyevale Garden Centre, 24 Wareham Rd, Galton, Dorchester, Dorset, DT2 8BY Tel: 01305 851541 Fax: 01305 851541 *Pine furniture*

Rural Solutions, The Stable Courtyard, Broughton Hall Business Park, Skipton, North Yorkshire, BD23 3AE Tel: (01756) 799955 Fax: (01756) 799988 E-mail: info@ruralsolutions.co.uk

Ruralcraft Furniture Ltd, Kimberley Road, Clevedon, Avon, BS21 6QJ Tel: (01275) 873869 Fax: (01275) 340969 *Wood machinists*

▶ Rusan, 70 Brunswick Street, Stockton-on-Tees, Cleveland, TS18 1DW Tel: (01642) 647330 Fax: (01642) 807788 E-mail: mike@aap4action.co.uk *Industrial Labelling Machines for many applications including Food,Chemicals,Cosmetics and Pharmaceutical Sectors*

Howard Ruse Associates Ltd, 2 Avery Hill Road, London, SE9 2BD Tel: (020) 8850 5678 E-mail: sales@hraconsulting.co.uk *Consulting engineers*

▶ Rush Courier Services, 7 Oakleigh Court, Bond Road, Surbiton, Surrey, KT6 7SH Tel: (020) 8241 1341 Fax: (020) 8241 1638 E-mail: info@rushcouriers.co.uk *UK sameday & nextday courier & international courier*

▶ Rush Drinks, Ashpool House, Sandy Lane, Lowton, Warrington, WA3 1BG Tel: (01942) 680006 Fax: (01942) 607412 E-mail: enquiries@rushdrink.com *Manufacturer of energy drink*

Rush Engineering, 126 Marjorie Street, Leicester, LE4 5GX Tel: 0116-268 2837 Fax: 0116-266 1781 *Precision engineers*

Rush Industrial Sales, 126 Station Road, Tempsford, Sandy, Bedfordshire, SG19 2AY Tel: (01767) 640779 Fax: (01767) 640617 E-mail: sales@rushind.com *Electric motor parts distributors, heater bands, cooling fans etc*

Ken Rush Associates, Bowman House, 191 South Street, Braintree, Essex, CM7 3QB Tel: (01376) 326789 Fax: (01376) 342711 E-mail: engineer@ken-rush-assoc.demon.co.uk *Structural engineers*

Rush Machine Co., Shelton House Barns, Shelton, Newark, Nottinghamshire, NG23 5JQ Tel: (01949) 850131 Fax: (01949) 850131 E-mail: johnandirush@yahoo.co.uk *Sewing machine repairs & maintenance*

▶ Rush & Warwick Ltd, 1 Acacia Close, Cherrycourt Way, Leighton Buzzard, Bedfordshire, LU7 4QE Tel: (01525) 372205 Fax: (01525) 852566 E-mail: sales@rushandwarwick.co.uk *Lithographic & digital printing services*

Rushall Protective Clothing Co. Ltd, 501 Bloxwich Road, Walsall, WS3 2XA Tel: (01922) 710055 Fax: (01922) 407885 *Protective clothing manufrs*

Rushall Tool & Engineering, Darlaston Central Trading Estate, Wednesbury, West Midlands, WS10 8XB Tel: 0121-526 3617 Fax: 0121-568 6015 *Press tool & work manufrs*

▶ Rushbrook Consultants Ltd, 216 West George Street, Glasgow, G2 2PQ Tel: (01357) 300633

Rushden Graphics Co., 25 Alfred Street, Rushden, Northamptonshire, NN10 9YS Tel: (01933) 418419 Fax: (01933) 317790 E-mail: sales@rgc.org.uk *Number plates & sign manufrs*

Rushden Pool Care Ltd, 7 Birchall Road, Rushden, Northamptonshire, NN10 9RQ Tel: (01933) 358256 Fax: (01933) 355911 E-mail: info@rushdenpoolcare.co.uk *Pool construction & maintenance*

Rushforth & Co. Ltd, Unit 3 Westfield Industrial Estate, Kirk Lane, Leeds, LS19 7LX Tel: 0113-250 9162 Fax: 0113-239 1394 *Precision engineers*

Rushforth John Plumbing Heating, 109 King Street, Drighlington, Bradford, West Yorkshire, BD11 1EJ Tel: 0113-285 4539 Fax: 0113-285 3627 *Drain cleaning & plumbing services*

Ray Rushin Ltd, Whiteley Road, Ripley, Derbyshire, DE5 3QL Tel: (01773) 512155 Fax: (01773) 512156 E-mail: sales@rayrushin.co.uk *Ductwork & ducting contractors*

Rushlift Mechanical Handling, Longfield Road, South Church Enterprise Park, Bishop Auckland, County Durham, DL14 6XB Tel: (01388) 777494 Fax: (01388) 770725 E-mail: sales@rushlift.co.uk *Materials handling*

Rushlift Mechanical Handling, Longfield Road, South Church Enterprise Park, Bishop Auckland, County Durham, DL14 6XB Tel: (01388) 777494 Fax: (01388) 770725 E-mail: sales@rushlift.co.uk *Fork lift truck services*

▶ Rushmere Fencing, 65 Linksfield, Rushmere St Andrew, Ipswich, IP5 1BA Tel: (01473) 623248 Fax: (01473) 623248 E-mail: will@forascape.co.uk *Domestic fencing, decking & garden architecture manufrs*

▶ Rushmore plc, Victoria Works, Victoria Road, Hebden Bridge, West Yorkshire, HX7 8LN Tel: (01422) 844866 Fax: (01422) 844466 E-mail: sales@rushmoreplc.com *Beverage dispense*

Rusholme Consoles Khan & Sons, 157 Dickenson Road, Manchester, M14 5HZ Tel: 0161-225 1475 Fax: 0161-225 1475 *Computer equipment retailers*

Rushpool Hall Hotel, Saltburn Lane, Saltburn-by-the-Sea, Cleveland, TS12 1HD Tel: (01287) 624111 Fax: (01287) 625255 E-mail: sales@rushpoolhall.com *Conference centre & hotel*

Rushton Electronic Solutions Ltd, Meadow Mill, Water Street, Stockport, Cheshire, SK1 2BU Tel: (0161) 429 6851 Fax: 0161-480 1855 E-mail: mail@restime.co.uk *Time recorder system manufrs*

Rushtons, Ashley Lane, Shipley, West Yorkshire, BD17 7DB Tel: (01282) 429977 Fax: (01274) 599474 E-mail: rushtonsinfo@btinternet.com *Specialist accountants & insolvency practitioners nationwide*

Rushworth Racing Dinghies, 141 Blandford Road, Poole, Dorset, BH15 4AT Tel: (01202) 776877 Fax: (01202) 483085 E-mail: sales@rushworthracing.co.uk *Boat building & boat repairers*

Ruskin Air Management Ltd, Stourbridge Road, Bridgnorth, Shropshire, WV15 5BB Tel: (01746) 761921 Fax: (01746) 766450 E-mail: sales@naco.co.uk Principal Export Areas: Worldwide *Louvre & ventilator distributors*

Rusmail Conveyor Systems Ltd, 33-35 Adams Street, Birmingham, B7 4LT Tel: 0121-359 1549 Fax: 0121-333 3104 E-mail: sales@rusmailconveyors.co.uk *Mechanical handling*

Russam G M S Ltd, 48 High St North, Dunstable, Bedfordshire, LU6 1LA Tel: (01582) 666970 Fax: (01582) 471757 E-mail: hq@russam-gms.co.uk *Interim management services*

H.& L. Russel Ltd, Russel House, Hornsby Way, Southfields Business Park, Basildon, Essex, SS15 6TF Tel: (01268) 889000 Fax: (01268) 889100 E-mail: sales@russel.co.uk *Shopfitting & home storage, coat hangers & housewares specialists*

Russell Ltd, 125 Business Park, Llanthony Road, Gloucester, GL2 5JQ Tel: (01452) 312851 Fax: (01452) 306388 E-mail: info@russell.co.uk *Commercial refrigeration equipment*

Russell Armer Ltd, Mintsfeet Place, Mintsfeet Road North, Kendal, Cumbria, LA9 6LL Tel: (01539) 722635 Fax: (01539) 740266 E-mail: sales@russell-armer.co.uk *Building contractors*

Russell Automation Engineering Ltd, The Stables, Batemans Lane, Wythall, Birmingham, B47 6NG Tel: (01564) 823513 Fax: (01564) 823238 *Automated screw driving machine manufacturers & general toolmakers*

▶ Russell C Soper, 57 Farringdon Road, Plymouth, PL4 9ER Tel: (01752) 268666

Russell Castings Ltd, Bonchurch Street, Leicester, LE3 5EP Tel: 0116-299 2000 Fax: 0116-299 8844 E-mail: general@russellductile.co.uk *Iron foundry services*

Russell & Chapple Ltd, 68 Drury Lane, London, WC2B 5SP Tel: (020) 7836 7521 Fax: (020) 7497 0554 E-mail: sales@randc.net *Artists & theatre canvas company*

F.W. Russell (Gauges) Ltd, 2-3 Avenue Industrial Estate, Gallows Corner, Romford, RM3 0HS Tel: (01708) 376888 Fax: (01708) 374050 *CNC turning services*

Russell Finex Ltd, Russell House, Browells Lane, Feltham, Middlesex, TW13 7EW Tel: (020) 8818 2000 Fax: (020) 8818 2060 E-mail: enquiries@russellfinexinc.com Purchasing Contact: A. Moss Sales Contact: D. McDonnell *Russell Finex, worldwide leaders in fine mesh separation technology, have designed and manufactured sieves, separators, filters and ultrasonic systems for over 75 years. With innovation at the core of the business, Russell Finex have produced market leading solutions to a wide variety of processing industries, including Food & Beverages, Pharmaceuticals, Chemicals, Coatings, Ceramics, Metallurgy and Environmental. With companies in the UK, USA and Belgium, and a strong network of experienced agents and distributors worldwide, the equipment is engineered for a global market supplied to over 140 countries. Russell Finex offer the widest range of sieves and filters, also providing custom built solutions to meet unique requirements. The product range includes check screeners, grading machines, liquid solid separation, ultrasonic sieve deblinding systems and self-cleaning filters. http:// www.russellfinex.com*

Russell Fire Ltd, 25-26 Second Drove Industrial Estate, Peterborough, PE1 5XA Tel: (01733) 310469 Fax: (01733) 897510 E-mail: sales@russellfire.co.uk *We offer total solution capability for your fire protection needs, providing reliable and cost-effective design, supply installation and maintenance. Our key areas include: Fire Alarms, Fire Extinguishers, Fire Detection, Suppression, Signs, Fire Extinguishers, Fire Suspension Systems, Fire Risk Assessment and Training, Russell Extinguisher Services Ltd. Chubb, Kidde, UK Fire, Dry Powder, Carbon Dioxide, Foam, Halon, Water Extinguisher, Hose Reel, Fire Blanket, Fm200, Smoke Detector, Heat Detector, Gas Suppression, Inert Gas, Health and Safety, Risk Assessment, Emergency Lighting, Flame, Nitrogen, Argon, Home and Office Fire, integrity testing, air sampling, fire trace, fire suppression, BS5306, BSen3, kitchen fire systems, kitchen fires, wet chemical, hydro spray, BS5839, stored pressure, extinguisher cabinets, fire extinguisher stands, fire extinguisher parts, intumescent, fire training, extinguisher maintenance, fire extinguishers in the UK.*

Russell Investments Ltd, Wrexhar, Lower Regent Street, London, SW1Y 4PE Tel: (020) 7024 6000 Fax: (020) 7024 6001 E-mail: rwhittaker@russell.com *Financial services*

Ivan Russell Joiners Ltd, Moycoft, Elgin, Morayshire, IV30 1XZ Tel: (01343) 549759 Fax: (01343) 549826 *Joinery services*

Ivor Russell Partnership, Royal Building, 10 Princess Way, Swansea, SA1 3LW Tel: (01792) 655888 Fax: (01792) 648384 E-mail: irp@themail.co.uk *Chartered quantity surveyors*

Russell Leisure Ltd, Newbridge Industrial Estate, Newbridge, Midlothian, EH28 8PJ Tel: 0131-335 5400 Fax: 0131-335 5401 E-mail: sales@russell-leisure.co.uk *Playground equipment manufrs*

▶ Russell Mainstream Supply Ltd, 8 Crown Square, Kingskettle, Cupar, Fife, KY15 7PW Tel: (01337) 831192 Fax: (01337) 371192 E-mail: wrussell@rmsupply.co.uk *Electrical test equipment distribution*

Russell Plastics, 8a High St, Harpenden, Herts, AL5 2TB Tel: (01582) 762868 Fax: (01582) 461086 E-mail: sales@russellplastics.co.uk *Manufacturers of furniture fittings (plastic); injection mouldings (plastic); plastic extrusions & plastic tubes*

▶ Russell Print Services Ltd, 105 Saltley Road, Birmingham, B7 4TJ Tel: 0121-359 2723

Russell Reynolds Associates Inc, 24 St James's Square, London, SW1Y 4HZ Tel: (020) 7839 7788 Fax: (020) 7839 9295 *Management recruitment agency services*

Russell Roof Tiles Ltd, Halleaths, Lockerbie, Dumfriesshire, DG11 1LR Tel: (01387) 810567 Fax: (01387) 811385 E-mail: christine.donaldson@rmc.co.uk *Manufacturer roof tiles*

Russell Sales Ltd, Truma House, Beechers Park, Eastern Avenue, Burton-On-Trent, Staffordshire, DE13 0BB Tel: (01283) 511883 Fax: (01283) 511329 E-mail: sales@miriadproducts.com *Caravan trailer parts distributors*

Russell Scientific Instruments Ltd, Rashs Green Industrial Estate, Dereham, Norfolk, NR19 1JG Tel: (01362) 693481 Fax: (01362) 698548 E-mail: sales@russell-scientific.co.uk *Manufacturers of barometers, barographs, mercury thermometers*

Russell Shutters Ltd, Unit 6 Sterling Industrial Estate, Dagenham, Essex, RM10 8TX Tel: (020) 8592 4545 Fax: (020) 8984 0378 E-mail: sales@lbsgroup.co.uk *Manufacturers & Installers of Security products including, manually & electrically operated Doors & Roller shutters, Fire shutters, Insulated & industrial Doors, Roller Grilles, PVC Curtains, Gates, Barriers, automatic doors and locks & Steel Hinged Doorsets. ISO 9001 registered, we offer a 24hr Repair Service*

Russell Signs Ltd, Units J-L Forest Industrial Park, Forest Road, Hainault, Ilford, Essex, IG6 3HL Tel: (020) 8501 2418 Fax: (020) 8500 4628 E-mail: vikki@russellsigns.co.uk *Sign manufrs*

Simon Russell, 5 The Hill, Kings Lane, Snitterfield, Stratford-upon-Avon, Warwickshire, CV37 0QB Tel: (01789) 730011 Fax: (01789) 730011 *Sign makers*

Russell Sub Surface Systems Ltd, Unit 2 Isbourne Way, Winchcombe, Cheltenham, Gloucestershire, GL54 5NS Tel: (01242) 603975 Fax: (01242) 602614 E-mail: rss-sales-uk@natoil.com *Electronic instruments*

Russell Systems Telecom, Communication House, The Watermark, Gateshead, Tyne & Wear, NE11 9SZ Tel: 0191-461 4200 Fax: 0191-461 4201 *Telecommunication systems provider & installation services*

▶ Russell Young Ifa Ltd, 18 Front Street, Low Pittington, Durham, DH6 1BQ Tel: 0191-372 3319 Fax: 0191-372 3319 E-mail: info@russellyoung-ifa.com *Russell Young IFA will help you find the mortgage you require. We specialise in mortgages for First Time Buyers, Remortgages and Credit Problems of all types.*

Russells Ltd, Eden Works, Old Malton, Malton, North Yorkshire, YO17 6RD Tel: (01653) 698000 Fax: (01653) 605499 E-mail: sales@russells.uk.com *Agricultural dealers*

▶ Russell's Garden Buildings, Gelsmoor Road, Coleorton, Coalville, Leicestershire, LE67 8JF Tel: (01530) 222295 E-mail: shedsrus@hotmail.co.uk *Sheds, summerhouses & wendy houses manufrs*

▶ Russell-Stoneham Photography, Suite 35, 2 Old Brompton Road, London, SW7 3DQ Tel: (020) 7413 9988 Fax: (020) 7581 4445 E-mail: puz.rs@btinternet.com *Established highly recommended photographers for weddings and events. "Story of the day" style and traditional posed photos. Also video.*

Russell-Webb Ltd, Fountain Drive, Hertford, SG13 7UB Tel: (01992) 551774 Fax: (01992) 554178 E-mail: info@russell-webb.com *Specialist manufacturers of anti set off powder*

Russels Automotive, 16 Bunyon Road, Kempston, Bedford, MK42 8HA Tel: (01234) 840655 Fax: (01234) 851358 *Motor factors distributors*

Russetts Developments Ltd, 27 Burners Lane, Kiln Farm, Milton Keynes, MK11 3HA Tel: (0870) 7702800 Fax: (0870) 7702801 E-mail: info@russetts.co.uk *Manufacturers of waterproof roofing membranes*

▶ Russia House, 61a Queen Mary Road, Sheffield, S2 1HQ Tel: (07814) 920071 Fax: 0114-283 5973 E-mail: anna@russia-house.co.uk *Russian to English Interpreter & Translator*

Russwood Ltd, Station Yard, Newtonmore, Inverness-Shire, PH20 1AR Tel: (01540) 673648 Fax: (01540) 673661 E-mail: sales@russwood.co.uk *Furniture & paper sawmill services*

Rust Industries, Unit 6 Lyon Road, Broadheath, Altrincham, Cheshire, WA14 5DG Tel: 0161-929 7550 Fax: 0161-929 7551 E-mail: sales@rustelectronics.co.uk *Electronic device manufrs*

Rust Proofing Company (Manchester) Ltd, Vauxhall Works, Greg Street, Reddish, Stockport, Cheshire, SK5 7BR Tel: 0161-480 8341 Fax: 0161-480 8820 *Stove enamelling & powder coating services & shot blasting contractors*

▶ Rustic Gardens, Wade Road, Clacton-on-Sea, Essex, CO15 4LT Tel: (01255) 434676 *Bird table & rabbit hutch manufrs*

Rustic Leather Co., 3 Penllwyngwent Industrial Estate, Saville Road, Ogmore Vale, Bridgend, Mid Glamorgan, CF32 7AX Tel: (01656) 842832 Fax: (01656) 841144 E-mail: sales@therusticleathercompany.co.uk *Leather furniture designers & manufrs*

Company Information

▶ Rustic Stone House Signs, 8 Burstow Park Business Centre, Antlands Lane, Shipley Bridge, Horley, Surrey, RH6 9TF Tel: (01293) 823673 Fax: (01293) 821462 E-mail: stone@rusticstone.net *House & estate signs*

Rusticraft Garden Furniture, 312a Brant Road, Lincoln, LN5 9AF Tel: (01522) 721014 Fax: (01522) 729122 *Garden furniture manufrs*

Rustin Allen Ltd, Darlaston Road, Wednesbury, West Midlands, WS10 7TN Tel: 0121-526 4048 Fax: 0121-526 4658 E-mail: sales@palextrusions.co.uk *Plastic extrusion manufrs*

Rustin Clark, 45 Waterloo Road, London, NW2 7TX Tel: (020) 8452 1091 Fax: (020) 8452 2008 E-mail: rustinclark@rustinclark.co.uk *Commercial printers*

Ruston Electronics Ltd, Unit 6, Sovereign Park, Laporte Way, Luton, LU4 8EL Tel: (01582) 506100 Fax: (01582) 506101 E-mail: sales@rustons.co.uk *Contract electronics manufrs*

▶ Ruth Lewis Complementary Therapy, 100 Manor Park Drive, Yateley, Hampshire, GU46 6JH Tel: 07879 465702 E-mail: ruth_lewis01@yahoo.co.uk *THERAPIES OFFERED: Therapeutic body massage (VTCT), and Indian Head Massage.*A mobile serivce is offered, within a reasonable distance.*

Gerald Rutherford Ltd, Unit 2 Rutherford House, Upton Street, Hull, HU8 7DA Tel: (01482) 323419 Fax: (01482) 214880 E-mail: sales@rutherfordvending.co.uk *Vending & catering equipment agents*

Rutherford Knitted Cape Specialists, Eastfield Mills, Mansfield Rd, Hawick, Roxburghshire, TD9 8AA Tel: 01450 376667 Fax: 01450 378532 *Knitwear manufrs*

Rutherford & Macpherson, 102 Bath Street, Glasgow, G2 2EP Tel: 0141-332 3223 Fax: 0141-332 3225 E-mail: administrator@arandem.co.uk *Sheriff officers services*

Rutherford The Pool People, Marley Lane, Battle, East Sussex, TN33 0TY Tel: (01424) 775060 Fax: (01424) 777066 E-mail: info@rutherfordpools.co.uk *Swimming pool equipment sales*

▶ Rutherfords, 3 Freetown Business Park, Hudcar Lane, Bury, Lancashire, BL9 6HD Tel: 0161-797 6952 E-mail: info@rutherfordsca.co.uk *Bakers & confectioners*

▶ rutherfordsofcoldstream.co.uk, D.M.I. Mechanical Engineers, Pinnaclehill Industrial Estate, KELSO, Roxburghshire, TD5 8DW Tel: (01573) 226255 Fax: (01573) 228255 E-mail: enquiries@dmi.gb.net *Spare Parts Supplied & Fitted for Rutherfords of Coldstream, John Rutherford & Sons, JR Grain Handling Equipment.*20/4 Grain Cleaners, 30/6 Grain Cleaners, Grain/Stone Separators, Barley De-awners, Heavy Duty Sieve Units, Dust Extraction Fan Units, Chain & Flight Conveyors, Deep Flight Conveyors, Flow & Return Conveyors, Belt Conveyors, Conveyor Accessories, Mechanical Intake Units, Grain Ducting & Accessories, Belt & Bucket Elevators, Grain Samplers, Etc*

R-Utility Software Consultants Ltd, 10 Charles Street, Rossendale, Lancashire, BB4 9JG Tel: (01706) 830565 Fax: (01706) 225306 E-mail: sales@r-utility.co.uk *Computer software developers*

Rutland Cutlery Co. Ltd, 73-101 Neepsend Lane, Sheffield, S3 8AT Tel: 0114-273 7056 Fax: 0114-273 1062 E-mail: shefcutler@aol.com *Cutlery manufrs*

Rutland Electric Fencing Co. Ltd, Unit 11 Brechin Bus Park, West Road, Brechin, Angus, DD9 6RJ Tel: (01356) 624109 Fax: (01356) 624109 E-mail: refscotsales@btclick.com *Electric fencing distributors & manufrs*

Rutland Electric Fencing Co Ltd, Fencing House, 8 Landsend Way, Oakham, Rutland, LE15 6RF Tel: (01572) 722455 Fax: (01572) 757614 E-mail: enquiries@rutland-electric-fencing.co.uk *Electric fence manufrs*

Rutland Engineering Services Ltd, Bridge Farm, Luffenham Road, Ketton, Stamford, Lincolnshire, PE9 3YA Tel: (01780) 721160 Fax: (01780) 722160 E-mail: sales@resl.fsnet.co.uk *Steel fabricators*

▶ Rutland Itc Computer Services Ltd, 4 Queen Street, Uppingham, Oakham, Leicestershire, LE15 9QR Tel: (01572) 821468 E-mail: support@rict.co.uk *IT Support services. Sales, repairs, upgrades, broadband, websites, training*

Rutland Lighting, 10-12 Watergate, Grantham, Lincolnshire, NG31 6PR Tel: (01476) 591049 Fax: (01476) 591049 *Lighting distribution*

Rutland Lighting, Thistleton Road Industrial Estate, Market Overton, Oakham, Leicestershire, LE15 7PP Tel: (01572) 767587 Fax: (01572) 767420 E-mail: Ab@rutlandlighting.sagehost.co.uk *Lighting retailers & manufrs*

▶ Rutland UK Trading Co, Whittington Way, Chesterfield, Derbyshire, S41 9AG Tel: 01246 261491

▶ Rutland Woodcraft, The Workshop, 31 Great North Road, Stibbington, Peterborough, PE8 6LS Tel: (01780) 784500 Fax: (01780) 784500 E-mail: info@rutlandwoodcraft.co.uk *We produce hand crafted made to order high quality bespoke furniture.products such as, tables, bookcases, beds, desks, garden, seats, kitchens, wardrobes, home office systems, hi-fi cabinets & tv cabinets, in a wide variety of designs, timbers & finishes*

Rutpen Ltd, Lambourn Woodlands, Hungerford, Berkshire, RG17 7TJ Tel: (01488) 71926 Fax: (01488) 71947 E-mail: mail@rutpen.co.uk *Chemical blending & mixing services*

Ruukki UK Ltd, The Old Granary, Riccall Grange King Rudding Lane, Riccall, York, YO19 6QL Tel: (01757) 249334 Fax: (01757) 249335 E-mail: claddingsalesuk@ruukki.com *Roofing & cladding manufrs*

▶ RVR Translation, 33 Leicester Close, Kettering, Northamptonshire, NN16 8EZ Tel: (0870) 2851687 E-mail: info@rvrtranslation.co.uk *Translation service*

RVT, 4 Halifax Place, Ryhope, Sunderland, SR2 0RD Tel: (07811) 207271 Fax: 0191-523 6333 *Electrical repairs*

RW Engineering, Threeways, High Street, Ixworth, Bury St. Edmunds, Suffolk, IP31 2HN Tel: (01359) 233098 Fax: (01359) 231832 *Mild steel fabrication engineers & manufrs*

RW Racing, 19a Bridge Industries, Fareham, Hampshire, PO16 8SX Tel: (01329) 236640 Fax: (01329) 236640 E-mail: neil@rwracing.freeserve.co.uk *Manufacturer & supplier of spare parts & accessories for radio controlled model cars*

RWB Engineering, Corona Works, Heaton Street, Denton, Manchester, M34 3RY Tel: 0161-320 7777 Fax: 0161-336 5255 *Precision machining services*

RWE npower, TS Ferrybridge, Old Great North Road, Knottingley, West Yorkshire, WF11 8PR Tel: (01977) 632201 Fax: (01977) 632311 E-mail: tsg@rwe.com Principal Export Areas: Worldwide *RWE Power International's Technical Support Group based at Ferrybridge provides a broad spectrum of engineering services available all year round, seven days a week. Our valuable experience derives from refurbishing, maintaining, modifying and providing emergency support for our own power plants and other major external power and industrial plants in the UK. **Our extensive workshop facilities include state-of-the-art machinery, which coupled with our vast experience enables us to offer a comprehensive, high quality service that includes: **1 Workshop services *2 Overhaul, repair and modification of plant and machinery *3 Manufacture of new components, spare parts and assemblies *4 Outage delivery and management *5 On-site machining *6 CNC and general machining *7 Gas Turbine services **RWE Power International is the brand name used by RWE npower to market its services to its customers.*

▶ Rxpharma, 17 Bury Lane, Withnell, Chorley, Lancashire, PR6 8RX Tel: (01254) 832321 Fax: (01254) 832322 E-mail: info@rxpharma.co.uk *Pharmaceutical manufrs*

▶ Ryan, Sandars Road, Heapham Road Industrial Estate, Gainsborough, Lincolnshire, DN21 1RZ Tel: (01427) 677556 Fax: (01427) 617773 E-mail: info@martinryan.co.uk *Furniture manufrs*

Ryan Car Services, C Taplow Road, Taplow, Maidenhead, Berkshire, SL6 0ND Tel: (01628) 669047 Fax: (01628) 605148 *Motor vehicle engineering services*

Ryan Jayberg Ltd, Delta House, Riverside Road, London, SW17 0BA Tel: (020) 8944 6288 Fax: (020) 8944 6295

Ryan Plastics, 21A Prince St, Northampton, NN6 0LL Tel: (01604) 811395 Fax: (01604) 812872 E-mail: john@ryanplastics.ssnet.co.uk *Plastics engineered products*

Ryan Scaffolding Co. Ltd, 132 St. Pauls Way, London, E3 4AL Tel: (020) 7987 2254 *Scaffolding contractors*

Ryans Move International Ltd, Unit 14 Gateway Industrial Estate, Hythe Road, London, NW10 6RJ Tel: (020) 8969 7047 Fax: (020) 8969 1326 E-mail: britannia@ryansmove.co.uk *Removal contractors & storage services*

Rybka Battle UK Ltd, 14-17 Wells Mews, London, W1T 3HF Tel: (020) 7637 1221 Fax: (020) 7637 2338 *Engineering consultants*

▶ Ryburn Associates, 23-25 Hob Lane, Soyland, Sowerby Bridge, Halifax, West Yorkshire, HX6 4LU Tel: 01422 823473 Fax: 01422 823473 E-mail: info@ryburnassociates.co.uk *Expediting and Engineering Services for the engineering and oil and gas industries*

Ryburn Concrete Ltd, 9 Woodman Works, Woodman Avenue, Elland, West Yorkshire, HX5 0PE Tel: (01422) 374423 Fax: (01422) 370249 *Concrete layers suppliers*

Ryburn Lapping, Riverside Ho, Queens Square Bus Pk, Huddersfield Rd, Honley, Huddersfield, HD9 6QZ Tel: (01484) 660878 Fax: (01484) 665373 *Flat plate lapping machine manufrs & sub contract lapping*

Ryburn Polythene Ltd, Oldham Road, Ripponden, Sowerby Bridge, West Yorkshire, HX6 4EL Tel: (01422) 823286 Fax: (01422) 823819 E-mail: ryburnpoly@btclick.com *Polythene bag manufrs*

▶ Ryburn Rubber Ltd, Watson Mill Lane, Sowerby Bridge, West Yorkshire, HX6 3BW Tel: (01422) 316323 Fax: (01422) 835898 E-mail: sales@ryburnrubber.co.uk *Recycled rubber manufrs*

Rycon Power Tools Ltd, Unit 13 Ely Valley Industrial Estate, Pontyclun, Mid Glamorgan, CF72 9DZ Tel: (01443) 230785 Fax: (01443) 237415 *Power tools suppliers*

Rycon Shipping & Forwarding Ltd, Rycon Warehouse, Rye Harbour Road, Rye, East Sussex, TN31 7TE Tel: (01797) 222747 Fax: (01797) 224535 E-mail: ryecon@btconnect.com *Warehousing & distribution packing*

Rycon Steels, 2 Alexandra Industrial Estate, Wentloog Road, Rumney, Cardiff, CF3 1EY Tel: (029) 2036 2311 Fax: (029) 2036 2322 E-mail: rycon@rsteels.fsnet.co.uk *Steel stockholders*

Rycote Microphone Windshields Ltd, Libbys Drive, Stroud, Gloucestershire, GL5 1RN Tel: (01453) 759338 Fax: (01453) 764249 E-mail: info@rycote.com *Microphone windshield manufrs*

Rycroft Associates LLP, 16 Queens Avenue, Shirley, Solihull, West Midlands, B90 2NT Tel: 0121 7458978 Fax: 0121 7443562 E-mail: mikestott@rycroftassociates.com *Specialist credit insurance brokers offering companies protection against bad debts through the insolvency of their customers.*

▶ Rycroft Distribution, Blackmore Road, Hill Barton Business Park, Clyst St. Mary, Exeter, EX5 1SA Tel: (01395) 233603 *Furniture manufrs*

Rydal Precision Tools Ltd, Unit 5 The Technology Centre, London Road, Swanley, Kent, BR8 7AN Tel: (01322) 614661 Fax: (01322) 614760 E-mail: sales@rydal.co.uk *Manufacturers of punch press tools & punch tools*

Ryden Property Consultants & Chartered Surveyors, Coronet House, Queen Street, Leeds, LS1 2TW Tel: 0113-243 6777 Fax: 0113-243 9323 E-mail: info@ryden.co.uk *Property management services* Also at: Aberdeen & Glasgow

▶ Ryder plc, 26-29 Morris Road, Nuffield Industrial Estate, Poole, Dorset, BH17 0GG Tel: (01202) 685181 Fax: (01202) 240841 E-mail: andrew_ellis@ryder.com *RENT ANYTHING FROM SMALL VANS UPTO LARGE TRUCKS. SPECIALISE IN EVERY RENTAL/ LEASING NEED WITH A SUPERIOR QUALITY OF SERVICE.*

Ryder & Chaddock, 6 162 Armley Road, Leeds, LS12 2QN Tel: 0113-231 1116 Fax: 0113-231 1118 E-mail: anything@ryderandchaddock.co.uk *Engraving & screen printing services*

Ryder Coachworks Ltd, Birchanger Industrial Estate, Bishop's Stortford, Hertfordshire, CM23 2TH Tel: (01279) 659059 Fax: (01279) 758460 *Motor vehicle repair & restoration services*

Ryders Autoservice International Ltd, 215 Knowsley Road, Bootle, Merseyside, L20 4NW Tel: 0151-933 4338 Fax: 0151-944 1424 E-mail: customerservices@ryders.co.uk *Car repairs & sales*

▶ Rydon Construction, Poughcombe Barns, Ogbourne St. Andrew, Marlborough, Wiltshire, SN8 1SE Tel: (01672) 841034 Fax: (01672) 841038

Rydon Signs Ltd, Unit 3 Peek House, Pinhoe Trading Estate, Exeter, EX4 8JN Tel: (01392) 466653 Fax: (01392) 466671 E-mail: sales@rydonsigns.com *Sign manufrs*

Rydon Springwater UK Ltd, Higher Mills, Crossley Moor Road, Kingsteignton, Newton Abbot, Devon, TQ12 3LE Tel: (01626) 367033 Fax: (01626) 203205 *Water cooler distributors*

▶ Rye Design, 107-109 High Street, Rochester, Kent, ME1 1JS Tel: (01634) 818168 Fax: (01634) 818178 E-mail: sales@ryedesign.co.uk *Graphic Design, Advertising, Corporate Identity, Printing, Brochures, Reports, Posters*

Rye Fires & Stoves, 20 Landgate, Rye, East Sussex, TN31 7LH Tel: (01797) 222041 Fax: (01797) 222041 E-mail: sales@ryefiresandstoves.co.uk *Wood stoves & fireplaces*

Rye Harbour Marine, The Point, Rye Harbour Village, Rye, East Sussex, TN31 7PU Tel: (01797) 227667 Fax: (01797) 227667 *Boat engine dealer*

The Rye Joinery Co. Ltd, Unit 3 Rother Iron Works, Fishmarket Road, Rye, East Sussex, TN31 7LR Tel: (01797) 229044 *Joinery manufrs*

Rye Oil Ltd, Rye Harbour Road, Rye, East Sussex, TN31 7TE Tel: (01797) 223374 Fax: (01797) 226991 E-mail: sales@rye-oil.ltd.uk *Oil distributors & oil tanks*

Rye Signs Ltd, 4 11 Fieldings Road, Cheshunt, Waltham Cross, Hertfordshire, EN8 9TL Tel: (01992) 636348 Fax: (01992) 621579 E-mail: dave@ryesigns.demon.co.uk *Sign manufrs*

▶ Rye Valley, 1 Garretts Green Industrial Estate, Granby Avenue, Birmingham, B33 0SU Tel: 0121-786 1664 Fax: 0121-786 1684

▶ Ryebrook Resins Ltd, Unit 4, Kelvin Bus Centre, Kelvin Way, Crawley, West Sussex, RH10 9SF Tel: (01293) 565500 Fax: (01293) 565472 E-mail: sales@ryebrook.co.uk *Industrial resin flooring suppliers*

Ryecomp Ltd, Woodside, Easthorpe Hall, Malton, North Yorkshire, YO17 6QX Tel: (01653) 697212 *Software developers*

Ryecroft Foods Ltd, Tudno Mill, Smith Street, Ashton-under-Lyne, Lancashire, OL7 0DB Tel: 0161-342 1600 Fax: 0161-342 1605 *Cereal food product manufrs*

▶ Ryedale Blinds, Unit 7 Showfield Lane, Malton, North Yorkshire, YO17 6BT Tel: (01653) 696955 Fax: (01653) 696955 *Blind manufrs*

Ryeford Engineering Ltd, 49 Arthur Street, Redditch, Worcestershire, B98 8JZ Tel: (01527) 517545 *Tube manipulators & exhaust manufrs*

Ryeford Engineering, 14 Ebley Road, Stonehouse, Gloucestershire, GL10 2LH Tel: (01453) 825841 Fax: (01453) 827732 E-mail: nick@ryefordeng.co.uk *Sheet metal & punching services*

Ryehill Farmservice, Unit 77 Manchester Road, Pocklington Industrial Estate, Pocklington, York, YO42 1NR Tel: (01759) 307447 Fax: (01759) 301155 *Agrochemicals sales*

Ryeland Toolmakers, Units 17-18 Barton Road, Water Eaton Industrial Estate, Milton Keynes, MK2 3JJ Tel: (01908) 647746 Fax: (01908) 270236 E-mail: info@ryelandtoolmakers.co.uk *Press tool manufrs*

Ryetec Industrial Equipment Ltd, 12-13 Town Green Lane, Settrington, Malton, North Yorkshire, YO17 8NR Tel: (01944) 768232 Fax: (01944) 768199 E-mail: info@ryetec.co.uk *Agricultural machinery importer & suppliers*

Ryetools Ltd, Westgate Carr Road, Pickering, North Yorkshire, YO18 8LX Tel: (01751) 476020 Fax: (01751) 477220 E-mail: ryetools@btinternet.co.uk *Injection mould toolmakers*

▶ Rygor Warehousing Ltd, 172-174 Chemical Road, West Wilts Trading Estate, Westbury, Wiltshire, BA13 4JN Tel: (01373) 826118 Fax: (01373) 823090

Rykneld Metals Ltd, Derby Road, Burton-on-Trent, Staffordshire, DE14 1RS Tel: (01283) 562745 Fax: (01283) 562745 *Scrap metal merchants*

Rykneld Tean Ltd, Hansard Gate, West Meadows Industrial Estate, Derby, DE21 6RR Tel: (01332) 542700 Fax: (01332) 542710 E-mail: sales@rykneldtean.co.uk *Manufacturers of braid*

Ryko International Ltd, Unit 11, Broadoak Industrial Estate, Broadbridge Heath, Horsham, West Sussex, RH12 3JR Tel: (01403) 240364 Fax: (01403) 246955 E-mail: sales@ryko.com *Automatic car washers maintenance*

Ryland Group Services Ltd, School House, St Philip's Court, Birmingham, B46 3AD Tel: (01675) 466566 Fax: (01675) 466568 *Holding company*

Ryland Saddlers Ltd, 5 Ashley Road, Cheveley, Newmarket, Suffolk, CB8 9DP Tel: (01638) 730113 Fax: (01638) 730113 *Saddlery & riding clothes manufrs*

Rylandes Engineering Ltd, Broomfield Barn, Coolham Road, Shipley, Horsham, West Sussex, RH13 8PF Tel: (01403) 741268 Fax: (01403) 741605 E-mail: sales@rylandesengineering.co.uk *Steel fabricators, sheet metalwork engineers & aluminium fabricators*

▶ Ian Rylands Ltd, Pitts House Farm, Pitts House Lane, Southport, Merseyside, PR9 7QT Tel: (01704) 226760 Fax: (01704) 231747 E-mail: ian.rylands@care4free.net *Plant hire & groundwork*

Ryman Control Systems Ltd, 4 Faygate Business Centre, Faygate Lane, Faygate, Horsham, West Sussex, RH12 4DN Tel: (01293) 851865 Fax: (01293) 851866 E-mail: info@rymancontrol.co.uk *Electrical wiring & manufacturing contractors*

Ryman The Stationer, 64 High Street, Bedford, MK40 1NT Tel: (01234) 216175 Fax: (01234) 351888 *Stationers suppliers*

Ryman The Stationer, 62 Old Christchurch Road, Bournemouth, BH1 1LL Tel: (01202) 295390 Fax: (01202) 554866 *Stationers*

Ryman The Stationer, 43 High Street, Bromley, BR1 1LE Tel: (020) 8460 6606 Fax: (020) 8460 6606 *Stationery retail outlet*

Ryman The Stationer, 53 Sidney Street, Cambridge, CB2 3HX Tel: (01223) 312095 Fax: (01223) 315130 *Stationery retailers*

Ryman The Stationer, 24 Burgate, Canterbury, Kent, CT1 2HA Tel: (01227) 470573 Fax: (01227) 470573 *Stationers*

Ryman The Stationer, 175-177 High Street, Guildford, Surrey, GU1 3AW Tel: (01483) 454088 Fax: (01483) 454088 *Retail stationers*

Ryman The Stationer, 63 Borough High Street, London, SE1 1NF Tel: (020) 7407 0288 Fax: (020) 7378 7960 *Retail stationers*

Ryman The Stationer, 191 Camden High Street, London, NW1 7BT Tel: (020) 7267 1276 Fax: (020) 7267 1276 *Retail stationers*

Ryman The Stationer, 57 Charing Cross Road, London, WC2H 0NE Tel: (020) 7439 2058 Fax: (020) 7439 2058 *Stationery retailers*

Ryman The Stationer, 146 Edgware Road, London, W2 1ET Tel: (020) 7723 2496 Fax: (020) 7723 0807 *Stationers*

Ryman The Stationer, 149 Fleet Street, London, EC4A 2BU Tel: (020) 7353 4985 Fax: (020) 7353 4985 *Stationers*

Ryman The Stationer, 19-20 High Holborn, London, WC1V 6BS Tel: (020) 7405 1642 Fax: (020) 7242 1463 *Retail stationers*

Ryman The Stationer, 96 Kensington High Street, London, W8 4SG Tel: (020) 7938 3531 Fax: (020) 7376 2284 E-mail: info@ryman.co.uk *Stationers*

Ryman The Stationer, 50 London Wall, London, EC2M 5TE Tel: (020) 7588 6707 Fax: (020) 7256 7010 *Retail stationers*

Ryman The Stationer, 336 North End Road, London, SW6 1NB Tel: (020) 7381 8885 Fax: (020) 7381 8885 *Stationers*

Ryman The Stationer, 68 Notting Hill Gate, London, W11 3HT Tel: (020) 7229 5308 Fax: (020) 7792 3044 *Stationers*

Ryman The Stationer, 64 Old Brompton Road, London, SW7 3LQ Tel: (020) 7581 0858 Fax: (020) 7581 0858 *Stationers*

Ryman The Stationer, 105 Putney High Street, London, SW15 1SS Tel: (020) 8788 6220 Fax: (020) 8789 8563 *Stationers*

Ryman The Stationer, 121 Queensway, London, W2 4SJ Tel: (020) 7229 5957 Fax: (020) 7727 0755 *Stationer retailers*

Ryman The Stationer, 4 Shepherd Market, London, W1J 7QB Tel: (020) 7493 2270 Fax: (020) 7493 2270 *Stationers wholesalers*

Ryman The Stationer, 430 The Strand, London, WC2R 0QN Tel: (020) 7240 4408 Fax: (020) 7497 0975 *Stationers*

Ryman The Stationer, 24-27 Thayer Street, London, W1U 2QL Tel: (020) 7935 8261 Fax: (020) 7224 3280 *Stationers*

Ryman The Stationer, 66 Tottenham Court Road, London, W1T 2EX Tel: (020) 7636 7306 Fax: (020) 7636 5120 *Retail stationers*

Ryman The Stationer, 31-35 Victoria Street, London, SW1H 0EU Tel: (020) 7222 4020 Fax: (020) 7630 0975 *Stationery*

Ryman The Stationer, 4 Montpelier Vale, London, SE3 0TA Tel: (020) 8318 1445 Fax: (020) 8318 3852 *Stationers*

Ryman The Stationer, 11 Regent Street, London, SW1Y 4ST Tel: (020) 7930 9538 Fax: (020) 7930 0975 *Stationers retailers*

Ryman The Stationer, 104 Baker Street, London, W1U 6TN Tel: (020) 7487 2570 Fax: (020) 7487 2570 *Stationers*

Ryman The Stationer, 6-10 Great Portland Street, London, W1W 8QL Tel: (020) 7636 3468 Fax: (020) 7637 0975 *Stationery*

Ryman The Stationer, 15 Hanover Street, London, W1S 1YJ Tel: (020) 7629 8397 Fax: (020) 7355 2081 *Retail stationery*

Ryman The Stationer, 26 New Broadway, London, W5 2XA Tel: (020) 8579 2839 Fax: (020) 8566 0934 *Stationers*

Ryman The Stationer, 48 Albemarle Street, London, W1S 4DH Tel: (020) 7493 9777 Fax: (020) 7493 9777 E-mail: info@ryman.co.uk *Stationers*

Ryman The Stationer, 27 Earl Street, Maidstone, Kent, ME14 1PF Tel: (01622) 750889 Fax: (01622) 766141 *Retail stationers*

Ryman The Stationer, High Street, Oxford, OX1 4AB Tel: (01865) 246571 Fax: (01865) 728427 *Retail stationers*

Ryman The Stationer, 3-5 Duke Street, Reading, RG1 4SA Tel: 0118-950 0493 Fax: 0118-950 0493 *Retail stationers*

Ryman The Stationer, 11 The Quadrant, Richmond, Surrey, TW9 1BP Tel: (020) 8948 8090 Fax: (020) 8948 8090 *Stationers*

Ryman The Stationer, 52 High Street, Staines, Middlesex, TW18 4DY Tel: (01784) 462981 Fax: (01784) 465208 *Stationers*

Ryman The Stationer, 119 High Street, Sutton, Surrey, SM1 1JF Tel: (020) 8643 5281 Fax: (020) 8643 5281 *Stationers*

Ryman The Stationer, 107 Peascod Street, Windsor, Berkshire, SL4 1DN Tel: (01753) 857310 Fax: (01753) 857310 *Retail outlet*

Ryman The Stationer, 23 Chertsey Road, Woking, Surrey, GU21 5AB Tel: (01483) 723608 Fax: (01483) 723608 *Stationary supplies*

Ryman The Stationer, 3 Middle Street, Yeovil, Somerset, BA20 1LE Tel: (01935) 431305 Fax: (01935) 477098 *Stationers*

Rystan Installations Ltd, Rystan House, The Opening, Codicote, Hitchin, Hertfordshire, SG4 8UF Tel: (01438) 820651 Fax: (01438) 821493 *Cable installators*

▶ Ryte Lynes Upholstery Co., 4 Shaftesbury Road, Leicester, LE3 0QN Tel: 0116-254 1063 Fax: 0116-255 2902 E-mail: robert-fenn@lineone.net *Upholstery & needlework shop*

Ryton Heating & Ventilating Co. Ltd, Sovereign House, 14 Warwick Street, Earlsdon, Coventry, CV5 6ET Tel: (024) 7667 7382 Fax: (024) 7667 7382 *Heating & ventilation engineers*

Rytons Building Products Ltd, Design House, Orion Way, Kettering Business Park, Kettering, Northamptonshire, NN15 6NL Tel: (01536) 511874 Fax: (01536) 310455 E-mail: vents@rytons.com *Roof sofit & cavity vent manufrs*

Ryvita Co., Ashton Road, Bredbury, Stockport, Cheshire, SK6 2SA Tel: 0161-494 5125 Fax: 0161-406 3288 *Crisp bread manufrs*

▶ Ryzex plc, Unit 1, Bumpers Way, Bumpers Farm, Chippenham, Wiltshire, SN14 6LH Tel: (01249) 465100 Fax: (01249) 659777 E-mail: infouk@ryzex.com *Sell, rent & install integrate barcode scanners, terminals & printers*

▶ S 1 Systems, Unit 15 Piccadilly Mill, Lower Street, Stroud, Gloucestershire, GL5 2HT Tel: (01453) 767006 E-mail: sales@s1systems.co.uk

▶ S.A.B. Print, 110 Albert Road, Widnes, Cheshire, WA8 6AX Tel: 0151-423 1403

S & A Bedding Ltd, 14 Honey Street, Cheetham Hill, Manchester, M8 8RG Tel: 0161-834 8249 Fax: 0161-834 7774 *Bedding accessory retailers*

S A C Marine International Ltd, 36 Ridleys Cross, Astley, Stourport-on-Severn, Worcestershire, DY13 0RF Tel: (01299) 825908 Fax: (01299) 878699 E-mail: sacmarine.com *Marine compressor pumps & engine suppliers*

S A Clough Ltd, 252-252a Newchurch Road, Bacup, Lancashire, OL13 0UE Tel: (01706) 875908 Fax: (01706) 875908 *Industrial & domestic sewing machines*

▶ S A Developments, 5 Peel Street, Failsworth, Manchester, M35 0UF Tel: 0161-681 0511 Fax: 0161-682 3919

▶ S & A Double Glazing Ltd, 111 Hopewell Drive, Chatham, Kent, ME5 7NP Tel: (01634) 843148 Fax: (01634) 818942

S A Ductwork, 1 Parc Y Nant, Nantgarw, Cardiff, CF15 7TJ Tel: (01443) 844210 *Heating & ventilation contractors*

S A Equipment Sales, Edison Point, Millmarsh Lane, Enfield, Middlesex, EN3 7QG Tel: (020) 8443 7420 Fax: (020) 8804 2655 *Visible & audible warning device suppliers*

S A F A Group Ltd, 59 Hill Street, Liverpool, L8 5SB Tel: 0151-708 0397 E-mail: sales@safa.co.uk *First aid equipment distributors*

S A F Power Tools Ltd, 5 Anjou Cresent, Fareham, Hampshire, PO15 5DA Tel: (01329) 844205 Fax: (01329) 844142 E-mail: netsales@safpt.co.uk *Power & hand tool distributors*

▶ S A Gas Engineers Ltd, Burma Road, Blidworth, Mansfield, Nottinghamshire, NG21 0RT Tel: (01623) 796545 Fax: (01623) 796546

S A I T Abrasives (UK) Ltd, Regent Street, Narborough, Leicester, LE19 2DL Tel: 0116-286 2325 Fax: 0116-275 0081 E-mail: info@sait-abrasives.co.uk *Abrasive coated product manufrs*

S & A Industrial Equipment Ltd, The Handling Center, Cardiff, CF11 8TW Tel: (029) 2071 1171 Fax: (029) 2070 6464 E-mail: sandadirect@ukonline.co.uk *Material handling equipment manufrs*

S A Jones, Unit 3 Gwyrfai Mills, Bontnewydd, Caernarfon, Gwynedd, LL54 7UN Tel: (01286) 678683 Fax: (01286) 678683 *Aluminium & stainless steel fabricators*

S A Labels Ltd, Station Road, Oakworth, Keighley, West Yorkshire, BD22 0ED Tel: (01535) 646177 Fax: (01535) 646739 E-mail: sales@salabels.co.uk *Self-adhesive label manufrs*

S A M Hydraulic UK Ltd, Planet House 910 Lakeside Drive, Centre Park, Warrington, WA1 1QX Tel: (01925) 624800 Fax: (01925) 624801 E-mail: sales@samhydraulik.co.uk *Hydraulic manufrs*

S A N Ltd, 42 Bloom Street, Manchester, M1 3HR Tel: 0161-236 2246 Fax: 0161-236 5528 E-mail: sasltd@lineone.net *Household textiles manufacturers & importers*

S A P A Profiles Ltd, Sawpit Lane, Tibshelf, Alfreton, Derbyshire, DE55 5NH Tel: (01773) 872761 Fax: (01773) 874389 E-mail: info@sapagroup.com *Aluminium extrusion & aluminium alloy tube manufrs*

S A Parsons Building Contractors Ltd, Mansfield Road, Killamarsh, Sheffield, S21 2BW Tel: 0114-247 9100 Fax: 0114-247 9101 E-mail: parsonsgroup@parsonsgroup.co.uk

S A S Components Ltd, 4 Saxon Business Park, Hanbury Road, Stoke Prior, Bromsgrove, Worcestershire, B60 4AD Tel: (01527) 575502 Fax: (01527) 575276 E-mail: sales@sascomponents.co.uk *Automotive electrical suppliers*

S A S Engineering Ltd, Fengate, Peterborough, PE1 5XB Tel: (01733) 312522 Fax: (01733) 314221 E-mail: sasfengate@aol.com *General & precision engineers & fabricators*

S A S Lawyers, 30 Greek Street, Stockport, Cheshire, SK3 8AD Tel: 0161-475 7676 Fax: 0161-475 7677 E-mail: help@saslawyers.co.uk *Solicitors*

S A S Materials Ltd, 956 Kingsbury Road, Erdington, Birmingham, B24 9QA Tel: 0121-377 6005 Fax: 0121-377 7402 E-mail: sales@easystick.co.uk *Sign contractors supply services* Also at: Kingsbury

S A S Refrigeration Ltd, 137-139 Harrowdene Road, Wembley, Middlesex, HA0 2JH Tel: (020) 8385 1355 Fax: (020) 8385 1344 *Air conditioning & refrigeration contractors*

▶ S A S (Safe and Secure) Ltd, 1 Yale Close, Owlsmoor, Sandhurst, Berkshire, GU47 0UJ Tel: (01276) 31749 Fax: (01276) 31749 E-mail: sasshop@btinternet.com *Security equipment suppliers*

S A Sewing Machines, 1 Halifax Road, Rochdale, Lancashire, OL12 9BD Tel: (01706) 355529 Fax: (01706) 355529 E-mail: sa.sewmac@ntlworld.com *Sewing machines sales & services*

S A V UK Ltd, Scandia House, Armfield Close, West Molesey, Surrey, KT8 2JR Tel: (020) 8941 4153 Fax: (020) 8783 1132 E-mail: info@savvalvessystems.co.uk *Valve distributors*

S A W Technologies Ltd, Express Works, Church St, Irthlingborough, Wellingborough, Northants, NN9 5SE Tel: 01933 653005 Fax: 01933 653391 *Bar top drinks dispenser manufrs*

S Ainsworth & Co., Chadwick Street, Blackburn, BB2 4AA Tel: (01254) 670668 Fax: (01254) 279887 E-mail: stan.ainsworth@zen.co.uk *Steel fabricators*

S Ashby & Co, 59 Sibson Road, Birstall, Leicester, LE4 4DX Tel: 0116-267 1122 Fax: 0116-267 1122 *Case manufrs & agents*

S B A Ltd, Freemens Common Road, Leicester, LE2 7SQ Tel: 0116-257 6595 Fax: 0116-247 0072 E-mail: sales@sba.co.uk Principal Export Areas: Worldwide *Gasket manufrs*

S B C Precision Engineering, 2 Kings Court Industrial Estate, Sedgley Road East, Tipton, West Midlands, DY4 8XA Tel: 0121-557 0456 Fax: 0121-557 0457 *Toolmaking services*

S B Chemicals Ltd, Altona Road, Lisburn, County Antrim, BT27 5QB Tel: (028) 9267 3331 Fax: (028) 9267 3939 E-mail: postmaster@sbchemicals.co.uk *Manufacturers of household detergents*

S B Cole, 24 Drury Lane, Biggin, Buxton, Derbyshire, SK17 0DL Tel: (01298) 84445 Fax: 01298 84445 *Walling contractors*

▶ S B Components International Ltd, Millennium Works, Enterprise Way, Wisbech, Cambridgeshire, PE14 0SB Tel: (01945) 475234 Fax: (01945) 476251 *Fuel tank manufrs*

S B Computers, 88 Wilsthorpe Road, Long Eaton, Nottingham, NG10 3JZ Tel: 0115-946 3898 Fax: 0115-972 2225 E-mail: steve@sb-computers.co.uk *Computer system builders & distributor*

▶ S B Consulting, Engineering & Acoustics, Vogelsang, Woodland Road, Ivybridge, Devon, PL21 9HB Tel: 07977 418945 E-mail: sbonline@tiscali.co.uk *Noise & Vibration Consultancy. Sound Testing to Part E. Occupational Assessments for Health & Safety, Environmental Noise Assessments (BS4142/ PPG24)for nuisance noise and Planning Applications. Noise Control Engineering.*

S & B E P S Ltd, Dudley, Cramlington, Northumberland, NE23 7PY Tel: 0191-250 0818 Fax: 0191-250 0548 E-mail: company@sandbeps.com *Polystyrene packaging, insulation & building merchants*

S B Electronic Systems Ltd, Arden Grove, Harpenden, Hertfordshire, AL5 4SL Tel: (01582) 769991 Fax: (01582) 461705 E-mail: sales@telepen.co.uk *Bar code reading systems manufrs*

S B Engineering (Precision) Ltd, 1 Dyke Road Mews, Brighton, BN1 3JD Tel: 01273 821397 Sales Contact: S. Boyle *Sheet metalwork engineers & fabricators*

S B H (SW) Ltd, 61D Ivy Court, High Street, Nailsea, Bristol, BS48 1AW Tel: (01275) 851739 Fax: (01275) 540211 E-mail: barbara@sbhcrushing.co.uk *Recycling services*

S & B Herba Foods Ltd, Berwick House, 8 - 10 Knoll Rise, Orpington, Kent, BR6 0EL Tel: (0870) 7243722 Fax: (0870) 7243622 E-mail: retail@sbhf.com *Produce merchants*

S B I Computers, 201-203 Park Lane, Kidderminster, Worcestershire, DY11 6TQ Tel: (01562) 829677 Fax: (01562) 862841 E-mail: sales@sbi-uk.net *Computer retail & services*

S B I Industries, Unit 10a Oakendene Industrial Estate, Bolney Road, Cowfold, Horsham, West Sussex, RH13 8AZ Tel: (01403) 864858 Fax: (01403) 864858 E-mail: richardball@sbindustries.co.uk *Stainless steel spray balls manufrs*

S B Joinery, The Forge, Nettlestone Hill, Seaview, Isle of Wight, PO34 5DU Tel: (01983) 562147 Fax: (01983) 812166 E-mail: sales@sb-joinery.co.uk *Joiners*

S B Lawrence, 5 Long Lane, Over Peover, Knutsford, Cheshire, WA16 8XB Tel: (01565) 722655 *Farm contractors services*

S B M Signmaking & Engraving, 8-9 Lawson Way, Middlesbrough, Cleveland, TS3 6LN Tel: (01642) 227268 Fax: (01642) 271033 E-mail: sbmsigns@sc.com *Sign manufrs*

S B Optical Ltd, 1 Mill Square, Catrine, Mauchline, Ayrshire, KA5 6QZ Tel: (01290) 551339 Fax: (01290) 552635 E-mail: hughk@sboptical.freeserve.co.uk *Ophthalmic lens manufrs*

▶ S & B Recovery, 118 Rossend Terrace, Burntisland, Fife, KY3 0DJ Tel: (0783) 2106600 E-mail: recovery1@hotmail.co.uk *FIFE BREAKDOWN RECOVERY*

▶ S & B Roller Shutters, Unit 16 Mayfair House, Redburn Road, Newcastle upon Tyne, NE5 1NB Tel: 0191-271 3777 Fax: 0191-271 4322 E-mail: enquires@sbrollershutters.co.uk *Roller shutter manufrs*

S B S Ltd, Woden Road, Wolverhampton, WV10 0AS Tel: (01902) 455655 Fax: (01902) 453760 E-mail: sales@sbstrailers.co.uk *Trailer manufrs*

▶ S B S Bathroom Centre, 34-40 Albert Street West, Grimsby, South Humberside, DN32 7SJ Tel: (01472) 241515 Fax: (01472) 241599 *Bathroom fitters*

S B S Computer Services, 23 Thistlecroft Gardens, Stanmore, Middlesex, HA7 1PJ Tel: (020) 8951 0564 Fax: (020) 8951 3962 E-mail: sales@sbsnet.com *Software developers*

S B S Engineering Services, Tynewydd, Horeb, Llandysul, Dyfed, SA44 4JG Tel: (01559) 363708 Fax: (01559) 363708 *Temperature control consultants*

S B S Technology, Hoo, Rochester, Kent, ME3 9DJ Tel: (01634) 256953 Fax: (01634) 256953 *Industrial grade computer retailers & manufrs*

▶ S & B Seafoods, Unit 7 Dales Industrial Estate, Peterhead, Aberdeenshire, AB42 3JF Tel: (01779) 491133 *Wholesale fish merchant & fish processors*

S B Services, 86 Chelwood Avenue, Hatfield, Hertfordshire, AL10 0RE Tel: (01707) 256644 Fax: (01707) 262599 E-mail: s.brayshaw@btopenworld.com *Engravers & hand made trophies*

S & B Sheds, 706 Oldham Road, Manchester, M40 2AA Tel: 0161-205 1642 *Garden sheds builders & manufrs*

S B Signs, 16 Blandford Square, Newcastle upon Tyne, NE1 4HZ Tel: 0191-222 0852 Fax: 0191-232 2065 *Sign manufrs*

S B T Engineering Services Ltd, Empress Street, Old Trafford, Manchester, M16 9EN Tel: 0161-877 7755 Fax: 0161-848 9225 E-mail: info@sbtengineering.co.uk *Repair, refurbishment of industrial gearboxes*

S B T Machine Co Stockport Ltd, Christie Street Industrial Estate, Christie Street, Stockport, Cheshire, SK1 4LR Tel: 0161-429 6929 Fax: 0161-480 6603 E-mail: sbtworldwide@aol.com *Sewing machine sales, service & rental merchants*

S & B Tools Ltd, Timmis Road, Stourbridge, West Midlands, DY9 7BQ Tel: (01384) 895555 Fax: (01384) 896675 *Precision grinding manufrs*

S & B UK Ltd, Labtec Street, Swinton, Manchester, M27 8SE Tel: 0161-793 9333 Fax: 0161-728 9149 E-mail: info@splusb.co.uk *Educational furniture manufrs*

S B Weston Ltd, 5 Cypress Court, Harris Way, Sunbury-on-Thames, Middlesex, TW16 7EL Tel: (01932) 785544 Fax: (01932) 761294 E-mail: sales@sbweston.com *Plastic injection mouldings manufrs*

S B Wheeler & Sons Ltd, 16 Commerce Way, Colchester, CO2 8HH Tel: (01206) 791559 Fax: (01206) 791500 *Scrap metal merchants non-ferrous*

S Barber & Co. Ltd, 66-68 Kitchen Street, Liverpool, L1 0AN Tel: 0151-709 7323 Fax: 0151-709 6608 E-mail: sales@barbersprn.co.uk *Computer stationery printing services & lithographic printers*

▶ S Barber & Co Shopfitters Ltd, Bangor Terrace, Leeds, LS12 5PS Tel: 0113-263 9996 Fax: 0113-279 0158 E-mail: info@sbarber.co.uk

S Bateman & Sons Ltd, Hart Street, Blackburn, BB1 1HW Tel: (01254 56153 Fax: (01254) 664416 *Toolmakers & patternmakers for the thermoform industry*

S Betts & Sons Ltd, 2 Hunsley Street, Sheffield, S4 8DY Tel: 0114-261 9766 Fax: 0114-261 7464 E-mail: sales@betts-tools.co.uk *Hand tools distributors & manufrs*

S Brannan & Sons Ltd, Leconfield Industrial Estate, Cleator Moor, Cumbria, CA25 5QE Tel: (01946) 816624 Fax: (01946) 816625 E-mail: sales@brannan.co.uk *Industrial bimetallic, dial & mercury thermometer manufrs*

▶ S Brash, Eshiels, Peebles, EH45 8NA Tel: (01721) 723400 Fax: (01721) 723378

S Buck, 36 Stanley Road, Warmley, Bristol, BS15 4NX Tel: 0117-967 4740 Fax: 0117-961 8050 *Wrought ironworker*

S Burvill & Son Ltd, The Forge Cossins Farm, Downside Road, Downside, Cobham, Surrey, KT11 3LZ Tel: (01932) 589666 Fax: (01932) 589669 *Wrought ironwork specialists manufrs*

S C A, Riverbank Works, Riverford Road, Glasgow, G43 1RP Tel: 0141-632 0999 Fax: 0141-632 8111 Principal Export Areas: Africa *Packaging solution services*

S C A Ltd, Etruscan Street, Stoke-on-Trent, ST1 5PG Tel: (01782) 202122 Fax: (01782) 224200 *Timber & sheet materials manufrs*

S C A Containerboard UK, East Mill, Aylesford, Kent, ME20 7PA Tel: (01622) 883661 Fax: (01622) 883660 E-mail: scacontainerboard.uk@sca.com *Packaging*

S C A Graphic Paper UK Ltd, 543 New Hythe Lane, Larkfield, Aylesford, Kent, ME20 7PE Tel: (01622) 883000 Fax: (01622) 883895 *Wood pulp & publication papers agent*

S C A Heavy Duty Ltd, Heanor Gate Industrial Estate, Heanor Gate Road, Heanor, Derbyshire, DE75 7RJ Tel: (01773) 836456 Fax: (01773) 530427 *Corrugated box manufrs* Also at: London & Stevenage

S C A Industrial, Dodwells Road, Hinckley, Leicestershire, LE10 3BX Tel: (01455) 251400 Fax: (01455) 251404 E-mail: info.industrial@sca.com *SCA Packaging Industrial Division manufacture heavy-duty corrugated packaging, developing solutions for industry - from design to supply. Applications vary from internal distribution and storage systems, to point of sale display packs in retail units, containing products from granular ingredients to industrial automotive components.*

▶ S C A Marine Ltd, 5 Millstream Trading Estate, Christchurch Road, Ringwood, Hampshire, BH24 3SB Tel: (0870) 6077772 Fax: (08702) 417124 *Scaffolding contractor within marine industry*

S C A Packaging, Brook Road, Speedwell, Bristol, BS5 7TD Tel: 0117-951 7415 Fax: 0117-935 4260 *Packaging manufrs*

S C A Packaging Ltd, North Road, Ellesmere Port, CH65 1AG Tel: 0151-355 2381 Fax: 0151-357 2676 *Corrugated cases*

S C A Packaging Ltd, 95a James Street, York, YO10 3WW Tel: (01904) 430915 Fax: (01904) 430921 *Cardboard converters*

S C A Packaging Bingham, Moorbridge Road, Bingham, Nottingham, NG13 8GG Tel: (01949) 838667 Fax: (01949) 838993 *Corrugated cardboard case & carton manufrs*

S C A Packaging Darlington Ltd, Faverdale Industrial Estate, Darlington, County Durham, DL3 0PE Tel: (01325) 284284 Fax: (01325) 460704 E-mail: enquiries@scapackaging.co.uk *Cardboard box manufrs* Also at: Peterlee

S C A Packaging Oldbury, Rood End Road, Oldbury, West Midlands, B69 4HT Tel: 0121-552 0696 Fax: 0121-552 0623 *Industrial packaging manufrs*

S C A Packaging Oxford, Unit 9 Stanton Harcourt Industrial Estate, Stanton Harcourt, Witney, Oxfordshire, OX29 5UX Tel: (01865) 882972 Fax: (01865) 882917 E-mail: oxford.salesoffice@sca.com *Corrugated packaging*

S C A Recycling UK Ltd, Lakeside Wharf, South Heighton, Newhaven, East Sussex, BN9 0HW Tel: (01273) 513863 Fax: (01273) 512030 *Waste paper process*

S C A Systems Ltd, 12 Littlehampton Road, Worthing, West Sussex, BN13 1QE Tel: (01903) 262688 Fax: (01903) 695311 E-mail: sales@scasystems.com *Computer systems house*

S C A T S, Winterborne Kingston, Blandford Forum, Dorset, DT11 9AZ Tel: (01929) 471789 Fax: (01929) 472202 E-mail: info@scatscountrystores.co.uk *Agricultural merchants & country stores*

▶ S C A Transport UK Ltd, 1-3 Branch Road, Lower Darwen, Darwen, Lancashire, BB3 0PR Tel: (01254) 680325 Fax: (01254) 680326

S C A Transport UK Ltd, Bath Road, Colthrop, Thatcham, Berkshire, RG19 4NQ Tel: (01635) 862244 Fax: (01635) 874165 *Road transport, haulage & freight services*

S & C Bennett Construction, The Workshop, Kingscote, Tetbury, Gloucestershire, GL8 8XZ Tel: (01453) 860180 Fax: (01453) 860180 *Groundworks contractors*

▶ S C Building Co., 207-209 Duckworth Street, Darwen, Lancashire, BB3 1AU Tel: (01254) 708338

S C Bus & Coach Builders, Hambledon Road, Waterlooville, Hampshire, PO7 7UB Tel: (023) 9225 8211 Fax: (023) 9225 5611 E-mail: sales@caetano.co.uk *Bus & coach repair, refurbishment & manufrs*

▶ S C C S, Great North Road, Eaton Socon, St. Neots, Cambridgeshire, PE19 8EB Tel: (01480) 404888 Fax: (01480) 404333 E-mail: sona@sccssurvey.co.uk *Surveying company*

S C C Transport (Devizes) Ltd, London Road, Hopton Estate, Devizes, Wiltshire, SN10 2EU Tel: (01380) 723324 Fax: (01380) 724850 *Warehousing & container self storage providers*

S C Chambers & Co. Ltd, 1 Water Street, Liverpool, L2 0RD Tel: 0151-236 4151 Fax: 0151-227 2921 E-mail: sandp@scchambers.co.uk *Ship brokers services*

S C Consultancy, Grey Tiles, Broad Oak, Heathfield, East Sussex, TN21 8SN Tel: (01435) 865527 *Computer consultants*

S C D Ltd, Navigation House, 4 Wilford Bridge Road, Melton, Woodbridge, Suffolk, IP12 1RJ Tel: (01394) 382600 Fax: (01394) 387672 E-mail: sales@scd-charts.co.uk *International chart agents*

▶ S C D Express, Whittle Road, Stoke-on-Trent, ST3 7QA Tel: (01782) 599967 Fax: (01782) 594445

S C F Ltd, Bellbrook Industrial Estate, Uckfield, East Sussex, TN22 1QL Tel: (01825) 761166 Fax: (01825) 765836 E-mail: sales@scf-print.co.uk *Printing services*

S C F Hardware Ltd, 3 Brook Park Estate, 27 Brook Road, Wimborne, Dorset, BH21 2BH Tel: (01202) 857140 Fax: (01202) 884419 E-mail: sales@scfhardware.com *Furniture fixings distributors*

S C F Supplies, Featherstone, Pontefract, West Yorkshire, WF7 6AH Tel: (01977) 700030 Fax: (01977) 700074 *Velcro brand distributor*

S C Grover Ltd, Grover House Burntmill Industrial Estate, Elizabeth Way, Harlow, Essex, CM20 2JH Tel: (01279) 420763 Fax: (01279) 416535 *Painting contractors*

S C H Bearings & Power Transmission, Unit 1 Great Bridge Business Park, Unit 1 Greatbridge Busn Park, Budds Lane, Romsey, Hampshire, SO51 0HA Tel: (01794) 830377 Fax: (01794) 830366 E-mail: sales@schgroup.com *Bearing & industrial engineering sales*

▶ S C H Digital, Hoghton Avenue, Bacup, Lancashire, OL13 9RD Tel: (01706) 870034 Fax: (01706) 870034 E-mail: steven.houghton1@ntlworld.com *RICOH COPIERS*RISO PRINTERS*PANASONIC COPIERS*

▶ S C H Site Services, Units G511 A, B & C, Whinbank Road, Aycliffe Industrial Estate, Newton Aycliffe, County Durham, DL5 6AY Tel: (01325) 327149 Fax: (01325) 327148 E-mail: b.smithies@schsiteservices.co.uk

S C H (Supplies) Ltd, S C H Supplies, Holbrook, Ipswich, IP9 2PT Tel: (01473) 328272 E-mail: enquiries@schsupplies.co.uk *Horticultural machinery manufrs*

▶ S & C Haulage, Enderby Road, Whetstone, Leicester, LE8 6JL Tel: 0116-286 3886

S C M Group UK Ltd, Dabell Avenue, Nottingham, NG6 8WA Tel: 0115-977 0044 Fax: 0115-977 0946 *Woodworking machinery distributors*

S C M Software, Ty Gwyn Pen Y Garnedd, Llanrhaeadr Ym, Oswestry, Shropshire, SY10 0AN Tel: (01691) 860583 Fax: (01691) 860456 *Industrial automation software writers*

S C Marsh Ltd, 2 Dorchester Road, Maiden Newton, Dorchester, Dorset, DT2 0AY Tel: (01300) 320268 Fax: (01300) 320268 *Agricultural*

S C Mitchell, 20a Castle Arcade Balcony, Cardiff, CF10 1BY Tel: (029) 2037 4838 *Jewellery repair & manufrs*

S & C Moulds, Southfield Lodge, Burnham Road, Althorne, Chelmsford, CM3 6DP Tel: (01621) 744165 Fax: (01621) 744165 *Garden ornament mould manufrs*

S C P Concrete Sealing Technology Ltd, Ver House, London Road, Markyate, St. Albans, Hertfordshire, AL3 8JP Tel: (01582) 842802 Fax: (01582) 842803

continued

Company Information

continuation
E-mail: sales@scp-consealtech.co.uk *Construction products manufr*

S C P UK Ltd, 15-19 Pelham Court, Pelham Place, Crawley, West Sussex, RH11 9SH Tel: (01293) 546126 Fax: (01293) 528442 E-mail: scpuk@scppool.com *Swimming pool equipment wholesalers*

▶ S C Packaging Supplies, Unit D 11 Seedbed Centre, Langston Road, Loughton, Essex, IG10 3TQ Tel: (020) 8418 9652 Fax: (020) 8521 7058

▶ S C Pointing Services, 6 Beswick Street, Droylsden, Manchester, M43 7FL Tel: 0161-370 2710 Fax: 0161-370 2710 *Pointing chemical cleaners*

S C R Retail Systems, 2 Kendal Road, Shrewsbury, SY1 4ER Tel: (01743) 441591 Fax: (01743) 468697 E-mail: paperway@tiscali.co.uk *Stationery & cash registers suppliers*

▶ S C S Haulage Ltd, 178 Avenue Road, Rushden, Northamptonshire, NN10 0SW Tel: (01933) 417920 Fax: (01933) 417921

S C S London Ltd, Success House, Works Road, Letchworth Garden City, Hertfordshire, SG6 1LP Tel: (01462) 484858 Fax: (01462) 485029 E-mail: bma@scs.co.uk *Nursery & safety equipment distributors*

S C S Machine Tool Services, 18 Deeming Drive, Quorn, Loughborough, Leicestershire, LE12 8NF Tel: (01509) 412108 Fax: (01509) 412108 *Plant machinery repairs*

S C Soffe & Sons, Sundew, Pollards Moor Road, Copythorne, Southampton, SO40 2NZ Tel: (023) 8081 2278 *Saw mill services*

S C W S Holdings Ltd, Greens Road, Dereham, Norfolk, NR20 3TG Tel: (01362) 696899 Fax: (01362) 692339 E-mail: email@scwsltd.com *Steel Stockholding, Design, Fabrication, Erection.*

S C Woodworking Machines (Kent) Ltd, Fairview Garage, 161 Fairview Avenue, Gillingham, Kent, ME8 0PX Tel: (01634) 386012 Fax: (01795) 558469 E-mail: info@sbwoodworkingmachinery.co.uk *Woodwork machinery sales*

S Calvert, 30 Elmwood Avenue, Barwick in Elmet, Leeds, LS15 4JT Tel: 0113-281 2281 Fax: (07971) 114375 E-mail: scalvert@tiscali.co.uk *Special computer software manufrs*

S Clarke & Son, 1 Kennel Lane, Newtownards, County Down, BT23 7HR Tel: (028) 9182 0333 Fax: (028) 9182 0333 *Glazing contractor & building maintenance*

S Cocker Tiles, Beckside Cottage, The Bridge, Bedale, North Yorkshire, DL8 1AN Tel: (01677) 424658 *Jobbing artists*

S.Cohen(Boxes)Limited, Unit 1b St Marks, Industrial Estate, London, E16 2BS Tel: (020) 7055 5330 Fax: (020) 7055 5331 E-mail: sales@scohenboxes.co.uk *Cardboard box manufrs*

S D C Builders, Limegrove House, Caxton Road, Elm Farm Industrial Estate, Bedford, MK41 0QQ Tel: (01234) 363155 Fax: (01234) 266385 E-mail: matt.clifford@sdc.co.uk *Builders & civil engineers*

S & D Chemicals Ltd, Cunningham House, 19-21 Westfield Lane, Harrow, Middlesex, HA3 9ED Tel: (020) 8907 8822 Fax: (020) 8927 0619 E-mail: sales@sdcldn.com *Pharmaceutical import & export agents*

S D Coatings, 1 Albion House, 9 Hexthorpe Business Park, Doncaster, South Yorkshire, DN4 0EJ Tel: (01302) 325758 Fax: (01302) 300522 *Textured coatings & masonry paint*

▶ S D Cooper Transport Ltd, Little London Lane, West Cowick, Goole, North Humberside, DN14 9EG Tel: (01405) 860506 Fax: (01405) 860061

S D Demolition Ltd, PO Box 65, Biggleswade, Bedfordshire, SG18 9BE Tel: (01767) 314166 Fax: (01767) 318511 E-mail: enquiries@sddemolition.net *Demolition, strip out & asbestos removal*

S & D Electronics, Unit 34, Winpenny Road, Parkhouse Industrial Estate East, Newcastle, Staffordshire, ST5 7RB Tel: (01782) 565797 Fax: (01782) 565181 E-mail: sales@sdelectronics.co.uk *Computer services*

S & D Fabricators Ltd, Greenbank CR, East Tullos Industrial Estate, Aberdeen, AB12 3BG Tel: (01224) 895564 Fax: (01224) 899065 *Welding & fabrication services*

▶ S D Flooring, 30 Guildford Road, Worthing, West Sussex, BN14 7LL Tel: (01903) 538201 E-mail: sales@sdflooring.co.uk *Wood floor refurbishment & laminate flooring specialists. Sanding & sealing, hardwood & laminate flooring, parquet flooring, floor tiling residential & commercial. We offer free estimates and a supply, supply & fit or fitting only service for all our services. We operate in and around Sussex. Choose S.D.Flooring, for a professional guaranteed service.*

S D Graphics, (c/o Complete Print), 3 Rawstorne Place, London, EC1V 7NL Tel: (020) 7837 4555 Fax: (020) 7837 4555 *Cartography & graphic design*

▶ S D I Ltd, Trinity Buoy Wharf, Orchard Place, London, E14 0JU Tel: (020) 8924 7722 E-mail: keith@safetydirectglobal.co.uk *Graffiti removal & prevention specialists*

S D I Displays Ltd, Ratcliffe Road, Sileby, Loughborough, Leicestershire, LE12 7PZ Tel: (01509) 813166 Fax: (01509) 816369 Principal Export Areas: Central/East Europe & West Europe *Point of sale, purchase & marketing display designers*

▶ S D I Equipment Ltd, Unit 13, Sovereign Enterprise Park, Salford Quays, Salford, M50 3UP Tel: 0161-873 8597 Fax: 0161-873 7261 E-mail: sdiequip@aol.com *Air compressors & generators*

S.D.I Plotter Supplies Sigma Graphics, Higher Hillgate, Stockport, Cheshire, SK1 3QY Tel: 0161-429 7404 Fax: 0161-402 9425 *Office equipment supplies*

S D International Logistics, 22 Freemans Close, Twyning, Tewkesbury, Gloucestershire, GL20 6JP Tel: (01684) 850146 Fax: (01684) 850146 E-mail: steveday@consultant.com *Logistics consultancy*

S D L Atlas (International) Ltd, Crown Royal, Crown Royal, Shawcross St, Stockport, Cheshire, SK1 3JW Tel: 0161-480 8485 Fax: 0161-480 8580 E-mail: stephen.combes@dial.pipex.com *Textile test equipment manufrs*

S D L Imports Ltd, 2-18 Windham Road, Bournemouth, BH1 4RW Tel: (01202) 291122 Fax: (01202) 293322 E-mail: sales@sdlimports.co.uk *Importers of giftware, toys, headwear*

S D L Trophies Ltd, Britannia Centre Bentley Wood Way, Network 65 Business Park, Hapton, Burnley, Lancashire, BB11 5ST Tel: (01282) 418418 Fax: (01282) 418419 E-mail: admin@midfield.bromley.sch.uk *Sports trophy distributor*

▶ S D M Building Contractors, 490 Calder Street, Glasgow, G42 0QD Tel: 0141-423 1444 Fax: 0141-423 7774 E-mail: sales@sdm-group.com

▶ S D M Building Contractors, 490 Calder Street, Glasgow, G42 0QD Tel: 0141-423 1444 Fax: 0141-423 7774 E-mail: sales@sdm-group.com

▶ S D M Images, 16 Blenheim Close, Chandler's Ford, Eastleigh, Hampshire, SO53 4LD Tel: (023) 8027 6828 E-mail: info@sdmimages.co.uk *Modern Wedding Photography*Creative Portrait Photogrpahy*Innovative Commercial Photography*SDM IMAGES - IMAGE IS EVERYTHING*

▶ S D Par Food Co. Ltd, Barlow Drive, Woodford Park Industrial Estat, Winsford, Cheshire, CW7 2RB Tel: (01606) 592299 *Sales & distribution*

S D Partners Ltd, The White House, 9a Belvedere Road, Southbank, London, SE1 8AB Tel: (020) 7401 9399 Fax: (020) 7401 9499 E-mail: sales@sd-partners.com *IT consultants*

S & D Plastics, 14 Huntspill Road, Highbridge, Somerset, TA9 3DD Tel: (01278) 781853 Fax: (01278) 782834 *Glass fibre custom moulders*

S D Precision, 3 Stevenage Enterprise Centre, Orchard Road, Stevenage, Hertfordshire, SG1 3HH Tel: (01438) 361587 Fax: (01438) 721217 E-mail: sales@sdprecision.co.uk *Beryllium copper & flat spring manufacture CNC machines*

S D Products, The Broadway, Mansfield, Nottinghamshire, NG18 2RL Tel: (01623) 655265 Fax: (01623) 420689 E-mail: sales@sdproducts.co.uk *Industrial fastener suppliers*

S D S Infotech Training Ltd, 5 Haig Court, Haig Road, Parkgate Industrial Estate, Knutsford, Cheshire, WA16 8XZ Tel: (01565) 654526 *Training provider (IT) & financial services*

▶ S D S Sound & Light, 6 Mellard Street, Newcastle, Staffordshire, ST5 2DN Tel: (01782) 713277 E-mail: sdsstoke@aol.com *Sale And Hire Of Sound And Lighting Equipment*

S & D Sealants Cotswold, St. James Trading Estate, Barton Street, Gloucester, GL1 4JJ Tel: (01452) 504344 Fax: (01452) 504355 *Sealant contractors*

S & D Solutions (UK) Ltd, Unit 3, New Line Road, Kirkby-In-Ashfield, NG17 8JQ Tel: (01623) 752837 Fax: (01623) 757584 E-mail: sale@sndsolutions.co.uk *Plastic engineering*

S D Tooling UK Ltd, Manor Lodge, Tabors Hill, Great Baddow, Chelmsford, CM2 7BP Tel: (01245) 471807 Fax: (01245) 475884 *Engineering cutting tools*

S D V Jewellers, 100 Lower Marsh, London, SE1 7AB Tel: (020) 7261 1718 Fax: (020) 7261 1718 *Jewellery repairs*

S D V UK Ltd, Building 673, Spur Road, Feltham, Middlesex, TW14 0SL Tel: (020) 8831 4900 Fax: (020) 8890 1111 E-mail: sdvlhr@sdv.co.uk *Air freight agents* Also at: Birmingham, Felixstowe, Leeds, Liverpool, Manchester & Southampton

▶ S D W Recruitment, 33 Currie House, Herbert Walker Avenue, Southampton, SO15 1HJ Tel: (023) 8033 6633 Fax: (023) 8033 6633 E-mail: info@sdwrecruitment.co.uk *Shipping & freight forwarding recruitment, import, export clerks*

S D West, Lower Pensworth Farm, Redlynch, Salisbury, SP5 2JU Tel: (01725) 510322 Fax: (01752) 510325 *Farmers*

S De Saulles & Son Ltd, St Johns Road, Stourbridge, West Midlands, DY8 1YS Tel: (01384) 393151 Fax: (01384) 393152 *Screw distributors, agents & stockholders*

S Dell & Sons Ltd, Unit 1 Canalside, North Bridge Road, Berkhamsted, Hertfordshire, HP4 1EG Tel: (01442) 863959 Fax: (01442) 862163

S E A C, 46 Chesterfield Road, Leicester, LE5 5LP Tel: 0116-273 9501 Fax: 0116-273 8373 E-mail: enquiries@seac.uk.com *Specialised industrial fasteners manufrs*

▶ S.E.A. consultants, Suite 15A, North Shields, Tyne & Wear, NE30 1HJ Tel: 07779 004374 E-mail: info@consult-sea.com *S.E.A. consultants provide environmental solutions for business. We uniquely balance the needs of business with those of our environment by offering environmental assessment and monitoring in addition to environmental marketing to develop the most effective strategy for your business.*

S E A Packaging, Lavenham Road, Yate, Bristol, BS37 5QY Tel: (01454) 314509 Fax: (01454) 325711 *Cardboard box manufrs*

S E A (UK) Ltd, Unit 6A Olton Wharf, Off Richmond Road, Solihull, West Midlands, B92 7RN Tel: 0121-706 9629 Fax: 0121-764 5603 E-mail: sales@seaukltd.co.uk *Wholesale supplier of gate automation, traffic barrier, access control and intercom equipment to the Trade. Full service and repair facilities available. 2nd Office located in London N21*

▶ S E A Windows & Doors, Unit 1a North Street, Reading, RG1 7DA Tel: 0118-957 3976 Fax: 0118-939 3610

S E Apex Ltd, 847-849 London Road, Westcliff-on-Sea, Essex, SS0 9SZ Tel: (01702) 477425 Fax: (01702) 480564 *Do-it-yourself wholesalers*

S E B International Ltd, Unity Road, Lowmoor Industrial Estate, Kirkby-in-Ashfield, Nottingham, NG17 7LE Tel: (01623) 754490 Fax: (01623) 753477 E-mail: contact@sebinternational.com Principal Export Areas: Worldwide *Cable drum handling equipment, jack & trailer manufrs*

S.E.C. Electrical Ltd, 15 Stafford Place, Moulton Park Industrial Estate, Northampton, NN3 6NN Tel: (01604) 491101 Fax: (01604) 790542 *Electrical contractors*

S E C Industrial Battery Co. Ltd, Thorney Weir House, Thorney Mill Road, Iver, Buckinghamshire, SL0 9AQ Tel: (01895) 431543 Fax: (01895) 431880 E-mail: info@secbattery.com *Rechargeable sealed battery manufrs*

▶ S & E Engineering, 22 Wentworth Road, Southpark Industrial Estate, Scunthorpe, South Humberside, DN17 2AX Tel: (01724) 858661 Fax: (01724) 281168 *Machinery*

S E G Digital Ltd, Unit 1 Willow Court, Bracewell Avenue, Poulton-le-Fylde, Lancashire, FY6 8JF Tel: (01253) 893688 Fax: (01253) 899226 E-mail: sales@sege.com *Visual display technology suppliers*

S E Gear Ltd, 19 Wenhill Heights, Calne, Wilts, SN11 0JZ Tel: 01249 811000 Fax: 01249 811000 *Equestrian products*

▶ S E H Europe Ltd, Wilson Road, Livingston, West Lothian, EH54 7DA Tel: (01506) 415555 Fax: (01506) 417171 E-mail: sales@sehe.com

▶ S E H Holdings Ltd, Crowcroft Road, Nedging Tye, Ipswich, IP7 7HR Tel: (01449) 740971 Fax: (01449) 741403

▶ S E H Windows & Doors Ltd, 1 Olimpus Close, Ipswich, IP1 5LJ Tel: (01473) 467171 Fax: (01473) 462240 *Home improvements*

S E I Interconnect Products Ltd, 10 Axis Court, Mallard Way, Riverside Business Park, Swansea, SA7 0AJ Tel: (01639) 822806 Fax: (01792) 794357 E-mail: nperkins@sumi-electric.com Principal Export Areas: Worldwide *Wire, coaxial, flat flexible, multi core & custom design cables*

S E Ison & Sons, Ebberns Road, Hemel Hempstead, Hertfordshire, HP3 9QS Tel: (01442) 264104 Fax: (01442) 233611 E-mail: office@seison.co.uk *Motor body repairers*

S E L Clarke Plant Hire, New Road, Bideford, Devon, EX39 5AA Tel: (01237) 476375 Fax: (01237) 421532 *Plant hire construction*

S E Manufacturing, Leek New Road, Stoke-on-Trent, ST6 2LB Tel: (01782) 213511 Fax: (01782) 287828 E-mail: general@serviceuk.com *General subcontract machining & fabrication, CNC, turning & milling*

▶ S E Marketing, 6 Hallas Grove, Manchester, M23 0GZ Tel: 0161-946 1116 E-mail: semarketing@postmaster.co.uk *Effective Search Engine Marketing With Guaranteed Top Three Positions on All Major Search Engines Including Google, Yahoo, Msn, Wanadoo, etc. Prices Start From £99.00 For The Whole Year.*

▶ S & E Mechanical & Fabrication Services Ltd, Dawes Lane, Scunthorpe, South Humberside, DN15 6UW Tel: (01724) 277408 Fax: (01724) 855669 E-mail: paulcloseartistic@hotmail.co.uk *Specialists in powder coated finishes*

S E N Marketing, 618 Leeds Road, Wakefield, West Yorkshire, WF1 2LT Tel: (01924) 871697 Fax: (01924) 871697 E-mail: info@sem.com *Educational supplier*

▶ S E O Computers, Waterside House, Falmouth Road, Penryn, Cornwall, TR10 8BE Tel: (01326) 378424 Fax: (01326) 376667 E-mail: info@seo-computers.com *IT computer company*

S E S Ltd, Unit 3 6 Clarence Street, Aberdeen, AB11 5DB Tel: (01224) 212132 Fax: (01224) 213031 E-mail: sales@ses-marine.com *Electronic marine equipment suppliers*

S E S Computing, 5 Market Street, Weymouth, Dorset, DT4 8DD Tel: (01305) 774402 Fax: (01305) 784502 E-mail: sales@sescomputors.com *PC manufrs*

S E S Multimetal Stock, 1 Caldershaw Centre, Ings Lane, Rochdale, Lancashire, OL12 7LQ Tel: (01706) 711999 Fax: (01706) 651999 E-mail: sales@sesmultimetal.co.uk *Metal stockholders*

S E S Precision Engineers Ltd, 206 Bromley Road, Catford, London, SE6 2XA Tel: (020) 8461 4240 Fax: (020) 8695 6561 *Precision engineers*

▶ S E S Quicktrak, 7 Longport Enterprise Centre, Scott Lidgett Road, Stoke-on-Trent, ST6 4NQ Tel: (01782) 826800 Fax: (01782) 813641 *Garage service equipment manufrs*

S E S Sterling Ltd, Halesfield 17, Harcourt Business Park, Telford, Shropshire, TF7 4PW Tel: (01952) 684196 Fax: (01952) 684286 E-mail: sales@ses-sterling.com *Cable management products & warning labels*

S E T Office Supplies Ltd, Asset House, 63 Penarth Road, Cardiff, CF10 5RA Tel: (029) 2022 5555 Fax: (029) 2022 1922 E-mail: sales@setofficesupplies.co.uk *Stationery suppliers*

▶ S E T S, 114 Canterbury Road, Worthing, West Sussex, BN13 1AL Tel: (07711) 674303 Fax: (01903) 523149 E-mail: transport.manager@ntlworld.com *National & International Road Transport Management & CPC Services: Est 1994.*Members of: - *CILT. IoTA. ICFM. AIRSO. TSUG.*

S E V Group Ltd, Houghton Road, North Anston Trading Estate, Dinnington, Sheffield, S25 4JJ Tel: (01909) 568006 Fax: (01909) 564781 E-mail: enquiry@sev.co.uk *Electric vehicle services & spare parts retailers*

S E W Eurodrive Ltd, 5 Sugarbrook Court, Aston Road, Bromsgrove, Worcestershire, B60 3EX Tel: (01527) 877319 Fax: (01527) 575245 E-mail: sales@sew-eurodrive.co.uk *Manufacturers of drive systems & pneumatic brakes*

S E W Eurodrive Ltd, 764 Finchley Road, London, NW11 7TH Tel: (020) 8458 8949 Fax: (020) 8458 7417 *Manufacturers of drive systems & pneumatic brakes*

S E W Eurodrive Ltd, Beckbridge Road, Normanton Industrial Estate, Normanton, West Yorkshire, WF6 1QR Tel: (01924) 893855 Fax: (01924) 893702 E-mail: sales@sew-eurodrive.co.uk *Electric motors, AC & fractional horse power & gear box manufrs*

S E W Eurodrive Ltd, Unit 37 Enterprise House, Springkerse Business Park, Stirling, FK7 7UF Tel: (01786) 478730 Fax: (01786) 450223 *Manufacturers of industrial & mechanical power transmission equipment*

S F C Ceramics Ltd, 4-6 Bethel Street, Brighouse, West Yorkshire, HD6 1JN Tel: (01484) 400377 Fax: (01484)400677 *Ceramics distributor*

S F Detection Ltd, Hatch Pond House, 4 Stinsford Road, Nuffield Estate, Poole, Dorset, BH17 0RZ Tel: (01202) 645577 Fax: (01202) 665331 E-mail: sales@sfdetection.com *Domestic gas alarm manufrs*

S & F Electrics, Office5 Rope Walk, Littlehampton, West Sussex, BN17 5DH Tel: (01903) 723593 Fax: (01903) 723593 *Electrical contractors*

S F J Systems Ltd, Andil House, Court Street, Trowbridge, Wiltshire, BA14 8BR Tel: (01225) 775103 Fax: (01225) 774877 E-mail: info@sfjsystems.co.uk *Computer software producers*

S F K Information, Langdale House, Lothersdale, Keighley, West Yorkshire, BD20 8HB Tel: (01535) 637390 E-mail: info@sfkinfo.co.uk *Software developers*

▶ S F Oakley Ltd, Bussavean Farm House, Kenwyn, Truro, Cornwall, TR4 9BY Tel: (01872) 240919 Fax: (01872) 240919 *Giftware suppliers*

S F R East Anglia, 22 Clements Way, Beck Row, Bury St. Edmunds, Suffolk, IP28 8AB Tel: (01638) 713758 Fax: (01638) 715541 E-mail: gary@sfrea.co.uk *Lubricants, CBM, speciality cleaners & phosphates*

▶ S F R Systems For Retailers Ltd, 23 Paterson Road, Finedon Road Industrial Estate, Wellingborough, Northamptonshire, NN8 4BZ Tel: (01933) 224101 Fax: (01933) 274598 E-mail: sales@sfr.co.uk

S F S Intect, Unit 13 Welshpool Enterprise Centre, Welshpool, Powys, SY21 7SL Tel: (01938) 556035 Fax: (01938) 556036 E-mail: hbob@sfsintec.biz *Specialists in the manufacture of Precision Cold Formed Parts, Engineered Fasteners, Sintered Parts (Powder Metallurgy) including Plastic Injection Mouldings specifically for the Automotive Industry. Inhouse Heat Treatment and Plating (inc. Crvi free) capabilities.* Also at: Leeds

S F Taylor & Co. Ltd, Whitehill Industrial Estate, Haigh Avenue, Stockport, Cheshire, SK4 1NU Tel: 0161-429 7200 Fax: 0161-429 5720 E-mail: gilltress@sftaylor.com *Commercial & colour printers*

S F Vehicle Builders Ltd, Crossways, Church Stretton, Shropshire, SY6 6PG Tel: (01694) 722804 Fax: (01694) 723583 *Steel & aluminium fabricators*

S Faulkner & Sons, Ashby Road East, Bretby, Burton-on-Trent, Staffordshire, DE15 0PS Tel: (01283) 550454 *Timber merchants*

S Frank Cook & Son, 215 West End Lane, London, NW6 1XJ Tel: (020) 7431 6565 Fax: (020) 7435 9862 E-mail: info@sfrankcook.co.uk *Textile agents*

S G, S G House, 41 Tower Hill, London, EC3N 4SG Tel: (020) 7676 6000 Fax: (020) 7762 4555 E-mail: firstname.second@sgcib.com *French international investment bank*

S G A Technologies Ltd, Shirehill Industrial Estate, Saffron Walden, Essex, CB11 3AQ Tel: (01799) 527264 Fax: (01799) 523064 E-mail: enquiries@sgatech.co.uk *Electroplating services*

S G Aluminium Ltd, Unit B Sett End Road West, Shadsworth Business Park, Blackburn, BB1 2QJ Tel: (01254) 691600 Fax: (01253) 340526 E-mail: info@sg-aluminium.co.uk *Aluminium & upvc specialists*

▶ S & G Aluminium Fabrications, Brooklands Road, Adwick-le-Street, Doncaster, South Yorkshire, DN6 7BA Tel: (01302) 330488 Fax: (01302) 330196

S G B plc, Unit 5 Pucklechurch Trading Estate, Pucklechurch, Bristol, BS16 9QH Tel: 0117-937 3218 Fax: 0117-937 2247 *Scaffold hire & sales service*

S G B Ltd, 40 Bayton Road, Exhall, Coventry, CV7 9EJ Tel: (024) 7636 2255 Fax: (024) 7658 8042 E-mail: info@sgb.co.uk *Contractors' plant hire, leasing & rental*

S G B plc, Pontefract Road, Leeds, LS10 1SP Tel: 0113-271 2951 Fax: 0113-270 7726 E-mail: rentalandsales@sgb.co.uk *Hire, sale & erection of scaffolding*

▶ S G B plc, 86-88 Gresham Road, London, SW9 7NP Tel: (020) 7924 9000 Fax: (020) 7738 4144 *Building (Temporary) Constructors or Fabricators*

▶ S G B plc, Richmond Walk, Plymouth, PL1 4LT Tel: (01752) 561575 Fax: (01752) 606892 *Building (Temporary) Constructors or Fabricators*

▶ S G B plc, Park Lane, Stoke-on-Trent, ST4 3JP Tel: (01782) 313104 Fax: (01782) 335164 E-mail: lpattyson@sgb.co.uk *Scaffolding*

S G B Formwork, 609 London Road, Grays, Essex, RM20 3BJ Tel: (01708) 861666 Fax: (01708) 869560 *Industrial fastener manufrs*

▶ S G B Group, Capper Yard, Bridge Lane, Woolston, Warrington, WA1 4BA Tel: (01925) 846260 Fax: (01925) 846270 E-mail: info@sgb.co.uk *Portable accommodation distributors*

▶ S G B Group Transport, 31 Hobbs Industrial Estate, Newchapel, Lingfield, Surrey, RH7 6HN Tel: (01342) 835555 Fax: (01342) 835003

S G B Hire Plus, High Street, West End, Southampton, SO30 3JF Tel: (023) 8047 0333 Fax: (023) 8047 3030 *Scaffolding contract suppliers*

▶ S G B Rental & Sales, 8 The Drift, Nacton Road, Ipswich, IP3 9QR Tel: (01473) 271313 Fax: (01473) 710979

S G B Rental & Sales, 104 Scrubs Lane, Willesden, London, NW10 6SF Tel: (020) 8969 3661 Fax: (020) 8960 6033 *Hire & sales access & groundwork equipment*

▶ S G B Rovacabin, Green Lane, Felling, Gateshead, Tyne & Wear, NE10 0EZ Tel: (0800) 585383 Fax: 0191-469 5175 *Building (Temporary) Constructors or Fabricators*

▶ S G B Rovacabin, 12 Dunnswood Road, Wardpark South, Cumbernauld, Glasgow, G67 3EN Tel: (01236) 729601 Fax: (01236) 738005 *Building (Temporary) Constructors or Fabricators*

▶ S G B Rovacabin, 609 London Road, Grays, Essex, RM20 3BJ Tel: (0800) 585383 Fax: (01708) 869560 *Building (Temporary) Constructors or Fabricators*

S G B Rovacabin, B Peterley Road, Cowley, Oxford, OX4 2TZ Tel: (01865) 337200 Fax: (01865) 337201 E-mail: rovasales@sgb.co.uk *Building (Temporary) Constructors or Fabricators* Also at: Branches throughout the U.K.

▶ S G B Rovacabin Haydock, Anglezarke Road, Sankey Valley Industrial Estate, Newton-le-Willows, Merseyside, WA12 8DJ Tel: (0800) 585383 Fax: (01925) 291045 *Building (Temporary) Constructors or Fabricators*

▶ S G B Rovacabin Hire Ltd, Ainleys Industrial Estate, Huddersfield Road, Elland, West Yorkshire, HX5 9BZ Tel: 0161-620 3047 Fax: (01454) 322948 *Building (Temporary) Constructors or Fabricators*

▶ S G B Rovacabin Hire Ltd, Ainleys Industrial Estate, Huddersfield Road, Elland, West Yorkshire, HX5 9BZ Tel: 0161-620 3047 Fax: (01422) 379142 *Building (Temporary) Constructors or Fabricators*

▶ S G B Services Ltd, Unit 3000, Academy Park, Gower St, Glasgow, G51 1PR Tel: 0141-419440

S G Baker Ltd, Union St, Friockheim, Arbroath, Angus, DD11 4TD Tel: (01241) 828681 Fax: (01241) 828349 E-mail: sales@sgbaker.co.uk *Paper, polythene and coated woven polypropylene sacks in both open mouth/block bottom and valve fill constructions.FIBC including our patented "Easilift" bag which allows single person operation. FIBC also available with ventilated fabric for agricultural products, e.g. potatoes. Hessian bags in our unique "Superbrite" colour. Woven polypropylene bags in a wide range of sizes. Net bags in a range of sizes, colours and constructions. Hessian (including rotproofed) and polypropylene sandbags. Crop cover in both mesh and fleece constructions. Many products available from stock and we offer a top quality overprinting service in up to 4 colours*

S G Blair & Co. Ltd, Davy Road, Astmoor Industrial Estate, Runcorn, Cheshire, WA7 1SL Tel: (01928) 503200 Fax: (01928) 715200 E-mail: sales@sgblair.com *Refractory engineers*

S & G Cables Co. Ltd, Unit 2D, Chilton Industrial Estate, Chilton, Ferryhill, County Durham, DL17 0SZ Tel: (01388) 722255 Fax: (01388) 722266 E-mail: fgcables@btinternet.com *Cable assembly services*

S G Cuttings, Unit E4 Europa Trading Estate, Stoneclough Road, Radcliffe, Manchester, M26 1GG Tel: (01204) 574030 Fax: (01204) 574031 E-mail: simon.leigh@john-holden.com *Cutting room consultants*

S G D Engineers, Unit 14c Whitebridge Industrial Estate, Whitebridge Lane, Stone, Staffordshire, ST15 8LQ Tel: (01785) 811104 Fax: (01785) 811104 E-mail: andrew.ward6@btconnect.com *General engineers*

S G D Security Ltd, 26-28 Dalcross Street, Cardiff, CF24 4SD Tel: (029) 2046 4120 Fax: (029) 2047 0843 E-mail: info@sgdsecurity.com *Electronic secure installation & maintenance*

S G Dieplas Ltd, J8 Dudley Central Trading Estate, Shaw Road, Dudley, West Midlands, DY2 8QX Tel: (01384) 258494 Fax: (01384) 258494 E-mail: gward.inet@court.co.uk *Plastics mould toolmakers*

S G E (Europe) Ltd, 1 Potters Lane, Kiln Farm, Milton Keynes, MK11 3LA Tel: (01908) 568844 Fax: (01908) 566790 E-mail: uk@sge.com *Chromatography accessories*

S G E (Seal) Ltd, Church Street, Seal, Sevenoaks, Kent, TN15 0AT Tel: (01732) 761724 Fax: (01732) 761422 E-mail: sales@sgeseal.com *Agricultural engineers & fabricators*

S & G Fabrications Lowestoft Ltd, Horn Hill, Lowestoft, Suffolk, NR33 0PX Tel: (01502) 566734 Fax: (01502) 573900 *Sheet metalwork fabricators*

S G H Moulds Ltd, Hypatia Street, Bolton, BL2 6AA Tel: (01204) 529374 Fax: (01204) 363356 E-mail: sgh@sghmoulds.freeserve.co.uk *Plastics mould toolmakers*

S G L Systems Ltd, Milton Industrial Estate, Lesmahagow, Lanark, ML11 0JN Tel: (01555) 894449 Fax: (01555) 894227 *Fire damper & air control equipment manufrs*

S G M, 23 Chelwood Drive, Leeds, LS8 2AT Tel: 0113-393 1999 Fax: 0113-393 1919 E-mail: sales@sgm.co.uk Principal Export Areas: Worldwide *SGM LTD , Have been supplying quality used Printing presses since 1988, and because of their attention to detail and customer care, have found themselves in one of the top ten U.K. used printing machinery specialists. They have supplied many customers both in the U.K and Overseas with quality machines, many of which have repeated orders, or have recommended them to other printing machinery buyers. All their machines are guaranteed free from cylinder damage.**We supply : AB DICK, ADAST , AKIYAMA , COLOUR METAL, CRABTREE , EBA , GESTETNER , HAMADA , HARRIS/AURELIA , HASIMOTO , HEIDELBERG , ITEK, KBA , KOMORI , MAN , MAN ROLAND , MIEHLE ROLAND , MILLER , MITSUBISHI, MULTILITH, NEBIOLO, OMCSA , PLANETA, POLAR , POLLY ROTAPRINT , RYOBI , SAKURAI , SHINOHARA FUJI, SHIVA , SOLNA , STAHL , WHOLENBERG , BOBST , CYLINDERS*

S G M Mapelli, 2 Como Place, Newcastle, Staffordshire, ST5 2QN Tel: (01782) 618101 Fax: (01782) 612616 E-mail: dougtee@mapelli.co.uk *Rubber machinery merchants & agents*

S G Magnets Ltd, Tesla House, 85 Ferry Lane, Rainham, Essex, RM13 9YH Tel: (01708) 558411 Fax: (01708) 554021 E-mail: sales@sgmagnets.com *Magnet manufrs*

S G O Decorative Glass, Unit 41 John Wilson Busn Park, Whitstable, Kent, CT5 3QY Tel: (01227) 265259 Fax: (01227) 265299 *Stain glass window over layers*

S G Print Ltd, PO Box 6068, Basildon, Essex, SS14 3WJ Tel: (01621) 773610 Fax: (01621) 773271 E-mail: sales@sgprint.ltd.uk *Printers, colour printing services*

S G Ray & Co. Ltd, Sheerlands House, Sheerlands Road, Finchampstead, Wokingham, Berkshire, RG40 4QX Tel: 0118-973 2515 *Gas engineering contractors*

S G S, Continental House, Oakridge, West End, Woking, Surrey, GU24 9PJ Tel: (01483) 485420 Fax: (01483) 485499 E-mail: gb.wkg@sgs.com *Employment agencies & employment business service providers*

▶ S G S Carbide Tool UK Ltd, Unit 1 Metro Centre, Toutley Road, Wokingham, Berkshire, RG41 1QW Tel: 0118-979 5200 Fax: 0118-979 5295 E-mail: sales@sgstool.com Principal Export Areas: Central Asia, Middle East, Africa, Central/East Europe & West Europe *Manufacturers of tungsten carbide tools, tungsten carbide rotary burrs, cutting tools & cutters (solid carbide)*

S G S Systems Ltd, Oakley Corner, 16 Kingswear Avenue, Perton, Wolverhampton, WV6 7RJ Tel: (01902) 745565 Fax: (01902) 757786 E-mail: simon@sgssystems.com *Specialists in all security aspects*

S G S (U K) Ltd, Rossmore Business Park, Ellesmere Port, CH65 3EN Tel: 0151-350 6666 Fax: 0151-350 6600 E-mail: ukenquiries@sgs.com *Petrochemical inspection/calibration laboratory services*

S G S UK Ltd, 7TH Floor, Westgate House, West Gate, London, W5 1YY Tel: (020) 8991 3410 Fax: (020) 8991 3417 E-mail: rolandstephan@sgsgroup.com *Consumer goods test services*

S G Scott, 46 Guycroft, Otley, West Yorkshire, LS21 3DS Tel: (01943) 461195 *Jewellery mounting repairers*

S G Springs Ltd, 43 Crossgate Road, Park Farm Industrial Estate, Redditch, Worcestershire, B98 7SN Tel: (01527) 500955 Fax: (01527) 510278 Principal Export Areas: Central/East Europe & West Europe *Wire formed, shaped component, spring clip & spring manufrs*

S & G Tate, 3 Pigot Road, Denbigh, Clwyd, LL16 3DG Tel: (01745) 814024 Fax: (01745) 814024 *Electrical alarm installers*

S G Waite, 6 Trummery Lane, Craigavon, County Armagh, BT67 0JN Tel: (028) 9261 1527 Fax: (028) 9261 1527 *Livestock transportation*

S G Welding & Fabrications, Freeman Road, North Hykeham, Lincoln, LN6 9AP Tel: (01522) 501569 Fax: (01522) 501560 *Steel fabricators*

S Gray & Son, Chapel Farm, Galhampton, Yeovil, Somerset, BA22 7AB Tel: (01963) 440347 Fax: (01963) 440347 E-mail: yarlington1@btopenworld.com *Agricultural contractors, groundwork's*

S Green & Sons Ltd, Fairfield Road, London, E3 2QA Tel: (020) 8981 7940 Fax: (020) 8981 3625 E-mail: sgreen@globalnet.o.uk *Wholesale linen merchants*

S H Coates, Selly Hill Depot, Guisborough Road, Whitby, North Yorkshire, YO21 1SG Tel: (01947) 820569 *Steel fabricators*

S & H Computers Ltd, Godfrey Drive, Ilkeston, Derbyshire, DE7 4HU Tel: 0115-875 8164 Fax: 0115-875 8164 E-mail: sales.shcomputers@ntlworld.com *Computer supplier*

S H & E Ltd, 210 High Holborn, London, WC1V 7EU Tel: (020) 7242 9333 Fax: (020) 7242 9334 E-mail: sales@sh-e.com *Air transport management consultants*

S H E Management, Barham Court, Teston, Maidstone, Kent, ME18 5BZ Tel: (01622) 618613 Fax: (01622) 205950 E-mail: info@formsmaster.com *Computer systems & software developers*

S H E Maritime Services Ltd, Unit 2 Town Quay Wharf, Abbey Road, Barking, Essex, IG11 7BZ Tel: (020) 8594 9325 Fax: (020) 8591 8369 E-mail: sales@she-maritime.com *Consolidation & freight forwarding*

▶ S H I Cyclo Drive Europe Ltd, Marfleet, Hull, HU9 5RA Tel: (01482) 788022

S H J Hospital Pipelines Ltd, 34 Springfield Rd., Chesham, Buckinghamshire, HP5 1PW Tel: (01494) 782168 Fax: (01494) 784478 E-mail: info@shj.co.uk *Pipe installation for medical gasses*

▶ S H Jenkins Ltd, 1 Rougham Industrial Estate, Rougham, Bury St. Edmunds, Suffolk, IP30 9ND Tel: (01359) 271234 Fax: (01359) 271235 *CNC & manual precision machining, welding & fabrication*

S & H Jig Boring Specialists, Hotchkiss Way, Binley Industrial Estate, Binley Industrial Estate, Coventry, CV3 2RL Tel: (024) 7663 5312 Fax: (024) 7663 6538 E-mail: office@shjigboring.co.uk *Jig & fixture construction*

▶ S H O Design, 57 Farringdon Road, London, EC1M 3JB Tel: (020) 7993 5472 E-mail: adam@sho-mail.com *Brand development & corporate identity specialists*

S H Rawnsley Ltd, Birkshead Mill, Wilsden, Bradford, West Yorkshire, BD15 0DH Tel: (01535) 273221 Fax: (01535) 273976 *Uniform fabric manufrs*

▶ S H S Ltd, Unit 15a Atlantic Trading Estate, Barry, South Glamorgan, CF63 3RF Tel: (01446) 735364 Fax: (01446) 745567

S H S Freight Services Ltd, Unit 20 Riverside Development, Chesterton Road, Eastwood Trading Estate, Rotherham, South Yorkshire, S65 1SU Tel: (01709) 377071 Fax: (01709) 820959 E-mail: davidmaw@aol.com *Road haulage & freight services*

S H S International Ltd, 1 Stubley Lane, Dronfield, Derbyshire, S18 1PE Tel: (01246) 413294 Fax: (01246) 414002 *Biscuit manufrs*

▶ S H S Overton Airfields Ltd, Grantham Road, Wellingore, Lincoln, LN5 0HH Tel: (01522) 810351

S H Service Hydraulics Ltd, 56 Pinfold Street, Wednesbury, West Midlands, WS10 8TQ Tel: 0121-526 6431 Fax: 0121-568 6683 *Hose fittings & hydraulic equipment distributors & manufrs*

▶ S H Somerscales Ltd, Roxton Lane, Keelby, Grimsby, South Humberside, DN41 8JB Tel: (01469) 560704 Fax: (01469) 561354 *Sawmill*

▶ S & H Storage & Haulage Ltd, 189 Dumbarton Road, Clydebank, Dunbartonshire, G81 4XJ Tel: 0141-952 1816 Fax: 0141-952 2102

S H Structures Ltd, Moor La Trading Estate, Sherburn in Elmet, Leeds, LS25 6ES Tel: (01977) 681931 Fax: (01977) 681930 E-mail: mail@shstructures.com *Structural engineers manufrs*

S & H Systems Design & Installation Ltd, Unit 1 Beechwood Business Park, Burdock Close, Cannock, Staffordshire, WS11 7GB Tel: (01543) 462620 Fax: (01543) 432630 E-mail: mail@s-and-h-systems.com *Control panel manufrs*

S.I.A. (Agencies) Ltd, Unit 2, 96 Beechill Road, Belfast, BT8 7QN Tel: (028) 9049 2744 Fax: (028) 9064 9401 E-mail: alison@siaagencies.com *Industrial portable power tools suppliers*

S I A Mould Tools Ltd, Russell Street, Sutton-in-Ashfield, Nottinghamshire, NG17 4BE Tel: 01623 553237 *Plastics injection moulds manufrs*

S I A S Building Services Ltd, Unit 4 Knowle Spring Industrial Estate, South Street, Keighley, West Yorkshire, BD21 1AQ Tel: (01535) 611336 Fax: (01535) 611361 E-mail: consultants@siasbuildingservices.co.uk *Mechanical service engineers*

S I Board Supplies, 4 Victoria Retail Park, Crown Road, Ruislip, Middlesex, HA4 0AF Tel: (020) 8839 4343 Fax: (020) 8839 4344 E-mail: ruislip@siboards.co.uk *Homes & industry insulations*

S I C Equipment Ltd, 5 St. Thomas Road, Belvedere, Kent, DA17 6AG Tel: (020) 8311 7081 Fax: (020) 8311 7082 *Fan coil manufrs*

▶ S I Evans & Son Ltd, 81 Lammas Street, Carmarthen, Dyfed, SA31 3AY Tel: (01267) 236253 Fax: (01267) 222727

▶ S I F A M (Fibre Optics) Ltd, Broomhill Way, Torquay, TQ2 7QL Tel: (01803) 407807 *Makers of fibre optics*

S I G Combibloc Ltd, Blackthorn Way, Houghton Le Spring, Tyne & Wear, DH4 6JN Tel: 0191-385 3131 Fax: 0191-385 4713 *Carton manufrs*

▶ S I G N, 28 Thistle Street, Edinburgh, EH2 1EN Tel: 0131-718 5090 E-mail: sign@sign.ac.uk *Produce medical evidence*

S I M Ltd, Albion House, Chertsey Road, Woking, Surrey, GU21 6BF Tel: (01483) 733100 Fax: (01483) 733101 E-mail: sales@simgroup.co.uk *Software testing consultancy & training*

▶ S I M Machine Tools Ltd, 5-6a Unit, London Terrace, Darwen, Lancashire, BB3 3DF Tel: (01254) 777117 Fax: (01254) 774841 E-mail: sales@simmachinetools.com *Supplier & purchaser pre-owned metal working machinery & equipment*

S I P Industrial Products Ltd, Gelders Hall Road, Shepshed, Loughborough, Leicestershire, LE12 9NH Tel: (01509) 500300 Fax: (01509) 503154 E-mail: sales@sip-group.com *Manufacturers & suppliers of industrial air compressors*

S I Pumps Ltd, Unit 5 Curtis Yard, North Hinksey Lane, Botley, Oxford, OX2 0LX Tel: (01865) 791719 Fax: (01865) 722299 E-mail: sales@sipumps.ltd.uk *Pump distributors, installation, repair & service*

S I S Chemicals Ltd, 1 The Square, Pennington, Lymington, Hampshire, SO41 8GN Tel: (01590) 674202 Fax: (01590) 679505 E-mail: info@sischem.co.uk *Chemical manufacturers & distributors* Also at: Bradford, Caerphilly, Fareham & Gloucester

S.I.S. Industrial Automation Ltd, 8 Amphion Court Hale Trading Estate, Lower Church Lane, Tipton, West Midlands, DY4 7HN Tel: 0121-520 7211 Fax: 0121-557 8146 *Bearings & power transmission stockists*

S I S Stafford, 1 North Avenue, Stafford, ST16 1NP Tel: (01785) 600113 Fax: (01785) 600113 E-mail: stafford.couriers@ntlworld.com *Home & National sameday delivery service. 24 hours, 7 days a week.*Documents & light haulage specialist. National coverage courier. Cheapest price in Stafford.*

S & I Structures, 4 Forge Way, Cleveland Trading Estate, Darlington, County Durham, DL1 2PJ Tel: (01325) 369930 Fax: (01325) 369940 *Steel fabricators*

S I Systems Ltd, 64 Killigrew Street, Falmouth, Cornwall, TR11 3PP Tel: (01326) 315200 E-mail: sisystems@btinternet.com *Computer hardware repair & retailers*

S I T A, Packington House, Packington Lane, Meriden, Coventry, CV7 7HN Tel: (01675) 434700 Fax: (01675) 465740 *Waste disposal*

S I T A Ltd, D12 Red Scar Industrial Estate, Longridge Road, Ribbleton, Preston, PR2 5NQ Tel: (01772) 703100 Fax: (01772) 703111 *Waste disposal contractors*

S I T Bray Ltd, Education Road, Meanwood Road, Leeds, LS7 2AN Tel: 0113-281 6700 Fax: 0113-281 6702 E-mail: sit.uk@sitgroup.it *Burner manufrs*

S J Aluminium Fabrications, Unit E., Area 6, Fort Fareham Business Park, Fareham, Hampshire, PO14 1AH Tel: (01329) 220828 Fax: (01329) 220828 E-mail: sales@shop-frontage.com *Commercial aluminium shop front & facade system fabricators*

S J Andrew & Sons, South Turnpike, Redruth, Cornwall, TR15 2LZ Tel: (01209) 213171 Fax: (01209) 219459 E-mail: nathan@sjandrew.com *Steel stockholders & engineers distributors*

▶ S J B Construction Ltd, Station Street, Treherbert, Treorchy, Mid Glamorgan, CF42 5HT Tel: (01443) 773570 Fax: (01443) 771739

▶ S J B Crane Co., Station Road, Halfway, Sheffield, S20 3GW Tel: 0114-247 9686 Fax: 0114-247 1527 *Crane hire specialists*

S J C Engineering Ltd, 5 Court Industrial Estate, Navigation Road, Chelmsford, CM2 6ND Tel: (01245) 492926 Fax: (01245) 494296 E-mail: enquiries@sjceng.co.uk *Precision engineers*

S J C Shopfitters, 3 Britannia Road, Waltham Cross, Hertfordshire, EN8 7NY Tel: (01992) 711151 Fax: (01992) 714441 E-mail: sales@sjcshopfitters.co.uk *Specialist joinery manufrs*

S J C Shopfitters, 3 Britannia Road, Waltham Cross, Hertfordshire, EN8 7NY Tel: (01992) 711151 Fax: (01992) 714441 E-mail: sales@sjcshopfitters.co.uk *Specialist paint sprayers*

S J Clifford & Co. Ltd, B 19 Bayton Road Industrial Estate, Bayton Road, Exhall, Coventry, CV7 9EL Tel: (024) 7636 3961 Fax: (024) 7664 4097 E-mail: sales@sjclifford.co.uk *Precision & general engineers*

S & J Contractors, 81 Vicarage Hill, Benfleet, Essex, SS7 1PD Tel: (01268) 755761 *Steel fabricators & erectors*

▶ S & J Couriers (North Devon), 63 East Ridge View, Bideford, Devon, EX39 4RS Tel: (07815) 814616 Fax: (01237) 420307 E-mail: jamie246@btinternet.com *WE ARE HERE TO DEAL WITH ALL YOUR UK NATION WIDE TRANSPORT REQUIREMENTS, WEATHER IT BE AN ENVONLOPE OR 30 PALLETS THEN USE THE INFORMATION ON OUR WEB SITE TO CONTACT US FOR A COMPETITIVE QUOTE.*

▶ S J D Commercial Interiors, 120 High Street, Lee-on-the-Solent, Hampshire, PO13 9DB Tel: (023) 9255 1469 *Ceiling contractors*

S.J Deegan Sons, Elstree Hill South, Edgwarebury House Farm, Elstree, Borehamwood, Hertfordshire, WD6 3DE Tel: (020) 8953 1042 Fax: (020) 8207 6550 *Civil engineers*

S. J. Dixon International Ltd, Dixon House, Old Heath Road, Wolverhampton, WV1 2RR Tel: (01902) 455114 Fax: (01902) 452602 *Decorators merchants & wholesale distributors*

S J Dixon & Son Ltd, Garden Street, Walsall, WS2 8EG Tel: (01922) 647244 Fax: (01922) 722965 *Decorators merchants & retailers* Also at: Branches throughout the Midlands

▶ S J Electronics, Unit 3 Vernon Court, Henson Way, Telford Way Industrial Estate, Kettering, Northamptonshire, NN16 8PX Tel: (01536) 416200 Fax: (01536) 416300 E-mail: sales@sjelectronics.co.uk Principal Export Areas: Worldwide *Educational (test & measurement) supplies/distributors/agents. Also oscilloscope & test equipment distributors or agents. Freephone 0800 5854455*

S & J Engineering Services, 1 Periwinkle Court, Church Street, Milton Regis, Sittingbourne, Kent, ME10 2JZ Tel: (01795) 431111 Fax: (01795) 431111 *Engineering machine shop*

▶ S & J European Haulage Ltd, Asfordby Business Park, Welby Road, Welby, Melton Mowbray, Leicestershire, LE14 3JL Tel: (01664) 810060 Fax: (01664) 810061

S J Floral Displays, 29 Newton Avenue, Tonbridge, Kent, TN10 4RR Tel: (01732) 356447 Fax: (01732) 356447 *Floral display services*

S J Gaskets Ltd, Tything Park, Tything Road East, Kinwarton, Alcester, Warwickshire, B49 6ES Tel: (01789) 763721 Fax: (01789) 764070 E-mail: sjgaskets@thesjgroup.com *Gaskets, rubber extrusion/rubber product manufrs*

▶ S & J Graveson Ltd, The Orchard, 1 Lyddington Road, Caldecott, Market Harborough, Leicestershire, LE16 8TE Tel: (01536) 770334 Fax: (01536) 771894

S J H Sparkes & Sons Ltd, 20 Devonshire Road, Cambridge, CB1 2BH Tel: (01223) 356172 Fax: (01223) 356172 *General engineers & locksmiths services*

S J Humphries Ltd, Portersfield Road, Cradley Heath, West Midlands, B64 7BN Tel: (01384) 569326 Fax: (01384) 74070 *Drop forging manufrs*

S & J Kidson, 7 Ingramgate, Thirsk, North Yorkshire, YO7 1DF Tel: (01845) 524610 *Agricultural contractors*

S & J Knitwear Ltd, Payne Street, Leicester, LE4 7RD Tel: 0116-261 1701 Fax: 0116-266 6965 *General leisure wear manufrs*

S.J.M. Eurostat (U.K.) Ltd, Unit 4b, Bramhall Moor Industrial Park, Hazel Grove, Stockport, Cheshire, SK7 5BW Tel: 0161-456 6088 Fax: 0161-456 6089 E-mail: sjm@sjmeurostat.co.uk *Anti-static packaging vacuum formers*

▶ S J Mcauley, 35 Vow Road, Ballymoney, County Antrim, BT53 7PB Tel: (028) 2766 6646 Fax: (028) 2766 6705 E-mail: info@mcauleyengineering.co.uk *Sheet metal engineering & machining services*

S J Maguire Groundwork, 20 Moseley Road, Naphill, High Wycombe, Buckinghamshire, HP14 4SQ Tel: (01494) 563056 *Ground workers*

S J Phillips Ltd, 139 New Bond Street, London, W1S 2TL Tel: (020) 7629 6261 Fax: (020) 7495 6180 E-mail: enquiries@sjphillips.com *Antique dealers*

S J Polishing, 39 Greville Street, London, EC1N 8PJ Tel: (020) 7404 0382 *Jewellery polishing services*

S J Products, Unit 2 Trench Lock 3, Telford, Shropshire, TF1 5ST Tel: (01952) 240656 Fax: (01952) 242281 E-mail: info@sjproductstoolanddie.co.uk *Wire eroding*

▶ S J Quick & Sons, Heather Lane, Canonstown, Hayle, Cornwall, TR27 6NQ Tel: (01736) 740272 Fax: (01736) 741311

S J Rolls Ltd, Plot 7, Wimbledon Avenue, Brandon, Suffolk, IP27 0NZ Tel: (01842) 811918 Fax: (01842) 811693 *Glass fibre reinforced plastic moulders*

▶ S J S Cannock Ltd, Unit 13, Cinder Road, Zone 3 Burntwood Business Park, Burntwood, Staffordshire, WS7 3FS Tel: (01543) 670066

S.J.S. Engineering, 114-116 Newhall Street, Willenhall, West Midlands, WV13 1LQ Tel: (01902) 606602 Fax: (01902) 606011 *General engineers & castings services*

S J S Newport Ltd, Avenue Road, Newport, Shropshire, TF10 7EA Tel: (01952) 814163

▶ S J S TV Services Ltd, 22 Becksbourne Close, Penenden Heath, Maidstone, Kent, ME14 2ED Tel: (01622) 664500 Fax: (01622) 664500 E-mail: sales@sjstv.co.uk *Maidstone TV repair. Also Video, Stereo etc. No Fix - No Fee*

S J Sharp (Nuneaton) Ltd, Weddington Road, Nuneaton, Warwickshire, CV10 0AE Tel: (024) 7638 3232 Fax: (024) 7638 2362 *Removal & storage specialists*

▶ S J T Medical, Spartan Works, 20 Carlisle Street, Sheffield, S4 7LJ Tel: 0114-272 8273 Fax: 0114-220 1172E-mail: info@sjtmedical.com *Wholesalers and distributors of Binocular Surgical Loupes for Vascular, ENT, plastic surgery and Dentists.*

S & J Webster, Spring Farm, Chellaston, Derby, DE73 6UE Tel: (01332) 700255 Fax: (01332) 690511 *Agricultural & industrial engineering & haulage services*

S Jones Transport Ltd, Anglian Road, Walsall, WS9 8ET Tel: (01922) 450000 Fax: (01922) 455920 E-mail: info@sjonestransport.com *Road transport contractors*

S K B Sails, The Sail Loft, Commercial Road, Penryn, Cornwall, TR10 8AG Tel: (01326) 372107 Fax: (01326) 373792 *Sail makers*

S K Bearings Ltd, Brewery Road, Pampisford, Cambridge, CB22 3HG Tel: (01223) 832851 Fax: (01223) 837668 E-mail: enquiries@skbearings.co.uk *Anti vibration mountings & anti vibration structural bearings manufrs*

S K C Ltd, Unit 11, Sunrise Park, Higher Shaftesbury Road, Blandford Forum, Dorset, DT11 8ST Tel: (01258) 480188 Fax: (01258) 480184 E-mail: info@skcltd.com *Air sampling equipment manufrs*

S K D Office Supplies Ltd, 71-75 Railway Road, Leigh, Lancashire, WN7 4AD Tel: (01942) 603326 Fax: (01942) 674961 E-mail: sales@skdoffice.co.uk *Office furniture & equipment suppliers & stationers*

S K Dodson, 2 Lower Green, Dane End, Ware, Hertfordshire, SG12 0PJ Tel: (01920) 830652 Fax: (01920) 830652 *Agricultural contractors*

S K Electronics Ltd, Regent Street, Oldham, OL1 3TZ Tel: 0161-620 5414 Fax: 0161-627 3237 E-mail: sales@skelectronics.co.uk *Electronic control systems manufrs*

S K Engineering, 16a Tamlaghduff Road, Bellaghy, Magherafelt, County Londonderry, BT45 8JQ Tel: (028) 7938 6561 Fax: (028) 7938 6561 *Motor engineers*

S & K Envelopes Ltd, Greatfield Farm, Single Street, Berrys Green, Westerham, Kent, TN16 3AA Tel: (01959) 575755 Fax: (01959) 574554 *Envelope printing*

S K F Spindle Service Centre (U K) Ltd, 8 Dencora Way, Sundon Business Park, Luton, LU3 3HP Tel: (01582) 494674 Fax: (01582) 494808 E-mail: skfspindleserviceuk@skf.com *Machine tool spindle reconditioning/rebuilding*

S K F (U K) Ltd, Sundon Park Road, Luton, LU3 3BL Tel: (01582) 490049 Fax: (01582) 848091 E-mail: marketing.uk@skf.com *SKF is the leading global supplier of products, customer solutions and services in the rolling bearing, seals, mechatronics and lubrication systems business. The Group's main competencies include technical support, maintenance services, condition monitoring and training. SKF also holds an increasingly important position in the market for linear motion products, as well as high precision bearings, spindles and spindle services for the machine tool industry, lubrication systems, and is an established producer of bearing steel* Also at: Birmingham, Glasgow & Wakefield

S K Fashions & Textiles, 33 Stonebridge Street, Leicester, LE5 3PB Tel: 0116-246 0960 Fax: 0116-274 2124 *Schoolwear manufrs*

S & K Fitted Furniture Ltd, 86 New Cleveland Street, Hull, HU8 7HE Tel: (01482) 227691 Fax: (01482) 589551 E-mail: designteam@skjoiners.karoo.co.uk *Manufacturers of kitchen & bedroom furniture*

S K Metal Works Ltd, 190 Courtauld Road, London, N19 4BA Tel: (020) 7263 1575 Fax: (020) 7263 1575 *Metal works*

S K N Electronics Ltd, Armoury Road, Birmingham, B11 2PP Tel: 0121-773 6672 Fax: 0121-766 8457 E-mail: technical@sknelectronics.co.uk *Electronic contract manufrs*

S K Plastics Ltd, Unit 18 Tanfield Lea Industrial Estate South, Tanfield Lea, Stanley, County Durham, DH9 9XB Tel: (01207) 236662 Fax: (01207) 236669 E-mail: sales@skplastics.co.uk *Plastic Fabrication Engineers*

▶ S K Print Ltd, Unit 25 Capitol Trading Park, Kirkby Bank Road, Knowsley Industrial Park, Liverpool, L33 7SY Tel: 0151-546 5532 Fax: 0151-546 5521 E-mail: skprintltd@hotmail.com *Printing services*

▶ S K Refrigeration, Churcham Business Park, Unit C8, Gloucester, GL2 8AX Tel: (01452) 750957 *Refrigeration & air conditioning service*

S K S Plant & Equipment Ltd, 11 Redehall Road, Smallfield, Horley, Surrey, RH6 9PY Tel: (01342) 843688 Fax: (01342) 842236 E-mail: jpeters@sks-group.co.uk *Engineers supplies distributors*

S K S Plant & Equipment Ltd, 11 Redehall Road, Smallfield, Horley, Surrey, RH6 9PY Tel: (01342) 843688 Fax: (01342) 842140 E-mail: sks@sks-group.co.uk Purchasing Contact: P. Denny Sales Contact: P. Denny Principal Export Areas: Worldwide *Workshop equipment suppliers/merchants; engineers' suppliers & hand tool distributors. Also export merchants or agents*

S K S Plant & Equipment Ltd, 11 Redehall Road, Smallfield, Horley, Surrey, RH6 9PY Tel: (01342) 843688 Fax: (01342) 842140 E-mail: export@fks-group.co.uk *Hand tool/ machine tool agents*

S K S Welding & Fasteners Supplies Ltd, Unit 33 Parkhouse Road East, Parkhouse Industrial Estate Ea, Newcastle, Staffordshire, ST5 7RB Tel: (01782) 566911 Fax: (01782) 561964 E-mail: sks.enquiries@btconnect.com *Welding consumables & equipment distributors*

S K (Sales) Ltd, Unit C1, Sapphire Way, Rhombus Business Park, Norwich, NR6 6NN Tel: (01603) 417522 Fax: (01603) 417524 E-mail: orders@sksales.co.uk *Ventilation fan suppliers*

▶ S K Scaffolding Dorset Ltd, 47 Enterprise Park, Piddlehinton, Dorchester, Dorset, DT2 7UA Tel: (01305) 849400 E-mail: sales@sk-scaffolding.co.uk

S K Signs & Labels Ltd, The Brookside Centre, Sumpters Way, Southend-on-Sea, SS2 5RR Tel: (01702) 462401 Fax: (01702) 662404 E-mail: info@sksigns.co.uk *Engravers (general); sign contractors/signmakers/suppliers/installers & signs including engraved metal & plastic. Also nameplate (metal) manufrs*

S Keeling & Co. Ltd, Forge Lane, Stoke-on-Trent, ST1 5PB Tel: (01782) 202660 Fax: (01782) 202019 *Timber merchants*

S Kempner Ltd, 498 Honeypot Lane, Stanmore, Middlesex, HA7 1JZ Tel: (020) 8952 5262 Fax: (020) 8952 8061 E-mail: sales@kempner.co.uk *Plastic packaging equipment distributors*

▶ S & L Ltd, Unit 13, Block 6, Old Mill Lane Industrial Estate, Mansfield Woodhouse, Mansfield, Nottinghamshire, NG19 9BG Tel: (01623) 652900 Fax: (01623) 652900 *Furniture & component manufrs*

▶ S L B Printing Services Ltd, 140 Molesey Avenue, West Molesey, Surrey, KT8 2RY Tel: (020) 8941 4115

S L Conyers & Son Ltd, Hawthorns Industrial Estate, Middlemore Road, Handsworth, Birmingham, B21 0BH Tel: 0121-551 2875 Fax: 0121-554 5267 E-mail: webmaster@conyers-labels.com *Self-adhesive labels manufrs*

▶ S L D Pumps Ltd, Ailsa Road, Irvine Industrial Estate, Irvine, Ayrshire, KA12 8LL Tel: (01294) 278986 Fax: (01294) 271324

▶ S L D Specialist Hire Service Ltd, 98 Turnhouse Road, Edinburgh, EH12 8ND Tel: 0131-339 1060

S L D Specialist Hires, Greenbank Road, East Tullos Industrial Estate, Aberdeen, AB12 4BS Tel: (01224) 248700 Fax: (01224) 890576 E-mail: aberdeen@sldpump.co.uk *Pump hire, leasing & rental*

S L E Ltd, Twin Bridges Business Park, 232 Selsdon Road, South Croydon, Surrey, CR2 6PL Tel: (020) 8681 1414 Fax: (020) 8649 8570 E-mail: admin@sle.co.uk *Electro-medical equipment manufrs*

S & L Fish, The Fish Market, The Quay, East Looe, Looe, Cornwall, PL13 1DT Tel: (01503) 262140 Fax: (01503) 263832 *Fish wholesalers*

S L Furnishing, 16 Church Walk, Lurgan, Craigavon, County Armagh, BT67 9AA Tel: (028) 3832 6556 Fax: (028) 3832 6556 *Furniture manufrs*

S L George Printers Ltd, 16 North Street, Leighton Buzzard, Bedfordshire, LU7 1EN Tel: (01525) 373057 Fax: (01525) 852387 E-mail: info@slgeorgeprinters.co.uk *Commercial printers*

S L Joinery, 24 Walbrook Road, Derby, DE23 8RY Tel: (01332) 773230 Fax: (01332) 773230 *Joinery manufrs*

S L K Kentex Fashions Ltd, 90-104 Constitution Hill, Hockley, Birmingham, B19 3JT Tel: 0121-236 6653 Fax: 0121-212 3530 E-mail: kentex@btinternet.com *Wholesalers of casual clothing*

▶ S L M, 22 Albion Street, Syston, Leicester, LE7 2AA Tel: 0116-260 4638

S L M Model Engineers Ltd, Chiltern Road, Prestbury, Cheltenham, Gloucestershire, GL52 5JQ Tel: (01242) 525488 Fax: (01242) 226288 E-mail: mail@slm.uk.com *Injection mouldings manufrs*

S L Mould Tools, 41 Albert Street, Syston, Leicester, LE7 2JA Tel: 0116-269 7080 Fax: 0116-269 8711 *Plastic injection mould toolmakers*

▶ S L R Consulting Ltd, No. 4 The Roundal, Roddinglaw Business Park, Gogar, Edinburgh, EH12 9DB Tel: 0131-335 6830 Fax: 0131-335 6831

S L S Fabrications Ltd, 2 Hythe Works, Diplocks Way, Hailsham, East Sussex, BN27 3JF Tel: (01323) 846061 Fax: (01323) 841009 *Sheet metal workers, engineers & fabricators*

S L S Precision Engineers Ltd, 1 Hermitage Way, Mansfield, Nottinghamshire, NG18 5ES Tel: (01623) 456601 Fax: (01623) 456602 E-mail: slsprec@aol.com *Precision engineers*

S L S Trailors, 29A Shanliss Road, Stewartstown, Dungannon, County Tyrone, BT71 5PZ Tel: (028) 8774 6078 Fax: (028) 8774 6078 E-mail: slsengineering@tiscali.co.uk *Agricultural machinery manufrs*

▶ S L Signs, 9 Georges Road, London, N7 8HD Tel: (020) 7697 0444 Fax: (020) 7697 0444

S L (Thermal Insulation) Contracts & Supplies Co. Ltd, Unit 16 Blue Chalet Industrial Park, London Road, West Kingsdown, Sevenoaks, Kent, TN15 6BT Tel: (01474) 854465 Fax: (01474) 854393 E-mail: les@slcontracts.com *Thermal insulation fire protection*

▶ S L V, The Barn, Fifield Farm, Marsiton Road, Marlston Hermitage, Thatcham, Berkshire, RG18 9UN Tel: (01635) 202500 Fax: (01635) 202088 E-mail: Info@s-l-v.co.uk *Technical production service for corporate events*

S L W Engineering, Dereham Road, New Costessey, Norwich, NR5 0SB Tel: (01603) 749346 *Engineering manufrs*

▶ S Luca, 32 High Street, Musselburgh, Midlothian, EH21 7AG Tel: 0131-665 2237 Fax: 0131-653 3828

S Lyles & Sons Co, Calder Bank Mills, Calder Bank Road, Dewsbury, West Yorkshire, WF12 9QW Tel: (01924) 436500 Fax: (01924) 436511 *Carpet yarn spinners & dyers*

▶ S Lyon & Son Haulage Ltd, Lincoln Road, Skellingthorpe, Lincoln, LN6 5SA Tel: (01522) 682519 Fax: (01522) 500041

S M A Roofing, 22 Thornhill Way, Plymouth, PL3 5NP Tel: (01752) 665918 Fax: (01752) 600123 E-mail: sales@hotmail.com *Roofing contractors*

S M Alexander Plastics Ltd, Little End Road, Eaton Socon, St. Neots, Cambridgeshire, PE19 8JH Tel: (01480) 473140 Fax: (01480) 406968 E-mail: smalexanderplastics@btinternet.com *HF plastic welding company*

▶ S M B Engineering Services, Unit G, Oldham Central Trading Park, Coulton Close, Oldham, OL1 4EB Tel: 0161-627 4640

▶ S M B Sheet Metal Co., Manor Farm, St Peters Road, Cowley, Uxbridge, Middlesex, UB8 3SG Tel: (01895) 440468 Fax: (01895) 422305 E-mail: mikeb@smbsheetmetal.co.uk *CNC punching & folding, sheet metal workers, fabricators, welders*

▶ S M Bayne & Co. Ltd, Orwell Bakery, Loanhead Avenue, Lochore, Lochgelly, Fife, KY5 8DD Tel: (01592) 860235

S M Bros Ltd, 1st Floor Union Mill, Cambrian St, Manchester, M40 7EG Tel: 0161-274 3112 Fax: 0161-274 3312 *Ladies', gent's & children's wear*

S M C Euro Clamps Ltd, Demmings Road, Cheadle, Cheshire, SK8 2PP Tel: 0161-428 8323 Fax: 0161-428 4513 E-mail: purchasing@smceuroclamps.com Principal Export Areas: Worldwide *Fork lift truck attachments manufrs*

S M C Pneumatics, Vincent Avenue, Crownhill, Milton Keynes, MK8 0AN Tel: (01908) 563888 Fax: (01908) 561185 E-mail: sales@smcpneumatics.co.uk *Air, pneumatic cylinders & pneumatic valves manufrs*

S & M Computer Cleaning Services Ltd, Midland House, New Road, Halesowen, West Midlands, B63 3HY Tel: 0121-550 4008 Fax: 0121-550 5272 E-mail: sales@computercleaners.co.uk *Computer cleaning services*

S & M Computer Cleaning Services Ltd, Midland House, New Road, Halesowen, West Midlands, B63 3HY Tel: 0121-550 4008 Fax: 0121-550 5272 E-mail: sales@computercleaners.co.uk *Computer cleaning product distributors*

S M Control Engineering Ltd, 1 Redhouse Industrial Estate, Middlemore Lane, Aldridge, Walsall, WS9 8DL Tel: (01922) 744020 Fax: (01922) 744001 E-mail: cbailey@smcontroleng.co.uk *Low voltage switchgear, & control panels manufrs*

S M Cooper & Associates, Churchfield House, 36 Vicar Street, Dudley, West Midlands, DY2 8RG Tel: (01384) 257227 Fax: (01384) 211973 *Structural engineers*

S M D Textiles Ltd, Pittman Way, Fulwood, Preston, PR2 9ZD Tel: (01772) 651199 Fax: (01772) 654034 E-mail: enquiries@swatchbox.co.uk *Soft furnishing fabric distributors*

▶ S M Davies, Acrefield Yard, Henfaes Lane, Welshpool, Powys, SY21 7BE Tel: (01938) 553446 Fax: (01938) 556842

S M E Ltd, Mill Road, Steyning, West Sussex, BN44 3GY Tel: (01903) 814321 Fax: (01903) 814269 E-mail: sales@sme.ltd.uk *Gramophone pick-up arm manufrs*

S M Engineering, 14 Courtyard Workshops, Bath Street, Market Harborough, Leicestershire, LE16 9PW Tel: (01858) 432211 Fax: (01858) 410305 *Engineering sub-contract services*

S M F, 62 Heming Road, Washford Industrial Estate, Redditch, Worcestershire, B98 0EA Tel: (01527) 514162 Fax: (01527) 514169 E-mail: info@smftools.com *Toolmakers*

S M G P.L.C., 200 Renfield Street, Glasgow, G2 3PR Tel: 0141-300 3000 Fax: 0141-300 3030 *Broadcasting services*

S M G Control Systems, 9 Smestow Bridge, Bridgnorth Road, Wombourne, Wolverhampton, WV5 8AY Tel: (01902) 326886 Fax: (01902) 326883 E-mail: smg@smgcontrolsystems.co.uk *Control systems, automatic & electrical engineers (industrial)/enginee*

S M Goodchild Ltd, East Common Lane, Scunthorpe, South Humberside, DN16 1DE Tel: (01724) 848200 Fax: (01724) 280274 *Industrial rubber products*

S M Group (Europe) Ltd, Mercator House, Brest Road, Plymouth, PL6 5XP Tel: (01752) 662129 Fax: (01752) 241040 E-mail: sales@smgeurope.com *Office furniture & equipment distributors*

▶ S M H Fleet Solutions Ltd, Building 140 Thurleigh Airfield, Business Park, Thurleigh, Bedford, MK44 2YP Tel: (01234) 353172 Fax: (01234) 357511 E-mail: thurleigh.logistics@smhfleet.com

S M H (Newcastle), S M H House, Maxwell St, South Shields, Tyne & Wear, NE33 4PU Tel: 0191-456 6000 Fax: 0191-456 7777 E-mail: sales@smh-products.demon.co.uk *Asbestos, fire safety equipment manufrs*

▶ S M H Products Ltd, 186 Drews Lane, Birmingham, B8 2SL Tel: 0121-328 6000 Fax: 0121-328 6800 E-mail: sales@smhproducts.com *Asbestos testing & removal services*

▶ S M I, 7 Gipping Close, Bedford, MK41 7XY Tel: (01234) 266255 Fax: (01234) 266255 E-mail: smiuk@btconnect.com *Sub contract machining & pump manufrs*

S M J Graphic Services Ltd, 113 Cecil Street, Watford, WD24 5AS Tel: (01923) 222886 Fax: (01923) 218948 *Lithographic plate makers*

S M J Products, Richardshaw Lane, Stanningley, Pudsey, West Yorkshire, LS28 6BZ Tel: 0113-236 0396 Fax: 0113-261 2357 *Leaf spring manufrs*

S M J Sheetmetal Fabrications, Wild Street, Dukinfield, Cheshire, SK16 4DL Tel: 0161-343 3109 Fax: 0161-343 3109 *Sheet metal engineering*

S M K Engineering Ltd, 4 Old Foundry Estate, Victoria Street, Widnes, Cheshire, WA8 7UE Tel: 0151-423 2320 Fax: 0151-420 8201 *Structural steel work manufrs*

S M L Ltd, 2 Red Rose Trading Estate, Lancaster Road, Barnet, Hertfordshire, EN4 8BZ Tel: (020) 8447 1199 Fax: (020) 8447 0880 E-mail: paulcarroll@sml.ltd.uk *Electrical engineers*

S M L, 3 Little Common, Stanmore, Middlesex, HA7 3BZ Tel: (020) 8954 7302 Fax: (020) 8954 1703 E-mail: punches@sml.co.uk *Hole punching distributors & manufrs*

S M L Engineering Co. Ltd, Benlow Works, Silverdale Road, Hayes, Middlesex, UB3 3BW Tel: (020) 8573 5907 Fax: (020) 8561 5033 *Metal work & steel fabricators*

S M M Propeller Services Ltd, Wharf Road, Gravesend, Kent, DA12 2RU Tel: (01474) 320192 Fax: (01474) 335047 *Marine propellers repairs & maintenance agents*

S M M Software Ltd, 42a High Street, Egham, Surrey, TW20 9DP Tel: (01784) 436234 Fax: (01784) 433315 E-mail: sales@smm.co.uk *Software programs & document management*

S & M Myers Ltd, 100-106 Mackenzie Road, London, N7 8RG Tel: (020) 7609 0091 Fax: (020) 7609 2457 *Carpet wholesalers & retailers*

S M P Plastics Fabrications Ltd, 51 Cyprus Street, Oldbury, West Midlands, B69 4XD Tel: 0121-552 0212 Fax: 0121-544 4863 E-mail: info@smp-plastics.co.uk *Plastics fabricators*

S M P Playgrounds Ltd, Thorpe Industrial Estate, Ten Acre Lane, Egham, Surrey, TW20 8RJ Tel: (01784) 489100 Fax: (01784) 431079 E-mail: sales@smp.co.uk *Playground equipment manufacturers.*

S M P Security Ltd, Halesfield 24, Telford, Shropshire, TF7 4NZ Tel: (01952) 585673 Fax: (01952) 582816 *Manufacturers of free standing cash safes*

▶ S M Partnership Ltd, East Lodge, Leylands Farm, Colden Common, Winchester, Hampshire, SO21 1TH Tel: (023) 8069 3969 Fax: (023) 8069 8969 E-mail: enquiries@smpartnership.com *Specialists in the design, manufacture & installation of canopies & walkways*

S M Plants Services Ltd, Hoo Marina Industrial Estate, Hoo, Rochester, Kent, ME3 9LB Tel: (01634) 253333 Fax: (01634) 253112 *Construction equipment suppliers*

▶ S M Plumbing & Heating Ltd, St Leonards House, St Leonards Place, Kinghorn, Burntisland, Fife, KY3 9UL Tel: (01592) 890000 Fax: (01592) 890023

S & M Products Ltd, Compstall Mills Estate, Andrew Street, Compstall, Stockport, Cheshire, SK6 5HN Tel: 0161-427 3864 Fax: 0161-426 0019 E-mail: info@brushclosures.com *Brush manufrs*

S M S Degreasers (Sheet Metal Structures) Ltd, Woodlands, Cliff Road, Salcombe, Devon, TQ8 8LD Tel: (01548) 842454 Fax: (01548) 843380 *Vapour degreasing equipment manufrs*

S M S Diesel Spares Ltd, Cabot Works, Bilton Way, Enfield, Middlesex, EN3 7NH Tel: (020) 8443 4442 Fax: (020) 8443 3667 E-mail: sales@smsdiesel.co.uk *Diesel vehicle parts distributors*

▶ S M S Maintenance Ltd, Faircross Offices, Stratfield Saye, Reading, RG7 2BT Tel: (01256) 880188 Fax: (01256) 880177 E-mail: sales@smsmaintenance.com

S M S Mevac (UK) Ltd, Road Four, Winsford Industrial Estate, Winsford, Cheshire, CW7 3RS Tel: (01606) 551421 Fax: (01606) 553078 E-mail: mail@sms-mevac.co.uk *Secondary steel making plant, design engineers*

▶ S M S Support, Support Centre, Tayside Software Centre, Technology Park, Dundee, DD2 1TY Tel: (01382) 598483 Fax: (01382) 598465

S M S Technologies Ltd, Elizabeth House, Elizabeth Way, Harlow, Essex, CM19 5TL Tel: (01279) 406000 Fax: (01279) 406001 E-mail: admin@smstl.com *Medical equipment manufrs*

S M Sewing Machines, 566 North Circular Road, London, NW2 7QA Tel: (020) 8452 4257 *Sewing machines & accessories*

S & M Specialist Joiners, Elvington Industrial Estate, York Road, Elvington, York, YO41 4AR Tel: (01904) 608677 *Shop fitting services*

S & M Springs, 3-4 Benner Road, Pinchbeck, Spalding, Lincolnshire, PE11 3TZ Tel: (01775) 712125 Fax: (01775) 712126 *Commercial vehicle part distributors*

S M T Associates Ltd, 17 Sandford Street, Lichfield, Staffordshire, WS13 6QA Tel: (01543) 250211 Fax: (01543) 257015 E-mail: sales@smtbadges.co.uk *Promotional gift house*

S M T Network Solutions Ltd, 20 Park Street, Princes Risborough, Buckinghamshire, HP27 9AH Tel: (01844) 275100 Fax: (01844) 275111 E-mail: info@smtnet.co.uk *Computer network installation*

S M Tech Ltd, 1 Ritchie Avenue, Monifieth, Dundee, DD5 4DJ Tel: (01382) 530999 Fax: (01382) 530752 E-mail: sales@findlers.co.uk *Fabrications, machinery services*

S M Thompson Ltd, Marathon Works, Newport Bridge, Middlesbrough, Cleveland, TS1 5TG Tel: (01642) 245161 Fax: (01642) 223392 E-mail: sales@smthompson.co.uk *Profiling steel stockholders*

S M Trailers, Bevis Lane, Wisbech St Mary, Wisbech, Cambridgeshire, PE13 4RR Tel: (01945) 410200 Fax: (01945) 410651 E-mail: sales@smtrailersltd.co.uk *Road trailer manufrs*

S M Upholstery Ltd, 212a Whitchurch Road, Cardiff, CF14 3NB Tel: (029) 2061 9813 Fax: (029) 2061 7579 E-mail: sales@smfoam.co.uk *Upholstery & foam sales*

S M W Autoblok, 8 The Metro Centre, Peterborough, PE2 7UH Tel: (01733) 394394 Fax: (01733) 394395 E-mail: sales@smwautoblok.co.uk *Chucking systems*

S M W Engineering Ltd, Unit 2c Durham Road Industrial Estate, Wolsingham, Bishop Auckland, County Durham, DL13 3JW Tel: (01388) 528930 *Wire rope manufrs*

S Mcconnell, 50 Glenavy Road, Lisburn, County Antrim, BT28 3UT Tel: (028) 9267 3757 Fax: (028) 9260 2590 *Agricultural merchants*

▶ S Mcconnell & Sons, 184 Carrigenagh Road, Kilkeel, Newry, County Down, BT34 4QA Tel: (028) 4176 3717 Fax: (028) 4176 5019

S Macneillie & Son Ltd, Stockton Close, Walsall, WS2 8LD Tel: (01922) 725560 Fax: (01922) 720916 *Motor body builders & vehicle reconstruction*

S Mason & Co., Bryndolau, Pumpsaint, Llanwrda, Dyfed, SA19 8BX Tel: (01558) 650230 Fax: (01558) 650230 *Animal & farm supply merchants*

S Morris Ltd, Tout Quarry, Tout Road, Charlton Adam, Somerton, Somerset, TA11 7AN Tel: (01458) 223991 Fax: (01458) 223181 E-mail: sales@smorris.co.uk *Concrete & concrete block suppliers*

S Murray & Co. Ltd, Holborn House, High Street, Old Woking, Woking, Surrey, GU22 9LB Tel: (01483) 740099 Fax: (01483) 755111 E-mail: sales@smurray.co.uk *Surgical instrument & laboratory equipment manufrs*

▶ S N B Electronic Services, Murton Lane, Murton, York, YO19 5UF Tel: (01904) 488820 Fax: (01904) 488467

S N E T Technology, 119 Cholmley Gardens, London, NW6 1AA Tel: (020) 7435 5855 *Computer consultants*

S N G Control Systems Ltd, 41 Dryden Terrace, Loanhead, Midlothian, EH20 9JH Tel: 0131-440 0416 Fax: 0131-440 0416 *Refrigeration & air conditioning*

S & N Signs, 133 Masons Hill, Bromley, BR2 9HT Tel: (020) 8460 8777 Fax: (020) 8460 8777 *Neon signs manufrs*

S Norton & Co., Bankfield Site, Regent Road, Bootle, Merseyside, L20 8RQ Tel: 0151-955 3300 Fax: 0151-955 3399 E-mail: s.norton@s-norton.co.uk *Ferrous & non-ferrous scrap processors & exporters*

S O P Edibles Ltd, 7 Aston Fields Road, Whitehouse Industrial Estate, Runcorn, Cheshire, WA7 3DL Tel: (01928) 712822 Fax: (01928) 719593 E-mail: sopinternational@btconnect.com *Edible oil & fat producers & exotic spices manufrs*

S O S Group, Westways Business Park, 2 Apollo Road, Belfast, BT12 6HP Tel: (028) 9066 1133 Fax: (028) 9068 2616 E-mail: sales@sosgroup.co.uk *Educational furniture manufrs*

S O S Hose Services, 30 Drome Road, Deeside Industrial Park, Deeside, Clwyd, CH5 2NY Tel: (01244) 280505 Fax: (01244) 281505 *Hydraulic hose assembly services*

S O S Refrigeration, 15 Thurston Avenue, Southend-on-Sea, SS2 4UJ Tel: (01702) 465061 Fax: (01702) 614000 *Refrigeration engineering services*

▶ S O S Saddlery, Little Pengelly Farm, Lower Sticker, St. Austell, Cornwall, PL26 7JJ Tel: (01726) 65022 Fax: (01726) 72727 *Established for 35 years, new & second hand saddles,problem fitting specialists, made to measure service at no extra cost, all other equestrian items*

S O S Talisman, 21 Grays Corner, Ley Street, Ilford, Essex, IG2 7RQ Tel: (020) 8554 5579 Fax: (020) 8554 1090 E-mail: sostalisman@btinternet.com *Safety & identification products*

S O T Mobile Link, 1 Tanners Road, Stoke-on-Trent, ST2 8DP Tel: (01782) 541271 Fax: (01782) 541346 E-mail: gary@mobile-link.co.uk *Communications equipment sales*

S P A Bristol Ltd, Unit 22, Barton Hill Trading Estate, Bristol, BS5 9RD Tel: 0117-955 3166 Fax: 0117-955 6053 *Automotive cash & carry*

S P Automation Ltd, 3 Omega Centre, Sandford Lane, Wareham, Dorset, BH20 4DY Tel: (01929) 550465 Fax: (01929) 550522 E-mail: sales@spautomation.co.uk Principal Export Areas: Africa, Central/East Europe & West Europe *Machinery designers & constructors*

S P B Metal Works, Unit 32a Bourne End Mills, Upper Bourne End Lane, Hemel Hempstead, Hertfordshire, HP1 2UJ Tel: (01442) 878165 Fax: (01442) 878444 E-mail: sales@spbmetalworks.co.uk *Sheet metalworkers*

S & P Blair & Son, Bayswell Park, Dunbar, East Lothian, EH42 1AE Tel: (01368) 862371 Fax: (01368) 862051 E-mail: sales@spblair.com *Electric welders & engineers*

S P Brown & Co. Ltd, 31 Lockhart Street, London, E3 4BL Tel: (020) 8981 2747 Fax: (020) 8981 2747 *Builders merchants*

S P C, Unit 1, Chalford Industrial Estate, Chalford, Stroud, Glos, GL6 8NT Tel: (01453) 885929 Fax: (01453) 731044 *Manufacturers of fire stopping material*

S P C Bearings Ltd, Unit 39 Coneygre Industrial Estate, Tipton, West Midlands, DY4 8XP Tel: 0121-557 1371 Fax: 0121-557 3793 *Bearing manufrs*

▶ S P C International, Unit 1-3, Station Road, Templecombe, Somerset, BA8 0JR Tel: (01963) 370504 Fax: (01963) 370101 E-mail: sales@spcint.com *Hardware support services*

S P C Patterns Ltd, 191 Vincent Road, Sheffield, S7 1BZ Tel: 0114-255 0040 Fax: 0114-255 8023 *Engineers' pattern makers*

S P C Systems, 69 Merton Hall Road, London, SW19 3PX Tel: (020) 8540 8409 E-mail: sales@spc-systems.com *Software systems*

S P C Tools, Unit B, Lyttleton Road, Northampton, NN5 7ET Tel: (01604) 583411 Fax: (01604) 758567 E-mail: spc001@hotmail.co.uk *Regrinding services & tools manufrs*

▶ S P Carpet & Upholstery Care, 64 Peasehill Road, Ripley, Derbyshire, DE5 3JH Tel: (01773) 749003 Fax: (01773) 749003 E-mail: forabetterclean@aol.com *Carpet & upholstery cleaning*

S P D S Ltd, Unit 4 Minto Drive, Altens Industrial Estate, Aberdeen, AB12 3LW Tel: (01224) 896106 Fax: (01224) 896112 E-mail: admin@spds.co.uk

S P D S Ltd, 20 Singer Road, Kelvin Industrial Estate, East Kilbride, Glasgow, G75 0XS Tel: (01355) 234807 Fax: (01355) 260525 E-mail: admin@spds.co.uk *UK Next-day pallet deliveries. *Timed deliveries to all major Scottish*

continued

*towns including Thurso & Wick. *Based in Scotland, nationwide service.*

▶ S P D Services, Birchfield Road, Kidderminster, Worcestershire, DY11 6PQ Tel: (01562) 756925 Fax: (01562) 756926

S & P Darwell Ltd, Scarborough Business Park, Hopper Hill Road, Eastfield, Scarborough, North Yorkshire, YO11 3YS Tel: (01723) 582000 Fax: (01723) 582828 E-mail: cad@darwells.fsnet.co.uk *Air conditioning engineers*

▶ S P Decorating, 78 Southbridge Road, Croydon, CR0 1AE Tel: (020) 8405 9676 E-mail: info@spdecorating.co.uk

S P E Ltd, 27 Dinghouse Wood, Buckley, Clwyd, CH7 3DH Tel: (01244) 549790 Fax: (01244) 549790 E-mail: s.mogridge@btinternet.com *Ventilation ductwork & dust extraction engineers*

S P Engineering, M Hawthorns Industrial Estate, Middlemore Road, Handsworth, Birmingham, B21 0BH Tel: 0121-554 1404 Fax: 0121-523 5834 *Pressworkers*

▶ S P Engineering, 9 Keyford Court, Manor Furlong, Frome, Somerset, BA11 4BD Tel: (01373) 474740 Fax: (01373) 471417 E-mail: enquires@spengineering.co.uk *General engineering services*

S P F Engineering Ltd, 29-30 Harvey Close, Crowther, Washington, Tyne & Wear, NE38 0AB Tel: 0191-419 4400 Fax: 0191-417 4799 E-mail: rgrspf@aol.com *Pipeline fitting stockholders*

S P Fibreglass, Station Road, Northiam, Rye, East Sussex, TN31 6QA Tel: (01797) 252476 Fax: (01797) 253093 *Glass fibre mouldings manufrs*

S.P Forming & Welding, Northwood Street, Birmingham, B3 1TT Tel: 0121-236 0582 Fax: (0121) 236 0582 *Forming & welding services*

S P Frames, Savile Street, Batley, West Yorkshire, WF17 6JS Tel: (01924) 502050 Fax: (01924) 503050 *Road traffic signs manufrs*

S P G Media Ltd, 57 North Wharf Road, London, W2 1LA Tel: (020) 7915 9660 Fax: (020) 7724 2089 E-mail: info@spgmedia.com *Book publishers*

▶ S P G Security Systems Ltd, 73 Meigle Street, Galashiels, Selkirkshire, TD1 1LN Tel: (01896) 759018 Fax: (01896) 668543 E-mail: enquires@spgltd.com *Security services*

S P Group, 9 Hedera Road, Redditch, Worcestershire, B98 9EY Tel: (01527) 508014 Fax: (01527) 508015 E-mail: enquiries@spgroup.co.uk *Screen printers & display producers*

S P I Security, 16 Saltmarket, Glasgow, G1 5LY Tel: 0141-564 1634 Fax: 0141-564 1636 *Alarm systems installation*

S P L Blacking, 420 Thurmaston Boulevard, Leicester, LE4 9LE Tel: 0116-223 6100 Fax: 0116-246 0803 E-mail: office@splblacking.co.uk *Chemical blacking specialist suppliers*

S & P M Signs & Graphics, Sign & Graphic Centre, Bath Road, Padworth, Reading, RG7 5HR Tel: 0118-971 4713 Fax: 0118-971 4723 E-mail: sales@spmsigns.com *Sign makers*

S P Neworks Ltd, 2 Wallingford Road, Uxbridge, Middlesex, UB8 2BB Tel: (01895) 259066 Fax: 01895 259150 *Telecommunication installation services*

S P P Extrusions, Timothys Bridge Road, Stratford-upon-Avon, Warwickshire, CV37 9NQ Tel: (01789) 298429 Fax: (01789) 414427 E-mail: sales@sp-plastics.co.uk *Plastics extrusion*

S P P Pumps Ltd, Unit 1, Stanstead Road, Boyatt Way Estate, Eastleigh, Hampshire, SO50 4RZ Tel: (023) 8061 6004 Fax: (023) 8061 4522 E-mail: sterlingreading@compuserve.com *Pump refurbishment*

S P P Pumps Ltd, Greg St, Reddish, Stockport, Cheshire, SK5 7BU Tel: 0161-480 4955 Fax: 0161-476 2193 *Valve & pump repairs & reconditioning services*

S P S, 63 Magna Road, Bournemouth, BH11 9ND Tel: (01202) 570142 Fax: (01202) 570142 E-mail: dave.robinson@spssecurity.org.uk *Security alarm installation*

S P S Ltd, Unit 9, Buildwas Road, Clayhill Light Industrial Park, Neston, CH64 3TU Tel: 0151-353 1775 Fax: 0151-353 1775 E-mail: pyeinc@supanet.com *Demount truck body system supplier*

▶ The S P S Group, 1 Nimrod Way, East Dorset Trade Park, Wimborne, Dorset, BH21 7SH Tel: (01202) 865100 Fax: (01202) 865111 E-mail: sales@thespsgroup.co.uk *Printing*

▶ S P S (Holdings) Ltd, 131 West Nile Street, Glasgow, G1 2RX Tel: 0141-332 9412

S P S Lamy, 123 Alders Gate Street, London, EC1A 4JQ Tel: (020) 7251 4171 Fax: (020) 7251 3778 E-mail: propertysales@spslamy.com *Surveyors, estate agents & property management*

S P S S Ltd, 65 Maygrove Road, London, NW6 2SP Tel: (020) 7625 7222 Fax: (020) 7624 5297 *Computer bureau services*

S & P Spanarc Ltd, Berwick House, 32 Dartford Road, Sevenoaks, Kent, TN13 3TQ Tel: (01732) 743456 Fax: (01732) 742922 E-mail: chris.guinane@spanarc.co.uk *Best known for our ranges of Knife Gate Valves we also supply Pinch Valves, Butterfly Valves, Swing Check Ball Check and Duckbill Check Valves, Expansion/Vibration Joints, Vulcanised Wedge Gate Valves, Lined and Unlined Diaphragm Valves. Size range generally up to DN1200. Large available stock.*

S P Stow Ltd, Portland Street, Kirkby-in-Ashfield, Nottingham, NG17 7AD Tel: (01623) 752258 Fax: (01623) 752258 *Builders merchants*

▶ S P Switchgear Ltd, The Courts, Western Access, Off Kestrel Road, Trafford Park, Manchester, M17 1SF Tel: 0161-872 4398 Fax: 0161-872 4550 *Suppliers of electrical goods*

S P T Machines Ltd, Brookside Ave, Rustington, Littlehampton, W. Sussex, BN16 3LF Tel: (01903) 784212 Fax: (01903) 770288 E-mail: info@sptmachines.co.uk Sales Contact: B. Wright Principal Export Areas: Worldwide

continued

Designers & Manufacturers of advanced machinery for the International Textile Industry.

S P Technology Ltd, Camperdown Industrial Park, George Buckman Drive, Dundee, DD2 3SP Tel: (01382) 880088 Fax: (01382) 880099 E-mail: info@sptechnology.co.uk *Custom built automation machinery constructors & manufrs*

▶ S P Toiletries Ltd, Appledore Road, Woodchurch, Ashford, Kent, TN26 3TG Tel: (01233) 861120 Fax: (01233) 861140

S P W Group Ltd, Victoria Works, Victoria Road, Stoke-on-Trent, ST4 2QR Tel: (01782) 847911 Fax: (01782) 744420 *Quarry plant manufrs*

S P Web Connections, Hazelwood House, Hazelwood Close, Crawley Down, Crawley, West Sussex, RH10 4HE Tel: (01342) 716971 E-mail: info@spwebco.com *Web site development, design, hosting & domain name registration*

S P Wound Components Ltd, Unit 12 Stanley Green Industrial Estate, Stanley Green Esc, Poole, Dorset, BH15 3TH Tel: (01202) 682828 Fax: (01202) 682828 E-mail: spwoundcomp@boltblue.com *Custom built transformer manufrs*

S P X Air Treatment Ltd, Hazleton Interchange, Lakesmere Road, Horndean, Waterlooville, Hampshire, PO8 9JU Tel: (023) 9257 2820 Fax: (023) 9257 2830 E-mail: enquiries@airtreatment.spx.com Principal Export Areas: Africa, Central/East Europe & West Europe *Manufacturers of compressed air, gas dryers & filters*

S P X Cooling Technologies UK Ltd, Gregory's Bank, Worcester, WR3 8AB Tel: (01905) 720200 Fax: (01905) 720201 E-mail: info@ct.spx.com *Cooling tower designers/contractors*

S Patterson, 58 Rathkeel Road, Broughshane, Ballymena, County Antrim, BT42 4QD Tel: (028) 2586 1254 Fax: (028) 2586 1574 *Road transport, haulage & freight services*

S Perviz & Co. Ltd, Solmar House, 7-9 Blackfriars Road, Salford, M3 7AG Tel: 0161-833 9910 Fax: 0161-839 0543 E-mail: mp@perviz.co.uk *Customised bag manufrs*

S Q A Engineering, 12 Benson Road, Nuffield Industrial Estate, Poole, Dorset, BH17 0GB Tel: (01202) 676520 Fax: (01202) 671234 *Precision engineers*

S Q L Ltd, Unit 1a, Stock Road, Southend-on-Sea, SS2 5QF Tel: (01702) 464978 Fax: (01702) 612929 E-mail: paul@sqlsouthend.co.uk *Label printers*

S Q W Ltd, Enterprise House, Vision Park, Histon, Cambridge, CB4 9ZR Tel: (01223) 209400 Fax: (01223) 209401 E-mail: mailbox@sqw.co.uk *Economic development consultants*

S R A Developments Ltd, Bremridge House, Ashburton, Newton Abbott, Devon, TQ13 7JX Tel: (01364) 652426 Fax: (01364) 653589 E-mail: mail@sra-developments.co.uk *Medical devices manufrs*

S R Air Conditioning Services, 11 New Road, Church Crookham, Fleet, Hampshire, GU52 6BH Tel: (01252) 622620 *Installers & suppliers of air conditioners*

S R B E Ltd, Stewkley Road, Soulbury, Leighton Buzzard, Bedfordshire, LU7 0DF Tel: (01525) 270591 Fax: (01525) 270727 E-mail: sales@srbe.co.uk *Contractors plant hire*

S R B Engineering 2000 Ltd, Unit 5 Enterprise Court, Newton Close, Park Farm Industrial Estate, Wellingborough, Northamptonshire, NN8 6UW Tel: (01933) 679161 Fax: (01933) 400363 E-mail: sales@srb-engineering.co.uk *Precision component manufacturers & toolmakers*

▶ S R Burke Engineering Ltd, Derwent Way, Wath-upon-Dearne, Rotherham, South Yorkshire, S63 6EX Tel: (01709) 877888 Fax: (01709) 877888 E-mail: info@srburke.co.uk *Steel fabrication*

S R C Systems Ltd, 5 Leslie Road, Ipswich, IP3 9PL Tel: (01473) 726445 Fax: (01473) 727278 E-mail: info@srcsystems.co.uk *Label slitting or rewinding machines*

▶ S R D Sound & Lighting, Dry Hill Farm, Shipbourne Road, Tonbridge, Kent, TN10 3DJ Tel: (01732) 373920 Fax: (01732) 373921 E-mail: info@srdgroup.co.uk *Suppliers of sound, lighting technical services for concerts, conferences and all events.*

S R Equipment, 33-35 Dawf Lane, London, NW7 4SD Tel: (020) 8906 6600 Fax: (020) 8906 6611 E-mail: admin@sreq.com *Plant & machinery dealers*

▶ S R Fabrications Ltd, Holm Industrial Estate, Barterholm Road, Paisley, Renfrewshire, PA2 6PF Tel: 0141-840 4934 Fax: 0141-840 4935 *Fabricators*

▶ S R Hire Centre Ltd, 15-19 West Bowling Green St, Edinburgh, EH6 5PQ Tel: 0131-555 3500

S R Industrial Ltd, Unit 42 Longshot Industrial Estate, Longshot Lane, Bracknell, Berkshire, RG12 1RL Tel: (01344) 860145 Fax: (01344) 305313 E-mail: srogers@srindustrial.co.uk *Property & facilities maintenance, builders' merchants*

S R Keig Ltd, 51 Strand Street, Douglas, Isle of Man, IM1 2EJ Tel: (01624) 673111 Fax: (01624) 662372 E-mail: sales@keigs.co.uk *Photographers & photographic printing*

S R M Peakland Ltd, Vulcan Way, Coalville, Leicestershire, LE67 3AP Tel: (01530) 838317 Fax: (01530) 835122 E-mail: sales@srmpeakland.co.uk *Rubber moulding manufrs*

S R Payne Non Ferrous Metals, Unit 8-10, Sibthorpe Street, Mansfield, Nottinghamshire, NG18 5DE Tel: (01623) 623354 Fax: (01623) 623354 *Non-ferrous metal merchant & recyclers*

S R S Aromatics Ltd, Boldero Road, Moreton Hall Industrial Estate, Bury St. Edmunds, Suffolk, IP32 7BS Tel: (01284) 760818 Fax: (01284) 750224 *Aromatic raw materials distributors*

S R S Automation, Daneside House, Riverdane Road, Congleton, Cheshire, CW12 1UN Tel: (01260) 281432 Fax: (01260) 281831 E-mail: srsautomation@btinternet.com *Electronic automation equipment repair service*

▶ S R S Computer Systems Ltd, 1 Dewar House, 1 Enterprise Way, Dunfermline, Fife, KY11 8PY Tel: (01383) 624446 Fax: (01383) 840880 E-mail: kellyanne@srsnet.co.uk *Sales, service & support for IT & copier equipment*

S R S Joinery High Wycombe Ltd, Wycombe Lane, Wooburn Green, High Wycombe, Buckinghamshire, HP10 0HE Tel: (01628) 520893 Fax: (01628) 810526 *Joinery manufrs*

▶ S R S Pensions, Broad Quay House, Broad Quay, Bristol, BS1 4DJ Tel: 0117-905 8734 Fax: 0117-963 7949 E-mail: sales@srs-pensions.co.uk *Pensions & actuarial recruitment services*

S R S Products P.L.C., 19 Mead Industrial Park, River Way, Harlow, Essex, CM20 2SE Tel: (01279) 635500 Fax: (01279) 635282 E-mail: sales@srs-products.co.uk *Electronic enclosure manufrs*

▶ S R S Shredder Repair Services, PO Box 4279, Dunstable, Bedfordshire, LU6 1WX Tel: (01582) 536346 Fax: (01582) 601448 E-mail: info@shredderrepair.co.uk *Office equipment repair services*

▶ S R Slating, Coneymead, Stalybridge, Cheshire, SK15 1HF Tel: 0161 3049731 E-mail: SRSlating@aol.com *From a Loft conversion to a Roof Window. All Roofing Works Undertaken.Modern & Traditional. Not Jack of all trades, We only undertake Roofing works. Master of One!*

S & R Transmissions Ltd, Old Stafford Road, Slade Heath, Wolverhampton, WV10 7PH Tel: (01902) 798877 Fax: (01902) 798088 E-mail: sales@transmissionunits.com *Commercial vehicle gear boxes*

S R Tubular Systems, Pioneer Mill, Kelly Street, Blackburn, BB2 4PJ Tel: (01254) 689922 Fax: (01254) 689933 *Office furniture components*

S R W (Sussex Refrigeration Wholesale) Ltd, Unit 4, Harbour Way, Shoreham-By-Sea, West Sussex, BN43 5HG Tel: (01273) 455530 Fax: (01273) 455575 E-mail: info@srw.co.uk *Refrigerator wholesalers*

S R Walsh, Chaddock Lane, Astley, Tyldesley, Manchester, M29 7JT Tel: (01942) 894070 Fax: (01942) 894073 E-mail: sales@srwalsh.co.uk *Protective clothing suppliers*

▶ S R Williams, 691-693 Warrington Road, Risley, Warrington, WA3 6AY Tel: (01925) 816700 Fax: (01925) 852961 E-mail: srwgarage@csemail.co.uk *Motor vehicle servicing & motor body repairs*

S Ransley & Sons, Elite, Hornash Lane, Shadoxhurst, Ashford, Kent, TN26 1HU Tel: (01233) 732921 Fax: (01233) 732921 *Hay & straw merchants*

S Redhead, Helsay Farm, Old Helsay, Warkworth, Morpeth, Northumberland, NE65 0SN Tel: (01665) 712952 E-mail: stephenredhead@aol.com *Plant hire, drainage, demolition & plant sales*

S Roberts Marine Ltd, Coburg Wharf, Liverpool, L3 4BP Tel: 0151-707 8300 Fax: 0151-707 8300 E-mail: stephen@robmar.freeserve.co.uk *Marine surveying company involved primarily in the small craft industry *Established by current proprieter 1985*

▶ S Russell, The Gables, Old Church Road, Bowers Gifford, Basildon, Essex, SS13 2EZ Tel: (01268) 725755 Fax: 01268 725755 E-mail: rikki.russell@blueyonder.co.uk *Fresh Fruit & Vegetables Delivered Daily To The Retail & Catering Trade. Essex Coverage*

S & S Burner Services Ltd, Unit 14 193 The Garth Road Industrial Centre, Garth Road, Morden, Surrey, SM4 4LZ Tel: (020) 8330 7992 Fax: (020) 8330 7993 *Heating engineers*

S S C S Lifting, Harfreys Road, Harfreys Industrial Estate, Great Yarmouth, Norfolk, NR31 0LS Tel: 0845 4940724 Fax: (01493) 443390 E-mail: sales@sscsystems.com Principal Export Areas: Africa *SSCS Lifting, Great Yarmouth inspects tests and certifies lifting equipment as well as manufacturing, servicing, and supplying all types of lifting gear. *SSCS Lifting is committed to the supply of complete lifting equipment and lifting accessories by both HIRE and by SALE and we have probably the largest capability in East Anglia and also for the Offshore Oil & Gas industry in the Southern North Sea. *SSCS Lifting manufactures their range of Ratchet Systems, Lashings and Cargo Restraint Systems from the finest quality, high tenacity polyester webbing with excellent abrasion resistance to comply with the European Community Machinery Directive. Systems are available in varying lengths with a choice of end fittings. Characteristically light weight and flexible, each lashing is quickly secured by a single operator, requiring very little effort or exertion. *As members of the Lifting Equipment Engineers Association (LEEA) we work to the LEEA Procedures and to BS EN ISO 9001.*

S S Central Coating Ltd, Unit 5 Oakhill Trading Estate, Euston Street, Freemens Common, Leicester, LE2 7ST Tel: 0116-255 4748 Fax: 0116-255 4769 E-mail: satu@sscoatings.com Principal Export Areas: Africa *Plastic finishing services*

S & S Distribution, 400 Vale Road, Tonbridge, Kent, TN9 1SW Tel: (01732) 358800 Fax: (01732) 770772 E-mail: traffic@ssdistribution.co.uk *Road haulage services*

S S E Precision Engineering, 37a Douglas Road, Poole, Dorset, BH12 2AU Tel: (01202) 463573 Fax: (01202) 463564 *Precision machining services*

S & S Electronics, Canal Works, Cadman Street, Sheffield, S4 7ZG Tel: 0114-275 8593 Fax: 0114-275 8593 *Electronic repair services*

▶ S S Engineering, Cleveland House, Cleveland Street, Darlington, County Durham, DL1 2NU Tel: (01325) 357465 Fax: (01325) 380327

S & S Engineering Ltd, Blackwell Industrial Estate, Station Road, Tilbrook, Huntingdon, Cambridgeshire, PE28 0JY Tel: (01480) 860426 Fax: (01480) 860355 *Welding services*

S & S Engineering, Unit 21 Such Close, Letchworth Garden City, Hertfordshire, SG6 1JF Tel: (01462) 675983 Fax: (01462) 675983 *Welding & fabricators*

Company Information

S & S Enterprises, Unit 23, Pontymister Industrial Estate, Risca, Newport, Gwent, NP11 6NP Tel: (01633) 612727 Fax: (01633) 612727 E-mail: none@none.com *Amusement machines hire*

S S F Forthside Ltd, Merlin Way, Hillend, Dunfermline, Fife, KY11 9JY Tel: (01383) 824181 Fax: (01383) 824722 *Building products suppliers*

S S I Solutions Ltd, Fordbrook Business Centre, Marlborough Road, Pewsey, Wiltshire, SN9 5NU Tel: (01672) 565300 Fax: (01672) 563001 E-mail: general.enquireis@ssi.co.uk *Document management solutions provider*

▶ S S Johal & Sons Ltd, 97 Monk Street, Derby, DE22 3QE Tel: (01332) 343005 Fax: (01332) 332950

S & S Joinery, Anglebury Business Park, Sandford Lane, Wareham, Dorset, BH20 4DY Tel: (01929) 553433 Fax: (01929) 550868 *Joinery*

S S M International, Tedstone Wafre, Bromyard, Herefordshire, HR7 4PY Tel: (01886) 853646 Fax: (01886) 853539 *Sports goods & shooting product retailer & manufrs*

S & S Marketing, B8-B10 Unit Tenterfields Business Park, Burnley Road, Luddendenfoot, Halifax, West Yorkshire, HX2 6EQ Tel: (01422) 882754 Fax: (01422) 884978 E-mail: sales@sandsmarketing.co.uk *Cutlery distributors & manufrs*

S S Motors (Fuels) Ltd, 2 Honeysome Road, Chatteris, Cambridgeshire, PE16 6RZ Tel: (01354) 693181 Fax: (01354) 694181 *Fuel oil merchants*

S S Oakes Fire Protection Ltd, Fourth Street, Bolton, BL1 7NW Tel: (01204) 845876 Fax: (01204) 845876 *Fire protection engineers*

S & S Precision Engineering Ltd, 23 Rainhill Close, East Stephenson Industrial Estate, Washington, Tyne & Wear, NE37 3HN Tel: 0191-416 2184 Fax: 0191-419 1586 E-mail: bob@ssprecision.com *CNC engineers*

S S S Consultants, Alfriston, Traps Lane, New Malden, Surrey, KT3 4RT Tel: (020) 8949 3753 Fax: (020) 8949 0809 E-mail: info@sss-it.co.uk *Software developers*

S S Scientific, 6 Granary Business Centre, North Street, Hellingly, Hailsham, East Sussex, BN27 4DU Tel: (01323) 441920 Fax: (01323) 441968 E-mail: sales@ss-sci.com *Scientific instrument manufrs*

▶ S & S Steel Fabrications, Greendale Mill, Brow Top, Grindleton, Clitheroe, Lancashire, BB7 4QR Tel: (01200) 440765 Fax: (01200) 440393 *Contact labour in steel fabrication*

S & S Steelstock Ltd, Dickens Street, Blackburn, BB1 1RN Tel: (01254) 699966 Fax: (01254) 674999 *Steel stockholders*

S S Systems, Sorby House, The Point, Rotherham, South Yorkshire, S60 1BP Tel: (01709) 362999 Fax: (0845) 4023789 *Fire & security alarm distributors & installers*

S & S Systems Ltd, Bretton Court, Manor Road, Wales, Sheffield, S26 5PS Tel: (08456) 441670 E-mail: info@astraaccounts.co.uk *Accounts software & computer dealers*

S S T Process Engineering Ltd, Unit 22 Autumn Park, Dysart Road, Grantham, Lincolnshire, NG31 7DD Tel: (01476) 590112 Fax: (01476) 590113 E-mail: sales@sstpe.co.uk *Heat exchanger & transfer equipment manufrs*

▶ S & S Tan Seakers, Wheatley House, Laughton, Gainsborough, Lincolnshire, DN21 3QF Tel: (01427) 628571 *Sunbed hire services*

S & S Tools Ltd, Units 9-10 Lupin Works, Worcester Road, Kidderminster, Worcestershire, DY10 1JR Tel: (01562) 60765 Fax: (01562) 60765 E-mail: sstools@virgin.net *Precision engineers*

▶ S & S Traders, 117 Williamson Street, Stoke-on-Trent, ST6 6AS Tel: (01782) 815581 Fax: (01782) 822881 *Janitorial equipment repairers*

S S U Equipment Ltd, Friars Mount, Friars, Jedburgh, Roxburghshire, TD8 6BN Tel: (01835) 862481 Fax: (01835) 863712 E-mail: davesharman@ssuequipment.co.uk *Second user PCB assembly equipment*

▶ S S White Technologies UK Ltd, 19 Heathfield, Stacey Bushes, Milton Keynes, MK12 6HP Tel: (01908) 525124 Fax: (01908) 319967 E-mail: insales@sswhite.co.uk Principal Export Areas: Worldwide *Manufacturers of concrete vibrating equipment*

S & S Windings Ltd, 5 Focus 303 Business Centre, South Way, Andover, Hampshire, SP10 5NY Tel: (01264) 334095 Fax: (01264) 334095 E-mail: sswindings@btclick.com *Coil windings & electro mechanical assembly specialists*

S & S Windows, Unit 19 Phoenix Industrial Estate, Cheetham Street, Failsworth, Manchester, M35 9DS Tel: 0161-684 7361 Fax: 0161-684 7361 *Joinery manufrs*

S S X Group P.L.C., 319 Vale Enterprise Park, Hayes Road, Sully, Penarth, South Glamorgan, CF64 5SY Tel: (01446) 741133 Fax: (01446) 740841 *Injection & plastics machinery manufrs*

▶ S Smith & Co. Ltd, Dowgate Wharf, 26 Orsman Road, London, N1 5QJ Tel: (020) 7739 1591

S T A International, Watson House, St. Leonards Road, Maidstone, Kent, ME16 0SS Tel: (01622) 718222 Fax: (01622) 718444 E-mail: enqueries@staonline.com *Debt collectors*

S T A S Ltd, Ryland Grange Farm, Fulbeck Heath, Grantham, Lincolnshire, NG32 3HJ Tel: (01400) 261745 Fax: (01400) 262287 E-mail: stasltd@aol.com *Agronomy*

S T B Construction, Low Field Farm Buildings, Ainderby Steeple, Northallerton, North Yorkshire, DL7 9SD Tel: 01609 776484 Fax: 01609 776484 *Builders & shopfitters*

S T B Engineering Ltd, Toadsmoor Road, Brimscombe, Stroud, Gloucestershire, GL5 2UF Tel: (01453) 885353 Fax: (01453) 886824 E-mail: sales@stbengineering.com *Materials handling specialist services*

S T B Foods Ltd, Ettingshall Road, Wolverhampton, WV2 2RB Tel: (01902) 490514 Fax: (01902) 354172 *Food wholesalers*

▶ S T C Energy Management Ltd, STC House, 38 Croydon Road, Beckenham, Kent, BR3 4BJ Tel: (020) 8662 6500 Fax: (020) 8662 6501 *Energy management*

S T C Tiles, 85 Chesterfield Road, Sheffield, S8 0RN Tel: 0114-258 9423 Fax: 0114-258 9423 *Ceramic tile suppliers*

▶ S T Clemens & Son Ltd, Providence Works, Lyndhurst Road, Chichester, West Sussex, PO19 7PF Tel: (01243) 782542 Fax: (01243) 773773

S T D Pharmaceutical Products Ltd, Plough Lane, Hereford, HR4 0EL Tel: (01432) 373555 Fax: (01432) 371314 E-mail: enquries@stdpharm.co.uk *Pharmaceutical product distributors*

S T Developments, 101 Leigh Road, Wimborne, Dorset, BH21 2AA Tel: (01202) 887048 Fax: (01202) 887048 E-mail: johnstd@globalnet.co.uk *Tools, jigs, fixtures designers & suppliers*

S T E UK Ltd, Staple Hurst Road, Sittingbourne, Kent, ME10 2NH Tel: (01795) 474700 Fax: (01795) 438901 E-mail: info@steuk.co.uk *Educational equipment suppliers*

▶ S & T Fullers Builders Ltd, The Old Stables, Crescent Road, Faversham, Kent, ME13 7AS Tel: (01795) 532562 Fax: (01795) 531924

S T G Fabrications Ltd, Monument Way East, Woking, Surrey, GU21 5LY Tel: (01483) 769222 Fax: (01483) 769666 E-mail: stgfab@btclick.com *Steel fabricators*

▶ S T L Communications Ltd, Park House, Station Lane, Witney, Oxfordshire, OX28 4LH Tel: (01993) 777100 Fax: (01993) 777101 E-mail: sryan@spireholdings.com *STL is a leading provider of the latest telephony solutions, with expertise in contact centres, IP telephony, customer relationship management, unified messaging and voice and video conferencing. **We take pride in providing leading edge, innovative solutions to organisations in a wide range of sectors working with world-leading partners, to help our customers achieve their objectives through the delivery of innovative, communications solutions that harness the latest advances in voice and data technology.* *From the latest IP-enabled solutions for the Lucky Strike BAR Honda and Jordan Formula 1 teams to a simple telephone system for a GP surgery or legal practice, STL is able to specify, install and maintain a telephony solution which maximises the efficiency of any organisation's communication requirements.*

S T L Midlands Ltd, 80 Lockhurst Lane, Coventry, CV6 5PZ Tel: (024) 7658 4800 Fax: (024) 7658 4848 E-mail: enquiries@stl-ltd.com *Analytical chemists*

S T L Stewart Transformers Ltd, 1 Townsend Industrial Estate, Waxlow Road, London, NW10 7NU Tel: (020) 8965 9505 Fax: (020) 8961 1499 E-mail: sales@stewart-transformers.co.uk *Transformer manufrs*

S T L Transtech Ltd, 64-66 Percy Road, Leicester, LE2 8FN Tel: 0116-283 3321 Fax: 0116-283 0730 E-mail: transtechsales@stlgroup.org *Transformer manufrs*

S T M Force Ltd, Rear of, 145-147 Northfield Road, Coventry, CV1 2BQ Tel: (024) 7652 0631 Fax: (024) 7663 3303 E-mail: sales@stmforce.co.uk *Martial art manufrs*

S T M Systems Ltd, 32 Bernard Street, Edinburgh, EH6 6PR Tel: 0131-467 7891 Fax: 0131-467 7448 E-mail: sales@systems.com *Software design & system support*

S T P Distribution, C Kelbrook Road, Manchester, M11 2QA Tel: 0161-223 8232 Fax: 0161-230 7814 *Door manufrs*

S T P Group Ltd, Watford Bridge Road, New Mills, High Peak, Derbyshire, SK22 4HJ Tel: (01663) 744030 Fax: (01663) 745295 E-mail: stpgroupltd@btinternet.com *Door agents, distributors & manufrs* Also at: Birmingham, Leeds & Manchester

▶ S T P Joinery Ltd, Mildred Sylvester Way, Normanton Industrial Estate, Normanton, West Yorkshire, WF6 1TA Tel: (01924) 891988 Fax: (01924) 897252

▶ S T Plumbing & Heating, 11 Hill Top, Knottingley, West Yorkshire, WF11 8EB Tel: (01977) 671859 Fax: (01977) 677699

S T Rawlings & Son, Puddletown, Haselbury Plucknett, Crewkerne, Somerset, TA18 7NZ Tel: (01460) 72466 *Agricultural contractor services*

S T Robotics, Orwell House, 11 Cowley Road, Cambridge, CB4 0PP Tel: (01223) 420288 Fax: (01223) 420291 E-mail: sales@strobotics.com *Robot & robotic system design, manufacture & installation*

S T S Computers, Tylney House, 23 High Street, Leatherhead, Surrey, KT22 8AB Tel: (01372) 378608 Fax: (01372) 374592 E-mail: info@stscomputers.co.uk *Computer hardware distributors*

S T S Defence Ltd, Amery House, Steeple Drive, Alton, Hampshire, GU34 1TN Tel: (01420) 88683 Fax: (01420) 89190 E-mail: sts@spacetechsys.co.uk *Meteorological* Also at: Wimborne

▶ S T S Defence, 12-20 Sharlands Road, Fareham, Hampshire, PO14 1RD Tel: (01329) 231310 Fax: (01329) 231300 *Metal fabricators*

S T S Eurolink, Andes Road, Nursling, Southampton, SO16 0YZ Tel: (023) 8073 0816 Fax: (023) 8073 0819 E-mail: stseurolink@dial.pipex.com *Transport & shipping agents*

S T S Recruitment Ltd, Radley House, 8 St Cross Road, Winchester, Hampshire, SO23 9HX Tel: (01962) 869478 Fax: (01962) 841982 E-mail: sales@stsrecruit.com *Employment agency*

S T S Signals Ltd, Unit 2 Teilo Works, Tyn Y Bonau Road, Pontarddulais, Swansea, SA4 8SA Tel: (01792) 885995 Fax: (01792) 885913 *Electric motor manufrs*

S T S Signals Ltd, 2 Stone Lane Industrial Estate, Stone Lane, Wimborne, Dorset, BH21 1HB Tel: (01202) 888402 Fax: (01202) 841717 E-mail: wimborne@spacetechsys.co.uk *Electronic equipment manufrs*

S T S Storage Systems Ltd, 49-51 Yew Tree Road, Slough, SL1 2AG Tel: (01753) 821166 Fax: (01753) 576192 E-mail: sales@stsstorage.co.uk *Used & new racking suppliers*

▶ S T S Switchgear Ltd, Doulton Road, Cradley Heath, West Midlands, B64 5QB Tel: (01384) 567755 Fax: (01384) 567710 E-mail: mark.mathews@sts-international.co.uk *Railway signalling equipment manufrs*

S T Services Ltd, Glasgow Road, Clydebank, Dunbartonshire, G81 1TS Tel: 0141-952 0055 Fax: 0141-952 9099 *Petrochemical bulk liquid storage*

▶ S T Services Ltd, Imperial Dock, Leith, Edinburgh, EH6 7DR Tel: 0131-553 2827

▶ S T Sheldon, Unit 31, Wren Court, Strathclyde Business Park, Bellshill, Lanarkshire, ML4 3NQ Tel: (01698) 747470 Fax: (01698) 747174 E-mail: enquiry@stsheldon.co.uk *Garage equipment suppliers*

S & T Shipping Ltd, 5 St. Annes Fort, King's Lynn, Norfolk, PE30 1QS Tel: (01553) 772661 Fax: (01553) 691074 E-mail: sandt01@aol.com *Freight forwarding agents*

▶ S T Sign Solutions, Unit B Paterson's Court, Broxburn, West Lothian, EH52 5HB Tel: (01506) 854966 Fax: (01506) 854966 E-mail: info@stsignsolutions.co.uk

S T T Associates, PO Box 18, Ledbury, Herefordshire, HR8 2YR Tel: (01531) 633604 Fax: (01531) 632790 *Specialised sales training management consultancy*

S & T Trimmings Ltd, 56-66 Cambridge Street, Coventry, CV1 5HW Tel: (024) 7622 3366 Fax: (024) 7666 4401 E-mail: info@sttrimmings.com *Trimming merchants & label suppliers*

S T V International Ltd, Forge House, Watton Road, Little Cressingham, Thetford, Norfolk, IP25 6ND Tel: (01953) 881580 Fax: (01953) 881452 E-mail: info@stvpestcontrol.com *Pest control products importers & manufrs*

S T V S, Unit 8, 2 Perry Way, Witham, Essex, CM8 3SX Tel: (01376) 517333 Fax: (01376) 517333 *Video consultants & electronic engineers*

S T V Videos, PO Box 299, Bromley, BR2 9EE Tel: (020) 8464 4287 E-mail: sales@stvvideos.co.uk *Video production with outside broadcasting*

S V I Ltd, 7 Chapel Street, Peterhead, Aberdeenshire, AB42 1TH Tel: (01779) 474000 Fax: (01779) 474800 E-mail: sales@svi.co.uk *Computer consultants*

S V M Consulting Engineers Ltd, 10 Kensworth Gate, Garden Road, Dunstable, Bedfordshire, LU6 3HS Tel: (01582) 660090 Fax: (01582) 660091 E-mail: solutions@svm.co.uk *Building services engineers*

▶ S V P Services, 106 Nevile Road, Salford, M7 3PL Tel: 0161-792 7501 E-mail: enquires@svpservices.co.uk *Service & repair inkjet printers*

S V R Coachworks, Unit U10, Rudford Industrial Estate, Ford Road, Ford, Arundel, West Sussex, BN18 0BF Tel: (01903) 734929 Fax: (01243) 545133 *Scrap metal merchants*

S V R Plastics Ltd, Units 5-6, Greenhey Place, Skelmersdale, Lancashire, WN8 9SA Tel: (01695) 50717 Fax: (01695) 50052 E-mail: sales@svrplastics.co.uk *SVR Plastics Ltd based in Skelmsdale, Lancashire are manufacturers of special pipe fittings for the Civil Engineering industry. Our experience enables us to fabricate with HDPE, polypropylene, ABS & PVC in a variety of sizes to individual requirements. We have completed projects on the channel tunnel, millennium dome, Severn bridge & supplied underground drainage pipes & fittings for several major football clubs across the UK & Ireland. E.g. West Ham, Kilmarnock, Wigan, Cardiff & Croke Park, Dublin. Our products include twin wall pipe fittings, twin wall inspection chambers, uPVC sewer pipe fittings, duct fittings and land drainage fittings, specialist fabrication work, uPCV flanges and valves including flap valves and puddle flanges, profiles including u channels and angles made to customer specification. SVR are becoming a market leader in their field, with the ability to increase production whilst maintaining their success rate at meeting deadlines and budget*

▶ S V Security Systems Ltd, Midway Offices, 68 Stone Road, Stoke-On-Trent, ST4 6SP Tel: (01782) 646455 Fax: (01782) 646564 E-mail: svelectrics@aol.com

▶ S W A T Distribution, 50 Providence Place, Brighton, BN1 4GE Tel: (01273) 690573 Fax: (01273) 690573 E-mail: sales@awat-distrubution.co.uk

S & W Agricultural Services, Royd Moor Farm, Royd Moor Lane, Badsworth, Pontefract, West Yorkshire, WF9 1AZ Tel: (01977) 610943 Fax: (01977) 612891 *Agriculture machinery merchants*

S W Asgood Engineering Ltd, Unit A1 Empress Park, Empress Road, Southampton, SO14 0JX Tel: (023) 8022 3880 Fax: (023) 8033 5131 *Sheet metal fabricators*

S W Brown, Topley Farm, Rushbury, Church Stretton, Shropshire, SY6 7EQ Tel: (01584) 841356 Fax: (01584) 841356 *Agricultural contractors*

S W C Health & Hygiene Ltd, Ripley Drive, Normanton Industrial Estate, Wakefield, West Yorkshire, WF6 1QT Tel: (01924) 891738 Fax: (01924) 220213 E-mail: mail@swc-online.co.uk *Cleaning chemical manufrs*

S W Ceiling Co., Hillsboro, Brockworth Rd, Churchdown, Gloucester, GL3 2NH Tel: (01452) 714334 Fax: (01452) 714334 E-mail: m.rickards@cableinet.co.uk *Suspended ceilings supply and fix*

▶ S & W Cutting Forms Nottingham Ltd, 3 Stamford Court, Nottingham, NG5 5LZ Tel: 0115-920 4959 Fax: 0115-967 0686

S W Durham Steelcraft Ltd, Old Colliery Buildings, Trimdon Grange Industrial Estate, Trimdon Grange, Trimdon Station, County Durham, TS29 6PA Tel: (01429) 881300 Fax: (01429) 883184 *Steel boat builders*

S W Electrical Repairs Ltd, Ashley Street Works, Ashley Street, Princess Way, Burnley, Lancashire, BB12 0BE Tel: (01282) 452411 Fax: (01282) 830167 E-mail: swrewinds@aol.com *Electric motor repairers & rewind specialists*

S W F Sales & Service, Office 6 Mill House Offices, Lichfield Street, Fazeley, Tamworth, Staffordshire, B78 3QA Tel: (01827) 61601 Fax: (01827) 312177 *Cleaning equipment suppliers*

S W G Ltd, Unit B6 Newbury Industrial Centre, Faraday Road, Newbury, Berkshire, RG14 2AD Tel: (01635) 30059 Fax: (01635) 521249 E-mail: sales@swgltd.co.uk *Industrial fastener distributors*

▶ S W G Cables, 70-71 Ennerdale Road, Shrewsbury, SY1 3LD Tel: (01743) 453000 Fax: (01743) 453009 E-mail: admin@swgcables.co.uk *Automotive, electrical & electronic*

S & W Garages Commercial Ltd, Printshop Lane, Atherton, Manchester, M46 9BJ Tel: (01942) 878961 Fax: (01942) 897955 *Commercial vehicle repairers*

S W Heating Equipment Ltd, Environmental Centre, 98 Holmesdale Street, Cardiff, CF11 7BU Tel: (029) 2023 7654 Fax: (029) 2023 7685 E-mail: mail@swgroup.org.uk *Heating equipment & air-conditioning engineers*

▶ S W L Engineering, 3 Holmfield Chase, Stanley, Wakefield, West Yorkshire, WF3 4QZ Tel: (07961) 170212 Fax: (01924) 824950 E-mail: swlengineering@msn.com *Metal railings, architectural castings manufrs*

S W & National Ventilation, 20 Brean Down Road, Peverell, Plymouth, PL3 5PX Tel: (01752) 201140 Fax: (01752) 201140 E-mail: swanvent@eurobell.co.uk *Ductwork contractor*

▶ S W P Hydraulics Ltd, 4 Bell Close, Newnham Industrial Estate, Plympton, Plymouth, PL7 4JH Tel: (01752) 338772 Fax: (01752) 336588

S W Plastics, Baldwins Yard, Noahs Ark, Kemsing, Sevenoaks, Kent, TN15 6PF Tel: (01732) 762260 Fax: (01732) 762025 E-mail: sales@swplasticsltd.com *Precision Engineers of plastics such as PTFE,PEEK,FEP,PFA,PCTFE,PVDF,PP,PE, HDPE,UHMWPE,ABS,ECTFE,NYLON, ACETAL,TUFNOL ETC...components ISO 9001/2000 to Space & Aerospace Standards. Medical,Military,Oil & Gas,Electronics,Telecommunications, Pharmaceutical,Aerospace and more*

▶ S W Property Repairs, 20 Cromford Road, Cosby, Leicester, LE9 1TL Tel: 0116-284 9542 Fax: 0116-284 9542 E-mail: helen@evertonhouse.wanadoo.co.uk *UPVC windows, doors & conservatories supply & fit garage doors*

S W S Ltd, Thomlinson Road, Hartlepool, Cleveland, TS25 1NS Tel: (01429) 864320 Fax: (01429) 864320 E-mail: sws.waste@themail.co.uk *Waste disposal & recycling services*

S W S Alloys & Metals Ltd, Progress Drive, Cannock, Staffordshire, WS11 0JE Tel: (01543) 572149 Fax: (01543) 573834 *Welding fabricators*

▶ S W S Machining Ltd, Progress Drive, Cannock, Staffordshire, WS11 0JE Tel: (01543) 504181 Fax: (01543) 573834 E-mail: sales@swsmachining.co.uk *Milling engineering services*

S W S Metal Treatments Ltd, Second Avenue, Trafford Park, Manchester, M17 1EE Tel: 0161-872 3569 Fax: 0161-848 7356 E-mail: enquiries@swsmetaltreatments.co.uk *Electroplating services*

S & W Services (Yorkshire) Ltd, 129/133 Manningham Lane, Bradford, West Yorkshire, BD8 7JA Tel: (01274) 722388 Fax: (01274) 722380 *Vehicle component parts distributors*

S W Witham & Sons, The Forge, Blacksmiths Lane, Erpingham, Norwich, NR11 7QF Tel: (01263) 761404 *Agricultural contractors*

▶ S Wade, Butterthwaite Lane, Ecclesfield, Sheffield, S35 9WA Tel: 0114-257 8190 Fax: 0114-257 8190

S Walters, Bearley Lane, Tintinhull, Yeovil, Somerset, BA22 8PE Tel: (01935) 822033 Fax: (01935) 826767 *Agricultural contractors*

S Ward & Co., 622 Commercial Road, London, E14 7HS Tel: (020) 7790 1172 Fax: (020) 7790 6616 E-mail: swardco@fsmail.net *Sheet metalworkers & ductwork contractors*

S Willetts (Fabrications) Ltd, Pleasant Street, Lyng, West Bromwich, West Midlands, B70 7DT Tel: 0121-553 2705 Fax: 0121-525 0581 *Steel fabricators*

S X 3, Queens Court, Wilmslow Road, Alderley Edge, Cheshire, SK9 7RR Tel: (01625) 587111 Fax: (01625) 587100 E-mail: sales@sx3.com Sales Contact: P. Bradbury *Software developers*

S X Consultancy Ltd, 5 White Oak Square, London Road, Swanley, Kent, BR8 7AG Tel: (01322) 407070 Fax: (01322) 660669 *Systems management & integration*

S Z Gears Ltd, Pontymister Industrial Estate, Risca, Newport, Gwent, NP11 6NP Tel: (01633) 612071 Fax: (01633) 612626 *Industrial gear manufacturing & reconditioning*

S Z N Pendle Automatics Ltd, 1 Stanhope Street, Birmingham, B12 0UZ Tel: 0121-772 2516 Fax: 0121-766 6310 *Automatic precision turned parts manufrs*

▶ S&S, 69 Cross Lane, Mountsorrel, Loughborough, Leicestershire, LE12 7BU Tel: 0116-210 6007 Fax: 0116-210 6779 E-mail: glensmith002@ntlworld.com *Cash registers sales & servicing*

S2 Engineering, 4 Derwenthaugh Marina, Blaydon-on-Tyne, Tyne & Wear, NE21 5LL Tel: 0191-414 2300 Fax: 0191-414 2287 E-mail: info@s2eng.co.uk *Machinery & special equipment manufrs*

S3 Interactive, Unit 1a Dunrobin Court, 14 North Avenue, Clydebank Business Park, Clydebank, Dunbartonshire, G81 2QP Tel: 0141-952 2111 Fax: 0141-952 5255

SA&R plc, Brickfield House, High Road, Thornwood, Epping, Essex, CM16 6TH Tel: 0845 331 2426 Fax: 0845 331 2427 E-mail: info@sarplc.com *SA&R is an*

continued

continuation
environmental consultancy and contractor that provides a complete service for the development and management of contaminated land. We undertake the whole spectrum of works from Phase 1 investigations through to the design and implementation of remediation schemes

Saa Consultants Ltd, The Computer Complex, Somerset Place, Plymouth, PL3 4BB Tel: (01752) 606000 Fax: (01752) 606838 E-mail: sales@saaconsultants.com *E-business software suppliers*

▶ SAA ELECTRICAL, 164 Ivyhouse Road, Dagenham, Essex, RM9 5RU Tel: 020 85937880 *Portable Appliance Inspection & Testing Specialists.*

Saacke Ltd, Marshlands Spur, Portsmouth, PO6 1RX Tel: (023) 9238 3111 Fax: (023) 9232 7120 E-mail: info@saacke.co.uk *Gas & industrial oil burner manufrs*

▶ Saat UK Ltd, 14 Chesterton Road, Brooklands, Manchester, M23 9LB Tel: 0161-945 5172 Fax: 0161-945 5172 E-mail: f.kaabipour@saatukltd.com *oil&gas equipments,axial flow vaves, safety fire doors,mineral,Iranian first class silk rugs.*

Saatchi & Saatchi, 80 Charlotte St, London, W1A 1AQ Tel: (020) 7636 5060 Fax: (020) 7436 1998 *Advertisers*

Saba Electrical Ltd, 10 1 Maltravers Road, Sheffield, S2 5AA Tel: 0114-278 7956 Fax: 0114-272 2040 E-mail: sales@sabacom.com *Communications*

Saban Photography, Charwell House, Wilsom Road, Alton, Hampshire, GU34 2PP Tel: (01420) 540227 E-mail: martin@saban.co.uk *Photography*

▶ Sabar UK Ltd, 17 Duckworth Street, Darwen, Lancashire, BB3 1AR Tel: (01254) 702456 Fax: (01254) 702456 E-mail: sabaruk@ntlworld.com *Import & distribution of electric motor & water pumps*

Sabel Cosmetics, Mount Pellon Works, Pellon Lane, Halifax, West Yorkshire, HX1 4TZ Tel: (01422) 366400 Fax: (01422) 366669 E-mail: sabel@sabel-cosmetics.co.uk *Cosmetics manufrs*

Sabell & Co., Saxon Way, Birmingham, B37 5AX Tel: 0121-770 1389 Fax: 0121-788 1970 *Office files & filing systems manufrs*

Saber Office Furniture Ltd, 21 Bath Lane, Leicester, LE3 5BF Tel: 0116-251 1121 Fax: 0116-251 2625 E-mail: sales@ukofficefurniture.co.uk *Office furniture suppliers*

Sabic Plastics, Bo'Ness Road, Grangemouth, Stirlingshire, FK3 9XF Tel: (01324) 483490 Fax: (01324) 667265 *Plastics materials manufrs*

Sabichi Homewares Ltd, Sabichi House, 5 Wadsworth Road, Greenford, Middlesex, UB6 7JD Tel: (020) 8991 9505 Fax: (020) 8991 9218 *Homeware products*

Sabine Bros Ltd, Heath Works, Hearthcote Road, Swadlincote, Derbyshire, DE11 9DU Tel: (01283) 217359 Fax: (01283) 550749 *Iron founders & general engineers*

Sabins Pine Furniture, 17 Church Road, Codsall, Wolverhampton, WV8 1EA Tel: (01902) 846027 *Pine antique furniture*

Sablon Fabrications, Unit 6 Laches Close, Four Ashes, Wolverhampton, WV10 7DZ Tel: (01902) 798894 Fax: (01902) 798895 *Industrial & commercial steel fencing, railing & gates*

Sabre, 122 Fieldside, Ely, Cambs, CB6 3AT Tel: 01353 667616 Fax: 01353 667444 *Soft furnishings manufr*

Sabre Advanced Micro Electronics Ltd, Unit 11 The Pines Trading Estate, Broad Street, Guildford, Surrey, GU3 3BH Tel: (01483) 535444 Fax: (01483) 535888 E-mail: sales@sabreadv.com *Microelectronic components distributors*

Sabre Engines Ltd, 22 Cobham Road, Ferndown Industrial Estate, Wimborne, Dorset, BH21 7PW Tel: (01202) 893720 Fax: (01202) 851700 E-mail: post@sabre-engines.co.uk *Marine & diesel engine manufrs*

Sabre Instrument Valves Ltd, Golf Road, Hale, Altrincham, Cheshire, WA15 8AH Tel: 0161-925 4000 Fax: 0161-925 4001 E-mail: info@sabre-valves.com *Valve manufrs*

Sabre International Ltd, Unit 9, Brookside Business Centre, Church Street, Swallowfield, Reading, RG7 1TH Tel: 0118-988 8818 Fax: 0118-988 8828 E-mail: david@sabre-international.com *Audio installation hire & sales services*

Sabre Leather Co. Ltd, 19-21 Sandwell Street, Walsall, WS1 3DR Tel: (01922) 629925 Fax: (01922) 723463 E-mail: sales@sabreleather.co.uk *Saddlery manufrs*

▶ Sabre Leisure, Home Orchard, Brim Hill, Maidencombe, Torquay, TQ1 4TR Tel: (01803) 316655 *Swimming pool equipment distributors*

▶ Sabre Mediacopy, 28 Shrewsbury Road, Edgmond, Newport, Shropshire, TF10 8HU Tel: (01952) 820453 Fax: (01952) 811438 E-mail: admin@mediacopy.co.uk *CD, DVD, video, floppy disk audio cassettes duplication & print services*

Sabre Plastics Ltd, Dockfield Road, Shipley, West Yorkshire, BD17 7AD Tel: (01274) 586815 Fax: (01274) 531397 E-mail: info@sabreplastics.co.uk Principal Export Areas: Africa *Plastics extrusion & plastic tube manufrs*

Sabre Rail Services Ltd, Grindon Way, Heighington Lane Business Park, Newton Aycliffe, County Durham, DL5 6SH Tel: (01325) 300505 Fax: (01325) 300485 E-mail: info@sabre-rail.co.uk *Railway engineers*

Sabre Repetitions Ltd, Golf Road, Hale, Altrincham, Cheshire, WA15 8AH Tel: 0161-925 4020 Fax: 0161-925 4021 E-mail: rep@sabreuk.com *Repetition work machinists*

Sabre Structures Ltd, 46a Bradford Road, Brighouse, West Yorkshire, HD6 1RY Tel: (01484) 722778 Fax: (01484) 722880 *Steel fabricators*

Sabre Supply Co., 35-37 Brent Street, London, NW4 2EF Tel: (020) 8457 1510 Fax: (020) 8201 7368 E-mail: sabre@sabresupply.co.uk *Toiletry product importers*

Sabre Systems (Heating) Ltd, Unit 9, Ruxley Corner Industrial Estate, Edgington Way, Sidcup, Kent, DA14 5BL Tel: (020) 8308 0708 Fax: (020) 8309 6727 E-mail: sales@sabresystems.co.uk *Sabre Systems - Central Heating and Boiler spare parts for trade and retail in Kent and the South East. A long established business with knowledgeable staff, (ex gas fitters) on hand to give help and a friendly service. Same day local/ next day national delivery offered. Extensive range of manufacturers available with 18,000 different stock items in our warehouse. Potterton/Baxi, Ideal, Ravenheat, Ariston, R M Solar and Worcester main dealers. Ebay shop. If we do hold the part we will use our extensive network to source it for you. Renewable energy equipment and solar thermal products both flat roof solar panels and evacuated tubes now in store. Come and see our renewable energy showroom with its working solar system. Competitively priced hot water storage cylinders available. Visit our Trade Counter located in South East London - Sidcup, next to A20, close to Junction 3 on M25. Easy free parking available. We specialise in Gas Safety Training Rigs for CORGI educational purposes.*

Sabre Technology (Hull) Ltd, 3a Newlands Science Park, Newlands Centre, Inglemire Lane, Hull, HU6 7TQ Tel: (01482) 801003 Fax: (01482) 801078 E-mail: info@sabretechnology.co.uk *Electronic designers*

Sabre Triad Ltd, 42 Roman Way Industrial Estate, Ribbleton, Preston, PR2 5BD Tel: (01772) 655328 Fax: (01772) 655326 E-mail: cmc@sabretriad.co.uk *Flexible packaging manufrs*

▶ Sabre Vending Ltd, Unit 27 South Hampshire Industrial Park, Totton, Southampton, SO40 3SA Tel: (023) 8086 0044 Fax: (023) 8066 7267 E-mail: sales@sabrevending.com

Sabrefame Ltd, Brook House, Duck Street, Wendens Ambo, Saffron Walden, Essex, CB11 4JU Tel: (01799) 542287 Fax: (01799) 541954 E-mail: sabrefame@aol.com *Computer consultancy*

Sabreglen Ltd, Unit 22 Marlowe Business Centre, Batavia Road, London, SE14 6BQ Tel: (020) 8694 1144 Fax: (020) 8694 8698 E-mail: sales@sabreglen.co.uk *Air-conditioning & refrigerators services*

Sabrina Traditional Oak Doors, Alma Yard, Alma Street, Shrewsbury, SY3 8QL Tel: (01743) 357977 Fax: (01743) 352233 E-mail: sales@oakdoors.co.uk *Oak door manufrs*

▶ Sabroe Ltd, 86 Melchett Road, Kings Norton Business Centre, Birmingham, B30 3HX Tel: 0121-683 7800 E-mail: sales@sabroe.co.uk

Sabtek International Ltd, Unit 9, 10 Badentoy Place, Portlethen, Aberdeen, AB12 4YF Tel: (01224) 782289 Fax: (01224) 781645 E-mail: info@sabtek.co.uk *Suppliers of instrumentation & pipeline equipment*

▶ Sabur Ink Systems Ltd, 2 Wharncliffe Park, Barnsley, South Yorkshire, S71 3HR Tel: (01226) 280999 Fax: (01226) 280888 E-mail: dsanger@fsmail.net *Screen printing supply services*

▶ SAC Consultancy & Design, 55 Olympia Close, Northampton, NN4 0RU Tel: (07733) 177743 E-mail: sacharlton@sac-consult-design.com *IT consultancy*

▶ Sac Heartland Environmental, Ferguson Building, Craibstone Estate, Bucksburn, Aberdeen, AB21 9YA Tel: (01224) 711095 Fax: (01224) 711268 E-mail: info@sac.ac.uk

Saccenda Group Ltd, High Street, Okeford Fitzpaine, Blandford Forum, Dorset, DT11 0RQ Tel: (01258) 860304 Fax: (01258) 861208 *Chicken processing factory*

S. Sacker (Claydon) Ltd, Railway Sidings, Gipping Road, Ipswich, IP6 0JB Tel: (01473) 830373 Fax: (01473) 832535 E-mail: recycle@sackers.co.uk *Metal reclaiming & processors*

Sackville Oak Ltd, 30 Store Street, London, WC1E 7QD Tel: (020) 7636 8723 Fax: (020) 7636 8726 E-mail: pdfprint@btclick.com *Printing & photocopying services*

▶ Sacranie.net, Flat1, 40 Woodstock Road, Golders Green, London, NW11 8ER Tel: 0208 9055523 Fax: 0871 2773305 E-mail: raheen@sacranie.net *Business & technology consultancy*

Sacrosanct Technology Ltd, 3 Sambourn Close, Solihull, West Midlands, B91 2SA Tel: 0121-711 2100 E-mail: robthomas@sacrosanct.co.uk *Project management services*

Saddle Rack, 93 Canterbury Road, Hawkinge, Folkestone, Kent, CT18 7BS Tel: (01303) 893659 Fax: (01303) 893659 *Saddlers & riding wear suppliers*

▶ Saddle Up, Unit 18 Hill Street, Ardrossan, Ayrshire, KA22 8HE Tel: (01294) 469999 Fax: (01294) 469999 E-mail: sales@saddlery-online.co.uk *Saddlery*

Saddlers Apprentice, Frankby Stiles, Wirral, Merseyside, CH48 1PL Tel: 0151-625 2551 Fax: 0151 625 6477 *Livery yard & feed kennels*

Saddlers Blinds, Station Road, Cowfold, Horsham, West Sussex, RH13 8DA Tel: (01403) 865353 Fax: (01403) 865352 E-mail: sales@saddlers-blinds.co.uk *Blinds suppliers*

▶ Saddleworth Bedrooms & Kitchens, 18 Broadbent Road, Oldham, OL1 4HU Tel: 0161-620 2600 *Suppliers & fitters of kitchens & bedrooms*

Saddleworth Burglar Alarm Systems, 162 Wall Hill Road, Dobcross, Oldham, OL3 5BL Tel: (01457) 870773 *Security alarm installers*

Saddleworth Meter Services, 62 Delph Lane, Delph, Oldham, OL3 5HX Tel: (01457) 871387 Fax: (01457) 871387 *Flow meter equipment service*

Sadlers Carton Stockholders Ltd, 10 Tilton Road, Small Heath, Birmingham, B9 4PE Tel: 0121-772 5200 Fax: 0121-771 4368 E-mail: sales@sadlers.co.uk *New & used corrugated cartons*

Saeloc Ltd, 9 Enterprise Court, Newton Close, Park Farm Industrial Estate, Wellingborough, Northamptonshire, NN8 6UW Tel: (01933) 678000 Fax: (01933) 678999 E-mail: sales@saeloc.co.uk *Bag closure machine packages & manufrs*

Saes Getters (GB) Ltd, Heritage House, Vicker Lane, Daventry, Northamptonshire, NN11 5AA Tel: (01327) 310777 Fax: (01327) 310555 E-mail: saes-gb@saes-group.com *High vacuum equipment distributors*

▶ SAF- Recuitment, Marvell Rise, Harrogate, North Yorkshire, HG1 3LT Tel: (01423) 550756 E-mail: stuart@saf-recruitment.com *Health & nutrition*

Saf Welding Products Ltd, 2 Low March Industrial Estate, Low March, Daventry, Northamptonshire, NN11 4SD Tel: (01327) 705511 Fax: (01327) 701310 E-mail: sales@saf-wp.co.uk *Distributor of welding & cutting equipment*

Safam 786 Ltd, 392a High Street, Cheltenham, Gloucestershire, GL50 3JD Tel: (01242) 693786 Fax: (01242) 252786 E-mail: safam786@dial.pipex.com *Software design & developers*

Safari, 44 Cascades, Portsmouth, PO1 4RR Tel: (023) 9282 9410 Fax: (023) 9281 6070 *Outdoor leisure suppliers*

▶ Safe Access, 136 Derbyshire Lane, Sheffield, S8 8SE Tel: 0114-280 2020 Fax: 0114-280 2010 E-mail: info@the-access-group.com *Access & safety system agents*

▶ Safe Access Scaffolding Midlands Ltd, Belfield Street, Ilkeston, Derbyshire, DE7 8DU Tel: 0115-932 7878 Fax: 0115-944 7812

▶ Safe Coatings Ltd, Bank House, High Street, Staplehurst, Tonbridge, Kent, TN12 0AE Tel: (01580) 893087 Fax: (01580) 893473 E-mail: enquiries@safecoatings.com *Asbestos encapsulation products distributors*

Safe Computing Ltd, 20 Freeschool Lane, Leicester, LE1 4FY Tel: 0116-262 9321 Fax: 0116-251 5535 E-mail: sales@safecomputing.co.uk *Computer software house*

Safe Guy, Simon Scotland Road, King's Lynn, Norfolk, PE30 4JF Tel: (01553) 774449 Fax: (01553) 761670 *Safety & corporate clothing*

Safe Handling, Unit 7-8 Pennine View Industrial Estate, of Shepley Lane, Marple, Stockport, Cheshire, SK6 7JW Tel: 0161-427 0639 Fax: 0161-427 0012 *Fork lift truck & plant operator training services*

Safe Homes UK, 1 Anker Court, Bonehill Road, Tamworth, Staffordshire, B78 3HP Tel: 0870 8580112 Fax: 0870 8580113 E-mail: info@safehomes.co.uk *Safe Homes UK is a leading independent provider of security solutions to UK businesses and properties.**We specialise in implementing cutting-edge intruder alarm and access control systems, including CCTV, digital storage, video transmission, and biometrics, and are trusted to protect the staff and premises of some of the UK's leading organisations nationwide. **We deliver peace of mind through our strict maintenance, monitoring and reporting regime, and we are audited and accredited to the highest professional and commercial standards by SSAIB, as well as the IS0 9001 quality assurance standard.*

Safe Lite (UK) Ltd, 7-11 Phoenix Business Park, Avenue Close, Birmingham, B7 4NU Tel: 0121-359 4034 Fax: 0121-333 3167 E-mail: enquiries@safelite.uk.com *Permanent signal manufrs*

▶ Safe N'Sound Security Systems Ltd, Head Office, 19 Hackford Walk, 119 - 123 Hackford Road, London, SW9 0QT Tel: (01424) 883275 Fax: (020) 7793 8188 E-mail: sales@safensoundsecurity.co.uk *Security services*

▶ Safe Remedies Ltd, 11 North Road Industrial Estate, Berwick-upon-Tweed, TD15 1UN Tel: (01289) 332888 Fax: (01289) 331888 E-mail: sales@saferemedies.net *Health food product suppliers*

Safe Security, 29 New Hall Lane, Preston, PR1 5NX Tel: (01772) 793792 Fax: (01772) 651886 E-mail: info@thesafeshop.co.uk *Safes & industrial fire cabinets suppliers*

Safe & Sound, 2 Moorhead Street, Colne, Lancashire, BB8 9AU Tel: (01282) 867830 *Burglar alarms & electrical*

Safe & Sound Car Technology, 247-249 Bradford Road, Keighley, West Yorkshire, BD21 4AW Tel: (01535) 691611 Fax: (01535) 610033 *Security engineers*

Safe & Sound Security Systems, 3 Chestnut Avenue, Manchester, M21 8BE Tel: 0161-861 8980 Fax: 0161-861 8980 E-mail: safeandsoundmcr@hotmail.com *Installation & repairers of alarm systems*

Safe & Sound Security Systems Security Alarms, 9 Devonshire Road, Gravesend, Kent, DA12 5AA Tel: (01474) 350613 Fax: (01474) 350613 *Security installers*

Safe & Sure Fire Protection Ltd, Mill Road, Langley Moor, Durham, DH7 8HE Tel: 0191-378 1153 Fax: 0191-378 9297 E-mail: info@safeandsurefire.com *sales and servicing of all types of fire fighting equipment, portable fire extinguishers, fire hose reels, fire blankets, fire alarm systems, emergency lighting, fire extinguisher training, fire risk assessments, safety signage, fire equipment storage*

Safe T Reach Ltd, Crucible Road, Corby, Northamptonshire, NN17 5TS Tel: (01536) 267686 Fax: (01536) 267686 *Access & working platforms*

Safe Textiles Ltd, 151 Whitechapel Road, London, E1 1DN Tel: (020) 7247 6641 Fax: (020) 7247 2497 *Textile convertors*

Safe & Warm Ltd, The Woodman Centre, 270 Vicarage Lane, Blackpool, FY4 4ND Tel: (01253) 792094 Fax: (01253) 292966 E-mail: sales@workwear-safety.co.uk *Work wear manufrs*

Safe Wear, Unit 13 Faraday Mill Business Park, Faraday Road, Plymouth, PL4 0ST Tel: (01752) 484045 Fax: (01752) 484045 E-mail: safewear@talk.to *Safety workwear, footwear, uniforms*

Safeandsound, Alma House, Perranporth, Cornwall, TR6 2QT Tel: (07854) 825599 E-mail: allysafeandsound@hotmail.co.uk *Safe & Sound are a community of holistic health practitioners, our aim is to spread useful information & provide a network of support in order to help people.*

Safechem Ltd, Drum Industrial Estate, Drum Industrial Estate, Chester le Street, County Durham, DH2 1SR Tel: 0191-410 8668 Fax: 0191-410 2934 E-mail: enquiries@safechem.co.uk *Chemical distributors & manufrs*

▶ Safecontrol Ltd, Tattershall Way, Fairfield Industrial Estate, Louth, Lincolnshire, LN11 0YZ Tel: (01507) 609944 Fax: (01507) 609579

Safefire Protection Ltd, 14 Kendal Way, Leigh-on-Sea, Essex, SS9 5QS Tel: (01702) 522183 E-mail: sales@safefireprotection.co.uk *Fire protection suppliers*

Safegard Security, 1a Old Torquay Road, Paignton, Devon, TQ3 2QY Tel: (01803) 523455 Fax: (01803) 556686 E-mail: info@safegardsecurity.co.uk *Security installation*

Safeguard Chemicals Ltd, Redkiln Close, Horsham, West Sussex, RH13 5QL Tel: (01403) 210204 Fax: (01403) 217529 E-mail: info@safeguardchem.com Principal Export Areas: Middle East & Africa *Manufacturers and distributors of specialist waterproofing and damp-proofing products, including Vandex cementitious waterproofing slurries, Oldroyd cavity drainage membranes and Dryzone damp-proofing cream. Solutions for basement waterproofing, swimming pools, green roofs and the treatment of rising damp.*

▶ Safeguard D & J Scaffolding Ltd, Station Goods Yard, Ham Road, Shoreham-by-Sea, West Sussex, BN43 6PA Tel: (01273) 465337 Fax: (01273) 453212

Safeguard Fire & Industrial, Silver Street, Gastard, Corsham, Wiltshire, SN13 9PY Tel: (01249) 715999 Fax: (01249) 715966 E-mail: sales@safeguardfireind.co.uk *Fire equipment suppliers*

Safeguard Pest Control, 3 Retreat Close, Harrow, Middlesex, HA3 0JQ Tel: (020) 8907 8922 *Pest control services*

Safeguard Screens, PO Box 2458, Wimborne, Dorset, BH21 5YG Tel: (01725) 551144 Fax: (01202) 892200 *Safeguard screen manufrs*

Safeguard Security Fencing Ltd, Safeguard House, Coldaville Road, Horbury Junction, Wakefield, West Yorkshire, WF4 5ER Tel: (01924) 264949 Fax: (01924) 264913 *Security mesh fencing*

Safeguard Security Systems, 17-19 Townhead, Kilmaurs, Kilmarnock, Ayrshire, KA3 2ST Tel: (01563) 523101 Fax: (01563) 523101 *Security systems installers*

Safeguard Solutions Ltd, 16 Larcombe Avenue, Wirral, Merseyside, CH49 6NB Tel: 0151-606 0457 Fax: 0151-604 0810 E-mail: safeguard-@btclick.com *Chemical suppliers*

Safehire Safety Netting Ltd, 96 Cobham Road, Ferndown Industrial Estate, Wimborne, Dorset, BH21 7RE Tel: (01202) 855330 Fax: (01202) 855331 *Industrial safety net contractors*

Safeholme Burglar Alarm Systems, 3 Lead Lane, Brompton, Northallerton, North Yorkshire, DL6 2TZ Tel: (01609) 772624 Fax: (01609) 761101 E-mail: sales@safeholme.co.uk *Electrical, security, repair & installers*

Safelab Systems Ltd, Unit 29, Lynx Crescent, Weston-super-Mare, Avon, BS24 9DJ Tel: (01934) 421340 Fax: (0870) 2402274 E-mail: sales@safelab.co.uk *Laboratory fume cupboard & furniture manufrs*

Safeland (Ground Rents) Ltd, 94/96 Great North Road, London, N2 0NL Tel: (020) 8815 1600 *Property developers*

Safelift Offshore Ltd, Forties Business Centre, School Road, Kintore, Inverurie, Aberdeenshire, AB51 0UX Tel: (01224) 775774 Fax: (01224) 775779 E-mail: sales@safelift.co.uk *Lifting engineers & mechanical/manual handling consultants*

▶ Safelincs Ltd, Unit 1, Farlesthorpe Road, Alford, Lincolnshire, LN13 9PS Tel: 01507 462176 Fax: 01507 463288 E-mail: service@safelincs.co.uk *Buy online Quality Fire Safety Equipment and Fire Resistant Safes. Best Price Guarantee! Free delivery of Fire Resistant Safes. Buy fire extinguishers, fire extinguisher cabinets and stands, smoke alarms, radio-interlinked smoke alarms, fire safes, fire chests, CO alarms, fire escape ladders, fire hoods, fire signs, fire door retainers, exit door fittings, fire escape signs, emergency lighting, fire blankets and many other fire safety products. We also offer nationwide installation and service for fire extinguishers. Safelincs Ltd is a member of The British Fire Consortium and the FPA and we pride ourselves in the quality of our products and the knowledge of our staff!*

Safeload (UK)Ltd, 26, Holton Road,, Holton Heath Trading Estate, Poole, Dorset, BH16 5SL Tel: (01202) 624422 Fax: (01202) 624569 *Machine mounts manufrs*

▶ Safely Workwear, Church Road, Worcester Park, Surrey, KT4 7RJ Tel: (020) 8337 5558 E-mail: sales@safelyworkwear.co.uk *Supplier of safety workwear, mens & ladies safety boots, big sizes, EN345 standards, steel toe cap boots, composite toe boots, gloves, hi-vi wear*

Safemark Computer Security, 92 Tadcaster Road, Dringhouses, York, YO24 1LT Tel: (01904) 778899 Fax: (01904) 778623 E-mail: sales@safemark.co.uk *Computer systems consultants*

Safemate Antislip Ltd, Unit 1 Bankhead Avenue, Bucksburn, Aberdeen, AB21 9ET Tel: (01224) 716283 Fax: (01224) 714653 E-mail: safemate@ifb.co.uk Principal Export Areas: Worldwide *For the past 20 years, Safemate International has provided a complete service in the manufacture and supply of a range of high quality antislip systems. Safemate products are designed to protect operators from slips and falls on decks, ladders, stairs and workstations.*

▶ Safepat, 26 Main Street, Wombwell, Barnsley, South Yorkshire, S73 8JS Tel: (07814) 916862 E-mail: enquiries@safepat *Portable appliance testing*

continued

continued

Company Information

▶ Safeplay Playground Equipment, Kelsey Park Depot, Manor Way, Beckenham, Kent, BR3 3LJ Tel: (020) 8658 5631 Fax: (020) 8658 9060 E-mail: playsafe@safeplay.co.uk *Inspection and Maintenance of playground equipment and safety surfacing*
▶ Safer Safety, Oaks Farm Lane, Calow, Chesterfield, Derbyshire, S44 5TA Tel: (01246) 201666 Fax: (01246) 201777 E-mail: safersafety@userve.net *Manufacturer of earplugs & anti slip footwear*
▶ Safer Systems UK Ltd, Units 7 & 8, Molyneux Business Park, Matlock, Derbyshire, DE4 2HJ Tel: (01629) 735577 Fax: (01629) 735588 E-mail: sales@safetysystems.co.uk *The threat of expensive vandalism and theft often restricts where you place a vending machine. Be free to place you machines where they'll work best for you rather than the 'safest' locations, with lower footfall and consequently lower sales.*
Saferad Ltd, 1 Saferad Ltd Development Off Meadowfi Eld Indust Estate, Durham, DH7 1KK Tel: 0191-378 2130 Fax: 0191-378 2130 E-mail: mwass@saferad.com *Radiographic equipment supply/maintenance/repair*
Saferide Saddlery Products, 2 Newfield Close, Walsall, WS2 7PB Tel: (01922) 646512 Fax: (01922) 646554 *Horse riding saddle manufrs*
Safescript Ltd, 2 Deanhill Road, London, SW14 7DF Tel: (020) 8876 7853 Fax: (020) 8876 3249 E-mail: info@safescript.co.uk *Medical computing*
Safestore, Brittanic House, Stirling Way, Borehamwood, Hertfordshire, WD6 2BT Tel: 0845 5314074 E-mail: info@safestore.co.uk *Secure storage, 24hr cctv & packing materials services*
▶ Safestore Ltd, Stirling Way, Borehamwood, Hertfordshire, WD6 2BT Tel: (020) 8732 1500 Fax: (020) 8732 1510 E-mail: borehamwood@safestoretrading.co.uk
▶ Safestore UK Limited, 1 Parkway Avenue, Sheffield, S9 4WA Tel: 01142 728181 Fax: 01142 728191 E-mail: sales@safestoreuk.co.uk *manufacturers and suppliers of hazardous storage solutions, drum stores, walk.in, reach in units*steel boxes, spill containment*
Safetech Systems Ltd, 97 Firs Drive, Hounslow, TW5 9TB Tel: (020) 8897 3317 Fax: (020) 8384 1660 *Fire alarm systems installations*
Safetell International Ltd, Unit 46, Fawkes Avenue, Dartford, DA1 1JQ Tel: (01322) 223233 Fax: (01322) 277751 *Security screen suppliers*
Safetrak Ltd, Wimbourne Road, Barry, Vale of Glamorgan, CF63 3Dh Tel: (01446) 723320 E-mail: info@safetrak.com *Safetrak - Asset Safety Management*Mobile computer systems utilising RFID tags for the inspection of assets and equipment to assist with the compliance to health & safety regulations and standards.*
Safety 1st Signs, 34 Millersdale Avenue, Mansfield, Nottinghamshire, NG18 5HS Tel: (01623) 429947 Fax: (01623) 640540 *Sign manufrs*
▶ Safety Barrier Erectors, Ballybrakes Indust Estate, Ballybrakes Road, Ballymoney, County Antrim, BT53 6LH Tel: (028) 2766 3164 Fax: (028) 2766 7815
Safety By Design, Safety House Aire & Calder Industrial Park, Lock Lane, Castleford, West Yorkshire, WF10 2JA Tel: (0800) 0858782 Fax: (01977) 555351 E-mail: sales@safetybydesign.co.uk *Safety barriers, pedestrian barriers, rack protection, traffic barriers, security products, safety products, Nationwide installation, Major contracts fullfilled, plastic barriers, polypropylene barriers, free survey, Leeds, uk, Morley, Safety by Design. Try our latest polypropylene safety barriers with a free no risk offer, contact us for details.*
Safety Engineers Ltd, 18 Dudley Wood Road, Dudley, West Midlands, DY2 0DB Tel: 01384 569024 *Machine guard manufrs*
Safety Equipment South West, Tinney Hall Cottage, Lewannick, Launceston, Cornwall, PL15 7QE Tel: (01566) 782393 Fax: (01566) 782401 *Safety equipment, power tools, hand tools suppliers*
Safety Equipment Supplies Ltd, 1 Manchester Row, Newton-le-Willows, Merseyside, WA12 8SD Tel: (0870) 1608130 Fax: (0870) 1608131 E-mail: sales@safety-supplies.co.uk *Suppliers of safety, industrial & janitorial products*
Safety First Aid Group Ltd, Unit 15-17 Garrick Industrial Centre, Irving Way, London, NW9 6AQ Tel: (020) 8202 7447 Fax: (0800) 281655 E-mail: sales@safetyfirstaid.co.uk *Workplace first aid & occupational health goods suppliers*
Safety First Extinguishers, Safety First Ho, Hawthorn Rd, Bognor Regis, W. Sussex, PO21 2UW Tel: (01243) 822215 Fax: (01243) 822215 E-mail: mrpcampbell@safetyfirstextinguishers. freeserve.co.uk *Fire extinguishers servicing & supplies*
Safety Flooring Supplies, 132-134 Stanwell Road, Ashford, Middlesex, TW15 3QP Tel: (01784) 244577 Fax: (0870) 4020124 *Slip resistant/ antislip flooring*
Safety Glass Replacements Ltd, Garden Street, Newcastle, Staffordshire, ST5 1BW Tel: (01782) 614693 Fax: (01782) 614633 *Glazing contractors*
Safety Industries (Oakwood) Ltd, Tonbridge Road, Harold Hill, Romford, RM3 8TS Tel: (01708) 381499 Fax: (01708) 381267 E-mail: sales@safetyindustries.co.uk *Asbestos equipment removal suppliers*
Safety Kleen UK Ltd, 9-10 Arkwright Road Industrial Estate, Arkwright Road, Bedford, MK42 0LQ Tel: (01234) 341292 Fax: (01234) 349200 *Industrial waste transfer*
Safety Kleen UK Ltd, 2 Broughton Industrial Estate, Broughton Mills Road, Bretton, Chester, CH4 0BY Tel: (01244) 660184 Fax: (01244) 661338 *Recycling equipment distributors*
▶ Safety Management & Assessments, 12 West Drive, Brandon, Suffolk, IP27 0JS Tel: (01842) 811435 E-mail: safetyman@risk-assessments.co.uk *A full range of H & S consultancy services is offered, including preparation of Safety Policies, Risk, COSHH, HAVS & Personal Noise*

continued

Assessments, Method Statements, plus industrial accident investigations & insurance style liability surveys. I also produce a range of DIY Safety Policy, Risk & COSHH Assessment kits.
Safety Screens Ltd, Unit 11a, 11b Greenfield Farm Industrial Estate, Congleton, Cheshire, CW12 4TR Tel: (01260) 295999 Fax: (01260) 295998 E-mail: sales@safetyscreens.co.uk *Insect screen & grille manufrs*
▶ Safety Simply, 23 Cock Close Road, Yaxley, Peterborough, PE7 3HJ Tel: (0845) 2600710 Fax: (0845) 2600711 E-mail: info@safetysimplifield.co.uk *Principal Export Areas: Middle East, Africa, West Europe, North America & South America Simple solutions to managing safety*
The Safety Site, Knightsbridge House, 229 Acton Lane, London, W4 5DD Tel: (0870) 2253000 Fax: (0870) 0770003 E-mail: enquiries@thesafetysite.co.uk *The Safety Site are distributors of Safety Equipment including: PPE, Home and Site safety, providing: First Aid equipment, head protection, hearing protection, respiratory protection, eye and face protection, workwear, protective workwear, fall arrest equipment, footwear and safety footwear, hand protection, road safety equipment and signs including: traffic signs, safety signs, site safety equipment and janitorial signs. We also offer our customers a health & safety consultancy service. Please contact us for further information to see how we can help you or see our website for additional information. Please mention Kellysearch.com when contacting us.*
▶ Safety Solutions Ni, Rathdown Close, Lissue Industrial Estate, Lisburn, County Antrim, BT28 2RB Tel: (028) 9262 2444 Fax: (028) 9262 2333 *Work wear retailers*
Safety Stairways Ltd, Unit 45 Owen Road Industrial Estate, Willenhall, West Midlands, WV13 2PX Tel: 0121-526 3133 Fax: 0121-526 2833 E-mail: info@safety-stairways.com *Safety Stairways Ltd - Designers, Manufacturers and Suppliers or Spiral Staircases, Cast Iron Staircases, Helical Stairs, Commercial and Domestic Stairs and Much More! Based in Willenhall, West Midlands, UK*
Safety Systems UK Ltd, Sharp Street, Worsley, Manchester, M28 3NA Tel: (01925) 820281 Fax: 0161-799 4335 E-mail: support@safetysystemsuk.com *Pressure reducing safety valves suppliers & manufrs*
Safety Tools Ltd, Highlands Road, Shirley, Solihull, West Midlands, B90 4NJ Tel: 0121-705 3508 Fax: 0121-713 2505 E-mail: info@safetytools.co.uk *Spark resistant tools & safety equipment (industrial) manufrs*
▶ Safety Train, 25 Raines Avenue, Worksop, Nottinghamshire, S81 7PA Tel: (01909) 532589 Fax: (01909) 532589 E-mail: thesafetyman@tiscali.co.uk *Health and Safety Training and Consultancy Service to Business and Industry. - CIEH (Chartered Institute of Environmental Health) accredited training centre. Nationally recognised qualifications by examination.**Safety Advice and Consultancy by qualified staff. Nationwide Service.**
▶ Safety Training Unit Ltd, 1062 Cornforth Drive, Sittingbourne Research Centre, Sittingbourne, Kent, ME9 8HL Tel: (01795) 438841 Fax: (0870) 131920 E-mail: enquiries@stunit.co.uk *Health & safety training services*
Safety Trolley Systems, 41 Praze Road, Leedstown, Hayle, Cornwall, TR27 6DS Tel: 01736 851050 E-mail: sales@sts-trolleys.co.uk *STS are the foremost experts in the design of manual handling equipment for drums, rolls, cylinders and all types of materials. We manufacture in the UK and can design and build the right piece of equipment that fulfills your specification.*
Safety Welding & Lifting International Ltd, Unit 3 Saville Street, Macclesfield, Cheshire, SK11 7LQ Tel: (01625) 422444 Fax: (01625) 618000 *Lifting equipment suppliers*
Safety Welding & Lifting (International) Ltd, Site 4 Inverbreakie Industrial Estate, Invergordon, Ross-Shire, IV18 0QR Tel: (01349) 852187 Fax: (01349) 853585 E-mail: info@safetyweldinglifting.co.uk *Lifting gear manufrs*
Safety-Kleen UK Ltd, 390 London Road, Isleworth, Middlesex, TW7 5AN Tel: (020) 8490 9084 Fax: (020) 8490 3859 E-mail: skuk@sk-europe.com *SafetyKleen provides top quality parts-cleaning, spraygun cleaning and industrial waste collection services through a country-wide network of branches in the United Kingdom, France, Italy, Spain, Germany, Belgium, and Ireland.*
Safetymark Consultancy Services, Sydney Cottages, Elm Road, Claygate, Esher, Surrey, KT10 0EJ Tel: (01372) 462277 Fax: (01372) 462288 E-mail: mark.snelling@safetymark.net *Consultancy services*
▶ Safetytags.co.uk, 1 Beverley Drive, Kimberley, Nottingham, NG16 2TW Tel: 0115-938 2810 Fax: 0115-938 2810 E-mail: sales@safetytags.co.uk *The NEW range of PPE safetytags provides employers and employees with a simple and effective method of visually checking that the PPE equipment is within its inspection period.*
▶ Safety-Train UK, 7 Belgravia Court, Oakthorpe Drive, Kingshurst, Birmingham, B37 6HY Tel: 0121-605 0598 E-mail: info@safety-trainuk.co.uk *ALL MATERIALS HANDLING TRAINING COVERED TO THE HIGHEST STANDARDS*FORKLIFT TRUCKS CONSTRUCTION SITE*MANUAL HANDLING RISK ASSESSMENTS*
▶ Safetywise Solutions Limited, Corner House, Main Road, South Reston, Louth, Lincolnshire, LN11 8JJ Tel: (01507) 4 50865 E-mail: info@safetywise.co.uk *Providing practical support to employers in the management of workplace health and safety; including policy, procedures, training, technical support and safety audits.*

Safetyworks GB Limited, P.O. Box 753, Aylesbury, Buckinghamshire, HP22 9BJ Tel: (01296) 655506 Fax: (01296) 655503 E-mail: david@safety-works.co.uk *Supplier of fireproof data safes or cabinets and document protection products, cash and jewellery safes, under floor and wall safes, security cabinets, shotgun safes, gun boxes and second hand items*
Safeway Office Services Ltd, 7 Leathermarket Street, London, SE1 3HN Tel: (020) 7403 2944 *Contract cleaning*
Safeway Security Services Ltd, 17 Hook Road, Goole, North Humberside, DN14 5JB Tel: (01405) 760664 Fax: (01405) 768727 E-mail: sales@safewaysecurityservices.com *Security equipment installers*
▶ Safeways Wirral Locksmiths Ltd, 10 Grange Mount, Prenton, Merseyside, CH43 4XW Tel: 0151-653 3414 Fax: 0151-653 3414 E-mail: inneng@aol.com *Caravan, motor home & vehicle lock manufacturers & locksmiths*
Safewear, Unit 1 Seaview Industrial Estate, Lewis Road, East Moors, Cardiff, CF24 5EB Tel: (029) 2049 6585 Fax: (029) 2049 4057 *Industrial clothing suppliers*
▶ Safewell, 31 Teesdale Avenue, Hull, HU9 3UG Tel: (01482) 792159 E-mail: sales@safewell.com *Safety & hygiene products manufrs*
▶ Saffery Champness, 40 Melville Street, Edinburgh, EH3 7TW Tel: 0131-225 2741 Fax: 0131-225 5376
▶ Saffron Computers Ltd, 4 Ash Drive, Haughton, Stafford, ST18 9EU Tel: (0871) 7233766 Fax: (01785) 780390 E-mail: sales@saffroncomputers.org *Suppliers of Quality PC Systems, Software, Hardware and IT Consultancy.*
▶ Saffron Design & Print Ltd, Chapel Works, Aldridge Road, Streetly, Sutton Coldfield, West Midlands, B74 2DU Tel: 0121-353 4446 Fax: 0121-353 5556 E-mail: sales@saffrondesign.co.uk *Printers*
Saffron Electronics Ltd, 3-04 St. Albans Road Industrial Estate, Stafford, ST16 3DR Tel: (0845) 1662314 Fax: (0845) 1662315 E-mail: sales@saffronelectronics.co.uk *We are a well established supplier of Hi-Technology Electronic Components and Batteries. We specialise in low volume component supply, PCB design, Component kitting, and the international sourcing of ""hard to find and obsolete parts"". Our component range is vast and includes batteries, bulbs, capacitors, chargers, connectors, diodes, fuses, ICs, LEDs, resonators, regulators, resistors, semiconductors, sensors, switches, surface mount, transformers, transistors, zeners, etc.*
Saffron Plastics Ltd, Bakers Court, Paycocke Road, Basildon, Essex, SS14 3EH Tel: (01268) 288874 Fax: (01268) 534592 E-mail: sales@saffronplastics.co.uk *High impact polystyrene suppliers*
▶ Saffron Scientific Equipment Ltd, GSPK Technology Park, Manse Lane, Knaresborough, North Yorkshire, HG5 8LF Tel: (01423) 796138 Fax: (01423) 798268 E-mail: sales@saffron-uk.com *Scientific equipment manufrs*
Saffron Security, Stanstead House, Shire Hill, Saffron Walden, Essex, CB11 3AQ Tel: (01799) 529911 Fax: (01799) 529912 *Security systems*
Saffron Tape Design, Epsilon House, 27 Fulfen Way, Saffron Walden, Essex, CB11 4DW Tel: (01799) 520170 Fax: (01799) 520170 E-mail: saffrontapedesign@tiscali.co.uk *Selling printed packaging tape & plain tapes*
SAFI Ltd, 35 Holton Road, Holton Heath Trading Park, Poole, Dorset, BH16 6LT Tel: (01202) 624618 Fax: (01202) 628500 E-mail: sales@safi-limited.com *SAFI has over 45 year's experience of manufacturing corrosion resistant valves and actuators. We are a thermo plastic valve supplier working in the following materials; PVC-U, PVC-C, ABS, PP (polypropylene), GRPP (Glass Reinforced PP), and PE (Polyethylene), PVDF & anti static PP & PVDF (ATEX approved). These materials are available in our comprehensive range of ball, butterfly and diaphragm valves, both manual and actuated (electric & pneumatic), swing check & non- return valves as well as bib taps, bulkhead fittings, tank fittings and access covers. *SAFI plastic valves and products are approved and widely used in agriculture (crop sprayers), water treatment, many chemical processes, chemical transportation, chemical storage, environmental, landfill, pharmaceutical, flexitank, boat building and power generation. Full technical & sales support is available from our manufacturing site in Poole, Dorset.*
Safpro Industrial Supply Co., Unit 4-5 Ashville Industrial Estate, Ashville Road, Gloucester, GL2 5EU Tel: (01452) 529050 Fax: (01452) 311221 *Protective clothing distributors*
Saft Ltd, 6th Floor Westgate House, West Gate, Harlow, Essex, CM20 1JN Tel: (01279) 772550 Fax: (01279) 420909 E-mail: sarah.carter@saftbatteries.com *Industrial, lithium, nickel cadmium & nickel metal hydride battery manufrs*
Saft, River Drive, South Shields, Tyne & Wear, NE33 2TR Tel: 0191-456 1451 Fax: 0191-456 6383 E-mail: enquiries@saftbatteries.com *Battery manufrs*
Saftek Brakes, 1 Rawfolds Industrial Estate, Bradford Road, Rawfolds, Cleckheaton, West Yorkshire, BD19 5LT Tel: (01274) 862666 Fax: (01274) 862444 *Manufacturers of brake & clutch linings*
Saftet Brakes, Unit D5 Halesfield 5, Telford, Shropshire, TF7 4QJ Tel: (01952) 581122 Fax: (01952) 585417 E-mail: sales@saftek.co.uk *Brake & clutch lining manufrs*
▶ Safyre Ltd, Unit 10 Tait Road Industrial Estate, Tait Road, Croydon, CR0 2DP Tel: (020) 8684 3080 Fax: (020) 8684 2634 E-mail: sales@safyre.co.uk *Fire alarm systems providers*
▶ Saga Fashions, Clarence House, 1 Hilda Road, Chatham, Kent, ME4 5PU Tel: (01634) 826520

Saga Group Ltd, The Saga Building, Middelburg Sqaure, Folkestone, Kent, CT20 1AZ Tel: (0800) 0150751 *Travel & insurance agents*
Sagar Marine Ltd, Victoria Works, Wharfe Street, Brighouse, West Yorkshire, HD6 1PP Tel: (01484) 714541 Fax: (01484) 400683 *Steel boat builders*
Sage Publications Ltd, 1 Olivers Yard, 55 City Road, London, EC1Y 1SP Tel: (020) 7374 0645 E-mail: info@sagepub.co.uk *Publishers*
▶ Sage Training Courses, 41 The Vale, Middlesbrough, Cleveland, TS4 2UE Tel: (01642) 519507 E-mail: info@sage-training-solutions.co.uk *We supply Homebased Sage accountancy training. Learning is done at home with the sent course materials, which include a 60day trial version of the sage software. course manuals and a floppy disk to submit all completed work back to ourselves for marking. Technical and Tutor support is available 5 days a week during office hours. If a client fails to reach the required standard a free re-sit will be allowed provided it falls within the 60day point of sale. Each level of sage training takes on average 8-10 hrs to learn. Courses are listed as follows.*Sage Line 50 (3 levels)£280*Sage Payroll (2 levels)*Sage Instant Accounts 1 (level)*Sage Instant Payroll (2 levels)*all courses dispatched within 5 days of payment with the client receiveing a competence certificate if successful with their training.*Also over 1000 other courses can be found by using the links found on website.*
▶ Sage Training Solutions, 183 Bosworth Drive, Chelmsley Wood, Birmingham, B37 5BT Tel: 01642 519507 E-mail: Info@sage-training-solutions.co.uk *We supply Homebased Sage accountancy training. Learning is done at home with the sent course materials, which include a 60day trial version of the sage software. course manuals and a floppy disk to submit all completed work back to ourselves for marking. Technical and Tutor support is available 5 days a week during office hours. If a client fails to reach the required standard a free re-sit will be allowed provided it falls within the 60day point of sale. Each level of sage training takes on average 8-10 hrs to learn. Courses are listed as follows.*Sage Line 50 (3 levels)£280*Sage Payroll (2 levels)*Sage Instant Accounts 1 (level)*Sage Instant Payroll (2 levels)*all courses dispatched within 5 days of payment with the client receiveing a competence certificate if successful with their training.*Also over 1000 other courses can be found by using the links found on website.*
Sagitech Designs Ltd, 120 Wolmer Gdns, Edgware, Middx, HA8 8QE Tel: (020) 8958 5747 *Gate automators & manufrs*
Sagittarian Embroidery, 27 Durham Road, Sacriston, Durham, DH7 6LN Tel: 0191-371 9371 Fax: 0191-371 2288 E-mail: sagittarianemb@clara.co.uk *Industrial & sport embroidered badge manufrs*
▶ Sagittarius Removals, 17 Darcy Close, Cheshunt, Waltham Cross, Hertfordshire, EN8 8UQ Tel: (020) 8372 2310 Fax: (01992) 419326 E-mail: Info@sagittariusexpress.com *Household removal, storage, office moves and shipping.*
Sahara Presentation Systems P.L.C., Williams House, Hailey Road, Erith, Kent, DA18 4AA Tel: (020) 8319 7777 Fax: (020) 8319 7775 E-mail: jsa@sahara-products.com *Manufacturer & distributor of audio visual & office equipment, including interactive whiteboards, projectors, plasma monitors, LCD TV's, screen with Moby-Go, CleverBoard, CleverTouch, CleverPad & TwinTrack*
Sahara Publications Ltd, 38 Greyhound Road, London, W6 8NX Tel: (020) 7610 1387 Fax: (020) 7610 0078 E-mail: sahara@btconnect.com *General publications*
Saharan Trading, 6 Blackburn Road, Rotherham, South Yorkshire, S61 2DR Tel: (01709) 557711 Fax: (01709) 557700 E-mail: info@saharantrading.co.uk *Scissor & surgical instrument manufrs*
Saharastorm, 25 Charles Avenue, Harrogate, North Yorkshire, HG1 4PE Tel: (01423) 552867 *Designer clothing on-line retailer selling top labels from top designers for Men, Women,Kids and accessories*
Sai Pac UK Ltd, Poly House, 88 Park Road, Ilford, Essex, IG1 1SF Tel: (020) 8553 4050 Fax: (020) 8553 5151 *Polythene packaging distributors*
▶ Saic Ltd, 5 Redwood Place, East Kilbride, Glasgow, G74 5PB Tel: (01355) 845000 Fax: (01355) 845001 *IT support service*
Saic Ltd, Berkshire House, Queen Street, Maidenhead, Berkshire, SL6 1NF Tel: (01628) 686100 Fax: (01628) 686200 *IT outsourcing & research*
Saic (UK) Ltd, 120 New Cavendish Street, London, W1W 6XX Tel: (020) 7533 3000 Fax: (020) 7533 3001 *IT outsources*
Saica Packaging UK Ltd, Road Three, Winsford Industrial Estate, Winsford, Cheshire, CW7 3RJ Tel: (01606) 562700 Fax: (01606) 562762 E-mail: reception@saica-packaging.co.uk *Corrugated board box manufacturers, bespoke packaging.*
Sail Loft, Port Edgar Marina, Port Edgar, South Queensferry, West Lothian, EH30 9SQ Tel: 0131-331 4949 Fax: 0131-331 4848 E-mail: info@sail-loft.co.uk *Sail care repair spray hoods & canvas manufacturers interior exterior fabrics*
Sail Register, 4 Yarborough Court, Ulceby, South Humberside, DN39 6RZ Tel: (01469) 589444 *Sail & cover manufrs*
Sail Style, 2 St. Marys Road, Unit 6, Hayling Island, Hampshire, PO11 9BY Tel: (023) 9246 3720 Fax: (023) 9246 6451 E-mail: info@sailstyle.co.uk *Sail manufrs*
▶ Sailcats, 2 Furzebeam Row, Torrington, Devon, EX38 8DH Tel: (01805) 624489 E-mail: info@sailcats.co.uk *Providers of day sails, sailing adventures & experiences*

Sailes Marketing Ltd, 15 Aintree Road, Keytec 7 Business Park, Pershore, Worcestershire, WR10 2JN Tel: (01386) 554210 Fax: (01386) 552461 E-mail: sales@sailesmarketing.com *Equipment manufrs*

Sails & Canvas, 10 The Quay, The Strand, Topsham, Exeter, EX3 0JB Tel: (01392) 877527 Fax: (01392) 876258 *Sail makers*

▶ Sainsbury Heating Ltd, Unit 11 Cambrian Court Ferryboat Close, Morriston Enterprise Park, Swansea Enterprise Park, Swansea, SA6 8PZ Tel: (01792) 793400 Fax: (01792) 793600

Sainsburys Supermarkets Ltd, Faraday Avenue, Hams Hall Distribution Park, Coleshill, Birmingham, B46 1AL Tel: (01675) 435800 *Distribution services* Also at: Aintree

St Albans Chamber Of Commerce, 3 Soothouse Spring, St. Albans, Hertfordshire, AL3 6PF Tel: (01727) 863054 Fax: (01727) 851200 E-mail: office@stalbans-chamber.co.uk *Chambers of commerce*

St. Albans Glass, 19A Elstow Road, Bedford, MK42 9NU Tel: (01727) 830325 Fax: (01582) 480980 *Glazing contractors*

The ST. Albans Meter Company Ltd, Lombardy House, The Ridgeway, St. Albans, Hertfordshire, AL4 9AL Tel: (01727) 899911 Fax: (01727) 899922 E-mail: stalbansmeters@ukgateway.net *Meters, panel suppliers*

St Andrews & Blackfriars Halls, St. Andrews & Blackfriars Hall, St. Andrews Hall Plain, Norwich, NR3 1AU Tel: (01603) 628477 Fax: (01603) 762182 E-mail: kingorders@norwich.gov.uk *Conference centres*

St Andrews Fire Equipment, 3 St Williams Way, Norwich, NR7 0AH Tel: (01603) 431122 Fax: (01603) 448640 *Fire protection equipment suppliers*

St Andrews Health Foods, 123 Market Street, St. Andrews, Fife, KY16 9PE Tel: (01334) 478887 Fax: (01334) 478887 *Health food merchants*

▶ St. Andrews House Rental, 10 Pipeland Farm, St. Andrews, Fife, KY16 8NL Tel: (01334) 473360 E-mail: webmaster@sKooF.co.uk *Golf Open 2005 This exclusive property rental is a light and airy four bedroom steadings villa situated on farmland on the edge of St Andrews.*

▶ St Annes, 26 St. Annes Road West, Lytham St. Annes, Lancashire, FY8 1RF Tel: (01253) 727575 Fax: (01253) 727575 E-mail: keycutters@blueyonder.co.uk *Shoe repairs, key cutting services & locksmiths*

St. Ann's Building Supplies, Bentalls Close, Sutton Road, Southend-On-Sea, SS2 5PT Tel: (01702) 463363 Fax: (01702) 469043 *Glass, tiles, bathrooms, kitchens & building materials suppliers*

▶ St Austell Couriers, 69 Thornpark Road, St. Austell, Cornwall, PL25 4DP Tel: (07876) 507355 *Sameday Courier company with full courier insurance and goods in transit upto 25k per load. For full details you can view our web site.*

▶ St Barnabas Press, Coldhams Road, Cambridge, CB1 3EW Tel: (01223) 413792 *Fine art printers*

St. Bernard Composites Ltd, 21 Invinsible Road, Farnborough, Hampshire, GU14 7QU Tel: (01252) 304000 Fax: (01252) 304001 E-mail: info@stbernard.co.uk *Composites aerospace manufrs*

▶ St Creative Ltd, 102 Frimley House 5 The Parade, Frimley, Frimley, Camberley, Surrey, GU16 7HY Tel: (0845) 3301920 Fax: (01276) 507157 E-mail: sales@st-creative.co.uk *Graphic designers & copywriters*

St Cross Electronics Ltd, 14 Mount Pleasant Industrial Estate, Mount Pleasant Road, Southampton, SO14 0SP Tel: (023) 8022 7636 Fax: (023) 8033 1769 E-mail: sales@st-cross-electronics.co.uk *Cable assemblies*

St Davids Assemblies Co. Ltd, Glasfryn Road, St. Davids, Haverfordwest, Dyfed, SA62 6RY Tel: (01437) 720555 Fax: (01437) 725500 E-mail: sales@stdavidsassemblies.co.uk *Light assembly & electronic component manufrs*

Saint Engineering Ltd, 73 Buckingham Avenue, Slough, SL1 4PN Tel: (01753) 578433 Fax: (01753) 822559 E-mail: sales@saint-eng.co.uk *Precision engineers*

St George Glass Co., 108 Halliwell Road, Bolton, BL1 3QN Tel: (01204) 383811 Fax: (01204) 394758 *Glass merchants & glazing contractors* Also at: Leigh

St George's Bakery, Worcester Road, Corse, Gloucester, GL19 3BZ Tel: (01452) 700234 Fax: (01452) 700562 *Wholesale bakery*

▶ St George's Press, 3 St. Georges Industrial Estate, White Hart Lane, London, N22 5QL Tel: (020) 8501 4411 Fax: (020) 8881 6658

St. Georges Woollen Mills Ltd, Glen Road, Laxey, Isle Of Man, IM4 7AR Tel: (01624) 861395 *Woollen manufacturers & retailers*

Saint Gobain Abrasives Ltd, Millbrook Close, Chandler's Ford, Eastleigh, Hampshire, SO53 4BZ Tel: (023) 8025 4777 Fax: (023) 8025 5930 E-mail: terry.hughes@saint-gobain.com *Tool manufrs*

Saint Gobain Bti UK Ltd, Unit 4-5 Walworth Industrial Estate, Crown Way, Andover, Hampshire, SP10 5LU Tel: (01264) 333400 Fax: (01264) 359610 E-mail: sales.uk.sgtfc@saint-gobain.com *Glass fibre reinforcement fabrics*

Saint Gobain Building Distribution Ltd, Merchant House, Binley Business Park, Harry Weston Road, Coventry, CV3 2TT Tel: (024) 7643 8400 Fax: (024) 7643 8505 E-mail: shelley.knowles@jewson.co.uk *Building distributors*

St. Gobain Building Products, Unit 18 Woodford Trading Estate, Southend Road, Woodford Green, Essex, IG8 8HF Tel: (020) 8550 8899 Fax: (020) 8550 3918 *Plastic laminate distributors* Also at: Bristol, Coventry, Darlington, Inverkething, Sevenoaks & Southampton

Saint Gobain Industrial Ceramics Ltd, Mill Lane, Rainford, St. Helens, Merseyside, WA11 8LP Tel: (01744) 882941 Fax: (01744) 883514 E-mail: andrew.smith.rainford@saint-gobain.com Principal Export Areas: Worldwide *Refractory,*

continued

ceramics, silicon carbide products & high temperature

Saint Gobain Performance Plastics, 13 Earlstrees Road, Earlstrees Industrial Estate, Corby, Northamptonshire, NN17 4AZ Tel: (01536) 276000 Fax: (01536) 203427 E-mail: pplcorbyuk@aol.com *Adhesive mounting tape*

Saint Gobain Solaglas Ltd, Catkin Way, Greenfields Industrial Estate, Bishop Auckland, County Durham, DL14 9TF Tel: (01388) 603667 Fax: (01388) 600594 E-mail: solaglas.gpd@saint-gobain-glass.com *glass processing, distribution, & glazing contractors*

Saint Gobain Technical Fabrics UK Ltd, 15-19 Pit Hey Place, Skelmersdale, Lancashire, WN8 9PS Tel: (01695) 723946 Fax: (01695) 723947 *Manufacturers of glass fibre fabrics & tapes*

▶ St Helens Electrical Supplies Ltd, 17 Peasley Cross Lane, St. Helens, Merseyside, WA9 3BG Tel: (01744) 613333 Fax: (01744) 613216

St. Ives Direct (Edenbridge) Ltd, Enterprise Way, Edenbridge, Kent, TN8 6HF Tel: (01732) 862788 Fax: (01732) 868868 E-mail: kevin.johnson@stivesdirect.com *Lithographic printers & mail order services*

▶ St Ives Direct Group Ltd, The Industrial Estate, Enterprise Way, Edenbridge, Kent, TN8 6HF Tel: (01732) 862788

St Ives Direct Romford Ltd, St Ives House, Faringdon Avenue, Romford, RM3 8XL Tel: (01708) 345599 Fax: (01708) 346025 *Lithographic printers* Also at: London SE1

St James Consultancy, 35 Thurloe Street, London, SW7 2LQ Tel: (020) 7589 1866 Fax: (020) 7589 8142 E-mail: recruit@stjc.co.uk *Recruitment & personnel management*

St James Foods Ltd, 67 Milmead Industrial Centre, Mill Mead Road, London, N17 9QU Tel: (020) 8808 3000 Fax: (020) 8808 3355 E-mail: info@theospastry.com *Manufacturers of fillo, samosa, strudel & kataifi pastry*

▶ St James Litho Ltd, 21 Wates Way, Mitcham, Surrey, CR4 4HR Tel: (020) 8640 9438 Fax: (020) 8685 1719

St James Lovell Partnership, Southbank House, Black Prince Road, London, SE1 7SJ Tel: (020) 7793 2330 Fax: (020) 7793 2335 E-mail: mail@stjameslovell.com *Civil & structural consulting engineers*

St. James Place, St. James Place House, Dollar Street, Cirencester, Gloucestershire, GL7 2AQ Tel: (01285) 640302 Fax: (01285) 640436 *Life assurance, pensions, investment*

St. James Property Development Ltd, 180 Brompton Road, London, SW3 1HQ Tel: (020) 7565 8000 Fax: (020) 7565 8008 *Business development consultants*

St. John Supplies, PO Box 707A, London, EC1V 7NE Tel: (020) 7278 7888 Fax: (020) 7278 0314 E-mail: customer-services@stjohnsupplies.co.uk *Emergency care & first aid suppliers*

St John's Engineering Ltd, Station Road, Auchtermuchty, Cupar, Fife, KY14 7DP Tel: (01337) 828980 Fax: (01337) 827032 E-mail: stj-eng@btconnect.com *Precision engineers* Also at: Auchtermuchty

St Josephs Workshop Ltd, 190-194 Bag Lane, Atherton, Manchester, M46 0JZ Tel: (01942) 883210 Fax: (01942) 878087 *Altar bread manufrs*

St Margarets, 11 Tower View, Kings Hill, West Malling, Kent, ME19 4UY Tel: (01732) 223820 Fax: (01732) 223821 E-mail: yachts@stminsurance.co.uk *Marine insurance brokers*

St Margarets Mill Retreats, St. Margarets Mill, Caister Road, Acle, Norwich, NR13 3AX Tel: (01493) 752288 *Cleaning materials suppliers*

St Martins Group Ltd, Shackleton House, 4 Battlebridge Lane, London, SE1 2HX Tel: (020) 7940 7700 Fax: (020) 7940 7744 E-mail: mail@samaprop.co.uk *Property company*

St. Martin's Marketing, 162 Langton Way, London, SE3 7JR Tel: (020) 8858 0577 Fax: (020) 8858 3991 *Advertising display manufrs*

▶ St Mary's Cathedral Workshop Ltd, 28 Manor Place, Edinburgh, EH3 7EB Tel: 0131-220 2227

St Micro Electronics Ltd, Planer House, Parkway, Marlow, Buckinghamshire, SL7 1YL Tel: (01628) 890800 Fax: (01628) 890391 *Semi-conductor manufrs*

St Microelectronics, 1000 Aztec West, Almondsbury, Bristol, BS32 4SQ Tel: (01454) 616616 Fax: (01454) 617910 E-mail: postmaster@st.com Principal Export Areas: Worldwide *Integrated circuit (MOS) (to specification) & semiconductor manufacturers & microprocessor chip*

St. Pauls Specialist Services, Suite 1 London Underwriting Centre, 3 Minster Court, Mincing Lane, London, EC3R 7YJ Tel: (020) 7617 5959 Fax: (020) 7617 5970 E-mail: info@unionamerica.co.uk *Property reinsurance*

▶ St Peters Community Partnership, Richmond Suite, Portland House, Katherine Street, Ashton-Under-Lyne, Lancashire, OL6 7BS Tel: 0161-343 7560 Fax: 0161-343 7560 *Computer trainers*

St Philips Litho, Unit 2, Minto Road Industrial Centre, Bristol, BS2 9YB Tel: 0117-955 4473 Fax: 0117-955 4473 *Lithographic trade printers*

St Regis Paper Co. Ltd, Higher Kings Mill, Cullompton, Devon, EX15 1QJ Tel: (01884) 836300 Fax: (01884) 836333 E-mail: sales@stregis.co.uk *Paper manufrs*

St Turier, Unit 7 Block 5 Shenstone Trading Estate, Bromsgrove Road, Halesowen, West Midlands, B63 3XB Tel: 0121-501 6880 Fax: 0121-501 6881 E-mail: sales@turierscales.co.uk *Weighing machine manufrs* Also at: Halesowen

St Vincents Insulation Ltd, 19 St Vincents Road, Dartford, DA1 1XF Tel: (01322) 225174 Fax: (01322) 221474 E-mail: sales@stvincents.co.uk *Packaging material manufrs*

▶ Saintel (UK) Ltd, Floor One, Meadowside, Lower Road, Cookham, Maidenhead, Berkshire, SL6 9HF Tel: (01628) 523666 Fax: (0870) 1315214 E-mail: saintel@dial.pipex.com *Microelectronics manufacturing equipment*

Saint-Gobain Abrasives Ltd, Albert Drive, Burgess Hill, West Sussex, RH15 9TN Tel: (01444) 259400 Fax: (01444) 232407 E-mail: sales@nimbus-diamond.co.uk *Blade manufrs*

Saint-Gobain Abrasives, Doxey Road, Stafford, ST16 1EA Tel: (01785) 223281 Fax: (01785) 213487 E-mail: sales.gloucester.uk@saint-gobain.com Principal Export Areas: Worldwide *Abrasive services*

▶ Saint-Gobain Quartz P.L.C, PO Box 6, Wallsend, Tyne & Wear, NE28 6DG Tel: 0191-262 5311 Fax: 0191-263 8040 E-mail: quartz.sales@saint-gobain.com Principal Export Areas: Worldwide *Saint-Gobain Quartz manufactures a range of Fused Quartz and Silica products for applications including: Fibre Optics, Optical, Semiconductor, Heating, Lighting, Laboratory, Foundry, Thermal Processing, etc. **Products include Ingots, Optical Components, Plate, Tubing, Rod, Fabricated Parts, Semiconductor Diffusion Components, Crucibles, Trays, Powders, Quartzel® fibres and textile products, Micaver® insulators, piezoceramics, etc.**

Saint-Gobain Solaglas, 11 Bridle Way, Bootle, Merseyside, L30 4UA Tel: (0151) 525 7241 Fax: (0151) 523 8212 *Glass processing services* Also at: Branches throughout the U.K.

Saipem Ltd, Saipem House, Station Road, Motspur Park, New Malden, Surrey, KT3 6JJ Tel: (020) 8296 5000 Fax: (020) 8296 5100 *Offshore pipeline contractors*

Saira Of Manchester Ltd, 4 Addington Street, Manchester, M4 5FQ Tel: 0161-839 9839 Fax: 0161-839 9839 *Clothing manufrs*

Sajemay Ltd, PO Box 528, York, YO24 2YH Tel: (01904) 778704 Fax: (01904) 778705 *Decorative wood veneer merchants*

▶ Säkerhetspartner UK Ltd, Noel House, West Lexham, King's Lynn, Norfolk, PE32 2QN Tel: (01760) 755112 Fax: (01760) 755112 E-mail: info@emergency-planning.net *Emergency planning software providers*

Saklok, Roughway Mill, Dunks Green, Tonbridge, Kent, TN11 9SG Tel: (01732) 810813 Fax: (01732) 810838 E-mail: roughway@btconnect.com *Specialised packaging & large format trade sheeting*

Sal Abrasives Technologies, 7 Drumhead Road, Chorley North Industrial Park, Chorley, Lancashire, PR6 7BX Tel: (01257) 271914 Fax: (01257) 260702 E-mail: sales@salgroup.co.uk *Abrasive product distributors*

Sal Europe Ltd, Houghton Road, Grantham, Lincolnshire, NG31 6JE Tel: (01476) 515550 Fax: (01476) 515551 E-mail: general@sal-europe.com *Autoclave & steriliser manufrs*

SAL Supplies, 40 Regent Quay, Aberdeen, AB11 5BE Tel: (01224) 574405 Fax: (01224) 212444 *EPOS cash registers suppliers*

Sala Consultancy, Forum House, Stirling Road, Chichester, West Sussex, PO19 7DN Tel: (01243) 775757 Fax: (01243) 787110 E-mail: info@ismc.co.uk *Computer consultants*

▶ Saladworks, Oak Spinney Park, Ratby Road, Leicester Forest East, Leicester, LE3 3JZ Tel: 0116-232 4300 Fax: 0116-232 4301 *Food m*

Salamander, 2-10 St. Johns Street, Bedford, MK42 0DH Tel: (0845) 3779160 Fax: (0845) 3779180 E-mail: info@salamanderpumps.co.uk *Power shower pumps & accessories*

Salamander (Engineering) Ltd, The Heath Business & Technical Park, Runcorn, Cheshire, WA7 4QX Tel: (01928) 583280 Fax: (01928) 562890 E-mail: enquiries@salamander-engineering.co.uk *Heating equipment manufacturers & water management*

The Salamander Organisation Ltd, 5 Innovation Close, York Science Park, York, YO10 5ZF Tel: (0870) 1611700 Fax: (0870) 1611701 E-mail: matthew.bosson@tsorg.com *Business transformation software & consultants*

Salamander Walking Ltd, Langley Drive, Birmingham, B35 7AD Tel: 0121-747 2603 Fax: 0121-748 4205 *Printing consultants*

Salamis International Ltd, 3 Greenhole Place, Bridge of Don Industrial Estat, Aberdeen, AB23 8EU Tel: (01224) 246001 Fax: (01224) 246100 *Insulation & scaffolding contractors & fabric maintainers services* Also at: Lowestoft

Salco, 17 Cutlers Road, South Woodham Ferrers, Chelmsford, CM3 5WA Tel: (0560) 0495051 Fax: (01245) 325208 E-mail: salcoengineering@btconnect.com *Tool makers/pressings & precision engineers*

▶ Salcombe 97 Ltd, Shadycombe Road, Salcombe, Devon, TQ8 8DX Tel: (01548) 843228

Sale Appliances Ltd, 343 Victoria Avenue, Southend-on-Sea, SS2 6NH Tel: (01702) 390845 Fax: (01702) 390845 E-mail: sales@saleappliances.co.uk *Domestic appliance sales*

Cecil Sale, The Mill, Roe Green, Sandon, Buntingford, Hertfordshire, SG9 0QQ Tel: (01763) 288206 Fax: (01763) 288422 E-mail: info@salesofsandon.co.uk *Agricultural merchants*

sale echo, Unit 30 Wolverton Mill East, Mill Park, High Park Drive Wolverton, Milton Keynes, MK12 5TT Tel: (0845) 124 1700 Fax: (01908) 441750 E-mail: enquires@echoltd.com Sales Contact: N Lamb *Express carriers*

H.B. Sale Ltd, 390 Summer Lane, Birmingham, B19 3PN Tel: 0121-236 5661 Fax: 0121-233 3817 *Commemorative medallions*

J.F. Sale Ltd, Newhouse Farm, Tompkin Lane, Stanley, Stoke-On-Trent, ST9 9LY Tel: (01782) 503206 Fax: (01782) 503206 *Heating & ventilation engineers*

Sale Print & Design, 5 Georges Road, Sale, Cheshire, M33 3NJ Tel: 0161-962 3365 *Commercial printers & graphic designers*

▶ Salem Automation Ltd, Sycamore Road, Eastwood Trading Estate, Rotherham, South Yorkshire, S65 1EN Tel: (01709) 538200 Fax: (01709) 376903 E-mail: sales@salemautomation.net *System integration services*

Salem Tube International Ltd, Unit 8, Regents Drive, Low Prudhoe Industrial Estate, Prudhoe, Northumberland, NE42 6PX Tel: (01661) 839240 Fax: (01661) 839248 E-mail: salem@btinternet.com *Stainless steel tube distributors*

▶ Sales 101, 7 Accommodation Road, London, NW11 8ED Tel: (020) 8209 3900 E-mail: info@sales101.co.uk *Online training courses*

Sales Force GB Ltd, 1 Haven Green, Ealing, London, W5 2UU Tel: (020) 8998 9646 Fax: (020) 8248 7796 E-mail: g.gedge@btconnect.com *Generalised sales recruitment agents*

M.W. Sales Ltd, 33-37 The Oval, Hackney Road, London, E2 0AS Tel: (020) 7739 5185 Fax: (020) 7729 3138 *Timber merchants & moulding manufrs*

▶ Sales Network (UK) Ltd, Globe Centre, Penistone Road, Sheffield, S6 3AE Tel: (0870) 4441074 Fax: E-mail: glenn@salesnetworkuk.co.uk *IT, software & telecoms market place sales recruitment specialists*

Sales Plus, PO Box 50, Knebworth, Hertfordshire, SG3 6UE Tel: (01438) 811657 Fax: (01438) 813320 E-mail: smedalsj@aol.com *Sales & marketing consultancy*

Sales Recruitment Services, 59 St. Peters Street, Bedford, MK40 2PR Tel: (01234) 270100 Fax: (01234) 270400 E-mail: salesrecruitmentservices@btinternet.com *Employment agency for construction industry*

Sales Stream, Independence House, Adelaide Street, Heywood, Lancashire, OL10 4HF Tel: (01706) 647462 Fax: (01706) 347956 E-mail: n.elliott@btclick.com *Computer chaining services*

▶ Sales Training UK, Davies Avenue, Leeds, LS8 1JZ Tel: (0870) 1998962 Fax: (0709) 2037133 E-mail: john.pykett@ntlworld.com *Specialist Sales and Sales Management Training throughout UK and Europe*

▶ SalesCentric, Worting House, Church Lane, Worting, Basingstoke, Hampshire, RG23 8PX Tel: (01256) 345575 Fax: (01256) 345553 *Computer software manufrs*

▶ SalesFirst Limited, Regency House, 6-7 Elwick Road, Ashford, Kent, TN23 1PD Tel: 01233 638888 E-mail: enquiries@salesfirst.co.uk *Sales outsourcing & telemarketing services*

Salesmark Ltd, Howard Road, Eaton Socon, St. Neots, Cambridgeshire, PE19 8ET Tel: (01480) 212888 Fax: (01480) 218585 E-mail: sales@salesmark.co.uk *Salesmark are major stockists and distributors of Unilin Quick-Step Laminate Flooring 120 mile radius of Cambridge*

Salesnet Ltd, Sterling House, Teddington, Middlesex, TW11 8PB Tel: (020) 8410 3200 Fax: (020) 8410 3211 E-mail: info@salesnet.ltd.uk *Business to business telephone marketing*

▶ Salespage Technologies Ltd, Chord Business Park, London Road, Godmanchester, Huntingdon, Cambridgeshire, PE29 2NX Tel: (01480) 424400 Fax: (01480) 424401 *Suppliers of CRM applications*

▶ Salestarget.co.uk, Holden House, 57 Rathbone Place, London, W1T 1LD Tel: 020 7769 9200 Fax: 020 7769 9008 E-mail: info@salestarget.co.uk *Salestarget.co.uk is a specialist recruitment website for sales professionals from Totaljobs Group. Launched in June 2005, the site is already established as the UK's leading source of quality sales jobs from hundreds of well known employers. The site covers all sales industry sectors including FMCG, construction and engineering, financial services, pharmaceutical and medical, recruitment and IT sales. To search for your next sales job, or for direct access to professional sales people, visit us today at www.salestarget.co.uk.*

▶ Salestarget.co.uk, Holden House, 57 Rathbone Place, London, W1T 1JU Tel: (020) 7769 9147 Fax: (020) 7769 9205 E-mail: sales@salestarget.co.uk *Online recruitment for the job board website*

Salesvacancies.Com, Charter House, Unit 1 South Bourne Business Park, Eastbourne, East Sussex, BN22 8UY Tel: (01323) 739995 Fax: (01323) 721990 E-mail: sales@salesvacancies.com *Job site specialising in sales vacancies*

Salford Electronic Systems Ltd, 48 Glastonbury Drive, Poyton, Stockport, Cheshire, SK12 1EN Tel: (01625) 877949 E-mail: roy.lowey@btinternet.com *Electronic contract manufacturing & design*

Salford Engineering Ltd, Unit 9 Seaford Industrial Estate, Seaford Road, Salford, M6 6AQ Tel: 0161-737 7670 Fax: 0161-745 9224 *Precision machinists*

Salford Fire & Safety Co. Ltd, 11 Vestris Drive, Salford, M6 8EL Tel: 0161-789 5550 *Fire fighting equipment distributors*

Salice UK Ltd, Kingfisher Way, Hinchingbrooke Business Park, Huntingdon, Cambridgeshire, PE29 6FN Tel: (01480) 413831 Fax: (01480) 451489 E-mail: info.salice@saliceuk.co.uk *Concealed hinge distributors*

▶ David Salisbury Joinery Ltd, Bennett Road, Isleport Business Park, Highbridge, Somerset, TA9 4PW Tel: (01278) 764400 Fax: (01278) 764422 E-mail: sales@davidsalisbury.com *Manufacture hardwood conservatories*

Salisbury Investment Castings Ltd, Building D Dinton Business Park, Catherine Ford Road, Dinton, Salisbury, SP3 5HZ Tel: (01722) 716151 Fax: (01722) 716509 E-mail: mark@casting.uk.com *Metal castings precision manufrs*

Salisbury Joinery, 3 Brunel Rd, Salisbury, SP2 7PU Tel: (01722) 337040 Fax: (01722) 337077 *Joinery manufacturers & timber merchants*

▶ Salisbury Printing Co. Ltd, 71a Greencroft Street, Salisbury, SP1 1JF Tel: (01722) 413330 Fax: (01722) 413242 E-mail: mail@salisburyprinting.co.uk *High quality printed products & services*

Salisbury Switchgear Ltd, Warminster Road, South Newton Industrial Estate, Salisbury, SP2 0QW Tel: (01722) 744388 Fax: (01722) 742882 E-mail: j.robinson@salisburyswitchgear.co.uk *Sheet metal fabricators*

Salisbury & Wood Ltd, Old Coach Road, Tansley, Matlock, Derbyshire, DE4 5FY Tel: (01629) 582272 Fax: (01629) 583989 *Building suppliers*

The Salix Cricket Bat Company Ltd, Butlers Farm, Horseshoes Lane, Langley, Maidstone, Kent, ME17 3JY Tel: (01622) 863380 Fax: (01622) 863380 *Sporting goods manufrs*

Sallco Tools Ltd, 3-4 Baddesley Park Industrial Estate, Botley Road, North Baddesley, Southampton, SO52 9NW Tel: (023) 8073 7355 Fax: (023) 8073 8647 E-mail: sales@sallcotools.co.uk *Power & hand tool suppliers*

Sallis Healthcare Ltd, Waterford Street, Nottingham, NG6 0DH Tel: 0115-978 7841 Fax: 0115-942 2272 E-mail: info@sallis.co.uk *Surgical appliance manufrs*

▶ Sally, Harbour Deck, Princes Quay, Hull, HU1 2PQ Tel: (01482) 620044 *Hairdressing accessory suppliers*

Sally, 7 Clifton Street, Lincoln, LN5 8LQ Tel: (01522) 542656 Fax: 01522 568918 *Hair & beauty products distributor*

▶ Sally, 138 Peascod Street, Windsor, Berkshire, SL4 1DS Tel: (01753) 832414

Sally Bourne Interiors, 10 Middle Lane, London, N8 8PL Tel: (020) 8340 3333 Fax: (020) 8340 9333 *Home interior retailers*

▶ Sally Hair & Beauty Supplies Ltd, 1b Broadway, Accrington, Lancashire, BB5 1JZ Tel: (01254) 391002 E-mail: admin@sallybeauty.co.uk *Hair & beauty product suppliers*

▶ Sally Hair & Beauty Supplies Ltd, 57 Grosvenor Shopping Centre, Northfield, Birmingham, B31 2JU Tel: 0121-476 5110 *Hairdressing & beauty accessory distributors*

Sally Hair & Beauty Supplies, 17 Canal Road, Bradford, West Yorkshire, BD1 4AT Tel: (01274) 739261 *Hair & beauty wholesalers*

▶ Sally Hair & Beauty Supplies Ltd, Sherbourne Arcade, Lower Precinct, Coventry, CV1 1DN Tel: (024) 7622 7077 *Hairdressing accessory suppliers*

Sally Hair & Beauty Supplies, 90- 92 Kilmarnock Road, Glasgow, G41 3NN Tel: 0141-636 5096 *Hairdressing products distributors*

Sally Hair & Beauty Supplies Ltd, 79 High Street, Hounslow, TW3 1RB Tel: (020) 8572 2476 *Hair & beauty wholesalers*

Sally Hair & Beauty Supplies, 537 Cranbrook Road, Ilford, Essex, IG2 6HA Tel: (020) 8554 1210 *Hairdressers equipment & supplies*

Sally Hair & Beauty Supplies Ltd, Unit 5 Bellsland Grove, Kilmarnock, Ayrshire, KA1 4BD Tel: (01563) 543211 *Hair & beauty suppliers*

▶ Sally Hair & Beauty Supplies Ltd, 28 Nicholsons Walk, Maidenhead, Berkshire, SL6 1LB Tel: (01628) 777456 *Hairdressing equipment suppliers*

Sally Hair & Beauty Supplies Ltd, 86 Stockwell Gate, Mansfield, Nottinghamshire, NG18 5QD Tel: (01623) 624300 *Hair & beauty product distributors*

▶ Sally Hair & Beauty Supplies, Unit 1 The Rex Trade Centre, Maskew Avenue, Peterborough, PE1 1AP Tel: (01733) 891765 *Hairdressing salon equipment manufrs*

Sally Hair & Beauty Supplies Ltd, Unit 11 The Gateway Industrial Estate, Parkgate, Rotherham, South Yorkshire, S62 6JL Tel: (01709) 528848 *Hairdressing accessories suppliers*

▶ Sally Hair & Beauty Supplies Ltd, Lord Street, Southport, Merseyside, PR8 1NH Tel: (01704) 538679 *Hairdressing services*

Sally Hair & Beauty Supplies Ltd, 675 Eskdale Road, Winnersh, Wokingham, Berkshire, RG41 5TS Tel: 0118-944 3600 Fax: 0118-944 3601 *Hair & beauty wholesalers* Also at: Branches throughout the U.K.

▶ Sally Hair & Beauty Supplies Ltd, 1 Ebor Industrial Estate, Hallfield Road, York, YO31 7XD Tel: (01904) 425653 *Hair salon equipment suppliers*

Sally Treloar, Southview, Whiteoak Green, Hailey, Witney, Oxfordshire, OX29 9XP Tel: 01993 869119 E-mail: support@firstideas.co.uk

▶ Sally Tweddle Training, 6 Ure Bank Terrace, Ripon, North Yorkshire, HG4 1JG Tel: (01765) 608114 E-mail: sally@twed6.freeserve.co.uk *IT training. Application training on Microsoft Word, Excel, Access, Outlook and PowerPoint. One to one or group IT training to suit your individual needs, at your premises.*

Sallys, Harwood Street, Blackburn, BB1 3BD Tel: (01254) 680138 *Hair & beauty equipment distributor*

Sally's, 5 The Brickyard Excelsior Road, Excelsior Industrial Estate, Cardiff, CF14 3AT Tel: (029) 2052 0259 *Hair & beauty suppliers*

Sally's, 1-2 Hope Street, Crewe, CW2 7DR Tel: (01270) 589206 *Hair & beauty products suppliers*

Sally's, 7 Margram Business Centre, Horne Street, Halifax, West Yorkshire, HX1 5UA Tel: (01422) 323077 *Hair & beauty accessories supplier*

Sallys, 2 Abacus Park, Forth Avenue Industrial Estate, Kirkcaldy, Fife, KY2 5NZ Tel: (01592) 260438 Fax: (01592) 260438 *Hair & beauty suppliers*

Sally's, Royds Lane, Leeds, LS12 6AD Tel: 0113-279 8441 *Hair & beauty accessory suppliers*

Sallys Hair & Beauty, 18 Derby Street, Manchester, M8 8RY Tel: 0161-832 5199 *Hair & beauty products wholesaler*

Salmon Consultancy, Littlewood Farm, Cheddleton, Leek, Staffordshire, ST13 7LB Tel: (01538) 361010 Fax: (01538) 361011 E-mail: salmonconsult@btconnect.com *Gear & gearbox manufacturers, bronze casting supplies*

Kurt Salmon Associates Ltd, Bruce Court, 25a Hale Road, Altrincham, Cheshire, WA14 2EY Tel: 0161-925 2727 Fax: 0161-927 7135 E-mail: manchester@kurtsalmon.com *Management consultants*

Salmon Poachers Ltd, Unit 1-4 Salisbury Road Business Park, Salisbury Road, Pewsey, Wiltshire, SN9 5PZ Tel: (01672) 562786 Fax: (01672) 564286 E-mail: sales@salmonpoachers.co.uk *Fresh food processors*

The Salmons Leap, Salmon Leap, Cenarth, Newcastle Emlyn, Dyfed, SA38 9JP Tel: (01239) 711242 *Fishing tackle & gifts suppliers*

Salmor Group Ltd, 150 Valley Money Rd, Banbridge, Co. Down, BT32 4HW Tel: (028) 4066 2999 Fax: (028) 4066 2298 *Manhole frame & cover manufrs*

▶ Salmor Industries, 4 Silverwood Industrial Area, Silverwood Road, Lurgan, Craigavon, County Armagh, BT66 6LN Tel: (028) 3831 3100 Fax: (028) 3831 7770 E-mail: sales@salmor.co.uk *Manufacturer of fabricated steel access covers*

▶ The Salon, PO Box 45, Leeds, LS15 8HN Tel: 0113-260 7318 Fax: 0113-243 4534 E-mail: info@salonweardirect.co.uk *Clothing manufrs*

▶ Salon Active, Tong Hall, Tong, Bradford, West Yorkshire, BD4 0RR Tel: 0113-287 9228 Fax: 0113-287 9595 E-mail: rob@email4group.com *Supply salon equipment*

▶ Salon Beauty Supplies, Equipment House, Marshfield Bank, Crewe, CW2 8UY Tel: (01270) 848535 Fax: (01270) 848613

Salon Centre, Unit 5-6 Riverside, Bolton, BL1 8TU Tel: (01204) 386004 Fax: (01204) 361750 *Salon wholesalers*

▶ Salon Connect, The Rear of, 157 High Street, Barkingside, Ilford, Essex, IG6 2AJ Tel: (020) 8418 2490 Fax: (020) 8551 5719 E-mail: salon@salonconnect.co.uk *Hair & beauty services*

▶ Salon Focus Ltd, 33 Gibbfield Park Avenue, Gibbfield Park, Atherton, Manchester, M46 0SY Tel: (01942) 886000 Fax: (01942) 888588 *Hair cosmetics suppliers*

▶ Salon Master Hot Water Systems, Unit B5, Bulwell Business Centre, Sellers Wood Drive, Bulwell, Nottingham, NG6 8GN Tel: 0115-975 4500 Fax: 0115-976 0300 E-mail: enquiries@salonmaster.info *Hot water systems suppliers for hairdressing industry*

▶ Salon Revolution, Stilebrook Road, Olney, Buckinghamshire, MK46 5EA Tel: (01234) 714010 Fax: (0845) 0714568 E-mail: info@salonrevolution.com *Hair products suppliers*

▶ Salon Services Ltd, Unit 15 Links Business Centre, Raynham Road, Bishop's Stortford, Hertfordshire, CM23 5NZ Tel: (01279) 658116 *Beauty products distributors*

▶ Salon Services Ltd, Brunel Way, Blackpool & Fylde Industrial E, Blackpool, FY4 5ES Tel: (01253) 695440 Fax: (01253) 695260 *Hair & beauty suppliers*

▶ Salon Services Ltd, Unit 3 Bolton Road, Bury, Lancashire, BL8 2AQ Tel: 0161-705 2015 *Suppliers of hair & beauty products*

▶ Salon Services Ltd, Unit 8 Cleveland Trading Estate, Darlington, County Durham, DL1 2PB Tel: (01325) 363333

▶ Salon Services Ltd, 3 Block 2 Maxwelltown Industrial Estate, Glasgow Road, Dumfries, DG2 0NW Tel: (01387) 256600 Fax: (01387) 255714 *Distributors of hair & beauty products*

▶ Salon Services Ltd, Units P Pitreavie Business Park, Queensferry Road, Dunfermline, Fife, KY11 8PU Tel: (01383) 622205 Fax: (01383) 620598 E-mail: dunfermline@salon-services.com *Hair & beauty suppliers*

Salon Services Ltd, Units P Pitreavie Business Park, Queensferry Road, Dunfermline, Fife, KY11 8PU Tel: (01383) 622205 Fax: (01383) 620598 *Hairdresser equipment suppliers*

▶ Salon Services Ltd, 45 Broomhall Drive, Edinburgh, EH12 7QL Tel: 0131-334 8237 Fax: 0131-334 9105

▶ Salon Services Ltd, Unit 1-2 Earls Park North, Earlsway, Team Valley Trading Estate, Gateshead, Tyne & Wear, NE11 0RQ Tel: 0191-487 3060 Fax: 0191-487 1118 *Hair & beauty wholesalers*

Salon Services Ltd, 8 Darland Avenue, Gillingham, Kent, ME7 3AL Tel: (01634) 854003 Fax: (01634) 854003 *Hairdresser's equipment & suppliers service*

▶ Salon Services Ltd, 17 Bridge Street, Glasgow, G5 9JB Tel: 0141-429 2686 Fax: 0141-429 0776 *Hair & beauty products & equipment suppliers*

Salon Services Ltd, 54-62 Broomielaw, Glasgow, G1 4QN Tel: 0141-248 5522 Fax: 0141-248 1785 *Hairdressing products supplier*

▶ Salon Services Ltd, 6a Rivergate, Irvine, Ayrshire, KA12 8EH Tel: (01294) 312330 Fax: (01294) 322817

▶ Salon Services Ltd, 28 Nelson Street, Kilmarnock, Ayrshire, KA1 1BA Tel: (01563) 558600

▶ Salon Services Ltd, Unit 2 Lammas Road, London, E10 7QT Tel: (020) 8558 2195 Fax: (020) 8556 2147

▶ Salon Services Ltd, 8 The Path, London, SW19 3BL Tel: (020) 8540 0867 Fax: (020) 8542 5012 *Hair & beauty wholesalers*

▶ Salon Services Ltd, 1 Pennyburn Industrial Estate, Londonderry, BT48 0LU Tel: (028) 7126 4195 Fax: (028) 7126 5104 E-mail: londonderry@salon-services.com *Hair dressing products*

▶ Salon Services Ltd, Unit 12 Seedbed Centre, Langston Road, Loughton, Essex, IG10 3TQ Tel: (020) 8502 2009 Fax: (020) 8418 0387 *Hair & beauty suppliers*

Salon Services Ltd, 91 Garamonde Drive, Wymbush, Milton Keynes, MK8 8DD Tel: (01908) 561962

▶ Salon Services Ltd, Unit 15 North Hinksey Lane, Oxford, OX2 0LX Tel: (01865) 249222 Fax: (01865) 249233 *Wholesale hair & beauty products & equipment*

▶ Salon Services Ltd, Unit E5 Seedbed Centre, Davidson Way, Romford, RM7 0AZ Tel: (01708) 714251 Fax: (01708) 755406

Salon Services Ltd, Unit 2 Brunel Avenue, Salford, M5 4BE Tel: 0161-737 7100 Fax: 0161-737 1362 *Hairdressing supplies services*

▶ Salon Services, Bessemer Drive, Unit 18, Stevenage, Hertfordshire, SG1 2DL Tel: (01438) 316960 *Hair & beauty products & equipment wholesale*

▶ Salon Services (Ballymena), Salisbury House, 26 Queen Street, Ballymena, County Antrim, BT42 2BD Tel: (028) 2565 1050 *Hair & beauty suppliers*

▶ Salon Services (Crawley), 18 Stanley Centre Royal, Kelvin Way Manor, Manor Royal, Crawley, West Sussex, RH10 2SE Tel: (01293) 612-488 *Wholesalers of salon products*

▶ Salon Services (Dumbarton Rd), 84 Dumbarton Road, Partick, Glasgow, G11 6NX Tel: 0141-357 5047 Fax: 0141-357 4185 E-mail: dumbartonroad@salonservices.com *Hair & beauty products & equipment suppliers*

▶ Salon Services (Dundee City), Sassi, 20 Castle Street, Dundee, DD1 3AF Tel: (01382) 226068 *Hair & beauty products & equipment suppliers*

▶ Salon Services (East Kilbride), Unit 2, Calderwood Square, Pollock Lane, East Kilbride, Glasgow, G74 3BQ Tel: (01355) 226266 *Hair & beauty products & equipment suppliers*

▶ Salon Services Hair & Beauty Supplies Ltd, Evanton Drive, Thornliebank, Glasgow, G46 8HL Tel: 0141-621 3600 Fax: 0141-882 8527 E-mail: info@salon-services.com *Hair & beauty products & equipment suppliers*

▶ Salon Services Hair & Beauty Supplies Ltd, Evanton Drive, Thornliebank, Glasgow, G46 8HL Tel: 0141-621 3600 Fax: 0141-882 8527 E-mail: info@salon-services.com *Hair & beauty suppliers*

▶ Salon Services Hair & Beauty Supplies Ltd, 201-205 Crystal Palace Road, London, SE22 9EW Tel: (020) 8693 2818 *Hair & beauty wholesalers*

▶ Salon Services Hairdressing Supplies Ltd, 3 Falcon Road, Belfast, BT12 6RD Tel: (028) 9068 1921 Fax: (028) 9068 2701 E-mail: belfast@salon-services.com *Hair & beauty products & equipment store*

▶ Salon Services Hairdressing Supplies Ltd, Unit 1-3 Kingstown Broadway, Kingstown Industrial Estate, Carlisle, CA3 0HA Tel: (01228) 532107 Fax: (01228) 592632 E-mail: carlisle@salon-services.com *Salon service providers*

▶ Salon Services Hairdressing Supplies Ltd, 2 Bonnington Business Centre, 108 Jane Street, Edinburgh, EH6 5HG Tel: 0131-554 6644 Fax: 0131-553 3955

▶ Salon Services Hairdressing Supplies Ltd, 1 Empress Court, St. Andrew Street, Greenock, Renfrewshire, PA15 4RW Tel: (01475) 785700 Fax: (01475) 784443 *Hairdressing & beauty supplies*

▶ Salon Services Hairdressing Supplies Ltd, 6 Fullwood Industrial Estate, Hamilton, Lanarkshire, ML3 9AZ Tel: (01698) 891458 Fax: (01698) 457368

▶ Salon Services Hairdressing Supplies Ltd, 6 Penton Grove, London, N1 9JX Tel: (020) 7713 5000 *Hair & beauty products & equipment suppliers*

▶ Salon Services Hairdressing Supplies Ltd, 10 Newport Way, Middlesbrough, Cleveland, TS1 5JW Tel: (01642) 243608 Fax: (01642) 232842

▶ Salon Services Hairdressing Supplies Ltd, 5 Woking Business Park, Albert Drive, Woking, Surrey, GU21 5JY Tel: (01483) 740932 Fax: (01483) 723536 E-mail: woking@salon-services.com *Hair & beauty product suppliers*

▶ Salon Services Ireland Ltd, Belmore Mews, 8 New Street, Enniskillen, County Fermanagh, BT74 6AH Tel: (028) 6632 6675 Fax: (028) 6632 9382 *Suppliers of hair & beauty products to the salon industry*

▶ Salon Services(Thornliebank) Ltd, Unit 7, Thornliebank Industrial Estate, Thornliebank, Glasgow, G46 8HZ Tel: 0141-621 3640 *Wholesale, hair & beauty products*

Salon Success, Kiln Pit Hill, Consett, County Durham, DH8 9SL Tel: (01207) 255333 Fax: (01207) 255366 *Hair care products distributor*

Salon Supplies, Unit 7, Tuffley Park, Lower Tuffley Lane, Gloucester, GL2 5DP Tel: (01452) 383383 Fax: (01452) 413228 *Hairdressing wholesalers*

Saloneasy.Com, 3 Pye Road, Wirral, Merseyside, CH60 0DB Tel: 0151-342 6271 Fax: 0151-342 1130 E-mail: sales@saloneasy.com *Hairdressing & beauty product wholesalers*

▶ Salonjunky Ltd, 15-17 Baslow Road, Sheffield, S17 4DL Tel: (0845) 4085390 E-mail: sales@salonjunky.co.uk *salonjunky supply ghd hair straighteners, shampoos and conditioners. we also supply fudge, tigi and other major brands.*

Salop Design & Engineering Ltd, Brixton Way, Shrewsbury, SY1 3LB Tel: (01743) 450501 Fax: (01743) 440904 E-mail: info@salopdesign.co.uk *Pressings & light assemblies*

▶ Salop Haulage Ltd, Brixton Way, Shrewsbury, SY1 3LB Tel: (01743) 466518 Fax: (01743) 440904

Salop Sand & Gravel Supply Co. Ltd, Station Road, Admaston, Telford, Shropshire, TF5 0AN Tel: (01952) 254101 Fax: (01952) 223932 E-mail: info@gravel.co.uk *Aggregate producers*

Salopia Heraldic Plaques Ltd, Severn House Business Centre, 66 Spring Gardens, Shrewsbury, SY1 2TE Tel: (01743) 232700 Fax: (01743) 271275 *Heraldic shield makers*

Salt Engineering (Midlands) Ltd, Unit 4, Macefield Close, Aldermans Green, Coventry, CV2 2PJ Tel: (024) 7661 6595 Fax: (024) 7660 2165 E-mail: vaughan@saltengineering.co.uk *Special purpose machinery manufacturers & tooling gauging*

Frank Salt & Co. Ltd, Sandy Lane, Stourport-on-Severn, Worcestershire, DY13 9QG Tel: (01299) 827006 Fax: (01299) 877901 E-mail: sales@franksalt.co.uk *Machinery merchants & auctioneers*

Salt Healthcare, 7 Connel Court, Ardconnel Street, Inverness, IV2 3EY Tel: (01463) 241756 Fax: (01463) 710345 E-mail: sales@salt.com *Medical equipment suppliers*

J.T. Salt Engineering Ltd, Woodbank Street, Burslem, Stoke-On-Trent, ST6 3AZ Tel: (01782) 577901 Fax: (01782) 790260 *Steel handrails, steel fabrication & steel fencing*

Salt Northwest, 147 Brownedge Road, Lostock Hall, Preston, PR5 5AH Tel: (01772) 311441 Fax: (01772) 697307 E-mail: sales@saltnw.com *Printers of adhesive & non adhesive tapes*

Salt Riley Ltd, High Street, Tunstall, Stoke-On-Trent, ST6 5PD Tel: (01782) 837390 Fax: (01782) 577534 *Building contractors*

Salt & Sadler Ltd, 71 Rea Street, Birmingham, B5 6BB Tel: 0121-622 3887 Fax: 0121-666 6530 E-mail: saltsadler@btconnect.com *Manufacturers of titanium jigs*

Salt Separation Services, Grosvenor House, Gorrell Street, Rochdale, Lancashire, OL11 1AP Tel: (01706) 655522 Fax: (01706) 654475 E-mail: sss@saltsep.co.uk *Desalination & water treatment plant manufrs*

Salt & Son Ltd, Blatchford Road, Horsham, West Sussex, RH13 5QR Tel: (01403) 274197 Fax: (01403) 218933 E-mail: salts@salts.co.uk *Medical supplies*

Salt & Son Ltd, 15 Harlesden Road, London, NW10 2BY Tel: (020) 8451 3348 Fax: (020) 8830 0635 E-mail: info@salt.co.uk *Surgical equipment service & supply*

▶ Saltash Construction, 110-116 Ormside Street, London, SE15 1TF Tel: (020) 7277 5661 Fax: (020) 7277 5662

▶ Mark Salter Ltd, PO Box 61, Swanley, Kent, BR8 8YZ Tel: (0870) 2406694 E-mail: sales@marksalter.com *Mail order merchandise wholesalers*

▶ Salter Roofing, Ebford Mews, Ebford, Exeter, EX3 0PF Tel: (01392) 875727 Fax: (01392) 875727 E-mail: salterroofing@aol.com *Roofing services, replacement & repair of slated, tiled roofs, reconstruct flat roofs*

Salter Weigh-Tronix Ltd, Unit 1 Tilson Road, Roundthorn Industrial Estate, Manchester, M23 9GF Tel: (0870) 4420000 Fax: 0161-946 0228 *Scales & weighing equipment manufrs*

▶ Saltern Sail Co., Gasworks Lane, Norton, Yarmouth, Isle of Wight, PO41 0SE Tel: (01983) 760120 Fax: (01983) 760120 *Sail manufrs*

Salters Refrigeration, 152 Preston Road, Whittle-le-Woods, Chorley, Lancashire, PR6 7HE Tel: (01257) 234000 Fax: (01257) 234111 E-mail: price.fridgeltd@btconnect.com *Industrial air conditioning design, installation, refrigeration services*

▶ Saltire Facilities Management Ltd, Unit 3, Arbroath Business Centre, 31 Dens Road, Arbroath, Angus, DD11 1RS Tel: (01241) 430987

Saltire Graphics, Brook St Studios, 60 Brook Street, Glasgow, G40 2AB Tel: 0141-556 3722 Fax: 0141-554 1621 E-mail: info@saltiregraphics-print.com *Graphic designers, typesetters & printers*

▶ Saltire International Ltd, Lower Bathville, Armadale, Bathgate, West Lothian, EH48 2JS Tel: (01501) 735222

Salton Europe Ltd, Sisson Street, Failsworth, Manchester, M35 0HS Tel: 0161-947 3000 Fax: 0161-682 1708 *Domestic electric appliance manufrs*

Salts Healthcare Ltd, Unit 2 Richard Street, Birmingham, B7 4AA Tel: 0121-333 2000 Fax: 0121-359 0830 E-mail: salt@salts.co.uk *Medical products manufacturers & distributors*

Saltwell Signs (North East) Ltd, Princesway North, Team Valley Trading Estate, Gateshead, Tyne & Wear, NE11 0TU Tel: 0191-482 5555 Fax: 0191-491 0246 E-mail: sales@saltwellsigns.co.uk *Engravers & sign manufrs*

Salty Yacht Productions Ltd, Victoria Wharf, River Bank, Old Town Dock, Newport, Gwent, NP20 2BS Tel: (01633) 250652 Fax: (01633) 842267 E-mail: sales@saltyyachts.com *Architectural glass fibre moulders & glass fibre flat roofing manufrs*

Saluki Ltd, 7 Lewisher Road, Leicester, LE4 9LR Tel: 0116-276 3509 Fax: 0116-246 0265 E-mail: saluki.leicester@virgin.net *Precision engineers*

▶ Salute Health Foods, 2 Cheam Common Road, Worcester Park, Surrey, KT4 8RW Tel: (020) 8337 5959 Fax: (020) 8337 5959 *Health food & supplement manufrs*

▶ The Salvage Doctor, Rowhurst Forge, Oxshott Road, Leatherhead, Surrey, KT22 0EN Tel: (01372) 360 191 Fax: (01372) 360 171 E-mail: info@salvagedoctor.com

Salvage, Gordon Ltd, Power House, Embley Lane, West Wellow, Romsey, Hampshire, SO51 6DN Tel: (01794) 522196 Fax: (01794) 511429 E-mail: gsl.metalcraft@btconnect.com *Steel fabricators*

Salvatex Holdings Ltd, 1 St. Marks Road, St. James Industrial Estate, Corby, Northamptonshire, NN18 8AN Tel: (01536) 400002 Fax: (01536) 400169 Principal Export Areas: Asia Pacific & Africa *Textile recycling services*

Salvesen Consumer Logistics, Parkhouse Industrial Estate We, Newcastle, Staffordshire, ST5 7DU Tel: (01782) 566099 Fax: (01782) 561184 *Warehousing services*

Salvo Design & Print Ltd, 4 Berrington Road, Leamington Spa, Warwickshire, CV31 1NB Tel: (01926) 429111 Fax: (01926) 450461 *Design & print services*

▶ Salvoscreen Ltd, 18b Highdown Road, Leamington Spa, Warwickshire, CV31 1XT Tel: (01926) 421402 Fax: (01926) 451447

Salzer UK Ltd, 44 Edison Road, Aylesbury, Buckinghamshire, HP19 8TE Tel: (01296) 399992 Fax: (01296) 392229 E-mail: info@salzeruk.co.uk *Low voltage switchgear manufrs*

Sam Electronics UK, 18 Dales Industrial Estate, Peterhead, Aberdeenshire, AB42 3JF Tel: (01779) 478233 Fax: (01779) 475060 *Marine Electronics & radar*

▶ Sam Mcgowan, 26 Dunrobin Place, Edinburgh, EH3 5HZ Tel: 0131-343 6536 Fax: 0131-343 6086 *Garden and landscape design consultant based in Scotland*

▶ Sam Moreton & Sons, Burnt Heath Farm, Long Itchington Road, Offchurch, Leamington Spa, Warwickshire, CV33 9AX Tel: (01926) 632269 Fax: (01926) 632023 E-mail: sales@farmerstyre.co.uk *Agricultural vehicle tyres & wheel manufrs*

▶ Samac Fixings, Capitol Industrial Centre, Fulmar Way, Wickford, Essex, SS11 8YW Tel: (01268) 764488 Fax: (01268) 562085 *Pre-pack nails & screws for builders merchants*

Samac Overseas Ltd, Alperton House, Bridgewater Road, Wembley, Middlesex, HA0 1EH Tel: (020) 8903 5611 Fax: (020) 8900 2373 E-mail: samac@stemcor.com *Steel merchants*

Samar Precision Engineering, Central Way, Andover, Hampshire, SP10 5AN Tel: (01264) 334410 Fax: (01264) 335315 E-mail: samar_mail@btconnect.com *Press tool manufacturing & metal pressings*

Samark Signs Sign Design, 6 Rosshill Industrial Park, Sutton Road, Southend-on-Sea, SS2 5PZ Tel: (01702) 616655 E-mail: samarksigns@yahoo.co.uk *Sign & shop front production company*

Samarose Engineering Services Ltd, Unit 3 West Side, Ash Industrial Estate, Flex Meadow, Harlow, Essex, CM19 5TJ Tel: (01279) 421395 Fax: (01279) 421612 E-mail: ses@samarose.co.uk *Shrink wrapping machine manufrs*

▶ Samba Sports, Walton Street Work, Walton Street, Colne, Lancashire, BB8 0EN Tel: (01282) 860077 Fax: (01282) 860033 E-mail: info@sambasports.co.uk *Sports goods manufrs*

Sambell Engineering Ltd, Winston Avenue, Croft, Leicester, LE9 3GQ Tel: (01455) 283251 Fax: (01455) 283908 E-mail: post@atacama-audio.co.uk *Hi-fi furniture manufrs*

Samco Industrial Rewinds, Irthlingborough Road, Wellingborough, Northamptonshire, NN8 1RA Tel: (01933) 442597 Fax: (01933) 225965 E-mail: samcorewinds@aol.com *Motor rewind specialists services*

Samco Products Ltd, Tir Llwyd Enterprise Park, Kinmel Bay, Rhyl, Clwyd, LL18 5JZ Tel: (01745) 362500 Fax: (01745) 362501 E-mail: enquiries@samcoproducts.co.uk *Protective clothing distributors & industrial merchants*

Samco Silicone Products, 4 Secton Court, Veasey Close, Attleborough Fields Industrial Estate, Nuneaton, Warwickshire, CV11 6RT Tel: (024) 7664 1270 Fax: (024) 7634 4992 E-mail: sales@samco.co.uk Principal Export Areas: Worldwide *Manufacturers of silicone rubber molding & extrusions*

Same Day Company Services, 9 Perseverance Works, Kingsland Road, London, E2 8DD Tel: (020) 7613 8161 Fax: (020) 7613 8162 E-mail: jw@samedaycompany.co.uk *Company registration agents*

Same Deuts Fahr (U K) Ltd, Barby Lane, Barby, Rugby, Warwickshire, CV23 8TD Tel: (01788) 891892 Fax: (01788) 891387 E-mail: info@sdf.co.uk *Agricultural tractor distributors*

▶ Sameday Co., Unit 16, Focus 303 Business Centre, Focus Way, Andover, Hampshire, SP10 5NY Tel: (01264) 352352 Fax: (01264) 369001 *Courier services*

▶ Same-day Dispatch Services, International House, 226 Seven Sisters Road, London, N4 3GG Tel: 0845 226 2994 E-mail: admin@samedaydispatch.uk.com *Courier service*

Sameday Service, 22 Brynn Street, Widnes, Cheshire, WA8 6BT Tel: (07800) 774224

▶ Sameday UK, 8 Elstow Close, Eastcote, Ruislip, Middlesex, HA4 9RA Tel: (0800) 435740 Fax: (01925) 292447 E-mail: info@samedayuk.com *we specialise in urgent sameday deliveries, whether it be a document or a pallet we have large and small vans available 24/7 to make that delivery for you nationwide the sameday*

Samfreight Ltd, Bath Road, West Drayton, Middlesex, UB7 0DB Tel: (020) 8750 2300 Fax: (020) 8750 2301 E-mail: lee.george@samfreight.co.uk *Freight forwarders*

Samina Fashions, 75 Tweedale Street, Rochdale, Lancashire, OL11 3TZ Tel: (01706) 644459 Fax: (01706) 644459 *Clothing manufrs*

Frank Sammeroff Ltd, 131 Woodhead Road, Glasgow, G53 7NN Tel: 0141-881 5701 Fax: 0141-881 4919 E-mail: info@sammeroff.co.uk *Surgical dressings & first aid kit manufacturers & distributors*

Samms Electronics, Unit C 7 Sandy Business Park, Gosforth Close, Sandy, Bedfordshire, SG19 1RB Tel: (01767) 680049 Fax: (01767) 680073 E-mail: sales@samms-electronics.co.uk *Electronic sub contractors*

Samoa Ltd, Asturias House Barrs Fold Road, Wingates Industrial Estate, Westhoughton, Bolton, BL5 3XP Tel: (01942) 850600 Fax: (01204) 812160 E-mail: sales@samoa.ltd.uk *Lubricating equipment manufrs*

John Samonas & Sons Ltd, Princeton Mews, 167-169 London Road, Kingston upon Thames, Surrey, KT2 6PT Tel: (020) 8547 2244 Fax: (020) 8547 1949 E-mail: samonas@johnsamonas.com *Ship brokers & agents*

▶ Paul Sample Corporate Communications Ltd, 4A Wilton Business Centre, Kingsway, Wilton, Salisbury, SP2 0AH Tel: (01722) 744033 Fax: (01722) 744031 E-mail: paul@paulsample.com *Public relations, advertising & marketing consultancy*

Sampson Engineering Co., Stanley Road, Bradford, West Yorkshire, BD2 1AS Tel: (01274) 723299 *Industrial machinery engineers*

Sampson Gaskets Ltd, Unit 22, Leigh Road, Ramsgate, Kent, CT12 5EU Tel: (01843) 854800 Fax: (01843) 854801 E-mail: uksales@sampsons.co.uk *Seal & Gasket manufrs*

Sampson Industrial Doors, 6-8 Ise Valley Industrial Estate, Meadow Close, Wellingborough, Northamptonshire, NN8 4BH Tel: (01933) 274276 Fax: (01933) 442676 E-mail: enquiries@dovegroup.co.uk *Industrial doors & roller shutters specialists*

Sampson International Machine Tools, Keeley Lane, Wootton, Bedford, MK43 9HS Tel: (01234) 851200 Fax: (01234) 851123 E-mail: sales@sampsonmachinetools.com Principal Export Areas: Worldwide *Machine tool merchants & sheet metalworking dealers*

▶ Nick Sampson, Braunton Road, Ashford, Barnstaple, Devon, EX31 4AU Tel: (01271) 376701 Fax: (01271) 328128 *Commercial plant repairs*

Sampson & Partners Fencing, Aubrey Works, 15 Aubrey Ave, London Colney, St. Albans, Herts, AL2 1NE Tel: (01727) 822222 Fax: (01727) 826307 E-mail: primasampson@compuserve.com *YSecurity fencing & CCTV manufrs*

Sampson Souvenirs Ltd, 77 Vanguard Way, Shoeburyness, Southend-on-Sea, SS3 9QY Tel: (01702) 296488 Fax: (01702) 293437 E-mail: csh@sampsonsouvenirs.ltd.uk *Souvenir distributors & manufrs*

T.F. Sampson Ltd, Creeting Road, Stowmarket, Suffolk, IP14 5BA Tel: (01449) 613535 Fax: (01449) 678381 E-mail: sales@t-f-sampson.co.uk *Ironmongers & blind manufrs* Also at: Ipswich

Samputensili (UK) Ltd, Rotherham, S. Yorkshire, S66 8XX Tel: (01709) 703707 Fax: (01709) 703232 E-mail: postbox@geartec.demon.co.uk *Gear cutting tools*

Samraj Fashions, 5 Ireton Road, Leicester, LE4 9ER Tel: 0116-220 7576 E-mail: samrajfashion@hotmail.com *Garments manufrs*

▶ Samrana Ltd, 74 Hoe Street, Walthemstow, London, E17 4PG Tel: (0845) 2307707 Fax: (0845) 2307706 E-mail: info@samrana.co.uk *CD & DVD cases & plastic wallet manufrs*

▶ Sams Blinds, 846 Green Lanes, London, N21 2RT Tel: (020) 8360 2888 Fax: (020) 8372 0786 E-mail: samsblinds@msn.com *Made 2 Measure Blinds*

▶ Sam's Brother Co., 18 Cannon Hill Road, Birmingham, B12 9NN Tel: (07786) 476273 Fax: 0121-078 0987 E-mail: sam888uk@yahoo.co.uk *Retail jewellery, scarves, ladies scarves*

Sam's Fabrication, Unit 17 Morgan Way, Bowthorpe Employment Area, Norwich, NR5 9JJ Tel: (01603) 743252 Fax: (01603) 746927 E-mail: sales@samsfabrications.co.uk *Sheet metalwork engineers or fabricators, stainless steel, aluminium, mild steel, sheet metal, fabrications, for more information about our products or services please visit our website.*

Samsons Transformers, 24 37 Hamilton Road, Twickenham, TW2 6SN Tel: (020) 8893 4053 Fax: (020) 8893 4054 E-mail: enquiries@samsons.co.uk *Transformers & outdoor lighting manufrs*

▶ Samsung Semi Conductors Ltd, Unit 5, Phoenix House, Phoenix Business Park, Paisley, Renfrewshire, PA1 2BH Tel: 0141-840 2424

Samsung Telecom UK Ltd, Unit B2 Brookside Business Park, Greengate, Middleton, Manchester, M24 1GS Tel: 0161-655 1100 Fax: 0161-655 1166 E-mail: marketing@samsungbusiness.co.uk *Telecommunication systems*

▶ Samtec Computer Maintenance, 11 King Street, Luton, LU1 2DW Tel: (01582) 402705 E-mail: samtec@aol.com *Computer maintenance services*

Samtec Europe Ltd, 117 Deerdykes View, Cumbernauld, Glasgow, G68 9HN Tel: (01236) 739292 Fax: (01236) 727113 E-mail: sales@samtec.com *Printed circuit (flexi-rigid) manufrs*

Samuel Bruce, 1-7 Corstorphine Road, Edinburgh, EH12 6DD Tel: 0131-313 3760 Fax: 0131-313 3721 *Business furniture manufrs*

Samuel Fields & Co., Croft Street, Willenhall, West Midlands, WV13 2NU Tel: (01902) 607177 Fax: (01902) 606582 *Bolt & nut distributors*

Samuel Grant Midlands Ltd, 22 Willow Road, Castle Donington, Derby, DE74 2NP Tel: (01332) 858200 Fax: (01332) 858292 *Packaging distributors*

Samuel Groves & Co. Ltd, Norton Street, Birmingham, B18 5RQ Tel: 0121-554 2001 Fax: 0121-523 2924 E-mail: sales@samuelgroves.co.uk *Catering equipment manufrs*

Samuel James Outdoor Centre, 75-77 Gisburn Road, Barrowford, Barrowford, Nelson, Lancashire, BB9 6DX Tel: (07939) 502602 Fax: (01282) 613415 E-mail: broomsticktrav@aol.com *Outdoor clothing, ski wear, walking boots & equipment suppliers*

Samuel Lamont & Sons Ltd, Victoria Street, Lurgan, Craigavon, County Armagh, BT67 9DA Tel: (028) 3832 9066 Fax: (028) 3834 3095 E-mail: mail@samuellamont.co.uk *Textile household goods manufactures & suppliers*

Samuel Pitt, 61 Albion St, Birmingham, B1 3EA Tel: 0121-236 7737 Fax: 0121-236 7737 *Jewellery manufrs*

Samuel Vickers, 15 Lealand Way, Boston, Lincolnshire, PE21 7SW Tel: (01205) 363289 Fax: (01205) 363289 *Electric motor repair & sales services*

SAMUK Lift Trucks Ltd, Park Road, Toddington, Dunstable, Bedfordshire, LU5 6HJ Tel: (01525) 877700 Fax: (01525) 874555 E-mail: admin@samuk.net *Lift trucks import & distributors*

Samwell Tooling Ltd, 29 Benson Road, Nuffield Industrial Estate, Poole, Dorset, BH17 0GB Tel: 01202 687258 Fax: 01202 665698 E-mail: sales@samwell.co.uk *Samwell Tooling Ltd have been leading UK providers of quality tool and cutter grinding services since 1983. Based in Poole, Dorset, South West England, we cover nationwide, with customers all over the UK. Our exceptional standards can help you produce quality components on time every time,* *continued* *not just in the regrinding sector but also in our capability to manufacture bespoke tooling. Whether it is in HSS, HSCo, TC tipped or solid carbide our expert staff produce special tooling to suit all your machining needs. With our Cyber grinding software complex cutters can be produced with ease where simulation of all grinding processes ensures correct form and geometry before machining takes place. This combined this with auto loading and on machine wheel dressing results in valuable savings in time and money, helping us to remain as competitive. We also modify customers own cutters and provide a full regrind service for all kinds of rotary and flat tooling, including horizontal milling cutters.*

San Electroheat, PO Box 259, Hereford, HR1 9AU Tel: (01432) 851999 Fax: (01432) 851299 E-mail: h_comerford@btconnect.com *Special purpose heating elements*

San Precision Engineering Co. Ltd, Units 9-10 Harnall Industrial Estate, Harnall Lane East, Coventry, CV1 5AE Tel: (024) 7622 0613 Fax: (024) 7652 0004 E-mail: sales@sanprecision.com *Hydraulic components & ball valve manufrs*

San & Sons Ltd, Argonaut House, 369 Burnt Oak, Broadway, Edgware, Middlesex, HA8 5XZ Tel: (020) 8951 6070 Fax: (020) 8951 6050 E-mail: pault@argonaut.com *Import & export agents*

Sanako Educational Equipment, Woodland Park, Bradford Road, Chain Bar, Cleckheaton, West Yorkshire, BD19 6BW Tel: (01274) 863380 Fax: (01274) 863381 E-mail: ukenquiries@sanako.com *Leading providers of language teaching technology, and solutions to motivate learning. Including digital language labs, classroom management software, whole-site teaching and learning solutions, audio accessories (headsets, MP3 player/recorders) and support services.*

Sanbar Signs Ltd, 21 Argyll Road, Westcliff-on-Sea, Essex, SS0 7HL Tel: (01702) 344611 Fax: (01702) 344611 E-mail: sanbarsignssouthend@aol.com *Sign manufrs*

▶ Sanchem Ltd, Orchard Works, Webber Road, Knowsley Industrial Park, Liverpool, L33 7SW Tel: 0151-546 1555 Fax: 0151-546 1666 *Chemical processors*

Sanctus Training, Sanctus House, Nympsfield, Stonehouse, Gloucestershire, GL10 3UP Tel: (01453) 828222 Fax: (01453) 827915 E-mail: info@sanctusltd.co.uk *Supply specialist services across construction & property industries*

Sand In A Bottle, 47 St. Denys Avenue, Sleaford, Lincolnshire, NG34 8AS Tel: (01529) 414861 Fax: (01529) 414861 E-mail: dave@sandinabottle.co.uk *Coloured sand, art & craft ideas*

Sand Point Marina, Woodyard Road, Dumbarton, G82 4BG Tel: (01389) 762396 Fax: (01389) 732605 E-mail: sales@sandpoint-marina.co.uk *Boat storage*

Sandal P.L.C., Number 5, Harold Close, The Pinnacles, Harlow, Essex, CM19 5TH Tel: (01279) 422022 Fax: (01279) 626304 E-mail: ctaylor@powerconnections.co.uk *Power cords & plug connectors*

Sandal Security Services Ltd, Otters Holt, Durkar, Wakefield, West Yorkshire, WF4 3QE Tel: (01924) 250350 Fax: (01924) 256217 E-mail: sales@sandalsecurity.co.uk *Security alarm systems installation & manufrs*

Sandalwood Gates & Timber Products, Unit G7 Elvington Industrial Estate, York Road, Elvington, York, YO41 4AR Tel: (01904) 608542 E-mail: enquiries@sandalwoodgates.co.uk *Timber manufrs*

▶ Sandawana Castings Ltd, Unit 4 Bromag Industrial Estate, Minster Lovell, Witney, Oxfordshire, OX29 0SR Tel: (01993) 775862 Fax: (01993) 776692 E-mail: sandawana@wlucy.co.uk *Grey & ductile iron castings manufacturers*

▶ The Sandbanks Estate Agents, PO Box 5561, Ringwood, Hampshire, BH24 2ZS Tel: (0870) 0114575 E-mail: info@SandbanksEstateAgents.com *Prime Sandbanks property for sale from the leading Sandbanks Estate Agents operating in Sandbanks, Branksome Park, Lilliput, Canford Cliffs areas of Poole Harbour*

The Sandbar, 120-122 Grosvenor Street, Manchester, M1 7HL Tel: 0161-273 1552 Fax: 0161 273 2814 E-mail: sales@sandbar-online.com *Import & export German beers*

Sandberg LLP, 40 Grosvenor Gardens, London, SW1W 0EB Tel: (020) 7730 3461 Fax: (020) 7565 7100 E-mail: ho@sandberg.co.uk *Consulting inspecting & testing engineers* Also at: London SW4

Sandblast Sign Co., The Lodge, Barking Road, Barking, Ipswich, IP6 8HG Tel: (01449) 722252 Fax: (01449) 722355 E-mail: lorrraine@ssc.gb.com *Sign manufrs*

Frank Sandell & Sons (Worthing) Ltd, Sandell House, Railway Approach, Worthing, West Sussex, BN11 1UR Tel: (01903) 231774 Fax: (01903) 823128 *Building contractors & property developers*

Sanden International Europe Ltd, Hampshire Int Business Park, Crockford Lane, Chineham, Basingstoke, Hampshire, RG24 8WH Tel: (01256) 708888 Fax: (01256) 708883 E-mail: sales@sanden-europe.com *Motor vehicle air conditioners*

B. Sanders (Bromsgrove) Ltd, 4 Sherwood Road, Aston Fields Industrial Estate, Bromsgrove, Worcestershire, B60 3DR Tel: (01527) 575757 Fax: (01527) 575539 *Badge manufrs*

Sanders Polyfilms Ltd, Westfields Trading Estate, Hereford, HR4 9NS Tel: (01432) 277558 Fax: (01432) 357409 E-mail: sales@polyfilms.co.uk *Shrink film manufacturers*

Sanders Pool Table Hire Ltd, 75 Hatherley Cresent, Fareham, Hampshire, PO16 9TN Tel: (01329) 239979 *Pool table hire & sales*

Ray Sanders Ltd, 550 Edge Lane, Old Swan, Liverpool, L13 1AJ Tel: 0151-259 1221 Fax: 0151-220 6856 E-mail: pottypots@aol.com *China, glass & earthenware merchants*

Sanders Sails, Bath Road, Lymington, Hampshire, SO41 3RU Tel: (01590) 673981 Fax: (01590) 676026 *Marine covers & upholstery manufrs*

Sanders Sails, Bath Road, Lymington, Hampshire, SO41 3RU Tel: (01590) 673981 Fax: (01590) 676026 E-mail: peter@sanders-sails.co.uk *Sail covers & upholstery makers manufrs*

Sanders & Sanders Ltd, Spencer Works, Spencer Road, Rushden, Northamptonshire, NN10 6AE Tel: (01933) 353066 Fax: (01933) 410355 E-mail: mail@sanders-uk.com *Military & fashion shoe manufrs*

Sanders & Co. (UK) Ltd, 181 Wellingborough Road, Northampton, NN1 4DX Tel: (01604) 630195 Fax: (01604) 633972 E-mail: sandersltd@aol.com *General & promotional printers*

Sander-Shade Blinds Ltd, Treadaway Tech Centre, Treadaway Hill, Loudwater, High Wycombe, Buckinghamshire, HP10 9QL Tel: (01628) 529676 Fax: (01628) 521684 E-mail: sales@blindfashion.co.uk *Window blind manufrs*

Sanderson Ltd, 720 Waterside Drive, Aztec West, Almondsbury, Bristol, BS32 4UD Tel: (01454) 892500 Fax: (01454) 892610 E-mail: enquiries@sanderson.com *Computer systems & software distributors*

Sanderson, Wellington Works, Plover Road, Huddersfield, HD3 3HW Tel: (01484) 653665 Fax: (01484) 654254 E-mail: sales@sandersonprecision.com *Precision engineers*

Sanderson & Co, High Street, Leyburn, North Yorkshire, DL8 5AQ Tel: (01969) 623143 Fax: (01969) 623364 *Decorators supplies merchants*

Sanderson, Sanderson House, Oxford Road, Denham, Uxbridge, Middlesex, UB9 4DX Tel: (01895) 830000 Fax: (01895) 830055 *Furnishing fabrics & wallpaper manufrs*

Sanderson Boat Hire, Riverside, Reedham, Norwich, NR13 3TE Tel: (01493) 700242 Fax: (01493) 701705 E-mail: sanderson_marine@amserve.com *Boat hire & engineers*

▶ Bob Sanderson Video Production, 82 Chapel Street, Wordsley, Stourbridge, West Midlands, DY8 5QP Tel: (01384) 271073 Fax: (01384) 271073 E-mail: bobsanderson@talk21.com *Bob Sanderson is a West Midland based producer of corporate videos. Clients include both companies and local authorities*

John Sanderson & Son (1929) Ltd, Eye Witness Works, 78 Milton Street, Sheffield, S3 7WJ Tel: 0114-272 2682 Fax: 0114-275 4187 E-mail: sales@harrison-fisher.co.uk *Cutlery table manufrs*

Sanderson P C S L Ltd, Batley Bus & Technology Centre, Technology Drive, Batley, West Yorkshire, WF17 6ER Tel: (01924) 520300 Fax: (01924) 520301 E-mail: info@sanderson.com *Fic business requirements suppliers*

Sanderson Recruitment P.L.C., Somerset House, 18 Canynge Road, Clifton, Bristol, BS8 3JX Tel: 0117-970 6666 Fax: 0117-970 6665 E-mail: mail@sandersonplc.com *Professional consultancy services*

Sanderson Retail Sytems Ltd, Lakeside House, Waltham Business Park Brickyard Road, Swanmore, Southampton, SO32 2SA Tel: (01489) 896266 Fax: (01489) 892045 E-mail: enquiries@megabyte.co.uk *Computer software & services*

Sandersons T C M, Unit 5 Wallis Court, Road Three, Winsford Industrial Estate, Winsford, Cheshire, CW7 3PD Tel: (01606) 550668 *Steel fabrications*

▶ Sanderum Centres Ltd, Sanderum House, 38 Oakley Road, Chinnor, Oxfordshire, OX39 4TW Tel: (01844) 353969 Fax: (01844) 353553 E-mail: cs@sanderum.com *Accountancy services, it support, secretarial & administrative support*

Sandess Water Treatment Co. Ltd, 70-72 Fearnley Street, Watford, WD18 0RD Tel: (01923) 236395 Fax: (01923) 818693 E-mail: sandess.@btconnect.co.uk *Water treatment services*

Sandford & Down, 24 Pier Street, Plymouth, PL1 3BT Tel: (01752) 266248 Fax: (01752) 226131 E-mail: dive@sandfordanddown.co.uk *Diving equipment suppliers*

▶ Sandford Electrical Services, Unit 2, Kelpatrick Road, Cippenham, Slough, SL1 6BW Tel: (01628) 668 808 E-mail: sales@sandfordelectrical.co.uk *Control panel services*

Sandford Partnership Ltd, 77-83 Walnut Tree Cl, Guildford, Surrey, GU1 4UH Tel: 01483 881600 Fax: 01483 881601 E-mail: ldon@sandford.co.uk *Computer consultants*

▶ Sandham Davies & Jones Ltd, 3 Park Square, Newport, Gwent, NP20 4EL Tel: (01633) 213063 Fax: (01633) 244316 E-mail: enquiries@sdandjones.co.uk *Mortgage & Insurance Brokers; Independent Financial Advisors*

Peter Sandham Associates, 2 Wesley Street, Castleford, West Yorkshire, WF10 1AE Tel: (01977) 519600 Fax: (01977) 555290 E-mail: paulsandham@totalise.co.uk *Chemical engineering consultants*

Sandhill Consultants Ltd, St Johns Court, Brewery Hill, Grantham, Lincolnshire, NG31 6DW Tel: (01476) 568708 Fax: (01476) 568620 E-mail: info@sandhill.co.uk *It & management consultancy services*

▶ Sandhurst Equipment Rental, Thames House, College Road, Northfleet, Gravesend, Kent, DA11 9AU Tel: (0845) 120 6622 Fax: (01474) 567611 E-mail: info@sandhurst-rent.co.uk *Hydraulic excavator attachment hire*

Sandhurst Instruments Ltd, 30 Sudley Road, Bognor Regis, West Sussex, PO21 1ER Tel: (01243) 820200 Fax: (01243) 860111 E-mail: sandhurst.instruments@freenet.co.uk *Flow meter & level control equipment manufrs*

Company Information

Sandhurst Manufacturing, Belchmire Lane, Gosberton, Spalding, Lincolnshire, PE11 4HG Tel: (01775) 840020 Fax: (01775) 843063 E-mail: info@sandhurst-mfg.com *Sandhurst Mfg Co Ltd manufacture & distribute a range of 'Telelight' Mobile Lighting Towers and 'Genpac' Diesel Powered Generators (8 to 2250kVA).*

▶ Sandhurst Plant, The Whitewall Centre, Whitewall Road, Medway City Estate, Rochester, Kent, ME2 4DZ Tel: (01634) 739590 Fax: (0845) 1206644 E-mail: info@sandhurst.co.uk *Plant & equipment sales (new & used)*

▶ Sandiacre Packaging Machinery Ltd, 101 Lilac Grove, Beeston, Nottingham, NG9 1PF Tel: 0115-967 8787 Fax: 0115-967 8707 E-mail: sandiacre.uk@molins.com *Leading designers & manufacturers of high speed, high quality horizontal and vertical form/fill/seal machines & integrated systems for the packaging of fast moving consumer goods (FMCG). We consider ourselves to be specialists in the provision of packaging systems for a wide range of product types, from fresh to frozen, granules to powders and fluids to solids.*

Sandiacre Packaging Machinery Ltd, 101 Lilac Grove, Beeston, Nottingham, NG9 1PF Tel: 0115-967 8787 Fax: 0115-967 8707 E-mail: sandiacre.uk@molins.com Principal Export Areas: Worldwide *Designers & manufacturers of vertical form/fill/seal machines & integrated systems for the packaging of fast moving consumer goods (FMCG). Provision of packaging systems*

Sandiford Son & Bannister Ltd, 153 Croydon Road, Caterham, Surrey, CR3 6PF Tel: (01883) 343545 Fax: (01883) 346808 *Joinery manufrs* Also at: Richmond (Surrey)

Sandilands Electric Ltd, 151 Stroud Green Road, London, N4 3PZ Tel: (020) 7272 4084 Fax: (020) 7263 1037 *Electrical contractors*

Sanding Wooden Floors, 127 Tarnwood Park, Eltham, London, SE9 5NX Tel: (020) 8859 4063 E-mail: simon.killgallon@btconnect.com *London floor sanding service high quality sanding to all types of wooden floors including floorboards,parquet,wood blocks, restoration, gap filling staining*

▶ SanDisk Scot Ltd, Links House, 15 Links Place, Edinburgh, EH6 7EZ Tel: 0131-555 5674

Sandland Packaging Ltd, 5 Phoenix Industrial Estate, Loxdale Street, Bilston, West Midlands, WV14 0PR Tel: (01902) 496925 Fax: (01902) 354760 E-mail: sales@sandlandpackaging.co.uk *Cardboard box manufrs*

Sandling Fireworks, Building Se16, Gloucestershire Airport, Staverton, Cheltenham, Gloucestershire, GL51 6SP Tel: (01452) 855915 Fax: (01452) 855917 E-mail: sundlingsfireworks@aol.com *Firework suppliers*

Sandmoor Textile Co. Ltd, 30 Low Hall Road, Horsforth, Leeds, LS18 4EF Tel: 0113-258 5228 Fax: 0113-239 0155 *Textile merchants*

Sandon Underwear & Hosiery Co., 21a St James Place, Mangotsfield, Bristol, BS16 9JB Tel: 0117-956 0835 Fax: 0117-961 6242 *Knitwear & underwear sales*

Sandons The Saddlery, Powleys Yard, Bintree Road, Foulsham, Dereham, Norfolk, NR20 5RL Tel: (01362) 683383 Fax: (01362) 683383 *Riding wear distributors*

Sandpiper Formulations Ltd, Harriott Drive, Heathcote Industrial Estate, Warwick, CV34 6TJ Tel: (01926) 334900 Fax: (01926) 334926 E-mail: mep.sandpiperformulationsltd@hotmail.co.uk *Foundry chemical suppliers*

Sandpiper Plastics, Unit 4, Heathfield I, Heathfield, Newton Abbot, Devon, TQ12 6UT Tel: (01626) 834342 Fax: (01626) 833724 E-mail: info@sandpiperplastics.co.uk *Plastic finished product manufrs*

Sandrair International Ltd, 18 Shield Road, Ashford, Middlesex, TW15 1AU Tel: (01784) 242081 Fax: (01784) 243335 E-mail: info@heathrow.sandrair.com *Airfreight services*

Sandretto UK Ltd, Leigh Road, Swift Valley Industrial Estate, Rugby, Warwickshire, CV21 1DS Tel: (01788) 544221 Fax: (01788) 542195 E-mail: welcome@sandretto.co.uk *Injection moulding machine suppliers*

Sandridge Blinds Ltd, 291 National Avenue, Hull, HU5 4JB Tel: (01482) 492662 Fax: (01482) 492667 E-mail: sales@sandridgeblinds.co.uk *Blind manufrs*

Sandring Ltd, 224 Burley Road, Leeds, LS4 2EU Tel: 0113-274 4488 Fax: 0113-275 8030 E-mail: sales@sandring.co.uk *Used & new storage systems, pallet racking, steel shelves. Design, delivery & installation services. Used storage equipment a speciality.*

Sandringham Soft Furnishings, 10 Barn Green, Wolverhampton, WV3 7AY Tel: (01902) 344522 *Soft furnishings manufr*

Sands Fabrics, 27 Gibson Road, High Wycombe, Buckinghamshire, HP12 4QW Tel: (01494) 521939 *Upholstery trimming merchants*

▶ Sands Home Search, PO Box 5561, Ringwood, Hampshire, BH24 1EN Tel: (01425) 462549 Fax: (0871) 6612892 E-mail: info@sandshomesearch.com *Property estate agents*

Sandsfield Ready Mix Ltd, Elvington Industrial Estate, York Road, Elvington, York, YO41 4AR Tel: (01904) 608772 Fax: (01904) 608998 *Concrete plant*

Sandtoft Holdings Ltd, Sandtoft, Doncaster, South Yorkshire, DN8 5SY Tel: (01427) 872696 Fax: (01427) 871222 E-mail: info@sandtoft.co.uk *Roofing tiles manufrs*

Sandvik Bioline, Longacre Way, Holbrook, Sheffield, S20 3FS Tel: 0114-263 3100 Fax: 0114-263 3111 *Steel stockholders & processors*

Sandvik Coromant UK, Manor Way, Halesowen, West Midlands, B62 8QZ Tel: 0121-504 5400 Fax: 0121-504 5555 E-mail: ukcoromant@sandvik.com *Tungsten carbide tool manufrs*

Sandvik Hard Materials Ltd, PO Box 89, Coventry, CV4 0XG Tel: (024) 7647 6000 Fax: (024) 7685 6950 *Tungsten carbide product manufrs*

Sandvik Material Technology UK, Manor Way, Halesowen, West Midlands, B62 8QZ Tel: 0121-504 5111 *Stainless steel stockholders*

Sandvik Materials Technology, Manor Way, Halesowen, West Midlands, B62 8QZ Tel: (01224) 725494 Fax: 0121-504 5152 E-mail: sales.smtuk@sandvik.com *Stainless steel stockholders*

Sandvik Materials Tecnology Ltd, Manor Way, Halesowen, Smethwick, West Midlands, B62 8QZ Tel: 0121-504 5000 Fax: 0121-504 5151 E-mail: sales.smtuk@sandvic.com *Stainless steel stockholders* Also at: Aberdeen, Colnbrook, Stockton-on-Tees & Widnes

Sandwell Doors 2000, 79 Grafton Road, West Bromwich, West Midlands, B71 4EG Tel: 0121-553 7470 Fax: 0121-525 9684 *Roller shutter installation & repairs*

Sandwell Insulation Services Ltd, Unit 1 Hale Trading Estate, Lower Church Lane, Tipton, West Midlands, DY4 7PJ Tel: 0121-520 3334 Fax: 0121-520 3334 E-mail: janxxx@ukonline.co.uk *Thermal insulation contractors*

Sandwell Scaffold Co. Ltd, Unit 2B, Charles Street, West Bromwich, West Midlands, B70 0AZ Tel: 0121-557 9464 Fax: 0121-522 3466 E-mail: westbromwich@sandwellscaffold.co.uk *Scaffolding erectors* Also at: Manchester & Northampton

Sandwell Stove Enamellers & Powder Coaters Ltd, Unit 12 Blankenhall Industrial Estate, Sunbeam Street, Wolverhampton, WV2 4PF Tel: (01902) 422899 Fax: (01902) 423380 *Stove enamelling & powder coating service providers*

▶ Sandwich Fillers, Unit D1 East Dorset Trade Park, Nimrod Way, Wimborne, Dorset, BH21 7SH Tel: (01202) 854774

Sandwich Fillings Ltd, Unit 22 Village Court, Village Farm Industrial Estate, Pyle, Bridgend, Mid Glamorgan, CF33 6BX Tel: (01656) 744944 Fax: (01656) 745454 *Manufacturers of sandwich fillings*

▶ Sandwich King, Enfield Street, Leeds, LS7 1RF Tel: 0113-242 6031 Fax: 0113-234 2047 E-mail: enquires@sandwichkinguk.com *Pre-pack sandwiches manufrs*

Sandwich Mowers Ltd, Homestead Farm, Woodnesborough Road, Sandwich, Kent, CT13 0AE Tel: (01304) 611000 Fax: (01304) 611000 E-mail: sandwichmowersltd@btinternet.com *Garden machinery sales & repairers*

▶ Sandy Allan Blacksmiths Ltd, 5 Small Holdings, Thornton Road, Kirkcaldy, Fife, KY1 3NN Tel: (01592) 655444 Fax: (01592) 655978 E-mail: joe.currie1@btopenworld.com *Welding fabrication services*

▶ Sandy Bedfordshire, Nursery House, Sandy, Bedfordshire, SG19 1BP Tel: 0845 2005165 Fax: 0845 2012190 E-mail: info@sandy-bedfordshire.co.uk *Sandy Bedfordshire UK lies approximately 50 mile (80km) North of London on the A1 trunk road (Great North Road). Sandy is famous for its connection with the Royal Society for the Protection of Birds (RSPB), which has Headquarters at the Lodge just outside Sandy on the Potton Road. This Community site is full of facts and useful information about Sandy & the local area. Please use our Feedback Form to make comments about the site or help to update its details.*

▶ Sandy Brown Associates, 16 West Terrace, South Queensferry, West Lothian, EH30 9LL Tel: 0131-331 2020 Fax: 0131-331 2187 E-mail: post@sandybrown.com *Acoustic Consultants*

▶ Sandy Bruce Trucking Ltd, Blackdog Centre, Bridge of Don, Aberdeen, AB23 8BT Tel: (01224) 824936 Fax: (01224) 820945

▶ Sandy Bruce Trucking, T2 Rudford Industrial Estate, Ford Road, Ford, Arundel, West Sussex, BN18 0BD Tel: (01903) 731303 Fax: (01903) 722049

Sandy Company Builders, Greyfriars Place, Stafford, ST16 2SD Tel: (01785) 258164 Fax: (01785) 256526 E-mail: info@sandy.co.uk *Building contractors & civil engineers*

▶ Sandy Mccracken & Son Ltd, Ayr Road, Rigside, Lanark, ML11 9NP Tel: (01555) 880890 Fax: (01555) 880891

▶ Sandy McCracken & Son Ltd, Canderside Toll, Larkhall, Lanarkshire, ML9 3PJ Tel: (01698) 791722

▶ Sandy Macgregor, 5 Saltoun Street, Wick, Caithness, KW1 5ET Tel: (01955) 602265 Fax: (01955) 606028

▶ Sandy Mclean & Co., 1 East High Street, Greenlaw, Duns, Berwickshire, TD10 6YF Tel: (01361) 810405 Fax: (01361) 810676

▶ Sandy Menzies Designer Jewellers Ltd, The Academy, Belmont Street, Aberdeen, AB10 1LB Tel: (01224) 641031 Fax: (01224) 641031 E-mail: shop@sandymenzies.co.uk *Design, manufacture & retail of quality contemporary jewellery*

▶ Sandy Morrison Engernering, The Pier, Uig, Portree, Isle of Skye, IV51 9YD Tel: (01470) 542300

Sandy Powder Coating, 14 Howard Road, Eaton Socon, St. Neots, Cambridgeshire, PE19 8ET Tel: (01480) 470555 Fax: (01480) 477155 *Powder coating services*

Sandy Press Ltd, 2 Handworth Street, Manchester, M12 6LH Tel: 0161-273 7535 Fax: 0161-274 3146 *Commercial printers*

Sandycott Pump Mnfrs, Manor House, Church Street, Eckington, Sheffield, S21 4BH Tel: (01246) 436632 Fax: (01246) 433372 E-mail: sales@hydron-pumps.com *Condensation pump manufrs*

▶ Sandy's Bake House Wholesale, Unit 1-2 Montford Enterprise Centre, Wynford Square, Salford, M50 2SN Tel: 0161-737 2700 Fax: 0161-737 4248 E-mail: sandysbakehouse@aol.com *Bakery*

▶ Sandywood Furniture, 8 Boundary Business Court, Church Road, Mitcham, Surrey, CR4 3TD Tel: (020) 8687 7070 Fax: (020) 8648 7020 E-mail: sandywoodfurnitureltd@gmill.com *Furniture bespoke manufrs*

Sanford Europe Parker Pen Co., 52 Railway Road, Newhaven, East Sussex, BN9 0AU Tel: (01273) 513233 Fax: (01273) 514773 E-mail: enquiries@parkerpen.co.uk *Writing instruments & inks manufrs*

▶ SANFORD SERVICES, 14 MOWBRAY CROFT,, BURNTWOOD, STAFFORDSHIRE, WS7 1QB Tel: 01543 304595 Fax: 01543 304596 E-mail: SANFORD-SERVICES@msn.com *Metal Detection Ltd ceased trading on the 27th May 2005, *Iam presently setting up an international *Servicing company for checkweighers, Beltweighers and *Metal Detectors under *Sanford Services. *with over 25 years of experience for all your *servicing requirements think first think *SANFORD SERVICES**

Sangamo Ltd, Auchenfoil Road, Port Glasgow, Renfrewshire, PA14 5XG Tel: (01475) 745131 Fax: (01475) 744567 E-mail: enquiries@sangamo.co.uk Principal Export Areas: West Europe *Time control manufrs*

Sanger Textile & Co., 74A Middlesex Street, London, E1 7EZ Tel: (020) 7247 8949 Fax: (020) 7247 8949 *Clothing & textile importers & exporting services*

Sangers of Maidstone Ltd, 24 Orsman Road, London, N1 5QJ Tel: (020) 7739 3411 Fax: (020) 7739 2079 *Pharmaceutical supplies distributors*

Sangers N Ireland Ltd, 2 Marshalls Road, Belfast, BT5 6SR Tel: (028) 9040 1111 Fax: (028) 9040 1240 E-mail: peter.surgenor@sangers.co.uk *Pharmaceuticals wholesalers*

Sangha Metrology, Blanche Street, Bradford, West Yorkshire, BD4 8DA Tel: (01274) 667785 Fax: (01274) 662523 *Manufacturing of measuring instruments*

Sangikyo Corporation, Highbridge Industrial Estate, Oxford Road, Uxbridge, Middlesex, UB8 1HR Tel: (01895) 876101 Fax: (01895) 876257 *Installation & maintenance of satellite systems*

Sangre Engineering Ltd, Unit 32c The Washford Industrial Estate, Heming Road, Redditch, Worcestershire, B98 0DH Tel: (01527) 524782 Fax: (01527) 510323 E-mail: sales@sangre.co.uk *Dust, fume & ventilation equipment*

Sangs Banff Ltd, 22 St Machar Road, Aberdeen, AB24 2UU Tel: (01224) 276699 Fax: (01224) 276100 E-mail: sales@sangs.co.uk *Spring water & soft drinks distributors*

Sangs Banff Ltd, Macduff Industrial Estate, Old Gamrie Road, Macduff, Banffshire, AB44 1GD Tel: (01261) 832911 Fax: (01261) 833637 E-mail: sales@sangs.co.uk *Mineral water (carbonated) manufrs*

Sangson Ltd, 221 Lozells Rd, Birmingham, B19 1RJ Tel: 0121-551 6530 Fax: 0121-551 6107 *Clothing manufacturers & textile merchants*

Sangwin Concrete Products Ltd, Dansom Lane, Hull, HU8 7LN Tel: (01482) 329921 Fax: (01482) 215353 E-mail: info@sangwin.co.uk *Mobile crane & plant hirers*

Sani UK Ltd, Unit B1 Link One Industrial Park, George Henry Road, Tipton, West Midlands, DY4 7BU Tel: (01384) 251175 Fax: (01384) 251300 *Component supplier for the blind*

▶ Sanico Building Services Ltd, 17 George Street, Croydon, CR0 1LA Tel: (020) 84072032 E-mail: info@sanico.co.uk *London Builder Company - High Quality House Refurbishment, Office Refurbishment, House Extension Basement Conversion and Loft Conversion for residential and commercial clients around London.*Sanico Building Services have certain core sectors in which we operate, one of which being commercial office refurbishment London. We have worked for commercial clients both on new builds, redevelopment of existing stock, office refurbishment London and refurbishment of health and educational sites.*

Sanitary Appliances Ltd, 3 Sandiford Road, Sutton, Surrey, SM3 9RN Tel: (020) 8641 0310 Fax: (020) 8641 6426 E-mail: info@sanitaryappliances.co.uk *Sanitary Appliances Ltd are specialist manufacturers, designers and suppliers to hHotel, commercial catering, sanitary equipment and hospital industry, together with specialised fittings for sports clubs, abattoirs, schools, old peoples' dwellings and nursing homes. Based in Sutton, Surrey, they can offer the most comprehensive range of specialised fittings in brass, stainless steel etc. Their standard range of fittings include terminal water fittings, self closing taps, lever action taps, pre-rinse spray units, guide and support rails, laboratory emergency equipment.*

Sanitary San Francisco Fudge Factory, 6 Church Street, Bath, BA1 1NL Tel: (01225) 425714 Fax: (01225) 332031 E-mail: sales@sanfranciscofudge.co.uk *Confectionary manufrs*

Sankey Carbide, Anchor Lane, Bilston, West Midlands, WV14 9NE Tel: (01902) 661144 Fax: (01902) 661100 E-mail: scd@cogent-power.com Sales Contact: S. Cooper Principal Export Areas: Worldwide *Precision press tool manufacturers*

Richard Sankey & Son Ltd, Bennerley Road, Bulwell, Nottingham, NG6 8PE Tel: 0115-927 7335 Fax: 0115-977 0197 E-mail: info@rsankey.co.uk *Horticultural plastics sundries manufrs*

▶ Sankofa Exchange Ltd, Africa House, 21 Shorwell Road, Nottingham, NG3 7HG Tel: 0115-911 0111 Fax: 0115-911 0110 E-mail: office@sankofa.co.uk *Specialists in HR equality and diversity, culture fair assessment and selection, psychometric testing, change management, team building and employee relations.*

Sankyo Oilless Industry (U K) Ltd, Huffwood Trading Estate, Billingshurst, West Sussex, RH14 9UR Tel: (01403) 785378 Fax: (01403) 784634 E-mail: sales@sankyo-oilless.co.uk *Maintenance free bronze bushes*

Sanmar Ltd, 29 Orleans Avenue, Glasgow, G14 9NF Tel: 0141-954 2944 Fax: 0141-959 9666 E-mail: sales@sanmar-chain.com *European representatives for the major anchor chain manufacturers from The Peoples Republic of China for the range of Offshore Mooring Chains manufactured by Zhenjiang Anchor Chain Factory, Asian Star Anchor Chain Factory - up to 152mm diameter in Grade R3, R3S and R4 including Stud link and studless chain and fittings*

continued

Sanmex (International) Plc, 5-9 Dalmarnock Road, Rutherglen, Glasgow, G73 1NY Tel: 0141-647 2244 Fax: 0141-613 1228 E-mail: info@sanmex.com *Manufacturers of toiletries & sundries*

▶ Sanmina Sci, 1-5 Crompton Way, North Newmoor Industrial Estate, Irvine, Ayrshire, KA11 4HU Tel: (01294) 224200 Fax: (01294) 221412 E-mail: info@samina-sci.com *Computer components manufrs*

▶ Sanmina Sci, 1-5 Crompton Way, North Newmoor Industrial Estate, Irvine, Ayrshire, KA11 4HU Tel: (01294) 224200 Fax: (01294) 221412 E-mail: info@samina-sci.com

Sanmor Communications Ltd, 37 The Drive, Ilford, Essex, IG1 3HA Tel: (020) 8554 7773 Fax: (020) 8554 7787 *Wholesalers Of Fibre Optic Componets*

Sanofi Synthelabo, Edgefield Avenue, Newcastle upon Tyne, NE3 3TT Tel: 0191-285 3931 Fax: 0191-284 9175 Principal Export Areas: Worldwide *Pharmaceutical chemicals suppliers* Also at: Branches throughout the U.K.

▶ Sanphire Design, 39 Sicily Park, Belfast, BT10 0AL Tel: (028) 9062 9325 E-mail: design@sanphire.co.uk *Dynamic Graphic and Web Design based in Belfast**Please see our site which includes examples of some of our advertising and design work **Our skills feed into a single goal which is to produce innovation and excellence for*our clients**On time and On Budget*

Sanquhar Tile Services Ltd, Blackaddie Road, The Industrial Estate, Sanquhar, Dumfriesshire, DG4 6DB Tel: (01659) 50497 Fax: (01659) 58384 *Carpet tile manufrs*

Sanroy Equipment Ltd, 1 Commerce Way, Highbridge, Somerset, TA9 4AG Tel: (01278) 780191 Fax: (01278) 792102 E-mail: mikesanroy@netscapeonline.co.uk *Display & exhibition stands supplier*

Sansol Foods Ltd, 101 Perth Road, Scone, Perth, PH2 6JL Tel: (01738) 567168 Fax: (01738) 567168 *Farm food suppliers*

Sansom Heating, Limber Road, Lufton Trading Estate, Yeovil, Somerset, BA22 8RR Tel: (01935) 444660 Fax: (01935) 433523 *Heating engineers*

Sansome Construction, Bond Street, Southampton, SO14 5AN Tel: (023) 8022 2349 *Ductwork & sheetmetal workers*

Sant Products Ltd, Unit 42 Coneygre Industrial Estate, Tipton, West Midlands, DY4 8XP Tel: 0121-557 7066 Fax: 0121-557 2007 *Diecastings & aluminium, alloy casting manufrs*

▶ Santa Letters UK, Unit 80, Speke Hall Industrial Estate, Liverpool, L24 1YA Tel: 0151-428 0638 E-mail: kmorrisroe@gmail.com *Santa Letters UK*

Santa-Cruz Travel & Shipping Agency Ltd, 2 Crampton Road, Pende, London, SE20 7AT Tel: (020) 8689 3373 Fax: (020) 8689 0493 E-mail: santacruzship@talk21.com *Shipping agents*

Santech Design Ltd, The Mount, Church Lane, Endon, Stoke-On-Trent, ST9 9HF Tel: (01782) 503388 Fax: (01782) 505234 E-mail: dm@santechdesign.co.uk *Ceramic consultants*

Santiki Ltd, Unit A4 The Connaught Business Centre, 22 Willow Lane, Mitcham, Surrey, CR4 4NA Tel: (020) 8685 0550 Fax: (020) 8640 7414 E-mail: sales@santiki.co.uk *Computer systems sales & support services*

Santima International, Globe House, 20-22 Cobb Street, London, E1 7LB Tel: (020) 7377 0166 Fax: (020) 7375 1906 E-mail: info@sanglobe.com *Promotional product suppliers*

Santronics Printed Circuit Services, Unit 8e New Yard, Clay Flatts Industrial Estate, Workington, Cumbria, CA14 3YE Tel: (01900) 870961 Fax: (01900) 870961 E-mail: sanmaral@tiscali.co.uk *Printed circuit assemblies*

Santype International Ltd, Harnham Trading Estate, Netherhampton Road, Salisbury, SP2 8PS Tel: (01722) 334261 Fax: (01722) 333171 E-mail: post@santype.com *Photo-typesetters*

▶ Sanyo Component Europe GmbH, Unit 1, Walton Lodge, Bridge Street, Walton-on-Thames, Surrey, KT12 1BT Tel: (01932) 233600 Fax: (01932) 230104 *Semiconductor components & display suppliers*

Sanyo Speechtek Ltd, Sanyo House, Otterspool Way, Watford, WD25 8JX Tel: (01923) 205900 Fax: (01923) 205935 E-mail: dictationsupport@sanyo.co.uk *Dictation machine distributors*

Sapa Pressweld Ltd, Spinnaker Park, Spinnaker Road, Hempsted, Gloucester, GL2 5DG Tel: (01452) 502502 Fax: (01452) 503503 E-mail: sales@pressweld.co.uk *Aluminium fabricators & metal finishers*

Sapa Profiles Ltd, Tewkesbury Road, Cheltenham, Gloucestershire, GL51 9DT Tel: (01242) 521641 Fax: (01242) 513304 E-mail: info.profiles.uk@sapagroup.com Principal Export Areas: Africa *Anodizing services, manufactures of alloy, aluminium bars, sections*

▶ Sapath Systems, 145 Vaughan Road, Harrow, Middlesex, HA1 4EG Tel: (0870) 9502936 Fax: (0870) 1281422 E-mail: info@sapath.com *We provide sale, repair, maintenance and networking services. Sapath Systems offer low-cost, convenient repair services as well as advice and assistance with system upgrades, preventive maintenance and other non-repair services.*

▶ Sapco, Seven Stars Road, Oldbury, West Midlands, B69 4JR Tel: 0121-544 7500 Fax: 0121-544 7499 *Shotblast & painting*

William Sapcote & Sons Ltd, 87 Camden Street, Birmingham, B1 3DE Tel: 0121-233 1200 Fax: 0121-236 2731 E-mail: enquiries@sapcote.co.uk *Building contractors services*

Saper Glass Industries Ltd, Thames House, Longreach Road, Barking, Essex, IG11 0JR Tel: (020) 8594 5757 Fax: (020) 8594 5252 E-mail: info@saperglass.co.uk *Glass merchants, glaziers & fire doors & fire screen suppliers*

▶ Sapient I.T Soultions, 119c High Street, Waltham Cross, Hertfordshire, EN8 7AN Tel: 01992 301550 E-mail: contact@sapientsolutions.co.uk *Systems, hardware, networks, internet, training*

Sapient Systems, 106 Queens Road, Carterton, Oxfordshire, OX18 3YF Tel: (01993) 845291 Fax: (01993) 845291 *Hardware & software constructions & services*

Sapio Solutions, New Brook House, 385 Alfreton Road, Nottingham, NG7 5LR Tel: 0115-875 8837 Fax: 0115-875 9900 E-mail: info@wowdesignsolutions.com *WOW Design Solutions Ltd provides creative web and print design, from logos and staionery to corporate web sites and exhibitions.*

Sapphire Ltd, Lambourne House, 7 Western Road, Romford, RM1 3LD Tel: (01708) 333700 Fax: (01708) 333800 E-mail: sales@dataease.com Principal Export Areas: Worldwide *Database software publishers* Also at: London & Worcester

▶ Sapphire Accounting Systems, New Manor Farm, West Harptree, Bristol, BS40 6HW Tel: (01761) 222010 Fax: (01761) 222011 *Computer software developers*

Sapphire Blinds, Unit D4, Olympic Business Park, Drybridge Road, Dundonald, Kilmarnock, Ayrshire, KA2 9BE Tel: (01563) 850258 Fax: (01563) 850258 *Manufacturer of blinds, fitting services*

Sapphire Communications Ltd, Herongate House, 76 Herongate Road, London, E12 5EQ Tel: (020) 8530 7272 Fax: (020) 8530 1141 *Telecommunications systems distributors*

▶ Sapphire Computing & Consulting Ltd, Shapphire House, 50 Leyes Lane, Kenilworth, Warwickshire, CV8 2QT Tel: (01926) 779700 *Software design & 3D solid modelling*

Sapphire Contractors Ltd, 18 Gladstone Road, Croydon, CR0 2BQ Tel: (020) 8665 6226 Fax: (020) 8665 6282 E-mail: enquiries@sapphirecontractors.co.uk *Partitioning services*

▶ Sapphire Controls Ltd, Sapphire House, Roundtree Way, Norwich, NR7 8SQ Tel: (01603) 480560

Sapphire Detection Systems Ltd, 263 Boundary Road, Loudwater, High Wycombe, Buckinghamshire, HP10 9QN Tel: (01628) 532830 *Fire alarms*

▶ Sapphire Document Solutions, Unit 4 5 Cae FFWT Business Park, Pendraw'R Llan, Glan Conwy, Colwyn Bay, Clwyd, LL28 5SP Tel: (0845) 8382501 Fax: (01492) 580052 E-mail: sales@sapphire-limited.co.uk *Authorised Main Dealer for Konica Minolta and Sharp.*Network Document Solutions, Full colour solutions, Digital copiers and printers, Document management software, System installation and support, Facilities Management, Office equipment and supplies.*

Sapphire Engineering, Atlas Works, Brieryfield Road, Preston, PR1 8SR Tel: (01772) 822133 Fax: (01772) 822144 *Fire protection equipment (sprinkler) engineers*

Sapphire Instrument Co., 25 Friar Road, Brighton, BN1 6NG Tel: (01273) 556008 Fax: (01273) 556008 *Computer system consultants & integrators*

Sapphire Knitwear, 445 St Saviours Road, Leicester, LE5 4HH Tel: 0116-273 3803 Fax: 0116-273 3803 *Ethnic knitwear manufrs*

Sapphire One Consulting Ltd, 5 Wordsworth Road, Addlestone, Surrey, KT15 2SW Tel: (01932) 857109 Fax: (0870) 0562324 E-mail: info@sapphireone.co.uk *Management consultants*

Sapphire Packaging, 28 Eldon Way, Hockley, Essex, SS5 4AD Tel: (01702) 205999 Fax: (01702) 562107 E-mail: sales@sapphirepackaging.com *Paper bag, polyethylene/polythene bag/carrier/sack & film/sheet manufacturers. Also packaging materials/goods/products merchants or agents & carrier bags including paper & polythene*

Sapphire Products Ltd, 4 Dunton Trading Estate, Mount Street, Birmingham, B7 5QL Tel: 0121-326 6000 Fax: 0121-328 5518 E-mail: sapphireproducts@boltblue.com *Manufacturers of rivets, industrial fasteners & cold headed products*

▶ Sapphire Signs Ltd, Bontoft Avenue, Hull, HU5 4HF Tel: (01482) 474888 Fax: (01482) 474889 E-mail: sales@saphiresigns.co.uk *Sign manufrs*

▶ Sapphire Sounds, 68 Lancaster Avenue, Accrington, Lancs, BB5 4BH Tel: (01254) 235868 E-mail: sapphire_sounds2003@yahoo.co.uk *Mobile Disco & Karaoke Services*Professional Disc Jockies*Reliable Service*

▶ Sapphire Systems (Scotland) Ltd, 272 Bath Street, Glasgow, G2 4JR Tel: 0141-354 8900 Fax: E-mail: info@s1sapphire.net *Bespoke software solutions services*

▶ Sapphire Tooling Ltd, Colndale Road, Colnbrook, Slough, SL3 0HQ Tel: (01753) 770004 Fax: (01753) 770005 *Machinery & plant equipment hire*

Sapsford Signs, 4 Mitre Avenue, London, E17 6QG Tel: (020) 8520 3739 Fax: (020) 8520 3739 *Sign manufrs*

Sapt Textile Products Co. Ltd, Bluepits Mills, Queensway, Castleton, Rochdale, Lancashire, OL11 2PG Tel: (01706) 632931 Fax: (01706) 640878 E-mail: sapt.uk@btclick.com *Fibre merchants*

Saputo Cheese UK Ltd, The Creamery, Aberarad, Newcastle Emlyn, Carmarthenshire, SA38 9DQ Tel: (01239) 710424 Fax: (01239) 710175 *Cheese manufrs*

Saqqara Technology Ltd, 47 Sandfield Road, Headington, Oxford, OX3 7RW Tel: (01865) 744505 Fax: (01865) 744505 *Development software & websites for retail*

Sar Ltd, Highfield, Row Dow Lane, Knatts Valley, Sevenoaks, Kent, TN15 6XN Tel: (01959) 524444 Fax: (01959) 524455 E-mail: sales@sarltd.co.uk *Import & export temperature recording*

Sara Lee Household & Body Care UK Ltd, 225 Bath Road, Slough, SL1 4AU Tel: (01753) 523971 Fax: (01753) 570340 E-mail: info@saralee.co.uk *Household & bodycare manufrs*

▶ Saracen Finance, The Old Barn, Hall Farm, Main Street, Kirklington, Newark, Nottinghamshire, NG22 8NN Tel: (01636) 815685 Fax: (01636) 817859 E-mail: vstrachan@saracenfinance.com Purchasing Contact: D. Bowman Sales Contact: V. Strachan *Vendor management & commercial asset finance providers. A new approach to financing commercial vehicles, construction & plant equipment*

Saracen Horse Feeds, The Forstal, Beddow Way, Aylesford, Kent, ME20 7BT Tel: (01622) 718487 Fax: (01622) 790321 E-mail: info@saracen-horse-feeds.co.uk *Agricultural merchants*

▶ Saracen International Ltd, Adamson House, Towers Business Park, Wilmslow Road, Didsbury, Manchester, M20 2YY Tel: 0161-955 4217 Fax: 0161-955 4201 E-mail: vigilant@saracen-int.com *Security investigation & distributors of security products*

Saracens Head Hotel, High Street, Chelmsford, CM1 1BE Tel: (01245) 262368 Fax: (01245) 262418 *Hotel & conference facilities*

Saracen's House Business Centre, Saracens House, 25 ST. Margarets Green, Ipswich, IP4 2BN Tel: (01473) 225951 Fax: (01473) 211508 E-mail: reception@saracens.co.uk *Office rental & business support services*

▶ Saraco Industries, PO Box 190, Bolton, BL1 8AH Tel: (01204) 381990 Fax: (01204) 525190 E-mail: info@saraco-industries.com *Wet wipes manufrs*

▶ Sarah Philips Bookkeeping Ltd, 51 Cissbury Avenue, Peacehaven, East Sussex, BN10 8TW Tel: 01273 297294 Fax: 01273 575388 E-mail: info@sarahphilipsbookkeeping.co.uk *Benefit your company by contacting the specialists in Bookkeeping, VAT and Payroll. Outsource your office tasks such as, typing, faxing and printing and allow us to be your virtual secretary. We use the most up to date software such as TAS, Sage and Excel, plus many others.*

▶ Sarah Smith, 2 Bell Cottages, High Street, Nutley, Uckfield, East Sussex, TN22 3NF Tel: (01825) 712143 Fax: (01825) 712143 E-mail: sarichel2@onetel.com *Chartered tax advisor*

▶ Sarahvee Gluten Free Foods Ltd, Unit 7, Sittingbourne Industrial Park, Crown Quay Lane, Sittingbourne, Kent, ME10 3JH Tel: (01795) 428417

▶ Saran Window Ltd, Unit 12, Dale Street Industrial Estate, Radcliffe, Manchester, M26 1AD Tel: 0161-724 6400

Sarasin Chiswell, Juxon House, 100 St. Pauls Church Yard, London, EC4M 8BU Tel: (020) 7038 7000 Fax: (020) 7038 6850 E-mail: mail@sarasin.co.uk *Investment services*

Saratoga Systems Ltd, Ashlyn House, Terrace Road North, Binfield, Bracknell, Berkshire, RG42 5JA Tel: (01344) 868700 Fax: (01344) 421171 E-mail: sales@saratoga.co.uk *Customer relationship management software*

Sarclad Ltd, Broombank Park, Chesterfield, Derbyshire, S41 9RT Tel: (01246) 457000 Fax: (01246) 457010 E-mail: sarclad@sarclad.com *Rolling mill plant & equipment manufrs* Also at: Birmingham

Sardar & Sons London Ltd, 31 New Road, London, E1 1HE Tel: (020) 7375 0246 Fax: (020) 7247 5239 *Children's clothing manufrs*

Sardon International Ltd, 28 Wylde Green Road, Sutton Coldfield, West Midlands, B72 1HD Tel: 0121-354 2165 Fax: 0121-354 2165 Principal Export Areas: Worldwide *Manufacturers of drying (industrial) plant or equipment*

Saren Engineering Ltd, Unit 10 Premier Trading Estate, 118 Dartmouth Middleway, Birmingham, B7 4AT Tel: 0121-359 4890 Fax: 0121-359 6951 E-mail: info@saren.co.uk *Pressings, general presswork; cable ties; assemblers*

Sarens UK Ltd, Dinsdale House, Riverside Park Road, Middlesbrough, Cleveland, TS2 1UT Tel: (01642) 621621 Fax: (01642) 621620 E-mail: sales@sarens.com *Heavy crane hire & contract lifting services*

Elliott Sargeant Ltd, 4 Rushington Business Park, Rushington Lane, Totton, Southampton, SO40 9AH Tel: (023) 8066 1666 Fax: (023) 8066 1567 *Specialist transport services*

Alfred Sargent & Sons Ltd, Portland Road, Rushden, Northamptonshire, NN10 0DQ Tel: (01933) 312065 Fax: (01933) 410207 *Men's shoe manufrs*

Sargents Factors Ltd, Birches Industrial Estate, East Grinstead, West Sussex, RH19 1XZ Tel: (01342) 321456 Fax: (01342) 321598 *Motor parts retailers*

Sarginsons Industries Ltd, Torrington Avenue, Coventry, CV4 9AG Tel: (024) 7646 6291 Fax: (024) 7646 8135 E-mail: keithb@sarginsons.co.uk *Aluminium casting foundry*

Sargom Fire, 6 Station Terrace, London, NW10 5RT Tel: (020) 8964 0808 Fax: (020) 8960 2113 E-mail: sales@sargom.com *Fire safety equipment distributors*

Sargrove Automation, The Chestnuts, 11 Eastern Road, Havant, Hampshire, PO9 2JE Tel: (023) 9247 1981 Fax: (023) 9247 1981 E-mail: sargrove@btinternet.com *Photometric & special purpose test equipment*

Sarian Systems, Beacon House, Riverside Business Park, Leeds Road, Ilkley, West Yorkshire, LS29 8JZ Tel: (01943) 605055 Fax: (01943) 605056 *Telecommunications manufrs*

Sarik Vacform, Unit 8-9 Pixash Business Centre, Pixash Lane, Keynsham, Bristol, BS31 1TP Tel: 0117-986 0404 Fax: 0117-986 0424 E-mail: info@sarik-vacform.com *Vacuum formers & plastics manufrs*

Sarka Tools, 14 Lodge Road, Atherton, Manchester, M46 9BL Tel: (01942) 894685 Fax: (01942) 894685 *Tool making*

▶ Sarkan Gardens, Vicarage Lane, Hessle, North Humberside, HU13 9LQ Tel: (01482) 649825

Sarlands Beds Ltd, Fletchampstead Highway, Tile Hill, Coventry, CV4 9BY Tel: 024 76717912 Fax: 024 76717912 *Bed manufrs*

▶ Sarll Metal Products, Leyton Avenue, Mildenhall, Bury St. Edmunds, Suffolk, IP28 7BL Tel: (01638) 718394 Fax: (01638) 718421 E-mail: info@sarl1.co.uk *Sheet metal working*

Sarnafil Ltd, 11 Robberds Way, Bowthorpe Employment Area, Norwich, NR5 9JF Tel: (01603) 748985 Fax: (01603) 743054 E-mail: sales@sarnafil.com *Roofing material*

Sarner Ltd, Metropolis House, 16 Southsea Road, Kingston Upon Thames, Surrey, KT1 2EH Tel: (0845) 0666444 Fax: (0845) 0666555 E-mail: rmagri@sarner.com *Audio visual systems suppliers*

▶ Saro Engineering Ltd, Unit 2, 64-66 Tregwilym Road, Rogerstone, Newport, Gwent, NP10 9EJ Tel: (01633) 892466

Saros Technology Ltd, 20-21 Market Place, Wallingford, Oxfordshire, OX10 0AD Tel: (01491) 837787 Fax: (01491) 837477 E-mail: info@saros.co.uk *Design tool suppliers*

Sarralle UK UK Ltd, 87 West Street, Oundle, Peterborough, PE8 4EJ Tel: (01832) 270371 Fax: (01430) 473027 E-mail: mail@sarralleuk.fsnet.co.uk *Workshop equipment & tool storage systems. Complete range including workbenches, tool trolleys, storage cabinets, shelving & lockers*

Sarsen Technology Ltd, 23 High Street, Marlborough, Wiltshire, SN8 1LW Tel: (01672) 511166 Fax: (01672) 511177 E-mail: sales@sarsen.net *We specialize in single board computing, FPGA, digital signal processing, data acquisition and high-speed data recording COTS technology. We support a wide range of high quality, high reliability products on formats including PCI, AMC, VME, CompactPCI, VPX, ATCA, PMC, PC/4-Plus, EBX, and VXS. Sarsen also provides complete integrated 19" rackmount embedded computing systems.*

Sarsfields Memorials, 1 Old Thomas Lane, Liverpool, L14 3NA Tel: 0151-259 2762 Fax: 0151-254 2067 *Stone masons*

▶ SARTAC Ltd, Manor House, Manor Street, Stoke-on-Trent, ST4 2JB Tel: (01782) 848100 E-mail: sales@jal.co.uk *Computer manufrs*

Sartec, Century Farmhouse, Reading Street, Tenterden, Kent, TN30 7HS Tel: (01233) 758157 Fax: (01233) 758158 E-mail: sales@sartec.co.uk *Analytical instrumentation distributors*

▶ Sartorius, Longmead Business Centre, Blenheim Road, Epsom, Surrey, KT19 9QQ Tel: (01372) 737102 Fax: (01372) 729927 E-mail: info@sartorius.co.uk *Weighing equipment for laboratory, industrial, educational & research*

Sarum Colourview Ltd, Unit 7-8 Woodford Centre Old Sarum Park, Lysander Way, Old Sarum, Salisbury, SP4 6BU Tel: (01722) 343600 Fax: (01722) 323604 E-mail: sales@colourview.co.uk *Lithographic printers*

Sarum D I Y Upholstery Supplies, 57 Fisherton Street, Salisbury, SP2 7SU Tel: (01722) 320633 Fax: (01722) 320633 *Upholstery suppliers*

Sarum Electronics Ltd, Clump Farm Industrial Estate, Higher Shaftesbury Road, Blandford Forum, Dorset, DT11 7TD Tel: (01258) 480802 Fax: (01258) 480803 E-mail: sarumelec@btopenworld.com *Air conditioning control system manufrs*

Sas, Wittington House, Henley Road, Medmenham, Marlow, Buckinghamshire, SL7 2EB Tel: (01628) 486933 Fax: (01628) 483203 *Software system distributors*

▶ SAS Amusements, 136-145 Central Parade, Herne Bay, Kent, CT6 8SS Tel: (01227) 375098 E-mail: info@sasamusements.co.uk *Amusement & gaming machines*

Sas International, Murray Gardens, Maybole, Ayrshire, KA19 7AZ Tel: (01655) 882555 Fax: (01655) 883781 *Ceiling manufrs*

▶ Sas Logistics Ltd, Poyle 14, Newlands Drive, Colnbrook, Slough, SL3 0DX Tel: (01753) 687317 Fax: (01753) 684165 E-mail: sales@saslogistics.co.uk

Sas Machine, Watton Road, Ware, Hertfordshire, SG12 0AE Tel: (01920) 465281 Fax: (01920) 465285 E-mail: sales@sasmachines.co.uk *Suppliers of machines & fasteners for leather related trades*

▶ Sas Paintball, Codsall Wood Road, Codsall Wood, Wolverhampton, WV8 1QR Tel: (01902) 844467 Fax: (01902) 713117 E-mail: info@saspaintball.co.uk *Indoor & outdoor paintball*

Sas Safe & Secure, Birchwoodmoor House, Roston, Ashbourne, Derbyshire, DE6 2EH Tel: (01889) 591595 Fax: (01889) 591595 E-mail: sales@legionnairesdisease.co.uk *Legionella control & tank refurbishment*

Sas Thermal Insulation Service, Greenhill Mills, Grange Road, Batley, West Yorkshire, WF17 6LH Tel: (01924) 443999 Fax: (01924) 478628 *Insulation contractors*

Sascal Displays Ltd, Unit 1 Hayes Metro Centre, Springfield Road, Hayes, Middlesex, UB4 0LE Tel: (020) 8573 0303 Fax: (020) 8569 1515 E-mail: sales@sascal.com *Electronic contract manufacturing services*

Sasex International, Sasex House, Haverhill Road, Horseheath, Cambridge, CB21 4QR Tel: (01223) 892319 Fax: (01223) 891535 E-mail: sales@sasex.co.uk *Exhibition display designers & contractors*

Sash Products UK Ltd, Ferrymoor Way, Grimethorpe, Barnsley, South Yorkshire, S72 7BN Tel: (01226) 715619 Fax: (01226) 780701 E-mail: sales@sashuk.com *PVCU windows supply, install & manufrs*

Sash Window Workshop, 4 Kiln Lane, Bracknell, Berkshire, RG12 1NA Tel: (01344) 868668 Fax: (01344) 868858 *Supplier & installation of sash windows*

Sasha Kagan Knitwear, The Studio, Y Fron, Llawr-y-Glyn, Caersws, Powys, SY17 5RJ Tel: (01686) 430436 *Designer knitwear*

Sasol UK Ltd, 1 Hockley Court, 2401 Stratford Road, Hockley Heath, Solihull, West Midlands, B94 6NW Tel: (01564) 783060 Fax: (01564) 784088 E-mail: sales@sasol.com *Chemical marketing & distribution*

▶ Sassen Engineering Ltd, 19 Aston Road North, Birmingham, B6 4DS Tel: 0121-359 7411 Fax: 0121-359 2404 E-mail: sales@sassenengineering.co.uk Principal Export Areas: Central/East Europe & West Europe *Precision turned parts manufrs*

▶ Sassi, 94 Brandon Parade East, Motherwell, Lanarkshire, ML1 1LR Tel: (01698) 258822 E-mail: info@sassijewellery.com

▶ Sassi, 40 Victoria Street, Wolverhampton, WV1 3PJ Tel: (01902) 311166 Fax: (01902) 712586 *Hairdressing beauty suppliers*

▶ Sassi By Salon Services, 10-12 Queen Street, Belfast, BT1 6ED Tel: (028) 9024 8245 Fax: (028) 9043 8639 *Retail*

▶ Sassi By Salon Services, 26 High Street, Lurgan, Craigavon, County Armagh, BT66 8AW Tel: (028) 3832 4212 Fax: (028) 3834 3078

▶ Sassi By Salon Services, 3 Damside Street, Lancaster, LA1 1PD Tel: (01524) 33337 Fax: (01524) 845783

▶ Sassi (Durham), 37 High Street, Durham, DH1 3UJ Tel: 0191-374 1108

▶ Sassi (Elgin), 43 High Street, Elgin, Morayshire, IV30 1EE Tel: (01343) 545055

▶ Sassi (Galasheils), 53 High Street, Galashiels, Selkirkshire, TD1 1RZ Tel: (01896) 757756 *Hairdressing & beauty suppliers*

▶ Sassi (Gravesend), 4 Railway Place, Windmill Street, Gravesend, Kent, DA12 1AP Tel: (01474) 566114 *Salon services*

Sassi Lift Systems Ltd, 5 Blackwell Drive, Braintree, Essex, CM7 2QJ Tel: (01376) 550666 Fax: (01376) 341219 *Lift component suppliers*

▶ Sassi (Omagh), 31 Market Street, Omagh, County Tyrone, BT78 1EE Tel: (028) 8225 9222

▶ Sat Technology, 105 Hyde Road, Woodley, Stockport, Cheshire, SK6 1NB Tel: 0161-494 0060 Fax: 0161-494 0018 E-mail: steve@sat24.co.uk *Computer hardware suppliers*

Satair Hardware Ltd, Shoreham Airport, Shoreham-by-Sea, West Sussex, BN43 5FF Tel: (01273) 441149 Fax: (01273) 464577 E-mail: enquiries@satair.com *Aircraft/aerospace industry fastener distributors or agents*

Satake Corporation (U K) Division, Horsefield Way, Bredbury Industrial Park, Stockport, Cheshire, SK6 2FG Tel: 0161-406 3800 Fax: 0161-406 3801 E-mail: sales@satake.co.uk *Cereal milling engineers*

Satalight Videography, Parkside Studio, Gotham Road, East Leake, Loughborough, Leicestershire, LE12 6JG Tel: (01509) 854004 Fax: (01509) 853111 E-mail: sales@satalight.co.uk *Environmental chamber & environmental test equipment manufrs. Also ovens laboratory & environmental chamber engineers/maintenance/refurbishment/service*

▶ Satara Ltd, Towcester, Northamptonshire, NN12 6WJ Tel: (07769) 973503 Fax: (01327) 358738 E-mail: dfdsatara@hotmail.co.uk *Electrical contractors*

Satchel Design Ltd, Whitley Lane, Walton, Street, Somerset, BA16 9RW Tel: (01458) 442371 Fax: (01458) 841245 *Leather goods manufacturer & supplier*

Satchrome Ltd, Unit 19 Birchills House Industrial Estate, Green Lane, Walsall, WS2 8LF Tel: (01922) 622721 Fax: (01922) 625353 E-mail: satchrome@yahoo.co.uk *Satchrome Ltd are specialists in Satin Chrome Finishing, Bright Decorative Chrome Plating and a wide range of Lacquer Finishes. *Satchrome supply many different industry sectors including; Brewery, Iron Mongery, Bright Sanitary Ware, Music Industry, Costume Jewellery and Leisure. *Satchrome Ltd have been a family run company for 50 years located in the heart of the black country, servicing nationwide.*

Satcom Distribution, 3 The Woodford Centre Old Sarum Park, Lysander Way, Old Sarum, Salisbury, SP4 6BU Tel: (01722) 410800 Fax: (01722) 410777 E-mail: sales@satcomdistribution.com *SatCom provide reliable satellite communications equipment and airtime for those working and travelling in remote areas.*The leading technologies we supply include Thuraya, Iridium, Inmarsat, Globalstar and VSAT systems.*We also supply airtime contracts for satellite phones.*With offices in the UK, US and Asia, worldwide support is available all day, every day.*

Satel Electronics, North East Suffolk Business Centre, Pinbush Road, Kessingland, Lowestoft, Suffolk, NR33 7NQ Tel: (01502) 513216 Fax: (01502) 513216 E-mail: satelelectronics@btclick.com *Electronic design & manufrs*

Satellite Business Systems Ltd, 11-13 Wakley Street, London, EC1V 7LT Tel: (020) 7417 2020 Fax: (020) 7417 2093 E-mail: sales@xenith.uk.com *Office equipment dealers*

▶ Satellite & Digital Services Ltd, Unit 5 Branhams Crescent, Roundswell, Barnstaple, Devon, EX31 3TD Tel: (01271) 325888 Fax: (01271) 329163

▶ Satellite GB Ltd, 15-20 The Oval, Bethnal Green, London, E2 9DX Tel: (020) 7739 5830 Fax: (020) 7739 5305 E-mail: roger@radar.gb.com *Furniture Design consultancy creating furniture products in the office, retail & contract sectors for UK & US manufacturers. System & seating design. Development & prototyping services.*

Satin Stainless Fabrications, Bridge Road, Weston-super-Mare, Avon, BS23 3NE Tel: 01934 632870 *Architectural metal workers*

Satoris Products Ltd, 25 Bradfield Close, Finedon Road Industrial Estate, Wellingborough, Northamptonshire, NN8 4RQ Tel: (01933) 274323 Fax: (01933) 274313 E-mail: edaids@aol.com *Metal fabrications services*

Satra Technology Centre Ltd, Satra House, Rockingham Road, Kettering, Northamptonshire, NN16 9JH Tel: (01536) 410000 Fax: (01536) 410626 E-mail: info@satra.co.uk *Laboratories-footwear, clothing, furniture & fabric research services*

Saturn Communications Ltd, Park House, 27 Hartswood Road, Warley, Brentwood, Essex, CM14 5AE Tel: (01277) 234131 Fax: (01277) 234156 E-mail: len@saturncomms.co.uk *Tower manufrs*

Saturn Engineering Ltd, 68 Wilbury Way, Hitchin, Hertfordshire, SG4 0TP Tel: (01462) 458511 Fax: (01462) 458515 E-mail: saturneng@hotmail.com *Electronic asembly wiring services*

▶ Saturn Facilities Ltd, Bedford Heights, Brickhill Drive, Bedford, MK41 7PH Tel: (01234) 244500 Fax: (01234) 244511 E-mail: tjordan@saturnfacilities.com *At Saturn Facilities Bedford business centre we provide: **-Conventional Lease Office Space*-Furnished and Serviced Offices *-Light production/ workshop units *-Document storage *-Self-Storage *-Conference Suite *-Meeting and Function Rooms to seat up to 200 *-Café-Restaurant *-Virtual Office Services *-Onsite Catering Facilities *-Onsite Health and Fitness Club *-Full on site services and facility manager *-Hotel **

▶ Saturn Facilities Ltd, 101 Lockhurst Lane, Coventry, CV6 5SF Tel: (024) 7658 2000 Fax: (024) 7658 2401 E-mail: sales@saturnfacilities.com *Saturn Facilities Coventry is situated just north of Coventry City Centre, within convenient access of the M6. The business centre offers a variety of excellent conventional and serviced office accommodation spread over two buildings. Dedicated conference facilities on the ground floor include a selection of conference suites and a 100-seater lecture theatre. Combining recent refurbishments with original period features the centre provides a modern working environment for businesses of all sizes.**Boasting an excellent range of business support services including a cafe-restaurant, extensive meeting rooms and ample parking the workspace is perfectly placed to suit the needs of today's businesses and their employees.*

Saturn Facilities Ltd, 8-10 Grosvenor Gardens, London, SW1W 0DH Tel: (020) 7861 0550 Fax: (020) 7861 0551 E-mail: enquiries@saturnfacilities.com *Operate multi-purpose business centres*

▶ Saturn Facilities, Saturn Centre, Spring Road, Ettingshall, Wolverhampton, WV4 6JX Tel: (01902) 493192 Fax: (01902) 402553 E-mail: tjordan@saturnfacilities.com *Saturn Facilities Wolverhampton business centre is a prestigious office building that lies on Spring Road, an established business park on the borders of the city centre. Within easy access of the M6 and Walsall, the building provides a selection of high quality office accommodation, conference facilities and virtual office requirements. It boasts an impressive reception area, a fully landscaped courtyard, ample parking and excellent views providing a healthy and vibrant working environment at the Wolverhampton business centre*

▶ Saturn Facilities Birmingham, Ephraim Phillips House, Bissell Street, Birmingham, B5 7UP Tel: 0121 6221366 E-mail: tjordan@saturnfacilities.com

▶ Saturn Facilities Mayfair, 5-6 Carlos Place, Mayfair, London, W1K 3AP Tel: (020) 7907 9700 E-mail: tjordan@saturnfacilities.com *Aurora House offers a full range of serviced offices and conventional office space in the heart of London Mayfair. Located in a superb Grade 2 listed building the offices are self contained, discreet and provide a 5 star corporate environment for any business looking for prestigious central London office space.**The centre in Mayfair also offers a range of conference rooms suitable for a variety of needs. **Our Mayfair centre also boasts virtual office services including telephone answering all handled by a professional management team ensuring it is one of the finest working environments in the West End of London.**

▶ Saturn Facilities Worthing, Columbia House, Columbia Drive, Worthing, West Sussex, BN13 3hd Tel: (01903) 262663 E-mail: tjordan@saturnfacilities.com *Columbia House, Worthing is a landmark five-storey purpose built office building which has recently undergone refurbishment to provide prestigious offices and conference rooms. Located 10 miles west of Brighton, the office space benefits from full air-conditioning, is fully equipped for network cabling, provides ample car parking and is set within landscaped grounds. This business centre is a superb environment for business.**

Saturn Music, The Old Vicarage, 24 Zetland Street, Wakefield, West Yorkshire, WF1 1QT Tel: (01924) 299214 Fax: (01924) 299214 E-mail: sales@saturnmusic.net *Musical instruments retailers*

Saturn Sales & Services Ltd, Unit 11 Morland Industrial Park, Morland Road, Highbridge, Somerset, TA9 3ET Tel: (01278) 794798 Fax: (01278) 788704 *Communications*

Saturn Security Installations Ltd, 678 Aigburth Road, Liverpool, L19 0NY Tel: 0151-427 5977 Fax: 0151-494 0766 *Security alarm installers*

Saudi Research & Marketing Ltd, Arab Press House, 182-184 High Holborn, London, WC1V 7AP Tel: (020) 7831 8181 Fax: (020) 7831 2310 E-mail: admin@hhsaudi.com *Newspaper publishers*

Sauer-Danfoss Ltd, Cheney Manor, Swindon, SN2 2PZ Tel: (01793) 530101 Fax: (01793) 481925 Principal Export Areas: Worldwide *Hydraulic pump & motors manufrs*

Saul D Harrison & Sons plc, 4 Langley Close, Romford, RM3 8XB Tel: (01708) 377330 Fax: (01708) 377220 E-mail: info@sauldharrison.com *Manufacturers & converters of textile & non-woven & polishing cloths*

Saul Trading, 427-431 Moseley Road, Balsall Heath, Birmingham, B12 9BX Tel: 0121-440 3276 Fax: 0121-440 3276 *Clothing manufrs*

Sauna Finn, 44 Napier Road, Poole, Dorset, BH15 4NA Tel: (01202) 675702 Fax: (01202) 675702 *Build saunas*

Saunders & Co. Ltd, 35-39 Trinity Street, Sheffield, S3 7AJ Tel: 0114-276 6733 Fax: 0114-275 0307 *Abrasives, machinery & forgings distributor*

Saunders & Associates Ltd, PO Box 6504, Basingstoke, Hampshire, RG22 4YZ Tel: (01256) 328881 E-mail: saceilings@btconnect.com *Office interior contractors refurbishment*

Saunders & Dolleymore, 7-9 Rickmansworth Road, Watford, WD18 0JU Tel: (01923) 238311 Fax: (01923) 246491 E-mail: sales@dolleymores.com *Patent agents services*

Saunders of Harpenden, 31 Frogmore, Park Street, St. Albans, Hertfordshire, AL2 2NH Tel: (01727) 875348 Fax: (01727) 875068 *Removal & storage contractors*

Jane Saunders & Manning Ltd, 1070-1072 London Road, Thornton Heath, Surrey, CR7 7ND Tel: (020) 8684 2364 Fax: (020) 8665 5968 E-mail: sales@jsmltd.co.uk *Surgical footwear manufrs*

Saunders & Taylor Ltd, 9 Boston Court, Kansas Avenue, Salford, M50 2GN Tel: 0161-848 9393 Fax: 0161-848 9696 E-mail: enquiries@saunders-taylor.co.uk *Heating engineers*

Saunders & Weeks Bristol Ltd, 265-267 Church Road, Redfield, Bristol, BS5 9HU Tel: 0117-955 7142 Fax: 0117-955 6064 E-mail: sales@saundersweeks.co.uk Principal Export Areas: Africa & South America *Manufacturers of gauges including pressure, vacuum & maintenance*

Sauter Automation, Trafford House, Chester Road, Stretford, Manchester, M32 0RS Tel: 0161-874 1300 Fax: 0161-848 0855 E-mail: ian.barstow@uk.sauter-bc.com *New & replacement control products to the HVAC industry*

Sauter Automations, Inova House Hampshire Int Business Park, Crockford Lane, Chineham, Basingstoke, Hampshire, RG24 8WH Tel: (01256) 374400 Fax: (01256) 374455 E-mail: info@uk.sauter-bc.com *Manufacturers of control regulator systems*

Sauvagnat UK Ltd, Unit 12 Weights Farm Business Park, Weights Lane, Redditch, Worcestershire, B97 6RG Tel: (0845) 0536000 Fax: (0845) 0536001 E-mail: sales@edencontractfurniture.co.uk *Sauvagnat UK Ltd are a leading UK supplier of furniture to the Leisure and Hospitality Industries offering a vast choice of indoor, outdoor and poolside furniture to suit all tastes, styles, designs and budgets. They also offer supply to the general public via their Retail Sales Division. Their main office is located in Redditch, Worcester. Examples of the products they offer include aluminium furniture, benches, giant umbrellas, pub furniture, table tops and table bases plus many more.*

Sauven Marking, 4 Wintersells Road, Byfleet, West Byfleet, Surrey, KT14 7LF Tel: (01932) 355191 Fax: (01932) 354511 E-mail: sales@sauven-marking.co.uk *Marking machine manufrs*

Savage Cranes Ltd, West Street, Hunton, Maidstone, Kent, ME15 0RR Tel: (01622) 820611 Fax: (01622) 820807 *Steel fabricators*

Savage Gate Automation, 8 Mulberry Road, Canvey Island, Essex, SS8 0PR Tel: (01268) 698182 Fax: (01268) 511722 *Automatic gate manufrs*

▶ Savage No.1, 89 Delphi Way, Crookhorn, Waterlooville, Hampshire, PO7 8AY Tel: (07745) 119063 E-mail: savageno1@ntlworld.com *Savage No.1 produces the latest in urban pocket fire. We manufacture the Lick-A-Shot cigarette lighter jackets for the Swan and Clipper lighter range. Lick-A-Shot, only from Savage No.1, only supplied to the wholesale trade*

Peter Savage Ltd, Liberty House, Liberty Way, Attleborough Fields Ind Estate, Nuneaton, Warwickshire, CV11 6RZ Tel: (024) 7664 1777 Fax: (024) 7637 5250 E-mail: sales@peter-savage.co.uk *Manhole covers & gulley gratings manufrs*

Savannah Web Design, Gatcombe Court, Dexter Close, St. Albans, Hertfordshire, AL1 5WA Tel: (01727) 763737 *Website designers*

Savant Distribution, Clayton Wood Close, Leeds, LS16 6QE Tel: 0113-388 5230 Fax: 0113-274 5777 E-mail: info@savant-health.com *Nutritional oil supplement distributors*

Savant Systems Ltd, 45a Chigwell Rd, London, E18 1NG Tel: (020) 8530 7809 E-mail: guy@savantsystems.co.uk *Computer consultants*

▶ Savant UK Ltd, 3-5 Rathbone Place, London, W1T 1HJ Tel: (020) 7291 0220 Fax: (020) 7291 0250 E-mail: sarah.briggs@savantinternational.co.uk *Specialists in cost management of design & construction projects*

Savcom Ltd, Little Acre, Coopers Hill Road, Nutfield, Redhill, RH1 4HS Tel: (01737) 822343 E-mail: martin@savcom.co.uk *Computer consultants*

Savcor Ltd, 8a Bridgend Road, Dingwall, Ross-Shire, IV15 9SL Tel: (01349) 867970 Fax: (01349) 867978 E-mail: info@savador.co.uk *Software design*

Save9 Ltd, Cayley Court, Hopper Hill Road, Eastfield, Scarborough, North Yorkshire, YO11 3YJ Tel: (01723) 588099 E-mail: sales@save9.com *IP communications*

Savecrest Machines Ltd, Stepney Grove, Bridlington, North Humberside, YO16 7PD Tel: 01262 671921 *Woodworking machinery agents*

Savetime Skip Company, Henrys House, Challenge Road, Ashford, Middlesex, TW15 1AX Tel: (01784) 247207 *Skip contractors*

Savill Cases, Units 14-17, Willow Farm Business Park, Rickinghall, Diss, Norfolk, IP22 1LQ Tel: (01379) 898898 Fax: (01379) 898466 E-mail: savillcases@aol.com *Custom made Transit/Protective Cases and Padded bags and*

continued

UK distributor of SKB Sports Cases and Bags for archery, golf, fishing and shooting.

Savill Fabrications Ltd, 2 Milton Avenue, Croydon, CR0 2BP Tel: (020) 8683 2929 Fax: (020) 8683 2555 E-mail: savill1@btconnect.com *Steel & metalwork fabricators & erectors*

Saville & Co., 1 Carey Lane, London, EC2V 8AE Tel: (020) 7920 0000 Fax: (020) 7920 0088 E-mail: mail@savillenotaries.com *Notaries public*

Saville Audio Visual, Scala Court, Leeds, LS10 1JD Tel: 0113-218 3600 Fax: 0113-242 6167 E-mail: leeds.hire@saville-av.com *Audio visual equipment hire, sales & service* Also at: Farnborough, Hull, Liverpool, Manchester, Middlesbrough, Sheffield & York

▶ Saville Group, 3 Swallowgate Business Park, Holbrook Lane, Coventry, CV6 4BL Tel: (024) 7670 5380 Fax: (024) 7670 5381 *Audio visual equipment & accessory suppliers*

Saville Heaton Ltd, Heaton House, Bradford Road, Dewsbury, West Yorkshire, WF13 2EE Tel: (01924) 466333 Fax: (01924) 456654 E-mail: sales@oakman.co.uk *Menswear distributors*

Saville Row Shirt Co (Castledowsan) Ltd, Curran Road, Castledawson, Magherafelt, County Londonderry, BT45 8AF Tel: (028) 7946 5000 Fax: (028) 7946 8074 *Shirt manufrs*

Saville Tractors Ltd, 67 Moira Road, Hillsborough, County Down, BT26 6DX Tel: (028) 9268 2220 Fax: (028) 9268 9333 E-mail: info@savillemac.com *Construction & agricultural machinery distributors*

Saville Whittle Ltd, Albion Bridge Works, Vickers Street, Manchester, M40 8EF Tel: 0161-205 1538 Fax: 0161-203 4159 E-mail: sales@savillewhittle.co.uk Sales Contact: W.T. Whittle Principal Export Areas: Asia Pacific, Middle East & South America *Pigment Preparations, Organic Pigments, Optical Brighteners, Metal Soaps, Lead Oxides, Inorganic Pigments, Dyestuffs, Chemicals, Anti - Corrosive Pigments, Titanium Dioxide, Fillers, Zinc Phosphates, Zinc Oxide + Zinc Dust. Most of the product range is stocked in our Manchester warehouse.*

Savilles Motor Factors Ltd, 15 Elders Street, Scarborough, North Yorkshire, YO11 1DZ Tel: (01723) 375010 Fax: (01723) 353798 *Brake lining distributors*

Savin Productions, 19 Woodlea Drive, Solihull, West Midlands, B91 1PG Tel: 0121-240 1100 Fax: 0121-240 4042 E-mail: sales@savinsproducts.com *Audio visual equipment hire*

Savoy Data Systems Ltd, 10 Leicester Road, Barnet, Hertfordshire, EN5 5DA Tel: (020) 8441 4426 Fax: (020) 8441 4428 E-mail: info@savoydata.co.uk *Computer consultants*

▶ Savoy Upholstery Ltd, South Parade Business Park, Grantham, Lincolnshire, NG31 6HT Tel: (01476) 591300

▶ Savu UK Ltd, 1 Green View Park, 1 Colin Crescent, Colindale, London, NW9 6EU Tel: (020) 8205 0890 Fax: (020) 8205 0890 E-mail: info@savu.co.uk *We are located in London as a representative company for many major factories in Turkey, China and Pakistan. Our product line comprises different kinds of woven fabrics such as denim, corduroy, ribs, twill, linen, saten, moleskin, which are produced in EU standarts.*

Savvas Georgiou, 207-209 Langham Road, London, N15 3LH Tel: (020) 8889 7999 Fax: (020) 8888 8927 *Wholesalers of shoe components*

Saw Centre Ltd, 650 Eglinton Street, Glasgow, G5 9RP Tel: (0870) 7280222 Fax: 0141-429 5609 E-mail: sales@thesawcentre.co.uk *Saw repairs & toll sharpening services* Also at: Edinburgh

Saw See Displays Ltd, 6 Speckled Wood, Hastings, East Sussex, TN35 5AH Tel: (0870) 1997726 Fax: (01424) 200521 E-mail: info@sawsee.net *Display systems supplier*

Saw & Tooling Services, 50a Sighthill CR, Edinburgh, EH11 4QB Tel: 0131-458 3886 Fax: 0131-458 3887 *Saw sharpening specialists services*

Sawcraft UK Ltd, Penncricket Lane, Rowley Regis, West Midlands, B65 0RE Tel: 0121-561 5616 Fax: 0121-561 5691 E-mail: sales@sawcraftukltd.co.uk *Machine & saw distributors*

Sawford Engineering Ltd, B1 Priors Haw Road, Corby, Northamptonshire, NN17 5JG Tel: (01536) 263211 Fax: (01536) 406266 E-mail: sales@sawfordengineering.co.uk *Subcontract engineering services*

Sawko Grinding Co., 1 Graham Cottages, Main Road, Lacey Green, Princes Risborough, Buckinghamshire, HP27 0PL Tel: (01844) 346823 Fax: (01844) 342396 E-mail: melebbles@hotmail.com *Sawblades service & repair*

Sawle & Vaughan, School House Farm, Littleham, Bideford, Devon, EX39 5HR Tel: (01237) 477181 Fax: (01237) 477181 E-mail: sales@sawleandvaughan.co.uk *Furniture & cabinet designers & makers*

Sawmatic Tool Sharpening, Commercial Way, Oakengates, Telford, Shropshire, TF2 6SG Tel: (01952) 615489 Fax: (01952) 613469 E-mail: info@sawmatic.com *Sawblade distributor & manufrs*

Sawmill UK Ltd, Ward Lane, Stanley, Wakefield, West Yorkshire, WF3 4LU Tel: (01924) 374953 Fax: (01924) 378294 *Wood yard*

Sawston Cleaning Services Ltd, 25 Brookfield Road, Sawston, Cambridge, CB22 3EH Tel: (01223) 832922 Fax: (01223) 830031 E-mail: enquiries@sawstoncleaning.co.uk *Commercial cleaning contractors*

▶ Sawtech North West, 9 Brown Street, Oldham, OL1 3QE Tel: 0161-624 1440 Fax: 0161-624 1440 E-mail: sales@sawtech.co.uk *Saw sales & service*

▶ Sawtooth, Unit 5, Victoria Works, Balls Street, Nottingham, NG3 3AR Tel: 0115-947 5184

▶ Sawtry Marquees, 4 Shawley Road, Sawtry, Cambridgeshire, PE28 5UH Tel: 01487 831852 E-mail: sawtrymarquees@btinternet.com *Low cost Marquee hire for whatever the weather*

A.K. Sawyer Consulting, 19 Capesthorne Rd, Hazel Grove, Stockport, Cheshire, SK7 6BP Tel: (01625) 263904 E-mail: alansawyer@ontel.net.uk *Media consultant*

J.T. Sawyer & Co. Ltd, Mottram Street, Stockport, Cheshire, SK1 3PA Tel: 0161-480 3366 Fax: 0161-480 9201 E-mail: boxes@sawyers.boxes.co.uk *Cardboard box manufrs*

Saxby Brothers Ltd, PO Box 15, Wellingborough, Northamptonshire, NN8 1LH Tel: (01933) 221700 Fax: (01933) 221702 E-mail: info@saxbys.co.uk *Saxby's are the market leader in the UK Chilled Pastry. We produce the best selling retail packs, Catering packs and bespoke B2B requirements. Chilled pastry takes the risk and time out of pastry making. The Quality of the cooked pastry is right first time, every time and there is no hassle to temper - as with those frozen alternatives. To find out local supplier or just to speak to Saxby's please call our Customer Care line on 0845 603 0821 or go to the website: www.saxbys.co.uk*

Mark Saxby Ltd, Spring Gardens, Higham Ferrers, Rushden, Northamptonshire, NN10 8EP Tel: (01933) 312176 Fax: (01933) 413260 *Leather manufrs*

Saxon Blinds Ltd, 7 Magee Street, Northampton, NN1 4JT Tel: (01604) 601888 Fax: (01604) 631212 E-mail: saxonblinds@hotmail.com *Window blind manufrs* Also at: Bradford

Saxon Carpets, Wilden Lane, Stourport-on-Severn, Worcestershire, DY13 9LW Tel: (01299) 827477 Fax: (01299) 827052 E-mail: sales@carpetsofkidderminster.com *Carpets manufrs*

Saxon Engineering, Unit 1, Bredgar Road, Gillingham, Kent, ME8 6PL Tel: (01634) 370023 Fax: (01634) 263250 E-mail: saxoneng@aol.com *Precision engineers*

Saxon Fire, 8 Newlands, Rushbrooke Lane, Bury St. Edmunds, Suffolk, IP33 2RS Tel: (01284) 704400 *Fire equipment sales & service*

Saxon Forge, Silver Snaffles, Verwood Road, Three Legged Cross, Wimborne, Dorset, BH21 6RR Tel: (01202) 826375 Fax: (01202) 826375 *Wrought iron manufrs*

Saxon Gate Motorist Centre, London Road Trading Estate, London Road, Biggleswade, Bedfordshire, SG18 8PS Tel: (01767) 314125 Fax: (01767) 314011 *Tyre & exhaust repairers*

Saxon Industries, Everland Road, Hungerford, Berkshire, RG17 0DX Tel: (01488) 684545 Fax: (01488) 684317 E-mail: sales@saxonind.co.uk *Horticultural products & car care products*

Saxon Lifts Ltd, Grand Union Works, Whilton Locks, Whilton, Daventry, Northamptonshire, NN11 2NH Tel: (01327) 843355 Fax: (01327) 843887 E-mail: sales@saxonlifts.com Sales Contact: S. Roe *Lift (scissor) manufacturers; air cargo handling service; disabled/handicapped person lift manufacturers; lift (motion platform) manufacturers; lift (goods) manufacturers; lift (hazardous area) (flameproof) manufacturers; lift (hydraulic) manufacturers; lift (theatre stage) manufacturers; lift vehicle moving manufacturers, and special engineering projects and motion platform for virtual reality videos.*

Saxon Packaging Ltd, 28 Harvest Drive, Lowestoft, Suffolk, NR33 7NJ Tel: (01502) 513112 Fax: (01502) 583627 E-mail: sales@saxonpackaging.ltd.uk *Corrugated packaging manufacturers & designers*

▶ Saxon Print Group, Saxon House, Hellesdon Park Road, Norwich, NR6 5DR Tel: (01603) 789560 Fax: (01603) 789561 E-mail: bruce.carpenter@saxongroup.com *Design*Repro*Proofing*Printing - 5 colour B1*Binding*lamination*Foiling & Embossing*

Saxon Security Locks, 208d Mitcham Road, London, SW17 9NN Tel: (020) 8767 6281 Fax: (020) 8767 7381 *Locksmiths*

▶ Saxon Steels Ltd, Callywhite Lane, Dronfield, Derbyshire, S18 2XR Tel: (01246) 418363 Fax: (01246) 290309 E-mail: enquiries@saxonsteels.com *Manufacturers of precision ground flat stock*

Saxton Drilling Ltd, Cardrew Industrial Estate, Redruth, Cornwall, TR15 1SS Tel: (01209) 315100 Fax: (01209) 315000 *Drilling contractors service* Also at: Exeter

Saxton Manufacturing Ltd, Unit 1 Bruntingthorpe Industrial Estate, Upper Bruntingthorpe, Lutterworth, Leicestershire, LE17 5QZ Tel: 0116-247 8665 *Cleaning chemicals*

▶ Peter Saxton & Co, 362 Church Road, London, SW19 2QF Tel: (020) 8648 5566 Fax: (020) 8648 7829 E-mail: peter@petersaxton.co.uk *Accountants*

William Say & Co. Ltd, 20-26 Verney Road, London, SE16 3DY Tel: (020) 7237 4500 Fax: (020) 7232 1568 E-mail: sales@pwcon.co.uk *Tin box manufrs*

Saybolt UK Ltd, Oliver Close, Grays, Essex, RM20 3EE Tel: (01708) 862611 Fax: (01708) 867401 *Inspection services*

Sayers Confectioners Ltd, Lorenzo Drive, Liverpool, L11 1BJ Tel: 0151-287 8700 Fax: 0151-270 2030 *Retail bakeries*

Sayes & Co. Ltd, Richardshaw Road, Grangefield Industrial Estate, Stanningley, Pudsey, West Yorkshire, LS28 6BR Tel: 0113-257 8411 Fax: 0113-256 9275 E-mail: contact@sayesandcoltd.co.uk *Heating, ventilation & air conditioning engineers*

Saygrove System & Technology, Units 9-10 Catheralls Industrial Estate, Brookhill Way, Buckley, Clwyd, CH7 3PS Tel: (01244) 550022 Fax: (01244) 549843 E-mail: info@saygrove.co.uk *High level electro-mechanical assembly sub contracts*

▶ Sayles & Booth Ltd, 312 Bradford Road, Huddersfield, HD1 6LQ Tel: (01484) 420670 Fax: (01484) 435065

Sayvol Chemicals Ltd, 111 Laurence Leyland Complex, Irthlingborough Road, Wellingborough, Northamptonshire, NN8 1RT Tel: (01933) 442069 Fax: (01933) 442070 E-mail: enquiries@sayvol.com *Water treatment chemicals & environmental services*

Saywell International, Aviation House, Woods Way, Goring-by-Sea, Worthing, West Sussex, BN12 4QY Tel: (01903) 705700 Fax: (01903) 705701 E-mail: sales@saywell.co.uk *Aircraft components stockholders*

SB Draughtproofing, Kintyre House, New Pentland, Loanhead, Midlothian, EH20 9NY Tel: 0131-440 3500 Fax: 0131-440 3500 *Joinery manufrs*

SB Fabrications, Unit 7 Hammond Business Centre, Hammond Close, Attleborough Fields Industrial Estate, Nuneaton, Warwickshire, CV11 6RY Tel: (024) 7632 9011 Fax: (024) 7632 9011 *Sheet metalwork engineers*

▶ SB Tek, 25 Hill Top CR, Doncaster, South Yorkshire, DN2 5SX Tel: (01302) 360461 Fax: (01302) 360461 E-mail: enquiries@sb-tek.co.uk *Specialise in the Installation of Electrical and Water Treatment systems*

▶ SBA Thermographics Scotland, 5 Pardovan Holdings, Linlithgow, West Lothian, EH49 6QZ Tel: (01506) 671707 Fax: (0700) 6313561 E-mail: sbrooker@sbathermal.com *Thermal imaging and thermographic surveying for predictive maintenance, energy and moisture surveys, condition monitoring and acquisition surveys. Based in Scotland covering UK and worldwide.*

SBC Group Ltd, City Gates, 2-4 Southgate, Chichester, West Sussex, PO19 8DJ Tel: (01243) 779526 Fax: (01243) 785503 E-mail: info@sbcgroup.co.uk *Computer consultants services*

SBJ Ltd, 100 Whitechapel Road, London, E1 1JG Tel: (020) 7816 2000 Fax: (020) 7816 2255 E-mail: info@sbjgroup.co.uk *Insurance brokers*

SBL, Eastmoor House Greenpark Business Centre, Goose Lane, Sutton-on-the-Forest, York, YO61 1ET Tel: (01347) 812100 Fax: (01347) 811220 E-mail: sales@softbox.co.uk *Software resellers*

▶ SBS Logistics Ltd, Inglesmaldie, Luthermuir, Laurencekirk, Kincardineshire, AB30 1QD Tel: (01674) 840007 Fax: (01674) 840009

▶ SC Consulting, Victoria House, 28-32 Desborough Street, High Wycombe, Buckinghamshire, HP11 2NF Tel: (01494) 601170 Fax: (01494) 601171 E-mail: mail@scceng.co.uk *SCconsulting provide Civil and Structural engineering design services for all types of building structures. We have experience in all types of projects in very many different sectors for both new build and refurbishment projects. We undertake both commercial and domestic surveys of building structures.*

SC Machinery, 16 Ranelagh Road, London, E6 2SL Tel: (020) 8552 9383 Fax: (020) 8552 6950 E-mail: frankcole@btconnect.com *Machinery merchants*

Sca Packaging Ltd, UK Central Office, Papyrus Way, Larkfield, Aylesford, Kent, ME20 7TW Tel: (01622) 883000 Fax: (01622) 716308 *Corrugated container manufrs* Also at: Corby, Edinburgh, Hartlepool, Histon, Langar, Lydbrook, Maidstone, Thatcham, War renport & Wigan

Sca Packaging Ltd, UK Central Office, Papyrus Way, Larkfield, Aylesford, Kent, ME20 7TW Tel: (01622) 883000 Fax: (01622) 793333 E-mail: publicity.packaging.uk@sca.com *Corrugated paper manufrs*

Sca Packaging Exeter, Kingfisher Way, Sowton Industrial Estate, Exeter, EX2 7LE Tel: (01392) 445141 Fax: (01392) 445125 E-mail: sales@scapackaging.co.uk *Corrugated box manufrs*

▶ Sca Packaging Telford, Halesfield 13, Telford, Shropshire, TF7 4PL Tel: (01952) 681950 *Packaging services*

Sca Recycling UK, Sca Packaging House, 543 New Hythe Lane, Aylesford, Kent, ME20 7PE Tel: (01622) 883000 Fax: (01622) 790905 *Waste paper merchants* Also at: Branches throughout the U.K.

Sca Recycling UK, Daneshill Industrial Estate, Armstrong Road, Basingstoke, Hampshire, RG24 8NU Tel: (01256) 351456 Fax: (01256) 842147 *Paper recycling services*

Scabal UK Ltd, 12 Savile Row, London, W1S 3PQ Tel: (020) 7734 1867 Fax: (020) 7439 0093 E-mail: info@scabaluk.com *Woollen merchants*

▶ Scadacentre, River Court, Brighouse Road, Riverside Park Industrial Estate, Middlesbrough, Cleveland, TS2 1RT Tel: (01642) 231111 Fax: (01642) 232211 E-mail: info@scadacentre.com *Scadacentre.com is the World's first online industrial automation superstore. A one-stop online shop for world leading automation products from multiple vendors, Scadacentre provides a flexible, easy to use shopping environment and specialist expertise in SCADA, DCS, Data Acquisition and PLC systems*

Scadin, 304 Upper Newtownards Road, Belfast, BT4 3EU Tel: (028) 9065 5105 Fax: (028) 9067 3370 E-mail: cadd@scadin.com *Surveyors*

▶ Scafclad Ltd, Canvas Works, Cox Lane, Chessington, Surrey, KT9 1SG Tel: (020) 8974 1271 Fax: (020) 8974 1957 E-mail: claire@protectivetextile.co.uk *Debris netting & cladding, scaffolding*

▶ ScaffCap, 12 Greenholm Road, Eltham, London, SE9 1UH Tel: (020) 8123 0505 E-mail: pcheek@scaffcap.co.uk *Protective covers that completely enclose round scaffolding joints manufrs*

▶ Scaffix & Access Kings Lynn Co, 177 St. Peters Road, West Lynn, King's Lynn, Norfolk, PE34 3JF Tel: (01553) 777879 E-mail: scaffix.access@btinternet.com *Scaffolding & Access, Fix & Hire.*Painting & Decorating.*General property maintenance.*

▶ Scaffold Alarms.Com, 168 Church Lane, London, NW9 8SP Tel: (0845) 1304591 Fax: (0845) 1304592 E-mail: sales@scaffoldalarms.co.uk *Scaffold alarm & security, secure a site, site alarms & security*

Scaffold Design Ltd, 409 Maltravers Road, Sheffield, S2 5AB Tel: 0114-281 3100 Fax: 0114-281 3104 E-mail: allen@scaffolddesignsltd.co.uk *Scaffold structure designers services*

Scaffold Erection Services Ltd, 225 Tyburn Road, Birmingham, B24 8NB Tel: 0121-322 2088 Fax: 0121-327 2592 E-mail: sales@scaffolder.co.uk *Traditional scaffolding contractors*

Scaffold Services Ltd, Hawarden Avenue, Leicester, LE5 4NN Tel: 0116-276 8125 Fax: 0116-274 2338 E-mail: sales@scaffoldservicesltd.co.uk *Scaffold contractors*

▶ Scaffold-towers.com, Unit 9 Haysbridge Farm, Brickhouse Lane, South Godstone, Godstone, Surrey, RH9 8JW Tel: (01342) 844218 Fax: (01342) 844588 E-mail: dan@scaffoldtowershop.co.uk *Scaffold tower sales*

Scaife Don Steel Fabrications, Pipwell Gate, Moulton Seas End, Spalding, Lincolnshire, PE12 6LU Tel: (01406) 371750 Fax: (01406) 371671 *Steel fabricators*

Jack Scaife, Stanfield Road, Waterfoot, Rossendale, Lancashire, BB4 7LR Tel: (0870) 1126881 Fax: (0870) 1126882 E-mail: sales@jackscaife.co.uk *Specialists in traditional & delicatessen meats*

▶ Scail, B Claylands Road, Bishops Waltham, Southampton, SO32 1BH Tel: (01489) 893453 Fax: (01489) 894730 E-mail: neil.stantiall@scail.co.uk

Scala Agenturen UK, West Midland House, Temple Way, Coleshill, Birmingham, B46 1HH Tel: (01675) 430300 Fax: (01675) 430444 E-mail: scalab46@yahoo.co.uk *Contraceptive & sex aids importers*

Scala Surgical Ltd, 200 Church Road, London, NW10 9NP Tel: (020) 8459 1816 Fax: (020) 8459 3416 E-mail: scala_impex@yahoo.co.uk *Medical & surgical suppliers*

▶ Scalable Communications, Wycombe Lane, Wooburn Green, High Wycombe, Buckinghamshire, HP10 0HH Tel: (01628) 852500 E-mail: info@scalablenetworks.co.uk *IT consultants*

▶ Scalar Technologies Ltd, 9 Cochrane Square, Brucefield Industrial Estate, Livingston, West Lothian, EH54 9DR Tel: (01506) 414806 Fax: (01506) 416279

▶ Scalderhurst Ltd, Ford Mill, The Street, Little Chart, Ashford, Kent, TN27 0QA Tel: (01233) 840711 Fax: (01233) 840794 E-mail: info@scalderhurst.co.uk *Paper merchants*

Scale Models Weston, The Wheel House, 10 Alfred St, Weston-super-Mare, Avon, BS23 1PU Tel: (01934) 413462 Fax: (01934) 643301 E-mail: workshop@scalemodelswestern.sfnet.co.uk *Industrial ship model making*

Scale Services, 33 Business Village, Wexham Road, Slough, SL2 5HF Tel: (01753) 511801 Fax: (01753) 694447 *Calibrate, hire & sell industrial scales*

Scales Plus, 25 Roundtree Close, Norwich, NR7 8SX Tel: (01603) 416569 Fax: (01603) 788045 E-mail: sales@scalesplus.co.uk *Scales equipment retailers & services*

Scalesmart Ltd, Unit 37, The Warren, East Goscote, Leicester, LE7 3XA Tel: (0800) 9154201 Fax: (0800) 9154202 E-mail: scales@scalesmart.com *Weigher/ weighing systems, scales, scales electronic/ mechanical, weigher/weighing systems hire/ leasing/rental*

Scaleways Leicester Ltd, 35 Carlisle Street, Leicester, LE3 6AH Tel: 0116-255 5092 Fax: 0116-255 5143 E-mail: sales@scaleways.co.uk *Weighing & scale maintenance, hire & leasing, distributors & agents*

▶ Scame UK Ltd, Jubilee Industrial Estate, Ashington, Northumberland, NE63 8UG Tel: (01670) 813351 Fax: (01670) 851199 E-mail: sales@scame.co.uk *Manufacturer of electrical installation accessories, to BS196 and IEC60309 standards*

▶ Scan Building Services Ltd, 35 Byron Street, Dundee, DD3 6QT Tel: (01382) 889700 Fax: (01382) 814980

Scan Coin Ltd, Dutch House, 110 Broadway, Salford, M50 2UW Tel: 0161-873 0500 Fax: 0161-873 0501 E-mail: sales@scancoin.co.uk *Coin handling equipment manufrs*

Scan Computers International Ltd, 27-28 Enterprise Park, Horwich, Bolton, BL6 6PE Tel: (01204) 474747 Fax: (01204) 474748 E-mail: sales@scan.co.uk *Computer component/ spare parts distributors or agents*

Scan & Design, 14 The Warren, Burgess Hill, West Sussex, RH15 0DZ Tel: (01444) 254750 Fax: (01444) 254750 E-mail: scan.design@fsbdial.co.uk *Printed circuit consultants & design services*

▶ Scan Hi Digital Ltd, Unit 48 100 Elderpark Street, Glasgow, G51 3TR Tel: 0141-425 1221 Fax: 0141-425 1050

Scan Logic Ltd, Shenstone Drive, Walsall, WS9 8TP Tel: (01922) 458158 Fax: (01922) 745110 E-mail: sales@scanlogic.co.uk *Document image & processing*

Scan Optics Ltd, 5 Brookside, Colne Way, Watford, WD24 7QJ Tel: (01923) 819581 Fax: (01923) 212633 *Computer systems & document scanners suppliers*

Scan Relation, 2 The Mews, 15a Liverpool Road, Southport, Merseyside, PR8 4AS Tel: (01704) 550500 Fax: (01704) 566958 E-mail: smithage@btinternet.com *Industrial, narrow fabric cutters, webbing cutting & sealing machines*

Scan Systems Ltd, Adswood Industrial Estate, Adswood Road, Stockport, Cheshire, SK3 8LF Tel: 0161-477 7750 Fax: 0161-477 7740 E-mail: sales@scansystems.co.uk *Quality control systems manufrs*

Scanachrome, 49 Glebe Road, Skelmersdale, Lancashire, WN8 9JP Tel: (01695) 725486 Fax: (01695) 722695 E-mail: sales@scanachrome.com *Ink jet printed images*

Scanbech Ltd, 44 Arkwright Road, Astmoor Industrial Estate, Runcorn, Cheshire, WA7 1NU Tel: (01928) 561747 Fax: (01928) 565672 E-mail: england@scanbech.com *Plastic bottle manufrs*

Scancad Services Ltd, Sussex House, Ewhurst Road, Cranleigh, Surrey, GU6 7AE Tel: (01483) 273770 Fax: (01483) 275931 E-mail: rbennet@btconnect.com *Sign makers & engravers*

Scancom Radio Communications, Beech House, 6 Banstead Road, Carshalton, Surrey, SM5 3NR Tel: (020) 8669 8212 Fax: (020) 8669 2918 *Radio communication equipment consultants*

Scandia Coldrooms, Brunel Road, Gorse Lane Industrial Estate, Clacton-on-Sea, Essex, CO15 4LU Tel: (01255) 433595 Fax: (01255) 222691 E-mail: enquiries@scandia-coldrooms.co.uk *Scandia Coldrooms - manufacturers of bespoke cold rooms, cold stores, food safe environments, coldroom flashings & doors, refrigerated trailers and shelving. With over three decades of industry experience Scandia has developed a range of highly efficient and cost effective products that are supported by a true commitment to customer services and after sales. We have provided cold room and food safe environments for many different industries and we are able to tailor make our products to meet your exact requirements, from reach in to drive in. Please do not hesitate to contact us with any enquires you may have from a new cold room storage solution, to new or replacement flashings and doors, as we are always happy to help.*

Scandia Hus, Felcourt Road, Felcourt, East Grinstead, West Sussex, RH19 2LP Tel: (01342) 838060 Fax: (01342) 838061 E-mail: sales@scandia-hus.co.uk *Timber frame house manufrs*

Scandic Foods, Beaufront Castle Flats, Hexham, Northumberland, NE46 4LT Tel: (01434) 608220 Fax: (01434) 608221 E-mail: sales@scandicfoods.com *Frozen food suppliers*

▶ Scandiflex UK, Keytec 7, Ascot Road, Pershore, Worcestershire, WR10 2JJ Tel: (01386) 565730 Fax: (01386) 565731 E-mail: craigs@scandiflex.co.uk *Suppliers of bespoke flexible packaging solutions*

The Scandinavian Door Co., 10 Willowhayne Crescent, East Preston, Littlehampton, West Sussex, BN16 1PJ Tel: (01903) 776894 Fax: (01903) 776894 *Door manufrs*

▶ Scandinavian Hardwood Flooring, 18 Blackford Road, Watford, WD19 6YN Tel: (020) 8428 9168 Fax: (020) 8421 6505 E-mail: gudnason.jorgen@btconnect.com *Sand & seal,stain,oil & maintain all wooden floors*

Scandinavian Log Cabins Direct Ltd, 6 North End, London Road, East Grinstead, West Sussex, RH19 1QQ Tel: (01342) 311131 E-mail: cabins@slcd.co.uk *Distributor of quality swedish manufactured log cabins*

Scandinavian Timber Ltd, 30a Roxborough Park, Harrow, Middlesex, HA1 3AY Tel: (020) 8864 0131 Fax: (020) 8426 9151 E-mail: enquiries@scandanaviantimber.com *Supplier of windows*

Scandura, St. James Road, Corby, Northamptonshire, NN18 8AW Tel: (01536) 267121 Fax: (01536) 266392 E-mail: sales@scandura.co.uk *Gasket manufrs*

Scanfit International Ltd, 11-14 Burton Close, Norwich, NR6 6AZ Tel: (01603) 480400 Fax: (01603) 424547 E-mail: mark@scanfit.co.uk Principal Export Areas: Worldwide *Pipeline fitters*

Scangrit, Eastfield Road, South Killingholme, Immingham, South Humberside, DN40 3NF Tel: (01469) 574715 Fax: (01469) 571644 E-mail: sales@scangrit.co.uk Principal Export Areas: Worldwide *Grit blasting abrasive & abrasive/metallic/shot blasting material manufacturers. In addition, industrial finishing abrasive products & blast cleaning media*

Scani GB Ltd, Royds Farm Road, Beeston Royds Industrial Estate, Leeds, LS12 6DX Tel: 0113-231 1411 Fax: 0113-231 1412 *Truck main dealers*

Scania (Great Britain) Ltd, Avonmouth Way, Bristol, BS11 8DB Tel: 0117-937 9800 Fax: 0117-982 4103 *GB scania trucks manufrs*

Scania (Great Britain) Ltd, Delaware Drive, Tongwell, Milton Keynes, MK15 8HB Tel: (01908) 210210 Fax: (01908) 215040 *Truck importers*

Scanlite Electronics, Data House, Mowbray Drive, Blackpool, FY3 7UZ Tel: (01253) 302723 Fax: (01253) 300484 E-mail: info@scanlite.co.uk *Electronic display suppliers*

Scanlock Overseas Property Agents, 208 Pensby Road, Heswall, Wirral, Merseyside, CH60 7RJ Tel: 0151-342 6530 Fax: 0151-342 6530 E-mail: sales@scanlock.com *Electric radiant heater distributors*

Scannedstick UK Ltd, Butterfly House, St. Neots, Cambridgeshire, PE19 6EE Tel: (01480) 362000 Fax: (01480) 217722 E-mail: sales@scannedstick.co.uk *Self adhesive paper manufrs*

Scanner Services Ltd, 7 Bluebell Court, Woking, Surrey, GU22 0HQ Tel: (01483) 762943 Fax: (01483) 871624 *Bar codes*

Scanners Television Outside Broadcast Ltd, 3 Chrysalis Way, Langley Bridge, Eastwood, Nottingham, NG16 3RY Tel: (01773) 718111 Fax: (01773) 716004 *Outside broadcasting equipment hire*

Scannest Ltd, 1 Horsewell Court, Moulton, Northampton, NN3 7XB Tel: (01604) 670064 Fax: (01604) 492767 *Communication aerial distributors*

Scantec Systems, Nicker Hill, Keyworth, Nottingham, NG12 5GD Tel: 0115-937 2023 *Alarm systems installation*

▶ Scantia, 78 Rainey Street, Magherafelt, County Londonderry, BT45 5AH Tel: (028) 7930 1143 E-mail: contact@scantia.com *Scantia stocks a wide range of exquisite luxury lingerie for all occasions and tastes. From lingerie sets, bridal lingerie, bras, thongs, stockings, suspenders right through to babydolls and basques.*

Scanvaegt N I Ltd, Unit 10 Mckibbin House, Eastbank Road, Carryduff, Belfast, BT8 8BD Tel: (028) 9081 3735 Fax: (028) 90813809 *Weighing system manufrs*

Scanway Engineering Ltd, 123 Vincent Street, Birmingham, B12 9SG Tel: 0121-440 3759 Fax: 0121-440 3759 E-mail: scanway.engineering@virgin.net *Press tools & presswork services*

Scapa, Manchester Road, Ashton-under-Lyne, Lancashire, OL7 0ED Tel: 0161-301 7400 Fax: 0161-301 7445 E-mail: sales@scapa.com *Cable components manufrs*

▶ Scape Developments Ltd, Windsor House, 1270 London Road, London, SW16 4DH Tel: (020) 8679 7111 Fax: (020) 8679 0221

Scappa (U K) Ltd, The Woodside Estate, Dunstable, Bedfordshire, LU5 4TP Tel: (01582) 478111 Fax: (01582) 471085 E-mail: carole.price@scapatapes.com *Scapa europe forms part of scapa group plc, a global manufacturer of specialist of adhesive tapes, foams, sealants & compounds, scapa europe is focused on meeting the requirements of its core market segments industrial, construction, printing & graphics, automotive, cable & medical* Also at: Lymington

Scarab Holdings Ltd, Pattenden Lane, Marden, Tonbridge, Kent, TN12 9QD Tel: (01622) 831006 Fax: (01622) 831417 E-mail: scarab@scarab-sales.com *Europes largest independant road sweeper manufacturer.*Range includes; Scarab Minor, Merlin, Merlin XP, Magnum, Mistral and Magnum Plus.*

Scaramanga Ltd, Etsome Barn, Etsome Road, Somerton, Somerset, TA11 6LU Tel: (01458) 273999 Fax: (01458) 272220 E-mail: scaramanga@mcmail.com *Furniture & kitchen manufrs*

Scarborough Fixings & Tool Hire, Lower William Street, Scarborough, North Yorkshire, YO12 7PL Tel: (01723) 360326 Fax: (01723) 374184 E-mail: sales@scarboroughfixings.co.uk *Architectural fixings distributors & manufrs*

Scarborough Laquers Co., Merry Lees, Staxton, Scarborough, North Yorkshire, YO12 4NN Tel: (01944) 710349 Fax: (01944) 710470 E-mail: sales@scarboroughlacquers.co.uk *Motor refinishing factors*

Scarborough Marine Engineers Ltd, 35-36 Sandside, Scarborough, North Yorkshire, YO11 1PQ Tel: (01723) 375199 Fax: (01723) 379734 E-mail: info@scarboroughmarine.co.uk *Boat builders marine engineers & chandlers*

Scarborough Minerals P.L.C., 1 Grosvenor Crescent, London, SW1X 7EF Tel: (020) 7152 6230 Fax: (020) 7152 6231 E-mail: info@scrbmin.com *Mining company*

▶ Scarf Enterprises Ltd, Colliery Road, Wolverhampton, WV1 2QY Tel: (01902) 871099 Fax: (01902) 871099 E-mail: info@scarf4art.co.uk *Art material suppliers*

Scarff Fire Safety UK Ltd, Unit 10 Cae FFWT Business Park, Pendraw'R Llan, Glan Conwy, Colwyn Bay, Clwyd, LL28 5SP Tel: (01492) 572992 Fax: (01492) 572992 *Fire fighting suppliers & maintenance*

Scaringbirds.com Ltd, Lower Upton, Ludlow, Shropshire, SY8 4BB Tel: (01584) 711701 Fax: (01584) 711478 E-mail: info@scaringbirds.com *Bird scarcer & rodent deterrent manufrs*

Scarness Fabrications Ltd, 3 Riverside Park, Reservoir Road, Hull, HU6 7QD Tel: (01482) 446662 Fax: (01482) 446268 *Steel & mezzanine flooring fabricators*

Scarthingwell Replicas, Scarthingwell Centre Scarthingwell, Barkston Ash, Tadcaster, North Yorkshire, LS24 9Pf Tel: (01937) 557877 Fax: (01937) 558084 E-mail: sales@scarthingwell.co.uk *Importers & wholesale of furniture*

Scartop Pine Furniture, 191 Station Road, Bamber Bridge, Preston, PR5 6LA Tel: (01772) 697111 Fax: (01772) 312369 E-mail: enquiries@scartop.com *Retailers of pine furniture*

Scartop Pine Villages, Moor Lodge, Oldfield, Keighley, West Yorkshire, BD22 0JL Tel: (01535) 642585 Fax: (01535) 644655 *Pine furniture suppliers*

Thomas Scatchard & Sons Ltd, Croft Mills, Batley Road, Heckmondwike, West Yorkshire, WF16 0EQ Tel: (01924) 402051 Fax: (01924) 406515 *Carpet manufrs*

Scatco Europa Ltd, Lowfield Road, Leeds, LS12 6BS Tel: 0113-243 5155 Fax: 0113-234 2170 E-mail: scatco@scatts.co.uk *Switchgear manufrs*

Scats, Hectors Way, Newbury, Berkshire, RG14 5AB Tel: (01635) 43436 Fax: (01635) 528502 *Agricultural merchants*

▶ SCC, 4 Redheughs Rigg, Edinburgh, EH12 9DQ Tel: 0131-339 0001 Fax: 0131-317 1683 *Computer software manufrs*

▶ SCC Construction, 83 Bell Lane, Broxbourne, Herts, EN10 7EX Tel: 01992 444588 Fax: 01992 444588 E-mail: shanieclark@hotmail.com *SCC Construction is a general building company specialising in all areas of the building trade. Please see our web site for more information or contact us to discuss your requirements.*

▶ Scenes Easy, Bath Road, Hare Hatch, Reading, RG10 9SB Tel: 0118-940 1700 *Retail outlet for giftware*

Scenetex Knitting Co Ltd, 17 Stephenson St, Thornaby, Stockton On Tees, Cleveland, TS17 6AL Tel: 01642 671417 Fax: 01642 646622 *Knitwear manufacturer*

▶ Scenic Blue, 13 Ferndene, Bradley Stoke, Bristol, BS32 9DG Tel: (0800) 7833428 Fax: E-mail: tracy_graham@scenicblue.co.uk *Professional garden designers*

▶ Scenic Compact, 3, Amarylis Close, Fareham, Hants, PO15 5LQ Tel: (01329) 849849

▶ Scenic Effect, Eyreswood Farm, Astwood Road, Cranfield, Bedford, MK43 0AU Tel: (01234) 750777 Fax: (01234) 752172 E-mail: martin@sceniceffects.com *Full design & build exhibition*

▶ SCENSION, 71 Bellegrove Road, Welling, Kent, DA16 3PG Tel: 0870 9914108 E-mail: enquiries@scension.co.uk *SCENSION is a highly successful company focusing on delivering advanced solutions across the new media industry. As a full service ISP, SCENSION*

continued

Company Information

continuation
has developed a product range that offers flexibility to all clients.

▶ Scent-Ible Solutions, 10 Sorrento Grove, Stoke-on-Trent, ST3 5XZ Tel: (01782) 594862 Fax: (01782) 599189 E-mail: Helen@scentsiblesolutions.co.uk *Aromatherapy products suppliers*

Schades Ltd, Brittain Drive, Ripley, Derbyshire, DE5 3RZ Tel: (01773) 748721 Fax: (01773) 745061 E-mail: schades@schades.co.uk *Paper converters*

Schal International Management Ltd, Elizabeth House, 39 York Road, London, SE1 7NQ Tel: (020) 7401 4800 Fax: (020) 7401 4900 *Project management consultants*

▶ Schawk, Kingsway North, Team Valley Trading Estate, Gateshead, Tyne & Wear, NE11 0JH Tel: 0191-491 7777 Fax: 0191-487 6673 E-mail: nclreception@schawk.com *Printing machine services*

Schawk, Kingsway North, Team Valley Trading Estate, Gateshead, Tyne & Wear, NE11 0JH Tel: 0191-491 7777 Fax: 0191-487 6673 *Global digital imagery plate manufrs*

Schawk Ltd, Boston Court, Kansas Avenue, Salford, M50 2GN Tel: 0161-872 9449 Fax: 0161-848 8441 *Flexographic plate designers*

▶ Scheelite Ltd, 2-3 Cursitor Street, London, EC4A 1NE Tel: (020) 7748 4408 E-mail: mail@scheelite.co.uk

Schefenacker Vision Systems UK Ltd, Portchester 2, Castle Trading Estate, Fareham, Hampshire, PO16 9SD Tel: (023) 9221 0022 Fax: (023) 9253 9522 *Car mirrors*

Schenectady (Europe) Ltd, Four Ashes, Wolverhampton, WV10 7BT Tel: (01902) 790555 Fax: (01902) 791640 E-mail: *Synthetic resin varnish manufrs*

Schenker B T L Ltd, Kelsey Close, Attleborough Fields Industrial Estate, Nuneaton, Warwickshire, CV11 6XN Tel: (024) 7635 7000 Fax: (024) 7635 4546 E-mail: enquiries@schenker.com *Road transport, haulage & freight services*

Schenkers Ltd, Schenkers House, Great South West Road, Feltham, Middlesex, TW14 8NT Tel: (020) 8890 8899 Fax: (020) 8751 0141 E-mail: enquires@schenker.com *International freight forwarders* Also at: Branches throughout the U.K.

Schiedel Right Vent Ltd, Crowther Road, Crowther Industrial Estate, Washington, Tyne & Wear, NE38 0AQ Tel: 0191-416 1150 Principal Export Areas: Worldwide *Manufacturers of flue linings, stainless tubes & insulated chimneys*

Schimmer Child, 31 Westward Road, Stroud, Gloucestershire, GL5 4JA Tel: (01453) 757333 Fax: (01453) 757333 E-mail: mail@schimmerchild.co.uk *Designers, interior design, cabinet manufrs*

Schindler, Benwell House, Green Street, Sunbury-on-Thames, Middlesex, TW16 6QT Tel: (01932) 785281 Fax: (020) 8818 7999 E-mail: marketing@schindler.com *Lift installation & maintenance services* Also at: Birmingham, Coventry, Glasgow & London E6

▶ Schindler Scotland, 2 Alderstone Business Park, Macmillan Road, Livingston, West Lothian, EH54 7DF Tel: (01506) 402800 Fax: 0141-641 9572 *Engineering*

Schippel Design Ltd, 21B Graham Street, Birmingham, B1 3JR Tel: 0121-236 2635 Fax: 0121-236 9289 *Textile designer*

Schischek Ltd, 1 Saddlestones, New Road, Princes Risborough, Buckinghamshire, HP27 0JJ Tel: (01494) 794904 Fax: (01494) 794905 E-mail: schischek@msn.com *Electric explosion proof equipment distributors: explosion proof products worldwide for heating, ventilating, air conditioning for industrial and offshore applications Especially explosion proof electric rotary actuators, linear actuators, sensors, magnets, transducers, explosion proof consultancy*

Schleifring Systems Ltd, Abex Road, Newbury, Berkshire, RG14 5EY Tel: (01635) 36363 Fax: (01635) 582118 E-mail: sales@schleifring.co.uk Principal Export Areas: Worldwide *Engineering slip rings suppliers*

Schleising Consultancy Ltd, 10 Victoria Mead, Thame, Oxfordshire, OX9 3HY Tel: (01844) 213492 Fax: (01844) 216751 E-mail: eddie.schleising@dsl.pipex.com *Corona discharge treatment specialists*

Schloetter Co. Ltd, Abbey Works, New Road, Pershore, Worcestershire, WR10 1BY Tel: (01386) 552331 Fax: (01386) 556864 E-mail: info@schloetter.co.uk *Electroplating chemical products*

Scholz+Bickenbach UK Ltd, Speedwell Industrial Estate, Staveley, Chesterfield, Derbyshire, S43 3JW Tel: (01246) 280280 Fax: (01246) 280445 *Steel stockholders*

▶ Schlumberger, Lambourn Court, Wyndyke Furlong, Abingdon, Oxfordshire, OX14 1UJ Tel: (01235) 559595 Fax: (01235) 535565 E-mail: info@geoquest.com *Manufacture software in the oil-fields*

Schlumberger Completions, Kirkton Avenue, Pitmedden Road Industrial Estate, Pitmedden Road Industrial Estate, Dyce, Aberdeen, AB21 0BF Tel: (01224) 723970 Fax: (01224) 770432 Principal Export Areas: Worldwide *Downhole completion products*

Schlumberger Evaluation & Production Services UK Ltd, Westhill Industrial Estate, Enterprise Drive, Westhill, Aberdeen, AB32 6TQ Tel: (01224) 741424 Fax: (01224) 840406 *Chemicals & oil production industry services*

Schlumberger Evaluation & Production Services UK Ltd, Unit 46 Howe Moss Terrace, Kirkhill Industrial Estate, Dyce, Aberdeen, AB21 0GR Tel: (01224) 406000 Fax: (01224) 723257 *Drilling monitoring services*

Schmidt Holdings Ltd, Southgate Way, Orton Southgate, Peterborough, PE2 6GP Tel: (01733) 363300 Fax: (01733) 363333 E-mail: sales@schmidt.co.uk *Road cleaning & sweeping machine manufrs*

Schmidt UK Ltd, 338 Polmadie Road, Glasgow, G42 0PH Tel: 0141-423 6002 Fax: 0141-423 5518 *Mechanical sweeping repairers*

Schmitt Europe Ltd, Sir William Lyons Road, University of Warwick Science Park, Coventry, CV4 7EZ Tel: (024) 7669 7192 Fax: (024) 7641 2697 E-mail: enquiries@schmitt.co.uk *Balancing equipment vibration control & laser measurement services*

Schneider Electric Ltd, 120 New Cavendish Street, London, W1W 6XX Tel: (0870) 6088608 Fax: (0870) 6088606 *Electrical manufrs*

Schofield Dyers & Finishers, Gala Mill, Huddersfield Street, Galashiels, Selkirkshire, TD1 3AY Tel: (01896) 754848 Fax: (01896) 754417 E-mail: galamill@aol.com *Fabric finishers*

Schofield Fabrications Bromsgrove Ltd, Sugarbrook Road, Bromsgrove, Worcestershire, B60 3DN Tel: (01527) 870220 Fax: (01527) 575409 E-mail: schofab@aol.com *Welding & fabrication engineers*

Schofield & Smith Huddersfield Ltd, Clough Road Mills, Slaithwaite, Huddersfield, HD7 5DB Tel: (01484) 842471 Fax: (01484) 842684 E-mail: sales@schofieldandsmith.co.uk *Worsted manufrs*

Scholar Engines, Blue House, Norwich Road, Mendlesham, Stowmarket, Suffolk, IP14 5NH Tel: (01449) 767711 Fax: (01449) 767772 E-mail: adwsre@aol.com *High performance car engine manufrs*

Scholle Europe Ltd, Princesway, Team Valley Trading Estate, Gateshead, Tyne & Wear, NE11 0UT Tel: 0191-491 0066 Fax: 0191-482 6626 E-mail: sales@scholle.com *Plastic bags for dairy industry*

School Colours Ltd, Manse Lane, 5 Monkswell Park, Knaresborough, North Yorkshire, HG5 8NQ Tel: (01423) 866906 Fax: (01423) 869319 E-mail: enquiries@schoolcolours.co.uk *Corporate identity clothing supplier*

The School Planner Co. Ltd, 80 Carolgate, Retford, Nottinghamshire, DN22 6EF Tel: (01777) 861980 Fax: (01777) 711782 E-mail: enquiries@school-planners.co.uk *Creators of top quality educational resources for schools & colleges. They include generic & customised student planners, homework diaries, homework planners, yearbooks, teacher planners, prospectuses, calendars, brochures, art materials, praise systems, merit stickers, certificates etc...*

School Shop, Prospect Hill, Kidderminster, Worcestershire, DY10 1PA Tel: (01562) 823763 Fax: (01562) 864637 *School uniforms retailers*

Schoolhill Hydraulic Engineering Co. Ltd, 3 Greenbank Place, East Tullos Industrial Estate, Aberdeen, AB12 3RJ Tel: (01224) 871086 Fax: (01224) 897135 E-mail: hydraulics@scheng.demon.co.uk *Designers & manufacturers of hydraulic cylinders*

Schort Industries Ltd, Trent Valley Industrial Estate, Rugeley, Staffordshire, WS15 3HA Tel: (01889) 583929 Fax: (01889) 583969 E-mail: sales@schort.co.uk *Electrical harness & assemblies*

Schott Industrial Glass Ltd, Ketton Way, Aycliffe Industrial Park, Newton Aycliffe, County Durham, DL5 6SR Tel: (01325) 300111 Fax: (01325) 300354 *Glass processors*

▶ Schott UK Ltd, Drummond Road, Stafford, ST16 3EL Tel: (01785) 223166 Fax: (01785) 223522 E-mail: info.uk@schott.com *Technical & specialist glass.*

Schottlander Dental Equipment Supplies, Fifth Avenue, Letchworth Garden City, Hertfordshire, SG6 2WD Tel: (01462) 480848 Fax: (01462) 482802 E-mail: service@schottlander.co.uk *Dental materials manufrs*

▶ Schrader S A Ltd, Unit 3 Castle Place, Adelaide Street, Coventry, CV1 5TS Tel: (024) 7655 0880 Fax: (024) 7655 1118 E-mail: jcarter@schrader-valves.co.uk *Established in 1844, Schrader is one of the worlds largest manufacturers of valves and associated products for tyre (including full range of repair material), air conditioning, aircraft, fuel injection, suspension systems and industrial applications.*

Schroff UK Ltd, Maylands Avenue, Hemel Hempstead Industrial Estate, Hemel Hempstead, Hertfordshire, HP2 7DE Tel: (01442) 240471 Fax: (01442) 213508 E-mail: sales_uk@schroff.co.uk *Electronic instrument case manufrs*

▶ Schtum Ltd, 11 Osram Road, East Lane Business Park, Wembley, Middlesex, HA9 7NG Tel: (020) 8904 4422 Fax: (020) 8904 3777 E-mail: info@schtum.co.uk *Schtum Ltd provides production co-ordination facilities for music and multimedia productions for TV, Film, DVD, CD and SACD.*

Schuco International KG, Whitehall Avenue, Kingston, Milton Keynes, MK10 0AL Tel: (01908) 282111 Fax: (01908) 282124 E-mail: info@schueco.de *Window system suppliers*

Schuco International London Ltd, Lyndhurst Avenue, London, N12 0NE Tel: (020) 8368 1642 Fax: (020) 8361 3761 E-mail: sales@schuco.co.uk *Medical equipment distributors*

▶ Schuf UK Ltd, 157 Park Road, Teddington, Middlesex, TW11 0BP Tel: (020) 8977 2992 Fax: (020) 8943 3898 E-mail: sales@schuf.co.uk *Valve manufacturers, including tank, tank drain & vessel outlet*

Schulmberger, Harlaw Road, Inverurie, Aberdeenshire, AB51 4TE Tel: (01467) 623059 Fax: (01467) 623062 *Cable protection manufrs*

Schunk UK Ltd, Richardshaw Drive, Pudsey, West Yorkshire, LS28 6QR Tel: 0113-256 7238 Fax: 0113-255 2017 E-mail: schunk.uk.sales@schunk-group.com *Manufacturers of carbon brushes & carbon related products*

Schwank Ltd, 62 Sunningdale Road, Sutton, Surrey, SM1 2JS Tel: (020) 8641 3900 Fax: (020) 8641 2594 E-mail: sales@schwank.co.uk *Infra red gas space heating equipment manufrs*

▶ Schwartz Ltd, 92 White Post Lane, London, E9 5EN Tel: (020) 8986 7429 Fax: (020) 8986 1125

Schwarzkopf, Oxford House, Oxford Road, Aylesbury, Buckinghamshire, HP21 8SZ Tel: (01296) 314000 Fax: (01296) 398012 *Hair preparations*

Schwenk Ltd, 70-71 Wells Street, London, W1T 3HN Tel: (020) 7580 3674 Fax: (020) 7580 2342 E-mail: schwenk.ltd@virgin.net *Button & buckle merchants*

Schwops Ltd, 34 Ashton Road, Luton, LU1 3QE Tel: (01582) 412622 Fax: (01582) 412095 E-mail: mo@schwops.co.uk *Visual communications*

Sci Lab Supplies, 14a Fifth Avenue, Bluebridge Industrial Estate, Halstead, Essex, CO9 2SZ Tel: (01787) 472068 Fax: (01787) 473970 E-mail: sci-labsupplies@btconnect.com *Laboratory suppliers*

Sci Tech Laboratories, The Grove, Craven Arms, Shropshire, SY7 8DA Tel: (01588) 672600 Fax: (01588) 672880 E-mail: enquiries@scitech-labs.com *Scientific services to poultry industry*

Sci Tek Instruments Ltd, N B House, 24 Stilebrook Road, Olney, Buckinghamshire, MK46 5EA Tel: (01234) 240765 Fax: (01234) 240965 *Scientific instrumentation distributors*

Sciaky Electric Welding Machines Ltd, 212 Bedford Avenue, Slough, SL1 4RH Tel: (01753) 525551 Fax: (01753) 821416 E-mail: sales@sciaky.co.uk *Welding equipment suppliers*

▶ Sciamed Ltd, Mart Road, Alford, Aberdeenshire, AB33 8BZ Tel: (01975) 564111 Fax: (01975) 564222

Sciclone Ltd, 24a Angel Hill, Bury St. Edmunds, Suffolk, IP33 1UZ Tel: (01284) 777432 Fax: (01284) 701080 E-mail: info@miuk.com *Analysis tool providers*

Science Exchange Service, Rutherford House, 43 Terrace Road, Walton-on-Thames, Surrey, KT12 2SP Tel: (01932) 246688 Fax: (01932) 246680 *Second-hand science equipment retailers*

Science In Sport Ltd, Ashwood, Brockhall Village, Old Langho, Blackburn, BB6 8BB Tel: (01254) 246060 Fax: (01254) 246061 E-mail: info@scienceinsport.com *Energy sports drinks manufacturer & marketing*

▶ Science Projects Ltd, 20 St. James Street, London, W6 9RW Tel: (020) 8741 2306 Fax: (020) 8741 2307 E-mail: info@science-projects.org *Non-profit company that designs & builds hands-on exhibitions*

▶ Science Recruitment Group, Buckland House, 10 Waterside Drive, Langley, Slough, SL3 6EZ Tel: (01753) 589700 Fax: (01753) 591900 E-mail: info@srg.co.uk *SRG is the UK's leading provider of technical and scientific staff to the pharmaceutical, biotechnology, engineering, environmental, food and beverage industries from junior to senior level appointments.*

Scientaire Thermal Systems Ltd, 40C Heath Road, Twickenham, TW1 4BZ Tel: (020) 8891 0450 Fax: (020) 8892 9168 *Air handling equipment*

Scientia Ltd, St. Johns Innovation Centre, Cowley Road, Cambridge, CB4 0WS Tel: (01223) 421221 Fax: (01223) 421218 E-mail: info@scientia.com *Timetabling software producers*

Scientific Atlanta Western Europe Ltd, 49 Suttons Park Avenue, Reading, RG6 1AZ Tel: (0870) 8325400 Fax: (0870) 8325444 *Global communications*

Scientific & Chemical Supplies Ltd, Carlton House, Livingstone Road, Bilston, West Midlands, WV14 0QZ Tel: (01902) 402402 Fax: (01902) 402343 E-mail: scs@scichem.com *Laboratory supplies distributors*

Scientific & Chemical Supplies Ltd, 39 Back Sneddon Street, Paisley, Renfrewshire, PA3 2DE Tel: 0141-887 3531 Fax: 0141-889 8706 E-mail: paisley@scichem.co.uk *Laboratory supply services & distributors*

Scientific Computers Ltd, Jubilee House, Jubilee Walk, Crawley, West Sussex, RH10 1LQ Tel: (01293) 403636 Fax: (01293) 403641 E-mail: info@scl.com *Computer software distributors*

Scientific Drilling Controls Ltd, Dyce Industrial Park, Wellheads Industrial Estate, Aberdeen, AB21 7GA Tel: (01224) 724535 Fax: (01224) 770581 E-mail: sales@scientific-drilling.co.uk *Oilwell survey contractors* Also at: Great Yarmouth

Scientific Games International Ltd, George Mann Road, Leeds, LS10 1DJ Tel: 0113-385 5000 Fax: 0113-385 5200 *Security printers*

Scientific Instruments Makers Co., 9 Montague Close, London, SE1 9DD Tel: (020) 7407 4832 Fax: (020) 7407 1565 E-mail: theclark@wcsim.co.uk *Charity*

Scientific Laboratory Supplies, Unit 14 Orchard House, The Square, Hessle, North Humberside, HU13 0AE Tel: (01482) 649665 Fax: (01482) 649667 E-mail: tcherry@scientific-labs.com *Scientific laboratory product suppliers*

Scientific Lesser Ltd, Hanworth Lane, Chertsey, Surrey, KT16 9JX Tel: (01932) 568122 Fax: (01932) 560818 E-mail: sllairskil@aol.com *Clean rooms, environmental instructors*

Scientific Lubricants Ltd, Glendene Depot, New Hey Road, Huddersfield, HD3 3YW Tel: (01422) 375401 Fax: (01422) 379666 E-mail: sales@scientificoil.co.uk *Lubricant distributors*

▶ Scientific Optical Ltd, Drury Lane, Pondswood Industrial Estate, St. Leonards-on-Sea, East Sussex, TN38 9YA Tel: (01424) 430371 Fax: (01424) 441639 E-mail: sales@scientificoptical.com *Optical lens & instruments manufrs* Also at: Bexhill-on-Sea

▶ Scientific Staffing Solutions (Scotland) Ltd, Suite 26D, 8-10 Glasgow Road, Kirkintilloch, Glasgow, G66 1SH Tel: 0141-578 3600 Fax: 0141-578 0049

▶ Scientific & Technical Gases Ltd, 1 Speedwell Road, Parkhouse Industrial Estate East, Newcastle, Staffordshire, ST5 7RG Tel: (01782) 564906 Fax: (01782) 564906 E-mail: info@stgas.eu *Precision custom-made gas & liquid mixtures for analytical & process applications, in a full range of container sizes*

Scientific & Technical Services Ltd, 3 Summerhill, Blaydon-on-Tyne, Tyne & Wear, NE21 4JR Tel: 0191-414 7801 Fax: 0191-414 1245 E-mail: sts@ststld.fsnet.co.uk *Corrosion prevention consultants*

Scientific Vacuum Systems Ltd, 12 Weller Drive, Hogwood Lane Industrial Estate, Wokingham, Berkshire, RG40 4QZ Tel: 0118-973 1946 Fax: 0118-973 1834 *Manufacturers, designers & sales of vacuum systems*

Scientific Wire Co. Ltd, 18 Raven Road, London, E18 1HW Tel: (020) 8505 0002 Fax: (020) 8559 1114 E-mail: wire@enterprise.net *Electric wire suppliers*

Scientifica, 9 Allied Business Centre, Coldharbour Lane, Harpenden, Hertfordshire, AL5 4UT Tel: (01582) 766888 Fax: (01582) 767888 E-mail: info@scientifica.uk.com *Scientific instrument sales & distributors*

Scientifics Ltd, 2-6 Langlands Place, Kelvin South Business Park, East Kilbride, Glasgow, G75 0YF Tel: (01355) 225488 Fax: (01355) 249669 E-mail: east.kilbride@scientifics.com *Metallurgists*

Scientifics, 4-6 Wharfside, Oldbury, West Midlands, B69 2BU Tel: 0121-552 1565 Fax: 0121-544 8581 E-mail: admin@scientifics.com *Independent analytical testing laboratory*

Scientifics Ltd, 52 Offerton Industrial Estate, Hempshaw Lane, Stockport, Cheshire, SK2 5TJ Tel: 0161-477 3004 Fax: 0161-480 4642 *Environmental consultants*

Scie-Plas Co. Ltd, Unit 3, Gainsborough Trading Estate, Old Road, Southam, Warwickshire, CV47 1HP Tel: (01926) 814093 Fax: (01926) 813975 E-mail: info@scie-plas.co.uk *Plastic product manufrs*

Scilabub Ltd, Unit 9 Huntingdon Court, Huntingdon Way, Measham, Swadlincote, Derbyshire, DE12 7NQ Tel: (01530) 279996 Fax: (01530) 270759 E-mail: sales@scilabub.com Principal Export Areas: Worldwide *Laboratory equipment suppliers & manufrs*

Scilly Linen Supplies Ltd, Porth Mellon, St. Mary's, Isles of Scilly, TR21 0JY Tel: (01720) 422211 Fax: (01720) 422211 *Laundry & cleaning*

▶ Scilutions, Trinafour, Abingdon Road, Marcham, Abingdon, Oxfordshire, OX13 6NU Tel: (01865) 391460 Fax: (01865) 391385 E-mail: kellysweb@scilutions.co.uk *Specialist electronics design and systems specification consultancy for high energy physics, cryogenics and space applications*

SciMAT Ltd, Dorcan 200, Murdoch Road, Dorcan, Swindon, SN3 5HY Tel: (01793) 511160 Fax: (01793) 533352 *Battery separators*

Scimed Ltd, Unit 5, Avon Business Park, Lodge Causeway, Fishponds, Bristol, BS16 3JP Tel: 0117-958 3754 Fax: 0117-958 4089 E-mail: enquiries@scimed-uk.com *Medical electronics*

Scimitar Construction Ltd, 105 Wentloog Road, Rumney, Cardiff, CF3 3HD Tel: (029) 2036 2221 Fax: (029) 2079 2100

Scimitar Engineering Co. Ltd, Power House, 87 Mansel Street, Swansea, SA1 5TZ Tel: (01792) 651781 Fax: (01792) 646229 *Power tool suppliers*

Sci-Net, Unit 5, Lakeside Farm, Middle Aston, Bicester, Oxfordshire, OX25 5PP Tel: (01869) 349949 Fax: (01869) 340063 E-mail: solutions@sci-net.co.uk *Network solutions services*

▶ Scion Electronics, 161 Hospital Street, Birmingham, B19 3XA Tel: 0121-359 6366 Fax: 0121-359 6448 E-mail: lee.davis@scionelectronics.co.uk *Manufacturer & supplier of GuardWatch. The U.Ks most succesful security guard patrol monitoring sytem. Reliable, rugged, cost effective and invaluable way of monitoring guards activities.*

Scipac Biosystems Ltd, Unit D7, Broad Oak Enterprise Village, Sittingbourne, Kent, ME9 8AQ Tel: (01795) 423077 Fax: (01795) 426942 E-mail: mail@scipac.com *Laboratory chemical product manufrs*

Sciss Ltd, Unit 9 Larkstore Park, Lodge Road, Staplehurst, Tonbridge, Kent, TN12 0QY Tel: (01580) 890582 Fax: (01580) 890583 E-mail: sales@sciss.co.uk Purchasing Contact: Gorsuch Sales Contact: Gorsuch *Waterjet cutting is an erosion process using a high pressure jet of water 0.6mm in diameter. Abrasive is fed into the water stream and self pierces for holes and internal cut-outs. Abrasive waterjet cutting cuts just about any material from plastic to hard tool steel. We are able to offer high production flexibility, so are pleased to accept single item, prototype cutting and repeat small batches. Tolerance +/-0.127mm. Variable cut finishes. Up to 100mm thick can be cut. Maximum part size up to 2.5m x1.4m . No heat generated during the cutting process so no hardening or distortion in the material. Accept drawings in DXF and other CAD formats. Engineering, Fabrication Parts. Sign, Art & Architectural Metal. Plastic, Stones & Composites.*

Sci-sys Ltd, Clothier Road, Bristol, BS4 5SS Tel: 0117-971 7251 Fax: 0117-972 1846 E-mail: marketing@scisys.co.uk *Bespoke computer software systems*

Sciteb Ltd, 18 Newton Man, Queens Club Gardens, London, W14 9RR Tel: (020) 7381 1481 Fax: (020) 7499 9253 E-mail: nicholas.beale@sciteb.com *Management consultancy*

Scitec Instruments, Bartles Industrial Estate, North Street, Redruth, Cornwall, TR15 1HR Tel: (01209) 314608 Fax: (01209) 314609 E-mail: info@scitec.uk.com *Specialist manufacturer of lock-in amplifiers and optical choppers which also distributes a wide range of photonic products including lasers, laser accessories and eyewear, ir sources, uv photodiodes and fibreoptic test products*

SCM Materials Handling Ltd, Unit 5, Albemarle Road, Taunton, Somerset, TA1 1BJ Tel: (01823) 325544 Fax: (01823) 333529 E-mail: a.watkins@scmhandling.com *Manufacturers of materials handling equipment*

Scobie & Mcintosh Catering Equipment Ltd, 15 Brewster Square, Brucefield Industrial Estate, Livingston, West Lothian, EH54 9BJ Tel: (01506) 426200 Fax: (01506) 426279 *Catering equipment manufrs*

▶ Scobies & Junor, 1 Singer Road, Kelvin Industrial Estate, East Kilbride, Glasgow, G75 0XS Tel: (01355) 237041 Fax: (01355) 263585 E-mail: info@scobie-junor.co.uk *Food manufrs*

Scobles, Anerley Railway Station, Anerley Station Road, London, SE20 8PY Tel: (020) 8676 7700 Fax: (020) 8676 7711 E-mail: sales@scobles.co.uk *Plumber materials, sanitary ware suppliers*

Scofish Ltd, Broadfold Road, Bridge-Of-Don, Aberdeen, AB23 8EE Tel: (01224) 222089 Fax: (01224) 222098 *Frozen fish processors*

Scomagg Ltd, Scomagg House, Crosshill Street, Motherwell, Lanarkshire, ML1 1RU Tel: (01698) 266199 Fax: (01698) 253672 E-mail: sales@scomagg.com *Computer software house*

Scomar Office Interiors Ltd, 18 Abbey Walk, Grimsby, North East Lincolnshire, DN31 1NB Tel: (01472) 500400 Fax: (01472) 500407 E-mail: scomar@scomar.co.uk *Supply & install office partitions & refurbishment*

▶ Scomi Group, Greenhead Site, Lerwick, Shetland, ZE1 0PY Tel: (01595) 692351 Fax: (01595) 693080 *Processing drill cuttings*

Scomo (Heating & Ventilating) Ltd, Escon House, 8 Fieldings Road, Cheshunt, Waltham Cross, Hertfordshire, EN8 9TL Tel: (01992) 635515 Fax: (01992) 635168 E-mail: esl@8escon.fsnet.co.uk *Heating & ventilation engineers*

Scooter Store Ltd, Unit 11 Italstyle Buildings, Cambridge Road, Harlow, Essex, CM20 2HE Tel: (01279) 453565 Fax: (01279) 454030 E-mail: albertwass@site-safe.co.uk *Security box manufrs*

▶ Scootles Bags, 19 High Street, Castle Donington, Derby, DE74 2PP Tel: 01332 811740 Fax: 01332 811740 E-mail: info@scootles.co.uk *Internet bag & fashion shop*

Scope Communications (UK) Ltd, Quantum House, Steamer Quay Road, Totnes, Devon, TQ9 5AL Tel: (01803) 860700 Fax: (01803) 863716 E-mail: sales@scope-uk.com *Communications suppliers*

▶ Scope GB Ltd, 70a Ilford Lane, Ilford, Essex, IG1 2LA Tel: (020) 8270 9891 Fax: (020) 8252 1727 E-mail: mansoor98@yahoo.com *Sports, leather, health & beauty instruments manufrs*

▶ Scope Security Systems Ltd, 66-68 Leigh Road, Leigh, Lancashire, WN7 1RX Tel: (01942) 674123 Fax: (01942) 680510

▶ Scopenet, Provender House, Unit Z, Paddock Wood Distribution Centre, Paddock Wood, Tonbridge, Kent, TN12 6UU Tel: (01892) 837968 Fax: (01892) 837226

ScopeNEXT Ltd, UWSP Barclay Centre, Sir William Lyons Road, Coventry, CV4 7EZ Tel: (0845) 4505406 Fax: (0845) 4505407 E-mail: info@scopenext.com *Suppliers of plastic pumps & dispensers*

Scorahs Ltd, 699 Huddersfield Road, Ravensthorpe, Dewsbury, West Yorkshire, WF13 3LQ Tel: (01924) 493222 Fax: (01924) 493222 *Plumbing, heating & electrical engineers*

Score Europe, Unit 8 Alpha Business Park, 20 White House Road, Ipswich, IP1 5LT Tel: (01473) 242460 Fax: (01473) 747644 E-mail: customersupport@score-group.com *Hydraulic valve actuator manufrs*

▶ Score Europe Ltd, Howley Park Road East, Morley, Leeds, LS27 0SW Tel: 0113-289 8420 Fax: 0113-253 5649

Score Europe Ltd, Glenugie Engineering Works, Burnhaven, Peterhead, Aberdeenshire, AB42 0YX Tel: (01779) 480000 Fax: (01779) 481111 E-mail: adm@score-group.com *Valve & actuator sales*

Score Research, 4 Meadway, Bramhall, Stockport, Cheshire, SK7 1LA Tel: 0161-439 3148 Fax: 0161-439 5032 E-mail: im@scoreresearch.com *Bench marking & performance improvements consultants*

Scorpio, 206a Watford Road, Croxley Green, Rickmansworth, Hertfordshire, WD3 3DD Tel: (01923) 212552 Fax: (01923) 468590 *Hairdressing wholesalers*

▶ Scorpio Business Solutions, 86 Mozart Close, Basingstoke, Hampshire, RG22 4HZ Tel: (07861) 215091 Fax: (01256) 410789 E-mail: scorpiosupplies@hotmail.com *Office furniture, stationery & logistics*

▶ Scorpio Computers, 2 Corporation Road, Plymouth, PL2 3NT Tel: (01752) 770027 *Computer suppliers & repairers*

Scorpio Computers, 6 Fore Street, Devonport, Plymouth, PL1 4DW Tel: (01752) 606011 Fax: (01752) 606011 E-mail: scorpio@myisp.co.uk *Computer retailers*

▶ Scorpio Signs (Design & Display) Ltd, Hartford House Yard, School Lane, Hartford, Northwich, Cheshire, CW8 1NP Tel: (01606) 74912 Fax: (01606) 76036 E-mail: mail@scorpiosigns.co.uk *Sign contractors/sign consultants or designers*

Scorpio Signs & Designs, Unit 28 Leeway Court, Leeway Industrial Estate, Newport, Gwent, NP19 4SJ Tel: (01633) 277599 Fax: (01633) 279669 E-mail: scorpiosigns@tiscalr.co.uk *Sign manufrs*

Scorpio Welding & Fabrications, 1 Old Wharf, Old Birchills, Walsall, WS2 8QD Tel: (01922) 643000 Fax: (01922) 643000 *Press brake facilities & services & fire escape installations contractors & fabricators*

Scorpion Bath Distributors Ltd, B Brookfield Park, Manvers Way, Wath-upon-Dearne, Rotherham, South Yorkshire, S63 7JY Tel: (01709) 878878 Fax: (01709) 879879

▶ Scorpion Compressed Air Co. Ltd, 9 Partington Street, Morris Green, Bolton, BL3 3LE Tel: (01204) 431846 E-mail: info@scorpioncompressors.co.uk *Compressed air compressors sales & services*

Scorpion Engineering Construction Ltd, Brunel Court, Elcot Lane, Marlborough, Wiltshire, SN8 2AZ Tel: (01672) 514471 Fax: (01672) 518518 E-mail: sales@scorpionstructures.co.uk *Erection & fabrication steel framed buildings*

▶ Scorpion Event Production, Castle Lane, Ripponden, Sowerby Bridge, West Yorkshire, HX6 4JZ Tel: (01422) 823399 E-mail: chris.smith@scorpion-events.co.uk

Scorpion H.T. Ltd, Unit 1 Ogles Yard, Victoria Road, Ripley, Derbyshire, DE5 3FW Tel: (01773) 570600 Fax: (01773) 570200 *Oil seal specialists*

▶ Scorpion Metal Fabrications Ltd, 8 Longside Lane, Bradford, West Yorkshire, BD7 1DF Tel: (01274) 730055 *Metal fabricators*

Scorpion Ribs Ltd, Haven Quay, Mill Lane, Lymington, Hampshire, SO41 9AZ Tel: (01590) 677080 Fax: (01590) 671911 E-mail: sales@scorpionribs.com *Boat builder*

Scorpion Tooling Services Ltd, Unit 7 & 9, Libbys Drive, Stroud, Gloucestershire, GL5 1RN Tel: (01453) 751511 Fax: (01453) 766676 *Precision grinding services*

Scorpion Vehicle Security Systems Ltd, Unit 1 Siemens Road, North Bank Industrial Estate, Manchester, M44 5AH Tel: 0161-777 9666 Fax: 0161-777 9473 E-mail: sales@selecto-parts.co.uk *Motor vehicle accessories*

▶ Scot Crest, Concept House, Old Monkland Road, Coatbridge, Lanarkshire, ML5 5EU Tel: (01236) 606560 Fax: (01236) 627711 *Embroidered work wear manufrs*

▶ Scot Pak Ltd, Unit 4 Hanson Street, Glasgow, G31 2JW Tel: 0141-550 4452 Fax: 0141-550 8836

Scot Seats Direct, Gainford Business Centre, Fenwick, Kilmarnock, Ayrshire, KA3 6AR Tel: (01560) 600100 Fax: (01560) 600100 E-mail: gainford@lineone.net *Extra seat kits for vans, 4x4's, estate cars & minibuses manufrs*

Scot Test Ltd, 12 Thomas Street, Paisley, Renfrewshire, PA1 2RE Tel: 0141-887 7925 Fax: 0141-889 0665 E-mail: scot-testltd@btconnect.com *Non-destructive testing services*

Scot Vent Ltd, 18-20 Boswell Square, Hillington Industrial Estate, Glasgow, G52 4BQ Tel: 0141-882 3243 Fax: 0141-810 5100 *Heating & ventilating engineers*

Scotair Balloons, The Old Farmhouse, Skirling, Biggar, Lanarkshire, ML12 6HB Tel: (01899) 860334 E-mail: info@scotair.com *Hot air balloons service*

▶ Scotaudio, Unit 2, Beta Centre, Stirling University Innovation Park, Stirling, FK9 4NF Tel: (01786) 442022 Fax: (01786) 458033 E-mail: andy@scotaudio.com *Retailers, installers & hirers of audio visual equipment*

▶ Scotavia Images, Birch View Cottage, High Street, Grantown-on-Spey, Morayshire, PH26 3EN Tel: (01479) 872144 E-mail: gary@smasher.demon.co.uk *Aerial photography service for Scotland.For tourism,construction,architects ,shipping etc. Can provide digital ,CD,large prints.Many examples on website.*

Scotbeef Ltd, 27 Glenburn Road, East Kilbride, Glasgow, G74 5BA Tel: (01355) 225381 Fax: (01355) 264327 E-mail: longleys@scotbeef.com *Meat (processed & cooked) products manufrs*

Scotcare Environmental Services, 670 Duke Street, Glasgow, G31 1JZ Tel: 0141-554 0375 Fax: 0141-554 0013 *Pest control services*

▶ Scotcare Health Solutions, 21 Carron Way, Paisley, Renfrewshire, PA3 4NW Tel: (07940) 223619 Fax: 0141-887 7197 E-mail: info@scotcare.co.uk *Occupational health, health promotion*

Scotch Lamb Marketing Ltd, Eastmains Farm, Newbigging, Carnwath, Lanark, ML11 8NB Tel: (01555) 840002 Fax: (01555) 840095 *Livestock dealers*

▶ Scotch Oven, 8 Main Street, Callander, Perthshire, FK17 8BB Tel: (01877) 339518

Scotech International Services, Craigshaw Road, West Tullos Industrial Estate, Aberdeen, AB12 3AR Tel: (01224) 248450 Fax: (01224) 248023 E-mail: sales@scotech.co.uk *Electronic instrument hire & leasing services*

Scotford & Teasdale, Unit 8 Thames Park, Lester Way, Wallingford, Oxfordshire, OX10 9TA Tel: 01491 821737 Fax: 01491 821730 *Refrigeration and air conditioning engineers*

Scotforms Computer Stationery Ltd, 3 Hatton Square, Livingston, West Lothian, EH54 9BJ Tel: (01506) 410871 Fax: (01506) 416805 E-mail: info@scotforms.co.uk *General printer & office suppliers*

Scotgrain Agriculture Ltd, Grampian Road, Elgin, Morayshire, IV30 1XJ Tel: (01343) 543281 Fax: (01343) 550849 *Grain merchants*

Scotgrain Agriculture Ltd, Rosehall, Turriff, Aberdeenshire, AB53 4HD Tel: 01888 568765 *Agricultural merchants*

Scotgrip (U K) Ltd, Units 8-9, North Deeside Road, Banchory, Kincardineshire, AB31 5YR Tel: (01330) 825335 Fax: (01330) 825260 E-mail: info@scotgrip.com *Safety product manufrs*

▶ Scotia Ceramics Ltd, Coll Pottery, Coll, Isle Of Lewis, HS2 0JP Tel: (01851) 820219

▶ Scotia Design Build Ltd, 175 Cocklaw Street, Kelty, Fife, KY4 0DH Tel: (01383) 831336 Fax: (01383) 831499

▶ Scotia Energy Saving Systems, 60 Mollinsburn Street, Glasgow, G21 4SF Tel: 0141-772 4621 Fax: 0141-557 3848

▶ Scotia Energy Saving Systems Ltd, 49 Nasmyth Road, Glenrothes, Fife, KY6 2SD Tel: (01592) 773623 Fax: (01592) 773562 E-mail: contracts@scotia-aircon.co.uk *Install heating & ventilation, air conditioning, refrigeration*

The Scotia Fencing Company Ltd, Howe Road, Kilsyth, Glasgow, G65 0TA Tel: (01236) 823339 Fax: (01236) 826434 *Fencing*

▶ Scotia Homes, Anderson Drive, Aberdeen, AB15 6BW Tel: (01224) 323954

Scotia Instrumentation Ltd, Aberdeen Science & Technology Park, Balgownie Road, Bridge of Don, Aberdeen, AB22 8GT Tel: (01224) 222888 Fax: (01224) 826299 E-mail: info@scotia-instrumentation.com *Instrument & hydraulic engineers*

Scotia Instrumentation Ltd, Unit 5c New York Way, New York Industrial Park, Newcastle upon Tyne, NE27 0QF Tel: 0191-296 3444 Fax: 0191-296 3555 E-mail: sales@scotia-instrumentation.com *Instrumentation house*

Scotia Marine, Clyde Marina, The Harbour, Ardrossan, Ayrshire, KA22 8DB Tel: (01294) 469584 Fax: (01294) 469584 E-mail: enquiries@scotiamarine.com *Yacht & motor cruiser charter, teambuilding events*

▶ Scotia Thermal Engineering Ltd, 1 Newark Road South, Glenrothes, Fife, KY7 4NS Tel: (01592) 770094 Fax: (01592) 770095

▶ Scotiathermel, 2B Craiglockhart Drive South, Edinburgh, EH14 1HZ Tel: 0131-455 7805 Fax: 0131-443 6190

▶ Scotish Provinsial Press Ltd, 13 Henderson Road, Inverness, IV1 1SP Tel: (01463) 224444

▶ Scotkleen Warwick Power Washers, 149a Glasgow Road, Wishaw, Lanarkshire, ML2 7QJ Tel: (0870) 8600600 Fax: (01698) 356697 E-mail: info@scotkleen.co.uk *Manufacturer of power washers*

Scotkleen Warwick Power Washers, 149a Glasgow Road, Wishaw, Lanarkshire, ML2 7QJ Tel: (0870) 8600600 Fax: (01698) 356697 E-mail: info@scotkleen.co.uk *Hot & cold static power washer manufrs*

Scotland Electronics (International) Ltd, 28 West Road, Greshop Industrial Estate, Forres, Morayshire, IV36 2GW Tel: (01309) 678900 Fax: (01309) 678909 E-mail: sales@scotlandelectronics.co.uk *Design & manufacture of electronic equipment & systems*

Scotland Gas Networks, 11 West Shore Road, Edinburgh, EH5 1RH Tel: 0131-559 6000 Fax: 0131-559 6000 *Gas pipe & meter installation*

▶ The Scotland Kilt Co., 93 -95 South Bridge, Edinburgh, EH1 1HN Tel: 0131-225 3555 E-mail: thescotlandkiltco@hotmail.com *Kilt retailer*

▶ Scotlee Transport, Portland Place, Heatherhouse Industrial Estate, Irvine, Ayrshire, KA12 8LW Tel: (01294) 311427 Fax: (01294) 271483

▶ Scotlog Sales, Shore Street, Inverness, IV1 1NF Tel: (01463) 712960 Fax: (01463) 711076

Scot-Nail Ltd, Pit Road, Kirkintilloch, Glasgow, G66 3ND Tel: 0141-777 6388 Fax: 0141-776 2581 *Fasteners*

Scotoil Services Ltd, Miller Street, Aberdeen, AB11 5AN Tel: (01224) 571491 Fax: (01224) 580861 E-mail: enquiries@scotoil.co.uk *Equipment decontamination contractors services*

▶ Scotprime, Murray Street, Grimsby, South Humberside, DN31 3RD Tel: (01472) 358100 Fax: (01472) 350328 E-mail: admin@scotprime.co.uk *Wholesale fish merchants*

Scotprime Seafoods Ltd, 11 Whitfield Drive, Heathfield Industrial Estate, Ayr, KA8 9RX Tel: (01292) 611161 Fax: (01292) 611039 E-mail: sales@scotprime.com *Seafood merchants*

▶ Scotprint Bookprinters, Gateside Commerce Park, Haddington, East Lothian, EH41 3ST Tel: (01620) 828800 Fax: (01620) 828801 E-mail: sales@scotprint.co.uk

Scotrad Car Radiator Repairs, 410 Gorgie Road, Edinburgh, EH11 2RN Tel: 0131-337 8887 Fax: 0131-337 9998 E-mail: sales@scotrad.co.uk *Car radiators & number plate manufrs*

▶ Scotram Cleaning Materials, 4 Scotram House Dumbryden Industrial Estate, Dumbryden Road, Edinburgh, EH14 2AB Tel: 0131-477 3588 Fax: 0131-477 3587 E-mail: sales@scotramltd.co.uk *Janitorial supplies*

Scotsafe Testing Ltd, 17 Woodlands Drive, Kirkhill Industrial Estate, Aberdeen, AB21 0GW Tel: (01224) 771200 Fax: (01224) 725511 E-mail: adrian@scotsafe.co.uk *Breathing apparatus specialists*

▶ Scotscraig BUSINESS SOLUTIONS, The Clock House, 87 Paines Lane, PINNER, Middlesex, HA5 3BZ Tel: 020 8933-9962 E-mail: reception@scotscraigsolutions.co.uk *INDEPENDENT BUSINESS DEVELOPMENT SERVICE, helping a Managing Director /Owner to articulate & resolve the most important "business problems'. The service allows the MD/ O to: gain an independent, perspective on options which offer the best returns for effort; identify & establish performance standards, matching needs; make changes which yield clear benefits. Our core expertise is in achieving effective resolution of business problems, where there is a clear need to improve or change direction. Scotscraig is an independent & ethical company, with a high delivery-capability, using an effective resource network. We have international credentials & accreditations to provide this service. We cherish our outstanding track record helping many ""well known"" companies to reach their goals. Please contact us for an appointment. We guarantee that: a)you will not be charged for a first appointment; b)you will be surprised by what we can achieve; c)how cost-effective we can be.*

▶ Scotserve Bottling Services Ltd, Unit 5, Lomond Industrial Estate, Alexandria, Dunbartonshire, G83 0TL Tel: 01389 756161 *Bottling machinery manufrs*

▶ Scotshield Ltd, Century House, Chapelhall Industrial Estate, Chapelhall, Airdrie, Lanarkshire, ML6 8QH Tel: (01236) 767788 Fax: (01236) 762233

Scotshield Burglar Alarm Systems, 1 Dryden Vale, Bilston Glen, Loanhead, Midlothian, EH20 9HN Tel: 0131-448 0583 Fax: 0131-448 0584 E-mail: admin@scotshield.com *Security services*

▶ Scotshield Fire & Security Systems, 9 Lotland Street, Inverness, IV1 1ST Tel: (01463) 709637 Fax: (01463) 709638

Scotsman Beverage Systems, 13 Halesowen Industrial Park, Chancel Way, Halesowen, West Midlands, B62 8SE Tel: 0121-501 2566 Fax: 0121-550 0873 *Cold drink dispenser manufrs*

▶ Scott, Back Lane, Mawdesley, Ormskirk, Lancashire, L40 3SY Tel: (01704) 823355 *Jewelers*

A.E. Scott Ltd, 65 Sienna, White Hart Avenue, London, SE28 0GU Tel: (020) 7232 1903 Fax: (020) 8301 8221 E-mail: info@scottscarpets.com *Industrial carpet contractors* Also at: London SE16

Scott Adam Systems Ltd, Ramsay House, 18 Vera Avenue, London, N21 1RA Tel: (020) 8360 6600 Fax: (020) 8360 6688 E-mail: sales@scottadam.co.uk *Computer consultants*

▶ Scott and Sons, 14 School Road, Faversham, Kent, ME13 8QZ Tel: (01795) 537221 E-mail: slarty@bardfast.wanadoo.co.uk *Carpentry Joinery Restoration*

Andrew Scott Ltd, The Grange, Margam, Port Talbot, West Glamorgan, SA13 2SP Tel: (01639) 889800 Fax: (01639) 889829 E-mail: asl@andrewscott.co.uk *Civil engineers*

Scott Bader Co. Ltd, Wollaston Hall, Wollaston, Wellingborough, Northamptonshire, NN29 7RL Tel: (01933) 663100 Fax: (01933) 663028 E-mail: sales@scottbader.com *Specialty chemicals manufrs*

▶ Scott Britten, 16 Pheonix House, Hyssop Close, Cannock, Staffordshire, WS11 7GA Tel: (01543) 579977 Fax: 01543 467260 E-mail: info@scottbritten.co.uk

Scott Bros, 94 Mill Hall, Aylesford, Kent, ME20 7JN Tel: (01622) 717007 Fax: (01622) 717007 *Concrete paving*

▶ Scott Bros Ltd, Annie House, Master Road, Thornaby, Stockton-on-Tees, Cleveland, TS17 0BE Tel: (01642) 750444 Fax: (01642) 766544

Scott Burridge Chick, Daniell House, 26 Falmouth Road, Truro, Cornwall, TR1 2HX Tel: (01872) 277397 Fax: (01872) 223342 E-mail: enq@sbcproperty.com *Commercial estate agents*

Charles Scott & Partners (London) Ltd, 23 Skylines, Limeharbour, London, E14 9TS Tel: (020) 7538 1333 Fax: (020) 7538 3747 E-mail: cspll@aol.com *Consulting engineers civil structural & building surveyors services*

Scott Closures International Ltd, Balena Close, Creekmoor Trading Estate, Poole, Dorset, BH17 7DZ Tel: (01202) 692428 Fax: (01202) 697944 E-mail: sales@scottclosures.com *Compression & injection moulded cap manufrs*

Scott Computer Supplies, Unit A3, Sumervell Street, Cambuslang, Glasgow, G72 7EB Tel: 0141-646 2690 Fax: 0141-646 2838 E-mail: info@scottcomputersupplies.co.uk *Office suppliers*

▶ Scott Consulting, Perranporth, Truro, Cornwall, TR6 0HX Tel: 01872 572564 E-mail: martin_scott@dsl.pipex.com *Electronics Design Services*

Scott Doors Ltd, York Street, Audenshaw, Manchester, M34 5TN Tel: 0161-882 9043 Fax: 0161-339 6366 E-mail: sales@scottdoors.com *Manufacturers of doors for the food industry*

Scott Electromech Ltd, 314 Ravenhill Road, Belfast, BT6 8GN Tel: (028) 9045 7225 Fax: (028) 9073 2031 E-mail: info@s-em.com Principal Export Areas: Worldwide *Electric motor repair services, installation & electric motors*

▶ Scott Engineering Co. Ltd, Block 3 Unit 1 Moorpark Industrial Estate, Moorpark Place, Stevenston, Ayrshire, KA20 3JT Tel: (01294) 602045 Fax: (01294) 604601 *Metalwork & fabrication services*

▶ Scott Ferguson Building Co., Unit 38 Work West Enterprise Centre, 301 Glen Road, Andersonstown, Belfast, BT11 8BU Tel: (028) 9030 2900 Fax: (028) 9030 2900

▶ Scott & Foggon Ltd, 11 Exchange Street, Jedburgh, Roxburghshire, TD8 6BH Tel: (01835) 863357 Fax: (01835) 862143

George Scott Architects, 378A Belmont Road, Belfast, BT4 2NF Tel: (028) 9076 0020 Fax: (028) 9076 1731 *Architects*

Scott Gibbin Ltd, Padholme Road, Peterborough, PE1 5XP Tel: (01733) 561569 Fax: (01733) 552065 *Engine test & development engineers*

Scott Glass, Kaimes Farm, Stirling, FK8 3AB Tel: (01786) 461700 Fax: (01324) 813743 E-mail: info@scottglass.co.uk *Scott Glass are manufacturers of scientific glassware. We are specialists in custom designed items such as Jacketed Reaction Vessels, Micro cells for analytical Chemistry, pilot plant components, as well general laboratory apparatus. Our range and services includes; Jacketed reaction vessel, Reaction Vessel, Decorative Glass, Glass Flask, Bespoke Glass, Custom Glass, Glass design, Jointed Glass, Glassware. Chromatography, PTFE, Laboratory apparatus, Custom Manufacture, Glass Repair., Flasks, Large separating funnels, glass laboratory bottles (up to 50 litres), Jacketed beakers (up to 50 litres),Borosilicate glass fabrication undertaken, Glass bubblers, amber glass staining, glass valves, Sintered glassware, Reaction vessel lids, Chromatography, Laboratory apparatus; Decorative items, Our repair service offers you a chance to save money on replacements. We also supply PTFE parts and O-rings., and much more.*

Scott Health & Safety Ltd, Pimbo Road, West Pimbo, Skelmersdale, Lancashire, WN8 9RA Tel: (01695) 727171 Fax: (01695) 711775 E-mail: plarge@tycoint.com *Industrial safety equipment manufrs*

Henry Scott & Son, 62 Doagh Rd, Newtownabbey, Co. Antrim, BT37 9NX Tel: (028) 9085 1604 *Joinery manufrs*

Scott Howard, Unit 15 Handlemaker Road, Frome, Somerset, BA11 4RW Tel: (01373) 466656 Fax: (01373) 47223 E-mail: scotthoward@compuserve.com *Office furnishers*

J. Scott Engineering Ltd, Little Wold, North Dalton, Driffield, East Yorkshire, YO25 9UZ Tel: (01377) 217197 Fax: (01377) 217790 *Steel fabricators*

▶ Scott James Glass Ltd, 12A-14 Armstrong Close, St. Leonards-On-Sea, East Sussex, TN38 9ST Tel: (01424) 854161 Fax: (01424) 853418 *Plastic products*

continued

▶ indicates data change since last edition

Scott Janitorial Supplies Ltd, Beecroft House, Dalton Lane, Keighley, West Yorkshire, BD21 4JH Tel: (01535) 607335 Fax: (01535) 690097 E-mail: info@scottjanitorial.co.uk *Janitorial products suppliers*

Scott Labels, The Old Saw Mill, Iping Road, Milland, Liphook, Hampshire, GU30 7NA Tel: (01428) 741741 Fax: (01428) 741742 *Label manufrs*

Scott Leathers Ltd, Unit 11 12, Industrial Estate, Stainton Grove, Barnard Castle, County Durham, DL12 8UJ Tel: (01833) 638913 Fax: (01833) 690375 *Motorcycle clothing manufrs*

Scott Office & Computer Services, Unit 11 Nortonthorpe Mills Nortonthorpe Industrial Estate, Wakefield Road, Scissett, Huddersfield, HD8 9LA Tel: (01484) 864205 Fax: (01484) 865684 *Office suppliers*

Scott Officer Knitwear, West Mill, Mill Wynd, Haddington, East Lothian, EH41 4DB Tel: (01620) 826111 Fax: (01620) 826777 *Knitwear, designer, manufrs*

Peter Scott & Co. Ltd, 11 Buccleuch Street, Hawick, Roxburghshire, TD9 0HJ Tel: (01450) 372311 Fax: (01450) 374610 E-mail: sales@peterscott.co.uk *Knitwear manufrs*

Scott Plant Hire Ltd, Kent Road, Pudsey, West Yorkshire, LS28 9DR Tel: 0113-257 1421 Fax: 0113-255 2690 *Plant hire*

▶ Scott & Rafferty, 66-68 Mains Street, Lockerbie, Dumfriesshire, DG11 2DQ Tel: (01576) 202613 Fax: (01576) 204720

Scott & Sargeant Wood Working Machinery Ltd, 1 Blatchford Road, Horsham, West Sussex, RH13 5QR Tel: (01403) 273000 Fax: (01403) 274444 E-mail: sales@machines4wood.com *New & used woodworking machinery, tooling & spare parts*

Scott Science & Healthcare Ltd, PO Box 83, Ashford, Kent, TN27 9XJ Tel: (01622) 765334 Fax: (01622) 765338 *Scientific instrument & chemical suppliers*

▶ Scott Stores, Station Industrial Estate, Newton Stewart, Wigtownshire, DG8 6ND Tel: (01671) 402038

Scott & Storey, 19 Norfolk Street, Sunderland, SR1 1EA Tel: 0191-565 8745 Fax: 0191-565 8745 *Hairdressing wholesalers*

▶ Scott Timber Group Ltd, Dundas Road, Rosyth, Dunfermline, Fife, KY11 2XS Tel: (01383) 435700 Fax: (01383) 435701 E-mail: sales@pallet.co.uk

Scott Toomebridge Ltd, 7 Creagh Road, Toomebridge, Antrim, BT41 3SD Tel: (028) 7965 0461 Fax: (028) 7965 0238 E-mail: sales@scottrooftiles.com *Concrete & roof tile manufrs*

Scott Trailers, 33 West End, Walcott, Lincoln, LN4 3ST Tel: (01526) 860741 Fax: (01526) 861357 E-mail: sales@scott-trailers.co.uk *Trailer manufacturer & sales*

▶ Scott Walker Perfumery, Carlton Buildings, Nangreaves Street, Leigh, Lancashire, WN7 4TN Tel: (01942) 676969 Fax: (01942) 676986

Scott Wilson, Central Boulevard, Blythe Valley Park, Shirley, Solihull, West Midlands, B90 8AH Tel: 0121-746 6200 Fax: 0121-746 6201 E-mail: birmingham@camerontaylor.co.uk *Consulting engineers*

Scott Wilson Kirkpatrick & Co. Ltd, Bayheath House, Rose Hill West, Chesterfield, Derbyshire, S40 1JF Tel: (01246) 209221 Fax: (01246) 209229 *Consulting engineers or designers*

Scott Wilson & kur Patrick Ltd, Scott House, Basing View, Basingstoke, Hants, RG21 4JG Tel: (01256) 461161 Fax: (01256) 460582 *Consulting engineers*

Scott Wilson Piesold Ltd, Kanthack House, 35-41 Station Road, Ashford, Kent, TN23 1PP Tel: (01233) 658200 Fax: (01233) 658299 *Consulting civil engineers* Also at: Ashford

Scott Wilson Railways, The Tri Centre, New Bridge Square, Swindon, SN1 1HN Tel: (01793) 508500 Fax: (01793) 508501 E-mail: rail.marketing@scottwilson.com *Rail consultancy*

▶ Scott Wilson Scotland Ltd, 23 Chester Street, Edinburgh, EH3 7ET Tel: 0131-225 1230 Fax: 0131-225 5582

▶ Scott Woyka Furniture, Falmouth Wharves, North Parade, Falmouth, Cornwall, TR11 2TF Tel: (01326) 311777 Fax: 01326 311777 *Design & making of fine furniture in native hardwoods*

Scottaspress Publishers Ltd, 15 Maberly Street, Aberdeen, AB25 1NA Tel: (01224) 637383 Fax: (01224) 643217 E-mail: info@theprinter.co.uk *Commercial printers*

Scot-Tech Surveillance Ltd, 6 Mead Avenue, Chryston, Glasgow, G69 0EZ Tel: (01236) 874870 Fax: (01236) 874870 *Cctv sales*

Scottex Precision Textiles Ltd, Bolholt Industrial Park, Walshaw Road, Bury, Lancashire, BL8 1PL Tel: 0161-763 6550 Fax: 0161-764 1365 E-mail: sales@scottex-filters.com *Filter, filter bag & sleeve manufrs*

▶ Scott-Grant Technical Services, Portland Tower, Portland Street, Manchester, M1 3LD Tel: 0161-234 2121 Fax: 0161-234 2125 E-mail: training@scott-grant.co.uk *Comprehensive range of training courses on Lean principles including SMED, SPC/Six Sigma, 5-S, Value Stream Mapping,TPM, courses on productivity improvement, the MOST(R) technique, IMS Certificate, PADS, PMT-X, Rating clinics & many other short courses. In-company or open programmes.*

Scottish Agronomy Ltd, Arlary Farmhouse, Milnathort, Kinross, KY13 9SJ Tel: (01577) 862759 Fax: (01577) 865129 *Agricultural consultants*

▶ Scottish Book Source, 32 Finlas Street, Cowlairs Industrial Estate, Glasgow, G22 5DU Tel: 0141-558 1366

Scottish Building, Carrongrange House, Carron Grange, Stenhousemuir, Larbert, Stirlingshire, FK5 3BQ Tel: (01324) 555550 Fax: (01324) 555551 E-mail: sales@scottish-building.co.uk *Trade association for the building industry in scotland*

▶ Scottish Coal Co. Ltd, Castlebridge Business Park Gartlove, Alloa, Clackmannanshire, FK10 3PZ Tel: (01259) 733800 Fax: (01259) 733850 E-mail: info@scottishcoal.co.uk

The Scottish Collection, Unit O & P Floors Street Industrial Estate, Floors Street, Johnstone, Renfrewshire, PA5 8PE Tel: (01505) 335861 Fax: (01505) 335861 *Textile manufrs*

Scottish Confectionery Co., Unit 18 South Parks Industrial Estate, Peebles, EH45 9ED Tel: (01721) 723691 Fax: 01721 723691 *Handmade confectionery*

Scottish Conference Centre Ltd, Exhibition Way, Glasgow, G3 8YW Tel: 0141-248 3000 Fax: 0141-226 3423 E-mail: info@secc.co.uk *Conference & exhibition venue*

Scottish Council For Development & Industry, 23 Chester Street, Edinburgh, EH3 7ET Tel: 0131-225 7911 Fax: 0131-220 2116 E-mail: enquiries@scdi.org.uk *Promoters of trade & industry services in scotland*

▶ The Scottish Crop Research Institute, Invergowrie, Dundee, DD2 5DA Tel: (01382) 562731 Fax: (01382) 562426

Scottish Data Systems, Bawer Drive, Old Minniguff, Newton Stewart, Wigtownshire, DG8 6AH Tel: (01671) 402483 Fax: (01671) 402283 E-mail: sales@scottishdatasystems.com *Legacy computer equipment services*

Scottish Development International, Dover House, Whitehall, London, SW1A 2AU Tel: (020) 7270 6838 Fax: (020) 7270 6790 *Inward investment agency*

Scottish Electric (Services) Ltd, Locarno Works, Brown Street, Dundee, DD1 5EE Tel: (01382) 228071 Fax: (01382) 322898 E-mail: scot.elec.grp@btconnect.com *Electrical engineers & distributors*

Scottish Enterprise, 3 Greenmarket, Dundee, DD1 4QB Tel: (01382) 223100 Fax: (01382) 305576 E-mail: set.reception@scotent.co.uk *Economic development agency*

▶ Scottish Enterprise, The Alba Centre, Livingston, West Lothian, EH54 7EG Tel: (01506) 407000

Scottish Enterprise Dunbartonshire, Spectrum House, 1a North Avenue, Clydebank Business Park, Clydebank, Dunbartonshire, G81 2DR Tel: 0141-951 2121 Fax: 0141-951 1907 E-mail: dunbartonshire@scotent.co.uk *Management training specialists*

▶ Scottish Enterprise Edinburgh & Lothian, Apex House, 99 Haymarket Terrace, Edinburgh, EH12 5HD Tel: 0131-313 4000 Fax: 0131-313 4231 E-mail: admin@scottish-enterprise.com *Business enterprise services*

Scottish Enterprise Forth Valley, Laurel House, Laurelhill Business Park, Stirling, FK7 9JQ Tel: (01786) 451919 Fax: (01786) 478123 E-mail: forthvalley@scotent.co.uk *Local economic developers*

▶ Scottish Enterprise Lanarkshire, Dove Wynd, Strathclyde Business Park, Strathclyde Business Park, Bellshill, Lanarkshire, ML4 3AD Tel: (01698) 745454 Fax: (01698) 842211 E-mail: paul.mccarthy@scotent.co.uk *Business development consultants*

Scottish Enterprise Network, 150 Broomielew, Atlantic Quay, Glasgow, G2 8LU Tel: 0141-248 2700 Fax: 0141-221 3217 E-mail: network.helpline@scotent.co.uk *Government agency, economic development agency services*

Scottish Enterprise Renfrewshire, 25 Causeyside Street, Paisley, Renfrewshire, PA1 1UL Tel: 0141-848 0101 Fax: 0141-848 6930 E-mail: network.helpline@scotent.co.uk *Economic development company*

▶ Scottish Equitable plc, Scottish Equitable House, 1 Lochside CR, Edinburgh, EH12 9SE Tel: (0870) 2426789

Scottish Equitable P.L.C., 1/3 Lockside Crescent, Edinburgh Park, Edinburgh, EH12 9SE Tel: 0131-339 9191 Fax: 0131-339 9567 E-mail: clientsolutions@scottishequitable.co.uk *Insurance company life pensions & investments services*

Scottish Executive, Meridian Court, 5 Cadogan Street, Glasgow, G2 6AT Tel: 0141-248 4774 Fax: 0141-242 5589 E-mail: ceu@scotland.gsi.gov.uk *Business support services*

Scottish Fisheries Protection Agency, Old Harbour Buildings, Scrabster, Thurso, Caithness, KW14 7UJ Tel: (01847) 895074 Fax: (01847) 894377 *Vessel agents*

Scottish Galvanisers Ltd, Maclellan Street, Glasgow, G41 1RR Tel: 0141-427 3041 Fax: 0141-427 4981 E-mail: scottish@wedge-galv.co.uk *Hot dip galvanising in Scotland*

▶ Scottish Health Innovations, Suite 342 Baltic Chambers, 50 Wellington Street, Glasgow, G2 6HJ Tel: 0141-248 7334 Fax: 0141-248 6454

▶ Scottish Hydro Electric plc, Inveralmond House, 200 Dunkeld Road, Perth, PH1 3AQ Tel: (0800) 444321 Fax: (01738) 457005

Scottish IT Jobs, 10 Paladin Av, Glasgow, G13 3HP Tel: 0141-954 6511 E-mail: mlow200@netscapeonline.co.uk *Recruitment website for IT & computing jobs*

The Scottish Life Guarantee Company Ltd, 19 St. Andrew Square, Edinburgh, EH2 1AU Tel: 0131-456 7777 Fax: 0131-456 7880 E-mail: enquiries@scottishlife.co.uk *Assurance company* Also at: Branches throughout the U.K.

▶ Scottish Milk Products Ltd, Townhead, Rothesay, Isle of Bute, PA20 9JH Tel: (01700) 503186 *Cheese manufrs*

Scottish Milk Products Ltd, Castle Kennedy, Stranraer, Wigtownshire, DG9 8SH Tel: (01581) 400208 Fax: (01581) 400208 *Cheese storage services*

▶ Scottish Motor Trimmers, Glenhead Road, Lenzie, Glasgow, Glasgow, G66 5AJ Tel: 07721 309744 Fax: 0141 578 7870 E-mail: p.james37@ntlworld.com *Car Seat Repairs. Complete leather retrim. All vehicle upholstery. Carpets, Headlinings Soft top Hoods. Boat Hoods & Caravan upholstery.*

Scottish Natural Stones Ltd, Westwood Estate, West Calder, West Lothian, EH55 8PN Tel: (01506) 874222 Fax: (01506) 874285 *Natural stone suppliers*

Scottish Night Riding Services Ltd, 138 Clydeholm Road, Glasgow, G14 0QQ Tel: 0141-959 0668 Fax: 0141-959 0668 *Heat treatment services*

▶ Scottish Packaging Solutions, Craigie Bank, Station Road, Maud, Peterhead, Aberdeenshire, AB42 5LY Tel: 01771 613707 E-mail: scottishpackagingsolutions@yahoo.co.uk *Packaging hall specialists, project management & equipment procurement*

Scottish Pest Control, Middle Grange, Culross, Dunfermline, Fife, KY12 8EL Tel: (01383) 851944 Fax: (01383) 851944 *Pest control services*

▶ Scottish Police College, Tulliallan Castle, Kincardine, Alloa, Clackmannanshire, FK10 4BE Tel: (01259) 732000 Fax: (01259) 732100

▶ Scottish Power plc, Glenlee Power Station, Dalry, Castle Douglas, Kirkcudbrightshire, DG7 3SF Tel: 0141-568 2800

▶ Scottish Power, Datacentre Cathcart Business Park, Spean Street, Glasgow, G44 4BE Tel: 0141-568 3718

Scottish Power P.L.C, Corporate Office, 1 Atlantic Quay, Glasgow, G2 8SP Tel: 0141-248 8200 Fax: 0141-248 8300 E-mail: contactus@scottishpower.co.uk *Electricity supply company*

Scottish Premier Fasteners, Unit 2 Block 2 Victoria Industrial Estate, Calderbank, Airdrie, Lanarkshire, ML6 9SE Tel: (01236) 751815 Fax: (01236) 751847 E-mail: scotspremfast@btconnect.com *Bolt & nut distributors*

▶ Scottish Prison Service, SPS HQ Industries, Central Store, Main Street, Fauldhouse, Bathgate, West Lothian, EH47 9DJ Tel: (01501) 773980 Fax: (01501) 771835 E-mail: anthony.apperley@sps.gov.uk *Manufacturer of gates, fencing, garden furniture, turned components*

Scottish Sea Food Processing Federation, South Esplanade West, Food Resource Centre, Aberdeen, AB1 1AA Tel: (01224) 897744 Fax: (01224) 871405 E-mail: rhona@aberdeenfish.co.uk *Trade association*

Scottish & Southern Energy P.L.C., Centenary House, 10 Winchester Road, Basingstoke, Hampshire, RG21 8UQ Tel: (0845) 7210220 Fax: (01256) 304269 E-mail: national.sales@scottish-southern.co.uk *Electricity supply companies & gas (natural) producers/suppliers*

Scottish & Southern Energy plc, Inveralmond House, 200 Dunkeld Road, Perth, PH1 3AQ Tel: (01738) 456000 Fax: (01738) 456520 E-mail: info@scottish-southern.co.uk *Energy company*

Scottish Stampings Ltd, East Park Road, Ayr, KA8 9HR Tel: (01292) 267971 Fax: (01292) 613408 *Drop, press & upset forgings manfurs*

Scottish Tanning Industries Ltd, 1 Seedhill, Paisley, Renfrewshire, PA1 1JL Tel: 0141-847 4520 Fax: 0141-848 7246 E-mail: enquiries@scottishleathergroup.com *Leather manufrs*

▶ Scottish Training Consultants, 28 Oldmill Crescent, Belmedie, Aberdeen, AB23 8WA Tel: (01358) 742470 Fax: (01358) 742775

▶ Scottish Water, 419 Balmore Road, Glasgow, G22 6NU Tel: (08457) 741741

Scottish Widows Fund & Life Assurance Society, 69 Morrison Street, Edinburgh, EH3 8YF Tel: (0845) 7678910 Fax: 0131-655 6878 E-mail: info@mcuk.panasonic.co.uk *Life & pension services* Also at: Branches throughout the U.K.

Scottish Widows Investment Partnership, 10 Fleet Place, London, EC4M 7RH Tel: (020) 7203 3000 Fax: (020) 7203 3000 *Investment management services*

Scottish Wool Growers, 1 Arkwright Way, North Newmoor Industrial Estate, Irvine, Ayrshire, KA11 4JU Tel: (01294) 203637 Fax: (01294) 203638 E-mail: sales@britishwools.org.com *Wool graders* Also at: Branches throughout the U.K.

Scottish Woolgrowers, Newton Road, Novar, Evanton, Dingwall, Ross-Shire, IV16 9XQ Tel: (01349) 830678 Fax: (01349) 830546 E-mail: mail@britishwool.org.uk *Agricultural services*

▶ ScottishJerky.Com, Unit 11A4, Balmakeith Industrial Estate, Nairn, IV12 5QW Tel: (07798) 934 920 E-mail: brian@scottishjerky.com *Beef and Venison Jerky - made in the Highlands of Scotland from prime wild Scotch beef and venison. Get it online at www.scottishjerky.com in six great flavours - Original, Chilli, Smoky, Cracked Black Pepper, Curry and Mild Mustard.*

John Scott-Nichol Ltd, Old Station Close, Shepshed, Loughborough, Leicestershire, LE12 9AJ Tel: (01509) 502261 Fax: (01509) 600364 E-mail: info@scott-nichol.com *Sock manufrs*

Scottoilers Scotland Ltd, 2 Riverside, Milngavie, Glasgow, G62 6PL Tel: 0141-955 1100 Fax: 0141-956 5896 E-mail: sales@scottoilers.com Principal Export Areas: Worldwide *Oil lubrication services*

Scotts Clothing Corp. Ltd, 15-19 Manor Street, Ardwick Green, Manchester, M12 6HE Tel: 0161-273 7677 Fax: 0161-273 7699 *Clothing importers & exporters*

Scotts Decorators Merchants Ltd, 5 Wharf Road, Avon Industrial Estate, Stratford-upon-Avon, Warwickshire, CV37 0AD Tel: (01789) 292171 Fax: (01789) 294073 *Decorative & paint merchants*

▶ Scotts Heavy Haulage Ireland Ltd, Whites Close, Alfreton, Derbyshire, DE55 7RB Tel: (01773) 606700 Fax: (01773) 608088

▶ Scotts Plant Hire Ltd, Radcliffe Bridge Yard, Radcliffe Road, Sutton, Macclesfield, Cheshire, SK11 0JE Tel: (01260) 252252 Fax: (01260) 252333

The Scotts Co. (UK) Ltd, Howden Dyke, Goole, North Humberside, DN14 7UF Tel: (01430) 433300 Fax: (01430) 431658 *Fertiliser & garden product manufrs*

Scott-White & Hookins, Fountain House, 26 St. Johns Street, Bedford, MK42 0AQ Tel: (01234) 213111 Fax: (01234) 213333 E-mail: bed@swh.co.uk *Structural & civil engineers*

Scottys Gates Ltd, Dixon Business Centre, 27 Dixon Road, Bristol, BS4 5QW Tel: 0117-977 8865 Fax: 0117-907 4698 E-mail: sales@scottys-gate.sagenet.co.uk *Metal gates & railings manufrs*

Scotvalve Services Ltd, Howemoss Cresent, Kirkhill Industrial Estate, Dyce, Aberdeen, AB21 0GN Tel: (01224) 722993 Fax: (01224) 723750 E-mail: sales@scotvalves.co.uk *Valve repair*

Scotwood Interiors Ltd, 48 Milton Road, East Kilbride, Glasgow, G74 5BU Tel: (01355) 241727 Fax: (01355) 241601 E-mail: sales@scotwood.com *Office interior refurbishments*

▶ Scrap N Craft, 21 Blackhills Road, Peterlee, County Durham, SR8 4DW Tel: 0191-518 4200 *Art craft suppliers*

▶ Scratch Wizard Bumper Repairs Service, Andover Green, Bovington, Wareham, Dorset, BH20 6LN Tel: (0800) 0076829 E-mail: michael.lane01@tiscali.co.uk *Mobile scratch repairs service*

Screeduct Ltd, Unit 8, Northcot Business Park, Blockley, Moreton-In-Marsh, Gloucestershire, GL56 9LH Tel: (01386) 701372 Fax: (01386) 701571 E-mail: sales@screeduct.com *Cable trunking systems*

▶ Screen and Digital Printers Ltd, Unit 2 Albion Trading Estate, Cobden Street, Salford, M6 6NA Tel: 0161-745 7887 Fax: 0161-745 7421

Screen Art Enterprises, Industrial Estate, St. Ives, Cambridgeshire, PE27 3LE Tel: (01480) 464649 Fax: (01480) 496426 *Screen printing machine & surface mounted manufrs*

Screen Art Enterprises, Industrial Estate, St. Ives, Cambridgeshire, PE27 3LE Tel: (01480) 464649 Fax: (01480) 496426 *Screen printers*

Screen Machine Supply Co., 6 Lyon Road, Bletchley, Milton Keynes, MK1 1EX Tel: (01908) 270600 Fax: (01908) 270601 E-mail: sales@screenmachinesupply.com *Suppliers to screen printers*

Screen Manufacturing Co Scotland Ltd, Old Station Yard, Friockheim, Arbroath, Angus, DD11 4SJ Tel: (01241) 828697 Fax: (01241) 828690 E-mail: sales.enquiries@screenmanufacturing.co.uk *Wire bonded screens manufrs*

Screen Print 2000, Northbridge Road, Berkhamsted, Hertfordshire, HP4 1EH Tel: (01442) 875879 Fax: (0845) 4567706 E-mail: fp2000@phillipsplastics.co.uk *Silk screen specialists*

Screen Pro Ltd, Unit 14 Shaftmoor Industrial Estate, Shaftmoor Lane, Hall Green, Birmingham, B28 8SP Tel: 0121-778 6808 Fax: 0121-778 5676 E-mail: sales@screenprouk.com *Screen print services*

Screen Solutions Ltd, Beaufort House, Newton Road, Peacehaven, East Sussex, BN10 8JQ Tel: (01273) 589922 Fax: (01273) 589921 E-mail: sales@screensolutions.co.uk *Office partitions & screening manufrs*

Screen Subtitling Systems Ltd, Old Rectory, Church Lane, Claydon, Ipswich, IP6 0EQ Tel: (01473) 831700 Fax: (01473) 830078 E-mail: sales@screen.subtitling.com *Subtitling equipment designers & manufrs*

Screen Systems Ltd, PO Box 237, Warrington, WA5 0JZ Tel: (01925) 659906 Fax: (01925) 571060 E-mail: info@screensystems.com *Manufacturer of woven wire mesh, wire screen, wire gauze*

Screen Technology, Maerdy Industrial Estate, Maerdy Road, Ferndale, Mid Glamorgan, CF43 4AB Tel: (01443) 730271 Fax: (01443) 730789 E-mail: info@screentec.co.uk *General & commercial printers & pvc welders*

Screenbond Ltd, 2 Serl Industrial Estate, London Road, Baldock, Hertfordshire, SG7 6NG Tel: (01462) 894600 Fax: (01462) 490463 E-mail: sales@screenbond.co.uk *Printed circuit manufrs*

Screencraft Publicity Hull, Reservoir Road, Hull, HU6 7QD Tel: (01482) 499999 Fax: (01482) 499994 E-mail: info@screencraft-display.co.uk *Design & Manufacture Point Of Sale Displays*

Screenmaster Ltd, 23 Hurlbutt Road, Heathcote Industrial Estate, Warwick, CV34 6TD Tel: (01926) 425325 Fax: (01926) 888792 E-mail: info@screenmaster.co.uk *Screen printers*

▶ Screenplus Design Ltd, 197-201 Reid Street, Glasgow, G40 4DX Tel: 0141-550 5180 Fax: 0141-550 5189

▶ Screenprint Ltd, Sandy Lane, Lowton, Warrington, WA3 1BG Tel: (01942) 602121 Fax: (01942) 260151

Screenprint Plus Ltd, Morton Peto Road, Harfreys Industrial Estate, Great Yarmouth, Norfolk, NR31 0LT Tel: (01493) 440292 Fax: (01493) 440269 E-mail: sales@screenprintplus.co.uk *Plastic & acrylic fabricators*

Screenprint Printers, Unit 14 Hall Barn Road Industrial Estate, Hall Barn Road, Isleham, Ely, Cambridgeshire, CB7 5RJ Tel: (01638) 780200 Fax: (01638) 780 300 E-mail: screenprint@mail.islehamnet.co.uk *Screen printers & t-shirt printers*

Screenprint Productions Ltd, The Print Mill, Rosebery Street, Elland, West Yorkshire, HX5 0HT Tel: (01422) 371751 Fax: (01422) 371702 E-mail: screenprint@demon.co.uk *Screen printing services*

Screenprint Studio, The Barns, 9 School Road, Great Massingham, King's Lynn, Norfolk, PE32 2JA Tel: (01485) 520455 *Graphics manufrs*

Screwbolt Fixing, Unit 1a Eastlands Industrial Estate, Leiston, Suffolk, IP16 4LL Tel: (01728) 832076 Fax: (01728) 833312 *Wholesale fixings & fasteners distributors*

Screwplan Ltd, Hazelwood St Works, Hazelwood Street, Todmorden, Lancashire, OL14 5BW Tel: (01706) 812299 Fax: (01706) 816258 E-mail: sales@screwplan.com *Industrial fasteners/screwdriving attachments*

▶ indicates data change since last edition

▶ Scribe Gifts, 1 Borehamgate King Street, Sudbury, Suffolk, CO10 2EG Tel: (01787) 373306 E-mail: sales@scribegifts.co.uk *Wholesale and retail supplier and engraver of crystal, glass, silverplate and other gift and trophy items.*Laser Crystal 3D engraver including portraits.*

Scrimsign Microelectronics Ltd, 8 Arkwright Way, North Newmoor Industrial Estate, Irvine, Ayrshire, KA11 4JU Tel: (01294) 216008 Fax: (01294) 219039 E-mail: sales@scrimsign.co.uk *Electronic information display*

Scriptus Ltd, 3 Campus Road, Listerhills Science Park, Bradford, West Yorkshire, BD7 1HR Tel: 0113-278 0367 Fax: (01274) 391973 E-mail: stylus.marketing@virgin.net *Sign manufrs*

Scriven Electrical Contractors Ltd, Unit 11, Brandon Way Industrial Estate, Brandon Way, West Bromwich, West Midlands, B70 9PW Tel: 0121-553 7243 Fax: 0121-553 7872 E-mail: building@scrivenelectric.demon.uk *Commercial & industrial contract service*

Scroby Fayre Ltd, 31 Clydesdale Rise, Bradwell, Great Yarmouth, Norfolk, NR31 9UG Tel: (01493) 652833 Fax: (01493) 441707 *Storage contractors*

Scrogie Scottaspress, 23 Broad Street, Peterhead, Aberdeenshire, AB42 1HY Tel: (01779) 490869 Fax: (01779) 477853 *Stationers & publishers*

Scroll Gates, Southampton Road, Eastleigh, Hampshire, SO50 5QT Tel: (023) 8061 2028 Fax: (023) 8061 2028 E-mail: sales@scrollgates.com *Gate systems, auto electric & manual*

H. Scrowcroft & Sons, Daisyfield Works, Rosslyn Avenue, Preesall, Poulton-Le-Fylde, Lancashire, FY6 0HE Tel: (01253) 810451 *Gate & railing manufrs*

Scruples, 40 Brook Street, Tavistock, Devon, PL19 0HE Tel: (01822) 618168 Fax: (01822) 613244 *Jewellery, gifts repairs & manufrs*

Scruse & Crossland Ltd, 2 Wingate Road, Gosport, Hampshire, PO12 4DR Tel: (023) 9250 2403 Fax: (023) 9251 1728 E-mail: sales@scruse.co.uk *Powder coating & stove enamelling*

Scruton & Co Builders Ltd, Redcliff House, Waterside Park, Hessle, North Humberside, HU13 0EG Tel: (01482) 644200 Fax: (01482) 647338 E-mail: annwelbourne@scruton.co.uk *House builders*

Wilfred Scruton Ltd, Providence Foundry, Foxholes, Driffield, North Humberside, YO25 3QQ Tel: (0844) 4770405 Fax: (01262) 470335 E-mail: sales@wilfredscruton.co.uk *Agricultural engineers* Also at: Weaverthorp

Scrutton Engineering Ltd, Duck Lees Lane Industrial Estate, 73 East Duck Lees Lane, Enfield, Middlesex, EN3 7SR Tel: (020) 8443 4010 Fax: (020) 8609 0050 E-mail: info@selfab.com *Sheet metalwork engineers or fabricators*

SCS Ltd, Multifreight House Cromwell Court, 16 St. Peters Street, Ipswich, IP1 1XG Tel: (01473) 212421 Fax: (01473) 212110 E-mail: sales@multifreight.com *Business systems house, software suppliers*

SCS Building Services Ltd, 6 Middlefield Road, Falkirk, FK2 9AG Tel: (01324) 888000 Fax: 01324 888030 E-mail: enquiries@scsbuildingservices.co.uk

▶ SCS Installation Ltd, 30 St Catherine Street, Gloucester, GL1 2BX Tel: (01452) 310990 Fax: (01452) 310998

SCS Structural Steel Ltd, Hotham Street, Hull, HU9 1RD Tel: (01482) 585599 Fax: (01482) 620100 E-mail: scs@scsfirm.co.uk *Structural steelwork engineers, erectors & fabricators*

SCS Technology Solutions Ltd, Unit 1 Exchange Close, North Hykeham, Lincoln, LN6 3TR Tel: (01522) 883636 Fax: (01522) 884467 E-mail: sales@scstechsolutions.co.uk *Computer maintenance*

SCT Systems, Balcarres House, 134-136 Balcarres Road, Leyland, PR25 3ED Tel: (01772) 450200 Fax: (01772) 450201 E-mail: sales@sctsystems.co.uk *Computer system building*

Scuba Dream Ltd, 18 Greasbrough Road, Parkgate, Rotherham, South Yorkshire, S62 6HN Tel: (01709) 525480 Fax: (01709) 529580 *Diving equipment suppliers*

Scubaaction, 9 Guy Place East, Leamington Spa, Warwickshire, CV32 4RG Tel: 01926 450193 Fax: 01926 435211 *Scuba diving centre equipment hire*

T.E. Scudder Ltd, Carey House, Great Central Way, Wembley, Middlesex, HA9 0HR Tel: (020) 8903 9722 Fax: (020) 8903 6311 E-mail: scudder@carey-plc.co.uk *Demolition & abestos removal contractors*

Scullion Bruce & Co., 8 Littlejohn Street, Aberdeen, AB10 1FF Tel: (01224) 624954 Fax: (01224) 624954 *Cabinet manufrs*

Scully UK, Unit 4 Road One, Winsford Industrial Estate, Winsford, Cheshire, CW7 3QE Tel: (01606) 553805 Fax: (01606) 553824 E-mail: sales@scullyuk.com *Liquid level control equipment*

Sculpture Studios, 3 Hornsby Square, Southfields Industrial Park, Laindon, Basildon, Essex, SS15 6SD Tel: (01268) 418837 E-mail: aden.hynes@virgin.net *Glass fibre mouldings & sculpture manufrs*

Scunthorpe Interior Design, 242 Ashby High Street, Scunthorpe, South Humberside, DN16 2SE Tel: (01724) 289556 Fax: (01724) 289556 *Interior design services*

▶ SCV Electronics Ltd, 40 Chigwell Lane, Loughton, Essex, IG10 3NY Tel: (020) 8418 0778 Fax: (020) 8418 0624 E-mail: info@scvlondon.co.uk *Audio visual equipment distributors*

Scytala Ltd, 181 St. Johns Road, Congleton, Cheshire, CW12 2EJ Tel: (01260) 276919 *Computer consultants*

SD Displays Ltd, 157 Boyn Valley Road, Maidenhead, Berkshire, SL6 4EG Tel: (01628) 673864 Fax: (01628) 674803 E-mail: sales@sd-displays.co.uk Principal Export Areas: Worldwide *Display modular systems*

▶ SDC Carpet & Upholstery Cleaning Systems, Park House, 26 Park Lane, Eastbourne, East Sussex, BN21 2UU Tel: (01323) 520044 Fax: (01323) 641775 E-mail: sdccleaning@hotmail.com *Quality carpet & upholstery cleaning services*

SDC Industries Ltd, 18 Colvilles Place, Kelvin Industrial Estate, East Kilbride, Glasgow, G75 0PZ Tel: (01355) 265959 Fax: (01355) 265484 E-mail: sales@sdcindustries.co.uk *Power factor correction equipment distributors*

SDC Trailers Ltd, Bradder Way, Mansfield, Nottinghamshire, NG18 5DQ Tel: (01623) 625354 Fax: (01623) 626946 E-mail: admin@sdctrailers.com *Trailer manufrs*

SDD Exhibitions, Marlborough House, 4 Marlborough Road, Sheffield, S10 1DD Tel: 0114-268 6040 Fax: 0114-266 2572 E-mail: sddex@sdd.co.uk *Exhibition designers & project managers*

▶ SDF-ASSIST, Daisyfield Business Centre, Appleby Street, Blackburn, BB1 3BL Tel: 01234 246396 Fax: 01234 246884 E-mail: info@sdfassist.com *We are a Tender & Business Partner Search Company*

SDS Group Ltd, 3 Courtlands Farm, Turnden Road, Cranbrook, Kent, TN17 2QL Tel: (01580) 715038 Fax: (01580) 712056 E-mail: sales@sdsgroupltd.co.uk *Suppliers of security equipment*

SDV Bernard Ltd, Convent Drive, Waterbeach, Cambridge, CB25 9QT Tel: (01223) 861460 Fax: (01223) 860985 E-mail: eastanglia@sdvbernard.co.uk *Shipping & forwarding agents*

Sea Bass Software Ltd, Abbotts Tower, Goring Heath, Reading, RG8 7RZ Tel: (01491) 682585 Fax: (01491) 682586 E-mail: sarah.bell@seabass.co.uk *Software consultants*

▶ Sea Blue Trading UK Ltd, New Park, Axminster, Devon, EX13 5UQ Tel: (01297) 32645 Fax: (0845) 2803125 *Swimming pool installer / contractor*

▶ Sea Chest, Dolphin Building, Queen Anne Battery, Plymouth, PL4 0LP Tel: (01752) 222012 Fax: (01752) 252679 E-mail: sales@seachest.co.uk *Charts & book services*

Sea Containers Railway Services Ltd, Containers House, 20 Upper Ground, London, SE1 9PF Tel: (020) 7805 5000 Fax: (020) 7805 5908 E-mail: info@seacontainers.com *International ferry & transportation services*

Sea Cruisers Of Rye, 28 Winchelsea Road, Rye, East Sussex, TN31 7EL Tel: (01797) 222070 E-mail: info@sea-cruisers.co.uk *Boat distributors & ship chandlers*

▶ Sea Design, Lansdowne Road, Falmouth, Cornwall, TR11 4BE Tel: (01326) 311658 E-mail: info@sea-studio.com *Graphic design services*

Sea Fab Ltd, Unit 4b Kings Court, Jarrow, Tyne & Wear, NE32 3QS Tel: 0191-489 9203 Fax: 0191-428 0357 E-mail: cfab@btclick.com *Steel fabricators*

Sea Fayre Cuisine, Unit 5 Marsh Lane, Hayle, Cornwall, TR27 4PS Tel: (01736) 755961 Fax: (01736) 755961 *Fish mongers*

Sea Pet Centre Ltd, 21 Beardmore Park, Martlesham Heath, Ipswich, IP5 3RX Tel: (01473) 610969 Fax: (01473) 610265 E-mail: sales@seapets.co.uk *Pets & aquatic leisure equipment retailers*

▶ Sea Screw, 4 Churchdale Road, Eastbourne, East Sussex, BN22 8PS Tel: (01323) 430294 Fax: (01323) 411778 *For Stainless Steel Fastenings & Fixings, Over 5,000 types & Sizes in Stock. Marine Hardware from Canvas Fasteners to Bow Thrusters. Also Marine Grade Stainless Steel Tub for Handrails, Pull Pits & Push Pits, Supplied to the UK & most of Europe.*

Sea Technik Ltd, Court House, 15 Glynne Way, Hawarden, Deeside, Clwyd, CH5 3NS Tel: (01244) 535787 Fax: (01244) 538908 E-mail: admin@seatechnik.com *Control systems manufrs*

The Sea of Tranquillity (Elaine Gradone), 42 Seaview Crescent, Edinburgh, EH15 2LT Tel: 0131 6696772 E-mail: info@theseaoftranquility.co.uk *The Sea of Tranquility can provide Complementary Therapies, in the workplace or home, in and around the Edinburgh area. Therapies available are Holistic Massage, Indian Head Massage,Reflexology (foot or hand), Reiki,Thai Foot Massage,Thermo Auricular Therapy (Hopi Ear Candles), Pamper parties*

▶ Sea Wing Cargo, Unit, 1 Beta Way, Thorpe Industrial Park, Egham, Surrey, TW20 8RE Tel: (01784) 435111 Fax: (01784) 439444 *Sea Wing are experienced international seafreight & airfreight forwarders, providing groupage & customs services to & from the UK*

▶ Sea Wing Cargo Services Ltd, Unit 1, Lakeside Industrial Estate, Colnbrook By Pass, Colnbrook, Slough, SL3 0ED Tel: (01753) 763488 Fax: (01753) 763489 E-mail: admin@seawing.co.uk *Sea & air freight forwarders*

Seabait Ltd, Woodhorn Village, Ashington, Northumberland, NE63 9NW Tel: (01670) 814102 Fax: (01670) 814102 E-mail: sales@seabait.co.uk *Fishing bait & aqua worm farm suppliers*

▶ Seablue Systems Ltd, 34 Redruth Drive, Stafford, ST17 0FJ Tel: (0845) 0568356 Fax: (01785) 229644 E-mail: info@seabluesystems.co.uk *Electrical inspection & testing service*

Seaborne Container Services & Supplies Ltd, Oliver Road, Grays, Essex, RM20 3ED Tel: (01708) 863388 Fax: (01708) 866779 E-mail: sales@bcsltd.co.uk *Container repair & storage*

Seabourne Group P.L.C., Unit 13, Saxon Way Trading Centre, Saxon Way, Harmondsworth, West Drayton, Middlesex, UB7 0LW Tel: (020) 7536 6360 Fax: (020) 7987 9889 *Freight forwarding express courier*

Seabourne Mailpack Worldwide, 13 Saxon Way, West Drayton, Middlesex, UB7 0LW Tel: (020) 8897 3888 Fax: (020) 8897 3898 E-mail: info@seabourne-express.com *Courier services*

▶ Seabrook Warehousing Ltd, Unit 2-5 Heath Park Industrial Estate, Freshwater Road, Dagenham, Essex, RM8 1RX Tel: (020) 8548 3540 Fax: (0870) 9901921

Seabrook Welding Supplies Ltd, 4-6 Cannock Street, Leicester, LE4 9HR Tel: 0116-276 4091 Fax: 0116-246 0492 *Welding suppliers*

Seacon Europe Ltd, Seacon House, Hewett Road, Great Yarmouth, Norfolk, NR31 0RB Tel: (01493) 652733 Fax: (01493) 652840 E-mail: sales@seaconeurope.com Principal Export Areas: Worldwide *Electrical cable assemblies, subsea connectors, fibre optic connectors services*

Seacon Shipping Ltd, Tower Warf, North Fleet, Gravesend, Kent, DA11 9BD Tel: (01474) 320000 Fax: (01474) 329946 E-mail: ships@seacon.co.uk *Shipping & transportation services brokers agents*

▶ Seacor Marine International Ltd, 87 Waterloo Quay, Aberdeen, AB11 5DE Tel: (01224) 576710

Seacor Marine International Ltd, Columbus Buildings, Waveney Road, Lowestoft, Suffolk, NR32 1BN Tel: (01502) 573366 Fax: (01502) 581500 E-mail: alan@bpos1.fsbusiness.co.uk *Marine engineers*

Seacore Ltd, Lower Quay, Gweek, Helston, Cornwall, TR12 6UD Tel: (01326) 221771 Fax: (01326) 221553 E-mail: sales@seacore.co.uk Principal Export Areas: Worldwide *Seacore - worldwide specialist marine contractors for offshore construction and exploration drilling. Geotechnical investigation and wind farm construction, marine construction for ports and harbours, drilled piling and socketing and marine pipeline installation.*

Seadrec Ltd, Blackhall House, Blackhall Lane, Paisley, Renfrewshire, PA1 1TA Tel: 0141-887 4131 Fax: 0141-887 6437 E-mail: info@lobnitz.com *Naval architects-dredge designers & suppliers*

Seaeye Marine Ltd, Seaeye House, Lower Quay Road, Fareham, Hampshire, PO16 0RQ Tel: (01329) 289000 Fax: (01329) 289001 *Underwater vehicle manufrs*

Seafab Consultants Ltd, Wellheads Terrace, Wellheads Industrial Estate, Aberdeen, AB21 7GF Tel: (01224) 770287 Fax: (01224) 723400 E-mail: info@seafab.co.uk *Pipework & steel fabricators*

Seafin Export & Import Agents, 52 Four Oaks Road, Sutton Coldfield, West Midlands, B74 2XX Tel: 0121-308 8340 Fax: 0121-308 8340 E-mail: seafin@totalise.co.uk *Export merchants*

Seafish UK, 45-55 Wassand Street, Hull, HU3 4AN Tel: (01482) 223648 Fax: (01482) 216230 E-mail: keith@sheltie.co.uk *Frozen fish & seafood products manufrs*

Seaflame Co. Ltd, Cameron House, 839-841 London Road, Sutton, Surrey, SM3 9DR Tel: (020) 8330 6055 Fax: (020) 8335 3052 E-mail: info@seaflame.co.uk *Ventilation engineers & gas servicing*

Seaflex Ltd, Samuel Whites, Bridge Road, Cowes, Isle of Wight, PO31 7RA Tel: (01983) 290525 Fax: (01983) 295853 E-mail: info@seaflex.co.uk *Air lift bags, water load bags & flexible tank manufrs*

Seaford Health Store, 26 Church Street, Seaford, East Sussex, BN25 1LD Tel: (01323) 893473 Fax: (01323) 893473 *Health products retailers*

Seaford Laboratories Ltd, Cradle Hill Industrial Estate, Seaford, East Sussex, BN25 3JE Tel: (01323) 896779 Fax: (01323) 490452 *Health food supplement manufrs*

Seaforth Saddlers, 23 Harbour Road, Inverness, IV1 1SY Tel: (01463) 223803 Fax: (01463) 223803 *Saddlery & riding wear distributors*

▶ Seaforth Services, Unit 6 Slader Business Park, Witney Road, Nuffield Industrial Estate, Poole, Dorset, BH17 0GP Tel: (01202) 330630 Fax: (01202) 679100

Seafresh Desalinators Ltd, A 4 Premier Centre, Romsey, Hampshire, SO51 9DG Tel: 01794 830363 *Desalination plant manufrs*

▶ Seaga UK Ltd, Unit 8 Cae Bach, Builder Street, Llandudno, Gwynedd, LL30 1DR Tel: (01492) 874010 *Seaga UK is your one-stop solution for bulk vending machines, snack vending machines, soda vending machines, medical vending machines, cold and frozen vending machines, cold beverage merchandisers, change machines and customized equipment. Through its vast network of vending distributors, Seaga UK is able to offer vending machines and cold beverage merchandisers globally to a multitude of international clients. Whether you are a private operator or a multi-national corporation, Seaga UK has equipment to fit your needs.*

Seagas Industries Ltd, 152 Abbey Lane, Leicester, LE4 0DA Tel: 0116-266 9988 Fax: 0116-268 2557 E-mail: sales@seagas.net *Seagas is domestic gas component supplier and manufacturer. *We can supply any gas appliance component such as for Boilers,Barbecues, cooking systems, decorative fires etc.**We specialise in CO-pilot systems. These are built on premises and can be adapted to your specification or requirement.**We also provide additional services of testing, done in our vitiation chamber and on site Quality Control.**

Seager Bearings Ltd, 52 Goldsmith Road, Birmingham, B14 7EL Tel: 0121-444 5391 Fax: 0121-443 5229 E-mail: sales@seager-bearings.co.uk *Ball bearing distributors* Also at: Redditch

Seaglaze Marine Windows Ltd, Wendover Road, Rackheath, Norwich, NR13 6LH Tel: (01603) 720745 Fax: (01603) 721770 E-mail: sales@seaglaze.co.uk *Marine doors & windows*

Seagoe Technology Ltd, Church Road, Portadown, Craigavon, County Armagh, BT63 5HU Tel: (028) 3833 3131 Fax: (028) 3835 1390 E-mail: info@jltgroup.com *Storage heating equipment & shower manufrs*

▶ Seagrave Metal Works Ltd, 60 Empress Road, Southampton, SO14 0JU Tel: (023) 8023 4434 Fax: (023) 8023 4242 E-mail: seagravemetal60@aol.com *Lift car refurbishments*

Seagull Fittings Ltd, 90 Roebuck Lane, West Bromwich, West Midlands, B70 6QX Tel: 0121-525 0020 Fax: 0121-525 1116 E-mail: sales@seagullfittings.co.uk *Hydraulic hose & stainless steel distributors*

Seagull Foods Ltd, Little Forge Road, Redditch, Worcestershire, B98 7SF Tel: (01527) 525154 Fax: (01527) 838100 *Wholesale distribution*

Seaham Harbour Dock Co., Cargo Durham Distribution Centre, Seaham, County Durham, SR7 7NZ Tel: 0191-516 1700 Fax: 0191-516 1701 E-mail: info@seahamharbour.com *Port distribution centre services*

Seal Graphics, Units 2-5, Watkins Close, Burnt Mills Industrial Estate, Basildon, Essex, SS13 1TL Tel: (01268) 722400 Fax: (01268) 725864 *Plastic coating processors & services*

Seal Sands Chemicals Ltd, Seal Sands Road, Seal Sands, Middlesbrough, Cleveland, TS2 1UB Tel: (01642) 546546 Fax: (01642) 546068 E-mail: george.christopherson@cambrex.com *Manufacturers of intermediate chemicals*

Seal Service Ltd, 1 & 2 Kingfisher Court, Kestrel Close, Quarry Hill Industrial Estate, Ilkeston, Derbyshire, DE7 4RD Tel: 0115-932 4308 Fax: 0115-944 0279 *Sealant distributors*

Seal Upvc Products Ltd, Unit 3-4 Heol Stanllyd, Cross Hands Industrial Estate, Cross Hands, Llanelli, Dyfed, SA14 6RB Tel: (01269) 845377 Fax: (01269) 845946 *PVC product manufrs*

▶ Sealability Concrete Repairing Services, Hirwaun Industrial Estate, Hirwaun, Aberdare, Mid Glamorgan, CF44 9UP Tel: (01685) 814345 E-mail: sales@sealability.co.uk

Sealand General Exporters, 78 New Oxford Street, London, WC1A 1HB Tel: (020) 7580 8663 Fax: (020) 7580 8662 E-mail: sales@sealand.co.uk *Overseas purchasing agents exporting manufrs*

Sealandair Transport Co., 101 Stephenson Street, London, E16 4SA Tel: (020) 7511 2288 Fax: (020) 7511 1466 E-mail: frt@sealandair.com *Air, road & deep sea transportation*

▶ Sealant & Construction Services Ltd, Framsden, Stowmarket, Suffolk, IP14 6LH Tel: (01728) 860198 Fax: (01728) 860203

Sealant Techniques Ltd, Harvey Road, Basildon, Essex, SS13 1EP Tel: (01268) 726500 Fax: (01268) 590226 *Sealant contractors & distributors*

▶ Sealcraft, 19 Willow Court, West Quay Road, Winwick, Warrington, WA2 8UF Tel: (01925) 634800 Fax: (01925) 634596 *Caskets seals manufrs*

Sealed Air Ltd, Clifton House, 1 Marston Road, St. Neots, Cambridgeshire, PE19 2HN Tel: (01480) 224000 Fax: (01480) 224063 Principal Export Areas: Worldwide *Plastic food packers*

Sealey UK Ltd, Kempson Way, Bury St. Edmunds, Suffolk, IP32 7AR Tel: (01284) 757500 Fax: (01284) 703534 E-mail: sales@sealey.co.uk *Tools & equipment import & export services*

Sealine International Ltd, Whitehouse Road, Kidderminster, Worcestershire, DY10 1HT Tel: (01562) 740900 Fax: (01562) 747709 E-mail: info@sealine.com *Glass fibre boat builders*

Sealing Solutions Ltd, 1 Wheatear, Perry Road, Witham, Essex, CM8 3YY Tel: (01376) 503633 Fax: (01376) 503733 *Manufacturers hydraulic, pneumatic seals & rubber*

▶ Sealking UK Ltd, Centrum House, Engine Lane, Brownhills, Walsall, WS8 7TE Tel: (01543) 453453 Fax: (01543) 452542 E-mail: uksales@seal-king-europe.com *Tape manufrs*

Sealmac Technology Ltd, 1645 Pershore Road, Kings Norton, Birmingham, B30 3DR Tel: 0121-459 4944 Fax: 0121-459 8420 E-mail: sales@sealmac.co.uk *Seal manufrs*

Sealock Ltd, Scott Close, Walworth Industrial Estate, Andover, Hampshire, SP10 5NU Tel: (01264) 358185 Fax: (01264) 332203 E-mail: sales@sealock.co.uk *Adhesive manufrs*

Sealocrete PLA Ltd, Greenfield Lane, Rochdale, Lancashire, OL11 2LD Tel: (01706) 352255 Fax: (01706) 860880 E-mail: bestproduct@sealocrete.co.uk *Building chemical manufrs*

Sealpoint Computing, 130 Highland Road, Southsea, Hampshire, PO4 9NH Tel: (023) 9287 7688 Fax: (023) 9287 7688 E-mail: enquiries@sealpoint-computing.co.uk *IT, computers & networking*

Sealproof Ltd, Dan Lane Mill, Tyldesley Road, Atherton, Manchester, M46 9DA Tel: (01942) 878012 Fax: (01942) 878298 *Textile waterproofing services & fabric manufrs*

Sealpump Engineering Ltd, Innovation Centre, Kirkleatham Business Park, Redcar, Cleveland, TS10 5SH Tel: (01642) 777720 Fax: (01642) 777730 E-mail: sales@sealpump.com Principal Export Areas: Worldwide *Spray nozzle & valve distributors or agents*

Seals & Components Ltd, Village Road, Norton, Shifnal, Shropshire, TF11 9ED Tel: (01952) 730685 Fax: (01952) 730665 *Hydraulic engineers*

Sealtight Gaskets Ltd, Unit 15 Calow Brook Drive, Hasland, Chesterfield, Derbyshire, S41 0DR Tel: (01246) 222400 Fax: (01246) 222401 E-mail: harveyslack@supernet.com *Gasket & cardboard box manufacturers & seal distributors*

Sealtite Sealants Ltd, 66 Woodbrooke Way, Corringham, Stanford-le-Hope, Essex, SS17 9DW Tel: (01375) 641607 Fax: (01375) 361283 *Sealant application, abseil access & fireproofing*

Sealy, Station Road, Aspatria, Wigton, Cumbria, CA7 2AS Tel: (0870) 7473259 Fax: (0870) 7429884 E-mail: salesorders@sealyuk.co.uk *Divan & mattress manufrs*

▶ Seamap (UK) Ltd, The Maltings, Lower Charlton Trading Estate, Shepton Mallet, Somerset, BA4 5QE Tel: (01749) 342223

Company Information

Seamark Nunn & Co., 400 High Road, Trimley St. Martin, Felixstowe, Suffolk, IP11 0SG Tel: (01394) 275327 Fax: (01394) 670329 E-mail: sales@seamarknunn.com *Boat equipment, chandlery, electronics, outboards, RIBS*

▶ SeaMark Systems Ltd, Uphall Depot, Broxburn, West Lothian, EH52 5NT Tel: (01506) 435888 Fax: (01506) 432520

Seament UK Ltd, Imperial Dock, Leith Docks, Edinburgh, EH6 7DR Tel: 0131-554 1555 Fax: 0131-553 2700 *Concrete distributors*

▶ J Seamer & Son Ltd, 35 Shaftesbury Street South, Derby, DE23 8YH Tel: (01332) 348303 Fax: (01332) 291617

Seamstress Playchutes Ltd, 23 Banbury Road, Byfield, Daventry, Northamptonshire, NN11 6XJ Tel: (01327) 263933 Fax: (01327) 263933 E-mail: sales@playchutes.com *Educational equipment suppliers*

Sean Feeney Furniture, The Old School House, Preston on Stour, Stratford-upon-Avon, Warwickshire, CV37 8NG Tel: (01789) 450519 E-mail: sales@seanfeeneyfurniture.co.uk *Cabinet manufrs*

▶ Sean Mcglone, 136 Lough Fea Road, Cookstown, County Tyrone, BT80 9ST Tel: (028) 8676 5116 Fax: (028) 8676 5057

Sean Murray, 9 Sandbank Road, Hilltown, Newry, County Down, BT34 5XU Tel: (028) 4063 0736 Fax: (028) 4063 0736 *Agricultural engineers*

▶ Sean Timoney & Sons Ltd, 144a Tattygare Road, Mullanaskea, Enniskillen, County Fermanagh, BT74 4JQ Tel: (028) 6632 9252 Fax: (028) 6632 7282 E-mail: seantimoney@yahoo.co.uk *PVC windows & doors*

▶ Sean's Usability Co., Level 5, 5 St Helen's Place, Bishopsgate, London, EC3A 6AU Tel: (020) 7036 0378 *loads and loads of usability stuff:**- usability testing*- heuristic evaluations*- card sort*- information architecture*- prototype design & testing*- focus groups*

Sea-Quipment International Sales Ltd, Bassett Road, Park Lane Industrial Estate, Halesowen, West Midlands, B63 2RE Tel: (01384) 562999 Fax: (01384) 568217 *Marine engineering equipment*

▶ Search Appliance, 398b Woodstock Road, Wolvercote, Oxford, OX2 8JW Tel: (0845) 2304560 Fax: 01926 490106 E-mail: sales@searchappliance.co.uk *All styles & designs of kitchen appliances to suit your kitchen. SearchAppliance is an easy to use searchable kitchen appliance site with detailed search options and 50 showrooms. Similar models shown. Each kitchen appliance has full specifications with clear pictures to ensure it is right for you.*

▶ Search Environmental Ltd, Centre Court, 1301 Stratford Road, Hall Green, Birmingham, B28 9HH Tel: (07821) 200228 Fax: 0121-702 1476 E-mail: enquiries@searchenvironmental.co.uk *Environmental consultants providing asbestos survey & sampling*

▶ Search Laboratory Ltd, 3 Littleway, Moortown, Leeds, LS17 6JN Tel: 0113-212 1211 E-mail: ian.harris@searchlaboratory.com *Search Engine Optimisation and Pay Per Click Management. Multilingual service if required.*

Search Liverpool Ltd, Hammond Road, Knowsley Industrial Park, Liverpool, L33 7UW Tel: 0151-546 3361 Fax: 0151-549 1914 E-mail: info@wgsearch.co.uk *Plant hire & leasing*

▶ Search & Supply Recruitment, The Sanctuary, Shelley Close, Armitage, Staffordshire, WS15 4UW Tel: 01543 304583 Fax: 01543 304583 E-mail: enquiry@searchandsupply.co.uk *Key person Search and Selection services for Exec, Non Exec, Interim, Contract or Permanent management positions within the Logistics, Supply Chain, Manufacturing, Project Management disciplines.*

Searchwise Ltd, 6 Broomiesburn Road, Ellon, Aberdeenshire, AB41 9RD Tel: (01358) 722990 Fax: (01358) 722933 E-mail: sales@searchwise.co.uk *Underwater equipment specialist*

Searcys Roof Garden Rooms, 30 Pavilion Road, London, SW1X 0HJ Tel: (020) 7584 4921 Fax: (020) 7823 8694 E-mail: rgr@searcys.co.uk *Hotel & private parties*

Seareach Ltd, Seareach House, 34a, The Broadway, Leigh-on-Sea, Essex, SS9 1AJ Tel: 01702 476286 Fax: 01702 476385 E-mail: info@seareach.plc.uk *Asset label and barcode label printing along with security printing solutions. Products include security ticket printing, holograms, security inks, concert tickets, certificates and other government documents and labels that require protection from tampering or alteration.*

Seargeant Bros Printers Ltd, Unit 12 Pontyfelin Industrial Estate, New Inn, Pontypool, Gwent, NP4 0DQ Tel: (01495) 752425 Fax: (01495) 763179 E-mail: sales@seargeants.co.uk *General printers*

Searle Manufacturing Co., 20 Davis Way, Newgate Lane, Fareham, Hampshire, PO14 1AR Tel: (01329) 823344 Fax: (01329) 821242 E-mail: sales@searle.co.uk *Refrigeration equipment manufrs*

Sears Seating, Unit 33, Rassau Industrial Estate, Ebbw Vale, Gwent, NP23 5SD Tel: (01495) 304518 Fax: (01495) 304452 E-mail: info@searsseating.co.uk *Manufacture of seats for off-road vehicles*

Seasafe Systems Ltd, Mar, Cowes, Isle of Wight, PO31 8PB Tel: (01983) 282388 Fax: (01983) 282399 E-mail: admin@seasafe.co.uk *Self inflating life jackets*

Seascope Insurance Services Ltd, 57 Mansell Street, London, E1 8AN Tel: (020) 7488 3288 Fax: (020) 7481 4499 E-mail: enquiries@seains.com *Insurance brokers*

Seascope Offshore, 25 Carden Place, Aberdeen, AB10 1UQ Tel: (01224) 628470 Fax: (01224) 621444 E-mail: sales@seascope.co.uk

Season Link Ltd, 15 Summer Lane, Birmingham, B19 3RZ Tel: 0121-236 7330 Fax: 0121-236 7370 E-mail: sales@seasonlink.co.uk *Children's & ladies wear manufrs*

Season Master, 1 Redan Hill Estate, Redan Road, Aldershot, Hampshire, GU12 4SJ Tel: (01252) 319670 Fax: (01252) 341983 E-mail: sales@seasonmaster.com *Double glazed window manufrs*

Season Master Windows Ltd, 1 Oaks Industrial Estate, Coventry Road, Narborough, Leicester, LE19 2GF Tel: 0116-286 7970 Fax: 0116-284 1693 E-mail: sales@seasonmasterwindows.co.uk *Pvcu window & door manufrs*

Seasonal Reflections Ltd, 30 High Street, Mold, Clwyd, CH7 1BH Tel: (01352) 756070 Fax: (01352) 757011 E-mail: seasonalreflectionsltd@yahoo.co.uk *Wedding & party shop*

▶ Seasons Textiles Ltd, 15 Gorst Road, London, NW10 6LA Tel: (020) 8965 6161 Fax: (020) 8961 6433 E-mail: enquiries@seasonstextiles.net

Seaspeed Technology Ltd, 2 City Business Centre, Basin Road, Chichester, West Sussex, PO19 8DU Tel: (01243) 784222 Fax: (01243) 784333 E-mail: info@seaspeed.co.uk *Marine consultants*

▶ Seasplash Herbalists, 1045 Manchester Road, Linthwaite, Huddersfield, HD7 5LS Tel: (01484) 846252 E-mail: seasplash@btconnect.com *Herbalists*

Seastyle, Unit 21 Three Springs Trading Estate, Vincent Road, Worcester, WR5 1BW Tel: (01905) 351528 Fax: (01905) 763776 E-mail: diving@seastyle.co.uk *Diving equipment manufrs*

Seatco Sales Ltd, Imperial Ho, Kings Court, King St, Leyland, PR25 2LE Tel: (01772) 434361 *Office chair manufrs*

Seaton Bay, 5 Burrow Road, Seaton, Devon, EX12 2NF Tel: (01297) 625081 E-mail: enquiries@seatonbay.com *an online guide to Seaton and East Devon U.K.*

Seaton Fire & Security, 11 Dorking Close, Blyth, Northumberland, NE24 3LX Tel: (01670) 797030 Fax: (01670) 797030 *Burglar alarms installers*

Seaton Heating & Engineering Services Ltd, Wilnecote Lane, Tamworth, Staffordshire, B77 2LE Tel: (01827) 286777 Fax: (01827) 288319 *Tool hire & sales*

Seaton Hobby Shop, Goulden Lion House, 23 Fore Street, Seaton, Devon, EX12 2LE Tel: (01297) 22025 Fax: (01297) 22025 E-mail: email@seatonhobbyshop.com *Stockists of a wide range of craft materials,fancy dress,dolls houses, Knitting Yarns,Card Making,R/C,Die-cast models,Paints,Glues,Airfix kits,Sugar Craft,Embrodary Kits & Threads,Matchstick Kits.Balsa Wood*

▶ Seaton Pets, 31 Fore Street, Seaton, Devon, EX12 2AD Tel: (01297) 22439 Fax: (01297) 22439 E-mail: seaton.petshop@members.v21.co.uk *Stockists Of;**James Wellbeloved,Royal Canin,Iams,Berties,Beta,Pedigree,*Pet Foods *And Forthglade Frozen Meats**Aquarium Products;**Clearseal,Juwel,Hagen,Ehiem,* Interpet,Algarde,Tetra,Arcadia,*Deltec,Kent,** Many Other Products Also Available To Order.**We Also Have A Well Stocked Fish House Containing;**Discus,Tropical Fish,Coldwater,Marine Fish,And Invertibrates. ******************

▶ Seatrax (UK) Ltd, Southtown Road, Great Yarmouth, Norfolk, NR31 0JJ Tel: 01493 443663

Seatronics Ltd, 4 Denmore Industrial Estate, Denmore Road, Denmore Industrial Estate, Aberdeen, AB23 8JW Tel: (01224) 853100 Fax: (01224) 853101 E-mail: david.currie@seatronics-group.com Principal Export Areas: Worldwide *Electronic underwater equipment suppliers*

▶ Seatstore Office Chairs, 7 Ravenstone Road, Camberley, Surrey, GU15 1SN Tel: 01276 23903 Fax: 01276 683799 E-mail: info@seatstore.co.uk *Office furniture & seating distributor*

Seaward Electronic Ltd, 11 Bracken Hill, South West Industrial Estate, Peterlee, County Durham, SR8 2LS Tel: 0191-586 3511 Fax: 0191-586 0227 E-mail: sales@seaward.co.uk *Seaward Electronic Ltd is the global market leader in manufacturer, sales, service of PAT testers together with full calibration of PAT testing equipment and 16th editions. Seaward has an extensive distribution network PAT testers and 16th electronic test equipment in the UK and represented in over 30 countries worldwide.*

▶ Seaward Engineering, 974 Pollokshaws Road, Glasgow, G41 2HA Tel: 0141-632 4910 Fax: 0141-636 1194

Seaward Safety Ltd, 24 Harvest Drive, Lowestoft, Suffolk, NR33 7NJ Tel: (01502) 512834 Fax: (01502) 512837 E-mail: mail@seawardsafety.co.uk *Safety signs manufrs*

Seaward Security Ltd, 40 Highwood Avenue, High Wycombe, Buckinghamshire, HP12 4LS Tel: (01494) 439886 Fax: (01494) 539269 *Burglar alarms*

▶ Seaway Transport, Station Brae, Macduff, Banffshire, AB44 1UL Tel: (01261) 832877 Fax: (01261) 833377 E-mail: sales@seawaygroup.co.uk

Seaways Diving & Marine, Commercial Road, Penryn, Cornwall, TR10 8AQ Tel: (01326) 375544 Fax: (01326) 375401 E-mail: colin@seawaysdiving.com *Diving equipment sales charters*

Seaweather Aviation Services Ltd, 625-649 Princes Road, Dartford, DA2 6EF Tel: (01322) 275513 Fax: (01322) 292639 E-mail: safety@seaweather.co.uk *Aircraft survival equipment*

Seaweld Engineering Ltd, The Limes, The Street, Acle, Norwich, NR13 3QJ Tel: (01493) 751421 Fax: (01493) 750064 E-mail: admin@seaweld.co.uk *Sub-sea engineering contractors*

Seaweld Fabrications, Mylor Yacht Harbour, Mylor Churchtown, Falmouth, Cornwall, TR11 5UF Tel: (01326) 373155 Fax: (01326) 373155 *Steel fabricators*

▶ Seawing Boats, 18 Darrowby Close, Thirsk, North Yorkshire, YO7 1FJ Tel: (01845) 527397 E-mail: info@seawingboats.co.uk *Plans & kits to build a beautiful cedar strip canoe or kayak*

▶ Seba Specialty Chemicals, Moody Lane, Grimsby, South Humberside, DN31 2SY Tel: (01472) 246000 Fax: (01472) 246001

Sebden Steel, Broad Quay Road, Felnex Industrial Estate, Newport, Gwent, NP19 4PN Tel: (01633) 276054 Fax: (01633) 283355 E-mail: newport@sebden.com *Steel stockholders*

Sebden Steel Midlands Ltd, Thorns Road, Brierley Hill, West Midlands, DY5 2PJ Tel: (01384) 424344 Fax: (01384) 892982 E-mail: brierleyhill@sebden.com *Steel processing sheet strip services & steel sheet stockholders*

Sebden Steel Service Centres Ltd, Craven Road, Broadheath, Altrincham, Cheshire, WA14 5HE Tel: 0161-928 8327 Fax: 0161-941 7061 E-mail: altrincham@sebden.com *Steel stockholders*

Sebden Steels, Chandler Road, Chichester, West Sussex, PO19 8UE Tel: (01243) 528311 Fax: (01243) 787038 E-mail: chichester@sebden.com *Delivering service and quality. 250,000 tonnes per annum of flat rolled products sourced from major European suppliers; cut to length panel flat decoiled sheet, precision sheared blanks, coil slitting. 30,000 tonnes of stock at any one time; hot rolled, cold reduced, hot dipped galvanised, aluminised, electro-zinc and other specialist coatings.*

Sebel Furniture Ltd, 7 Canon Harnett Court, Wolverton Mill, Milton Keynes, MK12 5NF Tel: (01908) 317766 Fax: (01908) 317788 E-mail: sales@sebel.com.au *Educational furniture suppliers & manufrs*

Sebix Ltd, 2 Crittle Drive, Springwood Industrial Estate, Braintree, Essex, CM7 2RD Tel: (01376) 550552 Fax: (01376) 550547 E-mail: mick-p@selbix.co.uk *Shop fitting equipment manufacturing*

▶ Sebolis Ltd, Swindon Innovation Centre, University of Bath in Swindon, Oakfield Campus, Marlowe Avenue, Swindon, SN3 3JR Tel: 01793 329927 E-mail: enquiries@sebolis.co.uk *Sebolis Ltd is a data networking company specialising in wireless and broadband technologies. We offer consultancy, design and support services. We can also provide a broadband equivalent service to businesses or individuals unable to obtain a "traditional" broadband connection.*

Sebor Absinth Ltd, PO Box 1111, Kingston Upon Thames, Surrey, KT1 4YX Tel: (020) 8943 9526 Fax: (020) 8977 3507 E-mail: info@seborabsinth.com *Spirit import & distributors*

Sebring International, Lotts Bridge, Threeholes, Wisbech, Cambridgeshire, PE14 9JG Tel: (01354) 638678 Fax: (01354) 638640 E-mail: sales@sebringcars.co.uk *Compounding cars manufr*

Sebserv Business Machine Repairs, Ramsay House, 18 Vera Avenue, London, N21 1RA Tel: (020) 8360 8845 Fax: (020) 8360 6688 E-mail: info@sebserv.com *Fax & printer service maintenance. Sales of office equipment, toners drums parts & maintenance kits. Nationwide maintenance contracts available*

▶ Sec Ltd, 6-8 Howard Chase, Basildon, Essex, SS14 3BE Tel: (01268) 533316 Fax: (01268) 531454 *Manufacture motor vehicle accessories or components*

▶ Seca PCS Ltd, Unit E 7 Craigend Place, Anniesland, Glasgow, G13 2UN Tel: 0141-959 1440 E-mail: info@secapcs.co.uk *Computer support, maintenance, repairs, upgrades & sales*

Seccombe (Builders' Merchants) Ltd, 158-164 St. James Road, Croydon, CR9 2RT Tel: (020) 8689 4421 Fax: (020) 8684 7411 *Building materials suppliers* Also at: Isleworth & Shirley

Secker & Sons (Norwich) Ltd, St. Johns Close, Norwich, NR1 2PR Tel: (01603) 616419 Fax: (01603) 622247 E-mail: servise@seckers.com *Refrigeration, air-conditioning & shopfitting services*

Seco Engineering Co. Ltd, 32 Reading Road South, Fleet, Hampshire, GU52 7QL Tel: (01252) 622333 Fax: (01252) 623888 E-mail: sales@secoeng.co.uk *Tools & machines*

Secol Engineering Ltd, Unit 6-9 Cubitt Way, St. Leonards-on-Sea, East Sussex, TN38 9SU Tel: (01424) 855144 Fax: (01424) 855155 E-mail: gary@secolengineering.co.uk *Sub-contract work, machinists & electronic engineers*

Secom plc, Unit 1 The Bell Centre, Newton Road, Crawley, West Sussex, RH10 9FZ Tel: (01293) 532249 Fax: (01293) 514416 E-mail: enquiries@secom.plc.uk *Security system installers*

Secom plc, 7 Hedge End Business Centre, Botley Road, Hedge End, Southampton, SO30 2AU Tel: (01489) 780396 Fax: (01489) 780397

Secomak Holdings Ltd, Unit 330, Centennial Park, Elstree, Borehamwood, Hertfordshire, WD6 3TJ Tel: (020) 8732 1300 Fax: (020) 8732 1301 E-mail: sales@secomak.com *Industrial Drying Solutions & Shrink Solutions. Air knife Systems, compressed air systems, fans, blowers, heaters, centrifugal fans.*

Secon Solutions Ltd, River House, 85 Esher Road, Walton-on-Thames, Surrey, KT12 4LN Tel: (020) 8255 0777 Fax: (020) 8255 7511 E-mail: sales@secon.co.uk *IT & software resellers*

Second Byte Computers, Market Square, Ellesmere Port, CH65 0HW Tel: 0151-356 8339 Fax: 0151-355 2851 *Software & peripherals*

▶ Second Byte It, Unit D2 Mercia Way, Foxhills Industrial Estate, Scunthorpe, South Humberside, DN15 8RE Tel: (01724) 280055 Fax: (01724) 852925 E-mail: secondbyteit@mail.com *Computer maintenance & repair services*

Second City Storage Systems Ltd, 108-110 Wood Lane, Erdington, Birmingham, B24 9QL Tel: 0121-382 7878 Fax: 0121-377 7758 *Forklift truck distributors & repairers*

Second Sight Video Ltd, The Old School House, Leicester Road, Sapcote, Leicester, LE9 4JE Tel: (01455) 274191 Fax: (01455) 273918 E-mail: sales@secondsight.co.uk *Video, photography, new media & conferencing*

Second To None, 25 Olive Street, Sunderland, SR1 3PE Tel: 0191-565 9176 Fax: 0191-510 8841 *Window blinds manufrs*

▶ Secondhome Ltd, 2 Beech Lane, Spofforth, Harrogate, North Yorkshire, HG3 1AN Tel: 01423 590574 Fax: 01423 590574 E-mail: peter.shackleton@secondhomeagency.com *Listing properties and land for sale including residential and commercial investment opportunities.*

Seconds & Co. Ltd, Europa House, 16a High Street, Tenterden, Kent, TN30 6AP Tel: (01580) 767700 Fax: (01580) 767709 E-mail: sales@seconds.co.uk *Building insulation*

▶ Seconsolar Ltd, Alexandra Building Business & Innovation Centre, Wearfield, Sunderland Enterprise Park, Sunderland, SR5 2TH Tel: 0191-516 6554 Fax: 0191-516 6558 E-mail: info@seconsolar.com *Solar water heating kits, components & distributor*

Secretarial Service, 43 Moselle Avenue, London, N22 6ES Tel: (020) 8889 6870 Fax: (020) 8889 6870 E-mail: emailforps@fsmail.net *WordProcessing, Typing, Editing*

▶ Secretarial Solutions, 6 Stonebridge Court, Blackbridge Lane, Horsham, West Sussex, RH12 1TX Tel: (01403) 253021 Fax: (01403) 253021 E-mail: tlnhome@hotmail.com *CV's, bookkeeping credit control pa & secretarial services*

▶ Secretariat Business Services, Suite 16, Folkestone Enterprise Centre, Shearway Business Park, Folkestone, Kent, CT19 4RH Tel: (0870) 3300615 E-mail: info@secretariatservices.net *Company formations, incorporations and registrations online using our electronic filing service approved by Companies House. We offer a range of packages and services to suit every business formation need.*

Sections & Tubes Ltd, Hall Street, West Bromwich, West Midlands, B70 7DW Tel: 0121-553 2721 Fax: 0121-500 5002 E-mail: admin@sectionsandtubes.co.uk *From a one-off stock requirement to continuous contracts Sections and Tubes Limited provide high quality cold roll formed solutions at competitive prices. Our commitment to customer satisfaction will guarantee a mutually beneficial partnership now and into the future. Our operation is located in the West Midlands with immediate access to the main motorway network which allows us to provide a comprehensive nationwide service. Your requirements may fall within our extensive range of standard profiles or alternatively you may instruct our in house design department to assist you in the development of a tailor made product. Our highly skilled toolmakers will then create the rolls and if required we can also build the rolling line itself. We can offer cold rolled sections, cold formed sections, rolled steel sections, steel channels, steel profiles, cold rolled steel sections, steel tubes, cold formed steel sections, cold rolled products to specification. Whatever your requirement, contact us or place an enquiry through our website www.sectionsandtubes.co.uk*

Sector Contracts Ltd, 12 Well Court, London, EC4M 9DW Tel: (020) 7489 0165 Fax: (020) 7236 2824 E-mail: mail@sector.co.uk *Computer personnel recruitment*

▶ Sector Lifts, 37 The Arcade, North Street, Keighley, West Yorkshire, BD21 3SL Tel: (01535) 606099 Fax: (01535) 606049 E-mail: info@sectorlifts.co.uk *Supply & installation of all types of lifts,*

▶ Sector Systems Ltd, 18 Milton Road, Caterham, Surrey, CR3 5JD Tel: (01883) 334641 Fax: (01883) 334641 E-mail: rdavies@sectorsystems.co.uk *Computer maintenance services*

Sectorguard plc, Gainsborough House, Sheering Lower Road, Sawbridgeworth, Hertfordshire, CM21 9RG Tel: (01279) 724777 Fax: (01279) 723977 E-mail: collette@sectorguard.plc.uk *Fire alarm manufrs*

Secuirdoor North East Ltd, Commercial Road, South Shields, Tyne & Wear, NE33 1RP Tel: 0191-425 0000 Fax: 0191-425 0037 *Steel door & shutter manufrs*

Secura Labels Ltd, Unit L2 Westminster Industrial Estate, Measham, Swadlincote, Derbyshire, DE12 7DS Tel: (01530) 515170 Fax: (01530) 515171 E-mail: sales@securalabels.co.uk *Self adhesive label printers*

Secure Alarm Co. Ltd, Unit 28 Shaftesbury St South, Derby, DE23 8YH Tel: (0870) 0429999 Fax: (0870) 0420099 E-mail: info@securealarm.co.uk *Security company*

Secure Bolts, Unit 18 Blenheim Way, Liverpool, L24 1YH Tel: 0151-486 3154 Fax: 0151-486 3154 *Industrial fixings & fasteners. In addition, nuts & bolts. Also nails*

▶ Secure Covers, Edgton, Craven Arms, Shropshire, SY7 8HN Tel: 01588 680661 Fax: 01588 680416 E-mail: gerardthomas@securecovers.com

Secure Engineering Ltd, Friday Street Barn, East Sutton, Maidstone, Kent, ME17 3DD Tel: (01622) 844244 Fax: (01622) 844567 E-mail: sales@secureeng.co.uk *A truly specialist CCTV supplier, Secure Engineering celebrated 20 years of business in September 2008. That confirms a wealth of CCTV knowledge and expertise enabling Secure Engineering to professionally carry out design, supply, installation and servicing of CCTV systems. Our technical expertise means that we are especially suited to larger CCTV systems on industrial sites for security and plant process monitoring. We are experienced in providing traffic monitoring systems from the central control room to remotely monitored camera positions and*

continued

continuation
managing all the connections in between. This experience includes Automatic Number Plate Recognition (ANPR) systems to facilitate traffic counting or to alert trigger mechanisms. We supply, install and maintain analogue and IP systems, control rooms, wireless, networked and fibre optic systems. Everything you would expect from a genuine CCTV specialist with industry leading customer satisfaction, backed up by UKAS ISO9000 certification.

Secure Fabrications, 1 Yew Street, Salford, M7 2HL Tel: 0161-705 0377 *Steel fabricators*

Secure I.T. Disposals Ltd, Unit 12, 53 Kettles Wood Drive, Woodgate Business Park, Woodgate Valley, Birmingham, B32 3DB Tel: (0870) 7271578 Fax: (0870) 7271469 E-mail: @sitd.co.uk *Secure computer recycling*

▶ Secure Ice, 159, Marsh Road, Luton, LU3 2QL Tel: (01582) 507860

Secure It All Ltd, 25 Howley Grange Road, Halesowen, West Midlands, B62 0HW Tel: 0121-423 1119 Fax: 0121-423 3393 E-mail: sales@secureitall.co.uk *Security products distributors & installers*

Secure Power Systems Ltd, 2A Watermoor Road, Cirencester, Gloucestershire, GL7 1JW Tel: (01285) 651768 Fax: (01285) 657053 E-mail: wknight756@aol.com *Uninterruptable power supplies*

Secure Shutters, 105 Richmond Road, Grays, Essex, RM17 6DN Tel: (01375) 397100 Fax: (01375) 397101 E-mail: sales@secureshutters.co.uk *Repairs, maintenance and installations of all types of industrial and commercial security shutters, doors, gates and grilles.*Manual, electrical and hand-chain operation covering all areas in the South of England, with a guaranteed 24 hour emergency response service.*We offer free quotations and conform to the operating standards of the Door and Shutter Manufacturers' Association.*

▶ Secure Solutions, 37 New Road, Burton Lazars, Melton Mowbray, Leicestershire, LE14 2UU Tel: 01664 568155 Fax: 01664 561990 *CCTV & intruder alarm specialists & digital surveillance*

Secure Track, Vaughan Trading Estate, Sedgley Road East, Tipton, West Midlands, DY4 7UJ Tel: 0121-522 2266 Fax: 0121-522 3344 *Secure overnight courier service*

▶ Secure-Axcess Ltd, 8 Westerman Close Sawtry, Huntingdon, Cambridgeshire, PE28 5PJ Tel: (01487) 830324 Fax: 01487 832906 E-mail: secure-axcess@dsl.pipex.com *Security System Installations, Commissioning and Project Management. JIB/CSCS Approved, ECS Assessed*

Securefast plc, Meadow Dale Works, Dimminsdale, Willenhall, West Midlands, WV13 2BE Tel: (01902) 607503 Fax: (01902) 609327 E-mail: sales@securefast.co.uk *Door & security lock manufrs*

▶ Securetec Ltd, 9 Firethorne Road, Liverpool, L26 7XE Tel: 0151-498 4845 Fax: 0151-284 1033 E-mail: securetec1@yahoo.co.uk *Specialist Electrical Maintenance contractor. For Fire Alarms, Entryphones, Intruder Alarms, Social Alarms, PAD testing and CCTV. *24hr 7 day week call out response.*

Securexe Security Systems, 24 Park Lane, Exmouth, Devon, EX8 1TH Tel: (01395) 227337 Fax: (01395) 260260 *Electronic security installation & service*

Securi Card, 2 Ings Croft, Low Fold, Ossett, West Yorkshire, WF5 9HZ Tel: (01924) 274007 Fax: (01924) 280868 *ID card manufrs*

Securi Plex Ltd, Swordfish Way, Sherburn in Elmet, Leeds, LS25 6NG Tel: (01977) 680700 Fax: (01977) 680701 E-mail: business@securi-plex.co.uk *Security installers*

Securicare Systems, 45 Shore Road, East Wittering, Chichester, West Sussex, PO20 8DY Tel: (01243) 672634 Fax: (01243) 672634 E-mail: securicaresystems@email.com *Installation & Maintenance of Security Systems for Commercial & Domestic Premises - Burglar Intruder Alarms to British Standard 4737 - CCTV - Door Entry/Access Systems - Locks - Safes - Security Lighting - Chichester - Witterings - Bognor - Littlehampton - Worthing - Emsworth - Portsmouth -Midhurst*

▶ Securiclear Systems Ltd, Forge Lane, Halesowen, West Midlands, B62 8EJ Tel: 0121-585 0822 Fax: 0121-585 0801

Securicor Cash Services, Unit 8, Blackburn Trading Estate, Northumberland Close, Stanwell, Staines, Middlesex, TW19 7LN Tel: (01784) 421311 Fax: (01784) 420324 *Security services*

▶ Securicor Omega Logistics Ltd, Irongray Road, Dumfries, DG2 0HS Tel: (01387) 721212

Securicorp Shutters Ltd, 43 Beacon Road, Romiley, Stockport, Cheshire, SK6 3ET Tel: 0161-494 2900 Fax: 0161-494 8300 *Roller shutters & doors manufrs*

Securi-Guard Ltd, Darklake View, Estover, Plymouth, PL6 7TL Tel: (01752) 204900 Fax: (01752) 204912 E-mail: david.campbell@securi-guard.co.uk *Security services*

Securikey Ltd, PO Box 18, Aldershot, Hampshire, GU12 4SL Tel: (01252) 311888 Fax: (01252) 343950 E-mail: sales@securikey.co.uk *Security stockists*

Securit Ropes & Packaging Ltd, Unit 6 Phoenix Court, Dominion Way, Rustington, West Sussex, BN16 3HQ Tel: 0845 5261818 Fax: (0845) 634 0262 E-mail: sales@securit-ropes-packaging.co.uk *Securit Ropes & Packaging Ltd serves the industrial and retail markets with Packaging Materials, Rope and all the associated services. *We are based in the UK in an office and warehouse facility, including a fully stocked Strapping Tool service and repair workshop. We are one of the fastest growing official stockist and distributors in the UK for SIGNODE a multinational manufacturer of steel and plastic strapping, stretch film and application equipment. We are probably the only distributor that will visit customer's sites under no obligation to work with and recommend the correct strapping and packaging products. We always bring and fund*
continued
all the necessary equipment to prove all the systems we offer thereafter. We pride ourselves on having a true understanding of our customer's needs and undertake to work with customers on long-term basis.

▶ Securit Security Systems Ltd, Unit 1, Sleaford Industrial Estate, Sleaford Road, Bracebridge Heath, Lincoln, LN4 2ND Tel: (01522) 569960

Securit World Ltd, Spectrum House, Hillview Gardens, London, NW4 2JQ Tel: (020) 8266 3300 Fax: (020) 8203 1027 E-mail: support@securitworld.com *Distributors of photo id card systems & visitor management systems*

Securitas Group, 203-205 Lower Richmond Road, Richmond, Surrey, TW9 4LN Tel: 0845 5314061 Fax: (020) 8876 4650 E-mail: jenny.campbell@securitas.uk.com *Security consultants & investigation services*

Securitel Fire Alarm Systems, 94 Warren Road, Brighton, BN2 6BA Tel: (01273) 888326 Fax: (01273) 887427 E-mail: info@securitel.co.uk *Fire alarm system installers*

Security 201, 332 Goring Road, Goring-by-Sea, Worthing, West Sussex, BN12 4PE Tel: (01903) 242902 Fax: (01903) 242618 E-mail: info@security201.co.uk *Alarm & security engineers*

▶ Security Air Express Ltd, Coppermill Court, Coppermill Lane, Rickmansworth, Hertfordshire, WD3 9XS Tel: (01895) 825258 Fax: (01895) 825259

▶ Security Centres Holdings G B Ltd, Portcullis House, Kingsway, Swansea, SA5 4DL Tel: (01792) 561111 Fax: (01792) 588555 E-mail: sales@securitycentres.co.uk *Alarm systems installers*

Security Closures, Barnack Trading Centre, Bedminster, Bristol, BS3 5QE Tel: 0117-963 5382 Fax: 0117-963 5395 *Door closing equipment suppliers*

Security Closures, 11 Heybridge Way, Leabridge Road, London, E10 7NQ Tel: (020) 8558 9350 Fax: (020) 8558 4815 *Door closing equipment distributors*

Security Composites Ltd, The Farriers, Annscroft, Shrewsbury, SY5 8AN Tel: (01743) 860778 Fax: 01743 860015 *Composites in safety environments*

▶ Security & Control Scotland, Block 15, West Avenue, Blantyre Industrial Estate, Glasgow, G72 0UZ Tel: 01698 713100 Fax: 01698 713111 E-mail: sales@security-control.co.uk *Supply, Installation, Service & Maintenance of Intruder & Fire Alarms, Access Control & CCTV Systems, (15% discount to your last years maintenance contract)Automation of Gates & Barriers, Structured Cabling & network, Electrical Contracting. 24 hour response, wireless and custom systems.*

Security D B S, Clyde Facilities, Howemoss Crescent, Kirkhill Industrial Estate, Dyce, Aberdeen, AB21 0EN Tel: (01224) 728400 Fax: (01224) 728487 *Oil drilling tool manufrs*

Security Design Centre Ltd, Falcon House, 10 Bloomfield Street West, Halesowen, West Midlands, B63 3RD Tel: 0121-550 8847 Fax: 0121-585 6142 E-mail: sales@securitydesigncentre.co.uk *Security systems supply & fit*

▶ Security Direct, 1 River Road Business Park, 33 River Road, Barking, Essex, IG11 0DA Tel: (020) 8522 0251 Fax: (020) 8507 9900 *CCTV & security product wholesalers*

▶ Security Direct, 347 Brighton Road, South Croydon, Surrey, CR2 6ER Tel: (020) 8662 8674 Fax: (020) 8407 0014 E-mail: enquiries@security-direct.co.uk

▶ Security Electronics Industries Ltd, Unit 19, Anniesland Business Park, Glasgow, G13 1EU Tel: 0141-959 5999 E-mail: sales@securityelectronicsonline.com *Cctv equipment manufrs*

Security Enforcement Services, 66 Lone Valley, Waterlooville, Hampshire, PO7 5EB Tel: (023) 9220 0924 Fax: (023) 9221 5154 E-mail: robert@security-enforcement.fsnet.co.uk *Security services*

Security Escorts Services, 6 Standard Road, London, NW10 6EU Tel: (020) 8965 3215 Fax: (020) 8961 5298 E-mail: sales@securityescorts.com *Palletised distribution, nationwide removals & storage*

Security First, 65 Bohemia Road, St. Leonards-on-Sea, East Sussex, TN37 6RG Tel: (01424) 427550 Fax: (01424) 427550 *Security alarms installers*

Security Group Distribution Ltd, 8 Oakenhill Road, Bristol, BS4 4LR Tel: 0117-914 1180 Fax: 0117-914 1181 E-mail: security@groupdistribution.fsnet.co.uk *CCTV alarms, fire alarms security products & installation services*

▶ Security Label, 76 High Street, Dunbar, East Lothian, EH42 1JH Tel: (01368) 869921 E-mail: enquiry@security-label.co.uk *Custom Printed asset tags /labels & security seals / labels. Barcoded or numbered in small/short runs. Tamper evident, warranty void, product authentication seal. FAST TURNAROUND.*

▶ Security Link Services Ltd, 124 Lea Vale Road, Norton, Stourbridge, West Midlands, DY8 2AU Tel: (0870) 2415883 E-mail: sales@securitylink.org.uk

▶ Security Matters, 1 Wellingborough Road, Broughton, Kettering, Northamptonshire, NN14 1PD Tel: (01536) 790999 Fax: (01536) 790710 *Acoustic fire door retainers manufrs*

▶ Security Park, Britannia House, 11 Glenthorne Road, London, W6 0LH Tel: 0870 7453380 *Security park publishes of online magazine*

Security Patrol Services Ltd, Roseland, Church Lane, Norton, Worcester, WR5 2PS Tel: (01905) 821000 Fax: (01905) 821408 *All types of security services*

▶ Security Printers Ltd, 185 Town Road, London, N9 0HQ Tel: (020) 8807 9333

R & I Security, 48a Westwood Park, Deans, Livingston, West Lothian, EH54 8QW Tel: (01506) 414793 Fax: (01506) 460007 *Security*

▶ Security Services Ltd, Bowmans House, Bessemer Drive, Stevenage, Hertfordshire, SG1 2DL Tel: (01474) 854444 Fax: (0870) 7374375 *Manufacture metal hardware & security products*

Security Shutter Systems, 49 Torquay Crescent, Stevenage, Hertfordshire, SG1 2RQ Tel: 0870 6092324 Fax: (01462) 638729 E-mail: cjanecolwill@aol.com *Security shutters, retractable gates, roller blinds, window bars, security gates, roller garage doors, gates folding, gates collapsible, door installation, garage doors automatic, garage doors roller, gates, gates commercial, electrically operated roller shutters, manually operated roller shutters, security cabinets, servery shutters, fixed grilles, removable window bars, garage doors domestic security, commercial security, security blinds, security grilles*

Security Shutters Ltd, Unit 2 Brooklands Approach, Romford, RM1 1DX Tel: (01708) 722334 Fax: (01708) 750900 E-mail: sales@securityshuttersltd.co.uk *Manufacture & repair of roller shutters & doors*

Security Specifier, 32 Portland Street, Cheltenham, Gloucestershire, GL52 2PB Tel: (01242) 236336 Fax: (01242) 222331 *Magazine publishers*

Security Surveillance Systems, Boundary Farm, Grave Yard Lane, Bickerstaffe, Ormskirk, Lancashire, L39 9EG Tel: (01695) 420968 Fax: (01695) 424790 E-mail: mark-fitzgerald@btconnect.com *Installers of security systems*

Securon Amersham Ltd, Winchmore Hill, Amersham, Buckinghamshire, HP7 0NZ Tel: (01494) 434455 Fax: (01494) 726499 E-mail: sales@securon.co.uk *Manufacturer of Seat Belts, Restraints and Harnesses*

▶ Sedac Construction Ltd, Triple House, Whitehill Road, Crowborough, East Sussex, TN6 1JP Tel: (01892) 669944

Seddon Ltd, PO Box 41, Bolton, BL4 0NN Tel: (01204) 570400 Fax: (01204) 570401 E-mail: p.winnington@seddonplant.co.uk *Contractors plant, ground care landscaping sales, parts & service* Also at: Birmingham, Birtley, Glasgow, Nottingham, Stoke-on-Trent & Wakefield

Seddon Design Ltd, Gelscoe Farm, Diseworth, Derby, DE74 2QQ Tel: (01530) 223777 Fax: (01530) 223666 E-mail: info@seddon-design.co.uk *Point of sale suppliers*

Seddon Packaging & Print Ltd, Orient House, Field Street, Kettering, Northamptonshire, NN16 8BD Tel: (01536) 517303 Fax: (01536) 410674 E-mail: info@seddon.co.uk *Jigsaw puzzle & cardboard box manufrs*

Seddon Stoke Ltd, PO Box 13, Stoke-on-Trent, ST4 3NN Tel: (01782) 599511 Fax: (01782) 599682 E-mail: transport@seddonstoke.co.uk *Building & painting contractors* Also at: Birmingham, Chester, Congleton, Newcastle upon Tyne & York

Seddons Plant & Engineers Ltd, Oldfields Business Park, Duke Street, Stoke-on-Trent, ST4 3NX Tel: (01782) 593444 Fax: (01782) 593555 *Garden machinery services*

Sedgbeer Processing Supplies, Unit 13, Mill Road, Radstock, BA3 5TX Tel: (01373) 812445 Fax: (01373) 812445 E-mail: info@sedgbeer.co.uk *Processing equipment suppliers*

▶ Sedgemoor Publicity, The Barn, 1 Sedgemoor Road, Weston-super-Mare, Avon, BS23 2TA Tel: (01934) 417352 Fax: (01934) 417352 E-mail: sales@sedgemoorpublicity.co.uk *promotional business gift specialist in weston super mare, somerset.*

Sedgemoor Stone Products Ltd, Pen Mill, Station Yard, Yeovil, Somerset, BA21 5DD Tel: (01935) 429797 Fax: (01935) 432392 E-mail: info@sedgemoorestone.co.uk *Reconstituted stone product manufrs*

Sedin UK Ltd, Burnley, Lancashire, BB11 5GY Tel: 01282 697979 *Machine tool engineers*

Sedis Co. Ltd, PO Box 6529, Wellingborough, Northamptonshire, NN8 4YS Tel: (0870) 1607840 Fax: (01604) 764162 E-mail: sedisco@sedis.com *Chains including conveyor & industrial suppliers*

▶ Sedo Systems Ltd, 19 Hertford Road, Stevenage, Hertfordshire, SG2 8RS Tel: (01438) 362033 Fax: (01438) 721888 E-mail: sales@sedosystems.com *Electronic manufrs*

▶ Seductive Lingerie, 14 Enderby Road, Scunthorpe, South Humberside, DN17 2HD Tel: (01724) 332874 E-mail: seller.seller@ntlworld.com *Online sales of lingerie*

See More Blinds, 24 Church Square, Midsomer Norton, Radstock, BA3 2HX Tel: (01761) 411063 Fax: (01761) 411063 E-mail: seemoreblinds@yahoo.com *Blinds manufrs*

▶ See Why Web Solutions, 5 Thorncliffe Lane, Chapeltown, Sheffield, S35 3XX Tel: 0798 5076233 *Web solution*

▶ Seearo Construction, Newmarket Road, Heydon, Royston, Hertfordshire, SG8 7PR Tel: (01763) 208332 Fax: (01763) 208880

Seeburger UK Ltd, Heathrow Boulevard 4, 280 Bath Road, West Drayton, Middlesex, UB7 0DQ Tel: (020) 8564 3914 E-mail: c.blomstedt@seeburger.co.uk *Business to business integration*

▶ Seed Developments Ltd, The Factory, Aller, Langport, Somerset, TA10 0QN Tel: (01458) 250762

Seeds Bakery Health Store, 35 High Street, Totnes, Devon, TQ9 5NP Tel: (01803) 862526 *Wholesaler & retail bakery, health food & health supplements*

Seedy Servey, 122 Hide Park Street, Glasgow, G3 8BW Tel: 0141-204 1744 Fax: 0141-204 1696 *Surveying equipment manufrs*

▶ Seefin Construction Ltd, 12 Royal Terrace, Glasgow, G3 7NY Tel: 0141-333 1744

▶ Seek & Find, 7 Broadmeadow House, Peneith Croft, Bartley Green, Birmingham, B32 3ND Tel: 0121-602 2783 Fax: 0121-602 2783 E-mail: seekandfind@blueyonder.co.uk

▶ Seeko Limited, Temple Court, Cathedral Road, Cardiff, CF11 9HA Tel: (0845) 3455312 Fax: (0845) 3455313 E-mail: theway@seeko.co.uk *Seeko is an international provider of conflict management, security, and close protection serveices.*

Seepex UK Ltd, Unit 3 Armtech Row, Houndstone Business Park, Yeovil, Somerset, BA22 8RW Tel: (01935) 472376 Fax: (01935) 479836 E-mail: sales@seepex.co.uk *Pump manufrs*

Seesaw Design, PO Box 100, Bury, Lancashire, BL8 2FU Tel: (01204) 882222 Fax: (01204) 882200 E-mail: mikeyounge@btconnect.com *Supplier of street furniture lighting & play equipment*

Seetrax Ltd, Old Buriton Line Works, Kiln La, Buriton, Petersfield, Hants, GU31 5SJ Tel: (01730) 260062 Fax: (01730) 267273 E-mail: sales@seetrax.com Principal Export Areas: Worldwide *Printed circuit production equipment manufrs*

Seevent Plastics Ltd, Units 2-5, Peter Road, Lancing, West Sussex, BN15 8TH Tel: (01903) 755877 Fax: (01903) 753673 E-mail: admin@seevent.co.uk *Polythene bag manufrs*

Sefar Ltd, Bury Business Centre, Kay Street, Bury, Lancashire, BL9 6BU Tel: 0161-705 1878 Fax: 0161-763 1382 E-mail: sales@sefar.co.uk *Textile products supplier*

Sefex International Ltd, 50 Frank Street, Preston, PR1 1PB Tel: (01772) 884020 Fax: (01772) 884020 E-mail: sales@sefexinternational.co.uk *Cable-trays, trunking & accessories*

Sefton Chamber of Commerce & Industry, 22 Hoghton Street, Southport, Merseyside, PR9 0PA Tel: (01704) 531710 Fax: (01704) 539255 E-mail: office@seftonchamber.org.uk *Chamber of commerce & industry*

▶ G. Segger Contracts Ltd, 6 Linden Drive, Hurworth Place, Darlington, County Durham, DL2 2DJ Tel: (01325) 720565 Fax: (01325) 720565 E-mail: seggercontracts@yahoo.co.uk *Plant & Machinery Hire, both operated and non-operated.*

Segmatic Engineering Ltd, 33a Ganton Way, Techno Trading Estate, Swindon, SN2 8ES Tel: (01793) 524175 Fax: (01793) 524168 *Precision subcontracting engineers services*

Seho UK Ltd, Unit C5, Brookside Business Park, Greengate, Middleton, Manchester, M24 1GS Tel: 0161-654 9117 Fax: 0161-654 7817 E-mail: pb@sehouk.demon.co.uk *Production soldering equipment distributors*

Seiko UK Ltd, S C House, Vanwall Road, Maidenhead, Berkshire, SL6 4UW Tel: (01628) 770001 Fax: (01628) 770655 E-mail: services@seiko.co.uk *Watch distributors*

Seimens Power Generation Ltd, C A Parsons Works, Shields Road, Newcastle upon Tyne, NE6 2YL Tel: 0191-276 1188 Fax: 0191-276 0276 E-mail: spgl@siemens.co.uk *Generating set installation services*

Seip UK Ltd, Unit 11 Monument Business Park, Warpsgrove Lane, Chalgrove, Oxford, OX44 7RW Tel: (01865) 400469 Fax: (01865) 400217 *Suppliers of electric garage door openers*

Seipel Ltd, Crescent Road, Dukinfield, Cheshire, SK16 4HQ Tel: 0161-330 9321 Fax: 0161-343 1287 E-mail: sales@seipel.co.uk *Ladies handbag manufrs*

Seivad Engineering Ltd, Meadow Road, Worthing, West Sussex, BN11 2RT Tel: (01903) 238845 Fax: (01903) 821529 E-mail: eng@seivad.co.uk *Sub-contract machinists*

Sekers Fabrics Ltd, Unit 7A, Nobel Road, West Gourdie Industrial Estate, Dundee, DD2 4UH Tel: (01946) 517500 Fax: (01946) 517503 E-mail: sales@sekers.co.uk *Furnishing fabric manufrs* Also at: London W1

Sekhon Savouries, 619 Foleshill Road, Coventry, CV6 5JR Tel: (024) 7666 7722 *Pre packed foods & snacks*

Sekisui Alveo, Queens Chambers, Eleanors Cross, Dunstable, Bedfordshire, LU6 1SU Tel: (01582) 600456 Fax: (01582) 600567 *Foam manufrs*

▶ Seko Ltd, Blackminster Business Park, Old Birmingham Road, Badsey, Evesham, Worcestershire, WR11 7RE Tel: (01386) 839010 Fax: (01386) 839011 E-mail: seko.uk@seko.com *Water treatment plant & equipment manufrs*

Sel Computers, Palace Building, Main Street, Grange-over-Sands, Cumbria, LA11 6AB Tel: (01539) 533222 Fax: (01539) 533303 *Computer networking services*

▶ Sel Tek, 31 Dellburn Street, Motherwell, Lanarkshire, ML1 1SE Tel: (01698) 262569 Fax: (01698) 259799 E-mail: enquiry@sel-tek.co.uk *Air conductor sales & service*

Selborne Biological Services Ltd, Goleigh Farm, Selborne, Alton, Hampshire, GU34 3SE Tel: (01420) 511535 Fax: (01420) 511537 E-mail: office@sbsuk.net *Pharmaceutical services*

Selborne Brickworks, Honey Lane, Selborne, Alton, Hampshire, GU34 3BT Tel: (01420) 478752 *Specialist brick manufrs*

Selby Engineering, 28 Dinglederry, Olney, Buckinghamshire, MK46 5ES Tel: (01234) 711773 Fax: (01234) 713992 *Machine tool repairers*

Selby Engineering & Lifting Services Ltd, 3 Lincoln Way, Sherburn in Elmet, Leeds, LS25 6PJ Tel: (01977) 684600 Fax: (01977) 685300 E-mail: sales@liftingsafety.co.uk *Lifting Equipment, Lifting Gear, Lifting Tackle, Lifting Hire, Test & Certification, Overhead & Jib Cranes, Manual Handling, Winching ,Fibre & Chain Slings, Fall Arrest, Fall Protection, Height Safety, Access Equipment, Working At Height, Restraint & Rescue, Fall Arrest Installations*

Selby Marketing Services, Ormonde St Works, Ormonde Street, Ashton-under-Lyne, Lancashire, OL6 8JQ Tel: 0161-339 5132 Fax: 0161-343 1005 E-mail: sales@selby-marketing.co.uk *Promotional handling services*

▶ Selby Transport, 32 Midland Road, Scunthorpe, South Humberside, DN16 1DQ Tel: (01724) 277577 Fax: (01724) 277720

Selclene, 7 Mandeville Courtyard, 142 Battersea Park Road, London, SW11 4NB Tel: (020) 7627 3874 Fax: (020) 7720 9800 E-mail: info@selclen.biz *Domestic cleaning service*

Selco, First Avenue, Minworth, Sutton Coldfield, West Midlands, B76 1BA Tel: 0121-313 2020 Fax: 0121-313 0523 *Builders merchants*

Selco Crystal Ltd, The Bond Street Silver Galleries, 111-112 New Bond Street, London, W1S 1DP Tel: (0870) 3307215 Fax: (0870) 3301003 E-mail: info@selcocrystal.com *Hand cut crystal importers*

Selco Trade Centres Ltd, 1 Charlote Road, Stirchley, Birmingham, B30 2BT Tel: 0121-433 3355 Fax: 0121-458 5996 *Builders' & timber merchants*

Selcom Systems, 65-71 York Road, Acomb, York, YO24 4LN Tel: (01904) 788181 Fax: (01904) 788194 E-mail: info@selcom.co.uk *IT consultants*

▶ Selcraft Ltd, Leigh Sinton, Malvern, Worcestershire, WR13 5XS Tel: (01886) 834850 Fax: (01886) 834851 E-mail: info@selcraft.com *Enamel badges, medals, corporate jewellery*

Selcrete Of Whitby, Selly Cottage, Guisborough Road, Whitby, North Yorkshire, YO21 1SE Tel: (01947) 603178 Fax: (01947) 821590 *Fireplace manufrs*

▶ Selcroft Reprographics Ltd, 22 Holmethorpe Avenue, Redhill, RH1 2NL Tel: (01737) 772773 Fax: (01737) 772774

Selden Masts Ltd, Lederle Lane, Gosport, Hampshire, PO13 0FZ Tel: (01329) 504000 Fax: (01329) 504049 E-mail: info@seldenmast.co.uk *Aluminium alloy fabricators*

▶ Seldos Computers, 211 Kingland Road, London, E2 8AN Tel: (07984) 340359 E-mail: sales@seldos.co.uk *Computer repair services*

Select Amusement Sales Ltd, Farmeloan Road, Rutherglen, Glasgow, G73 1DN Tel: 0141-647 3362 Fax: 0141-643 2250 E-mail: info@selectamuse.co.uk *Amusement machine supplier*

Select Appointments plc, Regent Court, Laporte Way, Luton, LU4 8SB Tel: (01582) 811600 Fax: (01582) 811611 E-mail: information@select.co.uk *Staffing services* Also at: Branches throughout the UK

Select Bio Sciences Ltd, 1 Bull La Industrial Estate, Bull Lane, Acton, Sudbury, Suffolk, CO10 0BD Tel: (01787) 319234 Fax: (01787) 319235 E-mail: admin@selectbiosciences.com *Laboratory equipment conference services*

Select Business Products Ltd, 65 Castle Street, Hull, HU1 1SE Tel: (01482) 586550 Fax: (01482) 211109 E-mail: info@selectgroup.co.uk *Computer software distributors*

Select Cables Ltd, Painter Close, Portsmouth, PO3 5RS Tel: (023) 9265 2552 Fax: (023) 9265 5277 E-mail: sales@selectcables.com *Select Cables specialise, with a wide ranging manufacturing capability, in producing any interconnection solution from phase matched microwave devices through low loss antenna feed cables to multi-way data harnesses. We also distribute a wide range of Coaxial Cables, Microwave and RF connectors, Test Equipment, Antennas and Wireless LAN equipment Distribution Times Microwave Inc - RF Cable & Connectors CM Srl. - RF Connectors Huber + Suhner - Antenna, Lightning Protectors, Surge Arrestors Test-Um - Test Equipment Re-Seller Pressmaster - Crimp Tools Netgear - Wireless Equipment Linksys - Wireless Equipment Belkin - Wireless Equipment D-Link - Wireless Equipment*

▶ Select Carpets, Unit F5 Hilton Main Industrial Estate, Bognop Road, Essington, Wolverhampton, WV11 2BE Tel: (01902) 737722 Fax: (01902) 737725 *Carpet retailers*

Select Computers, Suite 2 Rawmec Industrial Park, Plumpton Road, Hoddesdon, Hertfordshire, EN11 0EE Tel: (01992) 448899 Fax: (01992) 471314 E-mail: mailorder@selectcomputers.co.uk *Peripherals & hardware distributors*

Select Engineering, Broad Ground Road, Redditch, Worcestershire, B98 8YP Tel: (01527) 517157 Fax: (01527) 517145 E-mail: info@select-engineering.co.uk Principal Export Areas: Worldwide *Manufacturers of precision turned parts, turned parts & machined components (metal). Also repetition work (automatic) machinists, engineering sub-contract services & engineers, general engineering*

▶ Select Fabrications Ltd, Unit 3 2-3 King Edward Close, Worthing, West Sussex, BN14 8DJ Tel: (01903) 238225 Fax: (01903) 238225

▶ Select Gauges & Calibration Ltd, Select Works, Trevol Business Park, Torpoint, Cornwall, PL11 2PN Tel: (01752) 812147 Fax: (01752) 814892 Sales Contact: S. Jeynes Principal Export Areas: Worldwide *Gauge block manufacturers, Long Slip Gauges, Length Bars, Angle Gauges.*UKAS Calibration Laboratory*

▶ Select Intallations, 23 Duddington Park South, Edinburgh, EH15 3NY Tel: (01422) 823599 Fax: (01422) 823599

Select Kitchens & Bedrooms North East Ltd, 616 Durham Road, Gateshd, Gateshead, Tyne & Wear, NE9 6HY Tel: 0191-482 1889 Fax: 0191-482 1889 E-mail: info@selectkb.co.uk *Kitchens & bedrooms*

▶ Select London, 131a Weedington Road, London, NW5 4PQ Tel: (020) 7428 0505 Fax: (020) 7267 0232

Select Office Services, Forum House Business Centre, Stirling Road, Chichester, West Sussex, PO19 7DN Tel: (01243) 787932 Fax: (01243) 786930 E-mail: 100622.3205@compuserve.com *Secretarial & business services*

Select Recruitment (Aberdeen) Ltd, 11 Diamond Street, Aberdeen, AB10 1QU Tel: (01224) 638383 Fax: (01224) 658383 E-mail: select1@connectthree.co.uk *Recruitment agency*

Select Scales Ltd, 36 Skinner Street, Creswell, Worksop, Nottinghamshire, S80 4JH Tel: (01909) 725043 Fax: (01909) 724057 *Sales, service, repairs and calibration certification of industrial &* *continued* *commercial weighing equipment and weighbridges*

Select Signs, 68 Ballysallagh Road, Bangor, County Down, BT19 1UT Tel: (028) 9185 3301 Fax: (028) 9185 3301 *Sign makers*

Select Signs, 25 West Street, Newport, Isle of Wight, PO30 1PR Tel: (01983) 529477 Fax: (01983) 520177 *Design and print signs*

Select Software Ltd, Home Farm Road, Ellingham, Bungay, Suffolk, NR35 2EL Tel: (01508) 518112 Fax: (01508) 518113 E-mail: sales@selectsoftware.net *Software engineers services*

▶ Select Solutions, 27 Jersey Road, Rainham, Essex, RM13 7DR Tel: (01708) 878111 Fax: (01708) 878112 E-mail: martin-king@icomradios.co.uk *Supply, service and instillation of all two way radio communications equipment such as Icom, Motorola and there accessories such as headsets chargers and earpieces*

▶ Select Sourcing, The Technocentre, Coventry Technology Park, Puma Way, Coventry, CV1 2TT Tel: (024) 7623 6818 Fax: (024) 7623 6024 E-mail: info@selectsourcing.com *Provider of e-auction technologies and sourcing support services offers tailored solutions to significantly reduce company purchasing costs.*

Select Specs Ltd, PO Box 2, Westgate-on-Sea, Kent, CT8 8RX Tel: (01843) 835568 E-mail: reg1@selectspecs.com *Online prescription spectacles and sunglasses* *SelectSpecs.com is an online optical group based on the east coast of county of Kent - the Garden of England, and we are dedicated to bringing affordable designer and prescription spectacles and sunglasses to the public.* *Although our prices are inexpensive we only use the highest quality material with all lenses coming with the internationally recognised CE mark of quality. All frames are strong and substantial with fitting carried out by highly qualified staff of many years experience.*

Select Telecom, Colville House, 1 Lynn Road, Littleport, Ely, Cambridgeshire, CB6 1QG Tel: (0800) 0832228 Fax: (01353) 863535 E-mail: nkhokhar@selecttelecom.co.uk *Mobile phones - contract and pay as you talk, mobile phone repairs, mobile data, hands-free car kits,landline services**

▶ Select Telecommunications Ltd, 1 Lynn Road, Littleport, Ely, Cambridgeshire, CB6 1QG Tel: (0800) 0832228 Fax: (0870) 0337000 E-mail: info@selecttelecom.demon.co.uk *Installation service of hands free car kits*

Select Windows, Select House, Walsall Road, Walsall Wood, Walsall, WS9 9AQ Tel: (01543) 370666 Fax: (01543) 370270 E-mail: sales@selectwindows.co.uk *Industrial glassware manufrs*

The Select Yacht Group Ltd, Rock, Wadebridge, Cornwall, PL27 6NT Tel: (01208) 862666 Fax: (01208) 862375 E-mail: info@selectyachts.co.uk *Boat builders*

Selecta Ltd, 28 Duncrue Road, Belfast, BT3 9BP Tel: (028) 9077 1177 Fax: (028) 9037 0051 E-mail: sales@uk.slecta.com *Vending supply & services*

Selecta International, Dodgson Street, Rochdale, Lancashire, OL16 5SJ Tel: (01706) 350191 Fax: (01706) 525129 *Shower enclosures manufrs*

Selecta UK Ltd, Unit 7 Stockton Close, Minworth Industrial Park, Minworth, Sutton Coldfield, West Midlands, B76 1DH Tel: 0121-313 2442 Fax: 0121-313 5037 *Vending machine suppliers*

Selectactive Ltd, 67a Frimley Green Road, Frimley, Camberley, Surrey, GU16 8AL Tel: (01276) 683891 Fax: (01276) 683891 E-mail: alan@selectactive.co.uk

Selectaglaze Ltd, 1 Campfield Road, St. Albans, Hertfordshire, AL1 5HT Tel: (01727) 837271 Fax: (01727) 844053 E-mail: enquiries@selectaglaze.co.uk Sales Contact: Brian Steventon *Secondary Glazing Systems Specialists - Holder of Royal Warrant, ISO 9001, LPS 1175 Certified (Levels 1 and 2) and Red Book listing. Tailor-made windows to room side of primary windows provide noise insulation and thermal insulation. Unique Security Range offers anti-bandit and physical attack protection and blast resistance.*

Selectamark Security Systems Ltd, 1 Locks Court, 429 Crofton Road, Orpington, Kent, BR6 8NL Tel: (01689) 860757 Fax: (01689) 860693 E-mail: sales@selectamark.co.uk *Security systems distributors & manufrs*

Selected Rug & Matting Ltd, 74 Long Lane, London, SE1 4AU Tel: (020) 7407 8471 Fax: (020) 7378 0540 E-mail: srmlondon@aol.com *Rugs & matting distributors*

Selectequip Ltd, Unit 7, Brittannia Way, Brittania Enterprise Park, Lichfield, Staffordshire, WS14 9UY Tel: (01543) 416641 Fax: (01543) 416083 E-mail: sales@selectequip.co.uk *Engineers supplies & consumables*

▶ Selection & Development Ltd, Bronzeoak House, Stafford Road, Caterham, Surrey, CR3 6JG Tel: (01883) 332651 Fax: (01883) 332652 E-mail: info@selectionanddevelopment.com *Provision of outsourced HR management services*

▶ Selective Covers Ltd, G Lumley Close, Thirsk Industrial Park, Thirsk, North Yorkshire, YO7 3TD Tel: (01845) 522856 Fax: (01845) 574227 *Swimming pool equipment & waterproof covering manufrs*

Selective Koi Sales, 47 Waterloo Road, Hainford, Norwich, NR10 3AX Tel: (01603) 897453 Fax: (01603) 898523 E-mail: sales@selectivekoisales.co.uk *Ponds & aquarium supplier*

Selector Office Furniture, Harley Street, Todmorden, Lancashire, OL14 5JE Tel: (01706) 818821 Fax: (01706) 812099 E-mail: info@selectoroffice.co.uk *Furniture manufrs*

Selectricks Ltd, 98 Reginald Rd, Southsea, Hants, PO4 9HW Tel: 023 92738214 *Refrigeration installation & cold rooms*

Selectrobuild Precision Plating Ltd, Meadowside, Cultercullen, Udny, Ellon, Aberdeenshire, AB41 6QQ Tel: (01651) 842533 Fax: (01651) 842533 *Electrochemical metallising*

Selectron Ltd, 1 Davis Way, Fareham, Hampshire, PO14 1JF Tel: (01329) 230525 Fax: (01329) 822759 E-mail: sales@selectron-ltd.co.uk *PCB design & assembly*

Selectronic Ltd, Book End, Witney, Oxfordshire, OX29 0YE Tel: (01993) 778000 Fax: (01993) 772512 E-mail: sales@selectronic-ltd.co.uk *Optic electronic distributors*

Selectweb Computers, 51 Scotforth Road, Lancaster, LA1 4SA Tel: (01524) 383268 Fax: (01524) 382675 E-mail: sales@select.net *Computer systems suppliers*

Seletar Services, Queens Road, Great Yarmouth, Norfolk, NR30 3NW Tel: (01493) 857313 Fax: (01493) 332202 *Offshore & marine support services*

▶ Selex Centre At Airbourne Systems, Ferry Road, Edinburgh, EH5 2XS Tel: 0131-332 2411 Fax: 0131-343 4011

Selex Centre At Airbourne Systems, Ferry Road, Edinburgh, EH5 2XS Tel: 0131-332 2411 Fax: 0131-343 4011 *Radar equipment*

Selex Communications Ltd, Marconi House, New Street, Chelmsford, CM1 1PL Tel: (01245) 353221 Fax: (01245) 287125 E-mail: alan.heritage@selex-comms.com *Telecommunications equipment manufrs*

Selex Communications Ltd, Unit 26, Byker Business Development Centre, Albion Row, Byker, Newcastle Upon Tyne, NE6 1LQ Tel: 0191-265 0374 Fax: 0191-265 0382 E-mail: newcastle-marine@selexcomms.com *Marine electronics*

SELEX Communications, Green Park Business Centre, Sutton-On-Forest, York, YO61 1ET Tel: (01347) 811881 Fax: (01347) 811991 E-mail: davies.sales@selex-comms.com *Radio communications equipment manufrs*

Self Adhesive Supplies Ltd, 9 Southview Park, Caversham, Reading, RG4 5AF Tel: 0118-948 3833 Fax: 0118-948 1089 E-mail: sales@selfadhesive.co.uk *Adhesive tape stockists & distributors*

SelfDiagnosis Limited, P O Box 162, Stockport, Cheshire, SK7 3WJ Tel: 07699 392121 *Range of home diagnostic kits for prostate abnormalities, stomach ulcers, bowel disorders, male & female fertility, sexually transmitted diseases and many other conditions.*

Selfridges Retail Ltd, 400 Oxford Street, London, W1A 1AB Tel: (0870) 8377377 Fax: (020) 7495 8321 E-mail: paul.kelly@selfridges.co.uk *Departmental store*

Selfstyle, 54-57 Acorn Centre, Barry Street, Oldham, OL1 3NE Tel: 0161-626 7926 Fax: 0161-627 4732 E-mail: sales@selfstyle.co.uk *Printing services, blocking & stamping*

Selhide, Vulcan Works, Pollard Street, Manchester, M4 7AN Tel: 0161-273 1772 Fax: 0161-273 2437 *Upholstery furnishing & curtain fabric wholesaler*

Selkirk Blinds, 54 Forest Road, Selkirk, TD7 5DG Tel: (01750) 21732 *Blinds suppliers*

▶ Selkirk Mechanical Handling Ltd, Dairycoates Industrial Estate, Wiltshire Road, Hull, HU4 6PA Tel: (01482) 502010 Fax: (01482) 502011 E-mail: selkirk.mh@virgin.co.uk *Forklift trucks*

Selkom Ltd, Unit D1 Riverside Industrial Estate, Bridge Road, Littlehampton, West Sussex, BN17 5DF Tel: (01903) 723645 Fax: (01903) 721362 E-mail: tonyselkom@aol.com *Computer parts manufacturers & distributors*

▶ Sell My House Now, 20 Fairfield Avenue, Peverell, Plymouth, PL2 3QF Tel: 0800 0272393 E-mail: enquiries@sellmyhousenow.co.uk *Sell My House Now provides sellers with a quick cash settlement for property, which saves you time, money and hassle. All types of property and circumstances viewed favourably.*

Sellar Agricultural, Victoria Road, Maud, Peterhead, Aberdeenshire, AB42 4NL Tel: (01771) 613481 Fax: (01771) 613672 *Agricultural engineers*

Sellar Agriculture Ltd, Seabank Road, Invergordon, Ross-Shire, IV18 0HE Tel: (01349) 852577 Fax: (01349) 853856 *Agricultural machinery services*

John Sellars & Co, 4 Broadgate La, Deeping St James, Peterborough, PE6 8NW Tel: 01778 342608 Fax: 01788 341663 *Furnishing trade supplies*

▶ Sellec Special Cables Ltd, Dukeries Way, Worksop, Nottinghamshire, S81 7DW Tel: (01909) 483539 Fax: (01909) 500181 E-mail: sales@sellec.com Principal Export Areas: Worldwide *Cable distributors*

Seller Agricultural Ltd, Dundee Road, Letham, Forfar, Angus, DD8 2PP Tel: (01307) 818545 Fax: (01307) 818939 E-mail: admin@sellerle.net.uk *Agricultural machinery suppliers*

▶ SELLERS & CO. LTD, 2A BROOKFIELD AVENUE, BREDBURY, STOCKPORT, CHESHIRE, SK6 1DF Tel: 0161 612 1095 E-mail: n.sellers@ntlworld.com *Accountancy and taxation services for the smaller business.*

Sellers Engineering Ltd, Sellers Way, Chadderton, Oldham, OL9 8EY Tel: 0161-681 5846 Fax: 0161-683 5621 *Waste disposal container manufrs*

Sellers Engineers Ltd, Chapel Hill, Huddersfield, HD1 3EH Tel: (01484) 540101 Fax: (01484) 544457 E-mail: admin@sellersengineers.com *Textile machinery manufrs*

▶ Helen Sellers, The Dairy, Red House Farm, Priory Road, Fressingfield, Eye, Suffolk, IP21 5PH Tel: (0870) 4215709 E-mail: helen.sellers@crosspoint-resources.co.uk *Crosspoint is a specialist recruitment agency for Medical Sales Jobs, Nurse Advisors and Managers in the Medical equipment market*

Selles Removals & Storage, Dairycoates Industrial Estate, Wiltshire Road, Hull, HU4 6PA Tel: (01482) 562822 Fax: (01482) 562832

Selles Removals & Storage, Dairycoates Industrial Estate, Wiltshire Road, Hull, HU4 6PA Tel: (01482) 562822 Fax: (01482) 562832 E-mail: nicola.mason@selles-removals.co.uk *Removal & storage contractors*

Sellite Blocks Ltd, The Old Quarry, Long Lane, Great Heck, Goole, North Humberside, DN14 0BT Tel: (01977) 661631 Fax: (01977) 662155 E-mail: sales@sellite.co.uk *Manufacturers of building blocks*

Sellsem Training Consultants, 153 Finstall Road, Finstall, Bromsgrove, Worcestershire, B60 3DD Tel: (01527) 835685 Fax: (01527) 575955 E-mail: rmpowell@btinternet.com *Sales & training consultants*

▶ Selman Marine Design, 12 Oxhill Road, Dumbarton, G82 4DG Tel: (01389) 734245 Fax: (01389) 602947 E-mail: info@selman-marine.com *Naval architecture, marine surveying service*

Selo UK Ltd, Mulberry Road, Rock Ferry, Birkenhead, Merseyside, CH42 3YA Tel: 0151-644 9393 Fax: 0151-645 2202 E-mail: info@selo.co.uk *Food process & packaging machines services*

Sels College, 64 Long Acre, London, WC2E 9JD Tel: (020) 7240 2581 Fax: (020) 7379 5793 *English teaching college*

Selsea Fish & Lobster Co. Ltd, Lagoon Cottage, Kingsway, Selsey, Chichester, West Sussex, PO20 0SY Tel: (01243) 607444 Fax: (01243) 607333 *Shellfish dealers*

▶ J.B. Selsey, 6 Mixon Close, Selsey, Chichester, West Sussex, PO20 0TZ Tel: (01243) 601188 Fax: (01243) 601199 *Fish wholesalers*

▶ Selsey PC, 79 High Street, Selsey, Chichester, West Sussex, PO20 0QL Tel: (01243) 607605 Fax: (01243) 606597 E-mail: sales@selseypc.net *Computer software manufrs*

▶ Selsey Press Ltd, 84 High Street, Selsey, Chichester, West Sussex, PO20 0QH Tel: (01243) 605234 Fax: (01243) 605235

Selsmore (Marketing) Ltd, Unit 23 The Tanneries, Brockhampton Lane, Havant, Hampshire, PO9 1JB Tel: (023) 9249 2907 Fax: (023) 9247 3714 E-mail: selsmore@tiscali.co.uk *Injection moulders & designers*

Seltec Automation, Subway Street, Hull, HU3 4EL Tel: (01482) 225297 Fax: (01482) 212470 E-mail: sales@seltec.co.uk *Proximity & photoelectric switches*

Seltek Consultants, 25a Hockerill Street, Bishop's Stortford, Hertfordshire, CM23 2DH Tel: (01279) 657716 Fax: (01279) 651119 E-mail: sales@seltekconsultants.co.uk *Specialist recruiters in technical sales*

Seltek Solutions, Unit 25, Stockwood Business Park, Stockwood, Redditch, Worcestershire, B96 6SX Tel: (01386) 793274 Fax: (01386) 792154 E-mail: info@selteksolutions.co.uk *Maintenance software, mould chutes & curtains*

Selus Supplies & Equipment Ltd, Copper Beech, Black Hill, Lindfield, Haywards Heath, West Sussex, RH16 2HF Tel: (01444) 452390 Fax: (01444) 450654 E-mail: selus.supplies@btconnect.com *Foundry equipment distributors*

Selux UK Ltd, Harrison Way, Leamington Spa, Warwickshire, CV31 3HL Tel: (01926) 833455 Fax: (01926) 339844 E-mail: enquire@selux.co.uk *Lighting distribs*

Selva Engineering Ltd, Checketts Lane, Worcester, WR3 7JP Tel: (01905) 452877 Fax: (01905) 452699 *General engineers*

Selway Signs Ltd, Leonard House, Queen Street, Belper, Derbyshire, DE56 1NR Tel: (01773) 825445 Fax: (01773) 821619 E-mail: sales@selway-group.com *Screen process printers & print finishing services*

Selwell Computers (Software) Ltd, Selwood House, Hough Road, Frieston, Grantham, Lincolnshire, NG32 3DA Tel: (01400) 273311 Fax: (01400) 273312 *Software developers*

▶ Selwood Ltd, 32-36 Bournemouth Road, Chandler's Ford, Eastleigh, Hampshire, SO53 3ZL Tel: (023) 8026 6311 Fax: (023) 8026 0906

▶ Selwood Ltd, Derby Road, Langley Mill, Nottingham, NG16 4AA Tel: (01773) 714227 Fax: (01773) 716445 E-mail: nottingham@selwoodgroup.co.uk *Pump & plant hire*

▶ Selwood Ceramics Floor and Wall Tiling, 15 Havelock Road, Maidenhead, Berkshire, SL6 5BJ Tel: (01628) 782393 E-mail: sales@selwoodceramics.co.uk *Floor & wall tiling specialists*

Selwood Group, Hixon Industrial Estate, Church Lane, Hixon, Stafford, ST18 0QB Tel: (01889) 270524 Fax: (01889) 270063 *Contractors plant & pump hire services* Also at: Northwich, Nottingham, Preston, Queensferry, Rotherham, Sheffield, Wolverhampton & Wrexham

Selwood Pump Co. Ltd, 188 Robin Hood Lane, Birmingham, B28 0LG Tel: 0121-777 5631 Fax: 0121-702 2195 E-mail: graham.gallon@selwood-pumps.com *Pump distributors*

Selwyn Construction Engineering Ltd, Tarran Road, Tarran Industrial Estate, Wirral, Merseyside, CH46 4TU Tel: 0151-678 0236 Fax: 0151-678 8959 E-mail: enquiries@selwyngroup.co.uk *Design, fabrication & erection of structural steelwork & pipework*

Selwyn Electronics Ltd, Unit B8 Chaucer Business Park, Watery Lane, Kemsing, Sevenoaks, Kent, TN15 6QY Tel: (01732) 765100 Fax: (01732) 765190 E-mail: connect@selwyn.co.uk *Connector & cable assembly distributors*

Sem, Faraday House, Faraday Way, Orpington, Kent, BR5 3QT Tel: (01689) 884700 Fax: (01689) 884884 E-mail: info@sem.co.uk *Servo motor manufrs*

▶ Sem Logistics Milford Haven Ltd, Waterston Road, Milford Haven, Dyfed, SA73 1DR Tel: (01646) 692461 Fax: (01646) 695837

Semaphore Cardiff Ltd, Bessemer Road, Cardiff, CF11 8BA Tel: (029) 2022 4111 Fax: (029) 2022 5401

Sematic UK Ltd, Meadow Gate, Valley Park Industrial Estate, Wombwell, Barnsley, South Yorkshire, S73 0UN Tel: (01226) 344800 Fax: (01226) 344811 *Lift door manufrs*

Semb Corp Simon Carves Ltd, 34 Lowther Street, Whitehaven, Cumbria, CA28 7JS Tel: (01946) 692301 Fax: (01946) 599045 E-mail: info@simoncarves.com *Process engineers*

Semec Electrical, Northfleet Industrial Estate, Lower Road, Northfleet, Gravesend, Kent, DA11 9SN Tel: (01322) 382070 Fax: (01322) 382143 *Electric motor suppliers & repairers service providers*

Semefab (Scotland) Ltd, Newark Road North, Eastfield Industrial Estate, Glenrothes, Fife, KY7 4NS Tel: (01592) 630630 Fax: (01592) 775265 E-mail: sales@semefab.co.uk *Integrated circuit manufrs*

Semelab plc, Coventry Road, Lutterworth, Leicestershire, LE17 4JB Tel: (01455) 556565 Fax: (01455) 558371 E-mail: sales@semelab.co.uk Principal Export Areas: Worldwide *Manufacturers of semi-conductor components & integrated circuits* Also at: Glenrothes

▶ Semex UK Materials Ltd, Kilmartin Place, Tannochside Park, Uddingston, Glasgow, G71 5PH Tel: (01698) 811100 Fax: (01698) 816068 *Concrete & aggregate*

Semi Conductor Supplies International Ltd, 128-130 Carshalton Road, Sutton, Surrey, SM1 4TW Tel: (020) 8643 1126 Fax: (020) 8643 3937 E-mail: sales@ssi-uk.com *Electronic component distributors*

Semiconductor Specialists (UK) Ltd, Lincoln Business Park, Osbaldwick, York, YO10 3JB Tel: (01904) 436450 Fax: (01904) 436550 E-mail: sales@semispecs.com *Electronic components distribs*

▶ Semikron, Skipton Road, Keighley, West Yorkshire, BD20 6DT Tel: (01535) 691795 Fax: (01535) 691795 Sales Contact: D Shuttleworth

Semikron UK Ltd, Martin House, 7 Fountain Drive, Hertford, SG13 7UB Tel: (01992) 584677 Fax: (01992) 554942 E-mail: sales.skuk@semikron.com *Semiconductor component manufacturers. Also electronic power assembly & power solutions manufacturers*

▶ Semitool (Europe) Ltd, 509 Coldhams Lane, Cambridge, CB1 3JS Tel: (01223) 505000 Fax: (01223) 243026 *Manufacture semi-conductors*

Semore Classic Clothing, 104 Smawthorne Grove, Castleford, West Yorkshire, WF10 5AT Tel: (01977) 556307 E-mail: pamatsemoreclas6@aol.com *Ladies & girls clothing, design/pattern cutting, making up of samples & short runs. MADE IN UK!... ON THE PREMISES*

▶ Semper Vigil Security Ltd, Unit 9 Hardengreen Business Centre, Dalkeith, Midlothian, EH22 3NX Tel: 0131-660 9481 E-mail: semper.vigil@btconnect.com *Security system installers*

Semperit Industrial Products Ltd, Cottesbrooke Park, Heartlands Business Park, Daventry, Northamptonshire, NN11 8YL Tel: (01327) 313140 Fax: (01327) 313149 E-mail: paul.phillips@semperit.co.uk *Rubber hose, rubber sheeting, rubber mouldings, rubber extrusion, rubber products (industrial). Also gloves, medical/surgical & gloves, industrial*

▶ Semple P.L.C., 15 Fullerton Court, Drumhead Place, Glasgow East Investment Park, Glasgow, G32 8EY Tel: 0141-646 5252

Semta Centre, 14 Upton Road, Watford, WD18 0JT Tel: (01923) 238441 Fax: (01642) 566124 E-mail: infodesk@senta.org.uk *Training & engineers*

Semtech Ltd, 218 St. Vincent Street, Glasgow, G2 5SG Tel: 0141-229 5570 Fax: 0141-229 5571 *Semiconductor design engineers*

Semtron Services Ltd, Carlton House, 8 Gwash Way, Stamford, Lincolnshire, PE9 1XR Tel: (01780) 766736 Fax: (01780) 766736 E-mail: ken.swanson@semtron.co.uk *Scientific instrument services*

Senator Communications Ltd, 5 Newton Court, Wavertree Technology Park, Liverpool, L13 1EJ Tel: 0151-259 5959 Fax: 0151-259 0099 E-mail: sales@senatorinternational.uk *Radio paging & telemarketing services*

▶ Senator Homes Ltd, Hillcrest Avenue, Carlisle, CA1 2QJ Tel: (01228) 882200

Senator International Ltd, Sykeside Drive, Altham Business Park, Altham, Accrington, Lancashire, BB5 5YE Tel: (01282) 725000 Fax: (01282) 775039 E-mail: sales@senatorinternational.co.uk *Office furniture systems manufrs*

Senator Pens Ltd, Senator House, Stadium Way, Harlow, Essex, CM19 5GY Tel: (01279) 630700 Fax: (01279) 630750 E-mail: sales@senatorpens.co.uk *Manufacturers of writing instruments*

Senator Projects Ltd, The Door Centre, Discovery Park, Crossley Road, Stockport, Cheshire, SK4 5BW Tel: 0161-432 5080 Fax: 0161-432 6100 *Pattern manufrs*

Sencam UK Ltd, Unit 107 Cariocca Business Park, Hellidon Close, Ardwick, Manchester, M12 4AH Tel: 0161-273 5747 Fax: 0161-273 6077 E-mail: sales@sencam.co.uk *Computer maintenance & repairers*

▶ Sence Valley Consulting, 14 Nethercote, Newton Burgoland, Coalville, Leicestershire, LE67 2ST Tel: 01530 272561 E-mail: results@sencevalley.co.uk *Sence Valley Consulting has been specially formed to help companies grow by identifying strategies and plans to acquire new customers, retain existing customers and sell even more products and services through effective marketing communications.**Created to help companies that sell to other businesses (B2B), Sence Valley Consulting is ideally suited to those organisations that don"t have large marketing departments or access to large advertising agencies. Sence Valley Consulting adds a valuable resource that can be utilised as and when required, on an affordable, known-cost basis.* **

Sencon (UK) Ltd, Unit P, Blackpole Trading Estate East, Worcester, WR3 8SG Tel: (01905) 755525 Fax: (01905) 456393 E-mail: sales@sencon.co.uk *Control & instrumentation sensor manufrs*

Send The Light Ltd, PO Box 300, Carlisle, CA3 0QS Tel: (01228) 512512 Fax: (01228) 514949 E-mail: info@stl.org *Wholesalers, retailers & publishers of christian products*

▶ Send Me a Balloon, 23 Woodthorpe Road, Ashford, Middlesex, TW15 2RP Tel: (0870) 0117550 Fax: (0870) 0117660 E-mail: sales@staggerin.com *Send Me A Balloon is a 'Balloon in a Box' mail order service offered by the online fancy dress and party company Staggerin. Send someone special a Happy Birthday, congratulations, Valentines or get well balloon when you can't be there in person. Free UK Delivery.*

SeNd Technology Ltd, Hunters End, Cox Green Lane, Maidenhead, Berkshire, SL6 3EU Tel: (0870) 4587363 Fax: (07092) 383861 E-mail: sales@sendtech.co.uk *GSM modems & remote control devices specialists*

SendaCard, 19, Business Science Park, Nuns Corner, Grimsby, North East Lincolnshire, DN34 5FQ Tel: 01472 822554 E-mail: sales@sendacard.co.uk *Suppliers of quality cards for all occasions*

Sendean Photographic Equipment Repairs, 9-12 St. Annes Court, London, W1F 0BB Tel: (020) 7734 0895 E-mail: mail@sendeancameras.com *Camera repair services & used camera sales*

Sendt Ltd, Littlebrook Business Centre, Littlebrook Manorway, Dartford, DA1 5PZ Tel: (01322) 287347 Fax: (01322) 287493 E-mail: tony.blake@sendt.freeserve.co.uk *Non-destructive testing services*

Senior Aerospace Bird Bellows, Radnor Park Industrial Estate, Congleton, Cheshire, CW12 4UQ Tel: (01260) 271411 Fax: (01260) 270910 E-mail: info@bird-bellows.co.uk Principal Export Areas: Worldwide *Industrial bellows & expansion joint manufrs*

Senior Aluminium Systems, Eland Road, Denaby Main, Doncaster, South Yorkshire, DN12 4HA Tel: (01709) 772600 Fax: 01709 772601 E-mail: enquiries@senioraluminium.co.uk *Aluminium windows, doors & curtain walling systems*

Senior Automotive Products Division, 1 Oakwood Close, Pen-Y-Fan Industrial Estate, Crumlin, Newport, Gwent, NP11 3HY Tel: (01495) 241500 Fax: (01495) 241501 Principal Export Areas: Worldwide *Flexible motor vehicle exhaust coupling*

Senior Consultants, 113 Station Road, Ellon, Aberdeenshire, AB41 9AZ Tel: (01358) 725161 Fax: (01358) 725171 E-mail: sales@ellon.co.uk *Computer consultants*

Senior Design Associates Ltd, Unit 4 Dukes Street, Windsor, Berkshire, SL4 1SE Tel: (01753) 833382 Fax: (01753) 833709 E-mail: contactus@sda.uk.com *Manufacturers & constructors of custom built machinery & packaging*

Senior Engineering Investments Ltd, 59-61 High Street, Rickmansworth, Hertfordshire, WD3 1RH Tel: (01923) 775547 Fax: (01923) 896027 E-mail: info@seniorplc.com *Public holding company-mechanical engineers*

Senior Graphic Machinery Ltd, Thornes La Wharf, Wakefield, West Yorkshire, WF1 5RF Tel: (01924) 386386 Fax: (01924) 386800 *Printing equipment manufrs*

Senior Hargreaves Ltd, Lord Street, Bury, Lancashire, BL9 0RG Tel: 0161-764 5082 Fax: 0161-762 2333 E-mail: postbox@senior-hargreaves.co.uk *Ductwork contractors & manufrs* Also at: Branches throughout the U.K.

Senior Packaging Ltd, 4 Borrowdale Road, Dewsbury, West Yorkshire, WF12 7PF Tel: (01924) 430201 Fax: (01924) 510065 E-mail: info@seniorpackaging.co.uk *Strapping systems & packaging equipment distributors*

Senior Press & Tool Co. Ltd, Unit 34b Marlborough Road, Churchill Industrial Estate, Lancing, West Sussex, BN15 8TR Tel: (01903) 762835 Fax: (01903) 762835 *Metal pressings*

Senior Steel Ltd, Bamfurlong Industrial Park, Staverton, Cheltenham, Gloucestershire, GL51 6SX Tel: (01452) 712843 Fax: (01452) 856470 E-mail: sales@seniorsteel.co.uk *Structural steelworkers & fabricators*

Senlac Windows & Doors Ltd, Station Road, Battle, East Sussex, TN33 0DF Tel: (01424) 772362 Fax: (01424) 773615 E-mail: sales@senlac-windows.co.uk *Metal window manufrs*

Sennock Computer Services Ltd, 3 Nightingale Road, Kemsing, Sevenoaks, Kent, TN15 6RU Tel: (01959) 525153 Fax: (01959) 525153 E-mail: info@sennock.co.uk *Computer consultancy & software specialists*

▶ Senow Plastic Fabrications, Unit 25, Royds Enterprise Park, Future Fields, Bradford, West Yorkshire, BD6 3EW Tel: (01274) 355887 Fax: (01274) 355887 *THERMOPLASTIC WELDING/BENDING & MANUFACTURE IN PP/PVC/HDPE/FOAMEX.DISPLAY MANUFACTURING.ASBESTOS EQUIPMENT*

Sensa, Gamma House, Enterprise Road, Chilworth Science Park, Southampton, SO16 7NS Tel: (023) 8076 5500 Fax: (023) 8076 5501 *Fibre optic temperature sensor manufrs*

Sensaflow Ltd, P O Box 61, Bridgwater, Somerset, TA5 1YY Tel: (01278) 732620 Fax: (01278) 732647 *Water saving equipment manufrs*

Sensbey, 36 Carters Lane, Kiln Farm, Milton Keynes, MK11 3HL Tel: (01908) 569630 Fax: (01908) 562457 E-mail: sensbeyuk@compuserve.com *Soldering equipment distributors*

Sense Computer Systems, Corner House, Robey Close, Linby, Nottingham, NG15 8AA Tel: 0115-964 6646 Fax: 0115-964 6647 *Computer software resellers*

▶ Sense of Smell Ltd, 5 Wansbeck Cottages, Choppington, Northumberland, NE62 5JG Tel: 01670 522656 E-mail: info@senseofsmell.co.uk *Experience the wonderful aromas of Sense of Smell - Suppliers of Luxury bath bombs, natural soaps, scented candles and gifts.*

▶ Sense-Ability, Felin Brithdir, Rhydlewis, Llandysul, Dyfed, SA44 5SN Tel: 0151-652 1053 E-mail: post@sense-ability.co.uk *Sense-Ability provides a range of services with the aim of improving access to deaf and disabled people including: disability and deaf awareness training, sign language courses and access consultancy.*

continued

Sensible People, Romary House, 26 Church Road, Tunbridge Wells, Kent, TN1 1JP Tel: (01892) 612320 Fax: (01892) 612328 E-mail: sales@sensible-people.co.uk *Computer consultants*

Sensient Colors Ltd, Old Meadow Road, King's Lynn, Norfolk, PE30 4LA Tel: (01553) 669444 Fax: (01553) 770707 *Food colouring manufrs*

Sensine Flavors Ltd, Felinfach, Lampeter, Dyfed, SA48 8AG Tel: (01570) 470277 Fax: (01570) 470958 *Savoury food ingredients*

Sensing Devices Ltd, 97 Tithebarn Road, Southport, Merseyside, PR8 6AG Tel: (01704) 546161 Fax: (01704) 546231 E-mail: sales@sensing-devices.co.uk *Resistance temperature detector manufrs*

Sensitised Coatings Ltd, Bergen Way, North Lynn Industrial Estate, King's Lynn, Norfolk, PE30 2JL Tel: (01553) 764836 Fax: (01553) 760377 E-mail: sales@senco.co.uk *Recording chart manufrs*

Sensonics Ltd, North Bridge Road, Berkhamsted, Hertfordshire, HP4 1EF Tel: (01442) 876833 Fax: (01442) 876477 E-mail: sales@sensonics.co.uk *Manufacturers of condition monitoring equipment & vibration monitors*

Sensopart UK Ltd, Unit G8 The Arch, 48-52 Floodgate Street, Birmingham, B5 5SL Tel: 0121-772 5104 Fax: 0121-772 5126 E-mail: info@sensopart.co.uk *Electronic, photoelectric sensors & fibre optics sensors manufrs*

Sensor Technology Ltd, PO Box 36, Banbury, Oxfordshire, OX15 6JB Tel: (01295) 730746 Fax: (01295) 738966 E-mail: info@sensors.co.uk *Manufacturer of high performance torque sensors, using a radical new technology for rotary torque measurement, torqSense transducers are designed specifically for automotive, aerospace, motor control, viscosity & OEM applications*

Sensorbility Ltd, West Prawle House, East Portlemouth, Salcombe, Devon, TQ8 8PW Tel: (01548) 511498 Fax: (01548) 511393 E-mail: sales@sensor.co.uk *Sales of industrial proximity, opto & laser sensors & encoders*

▶ Sensorium Ltd, 9 Nethertown Broad Street, Dunfermline, Fife, KY12 7DS Tel: (01383) 720600 Fax: (01383) 739793 E-mail: info@sensorium.co.uk *Call systems, staff attack systems & local area paging service*

Sensors UK Ltd, 135-137 Hatfield Road, St. Albans, Hertfordshire, AL4 0DH Tel: (01727) 861110 Fax: (01727) 844272 E-mail: admin@sensorsuk.com *Industrial tachometer manufrs*

Sensorshop Automation Systems, 19 Orchard Close, East Hendred, Wantage, Oxfordshire, OX12 8JJ Tel: (01235) 833348 Fax: (01235) 835715 E-mail: sales@sensorshop.co.uk *Industrial automation equipment distribution*

▶ Sensortechnics UK & Ireland, McGowan House, Aspect Business Centre, 66c Somers Road, Rugby, Warwickshire, CV22 7DH Tel: (01788) 560426 Fax: (01788) 561228 E-mail: salesuk@sensortechnics.com *Sensortechnics is a leading manufacturer and distributor of a wide range of sensors and fluid control devices. The product portfolio includes basic pressure sensors, rugged transmitters, submersible level sensors and customised pressure sensing systems from 1 mbar up to 1000 bar as well as liquid level switches, oxygen, flow and force sensors. Additionally, Sensortechnics offers ultrasonic air bubble, air-in-line, liquid level and fluid monitoring sensors and detectors. Fluid control devices include miniature solenoid valves and diaphragm pumps, electronic pressure controllers and custom specific fluidic control systems. Sensortechnics has more than two decades of experience in providing highly customised sensing products and in the development of complex integrated fluid control systems for OEM customers worldwide.*

Sensor-Technik UK Ltd, Unit 10 The Granary, Sharnbrook, Bedford, MK44 1NN Tel: 01234 782049 *Hydraulic electrical controller specialists*

Sensotec Europe Ltd, Unit 7 Industrial Estate, Bala, Gwynedd, LL23 7NL Tel: (01678) 520022 Fax: (0870) 0740000 E-mail: technical@sensotec.co.uk *Fire alarm distributors*

Sensotec Europe Ltd, 6 Lumb Lane, Liversedge, West Yorkshire, WF15 7QH Tel: (01924) 412859 Fax: (0870) 0720000 E-mail: sales@sensotec.co.uk *Fire & safety smoke alarm manufrs*

Sensotemp Ltd, Plot 12, Woodford Halse, Daventry, Northamptonshire, NN11 3TZ Tel: 01327 261212 *Precision turned parts manufrs*

Sensotherm Europanel Ltd, Stafford Park 16, Telford, Shropshire, TF3 3BS Tel: (01952) 292219 Fax: (01952) 292128 E-mail: sales@sensotherm.co.uk *Specialist radiator supplier*

Senstronics Ltd, Unit 2, Angels Close, Aycliffe Industrial Park, Newton Aycliffe, County Durham, DL5 6BG Tel: (01325) 328500 Fax: (01325) 328504 E-mail: sales@senstronics.com *Pressure sensor manufrs*

▶ Sensual Reading.com Limited, 47 Manchester Road, Denton, Manchester, M34 2AF Tel: 07723 060498 E-mail: sensualreading@sensualreading.com *Offering sensual stories, sensual gifts and life balance information for discerning women to share with their partner.*

Sentinel Instruments Ltd, Unit 20 Howe Moss Drive, Kirkhill Industrial Estate, Dyce, Aberdeen, AB21 0GG Tel: (01224) 775830 Fax: (01224) 775831 *Instrumentation engineering services*

Sentinel Lightning Protection & Earthing Ltd, Sentinel House 19 Great, Northern Way Netherfield, Nottingham, NG4 2HD Tel: 0115-961 0520 Fax: 0115-961 3642 E-mail: enquiries@lightning-conductors.co.uk *Lightning conductor installation & servicing*

Sentinel Security Europe Ltd, 9 Oxhill Road, Shirley, Solihull, West Midlands, B90 1LR Tel: 0121-436 5999 Fax: 0121-436 5444 E-mail: info@sentinelgroup.co.uk *Security solutions*

Sentinel Security Systems, 7 Southern Avenue, Leominster, Herefordshire, HR6 0QF Tel: (01568) 615500 Fax: (01568) 610555 E-mail: sentinelss@btinternet.com *Electronic security systems*

▶ Sentripod Survey Company Ltd, The Lodge, 13 The Hamlet, Chippenham, Wiltshire, SN15 1BY Tel: (01249) 462039 Fax: (01249) 462039 E-mail: info@sentripod.co.uk *360 degree targets suppliers for electronic distance measuring instruments*

▶ Sentry Systems, Britannia Enterprise Centre, Waterworks Road, Hastings, East Sussex, TN34 1RT Tel: (01424) 720600 Fax: (01424) 440092 *Electronic component distributors*

Seohun Co Ltd, Excel Ho, 6 Pepys Rd, London, SW20 8NH Tel: 020 89479313 Fax: 020 88793958 *Computer repair & maintenance*

Sepal Ltd, 429 Lisburn Road, Belfast, BT9 7 EY Tel: (028) 9020 2333 *Hi-fi equipment distribution & tv & plasmas*

Separ Distribution, 428 Whippendell Road, Watford, WD18 7QU Tel: (01923) 819041 Fax: (01923) 255052 E-mail: filtration@separ.co.uk *Filtration systems for oil*

Seppi, 28 High Street, Meldreth, Royston, Hertfordshire, SG8 6JU Tel: (01763) 260326 Fax: (01763) 260035 E-mail: sales@seppities.co.uk *Screen printers & corporate neckwear*

Seppic UK Ltd, PO Box 338, Hounslow, TW4 6JQ Tel: (020) 8577 8800 Fax: (020) 8570 2106 E-mail: sales@seppic.com *Chemical distributors & manufrs*

Sepserv Ltd, 174 Liverpool Road, Southport, Merseyside, PR8 4NY Tel: (01704) 567401 Fax: (01704) 562644 *Dairy engineering services*

▶ Sepsure Ltd, 6 Duke Street, Hawick, Roxburghshire, TD9 9PY Tel: (01450) 373222 E-mail: info@sepsure.co.uk *Stainless steel filters & housings suppliers*

Septodont Ltd, Units R-S Orchard Business Centre, St. Barnabas Close, Allington, Maidstone, Kent, ME16 0JZ Tel: (01622) 695520 Fax: (01622) 686165 E-mail: information@septodont.co.uk *Suppliers of pharmaceuticals & technical dental products*

Sequani Ltd, Bromyard Road, Ledbury, Herefordshire, HR8 1LH Tel: (01531) 634121 Fax: (01531) 634753 E-mail: sales@sequani.com *Pharmaceutical contract research*

Sequel Technology Ltd, 2 Hart House, The Hart, Farnham, Surrey, GU9 7HJ Tel: (01252) 734321 Fax: (01252) 734355 E-mail: sales@seqtec.co.uk *Computer consultants*

Sequent Ltd, Kushi Koti, Court Road, Maidenhead, Berkshire, SL6 8LQ Tel: (01628) 628190 Fax: (01628) 623336 E-mail: seq1989@aol.com *Car suppliers & car finance services*

Sequoia Technology Ltd, Basingstoke Road, Spencers Wood, Reading, RG7 1PW Tel: 0118-976 9000 Fax: 0118-976 9070 E-mail: sales@sequoia.co.uk *Hybrid integrated circuit manufrs*

Sera Dosing UK Ltd, 7 Woodland Drive, Alma Park Road, Grantham, Lincolnshire, NG31 9SR Tel: (01476) 565512 Fax: (01476) 590171 E-mail: enquiries@liquiddosing.co.uk *Distributors of pumps including chemical injection*

▶ Seramis Hydroponics, Unit 11, Pentood Enterprise Park, Cardigan, Dyfed, SA43 3AG Tel: (0870) 0271980 Fax: (0870) 0271985 E-mail: sales@seramishydroponics.com *Clay granules suppliers for gardening*

Sercal MTMS Ltd, The Rubicon Centre, Redditch, Worcestershire, B98 8YP Tel: 01527 514015 *Calibration laboratory services*

Sercal NDT Equipment Ltd, 1 Littleton Business Park, Littleton Drive, Cannock, Staffordshire, WS12 4TR Tel: (01543) 570074 Fax: (01543) 465090 E-mail: sales@sercal.co.uk *Non-destructive test equipment supplier*

Serck Aviation, Oscar House, Wharfdale Road, Tyseley, Birmingham, B11 2DG Tel: 0121-623 6000 Fax: 0121-623 6100 E-mail: john.felton@dunlop-aerospace.com *Heat exchanger suppliers*

Serck Controls Ltd, Stonebridge Trading Estate, Rowley Drive, Coventry, CV3 4FH Tel: (024) 7651 1069 Fax: (024) 7630 2437 E-mail: sales@serck-controls.co.uk *Telemetry & SCADA systems manufrs*

▶ Serck Intertruck, 104 Hydepark Street, Glasgow, G3 8BW Tel: 0141-221 1127 Fax: 0141-248 1221

Serck Intertruck, 293 Elland Road, Leeds, LS11 8AX Tel: 0113-242 1463 Fax: 0113-385 5811 E-mail: si.leeds@unipart.co.uk *Commercial vehicle parts suppliers*

Serck Intertruck, Worrall Street, Salford, M5 4TA Tel: 0161-872 5726 Fax: 0161-873 8074 E-mail: si.manchester732@unipart.co.uk *Car radiator manufrs*

Serck Intertruck, Neachells Lane, Willenhall, West Midlands, WV13 3SH Tel: (01902) 862520 Fax: (01902) 306335 *Automotive radiator manufrs*

Serck Services, Units 9 & 10, Brook Industrial Estate, Bullsbrook Road, Hayes, Middlesex, UB4 0JZ Tel: (020) 8813 7470 Fax: (020) 8813 7499 E-mail: si@unipart.co.uk *Radiator manufrs*

▶ Serco Ltd, Shrewton, Salisbury, SP3 4DU Tel: (01980) 620985 Fax: (01980) 620890

Serco, Unit 63 Hillgrove Business Park, Nazeing Road, Nazeing, Waltham Abbey, Essex, EN9 2HB Tel: (01992) 893917 Fax: (01992) 893759 *Ductwork manufrs*

Serco, Unit A-B Wellington Gate, Silverthorne Way, Waterlooville, Hampshire, PO7 7XY Tel: (023) 9278 4950 Fax: (023) 9226 9859 *Automatic test systems including_automative & aerospace industry. Test systems/systems design services. In addition, manufrs of data acquisition systems*

Serco Ltd, Bar End Road, Winchester, Hampshire, SO23 9NP Tel: (01962) 828400 Fax: (01962) 843017 *Resource management services*

Serco Defence, Bartley Wood Business Park, Bartley Way, Hook, Hampshire, RG27 9XA Tel: (01256) 745900 Fax: (01256) 745995 E-mail: enquiries@serco.com *Aviation support services*

Serco Electrical Ltd, 93 Canwick Road, Lincoln, LN5 8HE Tel: (01522) 874874 Fax: (01522) 514732 *Electrical & refrigeration services*

Serco Geografix Ltd, Hurricane Way, Norwich, NR6 6EW Tel: (01603) 788940 Fax: (01603) 788964 E-mail: sales@premiergeografix.com *Tagging & monitoring equipment suppliers*

Serco Group P.L.C., Serco House, 16 Bartley Wood, Business Park, Hook, Hampshire, RG27 9UY Tel: (01256) 745900 Fax: (01256) 744111 *Facilities management & business support*

Serco Integrated Services, Building 37, Second Avenue, Pensnett Trading Estate, Kingswinford, West Midlands, DY6 7UL Tel: (01384) 401515 Fax: (01384) 404543 *Traffic signal installers*

Serco Integrated Transport Ltd, Cavendish House, Prince's Wharf, Stockton-On-Tees, Cleveland, TS17 6QY Tel: (01642) 636700 Fax: (01642) 636701 *Traffic management systems*

▶ Serco Medway Ltd, Victory House, Meeting House Lane, Chatham, Kent, ME4 4YU Tel: (01322) 303118 Fax: (01634) 835537 E-mail: paul@uk.serco-ai.com *Technical publications*

Serco Plastic Injection Moulders Ltd, Woden Road, Wolverhampton, WV10 0AU Tel: (01902) 351233 Fax: (01902) 351485 *Plastic mouldings manufrs*

Serco Ryan, Unit 45, Thornleigh Trading Estate, Dudley, West Midlands, DY2 8UB Tel: (01384) 459000 Fax: (01384) 456952 E-mail: dudley@sercoryan.co.uk *Fastener manufrs*

Serco Solutions, P O Box 57 Laburnum House, Birmingham, B30 2BD Tel: 0121-459 1155 Fax: 0121-459 2199 E-mail: mediaanddesign@serco.com *Information technology outsourcing & management*

▶ Sercombe Taxis, 4 Copland Meadows, Totnes, Devon, TQ9 6ER Tel: (01803) 864745 Fax: 01803 864745 E-mail: sales@sercombetaxis.co.uk

Sercon Controls Ltd, Clay Lane, Spar Fields, Slarthwate, Huddersfield, HD7 5BG Tel: (01484) 845548 Fax: (01484) 847846 E-mail: gln@serconcontrols.com *Control system manufrs*

▶ Serendipity Wholesale Co., Unit 12 Cambrian Industrial Estate East Side, Coedcae Lane, Pontyclun, Mid Glamorgan, CF72 9EW Tel: (01443) 230002 Fax: (01443) 230002 E-mail: paul@serendipity-wholesale.com *We are a family owned wholesaler of fancy goods,hand made designer interior pots/ vases,giftware,artificial,dried flowers,welsh gifts,childrens gifts also interior lighting etc*

Serene Paint, Serene Works, 67 Victoria Road, Burgess Hill, West Sussex, RH15 9YL Tel: (01273) 495393 Fax: (01273) 492853 *Paint manufrs*

▶ Serene Paints, Serene Works, 67 Victoria Road, Burgess Hill, West Sussex, RH15 9YL Tel: (01444) 870011 Fax: (01444) 871433 E-mail: sales@serenepaints.co.uk *Manufacturers of industrial & protective coatings*

▶ Serenity, 38 Clover Way, Harrogate, North Yorkshire, HG3 2WE Tel: 01423 528262 E-mail: heather@serenityofharrogate.co.uk *Complementary Therapies, Training Courses & Workshops. Natural Products & Hand Blended Skincare*

Serenity Computer Services, 86 Leyburne Road, Dover, Kent, CT16 1SH Tel: (01304) 242188 Fax: (01304) 242088 *Computer reseller & consultancy*

Serenity Wedding Tiaras, 19 Eltham Road, West Bridgford, Nottingham, NG2 5JP Tel: 0115 8461148 E-mail: info@serenity-wedding-tiaras.com *I specialise in Bespoke Designer Tiara"s and Wedding Accessories. All my tiara"s are individually designed for both the Bride and her Maid. I am also able to offer one on one consultations in the Nottingham area. Please feel free to take a look at my website and contact me for further information. I understand that it is the bride"s special day and I endeavour to do all I can to try and design a tiara to her unique specifications.*

Seres UK Ltd, 178 Dukes Ride, Crowthorne, Berkshire, RG45 6DS Tel: (01344) 762211 Fax: (01344) 761255 *On line analytical monitoring services*

▶ Serfice Engineering Consulting, 37 Leys Avenue, Desborough, Kettering, Northamptonshire, NN14 2PY Tel: (01536) 763567 *Metal finishing consultants, specialist manufacturing process advice*

Serfilco Europe Ltd, Broadoak Business Park, Ashburton Road West, Trafford Park, Manchester, M17 1RW Tel: 0161-872 1317 Fax: 0161-873 8027 E-mail: sales@serfilco-europe.com *Pump & filter distributors*

▶ Sergey Naumkin, 31 Wellington Road, Bollington, Macclesfield, Cheshire, SK10 5JR Tel: (01625) 576077 Fax: 0700 6051662 E-mail: sergey.naumkin@justice.com *Sergey Naumkin is a U.K. based Russian Business Lawyer specialising in the support of British companies who are looking to invest in trade in Russia, the Kaliningrad region and the Baltic Sea Countries.*

Series 4 Ltd, 9 Westwood Court, Caomoor Industrial Estate, Totton, Southampton, SO40 3WX Tel: (023) 8086 6377 Fax: (023) 8086 6323 E-mail: sales@series4.co.uk *Cable processing & pneumatic tools suppliers*

Serif Software Ltd, 141 St. James Road, Glasgow, G4 0LT Tel: 0141-552 3513 Fax: 0141-552 3506 *Computer software development*

Serigraphia Digital Ltd, Stonebridge Trading Estate, Sibree Road, Coventry, CV3 4FD Tel: (024) 7663 9425 Fax: (024) 7651 1582 E-mail: sales@serigraphia.co.uk *Screen & digital printers & printing designers*

Serin Computers Ltd, 4 Fairfax Court, Yarm, Cleveland, TS15 9QZ Tel: (01642) 650466 E-mail: serincomputers@aol.com *Computers manufacturers & distributors*

Serion Systems, St Francis Centre, Pembroke Road, Woking, Surrey, GU22 7DY Tel: (01483) 771151 Fax: (01483) 721722 *Business software provider*

Sermatech, Whisby Road, North Hykeham, Lincoln, LN6 3DL Tel: (01522) 878207 Fax: 01522 878250 E-mail: melissa.martin@sermatech.com *Coatings leaders in coating manufacture & applications to metal base materials. Offering anti-corrosion, erosion, wear, friction, fouling etc. Sermatech are ready to work with you to analyse and determine your coating requirements.*

Sermec Engineering Ltd, 2X South Nelson Road, Cramlington, Northumberland, NE23 1WF Tel: 01670 731000 *Hydraulic & pile driving equipment manufrs*

Serota Furniture, 92 Hilliard Road, Northwood, Middlesex, HA6 1SW Tel: (01923) 840697 E-mail: michael@serota.co.uk *Library furniture suppliers*

Serotec Ltd, Unit 22 Bankside, Station Approach, Kidlington, Oxfordshire, OX5 1JE Tel: (01865) 852700 Fax: (01865) 373899 E-mail: sales@serotec.co.uk *Immunological reagents manufrs*

Serpecon Ltd, 22 Fairmile Road, Halesowen, West Midlands, B63 3QJ Tel: 0121-550 5950 Fax: 0121-550 6222 E-mail: serpecon@btinternet.com *Supplier Worldwide of Conveyor Systems, Consultancy, Design, Manufacture, Erection, Maintenance Conveyors:- Screw Conveyors, Troughed Belt, Bucket Elevators, Drag Link, Flatbed, Vibratory, Roller, Slat, Magnetic, Screening, Sludge, Belt Conveyors a speciality.*

Serpell BC Engineering, New England Bungalow, Plympton, Plymouth, PL7 5BA Tel: (01752) 881060 Fax: (01752) 880060 *Wrought ironwork*

J.R. Serpell & Son, Blackpool Farm, Yealmpton, Plymouth, PL8 2LF Tel: (01752) 348376 E-mail: enquiries@serpells.co.uk *Agricultural & equestrian merchants*

▶ Serpentine Cars, 81 Hargate Way, Hampton Hargate, Peterborough, PE7 8DL Tel: (01733) 565058 E-mail: lee@serpentinecars.com *Private hire taxi company*

Sertec Birmingham Ltd, Gorsey Lane, Coleshill, Birmingham, B46 1JU Tel: (01675) 463361 Fax: (01675) 465539 E-mail: sertecgroup@sertec.co.uk *Pressings & welded assemblies*

Serto UK Ltd, Unit 3 West Court, Buntsford Park Road, Bromsgrove, Worcestershire, B60 3DX Tel: (01527) 573960 Fax: (01527) 870291 E-mail: sales@serto.co.uk *Distributors & assemblers of tube fittings*

Sertrix Tools Ltd, Clayton Road, Hayes, Middlesex, UB3 1BQ Tel: (020) 8848 9545 Fax: (020) 8561 7077 *Press tools manufrs*

Servacrane Investments Ltd, Bagnall Street Industrial Estate, George Henry Road, Tipton, West Midlands, DY4 7BZ Tel: 0121-557 4401 Fax: 0121-557 3788 *Crane repairers & manufrs*

Servair Ltd, Unit 6 Blackpole Trad Est East Blackpole, Worcester, WR3 8SG Tel: 01905 755400 *Air compressors & pneumatic equipment services*

Servais Silencers, 409 Harlestone Road, Northampton, NN5 6PB Tel: (01604) 754888 Fax: (01604) 759548 Principal Export Areas: Worldwide *Manufacturers of air filtration equipment to specification*

Servatruc Ltd, Church Street, Old Basford, Nottingham, NG6 0GA Tel: 0115-978 5504 Fax: 0115-942 2001 E-mail: sales@servatruc.co.uk *Fork lift truck distributors, hire & maintenance*

▶ Servcool Air Conditioning Equipment, 17 Upper Station Road, Bristol, BS16 4LY Tel: 0117-956 8444 Fax: 0117-956 4141 E-mail: sales@servcool.co.uk *Air conditioning equipment suppliers*

Servebrow Ltd, Bay 11 Central Works, Peartree Lane, Dudley, West Midlands, DY2 0XG Tel: (01384) 351453 Fax: (01384) 74948 *Plastic fabricators*

Servequip Ltd, 214 Purley Way, Croydon, CR0 4XG Tel: (020) 8686 8855 Fax: (020) 8681 7509 E-mail: info@servequip.co.uk *Catering equipment suppliers*

▶ Server Parts Ltd, Unit 1 Castle Grove Studios, 16 Castle Grove Drive, Leeds, LS6 4BR Tel: 0845 3457875 Fax: 0845 3457897 E-mail: sales@serverparts.co.uk *A new concept in hardware provision for Sun, HP, Cisco, 3Com, Compaq, DEC and IBM - Value-Added Supply. Server Parts will help you to specify what you want, help you to sell it, help you to install it, and help you to maintain it.*

Servex Ltd, Bellingdon Road, Chesham, Buckinghamshire, HP5 2NN Tel: (01494) 784501 Fax: (01494) 784086 E-mail: engineering@servexltd.co.uk *Electroplating & precision engineers*

Service Air Cargo Ltd, Dyce Airport, Dyce, Aberdeen, AB21 0PB Tel: (01224) 770518 Fax: (01224) 724737 E-mail: abzcargo@servisair.co.uk *Air line handling agents*

Service Aluminium Co Ltd, Eastbrook Road, Gloucester, GL4 3DD Tel: (01452) 423541 Fax: (01452) 501643 E-mail: office@serval.co.uk *Aluminium extrusion die manufrs*

Service Copier Supplies, 1 Swan Lane, Harleston, Norfolk, IP20 9AN Tel: (01379) 853713 Fax: (01379) 852158 E-mail: enq@servicesupplies.com *Office equipment & machinery*

Service Engineering Ltd, 45 Rosemary Terrace, Blyth, Northumberland, NE24 3DS Tel: (01670) 363309 Fax: (01670) 360528 E-mail: wldjrr@bun.com *Industrial boiler servicing engineers*

Service Engineering Co Grimsby Ltd, 56 Roberts Street, Grimsby, South Humberside, DN32 8AP Tel: (01472) 358596 Fax: (01472) 267359 *Engine reconditioning service*

Service Engines (Newcastle) Ltd, Great Lime Road, Killingworth, Newcastle Upon Tyne, NE12 6RU Tel: 0191-268 1000 Fax: 0191-216 0838 E-mail: admin@serviceengines.co.uk *Contractors plant merchants, repairs & hire* Also at: Thornaby

Service Graphics, 3 Osiers Road, London, SW18 1NL Tel: (020) 8877 6600 Fax: (020) 8871 3521 E-mail: scott.king@servicegraphics.co.uk *Exhibition printers* Also at: Bristol

Service Graphics Ltd, 1 Sarum Business Park, The Portway, Salisbury, SP4 6EA Tel: (01722) 321736 Fax: (01722) 330041 *Exhibition display designers*

Service Logic, Dunstable Road, Redbourn, St. Albans, Hertfordshire, AL3 7PR Tel: (01582) 792277 Fax: (01582) 792207 E-mail: info@servicelogic.co.uk *Bar code readers. Also repair*

Service Metals East Anglia Ltd, 4 Springwood Drive, Springwood Industrial Estate, Braintree, Essex, CM7 2YN Tel: (01376) 322795 Fax: (01376) 322804 *Aluminium stockholding services*

Service Metals (North) Ltd, 14 Tollpark Place, Cumbernauld, Glasgow, G68 0LN Tel: (01236) 453444 Fax: (01236) 453555 *Aluminium stockholders*

Service Metals (South) Ltd, Red Shute Hill, Hermitage, Thatcham, Berkshire, RG18 9QX Tel: (01635) 201811 Fax: (01635) 201894 *Aluminium stockholders*

Service Offset Supplies Ltd, Oakwood Hill Industrial Estate, Oakwood Hill, Loughton, Essex, IG10 3TZ Tel: (020) 8502 4291 Fax: (020) 8502 0200 E-mail: webmaster@sosuk.co.uk *Printing trade suppliers, distributors & agents*

Service Point, 16 Rivers St, Bath, BA1 2QA Tel: (01225) 311972 Fax: (01225) 310124 *Office equipment & reprographics*

Service Point, Enfield House, Enfield Road, Birmingham, B15 1QA Tel: 0121-456 4554 Fax: 0121-454 9908 E-mail: birmingham@servicepointuk.com *Reprographics service*

Service Point, 68 Whiteladies Road, Bristol, BS8 2NH Tel: 0117-970 6500 Fax: 0117-970 6182 E-mail: Bristol@servicepointuk.com *Office distributors & printers*

Service Point, 11-12 Enterprise Way, Cheltenham Trade Park, Cheltenham, Gloucestershire, GL51 8LZ Tel: (01242) 514813 Fax: (01242) 581752 E-mail: cheltenham@servicepointuk.com *Reprographic printing services*

Service Point, 3 Hursley Road, Chandler's Ford, Eastleigh, Hampshire, SO53 2FW Tel: (023) 8026 2000 Fax: (023) 8025 1195 E-mail: southampton@servicepointuk.com *Reprographic services*

▶ Service Point, 7 Leodis Court, Leeds, LS11 5JJ Tel: 0113-244 1140 Fax: 0113-247 1183

▶ Service Point, 2 Gartons Way, London, SW11 3SX Tel: (020) 7223 6104 Fax: (020) 7924 5815

Service Point, Unit 3, 8-14 William Road, London, NW1 3EN Tel: (020) 7387 6071 Fax: (020) 7387 1382 E-mail: williamrd@servicepointuk.com *Instant & reprographic printers*

Service Point, 161-165 Farringdon Road, London, EC1R 3AL Tel: (020) 7520 0200 Fax: (020) 7833 9781 E-mail: infouk@servicepointuk.com *Distributor & print reprographics*

Service Point, 32 Invincible Drive, Armstrong Industrial Park, Newcastle upon Tyne, NE4 7HX Tel: 0191-273 2834 Fax: 0191-272 3174 *Printing graphics*

▶ Service Point, Attenborough House, 15 Bennet Road, Reading, RG2 0QX Tel: 0118-975 3995 Fax: 0118-975 3997 E-mail: reading@servicepointuk.com *Copying & duplicating services*

Service Point UK, 49 Charles Street, Cardiff, CF10 2GD Tel: (029) 2022 4316 Fax: (029) 2034 2712 E-mail: info@servicepointuk.com *Supplies & reprographic services* Also at: Branches throughout U.K.

Service Point UK Ltd, 95 Fore Street, Exeter, EX4 3QY Tel: (01392) 250431 Fax: (01392) 410250 E-mail: exeter@servicepointuk.com *Drawing office equipment & reprographic suppliers* Also at: Branches throughout the U K

Service Point UK, 40-42 Mayflower Street, Plymouth, PL1 1QX Tel: (01752) 669701 Fax: (01752) 222117 E-mail: plymouth@servicepointuk.com *Drawing office equipment & plan printing & copying services*

Service Systems Ltd, 178 Oxford Road, Basford, Newcastle, Staffordshire, ST5 0QB Tel: (01782) 711077 Fax: (01782) 638538 E-mail: enquiries@servicesystemsltd.co.uk *Heating control installation services*

Service Systems UK Ltd, Chester Road, Sandycroft, Deeside, Clwyd, CH5 2QW Tel: (01244) 535095 Fax: (01244) 538987 E-mail: service@servicesystems.co.uk *Cleaning contractors & janitorial suppliers*

▶ Service Total, Unit 4b Kingsbridge Business Park, Gorseinon, Swansea, SA4 4HL Tel: (01792) 898882 Fax: (01792) 896308 E-mail: servicetotal@supanet.com

Service Works Ltd, 2 Burston Road, London, SW15 6AR Tel: (0870) 7360000 Fax: (0870) 7360001 E-mail: info@serviceworks.co.uk *Facilities management software company*

Servicecal Ltd, 19 Green Lane, Eccles, Manchester, M30 0RP Tel: 0161-789 8990 Fax: 0161-789 8991 E-mail: info@servicecal.co.uk *Test equipment calibration & repair*

Servicecare Support Services Ltd, Manchester Road, Hollinwood, Oldham, OL9 7AA Tel: 0161-688 1999 Fax: 0161-688 1998 *Computer servicing*

Servicecare UK, 551 Warwick Road, Tyseley, Birmingham, B11 2EX Tel: 0121-707 6011 Fax: 0121-707 6011 *Computer hardware services*

▶ Servicemaster Ltd, The Cleaning & Restoration Centre, Lime Avenue, Torquay, TQ2 5JL Tel: (01803) 200985 Fax: (01803) 200985 E-mail: office@cleanandrestore.co.uk *Cleaning & restoration*

Serviceplan Ltd, 1 Windmill Business Village, Brooklands Close, Sunbury-on-Thames, Middlesex, TW16 7DY Tel: (01932) 787871 Fax: (01932) 781071 E-mail: info@serviceplan.ltd.uk *Air conditioning, heating and ventillation maintenance.*Design, installation & commissioning of air conditioning systems*

Servicepoint, 81 Endell Street, London, WC2H 9AJ Tel: (020) 7836 9422 Fax: (020) 7836 4248 E-mail: coventgarden@servicepointuk.com *Drawing office services*

Servicepoint (U K) Ltd, 539-543 Sauchiehall St, Glasgow, G3 7PQ Tel: 0141-275 2424 Fax: 0141-204 3801 E-mail: glasgow@servicepointuk.com *Reprographic printing services*

Servicepower Ltd, Rosse Works, Moorhead Lane, Shipley, West Yorkshire, BD18 4JH Tel: (01274) 785500 Fax: (01274) 785544 E-mail: sales@servicepower.ltd.uk *Cable assemblies & inter-connect solutions*

Servicepower Business Solutions Ltd, Petersgate House, St. Petersgate, Stockport, Cheshire, SK1 1HE Tel: 0161-476 2277 Fax: 0161-480 8088 E-mail: info@servicepower.com *Developers of software scheduling*

▶ Services Ltd, 82 Trent BLVD, West Bridgfore, Nottingham, NG2 5BL Tel: 0115-945 5285 Fax: 0115-981 7137 E-mail: info@servicesltd.co.uk *Quality management consultancy & training*

▶ Services Management Ltd, Seymour House, 51 Praed Street, London, W2 1NR Tel: (020) 7565 5763 Fax: (020) 7565 5754 E-mail: c.bower@sml-ltd.com *Consultant building services engineers*

Services Online, 42 Kirby Drive, Luton, LU3 4AW Tel: (01582) 583823 Fax: (01582) 491384 E-mail: webmaster@services-online.co.uk *Internet hosting & web hosting*

Services Supply Co., 26 Penybont Road, Pencoed, Bridgend, Mid Glamorgan, CF35 5RA Tel: (01656) 860344 Fax: (01656) 862555 E-mail: sales@goldleafsupplies.com *Suppliers gold leaf & gilding sundry*

▶ Servicesound, 31 Turkey Road, Bexhill-On-Sea, East Sussex, TN39 5HB Tel: (01424) 216245 E-mail: contact@servicesound.com *Repair & service of all hi-fi's*

ServiceTec Ltd, ServiceTec House, 3 Rutherford Close, Medway Technology Park, Stevenage, Hertfordshire, SG1 2EF Tel: (01438) 341900 Fax: (01438) 341901 E-mail: info@servicetec.com *Computer maintenance & repair services*

Servicom (High Tech) Ltd, Unit 8 The I.O. Centre, Nash Road, Park Farm North, Redditch, Worcestershire, B98 7AS Tel: (01527) 510800 Fax: (01527) 510975 E-mail: sales@servicom.co.uk *Radio communication specialists*

Servier Laboratories Ltd, Wexham Springs, Framewood Road, Wexham, Slough, SL3 6RJ Tel: (01753) 662647 Fax: (01753) 663456 *Research laboratories*

Servis Heat Treatment Co. Ltd, 258b Ipswich Road, Trading Estate, Slough, SL1 4EP Tel: (01753) 521823 Fax: (01753) 531094 E-mail: sales@servisheattreatment.com *Established for 50 Years,Servis Heat Treatment has been providing a comprehensive range of heat treatment process that time. Our customers include those in tool making,mould making,aerospace,security,formula one,motorsport & general engineering.Members of our staff are either fully qualified metallurgists or are trained to a high standard in metallurgy. We offer various heat treatment processes from our high quality salt bath furnaces including,hardening & case hardening & our muffle furnaces cater for all our customers stress relieving & annealing requirements.Needless to say we also use top of the range free standing and hand held Rockwell and Vickers hardness testers. We also offer Normalising, Vaccum Hardening, Brinnel & Rockwell Testing, Tuftriding, Chemical Blacking, Shot Blasting & Plating (Bright Nickle,Electrolysis), Tempering & Mar-tempering, Solution & Precipitation Treatments, Carburising, Induction Hardening.*

Servis (U K) Ltd, Darlaston Road, Darlaston Road, Wednesbury, West Midlands, WS10 7TJ Tel: 0121-568 8333 Fax: 0121-568 8500 *Kitchen appliance distributors*

Servi-Sew, 38 The Chase, Stroud, Gloucestershire, GL5 4SB Tel: (01453) 757617 *Sewing machine repairs*

Servispak Ltd, Beadle Trading Estate, Hithercroft Road, Wallingford, Oxfordshire, OX10 9EZ Tel: (01491) 834000 Fax: (01491) 834054 E-mail: sales@sevispak.com *Corrugated cases, pallet containers, packers*

Servo, Oakwell Way, Birstall, Batley, West Yorkshire, WF17 9LU Tel: (01924) 422111 Fax: (0870) 1218302 E-mail: info@icm-computer.co.uk *Computer solution consultancy service*

Servo, Oakwell Way, Birstall, Batley, West Yorkshire, WF17 9LU Tel: (01924) 422111 Fax: (0870) 1218302 E-mail: info@icm-computer.co.uk *IT solutions & services* Also at: Kingswinford

Servo Chem Ltd, PO Box 221, Weston-super-Mare, Avon, BS22 9ZA Tel: (01934) 713999 Fax: (01934) 713990 E-mail: info@servo-chem.co.uk *Chemical manufrs*

Servo & Electronic Sales Ltd, Unit 1/5 Harden Road Industrial Estate, Harden Road, Lydd, Romney Marsh, Kent, TN29 9LX Tel: (01797) 322500 Fax: (01797) 321569 E-mail: r.egan@servoconnectors.co.uk *Electronic connectors distributor*

▶ Servo & Electronic Sales Ltd, Unit 1/5 Harden Road Industrial Estate, Harden Road, Lydd, Romney Marsh, Kent, TN29 9LX Tel: (01797) 322500 Fax: (01797) 321569

continued

continuation
E-mail: sam@servoconnectors.co.uk *Distributors of electrical connectors*

Servo & Electronic Sales Ltd, Unit 1/5 Harden Road Industrial Estate, Harden Road, Lydd, Romney Marsh, Kent, TN29 9LX Tel: (01797) 322500 Fax: (01797) 321569 E-mail: servo@plugs.demon.co.uk *Electronic test equipment manufrs*

Servomex Group Ltd, Crowborough Hill, Jarvis Brook, Crowborough, East Sussex, TN6 3DU Tel: (01892) 652181 Fax: (01892) 662253 E-mail: info@servomex.com *Analysis equipment manufrs*

▶ Servotek CNC, 16 Padgate, Thorpe End, Norwich, NR13 5DG Tel: 07860 408629 Fax: 01603 431992E-mail: mail@servotek.co.uk *CNC Machine Tool fault diagnosis and repairs / CNC Spares. CNC Retrofits and modifications. Fanuc Spares, Siemens Drive Spares, Beaver CNC Spares,*

Servotest Testing Systems Ltd, Unit 1 Beta Way, Thorpe Industrial Estate, Egham, Surrey, TW20 8RE Tel: (01784) 274410 Fax: (01784) 274438 E-mail: info@servotestsystems.com *Servohydraulic test & motion simulation systems-vibration test equip*

Servoto Warm Ltd, Coronation Road, High Wycombe, Buckinghamshire, HP12 3SU Tel: (01494) 474474 Fax: (01494) 492321 E-mail: sales@servowarm.co.uk *Central heating equipment repairers* Also at: Branches throughout the U.K.

Servtech Ltd, 2 Abbotswell Road, West Tullos, Aberdeen, AB12 3AB Tel: (01224) 878322 Fax: (01224) 895080 E-mail: info@servtech.co.uk *Non-destructive testing for offshore*

▶ SES Consultants, PO Box 5513, Ilkeston, Derbyshire, DE7 9ZT Tel: 0115-875 0848 Fax: 0115-875 0849 *Spill kits supplier for oil, general purpose & chemicals*

Ses Engine Services Ltd, 5 Wealdstone Road, Sutton, Surrey, SM3 9QN Tel: (020) 8641 0252 Fax: (020) 8644 3983 E-mail: sales@sesengines.co.uk *Petrol engines*

Ses Mechanical Services Ltd, Telford Way, Severalls Industrial Park, Colchester, CO4 9QP Tel: (01206) 845333 Fax: (01206) 844601 E-mail: sales@sesmechanical.co.uk *Heating & ventilating engineering services*

Ses Scarborough Ltd, Melrose Street, Scarborough, North Yorkshire, YO12 7SH Tel: (01723) 367341 Fax: (01723) 375758 E-mail: sales@s-e-s-ltd.co.uk *Engineers supply services*

▶ Sesame Access Systems Ltd, Units 10-12, Galleymead Road, Colnbrook, Slough, SL3 0EN Tel: (01784) 440088 Fax: (01784) 440088 E-mail: charlielyons@sesameaccess.plus.com *Disabled & elderly person aid manufrs*

Sesco Ltd, 3 Elm Road, Redhill, RH1 6AJ Tel: (01737) 763654 Fax: (01737) 772669 E-mail: enquiries@sesco.co.uk *Electrical & alarm services*

Sesmarine Ltd, 19A Harraton Terrace, Birtley, Chester Le Street, County Durham, DH2 2QG Tel: 0191-411 1141 Fax: 0191-411 4211 *Marine engineers & sea going maintenance*

Set (Cardiff) Ltd, 6-7 Duke St, Cardiff, CF10 1AY Tel: (029) 2037 3328 Fax: (029) 2038 3344 *Office equipment suppliers* Also at: Swansea

Set In Hand, Unit 1-2 Combs Tannery, Tannery Road, Combs, Stowmarket, Suffolk, IP14 2EN Tel: (01449) 675599 Fax: (01449) 678392 E-mail: james@setinhand.com *Warehouse, distribution & greeting cards packaging*

Set & Match Ltd, 46 Lower Tower Street, Birmingham, B19 3NH Tel: 0121-333 6329 Fax: 0121-333 6190 E-mail: info@setandmatch.net *Digital prepress*

▶ Set Solutions, 14 Bacon Street, London, E1 6LF Tel: (020) 7729 7906 E-mail: sales@s-e-t.co.uk

Set Square Fabrications, 19 Willow Road, Colnbrook, Slough, SL3 0BS Tel: (01753) 686212 Fax: (01753) 686212 *Wire wound filter manufrs*

Set To Brood, Turners House, Kingstone, Hereford, HR2 9HU Tel: (01981) 251720 Fax: (01981) 570598 E-mail: addisnicola@aol.com *Poultry house maintenance*

▶ SET Training, The Old Rectory, Springhead Enterprise Park, Springhead Road, Northfleet, Gravesend, Kent, DA11 8HN Tel: (01474) 708660 E-mail: info@settraining.co.uk *SET Training provide NVQ training for the Early Years and Schools sectors.*NVQ Children"s Care, Learning & Development levels II & III*Teaching Assistant Levels II & III*These are supported by short course programmes.*We are specialists in Child Protection Training*

Setco Automotive UK Ltd, Lipe Clutch Division, York Avenue Haslingden, Haslingden, Rossendale, Lancashire, BB4 4HU Tel: (01706) 237200 Fax: (01706) 229585 *Manufacturers & suppliers of commercial vehicle clutches*

▶ Setech Solutions Ltd, 53A High Street, Bugbrooke, Northampton, NN7 3PG Tel: (01604) 832623 Fax: (01604) 832623 E-mail: info@setechsolutions.com *Sales & marketing agency & electronic test equipment providers*

Setform Ltd, Europa House, 13-17 Ironmonger Row, London, EC1V 3QG Tel: (020) 7253 2545 Fax: (020) 7608 1600 E-mail: sales@setform.com *Publishers*

Sethia (London) Ltd, Sethia House, 105 St John St, London, EC1M 4AS Tel: (020) 7814 9014 Fax: (020) 7814 9016 E-mail: info@sethia-london.com *International commodity & consultants*

Setmasters Ltd, Lymington Saleroom, Emsworth Road, Lymington, Hampshire, SO41 9BL Tel: (01590) 675555 Fax: (01590) 682659 E-mail: collating@setmasters.co.uk *Collating machinery manufrs*

Setsquare Ltd, Tonbridge Road, Hadlow, Tonbridge, Kent, TN11 0AH Tel: (01732) 851888 Fax: (01732) 851853 E-mail: sales@setsquare.co.uk *Lighting & energy management supplier*

Setten & Durward Ltd, Ixl House, Waterloo Road, Llandrindod Wells, Powys, LD1 6BH Tel: (01597) 827800 Fax: (01597) 827847 E-mail: sales@ixl.uk.com *Commercial stationers & file manufrs*

Sev, 356d Dukesway Court, Gateshead, Tyne & Wear, NE11 0BH Tel: 0191-487 1311 Fax: 0191-482 0243 E-mail: sales@sev.co.uk *Electric vehicles design & manufrs* Also at: London, Manchester & Wem

Sev, Lilac Grove, Beeston, Nottingham, NG9 1QX Tel: 0115-907 8233 Fax: 0115-907 8823 *Shop fitting equipment importers*

Sevagram Ltd, 26 Hodder Drive, Greenford, Middlesex, UB6 8LH Tel: (020) 8998 5191 Fax: (020) 8998 5191 E-mail: info@sevagram.co.uk *Computer consultants*

Sevale Engineering Ltd, Business Park, Llanthony Road, Hempsted, Gloucester, GL2 5HJ Tel: (01452) 303180 Fax: (01452) 306250 *Component supplier to feed mills*

Sevarg Engineering Ltd, 14 The High Cross Centre, Fountayne Road, London, N15 4QN Tel: (020) 8801 0082 Fax: (020) 8801 9907 E-mail: sales@sevarg.com *Photo cutter manufrs*

Seven, 5Th Floor Big Peg, 120 Vyse Street, Hockley, Birmingham, B18 6NF Tel: 0121-236 1541 Fax: 0121-234 7775 E-mail: birmingham@sevenww.co.uk *Digital artwork & prepress studio services*

Seven Corners Communications Group, Penmark House, Woodbridge Meadows, Guildford, Surrey, GU1 1BL Tel: (01483) 576777 Fax: (01483) 567876 *Lithographic printers*

▶ Seven Day Signs Ltd, Millhall, Stirling, FK7 7LT Tel: (01786) 470111 Fax: (01786) 470111

Seven Internet Ltd, 35 Blanquettes Avenue, Worcester, WR3 8DA Tel: (01905) 745339 E-mail: sales@seveninternet.co.uk *Web & database design developers*

▶ Seven Oaks Sound Of Vision, 62 North Street, Leeds, LS2 7PN Tel: 0113-245 2775 Fax: 0113-242 5114 *Audio visual retail*

Seven Seas Ltd, Hedon Road, Hull, HU9 5NJ Tel: (01482) 375234 Fax: (01482) 374345 E-mail: terry.simpson@sseas.com *Health care products manufrs*

Seven Seas Chartering Ltd, Berger House, 38 Berkeley Square, London, W1J 5AD Tel: (020) 7495 6776 Fax: (020) 7491 9491 E-mail: sevenseas@sevsea.com.uk *Ship brokers*

Seven Stars Manufacturers, 2 Trafalgar Street, Rochdale, Lancashire, OL16 2EB Tel: (01706) 641628 Fax: (01706) 641628 *Children's & ladies wear manufrs*

Seven Worldwide Ltd, St. Marks House, Shepherdess Walk, London, N1 7LH Tel: (020) 7861 7777 Fax: (020) 7871 7777 E-mail: enquiries@sevenww.com *General printers & digital asset management*

▶ Sevenoaks, 3 The Mall, Bromley, BR1 1TR Tel: (020) 8313 1511 Fax: (020) 8466 5670 *Oak & pine furniture suppliers*

Sevenoaks Print Finishers Ltd, Enterprise Way, Edenbridge, Kent, TN8 6HF Tel: (01732) 866060 Fax: (01732) 867577 *Print finishers*

▶ Sevenwood, PO Box 1147, Luton, LU2 8WZ Tel: (01582) 420480 E-mail: enquiries@sevenwood.co.uk *Ladies online golf clothing company.*

Severfield-Reeve International Ltd, Dalton Airfield Industrial Estate, Dalton, Thirsk, North Yorkshire, YO7 3JN Tel: (01845) 577896 Fax: (01845) 578508 E-mail: admin@severfield-reeve.co.uk *Fabrication & structural steelwork*

Severn Biotech Ltd, 2 Park Lane Industrial Estate, Stourport Road, Kidderminster, Worcestershire, DY11 6TJ Tel: (01562) 825286 Fax: (01562) 825284 E-mail: admin@severnbiotech.com *Biotechnology products & services*

Severn Catering Equipment, 9 Suffolk Parade, Cheltenham, Gloucestershire, GL50 2AB Tel: (01242) 234307 Fax: (01242) 262656 *Catering equipment in the Gloucestershire area*

Severn Catering Services Ltd, Rivendel House, Saul, Gloucester, GL2 7LG Tel: 01452 740033 *Catering service & equipment maintenance*

Severn Electric Co. Ltd, 2 Lisle Avenue, Kidderminster, Worcestershire, DY11 7DN Tel: (01299) 877700 Fax: (01562) 865059 E-mail: sales@severnelectric.co.uk *Electrical contractors*

▶ Severn Engineering Co., 5 Grahamstown Road, Sedbury, Chepstow, Gwent, NP16 7AD Tel: (01291) 629670 Fax: (0870) 0850123 *Steel fabrication & installation*

Severn Environmental Engineering Ltd, Scan Buildings, Oldbury Road, Cwmbran, Gwent, NP44 3JU Tel: (01633) 866241 Fax: (01633) 874664 *Dust & fume extraction systems manufrs*

Severn Glocon Ltd, Olympus Park, Quedgeley, Gloucester, GL2 4NF Tel: (01452) 887900 Fax: (0845) 2232041 E-mail: sales@severnglocon.co.uk *Actuators & valve manufrs*

Severn Graphics, Unit 5, Windmill Business Park, Clevedon, Avon, BS21 6SR Tel: (01275) 879505 Fax: (01275) 340834 E-mail: richard@severngraphics.co.uk *Lithographic printers*

Severn Instruments, 4 Court Street, Upton-upon-Severn, Worcester, WR8 0JT Tel: (01684) 594164 Fax: (01684) 593364 *Process control engineers*

Severn Insulation Co. Ltd, Somerton Works, Lloyd Street, Newport, Gwent, NP19 0JN Tel: (01633) 274239 Fax: (01633) 275252 E-mail: sales@severninsulation.co.uk *Contractors & asbestos removal specialists* Also at: Ockenden

Severn Metals Ltd, Unit 22 Hither Green Industrial Estate, Clevedon, Avon, BS21 6XU Tel: (01275) 343430 Fax: (01275) 343469 E-mail: sales@severnmetals.co.uk *Stainless steel stockholders*

▶ Severn Signs Ltd, Unit 19 Innsworth Technology Park, Innsworth Lane, Gloucester, GL3 1DL Tel: (01452) 739156 Fax: (01452) 739153 *Sign manufrs*

Severn Trent Water Ltd, 2297 Coventry Road, Birmingham, B26 3PU Tel: 0121-722 4000 Fax: 0121-722 4800 E-mail: customer.relations@severntrent.co.uk *Water supply consultants*

Severn Trent Water Ltd, Park Lane, Minworth, Sutton Coldfield, West Midlands, B76 9BL Tel: 0121-722 4000 Fax: 0121-313 1938 E-mail: salesenq@severntrentservices.co.uk *Chlorination plant*

Severn Valley Lock & Safe, 9-10 Comberton Road, Kidderminster, Worcestershire, DY10 1UA Tel: (01562) 829406 Fax: (01562) 864089 E-mail: sales@severnlocks.co.uk *Locksmiths & safe engineers*

Severn Valley Metal Window & Door Maintenance Co., Faraday Drive, Bridgnorth, Shropshire, WV15 5BB Tel: (01746) 761127 Fax: (01746) 765652 *Maintenance of doors & windows*

▶ Severn Valley Storage Ltd, Alveley Industrial Estate, Alveley, Bridgnorth, Shropshire, WV15 6HG Tel: (01746) 780123 Fax: (01746) 781234 E-mail: info@severnvalleystorage.com *Storage services, self storage*

Severn Valley Trailers, Hanleaze Lodge, 73 Bristol Road, Keynsham, Bristol, BS31 2WD Tel: 0117-986 3256 Fax: 0117-986 3256 *Trailer manufrs*

Severn Ventilation Ltd, Rock Cottages, Hill Street, Kidderminster, Worcestershire, DY11 6TD Tel: (01562) 743869 Fax: (01562) 862018 *Dust extraction engineers, installation or service*

Severn & Wye Smokery Ltd, The Smoke House, Chaxhill, Westbury-on-Severn, Gloucestershire, GL14 1QW Tel: (01452) 760190 Fax: (01452) 760193 E-mail: info@severnandwye.co.uk *Fish smoking & curing*

▶ Severnprint Ltd, Unit 8-10 Ashville Industrial Estate, Ashville Road, Gloucester, GL2 5EU Tel: (01452) 416391 Fax: (01452) 307001

Severnside Fabrics Ltd, Gordon Road, Whitehall, Bristol, BS5 7DR Tel: 0117-951 0412 Fax: 0117-935 4165 E-mail: sales@severnsidefabrics.co.uk *Laundry industry textile manufrs*

Severnside Machinery Ltd, Unit 57, Ditton Priors, Bridgnorth, Shropshire, WV16 6SS Tel: 01746 712433 *New & used mobile crane services*

Severnside Recycling, The Pines, Heol-Y-Forlan, Cardiff, CF14 1AX Tel: (029) 2061 5871 Fax: (029) 2069 2120 E-mail: enquire@severnside.com *Recycling & waste management services*

Severnside Recycling, Unit 6 Bamfurlong Industrial Park, Staverton, Cheltenham, Gloucestershire, GL51 6SX Tel: (01452) 855767 Fax: (01452) 713197 E-mail: justin@severnside.com *Waste paper merchants*

Severnside Recycling UK, Folds Road, Bolton, BL1 2SW Tel: (01204) 372700 Fax: (01204) 372707 E-mail: bpbrecyclinguk@msn.com *Waste paper merchants* Also at: Basildon, Bolton, Durham, Glasgow, Jarrow, & Leeds

▶ Severnside Safety Supplies Ltd, Malmesbury Road, Kingsditch Trading Estate, Cheltenham, Gloucestershire, GL51 9PL Tel: (01242) 525811 Fax: (01242) 224184 E-mail: sales@sevsafe.co.uk *Importers & distributors of work wear,*

▶ Severnside Scaffolding Ltd, Morley House, Llanthony Road, Hempsted, Gloucester, GL2 5HL Tel: (01452) 529601 Fax: (01452) 305616

▶ Seville Design & Print Ltd, 10 Julian Road, Sheffield, S9 1FZ Tel: 0114-243 3995 Fax: 0114-243 8396 E-mail: sales@sevilledesign.co.uk

Sevtek Engineering Services, Unit 3t Innsworth Technology Park, Innsworth Lane, Gloucester, GL3 1DL Tel: (01452) 730457 Fax: (01452) 731706 E-mail: owencooper@sevtek.co.uk *Sevtek Engineering Services are based in Gloucester and cover the whole of the UK. We are precision engineers - some of the services we offer are CNC Milling, CNC Turning, Manual Milling, Manual Turning, CNC Plastic Machining, Milling Engineering Services, Metal CNC Machining, Grinding - small and medium batch. Sevtek covers all industries; Sub contract assemblies from design to fully assembled projects. All metals and plastics machined. We are able to produce a quick response upon receipt of an order and manufacture drawings.*

Sew Amazing Ltd, 80 St. Stephen's Road, London, E3 5JL Tel: (020) 8980 8898 Fax: (020) 8980 6989 E-mail: sewamazing@hotmail.co.uk *Sewing machines & pressing equipment*

Sew Europe, 88 Rice Lane, Walton, Liverpool, L9 1DD Tel: 0151-525 0511 Fax: 0151-525 0522 E-mail: seweurope@btopenworld.com *Solvent import & distribution*

Sew Knit, 9 Chapel Street, Lancaster, LA1 1NZ Tel: (01524) 64436 *Sewing machines & accessories retail*

▶ Sew Northampton, 173 Wellingborough Road, Northampton, NN1 4DX Tel: (01604) 637200 Fax: (01604) 637200 E-mail: sales@sewing-centres.co.uk *Sewing machine retailers*

Sew & Save, 12 King Street, Sutton-in-Ashfield, Nottinghamshire, NG17 1AT Tel: (01623) 554886 Fax: (01623) 554886 *Sewing machine retailers*

Sew & Sew Machine Co., 5 Olympia Arcade, High Street, Kirkcaldy, Fife, KY1 1QF Tel: (01592) 261352 Fax: (01592) 261352 *Sewing machines sell & repair*

Sew Systems Ltd, 53 Illiffe Avenue, Oadby, Leicester, LE2 5LH Tel: 0116-271 4098 Fax: 0116-271 2153 E-mail: info@sewsystems.co.uk *Design & development of lingerie manufacturing equipment*

Seward, 400 Poole Road, Branksome, Poole, Dorset, BH12 1DD Tel: (01202) 545700 Fax: (01202) 752934 *Car dealership*

Seward Ltd, The Technology Centre, Eastling Close, Worthing, West Sussex, BN14 8HQ Tel: (01903) 524616 Fax: (01903) 524603 E-mail: info@seward.co.uk *Laboratory equipment manufrs*

Seward Agricultural Machinery Ltd, Sinderby Station, Thirsk, North Yorkshire, YO7 4LB Tel: (01845) 567407 Fax: (01845) 567680 *Agricultural sales & services*

Seward Direct Mail Ltd, Unit 107 Cannon Workshops, 5 Cannon Drive, London, E14 4AS Tel: (020) 7538 5120 E-mail: sewardkj@aol.com *Direct mail services*

Seward Wyon Ltd, The Old Tannery, Kelston, Bath, BA1 9AN Tel: 0117-932 7565 Fax: 0117-932 7763 E-mail: sales@sewardwyon.co.uk Principal Export Areas: Worldwide *Lifting contractors & specialist services*

Sewcreative, 52 Prospect Rd, Market Drayton, Shropshire, TF9 3BH Tel: 01939 200266 Fax: 01939 200266 *Soft furnishing manufr*

Sewell Group plc, Geneva Way, Leads Road, Hull, HU7 0DG Tel: (01482) 701251 Fax: (01482) 707568

Sewing Is Fun, 77-79 High Street, Ruislip, Middlesex, HA4 8JL Tel: (01895) 634848 Fax: (01895) 632417 *Sewing machines*

Sewing Knitting & Handicraft Centre, 125 Mostyn Street, Llandudno, Gwynedd, LL30 2PE Tel: (01492) 875269 Fax: (01492) 875269 E-mail: wyn20@btinternet.com *Sewing machines suppliers*

Sewing & Knitting Machine Centre, 193 Burton Stone Lane, York, YO30 6DG Tel: (01904) 655751 Fax: (01904) 655751 *Sewing & knitting machines suppliers & repairers*

Sewing Machine Co., 17 Top Row, Kirkgate Market Hall, Leeds, LS2 7HN Tel: 0113-243 5798 *Sewing machine distributors*

▶ Sewing Machine Centre, Lisburn Enterprise Centre, Enterprise Crescent, Lisburn, County Antrim, BT28 2BP Tel: (028) 9260 1200 Fax: (028) 9260 1200 *Sewing machine manufrs*

Sewing Machine Exchange, 15 Daniel Owen Precinct, Mold, Clwyd, CH7 1AP Tel: (01352) 758925 Fax: (01352) 758925 *Sewing machine retail & repairs*

Sewing Machine Exchange, 21 Charles Street, Wrexham, Clwyd, LL13 8BT Tel: (01978) 266746 Fax: (01978) 266746 E-mail: enquiries@sewingmachinesdirect.co.uk *Sewing machines & overlockers distribution*

Sewing Machine Repair Co., 9 Morkinshire Cresent, Cotgrave, Nottingham, NG12 3HL Tel: 0115-989 2539 *Domestic sewing machine repairers*

Sewing Machine Services, 200 Studfall Avenue, Corby, Northamptonshire, NN17 1LJ Tel: (01536) 269080 *Sewing machine services*

Sewing Machine Services, Fallady Cottage, Idvies, Forfar, Angus, DD8 2SP Tel: (01307) 818853 Fax: (01307) 818720 *Sewing machines repairs*

Sewing Machine Services Luton Ltd, Unit 6-52 High Town Enterprise Centre, York Street, Luton, LU2 0HA Tel: (01582) 455112 *Sewing machine sales & services*

Sewing Machine Shop Ltd, 1 The Broadway, Brighton Road, Worthing, West Sussex, BN11 3EG Tel: (01903) 200771 Fax: (01903) 520036 E-mail: sales@sewingmachineshop.co.uk *Sewing machine repairs & retailers*

Sewing Machine Supplies, 4 Tai Rhos, Pentre Berw, Gaerwen, Gwynedd, LL60 6LN Tel: (01248) 421692 Fax: (01248) 421692 *Sewing machines & accessories*

Sewing Machine Trade Association, 24 Fairlawn Gro, Chiswick, London, W4 5EH Tel: (020) 8995 0411 Fax: (020) 8742 2396 E-mail: smta@netcomuk.co.uk

Sewing Safety Ltd, 1 Sherlock Lane, Wallasey, Merseyside, CH44 4ER Tel: 0151-638 0884 Fax: 0151-638 7888 E-mail: sewing.safety@freeuk.com *Sewing safety equipment specialists*

Sewing World, 308-310 Wimborne Road, Bournemouth, BH9 2HN Tel: (01202) 770055 Fax: (01202) 775590 E-mail: sales@sewingworld.co.uk *Sewing machines retailers*

Sewing World Industrial Bolton, 130 Belmont Road, Bolton, BL1 7AN Tel: (01204) 309598 Fax: (01204) 306933 *Sewing machines parts merchants*

▶ SewingChest.co.uk, 49 Balby Road, Doncaster, South Yorkshire, DN4 0RD Tel: (01302) 365949 E-mail: mail@sewingchest.co.uk *We sell a diverse number of products which are sewing related, with a particular interest to corset making, bra making, lingerie and period costume. We sell fabrics, haberdashery, lace, cord, tools, plastic and steel boning, spiral steel, bone casing, patterns and lots more. All are items are mail order only, with despatch within 24 hours, often the same day.*

Sewmatic Sewing Machine Repair Services, Harlington Centre, Harlington Way, Fleet, Hampshire, GU51 4AE Tel: (01276) 32564 *Sewing machine services*

Sewplant UK Ltd, 20 Whitcliffe Road, Cleckheaton, West Yorkshire, BD19 3NU Tel: (01274) 875218 Fax: (01274) 875218 *Industrial sewing machine agents*

Sew-Quick Sewing Machine Services Ltd, The Workshop, Waterloo Road, Falmouth, Cornwall, TR11 3NU Tel: (01326) 318450 Fax: (01326) 318450 E-mail: sew-quick@tiscali.co.uk *Industrial & domestic sewing machine repairs*

Sews Europe, Unit 1, Woodlands Business Pk, Ystradgynlais, Swansea, SA9 1JW Tel: (01639) 842281 Fax: (01639) 849853 E-mail: info@sewse.com *Wire harnesses*

Sewtec Automation Ltd, 3 Riverside Way, Dewsbury, West Yorkshire, WF13 3LG Tel: (01924) 494047 Fax: (01924) 480949 E-mail: sales@sewtec.co.uk *Special purpose machinery manufrs*

▶ Sextant Shipping Ltd, Mariners Street, Goole, North Humberside, DN14 5BW Tel: (01405) 769925 Fax: (01405) 763162

Sexton Sales Ltd, D Wiggenhall Road Goods Yard, Wiggenhall Road, Watford, WD18 0EZ Tel: (01923) 240434 Fax: (01923) 818454 E-mail: enquiries@sextonsales.com *Drainage & roofing suppliers*

Sextons, 69-71 Milton Road, Portsmouth, PO3 6AL Tel: (023) 9273 8262 Fax: (023) 9282 6110 *Car radio installer service provider*

Seychell Engineering & Fabrication Ltd, 8 Arkwright Road, Bicester, Oxfordshire, OX26 4SU Tel: (01869) 322035 Fax: (01869) 321174 E-mail: seychellgroup@btconnect.com *General & precision engineers*

▶ Seymour, 6 Mousebank Lane, Lanark, ML11 7PP Tel: (01555) 666123 Fax: (01555) 661302

Seymour & Castle Ltd, Tattershall Way, Fairfield Industrial Estate, Louth, Lincolnshire, LN11 0YZ Tel: (01507) 602491 Fax: (01507) 607717 E-mail: admin@seymour-castle.co.uk *Electrical engineers*

▶ Seymour Engineering Ltd, Phoebe Lane, Halifax, West Yorkshire, HX3 9AS Tel: (01422) 362135 Fax: (01422) 322511 E-mail: info@seymourengineering.co.uk *Machine tool manufacture & service*

Seymour Patterns & Castings, Oak St Trading Estate, Oak Street, Quarry Bank, Brierley Hill, West Midlands, DY5 2JQ Tel: (01384) 78768 Fax: (01384) 79138 E-mail: john.elwell@yesit.co.uk *Pattern maker engineers*

Seymour Refrigeration, 5 Hedgeway, Guildford, Surrey, GU2 7RB Tel: (01483) 567645 *Refrigeration & air conditioning installer*

S. Seymour (Electrics) Ltd, 50 Glentham Road, London, SW13 9JJ Tel: (020) 8748 7788 Fax: (020) 8741 0720 E-mail: seymourelectrics@aol.com *Exhibition electrical contractors*

▶ Ian Seymour (Salvage), c/o Queens Road Garage, Queens Road, Askern, Doncaster, South Yorkshire, DN6 0LX Tel: (01302) 700539 E-mail: salvage@seymour73.freeserve.co.uk *Supplier of used motor parts*

Seymour Transport Ltd, New Hythe Lane, Larkfield, Aylesford, Kent, ME20 6SB Tel: (01622) 716441 Fax: (01622) 715146 E-mail: mr@seymourtransport.co.uk *Road transport, haulage & freight services*

▶ Seymour Transport, Whaley Road, South Yorkshire Industrial Estate, Barnsley, South Yorkshire, S75 1HT Tel: (01226) 731100 Fax: (01226) 731344

▶ Seymour Windows Ltd, Unit 13, Wharton Street, Sherdley Road Industrial Estate, St. Helens, Merseyside, WA9 5AA Tel: (01744) 611211 Fax: (01744) 27576 E-mail: seymour.windows@btconnect.com *Manufacturers upvc conservatories, doors & windows*

▶ SF Consultants, 31 Austins Mead, Bovingdon, Hertfordshire, HP3 0JU Tel: 01442 380120 Fax: 01442 380334 E-mail: stephanie.farrer@ntlworld.com *Business services for the small business...*

SF Group, 4 Millennium Way West, Nottingham, NG8 6AS Tel: 0115-911 2082 Fax: 0115-975 8087 E-mail: registrations@registrations.com *Recruitment of clerical & accountancy personnel*

▶ SFG Structural Facade Glazing, Cedar House, Cedar Lane, Frimley, Surrey, GU16 7HZ Tel: 01276 671815 Fax: 01276 678743 E-mail: info@sfgltd.com *Bolted Structural Glazing *Automatic & Revolving Doors *Glass Canopies *Structural Glass Balustrades *Glass Floors *Supporting Steelwork *Internal Glass Partitioning*

SFS Intec Ltd, 153 Kirkstall Road, Leeds, LS4 2AT Tel: 0113-208 5500 Fax: 0113-208 5519 E-mail: gb.leeds@sfsintec.biz Principal Export Areas: Central/East Europe & West Europe *Fasteners & fixings for business trade manufrs*

▶ SG Consulting, 86 St. Peters Avenue, Sowerby Bridge, West Yorkshire, HX6 1DB Tel: (01422) 831765 E-mail: sgconsulting.halifax@btinternet.com *Fire Health and Safety Consultants, *Fire Risk Assessments, *Risk to Persons Assessments, *Safety Signs and Equipment,*

▶ SGB, Alfreton Road, Derby, DE21 4AP Tel: (01332) 831661 Fax: (01332) 835810

SGB plc, Crabtree Lane, Manchester, M11 4GU Tel: 0161-223 3151 Fax: 0161-231 7575 E-mail: sturner@sgb.co.uk *Scaffolding erection & hire*

SGB Island Scaffolding, Peel Road Industrial Estate, Douglas, Isle of Man, IM4 4LE Tel: (01624) 674528 Fax: (01624) 663815 *Scaffolding contractors*

SGB Rovacabin, 81 North Road, Yate, Bristol, BS37 7PS Tel: (01454) 325010 Fax: (01454) 322948 *Modular buildings design, hire & manufrs*

▶ SGB Rovacabin, Unit 54 Hobbs Industrial Estate, Newchapel, Lingfield, Surrey, RH7 6HN Tel: (01342) 833869 Fax: (01342) 835550 *Building (Temporary) Constructors or Fabricators*

▶ SGH Equipment, Unit 18, Beechcroft Avenue, Crewe, CW2 6SQ Tel: (01270) 651611 Fax: (01270) 651611 E-mail: sales@sghequipment.co.uk *Bulk solids & powders handling equipment suppliers*

SGL Carbon, 4 Arden Court, Arden Road, Alcester, Warwickshire, B49 6HN Tel: (01789) 400221 Fax: (01789) 400822 E-mail: enquiries@sglcarbon.co.uk Sales Contact: A James *Carbon & graphite components manufrs*

SGL Technic Ltd, Muir of Ord Industrial Estate, Great North Road, Muir of Ord, Ross-Shire, IV6 7UA Tel: (01463) 870000 Fax: (01463) 871402 *Advanced carbon fibres & acrylic yarns manufrs*

▶ Sgo (Glasgow) Ltd, 392 Swanston Street, Dalmarnock, Glasgow, G40 4HW Tel: 0141-554 5550

▶ SGP Computing Ltd, 1 Hinckley Road, Earl Shilton, Leicester, LE9 7LG Tel: (01455) 449372 Fax: (01455) 449372 E-mail: enquiries@sgpcomputing.com *IT Services, for SME companies, specialising in Microsoft products*

SGS UK Ltd, S G S House, Johns Lane, Tividale, Oldbury, West Midlands, B69 3HX Tel: 0121-520 6454 Fax: 0121-522 4116 E-mail: admin@sgsuk.com *Verification, inspection & certification services*

SGS UK Ltd, London Road, Purfleet, Essex, RM19 1QS Tel: (01708) 866855 Fax: (01708) 681910 *Cargo surveyors*

▶ SGW Security Consulting, The Innovation Centre, 217 Portobello, Sheffield, S1 4DP Tel: 0114-224 2421 Fax: (0845) 0097220 *Independent security & cctv consultants*

Shabaz Bedding & Carpets, Havelock Street, Oldham, OL8 1JR Tel: 0161-620 2800 Fax: 0161-627 4744 *Manufacturers of beds*

J.V. Shabetai Ltd, 34 Charlotte Street, Manchester, M1 4FD Tel: 0161-236 7758 Fax: 0161-737 6061 E-mail: zedfred@aol.com *Bed linen manufrs*

Shackerley (Holdings) Group Ltd, 139 Wigan Road, Euxton, Chorley, Lancashire, PR7 6JH Tel: (01257) 273114 Fax: (01257) 262386 E-mail: sales@shackerley.co.uk *Ceramics, marble & granite suppliers*

Shackleton Mortimer & Sons Ltd, 25 Pitcliffe Way, Bradford, West Yorkshire, BD5 7SG Tel: (01274) 726890 Fax: (01274) 390384 *Rolling shutters & exterior sunblinds*

Shad Fork Lifts, Faverdale Industrial Estate, Darlington, County Durham, DL3 0QQ Tel: (01325) 353894 Fax: (01325) 353894 *Fork lift truck servicing & repairs*

Shade Solutions Ltd, Oatley Trading Estate, Seymour Road, Kingswood, Bristol, BS15 1SD Tel: 0117-373 0599 Fax: 0117-330 9342 E-mail: sales@shadesolutions.co.uk *Supply & installation of domestic & commercial window blinds*

▶ Shademakers, 171 Cottonmill Lane, St. Albans, Hertfordshire, AL1 2EX Tel: (0800) 0851558 Fax: (0870) 4214097 E-mail: mike@shademakers.co.uk *Parasols & garden umbrellas*

▶ Shades Blinds, 30 Northfield Road, Reading, RG1 8AH Tel: 0118-958 3757 Fax: 0118-962 4621 E-mail: shadesblinds@hotmail.co.uk *Sell & install made to measure blinds*

▶ Shades Of Doncaster Ltd, Unit 3 Sandall Stones Road, Kirk Sandall Industrial Estate, Doncaster, South Yorkshire, DN3 1QR Tel: (01302) 887106 E-mail: tbell@shadesofdoncaster.co.uk *Light manufrs*

Shades Screenprint Ltd, Stur Mill, Broadstone Hall Road, Stockport, Cheshire, SK5 7BY Tel: 0161-477 4688 Fax: 0161-474 7629 E-mail: admin@shadesscreenprint.co.uk *Glass & perspex screen printers*

Shades Technics, 3 Marshgate Drive, Hertford, SG13 7AQ Tel: (01992) 501683 Fax: (01992) 501669 E-mail: sales@shades-technics.com *Coach interiors design & manufrs*

Shades Window Blind Specialists, 2B Chingford Road, London, E17 4PJ Tel: (020) 8527 3991 Fax: (020) 8523 4476 E-mail: info@shades-london.co.uk *Window blinds manufrs*

Shadewell Blinds Ltd, St Margarets Lane, Fareham, Hampshire, PO14 4BG Tel: (01329) 841199 Fax: (01329) 842299 E-mail: info@shadewell.co.uk *Manufacturers & distribution of awnings & canopies*

Shading Systems Ltd, Unit F5 Innsworth Technology Park, Innsworth Lane, Gloucester, GL3 1DL Tel: (01452) 536000 Fax: (01452) 731901 E-mail: sales@shadings.co.uk *Blinds, awnings, shutters & frills manufrs*

Shadow Blinds Ltd, Unit E Newark Road South, Glenrothes, Fife, KY7 4NS Tel: (01592) 630660 Fax: (01592) 630188 *Manufacturing window blinds*

Shadow Boatbuilders Ltd, Riverside Estate, Brundall, Norwich, NR13 5PL Tel: (01603) 712362 Fax: (01603) 717770 E-mail: swancraft@rjd.co.uk *Boat builders & repairers*

Shadow Sales & Service, 6 Lyttleton Court, Droitwich, Worcestershire, WR9 7BG Tel: (01905) 797898 Fax: (01905) 798399 E-mail: mike.ssslimited@btconnect.com *Industrial cleaners*

▶ Shady Palm Ltd, 31 Boscombe Road, London, W12 9HT Tel: 0870 4604969 Fax: 0870 1126573 E-mail: info@shadypalm.co.uk *Shady Palm is an online store offering luxury home products at extremely low prices, mostly 70% cheaper than those available in areas of London and Paris.*

Shaftec Automotive Components Ltd, 2 Cato Street, Birmingham, B7 4TS Tel: 0121-333 3555 Fax: 0121-359 3003 E-mail: shaftec@automotive8.freeserve.co.uk *Motor vehicle components manufrs*

Shaftesbury Engraving/Printing Unit 7, 7 Plaza Business Centre, Stockingswater Lane, Enfield, Middlesex, EN3 7XT Tel: (020) 8443 3970 Fax: (020) 8443 3972 E-mail: sales@shaftesburyengraving.co.uk *Engravers & die stampers*

Shaftesbury Garage Ltd, 65b East Barnet Road, Barnet, Hertfordshire, EN4 8RN Tel: (020) 8449 9111 Fax: (020) 8449 9922 E-mail: andy@shaftesburygarage.co.uk *Car service, repairs & MOT*

Shaftsbury P.L.C., Pegasus House, 37-43 Sackville Street, London, W1S 3DL Tel: (020) 7333 8118 Fax: (020) 7333 0660 E-mail: shaftesbury@shaftesbury.co.uk *Property investment*

▶ Shaggy Sheep, Cilwen, Abernant, Carmarthen, Dyfed, SA33 5RH Tel: (01267) 281202 E-mail: bookings@shaggysheep.com *tours of wales*

Shah & Co., 15 Stanier Street, Swindon, SN1 5QU Tel: (01793) 524084 E-mail: shahco@mrshah.com *Chartered certified accountants, taxation, company secretarial, management consultants, VAT, book keeping etc.*

Shah Trading, 146a Vine Place, Rochdale, Lancashire, OL11 1QZ Tel: (01706) 659774 *Children's fashion*

Shah-British Enterprises Ltd, 38 Upper Town Road, Greenford, Middlesex, UB6 9JF Tel: (020) 8575 0104 Fax: (020) 8575 6066 *Pharmaceutical manufrs*

▶ Shahina Textiles, Tivoli House, Derby Street, Bolton, BL3 6JY Tel: (01204) 361617 Fax: (01204) 261618 E-mail: sal92uk@yahoo.co.uk *Bulk & made to measure curtain manufrs*

Shahtex Leicester Ltd, Krishna Buildings, 7 Claymill Road, Leicester, LE4 9JJ Tel: 0116-274 1647 *Jersey knitted fabric manufrs*

Shairwood Contracts Ltd, Colchester Road, Tendring, Clacton-on-Sea, Essex, CO16 9AA Tel: (01255) 830704 Fax: (01255) 831047 E-mail: Office@sherwood.Co.uk *Civil engineering contractors*

▶ Shak Ltd, Unit D Grange Road, Walthamstow, London, E17 8AH Tel: (020) 8521 2900 Fax: (020) 8521 2010 E-mail: shak@theworldofwater.com *Modern & contemporary bathroom products suppliers*

▶ Shaker UK Ltd, Unit 213 Jubilee Trade Centre, 130 Pershore Street, Birmingham, B5 6ND Tel: 0121-622 2055 *Hospitality trainers*

Shakespear Finance Ltd, International House, 223 Regent Street, London, W1B 2EB Tel: (0808) 1602576 E-mail: webmaster@adverse-credit-business-loans.co.uk *Provider of Business Loans for both Homeowners and Tenants. Apply for one of the best Business Loan available in UK.*

Shakespeare Engineering, 91 Haltwhistle Road, South Woodham Ferrers, Chelmsford, CM3 5ZA Tel: (01245) 328118 Fax: (01245) 325696 *Electro-mechanical assembly services*

▶ Shakespeare finance ltd, 501 International House, 223 Regent Street, London, W1B 2EB Tel: (0808) 1602576 E-mail: webmaster@go4ukloans.co.uk *Helps you to check out a wide list of personal loan deals. Compare and choose the deal that perfectly matches your requirements.*

▶ Shakespeare Finance Ltd, 11 Parade House, 135 The Parade, High Street, Watford, WD17 1NA Tel: (020) 7097 3654 E-mail: m.wali@shakespearefinance.co.uk

Shakespeare International Ltd, Enterprise Way, Off Venture Road, Fleetwood, Lancashire, FY7 8RY Tel: (01253) 858787 Fax: (01253) 859595 *Thermoplastic yarn manufrs*

Shakespeare International Marine Ltd, Station Road, Hartlebury, Kidderminster, Worcestershire, DY11 7YJ Tel: (01299) 250685 Fax: (01299) 250509 *Boat builders*

Shakespeare & Sons, 291-295 Dudley Road, Birmingham, B18 4HA Tel: 0121-454 1341 Fax: 0121-454 1341 *DIY retail*

Shakespeares, Oak Lane, Kingswinford, West Midlands, DY6 7JS Tel: (01384) 296757 Fax: (01384) 401059 *Scrap metal merchants*

Shamley Saddlery, Fifield House Farm, Oakley Green Road, Oakley Green, Windsor, Berkshire, SL4 4QF Tel: (01628) 777664 Fax: (01628) 777664 E-mail: info@shamleysaddlery.co.uk *Saddlery manufrs*

Shamrock Horseboxes Ltd, 5 Soham Rd, Fordham, Ely, Cambs, CB7 5LB Tel: 01638 723050 Fax: 01638 723051 *Horse-box manufacturer*

Shand Engineering Ltd, Kiln Lane, Stallingborough, Grimsby, South Humberside, DN41 8DL Tel: (01469) 571586 Fax: (01469) 571073 *Pressure vessel & hose fittings manufrs*

Shand Higson & Co. Ltd, Lees Road, Knowsley Industrial Park North, Knowsley, Liverpool, L33 7SE Tel: 0151-549 2210 Fax: 0151-549 1405 E-mail: sales@shandhigson.co.uk Sales Contact: S.A. Fisher Principal Export Areas: Worldwide *Shand Higson & Co. Ltd Based in the North West we specialise in the conversion and distribution of all types of industrial adhesive tapes including cloth, pvc, paper, polypropylene, double-sided, foam, etc.Shand Higson are main distributors for Scapa and Tesa. We also supply all types of packaging materials including polythene film and bags, stretchwrap, shrinkwrap, bubble wrap, plastic and steel strapping, corrugated paper, packing foam,cardboard boxes and layer pads etc. We also supply a full range of dispensers, tools and automatic machinery for our products.We deliver across Liverpool, Manchester, Cheshire, Lancashire, Cumbria,Merseyside, the Wirral, Chester and North Wales, the North West and the rest of the UK. Please feel free to call*

▶ Andrew Shane Ltd, 157 Nottingham Road, Somercotes, Alfreton, Derbyshire, DE55 4JH Tel: (01773) 541414 Fax: (01773) 541415 E-mail: andrewshane@btconnect.com *Garment manufrs*

Shani Ltd, 2 Greycaine Road, Watford, WD24 7GT Tel: (01923) 228395 Fax: (01923) 228373 E-mail: shanimail@shani-fashions.com *Ladies fashion manufrs*

Shanick Engineering Co. Ltd, Byfield Place, Bognor Regis, West Sussex, PO22 9QY Tel: (01243) 863666 Fax: (01243) 827629 E-mail: shannick.eng@surfree.co.uk *CNC Precision turning & milling*

Alex Shanks, 2 Hagmill Crescent, East Shawhead Enterprise Park, Coatbridge, Lanarkshire, ML5 4NS Tel: (01236) 436017 Fax: (01236) 436017 E-mail: sales@alexshanks.com *Chemical & janitorial accessory suppliers*

Shanks Printers & Finishers Ltd, Unit 6/7 Martello Enterprise Centre, Courtwick Lane, Wick, Littlehampton, West Sussex, BN17 7PA Tel: (01903) 716442 Fax: (01903) 733019 E-mail: terri@shanksprinters.co.uk *Printers & finishers*

▶ T. Shanks Engineering Ltd, 141 Greengairs Road, Greengairs, Airdrie, Lanarkshire, ML6 7SY Tel: (01236) 830325 Fax: (01236) 830736 E-mail: sales@shanksgroup.co.uk *Engineering fabrications*

Shanks Waste Solutions, Loughborough Road, Bunny, Nottingham, NG11 6QN Tel: 0115-945 6069 Fax: 0115-940 5170 *Skip hire, landfill & recycling*

▶ Shannon Fine Art Photography, Norseman Studio Unit 8, Tedco Business Centre, Viking Industrial Park, Jarrow, Tyne & Wear, NE32 3DT Tel: 0191-428 3517 *photographers based in the north east of england,weddings portraiture,commercial,events, studio hire*

Shannon Installations, 10 Hillmeads Drive, Dudley, West Midlands, DY2 7TS Tel: (01384) 257475 Fax: (01384) 243908 E-mail: shannoninst@cs.com *Contract labour suppliers for the storage equipment industry*

Shanoc Electronic Systems Ltd, 1-3 Pond Close, Walkern Road, Stevenage, Hertfordshire, SG1 3QP Tel: (01438) 727244 Fax: (01438) 726565 E-mail: info@shannock.co.uk *Electronic contract manufrs*

Shanoc Precision Engineering, Unit 11 Bondor Business Centre, London Road, Baldock, Hertfordshire, SG7 6HP Tel: (01462) 895936 Fax: (01462) 895936 *Ceramic machining services*

Shape Design, Unit 1 Bankhall Lane, Liverpool, L20 8EW Tel: 0151-933 4438 Fax: 0151-933 4438 E-mail: dave@shapedesign.co.uk *Glass re-enforced plastics moulders*

▶ Shape Injection Mouldings, Unit 7-8 Thomas Gilchrist Court, Thomas Gilchrist Industrial Estate, Blaenavon, Pontypool, Gwent, NP4 9RJ Tel: (01495) 791369 Fax: (01495) 790582 E-mail: info@shapeplastics.co.uk *Manufacture, plastic & polyurethane foam mouldings*

Shaped Wires Ltd, Prospect Mills, Scholes, Cleckheaton, West Yorkshire, BD19 6NJ Tel: (01274) 855635 Fax: (01274) 851116 E-mail: sales@shapedwires.com *Precision rolled profile services*

Shapero Agencies Ltd, Salts Mill, Victoria Road, Shipley, West Yorkshire, BD18 3LB Tel: (01274) 531210 Fax: (01274) 531259 *Menswear agents*

M.& J. Shapero Ltd, 70 Thomas Street, Aston, Birmingham, B6 4TN Tel: 0121-359 7731 Fax: 0121-353 4557 E-mail: shapero@netcomuk.co.uk *Wholesale haberdashery & furnishings*

▶ Shapet Joinery Ltd, Booth Road, Bedminster, Bristol, BS3 1BP Tel: 0117-963 6953 Fax: 0117-963 6966 E-mail: shapetjoinery@btconnect.com *Bespoke joinery products suppliers*

Sharand Ltd, Churnetside Business Park, Station Road, Cheddleton, Leek, Staffordshire, ST13 7EE Tel: (01538) 360178 Fax: (01538) 360111 *Welding & fabrication engineers*

Shard Recruitment, 3 Cavendish Street, Keighley, West Yorkshire, BD21 3RB Tel: (01535) 690600 Fax: (01535) 610197 E-mail: info@shardrecruit.co.uk *Recruitment consultants & services*

▶ Sharemymemory.com, P.O. Box 3756, Sheffield, S6 9AB Tel: 08707 202 686 Fax: 08707 202 687 E-mail: mail@sharemymemory.com *Your own personalised baby, wedding, celebration or memorial website with a guestbook, text, photos and more, from award-winning Sharemymemory.com. Why not call us for a brochure or information about our gift certificates, or join our free trial at www.sharemymemory.com today?*

Sharetree Ltd, Unit 3 Meadow Mill Eastington Trading Estate, Churchend, Eastington, Stonehouse, Gloucestershire, GL10 3RZ Tel: (01453) 828642 Fax: (01453) 828076 E-mail: sales@sharetree.com Principal Export Areas: Worldwide *Environmental chambers & stress screening equipment manufrs*

Sharif Fashion, 15a Clark Street, London, E1 2HD Tel: (020) 7790 0546 Fax: (020) 7790 0546 *Ladies & childrens wear*

▶ Sharkey & Co Ltd, Vincent Court, Hubert St, Aston Locks, Birmingham, B6 4BA Tel: 0121-380 3700

▶ Sharkey Construction, The Paddocks, Ramsey Road, Laxey, Isle of Man, IM4 7PP Tel: (01624) 863113 Fax: (01624) 674131 E-mail: sharkey@manks.net

Sharkie & Huntbatch Ltd, Riverdane Road, Eaton Bank Trading Estate, Congleton, Cheshire, CW12 1PL Tel: (01260) 274747 Fax: (01260) 299017 E-mail: office@sharkies.co.uk *Porcelain & ceramic yarn guides distributors*

Sharley Domestics, 6 Green Lane, Radnage, High Wycombe, Buckinghamshire, HP14 4DN Tel: (01494) 485926 Fax: (01494) 484140 E-mail: sharleydomestics@btconnect.com *Domestic appliance sales & repairers*

Sharman & Co. Ltd, Newark Road, Peterborough, PE1 5TD Tel: (01733) 424949 Fax: (01733) 424948 *Contract newspaper printers*

H.D. Sharman Ltd, High Peak Works, Chapel-en-le-Frith, High Peak, Derbyshire, SK23 0HW Tel: (01298) 812371 Fax: (01298) 812237 E-mail: info@hdsharman.co.uk *Lining system manufrs*

Sharmans Agricultural Ltd, College Farm, Gonerby Moor, Grantham, Lincolnshire, NG32 2AB Tel: (01476) 562561 Fax: (01476) 590343 *Agricultural machinery dealers* Also at: Melton Mowbray & Stamford

Sharmans Of Stamford, Barnack Road, Stamford, Lincolnshire, PE9 2NA Tel: (01780) 762916 Fax: (01780) 752159 *Agricultural engineers*

Sharmic Engineering Ltd, Baldwin Road, Stourport-on-Severn, Worcestershire, DY13 9AX Tel: (01299) 878123 Fax: (01299) 879409 E-mail: info@sharmic.co.uk *Vibratory surface finishing machines, new and used, for vibratory deburring, polishing, degreasing and descaling. Also vibratory, abrasive plastic, ceramic, wood and steel medias, chemical compounds. Vibratory machinery repairs, service and relines.Nationwide service.ISO approved.*

Sharp & C0 Bagpipe Makers Ltd, 113 Barrack Street, Glasgow, G4 0UE Tel: 0141-553 0902 Fax: 0141-553 0903 E-mail: greig@kintail.co.uk *Bagpipe & kilt manufrs*

Chris Sharp Cabinets Ltd, Tillbridge Lane, Scampton, Lincoln, LN1 2SX Tel: (01522) 504505 Fax: (01522) 514958 *Solid wood furniture manufrs*

Sharp Electronics (UK) Ltd, Sharp House, Thorp Road, Manchester, M40 5BE Tel: 0161-205 2333 Fax: 0161-205 7076 *Electronic goods suppliers*

Sharp Interpack, Colley Lane, Bridgwater, Somerset, TA6 5YS Tel: (01278) 435000 Fax: (01278) 423019 E-mail: info@sharpinterpack.co.uk *Designers & manufacturers of rigid plastic packaging, food & non food use*

James Sharp & Co., 80 Bell Street, Dundee, DD1 1HW Tel: (01382) 226321 Fax: (01382) 202052 *Plumbers' hemp & plumbing services*

Sharp Labels Ltd, Woodhall Business Park, Sudbury, Suffolk, CO10 1WH Tel: (01787) 880291 Fax: (01787) 881841 E-mail: sales@sharplabels.co.uk *Label manufrs*

Sharp Maintenance Services, 57 Ballens Road, Chatham, Kent, ME5 8NX Tel: (01634) 683232 Fax: (01634) 200025 *Door repair services*

▶ Neil Sharp, Riverside Close, Weston-Super-Mare, Avon, BS22 7RZ Tel: (01934) 519278 Fax: (01934) 519278 *Auto electrical equipment suppliers*

Sharp & Nickless Ltd, 77 College Street, Long Eaton, Nottingham, NG10 4NN Tel: 0115-973 2169 Fax: 0115-973 2169 E-mail: sharp@brandysnap.co.uk *Sharp & Nickless is an undisputed specialist in the production of brandy snap and traditional biscuits. The range includes baskets, cones and rolls. They are available in catering packs. Old English Brandy Snaps and Honey Snaps are favourite items in many hamper selections. For the Christmas trade, there is a Festive Spiced Christmas Brandy Snap and the traditional biscuit range includes Ginger snaps, lemon, coconut and current biscuits, Local specialities are the Sherwood Spice Biscuit and the Grantham Gingerbread.*

▶ Sharp Photography, 14 Devonshire Place, Brighton, BN2 1QA Tel: (07775) 895477 E-mail: info@janesharp.com *Commercial & private photography commissions*

Sharp Printing, 8 The Green, Richmond, Surrey, TW9 1PL Tel: (020) 8940 7129 Fax: (020) 8940 8647 E-mail: sharppaint@london.com *Reprographic printers*

Sharp Site Services Ltd, 49 Mountain Road, Brynaman, Upper Brynamman, Ammanford, Dyfed, SA18 1AE Tel: (01269) 825932 Fax: (01269) 825932 E-mail: margaret@sharpsiteservices.com *Installation, repairs, refurbishment & maintenance services of GRP Housings & covers*

Walter Sharp & Sons, 498 Calder Street, Glasgow, G42 0QD Tel: 0141-423 8300 Fax: 0141-423 9200 *Catering equipment supply & engineers*

Andrew Sharpe Reproductions Ltd, The Old Carpenters Shop, The Cliff, Matlock, Derbyshire, DE4 5EW Tel: (01629) 55560 *Furniture manufrs*

Sharpe Appliance Spares, PO Box 182, Malvern, Worcestershire, WR13 5XX Tel: (01684) 576390 Fax: (01684) 576391 E-mail: info@sharpespares.co.uk *Spares for boilers*

Sharpe Haltham, Autumn Lodge, Wood Enderby Lane, Haltham, Horncastle, Lincolnshire, LN9 6JH Tel: (01507) 568485 Fax: (01507) 568485 *Agricultural merchants*

Sharpe Master Sportswear Shop, 49 St Helens Road, Swansea, SA1 4BD Tel: (01792) 414300 Fax: (01792) 414300 E-mail: enquiries@sharpemaster.co.uk *Sports clothing manufacturer & supplier*

Sharpe Media Ltd, 83-87 Cambridge Street, Coventry, CV1 5HU Tel: (024) 7622 4316 Fax: (024) 7652 5622 *Commercial printers*

▶ Sharpe Refinery Service Hydro Carbons Ltd, Arlington Works, Arlington Road, Twickenham, TW1 2BB Tel: (020) 8892 0502 Fax: (020) 8892 8193 E-mail: sales@sharpesoil.co.uk *Tank cleaning services*

▶ Sharpe Systems, Westthorpe Innovation Centre, Killamarsh, Sheffield, S21 1TZ Tel: 0114-251 4775 Fax: (0870) 1221505 E-mail: tim.sharpe@sharpe-systems.co.uk *IT consultancy*

Sharpening & Supply (Midlands) & Co., 1 Queen Street, Darlaston, Wednesbury, West Midlands, WS10 8JF Tel: 0121-526 6800 Fax: 0121-526 2256 E-mail: sharpsupplytool@westmids.fsbusiness.co.uk *Circular saw manufacturers & sharpeners*

Sharpenset Tool Sharpening, Dashwood Works Industrial Centre, Dashwood Avenue, High Wycombe, Buckinghamshire, HP12 3ED Tel: (01494) 530177 Fax: (01494) 463725 E-mail: info@sharpenset.co.uk *Knife sharpening & honing machine manufacturers*

Sharples Group, Tatton Court, Kingsland Grange, Woolston, Warrington, WA1 4RR Tel: (01925) 839599 Fax: (01925) 839580 E-mail: info@sharplesgroup.com *Office machinery & electronic management services*

▶ Sharples Street Salvage, Sharples Street, Blackburn, BB2 3QT Tel: (01254) 696824 Fax: (01254) 696824 E-mail: info@sssalvage.com *Dealers in accident damaged vehicles.*

Sharples Stress Engineers Ltd, Unit 29 Old Mill Industrial Estate, Bamber Bridge, Preston, PR5 6SY Tel: (01772) 323359 Fax: (01772) 316017 E-mail: sharplesstress@aol.com *Stress analysis services & equipment*

Sharples & Yates, Chorley Road, Westhoughton, Bolton, BL5 3PJ Tel: (01942) 815942 Fax: (01942) 815942 *Engineering & fabricators*

▶ Sharpline Solutions Ltd, Unit 2, Saturn House, Calleva Park, Aldermaston, RG7 8HA Tel: 0118-982 3930 Fax: 0118-981 2430 E-mail: sales@sharplinesolutions.co.uk *Photocopier suppliers*

▶ Sharpowl International, Wood Cottage Ketteringham Hall, Church Road, Ketteringham, Wymondham, Norfolk, NR18 9RS Tel: (01603) 813620 Fax: (01603) 813629 *Software author's*

▶ Sharpowl (International), Ketteringham Hall, Church Road, Ketteringham, Wymondham, Norfolk, NR18 9RS Tel: (01603) 813620 Fax: (01603) 813629 *Computer software developers*

▶ SharpOWL (Software International), Ketteringham Hall, Church Road, Ketteringham, Wymondham, Norfolk, NR18 9RS Tel: (0870) 2242574 Fax: (0870) 2242577 E-mail: info@sharpowl.com *Computer software developers*

Sharps Bedrooms Ltd, 12 High Street, Ashford, Kent, TN24 8TD Tel: (01233) 641033 *Manufacturers of bedroom & home office furniture*

Sharps Bedrooms Ltd, 58-60 High Street, Banstead, Surrey, SM7 2LX Tel: (01737) 370321 *Bedroom furniture retailers*

Sharps Bedrooms Ltd, Inside Allied Carpets, Barnstaple Retail Pk Station Rd, Sticklepath, Barnstaple, Devon, EX31 2AU Tel: 01271 321713 *Furniture manufacturers*

▶ Sharps Bedrooms Ltd, Albany Park, Camberley, Surrey, GU16 7PU Tel: (01276) 802000 *Sell & fit fitted bedroom & bathrooms*

Sharps Bedrooms Ltd, C/o, Portfield Way, Chichester, W. Sussex, PO19 7YH Tel: 01243 530936 *Fitted bedroom & home office furniture*

Sharps Bedrooms Ltd, Homebase, St Andrews Avenue, Colchester, CO4 3BG Tel: (01206) 861821 *Fitted bedroom furniture supplier*

Sharps Bedrooms Ltd, Homebase, Kingsway, Derby, DE22 3NF Tel: (01332) 383538 *Bedrooms furniture*

Sharps Bedrooms Ltd, Unit 11 Grahamston Retail Park, Grahams Road, Falkirk, FK1 1LW Tel: (01324) 626403 *Fitted bedrooms merchants*

Sharps Bedrooms Ltd, 44 Main Street, Milngavie, Glasgow, G62 6BU Tel: 0141-956 2242 *Fitted bedrooms provider*

Sharps Bedrooms Ltd, 62-68 Eden Street, Kingston upon Thames, Surrey, KT1 1EL Tel: (020) 8546 1238 *Fitted bedrooms*

▶ Sharps Bedrooms Ltd, 19 Haymarket, Leicester, LE1 3GD Tel: 0116-253 3099 *Furniture retailers*

Sharps Bedrooms Ltd, Homebase, 4 The Sidings, Lincoln, LN6 7TP Tel: (01522) 512181 *Bedroom sales fittings & manufrs*

Sharps Bedrooms Ltd, Wood Green Shopping City, High Road, London, N22 6YD Tel: (020) 8889 1657 *Bedrooms manufrs*

Sharps Bedrooms Ltd, 38-40 Old Church Road, London, E4 8DB Tel: (020) 8529 0162 *Fitted furniture manufacturers & installers*

Sharps Bedrooms Ltd, Enterprise Way, Luton, LU3 4BW Tel: (01582) 561345 *Fitted bedroom furniture distributor*

Sharps Bedrooms Ltd, 25 Swinton Hall Road, Swinton, Manchester, M27 4BL Tel: 0161-728 3561 Fax: 0161-728 3276 *Bedroom furniture distributors*

Sharps Bedrooms Ltd, Nene Valley Way, Northampton, NN3 5LU Tel: (01604) 408004 *Fitted bedrooms distributor*

Sharps Bedrooms Ltd, Madford Business Park, Mansfield Road, Daybrook, Nottingham, NG5 6AD Tel: 0115-967 1311 *Bedroom kitchen & bathroom furniture suppliers & manufrs*

Sharps Bedrooms, Inside Home Base, Horspath Driftway, Eastern Bypass, Headington, Oxford, OX3 7JN Tel: (01865) 777170 *Kitchen, bathroom, bedrooms showroom manufrs*

Sharps Bedrooms Ltd, Unit L Meadowhall Retail Park, Attercliffe Common, Sheffield, S9 2YZ Tel: 0114-244 4419 *Bedroom furniture retailer*

Sharps Bedrooms Ltd, 6 Thames Street, Staines, Middlesex, TW18 4SD Tel: (01784) 461791 Fax: (01784) 464073 *Bedroom furniture distributor & manufrs*

▶ Sharps Bedrooms Ltd, 1 East Street, Taunton, Somerset, TA1 3LQ Tel: (01823) 423862 *Furniture, Built In*

Sharps Bedrooms Ltd, Unit 9 Thorp Arch Trading Estate, Thorp Arch, Wetherby, West Yorkshire, LS23 7BJ Tel: (01937) 843245 *Furniture retailers*

Sharps Bedrooms Ltd, Hylton Road, Worcester, WR2 5JW Tel: (01905) 424502 *Joinery manufrs*

Sharps Bedrooms Ltd, 151-153 Montague Street, Worthing, West Sussex, BN11 3BZ Tel: (01903) 823438 *Fitted furniture retailers*

Sharps Bedrooms Ltd, Foss Bank, York, YO31 7JB Tel: (01904) 629574 *Fitted bedroom suppliers*

Sharps Moben & Dolphin, The Royals, Haygate Avenue, Southend-on-Sea, SS1 1DQ Tel: (01702) 464722 *Furniture wholesalers*

▶ Sharps World Of Wood, York Road Garage, York Road, Barmby Moor, York, YO42 4HS Tel: (01759) 305566 Fax: (01759) 306699 E-mail: paul@sharpsworldofwood.com *Timber product suppliers*

Richard Sharrock & Sons, Allied Bakeries, Ashton Road, Bredbury, Stockport, Cheshire, SK6 2RE Tel: 0161-430 5151 Fax: 0161-406 3117 *Bakery*

Sharrocks Ltd, 143-153 Whitehorse Road, Croydon, CR0 2LJ Tel: (020) 8684 4218 Fax: (020) 8689 6244 E-mail: sharrockslondon@btclick.com *Painters & decorators*

Arnold Sharrocks Ltd, 229 Spotland Road, Rochdale, Lancashire, OL12 7AQ Tel: (01706) 655411 Fax: (01706) 642452 E-mail: arnold-sharrocks@2binternet.co.uk *Painting contractors Also at: Aldershot, Bradford & Croydon*

Sharrod Hardchrome Co. Ltd, Hose Street, Tunstall, Stoke-on-Trent, ST6 5AL Tel: (01782) 815941 *Hard chrome plating services*

Sharrow Industries, Parkway Close, Sheffield, S9 4WJ Tel: 0114-203 9446 Fax: 0114-203 9448 *Kitchen units & PVCU window manufrs*

▶ Shaun Edwards, Unit 9 171 Evendons Lane, Wokingham, Berkshire, RG41 4EH Tel: 0118-979 2226 E-mail: info@shaunedwards.com *We specialise in contemporary portraiture and wedding photography. Our unique style reflects todays much more relaxed attitudes and lifestyles, producing stunning images for you to cherish.**

▶ Shaunsoft Computer Systems, Unit 18 Blencathra Business Centre, Threlkeld, Keswick, Cumbria, CA12 4TR Tel: (01768) 779988 *Computer software developers*

Shavrin Levatap Co. Ltd, 32 Watersides, Kings Langley, Hertfordshire, WD4 8HH Tel: (01923) 267678 Fax: (01923) 265050 E-mail: sales@shavinlevatap.co.uk *Kitchen, bathroom & washroom manufrs*

▶ Anna Shaw Associates Ltd, 9 Tramway Drive, Sutton-on-Sea, Mablethorpe, Lincolnshire, LN12 2GS Tel: (01507) 440278 Fax: (01507) 440278 E-mail: info@annashawassociates.co.uk *Computer accessories*

Anne Shaw Consultants Ltd, Adelphi Mill, Grimshaw Lane, Bollington, Macclesfield, Cheshire, SK10 5JB Tel: (01625) 576225 Fax: (01625) 576262 E-mail: consult@anneshaw.com *Management consultants*

Shaw Bros, Viaduct Works, Clay Lane, Linthwaite, Huddersfield, HD7 5BG Tel: (01484) 846442 Fax: (01484) 847774 E-mail: carole@shawbros.fsnet.co.uk *Aluminium window fabricators*

▶ Shaw Builders Ltd, Barnfield Road, Tipton, West Midlands, DY4 9DE Tel: 0121-520 5535 Fax: 0121-522 3485 *Building contractors*

Shaw Cutters, Ashwellthorpe Industrial Estate, Ashwellthorpe, Norwich, NR16 1ER Tel: (01508) 488400 Fax: (01508) 488058 E-mail: sales@dcdevs.co.uk *Glass cutter manufrs*

Shaw Design Services, Moorfield Mills, Chapel Lane, Heckmondwike, West Yorkshire, WF16 9JU Tel: (01924) 410938 Fax: (01924) 410178 *Engineering*

Shaw Electronic Development Co., 7 Market Street, Church, Accrington, Lancashire, BB5 0DP Tel: (01254) 393878 Fax: (01254) 393878 *Manufacture of electronic components for special applications*

F.W. Shaw & Sons (Worthing) Ltd, 3 Tudor Buildings, Aldwick Street, Bognor Regis, West Sussex, PO21 3AW Tel: (01903) 237174 Fax: (01243) 860267 E-mail: move@sussex-moving-services.com *Removal contractors*

Shaw Fabrication Ltd, Unit B4, Halesfield 9, Telford, Shropshire, TF7 4QW Tel: (01952) 580838 Fax: (01952) 581085 *Steel fabricators*

Frank Shaw (Bayonet) Ltd, Merse Road, North Moons Moat, Redditch, Worcestershire, B98 9HL Tel: (01527) 66241 Fax: (01527) 584455 E-mail: sales@frankshaw.co.uk Principal Export Areas: Worldwide *Manufacturers of wire nails, picture hooks & tacks*

Shaw Gears, Unit 5 Duchess St Industrial Estate, Shaw, Oldham, OL2 7UX Tel: (01706) 847220 Fax: (01706) 847220 *Gear cutting services*

George Shaw Engineering (Sheffield) 1994 Ltd, Carlisle Street East, Sheffield, S4 7QN Tel: 0114-276 7011 Fax: 0114-270 0365 E-mail: peter@shaweng.fsnet.co.uk *Steel fabricators engineers*

Shaw Group, Witan Gate House, 500-600 Witan Gate West, Milton Keynes, MK9 1BA Tel: (01908) 668844 Fax: (01908) 602211 E-mail: *Engineering & project management services*

Shaw Group UK Ltd, Stores Road, Derby, DE21 4BG Tel: (01332) 291122 Fax: (01332) 291123 E-mail: info@shawgrp.com *Pipe work erection fabricators*

Harry Shaw Business Computers Ltd, 29-31 Leicester Street, Bedworth, Warwickshire, CV12 8GG Tel: (024) 7631 6666 Fax: (024) 7631 6187 E-mail: info@harryshaw.net *Computer reseller hardware & software*

Isaac Shaw Ltd, Doulton Works, Marlborough Way, Tamworth, Staffordshire, B77 2HA Tel: (01827) 260915 Fax: (01827) 261039 E-mail: isl@tecweb.com *Non-ferrous scrap metal merchants*

Ivor Shaw Ltd, 300 City Gate Business Park, City Gate, Derby, DE24 8WY Tel: (01332) 794880 Fax: (01332) 794891 E-mail: ivorshawltd@penninehealthcare.co.uk *Hospital disposable products*

▶ Kevan Shaw Lighting Design, 4 Baltic Street, Edinburgh, EH6 7BW Tel: 0131-555 5553 Fax: 0131-555 5559 *Design lighting*

Shaw Marketing & Design Ltd, 18 Albany Street, Edinburgh, EH1 3QB Tel: 0131-557 5663 Fax: 0131-556 7379 E-mail: enquiries@shawltd.demon.co.uk *Marketing & design consultants*

Shaw Moisture Meters (UK) Ltd, Rawson Road, Westgate, Bradford, West Yorkshire, BD1 3SQ Tel: (01274) 733582 Fax: (01274) 370151 E-mail: mail@shawmeters.com *Dew point indicators & hygrometers*

Shaw Moor Yarns Ltd, Bryom Mill, Knowl Street, Stalybridge, Cheshire, SK15 3AW Tel: 0161-303 1770 Fax: 0161-303 1069 E-mail: 100436.327@compuserve.com *Yarn merchants*

Shaw Munster Ltd, Winster Grove, Great Barr, Birmingham, B44 9EG Tel: 0121-360 4279 Fax: 0121-360 4265 E-mail: office@shawmunstergroup.co.uk *Promotional gifts & souvenirs*

▶ Shaw Plant, 26 Poplar Place, Blantyre, Glasgow, G72 9QA Tel: (01698) 827406

▶ Shaw Printing, Unit F Pegswood Industrial Estate, Pegswood, Morpeth, Northumberland, NE61 6HZ Tel: (01670) 510271 Fax: (01670) 511759 E-mail: enquiries@azure-printing.co.uk

Shaw & Riley Ltd, Station Yard, New Road, Hessay, York, YO26 8JS Tel: (01904) 738700 Fax: (01904) 738001 *Cabinet makers*

▶ S. A. Shaw, Hoylake Business Centre, 38-42 Birkenhead Road, Hoylake, Wirral, Merseyside, CH47 3BW Tel: (0870) 0780202 Fax: 0151-632 4624 E-mail: enquiries@shawbusiness.co.uk *IT consultants*

Shaw Sheet Metal Rugby Ltd, 13 Paynes Lane, Rugby, Warwickshire, CV21 2UH Tel: (01788) 536033 Fax: (01788) 536922 E-mail: sales@shawsheetmetal.co.uk *Sheet metalwork engineers & fabrications*

Shaw & Sons Ltd, Shaway House, 21 Bourne Park, Bourne Road, Crayford, Dartford, DA1 4BZ Tel: (01322) 621100 Fax: (01322) 550553 E-mail: sales@shaws.co.uk *Publishers, printers & law stationers*

Sydney H. Shaw & Co. Ltd, Green Grove Mills, Kirkburton, Huddersfield, HD8 0QY Tel: (01484) 602614 Fax: (01484) 608459 E-mail: sydshaw.clothing@dial.pipex.com *Woollen fabric manufrs*

Shaw Timber Ltd, Bridge Street, Slaithwaite, Huddersfield, HD7 5JN Tel: (01484) 848484 Fax: (01484) 848494 E-mail: sales@shawtimber.com *Furniture components & timber shelf manufrs*

W. Shaw (Millinery), 58 Howard Street, Belfast, BT1 6PL Tel: (028) 9032 0135 Fax: (028) 9032 9026 *Wholesale milliners*

Shaw Water, Bristol House, 15 Ridge Way, Hillend, Dunfermline, Fife, KY11 9JH Tel: (01383) 820595 Fax: (01383) 820979 E-mail: shawwater@aol.com *Water treatment services*

Shawcross Ltd, Priory Street, Priory Industrial Estate, Birkenhead, Merseyside, CH41 5JH Tel: 0151-647 6692 Fax: 0151-666 1569 E-mail: info@shawcrosssigns.co.uk *Label manufacturers & sign makers*

Shawe Hall Textiles, 85 North Western Street, Manchester, M12 6DY Tel: 0161-273 6006 Fax: 0161-273 6006 *Rayon lining manufrs*

Shawgas Gas Companies, 29 Aismunderby Road, Ripon, North Yorkshire, HG4 1SQ Tel: (01765) 602621 Fax: (01765) 602621 *Gas refilling services*

Shawley Ltd, Suflex Estate, Newport Road, Risca, Newport, Gwent, NP11 6YD Tel: (01633) 619999 Fax: (01633) 619977 E-mail: sales@shawley.com *Closed circuit television manufrs*

Shawn Knitwear, 16-18 Hyde Road, Manchester, M12 6BW Tel: 0161-273 2841 Fax: 0161-273 7841 *Knitwear manufrs*

Shaws Of Darwen, Waterside, Darwen, Lancashire, BB3 3NX Tel: (01254) 771086 Fax: (01254) 873462 E-mail: sales@shaws-of-darwen.co.uk *Specialists ceramic manufrs*

Shaws Electrical, 349-353 Purley Way, Croydon, CR0 4NW Tel: (020) 8688 0491 Fax: (020) 8688 0492 E-mail: shawselectrical@compuserve.com *Electrical contractors*

Shaws Glass Ltd, 66 North Street, Horsham, West Sussex, RH12 1RD Tel: (01403) 211133 Fax: (01293) 852340 *Glazing contractors & glass merchants*

Shaws Metals Ltd, Hartland Works, Haydock Park Road, Derby, DE24 8HW Tel: (01332) 383341 Fax: (01332) 294085 E-mail: sales@shawsmetalsltd.sagenet.co.uk *Steel Stockholders To The House Building & Engineering Industries And Sales & Rental Of Used Jack Leg Cabins & Containers*

Shaws Pet Products Ltd, Unit 13 Bordesley Trading Estate, Bordesley Green Road, Birmingham, B8 1BZ Tel: 0121-326 7667 Fax: 0121-328 1734 E-mail: info@shawspet.co.uk *Brushware & grooming accessories manufrs*

Shawston International Ltd, Great Norbury Street, Hyde, Cheshire, SK14 1BW Tel: 0161-368 4545 Fax: 0161-367 8114 *Pipe work support systems manufrs*

Shayler Saddlery, Short Street, Premier Business Park, Walsall, WS2 9EB Tel: (01922) 631926 Fax: (01922) 630019 *Bridle manufacturer & leather luggage*

▶ Shaylor Construction Ltd, Frederick James House Units 52 Wharf Approach, Anchor Brook I, Aldridge, Walsall, WS9 8BX Tel: (01922) 741570 Fax: (01922) 745604 E-mail: admin@shaylorconstruction.co.uk

Shazminf Pies Manufacturers, 12 Gopsall Street, Leicester, LE2 0DL Tel: 0116-253 0058 Fax: 0116-212 3343 *Pie manufrs*

▶ She Software Ltd, The Nasmyth Building, Nasmyth Avenue, East Kilbride, Glasgow, G75 0QR Tel: (01355) 272444 Fax: (01355) 272445 *Software & hardware components suppliers*

Shea International Ltd, 31 King Street, Stanford-le-Hope, Essex, SS17 0HJ Tel: (01375) 642626 Fax: (01375) 361304 E-mail: sheaint@btconnect.com *Freight forwarders*

Sheaffer Pen (UK) Ltd, Chaplin House, Widewater Place, Harefield, Middlesex, UB9 6NF Tel: (01895) 827100 Fax: (01895) 827101 *Writing instrument manufrs*

Sheard Properties Ltd, Solar Works, Calder Street, Greetland, Halifax, West Yorkshire, HX4 8AQ Tel: (01422) 373649 Fax: (01422) 310090 E-mail: sales@sheard.co.uk *Security shredding services & manufrs*

Shearer Candles Ltd, 23 Robert Street, Glasgow, G51 3HB Tel: 0141-445 1066 Fax: 0141-445 1061 E-mail: sales@shearer-candles.com Sales Contact: J.G. Barnet *Church Candles, Decorative candles, Candle manufacturers, Candle maker, Candle supplier, Wedding Favours, Outdoor candles, BBQ candles, Dinner Candles Gift candles, Natural Wax candles, Floating Candles, Catering, Candle holders, Candle accessories, Scented candles. Scottish Scotland*

Shearer Mormet Ltd, 349 Shettleston Road, Glasgow, G31 5JL Tel: 0141-554 2401 Fax: 0141-556 3448 E-mail: shearermormet@btclick.com *Scrap metal merchants*

William Shearer, 71 Victoria Street, Kirkwall, Orkney, KW15 1DQ Tel: (01856) 873189 Fax: (01856) 870892 *Seed merchants*

Shearfab Ltd, Oldgate, St. Michaels Industrial Estate, Widnes, Cheshire, WA8 8TL Tel: 0151-420 5200 Fax: 0151-420 5190 E-mail: info@shearfab.co.uk *Control panel cabinet manufacturers, powder coatings & laser cutting*

Shearline Precision Engineering Ltd, Cambridgeshire Business Park, Angel Drove, Ely, Cambridgeshire, CB7 4EX Tel: (01353) 668668 Fax: (01353) 668203 E-mail: sales@shearline.co.uk *Shearline Precision Engineering Ltd., established in Cambridgeshire in 1973, provides contract manufacturing solutions for our industrial partners, 24 hours a day, 7 days a week.*

Shearline Steels Strip Ltd, 3 Gibbons Industrial Park, Dudley Road, Kingswinford, West Midlands, DY6 8XF Tel: (01384) 401533 Fax: (01384) 294892 E-mail: sales@shearlinesteel.com *Cold rolled steel stockholders*

▶ Shearwater Marine Ltd, Decoy Industrial Estate, Newton Abbot, Devon, TQ12 5ND Tel: (01626) 334980 Fax: (01626) 366250 E-mail: info@shearwater-marine.co.uk *Manufacturers of marine bearings*

Shearwell Ltd, Putham Farm, Wheddon Cross, Cutcombe, Minehead, Somerset, TA24 7AS Tel: (01643) 841552 Fax: (01643) 841628 E-mail: sales@shearwell.co.uk *Animal identification*

Shearwell Sheet Metal Works Ltd, 10 Boston Road, Leicester, LE4 1AU Tel: 0116-235 7669 Fax: 0116-235 7669 *Sheet metal workers*

Sheathed Heating Elements Holdings Ltd, Wardley Industrial Estate North, Worsley, Manchester, M28 2DP Tel: 0161-794 6122 Fax: 0161-794 8601 E-mail: sales@shealuk.free.com *Electric heating element manufrs*

▶ Shed Express, Roberts Yard, Off Crompton Road, Ilkeston, Derbyshire, DE7 4BG Tel: 0115-877 6696 Fax: 0115-930 8500 E-mail: terry@shedexpress.com *Garden*

continued

Company Information

continuation
buildings, sheds, summerhouses, playhouses manufrs

▶ Shed Scene, Brecklands Nursery, Siston Lane, Bristol, BS30 5LX Tel: (0845) 3108710 Fax: (0845) 3108711 E-mail: info@shedscene.com *Timber building suppliers*

▶ Sheds & Chalets, Llanelli Enterprise Workshops, Lower Trostre Road, Llanelli, Dyfed, SA15 2EA Tel: (01554) 759472 Fax: (01554) 775022 E-mail: sales@shedsnchalets.co.uk *Timber garden buildings manufrs*

▶ Sheds & Shelters, Pilgrims Way, Hollingbourne, Maidstone, Kent, ME17 1UT Tel: (01622) 880031 Fax: (01622) 880031

▶ Sheehan Haulage, Woodstock Road, Yarnton, Kidlington, Oxfordshire, OX5 1PH Tel: (01865) 379931

Sheen Equipment, Greasley Street, Nottingham, NG6 8NH Tel: 0115-927 2321 Fax: 0115-977 0671 *Cable laying equipment & flame guns manufrs*

Sheen Lane Motors Ltd, 194-198 Sheen Lane, London, SW14 8LF Tel: (020) 8876 1011 Fax: (020) 8392 2092 *Garage repairs & body work services*

Sheen Publishing Ltd, 50 Queens Road, Buckhurst Hill, Essex, IG9 5DD Tel: (020) 8504 1661 Fax: (020) 8505 4336 *Trade journal publishers*

Sheen Spark Ltd, 1 Ewhurst Avenue, Birmingham, B29 6EY Tel: 0121-472 6241 Fax: 0121-472 5396 *Spark erosion & wire erosion services*

Sheena Knitwear Ltd, 46 Hamilton Road, Manchester, M13 0PE Tel: 0161-224 1381 Fax: 0161-224 1674 E-mail: info@sheenaknitwear.com *Knitwear manufrs*

Sheepbridge Steel, Bleak Hill Sidings, Mansfield, Nottinghamshire, NG18 5EP Tel: (01623) 623144 Fax: (01623) 623144 *Steel fabricators*

Sheepy Farm Services Ltd, 155 Main Road, Sheepy Magna, Atherstone, Warwickshire, CV9 3QU Tel: (01827) 713142 *Agricultural engineers & haulage services*

▶ Sheer Elegance Soft Furnishings, 4 Prices Way, Brackley, Northamptonshire, NN13 6NR Tel: (07919) 157365 E-mail: caroline@sheer-e.co.uk *Curtains, roman blinds, cushions & other soft furnishings suppliers*

Sheerlyte Aggregates, Adelaide Street, Stoke-on-Trent, ST6 2BD Tel: (01782) 835369 Fax: (01782) 834496 E-mail: mark@timberandtile.com *Ceramic suppliers*

Sheerspeed Accounting Services, 45 Highgate, Kendal, Cumbria, LA9 4ED Tel: (01539) 720807 Fax: (01539) 740516 E-mail: linxroger@aol.com *Accountancy systems & services*

Sheerwater Glass Centre, 23-27 Dartmouth Avenue, Woking, Surrey, GU21 5PE Tel: (01932) 349247 Fax: (01932) 346580 *Glaziers & double glazing replacement windows*

▶ The Sheet Metal Co. Ltd, Holme End Works, Burnley Road, Hebden Bridge, West Yorkshire, HX7 8NX Tel: (01422) 846283 E-mail: accountants@sheetmet.co.uk *Sheet metal*

▶ Sheet Metal & General (Engineers), Unit D7-D8, Aldred Close, Killamarsh, Sheffield, S21 2JH Tel: 0114-251 1455 *Sheet Metal & General Engineers.*

Sheet Metal Products, St. Michaels Road, Newcastle upon Tyne, NE6 1QS Tel: 0191-276 3028 Fax: 0191-276 3028 *Sheet metalworkers*

Sheet Metal Services, Hill Street, Kidderminster, Worcestershire, DY11 6TD Tel: (01562) 824995 Fax: (01562) 743998 E-mail: sales@saferack-sheetmetalservices.com *Sheet metalwork & ductwork services*

▶ Sheet Metal Technology Ltd, Cradley Business Park, Overend Road, Cradley Heath, West Midlands, B64 7DW Tel: (01384) 411190 Fax: (01384) 412101 *Sheet metalwork engineers or fabricators*

Sheet Metals Sherwood Ltd, Dako House, Vernon Road, Nottingham, NG6 0AR Tel: 0115-978 4456 Fax: 0115-978 4456 *Sheet metalworkers*

▶ Sheet Tech Fabrications, 6 Doman Road, Camberley, Surrey, GU15 3DF Tel: (01276) 684800 Fax: (01276) 20696 *Sheet metal manufrs*

Sheet Tech Fabrications, 6 Doman Road, Camberley, Surrey, GU15 3DF Tel: (01276) 684800 Fax: (01276) 20696 E-mail: cliffdottson@sheettech.fsnet.co.uk *Steel fabricators*

Sheetfabs (Nottingham) Ltd, Nottingham Road, Attenborough, Beeston, Nottingham, NG9 6DR Tel: 0115-925 8101 Fax: 0115-943 0872 E-mail: sheetfabs@sheetfabs.co.uk Principal Export Areas: Worldwide *Architectural engineering projects*

Sheetmetal Developments, Unit 1 Wessex Park, Bancombe Road Trading Estate, Somerton, Somerset, TA11 6SB Tel: (01458) 272212 Fax: (01458) 272212 E-mail: rosser@aol.com *Sheet metalwork engineers*

Sheffield Art Metal Co., Charter Works, 20 Hodgson Street, Sheffield, S3 7WQ Tel: 0114-244 4444 Fax: 0114-270 1549 E-mail: sheff.artmetal@btconnect.com *Steel fabricators*

Sheffield Assay Office, 137 Portobello Street, Sheffield, S1 4DR Tel: 0114-275 5111 Fax: 0114-275 6473 E-mail: jarvisd@assayoffice.co.uk *Metallurgical analysts, assayers & analytical chemists*

Sheffield Bolt & Nut Co. Ltd, Unit G Harrison Street, Rotherham, South Yorkshire, S61 1EE Tel: (01709) 550101 Fax: (01709) 550176 E-mail: sales.sbn@btconnect.com *Fastening stockists & distributors*

Sheffield Ceilings S E Ltd, 165 Bow Road, Wateringbury, Maidstone, Kent, ME18 5EA Tel: (01622) 814477 Fax: (01622) 813555 E-mail: sheffield.ceilings@btinternet.com *Ceilings & linings specialists*

▶ Sheffield Deep Bore Ltd, Victoria Works, 31 Catley Road, Sheffield, S9 5JF Tel: 0114-261 9888 Fax: 0114-261 1181 E-mail: john.senior@essteel.co.uk *Oil fuel engineering*

▶ Sheffield Drain Services, 14 Grassington Drive, Sheffield, S12 4NE Tel: 0114-247 3131

Sheffield & Ford Builders Ltd, Mill Street, Duddington, Stamford, Lincolnshire, PE9 3QG Tel: (01780) 444666 Fax: (01780) 444567

Sheffield Forgemasters Engineering Ltd, PO Box 286, Sheffield, S9 2RU Tel: 0114-244 9071 Fax: 0114-242 2103 E-mail: sales@sfel.com *Heavy forged & cast steel products as well as stocking ingot & bar. Design, establish material requirements, produce material specifications & manufacture*

▶ Sheffield Gauge Plate Ltd, Bastock Road, Sheffield, S6 2AE Tel: 0114-233 5291

▶ Sheffield Independent Film & Television Ltd, 5 Brown Street, Sheffield, S1 2BS Tel: 0114-272 6304 Fax: 0114-279 5225 E-mail: admin.sif@workstation.org.uk *AV equipment hire, studio & workspace*

Sheffield Insulation Ltd, South Port, Forshore Way, Cardiff, CF10 5SP Tel: (029) 2049 3371 Fax: (029) 2066 2911 E-mail: cardiff@sheffins.co.uk *Insulation services*

Sheffield Insulations Ltd, Telford Way, Bedford, MK42 0PQ Tel: (01234) 761100 Fax: (01234) 272157 E-mail: bedford@sheffins.co.uk *Insulations distribs*

Sheffield Insulations Ltd, Lower Mill Street, Blairgowrie, Perthshire, PH10 6AQ Tel: (01250) 873611 Fax: (01250) 875252 E-mail: blairgowrie@sheffins.co.uk *Insulations distributors*

Sheffield Insulations Ltd, Cadleigh Close, Lee Mill Industrial Estate, Ivybridge, Devon, PL21 9GB Tel: (01752) 690969 Fax: (01752) 690527 *Insulation suppliers*

Sheffield Insulations Ltd, Hillsborough Works, Langsett Road, Sheffield, S6 2LW Tel: 0114-285 6300 Fax: 0114-285 6375 E-mail: info@sigplc.co.uk *Insulation & roofing related products distributors*

Sheffield Insulations Ltd, 303-305 Vale Road, Tonbridge, Kent, TN9 1TZ Tel: (01732) 370500 Fax: (01732) 370530 *Insulation distributors service*

Sheffield Magnet Co., Park Hill Works, Pottery Lane, Littlethorpe, Ripon, North Yorkshire, HG4 3LS Tel: (01765) 698698 Fax: (01765) 607922 E-mail: sheffield.magnet@virgin.net *Magnet manufrs*

Sheffield Metal Co., Smithfield, Sheffield, S3 7AR Tel: 0114-275 9566 Fax: 0114-275 4675 E-mail: shefcutler@aol.com *Table cutlery manufrs*

Sheffield Packaging Services Ltd, Sheffield Road, Woodhouse Mill, Sheffield, S13 9WH Tel: 0114-269 3977 Fax: 0114-269 3980 E-mail: sheffpack@btopenworld.com *Export packers & case makers*

Sheffield Shears Co. Ltd, 28 Trinity Street, Sheffield, S3 7AJ Tel: 0114-272 2644 Fax: 0114-272 2644 *Hand tool manufacturers of industrial hand knives*

Sheffield Testing Laboratories Ltd, 56 Nursery Street, Sheffield, S3 8GP Tel: 0114-272 6581 Fax: 0114-272 3248 E-mail: hq@sheffieldtesting.com *Testing & calibrating services*

▶ Sheffield Transmission Developments, Highfield Lane, Sheffield, S13 9NA Tel: 0114-288 9440 Fax: 0114-288 0319 E-mail: sales@sheffield-transmission.com *Repair industrial gearboxes*

Sheffield Wholesale Linoleum & Carpet Co. Ltd, 137 West Bar, Sheffield, S3 8PU Tel: 0114-272 8116 Fax: 0114-272 6558 E-mail: salesswlltd@btconnect.com *Linoleum, vinyl & carpet merchants*

Sheffiex Ltd, Club Mill Road, Sheffield, S6 2FH Tel: 0114-233 0332 Fax: 0114-285 2229 *Steel engineers*

Shefford Building Supplies Ltd, 44 High Street, Shefford, Bedfordshire, SG17 5DG Tel: (01462) 813381 Fax: (01462) 811655 *Builders' merchants*

Sheiling School, Beggars Roost, Horton Road, Ashley Heath, Ringwood, Hampshire, BH24 2EB Tel: (01425) 477488 Fax: (01425) 479536 *Educational services*

Shelana Fashions Ltd, 31 Eastcastle Street, London, W1N 8NL Tel: (020) 7580 0401 Fax: (020) 7436 5445 E-mail: shelanainvestments@talk21.com *Property investors*

Shelbourne Letheby & Co. Ltd, 154 New Kings Road, London, SW6 4LZ Tel: (020) 7736 4211 Fax: (020) 7371 0634 *Heating ventilation engineers*

Shelbourne Reynolds Engineering Ltd, Shepherds Grove Industrial Estate, Stanton, Bury St. Edmunds, Suffolk, IP31 2AR Tel: (01359) 250415 Fax: (01359) 250464 E-mail: info@shelbourne.com *Agricultural machinery manufrs*

▶ Sheldon & Clayton Ltd, Black Country Road, West Bromwich, West Midlands, B70 0BD Tel: 0121-520 7070

Sheldon Industrial Cleaners Ltd, 117-122 High Street, Bordesley, Birmingham, B12 0JU Tel: 0121-772 6001 Fax: 0121-771 0075 E-mail: mail@sheldon.uk.com *Holding company.*

Sheldon Reed Ltd, Seymore House, 4 Tudor Avenue, Watford, WD24 7NX Tel: (0870) 7454580 E-mail: admin@sheldonreed.com *Telephony payment system designers*

▶ Sheldon-Mann, 16 B Nuxley Road, Belvedere, Kent, DA17 5JF Tel: 01322 412157 Fax: 01322 412157 E-mail: sheldonmann@gmail.com *Graphic Design*

Sheldons Bakery Farnborough Ltd, 31 Queens Road, Farnborough, Hampshire, GU14 6DU Tel: (01252) 377577 Fax: (01252) 378262 *Wholesale bakers & confectioners*

Shelfguard Systems, 91 St Leonards Road, Windsor, Berkshire, SL4 3BZ Tel: (01753) 867257 Fax: (01753) 830024 E-mail: sales@shelfguard-systems.co.uk *We have supplied the industry since 1978 re-defined service & support. Our aim is to provide the very best choice in equipment, known tried & tested products, trusted & reliable support. Shelfguard Systems are one of the leading independent solution providers with nearly three decades of experience. Emerging from cash register*

continued

suppliers to innovative integration with chip & pin technology, wireless, loyalty schemes, front desk (hotels), cashless, door entry, e-commerce. We are constantly reviewing software development ensuring the right package is installed to your requirement. Every type of Retail or Hospitality environment is covered. We offer a greater choice of equipment than any other supplier. Ensuring the customer gets exactly what he requests, not a mis- match of incompatible hardware

Shelforce, Units 21-23 Erdington Industrial Park, Chester Road, Erdington, Birmingham, B24 0RD Tel: 0121-603 5262 Fax: 0121-603 2771 E-mail: sales@shelforce.co.uk *Manufacturer of UPVC windows*

Shelford Energy, 2 Station Road, Great Shelford, Cambridge, CB22 5LT Tel: (01223) 846846 Fax: (01223) 551161 E-mail: sales@shelford.co.uk *Fuel oil & petroleum distributors*

Shelfstore Shelving & Racking, 158 Finchley Road, London, NW3 5HD Tel: (020) 7794 0313 Fax: (020) 7435 3927 E-mail: info@shelfstore.co.uk *Shelving manufrs*

Shell UK Ltd, M1 Markham Lane, Duckmanton, Chesterfield, Derbyshire, S44 5HS Tel: (0870) 8301100 Fax: (0870) 8301101 E-mail: enquiries@shell.com *Liquefied petroleum gas distributors*

Shell UK Ltd, Shell Centre, York Road, London, SE1 7NA Tel: (020) 7546 5000 Fax: (020) 7934 8060 *Oil exploration company*

Shellbie Blinds, 2 The Parade Cannock Road, Wednesfield, Wolverhampton, WV10 8PZ Tel: (01902) 305400 Fax: (01902) 305400 *Blinds supply & installation*

Shellbourne Manufacturing Co. Ltd, Bolton Bus Centre, 44-49 Lower Bridgeman St, Bolton, BL2 1DG Tel: (01204) 546410 Fax: (01925) 740062 E-mail: sales@shellbourne.co.uk *Industrial metal fastener manufrs.*

Shelley Autonation Ltd, Block 1 Nortonthorpe Mill, Wakefield Road, Scissett, Huddersfield, HD8 9LA Tel: (01484) 860920 Fax: (01484) 860672 E-mail: shelleyauto@aol.com *Suppliers of pneumatic control equipment*

Shelley Engineering Redhill Ltd, Unit 31-33 Grace Business Centre, 23 Willow Lane, Mitcham, Surrey, CR4 4TU Tel: (020) 8685 0302 Fax: (020) 8687 0572 E-mail: mail@shelleyengineering.co.uk *Sheet metal fabricators*

Shelley (Halesowen) Ltd, 39 The Old Woodyard, Hagley Hall Hagley, Hagley, Stourbridge, West Midlands, DY9 9LQ Tel: (01562) 885905 Fax: (01562) 884941 *Presswork in all metals*

Shelley Signs Ltd, Eaton-on-Tern, Market Drayton, Shropshire, TF9 2BX Tel: (01952) 541483 Fax: (01952) 541755 E-mail: sales@shelleysigns.co.uk *Glass reinforced plastic & timber signs. Gauge boards. Sandblasted and routed signs. Interpretive panels. Interpretation signs.*

▶ Shelley Thermoformers International Ltd, Stonehill, Stukeley Meadows Industrial Es, Huntingdon, Cambridgeshire, PE29 6DR Tel: (01480) 453651 Fax: (01480) 52113 E-mail: sales@cannon-shelley.co.uk Principal Export Areas: Worldwide *CNC trimming, thermoforming packaging machines manufrs*

Shelleys Hotel, High Street, Lewes, East Sussex, BN7 1XS Tel: (01273) 472361 Fax: (01273) 483152 E-mail: info@the-shelleys.co.uk *Hotel, conference & function facilities*

▶ Shelley's Wood, 41 Kirtley, Tamworth, Staffordshire, B77 2HF Tel: (01827) 739050 Fax: E-mail: shelleyswood@yahoo.co.uk *Producers of natural, homemade personal care products. Suppliers of essential and carrier oils for aromatherapy.*

Shellscape Pyrotechnics Ltd, Butchers Lane, White Walthem, Maidenhead, Berkshire, SL6 3SD Tel: (01628) 829401 *Firework displays*

▶ Shelltown Productions Ltd, PO Box 21, Ballymoney, Co. Antrim, BT53 8TJ Tel: 0871 0971077 Fax: 0870 7627731 E-mail: admin@shelltown.co.uk *We are the owner of the IP of the children"s brand SHELLTOWN all products and services related to this*

Shelton House Saddlery, Starnhill Farm, Granby Lane, off Grantham Road, Bingham, NG13 8DH Tel: (01949) 838886 Fax: (01949) 838887 E-mail: sheltonsaddlery@bhtinternet.com *Saddlery*

J.G. Shelton & Co. Ltd, Unit 4, Gibbons Industrial Park, Kingswinford, West Midlands, DY6 8XF Tel: (01384) 293601 Fax: (01384) 293975 E-mail: terry.hawkins@btconnect.com *Crematorium furnace manufacturers & general engineers*

Ken Shelton Photography, 10 New Walk Terrace, Fishergate, York, YO10 4BG Tel: (01904) 630112 E-mail: ken@nwt10.demon.co.uk *Industrial & commercial photographers*

Sheltons Of Peterborough Ltd, 67 South Street, Stanground, Peterborough, PE2 8EX Tel: (01733) 565287 Fax: (01733) 560186 *Fishing tackle retailers*

▶ Shelving Direct, Element House, Napier Road, Elm Farm Industrial Estate, Bedford, MK41 0QS Tel: (0800) 214292 Fax: (01234) 270202 *Shelving, brackets & shop display furniture specialists*

Shenley Roofing Ltd, Shenley House, Cherrycourt Way, Stanbridge Road, Leighton Buzzard, Bedfordshire, LU7 4AB Tel: (01525) 374723 Fax: (01525) 851493 E-mail: dcook@shenley.co.uk *Roofing contractors & merchants*

Shenstone Pattern & Crafts Ltd, Little Cornbow, Halesowen, West Midlands, B63 3AJ Tel: 0121-503 0362 Fax: 0121-585 7440 *Pattern equipment manufrs*

Shep Associates, Long Barn, North End, Meldreth, Royston, Hertfordshire, SG8 6NT Tel: (01763) 261686 Fax: (01763) 262154 E-mail: sales@shep.co.uk *Audio & studio equipment manufrs*

Shep Plastics Ltd, The Old Pottery, Lower Dicker, Hailsham, East Sussex, BN27 4AT Tel: (01323) 440088 Fax: (01323) 841930 E-mail: sales@shep-plastics.co.uk *Plastic, components, fittings assem bly & design*

Shepcote Engineering Ltd, Davy Indust Park, Prince of Wales Road, Sheffield, S9 4EX Tel: 0114-256 2505 Fax: 0114-261 1910 E-mail: enquiries@shepcote-eng.com *Hydraulic cylinders design boring & honing manufrs*

Shepfield Batteries Ltd, 277 Stansted Road, Bishop's Stortford, Hertfordshire, CM23 2BT Tel: (01279) 652067 Fax: (01279) 758041 E-mail: info@shieldbatteries.co.uk *Battery manufrs*

Shephard Herriot, 12 Poverest Road, Orpington, Kent, BR5 2TP Tel: (01689) 877800 Fax: (01689) 877789 *Insurance brokers*

A.E. Shepherd, 108 Snakes Lane East, Woodford Green, Essex, IG8 7HY Tel: (020) 8504 1759 Fax: (020) 8504 1759 *Bakery & confectionery suppliers*

Andrew Shepherd & Sons Ltd, Restenneth House, Old Brechin Road, Forfar, Angus, DD8 3DX Tel: (01307) 474510 Fax: (01307) 474530

Shepherd Building Group Ltd, Huntington House, Jockey Lane, Huntington, York, YO32 9XW Tel: (01904) 650700 Fax: (01904) 650889 E-mail: information@shepherd-buildinggroup.com *Holding company for construction industries*

Shepherd Construction Ltd, Frederick House, Fulford Road, York, YO10 4EA Tel: (01904) 634431 Fax: (01904) 610256 E-mail: admin@shepherdsolutions.com *Building contractors* Also at: Birmingham, Cardiff, Darlington, Langley, Leeds, London W1R, Manchester, Northam pton, Nottingham, & Windsor

Shepherd Distribution Services, Birley Vale Avenue, Birley Vale Industrial Estate, Intake, Sheffield, S12 2AW Tel: 0114-264 3638 Fax: 0114-253 1326 E-mail: trafffic@shepherd-distribution.co.uk *Road transport, haulage, freight & services*

Shepherd Engineering Services Ltd, Mill Mount, York, YO24 1GH Tel: (01904) 629151 Fax: (01904) 610175 *Building services & process engineers*

▶ Shepherd General Builders Ltd, Restenneth House, Old Brechin Road, Forfar, Angus, DD8 3DX Tel: (01307) 474520 Fax: (01307) 474530

▶ Shepherd Homes Ltd, Huntington House, Jockey Lane, Huntington, York, YO32 9XW Tel: (01904) 650888 Fax: (01904) 650889 E-mail: sales@shepherd-homes.co.uk

Shepherd Interiors, Unit 4, 10 First Avenue, Bletchley, Milton Keynes, MK1 1DN Tel: (01908) 644688 Fax: (01908) 646606 E-mail: info@rgnsltd.co.uk *Partition contractors/ suppliers; ceiling (suspended) system constructors/manufacturers/contractors; office designers/fitters/planners/refurbishers; office furnishers/furniture distributors/agents; blinds (venetian); blind (vertical louvre) manufrs*

Shepherd & Miller, 94 Whyterose Terrace, Aberhill, Methil, Leven, Fife, KY8 3AS Tel: (01333) 426823 Fax: (01333) 423064 *Industrial suppliers*

Shepherd Offshore P.L.C., Offshore Technology Park, Walker, Newcastle Upon Tyne, NE6 3NL Tel: 0191-262 9614 Fax: 0191-263 9872 E-mail: headoffice@shepherdoffshore.com *Storage facilities*

Shepherd Widnes Ltd, Moss Bank Road, Widnes, Cheshire, WA8 0RU Tel: 0151-424 9156 Fax: 0151-495 1446 E-mail: sales@shepwidnes.co.uk *Chemicals including speciality & chemical based*

Shepherds (UK) Ltd, Eastbourne Road Industrial Estate, Eastbourne Road, Westham, Pevensey, East Sussex, BN24 5NH Tel: (01323) 768232 Fax: (01323) 768257 E-mail: abigail@shepherdsuk.co.uk *Plastic building product distributor*

Shepherds Windermere Ltd, Windermere Marina Village, The Marina, Bowness-on-Windermere, Windermere, Cumbria, LA23 3JQ Tel: (01539) 446004 Fax: (01539) 446005 E-mail: info@shepherdswindermere.co.uk *Motor boat & yacht retailers for sports*

Shepherdson Shades Ltd, Ellesmere Business Park, Swingbridge Road, Grantham, Lincolnshire, NG31 7XT Tel: 0161-928 0220 Fax: (01476) 593600 E-mail: sales@vbcblinds.com *Blinds, carpets & curtains retailers*

Sheplee Electrical Contractors Ltd, Unit 23, Jarman Way, Royston, Hertfordshire, SG8 5HW Tel: (01763) 243324 *Electrical contractors*

▶ Shepley Engineers Ltd, Westlakes Science & Technology Park, Moor Row, Cumbria, CA24 3JZ Tel: (01946) 599022 Fax: (01946) 591933 E-mail: engineers@sheepley.vhe.co.uk *Mechanical engineering*

Sheppard Moscow Personal Development Ltd, Enterprise House, 59-65 Upper Ground, London, SE1 9PQ Tel: (020) 7929 9650 Fax: (020) 7620 2200 E-mail: sml@sheppardmoscow.com *Management consultants*

▶ Sheppard Moscow Scotland Ltd, 57 Melville Street, Edinburgh, EH3 7HL Tel: 0131-226 3399 Fax: 0131-226 3344

Sue Sheppard, 2 Park Street, Bristol, BS1 5HS Tel: 0117-917 5900 Fax: 0117-917 5915 E-mail: post@sue-sheppard.co.uk *Recruitment agency*

Sheppee International Ltd, Airfield Industrial Park, York Road, Elvington, York, YO41 4AU Tel: (01904) 608999 Fax: (01904) 608777 E-mail: sales@sheppee.com *Bottle production plant rebuilders & suppliers*

▶ Shepperton Clerical Services, 7 Hawthorn Way, Upper Halliford, Shepperton, Middlesex, TW17 8QE Tel: 01932 429210 Fax: 01932 429210 E-mail: helen@sheppertonclerical.co.uk *Shepperton Clerical Services offers remote assistance to small businesses requiring occasional secretarial and administrative support. I can provide support on either a regular or an as and when required basis enabling companies to keep support costs to a minimum.*

Shepperton Marina Ltd, Shepperton Marina, Felix Lane, Shepperton, Middlesex, TW17 8NS Tel: (01932) 243722 Fax: (01932) 243152 E-mail: sales@boatshowrooms.com *Boats sales & services*

▶ Sheppey Dental Laboratory, 1a-2a Railway Terrace, Queenborough, Kent, ME11 5AY Tel: (01795) 662025 Fax: (01795) 583593

Sheppy Ltd, Rushenden Road, Queenborough, Kent, ME11 5HH Tel: (01795) 580181 Fax: (01795) 580649 E-mail: sales@sheppy.ltd.uk *Adhesive manufacturers & property developers*

Shepshed Knight Printing Service Ltd, 91 Charnwood Road, Shepshed, Loughborough, Leicestershire, LE12 9NL Tel: (01509) 502246 Fax: (01509) 503179 E-mail: sales@shepshedknight.com *Printers & stationers supplier*

Shepway District Council, Civic Centre, Castle Hill Avenue, Folkestone, Kent, CT20 2QY Tel: (01303) 853000 Fax: (01303) 853502 E-mail: jeremy.whittaker@shepway.gov.uk *Council*

Sheraton Blinds Ltd, Unit 3 High Cross Centre, Fountayne Road, London, N15 4QN Tel: (020) 8885 5518 Fax: (020) 8365 1108 E-mail: barry@sheraton-blinds.co.uk *Blind manufrs*

▶ Sheraz Iqbal, 6th Floor, Kings Gate House, Wellington Road North, Stockport, Cheshire, SK4 1LW Tel: (0800) 1386500 E-mail: marketing@consolidate-your-credit.com *Free professional debt advice from a UK leading financial management company get relief from the burden of instant debt consolidation, debt management or bankruptcy advice what ever your circumstances, we have a solution for you.**

Sherborne Metal Masters, Ash Lane, Little London, Tadley, Hampshire, RG26 5EL Tel: (01256) 880096 Fax: (01256) 880096 *Architectural metalwork engineers*

Sherborne Rubber Co. Ltd, Icknield Square, Ladywood, Birmingham, B16 0AB Tel: 0121-456 1565 Fax: 0121-452 1637 E-mail: sales@sherbourne.co.uk Principal Export Areas: Worldwide *Manufacturers of rubber products, anti vibration mountings*

Sherborne Upholstery Ltd, Pasture Lane, Clayton, Bradford, West Yorkshire, BD14 6LT Tel: (01274) 882633 Fax: (01274) 815129 E-mail: mail@sherbourne-uph.co.uk *Upholstered furniture manufrs*

Sherbourne Stone Co., Cleveland Road, Hartlepool, Cleveland, TS24 0SY Tel: (01429) 223276 *Concrete manufrs*

Sherbrook International Ltd, Unit 3, Upper Keys Business Park, Keys Park Road, Hednesford, Cannock, Staffordshire, WS12 2GE Tel: (01543) 495555 E-mail: export@sherbrook.co.uk *Import & export merchants*

Sherburn Hill Engineering Co. Ltd, Tanfield Lea Industrial Estate South, Tanfield Lea, Stanley, County Durham, DH9 9QT Tel: (01207) 236777 Fax: (01207) 231053 E-mail: sherburnhill@btconnect.com *Fabricators & precision engineers*

Shere Ltd, Guildford Indust Estate, Deaconfield, Guildford, Surrey, GU2 8YT Tel: (01483) 557400 Fax: (01483) 557401 E-mail: info@shere.com *Manufacturers of ticket machines*

▶ Shere Lighting, 5 Burrows Lea Farm, Hook Lane, Shere, Guildford, Surrey, GU5 9QQ Tel: (01483) 205333 Fax: (01483) 205334 E-mail: sherelightingltd@aol.com *Plastic defuses manufrs*

Shere Print, 8 West Street, Dorking, Surrey, RH4 1BL Tel: (01306) 888050 Fax: (01306) 888180 E-mail: info@shere.com *Colour, digital, printing & graphic design*

Sheridan Engineering, Unit 7, Hunters Lane Industrial Estate, Rugby, Warwickshire, CV21 1EA Tel: (01788) 579483 Fax: (01788) 579483 *Engineers & general engineers*

Sheridan Engineering Hereford, 4 Parkwood Court, Rotherwas Industrial Estate, Hereford, HR2 6NU Tel: (01432) 269683 Fax: (01432) 354410 E-mail: sales@sheridanengineering.co.uk *Engineering*

▶ Sheridan Fencing, 239 Lords Wood Lane, Chatham, Kent, ME5 8JU Tel: (01634) 660732 *A fast and reliable fencing and garden service.*

Sheridan Knitwear, Ground Floor, 371 Oldham Road, Manchester, M40 8EA Tel: 0161-203 5444 Fax: 0161-203 5557 *Ladies clothing manufrs*

▶ Sheridan UK Ltd, 40 Gold Street, Tiverton, Devon, EX16 6PY Tel: (01884) 255997 Fax: (01884) 255997 *Beds & bedding manufrs*

Sheridans, 213 Humberstone Lane, Leicester, LE4 9JR Tel: 0116-269 6198 Fax: 0116-269 6198 *Cabinet manufrs*

Sheriff Alarms Alarm Company, 33 Ockerby Street, Nottingham, NG6 9GA Tel: 0115-916 7777 *Burglar alarm systems installation*

Shering Weighing Group Ltd, Pitreavie Business Park, Queensferry Road, Dunfermline, Fife, KY11 8UL Tel: (01383) 621505 Fax: (01383) 620262 E-mail: sales@shering.com *Weighbridge manufrs*

Sherlock Ltd, 21 Station Road, Woodley, Stockport, Cheshire, SK6 1HN Tel: 0161-430 2647 Fax: 0161-430 8008 *Manufacturers of bandsaw blades*

Sherlock Computer Services Ltd, 28 Cornfield Road, Woodley, Reading, RG5 4QA Tel: 0118-954 0097 Fax: 0118-954 0097 *Computer services*

Sherlock Interiors Contracting Ltd, 20-22 Vestry Street, London, N1 7RE Tel: (020) 7336 7337 Fax: (020) 7336 7180 E-mail: info@sherlock.demon.co.uk *Interior fitting out & joinery*

▶ Sherlock & Neal Ltd, Ashmores Yard, Horsham Road, Rusper, Horsham, West Sussex, RH12 4PR Tel: (01293) 871343 Fax: (01293) 871298 E-mail: shirlock.neil@tiscali.co.uk *Building contractors*

Sherlock Of Oakwood, Oakwood, Chichester, West Sussex, PO18 9AL Tel: (01243) 786701 Fax: (01243) 775089 E-mail: sales@sherlocks.demon.co.uk *Manufacturers of timber & oak framed buildings*

Sherman Chemicals plc, Brickfields Business Park, Gillingham, Dorset, SP8 4PX Tel: (01747) 823293 Fax: (01747) 825383 E-mail: info@sherchem.co.uk *Chemical manufacturers, merchants & agents*

Sherman Treaters, Dormer Road, Thame Industrial Estate, Thame, Oxfordshire, OX9 3UW Tel: (01844) 213686 Fax: (01844) 217172 E-mail: sales@shermantreaters.co.uk *Plastics plant manufrs*

Shermaynes Welders Engineers Ltd, Units 2d 3a/3b Southgate Industrial Centre, Southgate, Lancaster, Morecambe, LA3 3PB Tel: (01524) 69333 *Sheet metalworkers & general engineers*

▶ Sherrens Printers, 2 Avon Court, Avon Close, Granby Industrial Estate, Weymouth, Dorset, DT4 9UX Tel: (01305) 785265 Fax: (01305) 761572

Sherriff Sales Agency, 1 The Limes, Porton, Salisbury, SP4 0LT Tel: (01980) 610844 Fax: (01980) 611866 E-mail: sherriff.sales@ntlworld.com *Stockholders of 316 stainless steel compression fittings*

T. Sherriff & Co. Ltd, West Barns, Dunbar, East Lothian, EH42 1UN Tel: (01368) 863708 Fax: (01368) 864799 E-mail: j.w.sherriff@talk21.com *Agricultural engineers*

Sherring-Lucas Dental Laboratory Ltd, 14 Mark Road, Hemel Hempstead, Hertfordshire, HP2 7BN Tel: (01442) 244706 Fax: (01442) 247014 E-mail: info@sherringlucas.co.uk *Dental laboratories*

Sherston Software Ltd, Angel House, High Street, Sherston, Malmesbury, Wiltshire, SN16 0LH Tel: (01666) 843200 Fax: (01666) 843216 E-mail: info@sherston.com *Computer software manufrs*

Sherwen Engineering Co. Ltd, Mile End Green, Dartford, DA2 8EB Tel: (01474) 703220 Fax: (01474) 705016 E-mail: sales@sherwen-engineering.co.uk *Steel fabricators*

Sherwin & Oliver Ltd, Midleton Industrial Estate, Guildford, Surrey, GU2 8XW Tel: (01483) 569241 Fax: (01483) 578232 *Optical manufacturing service*

Sherwood Agencies Ltd, Sherwood House Mutual Mills, Aspinall Street, Heywood, Lancashire, OL10 4HW Tel: (01706) 898100 Fax: (01706) 898101 E-mail: admin@sherwoodagencies.com *Promotional goods manufrs*

Sherwood Consulting Engineers, 26 Kings Meadow, Rainworth, Mansfield, Nottinghamshire, NG21 0FG Tel: (01623) 431128 Fax: (01623) 431129 E-mail: info@sherwoodce.com *Building engineering consultants*

Sherwood Control Panels, Lenton Business Centre, Lenton Boulevard, Nottingham, NG7 2BY Tel: 0115-978 1502 *Control panel manufrs*

Sherwood Enterprise, Unit 5a, Bailey Gate Industrial Estate, Sturminster Marshall, Wimborne, Dorset, BH21 4DB Tel: (01258) 857703 Fax: (01258) 858383 E-mail: yonkos@aol.com *Complete refurbishment of copper pots & pans, re-tinning*

Sherwood Group P.L.C., Fields Farm Road, Long Eaton, Nottingham, NG10 1GT Tel: 0115-946 1070 Fax: 0115-946 2720 E-mail: info@sherwoodgroup.co.uk *Lingerie, swimwear design & distributors*

Sherwood Interiors Ltd, 38 Churchill Park, Colwick, Nottingham, NG4 2HF Tel: 0115-987 0158 Fax: 0115-961 5505 E-mail: info@sherwoodinteriors.co.uk *Suspended ceiling contractors*

Sherwood Packaging Ltd, Amber Drive, Langley Mill, Nottingham, NG16 4BE Tel: (01773) 760101 Fax: (01773) 530527 E-mail: sales@sherwoodpkg.com *Polythene bag manufrs*

Sherwood Plastic Products Ltd, 25 Seavy Road, Goole, North Humberside, DN14 6TA Tel: (01405) 767338 Fax: (01405) 762222 E-mail: sherwoodplastic@btconnect.com *Plastic injection moulders & plastic component manufrs*

Sherwood Precision Co., 35 Wiverton Road, Nottingham, NG7 6NQ Tel: 0115-962 1758 Fax: 0115-962 1758 *Precision engineering*

Sherwood Scientific Ltd, Unit J1 The Paddocks, 347 Cherry Hinton Road, Cambridge, CB1 8DH Tel: (01223) 243444 Fax: (01223) 243300 E-mail: info@sherwood-scientific.com *Manufacturing*

Sherwood Services Ltd, Bolina Road, London, SE16 3LD Tel: (020) 7252 1293 *Metal polishers & finishers*

Sherwood Services UK Ltd, Parkway House, Wakefield Road, Ossett, West Yorkshire, WF5 9JA Tel: (01924) 267077 Fax: (01924) 261911 *Jet wash & chemical equipment*

Sherwood Transfer Co., 28 Victoria Road, Nottingham, NG5 2NB Tel: 0115-960 3995 Fax: 0115-969 1948 *Labels screens prints, water side, sign manufrs*

Sherwood Truck & Van Ltd, Berristow Lane, Blackwell, Alfreton, Derbyshire, DE55 5HP Tel: (01773) 863311 Fax: (01773) 580271 E-mail: enquiries@sherwoodtruckandvan.com *Commercial vehicle dealer, sales & repairers*

Sherwood Wholefoods, 1 Wilkinson Walk, Market Drayton, Shropshire, TF9 1PW Tel: (01630) 655155 *Health food supplies, herbal & homeopathic remedies*

Sherwood Windows Ltd, Unit A1, Enterprise Park, Brunel Drive, Newark, Nottinghamshire, NG24 2DZ Tel: (01636) 611611 Fax: (01636) 605976 E-mail: sales@sherwoodwindows.co.uk *Upvc windows, doors & conservatories install & manufrs*

▶ Sherwoods Fabrics, 39 Church Street, Malvern, Worcestershire, WR14 2AA Tel: (01684) 572379 Fax: (01684) 563295 E-mail: info@sherwoodsfabrics.co.uk *An extensive range of dress fabrics*

Shesto Ltd, 2 Sapcote Trading Centre, 374 High Road, London, NW10 2DH Tel: (020) 8451 6188 Fax: (020) 8451 5450 E-mail: sales@shesto.co.uk *Precision tool making services*

▶ Shetland Composites, Gremista Industrial Estate, Lerwick, Shetland, ZE1 0PX Tel: (01595) 696426 Fax: (01595) 692162

▶ Shetland Electrical Services, Rudda Park, Lerwick, Shetland, ZE1 0SD Tel: (01595) 692792 Fax: (01595) 695672

▶ Shetland Fudge, 11 Harbour Street, Lerwick, Shetland, ZE1 0LR Tel: (01595) 694324 Fax: (01595) 694324 *Confectionery manufrs*

▶ Shetland Island Council, Scord Quarry, Scalloway, Shetland, ZE1 0UR Tel: (01595) 880227

▶ Shetland Line Ltd, Garthspool, Lerwick, Shetland, ZE1 0NY Tel: (01595) 692869 Fax: (01595) 692234

▶ Shetland Litho, Gremista, Lerwick, Shetland, ZE1 0PX Tel: (01595) 742000 Fax: (01595) 742001

Shetland Seafish Ltd, 4a North Ness, Lerwick, Shetland, ZE1 0LZ Tel: (01595) 696949 Fax: (01595) 696929 E-mail: info@shetland-seafish.co.uk *White fish processor*

Shetland Smoked Salmon Ltd, Easterdale, Hamnavoe, Shetland, ZE2 9LB Tel: (01595) 859464 Fax: (01595) 859464 *Shellfish processors*

▶ Shetland Times Ltd, Gremista Industrial Estate, Lerwick, Shetland, ZE1 0PX Tel: (01595) 746700 Fax: (01595) 694637

▶ Shetland Transport Ltd, Greenhead, Lerwick, Shetland, ZE1 0PY Tel: (01595) 695792 Fax: (01595) 693722

Shibro Computer Consumables, 26 Tottenham Court Road, London, W1T 1BR Tel: (020) 7323 6948 Fax: (020) 7724 5087 E-mail: mmm@mmmltd.com *Computer accessories retailers distributors*

Shico (UK) Industrial Footwear Ltd, 35 Morris Road, Leicester, LE2 6BR Tel: (01933) 273800 Fax: (01933) 228179 E-mail: shico@shico.co.uk *Industrial footwear suppliers*

▶ Shield Corporate Finance, 25 Floral Street, London, WC2E 9DS Tel: (020) 7031 8265 Fax: (020) 7031 8268 E-mail: enquiries@shield.uk.com *Specialist in selling your business also advice on MBO"s,MBI"s,company valuation,negotiation and due dilligence.*

Shield Engineering, Wenlock Way, Leicester, LE4 9HU Tel: 0116-246 0660 Fax: 0116-246 1551 E-mail: shield@shield.eng.co.uk *Engineers*

Shield Environmental Services, Shield House, Crown Way, Warmley, Bristol, BS30 8XJ Tel: 0117-960 6366 Fax: 0117-960 5583 E-mail: enquiries@shieldenvironmental.co.uk *Asbestos removal & thermal insulation suppliers*

Shield Joinery Services, 30 Iverson Road, London, NW6 2QT Tel: (020) 7624 7098 Fax: (020) 7328 6309 *Joinery manufrs*

Shield Medicare Ltd, Hurlands Business Park, 5 Hurlands Close, Farnham, Surrey, GU9 9JE Tel: (01252) 717616 Fax: (01252) 715269 E-mail: info@shieldmedicare.com *Medical device manufrs*

Shield Pest Control UK Ltd, 10 Ewhurst Road, London, SE4 1AQ Tel: (020) 8690 4481 Fax: (020) 8690 7612 *Pest control services*

Shield Woodworking Ltd, Station Road, Kingham, Chipping Norton, Oxfordshire, OX7 6SX Tel: (01608) 658698 Fax: (01608) 658404 E-mail: shieldwood@btconnect.com *Bespoke joinery manufrs*

▶ Shielding Solutions Ltd, Unit 17, 46 Springwood Drive, Springwood Industrial Estate, Rayne Road, Braintree, Essex, CM7 2YN Tel: (01376) 330033 Fax: (01376) 339163 E-mail: info@shielding-solutions.com *Supply, design & manufrs*

▶ Shieldtone Ltd, Holbrook Rise, Holbrook Industrial Estate, Holbrook, Sheffield, S20 3FG Tel: 0114-251 3338 Fax: 0114-251 3341

▶ Shieldwell, Unit 5, Holloways, Bessemer Close, Ebblake Industrial Estate, Verwood, Dorset, BH31 6AZ Tel: (0870) 1626162 Fax: (0870) 1626163 E-mail: colin@shieldwell.com *Supplier of puncture sealants for pneumatic tyres like bikes, caravans & scooters*

Shiels Ltd, 16 St. Andrews Road South, St. Annes On Sea, Lytham St. Annes, Lancashire, FY8 1SR Tel: (01253) 726064 Fax: (01253) 722684 *Contact lens manufrs*

M.J. Shiers & Co., Rydene, Reigate Road, Dorking, Surrey, RH4 1SP Tel: (01306) 889464 *Joinery manufrs*

Shift F7 Ltd, 142 South Street, Dorking, Surrey, RH5 5EN Tel: (01306) 873900 Fax: (01306) 873910 *Computer resellers*

Shilchem Ltd, 217 Hinckley Road, Leicester, LE3 0TG Tel: 0116-251 8779 Fax: 0116-251 8779 *Chemist*

Shilldown Ltd, 16g Chalwyn Industrial Estate, Old Wareham Road, Poole, Dorset, BH12 4PE Tel: (01202) 722711 Fax: (01202) 722711 *General engineers*

Shillingbury Joinery & Restoration Ltd, Yarwood Works, Ledsam Street, Birmingham, B16 8DW Tel: 0121-455 6900 Fax: 0121-455 6900 *Joinery manufrs*

▶ Shillingford Bridge Hotel, Shillingford Hill, Wallingford, Oxfordshire, OX10 8LZ Tel: (01865) 858567 Fax: (01865) 858636

▶ Shiloh Active Care, Greensward House, 12 Brook Road, Rayleigh, Essex, SS6 7UR Tel: (01268) 771191 Fax: (01268) 771192

Shilton plc, 90 Peterborough Road, London, SW6 3HH Tel: (020) 7736 7771 Fax: (020) 7731 7683 E-mail: info@janeshilton.co.uk *Handbag, purse & wallet manufrs*

Shimadzu UK, Mill Court, Featherstone Road, Wolverton Mill, Milton Keynes, MK12 5RD Tel: (01908) 552200 Fax: (01908) 552211 E-mail: sales@shimadzu.co.uk *Scientific equipment supply & repair*

▶ Shimmee, Plough Road, Great Bentley, Colchester, CO7 8LG Tel: (01206) 250400 Fax: (01206) 250410 E-mail: sales@shimmee.co.uk

▶ Shimu Oriental Furniture Ltd, 3C-3D Harrogate Road, Rawdon, Leeds, LS19 6HW Tel: (0870) 2071433 Fax: 0113-250 8284 E-mail: info@shimu.co.uk *Importer of classical chinese furniture handcrafted reclaimed elm*

Shine Technologies, 21 Highcroft Industrial Estate, Enterprise Road, Waterlooville, Hampshire, PO8 0BT Tel: (023) 9257 2860 Fax: (023) 9257 2868 *Telecommunication systems & equipment manufrs*

Shinehill Ltd, 127 Ettingshall Road, Wolverhampton, WV2 2JP Tel: (01902) 451322 Fax: (01902) 870621 E-mail: shinehill@fsnet.co.uk *Commercial vehicle distribrs*

Shiner Ltd, 22 Church Road, Lawrence Hill, Bristol, BS5 9JB Tel: 0117-955 7432 Fax: 0117-955 4686 E-mail: admin@shiner.co.uk *Roller skate sales*

▶ Shiners Snobs Knobs, 81 Fern Avenue, Jesmond, Newcastle upon Tyne, NE2 2RA Tel: 0191-281 6474 Fax: 0191-281 9041 E-mail: onfo@snobsknobs.co.uk *Very Exclusive Antique & Period Door Furniture*

Shin-Etsu Handotai Europe Ltd, Wilson Road, Livingston, West Lothian, EH54 7DA Tel: (01506) 415555 Fax: (01506) 417171 *Silicon wafers manufrs*

▶ Shingle Berry Signs, Unit 4, Lloyd Court, Dunston, Gateshead, Tyne & Wear, NE11 9EP Tel: 0191-461 0084 Fax: 0191-460 3929 E-mail: sales@shingleberrysigns.com *Signs to specification*

Ship Inn, Thornbury Road, Alveston, Bristol, BS35 3LL Tel: (01454) 412521 Fax: (01454) 281664 E-mail: bristol.north@premierlodge.co.uk *Hotel & conference facilities*

Ship Shape Marine, 314-316 London Road, Hazel Grove, Stockport, Cheshire, SK7 4RF Tel: 0161-483 0666 Fax: 0161-483 0666 *Ship parts & service/repair*

Ship To Shore, Carnaby Industrial Estate, Lancaster Road, Carnaby, Bridlington, North Humberside, YO15 3QY Tel: (01262) 605896 Fax: (01262) 605896 E-mail: craig.davies8@btopenworld.com *Fish processors*

Shipaid Diesel Services Ltd, 9 Marjorie Avenue, Lincoln, LN6 7SD Tel: (01522) 533990 Fax: (01522) 544355 E-mail: shipaid.deisel@globaluk.net *Marine diesel engineers services*

Shipley Fabrications Ltd, Willoughby Road, Ancaster, Grantham, Lincolnshire, NG32 3RT Tel: (01400) 231115 Fax: (01400) 231220 *Structural steelwork*

Shipley Quarries, Rose Cottage, Lartington, Barnard Castle, County Durham, DL12 9BP Tel: (01833) 650529 Fax: (01833) 650529 *Natural stone product suppliers*

Shipley Transport Ltd, Castlefield Yard, Station Road, Hibaldstow, Brigg, South Humberside, DN20 9DU Tel: (01652) 651720 Fax: (01652) 651787 E-mail: jshiptransport@aol.com *Road transport, haulage & freight services*

▶ Shipmates, 2 Newcomen Road, Dartmouth, Devon, TQ6 9AF Tel: (01803) 839292 Fax: (01803) 832538 E-mail: admin@chandlery.co.uk *Shipmates chandlery for all your boating equipment needs*

Shipping Guides Ltd, 75 Bell Street, Reigate, Surrey, RH2 7AN Tel: (01737) 242255 Fax: (01737) 222449 E-mail: info@portinfo.co.uk *Marine consultants*

▶ Shipping Management Services, School Road, Aston Somerville, Broadway, Worcestershire, WR12 7JD Tel: (01386) 858600 Fax: (01386) 858616

Ships Electronic Services Ltd, Chichester House Waterside Court, Neptune Way, Medway City Estate, Rochester, Kent, ME2 4NZ Tel: (01634) 295500 Fax: (01634) 295537 E-mail: sales@ses-marine.com *Marine radio & navigational instruments*

▶ P Shipston & Sons, Victoria Mill, Watt Street, Sabden, Clitheroe, Lancashire, BB7 9ED Tel: (01282) 770225 Fax: (01282) 777146 *Manufacturers of furniture*

Shiptech (U K) Ltd, St. Andrews House, 33 Beverley Road, Hull, HU3 1XH Tel: (01482) 324964 Fax: (01482) 226679 E-mail: info@shiptech.co.uk *Marine consultants, engineers & naval architects*

Shipton & Co. Ltd, 27-33 Spencer Street, Birmingham, B18 6DL Tel: 0121-236 2427 Fax: 0121-212 0591 *Jewellers retail wholesale & manufrs*

Shipton Communications Ltd, 1 Frogmore Road, Hemel Hempstead, Hertfordshire, HP3 9TG Tel: (01442) 345600 Fax: (01442) 345663 *Telecommunication equipment suppliers*

Shire Business Interiors, Snowdown, PO Box 123 Dough Bank, Ombersley, Droitwich, Worcestershire, WR9 0HN Tel: (01905) 621691 Fax: (01905) 621345 E-mail: sales@shirebusinessinteriors.co.uk *Contract office furnishers, carpets, ceilings, partitions suppliers*

Shire Business Solutions, Shire House, Highlands Road, Shirley, Solihull, West Midlands, B90 4LR Tel: 0121-711 3030 Fax: 0121-711 3060 E-mail: sales@shire-bs.com *Printers & stationers interior designers*

▶ Shire Conservatories, Unit 7, Harlescott Barns, Battlefield Enterprise Park, Shrewsbury, SY1 3SY Tel: 01743 463333 Fax: 01743 462200 E-mail: info@shireconservatories.co.uk *UPVC windows, doors & conservatories installers*

▶ Shire Consulting, The Chapel, Barnsley Hall Road, Bromsgrove, Worcestershire, B61 0SZ Tel: (01527) 579933 Fax: (01527) 579537 E-mail: info@shire-uk.com *Telecoms consultants & structural engineers*

▶ Shire Consulting, 8 Spicer Street, St. Albans, Hertfordshire, AL3 4PQ Tel: (01727) 838455 Fax: (01727) 835047 E-mail: enquiries@shire-uk.com *Telecoms consultants & town planners*

Shire Fluid Power Ltd, 6 Racecourse Road, Pershore, Worcestershire, WR10 2EY Tel: (01386) 554744 Fax: (01386) 553743 *Hydraulic & pneumatic component distributors*

Shire Management Services, Centre Court, 1301 Stratford Road, Hall Green, Birmingham, B28 9HH Tel: 0121-702 2431 Fax: 0121-778 6668 E-mail: admin@shireman.com *Hospital database software manufrs*

Company Information

Shire Mechanical Ltd, Highfield Farm, Binley, Andover, Hants, SP11 6HA Tel: (01264) 738898 Fax: (01264) 738551

Shire Pressings Ltd, Doubak Works, Barton Industrial Estate, Bilston, West Midlands, WV14 7LH Tel: (01902) 490155 Fax: (01902) 490155 *General presswork, pressings, steel, non-ferrous & fabricated*

Shire Security Ltd, 2 Henson Park, Henson Way, Telford Way Industrial Estate, Kettering, Northamptonshire, NN16 8PX Tel: (01536) 410483 Fax: (01536) 412631 E-mail: info@shiresecurity.co.uk *Design & install intruder alarms, access control, cctv, fire detection*

▶ Shire Stoves, 71 High Street, Chobham, Woking, Surrey, GU24 8AF Tel: 01276 857879 *Stove manufrs*

▶ Shire Writing Services, 31 The Crescent, Stafford, ST16 1ED Tel: (01785) 252743 E-mail: george@shirewriting.co.uk *A complete range of freeelance writing services, Press Releases, Copywriting, Direct Mail, Articles and features newsletters etc.*

Shirecraft Designs, 159 Victoria Avenue, Borrowash, Derby, DE72 3HF Tel: (01332) 669136 E-mail: sales@shirecraft.co.uk *Manufacture Of Hand Made Pictures & Frames*

Shirehampton Village Bakery, 7 High Street, Shirehampton, Bristol, BS11 0DT Tel: 0117-907 0076 Fax: 0117-907 0076 *Bakers*

Shiremoor Compressors & Electrical Services Ltd, 11 Front Street, Seghill, Cramlington, Northumberland, NE23 7TQ Tel: 0191-237 7177 Fax: 0191-237 7178 E-mail: sylvo@talktalk.net *Compressed air sales-service-repairs*

Shires Art Printing Ltd, Brinksway Trading Estate, Stockport, Cheshire, SK3 0BZ Tel: 0161-480 8316 Fax: 0161-480 2357 E-mail: sales@shiresart.fsnet.co.uk *Screen printers & vehicle graphics & digital printers services*

Shires Bathrooms Ltd, Beckside Road, Bradford, West Yorkshire, BD7 2JE Tel: (01274) 521199 Fax: (01274) 521583 E-mail: marketing@shires-bathrooms.co.uk *Bathroom manufrs*

▶ Shires Crane Hire Ltd, Sheepbridge Lane, Chesterfield, Derbyshire, S41 9RX Tel: (01246) 452296 Fax: (01246) 451015 E-mail: louise@shirescrane.fsnet.co.uk *Mobile crane hire, repair & sales*

Shires Equestrian, 15 Southern Avenue, Leominster, Herefordshire, HR6 0QF Tel: (01568) 613600 Fax: (01568) 613599 E-mail: sales@shires-equestrian.co.uk *Equestrian product manufrs* Also at: Bromyard

Shires Fire & Safety Ltd, Unit F3 Oswestry Service Centre, Bank Top Industrial Estate, St. Martins, Oswestry, Shropshire, SY10 7BB Tel: (01743) 741741 Fax: (01691) 773144 E-mail: info@sfas.co.uk *Fire extinguisher & safety sign suppliers*

Shires Fire & Safety Ltd, Units 16-18 Business Development Centre, Stafford Park 4, Telford, Shropshire, TF3 3BA Tel: (01952) 292488 Fax: (01952) 292222 E-mail: info@ssaf.co.uk *Fire extinguishers, fire alarms & safety signs distributors*

Shires Vee & Inline Ltd, Royal Oak Way North, Royal Oak Industrial Estate, Daventry, Northamptonshire, NN11 8PQ Tel: (01327) 703235 Fax: (01327) 703281 E-mail: shiresveeinline@ukonline.co.uk *Industrial & reconditioned engine suppliers & truck dealers*

Jesse Shirley & Son Ltd, Etruria, Lower Bedford Street, Stoke-on-Trent, ST4 7AF Tel: (01782) 212473 Fax: (01782) 287308 E-mail: enquiries@jesseshirley.com *Processors service of ceramic raw materials for bone china*

Shirley Technologies Ltd, Unit 12 Westpoint Enterprise Park, Clarence Avenue, Trafford Park, Manchester, M17 1QS Tel: 0161-869 1610 Fax: 0161-872 6492 E-mail: info@shirleytech.co.uk *Textile research consultants* Also at: Manchester

Shirleys Ltd, Canterbury Street, Blackburn, BB2 2HP Tel: (01254) 59361 Fax: (01254) 697600 *Paper stock merchants*

▶ Shirlplass Ltd, Unit L Bury Close, Higham Ferrers, Rushden, Northamptonshire, NN10 8HQ Tel: (01933) 411814 Fax: (01933) 411914 E-mail: sales@shirlplass.co.uk *Packaging film printers*

Shiva Internet, 418 High Street, Smethwick, West Midlands, B66 3PJ Tel: 0121-565 4279 Fax: 0121-555 6149 E-mail: shiv@shivajewellers.co.uk *Jewellers manufrs*

Shivers Installation Ltd, 2 The Old School House, Southdown Road, Seaford, East Sussex, BN25 4JS Tel: (01323) 899888 Fax: (01323) 896810 *Air conditioning & refrigeration contractors*

SHL Refractories UK Limited, Celcius House, Lawn Road, Carlton-In-Lindrick, Worksop, Nottinghamshire, S81 9LB Tel: (01909) 731959 Fax: (01909) 731579 E-mail: sales@shl-refractories.co.uk *Refractory removal and installation. Furnaces, Incinerators, Kilns, Driers and Chimneys. Bricking, Spraying or guniting. Remote controlled Deomolition. 24/7 professional service.*

▶ Shobwood Engineering (Burton) Ltd, Crown Industrial Estate, Anglesey Road, Burton-on-Trent, Staffordshire, DE14 3NX Tel: 01283 516730

Shoe Zone Ltd, Haramead Business Centre, Humberstone Road, Leicester, LE1 2LH Tel: 0116-222 3000 Fax: 0116-222 3001 E-mail: info@shoezone.net *Shoe retailers*

▶ W.H. Shoebridge & Sons Ltd, 90 South Street, Stanground, Peterborough, PE2 8EZ Tel: (01733) 340281 Fax: (01733) 897002 E-mail: whshoebridge.pet@btconnect.com *Motor repairers*

Shogun International, 87 Gayford Road, London, W12 9BY Tel: (020) 8749 2022 Fax: (020) 8740 1086 *Martial arts sports equipment*

▶ Sholing Press, 180 Portsmouth Road, Southampton, SO19 9AQ Tel: (023) 8043 2997 Fax: (023) 8068 5907 E-mail: enquiries@sholingpress.co.uk

▶ Shomera, 63 Milton Road, London, SW14 8JP Tel: (020) 8332 3022 Fax: (020) 8487 8224 E-mail: info@shomera.com *Building relocaters*

Shonn Bros Manchester Ltd, Emperor House, 151 Great Ducie Street, Manchester, M3 1FB Tel: 0161-834 1394 Fax: 0161-832 1875 E-mail: shonnbros@yahoo.co.uk *Fancy goods distributors*

Shooshyne, 481 Meanwood Road, Leeds, LS6 2BH Tel: 0113-275 2283 Fax: 0113-275 2362 E-mail: shoeshine@compuserve.com *Shoeshine shoe polishers Boot cleaners boot scrapers boot washer.*

▶ Shooterbelts.Com, Hyde House, The Hyde, London, NW9 6LH Tel: (020) 8205 7049 Fax: (020) 8975 1025 E-mail: sales@shooterbelts.com *Importers & suppliers of leather & pvc shooter belts*

▶ Shooting Star, 18 Homfray Avenue, Morecambe, Lancashire, LA3 3AG Tel: (01524) 400181 E-mail: nickipilkington@yahoo.com *Wedding invitations*

▶ Shootyou Video Production, NO 1 Victory Park Road, Addlestone, Surrey, KT15 2AT Tel: (01932) 853696 Fax: (01932) 853648 E-mail: quint@shootyou.co.uk *Specialists in producing video for public relations*

Shop & Bakery Equipment Ltd, Adelaide St, Halifax, West Yorkshire, HX1 4LY Tel: 01422 356034 E-mail: sales@sabelhfx.demon.co.uk

Shop Fitting Suppliers Ltd, Aqueduct Street, Preston, PR1 7JH Tel: (01772) 886276 Fax: (01772) 201440 E-mail: sales@shopfittingsupplies.co.uk *Shop fitters*

Shop Fittings Warehouse, Derby Mill, 13 Thomas Street, Bolton, BL3 6JU Tel: (01204) 396395 Fax: (01204) 396395 E-mail: sales@shopfittingswarehouse.co.uk *Shop fittings retailers*

Shopfit UK Ktd, West End Works, Staithes Road, Preston, Hull, HU12 8TJ Tel: (01482) 896240 Fax: (01482) 896510 E-mail: info@shopfituk.co.uk *Shop fitters*

Shopfittings & Equipment, Waterloo Industrial Estate, Waterloo Road, Bidford-on-Avon, Alcester, Warwickshire, B50 4JH Tel: (01789) 778497 Fax: (01789) 490132 E-mail: sales@shopfittingsandequipment.co.uk *Display equipment & shop fitters*

Shopmobility, 6 Morris Mews, Leominster, Herefordshire, HR6 8LZ Tel: (01568) 616755

Shopper Trak Ltd, 42 Ivanhoe Road, Hogwood Industrial Estate, Finchampstead, Wokingham, Berkshire, RG40 4QQ Tel: (0870) 8908725 Fax: (0870) 4102604 E-mail: information@shoppertrak.co.uk *Computer consultants*

Shopstuff Cash Register Services, 75 Longford Road, Longford, Coventry, CV6 6DY Tel: (024) 7683 5666 Fax: (0845) 6443075 E-mail: sales@shopstuff.co.uk *Weighing scales, cash register, retail equipment supplies*

Shore Electronic Services, 32 Heacham Drive, Leicester, LE4 0LF Tel: 0116-235 1858 Fax: 0116-235 1858 E-mail: shoreelectronicservices@shoreb.freeserve.co.uk *Computer maintenance & repairs*

▶ Shore Scaffolding Ltd, 9 Harvey Road, Basildon, Essex, SS13 1DG Tel: (01268) 727633 Fax: (01268) 590958 E-mail: shorescaffold@talk21.com

▶ Shoreham Ferry Services Ltd, Basin Road South, Portslade, Brighton, BN41 1WF Tel: (01273) 417757

Shoreheat Ltd, Unit 5 226 Purley Way, Croydon, CR0 4XG Tel: (020) 8688 7438 Fax: (020) 8680 0663 *Heating spares distributors* Also at: Branches throughout Southern England

Shoreline UK Ltd, Unit 6-7 Martello Enterprise Centre, Courtwick Lane, Wick, Littlehampton, West Sussex, BN17 7PA Tel: (01903) 733877 Fax: (01903) 733891 E-mail: info@shoreline-uk.com *Refrigeration engineers*

Shorflow Engineering Co. Ltd, Unit 11, Step Bridge Road, Coleford, Gloucestershire, GL16 8PJ Tel: (01594) 839393 Fax: (01594) 839394 *Water jet cleaning equipment manufrs*

Shorrock's Bros, 210-212 Albert Road, Farnworth, Bolton, BL4 9JB Tel: (01204) 571386 *Fishing tackle retailers*

Short & Abbott Ltd, Agricultural Workshop, Bridge Mill, Bridgerule, Holsworthy, Devon, EX22 7EL Tel: (01288) 381485 Fax: (01288) 381486 E-mail: gary@shortandabbott.fsnet.co.uk *Agricultural machinery repairers service*

Shorts Group Ltd, Lyndhurst Road, Ascot, Berkshire, SL5 9ED Tel: (01344) 620316 Fax: (01344) 624572 E-mail: sales@shorts-services.co.uk *Contractors plant & tool hire demolition experts skip hire recycling wood recycling gritting agriculture*

Shorts Industries Ltd, PO Box 258, Bradford, West Yorkshire, BD2 1QR Tel: (01274) 305066 Fax: (01274) 736212 E-mail: sales@shorts-lifts.co.uk *Air conditioning unit suppliers*

▶ The Shortwave Shop Ltd, 18 Fairmile Road, Christchurch, Dorset, BH23 2LJ Tel: (01202) 490099 Fax: (01202) 490099 E-mail: sales@shortwave.co.uk *Hobby & business communications suppliers*

▶ Shot In The Dark, The Lodge, Beaumont Park Road, Huddersfield, HD4 7AY Tel: (01484) 651111 Fax: (01484) 643930 E-mail: info@shotinthedark.co.uk *Producers & suppliers of visual services*

Shotblast Supplies Ltd, 10-20 Kilton Terrace, Worksop, Nottinghamshire, S80 2DQ Tel: (01909) 530107 Fax: (01909) 482982 E-mail: sales@shotblast-supplies.co.uk *Shot blasting equipment manufrs*

▶ Shott Transport & Removals, The Lingfield Estate, Mcmullen Road, Darlington, County Durham, DL1 1RW Tel: (01642) 677780 Fax: (01325) 380346

▶ Shout, 24 Sparkford Gardens, London, N11 3GT Tel: (020) 8361 5222 Fax: (020) 8361 6177 E-mail: enquiries@shoutpm.co.uk *Printed promotional items & corporate gifts suppliers*

▶ Shout Business Promotions, 16 Fords Close, Bledlow Ridge, High Wycombe, Bucks, HP14 4AP Tel: (01494) 481166 Fax: (01494) 481433 E-mail: info@shout-promotions.com *Suppliers of a huge range of bespoke printed, engraved, embroidered promotional items, products, incentives and gifts, workwear, clothing and all advertising items. Fast turnaround and free brochures/samples.*

▶ Shout Business Promotions, 94 London Road, Headington, Oxford, OX3 9FN Tel: (0800) 0190967 Fax: (01494) 481433 E-mail: Sales@shout-promotions.com *Suppliers of a huge range of bespoke printed, engraved products*

▶ Shout Print, 2c Merrow Business Centre, Guildford, Surrey, GU4 7WA Tel: (01483) 450009 Fax: (01483) 455009

Show Business Software Ltd, 137 Euston Road, London, NW1 2AA Tel: (020) 7387 3888 Fax: (020) 7387 3883 *Business software suppliers*

The Show Business (UK) Ltd, 20 Folder Lane, Sprotbrough, Doncaster, South Yorkshire, DN5 7PB Tel: 01302 856330 Fax: 01302 856330 E-mail: info@theshowbusiness.co.uk *The Show Business (UK) Ltd has extensive experience of exhibition stand design & construction, conference & event management & video production. From our base in South Yorkshire, we provide a cost effective international service to clients who appreciate being able to arrive on site and immediately inhabit a comfortable, effective marketing environment. This includes graphics, special effects, fibre optics, moving displays, plasma screens and specialist lighting. We make interactive electronic 'Ad Games' to totally involve your customers and deliver your message in compelling and entertaining ways. Exhibition stand design and build, modular exhibition equipment, banner stands, pop up displays, graphics, exhibition furniture. Conference production, staging, lighting, sound systems, lecterns. Video production, animated graphics, corporate and training videos, dvd duplication, plasma screens. The Show Business - The experience, expertise and equipment to achieve your marketing objectives.*

Show Card, Fontana House, Works Road, Letchworth Garden City, Hertfordshire, SG6 1LD Tel: (01462) 677148 Fax: (01462) 480392 E-mail: sales@showcard.com *Point of sale display designers*

Show Connections Ltd, PO Box 74, Crowborough, East Sussex, TN6 3YE Tel: (01892) 653185 Fax: (01892) 652523 E-mail: sales@showconnections.com *Audio & visual installations services*

Show Hire, Station Lane, Milford, Godalming, Surrey, GU8 5AD Tel: (01483) 414337 Fax: (01483) 426926 *Suppliers of radio communication equipment*

Showboat Casino Slots, Unit 16 Meadow Walk, Halton Lea, Runcorn, Cheshire, WA7 2BU Tel: (01928) 795549 Fax: (01928) 713757 *Amusement arcade service providers*

Showbox Jewellery Manufacturers, 22 Miller Arcade, Preston, PR1 2QA Tel: (01772) 201061 Fax: (01772) 201061 E-mail: sales@showbox.co.uk *Jewellery manufrs*

Showell Packing Ltd, Showell Road, Wolverhampton, WV10 9JY Tel: (01902) 725895 Fax: (01902) 862962 E-mail: peterhoward@hoship.com *Packing case manufrs*

Showerdrape STD Ltd, Rammon House, 3 Longacre Street, Manchester, M1 2WN Tel: 0161-272 8700 Fax: 0161-272 8840 E-mail: info@showerdrape.co.uk *Shower curtains & rails manufrs*

Showerlux UK Ltd, Stonebridge Trading Estate, Sibree Road, Coventry, CV3 4FD Tel: (024) 7663 9400 Fax: (024) 7630 5457 E-mail: sales@showerlux.co.uk *Shower enclosures & baths*

Showpla Plastics Ltd, Landywood Lane, Cheslyn Hay, Walsall, WS6 7AL Tel: (01922) 419203 Fax: (01922) 419225 E-mail: info@showplaplastics.co.uk *Plastic injection mouldings manufrs*

▶ Showprice Accessories, J3-J4 Widnes Market Hall, Bradley Way, Widnes, Cheshire, WA8 6UE Tel: 0151-420 0544 Fax: 0151-420 0544 *Computer suppliers*

Showprint Photographics Ltd, 29 High Street, Hampton Wick, Kingston Upon Thames, Surrey, KT1 4DA Tel: (020) 8943 9572 Fax: (020) 8943 5372 *Digital graphic production*

▶ Showtech Sound & Light, Unit 1k Moss Industrial Estate, Woodbine St East, Rochdale, Lancashire, OL16 5LB Tel: (01706) 347159 Fax: 01706 347912 E-mail: info@showtechuk.com

Showtech Sound & Light Design, Unit 23 Hammond Business Centre, Hammond Close, Attleborough Fields Ind Estate, Nuneaton, Warwickshire, CV11 6RY Tel: (024) 7634 8890 Fax: (024) 7634 8890 E-mail: enquiries@ssld.co.uk *Lighting & sound equipment sales & hire. Consultancy on all aspects of sound, lighting & staging, including design & installation*

▶ Showtime Karaoke, 14 Filbert Street, Oldham, OL1 4HQ Tel: 0161-628 2652

The Shred Safe Ltd, Whitehall Farm Units, Cambridge Road, Croxton, St. Neots, Cambridgeshire, PE19 6SS Tel: (01480) 880088 Fax: (01480) 880044 E-mail: sales@shred-safe.co.uk *Confidential on site shredding*

Shredders Direct, Bath Road, Speen, Newbury, Berkshire, RG14 1QY Tel: (01635) 43828 Fax: 01635 43820 E-mail: shreddersdirect@talk21.com *Sales of shredders & bailers*

Shredhouse Gift Packaging, Salisbury Road Business Park, Salisbury Road, Pewsey, Wiltshire, SN9 5PZ Tel: (01672) 564333 Fax: (01672) 564301 *Manufacturers of presentation packaging*

Shreds, Station Yard, Station Road, Digby, Lincoln, LN4 3NF Tel: (01526) 320450 Fax: (01526) 320452 E-mail: information@shreds.co.uk *Promotional aprons & bags*

Shredsure Ltd, White House, Padhams Green, Mountnessing, Brentwood, Essex, CM13 1UL Tel: (01277) 354500 Fax: (01277) 356988 *Security shredding service*

Shrewsbury Tarpaulins Ltd, Unit 1ac Leaton Industrial Estate, Leaton, Bomere Heath, Shrewsbury, SY4 3AP Tel: (01939) 290692 Fax: (01939) 290692 *Tarpaulin repairers & manufrs*

Shrinkfast Ltd, Bridgewater Close, Hawkesworth TRDG Estate, Hawkesworth Trading Estate, Swindon, SN2 1ED Tel: (01793) 612072 Fax: (01793) 534649 E-mail: sales@shrinkfast.co.uk *Manufacturers of pallet covers & hoods*

Shrinkwrap Machinery Co. Ltd, 145 Sterte Road, Poole, Dorset, BH15 2AF Tel: (01202) 674944 Fax: (01202) 671891 E-mail: sales@shrinkwrap.co.uk *Manufacturers of shrinkwrap machines & packaging equipment*

▶ Shrinkwrap Services, Oswald Street, Burnley, Lancashire, BB12 0BY Tel: (01282) 434446 Fax: (01282) 434452

Shropshire Bearing Services, 6 Beveley Road, Oakengates, Telford, Shropshire, TF2 6AT Tel: (01952) 610157 Fax: (01952) 619669 E-mail: shropshirebearings@hotmail.com *Distributor & manufacturer of bearings*

Shropshire Ceilings, 50 Longden Coleham, Shrewsbury, SY3 7DH Tel: (01743) 343456 Fax: 01743 343456 E-mail: lee@shropshireceilings.co.uk *Suspended ceilings installation & supply*

Shropshire Flue & Duct Services, Unit 84, Condover Industrial Estate, Dorrington, Shrewsbury, SY5 7NH Tel: (01743) 718844 Fax: (01743) 718874 *Chimney & flue lining manufrs*

Shropshire Highland Seeds, Brockton Store, Brockton, Lydbury North, Shropshire, SY7 8BA Tel: (01588) 680371 Fax: (01588) 680345 *Potato seeds & daffodil bulb producers*

Shropshire Mini-Mix, Shawbury Heath, The Oaks, Shawbury, Shrewsbury, SY4 4EA Tel: (01939) 250986 Fax: 01939 251254 E-mail: sales@readymix.com *Ready mixed concrete suppliers*

▶ Shropshire Pine Company, The Mill, Heath Hill, Dawley, Telford, Shropshire, TF4 2JU Tel: (01952) 502361 Fax: (01952) 502359 E-mail: sales@shropshirepine.co.uk *Furniture manufrs*

Shropshire Scale Co., 27 Kestrel Drive, Shrewsbury, SY1 4TT Tel: (01743) 468928 *Scale services & repairers*

Shropshire Trophies Centre & Bowling Centre, 6 Milk Street, Shrewsbury, SY1 1SZ Tel: (01743) 369688 Fax: (01743) 360674 E-mail: stbc@lineone.net *Trophy retail & engraving services*

Shropshire Welding Supplies Ltd, Unit A10, Stafford Park 15, Telford, Shropshire, TF3 3BB Tel: (01952) 290610 Fax: (01952) 211960 E-mail: swsltd@compuserve.com *Welding suppliers*

Shropshire & West Midlands Agricultural Society, Berwick Road, Shrewsbury, SY1 2PF Tel: (01743) 289831 Fax: (01743) 289920 E-mail: mail@west-mid-show.org.uk *Agricultural event organisers*

Shrub Hill Fabrications, Unit 3 British Rail Industrial Estate, Tolladine Road, Worcester, WR4 9PT Tel: (01905) 20644 Fax: (01905) 20644 *Metal fabricators*

SHS, 4 The Centre, The Broadway, Farnham Common, Slough, SL2 3QQ Tel: (01753) 643451 Fax: (01753) 647140 *Security installation & monitoring services*

Shufflebottom Ltd, Heol Parc Mawr, Cross Hands Industrial Estate, Cross Hands, Llanelli, Dyfed, SA14 6RE Tel: (01269) 831831 Fax: (01269) 831031 E-mail: sales@shufflebottom.co.uk *Steel framed building installation engineers*

▶ Shuker Bass, 72 Arundel Street, Sheffield, S1 2NS Tel: 0114-275 8380

Shurflo Ltd, 5 Sterling Park, Gatwick Road, Crawley, West Sussex, RH10 9QT Tel: (01293) 424000 Fax: (01293) 421880 E-mail: sales@shurflo.com *Pump manufrs*

▶ Shurlok (UK), Unit 5 Oak Tree Park, Burns Medow Road, Moons Moat Industrial Estate, Redditch, Worcestershire, B98 9NW Tel: (01527) 592999 Fax: (01527) 592666 E-mail: sales@shurlok-keystorage.co.uk *Key safe storage boxes*

Shutter Door Repair & Maintenance Ltd, Lionel Works, 89-91 Rolfe Street, Smethwick, West Midlands, B66 2AY Tel: 0121-558 6406 Fax: 0121-555 7140 E-mail: sales@priory-group.com *Rolling shutters & security grills repair services & manufrs*

Shutter Door Services, Unit 15 Pant Industrial Estate, Dowlais, Merthyr Tydfil, CF48 2SR Tel: (01685) 375777 Fax: (01685) 373344 *Rolling shutter repairers*

▶ Shutter Point Photography, Milford Place, High Street, Kings Heath, Birmingham, B14 7LF Tel: (07759) 057549 E-mail: steve@shutterpoint.co.uk *Digital event photography*

Shuttersafe Roller Shutter Mnfrs, 3 Cae'R Odyn, Dinas Powys, South Glamorgan, CF64 4UF Tel: (029) 2081 1798 E-mail: shuttersafe@aol.com *Roller shutter door manufrs*

▶ Shuttle Bridge Logistics Ltd, Unit 15, Angerstein Business Park, Horn Lane, Greenwich, London, SE10 0RT Tel: 020 84655757 Fax: 020 84655858 E-mail: shuttlebridgeuk@yahoo.co.uk *As you can see from our website www.shuttlebridge.co.uk, Shuttle Bridge Logistics Ltd the international freight forwarding company based in UK, who can offer the full spectrum of international distribution services. We have offices situated at London and Felixstowe, as well as a global agency network representing us as reciprocal partners. Today we are poised to take our company and our clientele into the twenty first century by providing a range of services for forward thinking businesses. The range of services we have to offer includes Airfreight Operations, Sea Freight Logistics, Asia/European TIR Supply Chain Management, Asia/EU Distribution & Warehousing, Packing*

continued

continuation
Solutions, Insurance, Air Freight to door options services.

Shyamtronics Computer Systems, 246 Tottenham Court Road, London, W1T 7QU Tel: (020) 7637 1990 Fax: (020) 7637 0085 E-mail: sales@shyamtronicds.com *Computer retailers services*

▶ Si Fi, 463 Harrow Road, London, W10 4RG Tel: (020) 8962 0700 Fax: (020) 8964 2696 E-mail: sales@si-fi.com *Audio designers*

▶ Si Property Consultants Ltd, 39 Hermitage Way, Stanmore, Middlesex, HA7 2AX Tel: (020) 8930 1684 Fax: 020 84242557 E-mail: office@siproperty.co.uk *Building surveys, license for alterations, strategic property advice service*

Sia Abrafoam Ltd, Keys Road, Nixs Hill Industrial Estate, Alfreton, Derbyshire, DE55 7FQ Tel: (01773) 832524 Fax: (01773) 520776 E-mail: info@sia-abrafoam.co.uk *Manufacturers of abrasive blocks, coated products & products (industrial finishing). Also foam (abrasive coated) manufrs*

Sia Ni Ltd, 134 Finaghy Road South, Belfast, BT10 0DG Tel: (028) 9029 8999 Fax: (028) 9029 1617 E-mail: sales@sia.uk.com *CCTV & intruder alarms installers*

▶ Sian Fabrications, Deykin Avenue, Birmingham, B6 7HN Tel: 0121-328 9229 Fax: 0121-328 0990

Sian Saddlery, Coopers Green, Uckfield, East Sussex, TN22 4AT Tel: (01825) 732636 Fax: (01825) 732636 *Saddlery*

▶ Sibbasbridge Ltd, 175a Evesham Road, Stratford-upon-Avon, Warwickshire, CV37 9BS Tel: (01789) 205253 Fax: (01789) 298101

Sibcas Ltd, Chanters Indust Estate, Arley Way, Atherton, Manchester, M46 9BP Tel: (01942) 896688 Fax: (01942) 894967 *Portable accommodation hire services*

Sibcas Ltd, Brickyard Lane, Studley, Warwickshire, B80 7GA Tel: (01527) 850100 Fax: (01527) 850200 *Portable accommodation hire*

Sibert Technology, 2a Merrow Business Centre, Merrow Lane, Guildford, Surrey, GU4 7WA Tel: (01483) 440724 Fax: (01483) 440727 E-mail: NDT@sibtec.com *Scientific instrument designers manufrs*

▶ Sibley Haulage Ltd, Crabtree Lane, Lower End, Wavendon, Milton Keynes, MK17 8AP Tel: (01908) 583154 Fax: (01908) 587631

Sibley Material Movements Ltd, Andes Road, Nursling, Southampton, SO16 0YZ Tel: (023) 8073 7773 Fax: (023) 8074 0193 E-mail: sales@materialmovements.com *Road transport, haulage & freight services*

A.J. Sibthorpe & Co. Ltd, 22-42 Freshwater Road, Dagenham, Essex, RM8 1RY Tel: (020) 8597 7000 Fax: (020) 8597 7300 *Electrical contractors*

Sicame Electrical Developments Ltd, Riverholme Works, Huddersfield Road, Holmfirth, HD9 3TN Tel: (01484) 681115 Fax: (01484) 687352 E-mail: sales@sicame.co.uk *Electric cable jointing accessories manufrs*

Sicane Electrical Distribution Ltd, Amington Industrial Estate, Tamworth, Staffordshire, B77 4DS Tel: (01827) 68333 Fax: (01827) 65700 E-mail: barbara.shewan@sicame.co.uk *Power cable accessories distributor*

Sick UK Ltd, Waldkirch House, 39 Hedley Road, St. Albans, Hertfordshire, AL1 5BN Tel: (01727) 831121 Fax: (01727) 856767 E-mail: info@sick.co.uk *SICK is one of the world's leading producers of intelligent sensors & sensor solutions for factory, logistics & process automation. Based on years of practical experience, SICK assist clients to design their industrial processes more efficiently.*Factory automation sensors assist non-contact detecting, counting, classifying & positioning of any types of objects; accident protection & personal safety, as well as safety software & services. Industry innovators for photoelectric, proximity & ultrasonic sensors, vision systems, encoders & motor feed-back, safety light grids, laser scanners, interlocks, interfaces & relays.*Logistics automation devices offer automated identification with bar code & RFID for sorting & target control, & laser measurement systems to detect volume, position & contours of objects & surroundings in industrial material flows & optimization of sorting & warehousing processes.*In the area of process automation SICK offer complete systems for gas analysis, dust measurement & emissions monitoring, & volume flow rate measurement.*

▶ Sickle Cell Network, 85 Raeburn Road, Northampton, NN2 7EP Tel: (0870) 8502271 E-mail: theokeclub@hotmail.com *Investigation into the implementation of a health care policy concerning sickle cell anaemia disease years old. Health service which included nurses and doctors and the treatment of patients. Reporting on death, effects,sickle cell anaemia, disease, genetic condition, hereditary, people, health, police, education and pain*

▶ Sicl Ltd, S C L House, 131 Upper Wortley Road, Leeds, LS12 4JG Tel: 0113-238 9900 Fax: 0113-238 9910 E-mail: sales@sicl.co.uk *IT specialists*

SICO Europe Ltd, The Link Park, Lympne Industrial Estate, Lympne, Kent, CT21 4LR Tel: (01303) 234000 Fax: (01303) 234001 E-mail: sales@sico-europe.com *Established in 1951, today SICO and its associated companies worldwide are recognised as leading manufacturers of multi-purpose equipment. SICO Europe has secured major contracts with leading hotel chains, leisure developments, arenas and conference centres throughout the UK, Europe and Middle East.**Designed for one person operation, SICO products help save valuable staff resources and require minimal storage space. The folding, wheeling principle means rooms can be transformed from one use to another in a matter of minutes, helping you to maximise the potential revenue of your venue.**SICO's innovative product range includes mobile, folding banquet tables, as well as buffet, catering and room service tables. In addition SICO also manufactures mobile staging, portable dance floors and wallbeds.**All of SICO's products are renowned for their reliability, durability and minimum maintenance*

continued

requirements. Each product comes with its own warranty and is stringently tested for strength and stability.

Sicor International Ltd, 3 Murcar Industrial Estate, Denmore Road, Bridge of Don, Aberdeen, AB23 8JW Tel: (01224) 707560 Fax: (01224) 707561 E-mail: sales.sicorabdn@virgin.net *Industrial, sport, fishing netting & ropes suppliers*

Sidac Systems Ltd, New Road, Chorley, Bridgnorth, Shropshire, WV16 6PP Tel: (01746) 718737 Fax: (01746) 718737 E-mail: marie@cook120136.fsnet.co.uk *Automatic door & gate installation*

Siddall & Hilton Mesh Ltd, Birds Royd Lane, Brighouse, West Yorkshire, HD6 1LT Tel: (01484) 401610 Fax: (01484) 721028 E-mail: sales@shmesh.com *Security & razor barbed fencing manufrs*

Siddington Smithy, Smithy House, Siddington, Macclesfield, Cheshire, SK11 9LH Tel: 01260 224362 *Wrought iron furniture & curtain rails*

Siddons Packaging, Kingsley Street, Leicester, LE2 6DL Tel: 0116-244 8555 Fax: 0116-244 8575 E-mail: sales@sipak.co.uk *Corrugated containers*

Side Effects, 4 Camberwell Trading Estate, 117-119 Denmark Road, London, SE5 9LB Tel: (020) 7738 5199 Fax: (020) 7738 5198 *Special effect props & model makers*

Sidel (UK) Ltd, Lowesden Works, Lambourn Woodlands, Hungerford, Berkshire, RG17 7RU Tel: (01488) 72525 Fax: (01488) 72302 *Plastic blow moulding machinery manufrs*

Sidenor UK, Northside House, Mount Pleasent, Barnet, Hertfordshire, EN4 9EB Tel: (020) 8447 1444 Fax: (020) 8447 1555 *Steel merchants & agents*

Siderise Holdings Ltd, Unit 21 Lady Lane Industrial Estate, Hadleigh, Ipswich, IP7 6BQ Tel: (01473) 827695 Fax: (01473) 824143 E-mail: oem@siderise.com *Acoustic Insulation Solutions for OEMs, Marine and Vehicle Manufacturers.Including Acoustic Foams and barriers, and Thermal Insulation*

Sidevale (Building Contractors) Ltd, 43-45 Acre Lane, London, SW2 5TN Tel: (020) 7274 4255 Fax: (020) 7274 9159 *Building contractors*

▶ Sidewinder Ltd, Portswood House, Third Avenue, Southampton, SO15 0AH Tel: (023) 8077 5261 Fax: (023) 8078 0935 *Construction & refurbishment services*

▶ Sidey, 19 Feus Road, Perth, PH1 2AS Tel: (0800) 234400 Fax: (01738) 631335

Sidhu Fashions Ltd, Bentley Lane, Walsall, WS2 8SP Tel: (01922) 720854 Fax: (01992) 616314 E-mail: admin@sidhufashions.co.uk *Clothing wholesalers & manufrs*

Sidhu Textile Co. Ltd, 85-87 The Broadway, Southall, Middlesex, UB1 1LA Tel: (020) 8574 3385 Fax: (020) 8843 9229 E-mail: s_sidhu100@hotmail.com *Dress fabrics & soft furnishings*

▶ Sidlaw Windows Ltd, 2 Logie Avenue, Dundee, DD2 2AS Tel: (01382) 640200 Fax: (01382) 640118 *Upvc windows specialists*

Sidmouth Book Keeping Services, 6 Kings Avenue, Ottery St. Mary, Devon, EX11 1TA Tel: (01404) 813988 Fax: (01404) 813988 E-mail: tony@sbks.freeserve.co.uk *Book keeping & secretarial services, professional advisers for QuickBooks accountancy software & members of Clearlybusiness accountants*

Sidney Cubbage Heating & Ventilating Ltd, 37-43 Green Street, High Wycombe, Buckinghamshire, HP11 2RF Tel: (01494) 523661 Fax: (01494) 462707 E-mail: scl@sidneycubbage.com *Heating & ventilation equipment installers*

Sidney Darby, 4 Garman Close, Birmingham, B43 6NB Tel: 0121-357 2001 Fax: 0121-358 3011 E-mail: tony@sidneydarbyphotography.co.uk *Commercial & industrial photographers*

Sidney Graham Business Supplies Ltd, 236-240 Station Road, Kings Heath, Birmingham, B14 7TE Tel: 0121-443 3377 Fax: 0121-441 1456 E-mail: matt@sidneygraham.plus.com *Commercial stationers, printers & office refurbishment suppliers*

Sidney Harris Photography, 4 Brookland Close, London, NW11 6DJ Tel: (020) 8458 0137 Fax: (020) 8455 6220 *Photographers*

Sidney J George & Son, Moat Cottage, Beguildy, Knighton, Powys, LD7 1YU Tel: (01547) 510233 Fax: (01547) 510233 *Agricultural contractors*

Sidneyplus International Library System, Rodney House, Castle Gate, Nottingham, NG1 7AW Tel: 0115-955 5936 Fax: 0115-955 5937 E-mail: sales@sydneyplus.com *Software house*

Siebert Head Ltd, 80 Goswell Road, London, EC1V 7DB Tel: (020) 7689 9090 Fax: (020) 7689 9080 E-mail: info@sieberthead.com *Package design consultants*

▶ Siebert Industries Ltd, Blacksaulds House, Drumhead Place, Glasgow East Investment Park, Glasgow, G32 8EY Tel: (0870) 0502266 Fax: (0870) 0503366 *Telecommunications*

Siegel Laces & Fabric Ltd, Maiden Lane, Nottingham, NG1 1QJ Tel: 0115-950 3210 Fax: 0115-958 3969 E-mail: sales@siegel.demon.co.uk *Lace & fashion knit fabrics*

Siegling Ltd, Unit 4, Fifth Avenue, Tameside Park, Dukinfield, Cheshire, SK16 4PP Tel: 0161-331 3412 Fax: 0161-308 4385 E-mail: info@siegling.co.uk *Power transmission & conveyor belt manufrs*

Siegling (U K) Ltd, Unit 2, Pilton Industrial Estate, Pitlake, Croydon, CR0 3RY Tel: (020) 8681 8151 *Conveyors & conveyor belts manufrs*

▶ Siel Ups Systems Ltd, Unit H10 Draycott Business Park, Cam, Dursley, Gloucestershire, GL11 5DQ Tel: (01453) 899212 Fax: (01453) 899215 E-mail: enquiries@sielups.co.uk *Siel UPS is an established provider of UPS & associated systems for the continuous availability of power to essential services & mission critical applications, including UPS, central emergency lighting systems & static transfer switches (STS). Additional support services includes: system design/consultancy, installation, commissioning, maintenance & battery service/maintenance/replacements.*

Siemans Building Technologies Ltd, Hawthorne Road, Staines, Middlesex, TW18 3AY Tel: (01784) 461616 Fax: (01784) 464646 Principal Export Areas: Worldwide *Fire & security systems manufrs*

Siemans Technologies Ltd, Mersey House, 220-222 Stockport Road, Stockport, Cheshire, SK3 0LX Tel: 0161-428 3661 Fax: 0161-428 3662 E-mail: tom.wilkinson@siemens.com *Fire systems engineers*

Siemans V D O, 36 Gravelly Industrial Park, Birmingham, B24 8TA Tel: 0121-326 1234 Fax: 0121-326 1299 Principal Export Areas: Worldwide *Speedometer & tachometers manufrs*

Siemens P.L.C., Gatehouse Close, Aylesbury, Buckinghamshire, HP19 8DJ Tel: (01296) 339388 Fax: (01296) 339969 E-mail: marketing@moeller.co.uk Principal Export Areas: Worldwide *Busbar system manufrs*

Siemens Automation & Drive Training Centre, Sir William Siemens House, Princess Road, Manchester, M20 2UR Tel: 0161-446 5741 Fax: 0161-446 5742 E-mail: sales@siemens-industry.co.uk *Power transmission distributors*

▶ Siemens Building Technologies, Unit C19-C20, Poplar Business Park, 10 Prestons Road, London, E14 9RL Tel: (020) 7537 2888 Fax: (020) 7538 4118 *Heating & air conditioning services*

Siemens Business Services Ltd, 62 Boucher CR, Belfast, BT12 6HU Tel: (028) 9066 4331 Fax: (028) 9068 2168 E-mail: owen.mckenna@siemens.ie *Computer maintenance*

Siemens Communication, Turnells Mill Lane, Wellingborough, Northamptonshire, NN8 2RB Tel: (01933) 225000 Fax: (01933) 222650 *Telecommunications*

Siemens Communications, Technology Drive, Beeston, Nottingham, NG9 1LA Tel: 0115-943 0300 Fax: 0115-925 9610 E-mail: firstname.surname@siemens.com *Telecommunication equipment manufrs*

Siemens Financial Services Ltd, Townsend House, 160 Northolt Road, Harrow, Middlesex, HA2 0PG Tel: (020) 8422 7101 Fax: (020) 8422 4402 E-mail: enquiries.leasing@sfs-uk.com *Lease & finance business equipment*

Siemens Magnet Technology Ltd, Wharf Road, Eynsham, Witney, Oxfordshire, OX29 4BP Tel: (01865) 880880 Fax: (01865) 850176 *Magnet (medical usage) manufrs*

▶ Siemens Medical Solutions, Nasmyth Building, Nasmyth Avenue, East Kilbride, Glasgow, G75 0QU Tel: (01355) 353030 Fax: (01355) 353031 *Medical imaging*

Siemens Process Instruments, Century House, Bridgwater Road, Worcester, WR4 9ZQ Tel: (01905) 450500 Fax: (01905) 450501 *Level control equipment manufrs*

Siemens Products Life Cycle Management Software Iii (GB) Ltd, Park House, Castle Park, Cambridge, CB3 0DU Tel: (01223) 722600 Fax: (01223) 722601 E-mail: sales@d-cubed.co.uk *Software developers*

Siemens Protection Devices Ltd, PO Box 7, Hebburn, Tyne & Wear, NE31 1TZ Tel: 0191-401 5555 Fax: 0191-401 5575 *Industrial switch gear manufrs*

▶ Siemens Traffic Controls Ltd, 4 Edgewater Road, Belfast, BT3 9JQ Tel: (028) 9057 0570 Fax: (028) 9057 0571

▶ Siemens Traffic Controls plc, Block H2, 42 Nurseries Road, Baillieston, Glasgow, G69 6UL Tel: 0141-771 6555 Fax: 0141-771 8014 *Store & maintain traffic signals*

Siemens Transportation Systems, Sopers Lane, Poole, Dorset, BH17 7ER Tel: (01202) 846200 Fax: (01202) 846200 E-mail: internet@sts.siemens.com *Communication business*

▶ Siemens Transportation Systems, The Quadrangle, Cranmore Avenue, Shirley, Solihull, West Midlands, B90 4LE Tel: 0121-713 4300

Siemens V A I Metals Technologies Ltd, Loewy House 11 Enterprise Way, Aviation Park, Hurn, Christchurch, Dorset, BH23 6EW Tel: (01202) 331000 Fax: (01202) 581851 E-mail: sales@vai.co.at *Design engineers*

Siemens V D O Automotive Ltd, The Broadlands, 120 Holford Drive, Holford, Birmingham, B6 7UG Tel: 0121-344 2000 Fax: 0121-344 2072 E-mail: admin@vdodayton.com *Electronic instrument & instrumentation manufrs*

Siemens V D O Automotive Systems, Halesfield 25, Telford, Shropshire, TF7 4LP Tel: (01952) 683600 Fax: (01952) 580626 E-mail: sales@siemens.auto.com *Automotive plastic induction systems*

Siemens V D O Trading Ltd, Wiltshire House County Park, Shrivenham Road, Swindon, SN1 2NR Tel: (01793) 500100 Fax: (01793) 500101 E-mail: sales@siemens-datatrack.com *Vehicle tracking device suppliers*

Sienna Exhibitions Ltd, Unit 1r, Membury Business Park, Lambourn Woodlands, Hungerford, Berkshire, RG17 7TJ Tel: (01488) 73720 Fax: (01488) 73721 E-mail: sales@sienna-indigo.com *Exhibition & conference organisers*

▶ Siera-Training Org Ltd, Claro Court Business Centre, Claro Road, Harrogate, North Yorkshire, HG1 4BA Tel: (01423) 520201 E-mail: admin@sierra-training.org *Bespoke Training Providers to the Security Industry. City & Guilds/NOCN/SITO approved. SIA Security training specialists. Door Supervisor, Manned Guarding,CCTV Training.*

Sierra Blinds, 10 Openfields Cl, Liverpool, L26 7ZH Tel: 0151-487 3682 *Window blinds*

Sierra Leisure Products Ltd, Bridge Works, Mill Lane, Hasketon, Woodbridge, Suffolk, IP13 6HE Tel: (01473) 735773 Fax: (01473) 738316 E-mail: lisa.bean@sierraleisure.co.uk *Sierra Patio Heaters: Specially designed and manufactured in the UK to withstand the tough requirements of the hospitality industry. Our range includes: mobile LPG & Fixed natural gas heaters, overhead and bracketed heaters and our NEW remote control system.*

Sierra Saddle Co., 602 High Road, Benfleet, Essex, SS7 5RW Tel: (01268) 792769 Fax: (01268) 566775 *Gun leather*

Sifan System Ltd, Northwood Road, Windrush Industrial Park, Witney, Oxfordshire, OX29 7EE Tel: 01993 771336 Fax: 01993 771336 *Fan manufrs*

Sifbronze Ltd, Prentice Road, Stowmarket, Suffolk, IP14 1RD Tel: (01449) 771443 Fax: (01449) 771945 E-mail: sif@sifbronze.co.uk Principal Export Areas: Worldwide *Welding consumables, supplies & welding wire manufrs*

SIFCO Applied Surface Concepts (UK) Ltd, 38 Walkers Road, Moons Moat North, Moons Moat North Industrial Estate, Redditch, Worcestershire, B98 9HD Tel: (01527) 68008 Fax: (01527) 65924 E-mail: plating@sifco.co.uk *Electroplating equipment manufacturers*Sub contract services for selective electroplating*Repair of over-machined parts*Plating Chemical supplier**

Sifcon International plc, New Ford Road, Waltham Cross, Hertfordshire, EN8 7PG Tel: (01992) 718033 Fax: (01992) 718033 E-mail: sales@sil.demon.co.uk *Houseware & giftware importers*

Sig Pack Ltd, 1 Oakham Close, Derby, DE21 4DE Tel: (01332) 626262 Fax: (01332) 626288 *Packaging services*

▶ SIGHT International PLM Solutions Ltd, 12 York Gate, Regents Park, London, NW1 4QS Tel: (020) 7544 4853 Fax: (020) 7224 0553 E-mail: sales.uk@sightplm.com *With sightDSC we provide a complete PDM system at the Internet, which can be used for technical document management as well. The service sightDSC is meant for companies, who will exchange data internally and externally with suppliers, customers and external offices around the world. Even in the fast growing regions like China, Asia etc., the service can be used due to a technical feature to assure data transport even at poor bandwidths.*

Sight 'N' Sound, 11 Parkdale Drive, Sowerby Bridge, West Yorkshire, HX6 3HS Tel: (01422) 822734 Fax: (01422) 822442 *Audio visual hire services*

Sightguard I O W Ltd, 39 High Street, Wootton Bridge, Ryde, Isle of Wight, PO33 4LU Tel: (01983) 884000 Fax: (01983) 884000 *Security & fire alarm system fitters*

Sigma Ltd, 143 Westmoreland Road, Bromley, BR2 0TY Tel: (020) 8460 9191 Fax: (020) 8460 3969 E-mail: groupsigma@aol.com *Market research services*

Sigma Aerospace Ltd, 12 Imperial Way, Croydon, CR9 4LE Tel: (020) 8688 7777 Fax: (020) 8688 6603 E-mail: info@sigmaaerospace.com Principal Export Areas: Worldwide *Aircraft maintenance/repair specialist services*

▶ Sigma Coatings Ltd, Huddersfield Road, Birstall, Batley, West Yorkshire, WF17 9XA Tel: (01924) 354000 Fax: (01924) 354001 *Paint manufrs*

Sigma Computer Engineering & Maintenance Ltd, 316-318 Salisbury Road, Totton, Southampton, SO40 3ND Tel: (023) 8066 3636 Fax: (023) 8086 1213 *Computer maintenance & engineering*

Sigma Computer Services, 8 Adbolton Avenue, Gedling, Nottingham, NG4 3NB Tel: 0115-940 3041 E-mail: sigma@innotts.co.uk *Computer system consultants*

Sigma Consultancy Scotland Ltd, 18 Overton Crescent, Dyce, Aberdeen, AB21 7FW Tel: (01224) 723947 Fax: (01224) 773754 *Benchmarking, performance measurement & improvement*

▶ Sigma Electrical, Woodbine Road, Bolton, BL3 3JH Tel: (01204) 64322 Fax: (01204) 64612 E-mail: admin@sigma-electrical.co.uk *Control panel manufrs*

Sigma Electrical, 66 Cardinal Avenue, St. Budeaux, Plymouth, PL5 1UT Tel: (01752) 704529 Fax: (01752) 367515 *Burglar alarm systems installers & service*

Sigma Engineering Ltd, 26 Church Street, Altrincham, Cheshire, WA14 4DW Tel: 0161-928 9988 Fax: 0161-926 8726 E-mail: sigmapumps@aol.com *Industrial handpump worldwide distributors*

Sigma Exploration Ltd, 21 Chipstead Street, London, SW6 3SR Tel: (020) 7608 3883 Fax: (020) 7608 3883 E-mail: johnkiller@aol.com *Oil exploration consultants*

Sigma Group, PO Box 302, Guernsey, GY1 3SD Tel: (01481) 241111 Fax: (01481) 246391 E-mail: sales@sigma-aztec.com *Office equipment suppliers* Also at: St. Helier

Sigma Group, 12 Don Road, St. Helier, Jersey, JE2 4QD Tel: (01534) 733561 Fax: (01534) 768546 E-mail: cdpsigma@itl.net *Stationery & office equipment*

Sigma Industries Ltd, 19 Dunlop Road, Redditch, Worcestershire, B97 5XP Tel: (01527) 547771 Fax: (01527) 547772 E-mail: sales.sigmaind@btopenworld.com *Chain manufrs plastic modular belt & slat chain manufrs*

▶ Sigma Office Ltd, 20 West End, Ashwell, Baldock, Hertfordshire, SG7 5PJ Tel: (01462) 742783 Fax: (01462) 743321 E-mail: info@sigma-office.net *IT Consultancy*

▶ Sigma Projects, The Pines, Blairadam, Kelty, Fife, KY4 0JG Tel: (0870) 0540530 Fax: (0870) 0540531 E-mail: sales@sigmagroup.org *Security & digital archiving specialists*

Sigma Signs Ltd, Unit 4B, Arun Buildings, Arundel Road, Uxbridge, Middlesex, UB8 2RP Tel: (01895) 273268 Fax: (01895) 271614 E-mail: signs@sigmasigns.com *Signmaking contractors*

▶ Sigma Squared Solutions Ltd, Bedford Heights, Manton Lane, Bedford, MK41 7PH Tel: (0870) 4862682 Fax: (0870) 4862681 E-mail: enquiries@sigma2solutions.com *Engineers & agents to corrugated industry*

Sigma Studies Training, 121 Corringham Road, Stanford-le-Hope, Essex, SS17 0BA Tel: (01375) 671111 Fax: (07092) 380757 E-mail: info@sigmastudies.co.uk *Transport training & management services, forklift truck training services*

Company Information

Sigma Wireless (UK) Ltd, Unit 6, Bridgegate Business Park, Gatehouse Way, Aylesbury, Buckinghamshire, HP19 8XN Tel: (01296) 505505 Fax: (01296) 505500 E-mail: infouk@sigma.ie *Aerial antenna suppliers & manufrs*

Sigma-Aldrich Co. Ltd, Fancy Road, Poole, Dorset, BH12 4QH Tel: (01202) 712300 Fax: (01202) 712350 E-mail: ukcustsv@europe.sial.com *Chemical importers & manufrs*

Sigmacast Iron Ltd, Upper Church Lane, Tipton, West Midlands, DY4 9PA Tel: 0121-557 1293 Fax: 0121-522 2024 *Grey iron, castings manufrs*

SigmaKalon, 16D 16F Kilroot Business Park, Larne Road, Carrickfergus, County Antrim, BT38 7PR Tel: (028) 9335 1567 Fax: (028) 9335 1569 *Distributors of decorating materials*

▶ Sigmapi Systems Ltd, Poplar Grove, Newcastle, Staffordshire, ST5 1JW Tel: (01782) 740134 Fax: (01782) 619908 E-mail: ch@sigmapisystems.com *Computer software*

Sigmatek Europe Ltd, 16 University of Warwick Science Park, Coventry, CV4 7EZ Tel: (024) 7632 3065 Fax: (024) 7632 3060 E-mail: sales@sigmanest.com *Nesting & stock control software for laser cutting services*

Sigmatex (UK) Ltd, Unit 3, The Trafalgar Centre, Belfield Road, Rochdale, Lancashire, OL16 2UX Tel: (01706) 631128 Fax: (01706) 523691 E-mail: sigmatex@sigmatex.co.uk *Advanced fibre reinforced composites manufrs*

Sigmer, The Sussex Innovation Centre, Science Park Square, Falmer, Brighton, BN1 9SB Tel: (01273) 234663 Fax: (01273) 669 701 E-mail: info@sigmer.com *Bespoke IT development services*

▶ Sigmun, Unit 5 Dunhams Court, Dunhams Lane, Letchworth Garden City, Hertfordshire, SG6 1WB Tel: (01462) 678000 Fax: (01462) 678008 *Manufacturing castings*

▶ The Sign Co., Prism Buildings, 9 Nicol Street, Kirkcaldy, Fife, KY1 1NY Tel: (01592) 646454 Fax: (01592) 261333 E-mail: info@thesigncompany.info *Designers manufacturers & installers of all types of signs*

Sign Co., 18 Homedale Drive, Luton, LU4 9TE Tel: (01582) 492075 E-mail: sales@sign-co.com *Sign installation & design*

▶ The Sign Company, PO Box 50, Newport, Isle of Wight, PO30 1SS Tel: (01983) 520047 Fax: (01983) 523889 E-mail: info@signo-spt.com *Glass treatment services*

The Sign Co., 16 Parmington Close, Callow Hill, Redditch, Worcestershire, B97 5YL Tel: (01527) 550962 Fax: (01527) 402777 *Sign manufrs*

Sign 2000 Ltd, Maidstone Road, Paddock Wood, Tonbridge, Kent, TN12 6QJ Tel: (01892) 834383 Fax: (01892) 838349 E-mail: info@sign2000.co.uk *Sign manufacturers & installation nationwide*

Sign 7 Ltd, Unit 10 Fox Oak Enterprise Centre, Foxoak Street, Cradley Heath, West Midlands, B64 5DP Tel: (01384) 413704 Fax: (01384) 413705 *Sign manufrs*

▶ Sign A Rama, 100a Knaresborough Road, Harrogate, North Yorkshire, HG2 7NN Tel: (01423) 883700 Fax: (01423) 883075 E-mail: harrogate@signarama.co.uk *Signs manufrs*

Sign A Rama, 91 Ringway, Preston, PR1 2QD Tel: (01772) 258494 Fax: (01772) 259845 E-mail: preston@sign-a-rama.co.uk *Sign manufrs*

Sign A Rama, Unit A Whiteknights Retail Centre, Shinfield Road, Reading, RG2 8HA Tel: 0118-931 1122 Fax: 0118-931 4040 E-mail: reading@sign-a-rama.co.uk *Sign makers*

Sign A Rama, 328-330 Hobs Moat Road, Solihull, West Midlands, B92 8JT Tel: 0121-742 5888 Fax: 0121-742 5656 E-mail: birminghamsouth@sign-a-rama.co.uk *Sign manufrs*

▶ Sign A Rama, 128 London Road, Hazel Grove, Stockport, Cheshire, SK7 4DJ Tel: 0161-456 2003 Fax: 0161-456 2005 E-mail: info@signarama.uk.com *Full service vehicle, business and safety signs and graphic design including installation, full colour digital printing indoor and outdoor exhibition graphics*

Sign A Rama, 1 Parker Street, Warrington, WA1 1LT Tel: (01925) 445577 Fax: (01925) 244555 E-mail: signarama.warrington@talk21.com *Manufacture, design & installation of signs*

Sign A Rama, 35-36 Auster Road, York, YO30 4XA Tel: (0800) 0272588 Fax: (01904) 692155 *Sign manufrs*

The Sign & Blind Centre Ltd, 24 Cavendish Road, New Malden, Surrey, KT3 6DE Tel: (020) 8337 1538 E-mail: signblindcoltd@aol.com *Blind distributors & sign contractors*

The Sign Centre, Newark Road South, Glenrothes, Fife, KY7 4NS Tel: (01592) 630101 Fax: (01592) 630188 *Sign manufrs*

Sign Centre, 1 Farrier Road, Lincoln, LN6 3RU Tel: (01522) 500024 Fax: (01522) 500054 E-mail: enquires@signcentre-uk.com *Sign manufrs*

Sign Connections Ltd, Unit 5 Sinclair Court, Great Yarmouth, Norfolk, NR31 0NH Tel: (01493) 440285 Fax: (01493) 653888 E-mail: info@signconnections.com *Sign manufrs*

Sign Design, Unit 2 Pottery La West, Chesterfield, Derbyshire, S41 9BN Tel: (01246) 554334 Fax: (01246) 554334 E-mail: sign-design@btconnect.com *Designing & manufacturing vinyl graphics for cars*

Sign & Design, 31 Hospital Lane, Blaby, Leicester, LE8 4FE Tel: 0116-277 1957 Fax: 0116-277 5755 E-mail: signs@freenet.co.uk *Sign manufrs*

Sign & Design, 13 Crannog Lane, Oban, Argyll, PA34 4HB Tel: (01631) 562622 Fax: (01631) 562338 E-mail: sales@signx.com *Sign manufrs*

Sign Designs, 147-149 Hutcheon Street, Aberdeen, AB25 3RY Tel: (01224) 645361 Fax: (01224) 643647 E-mail: dundee@signdesigns.co.uk *Signs manufrs*

Sign Designs, 5 Whorterbank, Dundee, DD2 3AA Tel: (01382) 622407 Fax: (01382) 624344 *Industrial engravers & sign manufrs*

▶ Sign & Digital Print Solutions, The Sign Workshop, Rear of 78 Ham Lane, Longham, Ferndown, Dorset, BH22 9DP Tel: (01202) 572625 *Signmakers and large format print services in Dorset, We manufacture signs, labels, posters and much more, Also available for graphic design services, logo''s letterheads, business cards advertising and more.*

▶ Sign Directory, 38 Sandport Street, Edinburgh, EH6 6EP Tel: 0131-553 4224 Fax: 0131-554 5797 E-mail: signdirectory@btclick.com *Sign designers & printers*

Sign & Display, 2 Tenax Road, Trafford Park, Manchester, M17 1JT Tel: 0161-872 8585 Fax: 0161-876 4056 *Plastic materials, products & components*

Sign & Display Centre, 253 Barlow Moor Road, Manchester, M21 7GJ Tel: 0161-861 7311 Fax: 0161-861 7306 E-mail: sales@signanddisplay.co.uk *Sign contractors & suppliers*

Sign Engineering, George Street, High Wycombe, Buckinghamshire, HP11 2RZ Tel: (01494) 459915 Fax: (01494) 459915 *Sign manufrs*

The Sign Experience Ltd, 12 Dukes Court, Bognor Road, Chichester, West Sussex, PO19 8FX Tel: (01243) 779991 Fax: (01243) 779992 E-mail: info@sign-ex.co.uk *Signs*

▶ Sign Express Northampton, Collingwood Business Centre, Lower Harding Street, Northampton, NN1 2JL Tel: (01604) 472972 Fax: (01604) 472373 E-mail: northampton@signsexpress.co.uk *Vehicles grap signs services*

The Sign Factory, 86 Oxford Road, Clacton-on-Sea, Essex, CO15 3TG Tel: (01255) 429242 Fax: (01255) 429242 *Sign manufrs*

The Sign Factory, Burnbank Road, Bainsford, Falkirk, FK2 7PE Tel: (01324) 501950 Fax: (01324) 501951 E-mail: info@falkirk.gov.uk *Sign manufactures & general engravers*

Sign Factory, 1333 London Road, Leigh-on-Sea, Essex, SS9 2AD Tel: (01702) 716161 Fax: (01702) 716141 E-mail: sales@signfactory.ws *Neon sign specialists*

Sign Factory, Unit 12 Kingston Industrial Estate, Ardgowan Street, Port Glasgow, Renfrewshire, PA14 5DG Tel: (01475) 743624 Fax: (01475) 745677 E-mail: signfactory@btconnect.com *General sign makers*

Sign Fit, 482 Barking Road, London, E6 2LT Tel: (020) 8552 1194 Fax: (020) 8548 1047 *Sign makers & installers*

▶ Sign Focus, Unit 2 Gower Street, Bradford, West Yorkshire, BD5 7JF Tel: (01274) 747788 Fax: (01274) 747767 E-mail: sales@signfocusltd.com *Sign manufacturers & installers*

Sign Fx, Signs F X, Unit 4 Bradmash Court, Bradmarsh Way, Rotherham, South Yorkshire, S60 1BW Tel: (01709) 360057 E-mail: signfxsales@btconnect.com *sign manufacturers,shop signs,vehicle graphics,digital graphics,neon,illuminated box signs,pavement signs,vinyl lettering,design*

Sign Group, Cathedral Road, Cardiff, CF11 9HA Tel: (029) 2022 5250 Fax: (029) 2078 6666 *Sign manufrs*

▶ Sign Group, Unit 1del Guerra Courtgelligron Industrail Estatetonyrefa, Tonyrefail, Porth, Mid Glamorgan, CF39 8ES Tel: (01443) 670300 Fax: (01443) 670404 *Make & installing signs*

▶ Sign Guy, The Old School House, St Peters Lane, Bickenhill Village, Solihull, West Midlands, B92 0DP Tel: 07869 296579 Fax: 01675 443 080 E-mail: signguys@btinternet.com *Design, Build and Installation "Shop Fascias - Vehicle Liveries - Digital Printing - Built Up Letters - ""A"" Boards - Banners - Neons and L.E.D""s for Illuminated Signs*

Sign Here, Unit 1 & 2, 179 Fosse Road North, Leicester, LE3 5EZ Tel: 0116-225 9977 Fax: 0116-225 9966 E-mail: sales@sign-here.co.uk *Sign manufrs*

Sign House Ltd, Unit H Burley Hill Trading Estate, Leeds, LS4 2PU Tel: 0113-274 0476 Fax: 0113-274 0477 E-mail: enq@thesignhouse.com *Signmakers, large format printing*

Sign & Image Works, 115 Blackburn Road, Bolton, BL1 8HF Tel: (01204) 393824 Fax: (01204) 365123 E-mail: sales@silentimage.com *Sign & image works*

▶ Sign Impact, 1 High House Cottage, Woodham Road, Battlesbridge, Wickford, Essex, SS11 7QL Tel: (01268) 761116 E-mail: sales@sign-impact.co.uk *Design, manufacture & installation of all types of signs*

Sign Industries Ltd, Mains of Gardyne, Forfar, Angus, DD8 2SQ Tel: (01241) 828694 Fax: (01241) 828331 E-mail: info@signindustries.com *Engravers (chemical etchers)*

Sign Installations Ltd, Unit 2 1-7 Ernest Avenue, London, SE27 0DQ Tel: (020) 8681 1971 Fax: (020) 8670 7721 *Sign manufrs*

Sign It, 302 Union Road, Oswaldtwistle, Accrington, Lancashire, BB5 3JD Tel: (01254) 396325 Fax: (01254) 396325 *Advertising, neon & perspex signs*

Sign It, Beehive Works, Beehive Lane, Chelmsford, CM2 9JY Tel: (01245) 492294 Fax: (01245) 262147 E-mail: sales@sign-it.co.uk *Sign makers & designers*

▶ The Sign King, 35 charles street, Swinton, Manchester, M27 9UG Tel: 0161-278 0199 Fax: 0161-278 0199 E-mail: thesignking@ntlworld.com

Sign & Label Centre Ltd, Dock Road, Connah's Quay, Deeside, Clwyd, CH5 4DS Tel: (01244) 813660 Fax: (01244) 816812 E-mail: sales@signandlabelcentre.com *Sign, label & nameplate manufrs.*

▶ Sign & Light, Unit 5 Sherwood Industrial Estate, Bonnyrigg, Midlothian, EH19 3LW Tel: 0131-654 1122 Fax: 0131-654 0808 *Lighting & sign manufrs*

Sign Logic, Gatehead Business Park, Delph New Road, Delph, Oldham, OL3 5DE Tel: (01457) 878806 Fax: (01457) 820592 E-mail: sales@signlogic.co.uk *Sign manufrs*

Sign Maker, 82 York Road, Woking, Surrey, GU22 7XR Tel: (01483) 714389 Fax: (01483) 714389 E-mail: info@thesignmaker.co.uk *Sign manufrs*

Sign Makers Products Ltd, Hawthorne House, Ipswich Road, Long Stratton, Norwich, NR15 2XB Tel: (01508) 531183 Fax: (01508) 531139 E-mail: sales@sign-makers-products.co.uk *Sign & led manufrs*

Sign Nature Ltd, Monks Heath Hall Workshop, Chelford Road, Nether Alderley, Macclesfield, Cheshire, SK10 4SY Tel: (01625) 860921 Fax: (01625) 890255 E-mail: tim@sign-nature.co.uk *Exhibition sign producers*

Sign & Poster Specialists, 23 Meadow Place, Shrewsbury, SY1 1PD Tel: (01743) 353320 Fax: (01743) 235053 E-mail: david@signandposter.co.uk *Sign specialists*

▶ Sign & Print, 11 Colchester Road, Great Totham, Maldon, Essex, CM9 8BZ Tel: (01621) 891289 E-mail: sales@click4signs.co.uk

Sign & Print Centre, 162 Top Road, Calow, Chesterfield, Derbyshire, S44 5TD Tel: (01246) 209691 Fax: (01246) 209690 *Manufacturers of signs*

▶ Sign & Print Here, 4 Long Lane, Wrington, Bristol, BS40 5SA Tel: (01934) 861144 Fax: (01934) 861155

Sign Right Rugby, 47 High Street, Welford, Northampton, NN6 6HT Tel: (01858) 575715 Fax: (01858) 575705 *Sign manufrs*

Sign Services, Unit A4 Maidstone Industrial Centre, St Peter Street, Maidstone, Kent, ME16 0ST Tel: (01622) 681135 Fax: (01622) 678330 E-mail: sales@signservicesonline.co.uk *Neon sign manufrs*

Sign Shop, 93 West Main Street, Broxburn, West Lothian, EH52 5LE Tel: (01506) 853601 Fax: (01506) 853601 *Sign manufrs*

The Sign Shop (Horsham) Ltd, 55a Park Terrace East, Horsham, West Sussex, RH13 5DJ Tel: (01403) 268988 Fax: (01403) 253085 E-mail: enquiries@thesignshop.co.uk *Design, manufacture & installation of interior & exterior signs*

Sign Solutions, Unit 6-7, Brympton Way, Yeovil, Somerset, BA20 2HP Tel: (01935) 425864 Fax: (01935) 425533 E-mail: sales@ss4signs.co.uk *Sign makers*

Sign Specialists Ltd, 19 Oxleasow Road, East Moons Moat, Redditch, Worcestershire, B98 0RE Tel: (01527) 504250 Fax: (01527) 504251 E-mail: sales@sign-specialists.co.uk *Sign manufrs*

Sign Stop, 71 Station Road, Flitwick, Bedford, MK45 1JU Tel: (01525) 714949 Fax: (01525) 719498 *Sign manufrs*

The Sign Studio, The Ferrers Centre, Staunton Harold, Ashby-de-la-Zouch, Leicestershire, LE65 1RU Tel: (01332) 694545 Fax: (01332) 864863 E-mail: info@ferrerscentre.co.uk *Traditional sign writers*

Sign Studio, 5 Croft Street, Cheltenham, Gloucestershire, GL53 0EE Tel: (01242) 228866 Fax: (01242) 228777 E-mail: sales@chelt-signstudio.co.uk *Sign manufrs*

The Sign Studio, Coach Fold Works, Haley Hill, Halifax, West Yorkshire, HX3 6ED Tel: (01422) 345179 Fax: (01422) 365400 E-mail: phil.rushworth@msl-signstudio.co.uk *Manufacturers of display signs*

Sign Studio, 391 Durnsford Road, London, SW19 8EE Tel: (020) 8946 7193 *Sign manufrs*

Sign Studio, 158 Cromwell Road, Salford, M6 6DE Tel: 0161-792 7254 Fax: 0161-792 1873 *Sign manufrs*

The Sign Studio N E Ltd, 7 Tees Court, Skippers Lane Industrial Estate, Middlesbrough, Cleveland, TS6 6DX Tel: (01642) 465999 Fax: (01642) 465888 E-mail: sign.studio@btconnect.com *Sign makers*

Sign Studios Ltd, 16 Broomhills Industrial Estate, Rayne Road, Braintree, Essex, CM7 2RG Tel: (01376) 349529 Fax: (01376) 552635 E-mail: sign.studios@btinternet.com *Screen printing & sign contractors services*

Sign Supply Ltd, 20 Station Road, Chertsey, Surrey, KT16 8BE Tel: (0870) 2402678 Fax: (0870) 2402679 E-mail: sales@signsupply.co.uk *Sign manufrs*

Sign Systems, Unit 4a Shipley Court, Manners Avenue Industrial Estate, Manners Industrial Estate, Ilkeston, Derbyshire, DE7 8EF Tel: 0115-944 1678 Fax: 0115-944 1495 E-mail: enquiries@signsystems.uk.com *Sign manufrs*

Sign Trade Europe Ltd, Parker Street, Hucknall, Nottingham, NG15 7UF Tel: 0115-968 1000 Fax: 0115-968 1373 E-mail: email@signtrade.btconnect.com *Sign makers*

Sign Trade Supplies, Britannia House, Granville Road, Maidstone, Kent, ME14 2BJ Tel: (01622) 689410 Fax: (01622) 689416 E-mail: orders@signtradesupplies.co.uk Purchasing Contact: T. Spurgeon Sales Contact: T. Spurgeon *Sign making material distributors & agents. Vinyls, digital materials, banners, aluminium sections, traditional sign writers supplies, Saunex sheeting, Acrylic sheeting, Correx, Street Furniture, points of sale*

Sign Trading, 294grays Inn Road, London, WC1X 8DX Tel: (020) 7837 0703 Fax: (020) 7278 4717 E-mail: terrysigncentre@hotmail.com *Sign manufrs*

▶ Sign Update, 1 Allens Orchard, Chipping Warden, Banbury, Oxfordshire, OX17 1LX Tel: (01295) 660666 Fax: (0560) 1162164 E-mail: sb@freerbutler-gds.co.uk *Leading publication for the Sign Industry. Industry news, product reviews, shows and events, company profiles, classifieds.*

Sign Wizards, 27 Upper High Street, Cradley Heath, West Midlands, B64 5HX Tel: (01384) 413223 Fax: (01384) 413223 *Sign manufrs*

Sign Wizzard, Griffin Lane, Aylesbury, Buckinghamshire, HP19 0GH Tel: (01296) 398022 Fax: (01296) 398028 E-mail: sign.wizzard@virgin.net *Sign manufrs*

Sign Work Of Cambridge Sign Manufacturers, 303 St.Neots Road Hardwick, Hardwick, Cambridge, CB23 7QL Tel: (01954) 211611 Fax: (01954) 211010 E-mail: admin@signwork.co.uk *Sign & screen printing services*

Sign Works, 12 Clarendon Avenue, Leamington Spa, Warwickshire, CV32 5PZ Tel: (01926) 311791 Fax: (01926) 311791 E-mail: simon@thesignworks.co.uk *Sign makers*

Sign Workshop, 8 The Ridgeway, Hitchin, Hertfordshire, SG5 2BT Tel: (01462) 442440 Fax: (01462) 442440 E-mail: sales@thesignworkshop.co.uk *Signs designers & manufrs*

Sign Workshop The, Doods Road, Reigate, Surrey, RH2 0NT Tel: (01737) 240479 Fax: (01737) 223694 *Sign makers*

Sign World 2000, Drome Road, Deeside Industrial Park, Deeside, Clwyd, CH5 2NY Tel: (01244) 281955 Fax: (01244) 281949 E-mail: mail.signworld@btinternet.com *Signs makers & shop fitters*

▶ Sign Zone, 8 Worton Hall Industrial Estate, Worton Road, Isleworth, Middlesex, TW7 6ER Tel: (020) 8568 6898 Fax: (020) 8568 1070 E-mail: signzone@btconnect.com *ALL TYPES OF SIGNAGE*BANNERS SHOP FASCIAS*VEHICLE LIVERYS*VINYL LETTERING*EXHIBITION GRAPHICS*ENGRAVED PLAQUES*ETCHED GLASS VINYL*A BOARDS*ILLUMINATED SIGNS*

Signage Ltd, Units 31-32 Bloomfield Commercial Centre, 5 Factory Street, Belfast, BT5 5AW Tel: (028) 9045 0145 Fax: (028) 9073 2533 E-mail: signageltd@btconnect.com *Sign manufrs*

Signagraphic Signs & Nameplates, 7 Russell St North, Coventry, CV1 4GD Tel: (024) 7625 8802 Fax: (024) 7625 8802 E-mail: neil@signagraphic.co.uk *Sign manufrs*

Signal Ambitech Division, Ambitech Division, 9A Regal Way, Faringdon, Oxfordshire, SN7 7BX Tel: (01367) 242660 Fax: (01367) 242700 E-mail: ambitech@signal-group.com *Air pollution monitoring equipment manufrs*

Signal Business Systems Ltd, Swan Corner, Pewsey, Wiltshire, SN9 5HL Tel: (01672) 563333 Fax: (01672) 562391 E-mail: signalbusiness.systems@virgin.net *Planning board suppliers*

Signal Group Ltd, Standards House, 12 Doman Road, Camberley, Surrey, GU15 3DF Tel: (01276) 682841 Fax: (01276) 691302 E-mail: instruments@signal-group.com *Analysis equipment & analyser gas*

Signal House Ltd, Cherrycourt Way, Leighton Buzzard, Bedfordshire, LU7 4UH Tel: (01525) 377477 Fax: (01525) 850999 E-mail: admin@collis.co.uk *Railway signalling equipment manufrs*

Signal Management Ltd, Plumpton House, Plumpton Road, Hoddesdon, Hertfordshire, EN11 0LB Tel: (01992) 463603 Fax: (01992) 443824 E-mail: enquiries@signalman.co.uk *Matrix relays & systems*

Signam Ltd, Harris Road, Warwick, CV34 5FY Tel: (01926) 417300 Fax: (01926) 417333 E-mail: sales@signam.co.uk *Automotive & equestrian signage manufrs*

Signarama Ltd, 3b Burley Hill Trading Estate, Leeds, LS4 2PU Tel: 0113-230 7952 Fax: (0871) 2749370 E-mail: sales@signarama.demon.co.uk *Sign makers & large format digital printers*

Signarc Services, 1 Cording Street, London, E14 6NL Tel: (020) 7517 3979 Fax: (020) 7538 8657 E-mail: info@tcsigns.co.uk *Sign manufrs*

Signature Ltd, Signature House, Hainge Road, Tividale, Oldbury, West Midlands, B69 2NF Tel: 0121-557 0234 Fax: 0121-557 0995 E-mail: sales@signatureltd.com *Manufacturers of highway electrical & illuminated furniture*

Signature Aircraft Engineering, Hangar Road, Denham Airfield, Uxbridge, Middlesex, UB9 5DF Tel: (01895) 834777 Fax: (01252) 864399 *Helicopter maintenance*

Signature House Ltd, Signature House, 232A Rainhill Road, Rainhill, Prescot, Merseyside, L35 4LD Tel: 0151-430 7114 Fax: 0151-431 0515 E-mail: laurataylor@psignature.com *Business centre*

▶ Signature Image Consultants Ltd, Boughton Monchelsea, Maidstone, Kent, ME17 4XQ Tel: (01622) 744659 E-mail: results@signature.gb.com *Internet consultancy*

Signature Industries Ltd, Unit 19 Atlas Industrial Estate, Foundry Street, Glasgow, G21 4PR Tel: 0141-558 7272 Fax: 0141-558 9696 E-mail: info@sigcom.co.uk *Two-way radio communications services*

Signature Signs, Unit 79 Brasenose Road, Bootle, Merseyside, L20 8HJ Tel: 0151-933 7327 Fax: 0151-933 7323 *Sign makers*

Signature Signs, 188 Church Road, Hove, East Sussex, BN3 2DJ Tel: (01273) 774775 *Sign manufrs*

Signature Signs, Timbercot, Waterside, Bradwell-on-Sea, Southminster, Essex, CM0 7QT Tel: (01621) 776772 Fax: (01621) 776772 *Sign manufrs*

Signbox Ltd, 3 Egham Business Village, Crabtree Road, Egham, Surrey, TW20 8RB Tel: (01784) 438688 Fax: (01784) 471694 *Sign Manufrs*

Signbusters Of Ayr, 132 Hunters Avenue, Ayr, KA8 9EQ Tel: (01292) 281224 Fax: (01292) 477552 E-mail: signhouseayrcc@aol.com *Sign manufrs*

Signcast, 14 Sherwood Forest Art & Craft Centre, Forest Corner, Edwinstowe, Mansfield, Nottinghamshire, NG21 9RN Tel: (01623) 825595 Fax: (01623) 825595 E-mail: sales@signcast.co.uk *Sign Activities*

Signconex Ltd, St. Johns Works, Fern Street, Bury, Lancashire, BL9 5BP Tel: 0161-764 9500 Fax: 0161-764 9600 E-mail: sales@signconex.co.uk *Modular sign systems manufrs*

Signcraft, 172 St Sepulchre Gate West, Doncaster, South Yorkshire, DN1 3AQ Tel: (01302) 361078 Fax: (01302) 321804 E-mail: info@signcraft-doncaster.com *Sign manufrs*

Signcraft Ltd, St. Stephens Road, West Drayton, Middlesex, UB7 7RL Tel: (01895) 442768 Fax: (01895) 442153 E-mail: sales@signcraft.org *Sign contractors & suppliers*

Signcraft (Cheltenham) Ltd, Unit 40 Lansdale Industrial Estate, Gloucester Road, Cheltenham, Gloucestershire, GL51 8PL Tel: (01242) 513133 Fax: (01242) 227074 E-mail: sales@signcraftcheltenham.co.uk *Complete sign manufrs*

Signcraft Signs, 244 High Road, Romford, RM6 6AP Tel: (020) 8599 4747 Fax: (020) 8599 1616 E-mail: signcraft@signcraft.fsnet.co.uk *Sign & banners manufrs*

► Signcraft Signs & Graphics, 157 Heathhall Industrial Estate, Heathhall, Dumfries, DG1 3PH Tel: (01387) 251595 Fax: (01387) 251820 E-mail: sales@signcraft-signs.co.uk *Sign manufrs*

Signdisplay, Unit 7 Long Island Park, Carlisle, CA2 5AS Tel: (01228) 819144 Fax: (01228) 514145 E-mail: maurice@albanysigndisplay.wannado.co.uk *Sign designers & manufrs*

Signet A C Ltd, 5 Tower Road, Washington, Tyne & Wear, NE37 2SH Tel: 0191-417 4551 Fax: 0191-417 0634 E-mail: sales@signet-ac.co.uk *Voice alarm equipment design & maunfrs*

Signet Branded Tags Seals, 3-5 Aintree Road, Perivale, Greenford, Middlesex, UB6 7LA Tel: (020) 8810 7300 Fax: (0844) 9007301 *Promotional seals*

Signet Industrial Distribution Doncaster Ltd, Watch House Lane, Doncaster, South Yorkshire, DN5 9LZ Tel: (01302) 390002 Fax: (01302) 390003 *Bearing & power transmission*

Signet Joinery, Laing Close, Grangetown, Middlesbrough, Cleveland, TS6 7EA Tel: (01642) 456777 Fax: (01642) 452912 *Joinery manufrs*

Signet Signs Ltd, 45 West Town Road, Backwell, Bristol, BS48 3HG Tel: (01275) 463601 Fax: (01275) 462990 E-mail: mail@signetsigns.co.uk *Sign making*

Signet Signs, Unit 11 Islwyn Workshops, Pontymister Industrial Estate, Risca, Newport, Gwent, NP11 6NP Tel: (01633) 601305 Fax: (01633) 601305 E-mail: deansignet@aol.com *Sign manufrs*

► Signfab (UK) Ltd, Byford Road, Leicester, LE4 0DG Tel: 0116-261 0104

Signflair Ltd, 10-54 Ainsworth Avenue, Belfast, BT13 3EN Tel: (028) 9032 6007 Fax: (028) 9033 1936 E-mail: signflair@dnet.co.uk *Sign manufrs*

Signgrave Signs & Nameplates, Tudor Court, Harold Court Road, Romford, RM3 0AE Tel: (01708) 373827 Fax: (01708) 381069 E-mail: sign.grave@virgin.net *Engravers, sign & screen printers manufrs*

Significant Signs, Unit 34 Mahatma Gandhi Industrial Estate, Milkwood Road, London, SE24 0JF Tel: (020) 7924 9343 Fax: (020) 7924 9343 *Sign manufrs*

Signline, Unit 5a Ridge Hill Farm, Nash, Milton Keynes, MK17 0EH Tel: (01908) 379600 Fax: (01296) 715113 *Sign making manufrs*

Signline, Thistledown Farm, Tivetshall St. Margaret, Norwich, NR15 2DL Tel: (01379) 677699 Fax: (01379) 677879 E-mail: jason.signline@virgin.net *Sign manufacturers, digital printing, vehicle lettering*

Signline, Wayside House, Chapel Road, Meppershall, Shefford, Bedfordshire, SG17 5NQ Tel: (01462) 850718 Fax: (01462) 851212 E-mail: sales@signline.co.uk *General signage, digital printing services*

Sign-Maker.Net, Little Knowle Farm, High Bickington, Umberleigh, Devon, EX37 9BJ Tel: (01769) 560675 Fax: (01769) 560819 E-mail: enquiries@sign-maker.net *Huge range of signs by mail order. Prices & pictures on the website. House signs - wood, slate, granite, marble & brass. Engraved plaques in many materials wheel covers, vinyl & stainless, full colour or single. Full colour vinyl printing.*

► Signmaking Ltd, 9 Dee Road, Chester, CH2 4DL Tel: (0845) 2267251 E-mail: sales@signmaking.co.uk *Sign makers banner makers, vehicle graphics, neon, graphic designers*

The Signmaster, 25 Whessoe Road, Darlington, County Durham, DL3 0QP Tel: (01325) 351374 Fax: (01325) 351374 *Sign makers*

Signmaster, 276 Smithdown Road, Allerton, Liverpool, L15 5AJ Tel: 0151-722 4009 Fax: 0151-722 4008 E-mail: andyg@fitwell-ltd.co.uk *Sign makers*

Signmaster E D Ltd, Pinnaclehill Industrial Estate, Kelso, Roxburghshire, TD5 8DW Tel: (01573) 223227 Fax: (01573) 225014 *Sign fixers manufrs*

► Signode Machines Group Europe, Queensway, Fforestfach, Swansea, SA5 4ED Tel: (01792) 585758 Fax: (01792) 585078 E-mail: machinesuk@signodeuk.com Principal Export Areas: Worldwide *Signode Machines Group Europe is a dedicated business unit focused on the needs of a diverse range of industries with one common requirement - fast, efficient packaging of cartons, cases & palletized loads*

Signpost Engraving, 5 Dalton Court, Astmoor Industrial Estate, Runcorn, Cheshire, WA7 1PU Tel: (01928) 574777 Fax: (01928) 567314 E-mail: signpost.eng@btconnect.com *Industrial engravers*

Signpost Signs, 137 Upper Wickham Lane, Welling, Kent, DA16 3AL Tel: (020) 8854 8777 Fax: (020) 8855 0577 E-mail: enquiries@signpostsigns.co.uk *Sign manufrs*

SignRight, 157-161 West Road, Westcliff-On-Sea, Essex, SS0 9DH Tel: (01702) 308486 Fax: (0870) 7061711 E-mail: info@signright.co.uk *Banner & sign manufrs*

Signrise Signs & Nameplates, Tirmynydd Road, Three Crosses, Swansea, SA4 3PB Tel: (01792) 872536 Fax: (01792) 872536 *Graphic sign makers*

Signrite Ltd, 41C Green Street, Ayr, KA8 8BQ Tel: (01292) 285908 Fax: (01292) 261539 E-mail: mail@signritesignmakers.co.uk *Sign manufrs*

Signs Incorporated, 77 Lowfield Street, Dartford, DA1 1HP Tel: (01322) 221181 Fax: (01322) 221185 *Sign makers*

Signs 2000 Ltd, 6 North Street, Liverpool, L3 2AY Tel: 0151-227 1033 Fax: 0151-227 1032 E-mail: signs2000@cybase.co.uk *Sign manufrs*

Signs 2000, Unit 4 Kenworthy Road, Stafford, ST16 3DY Tel: (01785) 220561 Fax: (01785) 220969 E-mail: admin@signs2k.co.uk *Sign & nameplate manufrs*

Signs By Morrell Ltd, Tarran Way South, Tarran Industrial Estate, Wirral, Merseyside, CH46 4TP Tel: 0151-678 8989 Fax: 0151-678 8816 E-mail: sales@signs-by-morrell.com *Sign contractors & suppliers*

► Signs & Design Ltd, 22-23 King Street Trading Estate, Middlewich, Cheshire, CW10 9LF Tel: (01606) 738833 Fax: (01606) 738547 E-mail: info@golfcoursesigns.co.uk *Signage manufrs*

Signs & Designs, Riverside House, Lock Lane, Castleford, West Yorkshire, WF10 2JZ Tel: (01977) 512095 Fax: (01977) 603695 E-mail: sales@signs-designs.co.uk *Sign manufrs*

Signs & Designs Of Perth, 17 Main Street, Bridgend, Perth, PH2 7HD Tel: (01738) 633355 Fax: (01738) 577001 E-mail: sales@signsperth.co.uk *Sign manufrs*

Signs Direct, Commerce House, Bank Street, Long Eaton, Nottingham, NG10 1GY Tel: 0115-972 5001 Fax: 0115-972 3111 E-mail: sales@signsdirect-midlands.co.uk *Sign manufrs*

Signs Direct, 23 Kingsway, Scarborough, North Yorkshire, YO12 6SG Tel: (01723) 500425 Fax: (01723) 500425 E-mail: kevin@signsdirect.freeserve.co.uk *Sign manufrs*

Signs Direct Trade, 2 Rancorn Road, Margate, Kent, CT9 5DG Tel: (01843) 224400 Fax: (01843) 296092 *Sign manufrs*

► Signs Express Ltd, Unit 16 Anglo Business Park, Smeaton Close, Aylesbury, Buckinghamshire, HP19 8UP Tel: (01296) 339998 Fax: (01296) 331118 E-mail: aylesbury@signsexpress.co.uk *We offer a complete manufacture and fitting service for all forms of signage from interior and exterior signs to vehicle graphics, banners, window graphics and exhibition and display products. Part of the UK & Ireland''s largest sign company.*

► Signs Express Ltd, 11 Josselin Court, Josselin Road, Burnt Mills Industrial Estate, Basildon, Essex, SS13 1QF Tel: (01268) 729567 Fax: (01268) 729568

► Signs Express Ltd, 140 Appin Road, Birkenhead, Merseyside, CH41 9HJ Tel: 0151-650 2344 Fax: 0151-650 2355 E-mail: liverpool@signsexpress.co.uk *We specialise in vehicle graphics, interior and exterior signage, banners, window graphics, exhibition and display graphics, labels and stickers and also DDA compliant health and safety signage.**

► Signs Express Ltd, Unit 17 Avonbank Industrial Centre, West Town Road, Bristol, BS11 9DE Tel: 0117-982 4004 Fax: 0117-982 5005 E-mail: bristol.north@signsexpress.co.uk *Sign writers*

► Signs Express Ltd, Barnwell Drbarnwell Business Park, Cambridge, CB5 8UZ Tel: (01223) 414005 Fax: (01223) 413801 E-mail: cambridge@signsexpress.co.uk *Sign manufrs*

► Signs Express Ltd, 2 Ketlan Court, River Lane, Saltney, Chester, CH4 8SB Tel: (01244) 681682 Fax: (01244) 681600 E-mail: chester@signsexpress.co.uk *Sign manufrs*

Signs Express Ltd, Unit 16 Priory Industrial Park, Christchurch, Dorset, BH23 4HE Tel: (01425) 277676 Fax: (01425) 277694 E-mail: bournemouth@signsexpress.co.uk *We offer a complete manufacture and fitting service for all forms of signage from interior and exterior signs to vehicle graphics, banners, window graphics and exhibition and display products. Part of the UK & Ireland''''''''s largest sign company.*

Signs Express Ltd, 19a Westside Centre, London Road, Stanway, Colchester, CO3 8PH Tel: (01206) 213111 Fax: (01206) 212110 E-mail: colchester@signsexpress.co.uk *Sign makers*

Signs Express Ltd, Unit 4 Bishopgate Business Park, Widdrington Road, Coventry, CV1 4NN Tel: (024) 7622 3380 Fax: (024) 7625 6377 E-mail: coventry@signsexpress.co.uk *We offer a complete manufacture and fitting service for all forms of signage from interior and exterior signs to vehicle graphics, banners, window graphics and exhibition and display products. Part of the UK & Ireland''''s largest sign company.*

► Signs Express Ltd, 1 Henson Road, Darlington, County Durham, DL1 4QD Tel: (01325) 382444 Fax: (01325) 382777 E-mail: southdurham@signsexpress.co.uk *Manufacturers & fitting service for all forms of signage*

► Signs Express Ltd, 3 Parker Industrial Centre, 275-289 Watling Street, Dartford, DA2 6EP Tel: (01322) 221771 Fax: (01322) 221597 E-mail: dartford@signsexpress.co.uk *Sign manufrs*

Signs Express Ltd, Unit D1 Amberley Drive, Sinfin Lane, Sinfin, Derby, DE24 9RE Tel: (01332) 769450 Fax: (01332) 769470 E-mail: derby@signsexpress.co.uk *Sign manufrs*

Signs Express Ltd, Unit S2 & S4 Didcot Enterprise Centre, Hawksworth, Didcot, Oxfordshire, OX11 7PH Tel: (01235) 811177 Fax: (01235) 818805 E-mail: oxford@signsexpress.co.uk *Vehicle graphics, interior & exterior signage, banners, graphics*

Signs Express Ltd, 3 Guildhall Industrial Estate, Sandall Stones Road, Kirk Sandall Industrial Estate, Doncaster, South Yorkshire, DN3 1QR Tel: (01302) 888173 Fax: (01302) 888234 E-mail: doncaster@signsexpress.co.uk *Vehicle graphics, interior & exterior signage, banners,*

► Signs Express Ltd, Unit G2 Marabout Industrial Estate, Dorchester, Dorset, DT1 1YA Tel: (01305) 260042 Fax: (01305) 260052 E-mail: w.dorset@signsexpress.co.uk *Sign makers*

► Signs Express Ltd, 25 Dumbryden Road, Edinburgh, EH14 2AB Tel: 0131-453 1232 Fax: 0131-453 1238 E-mail: edinburgh.w@signsexpress.co.uk

Signs Express Ltd, 257b Dukesway, Team Valley Trading Estate, Gateshead, Tyne & Wear, NE11 0PZ Tel: 0191-487 4900 Fax: 0191-487 5900 E-mail: gateshead@signsexpress.co.uk *We offer a complete manufacture and fitting service for all forms of signage from interior and exterior signs to vehicle graphics, banners, window graphics and exhibition and display products. Part of the UK & Ireland''''s largest sign company.*

► Signs Express Ltd, 19 Eastville Close, Eastern Avenue, Gloucester, GL4 3SJ Tel: (01452) 309390 Fax: (01452) 309396 E-mail: gloucester@signsexpress.co.uk *Sign makers*

► Signs Express Ltd, Unit 2e Westmains Industrial Estate, Grangemouth, Stirlingshire, FK3 8YE Tel: (01324) 666966 Fax: (01324) 666969 E-mail: falkirk@signsexpress.co.uk *Sign specialists*

► Signs Express Ltd, 1 Maple River Industrial Estate, River Way, Harlow, Essex, CM20 2DP Tel: (01279) 641300 Fax: (01279) 641400 E-mail: info@signsexpress.co.uk *Vehicle, interior, exterior, banners, window, display graphics*

► Signs Express Ltd, 4 Hookstone Centre, Hookstone Chase, Harrogate, North Yorkshire, HG2 7HW Tel: (01423) 885111 Fax: (01423) 885222 E-mail: harrogate@signsexpress.co.uk *Specialists in vehicle graphics, signs, window graphics & banners*

► Signs Express Ltd, Unit 20 The Hawthorn Centre, Elmgrove Road, Harrow, Middlesex, HA1 2RF Tel: (020) 8424 9920 Fax: (020) 8424 9940 E-mail: wembley@signsexpress.co.uk *Sign makers*

► Signs Express Ltd, Unit 16 Priory Tec Park Saxon Way, Priory Park, Hessle, North Humberside, HU13 9PB Tel: (01482) 629966 Fax: (01482) 629967 E-mail: sales@signsexpress.co.uk *Graphics & signs services*

► Signs Express Ltd, 6 Greenwich Close, Ipswich, IP3 0DD Tel: (01473) 281414 Fax: (01473) 281456 E-mail: ipswich@signsexpress.co.uk *Sign makers*

Signs Express Ltd, 2 St Andrews Court, Rollesby Road, King's Lynn, Norfolk, PE30 4LS Tel: (01553) 761762 Fax: (01553) 761769 E-mail: kingslynn@signsexpress.co.uk *We offer a complete manufacture and fitting service for all forms of signage from interior and exterior signs to vehicle graphics, banners, window graphics and exhibition and display products. Part of the UK & Ireland''''s largest sign company.*

► Signs Express Ltd, Unit 30 Lake Enterprise Park, Ladies Walk, Lancaster, LA1 3NX Tel: (01524) 389966 Fax: (01524) 389977 E-mail: lancaster@signsexpress.co.uk *We specialise in vehicle graphics, interior and exterior signage, banners, window graphics, exhibition and display graphics, labels and stickers and also DDA compliant health and safety signage.**

► Signs Express Ltd, 2 Leodis Court, Leeds, LS11 5JJ Tel: 0113-243 6711 Fax: 0113-243 6744 E-mail: leeds.east@signsexpress.co.uk *Signs, design installation & manufrs*

► Signs Express Ltd, 3 Cardinal Close, Lincoln, LN2 4SY Tel: (01522) 530202 Fax: (01522) 539007 E-mail: lincoln@signsexpress.co.uk *Sign contractors*

► Signs Express Ltd, Unit 5 Simcox Court, Riverside Park Industrial Estate, Middlesbrough, Cleveland, TS2 1UX Tel: (01642) 249999 Fax: (01642) 240444 E-mail: teesside@signsexpress.co.uk *Vehicle interior & exterior graphics, banners, window graphics*

► Signs Express Ltd, 99 Alston Drive, Bradwell Abbey, Milton Keynes, MK13 9HF Tel: (01908) 221330 Fax: (01908) 221227 E-mail: miltonkeynes@signsexpress.co.uk *Sign makers*

Signs Express, Unit 14 Abbey Enterprise Park, Mill Road, Newtownabbey, County Antrim, BT36 7BA Tel: (028) 9086 5647 Fax: (028) 9086 9224 E-mail: belfast@signsexpress.co.uk *Supply signs for business to business*

Signs Express Ltd, 25 Kingsway, Norwich, NR2 4UE Tel: (01603) 762680 Fax: (01603) 762681 E-mail: norwich@signsexpress.co.uk *Sign manufrs*

► Signs Express Ltd, 1 2 The Old Church, St. Matthews Road, Norwich, NR1 1SP Tel: (01603) 625925 Fax: (01603) 613136 E-mail: sales@signsexpress.co.uk *With more than 80 centres throughout the UK and Ireland, Signs Express is in the unique position of being able to provide truly effective signage solutions for any situation, anywhere. Each centre is custom-designed and equipped with the kind of cutting-edge technology required to meet the most exacting customer requirement. At Signs Express, the UK and Ireland's market leader, we combine the highest standards of quality and professionalism with national coverage and local knowledge to offer you, our customer, an unbeatable service. From interior and exterior signs, exhibition graphics and banners to individual vehicle graphics or co-ordinated schemes for a nationwide chain of car showrooms, our signs are designed to raise the profile of national and local clients alike.*

► Signs Express Ltd, 9 Greenhill Road, Paisley, Renfrewshire, PA3 1RJ Tel: 0141-883 0304 Fax: 0141-840 1955 E-mail: info@signexpress.co.uk *Sign fittings*

Signs Express Ltd, 9-10 Fenlake Business Centre, Fengate, Peterborough, PE1 5BQ Tel: (01733) 340008 Fax: (01733) 340067 E-mail: peterborough@signsexpress.co.uk *Sign makers*

► Signs Express Ltd, Unit 14 Wolseley Business Park, Wolseley Close, Plymouth, PL2 3BY Tel: (01752) 563336 Fax: (01752) 500120 E-mail: plymouth@signsexpress.co.uk *Sign makers*

► Signs Express Ltd, Unit G3 Railway Triangle, Walton Road, Portsmouth, PO6 1TQ Tel: (023) 9238 3821 Fax: (023) 9238 3822 E-mail: portsmouth@signexpress.co.uk

► Signs Express Ltd, 14 Long Barn Lane, Reading, RG2 7SZ Tel: 0118-975 1155 Fax: 0118-975 1133 E-mail: reading@signsexpress.co.uk *Sign contractors, sign makers, suppliers & installers*

► Signs Express Ltd, Unit 27 Glenmore Business Park Churchfields Industrial Park, Salisbury, SP2 7BA Tel: (01722) 410410 Fax: (01722) 410234 E-mail: salisbury@signsexpress.co.uk *Sign makers*

► Signs Express Ltd, Unit 38 City Industrial Park, Southern Road, Southampton, SO15 1HA Tel: (023) 8022 7676 Fax: (023) 8022 7678 E-mail: southampton@signsexpress.co.uk *Specialist in vehicle graphics, signs, banners & window graphics*

► Signs Express Ltd, Unit 3 Crabtree Close, Fenton Industrial Estate, Stoke-on-Trent, ST4 2SW Tel: (01782) 416930 Fax: (01782) 416931 E-mail: stokeontrent@signsexpress.co.uk *Sign manufrs*

► Signs Express Ltd, 9-23 Third Cross Road, Twickenham, TW2 5DY Tel: (020) 8893 3221 Fax: (020) 8893 3233 E-mail: twickenham@signsexpress.co.uk *Sign makers*

Signs Express Ltd, Kingsland Grangeaston Ctwoolston, Woolston, Warrington, WA1 4SG Tel: (01925) 822990 Fax: (01925) 822120 E-mail: warrington@signsexpress.co.uk *Sign manufrs*

► Signs Express Ltd, Unit 4b Glover Industrial Estate, Spire Road, Washington, Tyne & Wear, NE37 3ES Tel: 0191-415 1234 Fax: 0191-415 3222 E-mail: wearside@signsexpress.co.uk *Specialise in vehicle graphics, interior & exterior signage*

► Signs Express Ltd, 2 Osbaldwick Industrial Estate, Outgang Lane, Osbaldwick, York, YO19 5UX Tel: (01904) 431343 Fax: (01904) 431344 E-mail: york@signsexpress.co.uk *Sign makers*

► Signs Express Stockport, Alpha Court, Windmill La Industrial Estate, Denton, Manchester, M34 3RB Tel: 0161-337 9988 Fax: 0161-337 0088 E-mail: stockport@signsexpress.co.uk *A complete sign manufacture and fitting service for all forms of signage including interior and exterior signs, vehicle graphics, banners, window graphics and exhibtition & display products. Part of the UK & Ireland''''s largest sign company.*

► Signs Express Taunton, 13a-13b Unit, Cornishway South, Galmington Trading Estate, Taunton, Somerset, TA1 5NQ Tel: (01823) 289366 Fax: (01823) 289377 E-mail: taunton@signsexpress.co.uk *Specialise in vehicle graphics*

► Signs & Imaging Ltd, Unit 2, Bredhurst Business Park, Westfield Sole Road, Boxley, Maidstone, Kent, ME14 3EH Tel: (0845) 4660473 Fax: (0845) 684686 E-mail: sales@anybanner.co.uk *LED's, a-boards, banners, stainless steel, perspex & neon suppliers*

Signs & Labels Ltd, Willow Business Park, 21 Willow Lane, Mitcham, Surrey, CR4 4NA Tel: (020) 8274 3700 Fax: (020) 8274 3702 E-mail: sales@signsandlabels.co.uk *Safety sign manufrs*

Signs & Labels Of Shrewsbury, Unit 7a Hardwicke Stables Industrial Estate, Hadnall, Shrewsbury, SY4 4AS Tel: (01939) 210230 Fax: (01939) 210231 *Sign makers*

Signs & Lighting Services, Easterton Farm, Stirling Road, Denny, Stirlingshire, FK6 6RG Tel: (01324) 824218 Fax: (01324) 823794 *Sign installation & maintenance*

Signs Now, 36a Ashley Road, Bournemouth, BH1 4LH Tel: (01202) 392727 Fax: (01202) 392728 E-mail: signsnowbmth@aol.com *Sign manufrs*

Signs Now, Unit 6 Kenn Court, Roman Farm Road, Hengrove, Bristol, BS4 1UL Tel: 0117-964 6644 Fax: 0117-964 6655 E-mail: sales@342.signsnow,co.uk *Sign manufrs*

Signs & Print, 21-23 Dudley Road, Brierley Hill, West Midlands, DY5 1HA Tel: (01384) 261333 Fax: (01384) 261666 *Sign manufrs*

Signs & Safety Ltd, Unit 6 Fairlawn Enterprise Park, Bonehurst Road, Redhill, RH2 7QT Tel: (01737) 246969 Fax: (01737) 247979 E-mail: info@signsandsafety.co.uk *Safety sign design, manufacture & installation*

Signs Of The Times, 25 Townhead, Glasgow, G66 1NG Tel: 0141-776 7962 Fax: 0141-776 3322 *Sign makers*

Signs Of The Times, Unit 6, 3 Campsie Rosd, Kirkintilloch, Glasgow, G66 1SL Tel: 0141-775 0456 Fax: 0141-776 3322 E-mail: signsofthetimes@aol.com *Sign manufrs*

Signs Of The Times Ltd, Wingfield Road, Tebworth, Leighton Buzzard, Bedfordshire, LU7 9QQ Tel: (01525) 874185 Fax: (01525) 875746 E-mail: enquiries@sott.co.uk *Letterbox & sign manufrs*

Signs Of The Times, 324 Smithdown Road, Liverpool, L15 5AJ Tel: 0151-734 4616 Fax: 0151-734 4616 *Sign manufrs*

Signs Of The Times, 43 Sidcup Hill, Sidcup, Kent, DA14 6HJ Tel: (020) 8309 5577 Fax: (020) 8309 5574 E-mail: mark@signsofthetimesuk.com *Sign manufrs*

Signs Of The Times, Whitchurch Business Park, Shakespeare Way, Whitchurch, Shropshire, SY13 1LJ Tel: (01948) 666609 Fax: (01948) 666681 E-mail: admin@signsofthetimes.uk.com *Sign manufrs*

Signs UK, Winsor Farm Studio, Yealmpton, Plymouth, PL8 2LL Tel: 01752 881144 Fax: 01752 881172 *Sign makers*

Signs Unlimited, 60 Lincoln Road, Birmingham, B27 6NZ Tel: 0121-706 9021 Fax: 0121-706 6192 *Sign writers*

Signs Xtra, Unit 6 Grange Lane Industrial Estate, Carrwood Road, Barnsley, South Yorkshire, S71 5AS Tel: (01226) 731334 Fax: (01226) 731335 E-mail: signsxtra@btconnect.com *Sign manufrs*

Signs4you, 35 East St, Crediton, Devon, EX17 3AY Tel: 01363 776877 Fax: 01363 776877 E-mail: shsigns@aol.com *Sign manufacturers & t-shirt printing*

Signsense, 240 Ashley Road, Poole, Dorset, BH14 9BZ Tel: (01202) 252627 Fax: (01202) 250300 *Sign manufrs*

Signshopuk.Com, 12 Crescent Road, Windermere, Cumbria, LA23 1EA Tel: (01539) 448884 Fax: (01539) 488884 E-mail: sales@signshopuk.com *Sign manufrs*

Signtec Signs & Nameplates, The Lawns, Chargrove Lane, Shurdington, Cheltenham, Gloucestershire, GL51 4XB Tel: (01242) 862008 Fax: (01242) 862008 *Sign manufrs*

Signtech, Hereford Way, King's Lynn, Norfolk, PE30 4JD Tel: (01553) 770800 Fax: (01553) 691931 E-mail: sales@signtech.uk.com *Sign manufrs*

Signtech Plastics & Signs, 82 Moorland Road, Weston-super-Mare, Avon, BS23 4HT Tel: (01934) 416137 Fax: (01934) 628008 E-mail: signtech1@tiscali.co.uk *Sign makers*

Signtech Sign Makers, 18-19 Lion Hill, Stourport-on-Severn, Worcestershire, DY13 9HG Tel: (01299) 827309 Fax: (01299) 877086 E-mail: sales@signtech.co.uk *Signs manufrs*

Signtek Sign Writers, Unit 5e Southbourne Business Park, Courtlands Road, Eastbourne, East Sussex, BN22 8UY Tel: (01323) 642625 Fax: (01323) 439559 E-mail: info@signtek.co.uk *Sign makers manufrs*

Signtrade Letters Ltd, 225 Long Lane, Finchley, London, N3 2RL Tel: (0500) 456700 Fax: (0208) 349 5806 E-mail: sales@signtrade.co.uk *SignTrade is widely regarded as the leading moulded acrylic letter company in the UK. We principally supply sign and exhibition companies with their acrylic dishes, acrylic domes/bubbles, flat cut and moulded letter requirements.*Our moulded letters are found enhancing the exteriors of pubs, clubs, restaurants, shops and businesses all over the UK. The moulded letters are made from high quality acrylics and plastics. Our sign supply service is second to none and we have prices to match. *Our highly experienced team can handle any complex fabrication or moulding projects, even those with tight deadlines. That is one of the many reasons we have so much repeat business and our clients return time and time again.*"SignTrade - You deserve the best" is our company motto and this is as true today as the day it was coined*

Signwaves Ltd, Lefevre Way, Great Yarmouth, Norfolk, NR31 0NW Tel: (01493) 419300 Fax: (01493) 419301 E-mail: equiries@signwavesgroup.com *Point of purchase signs & display services*

▶ Signway Signs, 103 Ashbourne Road, Derby, DE22 3FW Tel: (01332) 348830 Fax: (01332) 296342 *Plastic products & signs*

Signway Supplies (Datchet) Ltd, Signway House, Stroudley Road, Basingstoke, Hampshire, RG24 8UG Tel: (01256) 811234 Fax: (01256) 811299 *Sign manufrs*

Signwise, Unit 26 Enterprise Way, Newport, Gwent, NP20 2AQ Tel: (01633) 841766 Fax: (01633) 841766 E-mail: info@signwise.net *Signmakers & maintenance*

Signwise, Unit B3 Spectrum Business Estate, Anthonys Way, Medway City Estate, Rochester, Kent, ME2 4NP Tel: (01634) 297200 Fax: (01634) 297222 E-mail: info@signwise.co.uk *Sign installation & manufrs*

Signwise (Scotland) Ltd, 61 Dykehead Street, Queenslie Industrial Estate, Glasgow, G33 4AQ Tel: 0141-774 5261 Fax: 0141-774 9683 E-mail: signwise@cairnleck.co.uk *Sign Makers*

Signwise Sign Services Ltd, 4 Challenger Way, Peterborough, PE1 5EX Tel: (01733) 565770 Fax: (01733) 563384 E-mail: info@signwisesignservices.co.uk *Safety sign suppliers & contractors*

Signwise Sign Services Ltd, Unit 7 Bodolph Bridge Trading, Estate Oundle Road, Peterborough, PE2 9QP Tel: (01733) 558554 Fax: (01733) 563384 E-mail: sign.wise@btclick.com *Sign contractors & designers & manufrs*

Signwork, Crosshouse Road, Southampton, SO14 5GZ Tel: (023) 8063 8243 Fax: (023) 8023 4512 E-mail: info@signwork.net *Sign & screen printing services & digital printing*

Signworks Signs & Nameplates, Station Yard, Grange-over-Sands, Cumbria, LA11 6DW Tel: (01539) 534077 Fax: (01539) 535047 *Sign makers*

Signworld Screen Printers Ltd, Henson Way, Telford Way Industrial Estate, Kettering, Northamptonshire, NN16 8PX Tel: (01536) 527940 Fax: (01536) 527944 E-mail: sales@signworld.co.uk *Screen printers or Printing Services available from Signworld Screen Printers Ltd based in Kettering, Northamptonshire. Click the links below to visit our website or contact us via our profile page*

Signworx, Unit 16 Ellingham Industrial Centre, Ellingham Way, Ashford, Kent, TN23 6NF Tel: (01233) 632244 Fax: (01233) 632255 E-mail: info@msignworx.com *We design and manufacture high quality signs that WILL GET YOUR COMPANY NOTICED! In addition we also supply computer cut vinyl lettering, shop fascias, vehicle graphics, window graphics, interior /exterior signs, full colour digital graphics, exhibition panels, magnetic signs, banners, health & safety signs, traffic signs, street nameplates, pavement signs, illuminated signs, engraving, flat cut /built up lettering, stocklist of foamex, perspex & PVC, information and menu systems, t-shirts, polo shirts & sweatshirt printing, full colour business stationery and much more!*

▶ Signworx Scotland Ltd, Unit 4, Guards Road Industrial Estate, Coldstream, Berwickshire, TD12 4EE Tel: (01890) 885885 Fax: (01890) 882138 E-mail: signworx@ospreyco.com *Sign manufrs*

Sigram Flue Systems, Unit 8 Shepley Industrial Estate South, Audenshaw, Manchester, M34 5DW Tel: 0161-320 6515 Fax: 0161-320 6515 E-mail: sales@sigram.co.uk *Flue pipe manufacturers & installers*

Sigta Ltd, 26 Abinger Road, Portslade, Brighton, BN41 1RZ Tel: (01273) 420029 Fax: (01273) 423982 E-mail: sales@sigta.co.uk *Training development courses & nvq's*

▶ Sigtec Computer Systems, 121 Giles Street, Edinburgh, EH6 6BZ Tel: 0131-553 5599 Fax: 0131-553 5599 *Computer software suppliers*

Sigtel, Sensor House, Wrexham Technology Park, Wrexham, Clwyd, LL13 7YP Tel: (01978) 312488 Fax: (01978) 312494 E-mail: sigtel@esi-tec.com *Radio telemetry system manufrs*

Sihad Textiles Ltd, 3 Camden Street, Leicester, LE1 2AP Tel: 0116-253 9258 *Hosiery manufacturers & wholesalers*

Sika Ltd, Watchmead, Welwyn Garden City, Hertfordshire, AL7 1BQ Tel: (01707) 394444 Fax: (01707) 329129 E-mail: info@sika.com *Sika Limited, the U.K. representative of the worldwide Sika Group, provide solutions to local construction and building product requirements, based upon global expertise, innovation and quality.*

Sika Armorex, Riverside House, Bury Road, Lavenham, Sudbury, Suffolk, CO10 9QD Tel: (01787) 248005 Fax: (01787) 248315 *Flooring & grout material manufrs*

Siko Ltd, Unit 6, Cod Beck Estate, Dalton, Thirsk, North Yorkshire, YO7 3HR Tel: (01845) 578845 Fax: (01845) 577781 E-mail: sales@siko-uk.com *SIKO LTD offers customers a single source of supply of products to measure, display & control axis movement. Suppliers of linear absolute encoders, linear incremental encoders, rotary absolute encoders, rotary incremental encoders, magnetic linear encoders, magnetic rotary encoders, wire actuated sensors, geared potentiometers, shaft mounted geared motors, position controllers, mechanical position indicators, tilt sensors and electronic position displays.We are able to provide our customers with a total solution to all position measurement and control applications. Our key partners, recognised as world leaders within their chosen field:*SIKO GMBH*LIKA*ELAP*FRABA*DIGITRONIC* ERMA* ALTMANN*

▶ Sil Die Ltd, Fullbridge Quay, Maldon, Essex, CM9 4LE Tel: (01621) 858502 Fax: (01621) 851568

Silavent Ltd, 60 High Street, Sandhurst, Berkshire, GU47 8DY Tel: (01252) 878282 Fax: (01252) 871212 E-mail: admin@silavent.co.uk *Domestic electric ventilating fan manufrs*

Silavent Environmental, Pine Works, Pine Street, Hyde, Cheshire, SK14 4TG Tel: 0161-366 5903 Fax: 0161-367 8105 *Secondary glazing & ventilation services*

Silavent Ventilation Systems, Lea Mills, Lea Road, Batley, West Yorkshire, WF17 8BB Tel: (01924) 441874 Fax: (01924) 441892 *Extractor fans manufrs*

Silberline Ltd, Banbeath Industrial Estate, Leven, Fife, KY8 5HD Tel: (01333) 424734 Fax: (01333) 421369 E-mail: info@silberline.co.uk *Metallic pigment manufrs*

Silchrome Plating Ltd, Barras Garth Road, Leeds, LS12 4JW Tel: 0113-263 7808 Fax: 0113-263 2682 E-mail: sales@silchrome.co.uk *Electroplating & metal finishing*

Silcoms Ltd, Victoria Mill, Piggott Street, Farnworth, Bolton, BL4 9QN Tel: (01204) 571305 Fax: (01204) 861723 E-mail: pep@silcoms.co.uk *Industrial conveyor system manufrs*

▶ Silenster Building Services Ltd, 33A Whiffler Road, Norwich, NR3 2AW Tel: (01603) 482300

Silent Gliss Ltd, Pyramid Business Park, Poorhole Lane, Broadstairs, Kent, CT10 2PT Tel: (01843) 863571 Fax: (01843) 864503 E-mail: info@silentgliss.co.uk *Curtain rail & blind manufrs* Also at: London

Silent Night Beds, Longing Lane, Barnoldswick, Lancashire, BB18 6BJ Tel: (01282) 813051 Fax: (01282) 813466 E-mail: enquiries@silentnightgroup.co.uk *Bed manufrs*

Silent Power Systems Ltd, Unit 9 Dain Street, Stoke-on-Trent, ST6 3LN Tel: (01782) 822402 Fax: (01782) 577262 *Electronic equipment designers*

Silent Sleep Beds, Parkside Road, Bradford, West Yorkshire, BD5 8DY Tel: (01274) 733743 Fax: (01274) 733748 E-mail: sales@silentsleep.co.uk *Bed retailer & manufrs*

SilentCel, 137 Percy Avenue, Kingsgate, Broadstairs, Kent, CT10 3LE Tel: (07855) 358230 Fax: (01843) 603142 E-mail: enquiries@silentcel.co.uk *Professional installers of the highest quality domestic soundproofing*

▶ Silestone Of London, Unit 2 Octinum Business Park, Albert Drive, Woking, Surrey, GU21 5RW Tel: (01483) 757345 Fax: (01483) 757346 E-mail: sales@silestoneoflondon.co.uk *Kitchen worktops, granite & stone manufrs*

Silex Ltd, Units 4 & 5, Broxhead Trading Estate, Lindford, Bordon, Hants, GU35 0NY Tel: (01420) 487130 Fax: (01420) 489274 E-mail: info@silex.co.uk Purchasing Contact: N. Soudah Sales Contact: N. Soudah *Manufacturers of silicone products including silicone rubber tubing, sections, cords, sheets, sponges & hoses. In addition silicone rubber gaskets*

Silflex Ltd, Coedcae Lane, Pontyclun, Mid Glamorgan, CF72 9HJ Tel: (01443) 238464 Fax: 01443 238464 E-mail: silflex@silflex.com *Silicone hose manufrs*

Silgan White Cap UK Ltd, 1 Thames Side, Windsor, Berkshire, SL4 1QN Tel: (01753) 832828 Fax: (01753) 620825 *Bottle caps manufrs*

Silgo Lubricants Ltd, 20-22-24 Thurrock Commercial Centre, Purfleet Industrial Park, Aveley, South Ockendon, Essex, RM15 4YG Tel: (01708) 865665 Fax: (01708) 868996 E-mail: sales@silgo.co.uk *Lubricant & oil distributors*

Silicon 2000 (UK) Ltd, 82 Church Rd, Hove, E. Sussex, BN3 2EB Tel: 01273 388883 *Computer consultancy*

Silicon City Distribution, 50 Temple Avenue, London, N20 9EH Tel: (020) 8445 5251 Fax: (0870) 7052314 E-mail: sales@silcity.com *IT consultants*

Silicon Fabrication Services Ltd, Unit E Kingsway, Kingsway Industrial Estate, Luton, LU1 1LP Tel: (01582) 412697 Fax: (01582) 412277 E-mail: sfs.ltd@btinternet.com *Silicone fabrication services*

Silicon Glen Technologies Ltd, South Avenue, Blantyre Industrial Estate, Blantyre, Glasgow, G72 0XB Tel: (01698) 307070 Fax: (01698) 327979 E-mail: mail@sgtsiliconglen.com *Semiconductor processing equipment disk*

Silicon Group, 95 Whins Road, Alloa, Clackmannanshire, FK10 3RF Tel: (01259) 725200 Fax: (01259) 725270 E-mail: info@silicon-group.co.uk *Computer applications services*

Silicon Heart Ltd, 6-8 Sedley Pl, London, W1C 2HE Tel: (020) 7355 3344 Fax: (020) 7355 2266 *Computer consultancy*

▶ Silicon Sensor, 35 Orchard Close, Stanstead Abbotts, Ware, Hertfordshire, SG12 8AH Tel: (01920) 872090 E-mail: sales@silicon-sensor.de Sales Contact: P Nash

Silicon Systems, 31-33 Park Hill, Swallownest, Sheffield, S26 4UN Tel: 0114-269 6311 *Electronic control systems manufrs*

Silicon Valley Group plc, Lakeview House, Lightwater Road, Lightwater, Surrey, GU18 5XQ Tel: (01276) 455900 Fax: (01276) 455910 E-mail: svg@silicon-valley.co.uk *Computer consultants & recruitment*

Siliconepak Ltd, Amber Business Centre, Hill Top Rd, Riddings, Alfreton, Derbyshire, DE55 4BR Tel: (01773) 607967 Fax: (01773) 540283 *Silicon treated box, bakery papers & specialised packaging manufrs*

Silkmoth Ltd, Cara House, Crossall Street, Macclesfield, Cheshire, SK11 6QF Tel: (01625) 433388 Fax: (01625) 616760 E-mail: keith.jones@silkmoth.com *Multimedia internet & digital marketing*

Silks Of Northampton, 52 Tenter Road, Moulton Park Industrial Estate, Northampton, NN3 6AX Tel: (01604) 644488 Fax: (01604) 644488 *Artificial plants & floral displays*

Silkstream Water Treatment Equipment, 36 Spencer Close, Potton, Sandy, Bedfordshire, SG19 2QY Tel: (01767) 261942 E-mail: sales@silkstream.co.uk *Water filtration*

Sillaford Ltd, Martin House, 2 Martin Street, Brighouse, West Yorkshire, HD6 1DA Tel: (01484) 710231 Fax: (01484) 714607 E-mail: sales@sillaford.com *Filtration & technical textile agents & merchants*

Sillars Holdings Ltd, Graythorp Industrial Estate, Hartlepool, Cleveland, TS25 2DF Tel: (01429) 268125 Fax: (01429) 860693 E-mail: sillhold@sillaraol.com *Civil engineers*

▶ Sillars Iron Art, 42 Rannoch Place, Castlepark, Irvine, Ayrshire, KA12 9NQ Tel: (01294) 230774 E-mail: briansillars810@msn.com *specialist in wrought iron gates,railings,security grilles.rose arches,handrails,etc*

Sillavan Metal Polishes, Sillavan Works, Wood Street, Bury, Lancashire, BL8 2SL Tel: 0161-797 6666 Fax: 0161-797 3454 E-mail: bury@sillavan.co.uk *Metal polishing services*

Sillette Sonic, 2 Beverley Trading Estate, Garth Road, Morden, Surrey, SM4 4LU Tel: (020) 8337 7543 Fax: (020) 8330 9014 E-mail: sales@sillette.co.uk *Marine propulsion systems manufrs*

▶ Silly Billys, Knightsbridge Place, 3 Nottingham Road, Ripley, Derbyshire, DE5 3DJ Tel: (01773) 741222 *Furniture retailer*

Silly Jokes Ltd, Unit 11 Home Farm Park, Church Way, Whittlebury, Towcester, Northamptonshire, NN12 8XS Tel: (01327) 828205 Fax: (01327) 857400 E-mail: caroline@sillyjokes.co.uk *Online joke & party shops*

▶ Silocare Ltd, Grayingham Road, Blyborough, Gainsborough, Lincolnshire, DN21 4EY Tel: (01427) 668061 Fax: (01427) 668062 E-mail: silocare@aol.com *Silo maintenance contractors*

▶ Silom International Ltd, Unit 6 Abbey Park Industrial Estate, Abbey Road, Barking, Essex, IG11 7BT Tel: (020) 8594 3335 *Producers, importers & exporters of pipe working tools & equipment*

▶ Silprint Ltd, Halifax Road, Cullingworth, Bradford, West Yorkshire, BD13 5DE Tel: (01535) 272414

▶ Siltint Ind Ltd, 124 Longley Lane, Sharston, Manchester, M22 4SP Tel: 0161-945 4000 Fax: 0161-945 4040 E-mail: info@siltint.com *Optical ophthalmic coating & diamond turning services*

Silurian Scania, Whitchurch, Ross-On-Wye, Herefordshire, HR9 6EG Tel: (01600) 891257 Fax: (01600) 891251 *Commercial vehicles sales & services*

Silva Ltd, Fleming Road, Kirkton Campus, Livingston, West Lothian, EH54 7BN Tel: (01506) 419555 Fax: (01506) 415906 E-mail: info@silva.ltd.uk *Navigators*

Silvaflame Co. Ltd, Cannock, Staffordshire, WS11 0BX Tel: (01543) 431060 Fax: (01543) 509140 E-mail: silvaflame@cleervue.com *Machinery guard makers*

Silvan Ltd, 2 Coombe Road, Bushey, WD23 4SP Tel: (020) 8950 8160 Fax: (020) 8950 8163 E-mail: silvanltd@aol.com *Antique type lace merchants*

▶ The Silver Company, 25 Tabor Road, London, W6 0BN Tel: (020) 8748 7799 Fax: (020) 8834 7123 E-mail: info@silvercompany.co.uk *At The Silver Company we pride ourselves on providing only the highest quality silver plated gifts for the business promotions incentives. All of the business gifts come beautifully packed in a presentation box. Whatever statement you wish to make with a business gift , we have can source what you are looking for.**

▶ Silver Bullet Associates Ltd, 43 Temple Row, Birmingham, B2 5LS Tel: 0121 237 6073 E-mail: mark.bartrick@silverbulletassociates.com *"No saving: no Fee"advice on how to negotiate better software deals and so reduce your companys" software spend and costs.*

Silver By Coating, Unit 19, Whitworth Industrial Park, Tilton Road, Birmingham, B9 4PP Tel: 0121-772 1536 Fax: 0121-766 5771 *Powder coating services*

Silver Crane Co., 34a Black Moor Road, Ebblake Industrial Estate, Verwood, Dorset, BH31 6BB Tel: (01202) 825155 Fax: (01202) 823300 E-mail: sales@silvercrane.co.uk *Giftware designers & manufrs*

▶ Silver Dog Music, Chorlton, Manchester, M21 0AT Tel: 0161 8617182 E-mail: info@silverdogmusic.co.uk

Silver Dollar, Units 30-31 Byker Business Development Centre, Albion Row, Newcastle upon Tyne, NE6 1LQ Tel: 0191-224 3005 Fax: 0191-224 3005 *Clothing & fabrics manufrs*

Silver Fern Concrete, Milton Industrial Estate, Milton, Cambridge, CB4 4AZ Tel: (01223) 420669 *Concrete product manufacturer*

▶ Silver Fern Venues, 81 Westbury Road, Brentwood, Essex, CM14 4JS Tel: (01277) 222546 E-mail: greg@silverfernvenues.com *Silver Fern Venues is an independent venue sourcing consultancy. From our extensive database of venues we manage every detail of venue sourcing for your Meeting, Product Launch, Team Building & Training requirements.*The services of Silver Fern are provided to you Free of Charge, because our fees are paid by way of a commission collected from the venue.*

Silver Fox Ltd, Swallow Court, Swallowfields, Welwyn Garden City, Hertfordshire, AL7 1SA Tel: (01707) 373727 Fax: (01707) 372193 E-mail: sales@silfox.co.uk *Labelling printing solutions services*

▶ Silver Heaven, 20 Westham Road, Weymouth, Dorset, DT4 8NU Tel: (01305) 784005 E-mail: silverheaven@tesco.net *Sterling silver jewellery, plain and semi precious stoneset for men and women*

Silver Leaf Productions, 253 Lavender Hill, London, SW11 1JW Tel: (020) 7924 6544 Fax: (020) 7801 3105 E-mail: sales@silverleafp.co.uk *Event management & marketing services*

Silver Lining Workshops, Unit 5 Castle Farm, Cholmondeley, Malpas, Cheshire, SY14 8AQ Tel: (01948) 822150 Fax: (01948) 822151 E-mail: info@silverliningfurniture.com *Bespoke furniture manufrs*

▶ Silver Machines Scotland, Deanston House Lodge, Doune, Perthshire, FK16 6AD Tel: (0845) 0661662 Fax: (01786) 843009

Silver Productions Ltd, 29 Castle Street, Salisbury, SP1 1TT Tel: (01722) 336227 Fax: (01722) 336227 E-mail: info@silver.co.uk *TV film production services & organisers*

Silver Spoon Co., Silver Way, Bury St. Edmunds, Suffolk, IP32 7BZ Tel: (01284) 701621 Fax: (01284) 731200 *Packaging*

Silver Spring Mineral Water Co. Ltd, Park Farm Road, Park Farm Industrial Estate, Folkestone, Kent, CT19 5EA Tel: (01303) 856500 Fax: (01303) 256524 E-mail: eddie@silverspring.co.uk *Soft drink bottlers*

Silver Telecom Ltd, Imperial House, Imperial Way, Coedkernew, Newport, Gwent, NP10 8UH Tel: (01633) 811833 Fax: (01633) 811834 E-mail: sales@silvertel.com *Telecom circuits manufrs*

▶ Silver Television Ltd, 22 Green Street, Saltcoats, Ayrshire, KA21 5HQ Tel: (01294) 461508 Fax: (01294) 464829 E-mail: iain@silvertv.plus.com *Digital aerial & satellite dish installation & repair*

▶ Silver Toys & Allsorts, 21 Chapel Lane, Wimblington, March, Cambs, PE15 0QX Tel: 01354 742415 E-mail: paul_silvertoys@btinternet.com *Vintage & Rare Toys of allsorts*Corgi, Dinky, Matchbox, Marx, Batman, Thunderbirds, Books, Reproduction Boxes, Decals Spares loads.*TAKE A LOOK*

▶ Silverbirch Sameday Couriers, Silverbirch Estate, Middleton, Manchester, M24 5JU Tel: 0161-654 7439 E-mail: contact@sscouriers.co.uk *Based in Manchester specialising in same day deliveries both locally and throughout the U.K.From a document to a 1400kg laod.*

Silverburn Finance UK Ltd, 76 Winter Hey Lane, Horwich, Bolton, BL6 7PQ Tel: (01204) 432369 Fax: (01204) 693471 *Factoring services*

Silvercases, Daux Road, Billingshurst, West Sussex, RH14 9SR Tel: (01403) 784671 Fax: (01403) 785353 E-mail: info@woodcon.co.uk *Menu Cases, display cases, notice boards & sign system manufrs*

▶ Silvercoast Media, 12 Chainwalk Drive, Kenwyn, Truro, Cornwall, TR1 3ST Tel: 01872 271696 E-mail: mail@silvercoast.co.uk *We can offer lots of extended services such as product photography, corporate identity, design, type and content management.*

▶ Silverfish Solutions, Bullrushes, Main Street, Peasmarsh, Rye, East Sussex, TN31 6UL Tel: (01797) 230976 Fax: (01797) 230976 E-mail: info@silverfishsolutions.co.uk *Internet and IT Services company specialising in Web Design and Hosting. Other services include Database Solutions, Branding, Research Projects, Events Planning & Promotion and Technical Support. Professional Solutions to suit all sizes of company and budget.*

Silvergate Plastics, Unit 53 Clywedog Road South, Wrexham Industrial Estate, Wrexham, Clwyd, LL13 9XS Tel: (01978) 661496 Fax: (01978) 660462 E-mail: sales@silvergate-plastics.co.uk Principal Export Areas: Central/East Europe & West Europe *Master batch compounders manufrs*

Silverland Stone Ltd, Holloway Hill, Lyne, Chertsey, Surrey, KT16 0AE Tel: (01932) 569277 Fax: (01932) 563558 E-mail: gskilbeck@btinternet.com *Natural stone merchants*

Silverline Coachworks, Unit 4 Harrimans Lane, Lenton La Industrial Estate, Lenton Lane Industrial Estate, Nottingham, NG7 2SD Tel: 0115-970 3210 Fax: 0115-970 3210 *Lorry spraying*

Silverline Marine, Riverside Estate, Brundall, Norwich, NR13 5PL Tel: (01603) 712247 Fax: (01603) 716990 *Boat builders & repairers*

Silverline UK Ltd, Whitemoor, Iddesleigh, Winkleigh, Devon, EX19 8BN Tel: (01805) 804202 Fax: (01805) 804680 E-mail: enquiries@silverlineuk.co.uk *Water softener & filtering manufrs*

▶ Silverlink Software, Atmel Way, Wallsend, Tyne & Wear, NE28 9NZ Tel: 0191-280 4322 *Software developers*

Silverman's Ltd, Mile End, London, E1 4PS Tel: (020) 7790 0900 Fax: (020) 7791 0008 E-mail: info@silvermans.co.uk *Outdoor equipment mail order distributors*

▶ Silvers Marine Ltd, Silverhills, Rosneath, Helensburgh, Dunbartonshire, G84 0RW Tel: (01436) 831222 Fax: (01436) 831879 E-mail: enquiries@silversmarine.co.uk *Service yard for repairs, maintenance, refits & storage*

Silverson Machines Ltd, Waterside, Chesham, Buckinghamshire, HP5 1PQ Tel: (01494) 786331 Fax: (01494) 791452 E-mail: sales@silverson.co.uk *Mixer & industrial processors*

▶ Silverstar Services, 4 Palm Business Centre, Stock Lane, Chadderton, Oldham, OL9 9ER Tel: 0161-665 0828 *Scaffolding*

Silverstream Engineering, 60 Bridge Road East, Welwyn Garden City, Hertfordshire, AL7 1JU Tel: (01707) 322552 Fax: (01707) 334124 *Precision engineers*

Silverstream UK Ltd, Stretton Road, Greetham, Oakham, Leicestershire, LE15 7NP Tel: (01572) 812251 E-mail: sales@silverstream.uk.com *Computer brokers*

Silvertech Ltd, Holmwood Broadlands Business Campus, Langhurstwood Road, Horsham, West Sussex, RH12 4PN Tel: (01403) 211611 Fax: (01403) 211058 E-mail: sales@silvertech.co.uk *Computer systems designers & control engineers*

Silverthorn Services, 73 Whitehall Gardens, London, E4 6EJ Tel: (020) 8524 8481 Fax: (020) 8524 8481 *Commercial microwave oven repairs & espresso coffee machines*

Silverthorne Engineering Co., Attwood Street, Stourbridge, West Midlands, DY9 8RU Tel: (01384) 897639 Fax: (01384) 423980 E-mail: t.hoskins@virgin.net *Roll makers, precision engineers*

Silvertown UK Ltd, Horninglow Road, Burton-on-Trent, Staffordshire, DE13 0SN Tel: (01283) 510510 Fax: (01283) 510052 E-mail: sales.enq@silvertown.co.uk *Manufacturer of rubber & rubber to metal bonded components*

▶ SilverTripod.com, PO Box 553, Redhill, RH1 6XU Tel: 07793 155569 E-mail: info@silvertripod.com *SilverTripod.com designs and produces fun and eye-catching greeting cards; order online and delivered to your door.*

Silverts Ltd, 116-120 Goswell Road, London, EC1V 7DP Tel: (020) 7253 5766 Fax: (020) 7608 2230 E-mail: sales@silverts.co.uk *Ladies' coat & suits*

▶ The Silverware shop, 50a Tenby Street North, Hockley, Birmingham, B1 3EG Tel: 0121-248 7702 Fax: 0121-248 7701 E-mail: silverwareshop@aol.com *Manufacturers and discount retailers of high quality sterling silver giftware for every occasion*

Alan Silverwood Ltd, Ledsam House, Ledsam Street, Birmingham, B16 8DN Tel: 0121-454 3571 Fax: 0121-454 6749 E-mail: sales@alan-silverwood.co.uk *Manufacturers of bakeware*

Silverwood Exhibitions Ltd, 14 The Avenue, York, YO30 6AS Tel: (01904) 672700 Fax: (01904) 655800 E-mail: sales@silverwoodexhibitions.co.uk *Exhibition display designers, services & fabricators*

Silvester Engineering Ltd, Kingsmead, Marringdean Rd, Billingshurst, West Sussex, RH14 9HE Tel: (01403) 782255 Fax: (01403) 782703 E-mail: sales@silvesterengineering.co.uk *We provide a wide range of engineering services, from an individual repair, fabrication or machined component, to complete prototype and product manufacture. Our clients vary from local companies and authorities, to divisions of multi-national companies such as ADT and Siemens. We maintain close working relationships with both our clients and suppliers to achieve our aim of providing a complete engineering service - a range of services tailored to your needs. - Turning and Milling (Manual / CNC) - Folding and Punching (Manual /CNC) - Plasma and Laser Profiling - Pipe, Tube and Structural Bending - Heat Treatment - Plastic and Powder Coating - Electrolytic Plating - Galvanising - Product Assembly - Specially Designed Packaging - Nationwide Delivery We also work in close partnership with our sister companies. Southern Hydraulic Rams & Selvent*

Silvey Engineering Ltd, Redstones, Haywicks Lane, Hardwick, Gloucester, GL2 3QE Tel: (01452) 720439 *Precision engineers*

Thomas Silvey Ltd, 111-119 Newfoundland Road, Bristol, BS2 9LU Tel: 0117-954 8900 Fax: 0117-955 1436 E-mail: sales@silvey.co.uk *Fuel distribs*

Silvon Software Ltd, Pinewood Studios, Pinewood Road, IVER, Buckinghamshire, SL0 0NH Tel: 01753 631133 Fax: (01753) 653192 *Software house..*

Silwood Park Nurseries Ltd, Cheapside Road, Ascot, Berkshire, SL5 7QY Tel: (01344) 621354 Fax: (01344) 872740 *Floral & plant displays retailers*

Silwood Plastics Ltd, F Borough Road, Buckingham Road Industrial Estate, Brackley, Northamptonshire, NN13 7BE Tel: (01280) 844800 Fax: (01280) 700122 *Importers & distributors of plastics*

▶ Sim Building Group Ltd, Whitegates, Lenzie Road, Kirkintilloch, Glasgow, G66 3BL Tel: 0141-776 5151 Fax: 0141-777 8103

▶ Simanda Industrial Roofing & Cladding Ltd, Acreman Street, Little Hadham, Ware, Hertfordshire, SG11 2HD Tel: (01279) 461746 Fax: (01279) 461644 E-mail: sales@simanda.com *Industrial Roofing & Cladding*

Simark Engineering Co., Griffin Industrial Estate, Rowley Regis, West Midlands, B65 0SN Tel: 0121-559 1351 Fax: 0121-559 3205 E-mail: simark.engineering@virgin.net *Load restraint systems manufrs*

Simaron Engineering, Sunny Hill Road, Barnfields Industrial Estate, Leek, Staffordshire, ST13 5RG Tel: (01538) 386301 *Precision engineering service*

Simba International Ltd, Woodbridge Road, Sleaford, Lincolnshire, NG34 7EW Tel: (01529) 304654 Fax: (01529) 413468 E-mail: sales@simba.co.uk *Farming system providers & machinery manufrs*

Simbec Research Ltd, Clinical Research Organisation, Merthyr Tydfil Industrial Park, Merthyr Tydfil, Mid Glamorgan, CF48 4DR Tel: (01443) 690977 Fax: (01443) 692499 E-mail: alan.woodward@simbec.co.uk *Pharmaceutical researchers & testing services*

Simbeck Furniture Ltd, Spring Gardens Road, High Wycombe, Buckinghamshire, HP13 7AG Tel: (01494) 528617 Fax: (01494) 471737 E-mail: info@simbeck.com *Reproduction furniture manufrs*

Simbles Ltd, 76 Queens Road, Watford, WD17 2LD Tel: (01923) 226052 Fax: (01923) 817526 E-mail: sales@simbles.com *Tool & machinery merchants*

Simclar International Ltd, Pitreavie Business Park, Queensferry Road, Dunfermline, Fife, KY11 8UN Tel: (01383) 735161 Fax: (01383) 739986 E-mail: sales@simclar.com *Cables, fabrications & mouldings engineers*

R. Simcock Excavations, Delight Farm, Barkisland, Halifax, W. Yorkshire, HX4 0DZ Tel: (01422) 822260 Fax: (01422) 822260 *Hay & Straw*

▶ Simcoemedia, 14 Romans Court, Old Basford, Nottingham, NG6 0HF Tel: 07704 629906 E-mail: design@simcoe.co.uk *web design, video production, print design, advertising, multimedia, soundtrack production, corporate identity*

Simden Optical Ltd, Haugh Lane, Blaydon-on-Tyne, Tyne & Wear, NE21 4SA Tel: 0191-499 0122 Fax: 0191-414 4723 *Astronomical & scientific manufrs*

Sime Foundry Ltd, Stafford Street, Wednesbury, West Midlands, WS10 7JX Tel: 0121-502 5559 Fax: 0121-556 8079 E-mail: simefdy@aol.com *Non-ferrous aluminium castings manufrs*

James Sime & Co. Ltd, 29 Cow Wynd, Falkirk, FK1 1PT Tel: (01324) 622592 Fax: (01324) 612522 *Tool merchants*

Simer Environmental Services Ltd, 15 Arnside Road, Waterlooville, Hampshire, PO7 7UP Tel: (023) 9225 8059 Fax: (023) 9226 7059 E-mail: sales@simer-environmental.co.uk *Air conditioning distributors*

Simex Systems, Unit 44 Canal Bridge Enterprise Centre, Meadow Lane, Ellesmere Port, CH65 4EH Tel: 0151-356 3040 Fax: 0151-356 3049 E-mail: sales@pcmouse.co.uk *Retailers of computer accessories*

▶ Simextron, 4 Clune Road, Gowkhall, Dunfermline, Fife, KY12 9NZ Tel: (01383) 853130 Fax: (01383) 853130 E-mail: simextron@tiscali.co.uk *Anti static device suppliers*

Simister & Chorlton Ltd, 27 Edna Street, Hyde, Cheshire, SK14 1LD Tel: 0161-368 2309 Fax: 0161-367 8264 *Sheet metal fabricators*

▶ Simkiss Controls Systems Ltd, PLP House, Holmes Street, Rochdale, Lancashire, OL12 6AQ Tel: (01706) 719024 Fax: (01706) 719025 E-mail: office@simkis.co.uk *Manufacturers of electrical & electronic control panels*

Simm Engineering Group, Gilbertson Works, Jessell Street, Sheffield, S9 3HY Tel: 0114-244 0764 Fax: 0114-244 2725 E-mail: sales@simmengineeringgroup.co.uk *Air compressor repair services*

Simmatic Automation Specialists Ltd, 3 Heathfield Units, Sandy Lane, Titton, Stourport-on-Severn, Worcestershire, DY13 9QA Tel: (01299) 877770 Fax: (01299) 823273 E-mail: sales@simmatic.co.uk *Pneumatic control specialists*

▶ Simmetrics Ltd, 59 Cambridge Road, Carshalton, Surrey, SM5 3QR Tel: (020) 8642 8672 E-mail: hello@simmetrics.co.uk *Software development*

Simmonds Heath Company Estate Agents, 61 Grosvenor Street, London, W1K 3JE Tel: (020) 7491 8845 Fax: (020) 7493 6455 E-mail: robert@simmondsheath.com *Estate agents property investment consultants*

Simmonds Of Kensington, 4 Pembroke Place, London, W8 6ET Tel: (020) 7937 0122 Fax: (020) 7937 0322 *Building contractors*

Simmons plc, Simmons House Townsend Farm Road, Townsend Industrial Estate, Houghton Regis, Dunstable, Bedfordshire, LU5 5BQ Tel: (01582) 606163 Fax: (01582) 662175 E-mail: info@simmonsplc.com *Painting contractors*

Simmons Aerofilms, 32-34 Station Close, Potters Bar, Hertfordshire, EN6 1TL Tel: (01707) 648390 Fax: (01707) 648399 E-mail: library@aerofilms.com *Aerial photographers*

▶ Simmons Bakers Ltd, 1 Piggottshill Lane, Harpenden, Hertfordshire, AL5 1LG Tel: (01582) 713353 Fax: (01707) 274329 *Bakers*

Simmons Bedding Group P.L.C., Knight Road, Strood, Kent, ME2 2BP Tel: (01634) 723557 Fax: (01634) 290257 *Bedding manufrs*

Simmons & Hawker Ltd, Falcon House, Central Way, Feltham, Middlesex, TW14 0UQ Tel: (020) 8867 0070 Fax: (020) 8893 1987 E-mail: barryj@hma.co.uk *Estate owners & managers (industrial)*

▶ Simmons Industrial Services, C Anchor Business Centre, 102 Beddington Lane, Croydon, CR0 4YX Tel: (020) 8688 3553 Fax: (020) 8667 9241 E-mail: info@simmons-industrial.co.uk *Crane hire & machinery installation*

Simmons (Patternmakers) Ltd, Station Street West Business Park, Coventry, CV6 5BP Tel: (024) 7663 7028 Fax: (024) 7663 7030 E-mail: sales@epoxyworktops.com *Laboratory work surface manufrs*

Simmons (Patternmakers) Ltd, Station Street West Business Park, Coventry, CV6 5BP Tel: (024) 7663 7028 Fax: (024) 7663 7030 E-mail: sales@epoxyworktops.com *CAD/CAM pattern making engineers*

F.A. Simms & Partners P.L.C., Insol House, 39 Station Road, Lutterworth, Leicestershire, LE17 4AP Tel: (01455) 557111 Fax: (01455) 552572 *Business rescue & insolvency practitioners*

Simms Group UK Ltd, Foundry Road, Camborne, Cornwall, TR14 7XB Tel: (01209) 712333 Fax: (01209) 612512 *Scrap metal merchants*

T.A. Simms & Sons, Ballygorman Engineering Works, 160 Gosford Road, Loughgilly, Armagh, BT60 2DE Tel: (028) 3750 7258 Fax: (028) 3750 7307 *Repair services*

Simmtronic Ltd, Unit 3, Waterside Industrial Estate, Charlton Mead Lane, Hoddesdon, Hertfordshire, EN11 0QR Tel: (01992) 450126 Fax: (01992) 450127 E-mail: sales@simmtronic.com *Industrial & commercial control gear*

Simmy Ceramics, Sayer House, Oxgate Lane, London, NW2 7JN Tel: (020) 8208 0416 Fax: (020) 8450 1140 E-mail: sales@simmyceramics.com *Tiles, kitchen unit & worktop distributors*

Simon & Dean Ltd, Castle Works, Studley, Warwickshire, B80 7EE Tel: 01527 853131 *Storage equipment to the trade*

▶ Simon Distribution, Clough Lane, North Killingholme, Immingham, South Humberside, DN40 3JP Tel: (01469) 540760 Fax: (01469) 541680

▶ Simon Dunn, 2 Commercial Road, Hazel Grove, Hazel Grove, Stockport, Cheshire, SK7 4AA Tel: 0161-483 2228 Fax: 0161-483 2228 E-mail: info@simondunnschocolates.co.uk *Hand made chocolate for all occasions*

Simon Lewis Workshop, New House, 67-68 Hatton Garden, London, EC1N 8JY Tel: (020) 7831 4838 Fax: (020) 7405 5532 *Jewellery & diamond merchants*

▶ Simon Morris Photography, Two Stepps Cottage Studios, Old Road, Harbertonford, Totnes, Devon, TQ9 7TE Tel: (01803) 732171 E-mail: info@simonmorrisphotography.com *Contemporary photographic portraits of flowers and nature*A regular exhibitor in UK galleries and flower shows both in the UK and abroad; professional Fine Art and commercial photographer; Simon Morris, photographs spiritually stunning images of flowers, natural scenes, and sacred sites around the world.*As launched at the RHS Chelsea Flower Show 2004 view the stunning range of blank greetings cards on the Website.*Details of how to purchase the greetings cards, mounted and framed photographs and canvas prints can be found by following the links. *Information about the photographer, competitions, equipment, news of exhibitions, events and publications. can be found on www.simonmorrisphotography.com.*Limited Edition Fine art Photography on Canvas, Film and Glass*Prices Start from only £95*

Simon Price, 10 Straight Road, Old Windsor, Windsor, Berkshire, SL4 2RL Tel: (01753) 832542 Fax: (01753) 832542 *Joinery*

▶ Simon Rowe Copier Sales Aston Leys FM, Haddenham Road, Kingsey, Aylesbury, Buckinghamshire, HP17 8LS Tel: (01844) 290840 Fax: (01844) 292967 E-mail: sales@srcs-copier-resites.co.uk *Photocopiers & other office equipment suppliers*

Simon Storage Immingham West Ltd, West Riverside, Immingham Dock, Immingham, North East Lincolnshire, DN40 2QU Tel: (01469) 572615 Fax: (01469) 577019 *Oil & chemical storage contractors*

▶ Simon Storage (Seal Sands) Ltd, Seal Sands, Middlesbrough, Cleveland, TS2 1UB Tel: (01642) 546775

▶ Simon Transport Services Ltd, 43 Ember Road, Slough, SL3 8ED Tel: (01753) 547818 Fax: (01753) 545992

Simon West Interiors Ltd, Hendon Street, Sunderland, SR1 2NF Tel: 0191-514 3052 Fax: 0191-514 1989 *Shop fitting*

Simona (U K) Ltd, Unit 11, Telford Drive, Tollgate Industrial Estate, Stafford, ST16 3ST Tel: (01785) 222444 Fax: (01785) 222080 E-mail: sales@simona.de *Industrial plastic stockholders & distributors*

Simon-Carves Ltd, PO Box 17, Cheadle, Cheshire, SK8 5BR Tel: 0161-486 4000 Fax: 0161-486 1302 E-mail: simon.carves@simoncarves.com Principal Export Areas: Worldwide *Process engineering consultants & design service providers*

Simonds Industries Ltd, 3 Motorway Industrial Estate, Tyler Street, Sheffield, S9 1DH Tel: 0114-243 3701 Fax: 0114-243 3879 *Bandsaw, file & hacksaw manufrs*

Simons Construction Ltd, Outgang Lane, Osbaldwick, York, YO19 5GP Tel: (01904) 430200 Fax: (01904) 430210 E-mail: yorkhelpdesk@simonsgroup.com *Building contractors*

F. Simons Imports Ltd, Unit 10, The Parkwood Centre, Aston Road, Waterlooville, Hampshire, PO7 7HT Tel: (023) 9225 5339 Fax: (023) 9225 6800 *Costume jewellery import & export*

Simons Group Ltd, 401 Monks Road, Lincoln, LN3 4NU Tel: (01522) 510000 Fax: (01522) 521812 *Contractors developers design environmental*

Simons Reeve Holdings Ltd, Private Road No 2, Colwick Industrial Estate, Nottingham, NG4 2JR Tel: 0115-987 0970 Fax: 0115-961 1737 E-mail: mail@simons-reeve.co.uk *Simons Reeve Manufacture and Rent a wide range of Materials Handling Equipment including Roll Cages, Garment Rails, Plastic Pallets, Trays & Containers and Stillages.*

Simon's Workshop, 30 Royal Star Arcade, Maidstone, Kent, ME14 1JL Tel: (01622) 677841 Fax: (01622) 677841 *Jewellery sales, repairs & manufrs*

▶ Simonswerk UK Ltd, Burcot Works, Spring Street, Tipton, West Midlands, DY4 8TF Tel: 0121-522 2848 Fax: 0121-557 7042 E-mail: sales@simonswerk.co.uk *Agricultural iron monger manufrs*

Simorg Ltd, Room 13 Enterprise House, 7 Gordon St, Luton, LU1 2QP Tel: (01582) 484785 Fax: (01582) 484157 E-mail: admin@simorglimited.co.uk *Disabled access specialists suppliers*

Simpac Ltd, Spiersbridge Business Park, Spiersbridge Avenue, Glasgow, G46 8NL Tel: 0141-571 0220 Fax: 0141-571 0260 E-mail: packaging@simpac.co.uk *Paper sack manufrs*

▶ Simpers Ltd, 17 Mercers Row, Cambridge, CB5 8HY Tel: (01223) 351729 Fax: (01223) 311818 E-mail: info@simpers.co.uk *Outdoors, camping, furniture & catering hire services*

Simpkin & Icke Holdings Ltd, Glaisdale Works, Glaisdale Drive, Nottingham, NG8 4JU Tel: 0115-929 2106 Fax: 0115-929 0446 E-mail: boxes@simpkin-and-icke.co.uk *Presentation boxes & cartons manufrs*

Simplantex Healthcare, 145a Ashford Road, Eastbourne, East Sussex, BN21 3UA Tel: (0870) 8707140 Fax: (0870) 8707141 E-mail: sales@simplantex.co.uk *Disabled garments*

Simplas, Unit 8 Horcott Industrial Estate, Horcott Road, Fairford, Gloucestershire, GL7 4BX Tel: (01285) 713175 Fax: (01285) 713175 *Window & conservatory manufrs*

▶ Simple Kitchens, 4 Chruchill Crescent, Thame, Oxfordshire, OX9 3JN Tel: (01844) 217804 Fax: (01844) 217804 E-mail: thomas@simple-kitchens.co.uk *Designers & makers of quality bespoke kitchens*

▶ Simple Print, 54 Eldon Road, Winton, Bournemouth, BH9 2RU Tel: 01202 526200 E-mail: Patrick@fwd-design.co.uk *Printing, Marketing, Design and distribution of marketing material. Business Cards, Flyers, Brochures, etc.*

Simple Tech, The Brunel Building, The Scottish Enterprise Technology Park, East Kilbride, Glasgow, G75 0QD Tel: (01355) 572850 Fax: (01355) 572868 E-mail: salesuk@simpletech.com *Memory manufrs*

Simplex Ltd, Unit C Peter Road, Lancing, West Sussex, BN15 8TH Tel: (01903) 750333 E-mail: sales@simplexltd.com *Sign contractors & suppliers*

Simplex Knitting Ltd, Bye Pass Road, Beeston, Nottingham, NG9 5HN Tel: 0115-925 4980 Fax: 0115-943 0772 E-mail: enquiries@simplexknittingcompany.ltd.uk *Manufacturers of knitted & warp knitted fabric*

Simplex Marketing Ltd, Lowerclough Mill, Pendle Street, Nelson, Lancashire, BB9 8PH Tel: (01282) 697777 Fax: (01282) 699929 *Lighting company manufrs*

Simplex Security Systems, PO Box 33903, London, NW9 6ER Tel: (020) 8200 9991 Fax: (020) 8200 6598 E-mail: sales@simplex.org.uk *Security access control engineers*

▶ Simplicity Health, PO Box 4087, Kingswinford, West Midlands, DY6 9WY Tel: (0871) 2500120 Fax: (0871) 2500121 E-mail: info@simplicityhealth.co.uk *Range of home health tests including allergy, menopause, chlamydia, gonorrhoea, prostate and fertility plus vitamin supplements and drug testing kits. Online doctor service*

▶ Simplified Solutions, 80 Gathurst Road, Orrell, Wigan, Lancashire, WN5 8QH Tel: (0792) 1040857 *A small web design studio that creates simple, readable, usable web sites balanced with a standards-based methodology. Our services include; Web Design , Web Development , Web Hosting , Web Consultancy , Web Marketing*

Simply Agile, 25 Lindberg Way, Woodley, Reading, RG5 4XE Tel: 0118-969 7100 Fax: (0870) 1388551 E-mail: rod@train400.com *Computer consultants*

▶ Simply Bathrooms, Acan Way, Narborough, Leicester, LE19 2GW Tel: 0116-284 8880 Fax: 0116-284 8878 E-mail: sales@stuartplumbing.co.uk *Plumbers*

Simply The Best Entertainments, 1 Claypool Court, South Shields, Tyne & Wear, NE34 0XD Tel: 0191-456 6023 E-mail: elgood@hotmail.com *Karaoke equipment hire*

▶ Simply Blinds, 47 Rossall Road, Thornton-Cleveleys, Lancashire, FY5 1HG Tel: (01253) 863991 Fax: (01253) 863991 *Blind manufrs*

▶ Simply Computers, 1 Ferry Lane Industrial Estate, Wickford Way, London, E17 6HG Tel: (0870) 7274020 Fax: (0870) 7274002

▶ Simply Direct, Adelphi Mill, Grimshaw Lane, Bollington, Macclesfield, Cheshire, SK10 5JB Tel: (01625) 576527 Fax: (01625) 576545 E-mail: sales@simplydirect.net *Lockers & canteen furniture manufrs*

▶ Simply Direct, Adelphi Mill, Grimshaw Lane, Bollington, Macclesfield, Cheshire, SK10 5JB Tel: (01625) 576527 Fax: (01625) 576545 E-mail: sales@simplydirect.net *Canteen & school furniture*

▶ Simply Doughlightful, Unit 30 Barleylands Farm, Barleylands Road, Billericay, Essex, CM11 2UD Tel: (01268) 272766 *Artist materials retailers*

Simply Drinks Ltd, 17 Rufus Business Centre, Ravensbury Terrace, London, SW18 4RL Tel: (020) 8879 8300 Fax: (020) 8879 8301 E-mail: sales@simplydrinks.co.uk *Hot & cold bevarages, vending machines, vending cups*

Simply Foam Products Ltd, Harper Street, Willenhall, West Midlands, WV13 1SW Tel: (01902) 632060 Fax: (01902) 683383 *Plastic foam converters*

Simply Fresh Foods Ltd, Chaddock Lane, Worsley, Manchester, M28 1DR Tel: 0161-703 7023 Fax: 0161-703 7025 *Fresh food manufrs*

continued

▶ Simply Logo, 79 Rhyl Coast Road, Rhyl, Clwyd, LL18 3PW Tel: (01745) 361346 E-mail: enquiries@simplylogo.co.uk *Embroidery, printing services also wholesalers of work wear & sign makers*

▶ Simply Medical, 315 Centennial Park, Centennial Avenue, Elstree, Borehamwood, Hertfordshire, WD6 3TJ Tel: (020) 8236 3900 Fax: (020) 8953 4453 E-mail: info@simplymedical.co.uk *Medical equipment suppliers*

Simply Organic, Units 19-21, Dryden Vale, Bilston Glen, Loanhead, Midlothian, EH20 9HN Tel: 0131-448 0440 Fax: 0131-448 0441 E-mail: info@simplyorganic.co.uk *Organic food manufrs*

Simply Partitions, 2 Titchfield Park Road, Fareham, Hampshire, PO15 5RW Tel: (01489) 575993 E-mail: norman@simply-partitions.co.uk *Partition contractors & suppliers*

▶ Simply Pure Water, 4 Common Road, Skelmanthorpe, Huddersfield, HD1 5EU Tel: (01484) 868226 Fax: (01484) 866677 E-mail: sales@simplypurewater.co.uk *Water cooler manufrs*

Simply Read, Stanley Road, Hartlepool, Cleveland, TS25 1QP Tel: (01429) 868866 Fax: (01429) 868866 E-mail: sales@simply-read.com *Health & safety sign manufrs*

Simply Refrigeration & Air Conditioning Ltd, 10 Samsons Close, Brightlingsea, Colchester, CO7 0RP Tel: (0800) 0265140 Fax: (0870) 0520855 E-mail: info@simply-fridge.demon.co.uk *Air conditioning suppliers & installation*

▶ Simply Rugs, Unit 7 Skein Enterprise Park, Hodsoll Street, Sevenoaks, Kent, TN15 7LB Tel: (01732) 820304 *Saddlery*

Simply Scuba, Unit 111 112 John Wilson Business Park, Harvey Drive, Chestfield, Whitstable, Kent, CT5 3QY Tel: (0870) 9707000 Fax: (0870) 9707001 E-mail: customer.services@simplyscuba.com *Scuba diving*

▶ Simply Signs Ltd, The Old Dairy, Well Street, Winsford, Cheshire, CW7 1HN Tel: (01606) 869123 Fax: (01606) 869169 *Sign manufrs*

▶ Simply Stainless, 40 Walter Way, Silver End, Witham, Essex, CM8 3RJ Tel: (01376) 585602 Fax: (01376) 585529 E-mail: sales@simplystainlessltd.co.uk *Internet based distributors of stainless steel products*

▶ Simply Stone Ltd, 48 King Street, Larbert, Stirlingshire, FK5 4HD Tel: (01324) 579700 *Retail garden furniture*

Simply Stripes Signmakers Ltd, Unit 33 Enterprise City, Meadowfield Avenue, Spennymoor, County Durham, DL16 6JF Tel: (01388) 420460 Fax: (01388) 420009 *Sign manufrs*

▶ Simply Summerhouses, 130C High Street, Tranent, East Lothian, EH33 1HJ Tel: (01875) 613090 Fax: (01875) 617492 E-mail: enquiries@simply-summerhouses.co.uk *Timber products for outdoors*

▶ Simply Sweets, 334 Moorhey Road, Liverpool, L31 5LR Tel: 0151-520 0202 Fax: 0151-520 0202

▶ Simply Umbrellas, 17 Hampstead Gardens, Chadwell Heath, RM6 4FE Tel: (020) 8598 2811 E-mail: enquiries@simplyumbrellas.co.uk *On-line retailer umbrellas for day-to-day use, special occasions*

▶ Simply Wood Ltd, The Showroom, Kilkhampton, Bude, Cornwall, EX23 9QN Tel: (01288) 321772 Fax: (01288) 321782 E-mail: info@simplywoodltd.co.uk *Kitchen manufrs*

Simportex, 452a Finchley Road, London, NW11 8DG Tel: (020) 8457 8770 Fax: (020) 8457 7484 E-mail: sales@simportex.com *Commodity dealers*

▶ Simpson, 27 Sinclair Road, Aberdeen, AB11 9PL Tel: (01224) 890221 Fax: (01224) 871516

A.C. Simpson (Transformers) 1981 Ltd, Unit 20, Olds Close, Watford, WD18 9RU Tel: (01923) 777495 Fax: (01923) 771257 E-mail: info@acstx.co.uk *Transformer manufacturers including air cooled, bespoke/ custom built, dry type & power*

Simpson Environmental Services Ltd, Simpsons Way, Stoke Poges Lane, Slough, SL1 3GD Tel: (01753) 533311 Fax: (01753) 533311 E-mail: jeff@simpsonrecycling.com *Skip hire*

J.P. Simpson & Co. (Alnwick) Ltd, Tweed Valley Maltings, Tweedside Trading Estate, Berwick-upon-Tweed, TD15 2UZ Tel: (01289) 330033 Fax: (01289) 306602 E-mail: malt@simpsonsmalt.co.uk *Malt manufrs*

Simpson John Junior Glasgow Ltd, 28 Coxhill Street, Glasgow, G21 1HN Tel: 0141-332 3231 Fax: 0141-332 7325 E-mail: sales@simpsonsteel.co.uk *Steel stockholders*

Simpson Label Co. Ltd, Newbattle Industrial Estate, Mayfield, Dalkeith, Midlothian, EH22 4AF Tel: 0131-654 2800 Fax: 0131-663 6185 E-mail: mail@simpsonlabel.co.uk *Self-adhesive label, tag printers, digital & multicolour suppliers*

▶ Simpson Oils Ltd, South Quay, Fishmart, Wick, Caithness, KW1 5HA Tel: (01955) 604444 Fax: (01955) 602316

Simpson Packaging, Shawcross, Owl Lane, Dewsbury, West Yorkshire, WF12 7RQ Tel: (01924) 869010 Fax: (01924) 437666 E-mail: sales@simpson-packaging.co.uk *Packaging material suppliers*

▶ Simpson Plant Hire & Civil Engineering, 61 Trevithick Estate, St. Merryn, Padstow, Cornwall, PL28 8NN Tel: (01841) 520786 Fax: (01841) 521255

Simpson Refractories, Wood Croft, The Hills, Bradwell, Hope Valley, Derbyshire, S33 9HZ Tel: (01433) 621171 Fax: (01433) 623292 *Refectory installers*

Samuel Simpson & Co. Ltd, 30 Broughton Street, Manchester, M8 8NN Tel: 0161-834 4920 Fax: 0161-834 3056 E-mail: sales@samuelsimpson.com *Curtain lining & fabrics wholesalers*

Simpson Strong-Tie International Inc, Cardinal Point, Winchester Road, Tamworth, Staffordshire, B78 3HG Tel: (01827) 255600 Fax: (01827) 255616 E-mail: swilkes@strongtie.com *Builders ironwork manufrs*

Simpson Thomson Filtration, Virginia Mills, 187 Higher Hillgate, Stockport, Cheshire, SK1 3JG Tel: 0161-480 8991 Fax: 0161-429 8413 *Filter bag manufrs*

W.M. Simpson (Oldham) Ltd, 1-3 St. Chad's High St, Uppermill, Oldham, OL3 6AP Tel: (01457) 870478 Fax: (01457) 871057 *Machine tool dealers*

Simpsons, Clapper Lane, Staplehurst, Tonbridge, Kent, TN12 0JS Tel: (01580) 890747 Fax: (01580) 890667 E-mail: simpsonssolutions@supanet.com *Manufacturers of promotional packaging*

Simpsons, Trowbridge Road, Westbury, Wiltshire, BA13 3AY Tel: (01373) 826578 Fax: (01373) 865315 E-mail: simpson1979@aol.com *Cleaning machine distributors & agents*

Simpsons Of Aberdeen, 30 Anderson Drive, Aberdeen, AB15 4TY Tel: (01224) 316260 Fax: (01224) 316260 *Signmakers & engravers*

Simpsons Engineering, Vowels Lane, Kingscote, East Grinstead, West Sussex, RH19 4LF Tel: (01342) 811040 Fax: (01342) 811040 *Fabrication, installation, design & manufrs*

▶ Simpsons Excavating Contractors Woolacombe Ltd, Chilworth House, Woolacombe Station Road, Woolacombe, Devon, EX34 7HH Tel: (01271) 870386 *Plant hire & road haulage contractors*

▶ Simpsons Of Greenfield Mill Ltd, Greenfield Mill, Greenfield Road, Colne, Lancashire, BB8 9PW Tel: (01282) 863988 Fax: (01282) 863338 E-mail: sales@simpsonsfurniture.co.uk *Kitchen & furniture manufrs*

Simpsons Of Norfolk, Unit G1-G4, Abbey Farm Commercial Park, Southwell Road, Horsham St. Faith, Norwich, NR10 3JU Tel: (01603) 270270 Fax: (01603) 893538 E-mail: sales@simpsonsofnorfolk.co.uk *Furniture manufrs*

Simpson's Paints Ltd, 122-124 Broadley Street, London, NW8 8BB Tel: (020) 7723 6657 Fax: (020) 7706 4662 *Decorators merchants*

Simpson's Printers, Transfer Bridge Industrial Estate, County Road, Swindon, SN1 2EL Tel: (01793) 536305 Fax: (01793) 532543 E-mail: sales@simpsonprinters.co.uk *Screen & litho printers*

Simpson's Printers, Transfer Bridge Industrial Estate, County Road, Swindon, SN1 2EL Tel: (01793) 536305 Fax: (01793) 532543 *Screen & lithographic printers*

Simrad Ltd, Star Lane, Margate, Kent, CT9 4NP Tel: (01843) 290290 Fax: (01843) 290471 *Marine electronics manufacturers & distributors*

Simrad Marine Electrical Services, Fish Market Quay, Commercial Road, Buckie, Banffshire, AB56 1UR Tel: (01542) 834888 Fax: (01542) 839005 *Marine electronic services*

Simrad Optronics Ltd, 3 Medowbrook Industrial Estate, Maxwell Way, Crawley, West Sussex, RH10 9SA Tel: (01293) 560413 Fax: (01293) 560418 *Optical equipment*

Sims Automatics Ltd, 46 Dalsholm Road, Glasgow, G20 0TB Tel: 0141-946 0444 Fax: 0141-946 8155 E-mail: sales@simsautomatics.co.uk *Gaming equipment hire*

Sims Garden Machinery Ltd, 2 Western Road, Stratford-upon-Avon, Warwickshire, CV37 0AH Tel: (01789) 205671 Fax: (01789) 299006 *Garden machinery services & sales*

Sims Group (U K) Ltd, Whitelands Road, Ashton-under-Lyne, Lancashire, OL6 6UG Tel: 0161-343 2316 Fax: 0161-343 3272 *Recycling of tyres & electronics*

Sims Metal Management, Long Marston, Stratford-upon-Avon, Warwickshire, CV37 8AQ Tel: (01789) 720431 Fax: (01789) 720940 E-mail: info.uk@simsmm.com *Metal recycling & waste disposal*

Sims Metal UK Ltd, Gatton Road, Bristol, BS2 9SH Tel: 0117-955 7767 Fax: 0117-955 8098 E-mail: info@simsmetal.com.au *Scrap metal merchants*

Sims Metal UK Ltd, 7 Christow Road, Marsh Barton Trading Estate, Exeter, EX2 8QT Tel: (01392) 276292 Fax: (01392) 422420 E-mail: sales@sims-group.com *Scrap iron & metal merchants* Also at: Barnstaple, Bristol, Plymouth, Taunton & Torquay

Sims Metal UK Ltd, Alexandra Docks, Newport, Gwent, NP20 2WE Tel: (01633) 250650 Fax: (01633) 250850 *Scrap metal merchants*

Sims Metal UK Ltd, Blackbushe House, Vigo Lane, Yateley, Hampshire, GU46 6ED Tel: (01252) 873222 Fax: (01252) 876072 *Metal recycling*

Sims Metals UK Ltd, Paget Street, Burton-On-Trent, Staffordshire, DE14 3TQ Tel: (01283) 568549 Fax: (01283) 511989 *Metal recyclers*

Raymond Sims Ltd, Trent Side North, West Bridgford, Nottingham, NG2 5FA Tel: 0115-981 0992 *Racing rowing boat manufrs*

Ron Sims, Gregorys Mill Street, Worcester, WR3 8BA Tel: (01905) 25214 Fax: (01905) 22284 *Heating & electrical installation service providers*

W.J. Sims Ltd, 10 Endeavour Way, Croydon, CR0 4TR Tel: (020) 8689 2198 Fax: (020) 8689 4027 *Road transport contractors*

▶ Simstler, Riverside Way, Riverside Business Park, Irvine, Ayrshire, KA11 5DJ Tel: (01294) 557911

Simtech Simulation Techniques, Westcott Venture Park, Westcott, Aylesbury, Buckinghamshire, HP18 0XB Tel: (01296) 655787 Fax: (01296) 651729 E-mail: info@simtech-simulation.com *Autotutor vehicle simulator manufrs*

▶ Simtek Ems Ltd, Unit 5 Ocivan Way, Star Lane, Margate, Kent, CT9 4NP Tel: (01843) 233120

▶ Simulations.co.uk, 11 Colmans Wharf, 45 Morris Road, London, E14 6PA Tel: (020) 7537 2982 E-mail: jeremyhall@simulations.co.uk *Computer simulations for management development & management games for all levels training & education on courses & universities*

Simutech Electronics Ltd, Unit 42 Louis Pearlman Centre, Goulton Street, Hull, HU3 4DL Tel: (01482) 212961 Fax: (01482) 585608 E-mail: simutechpt@compuserve.com *Manufacturers of marine training simulators*

Sinar Technology Ltd, Unit 8 Camberley Business Centre, Bracebridge, Camberley, Surrey, GU15 3DP Tel: (01276) 63957 Fax: (01276) 29941 E-mail: office@sinar.co.uk *Agricultural moisture meters manufrs*

Sinara Consultants Ltd, 63 Tanner Street, London, SE1 3PL Tel: (020) 7940 7950 Fax: (020) 7378 1074 E-mail: sales@sinara.co.uk *IT consultants*

▶ SinCity Records UK, Polaris Studio's, Milestone Cottage, 61 London Road, Calne, Wiltshire, SN11 0AA Tel: 01249 816026 Fax: 01249 816026 E-mail: sincity@pobox.com *Record Labal **www.Finaldemand.net*

▶ Sinclair Ltd, Corse Industrial Estate, Gloucester Road, Corse, Gloucester, GL19 3RD Tel: (01452) 840771 Fax: (01452) 840315 E-mail: sales@hirose.co.uk *Optical manufrs*

▶ Andrew Sinclair, Hatston Industrial Estate, Kirkwall, Orkney, KW15 1RE Tel: (01856) 873178 Fax: (01856) 873351

▶ Sinclair Cleaning Services, Unit 2 Barleycroft End, Furneux Pelham, Buntingford, Hertfordshire, SG9 0LG Tel: (01279) 777115 Fax: (01279) 778006 E-mail: mail@jsld.co.uk *John Sinclair landscape and garden design services*

▶ Sinclair Computers, 16 Nisbet Drive, Denny, Stirlingshire, FK6 6AQ Tel: (01324) 829829 *Computer suppliers & repairers*

Sinclair Decorators, Roscoe Street, Scarborough, North Yorkshire, YO12 7BY Tel: (01723) 367361 Fax: (01723) 370848 E-mail: admin@sinclair.co.uk *General building contractors* Also at: Hull

Sinclair Electrics, 130 Embankment Rd, Plymouth, PL4 9JF Tel: (01752) 268887 Fax: (01752) 268887 *Electrical engineers*

Sinclair Fabrics, London Road, Bozeat, Wellingborough, Northamptonshire, NN29 7JR Tel: (01933) 663533 Fax: (01933) 663657 *Curtain makers manufrs*

Sinclair & Hay Ltd, Poynernook Road, Aberdeen, AB11 5QX Tel: (01224) 580940 Fax: (01224) 584453 *Scrap metal merchants*

Sinclair Horticulture & Leisure Ltd, Moss Lock Road, Ravenstruther, Lanark, ML11 8NP Tel: (01555) 870780 Fax: (01555) 870552 *Peat excavation*

▶ John Sinclair, 7 Hillborough Business Park, Sweechbridge Road, Herne Bay, Kent, CT6 6TE Tel: (01227) 749808 Fax: (01227) 749909 *Furnishings*

Sinclair Johnston & Partners, Eagle House, 2b Narbonne Avenue, London, SW4 9JS Tel: (020) 8682 8920 Fax: (020) 8673 1419 E-mail: email@sjandp.co.uk *Consulting structural engineers*

Sinclair Print, 396 Ashley Road, Poole, Dorset, BH14 0AA Tel: (01202) 730221 Fax: (01202) 380600 E-mail: sales@sinclairprint.co.uk *Quality printers & stationers*

▶ Sinclair Scott Ltd, 6 Borthwick View, Pentland Industrial Estate, Loanhead, Midlothian, EH20 9QH Tel: 0131-448 0868 Fax: 0131-448 0869

Sinclair Stainless Fabrications Ltd, Chalk Lane, Snetterton, Norwich, NR16 2JZ Tel: (01953) 887473 Fax: (01953) 888405 E-mail: info@sinclair-stainless.com *Stainless steel vessel manufrs*

Sinclair Systems Ltd, 74 Bewsey Street, Warrington, WA2 7JE Tel: (01925) 575543 Fax: (0845) 4567025 E-mail: info@sinclairsystems.co.uk *Air conditioning suppliers*

Sinclair Technologies Ltd, William James House, Cowley Road, Cambridge, CB4 0WX Tel: (01223) 420303 Fax: (01223) 420606 E-mail: salesuk@sinctech.com *Radio systems sales & manufrs*

Sinclair Voicenet Ltd, 2 Orbital Court, Peel Park, East Kilbride, Glasgow, G74 5PH Tel: (01355) 900000 Fax: (01355) 900001 E-mail: enquiries@voicerecording.co.uk *Electronic equipment distributors, call recording*

Morgan Sindall P.L.C., 77 Newman Street, London, W1T 3EW Tel: (020) 7307 9200 Fax: (020) 7307 9201 *Holding company & specialist construction group* Also at: Banbury, London W11, Norwich, Oxford & Portsmouth

Sinderby Stainless Ltd, J Alanbrooke Business Park, Station Road, Topcliffe, Thirsk, North Yorkshire, YO7 3SE Tel: (01845) 577550 Fax: (01845) 577800 E-mail: sales@sinderbystainless.co.uk *Stainless steel stockholders*

Sinelco Ltd, 16 Carlyle Avenue, Hillington Industrial Estate, Glasgow, G52 4XX Tel: 0141-810 1441 Fax: 0141-810 1711 *Control gear agents & distributors*

Sinergy Ltd, Station Road, Strines, Stockport, Cheshire, SK6 7GP Tel: (01663) 764833 Fax: (01663) 765885 *Energy system manufrs*

Singapore Airlines, 578-586 Chiswick High Road, London, W4 5RP Tel: (020) 8563 6767 Fax: (020) 8563 6753 *Airline* Also at: London W1

Singapore Economic Development Board, 30 Charles Ii Street, London, SW1Y 4AE Tel: (020) 7839 6688 Fax: (020) 7839 6162 E-mail: edbln@edb.gov.sg *Investment promoters*

Singer Instrument Co. Ltd, Roadwater, Watchet, Somerset, TA23 0RE Tel: (01984) 640226 Fax: (01984) 641166 E-mail: yeast@singerinst.co.uk Principal Export Areas: Worldwide *Scientific instrument manufrs*

Singer & James Ltd, 33 Roebuck Road, Ilford, Essex, IG6 3TZ Tel: (020) 8500 4115 Fax: (020) 8501 2456 E-mail: info@singerandjames.co.uk *Architectural metalworkers*

Singer & Partners Ltd, Harrison Trading Estate, Longworth Street, Preston, PR1 5DL Tel: (01772) 651188 Fax: (01772) 652577 E-mail: info@singerpartners.com *Direct marketing services & contract packaging*

Singer Sewing Centre, 14 Donegall Road, Belfast, BT12 5JN Tel: (028) 9032 6002 Fax: (028) 9032 6002 *Sewing machine suppliers*

Singer Sewing Centre, 94 Church Street, Croydon, CR0 1RD Tel: (020) 8688 1128 Fax: (020) 8688 1128 *Sewing machine retailers*

Singer Sewing Centre, 7 Vine Street, Evesham, Worcestershire, WR11 4RE Tel: (01386) 765844 Fax: (01386) 765844 *Sewing machines & accessories*

Singer Sewing Centre, 59 Green Street, Gillingham, Kent, ME7 1AE Tel: (01634) 570254 *Sewing machine retailers*

Singer Sewing Centre, 60 Fife Road, Kingston upon Thames, Surrey, KT1 1SP Tel: (020) 8546 1828 Fax: (020) 8546 8029 *Sewing machine manufrs*

Singer Sewing Centre, 4 Market Street, Rhyl, Clwyd, LL18 1RL Tel: (01745) 351175 *Sewing machines & equipment suppliers*

▶ Singer Sewing Centre, 126 Park View, Whitley Bay, Tyne & Wear, NE26 3QN Tel: 0191-252 5825 Fax: 0191-292 5826 E-mail: sales@singermachines.co.uk *Retail sewing machines*

Single Source Binding Ltd, 223 East India Dock Road, London, E14 0ED Tel: (020) 7515 0539 Fax: (020) 7537 9839 E-mail: sales@single-source.co.uk *Binding machines, plastic comb & plastic spiral or coil systems*

Singleton Birch Ltd, South Thoresby, Alford, Lincolnshire, LN13 0AR Tel: (01507) 480651 Fax: (01507) 480324 E-mail: sh@singletonbirch.co.uk *Quarry operators*

Singleton Birch Ltd, Melton Ross Quarries, Barnetby, South Humberside, DN38 6AE Tel: (01652) 688386 Fax: (01652) 686081 *Lime burners*

Charles Singleton Ltd, 1 Church Lane, Hackenthorpe, Sheffield, S12 4AN Tel: 0114-248 7976 Fax: 0114-248 6717 *Pearl button suppliers*

▶ Singleton Services, Unit E, The Sidings Industrial Estate, Settle, North Yorkshire, BD24 9RP Tel: (01729) 823939 Fax: (01729) 823939 E-mail: sales@beerengines.com *Fully refurbished & tested hand pumps parts & cellar ware*

▶ Sinks & Appliances (UK) Ltd, 9 Tudor Court, Church Lane, Ash Green, Coventry, CV7 9GX Tel: (024) 7636 1721 Fax: (024) 7636 5214 E-mail: sales@sinksandappliances.com *retailers of appliances*

Sino West Business Consultancy Ltd, 32 William Bristow Road, Coventry, CV3 5LQ Tel: (024) 7650 2465 Fax: (024) 7650 3215 E-mail: enquiry@sinowest.co.uk *Consultancy & services of Chinese manufacturing*

Sintamesh Ltd, Unit 2, Bentinck Workshops, Park Lane, Kirkby-in-Ashfield, Nottingham, NG17 9LE Tel: (01623) 753401 Fax: (01623) 753408 E-mail: sinta@btconnect.com *Our regular pattern & customised high quality filters are found at critical points in a variety of manufacturing & processing technologies from foam rubber making to lubricant purification*

Sintec Keramik Ltd, Lake Road, Leeway Industrial Estate, Newport, Gwent, NP19 4SR Tel: (01633) 636500 Fax: (01633) 636501 E-mail: info.uk@sintec-keramik.com *Chemical & ceramics manufrs*

Sintercast Ltd, 30 Anyards Road, Cobham, Surrey, KT11 2LA Tel: (01932) 862100 Fax: (01932) 862146 E-mail: info@sintercast.com *CGI marketing*

Siop Newydd, 50 High Street, Criccieth, Gwynedd, LL52 0EY Tel: (01766) 522737 *Delicatessen*

Siop Y Bont, 69-70a, The Market Market Street, Pontypridd, Mid Glamorgan, CF37 2SP Tel: (01443) 402584 E-mail: siopybont@yahoo.com *Book sales*

Sip (UK) Ltd, 1-2 Mercia Business Village, Torwood Close, Westwood Business Park, Coventry, CV4 8HX Tel: (024) 7647 4545 Fax: (024) 7647 0353 E-mail: peter.carnall@sipuk.com *Machine tool merchants or agents*

▶ Sipher Computer Maintenance, 39 English Street, Dumfries, DG1 2BU Tel: (01387) 253353 Fax: (01387) 270999 E-mail: enquiries@siphercomputing.co.uk *Computer maintenance consultants*

Sipson Group Ltd, Stone Close, West Drayton, Middlesex, UB7 8JU Tel: (01895) 441661 Fax: (01895) 431140 *Motor vehicle repair services, crash repair, body work*

Sir Ltd, 4 Carron Place, Kelvin Industrial Estate, East Kilbride, Glasgow, G75 0YL Tel: (01355) 264422 Fax: (01355) 244744 E-mail: sales@sir.ltd.uk *Supply wide format engineer drawing, printers, scanners copiers*

▶ Sir Bounce A Lot, 16 Portnalls Rise, Coulsdon, Surrey, CR5 3DA Tel: (01737) 554691 *Bouncy castle hirers*

Sir Jacob Behrens & Sons Ltd, Newhaven Business Park, Barton Lane, Eccles, Manchester, M30 0TH Tel: 0161-786 1000 Fax: 0161-787 7613 E-mail: sales@behrens.co.uk *Fabric converters*

SIR Learning Systems Ltd, Blackbrook House, Ashbourne Road, Blackbrook, Belper, Derbyshire, DE56 2DB Tel: (01773) 820011 Fax: (01773) 820206 E-mail: sales@sirplc.co.uk *Developers & marketers of educational multimedia software*

▶ Sir Robert Mcalpine Ltd, Yorkshire House, Grosvenor CR, London, SW1X 7EP Tel: (020) 7225 0064 Fax: (020) 7838 9157

▶ Sir Robert Mcalpine Ltd, Sellafield, Seascale, Cumbria, CA20 1PG Tel: (01946) 728080 Fax: (01946) 727295

▶ Siramics Ceramic Supplies & Services, Shawclough Road, Rochdale, Lancashire, OL12 6LN Tel: (01706) 351122 Fax: (01706) 351123 *Ceramics tiles distributors & retailers*

Sirch Tool & Design Ltd, 1 Park St Industrial Estate, Osier Way, Aylesbury, Buckinghamshire, HP20 1EB Tel: (01296) 330868 Fax: (01296) 330828 *Press toolmakers*

Sirco Controls Ltd, Swaines Industrial Estate, Ashingdon Road, Rochford, Essex, SS4 1RQ Tel: (01702) 545125 Fax: (01702) 546873 E-mail: sales@sirco-controls.co.uk *Pressure switch & pollution controller manufrs*

Siren Technology, 167 Radclifffe New Road, Whitefield, Manchester, M45 7RG Tel: 0161-796 5279 Fax: 0161-796 3208 E-mail: enquiries@sirentechnology.co.uk *Computer manufrs*

▶ Siriba Communications Ltd, 8 Whitefield Close, Lymm, Cheshire, WA13 9QG Tel: 08707 508842 Fax: 08707 508843
E-mail: richardball@siriba.co.uk *Siriba Communications specialise in the design, installation and implementation of Structured cabling systems including the supply and installation of active network equipment.*
Sirius, 3 Minster Court, London, EC3R 7DD Tel: (020) 7617 4900 Fax: (020) 7617 4919 *Insurance company*
Sirius Analytical Instruments, Riverside Forest Row Business Park, Station Road, Forest Row, East Sussex, RH18 5DW Tel: (01342) 820720 Fax: (01342) 820725
E-mail: sales@sirius-analytical.com *Chemical analysing instruments designers*
▶ Sirius Concepts Ltd, Oswald Hall, Auchincruive, Ayr, KA6 5HW Tel: (01292) 521376 Fax: (01292) 525939 E-mail: enquiries@sircon.co.uk *Software development diagnostic action plan provider*
Sirius Corporation, Rivermead House, Hamm Moor Lane, Addlestone, Surrey, KT15 2SF Tel: (01932) 820467 E-mail: mail@siriusit.co.uk *Computer consultants*
Sirius Yachts Ltd, Sandy La Industrial Estate, Stourport-on-Severn, Worcestershire, DY13 9QB Tel: (01299) 871048 Fax: (01299) 871048
E-mail: bryan@siriusyachts.com *Yacht & boat builders services*
Sirocco 2000 Ltd, Imperial Mill, Liverpool Road, Burnley, Lancashire, BB12 6HH Tel: (01282) 441771 Fax: (01282) 441770 *Gas appliances manufrs*
Sirocco Air Co. Ltd, Unit 4, Carew Street Industrial Estate, London, SE5 9DF Tel: (020) 7326 1272 Fax: (020) 7326 1272 *Air conditioning contractors*
Sirocco Signs, 5 Strathpeffer Road, Dingwall, Ross-Shire, IV15 9QF Tel: (01349) 866726 Fax: (01349) 866727
E-mail: info@siroccosigns.com *Sign makers*
Sirona Consulting, 80 Bulkington Avenue, Worthing, West Sussex, BN14 7HZ Tel: (01903) 206249 Fax: (01903) 206249
E-mail: andy@sironaconsulting.com *Specialists in recruitment within the credit card industry*
▶ SIRRIS Golf Tpa Ltd, 44 Heightington Place, Stourport-On-Severn, Worcestershire, DY13 0BE Tel: (07813) 117649
E-mail: info@SIRRISgolf.com *UK Supplier of SIRRIS performance technology golf products. Titanium Drivers, Irons, putters, bags and accessories.*
Sirsi, Unicorn House, Station Close, Potters Bar, Hertfordshire, EN6 3JW Tel: (01707) 646848 Fax: (01707) 858111 E-mail: sirsi@sirsi.co.uk *Provide software for library systems*
Sirton Computer Services Ltd, Unit 19 Windsor Park Indutrail Estate, 50 Windsor Avenue, London, SW19 2TJ Tel: (020) 8542 2255 Fax: (020) 8542 2266
E-mail: office@sirton.co.uk *Computer maintenance services*
Sirus Microtech, The Old Stables, Linden Hill, Wellington, Somerset, TA21 0DW Tel: (01823) 660665 Fax: (01823) 665321
E-mail: sales@sirus.co.uk *Static control equipment manufrs*
Sisis Equipment Macclesfield Ltd, Hurdsfield Industrial Estate, Macclesfield, Cheshire, SK10 2LZ Tel: (01625) 503030 Fax: (01625) 427426 E-mail: info@sisis.com *Engineering*
Franke Sissons Ltd, Carrwood Road, Chesterfield, Derbyshire, S41 9QB Tel: (01246) 450255 Fax: (01246) 451276
E-mail: ws.uk@franke.com Sales Contact: D. Howie Principal Export Areas: Worldwide *Stainless steel catering equipment & sanitary ware manufacturers*
▶ Sissons & French Transport Services Ltd, Lows Lane, Stanton-by-Dale, Ilkeston, Derbyshire, DE7 4QU Tel: 0115-932 3535 Fax: 0115-932 3535
▶ SISTech, Heriot Watt University, Edinburgh, EH14 4AS Tel: 0131-451 8162 Fax: 0131-451 8150
Sisys, Patrick House, West Quay Road, Poole, Dorset, BH15 1JF Tel: (01202) 660666 Fax: (01202) 330290 *Strategic imaging systems manufrs*
Sita, Wallsend Road, North Shields, Tyne & Wear, NE29 7SH Tel: 0191-257 8426 Fax: 0191-296 3402 *Waste management*
Sita Advanced Travel Solutions, Thornbrook House Weyside Park, Catteshall Lane, Godalming, Surrey, GU7 1XE Tel: (020) 8756 8000 Fax: (01483) 414122 *Travel industry software services*
Sita Recycling Services Ltd, Unit 34 Coneygre Industrial Estate, Tipton, West Midlands, DY4 8XP Tel: 0121-522 2216 Fax: 0121-522 2942 *Shredding services & waste paper merchants*
Sita Security Shredding Ltd, 64-76 River Road, Barking, Essex, IG11 0DS Tel: (020) 8532 7990 Fax: (020) 8591 9345
E-mail: securityshredding@sita.co.uk *Confidential document disposal agents*
Sita Security Shredding, Sinon House, The Hyde, Lower Bevendean, Brighton, BN2 4JE Tel: (01273) 699969 Fax: (01273) 690999 *Confidential waste disposers*
Sita South Gloucestershire Ltd, Grenfell Road, Maidenhead, Berkshire, SL6 1ES Tel: (01628) 513100 Fax: (01628) 513101 *Waste reclamation & disposal consultants*
Sitara & Co., 83 Howard Avenue, Mannar Park, Slough, SL2 1LD Tel: (01753) 774533 Fax: (01753) 673857
E-mail: sitara_co@yahoo.co.uk *Providers of labour assistance to companies for packaging work or for nursery work*
Site Data Sutton Coldfield Ltd, The Courtyard, Roman Way, Coleshill, Birmingham, B46 1HQ Tel: (01675) 430043 Fax: (01675) 430133
E-mail: site-data@dial.pipex.com *Industrial & residential site surveys*
Site Engineering Crane Hire, 11 Back Lane, Sileby, Loughborough, Leicestershire, LE12 7RB Tel: (01509) 816655 Fax: (01509) 816060 *We handle engineering inquiries from the local area, UK and Europe. We specialise in the installation, refurbishment and maintenance of plastic extrusion machinery. We also handle fabrication, sheet metal work, welding and general engineering.*
Site Engineering Services, Reverdane Road, Congleton, Cheshire, CW12 1UN Tel: (01260) 275252 Fax: (01260) 270111
E-mail: sales@phoenixengineering.co.uk *Fabricating & precision engineers*
Site Equipment Ltd, King Road Avenue, Avonmouth, Bristol, BS11 9HG Tel: 0117-982 8236
▶ Site Equipment Ltd, Bowerhurst, Mill Lane, Crondall, Farnham, Surrey, GU10 5RP Tel: (01252) 851988 Fax: (01252) 851989
E-mail: hire@site-equip.co.uk *Toilet hire*
Site Safe Supplies Ltd, 26 Sollershott East, Letchworth Garden City, Hertfordshire, SG6 3JN Tel: 01462 685544 *Lifting gear services*
Site Services Construction Ltd, 3 Inglewhite Road, Goosnargh, Preston, PR3 2EB Tel: (01772) 782583 Fax: (01772) 784166
E-mail: fredwareing@aol.com *Steel site construction service specialists*
Site Space Ltd, Meresborough Lane, Rainham, Gillingham, Kent, ME8 8PR Tel: (01634) 389440 Fax: (01634) 373151
E-mail: sales@sitespace.co.uk *Portable toilet hire*
▶ The Site Supply Co. Ltd, Unit 20, Haigh Park, Whitehill Industrial Estate, Stockport, Cheshire, SK4 1QR Tel: (0845) 0096750 Fax: (0845) 0096751 E-mail: info@sitesuppyco.com *Industrial fasteners & protective clothing manufrs*
Site Unit Rentals Ltd, Watlington Road, Cowley, Oxford, OX4 6SR Tel: (01865) 747025 Fax: (01865) 774562
E-mail: sales@surhire.com *Site unit rentals*
Site Weld, Manor Farm, Andover, Hampshire, SP11 7DB Tel: (01264) 710194 *Welding service, trailers & spares*
▶ Site Wizard, Ascot House, 22-24 Albion Place, Maidstone, Kent, ME14 5DZ Tel: (01622) 200045 Fax: (01622) 206700
E-mail: info@sitewizard.co.uk *Web site designers*
Sitec International Ltd, Unit 11 Lansdowne Court, Bumpers Way, Bumpers Farm, Chippenham, Wiltshire, SN14 6RZ Tel: (01249) 464150 Fax: (01249) 464160
E-mail: sales@sitec-int.co.uk *Railway signal testers & designers*
Sitecom UK Ltd, Falcon House, 16 Fernhill Road, Farnborough, Hampshire, GU14 9RX Tel: (01252) 551050 Fax: (01252) 511333
E-mail: sales@sitecom.com *Computer networkers*
Siteguard UK Ltd, Unit 30 Canal Bridge Enterprise Centre, Meadow Lane, Ellesmere Port, CH65 4EH Tel: 0151-355 3456 Fax: 0151-355 7809 E-mail: info@siteguarduk.com *Temporary CCTV installation for construction & vacant sites using remote site monitoring technology, central station connections, nationwide coverage with Group 4 National Rapid Response. Short term NO LEASE RENTAL. Long term rents available. Consultation-design-installation-rental-excellence through engineering*
▶ Sitel UK Ltd, Sitel House, Timothys Bridge Road, Stratford-upon-Avon, Warwickshire, CV37 9HY Tel: (01789) 299622 Fax: (01789) 292341
E-mail: info@sitel.com *Direct marketing*
Sitelink Communications, 14 Collingwood Court, Riverside Park Industrial Esta, Middlesbrough, Cleveland, TS2 1RP Tel: (01642) 232468 Fax: (01642) 226155
E-mail: teeside@sitelink.co.uk *Communication equipment sales, service & hire providers*
▶ Sitelink Communications Ltd, Radiophone Centre, 179 Hall Street, Stockport, Cheshire, SK1 4JG Tel: 0161-477 9229 Fax: 0161-480 7988 E-mail: manchester@sitelink.co.uk
▶ Sitemech Fabrications Ltd, Porritt Street, Bury, Lancashire, BL9 6HJ Tel: 0161-764 3901 Fax: 0161-763 3109
E-mail: sales@sitemechfabs.co.uk
▶ Site-Seeing Ltd, Ayston House, Ayston Road, Uppingham, Oakham, Rutland, LE15 9RL Tel: (01572) 821374 Fax: (01572) 821491
E-mail: cw@site-seeing.co.uk *Specialists in educational holidays in southern Greece.*We also cater for groups of retired people.*We only use quality hotels based in Tolon, with a beautiful snady beach, great facilities, and a few minutes drive to some of the countries most important archaeological sites. Visit our website for greater detail @ www.site-seeing.co.uk*
Sitest Ltd, Unit 9 Minster Park Collingwood Road, Verwood, Dorset, BH31 6QF Tel: (01202) 861733 Fax: (01202) 861734
E-mail: info@sitest.co.uk *Automatic test equipment distributors*
▶ sitewriters.co.uk, 42 North Street, Haworth, Keighley, West Yorkshire, BD22 8EP Tel: (01535) 210472 Fax: (01535) 210472
E-mail: john@sitewriters.co.uk *Web designers & services for charitable & small business sectors*
Sitting Firm Ltd, The Old Saw Mill, Harvest Hill Lane, Allesley, Coventry, CV5 9DD Tel: (024) 7640 7930 Fax: (024) 7640 7940
E-mail: info@sittingfirm.co.uk *Furniture manufrs*
Situations Upholsterers, Delvin End, Sible Hedingham, Halstead, Essex, CO9 3LN Tel: (01787) 462141 Fax: (01787) 462141
E-mail: enquiries@situations-uk.com *Upholsterers & polishers*
Sivil & Marine Ltd, Gibson Lane, Melton, North Ferriby, East Yorkshire, HU14 3HN Tel: (01482) 633305 Fax: (01482) 634835
E-mail: info@sivilandmarine.co.uk *Grinding media manufrs*
Sivyer Waste Management, Unit D2 Kent Kraft Industrial Estate, Lower Road, Northfleet, Gravesend, Kent, DA11 9SR Tel: (01322) 386265 *Paper recycling*
Siwgr A Sbeis Bakery, Parc Ty Gwyn, Betws Road, Nant y Rhiw, Llanrwst, Gwynedd, LL26 0PQ Tel: (01492) 641940 *Hotel & restaurant desserts manufrs*
Six Am Tackle & Bait Ltd, 82 Worksop Road, Swallownest, Sheffield, S26 4WD Tel: 0114-287 3070 Fax: 0114-287 3070 *Fishing tackle & angling suppliers*
▶ Six Hills Pallets, South Leicester Industrial Estate, South Street, Ellistown, Coalville, Leicestershire, LE67 1EU Tel: (01530) 263775 Fax: (01530) 263710
Six Hills Welding Supplies Ltd, 7 Pate Road, Melton Mowbray, Leicestershire, LE13 0RG Tel: (01664) 480801 Fax: (01664) 481833 *Welding suppliers*
Six Mile Excavators, Little North Leigh Farm, Stelling Minnis, Canterbury, Kent, CT4 6BZ Tel: (01227) 709611 Fax: (01227) 709820 *Plant hire company*
Sixaxis Ltd, 3 Hinton Way, Houghton Regis, Dunstable, Bedfordshire, LU5 5RB Tel: (07801) 719853 Fax: (07808) 769198
E-mail: sales@sixaxis.ltd.uk *Industrial robot programmers*
Sixty Six Software, 128 Melton Road, West Bridgford, Nottingham, NG2 6EP Tel: 0115-945 5150 Fax: 0115-945 5152 *Software consultants*
Sizerite Timber, Long Lane, South Hykeham, Lincoln, LN6 9NX Tel: (01522) 685349 Fax: (01522) 682520
E-mail: sizerite@southhykeham.freeserve.co.uk *Pine furniture manufrs*
Sizma Ltd, Unit 2 Upper Wingbury Courtyard, Wingrave, Aylesbury, Buckinghamshire, HP22 4LW Tel: (01296) 688303 Fax: (01296) 682119 E-mail: sales@sizma.co.uk *Pet & cotton products distributors*
▶ SJ Consultancy, 6 Flaxfields End, Fordingbridge, Hampshire, SP6 1RT Tel: 01425 652961 Fax: 01425 652961
E-mail: enquiries@sjcfb.co.uk *Computer repairs, uogrades and serviceing. New computer systems, virus removal and fault finding. One to One tuition and anything computer related.*
SJ Technologie, 10 Westminster Drive, Barton Seagrave, Kettering, Northamptonshire, NN15 6GE Tel: (08451) 304640 Fax: (08451) 304650 E-mail: sales@sjtechnologie.co.uk *Microwave components suppliers*
▶ Sja Film Technologies, 7 Laneside Metcalf Drive, Altham Industrial Estate, Accrington, Lancashire, BB5 5TU Tel: (01282) 774364 Fax: (01282) 772214 E-mail: dave.hoy@sjafilmtech.com *Film slitting services*
▶ SJA UK Ltd, 5 Lupton Road, Thame Industrial Estate, Thame, Oxfordshire, OX9 3SE Tel: (01844) 218275
E-mail: steve@sjalimited.co.uk *CNC milling & turning engineering services, prototype to production*
SJD Computers, Medford House, East Common Lane, Scunthorpe, South Humberside, DN16 1DE Tel: (01724) 854424 Fax: (01724) 854424 E-mail: sjd@cwcom.net *Suppliers of tacograph charts & transport consultants*
▶ SJD Creative Ltd, 31 Epworth Road, Copnor, Portsmouth, PO2 0HD Tel: 023 92350812 *Full service, creative and design agency based in Portsmouth, UK. Specialise in direct mail, branding and logos, advertising, brochures, business stationery, online media including e-commerce and exhibition graphics. ***
SJH Engraving, 74 Cecil Street, Birmingham, B19 3SU Tel: 0121-359 1321 Fax: 0121-333 4668 *Engravers*
▶ SJM French Polishers Ltd, 30 Marion CR, Orpington, Kent, BR5 2DD Tel: (01689) 897210 Fax: (01689) 890119
E-mail: sales@sjmltd.co.uk
▶ SJM Secretarial Services, Nelson Street, Burton-on-Trent, Staffordshire, DE15 0DE Tel: (01283) 509854 *Experienced legal secretary providing fast, accurate typing service to businesses and indviduals. Services include, letters, invoices, quotations, CVs, theses, dissertations, manuscripts and mail shots.*
▶ SJP Business Supplies Ltd, 6 Acorn Drive, Leeds, LS14 2HH Tel: (0800) 0431044 Fax: (0870) 0429348
E-mail: sjpbusinesssupplies@ntlworld.com *Toner cartridges, adhesive labels & tapes, printer & thermal ribbons suppliers*
▶ Skaala Windows & Doors, Diss Business Centre, Dark Lane, Scole, Diss, Norfolk, IP21 4HD Tel: (01379) 640580 Fax: (01379) 640590
E-mail: sales@skaala.com *Window & door manufrs*
Skagerak Co., 13 Byemoor Avenue, Great Ayton, Middlesbrough, Cleveland, TS9 6JP Tel: (01642) 723819 Fax: (01642) 722324
E-mail: info@skagerak.co.uk *Marine engineers*
▶ Skaino Ltd, West March Industrial Estate, West March, Daventry, Northamptonshire, NN11 4SA Tel: (01327) 871335 Fax: (01327) 706029 *Construction, heating & plumbing services*
Skako A/S (UK), PO Box 563, Bury St. Edmunds, Suffolk, IP33 9AW Tel: (01284) 723846 Fax: (01284)) 723846 E-mail: rta@skako.com *Leading manufacturer of concrete mixing & batching plants & associated equipment for the readymix & precast industries.*
▶ Skamem and Durham, Unit 7, Park 2000, Millennium Way, Newton Aycliffe, County Durham, DL5 6AR Tel: (01325) 375140 Fax: (01325) 375161 *Printing manufrs*
Skan Processing, The Howard John Glass Centre, Bodmin Road, Coventry, CV2 5DB Tel: (024) 7660 4999 Fax: (024) 7660 4888 *Precision machining of glass & ceramics*
Skandiaverken Ltd S K V, Cartside Avenue, Inchinnan, Renfrew, PA4 9RW Tel: 0141-812 8121 Fax: 0141-812 8124
E-mail: spares@skvuk.com *Diesel engine component manufrs*
Skandinaviska Enskilda Banken, Scandinavian House, 2-6 Cannon Street, London, EC4M 6XX Tel: (020) 7246 4000 Fax: (020) 7588 0929 *Investment banking services*
Skanem, 2 Princesway, Team Valley Trading Estate, Gateshead, Tyne & Wear, NE11 0TU Tel: 0191-482 8000 Fax: 0191-482 8001
E-mail: reception.newcastle@skanem.com *Self-adhesive label manufrs*
Skanem Cardiff, Bedwas House Industrial Estate, Bedwas, Caerphilly, Mid Glamorgan, CF83 8DW Tel: (029) 2086 5567 Fax: (029) 2086 5543
E-mail: gavin.braddon@selabelimage.co.uk *Specialist label printers*
Skanska Construction, 8 Dysart Street, London, EC2A 2BX Tel: (020) 7377 1444 Fax: (020) 7377 1999 *Building refurbishment contractors*
Skanska Construction, Maple Cross House, Denham Way, Maple Cross, Rickmansworth, Hertfordshire, WD3 9SW Tel: (01923) 776666 Fax: (01923) 777834
E-mail: skanska.construction@skanska.co.uk *Mechanical construction service*
▶ Skanska Rashleigh Weatherfoil Ltd, 160 Blackswarth Road, Bristol, BS5 8AG Tel: 0117-954 1175 Fax: 0117-955 1672
▶ Skanska Rashleigh Weatherfoil Ltd, 7 Colquhoun Avenue, Hillington Industrial Estate, Glasgow, G52 4BN Tel: 0141-810 1100 Fax: 0141-882 2200
Skanska Rashleigh Weatherfoil Ltd, West Lodge, Station Approach, West Byfleet, Surrey, KT14 6NG Tel: (01932) 791800 Fax: (01932) 791810 E-mail: krw.receptionist@skanska.co.uk *Electrical contractors & mechanical engineers*
Skar Precision Mouldings Ltd, Lady Lane Industrial Estate, Hadleigh, Ipswich, IP7 6AZ Tel: (01473) 828000 Fax: (01473) 828001
E-mail: sales@skar.co.uk *Injection mouldings manufrs*
Skate Systems Ltd, 55 London Road, Hurst Green, Etchingham, East Sussex, TN19 7QP Tel: (01580) 860020 Fax: (01580) 860021
E-mail: sales@skatesystems.co.uk *Machinery removal contractors*
▶ Skater Motor Sport, 1 Flight Path Farm, Broadbridge Lane, Smallfield, Horley, Surrey, RH6 9RF Tel: (01342) 844077 Fax: (01342) 844887 E-mail: sales@skatermotorsport.co.uk *Dry storage for all models of car & specialise in the repair of classic & high performance sports cars*
Skatoskalo International, 6 Morris Road, Royal Oak Industrial Estate, Daventry, Northamptonshire, NN11 8PD Tel: (01327) 312443 Fax: (01327) 314140 E-mail: sales@skatoskalo.com Principal Export Areas: Worldwide *Boiler cleaning apparatus manufrs*
▶ Skechers Usa Ltd, Katherine House Darkes Lane, 9 - 11 Wyllyotts Place, Potters Bar, Hertfordshire, EN6 2JD Tel: (01707) 655955 Fax: (01707) 647986
Skeens Precision Engineering Ltd, 55-55a Jubilee Road, Waterlooville, Hampshire, PO7 7RE Tel: (023) 9226 2191 Fax: (023) 9225 4219
E-mail: skeens@deans.freeserve.co.uk *Special purpose machinery manufrs*
Skegness Springs Ltd, Hassall Road, Skegness, Lincolnshire, PE25 3TB Tel: (0845) 4305000 Fax: (01754) 610584
E-mail: sales@skegsprings.co.uk Principal Export Areas: Africa, North America & South America *Spring manufacturers including stainless steel, compression & nickel alloy springs*
▶ Skelair International Ltd, Unit 1 Manor Lane, Holmes Chapel, Crewe, CW4 8AB Tel: (01477) 539100 Fax: (01477) 539101
Skelding's Ltd, 126 Oldbury Road, Smethwick, West Midlands, B66 1JE Tel: 0121-558 0622 Fax: 0121-558 6115 *Pressings & spring manufrs*
▶ Skeleton Coast, Unit B11, The Seedbed Centre, Wyncolls Road, Severalls Industrial Park, Colchester, CO4 9HT Tel: (01206) 855333
E-mail: terry@skeletoncoast.co.uk *Extreme sports*
Skelox Productions Ltd, Platts Common Industrial Estate, Barrowfield Road, Hoyland, Barnsley, South Yorkshire, S74 9TH Tel: (01226) 743993 Fax: (01226) 748974
E-mail: enquiries@skelox.co.uk *Injection moulding manufrs*
▶ The Skelton Group, Cooting Road, Aylesham, Canterbury, Kent, CT3 3EP Tel: (01303) 249561 Fax: (01303) 245007
▶ Skelton Group, Aylesham Industrial Estate, Aylesham, Canterbury, Kent, CT3 3EP Tel: (01304) 840640 Fax: (01304) 840440
H.J. Skelton & Co. Ltd, 9 The Broadway, Thatcham, Berkshire, RG19 3JA Tel: (01635) 865256 Fax: (01635) 865710
E-mail: info@hjskelton.com Principal Export Areas: Worldwide *Suppliers of crane rails railway rails tram rails*
Skelton T.J Ltd, 16 Well Street, Birmingham, B19 3BJ Tel: 0121-554 0487 Fax: 0121-523 3585 E-mail: info@whderby.co.uk *HIGH QUALITY CRAFTSMANSHIP AND SERVICE SPANNING THREE CENTURIES. Your best guarantee of prompt, high quality services the reputation we have developed over three centuries. From the earliest days, the company has run on the foundations of craftsmanship and service, and we remain true to these traditions today. Still in family ownership, the company has faithfully maintained the standards of quality, attention to detail and service that were set two centuries ago. We have built on these foundations and have developed complimentary skills to become one of the foremost names in manufacturing Medals, badges, insignia and other presentational products, backed up by standards of service others find hard to match.*
Skeltonhall Systems Ltd, 70 Carwood Road, Sheffield, S4 7SD Tel: 0114-243 1332 Fax: 0114-244 9579
E-mail: info@skeltonhall-systems.com *Design & supply of gas & liquid metering systems*
▶ Skene Blair & Son Forfar Ltd, Unit 1 Station Place, Forfar, Angus, DD8 3TB Tel: (01307) 463431 Fax: (01307) 468595
▶ Skerritt Ltd, 24 Union Road, Nottingham, NG3 1FH Tel: 0115-950 6722 Fax: 0115-958 8149 E-mail: info@skerritt.co.uk *Mechanical, electrical, plumbing & property care services*
Skerritt Electrical Ltd, 1087 Kingsbury Road, Castle Vale, Birmingham, B35 6AJ Tel: 0121-776 5710 Fax: 0121-322 2216
E-mail: admin@skerrittelectrical.co.uk *Electrical engineers & contractors*
▶ Sketch 3D Design & Drafting, 130 Cambridge Street, Wolverton, Milton Keynes, MK12 5AQ Tel: (07789) 002945
E-mail: info@sketch3d.co.uk *Architectural services*
▶ SKF Economos U.K. Ltd, Unit 20 Avonbank Industrial Estate, West Town Rd, Bristol, BS11 9DE Tel: 0117-982 5729 Fax: 0117-982 5730 E-mail: bristol@economos.com *Manufacturers of seals, high pressure, high temperature, hydraulic/fluid, pneumatic air, oil,*

continued

continuation
special purpose, food/beverage/pharmaceutical/ healthcare industries, and to specification. Also manufacturers of gaskets, gland packing, PTFE products/components/fittings. In addition, water jet (high pressure) cutting services, and machinists of plastics and elastomers.

▶ SKF Economos U.K. Ltd, Unit B2, Connaught Business Centre, 22 Willow Lane, Mitcham, Surrey, CR4 4NA Tel: (020) 8648 0252 Fax: (020) 8648 0248 E-mail: mitcham@economos.com *Manufacturers of seals, high pressure, high temperature, hydraulic/fluid, pneumatic air, oil, special purpose, food/beverage/pharmaceutical/ healthcare industries, and to specification. Also manufacturers of gaskets, gland packing, PTFE products/components/fittings. In addition, water jet (high pressure) cutting services, and machinists of plastics and elastomers.*

▶ SKF Economos U.K. Ltd, Unit 32, Stirling Close, Pattinson South Industrial Estate, Washington, Tyne & Wear, NE38 3QD Tel: 0191-417 1094 Fax: 0191-417 1118 E-mail: washington@economos.com *Based in the North East of the UK, covering Tyneside, Teesside, Durham, Northumberland & Cumbria, we are manufacturers of Seals, High & Low Pressure and Temperature's for use with water and all types of hydraulic fluids and in pneumatic applications. Due to our innovative manufacturing process, we are able to offer all types of seal profile and any special purpose or R & D seals from small to large batch quantities and sizes up to 4 meters in diameter! We cover all industries including Food/Beverage/ Pharmaceutical/Healthcare as well as heavy Engineering/Shipbuilding/Iron & Steel etc. We are also manufacturers of Gaskets, gland packings, PTFE products, components and fittings. In addition we offer a High Pressure Water Jet cutting service and Engineered Plastic Solutions with our state of the art multi axis machining centres for the machining of plastics and elastomers.*

▶ SKF Economos U.K. Ltd, Unit 17, Block D Wednesbury Trading Estate, Darlaston Rd, Wednesbury, W. Midlands, WS10 7JN Tel: 0121-505 2112 Fax: 0121-505 2045 E-mail: wednesbury@economos.com *Manufacturers of seals, high pressure, high temperature, hydraulic/fluid, pneumatic air, oil, special purpose, food/beverage/pharmaceutical/ healthcare industries, and to specification. Also manufacturers of gaskets, gland packing, PTFE products/components/fittings. In addition, water jet (high pressure) cutting services, and machinists of plastics and elastomers.*

▶ SKF Economos UK Ltd, Unit 2 Airport Commerce Park, Howmoss Drive, Kirkhill Industrial Estate, Dyce, Aberdeen, AB21 0GL Tel: (01224) 725400 Fax: (01224) 725686 E-mail: aberdeen@economos.com *Oil & gas engineering services*

▶ SKF Economos UK Ltd, Unit 5-6, Armley Link, Armley Road, Leeds, LS12 2QN Tel: 0113-231 0303 Fax: 0113-231 0395 E-mail: leeds@economos.com *Manufacturers of seals, high pressure, high temperature, hydraulic/fluid, pneumatic air, oil, special purpose, food/beverage/pharmaceutical/ healthcare industries, and to specification. Also manufacturers of gaskets, gland packing, PTFE products/components/fittings. In addition, water jet (high pressure) cutting services, and machinists of plastics and elastomers.*

▶ SKF Economos UK Ltd, 83 Buckingham Avenue, Trading Estate, Slough, SL1 4PN Tel: (01753) 696565 Fax: (01753) 696181 E-mail: uk.sales@economos.com *Economos UK is the world leader in machined seal technology. With 11 manufacturing units located throughout the UK, we can produce any type of seal in a wide variety of materials on demand without delays for tooling or stocks. We offer engineers and buyers in both the OEM and MRO industries the ability to solve sealing problems and reduce costs. Our products include; Piston seals, Rod seals, Wiper seals, O rings, wear rings. Other seals such as High temperature seals in PTFE compounds and PEEK materials can also be supplied. Any quantity can be produced either by machining or for high volumes injection moulding. Economos also specialise in Machined Plastics components and machined elastomers components using state-of-the-art CNC equipment. In addition, we operate a Water Jet cutting facility for producing gaskets and other flat components. Call Economos and ask for our extensive literature or request a visit from one of our sales engineers Also at: Branches throughout the U.K.*

▶ Ski Rack Surfboard Car Roof Rack Cheap Car Roof Rack, 15 Ambridge Close, Northampton, NN4 9RW Tel: (01604) 710106 E-mail: sales@rackinabag.co.uk *Ski Rack, Ski car roof rack. Surfboard Car roof rack. Surfboard Car roof rack in your boot. Ski and Surfboard rack.*

▶ Ski Slope Services Ltd, Woodlands, Woodlands Road, Blairgowrie, Perthshire, PH10 6JU Tel: (01250) 873028 Fax: (01250) 874723 E-mail: info@sss.uk *Ski lift engineers*

Skiathos Villa Rentals, 1 Tower View, Uckfield, East Sussex, TN22 1TP Tel: (01825) 763328 E-mail: webmaster@skiathosvillarentals.com *Quiet hillside greek villa on Skiathos island for villa rentals sleeping 4-6. Our greek villa has two bedrooms with balconies and two bathrooms.*

Skidmarx, 16-18 Cambridge Road, Granby Industrial Estate, Weymouth, Dorset, DT4 9TJ Tel: (01305) 780808 Fax: (01305) 787499 E-mail: info@skidmarx.co.uk *Motorbike components manufrs*

Skidmore Lifting Equipment, 60 Sandwell Street, Walsall, WS1 3EB Tel: (01922) 613633 Fax: (01922) 626991 E-mail: sales@lodar.com *Winch & lifting equipment suppliers*

Skiffy, 5 Wombourne Enterprise Park, Bridgnorth Road, Wombourne, Wolverhampton, WV5 0AL Tel: (01902) 894658 Fax: (01902) 894661 E-mail: skiffyuk@btconnect.com *Nylon component parts distributors*

▶ Skill Express Ltd, Unit 17, Enterprise Centre, 1 Dryden Road, Loanhead, Midlothian, EH20 9LZ Tel: 0131-440 9889

▶ Skill Scaffolding Ltd, Third Avenue, Southampton, SO15 0JX Tel: (023) 8077 7750 Fax: (023) 8070 4535 E-mail: skill.foton@btconnect.com

▶ Skill Scaffolding Ltd, Third Avenue, Southampton, SO15 0JX Tel: (023) 8077 7750 Fax: (023) 8070 4535

▶ Skillbase, 106 Fintry Road, Dundee, DD4 9EZ Tel: (01382) 506676 Fax: (01382) 500884

▶ Skillbase Training Ltd, PO Box 8325, Leicester, LE9 7FG Tel: (01455) 846434 Fax: (0871) 661 7209 E-mail: info@skillbasetraining.co.uk *SkillBase Training Ltd, providers of First Aid, Health & Safety, and Food Hygiene Training accross the UK. SkillBase prides itself on being a professional, yet affordable company, offering certified training, allowing you to meet your statutory requirements, at a competitive price. It's not only our prices that are competitive, our service is great too, our feedback indicates that 97% of delegates rate our courses as excellent - with the other 3% rating them as very good!*

Skilled Manufacturing Ltd, Victoria Road, Halesowen, West Midlands, B62 8HY Tel: 0121-559 0776 Fax: 0121-559 0801 *Fire trim manufrs*

Skiller Engineering Ltd, Unit 1, Pig Lane, Bishop'S Stortford, Hertfordshire, CM23 3HG Tel: 01279 501631 *Tool makers*

Skillforce Ltd, Eton Hill Road, Radcliffe, Manchester, M26 2ZT Tel: 0161-724 6634 Fax: 0161-723 1661 E-mail: sales@parsonsreiss.com *Engineers to the paper industry & steel fabricators*

Skillframe Ltd, 138 Walton Road, East Molesey, Surrey, KT8 0HP Tel: (020) 8941 7733 Fax: (020) 8941 3301 E-mail: info@skillframe.co.uk *Recruitment consultants*

Skillion Ltd, Southbank Commercial Centre, 140 Battersea Park Road, London, SW11 4NB Tel: (020) 7622 5511 Fax: (020) 7738 8272 E-mail: southbankcc@easynet.co.uk *Property management*

▶ Skillmarque Ltd, 27, East Street, Chichester, W. Sussex, PO19 1HS Tel: 0845-129 7299 Fax: 0845-129 7298

▶ Skillquest Ltd, Bordesley Hall, The Holloway, Alvechurch, Birmingham, B48 7QA Tel: (01527) 585855 Fax: (01527) 60140 E-mail: skillquest@btconnect.com *IT Staff Recruitment, mainly Permanent employees at all levels from Graduate to IT Director*

The Skills Centre, 3 The Adelaide, Higham, Rochester, Kent, ME3 7LU Tel: (01474) 824555 *IT training*

Skills For Security Recruitment Ltd, Security House, Barbourne Road, Worcester, WR1 1RS Tel: (01905) 27289 Fax: (01905) 724949 E-mail: info@skillsforsecurity.org.uk *Security industry training services*

▶ Skills UK, 17 Britannia Road, Burbage, Hinckley, Leics, LE10 2HE Tel: 01455 617776 E-mail: ted@skills.uk.com *Sooner or later, someone has to provide the kind of service that Recruitment Agencies need when advertising or database searches don"t meet a particular need. The talents of Skills UK addresses this need, often costing less than your own in-house solution, but providing a swifter and better result.*

Skils Ltd, 8 Mead Park, Mead Road, Leckhampton, Cheltenham, Gloucestershire, GL53 7EF Tel: (01242) 231231 Fax: (01242) 251212 *Hiring of inflatable toys*

Skilton Bros, 13 Thurstons Estate, Binsted, Alton, Hampshire, GU34 4PD Tel: (01420) 22290 *Heavy plant repairs*

Skincross (Cheshire) Ltd, 6 Riverside, Dukinfield, Cheshire, SK16 4HE Tel: 0161-343 7323 Fax: 0161-343 7324 *Shrink, skin & blister packaging*

Skinner Board & Co. Ltd, Sussex Street, Bristol, BS2 0RE Tel: 0117-955 1592 Fax: 0117-935 1408 *Heating, cooling & ventilation*

Omar Skinner & Sons, Warfield Park, Bracknell, Berkshire, RG42 3RG Tel: (01344) 882207 Fax: (01344) 882207 *Loudspeaker systems manufrs*

Skinners Sheds Ltd, 161 Bexhill Road, St. Leonards-On-Sea, East Sussex, TN38 8BG Tel: (01424) 716716 Fax: (01424) 716716 E-mail: info@skinners-sheds.com *Order your 100% pressure treated sheds on-line today! We even include Free delivery throughout Sussex, Kent, Surrey and South London, check our delivery page for more information. Our quality sheds are built at our factory site in St. Leonards-on-Sea in East Sussex and built to a high standard. Why not visit one of our many show sites and see for yourself. Hopefully you can find and order the shed you like, however if you cannot find what you are looking for or need help then please do not hesitate to call us on 01424 716716..*

Skip Units Ltd, Industrial Estate, Sinfin Lane, Derby, DE24 9GL Tel: (01332) 761361 Fax: (01332) 270013 E-mail: sales@skipunits.co.uk *Waste container manufrs*

▶ Skippers, Manor Lane, Rochester, Kent, ME1 3JN Tel: (01634) 815522 Fax: (01634) 815533 *Distributors of the Italian Marine Coatings brand Skipper"s Line, providing a large range of high performace coatings to the marine industry, including Yacht paints and varnishes, primers, antifoulings, undercoats, epoxy coatings*

Skippy's Machine Tools, 12 Queens Road, Erdington, Birmingham, B23 7JP Tel: 0121-386 3622 Fax: 0121-386 3623 E-mail: service@skippysmt.com *We repair all CNC machine tools including, EMI-MEC, Bermak, Feeler, Fanuc, Heidenhain, Siemens, Fagor, Allen Bradley, Mitsubishi & other CNC & PLC. Breakdowns, rebuilding, retrofitting & preventative maintenance contracts plus all EMI-MEC spares*

Skipton Bed & Suite Centre, 17 Water Street, Skipton, North Yorkshire, BD23 1PQ Tel: (01756) 794719 Fax: (01756) 796284 *Beds & suites retail & distributors*

SKM Products Ltd, Unit N3 Troon Way Business Centre, Humberstone Lane, Leicester, LE4 9HA Tel: 0116-246 1727 Fax: 0116-246 0313 *Welding stud fasteners manufrs*

Skorpion Sports Ltd, 103a Oak Lane, Bradford, West Yorkshire, BD9 4QU Tel: (01274) 548761 Fax: (01274) 544301 E-mail: info@skorpionsports.com *Sports gloves manufrs*

E. Skorski & Son Ltd, Cortress House, Julia Street, Strangeways, Manchester, M3 1DQ Tel: 0161-831 7017 Fax: 0161-832 7097 E-mail: mark@skorski.freeserve.co.uk *Promotional & sports bag manufrs*

Skot Chemist, 139 Victoria Road, London, N9 9BA Tel: (020) 8803 3221 Fax: (020) 8807 2946 *Dispensing chemist*

Skotland Joinery Ltd, Lochshore Indust Estate, Caledonian Place, Glengarnock, Beith, Ayrshire, KA14 3AZ Tel: (01505) 682829 Fax: (01505) 685331 *Joiners*

SKS Uk Ltd, Tweed Road, Clevedon, Avon, BS21 6QQ Tel: (01275) 876021 Fax: (01275) 878480 E-mail: mail@ampep.co.uk *Manufacturers of flying controls*

SKTS, 451 Bushey Mill Lane, Bushey, WD23 2AT Tel: (01923) 223657 Fax: (01923) 333731 E-mail: enquiries@shkata.com *Computer consultancy & service providers*

Sky Electronic Systems Ltd, Unit D Cavendish Courtyard, Weldon North Industrial Estate, Corby, Northamptonshire, NN17 5DZ Tel: (01536) 267000 Fax: (01536) 267666 E-mail: ian@skyd.fsnet.co.uk *Manufacturers of control signal conditioning instrumentation*

▶ Sky Eye Aerial Photography Ltd, PO Box 10, Reading, RG8 0EF Tel: (01491) 873277 Fax: (01491) 873430 E-mail: skyeyephoto@aol.com *Specialist aerial photography company*

▶ Sky Fashion Garments, 36 Cyprus Road, Leicester, LE2 8QS Tel: 0116-283 7755 Fax: 0116-283 8322 E-mail: dazzle.europe@totaliser.co.uk *Clothing manufrs*

Sky Films, 49 Butt Lane, Hinckley, Leicestershire, LE10 1LB Tel: (01455) 890081 Fax: (01455) 611227 E-mail: admin@skyfilmsnational.co.uk *Aerial photos & surveys*

▶ Sky High Leisure Hot Air Balloon Team, Watery Lane Cottage, Wrexham, LL13 OSL Tel: (0845) 3302994 E-mail: info@skyhighleisure.com *Visit our web site @ www.skyhighleisure.com*Champagne Hot Air Balloon Pleasure Flights*The Perfect Gift that will be remembered for a life time.**Gift Vouchers*

Sky Plastics Ltd, Eastfield Side, Sutton-in-Ashfield, Nottinghamshire, NG17 4JR Tel: (01623) 553527 Fax: (01623) 556737 E-mail: sales@skyplastics.demon.co.uk Principal Export Areas: Worldwide *Plastic injection moulding manufrs*

Sky Signs Ltd, Broadgate House, Church Street, Deeping St. James, Peterborough, PE6 8HD Tel: (01778) 345464 Fax: (01778) 341198 E-mail: enquiries@icarusballoons.co.uk *Balloon & banner company*

Sky Trade International Ltd, Cheriton Fitzpaine, Crediton, Devon, EX17 4BQ Tel: (01363) 866573 Fax: (01363) 866860 *Vintage aircraft spare parts stockist*

▶ Sky Wind, 34 Buckingham Palace Road, London, SW1W 0RH Tel: 07092 015632 Fax: 07092 015637 E-mail: info@skywind.co.uk

Skyblue, 23 Tavistock Street, London, WC2E 7NX Tel: (08701) 285430 Fax: (0870) 1285240 E-mail: ask@skybluesoloutions.com *Recruitment agency*

Skyburst Illuminations Ltd, 16 Chestnut Drive, Claverham, Bristol, BS49 4LN Tel: (01934) 877359 E-mail: info@skyburst..co.uk *Firework company, distributors & displays*

Skycraft Services Ltd, Albany House, 12 Silver Street, Litlington, Royston, Hertfordshire, SG8 0QE Tel: (01763) 852150 Fax: (01763) 852593 *Propeller manufrs*

Skydrift Ltd, Norwich Airport, Norwich, NR6 6EP Tel: (01603) 407424 Fax: (01603) 418687 E-mail: ops@skydrift.co.uk *Air charter operators & air brokers*

▶ Skye Transport, Crossal, Drynoch, Carbost, Isle of Skye, IV47 8SP Tel: (01478) 640243 Fax: (01478) 640473

Skyetime Computer Maintenance, Clock House, Wadhurst Road, Frant, Tunbridge Wells, Kent, TN3 9EJ Tel: (01892) 750800 Fax: (01892) 750076 E-mail: info@skyetime.co.uk *Computers*

Skyewright, 24 Elgol, Isle of Skye, IV49 9BL Tel: (01599) 534046 *Computer software development*

Skyforce Ltd, Old Mill Lane Industrial Estate, 15 Millway, Mansfield, Nottinghamshire, NG19 9AL Tel: (0800) 622752 Fax: (01623) 420672 *Aerial installation contractors*

▶ Skyform, Unit 7C, Beechcroft Farm Industrial Estate, Chapel Wood Road, Ash, Sevenoaks, Kent, TN15 7HX Tel: (01474) 879990 *Access equipment services*

Skyglass Ltd, Morgans Yard, Arundel Road Industrial Estate, Uxbridge, Middlesex, UB8 2RP Tel: (01895) 234432 Fax: (01895) 271118 *Welded fabrications of steel skips*

Skyhigh Traffic Data, 28 High Street, Tadcaster, North Yorkshire, LS24 9AT Tel: (01937) 833933 Fax: (01937) 832275 E-mail: mail@skyhightraffic.co.uk *Traffic & pedestrian surveys, manuals & videos*

▶ Skylark Energy Systems Ltd, PO Box 11033, Banchory, Kincardineshire, AB31 5WS Tel: (01330) 823950 Fax: (01330) 823966 E-mail: info@skylark.co.uk *Power electronics, batteries & UPS*

Skylark Motor Services, The Ridge, Woodfalls, Salisbury, SP5 2LW Tel: (01725) 510282 Fax: (01725) 512844 *MOT station services motor vehicle repair & coach operator*

Skyline, Unit 16 First Avenue, Drum Industrial Estate, Chester le Street, County Durham, DH2 1AG Tel: 0191-410 7917 Fax: 0191-492 0620 *Scaffolding contractors & erectors*

▶ Skyline International Electronics, Harbour House, Coldharbour Lane, Rainham, Essex, RM13 9YA Tel: (01708) 522211

Skyline Models, Wycombe Road, Studley Green, High Wycombe, Buckinghamshire, HP14 3XB Tel: (01494) 484545 Fax: (01494) 484545 E-mail: sales@skylinemodels.co.uk *Model shop*

Skyline Relocation Services Ltd, Unit 2, Inchinnan Road, Paisley, Renfrewshire, PA3 2RE Tel: 0141-887 5444 Fax: 0141-887 3730

Skymark Packaging International Ltd, Southern Avenue, Leominster, Herefordshire, HR6 0QF Tel: (01568) 611393 Fax: (01568) 611602 E-mail: info@skymark.co.uk *Flexible film manufrs*

Skymark Packaging Solutions, Manners Avenue, Manners Industrial Estate, Ilkeston, Derbyshire, DE7 8EF Tel: 0115-930 2020 Fax: 0115-907 1525 E-mail: admin@skymark.co.uk *Polythene bag manufrs*

▶ Skymark Performance Films Ltd, Mannaberg Way, Scunthorpe, South Humberside, DN15 8XF Tel: (01724) 270777 Fax: (01724) 289554 E-mail: admin@skymark.co.uk *Extruded plastic laminating manufrs*

Skymasts Antennas Ltd, Equilibrium House, Mansion Close, Moulton Park Industrial Estate, Northampton, NN3 6RU Tel: (01604) 494132 Fax: (01604) 494133 E-mail: info@skymasts.com *Design, Manufacture and Global Distribution of professional Land, Sea and Vehicular Based Wireless Communication Antennas within the frequency ranges of 27Mhz up to 5.8GHz.**

Skymetals Non Ferrous Metals, Unit 3 Trillennium Highway Point, Gorsey Lane, Coleshill, Birmingham, B46 1JU Tel: (01675) 430140 Fax: (01675) 430346 E-mail: birmingham@allmetal.co.uk Principal Export Areas: Worldwide *Aluminium & bronze stockholders*

Skynet Worldwide Express, Unit 8-9 Maple Grove Business Centre, Lawrence Road, Hounslow, TW4 6DR Tel: (020) 8538 1988 Fax: (020) 8538 1921 E-mail: tustserv@deltec-international.com *International courier - import & export*

▶ Skypark, Sycamore Trading Estate, Squires Gate Lane, Blackpool, FY4 3RL Tel: (01253) 310647 Fax: (01253) 362858 E-mail: webmaster@skyparksecure.com *Airport parking services*

▶ Skypark Freight, 16 Owen Drive, Liverpool, L24 1YL Tel: 0151-448 0048 Fax: 0151-448 0007 E-mail: steve@skylog.freeserve.co.uk

Skyscene, Flat 5 Napier Court, Gefle Close, Bristol, BS1 6XY Tel: 0117-929 0735 Fax: 0117-914 3775 E-mail: info@skyscene.co.uk *High Quality Aerial Photography through-out United Kingdom and Ireland.*

▶ Skyscope, 196 Morris Green Lane, Bolton, BL3 3LB Tel: (01204) 654901 E-mail: paul@skyscope.co.uk *foreign channels from europe middle east and asia.italian spanish german thai french greek and many more.premiership football motorised and fixed dish systems.adult channels.sky digital.tv aerials.for all your satellite requirements contact skyscope.*

▶ Skyscrapers UK Ltd, 81 Cheam Road, Epsom, Surrey, KT17 3EG Tel: (020) 8786 7456 Fax: (020) 8786 7456 E-mail: info@skyscrapersuk.com *Lift maintenance, repairs & installation*

Skysearchers Radio Communication Equipment, 1 Oak Street, South Bank, Middlesbrough, Cleveland, TS6 6PB Tel: (01642) 453613 Fax: (01642) 453613 *Radio communication equipment suppliers*

Skytec Aviation Ltd, Unit 23 Langlands Avenue, Kelvin South Business Park, East Kilbride, Glasgow, G75 0YG Tel: (01355) 279633 Fax: (01355) 279634 E-mail: skytecaviation@btconnect.com *Turbine maintenance & repair services*

Skytrex Model Makers, 1 Charnwood Business Park, North Road, Loughborough, Leicestershire, LE11 1LE Tel: (01509) 213789 Fax: (01509) 230874 E-mail: sales@skytrex.com *Metal model manufrs*

Skytronic Ltd, Containerbase, Barton Dock Road, Urmston, Manchester, M41 7BQ Tel: 0161-749 8180 Fax: 0161-749 8181 E-mail: sales@skytronic.co.uk *Public address equipment distributor*

▶ Skyway Scaffold Ltd, Unit 1 Sams Lane, West Bromwich, West Midlands, B70 7EG Tel: 0121-525 2666 Fax: 0121-580 4666

John Slack Ltd, Bank Vale Mill, Swallow House Lane, Hayfield, High Peak, Derbyshire, SK22 2HA Tel: (01663) 744211 Fax: (01663) 745139 *Quality converters of papers & fabrics*

Slack & Parr Hydraulics Ltd, Long Lane, Kegworth, Derby, DE74 2FL Tel: (01509) 672306 Fax: (01509) 673357 E-mail: info@slack-parr.com *Manufacturers of drill heads, machine tool accessories, multi-spindle drilling & tapping attachments & tapping attachment (machine tools)*

W. Slack & Sons, 38 Rosemary Street, Mansfield, Nottinghamshire, NG18 1QL Tel: (01623) 624449 *Outdoor leisure retailer*

▶ Slade Edwards & Co Insurance Brokers Ltd, 10 East Street, Horsham, West Sussex, RH12 1HL Tel: (01403) 250606 Fax: (01403) 210539 E-mail: anthony.birch@sladeedwards.co.uk *Slade Edwards are a Health & Safety Consultancy in West Sussex. We offer Health & Safety Training, assistance with Risk Assessments and Writting Health & Safety Policies. **Slade Edwards can offer assistance in Construction and office safety and are qualified to act as Planning Supervisors under the CDM Regulations.**Health & Safety Audits can be undertaken by our staff to ensure legal compliance and assess the safety of your business.**Fire Safety and Fire Safety training can also be arranged through Slade Edwards.**All of our Consultants are trained to NEBOSH Diploma leval amd are members of I.O.S.H.*

Slade & Kempton, 1 New Brent Street, Hendon, London, NW4 2DF Tel: (020) 8202 9000 Fax: (020) 8202 1500 E-mail: sales@slade-kempton.com *Manufacturing jewellers*

▶ Slaney & Co., 3 Queen Street, Worksop, Nottinghamshire, S80 2AW Tel: (01909) 472105 Fax: (01909) 482907 E-mail: worksop@slaneyandco.co.uk *We are a 3 Partner firm of Chartered Accountants who work with small business and personal clients to help them meet their business and financial goals.*

Slatebond Ltd, Unit 27 Leafield Industrial Estate, Leafield Way, Neston, Corsham, Wiltshire, SN13 9RS Tel: (01225) 810099 Fax: (01225) 811413 E-mail: sales@slatebond.com *Plastic & rubber moulding manufrs*

Slater, 13 Fort Dunlop, Birmingham, B24 9FD Tel: 0121-384 9700 Fax: 0121-384 9790 E-mail: golleyslater@golleyslater.co.uk *Advertising agents*

Slater Bros, 20 Highgate Place, Birmingham, B12 0DD Tel: 0121-440 5665 Fax: 0121-440 5005 *Scrap metal merchants & car dismantlers services*

▶ Slater & Crabtree Ltd, Thornes Lane, Wakefield, West Yorkshire, WF1 5RW Tel: (01924) 374874 Fax: (01924) 378288 E-mail: precision@slatercrabtree.co.uk *Providers of precision & subcontract engineering & machining services*

Slater Drive Systems Ltd, 6a Dukesway, Prudhoe, Northumberland, NE42 6PQ Tel: (01661) 835566 Fax: (01661) 833868 E-mail: sales@slater-drives.com *Drive system centre*

Slater Eyre, 105 Eastgate, Louth, Lincs, LN11 9QE Tel: 01507 603823 Fax: 01507 603 823 *Bakery & confectionary supplies*

Slater & Green, Bath Mill, Byron Street, Royton, Oldham, OL2 6QZ Tel: 0161-624 7160 Fax: 0161-628 7552 *Blacksmiths*

Slater Harrison & Co. Ltd, Lowerhouse Mills, Bollington, Macclesfield, Cheshire, SK10 5HW Tel: (01625) 578900 Fax: (01625) 578972 E-mail: l.preston@slater-harrison.co.uk *Coated paperboard processors or services, fluorescent paper/boards & paperboard/cardboard manufrs*

Herbert M. Slater Ltd, 332 Coleford Road, Sheffield, S9 5PH Tel: 0114-261 2308 Fax: 0114-261 2305 E-mail: info@slaterknives.co.uk *Trade knife manufrs*

Slater Safety Supplies, 238 Woodplumpton Road, Woodplumpton, Preston, PR4 0TA Tel: (01772) 691000 Fax: (01772) 691436 *Work & safety wear supplier*

Slater Signs, Unit 32 Crayford Industrial Estate, Swaisland Drive, Crayford, Dartford, DA1 4HS Tel: (01322) 558409 Fax: (01322) 554474 E-mail: sales@slatersigns.co.uk *Silk screen printers & safety signs manufrs*

Slater Yendall Ltd, Howard Road, Park Farm North, Redditch, Worcestershire, B98 7SE Tel: (01527) 529069 Fax: (01527) 510359 *Machinists*

Slatter & Sons, 61a Spencer Bridge Road, Northampton, NN5 7DP Tel: (01604) 753333 Fax: (01604) 753333 *Wrought iron works*

Slave to Design, Suite 5, Unit 9, Oldham Street Business Centre, Hanley, Stoke-on-Trent, ST1 3EY Tel: (01782) 207884 Fax: (01782) 207884 E-mail: info@slavetodesign.com *A full range of creative and professional services are provided for your advertising and marketing needs. Based on over 15 years of experience in advertising, print and new media, "Slave to Design" always supplies advice and guidance to help you create a solution. If you have any questions or would like to discuss a project... Slave is at your service!*

▶ Sleek Marketing, First Floor Cedar House Aire Valley Business Centre, Lawkholm, Keighley, West Yorkshire, BD21 3DD Tel: (0845) 6381301 Fax: (01535) 605005 E-mail: info@sleekmarketing.co.uk *An extensive, cost-effective range of marketing, communication and promotional services offered in support of companies wishing to enhance their business opportunities and bottom line profits From design concept to completion of product, our culture and work ethic enable us to keep control of costs and meet your deadlines.*

Sleeman Engineering Ltd, Dawes Lane, Scunthorpe, South Humberside, DN16 1DN Tel: (01724) 272100 Fax: (01724) 272101 E-mail: info@firthrixson.com *Steel plate stockholders*

Sleep At Ease Ltd, Clifton Road, Blackpool, FY4 4QZ Tel: (01253) 792600 Fax: (01253) 767590 *Bed manufacturers & retailers*

▶ The Sleep Factory, PO Box 28859, London, SW13 0YX Tel: (020) 8332 7467 *Children's nightwear, Snuggle Sacs and bedroom and bathroom gifts.*

▶ Sleep Heaven Beds, 115 Birleywood, Skelmersdale, Lancashire, WN8 9HR Tel: (01695) 722772 *Bed distributors*

▶ Sleep Right, Shop 4 Marine Court, St. Leonards-on-Sea, East Sussex, TN38 0DN Tel: (01424) 447246 Fax: (01424) 447246 E-mail: sales@futonsfirst.co.uk *We do Modern and Traditional futons. Every futon comes in a broad range of colours to suit most styles. We also offer a delivery service anywhere in the UK.*

▶ Sleep Sound Beds Ltd, Elm Street Mill, Burnley, Lancashire, BB10 1NY Tel: (01282) 416666

▶ Sleepcraft Ltd, 8 Brook Lane Industrial Estate, Westbury, Wiltshire, BA13 4EP Tel: (01373) 825504 Fax: (01373) 825514

▶ Sleepmasters Ltd, 47-49 Stamford New Road, Altrincham, Cheshire, WA14 1DS Tel: 0161-928 3640 Fax: 0161-928 3640 *Bed suppliers*

Sleepmasters Ltd, Oxford Square, Blackpool, FY4 4DP Tel: (01253) 698987 Fax: (01253) 698987 *Bed distributors*

Sleepmasters Ltd, 11-12 Derby Street, Burton-on-Trent, Staffordshire, DE14 2LA Tel: (01283) 512131 Fax: (01283) 512131 *Bed retailers*

Sleepmasters Ltd, 25 Gravel Street, Leicester, LE1 3AG Tel: 0116-253 2523 Fax: 0116-251 3684 *Bed suppliers*

Sleepmasters Ltd, Unit 7 Great Eastern Way, Parkgate, Rotherham, South Yorkshire, S62 6JD Tel: (01709) 780802 Fax: (01709) 780802 *Bed Retail*

Sleepmasters Ltd, 8 Riverside Retail Park, Wharf Street, Warrington, WA1 2GZ Tel: (01925) 445524 Fax: (01925) 445524 *Retailer of beds*

Sleepmasters Ltd, 27 Loire Drive, Robin Park, Wigan, Lancashire, WN5 0UH Tel: (01942) 218800 Fax: (01942) 218800 *Bed distributors*

▶ Sleeptime Bedding Co. Ltd, Winstanley Way, Basildon, Essex, SS14 3BP Tel: (01268) 270813 Fax: (01268) 534793

▶ Sleepythings, 1 Wood Farm Cottages, Bramdean, Alresford, Hampshire, SO24 0JL Tel: 01962 771784 Fax: 01962 771784 E-mail: info@sleepythings.co.uk *Timeless Designs Sleapwear And Gifts for Baby And Child*

▶ Sleetree Ltd, Edward House, Cores End Road, Bourne End, Buckinghamshire, SL8 5AL Tel: (01628) 529323 Fax: (01628) 850064 E-mail: enquiries@sleetree.co.uk

Slencrest Ltd, Broad Oak House, Pheasant Lane, Maidstone, Kent, ME15 9QR Tel: (01622) 741122 Fax: (01622) 747722 E-mail: sales@slencrest.com *Electronic equipment & distribution of electronic components*

▶ Robert Sleven, Butlers Farm Buildings, Butlers Lane, Saffron Walden, Essex, CB10 2ND Tel: (01799) 529440 E-mail: info@robertsleven.co.uk *Cabinet manufrs*

▶ Sli Developments, 94 Dawpool Road, London, NW2 7JY Tel: (020) 8830 6943

▶ Sliced Ltd, 91 Western Road, Brighton, BN1 2NW Tel: (01273) 776373 Fax: (01273) 706030 E-mail: info@slicedcreative.co.uk *Website design, search engine marketing & web development*

Slicer Maintenance Services, PO Box 152, Macclesfield, Cheshire, SK10 4LX Tel: (01625) 827827 Fax: 01625 820011 E-mail: enquiries@smsfoodequip.com *sale of food processing machinery spare parts,meat mincers,vacuum packers,slicing machines,sausage fillers,mixer grinders,butchers blocks,veg prep machines,scales & labellers.new & used*

▶ Slick-Click Ltd, Suite 14 Orion Building, Enterprise Way, Newport, Gwent, NP20 2AQ Tel: (0870) 1126272 E-mail: mailbox@slick-click.net *Web design, applications, internet connections, e-commerce web sites*

Slidaway, 5 Gardener Industrial Estate, Kent House Lane, Beckenham, Kent, BR3 1QZ Tel: (020) 8778 7566 Fax: (020) 7778 1839 *Ventilation engineers*

Slide Show, 24 Middle Street, London, EC1A 7JA Tel: (020) 7796 4664 Fax: (020) 7796 3816 E-mail: info@slideshow.co.uk *Presentation & internet designers*

Sliderobes, Unit 3C, Deacon Trrading Estate, Forstall Road, Aylesford, Maidstone, Kent, ME20 7SP Tel: (01622) 718987 Fax: (01622) 882114 E-mail: maystone@sliderobes.com *Manufacturers of luxury fitted bedrooms*

Slideway Grinding Services, Unit 4, Fullwood Close, Aldermans Green Industrial Estate, Coventry, CV2 2SS Tel: (024) 7661 3541 Fax: (024) 7660 2649 *Slideway grinding services*

▶ Sliding Door Wardrobes Ltd, Unit H2-H3, Cowlairs, Nottingham, NG5 9RA Tel: 0115-928 3987 E-mail: slidingwardrobe@aol.com *Wardrobes designers & installers*

Slik Fasteners Ltd, Units B2-B3 The Dresser Centre, Whitworth Street, Openshaw, Manchester, M11 2NE Tel: 0161-230 6878 Fax: 0161-230 7636 E-mail: info@slik.co.uk *Zip fasteners & garment accessories*

SlimDril Ltd, Unit 4 Marine Park, Gapton Hall Road, Great Yarmouth, Norfolk, NR31 0NL Tel: (01493) 656145 Fax: (01493) 601772 E-mail: sdi@slimdril.co.uk *Oillwell drilling equipment distributors*

Slimma plc, PO Box 30, Leek, Staffordshire, ST13 8AR Tel: (01538) 399141 Fax: (01538) 385438 E-mail: admin@slimma.com *Ladies wear manufrs*

▶ SlimSeekers, 11 Huntleys Park, Tunbridge Wells, Kent, TN4 9TD Tel: (01892) 535300 Fax: (01892) 535311 E-mail: suehay@slimseekers.co.uk *We can help you to achieve permanent weight loss. Have a Personal Advice Plan created just for you. No fad diets. No products. Just a healthier lifestyle. Full back-up and support given.*

Slinden Services, 3 Riverside Court, Westminster Industrial Estate, Measham, Swadlincote, Derbyshire, DE12 7DS Tel: (01530) 274646 Fax: (01530) 274647 E-mail: info@slindenservices.co.uk *CAST IRON REPAIRS - We are a specialised company who repair and recondition cast iron components by fusion welding and metal stitching to cylinder heads, engine blocks, castings, machinery etc. serving the marine, automotive, classic car, industrial & agricultural sectors. Lloyds EMEA approved welding procedure. Full machining facilities. 12 months guarantee & FREE UK collection.*

Sling & Tackle, Unit 57, Third Avenue, Bletchley, Milton Keynes, MK1 1DR Tel: (01908) 449300 Fax: (01908) 449301 E-mail: sales@slingandtackle.co.uk *Lifting equipment manufr*

Slingsby Aviation Ltd, Ings Lane, Kirkbymoorside, York, YO62 6EZ Tel: (01751) 432474 Fax: (01751) 431173 E-mail: sal1@slingsby.co.uk *Hovercraft builders & composite manufrs*

Slingtak Hoists Ltd, Quarry Road, Westgate, Cleckheaton, West Yorkshire, BD19 5HP Tel: (01274) 851724 Fax: (01274) 851724 E-mail: info@slingtak.co.uk *Lifting gear manufrs*

Slioch Outdoor Equipment Ltd, Cliffton Place, Poolewe, Achnasheen, Ross-Shire, IV22 2JU Tel: (01445) 781412 Fax: (01445) 781412 *Waterproof & outdoor clothing manufrs*

Slip A Way, Slip Away, Lansallos Street, Polperro, Looe, Cornwall, PL13 2QU Tel: (01503) 272958 *Clothes retailer*

▶ Slipped Discs, 2 Broomfield Court, Broomfield Park, Ascot, Berkshire, SL5 0JP Tel: (01344) 622131 Fax: (01344) 622131 E-mail: sales@slipped-discs.com *Gift packaging for cds, dvds & computer games*

▶ The Slipper . Com, Brantwood Lodge, Coniston, Cumbria, LA21 8AD Tel: 015394 41997 Fax: 015394 41998 E-mail: lasts@theslipper.com

Slipstop (European) Ltd, Whitwick Business Park, Stenson Road, Coalville, Leicestershire, LE67 4JP Tel: (01530) 813500 Fax: (01530) 813400 E-mail: info@slipstop.co.uk *Anti slip floor treatments*

Slipstop (European) Ltd, Whitwick Business Park, Stenson Road, Coalville, Leicestershire, LE67 4JP Tel: (01530) 813500 Fax: (01530) 813400 E-mail: info@slipstop.co.uk *Anti-slip floor treatments*

Slipstream Ltd, Pooley Hall Farm, Pooley Lane, Polesworth, Tamworth, Staffordshire, B78 1JA Tel: (01827) 330027 Fax: (01827) 330027 *Glass fibre product fabricators*

▶ SLJ Commercial Finance, 72 Manor Avenue South, Kidderminster, Worcestershire, DY11 6DG Tel: (01562) 744300 Fax: (01562) 744300 E-mail: admin@sljcf.co.uk *Independent commercial finance broker, with over 30 years of business banking experience.**If your business needs to borrow money, for whatever purpose, I can arrange it.*

SLK Engineering & Manufacturing Services Ltd, 4 Castle Road, Ellon, Aberdeenshire, AB41 9EY Tel: (01358) 724002 Fax: (01358) 720166 E-mail: sales@sltengineering.co.uk *Pump & meter maintenance services*

Sloan Agencies Ltd, Unit 3 Duncrue Industrial Park, Duncrue Road, Belfast, BT3 9BP Tel: (028) 9037 0377 Fax: (028) 9037 0344 *Heating & plumbing agents*

Sloan Electronics Ltd, 241 Kells Lane, Gateshead, Tyne & Wear, NE9 5HU Tel: 0191-491 0191 Fax: 0191-482 6762 E-mail: info@sloanelectronics.co.uk *Design & manufr electronic solutions*

Sloan Molyneaux & Co. Ltd, Maldon Street, Belfast, BT12 6HE Tel: (028) 9032 6868 Fax: (028) 9043 8107 E-mail: office@sloanmolyneaux.co.uk *Clothing retailers*

Sloane Cleaning Services, Anerley Town Hall, Anerley Road, London, SE20 8BD Tel: (020) 7584 6500 Fax: (020) 7527 7918 *Office cleaning contractors*

Sloane Group (Holdings) Ltd, 2-20 Booth Drive, Park Farm Estate, Wellingborough, Northamptonshire, NN8 6GR Tel: (01933) 401555 Fax: (01933) 400507 E-mail: info@sloanegroup.co.uk *Shop fitter services*

Slocombe Buildbase, Searle Crescent, Winterstoke Commercial Centre, Weston-Super-Mare, Avon, BS23 3YX Tel: (01934) 626503 Fax: (01934) 635334 E-mail: westonsupermare@buildbase.co.uk *Buildbase is one of the UK's fastest growing builders merchants. All of our branches are long established companies which have been serving local trades people for many years, with knowledge and experience to match. We believe strongly in understanding the needs of trades professional and our business has been developed specifically to meet those demands. Massive stocks, top quality products, competitive pricing, reliable delivery, specialist staff and exceptional customer service.*

Slotted Nut Service Ltd, Woden Road South, Wednesbury, West Midlands, WS10 0AH Tel: 0121-556 0865 *Bolt & nut manufrs*

Slottseal Extrusions Ltd, Tyne Road, Weadon Road Industrial Estate, Northampton, NN5 5AF Tel: (01604) 759535 Fax: (01604) 752780 E-mail: tecplastics@btinternet Principal Export Areas: Asia Pacific, Central/East Europe & West Europe *Plastic extrusions manufrs*

Slough Computers, The Observatory, High Street, Slough, SL1 1LE Tel: (01753) 521594 Fax: (01753) 694633 *Computer games retailers*

Slough Estates P.L.C., 234 Bath Road, Slough, SL1 4EE Tel: (01753) 537171 Fax: (01753) 820585 E-mail: property@sloughestates.co.uk *Property development & investment*

Slough International Freight & Packing Ltd, 820 Yeovil Road, Slough, SL1 4JA Tel: (01753) 691011 Fax: (01753) 825669 E-mail: sloughinter@btconnect.com *Freight forwarders*

Slough & Langley Express, 256 Ipswich Road, Slough, SL1 4EP Tel: (01753) 825111 Fax: (01753) 692254 E-mail: sales@sloughexpress.co.uk *Newspaper publishers*

Slough Plastering Co. Ltd, 19 Willoughby Road, Langley, Slough, SL3 8JH Tel: (01753) 543947 Fax: (01753) 594135 *Plastering contractors*

Slough Plastic Coatings, 2 David Road, Colnbrook, Slough, SL3 0DG Tel: (01753) 683907 Fax: (01753) 682571 E-mail: sloughplastic@btconnect.com *Slough Plastic coatings offer powder coating, stove enamelling and air dry coatings to UK industry as well as shot blasting, chemical stripping and assembly work.*

▶ SLP, 23 West View, Chirk, Wrexham, LL14 5HL Tel: (01691) 774778 Fax: (01691) 774849

SLR Sportequip Co., 21 Ferndale Drive, Ratby, Leicester, LE6 0LH Tel: 0116-239 5020 Fax: 0116-239 0489 E-mail: sales@slrsportequip.co.uk *Sports ground equipment distributors.*

▶ SLS Construction, Orchard Lodge, Brinsea, Bristol, BS49 5JP Tel: 01934 853331

Slumberfleece Bedding & Blankets, Arkwright Industrial Estate, Arkwright Road, Bedford, MK42 0LE Tel: (01234) 210879 Fax: (01234) 217983 E-mail: samirvine6@netscape.net *Mattress protector manufrs*

Sly Development Ltd, 15 The Avenue, Acocks Green, Birmingham, B27 6NG Tel: 0121-707 0060 Fax: 0121-707 0032 E-mail: info@slynet.co.uk *EPOS & stock control systems retailers*

Sly Filters Europe Ltd, 16 The Warren, East Goscote, Leicester, LE7 3XA Tel: 0116-260 8187 Fax: 0116-264 0543 E-mail: sly@ridgep.fsbusiness.co.uk *Air pollution control equipment manufrs*

▶ SM Creative Ltd, 4 Raven Close, Chorley, Lancashire, PR7 2RE Tel: (01257) 232392 Fax: (01257) 232392 E-mail: design@smcreative.co.uk *Design agency*

▶ Smaart Associates, 1 Farnham Road, Guildford, Surrey, GU2 4RG Tel: (01483) 549815 Fax: (01483) 549115 E-mail: info@smaart.info *Independent mortgage brokers*

F. Smales & Son Ltd, 30 West Dock Street, Hull, HU3 4HL Tel: (01482) 324997 Fax: (01482) 323765 E-mail: info@smales.co.uk *Frozen food processors*

Small Back Room, 88 Camberwell Road, London, SE5 0EG Tel: (020) 7701 4227 Fax: (020) 7703 3474 E-mail: sbr@smallbackroom.co.uk *Integrated communication services*

Small Batch Polishing & Plating, No 2 Arcade Workshops, Atlantic Trading Estate, Barry, S. Glam, CF63 3RF Tel: (01446) 720905 *Electroplaters of resins & antiques*

▶ The Small Battery Co., 70 Cromford Road, London, SW18 1NY Tel: (020) 8871 3730 Fax: (020) 8871 3686 E-mail: info@smallbattery.company.org.uk *Battery on-line sales*

▶ Small Biz It Ltd, 13 Avenue Road, Trowbridge, Wiltshire, BA14 0AQ Tel: (01225) 765182 Fax: (01225) 765340 *Computer systems consultants*

Small Geared Motors Ltd, Villa Nova, Spurlands End Rd, Great Kingshill, High Wycombe, Bucks, HP15 6HX Tel: 01494 715642 Fax: 01494 711527 *Light engineering*

Small Life Supplies, Station Buildings, Station Road, Bottesford, Nottingham, NG13 0EB Tel: (01949) 842446 Fax: (01949) 843036 E-mail: emma@small-life.co.uk *Pet requisites manufrs*

Small Loads Concrete, Haye Quarry, Stag Lane, Plymouth, PL9 8AX Tel: (01752) 481723 Fax: (01752) 848862 *Ready mix concrete suppliers*

Small Removal Co., 2 Southdown Industrial Estate, Southdown Road, Harpenden, Hertfordshire, AL5 1PW Tel: (01582) 760783 Fax: (01582) 760783

▶ Small Screen Film & Video, 17 Knole Road, Dartford, DA1 3JN Tel: (01322) 419353 E-mail: sales@smallscreenvideo.com *Filming services*

Small & Co. Shipping Ltd, Europa House, 40 South Quay, Great Yarmouth, Norfolk, NR30 2RL Tel: (01502) 572301 Fax: (01493) 857533 E-mail: smallandcoshipping@halcyonshipping.com *International freight forwarder*

Small & Tidmas Ltd, Vicarage Street, Barnstaple, Devon, EX32 7HA Tel: (01271) 375972 Fax: (01271) 379753 E-mail: info@smallandtidmas.co.uk *Warp knitted textile manufrs* Also at: Bodmin

Small World Connections Ltd, PO Box 132, Manchester, M20 3BB Tel: 0161-445 0630 E-mail: info@swcltd.co.uk *Management consultants*

Smallbone & Co Devizes Ltd, 10 Princes Street, Harrogate, North Yorkshire, HG1 1NH Tel: (01423) 529222 Fax: (01423) 524443 E-mail: harrogate.showroom@smallbone.co.uk *Kitchen manufrs*

▶ Smalldene Midlands Ltd, Houndsfield Lane, Hollywood, Birmingham, B47 5QR Tel: (01564) 823085

Smallpiece Enterprises, 27 Newbold Terrace, Leamington Spa, Warwickshire, CV32 4ES Tel: (01926) 336423 Fax: (01926) 450679 E-mail: train@smallpeice.co.uk *Training, engineering & project management*

Smallthorne Joinery Manufacturers, Unit A4 Fraylings Business Park, Davenport Street, Stoke-on-Trent, ST6 4LN Tel: (01782) 577225 Fax: (01782) 865855 *Wooden windows & PVC suppliers*

▶ Smallwood Storage Ltd, Moss End Farm, Moss End, Smallwood, Sandbach, Cheshire, CW11 2XQ Tel: (01477) 500376 Fax: (01477) 500444 E-mail: info@smallwoodstorage.co.uk *A haulage company based in the UK. Handles various products including hazardous chemicals, food products and air conditioning units. Specialises in abnormal loads. Also has 40,000 sq ft of warehousing to let.*

Smart 421, North Felaw Malting, 48 Felaw Street, Ipswich, IP2 8HE Tel: (01473) 421421 Fax: (01473) 421422 E-mail: info@smart421.com *Internet services & systems integrator*

▶ Smart Alloys, Unit 5 Harrison Street, Blackburn, BB2 2JN Tel: (01254) 589626 Fax: (0845) 3891161 E-mail: info@smartalloys.co.uk *Alloy wheel refurbishing, scuffs, scrapes & dents*

▶ Smart Cartridge, 119 Bruntsfield Place, Edinburgh, EH10 4EQ Tel: 0131-466 0067 Fax: 0131-466 0989 *Printing & accessory retailers*

▶ Smart Cartridge, Unit 6, B S S House, Cheney Manor Industrial Estate, Swindon, SN2 2PJ Tel: (01793) 532251 Fax: (01793) 532258 E-mail: enquiries@smart-cartridge.com *Refill ink & toner cartridges*

▶ Smart Cartridge, 15 Ardsheal Road, Worthing, West Sussex, BN14 7RN Tel: (01903) 202292 Fax: (01903) 202303 E-mail: info@smart-cartridge.com *Computer accessories suppliers*

▶ Smart Cartridge Hitchin, 43 Hermitage Road, Hitchin, Hertfordshire, SG5 1BY Tel: (01462) 434007 Fax: (01462) 451117 *Computer consultants*

▶ Smart Cleanings UK Ltd, 66 Queen''s Park, Aylesbury, Buckinghamshire, HP21 7RT Tel: 08448 442548 Fax: 01296 580632 E-mail: admin@smart-cleanings.co.uk *Office & Commercial Cleaning Company in Aylesbury,Buckinghamshire,UK*

Smart Computers Ltd, Enterprise Way, Cheltenham Trade Park, Cheltenham, Gloucestershire, GL51 8LZ Tel: (01242) 580654 Fax: (01242) 580652 *Computer hardware & software rental & support*

▶ Smart Construction, Inchinnan House, Inchinnan Road, Paisley, Renfrewshire, PA3 2RA Tel: 0141-840 4044

Smart Cool Systems (UK) Ltd, Westgate, 104 High Street, Alton, Hampshire, GU34 1EN Tel: (01420) 544868 Fax: (01420) 544723 E-mail: enquries@smartcool.co.uk *Energy consultants*

Company Information

▶ Smart Design & Print Ltd, 11 West Gorgie Parks, Edinburgh, EH14 1UT Tel: 0131-538 8020 Fax: 0131-538 8050 E-mail: sales@smartdesignandprint.com

▶ Smart Electrics, 41 Britannia Drive, Hatch Warren, Basingstoke, Hampshire, RG22 4FW Tel: (01256) 398571

Smart & Emanuel, 93 Francklyn Gardens, Edgware, Middlesex, HA8 8SB Tel: (020) 8905 4114 Fax: (020) 8958 5100 *Timber importers & exporters*

▶ Smart Fibres Ltd, 12 The Court Yard, Eastern Road, Bracknell, Berkshire, RG12 2XB Tel: (01344) 484111 Fax: (01344) 423241 E-mail: info@smartfibres.com *Optical fibre sensor manufrs*

Smart Frame Tectonics, Burnmill Road, Leven, Fife, KY8 4RA Tel: (01333) 421525 Fax: (01333) 423886 *House & store construction*

G.S. Smart & Co. Ltd, Ardath Road, Birmingham, B38 9PN Tel: 0121-459 0983 Fax: 0121-459 8559 E-mail: info@metalrax-group.co.uk *Occasional furniture manufrs*

Smart Golf, 30 Hopefield Avenue, Belfast, BT15 5AP Tel: (028) 9087 8001 Fax: (028) 9087 8001 E-mail: info@smartgolf.co.uk *Computer software developers*

▶ Smart Holograms, 291 Science Park, Milton Road, Cambridge, CB4 0WF Tel: (01223) 393400 Fax: (01223) 393401 E-mail: info@smartHolograms.com *Technology developers in medical devices & diagnostics sectors*

▶ Smart Interior, Watson House, 33 Burton Road, Sheffield, S3 8BX Tel: 0114-272 3929 Fax: 0114-272 3894 E-mail: john@smartinterior.net *Commercial suspended ceiling installation services*

Smart Manufacturing Ltd, Clovelly Road Ind Estate, Bideford, Devon, EX39 3HN Tel: 01237 471977 *Stainless steel manufrs*

Smart Metals Ltd, 3 Victoria Trading Estate, Drury Lane, Chadderton, Oldham, OL9 7PJ Tel: 0161-684 9545 Fax: 0161-684 9969 *Fabrication engineers*

▶ Smart Modular Technologies Europe Ltd, 5 Kelvin Park South, Block 1, East Kilbride, Glasgow, G75 0RH Tel: (01355) 595000

▶ Smart Move, 23 Nash Gardens, Dawlish, Devon, EX7 9RR Tel: (01626) 889171 Fax: E-mail: enquiries@smartmoveremovals.com *Domestic removal, rubbish, waste removal, delivery & collection service*

Smart Packaging Ltd, Units 15-16, Beeches Industrial Estate, Lavenham Road, Yate, Bristol, BS37 5QX Tel: (01454) 311811 Fax: (01454) 311822 E-mail: smartpackaging@breathemail.net *Packaging materials & products manufrs*

Smart People Time plc, Node Court, Drivers End, Codicote, Hitchin, Hertfordshire, SG4 8TR Tel: (01438) 822222 Fax: (01438) 822240 E-mail: info@smarthumanlogistics.com *Time management & labour productivity software*

▶ Smart Refinishers (Aberdeen) Ltd, Kirkhill Indust Estate, Aberdeen, AB21 0HP Tel: (01224) 772999 Fax: (01224) 772007 E-mail: sales@smartrefinishers.co.uk *Accident, repair & refinishing car, commercial motor body shop*

Smart Screw Ltd, Portland House, Floodgate Street, Digbeth, Birmingham, B5 5SL Tel: 0121-772 2115 Fax: 0121-766 5828 E-mail: sales@smartscrew.co.uk *Screw & fastener manufrs*

Smart Shading Systems, Crown Business Centre, 195 Horton Road, West Drayton, Middlesex, UB7 8HP Tel: (01895) 448217 Fax: (01895) 448503 E-mail: sales@smartshading.co.uk *Electronic curtain & blinds suppliers*

▶ Smart Shape International, Millett Street, Bury, Lancashire, BL9 0JB Tel: (07932) 346710 E-mail: jefstudent@hotmail.com *Herbalife offers individual weight management programs and weight loss programs as well as nutritional supplements for overall good health. Become an Herbalife Distributor and start your own home based business*

▶ Smart Source UK, Sherbrook Enterprises, Sherbrook Road, Daybrook, Nottingham, NG5 6AB Tel: 0115-926 4014 Fax: 0115 9263986 E-mail: sales@smartsource.uk.com *Smart Source UK can help your business by generating fully qualified leads and appointments with prospective clients who are in the market for your services or products immediately, thus making sure that you are always talking to qualified potential clients..*

Smart Supplies Ltd, The Field House, Upper Sapey, Worcester, WR6 6XT Tel: (01886) 853003 Fax: (01886) 853001 *Disposable cleaning & hygiene products suppliers*

Smart Systems Distribution, Arnolds Way, Bristol, BS49 4BP Tel: (01934) 876023 Fax: (01934) 835169 E-mail: sales@smartsystems.co.uk *Window & door extrusion suppliers*

Smart Systems (Essex) Ltd, 33 President Road, Colchester, CO3 9ED Tel: (01206) 549291 Fax: (01206) 769749 *Computer programmers*

Smart Technologies, 94 Sandy Lane, Higher Kinnerton, Chester, CH4 9BS Tel: (0800) 0186511 Fax: (0870) 7708332 E-mail: sales@smartserve.net *Internet service & solution providers*

▶ Smart Upper Closes, 8a, North Way, Claverings Industrial Estate, London, N9 0AD Tel: (020) 8803 1116 Fax: (020) 8803 1116

▶ Smart Valeting, 28 Cosby Road, Littlethorpe, Leicester, LE19 2HF Tel: 0116-286 6338 E-mail: spencer@smartvaleting.co.uk *Suppliers of auto smart & smart wax range of car care products*

▶ Smart Valves Ltd, Uxbridge Road, Leicester, LE4 7ST Tel: 0116-268 8120 Fax: 0116-261 0050 E-mail: sales@smartvalves.co.uk *Electric actuators & steam systems manufacturers*

Smart Valves & Controls Ltd, Uxbridge Road, Leicester, LE4 7ST Tel: 0116-268 8130 Fax: 0116-261 0050 E-mail: sales@northvalekorting.co.uk *Suppliers & installers of steam systems*

Smart Vision, 40 Hamlet Court Road, Westcliff-on-Sea, Essex, SS0 7LX Tel: (01702) 343260 Fax: (01702) 343260 *Optical appliance retailers*

Smart Visual Presentation Products Ltd, Unit 18, Kempton Road, Pershore, Worcestershire, WR10 2TA Tel: (0870) 0800612 Fax: (0870) 0800613 E-mail: sales@smartvisual.co.uk *Suppliers of presentation equipment such as, multimedia projectors, plasma screens, interactive white boards, projection screens & pc's*

▶ Smart Wise UK Ltd, 5 Ashwyn Business Centre, Marchants Way, Burgess Hill, West Sussex, RH15 8QY Tel: (01444) 257342 Fax: (01444) 257673 E-mail: sales@smartwise.com *Automotive equipment distributors*

Smartcomm Ltd, 45 Cressex Enterprise Centre, Lincoln Road, High Wycombe, Buckinghamshire, HP12 3RL Tel: (01494) 471912 Fax: (01494) 472464 E-mail: lucy.jenner@smartcomm.co.uk *Audio & visual installations services*

▶ Smartdata, Abertechnium, Y Lanfa, Trefechan, Aberystwyth, Dyfed, SY23 1AS Tel: (0845) 6128061 Fax: (01970) 613480 E-mail: enquiries@smartdata.co.uk *Smart data uk manufactures bespoke software & database solutions*

▶ SmartDent Paintless Dent Removal Training Ltd, Unit 5, Ashwyn Business Centre, Marchants Way, Sheddingdean Industrial Estate, Burgess Hill, West Sussex, RH15 8QY Tel: (01444) 257342 Fax: (01444) 257673 E-mail: colm@smartwise.com *Nationwide training, paint less dent removal & pdr tools*

▶ Smartdesignz, Railside, Scunthorpe, South Humberside, DN16 1TB Tel: (07749) 291839 *We Provide professional web site hosting, design, development & search engine optimisation services*

Smartdrive Ltd, 8 Colne Road, Earith, Huntingdon, Cambridgeshire, PE28 3PX Tel: (01487) 843663 Fax: (01487) 843661 E-mail: info@smartdrive.co.uk *Motion control systems*

▶ Smartekh, 256 Carmel Road North, Darlington, County Durham, DL3 9TD Tel: (01325) 778161 E-mail: info@smartekh.co.uk *Mobile smart repairs,minor car body repairs,scratches,scuffs,dents,interior and exterior trim,upholstery,alloy wheel refurbishment.*

▶ SmartGauge Electronics, Nantwich Canal Centre, Basin End, Chester Road, Nantwich, Cheshire, CW5 8LB Tel: 07951 995475 E-mail: chris.gibson@smartgauge.co.uk *Manufacturer of the SmartGauge deep cycle battery monitor, the SmartBank intelligent split charge controller and the SmartGuard and PowerGuard flat battery protection systems.*

▶ Smartlock Access Control Ltd, 3A Thame Road, Long Crendon, Aylesbury, Buckinghamshire, HP18 9AS Tel: (01844) 201145 Fax: (01844) 201155 E-mail: sales@smart-lock.co.uk *Electronic access control product suppliers*

Smarts Of Northolt, Unit 15 The Metropolitan Centre, Derby Road, Greenford, Middlesex, UB6 8UJ Tel: (0500) 030609 Fax: (020) 8575 8804 E-mail: sales@smartsremovals.co.uk *Office removal contractors & domestic removals*

Smartstone Drives, 23 Church Street, Owston Ferry, Doncaster, South Yorkshire, DN9 1RG Tel: (01427) 728767 E-mail: elliottbaggy@aol.com *Resin bound & bonded drives, paths, patios & natural stone driveways suppliers*

Smartstream Technologies, 1690 Park Avenue, Aztec West, Bristol, BS32 4RA Tel: (01454) 855100 Fax: (01454) 888503 *Software house*

Smartstream Technologies Ltd, 3 St Helens Place, London, EC3A 6AB Tel: (020) 7847 8000 Fax: (020) 7847 8003 *Computer software suppliers*

Smartt Software Ltd, 3 Queens Road, Exeter, EX2 9ER Tel: (01392) 424299 Fax: (01392) 425254 E-mail: sales@exetermicro.co.uk *Software designers*

▶ Smarttalk Communications, 23 Burlington Lane, London, W4 2RN Tel: (020) 8742 0321 Fax: 0870 2854888 E-mail: solutions@smarttalkuk.com *Supplier of Telecom Solutions and Services - in strategic partnerships with major Tier 1 Carriers & Service Providers, we provide the most appropriate and cost-effective products and services in any scenario including: Voice (Least Cost Routing / Carrier Pre Select) Mobile & Data Business Broadband Corporate TPS Auto Screening VPN/ MPLS Solutions Telephone Systems 0800, Non-Geo & Premium Rate Numbers, Unified Communications, Fax to Email, Wireless Solutions, Call Centre Solution and Text Messaging Solutions. For more info call 020 8742 0321*

▶ Smartways Pharmaceuticals Pharmaceutical Suppliers, 130 Northcote Road, London, SW11 6QZ Tel: (020) 7924 7475 Fax: (020) 7564 8890 E-mail: 1nfo@Smartway-pw.co.uk *Pharmaceutical wholesaler*

▶ Smartways Technology Ltd, 1 Scirocco Close, Northampton, NN3 6AP Tel: (01604) 670500 Fax: (01604) 670567 E-mail: admin@a-i-t.co.uk *Information technology services & solutions providers*

▶ Smartwood Lesiure Products, Belle Vue Barn, Mansergh, Carnforth, Lancashire, LA6 2EJ Tel: (01524) 273333 Fax: (01524) 273303 *Importers of garden furniture*

SMB Design, Coombe Lodge, Bourne Lane, Blagdon, Bristol, BS40 7RG Tel: (01934) 413617 Fax: (01761) 463399 E-mail: sales@smbdesigns.co.uk *Printed circuit assembly services*

S M B Couriers, 683 Tonbridge Road, Barming, Maidstone, Kent, ME16 9DQ Tel: (07930) 281229 E-mail: info@smbcouriers.com *Courier services, 24-7 same day courier service*

SMD, Merse Road, Moons Moat North Industrial Es, Redditch, Worcestershire, B98 9HL Tel: (01527) 69548 Fax: (01527) 584884 *Sliding door manufrs*

SMD Hydrovision Ltd, Davy Banks, Wallsend, Tyne & Wear, NE28 6UZ Tel: +44 (0) 1224 772150 Fax: +44 (0) 1224 772166 E-mail: smd@smdhydrovision.com Principal Export Areas: Worldwide *Manufacturers of electronic equipment for subsea & underwater surveys & ROV operators*

Smeaton Hanscomb & Co. Ltd, Lisle Road, Hughenden Avenue, High Wycombe, Buckinghamshire, HP13 5SQ Tel: (01494) 521051 Fax: (01494) 461176 E-mail: sales@smeathans.plus.com *Woodworking machinery sellers*

John Smedley Ltd, Eldon Street, Clay Cross, Chesterfield, Derbyshire, S45 9PE Tel: (01246) 862599 Fax: (01246) 862963 *Knitwear manufrs*

John Smedley Ltd, Rands Lane, Armthorpe, Doncaster, South Yorkshire, DN3 3DY Tel: (01302) 832346 Fax: (01302) 300384 *Knitwear manufrs*

Smelly Rug Co., Millmount Farm, Melrose, Roxburghshire, TD6 9BZ Tel: (01896) 822467 E-mail: info@thesmellyrugco.co.uk *Horse rugs washing*

Charles Smethurst Ltd, Castlemill Street, Oldham, OL1 3HL Tel: 0161-624 4505 Fax: 0161-628 4282 E-mail: info@charlessmethurst.co.uk *Sheet metalworkers*

Smethwick Maintenance Co. Ltd, 336 Spon Lane South, West Bromwich, West Midlands, B70 6AZ Tel: 0121-553 3941 Fax: 0121-553 5371 E-mail: sales@sis-group.co.uk *Industrial contractors*

▶ Smews, 108 Nalders Road, Chesham, Buckinghamshire, HP5 3DA Tel: (01494) 776732 E-mail: sales@smews.com *Software development consultants*

▶ SMG Ltd, Archery House, 2 Archery Lane, Eastbourne, East Sussex, BN22 7GA Tel: (01323) 411298

SMG Computers, 34 Hallen Close, Emersons Green, Bristol, BS16 7JE Tel: (0788) 0731672 E-mail: smg@smg-computers.com *It support*

▶ SMG International, Imex Block 32, Dryden Road, Loanhead, Midlothian, EH20 9LZ Tel: 0131 4480505 *European Remy Hair Extensions, 0% Human hair, next working day delivery.*

Smiffy's, Heapham Road South, Caldicott Drive, Heapham Road Industrial Estate, Gainsborough, Lincolnshire, DN21 1FJ Tel: (01427) 616831 Fax: (01427) 617190 E-mail: info@smiffys.com *Jokes, novelties, party goods & wigs suppliers*

Smilde Food Group Ltd, PO Box 27, Crowborough, East Sussex, TN6 3DZ Tel: (01892) 669616 Fax: (01892) 669617 E-mail: bobwilliams@smildefood.uk.com *Edible oil, fat producer & refiners*

Smileberry Interiors, 18 Church Street, Warnham, Horsham, West Sussex, RH12 3QW Tel: (01403) 242600 Fax: (01403) 264856 *Partitions fit outs installers services*

Smillie & Cuthbertson Ltd, 17 James Little St, Kilmarnock, Ayrshire, KA1 4AU Tel: 01563 521819 *General engineers*

John Smillie Ltd, 40 Carmichael Street, Glasgow, G51 2QT Tel: 0141-445 2574 Fax: 0141-425 1315 *Road transport, haulage & freight services*

Smit International (Scotland) Ltd, The Exchange, 62 Market Street, Aberdeen, AB11 5PT Tel: (01224) 560400 Fax: (01224) 581485 *Marine management & crew services*

Smit Salvage BV, 65 Fenchurch Street, London, EC3M 4BE Tel: (020) 7480 7648 Fax: (020) 7702 1842 E-mail: sales@smit.com *Towage & salvage*

Smith, Inchbreck House, Drumlithie, Stonehaven, Kincardineshire, AB39 3YQ Tel: (01569) 740441

▶ A.O. Smith Water Products Co. UK, Unit B8, Armstrong Mall, Southwood Business Park, Farnborough, Hampshire, GU14 0NR Tel: (0870) 2676484 Fax: (0870) 2676485 E-mail: sales@aosmith.co.uk *Water heaters manufrs*

Smith Aerospace Actuation Systems, Arle Court, Cheltenham, Gloucestershire, GL51 0TP Tel: (01242) 221155 Fax: (01242) 277577 *Specialists in integrated aircraft landing gear and door actuation systems, including hydraulic energy*

Smith & Allan, 1a Valley St, Darlington, County Durham, DL1 1QE Tel: (01325) 462228 Fax: (01325) 368122 E-mail: stevearcher@smithandallan.com *Oils & paints manufrs*

▶ Allan Smith, 85 Clerk Street, Loanhead, Midlothian, EH20 9RE Tel: 0131-440 0302 *Retail bakery*

▶ Smith and Jones, Devonshire Lavenders, Exmouth Road, West Hill, Ottery St. Mary, Devon, EX11 1JZ Tel: 01404 823975 Fax: 01404 823335 E-mail: sales@smithnjones.co.uk *Irrigation services*

▶ Smith Anderson & Co. Ltd, St Johns Works, Falkland, Ladybank, Cupar, Fife, KY15 7AY Tel: (01337) 858201 Fax: (01337) 857172 *Paper bag manufrs*

Smith Anderson Envelopes Ltd, Whiteside Industrial Estate, Bathgate, West Lothian, EH48 2RX Tel: (01506) 634463 Fax: (01506) 634366 E-mail: sales@eagle-envelopes.com *Envelope manufacturers & printers*

Andrew & Mark Smith Metals Ltd, Darbishire Street, Bolton, BL1 2TN Tel: (01204) 533662 Fax: (01204) 392480 E-mail: mark@smithmetals.co.uk *Scrap metal merchants*

Andrew Smith & Schultze Ltd, 54 Broad Street, Peterhead, Aberdeenshire, AB42 1BX Tel: (01779) 472210 Fax: (01779) 470638 E-mail: stevedores@rapidial.co.uk *Shipping agents & stevedoring services*

▶ Andy Smith Photography, 53 Caer Wenallt, Pantmawr, Cardiff, CF14 7HP Tel: (029) 2062 4860 *Andy Smith Photography for all wedding and photgraphy needed in wales, andy smith photography, andy smith photographer, photography cardiff, cardiff photography, wedding photographer in cardiff, cardiff weddings, Graduation Portraits, *Graduation Photography, Family Portraits, Portrait photography, VIP Portraiture, Commercial photography, Pet Photography, Birthday Photography, Wedding Photography, Presentations, Press Photography, Location Photography, Celebration Photography, Glamour Photography, Christenings, Media Photography, School photography*

continued

Arthur C. Smith Ltd, Oldmedow Road, Hardwick Industrial Estate, King's Lynn, Norfolk, PE30 4LD Tel: (01553) 817220 Fax: (0845) 0500864 E-mail: sales@acssupplies.com *Computer & word processing supplies*

▶ Smith & Austin Engineering Products Ltd, 11 Church Road, Hayling Island, Hampshire, PO11 0NN Tel: (023) 9246 2451 Fax: (023) 9246 1431 Sales Contact: A. Austin *Sheet metalworking engineers/fabricators specializing in aircraft ground support equipment, aircraft maintenance equipment & aircraft gallery equipment. Also, suppliers to the defence, MOD & marine industries*

Smith Brothers Ltd, Osbaldwick Link Road, York, YO10 3WA Tel: (01904) 415222 Fax: (01904) 413219 E-mail: admin@smithbrothersyork.com *Smith Brothers of York supplying Bathroom & showers Design & installation, Kitchens & appliances, Bedrooms & studies dinging, Lounge & soft furniture, Bedroom Furniture, Interior Design, Plumbers Merchants & heating supplies.*

Smith Bros. Joinery Ltd, Pope Iron Road, Worcester, WR1 3HB Tel: (01905) 619830 Fax: (01905) 617294 E-mail: raymondwillden@smithbrothersjoinery.com *Joinery manufrs*

Smith Bros Quinton Scotland, Bridgeness Road, Bo'Ness, West Lothian, EH51 9TD Tel: (01506) 822214 Fax: (01506) 826307

Smith Bros (Staincliffe) Ltd, Mohair Mills, Gibson Street, Bradford, West Yorkshire, BD3 9TS Tel: (01274) 662281 Fax: (01274) 656299 E-mail: strossltd@aol.com *Textile waste reclaimers*

Smith Brothers Stores Ltd, Battern Street, Aylestone Road, Leicester, LE2 7PB Tel: 0116-283 3511 Fax: 0116-244 0430 E-mail: sales@sbs-1897.co.uk *Tube fittings & valves distributors* Also at: Northampton

▶ Smith Brothers Stores, Empson Road, Eastern Industry, Peterborough, PE1 5UP Tel: (01733) 311711 Fax: (01733) 345293 E-mail: david@airplants.co.uk *Industrial pipeline suppliers*

Smith Bros & Webb Ltd, 22 Tything Road East, Kinwarton, Alcester, Warwickshire, B49 6EX Tel: (01789) 400096 Fax: (01789) 400231 E-mail: sales@vehicle-washing-systems.co.uk *Vehicle washing system manufacturers.*

▶ Smith & Brown, 21 Regent Park Square, Glasgow, G41 2AF Tel: 0141-424 3107 Fax: 0141-424 0610 E-mail: fiona@smithandbrown.co.uk *Design consultancy*

Smith & Co Carlisle Ltd, Junction Street, Carlisle, CA2 5UQ Tel: (01228) 522213 Fax: (01228) 515388 *Repairers of electrical plant*

Smith & Choyce Ltd, 280 Barton Street, Gloucester, GL1 4JJ Tel: (01452) 523531 Fax: (01452) 310032 E-mail: m.choyce@btconnect.com *Joinery manufrs*

▶ Smith Construction Heckington Ltd, Station Road, Heckington, Sleaford, Lincolnshire, NG34 9NF Tel: (01529) 461500 Fax: (01529) 461463 E-mail: info@smithsportscivils.co.uk

D.S. Smith Packaging, Meadow Close, Ise Valley Industrial Estate, Wellingborough, Northamptonshire, NN8 4BH Tel: (01933) 440488 Fax: (01933) 441202 *Corrugated box & case manufrs*

David S. Smith Norpack, Unit 4, 3A West Chirton Trading Estate, North Shields, Tyne & Wear, NE29 7UD Tel: 0191-257 1141 Fax: 0191-258 6193 *Packaging manufrs*

David Smith St. Ives Ltd, Marley Road, St. Ives, Cambridgeshire, PE27 3EX Tel: (01480) 462323 Fax: (01480) 494832 E-mail: info@davidsmith.co.uk *Timber manufrs*

Smith & Deakin Plastics, 75 Blackpole Trading Estate West, Worcester, WR3 8TJ Tel: (01905) 458886 Fax: (01905) 458889 E-mail: sales@smithanddeakin.co.uk *Glass fibre moulders & fabricators*

▶ Dick Smith Services Ltd, 3 Shannon Centre, Shannon Way, Canvey Island, Essex, SS8 0PE Tel: (01268) 510963 Fax: (01268) 510977 E-mail: sales@dicksmithservices.co.uk *Specialists suppliers in shrink wrapping equipment*

▶ Eddie Smith & Associates Ltd, 11 Robin Way, Chipping Sodbury, Bristol, BS37 6JN Tel: (01454) 314345 Fax: (01454) 314345 E-mail: e.y.smith@btinternet.com *Designers and manufactures of workholding and toolholding equipment including :Expanding Mandrels,Angle Heads,Prismatic Fixtures,Gauges Etc*

D. Smith Engineering, 90 Nuffield Road, Poole, Dorset, BH17 7SX Tel: (01202) 687123 Fax: (01202) 685042 *Precision engineers*

Smith Engineering GB Ltd, Solway Trading Estate, Maryport, Cumbria, CA15 8NF Tel: (01900) 815831 Fax: (01900) 815553 E-mail: r.smith@moonbuggy.com *Light engineering/powder coating services*

F.P. Smith (Holdings) Ltd, Garton House, 179A Newark Avenue, Peterborough, PE1 4NL Tel: (01733) 344800 Fax: (01733) 560392 *Holding company*

Smith Flow Control Ltd, 6 Waterside Business Park, Eastways, Witham, Essex, CM8 3YQ Tel: (01376) 517901 Fax: (01376) 518720 E-mail: sales@smithflowcontrol.com Principal Export Areas: Worldwide *Interlocking safety devices manufrs*

G.W.& S. Smith, Lambert St, Greetland, Halifax, W. Yorkshire, HX4 8AA Tel: 01422 370464 Fax: 01422 370464 *Tool making*

George Smith, Easter Tullochs, Rafford, Forres, Morayshire, IV36 2SL Tel: (01309) 674741 E-mail: info@georgecsmith.co.uk *Woodworking manufrs*

Gordon Smith, 9 Manchester Road, Partington, Manchester, M31 4FB Tel: 0161-777 9438 Fax: 0161-777 6871 E-mail: gordonsmith@tesco.net *Musical instrument manufrs*

H. Smith Engineers Ltd, Fordcroft Road, Orpington, Kent, BR5 2DB Tel: (01689) 833581 Fax: (01689) 820218 E-mail: mail@hsmith.co.uk *Demolition contractors*

H. Smith Plastics Ltd, Mayphil Industrial Area, Battlesbridge, Wickford, Essex, SS11 7RJ Tel: (01268) 733088 Fax: (01268) 560561 E-mail: hsp@plantcell.co.uk *Horticultural container manufrs*

H.R. Smith Technical Development Ltd, Street Court, Kingsland, Leominster, Herefordshire, HR6 9QA Tel: (01568) 708744 Fax: (01568) 708713 E-mail: sales@hr-smith.com *Microwave component manufrs*

H.R. Smith Techtest Ltd, Street Court, Kingsland, Leominster, Herefordshire, HR6 9QA Tel: (01568) 708744 Fax: (01568) 708713 E-mail: sales@hr-smith.com *Aerospace test equipment*

Smith & Harris, 31 Hatton Garden, London, EC1N 8DH Tel: (020) 7405 1056 Fax: (020) 7405 1056 *Goldsmiths & silversmiths*

Smith Harrison Shade Cards Ltd, Unit 2 Factory Street, Bradford, West Yorkshire, BD4 9NW Tel: (01274) 683579 Fax: (01274) 688936 E-mail: info@smithharrison.co.uk *Shade card makers*

Smith & Healey, 7 Upper Northgate Street, Chester, CH1 4EE Tel: (01244) 372684 *Jewellery repairers*

Smith, Hogg & Co. Ltd, Dock Offices, Cleveland Road, Hartlepool, Cleveland, TS24 0UZ Tel: (01429) 273157 Fax: (01429) 270693 *Ship brokers* Also at: Middlesbrough & Seaham

Smith & Co. (Holdings) Ltd, Cauldwell Walk, Bedford, MK42 9DT Tel: (01234) 272572 Fax: (01234) 271891 E-mail: info@emrltd.com *Scrap metal merchants*

Ian Smith Plant Ltd, Scotter Common, Gainsborough, Lincolnshire, DN21 3JF Tel: (01724) 764185 Fax: (01724) 764649 *Used construction plant sales*

Ian Smith Stationers Ltd, 205 Great Bridge Street, West Bromwich, West Midlands, B70 0DJ Tel: 0121-557 5451 Fax: 0121-557 2507 E-mail: head.office@iansmithstationers.btinternet.com *Commercial stationers & retail services* Also at: Colchester, Newcastle, Norwich & Peterborough

▶ Smith Ivanson, 28 New Road, Penn, High Wycombe, Buckinghamshire, HP10 8DJ Tel: (01494) 817103 *IT consultants*

J.E. Smith (Higham Ferrers) Ltd., 24 Saffron Road, Higham Ferrers, Rushden, Northamptonshire, NN10 8ED Tel: (01933) 312495 Fax: (01933) 410424 E-mail: aircon@jesmith.sagehost.co.uk *Industrial air conditioning heating & ventilation services*

Smith Jigboring Ltd, Unit 20 Phoenix Industrial Estate, Charles Street, West Bromwich, West Midlands, B70 0AY Tel: 0121-557 0211 Fax: 0121-557 1941 *Precision engineers*

John B. Smith Ltd, Dugdale Street, Stockton-On-Tees, Cleveland, TS18 2NE Tel: (01642) 675096 Fax: (01642) 617701 E-mail: enquiries@johnbsmith.co.uk *Roof truss manufrs*

John Smith & Sons (New Pitsligo) Ltd, 96-102 High Street, New Pitsligo, Fraserburgh, Aberdeenshire, AB43 6NN Tel: (01771) 653207 Fax: (01771) 653684 *Bakers retail & wholesale*

Smith & Jones Joinery, 1 Furnham Road Trading Estate, Furnham Road, Chard, Somerset, TA20 1AX Tel: (01460) 62262 Fax: (01460) 66355 E-mail: smithjonesjoinery@lineone.net *Purpose-made joinery*

▶ Josh Smith, 1St Galaxy Fireworks, Pyro Plot, Nottingham Road, Ravenshead, Nottingham, NG15 9HP Tel: (0870) 4430210 *Fireworks display company*

▶ Smith Kellett Ltd, Westholme House, Westholme Road, Halifax, West Yorkshire, HX1 4ER Tel: (01422) 349029

▶ Smith & Latimer Ltd, 1 Avebury Court Mark Road, Hemel Hempstead Industrial Estate, Hemel Hempstead, Hertfordshire, HP2 7TA Tel: (01442) 212966

Smith & McLaurin Ltd, Cartside Mill, Kilbarchan, Renfrewshire, PA10 2AF Tel: (01505) 707700 Fax: (01505) 704992 E-mail: info@smcl.co.uk *Manufacturers of paper coating, self-adhesive paper*

Smith Medical Ltd, 52 Grayshill Road, Westfield, Cumbernauld, Glasgow, G68 9HQ Tel: (01236) 737138 Fax: (01236) 738503 E-mail: info@smiths-medical.com *Disposable drape & surgical pack manufrs*

Smith Melzack Pepper Angliss Services Ltd, 7-10 Chandos Street, Cavendish Square, London, W1G 9AJ Tel: (020) 7546 1996 Fax: (020) 7546 1900 E-mail: enquiries@sm-pa.co.uk *Property consultants*

▶ Smith Metal Centres, Unit 7-10, Eldon Road, Beeston, Nottingham, NG9 6DZ Tel: 0115-925 4801 Fax: 0115-925 5370 E-mail: nottingham-sales@smithmetal.com *Non ferrous metals stock holders*

Michael Smith Engraving Services Ltd, Unit 3, Leicester, LE2 8AA Tel: 0116-283 0712 Fax: 0116-244 0198 E-mail: sales@michaelsmithswitchgear.co.uk *Industrial engravers*

Mike Smith Designs Ltd, Unit 10 Fordhouse Road Industrial Estate, Steel Drive, Wolverhampton, WV10 9XE Tel: (01902) 784400 Fax: (01902) 785980 E-mail: sales@mikesmithdesigns.com *External lighting & street furniture manufrs*

Smith & Moore, 82-86 New Street, West Bromwich, West Midlands, B70 7PT Tel: 0121-553 0337 Fax: 0121-500 5463 E-mail: smithmoore@supernet.com *Janitorial suppliers*

Neil Smith Ltd, 370 Gallowgate, Glasgow, G4 0TX Tel: 0141-552 1141 Fax: 0141-552 0623 *Carpet & curtain fittings distribs*

▶ Smith & Nephew Extruded Films Ltd, Gateway To Humberside Trading Estate, Gilberdyke, Brough, North Humberside, HU15 2TD Tel: (01430) 440757 Fax: (01430) 440211 E-mail: phil.redshaw@smith-nephew.com *A specialist supplier of film, foam, polymeric nets and tapes for the medical and industrial sectors.*

Noel Smith, Stratford Road, Milford Haven, Dyfed, SA73 2JA Tel: (01646) 690097 Fax: (01646) 695599 E-mail: nsjoinery@aol.com *Joinery manufrs*

Smith & Ouzman Ltd, 45 Brampton Road, Eastbourne, East Sussex, BN22 9AH Tel: (01323) 524000 Fax: (01323) 524024 E-mail: print@smith-ouzman.com *Security printers & business forms* Also at: Danbury

Smith Pack, Units 43-44, Brook House Road, Parkhouse Industrial Estate West, Newcastle, Staffordshire, ST5 7EF Tel: (01782) 565123 Fax: (01782) 565124 E-mail: northweston@wsmith.co.uk *Cardboard boxes & containers manufrs*

Smith Packaging Services, Lochlands Industrial Estate, Larbert, Stirlingshire, FK5 3NS Tel: (01324) 555521 Fax: (01324) 555988 E-mail: smith.packaging@btinternet.com *Export packers*

Pat Smith Enterprises, DP3, Aghnashammer, Rosslea, Enniskillen, County Fermanagh, BT92 7HF Tel: (028) 6775 1010 Fax: (028) 6775 1996 *Tile adhesive products manufrs*

Paul Smith Furniture, C4 Newton Road, Peacehaven, East Sussex, BN10 8JQ Tel: (01273) 580454 Fax: (01273) 586994 E-mail: sales@paulsmithfurn.com *Reproduction furniture manufrs*

Peter Smith Photography, George House, Derwent Road, York Road Business Park, Malton, North Yorkshire, YO17 6YB Tel: (0870) 2201249 Fax: (01653) 600314 E-mail: peter@petersmith.com *Aerial & commercial photographer & video*

Peter Smith Valve Co. Ltd, Occupation Road, Nottingham, NG6 8RX Tel: 0115-927 2831 Fax: 0115-977 0233 E-mail: sales@petersmithvalve.co.uk *Valves globe, marine & steam manufrs*

▶ Smith Property Maintenance, 129 Albany Road, Hornchurch, Essex, RM12 4AQ Tel: (01708) 477764 Fax: (01708) 442100 E-mail: lg_smiths@hotmail.com *Building maintenance*

Smith Rea, 78 Carden Place, Aberdeen, AB10 1UL Tel: (01224) 612400 Fax: (01224) 612401 E-mail: info@srel.co.uk *Oil & gas industry advisers*

Charles Smith & Reddish Ltd, 11a Lever Street, London, EC1V 3QU Tel: (020) 7253 2457 Fax: (020) 7490 4612 E-mail: info@csr-chartinstruments.co.uk *Nautical & survey instrument manufrs*

▶ Smith & Rhodes, Kirk Syke Farm, Lothersdale, Keighley, West Yorkshire, BD20 8HX Tel: (01535) 633636 Fax: (01535) 633784

Smith & Rodger Ltd, 34 Elliott Street, Glasgow, G3 8EA Tel: 0141-248 6341 Fax: 0141-248 6475 E-mail: info@smithandrodger.co.uk *Lacquer, paint, wood finishes & polish manufrs*

Smith & Sons (Bletchington) Ltd, Enslow, Kidlington, Oxfordshire, OX5 3AY Tel: (01869) 331281 Fax: (01869) 331734 *Sand & gravel, merchants & producers*

T.A. Smith & Co. Ltd, 53-55 Scrutton Street, London, EC2A 4PJ Tel: (020) 7739 1702 Fax: (020) 8500 4634 *Builders merchants*

Walter Smith Joinery Ltd, Westerby Road, East Middlesbrough Industrial Estate, Middlesbrough, Cleveland, TS3 8BQ Tel: (01642) 221171 Fax: (01642) 231342 E-mail: sales@waltersmithjoineryltd.co.uk *Laminated plastics fabricators & joinery manufrs*

▶ Smith of Whiteinch Ltd, 85 Clydeholm Road, Glasgow, G14 0SE Tel: 0141-954 8071

Smith & Williamson Investment Management, 25 Moorgate, London, EC2R 6AY Tel: (020) 7776 8700 Fax: (020) 7131 4001 E-mail: info@smith.williamson.co.uk *International securities dealers*

Smith & Co Woollen Ltd, 16a Dufours Place, London, W1F 7SP Tel: (020) 7437 6226 Fax: (020) 7287 5324 *Woollen merchants*

Smithbrewer Ltd, Sunnyside Road North, Weston-super-Mare, Avon, BS23 3PZ Tel: (01934) 642642 Fax: (01934) 642646 E-mail: sales@smithbrewer.co.uk *Shop fitters & sign designers, installers & manufrs*

Smithbrook Ltd, Unit 10, Manfield Park, Cranleigh, Surrey, GU6 8PT Tel: (01483) 272744 Fax: (01483) 267863 E-mail: smithbrook@smithbrooklighting.co.uk *Lighting manufrs*

Smithbrook Building Products Ltd, Shoreham-By-Sea, West Sussex, BN43 9BD Tel: (01273) 573811 Fax: (01273) 689021 E-mail: info@smithbrookproducts.com *Specialists in the supply of glazed clay roof tiles & ridge tiles*

Smithers Rapra, Shawbury, Shrewsbury, SY4 4NR Tel: (01939) 250383 Fax: 01939 251118 E-mail: info@rapra.net *Plastic & rubber consultants*

Smithfield Casings & Sundries, Unit 6 West Smithfield, Welwyn Garden City, Hertfordshire, AL7 4TW Tel: (01707) 328557 Fax: (01707) 335801 *Butchers accessories & food industry suppliers*

Smithfield Tractors Builth Wells Ltd, Llanelwedd, Builth Wells, Powys, LD2 3SR Tel: (01982) 553221 Fax: (01982) 552048 E-mail: sales@smithfieldtractors.co.uk *Agricultural engineers*

Smithpack Ltd, 1 Pegasus Way, Bowerhill, Melksham, Wiltshire, SN12 6TR Tel: (01225) 709628 Fax: (01225) 709884 *Cardboard & corrugated packaging cases*

Smiths & Bateson Ltd, Kitling Road, Knowsley Business Park, Prescot, Merseyside, L34 9JA Tel: 0151-547 1801 Fax: 0151-547 7171 E-mail: sales@smithbateson.co.uk *Packaging material merchants*

Smiths Of Buckie, 27 East Church Street, Buckie, Banffshire, AB56 1ET Tel: (01542) 832488 Fax: (01542) 834896 *Sign manufrs*

▶ Smiths Building Contractors, 36 King Harald Street, Lerwick, Shetland, ZE1 0EQ Tel: (01595) 692251

▶ Smith's Cleaning, 17 Lytchett Way, Poole, Dorset, BH16 5LS Tel: (01202) 620895 E-mail: smithscleaning@ntlworld.com *Carpet & upholstery cleaning services*

Smith's Coffee Co. and The Natural Coffee Co., Arabica House, Ebberns Road, Apsley, Hemel Hempstead, Herts, HP3 9RD Tel: (01442) 234239 Fax: (01442) 248614 E-mail: sales@smiths-coffee.demon.co.uk *Smith's Coffee Co. and The National Coffee Co. are based in Hemel Hempstead and are delighted to offer their customers a comprehensive range of the highest quality coffees from around the world. This includes single estate, speciality, Fairtrade and organic coffees as well as a wide range of blends to suit every occasion. A range of flavoured coffees, teas and syrups are also available. They also offer a range of coffee making equipment including filter machines, jugs, coffee grinders, espresso accessories, cleaning products, cafetieres and espresso machines.*

Smiths Concrete Ltd, Southam Road, Banbury, Oxfordshire, OX16 2RR Tel: (01295) 278177 Fax: (01295) 271402 E-mail: info@smithsconcrete.co.uk *Ready mixed concrete service & aggregate producers* Also at: Barford, Bicester, Bobenhall & Cassinton

Smiths Concrete Ltd, Waverley Wood Quarry, Weston Lane, Bubbenhall, Coventry, CV8 3BN Tel: (01926) 633186 Fax: (01926) 633478 E-mail: info@smithsconcrete.co.uk *Sand & gravel quarry suppliers*

▶ Smiths Design Group Ltd, Saxon Business Park Hanbury Road Unit 9, Alfred Court, Stoke Prior, Bromsgrove, Worcestershire, B60 4AD Tel: (01527) 837873 Fax: (01527) 837971 E-mail: enquiries@smithsdesigngroup.com *Design services for printing signs, exhibition, point of sale*

▶ Smiths Distribution Ltd, Laughton Road, Blyton, Gainsborough, Lincolnshire, DN21 3LQ Tel: (01427) 622000 Fax: (01427) 629609

▶ Smiths Engineering Works N I Ltd, Larne Road, Ballymena, County Antrim, BT42 3HA Tel: (028) 2564 1621 Fax: (028) 2564 3724 E-mail: info@smiths-engineering.com *Precision engineering services*

Smiths Engineering Works N I Ltd, Larne Road, Ballymena, County Antrim, BT42 3HA Tel: (028) 2564 1621 Fax: (028) 2564 3724 *Engine reconditioning specialists*

Smiths Equipment Hire Ltd, 245 Fleetwood Road, Thornton-Cleveleys, Lancashire, FY5 1NJ Tel: (01253) 862445 Fax: (01253) 853496 *Tool hire services*

Smiths Group plc, 765 Finchley Road, Childs Hill, London, NW11 8DS Tel: (020) 8458 3232 Fax: (020) 8458 4380 E-mail: plc@smiths-group.com *Fuel control, management, aircraft components & instruments manufrs*

Smith's (Harlow) Aerospace Ltd, Interstate House, Horsecroft Road, The Pinnacles, Harlow, Essex, CM19 5BZ Tel: (01279) 414999 Fax: (01279) 421411 *Aircraft repair service*

Smiths Medical International Ltd, Bramingham Business Park, Enterprise Way, Luton, LU3 4BU Tel: (01582) 430000 Fax: (01582) 430001 E-mail: info@pneupac.co.uk Principal Export Areas: Worldwide *Medical equipment*

Smiths Medical International, The Belfry, Colonial Way, Watford, WD24 4LG Tel: (01706) 233821 Fax: (01706) 218834 E-mail: ukcs@smiths-medical.com Principal Export Areas: Worldwide *Hospital disposable products*

▶ Smiths Metal Centres Ltd, Straton Business Park, London Road, Biggleswade, Bedfordshire, SG18 8QB Tel: (01767) 604704 Fax: 01767 600466 E-mail: sales@smithsselect.com *Supply non-ferrous metals & all forms of engineering raw materials*

▶ Smiths Metal Centres Ltd, Straton Business Park, London Road, Biggleswade, Bedfordshire, SG18 8QB Tel: (01767) 604704 Fax: (01767) 315271 E-mail: biggleswade@smithmetal.com *Suppliers of engineering raw materials*

▶ Smiths Metal Centres Ltd, Straton Business Park, London Road, Biggleswade, Bedfordshire, SG18 8QB Tel: (01767) 604704 Fax: (01767) 312885 E-mail: sales@smithshp.com *Suppliers of all forms of high performance engineering raw materials*

▶ Smiths Metal Centres Ltd, 10 Unicorn Park, Unicorn Park Avenue, Brislington, Bristol, BS4 4EX Tel: 0117-971 2800 Fax: 0117-971 6300 E-mail: info@smithsmetal.com *Suppliers of all forms of engineering raw materials*

▶ Smiths Metal Centres Ltd, Argyll Road, Chelmsford, CM2 6PY Tel: (01245) 466664 Fax: (01245) 465916 E-mail: chelmsford@smithmetal.com *Stockists & distributors of all forms for engineering raw materials*

▶ Smiths Metal Centres Ltd, 3 Epsom Court, Leeds Twenty Seven Industrial Estate, Bruntcliffe Avenue, Morley, Leeds, LS27 0LL Tel: 0113-307 5167 Fax: 0113-307 5327 E-mail: leeds@smithmetal.com *Engineering raw materials non-ferrous metals & stainless steel*

Smiths Metal Centres Ltd, 42-56 Tottenham Road, London, N1 4BZ Tel: (020) 7241 2430 Fax: (020) 7254 9608 *Non-ferrous metals, stainless steel & engineering raw materials*

▶ Smiths Metal Centres Ltd, 8-9 Cedar Trade Park, Cobham Road, Ferndown Industrial Estate, Wimborne, Dorset, BH21 7SD Tel: (01202) 893755 Fax: (01202) 893712 E-mail: ferndown@smithmetal.com *Suppliers of non-ferrous metals & engineering plastics*

Smiths Office & Commercial Furniture, Windsor Road, Redditch, Worcestershire, B97 6DJ Tel: (01527) 66663 Fax: (01527) 69333 E-mail: info@smithseating.co.uk *Commercial & office furniture suppliers & manufrs*

Smiths Of Peterhead Ltd, Kirkburn Mills, Wevers Lane, Peterhead, Aberdeenshire, AB42 1SA Tel: (01779) 871400 Fax: (01779) 478989 E-mail: smithsofpeterhead@btconnect.com *Clothing & fabric weavers*

▶ Smiths Profiles, Cheltenham Film Studios, Arle Court, Hatherley Lane, Cheltenham, Gloucestershire, GL51 6PN Tel: (01242) 541380 Fax: (01242) 515480 E-mail: sales@smithsprofiles.com *Suppliers of bespoke aluminium profiles.*

Smith's Solutions, 27 Kiln Lane, Hope, Wrexham, Clwyd, LL12 9PH Tel: (01978) 769090 Fax: 01978 769173 E-mail: sales@smiths-solutions.co.uk *Freight, import & export, freight forwarders, customs clearance*

Smiths Timber & Joinery Ltd, Misterton Way, Lutterworth, Leicestershire, LE17 4JA Tel: (01455) 550194 Fax: (01455) 553974 *Timber hardware suppliers*

F. Smithson, Anchor Mills Foundry, Watergate, Dewsbury, W. Yorkshire, WF12 9DY Tel: (01924) 462439 *Non-ferrous metal founder*

▶ Smithsonia Designers, 14-16 Piccadilly Arcade, Birmingham, B2 4HD Tel: 0121-643 8405 Fax: 0121-643 8194 *Semi-precious gemstone jewellery handcrafted sterling silver manufrs*

▶ Smithy Joinery, The Barn, Blackleach Lane, Bartle, Preston, PR4 0RY Tel: (01772) 690417 Fax: (01772) 691797 *Joinery manufrs*

▶ Smithys Bakery, Unit 3, The George Shopping Centre, Crewkerne, Somerset, TA18 7LU Tel: (01460) 77962

Smithz Pac, Unit 33, Darwin Enterprise Centre, Railway Road, Darwen, Lancashire, BB3 3EH Tel: (01254) 703311 E-mail: smithzpac@yahoo.co.uk *Contract packing services*

▶ SMJ Classic Cadillac Hire, Unit C1, Cromer House, Caxton Way, Stevenage, Hertfordshire, SG1 2DF Tel: 01438 356925 Fax: 01438 236023 E-mail: smjclassiccad64@aol.com *Wedding Car Hire, School Proms, Special Occasions, TV & Promotional Work.*

SMJ Fabrications Ltd, Unit 12 Rookwood Hall, Abbess Roding, Ongar, Essex, CM5 0JL Tel: (01279) 876497 Fax: (01279) 876419 *Sheet metalwork engineers & fabricators*

Smoke & Solar Controls Systems UK Ltd, PO Box 2143, Atherstone, Warwickshire, CV9 1YB Tel: (01827) 714513 Fax: (01827) 714513 *Smoke containment curtain fitting*

Smoke Vent Services Ltd, 27 Pandy Road, Bedwas, Caerphilly, Mid Glamorgan, CF83 8EH Tel: (029) 2088 9173 Fax: (029) 2088 5026 E-mail: sales@smokevent.co.uk *Ventilation equipment repairers*

▶ Smokeson Glass, Dart Mills, Buckfastleigh, Devon, TQ11 0NF Tel: (01364) 644673 Fax: (01364) 642162 E-mail: mail@smokesonglass.co.uk *Welcome to Smokeson Glass. Whether you are a commercial Double Glazing business or a residential customer we are able to supply you with the highest quality sealed units, decorative glass and mirrors.***

▶ Smoking Barrels Leicestershire & Rutland, Glebe Farm, North End, Hallaton, Market Harborough, Leicestershire, LE16 8UZ Tel: 0116-247 8714 E-mail: max@jacquespad.fsnet.co.uk *Experience simulated game shooting in Rutland and Leicestershire. Corporate entertainment for small *or large groups.*

▶ Smooth Move Ltd, Unit 2, 9 Paul Street, Liverpool, L3 6DX Tel: 0151-236 7666

SMP Metallurgical Ltd, Surrey Street, Glossop, Derbyshire, SK13 7AL Tel: (01457) 852333 Fax: (01457) 855655 E-mail: sales@smp-metallurgical.com Principal Export Areas: Central/East Europe & West Europe *Ferro alloy producers*

Smr Marine Limited, Unit 1A East Lockside, East Lockside, Brighton Marina, Brighton, BN2 5UG Tel: (01273) 668900 Fax: (01273) 668905 E-mail: boatsales@smrmarine.co.uk *Yacht riggers & chandlery services*

▶ Smr2 Computer Consultants, 44 High Street, Aylesbury, Buckinghamshire, HP20 1SE Tel: (01296) 428525

SMS Ltd, 1 Lytham Road, Warton, Preston, PR4 1AH Tel: (01772) 634042 Fax: (01772) 635942 *Steel fabrication engineers*

SMS Scotland Ltd, 6 Albion Way, Kelvin Industrial Estate, East Kilbride, Glasgow, G75 0YN Tel: (01355) 264949 Fax: (01355) 264545 E-mail: sales@stockmetal.co.uk *Stainless steel*

▶ SMT Electrical Ltd, Great Lime Road, Newcastle upon Tyne, NE12 6RU Tel: 0191-268 5999 Fax: 0191-268 4440 E-mail: sales@smtelectrical.co.uk

Smurfit Cartons UK, Freebournes Road, Witham, Essex, CM8 3DA Tel: (01376) 512501 Fax: (01376) 520442 *Folder presentation services*

Smurfit Composites, Richmond Works, Moresby Road, Hensingham, Whitehaven, Cumbria, CA28 8TS Tel: (01946) 61671 Fax: (01946) 592281 *Cardboard & composite tube manufrs*

Smurfit Corrugated, Lattersey Hill Trading Estate, Benwick Road, Whittlesey, Peterborough, PE7 2JA Tel: (01733) 206050 Fax: (01733) 202770 E-mail: mike.dench@smurfitkappa.co.uk *Corrugated cardboard*

Smurfit Corrugated Sheet Sales Windrush Ltd, Windrush Park Road, Witney, Oxfordshire, OX29 7EX Tel: (01993) 771188 Fax: (01993) 701201 *Corrugated materials manufrs*

Smurfit Kappa, 24-26 Robjohns Road, Chelmsford, CM1 3BB Tel: (01245) 493777 Fax: (01245) 353427 *Corrugated fibreboard containers*

Smurfit Sheet Feeding, Fishergate, Norwich, NR3 1SJ Tel: (01603) 660041 Fax: (01603) 679876 E-mail: sales@smurfitgroup.com *Corrugated cardboard manufrs*

Smurfit South West, Riverside Road, Pottington Business Park, Barnstaple, Devon, EX31 1LX Tel: (01271) 345011 Fax: (01271) 346665 *Corrugated container manufrs*

Smurfit Townsend Hook, Paper Mills, Mill Street, Snodland, Kent, ME6 5AX Tel: (01634) 240205 Fax: (01634) 243458 E-mail: sales@smurfit-europe.com *Coated paper & board processors or services & packaging material, goods & products manufrs*

Smyth Steel Ltd, 15 Gorran Road, Garvagh, Coleraine, County Londonderry, BT51 4HA Tel: (028) 7086 8544 Fax: (028) 7086 8102 E-mail: mail@smyth-steel.co.uk *Structural steelwork fabricators & erectors*

Smyth's Equipment Supply Co., Tamar Commercial Centre, Chater Street, Belfast, BT4 1BL Tel: (028) 9045 1355 Fax: (028) 9045 4838 E-mail: sescobelfast@aol.com *Coach building suppliers*

Frank Smythson Ltd, 40 New Bond Street, London, W1S 2DE Tel: (020) 7629 8558 Fax: (020) 7495 6111 E-mail: 101451.2265@compuserve.com *Luxury leather goods & bespoke stationers suppliers*

continued

▶ indicates data change since last edition

SNA Europe Ltd, Bahco Thorne, Moorhead Way, Bramley, Rotherham, South Yorkshire, S66 1YY Tel: (01709) 731731 Fax: (01709) 731741 E-mail: uksales@bahco.com *Hand tools & saws manufrs*

Snackcakes, Unit X2, Herald Way, Binley Ind Est, Coventry, CV3 2RZ Tel: 024 76651991 Fax: 024 76651306 *Cakes*

▶ Snacks Unlimited, Standard Road, London, NW10 6EX Tel: (020) 8838 3380 Fax: (020) 8961 3866

▶ Snafu Design, 8 South Street, Torrington, Devon, EX38 8HE Tel: (01805) 623387 E-mail: rob@snafudesign.co.uk *Creative design for print & web*

Snai International Ltd, 5 Berners Rd, London, N1 0PW Tel: 020 73541991 Fax: 020 73542474 *Technology provider*

Snamprogetti Ltd, Snamprogetti House, Basingview, Basingstoke, Hampshire, RG21 4YY Tel: (01256) 461211 Fax: (01256) 482211 E-mail: sales@snampro.co.uk *Petrochemical plant contractors & designers*

Snap On Tools, Telford Way, Telford Way Industrial Estate, Kettering, Northamptonshire, NN16 8SN Tel: (01536) 413800 Fax: (01536) 413900 E-mail: max.christmas@snapon.com *Hand tool distributors & manufrs*

Snap Survey Software Mercator Research Group Ltd, 5 Mead Court, Cooper Road, Thornbury, Bristol, BS35 3UW Tel: (01454) 280800 Fax: (01454) 281216 E-mail: info@snapsurveys.com *Computer software house for market research*

▶ Snape Maltings, Snape, Snape, Saxmundham, Suffolk, IP17 1SR Tel: (01728) 688305 Fax: (01728) 688930 E-mail: admin@snapemaltings.co.uk

Snapfast Fasteners & Fixing Devices, Unit 1-2 Park Court, Ninth Avenue, Team Valley Trading Estate, Gateshead, Tyne & Wear, NE11 0EH Tel: 0191-482 4075 Fax: 0191-491 1799 E-mail: snapfast@natlineuk.net *Fastener & street lighting distributors*

Snap-On Finance UK Ltd, Telford Way, Industrial Estate, Kettering, Northamptonshire, NN16 8SN Tel: (01536) 516651 Fax: (01536) 413874 E-mail: industrialuk@snapon.com *Supply hand tools, power tools, workshop equipment, tool storage units, mobile workshops & tools at height safety systems to general industry, the oil & gas, energy, construction, rail, aerospace, military & many other sectors*

Snapple Europe Ltd, 1 Castle Yard, Richmond, Surrey, TW10 6TF Tel: (020) 8332 9990 Fax: (020) 8332 6998 E-mail: snapple_europe@compuserve.com *Beverage manufrs*

Snashall Steel Fabrications Co. Ltd, Pulham Business Park, Pulham, Dorchester, Dorset, DT2 7DX Tel: (01300) 345588 Fax: (01300) 345533 E-mail: malcolm@snashallsteel.co.uk *Structural steel fabricators*

SNC, 2 Denston Close, Prenton, Merseyside, CH43 9XU Tel: 0151-678 6471 Fax: 0151-257 9453 *Telecommunications equipment & systems installers*

SNC Lavalin UK Ltd, Knollys House, Addiscombe Road, Croydon, CR0 6SR Tel: (020) 8681 4250 Fax: (020) 8681 4299 E-mail: sncl.uk@snclavalin.com *Project management consultants*

▶ Snedden, 1c Lockharton Gardens, Craiglockhart, Edinburgh, EH14 1AU Tel: 0131-443 3712 Fax: 0131-443 3712

▶ Sneddon Transport, Unit 1, Block 1, Brownsburn Industrial Estate, Airdrie, Lanarkshire, ML6 9SE Tel: (01236) 759036

▶ Darren Snell, Ground Floor, Clair House, Haywards Heath, West Sussex, RH16 3DP Tel: (01444) 415559 Fax: (01444) 415180 E-mail: enquiries@artconsulting.com *Recruiting specialist staff for the financial services*

▶ Snell & Mackay, 2A Sivell Place, Heavitree, Exeter, EX2 5ER Tel: (01392) 211882

Snell & Prideaux Ltd, 6-9 Ernest Street, Birmingham, B1 1NS Tel: 0121-622 3824 Fax: 0121-666 6630 *Anodises & metal finishers*

Snell Signs & Supplies Ltd, 243-245 Cleethorpe Road, Grimsby, South Humberside, DN31 3BE Tel: (01472) 342000 Fax: (01472) 240027 *Sign contractors*

Snell & Wilcox Ltd, Durford Mill, Petersfield, Hants, GU31 5AZ Tel: (01730) 821188 Fax: (01730) 821199 *Video Manufacturers*

▶ Sneyd Builders, 113-121 Garner Street, Stoke-on-Trent, ST4 7AX Tel: (01782) 272137 Fax: (01782) 201695

Sneyd Oxides Ltd, Sneyd Mills, Leonora Street, Stoke-On-Trent, ST6 3BZ Tel: (01782) 577600 Fax: (01782) 835742 E-mail: ceramics@sneydoxides.co.uk Principal Export Areas: Worldwide *Manufacturers of ceramic glaze*

Snfa Bearings Ltd, Wotton Road, Charfield, Wotton-under-Edge, Gloucestershire, GL12 8SP Tel: (01453) 843501 Fax: (01453) 842577 E-mail: sales@snfa-bearings.co.uk *High precision, ceramic & aerospace bearings*

Snickers Original Ltd, Unit N3 Meltham Mills Industrial Estate, Meltham, Holmfirth, HD9 4DS Tel: (01484) 854488 Fax: (01484) 854733 *Electrical protective clothing*

▶ Snooker Direct, 52 Kingfisher Way, Upton, Wirral, Merseyside, CH49 4PR Tel: (0845) 2751741 E-mail: sales@snookerdirect.co.uk *Snooker Solutions is a one stop shop for all your Snooker, Pool table and Accessories.*

Snooze UK Ltd, 14 Harcley Street, Dewsbury, West Yorkshire, WF13 2VB Tel: (01924) 467149 *Bed manufrs*

▶ Snout Ltd, 9 The Lime Kilns, Barrow upon Soar, Loughborough, Leicestershire, LE12 8YF Tel: (01509) 415643 E-mail: info@snoutthings.co.uk *Snout designs and manufactures a range of interior and fashion accessories.*

▶ Snow + Rock - Romford, Unit 1A, Davidson Way, Rom Valley Way, Romford, RM7 0AZ Tel: (01708) 436400 E-mail: direct@snowandrock.com *Outdoor sports clothing & equipment retailer*

▶ Snow + Rock - Wirral Ltd, Unit 1, Eastham Point, 1062 New Chester Road, Wirral, Merseyside, CH62 8HJ Tel: 0151-328 5500 Fax: 0151-328 5501 E-mail: manager.liverpool@snowandrock.com *Retail sports goods & equipment, accessories*

Snow Hunter Automation, PO Box 260, Scarborough, North Yorkshire, YO12 5YA Tel: (07944) 085848 Fax: (01723) 371696 E-mail: john@snowhunter.freeserve.co.uk *Special purpose machine designers*

▶ Snow & Rock, 188 Kensington High Street, London, W8 7RG Tel: (020) 7937 0872 Fax: (020) 7938 2758 E-mail: manager.kensington@snowandrock.com *Selection of winter clothing in addition to ski & snowboard equipment*

▶ Snow & Rock, 150 Holborn, London, EC1N 2LR Tel: (020) 7831 6900 Fax: (020) 7831 8545 E-mail: phil@mackechnie.co.nz *Holborn branch is a boutique style store aimed at the City market catering for people who want the best in outdoor equipment and have little time. During the winter, our Holborn store specialises in ski and snowboard clothing and equipment, including backcountry, ensuring accurate service and advice.*

▶ Snow & Rock, 4 Mercer Street, London, WC2H 9QA Tel: (020) 7420 1444 Fax: (020) 7420 1445 E-mail: manager.coventgarden@snowandrock.com *Ski & outdoor retailer*

▶ Snow & Rock Sports Ltd, 14-16 The Priory Queensway, Birmingham, B4 6BS Tel: 0121-236 8280 Fax: 0121-212 2177 *This is one of our longer established shops and is located in central Birmingham with parking available close by on street meters or NCP car parks. Informative staff and careful shop layout allow us to fully maximise our floor space, allowing a wide range of our outdoor and winter sports ranges to be featured. Our Birmingham store carries a good selection of tents, backpacks and footwear in addition to ski and snowboard equipment and clothing.*

▶ Snow & Rock Sports Ltd, Units 1-3, Gloucester Road North, Filton, Bristol, BS34 7BQ Tel: 0117-914 3000 Fax: 0117-907 4278 *Our Bristol superstore offers plenty of free space to move around and relax. The shop features large departments for our outdoor and winter ranges, giving you all the choice you'll need for winter sports or making the most of the outdoors. This store's location at the gateway to the West Country and South Wales makes it the ideal jumping off point for your forays into the wild.*

▶ Snow & Rock Sports Ltd, 97 Fordwater Road, Chertsey, Surrey, KT16 8HH Tel: (01932) 566886 Fax: (01932) 561553 *Located within a couple of minutes of the M25 in Surrey, our Chertsey superstore boasts over ,000sq ft of retail space. We have plenty of free parking on site and the store also offers a café, allowing you to take a load off mid-shop or just to double-check that you know exactly what you want! The Chertsey store also features the second of our BodyFactor clinics (www.bodyfactor.co.uk) offering professional sports rehabilitation services. **Chertsey is able to offer our customers the vast majority of all our outdoor range, from convertible hiking pants to multifuel stoves and expedition down sleeping bags, making it a great place to get yourself quickly and easily kitted out for your adventures. This is of course on top of the full range of Winter Ski, Snowboard and Backcountry clothing and equipment, all backed up by knowledgeable and friendly staff.*

▶ Snow & Rock Sports Ltd, Thorneberry Way, Guildford, Surrey, GU1 1QB Tel: (01483) 445200 Fax: (01483) 445336 E-mail: admin@snowandrock.com *Outdoor sports equipment & clothing retailers*

▶ Snow & Rock Sports Ltd, 31 The Boardwalk, Port Solent, Portsmouth, PO6 4TP Tel: (023) 9220 5388 Fax: (023) 9220 5399 *Ski & outdoor retail shop*

▶ Snow & Rock Sports Ltd, Sheffield Ski Village, Vale Road, Sheffield, S3 9SJ Tel: 0114-275 1700 Fax: 0114-273 0003 *Based at the Sheffield Ski Village, this store is split over two levels offering a strong selection of clothing and equipment. Free parking is available on site and the store is open long hours to complement the ski centre.*

Snow White Laundries Ltd, 69 The Highway, New Inn, Pontypool, Gwent, NP4 0PN Tel: (01495) 764652 Fax: (01495) 762494 *Laundry & dry cleaning service*

▶ Snowcrest Ice Cream Manufacturers, 1-7 Garman Road, London, N17 0UR Tel: (020) 8365 0000 Fax: (020) 8808 9789

Edwin Snowden & Co. Ltd, 173 Fountain Road, Hull, HU2 0LJ Tel: (01482) 320143 Fax: (01482) 225589 E-mail: info@edwin-snowden.co.uk *Based in Hull, for over a century Edwin Snowden & Co Limited have built up a reputation for boiler repairs and the fabrication of custom made storage tanks and pressure vessels. More recently fabricated environmental vessels and hyperbaric chambers have expanded their product range. Edwin Snowden's technology advances alongside their product range, which continues to expand and diversify and now offer products to a range of sectors including petrochemical; paint; pharmaceutical; food; medical; horticultural and marine. The company manufactures to PD5500:2000 or ASME VIII construction standards, including P.E.D requirements and work to the European quality standard BS EN IS09001:2000.obtained in 1993. Continual staff development is key to the company's progress. All welders are coded to BS EN 288 and ASME IX and all employees are certified to work in confined spaces and hold health and safety passports.*

▶ Snowdrop Gardening & Design Services, 3 Stapeley Farm Cottages, Odiham, Hampshire, RG29 1JE Tel: (01256) 862020 E-mail: info@snowdropgardening.co.uk *Snowdrop Gardening & Design Services offers all types of gardening work to high professional standards. Serving all of the Northern Hampshire area, plus the Reading, Farnham, Guildford and Epsom areas, they provide weekly, fortnightly or*

continued

*monthly visits to keep your garden looking beautiful.*One-off services such as clearing overgrown gardens, pre-house sale tidy - ups, and providing a garden -sitting service, for when you are away, are also popular offerings.*Snowdrop offer free written estimates.*Snowdrop has 2 million pound liability insurance and are also members of the Institute of Gardening, the Institute of Garden Design and The Guild of Master Craftsmen.*A Fast, Friendly And Reliable Service is guaranteed! With Snowdrop Gardening & Design Services - *'You Take Pleasure - We Take Pride'***

Snowflake Animal Bedding Ltd, Riverside Industrial Estate, Marsh Lane, Boston, Lincolnshire, PE21 7ST Tel: (0870) 3003355 Fax: (01205) 310298 E-mail: snowflakesales@plevin.co.uk *Wood shavings & cat litter suppliers* Also at: Bristol, Oakhampton, Rotherham, Shipley & Widnes

Snowflake Animal Bedding Ltd, Slimbridge Crossroads, Bristol Road, Slimbridge, Gloucester, GL2 7DW Tel: (0870) 3003355 Fax: (01453) 890047 E-mail: snowflakesales@plevin.co.uk *Wood shavings & sawdust contractors*

▶ Snowie Ltd, East Gogar Farm, Blairlogie, Stirling, FK9 5QB Tel: (01259) 723240 Fax: (01259) 211684

▶ Snowie Logistics (Scotland), Grange Lane, Grangemouth, Stirlingshire, FK3 8EG Tel: (01324) 483774

▶ SnowPrince Document Management, 1-3 Lime Hill Road, Tunbridge Wells, Kent, TN1 1LJ Tel: 0870 760 7879 E-mail: info@SnowPrince.co.uk *Document Management consultancy and systems, PDF Reference Manuals, Document Scanning, Electronic Archiving etc.*

Snows Office Supplies, Unit 8 Hounsdown Business Park, Newmans Copse Road, Totton, Southampton, SO40 9LX Tel: (0870) 6092027 Fax: (0870) 6092028 E-mail: sales@snowsoffice.co.uk *Machines, furniture & stationery*

▶ SnowTubes.co.uk, Hill Cottage, Lanfine Estate, Newmilns, Ayrshire, KA16 9JR Tel: 08700 664373

▶ SNS It, 18 Mount Close, Mount Avenue, London, W5 2RQ Tel: (020) 8991 4200 E-mail: info@snsitltd.com *IT Support London provided by SNS IT LTD. Including technical outsourcing and PC support services covering London and the UK, with extensive resources in Microsoft Technologies, Firewalls and email systems*

Snug Company Ltd, Stonegate House, Stoneygate Lane, Gateshead, Tyne & Wear, NE10 0HJ Tel: 0191-495 2322 Fax: 0191-495 2321 E-mail: admin@snug-ltd.com *Quilt, pillow & cushion manufrs*

▶ SnuggleSafe, Unit 10, Thorgate Road, Wick, Littlehampton, West Sussex, BN17 7LU Tel: (01903) 730811 Fax: (01903) 726486 E-mail: info@lenricc21.com *Pet products manufacturers & importers*

▶ Snugglytots, 4 Ffordd Derwen, Margam, Port Talbot, West Glamorgan, SA13 2TX Tel: (07709) 656139 *Fleece and Fur Cosytoes made especially for you. Choose from our large selection of plain and patterned fabrics*

Snyder William Publishing Associates Information Services, 5 Five Mile Drive, Oxford, OX2 8HT Tel: (01865) 311015 Fax: (01865) 513186 E-mail: snyderpub@cs.com *Directory publishers*

▶ So Estates, 20 Russell Road, West Wittering, Chichester, West Sussex, PO20 8EF Tel: (01243) 674444 Fax: (01243) 674444 E-mail: info@soestates.co.uk *we sell property & holiday homes in west sussex*

▶ So Raise Your Glasses, 9 The Courtyard, St. James Street, Taunton, Somerset, TA1 1JR Tel: (01823) 335144 *Calibration products retailers*

Soabar Marking Systems, 7 Ashville Way, Whetstone, Leicester, LE8 6NU Tel: 0116-284 7000 Fax: 0116-284 7001 E-mail: sales@soabar.co.uk *Label manufrs*

Soames Chris Ltd, Randall House, New Road, Whaley Bridge, High Peak, Derbyshire, SK23 7JG Tel: (01663) 733599 Fax: (01663) 735480 E-mail: mail@chrissoames.co.uk *Jeans packaging.*

Soanes Signs, Unit 15 Woodland Park Industrial Estate, Shortthorn Road, Stratton Strawless, Norwich, NR10 5NU Tel: (01603) 754544 Fax: (01603) 754127 *Sign manufrs*

▶ Soapbox Creative Marketing Ltd, 6 Billing Road, Northampton, NN1 5AN Tel: (01604) 638989 Fax: (01604) 638553 E-mail: jo@soapbox-creative.com *Creative & strategic marketing*

▶ The Soap-Hut, Wayside, The Slough, Redditch, Worcestershire, B97 5JT Tel: 07835 555775 E-mail: thesoaphut@hotmail.com *Wholesalers of handmade, fun, unique soaps and toiltries. Starter Retail stands, soap logs/bars, hair care, bath bombs, lip balm and much more. Ideal for establishments. We are against animal testing.*

Soapworks Ltd, Coltness Street, Glasgow, G33 4JD Tel: 0141-774 2282 Fax: 0141-774 9273 *Soap manufrs*

▶ Soar Valley Steel Boats, Brimington Road, Chesterfield, Derbyshire, S41 7JG Tel: (01246) 274125 Fax: (01246) 274125 *Boat builders*

Social Climbers Ltd, Parsonage Farm, Childrey, Wantage, Oxfordshire, OX12 9PH Tel: (01235) 751717 Fax: (01235) 751999 *Children's climbing frames*

▶ societás limited, Suite 2, 27 James Street, Mayfair, London, W1U 1DX Tel: 0870 910 4904 Fax: 0870 910 4904 E-mail: info@societas.ltd.uk *Societás > Specialists in Creative Business Strategy, Marketing, Public Relations, Sponsorship, Branding, Design, Media and Event Production. Represent leading figures from the creative fields. Represented in Berlin, Doha, Abu Dhabi, LA and New York.*

Society Of British Gas Industries, 36 Holly Walk, Leamington Spa, Warwickshire, CV32 4LY Tel: (01926) 334357 Fax: (01926) 450459 E-mail: sales@sbgi.org.uk *Gas trade association*

Society Of Consulting Marine Engineers, 202 Lambeth Road, London, SE1 7JW Tel: (020) 7261 0869 Fax: (020) 7261 0871 E-mail: scc@scmshq.org *Professional society*

Society Of Maritime Industries, Great Guildford Business Square, 30 Great Guildford Street, London, SE1 0HS Tel: (020) 7928 9199 Fax: (020) 7928 6599 E-mail: sales@maritimeindustries.org *Trade association*

Society Of Motor Manufacturing & Traders Ltd, Forbes House, Halkin Street, London, SW1X 7DS Tel: (020) 7235 7000 Fax: (020) 7235 7112 E-mail: cford@smmt.co.uk *Trade association*

Society Of Operations Engineers, 22 Greencoat Place, London, SW1P 1PR Tel: (020) 7630 1111 Fax: (020) 7630 6677 E-mail: soe@soe.org.uk *Professional institution*

Socket & Allied Screws Ltd, 121 Camden Street, Birmingham, B1 3DJ Tel: 0121-200 2880 Fax: 0121-236 8991 E-mail: sales@socket-allied.com *Special socket screw manufrs*

Soco System UK Ltd, Unit 18 Palmerston Street, Joiners Square Industrial Estate, Stoke-on-Trent, ST1 3EU Tel: (01782) 274100 Fax: (01782) 272696 E-mail: paul.bangs@socosystem.co.uk *Manufacturers s, carton sealers, pallet loaders*

Socomec Ltd, Knowl Piece, Wilbury Way, Hitchin, Hertfordshire, SG4 0TY Tel: (01462) 440033 Fax: (01462) 431143 E-mail: sales@socomec.com *Industrial switching & protection systems*

Socomec Sicon Ltd, 401-402 Love Lane, Cirencester, Gloucestershire, GL7 1YG Tel: (01285) 644444 Fax: (01285) 644414 E-mail: enquires@socomec.com *Sales of UPS*

Soda Creative Ltd, 17-25 Cremer Street, London, E2 8HD Tel: (020) 7739 6217 Fax: (020) 7739 8650 E-mail: info@soda.co.uk *Computer systems & software developers*

Soderhamn Errikson, Unit 17 Vauxhall Industrial Estate, Greg Street, Reddish, Stockport, Cheshire, SK5 7BR Tel: 0161-429 9437 Fax: 0161-477 0641 E-mail: info@se-saws.co.uk *Saw mill equipment suppliers*

Sodexho Ltd, Buchanan Tower Buchanan Business Park, Cumbernauld Road, Stepps, Glasgow, G33 6HZ Tel: 0141-779 8200 Fax: 0141-779 8201 *Catering & support services* Also at: Aberdeen

▶ Soewitos Hair And Beauty Salon, Brunel Centre, Bletchley, Milton Keynes, MK2 2ES Tel: 01908 642985

Sofa Bed Factory Shop, Oxford House, Lower Oxford Street, Hartlepool, Cleveland, TS25 1PT Tel: (01429) 866607 Fax: (01429) 297001 E-mail: sales@sofabedfactoryshop.co.uk *Sofa beds & bedroom furniture manufrs*

Sofa Design, 1a Queen Street, Stourbridge, West Midlands, DY8 1TP Tel: (01384) 440546 Fax: (01384) 440546 E-mail: enquiries@sofadesign.co.uk *Sofa retailers & manufrs*

▶ Sofa Plan, 39 Phoenix Road, Washington, Tyne & Wear, NE38 0AD Tel: 0191-417 3511 Fax: 0191-417 5477

Sofa Workshop Ltd, Llantrisant Business Park, Llantrisant, Pontyclun, Mid Glamorgan, CF72 8LF Tel: (01798) 345345 Fax: (01443) 237752 E-mail: sales@sofaworkshop.co.uk *Mail order sofa distributors*

Sofa Workshop Ltd, 10 Coppergate, York, YO1 9NR Tel: (01904) 612189 Fax: (01904) 627142 E-mail: enquiries@sofaworkshopdirect.co.uk *Retail upholsterer*

Soft Adventure Play, 19 Jack Lane, Davenham, Northwich, Cheshire, CW9 8LA Tel: (01606) 44440 Fax: (01606) 330388 *Protective play equipment providers*

Soft Brands ' Evolution, Glenfield Park 2, Blakewater Road, Blackburn, BB1 5QH Tel: (01254) 724400 Fax: (01254) 724404 E-mail: joanne.slater@softbrands.com *Software house*

Soft Control Ltd, Market Chambers, Market Place, Shifnal, Shropshire, TF11 9AZ Tel: (01952) 462976 Fax: (01952) 462797 E-mail: technical@softcontrol.co.uk *Process controller, control systems engineers, installers or services*

Soft Machine Ltd, Tilshead Ho, High St, Tilshead, Salisbury, SP3 4RX Tel: (01980) 621300 Fax: (01980) 621340 E-mail: hrh@softmachine.co.uk *Computer software house*

Soft Option Technology, 2 The Old School, High Street, Wilburton, Ely, Cambridgeshire, CB6 3RB Tel: (01353) 741641 Fax: (01353) 741341 E-mail: info@softoption.com *Software computers*

Soft Options Custom Software, Wood Lodge, Calmore, Southampton, SO40 2UP Tel: (023) 8087 1580 Fax: (023) 8087 1582 *Computer software design & consultancy services*

▶ Soft Point Multi Media, Green Dragon House, 64-70 High Street, Croydon, CR0 9XN Tel: (020) 8681 7100 Fax: (020) 8681 8080 *Computer software consultants sales promotions & marketing*

Soft Priced Hardware, 209-215 Padiham Road, Burnley, Lancashire, BB12 0HB Tel: (01282) 431113 Fax: (01282) 425550 E-mail: sphard@tiscali.co.uk *Computer suppliers*

Soft Sell Computers, 74 Darwen St, Blackburn, BB2 2BL Tel: (01254) 693593 Fax: (01254) 668975 E-mail: info@soft-sell.co.uk *Computer solutions providers*

Soft Sheen Carson Europe, 11a Hagley Road, Stourbridge, West Midlands, DY8 1QH Tel: (01384) 372466 Fax: (01384) 440513 *Hair care products distributors*

Soft Solutions International Ltd, 123 Mudford Road, Yeovil, Somerset, BA21 4AQ Tel: (01935) 474469 Fax: (01935) 426228 E-mail: enquiries@ssi-ltd.com *Internet consultancy & web application design*

▶ Soft Touch Clothing Ltd, Unit 4, Lancaster Street, Leicester, LE5 4GA Tel: 0116-276 0548 Fax: 0116-276 9038

Soft Waterworks Co. Ltd, Chorlton House, 149 Bridgnorth Road, Stourton, Stourbridge, West Midlands, DY7 6RY Tel: (01384) 872548 Fax: (01384) 878105 E-mail: ipayton@softwaterworks.fsbusiness.co.uk *Water treatment service providers*

SoftBrands Ltd, SoftBrands House, 11 Worton Drive, Reading, RG2 0LX Tel: 0118-975 4000 Fax: 0118-975 4011 E-mail: info.emea@softbrands.com *Computer software distributors*

Softcase Consulting, 32 Canford Cliffs Road, Poole, Dorset, BH13 7AA Tel: (01202) 749643 Fax: (01202) 749643 E-mail: howard@softcase.co.uk *Software consultants*

▶ Softcaw Computer Systems, 7 Wetherby Close, Chippenham, Wiltshire, SN14 0SU Tel: (01249) 444496 Fax: (07043) 326267 E-mail: enquiries@softcaw.co.uk *Computer software developers*

Softech Global, Softech House, London Road, Albourne, Hassocks, West Sussex, BN6 9BN Tel: (01273) 833844 Fax: (01273) 833044 E-mail: info@softechglobal.com *Computer software, system development & training services*

▶ Softedge Technology, Unit 6, Mavros House, 95 Vale Road, London, N4 1TG Tel: (020) 8809 1666 Fax: (020) 8809 5984

Softek Computer Security, La Rue Du Pont Marquet, St. Brelade, Jersey, JE3 8DS Tel: (01534) 811182 Fax: (01534) 811183 E-mail: sales@softek.co.uk *Distributing & supporting carefully selected security*

Softel Ltd, 7 Horseshoe Park, Pangbourne, Reading, RG8 7JW Tel: 0118-984 2151 Fax: 0118-984 3939 E-mail: sales@softel.co.uk *Broadcasting equipment manufrs*

Soft-Ex UK Ltd, Unit 3b Juno House, Calleva Park, Aldermaston, Reading, RG7 8RA Tel: 0118-981 5555 Fax: 0118-981 5577 E-mail: sales@soft-ex.net *Telecommunications software*

Softflow Water Treatment Equipment, Wantz Stores, Main Road, Woodham Ferrers, Chelmsford, CM3 8RP Tel: (01245) 322816 Fax: (01245) 320008 E-mail: info@softflowsofteners.co.uk *Water softening services*

Softgen Ltd, 92 Harrowdene Road, Wembley, Middlesex, HA0 2JF Tel: (020) 8900 0333 Fax: (020) 8900 9646 E-mail: admin@softegenltd.co.uk *Computers consultants systems developers*

Softlink Solutions Ltd, 417 Baddow Road, Chelmsford, CM2 7QL Tel: (01245) 475669 Fax: (01245) 473993 E-mail: info@softlinksolutions.co.uk *Computer network designers*

Softlogic Solutions Ltd, 1 Bath Road, Stonehouse, Gloucestershire, GL10 2JD Tel: (01453) 827366 *Computer software developers*

Softrilogy Ltd, 16 Albert Road, London, NW4 2SG Tel: (020) 8202 8431 Fax: (020) 8202 8431 E-mail: info@softrilogy.com *Computer software development*

Softronic Systems Ltd, Unit 2 & 3 Enterprise Estate, Station Road West, Ash Vale, Aldershot, Hampshire, GU12 5QJ Tel: (01252) 513884 *Electronic equipment consultants & designers*

Softsell Computers Ltd, 199 High Street, Blackwood, Gwent, NP12 1AA Tel: (01495) 221166 Fax: (01495) 221177 *Computer hardware retailers*

Softsmart Ltd, Minster House, York Road, Eastbourne, East Sussex, BN21 4ST Tel: (01323) 419682 Fax: (01323) 419558 E-mail: sales@softsmart.co.uk *Computer software training for small businesses*

Softsol Ltd, 27 Buckingham Road, Shoreham-by-Sea, West Sussex, BN43 5UA Tel: (01273) 440100 Fax: (01273) 454709 E-mail: softsol@softsol.ltd.uk *Software engineers*

▶ Software Central Ltd, 28 Vista Drive, Ilford, Essex, IG4 5JF Tel: (020) 8551 6262 *Computer software retailers*

▶ Software Consulting Ltd, 10 Lime Kiln Road, Mannings Heath, Horsham, West Sussex, RH13 6JH Tel: (01403) 263269 E-mail: sales@scss.co.uk *Computer consultancy providing software development, web site design, IT support, IT systems, computer maintenance and training in Sussex and Surrey.*

Software Futures Ltd, 2 Waterloo Way, Cheltenham Road, Bredon, Tewkesbury, Gloucestershire, GL20 7NA Tel: (01684) 772691 Fax: (01684) 772639 E-mail: information@softwarefutures.ltd.uk *IT consultants*

Software Generation Training, 339 Plungington Road, Fulwood, Preston, PR2 3PS Tel: (01772) 712499 Fax: (01772) 787943 E-mail: info@sgtoday.co.uk *End user & technical computer training*

Software Index Ltd, Matrix House, Gelders Hall Road, Shepshed, Loughborough, Leicestershire, LE12 9NH Tel: (01509) 505333 Fax: (01509) 505444 *Business solutions software development**

Software Integrators Ltd, New London Bridge House, 25 London Bridge Street, London, SE1 9SG Tel: (020) 7378 9309 Fax: (020) 7378 9310 E-mail: admin@software-integrators.co.uk *Software programming*

Software International Training Ltd, 8 Thorpe Road, Norwich, NR1 1RY Tel: (01603) 667308 Fax: (01603) 761281 E-mail: training@softwareinternational.co.uk *Providers of IT training courses*

▶ The Software Practice, Bullbeck Mill, Mill Lane, Barrington, Cambridge, CB2 5QY Tel: (01223) 872874 Fax: (01223) 872876 E-mail: enquiries@softwarepractice.co.uk *IT training services provider & the regions only gold member of the institute of IT training, we provide a wide range of services on microsoft, macromedia, adobe & other vendors software for end-users.*

Software Production Associates Ltd, PO Box 59, Tewkesbury, Gloucestershire, GL20 6AB Tel: (01684) 833700 Fax: (0845) 2301306 E-mail: sales@spasoft.co.uk *Educational software*

▶ Software Skills Centre, Unit 5, Zurich House, 299 High Street, Sutton, Surrey, SM1 1LG Tel: (020) 8770 9817 Fax: (020) 8652 7374 E-mail: judy@softwareskills.info *Software training services*

Software Spectrum Ltd, Mallard House, Peregrine Business Park, Gomm Road, High Wycombe, Buckinghamshire, HP13 7DL Tel: (0870) 5771100 Fax: (0870) 5771104 *Computer consultants*

Software & Training Ltd, 71 Crombey Street, Swindon, SN1 5QW Tel: (01793) 485761 Fax: (01793) 421725 E-mail: arun.bedi9@ntlworld.com *Computer software developers*

▶ Softwide, Unit 134 The Harlequin, Watford, WD17 2UB Tel: (01923) 630259 Fax: (01923) 630261 *Computer software manufrs*

▶ Softworks Business Systems Solutions Ltd, 47 St Marys Court, Huntly Street, Aberdeen, AB10 1TH Tel: (01224) 212090

Sogefi Filtration Ltd, Llantrisant Industrial Estate, Llantrisant, Pontyclun, Mid Glamorgan, CF72 8YU Tel: (01443) 223000 Fax: (01443) 225459 E-mail: stuart.hobbs@sogefifiltration.com Principal Export Areas: Worldwide *SOGEFI is an Italian Group, leader in the auto parts components, specialized and first on the worldwide markets in two product lines: the systems of engine and cabin filtration and the suspensions components. * SOGEFI is a multinational company, partner of the most important car manufacturers in the world. *The Company has a global presence: 4 continents and 14 countries, with 50 offices of which 41 plants. *Leader in its core business in Europe and South America, SOGEFI is active on the markets of the first equipment and the original and independent replacement.*

Sogi Clothing Co, 24 Heathfield Road, Handsworth, Birmingham, B19 1HB Tel: 0121-515 1225 Fax: 0121-515 1225 *Clothing manufrs*

Sohal Trading UK Co., 132 Tew Park Road, Birmingham, B21 0TR Tel: 0121-523 0622 Fax: 0121-523 0622 *Clothing manufrs*

Soham Joinery, 119 Mereside, Soham, Ely, Cambridgeshire, CB7 5EG Tel: (01353) 720396 Fax: (01353) 624941 *Joinery manufrs*

Soham Pest Control, Fordham Road, Soham, Ely, Cambridgeshire, CB7 5AJ Tel: (01353) 720877 *Pest control services*

Soham Security Products Ltd, 22 Regal Drive, Soham, Ely, Cambridgeshire, CB7 5BE Tel: (01353) 722930 Fax: (01353) 624429 E-mail: sales@sohamsecurity.co.uk *Fire exit & high security door manufrs*

▶ Soho Computer Services, 164 Dulverton Avenue, Coventry, CV5 8HB Tel: (024) 7626 9533 E-mail: sales@soho-computer-services.co.uk *Computer services*

Soho Sheet Metal Ltd, Furlong Lane, Stoke-on-Trent, ST6 3LE Tel: (01782) 817930 Fax: (01782) 575656 *Dust extraction plant & equipment manufrs*

▶ Soil, The Nano Tech Centre Herschal Building, Kings Road, Newcastle upon Tyne, NE1 7RU Tel: 0191-243 0686 Fax: 0191-222 3528 E-mail: rd@soilenvironmentservices.co.uk *Soil survey, land classification, contaminated land risk assessment, soil erosion survey, soil research, recycling waste to land, specialist soil investigations*

▶ Soil Essentials Ltd, Nether Careston Farm, Brechin, Angus, DD9 6SB Tel: (01241) 890204 E-mail: robert@soilessentials.com

Soil Fertility Dunns Ltd, North Harbour Street, Ayr, KA8 8AH Tel: (01292) 611622 Fax: (01292) 619990 *Fertiliser manufrs*

Soil Mechanics, Glossop House, Hogwood Lane, Finchampstead, Wokingham, Berkshire, RG40 4QW Tel: 0118-932 8888 Fax: 0118-932 8383 E-mail: sm@wokingham.mesgl.co.uk *Geotechnical consultants* Also at: Bristol, Bromsgrove & Doncaster

▶ Soil Models Ltd, 19 Llwyncelyn Close Capel, Hendre Ammanford, Capel Hendre, Ammanford, Dyfed, SA18 3SS Tel: (01279) 419934 E-mail: Richard.Dean@soilmodels.co.uk *Civil engineering consultancy, especially**Geotechnical /Foundations*Offshore / Coastal*

Sojitz P.L.C., Old Change House, 128 Queen Victoria Street, London, EC4V 4HR Tel: (020) 7886 7000 Fax: (020) 7634 0490 *Import & export merchants & agents*

Sol Construction Ltd, Vale Road, Colwick, Nottingham, NG4 2EG Tel: 0115-961 3100 Fax: 0115-961 3400

Sol Systems, Unit 4 Mallorie House, Beaumont Road, Banbury, Oxfordshire, OX16 1RH Tel: (01295) 255536 Fax: (01295) 276492 E-mail: bworsley@btinternet.com *Polycarbonate sheet distribs*

Sola Wet Suits & Leisure Wear Ltd, Saltash Industrial Estate, Saltash, Cornwall, PL12 6LF Tel: (01752) 854418 Fax: (01752) 854401 E-mail: info@sola.co.uk *Wet-suits distributors*

▶ Sol-Ace Window Tinting Ltd, Slough Road, Iver, Buckinghamshire, SL0 0DR Tel: (01753) 783715 E-mail: sales@sol-ace.co.uk *Supply & fitting of security & tinted window films to cars & windows*

▶ Solaglas Ltd, 6 James Street, Righead Industrial Estate, Bellshill, Lanarkshire, ML4 3LU Tel: (01698) 300300 Fax: (01698) 300350

Solaglas Ltd, Unit 1 Binley Way, Binley, Coventry, CV3 2ZG Tel: (024) 7654 7400 Fax: 024 7654 7793 E-mail: solaglas.gpd@saint-gobain-glass.com *glass processing and distribution*

Solaglas Ltd, Guild House, Cradley Road, Dudley, West Midlands, DY2 9TH Tel: (01384) 411511 Fax: (01384) 411234 E-mail: midlandsales@solaglass.co.uk *Glass merchants* Also at: Birmingham

Solaglas Ltd, Treefield Industrial Estate, Gelderd Road, Morley, Leeds, LS27 7JU Tel: 0113-253 8030 Fax: 0113-253 7659 E-mail: solaglas.gpd@saint-gobain-glass.com *glass processing and distribution*

Solaglas Ltd, Trinity Trading Estate, Mill Way, Sittingbourne, Kent, ME10 2PD Tel: (01795) 421534 Fax: (01795) 473651 *Security & safety glass manufrs*

Solaglas Ltd, Horton Road, West Drayton, Middlesex, UB7 8JL Tel: (01895) 424900 Fax: (01895) 421937 E-mail: solaglas.gpd@saint-gobain-glass.com *glass processing and distribution*

Solair Ltd, Pennington Close, West Bromwich, West Midlands, B70 8BG Tel: 0121-525 2722 Fax: 0121-525 6786 E-mail: sales@solair.co.uk *Windows & doors manufrs*

Solaire Performance Films, 7 Lincoln Road, Navenby, Lincoln, LN5 0LA Tel: (01522) 811175 Fax: (01522) 811175 *Installation of glass film*

▶ Solak Technology Solutions, 25 Merryfields, Strood, Rochester, Kent, ME2 3ND Tel: (01634) 290983 Fax: (01634) 290983

Solalighting Ltd, 17 High Street, Olney, Buckinghamshire, MK46 4EB Tel: (0845) 4580101 Fax: (01234) 241766 *Tubular skylight suppliers*

▶ Solar Century, 91-94 Lower Marsh, London, SE1 7AB Tel: (020) 7803 0100 Fax: (08707) 358101 E-mail: info@solarcentury.co.uk *Solar photovoltaic company manufrs*

Solar Energy Alliance, 8 Battery Green Road, Lowestoft, Suffolk, NR32 1DE Tel: (01502) 515532 Fax: (01502) 589159 E-mail: info@solarenergyalliance.com *Renewable energy products retailers & installers*

Solar Graphics, 8 Finch Drive, Braintree, Essex, CM7 2SF Tel: (01376) 552209 Fax: (01376) 320077 E-mail: sales@solargraphics.net *Sign manufrs*

Solar Illuminations, P.O. Box 19, Rye, East Sussex, TN31 6WZ Tel: (020) 8144 0847 E-mail: sales@solarilluminations.co.uk *Solar Illuminations offers a large range of high quality, unique and exclusive solar lights, solar garden lights and outdoor lighting products. UK & Ireland home delivery. Secure on-line ordering.*

Solar Marine Services, 4 Barratt Industrial Park, Gillender Street, London, E3 3JX Tel: (020) 7987 2244 Fax: (020) 7987 0242 *Shipping & forwarding agents*

Solar Microfilm Equipment Ltd, 1 Laser Quay, Culpeper Close, Medway City Estate, Rochester, Kent, ME2 4HU Tel: (01634) 290099 Fax: (01634) 290110 E-mail: info@solar-imaging.com *Microfilm & digital equipment manufrs*

Solar Petroleum Ltd, Ditton Road, Widnes, Cheshire, WA8 0NN Tel: 0151-424 2488 Fax: 0151-495 1007 E-mail: sales@solar-lubricants.com *Lubricant manufrs*

Solar Signs, Normanby Road, Nettleton, Market Rasen, Lincolnshire, LN7 6TB Tel: (01472) 851914 Fax: (01472) 851037 E-mail: enquires@solarsigns.co.uk *Sign manufrs*

▶ Solar Signs UK Ltd, Doodys Yard, Park Road, Haltwhistle, Northumberland, NE49 9LD Tel: (07860) 606549 Fax: (01434) 322104 E-mail: janetdoody@solarsignsuk.com *Traffic management & events services*

Solar Soft PMS Ltd, Hampshire Int Business Park, Crockford Lane, Chineham, Basingstoke, Hampshire, RG24 8WH Tel: (01256) 685200 Fax: (01256) 685201 E-mail: sales@ssi-world.com Principal Export Areas: Central/East Europe & West Europe *Computer software suppliers*

Solar Turbines Europe Sa, Suite H Centennial Court, Easthampstead Road, Bracknell, Berkshire, RG12 1YQ Tel: (01344) 782920 Fax: (01344) 782930 *Gas turbine manufacturers.*

▶ Solar Watts Ltd, Holly Road, Horsham, West Sussex, RH12 4PA Tel: (0796) 6160126 *We sell ranges of solar panels, solar controllers and inverters at great value for money.*

Solardome Industries, Unit 3 Hammerley Enterprise Park, Burnetts Lane, Horton Heath, Eastleigh, Hampshire, SO50 7DJ Tel: (023) 8069 7128 Fax: (023) 8069 7129 E-mail: sales@solardome.co.uk *Dome designers & greenhouse manufrs*

Solaris Sunblinds Ltd, 48 Victoria Road, Woolston, Southampton, SO19 9DX Tel: (023) 8043 1739 Fax: (023) 8043 7531 E-mail: info@solarissunblinds.co.uk *Venetian & sun blind manufrs*

Solarsoft Ltd, Unit 3, Maridian Office Park, Osbourne Way, Hook, Hampshire, RG27 9HY Tel: (01256) 769769 Fax: (0870) 8728210 *Software publisher specialising security*

▶ Solartek Films, Unit 10, High Street, Ware, Hertfordshire, SG12 9BA Tel: (01920) 466999 Fax: (01920) 464488 E-mail: enquiries@solartekfilms.co.uk *Solar, safety, bomb blast, security & privacy glass film manufrs*

▶ Solartron Metrology Ltd, 1 Steyning Way, Bognor Regis, West Sussex, PO22 9ST Tel: (01243) 833300 Fax: (01243) 861244 *Solartron Metrology is a world leader in precision dimensional and position measurement transducers & instrumentation. Solartron Analogue & Digital Gauge Probes are renowned for their accuracy and long life in shop floor applications world-wide. Linear Encoders offer accuracies to 0.4 μm with measuring ranges to 100 mm. Our extensive range of displacement transducers are used in numerous applications where position or size need to be determined. Networked, digital versions of these products are available to simplify connection, using our Orbit Network.*

▶ Solartron Mobrey Ltd, 158 Edinburgh Avenue, Slough, SL1 4UE Tel: (01753) 756600 Fax: (01753) 823589 Principal Export Areas: Africa *Manufacturers of level control equipment, flow & pressure*

Solcom Ltd, 79 George Street, Ryde, Isle Of Wight, PO33 2JF Tel: (01983) 817000 Fax: (01983) 817001 E-mail: info@solcom.com *Computer software suppliers*

Soldier Of Fortune Adventure, 8-10 Lower Bridge Street, Chester, CH1 1RS Tel: (01244) 328205 Fax: (01244) 328205 *Military equipment suppliers*

▶ Sole Air, 25 Lacewing Close, Pinewood, Ipswich, IP8 3UD Tel: (01473) 602888

Sole Bay Pine Co., Red House Farm, Hinton, Saxmundham, Suffolk, IP17 3RF Tel: (01502) 478077 Fax: (01502) 478006 *Pine furniture distributors*

Solectron Systems UK, Arisdale Avenue, South Ockendon, Essex, RM15 5TT Tel: (01708) 852223 Fax: (01708) 850217 *Telecoms manufrs*

Solent, The Sanderson Centre, Lees Lane, Gosport, Hampshire, PO12 3UL Tel: (023) 9251 1924 Fax: (023) 9251 1924 E-mail: peter@solentpowdercoatings.co.uk *Powder coating services*

Solent, The Sanderson Centre, Lees Lane, Gosport, Hampshire, PO12 3UL Tel: (023) 9251 1924 Fax: (023) 9251 1924 E-mail: sales@solentcomputers.com *Supplying Blank Dvds, Cds, DVD-r +R , CD-R, Ink & Ink Cartridges Throughout Hampshire & The South Coast Visiting Gosport, Fareham, Eastleigh, Havant & Worthing Markets weekly where you can order online or simply come to the Market saving delivery Charges making it the cheapest way to order online.*

Solent Audio Visual, Meadowsweet Cottage, Hambledon Road, Denmead, Waterlooville, Hampshire, PO7 6QA Tel: (023) 9223 0999 Fax: (023) 9223 0555 E-mail: colin@solentav.demon.co.uk *Audio visual ccvt equipment distribs*

Solent Body Builders Ltd, 4 Cockerell Close, Fareham, Hampshire, PO15 5SR Tel: (01489) 575611 Fax: (01489) 578780 E-mail: kevin@solentbodybuilders.co.uk *Commercial vehicle bodybuilders & repairers*

Solent Business Supplies, 2 Marples Way, Havant, Hampshire, PO9 1UH Tel: (023) 9248 9933 Fax: (023) 9248 9934 E-mail: sales@solentbs.co.uk *Solent Business Supplies are a specialist office furniture supplier. We hold large stocks of desking, seating, storage and tables available for 24-48 hour delivery and an extensive catalogue of ranges available on a 10 day delivery. We supply many different markets including education, local government and medical. We offer a vast selection of furniture styles including bespoke and made-to-measure reception and boardroom furniture.*We also offer an office refurbishment, planning and fitout service.*Solent Business Supplies is a Havant-based company established in 1975. We cover Hampshire, West Sussex, Surrey, Berkshire, Wiltshire and Dorset including Portsmouth, Southampton, Chichester, Guildford, Basingstoke and Reading. We also offer national coverage.*Solent Business Supplies are ISO9001 and ISO14001 accredited and are approved suppliers to Hampshire County Council.*Please call today to discuss your particular requirements, or visit our showrooms.*

Solent Computer Services Ltd, 70 Church Lane, Fawley, Southampton, SO45 1DH Tel: (07838) 125609 *Computer services*

Solent Electrical Ltd, Shepherds Road, Bartley, Southampton, SO40 2LH Tel: (023) 8081 4151 Fax: (023) 8081 3918 *Electrical contractors*

Solent Environmental Services Asbestos Ltd, 151-153 Long Lane, Holbury, Southampton, SO45 2NZ Tel: (023) 8089 9932 Fax: (023) 8089 9934 *Asbestos removal services*

Solent Fluid Power, 9 Enterprise Industrial Estate, Enterprise Road, Waterlooville, Hampshire, PO8 0BB Tel: (023) 9259 7437 Fax: (023) 9259 9899 E-mail: sales@solentfluidpower.co.uk *Hydraulic & pneumatic engineers*

Solent Forklift Trucks Ltd, Paultons Park, Ower, Romsey, Hampshire, SO51 6AL Tel: (023) 8081 4545 Fax: (023) 8081 3935 E-mail: solents@forkway.co.uk *Fork lift truck hire, repairs & sales specialists*

Solent Glass & Glazing Ltd, 1 Hackett Way, Fareham, Hampshire, PO14 1TH Tel: (01329) 828210 Fax: (01329) 828838 *UPVC windows & doors manufrs*

Solent Groundworks Ltd, 32 Dean Road, Southampton, SO18 6AP Tel: (023) 8044 8446 Fax: (023) 8044 3226 E-mail: solentgroundworks@btconnect.com *Groundwork, foundations & drainage services*

Solent Manufacturing Ltd, Unit 4-5 Pipers Wood Industrial Park, Waterberry Drive, Waterlooville, Hampshire, PO7 7XU Tel: (023) 9223 2348 Fax: (023) 9223 2358 E-mail: pam.a@solentmanufacturing.co.uk *Specialists in steel fabrication & welding*

Solent Marine Chandlery Ltd, Mumby Road, Gosport, Hampshire, PO12 1AQ Tel: (023) 9258 4622 Fax: (023) 9258 2325 E-mail: info@solentmarine.co.uk *Yacht chandlers*

Solent Mould Tools Ltd, 1 Relay Road, Waterlooville, Hampshire, PO7 7XA Tel: (023) 9223 9950 Fax: (023) 9223 9951 E-mail: solentmd@tcp.co.uk *Toolmaking services*

Solent Plastics, Manor House Avenue, Southampton, SO15 0LF Tel: (023) 8057 2500 Fax: (023) 8057 7775 E-mail: sales@solentplastics.co.uk *Storage equipment distrubuters.*

▶ Solent Powder Finishers Ltd, 3 Brookwood Industrial Estate, Brookwood Avenue, Eastleigh, Hampshire, SO50 9EY Tel: (023) 8064 2632 Fax: (023) 8064 2631 E-mail: enquiries@s-p-f.co.uk *Powder coating services*

Solent Print Engineering Ltd, 1 Pytchley Close, Fareham, Hampshire, PO14 3SF Tel: (07917) 784595 E-mail: print.eng@ntlworld.com *Print Engineering ideally situated for quick response for customers in Portsmouth, Southampton and surrounding areas.*Specialising in the latest Heidelberg sheet fed presses.*Preventitive maintenance programs,and a quick breakdown response to keep your presses printing.*

▶ Solent Printer Services, 12b Walworth Enterprise Centre, West Way, Andover, Hampshire, SP10 5AP Tel: (0870) 7667511 E-mail: sales@solent-printer-services.co.uk *Servicing & repairs to hp laser jet printers & design jet plotters*

Solent Rigging Services Ltd, 21 Shamrock Quay, William Street, Southampton, SO14 5QL Tel: (023) 8055 0444 Fax: (023) 8023 0608 *Yacht & commercial riggers*

Solent Scientific Ltd, 14 Matrix Park, Talbot Road, Segensworth, Fareham, Hampshire, PO15 5AP Tel: (0870) 7747140 Fax: (0870) 7747150 E-mail: sales@solentsci.com *Scientific equipment suppliers*

Solent Sign Ltd, 174 The Dale, Waterlooville, Hampshire, PO7 5JD Tel: (023) 9264 5796 Fax: (023) 9264 5796 E-mail: sales@solent-signs.co.uk *Sign manufrs*

Solent Time Recorders, 20 St Johns Road, Locks Heath, Southampton, SO31 6NF Tel: (01489) 572717 Fax: (01489) 572717 *Sales & service of time recording equipment*

Solent Tools Ltd, Unit 009, Solent Business Centre, 343 Millbrook Road West, Southampton, SO15 0HW Tel: (023) 8057 8057 Fax: (023) 8057 4470E-mail: martinnoland@btconnect.com *Power tools & spares specialists. Black and Decker, Flymo, Qualcast, Performance Power, Silverline, Dewalt, Mountfield, Hayter, Bosch.Mower bladesStrimmer sparesSaw bladesdrive beltsFixingsBolts Nuts Washers*

Solent tools, UNIT 009 SOLENT BUSINESS CENTRE, MILLBROOK ROAD WEST, SOUTHAMPTON, SO15 0HW Tel: 023 80578057 Fax: 023 80574470 E-mail: SALES@SOLENTTOOLS.CO.UK *Black and Decker, Dewalt, Elu, Makita, Bosch, Metabo, Hitachi, Qualcast, Flymo power tool sales service & spares, mail order next day.Performance Power spares Carbon BrushesDrive BeltsGarben blow vac bags mower blades saw blades strimmer spares.*

▶ Solent & Wight Line Cruises, Thetis Wharf, Medina Road, Cowes, Isle of Wight, PO31 7BP Tel: (01983) 289966

Solentec Ltd, 82a Jubilee Road, Waterlooville, Hampshire, PO7 7RE Tel: (023) 9226 1651 Fax: (023) 9226 9487 E-mail: sales@solentec.co.uk *Solenoid manufrs*

▶ Solex Manufacturing, Unit 8, Tower Road, Gluther Industrial Estate, Washington, Tyne & Wear, NE37 2SH Tel: 0191-419 4499 Fax: 0191-419 4466 E-mail: sales@solexltd.com *Manufacture & install aluminium windows & roller shutters*

Solgar Vitamins & Herbs, Aldbury, Tring, Hertfordshire, HP23 5PT Tel: (01442) 890355 Fax: (01442) 890366 *Vitamins & herbs*

Solid Solutions Management Ltd, Innovation Centre Warwick Technology Park, Gallows Hill, Warwick, CV34 6UW Tel: (01926) 623160 Fax: (01926) 623161 E-mail: sales@solidsolutions.co.uk *Computer aided design services*

Solid Stampings Ltd, Porters Field Road, Cradley Heath, West Midlands, B64 7BL Tel: (01384) 636421 Fax: (01384) 639163 E-mail: info@solidswivel.co.uk Principal Export Areas: Worldwide *Lifting lashing & rigging tackle manufrs*

▶ Solid Timber Products, Heathfield Way, Gladstone Industry, Northampton, NN5 7QP Tel: (0845) 1297171 Fax: (0845) 1249499 E-mail: adam@solidonline.co.uk *Wooden materials & buildings suppliers*

Solidbase (UK) Ltd, Egerton Court, Haig Road, Knutsford, Cheshire, WA16 8FB Tel: (01565) 621150 Fax: (01565) 653950 E-mail: info@solidbase.co.uk *Business solutions provider & CAD re-seller*

Solideal UK Ltd, Vale Business Park, Llandow, Cowbridge, South Glamorgan, CF71 7PF Tel: (01446) 774914 Fax: (01446) 775410 E-mail: sales@solidealuk.com *Industrial tyre, wheel & rubber track*

▶ Solids Control Services Ltd, 4 International Base, Greenwell Road, East Tullos Industrial Estate, Aberdeen, AB12 3AX Tel: (01224) 249220 Fax: (01224) 249221

▶ Solidtech Solutions, Southgate House, Plough Road, Great Bentley, Colchester, CO7 8LG Tel: (01206) 252062 Fax: (0870) 1314474 *IT consultants*

Solihull Blinds Ltd, A 85, Skelcher Road, Shirley, Solihull, West Midlands, B90 2EY Tel: 0121-733 1001 Fax: 0121-733 3062 E-mail: solihullblinds@blueyonder.co.uk *Window blind manufacturers & installers*

Solihull Rail Supplies & Services Ltd, Earlswood Trading Estate, Poolhead Lane, Earlswood, Solihull, West Midlands, B94 5EW Tel: (01564) 700222 Fax: (01564) 702341 E-mail: neil-willets@solrail.fsbusiness.co.uk *Railway material contractors*

Solihull Roofing & Building Co. Ltd, 236 Wharfdale Road, Tyseley, Birmingham, B11 2EG Tel: 0121-707 8600 Fax: 0121-706 4693 E-mail: sales@solihullroofing.co.uk *General roofing & building contractors*

Solihull Signs, 270 Lode Lane, Solihull, West Midlands, B91 2HY Tel: 0121-704 1624 Fax: 0121-704 1624 E-mail: sales@solihullsigns.co.uk *Hand painted signmakers*

Solihull Storage Ltd, Beresford House, Highlands Road, Shirley, Solihull, West Midlands, B90 4ND Tel: 0121-705 2323 Fax: 0121-705 7683 E-mail: sales@storage-removals.co.uk *Self access storage contractors*

▶ Solihull Transport Ltd, 337 Tanworth Lane, Solihull, West Midlands, B90 4DU Tel: 0121-733 8248

Solitaire Communications Ltd, 1 Yardley Business Park, Luckyn Lane, Basildon, Essex, SS14 3GL Tel: (0845) 8800180 Fax: (01268) 243903 *Telecommunications software*

▶ Solitaire Entertainments Ltd, 11 Mitford Close, Reading, RG2 8JQ Tel: 0118-986 4595 Fax: 0118-967 2498 E-mail: info@solitaireentertainments.co.uk

▶ Solitec Engineering, Unit 8 Gilchrist Thomas Industrial Estate, Blaenavon, Pontypool, Gwent, NP4 9RL Tel: (01453) 828727 Fax: (01495) 790666

Solitec Engineering, Unit 8 Gilchrist Thomas Industrial Estate, Blaenavon, Pontypool, Gwent, NP4 9RL Tel: (01453) 828727 Fax: (01495) 790666 E-mail: solitec@aol.com *Materials handling equipment manufrs*

Solitek Ltd, Watermill House, Restmoor Way, Wallington, Surrey, SM6 7AH Tel: (020) 8669 6669 Fax: (020) 8669 6961 E-mail: sales@solitek.co.uk *Telecommunication spares & electronic component distribs*

Solito Graphics, 1137 Yardley Wood Road, Birmingham, B14 4LS Tel: 0121-474 4640 Fax: 0121-474 4640 *Sign makers*

Soliton Associates Ltd, Coventry Point, Market Way, Coventry, CV1 1EA Tel: (024) 7622 0018 *Software support services*

Sollatek (UK) Ltd, Units 10 Poyle, 14 Industrial Estate, Newlands Drive, Poyle, Slough, SL3 0DX Tel: (01753) 688300 Fax: (01753) 685306 E-mail: sales@sollatek.co.uk *Electronics manufrs*

▶ Solley's Farms Ltd, The Dairy, Ripple, Deal, Kent, CT14 8JL Tel: (01304) 374100 Fax: (01304) 379611 E-mail: sc.solley@solleysicecream.co.uk *Ice cream suppliers & manufrs*

Solmedia Laboratory Supplies, 6 The Parade, Colchester Road, Romford, RM3 0AQ Tel: (01708) 343334 Fax: (01708) 372785 E-mail: labsupplies@solmedialtd.com Principal Export Areas: Africa *Laboratory supplies distributor.*

Solo Blinds, 5 Northumbria House, Manor Walks Shopping Centre, Cramlington, Northumberland, NE23 6UR Tel: (01670) 730077 Fax: (01670) 590555 *Blind retailers*

Solo Europe, Tower Close, Huntingdon, Cambridgeshire, PE29 7BZ Tel: (01480) 459413 Fax: (01480) 459274 E-mail: sales@soloeurope.co.uk *Disposable food containers*

▶ Solo Glass Ltd, Horton Road, West Drayton, Middlesex, UB7 8EQ Tel: (01895) 424900 Fax: (01895) 424960

Solo Interiors Ltd, Unit 3b, Brookfield Farm Industrial Estate, Gravel Pit Lane, Cheltenham, Gloucestershire, GL52 3NQ Tel: (01242) 220440 Fax: (01242) 220441 E-mail: info@solointeriors.com *Solo Commercial Interiors has been trading since 1993 from our base in Cheltenham. In that time we have built up a regular and loyal customer base of end users and contractors. *Our core business and experience is in all types of suspended ceilings, the full spectrum of partition systems and all associated decorations and electrical services. We also supply and install 'Altro' hygenic lining systems, carpentry work and minor building works.*

▶ Solo Lighting & Sound Ltd, 7 Derby Road, Stapleford, Nottingham, NG9 7AS Tel: 0115-917 1718 Fax: 0115-913 3577 E-mail: sales@lifeismusic.co.uk *Life is Music is an online music superstore that offers the music enthusiast everything from musical instruments (both electric and acoustic), audio equipment such as amplifiers and lighting products for shows, concerts and other events.*

Solo Manufacturing Ltd, 18 South Nelson Road, South Nelson Industrial Estate, Cramlington, Northumberland, NE23 1WF Tel: (01670) 733788 Fax: (01670) 590555 *Blind manufacturers & installers*

▶ Solo Music Superstore, 137 Derby Road, Stapleford, Nottingham, NG9 7AS Tel: 0115-917 1718 Fax: 0115-913 3577 E-mail: info@solomusicstore.co.uk *Retail sales of guitars, basses, amplifiers, keyboards & pa systems*

Solo Product Finishing, 4 Highbury Road, Brandon, Suffolk, IP27 0ND Tel: (01842) 813355 Fax: (01842) 813377 *Stove enamelling services*

Solo Security Security Alarms, 7 Green Lane, Oaklands, Mossley Hill, Liverpool, L18 6HA Tel: 0151-724 6262 Fax: 0151-724 2333 E-mail: sales@solosecurity.co.uk *Security system installers*

Solo Sprayers Ltd, 4 Brunel Road, Leigh-on-Sea, Essex, SS9 5JN Tel: (01702) 525740 Fax: (01702) 522752 E-mail: solo.sprayers@fsbdial.co.uk *Spray equipment manufrs*

Solo Window Blinds, 120 London Road, Long Sutton, Spalding, Lincolnshire, PE12 9EE Tel: (01406) 364447 Fax: (01406) 364447 *Blind manufrs*

Soloheat Electrical Heating Equipment, Units 1 & 2 Lightpill Trading Estate, Bath Road, Stroud, Gloucestershire, GL5 3LL Tel: (01453) 752459 Fax: (01453) 752458 E-mail: heatit@aol.com *Heating elements including plastics processing services*

Solomon Holdings Ltd, Knowlsey Road Industrial Estate, Haslingden, Rossendale, Lancashire, BB4 4RX Tel: (01706) 211211 Fax: (01706) 831518 E-mail: sales@solocom.co.uk *Refrigerated vehicle body builders*

David L. Solomons Ltd, 5 Hatton Place, London, EC1N 8RU Tel: (020) 7242 7659 Fax: (020) 7831 6647 E-mail: dsolo34962@aol.com *Manufacturing & wholesale jewellers diamond merchants*

Solopark plc, Station Road, Pampisford, Cambridge, CB22 3HB Tel: (01223) 834663 Fax: (01223) 834780 E-mail: sales@solopark.co.uk *Reclaimed building materials* Also at: Ipswich

Soloprint Ltd, 105 Great North Road, Eaton Socon, St. Neots, Cambridgeshire, PE19 8EL Tel: (01480) 213555 Fax: (01480) 218887 E-mail: sales@tsgcf.co.uk *General & fine colour printers*

Solsoft Computers, 2 Bosuen Road, Newquay, Cornwall, TR7 3BA Tel: (01637) 878933 Fax: (01637) 852666 E-mail: admin@solsoftsw.com *Computer, repairs, construction & sales*

Solsoft S W Bespoke Software Systems, 2 Bosuen Road, Newquay, Cornwall, TR7 3BA Tel: (01637) 852666 Fax: (01637) 852666 E-mail: info@solsoftaw.com *PC repairs & computer building*

Solstice Energy Ltd, 14 Gladwyn Road, Putney, London, SW15 1JY Tel: 020 8789 4717 Fax: 020 8789 4717 E-mail: info@solsticeenergy.co.uk *Photovoltaic (solar electrical) systems, design & installation*

Solstone Plus, 48a Old Steine, Brighton, BN1 1NH Tel: (01273) 206555 Fax: (01273) 387769 E-mail: solestoneplus@solestonegroup.com *Computer consultants*

Solstrand Industries Ltd, J J Building, Hillbottom Road, Sands Industrial Estate, High Wycombe, Buckinghamshire, HP12 4HJ Tel: (01494) 522030 Fax: (01494) 472685 *Precision engineering electronic components & sub-contractors services*

▶ Solubus Ltd, Laggan, Sunnyside Road, Falkirk, FK1 4BG Tel: (01324) 871667 Fax: (01324) 871667 E-mail: stuart@solubus.co.uk *Business advisors & consulting services*

Soluis Technologies Ltd, 31a King Street, Stenhousemuir, Larbert, Stirlingshire, FK5 4HD Tel: (01324) 878788 Fax: (01324) 878799 E-mail: martin@soluis.com *Photo-realistic visualisation & 3d animation services*

Solus Garden & Leisure Ltd, Bluebird Park, Bromsgrove Road, Hunnington, Halesowen, West Midlands, B62 0EW Tel: 0121-504 2700 Fax: 0121-585 5971 E-mail: sales@solusgl.com *Garden furniture wholesalers & distributors*

Solus Norwich Union, 16 Blenheim Road, Epsom, Surrey, KT19 9AP Tel: (01372) 727133 Fax: (01372) 745048 E-mail: info@longmead.co.uk *Motor body repairers & service*

Solution, Claydon Court, Old Ipswich Road, Claydon, Ipswich, IP6 0AE Tel: (01473) 833070 Fax: (01473) 833053 E-mail: sales@sw4it.com *Raising performance through IT*

Solution & Communications Services Ltd, 57 Crwys Road, Cardiff, CF24 4NE Tel: (029) 2066 6133 Fax: (029) 2066 6017 E-mail: sales@solutions-and-communications.com *Computer maintanence & repair services*

Solution House Ltd, 359 Nuthall Road, Nottingham, NG8 5BU Tel: 0115-910 1010 Fax: 0115-910 1012 E-mail: will.pickles@soloutionhouse.co.uk *Computer reselling software & suppliers*

▶ Solution Management Ltd, Ferryview, Grantown Road, Forres, Morayshire, IV36 2PG Tel: (01309) 672547

Solution Product Systems Ltd, Unit 34, Walker Avenue, Wolverton Mill, Milton Keynes, MK12 5TW Tel: (01908) 682700 Fax: (01908) 682739 E-mail: sales@spslretail.com *People counter manufrs*

▶ Solution Rail Ltd, 4 Raleigh Close, Pinner, Middlesex, HA5 1NR Tel: (07951) 361723 Fax: (0871) 9895700 E-mail: enquiries@solutionrail.co.uk *Project management consultancy*

Solutions, 29 James Carter Road, Mildenhall, Bury St. Edmunds, Suffolk, IP28 7DE Tel: (01638) 717798 Fax: (01638) 713603 E-mail: sales@solutions-c-s.co.uk *Suppliers of janitorial, cleaning & hygiene products operating with minimum possible impact on the environment. Free delivery within Newmarket, Thetford, Braunton & Bury St. Edmunds*

plc Solutions, Unit 3 Oakford Place, Tog Lane, Great Horkesley, Colchester, CO6 4BX Tel: (01206) 273644 Fax: 01206-273655 *Industrial solutions*

Solutions, Unit 8 Albion Works, Havannah Street, Buglawton, Congleton, Cheshire, CW12 2AQ Tel: (01260) 299099 Fax: (01260) 291144 E-mail: info@solns.co.uk *CAD design services, solid modelling, 2D to 3D conversion. product prototype development, rapid prototyping, fabrication development, metal product development, plastic product development. Electrical and electronic design services. Special machinery design, machine and process automation.*

▶ Solutions Inc, 255 Old Shoreham Road, Hove, East Sussex, BN3 7ED Tel: (01273) 200800 Fax: (01273) 889030 E-mail: richard@solutionsinc.co.uk *Apple premium re-seller*

▶ Solutions, The Trent Business Centre, Canal Street, Long Eaton, Nottingham, NG10 4HN Tel: 0115-946 3215 Fax: 0115-946 3332

▶ Solutions 2 Enterprise Ltd, Church Road, Rainford, St. Helens, Merseyside, WA11 8HE Tel: (01744) 885860 Fax: (01744) 885872 *Computer software consultants*

▶ Solutions Audio Visual Ltd, Unit 4 Bowdens Business Centre, Hambridge, Langport, Somerset, TA10 0BP Tel: (01458) 252000 Fax: (01458) 254461 *Audio visual hire*

Solutions For Business, Royston Business & Design Centre, 8 Priory Lane, Royston, Hertfordshire, SG8 9DU Tel: (01763) 242939 Fax: (01763) 243332 E-mail: sales@solutions-for-business.co.uk *Colour copying bureau, printers & publishers*

Solutions Display Ltd, Hayseech Road, Halesowen, West Midlands, B63 3PD Tel: 0121-550 5088 Fax: 0121-585 0850 E-mail: info@solutions-display.co.uk *Acrylic & display manufrs*

▶ Solutions Distributors Ltd, Unit 1 Hixon Industrial Estate, Church Lane, Hixon, Stafford, ST18 0PY Tel: (0871) 4341510 Fax: (0871) 4341514 E-mail: sales@solutions-distributors.co.uk *Security products, tagging systems, tags & labels suppliers*

▶ Solutions Fire Safety Ltd, PO Box 5963, Basildon, Essex, SS14 3GW Tel: 0845 6012632 Fax: 0845 6012659 E-mail: sales@solutionsfiresafety.co.uk *Leading UK fire safety consultancy, providing help and support with the complications of fire safety legislation. We offer Fire Risk Assessment, Fire Safety Log Books, Photoluminescent Safety Signs and Warden/Marshall training.*

▶ Solutions for Management, Upper Leigh View, 195 Coronation Road, Southville, Bristol, BS3 1RQ Tel: 07970 262938 E-mail: jen@solutions4management.co.uk *A strategic consultancy for small to medium companies providing the means for corporate and departmental improvement by streamlining processes, increasing profitability, re-aligning end to end management, undertaking rapid business development and turnarounds, trouble-shooting and personal /corporate mentoring.*

Solutions Play By Design, Ninelands La, Garforth, Leeds, LS25 1NX Tel: 0113-287 7565 Fax: 0113-287 7565 E-mail: nev@fsbusiness.co.uk *Playground equipment manufrs*

Solutions PT, Unit 1, Oakfield Road, Cheadle Royal Business Park, Cheadle, Cheshire, SK8 3GX Tel: 0161-495 4600 Fax: 0161-495 4690 E-mail: sales@solutionspt.co.uk *Computer software distributors for industry*

▶ Solutions To Packaging Ltd, 44 Victoria Park Avenue, Leyland, PR25 1UG Tel: (01772) 458046 Fax: (01772) 458743 E-mail: sol2pac@msn.com *Packaging Consultancy Specialising in:*Capital project management.*Packaging design and development.*Cost reduction and procurement **

Solutions With Software, 4 Yonder Way, Wanborough, Swindon, SN4 0BX Tel: (01793) 790379 Fax: (01793) 790379 *Computer software consultants*

Solvay Healthcare Ltd, Mansbridge Road, West End, Southampton, SO18 3JD Tel: (023) 8046 7000 Fax: (023) 8046 5350 E-mail: enquiries.shl@solvay.com *Pharmaceutical suppliers*

Solvay Interox Ltd, PO Box 7, Warrington, WA4 6HA Tel: (01925) 651277 Fax: (01925) 655856 E-mail: peroxide.warrington@solvay.com *Chemical manufrs*

Solvay Speciality Chemicals Ltd, Lostock Works, Works Lane, Northwich, Cheshire, CW9 7ZR Tel: (01606) 723331 Fax: (01606) 723336 E-mail: sales@solvay.com *PCC manufrs*

Solvent Resource Management Ltd, Middleton Road, Middleton, Morecambe, Lancashire, LA3 3JW Tel: (01524) 853053 Fax: (01524) 851284 E-mail: sales@srm-ltd.com *Solvent recovery & contract distillation service providers*

Solvent Resource Management Ltd, Rye Harbour Road, Rye, East Sussex, TN31 7TE Tel: (01797) 223936 Fax: (01797) 223017 E-mail: sales@srm-ltd.com *Solvent manufrs*

Solvent Resource Management Ltd, Hendon Dock, Sunderland, SR1 2EW Tel: 0191-566 0000 Fax: 0191-566 0025 E-mail: sales@srm-ltd.com *Solvent recovery & contract distillation*

Solvents With Safety Ltd, Plumtree Road, Bircotes, Doncaster, South Yorkshire, DN11 8EW Tel: (01302) 711733 Fax: (01302) 711744 E-mail: sales@solventswithsafety.co.uk *Waste removal services & solvents suppliers*

Solvers Accounting Services Ltd, Bridge House, 119-123 Station Road, Hayes, Middlesex, UB3 4BX Tel: (020) 8589 0786 Fax: (020) 8561 9034 E-mail: mail@taxsolvers.co.uk *Accountancy & taxation services*

Solvitol Ltd, Shadon Way, Birtley, Chester Le Street, County Durham, DH3 2RE Tel: 0191-410 9131 Fax: 0191-492 0503 *Suppliers of industrial cleaning products*

Sol-Vox, 13 Station Rd, Horsforth, Leeds, LS18 5PA Tel: 0113-225 2266 *Computer software developers*

Solvwaste Environmental Ltd, Cogdean Elms Industrial Estate, Higher Merley Lane, Corfe Mullen, Wimborne, Dorset, BH21 3EG Tel: (01202) 840084 Fax: (01202) 841282 E-mail: sales@iswgroup.co.uk *Chemical waste management & disposal consultants*

Solway Instrument Services, South End, Wigton, Cumbria, CA7 9PZ Tel: (01697) 344168 Fax: (01697) 345242 E-mail: sales@solwayinstrumentservices.co.uk *Technical instruments distributors*

▶ Solway Offset Services, 11 Catherinefield Industrial Estate, Dumfries, DG1 3PQ Tel: (01387) 264959 Fax: (01387) 261112

▶ Solway Precast, Braehead, Barrhill, Girvan, Ayrshire, KA26 0QR Tel: (01465) 821348 Fax: (01465) 821383 *Pre-cast manufrs*

Solway Sea Foods, Bladnoch Bridge Industrial Estatae, Bladnoch, Wigtown, Newton Stewart, Wigtownshire, DG8 9AB Tel: (01988) 402661 Fax: (01988) 402662 E-mail: enquiries@solwayseafoods.co.uk *Scampi processors*

Solway Signs & Shop Equipment, 79 Blackwell Road, Carlisle, CA2 4AJ Tel: (01228) 528865 Fax: (01228) 528865 E-mail: solway.signs@tiscali.co.uk *Suppliers of cash registers & sign manufrs*

▶ Solweb Ltd, Suite 8a Bourne Gate, 25 Bourne Valley Road, Poole, Dorset, BH12 1DY Tel: (01202) 269879 Fax: 01202 762233 E-mail: info@solweb.co.uk *Solweb Ltd are a bespoke software development company specialising in web and application integration.*

▶ Soma Contract Services Ltd, 6 The Green, Dunchurch, Rugby, Warwickshire, CV22 6NX Tel: (01788) 817811 Fax: (01788) 817282 E-mail: maggieholman@somacontracts.co.uk *Established in 1990, SOMA has a reputation for providing an efficient and cost-effective contract dispute resolution service, based on extensive experience and expertise in contractual, technical and financial matters.*

Somac Threads Manufacturing Ltd, Unit 2-3 Brymau Four Trading Estate, River Lane, Saltney, Chester, CH4 8RF Tel: (01244) 680506 Fax: (01244) 680202 E-mail: sales@somac.co.uk *Sewing thread manufrs*

Somar International Ltd, Somar House, Heron Way, Newham, Truro, Cornwall, TR1 2XN Tel: (01872) 223000 Fax: (01872) 264325 E-mail: enquiries@somar.co.uk *Motor controller distributor*

Somat Systems (UK) Ltd, 230 Woodburn Road, Sheffield, S9 3LQ Tel: 0114-275 5292 Fax: 0114-275 8272 E-mail: ajb@somat.com Sales Contact: G. Smith Principal Export Areas: Africa *Data acquisition systems & data logging equipment distributors. Also computer software (post processing) producers or suppliers, computer software (data acquisition) producers or suppliers, process controller/control systems manufacturers & data acquisition systems manufrs*

Somdor Engineering Ltd, Gibbs Marsh Trading Estate, Stalbridge, Sturminster Newton, Dorset, DT10 2RY Tel: (01963) 362210 Fax: (01963) 362388 *Steel fabricators & welding engineers*

Leroy Somer Ltd, Heathrow Interchange, Bullsbrook Road, Hayes, Middlesex, UB4 0JR Tel: (020) 8756 7000 Fax: (020) 8756 7028 E-mail: leroy-somer@leroy.somer.co.uk *Electric motor/alternator suppliers* Also at: Skelmersdale, Southampton, Stamford & Warwick

Somerco Industrial Ltd, 34 Tollpark Road, Cumbernauld, Glasgow, G68 0LW Tel: (01236) 728445 Fax: (01236) 728445 E-mail: somerco@aol.com *Surface coating contractors*

▶ Somercourt Office, 7 Castle Road, Chelston Business Park, Wellington, Somerset, TA21 9JQ Tel: (01823) 668428 Fax: (01823) 668420 E-mail: enq@somercourt.co.uk *Office furniture manufrs*

Somerdell Furniture, 98 Radstock Road, Midsomer Norton, Radstock, BA3 2AU Tel: (01761) 418969 Fax: (01761) 418969 E-mail: somerdell@aol.com *Furniture manufrs*

Somerfield Merchant Services Ltd, Summerfield House, Whtchurch Lane, Bristol, BS14 0TJ Tel: 0117-935 9359 Fax: 0117-978 0629 *Supermarket & retail*

Somerford Laboratories Ltd, 9 Horcott Industrial Estate, Horcott Road, Fairford, Gloucestershire, GL7 4BX Tel: (01285) 713737 Fax: (01285) 713733 E-mail: test@somlab.com *Environmental test facility*

Somerlap Forest Products, Wells Road, Mark, Highbridge, Somerset, TA9 4NR Tel: (01278) 641671 Fax: (01278) 641629 E-mail: admin@somerlap.net *Pallet & fencing manufrs*

Somers Forge Ltd, Haywood Forge, Prospect Road, Halesowen, West Midlands, B62 8DZ Tel: 0121-585 5959 Fax: 0121-585 7154 E-mail: sales@somersforge.com *Steel forging manufrs*

Somers Totalkare Ltd, Unit 15 Forge Trading Estate, Mucklow Hill, Halesowen, West Midlands, B62 8TR Tel: 0121-585 2700 Fax: 0121-501 1458 E-mail: sales@somerstotalkare.co.uk *Mobile vehicle lifting equipment manufrs*

▶ Somerset Bouncy Castles, 1 Buller Avenue, Houndstone, Yeovil, Somerset, BA22 8SN Tel: (0845) 0000447 E-mail: sales@sommersetbouncycastles.co.uk *Bouncy castles provider*

Somerset Camping Ltd, Walford Cross, Taunton, Somerset, TA2 8QR Tel: (01823) 413333 Fax: (01823) 413344 E-mail: enquiries@somersetcaravans.co.uk *Caravan & camping equipment dealers*

▶ Somerset Computers, 168 Southdown Road, Southdown, Bath, BA2 1JL Tel: 01225 424887

David Somerset Skincare, Henley-On-Thames, Oxfordshire, RG9 6YZ Tel: (01491) 578080 E-mail: info@somersets.com *Skincare products manufrs*

Somerset Fire Extinguishers, Covert End Westleigh Court, Westleigh Close, Yate, Bristol, BS37 4PR Tel: (01458) 443942 Fax: (01454) 273312 E-mail: sales@bristolfire.co.uk *Fire alarms suppliers*

▶ Somerset Footwear Ltd, Unit 15 Canvin Court, Bancombe Road, Somerton, Somerset, TA11 6SB Tel: (01458) 273997 Fax: (01458) 274483 *Footwear suppliers*

▶ Somerset Gas Co. Ltd, 17 Knights Road, Chelston Business Park, Wellington, Somerset, TA21 9JH Tel: (01823) 661144 Fax: (01823) 661155 E-mail: info@somersetgas.eclipse.co.uk *Gas installation maintained*

Somerset Hotel, 6 Dorset Square, London, NW1 6QA Tel: (020) 7723 0741 Fax: (020) 7723 6081 *Hotel & restaurant & conference facilities*

Somerset Lifting Supplies, Riverside, Bathpool, Taunton, Somerset, TA1 2DX Tel: (01823) 352029 Fax: (01823) 352029 *Lifting equipment & crane hire service*

Somerset Machine Tools, 29 Brimbleworth Lane, St. Georges, Weston-super-Mare, Avon, BS22 7XS Tel: (01934) 510686 Fax: (01934) 522279 E-mail: smtcnc@aol.com *Machine tool sales*

Somerset Scaffolding Ltd, Southwood, Evercreech, Shepton Mallet, Somerset, BA4 6LX Tel: (01749) 830159 Fax: (01749) 831159 E-mail: somersetscaff@btinternet.com *Scaffolding specialists*

Somerset Shipbrokers Ltd, Walsingham House, 35 Seething Lane, London, EC3N 4AN Tel: (020) 7488 4401 Fax: (020) 7265 0238 *Ship brokers*

Somerset Willow Co., Wireworks Estate, Bristol Road, Bridgwater, Somerset, TA6 4AP Tel: (01278) 424003 Fax: (01278) 446415 E-mail: enquires@sumersetwillows.co.uk *Basket manufrs*

Somersham G R P Mouldings, Somersham Road, Little Blakenham, Ipswich, IP8 4NF Tel: (01473) 831333 Fax: (01473) 832466 *Glass fibre moulding*

Somerton Paper Services, Unit 15 Samuel Whites Business Estate, Bridge Road, Cowes, Isle of Wight, PO31 7DU Tel: (01983) 294702 Fax: (01983) 294702 *Janitorial distributors*

Somerville Models, Westfield Ho, 104 High St, Billinghay, Lincoln, LN4 4ED Tel: 01526 860348 Fax: 01526 860315 *Model car collector manufrs*

Philip Somerville Ltd, 38 Chiltern Street, London, W1U 7QL Tel: (020) 7224 1517 Fax: (020) 7486 5885 E-mail: info@philipsomerville.com *Ladies hats retail & manufrs*

Somerwood Ltd, 52a Summerhill Road, Saffron Walden, Essex, CB11 4AJ Tel: (01799) 500180 *Mobility accessories*

▶ Something Special, 47 Hereward Cross, Peterborough, PE1 1TQ Tel: (01733) 319099 Fax: (01733) 319099

Somic plc, PO Box 8, Preston, PR1 5PS Tel: (01772) 790000 Fax: (01772) 795677 E-mail: somic@somic.co.uk *Paper yarn spinners, weavers & textile coaters*

Sommerwest Technical Services Ltd, 32 Garrett Road, Lynx Trading Estate, Yeovil, Somerset, BA20 2TJ Tel: 01935 412595 *Subcontract machining*

▶ Sona Jewellers, 1 Morris Street, Oldham, OL4 1EL Tel: 0161-620 7049 E-mail: sales@hannahjewellers.co.uk

▶ Sona Vision, Unit 16 Denmore Industrial Estate, Denmore Road, Bridge of Don, Aberdeen, AB23 8JW Tel: (01224) 707737 Fax: (01224) 827289 E-mail: sales@sonavision.co.uk

Sonalux Systems, Tanglewood, Hophurst Hill, Crawley Down, Crawley, West Sussex, RH10 4LP Tel: (01342) 717691 Fax: (01342) 717094 E-mail: rob@sonalux.tv *CCTV installers*

▶ Sonaptic Ltd, Chancery Court, Lincolns Inn, Lincoln Road, High Wycombe, Bucks, HP12 3RE Tel: 01494 429368 E-mail: mail@sonaptic.com *Sonaptic is the home of Sonaptic SoundTM, a unique set of technologies which allow mobile devices to produce three-dimensional, positional sound. The technology is in use by handset and games developers and has applications in mobile speech, music, gaming and conferencing.*

▶ Sonardyne, Units 12-13, The Technology Centre, Claymore Drive, Bridge of Don, Aberdeen, AB23 8GD Tel: (01224) 707875 Fax: (01224) 707876 *Sub sea acoustic navigation & control service*

Sonardyne Group Ltd, Ocean House, Blackbush Business Park, Yateley, Hampshire, GU46 6GD Tel: (01252) 872288 Fax: (01252) 876100 E-mail: sales@sonardyne.co.uk *Underwater navigation & positioning systems*

Sonatest plc, Dickens Road, Old Wolverton, Milton Keynes, MK12 5QQ Tel: (01908) 316345 Fax: (01908) 321323 E-mail: info@sonatest-plc.com Principal Export Areas: Worldwide *Sonatest Limited has one over-riding and driving motivation - to design, manufacture and market the worlds best 'Non Destructive Evaluation' (NDE or NDT) products. From our UK based HQ, we design and produce a wide range of high performance ultrasonic equipment and NDT accessories, employing cutting edge technology in our range of non-destructive testing equipment*

Sonatrach Petroleum Corporation, 5 Princes Gate, London, SW7 1QJ Tel: (020) 7823 8030 Fax: (020) 7823 7069 E-mail: enquiries@sonatrach.co.uk *Oil trading company*

Sondex Ltd, Ford Lane, Bramshill, Hook, Hampshire, RG27 0RH Tel: 0118-932 6755 Fax: 0118-932 6704 E-mail: sondex@sondex.com *Well logging tools & equipment*

Sondia Lighting Ltd, 45 Portland Place, Hull, HU2 8QP Tel: (01482) 223353 Fax: (01482) 225681 E-mail: sales@sondialighting.com *Marine fluorescent lighting manufrs*

Sondom Development Co. Ltd, The Depot, Windsor Road, Bedford, MK42 9SU Tel: (01234) 350307 Fax: (01234) 262025 E-mail: buildright@sondom.demon.co.uk *Building contractors*

Soneck Electronics Ltd, 3A Cumberland Works, Wintersells Road, Byfleet, Byfleet, Surrey, KT14 7LF Tel: (01932) 355925 Fax: (01932) 336675 E-mail: soneck@tesco.net *Electronic equipment sub-contracting services*

▶ Soneric Communications, Unit 24 Wren Court, Strathclyde Business Park, Bellshill, Lanarkshire, ML4 3NQ Tel: (01698) 742210 Fax: (01698) 840080 E-mail: sales@soneric.com *Telecommunication services*

Sonet Prebbles Ltd, St. John'S Road, Bootle, Merseyside, L20 8BH Tel: 0151-922 8606 Fax: 0151-944 1048 *Pharmaceutical & dressings manufrs*

▶ Soni Exports Ltd, PO Box 7923, Leicester, LE4 9LS Tel: 0116-276 4000 Fax: 0116-276 4002 E-mail: sales@soniexports.co.uk *Import & export of commercial engines*

Sonic Air Systems (Europe) Ltd, 227 Sunderland Road, South Shields, Tyne & Wear, NE34 6AL Tel: 0191-455 1628 Fax: 0191-427 1994 E-mail: priley@sonicairsystems.com *Air knife drying systems & blowers*

Sonic Communications International Ltd, Starley Way, Birmingham, B37 7HB Tel: 0121-781 4400 Fax: 0121-781 4404 E-mail: sales@sonic-comms.com *Sonic intercom systems manufrs*

▶ Sonic Drilling Supplies Ltd, 141 St Johns Road, Congleton, Cheshire, CW12 2EH Tel: (01260) 273956 Fax: (01260) 276923 E-mail: info@sonicdrill.co.uk *Supply of Drilling Equipment and Supply of Sonic Drilling systems.*

Sonic Party Time, 2a North Street, Heavitree, Exeter, EX1 2RH Tel: (01392) 848785 *Entertainment services*

Sonic Technologies Ltd, Ty Coch Farm, Pembrey Rd, Kidwelly, Dyfed, SA17 4TF Tel: (01554) 890612 Fax: (01554) 890612 *Ultrasonic design & consultancy*

▶ Sonic Works, 2a The Grove, Breaston, Derby, DE72 3AE Tel: (01332) 872543

▶ Sonics & Materials (UK) Ltd, Unit 18 Tomo Business Park, Creeting Road, Stowmarket, Suffolk, IP14 5EP Tel: (01449) 770055 Fax: (01449) 770333 E-mail: sales@sonicsandmaterials.co.uk *Suppliers of plastic welding equipment*

Sonifex Ltd, 61 Station Road, Irthlingborough, Wellingborough, Northamptonshire, NN9 5QE Tel: (01933) 650700 Fax: (01933) 650726 E-mail: sales@sonifex.co.uk *Broadcasting equipment manufrs*

Sonneborn & Rieck Ltd, 91-95 Peregrine Road, Ilford, Essex, IG6 3XH Tel: (020) 8500 0251 Fax: (020) 8500 3696 E-mail: export@sonneborn-rieck.co.uk *Industrial paint & lacquer manufrs* Also at: Bristol, Chesterfield & Glasgow

Sonnet Furniture, Units 1-5, Blackfriars Road, Nailsea, Bristol, BS48 4DJ Tel: (01275) 858131 Fax: (01275) 811834 *Furniture designers & manufrs*

Sonnet Furniture, Units 1-5, Blackfriars Road, Nailsea, Bristol, BS48 4DJ Tel: (01275) 858131 Fax: (01275) 811834 *Flat pack furniture manufrs*

Sonning Fireworks Ltd, The Old Cottage, Sonning Eye, Reading, RG4 6TN Tel: (0800) 0743140 E-mail: enquiries@sonningfireworks.co.uk *Firework displays*

▶ Sonning Flowers, 2 The Old Forge, Pearson Road, Sonning, Reading, RG4 6UH Tel: 0118-944 8400 E-mail: info05@sonningflowers.com *Florist*

Sonning Heating Co. Ltd, Mayflower Close, Chandler's Ford, Eastleigh, Hampshire, SO53 4AR Tel: (023) 8026 2826 Fax: (023) 8027 3869 E-mail: sonnaire@sonning-heating.demon.co.uk *Heating engineers*

Sono UK Ltd, Enterprise House, Murdock Road, Dorcan, Swindon, SN3 5HY Tel: (01793) 488488 Fax: (01793) 522868 E-mail: info@sono-uk.com Purchasing Contact: J. Maule Sales Contact: I. Street *Manufacturers of workbenches including steel benches. Also mobile storage equipment/ systems manufrs*

Sonoco Board Mills, Holywell Green, Halifax, West Yorkshire, HX4 9PY Tel: (01422) 374741 Fax: (01422) 371495 *Paperboard manufrs*

Sonoco Consumer Products Ltd, Stokes Street, Manchester, M11 4QX Tel: 0161-230 7000 Fax: 0161-230 1200 E-mail: info@sonoco.com *Packaging manufrs*

Sonoco Industrial Products, 4 Portadown Road, Lurgan, Craigavon, County Armagh, BT66 8QW Tel: (028) 3832 3501 Fax: (028) 3832 3781 E-mail: info@sonoco.co.uk *Paperboard converters*

Sonoscan (Europe) Ltd, The Wincombe Business Centre, Shaftesbury, Dorset, SP7 9QJ Tel: (01747) 855988 Fax: (01747) 855938 E-mail: info@sonoscan.com *Ultrasonic equipment suppliers*

Sontay Ltd, Four Elms Road, Edenbridge, Kent, TN8 6AB Tel: (0845) 3457253 Fax: (0845) 3457353 E-mail: sales@sontay.com *Sensing products for temperature & relative humidity*

Sontec Electronics Ltd, Sontec House, Concorde Road, Norwich, NR6 6BE Tel: (01603) 483675 Fax: (01603) 788937 E-mail: enquire@sontec.co.uk *Consumer electronic service agent*

Sontex Machinery Ltd, 61 Westgate, Cleckheaton, West Yorkshire, BD19 5JZ Tel: (01274) 872299 Fax: (01274) 862829 E-mail: info@sontex.co.uk *UK distributors of packaging machinery & materials.*

▶ Sontrest Surrounds, Mount Road, Kidsgrove, Stoke-on-Trent, ST7 4AZ Tel: (01782) 776271 Fax: (01782) 783357 *Metal components for fires manufrs*

Sony Business Europe, Viables Industrial Estate, Jays Close, Basingstoke, Hampshire, RG22 4SB Tel: (01256) 355011 Fax: (01256) 474585 *Broadcasting equipment & marketing agents*

Sony Centre, 134 Baker Street, London, W1U 6UB Tel: (020) 7486 2526 Fax: (020) 7487 5603 E-mail: admin@audiovisual4u.co.uk *TV, hi-fi & video suppliers*

Sony DADC Ltd, Southwater Business Park, Worthing Road, Southwater, Horsham, West Sussex, RH13 9YT Tel: (01403) 732302 Fax: (01403) 732313 *Audio cd's CD roms dvd mastering & manufacturing*

Sony Music Entertainment UK Ltd, 10 Great Marlborough Street, London, W1F 7LP Tel: (020) 7911 8400 Fax: (020) 7911 8600 *Computer entertainment manufrs*

Sony UK Ltd, The Heights, Brooklands, Weybridge, Surrey, KT13 0XW Tel: (01932) 816000 Fax: (01932) 817000 *Domestic hardware manufrs*

▶ Soo Consultant Ltd, 54-57, Key Hill, Birmingham, B18 5NX Tel: 0121-507 1512 Fax: 0121-554 4982

Sophos plc, Pentagon West, The Pentagon, Abingdon, Oxfordshire, OX14 3YP Tel: (01235) 559933 Fax: (01235) 559935 E-mail: sales@sophos.com *Data security & anti-virus areas*

▶ Sopra Group Ltd, Northbrook House, Robert Robinson Avenue, Oxford, OX4 4GA Tel: (01865) 781781 Fax: (01865) 781777 E-mail: jim.wicks@thefluidgroup.com *Software, fluid or flow simulation manufrs*

Sopra Group Ltd, Northbrook House, Robert Robinson Avenue, Oxford, OX4 4GA Tel: (01865) 781781 Fax: (01865) 781777 *Computer systems & software services*

Soptralentz UK Ltd, Ravell Drum Works, Gelderd Road, Leeds, LS12 6DL Tel: 0113-263 8573 Fax: 0113-263 7842 E-mail: ken@peaserecycling.co.uk *Drum & tank manual recycling*

Sor Europe Ltd, Farren Court, The Street, Cowfold, Horsham, West Sussex, RH13 8BP Tel: (01403) 864000 Fax: (01403) 710177 E-mail: sales@soreur.co.uk *Switch manufrs*

▶ Soralex Technologies, London, E6 3QJ Tel: 0870-350 0065 Fax: 0870-350 0064 *Audio equipment installers*

▶ Sorba UK, The Barn, Witham, Essex, CM8 2BU Tel: 01376 507750 *Aluminum & stainless steel cladding suppliers*

Sorba-Freeze Ltd, Unit 5 Girdleness Trading Estate, Girdleness Road, Aberdeen, AB11 8DG Tel: 01224 894417 E-mail: info@sorbafreeze.com *Refrigerated pads for insulated packaging systems. Ideal for use when sending food by mail order.*

▶ Sorbican Distribution, 27 Priory Lane, Hartley Wintney, Hook, Hampshire, RG27 8EX Tel: (01256) 762435 *Supplier of natural, organic oil absorbents & cat litters*

Sorby (UK) Ltd, 7 Orgreave Close, Handsworth, Sheffield, S13 9NP Tel: 0114-269 3803 Fax: 0114-254 0523 E-mail: sales@sorbyuk.co.uk *Tungsten carbide tool manufrs*

Soreen Ltd, Taylor Road, Urmston, Manchester, M41 7WS Tel: 0161-748 1235 Fax: 0161-746 7067 *Bakers wholesale manufrs*

Sorex Ltd, Oldgate, Widnes, Cheshire, WA8 8TJ Tel: 0151-424 4328 Fax: 0151-495 1163 E-mail: enquiries@sorex.com *Rodenticide & pesticide manufrs*

Sorokin Joinery & Glazing Ltd, Unit 3 Monastery Business Centre, Monastery Road, Neath Abbey, Neath, West Glamorgan, SA10 7DP Tel: (01792) 815661 Fax: (01792) 816636 *Joinery manufrs*

Soron Ltd, Unit 2d Payne Street, Glasgow, G4 0LE Tel: 0141-333 9518 Fax: 0141-332 2711 *Mechanical engineers*

▶ Soros Limited, 142 Abbey Road, Macclesfield, Cheshire, SK10 3PA Tel: 01625 501098 Fax: 01625 501098 E-mail: enquiries@soros.co.uk *Your one stop*

continued

business administration, secretarial, technical and commercial documentation support service. We specialise in providing virtual business solutions world-wide. Our clients include Surveyors, construction companies, local authorities, estate agents, business managers, directors and many more. Please view our web-site to see how we can help.

Sorrill & Coley, 22 New John St West, Birmingham, B19 3NB Tel: 0121-359 7428 Fax: 0121-359 5508 *Silver plated giftware manufrs*

▶ Sorsis Ltd, 20 Normandy Close, Northwold, Thetford, Norfolk, IP26 5NN Tel: (01366) 727661 Fax: (01366) 727661 *Financial software consultants & developers*

Sorsky Ltd, Yeoward House, Dennis Road, Tanhouse Estate, Widnes, Cheshire, WA8 0SF Tel: 0151-257 2222 Fax: 0151-257 2233 E-mail: sales@sorsky.com Principal Export Areas: Worldwide *"Sorsky supplies a full range of workwear, PPE & hygieneproducts for user companies in all business sectors. We have the capability to supply a wide range of products efficiently & quickly at competative prices"*

▶ Sort IT, 120 Holmes Avenue, Hove, East Sussex, BN3 7LE Tel: 01273 227709 E-mail: info@sortitquick.co.uk

▶ Sorted Technical Services Ltd, Brafield on the Green, Northampton, NN7 1BT Tel: (01604) 890260 E-mail: enquiries@sortedtech.co.uk *Providing technical support and equipment hire to the conferences, theatre and outdoor entertainment industries.*

Sortex Ltd, Pudding Mill Lane, London, E15 2PJ Tel: (020) 8519 0525 Fax: (020) 8519 5614 E-mail: sales@sortex.com *Colour sorting machine manufrs*

Sortimo International Ltd, Old Sarum Park, Old Sarum, Salisbury, SP4 6EB Tel: (01722) 411585 Fax: (01722) 320831 E-mail: sales@sortimo.co.uk *Supplier & installer of secure van equipment as secure storage system*

Sos Derby Ltd, 21 Noel Street, London, W1F 8GP Tel: (020) 7734 2882 Fax: (020) 7734 1441 *Clothing company retail*

Sos Internet Ltd, Sosi House, Hacche Mill, South Molton, Devon, EX36 3NA Tel: (0870) 7442961 Fax: (0870) 9911730 E-mail: sosi@sosi.net *Computer & internet services*

▶ SOS Response Ltd, 14-30 Hyde Street, Winchester, Hampshire, SO23 7TA Tel: (0870) 1657452 Fax: (0870) 1657453 E-mail: info@sosresponse.com *Security services*

Sotech Ltd, 4 Mill Hill, North West Industrial Estate, Peterlee, County Durham, SR8 2HR Tel: 0191-587 2287 Fax: 0191-518 0703 E-mail: mail@sotech-optima.co.uk *Architectural sheet metal rain screen cladding*

Soth Tyneside College, Marine Safety Training Centre South Tyneside College, Wapping, South Shields, Tyne & Wear, NE33 1LQ Tel: 0191-427 3664 Fax: 0191-427 3600 E-mail: marine_safety_at_stc@compuserve.com *Survival training centre*

Sotham Engineering Services Ltd, Home End, Fulbourn, Cambridge, CB21 5BS Tel: (01223) 881081 Fax: (01223) 880169 E-mail: info@sotham.co.uk *Mechanical engineering services*

▶ Sottek Ltd, 16 Warren Avenue, Sutton, Surrey, SM2 7QL Tel: (020) 8643 3487 Fax: (020) 8770 3997

Soudal Ltd, Telford Way, Stephenson Industrial Estate, Coalville, Leicestershire, LE67 3HE Tel: (01530) 510502 Fax: (01530) 510970 E-mail: sales@soudal.co.uk *Packaging machinery suppliers*

Soul Traders Workshops, Unit 267b Wenta Business Centre Colne Way Watford Herts, Colne Way, The Wenta Business Centre, Watford, WD24 7ND Tel: (0870) 3503803 Fax: (0870) 3503813 E-mail: info@soultradersworkshops.com *Enterprise Learning Programme for schools, FE, Adult learners (Disabled/NEET). Schools may access Standards Fund (LEA) - free at point of delivery. LSC/RDA/Prince"s Trust endorsed programme; flexible on/off timetable direct delivery of events or modular sessions/tutor training; KS3/KS4+; meets WRL/QCA requirements; interactive content, online resources, prizes, entrepreneur visits, etc. Territories available under license to individual trainers/training providers with education/ business background.*

▶ Sound Absortion, Melville House, Queens Avenue, Macclesfield, Cheshire, SK10 2BN Tel: (01625) 432255 Fax: (01625) 432255 E-mail: roland@quietstone.co.uk *Sound absorption production & manufrs*

▶ Sound Broadcast Services, Lauriston House, Pitchill, Evesham, Worcestershire, WR11 8SN Tel: (01386) 871650 Fax: (01386) 871987 E-mail: sales@sbsfm.com *Broadcast equipment suppliers*

Sound Business Audio Ltd, Fitzroy House, Coombe Lane, Hughenden Valley, High Wycombe, Buckinghamshire, HP14 4NX Tel: (01494) 564497 Fax: (01494) 563497 E-mail: sales@soundbusinessaudio.co.uk *Producers of audio information*

Sound Concepts, 56 St. Saviours Crescent, Luton, LU1 5HG Tel: (01582) 416964 Fax: (01582) 480841 *Electronic communication system manufrs*

▶ Sound Control Services, White Lodge Farm, Nottingham Road, Ab Kettleby, Melton Mowbray, Leicestershire, LE14 3JB Tel: (01664) 823704 Fax: (01664) 823663 E-mail: sales@soundcontrolservices.co.uk *Sound proofing, damping materials, sound & vibration consultants*

▶ Sound Deli, Unit 2, Victoria Grove, Hove, Brighton, BN3 2LJ Tel: (01273) 746506 E-mail: info@sounddeli.co.uk *We supply & install sound systems*

Sound Image UK Ltd, 52 Milton Road, London, SW14 8JR Tel: (020) 8255 6868 E-mail: sales@choicehifi.com *Hi fi equipment distributors*

Sound Interiots Ltd, 4 Levens Road, Newby Road Industrial Estate, Hazel Grove, Stockport, Cheshire, SK7 5DL Tel: 0161-456 8282 Fax: 0161-456 3030 E-mail: all@sound-interiors.co.uk *Suspended ceiling systems & partition fabricators*

Sound Leisure Ltd, Sandlees Way, Leeds, LS15 8AR Tel: (0845) 2301775 Fax: (0845) 2301776 E-mail: sales@soundleisure.com *Juke box manufrs*

Sound & Light Hire Pa Co, 14 Exeter St, North Tawton, Devon, EX20 2HB Tel: (01837) 89066 Fax: (01837) 89065 *Sound & light hire*

Sound Network, 131-151 Great Titchfield Street, London, W1W 5BB Tel: (020) 7665 6463 Fax: (020) 7890 7071 E-mail: info@soundnetwork.co.uk *Professional audio sales*

Sound Research Laboratories Ltd, Holbrook House, Holbrook Hall Park, Little Waldingfield, Sudbury, Suffolk, CO10 0TH Tel: (01787) 247595 Fax: (01787) 248420 E-mail: srl@soundresearch.co.uk *Environmental, acoustic consultants & noise control consultants* Also at: Birmingham, Manchester & Newcastle

Sound & Secure Ltd, 454-456 Thornton Road, Bradford, West Yorkshire, BD8 9BS Tel: (01274) 775005 Fax: (01274) 770051 *Hi-fi systems, car navigation systems & alarm retailers & fitters*

▶ Sound & Secure, Robins Park, Loddiswell, Kingsbridge, Devon, TQ7 4RT Tel: (07966) 033718 E-mail: jason@soundandsecure.freeserve.co.uk *Alarm systems installers*

Sound Sense Training, The Old Manor Ho, Bush Rd, London, SE8 5AP Tel: 020 73940131 *Supply computer training & consultants for blind*

Sound Services, Button Street, Swanley, Kent, BR8 8DX Tel: (01322) 667709 Fax: 0208-196 2387 E-mail: mail@sound-services.co.uk *Professional public address audio equipment hire sales and installation company based in Kent covering London/SE England. Dry/wet hire to bands, DJ's, conferences, schools & clubs. PAT testing service available. Microphones, mixers, decks, speakers, amplifiers & CD players for hire. Sound engineers available*

▶ Sound Space Design, Unit 2 St. George's Court, 131 Putney Bridge Road, London, SW15 2PA Tel: (020) 8877 5868 Fax: (020) 8875 9385 E-mail: acoustics@soundspacedesign.co.uk *Design, consulting and research in acoustics for the built environment, music and theatre*

▶ Sound Surround, 12 Belvedere Crescent, Bewdley, Worcestershire, DY12 1JX Tel: 01299 405077 E-mail: soundsurround@bewdley12.freeserve.co.uk *Specialists in Installation, Service, Upgrades and Maintenance of Background Music (BGM) systems in Public Houses, Clubs and Retail environments. Sales of high quality professional audio products. We offer very competitive rates while maintaining a fantastic level of customer service.*

Sound Systems, 30 Station Road, Alvechurch, Birmingham, B48 7SD Tel: 0121-445 2757 Fax: 0121-445 2757 *Sound systems hire installations & sale*

Sound Tech Ltd, 137 Western Road, Hockley, Birmingham, B18 7QD Tel: 0121-523 6344 Fax: 0121-507 0151 E-mail: chris@soundtech-ltd.freeserve.co.uk *Sound & lighting designers*

Sound Technology, 23 Townhead Street, Hamilton, Lanarkshire, ML3 7BQ Tel: (01698) 458754 Fax: (01698) 421116 *Computer systems manufrs*

Sound Technology plc, 17 Letchworth Point, Dunhams Lane, Letchworth Garden City, Hertfordshire, SG6 1ND Tel: (01462) 480500 Fax: (01462) 480800 E-mail: sales@soundtech.co.uk *Sound recording equipment & musical instruments distribution*

Sound Vision (UK) Ltd, 86 Kingsley Road, Hounslow, TW3 1QA Tel: (020) 8570 1999 Fax: (020) 8577 3033 *Educational videos & entertainment distribution*

▶ Sound & Visual Ltd, 326 Hook Rise North, Surbiton, Surrey, KT6 7LN Tel: (020) 8391 4052 E-mail: info@soundandvisual.co.uk *Audio visual installations service*

▶ SoundAV, 9 Scriven Road, Knaresborough, North Yorkshire, HG5 9EQ Tel: (0772) 5050322 E-mail: info@soundav.co.uk *Sales, hire & service provider for audio visual equipment*

▶ Soundbarrier Systems, 4 Knowsley Crescent, Portsmouth, PO6 2PJ Tel: (07709) 815242 E-mail: simon@soundbarriersystems.com *We are a Disco based in Portsmouth, UK. We have setups for local pubs/clubs to concert sized rigs for the largest of events. We cater for any event around the UK, and meet the highest standards of equipment, engineers, presentation and back-up.*

Soundcraft, Cranbourne House Cranborne Industrial Estate, Cranborne Road, Potters Bar, Hertfordshire, EN6 3JN Tel: (01707) 665000 Fax: (01707) 660482 E-mail: sales@soundcraft.com *Professional audio equipment manufrs*

▶ Soundguard, 3 Rectory Park, Bideford, Devon, EX39 3AJ Tel: 01237 478142 E-mail: info@soundguard.co.uk *Industrial audiologists provide surveys & assessments*

Soundlite Equipment, YBS House, Unit 3 Gladstone Terrace, Stanningley, Pudsey, West Yorkshire, LS28 6NE Tel: 0113-236 1157 Fax: 0113-236 3942 *Loud speaker cabinet manufrs*

Sounds Inc, Poundsbridge, Penshurst, Tonbridge, Kent, TN11 8AP Tel: (01892) 861099 Fax: (01892) 863485 E-mail: sales@soundsinc.co.uk *Vintage sound equipment*

Sounds Good Ltd, Chiltern Enterprise Centre, 12 Station Road, Theale, Reading, RG7 4AA Tel: 0118-930 1700 Fax: 0118-930 1709 E-mail: info@sounds-good.co.uk *CD manufrs*

▶ Sounds in Scale, Trefaes Bellaf, Sarn, Pwllheli, Gwynedd, LL53 8RL Tel: 01758 730529 E-mail: enquiries@soundsinscale.com *Luthier specialising in custom built electric guitars to customers own specifications.Also repairs.*

Sounds Wholesale Ltd, Unit 2 Park Street, Burton-on-Trent, Staffordshire, DE14 3SE Tel: (01283) 566823 Fax: (01283) 568631 *Replacement case suppliers*

Soundsleep Ltd, Aloe Farm, Mile Road, Winfarthing, Diss, Norfolk, IP22 2EZ Tel: (01953) 861177 Fax: (01953) 861186 E-mail: sales@sound-sleep.co.uk *Bed manufrs*

▶ Soundsounds, Balmoral Close, Earls Barton, Northampton, NN6 0LZ Tel: (01604) 811768 E-mail: sales@soundsounds.com *Providing Sound engineering and AV services to Corporate sector, bands venues, and performers. Set design /build, lighting, staging, and mains distribution.*

Soundswright Entertainers, 66 Church Street, Hartlepool, Cleveland, TS24 7DN Tel: (01429) 231133E-mail: enquiries@soundswrightday.com *Media consultancy & after-dinner speaker services*

Souness & Boyne Interiors Ltd, Suite 8, Adam Ferguson House, Station Road, Musselburgh, Midlothian, EH21 7PQ Tel: 0131-653 2228 Fax: 0131-653 2229 *Office interiors*

Source, 1 Oak Court, Pennant Way, Lee Mill Industrial Estate, Ivybridge, Devon, PL21 9GP Tel: (01752) 698698 Fax: (01752) 698001 E-mail: sales@cable-accessories.com *Cable accessories manufrs*

Source Ltd, The Old Stables, 10 Beulah Road, London, SW19 3SB Tel: (020) 8540 4201 Fax: (020) 8540 7380 E-mail: sales@sbsource.co.uk *Advertising gift suppliers*

▶ Source Internet Development Ltd, 33A Regent Street, Hinckley, Leicestershire, LE10 0BA Tel: (01455) 614711 E-mail: info@sourcedesign.co.uk *Source Internet Development is an independent web, multimedia & software design company based in Hinckley, Leicestershire. **We bring a fresh attitude to our work, coupled with extensive experience in successfully promoting a diverse range of businesses.*

Source Logistics Ltd, 75 Bothwell Street, Glasgow, G2 6TS Tel: 0141-572 2100 Fax: 0141-572 2101 E-mail: mail@sourceuk.com *Recruitment agency*

Sourcing Partnership, 24 Alva Street, Edinburgh, EH2 4PY Tel: 0131-226 4747 Fax: 0131-226 4708 E-mail: admin@sourcingpartners.co.uk *Information technology sourcing recruitment*

Sous Vide, 48-50 Edison Road, Rabans Lane Industrial Area, Aylesbury, Buckinghamshire, HP19 8TE Tel: (0845) 1212213 Fax: (01296) 431133 E-mail: lucy@sous-vide.co.uk *Chef prepared sous-vide dishes.*

▶ Souterrain Archaeological Services Ltd, 50 Rectory Drive, Exhall, Coventry, CV7 9PD Tel: (024) 7631 1567 Fax: (01794) 523528 E-mail: gps@souterrain.biz *GPS surveying services for archaeology & gis mapping services*

▶ Souters Sports Ltd, Unit 80, Bandeath Industrial Estate, Stirling, FK7 7NP Tel: (01786) 480720

South Advertising Group, PO Box 118, Congleton, Cheshire, CW12 3RQ Tel: (01260) 273813 Fax: (01260) 273813 E-mail: south@m-i-6.co.uk *Advertising & promotions*

South African Airways, St. Georges House, 61 Conduit Street, London, W1S 2NE Tel: (020) 7312 5005 Fax: (020) 7312 5008 E-mail: carriehopkins@lon.flysaa.com *Civil airline*

South Anglia Marketing Co. Ltd, Eastlodge, 110 Dunmow Road, Bishop's Stortford, Hertfordshire, CM23 5HN Tel: (01279) 656523 Fax: (01279) 653179 E-mail: enquires@sancoshrim.com *Farmers co-operative*

South Bank Alarms Ltd, 47 Church Lane, Humberston, Grimsby, South Humberside, DN36 4HZ Tel: (01472) 210031 Fax: (01472) 230772 *Alarm systems engineers*

South Bank Systems P.L.C., Compass Centre North, Chatham Maritime, Chatham, Kent, ME4 4YG Tel: (01634) 880141 Fax: (01634) 880383 E-mail: corporate@southbanksystems.com *Software systems*

South Caernarfon Creameries Ltd, Chwilog, Pwllheli, Gwynedd, LL53 6SB Tel: (01766) 810251 Fax: (01766) 810578 E-mail: mail@sccwales.co.uk *Cheese producers*

South Cave Tractors Ltd, Main Road, Brough, North Humberside, HU15 2RD Tel: (01430) 424233 Fax: (01430) 424200 E-mail: tony.levitt@btconnect.com *Agricultural sales & repairs*

South Central Cleaning Services, 7 Acorn Workshops, Empress Road, Southampton, SO14 0JY Tel: (023) 8032 2752 Fax: (023) 8032 2752 E-mail: russellbowley@hotmail.com *Cleaning & maintenance services*

South Coast, The Docks, Fowey, Cornwall, PL23 1AL Tel: (01726) 832121 Fax: (01726) 833474 E-mail: agency.foy@denholm-barwil.com *Shipping agents* Also at: Par

South Coast Alarms Ltd, 54 Overcombe Drive, Weymouth, Dorset, DT3 6QF Tel: (01305) 832614 E-mail: admin@southcoastalarms.co.uk *Intruder alarms, servicing, installation & upgrades. CCTV & access control*

South Coast Cartons, Unit 36, Bailey Gate Industrial Estate, Sturminster Marshall, Wimborne, Dorset, BH21 4DB Tel: (01258) 858445 Fax: (01258) 858223 *Carton manufrs*

South Coast Catering, 43 Seaside, Eastbourne, East Sussex, BN22 7NB Tel: (01323) 444530 Fax: (01323) 641176 E-mail: info@sccuk.com *Catering equipment*

▶ South Coast Construction, Ford House, 54 High Street, Fordingbridge, Hampshire, SP6 1AX Tel: (01425) 657272 Fax: (01425) 656788

▶ South Coast Fencing Ltd, Corn Dryer, Alresford Road, Winchester, Hampshire, SO21 1HH Tel: (01962) 843231 Fax: (01962) 843294 E-mail: sales@southcoastfencing.co.uk *Fencing materials*

South Coast Hydraulics Ltd, Unit 1, Kings Crescent, Shoreham-by-Sea, West Sussex, BN43 5LE Tel: (01273) 446444 Fax: (01273) 446555

South Coast Roofing Supplies Ltd, Daveys Lane, Lewes, East Sussex, BN7 2BQ Tel: (01273) 488888 Fax: (01273) 489999 *Roofing material distributors*

South Coast Seals Services Ltd, 16 Fareham Enterprise Centre, Hackett Way, Fareham, Hampshire, PO14 1TH Tel: (01329) 230916 Fax: (01329) 823783 *Mechanical seal suppliers*

▶ South Coast Web Solutions, 5 County Gardens, Fareham, Hampshire, PO14 3JA Tel: 01329 314226 E-mail: scws-uk@ntlworld.com *South Coast Web Solutions - Web design and hosting services - Fareham, Hampshire. Professional web design and hosting services for the south of England.*

▶ South Coast Windows & Conservatories Ltd, 81 South Coast Road, Peacehaven, East Sussex, BN10 8UR Tel: (01273) 585077 Fax: (01273) 589555 E-mail: info@southcoastwindows.co.uk *Install conservatories & windows*

South Coat Optical Ltd, 26 Highcroft Industrial Estate, Enterprise Road, Waterlooville, Hampshire, PO8 0BT Tel: (023) 9259 9411 Fax: (023) 9259 9011 *Optical manufrs*

South Darenth Farms & Coldstores Co. Ltd, St. Margarets Farm, St. Margarets Road, South Darenth, Dartford, DA4 9LB Tel: (01322) 863267 Fax: (01322) 861200 E-mail: sdfarms@btconnect.com *Farming & storage*

South Devon & Cornwall Institution For The Blind, 2 Stonehouse Street, Plymouth, PL1 3PY Tel: (01752) 662317 Fax: (01752) 662317 E-mail: sdcib@zoom.co.uk *Sewing & hospital supplies packing*

South Devon Craft & Furniture Centre, New Road, Modbury, Ivybridge, Devon, PL21 0QH Tel: (01548) 830405 *Cabinet makers*

▶ South Devon Solutions, 6a Prings Court, Market Street, Brixham, Devon, TQ5 8ET Tel: (01803) 850875 E-mail: enquiries@southdevonsolutions.com *computer repair,fix computer,computer health check,torbay,devon,torquay,brixham,paignton, south west,computer training,internet security,computer security,privacy,computer installation,computer service,computer support,computer help,infection,virus removal,spyware removal,business services,crash,computer problem,computer solutions,technology solutions,computer technology,computer software,software design,software development,database design,database development,business services,south hams,cornwall,south devon solutions*

South Durham Refrigeration, Unit 2b Trimdon Grange Industrial Estate, Trimdon Grange, Trimdon Station, County Durham, TS29 6PA Tel: (01429) 880544 Fax: (01429) 880544 *Commercial refrigeration repair*

South Durham Structures Ltd, South Church Enterprise Park, Bishop Auckland, County Durham, DL14 6XR Tel: (01388) 777350 Fax: (01388) 775225 E-mail: name@southdurhamstructures.co.uk *Structural steelwork fabricators & erectors*

South East Cooling Ltd, 6 Southwinds House, Barrack Lane, Bognor Regis, West Sussex, PO21 4BZ Tel: (01243) 268888 Fax: (01243) 268843 E-mail: sales@southeast-cooling.co.uk *Air conditioning design installation & maintenance*

South East Disco Supplies, 85 Baden Road, Gillingham, Kent, ME7 1QZ Tel: (01634) 281877 *Disco equipment suppliers*

▶ South East Galvanizers Ltd, Weston Industrial Estate, Crittall Road, Witham, Essex, CM8 3AW Tel: (01376) 501501 Fax: (01376) 513410 E-mail: lionel.bell@wedge-galv.co.uk *Hot dip galvanizing services*

South East Labels, 7 Broomers Hill Park, Broomers Hill Lane, Pulborough, West Sussex, RH20 2RY Tel: (01798) 873738 Fax: (01798) 874538 E-mail: sales@southeastlabels.co.uk *Labels manufrs*

South East Power Transmissions Ltd, Network House, Perry Road, Harlow, Essex, CM18 7ND Tel: (01279) 418300 Fax: (01279) 418100 E-mail: stransltd@aol.com *Gear cutters*

▶ South East Solar, Alterchrome House, Murray Road, Orpington, Kent, BR5 3QY Tel: (01689) 896345 Fax: (01689) 806549 E-mail: sales@sesolar.co.uk *Window film installers ,interior curtains & blinds*

South East Steel Fabrication & Engineering, Legge Street, London, SE13 6NP Tel: (020) 8690 6229 Fax: (020) 8690 6229 *Structural steelwork engineers*

South East Ties Ltd, The Old Forge House, Manston Road, Manston, Ramsgate, Kent, CT12 5HG Tel: (0845) 8387442 Fax: (0845) 8387443 *Structural repairers services*

South Eastern Auto Ltd, Bridge Industrial Centre, Wharf Road, Tovil, Maidstone, Kent, ME15 6RR Tel: (01622) 690010 Fax: (01622) 690683 E-mail: seaes@aol.com *Auto-electrical engineers & automotive parts distributors*

South Eastern Carriage Co. Ltd, Unit 11, 71-73 Nathan Way, London, SE28 0BQ Tel: (020) 8854 4655 Fax: (020) 8854 0614 *Road transport/ haulage/freight services*

South Eastern Finecast, Glenn House, Hartfield Row, Forest Row, East Sussex, RH18 5DZ Tel: (01342) 824711 Fax: (01342) 822270 *Model kits manufrs*

South Eastern Hydraulics Ltd, 40b Holmethorpe Avenue, Redhill, RH1 2NL Tel: (01737) 768011 Fax: (01737) 773469 E-mail: mail@seh-ltd.co.uk *Hydraulic component & equipment distributors & manufrs*

South Eastern Marine Services Ltd, Olympic Business Centre, Paycocke Road, Basildon, Essex, SS14 3EX Tel: (01268) 534427 Fax: (01268) 281009 E-mail: sems@btinternet.com *Marine & aviation survival equipment*

South Eastern Printing & Stationery Co. Ltd, Unit 5H Horndon Industrial Park, Station Road, West Horndon, Brentwood, Essex, CM13 3XL Tel: (01277) 812111 Fax: (01277) 811388 *Wholesale stationers & printers*

South Eastern Road & Groundworks Ltd, Highlands Yard, Queenborough Road, Southminster, Essex, CM0 7AD Tel: (01621) 774901 Fax: (01621) 773988 *Ground workers*

South Eastern Saws (Industrial) Ltd, Unit 6 Spectrum, Parkwood Industrial Estate, Maidstone, Kent, ME15 9XZ Tel: (01622) 750177 Fax: (01622) 688112 *Industrial tooling sales & services*

South Eastern Security, 90 Canterbury Road, Hawkinge, Folkestone, Kent, CT18 7BN Tel: (01303) 891155 Fax: (01303) 891155 E-mail: enquiries@southeasternsecurity.co.uk *Security alarm installation & monitoring*

South Eastern Tools, Old Odiham Road, Alton, Hampshire, GU34 4BU Tel: (01420) 89555 Fax: (01420) 84463 *Supply & repair garage equipment*

South Ferriby Marina Ltd, South Ferriby Marina, Red Lane, South Ferriby, Barton-Upon-Humber, South Humberside, DN18 6JH Tel: (01652) 635620 Fax: (01652) 660517 E-mail: tfertuson_ie@yahoo.co.uk *Yacht builders, marina operators & chandlers*

▶ South Haven Construction Ltd, Stockwell Road, Pembroke Dock, Dyfed, SA72 6TQ Tel: (01646) 686838 Fax: (01646) 686296

South Herts Waste Management Ltd, 12 Barbers Road, Stratford, London, E15 2PH Tel: (020) 8519 5622 Fax: (020) 8519 8269 E-mail: info@shwm.co.uk *Waste management contractors*

▶ South Holland Marine & Fabrication Ltd, Poplars Farm, Donington Road, Swineshead, Boston, Lincolnshire, PE20 3HL Tel: (01529) 460758 Fax: (01529) 460927 E-mail: info@southhollandmarine.co.uk *Boat builders*

John South (Boats) Ltd, 89 Condover Industrial Estate, near Shrewsbury, Dorrington, Shrewsbury, SY5 7NH Tel: (01743) 718415 Fax: (01743) 718415 *Boat builders*

South Lincs Construction Ltd, Bars Bridge, Bourne Road, Spalding, Lincolnshire, PE11 3NQ Tel: (01775) 640555 Fax: (01775) 640679 E-mail: info@aldesignandbuild.com *Steel work & cladding*

South Lincs Patterns, Ivanhoe, Spalding Common, Spalding, Lincolnshire, PE11 3AS Tel: (01775) 722988 Fax: (01775) 760386 E-mail: sales@southlincsfoundry.co.uk *Ferrous & non-ferrous castings & pattern makers*

South Lincs Plant Hire & Sales Ltd, Enterprise Way, Pinchbeck, Spalding, Lincolnshire, PE11 3YR Tel: (01775) 766131 Fax: (01775) 711305 *Plant hire & sales*

▶ South Link Distribution, Units 11-12 Winston Business Centre, Chartwell Road, Lancing, West Sussex, BN15 8TU Tel: (01903) 851852 Fax: (01903) 851444

▶ South Lodge, 19 The Vale, Broadstairs, Kent, CT10 1RB Tel: (01843) 600478 E-mail: Info@VisitSouthLodge.co.uk *Bed and Breakfast in Broadstairs*Welcome to the South Lodge Guest House * **A place to stay where you will experience the comfort of home,*a sense of space, relaxation and time for yourself.***A feeling of luxury that comes from quality surroundings.***All only 6 minutes walk from Broadstairs main beach,*the glorious Viking Bay and only 5 minutes from the town centres many*restaurants, pubs, cafes and interesting shops.***

South London Auto Paints, 40 Deptford Broadway, London, SE8 4PQ Tel: (020) 8692 6940 Fax: (020) 8692 7862 *Car paint manufrs*

▶ South London Fencing, 288 Addington Road, South Croydon, Surrey, CR2 8LF Tel: (020) 8657 9449 Fax: 0208 6579449 E-mail: stuart@south-london-fencing.co.uk *Fencing and gates contractors based in South Croydon Surrey serving south London. Supplying and installing fences, gates, pergolas and trellises for homes and businesses.*

South London Lock Service Ltd, 190 High Street, London, SE20 7QB Tel: (020) 8778 6657 Fax: (020) 8778 6657 *Locksmiths*

▶ South Meadow Homes Ltd, 1 Gibbas Way, Upper Lamphey Road, Pembroke, Dyfed, SA71 5JA Tel: (01646) 682053 Fax: (01646) 682066

South Midland Saws Ltd, Lincoln Road, Cressex Business Park, High Wycombe, Buckinghamshire, HP12 3RQ Tel: (01494) 520612 Fax: (01494) 465373 E-mail: sales@scsaws.co.uk *Circular saws, distribute, repair & manufrs*

South Midland Steel Ltd, 19 Oaklands Avenue, Watford, WD19 4SD Tel: (01923) 252089 Fax: (01923) 250525 E-mail: smsteel@freeuk.com *Steel stockholders* Also at: Luton

South Midlands Communications Ltd, SM House, School Close, Chandler's Ford, Eastleigh, Hampshire, SO53 4RA Tel: (023) 8024 6200 Fax: (023) 8024 6206 E-mail: sales@smc-comms.com *Mobile radio communications service*

South Midlands Group plc, 48 Oakley Road, Luton, LU4 9PU Tel: (01582) 490606 Fax: (01582) 581305 E-mail: info@smgplc.co.uk *Cleaning & maintenance contractors*

South Notts Computers, 246-248 Southchurch Drive, Nottingham, NG11 8AA Tel: 0115-914 7066 Fax: 0115-914 7077 E-mail: info@southnottscomputers.co.uk *Computer systems & software retailers*

South Ribble Cash Registers, Middleforth, Penwortham, Preston, PR1 9QR Tel: (01772) 740588 Fax: 01772 740588 E-mail: info@srcr.co.uk *Electronic cash register suppliers*

South River Marine, Reed Lane, St. Olaves, Great Yarmouth, Norfolk, NR31 9HG Tel: (01493) 488469 Fax: (01493) 488499 E-mail: southrivermarine@broadlyboats.com *Boat builders & repairers*

South Scotland Valve & Fitting Co Ltd, 9-11 Macadam Place, Irvine, Ayrshire, KA11 4HP Tel: (01294) 213341 Fax: (01294) 213484 E-mail: enquiries@ssvf.co.uk *Tube fittings & hose assembley distributors*

South Staffordshire Fencing Co. Ltd, Unit 12, Brookfield Drive, Cannock, Staffordshire, WS11 0JN Tel: (01543) 462008 Fax: (01543) 462341 *Fencing contractors*

South Staffs Group Ltd, Churchfield House, 36 Vicar Street, Dudley, West Midlands, DY2 8RG Tel: (01384) 458300 Fax: (01384) 233670 E-mail: sales@southstaffsindustries.com *Metal finishing & general engineers* Also at: Tipton

▶ South Staffs Industries Ltd, Bloomfield Road, Tipton, West Midlands, DY4 9EE Tel: 0121-522 2373 Fax: 0121-522 3528 *Pipes & tubes*

South Staffs Supplies, Langley Heath Business Park, Eastern Avenue, Lichfield, Staffordshire, WS13 6RL Tel: (01543) 258883 Fax: (01543) 417444 *Protective clothing distributors*

South Wales Brush Co Ltd, 1 Ely Distribution Centre, Argyle Way, Cardiff, CF5 5NJ Tel: (029) 2059 9199 Fax: (029) 2059 9299 E-mail: sales@brush.co.uk *Industrial brush manufactures, design & manufacture service for bespoke products.*

▶ South Wales Cameras Ltd, Unit 2, Bessemer Workshop, Bessemer Close, Cardiff, CF11 8CL Tel: (029) 2034 2681 Fax: (029) 2034 2486 E-mail: southwalescamera@btconnect.com *Security manufrs*

South Wales Computer Repairs, 1-2 Usk Street, Newport, Gwent, NP19 7BE Tel: (01633) 252306 Fax: (01633) 252304 E-mail: jeoff@swcr.net *Computer maintenance, sales & repairs*

South Wales Fork Trucks, Oaktree Workshops, Main Road, Crynant, Neath, West Glamorgan, SA10 8PF Tel: (01639) 750161 Fax: (01639) 750612 E-mail: admin@southwalesforktrucks.co.uk *Fork trucks sales service & hire*

South Wales Marine, Unit 4, Vale Court Alamein Road Morfa Industrial Estate, Landore, Swansea, SA1 2HY Tel: (01792) 463000 E-mail: info@sw-marine.co.uk *Rope & rigging suppliers for the commercial and leisure industries*

South Wales Microwaves, 47 St. Helens Road, Swansea, SA1 4BD Tel: (01792) 651422 Fax: (01792) 475205 *Microwave oven distribution & services*

South Wales Photocopiers, 32 Elgin St, Swansea, SA5 8QF Tel: (01792) 476065 Fax: (01792) 456849 E-mail: enquiries@southwalesphotocopiers.co.uk *Photocopier sales & services*

South Wales Sack & Bag, 4 Rhymney River Bridge Road, Cardiff, CF23 9AF Tel: (029) 2049 5060 Fax: (029) 2049 5055 E-mail: andrew_manuel@amserve.net *Polythene bag & sack suppliers*

South Wales Suppliers, Unit 40 Penmaen Business Centre, Pontllanfraith, Blackwood, Gwent, NP12 2DZ Tel: (01495) 229919 Fax: (01495) 229919 *Industrial work wear suppliers*

South Wales Time Recorders Sales & Services Ltd, Time House, Regent Street, Barry, South Glamorgan, CF62 8DT Tel: (01446) 721446 Fax: (01446) 744678 E-mail: sales@swtr.co.uk *Time recording sale & services*

▶ South Wales Time Recorders Sales & Services Ltd, Time House, Regent Street, Barry, South Glamorgan, CF62 8DT Tel: (01446) 721446 Fax: (01446) 744678 E-mail: sales@swtr.co.uk *Based in Barry, Cardiff, Time Recorders Direct are Wales' largest time recorder supplier. A leading supplier of cost effective solutions for Time & Attendance, Shop Floor Data Collection and Access Control markets. Product range includes Time Card Systems, P.C Systems, Access Control, Time Cards and Accessories, I.D Card Production, and Wall Clocks. Fully trained engineers install and repair all equipment, and after sales service contracts support all equipment. Visit our website for information on leading makes and the latest special offers*

South Wales Waterbeds Ltd, 124A Lower Dock Street, Newport, Gwent, NP20 1EN Tel: (01633) 211448 Fax: (01633) 841083 *Waterbed sales*

South Wales Window Blind Centre Ltd, 77 Fleet Street, Swansea, SA1 3US Tel: (01792) 648334 Fax: (01792) 460334 *Window blind manufrs*

▶ South West Adult Placement Scheme, Zeally House, Greenhill Way, Kingsteignton, Newton Abbot, Devon, TQ12 3SB Tel: (01626) 360170 Fax: (01626) 368252 E-mail: enquiries@swaps.org.uk *SWAPS provides adult placements in the South West of England. SWAPS is a registered charity & a not for profit company. It currently operates within the geographical areas of Devon & Cornwall. SWAPS makes & supports family based placements for vulnerable and disabled people over the age of 18 who may have learning disabilities, mental health problems &/or physical disabilities & for older people. At present SWAPS is only supporting long stay placements but we hope to be able to offer short term placements & respite breaks in the future.*

▶ South West Areas Services, Lower Upton Farm, Old Village, Cullompton, Devon, EX15 1RA Tel: (01884) 839393 Fax: (01884) 839399 *Dairy plant & equipment manufrs*

South West Audio Ltd, Vine House, Northwick Road, Pilning, Bristol, BS35 4HA Tel: (01454) 633635 Fax: (01454) 633668 *Public announcement equipment hire*

South West Business Centre Ltd, Queensgate House, 48 Queen Street, Exeter, EX4 3SR Tel: (01392) 215541 Fax: (01392) 410436 E-mail: mpurton@swbus.co.uk *Property agents*

▶ South West Coatings Ltd, 8a The Lawn, Budleigh Salterton, Devon, EX9 6LR Tel: (0870) 0802978 E-mail: info@southwestcoatings.co.uk

South West Crane Hire Ltd, Tan Lane, Exeter, EX2 8EG Tel: (01392) 256148 Fax: (01392) 270603 E-mail: info@sw-crane-hire.co.uk Sales Contact: M. Jeffery *With crane hire depots in Exeter, Plymouth, Yeovil, Taunton, Barnstaple and Bristol, South West Crane Hire Ltd provide a professional and comprehensive Crane Hire service for the South West of the UK. With cranes ranging from 8 ton to 200 ton capacity, mobile cranes, truck mounted cranes, lorry mounted cranes, all terrain cranes, we will cater for all your lift requirements under CPA contract lift or CPA crane hire terms. Our transportation division boasts a fleet of heavy hiabs, lorry mounted cranes, flat beds and trailers for heavy load transportation. Our machinery removal team will handle the dismantle, transport and*

continued

assembly of machines, factory equipment and heavy plant, machine moves of all types considered. So for a complete, professional lift and transport service look no further than South West Crane Hire, no job too small or too big

South West Doors, 112 Eden Vale Road, Westbury, Wiltshire, BA13 3QE Tel: (01373) 865067 Fax: (01373) 301811 E-mail: sales@southwestdoors.co.uk *Industrial & commercial doors*

South West Fasteners, 1 Shepherd Road, Gloucester, GL2 5EL Tel: (01452) 424346 Fax: (01452) 309313 *Threaded product specialists*

South West Fencing & Sheds, Unit 1A Plum Lane, Dunwear, Bridgwater, Somerset, TA6 5HL Tel: (01278) 447031 *Fence & shed sellers*

South West Galvanizers Ltd, Marsh End, Lords Meadow Industrial Estate, Crediton, Devon, EX17 1DN Tel: (01363) 774574 Fax: (01363) 775070 E-mail: south.west@wedge-galv.co.uk *Hot dip galvanizing organisation, part of nation-wide Wedge Group*

South West Glassfibre, The Former Mine Compressor House, Dolcoath, Camborne, Cornwall, TR14 8RR Tel: (01209) 613033 Fax: (01209) 613033 *Car styling accessories manufrs*

▶ South West Highways Ltd, Rydon Depo, Rydon Road, Kingsteignton, Newton Abbot, Devon, TQ12 3QG Tel: (01626) 351636 Fax: (01626) 332154

South West Highways Signs, Upcott Avenue, Barnstaple, Devon, EX31 1HN Tel: 01271 342607 *Sign manufrs*

South West Industrial Finishers Co. Ltd., 117-119 Severn Road, Weston-Super-Mare, Avon, BS23 1DS Tel: (01934) 414613 Fax: (01934) 636243 *Paint finishers*

South West Instrumentation, Swi House, High Street, Market Lavington, Devizes, Wiltshire, SN10 4AF Tel: (01380) 816444 Fax: (01380) 816999 E-mail: sales@swi.org.uk *Pressure Transducers in twenty four hours. Instrumentation Distributors.*

South West Metal Finishing Ltd, Alphinbrook Road, Marsh Barton Trading Estate, Exeter, EX2 8TJ Tel: (01392) 258234 Fax: (01392) 421538 E-mail: swmf@eicgroup.co.uk *Electroplaters & metal finishers*

South West Metallurgical Services, Sancreed Business Centre, Grumbla, Sancreed, Penzance, Cornwall, TR20 8QU Tel: (01736) 810812 Fax: (01736) 810810 E-mail: swmet@swmet.com *Mineral engineers*

▶ South West Mortgage Solutions, 12 Court View, Brixton, Plymouth, PL8 2NY Tel: (01752) 881647 Fax: (01752) 881647 E-mail: enquiry@justmortgagesplus.com *We are a small, friendly, client orientated team, qualified in mortgage brokerage & administration. We aim to provide the best possible mortgage & insurance related advice, tailored to fit each client's requirements, from first enquiry to completion*

South West Motors Ltd, 1 Cornishway North, Galmington Trading Estate, Taunton, Somerset, TA1 5LY Tel: (01823) 327805 Fax: (01823) 321791 *Motor trade repairs & recovery*

▶ South West Motorsport, St. Johns Business Park, Penzance Road, Helston, Cornwall, TR13 8HN Tel: (01326) 561802 E-mail: info@southwestmotorsport.com *Supply & fit car parts & accessories*

South West Precision, Mill Road, Barnstaple, Devon, EX31 1JQ Tel: (01271) 344221 Fax: (01271) 344355 *Precision engineers & spring manufrs*

South West Sound & Light, The Old Smithy, Cockwood, Starcross, Exeter, EX6 8RA Tel: (01626) 890806 Fax: (01626) 891465 E-mail: sales@swlighting.co.uk *Entertainment industry sales & repair*

South West Storage Equipment, Unit 1-2 Rowan Court, Armstrong Way, Yate, Bristol, BS37 5NG Tel: (01454) 310536 Fax: (01454) 322090 E-mail: enquiries@southweststorage.co.uk *Floor & racking manufrs*

South West Surveys Projects Ltd, 43 Lower Fore Street, Saltash, Cornwall, PL12 6JQ Tel: (01752) 849190 Fax: (01752) 849229 E-mail: office@swsurveys.co.uk *Hydrographic & land surveyors & project management*

▶ South West Tourism, Tourism House Pynes Hill, Rydon Lane, Exeter, EX2 5WT Tel: (01392) 360050 Fax: (01392) 445112 E-mail: info@swtourism.co.uk *A speciality service introducing buyers and sellers of tourism/ hospitality related*

South West Tractors Ltd, Thorne Cross Farm, Cheriton Bishop, Exeter, EX6 6HA Tel: (01647) 24007 Fax: (01647) 24107 E-mail: chris@southwesttractors.co.uk *Sales & export, tractors, construction equipment & shipping containers*

▶ South West Yacht Brokers, Breakwater Road, Plymstock, Plymouth, PL9 7HJ Tel: (01752) 401421 Fax: (01752) 401421 E-mail: enquiries@south-west-rib-rides.co.uk *Fly over the waves at up to 30 knots in a Rigid Inflatable Boat similar to an inshore lifeboat.*Hold on as you are taken into breathtakingly exciting turns at your request.*Rides are from the Mount Batten Centre and Barbican Plymouth. Visit the beautiful River Yealm and numerous beaches on the 1 hour ride.*Gift Vouchers available.*Services provided include Corporate Entertainment, Stag /Hen Parties, Childrens Parties, Ferrying and large groups where the leaders travel free.*Area covered:- Salcombe to Fowey* Open all year*½ hr rides Adults £10, Children £5, 1 hr rides Adults £15 Children £10. Family Discounts. **

South Western Equipment Catering Services, Southlands Farm, Cockers Hill, Compton Dando, Bristol, BS39 4JX Tel: (01761) 490167 Fax: (01761) 490167 *Repairers sales & service of catering equipment*

South Western Flooring Services, 145-147 Park Lane, Frampton Cotterell, Bristol, BS36 2ES Tel: (01454) 880982 Fax: (01454) 880982 E-mail: swflooring@blueyonda.co.uk *Flooring services*

South Western Industrial Plasters, 63 Netherstreet, Bromham, Chippenham, Wiltshire, SN15 2DP Tel: (01380) 850616 *Casting plaster suppliers*

South Western Joinery, The Barn, Pymore Road, Bridport, Dorset, DT6 3GR Tel: (01308) 425543 *Joinery manufrs*

South Western Plastics Ltd, The Old Jail, Willway Street, Bristol, BS3 4BG Tel: 0117-953 1811 *Plastics coating services*

South Western Supplies, Collett Way, Newton Abbot, Devon, TQ12 4PH Tel: (01626) 333900 Fax: (01626) 324297 *Architectural ironmongers*

South Western Tools Ltd, 26 New Station Road, Bristol, BS16 3RU Tel: 0117-965 9596 Fax: 0117-965 9566 *Toolmakers & precision engineering services*

South Western Windows Ltd, Panteg Industrial Estate, Station Road, Griffithstown, Pontypool, Gwent, NP4 5LX Tel: (01495) 756868 Fax: (01495) 758274 E-mail: swwindows@aol.com *Upvc & aluminum windows installers & manufrs*

South Wirral Joinery, 1 Newton Road, Ellesmere Port, CH65 4AP Tel: 0151-355 2541 *Joinery*

▶ South Yorks Tarmacadam Contractors Ltd, Wentworth Industrial Estate, Wentworth Way, Tankersley, Barnsley, South Yorkshire, S75 3DH Tel: (01226) 748748

▶ South Yorkshire Cash Registers & Scales, Unit 2 Longacre Way, Holbrook Industrial Estate, Holbrook, Sheffield, S20 3FS Tel: 0114-288 0854 Fax: 0114-247 8777 E-mail: sycr@btconnect.com *Cash register manufrs*

▶ South Yorkshire Home Improvements, Hoyle Mill Lane, Thurlstone, Sheffield, S36 9PZ Tel: (01226) 370270 Fax: (01226) 370377 E-mail: sales@syhi.co.uk *Timber merchants services*

South Yorkshire Laser Cutting Ltd, Unit 22-23, Bookers Way, Todwick Road Industrial Estate, Dinnington, Sheffield, S25 3SH Tel: (01909) 568682 Fax: (01909) 565648 E-mail: sylc.laser@virgin.net *Laser cutting sub-contractors*

South Yorkshire Pattern Co. Ltd, Nimrod Works, Trinity Street, Sheffield, S3 7AJ Tel: 0114-272 1999 Fax: 0114-272 1999 *Engineers pattern makers*

▶ South Yorkshire Printers Ltd, Digital Works, Arvis Lane, Sheffield, S3 8EG Tel: 0114-272 1105 Fax: 0114-276 0633 E-mail: design@southyorkshireprinters.co.uk *Commercial printing for business use*

Southam Agricultural Services, Fields Farm, Station Road, Southam, Warwickshire, CV47 2DH Tel: (01926) 813426 Fax: (01926) 817908 E-mail: sales@southamagri.co.uk *Agricultural engineers*

▶ Southam Hire Services Ltd, Manor Farm, Beachampton, Milton Keynes, MK19 6DT Tel: (01908) 262224 Fax: (01908) 240003 E-mail: info@southamhireservices.co.uk *Southam hire services is a company which specialise in the hire of plant & tools for the trade & diy, specialising in mini excavators,skid steer loaders,dumpers & ground clearing equipment, nationwide coverage*

Southampton Container Terminals Ltd, Berth 204-206 Prince Charles Container Port, Western Docks, Southampton, SO15 1DA Tel: (023) 8070 1701 Fax: (023) 8052 8285 E-mail: admin@sct.uk.com *Containers loading & unloading specialists*

▶ Southampton Containers Limited, Eling Container Base, Eling Wharf, High Street, Totton, Southampton, SO40 4TE Tel: (023) 8066 8505 Fax: (023) 8066 8504 E-mail: info@southamptoncontainers.co.uk *Container storage*

Southampton & Fareham Chamber Of Commerce & Industry Ltd, 53 Bugle Street, Southampton, SO14 2LF Tel: (023) 8022 3541 Fax: (023) 8022 7426 E-mail: info@soton-chamber.co.uk *Chamber of commerce*

Southampton Industrial Draughting Ltd, 33A Salisbury Road, Totton, Southampton, SO40 3HX Tel: (023) 8086 1651 Fax: (023) 8086 1651 *Technical designers*

▶ Southampton Mazda, Bursledon Road, Southampton, SO19 7LW Tel: (023) 8042 2777 Fax: (023) 8044 3320 E-mail: sales@southamptonmazda.co.uk *Whether a business or a private motorist we can help you acquire your next Car. Choose a new car from the stunning Mazda range or ofrom a selection of used cars. In addition we can arrange a finance packge to suit your pocket and needs. *We offer an excellent service and maintenance facilities.*

▶ Southampton Rubber Stamp Co., 23a Rumbridge Street, Totton, Southampton, SO40 9DQ Tel: (023) 8086 2993 Fax: (023) 8086 9998 E-mail: sales@southamptonrubberstamp.com *Office equipment & rubber stamps suppliers*

▶ Southampton Tools, 159-161 Obelisk Road, Southampton, SO19 9DN Tel: (023) 8043 5700 Fax: (023) 8044 7081 *Tool sales - marine, plumbing distributors*

Southams Of Haworth, 202 Long Lee Lane, Keighley, West Yorkshire, BD21 4TT Tel: (01535) 603491 Fax: (01535) 647255 *Bakers*

▶ Southborough Builders (2004) Ltd, Unit 1, Woodfalls Industrial Estate, Gravelly Ways, Laddingford, Maidstone, Kent, ME18 6DA Tel: (01622) 870167

Southbound Print Finishers, 42A Commercial Road, Eastbourne, East Sussex, BN21 3XF Tel: (01323) 647824 Fax: (01323) 647963 *Printers services & supplies*

Southco Europe, Farnham Trading Estate, Farnham, Surrey, GU9 9PL Tel: (01252) 714422 Fax: (01252) 712738 E-mail: info@dzus.com *Manufacturers of fasteners*

Southco Manufacturing Co., Shire Business Park, Wainwright Road, Worcester, WR4 9FA Tel: (01905) 751000 Fax: (01905) 751090 E-mail: info@southco.com *Fastener-latch & rivet manufrs*

Southcombe Bros Ltd, Cole Lane, Stoke-sub-Hamdon, Somerset, TA14 6QD Tel: (01935) 823567 Fax: (01935) 822918 E-mail: sales@southcombe.com *Dress gloves & all types of gloves*

Southcroft Engineering Co. Ltd, Thurcroft Industrial Estate, New Orchard Road, Thurcroft, Rotherham, South Yorkshire, S66 9HY Tel: (01709) 545147 Fax: (01709) 700259 *Stainless steel catering equipment manufrs*

▶ Southdale Homes Ltd, Westholme Road, Halifax, West Yorkshire, HX1 4JF Tel: (01422) 380090 Fax: (01422) 321636

Southdown Composites Ltd, Lasham Airfield, Lasham, Alton, Hampshire, GU34 5SR Tel: (01256) 381359 Fax: (01256) 381359 E-mail: sales@southdowncomposites.com *Glider & aircraft maintenance & repairers*

Southdown Composites Ltd, Lasham Airfield, Lasham, Alton, Hampshire, GU34 5SR Tel: (01256) 381359 Fax: (01256) 381359 E-mail: sales@southdowncomposites.com *Composite manufacturer of fibreglass & reinforced plastics*

▶ Southdown Construction Ltd, Mill Road, Portslade, Brighton, BN41 1PD Tel: (01273) 429200 Fax: (01273) 429222 E-mail: sales@southdownconstruction.com *Architectural metalwork*

Southdown House Software Ltd, Southdown House, Guildford Road, Westcott, Dorking, Surrey, RH4 3NR Tel: (01306) 877998 Fax: (01306) 887755 E-mail: info@southdown.co.uk *Software reseller & web developers*

Southdown Oil Supplies Ltd, Pound Lane, Thatcham, Berkshire, RG19 3TQ Tel: (01635) 877456 Fax: (01635) 861352 *Oil distributors*

Southdown Plant Hire Ltd, Daveys Lane, Lewes, East Sussex, BN7 2BQ Tel: (01273) 472177 *Construction plant hire*

Southdown Tractors, Burndell Road, Yapton, Arundel, West Sussex, BN18 0HR Tel: (01243) 551835 Fax: (01243) 553517 *Repair agricultural machinery suppliers*

Southeast Plant Ltd, Unit B1, Sweechbridge Road, Herne Bay, Kent, CT6 6TE Tel: (01227) 749009 Fax: (01227) 749009 *Plant & machinery dealers*

Southend Aluminium Co., 24 Milton Road, Westcliff-on-Sea, Essex, SS0 7JX Tel: (01702) 331601 Fax: (01702) 330525 *Metal stockholders*

Southend Paper Bag Co., 90 Archer Avenue, Southend-on-Sea, SS2 4QT Tel: (01702) 463830 *Paper bag wholesalers, polythene tissue*

Southend Sports Trophies, 536 Sutton Road, Southend-on-Sea, SS2 5PW Tel: (01702) 616046 Fax: (01702) 616046 *Trophies medals & rosettes*

Southend Total Engineering & Fabrication, 14 Terminal Close, Shoeburyness, Southend-on-Sea, SS3 9BN Tel: (01702) 299499 Fax: (01702) 299561 *Engineers & fabricators*

Southern Antennae Ltd, 15 Grosvenor Road, Broadstairs, Kent, CT10 2BT Tel: (01843) 865673 Fax: (01843) 864542 E-mail: sales@southern-antenna.demon.co.uk *CCTV installation & tv aerial, satellite system*

Southern Asbestos Services Ltd, Riverside Business Centre, River Lawn Road, Tonbridge, Kent, TN9 1EP Tel: (01732) 357468 Fax: (01732) 358377 *Asbestos Removal Contractors*

▶ Southern Auto Repairs Ltd, Unit 7 Quay Lane, Hardway, Gosport, Hampshire, PO12 4LJ Tel: (023) 9252 6223 Fax: (023) 9251 0919 E-mail: info@automation4industry.co.uk *Southern Automation & Control is an industrial automation company focused to be the most valued provider of control and information solutions. With a focus on automation solutions that help customers meet productivity objectives, the company brings together leading brands in industrial automation, engineering services and factory management software. Our complete automation solutions include specialty products designed for industry-specific applications.*

Southern Automatic Transmission Services, 2 Avocet Way, Diplocks Way, Hailsham, East Sussex, BN27 3JF Tel: (01323) 843178 Fax: (01323) 843178 *Automatic transmission re-manufrs*

Southern Bearings Ltd, Unit 11 Waldeck House, Waldeck Road, Maidenhead, Berkshire, SL6 8BR Tel: (01628) 674123 Fax: (01628) 776502 E-mail: cmay@southernbearing.co.uk *Bearing distributors & stockholders*

Southern Brick Cutting Services Ltd, Kennel Lane, Reigate Road, Hookwood, Horley, Surrey, RH6 0AY Tel: (01293) 776888 Fax: (01293) 776598 *Specialist brick cutting service*

Southern Business Communications, Unit 2 The Broadway, Andover, Hampshire, SP10 2JF Tel: (01264) 336644 Fax: (01264) 332083 E-mail: sbc-ltd@btconnect.com *Cellular telephones retailers*

Southern Cables, 5 Burwood Grove, Hayling Island, Hampshire, PO11 9DS Tel: (023) 9246 7337 *Telecommunication equipment suppliers*

Southern Calibration Laboratories Ltd, 7 Solent Industrial Estate, Shamblehurst Lane, Hedge End, Southampton, SO30 2FX Tel: (01489) 790296 Fax: (01489) 790294 E-mail: info@southcal.co.uk Sales Contact: Lesley King *We guarantee a five working day turnaround on calibration of electrical/ dimensional/pressure/torque/crimp/force & balances etc/Including a dedicated repair facility. SCL also supply new instrumentation by most manufacturers, contact sales for advice on selection and a quotation.*

Southern Care Systems Ltd, Spectra House Unit 1a, Hightown Industrial Estate, Ringwood, Hampshire, BH24 1NZ Tel: (01425) 471522 Fax: (01425) 479130 E-mail: sales@southerncaresystems.co.uk *Disabled person lifting equipment manufrs*

Southern Chemical Services Ltd, 16 Williams Industrial Park, Gore Road, New Milton, Hampshire, BH25 6SH Tel: (01425) 617197 Fax: (01425) 617197 E-mail: scsltd@scsltd.fsnet.co.uk *Industrial cleaning chemical suppliers*

Southern Cleaning Supplies, 8 Lindbergh Road, Ferndown Industrial Estate, Wimborne, Dorset, BH21 7SP Tel: (01202) 861769 Fax: (01202) 870436 *Janitorial suppliers*

Southern Commutators Ltd, 16B Mill Lane, Carshalton, Surrey, SM5 2JY Tel: (020) 8669 3876 Fax: (020) 8773 4082 E-mail: southerncommutators@tiscali.co.uk *Electric commutator & slip ring manufrs*

Southern Computer Service Ltd, 15 Blandford Gardens, Sittingbourne, Kent, ME10 4HW Tel: (01795) 429398 *Computer consultants*

Southern Confectioners, 9 East Howe Lane, Bournemouth, BH10 5HX Tel: (01202) 581126 Fax: (01202) 582025 *Confectionery manufrs*

▶ Southern Conveyors, Unit 2 Denton Slipways Site, Wharf Road, Gravesend, Kent, DA12 2RU Tel: (01474) 564145 *Conveyor designers & manufrs*

Southern Counties Automatics, Great Hills Farm, Swallowfield Road, Beech Hill, Reading, RG7 2BG Tel: (01256) 882020 Fax: (01256) 881112 E-mail: ian@amusementsrus.co.uk *Amusement equipment suppliers*

▶ Southern Counties Engineering Services Ltd, Ailwood, Corfe Castle, Wareham, Dorset, BH20 5JA Tel: (01929) 481440 Fax: (01929) 425688 E-mail: keithshaw@shellbay.unioffice.co.uk *Agricultural engineering, forestry, plant & commercial vehicles*

Southern Counties Fuels Ltd, Colwood Lane, Warninglid, Haywards Heath, West Sussex, RH17 5UE Tel: (0845) 6004006 Fax: (01870) 7584442 E-mail: sales@scf.co.uk *Distributors heating fuel & kerosene gas*

▶ Southern Counties Fuels, Ipswich Depot, Holywells Site, Cliff Quay, Ipswich, IP3 0BE Tel: (0845) 6004006 Fax: (01473) 885030 E-mail: jonathan@scf.co.uk *Fuel oils*

Southern Counties Glass, Unit I Foundry Close, Horsham, West Sussex, RH13 5TX Tel: (01403) 264723 Fax: (01403) 268153 E-mail: derek@southerncountiesglass.co.uk *Glazing contractors, conservatory & double glazing* Also at: Crawley

Southern Counties Scientific Services Ltd, 15-17 Lansdowne Road, Shirley, Southampton, SO15 4HD Tel: (023) 8077 5535 Fax: (023) 8077 5545 E-mail: davidbelgrovelee@aol.com *Analytical chemists service*

Southern Counties Shooting Ltd, Wardon Hill, Evershot, Dorchester, Dorset, DT2 9PW Tel: (01935) 83625 Fax: (01935) 83756 E-mail: scshooting@aol.com *Clay shooting club*

Southern Counties Steel Fabrications, Unit 1-2 17 Bessemer Close, Ebblake Industrial Estate, Verwood, Dorset, BH31 6AZ Tel: (01202) 820983 Fax: (01202) 820001 E-mail: info@southernsteel.co.uk *Steel fabricating specialists*

▶ Southern Court Furniture Co. Ltd, 14 Newport Industrial Estate, Launceston, Cornwall, PL15 8EX Tel: (01566) 779880 Fax: (01566) 779880 E-mail: sales@southerncourtfurniture.co.uk *Reproduction antique furniture*

Southern Crafts, Durweston, Blandford Forum, Dorset, DT11 0QE Tel: (01258) 453987 *Interior Furniture Design/manufacture*

Southern Credit Services Kent Ltd, 64 Highfield Road, Willesborough, Ashford, Kent, TN24 0JU Tel: (01233) 631998 E-mail: scs_ashford@hotmail.com *Debt collectors*

Southern & Darwent, Lissadel Street, Salford, M6 6BR Tel: 0161-745 9287 Fax: 0161-737 9744 *Timber merchants*

▶ Southern Despatch, 87 Palmerston Road, Bournemouth, BH1 4HP Tel: (01202) 394357 Fax: (01202) 398954 E-mail: sales@southerndespatch.co.uk *Bournemouth leading Courier company offer a same day service locally and nationwide, we also have an out of hours call out service, from single jobs to company contracts, bikes, vans & trucks are available*

Southern Drilling Services Ltd, The Factory, Ford Airfield Industrial Estate, Ford, Arundel, West Sussex, BN18 0HY Tel: (01903) 732359 Fax: (01903) 732476 E-mail: info@southern-drilling.co.uk *Water well drilling equipment manufrs*

▶ Southern Driver Training, 87 Wrestwood Road, Bexhill-on-Sea, East Sussex, TN40 2LP Tel: (01424) 732952 E-mail: southerndrivertraining@hotmail.com *Driving tuition*

Southern Drylining, 32 North Poulner Road, Ringwood, Hampshire, BH24 1SP Tel: (07739) 605060 Fax: (0781) 2245583 E-mail: info@southerndrylining.co.uk *Southern Drylining offers a complete, competitive & reliable contract plastering & dry lining service. We have public & employers liability insurance, up to date Health & Safety policies, CDM method statements and cash reports.*

Southern Ductwork Manufacturing Ltd, Unit 15, Woodlands Business Park, Maidenhead, Berkshire, SL6 3UA Tel: (01628) 828446 Fax: (01628) 828448 E-mail: southernductwork@btconnect.com *Sheet metalwork & ductwork manufrs*

▶ Southern Electric, Hambridge Road, Newbury, Berkshire, RG14 5TP Tel: (01635) 572382 Fax: (01635) 572383

▶ Southern Electric, Benett Street, Ryde, Isle of Wight, PO33 2BJ Tel: (01983) 617000 Fax: (01983) 566324

▶ Southern Electric Power Distribution plc, Inveralmond House, 200 Dunkeld Road, Perth, PH1 3GH Tel: (0845) 6002006

▶ Southern Exhaust Supplies Ltd, Avonside Indust Estate, St. Philips Marsh, Bristol, BS2 0TS Tel: 0117-972 8844 Fax: 0117-971 7112 *Exhausts supplies & components*

Southern Exhaust Supplies, Unit 22, Phase 2, Fairfax Road, Heathfield Industrial Estate, Heathfield, Newton Abbot, Devon, TQ12 6TT Tel: (01626) 833300 Fax: (01626) 835814 *Exhaust system distributors*

Southern Express, Express House, 832 Yeovil Road, Slough, SL1 4JG Tel: (01753) 820022 Fax: (01753) 691276 E-mail: sales@palletforce.com *A member of the PalletFORCE distribution network- palletised distribution, timed, next day, economy, tail loft, Ireland and services to mainland Europe. Through its expanding shareholder member depot network, full and part loads, warehouse and logistics services are available.*

▶ Southern File & Data Management, 1 Elgar Estate, Preston Road, Reading, RG2 0BE Tel: 0118-975 9200 Fax: 0118-975 9300

Southern Fire Security Ltd, 4 The Old Saw Mill Industrial Estate, The Street, Broughton Gifford, Melksham, Wiltshire, SN12 8PY Tel: (01225) 782020 Fax: (01225) 782007 *Fire safety*

Southern Flamecuts, 28 Uddens Trading Estate, Wimborne, Dorset, BH21 7NL Tel: 01202 895895 *Profile cutting services*

Southern Fluid Power, E Altbarn Industrial Estate, Revenge Road, Chatham, Kent, ME5 8UD Tel: (01634) 686060 Fax: (01634) 683332 E-mail: info@s-f-p.co.uk *Hydraulic & pneumatic components distributors & agents*

▶ Southern Foam, Dial Post Park, Horsham Road, Rusper, Horsham, West Sussex, RH12 4QX Tel: (01293) 871875 Fax: (01293) 871995

Southern Gilcrest Services, 63 Silverberry Road, Weston-super-Mare, Avon, BS22 6RY Tel: (01934) 521682 Fax: (01934) 513268 *Computer training services*

Southern Group (UK) Ltd, 23 Caker Stream Rd, Alton, Hampshire, GU34 2QA Tel: (01420) 88344 Fax: (01420) 88348 E-mail: info@southerngroupuk.com *Southern Group (UK) Ltd are based in the South of England with regional offices in Hampshire and Surrey. We are one of the South's leading Asbestos consultants. We carry out Asbestos removal, Asbestos surveys, Asbestos air sampling, Asbestos management and Asbestos collection and disposal. We have a dedicated Asbestos survey organisation within the group along with an Asbestos air monitoring facility which also carries out all aspects of environmental pollution control. We have held full, 3 year Asbestos removal licences, consecutively for 20 years and carry full insurance with Professional Indemnity cover in all disciplines. We also carry out all types of demolition and strip out works and offer a complete turnkey service starting with the initial Asbestos survey through Asbestos removal and then complete demolition. Please see our website for the full range of our services.*

Southern Heating Co., 272 South Coast Road, Peacehaven, East Sussex, BN10 7PD Tel: (01273) 588123 Fax: (01273) 588121 E-mail: southtg@fastnet.co.uk *Heating, plumbing & electrical contractors*

▶ Southern Hoist Services, A Culverlands Corner, Winchester Road, Shedfield, Southampton, SO32 2JF Tel: (01329) 833223 Fax: (01329) 833683

Southern Industrial Controls, 118 Faulds Industrial Estate, Tutbury, Burton-on-Trent, Staffs, DE13 9HS Tel: (01283) 814488 Fax: (01283) 814480 *Control panel manufrs*

Southern Insulations, 2 Grove Rd, Strood, Rochester, Kent, ME2 4BY Tel: (01634) 291100 Fax: (01634) 290680 *Asbestos removal specialists*

▶ Southern IT Ltd, Estate Office, Eridge Park, Eridge Green, Tunbridge Wells, Kent, TN3 9JT Tel: (01892) 750880 Fax: (0845) 2600644 E-mail: info@southernit.co.uk *Computer software developers*

▶ Southern IT Ltd, Estate Office, Eridge Park, Eridge Green, Tunbridge Wells, Kent, TN3 9JT Tel: (0845) 2600633 Fax: (0845) 2600644 E-mail: info@southern-it.com *IT software & services*

▶ Southern IT Networks Ltd, Link House,, Link Place, Upper Hollingdean Road, Brighton, BN1 7DX Tel: (0870) 7661061 E-mail: mail@southernit.com *Network installations*

Southern J G & Tool Ltd, Edge Lane, Henley-in-Arden, West Midlands, B95 5DT Tel: (01564) 792651 Fax: (01564) 794403 *Sub contracting engineers*

Southern Lightning Engineers, Unit D2 Bearsted Green Business Centre, The Green, Bearsted, Maidstone, Kent, ME14 4DF Tel: (01622) 631312 Fax: (01622) 631313 E-mail: ian-barker@btconnect.com *Lightning conductors engineers*

Southern Media Maintenance Ltd, Bridge House, R/O 1A Bensham Manor Road, Thornton Heath, Surrey, CR7 7AA Tel: (020) 8665 6760 Fax: (020) 8689 9541 *Computer consumables*

Southern Metals, 29 St. James Industrial Estate, Westhampnett Road, Chichester, West Sussex, PO19 7JU Tel: (01243) 781814 Fax: (01243) 781814 *Steel stockholders & fabricators*

▶ Southern Metropolitan, 2 Salisbury Road, Moseley, Birmingham, B13 8JS Tel: 0121-442 4200 Fax: 0121-442 4611

Southern Monitoring Services Ltd, 212-218 London Road, Waterlooville, Hampshire, PO7 7AJ Tel: (0870) 2422220 Fax: (0870) 2433330 E-mail: info@security-house.demon.co.uk *Alarm monitoring services*

Southern Motor Factors Ltd, 25 Lower Gravel Road, Bromley, BR2 8LR Tel: (020) 8462 6372 Fax: (020) 8462 7919 E-mail: info@smfuk.com *Motor spares suppliers*

Southern Motor Group Van Centre, 22 Lansdowne Road, Croydon, CR0 2BD Tel: (020) 8680 5533 Fax: (020) 8688 3840 E-mail: sales@smguk.co.uk *Car & truck hirer services* Also at: Battersea & Crawley

Southern Nail Supplies, Ikon House, 3 Arkwright Road, Reading, RG2 0LU Tel: 0118-987 3344 *Specialist building product suppliers*

Southern Neon Lights, 57a Rockstone Lane, Southampton, SO14 6JA Tel: (023) 8071 0300 Fax: (023) 8033 8481 E-mail: sales@southernneon.com *Sign manufrs*

Southern Overall Service, Unit D Foundry Close, Horsham, West Sussex, RH13 5TX Tel: (01403) 263108 Fax: (01403) 254539 E-mail: sales@horshamanddistrictlaundry.co.uk *Commercial laundry service*

Southern Paper Ltd, 32 Factory Lane, Croydon, CR0 3RL Tel: (020) 8681 7979 Fax: (020) 8681 8235 *Paper merchants*

Southern Paper Group Ltd, 14-16 Admiralty Way, Camberley, Surrey, GU15 3DT Tel: (01276) 36464 Fax: (01276) 600065 *Paper merchants*

Southern Plastics Ltd, Unit 3, Unit 3 Holton Heath Industrial Estate, Poole, Dorset, BH16 6LT Tel: (01202) 622311 Fax: (01202) 622102 *Industrial plastic coaters*

Southern Platform, Unit 16 Vulcan Business Centre, Vulcan Way, New Addington, Croydon, CR0 9UG Tel: (01689) 800181 Fax: (01689) 800401 E-mail: sales@southernplatforms.co.uk *Advertising gifts/business incentives*

Southern Pneumatics, 496 Ipswich Road, Slough, SL1 4EP Tel: (01753) 511255 Fax: (01753) 511755 E-mail: admin@southern-pneumatics.co.uk *Pneumatic control systems manufrs*

Southern Power Tools & Abrasives Ltd, Unit A Nickel Close, Winchester, Hampshire, SO23 7RJ Tel: (01962) 856022 Fax: (01962) 842395 *Power tool distributors & agents*

Southern Precast Concrete Ltd, Unit 6 Holm Farm, Stansted, Rowland's Castle, Hampshire, PO9 6DT Tel: (023) 9241 3544 Fax: (023) 9245 3779 *Concrete product manufrs*

Southern Pricing Systems Ltd, 28 Eastwell Close, Paddock Wood, Tonbridge, Kent, TN12 6UH Tel: (01892) 834189 Fax: (01892) 835355 *Labels, applicators & scale label retailers*

Southern & Redfern Ltd, Forward House, Mount Street, Bradford, West Yorkshire, BD3 9SR Tel: (01274) 733333 Fax: (01274) 731300 E-mail: bernard.davis@southern-redfern.co.uk *Electrical engineers & building services* Also at: York

Southern Refining Services Ltd, Membury Airfield, Lambourn Woodlands, Hungerford, Berkshire, RG17 7TJ Tel: (01488) 72898 Fax: (01488) 72762 E-mail: richard.srs@btconnect.com *Solvent recovery & chemical services*

Southern Safety Centres Ltd, 3 South Parade, Stafford Road, Wallington, Surrey, SM6 9AJ Tel: (020) 8395 8913 Fax: (020) 8773 2937 E-mail: safety@ssctld.fsnet.co.uk *Industrial & safety wear distributors*

Southern Sales & Services Ltd, Sterling House, Mayflower Close, Chandler's Ford, Eastleigh, Hampshire, SO53 4AR Tel: (023) 8026 1188 Fax: (023) 8025 4054 E-mail: jules@southernsales.co.uk *Parts for transport refrigeration suppliers*

Southern Scales & Equipment Co., 15 Chorley Avenue, Saltdean, Brighton, BN2 8AQ Tel: (01273) 303692 Fax: (01273) 279578 *Scales leasing suppliers*

Southern Sheeting Supplies (Roofing and Cladding), Hill Place Farm, Turners Hill Road (B2110), East Grinstead, West Sussex, RH19 4LX Tel: (01342) 315300 Fax: (01342) 410560 E-mail: sales@southernsheeting.co.uk *Established in 1979, we are an independent, family owned and operated business specialising in the stocking & supply of roofing & cladding materials. From our yard & warehouses in West Sussex we supply materials throughout the South-East, as well as the rest of the UK. We also offer an international export shipping service. Supplying over 2000 tonnes of steel into the industrial, commercial, agricultural & domestic marketplace annually, we are well placed to service the roofing & cladding industry, whatever the requirements. With our friendly, personal service we have firmly established ourselves as the South-East leading cladding supplier.*Products include: cut-to-length Painted and Plastic-Coated Profiled Roofing & Cladding Sheets in a full range of colours plus MANY FACTORY SECONDS, Flashings/Trims, Pre-Insulated Panels, Z Purlins & C Sections, Eternit Fibre Cement & Accessories, Rooflights, Onduline, PVC & Galvanised Guttering & Polycarbonate. VISIT OUR WEBSITE NOW*

Southern Sheetmetal Ltd, Unit 9 Bury Farm, Curbridge, Botley, Southampton, SO30 2HB Tel: (01489) 789143 Fax: (01489) 789069 *Sheet metal fabricators*

Southern Shipping & Finance Co. Ltd, Fourth Floor, 3 London Wall Buildings, London, EC2M 5RL Tel: (020) 7588 3711 Fax: (020) 7696 9971 E-mail: mail@southershipping.co.uk *Ships management*

▶ Southern Smiles Ltd, 9a Catherine Street, Salisbury, SP1 2DF Tel: (01722) 410430

Southern Springs & Pressings Ltd, Stem Lane, New Milton, Hampshire, BH25 5NE Tel: (01425) 611517 Fax: (01425) 638142 E-mail: enquiries@southernsprings.co.uk *Spring manufrs*

Southern Staircases, 81 Dudley Road, Brighton, BN1 7GL Tel: (01273) 551556 *Fire escapes & fire equipment manufrs*

Southern Steamship, Victoria House, 1-3 College Hill, London, EC4R 2RA Tel: (020) 7236 2955 Fax: (020) 7248 4383 E-mail: southern@southernsteam.co.uk *Ship brokers*

Southern Supplies Ltd, Eastern Industrial Estate, South Woodham Ferrers, Chelmsford, CM3 5UF Tel: (01245) 321451 Fax: (01245) 329465 *Garage equipment sales*

Southern Suspended Ceilings Ltd, 151 Burges Road, Southend-on-Sea, SS1 3JN Tel: (01702) 584392 Fax: (01702) 584392 *Suspended ceiling systems constructors*

Southern Tank Services Ltd, Deptford Field Barn, Deptford Farm, Wylye, Warminster, Wiltshire, BA12 0QQ Tel: (01985) 248555 *Supply and installation of oil tanks, replacement fuel tanks and waste oil tanks in the Wiltshire, Hampshire, Dorset, Somerset and Bath areas.*

Southern Testing Laboratories Ltd, Keeble House, Stuart Way, East Grinstead, West Sussex, RH19 4QA Tel: (01342) 333100 Fax: (01342) 410321 E-mail: enquiries@southerntesting.co.uk *Southern Testing is an independent*

continued

Geo-Environmental Consultancy specialising in Ground Investigation, Contaminated Land Assessment and Remediation Validation. The Company also carries out Desk Studies, Environmental Impact Assessments, Risk Assessments, Geotechnical and Slope Stability Analysis, Asbestos Surveys, Soakaway Testing and Assessment, Installation and Assessment of Borehole Soakaways, Soils Testing, CBR Testing, and Contamination Testing. The Company has two Specialists in Land Condition (SiLC). The Company is ISO 9001 registered, has a turnover of about £4 million, and has many longstanding Private Sector clients eg Housing Developers, Consulting Engineers, NHBC, and Water Companies. The Company has all the necessary Insurances and follows appropriate Health & Safety procedures so that the Client's risks are minimised. In September 2006 the Company won a Brownfield Briefing Remediation Innovation Award for Best Use of Combined Systems. A second office was opened in Northampton in February 2006 Tel 01604 500020. This office operates under the name ST Consult.

Southern Timber Frame, Longdown Estate Yard, Longdown, Marchwood, Southampton, SO40 4UH Tel: (023) 8029 3062 Fax: (023) 8029 3969 E-mail: mail.stf@virgin.net *Timber frame buildings manufrs*

▶ Southern Time Recorders, Westwood House, Thurnham Lane, Bearsted, Maidstone, Kent, ME14 4QZ Tel: (01622) 737177 Fax: (01622) 735424 E-mail: info@southerntime.co.uk *Electronic systems, time recorders, time & date stamps*

Southern Tools Ltd, 32 Kimpton Road, Sutton, Surrey, SM3 9RB Tel: (020) 8644 1133 Fax: (020) 8641 1914 E-mail: stl@tools64.freeserve.co.uk *Precision engineers*

Southern Tractors, Ruthwell, Dumfries, DG1 4NZ Tel: (01387) 870216 Fax: (01387) 870306 *Agricultural engineers*

Southern Trading (London) Co Ltd, 34 Eastdown Park, London, SE13 5HS Tel: 020 88528563 *Cycle manufrs*

Southern Weighing Group, Calibra House, Splott Industrial Estate, Splott, Cardiff, CF24 5FF Tel: (029) 2048 8124 Fax: (029) 2048 1115 E-mail: sales@calibraweighing.co.uk *Weigher & weighing systems manufrs* Also at: Bristol, Swansea & Taunton

▶ Southern Workforce UK Ltd, Ashlands, The Street, Ash, Sevenoaks, Kent, TN15 7HB Tel: (01474) 873517 Fax: (01474) 872335 E-mail: kevin@swf.gb.com *Labour & workforce services*

Southernwood Furnishings, The Rocks, Ashwicke, Chippenham, Wiltshire, SN14 8AP Tel: (01225) 852213 Fax: (01225) 859699 *Furniture & joinery manufrs*

James Southerton Ltd, Unit 24A, Reddicap Trading Estate, Sutton Coldfield, West Midlands, B75 7BU Tel: 0121-378 0194 Fax: 0121-378 3438 E-mail: rjsd@southertons.com *Gas fittings manufrs*

Southfields Tyre & Battery Service, 288-290 Merton Road, London, SW18 5JN Tel: (020) 8874 5656 *Motor tyre distributors*

A.E. Southgate Ltd, Station Road, Coleshill, Birmingham, B46 1HT Tel: (01675) 463096 Fax: (01675) 467455 *Brush ware*

Southgate Accounting & Computer Consultants Ltd, The Grange, 100 High Street, London, N14 6TG Tel: (0870) 8506007 Fax: (0870) 8506008 E-mail: info@southgate.sagehost.co.uk *Accounting & computer consultants*

Southgate Lighting Ltd, Southgate, Moorland Road, Drighlington, Bradford, West Yorkshire, BD11 1JY Tel: 0113-285 4000 Fax: 0113-285 3434 *Lighting manufrs*

Southill Saw Mills Ltd, Southill Park, Southill, Biggleswade, Bedfordshire, SG18 9LJ Tel: (01462) 819173 Fax: (01462) 851873 *Timber yard fencing manufrs*

▶ Southmead Poultry, Southmead, Leatherhead, Surrey, KT22 Tel: 01372 458320 E-mail: southmead@dsl.pipex.com

Southon Engineering Ltd, Aveley Indust Estate, Ardmore Road, Sth Ockendon, South Ockendon, Essex, RM15 5TH Tel: (01708) 858757 Fax: (01708) 858757 E-mail: john@southonengineering.co.uk *Light engineering, structural engineering*

Southpark Signs, 258 Green Lane, Ilford, Essex, IG1 1YF Tel: (020) 8553 1123 Fax: (020) 8553 0789 *Sign designers, installers & manufrs*

Southport Electronics Ltd, 22 Glebe Lane, Banks, Southport, Merseyside, PR9 8EU Tel: (01704) 228510 Fax: (01704) 211057 *Printed circuit manufrs*

Southport Glass, 19 St James Street, Southport, Merseyside, PR8 5AE Tel: (01704) 537474 Fax: (01704) 534418 *Double glazing, frames & doors in pvc manufrs*

▶ Southport Marquees, PO Box 356, Southport, Merseyside, PR9 7WD Tel: (01704) 508646 Fax: (01704) 508646

Southridge Interiors Ltd, The Kiln, Pencroft, Crondall, Farnham, Surrey, GU10 5PX Tel: (01252) 852010 Fax: (01252) 852015 *Office furnishing service*

Southsea Deck Chairs Ltd, The Old Council Depot, Burrfields Road, Portsmouth, PO3 5LZ Tel: (023) 9265 2865 Fax: (023) 9265 5830 E-mail: info@deckchairs.co.uk *Deckchair manufacturers & distributor*

Southwark & Boon Ltd, 23 Tallon Road, Hutton, Brentwood, Essex, CM13 1TE Tel: (01277) 225661 Fax: (01277) 233620 E-mail: sales@southwarkandboon.com *Office design, spaceplanning refurbishment & furniture & seating*

Southwark Chamber Of Commerce, 21 Potier Street, London, SE1 4UX Tel: (020) 7403 5500 Fax: (020) 7403 5500 E-mail: admin@southwarkcommerce.com *Chamber of commerce*

▶ Southway Engineering Cornwall Ltd, Station Road, Kelly Bray, Callington, Cornwall, PL17 8ER Tel: (01579) 382261 Fax: (01579) 383935

▶ Southwest Ceilings Ltd, 1, Queen Victoria Street, Bristol, BS2 0QR Tel: 0117-955 8552 Fax: 0117-955 8552

▶ Southwest Conservation, 15 Richmond Road, Taunton, Somerset, TA1 1EN Tel: (01823) 337447

Southwest Fasteners Ltd, Unit 7-8 306 Industrial Estate, 242-244 Broomhill Road, Bristol, BS4 5RG Tel: 0117-972 3242 Fax: 0117-971 7555 E-mail: southwestfastners@dial.pipex.com *Industrial fastener distributors*

Southwest Glass, The Old Saw Mill Industrial Estate, The Street, Broughton Gifford, Melksham, Wiltshire, SN12 8PY Tel: (01225) 783207 Fax: (01225) 783273 E-mail: sales@swglass.co.uk *Double glazing unit manufrs*

▶ Southwest Marine, Shealinghill, Lochfoot, Dumfries, DG2 8NJ Tel: (01387) 250602 Fax: (01387) 250155

▶ Southwest Roofing Services Ltd, 6 Green Street Lane, Ayr, KA8 8BL Tel: (01292) 287936 Fax: (01292) 619719 *Roofing services*

▶ Southwest Roofing Services Ltd, Commerce Road, Stranraer, Wigtownshire, DG9 7DZ Tel: (01387) 256176 Fax: (01776) 703523 *Roofing contractors*

▶ Southwest Roofing Services Ltd, Commerce Road, Stranraer, Wigtownshire, DG9 7DZ Tel: (01387) 256176 Fax: (01776) 703523 *Roofing specialists*

Southwest Service Centre, Unit 2 Merlin Business Park, Fair Oak Close, Clyst Honiton, Exeter, EX5 2UL Tel: (0800) 7839520 Fax: (01392) 445494 *Vacuum cleaners sales*

Southwest Sumo Hire, Lower Brexworthy, Bradworthy, Holsworthy, Devon, EX22 7TR Tel: (07779) 782716 E-mail: Budesumo@hotmail.co.uk *Sumo wrestling suits hire*

Southwest Waterbeds, Church Farm Barn, East Stoke, Stoke-sub-Hamdon, Somerset, TA14 6UF Tel: (01935) 829777 *Waterbed suppliers*

Southwold Angling Centre, 9 Station Road, Southwold, Suffolk, IP18 6AX Tel: (01502) 722085 Fax: (01502) 722085 *Fishing equipment retail*

Southwood quality and regulatory solutions, 1 Hall Cottages, Freethorpe road, Southwood, Norwich, NR13 3LR Tel: (01493) 701452 Fax: (01493) 701452 E-mail: mark.read@southwood-qrs.co.uk *Writing and institution of ISO 9001, ISO13485 and FDA Title 21CFR820 quality systems. **CE marking for EC product directives.**Technical documentation.*

Southworth Developments Ltd, 2e 261 Sileby Road, Barrow upon Soar, Loughborough, Leicestershire, LE12 8LP Tel: (01509) 815196 Fax: (01509) 815210 *Double glazing & conservatory manufrs*

Sovereign Alarms Ltd, 142 Saltdean Vale, Saltdean, Brighton, BN2 8HF Tel: (01273) 301303 Fax: (01273) 300937 *Fire alarm systems installation & maintenance*

▶ Sovereign Brush Co Ltd, 29-43 Sydney Road, Watford, WD18 7PZ Tel: (01923) 227301 Fax: (01923) 817121 E-mail: sales@sovereignbrush.com Sales Contact: B. Barr *Sovereign Brush specializes in first quality British made brushes. We can produce to your specification, supply our own or make to BS 2992 standards. We offer a full range of decorator brushes for the professional and home decorator. We also supply rollers, artist brushes and all sundry products. Over 200 years of experience in brush making, over 40 here at our factory in Watford Hertfordshire. We supply many local and national authorities and hold detailed specifications for brushes used by the rail industry and MOD having held contracts for over 25years. We also offer a full service to our wholesalers, including branding and specialist packaging together with labelling and bar codes as required.*

Sovereign Business Equipment, Unit 3 Leigh Park, Fulflood Road, Havant, Hampshire, PO9 5AX Tel: (023) 9247 4272 E-mail: sovbus.equip@ntlworld.com *Cash register suppliers & repairers*

▶ Sovereign Business Integration, 1a Chalk Lane, Cockfosters, Barnet, Hertfordshire, EN4 9JQ Tel: (020) 8216 3333 Fax: (020) 8216 3300 E-mail: jhambleton@sovereign-plc.co.uk *Air Charter service for business, pleasure, corporate hospitality and incentive travel. Flying you from an airport of choice in comfort and style to your destination, saving you hours. Give us a call!*

▶ Sovereign Business Integration, 1a Chalk Lane, Cockfosters, Barnet, Hertfordshire, EN4 9JQ Tel: (020) 8216 3333 Fax: (020) 8216 3300 E-mail: sales@sovereign-plc.co.uk *Insurance & professional services*

Sovereign Chemical Ltd, Park Road, Barrow-In-Furness, Cumbria, LA14 4EQ Tel: (01229) 870800 Fax: (01229) 870850 E-mail: sales@sovchem.co.uk Principal Export Areas: Worldwide *Building chemical products manufrs*

Sovereign Cleaning Services, 56 Silverknowes Parkway, Edinburgh, EH4 5LA Tel: 0131-336 2492 Fax: 0131-336 2492 *Cleaning contractors*

Sovereign Commercial Installation, Avenue Lane, Eastbourne, East Sussex, BN21 3UL Tel: (01323) 439090 Fax: (01323) 721967 *Floors, ceilings & partitions installations*

▶ Sovereign Commercial Printers Ltd, 579 Kingston Road, London, SW20 8SD Tel: (020) 8544 9391 Fax: (020) 8542 1647 E-mail: info@sovereignprinters.co.uk

▶ Sovereign Communication Systems Ltd, Merlin Way, Bowerhill Industrial Estate, Melksham, Wiltshire, SN12 6TJ Tel: (01225) 700700 Fax: (01225) 700727 E-mail: sales@sovereigncomms.co.uk *Structured cabling systems*

Sovereign Cosmetics Ltd, Unit 3 Gainsborough Close, Long Eaton, Nottingham, NG10 1PX Tel: 0115-973 0195 Fax: 0115-946 1935 E-mail: sales@dutyfreeperfume.co.uk *Wholesaler of cosmetics*

Sovereign Diamond Services Ltd, 13 Duddingston Square West, Edinburgh, EH15 1RS Tel: 0131-669 4365 Fax: 0131-669 4365 *Diamond tool manufrs*

▶ Sovereign Electrical Services, 22 Holifast Road, Sutton Coldfield, West Midlands, B72 1AP Tel: 0121-384 6285 Fax: 0121-350 1859

Sovereign Excel Ltd, Globe Lane, Dukinfield, Cheshire, SK16 4RQ Tel: 0161-330 3091 Fax: 0161-343 1610 E-mail: info@sovereignshowers.co.uk *Shower cubicle manufrs*

Sovereign Fasteners Ltd, 70 Morgan Close, Willenhall, West Midlands, WV12 4LH Tel: (01902) 636191 Fax: (01902) 634508 *Bolt & nut manufrs*

Sovereign International Ltd, 86 Church Road, Formby, Liverpool, L37 3NG Tel: (01704) 832800 Fax: (01704) 832700 E-mail: sales@sovereign-cctv.co.uk *CCTV distribution*

Sovereign Lubricants UK Ltd, Sovereign House, Crowtrees Lane, Brighouse, West Yorkshire, HD6 3LZ Tel: (01484) 718674 Fax: (01484) 400164 E-mail: schesters@btconnect.com *Lubricant & seals distributor*

Sovereign Rotating Electrics Ltd, Unit 1-2 Christie Place, Bognor Regis, West Sussex, PO22 9RT Tel: (01243) 833420 Fax: (01243) 833421 E-mail: sales@sovereignltd.co.uk *Rotating electrics manufrs*

Sovereign Security Services Ltd, 28 Station Road, Shirehampton, Bristol, BS11 9TX Tel: 0117-982 6618

Sovereign Sewing Machines Ltd, 32 Stoke Newington Road, London, Greater London, N16 7XJ Tel: 020 72491839 *Sewing machine hire & retailers*

Sovereign Software Solutions Ltd, 12 Bank Crescent, Burntwood, Staffordshire, WS7 4TL Tel: (01543) 677070 Fax: (01543) 677671 E-mail: info@sovsoft.co.uk *Computer software (sage) & printers*

Sovereign Specialty Chemicals Ltd, Winthorpe Road, Newark, Nottinghamshire, NG24 2AL Tel: (01636) 646711 Fax: (01636) 605187 Principal Export Areas: Worldwide *Adhesive manufrs*

Sovereign Stainless Fabrications Ltd, Canal Works, Cadman St, Sheffield, S4 7ZG Tel: 0114-276 9192 Fax: 0114-276 3700 E-mail: ssfl@sovereign-stainless.co.uk *Architectural metal work*

Sovereign UK Ltd, 38 Smith Street, Birmingham, B19 3ER Tel: 0121-551 4124 Fax: 0121-445 8433 *Watch & jewellery manufrs*

Sovereign Rubber, Hillgate Industrial Estate, Carrington Field St, Stockport, Cheshire, SK1 3JN Tel: 0161-429 8787 Fax: 0161-480 3573 E-mail: salessov@sovereign-rubber.co.uk Sales Contact: P. Simpson Principal Export Areas: Worldwide *Manufacturers of boat/ship/ yacht & rubber fenders, rubber matting, slip resistant matting & rubber extrusions*

▶ Sovrin First Aid Training, Carreg Cwrnach, Pentrefelin, Amlwch, Gwynedd, LL68 9PF Tel: (01407) 830165 E-mail: office@sovrintraining.co.uk *First aid, health & safety and food hygeine training*

Sovrin Plastics Ltd, Stirling Road, Slough, SL1 4ST Tel: (01753) 825155 Fax: (01753) 654923 E-mail: sales@sovrin.com *Plastics injection mouldings manufrs*

Peter Sowter & Co. Ltd, Components House, 5 Holmes Close, Wokingham, Berkshire, RG41 2SG Tel: 0118-978 2691 Fax: 0118-978 2691 *Metal & plastic components manufrs*

Spa Advanced Systems Ltd, 40 Holden Park Road, South Borough, Tunbridge Wells, Kent, TN4 0ER Tel: (01892) 548998 Fax: (01892) 548175 E-mail: spa@spadata.co.uk *Computer maintenance*

Spa Aluminium Ltd, Unit 1, Chapman Way, Tunbridge Wells, Kent, TN2 3EG Tel: (01892) 533911 Fax: (01892) 542019 E-mail: sales@spaaluminium.co.uk Principal Export Areas: Worldwide *Stockholder and Stockists of Aluminium Extrusions and Sheet including the following variations: -Sections -Angles -Flats -Round Tubes -Square & Rectangular Tubes -Bars & Rods -Strip -Tees & Zeds -Pattern Sheet & Treadplate -Channels -Mouldings -Shop Front Systems -Custom Made Profiles The majority of our stocks of extrusion & sheet can be supplied in standard anodised finishes, plus a range of exciting colours produced by the revolutionary Spectrocolour 2000 process. Power Coated finishes are also available.*

▶ Spa City, Beechwood Nurseries, Broxburn, West Lothian, EH52 6PA Tel: (01506) 811170 E-mail: info@spaconnection.co.uk *Provide hot tubs & swimming pools*

Spa Display Ltd, 23 North Street Industrial Estate, Droitwich, Worcestershire, WR9 8JB Tel: (01905) 775428 Fax: (01905) 795417 E-mail: signs@spa-display.sagehost.co.uk *Sign manufrs*

Spa Engineering, Eastfield Fcty, Frank Perkins Way, Peterborough, PE1 2TD Tel: (01733) 345798 Fax: (01733) 345798 E-mail: spaengineering@btinternet.com *Grit blasting contractors, show & exhibition work services*

Spa Fabrics Ltd, Unit 4c, 40 Sawday Street, Leicester, LE2 7JW Tel: 0116-285 8637 Fax: 0116-254 6931 E-mail: spafabrics@aol.com *Fabric manufrs*

Spa Fasteners Ltd, 26 Hurlbutt Road, Heathcote Industrial Estate, Warwick, CV34 6TD Tel: (01926) 883671 Fax: (01926) 430953 E-mail: postmaster@spafasteners.co.uk *Industrial fasteners distributors, agents & stockbrokers*

▶ Spa Laminates Limited, 59 Pepper Road, Leeds, LS10 2TH Tel: 0113-271 8311 Fax: 0113-270 3968 E-mail: info@spalaminates.co.uk *Specialised veneered panel manufrs*

▶ SPA MOMENTS UK (Pure Fiji Retailers), c/o The Perfect Balance, Dunston Hole Farm, Dunston Road, Chesterfield, Derbyshire, S41 9RL Tel: 01246 269819 E-mail: products@spamoments.co.uk *Pure Fiji products represent the lifestyle in the Pacific. For centuries South Pacific Islanders have used a blend of pure coconut oil and local nut extracts infused with tropical flowers to soften, moisturise and protect the skin. Pure Fiji products brings you the best of these ancient traditions for today''s natural body care, giving you the ultimate tropical spa experience.*

Spa Plastics Ltd, 4 Herald Business Park, Golden Acres Lane, Coventry, CV3 2SY Tel: (024) 7665 0670 Fax: (024) 7665 0680 E-mail: sales@spaplastics.com Principal Export Areas: Africa *Distributors of plastic tube fittings & plastic tubes*

▶ Spa Security Solutions, 8 Spa Road, Ballynahinch, County Down, BT24 8LU Tel: (028) 9756 1065 Fax: (028) 9756 1065 E-mail: sales@spacctv.com *Security installations, cctv, control room installation & fit out*

▶ Spa Speakers, Calcutt Locks Cottage, Tomlow Road, Stockton, Southam, Warwickshire, CV47 8HX Tel: (07973) 286509 *Learn how to get your message across - for Presentations, Interviews, Meetings, or Just for Fun!*Speaking confidently to groups of people, whether in a business or social setting, is a valuable and enjoyable skill. *Spa Speakers is based in Leamington, and run by and for people who want to improve their speaking skills, and to have fun doing it! Our diverse group of members each progresses at their own pace. We all benefit from a supportive, encouraging, and friendly atmosphere where everyone learns together. *Spa Speakers is open to anyone over 18, and is part of Toastmasters International, a not for profit organisation. Coming along as a visitor is free, and will give you an opportunity to meet us and make up your own mind!*We meet at the Helen Ley Care Centre, Bericote Road, Leamington Spa, on the 2nd and 4th Wednesdays of each month, at 7.15pm. *Visit our website www.spaspeakers.org for more information and directions; feel free to call us.*We look forward to meeting you.**

Spa Vending, Bona Vista, Kirkby Malzeard, Ripon, North Yorkshire, HG4 3RY Tel: (01765) 658113 Fax: (01765) 658219 *Vending machine distributors*

Spa Web Ltd, Metcalf Drive, Altham Industrial Estate, Accrington, Lancashire, BB5 5TU Tel: (01282) 688100 Fax: (01282) 688105 E-mail: sales@spaweb.co.uk *Industrial webbing manufrs*

▶ Spa Welding Supplies, Marlborough House, Marlborough Road, Lancing, West Sussex, BN15 8UF Tel: (01903) 766909 Fax: (01903) 756180 *Welding equipment, service, repair & hire*

Space Airconditioning plc, Willway Court, 1 Opus Park, Moorfield Road, Guildford, Surrey, GU1 1SZ Tel: 01483 504883 Fax: 01483 574835 E-mail: marketing@spaceair.co.uk *Space Air-conditioning plc is one of the UK's largest independent distributors of air conditioning equipment and systems. Celebrating its 25th anniversary in 2005, the company has its headquarters in Guildford, Surrey, and regional offices in Birmingham, Bristol, Leeds and Manchester.*Distributing the comprehensive Daikin range of products, Space Air provides air conditioning solutions for all buildings in both public and private sectors.**

Space Control Ltd, Oak Court, Pennant Way, Lee Mill Industrial Estate, Ivybridge, Devon, PL21 9GP Tel: (01752) 690023 Fax: (01752) 690027

▶ Space Cooling Systems Ltd, 9 Meadow Close, Langage Business Park, Plympton, Plymouth, PL7 5EX Tel: (01752) 231680 Fax: (01752) 348990 E-mail: space@engineering.co.uk *Heating & ventilation services*

Space Craft Projects Ltd, Sandbeck Way, Wetherby, West Yorkshire, LS22 7DN Tel: (01937) 584554 Fax: (01937) 580012 E-mail: info@space-craft.co.uk *Interior refurbishment contractors*

Space Decks Holdings Ltd, Leach Road, Chard Business Park, Chard, Somerset, TA20 1FA Tel: (01460) 260800 Fax: (01460) 66123 E-mail: skysystems@spacedecks.co.uk *Space frame roofing & glazing manufrs*

Space Industries Ltd, 748 Wimborne Road, Bournemouth, BH9 2DZ Tel: (01202) 517616 Fax: (01202) 533955 E-mail: sales@spaceindustries.co.uk *Construction services*

▶ Space Is LLP, 17 Richmond Road, Towcester, Northamptonshire, NN12 6EX Tel: (01327) 353638 E-mail: info@space-is.co.uk *Aluminium shelving systems*

▶ Space Makers Garage Conversions, Unit 16, Mayfield, 1 East Avenue, Carfin Industrial Estate, Motherwell, Lanarkshire, ML1 4UE Tel: (01698) 833603 E-mail: smc_limited@btinternet.com *Reliable & reputable builders based in motherwell specialising in garage & lift conversions, extension building, site clearing / preparation & general building services.*

Space Models Ltd, Pier Road, North Feltham Trading Estate, Feltham, Middlesex, TW14 0TW Tel: (020) 8890 5542 Fax: (020) 8751 1731 E-mail: enq@spacemodels.co.uk *Industrial & display model makers*

Space Plan Interiors Ltd, Henstaff House, Groesfaen, Pontyclun, Mid Glamorgan, CF72 8NG Tel: (029) 2089 2222 Fax: (029) 2089 2233 E-mail: sales@spaceplan.co.uk *Partitioning system distributors*

▶ Space Planning UK, 32 Batemans Road, Brighton, BN2 6RD Tel: (0845) 1668381 Fax: (0870) 7620832 E-mail: enquiry@spaceplanning.org *Space Planning UK are a Brighton based office design consultancy. We offer space planning, cad services and office design advice throughout the UK.*

▶ Space Solutions Ltd, 23 Ampthill Road, Shefford, Bedfordshire, SG17 5BD Tel: 01462 815206 Fax: 01462 641176 E-mail: space@space-solutions.co.uk *Space Solutions, a Trading Standards Approved Company, specialises in custom-designing and constructing stylish Conservatories and Garage Conversions for its clients in Hertfordshire, Bedfordshire, Cambridgeshire and Buckinghamshire.**

▶ Space Station, Brewery Lane, Gateshead, Tyne & Wear, NE10 0EY Tel: 0191-438 1616 Fax: 0191-438 2626 E-mail: sales@spacestationstorage.co.uk

Spacelabs Healthcare Ltd, 3 Chiltern Court Asheridge Road Industrial Estate, Asheridge Road, Chesham, Buckinghamshire, HP5 2PX Tel: (01494) 784422 Fax: (01494) 791497 E-mail: advsales@spacelabs.com *Medical equipment manufrs*

Spacemaker Bedrooms Ltd, Ilford Trading Estate Paycocke Road, Basildon, Essex, SS14 3DR Tel: (01268) 476705 Fax: (01268) 472010 E-mail: sales@spacemakerfurniture.co.uk *Furniture manufrs*

Spacemaker Bedrooms Ltd, 160-162 Hornchurch Road, Hornchurch, Essex, RM11 1QH Tel: (01708) 473020 *Bedroom designers*

▶ Spacemax Cranleigh Ltd, 23 Hewitts Estate, Elmbridge Road, Cranleigh, Surrey, GU6 8LW Tel: 01483 542900 Fax: 01483 542901 E-mail: space@spacemax.co.uk *Spacemax offers Self Storage rooms of to ,000sq ft on flexible, all inclusive terms for use from a day to a decade.*Our handy delivery reception service can prove particularly handy at only £1 per delivery received - be in when you''re out.*We also offer a range of services and virtual office services, mailboxes, meeting rooms and packaging supplies for sale.*

Space-Ray UK, 4-6 Chapel Lane, Claydon, Ipswich, IP6 0JL Tel: (01473) 830551 Fax: (01473) 832055 E-mail: info@spaceray.co.uk *Heating apparatus manufrs*

▶ Spacesaver Furniture, 149-153 High Holborn, London, WC1V 6PJ Tel: (020) 7404 7552 Fax: (020) 7404 7442

Spacetime Interiors Ltd, Unit 1, Sunderleigh Farm, Bampton, Tiverton, Devon, EX16 9DT Tel: (0845) 8620326 Fax: (0845) 8689369 E-mail: sales@space-time.co.uk *Suppliers of office furniture, workstations, desks & storage*

Spacewise, Unit 2, The Business Center, Corinium Industrial Estate, Raans Road, Amersham, Buckinghamshire, HP6 6FB Tel: (01494) 431200 Fax: (01494) 431203 E-mail: sales@quintoncav.co.uk *Office furnishers*

▶ Spaciotempo UK Ltd, Dovefields, Dovefields Industrial Estate, Uttoxeter, Staffordshire, ST14 8HU Tel: (01889) 569569 Fax: (01889) 569555 E-mail: sales@spaciotempo.com *Spaciotempo UK Ltd is the UK's No1 choice for multi-purpose temporary buildings, temporary warehouses, modular storage buildings, canopies and retractable tunnels.*We are part of a European company, Spaciotempo®, specialising in the manufacture, hire and sale of high quality temporary modular buildings. Budget stock items through to bespoke design solutions available all delivered to your site and installed by our own qualified installation teams. Our range includes; Temporary buildings, Prefabricated buildings, Portable buildings, Re-locatable buildings, Modular buildings, Modular storage structures, Portable storage units, Canopies, Sports Buildings, Sports Halls, Temporary gyms, Temporary supermarkets, Temporary Showrooms, Portable warehouses, Temporary warehouses, Modular warehouses, Prefabricated warehouses, Re-locatable warehouses*

Spafax International Ltd, Kingsland Industrial Park, Stroudley Road, Basingstoke, Hampshire, RG24 8UG Tel: (01256) 814400 Fax: (01256) 814141 E-mail: sales@spafaxmirrors.com *Unbreakable commercial vehicle mirror manufrs*

Spafield Displays Ltd, 404 Bretton Park Way, Dewsbury, West Yorkshire, WF12 9BS Tel: (01924) 452386 Fax: (01924) 465713 E-mail: hazel@sparfield.com *Plastic extrusion fabricators*

▶ Spaford Electro & Mechanic Services Ltd, Unit 7d, Beechcroft Industries, Chapelwood Road, Sevenoaks, Kent, TN15 7HX Tel: (01474) 879922

▶ Spain Building & Maintenance Ltd, 96 Keighley Road, Colne, Lancashire, BB8 0PH Tel: (01282) 866466

▶ Spain Property, PO Box 46, Wirral, Merseyside, CH60 9LR Tel: 0774 788 8181 *Golf property for sale and to Let.*

Spaldings Trustees Ltd, 25-35 Sadler Road, Lincoln, LN6 3XJ Tel: (01522) 500600 Fax: (01522) 509300 E-mail: sales@spaldings.co.uk *Agricultural wearing parts factors*

Spanboard Products Ltd, Hillmans Way, Coleraine, County Londonderry, BT52 2ED Tel: (028) 7035 5126 Fax: (028) 7035 8670 E-mail: faels@stanboard.co.uk *Chipboard manufrs*

Spanclad Construction Ltd, 337 Heath Street, Smethwick, West Midlands, B66 2QY Tel: 0121-558 2131 Fax: 0121-555 5604 E-mail: spanclad@compuserve.com *Industrial roofing, insulation & street erection*

Spanesi Automotive Mechanic Ltd, 33-37 Second Avenue Ind Estate, Chatham, Kent, ME4 5AY Tel: (01634) 845580 Fax: (01634) 401515 *Solder & fluxe distributors*

▶ Spanish Costa Properties, 9 Castle Hill Court, 21-23 Castle Hill Avenue, Folkestone, Kent, CT20 2QU Tel: 01303 241025 *Spanish properties for sale in Costa Blanca, Costa Calida, Costa de Almeria and Costa del Sol. Wide selection of new and resale properties. Viewing trips arranged.*

▶ Spanish Machine, 115 Greenwich South Street, London, SE10 8NX Tel: (020) 8692 3918 E-mail: felipe@thespanishmachine.co.uk *Learn Spanish in London. Spanish classes. Spanish tuition. Spanish course London.*

Spanish & Portuguese At Fultons, The Chase, Behoes Lane, Woodcote, Reading, RG8 0PP Tel: (01491) 680042 Fax: (01491) 680085 E-mail: mike@mikefulton.co.uk *Translating, interpreting & editing services* Also at: London EC2

▶ Spanish Removals, Hellman House, Lakeside Estate, Colnbrook, Slough, SL3 0EL Tel: (0870) 4202950 Fax: (08704) 202951 E-mail: info@spanishremovals.com *Specialist*

continued

continuation removals to Spain and France. Full export packing service, storage facilties. Also local and national moves. Competitive prices, free estimates and advice

Spanjaard UK Ltd, PO Box 21, Huntingdon, Cambridgeshire, PE29 2EQ Tel: (01480) 457022 Fax: (01480) 457022 *Lubricant manufrs and suppliers*

▶ Spanks Foods, Mead Lane, Saltford, Bristol, BS31 3ER Tel: (01225) 874466 Fax: (01225) 874466 *Food processors*

Spanset Ltd, Telford Way, Middlewich Bus Industrial, Park, Middlewich, Cheshire, CW10 0HX Tel: (01606) 737494 Fax: (01606) 737502 E-mail: sales@spanset.com *Safety harness manufrs*

Spantech Products Ltd, Spantech House, Lagham Road, South Godstone, Godstone, Surrey, RH9 8HB Tel: (01342) 893239 Fax: (01342) 892584 E-mail: spantech-acd@tiscali.co.uk *Special gas mixtures & trace gas oxygen analyses suppliers*

▶ Spar, 1 62 Swindon Road, Cheltenham, Gloucestershire, GL50 4AY Tel: (01242) 234323 Fax: (01242) 234323 *Office furniture suppliers*

Spar Plastics, 7 Park Trading Estate, Park Road, Hockley, Birmingham, B18 5HB Tel: 0121-551 6220 Fax: 0121-551 6220 *Badge & plastic injection mould manufrs*

▶ Sparc Systems Ltd, 430 Allesley Old Road, Coventry, CV5 8GF Tel: (07930) 854033 E-mail: wilson@sparcsys.co.uk *We develop electronic solutions using state of art Open Source technologies. Linux Security Solutions, Open Source Business Solutions,Wireless Handhelds, Communication systems, Embedded Systems and sophisticated physical security systems.*

▶ SpareRIBs RIB Hire Agency, PO Box 1352, Southampton, SO19 9WX Tel: (023) 8042 0303 E-mail: sparerbs@sparerbs.info *SpareRIBs provides an online database of powerboats available for charter or sale, internationally. Boat owners may post adverts for their boats to hire or sell and those looking to hire a boat or RIB may select a fleet or one from the current online listing.*

▶ Spares2Go, Unit 1 Fordingbridge Business Park, Ashford Road, Fordingbridge, Hampshire, SP6 1BZ Tel: (0870) 4449873 Fax: (0870) 4449874 E-mail: enquiries@spares2go.co.uk *Spares and spare parts for domestic electrical appliances.*

▶ Spares-Direct-2-U, 20 Allerton Grange Gardens, Moortown, Leeds, LS17 6LL Tel: 0113 2263384 Fax: 0113 2955753 E-mail: info@sparesdirect2u.com *Spares-Direct-2-U offer specialist procurement services, predominantly for current and commercially obsolete electrical distribution and automation products from manufacturers such as Yorkshire Switchgear, Telemechanique, Merlin Gerin, ABB, Siemens, MK, Legrand, and many more.*

▶ Sparesforhome Co UK, 2 Cross Coates Road, Grimsby, South Humberside, DN34 4QG Tel: (01472) 240001 E-mail: enquiries@sparesforhome.co.uk *Online shop selling domestic appliance spare parts*

Sparex Agricultural Machinery, 56 Seskanore Road, Omagh, County Tyrone, BT78 1RW Tel: (028) 8225 2565 Fax: (028) 8225 2946 E-mail: inpost@sparex.co.uk *Agricultural machinery spares*

Alan Spargo Ltd, Coronation Road, Cressex Business Park, High Wycombe, Buckinghamshire, HP12 3TA Tel: (01494) 529808 Fax: (01494) 464077 E-mail: bobw@alanspargoltd.com *Precision engineers & press tool manufrs*

▶ Spark Promotions Ltd, Building 3.1 Power Road Studio, Power Road, London, W4 5PY Tel: (020) 8742 5920 E-mail: spriestman@blackjack.co.uk *Field marketing specialists providing brand experience, brand ambassadors, on airport and event promotional staffing experts.*

Spark Response Ltd, Follingsby Avenue, Gateshead, Tyne & Wear, NE10 8HQ Tel: 0191-495 9999 Fax: 0191-495 9900 E-mail: enquiries@sparkresponse.co.uk *Mail order & fulfillment services*

Sparkford Chemicals Ltd, Sparkford House, 58 The Avenue, Southampton, SO17 1XS Tel: (023) 8022 8747 Fax: (023) 8021 0240 E-mail: info@sparkford.co.uk *Chemical merchants & fibre merchants*

Sparkford Sawmills Ltd, Sparkford, Yeovil, Somerset, BA22 7LH Tel: (01963) 440414 Fax: (01963) 440982 E-mail: enquiries@sparkford.com *Timber product manufacturers & sawmills*

Sparkle, 37 High Street, Fordingbridge, Hampshire, SP6 1AS Tel: (01425) 657658 Fax: 01202 824171 E-mail: david@wesparkle.co.uk *Contract cleaners, carpet and upholstery cleaning. Floor maintenance specialists for all types of flooring. Specialists in builders and sparkle cleans for contractors and refurbishers*

▶ Sparklebright Ltd, 26 The Courts, Margate, Kent, CT9 5HP Tel: (0845) 6442147 E-mail: info@sparklebright.biz *Commercial & domestic window cleaners*

Sparkling Spring Water UK Ltd, Unit M, Progress Road, High Wycombe, Buckinghamshire, HP12 4JD Tel: (01494) 473111 Fax: (01494) 539356 *Market & spring water bottlers*

Sparks Ltd, Bullingdon House, 174b Cowley Road, Oxford, OX4 1UE Tel: (01865) 242406 Fax: (01865) 242407 E-mail: sales@sparks.co.uk *Multi media publishers*

Sparks Business Systems, Kingsway House, Bank Buildings, Bridgend Industrial Estate, Bridgend, Mid Glamorgan, CF31 3SB Tel: (01656) 767231 Fax: (01656) 661106 *Telecommunication services*

Sparks Fire Protection, 89 Llewellyn Street, Port Talbot, West Glamorgan, SA12 8SG Tel: (01639) 885837 E-mail: kevin@sparksfire.org.uk *Disabled facility installers*

John A. Sparks & Co. Ltd., Western Industrial Estate, Caerphilly, CF83 1BQ Tel: (0845) 8503434 Fax: (029) 2080 7081 E-mail: tonysparks@a-sparks.com *CHP units generating sets diesel & gas engines suppliers*

Sparks Marine Trimmers, Old School House, Thame Road, Chilton, Aylesbury, Buckinghamshire, HP18 9LX Tel: (01844) 208731 Fax: (01844) 208510 *Soft furnishings for boats manufrs*

Sparks Mechanical Services Ltd, Broadfold Road, Bridge of Don, Aberdeen, AB23 8EE Tel: (01224) 704448 Fax: (01224) 703864 E-mail: info@sparksms.co.uk *Refrigeration, air-conditioning, electrical, heating & plumbing*

▶ Spark's Mechanical Services Ltd, Unit 12 Tyock Industrial Estate, Elgin, Morayshire, IV30 1XY Tel: (01343) 547840 Fax: (01343) 549525

R.J. Sparks, Holly Farm, Partridge Lane, Newdigate, Dorking, Surrey, RH5 5BN Tel: (01293) 862608 *Plant machinery services*

R.J. Sparks, 2 Winfield Gro, Newdigate, Dorking, Surrey, RH5 5AZ Tel: 01306 631256 *Agricultural contractors*

▶ Sparkys Karaoke & Disco Supplies, 5 Meadow Gardens, Portstewart, County Londonderry, BT55 7SS Tel: (028) 7083 8197 Fax: (028) 7083 8197

Gordon Sparrow Plant Sales Ltd, 3-4 Newlands House, Lansdown Hill, Lansdown, Bath, BA1 5RE Tel: (01225) 429522 Fax: (01225) 429496 *Cranes & equipment sale & hire*

Ian Sparrow Equipment Ltd, Grantham Road, Bottesford, Nottingham, NG13 0EE Tel: (01949) 842385 Fax: (01949) 843436 *Importers of concrete machinery*

Sparrow Quality Water Solutions, The Abbey, Preston Road, Yeovil, Somerset, BA20 2EN Tel: (01935) 479395 Fax: (01935) 848523 *Water services*

C.F. Sparrowhawk Ltd, 24 Epsom Lane North, Tadworth, Surrey, KT20 5EH Tel: (01737) 352889 Fax: (01737) 371088 *Steel stockholders/ scrap metal merchants*

Sparrows Offshore Services Ltd, Woodside Road, Bridge Of Don Industrial Estate, Aberdeen, AB23 8BW Tel: (01224) 826032

▶ Sparrows Offshore Services Ltd, Denmore Road, Bridge of Don, Aberdeen, AB23 8JW Tel: (01224) 704868 Fax: (01224) 825191 E-mail: sales@sparrows.co.uk *Crane test inspection, maintenance & modification services. Also bolt torque/tensioning services, lifting gear design & lifting contractor specialist services. In addition, machining/planing/turning (metal) services (including on site), steel fabricators & hydraulic test & refurbishment.*

Sparta Ltd, Victoria Works, Hill End Lane, Rossendale, Lancashire, BB4 7AG Tel: (01706) 221111 Fax: (01706) 222309 E-mail: enquiries@sparta.co.uk *Steel fabricators*

▶ Sparta Database Development, 17 Cyncoed Close, Dunvant, Swansea, SA2 7RS Tel: 01792 425730 E-mail: enquiries@sparta-development-db.co.uk *We are specialized in designing Access databases, web sites, online store's and database driven web sites for small to medium sized companies. We also supply other IT services, like spreadsheets and presentations.*

Spartan Europe Ltd, Unit A13 Railway Triangle, Walton Road, Portsmouth, PO6 1TN Tel: (023) 9221 0053 Fax: (023) 9221 0057 E-mail: sales@spartaneurope.com *Electronic components distributors*

Spartan Storage Ltd, Fairgate House, 205 Kings Road, Birmingham, B11 2AA Tel: 0121-706 3591 Fax: 0121-707 8950 *Storage equipment*

Spartan Tiles Ltd, Martells Pit, Slough Lane, Ardleigh, Colchester, CO7 7RU Tel: (01206) 230553 Fax: (01206) 230516 E-mail: david@spartantiles.com *Concrete tiles manufrs*

Sparton Metal Polishers, Unit 11 Croydon Street, Leeds, LS11 9RT Tel: 0113-244 6975 Fax: 0113-244 5629 E-mail: ash@amsspartan.com *Polishing & buffing services*

Spatial Air Brokers & Forwarders Ltd, Unit 7c Willow Farm Business Park, Castle Donington, Derby, DE74 2TW Tel: (01332) 850925 Fax: (01332) 812427 E-mail: sales@the-spatial-group.com *Air & sea freight brokers*

Spatz Shop, Unit 9 Brook Street, Redditch, Worcestershire, B98 8NG Tel: (01527) 68168 Fax: (01527) 60026 E-mail: sales@spatz.uk.com *Plastic vacuum forming services*

Spax Performance Ltd, 2 Launton Business Centre, Murdock Road, Bicester, Oxfordshire, OX26 4PL Tel: (01869) 244771 Fax: (01869) 240536 E-mail: sales@spaxperformance.com *Shock absorber & spring specialists manufrs*

Spazio Folding Door Co., 3 Barnfield, St. Michaels, Tenterden, Kent, TN30 6NH Tel: (01580) 763593 Fax: (01580) 765883 E-mail: susie@spazio.co.uk *Retail of folding doors & folding walls*

SPC International Ltd, 106 Oxford Road, Uxbridge, Middlesex, UB8 1NA Tel: (01895) 454850 Fax: (01895) 454851 E-mail: sales@spcint.com *Electronic equipment repairers*

SPC International Food Ltd, 35 Pinfold Lane, Grimsby, South Humberside, DN33 2EW Tel: (01472) 505080 Fax: (01472) 505088 *Industrial specialist suppliers & brokers of food processing equipment*

Spea (UK) Ltd, Spea Ho, Sanford La, Wareham, Dorset, BH20 4DY Tel: (01929) 554444 Fax: (01929) 554446 E-mail: spea@spea.co.uk *Electronic measuring instrument services*

▶ Speak Easy School Of English, 24 Chiswick High Road, London, W4 1TE Tel: (020) 8995 8772 Fax: (020) 8995 7363 E-mail: info@speakeasyschool.co.uk

Speak & Enter Services Ltd, 457 Alexandra Avenue, Rayners Lane, Harrow, Middlesex, HA2 9RY Tel: (020) 8429 2976 Fax: (020) 8429 3703 E-mail: derrick01@btconnect.com *Access control systems*

J. Speak & Co. Ltd, North Dean Mills, West Vale, Greetland, Halifax, West Yorkshire, HX4 8LS Tel: (01422) 378228 Fax: (01422) 370720 *Wool merchants*

Speake & Co. Llanfaply, 6 Firs Road, Llanfapley, Abergavenny, Monmouthshire, NP7 8SL Tel: (01600) 780150 Fax: (01600) 780150 E-mail: speake@elvicta.fsnet.co.uk *Manufacturer & supplier of magnetic field sensors, gradiometers*

Speakeasy Productions Ltd, Wildwood House, Stanley, Perth, PH1 4PX Tel: (01738) 828524 Fax: (01738) 828419 E-mail: info@speak.co.uk *Video & television production company live events service*

▶ Speakmans Ltd, Phoenix Way, Burnley, Lancashire, BB11 5SX Tel: (01282) 427529

▶ Speakmans Ltd, Phoenix House, 32 Broughton Street, Manchester, M8 8NN Tel: 0161-830 8300 Fax: 0161-839 3560

Alan Spear Ltd, Broadley Park Road, Roborough, Plymouth, PL6 7EZ Tel: (01752) 696500 Fax: (01752) 696777 E-mail: info@alanspear.co.uk *Fabricators & installers of aluminium windows, doors & automatic doors*

▶ Spear Engineering (Scotland) Ltd, Christianhall, Cuminestown, Turriff, Aberdeenshire, AB53 5UE Tel: (01888) 544398 Fax: (01888) 544012 *Hydraulic equipment, hydraulic control systems, offshore & subsea hydraulic control systems, fluid contamination control, hydraulic distributors, agents*

▶ Spear Europe Ltd, Christopher Grey Court, Lakeside, Llantarnam Industrial Park, Cwmbran, Gwent, NP44 3SE Tel: (01633) 627600 Fax: (01633) 627601 E-mail: sales@spearsystem.com *Manufacturing services*

Spear & Jackson Ltd, St Pauls Road, Wednesbury, West Midlands, WS10 9RA Tel: 0121 5561414 *Garden tool manufrs*

▶ Spear & Jackson International Ltd, The Mill Race, 346 Brightside Lane, Sheffield, S9 2SP Tel: 0114-225 0862 Fax: 0114-225 0861 E-mail: pjones@sjint.com *Manufacturing machine knifes*

▶ Spear Technologies Ltd, Station Rise, York, YO1 6HT Tel: (01904) 624009 Fax: (01904) 655411 E-mail: admin@speartechnologies.com *Computer support services*

▶ Spear Trent, 29 Kestrel Drive, Bingham, Nottingham, NG13 8QD Tel: (0800) 8048236 Fax: (0871) 4310507 E-mail: enquiries@speartrent.co.uk *Website design services*

Spearhead Training, 19 Cheriton House Cromwell Park Banbury Road, Chipping Norton, Oxfordshire, OX7 5SR Tel: (01608) 644144 Fax: (01608) 649680 E-mail: info@spearhead-training.co.uk *Management & personal development training*

▶ Spec Check Europe Ltd, Lion Buildings, 8 Market Place, Uttoxeter, Staffordshire, ST14 8HP Tel: (01889) 569666 Fax: (01889) 569777 E-mail: sales@spec-checkeurope.com *Technical publishers*

Spec Tools Europe, Petersfield Road, Greatham, Liss, Hampshire, GU33 6AA Tel: (01420) 538539 Fax: (01420) 538111 E-mail: nsb@eurotec-intl.co.uk *Hand tool distributors*

Specac Ltd, River House, 97 Cray Avenue, Orpington, Kent, BR5 4HE Tel: (01689) 873134 Fax: (01689) 878527 E-mail: sales@specac.co.uk *Laser optical equipment manufrs*

Specfab (Pershore) Ltd, Unit 5A, Pershore Trading Estate, Pershore, Worcestershire, WR10 2DD Tel: (01386) 552790 Fax: (01386) 556827 E-mail: sales@specfab.co.uk *Specialist metal fabricators*

Special Alloys Northern Ltd, Greasbrough Road, Rotherham, South Yorkshire, S60 1RW Tel: (01709) 828333 Fax: (01709) 829915 E-mail: nickeightyatspecialalloys@fsmail.net *Scrap metal merchants*

▶ Special Blue Ltd, Unit 30, Cranwell Close, Violet Road, London, E3 3QY Tel: (020) 7538 0330

Special Branch, 5 Brailwood Close, Bilsthorpe, Newark, Nottinghamshire, NG22 8UG Tel: (01623) 871306 *Pine furniture*

Special Carrier, Express House, Kedlestone Road, Whitfield, Dover, Kent, CT16 3NX Tel: (01304) 820999 Fax: (01304) 820990 E-mail: info@specialcarrier.co.uk *European express carriers*

Special Delivery Ltd, 531 Kings Road, London, SW10 0TZ Tel: (020) 7351 5133 Fax: (020) 7351 6076 *Courier services*

Special Efx Ltd, Ettington Park Bus Centre, Stratford-upon-Avon, Warwickshire, CV37 8BT Tel: (01789) 450005 *Advertising gifts, business incentives & souvenir designers*

Special Equipment Ltd, 1 United Mill, Suffolk Street, Oldham, OL9 7DJ Tel: 0161-624 6636 Fax: 0161-628 6340 *Special purpose machinery*

▶ Special Event Services, Grove Farm, Westbury, Brackley, Northamptonshire, NN13 5JH Tel: (01280) 841215 Fax: (01280) 841217 E-mail: info@sesltd.net *Exhibition trailer design, hire & manufrs*

▶ Special Fire Systems, Baston Hall, Crews Hill, Alfrick, Worcester, WR6 5HF Tel: (01886) 884747 Fax: (01886) 884125 E-mail: enquiries@special-fire.com *Suppliers: certificated flame retardant temporary protection materials*

Special Formwork Ltd, Stubbers Green Road, Aldridge, Walsall, WS9 8BN Tel: (01922) 451909 Fax: (01922) 454520 E-mail: info@formwork.co.uk *Steel formwork suppliers, working for the Civil Engineering and Construction industries across the UK. Quick response and Quick turnaround of purpose made steel formwork.*

▶ Special FX Entertainments, Unit 3, New Found Out Farm, Whiteoak Green, Witney, Oxfordshire, OX29 9XP Tel: (07785) 266702 Fax: (08456) 106406 E-mail: enquiries@special-f-x.co.uk *Lighting, sound & engineering suppliers & services*

Special Metal Welding Products, Waterloo Road, Bidford-on-Avon, Alcester, Warwickshire, B50 4JN Tel: (01789) 491780 Fax: (01789) 491781 E-mail: sales.uk@iaiwpc.com *Welding consumables supplies manufrs*

Special Occasions, 105 High Street, Rowley Regis, West Midlands, B65 0EG Tel: 0121-559 2573 Fax: 0121-559 2878 *Greeting cards gifts & balloons suppliers*

Special Occasions, Rambleside, Patmore Heath, Albury, Ware, Hertfordshire, SG11 2LY Tel: (01279) 771944 Fax: (01279) 771944 *Balloon decorating services*

Special Piping Materials Ltd, Broadway, Dukinfield, Cheshire, SK16 4UU Tel: 0161-343 7005 Fax: 0161-343 7011 E-mail: sales@spm.co.uk Principal Export Areas: Worldwide *Pipes fitters*

Special Purpose Equipment Ltd, 3 Loaland Business Centre, Maritime Close, Medway City Estate, Rochester, Kent, ME2 4AZ Tel: (01634) 295396 Fax: (01634) 718879 E-mail: johnlambell@special-purpose-equipment.co.uk *Computer controlled assembly & test equipment*

Special Quality Alloys Ltd, Colwall St, Sheffield, S9 3WP Tel: 0114-243 4366 Fax: 0114-244 1199 E-mail: sales@specialqualityalloys.com *Nickel alloy & stainless steel manufrs*

Special Security Products, 37 Warren Hill Road, Birmingham, B44 8HA Tel: 0121-344 4593 Fax: 0121-356 0867 E-mail: enquiries@special-locks.com *Security & general lock manufrs*

▶ Special Source Ltd, 58A Chaplin Road, London, NW2 5PN Tel: (0845) 0573136 E-mail: info@special-source.co.uk *Computer software development*

Special Steels Ltd, Woodbourn Hill, Attercliffe, Sheffield, S9 3NE Tel: 0114-272 0321 Fax: 0114-275 8354 *Heat treatment specialists services*

Special Testing Works Ltd, Bacon Lane, Sheffield, S9 3NH Tel: 0114-244 1061 Fax: 0114-244 0444 *Testing & proving contractors*

Special Tooling Services, Exchange Road, Lincoln, LN6 3JZ Tel: (01522) 693993 Fax: (01522) 500993 *Cutting tool manufrs*

Special Touch, Ivydene, Whelpley Hill, Chesham, Bucks, HP5 3RN Tel: 01442 831585 *Bouncy castle hire & balloon decoration*

▶ Special Treasures, 193 Hylton Road, Millfield, Sunderland, SR4 7YE Tel: (07931) 756051 E-mail: emahoward@yahoo.co.uk

▶ Specialcards4you, 65 Oakfield Road, Benfleet, Essex, SS7 5NS Tel: (01268) 752104 Fax: (01268) 752104 E-mail: specialcards4you@googlemail.com *Personalised greeting cards & gifts designers & manufrs*

Specialised Aerosols Co. Ltd, Carr Green Lane, Mapplewell, Barnsley, South Yorkshire, S75 6DY Tel: (01226) 387101 Fax: (01226) 387100 E-mail: sales@specialised-aerosols.co.uk *Cleaning material for industry*

Specialised Assemblies (Wellingborough) Ltd, Engineering Works, Higham Road, Burton Latimer, Kettering, Northamptonshire, NN15 5PU Tel: (01536) 420102 Fax: (01536) 420097 E-mail: markv@specassy.com *Laser cutting services/general engineering*

Specialised Belting Supplies Ltd, 26 Brunel Way, Thetford, Norfolk, IP24 1HP Tel: (01842) 754392 Fax: (01842) 765264 E-mail: sales@sbsbelting.com *Conveyor belting manufrs*

Specialised Belting Supplies (Doncaster), Wheatcroft Farm, Hayfield Lane, Auckley, Doncaster, South Yorkshire, DN9 3NP Tel: (01302) 869090 Fax: (01302) 867373 E-mail: sales@sbsbelting.com *Rubber belting manufrs*

Specialised Car Covers Ltd, Concourse House, Main Street, Burley in Wharfedale, Ilkley, West Yorkshire, LS29 7JP Tel: (01943) 864646 Fax: (01943) 864365 E-mail: sales@carcoversuk.com *Car cover manufrs*

▶ Specialised Castings, Headswood Mill, Denny, Stirlingshire, FK6 6BL Tel: (01324) 820077 Fax: (01324) 820077 E-mail: sales@specialisedcastings.co.uk *Foundry services*

Specialised Chemicals Ltd, Spittlegate Level, Grantham, Lincolnshire, NG31 7UH Tel: (01476) 567615 Fax: (01476) 560837 E-mail: sales@specialisedchemicals.com *Aerosol filling services*

Specialised Cutting & Creasing, Unit 16 Hillgate Business Centre, Swallow Street, Stockport, Cheshire, SK1 3AU Tel: 0161-474 7246 *Printing trade finishing services*

Specialised Electrical Services, 52 Belhaven Terrace, Wishaw, Lanarkshire, ML2 7AY Tel: (01698) 374718 Fax: (01698) 373984 *Electrical repairs*

Specialised Engineering Products, Unit C3-7 The Premier Centre, Premier Way, Romsey, Hampshire, SO51 9DG Tel: (01794) 830757 Fax: (01794) 830736 E-mail: sales@specialisedengineering.co.uk *Fluid sealing specialists suppliers*

Specialised Engineering Services, 129 Monk Street, Derby, DE22 3QE Tel: (01332) 370994 Fax: (01332) 294513 E-mail: sales@ukbollards.com *Steel fabricators*

Specialised Engines Ltd, 15 Curzon Drive, Grays, Essex, RM17 6BG Tel: (01375) 378606 Fax: (01375) 381249 E-mail: specialisedengines@talk21.com *Car petrol engine manufrs*

Specialised Fixing (East Anglia) Ltd, Unit 9, Farthing Road, Ipswich, IP1 5AP Tel: (01473) 461461 Fax: (01473) 240518 E-mail: spencer.priestley@omnico.co.uk *Installation plastic, aluminium & rainwater systems*

Specialised Industrial Chemicals Ltd, 44 Henver Road, Newquay, Cornwall, TR7 3BN Tel: (01637) 850643 Fax: (01637) 880040 E-mail: sales@sic-uk.com *Industrial chemicals paint & ink manufrs*

▶ Specialised Investment Property Services Ltd, Suite 5c, Deer Park Business Centre, Eckington, Pershore, Worcestershire, WR10 3DN Tel: (01386) 750990 Fax: 01386 751321 E-mail: admin@sips-ltd.co.uk *Residential Property Lettings, management and consultancy services*

Specialised Laser Products Ltd, Unit 6 Ford Park, Canklow Road, Rotherham, South Yorkshire, S60 2JB Tel: (01709) 720799 Fax: (01709) 837444 E-mail: sales@slp-ltd.co.uk *Laser cutting services*

Specialised Latex Services Ltd, Lupton Road, Thame Industrial Estate, Thame, Oxfordshire, OX9 3SE Tel: (01844) 212489 Fax: (01844) 212489 E-mail: sales@specialisedlatex.co.uk *Dipped rubber goods manufrs*

Specialised Management Services, Harfreys Road, Great Yarmouth, Norfolk, NR31 0LS Tel: (01493) 655515 Fax: (01224) 657408 *Hydraulic hose refurbishers & distributors*

Specialised Paving Services, 31 Lordscroft Lane, Haverhill, Suffolk, CB9 0ER Tel: (07957) 895397 E-mail: info@specialisedpaving.co.uk *We specialise in domestic and commercial paving maintenance. We can clean all types of paving using commercial high pressure water compressors coupled with state-of-the art flat surface cleaners for unsurpassable cleaning and efficiency. Oil and diesel spills can be treated and cleaned using advanced biological cleaners for outstanding results and minimal environmental impact. Tarmac areas can be coated with sealant to extend useful lifespan of car parks and improve visual impact.*

Specialised Pipe & Services Ltd, F1 Folland Way, Hull, HU9 1NB Tel: (01482) 587060 Fax: (01482) 587099 E-mail: sales@spsworld.com *Instrument equipment, tube/valve fittings*

Specialised Polishing Services, 10 Lodge Way, Thetford, Norfolk, IP24 1HE Tel: (01842) 762700 Fax: (01842) 762700 *Metal finishing contractors*

Specialised Production Technology Ltd, 3 Monometer Business Park, Woodrolfe Road, Tollesbury, Maldon, Essex, CM9 8SB Tel: (01621) 868200 Fax: (01621) 868860 *Fabrication*

Specialised Security Manufacturing Ltd, 5 David Wright Close, Great Dunmow, Dunmow, Essex, CM6 1DB Tel: (01371) 874600 Fax: (01371) 873006 *Physical security manufrs*

Specialised Security Systems Ltd, Carmichael House, Village Green, Inkberrow, Worcester, WR7 4DZ Tel: (01386) 792522 Fax: (01386) 792729 E-mail: info@specialisedsecurity.co.uk *Installers, maintainers & suppliers of burglar alarms*

Specialised Sideloader Products Ltd, Units 2-4 Wilton Court Industrial Estate, 851 Bradford Road, Batley, West Yorkshire, WF17 8NN Tel: (01924) 477499 Fax: (01924) 473220 E-mail: sales@sspsideloaders.com *Manufacturers of side loaders*

Specialised Wheel Services, Buntings Lane, Methwold, Thetford, Norfolk, IP26 4PR Tel: (01366) 727393 Fax: (01366) 728256 E-mail: lisag@fieldens.co.uk *Agricultural services*

Specialist Anodising Ltd, New Hall Works, Elm Street, Burnley, Lancashire, BB10 1NY Tel: (01282) 412500 Fax: (01282) 422804 E-mail: saco@sacoltd.com *Metal pressings toiletries & cosmetics manufrs*

▶ Specialist Antenna Solutions, Unit 19, Hillcrest Way, Buckingham Industrial Park, Buckingham, MK18 1HJ Tel: (01280) 818768 Fax: (01280) 817179 E-mail: sales@specialistantennas.co.uk *Mobile & base station antennas suppliers*

▶ Specialist Appointments, Unit 1 The Old Bakery, South Road, Reigate, Surrey, RH2 7LB Tel: (01737) 223305 Fax: (08704) 296873 E-mail: recruit@specialistappointments.co.uk *Providing bespoke recruitment solutions to call centres. Specialist Appointments delivers a first class recruitment experience to companies and candidates.*

Specialist Bearings & Transmissions Ltd, Lees Road, Knowsley Industrial Park, Liverpool, L33 7SE Tel: 0151-546 9787 Fax: 0151-546 2861 *Gearbox & unit rebuilders & suppliers*

Specialist Building Products, 24 Beaufort Drive, London, NW11 6BU Tel: (020) 8458 8212 Fax: (020) 8458 4116 E-mail: sbpchemicals@yahoo.com *Supply chemicals for building, paint & agro*

Specialist Coating Ltd, All Saints Industrial Estate, Darlington Road, Shildon, County Durham, DL4 2RD Tel: (01388) 774034 Fax: (01388) 777010 E-mail: sales@specialistcoatings.co.uk *Powder coaters & stove enamellers*

Specialist Coatings UK Ltd, 5 Tramsheds Industrial Estate, Coomber Way, Croydon, CR0 4TQ Tel: (020) 8665 5888 Fax: (020) 8665 6888 E-mail: info@specialistcoatingsuk.com *Structural fire protection services*

Specialist Coding P.L.C., Greenbank Rd, East Tullos Ind Est, Aberdeen, AB12 3BQ Tel: 01224 894523 Fax: 01224 894358 *Supplier of bar-coding*

Specialist Computer Centre, 16 Dargan Crescent, Belfast, BT3 9JP Tel: (028) 9037 0160 Fax: (028) 9037 0195 E-mail: belfast.sales@scc.com *Computer hardware contractors*

Specialist Computer Centre, Kingsway House, Kingsway North, Team Valley Trading Estate, Gateshead, Tyne & Wear, NE11 0JS Tel: 0191-497 0000 Fax: 0191-497 0001 *IT reseller*

Specialist Computer Centres Ltd, Applied House, Killingbeck Drive, York Road, Leeds, LS14 6UF Tel: 0113-240 5250 Fax: 0113-240 1093 *Sales & engineers*

Specialist Computer Holdings UK plc, James House, Warwick Road, Birmingham, B11 2LE Tel: 0121-766 7000 Fax: 0121-773 3986 E-mail: pete_read@scc.co.uk *IT training solutions*

▶ Specialist Contractors Supplies Ltd, Unit 29 Fallings Park Industrial Estate, Park Lane, Wolverhampton, WV10 9QB Tel: (01902) 728381 Fax: (01902) 728401 E-mail: sales@s-c-s.co.uk *Industrial diamond tools manufrs*

Specialist Crafts, PO Box 247, Leicester, LE7 1PD Tel: 0116-269 7711 Fax: 0116-269 7722 E-mail: sales@speccrafts.co.uk *Art & craft material suppliers*

▶ Specialist Digital Imaging, Unit 8 Little Row, Fenton Industrial Estate, Stoke-on-Trent, ST4 2SQ Tel: (01782) 746305 Fax: (01782) 747235 *Digital ceramic decal manufrs*

▶ Specialist Electronics Services Ltd, 25 Craven Court, Stanhope Road, Camberley, Surrey, GU15 3BS Tel: (01276) 63483 Fax: (01276) 63327 E-mail: stinsonm@sesltd.com *Avionics electronics industry*

Specialist Engineering, Unit 17, Little Ridge, Knella Road Industrial Estate, Welwyn Garden City, Hertfordshire, AL7 2BH Tel: (01707) 336075 Fax: (01707) 330215 *Prototype engineers*

▶ Specialist Engineering Plastics, Unit 4, Swingbridge Road, Grantham, Lincolnshire, NG31 7XT Tel: (01476) 574476 Fax: (01476) 592262 E-mail: sep@amariplastics.com *Distributor of Semi finished engineering plastics nationwide*

Specialist Environmental Flooring Ltd, 38 Fowler Avenue, Spondon, Derby, DE21 7GR Tel: (01332) 669353 Fax: (01332) 669011 *Flooring contractors*

Specialist Equipment, 18 Derwent Road, Honley, Holmfirth, HD9 6HS Tel: (01484) 661962 Fax: (01484) 329468 E-mail: sales@specialistequipment.com *Fire protection company, supply and service of fire extinguishers and related fire products along with portable appliance testing (PAT testing)*

Specialist Fabrications Ltd, Unit 4b, Heritage Business Park, Heritage Way, Gosport, Hampshire, PO12 4BG Tel: (023) 9252 5555 Fax: (023) 9250 3333 E-mail: sales@specfabs.co.uk *Steel fabricators*

Specialist Fastener Systems Ltd, 5 The Forward Industrial Estate, Talbot Road, Leyland, PR25 2ZJ Tel: (01772) 622194 Fax: (01772) 623189 E-mail: info@specialistfastenersystems.co.uk *Industrial fastener distributors*

Specialist Heat Exchangers Ltd, Freeman Road, North Hykeham, Lincoln, LN6 9AP Tel: (01522) 881100 Fax: (01522) 684900 E-mail: info@specheat.co.uk *Heat exchanger & transfer equipment manufrs*

Specialist Heavy Engineers plc, Alexandra Docks, Newport, Gwent, NP20 2NP Tel: (01633) 262961 Fax: (01633) 246342 E-mail: she.industrial@btinternet.com *Ship repair services/general engineers*

Specialist Induction Refractories Ltd, Wednesbury Trading Estate, Wednesbury, West Midlands, WS10 7JW Tel: 0121-556 6288 Fax: 0121-556 5326 *Induction refractories manufrs*

Specialist Laminates Ltd, Station Road, Gordon, Berwickshire, TD3 6LR Tel: (01573) 410243 Fax: (01573) 410243 E-mail: sales@speclams.co.uk *Fibreglass & laminating services*

Specialist Lighting Co. Ltd, 49 The Broadway, Cheam, Sutton, Surrey, SM3 8BL Tel: (020) 8643 3110 Fax: (020) 8770 1911 E-mail: sic-@hotmail.com *Lamp wholesalers providing specialist & general lighting*

Specialist Lighting Co. Ltd, 49 The Broadway, Cheam, Sutton, Surrey, SM3 8BL Tel: (020) 8643 3110 Fax: (020) 8770 1911 E-mail: elc-ltd@hotmail.com *Lamp wholesalers providing specialist & general lighting*

Specialist Materials Processing, Unit 22 Podington Airfield, Hinwick, Wellingborough, Northamptonshire, NN29 7JQ Tel: (01234) 782026 Fax: (01234) 782028 *Tin box manufrs*

Specialist Mirror Shop, Mediterranean Village, Metrocentre, Gateshead, Tyne & Wear, NE11 9XG Tel: 0191-460 9328 Principal Export Areas: Worldwide *Mirror manufrs*

Specialist On Site Services Ltd, 3 Park Lane, Spalding, Lincolnshire, PE11 1PJ Tel: (01775) 680608 Fax: (01775) 680825 *Valve services*

Specialist Precast Products Ltd, Pantglas Industrial Estate, Bedwas, Caerphilly, Mid Glamorgan, CF83 8DR Tel: (029) 2088 0800 Fax: (029) 2088 0700 E-mail: consolidated.specialist@virgin.net *Concrete product manufrs*

Specialist Print Sevices Ltd, Mallard Close, Birmingham, B27 6BW Tel: 0121-707 7166 Fax: 0121-706 1363 E-mail: specialist-print@aol.com *Trade printers*

Specialist Pumping Services, Walkers Yard, Castle Road, Kidderminster, Worcestershire, DY11 6TH Tel: (01562) 67935 Fax: (01562) 515554 *Pump engineers*

Specialist Services (South West) Ltd, Mardle Way, Buckfastleigh, Devon, TQ11 0JS Tel: (01364) 644101 Fax: (01364) 644080 *Lifting equipment hire*

Specialist Sports Cars Ltd, Old School Yard, Smithfield Street, Llanidloes, Powys, SY18 6EJ Tel: (01686) 413000 Fax: (01686) 413000 *Small sports car manufrs*

Specialist Switchgear Systems Ltd, 9 Kay Street, Bury, Lancashire, BL9 6BU Tel: 0161-764 1297 Fax: 0161-762 9807 *Switchgear distributors & manufrs*

Specialist Tackle Ltd, 93 Chase Cross Road, Romford, RM5 3RP Tel: (01708) 752277 Fax: (01708) 754714 E-mail: info@specialist-tackle.co.uk *Fishing tackle retailers*

▶ Specialist Training Consultants Ltd, The Sycamores, 7 Rugby Close, Seaford, East Sussex, BN25 3PQ Tel: (01323) 873043 Fax: (01323) 872308 E-mail: pgwilliam@aol.com *Rollgliss rescue equipment,Rope rescue equipment,Fall Arrest sales, training and maintenance, Road Traffic Accident training, Confined Space Training & certification. Training undertaken by Ex-Fire service instructors, all highly skilled in their respective disiplines.*

▶ Specialist Woodworks, Unit 12a, Brookfield Industrial Estate, Tansley, Matlock, Derbyshire, DE4 5ND Tel: (01629) 583769 Fax: (01629) 583769

▶ Co Specialists, 53 Rodney Street, Liverpool, L1 9ER Tel: 0151-703 0303 Fax: 0151-703 0404 E-mail: info@thecompanyspecialists.com *Company formation & corporate services*

▶ Specialists In Traditional Sash Windows, 5 Bramley Hedge Farm, Redhill Road, Cobham, Surrey, KT11 1EQ Tel: (01932) 866684 Fax: (01932) 590483 E-mail: sales@sashwindowspecialists.co.uk *Manufacture of traditional hardwood sash windows*

Specialists In Traditional Sash Windows, 24 Stoughton Road, Guildford, Surrey, GU1 1LL Tel: (01483) 823161 Fax: (01483) 823161 *Sash windows manufrs*

▶ Speciality Breads By FDC, Unit J2 Westwood Industrial Estate, Margate, Kent, CT9 4JS Tel: (01843) 209442 Fax: (01843) 231378 E-mail: sales@specialitybreads.co.uk *Bread manufacturers*

Speciality Chemicals, 6 Faraday Road, Business Park, Little Port, Ely, Cambridgeshire, CB6 1PE Tel: (01353) 863686 Fax: (01353) 863990 E-mail: sales@capricorn.co.uk *Specialist chemicals & pigments manufactures & distribution*

Speciality Coatings Darwen Ltd, Dewhurst Street, Darwen, Lancashire, BB3 2EN Tel: (01254) 706026 Fax: (01254) 777132 E-mail: sales@sclgroup.com Principal Export Areas: Asia Pacific, Central/East Europe & West Europe *Vinyl wall covering manufrs*

Speciality Filaments Ltd, St. Helen Industrial Estate, Bishop Auckland, County Durham, DL14 9AD Tel: (01388) 661818 Fax: (01388) 450733 *Brush fibre manufrs*

Speciality Welds Ltd, Unit 18, Moorlands Business Centre, Cleckheaton, West Yorkshire, BD19 4EW Tel: (01274) 879867 Fax: (01274) 855975 E-mail: sales@specialwelds.com *Welding engineers & consultancy services*

Specialized Door & Window Services, Unit 5-6 Merlin Way, Hillend Industrial Park, Hillend, Dunfermline, Fife, KY11 9JY Tel: (01383) 829912 Fax: (01383) 825372 *Door & window installation & repair*

Specialized Geared Motors Ltd, Appletree Cottage Blakeshill, Road Landkey, Barnstaple, Devon, EX32 0NE Tel: (01271) 831070 Fax: 01271 831070 E-mail: sales@specializedgm.com *Manufacturers and Suppliers of shaded pole geared motors. Available in many configurations, most of which are stock lines. Custom solutions and fast delivery are a specialty. Supplied worldwide in any volume from one to thousands.*

Specialized & General Welding, Unit 35 The Wallows Industrial Estate, Brierley Hill, West Midlands, DY5 1QA Tel: (01384) 480408 Fax: (01384) 480828 *Welding equipment distributors*

▶ Specialized Glazing Ltd, Unit 6, Marshlands Road, Portsmouth, PO6 1ST Tel: (023) 9221 4113 Fax: (023) 9221 4118 E-mail: sales@specializedglazing.co.uk

Specialized Security Products Ltd, Unit 18, Park Farm Industrial Estate, Ermine Street, Buntingford, Hertfordshire, SG9 9AZ Tel: (01763) 274223 Fax: (01763) 273515 E-mail: sales@specialized-security.co.uk *Security equipment suppliers*

Specialty Coating Systems Ltd, Forsyth Road, Woking, Surrey, GU21 5RZ Tel: (01483) 541000 Fax: (01483) 541050 *Parylene conformal coatings*

Specialty Electric Motor Sales, 23 Winston Business Centre, Chartwell Road, Lancing, West Sussex, BN15 8TU Tel: (01903) 765652 Fax: (01903) 765654 E-mail: info@sp-t.co.uk *Manufacturers of electric motors, geared motors, electric, electric motors, DC & armature. In addition electric motor stockists/distributors/agents*

Specialty Fasteners & Components Ltd, Seymour Wharf, Steamer Quay Road, Totnes, Devon, TQ9 5AL Tel: (01803) 868677 Fax: (01803) 868678 E-mail: sales@specialty-fasteners.co.uk Principal Export Areas: Asia Pacific, Middle East, Africa, Central/East Europe, West Europe, North America & South America *Fitting manufrs*

Specialty Fasteners & Components Ltd, Seymour Wharf, Steamer Quay Road, Totnes, Devon, TQ9 5AL Tel: (01803) 868677 Fax: (01803) 868678 E-mail: sales@specialty-fasteners.co.uk Purchasing Contact: M. Langdon Sales Contact: P. Boote Principal Export Areas: Asia Pacific, Middle East, Africa, Central/East Europe, West Europe, North America & South America *Fastener (quick release), hardware (security), shock absorber (industrial) & vibration damper manufr*

Specialty Gases Ltd, Buiding 940 Kent Science Park, Sittingbourne, Kent, ME9 8PS Tel: (01795) 599099 Fax: (01795) 411525 E-mail: sales@specialty-gases.com *Producers of calibration gas mixtures in non-refillable cylinders. For use with gas detection equipment, medical gas analysers & other analytical equipment. MicroGas are ISO 9001-2000 approved and members of the BCGA (British Compressed Gas Association). Based in the South East of England supply gas worldwide through chain of distributors and a Sister company located in Germany. MicroGas supply cans that are manufactured & approved to either ISO or SOT standards.*

Specific Components, Unit 23, Common Bank Industrial Estate, Ackhurst Road, Chorley, Lancashire, PR7 1NH Tel: (01257) 279944 Fax: (01257) 279922 E-mail: sales@specific-components.co.uk *S.C.L. Services® Tape & Reeling · Tape & Reel Re-Counting ·De-Reeling · Re-Labelling · Programming · BGA Re-Balling · BGA Re-Balling Testing · Solder Ability Testing · Solder Ability Re-Working ·Lead-free Technologies ·Lead-Free Re-Working · Lead-Free Solution · Lead-Free Re-Dipping · Reforming Damaged IC's · Dry Packaging · Vacuum Packaging · IC's Trays · Waffle Trays · Oven Baking · Labelling · Paint Marking · IC-Sourcing*

Specific Environments Ltd, Gallows Lane, High Wycombe, Buckinghamshire, HP12 4BX Tel: (01494) 464411 Fax: (01494) 523933 E-mail: sel@specific-environments.co.uk *Air-conditioning equipment & system services*

Robert Speck Ltd, Little Ridge, Whittlebury Road, Silverstone, Towcester, Northamptonshire, NN12 8UD Tel: (01327) 857307 Fax: (01327) 858166 E-mail: info@robertspeck.com *Flow drill distributors & manufacturers, tapping machines*

▶ Specnet, 27 The Poplars, Earl Shilton, Leicester, LE9 7ET Tel: (01455) 447928 Fax: (01455) 447928 E-mail: info@specnet.co.uk *Web site design & hosting aimed at small businesses*

Specthread Ltd, Unit 20, Field Close, Bloxwich, Walsall, WS3 3JS Tel: (01922) 710180 Fax: (01922) 710181 *Specialised fasteners manufrs*

Spectile Ltd, 2 Poplar Grove, Crewe, CW1 4AZ Tel: (01270) 587222 Fax: (01270) 250888 E-mail: sales@spectile.co.uk *Ceramic tile distributors*

Spectra Displays Ltd, 194 Station Road, Willingham, Cambridge, CB4 5HQ Tel: (01954) 261402 Fax: (01954) 261403 E-mail: sales@spectra-displays.co.uk *Fantastic range of LED Signs & Displays for use indoor & outdoor. From simple scrolling or moving message signs to full colour LED video - Spectra have a product to suit your requirement.*

Spectra Group Ltd, Duchess Industrial Estate, Sievewright Street, Rutherglen, Glasgow, G73 1LL Tel: 0141-647 0831 Fax: 0141-643 0047 E-mail: office@spectragroup.co.uk *Suspended ceilings supplier*

Spectra Masterbatch Ltd, 5 Blyth Road, Halesworth, Suffolk, IP19 8EN Tel: (01986) 875100 Fax: (01986) 875700 E-mail: sales@spectra-masterbatch.co.uk *Masterbatch manufrs*

Spectra Plastics Ltd, Southam Road, Long Itchington, Southam, Warwickshire, CV47 9QL Tel: (01926) 812195 Fax: (01926) 817401 E-mail: sales@spectra-plastics.co.uk *Plastic materials, products, components services*

Spectra Sensortech Ltd, Cowley Way, Crewe, CW1 6AG Tel: (01270) 250150 Fax: (01270) 251939 *Gas analyser manufrs*

Spectra Sound, Unit 1-2 The Chambers, St. Edmunds Road, Northampton, NN1 5ET Tel: (01604) 634100 Fax: E-mail: dondix@lineone.net *Sound & lighting maintenance services*

Spectral Dynamics UK Ltd, Fulling Mill, Fulling Mill Lane, Welwyn, Hertfordshire, AL6 9NP Tel: (01438) 716626 Fax: (01438) 716628 E-mail: sales@spectraldynamics.co.uk *Vibration test equipment & transducer manufrs*

Spectral Fusion Technologies Ltd, Unit 45 Coleshill Industrial Estate, Station Road, Coleshill, Birmingham, B46 1JT Tel: (01675) 466111 Fax: (01675) 467111 *Laboratory research services*

Spectral Line Systems Ltd, Units 1-3 Scott Road, Tarbert, Isle of Harris, HS3 3DL Tel: (01859) 502533 Fax: (01859) 502533 E-mail: slsltd@lineone.net *Microwave/R F frequency sources manufacturing*

Spectrex Inc, 6 Applecross Road, Kirkintilloch, Glasgow, G66 3TJ Tel: 0141-578 0693 Fax: 0141-578 9689 E-mail: ian@spectrex-inc.com *Flame detection consultants*

Spectro Analytical UK Ltd, Fountain House, Great Cornbow, Halesowen, West Midlands, B63 3BL Tel: 0121-550 8997 Fax: 0121-550 5165 E-mail: sales@spectro.co.uk *Spectrometers, sales & service*

▶ Spectro Service Ltd, Top Station Road, Top Station Road Industrial Estate, Brackley, Northamptonshire, NN13 7UG Tel: (01280) 705577 Fax: (01280) 705510 E-mail: sales@spectroservice.co.uk *Service & repair of analytical equipment*

Spectroform Engineering Services Ltd, 1a Saxby Road Industrial Estate, Hudson Road, Melton Mowbray, Leicestershire, LE13 1BS Tel: (01664) 500728 Fax: (01664) 410509 E-mail: sales@spectroform.co.uk *General engineering, machining & fabricators*

Spectronic Analytical Insruments, Tudor House, Barley Hill Road, Garforth, Leeds, LS25 1DX Tel: 0113-286 4536 Fax: 0113-232 0424 E-mail: spectrouk@aol.com *Suppliers of scientific instruments*

Spectrum, Unit 26 Small Heath Trading Estate, Armoury Road, Birmingham, B11 2RJ Tel: (0121) 772 3867 *Kitchen furniture distributors & manufrs*

Spectrum, 540 London Road, Grays, Essex, RM20 3BJ Tel: (01708) 868306 Fax: (01708) 860118 E-mail: spectrumvr@aol.com *Commercial vehicle bodybuilders & repairers*

Spectrum Alloys Ltd, Milton Road, Stoke-on-Trent, ST1 6LE Tel: (01782) 532800 Fax: (01782) 532809 E-mail: info@spectrumalloys.co.uk *Aluminium, stainless steel, brass & bronze stockholders*

▶ Spectrum Architectural Coatings, High Street, Princes End, Tipton, West Midlands, DY4 9HG Tel: 0121-522 2244 Fax: 0121-522 2243

Spectrum Blinds, Millers Avenue, Brynmenyn, Bridgend, CF32 9TD Tel: (01656) 723898 Fax: (01656) 723079 *Blind manufrs*

Spectrum Blinds, 519 Leeds Road, Outwood, Wakefield, West Yorkshire, WF1 2PN Tel: (0800) 0965480 Fax: (01924) 372728 *Blind retailers & manufrs*

Spectrum Colors, Merrivale House, Kinburn Drive, Egham Hill, Egham, Surrey, TW20 0BD Tel: (01784) 431273 Fax: (01784) 431103 E-mail: sales@spectrum.co.uk *Computer resellers*

Spectrum Computer Services plc, PO Box 199, Bradford, West Yorkshire, BD1 5RJ Tel: (01274) 308188 Fax: (01274) 307264 E-mail: admin@spectrumplc.co.uk *Computer services & products*

Spectrum Control GmbH, PO Box 34, Great Yarmouth, Norfolk, NR29 5RE Tel: (01692) 678041 Fax: (01692) 678042 E-mail: sales@spectrumcontrol.co.uk *Electronic component suppliers*

▶ Spectrum Electrical Engineers, 10 Coton Lane, Birmingham, B23 6TP Tel: 0121-350 9929 Fax: 0121-350 4929

Spectrum Engineering & Transmission Co. Ltd, Unit 43 Purfleet Industrial Park, London Road, Aveley, South Ockendon, Essex, RM15 4YA Tel: (01708) 861718 Fax: (01708) 867540 E-mail: bob@spectrum-engineering.co.uk *Engineers merchants & electrical wholesalers*

Spectrum Fire Protection Ltd, Middlemore Lane, Walsall, WS9 8SP Tel: (01922) 744466 Fax: (01922) 744477 E-mail: sales@spectrumfire.co.uk *Fire fighting equipment suppliers*

Spectrum Fitted Furniture Ltd, Rosehill, Henley-On-Thames, Oxfordshire, RG9 3EB Tel: (01628) 820240 Fax: (01628) 820241 *Furniture manufrs*

Spectrum Industrial Ltd, Unit 19-24 Bedesway, Bede Trading Estate, Jarrow, Tyne & Wear, NE32 3EG Tel: 0191-430 1111 Fax: 0191-483 7422 E-mail: sales@spectrum-ind.co.uk *Janitorial supply services*

Spectrum Investigations, 1 The Arches, Park Street, Wellington, Telford, Shropshire, TF1 3PE Tel: (01952) 276493 Fax: (01952) 412674 E-mail: specrumpi@blueyonder.co.uk *Professional investigation agency*

Spectrum Laser Ltd, 2 Aysgarth Road, Waterlooville, Hampshire, PO7 7UG Tel: (023) 9225 2900 Fax: (023) 9223 3766 E-mail: sales@spectrumlaser.co.uk *Laser cutting services*

▶ Spectrum Marketing Ltd, PO Box 274, Blackburn, BB1 8XB Tel: 01254 249991 Fax: 01254 249417 E-mail: info@spectrummarketing.co.uk *Everything we do is based on strategy and research. The first question we ask is Why? We don't have a 'catch all' solution or templates that we 'tweak'. We won't guide you down paths where we can maximise our profit. We will look at what you need. We decide this by looking at your products and/or services and your existing customer base or proposed market. We don"t assume. What have you already got? What are you doing well? Where can we help you improve? **The strategies we develop are based on our clients" ability to implement them. Our clients are sole traders, small companies, SME"s and Plcs. They are in different markets, different countries with different products and different objectives. This is why we have to be different. To achieve this we have developed partner companies and currently have bases in the Balti states, Poland and Hungary, ***

Spectrum Menu Systems Ltd, Units 12 &13, Hixon Industrial Estate, Church Lane, Hixon, Stafford, ST18 0PY Tel: (01889) 271440 Fax: (01889) 271449 *Sign manufrs*

Spectrum O A Ltd, 7 121 Lansdowne Road, London, W11 2LF Tel: (020) 7221 3877 Fax: (020) 7221 6568 *Computer consultants*

▶ Spectrum Personnel Ltd, 154 Merry Street, Motherwell, Lanarkshire, ML1 1NA Tel: (01698) 304545 Fax: (01698) 304646 E-mail: garytelfer@spectrum-personnel.com *Providing professional recruitment services to the distribution, industrial, technical/engineering and office business sectors throughout central Scotland. Members of the REC, our service is available 24/7.*

▶ Spectrum Photographic, Unit 10 Hove Business Centre, Fonthill Road, Hove, East Sussex, BN3 6HA Tel: (01273) 708222 Fax: (01273) 888515 E-mail: info@spectrumphoto.co.uk *High quality photographic laboratory*

Spectrum Photos, Belgrave Gate, Leicester, LE1 3GQ Tel: 0116-251 9478 Fax: 0116-251 9478 E-mail: spectrumphoto@virginnet.co.uk *Picture frame & mirror gallery & photographers services*

Spectrum Printing & Mailing Services, 1 50 Station Road, Chertsey, Surrey, KT16 8BE Tel: (01932) 569123 Fax: (01932) 569123 E-mail: spectrumpms@btconnect.com *Fulfillment & marketing specialists*

Spectrum Printing Services Ltd, Hamilton Business Park, Waterside Road, Hamilton, Leicester, LE5 1TL Tel: 0116-246 1717 Fax: 0116-246 1575 E-mail: info@spectrumprinting.co.uk *Lithographic printers*

▶ SPECTRUM PRODUCTS LTD, The Workshop, 8 Church Street, Little Lever, Bolton, BL3 1BE Tel: 01204 452731 Fax: 01204 452731 E-mail: spectrummail@aol.com *Stainless Steel Water Features*

Spectrum Resin Systems Ltd, 69a Huddersfield Road, Elland, West Yorkshire, HX5 9AA Tel: (01422) 375851 Fax: (01422) 310291 *Contractors & suppliers for flooring*

Spectrum Robotic Systems Ltd, Spithead Business Centre, Newport Road, Sandown, Isle of Wight, PO36 9PH Tel: (01983) 401188 Fax: (01983) 408450 *Manufacturers of Vectaspark EDG/EDM spark erosion machines & flat bed cutting systems.*

Spectrum Security Services Ltd, 111 Magdalen Street, Colchester, CO1 2LF Tel: (01206) 793915 Fax: (01206) 795974 *Burglar alarm installation services & lock smiths*

▶ Spectrum Services UK Ltd, 11 Sandown Road, Brislington, Bristol, BS4 3PL Tel: 0117-907 1644 Fax: 0117-907 1646 *Builders*

Spectrum Sign & Display Ltd, 11a Brindley Road, Reginald Road Industrial Estate, St. Helens, Merseyside, WA9 4HY Tel: (01744) 815005 Fax: (01744) 813920 E-mail: sales@spectrumsigns.net *Sign manufrs*

Spectrum Signs, 290 Northholt Road, South Harrow, Harrow, Middlesex, HA2 8EB Tel: (020) 8422 1168 Fax: (020) 8864 4220 E-mail: spectrumsigns@webtribe.net *Sign & banner manufrs*

Spectrum Signs, 22 Bladon Road, Southampton, SO16 6QD Tel: (023) 8077 2264 Fax: (023) 8032 2264 E-mail: sales@spectrum-signs.co.uk *General sign manufacturers & digital printers, work wear suppliers*

Spectrum Signs, Unit R5 Elvington Industrial Estate, York Road, Elvington, York, YO41 4AR Tel: (01904) 607000 Fax: (01904) 607060 E-mail: sales@signsbyspectrum.com *Sign manufrs*

Spectrum Weighing Technology Industrial Weighing Equipement, Newbigging Road, Carnock, Dunfermline, Fife, KY12 9GD Tel: (01383) 851600 Fax: (01383) 851600 *Industrial Weighing Equipment*

Spectrum Welding Supplies Ltd, Spectrum House, Chesterfield, Derbyshire, S40 2WB Tel: 01246 205267 *Suppliers of welding equipment*

▶ Spectus Construction, Upton Snodsbury, Worcester, WR7 4NH Tel: (01905) 380056 Fax: (01905) 381933

Spectus Windows Systems Ltd, Pinewood Court, Cycherington Business Park, Macclesfield, Cheshire, SK10 2XR Tel: (01625) 420400 Fax: (01625) 501418 *UPVC window & door extrusion manufrs*

Spedition Services, 32 Anyards Road, Cobham, Surrey, KT11 2LA Tel: (01932) 584458 Fax: (01932) 584459 E-mail: info@spedition.co.uk *Freight forwarding services*

Speech Centre, Croft Road, Crowborough, East Sussex, TN6 1DL Tel: (01892) 661116 Fax: (01892) 668177 E-mail: info@speechcentre.co.uk *Computer services*

Speech & Data Communications, 135 Glendale Gardens, Leigh-on-Sea, Essex, SS9 2BE Tel: (01702) 473478 Fax: (01702) 473478 *Telephone distribution*

Speech Machines Ltd, Merebrook Business Park, Hanley Road, Welland, Malvern, Worcestershire, WR13 6NP Tel: (01684) 312300 Fax: (01684) 312301 *Dictation recording application service providers*

Speed Alarm Ltd, 94-98 Sandon Street, Nottingham, NG7 7AN Tel: 0115-978 0791 Fax: 0115-942 2423 E-mail: sales@speedalarm.com *Security retailers*

▶ Speed Alloys Ltd, Marsh Road, Burnham-on-Crouch, Essex, CM0 8NB Tel: (01621) 785578 Fax: (01621) 785588 E-mail: keith@speedalloys.com *stockholder of stainless steel aluminium and non ferrous metals*

Speed Bird Engineering, 21 Cunliffe Drive Industrial Estate, Cunliffe Drive, Kettering, Northamptonshire, NN16 8LD Tel: (01536) 524240 Fax: (01536) 520689 E-mail: nitulpanchal@speedbird-engineering.com *Precision engineering of medical equipment*

Speed Drill Ltd, Unit 17-18 Chingford Industrial Centre, Hall Lane, London, E4 8DJ Tel: (020) 8524 0004 Fax: (020) 8524 6778 *Concrete drilling contractors*

Speed Engineering, Station Yard, Broome, Aston-on-Clun, Craven Arms, Shropshire, SY7 0NT Tel: (01588) 660427 Fax: (01588) 660771 *Machinists & general engineers*

▶ SPEED Laboratory, University Of Glasgow, Oakfield Avenue, Glasgow, G12 8LT Tel: 0141-330 3157 Fax: 0141-330 3158 *Electric motors & software for electric motors*

▶ Speed Print, Unit 29, Dinan Way Trading Estate, Exmouth, Devon, EX8 4RS Tel: (01395) 263831 Fax: (01395) 274064

▶ Speedbird Supplies, 15 Thistledown Drive, Ixworth, Bury St. Edmunds, Suffolk, IP31 2NH Tel: (01359) 235170 Fax: (01359) 232015 E-mail: sales@speedbird-supplies.co.uk *Speedbird Supplies offer personalised services for Promotional Die-Cast Model Trucks of the highest-quality.**We also have extensive stocks on Printer and Office Supplies at competitive prices*

Speedbore Diamond Drilling (Northern) Ltd, Unit 7, Wood St, Poulton-le-Fylde, Lancashire, FY6 8JY Tel: (01253) 891206 Fax: (01253) 893848 E-mail: peter@speedbore.com *Concrete drilling & sawing contractors*

Speedfab Ltd, Unit 10, Credenda Road, West Bromwich, West Midlands, B70 7JE Tel: 0121-541 1761 Fax: 0121-544 0028 E-mail: speedfabltd@aol.com *Specialist stainless steel fabricators engineering & installation*

Speedform Tools (Midlands) Ltd, Windmill Street, Walsall, WS1 3EE Tel: (01922) 635499 Fax: (01922) 722878 E-mail: info@speedform.co.uk *Precision toolmakers*

Speedgold Ltd, Pierhead, The Docks, Port Talbot, West Glamorgan, SA13 1RH Tel: (01639) 898519 Fax: (01639) 891611 *General engineers*

Speedibake Ltd, 6 Cross Lane, Bradford, West Yorkshire, BD4 0SG Tel: (0870) 8307600 Fax: (0870) 8307601 *Bakery & cake manufrs*

▶ Speedier Scaffolding Ltd, Manchester Road, Westhoughton, Bolton, BL5 3QH Tel: (01942) 841919

Speedings Flags Poles & Masts, 4 Carrmere Road, Leechmere Industrial Estate, Sunderland, SR2 9TW Tel: 0191-523 9933 Fax: 0191-523 9955 E-mail: speedingsltd@btconnect.com *Tarpaulin & fire fighting equipment manufrs*

Speedlaw Services, 43 Ainsdale Road, Ealing, London, W5 1JY Tel: (020) 8991 1111 *Same day delivery telegram services*

▶ Speedline Graphics, 81 Queens Road, Buckhurst Hill, Essex, IG9 5BW Tel: (020) 8504 8070 E-mail: speedline1@hotmail.co.uk *Sign writers*

Speedlith Ltd, Longford Trading Estate, Thomas Street, Stretford, Manchester, M32 0JT Tel: 0161-864 2233 Fax: 0161-864 5238 E-mail: speedlith@aol.com *Photo litho reproduction & pre-press services*

▶ speed-networking.net, 47 Bluebell Close, Gateshead, Tyne & Wear, NE9 6RH Tel: 0191 4821709 E-mail: info@speed-networking.net *Speed-networking.net was setup to be the fastest and most cost effective way to generate successful new business contacts. It offers the unique chance to voice your pitch for 5 minutes face to face with people you would normally not get the opportunity to meet.*

Speedo International Ltd, Ascot Road, Nottingham, NG8 5AJ Tel: 0115-916 7000 Fax: 0115-910 5005 E-mail: speedoinfo@pentland.com *Swimwear manufrs*

Speedograph Ltd, 104 Rolleston Drive, Arnold, Nottingham, NG5 7JR Tel: 0115-926 4235 Fax: 0115-920 9912 E-mail: info@speedograph-richfield.co.uk *Speedometer cable specialists*

Speedpac, Sywell Airport Business Park, Wellingborough Road, Sywell, Northampton, NN6 0BN Tel: (01604) 746999 Fax: (01604) 746900 E-mail: sales@speedpac.co.uk *Contract packers*

▶ SpeedPlumb.co.uk, Casemill, Temeside, Ludlow, Shropshire, SY8 1JW Tel: 0845 3732738 *SpeedPlumb stock a huge range of plumbing supplies, at the best prices. Our range includes taps, showers, heating controls, towel radiators and every type of fitting. We have all the top brands, including Bristan, Mira, Triton, Honeywell and Saniflo.*

Speedprint Services Ltd, Brook Street, Failsworth, Manchester, M35 0BS Tel: 0161-683 4111 Fax: 0161-683 4570 *General printers*

Speedstick Adhesive Labels Ltd, The Street, Ulcombe, Maidstone, Kent, ME17 1DX Tel: (01622) 843705 Fax: (01622) 843751 E-mail: speedstick@blueyonder.co.uk *Adhesive label manufrs*

Speedwater Ltd, Silverdale, Glynleigh Road, Hankham, Pevensey, East Sussex, BN24 5BJ Tel: (01323) 761475 Fax: (01323) 760020 E-mail: sales@speedwater.co.uk *Water cooler (drinking) manufrs*

▶ Speedwell Couriers, 23 Plough Lane, Whitstable, Kent, CT5 2NZ Tel: (01227) 792790 E-mail: speedwellcouriers@yahoo.co.uk *We are a family run same day courier service. We specialize in high value deliveries of fragile and delicate products.*We are available for uk mainland deliveries 24 hours a day 7 days a week*

Speedwell Reinforcement Ltd, White Lane, Chapeltown, Sheffield, S35 2YG Tel: 0114-246 7551 Fax: 0114-240 2519 E-mail: enquiries@speedwellreinforcement.co.uk *Steel reinforcement wire & mesh manufrs*

Speedwell Tool Co, 62 Meadow Street, Preston, PR1 1SU Tel: (01772) 252951 Fax: (01772) 254861 *Tool distributors*

▶ Speedy Hire plc, Chase House, 16 The Parks, Newton-le-Willows, Merseyside, WA12 0JQ Tel: (01942) 720000 Fax: (01942) 720077 E-mail: customer.services@speedyhire.co.uk *Tool hire and equipment hire.* Also at: Brierley Hill, Ilkley & Swindon

Speedy Hire Centres Ltd, Tollgate House, Tollgate Lane, Bury St. Edmunds, Suffolk, IP32 6DG Tel: (01284) 766254 Fax: (01284) 700542 E-mail: customer.services@speedyhire.co.uk *Industrial tool hire & sales*

Speedy Hire Centres Ltd, 572 Melton Road, Thurmaston, Leicester, LE4 8BB Tel: 0116-260 1019 Fax: 0116-260 0109 *Tool & plant hire*

Speedy Hire Centres Ltd, 56 Christchurch Road, Reading, RG2 7AZ Tel: 0118-931 2636 Fax: 0118-986 1555 *Tool hire services*

▶ Speedy Hire Centres Ltd, Brigg Road, Scunthorpe, South Humberside, DN16 1AX Tel: (01724) 865432 Fax: (01724) 289569 *Power generation, compressor & lighting hire services*

Speedy Hire Centres Ltd, Hilton Industrial Estate, 1 Hepworth Road, Sunderland, SR5 3JT Tel: 0191-548 4114 Fax: 0191-516 0384 *Tool hire company*

Speedy Hire Centres Ltd, Unit 3 Ironbridge Road, West Drayton, Middlesex, UB7 8DU Tel: (01895) 440046 Fax: (01895) 431417 *Tool hire*

Speedy Hire Centres Northern Ltd, Lakeside Buildings, St. Helens, Merseyside, WA10 3TT Tel: (01744) 697000 Fax: (01744) 739975 *Tool hire* Also at: Branches throughout the U.K.

▶ Speedy Hire Centres Southern Ltd, 6 Broadfields, Aylesbury, Buckinghamshire, HP19 8ZU Tel: (01296) 331007 Fax: (01296) 393930 E-mail: ellesby-southern@speedydepots.co.uk *Tool & equipment hire services*

Speedy Hire Centres Southern Ltd, 6 Bedford Road, Kempston, Bedford, MK42 8AD Tel: (01234) 353148 Fax: (01234) 363285 *Tool & plant hire*

▶ Speedy Hire Centres Southern Ltd, Dukes Ride, Crowthorne, Berkshire, RG45 6NZ Tel: (01344) 779004 Fax: (01344) 779073 *Tool & equipment hire services*

Speedy Hire Centres Southern Ltd, Accademy House, Fengate, Peterborough, PE1 5SW Tel: (01733) 551092 Fax: (01733) 352089 *Tool hire*

▶ Speedy Hire (Southern) Ltd, Overthorpe Road, Banbury, Oxfordshire, OX16 4SY Tel: (01295) 267977 Fax: (01295) 250045 *Tool & equipment hire services*

Speedy Hire UK, 101 Blackhorse Lane, London, E17 6DJ Tel: (020) 8531 7621 Fax: (020) 8503 2599 *Tool hire*

Speedy L G H, Unit 13, Royce Road, Fleming Way, Crawley, West Sussex, RH10 2NX Tel: (01293) 615898 Fax: (01293) 615818 E-mail: crawley@lgh.co.uk *Lifting equipment hire sales & service for the construction industry*

Speedy L G H, Unit 2, Crescent Industrial Park, Peartree Lane, Dudley, West Midlands, DY2 0QQ Tel: (01384) 239966 Fax: (01384) 455782 E-mail: rob.langford@lgh.co.uk *Lifting gear hire services*

Speedy LGH, Bentley Avenue, Cowpen Bewley Industrial Estate, Billingham, Cleveland, TS23 4BU Tel: (01642) 561611 Fax: (01642) 566032 E-mail: teeside@lgh.co.uk *Lifting gear hire*

Speedy LGH, Units 36-37, Millers Bridge Industrial Estate, Bootle, Merseyside, L20 1EE Tel: 0151-922 5596 Fax: 0151-922 0361 E-mail: liverpool@lgh.co.uk *Lifting gear hire*

Speedy LGH, Long Island Park, Carlisle, CA2 5AS Tel: (01228) 599766 Fax: (01228) 599788 E-mail: info@lgh.co.uk *Lifting gear hire contractors*

Speedy LGH Ltd, Unit A, Castleblair Works, Inglis Lane, Dunfermline, Fife, KY12 9DP Tel: (01383) 721079 Fax: (01383) 732781 *Lifting gear hire services*

Speedy LGH, 100 Brook Street, Glasgow, G40 3AP Tel: 0141-554 6477 Fax: 0141-554 6162 *Lifting gear hire services*

Speedy LGH, Unit 2, 40 Adam Smith Street, Grimsby, South Humberside, DN31 1SJ Tel: (01472) 362685 Fax: (01472) 342612 E-mail: grimsby@lgh.co.uk *Lifting gear hire contractors*

Speedy LGH Ltd, Unit 5, Farthing Road, Ipswich, IP1 5AP Tel: (01473) 461083 Fax: (01473) 240532 E-mail: ipswich@lgh.co.uk *Lifting gear hire services*

Speedy LGH, West Thamesmead Business Park, 7 Kellner Road, London, SE28 0AX Tel: (020) 8854 6248 Fax: (020) 8316 0501 E-mail: south-thames@lgh.co.uk *Lifting gear hire*

Speedy LGH, Unit 1, Dewsbury Road, Fenton Industrial Estate, Stoke-on-Trent, ST4 2TE Tel: (01782) 272954 Fax: (01782) 260713 E-mail: stoke@lgh.co.uk *Lifting gear hire*

▶ Speedy Lift, Unit B North Sea Supply Base, Riverside Park Road, Middlesbrough, Cleveland, TS2 1UT Tel: (01642) 246111 Fax: (01642) 249123 E-mail: teeside-lifting@speedydepots.co.uk *Lifting equipment hire.*

Speedy Lifting Ltd, Cronin Road, Weldon South Industrial Estate, Corby, Northamptonshire, NN18 8AQ Tel: (01536) 206306 Fax: (01536) 264513 E-mail: corby-lifting@speedydepots.co.uk *Lifting gear hire*

Speedy Lifting Ltd, Pentagon Island, Nottingham Road, Derby, DE21 6BW Tel: (01332) 380493 Fax: (01332) 372615 *Small plant & tool hire* Also at: Ashbourne, Burton-on-Trent & Nottingham

Speedy Lifting, 3 Vulcan House, Vulcan Road North, Norwich, NR6 6AQ Tel: (01603) 764642 Fax: (01603) 620839 E-mail: norwich@lgh.co.uk *Lifting gear hire*

Speedy Lifting, Unit 1, Llewellyns Quay, The Docks, Port Talbot, West Glamorgan, SA13 1RF Tel: (01639) 890875 Fax: (01639) 895009 E-mail: port-talbot@lgh.co.uk *Lifting gear hire*

Speedy Lifting, Unit 4 Meridian Park, Neptune Close, Rochester, Kent, ME2 4LE Tel: (01634) 297373 Fax: (01634) 296638 E-mail: medway@lgh.co.uk *Lifting gear hire contractors*

Speedy Lifting, Unit 10, Central Trading Estate, Marine Parade, Southampton, SO14 5JP Tel: (023) 9223 8236 Fax: (023) 8063 1712 E-mail: southampton-lifting@speedydepos.co.uk *Lifting gear hire services*

▶ Speedy Mortar, Unit 14, Currock Road Trade Centre, Currock Road, Carlisle, CA2 5AD Tel: (01228) 548001 Fax: (01228) 548001 *Concrete ready mixed distributors*

▶ Speedy Parcels, Field Way, Greenford, Middlesex, UB6 8UN Tel: (020) 8813 4111 Fax: (020) 8833 7222 *We are a courier company, forwarding UK, European and International freight on a daily basis.*

Speedy Sheet Metal Ltd, 5 Teknol House, Victoria Road, Burgess Hill, West Sussex, RH15 9LH Tel: (01444) 248764 Fax: (01444) 247767 *Fine limit sheet metal engineers & fabrication*

Speedy Signs, 1 Moor Lane, Dungannon, County Tyrone, BT71 6HS Tel: (028) 8772 7511 Fax: (028) 8772 9511 *Sign makers*

Speedy Signs Ltd, 39 Waterhead Road, Stoke-on-Trent, ST3 5NG Tel: (01782) 327077 Fax: (01782) 593276 *Sign manufrs*

Speedy Space Ltd, The Premier Partnership Estate, Leys Rd, Brockmoore, Brierley Hill, W. Midlands, DY5 3UP Tel: (01384) 572635 Fax: (01384) 480434 *Portable accommodation and storage hire.*

▶ Speedy Space Ltd, 57 East Parade, Ilkley, West Yorkshire, LS29 8JP Tel: (01943) 600511 Fax: (01943) 817118 *Portable accommodation & storage hire services*

Speedy Survey Ltd, 6 Power Court, Luton, LU1 3JJ Tel: (01582) 722365 Fax: (01582) 424341 *Surveying instruments & equipment.*

▶ Speedy Survey Ltd, Unit 3 12 Popes Lane, Oldbury, West Midlands, B69 4PN Tel: 0121-544 7726 Fax: 0121-552 0250 E-mail: sales@speedysurvey.co.uk *Survey equipment manufrs*

Speedy/LGH, Unit 1C, Walney Road Industrial Estate, Barrow-In-Furness, Cumbria, LA14 5UG Tel: (01229) 835407 Fax: (01229) 811236 E-mail: cumbria@lgh.co.uk *Lifting gear hire services*

Speedyprint Ltd, 67 Stockport Road, Stockport, Cheshire, SK3 0JG Tel: 0161-480 6038 Fax: 0161-480 5166 E-mail: sales@speedyprint.co.uk *Printers & label manufrs*

Speights Classic Lighting, Huddersfield Road, Mirfield, West Yorkshire, WF14 8BJ Tel: (01924) 494176 Fax: (01924) 480691 *Lampshade manufrs*

Speirs Robertson Ltd, 42 Bedford Road, London, N2 9DA Tel: (01234) 823410 Fax: (0870) 7624234 E-mail: sales@robertson.co.uk *Honeycomb core boards & panel manufrs*

▶ Spektaglaze Ltd, 137-139 Richmond Row, Liverpool, L3 3BU Tel: 0151-207 4066 *Glazers*

Spel Lighting Mnfrs, Beecham Close, Walsall, WS9 8UZ Tel: (0870) 5168214 Fax: (0870) 5168519 E-mail: sales@spelonline.co.uk *Emergency lighting manufrs*

Spel Products Ltd, Lancaster Road, Shrewsbury, SY1 3NQ Tel: (01743) 445200 Fax: (08451) 300442 *Glass fibre tank manufrs*

Spen Bearings, 129 Westgate, Cleckheaton, West Yorkshire, BD19 5EJ Tel: (01274) 851700 Fax: (01274) 869736 E-mail: admin@spen-bearings.co.uk *Ball bearing distributors & agents*

▶ Spence, Audrey House, 16-20 Ely Place, London, EC1N 6SN Tel: (020) 7440 4670 Fax: (020) 7440 4671

▶ Spence Associates, 41 Francis Gardens, Winchester, Hampshire, SO23 7HD Tel: (01962) 867425 Fax: (01962) 841425 E-mail: sales@spencea.com *Management training consultancy*

Spence Bryson Ltd, Unit 14a Seagoe Industrial Area, Portadown, Craigavon, County Armagh, BT63 5QD Tel: (028) 3833 2521 Fax: (028) 3835 1043 E-mail: sales@spencebryson.co.uk *Handkerchief & gift manufrs*

George Spence & Sons Ltd, 105 Wellington Road, Leeds, LS12 1DX Tel: 0113-279 0507 Fax: 0113-263 6817 E-mail: sales@geospence.co.uk *Tools ironmongery & storage equipment wholesalers*

▶ Spence & Grant Ltd, New Elgin Road, Elgin, Morayshire, IV30 6BA Tel: (01343) 541716 *Carpentry & joinery*

J.E. Spence Ltd, Church Lane, Adel, Leeds, LS16 8DE Tel: 0113-267 4110 *Cabinet manufrs & undertakers*

Spencer & Co., The Green, Long Lawford, Rugby, Warwickshire, CV23 9BL Tel: (01788) 560782 Fax: (01788) 537917 E-mail: enquiries@spencerfurniture.co.uk *Furniture & furnishing projects specialists*

Spencer Coatings Ltd, Froghall Terrace, Aberdeen, AB24 3JN Tel: (01224) 788400 Fax: (01224) 648116 E-mail: info@spencercoatings.co.uk *Paint manufrs*

Spencer Commercial Property P.L.C., Spencer House, Millbrook Business Park, Rainford, St. Helens, Merseyside, WA11 8LZ Tel: (01744) 887980 Fax: (01744) 887981 E-mail: info@spencerholdingsplc.com *Investment companies & investment property*

Spencer Construction & Engineering, Royal Albert Works, Bradfield Road, London, E16 2AT Tel: (020) 7511 1711 Fax: (020) 7474 2195 *Storage tank manufrs*

Spencer Davis Handling Ltd, Glanmor Terrace, Burry Port, Dyfed, SA16 0LS Tel: (01554) 833358 Fax: (01554) 835338 E-mail: sales@sde.co.uk *Material handling equipment manufrs*

▶ The Spencer Group Ltd, 308-314 Kings Road, Reading, RG1 4NR Tel: 0118-935 9444 Fax: 0118 935 9445 E-mail: sales@spencergroup.co.uk Sales Contact: M. Trott *Specialist Recruitment Solutions provider & search and selection firm - partnering with key clients to deliver superior recruitment solutions - IT - HR - Science - Sales - Marketing - Content Management. Permanent & Interim. Executive Search. Throughout Europe.*

John Spencer (Hazelhurst) Ltd, Hazelhurst Engraving Works, 258 Bolton Road West, Ramsbottom, Bury, Lancashire, BL0 9PX Tel: (01706) 823244 Fax: (01706) 828529 E-mail: jshlaser@compuserve.com *Manufacturer of laser engraved screens*

Spencer Manufacturing Co Ltd, Wilson Street, Oldham, OL8 1HN Tel: 0161-627 2918 Fax: 0161-627 2137 *Clothing manufacturers for next export*

Spencer Press Tools, 188-192 Barr Street, Hockley, Birmingham, B19 3AE Tel: 0121-554 0606 Fax: 0121-554 9129 *Specialised press tool manufrs*

Spencer Rigging Ltd, Empire Buildings, St. Mary's Road, Cowes, Isle Of Wight, PO31 7SX Tel: (01983) 292022 Fax: (01983) 291589 E-mail: info@spencerrigging.co.uk *Industrial & yacht rigging manufrs*

Spencer Signs Ltd, Courtney Street, Hull, HU8 7QF Tel: (01482) 325797 Fax: (01482) 323077 *Sign manufrs*

▶ Spencer Synthetics Ltd, Hud Hey Indust Estate, Hud Hey Road, Haslingden, Rossendale, Lancashire, BB4 5JH Tel: (01706) 229895 Fax: (01706) 229895 E-mail: enquiries@spencersynthetics.com *Recycling services*

Spencers Drinks, 11 Rawson Street, Nottingham, NG7 7FR Tel: 0115-979 0358 Fax: 0115-979 1140 *Wholesalers of beers wines & spirits*

Spenco Engineering Co Ltd, Clyst Honiton, Exeter, EX5 2DX Tel: (01392) 369795 Fax: (01392) 364439 E-mail: post@spenco.co.uk *Manufacturers & engineers of agricultural components*

Spenco Healthcare International, Brian Royd Mills, Saddleworth Road, Greetland, Halifax, West Yorkshire, HX4 8NF Tel: (01422) 378569 Fax: (01422) 376064 E-mail: sales@spenco-healthcare.co.uk *General healthcare products*

Spensall Engineering Ltd, Kitson Road, Leeds, LS10 1NR Tel: 0113-245 0726 Fax: 0113-242 0047 *Nuts & bolts manufrs*

Spentex B C A Ltd, Thorp Arch Trading Estate, Thorp Arch, Wetherby, West Yorkshire, LS23 7BJ Tel: (01937) 845848 Fax: (01937) 541237 E-mail: sales@spentex.co.uk *Haberdashery & textile materials service*

▶ Spentronics, 93 Waveney Road, St. Ives, Cambridgeshire, PE27 3FN Tel: (01480) 389802 E-mail: robert@spentronics.co.uk *Service & repair of electron beam welders*

Sperrin Knitwear Ltd, 57 Oldtown Street, Cookstown, County Tyrone, BT80 8EE Tel: (028) 8676 1634 *Clothing manufrs*

Sperrin Metal Products Ltd, Cahore Road, Draperstown, Magherafelt, County Londonderry, BT45 7AP Tel: (028) 7962 8362 Fax: (028) 7962 8972 E-mail: sales@sperrin-metal.com *Storage products*

Sperrin Switchgear, 1 20 Cahore Road, Draperstown, Magherafelt, County Londonderry, BT45 7LS Tel: (028) 7962 7770 Fax: (028) 7962 7771 *Switchgear & control panels manufrs*

Sperring Engineering Ltd, Unit 14, Knightcott Industrial Estate, Banwell, Avon, BS29 6JN Tel: (01934) 820233 Fax: (01934) 820374 E-mail: info@sperringengineering.co.uk *Engineers*

▶ Sperry Drilling Services, Tates Facility, Howemoss Drive, Dyce, Aberdeen, AB21 0GL Tel: (01224) 727347 Fax: (01224) 724359 *Drilling services*

Sperry Marine Systems, Burlington House, 118 Burlington Road, New Malden, Surrey, KT3 4NR Tel: (020) 8942 2464 Fax: (020) 8329 2415 *Navigation instrument manufrs*

Sperry Springs (Sussex) Ltd, Unit 4 Kingston Industrial Estate, Easton Road, Aldershot, Hampshire, GU12 4YA Tel: (01903) 762272 Fax: (01252) 327773 *Spring distributors & manufrs*

Spey Fish Ltd, 6 March Lane, Buckie, Banffshire, AB56 4BB Tel: (01542) 834524 Fax: (01542) 834970 *Fish processors*

▶ Spey Valley Hire Centre, Myrtlefield, Aviemore, Inverness-Shire, PH22 1SB Tel: (01479) 810555 Fax: (01479) 810789

▶ Speyroc, 120 Strathmore Road, Balmour Industrial Estate, Glasgow, G22 7DW Tel: 0141-347 1033 Fax: 0141-347 1050

Speyside Cooperage Ltd, Dufftown Road, Craigellachie, Aberlour, Banffshire, AB38 9RS Tel: (01340) 881264 Fax: (01340) 881303 E-mail: info@speyside-cooperage.demon.co.uk *Used casks reconditioning & suppliers*

SPG Ltd, Little End Road, Eaton Socon, St. Neots, Cambridgeshire, PE19 8JH Tel: (01480) 403099 Fax: (01480) 406638E-mail: sales@spgltd.co.uk *Refrigeration manufrs*

▶ Sphere, 1 Crown Centre, Bond Street, Macclesfield, Cheshire, SK11 6QS Tel: (01625) 425676 Fax: (01625) 511375

Sphere IT Ltd, Fernhill House, St. Catherines Hill Lane, Christchurch, Dorset, BH23 2NL Tel: (08707) 373001 Fax: (08707) 373002 E-mail: admin@sphereit.com *Computer software developer*

Spheric Trafalgar Ltd, Bentley House Wiston Business Park, London Road, Ashington, Pulborough, West Sussex, RH20 3DJ Tel: (01903) 891200 Fax: (01903) 891220 E-mail: sales@ballbiz.co.uk Sales Contact: I. Weston *Spheric-Trafalgar: the flexible ball company. Manufacturers of high precision stainless steel, tungsten carbide, silicon nitride, chrome steel, ceramic & plastic balls*

▶ Spheroid (UK) Ltd, Unit 27, Balfour Road, Balfour Business Centre, Southall, Middlesex, UB2 5BD Tel: (0870) 4582222 Fax: (020) 8893 5588 E-mail: sales@compubits.com *Computer parts suppliers*

Sphinx C S T, Woodside House, Osier Drive, Annesley, Nottingham, NG15 0DS Tel: (01623) 726282 Fax: (01623) 726292 E-mail: sales@sphinx.co.uk *Software distributors*

Sphinx Welding Repair & Supplies, 37B Broad Street, Coventry, CV6 5AX Tel: (024) 7666 3365 Fax: (024) 6666 3365 E-mail: joefletch@tiscali.co.uk *Welding service engineers & suppliers*

Spic 'N' Span, 20 Edith Avenue, Plymouth, PL4 8TH Tel: (01752) 666707 Fax: (01752) 666707 *Industrial cleaning & maintenance services*

Spice Design Consultants, Hop Studios, 2 Jamaica Road, London, SE1 2BX Tel: (020) 7252 0808 Fax: (020) 7237 7199 E-mail: studio@spicehop.com *Interior, graphic & industrial designers*

Spice Hawk Steel Sections Ltd, Gupta Trading Estate, West Bromwich Street, Oldbury, West Midlands, B69 3AP Tel: 0121-552 5151 Fax: 0121-544 4994 *Steel section manufrs*

Spicer Arts, Wharley Farm, College Road, Cranfield, Bedford, MK43 0AH Tel: (01234) 750029 Fax: (01234) 750029 *House signs manufrs*

Spicer Driveshaft UK Ltd, Rutherford Drive, Park Farm Industrial Estate, Wellingborough, Northamptonshire, NN8 6AQ Tel: (01933) 402000 Fax: (01933) 401322 *Driveshaft manufacturers for road applications*

Spicer Global Systems Ltd, Elmdon House, Airport Cargo, Birmingham International Airport, Birmingham, B26 3QN Tel: 0121-782 2882 Fax: 0121-782 2103 E-mail: spicerg@spicer-global.co.uk *Freight forwarders*

Spicer Hallfield, Banks Road, Haddenham, Aylesbury, Buckinghamshire, HP17 8EG Tel: (01844) 299600 Fax: (01844) 299670 E-mail: sales@spicerhallfield.com *Manufacturers of photograph albums & frames* Also at: Bradford

Spicers Builders Ltd, Checketts Lane, Worcester, WR3 7JP Tel: (01905) 755744 Fax: (01905) 754005 *Building contractors/joinery manufacturers*

Spick 'N' Span, 121 Kentish Town Road, London, NW1 8PB Tel: (020) 7485 5203 *Dry cleaners*

Spick & Span, 375 Tunstall Road, Knypersley, Stoke-on-Trent, ST8 7PT Tel: (01782) 815800 Fax: (01782) 822881 *Industrial cleaners*

Spick & Span Supplies, Oakhurst, Bourton Road, Frankton, Rugby, Warwickshire, CV23 9NX Tel: (01926) 633090 Fax: (01926) 633090 *Cleaning materials & dispersal products distributors*

▶ Spicnspan, 5 Christie Avenue, Morecambe, Lancashire, LA4 5UR Tel: (01524) 310749 E-mail: cleaningcleanse@yahoo.co.uk *office and domestic cleaning*

Spider Security Alarms, 8 Girtrell Road, Wirral, Merseyside, CH49 4LQ Tel: 0151-604 0344 *SSAIB national inspectorate member selling burglar alarms*

▶ SpiderWeb Business Admin, 16 Allerton Close, Coventry, CV2 5DH Tel: (07981) 785717 Fax: E-mail: info@spideradmin.co.uk *We offer a range of administration services: word processing, spreadsheets,general administration, desktop publishing. We can also provide services relating to Human Resource tasks. You can use us for a one-off task or we can provide a regular service to your business, allowing you the flexibility to get help when you need it.***

▶ SpiderWeb Recruitment Ltd, Kingfisher House, 2 Yarrow Road, Chatham, Kent, ME5 0SJ Tel: 01634 353131 E-mail: info@spiderweb-recruitment.co.uk *Engineering & Technical Recruitment Consultants, based in Kent covering London and the South East. We specialise in Engineers, Skilled Production Workers and Technical Personnel to the Power Generation, Oil and Gas and Manufacturing Industries (FMCG) Jobs for Welders to Directors.*

▶ Spike Events Ltd, 419 London Road, Hemel Hempstead, Herts, HP3 9BD Tel: 01442 261851 Fax: 01442 397138 E-mail: info@spikeevents.co.uk *Live event production company specialising in conferences, roadshows, product launches, award shows and video*

▶ Spike Outdoors Ltd, 20 Castle Gates, Shrewsbury, SY1 2AD Tel: (01743) 364455 Fax: (01743) 350550 E-mail: info@spikeoutdoors.co.uk *Retail of specialist outdoor clothing & equipment*

▶ Spiky, 116A Fillongley Road, Meriden, Meriden, Coventry, CV7 7LT Tel: 01676 523759 Fax: 01676 523759 E-mail: spiky@myspiky.co.uk *Development and supply of mobile phone applications and games.*

Spiller & Webber Ltd, Viney Court, Victoria Street, Taunton, Somerset, TA1 3JA Tel: (01823) 337333 Fax: (01823) 321364 *Kitchens & bathrooms suppliers*

▶ Spillers Of Chard Ltd, The Aga Cooker Centre Chard Business Park, Leach Road, Chard, Somerset, TA20 1FA Tel: (01460) 67878 Fax: (01460) 65252 *Spillers the cooker centre, have over 300 appliances on display in over 12,000 square feet of truly inspirational showrooms based in Somerset. Features AGA and Rayburn cooker sets in custom designed kitchen settings. Products also include, dishwashers, ovens, washing machines, and refrigerators.*

Spimin Development Ltd, Spimin House, Beacon Road, Poulton Industrial Estate, Poulton-Le-Fylde, Lancashire, FY6 8HD Tel: (01253) 881001 Fax: (01253) 881019 E-mail: sales@spimin.co.uk *PCB assembly work, control systems & lighting manufrs*

Spina, 8 Hillside Road, Pannal, Pannal, Harrogate, North Yorkshire, HG3 1JP Tel: (07780) 734797 Fax: (01423) 870392 E-mail: tracy@spina.co.uk *Web design*

Spinamex, Unit 2 B B W Estates, Oldmixon CR, Weston-super-Mare, Avon, BS24 9BA Tel: (01934) 635077 Fax: (01934) 635077 E-mail: deedazfinn@aol.com *Metal Spinners with over 35 years experience we can manufacture to your designs and drawings and can deal with prototypes up to large production runs. With nationwide coverage please call us quoting Kellysearch to discuss your requirements.*

▶ Spindle Services, Unit 9-10 Central City Industrial Estate, Red Lane, Coventry, CV6 5RY Tel: (024) 7663 7771 Fax: (024) 7663 7772 E-mail: simon.emms@btconnect.com *Spindle manufacturer (machine tools)*

Spindrift Ltd, Unit 17 Park Farm, Hundred Acre Lane, Wivelsfield Green, Haywards Heath, West Sussex, RH17 7RU Tel: (01273) 890932 Fax: (01273) 890931 E-mail: lockerlexus@aol.com *Wholesale of agricultural spraying equipment*

Spinflo Ltd, Unit 19, Oakham Drive, Sheffield, S3 9QX Tel: 0114-273 8157 E-mail: sales@spinflo-group.co.uk *Kitchen equipment sheet metal workers*

Spink & Son Ltd, 69 Southampton Row, London, WC1B 4ET Tel: (020) 7563 4000 Fax: (020) 7563 4066 E-mail: sales@spink-online.com *Collectables dealers* Also at: Croydon & Raynes Park

▶ Spinks Compak Ltd, 9 Shannon Street, Leeds, LS9 8SS Tel: 0113-235 0662 Fax: 0113-249 3845 *Stockists of various glass & plastic containers*

James Spinks & Sons Ltd, Bramshot House, Clemence Lane, Tamworth, Staffordshire, B79 9DH Tel: (01827) 382850 Fax: (01827) 382855 E-mail: data.resource@virgin.net *Commercial database developers*

Spinlock Ltd, 41 Birmingham Road, Cowes, Isle of Wight, PO31 7BH Tel: (01983) 295555 Fax: (01983) 295542 E-mail: prosupport@spinlock.co.uk *Yacht fitting manufrs*

Spinnaker Products Ltd, Unit 15, Rylands Farm Industrial Estate, Bagley Road, Rockwell Grove, Wellington, Somerset, TA21 9PZ Tel: (01823) 400969 Fax: (01823) 665268 *Manufacturer of garden toys, rotary lines & hardware*

▶ Spirac Ltd, Tapper House, Thorpe Mead, Banbury, Oxfordshire, OX16 4AB Tel: (01295) 270335 Fax: (01295) 273334 E-mail: info@spirac.co.uk

Spiral Computers Ltd, 22 London Street, Southport, Merseyside, PR9 0UE Tel: (01704) 500977 Fax: (01704) 540977 E-mail: steve@spiral.co.uk *Computer software development*

Spiral Hardware Ltd, Unit 36, Wimbledon Avenue, Brandon, Suffolk, IP27 0NZ Tel: (01842) 816086 Fax: (01842) 813867 E-mail: info@spiralhardware.co.uk *Hardware services online*

Spiralock Europe, 11 Court Yard Workshops, Bath Street, Market Harborough, Leicestershire, LE16 9EW Tel: (01858) 468646 Fax: (01858) 466808 E-mail: sl-europe@spiralock.com *Industrial fastener manufrs*

Spirax Binding (Scotland) Ltd, Inveralmond Road, Inveralmond Estate, Perth, PH1 3XA Tel: (01738) 626281 Fax: (01738) 630575 E-mail: sales@spirax.co.uk *Trade print finishing services*

Spire Bearings, 94 Storforth La Trading Estate, Hasland, Chesterfield, Derbyshire, S41 0SN Tel: (01246) 274183 Fax: (01246) 202898 E-mail: sales@spirebearings.co.uk *Bearing-ball & bearing distributors, agents & stockholders*

▶ Spire Hydraulics Ltd, Brimington Road North, Chesterfield, Derbyshire, S41 9BE Tel: (01246) 208400 Fax: (01246) 559428

Spire Marketing, Unit 36 Coney Green Business Centre, Wingfield View, Clay Cross, Chesterfield, Derbyshire, S45 9JW Tel: (01246) 865500 Fax: (01246) 865585 E-mail: info@spiremarketing.co.uk *Work wear safety footwear & promotional leisurewear suppliers*

Spire Technology Ltd, 5 Black Moor Road, Verwood, Dorset, BH31 6AX Tel: (01202) 821300 Fax: (01202) 813966 E-mail: pcsales@spire.co.uk *Computer components distributors*

▶ Spire Window Systems Ltd, Tattershall Way, Fairfield Industrial Estate, Louth, Lincolnshire, LN11 0YZ Tel: (01507) 607291 Fax: (01507) 600159 *Conservatories, doors & windows manufrs*

Spire-View.Com, 1 Challands Close, Hasland, Chesterfield, Derbyshire, S41 0ET Tel: (01246) 221681 *Suppliers of sublimation imprintable items, heat presses, clothing and more for small, medium and large businesses. Also producers of personalised and corporate gifts, discounted personal quotes on multi-item orders. Hundreds of unique items from t shirts, glassware, clocks, keyrings and more*

Spirex Metal Products Ltd, Marsh Lane, Ware, Hertfordshire, SG12 9QQ Tel: (01920) 460516 Fax: (01920) 487028 E-mail: info@spirex.co.uk *Sheet metal workers*

▶ Spirit Advertising Ltd, Great Titchfield House, 14-18 Great Titchfield Street, London, W1W 8BD Tel: (020) 7299 1260 Fax: (020) 7299 1261 E-mail: richardh@spiritads.com *Creative Advertising*

▶ Spirit Displays Ltd, 14 Victory Road Wimbledon, London, SW19 1HN Tel: (020) 8542 7279 Fax: (020) 8542 1680 E-mail: info@spirit-displays.com *Trade suppliers of banner tensioning system, flex face signage system*

▶ Spirit Yachts, New Cut East, Ipswich, IP3 0EA Tel: (01473) 214715 Fax: (01473) 214713 *Boat builders & repairers*

Spiro GB Ltd, Harlescott Lane, Shrewsbury, SY1 3AR Tel: (01743) 443051 Fax: (01743) 443053 E-mail: steve@spirogb.enta.net *Poultry equipment suppliers*

Spirol Industries Ltd, 17 Princewood Road, Earlstrees Industrial Estate, Corby, Northamptonshire, NN17 4ET Tel: (01536) 444800 Fax: (01536) 203415 E-mail: info@spirol.co.uk Principal Export Areas: Asia Pacific, Middle East & Africa *Standard & specialised fastening solutions*

Spiroll Precast Services Ltd, 2 Kingsway Industrial Park, Kingsway Park Close, Derby, DE22 3FP Tel: (01332) 365131 Fax: (01332) 291736 E-mail: enquiries@spiroll.co.uk *Pre stressing & pre cast technology specialists services* Also at: Dronfield

Spitfire Technology Group, Unit 6-7 Southbank Business Centre, Ponton Road, London, SW8 5BL Tel: (020) 7501 3000 Fax: (020) 7501 3001 E-mail: sales@spitfire.co.uk *Data communication, security & telecommunication systems*

R. Spivey & Sons Ltd, 30 Pheasant Drive, Birstall, Batley, West Yorkshire, WF17 9LT Tel: (01924) 423200 Fax: (01924) 420006 E-mail: david@spiveydrums.co.uk Principal Export Areas: Africa *Polyethylene, steel drums & drum dealers*

SPJ Enterprises Ltd, Unit 14-15 Oakleigh Trading Estate, Anchor Road, Bilston, West Midlands, WV14 9NA Tel: (01902) 491818 Fax: (01902) 491818 *Steel fabricators*

▶ SPL Audio Services, 2 Sidmouth Road, Sale, Cheshire, M33 5FX Tel: 0161 9625151 Fax: 0161 9698407 E-mail: banthony@globalnet.co.uk *Sound equipment hire & installation*

Splash Aquatics, 1 James Street, Pontardawe, Swansea, SA8 4LR Tel: (01792) 869779 Fax: (01792) 869779 *Aquatic suppliers*

▶ Splash Display Ltd, 1 Hartley Close, Dibden Purlieu, Southampton, SO45 4LU Tel: (0845) 2261936 Fax: (0845) 2261937 E-mail: sue@splashdisplay.com *Point of purchase & display solutions service*

▶ Splash Winery Ltd, 16 Briar Avenue, Meltham, Holmfirth, HD9 5LQ Tel: (01484) 323814 Fax: (01484) 323814 *Wine producers*

▶ Splasher Pools, Culver Garden Centre, Cattlegate Road, Enfield, Middlesex, EN2 9DS Tel: (020) 8363 7249 Fax: (020) 8303 1398 E-mail: sales@splasherpools.com

Splashsports Services, 5 8 Meadow Road, Glasgow, G11 6HX Tel: 0141-337 2828 Fax: 0141-339 7788 E-mail: sales@splashsports.co.uk *Splash sports equipment*

Splice (UK) Ltd, The Coach House, Whitehall Road, Drighlington, Bradford, West Yorkshire, BD11 1LN Tel: 0113-285 2536 Fax: 0113-285 2741 E-mail: info@spliceuk.com *Fibre optics telecommunication services*

Spline Gauges, Piccadilly, Tamworth, Staffordshire, B78 2ER Tel: (01827) 872771 Fax: (01827) 874128 E-mail: sales@splinegauges.co.uk *Manufacturers splinegauges*

Splinter Group, 3 Lombard Trading Estate, 51 Anchor & Hope Lane, London, SE7 7SN Tel: (020) 8305 2702 Fax: (020) 8858 1922 E-mail: enquiries@thesplintergroup.com *Joinery manufrs*

Spoken Image Ltd, The Design Centre, 44 Canal St, Manchester, M1 3WD Tel: 0161-236 7522 Fax: 0161-236 3386 E-mail: multimedia@spoken-image.com *Multimedia production service*

▶ Spook Ltd, Ayleswade Lane, Biddenden, Ashford, Kent, TN27 8LE Tel: (01580) 292202 Fax: (01580) 292202 E-mail: sales@spook.eu.com *Environmental monitoring services*

▶ Spooner Bros, Hawksworth Trading Estate, Swindon, SN2 1EJ Tel: (01793) 336333 Fax: (01793) 336333 E-mail: Sales@spoonerbrothers.co.uk *The Spooner Brothers name is synonymous with the best in high quality hardwood or PVCu conservatory using state of the art software and many years of experience. We offer a personal service from concept to completion, including local authority planning, building regulations and listed building consent using architectural drawings for domestic and commercial installations.*We offer a free site survey, free advice on design, complete with a virtual conservatory pictured on your property for you to keep , followed up with a quotation.**

Spoors Ltd, Railway Street, Bishop Auckland, County Durham, DL14 7LR Tel: (01388) 603865 Fax: (01388) 608029 E-mail: spoors@onyxnet.co.uk *Distributor of butane, propane & industrial gas & drinks dispensers*

Sportcal Global Communications Ltd, 56 High St Wimbledon, London, SW19 5EE Tel: (020) 8944 8786 Fax: (020) 8944 8740 E-mail: sales@sportcal.com *Sport business information & computer consultants*

▶ sportdiscount.com, 217 Chestergate, Stockport, Cheshire, SK3 0AN Tel: (0870) 4207961 E-mail: sales@sportdiscount.com *Offer the most extensive range of sportswear & sports equipment*

Sportfish Ltd, Winforton, Hereford, HR3 6SP Tel: (01544) 327111 Fax: (01544) 327093 E-mail: orders@sportfish.co.uk *Fishing equipment distributors*

▶ The Sporting Experience, 4 Meadow La, Lapworth, Solihull, W. Midlands, B94 6LS Tel: (01564) 782234 Fax: (01564) 782234 E-mail: info@thesportingexperience.co.uk *Camouflage, sporting clothing & accessories*

Sports Crest, 8 Balloo Drive, Bangor, County Down, BT19 7QY Tel: (028) 9127 1131 Fax: (028) 9127 0799 E-mail: sales@sportscrest.net *Embroidered badge manufrs*

Sports Express GWCC, 75 Commercial Road, Oldgate, London, E1 1RD Tel: (020) 7377 5037 Fax: (020) 7247 1951 *Screen printing & embroidery for sportswear*

Sports Surfaces (UK) Ltd, PO Box 1010, Chester, CH1 3WN Tel: (01244) 321200 Fax: (01244) 347735 E-mail: info@sportssurfacesuk.com *Suppliers of synthetic sports surfaces*

▶ Sports Turf Services, Bellfield Park, Kinross, KY13 0NL Tel: (01577) 863864

▶ Sportsground Drainage Contractors, Backhill Farm, Carberry, Musselburgh, Midlothian, EH21 8QD Tel: 0131-654 2882 Fax: 0131-654 0466

▶ SportsMania, Mercury House, Shipstone Business park, Northgate, New Basford, Nottingham, NG7 7FN Tel: (0845) 6733346 E-mail: info@sportsmania.biz *Online sport specialist selling rugby, cricket and football equipment at permanently low prices. Football, rugby and cricket equipment includes, balls, clothing, protective and training equipment and accessories - all at discounted prices. Clubs and individuals are catered for and discounts given for bulk orders of sports equipment.**All sports equipment is of the highest quality and includes all major brands. Sportsmania strive to be the best online sports equipment supplier providing excellent quality and value for money. *Why not visit us at www.sportsmania.biz ***

Sportsmatch UK Ltd, 16 Summer Street, Leighton Buzzard, Bedfordshire, LU7 1HT Tel: (01525) 381638 Fax: (01525) 851236 E-mail: info@sportsmatch-uk.com *Skin packaging & sub-contract engineers*

▶ Sportswear, Unit 12 Sharpes Industrial Estate, Alexandra Road, Swadlincote, Derbyshire, DE11 9AZ Tel: (01283) 225234 Fax: (01283) 552132 E-mail: k3552_@hotmail.com *Sportswear suppliers*

▶ Sportsworld Promotions, 18 Truemper Grove, Caversfield, Bicester, Oxfordshire, OX27 8FD Tel: (01869) 320321 Fax: (01869) 320321

▶ Sportzone Marketing, PO Box 332, Bushey, WD23 3XZ Tel: 0700 5938868 Fax: 0700 5938869 E-mail: john@sportzone-marketing.co.uk *Fantastic new Soccer Lockers.......**The absolute coolest thing to tidy your stuff away...**Football, Soccer, Hockey, Baseball...**Three great sizes...**4"0 wardrobe, 2"0 bedside cabinet, 1"0 CD holder*

▶ Spot On, 167-169 Union Street, Torquay, TQ1 4BX Tel: (01803) 407407 Fax: (01803) 407405 E-mail: info@spotondisplay.com *Display graphics printer, digital printers,traditional full colour printing, exhibition manufacturer, portable displays distributors, internet services & web hosting.*Graphic designers, exhibition designers, design for print, web designers. marketing consultants*

Spot On Ceramics Ltd, 1 Moorview Court, Estover Close, Plymouth, PL6 7PL Tel: (01752) 692170 Fax: (01752) 788785 E-mail: enquiries@spotonceramics.co.uk *Tiling contractors*

Spot On Computers Ltd, 122 Waterloo Road, Manchester, M8 8AF Tel: (0845) 3453111 Fax: (0870) 1121953 E-mail: sales@spotonuk.com *Computer systems & software supplies*

▶ Spot On Digital Imaging, Gomm Road, High Wycombe, Buckinghamshire, HP13 7DJ Tel: (01494) 435060 Fax: (01494) 443284

Spot On Supplies Industrial Consumables Ltd, Willand Industrial Estate, Willand, Cullompton, Devon, EX15 2QW Tel: (01884) 821169 Fax: (01884) 821276 E-mail: admin@spotonsupplies.com *Hygiene materials distributors*

▶ Spotless Cleaning Services, 317 Coalburn Road, Coalburn, Lanark, ML11 0NF Tel: (01555) 820032 Fax: (01555) 820032 E-mail: spotless@email.com *Reliable, Discreet, Professional, Value for Money.**Our service portfolio comprises of: Domestic Support (cleaning, shopping, ironing, oven cleaning, etc)*Commercial/Contract Cleaning to offices, salons, letting agencies as well as Builder Cleans.**Whatever your requirements give us a call and we will be happy to quote you.**T: 01555 820032*M: 07851 124691 /07738 409154*E: spotless@email.com*

Spotlight Casting Directories & Contacts, 7 Leicester Place, London, WC2H 7RJ Tel: (020) 7437 7631 Fax: (020) 7437 5881 E-mail: sales@spotlightcd.com *Directory publishers*

Spotlight Design Services Ltd, 118 Queens Road, Walton-on-Thames, Surrey, KT12 5LL Tel: (01932) 245934 *Graphic design & applied marketing*

▶ SPOTLIGHT IMPRESSIONS, 1BARONS CLOSE, FAKENHAM, NORFOLK, NR21 8BE Tel: 01328 851468 E-mail: spotlightimps@btconnect.com *Family run printing business specialising in Hot Foil printing. Customised printing for Business; Personal and Promotional.*

Spotmix, 99 Carstairs Street, Glasgow, G40 4JQ Tel: 0141-550 1444 Fax: 0141-550 1555 E-mail: sales@spotmix.co.uk *Concrete ready mix suppliers*

▶ Spotmix UK Ltd, 10 Llanddulas Avenue, Kinmel Bay, Rhyl, Clwyd, LL18 5HH Tel: (01745) 356800 E-mail: info@spotmixuk.com *Suppliers of ready mixed concrete*

Spotnails Ltd, Unit 21, Pantglas Industrial Estate, Bedwas, Caerphilly, Mid Glamorgan, CF83 8DR Tel: (029) 2086 0222 Fax: (029) 2086 0999 E-mail: sales@spotnails.co.uk *Established 1952.*

continued

*The UK"s only independent manufacturer of collated staples. Supplying Collated Nailing and Stapling Systems. Packaging Staples and Staplers. Collated Screwdriving systems. Suppliers to the Flooring, Building, Furniture, Pallet, Packaging and associated timber and cardboard using industries.**Nails, Staples, Nailing Tools, Frame Nailers, Framing Tools, Stapling Tools, Nailgun, Staplegun, Flooring, Autofeed Screwdrivers, Collated Nails, Industrial Staples, Brads, Corrugated Fasteners, Packaging Staples. Nailers, Staplers, Omer, Hitachi, Makita, MAX, Haubold, Nikema, ***

▶ Spots Consulting, Knaves Beech Business Centre, Loudwater, High Wycombe, Buckinghamshire, HP10 9ZN Tel: (01628) 530404 Fax: (01628) 530404 E-mail: info@spots.co.uk *Computer systems consultants*

▶ Spotstudio, 70-72 Kingsland Road, Shoreditch, London, E2 8DP Tel: (020) 8459 4301 E-mail: info@spotstudio.net *Spotstudio create uniquen modeling portfolio for models.*

▶ Spotty Dog Tackle, 15 Yarm Lane, Stockton-on-Tees, Cleveland, TS18 3DR Tel: (01642) 601171 Fax: (01642) 601172 E-mail: sales@spottydogtackle.com *Fishing tackle retailers*

▶ SPP Folding Tables, 8 Castle Street, Castle Gate, Hertford, SG14 1HD Tel: (01992) 410333 E-mail: enquiries@tables4sale.com *Trestle & round tables with plywood tops & wishbone legs manufrs*

Sprague Equipment Ltd, 2 Roberts Street, Liverpool, L3 7AS Tel: 0151-236 0317 Fax: 0151-236 0260 *Sheet metalworkers & general engineers*

Sprague & Ouseley, 1 Knowle Business Units, Silverton Road, Exeter, EX2 8HD Tel: (01392) 825930 Fax: (01392) 825629 E-mail: info@spragueandouseley.co.uk *Heating engineers & plumbers mechanical services*

▶ J. Spratt & Co., 25 Ballybeen Road, Comber, Newtownards, County Down, BT23 5PY Tel: (028) 9044 8505 Fax: (028) 9044 8891 E-mail: spratt.j.co@btconnect.com *Engineering & fabrication services*

Spray Art Ltd, Grove Farm, The Street, Crookham Village, Fleet, Hampshire, GU51 5SD Tel: (01202) 580942 Fax: (01252) 811796 E-mail: action@sprayart.co.uk *Electrostatic paint spraying equipment manufrs*

Spray Finishers (Poole), 14 Abingdon Road, Nuffield Industrial Estate, Poole, Dorset, BH17 0UG Tel: (01202) 685488 Fax: (01202) 676260 E-mail: info@sprayfinishes.co.uk *Stove enamelling services & powder coating services*

Spray Glass International, 3 Beckley Hill Works, Canal Road, Higham, Rochester, Kent, ME3 7HX Tel: (01474) 824499 Fax: (01474) 824482 E-mail: sales@sprayglass.co.uk *Corrosion engineers & specialist coating applicators*

Spray Processes Ltd, 49A Bromham Road, Bedford, MK40 2AA Tel: (01234) 273922 Fax: (01234) 269436 E-mail: sales@spraypro.com *Manufacturers of drying plant/equipment*

Spray Systems, Merlin Centre, Gatehouse Close, Gatehouse Industrial Area, Aylesbury, Buckinghamshire, HP19 8DP Tel: (01296) 393822 Fax: (01296) 399757 E-mail: spraysys@btconnect.com *Chemical application equipment manufrs*

Spraybake JRC, 1 Boarshurst Business Park, Boarshurst Lane, Greenfield, Oldham, OL3 7ER Tel: (01457) 870779 Fax: (01457) 875477 E-mail: info@spraybakejrc.co.uk *Powder coating services*

Spraybake Spraybooth Manufacturers, Unit 1, Milner Road Chilton Road Indust Area, Sudbury (Suffolk), Sudbury, Suffolk, CO10 2XG Tel: (01787) 888650 Fax: 01787 882305 E-mail: b.baird@spraybake.co.uk *Spray booth manufacturer & distributors, servicing and filters.*

Spraycare, Roughton Moor, Woodhall Spa, Lincolnshire, LN10 6YQ Tel: (01526) 353671 Fax: (01526) 353963 E-mail: sales@spraycare.com *Crop spraying machinery*

Spraychem Ltd, Cardrew Industrial Estate, Redruth, Cornwall, TR15 1ST Tel: (01209) 315222 Fax: (01209) 314333 E-mail: sales@contico.co.uk *Cleaning equipment manufrs*

Spraying Systems Ltd, Farnham Business Park, Weydon Lane, Farnham, Surrey, GU9 8QT Tel: (01252) 727200 Fax: (01252) 712211 E-mail: info.uk@spray.com *Manufacturers of spray nozzles, air knives & tank cleaning equipment*

Sprayrite, Greshop Industrial Estate, Forres, Morayshire, IV36 2GW Tel: (01309) 674217 Fax: (01309) 675262 *Agricultural chemical distributors*

Sprayseal Contracts Ltd, Bollin House, Blakeley Lane, Mobberley, Knutsford, Cheshire, WA16 7LX Tel: (01565) 872303 Fax: (01565) 872599 E-mail: sales@sprayseal.co.uk *Roof protection & renovation services*

▶ Spraytek, Frith Farm, Frith Lane, Wickham, Fareham, Hampshire, PO17 5AW Tel: (01329) 836300 Fax: (01329) 836301 *Commercial vehicle spraying services*

Spray-Trac Systems Ltd, Legram Lane, Marton-Cum-Grafton, Boroughbridge, York, YO51 9PS Tel: (01423) 322377 Fax: (01423) 324678 E-mail: sales@spraytrac.com *Spray machinery manufrs*

Spread Garden Supplies Ltd, Edward Street, St. Helens, Merseyside, WA9 3DS Tel: (01744) 753431 Fax: (01744) 24513 E-mail: kenb@spread.co.uk *Horticultural wholesalers* Also at: Newbury

Spree Engineering Ltd, The Laboratory, Castle Road, Sittingbourne, Kent, ME10 3RL Tel: (01795) 421441 Fax: (01795) 470479 *Non-destructive testing engineers*

Sprezzatura Ltd, 45 St Mary's Road, Ealing, London, W5 5RG Tel: (020) 8912 1010 Fax: (020) 8912 1011 E-mail: info@sprezzatura.com *Computer consultants*

▶ Spriegel Associates, 27 Downs Way, Tadworth, Surrey, KT20 5DH Tel: (01737) 817799 Fax: (01737) 817799

▶ Spring Associates, Roland Road, St. Sampson, Guernsey, GY2 4PF Tel: (07781) 149134 *Computer systems consultants*

▶ Spring Dale, 46 Theydon Road, London, E5 9NA Tel: (020) 8815 4411

Spring Developments Ltd, Lyng Lane, West Bromwich, West Midlands, B70 7RP Tel: 0121-553 6543 Fax: 0121-553 7552 *Spring, pressings & wire forms manufrs*

▶ Spring Distribution Ltd, 14a Blackburn Road, Bathgate, West Lothian, EH48 2EY Tel: (01506) 631875 Fax: (01506) 652245

Spring Field Catering Butchers Ltd, 182 Herbert Avenue, Poole, Dorset, BH12 4HU Tel: (01202) 744910 Fax: (01202) 716588 *Butchers*

Frederick Spring Co., Princes End Industrial Park, Nicholls Road, Tipton, West Midlands, DY4 9LG Tel: 0121-557 4080 Fax: 0121-557 6959 E-mail: robjenkins@btclick.com *Spring manufrs*

Spring Group Ltd, Hazlitt House, 4 Bouverie Street, London, EC4Y 8AX Tel: (020) 7300 9000 Fax: (020) 7300 9090 E-mail: info@spring.com Principal Export Areas: Worldwide *Management consultancy*

Spring Grove Forge Ltd, Spring Grove Forge, Coombe Road, Puddletown, Dorchester, Dorset, DT2 8RZ Tel: (01305) 848328 Fax: (01305) 848328 *General blacksmiths*

Spring It Solutions Ltd, 1-3 Museum Place, Cardiff, CF10 3BD Tel: (029) 2064 9400 Fax: (029) 2038 3750 E-mail: pete-heaven@spring.com *IT consultancy*

Spring Personnel, 15-17 South John Street, Liverpool, L1 8BN Tel: 0151-708 8800 Fax: 0151-708 7122 E-mail: personnel_liverpool@spring.com *Consultancy, recruitment & training services*

Spring & Press Developments Ltd, Unit 49 Enfield Industrial Estate, Redditch, Worcestershire, B97 6DE Tel: (01527) 67602 Fax: (01527) 60183 E-mail: sales@kn-products.co.uk *Presswork & spring manufacturers*

Spring Technology Staffing Services, First Floor, Bishops Weald House, Albion Way, Horsham, West Sussex, RH12 1AH Tel: (01403) 262345 E-mail: itpersonnel-birmingham@spring.com *IT recruitment*

Spring Tooling Ltd, Alfred Court Saxon Business Park, Hanbury Road, Stoke Prior, Bromsgrove, Worcestershire, B60 4AD Tel: (01527) 876412 Fax: (01527) 878990 E-mail: andy@spring-tooling.co.uk *Tool manufrs*

Spring Vale Engineering (Brighouse) Ltd, Spring Vale Industrial Estate, Elland Road, Brighouse, West Yorkshire, HD6 2RA Tel: (01484) 720205 Fax: (01484) 400056 E-mail: enquiries@springvalegroup.com *Material handling equipment manufrs*

Springboard Design, Unit4 Point 2, The Paint Works, Bath Road, Bristol, BS4 3EH Tel: 0117-958 8500 Fax: 0117-958 8501 E-mail: info@springboard-design.co.uk *Graphic, exhibition & industrial designers*

Springboard Marketing Ltd, 1 Tonbridge Chambers, Pembury Road, Tonbridge, Kent, TN9 2HZ Tel: (01732) 363399 Fax: (01732) 352304 E-mail: info@springboard-marketing.co.uk *Marketing & PR consultancy*

Springco (N I) Ltd, Tavanagh Factory, Armagh Road, Craigavon, County Armagh, BT62 3EG Tel: (028) 3833 3482 Fax: (028) 3833 8721 E-mail: sales@springco.co.uk *Spring manufacturer, including compression, flat, nickel alloy, tension & torsion.*

Springcoil Spring Distributors, 2 Woodbourn Hill, Sheffield, S9 3NE Tel: 0114-273 1111 Fax: 0114-273 0222 E-mail: enquiries@springcoil.co.uk *Since 1983 Springcoil has supplied Compression, Extension, Torsion and Suspension coil Springs to a wide spectrum of engineering trades. Our Quality is assured through regular independent auditing to BS EN ISO 9001 : 2000. Product range is from 0.5 mm wire to 19 mm bar and Materials comprise High carbon Steel, Stainless steel, Phosphor bronze, Inconel X750, Hastalloy C276, Nimonic 90 and Titanium alloys. We serve a wide variety of diverse markets ranging from high powered Diesel Engine Valve springs and Lowered & Uprated Suspension coil springs for Racing cars to the smaller engineering tool applications. Our design department will be pleased to advise on any spring related problem, no matter how small or exacting and even production of one off presents no problem to our versatile work force of skilled Sheffield springmakers.*

Springdata, 116a Groby Road, Glenfield, Leicester, LE3 8GL Tel: 0116-232 0116 *Computer software distributors*

Springdew Ltd, Unit 9 10, Woodlands Business Park, Ystradgynlais, Swansea, SA9 1JW Tel: (01639) 849676 Fax: (01639) 845662 E-mail: mail@springdewfreeserve.co.uk *Contract packers*

▶ Springdot Ltd, 14 Barham Close, Bromley, BR2 8LU Tel: (020) 8462 0682 E-mail: enquiries@springdot.co.uk *Springdot Limited provide UK web design and hosting solutions for everyone from the smallest business upwards. They have a friendly and personal service, that will guide you through getting online. Springdot can also provide IT Support and Consultancy services in the Bromley or London regions.*

Springetts Brand Design Consultants, 13 Salisbury Place, London, W1H 1FJ Tel: (020) 7486 7527 Fax: (020) 7487 3033 E-mail: all@springetts.co.uk *Design consultants*

Springfast Ltd, Unit 6F, Morelands Trading Estate, Bristol Road, Gloucester, GL1 5RZ Tel: (01452) 416688 Fax: (01452) 308723 E-mail: admin@springfast.co.uk *Spring clips & industrial fastener manufrs*

Springfield Appointments, 11 Station Road, Ashford, Middlesex, TW15 2UW Tel: (01784) 256144 Fax: (01784) 240936 *Recruitment*

Springfield Camping, Denholme Mill, Burnley Road, Luddendenfoot, Halifax, West Yorkshire, HX2 6AR Tel: (01422) 883164 Fax: (01422) 886698

continued

E-mail: sales@springfield-camping.co.uk *Camping goods & outdoors clothing manufrs*

Springfield Cartons Ltd, Cottenham Lane, Salford, M7 1TW Tel: 0161-833 9857 Fax: 0161-832 1831 *Carton manufrs*

Springfield Construction, 10 The Fields, Donnington Wood, Telford, Shropshire, TF2 7PW Tel: (01952) 603233 Fax: (01952) 603233 *Groundwork & demolition contractors*

Springfield Hire (Lancs) Ltd, Collins Industrial Estate, Merton Bank Road, St. Helens, Merseyside, WA9 1HY Tel: (01744) 731215 Fax: (01744) 451842 E-mail: michael@spring-field.co.uk *Prefabricated buildings manufrs*

Springfield Stainless, Springfield Works, Stocks Lane, Batley, West Yorkshire, WF17 8PA Tel: (01924) 420303 Fax: (01924) 423333 E-mail: info@springfield-stainless.co.uk Principal Export Areas: Worldwide *Water jet, plasma & profile cutting services*

Springfield Stores, Buck Street, Challock, Ashford, Kent, TN25 4AR Tel: (01233) 740327 Fax: (01233) 740327 *Foam & vinyl specialists*

Springfield Timber & Building Supplies, Broughton Works, Chester Road, Bretton, Chester, CH4 0DH Tel: (01244) 660351 Fax: (01244) 661276 *Building material suppliers*

Springfield Tools Ltd, Unit 14B, 54 College Road, Perry Barr, Birmingham, B44 8BS Tel: 0121-356 3403 Fax: 0121-356 2215 E-mail: andrewregan@btconnect.com *Spark erosion machining*

Springfields Supplies, 11 Bangor Road, Overton, Wrexham, Clwyd, LL13 0HB Tel: (01978) 710291 Fax: (01978) 710292 E-mail: sales@springfieldsupplies.co.uk *Engineers supplies & agricultural merchants*

▶ Springhill Ltd, 1 Main Street, Clarkston, Glasgow, G76 8DS Tel: 0141-644 2046 Fax: 0141-644 4062

Springhill Mills, 12 Harts Road, Haddenham, Aylesbury, Buckinghamshire, HP17 8HJ Tel: (01844) 299406 Fax: (01844) 299406 E-mail: gbsmr521@attgolbal.net *Stone grain mills importers*

Springlab Ltd, 2 Whitting Valley Road, Old Whittington, Chesterfield, Derbyshire, S41 9EY Tel: (01246) 455399 Fax: (01246) 452397 E-mail: enquiries@springlab.co.uk *Plastic test tube rack manufrs*

Springline, 20 Blacker Crescent, Netherton, Wakefield, West Yorkshire, WF4 4EY Tel: (07711) 138209 E-mail: brian.springline.@fsnet.co.uk *Laminated springs suppliers* Also at: West Bromwich

Springlynn, Manor Road, Woodley, Stockport, Cheshire, SK6 1RT Tel: 0161-430 6719 Fax: 0161-406 6193 E-mail: david@springlynn.fsbusiness.co.uk *Non-ferrous founders*

Springmakers Redditch Ltd, Unit 2b Ipsley Street, Redditch, Worcestershire, B98 7BU Tel: (01527) 65300 Fax: (01527) 65300 *Spring manufrs*

Springmakers Redditch, Doward Crest, The Doward, Whitchurch, Ross-on-Wye, Herefordshire, HR9 6DZ Tel: (01600) 890325 Fax: (01600) 890325 *Spring manufrs*

Springmasters Ltd, Arthur Street, Redditch, Worcestershire, B98 8LF Tel: (01527) 521000 Fax: (01527) 528866 E-mail: sales@springmasters.com Purchasing Contact: D.C. Clarke Sales Contact: D.C. Clarke Principal Export Areas: Africa *Manufacturers of springs, wire forms and pressings including compression, extension, torsion and die springs; and distributors of circlips, hose clamps, disc springs and belleville washers*

Springpack, New Road, Pershore, Worcestershire, WR10 1BY Tel: (01386) 552550 Fax: (0870) 7747402 *Packaging material merchants*

Springpart Manufacturing Ltd, 50 Heming Road, Redditch, Worcestershire, B98 0EA Tel: (01527) 527302 Fax: (01527) 520215 E-mail: info@springpart.com *Manufacturers of aerosol components*

Springs Smoked Salmon, Edburton Road, Edburton, Henfield, West Sussex, BN5 9LN Tel: (01273) 857338 Fax: (01273) 857228 *Smoked salmon merchants & frozen sea products*

Springstop Ltd, Unit 11 Block 3, Nuneaton Street, Glasgow, G40 3JU Tel: 0141-554 4424 Fax: 0141-554 4423 E-mail: springstop1@aol.com *Spring manufrs*

Springvale Eps Ltd, 75 Springvale Road, Doagh, Ballyclare, County Antrim, BT39 0SS Tel: (028) 9334 0203 Fax: (028) 9334 1159 E-mail: sales@springvale.com *Expanded polystyrene manufrs*

Springvale EPS Ltd, Hazlerigg, Newcastle Upon Tyne, NE13 7AP Tel: 0191-217 1144 Fax: 0191-217 1212 E-mail: sales@springvale.com *Expanded polystyrene manufrs*

Springvale Eps Ltd (Glossop Division), Dinting Vale Business Park, Glossop, Derbyshire, SK13 6LG Tel: (01457) 863211 Fax: (01457) 869269 *Polystyrene manufrs*

Springvale Metals, 55 Springvale Street, Willenhall, West Midlands, WV13 1EJ Tel: (01902) 606562 Fax: (01902) 606619 *Non-ferrous scrap metal merchants*

Springvale Weatherproofing Ltd, 5 Broad Street, Newport, Gwent, NP20 2DQ Tel: (01633) 213433 Fax: (01633) 212005 *Flat roofing contractors*

Springwater Direct Ltd, 152 Park Road, Kirkcaldy, Fife, KY1 3EP Tel: (01592) 650022 Fax: (01592) 653664 *Bottle water cooler & equipment suppliers*

Springwater Software Ltd, 101 Park St, Luton, LU1 3HG Tel: 01582 483399 *Computer software development*

▶ Springwell Microelectronics Ltd, 197 Raikes Lane, Birstall, Batley, West Yorkshire, WF17 9QF Tel: (01924) 420029 Fax: (0870) 7062353 E-mail: sales@springwellmicro.co.uk *Manufactures of water urinal products*

Springwood Engineering, Bunces Lane, Burghfield Common, Reading, RG7 3DH Tel: 0118-983 2411 Fax: 0118-983 4731 E-mail: springwood.eng@btopenworld.com *Road marking equipment manufrs*

Sprint Ltd, PO Box 2452, Hove, East Sussex, BN3 7WB Tel: (0870) 6082801 Fax: (0870) 6082802 E-mail: sales@scsl.co.uk *Telecommunications*

Sprint Communications, Unit F, Hove Technology Centre, St. Josephs Close, Hove, East Sussex, BN3 7ES Tel: (0870) 6082801 Fax: (0870) 6082802 E-mail: sales@scsl.co.uk *Telecommunications equipment & systems manufrs*

Sprint Data Systems, Bridge Road, Ashford, Kent, TN23 1JA Tel: (01233) 665822 Fax: (01233) 665821 E-mail: sales@sprint-data.co.uk *Data recording system*

▶ Sprint Design Ltd, Unit 46 John Player Building, Stirling Enterprise Park, Stirling, FK7 7RP Tel: (01786) 447707 Fax: (01786) 447707 E-mail: info@sprintdesign.co.uk

Sprint Electric Ltd, Unit C2 Rudford Industrial Estate, Ford Road, Ford, Arundel, West Sussex, BN18 0BD Tel: (01903) 730000 Fax: (01903) 730893 E-mail: sales@sprint-electric.com *Controlled variable speed drive manufrs*

Sprint Engineering Services Ltd, Unit G3 Imperial Business Estate, West Mill, Gravesend, Kent, DA11 0DL Tel: (01474) 534251 Fax: (01474) 534566 E-mail: info@sprint-uk.com *Sprint engineering & lubricants manufrs*

Sprint Graphics, Station Road, Irthlingborough, Wellingborough, Northamptonshire, NN9 5QE Tel: (01933) 651908 Fax: (01933) 655688 E-mail: sales@sprintgraphics.co.uk *Exhibition designers*

Sprint Industrial Sales Ltd, 1 Rosehill, Willenhall, West Midlands, WV13 2AR Tel: (01902) 636106 Fax: (01902) 636137 E-mail: sprint@btclick.com *Ball bearing distributors* Also at: Smethwick & Willenhall

Sprint Labels & Co., 4 Barn Road, Carmarthen, Dyfed, SA31 1DE Tel: (01267) 231920 Fax: (01267) 231921 *Computer label supply & manufrs*

Sprint Lifting Equipment Ltd, 16 Pinfold Road, Thurmaston, Leicester, LE4 8AS Tel: 0116-260 4100 Fax: 0116-260 4111 *Manufacture lifting equipment & crane hire*

Sprint Manufacturing, 30b, Upton Lovell, Warminster, Wiltshire, BA12 0JW Tel: (01985) 850821 Fax: (01985) 850821 E-mail: enquiries@sprintmanufacturing.co.uk *Motor cycle component manufrs*

▶ Sprint Print Co. Ltd, 8b Okehampton Place, Exeter, EX4 1AY Tel: (01392) 276144 Fax: (01392) 420737

Sprint Signs Ltd, Holmes Way, Horncastle, Lincolnshire, LN9 6JW Tel: (01507) 522247 Fax: (01507) 522017 E-mail: sales@sprintsigns.co.uk *Sign manufrs*

Sprint Systems, Unit 8 Bath Road Business Centre, Bath Road, Devizes, Wiltshire, SN10 1XA Tel: (01380) 729365 Fax: (01380) 729616 *Computer consultants & services*

Sprintprint Printers, Aston Road, Waterlooville, Hampshire, PO7 7UD Tel: (023) 9226 7131 Fax: (023) 9224 1448 E-mail: sales@sprintprint.co.uk *General printers & stationers*

Sprite Engineering Ltd, 10 Lenziemill Road, Cumbernauld, Glasgow, G67 2RL Tel: (01236) 457970 Fax: (01236) 457970 *Engineering services*

Sprockets Unlimited, Claybrook Farm Cottage, 103 Brett Forton Road, Badsey, Evesham, Worcestershire, WR11 7XQ Tel: (01386) 831341 *Chain sprocket distributors*

Spromak, 11g Wilson Road, Liverpool, L36 6AN Tel: 0151-480 0592 Fax: 0151-480 0656 *Steel forging manufrs*

▶ Spruce Engineering Co. Ltd, Flanshaw Lane, Wakefield, West Yorkshire, WF2 9JE Tel: (01924) 378637 Fax: (01924) 383157 E-mail: mail@spruceeng.co.uk *Sub contract machining services*

Spruce Technology, 40 High Street, Langholm, Dumfriesshire, DG13 0JH Tel: (01387) 381529 Fax: (01387) 381779 E-mail: office@sprucetechnology.com *PC & network builders & retailers*

▶ Spruce Work & Leisure Wear, Ground Floor, Kyme Mill, Johnson Street, Bradford, West Yorkshire, BD3 8HW Tel: (01274) 667788 *Promotional clothing suppliers*

Sprue Aegis P.L.C., The Techno Centre, Puma Way, Coventry, CV1 2TT Tel: (024) 7623 6600 Fax: (024) 7623 6603 E-mail: info@sprueaegis.com *Safety product distributors*

Ivor Spry & Co. Ltd, The Granary, Cornwells Farm, Sheephurst Lane, Marden, Tonbridge, Kent, TN12 9NS Tel: (01622) 833414 E-mail: sales@spry.co.uk *Importers*

SPS Technologies Ltd, Troon Industrial Area, 191 Barkby Road, Leicester, LE4 9HX Tel: 0116-276 8261 Fax: 0116-274 0243 *Aircraft fastener manufrs*

▶ SPSL Customer Counting, 47 Burners Lane South, Kiln Farm, Milton Keynes, MK11 3HA Tel: 01908 265007 E-mail: info@spslretail.com *Provides people counting and customer tracking systems for staff scheduling, ad-tracking and market research. Use the Retail Traffic Index to improve your retail performance.*

Spunalloys Ltd, PO Box 1, Cradley Heath, West Midlands, B64 5QS Tel: (01384) 410111 Fax: (01384) 410116 E-mail: sales@spunalloys.co.uk *Centrifugal casting manufrs*

Spunhill Farm Sales, Ruthin Road, Mold, Clwyd, CH7 1QQ Tel: (01352) 759189 *Agricultural farm suppliers*

Spur Engineering Services Ltd, River Gardens Business Centre, Spur Road, Feltham, Middlesex, TW14 0SN Tel: (020) 8844 0887 Fax: (020) 8844 0887 E-mail: sales@spurengineering.co.uk *Precision engineers*

▶ Spur Information Solutions Ltd, Hayward House 2a-2b Hayward Business Centre, New Lane, Havant, Hampshire, PO9 2NL Tel: (023) 9245 5564 Fax: (023) 9247 0874 E-mail: info@spursolutions.com *Bespoke software solutions & programming*

▶ Spurcroft Ltd, Waterside Mill, Lower Bank Street, Macclesfield, Cheshire, SK11 7HL Tel: (01625) 615056 Fax: (01625) 613452 E-mail: sales@spurcroft.co.uk *Textile weaving services & tie manufrs*

Spurgeon Walker Ltd, 67 High Street, Sevenoaks, Kent, TN13 1JY Tel: (01732) 459821 Fax: (01732) 459496 E-mail: info@spurgeonwalker.com *Advertising & public relations agency*

Spurgeons Clean-Plan Ltd, 3 Royce Road, Crawley, West Sussex, RH10 9NX Tel: (01293) 437511 Fax: (01293) 437517 *Cleaning services*

Harry Spurr Ltd, Harvest Lane, Sheffield, S3 8EF Tel: 0114-272 4581 Fax: 0114-276 6246 E-mail: info@spurrs.co.uk *Shop fitters, joinery contractors, manufacturing joinery, IPS systems, building maintenance etc*

John Spurrier & Co. Ltd, 3 Turners Hill Road, Craven Arms Business Park, Craven Arms, Shropshire, SY7 8DZ Tel: (01588) 673332 Fax: (01588) 673333 E-mail: gspurrier@aol.com *Industrial leather good suppliers*

▶ SPX Contech, Buttington Cross Enterprise Park, Buttington, Welshpool, Powys, SY21 8SL Tel: (01938) 557557 Fax: (01938) 557558 *Aluminium dye setters*

Spy Alarms Ltd, 5 Sevenoaks Business Centre, Cramptons Road, Sevenoaks, Kent, TN14 5DQ Tel: (01732) 464649 Fax: (01732) 779568 E-mail: info@spyalarms.co.uk *Security alarm suppliers*

Spy Machinery, Albion Street, Willenhall, West Midlands, WV13 1NN Tel: (01902) 633233 *New & used machine tools suppliers*

Spyder Engineering Ltd, Fenland District Industrial Estate, Station Road, Whittlesey, Peterborough, PE7 2EY Tel: (01733) 203986 Fax: (01733) 350662 *Motor chassis builders & general fabricators*

Spyx Audio Equipment, 36 Shaftesbury Road, Coventry, CV5 6FN Tel: (024) 7667 7896 Fax: (024) 7667 7896 E-mail: spyx@btinternet.com *For exhibitions, presentations & training services*

▶ Squallstar Ltd, 1A George Road, Alvechurch, Birmingham, B48 7PB Tel: 0121-445 3762 Fax: 0121-445 3762 E-mail: pete@squallstar.co.uk *Installers of television equipment*

Square 1 Cleaning Services, Botany Bay Ii, Playhatch, Reading, RG4 9QU Tel: 0118-946 1503 E-mail: square1@botanybayii.freeserve.co.uk *Commercial cleaning services*

▶ The Square Design & Print Co Ltd, Caxton Court, 43 Garamonde Drive, Wymbush, Milton Keynes, MK8 8DD Tel: (01908) 305018 Fax: (01908) 260901 E-mail: ksthefoodie@thesquareguide.co.uk *The Square Design & Print Co Ltd are designers, printers and publishers of THE FOODIE Square Guide - a restaurant reviews guide. Based in Milton Keynes, UK, we have over 25 years experience in the printing industry behind us and as well as producing the local Square Guides we can give you a no obligation quote on any of your printing requirements. From single colour business cards to full colour brochures. If you have a printing requirement or want to advertise in THE FOODIE Square Guide, just click on the Square Design logo and fill in your details and we will get straight back to you.*

Square Group Ltd, 78 New Oxford Street, London, WC1A 1HB Tel: (020) 7692 9990 Fax: (020) 7692 6636 E-mail: sales@squaregroup.co.uk *Applemac sales & services*

▶ Square Mile Marine Co., 1 Willett Close, Orpington, Kent, BR5 1QH Tel: (01689) 890888 Fax: (01689) 891100 E-mail: sales@smm.co.com *Computer software*

Square One Advertising & Design Ltd, 134 Archer Road, Sheffield, S8 0JZ Tel: 0114-258 4557 Fax: 0114-258 3076 E-mail: info@squareone.co.uk *Advertising, direct marketing, public relations & printers*

Square One Computer Training, Egerton House, Tower Road, Birkenhead, Merseyside, CH41 1FN Tel: 0151-650 6907 Fax: 0151-649 8567 E-mail: sales@squareonetraining.com *Computer training services*

Square One Sealants Ltd, Elfords, Heightington, Bewdley, Worcestershire, DY12 2XW Tel: (01299) 878900 Fax: (01299) 871144 E-mail: sossealants@aol.com *Sealing compound contractors*

▶ Square Peg International Ltd, 40 Brockham Lane, Brockham, Betchworth, Surrey, RH3 7EH Tel: (0870) 2424206 E-mail: doug.ross@squarepegint.com *Square Peg, is an international boutique consulting practice that provides an integrating force in the alignment and effectiveness of organisations. Our services are based on the interrelationship between business strategy, leadership and HR - our focus is to help clients improve performance and drive value.**As business consultants focused on the people side of change, we support clients managing a variety of enterprise-wide changes such as M&A"s, establishing new mandates, and meeting new expectations.**We maximise productivity, performance and morale and drive value by accelerating results, ensuring their quality, and measuring their impact. From our offices in the UK and North America we assist companies to capture the full value of their investment in people.*

▶ Square Sail Ship Yard Ltd, Charlestown Harbour, St. Austell, Cornwall, PL25 3NJ Tel: (01726) 70241 Fax: (01726) 61839 E-mail: info@square-sail.com *The Square Sail fleet of historic sailing ships can be hired for publicity events and corporate entertainment. The ships are also available for TV/film work with accompanying vessels and crew.*

▶ Squareone Scenic Service Ltd, Production House, Enterprise Way, Leighton Buzzard, Bedfordshire, LU7 4SZ Tel: (0870) 2432623 Fax: (01525) 371663 E-mail: info@squareone.uk.com *Specialist design*

▶ Squashee Co. Ltd, 8 Portmore Lea, Ballinderry Lower, Lisburn, County Antrim, BT28 2LX Tel: (028) 9265 2985

▶ Squeaky Clean, 34 Dean Road, Wrexham, Clwyd, LL13 9EH Tel: (07713) 922158 E-mail: info@squeaky-clean.me.uk *Car valeting services*

Squeegee Clean Direct, 76 Leyland Rd, Penwortham, Preston, PR1 9XS Tel: 01772 491431 *Cleaning product manufrs*

Squeezyball Merchandising, 2 The Linen House, 253 Kilburn Lane, London, W10 4BQ Tel: (0870) 7512538 Fax: (020) 8960 6077 E-mail: sales@squeezyball.com *Stress ball wholesaler*

▶ Squibnocket Ltd, 17 The Grove, Barry, South Glamorgan, CF62 6RD Tel: (01446) 735903 Fax: (01446) 735903 E-mail: sales@squibnocket.co.uk *Website designers*

Squink, West Winds, Gong Hill Dr, Lower Bourne, Farnham, Surrey, GU10 3HQ Tel: 01252 792900 Fax: 01252 792022 *Designers*

Squire A Radcliffe & Sons Ltd, Gillbridge Works, Lowlands Road, Mirfield, West Yorkshire, WF14 8LU Tel: (01924) 491491 Fax: (01924) 498940 *Oil lubricants retailers*

▶ Squire International Ltd, Skillion Business Centre, Hawley Road, London, N18 3SB Tel: (020) 8345 7474 Fax: (020) 8345 7373 E-mail: sales@squire.co.uk *We supply blank DVD media throughout the UK.*

Squirealarms Ltd, 165-171 Humberstone Road, Leicester, LE5 3AF Tel: 0116-262 3916 E-mail: info@squirealarms.co.uk *Security installation service*

Squires, Closglas, Llanarthney, Carmarthen, Dyfed, SA32 8HJ Tel: (01558) 668005 Fax: (01558) 668005 *Mechanical handling equipment design & manufrs*

Squires Gear & Engineering Ltd, 98 Swan Lane, Coventry, CV2 4GB Tel: (024) 7623 1110 Fax: (024) 7623 1112 E-mail: djs@squires-gear.co.uk Principal Export Areas: Central/East Europe & West Europe *CNC engineering services*

Squires Metal Fabrications Ltd, 6 Burgess Road, Hastings, East Sussex, TN35 4NR Tel: (01424) 428794 Fax: (01424) 431567 E-mail: squires@squiresmetal.freeserve.co.uk *Metal fabrications manufrs*

Phil Squires Dairy & Electronic Engineers, Unit 1b, Dulford, Cullompton, Devon, EX15 2DY Tel: (01884) 266796 Fax: (01884) 266797 *Dairy engineers*

Squirrel Films Ltd, 119 Rotherhithe Street, London, SE16 4NF Tel: (020) 7231 2209 Fax: (020) 7231 2119 E-mail: ostockman@sandsfilms.co.uk *Film studio*

▶ Squirrel Storage Ltd, Unit 10 Forest Trading Estate, Priestley Way, London, E17 6AL Tel: (020) 8527 9261 Fax: (020) 8527 9251

▶ Squirrel Storage Ltd, Units 3-4-5, Wardley Industrial Estate, Shield Drive, Worsley, Manchester, M28 2QB Tel: (0800) 3284242 Fax: 0161-728 3762 E-mail: info@squirrel.co.uk

▶ SR Designs, 1 Hook Hill Park, Woking, Surrey, GU22 0PX Tel: (01483) 750611 Fax: (01483) 770919 E-mail: golfprizes@aol.com *Mail order*

SR Electromatics, 511 Fulbridge Road, Peterborough, PE4 6SB Tel: (01733) 579591 Fax: (01733) 571958 *Electronics repair service*

SRB Technologies, 6 Portland Business Centre, Manor House Lane, Datchet, Slough, SL3 9EG Tel: (01753) 592492 Fax: (01753) 592692 E-mail: sales@betalight.com *Self powered lighting*

SRC Ltd, Buckingham Road, Stockport, Cheshire, SK4 4QZ Tel: 0161-432 3222 Fax: 0161-443 2025 E-mail: sales@src.ltd.uk *Rubber manufrs*

SRCL, The Incinerator Building, Kennington Road, Willesborough, Ashford, Kent, TN24 0LZ Tel: (0845) 1242020 Fax: 0113-235 1286 E-mail: mwardle@srcl.com *SRCL is the new name for White Rose Environmental and Sterile Technologies Group and is one of the leading clinical waste management companies in the UK and Ireland. We offer customers fully intergrated collection and disposal services and solutions to address all legislative needs.*

SRCL, Bolton Incinerator, Incinerator Building, Bolton General Hospital, Minerva Road, Bolton, BL4 0JR Tel: (0845) 1242020 Fax: 0113-235 1286 E-mail: mwardle@srcl.com *SRCL is the new name for White Rose Environmental and Sterile Technologies Group and is one of the leading clinical waste management companies in the UK. We offer customers fully intergrated collection and disposal services and solutions to address all legislative needs.*

▶ Sri Toy Europe, P. O Box 36957, London, SE6 4WT Tel: 020 8690 6995 Fax: 020 8690 8990 E-mail: sales@sritoyseurope.com *Supplier Of Wooden Educational Toys, Puzzles and Furniture.*

SRM, Northumberland Dock, Hayhole Road, North Shields, Tyne & Wear, NE29 6DY Tel: 0191-258 4579 Fax: 0191-257 1646 *Solvent recovery & recycling*

SRM Gaskets Ltd, Station Road, Hatton, Derby, DE65 5EL Tel: (01283) 812946 Fax: (01283) 813172 *Gasket manufrs*

SRS, 3 Heol Mostyn, Village Farm Industrial Estate, Pyle, Bridgend, Mid Glamorgan, CF33 6BJ Tel: (01656) 745514 Fax: (01656) 749741

SRS Cooling, Archard House, Waverley Road, Weymouth, Dorset, DT3 5HL Tel: (01305) 750020 Fax: (01305) 750021 E-mail: sales@southernrefrigeration.freeserve.co.uk *Refrigeration & air conditioning repairs*

SSAB Swedish Steel UK (Dobel), Unit 17 Narrowboat Way, Hurst Business Park, Brierley Hill, West Midlands, DY5 1UF Tel: (01384) 74660 Fax: (01384) 77575 E-mail: sales@dobel.co.uk *Coated steel sheet*

SSC Laser Cutting, Hangar 5, New Road, Hixon, Stafford, ST18 0PJ Tel: (01889) 270241 *Laser cutting services*

SSD Drives Ltd, New Courtwick Lane, Wick, Littlehampton, West Sussex, BN17 7RZ Tel: (01903) 737000 Fax: (01903) 737100 E-mail: *SSD Drives (formerly Eurotherm Drives) & Parvex, design & manufacture AC drives (AC inverters, VSD's) servo drives & motors (AC*

continued

brushless & DC brushed), DC thyristor drives & variable speed drive systems. SSD Drives have full service support in

Sse Pipe Fittings Ltd, Pedmore Road, Dudley, West Midlands, DY2 0RE Tel: (01384) 480333 Fax: (01384) 480805 E-mail: sales@ssepipefittings.co.uk *Stainless steel tube & pipe fittings manufrs*

▶ Ssed Ltd, 242 Trelawney Avenue, Langley, Slough, SL3 7UD Tel: (01753) 542727 Fax: (01753) 542727 E-mail: raj@gx-security.com *GX Security offer a wide range of electronic security services including Intruder alarms ,closed circuit television (CCTV), access control, fire alarms and door entry systems. We can provide to Domestic, Retail & Commercial sites. We also provide high security solutions to even the most complex sites.***We have NSI Silver (NACOSS) accreditation for Intruder Alarms and are regularly inspected. (NSI have ukas accreditation) *All security systems provided by GX Security have the latest technology *All our installations and servicing is to British & European standards for intruder alarms - BS4737,DD243,PD6662,EN501, etc. *We have full 24 hour Emergency call out service. *All our technicians carry a Company Identity Card. They are also trained to carry out their work causing the minimum of disruption. *All our alarm installers & Surveyors are sent on regular training courses *to keep them up to date with all new technology. **

Sshteel, The Lodge, Cefn Bychan Woods, Pantymwyn, Mold, Clwyd, CH7 5EP Tel: (01352) 742111 Fax: (01352) 742101 *Stainless steel furnishings*

SSI Projects Ltd, 40 Dodington, Whitchurch, Shropshire, SY13 1EF Tel: (01948) 665331 Fax: (01948) 663001 E-mail: cme@ssi.uk.com *Steelwork consultants contractors*

Ssi Schaefer Ltd, 83-84 Livingstone Road, Walworth Industrial Estate, Andover, Hampshire, SP10 5QZ Tel: (01264) 386600 Fax: (01264) 386611 E-mail: solutions@ssi-schaefer.co.uk *Storage equipment manufrs*

SSL International plc, Venus Building, 1 Old Park Lane, Manchester, M41 7HA Tel: 0161-638 2560 Fax: 0161-615 8817 E-mail: andrea.smith@durex.co.uk *Durex the brand is owned by SSL International. SSL International Plc (SSL) was formed in July 1999 through the merger of Seton Scholl Healthcare plc and the London International Group plc. SSL is a multinational healthcare business, manufacturing well-known brands including Durex condoms, Scholl foot-care and footwear products, Marigold household gloves and a number of over the counter consumer products. SSL is the world's leading condom manufacturer with its Durex brand of condoms. Sold in over 150 countries worldwide and market leader in more than 40 markets, the Durex brand accounts for 26% of the world's four billion condom market, making it the No 1 condom brand in the world. SSL currently operates 17 either wholly owned or jointly owned manufacturing facilities in eight countries and has offices in 35 countries.*

SSP Powar Forge Ltd, 1A Denaby Main Industrial Estate, Coalpit Lane, Denaby Main, Doncaster, South Yorkshire, DN12 4LH Tel: 0114-244 8371 Fax: 0114-242 6714 E-mail: ssppowarforge@btconnect.com *Motor vehicle accessory manufrs*

▶ SSP Specialised Sports Products Ltd, Po Box 998, Canterbury, Kent, CT1 9EU Tel: (0870) 7501432 Fax: (0870) 7518935 E-mail: info@ssp-uk.co.uk *Installation wet pour rubber and artificial grass playground surfaces and muga . Maintenance of artificial grass sport pitched and tennis courts*

SSR Personnel Services Ltd, 5 Blackhorse Lane, London, E17 6DN Tel: (020) 8626 3100 Fax: (020) 8626 3101 E-mail: sales@ssrpersonnel.com *Recruitment consultancy & contract hire*

SSR Stainless Steel Reinforcement Ltd, Units B & C Burnt Common, London Road, Send, Woking, Surrey, GU23 7LN Tel: (01483) 226426 Fax: (01483) 226427 E-mail: ssr@btconnect.com *Fixing systems manufrs*

Stabel Ltd, Coney Green, Oswestry, Shropshire, SY11 2JL Tel: (01691) 650200 Fax: (01691) 654839 E-mail: george@stabel.co.uk *Textile machinery*

Stabilag (E.S.H.) Ltd, 34 Mark Road, Hemel Hempstead, Hertfordshire, HP2 7DD Tel: (0870) 9906763 Fax: (0870) 9906762 E-mail: sales@stabilag.com *Electric surface heating specialists since 1949, serving process engineering, transport and building services sectors. We manufacture heating equipment for drums, mantles, pre-melters. We install and maintain trace heating, leak detection systems and electric underfloor heating.*

Stabilus, Unit 4 Canada Close, Banbury, Oxfordshire, OX16 2RT Tel: (01295) 700100 Fax: (01295) 700106 E-mail: info@uk.stabilus.com *Gas operated springs*

Stable Co., Outgang Lane, Osbaldwick, York, YO19 5UP Tel: (01904) 430630 Fax: (01904) 430363 E-mail: enquire@thestablecompany.com *Timber stable designers & manufrs*

Stable Engineering Ltd, Dinas Road, Tonypandy, Mid Glamorgan, CF40 1JQ Tel: (01443) 682364 Fax: (01443) 686109 *General engineers*

▶ Stable Precision, 7 Silver Business Park, Airfield Way, Christchurch, Dorset, BH23 3TA Tel: (01202) 487755 Fax: (01202) 485522 E-mail: sales@stableprecision.co.uk *Precision CNC milling*

Stable Software, Stable Cottage, 3 Blind Lane, Hurworth, Darlington, County Durham, DL2 2JB Tel: (01325) 720039 E-mail: office@stablesoft.co.uk *Computer software*

▶ Stable Tapes, 557 Aspley Lane, Nottingham, NG8 5RX Tel: 0115-929 8782 Fax: 0115-929 8783 *Adhesive tape manufrs*

▶ Stablemate Systems, 63-65 Chilton Business Centre, Woodside Road, Amersham, Buckinghamshire, HP6 6AA Tel: (01494) 434323 Fax: (01494) 434643 E-mail: stablemateltd@aol.com *Software developers*

David Stabler, 12B Salamanca Road, Long Stratton, Norwich, NR15 2PF Tel: (01508) 532122 *Machinery services refurbishing*

Stables Garage, Stone Street, Cleckheaton, West Yorkshire, BD19 5EE Tel: (01274) 869601 Fax: (01274) 869601 *Commercial vehicle painting*

Stacarac UK Ltd, Industrial Estate, Steeple Road, Mayland, Chelmsford, CM3 6AX Tel: (01621) 741250 Fax: (01621) 742768 E-mail: sales@stacarac.com *Manufacturers of storage systems in plastic & aluminium also cloakroom seating with hooks or hangers*

Stace, 273 High Street, Epping, Essex, CM16 4DA Tel: (01992) 565565 Fax: (01992) 560597 E-mail: epping@stace.co.uk *Chartered quantity surveyors*

Stace Yates Ltd, Unit 24 Bamfurlong Industrial Park, Staverton, Cheltenham, Gloucestershire, GL51 6SX Tel: (01452) 713722 Fax: (01452) 713282 *Sheet metal fabrication specialists*

Stacey Arts Ltd, 128 Kensington Church Street, London, W8 4BH Tel: (020) 7221 7166 Fax: (020) 7221 9288 E-mail: sales@stacey-international.co.uk *Book publishers*

▶ Stacey Construction Ltd, Station Road, Wiveliscombe, Taunton, Somerset, TA4 2LX Tel: (01984) 623802 Fax: (01984) 624497

Richard Stacey, The Workshop, Easthampnett Lane, Easthampnett, Chichester, West Sussex, PO18 0JY Tel: (01243) 533132 Fax: (01243) 538204 E-mail: sales@richardstacey.com *Brick cutting & miniature brick products manufrs*

▶ Stacey Security Ltd, Lancaster Fields, Crewe, CW1 6FF Tel: (01270) 251254 Fax: (01270) 505998

▶ Staceys Bread Shop, 59 South Street, Ilkeston, Derbyshire, DE7 5QT Tel: 0115-932 5624 Fax: 0115-932 5624 *Retail bakery*

Stack Computer Solutions Ltd, Bridle House, Bridle Way, Bootle, Merseyside, L30 4UA Tel: 0151-521 2202 Fax: 0151-525 2298 E-mail: sales@stack.co.uk *Computer Installation services*

▶ Stackright Portable Buildings, 2 Bloxwich Road, Walsall, WS2 7BD Tel: (01922) 474455 Fax: (01922) 474477 E-mail: sales@stackright.co.uk *Timber manufrs*

Stackright Services Ltd, P O Box 456, Derby, DE24 8UP Tel: 0870 428 2479 Fax: 01332 830132 E-mail: sales@stackrightservices.co.uk *Bulk handling equipment manufrs*

▶ Stacks, Providence Mill, Alexandra Street, Hyde, Cheshire, SK14 1DX Tel: 0161-368 4948 Fax: 0161-368 4948

Stackwell Forge, Front Road, Parson Drove, Wisbech, Cambridgeshire, PE13 4JQ Tel: (01945) 700666 Fax: (01945) 701242 E-mail: sales@stackwellforge.com *Ornamental architecture manufrs*

Stadco Ltd, 21 Renaissance Way, Liverpool, L24 9PX Tel: 0151-728 4500 *Automotive metal assembly services*

Stadco Ltd, Harlescott Lane, Shrewsbury, SY1 3AS Tel: (01743) 462227 Fax: (01743) 447709 E-mail: cooling@stadco.co.uk Principal Export Areas: Worldwide *Stadco Cooling offers a solution for all industrial and commercial water cooling requirements: cooler system design, consultancy, development and manufacture of low maintenance and environmentally friendly cooling systems. We offer extensive experience of sealed and open cooling systems, individually designed and engineered. The industrial cooling equipment systems we can design and supply include: coolers - air blast coolers, evaporative coolers, oil coolers, liquid coolers, water coolers, dry air coolers: and also closed circuit cooling towers, open circuit cooling towers, water chillers, air cooled chillers, air blast heat exchangers, plate heat exchangers, shell and tube heat exchangers. We specialise in total sealed air blast cooler systems, which offer the following benefits: zero water consumption, elimination of limescale, vapour free and therefore not a risk to health, no chemical treatment required. Applications supplied include manufacturing, pharmaceutical, food, drink, catering, aerospace, heat recovery plant.*

▶ Stadco Ltd, Harlescott Lane, Shrewsbury, SY1 3AS Tel: (01743) 462227 Fax: (01743) 447709 E-mail: info@stadco.co.uk *Stadco is a multi-site manufacturer of automotive body panels and sub-assemblies for leading vehicle producers including Ford, Jaguar, BMW, Land Rover, MG Rover and Volkswagen. Stamping, welding and robotic assembly are the company's core activities.*

Stadex Industries Ltd, Coed Aben Road, Wrexham Industrial Estate, Wrexham, Clwyd, LL13 9UH Tel: (01978) 660266 Fax: (01978) 660316 E-mail: sales@stadex.co.uk *Foam product & adhesive manufrs*

Stadia Sports, 19-20 Lancaster Way Business Park, Ely, Cambridgeshire, CB6 3NW Tel: (01353) 668686 Fax: (01353) 669444 E-mail: sales@stadia-sports.co.uk *Joinery manufrs*

▶ Stadium, Hannington Works, Longrigg, Swalwell, Newcastle upon Tyne, NE16 3AS Tel: 0191-496 1321 Fax: 0191-488 4127 E-mail: sales-gh@stadium-packing.co.uk *Packing, timber case & crate manufrs*

Stadium Chalk & Crayon Co. Ltd, Endle Street, Southampton, SO14 5AW Tel: (023) 8022 6765 Fax: (023) 8063 0304 E-mail: sales@stadium-chalk.fsnet.co.uk *Crayon & billiard chalk manufrs*

Stadium Consumer Products, Stadium North, Tofts Farm Industrial Estate East, Hartlepool, Cleveland, TS25 2DH Tel: (01429) 862616 Fax: (01429) 272126 E-mail: julie.morrissey@stadiumcp.co.uk *Vehicle security system manufrs*

Stadium Disposables Ltd, 161-162 Dukes Road, Acton, London, W3 0SL Tel: (020) 8993 7686 Fax: (0845) 450 0694 Principal Export Areas: Worldwide *Catering equipment/janitorial supply services*

Stadium Plastics Midlands Ltd, Unit 4-6 Southways Industrial Estate, Coventry Road, Hinckley, Leicestershire, LE10 0NJ Tel: (01455) 234202 Fax: (01455) 234191 E-mail: chris@spfd.fsbusiness.co.uk *Plastic finishing services*

Stadium Plastics South West Ltd, Forde Road, Newton Abbot, Devon, TQ12 4AE Tel: (01626) 333338 Fax: (01626) 331487 *Plastic mouldings manufrs*

Stadium Power Ltd, 23-29 Owen Road, Vinces Road Industrial Estate, Diss, Norfolk, IP22 4YU Tel: (01379) 644233 Fax: (01379) 650118 E-mail: sales@stadiumpower.co.uk *Power supplies manufrs*

Stadium Transformers P.L.C., Chin Bridge Road, Blaydon-On-Tyne, Tyne & Wear, NE21 5SD Tel: 0191-414 2971 Fax: 0191-499 0087 E-mail: terry.french@interservice.co.uk *Scaffolders*

Staedler (UK) Ltd, Cowbridge Road, Pontyclun, Mid Glamorgan, CF72 8YJ Tel: (01443) 235011 Fax: (01443) 237668 E-mail: terry.james@uk.staedler.com Principal Export Areas: Worldwide *Writing instrument manufrs*

Staff Smart, Goodacre Son, Church Street, Donington, Spalding, Lincolnshire, PE11 4UA Tel: (01775) 820786 Fax: (01775) 820512 E-mail: info@staffsmartuk.com *Nationwide suppliers of staff to industry, staffing at the highest level. Factory workers, food processing, crop and field work.*

▶ Staff Solution Limited, Lasyard House, Underhill Street, Bridgnorth, Shropshire, WV16 4BB Tel: 01746 767107 Fax: 01746 769217 E-mail: sales@staffsolution.co.uk

Staffhunt, 30 Birch Grove, Menstrie, Clackmannanshire, FK11 7DW Tel: (01786) 834776 E-mail: info@staffhunt.org *Recruitment for manufacturing, engineering and oil and gas personnel from both client and candidate perspective. Translation service also offered.*

Stafflink (UK) Ltd, 138 Lower Road, London, SE16 2UG Tel: (020) 7252 2212 Fax: (020) 7252 2901 E-mail: info@staff-link.co.uk *London's leading recruitment consultancy. Specialist divisions include retail sales, office administration staff, warehouse personnel, cleaning staff, domestic and care staff, catering staff. Skilled and semi-skilled across all areas. Also supply personnel for housing associations.*

▶ Stafforce Recruitment, 39A Minerva Road, London, NW10 6HJ Tel: (020) 8537 9070 Fax: (020) 8537 9071 E-mail: parkroyal@stafforce.co.uk *Outsource centre*

Stafford Ltd, Overbrook Court, Overbrook Lane, Knowsley, Prescot, Merseyside, L34 9FB Tel: 0151-907 0027 Fax: 0151-907 0028 E-mail: paul.spooner@staffords.ltd.uk *Office equipment suppliers*

Stafford Automatic Systems Ltd, Stafford House, Freeman Street, Stafford, ST16 3HY Tel: (01785) 251045 Fax: (01785) 212152 *Fire alarms installation*

▶ Stafford Bridge Doors Ltd, Bedford Road, Pavenham, Bedford, MK43 7PS Tel: (01234) 826316 Fax: (01234) 826319 E-mail: sales@sbdoors.com

▶ Stafford Construction Ltd, 107 Bethania Street, Maesteg, Mid Glamorgan, CF34 9EX Tel: (01656) 735235 Fax: (01656) 735235

▶ Stafford & Coomber Electrical Contractors, 112 Lambrook Road, Taunton, Somerset, TA1 2AD Tel: (01823) 284620 Fax: (01823) 331283

▶ Stafford Hygiene Solutions, Unit 5 Greyfriars Business Park, Greyfriars Way, Stafford, ST16 2RF Tel: (01785) 227272 Fax: (01785) 257725

Stafford Outdoor Leisure, 38 Mill Street, Stafford, ST16 2AJ Tel: (01785) 240594 Fax: (01785) 213420 E-mail: sales@staffordoutdoor.com *Camping equipment suppliers*

Stafford Rubber Co. Ltd, Belsize Close, Norton Canes, Cannock, Staffordshire, WS11 9TQ Tel: (01543) 270002 Fax: (01543) 278046 E-mail: sales@stafford-rubber.co.uk *Industrial rubber product manufrs*

Stafford Stainless Steels, Meaford Power Station, Meaford, Stone, Staffordshire, ST15 0UU Tel: (01782) 796868 Fax: (01782) 374410 E-mail: sales@stainless.st *Stainless steel strip processors & stockists*

▶ Stafford Uniprint, 2 Willoughby Court, Bramshall, Uttoxeter, Staffordshire, ST14 5NH Tel: (01889) 567532 Fax: (01782) 395801 E-mail: uniprint@tesco.net *Specialist security printers specialising in Vistor and Contractor management systems, permits to work, and a full range of ID sysems and accessories*

Staffordshire Figure Co., 70-72 Hospital St, Nantwich, Cheshire, CW5 5RP Tel: 01270 625006 Fax: 01270 629603 *Pottery figurines*

▶ The Staffordshire Hog Roast, Birches Road, Codsall, Wolverhampton, WV8 2JW Tel: 01902 844853 E-mail: staffordshire.hogroast@btinternet.com *Provides Hog Roasts and BBQ''s for all occassions.*

Staffordshire Marketing Ltd, Charrington House, 17 Market Street, Lichfield, Staffordshire, WS13 6JX Tel: (01543) 263942 Fax: (01543) 415249 E-mail: info@stratford-marketing.co.uk *Advertising & public relations agents*

Staffordshire Newsletter Ltd, Publishing Centre, Derby Street, Stafford, ST16 2DT Tel: (01785) 257700 Fax: (01785) 253287 E-mail: admin@staffordshirenewsletter.co.uk *Newspaper & magazine publishers*

Staffordshire Porcelain & China, 70-72 Williamson Avenue, Stoke-on-Trent, ST6 8AU Tel: (01782) 536336 Fax: 01782 536336 *Bone china manufrs*

Staffordshire Precision Engineering Ltd, 4 Red Mine Close, Newcastle, Staffordshire, ST5 9HZ Tel: (01782) 630500 Fax: (01782) 638440 E-mail: sales@staffsprecision.co.uk *Precision engineers*

Staffordshire Property Development, Spot Service Stations, Sutherland Road, Stoke-on-Trent, ST3 1HZ Tel: (01782) 311562 Fax: (01782) 598316 *Ceramic engineering services*

Staffordshire Signs & Graphics Ltd, 154 Lime Lane, Pelsall, Walsall, WS3 5AP Tel: (01543) 373006 Fax: (01543) 374550 E-mail: richard@signs-and-graphics.co.uk *Sign manufacturers & installers*

Staffordshire Stone Hollington Ltd, Quarry Bank, Hollington, Stoke-on-Trent, ST10 4HQ Tel: (01889) 507435 Fax: (01889) 507365 *Quarry & masonry work* Also at: Birmingham

▶ Staffs Concrete Ltd, Litchfield Street, Hanley, Stoke-On-Trent, ST1 3JE Tel: (01782) 849993 Fax: (01782) 398048 *Concrete manufrs*

▶ Staffs Operator Training, Mill Farm, Gratton Lane, Endon, Stoke-on-Trent, ST9 9AG Tel: (01782) 503500 Fax: (01782) 503979 E-mail: email@operatortraining.co.uk *Staffordshire Operator Training offer CPCS courses for over 60 categories of plant and machinery including: 360 excavator, telehandler / loadall, 180 backhoe loader, 3CX, forward tip dumper, ride-on-roller and fork lift to name just a few.*

Staffs Timber Products Ltd, New Park House, Newstead Industrial Trading Estate, Stoke-on-Trent, ST4 8HX Tel: (01782) 641241 Fax: (01782) 642982 E-mail: info@pallets4u.com *Pallet suppliers*

▶ Stag Bakeries Ltd, 60 Bayhead Street, Stornoway, Isle of Lewis, HS1 2DZ Tel: (01851) 702733 Fax: (01851) 701808

Stag Chem Ltd, 6b Mid Road, Cumbernauld, Glasgow, G67 2TT Tel: (01236) 457900 Fax: (01236) 727955 E-mail: sales@stagchem.co.uk *Cleaning, maintenance product manufrs*

Stag Commercial Body Manufacturers Ltd, Unit 1a Cockshute Industrial Estate, Shelton New Road, Stoke-on-Trent, ST4 7AW Tel: (01782) 287528 Fax: (01782) 283504 E-mail: stagcommercial@yahoo.co.uk *Commercial body builders*

Stag Glass & Windows Ltd, 6 High Street, Chapel-en-le-Frith, High Peak, Derbyshire, SK23 0HE Tel: (01298) 816400 Fax: (01298) 816400 E-mail: info@stagglass.fsnet.co.uk *PVCu doors, windows & conservatories*

▶ Stag & Hen UK, Park House Farm, Lenham Road, Headcorn, Ashford, Kent, TN27 9LJ Tel: (0845) 3300431 Fax: (0845) 3300432 E-mail: marketing@stagandhenuk.com *Organise outdoor stag or hen parties*

Stag Shopfronts Ltd, 16B Kings Mill Way, Mansfield, Nottinghamshire, NG18 5ER Tel: (01623) 631356 Fax: (01623) 421653 *Aluminium shop fronts manufrs*

Stag Specialised Joinery, 47a High Street, Ongar, Essex, CM5 9AQ Tel: (01277) 365551 Fax: (01277) 365551 *Joinery manufrs*

▶ Stage Electrics, Yeoford Way, Marsh Barton Trading Estate, Exeter, EX2 8LB Tel: (01392) 824100 Fax: (01392) 825230

Stage Plan Of London, 26-30 The Swan Centre, Rosemary Road, London, SW17 0AR Tel: (020) 8944 0899 Fax: (020) 8946 5454 *Sets & stages for conferences*

Stage Services, C8 Ford Airfield Industrial Estate, Ford, Arundel, West Sussex, BN18 0HY Tel: (01903) 716333 Fax: (01903) 717187 E-mail: sales@stage-services.co.uk *Theatre sound & lighting installers*

Stage Two Ltd, Unit J Penfold Trading Estate, Imperial Way, Watford, WD24 4YY Tel: (01923) 230789 Fax: (01923) 255048 E-mail: info@stage-two.co.uk *Audio visual equipment hire*

Stagecraft Ltd, Ashfield Trading Estate, Salisbury, SP2 7HL Tel: (01722) 326055 Fax: (01722) 414076 E-mail: myran@stagecraft.co.uk *Conference organizers*

▶ Stagonset, 276 Lichfield Road, Sutton Coldfield, West Midlands, B74 2UG Tel: 0121-240 4603 Fax: (0870) 7627532 E-mail: spratt@stagonset.co.uk *Specialist suppliers for stainless steel nuts, bolts, screws & washers*

Stahlwille Tools Ltd, Albany Park, Camberley, Surrey, GU16 7PD Tel: (01276) 24080 Fax: (01276) 24696 E-mail: sales@stahlwille.co.uk *Hand tool manufrs*

Stained Glass Experience, Studio 7 Art At Cedar Farm, Back Lane, Mawdesley, Ormskirk, Lancashire, L40 3SY Tel: (01704) 823121 Fax: (01704) 823121 E-mail: enquiries@stainedglassexperience.co.uk *Stained glass & leaded lights*

Staines Machine Tool Co. Ltd, 131 Ashford Road, Staines, Middlesex, TW18 1RS Tel: (01784) 245669 Fax: (01784) 241291 *Machine tool merchants*

▶ Staines Steel Gate Co. Ltd, 18-24 Ruskin Road, Staines, Middlesex, TW18 2PX Tel: (01784) 454456 Fax: (01784) 466668

Stainfab Sheet Metal Ltd, 50 Offerton Industrial Estate, Hempshaw Lane, Stockport, Cheshire, SK2 5TJ Tel: 0161-480 5009 Fax: 0161-480 5509 E-mail: sales@stainfab.com *Stainless steel metalwork engineers or fabricators*

Stainfree Fabrications Ltd, Cockersdale Works, Whitehall Road, Drighlington, Bradford, West Yorkshire, BD11 1NQ Tel: 0113-285 4299 Fax: 0113-285 2706 E-mail: mail@stainfree-fabrications.ltd.uk *Stainless steel fabricators*

Stainless & Alloy (Aberdeen) Ltd, 1 Crombie Road, Aberdeen, AB11 9QQ Tel: (01224) 874666 Fax: (01224) 874699 E-mail: sales@stainlessandalloy.co.uk Principal Export Areas: Worldwide *Flange, bolts & nuts manufrs*

Stainless & Alloy Products Ltd, 8 Greets Green Road Industrial Estate, Greets Green Road, West Bromwich, West Midlands, B70 9EW Tel: 0121-557 0033 Fax: 0121-557 7775 *Stainless steel sheetmetal workers*

Stainless & Alloy Supplies, Unit 75 Percy Business Park, Rounds Green Road, Oldbury, West Midlands, B69 2RE Tel: 0121-544 9969 Fax: 0121-544 9979 E-mail: stainandalloy1@btconnect.com *Stainless steel stockholders*

continued

The Stainless Centre, Hurricane Way, Wickford, Essex, SS11 8YB Tel: (01621) 785578 E-mail: sales@stainless-centre.co.uk *Stainless steel stockholders*

Stainless Design Services Ltd, C The Old Bakery, Kiln Lane, Swindon, SN2 2NP Tel: (01793) 692666 Fax: (01793) 487242 E-mail: sds@stainlessdesign.co.uk *Manufacturers of stainless steel equipment*

Stainless Equipment Co. (Metal Finishers) Ltd, Alma Road, Ponders End, Enfield, Middx, EN3 7BB Tel: (020) 8805 0884 Fax: (020) 8804 8167 E-mail: david@stainlesssteelpolishers.co.uk *Metal & stainless steel finishing/polising services. Also architectural finishing, metal.*

Stainless International Ltd, George Henry Rd, Great Bridge, Tipton, West Midlands, DY4 7BU Tel: 0121-522 3111 Fax: 0121-522 3377 E-mail: a.holland@stainlessinternational.com *Stainless International is one of the UK's major independent stockholders and processors of stainless steel flat-rolled and long products. We supply stainless steel sheet, polished sheet, coloured sheet, coil, strip in coil, hollow section, welded tube, round bar and stainless steel flat bar. We also provide a slitting and distribution service through our subsidiaries, Shear Pro and Pallet Pro. For further details please visit our website at www.stainlessinternational.com or call us on 0800 037 9117. Thank you for taking the time to learn about Stainless International.*

Stainless Metalcraft, Chatteris Engineering Works, Honeysome Road, Chatteris, Cambridgeshire, PE16 6SA Tel: (01354) 692391 Fax: (01354) 695281 E-mail: infoline@metalcraft.co.uk *Stainless steel & engineering fabricators services*

Stainless Plating Ltd, 24 Don Road, Sheffield, S9 2UB Tel: 0114-242 2000 Fax: 0114-242 2003 E-mail: brenda@stainlessplating.co.uk *Electroplaters & metal finishers*

Stainless Steel Centre Ltd, Renown Close, Chandler's Ford, Eastleigh, Hampshire, SO53 4HZ Tel: (023) 8027 1155 Fax: (023) 8027 1110 E-mail: sales@stainlesssteelcentre.co.uk *Specialist supplier of non corrosive fasteners & fixings*

Stainless Steel Fasteners Ltd, Broombank Road, Chesterfield, Derbyshire, S41 9QJ Tel: (01246) 451818 Fax: (01246) 455268 E-mail: sales@ssfast.co.uk *Bolts & nut manufrs*

Stainless Steel Fixings Ltd, 10 Charlwoods Road, East Grinstead, West Sussex, RH19 2HU Tel: (01342) 328608 Fax: (01342) 314861 *Fixings & fastenings manufrs & fabricators*

Stainless Steel Services Ltd, Middlemore Road, Handsworth, Birmingham, B21 0BH Tel: 0121-523 8100 Fax: 0121-523 8102 E-mail: info@stainlesssteelservices.co.uk *Stockists & processors of stainless steel & aluminium*

Stainless Threaded Fasteners Ltd, 7 Beldray Park, Beldray Road, Bilston, West Midlands, WV14 7NH Tel: (01902) 490490 Fax: (01902) 496583 E-mail: sales@stf.fasteners.co.uk *Stainless steel fastener distributors*

Stainless UK Ltd, Newhall Works, Newhall Road, Sheffield, S9 2QL Tel: 0114-244 1333 Fax: 0114-244 1444 *Stainless steel suppliers*

The Stainless Wire Tie Company Ltd, 3 Fife Street, Sheffield, S9 1NJ Tel: 0114-261 9966 Fax: 0114-242 6333 E-mail: sales@wiretie.com *Construction product manufrs*

Stair Place, 86 Knights Hill, London, SE27 0JD Tel: (020) 8761 8855 Fax: (020) 8761 8855 E-mail: info@stairplace.co.uk *Staircase distributors*

Stair Well Ltd, Olympic Industrial Estate, 3 Watkin Road, Wembley, Middlesex, HA9 0YG Tel: (020) 8902 7885 *Staircase manufrs*

Staircase Co., Unit 4 Silver Royd Business Park, Silver Royd Hill, Leeds, LS12 4QQ Tel: 0113-279 9092 Fax: 0113-279 9095 *Joinery manufrs*

Staircase & Balustrades Ltd, Slaney Street, Oakengates, Telford, Shropshire, TF2 6ET Tel: (01952) 610370 Fax: (01952) 610370 *Architectural metalworkers*

▶ Stairglide, Unit 8, Barshaw Park, Leycroft Road, Leicester, LE4 1ET Tel: (0800) 7812020 E-mail: info@equilift.com *Supply affordable stair lifts to fit all stair types*

StairRopes.com, Tallowater, Braddock, Lostwithiel, Cornwall, PL22 0RH Tel: (07624) 172799 E-mail: jameswatson@stairropes.com *Stair rope manufrs*

Stairway Projects, Unit 16 Taylors, Gravel Lane, Chigwell, Essex, IG7 6DQ Tel: (020) 8559 9226 Fax: (020) 8559 9226 *Staircase manufrs*

Stakeholder Communications Ltd, 2 Donegall Square East, Belfast, BT1 5HB Tel: (028) 9033 9949 Fax: (028) 9033 9959 E-mail: gayle.armstrong@stakeholdergroup.com *Public relations & event management services & design*

Staley Radford & Co. Ltd, Blackburn House, 22-26 Eastern Road, Romford, RM1 3PJ Tel: (01708) 737333 Fax: (01708) 737334 *Freight forwarders*

Stalham Engineering Co. Ltd, The Green, Stalham, Norwich, NR12 9QG Tel: (01692) 580513 Fax: (01692) 581770 E-mail: mgn@stalhameng.co.uk *Agricultural machinery dealers & car dealers*

Stalite Signs Ltd, 7 Apple Lane, Exeter, EX2 5GL Tel: (01392) 447001 Fax: (01392) 447002 E-mail: sales@stalite.co.uk *General neon sign manufrs*

Stalkers Transport Ltd, Townfoot Industrial Estate, Brampton, Cumbria, CA8 1SW Tel: (01697) 73699 Fax: (01697) 73176 E-mail: enquiries@stalkerstransport.co.uk *Haulage company*

Stallingborough Construction Ltd, Unit 5, Prince Edward Drive, Immingham, South Humberside, DN40 1QU Tel: (01469) 574867 Fax: (01469) 577760 *Welders & fabricators*

Stallion Hydraulic Services Ltd, Wharf Road, Gravesend, Kent, DA12 2RU Tel: (01474) 564707 Fax: (01474) 564752 E-mail: sales@stallion-group.com *Manufacturers & distributors of hydraulic equipment & pumps*

▶ Stall-Mech Engineering Services Ltd, 8 Anthony Way, Stallingborough, Grimsby, South Humberside, DN41 8BD Tel: (01472) 886030 Fax: (01472) 886020

Stalum Engineering Ltd, 3 Darnall Works, Leathley Road, Leeds, LS10 1BG Tel: 0113-242 2289 Fax: 0113-234 7951E-mail: sales@stalum.co.uk Principal Export Areas: Worldwide *Manufacturers of bucket type elevators & materials handling equipment.*

Stalwart Commission Carpets, Primrose Works, Primrose Road, Clitheroe, Lancashire, BB7 1BT Tel: (01200) 423721 Fax: (01200) 420804 E-mail: sales@stalwartcarpets.co.uk *Carpet manufrs*

▶ Stalwart Impex, 35 Stadium Business Centre, North End Road, Wembley, Middlesex, HA9 0AT Tel: (020) 8903 7711 Fax: 08707 66 17 19 E-mail: info@stalwartimpex.com *Architectural Ironmongers**Suppliers of quality Door Handles and Locks, Door Hinges + Bathroom Mixers*

▶ Stalwart Productions, Barclay House, 35 Whitworth Street West, Manchester, M1 5NG Tel: 0161-228 0507 Fax: 0161-236 2836 *Audio visual services & programme producers*

Stalwart Products, 179 Radstock Road, Southampton, SO19 2HW Tel: (023) 8044 5656 Fax: (023) 8042 2360 *Plastic materials distributor*

Stalwart Signs & Industrial Supplies Ltd, Anglian House Admiralty Road, Great Yarmouth, Norfolk, NR30 3DY Tel: (01493) 857410 Fax: (01493) 852383 E-mail: stalwartsafety@dsl.pipex.com *Safety signs, industrial equipment distributors, marine & offshore*

Stambermill Autocraft, Building 80, First Avenue, Pensnett Trading Estate, Kingswinford, West Midlands, DY6 7FQ Tel: (01384) 298682 Fax: (01384) 866003 *Commercial vehicle repairers*

Stamford Fabrications Ltd, Oliver Close, Grays, Essex, RM20 3EE Tel: (01708) 861665 Fax: (01708) 864123 *Steel fabricators*

Stamford Homes, Ashurst Southgate Park, Bakewell Road, Orton Southgate, Peterborough, PE2 6YS Tel: (01733) 396600 Fax: (01733) 396669 E-mail: sales@stamford-homes.co.uk *Building contractors*

Stamford International Export Ltd, Jack Haws Lane, Barnack, Stamford, Lincolnshire, PE9 3DY Tel: (01780) 740400 Fax: (01780) 740460 E-mail: sales@stamfordint.demon.co.uk *Fuel equipment & parts suppliers*

Stamford Plant Hire Ltd, Uffington Road, Stamford, Lincolnshire, PE9 2HA Tel: (01780) 482888 Fax: (01780) 480066 E-mail: shgilmer@atglobal.net *Ready mixed concrete distributor*

▶ Stamford Stone Co. Ltd, Stamford Road, Marholm, Peterborough, PE6 7HX Tel: (01780) 740970 Fax: (01780) 740755 E-mail: sales@stamfordstone.co.uk *Operators of Clipsham Medwells Limestone Quarry and producer of natural stone building products including walling stone and masonary.*

Bruce Stamp, Station Yard, Pinchbeck, Spalding, Lincolnshire, PE11 3RF Tel: (01775) 723096 Fax: 01755 723096 *Portacabins*

Stamp It UK, Davyhulme Road East, Stretford, Manchester, M32 0DN Tel: 0161-610 9405 Fax: 0161 610 9406 E-mail: sales@stampituk.co.uk *StampIt UK - the UK's premier manufacturer of self-inking rubber stamps. Based centrally in Manchester, England we endeavour to provide our customers with the best in quality, service and Price.*- 600dpi Quality Stamps.*- 0's of stock designs to choose from!*- Custom designs made to your requirements!*- Anything you can put on a computer can be made on a stamp!*Stamps are made and dispatched in 24 Hours!*Our client list includes schools, colleges, offices, warehouses, stationers and even individuals - all of whom have been supplied with stamps created to their exact designs. Through the years of experience and knowledge shared by our staff we hope that StampIt UK will be your choice of supplier for your Self-inking rubber stamp needs **

Stampiton Group Of Companies Ltd, Bingswood Industrial Estate, Whaley Bridge, High Peak, Derbyshire, SK23 7SP Tel: (01663) 733535 Fax: (01663) 734253 E-mail: enq@stampiton.co.uk *General labels to the trade*

Stampreo Rubber Ltd, Plexus House, Stockholm Road, Hull, HU7 0XW Tel: (01482) 348134 Fax: (01482) 446453 E-mail: stamps@plexus-net.co.uk *Rubber stamp makers & laser engravers*

Stamps Direct Ltd, 125 Carholme Road, Lincoln, LN1 1RT Tel: (01522) 534729 Fax: (01522) 521038 E-mail: linc@rubber-stamps.co.uk *Rubber stamp manufrs* Also at: Cambridge, Norwich & Nottingham

Stamps Direct, 24 Halls Road, Stapleford, Nottingham, NG9 7FQ Tel: 0115-939 0333 Fax: 0115-949 0415 E-mail: nott@rubber-stamps.co.uk *Rubber stamp manufrs*

▶ Stan Randell & Co. Ltd, 71-73 Clarendon Road, Christchurch, Dorset, BH23 2AD Tel: (01202) 481871 Fax: (01202) 481874 E-mail: admin@stanrandellandco.co.uk

▶ Stan Robinson Ltd, Morton Road, Darlington, County Durham, DL1 4PT Tel: (01325) 480100 Fax: (01325) 480787 E-mail: sales@stanrobinson.com

▶ Stan Robinson Stafford Ltd, Tiverton Junction, Cullompton, Devon, EX15 2QD Tel: (01884) 821777 Fax: (01884) 821787

▶ Stan Robinson Stafford Ltd, Drumhead Road, Glasgow East Investment Park, Glasgow, G32 8EX Tel: 0141-641 6141 Fax: 0141-641 8641

Stanair Industrial Door Services Ltd, Unit 2 Henson Way, Telford Way Industrial Estate, Kettering, Northamptonshire, NN16 8PX Tel: (01536) 482187 Fax: (01536) 411799 E-mail: admin@shiresecurity.co.uk *Industrial door repair, service & installation*

Stanair Industrial Door Services Ltd, Unit 11, Blundells Road, Bradville, Milton Keynes, MK13 7HA Tel: (01908) 222070 Fax: (01908) 222621 E-mail: info@stanair.co.uk *Industrial door repair, service & installation*

Stanair Industrial Door Services Ltd, 5 Fairweather Court, Peterborough, PE1 5UN Tel: (01733) 314097 Fax: (01733) 314097 E-mail: info@stanair.co.uk *Industrial door repair, service & installation services*

Stanair Industrial Door Services Ltd, Unit A-D Great Central Indust Estate, Great Central Way, Rugby, Warwickshire, CV21 3XH Tel: (01788) 568888 Fax: (01788) 568999 E-mail: sales@stanair.co.uk *Industrial door repair, service & installation services*

Stanborough Press Ltd, Londonthorpe Road, Grantham, Lincolnshire, NG31 9SL Tel: (01476) 591700 Fax: (01476) 577144 E-mail: stanborg@aol.com *Publishers of childrens & adult books*

Stanbridge Precision Turned Parts Ltd, 20 Bilton Way, Luton, LU1 1UU Tel: (01582) 617000 Fax: (01582) 401630 E-mail: info@stanbridge-precision.co.uk *Turned part manufrs*

Stanco Exhibitions Ltd, 4 Tregwilym Industrial Estate, Tregwilym Road, Rogerstone, Newport, Gwent, NP10 9DQ Tel: (01633) 890300 Fax: (01633) 890301 E-mail: reception@stanco.co.uk *National exhibition & display contractors*

Stancold, Portview Road, Bristol, BS11 9LQ Tel: 0117-316 7000 Fax: 0117-316 7001 E-mail: sales@stancold.co.uk *Cold room manufrs*

▶ Stancombe Stone Ltd, The Camp, Stroud, Gloucestershire, GL6 7EW Tel: (01285) 821839 Fax: (01285) 821841

Standall Tools Ltd, Mickley Lane, Dronfield Woodhouse, Dronfield, Derbyshire, S18 8XB Tel: 0114-262 0626 Fax: 0114-262 0520 E-mail: sales@standall.com *Contractors tool manufrs*

Standaparts Ltd, 7A South Bank, Thames Ditton, Surrey, KT7 0UD Tel: (020) 8398 7812 Fax: (020) 8398 7813 E-mail: standaparts@btclick.com *Standard components for machines*

▶ Standard Cash Registers & Scales, 141 Tarring Road, Worthing, West Sussex, BN11 4HG Tel: (01903) 208969 Fax: (01903) 233144 E-mail: sales@scr-epos.com *Cash register suppliers & repairers*

▶ Standard Chartered Africa plc, 1 Aldermanbury Square, London, EC2V 7SB Tel: (020) 7280 7500 Fax: (020) 7280 7791 E-mail: sales@standardchartered.com *Worldwide banking services & authorised banking institution*

Standard Engineering Ltd, Lawson Street, Kettering, Northamptonshire, NN16 8XU Tel: (01536) 517070 Fax: (01536) 410755 *Shoe repairing machinery*

▶ Standard English, Clark House, Higher Kingsbury, Milborne Port, Sherborne, Dorset, DT9 5EB Tel: (07709) 935909 Fax: (0870) 7461291 E-mail: lisa@galventures.com *Proofreading and copy writing specifically for web sites. All types of commercial web sites can be proofed and updated, plus I can offer a bespoke service to small businesses starting out on the web, from wording, planning and selecting/enhancing images until the final copy is sent to the design company.*

Standard Fencing (Glasgow) Ltd, Downiebrae Road, Rutherglen, Glasgow, G73 1PW Tel: 0141-613 1555 Fax: 0141-613 1811 E-mail: standardfencing@btconnect.com *Security fencing manufrs*

Standard Freight Forwarders Ltd, 73 Maltings Place, London, SW6 2BY Tel: (020) 7384 1212 Fax: (020) 7384 1030 E-mail: exports@standardfreight.com *International freight forwarding agents, road, sea, air freight*

▶ Standard Industrial Systems Ltd, Stanton House, Eastham Village Rd, Eastham, Wirral, Merseyside, CH62 0DE Tel: (0845) 2571985 Fax: (0845) 2571986 E-mail: sales@standardindustrial.co.uk Purchasing Contact: A. Forbes Sales Contact: G. Greenlees *Solvent, aqueous industrial cleaning. Washing, hermetically sealed, zero emission vapour degreasing. Vacuum drying degreasing systems. Spray, ultrasonic cleaming. Perchlorethylene, methylene chloride, dichloromethane, hydrocarbon, modified alcholol, DOWCLENE. Carbon dioxide cleaning. Cryogenic, dry ice blasting. Solvent cleaning technology. Tube cleaning. Automotive, aerospace approved cleaning processes. VOC compliant degreasing. Solvent emissions directive compliance**

Standard Laundry (N I) Ltd, 213 Donegall Avenue, Belfast, BT12 6LU Tel: (028) 9032 7295 Fax: (028) 9031 4026 *Laundry domestic & dry-cleaning services*

▶ Standard Life Assurance Co., 5-15 Thistle Street, Edinburgh, EH2 1DF Tel: 0131-245 1456

Standard Motor Product Europe, Occupation Road, Hucknall, Nottingham, NG15 6DZ Tel: 0115-952 8000 Fax: 0115-952 0050 E-mail: sales@intermotor.co.uk Principal Export Areas: Worldwide *Autoelectrical & electronic equipment manufrs*

Standard Motor Transport, 15 Lisle Avenue, Kidderminster, Worcestershire, DY11 7DJ Tel: (01562) 745308 Fax: (01562) 754546 E-mail: rob@standardmotortransport.co.uk *Road transport, haulage & freight services*

Standard Patent Glazing Co. Ltd, Forge Lane, Dewsbury, West Yorkshire, WF12 9EL Tel: (01924) 461213 Fax: (01924) 458083 E-mail: enquiries@patent-glazing.com *Patent glazing contractors* Also at: Welling & Worthing

Standard & Pochin Ltd, 6-7 Westminster Road, Wareham, Dorset, BH20 4SP Tel: 0845 1306660 Fax: (01929) 556726 E-mail: sales@standard-pochin.co.uk *Fan & impeller manufrs*

Standard & Pochin Ltd, 94 Lyde Road, Yeovil, Somerset, BA21 5DS Tel: (01935) 421481 Fax: (01935) 428030 E-mail: info@ijmcgilltransport.com *Providing total sheet metal work, welding, bespoke shop fitting services*

Standard Power Ltd, Unit 13 Riverside, Bolton, BL1 8TU Tel: 01204 527521 *Industrial pneumatic hand tools sales*

▶ Standard Scaffolding Specialists Ltd, 131 Church Street, Little Lever, Bolton, BL3 1BW Tel: (01204) 574064 Fax: (01204) 862612

Standard Soap Co. Ltd, Derby Road, Ashby-de-la-Zouch, Leicestershire, LE65 2HG Tel: (01530) 410000 Fax: (01530) 410001 E-mail: sales@standardsoap.co.uk *Manufacturers of soap*

Standard Wool UK Ltd, Carlton Bulidings, Bradford, West Yorkshire, BD8 7DB Tel: (01274) 495511 Fax: (01274) 493310 E-mail: woolinfo@standard-wool.co.uk *Wool merchants & wool top manufrs*

Standardair Ltd, Harleyford Estate, Henley Road, Marlow, Buckinghamshire, SL7 2DZ Tel: (01628) 472055 Fax: (01628) 473900 E-mail: sales@standardair.co.uk *Air compressors & parts*

▶ Standards Group, Bentley Hall Barn, Alkmonton, Ashbourne, Derbyshire, DE6 3DJ Tel: (01335) 330263 Fax: (01335) 330922 E-mail: uk@standardsgroup.co.uk *Spanish joinery & allied products*

▶ Standel Dawman Ltd, Pasture Lane Works, Factory La, Barrowford, Nelson, Lancs, BB9 6ES Tel: (01282) 613175 Fax: (01282) 615429 E-mail: sales@standeldawman.uk.com *Manufacturers of parts for electric golf trolleys, including wheels, plastic & pneumatic; gear motor units, differential units, speed controllers, battery chargers & plastic rotational moulding manufrs*

Standen Engineering Ltd, Hereward Works, 47-49 Station Road, Ely, Cambridgeshire, CB7 4BP Tel: (01353) 661111 Fax: (01353) 662370 E-mail: sales@standen.co.uk *Agricultural implement manufrs*

Standen Reflex Ltd, Hereward Works, 47-49 Station Road, Ely, Cambridgeshire, CB7 4BP Tel: (01353) 666200 Fax: (01353) 666202 E-mail: sales@standenreflex.com *Agricultural machinery, equipment import & distribution*

Standeven & Mathers Ltd, 49a Westfield Road, Leeds, LS3 1DF Tel: 0113-245 4578 Fax: 0113-245 4580 *Bakers suppliers*

Standex Electronics (U.K.) Ltd, 40 Morley Road, Tonbridge, Kent, TN9 1RA Tel: (01732) 771023 Fax: (01732) 770122 E-mail: sales@standex.co.uk *Reed relay & switch manufrs*

▶ Standfast Access Equipement, Brendon Road, Bristol, BS3 4PX Tel: 0117-953 9533 *Access equipment suppliers*

Standfast Barracks, Caton Road, Lancaster, LA1 3PA Tel: (01524) 64334 Fax: (01524) 380157 *Bleachers, dyers & printers*

Standfast Security Systems Ltd, 120 Coldharbour Road, Redland, Bristol, BS6 7SL Tel: 0117-942 3366 Fax: 0117-944 6241 E-mail: sales@standfast.co.uk *Security services*

Standguard Security Systems, 340 Broxtowe Lane, Aspley, Nottingham, NG8 5ND Tel: 0115-913 0372 Fax: 0115-942 5590 E-mail: standguard@ntlworld.com *Electric gates & barriers supply & installation & security systems*

Standing Stone, Llwynteg, Ffynnonddrain, Carmarthen, Dyfed, SA33 6EE Tel: (01267) 223226 Fax: (01267) 223495 E-mail: sales@standingstone.co.uk *Sign manufrs*

Standing Stone, Uni G10 Morton Park Way, Darlington, County Durham, DL1 4PJ Tel: (01325) 288877 Fax: (01325) 288855 E-mail: sales@standing-stone.co.uk *Drawing office suppliers*

Standing Stone Drawing Office Supplies, Unit 1-2 Standing Stone, Matfen, Newcastle upon Tyne, NE20 0RQ Tel: (01661) 886653 Fax: (01661) 886988 E-mail: sales@standing-stone.co.uk *Drawing office equipment & materials service*

Standish Engineering Co. Ltd, Mayflower Works, Bradley Lane, Standish, Wigan, Lancashire, WN6 0XF Tel: (01257) 422838 Fax: (01257) 422381 E-mail: enquiries@cnc-machining.co.uk *Precision engineering specialists*

Standish Metal Treatments, Potter Place, Skelmersdale, Lancashire, WN8 9PW Tel: (01695) 455977 Fax: (01695) 728835 E-mail: smtltd@aol.com *Shot blasting & metal protection contractors*

Standpoint Ltd, Unit 22A, Park Avenue Estate, Sundon Park, Luton, LU3 3BP Tel: (01582) 561754 Fax: (01582) 563296 E-mail: info@standpoint.uk.com *Exhibition stand contractors*

Standring Bros Ltd, Wellington Road, Greenfield, Oldham, OL3 7AG Tel: (01457) 877227 Fax: (01457) 877204 E-mail: standring.brothers@btopenworld.com *PVC extrusion manufrs*

Stanelco R F Technologies, Marchwood Industrial Park, Marchwood, Southampton, SO40 4PB Tel: (023) 8086 7100 Fax: (023) 8086 7070 E-mail: sales@stanelco.co.uk *Bottle cap induction sealing equipment manufrs*

Stanfield Building Services Ltd, Imex Technology Park, Unit 7 Bellringer Road, Trentham, Stoke-on-Trent, ST4 8LJ Tel: (01782) 658877 Fax: (01782) 658899 E-mail: info@stanfieldbs.co.uk *Chemical, Process Waste,Syphonic drainage and Plumbing Engineers.*Manufacturer of SGD Borosilicate Glass Traps for disposal of Condensate Waste.*

Stanford Design & Construct Ltd, 5 Richmond St South, West Bromwich, West Midlands, B70 0DG Tel: 0121-522 2220 Fax: 0121-522 2020 E-mail: sales@stanford-flooring.co.uk *Industrial flooring contractors*

▶ Stanford Logistics Ltd, Blantyre Industrial Estate, Blantyre, Glasgow, G72 0XB Tel: (01698) 712504 Fax: (01698) 712877 E-mail: sales@stanford-logistics.com

Stanford Marsh Ltd, Buckholt Drive, Worcester, WR4 9ND Tel: (01905) 458000 Fax: (01905) 754057 E-mail: sales@stanfordmarsh.co.uk *Reprographic & computer aided design systems* Also at: Birmingham & Bristol

Stanford Signs, 13 Gideons Way, Stanford-le-Hope, Essex, SS17 8EE Tel: (01268) 753810 Fax: (01268) 753810 *Signmakers & banner manufrs*

Stanford Technologies Ltd, Rayner House, Higher Hillgate, Stockport, Cheshire, SK1 3ER Tel: 0161-480 4051 Fax: 0161-429 0966 E-mail: sales@stanfordtec.co.uk *Software designers*

Stanfords Digital, 12-14 Long Acre, London, WC2E 9LP Tel: (020) 7836 2260 Fax: (020) 7379 4776 E-mail: sales@stanfords.co.uk *Map & travel retailers*

Stanham Engineering Ltd, 31a Cobble Lane, London, N1 1SF Tel: (020) 7226 3730 Fax: (020) 7226 2746 *Sheet metalwork (precision) engineers*

Stanhope Press, Railway Arch 89-90, Enid Street, London, SE16 3RA Tel: (020) 7252 3838 Fax: (020) 7232 1056 *Lithographic printers*

Samuel Staniforth Ltd, Old Lane, Halfway, Sheffield, S20 3GZ Tel: 0114-248 8250 Fax: 0114-258 6066 E-mail: info@s-stainiforth.co.uk *Catering equipment manufrs*

Staniland Marina, Staniland Marina, Lock Hill, Thorne, Doncaster, South Yorkshire, DN8 5EP Tel: (01405) 813150 Fax: (01405) 740592 E-mail: sales@staniland-marina.co.uk *Boat builders, repairs & chandlers*

Stanler Components Ltd, Crittal Court, Crittal Drive, Braintree, Essex, CM7 2SE Tel: (01376) 340902 Fax: (01376) 322510 E-mail: sales@stanler.co.uk *Electronic component suppliers*

Stanley Acmetrack, Drake House, Beighton Rd. East, Sheffield, S19 6GJ Tel: 0114-251 0570 Fax: (08701) 654654 *There is more to Stanley than trimming knives: Hand tools, decorating products, sliding wardrobe doors, pneumatic fasteners & mechanics tools*

Stanley Agriculture, Thorn Rise Farm, Sandon Road, Hopton, Stafford, ST18 9TH Tel: (01785) 229140 Fax: (01785) 251620 *Sellers of agricultural machinery*

Stanley Assembly Technologies, Gowerton Road, Brackmills, Northampton, NN4 7BW Tel: (01604) 827255 Fax: (01604) 827277 E-mail: sholliday@stanleyworks.com *Automotive industry tool manufrs*

Stanley Bros, Long Street, Premier Business Park, Walsall, WS2 9DX Tel: (01922) 621788 Fax: (01922) 723560 E-mail: info@stanley-brothers.com *Metal buckle manufrs*

Stanley Butchers Supply Co., 364 Prescot Road, Old Swan, Liverpool, L13 3AP Tel: 0151-228 1209 Fax: 0151-475 2343 E-mail: sbssupply@hotmail.com *Food ingredients for the butchers trade*

Stanley Charleston, Treglossack Farm, St. Keverne, Helston, Cornwall, TR12 6PS Tel: (01326) 280017 Fax: (01326) 280017 *Commercial garage*

Stanley Cookers Ni, 5 Moygashel Mills Park, Moygashel, Dungannon, County Tyrone, BT71 7DH Tel: (028) 8772 2195 Fax: (028) 8775 2022 E-mail: sales@stanley-cookers.com *Cooker wholesalers*

Stanley Cylinders Ltd, 82 Lime Pit Lane, Stanley, Wakefield, West Yorkshire, WF3 4DF Tel: (01924) 823320 Fax: (01924) 825283 E-mail: stanleycylinders@aol.com *Copper & stainless steel cylinders manufrs*

Stanley Gibbons Holdings plc, 399 Strand, London, WC2R 0LX Tel: (020) 7836 8444 Fax: (020) 7836 7342 E-mail: info@stanleygibbons.co.uk *Stamp dealers, auctioneers & publishers*

▶ Stanley J Murphy Ltd, Crompton Road, Stevenage, Hertfordshire, SG1 2EE Tel: (01438) 359923 Fax: (01438) 350651 E-mail: enquiries@sjmgroup.co.uk *Shop fitters commercial & domestic glazing*

Stanley Land Drainage Ltd, Crow Royd Farm, North Moor Lane, Huddersfield, HD5 0PZ Tel: (01924) 497283 Fax: (01924) 493481 *Land drainage consultants*

Stanley Plastics Ltd, Units 4-7, Holmbush Industrial Estate, Midhurst, West Sussex, GU29 9HX Tel: (01730) 816221 Fax: (01730) 812877 E-mail: sales@stanleyplastics.co.uk *Acrylic manufrs*

Stanley Press Equipment Ltd, Sutton Mill, Byrons Lane, Macclesfield, Cheshire, SK11 7JL Tel: (01625) 619094 Fax: (01625) 619094 E-mail: sales@s-p-e.co.uk *Label printing equipment distributors*

Stanley Tools, The Stanley Works, Woodside, Sheffield, S3 9PD Tel: (0870) 1650650 Fax: (0870) 1654654 *Hand tool manufrs*

Stanley Vickers Ltd, Snowdon Road, Middlesbrough, Cleveland, TS2 1LG Tel: (01642) 247353 Fax: (01642) 231571 E-mail: info@sv-ltd.co.uk *Extruder screw & barrel manufrs*

Stanley Welch & Son Ltd, 9 Greenway, Barton-upon-Humber, South Humberside, DN18 5HY Tel: (01652) 632933 Fax: (01652) 632933 *Joiners*

▶ Stanleys Quarry, Westington Hill, Broad Campden, Chipping Campden, Gloucestershire, GL55 6UR Tel: (01386) 841236 Fax: (01386) 841845

Stanlow Pallets Ltd, Indigo Road, Ellesmere Port, CH65 4AJ Tel: 0151-356 3932 Fax: 0151-357 2667 *Reconditioned pallet rebuilders & suppliers & pallet recovery services*

Stanmark Engraving, Unit 8, Catherington Business Park, Catherington, Waterlooville, Hampshire, PO8 0AQ Tel: (023) 9259 8414 Fax: (023) 9259 4791 E-mail: stanmark@crossmanm.freeserve.co.uk *General engravers*

Stanmor Floors Ltd, Holly Park Industrial Estate Unit 6, Spitfire Road, Birmingham, B24 9PB Tel: 0121-384 8868 Fax: 0121-384 6424 E-mail: bmorton@stanmorfloors.co.uk *Flooring contractors*

Stannah Lift Service Ltd, Unit 6 Ambassador Industrial Estate, 9 Airfield Road, Christchurch, Dorset, BH23 3TG Tel: (01202) 476781 *Lift maintenance division*

Stannah Lift Service Ltd, 46-47 Acorn Industrial Park, Crayford Road, Dartford, DA1 4AL Tel: (01322) 555777 Fax: (01322) 555444 *For service of passenger and access lifts, escalators and moving walkways*

Stannah Lift Service Ltd, 48 Bleak Hill Way, Mansfield, Nottinghamshire, NG18 5EZ Tel: (01623) 631010 Fax: (01623) 636182 *Elevator & lift manufrs*

Stannah Lift Service Ltd, 27-28 Morgan Way, Bowthorpe Employment Area, Norwich, NR5 9JJ Tel: (01603) 748021 Fax: (01603) 743097

Stannah Lift Services, 45 Carlyle Avenue, Hillington Industrial Estate, Glasgow, G52 4XX Tel: 0141-882 9946 Fax: 0141-882 7503 *Stair lifts & lifts manufacturers*

Stannah Stairlifts LTS, Watt Close, Andover, Hampshire, SP10 3SD Tel: (0800) 715492 E-mail: nigel_dickinson@stannah.co.uk *Manufacturers of the world's most chosen stairlifts*

Stanneylands Livery, Stanneylands Road, Wilmslow, Cheshire, SK9 4ER Tel: (01625) 533250 *Livery & stables*

Stanref International Ltd, Northern Way, Bury St. Edmunds, Suffolk, IP32 6NL Tel: 01284 763501 *Refrigeration, Pressure Vessel & Heat Exchanger design & manufacture* Also at: Blunham

John Stansfeld Ltd, Springwell Works, Buslingthorpe Lane, Leeds, LS7 2DF Tel: 0113-262 8155 Fax: 0113-262 9730 E-mail: sales@gheuk.co.uk *Steel stockholders*

Stansons Indoor Blinds, Sterling House, School Road, Hampton Hill, Hampton, Middlesex, TW12 1QL Tel: (020) 8941 8895 Fax: (020) 8979 8156 *New commercial & industrial blind fitters*

Stansted All-Steel Ltd, Unit 1 Parsonage Farm Industrial Estate, Forest Hall Road, Stansted, Essex, CM24 8TY Tel: (01279) 817801 Fax: (01279) 815704 *Precision engineers*

▶ Stansted Laboratories, Unit 9, Riverside Industrial Estate, 27, Thames Road, Barking, Essex, IG11 0ND Tel: (020) 8594 5104 Fax: (020) 8591 8762 E-mail: sales@stanstedlabs.co.uk *Water system maintenance including chemical analysis*

Stansted Pine, Stansted Saw Mills, Stansted Park, Rowland's Castle, Hampshire, PO9 6DU Tel: (023) 9241 3595 *Pine furniture & shop fittings*

Stansted Sawmill Ltd, Stansted Park, Rowland's Castle, Hampshire, PO9 6DU Tel: (023) 9241 2445 Fax: (023) 9241 3434 *Timber yard*

▶ Stant Ltd, Skewfields, New Inn, Pontypool, Gwent, NP4 0XZ Tel: (01495) 757555 Fax: (01495) 757609

Stanton Bonna Concrete Ltd, Littlewell Lane, Stanton-by-Dale, Ilkeston, Derbyshire, DE7 4QW Tel: 0115-944 1448 Fax: 0115-944 1466 E-mail: sbc@stanton-bonna.co.uk *Pre-cast concrete manufrs*

Stanton Chase International, 56 Haymarket, London, SW1Y 4RN Tel: (020) 7930 6314 Fax: (020) 7930 9539 E-mail: london@stantonchase.com *Recruitment agency*

Stanton Engineering Coventry 1999 Ltd, 9 Lythalls La Industrial Estate, Lythalls Lane, Coventry, CV6 6FL Tel: (024) 7668 8552 *Slotting & precision engineers*

Stanton Group, Laxcon Close, London, NW10 0TG Tel: (020) 8459 4640 Fax: (020) 8830 3377 E-mail: sales@stantongroup.co.uk *Glazed partitioning*

Stanton Hope Ltd, 11 Seax Court, Southfields, Laindon, Basildon, Essex, SS15 6LY Tel: (01268) 419141 Fax: (01268) 545992 E-mail: sales@stantonhope.co.uk *Stanton Hope Ltd - your first choice in the UK for chainsaws, brushcutters, hedgetrimmers, forestry, tree surgery and arboricultural tools, equipment and PPE, from Stihl, Husqvarna, Silky, Felco, Oregon saw chain, Windsor and other leading brands*

Stanton Kilns, Foley Works, King Street, Stoke-on-Trent, ST4 3DE Tel: (01782) 312316 Fax: (01782) 598978 E-mail: sales@stanton-kilns.co.uk Principal Export Areas: Central/East Europe & West Europe *Kilns & temperature controllers manufrs*

Stanton Media Sales, 10 Grazing Lane, Redditch, Worcestershire, B97 5PE Tel: (01527) 404295 Fax: (01527) 540503 E-mail: sales@stantonmedia.co.uk *Advertisement managers for publishers of technical magazines, journals and web sites*

Stantondown Ltd, Shafton Lane, Leeds, LS11 9QY Tel: 0113-243 5746 Fax: 0113-242 1706 E-mail: stantondown@btclick.com *Professional hair product manufrs*

Stantone Mechanical Handling Ltd, 3 Rothersthorpe Avenue, Rothersthorpe Avenue Industrial Estate, Northampton, NN4 8JW Tel: (01604) 761001 Fax: (01604) 762318 *Mechanical handling equipment*

▶ Stanton's brick cutting & bonding service, sunny avenue upton, pontefract west yorkshire, pontefract, west yorkshire, WF9 1DJ Tel: 01977 649760 E-mail: stanny2@tiscali.co.uk *brick specials cut & bonded to your specification. quick turn around time. free local collection & delivery. special rates for bulk*

Stantons Weybridge Ltd, Canal Bridge, Byfleet Road, New Haw, Addlestone, Surrey, KT15 3JE Tel: (01932) 848131 Fax: (01932) 848447 *Plastic panel manufrs*

Stanton-Thompson (Agencies) Ltd, 14 Watcombe Road, Watlington, Oxfordshire, OX49 5QJ Tel: (01491) 613515 Fax: (01491) 613516 E-mail: diana@stanthom.freeserve.co.uk *Engineers distributors*

Stantree Precision Ltd, Unit F4 Anchor Brook Industrial Park, Aldridge, Walsall, WS9 8BZ Tel: (01922) 455775 Fax: (01922) 455323 E-mail: garymills@stantreeprecision.co.uk *We are a sub contract machining company engaged in the manufacture & assembly of machined components for a wide range of different products, with a varied customer base.*

continued

Components produced are consistent to the highest quality, & dimensional accuracy is achieved by the application of comprehensive quality control procedures. Stantree has carried an excellent reputation for providing service & quality at the right price

Stanway Screens Ltd, Oil Croft Orchard, Main Road, Bredon, Tewkesbury, Gloucestershire, GL20 7LX Tel: (01684) 772378 Fax: (01684) 772013 E-mail: marcuspriest@hotmail.com *Caravan window manufrs*

▶ Stanwell Trailers, 3 Bedfont Road, Stanwell, Staines, Middlesex, TW19 7LR Tel: (01784) 252145 Fax: (01784) 244217 E-mail: mick@stanwelltrailers.co.uk *supply towbars 40%discount *SUNVISORS *STAINLESS STEEL NUDGE BARS*REAR STEP BUMPERS*ROOF RACKS*LIGHT GUARDS*WINDOW GUARDS*ROOF MOUNTED LIGHT BARS*TOW BARS FOR MOTORHOMES***

Stanwood Engineering Ltd, 21 Church Street, Bawtry, Doncaster, South Yorkshire, DN10 6HR Tel: (01302) 710661 Fax: (01302) 711663 *Reconditioned engine machinists*

Stanworth Engineers Ltd, Brown Street, Burnley, Lancashire, BB11 1PN Tel: (01282) 421427 Fax: (01282) 458318 E-mail: info@stanworth.co.uk *Aerospace engineering services*

Stapak Services, Bankside, Youlgrave, Bakewell, Derbyshire, DE45 1WD Tel: (01629) 636855 Fax: (01629) 636187 E-mail: stapakservices@aol.com *Foundry suppliers*

Staple Dairy Products Ltd, Main Road, Orpington, Kent, BR5 3HS Tel: (01689) 888700 Fax: (01689) 888710 E-mail: sales@stapledairy.co.uk *Exporters & importers of dairy products*

Staples Disposables Ltd, East Road, Sleaford, Lincolnshire, NG34 7EQ Tel: (01529) 411600 Fax: (01529) 411607 E-mail: admin@staplesdisposables.com *Paper converting & chemical production services*

Staples Uk Ltd, Heights of Alma, Stanley, Crook, County Durham, DL15 9QW Tel: (01388) 768990 *Furniture & cabinet makers manufrs*

Staples Uk Ltd, Windover Road, Huntingdon, Cambridgeshire, PE29 7EF Tel: (01480) 442222 Fax: (01480) 442266 E-mail: enquiries@staplesbeds.co.uk *Bedding manufrs*

Staples Uk Ltd, Lady Bay Retail Park, Meadow Lane, Nottingham, NG2 3GZ Tel: 0115-986 0714 Fax: 0115-986 0721 *Stationary retailers*

Stapleton Engineering, 13 Orwell Court, Hurricane Way, Wickford, Essex, SS11 8YJ Tel: (01268) 764985 Fax: (01268) 764985 *Injection moulding specialists*

Stapletons, 14 Rhodes Way, Watford, WD24 4TJ Tel: (01923) 801039 Fax: (01923) 818416 *Tyre wholesalers*

Stapleton's Commercial & Agricultural Depot, Fourth Avenue, Letchworth Garden City, Hertfordshire, SG6 2TT Tel: (01462) 488844 Fax: (01462) 488845 E-mail: admin@stapletons-tyres.co.uk *Tyres & exhausts wholesale & retail* Also at: Aylesbury, Barnet, Biggleswade, Ely, Harpenden, Hitchin, Letchworth & Maidenhead

Stapletons Systems Ltd, Queniborough Road Industrial Estate, 1489 Melton Road, Queniborough, Leicester, LE7 3FP Tel: 0116-260 6909 Fax: 0116-264 0165 E-mail: enquiries@stapletons-group.co.uk *Complete range of decorating work*

Stapling Centre P.L.C., Rapesco House, One Connections Business Place, Otford Road, Sevenoaks, Kent, TN14 5DF Tel: (01732) 464800 Fax: (01732) 464888 *Stapling equipment*

▶ Star Accountancy, Park Royal Metro Centre, Britannia Way, London, NW10 7PA Tel: (020) 8961 5151 Fax: (020) 8961 4546 E-mail: info@sacs-uk.com *Accountants*

▶ Star Beds Ltd, Queens Mills, Mill Street East, Savile Town, Dewsbury, West Yorkshire, WF12 9AQ Tel: (01924) 457794

▶ Star Building Services Ltd, Thermal House, 89 Wellington Street, Leicester, LE1 6HJ Tel: 0116-254 2013 Fax: 0116-254 4866 E-mail: sales@starbuildingservs.co.uk

▶ Star Business Support, 6 Werner Court, Aylesbury, Buckinghamshire, HP21 9QS Tel: (01296) 483352 *STAR Business Support can offer you all the skills, time and professionalism you will ever need from a virtual office environment.**From typing a single report to regular spreadsheet updates, we can help on a one-off or ongoing basis to meet your requirements.**

Star Ceilings Ltd, P O Box 6, Banbury, Oxfordshire, OX15 4RU Tel: (01295) 722777 Fax: (01295) 722778 *Suspended ceiling sub-contractors*

▶ Star Child, Unit 18 The Oak Business Centre, 79-93 Ratcliffe Road, Sileby, Loughborough, Leicestershire, LE12 7PU Tel: (01509) 817601 Fax: (01509) 817602 E-mail: info@starchildshoes.co.uk *Production, wholesale and mail order of baby and childrens soft leather shoes. Designed and handmade in England.*

Star Civil Engineering Ltd, Templar Indust Park, Torrington Avenue, Coventry, CV4 9AP Tel: (024) 7642 1122 Fax: (024) 7645 4973 E-mail: info@starcivil.co.uk *Civil engineering contractors*

Star Computer Group plc, King Edward Court, 23 High Street, Sutton Coldfield, West Midlands, B72 1XS Tel: 0121-355 6171 Fax: 0121-354 4656 E-mail: info@starplc.co.uk *Computer systems & software developers*

Star Computer Group plc, 2 Spar Centre Boulevard, Blackmoor Lane, Watford, WD18 8UX Tel: (01923) 246414 Fax: (01923) 254301 E-mail: sales@starplc.com *Computer software manufrs*

Star Computer Services (U K) Ltd, Unit 21 Woodside Park, Rugby, Warwickshire, CV21 2NP Tel: (01788) 551522 Fax: (01788) 551523 *Bespoke computer systems & hardware integrator*

Star Covers Ltd, 12 Manor Workswhitehall Road, Drighlington, Bradford, West Yorkshire, BD11 1LN Tel: 0113-285 4747 Fax: 0113-285 2293 *Tarpaulin manufrs*

Star Credit Services Ltd, 10-12 Lombard Road, London, SW19 3TZ Tel: (020) 8540 9691 Fax: (020) 8540 6021 E-mail: info@star-serv.com *Process servers & debt collectors*

Star Diamond Co Ltd, 91-94 Saffron Hill, London, EC1N 8PT Tel: (020) 7404 2222 Fax: (020) 7404 2950 E-mail: info@stardiamond.com *Jewellery wholesalers*

Star Electrical Repairs, 5 Englehard Industrial Estate Valley Road, Bilson, Cinderford, Gloucestershire, GL14 2PB Tel: (01594) 826433 Fax: (01594) 826433 *Electrical repairs*

▶ Star Electrical Services, Unit 1a Motherwell Business Centre, Coursington Road, Motherwell, Lanarkshire, ML1 1PW Tel: (01698) 267865 Fax: (01698) 264354

▶ Star Electrics, 22 Mcgowan Street, Paisley, Renfrewshire, PA3 1QJ Tel: 0141-889 0947 Fax: 0141-887 2526

Star Engineers, 157 Main Road, Broomfield, Chelmsford, CM1 7DJ Tel: (01245) 440501 Fax: (01206) 549167 E-mail: carhire@jdrobertson.freeserve.co.uk *Cylinder borers & crankshaft grinders*

▶ Star Environmental Systems Ltd, Gaia Lodge, Blairs, Aberdeen, AB12 5YT Tel: (01224) 860260 Fax: (01224) 860265

Star Executives Ltd, 7 Fitz Roy Mews, London, W1T 6DQ Tel: (020) 7387 6999 Fax: (020) 7387 6999 E-mail: info@starexecutives.com *Management selection services*

Star Garments Co. Ltd, Caressa House, Cemetery Road, Pudsey, West Yorkshire, LS28 7XD Tel: 0113-257 8234 Fax: 0113-239 3421 E-mail: wwg@wwgroup.co.uk *Garment design development & distribution*

Star Hydraulics Ltd, 8a Beta Close, Tewkesbury, Gloucestershire, GL20 8SR Tel: (01684) 296176 Fax: (01684) 850714 E-mail: sales@star-hydraulics.co.uk *Hydraulic servo valve repairers & manufrs*

Star Industrial Tools Ltd, 42 Westfield Road, Kings Heath, Birmingham, B14 7ST Tel: 0121-444 4354 Fax: 0121-441 1838 E-mail: sales@starindustrialtools.co.uk *Industrial diamond tool manufrs*

Star Installation Ltd, Unit B Progress Business Centre, Cannock, Staffordshire, WS11 0JR Tel: (01543) 574146 Fax: (01543) 469312 *Thermal insulation contractors, fire protection board*

Star Instruments Ltd, Dunmurry Industrial Estate, Dunmurry, Belfast, BT17 9HU Tel: (028) 9061 8221 Fax: (028) 9060 1803 E-mail: sales@star-instruments.co.uk *Thermometer & pressure gauge manufrs*

Star Instruments Ltd, Barkway, Royston, Hertfordshire, SG8 8EH Tel: (01763) 848886 Fax: (01763) 848881 E-mail: sales@star-instruments.co.uk *Flow switch & gauges distributors* Also at: Dunmurry

Star Litho Plates Ltd, Unit 10 Orient Industrial Park, Simonds Road, London, E10 7DE Tel: (020) 8532 8686 Fax: (020) 8556 5568 E-mail: starlitho@btconnect.com *Litho plate makers*

▶ Star Mechanical & Electrical, Fryern House, 125 Winchester Road, Chandler's Ford, Eastleigh, Hampshire, SO53 2DR Tel: (023) 8027 3050 Fax: (023) 8027 3051 E-mail: admin@dagenhammotors.co.uk

Star Metal Polishing Ltd, Hilton Trading Estate, Birmingham New Road, Wolverhampton, WV4 6BW Tel: (01902) 408455 *Polishing, buffing, grinding services & casting*

Star Micronics GB Ltd, Chapel Street, Melbourne, Derby, DE73 8JF Tel: (01332) 864455 Fax: (01332) 864005 E-mail: sales@stargb.net *Precision machines distributors*

Star Pac Ltd, 23 Fernwood Close, Redditch, Worcestershire, B98 7TN Tel: (01527) 850022 Fax: (01527) 850033 E-mail: sales@starpac.co.uk *Heavy duty packing case manufrs*

Star Pallets, Shawlands Farm, Newchapel Road, Lingfield, Surrey, RH7 6BL Tel: (01342) 833704 Fax: (01342) 833704 *Suppliers of pallets for the industry including wooden, new & reconditioned*

Star Polishing, Graiseley House, Graiseley Row, Wolverhampton, WV2 4HJ Tel: (01902) 421137 Fax: (01902) 421137 *Polishing & plating service providers*

▶ Star Property Maintenance Ltd, Unit 4 Parc-Y-Bont, Millers Avenue, Brynmenyn, Bridgend, CF32 9TD Tel: (01656) 729900 Fax: (01656) 729901 E-mail: star.property.services@virgin.net

▶ Star Quality Entertainment Agency UK, 10 Park Meadow Avenue, Bilston, West Midlands, WV14 6HA Tel: (01902) 578959 E-mail: info@starqualityentertainment.net *supplier of entertainment for the Corporate Hospitality, corporate Functions, Corporate Agent, Themed Nights, Tribute Bands, Quality Acts, Disco, Hotels, Pubs, Clubs and the Wedding industry. Also any public or private event you may be organizing.we supply*

Star Quality Video Productions, 36 Mount Ephraim Lane, London, SW16 1JD Tel: (020) 8769 6425 Fax: (020) 8769 6425 E-mail: starqualityvideo@aol.com *Video production services*

R. & B. Star Ltd, 14 Kennet Road, Crayford, Dartford, DA1 4SD Tel: (01322) 555125 Fax: (01322) 522465 *Electrical wholesalers to the trade* Also at: London SE13 & Norwich

Star Refrigeration Ltd, 4 Murray Place, Righead Industrial Estate, Bellshill, Lanarkshire, ML4 3LP Tel: (01698) 841535 Fax: (01698) 842074 *Refrigeration manufrs*

▶ Star Refrigeration Ltd, Wincanton Close, Derby, DE24 8NB Tel: (01332) 756041 Fax: (01332) 757289

Star Refrigeration Ltd, Thornliebank Industrial Estate, Nitshill Road, Glasgow, G46 8JW Tel: 0141-638 7916 Fax: 0141-638 8111 E-mail: star@star-ref.co.uk *Refrigeration engineers*

▶ Star Refrigeration Ltd, A8 Imperial Business Estate, West Mill, Gravesend, Kent, DA11 0DL Tel: (01474) 568221 Fax: (01474) 363004 *Industrial refrigeration services*

▶ Star Refrigeration Ltd, 15 Tower Road, Washington, Tyne & Wear, NE37 2SH Tel: 0191-415 7755 Fax: 0191-415 0446 E-mail: jwilson@ref.co.uk *Refrigeration, cold stores, ice ring maintenance*

Star Seaford, 10 Broad Street, Seaford, East Sussex, BN25 1ND Tel: (01323) 490565 Fax: (01323) 491599 *Computer systems & software developers*

▶ Star Seating Ltd, 5 Two Woods Trading Estate, Talbots Lane, Brierley Hill, West Midlands, DY5 2YX Tel: (01384) 485672 Fax: (01384) 485673 E-mail: sales@starseating.com *Manufacturing*

Star Security Systems Ltd, 40E Kilburn High Road, London, NW6 5UA Tel: (020) 7625 1001 Fax: (020) 8076 5122 E-mail: enquiries@starlocks.co.uk *Locksmiths*

Star Security (UK) Ltd, Somerset House, School Lane, East Harling, Norwich, NR16 2LU Tel: (01953) 718600 Fax: (01953) 718662 E-mail: steve@starsecurity.co.uk *Designers & installers of integrated fire alarms, CCTV & audio systems*

Star Services UK Ltd, 108 Riverbank House, 1 Putney Bridge Approach, London, SW6 3JD Tel: (020) 7731 2361 Fax: (020) 7384 2213 E-mail: janstarren@msn.com *Export merchants for electrical engineering industry*

Star Signs, Pioneer Business Park, Princes Road, Ramsgate, Kent, CT11 7RX Tel: (01843) 579003 Fax: (01843) 583002 *Sign manufrs*

Star Suspended Ceilings Ltd, 4 Lockwood Street, Hull, HU2 0HJ Tel: (01482) 229788 Fax: (01482) 588155 E-mail: info@star.co.uk *Suspended ceilings*

Star Transport & Warehousing Ltd, Brunel Way, Thetford, Norfolk, IP24 1HP Tel: (01842) 752603 Fax: (01842) 765085 E-mail: traffic@star-transport.co.uk *Road transport & warehousing*

Star Trophies, 61 High Street, Bilston, West Midlands, WV14 0EZ Tel: (01902) 403655 Fax: (01902) 403655 *Trophy makers & engraver*

Star Tubes (Southern) Ltd, Lilliput Road, Brackmills, Northampton, NN4 7DT Tel: (01908) 311777 Fax: (01908) 321874 E-mail: sales@startubes-southern.co.uk *Steel tubes stockholders*

Star Tubes (UK) Ltd, Airfield Industrial Estate, York Road, Elvington, York, YO41 4AU Tel: (01904) 608681 Fax: (01904) 608649 E-mail: enkayo@aol.com *Steel tube stockholders*

Star Universal Gosport Ltd, 2 Clarence Wharf, Mumby Road, Gosport, Hampshire, PO12 1AJ Tel: (023) 9258 2857 Fax: (023) 9251 1731 E-mail: sales@staruniversal.com *Designers & manufacturers in the UK of a wide range of packaging machinery for heavy-duty bag sealing, sack sealing & vacuum sealing. Impulse sealers up to 4500mm long & constant heat machines for medical & industrial applications*

▶ Starbelt (UK) Ltd, 4 Yarrow Close, Rugby, Warwickshire, CV23 0TU Tel: (07747) 627587 Fax: (01788) 570009 E-mail: starbeltuk@aol.com *Supply, service conveyor belts*

▶ Starbridge Systems Ltd, Techneum 2, Kings Road, The Docks, Swansea, SA1 8PJ Tel: (01792) 485530 Fax: (01792) 485531 E-mail: info@labstar.co.uk *Micro pumps medical consultants*

Starbrite Chemicals Ltd, X L House, Rutherford Way, Crawley, West Sussex, RH10 9PB Tel: (01293) 434250 Fax: (01293) 434252 E-mail: sales@starbrite.co.uk *Cleaning equipment distributors*

Starbuck Distribution Ltd, Queen Street, Walsall, WS2 9NS Tel: (01922) 612194 Fax: (01922) 630503 *Motor accessories factors*

Starchem Ltd, Strawberry Lane, Willenhall, West Midlands, WV13 3RS Tel: (01902) 838880 Fax: (01902) 838881 E-mail: sales@starchem.co.uk *Car refinishing contractors*

H C Starck Ltd, Unit 1 Harris Road, Calne, Wiltshire, SN11 9PT Tel: (01249) 822122 Fax: (01249) 823800 E-mail: sally.field@hcstarck.co.uk *Molybdenum component manufrs*

▶ Starco DML Ltd, Marshfield Bank Employment Park, Middlewich Road, Crewe, CW2 8UY Tel: (01270) 253589 Fax: (01270) 253589 E-mail: paul@dmluk.com *Plastic mould sub-contractors*

Starcol Ltd, 7 Cork Place, Bath, BA1 3BB Tel: (01225) 311276 Fax: (01225) 446828 E-mail: info@starcol.com *Computer consultants*

Stardes Ltd, Ashes Building, Old Lane, Sheffield, S20 3GZ Tel: 0114-251 0051 Fax: 0114-251 0555 E-mail: info@stardes.co.uk *Specialist road transport, haulage & freight services*

Stardust Leisure Ltd, 52 Holton Road, Barry, South Glamorgan, CF63 4HE Tel: (01446) 734862 *Fruit machines distributors*

Starfrost UK Ltd, Starfrost House, Newcombe Road, Lowestoft, Suffolk, NR32 1XA Tel: (01502) 562206 Fax: (01502) 584104 E-mail: info@starfrost.co.uk *Freezer & refrigerator manufrs*

Starglaze Midlands Ltd, Unit 5 Waterside South, Lincoln, LN5 7JD Tel: (01522) 512525 Fax: (01522) 567651 E-mail: sales@sternfenster.co.uk *PVC window & door manufrs*

Stargrade Constuction, 2 Morrison Court, Crownhill, Milton Keynes, MK8 0DA Tel: (01908) 560774 Fax: (01908) 567136 *Civil engineers*

▶ Starida Sea Services, Bryn y Mor, West End, Beaumaris, Gwynedd, LL58 8BG Tel: (01248) 810254 E-mail: Jasonzalot03@aol.com *Workboat, safety boat contract, coastal survey work, passenger carrying etc*

▶ Stark & Mccormick Ltd, 92 Liverpool Road North, Liverpool, L31 2HN Tel: 0151-531 8505 Fax: 0151-527 2233

Bruce Starke & Co. Ltd, Langton Green, Eye, Suffolk, IP23 7HL Tel: (01379) 870209 Fax: (01379) 871232 E-mail: info@bruce-starke.com *Matting merchants*

Starkey Laboratories Ltd, William F Austin House, Pepper Road, Hazel Grove, Stockport, Cheshire, SK7 5BX Tel: 0161-483 2200 Fax: 0161-483 9833 E-mail: sales@starkey.co.uk *Hearing aid manufrs*

A.L. Starkie Ltd, Wellington Works, Wellington Rd, Ashton-under-Lyne, Lancs, OL6 7EF Tel: 0161-339 4549 Fax: 0161-343 3305 E-mail: sales@superheater.co.uk *Our products includes boiler superheaters, reheaters and economisers, elements and heaters, generating tubes, heater coils and batteries as well as pressure vessels, heat exchangers, pipework and plate fabrication. Accustomed to working with all the major inspection companies our quality control systems inspire customer confidence.*

Starkie & Palmer, 16 Fairfield Road, Market Harborough, Leicestershire, LE16 9QQ Tel: (01858) 469508 Fax: (01858) 469508 *General garage services*

Starkstrom (London) Ltd, 256 Field End Road, Eastcote, Ruislip, Middlesex, HA4 9UW Tel: (020) 8868 3732 Fax: (020) 8868 3736 E-mail: sales@starkstrom.com *Earth leakage equipment & insulation & monitoring equipment manufrs*

▶ Starlight, 5 Gateway Trading Estate, Hythe Road, London, NW10 6RJ Tel: (020) 8960 6078 Fax: (020) 8960 7991

Starlight Garments, Jubilee Centre, Gate Street, Blackburn, BB1 3AQ Tel: (01254) 690227 Fax: (01254) 690227 *Children's clothing manufrs*

Starlight Music, 2 Humphrey Street, Ince, Wigan, Lancashire, WN2 2HS Tel: (01942) 242450 Fax: (01942) 242450 *Amusement machine repairs & hire*

Starline, Mowbray Drive, Blackpool, FY3 7UN Tel: (01253) 307100 Fax: (01253) 307149 E-mail: sales@starlinesales.co.uk *Advertising business gifts manufrs*

Starline Blinds West Ltd, Unit 16-17 Western Industrial Estate, Lon-Y-Llyn, Caerphilly, Mid Glamorgan, CF83 1BQ Tel: (029) 2086 0631 Fax: (029) 2086 2000 E-mail: sales@starlineblinds.co.uk *Blind manufrs*

Starlit, 2 Dutton Street, Manchester, M3 1LE Tel: 0161-832 0112 Fax: 0161-832 0112 *Ladies & children's clothing manufrs*

▶ Starlite Express Transport, 247 Rochford Garden Way, Rochford, Essex, SS4 1QR Tel: 01702 530848 E-mail: admin@starlite-express.co.uk *Store to door delivery service. We collect your purchases from the store and bring them to your door.*We also provide a customer delivery service to retailers. We will collect your customer orders from your shop or warehouse and deliver them to your customers door.*

Starmaker Welding Services, 16 Pembroke Avenue, Waterbeach, Cambridge, CB25 9QR Tel: (01223) 860662 Fax: (01223) 440009 E-mail: sales@starmake-rwelding.fsnet.co.uk *Welding equipment suppliers*

▶ Starplan Furniture, 173 Killyman Road, Dungannon, County Tyrone, BT71 6LN Tel: (028) 8772 5497 Fax: (028) 8772 5606 E-mail: enquiries@starplanfurniture.net *Beds & bedroom furniture manufrs*

Starpoint Electrics Ltd, Units 1-5 King George's Trading Estate, Davis Road, Chessington, Surrey, KT9 1TT Tel: (020) 8391 7700 Fax: (020) 8391 7760 E-mail: sales@starpoint.uk.com Principal Export Areas: Worldwide *Push button switch manufrs*

Starr Pyrometers Ltd, 31 Spring Hill, Sheffield, S10 1ET Tel: (07973) 726785 *Temperature sensor & controller dealers*

Starragheckert UK Ltd, Unit 1a-1b Haddenham Business Park, Thame Road, Haddenham, Aylesbury, Buckinghamshire, HP17 8LJ Tel: (01844) 296575 Fax: (01844) 296579 E-mail: sales@starragheckert.com *Agents & distributors of milling machines*

▶ Starrant Building Services Ltd, 8 The Parade, Shifnal, Shropshire, TF11 8DL Tel: (01952) 460808

▶ Starry Night Ceilings, 37A Bolton Street, Ramsbottom, Bury, Lancashire, BL0 9HU Tel: (07904) 811480 E-mail: info@starrynightceilings.net *Interior design, light fitting & effects etc*

▶ Starscape, 7 Main Street, Lowick, Berwick-upon-Tweed, TD15 2UD Tel: (01289) 388399 E-mail: info@starceiling.co.uk *Fibre optic lighting manufacturers, designers & suppliers*

Starseal Window Systems, 37 Hoylake Road, Scunthorpe, South Humberside, DN17 2AZ Tel: (01724) 873500 Fax: (01724) 873600 *Plastic window manufrs*

Starsmore Ltd, Main Road, Rookley, Ventnor, Isle of Wight, PO38 3NL Tel: (01983) 721445 Fax: (01983) 721912 E-mail: sales@starsmore.com *Computer software development*

Start Spellman Ltd, Unit 14 Broomers Hill Park, Broomers Hill Lane, Pulborough, West Sussex, RH20 2RY Tel: (01798) 873986 Fax: (01798) 872479 E-mail: hvsales@start-spellman.co.uk *High voltage power manufrs*

Start & Tremayne, 178 High Street, Burton-on-Trent, Staffordshire, DE14 1HN Tel: (01283) 563650 Fax: (01283) 561144 *Leather goods retailers*

Startech Engineering Consultancy Ltd, 2 Drayton Ford, Rickmansworth, Hertfordshire, WD3 8FE Tel: (01923) 897903 Fax: (01923) 897904 E-mail: startech@btinternet.com *Design & project management in the food & drinks industries*

▶ Starter Mart, 994 Astley Street, Globe Square, Dukinfield, Cheshire, SK16 4QS Tel: (0870) 8034101 Fax: 0161-343 5755 E-mail: enquires@startermart.co.uk *Starter motor specialists delivered to your door, next day service*

Startin & Co. Ltd, 2 Sylvan Road, Wanstead, London, E11 1QN Tel: (020) 8989 5125 Fax: (020) 8989 5657 *Mica produce brokers*

Startin Tractors Ltd, Ashby Road, Twycross, Atherstone, Warwickshire, CV9 3PW Tel: (01827) 880088 Fax: (01827) 880572 E-mail: sales@startintractors.co.uk *Agricultural machinery distributors*

Startmaze Ltd, Unit 2, Glaholm Industrial Estate, Glaholm Road, Hendon, Sunderland, SR1 2NX Tel: 0191-567 3649 Fax: 0191-510 3917 *Paint wholesalers*

▶ Startright Scaffold Hire Ltd, Unit 7 Lyon Road Industrial Estate, Kearsley, Bolton, BL4 8NB Tel: (01204) 604441 Fax: (01204) 604442

Startrite Designs Ltd, 76 Bissell Street, Birmingham, B5 7HP Tel: 0121 6666865 *Precision engineers*

Startrite Designs Ltd, Courteney Road, Hoath Way, Gillingham, Kent, ME8 0RZ Tel: (01634) 233216 Fax: (01634) 373516 E-mail: startritedesigns@btinternet.com *Tool & gauge manufrs*

▶ Startrite Machine Tool Co Ltd, Garratt Street, Brierley Hill, West Midlands, DY5 1JU Tel: 0870 870 2550 Fax: 0870 870 2660 E-mail: sales@startrite.com *MANUFACTURERS OF ORIGINAL SPARES FOR STARTRITE VERTICAL & HORIZONTAL BANDSAWS. STARTRITE DRILLING MACHINES, *STARTRITE MEBA 250/320 BANDSAW. NEW HEAVY DUTY BANDSAWS.*

▶ Startwell Learning Resources Ltd, Unit G1b Heaton St Mill, Heaton Street, Denton, Manchester, M34 3RG Tel: 0161-335 9400 Fax: 0161-335 9404

Starvac, 13 Thornhill Park Road, Bitterne, Southampton, SO18 5TP Tel: (023) 8036 6848 Fax: (023) 8036 7684 E-mail: sales@starmix.co.uk *Distributors of wet & dry vacuum cleaners*

Starweld Engineering Ltd, 46 Harleston Street, Sheffield, S4 7QB Tel: 0114-272 0283 Fax: 0114-275 0383 E-mail: sales@starweld.com *Welding & metal fabrication services Cast iron, aluminium, stainless, carbon steel Lancing, brazing, hardfacing, bending Heat resisting, corrosion resistant Profiling, mobile welding Alloy wheel repair Plant repairs Furnace work Heat treatment baskets & electrodes*

▶ Stas Partnership Ltd, 19 Eastern Industrial Estate, Hailey Road, Erith, Kent, DA18 4AA Tel: (020) 8311 3747 Fax: (020) 8311 6372 *Chocolate manufrs*

Stasys Ltd, The Granary, 1 Waverley Lane, Farnham, Surrey, GU9 8BB Tel: (01252) 732500 Fax: (01252) 732501 E-mail: stasys@stasys.co.uk *Consultants*

Stat Plus Ltd, Greenlea Park, Prince Georges Road, London, SW19 2PU Tel: (020) 8646 5500 Fax: (020) 8640 2905 E-mail: enquiries@statplus.co.uk *Law stationers & office suppliers* Also at: Birmingham, Bristol, Leeds & Leicester

Stat Plus, A1 New Pudsey Square, Bradford Road, Stanningley, Pudsey, West Yorkshire, LS28 6PX Tel: 0113-256 9494 Fax: 0113-204 7044 *Law stationers* Also at: London

Stat Shop, 3-9 Station Street, Sittingbourne, Kent, ME10 3DU Tel: (01795) 425424 Fax: (0870) 7777827 E-mail: admin@statshop.co.uk *Rubber stamp manufacturers, stationers & printing services*

Statco, Evett Close, Stocklake, Aylesbury, Buckinghamshire, HP20 1DN Tel: (01296) 392379 Fax: (01296) 435940 E-mail: statco@uk.uumail.com *Commercial stationery*

Statcom Telecommunication Consultants, Unit 17d Shrub Hill Industrial Estate, Worcester, WR4 9EL Tel: (0870) 9909460 Fax: (08707) 872330 *Telecommunications systems suppliers*

State Of The Art Hair Products Ltd, Unit 2, Nelson Park Network Centre, Cramlington, Northumberland, NE23 1WD Tel: (01670) 716234 Fax: (01670) 716234 *Hair dressing equipment suppliers*

State Securities plc, Jellicoe House, Grange Drive, Hedge End, Southampton, SO30 2AF Tel: (01489) 775600 Fax: (01489) 775601 E-mail: jmacklin@statesecurities.plc.uk *Asset finance, Commercial Mortgages, Factoring, Small Firms Loan Guarantee, Factoring, Turnaround Finance*

Statebourne Cryogenics Ltd, 18 Parsons Road, Washington, Tyne & Wear, NE37 1EZ Tel: 0191-416 4104 Fax: 0191-415 0369 E-mail: sales@statebourne.com *Cryogenic equipment & liquified gas container manufrs*

Stately Albion Ltd, Prince of Wales Industrial Estate, Abercarn, Newport, Gwent, NP11 5AR Tel: (01495) 244472 Fax: (01495) 248939 E-mail: sales@stately-albion.co.uk *Prefabricated building manufrs*

Stately Gates Inc 'Urswick Engineering, Long Lane, Barrow-in-Furness, Cumbria, LA13 0PF Tel: (01229) 462646 Fax: (01229) 462646 *Gate & railing manufrs*

Stateside Foods Ltd, 31-32 Great Bank Road, Wingate South, Bolton, BL5 3XU Tel: (01942) 841200 Fax: (01942) 841201 E-mail: sales@stateside-foods.co.uk *Food manufrs*

▶ Statesoft, 150-151 New Bond Street, London, W1S 2TX Tel: (020) 7318 7600 Fax: (020) 7491 7170 E-mail: mhogan@statesoft.com *Statesoft"s technology reduces the risk and cost associated with delivering computer applications on time and is the most reliable and secure system available in the market today.**Statesoft's professional services team use statesoft technology to automate work processes reducing the risk of human error and poor training.**

Statestrong Ltd, Boundary Road, Lytham St. Annes, Lancashire, FY8 5LT Tel: (01253) 741806 Fax: (01253) 794542 *Aerosol & toiletry manufrs*

Statham Engineering Services Ltd, Warrington Lane, Lymm, Cheshire, WA13 0SW Tel: (01925) 754965 Fax: (01925) 754127 E-mail: info@stathameng.co.uk *Pipework contractors*

Static Safe, 6 Timmis Road, Stourbridge, West Midlands, DY9 7BQ Tel: (01384) 898599 Fax: (01384) 898577 E-mail: sse@static-safe.demon.co.uk *Anti-static floor covering manufrs*

Static Scotland Ltd, 16 Cromarty Campus, Rosyth, Dunfermline, Fife, KY11 2WX Tel: (01383) 419833 Fax: (01383) 413028 E-mail: staticscotland@aol.com *Fami, Static Scotland, EPA, Fami, Wez, antistatic storage antistatic packaging, antistatic,conductive storage,Anti-static products & plastic container, ESD, Conductive packaging, Static, cleanroom, ESD Matting,Dima, assembleon, x-tek vac forming, ionisation, ionisers grounding, products,PPE, customised packaging, fami, wez, utz,linn bin, picking bin,storage,wriststraps,heelstraps,conductive foam.*

Statiflo International Ltd, Crown Centre, Bond Street, Macclesfield, Cheshire, SK11 6QS Tel: (01625) 433100 Fax: (01625) 511376 E-mail: sales@statiflo.co.uk *Chemical & industrial mixer manufrs*

▶ Station Garage, Wilbraham Road, Fulbourn, Cambridge, CB21 5ET Tel: (01223) 880747 Fax: (01223) 880885 E-mail: mail@stationgaragefulbourn.co.uk *4 X 4 specialist used car sales, servicing, general repairs, welding, MOT's including diesels.*

Station Kitchens Ltd, 47 Station Road, Erdington, Birmingham, B23 6UE Tel: 0121-373 9160 Fax: 0121-377 7530 *Kitchen & bathroom distributors*

Stationery Express, 15 The Metro Centre, St. Johns Road, Isleworth, Middlesex, TW7 6NJ Tel: (020) 8568 1771 Fax: (020) 8569 8168 E-mail: sales@stationeryexpress.net *Office furniture & stationery & computer consumables suppliers*

▶ Stationery Office, Mandela Way, London, SE1 5SS Tel: (020) 7394 4200 Fax: (020) 7231 0902

Statoil (U K) Ltd, 11 Regent St, London, SW1Y 4ST Tel: (020) 7766 7777 Fax: (020) 7766 7862 E-mail: info@statoil.com *Oil & gas exploration services*

Stator Systems, 7 Potton Road, Abbotsley, St. Neots, Cambridgeshire, PE19 6TX Tel: (01767) 679076 Fax: (01767) 679162 *Process machinery manufrs*

Stats NNC Ltd, South House, 2 Bond Avenue, Bletchley, Milton Keynes, MK1 1SW Tel: (01908) 271660 Fax: (01908) 271332 E-mail: diane.quick@stats-nnc.co.uk *Technical documentation services*

Status Alarms Ltd, Holbrook Lane, Coventry, CV6 4AF Tel: (024) 7668 5523 Fax: (024) 7666 1127 *Burglar alarm engineers & cctv installation*

▶ Status Blinds, Unit 3, Rivington Works, Rivington Avenue, St. Helens, Merseyside, WA10 6UU Tel: (01744) 754794 Fax: (01744) 753683 E-mail: enquiries@statusblinds.co.uk *Blind manufacturers & retailers*

Status Credit Reports Ltd, 21 Whitchurch Road, Cardiff, CF14 3JN Tel: (029) 2054 4333 Fax: (029) 2054 4300 E-mail: orders@statuscredit.com *Credit reporting agents*

▶ Status Design & Print, Pelham Street, Bolton, BL3 3JB Tel: (01204) 655995 Fax: (01204) 655229

Status Graphite, Unit 6a, Commerce Way, Colchester, CO2 8HR Tel: (01206) 868150 Fax: (01206) 868160 Principal Export Areas: Worldwide *Musical instrument*

▶ Status Heating Ltd, 178 Sladepool Farm Road, Birmingham, B14 5EE Tel: 0121-430 3668 Fax: 0121-436 6765 E-mail: info@statusheating.co.uk

▶ Status Mechanical Services, Lightning Works Birmingham Road, Hopwood, Alvechurch, Birmingham, B48 7AL Tel: 0121-447 7677 Fax: 0121-447 7432

Status Pine, 587 Warwick Road, Tyseley, Birmingham, B11 2EX Tel: 0121-707 2077 Fax: 0121-707 4022 *Bedroom & kitchen furniture manufrs*

Status Scientific Controls, Hermitage Lane Inudst Estate, Kings Mill Way, Mansfield, Nottinghamshire, NG18 5ER Tel: (01623) 651381 Fax: (01623) 421063 E-mail: sales@status-scientific.com Principal Export Areas: Worldwide *Gas detection equipment manufrs*

Staub Precision, 4 Vincients Road, Bumpers Farm, Chippenham, Wiltshire, SN14 6NQ Tel: (01249) 658197 Fax: (01249) 443408 E-mail: sales@staub.co.uk *Sub-contract precision engineers*

Staubli Unimation Ltd, Lodge Park, Telford, Shropshire, TF1 7ET Tel: (01952) 604827 Fax: (01952) 608579 E-mail: connectors.uk@staubli.com *Quick release couplings & connectors sales*

▶ Stauff, 332 Coleford Road, Sheffield, S9 5PH Tel: 0114-251 8518 Fax: 0114-251 8519 E-mail: sales@stauff.co.uk *Pipe work distributors sales & technical support on site design, development for complete pipe work systems*

Stauff, Unit 30-31, Point Pleasant Industrial Estate, Wallsend, Tyne & Wear, NE28 6HA Tel: 0191-262 6390 Fax: 0191-262 8825 E-mail: enquiries@stauff.co.uk *Hydraulic accessory suppliers*

Stauff Scotland, Unit 3-4 Altens Trade Centre, Hareness Circle, Altens Industrial Estate, Aberdeen, AB12 3LY Tel: (01224) 238518 Fax: (01224) 238500 E-mail: sales@stauffscotland.co.uk *Hydraulic component distributors*

Stauff UK, 3 Rennie Place, East Kilbride, Glasgow, G74 5HD Tel: (01355) 244445 Fax: (01355) 243399 E-mail: sales@stauffuk.co.uk *Hydraulic component distributors*

Stauff UK Southampton, Unit 1-2 Millbrook Trading Estate, Third Avenue, Southampton, SO15 0LD Tel: (023) 8079 9518 Fax: (023) 8079 9519 E-mail: sales@stauffsouthampton.co.uk *Hydraulic hose distributors*

Stave-Con Ltd, 6-7 Spring Road Industrial Estate, Lanesfield, Wolverhampton, WV4 6JT Tel: (01902) 493749 Fax: (01902) 401466 *Civil engineering contractors*

Stàvekirk Ltd, Studio, Pale Lane, Winchfield, Hook, Hampshire, RG27 8SW Tel: (01252) 844808 Fax: (01252) 844705 E-mail: enquiries@stavekirk.co.uk *Audio visual equipment distributors*

Staveley NDT Technologies, 3 Cromwell Park, Banbury Road, Chipping Norton, Oxfordshire, OX7 5SR Tel: (01608) 642001 Fax: (01608) 644752 E-mail: sales@sndt.co.uk Principal Export Areas: Worldwide *Non-destructive test equipment manufrs*

Staveley Timber Ltd, Back Lane, Staveley, Kendal, Cumbria, LA8 9LR Tel: (01539) 821234 Fax: (01539) 821898 E-mail: broc@broc.co.uk *Wooden handle manufrs*

Staveley Tools, Bailey Drive, Norwood Industrial Estate, Killamarsh, Sheffield, S21 2JF Tel: 0114-247 3367 *Clamp manufrs*

Stax Trade Centre, Brades Road, Oldbury, West Midlands, B69 2HN Tel: 0121-569 7000 Fax: 0121-569 7010 *Cash & carry hardware wholesalers*

Stay Cool Refrigeration, Manchester Road, Preston, PR1 4HL Tel: (01772) 827722 Fax: (01772) 827720 *Transport refrigeration services*

▶ Stay Fit and Healthy, 160 Goring Road, Colchester, CO4 0DB Tel: 0207 6640538 E-mail: stayfitandhealthy@ntlworld.com *WANT TO LOSE OR GAIN WEIGHT? Try ShapeWorks the weight management programme that is tailored to your needs and you"ll feel a difference in a matter of days. All products are natural herbal products, receive full customer follow up, 30 days money back guarantee. Herbalife operates in 60 countries, with over 50+ million satisfied customers. We can help you to acheieve your goals.**WANT TO IMPROVE YOUR SKIN? IS IT DRY OR OILY? The secrect to looking great is good nutrition - inside and out. NouriFusion products are designed to help you loo and feel your radiant best. Discover botanical-based formulas to revitalise, soothe, smooth and pamper every inch of you.*

▶ Stay Tensioner Services, 3 Tresidder Close, Tregoniggie Industrial Estate, Falmouth, Cornwall, TR11 4SP Tel: (01326) 373310 Fax: (01326) 373124 *Hydraulic rigging tension manufrs*

▶ Staybrite Conservatories, 16 Warwick Row, Coventry, CV1 1EJ Tel: (024) 7622 2956 Fax: (024) 7622 3290

Staybrite Windows, Weston Road, Norwich, NR3 3TP Tel: (0800) 0832656 Fax: (01603) 406185 E-mail: mike.holmes@zsltd.co.uk *Window manufrs*

▶ Stayclean Window Cleaning, Freepost, Bristol, BS11 9XB Tel: 0117-982 1857 E-mail: info@staycleanwindows.co.uk *Bristol Commercial Window Cleaning is carried out by using our Reach and Wash ladderless window cleaner system. Fully insured. BWCA and SAFEcontractor accredited. Stayclean provide a bespoke window cleaning service to both commercial and domestic clients in the Bristol area. Properties ranging from the smallest shop window to large multi-storey office buildings, including private houses, stately homes, apartment blocks, schools, factories, pubs, restaurants, hotels and many more.*

Staycool Refrigeration, 320 Spring Lane, Mapperley, Nottingham, NG3 5RQ Tel: 0115-920 0166 Fax: 0115-920 0166 *Refrigerator engineering*

Stayprint Labels & Tags, Brow Lane, Shelf, Halifax, West Yorkshire, HX3 7QJ Tel: (01274) 699200 Fax: (01274) 699209 E-mail: sales@stayprint.com *Label & nameplate manufrs*

▶ Stayput Covers Ltd, PO Box 7884, Leicester, LE4 4WY Tel: 0116-267 2121 Fax: 0116-220 9849 E-mail: sales@seatguard.com *Manufacturers of protective seat covers*

Staystrip Group Ltd, 11-16 Eyre Street, Birmingham, B18 7AA Tel: 0121-455 0111 Fax: 0121-454 5524 E-mail: sales@staystrip.co.uk *Stainless steel strips & flat bars*

Staytite Ltd, Unit B Coronation Road, Cressex BSNS Park, High Wycombe, Buckinghamshire, HP12 4PR Tel: (01494) 462322 Fax: (01494) 464747 E-mail: fasteners@staytite.com Purchasing Contact: Plummer *Distributors of screws, screw & washer assemblies, serrated flange nuts, self-locking nuts, stainless steel screws, stainless steel bolts & nuts, pressed nuts, lock nuts, dome nuts & industrial fasteners. Also general/standard bolts & nuts, machine screws, thread forming screws, self-tapping screws & bolt & nut distributors. We supply to end-users. Supply Technical products.*

▶ Stead Experience, 1 Nicholas Street, Barnsley, South Yorkshire, S70 6DU Tel: (07717) 004065 E-mail: steadexperience@hotmail.com

Stead & Wilkins Fabrications Ltd, Jolly Farmers Wharf, Thames Road, Crayford, Dartford, DA1 4QH Tel: (01322) 529134 Fax: (01322) 550314 E-mail: alanbaynton@steadandwilkins.co.uk *Sheet metalworkers & mechanical engineers*

▶ Steadblast Special Projects, 4 Buckland Road, Parkside, Stafford, ST16 1TZ Tel: 0788 4433851 Fax: 01785 603506 E-mail: doctorearwax60@hotmail.com

▶ Steadfast Courier Services, 34 Caerhendy Street, Merthyr Tydfil, Mid Glamorgan, CF47 9NJ Tel: (07782) 162061 E-mail: steadfastcourier@aol.com *The key features of my service are as follows:**-LDV Convoy high top L.W.B van *-Fully Comprehensive vehicle insurance, Goods-in-transit cover up to value of £25000 (more on request), £2 million public liability and £1million employer liability.*-Short notice availability 7 days-a-week *-UK-wide delivery*-Professional and well-presented driver and vehicle**I pride myself on a good working knowledge of courier services, maintain a professional approach and, most importantly, ensure the very highest standards of customer care. In addition, my rates are very competitive. I would be happy to discuss any requirements with you personally or over the phone - whichever you prefer. **Thank you for taking the*

continued

continuation
time to read this. I hope to hear from you soon and look forward to the opportunity of working with your team in the near future."

▶ Steadfast Engineering Co. Ltd, Broadway, Hyde, Cheshire, SK14 4QQ Tel: 0161 3683636 *Bolts & nuts manufrs*

Steadfast Fastenings, 167 Junction Road, Burgess Hill, West Sussex, RH15 0JW Tel: (01444) 247755 Fax: (01444) 248022 *Industrial fasteners & fixing systems distributor*

Steadfast Scotland Ltd, Units 7-8, Barratt Trading Estate, Denmore Road, Bridge Of Don, Aberdeen, AB23 8JW Tel: (01224) 823555 Fax: (01224) 823666 E-mail: brian.sherwood@steadscott.co.uk *Fastener suppliers & manufrs*

Steadhall Finishing, Unit 1, Bay Close, Progress Way, Luton, LU4 9UP Tel: (01582) 561518 Fax: (01582) 493350 E-mail: rainbowfinishers@aol.com *Stove enamellers & powder coaters*

Steadlands International Marketing Ltd, PO Box 41, Blyth, Northumberland, NE24 3YE Tel: (01670) 361261 Fax: (0870) 9006097 E-mail: info@steadlands.com *Computer peripheral distributor*

A. Steadman & Son Ltd, Warnell, Welton, Carlisle, CA5 7HH Tel: (01697) 478277 Fax: (01697) 478530 E-mail: info@steadmans.co.uk *Steel sheet manufrs*

Steadman Engineering Ltd, Steadman House, Dockfield Road, Shipley, West Yorkshire, BD17 7AZ Tel: (01274) 531531 Fax: (01274) 531044 *General engineers*

▶ Steadman Transport, 732 London Road, Grays, Essex, RM20 3NL Tel: (01708) 869600

Steads Fibrous Plasterers, Victoria Plaster Works, Victoria Road, Bradford, West Yorkshire, BD2 2DJ Tel: (01274) 637222 Fax: (01274) 637222 E-mail: enquiries@steadsplasterers.co.uk *Fibrous plaster manufrs*

▶ Steadvale Air Systems Ltd, Boston Road, Glenrothes, Fife, KY6 2RE Tel: (01592) 771891 Fax: (01592) 772759 E-mail: sales@steadvale.co.uk

Steadvale Air Systems Ltd, Boston Road, Glenrothes, Fife, KY6 2RE Tel: (01592) 771891 Fax: (01592) 772759 E-mail: sales@steadvale.co.uk *Compressor manufacturers & suppliers of spares parts & valves*

▶ Steady Networking, PO Box 7025, London, WC2R 0DZ Tel: (0845) 2265983 Fax: 0871 2778988 E-mail: sales@steadynetworking.com *The essential mission of Steady Networking is to provide affordable and quality IT solutions for small and medium enterprises, including remote and home working professionals. Our company's expertise spans the full gamut of the Information Technology market, from simple, but necessary memory upgrade for a stand-alone computer, to a full cost-effective multi-site network system.**Steady Networking can offer your business a service tailored to your specific needs. This could be a basic support service just to let you know about current potential problems. Or maybe one of our comprehensive, fully managed, support solutions which is a proactive preventative support that aims to identify and fix the problems before you even know about them. This effectively minimising downtime and more importantly saves you time by providing a reliable effective IT system.*

▶ Steamrail IT Solutions, 57 Norburn Park, Witton Gilbert, Durham, DH7 6SG Tel: 0191-371 1011 E-mail: peter.russell@steamrail.co.uk *Computer repair*

Steanne Solutions, Hyde Park House, Cartwright Street, Hyde, Cheshire, SK14 4EH Tel: 0161-367 8137 Fax: 0161-367 8717 E-mail: info@steanne.co.uk *Computer software manufrs*

Stear & Bright Silversmiths, Studio 1 Clevedon Craft Centre, Moor Lane, Clevedon, Avon, BS21 6TD Tel: (01275) 872149 *Jewellery manufrs*

R.J. Stearn & Sons (Luton) Ltd, Unit 9 Windmill Trading Estate, Thistle Road, Luton, LU1 3XJ Tel: (01582) 729458 Fax: (01582) 455582 *Commercial electrical engineers*

Stebon Ltd, Unit 2C Chase Park Industrial Estate, Ring Road, Burntwood, Staffordshire, WS7 8JQ Tel: (01543) 677211 Fax: (01543) 675005 E-mail: sales@stebon.net *Electric motor manufrs*

Stebro Flooring Co. Ltd, Station Road Industrial Estate, Station Road, Rowley Regis, West Midlands, B65 0JY Tel: 0121-559 0544 Fax: 0121-559 0705 E-mail: sales@stebro-flooring.co.uk *General flooring contractors*

Stedall Vehicle Fittings Ltd, Unit 1a Badminton Road Trading Estate, Yate, Bristol, BS37 5JS Tel: (01454) 314646 Fax: (01454) 312077 E-mail: info@stedall.co.uk *Commercial vehicle components distributors*

Stedeford Ceilings, 11 Carsic Lane, Sutton-in-Ashfield, Nottinghamshire, NG17 2AS Tel: (01623) 515355 Fax: (01623) 403046 *Suspended ceiling manufrs*

▶ The Stedifix, Unit 12 Marbury House Farm, Bentleys Farm Lane, Higher Whitley, Warrington, WA4 4QW Tel: (01925) 730938 Fax: (0845) 0092670 E-mail: stedifix@tiscali.co.uk *Fasteners & fixing suppliers*

Steel & Alloy Processing Ltd, Trafalgar Works, Union Street, West Bromwich, West Midlands, B70 6BZ Tel: 0121-553 5292 Fax: 0121-553 3864 E-mail: info@steelalloy.co.uk *Coil steel stockholders*

Steel Appeal, Rear Of 116-118 Highfield Road, Blackpool, FY4 2JF Tel: (01253) 341225 Fax: (01253) 405378 E-mail: angleace@btconnect.com *Steel manufrs*

Steel City Marketing Ltd, Allen Street, Sheffield, S3 7AW Tel: 0114-275 4150 Fax: 0114-275 0010 E-mail: sales@steel-city.co.uk Principal Export Areas: Africa *Promotion incentive products*

Steel Construction, Molehill Road, Chestfield, Whitstable, Kent, CT5 3PB Tel: (01227) 792556 Fax: (01227) 794361 *Steel fabricators*

Steel Craft, Greenhill Mills, Grange Road, Batley, West Yorkshire, WF17 6LH Tel: (01924) 441770 Fax: (01924) 441770 *Fire escape manufrs*

Steel Engineering Services Ltd, Unit 7f Block Westway, Porterfield Road, Renfrew, PA4 8DJ Tel: 0141-885 0885 Fax: 0141-886 3322 E-mail: info@steeleng.com *Welded fabrication manufrs*

▶ Steel Erecting Services Ltd, 32 Woodcote Avenue, Wallington, Surrey, SM6 0QY Tel: (020) 8773 0667 Fax: (020) 8773 0668 E-mail: info@seslimited.net *Steel erecting*

Steel Fab U K, Bold Street, Preston, PR1 7NX Tel: (01772) 883380 Fax: (01772) 883225 E-mail: sales@steelfabuk.co.uk *Steel fabricators*

Steel Forgings, 2 Stocks Lane, Rawmarsh, Rotherham, South Yorkshire, S62 6NL Tel: (01709) 522284 Fax: (01709) 522285 E-mail: steel_forgings@yahoo.co.uk *Manufacturers & suppliers of steel forge products*

The Steel Grating Company Ltd, 9a Between Streets, Cobham, Surrey, KT11 1AA Tel: (01932) 868403 Fax: (01932) 863528 E-mail: adminco@aol.com *Supplier of steel gratings*

Steel Line Ltd, 415 Petre Street, Sheffield, S4 8LL Tel: 0114-231 7330 Fax: 0114-256 0330 E-mail: enquiries@steelline.co.uk *Steel Line, a company specialising in stainless steel metalwork, tube manipulation & metal polishing. The Company's skills range from simple grab handles for the caravan industry to Veterinary tables & equipment specialists in street furniture. Also Catering Equipment, Construction - handrailing, ballustrading, canopies, architectural metalwork, Office, Hotel & Shopfitting, Process Plant, Swimming pools, Medical, mortuary Equipment & Playground equipment*

Steel Options Ltd, Orion Business Centre, Surrey Canal Road, London, SE14 5RT Tel: (020) 7232 0293 *Architectural steel workers*

Steel People Ltd, Unit 3e Priory Park, Mills Road, Aylesford, Kent, ME20 7PP Tel: (01622) 715900 Fax: (01622) 715905 E-mail: mail@thesteelpeople.com *Steel fabricators & stockists structural steel contractors*

Steel Plate & Sections Ltd, Mill House Forge Lane, Minworth Industrial Park, Minworth, Sutton Coldfield, West Midlands, B76 1AH Tel: 0121-313 4300 Fax: 0121-351 7924 E-mail: sales@steelplate.co.uk *Steel stockholders*

Steel Security Services, 121 Boothferry Road, Hull, HU4 6EX Tel: (01482) 563732 Fax: (01482) 568353 *Security services*

Steel Services Associates Ltd, 6 Barton Road Industrial Units, Barton Road, Torquay, TQ2 7NS Tel: (01803) 313383 Fax: (01803) 322299 *Steel fabricators services*

Steel Services Great Yarmouth Ltd, South Denes Road, Great Yarmouth, Norfolk, NR30 3PF Tel: (01493) 856180 Fax: (01493) 852237 E-mail: info@steelservices.co.uk *Steel fabricators, engineers & manufrs*

Steel Services Winchester Ltd, London Road, Kings Worthy, Winchester, Hampshire, SO23 7QA Tel: (01962) 884588 Fax: (01962) 889366 *Steel fabricators*

Steel Spinnings Ltd, 94-96 Steward Street, Birmingham, B18 7AF Tel: 0121-456 3737 Fax: 0121-452 1616 E-mail: info@steelspinnings.com Principal Export Areas: North America *Manufacturers of aluminium & stainless spinning*

Steel Stamping Products Ltd, 15-17 Highmeres Road, Troon Industrial Estate, Leicester, LE4 9LZ Tel: 0116-276 6572 Fax: 0116-276 1624 E-mail: info@steelstampings.co.uk *Presswork manufrs*

Steel Stop Ltd, Methley Road, Castleford, West Yorkshire, WF10 1LX Tel: (01977) 555333 Fax: (01977) 603960 *Steel stockholders & processors*

▶ Steel Storage (UK) Ltd, Unit C1, Twickenham Trading Estate, Rugby Road, Twickenham, TW1 1DG Tel: (020) 8744 9444

Steel Supplies Ltd, Arksey Lane, Bentley, Doncaster, South Yorkshire, DN5 0ST Tel: (01302) 874321 Fax: (01302) 876287 E-mail: sales@steelsupplies.co.uk *Steel stockholders & distrbutors*

Steel Technic Ltd, Mells, Frome, Somerset, BA11 3RH Tel: (01373) 813323 Fax: (01373) 813325 *Fabrication, welding in carbon & stainless steel*

Steel Windows Service & Supplies Ltd, 30 Oxford Road, London, N4 3EY Tel: (020) 7272 2294 Fax: (020) 7281 2309 E-mail: post@steelwindows.co.uk *Steel window consultants services*

Steelcase Strafor plc, Second Floor 2 Carriage Row, 183 Eversholt St, London, NW1 1BU Tel: (020) 7874 0000 Fax: (020) 7380 0153 *Office furniture manufrs*

Steelco UK Ltd, 12 Blackbrook Business Park, Narrowboat Way, Dudley, West Midlands, DY2 0XQ Tel: (01384) 455535 Fax: (01384) 456860 E-mail: steelco@fowle.btinternet.com *Steel stockholders & processors*

Steelcraft Ltd, Unit 2-6 Drum Industrial Estate, Chester le Street, County Durham, DH2 1AG Tel: 0191-410 9996 Fax: 0191-410 9228 E-mail: sales@steelcraft.ltd.uk *Metal gate & railing manufrs*

Steelcraft Precision, Unit A Mortimer Road, Narborough, Leicester, LE19 2GA Tel: 0116-284 1025 Fax: 0116-286 9781 E-mail: info@steelcraft.co.uk *Precision component manufrs*

▶ Steelcraft Site Service Ltd, 6 Dollymans Farm House, Doublegate Lane, Rawreth, Wickford, Essex, SS11 8UD Tel: (01268) 560100 Fax: (01268) 560102 *Steel fabricators*

Steeldeck, Kings Cross Freight Depot, York Way, London, N1 0UZ Tel: (020) 7833 2031 Fax: (020) 7278 3403 E-mail: info@aolsteeldeck.co.uk *Modular staging systems & scenery maker*

Steeldeck Ltd, 30 Arklow Road, London, SE14 6EB Tel: (020) 8692 9721 Fax: (020) 7278 3403 *Staging manufrs*

Steele & Bray Ltd, 59-67 Moore Street, Northampton, NN2 7HU Tel: (01604) 716808 Fax: (01604) 712434 *Building contractors*

▶ Steele Electrics Ltd, 3 Ambassador Industrial Estate, 9 Airfield Road, Christchurch, Dorset, BH23 3TG Tel: (01202) 487766 Fax: (01202) 490305 E-mail: info@steele-electrics.co.uk

Steelfast, Kings Farm Estate, Stanbridge Road, Great Billington, Leighton Buzzard, Bedfordshire, LU7 9JH Tel: (01525) 851603 Fax: (01525) 851836 *Steel stockholders*

Steelfix Ltd, Prestwick Old Plant Yard, Prestwick Road Ends, Ponteland, Newcastle upon Tyne, NE20 9BX Tel: (01661) 860660 Fax: (01661) 820083 E-mail: enquiries@wroughtirongates.co.uk *Steel fabrications*

Steelform Ventilation Ltd, Unit 13 Attenburys Park Estate, Attenbury Lane, Timperley, Altrincham, Cheshire, WA14 5QE Tel: 0161-962 8639 Fax: 0161-973 6742 E-mail: sales@steelformvetilation.com *Dust, fume & ventilation engineers*

Steelkit, Abberleri Boatyard, Ynyslas, Borth, Dyfed, SY24 5JU Tel: (01970) 871713 Fax: (01970) 871879 E-mail: info@steelkit.com *Steel, aluminium boat kits & builders, turnkey solutions & marine project management*

Steelmans Broaches UK Ltd, The Old Nurseries, Ravenstone, Coalville, Leicestershire, LE67 2LA Tel: (01530) 830593 Fax: (01530) 838958 E-mail: sales@steelmans.co.uk *Special & standard broaches, broaching machines, broach regrinding etc*

Steelock Engineering Ltd, Unit 42 Pioneer Mills, Milltown Street, Radcliffe, Manchester, M26 1WN Tel: 0161-724 4066 Fax: 0161-724 4066 *Architectural metalworkers, general & precision engineers*

▶ Steels Engineering Services Ltd, Unit 4b Apollo House, Calleva Park, Aldermaston, Reading, RG7 8TN Tel: 0118-981 7868 Fax: 0118-981 6291

Steelsoft Computing, Willowdene, Thornton-Cleveleys, Lancashire, FY5 3NB Tel: (01253) 828000 Fax: (01253) 867821 E-mail: sales@steelsoft.co.uk *Computer software manufrs*

Steeltech Ltd, Pitts Cleave, Tavistock, Devon, PL19 0PW Tel: (01822) 611144 Fax: (01822) 611188 *Steel fabricators, structural & mechanical installation*

Steeltech Kinetix Ltd, Dancroft Works, Gauxholme Fold, Todmorden, Lancashire, OL14 7PW Tel: (01706) 817144 Fax: (01706) 817522 E-mail: mail@steeltech-kinetix.co.uk *Steel & stainless steel fabricators*

Steeltek, Serpentine Works, Serpentine Road, Cleckheaton, West Yorkshire, BD19 3HU Tel: (01274) 852131 Fax: (01274) 851486 *Structural steel fabricators*

Steelware Co. UK Ltd, 36 Normandy Way, Walker Lines Industrial Estate, Bodmin, Cornwall, PL31 1EX Tel: (01208) 77766 Fax: (01208) 77779 *Tubular steel fabricators*

Steelwise Steel Fabricators, Centurion House, Centurion Way, Farington, Leyland, PR25 3GR Tel: (01772) 454929 Fax: (01772) 454929 *Steel fabricators*

▶ Steelwood (UK) Ltd, Units 7-8, Venture Court, Metcalf Drive, Altham Industrial Estate, Accrington, Lancashire, BB5 5WH Tel: (01282) 777781 Fax: (01282) 777889 E-mail: sales@steelwood.com *Manufacturers of doors*

▶ Steelworks lt, C23 Houghton Enterprise Centre, Lake Road, Houghton le Spring, Tyne & Wear, DH5 8BJ Tel: 0191-584 8811 Fax: 0191-584 7856 E-mail: sales@switcms.co.uk *Website design & it consultancy*

▶ Steen & Co., Magdalen Centre, The Oxford Science Park, Oxford, OX4 4EA Tel: (01865) 784101 Fax: (01865) 784103 E-mail: mail@steenandco.co.uk *Specialist employment law solicitors*

Steenbergs Organic, 1 Hallikeld Close, Melmerby, Ripon, North Yorkshire, HG4 5GZ Tel: (01765) 640101 Fax: (01765) 640101 E-mail: enquiriesl@steenbergs.co.uk *Organic & fair trade tea*

▶ Steenbergs Organic, Unit 6-7, Melmerby Green Lane, Barker Business Park, Ripon, North Yorkshire, HG4 5GZ Tel: (01765) 640088 Fax: (01765) 640101 E-mail: sales@steenbergs.co.uk *Wide range of organic pepper, spice, herbs, blends & traditional seasalt - many sourced direct from farmers to ensure freshness & provenance, supplied packed in glass & stainless steel for retail - bulk for food service, gift packs & ideas available for retail. UK"s first and largest range of spices carrying the FAIRTRADE Mark.*

Steerforth Sales Ltd, Unit 7, Holder Road, Aldershot, Hampshire, GU12 4RH Tel: (01252) 333633 Fax: (01252) 343080 E-mail: sales@steerforth.co.uk *Hydraulic cylinder manufrs*

Steering Developments Group Ltd, Unit 5 Eastman Way, Hemel Hempstead, Hertfordshire, HP2 7HF Tel: (01442) 212918 Fax: (01442) 240254 E-mail: enquiries@steeringdevelopments.co.uk *Disability conversions & wheelchair suppliers*

Steering Rack Services Ltd, 100 Borron Street, Port Dundas Business Park, Glasgow, G4 9XG Tel: 0141-353 1202 Fax: 0141-353 3159 *Supply car parts*

▶ Steertrak Commercial Vehicle Servicing, Commercial House Station Road Business Park, Station Road, Tewkesbury, Gloucestershire, GL20 5DR Tel: (01684) 276900 Fax: (01684) 276500 E-mail: sales@steertrak.co.uk

Steetley Bentonite & Absorbents Ltd, Woburn Road, Woburn Sands, Milton Keynes, MK17 8TU Tel: (01908) 583939 Fax: (01908) 585231 *Quarry*

Steetley Bentonite & Absorbents Ltd, West Carr Road, Retford, Nottinghamshire, DN22 7ZF Tel: (01777) 712828 Fax: (01777) 700344 E-mail: hq@steetley.com Principal Export Areas: Worldwide *Distributors for absorbents, foundry clay & paint additives*

Stef Plastics Ltd, Unit 5, Lakes Road, Braintree, Essex, CM7 3QS Tel: (01376) 349315 Fax: (01376) 349315 *Injection moulders*

Stef's Models, Reeth Dale Centre, Silver Street, Reeth, Richmond, North Yorkshire, DL11 6SP Tel: (01748) 884498 Fax: (01748) 884334 E-mail: sales@stefsmodels.co.uk *Manufacturers of animal models & sculptures*

Stega Engineering Ltd, Sendalls Yard, Crawley Road, Horsham, West Sussex, RH12 4HG Tel: (01403) 269271 Fax: (01403) 269364 E-mail: info@stega.co.uk

▶ Steggles Larner, 25 Charing Cross, Norwich, NR2 4AX Tel: (01603) 724724 Fax: (01603) 724700

Stehlin Hostag Inc UK Ltd, 4 Linkmell Close, Longwall Avenue, Queens Drive Industrial Estate, Nottingham, NG2 1NA Tel: 0115-986 0477 Fax: 0115-986 2681 *Printing ink distributors & manufrs*

▶ Stein Atkinson Stordy Ltd, Heath Mill House, Heath Mill Road, Wombourne, Wolverhampton, WV5 8AP Tel: (01902) 892388 Fax: (01902) 894880 E-mail: chris.baldwin@sas-eng.com *Stein Atkinson Stordy (SAS), which is now embodied in the main name of the company, was founded in the beginning of the last century. Our Product Range includes - Coil Coating - Muffle furnaces - Finishing Systems - IR Drying - Atmospheric Generators - Continuous Roller Hearth*

Steinel (UK) Ltd, 25 Manasty Road, Axis Park, Orton Southgate, Peterborough, PE2 6UP Tel: (01733) 366700 Fax: (01733) 366701 E-mail: steinel@steineluk.co.uk *Manufacturer & distributors of: heat & hot air guns*

Steinlock Ltd, Danbury Mews, Wallington, Surrey, SM6 0BY Tel: (020) 8773 4966 Fax: (020) 8773 4968 *Industrial hoses, fittings & protective clothing*

Stekko Co Ltd, 4 Avocet Trading Estate, Richardson Street, High Wycombe, Buckinghamshire, HP11 2SB Tel: (01494) 459332 Fax: (01494) 459313 E-mail: sales@stekko.co.uk *Manufacturers of stainless steel products*

Stelex Construction Equipment Ltd, Prees Industrial Estate, Shrewsbury Rd, Prees, Whitchurch, Shropshire, SY13 2DJ Tel: (01948) 840840 Fax: (01948) 841147 E-mail: info@stelex.co.uk *Stelex Ltd based in Whitchurch, Shropshire offer subcontract engineering services and concrete batching plant hire. They manufacture high quality steel products from small components through to complete engineered machines for a diverse market incorporating industries such as mining, quarrying, recycling, water and power.*

▶ Stella Blast, Stella Gill Industrial Estate, Pelton Fell, Chester le Street, County Durham, DH2 2RH Tel: 0191-389 4677 Fax: 0191-389 1999 *Powder coatings*

Stella Foods Holding Ltd, 6 Tileyard Road, London, N7 9AH Tel: (020) 7692 4455 Fax: (020) 7692 4470 E-mail: info@negroni.co.uk *Italian food importers & distribs*

▶ Stelladreams, 26 Wordsworth Road, Diss, Norfolk, IP22 4QA Tel: (01239) 677854

Stellafoam Ltd, Manor Way, Rainham, Essex, RM13 8RH Tel: (01708) 522551 Fax: (01708) 522162 E-mail: sales@stellafoam.ltd.uk *Melamine faced chipboard distributors*

▶ Stellar Environmental Solutions Ltd, 1 Main Street, Ayston, Oakham, Rutland, LE15 9AE Tel: (07747) 125780 *Stellar Environmental Solutions Ltd is a family run business, that has been in the fishery trade for a few years. We always work closely with the Environment Agency and will not stock or move fish without relevant section 28 and 30 paperwork. We always aim to achieve the higest standard of service for our customers. We provide services in all aspects of fisheries management including de-silting, fish rescues, health checks and fish stocking. Please check out our website for more information.*

▶ Steller Performance Ltd, Unit 13 Silwood Park, Buckhurst Road, Ascot, Berkshire, SL5 7PW Tel: (01344) 870350 Fax: (01344) 870359

Stellex Ltd, Hadston Industrial Estate, Hadston, Morpeth, Northumberland, NE65 9YG Tel: (01670) 760082 Fax: (01670) 761404 E-mail: sales@stellex.co.uk *Stainless steel catering equipment manufrs*

Stellier Stainless Services, 6 Shipston Close, Brockhill, Redditch, Worcestershire, B97 6UN Tel: 07966 665974 E-mail: contact@stellierstainless.com *Stellier Stainless Services started in 2003 and is now a healthy, growing on-line business. **We supply all types of top quality stainless steel fabrications for your home, including stainless steel splash backs, work tops, door kick plates,*up-stands, and other items. **We make to order and our aim is to give total quality and a fantastic service at a competitive price.*

Stelling Joinery Ltd, Green Copse, Etherley, Bishop Auckland, County Durham, DL14 0LT Tel: (01388) 832792 Fax: (01388) 835954 *Joinery manufrs*

Stellram, Bowerhill, Melksham, Wiltshire, SN12 6YH Tel: (01225) 897100 Fax: (01225) 897111 *Precision tools manufrs*

Stelmax Ltd, 21-23 Gloster Road, Martlesham Heath, Ipswich, IP5 3RD Tel: (01473) 626651 Fax: (01473) 610651 E-mail: stelmaxltd@aol.com *Paints & adhesive manufrs*

Steloc Tooling Co, 3 Brunswick Trading Estate, Hertford Street, Sparkbrook, Birmingham, B12 8NP Tel: 0121-440 3467 Fax: 0121-440 5194 *Precision engineers' cutting tools manufrs*

▶ Stem Drive Ltd, Solway Works, Annan Road, Eastriggs, Annan, Dumfriesshire, DG12 6NJ Tel: (01461) 40904 Fax: (01461) 40801 E-mail: sales@stemdrivemixer.co.uk *Gas & air mixing equipment*

Stemet Earthing Co. Ltd, 6 Downs View, Bow Brickhill, Milton Keynes, MK17 9JS Tel: (01908) 373907 Fax: (01908) 378658 *Electrical earthing engineers*

Stena Drilling, Greenbank Crescent, East Tullos Industrial Estate, Aberdeen, AB12 3BG Tel: (01224) 401180 Fax: (01224) 897089 E-mail: stena.commercial@sdlabz.com *Drilling contractors service*

Stencel Furniture, 315 Finchley Road, London, NW3 6EH Tel: (020) 3112 0112 Fax: (020) 3112 0112 E-mail: sales@stencel.co.uk *At Stencel Furniture we design & manufacture an exclusive & extensive range of furniture for the home, & to the trade & commercial customers. Our ranges include; dining furniture, cabinets, sofas, tables, kitchen & bedroom furnishings. In addition we offer a bespoke service for all office, commercial & retail applications. Ranges include modern, contemporary & traditional, with a wide choice of colours, fabrics & leathers. We provide a first class product & service at a competitive price. Please call, see us on line or visit our London showroom for advice & further information.*

Stencil Tech, 1 Upland Industrial Estate, Mere Way, Wyton, Huntingdon, Cambridgeshire, PE28 2JZ Tel: (01480) 435919 Fax: (01480) 435922 E-mail: sales@stencil-tech.co.uk *National driveway installations. Specialist in stencil pattern concrete, spray on paving and printed concrete. Full certificated training courses available. Concrete never looked so good.*

Stenco Furniture, Harvest Works, Vale Road, London, N4 1PL Tel: (020) 8800 2277 Fax: (020) 8809 5612 *Furniture makers*

Stenic Trading, 6 Stareton, Kenilworth, Warwickshire, CV8 2LL Tel: (01926) 450221 Fax: (01926) 429992 *Agricultural irrigation contractors*

▶ Stenna Line Ltd, Sea Terminal, Stranrear Harbour, Stranraer, Wigtownshire, DG9 8EL Tel: (01776) 802180

Stenner Ltd, Lowman Works, Tiverton, Devon, EX16 4JX Tel: (01884) 255700 Fax: (01884) 257794 E-mail: stenner@stenner.co.uk *Saw milling machinery manufrs*

Stennett Self Drive Hire, Blakeney, Guildford Road, Cranleigh, Surrey, GU6 8QZ Tel: (01483) 273814 Fax: (01483) 275912 E-mail: sales@stennetts.com *Contractors plant hire, leasing & rental*

Stenochair Ltd, 30 Stilebrook Road, Industrial Estate, Olney, Buckinghamshire, MK46 5EA Tel: (01234) 711354 Fax: (01234) 713652 E-mail: sales@stenochair.co.uk *Office seating & tables manufacturers*

▶ Stenson Laurencekirk Ltd, Station Road, Laurencekirk, Kincardineshire, AB30 1BE Tel: (01561) 377327 Fax: (01561) 378057

▶ Stent Foundations Ltd, Pavilion C2, Ashwood Park, Ashwood Way, Basingstoke, Hampshire, RG23 8BG Tel: (01256) 400200 Fax: (01256) 400201 E-mail: foundations@stent.co.uk *Stent is one of the UK's largest ground engineering contractors with an annual turnover in excess of £60 million. The company designs and constructs foundations for all types of building, structures and civil engineering works. Its wide range of piling techniques includes rotary bored piling, CFA piling, precast driven piling, vibropiling and retaining wall piling. In addition the company carries out diaphragm walling and ground improvement utilising environmental techniques. Stent has successfully completed some of the UK's most demanding and innovative piling projects ranging from foundations for the Emirates Stadium and Wembley Stadium to retaining structures for the Channel Tunnel Rail Link. Stent also operate the Industries' largest manufacturing facilities based in Nottinghamshire and Scotland for the production of Precast Concrete piles for delivery throughout the UK.*

Stento (U K) Ltd, 3 Baird Close, Maxwell Way, Crawley, West Sussex, RH10 9XE Tel: (01293) 545911 Fax: (01293) 545914 E-mail: intercom@globalnet.co.uk *Telecommunications*

Stentorgate, Beech Grove, Eldwick, Bingley, West Yorkshire, BD16 3EG Tel: (01274) 560600 *Speech units & indicator manufrs*

▶ Step By Step Nursery, Watford College Site, Park Avenue, Bushey, WD23 2DD Tel: (01923) 639333 Fax: (01923) 639334 E-mail: enquiries@sbsnursery.com *Daycare nursery looking after children aged 3 months to 5 years.*

▶ Step Forward, 3 Langdon Hills Business Park, Florence Way, Basildon, Essex, SS16 6AJ Tel: (01268) 544044 Fax: (01268) 544045 E-mail: sales@sfruk.com *Recruitment service*

Step Pest Control, 92 Meldreth Road, Whaddon, Royston, Hertfordshire, SG8 5RP Tel: (01223) 208349 Fax: (01223) 207373 *Pest control*

Stepan UK Ltd, Bridge House, Bridge Street, Stalybridge, Cheshire, SK15 1PH Tel: 0161-338 5511 Fax: 0161-338 4245 E-mail: sales@stepanuk.com *Specialist cases & covers*

Stepart Plastics, Riverside House, Wye Business Park, Churchfield Way, Wye, Ashford, Kent, TN25 5BX Tel: (01233) 813353 E-mail: stepart@tiscali.co.uk *Plastic fabrication*

Stephar UK Ltd, 3 Hewett Road, Harfreys Industrial Estate, Great Yarmouth, Norfolk, NR31 0NN Tel: (01493) 650069 Fax: (01493) 655479 E-mail: stepher@ukpharm.freeserve.co.uk *Pharmaceutical merchants & importers*

Stephen A Hughes, 2 Oak Street, Gilfach Goch, Porth, Mid Glamorgan, CF39 8UG Tel: (01443) 672111 *Blacksmiths*

▶ Stephen Anthony, 4 Ridge Farm, Horsham Road, Rowhook, Horsham, West Sussex, RH12 3QB Tel: (01306) 627502 Fax: (01306) 627502 *Furniture designers & manufrs*

Stephen Betts, 49-63 Spencer Street, Birmingham, B18 6DE Tel: 0121-233 9856 Fax: 0121-236 2265 E-mail: admin@bettsmetals.co.uk *Bullion dealers* Also at: Kidderminster

▶ Stephen Christian & Sons Ltd, Fuchsia Cottage, Kirk Michael, Isle of Man, IM6 1AX Tel: (01624) 878223 Fax: (01624) 878189

▶ Stephen Clark Fabrication Ltd, Castle Street, Alloa, Clackmannanshire, FK10 1EU Tel: (01259) 729729 Fax: (01259) 210000 E-mail: sales@scfabs.com Principal Export Areas: Asia Pacific, Middle East, Central/East Europe & West Europe *Precision sheet metal, fabrications & enclosures in mild steel*

Stephen Dalton Scrap Metal Merchants, Station Road, Gogarbank, Edinburgh, EH12 9BU Tel: 0131-339 5355 Fax: 0131-317 7168 E-mail: dalton@daltondemo.co.uk *Scrap iron & steel merchants services*

Stephen Glover & Co. Ltd, Long Street, Walsall, WS2 9DU Tel: (01922) 611311 Fax: (01922) 721824 E-mail: verglo@btconnect.com *Conduit electric fittings or accessories manufrs*

Stephen Goldsbrough Boats, 200 Kenilworth Road, Knowle, Solihull, West Midlands, B93 0JJ Tel: (01564) 778210 Fax: (01564) 770557 E-mail: russ@sgboats.com *Boat builders*

Stephen J Fawcett, 7 Great John Street, Lancaster, LA1 1NQ Tel: (01524) 32033 Fax: (01524) 843470 E-mail: sales@fawcettonline.com *Outdoor clothing, fishing tackle & gun retail*

▶ Stephen Kinsella, 200 Garston Old Road, Garston, Liverpool, L19 1QL Tel: 0151-427 4698 E-mail: ste.kinsella@ntlworld.com *Superior quality window cleaning services throughout Liverpool, Merseyside, Cheshire. Office suites, business units, large executive property, schools, shops.*Conservatory roof cleaning and difficult access window cleaning.*We clean your windows as and when required. For a no obligation quotation, please call Steve Kinsella on 24hr Mobile: 0789 1502 961 or visit our website at www.executivewindowcleaning.com for further contact details and information.*

Stephen Morris, Unit 4 Brent Trading Centre, 390 North Circular Road, London, NW10 0JF Tel: (020) 8830 1919 Fax: (020) 8830 1999 E-mail: enquiries@shipsms.co.uk *Packing & shipping of antiques, fine art and corporate removals.*

Stephen P Wales, The Old Brewery Works, Lower Ellacombe Church Road, Torquay, TQ1 1JH Tel: (01803) 295430 Fax: (01803) 212819 E-mail: steve@stephenpwales.co.uk *Electricity meter wholesalers & retailers*

▶ Stephen Quinn Associates Ltd, 4 Fitzroy Place, Glasgow, G3 7RH Tel: 0141-221 6611 Fax: 0141-882 5192

▶ Stephen Roberts, Watton Salerooms Breckland House, Norwich Road, Watton, Thetford, Norfolk, IP25 6JT Tel: (01953) 885676 Fax: (01953) 885676 E-mail: watton.salerooms@eidosnet.co.uk *Weekly general auction of antique, new and house clearance, furniture, pictures, clocks, china, glassware, colelctable items, timber, toold, garden & DIY machinery, electrical goods and garden plants.*House Clearance Service.*Freelance Auctioneering Services.*Valuations.*Dispersal Sales "On The Premises"*

▶ Stephen Robertson & Co., PO Box 55, Whitley Bay, Tyne & Wear, NE26 3WR Tel: 0191-251 1135 Fax: (0870) 1602759 E-mail: sr@srco.co.uk *Food flavouring and preservation techniques. *Electrostatic flavouring systems for food, pharmaceutical and agricultural sectors.*On site gas generators for Modified Atmosphere Packaging (MAP)*

Stephen Simpson, 50 Manchester Road, Preston, PR1 3YH Tel: (01772) 556688 Fax: (01772) 204738 *Masonic embroidery manufrs*

▶ Stephen Ward & Company, Warwick Corner, 42 Warwick Road, Kenilworth, Warwickshire, CV8 1HE Tel: 01926 866610 Fax: 01926 851534 E-mail: mail@stephen-ward.com *Our business maximises the success of clients (whether organisations or individuals), through offering the following: Individual Career Coaching, strategic advice and support to entrepreneurs and small businesses, precision recruitment consultancy for senior and specialist roles, and support for personal development.***We combine over 2 decades of people based consultancy, coaching expertise, MBA training and first hand business experience to support these services, and have built a strong reputation for care, empathy and professionalism with individuals as well as large and smaller client businesses.**

▶ Stephen Wormell, Langenhoe Hall, Hall Lane, Langenhoe, Colchester, CO5 7NA Tel: (01206) 735687 Fax: (01206) 735487

▶ Stephens Associates, 14 Buckingham Street, London, WC2N 6DF Tel: (020) 7925 0200 Fax: (020) 7925 0235 E-mail: stephens@stephens.co.uk *M & A & executive search consultants*

E. Stephens Gutter Repairs, Little Clanfield Mill, Little Clanfield, Bampton, Oxfordshire, OX18 2RX Tel: (01367) 810380 Fax: (01367) 810390 E-mail: sales@gutter-repairs.co.uk *Rainwater goods*

John A. Stephens Ltd, 43 Radcliffe Road, West Bridgford, Nottingham, NG2 5FF Tel: 0115-981 4313 *Builders merchants*

Stephens (Midlands) Ltd, Greets Green Industrial Estate, West Bromwich, West Midlands, B70 9EW Tel: 0121-522 2221 Fax: 0121-557 6861 E-mail: info@stephenslube.co.uk *Lubricating systems equipment suppliers. We have over 50 years" experience in the supply and installation of lubrication equipment. Our online, priced, catalogue details a small selection of our range of products.*

Stephens Plastics Ltd, Old School House, Sinclair Street, Halkirk, Caithness, KW12 6XT Tel: (01847) 831216 Fax: (01847) 831305 E-mail: info@stephens-plastics.co.uk *Work wear manufrs*

▶ Stephens & Stuart Engineering, Nutsey Lane, Totton, Southampton, SO40 3NB Tel: (023) 8086 3666 Fax: (023) 8086 3777 E-mail: info@stephensandstuartseng.co.uk *Steelwork suppliers*

▶ Stephens Sunblinds, Unit Factory Estate, Argyle Street, Hull, HU3 1HD Tel: (01482) 321298 Fax: (01482) 321298 *Sun blind manufrs*

Stephens Umbrellas, Sandall Stones Road, Kirk Sandall Industrial Estate, Kirk Sandall, Doncaster, South Yorkshire, DN3 1QR Tel: (01302) 790790 Fax: (01302) 790088 E-mail: sue@oasisleisure.ltd.uk Principal Export Areas: Worldwide *Manufacturers of umbrellas*

Stephenson Ltd, Oakwood House, Bucks Green, Rudgwick, Horsham, West Sussex, RH12 3JJ Tel: (01403) 824960 Fax: (01403) 824961 E-mail: m.s@stephenson-ssc.co.uk *Reinforcing concrete frame builders*

Stephenson Blake & Co. Ltd, 199 Upper Allen St, Sheffield, S3 7GW Tel: 0114-272 8325 Fax: 0114-272 0065 E-mail: sales@stephensonblake.co.uk *Brass tool rule plastic welders*

Stephenson Gobin Engineering Ltd, South Road, High Etherley, Bishop Auckland, County Durham, DL14 0HY Tel: (01388) 830900 Fax: (01388) 834220 E-mail: sales@stephensongobin.com *Electro-magnetic brake & clutch manufrs*

Stephenson Group Ltd, PO Box 305, Bradford, West Yorkshire, BD7 1HY Tel: (01274) 723811 Fax: (01274) 370108 E-mail: group@stephensongroup.co.uk *Rubber production industry chemicals*

Stephenson Group Ltd, PO Box 305, Bradford, West Yorkshire, BD7 1HY Tel: (01274) 723811 Fax: (01274) 370108 E-mail: src@stephensongroup.co.uk *Chemical manufrs*

▶ Stephenson IT, 54 St James Drive, Romanby, Northallerton, North Yorkshire, DL7 8YW Tel: (01609) 898158 E-mail: info@stephensonit.co.uk *Computer repair*

Stephenson & Johnson Ltd, Malaga House, Pink Bank Lane, Manchester, M12 5GH Tel: 0161-223 0011 Fax: 0161-223 0404 *Photographers & printers*

Stephenson Plastics, The Workshop Pickards Farm, Sandy Lane, Guildford, Surrey, GU3 1HJ Tel: (01483) 565277 Fax: (01483) 505047 E-mail: stephensonplastics@talk21.com *Plastics & work in acrylic specialists*

Stephenson & Wilson Ltd, Louvic Works, 44 Garden Street, Sheffield, S1 3HL Tel: 0114-249 3889 Fax: 0114-249 3891 E-mail: stephenson@wilsonltd.freeserve.co.uk *Pocket knife manufacturers, promotional & premium product designers*

Stephensons Enterprise Fork Trucks, Unit 1, Great Bank Road, Westhoughton, Bolton, BL5 3XU Tel: (01942) 276711 Fax: (01942) 276728 E-mail: enterpriseforktruck@lineone.net *Fork lift truck services*

Stepnell Estates Ltd, Lawford Road, Rugby, Warwickshire, CV21 2UU Tel: (01788) 574511 Fax: (01788) 541364 E-mail: gailb.@stepnell.co.uk *Building contractors*

Steppin Out Entertainment & Corporate Events, 11 Beaumont Court, The Avenue, South Hinksey, Oxford, OX1 5AL Tel: (01865) 327772 Fax: (01865) 327772 E-mail: enquiries@steppin-out.co.uk *Entertainment agents, entertainment nationwide, internationally*

Steptronik UK Ltd, 1 & 2 Baird Close, District 12, Washington, Tyne & Wear, NE37 3HL Tel: 0191-417 8990 Fax: 0191-417 8202 E-mail: peter@steptronik.co.uk *Industrial electronic repairers*

▶ Steratape Ltd, Carnaby Industrial Estate, Lancaster Road, Carnaby, Bridlington, East Yorkshire, YO15 3QY Tel: (01262) 603721 Fax: (01262) 400028 E-mail: carl@steratape.com Principal Export Areas: Worldwide *Manufacturers of Double Sided Self Adhesive Tapes and Bonding Systems. Products include a full range of Fingerlift Tapes, Heat Cuttable Tapes for Poly Bags, Forms Tapes, Tape for Print Finishing, Splicing Tapes, Box Sealing Tapes, Tape for Postage Bags and Boxes, and Tapes for Arts and Krafts. Converting and Coating capability includes Zone Coating, Spooling, Customised Coating and Finishing.*

Sterchi's Cake Shop, 40 Murray Street, Filey, North Yorkshire, YO14 9DG Tel: (01723) 513120 E-mail: admin@sterchis.co.uk *Bakery & confectionary suppliers & manufrs*

Stereomatics Ltd, Seven Stars Industrial Estate, Wheler Road, Coventry, CV3 4LB Tel: (024) 7630 4000 Fax: (024) 7630 4455 E-mail: sales@stereomatic.co.uk *Precision engineers*

Sterex Electrolysis International Ltd, 174 Kings Road, Tyseley, Birmingham, B11 2AP Tel: 0121-708 2404 Fax: 0121-707 0028 E-mail: info@sterex.demon.co.uk *Epilation needles manufrs*

Steri Products Ltd, 10 Towerfield Road, Shoeburyness, Southend-on-Sea, SS3 9QE Tel: (01702) 296266 Fax: (01702) 296267 E-mail: steriproducts@btconnect.com *Steriliser manufrs*

Sterigenics (U K) Ltd, Cotes Park Industrial Estate, Somercotes, Alfreton, Derbyshire, DE55 4NJ Tel: (01773) 543200 Fax: (01773) 543210 *Sterilisation & supply disposable supplies to the health service*

▶ Sterile Technologies Group, Block 5 Units 1-2, Elliot Industrial Estate, Arbroath, Angus, DD11 2NJ Tel: (01241) 877222 Fax: (01241) 879944

Sterilox Technologies International Ltd, Montrose House, Montrose Street, Stoke-on-Trent, ST4 3PB Tel: (01782) 595969 Fax: (01782) 595979 *Medical supplies distributors*

Sterimatic Ltd, Griffin Mill, London Road, Stroud, Gloucestershire, GL5 2AZ Tel: (01453) 884944 Fax: (01453) 886481 E-mail: sterimatic@sterimatic.com *Safety veterinary & medical products*

Sterimedix Ltd, Unit 6/7, Kingfisher Business Park, Arthur Street, Redditch, Worcestershire, B98 8LG Tel: (01527) 501480 Fax: (01527) 501491 E-mail: sales@sterimedix.com *Ophthalmic instrument manufrs*

Steritouch, Unit 15 Roseheyworth Business, Abertillery, Gwent, NP13 1SP Tel: (01495) 211400 E-mail: info@steritouch.com *Antibacterial additives manufrs*

Sterland & Elgar, 46 Church Street, Shipston-on-Stour, Warwickshire, CV36 4AS Tel: (01608) 663341 Fax: (01608) 661212 *Installation & distribution of stoves & cookers*

Sterling Coach Works, Ellerbeck Way, Stokesley Industrial Park, Stokesley, Middlesbrough, Cleveland, TS9 5JZ Tel: (01642) 713333 Fax: (01642) 713805 E-mail: info@worldwidetrots.co.uk *Commercial vehicle sales body building*

▶ Sterling Collection, Unit 401 Via Gellia Mill, Via Gellia Road, Bonsall, Matlock, Derbyshire, DE4 2AJ Tel: (01629) 824994 Fax: (01629) 824994 *Gift ware manufrs*

Sterling Corporation, 2 Law Street, Leicester, LE4 5GR Tel: 0116-261 0330 Fax: 0116-261 0259 E-mail: sales@sterlingbearings.com *Bearing distributors & manufrs*

Sterling Electrical Centre, 16 North Street, Leighton Buzzard, Bedfordshire, LU7 1EN Tel: (01525) 376895 Fax: (01525) 853358 E-mail: peter.sinclair@shop4electricals.co.uk *On-line shop for electrical and domestic appliances, including washing machines, dishwashers, ovens, microwave ovens, fridges and freezers. Suppliers of Hotpoint, Bosch, Zanussi, Whirlpool, Indesit and many more!*

Sterling Enterprises Precious Stone Merchants, 26-27 Hatton Garden, Minerva House, London, EC1N 8BR Tel: (020) 7405 5255 Fax: (020) 7405 5255 *Precious stone merchants*

Sterling Environmental Engineering Ltd, Sterling House, 12 Gate Lane, Sutton Coldfield, West Midlands, B73 5TT Tel: 0121-321 2244 Fax: 0121-321 3151 E-mail: enquiries@sterling.uk.com *Air conditioning engineers*

▶ Sterling Financial Ltd, Church Farm, Little Sodbury, Chipping Sodbury, Bristol, BS37 6QA Tel: (01454) 317272 Fax: (07884) 500629 E-mail: mail@sterlingfinancial.ltd.uk *The Complete Financial Service for Business*The services provided include Credit control & Cashflow management, Book-keeping & VAT, Payroll Service, Management Accounting, Forecasting & Preparation for Statutory Accounts**These services can be provided in your offices or ours*

Sterling Fluid Systems UK Ltd, Atlantic Street, Broadheath, Altrincham, Cheshire, WA14 5DH Tel: 0161-928 6371 Fax: 0161-925 2129 E-mail: sales@sterlingfluid.com *Pumps*

Sterling Foodservice Design Ltd, 2 Wheeley Ridge, Wheeley Road, Alvechurch, Birmingham, B48 7DD Tel: 0121-445 0900 Fax: 0121-445 0901 E-mail: info@sterlingfoodservice.com *Birmingham-based Sterling Foodservice Design Ltd are International foodservice consultants, kitchen designers and planners.*

Sterling Group Ltd, Boulevard Works, Radford Boulevard, Nottingham, NG7 3AE Tel: 0115-978 2221 Fax: 0115-978 5034 *Lingerie & menswear manufrs*

Sterling Hamilton Wright Ltd, City Reach, 5 Greenwich View Place, Mill Harbour, London, E14 9NN Tel: (020) 7716 5000 Fax: (020) 7716 5001 E-mail: info@shwgroup.co.uk *Lloyds insurance brokers* Also at: Herne Bay

▶ Sterling Hydraulics Ltd, Sterling House, Blacknell Lane, Crewkerne, Somerset, TA18 8LL Tel: (01460) 271800 Fax: (01460) 271801 E-mail: mktng@sterling-hydraulics.co.uk *Hydraulic cartridge valve & custom manifold block designers & manufacturers*

Sterling Installations Ltd, 128-129 Leyland Complex, Irthlingborough Road, Wellingborough, Northamptonshire, NN8 1RT Tel: (01933) 226227 Fax: (01933) 226447 E-mail: sterling@computalynx.co.uk *Industrial & commercial pipework installers*

Sterling Insurance Co. Ltd, 3rd Floor Blackburn House, 22-26 Eastern Road, Romford, RM1 3PJ Tel: (01708) 777900 Fax: (01708) 777949 E-mail: commercial@sterlinginsurancegroup.com *Insurance services*

▶ Sterling Labels, Lubbards Lodge, Hullbridge Road, Rayleigh, Essex, SS6 9QG Tel: (01268) 782783 Fax: (01268) 783444 *Label manufrs*

Sterling (Mechanical & Electrical) Contractors Ltd, 1 Queen Victoria Street, Bristol, BS2 0QR Tel: 0117-941 3111

Sterling Packaging Ltd, Unit 3-4 Catherine Street, Warrington, WA5 0LH Tel: (01925) 575520 Fax: (01925) 575521 *Polyethylene & polythene converters & packaging suppliers*

Sterling Plastics, 5 Crocus Place, Crocus Street, Nottingham, NG2 3DE Tel: 0115-985 1101 Fax: 0115-985 1101 *Coin handling component manufrs*

Sterling Power Tools & Fixings, 103 Newland Road, Worthing, West Sussex, BN11 1LB Tel: (01903) 211543 Fax: (01903) 523066 *Fixing systems, bolt & nut distributors*

Sterling Precast Ltd, Springkerse Works, Springkerse Industrial Estate, Stirling, FK7 7SX Tel: (01786) 472191 Fax: (01786) 451284 E-mail: general@stirlingprecast.com *Pre-cast concrete manufrs*

Sterling Products Ltd, Richmond Street, West Bromwich, West Midlands, B70 0DD Tel: 0121-557 0022 Fax: 0121-557 0222 *Suppliers of trade valeting materials & equipment*

Sterling Saddlery, Court Lodge Farm, Bodiam, Robertsbridge, East Sussex, TN32 5UJ Tel: (01580) 830891 Fax: (01580) 830186 *Saddlery distributors*

Sterling Security Shutters, 42 Huddersfield Road, Barnsley, South Yorkshire, S75 1DW Tel: (01226) 207030 Fax: (01226) 770088 *Marketing & selling shutters*

Sterling Security Systems Ltd, PO Box 999, Tamworth, Staffordshire, B79 8EY Tel: (01827) 310059 Fax: (0870) 0558852 E-mail: info@sterling-security.co.uk *Security systems equipment installers*

Sterling Sensors Ltd, Fitmec Works Hawksley Street, Oldham, OL8 4PQ Tel: 0161-627 0507 Fax: 0161-627 0507 E-mail: sales@sterlingsensors.co.uk *Thermocouple manufrs*

Sterling Signs Ltd, Millmead Business Centre, Milmead Industrial Centre, London, N17 9QU Tel: (020) 8885 4206 Fax: (020) 8801 8714 E-mail: tim@sterlingsigns.co.uk *Sign makers*

Sterling Solutions, Kettering Parkway, Kettering Venture Park, Kettering, Northamptonshire, NN15 6XU Tel: (0870) 0842100 Fax: (0870) 0842094 E-mail: ctimm@sterlingsolutions.co.uk *Sterling provides creative communication, print production, direct mail and fulfilment solutions to a wide range of organisations across several industry sectors through both traditional and new media.*

Sterling Swimming Pools, Daniels Road, Norwich, NR4 6QP Tel: (01603) 503908 Fax: (01603) 811507 E-mail: duncan@sterlingpools.co.uk *Swimming pool installation, repairs & services*

Sterling Technology Ltd, Europa Gate, Trafford Park, Manchester, M17 1DU Tel: 0161-848 8411 Fax: 0161-848 0966 E-mail: sales@sterling-tech.com *Manufacturers of epoxy resin*

Sterling Timber Ltd, White House, Bleasby Moor, Market Rasen, Lincolnshire, LN8 3QJ Tel: (01673) 844007 Fax: (01673) 844007 E-mail: admin@sterlingtimber.fsnet.co.uk *Sectional timber buildings supply & erection*

▶ Sterling Travel Management, H Medina Chamber, Town Quay, Southampton, SO14 2AQ Tel: (023) 8033 0111 Fax: (023) 8033 7397 E-mail: info@sterlingtravel.co.uk *Sterling Travel Management is an independent company specialising in Business Travel and Event Management (www.stmevents.com). We are both creative and committed in our approach and place strong emphasis on choice, quality, budgetary control and cost reduction. Our company continually invests in the latest technology to provide you with easy access on-line travel information and time saving interactive e-services. Equally we invest substantially in our staff who take great pride in delivering a swift, highly efficient personal service.*

Sterling Upper Co Surgical Ltd, 2 36-38 Beaconsfield Road, St. George, Bristol, BS5 8ER Tel: 0117-955 6520 Fax: 0117-941 2060 *Surgical shoe manufrs*

▶ Sterling Ward, 18 Charlotte Road, London, EC2A 3PB Tel: (020) 7729 4513 Fax: (020) 7033 0589 E-mail: gary.ward@stirling-ward.com

Sterlings D F C Ltd, Ynys Bridge, Hoel-Yr-Ynys, Tongwynlais, Cardiff, CF15 7NT Tel: (029) 2081 3131 Fax: (029) 2081 3598 E-mail: rvs@easynet.co.uk *Refrigeration engineers & transport repair*

Sterma M, Reed Point, Sutterton, Boston, Lincolnshire, PE20 2EP Tel: (01205) 460418 *Agricultural contractors*

J. & J. Stern Glass, Hanway House, 306-308 West Hendon Broadway, Edgware Road, London, NW9 6AE Tel: (020) 8202 2177 Fax: (020) 8202 2719 E-mail: sales@jj-stern.co.uk *Button merchants*

Sternpower Marine Drives Ltd, 51 Victoria Road, Portslade, Brighton, BN41 1XY Tel: (01273) 411765 Fax: (01273) 430290 E-mail: sternpower@lancingmarine.com *Marine transmission suppliers & manufrs*

Steroma International Ltd, 16 Metelr Close, Airport Industrial Estate, Norwich, NR6 6HG Tel: (01603) 612655 Fax: (01603) 618530 E-mail: sales@steroma.com *Injection mouldings manufrs*

Steroplast, Alpha Point, Bradnor Road, Sharston Industrial Area, Manchester, M22 4TE Tel: 0161-902 3030 Fax: 0161-902 3040 E-mail: sales@steroplast.co.uk *First aid dressing wholesale*

Stevana Ltd, Leverton Buildings, Leverton, Hungerford, Berkshire, RG17 0TA Tel: (01488) 684444 Fax: (01488) 684444 E-mail: mail@stevana.co.uk *Furniture manufrs*

Steve Amin Glaziers, 14-16 St. Ronans Road, Whitley Bay, Tyne & Wear, NE25 8AX Tel: 0191-251 4893 Fax: 0191-251 4893 E-mail: stevenamin@hotmail.com *Stained glass, studio glaziers, handmade lamps, tiffany lamps*

Steve Church Carpentry & Interior Contractors, 15 Lampits Hill Avenue, Corringham, Stanford-le-Hope, Essex, SS17 7NY Tel: (07960) 140338 Fax: (01375) 678513 E-mail: enquiries@steve-church.com *Carpentry contractors*

▶ Steve Cornish Solutions, Imex Business Centre, Brookfield Road, Arnold, Nottingham, NG5 7ER Tel: 0115-920 5740 Fax: 0115-966 7427 E-mail: steve@stevecornish.com *Telecommunications*

▶ Steve Cornish Solutions, Imex Business Centre, Brookfield Road, Arnold, Nottingham, NG5 7ER Tel: 0115-920 5740 Fax: 0115-966 7427

Steve Downer Photography & Video, The Gatehouse, High Street, Ratley, Banbury, Oxfordshire, OX15 6DT Tel: (01295) 670836 Fax: (01295) 670836 E-mail: downerfilm@aol.com *Digital photography and video production.*

▶ Steve Foster Crane Hire, Dovefields, Derby Road, Dovefields Industrial Estate, Uttoxeter, Staffordshire, ST14 8HU Tel: (01889) 568163 Fax: (01889) 568853 E-mail: sales@stevefostercranes.co.uk *Crane-hire*

Steve Foster Crane Hire, Dovefields, Derby Road, Dovefields Industrial Estate, Uttoxeter, Staffordshire, ST14 8HU Tel: (01889) 568163 Fax: (01889) 568853 E-mail: sales@stevefostercranes.co.uk *Crane hire manufrs*

▶ Steve Hoskin Ltd, Pensilva Industrial Estate, St Ive Road, Pensilva, Liskeard, Cornwall, PL14 5RE Tel: (01579) 362630 Fax: (01579) 362644

Steve Hyde, Unit C Cophall Farm Business Park, Effingham Road, Copthorne, Crawley, West Sussex, RH10 3HZ Tel: (01342) 714230 Fax: (01342) 716760 E-mail: stevehydestudios@btconnect.com *Screen process & litho printers*

Steve Nunn Electrical Electric Contractors/Installers, 3 Forest End, Kennett, Newmarket, Suffolk, CB8 7RG Tel: (01638) 552110 *Burglar & intruder alarm system installation services*

▶ Steve Parker ICD International Company Development, 24 Shearwater Drive, Amblecote, Brierley Hill, West Midlands, DY5 2RD Tel: 01384 893346 Fax: 01384 893346 E-mail: steveparker1@ukonline.co.uk *International market development,sales & marketing, strategy planning, management, product development and finance help where it is needed. Implementing not just advising! 25 + years expertise & success.*

▶ Steve Robertson Training Services, Peamore Truck Centre, Alphington, Exeter, EX2 9SL Tel: 01392 833369 E-mail: lorrydrivertraining@tiscali.co.uk *Professional Driver & Operator training for LGV PCV FORKLIFT and Lorry Mounted Cranes (HIAB) **www.lorrydrivertraining.co.uk*

▶ Steve Wall Plumbing & Heating Ltd, Furlong Road, Stoke-on-Trent, ST6 5UN Tel: (01782) 821730 Fax: (01782) 812155

▶ Steven Burrows, 12 Henderson Road, Bangor, County Down, BT19 1NN Tel: (07931) 362847 Fax: (08715) 227115 E-mail: info@steveburrows.co.uk *Graphic design and web development services, from accessible websites to complete branding for your business*

Steven Cambage, Willow Garth, Roecliffe, York, YO51 9LY Tel: (01423) 323640 *Agricultural engineering services*

Steven Mooney Machinery, Edwards House, Marchants Way, Burgess Hill, West Sussex, RH15 8QY Tel: (01444) 245414 Fax: (01444) 247518 E-mail: stevenmooney@compuserve.com. *Machinery merchants*

▶ Steven R Paterson Ltd, 10 Crowness Road, Hatston, Kirkwall, Orkney, KW15 1RG Tel: (01856) 870088 Fax: (01856) 870066

Steven Stone Ltd, 142 Bury Old Road, Whitefield, Manchester, M45 6AT Tel: 0161-766 1700 Fax: 0161-766 1330 E-mail: info@steven-stone.com *Jewellery manufrs*

Stevenage Business Initiative, The Business & Technology Centre, Bessemer Drive, Stevenage, Hertfordshire, SG1 2DX Tel: (01438) 315733 Fax: (01438) 313001 E-mail: sbienq@stevbtc.demon.co.uk *Business advisory services*

Stevenage Circuits Ltd, Caxton Way, Stevenage, Hertfordshire, SG1 2DF Tel: (01438) 751800 Fax: (01438) 728103 E-mail: sales@stevenagecircuits.co.uk *Printed circuit board manufrs*

Stevenage Fencing Co., 105 Mobbsbury Way, Stevenage, Hertfordshire, SG2 0HZ Tel: (01438) 725918 Fax: (01438) 235081 E-mail: stevefencing@aol.com *Fencing contractor*

Stevenage Knitting Co. Ltd, 18 Sish Lane, Stevenage, Hertfordshire, SG1 3LS Tel: (01438) 353240 Fax: (01438) 748364 *Knitted outerwear manufrs*

Stevenage Machine Tools Ltd, Unit 12, Ironcraft Industrial Estate, Stotfold, Hitchin, Hertfordshire, SG5 4NZ Tel: (01462) 731691 Fax: (01462) 835214 *Machine tool accessories & hand tool distributors*

Stevenage Sheet Metal Co. Ltd, Unit 1, Jubilee Trade Centre, Jubilee Road, Letchworth Garden City, Hertfordshire, SG6 1SP Tel: (01462) 674794 Fax: (01462) 481132 E-mail: richard@stevenagesheetmetal.com *Fine Limit Sheet Metalworkers*

Stevenage Spring Co. Ltd, 9 Hyatt Trading Estate, Babbage Road, Stevenage, Hertfordshire, SG1 2EQ Tel: (01438) 740078 Fax: (01438) 741065 E-mail: stan.copper@stevenagesprings.co.uk *Spring manufrs*

Stevend Ltd, Fieldhouse Lane, Marlow, Buckinghamshire, SL7 1LW Tel: (01628) 472374 Fax: (01628) 475050 E-mail: ralph@stevend.co.uk *Stainless steel fabricators*

Steveni Kessler Insurance Services Ltd, Steveni Kessler House Dominion Business Park, Goodwin Road, London, N9 0BG Tel: (020) 8345 5500 Fax: (020) 8482 2000 E-mail: sales@steveni-kessler.co.uk *Insurance brokers specialising in commercial insurance*

Stevens A & Co Yeovil Ltd, Woodland Grove, Yeovil, Somerset, BA20 1NZ Tel: (01935) 476151 Fax: (01935) 422648 E-mail: peter@stevensboxes.com *Printed carton & rigid boxes manufrs*

▶ Stevens Bros Builders Ltd, St. Johns Road, Crowborough, East Sussex, TN6 1RP Tel: (01892) 653614 Fax: (01892) 667921

▶ Stevens Construction Ltd, Benover Road, Yalding, Maidstone, Kent, ME18 6AS Tel: (01892) 730634 Fax: (01892) 730540

Stevens & Gill Panelcraft, Unit 54, Barking Industrial Park, Alfreds Way, Barking, Essex, IG11 0TJ Tel: (020) 8594 0357 Fax: (020) 8594 0357 *Motor body refinishing services, cars*

Stevens Graham Picture Framers, 5 Middle Row, East Grinstead, West Sussex, RH19 3AX Tel: (01342) 300685 E-mail: grahamstevensgallery@msn.com *Picture framers & gallery services*

Stevens Group Ltd, Challenge Way, Blackburn, BB1 5QB Tel: (01254) 685200 Fax: (01254) 685202 E-mail: sales@stevensgroup.com *Weighing systems*

Stevens Hewlett & Perkins, 20-23 Holborn, Halton House, London, EC1N 2JD Tel: (020) 7936 2499 Fax: (020) 7404 1844 E-mail: mail@shplondon.co.uk *Chartered patent agents*

Leonard Stevens, 16 Crown Street, Eastbourne, East Sussex, BN21 1NX Tel: (01323) 734496 *Saddlers workshop manufrs*

Stevens Machine Tools, 37-41 Anne Road, Smethwick, West Midlands, B66 2NZ Tel: 0121-555 6392 Fax: 0121-565 2438 E-mail: info@stevensmachinetools.co.uk *Supplier of good quality used machinery*

Stevens Metal Co Ltd, 33-35 Overton Road, Leicester, LE5 0JB Tel: 0116-276 7418 Fax: 0116-276 7418 *Non-ferrous & ferrous scrap metal*

Robert Stevens & Sons Ltd, Unit 5 Crescent Court Business Centre, North Crescent, London, E16 4TG Tel: (020) 7511 6300 *Steel fabricators*

Stevens Saw & Tool Services, 1 Pope Iron Road, Worcester, WR1 3HB Tel: 01905 26413 *Saw sharpening*

▶ Stevenson Bros, Blackston Road, Avonbridge, Falkirk, FK1 2NB Tel: (01324) 861331 Fax: (01324) 861666 E-mail: sales@stevensonbros.co.uk

Stevenson & Cheyne, Unit 7 Butlerfield Industrial Estate, Bonnyrigg, Midlothian, EH19 3JQ Tel: (01875) 822822 Fax: (01875) 823723 E-mail: sales@platerolling.co.uk *Heavy plate workers*

James Stevenson Flags Ltd, 75 Westmoreland Street, Glasgow, G42 8LH Tel: 0141-423 5757 Fax: 0141-946 3741 E-mail: john@stevensonflags.com *Flag makers & flagpole suppliers*

Stevenson Office Furniture, 863-865 Harrow Road, London, NW10 5NG Tel: (020) 8969 3850 Fax: (020) 8968 1790 *Office furniture distributors*

Stevenson Reeves Ltd, 40 Oxgangs Bank, Edinburgh, EH13 9LH Tel: 0131-445 7151 Fax: 0131-445 7323 E-mail: sales@stevenson-reeves.co.uk *Hydrometer manufrs*

Stevensons, Amber Dye Works, Bullbridge, Ambergate, Belper, Derbyshire, DE56 2EX Tel: (01773) 852222 Fax: (01773) 857078 E-mail: gordon.cawood@quantumclothing.com *Garment dyers & finishers textile traders*

▶ Stevensons, 26 Barony Road, Auchinleck, Cumnock, Ayrshire, KA18 2LL Tel: (01290) 426009 Fax: (01290) 425988

Stevensons Of Norwich Ltd, Roundtree Way, Norwich, NR7 8SQ Tel: (01603) 400824 Fax: (01603) 405113 E-mail: sales@stevensons-of-norwich.co.uk *Stevensons of Norwich Limited is an English company specialising in the design, manufacture and installation of standard and bespoke mouldings and products for interior and exterior use in: Fibrous Plaster, GRG (glass reinforced gypsum), Jesmonite - both interior and exterior uses, GRP (glass reinforced polyester) We restore and repair historic plasterwork. We carry out lime plasterwork using traditional methods and materials. The company has been established for 25 years and has a reputation for top quality and reliability. Stevensons of Norwich Limited was formed to provide a specialist design, manufacturing and installation service to architects, designers, contractors and private clients. Based in Norwich, the company produces high quality products in fibrous plaster, GRG, GRP, Jesmonite and Glass Reinforced Cement for distribution and installation throughout the UK and overseas. We have done business in 25 different countries and our services are available around the world.*

Steves Bees, 131 Wellington Street, Peterborough, PE1 5DU Tel: (01733) 891155 Fax: (01733) 709709 E-mail: enquiries@englishhoney.co.uk *Bee farmers*

Steve's Joinery, Morgan Street Works, Morgan Street, Llanbradach, Caerphilly, Mid Glamorgan, CF83 3QT Tel: (029) 2085 1566 *Joinery manufrs*

▶ Steves Transport Services (Wraysbury) Ltd, John Taylor House, Blackthorne Road, Colnbrook, Slough, SL3 0AH Tel: (01753) 685544

Stevesound Communications Services Ltd, 103 Comer Road, Worcester, WR2 5HY Tel: (01905) 425300 Fax: (01905) 425300 *Radio communications hire*

Steveweld Ltd, 3 Hillview Road, East Tullos Industrial Estate, Aberdeen, AB12 3HB Tel: (01224) 899944 Fax: (01224) 898998 E-mail: sales@steveweld.co.uk *Welding equipment distributors*

Stevron Marine, 38 Farriers Way, Bootle, Merseyside, L30 4XL Tel: 0151-525 9555 Fax: 0151-521 7190 E-mail: sales@stevron.co.uk *Rubber seals, sheeting & gaskets*

Steward Ltd, 5 Cochrane Square, Brucefield Industrial Estate, Livingston, West Lothian, EH54 9DR Tel: (01506) 414200 Fax: (01506) 410694 E-mail: europe@steward.com *Ferrite component distributors*

Stewardsons, Main Street, Hawkshead, Ambleside, Cumbria, LA22 0NT Tel: (01539) 436741 Fax: (01539) 436675 E-mail: sales@stewardsons.co.uk *Outdoor clothing retail*

Stewart, Elliot Industrial Estate, Arbroath, Angus, DD11 2NJ Tel: (01241) 873905 Fax: (01241) 875770 E-mail: jjselliot@fsbdial.co.uk *Blacksmiths*

Stewart & Allen Ltd, The Runnings, Cheltenham, Gloucestershire, GL51 9NW Tel: (01242) 523298 Fax: (01242) 224416 *Aircraft sheet metalwork engineers & fabricators*

Stewart Anthony, Data House, 2 Waldeck Road, Dartford, DA1 1UA Tel: (01322) 293005 Fax: (01322) 293879 E-mail: peterdavison@stewartanthony.co.uk *Installation and maintenance of, air conditioning, gas and oil fired heating, gas and electrical inspections.*

▶ Stewart Associates, Ladywell, Abbotskerswell, Newton Abbot, Devon, TQ12 5PE Tel: (01626) 363200 Fax: (01626) 360633 E-mail: jamie.stewart@stewart-associates.co.uk *Supplying consultancy for executive development, including leadership and team development, executive coaching, organisational development and cultural change, including online 360 questionnaire design and processing*

▶ Stewart Burn Distillers Ltd, Bunnahabhain Distillery, Port Askaig, Isle of Islay, PA46 7RP Tel: (01496) 840646 Fax: (01496) 840248 *Distillers*

▶ Stewart Christie & Co. Ltd, 63 Queen Street, Edinburgh, EH2 4NA Tel: 0131-225 6639 Fax: 0131-220 2397 *Men's clothing & tailoring services*

Stewart Downie Sutton Coldfield, 87 Jockey Road, Sutton Coldfield, West Midlands, B73 5PH Tel: 0121-354 8610 Fax: 0121-681 2235 E-mail: stewartdownie@blueyonder.co.uk *Photographers*

Stewart Energy Insulation Ltd, Connect House, 21 Willow Lane, Mitcham, Surrey, CR4 4NA Tel: (020) 8648 6601 Fax: (020) 8648 6602 E-mail: info@stewart-energy.com *Insulation equipment manufrs*

Stewart Furneaux, 16E Portland Road, Holland Park, London, W11 4LA Tel: (020) 7792 9000 Fax: (020) 7792 9270 *Exhibition display designers*

▶ Stewart George Upholstery Ltd, Stanhope Mill, Stanhope Street, Long Eaton, Nottingham, NG10 4QN Tel: 0115-946 4818

Stewart Gill Conveyor Ltd, 2 Christy Estate, Ivy Road, Aldershot, Hampshire, GU12 4TX Tel: (01252) 332221 Fax: (01252) 334387 E-mail: info@stewart-gill.co.uk Principal Export Areas: Worldwide *Conveyor systems manufrs*

Stewart Harvey & Woodbridge Ltd, Eldenwall Industrial Estate, Whalebone La South, Dagenham, Essex, RM8 1AU Tel: (020) 8517 0011 Fax: (020) 8592 0827 E-mail: shw@shwlondon.co.uk *Overseas furniture removers & warehousing*

▶ Stewart Homes (Scotland) Ltd, Atrium House, Callendar Business Park, Falkirk, FK1 1XR Tel: (01324) 670000

James Stewart & Co. (Printers) Ltd, 151 Hertingfordbury Road, Hertford, SG14 1NL Tel: (01992) 582531 Fax: (01992) 500549 E-mail: sales@james-stewart.demon.co.uk *Copperplate, litho & foil printers*

L.R. Stewart & Sons Ltd, Hampden Road, Hornsey, London, N8 0HG Tel: (020) 8348 5267 Fax: (020) 8340 7774 E-mail: info@lrstewartandsons.co.uk *Steel stockholders*

Stewart Linford Chair Maker Ltd, Kitchener Works, Kitchener Road, High Wycombe, Buckinghamshire, HP11 2SJ Tel: (01494) 440408 Fax: (01494) 451555 *Furniture manufrs*

Lorne Stewart P.L.C., Stewart House, Kenton Road, Harrow, Middlesex, HA3 9TU Tel: (020) 8759 9988 Fax: (020) 8759 9987 *Building services engineers*

▶ Stewart McNee (Dunoon) Ltd, Sandbank Industrial Estate, Sandbank, Dunoon, Argyll, PA23 8PB Tel: (01369) 702578

▶ Stewart Miller Associates, Na Mara, Innellan, Dunoon, Argyll, PA23 7QN Tel: (01369) 830000

▶ Stewart Milne Group, Kestrel House, 3 Kilmartin Place, Tannochside Business Park, Glasgow, G71 5PH Tel: (01698) 804804

Stewart Offshore Services, 1 Tranquil Bale, Black Heath, London, SE3 0BU Tel: (020) 8297 7474 *Ship brokers & services* Also at: Aberdeen & Yarmouth

▶ Stewart & Partners, 6 Regent Gate, High Street, Waltham Cross, Hertfordshire, EN8 7AF Tel: (0870) 0508091 Fax: (0845) 2050033 E-mail: mail@stewartpartners.co.uk *We are an accessable and practical firm of Chartered Accountants specialising in all aspects of accounts and tax for familly run businesses and the SME sector.**Specialisms include: accounts, audit, personal and corporate tax, payroll, sub-contractors.*

▶ Stewart Pearl & Associates, 3 Sandy Lane, Prestwich, Manchester, M25 9RU Tel: 0161-798 8811 Fax: 0161-798 4877 E-mail: sales@stewartpearl.co.uk *Chartered Building Consultants covering Quantity Surveyors, Planning Supervisors (CDM), Project Management*

Stewart Plant Sales Ltd, Townmill Road, Glasgow, G31 3AR Tel: 0141-554 6881 Fax: 0141-550 2358 E-mail: enquiries@stewart-plant-sales.co.uk *Contractors' plant distributors*

▶ Stewart Property Services Ltd, 45 Polwarth CR, Edinburgh, EH11 1HS Tel: 0131-228 2867 Fax: 0131-228 2812

Stewart R Trophies, 90 Titchfield Street, Kilmarnock, Ayrshire, KA1 1PH Tel: (01563) 522594 Fax: (01563) 522594 E-mail: ltd@btconnect.com *Engraving services & sports trophies retailers & manufrs*

Stewart & Ramsden Ltd, North Wheatlands Mill, Wheatlands Road, Galashiels, Selkirkshire, TD1 2HQ Tel: (01896) 754898 Fax: (01896) 758767 *Wool brokers service & retailer's*

Stewart Of Reading, 17 King Street, Mortimer Common, Reading, RG7 3RS Tel: 0118-933 1111 Fax: 0118-933 2375 E-mail: dwayn@stewart-of-reading.co.uk *Second hand electronic retailers*

Stewart Rewinds Ltd, 1 Mafeking Street, Glasgow, G51 2UZ Tel: 0141-445 3055 Fax: 0141-445 3008 *Electric motor rewinders*

▶ Stewart S Redman Dental Engineering Services, 63A Steam Mill Lane, Ripley, Derbyshire, DE5 3JR Tel: 07904 048102 E-mail: enquiries@ssredman.co.uk *Repair, installation and maintenance of a large range of dental products. Chairs, delivery, Autoclaves, X-ray, Aspiration and more.*

Stewart Scott Fabrications Ltd, 16 East Cromwell Street, Edinburgh, EH6 6HD Tel: 0131-555 0375 Fax: 0131-553 7958

▶ Stewart Shaw Ltd, 10 Jane Street, Dunoon, Argyll, PA23 7HX Tel: (01369) 702085

▶ Stewart & Shields Ltd, 27 East King Street, Helensburgh, Dunbartonshire, G84 7QQ Tel: (01436) 672356 Fax: (01436) 679196

Stewart Signs Ltd, Trafalgar Close, Chandler's Ford, Eastleigh, Hampshire, SO53 4BW Tel: (023) 8025 4781 Fax: (023) 8025 5620 E-mail: sales@stewartsigns.co.uk *Sign contractors & suppliers & manufrs*

Stewart Technology Ltd, Tweedside Park, Tweedbank, Galashiels, Selkirkshire, TD1 3TE Tel: (01896) 668100 Fax: (01896) 668101 E-mail: sales@stewart-technology.co.uk *Electronic design & manufacturing services*

W. Stewart, 126 Irish Hill Road, Newtownabbey, Co. Antrim, BT36 5SH Tel: (028) 9083 6047 *Agricultural Contractors*

Stewart Wales Somerville Ltd, 28 Glenburn Road, East Kilbride, Glasgow, G74 5BA Tel: (01355) 222101 Fax: (01355) 233847 E-mail: sales@sws-ltd.com *Specialist surface coating manufrs*

▶ Stewart & Williamson, 5 Clairmont Gardens, Glasgow, G3 7LW Tel: 0141-332 7475 Fax: 0141-332 6625

Stewarts of Edinburgh Ltd, Meadowbank Works, 67 Marionville Road, Edinburgh, EH7 6AJ Tel: 0131-659 6010 Fax: 0131-652 1348 E-mail: mail@stewarts.eu.com *Printers & stationers*

▶ Stibbards Consultancy Ltd, 26 Downs Court Road, Purley, Surrey, CR8 1BB Tel: (020) 8660 3440 E-mail: stibbardsconsultancy@yahoo.co.uk

continued

continuation
General Insurance Compliance to meet FSA rules

Stick 'Em Signs, Hyde Bank Road, New Mills, High Peak, Derbyshire, SK22 4NN Tel: (01663) 741160 Fax: (01663) 741162 *Sign manufrs*

▶ Sticks & Stones, Colchester Main Road, Alresford, Colchester, CO7 8DD Tel: (01206) 826835 Fax: (01206) 827655 E-mail: info@stixandstones.co.uk *Garden building, home office, shed, beach hut summer house & fencing suppliers*

▶ Sticky Letter Co., 35 Bridgefield, Farnham, Surrey, GU9 8AW Tel: (01252) 713683 Fax: (01252) 713683 E-mail: ideas@stickyletter.co.uk *Sign makers for exhibitions*

Stiebel Eltron UK Ltd, Unit 12, Stadium Court Stadium Road, Wirral, Merseyside, CH62 3RP Tel: 0151-346 2300 Fax: 0151-334 2913 E-mail: aeinfo@appied-engery.com *Water & space heating distributors*

Stieber Brakes, Wichita Building, Ampthill Road, Bedford, MK42 9RD Tel: (01234) 355499 Fax: (01234) 214264 E-mail: diane.lawman@wichita.co.uk *Power transmission equipment manufrs*

Stiefel Laboratories (UK) Ltd, Holtspur Lane, Wooburn Green, High Wycombe, Buckinghamshire, HP10 0AU Tel: (01628) 524966 Fax: (01628) 810021 E-mail: general@stiefel.co.uk *Pharmaceutical distributors*

Stiell Ltd, Cannock Side Park, Uddingston, Glasgow, G71 5PW Tel: (01698) 805100 Fax: (01698) 805111 E-mail: ho@stiell.co.uk *Electrical engineers* Also at: Coatbridge, Dunfermline & Glasgow

Stigwood & Sons, Grafton Street, Oldham, OL1 4SD Tel: 0161-633 3398 Fax: 0161-633 3398 *Potato peeling machine manufrs*

Andreas Stihl Ltd, Stihl House, Stanhope Road, Camberley, Surrey, GU15 3YT Tel: (01276) 20202 Fax: (01276) 670510 E-mail: postmaster@stihl.co.uk *Chain saw suppliers*

▶ Stikatak Ltd, J Braintree Industrial Estate, Braintree Road, Ruislip, Middlesex, HA4 0EJ Tel: (020) 8839 4405 Fax: (020) 8842 1387 E-mail: enquiry@stikatak.co.uk *Flooring equipment*

▶ Stik-Chik Agency, Old Straw Barn, 5 Greenacre Drive, Rushden, Northamptonshire, NN10 0TQ Tel: (07866) 718132 E-mail: enquiries@ntlworld.co.uk *Full marketing & design creative agency*

▶ Stilcan Industrial Conveyors, 10 Westgarth Place, East Kilbride, Glasgow, G74 5NT Tel: (01355) 270788 Fax: (01355) 270789

Stiles Metal Craft, Brickfield Industrial Estate, New Road, Gillingham, Dorset, SP8 4LT Tel: (01747) 824240 Fax: (01747) 824240 *General sheet metalwork general*

Still Frame, Knight House, Farren Court, Cowfold, Horsham, West Sussex, RH13 8BT Tel: (01403) 865268 Fax: (01403) 865269 E-mail: info@stillframe.co.uk *Cctv Installators*

Still Materials Handling, Aston Way, Moss Side Industrial Estate, Leyland, PR26 7UX Tel: (01772) 644300 Fax: (01772) 454668 E-mail: sales@still.co.uk *Fork lift truck hire & manufrs* Also at: Glasgow & London

▶ Still Works Ltd, 76 Wells Street, Cardiff, CF11 6DY Tel: (029) 2035 3940 Fax: (029) 2035 3941 E-mail: info@stillsdesign.com *Communications agency specialising in branding*

Stiller Group Ltd, Vulcan Road, Bilston, West Midlands, WV14 7LB Tel: (01902) 491151 Fax: (01902) 402613 *Road transport contractors* Also at: King's Lynn & Leicester

Stiller Group, Boeing Way, Preston Farm Industrial Estate, Stockton-on-Tees, Cleveland, TS18 3TE Tel: (01642) 607777 Fax: (01642) 607711 E-mail: enquiries@stiller.co.uk *Haulage & warehousing contractors*

Stilo Technology, North Quay, Temple Back, Bristol, BS1 6FL Tel: 0117-311 6500 Fax: 0117-311 6599 E-mail: info@stilo.com *Software developers*

▶ Stilton Surveys Ltd, 2 Turpins Ride, Stilton, Peterborough, PE7 3RE Tel: (01733) 240072 Fax: (01733) 240072 E-mail: info@stiltonsurveys.co.uk *PR & marketing services to plant & tool hire industry copy writing*

Stinchcombe Furnaces Ltd, Unit 9 Mount Road Industrial Estate, Mount Road, Burntwood, Staffs, WS7 9QF Tel: 01543 674031 Fax: 01543 683846 E-mail: stinchcombeltd@aol.com *Furnace builders**

Stirchley Machine Tool Co. Ltd, 401-407 Tyburn Road, Birmingham, B24 8HJ Tel: 0121-328 2424 Fax: 0121-327 6200 *New & used machine tool suppliers*

▶ Stirling, 7 Cunningham Road, Stirling, FK7 7SW Tel: (01786) 445349 Fax: (01786) 445349 E-mail: sales@fergusons450222.com *Car parts suppliers*

Stirling Business Solutions Ltd, Lasyard House, Underhill Street, Bridgnorth, Shropshire, WV16 4BB Tel: (01746) 769301 Fax: (01746) 769302 E-mail: sales@tmssolutions.co.uk *Consultants & training*

Stirling Evp Ltd, 222 West Road, Westcliff-on-Sea, Essex, SS0 9DE Tel: (01702) 300999 Fax: (01702) 303039 E-mail: info@stirlingevp.com *Emergency warning equipment manufrs*

Stirling Group P.L.C., Union Bank, King Street, Knutsford, Cheshire, WA16 6EF Tel: (01565) 633111 Fax: (01565) 633555 E-mail: adrian.pettiford@stirlinggroup.com *Water proofing services*

Stirling Hamilton Wright, City Reach, 5 Greenwich View Place, Millharbour, London, E14 9NN Tel: (020) 7712 6000 Fax: (020) 7712 6001 E-mail: info@shwgroup.co.uk *Insurance broker*

Stirling Health Food Store, 29 Dumbarton Road, Stirling, FK8 2LQ Tel: (01786) 464903 Fax: (01786) 464903 *Health food retail*

Stirling Highland Hotel Ltd, Spittal Street, Stirling, FK8 1DU Tel: (01786) 272727 Fax: (01786) 272829 E-mail: stirling@paramount-hotels.co.uk *Hotel & conference facilities*

Stirling Industrial Doors, Stirling House, Eridge Road, Crowborough, East Sussex, TN6 2SY Tel: (01892) 665530 Fax: (01892) 665520 *Industrial doors installation & manufrs*

Stirling Maynard & Partners Ltd, Stirling House, Rightwell, Bretton, Peterborough, PE3 8DJ Tel: (01733) 262319 Fax: (01733) 331527 E-mail: enquires@stirlingmaynard.com *Civil & structural engineers*

Stirling Moulded Composites Ltd, Unit 10 Alliance Business Park, Corporation Street, Accrington, Lancashire, BB5 0RR Tel: (01254) 395550 Fax: (01254) 398584 E-mail: daryl@stirlingmoulded.com *Plastic moulders*

▶ Stirling Precast Ltd, Whitehouse Road, Stirling, FK7 7SX Tel: (01786) 472191 Fax: (01786) 451284 E-mail: general@sterlingprecast.com

Stirling Recruitment, 49 Old Steine, Brighton, BN1 1NH Tel: (01273) 324255 Fax: (01273) 325656E-mail: info@duneofficerecruitment.co.uk

▶ Stirling Sensors, Cowling Street, Oldham, OL8 1UY Tel: 0161-785 8788 Fax: 0161-627 0507 E-mail: sales@stirlingsensors.co.uk *Temperature monitoring system manufrs*

Stirling Solent Communications, 33 Portsmouth Enterprise Centre, Quartremaine Road, Portsmouth, PO3 5QT Tel: (0870) 7701702 Fax: (023) 9267 3518 E-mail: csil@csil-uk.com *Electronic warfare simulators & stimulators*

Stirling Steelcraft (Liverpool) Ltd, 11-13 Cheapside, Liverpool, L2 2DY Tel: 0151-236 4752 Fax: 0151-236 5466 *Catering equipment fabricators*

▶ Stirling University Innovation Park, 4 Scion House, Stirling University Innovation Park, Stirling, FK9 4NF Tel: (01786) 448333 E-mail: info@forthright.co.uk

▶ Stirling Water Ltd, Hillside House, Laurelhill Business Park, Stirling, FK7 9JQ Tel: (01786) 445591

▶ Stitt Bros Ltd, Station Yard, Main Street, Killin, Perthshire, FK21 8UH Tel: (01567) 820344 Fax: (01567) 820944

Stix & Stones Garden Products Ltd, The Yard, Colchester Main Road, Alresford, Colchester, CO7 8DD Tel: (01206) 826835 Fax: (01206) 827655 *Fencing manufrs*

STL INTERNATIONAL LTD, Hill Farm, Linton Hill, Linton, Maidstone, Kent, ME17 4AL Tel: 01622 749633 Fax: 01622 746800 E-mail: solutions@stl-int.co.uk *STL International Ltd has SAFE answers to HAZARDOUS questions.*The company has over 30 years experience in hazardous area and industrial environments. *STL provides complete solutions by combining expert advice with application research and high service levels for the supply of competitive and technically innovative products. These include maintenance free and low maintenance lighting systems and explosion proof enclosures.**

STM Power Transmission Ltd, Unit 10 Hartford Business Centre, Chester Road, Hartford, Northwich, Cheshire, CW8 2AB Tel: (01606) 557200 Fax: (01606) 301260 E-mail: info@stmuk.co.uk *Power transmission distributors*

Stoakes Systems Ltd, 1 Banstead Road, Purley, Surrey, CR8 3EB Tel: (020) 8660 7667 Fax: (020) 8660 5707 E-mail: admin@stoakes.co.uk *Curtain walling & roof glazing systems suppliers*

Stoate & Bishop Printers)Ltd, Shaftesbury Indust Estate, The Runnings, Cheltenham, Gloucestershire, GL51 9NH Tel: (01242) 236741 Fax: (01242) 222032 E-mail: stoatprint@btinternet.com *Lithographic printers*

▶ Stocade, Unit 3, Heron Industrial Estate, Basingstoke Road, Spencers Wood, Reading, RG7 1PJ Tel: 0118-988 1490

Stocdon Ltd, 2 Mackenzie Way, Swindon Village, Cheltenham, Gloucestershire, GL51 9TX Tel: (01242) 241123 Fax: (01242) 241133 E-mail: info@stocdon.co.uk *Cutting tool & workholding system distributors*

Stock Associates Print Finishers Ltd, Unit 2-3, Perry Way, Witham, Essex, CM8 3SX Tel: (01376) 500123 Fax: (01376) 501744 E-mail: sales@stock.uk.com *Printing trade finishing services*

Stock Blinds, 38 Bedford Street, Bognor Regis, West Sussex, PO21 1RP Tel: (01243) 863091 Fax: (01243) 840976 *Furnishings & blinds retailers*

Stock Electronics Ltd, 10 Edison Road, Salisbury, SP2 7NU Tel: (01722) 321758 Fax: (01722) 413079 E-mail: enquiries@stockelectronics.co.uk *Speed control manufrs*

Stock Films, PO Box 11, Barnet, Hertfordshire, EN4 8AR Tel: (020) 8441 0449 Fax: (020) 8441 4888 *Solar control & safety film distributors*

▶ Stock Optics Ltd, Unit 430, Thorp Arch Estate, Wetherby, West Yorkshire, LS23 7BJ Tel: (01937) 849421 Fax: (01937) 849836 E-mail: optics1@btconnect.com *Scientific optic military to medical*

Stockall Electronics Ltd, Bond House, Howsell Road, Malvern, Worcestershire, WR14 1TF Tel: (01684) 574977 Fax: (01684) 574977 E-mail: enquiries@stockallelectronics.com *Weld monitor equipment & electronic designers*

Stockall Precision Sheet Metal Work Ltd, Unit 10 Wansdyke Business Centre, Oldfield Lane, Bath, BA2 3LY Tel: (01225) 422404 Fax: (01225) 422404 E-mail: sales@stockall.co.uk *Precision sheet metal engineers*

Stockbridge Airco Ltd, Blossom Street Works, Ancoats, Manchester, M4 6AE Tel: 0161-236 9314 Fax: 0161-228 0009 E-mail: mark@stockbridge-airco.com *Manufacturers of fans*

Stockbridge Mill Co. Ltd, Green Lane, Padiham, Burnley, Lancashire, BB12 7AE Tel: (01282) 772231 Fax: (01282) 771084 E-mail: sales@stockbridgemill.com *Handkerchief manufrs*

Stockbridge Racing Ltd, Grosvenor Garage, High Street, Stockbridge, Hampshire, SO20 6HE Tel: (01264) 810712 Fax: (01264) 810247 E-mail: sales@willansharness.co.uk *Competition seat belt manufrs*

Stockbridge Workwear, 6 House O'Hill Avenue, Edinburgh, EH4 5DD Tel: 0131-343 1039 Fax: 0131-332 6766 E-mail: richie.pearson@virgin.net *Clothing supplier & manufrs*

Stockcare Ltd, 83 West Street, Leven, Beverley, North Humberside, HU17 5LR Tel: (01964) 543924 Fax: (01964) 542750 E-mail: sales@goldlabeluk.com *Principal Export Areas: Central America Heath care products for horses*

Stockeld Farms Ltd, Kingbarrow Farm, Harrogate Road, Wetherby, West Yorkshire, LS22 4AL Tel: (01937) 586101 Fax: (01937) 580084 E-mail: peterstockeld@bigfastweb.net *Christmas tree growers and wholesalers. Online sales of Christmas trees and decorations.*

Stockfarm Equestrian Supplies, 38 Upton Lane, Upton, Chester, CH2 1EE Tel: (0800) 0899020 *Equestrian supplies*

Stockfarm Supplies, 1 Highfield Close, Stockport, Cheshire, SK3 8UB Tel: 0161-483 1011 *Farm supplies*

Stockfield Fencing Products Ltd, Stockfield Road, Chadderton, Oldham, OL9 9HD Tel: 0161-620 4034 Fax: 0161-620 4034 *Manufacturers of fencing accessories & equipment*

Stockfield Manufacturing Co. Ltd, Sherbourne Road, Balsall Heath, Birmingham, B12 9DJ Tel: 0121-440 1333 Fax: 0121-440 8221 E-mail: info@stockfield.com *CNC & hand spinning custom metal spinners manufrs*

▶ Stockfolder.com, 1 North Avenue, Ealing, London, London, W13 8AP Tel: 0208 998 3445 E-mail: info@stockfolder.com *Internet service for buyers and retailers to source low cost stock fabrics worldwide.*

▶ Stockies Inventory Services, 105 Birkdale, Whitley Bay, Tyne & Wear, NE25 9LZ Tel: 0191-251 5584 E-mail: sales@stockies.com *Periodical stocktaking & business transfer services*

Stocking Beer & Oborn Dental Laboratories, 120a Marylebone Lane, London, W1U 2QG Tel: (020) 7486 2097 Fax: (020) 7224 6382 E-mail: lab@sbodentallaboatory.co.uk *Dental laboratory*

▶ The Stocking Shop Ltd, 1 Chantry Road Thornbury, Thornbury, Bristol, BS35 1ER Tel: (07771) 822972 E-mail: sales@the-stocking-shop.com *Wholesalers and retailers of lingerie and hosiery. Ranges being added and updated daily.*

▶ Stockle Colour Printers Ltd, Linton Street, Bradford, West Yorkshire, BD4 7EZ Tel: (01274) 308100

Stockley Electrics Ltd, 154 Bedworth Road, Bulkington, Bedworth, Warwickshire, CV12 9LQ Tel: (024) 7631 2639 Fax: (024) 7631 2639 *Electrical engineers*

Stockley Sweets Ltd, Moscow Mill, Colliers St, Oswaldtwistle, Accrington, Lancashire, BB5 3DF Tel: (01254) 232807 Fax: (01254) 382220 *Confectionery manufrs*

Stockline Plastics Ltd, Grovepark Mills, Hopehill Road, Glasgow, G20 7NF Tel: 0141-332 9077 Fax: 0141-332 9079 E-mail: sales@stockline-plastics.co.uk *Plastics distributing services*

G. Stockman, 137 Stoke Newington Road, London, N16 8BP Tel: (020) 7249 6017 Fax: (020) 7254 8895 *Clothing manufrs*

Stockmart Plastics, 184 Kingston Road, Portsmouth, PO2 7LP Tel: (023) 9266 0736 Fax: (023) 9266 0736 *Laminated plastics & materials worktops*

▶ Stockmill Widows Ltd, Alexa Court, Aston Road, Bedford, MK42 0LW Tel: (01234) 356995 Fax: (01234) 267873

Stockport Binocular & Telescope Centre, Mercian Way, Stockport, Cheshire, SK3 9DF Tel: 0161-429 8002 Fax: 0161-474 0440 E-mail: tloptics@aol.com *Binoculars & telescope retailers*

Stockport Chamber of Commerce & Industry, Stockport Business Centre, 1 St. Peters Square, Stockport, Cheshire, SK1 1NN Tel: 0161-474 3780 Fax: 0161-476 0138 *Chamber of commerce*

Stockport Engineering Training Association Ltd, Hammond Avenue, Stockport, Cheshire, SK4 1PQ Tel: 0161-480 9822 Fax: 0161-477 4720 E-mail: julie-burns@lineone.net *Industrial engineering training services*

Stockport Fire Extinguishers, Unit 14 Haigh Park, Haigh Avenue, Stockport, Cheshire, SK4 1QR Tel: 0161-476 2004 Fax: 0161-429 7239 *Fire extinguisher distributors*

Stockport Fire Protection, 14 Hade Park, White Hill Industrial Estate, Stockport, Cheshire, SK4 1QR Tel: 0161-477 0061 Fax: 0161-429 7239 E-mail: safe@globalnet.co.uk *Fire extinguisher supply, refill & maintenance*

▶ Stockport Joinery Co., 10-16 King St West, Stockport, Cheshire, SK3 0DY Tel: 0161-477 5480 Fax: 0161-474 7248 E-mail: info@stockportjoinery.co.uk

Stockport Lifting Gear, Unit 14 Bamford Business Park, Whitehill Industrial Estate, Stockport, Cheshire, SK4 1PL Tel: 0161-429 0737 Fax: 0161-476 3315 E-mail: info@rossendalegroup.co.uk *Lifting equipment hire services* Also at: Burnley, Ellesmere Port, Liverpool & Rossendale & Wrexham

Stockport Printing Co. Ltd, 9 Enterprise Centre Two, Chester Street, Stockport, Cheshire, SK3 0BR Tel: 0161-477 2391 Fax: 0161-480 1600 E-mail: sales@stockportprint.co.uk *Printing services*

Stockport Racking Co. Ltd, 12 Hammond Avenue, Whitehill Industrial Estate, Stockport, Cheshire, SK4 1PQ Tel: 0161-477 0155 Fax: 0161-477 0159 *Pallet racking & shelving distributors*

Stockport Signs, 26 Middle Hillgate, Stockport, Cheshire, SK1 3AY Tel: 0161-429 7604 Fax: 0161-429 7604 E-mail: cheshiresigns@aol.com *Sign retailers & manufrs*

Stockport Window Co., 10-16 King St West, Stockport, Cheshire, SK3 0DY Tel: 0161-480 7011 Fax: 0161-474 7248 E-mail: info@stockportwindows.co.uk *Joinery manufacturers & window fitters (UPVC)*

▶ Stocks Bros Ltd, Pontefract Road, Leeds, LS10 1SW Tel: 0113-271 7249 Fax: 0113-271 7249

Stocks Bros Ltd, Blocks, 5 Ninelands Lane, Garforth, Leeds, LS25 1NT Tel: 0113-232 0022 Fax: 0113-287 0839 E-mail: sales@stocks-blocks.co.uk *Breeze block & paving slab manufrs* Also at: Stourton

Stocks Fly Fishery, Bank House Lancaster Road, Caton, Lancaster, LA2 9HX Tel: (01524) 770412 Fax: (01524) 770412 *Day tickets for trout fishing*

Stocks Sewing Machines, King House, 17 Regent Street, Leeds, LS2 7UZ Tel: 0113-243 6800 Fax: 0113-242 9830 E-mail: accounts@stocks.co.uk *Industrial & domestic sewing machinery*

Stockshop Livestock Equipment Ltd, Lodge Trading Estate, Broadclyst Station, Exeter, EX5 3BS Tel: (01392) 460077 Fax: (01392) 460966 E-mail: nathalie.andre@stockshop.co.uk *Husbandry equipment wholesalers*

Stockton Drilling Ltd, Unit 15 Navigation Court, Calder Park, Wakefield, West Yorkshire, WF2 7BJ Tel: (01924) 242128 Fax: (01924) 253177 E-mail: info@stocktondrilling.com *Horizontal drilling services*

Stockton Engineering Ltd, 84 Barford Street, Birmingham, B5 6AH Tel: 0121-622 7474 Fax: 0121-666 6264 E-mail: peter@stocktonengineering.co.uk Purchasing Contact: Burchell Sales Contact: M. Brookin Principal Export Areas: Africa, Central/East Europe & West Europe *Stockton Engineering Ltd, Birmingham, Midlands, United Kingdom. Manufacturers of component products, wire, pressed, pressings, formed, welded, assemblies, turned parts, tube bending tools, pipe bending tools, garage door locks. Quality accredited to BSI ISO 9001-2000*

Stockton Fencing, Park Farm, Riseley Road, Bletsoe, Bedford, MK44 1QU Tel: (01234) 708318 Fax: (01234) 709917 E-mail: sales@stocktonfencing.co.uk *Fencing contractors*

Stockwell Motor Accessories, 226-236 Clapham Road, London, SW9 0PZ Tel: (020) 7582 3666 Fax: (020) 7735 6484 *Motor accessory retailers for public & trade*

Stockwell Mouldings, 4 Oughton Road, Birmingham, B12 0DF Tel: 0121-440 6555 Fax: 0121-440 6555 E-mail: info@stockwell-mouldings.co.uk *Manufacturers of rubber mouldings*

Stockwell Steel, Goods Yard, Bangor, Gwynedd, LL57 2TX Tel: (01248) 364041 Fax: (01248) 353100 E-mail: bangor@bmsteel.co.uk *Steel stockholders*

▶ Stoctech Solutions, 21 Naples Road, Stockport, Cheshire, SK3 0TN Tel: (0800) 4583548 Fax: (07792) 528875 *Computer services maintenance & repairers*

Stoddard International P.L.C., Barbados Road, Kilmarnock, Ayrshire, KA1 1SX Tel: (01563) 578000 Fax: (01563) 578015 E-mail: enquires@stoddardintl.co.uk *Carpet & fabric manufrs*

Stoddard Manufacturing Co. Ltd, Denturax Works, Icknield Way, Letchworth Garden City, Hertfordshire, SG6 4AH Tel: (01462) 686221 Fax: (01462) 480711 E-mail: admin@stoddard.co.uk *Dental brush & polisher manufrs*

Stoddards Ltd, Greenhill Garage, Leek Road, Cheadle, Stoke-on-Trent, ST10 1JF Tel: (01538) 754420 Fax: (01538) 750375 E-mail: sales@stoddards.co.uk *Coach hire & fuel oil distributors*

Fred Stoddart Ltd, 28 Wilson Street North, Sunderland, SR5 1BB Tel: 0191-567 3960 Fax: 0191-564 1624 E-mail: enquiries@fredstoddartltd.co.uk *Plumbing & heating installations*

Mark Stoddart International Designer, Ladybank House, Girvan, Ayrshire, KA26 9JJ Tel: (01292) 443103 Fax: (01292) 441266 E-mail: info@markstoddart.com *Bronze sculptors & furniture designers services*

S.J. Stoddart Insurance Ltd, St. Peter's House, 119 High Street, Berkhamsted, Hertfordshire, HP4 2DJ Tel: (01442) 872331 Fax: (01442) 871025 *Insurance brokers & agencies*

Stoke Galvanising Ltd, Nevada Lane, Hot Lane, Hot Lane Industrial Estate, Stoke-on-Trent, ST6 2BN Tel: (01782) 811226 Fax: (01782) 836686 *Galvanisers & galvanising processors or services*

Stoke Hall Quarry (Stone Sales) Ltd, Eyam Road, Grindleford, Hope Valley, Derbyshire, S32 2HW Tel: (01433) 630313 Fax: (01433) 631353 E-mail: design@stokehallquarry.co.uk *Suppliers of natural stone*

Stoke On Trent Workshops For The Blind, 211 City Road, Stoke-on-Trent, ST4 2PN Tel: (01782) 233900 Fax: (01782) 234900 E-mail: sales@stokeworkshops.co.uk *Point of sale stands*

▶ Stokergate, 36 Geoffrey CR, Fareham, Hampshire, PO16 0QQ Tel: (01329) 519669 E-mail: stokers3@ntlworld.com *Gates & railings manufrs*

A.W. Stokes & Son (Drums) Ltd, Hall Street, West Bromwich, West Midlands, B70 7DN Tel: 0121-553 1713 Fax: 0121-553 0825 E-mail: sales@awsdrums.co.uk *Manufacturers of drums*

▶ Stokes Clarkson Electrical Ltd, Unit D1 Admin Buildings, Admin Road, Knowsley Industrial Park, Liverpool, L33 7TX Tel: 0151-548 9377 Fax: 0151-548 6377

Stokes Forgings Ltd, Northcote St, Walsall, WS2 8BH Tel: (01922) 704800 *Drop forging manufrs*

Stokes & Parry Ltd, Kelsey Close, Attleborough Fields Industrial Estate, Nuneaton, Warwickshire, CV11 6RS Tel: (024) 7638 2096 Fax: (024) 7634 2006 E-mail: stokesandparry@tiscali.co.uk *Sheet metalworkers*

▶ Stokes Removals & Storage Ltd, 115 Waterside Road, Hamilton, Leicester, LE5 1TL Tel: 0116-274 1111 Fax: 0116-270 6099

Company Information

▶ Stokes Vehicle Services, 13a River Road, Barking, Essex, IG11 0HE Tel: (020) 8507 0577 Fax: (020) 8591 5898 E-mail: sales@stokesvehicle.co.uk *Air conditioning & refrigeration services*

Stokke Furniture, 3 Shredding Green Farm, Langley Park Road, Iver, Buckinghamshire, SL0 9QS Tel: (01753) 655873 Fax: (01753) 655878 E-mail: stokkeuk@stokke.com *Furniture manufrs*

Stokplas Ltd, Sandall Park, Barnby Dun Road, Doncaster, South Yorkshire, DN2 4QL Tel: (01302) 816040 Fax: (01302) 816050 E-mail: stokplas@crossling.co.uk *Distributors of thermoplastic pipe & fittings*

Stolk & Reese Kubert BV, D T E House, Hollins Lane, Bury, Lancashire, BL9 8AT Tel: 0161-877 4060 Fax: 0161-877 4090 E-mail: enquires@vsr.nl *Envelope manufrs*

Stoll UK Ltd, Craven Street, Leicester, LE1 4BX Tel: 0116-253 8296 Fax: 0116-253 8219 E-mail: sales@stolluk.co.uk *Knitting machine agents*

Stoltzman & Thomas Sculptural Ceramics, Unit F21 Park Hall Road Trading Estate, 40 Martell Road, London, SE21 8EN Tel: (020) 8670 6464 Fax: (020) 8670 6464 E-mail: stoltzmanthomas@onetel.com *Garden ceramic products manufrs*

Stolzle Flaconnage Ltd, Weeland Road, Knottingley, West Yorkshire, WF11 8AP Tel: (01977) 607124 Fax: (01977) 672879 *Glass bottles manufrs*

Stomet Industries Ltd, Thorpe House, Thorpe Way, Banbury, Oxfordshire, OX16 4SP Tel: (01295) 257565 Fax: (01295) 271762 E-mail: sales@oastdeck.com *Mezzane floors & office partitions manufrs*

Stonaco Fabrications Ltd, Wilton Road, Haine Industrial Estate, Ramsgate, Kent, CT12 5HG Tel: (01843) 596448 Fax: (01843) 593548 *Fire escape welding & fabrications*

Stonbury Ltd, 4 Phoenix Enterprise Park, Grovehill Road, Beverley, North Humberside, HU17 0JG Tel: (01482) 881198 Fax: (01482) 868457 E-mail: admin@stonbury.co.uk *Concrete repair & blast cleaning*

▶ Stone, 24b Hamilton Street, Carluke, Lanarkshire, ML8 4HA Tel: (01555) 752068 Fax: (01555) 752266 *Joiners*

Stone Acre, Barnby Dun Road, Doncaster, South Yorkshire, DN2 4QP Tel: (01302) 327111 Fax: (01302) 340460 E-mail: sales@stoneacre.com *Car dealers*

Stone Adrian, Cowes Yacht Haven, Cowes, Isle of Wight, PO31 7BD Tel: (01983) 297898 Fax: (01983) 280499 E-mail: adrianstone.yachts@virgin.net *Yacht repairs*

Alexandra Stone Co. Ltd, Kirby Muxloe, Leicester, LE9 2BR Tel: 0116-239 2513 Fax: 0116-239 3993 *Concrete products manufrs*

Stone & Associates, 40 Beaulieu Drive, Pinner, Middlesex, HA5 1NG Tel: (020) 8866 8631 E-mail: sales@stone-associates.co.uk *Computer accountancy software specialists services*

Stone Boat Building Co. Ltd, Newcastle Road, Stone, Staffordshire, ST15 8JZ Tel: (01785) 812688 Fax: (01785) 811317 E-mail: sales@stoneboatbuilding.co.uk *Boat chandlery, calorifiers & caravan accessories*

Stone Bros, Unit 9 Withy Road Trading Estate, Bilston, West Midlands, WV14 0RX Tel: (01902) 496651 Fax: (01902) 496651 *Scrap metal merchants*

Stone & Ceramic Ltd, Unit 3 Kingside, Ruston Road, Woolwich, London, SE18 5BX Tel: (020) 8855 5400 Fax: (020) 8855 5404 E-mail: info@stone-ceramic.co.uk *Stone & ceramic importer & contractor*

Stone The Crows, Callywhite Lane, Dronfield, Derbyshire, S18 2XR Tel: (01246) 299800 Fax: (01246) 299809 E-mail: enquiries@stonethecrows.co.uk *Ceramics retailer*

▶ Stone Essentials Ltd, Mount Spring Works, Off Burnley Road East, Waterfoot, Rossendale, Lancashire, BB4 9LA Tel: (01706) 210605 Fax: (01706) 228707 E-mail: stoneessentials@btconnect.com *Providers of headstones gravestones, grave markers*

Stone Fasteners Ltd, Woolwich Road, London, SE7 8SL Tel: (020) 8293 5080 Fax: (020) 8293 4935 E-mail: sales@stonefasteners.com *Nail & rivet manufrs*

Stone Food Equipment, 40 High Street, Stone, Staffordshire, ST15 8AU Tel: (01785) 817258 Fax: (01785) 817258 *Butchers equipment suppliers*

Stone Foundries Ltd, Woolwich Road, London, SE7 8SL Tel: (020) 8853 4648 Fax: (020) 8305 1934 E-mail: enquiries@stone-foundries-limited.com *Casting manufrs*

George Stone Ltd, 10 Tower Road West, St. Leonards-On-Sea, East Sussex, TN38 0RG Tel: (01424) 436166 Fax: (01424) 420603 E-mail: info@georgestone.co.uk *Building contractors*

Stone Group, 58 Edison Road, Rabans Lane Industrial Area, Aylesbury, Buckinghamshire, HP19 8TE Tel: (01785) 812100 Fax: (01296) 424165 E-mail: info@compusys.co.uk *Manufacturers of computer graphic (design etc) systems, computer installation local area network systems, computer systems bespoke/ turnkey & computer protection UPS power supply systems. Also computers, general purposes; internet/electronic comerce services; computer support services; computer storage services; computer solutions house; computer outsourcing services; computer network services; computers, industrial & power supply (uninterruptible) (computer) systems/unit manufrs*

Stone Hardy, London House, Chittening Industrial Estate, Chittening, Bristol, BS11 0YB Tel: 0117-938 0802 Fax: 0117-938 6229 *Tailor repairers*

▶ Stone Hardy, 1 Aubrey Street, Salford, M50 3UT Tel: 0161-868 2880 Fax: 0161-868 2899 *Commercial repairers*

▶ Stone House Tiles Ltd, Unit 42 Enterprise Industrial Estate, Bolina Road, London, SE16 3LF Tel: (020) 7237 5375 Fax: (020) 7231 7597 E-mail: info@stonehousetiles.co.uk *Nature stone tiles wholesalers*

Stone Industry Supplies Ltd, 3 The Sidings Industrial Park, Birds Royd Lane, Brighouse, West Yorkshire, HD6 1LQ Tel: (01484) 723730 Fax: (01484) 723760 E-mail: sales@stoneindustrysupplies.com *Suppliers of tools and consumables to the Granite, Marble, Natural Stone, Kitchen, Fireplace and Monumental trades.*

▶ Stone Installations.co.uk, 9 Talbot Road, Rushden, Northamptonshire, NN10 6DQ Tel: 01933 387059 Fax: 01933 387059 *We are traditional stone masons who specialize in supplying and installing granite and marble kitchen worktops, fireplaces, floors and other stone products for the home and garden.*

▶ Stone Junction, 33 Kirkdale, London, SE26 4BT Tel: (020) 8699 7743 Fax: (020) 8699 7743 E-mail: richards@stonejunction.co.uk *Public relations consultancy*

Stone Manganese Marine Ltd, Dock Road, Birkenhead, Merseyside, CH41 1DT Tel: 0151-652 2372 Fax: 0151-652 2377 E-mail: sales@stonemanganese.co.uk *Marine propeller manufrs*

▶ Stone Mine Ltd, 22 Blackfriars Street, Facing Travelodge, City Centre, Manchester, M3 5BQ Tel: 0161-833 2333 Fax: 0161-870 6340 E-mail: alex@stonemine.co.uk *Stone suppliers*

▶ Stone Polishing, 16 Laity Road, Troon, Camborne, Cornwall, TR14 9EL Tel: (01209) 614511 E-mail: office@stonepolishing.co.uk *We supply individuals with abrasive materials*

Stone Products Ltd, Nab Works, Long Lane, Pott Shrigley, Macclesfield, Cheshire, SK10 5SD Tel: (01625) 560757 Fax: (01625) 576494 *Concrete precasters & landscaping centre*

▶ Stone Studio, 45 High Street, Petersfield, Hampshire, GU32 3JR Tel: (01730) 269966 Fax: (01730) 269966 E-mail: mail@thestonestudio.co.uk *Photographic services*

▶ Stone Tec Ltd, 34 Russell Road, Edinburgh, EH11 2LP Tel: 0131-313 4111 Fax: 0131-313 4222 *Stone & building preservations*

Stonebridge Cabinet Works (Rowntrees) Ltd, 118 Battlehill Rd, Richhill, Armagh, BT61 8QL Tel: (028) 3887 1229 Fax: (028) 3887 0402 *Furniture manufrs*

Stonebridge Joinery Works Ltd, 190-206 Acton Lane, London, NW10 7NH Tel: (020) 8965 4349 Fax: (020) 8961 1619 E-mail: info@stonebridge-ltd.com *Pre-formed plywood manufrs*

▶ Stonecraft Weston, Unit 21 Kewstoke Quarry, Kewstoke Road, Worle, Weston-super-Mare, Somerset, BS23 4QA Tel: (07778) 302672 Fax: (01934) 413295 E-mail: nickstonecraft@aol.com *Property & development supplies*

Stonedale Property Management Ltd, Romshed Courtyard, Underriver, Sevenoaks, Kent, TN15 0SD Tel: (01732) 746035 Fax: (01732) 454136 E-mail: spm@weald.co.uk *Property management*

Stoneflex URP Ltd, Units 1-4, Vauxhall Industrial Estate, Ruabon, Wrexham, Clwyd, LL14 6HA Tel: (01978) 812111 Fax: (01978) 810399 E-mail: info@stoneflex.com *Fibre reinforced composite panel systems*

Stonegalleon plc, The SPS Building, Burnaby Road, Coventry, CV6 4AE Tel: (024) 7658 4584 Fax: (024) 7657 4585 E-mail: stonegalleon@plc.com *Import & export agents*

▶ Stoneglen Demolition & Co. Ltd, 10 Queens Road, London, SE15 2PT Tel: (020) 7639 2267 Fax: (020) 7639 4323

Stonegrove Ltd, 3 Boyd Business Centre, Whitewall Road, Medway City Estate, Rochester, Kent, ME2 4DZ Tel: (01634) 291151 Fax: (01634) 719430 E-mail: chris@stonegrove.co.uk *Control panel manufrs*

Stonehage Ltd, 21 Dartmouth Street, London, SW1H 9BP Tel: (020) 7799 3159 Fax: (020) 7799 3236 *Financial consultants*

Stoneham plc, Powerscroft Road, Sidcup, Kent, DA14 5DZ Tel: (020) 8300 8181 Fax: (020) 8300 8183 E-mail: kitchens@stoneham.plc.uk *Kitchen furniture manufrs*

Stoneham Construction Ltd, Station Road, Havenstreet, Ryde, Isle of Wight, PO33 4DT Tel: (01983) 883723 Fax: (01983) 883761 E-mail: info@stonehamconstruction.co.uk *Building contractors*

▶ Stonehaven Engineering Ltd, 2 Spurryhillock Industrial Estate, Broomhill Road, Stonehaven, Kincardineshire, AB39 2NH Tel: (01569) 766700 Fax: (01569) 766147 E-mail: info@stonehaven-eng.com *Mobile defence camp manufacturers & specialists*

▶ Stonehenge Services Ltd, Faraday Road, Salisbury, SP2 7NR Tel: (01722) 414161 Fax: (01722) 335343 E-mail: stonehenge.serve@btconnect.com *General engineering services*

Stonehill Estates Ltd, Stonehill Business Park, Harbet Road, Edmonton, London, N18 3LD Tel: (020) 8807 1020 Fax: (020) 8884 3528 *Industrial agents*

Stonehill Office Supplies, Unit 16, Chapel Way, St. Annes Park, Bristol, BS4 4EU Tel: 0117-300 5661 Fax: 0117-300 5662 E-mail: mo@stonehill.co.uk *Stationery & office suppliers*

Stonehouse Paper & Bag Mills Ltd, Lower Mills, Stonehouse, Gloucestershire, GL10 2BD Tel: (01453) 822173 Fax: (01453) 822174 E-mail: stonehousepaper@aol.com *Paper bag manufrs*

Stonehouse Tablet Manufacturing Co. Ltd, Nottingham Road, Beeston, Nottingham, NG9 6DT Tel: 0115-925 4552 Fax: 0115-922 4226 E-mail: info@stonehousetablet.co.uk *Powder blending services & industrial tablet manufrs*

▶ Stoneledge (South Bank) Ltd, Estate Road 4, South Humberside Industrial Es, Grimsby, South Humberside, DN31 2TB Tel: (01472) 240265

Stoneleigh Concrete Products Ltd, 26 Dalston Close, Camberley, Surrey, GU15 1BT Tel: (01276) 21053 Fax: (01276) 517332 *Concrete product manufrs*

Stoneleigh Consultancy Ltd, The Ditches Hall, Ellesmere Road, Wem, Shrewsbury, SY4 5TX Tel: (01939) 238800 Fax: (01939) 235123 E-mail: sales@stoneleigh.co.uk *Networking*

Stoneleigh Engineering Services Ltd, Unit 10 Lansdowne Workshops, Lansdowne Mews, London, SE7 8AZ Tel: (020) 8305 0792 Fax: (020) 8858 6665 *Valve reconditioning & supply services*

Stoneman Engineering Ltd, Parks Works, Station Road, Tiverton Junction, Cullompton, Devon, EX15 2QA Tel: (01884) 820369 Fax: (01884) 821533 E-mail: sales@stoneman-engineering.co.uk *Stainless steel fabricators*

Stoneman Refrigeration, 10 Fore Street, Witheridge, Tiverton, Devon, EX16 8AH Tel: (01884) 860595 Fax: (01884) 860676 *Refrigeration designers & installers*

Stonemarket Driveway Contractors Ltd, Old Gravel Quarry, Oxford Road, Ryton on Dunsmore, Coventry, CV8 3EJ Tel: (024) 7651 8700 Fax: (024) 7651 8777 E-mail: sales@stonemarket.co.uk *Stockist of Garden landscape products - We have combined in-depth landscape experience and technical knowledge to create a range of garden landscape products that are renowned for outstanding quality and beauty.*

Stoner Benton Concrete Ltd, Tilley Lane, Boreham Street, Hailsham, East Sussex, BN27 4UU Tel: (01323) 832334 Fax: (01323) 873791 E-mail: info@stonerbenton.co.uk *Concrete products manufrs*

Stoneridge Pollak Ltd, The Moors, Tewkesbury Road, Cheltenham, Gloucestershire, GL51 9BP Tel: (01242) 283000 Fax: (01242) 283023 E-mail: stuart.felton@stoneridgepollak.co.uk *Electric automotive switch manufrs* Also at: Northampton

Stones Bros, Garratt Street, Brierley Hill, West Midlands, DY5 1JU Tel: (01384) 79888 Fax: (01384) 77966 *Bolt & nut stockists*

▶ Lawrence Stones, 30 Lucerne Close, Worcester, WR3 7NA Tel: (01905) 456906 E-mail: lawrence@stone1012.freeserve.co.uk *are you ready to explode your income? check out the 7 minute movie that could change your life at www.myepi.biz/158348 and prepare to be amazed free brochure upon request*

Stones The Printers Ltd, 10 Wates Way, Banbury, Oxfordshire, OX16 3ES Tel: (01295) 819300 Fax: (01295) 819390 E-mail: lbrown@stonestheprinters.co.uk *Promotional printers*

▶ R.G. Stones (Buildings) Ltd, Rhoswiel Sawmills, Weston Rhyn, Oswestry, Shropshire, SY10 7TG Tel: (01691) 773391 Fax: (01691) 774316 E-mail: rgstones@btconnect.com *Timber products, building contractors*

▶ Stonetext Ltd, 17 Port Street, Clackmannan, FK10 4JH Tel: (07719) 815636 E-mail: enquiries@stonetext.f2s.com *Virtual administrative services tailored to your requirements*

▶ Stoneville Stone Merchants, Unit 12 Set Star Estate, Transport Avenue, Brentford, Middlesex, TW8 9HF Tel: (020) 8560 1000 Fax: (020) 8560 4060 E-mail: info@stvl.co.uk *Stone installation stones, marble, limestone, granite, travertine*

Stoneway Engineering, Unit 2 The Warehouse, Benson Lane, Normanton, West Yorkshire, WF6 2HX Tel: (01924) 895959 Fax: (01924) 890721 *Pneumatic equipment distributors & engineering*

Stonewest Holdings Ltd, Lamberts Place, St James's Road, Croydon, CR9 2HX Tel: (020) 8684 6646 Fax: (020) 8684 9323 E-mail: info@stonewest.co.uk *Building restoration services*

Stonewood Trading Ltd, Dunmere Road, Bodmin, Cornwall, PL31 2QN Tel: (01208) 73258 Fax: (01208) 74223 E-mail: stonewoodtrading@btconnect.com *Candle manufrs*

▶ Stoney Brook, The Maltings, Main Road, Narborough, King's Lynn, Norfolk, PE32 1TE Tel: (01760) 339469 Fax: (0871) 4310456 E-mail: rachael@stoneybrook.co.uk *Suppliers of horse riding equipment*

Stoneycroft Diesels Ltd, 9 Empress Road, Anfield, Liverpool, L6 0BX Tel: 0151-260 9066 Fax: 0151-260 9066 *Repair fuel injection equipment diesels*

Stonham Hedgerow Ltd, Hemingstone Fruit Farm, Main Road, Hemingstone, Ipswich, IP6 9RJ Tel: (01449) 760330 Fax: (01449) 760330 E-mail: enquiries@stonhamhedgerow.co.uk *Preserves producers*

▶ The Stop, 2 East Street, Crowland, PETERBOROUGH, PE6 0EN Tel: 01733 212155 E-mail: enquiries@thestop.biz

Stop Choc Ltd, Banbury Avenue, Slough, SL1 4LR Tel: (01753) 533223 Fax: (01753) 693724 E-mail: sales@stop-choc.co.uk Sales Contact: C. Turner *Antivibration mounting, antivibration/ shock mount & rubber/metal bonded products. Also antivibration services/consultants/designers/ installation engineers & aeronautical designing/ engineering services*

▶ Stop Gap, 18 Hillcrest Drive, Little Sutton, Ellesmere Port, CH66 4QD Tel: 0151-347 1974 Fax: 0151-347 1974 *Secretarial Service designed for small or large companies. No amount of work too small. Virtual Secretarial work or routine copy/audio typing undertaken. Telephone messaging service, faxing*

▶ Stopbox Ltd, Verney House, 1B Hollywood Road, London, SW10 9HS Tel: (020) 7183 0000 Fax: (020) 7183 0100 E-mail: info@stopbox.co.uk *Distribute light fittings*

Stopford Graham & Co. Ltd, Chapel House, 1 Borough Road, Altrincham, Cheshire, WA15 9RA Tel: 0161-941 1024 Fax: 0161-926 9773 *Marketing, public relations & promotional consultants*

Stopps Ltd, Lyon Road, Walton-on-Thames, Surrey, KT12 3RU Tel: (01932) 242086 Fax: (01932) 228893 E-mail: mail@stopps.co.uk *Shop fitters & architectural joiners refurbishments*

Stor Tech, Unit A Castle Park Industrial Estate, Bower Street, Oldham, OL1 3LN Tel: 0161-678 8597 Fax: 0161-665 0579 E-mail: info@stortech.ltd.uk *Storage & material handling systems*

Storacall Teleacoustics, 6 Enterprise Way, Cheltenham Trade Park, Cheltenham, Gloucestershire, GL51 8LZ Tel: (01242) 570995 Fax: (01242) 226131 E-mail: storacall.telea@btinternet.com *Manufacturers of telephone cabinets, kiosks & hoods*

Storaenso, Enso House, New Mill Road, Orpington, Kent, BR5 3TW Tel: (01689) 892700 Fax: (01689) 897290 *Paper agents & distributors*

Storaenso UK Ltd, 1 Phoenix Place, Nottingham, NG8 6BA Tel: 0115-964 7100 Fax: 0115-964 7170 *Paper agents*

Storage Concepts Ltd, Pate Road, Melton Mowbray, Leicestershire, LE13 0RG Tel: (01664) 410414 Fax: (01664) 569969 E-mail: sales@storageconcepts.co.uk *Pallet racking services*

Storage Designs, Station Road, Clive, Shrewsbury, SY4 3LD Tel: (01939) 220269 Fax: (01939) 220484 *Shelving & racking equipment retail*

▶ Storage Direct Ltd, 6 Russell Place, Trinity, Edinburgh, EH5 3HA Tel: 01506 871757 Fax: 01506 873400 E-mail: sales@mgk-storagedirect.co.uk *For all enquiries regarding storage direct limited please call 01506 871757*

▶ Storage Equipment Centre, Entrance Two, Gunnels Wood Road, Stevenage, Hertfordshire, SG1 2BT Tel: (0870) 2410872 Fax: (0870) 2410873 E-mail: info@sec-online.co.uk *At SEC we design & build storage solutions to solve materials handling problems through the use of pallet racking, conveyors, mezzanine floors etc., and also provide interior partitioning and office refurbishment services to suit our varied clients' needs.*

Storage Equipment Safety Service Ltd, Trafalgar Court, South Nelson Road, South Nelson Industrial Estate, Cramlington, Northumberland, NE23 1WF Tel: (01670) 736444 Fax: (01670) 739903 E-mail: sess@sess.co.uk *Industrial storage system inspectors*

Storage Equipment Systems, A Bumpers Farm Industrial Estate, Bristol Road, Bumpers Farm, Chippenham, Wiltshire, SN14 6LH Tel: (01249) 445593 Fax: (01249) 658779 E-mail: aashelving@aol.com *Pallet racking & storage equipment systems*

▶ Storage Industries Ltd, Sunrise House, Hulley Road, Macclesfield, Cheshire, SK10 2LP Tel: (01625) 505935 Fax: (01625) 268317 E-mail: info@storageindustries.co.uk *Shelving and pallet racking by Link 51, Dexion, Redirack, Hilo, Planned Storage and Apex Linpac*

Storage King, Orchard Works, Badsell Road, Orchard Business Centre, Five Oak Green, Tonbridge, Kent, TN12 6QU Tel: (01892) 832700 Fax: (01892) 838700 E-mail: fiveoak@storageking.co.uk *Self storage company*

Storage Logic, 24 High Street, Bovingdon, Hemel Hempstead, Hertfordshire, HP3 0HG Tel: (01442) 831133 Fax: (01442) 831144 E-mail: info@storage-logic.co.uk *Storage & materials handling equipment*

▶ Storageshop, Brookfield, Horsham Road, Alfold, Cranleigh, Surrey, GU6 8JE Tel: (07767) 821194 E-mail: sales@storageshop.co.uk *Suppliers of all shelving, racking & storage equipment*

Storagetek Ltd, 36 South Gyle Crescent, Edinburgh, EH12 9EB Tel: 0131-338 6515 Fax: 0131-339 3900 *Computer data storage services*

Store Forge, 15 Lintonville Terrace, Ashington, Northumberland, NE63 9UN Tel: (01670) 522088 Fax: (01670) 522088 *Steel fabricators*

Storefast Ltd, North End Park Corner Road, Betsham, Southfleet, Gravesend, Kent, DA13 9LJ Tel: (01474) 833824 Fax: (01474) 833236 E-mail: sales@storefast.co.uk *Cold storage warehouse services*

Storehire UK Ltd, Stansted Distribution Centre, Start Hill, Great Hallingbury, Bishop's Stortford, Hertfordshire, CM22 7DG Tel: (01279) 505202 Fax: (01279) 505233 *Self service storage centre*

Charles Storer Ltd, Coopers Lane, Northaw, Potters Bar, Hertfordshire, EN6 4NE Tel: (01707) 656261 Fax: (01707) 652919 E-mail: chasstorer@freeuk.com *Waste paper merchants*

Storer Refrigeration & Catering Manufacturers Ltd, Newstead Industrial Estate, Brookfield Road, Arnold, Nottingham, NG5 7ER Tel: 0115-920 0329 Fax: 0115-967 0676 E-mail: tedblake@supanet.com *Serveries, counters, refrigerated displays, heated displays, catering equipment, cold rooms, freezer rooms, temporary refrigeration hire, catering design, refrigeration, blast chillers*

Edwin Storey Builders Ltd, 1a Haslemere Road, Thornton Heath, Surrey, CR7 7BF Tel: (020) 8664 8277 Fax: (020) 8664 8279 *Foundation ground building contractors*

Storey Evans & Co. Ltd, Robin Mills, Leeds Road, Idle, Bradford, West Yorkshire, BD10 9TE Tel: (01274) 622222 Fax: (01274) 620444 E-mail: sales@storeyevans.co.uk

Storeys Industrial Products Ltd, Brantham, Manningtree, Essex, CO11 1NJ Tel: (01206) 392401 Fax: (01206) 395288 E-mail: info@wardlestoreys.com *Plastic & pvc manufrs*

Stork Bros Ltd, Bay Hall Mills, Bay Hall Common Road, Huddersfield, HD1 5EP Tel: (01484) 424283 Fax: (01484) 542876 *Woollen yarn spinners*

Storm Cutting Formes, Unit 2 Roe Street, Congleton, Cheshire, CW12 1PS Tel: (01260) 291793 Fax: (01260) 291794 *Packaging material manufrs*

▶ Storm Kayaks and Equipment, Unit 8 Harbour House, Harbour Way, Shoreham-by-Sea, West Sussex, BN43 5HZ Tel: (01273) 465406 E-mail: tony@stormkayaks.co.uk *Storm kayaks*

continued

continuation
have a great range of Sit-on-Top, White Water, Touring and Sea Kayaks, as well as a comprehensive range of Clothing and Equipment.

▶ Storm Lightning Protection, Droylsden, Manchester, M43 6XE Tel: 0161-370 9944 Fax: 0161-370 9955 E-mail: stormlighningprotection@hotmail.com *Lightning conductors manufrs*

▶ Storm Of London, 53a Neal Street, London, WC2H 9PJ Tel: (020) 7240 0888 Fax: (020) 7240 8586 *Watchers*

Storm Power, 13 Pendyffryn Road, Rhyl, Clwyd, LL18 4RU Tel: (01745) 354405 Fax: (01745) 361219 E-mail: sales@stormpower.co.uk *Electronic design consultants*

Storm Products, 28 Hawbank Road, East Kilbride, Glasgow, G74 5EX Tel: (01355) 249358 Fax: (01355) 249197 E-mail: sales@cvcs.co.uk *Data logging equipment manufrs*

▶ Stormcheck, 26a Bondgate Green, Ripon, North Yorkshire, HG4 1QW Tel: 01765 692053 Fax: 01765 692053 E-mail: sales@stormcheck.co.uk *Flat roof repairs using EPDM rubber membrane with a 50 year plus life expectancy and 20 year guarantee. Local Tradesmen with national company back up. Satisfaction guaranteed.*

Stormleaf Ltd, Unit 7 Premier House Midland Business Units, Finedon Road, Wellingborough, Northamptonshire, NN8 4AD Tel: (01933) 274499 Fax: (01933) 277794 *Timber merchants*

Stormont Truck & Van Ltd, Ellen Street, Portslade, Brighton, BN41 1DW Tel: (01273) 430828 Fax: (01273) 411490 *Motor vehicle accessory distributors service*

▶ Stornoway Plastics, Rigs Road, Stornoway, Isle of Lewis, HS1 2RF Tel: (01851) 702122 Fax: (01851) 701287 E-mail: info@stornowayplastics.com *Manufacturers of plastics for the fishing industry*

Storofile, Shirewood Store, Woodlands, Wimborne, Dorset, BH21 8LX Tel: (01202) 822115 Fax: (01202) 822866 E-mail: sales@storofile.com *Document management systems*

Sto-Rose Ltd, Unit 8, Park Farm, Wellham Road, Black Knotley, Braintree, Essex, CM77 8LQ Tel: (01376) 328256 Fax: (01376) 329256 E-mail: sales@fantasiaballoons.com *Toy balloon distributors*

Storplan Racking Ltd, The Airfield, Full Sutton, York, YO41 1HS Tel: (01759) 371553 Fax: (01759) 372451 E-mail: storplan@ic24.net *Storage & security equipment manufrs*

Storrington Auto Repairs, M J House, Old Mill Drive, Storrington, Pulborough, West Sussex, RH20 4RH Tel: (01903) 746694 Fax: (01903) 741101 *Garage repairers*

▶ Storrm Industrial, 7 Axis Way, Eaton Socon, St. Neots, Cambridgeshire, PE19 8QE Tel: (01480) 216056 Fax: (01480) 352332 *Work wear suppliers*

Storsack UK Ltd, Dalton Airfield, Dalton, Thirsk, North Yorkshire, YO7 3HE Tel: (01845) 577464 Fax: (01845) 578175 E-mail: info@storsack.co.uk *Bulk container & sack manufrs*

Stortex (UK) Ltd, Caird Centre, Caird Park, Hamilton, Lanarkshire, ML3 0EU Tel: (01698) 455821

Stortext FM, Hikenield House, Icknield Way, Andover, Hampshire, SP10 5AH Tel: (01264) 360900 Fax: (01264) 360901 E-mail: richard.butler@stortextfm.com *Using our 20 years of experience in document management we partner a number of major organisations providing; Automated document scanning and data capture services specialising in invoice processing (to feed AP systems and ebilling hubs); Mailroom management (electronic distribution of incoming post); Compiance process management (FSA and HMR&C rules), Sales Ledger invoices and proof of delivery; and Customer management. We deliver documents electronically to offshore (BPO) service providers and provide service delivery performance data and management. Scanned documents feed into cleint DM systems or we host them. Captured data updates our client systems (AP /Sales / Client /Member databases)*

▶ Stortford Computer Services Ltd, 9 Boundary Road, Bishop's Stortford, Hertfordshire, CM23 5LE Tel: (01279) 657855 E-mail: contact@stortfordcomputerservices.co.uk *IT Consultancy and Software Development.*

Storwave Ltd, 1 Flowers Hill Close, Flowers Hill Trading Estate, Bristol, BS4 5LF Tel: 0117-972 8855 Fax: 0117-916 9234 E-mail: sales@theedmgroup.co.uk *Image processing equipment documents* Also at: Newport (Gwent) & Stroud

▶ Story Construction Ltd, Catherinefield Road, Dumfries, DG1 3PJ Tel: (01387) 249699 Fax: (01387) 249701 E-mail: admin@storyconstruction.co.uk

Storysacks Support Project, Pinehurst Infant School, Beech Av, Swindon, SN2 1JT Tel: 01793 421168 Fax: 01793 421168 *Educational equipment & supplies*

▶ Karl Storz Endoscopy UK Ltd, Ninewells, Thomas Wise Place, Dundee, DD2 1UB Tel: (01382) 647500 Fax: (01382) 644999 E-mail: sales@karlstorz-uk.com *Medical suppliers*

▶ Karl Storz Endoscopy (UK) Ltd, 392 Edinburgh Avenue, Slough, SL1 4UF Tel: (01753) 503500 Fax: (01753) 578124 E-mail: customerservices@karlstorz-uk.com *Video imaging equipment suppliers*

▶ Stotfold Plating Co. Ltd, Taylors Road, Stotfold, Hitchin, Hertfordshire, SG5 4AX Tel: (01462) 732158 Fax: (01462) 835330 *Electroplating services*

Stothert & Pitt, Lower Bristol Road, Bath, BA2 3DJ Tel: (01225) 314400 Fax: (01225) 332529 *Mechanical handling equipment manufrs*

Stotron Ltd, York Road Industrial Park, Derwent Road, Malton, North Yorkshire, YO17 6YB Tel: (01653) 600492 Fax: (01653) 690980 *Electronic component distributors*

Stott Concrete Pumping Ltd, PO Box 393, Wigan, Lancashire, WN6 7LA Tel: (01942) 497776 Fax: (01942) 515952 E-mail: enquiries@stottconcretepumping.co.uk *Plant hire*

J. Stott & Sons Ltd, 7 Richmond Hill, Blackburn, BB1 7LB Tel: (01254) 51567 Fax: (01254) 682780 E-mail: tony@jstott.com *Cash & carry wholesalers*

Stott O'Connell, 1 Nesfield Street, Bradford, West Yorkshire, BD1 3ET Tel: (01274) 722549 Fax: (01274) 724524 *Carton manufrs*

Stour Computer Services, Croft Road, Sudbury, Suffolk, CO10 1HJ Tel: (01787) 374959 *Computers & computer repairs services*

Stour Precision Tools Ltd, George Baylis Road, Berry Hill Industrial Estate, Droitwich, Worcestershire, WR9 9RB Tel: (01905) 773932 Fax: (01905) 776434 *Cavity mould tooling designers & manufrs*

Stour Precision Tools Ltd, George Baylis Road, Berry Hill Industrial Estate, Droitwich, Worcestershire, WR9 9RB Tel: (01905) 773932 Fax: (01905) 776434 *Press tool manufrs*

▶ Stour Valley Trophies, 6 Springfield Terrace, East Street, Sudbury, Suffolk, CO10 2TS Tel: (01787) 377139 *Sports trophies engravers*

Stourbridge Engineering Services Ltd, 19a Oak Street, Quarry Bank, Brierley Hill, West Midlands, DY5 2JN Tel: (01384) 561600 Fax: (01384) 561600 *Machinery reconditioning services & machinery removal contractors*

Stourbridge Fork Lift Co. Ltd, Knoll Hill, Belbroughton Road, Blakedown, Kidderminster, Worcestershire, DY10 3LN Tel: (01562) 700099 Fax: (01562) 700915 *Fork lift truck distributors*

Stourbridge Navigation Trust, 2 Canal Street, Stourbridge, West Midlands, DY8 4LU Tel: (01384) 395216 Fax: (01384) 395216 *Hospitality event organisers*

Stourport Sign Studio, 3 Sandy La Industrial Estate, Stourport-on-Severn, Worcestershire, DY13 9QB Tel: (01299) 826044 Fax: (01299) 826044 *Signwriters, sign & t-shirt printers*

▶ Stourton Grange Scaffolding Ltd, Unit 3 Long Close Ind Estate, Dolly Lane, Leeds, LS10 4SF Tel: 0113- 277 9045 Fax: 0113-277 9993 E-mail: john@sgsltd.co.uk *Scaffolding erectors*

Stovax Ltd, Falcon Road, Sowton Industrial Estate, Exeter, EX2 7LF Tel: (01392) 474011 Fax: (01392) 219932 E-mail: info@stovax.com *Manufacturers & distributors of fireplaces & stoves*

The Stove Gallery, 41-43 High Street, Starbeck, Harrogate, North Yorkshire, HG2 7LQ Tel: (01423) 887799 Fax: (01423) 889416 E-mail: sales@thestovegallery.com *Stove manufrs*

▶ Stovesonline Ltd, Box and Rose Cottage, Capton, Dartmouth, Devon, TQ6 0JE Tel: 0845 226 5754 Fax: 0870 220 0920 E-mail: info@stovesonline.co.uk *Stovesonline supplies woodburning stoves and multifuel stoves, flue pipe, flexible chimney liner, pumice chimney and insulated stainless steel chimney systems. We offer a flue and chimney design service for domestic situations and architects both for new build and when re-lining existing chimneys or making a chimney in an existing house. Based on twenty five years experience in supplying and installing stoves and flues we specialise in offering expert and impartial advice and follow that up with being able to deliver everything needed for the job to both private and trade customers.*

Stow Agricultural Services, Lower Swell Road, Stow on the Wold, Cheltenham, Gloucestershire, GL54 1LD Tel: (01451) 830400 *General farm & estate hardware*

Stowell Concrete, Arnolds Way, Yatton, Bristol, BS49 4QN Tel: (01934) 833340 Fax: (01934) 835474 E-mail: sales@stowellconcrete.co.uk *Manufacturers of concrete products*

Stowell Concrete Ltd, Edford Green, Holcombe, Radstock, BA3 5DA Tel: (01761) 232282 Fax: (01761) 232806 E-mail: enquiries@stowellconcrete.co.uk *Concrete product manufrs*

▶ Stowell Concrete, Winterstoke Road, Weston-super-Mare, Avon, BS23 3YW Tel: (01934) 628185

W. Stowell (Shipping) Ltd, 37 Coleridge Avenue, Low Fell, Gateshead, Tyne & Wear, NE9 6EN Tel: 0191-487 3222 Fax: 0191-491 0056 E-mail: sparestan@stowellshipping.co.uk *Ship & forwarding agents*

Tim Stower & Partners Ltd, Unit A, Waterfront House, New Brunswick Street, Wakefield, West Yorkshire, WF1 5QW Tel: (01924) 375947 Fax: (01924) 382707 E-mail: stower.tprs@btconnect.co.uk *Civil & structural engineering consultants services*

Stowfledge Ltd, Mill Works, Mountsorrel Lane, Sileby, Loughborough, Leicestershire, LE12 7NF Tel: (01509) 812915 Fax: (01509) 816648 *Pressings & general engineers*

Stowlin Ltd, Radnor Road, Wigston, Leicestershire, LE18 4XY Tel: 0116-278 5373 Fax: 0116-277 2616 E-mail: kate@stowlin.com *Chemical suppliers*

STR Ambergate, Dylan Laboratories, Ambergate, Belper, Derbyshire, DE56 2EY Tel: (01773) 854000 *Textile technology services*

▶ Strachan Antiques, 40 Darnley Street, Glasgow, G41 2SE Tel: 0141-429 4411 Fax: 0141-429 4411 E-mail: sales@strachanantiques.co.uk *Antiques distributors*

Strachan & Livingston, 23-25 Kirk Wynd, Kirkcaldy, Fife, KY1 1EP Tel: (01592) 261451 Fax: (01592) 204180 *Newspaper publishers*

Strad Concrete, 125 Straid Road, Bushmills, County Antrim, BT57 8XU Tel: (028) 2073 1751 Fax: 028 20731751 *Building contractor & premix concrete supplier*

▶ Stradform Ltd, The Conference Centre, East Moors Road, Cardiff, CF24 5SL Tel: (029) 2049 3989

Stradway Vending Ltd, Stradway Buildings, Hume St, Kidderminster, Worcestershire, DY11 6RD Tel: (01562) 822272 *Vending machine sales & services*

Straight Eight Precision, Unit F2 Phoenix Trading Estate, London Rd, Thrupp, Stroud, Glos, GL5 2BN Tel: (01453) 884762 Fax: (01453) 884763 *Precision engineers*

Straight Line Products Ltd, Unit 39 Uxbridge Trading Estate, Arundel Road, Uxbridge, Middlesex, UB8 2RP Tel: (01895) 850577 Fax: (01895) 850766 E-mail: george@straightlineproducts.co.uk *Manufacturers of plastic mouldings*

Straight Line Services Ltd, Westwood Farm, Highcross Road, Southfleet, Gravesend, Kent, DA13 9PH Tel: (01474) 832244 Fax: (01474) 834414 *Fabricating engineers*

C.J. Strain & Son Ltd, Lugton Road, Shillford, Hamlet, Glasgow, G78 3BA Tel: (01505) 850950 Fax: (01505) 850951 E-mail: cjstrain@btconnect.com *Sign manufrs*

▶ Strain Measurement Devices Ltd, Bury Road, Chedburgh, Bury St. Edmunds, Suffolk, IP29 4UQ Tel: (01284) 852000 Fax: (01284) 852371 E-mail: askus@smdsensors.co.uk Principal Export Areas: Worldwide *Located in Chedburgh, UK, and trading worldwide, we specialise in the design and manufacture of custom and standard load cells and pressure sensors, all based on our own thin-film strain-gauge technology, together with a wide range of liquid level sensors. Our sensors are applied in industrial measurements, process control, medical, subsea, test-system, aerospace, education, vehicle and research applications. Gauge characteristics of high stability, rugged reliability, low power consumption, high temperature and high resistance, plus a UK-based volume manufacturing capability supported by specialist design engineering, make our services ideal for OEM's. Precision medical scales, non-invasive pressure sensors, infusion-pump sensors, enteral feed pump sensors, irrigation-pump sensors, tocodynamometers, orthopaedic sensors, exercise equipment sensors, contact-force sensors and patient-weighing sensors have all been supplied for medical device applications.*

Strainstall UK Ltd, 10 Mariners Way, Cowes, Isle of Wight, PO31 8PD Tel: (01983) 203600 Fax: (01983) 291335 E-mail: sales@strainstall.co.uk *Manufacturers of load cells & crane safety, load & marine buoy monitoring systems. Also stress analysis, structural monitoring & specialised engineering services. System manufacturers including ships' hull stress monitoring, moving/docking, winch safety, data acquisition, temperature measuring & noise analysis. In addition, geotechnical consulting engineers* Also at: Bath

Straits Construction, Bloomfield Road, Tipton, West Midlands, DY4 9ET Tel: 0121-557 8758 Fax: 0121-520 0435 *Structural steelwork & cladders*

▶ Strakan Group plc, Buckholm Mill, Galashiels, Selkirkshire, TD1 2HB Tel: (01896) 668060 Fax: (01896) 668061

▶ Straker Cleaning, 41 Abbotts Road, Sutton, Surrey, SM3 9SJ Tel: (020) 8644 8892 E-mail: chris@strakercleaning.co.uk *A NEW level in cleaning for carpets, curtains, upholstery & rugs.*AllergSTOP Authorised Network Member covering Surrey & SW London.*NCCA member 97.*MoD vetted & cleared.*Fully insured for liability & treatment risk.*Appointments available 7 days a week.*

Straker Systems Ltd, 9 Mollins Court, Cumbernauld, Glasgow, G68 9HP Tel: (01236) 456666 Fax: (01236) 722912 E-mail: sales@straker.com *Computer manufrs*

Stralfors P.L.C., Cardew Way, Redruth, Cornwall, TR15 1SH Tel: (01209) 312800 Fax: (01209) 312900 E-mail: enquiries@stralfors.co.uk *Core printing company*

Stramit International Ltd, Creeting Road, Stowmarket, Suffolk, IP14 5BA Tel: (01449) 613564 Fax: (01449) 678381 E-mail: sales@stramit-int.com *Building material suppliers*

Strand Business Systems Ltd, 542 Chigwell Road, Woodford Green, Essex, IG8 8PA Tel: (020) 8559 2555 Fax: (020) 8506 0561 *Computer software suppliers*

Strand Engineering North West Ltd, Ironworks Road, Barrow-in-Furness, Cumbria, LA14 2PH Tel: (01229) 821991 Fax: (01229) 811104 E-mail: strandeng@yahoo.co.uk *Quality machining sheetmetal workers*

Strand Refrigeration, 82 Marlborough Rd, Hyde, Cheshire, SK14 5HX Tel: 0161-366 0037 *Refrigeration & air conditioning*

Strand Technology Group, 10-12 Westgate, Skelmersdale, Lancashire, WN8 8AZ Tel: (0845) 6607968 E-mail: mail@standtech.co.uk *Software developers*

▶ Strandhill Civil Engineering Ltd, 3 Dukes Road, Southampton, SO14 0SQ Tel: (023) 8055 9121 Fax: (023) 8055 9660

Alex Strang Dental Laboratory, Cross Street, Venture House, Macclesfield, Cheshire, SK11 7PG Tel: (01625) 421368 *Dental laboratory*

Strange & Dawson Advertising Ltd, Ninth Floor Clifton Heights, Triangle West, Clifton, Bristol, BS8 1EJ Tel: 0117-925 3830 Fax: 0117-925 3851 *Advertising agencies*

▶ Ian Strange (Tansley) Ltd, Holly Lane, Tansley, Matlock, Derbyshire, DE4 5FF Tel: (01629) 583835 Fax: (01629) 583835 E-mail: admin@fosterfridge.co.uk *Commercial refrigeration suppliers & general engineers*

Strange Jeens & Mathison, 84 Warwick Road, Carlisle, CA1 1DE Tel: (01228) 524406 Fax: (01228) 548057 E-mail: sj_m@btconnect.com *Vehicle assessors & valuers*

Strank's Removals, Unit 5 Wotton Trading Estate, Ashford, Kent, TN23 6LL Tel: (01233) 646478 Fax: (01233) 645653 E-mail: admin@stranks-removals.co.uk *Office removals & crate hire services*

Stransky Thompson Public Relations, The Chemistry Lab, 57 Kingsway Place, Sans Walk, London, EC1R OLY Tel: (020) 7689 5159 Fax: (020) 7689 5156 E-mail: enquiries@clear-group.co.uk *Public relations consultants*

▶ Strap Trap, Stanmore Road, London, E11 3BU Tel: (020) 8530 3484 E-mail: info@straptrap.co.uk *Haberdashery manufrs*

Strapex, Unit 50 Empire Industrial Park, Aldridge, Walsall, WS9 8UQ Tel: (01922) 742500 Fax: (01922) 742501E-mail: info@strapex.co.uk *Strapex supplies strapping and stretchwarpping machinery and products for securing merchandise for transport.*

Strata Communications, 25 Hibson Avenue, Rochdale, Lancashire, OL12 7RU Tel: (01706) 344375 Fax: (01706) 633172 E-mail: info@stratacommunications.co.uk *Telephone engineers & installers*

▶ Strata Contracts Ltd, Copsham House, 53 Broad Street, Chesham, Buckinghamshire, HP5 3EA Tel: (01494) 778712 Fax: (01494) 778925 E-mail: stratacontracts@btconnect.com

▶ Strata Financial, 11 Reynolds Wharf, Coalport, Telford, Shropshire, TF8 7HU Tel: (0845) 2260125 E-mail: info@strataifa.co.uk *Financial planning consultants*

Strata Flame Cutting & Fabrications, 101 York Road, Hall Green, Birmingham, B28 8LH Tel: 0121-778 5022 Fax: 0121-777 8241 *Profile cutting flame services*

Strata Products Ltd, Strata Building, Waterloo Road, London, NW2 7UH Tel: (020) 8450 7829 Fax: (020) 8450 3114 E-mail: sales@strataproducts.co.uk *Plastic household goods manufrs*

▶ Strata Products Ltd, Brookhill Industrial Estate, Pinxton, Nottingham, NG16 6NT Tel: (01773) 510520 Fax: (01773) 510502 E-mail: sales@strata.co.uk *Classic injection moulding*

Stratascan, Vinyard House, Upper Hook Road, Upton-Upon-Severn, Worcester, WR8 0SA Tel: (01684) 592266 Fax: (01684) 594142 E-mail: info@stratascan.co.uk *Geophysical surveyors*

Stratec Medical Ltd, 20 Tewin Road, Welwyn Garden City, Hertfordshire, AL7 1LG Tel: (01707) 332212 Fax: (01707) 338504 *Surgical & orthopedic implant distributors*

Strategem Ltd, Hough End Hall, 95 Nell Lane, Manchester, M21 7AZ Tel: 0161-860 0344 Fax: 0161-860 0888 E-mail: strategem@strategem.co.uk *Management consultants*

▶ Strategic Insight, Orchard Lodge, Roydon, Diss, Norfolk, IP22 5XL Tel: 01379 641168 E-mail: m.lawton@strategic-insight.org *We deliver cost effective market research services to a wide range of UK organisations. Our specialist areas include mystery shopping, customer satisfaction and new product/service development*

Strategic Maintenance Planning Ltd, Stanton Court, Stirling Road South Marston Indust Estate, Swindon, SN1 1PZ Tel: (01793) 823013 Fax: (01793) 823014 E-mail: info@smpltd.co.uk *Strategic Maintenance Planning is renowned for offering Quality, Solutions and Value. We are the leading provider of Maintenance and IT Solutions, not just software systems. Whether it is Computerised Maintenance Management Software CMMS, developing maintenance strategies or implementing systems, all require a proven and effective methodology to ensure success and demonstrably improve performance. Our dedicated team of professional Engineers and IT Consultants listen first to understand customer requirements and in partnership, deliver a product and service beyond expectations. From blue-chip multi-nationals, to single site organisations in both the private and public sectors, Strategic Maintenance Planning offer IT and Project Management solutions that fit.*

▶ Strategic Marine Services Ltd, Marine House, Station Road, Hoylake, Wirral, Merseyside, CH47 4AA Tel: 0151-632 3355 Fax: 0151-632 3399 E-mail: hq@stratmarine.com *Marine Consultants - Promoting High Standards in the Maritime Industries*

Strategic Sourcing International Limited, Unit A46, Western Avenue, Bridgend Industrial Estate, Bridgend, Mid Glamorgan, CF31 3RT Tel: 0870 2111195 Fax: 0870 2111197 E-mail: sales@sourcewithus.com *Contract packaging services**

Strategic Systems Technology Ltd, 14 Landons Close, London, E14 9QQ Tel: (020) 7538 8228 Fax: (0870) 2351411 E-mail: info@sst.co.uk *Computer systems & software developers*

Strategic Thought Group plc, Old Town Hall, Centre Court Shopping Centre, Queens Road, London, SW19 8YB Tel: (020) 8410 4000 Fax: (020) 8410 4030 E-mail: sales@strategicthought.com *Computer consultants*

Strategix, Regatta Place, Marlow Road, Bourne End, Buckinghamshire, SL8 5TD Tel: (01628) 532565 Fax: (01628) 551490 E-mail: strategix@tissoft.co.uk *Distribution, financial accounting & service management*

▶ Strategy Consulting Ltd, The Haven Scotland House Farm, Stockwood Road, Bristol, BS4 5LU Tel: (0845) 8386906 Fax: (0870) 1369549 E-mail: info@strategyconsultinglimited.co.uk *Management consultants services*

Strategy In Computing Ltd, Mooring Business Centre Willows End House, 9 Carolus Creek, Penn Island, Milton Keynes, MK15 8AZ Tel: (01908) 201202 Fax: (01908) 201170 E-mail: reply@strategy-in-computing.co.uk *Computer software consultancy document handling specialists*

Strategy International Ltd, The Ivory Ho, St. Katherine Docks, London, E1W 1BN Tel: (020) 7480 5652 Fax: (020) 7488 9643 E-mail: ej@dgroup.co.uk *Management consultants*

Strategy Partners International Ltd, Chappell House, The Green, Datchet, Slough, SL3 9EH Tel: (01753) 592787 Fax: (01753) 592789 *IT analysts programming & networking*

Strategy Partners International Ltd, Chappell House, The Green, Datchet, Slough, SL3 9EH Tel: (01753) 592787 Fax: (01753) 592789 *IT industrial analyst*

continued

Stratford Paper Co. Ltd, 50 Holness Road, London, E15 4EW Tel: (020) 8534 1639 Fax: (020) 8519 1810 *Wholesale stationers*

▶ Stratford Precision Engineering Ltd, 5 The Rubicon Centre, Broad Ground Road, Redditch, Worcestershire, B98 8YP Tel: (01527) 502567 Fax: (01527) 501921 E-mail: info@stratfordprecision.co.uk *Metal pressing*

▶ Stratford Repro Ltd, 42 Greenhill Street, Stratford-upon-Avon, Warwickshire, CV37 6LE Tel: (01789) 269650 Fax: (01789) 414342 E-mail: sales@stratfordrepro.co.uk

Stratford Wire Works, Rowse Close, London, E15 2HX Tel: (020) 8534 1950 Fax: (020) 8534 8280 *Roller shutter manufrs*

Strathaird Salmon Ltd, 21-23 Longman Drive, Inverness, IV1 1SU Tel: (01463) 715123 Fax: (01463) 230867 E-mail: reception@strathaird.com *Fish processors*

Strathaven Belting Co. Ltd, 33 Colvilles Place, East Kilbride, Glasgow, G75 0PZ Tel: (01357) 529936 Fax: (01357) 521188 *Conveyor belting manufrs*

Strathclyde Auto Supplies Ltd, Townholm Kilmarnock, Kilmarnock, Ayrshire, KA3 1BB Tel: (01563) 534440 Fax: (01563) 534361 E-mail: info@acs-auto.co.uk *Car paint & Sundries suppliers*

Strathclyde Fans Ltd, Unit B4 Somervell Trading Estate, Somervell Street, Cambuslang, Glasgow, G72 7EB Tel: 0141-641 0224 Fax: 0141-641 7796 *Fans, heating & ventilation materials* Also at: Aberdeen

Strathclyde Firemans Personal Alarm Co. Ltd, 234 Allison Street, Glasgow, G42 8RT Tel: 0141-423 7011 E-mail: ellis.cohen@amserve.net *Fire-fighters safety equipment manufrs*

Strathclyde Hydraulics Ltd, 3 Bonnyton Industrial Estate, Munro Place, Kilmarnock, Ayrshire, KA1 2NP Tel: (01563) 543349 Fax: (01563) 533226 *Hydraulic engineers*

▶ Strathclyde Passenger Transport, Glasgow Subway Broomloan Depot, Robert Street, Glasgow, G51 3HB Tel: 0141-333 3164 Fax: 0141-425 1023 E-mail: sales@spt.co.uk

Strathclyde Pest Services, 53 High Street, Paisley, Renfrewshire, PA1 2AN Tel: 0141-889 1990 Fax: 0141-889 1990 *Pest control services*

Strathclyde Powder Coatings Scotland Ltd, 40-42 Telford Road, East Lenziemill Industrial Estate, Glasgow, G67 2NH Tel: (01236) 734242 Fax: (01236) 720619 E-mail: douglas.spc@btconnect.com *Power coating services*

Strathcona Conveyors Ltd, UNIT 3A, 95 Westburn Drive, Camduslamg, Glasgow, G72 7NA Tel: 0141-876 4525 Fax: 0141-620 2165 *Conveyor belting suppliers*

Strathmore Mineral Water Co. Ltd, 126 West High St, Forfar, Angus, DD8 1BP Tel: (01307) 466147 Fax: (01307) 466072 E-mail: bobwatson@matthewclark.co.uk *Mineral water (carbonated) manufrs*

Strathmore Woollen Co. Ltd, Station Works, North Street, Forfar, Angus, DD8 3BN Tel: (01307) 462135 Fax: (01307) 468603 E-mail: info@tartanbystrathmore.co.uk *Worsted tartan manufrs*

Stratos Control System, Great Harrowden Lodge, The Slips, Great Harrowden, Wellingborough, Northamptonshire, NN9 5AE Tel: (01933) 677550 Fax: (01933) 677884 *Control systems manufrs*

Stratstone Of Mayfair, 14 Berkeley Street, London, W1J 8DX Tel: (020) 7514 0400 Fax: (020) 7491 1410 E-mail: sales-mayfair@pendragon.uk.com *Jaguar dealership*

Stratton Sales Ltd, 1 Station Road, Shepton Mallet, Somerset, BA4 5DD Tel: (01749) 344071 Fax: (01749) 346134 E-mail: info@strattonsales.co.uk *Cheese textiles products & manufrs*

Stratton Woodcraft, Foxcote House, Broad Lane, East Chinnock, Yeovil, Somerset, BA22 9ES Tel: (01935) 862776 Fax: (01935) 862776 *Kitchen & furniture manufrs*

Stratus Computer Systems Ltd, Stratus House, 47 Woodthorpe Road, Ashford, Middlesex, TW15 2RP Tel: (01784) 266500 Fax: (01784) 266555 E-mail: infouk@stratus.com *Server hardware manufrs*

Philip Straughton, 8 High Sand Lane, Cockermouth, Cumbria, CA13 9NA Tel: (01900) 825444 *Joinery*

▶ The Strawberry Card Co., 8 Clarence Road, Exmouth, Devon, EX8 1LE Tel: (01395) 274923 Fax: (01395) 274923 E-mail: sian@thestrawberrycardcompany.co.uk *Designers of greetings cards*

▶ Strawberry Global Technology, 1-2 219 High Street, Hampton Hill, Hampton, Middlesex, TW12 1NP Tel: (020) 8973 1414 Fax: (020) 8973 1515 E-mail: sales@strawberrygt.com *Computer systems consultants*

Strax Gas Ltd, Longfield Road, Sydenham Industrial Estate, Leamington Spa, Warwickshire, CV31 1XB Tel: (01926) 477511 Fax: (01926) 477510 E-mail: sales@straxgas.co.uk *Gas fir manufrs*

▶ Streaker Promotions, Bentwaters Parks, Rendlesham, Woodbridge, Suffolk, IP12 2TW Tel: (01394) 460612 Fax: (01394) 460816 *Promotional items manufrs*

▶ Stream, Fishburn Industrial Estate, Fishburn, Stockton-on-Tees, Cleveland, TS21 4AJ Tel: (01740) 623311 Fax: (01740) 623311 E-mail: enquiries@streamsupplies.f2s.com

Stream Environmental, 100-102 Headstone Road, Harrow, Middlesex, HA1 1PF Tel: (020) 8933 6611 Fax: (020) 8424 8001 E-mail: sales@streamenvironmental.co.uk *Design & engineering solutions specialists*

▶ stream:20, Southbank house, Blackprince Road, London, SE1 7SJ Tel: 0207 7932450 *stream:20 specialises in delivering direct online revenue to your online business. We focus on affiliate marketing, email marketing, partnership marketing and pay per click marketing*

▶ Streamline Computer Solutions Ltd, Orchard House, Barncroft Road, Berkhamsted, Hertfordshire, HP4 3NL Tel: (01442) 405768 E-mail: alan@streamline-solutions.co.uk *Professional & logical business software solutions*

Streamline Dispence Ltd, Brunel Court, Stroudwater Business Park, Stonehouse, Gloucestershire, GL10 3SW Tel: (01453) 821155 Fax: (01453) 821166 E-mail: dispense@enterprise.net *Specialists in bar & cellar equipment*

▶ Streamline Fishing, Forest Road, New Ollerton, Newark, Nottinghamshire, NG22 9QT Tel: (01623) 869363 Fax: (01623) 869363 *Fishing tackle suppliers*

Streamline Graphics, Banhaw Wood Lodge, Lower Benefield, Peterborough, PE8 5AG Tel: (01832) 205363 Fax: (01733) 205216 E-mail: streamline-graphics@tiscali.co.uk *Silk screen & hot press printing services*

Streamline Outsource Ltd, The Innovation Centre, Rennes Drive, University Of Exeter Campus, Exeter, EX4 4RN Tel: (07743) 845124 Fax: (0870) 4584046 E-mail: sales@streamlineoutsource.com *Full design for manufacture using solid works*

Streamline Precision Ltd, Spedding Road, Fenton Industrial Estate, Fenton, Stoke-On-Trent, ST4 2ST Tel: (01782) 847408 Fax: (01782) 749261 *Precision & cnc engineers*

▶ Streamline Press Ltd, 11 Boston Road, Leicester, LE4 1AA Tel: 0116-235 5003 Fax: 0116-235 5004 E-mail: enquiries@streamlinepress.co.uk

▶ Streamline Shipping Agencies Ltd, 7 Fairfield Place, East Kilbride, Glasgow, G74 5LP Tel: (01355) 276710

Streamline Waterjet & Laser Cutters Ltd, Kingsway South, Team Valley Trading Estate, Gateshead, Tyne & Wear, NE11 0JL Tel: 0191-491 4422 Fax: 0191-497 3421 E-mail: streamline@responsive-engineering.com *Streamline combines the Waterjet and Laser processes with many years of experience, expertise and technology to offer an unrivalled precision profiling service. CNC Bending complements the core processes and enhances Streamline's total capability. Waterjet cutting accurately cuts materials up to 150mm thick including armour plate. Laser capability includes rotary cutting for Tubes and Section. Streamline is part of the Responsive Engineering group of companies*

Strebel Ltd, Unit 1f Albany Park, Camberley, Surrey, GU16 7PB Tel: (01276) 685422 Fax: (01276) 685405 E-mail: andy.parker@strebel.co.uk *Boiler & radiator manufrs*

Strebor Fire Protection (Intl) Ltd, 20 Brook Road, Wimborne, Dorset, BH21 2BH Tel: (01202) 886797 Fax: (01202) 889329 E-mail: sales@streborfire.com *Fire protection equipment manufrs*

Street Express Ltd, Roman Ridge Road, Sheffield, S9 1GA Tel: 0114-243 1142 Fax: 0114-256 1739 E-mail: info@scx.co.uk *Material & mechanical handling solutions*

▶ Street Workz, Silver Wing Industrial Estate, Horatius Way, Croydon, CR0 4RU Tel: (020) 8603 7272 Fax: (020) 8603 7272

Streethay Wharf Ltd, Burton Road, Streethay, Lichfield, Staffordshire, WS13 8LT Tel: (01543) 414808 Fax: (01543) 414770 *Narrow boat suppliers*

Streetly Windows Ltd, 338 Aldridge Road, Streetly, Sutton Coldfield, West Midlands, B74 2DT Tel: 0121-353 5886 Fax: 0121-353 2908 *UPVC double glazed windows & conservatories manufrs*

Streets Heaver Computer Systems Ltd, 4 Low Moor Road, Lincoln, LN6 3JY Tel: (01522) 872000 Fax: (01522) 872255 E-mail: control@streetsheaver.com *Software developers*

▶ Streets Printers Ltd, Royston Road, Baldock, Hertfordshire, SG7 6NW Tel: (01462) 893771 Fax: (01462) 894660 E-mail: sales@streetsprinters.co.uk *Well established printing company with reputation for quality, reliability and competitive pricing. Our comprehensive service includes a creative design team, litho and digital printing and now the latest poster printing. From one copy to a million, we are your printers. If you're looking for a printer you can trust? You have just found them!*

Streetwise Courier Services, 25 Johns Mews, London, WC1N 2NS Tel: (020) 7404 6161 Fax: (020) 7404 6045 E-mail: mach1ltd@aol.com *Courier services*

Strella Fabrics Ltd, Radford Boulevard, Nottingham, NG7 5QG Tel: 0115-955 4444 Fax: 0115-955 4500 E-mail: enquiries@strella-fabrics.ltd.uk *Embroidery & lace manufrs*

Strenco Tools Ltd, 1 Kelston Road, Bristol, BS10 5EP Tel: 0117-950 7447 Fax: 0117-949 6494 E-mail: sales@strencotools.co.uk *Toolmakers, support & solid modeling equipment services*

▶ Stress Engineering Services (Europe) Limited, Bracken Lodge, Brookside Close, Runcton, Chichester, West Sussex, PO20 1PY Tel: 01243 778231 E-mail: info@seseurope.com *An independent company specialising in structural integrity support for through-life asset management.*We offer design and materials evaluation, fitness for service, life prediction, life extension and performance optimisation, safety risk and reliability management, and trouble-shooting and problem-solving. This includes failure analysis and litigation advice.*We primarily serve the power generation, petrochemical/refining, defence and transport sectors.*

Stressline Ltd, Lunds Field Quarry, Carnforth, Lancashire, LA5 9NB Tel: (01524) 732204 Fax: (01524) 735831 E-mail: mail@stressline.ltd.uk *Pre-stressed concrete lintel & floor beams manufrs*

Stressline Ltd, Station Road, Stoney Stanton, Leicester, LE9 4LX Tel: (01455) 272457 Fax: (01455) 274564 E-mail: info@stressline.ltd.uk *Concrete products manufrs*

Streten Hills Mineral Water Co., Shrewsbury Road, Church Stretton, Shropshire, SY6 6HD Tel: (01694) 722935 Fax: (01694) 724318 *Mineral water producers*

▶ Stretford Angling Centre, 854 Chester Road, Stretford, Manchester, M32 0QJ Tel: 0161-865 2646 *Fishing tackle manufrs*

Stretford Industrial Services Ltd, 8 Radnor Street, Stretford, Manchester, M32 8LE Tel: 0161-865 4235 Fax: 0161-865 0139 E-mail: sales@sisgroup.co.uk *Signs makers, playground & road marking contractors*

▶ Strettle Memorials, Moor Edge Road, Shiremoor, Newcastle upon Tyne, NE27 0HU Tel: 0191-253 3222 Fax: 0191-297 1775

▶ Stretton Bros Ltd, Hamilton Street, Oldham, OL4 1DA Tel: 0161-633 3990 Fax: 0161-627 4772

▶ Stretton Bros Leicester, 27 Lunsford Road, Leicester, LE5 0HW Tel: 0116-274 1166 Fax: 0116-246 0299

Stretton Engineering Co. Ltd, 365 Old Church Road, Coventry, CV6 7DT Tel: (024) 7668 9664 Fax: (024) 7668 9664 *Production engineers*

▶ Stretton Gates & Automation, Unit 11 Manor Industrial Estate, Lower Wash Lane, Warrington, WA4 1PL Tel: (01925) 268414 *Iron workers*

Stribbons Ltd, 99 Sanders Road, Finedon Road Industrial Estate, Wellingborough, Northamptonshire, NN8 4NL Tel: (01933) 443446 Fax: (01933) 443435 E-mail: info@stribbons.co.uk Purchasing Contact: G.I. Curtis Sales Contact: G.I. Curtis Principal Export Areas: Worldwide *Manufacturers of bows (fashion/decorative), carry handles (tagged cord), cord (fancy), elastic braid, gift wrappings or accessories, packaging fancy accessories (ribbon/bow etc), ribbon (decorative), tassels & trimmings. Also point of sale/purchase/marketing display designers/ producers/services & ribbon products to customer design*

Strickland Direct Ltd, 5 Main Road, Cropthorne, Pershore, Worcestershire, WR10 3NE Tel: (01386) 860349 Fax: (01386) 860057 E-mail: sales@stricklanduk.com *Bucket & excavator attachment manufrs*

Strickland Direct Ltd, 5 Main Road, Cropthorne, Pershore, Worcestershire, WR10 3NE Tel: (01386) 860349 Fax: (01386) 860057 *Manufacturers of earth moving equipment*

Strickland & Co. (Electrical) Ltd, 113-117 Springfield Road, Windsor, Berkshire, SL4 3PZ Tel: (01753) 830040 Fax: (01753) 867894 E-mail: ccelectrical@btconnect.com *Electrical supplies to the trade*

▶ Stride Ltd, The Briars, Waterberry Drive, Waterlooville, Hampshire, PO7 7YH Tel: (023) 9224 8790 Fax: (023) 9224 8799 E-mail: info@stride.co.uk *Leading commercial insurance broker. Specialists to the property market. Our proffesional service is unrivalled and our prices amongst the best in the insurance market.*

Stride Supplies Ltd, 33 Monkspath Business Park, Highlands Road, Shirley, Solihull, West Midlands, B90 4NZ Tel: 0121-733 3010 Fax: 0121-733 3360 E-mail: sales@stride-technical.co.uk *Spring wire stockholders*

Strike Club Correspondents London Ltd, 108 Fenchurch Street, London, EC3M 5JR Tel: (020) 7428 7708 Fax: (020) 7709 9401 E-mail: scc.lon@dial.pipex.com *Insurance correspondents*

Striking Displays UK Ltd, Display House, North Street, Portslade, Brighton, BN41 1DH Tel: (01273) 423623 Fax: (01273) 420424 E-mail: sales@strikingdisplays.com *Designers, manufacturers & Stockists of display products. Specialist fabricators in acrylic (perspex) & other plastics for all point of sale products, leaflet dispensers, display cases, exhibition & estate agents display systems, pavement signs & much more.*

Strimech Engineering Ltd, Longmore Avenue, Walsall, WS2 0BW Tel: (01922) 649700 Fax: (01922) 649802 E-mail: info@strimech.com *Fork lift truck & loader attachments supplier*

▶ String Clean, Unit 2 Quarry Farm, Bodiam, Robertsbridge, East Sussex, TN32 5RA Tel: (01580) 831804 E-mail: sales@stringclean.com *Musical instrument accessories*

H.E. Stringer Ltd, Icknield Way, Tring, Hertfordshire, HP23 4JZ Tel: (01442) 822621 Fax: (01442) 822727 E-mail: info@stringer-flavour.com *Food flavourings extracts*

Strings & Things Ltd, Unit 3, 202-210 Brighton Road, Shoreham-By-Sea, West Sussex, BN43 6RJ Tel: (01273) 440442 Fax: (01273) 440278 E-mail: strings@stringsandthings.co.uk *Musical instrument distributors*

Strip Tinning Ltd, Heath Street South, Springhill, Birmingham, B18 7PY Tel: 0121-454 8008 Fax: 0121-454 7600 E-mail: richard@stuk.demon.co.uk *Tinning services* Also at: London SE18

▶ Stripes, 1a Old Church Buildings, Cramlington, Northumberland, NE23 1DN Tel: (01670) 737014 Fax: (01670) 734026

Strix UK Ltd, Taylor House, Minerva Close, Chester West Employment Park, Chester, CH1 4QL Tel: (01244) 394333 Fax: (01244) 390137 E-mail: sales@strix.com *Thermostat manufrs* Also at: Castletown & Ramsey

Strom International Ltd, Unit B3 Connaught Business Centre, Edgware Road, London, NW9 6JL Tel: (020) 8205 9697 Fax: (020) 8905 8189 E-mail: sales@strom.co.uk *Children's & menswear manufrs*

▶ Stroma, Stroma Unit 4, Pioneer Way, Pioneer Business Park, Wakefield, West Yorkshire, WF10 5QU Tel: 0845 6211111 Fax: 0845 6211112 E-mail: info@stroma.com *STROMA Accreditation provides training, assessment and licensing of Code for Sustainable Homes, amongst all the commercial and domestic energy assessment accreditations. *Meanwhile, STROMA Technology specialise in helping builders & contractors achieve air-tightness & acoustic compliance. Beyond the traditional architectural services, STROMA Architecture offer sustainable architecture, general design services, planning consultancy and advice on all aspects of sustainability.*Explore options for renewable energy with STROMA LZC, who supply latest solar thermal system, under-floor heating, geo-thermal & air-source heat pumps. *STROMA Contracting provide a comprehensive*

continued

range of specialist sub-contract packages including dry-lining and partitioning, suspended ceilings, all forms of passive fire protection, cavity barriers, acoustic and air sealing. Whilst delivering Part L, B and E compliance as part of the solution.

Stroma Engineering Ltd, 21 Bickford Road, Birmingham, B6 7EE Tel: 0121-327 5550 Fax: 0121-327 2314 *General & precision engineers*

Stromag Ltd, 29 Wellingborough Road, Rushden, Northamptonshire, NN10 9YE Tel: (01933) 350407 Fax: (01933) 358692 E-mail: sales@stromag.com Principal Export Areas: Asia Pacific & Central Asia *Power transmission equipment & electro-magnetic clutch, clutch brake unit, limit switches, flexible coupling & clutch plate manufrs*

Strong Holdings plc, Caspian Wharf, Violet Road, London, E3 3QQ Tel: (020) 7987 7113 Fax: (020) 7987 9060 E-mail: info@strongcases.com *Packing case manufrs*

▶ Strong Team, Marsden House, Elmdon Lane, Birmingham, B37 7DL Tel: 0121-505 5520 Fax: 0121-505 4333

Strong Vend Ltd, 8 St Marks Industrial Estate, 439 North Woolwich Road, London, E16 2BS Tel: (020) 7511 3511 Fax: (020) 7473 0573 E-mail: info@strongvend.co.uk *Drinks vending machines & ingredients distributors*

Stronga Ltd, Ashendene Farm, White Stubbs Lane, Bayford, Hertford, SG13 8PZ Tel: (01992) 519000 Fax: (01992) 519011 E-mail: info@stronga.co.uk *Steel fabrications including Architectural (straight and spiral staircases, balustrades, fire escapes); Fencing (perimeter, ornamental); Forklift & Telehandler Attachments (buckets, forks, access platforms); Waste Containers (skips, hooklifts).*

▶ Strongbar, 2 Banningham Road, Aylsham, Norwich, NR11 6PE Tel: (01263) 734034 Fax: (01263) 734790 E-mail: sales@strongbar.co.uk *Steel bars, precision ground; bearings, linear & linear guide (machine tool) manufrs*

Strongbond Adhesives Ltd, Beehive Works, Hollins Lane, Bury, Lancashire, BL9 8AA Tel: 0161-766 2618 Fax: 0161-767 9024 E-mail: sales@strongbond.co.uk *Adhesive manufrs*

▶ Strongcastle Builders, 120 Whitehorse Road, Croydon, CR0 2JF Tel: (020) 8665 7129 Fax: (020) 8665 6907

Strongfield Technologies Ltd, Strongfield House, Unit 2 Inovation Park, 89 Manor Farm Road, Wembley, Middlesex, HA0 1BA Tel: (020) 8813 2684 Fax: (020) 8799 8901 E-mail: anu@strongfield.com *Specialist recruitment within the electronics, aerospace, automotive & communication industries*

Stronghold International, Nicholson Court, Geddings Road, Hoddesdon, Hertfordshire, EN11 0NE Tel: (01992) 460274 Fax: (01992) 479471 E-mail: sales@stronghold.co.uk *Commercial tarpaulin manufrs*

Stronghold Safety Workwear, Cocklebury Road, Chippenham, Wiltshire, SN15 3NT Tel: (01249) 655976 Fax: (01249) 460623 *Health & safety products, advise & corporate clothing*

Stronghold Welding & Engineering Co., Overend Road, Halesowen, West Midlands, B63 2SA Tel: (01384) 569441 *Steel fabricators*

Strongpoint Fencing Ltd, Unit 1 Boarshaw Industrial Estate, Clough Road, Middleton, Manchester, M24 2WH Tel: 0161-643 0045 Fax: 0161-653 8162 *Steel industrial fencing manufrs*

Strong's Plastic Products Ltd, 18 Silica Road, Amington Industrial Estate, Tamworth, Staffordshire, B77 4DT Tel: (01827) 302490 Fax: (01827) 54999 E-mail: myles@strongs.co.uk Principal Export Areas: Worldwide *Plastic fabricators, plastic machinists & plastic battery containers distributors*

George Stross Ltd, Providence Mills, Bradford Street, Dewsbury, West Yorkshire, WF13 1EN Tel: (01924) 466031 Fax: (01924) 466029 E-mail: sales@fabworks.co.uk *Textile waste management & recycling*

▶ Stroud A & M, 2a The Old Brickworks, Ebley Road, Stonehouse, Gloucestershire, GL10 2LW Tel: (01453) 825111 *Concrete suppliers*

Stroud Green Joinery, 178 Stroud Green Road, London, N4 3RS Tel: (020) 7281 1800 Fax: (020) 7263 8388 *Joinery manufrs*

Stroud Metal Co. Ltd, Dudbridge, Stroud, Gloucestershire, GL5 3EZ Tel: (01453) 763331 Fax: (01453) 753804 E-mail: enquiries@stroudmetal.co.uk *Seat stick manufrs*

Stroud Office Interiors Ltd, Alder Ho, Inchbrook Trading Estate, Woodchester, Stroud, Glos, GL5 5EY Tel: (01453) 834867 Fax: (01453) 835818 E-mail: derek@stroudofficeinteriors.co.uk *Office fitters, planners & refurbishers. Also partitionings & ceilings.*

▶ Stroud PC (Cinderford), 20 Victoria Street, Cinderford, Gloucestershire, GL14 2HQ Tel: (0870) 8034246 Fax: (07092) 812233 E-mail: bryan@stroud-pcs.com *Spreadsheet & database design**

Stroud Sewing Services, 5 Meadow Mills Eastington Trading Estate, Churchend, Eastington, Stonehouse, Gloucestershire, GL10 3RZ Tel: (01453) 791487 Fax: (01453) 791487 E-mail: stroudsewingservices@tiscali.co.uk *Sewing contractors to the traders*

Stroud Switchgear Developments Ltd, Unit 3, Lightpill Trading Estate, Stroud, Gloucestershire, GL5 3LL Tel: (01453) 762709 Fax: (01453) 751977 E-mail: sales@stroud-switchgear.com *Switchboard & control panel manufrs*

▶ Stroud-PC's (RuralDean), 27 Victoria Street, Cinderford, Gloucestershire, GL14 2ET Tel: (0845) 2260173 E-mail: info@stroud-pcs.com *Computer services & repairs*

Strouds Woodworks, Ashmansworthy, Woolsery, Bideford, Devon, EX39 5RE Tel: (01409) 241624 *Joinery manufrs*

Strowger Ltd, 395-397 London Road, Mitcham, Surrey, CR4 4BG Tel: (020) 8648 2401 Fax: (020) 8648 2401 *DIY & plumbers' merchants*

▶ Strowger & Smith, 5 Seaview Road, Sandend, Banff, AB45 2UE Tel: (01261) 842226 Fax: (01261) 842226

Strowmar Ltd, Scottish Mutual House, North Street, Hornchurch, Essex, RM11 1RS Tel: (01708) 446253 Fax: (020) 8534 0652 E-mail: martine@strowmar.co.uk *Shipping & forwarding agents*

▶ Stroz Friedberg, Baird House, 15-17 St. Cross Street, London, EC1N 8UW Tel: (020) 7841 5870 Fax: (020) 7242 7860 E-mail: mail@strozfriedberg.co.uk *Software consultancy*

Structherm Ltd, Bent Ley Road, Meltham, Holmfirth, HD9 4AP Tel: (01484) 850098 Fax: (01484) 851388 E-mail: sales@structherm.co.uk *Structural manufrs*

Structura UK Ltd, Phoenix Works, Davis Road, Chessington, Surrey, KT9 1TH Tel: (020) 8397 4361 Fax: (020) 8391 5805 E-mail: sales@structura-uk.com *Aluminium fabricators*

Structural Accessories Ltd, Unit 2a Bilston Key Industrial Estate, Oxford Street, Bilston, West Midlands, WV14 7DW Tel: (01902) 492298 Fax: (01902) 354055 *Presswork & fabricators*

Structural Metal Decks Ltd, Mallard House, Duck Island Lane, Ringwood, Hampshire, BH24 3AA Tel: (01425) 471088 Fax: (01425) 471408 E-mail: contactus@smdltd.co.uk *Composite metal deck distributors & contractors*

Structural Sealant Services Ltd, Grove Farm, North Road, South Ockendon, Essex, RM15 6SR Tel: (01708) 853285 Fax: (01708) 851142 E-mail: sales@structuralsealants.co.uk *Sealants, waterproofing contracts & fireproofing*

Structural Space Ltd, Trident House, Neptune Business Estate, Dolphin Way, Purfleet, Essex, RM19 1NZ Tel: (01708) 683041 Fax: (01708) 683068 E-mail: info@structuralspace.co.uk *Durasteel fire rated ductwork contractors*

Structural Stairways Ltd, The Premier Estate, Leys Road, Brierley Hill, West Midlands, DY5 3UP Tel: (01384) 79256 Fax: (01384) 482412 E-mail: metalwork@stairways18.fsnet.co.uk *Architectural metalworkers*

Structural Statics Ltd, Burntwood, Martyr Worthy, Winchester, Hampshire, SO21 1AD Tel: (01962) 886644 Fax: (01962) 886788 E-mail: info@structuralstatics.co.uk *Structural monitoring systems*

Structural Steel Fabrications, Shilton Industrial Estate, Bulkington Road, Coventry, CV7 9JY Tel: (024) 7660 2900 Fax: (024) 7662 2111 *Steel fabricators*

▶ Structural Surveys Direct, 1-2 Aire House, Richmond Business Park, Sidings Court, Doncaster, South Yorkshire, DN4 5NL Tel: (0808) 144 8899 Fax: 08081 448898 E-mail: info@structuralsurveysdirect.co.uk *CCTV drain, asbestos surveys & damp & timber surveys*

Structured Cabling Services Ltd, 13 Portland Road, Birmingham, B16 9HN Tel: (0845) 2300041 Fax: (0845) 2300042 E-mail: info@structured-cabling.co.uk *Computer installers*

▶ Structured Lan, The Garage, Crag Lane, Beckwithshaw, Harrogate, North Yorkshire, HG3 1QA Tel: (01423) 508011 Fax: (01423) 508011 E-mail: structuredlan@btconnect.com *Computer networking & installation of data communications*

Structure-Flex Ltd, Peacock Way, Melton Constable, Norfolk, NR24 2AZ Tel: (01263) 863100 Fax: (01263) 863120 E-mail: enquiries@structure-flex.co.uk *Intermediate bulk container & flexible tank manufrs*

Structures (Cordell) Ltd, Sotherby Road, Skippers Lane Industrial Estate, South Bank, Middlesbrough, Cleveland, TS6 6LP Tel: (01642) 452406 Fax: (01642) 464118 E-mail: structures@cordellgroup.com *Structural steelwork engineers*

▶ Structures (Teesside) Cordell Ltd, Skippers Lane Industrial Estate, Middlesbrough, Cleveland, TS6 6LP Tel: (01642) 452406 Fax: (01642) 464118 E-mail: stuctures@cordellgroup.com *General construction services*

▶ Struer Consulting Engineers Ltd, 113 St. Georges Road, Glasgow, G3 6JA Tel: 0141-445 5621 Fax: 0141-331 1171

Struthers & Carter Ltd, Erimus Works, Valletta Street, Hedon Road, Hull, HU9 5NU Tel: (01482) 795171 Fax: (01482) 708926 E-mail: enquiries@struthers-carter.co.uk *Steel stockholders*

Struture-flex Ltd, 24 Grove Lane, Holt, Norfolk, NR25 6EG Tel: (01263) 712911 Fax: (01263) 710015 E-mail: enquiries@structure-flex.co.uk *Lifting gear manufrs*

Stryker UK Ltd, Stryker House, Hambridge Road, Newbury, Berkshire, RG14 5EG Tel: (01635) 262400 Fax: (01635) 580300 E-mail: sales@emea.strykercorp.com *Orthopaedic implant manufrs*

▶ Strysen Heating & Plumbing, 4 St James Rd, Sutton Coldfield, West Midlands, B75 5EH Tel: 0121-308 0962 Fax: 0121-323 2838

STS, Unit 175 Dean Clough Office Park, Halifax, West Yorkshire, HX3 5AX Tel: (01422) 383071 Fax: (01422) 383072 *Telecommunications*

STS 2000 Ltd, Unit 11 Bowmans Trading Estate, Bessemer Drive, Stevenage, Hertfordshire, SG1 2DL Tel: (01438) 747474 Fax: (01438) 747476 *Computer industry epos*

STS Alarm Systems, 435 Old Walsall Road, Birmingham, B42 1HX Tel: 0121-357 8390 Fax: 0121-686 9278 *Burglar & intruder alarm systems*

Sttop Filters Ltd, Woodmere, 7 Moor Close, Acton Trussell, Stafford, ST17 0QZ Tel: (01785) 714687 Fax: (01785) 716499 E-mail: peter@sttopfilters.co.uk *Air filter distributors*

Stuart Brumby Cover Makers, 18 Park Farm Road, Foxhills Industrial Estate, Scunthorpe, South Humberside, DN15 8QP Tel: (01724) 280440 Fax: (01724) 280440 *Tarpaulin & canvass good manufrs*

Stuart Building Services, Duncrub, Dunning, Perth, PH2 0QN Tel: (01764) 684840 Fax: (01764) 684841 E-mail: info@stuartbuildingservices.co.uk *Civil engineers & steelwork building*

Stuart Canvas Products, Warren Works, Hardwick Grange, Woolston, Warrington, WA1 4RF Tel: (01925) 814525 Fax: (01925) 831709 *Tarpaulin & sports ground cover manufrs*

▶ Charles Stuart Phone Services, 18 Harewood Avenue, Newark, Nottinghamshire, NG24 4BE Tel: (01636) 705313 Fax: (08714) 335235 E-mail: sales@charles-stuart.com *Low prices don"t just stop at design with our sister company Charles Stuart Design Services. Now there is an extension to our services, with the launch of Charles Stuart Phone Services. 0845, 0800, 0870 and Regional Numbers. Have a virtual office in London, Birmingham or Lincoln. You can have these LOW COST numbers routed anywhere! Yes, you could be on the train. Let us save you money and see what we can do for your business. Why not combine a new logo with a new number to promote your business cost-effectively?*

Stuart Edwards Fullermoon, 102-104 High Street, Croydon, CR9 1TN Tel: (020) 8686 4771 Fax: (020) 8688 7121 E-mail: sales@stuart-edwards.com *Estate agents & chartered surveyors* Also at: Beckenham & Sanderstead

Stuart Engineering, Unit B4 Chadwell Heath Industrial Park, Kemp Road, Dagenham, Essex, RM8 1SL Tel: (020) 8590 7412 Fax: (020) 8598 1787 *Aluminium welding engineers*

George Stuart Ltd, Central Drive, Walsall, WS3 2QJ Tel: (01922) 711919 Fax: (01922) 473147 E-mail: sales@georgestuart.co.uk *Leather good manufrs*

▶ Stuart Group Ltd, Stuart House, Crowshall Lane, Attleborough, Norfolk, NR17 1AD Tel: (01953) 454540 Fax: (01953) 456968 E-mail: info@stuartpumps.co.uk *Engine Sales, Petrol 4.5/10.5HP, Diesel 4.2/9.9HP*

▶ Stuart Harris Cabinet Maker, Ilex Farm Workshop, Waterhouse Lane, Ardleigh, Colchester, CO7 7NE Tel: (01206) 230078 Fax: (01206) 231177 E-mail: info@harriscabinetmaker.co.uk *BESPOKE FURNITURE AND FITMENTS, CHURCH FURNISHINGS,*SPECIALIST JOINERY*

Stuart Interiors Ltd, Barrington Court, Barrington, Ilminster, Somerset, TA19 0NQ Tel: (01460) 240349 Fax: (01460) 242069 E-mail: design@stuartinteriors.com *Period furniture manufrs*

▶ Stuart Kennedy Heating Services, 14 Hillview Place, Dumfries, DG1 4DU Tel: (01387) 268852

Stuart Neal Chartered Loss Adjusters Ltd, 26 White Horse Lane, Maldon, Essex, CM9 5QP Tel: (01621) 857111 Fax: (01621) 858111 E-mail: claims@stuartneal.co.uk *Loss adjusters*

Stuart Neal Chartered Loss Adjusters Ltd, 26 White Horse Lane, Maldon, Essex, CM9 5QP Tel: (01621) 857111 Fax: (01621) 858111 E-mail: stuartneilclaims@hotmail.com *Loft adjusters*

Stuart Pease Fibreglass Ltd, Unit 1 Taylors Close, Parkgate, Rotherham, South Yorkshire, S62 6NW Tel: (01709) 527761 Fax: (01709) 522147 E-mail: stuartpeaseltd@btinternet.com *GRP moulds & products also wooden patterns suppliers & manufrs*

▶ Peter Stuart, Falkners, Rectory Lane, Bramshott, Liphook, Hampshire, GU30 7QZ Tel: (01428) 727089 *Hog-roast.com is an outside caterer to corporate and domestic consumers looking for 0% reliability and professionalism.*

▶ Stuart Plant Ltd, Stuart House, Crowshall Lane, Attleborough, Norfolk, NR17 1AD Tel: (01953) 458963 Fax: (01953) 456968

Stuart Pumps Ltd, Stuart House, Crowshall Lane, Attleborough, Norfolk, NR17 1AD Tel: (01953) 454540 Fax: (01953) 456968 E-mail: info@stuartpumps.co.uk *Pump suppliers & diesel pump hire services*

Stuart Shop Fittings Ltd, Unit 10 Alexandra Mill, Baker Street, Morley, Leeds, LS27 0QH Tel: 0113-259 7092 Fax: 0113-259 7093 *Shop fittings distributor & manufrs*

▶ Stuart Taylor, Lane Ends Cottage, Nightfield Lane, Balderstone, Blackburn, BB2 7LJ Tel: (01254) 813175 Fax: (01254) 813479 E-mail: stuarttaylor@freeola.com *Commercial ride on lawnmowers sales & hire services*

Stuart Wright, Warp Farm, Newsholme, Goole, North Humberside, DN14 7JS Tel: (01757) 638205 Fax: (01757) 630412 E-mail: stuart@dn14.co.uk *Computer consultants*

Stubbings Bros., Chale Green, Ventnor, Isle Of Wight, PO38 2JN Tel: (01983) 551400 Fax: (01983) 551400 E-mail: sales@stubbings-bros.co.uk *Agricultural & horticultural engineers*

▶ Stubbs Tickets, Streethay Farm, Burton Road, Streethay, Lichfield, Staffordshire, WS13 8RJ Tel: 01543 410107 Fax: 01543 410180 E-mail: sales@stubbsticlkets.com *Printers of raffle tickets & lottery tickets*

Stubbs & Co UK Ltd, Assay House, 28 Greville Street, London, EC1N 8PQ Tel: (020) 7404 4000 Fax: (020) 7421 6901 E-mail: sales@stubbs.co.uk *Jewellery importers*

Peter Stubs Ltd, Causeway Avenue, Warrington, WA4 6QB Tel: (01925) 653939 Fax: (01925) 413870 E-mail: sales@peterstubs.com *Steel manufrs*

▶ Studer Ltd, 2 Commerce Way, Flitwick, Bedford, MK45 5BP Tel: (01525) 719719 Fax: (01525) 718180 E-mail: info@studerfurniture.co.uk *Furnishings supplier*

Studfast Studwelding Ltd, 5 Low Farm Place, Moulton Park Industrial Estate, Northampton, NN3 6HY Tel: (01604) 790901 Fax: (01604) 492946 E-mail: sales.studfast@btconnect.com *Stud welding equipment distributors*

Studio, Gill Lane, Mersham, Ashford, Kent, TN25 7HZ Tel: (01233) 721511 Fax: (01303) 721662 E-mail: jan@studio2uk.com *Design & photography studio service*

The Studio, 21 Cabul Road, London, SW11 2PR Tel: (020) 7228 5228 Fax: (020) 7228 9975 *Film & photographic studio*

▶ The Studio, 6 Charlotte Square, Newcastle Upon Tyne, NE1 4XF Tel: 0191-211 1976 *Advertising agency service*

▶ Studio, Riverside Works, Forde Road, Newton Abbot, Devon, TQ12 4AD Tel: (01626) 358600 Fax: (01626) 358601

Studio 127, 127 East Parade, Keighley, West Yorkshire, BD21 5HX Tel: (01535) 605148 Fax: (01535) 691521 E-mail: enquiries@studio127.co.uk *Sign manufrs*

Studio 2, 101 Lockhurst Lane, Coventry, CV6 5SF Tel: (024) 7663 8144 Fax: (024) 7666 1457 E-mail: sales@studio2exhibitions.co.uk *Exhibition graphics & point of sale designers*

Studio 2, 5 Sizes Court, Henshaw Lane, Yeadon, Leeds, LS19 7DP Tel: 0113-239 1859 Fax: 0113-250 9688 *Natural stone tiles importers & distributors*

Studio Argent Ltd, School Lane, Knowsley, Prescot, Merseyside, L34 9EN Tel: 0151-548 7722 Fax: 0151-549 1713 E-mail: sales@studioargent.co.uk *Commercial photographers*

▶ Studio Art, 65 The Parkway, Cottingham, North Humberside, HU16 5HD Tel: (07834) 839727 E-mail: info@studioartwork.co.uk *Studio Art produce high quality Websites at low costs.*Studio Art produce high quality contemporary artwork using acrylic paints on stretched canvas. targeted towards: cafe bars . hotels . restaurants . conference rooms . offices . home... all artwork is hand painted and is original or based upon an original.*

▶ Studio Box, Far End, Priest Hill, Caversham, Reading, RG4 7RY Tel: 0118-946 3336 Fax: 0118-948 2556 E-mail: studio@studiobox.com *Computer software developers*

Studio Ceramics Ltd, 72 Fosse Road, Farndon, Newark, Nottinghamshire, NG24 4ST Tel: (01636) 673527 Fax: (01636) 612871 E-mail: sales@studioceramics.com *Ceramic tile importers*

▶ Studio Designers, Shireshead Old Church, Stony Lane, Forton, Preston, PR3 1DE Tel: (01524) 792020 Fax: (01524) 792305 E-mail: info@studio-designers.co.uk *Studio design, construction & installation*

Studio Digital Media Ltd, Windsor Park, Trent Valley Road, Lichfield, Staffordshire, WS13 6EU Tel: (01543) 416912 Fax: (01543) 416914 E-mail: info@studiodm.co.uk *New media & web*

▶ Studio Emergence, PO Box 139, Thornton-Cleveleys, Lancashire, FY5 4WU Tel: (07834) 986958 E-mail: interest@studioemergence.net *We create internet sites for all kinds of business and commerce, combining functionality with maximum visual appeal.**We offer dynamic, database driven websites, online marketing and promotion and search engine submission.**Online same day quote available at site.*

Studio Four Regency Design, Dormston Trading Estate, Burton Road, Dudley, West Midlands, DY1 2UF Tel: (01902) 663913 *Plaster work specialists*

▶ Studio K, The Lodge, 145 Westgate, Cleckheaton, West Yorkshire, BD19 5EJ Tel: 01274 861433 E-mail: imelda@studiok.fsbusiness.co.uk *Exhibition designers*

▶ Studio Limonard, The Residence 43 Royal Clarence Yard, Weevil Lane, Gosport, Hampshire, PO12 1AX Tel: (023) 9258 9910 Fax: (023) 9258 9910 *Studio Limonard - A graphic design consultancy providing the design and production of brochures, stationery, websites, copywriting and exhibitions. With offices in Chichester, West Sussex and Gosport, Hampshire.*

Studio Ninety Two Ltd, The Barns, Belmont Farm, Stud Green, Holyport, Maidenhead, Berkshire, SL6 2JH Tel: (01628) 676567 Fax: (01628) 676568 E-mail: studio92@clara.co.uk *Lithographic plate makers*

Studio North, 41 Cecil Street, Carlisle, CA1 1NS Tel: (01228) 533344 E-mail: sales@studionorthphotographers.co.uk *Photographers*

Studio One Screen, 13 Paramount Industrial Estate, Sandown Road, Watford, WD24 7XA Tel: (01923) 494944 Fax: (01923) 494940 *Silk screen printers*

Studio Signs, 10-12 High Street, Goldthorpe, Rotherham, South Yorkshire, S63 9LR Tel: (01709) 891160 Fax: (01709) 891160 E-mail: dean@studiosigns.co.uk *Manufacture all types of signs*

▶ Studio Stone, The Stone Yard, Alton Lane, Four Marks, Alton, Hampshire, GU34 5AJ Tel: (01420) 562500 Fax: (01420) 563192 E-mail: info@studiostone.co.uk *Granite, marble & limestone kitchen worktops, bathrooms, fireplaces suppliers*

▶ Studio Tone Ltd, 6-8 Crown Close Business Centre, Crown Close, London, E3 2JQ Tel: (020) 8980 4242

Studiocare Professional Audio Ltd, Unit 9, Century Building, Summers Road, Brunswick Business Park, Liverpool, L3 4BL Tel: (0845) 3458910 Fax: (0845) 3458911 E-mail: sales@studiocare.com *Professional audio equipment hire, sales & services*

Studiocraft Ltd, 17 Arden Business Centre, Arden Forest Industrial Estate, Alcester, Warwickshire, B49 6HW Tel: (01283) 840380 Fax: (01283) 840980 E-mail: sales@studiocraft.co.uk *Education contractors*

▶ Studiohope, 2 Oolite Grove, Bath, BA2 2UF Tel: (01225) 830634 Fax: (01225) 830634 E-mail: mcmaster@studiohope.co.uk *Graphic design agency*

Andrew Studley, Castle Lodge Farm, Llancarfan, Barry, South Glamorgan, CF62 3AW Tel: (01446) 781229 *Agricultural engineers*

Studley Engineering Ltd, 17 Vulcan Street, Liverpool, L3 7BG Tel: 0151-236 7825 Fax: 0151-255 0597 *Pipework fabricators*

▶ Studley Fish & Tackle, 10 High Street, Studley, Warwickshire, B80 7HJ Tel: 01527 854244 *Fishing tackle retailers*

Studwelders, Millennium House Severn Link Distribution Centre, Newhouse Fa, Mathern, Chepstow, Gwent, NP16 6UN Tel: (01291) 626048 Fax: (01291) 629979 E-mail: info@studwelders.co.uk *Manufacturers of stud welding equipment, fasteners & studding*

Studweldpro UK Ltd, Ollerton Road, Tuxford, Newark, Nottinghamshire, NG22 0PQ Tel: (01777) 874500 Fax: (01777) 874555 E-mail: sales@swpuk.com *Stud weld equipment suppliers*

Stuff 4 Offices, 11 Queen Street, Ripon, North Yorkshire, HG4 1ED Tel: (01765) 608122 Fax: (01765) 690292 E-mail: stuff4offices@f2s.com *Stationery, Office Supplies, Printer Cartridges, Paper, Envelopes, Toners, Books, Pads, Filing, Storage, Pens, Pencils, Staplers, Staples, Hole Punches, Labels, Conference, Presentation, Seating*

Stuma Plastics Ltd, Atlas Works, Mornington Road, Bolton, BL1 4EZ Tel: (01204) 492862 Fax: (01204) 493090 E-mail: enquiries@stuma.co.uk *Injection moulders services*

Stump Co - Tree Stump Removal Services, 6 Holt Park Approach, Leeds, LS16 7PW Tel: 0113-293 7510 E-mail: sales@stumpco.co.uk *Stump Co offer a full tree stump grinding and removal service, based in Leeds we cover a large geographical area.*

Peter Stunt, Beam Wireless Station, North Petherton, Bridgwater, Somerset, TA7 0DX Tel: (01278) 663344 Fax: (01278) 663343 E-mail: sales@peterstunt.co.uk *Musto performance clothing retailers*

Sturdy Joinery & Display, Unit 6 The Barns, Hewell Lane, Tardebigge, Bromsgrove, Worcestershire, B60 1LP Tel: (01527) 579306 Fax: (01527) 574492 *Joinery manufrs*

Sturges Tooling, 9 Priestley Way, Crawley, West Sussex, RH10 9NT Tel: (01293) 527229 Fax: (01293) 553668 *Precision engineers*

John Sturman Ltd, Park Street, Rowley Regis, West Midlands, B65 0LU Tel: 0121-559 1175 Fax: 0121-559 1175 *Agricultural merchants*

Sturrock Power Installations Ltd, 15 Bankhead Drive, Edinburgh, EH11 4DW Tel: 0131-453 5050 Fax: 0131-458 5066 *Electrical contractors*

Stutley Bros Ltd, Elms Depot, Stevenage Road, Little Wymondley, Hitchin, Hertfordshire, SG4 7HZ Tel: (01438) 354495 Fax: (01438) 354495 E-mail: stutleybros@aol.com *Waste disposal contractors*

Stuttaford Ltd, Unit 31, East Lane, Wembley Commercial Centre, Wembley, Middlesex, HA9 7UR Tel: (020) 8904 2300 *Cable management system manufrs*

Stuvex Safety Systems Ltd, 48 Church Street, Weybridge, Surrey, KT13 8DP Tel: (01932) 849602 Fax: (01932) 852171 E-mail: sales@stuvex.com Sales Contact: S. Cooper Principal Export Areas: Central/East Europe & West Europe *Explosion suppression & protection equipment manufrs*

▶ Stva UK Ltd, 26 1 Whitburn Road, Bathgate, West Lothian, EH48 1HH Tel: (01506) 650505 Fax: (01506) 650905

▶ Stva UK Ltd, Cva House, 2 Cooper Road, Thornbury, Bristol, BS35 3UP Tel: (01454) 410200 Fax: (01454) 410230 E-mail: sales@stva.com

▶ Styan Builders Ltd, Builders Yard, Crabmill Lane, Easingwold, York, YO61 3DE Tel: (01423) 322711 Fax: (01423) 323985 E-mail: styanbuilders@btinternet.com

Style Cafe Ltd, Vivary Mill, Vivary Way, Colne, Lancashire, BB8 9NW Tel: (01282) 869641 Fax: (01282) 869616 E-mail: sales@stylecafe.co.uk *Coffee machine distributors*

Style Engravers, Unit 2 Warneford Avenue, Ossett, West Yorkshire, WF5 9NJ Tel: (01924) 270506 Fax: (01924) 265156 E-mail: sales@engravers.fsbusiness.co.uk *Sign makers & engravers*

Style Graphics Ltd, 38 Decima Street, London, SE1 4QQ Tel: (01689) 609477 Fax: (020) 7407 7625 *Sign manufrs*

▶ Style Improvements Ltd, Dunfords Yard, Main Road, Colden Common, Winchester, Hampshire, SO21 1TB Tel: (01962) 715435 Fax: (01962) 711021

Style Machine Tools Ltd, 30a Centurion Industrial Estate, Centurion Way, Farington, Leyland, PR25 4GU Tel: (01772) 624114 Fax: (01722) 624114 E-mail: enquiries@stylemachinetools.co.uk *Machine tools service engineers*

▶ Style Midlands, Unit 3, Phoenix Park, Telford Way, Stephenson Industrial Estate, Coalville, Leicestershire, LE67 3HB Tel: (01530) 831144 Fax: (01530) 831184 E-mail: midlands@style-partitions.co.uk *Sliding, folding & moving partions distributors*

▶ Style Overload, The Lodge, Links Rd, Worthing, West Sussex, BN14 9QY Tel: 0207 6694181 E-mail: info@styleoverload.com *We specialise importing Jewellery to the UK and Europe*

Style Seating Ltd, Algores Way, Wisbech, Cambridgeshire, PE13 2TQ Tel: (01945) 580099 Fax: (01945) 580127 E-mail: sales@styleseating.co.uk *Style Seating Ltd based in Wisbech, Cambridgeshire are furniture suppliers for banquets and functions. They are manufacturers of stacking chairs and folding tables for the hospitality industry.*

Stylebord Ltd, 34 London Road, Great Shelford, Cambridge, CB22 5DD Tel: (01223) 843341 *Electronic contract manufacturing services*

Stylecharm Fireplaces, 14 Bowlers Croft, Basildon, Essex, SS14 3EE Tel: (01268) 287673 Fax: (01268) 287710 E-mail: carl@beeb.net *Marble importers & fireplaces manufrs*

Styleguard Ltd, 7 Long Acre Trading Estate, Long Acre, Birmingham, B7 5JD Tel: 0121-327 3222 Fax: 0121-328 4312 *Plastic vacuum formed products manufrs*

Charles Styles Ltd, New Bond Street, Birmingham, B9 4EJ Tel: 0121-772 2424 Fax: 0121-771 2597 E-mail: sales@hexasports.co.uk *Providers of services in universal grinding, internal grinding, surface grinding & honing*

▶ Styles & Wood, Merlin Court, Atlantic Street, Altrincham, Cheshire, WA14 5NL Tel: 0161-924 1800

Styletype Printing Ltd, Glengormley Park, Newtownabbey, County Antrim, BT36 7RJ Tel: (028) 9034 2725 Fax: (028) 9084 8225 E-mail: sales@styletype.co.uk *Printers & publishers journals*

Styleware Ltd, 28 Wittering Road, Hayling Island, Hampshire, PO11 9SP Tel: (023) 9246 1561 Fax: (023) 9246 1501 E-mail: sales@styleware.co.uk *Web designers*

Stylewrite Press Ltd, 44 Howard Street, Birmingham, B19 3HH Tel: 0121-236 5557 Fax: 0121-236 5717 E-mail: stylewritepress@yahoo.co.uk *Design typesetting & litho printing*

Stylex, 49 Berwick Street, London, W1F 8SH Tel: (020) 7437 2428 Fax: (020) 7437 0649 E-mail: sales@style-x.co.uk *Urban, street, gothic, punk & club wear & studded leather accessories*

Stylographics Ltd, 134 St Albans Road, Watford, WD24 4AE Tel: (01923) 800666 Fax: (01923) 800777 E-mail: admin@stylographics.co.uk *Exhibition consultants*

▶ Styro Park (UK), Aberamon Park Industrial Estate, Aberdare, Mid Glamorgan, CF44 6DA Tel: (01685) 881022 Fax: (01685) 871515

Styropack UK Ltd, Craigshaw Road, West Tullos Industrial Estate, Aberdeen, AB12 3AS Tel: (01224) 873166 Fax: (01224) 873361 E-mail: aberdeen@styropack.co.uk *Polystyrene packaging manufrs* Also at: Arundel

Styropack UK Ltd, Unit A Rudford Industrial Estate, Ford Road, Ford, Arundel, West Sussex, BN18 0BD Tel: (01903) 725282 Fax: (01903) 731628 E-mail: ford@styropack.co.uk *Polystyrene manufrs*

Styropack UK Ltd, 1 Stephenson Street, Hillington Industrial Estate, Glasgow, G52 4JD Tel: 0141-882 9166 Fax: 0141-882 7022 E-mail: glasgow@styropack.co.uk *Packaging manufrs*

Styx Information Systems Ltd, 12 St Giles Grove, Haughton, Stafford, ST18 9HP Tel: (01785) 780583 Fax: (01785) 780641 E-mail: styx@styx.co.uk *Computer consultants*

Sub Aqua Divers, Rescuestation House, Station Road, Wath-upon-Dearne, Rotherham, South Yorkshire, S63 7DG Tel: (01709) 877222 Fax: (01709) 877555 *Diver training & equipment hire*

▶ Sub Aqua Products Ltd, Lycroft Farm, 8 Upper Swanmore, Swanmore, Southampton, SO32 2QQ Tel: (01489) 878055 Fax: (01489) 878002 E-mail: info@subaqua-products.com *Diving equipment manufrs*

Sub Soil Consultancy Services Ltd, Kennedy Road, Off Chaddocks Lane, Manchester, M29 7LD Tel: (01942) 883565 Fax: (01942) 883566 E-mail: richard@subsoil.co.uk *Geotechnical consultants*

Subak Signs, 9a Stocks Street, Manchester, M8 8GW Tel: 0161-835 9993 Fax: 0161-835 9994 E-mail: info@subaksigns.co.uk *Sign making services*

▶ Sub-Atlantic, Blackburn Business Park, Woodburn Road, Blackburn, Aberdeen, AB21 0PS Tel: (01224) 798660 Fax: (01224) 798661 *ROV equipment suppliers*

▶ Subcircle Creative, 5 Luther Mews, Brighton, BN2 9YR Tel: 01273 675428 *Subcircle Creative are a brand communications organisation that formulates brand identity and creative solutions across every medium from design for print and web to events management.*

Subcon Laser Cutting Ltd, Unit 7, Trident Business Park, Park St, Nuneaton, Warwickshire, CV11 4NS Tel: (024) 7664 2221 Fax: (024) 7634 2180 E-mail: info@subconlaser.co.uk Sales Contact: T. Mongan *Laser cutting/profile cutting services*

▶ Sub-K Civil Engineering/Building Contractors Ltd, 40 Mellerstain Road, Kirkcaldy, Fife, KY2 6UA Tel: (01592) 200245

▶ Sublime Scuba Photography, PO Box 21524, Stirling, FK8 3YW Tel: 01786 860786 *Underwater photography. Image bank and library. Courses in underwater photography and other diver training. PADI instructor. Commissions accepted.*

Submersible Television Surveys Ltd, 4 Barratt Trading Estate, Denmore Road, Bridge of Don, Aberdeen, AB23 8JW Tel: (01224) 823333 Fax: (01224) 824639 E-mail: admin@stsrov.com *Underwater electronic equipment manufrs*

Subsea Components, 59 Clivemont Road, Maidenhead, Berkshire, SL6 7BZ Tel: (01628) 506560 Fax: (01628) 506501 E-mail: sales@subsea-components.co.uk *Subsea Oil Production Valves, Couplings & Stabplates.*

Subsea Vision Ltd, 15 Southlands Avenue, Corfe Mullen, Wimborne, Dorset, BH21 3JB Tel: (01202) 656861 Fax: (01202) 601530 E-mail: enquiries@subseavision.co.uk *Remotely operated marine vehicle services*

▶ Subsidence Forum, Tournai Hall, Evelyn Woods Road, Aldershot, Hampshire, GU11 2LL Tel: (01252) 357843 Fax: (01252) 357831 E-mail: admin@subsidenceforum.org.uk *Forum representing subsidence industry for a coordinated response*

Subspection Ltd, Shelf House, New Farm Road, Alresford, Hampshire, SO24 9QE Tel: (01962) 734977 Fax: (01962) 735277 E-mail: sales@subspection.com Purchasing Contact: R. Holt Sales Contact: R.J. Holt Principal Export Areas: Asia Pacific, Africa & North America *Manufacturers of cathodic protection systems & survey (subsea/ underwater) electronic equipment/systems. Also cathodic protection services & pipeline surveyors*

▶ Substructure Protection Ltd, Warth Mill, Huddersfield Road, Diggle, Oldham, OL3 5PJ Tel: (01457) 878200 Fax: (01457) 879132 E-mail: sales@spsltd.co.uk *Structure protection service*

Subtech Safety Ltd, Unit 16e Top Barn Business Centre, Worcester Road, Holt Heath, Worcester, WR6 6NH Tel: (01905) 621553 E-mail: info@subtech.co.uk *Repair, hire & sales of safety equipment to the construction industry*

Suburban Ironcraft, Heavy Metal House, Rolling Mill Road, Bettys Lane Norton Canes, Cannock, Staffordshire, WS11 3UH Tel: (01543) 495250 Fax: (01543) 495251 E-mail: subironcraft@aol.com *Ironwork services*

Subway, 6a Friargate Arches, Derby, DE1 1BU Tel: (01332) 347472 *Motor vehicle repairs*

Successful Security Ltd, 73 Rowantree Road, Dromore, County Down, BT25 1NW Tel: (028) 9269 8090 Fax: (028) 9269 8241 E-mail: sales@successfulsecurity.com *Retail fraud consultants*

Sucden UK Ltd, 5 London Bridge Street, London, SE1 9SG Tel: (020) 7940 9400 Fax: (020) 7940 9500 E-mail: info@sucden.co.uk *Commodity brokers*

Sucre Export London Ltd, Greencoat House, Francis Street, London, SW1P 1DH Tel: (020) 7873 0088 Fax: (020) 7873 0100 E-mail: sucre@sopex.co.uk *Commodity traders*

Sud Chemie UK Ltd, 3 Drake Mews, Gadbrook Park, Rudheath, Northwich, Cheshire, CW9 7XF Tel: (01606) 813060 Fax: (01606) 813061 E-mail: info.uk@sud-chemie.com *Chemical exporters & importers*

Sudak Printers Ltd, Unit 5A, Princess Drive Industrial Estate, Coventry Road, Kenilworth, Warwickshire, CV8 2FD Tel: (01926) 513131 E-mail: info@sudak.co.uk *Lithographic printers*

Sudatek Ltd, 59 Barn Meadow Lane, Bookham, Leatherhead, Surrey, KT23 3EZ Tel: (01372) 450008 Fax: (01372) 450006 E-mail: sales@sudatek.com *Electric commutator manufrs*

Sudburys Gloves Ltd, Calvesford Road, Greenbank, Torrington, Devon, EX38 7DP Tel: (01805) 622006 Fax: (0870) 4100089 E-mail: sales@sudburys-gloves.co.uk Sales Contact: R. Booth Principal Export Areas: Central/East Europe & West Europe *Sudburys are UK manufacturers of fashion knitted accessories under their Chimera brand as well as suppling fabric gloves, hats, scarves and accessories into fashion, corporate and protective clothing markets. Customers own requirements also catered for.*

Sudden Impact Computer Services Ltd, Unit 59 Brick Kiln Lane, Parkhouse Indust Estate, Newcastle, Staffordshire, ST5 7AS Tel: (01782) 571900 Fax: 0845 3707702 E-mail: sales@siprinters.co.uk *Sudden Impact offer a printer repair service for a wide range of printers, plotters etc. We supply Refurbished Fusers, Maintenance kits, 2nd User Printers, spares and parts. We offer a tailored printer exchange service.*

Sudeco International Ltd, Unit 1-2 Progress Business Park, Progress Way, Croydon, CR0 4XD Tel: (020) 8686 7000 Fax: (020) 8680 0068 E-mail: info@sudeco.com *Manufacturers, designers & installers of sugar machinery*

Sudlows Carriers Ltd, Stamford Mill, Bayley Street, Stalybridge, Cheshire, SK15 1QQ Tel: 0161-344 2600 Fax: 0161-330 5407 *Road transport/ haulage/freight services*

▶ Sudpack UK Ltd, 40 High Park Drive, Wolverton Mill, Milton Keynes, MK12 5TT Tel: (01908) 525720 Fax: (01908) 525721 E-mail: info@suedpack.com *Vacuum packaging materials manufrs*

Sue & John Jorgensen, 9 Canham Road, London, W3 7SR Tel: (020) 8749 6306 Fax: (020) 8749 6754 *Photographers*

Sueco UK Domestic & Industrial Sewing Machines, 162b Copnor Road, Portsmouth, PO3 5BZ Tel: (023) 9269 7621 Fax: (023) 9269 7621 E-mail: info@sueco.co.uk *Sewing machine repairers*

▶ suesnaughties.com, P.O. Box 88, Lyde, Hereford, HR1 3YS Tel: (01432) 378419 E-mail: sue.price3@btinternet.com *www.suesnaughties.com. Lingerie, sex toys, naughty uniforms & bondage equipment for a fun night in, pole dancing, fetish, p.v.c., rubber, leather & clubbing gear for a great night out if you dare!! Fool around on our Just4Fun page, see our offers page or claim a FREE thong! See website for details. www.suesnaughties.com.*

Suface Specialists P.L.C., Bath Road, Bridgwater, Somerset, TA6 4PA Tel: (01278) 424321 Fax: (01278) 421999 *Bio-degradable packaging materials*

Suff Marine (Europe) Ltd, 15 Allanfield Drive, Newton Stewart, Wigtownshire, DG8 6BP Tel: (01671) 401216 Fax: (01671) 401216 E-mail: sales@suffmarine.com *Supply synthetic lubricants, lube pumps & lube fittings for valves*

Suffolk Chamber Of Commerce, Felaw Maltings, 42 Felaw Street, Ipswich, IP2 8SQ Tel: (01473) 694807 Fax: (01473) 603888 E-mail: info@suffolkchamber.co.uk *Chamber of commerce*

Suffolk Fastener & Engineering Co. Ltd, Unit 17 Hummable Industrial Estate, Toppesfield Road, Great Yeldham, Halstead, Essex, CO9 4HD Tel: (01787) 237007 Fax: (01787) 238052 *Fastener distributors*

▶ Suffolk Films Ltd, The Street, Wenhaston, Halesworth, Suffolk, IP19 9ED Tel: (01986) 875875 E-mail: sales@suffolkfilms.co.uk *Audio visual services*

▶ Suffolk Fleet Maintenance, Blyth Road, Halesworth, Suffolk, IP19 8EN Tel: (01986) 874427 Fax: (01986) 873279

Suffolk Gate Co., Bridge Farm, Rushbrooke, Bury St. Edmunds, Suffolk, IP30 0BP Tel: (01284) 388399 Fax: (01284) 388400 E-mail: sales@suffolkgatecompany.co.uk *Wooden gate manufrs*

▶ Suffolk Heritage Joinery Ltd, Bay 3 Building 89, Anglia Int Airpark, Rendlesham, Woodbridge, Suffolk, IP12 2TW Tel: (01394) 460331 Fax: (01394) 460661 E-mail: dean@sh-joinery.com *Joinery services*

Suffolk Masonery Services, 31 Woolner Close, Barham, Ipswich, IP6 0DL Tel: (01473) 831719 E-mail: r.templeton@ntlworld.com *Stone carvers. Suppliers of stone, marble and granite. Church restoration and repair. Memorials in stone and granite.*

Suffolk Pricing Systems, 66a Canhams Road, Great Cornard, Sudbury, Suffolk, CO10 0ES Tel: (01787) 375192 Fax: (01787) 375192 *Self adhesive label manufrs*

Suffolk Steel Stockholders Ltd, Woodhall Business Park, Sudbury, Suffolk, CO10 1WH Tel: (01787) 370015 Fax: (01787) 379109 *Steel stockholders*

Suffolk Stove Enamellers, Bridge Works, Hasketon, Woodbridge, Suffolk, IP13 6HE Tel: (01473) 735585 Fax: (01473) 735585 *Powder coating services*

▶ Suffolk Webs, 8 Warwick Drive, Bury St. Edmunds, Suffolk, IP32 6TF Tel: (01284) 717162 Fax: (01284) 717162 E-mail: sales@suffolkwebs.co.uk *Web Design, Hosting & Domain Name Registration*

Suffolk Wire, River Hill, Bramford, Ipswich, IP8 4BB Tel: (01473) 748713 Fax: (01473) 748713 *Wire product stockers & retailers*

Sugar Bureau, Duncan House, Dolphin Square, London, SW1V 3PW Tel: (020) 7828 9465 Fax: (020) 7821 5393 E-mail: info@sugar-bureau.co.uk *Trade association*

Sugar Shack, 87 Burnt Oak Broadway, Edgware, Middlesex, HA8 5EP Tel: (0800) 5975097 Fax: (020) 8951 4888 E-mail: sales@sugarshack.co.uk *Cake decorating & bakery supplies*

The Sugarcraft Centre, 106 Lower Road, Hullbridge, Hockley, Essex, SS5 6DD Tel: (01702) 231967 Fax: (01702) 231967 *Cake decorating services*

▶ Sugarfayre Cake Decorating Equipment, 11 Wrexham Street, Mold, Clwyd, CH7 1ET Tel: (01352) 757305 *Cake decorations & equipment suppliers*

Sugarich, Wildmoor Mill Farm, Mill Lane, Wildmoor, Bromsgrove, Worcestershire, B61 0BX Tel: (01527) 576077 Fax: (01527) 575269 *Animal feed manufrs*

▶ Sugaring Practitioner Vanessa Williams, 24 Holland Way, Blandford Forum, Dorset, DT11 7RU Tel: 01258 458528 *Sugaring is the ancient art of hair removal suitable for the face or body.*

Sugarman Medical, 14 Devonshire Square, London, EC2M 4YT Tel: (020) 7456 8777 Fax: (020) 7456 8787 E-mail: info@sugarman.co.uk *Employment agency*

Sugden Ltd, Pasture Lane, Barrowford, Nelson, Lancashire, BB9 6ES Tel: (01282) 611199 Fax: (01282) 613373 E-mail: sales@sugden.ltd.uk *Food process plant equipment services*

Sugg Lighting Ltd, Sussex Manor Business Park, Gatwick Road, Crawley, West Sussex, RH10 9GD Tel: (01293) 540111 Fax: (01293) 540114 E-mail: admin@sugglighting.co.uk *Gas & electric lighting manufrs*

Sugro Robertson Ltd, Tynycoed, Llanrhos, Llandudno, Gwynedd, LL30 1SA Tel: (01492) 581811 Fax: (01492) 583416 E-mail: info@fugro-robertson.com *Petroleum exploration & production consultants* Also at: London W1

Suhner Electronics Ltd, Telford Road, Bicester, Oxfordshire, OX26 4LA Tel: (01869) 364100 Fax: (01869) 249046 E-mail: info.uk@hubersuhner.co.uk *The HUBER+SUHNER Group is a leading global supplier of components and systems for electrical and optical connectivity in communications, industrial applications, and transportation. HUBER+ SUHNER can draw on core competencies in the areas of high frequency technology, fibre optics, cables and polymers. Working in close collaboration with its customers around the globe, HUBER+SUHNER strives for excellence in the development and manufacturing of high quality products.*

Suhner UK Ltd, Pool Road Business Centre, Pool Road, Nuneaton, Warwickshire, CV10 9AQ Tel: (024) 7638 4333 Fax: (024) 7638 4777 E-mail: admin@suhner.com *Hand held power tools distributors*

Sui Generis, Redbanks, Eday, Orkney, KW17 2AA Tel: (01857) 622219 Fax: (01857) 622219 *Cabinet maker*

Suilven Associates Computer Systems, PO Box 1, Leominster, Herefordshire, HR6 9YP Tel: (01568) 720194 Fax: (01568) 720195 E-mail: sales@suilven.com *Computer software developers*

Suite Illusions, 25 Hamilton Road, Rutherglen, Glasgow, G73 3DF Tel: 0141 6470427 Fax: 0141 6470427 E-mail: info@suiteillusions.co.uk *Upholstery*

▶ Suite Leather, New Victoria Mills, Wellington Street, Bury, Lancashire, BL8 2AL Tel: 0161-763 4500 Fax: 0161-763 3500 E-mail: suiteleatheruk@btconnect.com *Suppliers of leather suites, and furniture at wholesale prices. we also sell reconditioned and seconds. Unbeliveably low prices.*

Suite Seat, 12a West Newington Place, Edinburgh, EH9 1QU Tel: 0131- 667 9923 Fax: 0131- 667 9923 *Upholsterers*

Sujitsu Services Ltd, Viables Industrial Centre, Jays Close, Basingstoke, Hampshire, RG22 4BY Tel: (0870) 234 5555 Fax: (0870) 853 3262 *Computer software & hardware distributors*

▶ Suki Teahouse, Unit 6a, Northumberland Street, Belfast, BT13 2JF Tel: (028) 9033 0938 Fax: (028) 9027 8491 E-mail: oscar@suki-tea.com *Fairtrade and Organic Tea merchants*

Sulectric Control Panel Mnfrs, 52 Sherwell Road, Bristol, BS4 4JZ Tel: 0117-971 3917 Fax: 0117-983 4775 *Control panel manufrs*

Sullis Health, The Hollies, Mill Hill, Wellow, Bath, BA2 8QJ Tel: (01225) 833150 Fax: (01225) 833150 E-mail: sullis-health@sullis-health.co.uk *Mail order health products*

Sullivan Engineering Co., 9 Doman Road, Camberley, Surrey, GU15 3DF Tel: (01276) 20931 Fax: (01276) 27168 E-mail: sullivaneng42@netscapeonline.co.uk *Sheet metalwork engineers*

▶ Sullivan Holdings Ltd, West Coppice Road, Walsall, WS8 7HB Tel: (01543) 377280 Fax: (01543) 373079 E-mail: sullivan.holdings@tiscali.co.uk *Road Haulage Services. Factory Relocation Specialist. Low loaders, Hiabs, Mobile Cranes, Artics, Trailers, Rigids, Pallet Network, Back Loads, Good rates to Scotland and Ireland.*

Sullivan Signs, Unit 8 Coatbank Way, Coatbridge, Lanarkshire, ML5 3AG Tel: (01236) 432892 Fax: (01236) 440744 E-mail: jimsullivansigns@btopenworld.com *Sign contractors*

Sullivans Ceilings Ltd, 105 Hilldene Avenue, Romford, RM3 8DL Tel: (01708) 371038 Fax: (01708) 371038 *Suspended ceiling installation & partitions*

D. Sully & Son Ltd, Unit 4 Coldharbour Lane Industrial Estate, 129 Coldharbour Lane, London, SE5 9NY Tel: (020) 7733 3559 E-mail: sales@sully.co.uk *Removal contractors*

▶ SullyVin, 19 Birchwood Avenue, Hutton, Preston, PR4 5EE Tel: (01772) 612152 E-mail: enquiries@sullyvin.com *Importers and distributors of French wine from small producers.**Services include wholesale, mail order, tastings, events and gifts.**Buy wine online.*

Sulzer Metco (UK) Ltd, Suflex Estate, Newport Road, Risca, Newport, Gwent, NP11 6YD Tel: (01633) 600970 Fax: (01633) 601717 E-mail: simon.hiiemal@sulzer.com *Metal spraying equipment, powder & wires suppliers* Also at: York

Sulzer Precision Engineers, 7 Twenty Twenty Industrial Estate, St Laurence Avenue, Allington, Maidstone, Kent, ME16 0LL Tel: (01622) 679562 Fax: (01622) 766306 *Pump maintenance & repair services*

▶ Sulzer Pumps, 18d Challenge House, Sherwood Drive, Bletchley, Milton Keynes, MK3 6DP Tel: (01908) 632775 Fax: (01908) 274957 *Pump manufrs*

Sulzer Pumps UK Ltd, Manor Mill Lane, Leeds, LS11 8BR Tel: 0113-270 1244 Fax: 0113-272 4404 E-mail: sales@sulzerpumps.com *Precision engineers*

Sum & Difference Ltd, 111 Yeolands Drive, Clevedon, Avon, BS21 7XL Tel: (01275) 870378 Fax: (01275) 870378 E-mail: ian.fisher@sumanddifference.co.uk *Audio recording & outside broadcasts*

Suma Containers, Plot Z Robian Way, Swadlincote, Derbyshire, DE11 9DH Tel: (01283) 224114 Fax: (01283) 218280 E-mail: sales@sumacontainers.co.uk *IBC plastic drums & containers suppliers*

Suma Designs, 95 Main Road, Baxterley, Atherstone, Warwickshire, CV9 2LE Tel: (01827) 714476 Fax: (01827) 714476 E-mail: sales@suma-designs.co.uk *Electronic surveillance equipment suppliers*

▶ Sumari Business Systems Ltd, Branston Court, Branston Street, Birmingham, B18 6BA Tel: 0121-244 8111 Fax: 0121-244 8811 E-mail: sumari@sumari.co.uk *Metal finishing software suppliers*

Sumark Services, 221 Ware Road, Hoddesdon, Hertfordshire, EN11 9AF Tel: (01992) 421756 Fax: (01992) 421756 *Equipment service & maintain*

Sumfield & Day Ltd, Park View, Alder Close, Eastbourne, East Sussex, BN23 6QE Tel: (01323) 720455 Fax: (01323) 411230 E-mail: sales@sumfieldandday.com *Sheet fed litho printers, digital printers & stationers*

Sum-It Computer Systems Ltd, Samuel House, Chinnor Road, Thame, Oxfordshire, OX9 3NU Tel: (01844) 213003 Fax: (01844) 214722 E-mail: sales@sum-it.co.uk *Agricultural computer software house*

Sumitomo Corporation Europe Holding Ltd, Vintners Place, 68 Upper Thames Street, London, EC4V 3BJ Tel: (020) 7246 3600 Fax: (020) 7246 3925 E-mail: info@sumitomocorp.co.uk Principal Export Areas: Asia Pacific *Importing/exporting primarily in steel, non-ferrous metals, machinery, foodstuffs.*

Sumitomo Drive Technologies SM Cyclo (UK) Ltd, Unit 29, Bergen Way, Hull, HU7 0YQ Tel: (01482) 790340 Fax: (01482) 790321 E-mail: marketing@sumitomoeurope.com *Power transmission equipment*

Sumitomo Electric Europe Ltd, Unit 220 Centennial Park, Elstree, Hertfordshire, WD6 3SL Tel: (020) 8953 4489 Fax: (020) 8207 5950 E-mail: a.bayram@sumielectric.com *Fibre optics & optical components*

Sumitomo Electric Hardmetal Ltd, 50 Summerleys Road, Princes Risborough, Buckinghamshire, HP27 9PW Tel: (01844) 342081 Fax: (01844) 342415 E-mail: enquiries@sumitomo-hardmetal.co.uk *CBN tungsten carbide & cutting tools distributors*

Sumitomo Electrical Wiring Systems Europe Ltd, Unit1 Woodlands Business Park, Ystradgynlais, Swansea, SA9 1GW Tel: (01639) 842281 Fax: (01639) 849853 *Automotive electrical products*

Summer Garden & Leisure Buildings, High Street, Horningsea, Cambridge, CB25 9JG Tel: (0800) 9777828 Fax: (01223) 441141 E-mail: enquiries@summergardenbuildings.co.uk *Summerhouses, log cabins, garden sheds, garden offices, garden rooms, greenhouses, childrens playhouses, gazebos, timber garages, concrete garages and DIY conservatories. Free UK delivery. Show Centres in Cambridge and Norwich.*

▶ Summer Isles Foods Ltd, The Smoke House, Altandhu, Achiltibuie, Ullapool, Ross-Shire, IV26 2YR Tel: (01854) 622353 Fax: (01854) 622335

Summercliff Ltd, Bilport Lane, Wednesbury, West Midlands, WS10 0NT Tel: 0121-556 0888 Fax: 0121-556 5779 E-mail: sales@summercliffe.co.uk *Steel bar stockholders*

Summerfield & Lang Ltd, 60 Allerton Road, Woolton, Liverpool, L25 7RG Tel: 0151-428 7000 Fax: 0151-428 7172 E-mail: peter.summerfield@btinternet.com

continued

▶ indicates data change since last edition

continuation
Suppliers of filter media for use in wastewater treatment works

Summerhill Steels Ltd, Chiltern House, Leys Road, Brierley Hill, West Midlands, DY5 3UP Tel: (01384) 482048 Fax: (01384) 482022 E-mail: pmale@aol.com *Steel stockholders mild steel products suppliers*

The Summerleaze Waste Company Ltd, Lakeside, Summerleaze Road, Maidenhead, Berkshire, SL6 8HZ Tel: (01628) 630444 Fax: (01628) 773160 E-mail: info@summerleaze.co.uk *Gravel merchants*

▶ Summers Training, 7 Woodlands, Pickwick, Corsham, Wiltshire, SN13 0DA Tel: (01249) 712037 *Professional skills for technical people, including: Project Management; Requirements Management; Negotiating Skills; etc. In total, 16 courses for the technical professional.*

Summit, Unit 5 Vulcan Road, Solihull, West Midlands, B91 2JY Tel: 0121-709 1898 Fax: 0121-711 1429 E-mail: enquires@summit-precision.co.uk *Production engineers & engineering services*

Summit Accessories, 1 Lombard Way, Banbury, Oxfordshire, OX16 4TJ Tel: (01295) 275469 Fax: (01295) 270249 E-mail: sales@summit-auto.com *Motor accessories manufrs*

▶ Summit Asset Management Ltd, Melita House, 124 Bridge Road, Chertsey, Surrey, KT16 8LA Tel: (01932) 575888 Fax: (01932) 575889

Summit Directions, The Innovation Centre, 217 Portobello, Sheffield, S1 4DP Tel: 0114-224 2624 Fax: 0114-224 2222 E-mail: innovations@the-summit.co.uk *Computer software developer*

Summit Drawing Office Supplies Ltd, 1 Grove Street, Woodston, Peterborough, PE2 9AG Tel: (01733) 555789 Fax: (01733) 555004 E-mail: summit@summitdos..co.uk *Drawing office equipment suppliers*

Summit Engineering Co., Wharf Way, Glen Parva, Leicester, LE2 9TF Tel: 0116-277 1083 Fax: 0116-277 3518 E-mail: summit@webleicester.co.uk *Sheet metalwork fabricators*

▶ Summit Engineering Services, 39 Glenburn Road, East Kilbride, Glasgow, G74 5BA Tel: (01355) 260200 Fax: (01355) 260456

Summit Equipment Supplies Ltd, Clover Nook Road, Clover Nook Industrial Estate, Alfreton, Derbyshire, DE55 4RF Tel: (01773) 520488 Fax: (01773) 831004 E-mail: sumhyd@lineone.net *Hydraulic equipment distributors & manufrs*

Summit Hygiene, Cameron Road, Chesham, Buckinghamshire, HP5 3BX Tel: (01494) 793414 Fax: (0870) 3001143 *Cleaning materials suppliers*

Summit Patternmaking Co. Ltd, Paper Mill End Industrial Estate, Birmingham, B44 8NH Tel: 0121-344 3943 Fax: 0121-344 3944 *Engineers pattern makers*

Summit Retail Display Ltd, Church Street, Milton Regis, Sittingbourne, Kent, ME10 2JZ Tel: (01795) 425552 Fax: (01795) 475552 *Shop fitters*

▶ Summit Seven Ltd, 5 Vine Street, King Charles Court, Evesham, Worcestershire, WR11 4RF Tel: (01386) 765488 E-mail: info@summit7.co.uk *Design agency*

Summit Solder Products, Rail Works, Railway Sidings, Biggleswade, Bedfordshire, SG18 8BD Tel: (01767) 318999 Fax: (01767) 318912 E-mail: summit@mountstar.com *Solder manufrs*

Summit Systems Ltd, F Tame Park, Vanguard, Wilnecote, Tamworth, Staffordshire, B77 5DY Tel: (01827) 265800 Fax: (01827) 265801 E-mail: info@summitsystems.co.uk *Plastics machinery & ancillary equipment*

George Sumner Ltd, Bridge Street, Oldham, OL1 1EB Tel: 0161-678 6111 Fax: 0161-624 7773 E-mail: terry@georgesumner.co.uk *Sub-contract engineers*

Sun Blinds, 42 Bellevue Road, Prestwick, Ayrshire, KA9 1NJ Tel: (01292) 477807 *Window blind manufrs*

Sun Chemical Ltd, Head Office, 3 High View Road, South Normanton, Alfreton, Derbyshire, DE55 2DT Tel: (01773) 813704 Fax: (01773) 580045 E-mail: gbsn_info@eu.suncham.com *Printing ink manufrs*

Sun Chemical, 6 South Crescent, London, E16 4TL Tel: (020) 7712 7121 Fax: (020) 7712 7122 *Newspaper & water-based printing ink manufrs* Also at: Glasgow, Manchester, Sutton Coldfield & Wetherby

Sun Chemical Gibbon, 151 South Liberty Lane, Bristol, BS3 2TL Tel: 0117-966 9987 Fax: 0117-966 9880 *Printing ink manufrs*

Sun Chemical Screen, Cray Valley Road, St. Mary Cray, Orpington, Kent, BR5 3TT Tel: (01689) 899666 Fax: (01689) 878262 E-mail: orpington@coates.com Principal Export Areas: Worldwide *Screen printing ink manufrs*

Sun Chemical Swale, Taylor Road, Urmston, Manchester, M41 7SW Tel: 0161-748 7340 Fax: 0161-748 7685 *Ultra-violet coating & ink manufrs*

▶ Sun Chemicals Coates Ltd, Chicester Street, Rochdale, Lancashire, OL16 2IU Tel: (01706) 715060 Fax: (01706) 711178 *Ink manufrs*

Sun Diagnostic, Unit 12 Horsleys Fields, King's Lynn, Norfolk, PE30 5DD Tel: (01553) 692422 Fax: (01553) 691844 E-mail: uksales@snapon.com *Automotive testing equipment manufrs*

▶ Sun Electrical Ltd, 17 Heol Nant Bran, Birchgrove, Swansea, SA7 9LS Tel: (01792) 815962 Fax: (01792) 815962 E-mail: sunelectrical@ntlworld.com *Domestic appliances*

Sun Interiors Ltd, Unit 8, Plaxton Park, Cayton Low Road, Eastfield, Scarborough, North Yorkshire, YO11 3BQ Tel: (01723) 585808 Fax: (01723) 585807 E-mail: info@sun-blinds.co.uk *Blinds manufrs*

Sun Life Financial Of Canada, Head Office, Basing View, Basingstoke, Hampshire, RG21 4DZ Tel: (01256) 841414 Fax: (0870) 1611122 *Assurance services* Also at: Branches throughout the U.K.

Sun Micro Systems, Units 27-30, Number One Industrial Estate, Consett, County Durham, DH8 6TJ Tel: (01207) 580000 Fax: (01207) 591002 E-mail: postmaster@uk.sun.com *Computer sales*

Sun Microsystems Ltd, Solaris House, Minley Road, Blackwater, Camberley, Surrey, GU17 9QG Tel: (01252) 420000 Fax: (01252) 420001 *Software & hardware operating & network systems*

▶ Sun Microsystems Scotland Ltd, Springfield, Linlithgow, West Lothian, EH49 7LR Tel: (01506) 670000 Fax: (01506) 670011 E-mail: sales@sun.com

Sun Safe Play Systems Ltd, Cedars Coach House, Church Road, Windlesham, Surrey, GU20 6BL Tel: (01276) 489999 Fax: (01276) 489999 E-mail: sales@sunsafe.co.uk *Playground equipment distributors*

▶ Sun Save, 37 The Meadway, Shoreham-by-Sea, West Sussex, BN43 5RN Tel: (01273) 455500 Fax: (01273) 441631 E-mail: sales@sun-save.co.uk *Sales of Vaccum tube solar collectors & associated components for Water heating. Commercial & home use. Swimming pool heating /Hot water heating*

Sun Screens Ltd, 72 Silver Street, Newport Pagnell, Buckinghamshire, MK16 0EG Tel: (01908) 216808 Fax: (01908) 210447 *Sun screen blinds manufrs*

▶ Sun Signs & Blinds Ltd, Unit 27 Sheraton Business Centre, Wadsworth Road, Greenford, Middlesex, UB6 7JB Tel: (020) 8998 3368 Fax: (020) 8998 3365 E-mail: info@sun-sign.co.uk *Sign & Blind Makers, Awnings, Canopies & all kinds of signs*

▶ Sun Star Models Europe, The Vicarage, Lounts CR, Great Easton, Market Harborough, Leicestershire, LE16 8SX Tel: (01536) 772490 Fax: (01536) 772491 E-mail: sales@sunstartoys.com

Sun X UK Ltd, 2 Madeira Parade, Madeira Avenue, Bognor Regis, West Sussex, PO22 8DX Tel: (01243) 826441 Fax: (01243) 829691 E-mail: sales@sun-x.co.uk *Solar blinds installers & manufrs*

▶ Suna Supplies Ltd, B 91 Ewell Road, Surbiton, Surrey, KT6 6AH Tel: (020) 8390 8811 Fax: (020) 8390 4331 E-mail: sales@suna.co.uk

Suna Supplies Ltd, B 91 Ewell Road, Surbiton, Surrey, KT6 6AH Tel: (020) 8390 8811 Fax: (020) 8390 4331 E-mail: sales@suna.co.uk *Computer cable distributors*

Sunag Corporation Europe Ltd, Middlesex House, 29-45 High Street, Edgware, Middlesex, HA8 7UU Tel: (020) 8381 1232 Fax: (020) 8381 1632 *Engineering export house*

Sunbeam Timber Products, 119 Bristol Road, Frampton Cotterell, Bristol, BS36 2AU Tel: (01454) 273300 Fax: (01454) 273300 *Fencing manufrs*

▶ Sunbeam Woodworks Ltd, 17 & 21 Sunbeam Road, Park Royal, London, NW10 6JP Tel: (020) 8357 1000 Fax: (020) 8357 1021 E-mail: admin@sunbeamgroup.com *Architectural metalwork & shopfittings*

Sunbright Blinds, 56 Gloucester Road, Urmston, Manchester, M41 9AE Tel: 0161-881 8181 Fax: 0161-748 2227 E-mail: ged.sunbright@virgin.net *Window blind manufrs*

Sunbury Engineering Co. Ltd, Town Mill Works, Hanbury Street, Droitwich, Worcestershire, WR9 8PL Tel: (01905) 773341 Fax: (01905) 779072 *General engineers*

Sunbury Tubing & Pneumatics Ltd, Unit 11 Littleton House, Littleton Road, Ashford, Middlesex, TW15 1UU Tel: (01784) 256309 Fax: (01784) 246470 *Pneumatic equipment distributors*

Suncleen Specialist Cleaning Centre, 119 Seamer Road, Scarborough, North Yorkshire, YO12 4EY Tel: (01723) 352211 Fax: (01723) 352211 *Cleaning janitorial supplies retailers*

Suncolor Blinds, Almond Business Centre, Craigshill Road, Livingston, West Lothian, EH54 5DT Tel: (0800) 3898825 Fax: (01506) 497265 E-mail: sales@suncolor.co.uk *Blinds suppliers*

Suncombe Ltd, Jade House, Lockfield Avenue, Brimsdown, Enfield, Middlesex, EN3 7JY Tel: (020) 8443 3454 Fax: (020) 8443 3969 E-mail: sales@suncombe.com *CIP & food & industrial engineers*

▶ Suncream Holdings Ltd, Glascote Road, Glascote, Tamworth, Staffordshire, B77 2BS Tel: (01827) 54196 Fax: (01827) 61327

▶ Suncrest, Unit B Britannia Trading Estate, Printing House Lane, Hayes, Middlesex, UB3 1AP Tel: (020) 8848 0099 Fax: (020) 8848 4990 E-mail: sales@suncrestdrinks.com *Specialists in exotic fruit & yogurt drinks*

Sundance Multiprocessor Technology Ltd, Chiltern Ho, Waterside, Chesham, Buckinghamshire, HP5 1PS Tel: (01494) 793167 Fax: (01494) 793168 E-mail: sales@sundance.com *Computer manufrs*

▶ Sundance Spas, Unit 23 Waterhouse Business Centre, Cromar Way, Chelmsford, CM1 2QE Tel: (01245) 392288 *Spas & hot tub manufrs*

Sunderland Bedding Centre, 7-9 Olive Street, Sunderland, SR1 3PE Tel: 0191-514 2056 Fax: 0191-510 1317 E-mail: sales@sunderlandbeddingcentre.co.uk *Bed manufrs*

Sunderland Mobile Communication, East Cross Street, Sunderland, SR1 1XB Tel: 0191-567 5675 Fax: 0191-567 5675 *Two way radio's service & manufrs*

Sunderland Paper Mill, Ocean Road, Grangetown, Sunderland, SR2 9RZ Tel: 0191-514 4944 Fax: 0191-510 8012 E-mail: patb@edward-thompson.com *Paper manufrs*

Sundernote Ltd, HRS House, Garrets Green Lane, Birmingham, B33 0UE Tel: 0121-783 3896 Fax: 0121-783 5801 E-mail: info@trogenltd.com *Corporate clothing manufrs*

Sundial Workshop, Valley Farm, Bix, Henley-on-Thames, Oxfordshire, RG9 6BW Tel: (01491) 576956 Fax: (01491) 413524 E-mail: enquiry@sundial-workshop.com *Beautiful affordable sundials to buy online. Solid brass* *continued* *armillary spheres and contemporary stainless steel sundials.*

Sundolitt Ltd, 8 Broomfield Road, Montrose, Angus, DD10 8SY Tel: (01674) 676006 Fax: (01674) 676686 *Packaging materials manufrs* Also at: Aberdeen

Sundolitt, Mirren Court (Three), 123 Renfrew Road, Paisley, Renfrewshire, PA3 4EA Tel: 0141-887 1123 Fax: 0141-889 9878 E-mail: enquiries@sundolitt.co.uk *Expanded polystyrene manufrs*

▶ Sundown Services, Unit 29 Carcroft Enterprise Park, Carcroft, Doncaster, South Yorkshire, DN6 8DD Tel: (01302) 729436 Fax: (01302) 725635 E-mail: sales@sundownservices.co.uk *Suppliers of fork lift trucks, service, rental, contract hire, parts*

Sundwell Solar Ltd, 7 Tower Road, Washington, Tyne & Wear, NE37 2SH Tel: 0191-416 3001 Fax: 0191-415 4297E-mail: solar@sundwel.com *Solar heating equipment manufrs*

▶ Sunflair Camping Equipment Suppliers, Parham Airfield, Parham, Woodbridge, Suffolk, IP13 9AF Tel: (01728) 720773 Fax: (01728) 720774 *Camping equipment distributors*

▶ Sunflex, Sapphire Way, Rhombus Business Park, Norwich, NR6 6NN Tel: (01603) 424434 Fax: (01603) 408839 *Folding & sliding doors manufrs*

Sunflower Consulting Ltd, 2 Days Folley, Haytor, Newton Abbot, Devon, TQ13 9XR Tel: (01364) 661422 Fax: (01364) 661461 *Computer programming & consultant services*

▶ Sunflower Medical, Headway Business Centre, Knowles Lane, Bradford, West Yorkshire, BD4 9SW Tel: (01274) 684004 Fax: (01274) 684006 E-mail: info@sunflowermedical.co.uk *Medical equipment manufrs*

Sunfold Systems, Unit 12 Chestnut Drive, Wymondham, Norfolk, NR18 9SB Tel: (01953) 423423 Fax: (01953) 423430 E-mail: info@sunfold.com *Sunfold Systems, Norfolk are manufacturers of Folding Sliding Doors.*

Sungard Availability Services Ltd, Unit B, Heathrow Corporation Park, Green Lane, Hounslow, TW4 6ER Tel: (020) 8080 8080 Fax: (020) 8080 8112 E-mail: sas.customeruk@sungard.com *Business i t*

Sungold Auto Electrics, Bishops Road, Newcastle upon Tyne, NE15 6RY Tel: 0191-273 5667 Fax: 0191-273 1900 E-mail: sales@sungoldautoelectrics.co.uk *Auto electrical services*

Sunguard Systems Ltd, 33 St. Mary Axe, London, EC3A 8AA Tel: (020) 7337 6000 Fax: (020) 7337 6010 *Computer software distributors*

Sunhill Fashion, 342 Main Street, Glasgow, G40 1LN Tel: 0141-556 4040 Fax: 0141-556 4040 *Clothing manufrs*

Sunit Glass, Napier Close, Hawkesworth Trading Estate, Swindon, SN2 1TY Tel: (01793) 615445 Fax: (01793) 491414 *Double glazers*

Sunitek Marshan Ltd, 176 Newhampton Road East, Wolverhampton, WV1 4PQ Tel: (01902) 773329 Fax: (01902) 773328 *Computer manufrs*

Sunland Airport Transfers, Castle Lane, Littleham, Exmouth, Devon, EX8 5BR Tel: 01395 269301 E-mail: sunlandcars@centralpets.com

Sunlight Ltd, Buckwell End, Wellingborough, Northamptonshire, NN8 4LR Tel: (01933) 279813 Fax: (01933) 274111 *Linen hire services*

Sunlight Service Group Ltd, 9 Castle Lane, Bournemouth, BH9 1PQ Tel: (01202) 512544 Fax: (01202) 547312 E-mail: winton@sunlight.co.uk *Laundry services*

The Sunlight Service Group Ltd, Hotel Division, 72 Thornliebank Road, Glasgow, G43 1LB Tel: 0141-632 1281 Fax: 0141-649 1151 *Industrial linen rental*

The Sunlight Service Group Ltd, Shap Road, Kendal, Cumbria, LA9 6DQ Tel: (01539) 723378 Fax: (01539) 740921 E-mail: kendal@sunlight.co.uk *Washroom hygiene services* Also at: Branches throughout the North

The Sunlight Service Group, 47-49 Lomond Grove, London, SE5 7HW Tel: (020) 7701 6481 Fax: (020) 7708 5954 *Hospital laundry services*

The Sunlight Service Group Ltd, 9 Deer Park Road, London, SW19 3UY Tel: (020) 8542 4646 Fax: (020) 8543 3984 *Laundry*

The Sunlight Service Group Ltd, Princes Street, Penrith, Cumbria, CA11 7BQ Tel: (01768) 862744 Fax: (01768) 891881 E-mail: penrith@sunlight.co.uk *Laundry & dry cleaners*

The Sunlight Service Group Ltd, Victoria Works, Victoria Road, Sowerby Bridge, West Yorkshire, HX6 3AE Tel: (01422) 831151 Fax: (01422) 839101 *Laundry & dry cleaning services*

Sunlight Service Group Ltd, 129 St. Leonards Road, Windsor, Berkshire, SL4 3JT Tel: (01753) 861151 Fax: (01753) 833608 *Laundry services*

Sunlight Services Group Ltd, 226 Whitehorse Road, Croydon, CR9 2NE Tel: (020) 8684 2255 Fax: (020) 8683 4050 E-mail: croydon@sunlight.co.uk *Work wear cleaning contractors*

▶ Sunlight Windows, Lloyd House, Gate Lane, Sutton Coldfield, West Midlands, B73 5TT Tel: 0121-355 5509 Fax: 0121-355 5518 *Window manufrs*

Sunline Blinds & Shutters Ltd, 1200 Lincoln Road, Peterborough, PE4 6LA Tel: (01733) 320822 Fax: (01733) 578732 *Blind fitters*

Sunlite Blinds, Ravensby Road,, Carnoustie, Carnoustie, Angus, DD7 7KK Tel: (01307) 477888 Fax: (01382) 200833 *Manufacturers of blinds*

Sunlite Blinds, 43 Foregate Street, Stafford, ST16 2PJ Tel: (01785) 259345 Fax: (01785) 253363 *Blinds distributors & manufrs*

Sunlock Blinds & Interiors, 9 Gerald Road, Gravesend, Kent, DA12 2HT Tel: (01474) 564614 Fax: (01474) 564614 *Blind manufrs*

Sunnen Products Ltd, Enterprise House, Maxted Road Hemel Hempstead Industrial Estate, Hemel Hempstead Industrial Estate, Hemel Hempstead, Hertfordshire, HP2 7BT Tel: (01442) 393939 Fax: (01442) 391212 E-mail: sales@sunnen.com *A wide variety of engine rebuilding & bore-sizing machines*

Sunningdale Blinds, 3 Henblas Street, Wrexham, Clwyd, LL13 8AE Tel: (01978) 366661 *Domestic & commercial blind retailers & manufrs*

Sunningdale Joineries Ltd, The Timber Yard, Lucas Green, West End, Woking, Surrey, GU24 9YB Tel: (01483) 476444 Fax: (01483) 799967 *Joinery building & decorating*

▶ Sunningvale Coach Works, 274 Davidson Road, Croydon, CR0 6DF Tel: (020) 8663 8800 Fax: (020) 8663 8829 *Vehicle body repairers*

▶ Sunny Aspects Ltd, 36 Udney Park Road, Teddington, Middlesex, TW11 9BG Tel: (020) 8977 4149 E-mail: info@sunnyaspects.co.uk *Semi-transparent garden screens, garden furniture, wooden, manufrs*

Sunny Blinds, 127 Drummond Road, Skegness, Lincolnshire, PE25 3EX Tel: (01754) 896558 E-mail: sunny_blinds@btinternet.com *Blinds, awnings & window film retail*

Sunny Hires, 12 Davenport Road, Sidcup, Kent, DA14 4PW Tel: (07796) 574918

Sunny Textiles Ltd, 115 Soho Hill, Hockley, Birmingham, B19 1AY Tel: 0121-523 9921 *Ladies & children's leisurewear manufrs*

▶ Sunnyfield International. Ltd, Sunnyfield Farm, Ince Lane, Liverpool, L23 4UJ Tel: 0151-924 3692 Fax: 0151-924 8305 E-mail: enquiries@setting-out.com *Survey equipment sales*

Sunnyside Tiles, Sunnyside, Southrop, Lechlade, Gloucestershire, GL7 3PG Tel: (01367) 850510 Fax: (01367) 850508 *Roofing tile manufrs*

▶ Sunnyville Clothing Ltd, East Park Works, 69 St. Barnabas Road, Leicester, LE5 4BE Tel: 0116-246 1988 Fax: 0116-246 1988

Sunray Engineering Ltd, Wotton Road, Ashford, Kent, TN23 6LL Tel: (01233) 639039 Fax: (01233) 625137 E-mail: sales@sunraydoors.co.uk *Steel security & fire rated doors manufrs*

Sunray Home Bakery, Carnbane Industrial Estate, Newry, County Down, BT35 6EF Tel: (028) 3026 2614 *Confectionery manufrs*

Sunrider Europe Incorporated, 14-20 Shand Street, Shand House, London, SE1 2ES Tel: (020) 7940 8000 Fax: (020) 7940 8040 E-mail: info@sunrider.co.uk *Herbal foods manufrs*

Sunrise, Unit 49g Pipers Road, Park Farm Industrial Estate, Redditch, Worcestershire, B98 0HU Tel: (01527) 522354 Fax: (01527) 517265 *PVC window, patio door & conservatory manufrs*

Sunrise Fine Foods, Unit 5 The Business Centre, Morgans Vale Road, Redlynch, Salisbury, SP5 2HA Tel: (01725) 513122 Fax: (01725) 513322 E-mail: admin@wiltonwholefoods.co.uk Principal Export Areas: Central/East Europe *Food*

Sunrise Medical Ltd, Sunrise Business Park, High Street, Wollaston, Stourbridge, West Midlands, DY8 4PS Tel: (01384) 446688 Fax: (01384) 446699 E-mail: sunmail@sunmed.co.uk *Stairlift, wheelchair & scooter manufrs*

▶ Sunrise Music Group, 11 Redstock Close, Westhoughton, Bolton, BL5 3UX Tel: 01942- 810 820 E-mail: sales@sunrisemusicgroup.co.uk *Online music retailers*

Sunrise Software Ltd, 50 Barwell Business Park, Leatherhead Road, Chessington, Surrey, KT9 2NY Tel: (020) 8391 9000 Fax: (020) 8391 4445 E-mail: enquiries@sunrisesw.com *Software developers*

Sunrise Systems Ltd, Flint Bridge Bus Centre, Flint Lane, Ely Road, Cambridge, CB5 9QZ Tel: (01223) 441311 Fax: (01223) 441297 E-mail: info@sunrise-sys.com *Computer software developers*

▶ Sunrise Systems, 52 Albany Street, Edinburgh, EH1 3QR Tel: 0131-478 7781 Fax: 0131-478 0239

▶ Sunrise Systems (Scotland), Arbikie Farm, Inverkeilor, Arbroath, Angus, DD11 4UZ Tel: (01241) 830770 Fax: (01241) 830755 E-mail: sales@sunsys.com

Sunrite Blinds, 11 Caledonian Lane, Aberdeen, AB11 6XF Tel: (01224) 575201 Fax: (01224) 575201 E-mail: sales@sunrite-blinds-aberdeen.com *Rollers & vertical blind manufrs*

Sunrite Blinds Ltd, 4 Newhailes Industrial Estate, Musselburgh, Edinburgh, EH21 6SY Tel: 0131-669 2345 Fax: 0131-665 7711 E-mail: info@sunrite.co.uk *Manufactures blinds & curtains*

▶ Sunrite Blinds Ltd, Caxton Way, Cromer House, Stevenage, Hertfordshire, SG1 2DF Tel: (01438) 722221 Fax: (01438) 740794

▶ Sunscan Ltd, Unit 9D, Brindley Road, Reginald Road Industrial Estate, St. Helens, Merseyside, WA9 4HY Tel: (01744) 811788 Fax: (0870) 3212406

Sunseal Blinds, 8 Lymington Road, Willenhall, West Midlands, WV13 2SB Tel: (01902) 607798 *Blind manufrs*

Sunseeker Caravans Ltd, 72-84 Station Road, Burton Latimer, Kettering, Northamptonshire, NN15 5NX Tel: (01536) 722316 Fax: (01536) 725883 *Doors windows conservatories manufrs*

Sunseeker Exhibitions Ltd, 27-31 West Quay Road, Poole, Dorset, BH15 1HX Tel: (01202) 381111 Fax: (01202) 382222 E-mail: admin@sunseeker.com *Boat builders*

Sunset Blinds, 48 Gordon Terrace, Invergordon, Ross-Shire, IV18 0DA Tel: (01349) 854888 Fax: (01349) 854777 E-mail: info@sunsetblinds.com *Window blinds*

Sunset Blinds, Rugby House, Hinckley Road, Sapcote, Leicester, LE9 4FS Tel: (01455) 274927 Fax: (01455) 274948 *Blind manufrs*

Sunset Packaging Supplies Ltd, Unit 4 Witan Park, Avenue Two, Witney, Oxfordshire, OX28 4FN Tel: (01993) 776641 Fax: (01993) 779834 E-mail: enquiries@sunsetpackaging.co.uk *Merchant packers*

Sunsetters Of Nottingham, 130 Davies Road, West Bridgford, Nottingham, NG2 5HY Tel: 0115-974 4402 Fax: 0115-974 4402 *Retractable all weather awnings*

Sunshade Blinds, 592 Kingstanding Road, Birmingham, B44 9SH Tel: 0121-373 1919 Fax: 0121-373 1919 *Blind manufrs*

Sunshine, 27 The Grove, Biggin Hill, Westerham, Kent, TN16 3TA Tel: (01959) 570489

▶ indicates data change since last edition

▶ Sunshine Au Pair, Wardwick, Derby, DE1 1HA Tel: (0845) 0066245 Fax: (01332) 231320 E-mail: info@sunshineaupairs.co.uk *We provide au pairs to clients across the UK*

Sunshine Solutions Ltd, 1 Hatchfield Cottages, Knighton Road, Broad Chalke, Salisbury, SP5 5DU Tel: (01722) 780885 Fax: (01722) 780886 E-mail: enquiries@sunshine-solutions.co.uk *Computer software suppliers*

▶ Sunsmart Spray Tanning Systems, 2 Airebank, Bingley, West Yorkshire, BD16 2RA Tel: (07716) 380034 E-mail: richard@theairbrushtan.co.uk *Suppliers of sunless tanning systems & other sunless tanning supplies*

▶ Sunspar Services, Elswick Road, Fenton Industrial Estate, Stoke-on-Trent, ST4 2PZ Tel: (01782) 415733 Fax: (01782) 417042

▶ SunSpecs2u, 63 High West Street, Dorchester, Dorset, DT1 1UY Tel: (01305) 264922 E-mail: info@sunspecs2u.co.uk *Designer sunglasses manufrs*

Sunspel Menswear Ltd, Cavendish House, Canal Street, Long Eaton, Nottingham, NG10 4HP Tel: 0115-973 5292 Fax: 0115-946 1211 E-mail: sales@sunspel.com *Mens undershorts, pyjamas & leisurewear*

Suntech Computer Services, 9 St. Colmans Park, Newry, County Down, BT34 2BX Tel: (028) 3026 6650 Fax: (028) 3083 4974 E-mail: messages@suntech.co.uk *Computer installers & maintenance*

▶ Sun-Togs, Litton House, Saville Road, Peterborough, PE3 7PR Tel: (01733) 765030 Fax: (01733) 765210 E-mail: sales@sun-togs.co.uk *Clothes mail order*

Sunvic Controls Ltd, Bellshill Road, Uddingston, Glasgow, G71 6NP Tel: (01698) 812944 Fax: (01698) 813637 E-mail: sales@sunvic.co.uk *Domestic appliance controls & thermostats manufrs*

Supa Roofing & Power Tools Ltd, Aller Mills, Aller Road, Kingskerswell, Newton Abbot, Devon, TQ12 5AU Tel: (01803) 873288 Fax: (01803) 875277 E-mail: clive@suparoofing.co.uk *Roofing contractors, power tools & screws suppliers*

Supablast Nationwide Ltd, 11 Gorsey Lane, Coleshill, Birmingham, B46 1JU Tel: (01675) 464446 Fax: (01675) 464447 E-mail: enquiries@supablast.co.uk *Sandblasting services*

Supaclad Ltd, Timmis Road, Stourbridge, West Midlands, DY9 7BQ Tel: (01384) 896647 Fax: (01384) 892457 *External & internal composite panels*

Supacleen Ltd, 1 Bessemer Close, Cardiff, CF11 8DL Tel: (029) 2066 6663 Fax: (029) 2066 6663 E-mail: supacleen@onetel.net.uk *Office cleaning contractors*

Supagard Ltd, 23-25 Gavinton Street, Glasgow, G44 3EF Tel: 0141-633 5933 Fax: 0141-637 7219 E-mail: info@supagard.co.uk *Car care products supplier*

▶ Supaglazing Ltd, Units 29 & 10, Deacon Trading Centre, Knight Road Strood, Rochester, Kent, ME2 2AU Tel: (01634) 727406

Supapak Ltd, 24 Jubilee Way, Shipley, West Yorkshire, BD18 1QG Tel: (01274) 531314 Fax: (01274) 532008 E-mail: sales@supapak.com *Packaging materials distributors*

Supaseal Glass Ltd, 1-3 Lovat Place, Hillington Industrial Estate, Glasgow, G52 4DS Tel: 0141-810 5010 Fax: 0141-810 5020 E-mail: sales@supasealglass.co.uk *Sealed glass unit manufrs*

Supaseal (U K) Ltd, PO Box 5329, Market Harborough, Leicestershire, LE16 7PT Tel: (01858) 434141 Fax: (01858) 434717 E-mail: admin@supaseal.co.uk *Seal distributors*

Supaturf Products Ltd, Office 7 Grange Farm Business Park, Desford Road, Newtown Unthank, Leicester, LE9 9FL Tel: (01455) 825440 Fax: (01455) 828945 E-mail: sales@supaturf-products.co.uk *Sports turf supplies*

▶ Super Clean Commercial, 45 Phipps Road, Oxford, OX4 3HJ Tel: (01865) 712169 Fax: (01865) 712169 E-mail: superclean_oxford@hotmail.com *We are Commercial Window Cleaning Specialists who have been cleaning windows and carpets throughout Oxfordshire and the South of England for over 20 years.*All our work comes with full money back guarantee*

Super Finish Elastics Ltd, 42 London Street, Leicester, LE5 3RU Tel: 0116-276 1007 Fax: 0116-276 1005 E-mail: sales@superfinishelastics.co.uk *Elastic lace & trimmings manufrs*

Super Gear Co. Ltd, Unit 2 Nine Trees Trading Estate, Morthen Road, Thurcroft, Rotherham, South Yorkshire, S66 9JG Tel: (01709) 702320 Fax: (01709) 700733 *Gear & sprocket manufrs*

Super Hanger Manufacturing Co. Ltd, 100 Vale Road, Windsor, Berkshire, SL4 5JL Tel: (01753) 622500 Fax: (01753) 622770 E-mail: sales@super-hanger.co.uk *Coat hanger distributors*

Super Service, Frogs Island, Old Didcot Road, Brightwell-cum-Sotwell, Wallingford, Oxfordshire, OX10 0SW Tel: (01491) 837000 Fax: (01491) 839900 *Cleaning equipment, pressure washers, floor care equipment, chemicals*

▶ Super Shade Blinds & Awnings, 3 Miglo Industrial Estate, Yalberton Road, Paignton, Devon, TQ4 7QW Tel: (01803) 522887 Fax: (01803) 522887 E-mail: tony@super-shade.co.uk *Blinds & awning retailers*

Super Sharp Saw Service, 174 London Road, Mitcham, Surrey, CR4 3LD Tel: (020) 8648 2154 Fax: (020) 8648 2154 *Tool grinders*

▶ Super Slitters, 7-8 Lessarna Court, Bowling Back Lane, Bradford, West Yorkshire, BD4 8ST Tel: (01274) 735290 Fax: (01274) 740193 E-mail: superslitters@hotmail.com *Specialist slitting services*

Super Spares Ltd, Brookfield Industrial Estate, Peggys Loaning, Banbridge, County Down, BT32 3AP Tel: (028) 4066 2166 Fax: (028) 4062 6642 E-mail: info@super-spares.com *Engineering & mechanical supplies*

Super Stickers, PO Box 55, Bangor, County Down, BT19 7PJ Tel: (028) 9145 4344 Fax: (028) 9146 6474 E-mail: info@motivationinlearning.co.uk *Motivational learning sticker manufrs*

Super Stork I P T Ltd, Carlisle Road, London, NW9 0HD Tel: (020) 8200 1144 Fax: (020) 8200 4385 E-mail: sales1@superstork.co.uk *Industrial power tool distributors*

Super Systems UK Ltd, 120 Rectory Road, Sutton Coldfield, West Midlands, B75 7RS Tel: 0121-240 1591 Fax: 0121-240 1591 E-mail: matthew.cross@which.net *Oxygen probes, sensors and control instrumentation for most heat treatment applications;esp. carburising, nitriding, nitrocarburising and carbonitriding.*

Super Tan, Unit 17b Asquith Bottom, Sowerby Bridge, West Yorkshire, HX6 3BT Tel: (01422) 831122 Fax: (01422) 831122 *Sun bed hire services*

Super Trucks Ltd, Beaufort Street, St. Helens, Merseyside, WA9 3BQ Tel: (01744) 25348 Fax: (01744) 27772 E-mail: supertrucks@btinternet.com *Commercial vehicle body builders*

▶ Super Wide Digital, Cromer Industrial Estate, Hilton Fold Lane, Middleton, Manchester, M24 2LE Tel: 0161-653 6500 Fax: 0161-654 9500 E-mail: sales@super-wide.co.uk *Super-wide banners, mesh, pvc, building wrap.*

▶ Super Yacht Doc's, 6 Lester Avenue, Havant, Hampshire, PO9 3HE Tel: (023) 9247 6566 Fax: (023) 9248 1884 E-mail: info@superyachtdoc.com *Atlas carbon fibre portable davits, solid stainless steel anchor, stainless steel chairs & table pedestals, spares service, general wholesale chandlery available, Osculati agents*

Superchips Ltd, 2-16 Homestall, Buckingham Industrial Estate, Buckingham, MK18 1XJ Tel: (01280) 816781 Fax: (01280) 816764 E-mail: sales@superchips.co.uk *Auto electrical component manufrs*

Supercraft Ltd, Canada Road, Byfleet, West Byfleet, Surrey, KT14 7JL Tel: (01932) 351941 Fax: (01932) 340807 E-mail: sales@supercraft.co.uk *Aerospace manufrs*

Supercrafts Cane Goods, Harlestone Road, Northampton, NN5 6NU Tel: (01604) 581757 Fax: (01604) 581554 E-mail: supercrafts@btinternet.co.uk *Retail cane furniture manufrs*

▶ Supercross Ltd, 3 Babington Close, Middleton, Milton Keynes, MK10 9HE Tel: (01908) 308180 Fax: (01908) 230750 *Telecommunications & products*

Superdrug Stores plc, 118 Beddington Lane, Croydon, CR0 4TB Tel: (020) 8684 7000 Fax: (020) 8684 6102 *Retail health & beauty chemists retailers*

▶ SuperEtrader, PO Box 4788, Walsall, WS1 9DZ Tel: (0870) 4438446 Fax: (0870) 4438445 E-mail: sales@superetrader.co.uk *GPS satellite navigation systems specialising in vehicles*

Superfine Tapes Co. Ltd, Batford Mill, Lower Luton Road, Harpenden, Hertfordshire, AL5 5ES Tel: (01582) 460808 Fax: (01582) 766535 *Distributors of packaging materials*

Superform Aluminium, Cosgrove Close, Worcester, WR3 8UA Tel: (01905) 874300 Fax: (01905) 874301 E-mail: sales@superform-aluminium.com *Aluminium pressings superplastic forming process*

Superfos Runcorn Ltd., Edison Road, Astmoor Industrial Estate, Runcorn, Cheshire, WA7 1PY Tel: (01928) 575051 Fax: (01928) 572038 E-mail: steve.winstanley@superfos.co.uk *UK based manufacturers of plastic injection moulded buckets & containers.*

Superframe Ltd, The Old Electricity Works, Campfield Road, St. Albans, Hertfordshire, AL1 5HJ Tel: (01727) 865555 Fax: (01727) 865566 E-mail: sales@sf2.co.uk *Plastics fabricators*

▶ Supergreenthumb, London, London, N22 6SD Tel: 0800 917 4252 *Supergreenthumb.co.uk specialises in the following brands for all your online gardening needs. Weber, Gloster, Gardena, Phostrogen, Town and Country, Bonsai, Baby Bio, Felco and Wolf Garten.*

▶ Superior Cleaning Services, 111 George Street, Edinburgh, EH2 4JN Tel: 0131-624 7169 Fax: 0131-624 7168 E-mail: info@superiorcs.co.uk *Superior Cleaning Services, one of the largest independent Window Cleaning Contractors -*where the principals actively manage the business. Our company has Teams operating throughout the United Kingdom. *We maintain Hundreds of facilities, employ a large professional Window Cleaning staff and have been serving customers for more than 20 years.**Superior Cleaning Services provides industrial, retail, commercial, and professional window cleaning services, *with local expertise, through our many local locations across the U.K. *We've been a leader in the business for over 20 years, serving customers of all sizes, from Blue Chip companies to local start-ups.**Our method involves a detailed consultation and site survey, we provide you with a comprehensive*proposal together with detailed costings, specific to your individual needs.***

Superior Plant Sales Services Ltd, Unit 2-3 Cornwall St Industrial Estate, Cornwall Street, Manchester, M11 2WL Tel: 0161-343 3312 Fax: 0161-231 1133 *Powder coating suppliers*

▶ Superior Plumbing Installations Ltd, 7 High Street, Chasetown, Burntwood, Staffordshire, WS7 3XE Tel: (01543) 677161 Fax: (01543) 685730

▶ Superior Plumbing Installations Ltd, Unit1 Wheeler Road, Binley Industrial Estate, Whitley, Coventry, CV3 4LA Tel: (024) 7621 7980 Fax: (024) 7663 9766

Superior Radiator Co., 86a Victoria Road, London, N4 3SW Tel: (020) 7272 1995 Fax: (020) 7272 7554 *Motor radiator sales & repairs*

Superior Seals, 7 Nimrod Way, East Dorset Trade Park, Wimborne, Dorset, BH21 7SH Tel: (01202) 854300 Fax: (01202) 854313 E-mail: sales.seals@superiorltd.com *O-ring manufrs*

Superior Sections Ltd, 32 Regal Drive, Walsall Enterprise Park, Walsall, WS2 9HQ Tel: (01922) 620333 Fax: (01922) 610555 E-mail: sales@superiorsections.co.uk *Machinery manufrs*

Superior Signs Ltd, 1-7 Taylor Street, Bury, Lancashire, BL9 6DT Tel: 0161-764 5170 Fax: 0161-762 9068 E-mail: sales@superiorsigns.co.uk *Signs manufrs*

▶ Superior Systems, 39 Deerhurst Road, Coventry, CV6 4EJ Tel: (024) 7666 3321 Fax: (024) 7666 3321 E-mail: sales@superior-systems.co.uk *Design and Supply of Control Systems (PLC based), Industrial Control Systems, Process Control, Factory Automation, HMI Terminals, Control Panels, DVT Machine Vision.*

Superite Tools, Unit 3 Hayward Industrial Park, Vigo Place, Walsall, WS9 8UG Tel: (01922) 455769 Fax: (01922) 743176 E-mail: enquiries@superite.co.uk *Plastic & pressure die toolmakers*

Super-Max Ltd, 5-11 Mono Lane, Feltham, Middlesex, TW13 7LR Tel: (020) 8844 1433 Fax: (020) 8844 1479 E-mail: stirlingfour@aol.com *Razor blade packaging & distributors*

Supermix Concrete, 76 Strabane Road, Newtownstewart, Omagh, County Tyrone, BT78 4JZ Tel: (028) 8166 1391 Fax: (028) 8166 1391 *Concrete product manufrs*

Superplants Ltd, Chart House, Shaftesbury Lane, Stoke Trister, Wincanton, Somerset, BA9 9PL Tel: (01963) 34842 Fax: (01963) 34673 E-mail: info@superplants.co.uk *Floral suppliers*

Superplate Graphics Ltd, 2 Apex Business Park, Apex Way, Leeds, LS11 5LN Tel: 0113-234 0800 Fax: 0113-234 0944 *Computer graphic design services*

▶ Superseal Anglia Ltd, 40 Mansell Close, Spalding, Lincolnshire, PE11 1NE Tel: (01775) 722116 Fax: 07883 399444 E-mail: info@supersealanglia.co.uk *Superseal tyre sealant.The World Leaders in Puncture Protection.Prevents losses through punctures,Extends Tyre life upto 25% and saves Fuel too.*

Superseal Windows Ltd, 5 Bridge Street, Castledawson, Magherafelt, County Londonderry, BT45 8AD Tel: (028) 7946 9606 Fax: (028) 7946 9796 *Windows manufrs*

Supershades Blinds & Awnings, 167 Alexandra Road, Farnborough, Hampshire, GU14 6SD Tel: (01252) 518493 Fax: (01252) 518493 *Window blind retailer & manufrs*

▶ Supersigns Sign Writers, 114-116 The Hornet, Chichester, West Sussex, PO19 7JR Tel: (01243) 532045 Fax: (01243) 532062 E-mail: sales@supersignschichester.co.uk *Manufacturers & retailers of signs & displays*

▶ Supersine Duramark Ltd, Freemantle Road, Lowestoft, Suffolk, NR33 0EA Tel: (01502) 501234 Fax: (01502) 560620 E-mail: info@ssdm.co.uk *Suppliers of Banner stands, Pop ups & Exhibition display. Large format graphics, Decorative finishes, Retail graphics. Corporate Identity and Branding mulitple rollout programmes National and International .*Fleet graphics, Vinyl graphics, Vending machine graphics, Banners, Hoarding, Building, and Developer graphics.Screenprinting and Internal signs.*

Supersine Duramark Ltd, Freemantle Road, Lowestoft, Suffolk, NR33 0EA Tel: (01502) 501234 Fax: (01502) 560620 E-mail: info@ssdm.co.uk *Vinyl graphics converters & digital format printing services*

▶ Supersounds Roadshow, 112 Tamarisk Road, South Ockendon, Essex, RM15 6HX Tel: (01708) 670582 E-mail: supersounds@btinternet.com *For the very best in mobile discos for all occasions specialists in weddings with various packages call today for a brochure*

Supertron Ltd, 19-21 Fosse Way, London, W13 0BZ Tel: (020) 8998 4372 *Invention & patent searchers & developers*

Supertube, Darby House, Darby Way, Narborough, Leicester, LE19 2GP Tel: 0116-286 6611 Fax: 0116-275 0216 *Display modular system manufrs*

Supertune Automotive Ltd, 291 Elland Road, Leeds, LS11 8AX Tel: 0113-277 4311 Fax: 0113-272 0400 *Car body shop suppliers*

Superwinch Ltd, Union Mine Road, Pitts Cleave, Tavistock, Devon, PL19 0PW Tel: (01822) 614101 Fax: (01822) 615204 E-mail: sales@superwinch.net Principal Export Areas: Worldwide *Winches manufrs*

Supotco Design Ltd, 3-5 Valentine Place, London, SE1 8QH Tel: (020) 7928 5474 Fax: (020) 7928 6082 E-mail: info@supotco.co.uk *Theatrical production services & fashion show*

Supplie Direct UK Ltd, Unit 5, Commondale Way, Euroway Industrial Estate, Bradford, West Yorkshire, BD4 6SF Tel: (01274) 652000 Fax: (01274) 685632 *Garage equipment sales*

Supplies House Ltd, Unit 21 Interchange East Business Park, Grosvenor Way, London, E5 9ND Tel: (020) 8806 8666 Fax: (020) 8806 8686 E-mail: sales@supplieshouse.com *Janitorial suppliers*

▶ Supplies Team, 66-70 Vicar Lane, Little Germany, Bradford, West Yorkshire, BD1 5AG Tel: (01274) 741111 E-mail: info@supplies-team.co.uk *Office supplies from laser toner cartridges to lever arch files*

Supplies Team Scotland, Custom House, Union Street, Bo'Ness, West Lothian, EH51 9AQ Tel: (0870) 8715929 Fax: (0870) 8715928 E-mail: sales@supplies-team.co.uk *Computer consumables distributors*

▶ Supply Co. Ltd, Brookfield Industrial Estate, Peakdale Road, Glossop, Derbyshire, SK13 6LQ Tel: (01457) 869875 Fax: (01457) 855852 E-mail: service@supplycompany.co.uk *Specialist designers & manufacturers of garment presentation packaging*

Supply Chain & Logistics Consulting Ltd, The Chimes, 1 Park Road, Congleton, Cheshire, CW12 1DS Tel: (01260) 276469 E-mail: info@supplychainlogistics-consulting.co.uk *Supply Chain Logistics Consulting Limited is an independent consultancy in logistics and*

continued

supply chain disciplines working with major domestic and multi-national organisations within the UK and Europe

Supply Control Ltd, Broomlea, Pacemuir Road, Kilmacolm, Renfrewshire, PA13 4JJ Tel: (01505) 873255 E-mail: neilm@supplycontrol.com *Supply chain management consultants specialising in interim management, purchasing, materials management,& logistics with experience in high-tech industries*

Supply Direct Ltd, 8 Priory House, Cloisters Business Park, 8 Battersea Park Road, London, SW8 4BH Tel: (020) 7622 9119 Fax: (020) 7622 0567 E-mail: info@supplydirect.com *Supply Direct are contract caterers, supplying the NHS and schools with a comprehensive one stop shop solution. They are catering consultants & food distributors/agents/packers based in London.*

▶ Support Communications Ltd, Suite 21 Elite House, 70 Warwick Street, Birmingham, B12 0NL Tel: 0121-766 3168 Fax: 0121-766 3086 E-mail: t.foley@supportcomms.co.uk *Cable containment systems*

Support & Development Ltd, 43 Cottesford Clo, Hadleigh, Ipswich, IP7 5JA Tel: 01473 824642 *Computer consultants*

▶ Support Force, Nionisle House, Station Road, Betchworth, Surrey, RH3 7BZ Tel: (0870) 7594357 E-mail: sales@thesupportforce.com

Support In Sport (U K) Ltd, Tavistock Works, Glasson Industrial Estate, Maryport, Cumbria, CA15 8NT Tel: (01900) 812796 Fax: (01900) 815509 *Artificial turf & synthetic grass manufrs*

Support Instrumentation Ltd, 52 Westhall Rd, Warlingham, Surrey, CR6 9BH Tel: 01883 623399 Fax: 01883 624499 *Instrumentation distributor*

Support Site P.L.C., Pedmore Road, Dudley, West Midlands, DY2 0RN Tel: (01384) 472250 Fax: (01384) 472251 E-mail: birmingham@supportsite.co.uk *Building construction*

Support Stool, 13 Madeley Road, Aylesbury, Buckinghamshire, HP21 8BP Tel: (01296) 581764 Fax: (01296) 586583 E-mail: sales@supportstool.co.uk *Surgeons stools & medical equipment suppliers*

Support Systems Nottingham Ltd, Nottingham Road, Beeston, Nottingham, NG9 6DP Tel: 0115-922 9067 Fax: 0115-925 5555 *Pipe work support fixings & steel fabrications services*

Supportive Ltd, Old Studios, Hyde Park Road, Leeds, LS6 1RU Tel: 0113-245 7302 Fax: 0113-245 7304 E-mail: post@supportive.co.uk *IT consultants*

▶ Supportkey Ltd, Ladywell Business Centre, 94 Duke Street, Glasgow, G4 0UW Tel: 0141-552 8505 Fax: 0141-552 0246 E-mail: sales@supportkey.com *IT consultants*

Suppression Devices, Unit 8, York Street Business Centre, Clitheroe, Lancashire, BB7 2DL Tel: (01200) 444497 Fax: (01200) 444330 E-mail: sales@suppression-devices.com *EMC filters, mains & interference, capacitors manufrs*

Suprafilt Ltd, Units 2 Rochdale Industrial Estate, Albion Road, Rochdale, Lancashire, OL11 4JB Tel: (01706) 640909 Fax: (01706) 640683 E-mail: sales@suprafilt.com *Waste water systems design & manufrs*

Supreme Blinds, 62 Shepherds Way, Rickmansworth, Hertfordshire, WD3 7NL Tel: (01923) 773461 Fax: (01923) 773461 *Blinds manufrs*

Supreme Bodies Midlands Ltd, Ablow Street, Wolverhampton, WV2 4ER Tel: (01902) 426244 Fax: (01902) 710669 *Commercial vehicle body builders*

▶ Supreme Clean, 8 Enterprise Court, Lakes Road, Braintree, Essex, CM7 3QS Tel: (01376) 339719 Fax: (01376) 320600 E-mail: info@supremeclean-ltd.co.uk *Contract cleaning, janitorial supplies, cleaning machine sales & hire*

Supreme Concrete Ltd, Coppingford Hall, Coppingford Road, Sawtry, Huntingdon, Cambridgeshire, PE28 5GP Tel: (01487) 833300 Fax: (01487) 833305 E-mail: sales@supremeconcrete.co.uk *Concrete product manufrs*

▶ Supreme Concrete Ltd, Andall Road, Barnwell, Peterborough, PE8 5PD Tel: (01832) 270107

Supreme Concrete Ltd, Crown Quay Lane, Sittingbourne, Kent, ME10 3SL Tel: (01795) 475255 Fax: (01795) 433599 E-mail: enquiries@bourncrete.co.uk *Concrete products manufrs*

▶ Supreme Concrete Ltd, Unit 2 Tweedale Industrial Estate, Madeley, Telford, Shropshire, TF7 4JR Tel: (01952) 684282 Fax: (01952) 580834 *Concrete casting suppliers*

Supreme Conveyor Belts, Unit 2G, Halas Industrial Estate, Forge Lane, Halesowen, West Midlands, B62 8EB Tel: 0121-585 5227 Fax: 0121-585 5244 E-mail: supremebelts@aol.com *Manufacturer & supplier of metalic conveyor belts & sprockets*

Supreme Die Cutters, Unit 7 Forest Hill Business Centre, Clyde Vale, London, SE23 3JF Tel: (020) 8291 0473 Fax: (020) 8291 0402 *Cutting & creasing form makers*

Supreme Distributing Co. Ltd, 235-237 Coldharbour Lane, London, SW9 8RR Tel: (020) 7274 2516 Fax: (020) 7737 5377 *Motor car spares & accessories factors*

▶ Supreme Fireworks, Tree Tops, Golden Ball Lane, Maidenhead, Berkshire, SL6 6NW Tel: (01628) 625261 Fax: (01628) 625261 E-mail: sales@supremefireworks.com *Firework displays for any event & firework sales*

▶ Supreme Food Ingredients, 5 Moor Close, Holmewood Industrial Park, Holmewood, Chesterfield, Derbyshire, S42 5UX Tel: (01246) 855552 Fax: (01246) 855664 *Food ingredient manufrs*

▶ Supreme Grinding Machines, Church Gates, Church Street, Mexborough, South Yorkshire, S64 0ER Tel: (07710) 945439 Fax: (01709) 570475 E-mail: supremegrindingmachines@hotmail.co.uk *Specialist grinding machine repairs (lawn mower blades)*

Supreme Ironcraft Ltd, Unit 26 Brook Road Industrial Estate, Brook Road, Rayleigh, Essex, SS6 7XL Tel: (01268) 747774 Fax: (01268) 770449 *Steel fabricators*

Supreme Plastics Ltd, Stainsacre Lane, Whitby, North Yorkshire, YO22 4PT Tel: (01947) 604161 Fax: (01947) 606168 E-mail: sales@supremeplastics.com *Re-sealable plastic packaging manufacturers & distributors*

Supreme Plastics Group plc, Supreme House, 300 Regents Park Road, London, N3 2JX Tel: (020) 8346 3291 Fax: (020) 8346 1624 E-mail: info@supremeplastics.com *Re-sealable flexible packaging manufrs*

Supreme Quilting Co plc, Brittania Works, Whitehall Road, Tipton, West Midlands, DY4 7JR Tel: 0121-520 7227 Fax: 0121-522 4245 *Quilters & textile merchants*

Supreme Rubber Stamp Co., 1 Valley End Business Centre, Nunn Brook Road, Huthwaite, Sutton-in-Ashfield, Nottinghamshire, NG17 2HU Tel: (01623) 514942 Fax: (01623) 559849 E-mail: faststampsuk@yahoo.co.uk *Rubber stamp & marking device manufrs*

Supreme Saws Ltd, Detection House, Brooklands Approach, Romford, RM1 1DX Tel: (01708) 736220 Fax: (01708) 745726 E-mail: sales@supremesaws.co.uk *Cutting tool manufrs*

Supreme Seating & Desking Ltd, 4 40 Wilton Road, Reading, RG30 2SS Tel: 0118-959 5535 Fax: 0118-950 3271 E-mail: info@supremeseating.com *New office furniture & office re upholstery services*

Supreme Sewing & Knitting Machines Ltd, 114-116 Narborough Road, Leicester, LE3 0BS Tel: 0116-254 9029 Fax: 0116-254 9029 *Sewing machine repairs & supplies*

Supreme Steels, 578 Queslett Road, Birmingham, B43 7DY Tel: 0121-325 1393 Fax: 0121-325 1409 E-mail: supremesteels@aol.com *Steel trader, suppliers & buyer*

Supreme Tools Ltd, Lincoln Ho, Lincoln Rd, High Wycombe, Bucks, HP12 3RA Tel: (01494) 465423 Fax: (01494) 447560 *Injection toolmakers & injection moulders*

▶ Supreme Windows Ltd, 1 Lowercroft Warehouse, Lowercroft, Bury, Lancashire, BL8 3PA Tel: 0161-797 1995 Fax: 0161-763 1385 E-mail: sales@supremewindows.co.uk

Supreme-O-Glaze Home Products Ltd, 4 Lyon Road, Romford, RM1 2BA Tel: (0208) 518 2221 Fax: (01708) 739 363 *Double glazing manufrs*

Sur Clean Systems Ltd, Jublilee House, First Avenue, Poynton, Stockport, Cheshire, SK12 1YJ Tel: (01625) 877777 Fax: (01625) 877788 E-mail: sales@manchesterpressurewashers.co.uk *Cleaning equipment service*

▶ Sure Connects Systems, 1200 Rochdale Road, Manchester, M9 6FR Tel: 0161-795 6060 Fax: 0161-795 6161

▶ Sure Count Stocktakers, Unit 8, 88 Clyde Road, Didsbury, Manchester, M20 2JN Tel: 0161-448 9491 E-mail: info@surecount.co.uk *Stocktakers and stocktaking services from Sure Count. Welcome to Sure Count. As stocktakers we are here to cater for all your retail stocktaking and inventory requirements*

Sure Enterprises (UK) Ltd, 2 Chilton Corner, Chilton, Sudbury, Suffolk, CO10 0RL Tel: (01787) 881321 Fax: (01787) 881332 E-mail: amanda@sureenterprises.co.uk *Fleet markings, commercial vehicle signage*

Sure Punch Precision Ltd, Tameside Mills, Park Road, Dukinfield, Cheshire, SK16 5PU Tel: 0161-343 7999 Fax: 0161-343 8999 E-mail: surepunch@surepunch.co.uk *Precision sheetmetal CNC punching & bending*

Sure Safe Ltd, College Farm Business Centre, North End, Meldreth, Royston, Hertfordshire, SG8 6NT Tel: (01763) 262649 Fax: (01763) 263134 E-mail: henrik@sure-safe.com *Gas detection service providers*

▶ Sure Safe Fire Systems Ltd, 53 Highcroft Lane, Horndean, Waterlooville, Hampshire, PO8 9PU Tel: (023) 9259 9113 Fax: (023) 9259 7757 E-mail: info@suresafefire.co.uk *Design, supply & installation of complete security systems*

Sure Shutters & Blinds Ltd, 24 High Street, Wallingford, Oxfordshire, OX10 0BP Tel: (01491) 824786 Fax: (01491) 824786 *Manufacturers & distributors of security blinds & shutters*

Surebasic Ltd, Units 2 & 3, Castlemeadows Park, Abergavenny, Gwent, NP7 7RZ Tel: (01873) 852663 Fax: (01873) 859128 E-mail: laser@change.co.uk *Supply of computer printer consumables*

Sure-Can Ltd, Unit 6, 8 & 9 Adam Business Centre, Henson Way, Telford Way Industrial Estate, Kettering, Northamptonshire, NN16 8PX Tel: (01536) 411882 Fax: (01536) 518086 E-mail: sales@sure-can.co.uk *Sure-can is a manufacturer and supplier of cylindrical tin cans. We also supply other tin plate products such as plate panels, various lids and enclosures such as screw tops, ring pulls and bergs and also products such as lid clips, and lever lid clips for various tins such as paint tins. From ejector seat cartridges to body filler tins, to candle tin containers. As well as tin manufacturing and supplying we also have a range of coatings and finishes to make your product just what you need. We have many choices from tin plate coating, printed designs, lacquer coating, to embossing. We work to customer specification and can supply a 'certificate of conformance to specification' on request.*

Surecast Devizes Ltd, Roundway Mill, London Road, Devizes, Wiltshire, SN10 2EA Tel: (01380) 723402 Fax: (01380) 729063 E-mail: sales@surecast.co.uk *Pump & diecasting manufrs*

▶ Surechem Products (Holdings) Ltd, Lion Barn Industrial Estate, Needham Market, Ipswich, IP6 8NZ Tel: (01449) 722143 Fax: (01449) 722483 E-mail: sales@surechem.co.uk *Manufacturers & suppliers of laboratory chemicals & consumables*

Sureclean Ltd, 10 River Drive, Alness, Ross-Shire, IV17 0PG Tel: (01349) 884480

Surecoat Powder Coatings, Unit 13 Bolton Textile Mill, Cawdor Street, Farnworth, Bolton, BL4 7EA Tel: (01204) 793339 Fax: (01204) 793339 *Powder, gates, stair casings & billings manufrs*

Surefast Freight Ltd, 2 Abercorn Avenue, Hillington Industrial Estate, Glasgow, G52 4XZ Tel: 0141-883 4660

Surefil Beauty Products, The Bedford Centre, Bedford Street, Parr Industrial Estate, St. Helens, Merseyside, WA9 1PN Tel: (01744) 758820 Fax: (01744) 451859 E-mail: surefil@aol.com *Cosmetic & toiletries manufrs*

Surefold Partitions, Cavendish House Cavendish Avenue, Birchwood Park, Birchwood, Warrington, WA3 6BU Tel: (01925) 810022 Fax: (01925) 818050 *Partitions & folding screens manufrs*

▶ Sureframe Windows Ltd, Oxford Works, Oxford Street, Accrington, Lancashire, BB5 1QX Tel: (01254) 235390 Fax: (01354) 388084 *Double glazing suppliers & installation*

▶ Suregrave UK Ltd, Unit 4 Faraday Close, Washington, Tyne & Wear, NE38 8QJ Tel: 0191-417 4505 Fax: 0191-415 3410 *Engraving machines manufrs*

Surekill Pest Control Services, Annerley, Oakfield Road, Edenbridge, Kent, TN8 6JG Tel: (01732) 863206 Fax: (01732) 863206 E-mail: surekill@tinyonline.co.uk *Pest control services*

▶ Surelift Lifting Equipment, Peterhead Offshore Supply Base, Peterhead, Aberdeenshire, AB42 2PF Tel: (01779) 477775 Fax: (01779) 477771 *Lifting equipment manufrs*

Sureline Finishing, 1-2 Quarry CR, Pennygillam Industrial Estate, Launceston, Cornwall, PL15 7PF Tel: (01566) 776630 Fax: (01566) 777773 *Power coating stove enameling services*

Surelock Casting Repairs, Unit 3, Pillings Road Industrial Estate, Oakham, Leicestershire, LE15 6QF Tel: (01572) 722051 Fax: (01572) 722051 E-mail: surelock@onetel.com *Casting repair & restoration*

Surelock Mcgill Ltd, 26 The Business Centre, Molly Millars Lane, Wokingham, Berkshire, RG41 2QY Tel: 0118-977 2525 Fax: 0118-977 1913 E-mail: info@surelock.co.uk *The Surelock McGill Group has specialised primarily in the physical security market for over thirty years and recognised as a leading organisation on meeting the collective requirements of Security, Fire and Safety door solutions. Members of the group are Surelock McGill Ltd, Stafford Bridge, Doors Ltd, TS Systems (UK) Ltd.*

Surepart S V G Ltd, Morda Mill Business Centre, Beaconsfield Terrace, Morda, Oswestry, Shropshire, SY10 9PE Tel: (01691) 655300 Fax: (01691) 653838 *Motor panel distribs*

Sureparts Motor Component Distribution, 12 Howard Road, Park Farm Industrial Estate, Redditch, Worcestershire, B98 7SE Tel: (01527) 501333 Fax: (01527) 522848 *Motor component distributors*

Surespan Ltd, Leamore Industrial Estate, Leamore Close, Walsall, WS2 7NL Tel: (01922) 711185 Fax: (01922) 497943 *Access cover manufrs*

▶ Surestart Technology, The School House, Main Street, Hill of Beath, Cowdenbeath, Fife, KY4 8DP Tel: (01383) 610318 Fax: (01383) 610318 E-mail: ss@surestartechnology.com *Independent & privately owned coating & corrosion consultancy*

▶ SureState Ltd, The Drill Hall, 25 Lion Street, Hay-on-Wye, Hereford, HR3 5AD Tel: (07779) 718457 E-mail: studio@surestate.co.uk *Website design, website hosting and e-mail services, e-commerce solutions, online accounting and fincial systems, online streatgy consulting*

Surestep Sheet Metal Ltd, Unit J2 Northfleet Industrial Estate, Lower Road, Northfleet, Gravesend, Kent, DA11 9BL Tel: (01474) 560511 Fax: (01474) 354396 E-mail: info@surestepsheetmetal.com *Sheet metalwork engineers & enclosure manufrs*

▶ Surestore, 7, Kingsway, Hayling Island, Hampshire, PO11 0LZ Tel: (023) 9246 3239 Fax: (023) 9246 0302 *Shelving distributors*

▶ Suretech Services Ltd, 12 Florence Road, Codsall, Wolverhampton, WV8 1JD Tel: (01902) 840684 Fax: (01902) 847088 E-mail: info@suretechservices.co.uk *A professional furniture repair company in the UK, specialising in leather repairs.*www.suretechservices.co.uk*

Suretel Systems Ltd, 39 Chedworth Crescent, Portsmouth, PO6 4ES Tel: (023) 9264 6646 Fax: (023) 9264 6646 *Telecommunication installation*

Sureway Scaffolding Co., Vale Lane, Hartcliffe Way, Bristol, BS3 5RU Tel: 0117-966 8393 Fax: 0117-963 7043 E-mail: sales@surewayscaffolding.co.uk

Sureweld UK Ltd, Sanders Lodge Industrial Estate, Rushden, Northamptonshire, NN10 6BQ Tel: (01933) 357005 Fax: (01933) 357606 E-mail: info@surerweld.co.uk *Welding equipment & air tools distributors*

Surex (International) Ltd, Unit 5, Airport Trading Estate, Westerham, Kent, TN16 3BW Tel: (01959) 576000 Fax: (01959) 571000 E-mail: info@surex.co.uk *Swimming pool equipment suppliers*

▶ Surf4apropety, Leeds, LS17 1BX Tel: 0113-266 9639 Fax: 0113-266 9639 E-mail: info@surf4aproperty.com *Property website*

Surface Dynamics (UK) Ltd, 348 SPON LANE SOUTH, WEST BROMWICH, WEST MIDLANDS, B70 6AZ Tel: (0121) 553 7772 Fax: (0121) 553 4746 E-mail: sales@surfacedynamics.co.uk *Shot blasting equipment manufrs*

Surface Engineering Process Equipment Ltd, Bennetts Field Trading Estate, Bennetts Field, Wincanton, Somerset, BA9 9DT Tel: (01963) 31274 Fax: (01963) 31288 *Heath exchanger (HE) production equipment, fluxing machine & industrial washing machines. Also waste water recovery/treatment plant contractors or designers & process plant contractors or designers*

Surface Engineers Manchester Ltd, Globe Works Off Astley Street, Dukinfield, Cheshire, SK16 4QZ Tel: 0161-330 9224 Fax: 0161-343 2650 *Metal spraying contractors*

▶ Surface Heating Systems Ltd, 129-130 Whitehill Road, Whitehill Industrial Estate, Glenrothes, Fife, KY6 2RP Tel: (01592) 770003 Fax: (01592) 773339 *Heating systems distributors & manufrs*

Surface Heating Systems Ltd, 1 Heath Mill Enterprise Park, Heath Mill Road, Wombourne, Wolverhampton, WV5 8AP Tel: (01902) 326062 Fax: (01902) 892866 E-mail: surfheat@aol.com *Surface heating manufrs*

Surface Inspection Ltd, Unit 6 St. Philips Central, Albert Road, St. Philips, Bristol, BS2 0XJ Tel: 0117-916 9900 Fax: 0117-916 9907 E-mail: sil@surface-inspection.com *Ceramic tile inspection systems*

Surface Technik (Old Hill) Ltd, Sovereign Works, Deepdale Lane, Lower Gornal, Dudley, West Midlands, DY3 2AF Tel: (01384) 457610 Fax: (01384) 238563 *Shot blasting & painting contractors bead blasting & anti corrosion coatings*

Surface Technik (Tamworth) Ltd, Ninian Way, Wilnecote, Tamworth, Staffordshire, B77 5ES Tel: (01827) 250736 Fax: (01827) 283384 *Shotblasting & anticorrosion coatings*

Surface Technology plc, Godiva Place, Coventry, CV1 5PN Tel: (024) 7625 8444 Fax: (024) 7655 1402 E-mail: sales@ultraseal.co.uk *Electroplaters*

▶ Surface Technology plc, 15-17 Colvilles Place, Kelvin Industrial Estate, East Kilbride, Glasgow, G75 0PZ Tel: (01355) 248223 Fax: (01355) 237141 E-mail: ronald.ross@surface-technology.co.uk *Electroplating specialists & PTFE processors*

▶ Surface Technology plc, Long Causeway, Leeds, LS9 0NY Tel: 0113-248 0555 Fax: 0113-235 0169 E-mail: sales@armourcote.co.uk *PTFE processors*

Surface Technology Products Ltd, 244 Heneage Street, Birmingham, B7 4LY Tel: 0121-359 4322 Fax: 0121-359 1817 E-mail: sales@surtech.co.uk *Suppliers of Abrasive grinding, deburring and polishing machines for all types of uses. Extensive range with the added ability to be able to adapt machines to the needs of the consumer. Over 30 years experience in finding solutions to all grinding, polishing and deburing needs.*

Surface Technology Systems plc, Imperial Park, Newport, Gwent, NP10 8UJ Tel: (01633) 652400 Fax: (01633) 652405 E-mail: webenquiries@stsystems.com *Semi-conductor production equipment manufrs*

Surface Technology P.L.C. (Ultraseal), Godiva Place, Coventry, CV1 5PN Tel: (024) 7655 1401 Fax: (024) 7663 3411 E-mail: surfacetech@ultraseal.co.uk *Vacuum impregnation services*

▶ Surface Treatment Specialists Ltd, 1B Nelson Street, Widnes, Cheshire, WA8 0QD Tel: 0151-424 1200

Surfair Freight Services Ltd, Wilson Road, Wigston, Leicestershire, LE18 4TQ Tel: 0116-278 6206 Fax: 0116-277 7784 E-mail: transport@surfair.co.uk *Freight forwarding & export packers*

Surgecam Ltd, Cold Hesledon Industrial Estate, Cold Hesledon, Seaham, County Durham, SR7 8ST Tel: 0191-513 0666 Fax: 0191-513 0862 E-mail: david.watson@surgecam.co.uk *Electrical engineers*

Surgecrown Ltd, J The Wallows Industrial Estate, Fens Pool Avenue, Brierley Hill, West Midlands, DY5 1QA Tel: (01384) 483712 Fax: (01384) 483712 *Plastic mould toolmakers*

Surgetech Ltd, Durlston House, North Street, Westbourne, Emsworth, Hampshire, PO10 8SN Tel: (01243) 379613 Fax: (01243) 370003 E-mail: bill.jones@surgetech.co.uk *Lightning protection equipment suppliers & manufrs*

Surgical Holdings Ltd, 8 Parkside Centre, Potters Way, Southend-on-Sea, SS2 5SJ Tel: (01702) 602050 Fax: (01702) 460006 E-mail: office@surgicalholdings.co.uk *Surgical, veterinary instrument manufrs*

Surgical Instrument Group Holdings Ltd, 89a Gloucester Road, Croydon, CR0 2DN Tel: (020) 8683 1103 Fax: (020) 8683 1105 *Ophthalmic surgical instrument manufrs*

Surin Fashions Ltd, 4 Belgrave Commercial Centre, 160 Belgrave Road, Leicester, LE4 5AU Tel: 0116-266 6191 Fax: 0116-261 1699 *Import & wholesaler of Asian clothes*

Surlyt, 5 The Cross, Dalry, Ayrshire, KA24 5AL Tel: (01294) 832322 Fax: (01294) 832101 E-mail: jim_langlands@1stlam.com *Mirrors & decorative glass distributors & manufrs*

Surman Building Services, Queens Avenue, Factory Road, Birmingham, B18 5JX Tel: 0121-554 0390 Fax: 0121-554 3277 *Building contractors*

▶ Surplex UK Ltd, Quest Hills Road, Malvern, Worcestershire, WR14 1RN Tel: (01684) 575665 E-mail: info@surplex.co.uk *Collection and recycling of IT equipment, computers and electronic equipment in the UK.**Removal and recycling of obsolete, surplus and excess IT and electronic equipment in accorance with the WEEE Directive. Fast and friendly service.*

▶ Surplus Apparels, Stanley Terrace, Bedminster, Bristol, BS3 3PJ Tel: (0783) 5088854 *apparel designer authentic fashion*

Surprise Balloons, 82 Newton Rd, Rushden, Northants, NN10 0HQ Tel: 01933 411457 *Party equipment*

▶ Surrex Financial Management, 2 Paddock Road, Ashford, Kent, TN23 5WH Tel: (01233) 665812 Fax: (01903) 261550 E-mail: walterb@surrexfm.com *Surrex Financial Kent based independent financial advisers.**We provide independent financial advice, planning and investment for large and small businesses and on a personal individual basis. Other services include an unbiased mortgage or buy to let mortgage advice from our mortgage broker for personal or commercial, loans and an array of building and contents, home, car, life and travel insurance.**View our website and speak to one of our professional advisers. ***

Surrey Car Telephones Ltd, 3 The Riverside Business Centre, Walnut Tree Close, Guildford, Surrey, GU1 4UG Tel: (01483) 563999 Fax: (01483) 300813 E-mail: info@sctcomms.co.uk *Radio telephone contractors, installation, rental, services*

Surrey Chamber Of Commerce Ltd, 5th Floor Hollywood House, Church Street East, Woking, Surrey, GU21 6HJ Tel: (01483) 726655 Fax: (01483) 740217 E-mail: info@surrey_chambers.co.uk *Chamber of commerce & industry*

▶ Surrey Downs Food, Units 79-80, Dunsfold Park, Stovolds Hill, Cranleigh, Surrey, GU6 8TB Tel: (01483) 273000 Fax: (01483) 273022 E-mail: info@surreydownsfoods.com *Food processors*

Surrey Embroidery Co. Ltd, 7 Linkfield Corner, Redhill, RH1 1BD Tel: (01737) 766691 Fax: (01737) 780666 E-mail: enquiries@surreyembroidery.co.uk *Suppliers of embroidered garments & promotional wear*

Surrey Engineering, Lambs Green, Rusper, Horsham, West Sussex, RH12 4RG Tel: (01293) 871594 Fax: (01293) 871401 *Agricultural engineers services*

Surrey Fastners, Course Road, Ascot, Berkshire, SL5 7HQ Tel: (01344) 876104 Fax: (01344) 620185 E-mail: surreyfast@aol.com *Industrial fastener stockists*

▶ Surrey Films Ltd, Valley Farm, Green Lane, Churt, Farnham, Surrey, GU10 2LT Tel: (01428) 609532 E-mail: pete@surreyfilms.co.uk *Film & web production services*

Surrey Fire & Rescue Service, Wray Park Centre, 70 Wray Park Road, Reigate, Surrey, RH2 0EJ Tel: (01737) 224024 Fax: (01737) 224092 E-mail: wraypark@surreycc.gov.uk *Fire protection consultants*

▶ Surrey Foam, 54 Croydon Road, Caterham, Surrey, CR3 6QB Tel: (01883) 349456 E-mail: simon@surreyfoam.com *Foam, fabric & craft item retailers*

Surrey Glasshouse, 288b Woodham Lane, New Haw, Addlestone, Surrey, KT15 3NT Tel: (01932) 336086 Fax: (01932) 336086 E-mail: enquiries@surreyglasshouse.co.uk *Glass installation services*

Surrey Hants & Cleaning Supplies, Hygiene House, 14 St. Josephs Road, Aldershot, Hampshire, GU12 4LG Tel: (01252) 313131 Fax: (01252) 334433 E-mail: sales@tiagroup.co.uk *Janitorial supply services*

Surrey Harley Davidson Buell, 285-293 High Street, Dorking, Surrey, RH4 1RL Tel: (01306) 883825 Fax: (01306) 881397 *Specialist motorcycle distributors*

▶ Surrey Home Entertainment, 6 William Road, Caterham, Surrey, CR3 5NN Tel: (01883) 345102 E-mail: surreyhomeent@btconnect.com *Audio & visual custom installers*

▶ Surrey Homefinder, 96 Manor Green Road, Epsom, Surrey, KT19 8LN Tel: (01372) 806643 Fax: (01372) 819981 E-mail: mail@surreyhomefinder.co.uk *An affordable effective homefinding service. An ideal choice in the current "buyers market" if you are moving into or within Surrey.*

▶ Surrey Kitchen Installation, 19 Breech Lane, Walton on the Hill, Tadworth, Surrey, KT20 7SJ Tel: (01737) 813425 Fax: (01737) 813425 E-mail: johnantill@hotmail.co.uk *We fit kitchens to a high standard in Surrey & Sussex. For a free estimate call John on 07979 551593 or visit our website*

Surrey Laminators Ltd, 7 Saxon Way Trading Estate, Harmondsworth, West Drayton, Middlesex, UB7 0LW Tel: (020) 8759 5995 Fax: (020) 8564 7049 E-mail: harmondsworth@surreylaminators.co.uk *Laminated paper finishers*

▶ Surrey Lighting Centre, 13-14 Castle Parade, Ewell By Passage, Epsom, Surrey, KT17 2PR Tel: (020) 8393 0953 Fax: (020) 8394 2181 E-mail: sales@surreylighting.co.uk *Lighting wholesalers*

Surrey Management Consultants Ltd, Newmet House, Rue de St Lawrence, Waltham Abbey, Essex, EN9 1PF Tel: (01992) 703401 Fax: (01992) 768393 E-mail: materials@newmet.co.uk *Electronic consultants*

Surrey Materials, Newmet House, Rue De St. Lawrence, Waltham Abbey, Essex, EN9 1PF Tel: (01992) 711111 Fax: (01992) 768393 E-mail: materials@newmet.co.uk *Boardroom & conference facilities distributors* Also at: Ripley

Surrey Pattern & Mould Co., Chiltern House, Drake Avenue, Staines, Middlesex, TW18 2AW Tel: (01784) 457799 Fax: (01784) 458728 E-mail: surreypatternandmould@aol.com *Vacuum forming toolmakers*

Surrey Scales Co, 2 The Parade, Philanthropic Road, Redhill, RH1 4DN Tel: (01737) 769745 Fax: (01737) 760390 *Industrial weighing machines suppliers*

Surrey Security Systems, 37 Woodbridge Hill, Guildford, Surrey, GU2 9AA Tel: (01483) 303012 Fax: (01483) 303013 *Security alarm installers*

Surrey Stainless Steels Ltd, Unit 5 Stirling Way, Beddington Farm Road, Croydon, CR0 4XN Tel: (020) 8684 9596 Fax: (020) 8689 9651 E-mail: surreystainless.steels@btinternet.com *Stainless steel stockholders*

▶ Surrey Technology Management, Sandy Farm Business Centre, Sands Road, The Sands, Farnham, Surrey, GU10 1PX Tel: (08458) 904040 E-mail: info@surreytm.com *Home & small business IT support services*

▶ Surrey Wedding Marquees, Unit 12, Church Road, Bookham, Leatherhead, Surrey, KT23 3JT Tel: (07712) 625127 E-mail: info@surreyweddingmarquees.co.uk *Wedding marquee hire & event equipment hire*

Surrey Wholesale, Fleming Way, Crawley, West Sussex, RH10 9JY Tel: (01293) 611111 Fax: (01293) 550555 *Distributors & agents of bubble film, adhesive tapes, printed & packaging material*

Company Information

Surrounds Picture Framing, 13 Old Woking Road, West Byfleet, Surrey, KT14 6LW Tel: (01932) 400555 Fax: (01932) 400554 E-mail: info@surrounds.co.uk *Picture framing services*

Surtech Distribution Ltd, Glenmore Business Park, Colebrook Way, Andover, Hampshire, SP10 3GZ Tel: (01264) 369991 Fax: (01264) 369992 E-mail: enquiries@surtechdist.co.uk *Electronic component distributors & agents*

Surtees Bournemouth Ltd, 6 Whittle Road, Ferndown Industrial Estate, Wimborne, Dorset, BH21 7RU Tel: (01202) 890074 Fax: (01202) 890076 E-mail: hire@surteeshire.com *Audio & video services* Also at: London & Rochester

Surtees Presentation Services Ltd, 6 Whittle Road, Ferndown Industrial Estate, Wimborne, Dorset, BH21 7RU Tel: (01202) 890074 Fax: (01202) 890076 E-mail: sales@surteeshire.com *Audio visual equipment sales & hire services*

Survair Services, Caolils, Glendevon, Dollar, Clackmannanshire, FK14 7JY Tel: (01259) 781282 Fax: (01259) 781291 E-mail: info@survair.co.uk *Property maintenance services*

▶ Survair South Manchester Ltd, 17 Hawthorn Lane, Ashton-On-Mersey, Sale, Cheshire, M33 5WW Tel: 0161-286 9629 E-mail: brian.kiely@survair.co.uk *Surface Coatings*

▶ Survair Yorkshire Ltd, Rose Cottage Front Street, Ingleton, Darlington, County Durham, DL2 3HL Tel: (01325) 733141 E-mail: steven.baker@survair.co.uk *Anti Slip Flooring*Water Repellent Coatings*Industrial Resin Flooring*Anti Graffiti Coatings*Hygienic Wall Coatings*Chemical Protection Systems*Asbestos Encapsulation*

Surveillance Solutions Ltd, 127 Ouzlewell Green, Lofthouse, Wakefield, West Yorkshire, WF3 3QW Tel: (0845) 1304631 Fax: (0870) 1333608 E-mail: chris@ssl-cctv.co.uk *CCTV & access control installers*

Survequip.com, Centrix House, Ash 05, 26 Crow Lane East, Newton-le-Willows, Merseyside, WA12 9UY Tel: (0800) 13 13 435 Fax: (01925) 273001 E-mail: sales@survequip.com *The UK's Largest Online Surveying Super Store!! For the best in GPS, Surveying, Levelling, Measuring, Inspection & Detection, Moisture Meters, Telescopic Ladders, Surveyors Ladders, General Ladders & steps and all types of Access Equipment, Instruments, Accessories and Consumables, Hand & Power Tools, Clothing etc etc. All well known brands such as Leica - Topcon - Pentax - Radio Detection - Theis - DeWALT Trimble - SpectraSokkia - Agatec - Robotoolz - Thales - C-Scope - Nikon - CST/ Berger - Stanley - Crowcon - Oldham - Little Giant Ladder Systems - Elcometer - South - Stabila - Trumeter and more at discount prices. Eg The Cheapest Dumpy Level Kit in the UK only £99.00, Line Marking Paint ONLY £2.87/can and lots more. We can also offer our unique Lease Purchase Scheme. 30 Day No Quibble Money Back Guarantee and Promise to match any "Like for Like" price. Call us on Free 0800 13 13 435. BUY Securely Online - FULL eCommerce website.*

▶ Survey Analysis (UK) Ltd, Old School House, 89 Main Road, Glengarnoch, Beith, Ayrshire, KA14 3AH Tel: 01505 682582 Fax: 01505 682681 E-mail: info@surveyanalysis.co.uk *Data entry and analysis of social and market research surveys. Online surveys, computer assisted telephone interviewing and employee surveys*

Survey Connection Scotland Ltd, Paragon House, Oakbank, Livingston, West Lothian, EH53 0JS Tel: (01506) 881090 Fax: (01506) 884488 *Surveying equipment hire & suppliers*

Survey Express Services, 9 Manor Parade, Hatfield, Hertfordshire, AL10 9JS Tel: (01707) 273172 Fax: (01707) 270085 *Surveying equipment*

Survey Supplies Ltd, 1-5 Bankfield Drive, Spondon, Derby, DE21 7QZ Tel: (01332) 675888 Fax: (01332) 661381 E-mail: info@surveysupplies.co.uk Principal Export Areas: Worldwide *Surveying services*

Survey Supplies Ltd, The Forge, 1 Cross Street, Eye, Suffolk, IP23 7AB Tel: (01379) 870111 Fax: (01379) 870935 *Survey equipment suppliers*

Survey Systems Ltd, Willow Bank House, Old Road, Handforth, Wilmslow, Cheshire, SK9 3AZ Tel: (01625) 533444 Fax: (01625) 526815 E-mail: sales@survsys.co.uk *Survey & geophysical consultants*

▶ Survey Technology, Westmere Drive, Crewe, CW1 6ZG Tel: (01270) 250525 Fax: (01270) 580700 E-mail: info@surveytechnology.co.uk *Survey Technology are the leading independent provider for hire, sale, service and repair of surveying instruments within the UK. We stock all leading European manufacturers including Sokkia, Leica and Topcon. *Survey Technology offer a full range of instrumentation including; Auto Levels; Exterior Lasers; Total Stations, Theodolites; Pipe Lasers; Interior Lasers; Grade Lasers; Machine Control Receivers; Digital Levels; Distance Metres; Receivers; Tripods and a full range of accessories.*

Surveyplan Market Research, Summit House, Tower Hill, Dorking, Surrey, RH4 2AN Tel: (01306) 876211 Fax: (01306) 740643 E-mail: info@surveyplan.co.uk *Market research services*

▶ Surveys, Sussex Innovation Centre, Science Park Square, Falmer, Brighton, BN1 9SB Tel: (01273) 704438 Fax: (01273) 704499 E-mail: sales@summitsolutions.co.uk *Flood risk assessments service*

Survirn Engineering Ltd, 1581 Bristol Road South, Rednal, Birmingham, B45 9UA Tel: 0121-453 7718 Fax: 0121-453 6915 E-mail: sales@survirn.co.uk *Large CNC machinists*

Survival Craft, Findon Shore, Findon/Portlethen, Portlethen, Aberdeen, AB12 3RL Tel: (01224) 784488 Fax: (01224) 784111 E-mail: info@survivalcraft.com *Repair & maintenance to life boats*

Survival Systems International UK Ltd, Viking Road, Great Yarmouth, Norfolk, NR31 0NU Tel: (01493) 659411 Fax: (01493) 655425 E-mail: admin@survivalsystemsint.com *Survival capsule service agents*

▶ SUS IT, PO Box 114, Cheadle, Cheshire, SK8 7WQ Tel: 0161-439 0783 Fax: 0161-439 0783 E-mail: enquiries@sus-it.uk.com *IT training provider*

Susan's Bakery, 6a Henry Wells Square, Hemel Hempstead, Hertfordshire, HP2 6BJ Tel: (01442) 245400 Fax: (01442) 245400 *Bakery manufrs*

▶ Susieart, 38 Hill Close, Lightpill, Stroud, Gloucestershire, GL5 3PG Tel: (01453) 762013 E-mail: sue-halliday@tiscali.co.uk *Greetings cards specialists*

▶ SUSPENDED CEILING INSTALLATIONS., Lordshill,, Southampton, SO16 8GW Tel: 023 80735029 E-mail: ddigweed16@yahoo.com *The installation of suspended ceilings,within a thirty mile radius of Southampton.*

Suspended Ceiling Co Wales Ltd, 74a Westbourne Road, Penarth, South Glamorgan, CF64 3HB Tel: (029) 2071 1708 Fax: (029) 2071 2607 *Suspended ceiling supply & service*

▶ Sussex Alarms, 51, 53 Church Road, Hove, East Sussex, BN3 2BD Tel: (0500) 099965 Fax: (01273) 747997 E-mail: admin@sussexalarms.co.uk *Communication equipment*

Sussex Asphalte, Clarendon Place, Portslade, Brighton, BN41 1DJ Tel: (01273) 417315 Fax: (01273) 422304 E-mail: info@sussexasphalte.co.uk *Asphalt & roofing contractors*

▶ Sussex Astronomy Centre, 16 Mulberry Lane, Goring By Sea, Worthing, West Sussex, BN12 4JL Tel: (01903) 247317 E-mail: worthingastronomy@tiscali.co.uk *The south coasts largest astronomy centre, Meade, Celestron & SkyWatcher main dealer.*

Sussex Blast Cleaning Ltd, 35 Industrial Estate, Station Road, Hailsham, East Sussex, BN27 2ER Tel: (01323) 849229 Fax: (01323) 442442 *Plaster cleaning & powder coating services*

▶ Sussex Blinds & Awnings Ltd, 53 East Street, Horsham, West Sussex, RH12 1HR Tel: (01403) 256000 Fax: (01403) 256252 E-mail: sussexblinds@btconnect.com *Suppliers & installation of window blinds & awnings*

Sussex Computers Ltd, Suite F10, Waterside Centre, North Street, Lewes, East Sussex, BN7 2PE Tel: (01273) 407360 Fax: (01273) 464880 E-mail: gm@sussexcomputers.co.uk *Bespoke packaged software distributors authors*

Sussex County, Bookers Yard, Bersted Street, Bognor Regis, West Sussex, PO22 9PS Tel: (01243) 827131 Fax: (01243) 827131 *Joinery manufrs*

▶ Sussex Disco, The Templars, Worthing, West Sussex, BN15 0DT Tel: (01903) 200850 Fax: (01903) 200850 E-mail: info@sussexdisco.co.uk *Sussex Disco are Sussex''s number one Roadshow, supplying quality disco entertainment*

Sussex Electrical Supplies Ltd, Unit 34 Cradle Hill Industrial Estate, Seaford, East Sussex, BN25 3JE Tel: (01323) 873333 Fax: (01323) 873344 E-mail: sussex.elec@virgin.net *Electrical equipment distributor*

Sussex Fencing & Construction Co., 1 Beaconsfield Road, Portslade, Brighton, BN41 1XA Tel: (01273) 418878 Fax: (01273) 881858 *Fencing construction*

Sussex Hand Made Bricks, Fourteen Acre Lane, Three Oaks, Hastings, East Sussex, TN35 4NB Tel: (01424) 814344 Fax: (01226) 700350 *Brick manufrs*

▶ Sussex Homesearch Ltd, Fairyhill, Old Broyle Road, Chichester, West Sussex, PO19 3PJ Tel: 01243 771321 Fax: 01243 771321 E-mail: info@sussexhomesearch.co.uk *A proactive property search agent finding properties to buy in West Sussex.*

▶ Sussex Horseboxes, 1 Woollett Street, Maidstone, Kent, ME14 1UX Tel: (01622) 206006 E-mail: sussex_horseboxes@hotmail.com *We design, develop and build horseboxes in the Kent and Sussex areas. We also maintain and prepare and present your horsebox for its annual MOT. We specialise in all aspects of electrical work. WE NOW HAVE A WORKSHOP IN HEADCORN, KENT. WE ARE ADVERTISING IN LOCAL RIDER EVERY MONTH. TAKE A LOOK AT THIS MONTHS FOR OUR DETAILS.*

▶ Sussex Interior Fixings Ltd, Unit 5b Sewells Farm, Barcombe, Lewes, East Sussex, BN8 5TJ Tel: (01273) 400000 Fax: (01273) 401549

▶ Sussex Internet Ltd, Enterprise Works Ltd, Beach Road, Newhaven, East Sussex, BN9 0BX Tel: (01273) 514710 E-mail: info@sussex-internet.net *Internet & web site development services*

Sussex Ironcraft South Eastern Ltd, 31b Avis Way, Newhaven, East Sussex, BN9 0DJ Tel: (01273) 515931 Fax: (01273) 513811 *Balustrade manufacturers & steel fabricators*

Sussex Marble Co. Ltd, 16 Wainwright Close, St. Leonards-on-Sea, East Sussex, TN38 9PP Tel: (01424) 852575 Fax: (01424) 852798 E-mail: sales@sussexmarble.co.uk *Marble & granite suppliers*

Sussex Model Makers, 14 Hertford Close, Bognor Regis, West Sussex, PO21 5SF Tel: (01243) 841862 *Model manufrs*

Sussex Pattern Co. Ltd, 70 Victoria Road, Burgess Hill, West Sussex, RH15 9LY Tel: (01444) 245292 Fax: (01444) 247168 E-mail: info@sussexpattern.co.uk *Manufacturers of composite components*

Sussex Port Forwarding Ltd, Shoreham Port, Harbour Office, 84-86 Albion Street, Southwick, Brighton, BN42 4ED Tel: (01273) 598100 Fax: (01273) 592492 E-mail: info@shoreham-port.co.uk *Stevedores & haulage contractors* Also at: Chichester

Sussex Radiators, Stephenson Way, Crawley, West Sussex, RH10 1TN Tel: (01293) 528225 *Vehicle radiator repairers & manufrs*

Sussex Refrigeration Wholesale Ltd, The Glen, Halwill, Beaworthy, Devon, EX21 5TJ Tel: 01409 221195 *Refrigeration wholesalers*

▶ Sussex Saddlery, Cowfold Road, West Grinstead, Horsham, West Sussex, RH13 8LP Tel: (01403) 865961 E-mail: info@sussexsaddlery.com *Horse tack retailers*

Sussex Safetywear, East Lodge Farm, Malthouse Lane, Hurstpierpoint, Hassocks, West Sussex, BN6 9LA Tel: (01273) 831800 Fax: (01273) 831880 *Industrial protective clothing*

Sussex Sewing Machines, 148 Willingdon Park Drive, Eastbourne, East Sussex, BN22 0DG Tel: (01323) 509874 Fax: (01323) 509874 *Sewing machine repairers*

Sussex Sign Centre, 4 Mill Road, Burgess Hill, West Sussex, RH15 8DR Tel: (01444) 246884 Fax: (01444) 871871 E-mail: sales@sussexsigncentre.co.uk *Sign makers and lettering services. Same ownership since 1974. Products & services include, illuminated signs, banners, commercial vehicles, fascias, engraving, printing, vinyl lettering, acrylic letters, trade boards, magnetic signs, pavement signs, business cards, letterheads & full colour digital printing. Free quotations.*

▶ Sussex Steam Co., 94 North Lane, East Preston, West Sussex, BN16 1HE Tel: 01903 770848 Fax: 01903 770848 E-mail: john@sussexsteam.co.uk *Designer and Supplier of Live Steam Model Steam Engines. Newcomen Atmospheric Engine, Beam Engines and Mill Engines.*

Sussex Terracotta, Aldershaw Farm, Kent St, Sedlescombe, Battle, E. Sussex, TN33 0SD Tel: (01424) 756777 Fax: (01424) 756888 *Tile manufrs*

Sussex Timber Preservation Co. Ltd, Baltic Wharf, Wellington Road, Portslade, Brighton, BN41 1DX Tel: (01273) 420230 Fax: (01273) 430612 *Timber preservation*

Sussex Water Treatment Systems, 17 Harefield Road, Bognor Regis, West Sussex, PO22 6EE Tel: (01243) 587928 Fax: (01243) 587928 *Water softeners, filters & purifiers*

▶ Sussex Woodstoves, 44 Pondtail Road, Horsham, West Sussex, RH12 5HR Tel: (01403) 240300 E-mail: info@sussexwoodstoves.co.uk *Woodstoves, Coalstoves, Chimney liners...... HETAS specialists*

Sustainable Life, 12 Catherine Street, St. Davids, Haverfordwest, Dyfed, SA62 6RJ Tel: (01437) 721849 Fax: (01437) 721849 E-mail: sales@sustlife.com *Distributors of health food products*

▶ Sustain-World Ltd, 1 Church Lane, Cliddesden, Basingstoke, Hampshire, RG25 2JQ Tel: (01256) 475522 E-mail: gtaylor@sustainworld.com *Sustainworld is a unique web based resource covering sustainable products and services. More specifically, Sustainworld focuses on sustainable construction, sustainable finance, sustainable energy, Sustainable property and sustainable motoring products and services.*

Sutch & Searle Shipping Ltd, Highwood Road, Writtle, Chelmsford, CM1 3PT Tel: (01245) 421770 Fax: (01245) 422734 E-mail: keith.davis@sutchanddsearle.com *Freight forwarders & warehousing services* Also at: Heathrow Airport

Sutcliffe Bros Bradford Ltd, Paradise Works, 164 Sunbridge Road, Bradford, West Yorkshire, BD1 2HF Tel: (01274) 733063 Fax: (01274) 304434 E-mail: sutbros@aol.com *Steel fabricators*

Sutcliffe Farrar & Co. Ltd, Banksfield Works, Mytholmroyd, Hebden Bridge, West Yorkshire, HX7 5LT Tel: (01422) 883363 Fax: (01422) 885479 E-mail: sales@fieldclassics.com *Clothing manufrs* Also at: Huddersfield

Henry Sutcliffe Ltd, Hulme Street, Salford, M5 4PX Tel: 0161-736 1337 Fax: 0161-745 7724 E-mail: sales@hsltd.co.uk *Heavy duty packing cases manufrs* Also at: Prescot

▶ Sutcliffe Properties Ltd, Hellifield, Skipton, North Yorkshire, BD23 4JR Tel: (01729) 850817 Fax: (01729) 850323

Sutcliffe Speakman Ltd, Edgar House, Lockett Road, Ashton-In-Makerfield, Wigan, Lancashire, WN4 8DE Tel: (01942) 275400 Fax: (01942) 275600 E-mail: immisioncontrols@waterlink.com *Activated carbon suppliers & manufrs*

Suter Ltd, 38 Vyse Street, Hockley, Birmingham, B18 6JY Tel: 0121-523 5039 Fax: 0121-523 5039 *Jewellery repairers*

Sutherland Trading Co., Bedwas House Industrial Estate, Bedwas, Caerphilly, Mid Glamorgan, CF83 8XQ Tel: (029) 2088 7337 Fax: (029) 2085 1056 E-mail: info@sutherlandtrading.com *Musical instrument distributors*

B.S. Suthi & Brothers Ltd, Unit H1, 80 Rolfe Street, Smethwick, West Midlands, B66 2AR Tel: 0121-558 2420 Fax: 0121-555 5319 E-mail: info@bsssuthi.com *Country clothing & equestrian clothing manufrs*

▶ The Sutlers Stores, Unit 35 Wessex Trade Centre, Ringwood Road, Poole, Dorset, BH12 3PG Tel: (01202) 711660 Fax: (01202) 741137 E-mail: sales@sutlers.co.uk *We are Europe's leading supplier to film, re-enactors, television and museum. Our chosen specialist period is 1700-1950.*we are also a venue for civil weddings*And also a photographic studio**

Sutronics, 62 Park Road, Swanage, Dorset, BH19 2AE Tel: (01929) 426400 E-mail: sales@sutronics.com *Heating & ventilation control distributors*

Sutterton Camping Equipment, Post Office Lane, Sutterton, Boston, Lincolnshire, PE20 2EB Tel: (01205) 460485 Fax: (01205) 460162 E-mail: sales@sutterton-camping.com *Camping equipment suppliers*

Sutterton Labels, Pinfold Road, Bourne, Lincolnshire, PE10 9HT Tel: (01778) 391637 Fax: (01778) 391638 E-mail: sales@slpp.co.uk *Label printers & packaging*

▶ Suttle Stone Quarries, Swanworth Quarry, Worth Matravers, Swanage, Dorset, BH19 3LE Tel: (01929) 439444 Fax: (01929) 439446

Suttle, Willis & Co. Ltd, 28 Goodge Street, London, W1T 2QQ Tel: (020) 7636 5391 Fax: (020) 7636 7723 E-mail: info@conserverframe.com *Picture frame manufrs*

Sutton Cars, 302 High Street, Sutton, Surrey, SM1 1PQ Tel: (020) 8643 7004 Fax: (020) 8643 9000 *Mini cab service*

▶ Sutton Domestic Ironing Services, 28, Ringstead Road, Sutton, Surrey, SM1 4SJ Tel: 07 709 216338 E-mail: sdis@blueyonder.co.uk *Professional and efficient ironing service based in the London Borough of Sutton. Call for quote and ask about our free collection and delivery service for Sutton and some surrounding areas.*

Sutton & East Surrey Water, London Road, Redhill, RH1 1LJ Tel: (01737) 772000 Fax: (01737) 766807 E-mail: sesw@waterplc.com *Water companies & management services*

P.B. Sutton Engineering Co, 3 Hedley Road, St. Albans, Hertfordshire, AL1 5JL Tel: (01727) 858731 Fax: (01727) 847064 E-mail: hazel@pbsuttonsagehost.co.uk *Precision turned parts manufrs*

Sutton Gears Ltd, Unit 2 Lifford Way, Binley Industrial Estate, Binley Industrial Estate, Coventry, CV3 2RN Tel: (024) 7643 1331 Fax: (024) 7665 1000 *Gear manufacturers, cutters & precision gears*

Sutton Hydraulics, Unit 4a Alton Road Industrial Estate, Ross-on-Wye, Herefordshire, HR9 5NB Tel: (01989) 768545 Fax: (01989) 762202 *Hydraulic engineers*

Maurice Sutton Crane Hire, 1 Newstead Road, Urmston, Manchester, M41 0QQ Tel: 0161-748 1848 Fax: 0161-748 1848 *Crane hire*

Sutton Mouldings Ltd, Brook Road Industrial Estate, Totman Cresent, Rayleigh, Essex, SS6 7UY Tel: (01268) 779655 Fax: (01268) 779633 *Glass fibre moulders*

Sutton & Phillips Ltd, 5 Stowupland Road, Stowmarket, Suffolk, IP14 5AQ Tel: (01449) 613205 Fax: (01449) 770350 *Manufacturing chemists*

▶ Sutton Service International Ltd, 48 Darnley Street, Glasgow, G41 2SE Tel: 0141-420 3277

Sutton & Smith Ltd, Bullmans Wharf, Great Wakering, Southend-on-Sea, SS3 0DA Tel: (01702) 219422 Fax: (01702) 219050 *Boat mooring & sales services*

Sutton & Son Ltd, Sutton Heath, St. Helens, Merseyside, WA9 5BW Tel: (01744) 811611 Fax: (01744) 813324 *Road transport, haulage & freight services*

▶ Sutton & Son St Helens Ltd, Wilson Street, Thornaby, Stockton-on-Tees, Cleveland, TS17 7AR Tel: (01642) 606160

Sutton Tooling Ltd, Reservoir Road, Hull, HU6 7QD Tel: (01482) 342879 Fax: (01482) 446911 E-mail: suttontool@aol.com Principal Export Areas: Worldwide *Press tools manufrs*

Sutton-In-Ashfield Supply Stores Ltd, 9 Market Street, Huthwaite, Sutton-in-Ashfield, Nottinghamshire, NG17 2LB Tel: (01623) 554238 Fax: (01623) 550464 E-mail: sss-ltd@tiscali.co.uk *Camping equipment retailer*

Suttons Buildings, 66 Blackgate Lane, Tarleton, Preston, PR4 6UT Tel: (01772) 814865 Fax: (01772) 815643 *Agricultural builders services*

Suttons Furnishings Ltd, 56 Church Road, Hove, East Sussex, BN3 2FP Tel: (01273) 723728 Fax: (01273) 730837 *Interior soft furnishers*

Sutton's Jewellery Workshop, 1a Upper Brook Street, Rugeley, Staffordshire, WS15 2DP Tel: (01889) 585065 Fax: (01889) 585065 *Jewelery suppliers*

▶ Sutton's Packaging, Unit 33 Dinan Way Trading Estate, Concorde Road, Exmouth, Devon, EX8 4RS Tel: (01395) 223405 Fax: (01395) 446546 E-mail: sales@suttonswrap.co.uk *Luxury gift wrapping services*

Suttons Performance Packaging, 16 Albert Way, Chatteris, Cambridgeshire, PE16 6US Tel: (01354) 693171 Fax: (01354) 695430 E-mail: info@suttonspp.co.uk *Instrument pack manufrs*

▶ Sutton's Removals, 12 Sandiford Road, Sutton, Surrey, SM3 9RD Tel: (020) 8641 6767 Fax: (020) 8644 4018 E-mail: sales@sutton-removals.com

▶ Suzanne Grala Photography, PO Box 458, Epsom, Surrey, KT17 4WY E-mail: suzi@suzanne.grala.co.uk *Personal artistic photography in the comfort of your own home by award*winning Epsom based photographer Suzanne Grala. Family portraits, pregnancy*& baby and expressive shots. Colour and black & white, reprints and framing*available. Commercial work also undertaken.*

▶ Suzuki Europe, Unit 18 Lodge Farm Business Centre, Wolverton Road, Castlethorpe, Milton Keynes, MK19 7ES Tel: (01908) 511488 Fax: (01908) 511904 *Musical instrument suppliers*

Suzuki GB P.L.C., Steinbeck Crescent, Snelshall West, Milton Keynes, MK4 4AE Tel: (01908) 336600 Fax: (01908) 336719 *Motorcycle manufrs*

Sven Christiansen plc, Riverway Industrial Estate, Portsmouth Road, Peasmarsh, Guildford, Surrey, GU3 1LZ Tel: (01483) 302728 Fax: (01483) 569903 E-mail: info@sven.co.uk *Office furniture manufrs*

Svenska Petroleum Exploration, 1 Hamilton Mews, London, W1J 7HA Tel: (020) 7647 2500 Fax: (020) 7647 2501 E-mail: info@speuk.co.uk *Oil exploration*

▶ SVG Systems Ltd, Mill Road Industrial Estate, Linlithgow Bridge, Linlithgow, West Lothian, EH49 7SF Tel: (01506) 671555

Svitzer Towage Ltd, 11 Marina Court, Castle Street, Hull, HU1 1TJ Tel: (01482) 337650 Fax: (01482) 337683 E-mail: info@adsteamuk.co.uk *Ship assist services* Also at: Immingham & Selby

SVR, Unit 1 35 Little London, Spalding, Lincolnshire, PE11 2UE Tel: (01775) 760999 Fax: (01775) 724547 *Valve (reconditioned) rebuilders or suppliers, pump (reconditioned) rebuilders or suppliers & heat exchangers & repair/retubing services*

SW Blinds & Interiors Ltd, Unit 60-61 Faraday Mill Business Park, Faraday Road, Plymouth, PL4 0ST Tel: (01752) 663517 Fax: (01752) 226150 E-mail: info@swblinds.com *Blind & curtains manufrs*

SW Courier Services, 1 Willowbank, Favordale Road, Colne, Lancashire, BB8 7AG Tel: (01282) 861147 Fax: (01282) 861147 *SW Courier Services offers a dedicated same-day delivery service to both Pendle and Craven districts.**

Swada London, High Street, London, E15 2PP Tel: (020) 8534 7171 Fax: (020) 8519 2818 *Fluorescent pigment manufrs*

Swagelock London, Unit 11, Kingley Park, Station Road, Kings Langley, Hertfordshire, WD4 8GW Tel: (020) 8200 1677 Fax: (020) 8200 9819 E-mail: info@london.swagelock.com *Biomechanical plant & equipment manufrs*

▶ Swaggers, 51 St. Martins Street, Wallingford, Oxfordshire, OX10 0AJ Tel: (01491) 824022 Fax: (01491) 613039 E-mail: sales@swaggers.co.uk *Ladies fashion accessories supplier*

▶ Swaggs & Tails, Unit 26, Rake Industries, Rogate, Petersfield, Hampshire, GU31 5DU Tel: (01730) 891006 Fax: (01730) 891006

R. Swain & Sons Ltd, Medway Freight Terminal, Corys Road, Rochester, Kent, ME1 1PZ Tel: (01634) 830531 Fax: (01634) 829318 E-mail: davidmorton@rswain.com *Road transport contractors & warehousing*

▶ R. Swain & Sons Ltd, Occupation Lane, Woodville, Swadlincote, Derbyshire, DE11 8EU Tel: 0121-505 3894

Swaine Adeney Brigg Ltd, Viking Way, Bar Hill, Cambridge, CB23 8EL Tel: (01799) 530521 Fax: (01799) 530320 E-mail: sales@swaine-adeney-brigg.co.uk *Umbrella & leather goods retailer & manufrs*

Swaine Photographic, 139 Pinks Hill, Swanley, Kent, BR8 8NP Tel: (0800) 9567310 Fax: (01474) 872154 E-mail: alanswaine@aol.com *Professional photography (commercial & social)*

Swaingrove Ltd, Unit 3-4 Fourwheel Drive, Rougham Industrial Estate, Rougham, Bury St. Edmunds, Suffolk, IP30 9ND Tel: (01359) 271385 Fax: (01359) 271327 E-mail: systems@swaingrove.co.uk *Digital printers & reprographic producers services*

R. Swains & Son, The Pool Works, Occupation Lane, Woodville, Swadlincote, Derbyshire, DE11 8EU Tel: (01283) 214776 Fax: (01283) 222112 E-mail: ensor@rswains.com *Transport supplies*

Swale Borough Council, Swale House, East Street, Sittingbourne, Kent, ME10 3HT Tel: (01795) 417398 Fax: (01795) 417130 E-mail: edu@swale.gov.uk *Council*

Swale Components Ltd, Unit 88 John Wilson Business Park, Chestfield, Whitstable, Kent, CT5 3QT Tel: (01227) 771100 Fax: (01227) 771117 E-mail: sales@swalecomponents.com *Interconnection device suppliers*

SWALEC, Ty Meridian, Malthouse Avenue, Cardiff Gate Business Park, Cardiff, CF23 8AU Tel: (0800) 7834121 Fax: (01920) 249760 E-mail: ian.mason@scottish-7.co.uk *Electrical & gas wholesalers*

▶ Swales Haulage Ltd, Unit 53 Youngs Industrial Estate, Paices Hill, Aldermaston, Reading, RG7 4PW Tel: 0118-970 8000 Fax: 0118-982 0829 E-mail: admin@swaleshaulage.com

Swallow Bros (Plastics) Ltd, Clay La, Slaithwaite, Huddersfield, HD7 5BG Tel: (01484) 842817 Fax: (01484) 845350 *Plastics injection moulders*

Swallow Churchgate Hotel, Churchgate Street, Old Harlow, Harlow, Essex, CM17 0JT Tel: (01279) 420246 Fax: (01279) 437720 E-mail: swallow.oldharlow@swallowhotels.com *Conference centres & hotels*

Swallow Cleaning Contractors, Spa Road, Lincoln, LN2 5TB Tel: (01522) 540056 Fax: (01522) 546846 E-mail: enquiries@swallowcleaning.com *Contract cleaning services*

Swallow Furniture, Mill Farm, St. Mellons Road, Lisvane, Cardiff, CF14 0SH Tel: (029) 2076 3782 *Pine furniture manufrs*

Swallow Hosiery, 2 Swallow Street, Manchester, M12 4GH Tel: 0161-225 6336 Fax: 0161-225 6336 *Sock manufrs*

Swallow Security Services Ltd, Swallow House, Theaklen Drive, St. Leonards-on-Sea, East Sussex, TN38 9AZ Tel: (01424) 425999 Fax: (01424) 421666 E-mail: swallowsecurity@btconnect.com *Security services*

Swallow Tapes Ltd, 2 Cotton Hall Barns, Middlewich Road, Holmes Chapel, Crewe, CW4 7ET Tel: (01477) 535599 Fax: (01477) 535440 E-mail: sales@swallowtapes.sagehost.co.uk *Plain/printed adhesive tape suppliers*

Swallowfield P.L.C., Station Road, Wellington, Somerset, TA21 8NL Tel: (01823) 662241 Fax: (01823) 663642 E-mail: scp@swallowfield.com *Aerosol contract fillers manufrs*

▶ The Swallows Nest Holiday Cottage, Middlewood House, Linton Woods Lane, Linton On Ouse, York, YO30 2BE Tel: (01347) 848787 E-mail: chrismas@btconnect.com *Self catering holiday cottage, sleeps 2 & 2 north west of york*

Swallows Tiles Cranleigh Ltd, Bookhurst Hill, Bookhurst Road, Cranleigh, Surrey, GU6 7DP Tel: (01483) 274100 Fax: (01483) 267593 E-mail: sales@swallowsrooftiles.co.uk *Roofing tile manufrs*

Swan C D Computers, 36 Carnglas Road, Sketty, Swansea, SA2 9BW Tel: (01792) 521158 Fax: (01792) 522957 E-mail: swancd@swancd.co.uk *Computer manufrs*

Swan Castings & Engineering (Banbury) Ltd, Swan Close Road, Banbury, Oxfordshire, OX16 5AL Tel: (01295) 263134 Fax: (01295) 270461 E-mail: info@swangroup.co.uk *Castings manufrs*

Swan Engineering, 70 Scarborough Street, Hull, HU3 4TG Tel: (01482) 890140 Fax: (01482) 323077 E-mail: sales@swan-engineering.co.uk *Sheet metal fabricators*

Swan Enviro Freshmesh Systems, 10 Engine Road, Loanhead, Midlothian, EH20 9RF Tel: 0131-440 3812 Fax: 0131-448 2119 E-mail: sales@swanenviro.com *Ventilation equipment manufrs*

▶ Swan Hill Homes Ltd, Unit B, Gifford Court, Fox Den Road, Stoke Gifford, Bristol, BS34 8TT Tel: 0117-944 8700

▶ Swan Hill Homes Ltd, Swans Court, Watermans Business Park, Kingsbury C.R., Staines, Middlesex, TW18 3BA Tel: (01784) 464351

Swan Hunter Tyneside Ltd, Station Road, Wallsend, Tyne & Wear, NE28 6EQ Tel: 0191-295 0295 Fax: 0191-262 0374 E-mail: john.mitchell@swanhunter.com Principal Export Areas: Worldwide *Offshore engineering services & ship building services*

Swan Lake Ltd, Harris Way, Sunbury-on-Thames, Middlesex, TW16 7EL Tel: (01932) 783620 Fax: (01932) 772207 E-mail: swanlake@totalise.co.uk *Upholstery & soft furnishings manufrs*

Swan Mill Holdings Ltd, Swan Mill, Goldsel Road, Swanley, Kent, BR8 8EU Tel: (01322) 665566 Fax: (01322) 666460 E-mail: sales@swantex.com *Serviette manufrs*

Swan Mill Paper Co. Ltd, Goldsel Road, Swanley, Kent, BR8 8EU Tel: (01322) 665566 Fax: (01322) 661406 E-mail: sales@swantex.com *Swan Mill Paper Company, based in Swanley, Kent, is a long-established privately-owned company. As a market leader within the paper tableware manufacturing industry Swantex provides a range of high quality retail and catering disposable products along with professional service and flexibility, and supplying tableware, party products, crackers, gift wrap and hygiene products all produced under the Swantex brand as well as own label.*

Peter Swan & Sons Ltd, 3 Dryden Loan, Loanhead, Midlothian, EH20 9HR Tel: 0131-448 0880 Fax: 0131-448 0881 *Hospital & laboratory refrigeration retailers & manufrs*

Swan Petroleum, Wood Lane, Ellesmere, Shropshire, SY12 0HY Tel: (01691) 626201 Fax: (01691) 626365 E-mail: swanpetroleum@tggroup.co.uk *Fuel oil distributors* Also at: Kingsbury & Middlewich

Swan Portaforge, Units 1 & 2 Gamma, Orchard Trading Estate, Toddington, Cheltenham, Gloucestershire, GL54 5EB Tel: (01242) 621590 Fax: (01242) 621591 E-mail: swan@swan-portaforge.co.uk Principal Export Areas: Middle East, Central/East Europe, West Europe & North America *Manufacturers of portable gas forges*

Swan Signs Ltd, Lynton House, Golden Hill, Leyland, PR25 3NN Tel: (01772) 455011 Fax: (01772) 457936 *Display systems & sign manufrs*

Swan Stabilo Ltd, 75 Buckingham Avenue, Slough, SL1 4PN Tel: (01753) 605656 Fax: (01753) 605657 E-mail: marketing@stabilo.co.uk *Pens, stationery & graphic materials manufrs*

Swan Upholstery, 5-9 George Street, Romford, RM1 2DT Tel: (01708) 740569 Fax: (01708) 740569 *Upholsterers services*

Swan Windows, 9 Mandervell Road, Oadby, Leicester, LE2 5LQ Tel: 0116-271 4292 Fax: 0116-271 0611 E-mail: enquiries@swanwindows.co.uk

Swanells & Grylls Ltd, 330-332 Selborne Road, Luton, LU4 8NU Tel: (01582) 573066 *Sheet metalworkers & powder coating services, security product manufrs*

Swanglen Furniture Ltd, Ashmead Business Park, Ashmead Road, Keynsham, Bristol, BS31 1SX Tel: 0117-986 0200 Fax: 0117-986 6100 E-mail: sales@swanglen.co.uk *Furniture manufrs*

▶ Christopher Swann, 408-410 Corn Exchange Building, Fenwick Street, Liverpool, L2 7QS Tel: (0845) 1259010 Fax: (0845) 1259014 E-mail: sales@christopherswann.com *Managers profess development modular form mentoring services*

Swann Engineering Group Ltd, Springwood Drive, Braintree, Essex, CM7 2YN Tel: (01376) 320100 Fax: (01376) 347995 *Steel fabricators*

Swann Technology Ltd, 3 The Quadrant, Newark Close, Royston, Hertfordshire, SG8 5HL Tel: (01763) 249967 Fax: (01763) 249626 E-mail: swancygnet@cs.com *Export buying agents services*

▶ Swann-Morton Europe Ltd, Owlerton Green, Sheffield, S6 2BJ Tel: 0114-234 4231 Fax: 0114-231 4966 E-mail: exportsales@swann-morton.com *Surgical blade manufrs*

Swann-Morton Europe Ltd, Owlerton Green, Sheffield, S6 2BJ Tel: 0114-234 4231 Fax: 0114-231 4966 E-mail: services@swann-morton.com *Contract Irradiation /Sterilisation Services.*

Swans Nest, Bridgetown, Stratford-upon-Avon, Warwickshire, CV37 7LT Tel: (0870) 4008183 Fax: (01789) 414547 *Hotel with conference facilities*

Swansea Bakeries Ltd, Unit 10-11 St. Davids Industrial Estate, St. Davids Road, Swansea Enterprise Park, Swansea, SA6 8RX Tel: (01792) 798042 Fax: (01792) 700105 E-mail: jdhughes@btconnet.com *Bakery products*

Swansea Bar & Catering Supplies, Unit 2 Celtic Form Business Park, Carlton Terrace, Swansea, SA1 6AE Tel: (01792) 477777 Fax: (01792) 464500 *Bar equipment & catering equipment suppliers*

Swansea Fastners, Unit 8, Horizon Park, Swansea Enterprise Park, Swansea, SA6 8RG Tel: (01792) 310284 Fax: (01792) 310291 E-mail: sales@swanseafasteners.com *Industrial fasteners & engineers' supplies distributors*

Swansea Industrial Components Ltd, 66-70 Morfa Road, Swansea, SA1 2EF Tel: (01792) 458777 Fax: (01792) 456252 *Electronic cable assembly manufrs*

Swansea Itec Ltd, 250 Carmarthen Road, Swansea, SA1 1HG Tel: (01792) 464561 Fax: (01792) 648375 E-mail: info@swansea-itec.co.uk *Computer consultancy & training services*

Swansea Precision Engineering Services Ltd, Unit 11 Oxwich Court, Fendrod Business Park, Swansea, SA6 8QW Tel: (01792) 774817 Fax: (01792) 412282 *Precision toolmakers*

Swansea Tribology Services, Unit 5 Penrice Court, Swansea Enterprise Park, Swansea, SA6 8QW Tel: (01792) 799036 Fax: (01792) 799034 E-mail: swansea_tribology@compuserve.com *Petroleum condition services*

Swansea Truck Centre Ltd, Unit 43 Cwmdu Industrial Estate, Carmarthen Road, Gendros, Swansea, SA5 8LG Tel: (01792) 582255 Fax: (01792) 579895 E-mail: sgc@swanseatrucks.co.uk *Commercial vehicle distributors*

Swansea Water Bed Centre, Gorseinon Road, Penllergaer, Swansea, SA4 9GE Tel: (01792) 899110 Fax: (01792) 899110 E-mail: sales@swanseawaterbeds.co.uk *Water beds retail*

Swantex Ltd, Bromley Ho, Spindle St, Congleton, Cheshire, CW12 1QN Tel: (01260) 291110 Fax: (01260) 291112 E-mail: dave@swantex1.fsnet.co.uk *Specialised sewing services*

Swarland Grain Driers Ltd, Kitswell Dene, Felton, Morpeth, Northumberland, NE65 9NZ Tel: (01670) 787698 Fax: (01670) 787281 E-mail: richard@swarlandgrange.fsnet.co.uk *Grain driers*

▶ Swarovski Store Guilford, 10 White Lion Walk, Guildford, Surrey, GU1 3DN Tel: (01483) 568200 E-mail: swarovskiguildford@ntlworld.com *SWAROVSKI(Guildford)*The wonderful range of timeless jewellery & crystal, now available in the historic county town of Guildford, Surrey.*

Swatchways Ltd, Unit 13 Ely Industrial Estate, Williamstown, Penygraig, Tonypandy, Mid Glamorgan, CF40 1BY Tel: (01443) 423111 Fax: (01443) 440939 *Books & silk screens*

Swatkins Group Ltd, Leamore House, Leamore Lane, Walsall, WS2 7DQ Tel: (01922) 711700 Fax: (01922) 710410 E-mail: sales@swatkins.com *Silverware & sports trophy manufrs*

▶ Swatman Groundworks Ltd, Fairfield, North Cove, Beccles, Suffolk, NR34 7QG Tel: (01502) 476208 Fax: (01502) 476580

▶ - Swayo - Internet Solutions, PO Box 37491, London, United Kingdom, N3 2XR Tel: 0845 257 0392 Fax: 0871 242 5970 E-mail: sales@swayo.co.uk *Internet Software Services, Website development, Multimedia, E-business strategies. Technology for business, entertainment and education.*

▶ SWB Cymru Ltd, Nant Y Felin, Swansea, SA5 4HG Tel: (01792) 580100 Fax: (01792) 701900 E-mail: sales@swbcymru.com *Distributors for glazing components, adhesives & business forms*

▶ SWC Trailers & Spares, Manor Farm, Abbotts Ann, Andover, Hampshire, SP11 7DB Tel: (01264) 710610 *Trailer sales& steel fabrication*

Swedecor Ltd, Manchester Street, Hull, HU3 4TX Tel: (01482) 329691 Fax: (01482) 212988 E-mail: info@swedecor.com *Ceramic tiles distributors*

▶ Swedish Match UK Ltd, Sword House, Totteridge Road, High Wycombe, Buckinghamshire, HP13 6DG Tel: (01494) 533300 Fax: (01494) 437459 E-mail: gareth.newton@swedishmatch.co.uk *Tobacco products & accessories retailers*

Swedish Match UK Ltd, Sword House, Totteridge Road, High Wycombe, Buckinghamshire, HP13 6DG Tel: (01494) 533300 Fax: (01494) 437459 *Promotional product manufrs*

Swedish Steel, De Salis Court, De Salis Drive, Hampton Lovett, Droitwich, Worcestershire, WR9 0QE Tel: (01905) 795794 Fax: (01905) 794736 E-mail: ssabuk@ssab.com *Steel plate, abras resistant steel coil & armour plate manufrs*

Sweeney & Blocksidge (Power Presses) Ltd, 126 Parkfield Road, Saltley, Birmingham, B8 3AZ Tel: 0121-327 3231 Fax: 0121-327 4329 E-mail: enquires@sweeneyandblocksidge.co.uk *Mechanical press manufacturer (up to 160 tons capacity)*

Sweeney First Aid Supplies Ltd, 13 Scar Bank, Warwick, CV34 5DB Tel: (01926) 497108 Fax: (01926) 497109 E-mail: sales@sweeneyfirstaid.co.uk *First aid supply services*

M.P. Sweeney, 123 Burnham La, Slough, SL1 6LA Tel: 01628 602390 *Plant hire & engineering*

▶ Sweeney Plant Ltd, 1 A Petersburn Road, Airdrie, Lanarkshire, ML6 8RD Tel: (01236) 762290

Sweeney & Sherlock, Unit 25 Whitworth Industrial Park, Tilton Road, Birmingham, B9 4PP Tel: 0121-753 0960 Fax: 0121-753 0961 E-mail: sales@sweeneysherlock.co.uk *Sweeney & Sherlock Ltd are a powder coating company centrally located in Birmingham (free parking), we have have been established for over 25 years. Our services include; Alloy refurb, alloy refurbishment, powder coating services, aluminium powder coating services, motorcycle wheel refurbishment, architectural powder coating services, metal powder coating services, PPC, EPPC, polyester powder coating services, special batches powder coating, metal fabrications powder coating, coating up to 7 metres in length , plastic coating, vintage powder coating, dust extraction equipment coating, air movement equipment coating, handrail coatings, balustrade coating, and much more.*

▶ Sweeny's Cruises, Balloch Road, Balloch, Alexandria, Dunbartonshire, G83 8SS Tel: (01389) 752376 Fax: (01389) 721082

▶ The Sweeper Centre Ltd, Broomlands Farm, West Kilbride, Ayrshire, KA23 9NX Tel: (01294) 829333

▶ Sweet Dreams Ltd, Martin Street, Burnley, Lancashire, BB10 1SH Tel: (01282) 830033 Fax: (01282) 830055

Sweet Dreams Bed Centre, 55-57 New Road, Skewen, Neath, West Glamorgan, SA10 6EP Tel: (01792) 815080 Fax: (01792) 324177 *Bed retailers*

▶ Sweet Sensations Ltd, Unit 53 Britannia Way, Britannia Enterprise Park, Lichfield, Staffordshire, WS14 9UY Tel: (01543) 417822 Fax: (01543) 417889

Sweet Success, Unit 7 Gauntley Court, Ward Street, Nottingham, NG7 5HD Tel: 0115-845 0660 Fax: 0115-845 0661 E-mail: info@sweetsuccess.uk.com *Fruit cake bases in every shape & size*

Sweet Thoughts, Hawthorn Road, Skegness, Lincolnshire, PE25 3TD Tel: (01754) 896667 E-mail: info@sweetthoughts.co.uk *Sweet Thoughts manufacturers of corporate rock, promotional sweets, rock candy and personalised rock*

Sweet Valley Solutions Ltd, East Lodge House, 116 High Street, Cranleigh, Surrey, GU6 8AJ Tel: (01483) 273838 Fax: (01483) 275983 E-mail: sales@sweetvalley.co.uk Principal Export Areas: Central/East Europe *Computer systems consultants*

Sweetdreams Waterbeds, 115 Glasgow Road, Dumbarton, G82 1RG Tel: (01389) 742241 Fax: (01389) 742241 E-mail: sales@waterbeds.ws *Furniture & beds*

Sweetheat Technology Ltd, 16 Millwater Avenue, Dewsbury, West Yorkshire, WF12 9QN Tel: (01924) 488619 Fax: (01924) 488619 E-mail: nazim@sweetheat.co.uk *SweetHeat, Dewsbury, West Yorkshire, are manufacturers of heated delivery bags and are authorised distributors of commercial catering equipment and refrigerated products.*

Sweetland, Farway, Colyton, Devon, EX24 6JD Tel: (01404) 871436 Fax: (01404) 871436 *Caterers*

Sweetmans Retail Ltd, 59 Herbert Street, Pontardawe, Swansea, SA8 4ED Tel: (01792) 869552 Fax: (01792) 869552 *Bakers*

Sweetnam & Bradley Ltd, Gloucester Road, Malmesbury, Wiltshire, SN16 0DY Tel: (01666) 823491 Fax: (01666) 826010 E-mail: mike@sweetnam-bradley.com *Precision sheet metalwork specialists*

Sweets For U, Unit 9, Bradley Hall Trading Estate, Bradley Lane, Standish, Wigan, Lancashire, WN6 0XQ Tel: (01257) 400780 E-mail: julierose_4@hotmail.com *Sweets manufrs*

Swefco Ltd, 188 Corporation Road, Newport, Gwent, NP19 0DQ Tel: (01633) 250170 Fax: (01633) 250171 E-mail: swefco@aol.com *CNC sheet metalwork engineers*

▶ Swemko (U K) Ltd, Unit 2, Crimscott St, London, SE1 5TE Tel: (020) 7231 2381

Swemko (UK) Ltd, 29 Bonville Road, Brislington, Bristol, BS4 5QH Tel: (0845) 0760960 Fax: 0117-972 0470 E-mail: sales@swemkoknifes.com *Machine knife manufacturers & sharpeners*

Swesco, Unit 3E Treloggan Industrial Estate, Newquay, Cornwall, TR7 2SX Tel: (01637) 878160 Fax: (01637) 871115 E-mail: sales@swesco.net *Sign manufrs*

Swift, Unit 13 Glover Centre, Egmont Street, Mossley, Ashton-under-Lyne, Lancashire, OL5 9PY Tel: (01457) 834005 Fax: (01457) 836617 E-mail: enquiries@swiftengineering.co.uk *Precision sub-contract engineers*

Swift Ltd, Mistral House, Parsons Lane, Hinckley, Leicestershire, LE10 1XT Tel: (01455) 238398 Fax: (01455) 238866 *Uniform wholesale & retail*

Swift Ltd, 150 Walkden Road, Worsley, Manchester, M28 7DP Tel: 0161-790 3428 Fax: 0161-703 8793 *Portable toilet suppliers*

▶ Swift, Matthew Elliott House, 64 Broadway, Salford, M50 2TS Tel: 0161-872 6262 Fax: 0161-877 2424 E-mail: info@swiftsecurity.com *MAIN INTEGRATER FOR GENT FIRE SYSTEMS. DESIGN, INSTALLATION AND COMMISSIONING.**CORE DISCIPLINES-FIRE DETECTION ,FIRE SUPPRESSION, PAVA, CCTV, ACCESS CONTROL, INTRUDER SYSTEMS, CCTV MONITORING.*

Swift Abrasive Wheels, Toll End Road, Tipton, West Midlands, DY4 0HF Tel: 0121-557 8337 Fax: 0121-520 4770 E-mail: swiftandwhitmore@virgin.net *Abrasive products, abrasive coated products & grinding wheel dressers*

▶ Swift Aerospace Ltd, Metro Centre, Ronsons Way, St. Albans, Hertfordshire, AL4 9QT Tel: (01727) 868293 Fax: (01727) 868292 E-mail: sales@swiftaero.com Principal Export Areas: Worldwide *Aerospace & motor sport fastenings stockists*

▶ Swift Air Ventilation Ltd, 1 Station Yard, Station Road, Lenwade, Norwich, NR9 5LY Tel: (01603) 872706 Fax: (01603) 871742 *Ventilation engineers*

Swift Asbestos Services Ltd, 13 Test Valley Business Centre, Test Lane, Southampton, SO16 9JW Tel: (023) 8066 9357 Fax: (023) 8066 9358 *Swift Asbestos Services Ltd have been established for over 10 years. Trading successfully as a Licensed Asbestos Removal Contractor and now expanding out as a one-stop-shop for all/any asbestos-related works. With the advent of new legislation the "Duty to manage asbestos in non-domestic premises" in particular (regulation 4 of the control of asbestos at work regulations, 2002), we continue to grow with the continued development of our asbestos surveying division. We are happy to help and guide you through the implications of this new legislation and can advise on the strategies needed to ensure compliance. We are happy to help with any asbestos-related enquiry. Call us for straightforward, honest and impartial professional advice about asbestos.*

Swift Brickwork Contractors Ltd, Hampton House, Chelmsford, CM2 9RX Tel: (01245) 255000 Fax: (01245) 255001 E-mail: construction@swiftgroup.co.uk *Scaffolding contractors*

Swift Building Maintenance Services Ltd, 74 High St Colliers Wood, London, SW19 2BY Tel: (020) 8288 0919 Fax: (020) 8715 9963 E-mail: swift@ollierswood98.freeserve.co.uk *Building maintenance services*

Swift Business Equipment Ltd, Northgate, Aldridge, Walsall, WS9 8TR Tel: (01922) 743454 Fax: (01922) 743134 E-mail: sales@swiftbe.co.uk *Office furnishers*

Swift Catering Equipment, Harper Hill Industrial Estate, Buxton, Derbyshire, SK17 9JN Tel: (01298) 79381 *Stainless steel manufrs*

Swift Coatings, Empire Works, Church Street, Darfield, Barnsley, South Yorkshire, S73 9JX Tel: (01226) 752016 Fax: (01226) 752016 E-mail: enquiries@swiftcoatings.co.uk *Powder coating services*

Swift Creative Print Ltd, 2 Albright Road Off Newstead, Road Speke Approach Ditton, Widnes, Cheshire, WA8 8FY Tel: 0151-423 8300 Fax: 0151-423 8329 *Screen printers*

Swift Credit Services, Hazeldene, 2 High Street, Penydarren, Merthyr Tydfil, Mid Glamorgan, CF47 9AH Tel: (01685) 721900 Fax: (0870) 0006210 E-mail: sales@swift-credit.com *Certified bailiffs & debt recovery services*

David B. Swift Ltd, 63 Byward Drive, Crossgates, Scarborough, North Yorkshire, YO12 4JG Tel: (01723) 862089 E-mail: bramley_swift@btinternet.com *Machine tool repair* Also at: Leicester

▶ Swift Digital Solutions Ltd, 1st Floor, 3 Chase Side, Southgate, London, N14 5BP Tel: (020) 8886 9049 Fax: (020) 8882 8296 E-mail: info@swift-ds.co.uk *Swift Digital Solutions Limited focuses initially on the Infrastructure. This is the base for all others services including Telephones, Email, Internet, Databases etc. Whatever Service the client is looking to introduce or upgrade, the infrastructure must be stable and capable of the change. Many companies make the mistake of neglecting the infrastructure and encounter problems at a later date. SDS informs the client of any changes that need to be made before any work commences.*

Swift Electrical, Unit 1 Craven Way, Newmarket, Suffolk, CB8 0BW Tel: (01638) 661001 Fax: (01638) 560195 E-mail: swiftsescrubes@hotmail.com *Electric motor & pump repairs contractors*

Swift Engineering Co., 35 River Road, Barking, Essex, IG11 0DA Tel: (020) 8594 7626 Fax: (020) 8594 6207 *Precision engineers*

▶ Swift Engineering Services Ltd, 4 Holgate Court, Western Road, Romford, RM1 3JS Tel: (01708) 764573

Swift Fasteners Ltd, Unit 20 Oldends Industrial Estate, Oldends, Stonehouse, Gloucestershire, GL10 3RQ Tel: (01453) 825222 Fax: (01453) 827824 E-mail: sales@swift-fasteners-ltd.co.uk *Bolts & nuts & fasteners distributors & agents & stockholders*

▶ Swift FM Ltd, Swift Park, Old Leicester Road, Rugby, Warwickshire, CV21 1DZ Tel: (01788) 820200 Fax: (01788) 820222

Swift Forwarders (Midlands) Ltd, Unit 7 Greets Green Industrial Estate, Greets Green Road, West Bromwich, West Midlands, B70 9EW Tel: 0121-522 4499 Fax: 0121-522 4490 E-mail: info@swiftforwarders.freeserve.co.uk *Freight forwarders*

▶ Swift & French, 23a Church Road, Kingston upon Thames, Surrey, KT1 3DJ Tel: (020) 8549 2536 Fax: (020) 8547 1585

Swift Holdings Ltd, Dunswell Road, Cottingham, North Humberside, HU16 4JX Tel: (01482) 847332 Fax: (01482) 876335 E-mail: enquire@swiftleisure.co.uk *Touring caravans, motor homes retailers & manufrs*

Swift Industrial Suppliers, Anstey Mill Lane, The Mill House, Alton, Hampshire, GU34 2QQ Tel: (01420) 592500 Fax: (01420) 592501 *Safety equipment, protective clothing & corporate clothing suppliers*

▶ Swift Inline, 123 Walkern Road, Stevenage, Hertfordshire, SG1 3RE Tel: (01438) 244721 Fax: (01438) 244698 E-mail: scott@swiftinline.co.uk *suppliers of flexographic printing plates*and computer ready graphics*

▶ Swift Joinery, Mylord CR, Camperdown Industrial Estate, Newcastle upon Tyne, NE12 5UJ Tel: 0191-216 9631

▶ Swift Joinery Manufacturers Ltd, 6 Carr Wood Industrial Estate, Carr Wood Road, Castleford, West Yorkshire, WF10 4SB Tel: (01977) 551319 Fax: (01977) 556245 E-mail: sales@swift-windows.co.uk *Window manufrs*

Swift Levick Magnets Ltd, High Hazels Road, Barlborough, Chesterfield, Derbyshire, S43 4UZ Tel: (01246) 570500 Fax: (01246) 573000 E-mail: sales@arnoldengr.com Sales Contact: T. Gallagher *Manufacturers of magnets including industrial, permanent & neodymium. Also, magnetic sheet manufrs*

▶ The Swift Lift Company U K Ltd, Unit 60-69 Old Bexley Business Park, Bourne Road, Bexley, Kent, DA5 1LR Tel: (01322) 551379 Fax: (01322) 551381

▶ Swift Line Engineering, 5 Wellesely Court, Atcheley Way, Staples Corner, London, NW2 7PH Tel: (020) 8452 4080

▶ Swift Machinery Maintenance, 98 Recreation Way, Kemsley, Sittingbourne, Kent, ME10 2TG Tel: (01795) 420066 Fax: (0560) 1160925 *Machine tool engineers*

Swift Maintenance Services, Unit 2 Albert Street, Wednesbury, West Midlands, WS10 7EW Tel: 0121-505 4001 Fax: 0121-502 2065 *Catering engineers*

▶ Swift Micro Products Ltd, 26 Charnwood Road, Shepshed, Loughborough, Leicestershire, LE12 9QF Tel: (01509) 507007 Fax: (01509) 507007 *Tool design services*

▶ Swift Parts, 3 Rawfolds Industrial Estate, Bradford Road, Rawfolds, Cleckheaton, West Yorkshire, BD19 5LT Tel: (01274) 876777 Fax: (01274) 876505 *Bottling industry parts suppliers*

Swift Precision Engineering, Dogflud Way, Farnham, Surrey, GU9 7UD Tel: (01252) 713695 Fax: (01252) 734754 *Precision engineers*

Swift Press Tools, Oldbury Road Industrial Park, 136 Oldbury Road, Smethwick, West Midlands, B66 1JE Tel: 0121-555 5979 Fax: 0121-555 6798 *Press tool manufrs*

Swift Printers, 7 Stephenson Way, Crawley, West Sussex, RH10 1TN Tel: (01293) 516507 *General printers*

Swift Roofing Contracts Ltd, Kent House, Ware Street, Bearsted, Maidstone, Kent, ME14 4PA Tel: (01622) 632420 Fax: (01622) 632510 *Roofing contractors*

Swift Screw Products, Dunmore, Alexandra Park Avenue, Belfast, BT15 3GD Tel: (028) 9077 0721 Fax: (028) 9037 0914 E-mail: sales@swiftscrewproducts.co.uk *Screw & fastener stockists & distributors*

Swift Security Systems (Midlands) Ltd, 6-10 Rising Lea, Derby Road, Risley, Derby, DE72 3SS Tel: 0115-949 9449 Fax: 0115-939 7620 *Alarm installers*

▶ Swift Shutters, Unit 3-4 Harp Industrial Estate, Queensway, Rochdale, Lancashire, OL11 2QQ Tel: (01706) 653777 Fax: (01706) 653666 *Manufacturers of roller shutters*

Swift Signs Ltd, Vere Court, Grantham, Lincolnshire, NG31 8FB Tel: (01476) 563981 Fax: (01476) 590655 *Aluminium sign manufrs*

Swift Signs, 26 Stradey Park Avenue, Llanelli, Dyfed, SA15 3EF Tel: (01554) 757781 Fax: (01554) 774024 *Sign makers*

Swift Signs, 73 Kingsmead Avenue, Worcester Park, Surrey, KT4 8UZ Tel: (020) 8337 1080 Fax: (020) 8337 1080 E-mail: swifsign@btconnect.com *Sign makers*

Swift Signs & Shirts, Tutin Road, Leeming Bar Industrial Estate, Northallerton, North Yorkshire, DL7 9UJ Tel: (01677) 424175 Fax: (01677) 426550 E-mail: swiftsigns@tiscali.co.uk *Sign designers & manufrs*

▶ Swift Software Solutions Ltd, 2 Warner House, Harrovian Business Village, Bessborough Road, Harrow, Middlesex, HA1 3EX Tel: (020) 8423 8333 Fax: (020) 8423 9627 *Computer maintenance specialists*

▶ Swift Specialist Interiors Ltd, Bramley House, 91-99 Bradford Road, East Ardsley, Wakefield, West Yorkshire, WF3 2JD Tel: (01924) 828677 Fax: (01924) 828877 *Partitions installers*

Swift Steels Services Ltd, Unit 9 Leeway Industrial Estate, Newport, Gwent, NP19 4SL Tel: (01633) 271188 Fax: (01633) 278311 *Steel stockholders & processors*

▶ Swift Timber Homes Ltd, North Bridge House, North Bridge, St. Helen Auckland, Bishop Auckland, County Durham, DL14 9EY Tel: (01388) 835222 Fax: (01388) 835444 E-mail: enquires@swifttimberhomes.com *Manufacturers of timber frames*

Swift Vulcanising Services, Unit 10 Littleton Business Park, Littleton Drive, Cannock, Staffordshire, WS12 4TR Tel: (01543) 468018 Fax: (01543) 468018 E-mail: petrasedgley@btconnect.com *Vulvanising services*

Swiftclean (UK) Ltd, Aviation Way, Southend-On-Sea, SS2 6UN Tel: (01702) 531221 Fax: (01702) 531220 E-mail: info@swiftclean.co.uk *Building & hygiene cleaning services*

▶ Swiftec, Pennine House, Tilson Road, Roundthorn Industrial Estate, Manchester, M23 9GF Tel: 0161-945 1500 Fax: (0800) 0740005 *Builders' merchants*

▶ Swiftfix, 18 Newtown Road, Southampton, SO19 9HQ Tel: (023) 8044 8444 Fax: (023) 8044 8444 E-mail: sales@swiftfix.co.uk *Fasteners & Fixings,Drill Bits,Anchor Bolts ,Abrasives,Hand Tools,Power Tools,Sealants,Aerosols.*

Swiftkill Pest Control, Brookmill Road, London, SE8 4JH Tel: (020) 8694 3666 Fax: (020) 8305 6728 *Pest control service providers*

Swiftkill Pest Control Ltd, 50 Friendly Street, London, SE8 4DR Tel: (020) 8692 2935 Fax: (020) 8692 8891 E-mail: swiftkill@yayoo.co.uk *Pest control*

Swiftlight Charcoal, Marley Lane, Battle, East Sussex, TN33 0RE Tel: (01424) 870333 Fax: (01424) 870527 E-mail: steve@swift-lite.com Principal Export Areas: Worldwide *Charcoal suppliers*

Swiftnet Ltd, Britannia House, 958-964 High Road, London, N12 9RY Tel: (020) 8446 9494 Fax: (020) 8446 7010 E-mail: sales@swiftnet.co.uk *Telecommunications provider*

Swiftool Precision Engineering Ltd, Unit 1, Brierley Indust Park, Stanton Hill, Sutton-in-Ashfield, Nottinghamshire, NG17 3FW Tel: (01623) 515544 Fax: (01623) 442166 E-mail: sales@swifttool.co.uk *Precision engineers*

▶ Swiftpass Digital, County Gates, Ashton Road, Bristol, BS3 2JH Tel: 0117-944 9850 Fax: 0117-944 9851 E-mail: info@swiftpass.com *Leading provider of mobile ticketing worldwide*

Swiftprint, 186 Campden Hill Road, London, W8 7TH Tel: (020) 7229 5012 Fax: (020) 7229 3068 E-mail: mail@swiftprint.co.uk *Reprographic printers*

▶ Swiftpro, 2 Warner House, Harrovian Business Village, Bessborough Road, Harrow, Middlesex, HA1 3EX Tel: (0870) 8731270 Fax: (0870) 8731271 E-mail: sales@swiftpro.com *Software development services*

Swiftread Metals Ltd, 87 High View Road, London, E18 2HL Tel: (020) 8989 1113 Fax: (020) 8989 0875 *Scrap metal merchants & processors*

Swimco A R Penny Ltd, 12 Coombend, Radstock, BA3 3AJ Tel: (01761) 432838 Fax: (01761) 437216 E-mail: info@swimcopools.co.uk *Swimming pool contractors*

▶ Swimming Hippo Design, Eagle Tower, Montpellier Drive, Cheltenham, Gloucestershire, GL50 1TA Tel: (01242) 263102 Fax: (01242) 262491 E-mail: create@swimminghippo.co.uk *Web design*

▶ Swimming Pool Supplies, 224e Havant Road, Drayton, Portsmouth, PO6 1PA Tel: (023) 9238 7771 Fax: (023) 9238 7772 *Swimming pool equipment & accessory distributors*

Swindell & Pearson, 48 Friargate, Derby, DE1 1GY Tel: (01332) 367051 Fax: (01332) 345200 E-mail: sales@patent.co.uk *Patent & trade mark attorneys* Also at: Burton-on-Trent, Stafford, Stoke-on-Trent & Walsall

Swindens Revolving Head Vices Ltd, Suite 401 Langham Ho, 302 Regent St, London, W1B 3AT Tel: (020) 7580 6491 Fax: (020) 7580 4729 E-mail: am@swindens-vices.co.uk *Revolving head vices, hand vices & clamp manufrs*

Swindon Aerials, 31 Newport Street, Swindon, SN1 3DP Tel: (01793) 531400 Fax: (01793) 431831 E-mail: roysas777@yahoo.com *Communications aerial supply & installation*

D.J.T. Swindon Ltd, Unit 12 Ash Phase, Kembrey Park, Kembrey Street, Swindon, SN2 8UN Tel: (01793) 432543 Fax: (01793) 435397 E-mail: djt@djt-engineering.fsnet.co.uk *Precision & backshell design engineers*

Swindon Engineering Metalworkers, Unit 10 Bramble Close, Swindon, SN2 8DW Tel: (01793) 641808 Fax: (01793) 513029 *Metal fabricators*

Swindon Engineering Metalworkers, Unit 10 Bramble Close, Swindon, SN2 8DW Tel: (01793) 641808 Fax: (01793) 513029 *Precision engineers*

Swindon Lifting Gear Ltd, 9-11 Station Industrial Estate, Sheppard Street, Swindon, SN1 5DB Tel: (01793) 542051 Fax: (01793) 497187 *Lifting machinery suppliers*

Swindon Pressings, Bridge End Road, Swindon, SN3 4PE Tel: (01793) 536281 Fax: (01793) 551888 E-mail: info@swindon-pressings.co.uk *Producers of panels*

Swindon Racing Engines Ltd, Crampton Road, Greenbridge Estate, Swindon, SN3 3JJ Tel: (01793) 531321 Fax: (01793) 528484 E-mail: info@swindon-engines.com *Race engineers*

Swindon Security Systems, 2 Kitefield, Cricklade, Swindon, SN6 6NF Tel: (01793) 752820 Fax: (01793) 752820 *Installation & maintenance of security*

Swindon Silicon Systems Ltd, Radnor Street, Swindon, SN1 3PR Tel: (01793) 649400 Fax: (01793) 616215 E-mail: info@sssl.co.uk *ASIC devices design & supply*

Swindon Woodworking Co. Ltd, 9 Regal Way, Faringdon, Oxfordshire, SN7 7BX Tel: (01367) 240272 Fax: (01367) 243290 E-mail: info@swindonwoodworking.co.uk *Joinery manufrs*

Swinford Engineering Ltd, 191 Hagley Road, Stourbridge, West Midlands, DY8 2JJ Tel: (01384) 397531 Fax: (01384) 440118 *Iron casting manufrs*

Swinnertons Of Walsall, 1 Holtshill Lane, Walsall, WS1 2JA Tel: (01922) 626081 Fax: (01922) 626082 *Party goods distributors & engravers*

Swinton Fabrications Ltd, Unit 10 Cliffton Units, Rake Lane, Manchester, M27 8LJ Tel: 0161-793 9969 *Fabricating engineers*

▶ Swinton Technology Ltd, Unit 3 Park Farm Courtyard, Easthorpe, Malton, North Yorkshire, YO17 6QX Tel: (01653) 698844 Fax: (01653) 605679 E-mail: allison_knaggs@swintontechnology.co.uk *Supplying software computer systems*

John Swire & Sons Ltd, Swire House, 59 Buckingham Gate, London, SW1E 6AJ Tel: (020) 7834 7717 Fax: (020) 7630 0353 *Far East merchants & ship owners*

Swire Oil Field Services, Swire House, Souter Head Road, Altens Industrial Estate, Aberdeen, AB12 3LF Tel: (01224) 872707 Fax: (01224) 874516 E-mail: jlucas@swireos.com *Helicopter fuel services & offshore container hire*

Swiscot Textiles Ltd, Canada House, 3 Chepstow Street, Manchester, M1 5FW Tel: 0161-236 1025 Fax: 0161-236 6635 E-mail: info@swiscot.com *Grey household textiles & yarns*

▶ Swisher (Bath), Unit Mill Road Ind Estate, Radstock, BA3 5TX Tel: 01761 436791 E-mail: contact@swisherbath.co.uk *Unique weekly sanitation service to deep clean washrooms maintaining clean, sanitised and fresh smelling facilities. Air fresheners, soaps, feminine hygiene and paper delivered, installed and maintained.*

Swisher Wessex, Foredown House, High Street, Winterbourne Stoke, Salisbury, SP3 4TB Tel: (01980) 620091 Fax: (01980) 620070 E-mail: gcroft@dircon.co.uk *Swisher provides a unique weekly washroom hygiene service for any non-residential washroom. We sanitise commercial washrooms better and more cost-effectively. We offer a specialist service that is aimed at improving not only the cleanliness of the washroom, but also the overall image of the business. In addition, we stock a range of specialist washroom products which together with the Swisher service - makes Swisher a "One-stop shop" for its customers.*

Swiss Mimic Co Ltd, 26 Highfield Road, Chertsey, Surrey, KT16 8BU Tel: (01932) 569100 Fax: (01932) 569100 E-mail: swiss.mimic@tiscarly.co.uk *Mimic displays*

Swiss Pack Ltd, 312a London Road, Waterlooville, Hampshire, PO7 7DU Tel: (023) 9224 0200 Fax: (023) 9224 0288 E-mail: sales@swisspack.co.uk *Supply plastic vending cups*

Swiss Tech UK Ltd, Harmill House, 31 Pebblemoor, Edlesborough, Dunstable, Bedfordshire, LU6 2HZ Tel: (01525) 222556 Fax: (01525) 221749 E-mail: fletcherswisstec@aol.com *Surveying equipment distributors*

▶ Swiss Valley Print Ltd, Unit 9 Trostre Industrial Park, Llanelli, Dyfed, SA14 9UU Tel: (01554) 758758 Fax: (01554) 758758 E-mail: cambrian@clara.net *Design & print service, same day full colour printing*

▶ Swiss Valve Supply Ltd, 2 Rose Court Maytum Farm, Vanity Lane, Linton, Maidstone, Kent, ME17 4BP Tel: (01622) 746945 Fax: (01622) 749406 E-mail: swissvalvesupply@btconnect.com *Valves, knife gate suppliers*

Swisshealth Health Foods, 11 St Mary Abbots Terrace, London, W14 8NX Tel: (020) 7602 5344 Fax: 020 7602 5344 *Health food suppliers*

Swisslog, 707 Stirling Road, Slough, SL1 4SY Tel: (01753) 528545 Fax: (01753) 570407 E-mail: sales@teleliftuk.com *Automated materials & document systems distributors*

Swisslog Digitron Ltd, Regents Court, Farmoor Lane, Redditch, Worcestershire, B98 0SD Tel: (01527) 517333 Fax: (01527) 517344 E-mail: info@digitron.ltd.uk *Manufacture automated handling equipment & guided vehicles*

Swisstulle UK plc, Pelham Road, Nottingham, NG5 1AP Tel: 0115-969 2500 Fax: 0115-969 3270 E-mail: sales@swisstulle.co.uk *Mosquito & net fabric manufrs*

Swissvac (G B) Ltd, Marish Wharf, St Marys Road, Middlegreen, Slough, SL3 6DA Tel: (01753) 546777 Fax: (01753) 585564 E-mail: mail@swissvac.co.uk *Vacuum packaging & sealing machines* Also at: Edinburgh

Switch 2 Energy Solutions Ltd, High Mill, Mill Street, Cullingworth, Bradford, West Yorkshire, BD13 5HA Tel: (01535) 270266 Fax: (01535) 270282 E-mail: sales@switch2.com *Meter, valve & control services*

Switch Alarms, 8 Boothroyden Road, Middleton, Manchester, M24 4RY Tel: 0161-653 2541 *Security alarms specialists*

▶ Switch Soultions Ltd, 15 Richmond Road, Croydon, CR0 4SQ Tel: (07813) 055470 Fax: (020) 8680 4985 E-mail: enquiries@switchsolutions.co.uk *Telecom & data communications services*

▶ Switch Utilities Ltd, New Brook House, 385 Alfreton Road, Nottingham, NG7 5LR Tel: (0845) 6341005 Fax: (0845) 6341006 E-mail: james@switchutilities.com *Electricity, gas & telecom consultants*

▶ Switch2save.Co.Uk, 171 Robin Hood Lane, Birmingham, B28 0JE Tel: 0121-778 2722 Fax: (0871) 2427376 E-mail: savemoney@switch2save.co.uk *FREE independent service GUARANTEES to find you the cheapest gas and electricity prices in the UK Other services include, cheapest telephone and broadband rates and cheapest quotes for business users.*

Switchbox Vision Co., 6 Crown Court, Castle Street, Hinckley, Leicestershire, LE10 1DD Tel: (01455) 633505 *Alarms installation*

Switchcraft Incorporated, Robinson Way, Portsmouth, PO3 5TD Tel: (023) 9266 1579 Fax: (023) 9227 4731 E-mail: intsales@switchcraft.com *Electronic components manufrs*

Switchgear Engineering Services Ltd, Wright Street, Audenshaw, Manchester, M34 5TT Tel: 0161-371 0833 Fax: 0161-371 0834 *Switchgear maintenance & repair services*

Switchgear & Instrumentation Ltd, Ripley Road, Bradford, West Yorkshire, BD4 7EH Tel: (01274) 734221 Fax: (01274) 731390 E-mail: sales@switchgear.co.uk *Control panel manufrs*

Switchgear International Ltd, Farthing Road Industrial Estate, Ipswich, IP1 5AP Tel: (01473) 240280 Fax: (01473) 242929 E-mail: sales@switchgearinternational.co.uk *Control panels & switchboard manufrs*

Switchgear Services Ltd, Reme Drive, Heathpark Industrial Estate, Honiton, Devon, EX14 1SE Tel: (01404) 44337 Fax: (01404) 45993 E-mail: hq@switchgear-services.co.uk *Industrial switchgear & controls*

Switchit Service Ltd, 34 Brunswick Street West, Hove, East Sussex, BN3 1EL Tel: (01273) 325442 Fax: (01273) 208450 *Television aerial services*

▶ SwitchMode Ltd, 41 Kidderminster Road, Bewdley, Worcs, DY12 1BU Tel: (0793) 1506665 E-mail: sales@switch-mode.co.uk *Switchmode Power Supplies Ltd is managed by its owners. We all take an active part in the running of the business. This hands-on approach aims to ensure that our customers receive the best possible service. We consider each of our customers unique and seek to design solutions that reflect their varying business circumstances. We aim to offer solutions that are created to meet your needs.**Also, we aim to develop long-term relationships with our customers. We desire to develop a long-term relationship that will benefit both the company and it's employees.***

▶ Switchnet Systems Ltd, 5 Cecil Court, Pegrams Road, Harlow, Essex, CM18 7QR Tel: (01279) 306060 Fax: (01279) 309180 E-mail: info@switchnetsys.com *Providers of network solutions & infrastructure*

Switchtec Electronics Ltd, Brooms Road, Stone Business Park, Stone, Staffordshire, ST15 0SH Tel: (01785) 818600 Fax: (01785) 811900 E-mail: sales@switchtec.co.uk *Electric connector manufrs*

Swithland Spring Water Ltd, Hall Farmmain Streetswithland, Swithland, Loughborough, Leicestershire, LE12 8TQ Tel: (01509) 891189 Fax: (01509) 891189 E-mail: spring.water@btconnect.com *Spring water bottling & distribution*

Switzer Industrial Instruments, 14 Station Road, Lostock Gralam, Northwich, Cheshire, CW9 7PN Tel: (01606) 48950 Fax: (01606) 49581 E-mail: sswitzer1@aol.com *Industrial instrumentation maintenance & repair*

▶ SWL Lifting Services, 2 Nations Farm, Curdridge Lane, Curdridge, Southampton, SO32 2BH Tel: (01489) 891333 Fax: (01489) 891444 *Hire, sales, repair, tests & examinations of lifting equipment*

SWM Distribution Ltd, 5 Goodwood Road, Eastleigh, Hampshire, SO50 4NT Tel: (023) 8065 3283 Fax: (023) 8065 3285 E-mail: info@swm.co.uk *Air conditioning distributors*

Sword Business Technology Solutions Ltd, Johnston House, 52-54 Rose Street, Aberdeen, AB10 1UD Tel: (01224) 704704 Fax: (01224) 704604 E-mail: enquiries@realtimeengineering.co.uk *Computer software designers*

Sword Sealant Services Ltd, 8 Fryern Wood, Chaldon, Caterham, Surrey, CR3 5AR Tel: (01883) 348311 Fax: (01883) 340872 E-mail: swordsealant@btconnect.com *Sealant applicators*

SWR Ltd, 3 Eastman Way, Hemel Hempstead Industrial Estate, Hemel Hempstead, Hertfordshire, HP2 7DU Tel: (01442) 219611 Fax: (01442) 259918 E-mail: sales@swrgaragedoors.com Purchasing Contact: J. Lee Sales Contact: J. Lee Principal Export Areas: Worldwide *Manufacturers of wire rope assemblies & wire rope slings. Also lifting gear distributors/agents/stockholders & lifting gear inspection/maintenance/repair/test services. In addition wire rope stockholders*

Syan Ltd, The Mill, King Coughton, Alcester, Warwickshire, B49 5QG Tel: (01789) 400464 Fax: (01789) 400470 *Computer systems specialists*

Syan Ltd, Holton Wood 37, Telford, Shropshire, TF1 7GT Tel: (01952) 607000 Fax: (01952) 677278 E-mail: administration.team@syansmb.co.uk *Computer maintenance repair services*

Syan Data Centre Ltd, Orton Wood, Telford, Shropshire, TF1 7TT Tel: (01952) 602510 Fax: (01952) 404200 E-mail: info@nsoft.co.uk *IT support*

Syan Technology Ltd, Unit 2, Stafford Park 17, Telford, Shropshire, TF3 3DG Tel: (01952) 291670 Fax: (01952) 291845 *Computer services*

Sycamore Mouldings Ltd, Sycamore Industrial Estate, Sycamore Road, Handsworth, Birmingham, B21 0QW Tel: 0121-523 0732 Fax: 0121-523 5918 E-mail: ralph@sycamore76.freeserve.co.uk *Manufacturers of glass fibre mouldings*

Sycamore Products Ltd, Unit 6a Astra Park, Parkside Lane, Leeds, LS11 5SZ Tel: 0113-271 3200 Fax: 0113-276 1195 *Furniture fittings suppliers*

Sychron Ltd, Southern House, 1 Cambridge Terrace, Oxford, OX1 1RR Tel: (01865) 200211 Fax: (01865) 249666 *Computer software*

Sycon Ltd, Underleys, Beer, Seaton, Devon, EX12 3NA Tel: (01297) 21391 Fax: (01297) 625991 *Plastics moulders*

Sycopel International, Viking Industrial Park, Jarrow, Tyne & Wear, NE32 3DT Tel: 0191-428 5004 Fax: 0191-483 5995 E-mail: sycopelint@aol.com *Electronic component manufrs*

Sycopel Scientific Ltd, 15 Sedling Road, Wear Industrial Estate, Washington, Tyne & Wear, NE38 9BZ Tel: 0191-417 8788 Fax: 0191-417 6627 E-mail: sales@sycopel.com *Elector-chemical instrumentation designers & manufrs*

Sycos (UK) Ltd, Kensworth Gate, Garden Road, Dunstable, Bedfordshire, LU6 3JD Tel: (01582) 600640 Fax: (01582) 665210 E-mail: sales@sycos.co.uk *Aircraft electrical equipment manufrs*

Syddal Engineering Ltd, Palatine Street, Denton, Manchester, M34 3LY Tel: 0161-336 4205 Fax: 0161-320 9525 E-mail: info@syddalengineering.co.uk *Pipe repair clamp manufrs*

Sydenhams Ltd, 45-55 Ashley Road, Bournemouth, BH1 4LG Tel: (01202) 397454 Fax: (01202) 396465 *Building material suppliers*

Sydenhams Ltd, Mislingford, Fareham, Hampshire, PO17 5BA Tel: (01329) 832002 Fax: (01329) 834255 *Timber merchants*

Sydney Free (Saddlers) Ltd, 54 Querns Lane, Cirencester, Gloucestershire, GL7 1RH Tel: (01285) 655384 Fax: (01285) 650213 E-mail: enquiries@sydneyfree.co.uk *Saddlery & repairs*

Syfer Technology Ltd, Old Stoke Road, Arminghall, Norwich, NR14 8SQ Tel: (01603) 629721 Fax: (01603) 665001 E-mail: sales@syfer.co.uk Principal Export Areas: Worldwide *Capacitors*

Sygnet Signs Ltd, 129 Humberstone Rd, Leicester, LE5 3AP Tel: 0116-262 6288 Fax: 0116 262 6061 *Laser cutting & profile cutting services. Also sign contractors/sign makers suppliers/ installers*

▶ Syk Components, Unit 27 Commerce Court, Challenge Way, Bradford, West Yorkshire, BD4 8NW Tel: (01274) 662333 Fax: (01274) 664280 E-mail: sykcompsales@aol.com *Building products, fastener, sealants, adhesives specialists*

▶ Sykam Solutions Ltd, 1 Thomson Green, Deer Park, Livingston, West Lothian, EH54 8TA Tel: (01506) 201327 Fax: (01506) 442248

Sykes & Dyson, Albert Street, Lockwood, Huddersfield, HD1 3QG Tel: (01484) 541131 Fax: (01484) 512426 E-mail: sykes_dyson@shawvalves.co.uk *Jigs & fixtures to specification*

Sykes & East Ltd, Cleeve Court, 1 Cleeve Road, Leatherhead, Surrey, KT22 7UD Tel: (01372) 363054 Fax: (01372) 362920 *Clothing & utilities exporters*

Sykes Fabrications, West Street, Morley, Leeds, LS27 9EU Tel: 0113-238 3079 Fax: 0113-238 3081 *Metal fabricators*

Graham Sykes Insurance, 37 Rolle Street, Exmouth, Devon, EX8 2SN Tel: (01395) 266621 Fax: (01395) 268829 E-mail: info@graham-sykes.co.uk *Motor, household, commercial & general insurance, business insurance*

Sykes International Group Ltd, Swan Road, Mercer House, Harrogate, North Yorkshire, HG1 2SA Tel: (01423) 503333 Fax: (01423) 501111 E-mail: sales@sykesinternational.co.uk *Plant & machinery dealers*

▶ Sykes Leisure Projects, 34 Castle View Drive, Cromford, Matlock, Derbyshire, DE4 3RL Tel: (01629) 823700 Fax: (01629) 823700

Sykes Marine Hydromaster Ltd, B6 Fleet House Trading Estate, Motherwell Way, Grays, Essex, RM20 3XD Tel: (01708) 862651 Fax: (01708) 867905 E-mail: sykes.sales@sykeshydromaster.com *Transport equipment infrastructure*

Sykes Pickervant Ltd, Lancaster House, Bowerhill Industrial Estate, Bowerhill, Melksham, Wiltshire, SN12 6TT Tel: (01225) 700750 Fax: (01225) 791845 *Diagnostic equipment manufrs*

Sykes Purston Ltd, 37 Ackworth Road, Featherstone, Pontefract, West Yorkshire, WF7 5LN Tel: (01977) 791922 *Joinery manufrs*

Sykes R.O, 62b Feltwell Road, Southery, Downham Market, Norfolk, PE38 0NS Tel: (01366) 377591 Fax: 01366 377592 *Potato consultancy*

Sykes Timber, Carlyon Road, Atherstone, Warwickshire, CV9 1JD Tel: (01827) 718951 Fax: (01827) 714257 E-mail: wood@sykestimber.co.uk *Timber importers & merchants*

Sykes & Tunnicliffe Rugs Ltd, Chapel House, Chapel Street, Taylor Hill, Huddersfield, HD4 6HL Tel: (01484) 428433 Fax: (01484) 435280 *Woven pile rugs & mats*

Sylvasprings Watercress Ltd, Manor Farm, Southbrook, Bere Regis, Wareham, Dorset, BH20 7LH Tel: (01929) 471381 *Watercress growers & suppliers*

▶ Sylvia Jeffreys, Queensway, Wrexham, Clwyd, LL13 8YR Tel: (01978) 360390 Fax: (01978) 361684

Sylvia Plant Hire Ltd, 46 Sheepcote Dell Road, Holmer Green, High Wycombe, Buckinghamshire, HP15 6TL Tel: (01494) 717881 Fax: (01494) 488516 *Ground work contractors*

▶ Sylvias Fish Supplies, 469 Winchester Road, Southampton, SO16 7EH Tel: (023) 8076 0788 Fax: (023) 8076 0755 *Fish broker*

Symantec Ltd, Green Park, 350 Brook Drive, Reading, RG2 6UH Tel: (0870) 2431080 Fax: (0870) 2431081 *Manufacturing software*

▶ Symark Builders Ltd, Dunleigh House, Butts Green, Lockerley, Romsey, Hampshire, SO51 0JG Tel: (01794) 341833

▶ Symbiant Technologies, 10 Upper Bridge Street, Canterbury, Kent, CT1 2NA Tel: (01227) 455002 Fax: (01227) 454367 *Computer software development*

Symbol Signs, Unit 18 Abenglen Industrial Estate, Betam Road, Hayes, Middlesex, UB3 1SS Tel: (020) 8561 0240 Fax: (020) 8561 0920 E-mail: symbolsign@aol.com *Sign manufrs*

Symbol Signs, 3 Rennie Road, Skippers Lane Industrial Estate, Middlesbrough, Cleveland, TS6 6PX Tel: (01642) 467533 Fax: (01642) 463393 E-mail: symbolsigns@btconnect.com *Safety & industrial sign manufrs*

Symbol Signs, 21 St. Peters Street, Nottingham, NG7 3EN Tel: 0115-979 1456 Fax: 0115-979 0987 E-mail: info@symbol-signs.freeserve.co.uk *Screen process printers*

Symbol Technologies Ltd, Symbol Place, Wharfedale Road, Winnersh, Wokingham, Berkshire, RG41 5TP Tel: 0118-945 7000 Fax: 0118-945 7500 *Mobile computing wireless networkers*

Symdex Ltd, 3 Mill Lane, Broxbourne, Hertfordshire, EN10 7AZ Tel: 01992 451515 E-mail: info@symdex.co.uk *Software consultancy & supply*

Symicron Computer Communications Ltd, Technical Support Green Lane Business Park, 238 Green Lane, London, SE9 3TL Tel: (020) 8857 5577 Fax: (020) 8857 1945 E-mail: sales@symicron.com Principal Export Areas: Worldwide *Hardware & software*

Symm & Co. Ltd, Osney Mead, Oxford, OX2 0EQ Tel: (01865) 254900 Fax: (01865) 254935 E-mail: mailbox@symm.co.uk *Builders & contractors*

▶ Symmetry Communication, Chalfont House, Hampden Road, Chalfont St. Peter, Gerrards Cross, Buckinghamshire, SL9 9RY Tel: (01753) 279200 Fax: (01753) 279301 E-mail: info@symmetryplc.com *Virtual secretary services, call answering and outbound telephone services for business.*

Symmetry Medical, Beulah Road, Sheffield, S6 2AN Tel: (0114) 285 5881 Fax: (0114) 233 6978 E-mail: info@tpcl.com *Precision forging & casting machining*

Symology Ltd, Cotswold Farm Business Park, Millfield Lane, Caddington, Luton, LU1 4AJ Tel: (01582) 842626 Fax: (01582) 842600 E-mail: webmaster@symology.co.uk *Software house*

Symon Of Edinburgh, Hardengreen, Dalkeith, Midlothian, EH22 3JY Tel: 0131-660 6611 Fax: 0131-663 9966 E-mail: sales@symon-edinburgh.co.uk *Manufacturers & distributors of textiles*

▶ Symonds Group Ltd, Unit 28-32 Concourse House 432, Dewsbury Road, Leeds, LS11 7DF Tel: 0113-385 7000 Fax: 0113-270 1597

Symonds Trolley Services Ltd, Wern Trading Estate, Rogerstone, Newport, Gwent, NP10 9XX Tel: (01633) 892362 Fax: (01633) 896618 E-mail: symonds@symondshydroclean.co.uk Principal Export Areas: Central/East Europe & West Europe *Trolley maintenance & refurbishment services*

▶ Symphony Blinds, Unit 6 Highfield Works, Highfield Road, Yeovil, Somerset, BA21 4RJ Tel: (01935) 700000 Fax: (01935) 700000 E-mail: enquiries@symphonyblinds.co.uk *Window blinds manufrs*

The Symphony Group plc, Gelderd Lane, Leeds, LS12 6AL Tel: 0113-230 8000 Fax: 0113-231 0138 *Furniture manufrs*

Symphony Plastic Technologies Plc, Elstree House, Elstree Way, Borehamwood, Hertfordshire, WD6 1LE Tel: (020) 8207 5900 Fax: (020) 8207 5960 E-mail: sales@degradable.net *Degradable packing/polythene bag manufrs*

Symphony Telecom Ltd, Telford House, Corner Hall, Hemel Hempstead, Hertfordshire, HP3 9HN Tel: (01442) 283300 Fax: (01442) 283328 E-mail: symphony@symphony.com *Telecommunication consultants*

▶ Symplest Ltd, PO Box 922, Guildford, Surrey, GU2 9JT Tel: 01483 452525 Fax: 01483 452525 E-mail: sales@symplest.com *Art, the meaningful alternative. Symplest has taken a very pragmatic and simple approach to the opportunity presented by the 'blank wall' syndrome and has developed a service that delivers meaningful art at affordable prices, and without the usual costs associated with consultants and design agencies.*

Symsmetal, Candys Lane, Corfe Mullen, Wimborne, Dorset, BH21 3EF Tel: (01202) 885019 Fax: (01202) 889400 *Scrap metal merchants*

Symtag, Unit 9, Mendip Industrial Estate, Mendip Road, Rooksbridge, Axbridge, Somerset, BS26 2UG Tel: (01934) 750410 Fax: (01934) 750404 E-mail: info@symtag.co.uk *Sheep ID tag manufrs*

Synapse Electronics, Old Crofters Yard, Combi Street, Oban, Argyll, PA34 4HU Tel: (01631) 565055 *TV repairers*

The Synapse Partnership Ltd, 1A Cecil Road, Hale, Altrincham, Cheshire, WA15 9NY Tel: 0161-929 5777 Fax: 0161-929 0805 *Computer consultants*

▶ Synapsys Solutions Ltd, 23 Cuckfield Road, Hurstpierpoint, Hassocks, West Sussex, BN6 9RW Tel: (01273) 831831 Fax: (01273) 831631 E-mail: sales@synapsys-solutions.com *BMS systems integrators*

▶ Synaptics (UK) Ltd, 7340 Cambridge Research Park, Beach Road, Waterbeach, Cambridge, CB5 9TB Tel: (01223) 204900

Synatel Instrumentation Ltd, Walsall Road, Norton Canes, Cannock, Staffordshire, WS11 9TB Tel: (01543) 277003 Fax: (01543) 271217 E-mail: sales@synatel.co.uk *Level control equipment manufrs*

▶ Synchro Ltd, Design Centre 2.3, Coventry Universtiy, Technology Park, Puma Way, Coventry, CV1 2TT Tel: (024) 7679 2200 E-mail: info@synchroltd.com *Construction planning software*

Synchro Arts, 13 Links Road, Epsom, Surrey, KT17 3PP Tel: (01372) 811934 Fax: (01372) 817976 E-mail: info@synchroarts.com *Computer software manufrs*

Synchrodata Ltd, 25 Long Street, Bulkington, Bedworth, Warwickshire, CV12 9JZ Tel: (024) 7631 2218 Fax: (024) 7664 3211 E-mail: sychrodata@rukonline.co.uk *Machine tool rebuilders or suppliers*

▶ Syncro Ltd, 175 Trident House, Renfrew Road, Paisley, Renfrewshire, PA3 4EF Tel: 0141-849 7800 Fax: 0141-849 7844 E-mail: admin@letsco-operate.com *Construction of refurbishment offices*

Syncro Ltd, 6th Floor Furness House, Furness Quay, Salford, M50 3XZ Tel: 0161-786 4400 Fax: 0161-877 5233 *Refrigeration designers & installers*

Syncron UK Ltd, Baskerville House, Centenary Square, Birmingham, B1 2ND Tel: 0121-503 2650 Fax: 0121-503 2651 *Logistics software developers*

Syne Qua Non Ltd, Navire House, Mere Street, Diss, Norfolk, IP22 4AG Tel: (01379) 644449 Fax: (01379) 644445 E-mail: sales@synequanon.com *Clinical trials*

Synectics Solutions Ltd, Synectics House The Hollies, The Brampton, Newcastle, Staffordshire, ST5 0QY Tel: (01782) 664000 Fax: (01782) 664050 E-mail: enq@synectics-solutions.com *IT consultants*

Synektics Ltd, 4 Brinksway, Fleet, Hampshire, GU51 3LZ Tel: (01252) 815281 Fax: (01252) 624433 E-mail: sales@synektics.co.uk *High quality awnings. Garage Doors.*

Synergie Ltd, Digital House, The Loddon Centre, Wade Road, Basingstoke, Hampshire, RG24 8QW Tel: (01256) 467771 Fax: (01256) 840383 E-mail: alison@synergie.uk.com *Specialist commercial printers*

Synergie Healthcare Ltd, Lyon Mill, Fitton Street, Royton, Oldham, OL2 5JX Tel: 0161-624 5641 Fax: 0161-627 0902 *'J-suit' protective clothing manufrs*

Synergie-Cad UK Ltd, Greetwell Place, 2 Lime Kiln Way, Lincoln, LN2 4US Tel: (01522) 520222 Fax: (01522) 531222 E-mail: rogercooke@synergie-cad.co.uk *Printed circuit board designers & consultancy*

▶ Synergis Group, Rutherglen, Glasgow, G73 1NP Tel: 0141-613 1333

Synergistic Software Co Ltd, Hughenden House, Main Street, Collingham, Wetherby, West Yorkshire, LS22 5AS Tel: (01937) 573446 Fax: (01937) 574211 E-mail: tony@syn.co.uk *Complete business broadband solution (dedicated server, neat applications and full security).*We can save you money on Internet dial-up /satellite /leased line and office-to-office intranet.*We install phone systems, CRM with workflow and CTI.*We also develop Content Management Systems and eCommerce websites.*

Synergix Peripheral Systems Ltd, Unit 3 The Sapphire Centre, Fishponds Road, Wokingham, Berkshire, RG41 2QL Tel: 0118-979 0992 Fax: 0118-989 2187 E-mail: info@synergix.co.uk *Bar code product distributors*

Synergy, 57 Cotton Street, Aberdeen, AB11 5EG Tel: (01224) 211841 Fax: (01224) 211841 *Hairdressers equipment & suppliers*

▶ Synergy Coaching Ltd, 1 Ryding Close, Farington Moss, Leyland, PR26 6QZ Tel: (01772) 641234 Fax: (01772) 641234 *Synergy Coaching is a Business Coaching and personal coaching company. We assist companies on business growth and sales and marketing strategies, we offer coaching for all types of companies and executives within small or large enterprises.*Our coaching is proven by thousands of companies who have seen rapid sales improvement as well as in many other key performance areas. Our coaches are qualified and highly experienced, senior professionals.*

▶ Synergy Components Ltd, 6 Bolsover Business Park, Intake Road, Bolsover, Chesterfield, Derbyshire, S44 6BB Tel: (01246) 241414

▶ Synergy Devices Ltd, Unit 2 Network 4, Lincon Road, Cressex Business Park, High Wycombe, Buckinghamshire, HP12 3RF Tel: (01494) 769020 Fax: (01494) 528611 E-mail: sales@speedmixer.co.uk *Mixers suppliers*

Synergy Financial Systems Ltd, 8-9 Edison Village, Nottingham Science Technology Park, Nottingham, NG7 2RF Tel: 0115-967 7933 Fax: 0115-967 7933 E-mail: info@synergy-sf.com *Software producers*

Synergy Flavours, Synergy House, 2 Hillbottom Road, Sands Industrial Estate, High Wycombe, Buckinghamshire, HP12 4HJ Tel: (01494) 492222 Fax: (01494) 492111 E-mail: info@synergyflavours.com *Food flavouring manufrs*

Synergy Plastics Ltd, 8 Willow Road, Pen-Y-Fan Industrial Estate, Crumlin, Newport, Gwent, NP11 4EG Tel: (01495) 248888 Fax: (01495) 245678 E-mail: sales@synergy-plastics.com *Injection plastics services*

▶ Synergy Salon Supplies, 3 Ladeside Business Centre, St. Catherines Road, Perth, PH1 5RY Tel: (01738) 440187 Fax: (01738) 440147 *Hairdressing salon equipment suppliers*

Synergy Sign Design Ltd, Hi-Spec House, Liverpool Road, Great Sankey, Warrington, WA5 1EE Tel: (01925) 497879 Fax: (01925) 492794 E-mail: sales@synergysigns.com *Sign manufrs*

Synergy Systems Ltd, 43 Ashbarn Cresent, Winchester, Hampshire, SO22 4QH Tel: (01962) 840174 Fax: (01962) 877266 E-mail: admin@synsys.com *Computer consultants & software developers*

Synergy Systems Manchester Ltd, 219 Stockport Road, Stockport, Cheshire, SK3 0RH Tel: 0161-428 1517 Fax: 0161-428 8528 *Computer software developers*

▶ Synetix Group, Unit C1, Aven Industrial Park, Tickhill Road, Maltby, Rotherham, South Yorkshire, S66 7QR Tel: (01709) 819933 Fax: (01709) 798804 *IT support services*

Synetrix Ltd, Innovation Centre, University of Keele, Keele, Newcastle, Staffordshire, ST5 5NB Tel: (01782) 338200 Fax: (01782) 629600 E-mail: enq@synetrix.co.uk *Computer consultants*

▶ Syngenta Ltd, PO Box A38, Huddersfield, HD2 1FF Tel: (01484) 537456 Fax: (01484) 517067

Syngenta Crop Protection UK Ltd, CPC4 Capital Park, Fulbourn, Cambridge, CB21 5XE Tel: (01223) 883400 Fax: (01223) 882195 E-mail: cropmarketing-uk@syngenta.com *Corp protection product distributors*

Synlatex Ltd, Unit M2 Innsworth Technology Park, Innsworth Lane, Gloucester, GL3 1DL Tel: (01452) 730068 Fax: (01452) 730048 E-mail: enquiries@slguk.com *Make-up applicators & powder puffs manufrs*

Synnex Information Technology Ltd, Synnex House, Nedge Hill, Telford, Shropshire, TF3 3AH Tel: (01952) 207200 E-mail: enquiries@smartwater.com *Forensic security crime detection systems*

Synoptics Ltd, Beacon House, Nuffield Road, Cambridge, CB4 1TF Tel: (01223) 727100 Fax: (01223) 727101 E-mail: sales@synoptics.co.uk *Image processing systems*

Synpac Ltd, Priory Tec Park Saxon Way, Priory Park, Hessle, North Humberside, HU13 9PB Tel: (01482) 640606 Fax: (01482) 642768 E-mail: sales@synpac.ltd.uk Principal Export Areas: Worldwide *Flexible packaging manufrs*

Synprotec Ltd, 303 Clayton Lane, Clayton, Manchester, M11 4SX Tel: 0161-223 3344 Fax: 0161-220 8778 E-mail: sales@synprotec.com *Chemical manufrs*

Synrein Plastics Ltd, Grosvenor Works, Grosvenor Street, Ashton-Under-Lyne, Lancashire, OL7 0RG Tel: 0161-330 8573 Fax: 0161-343 2195 E-mail: sales@synrein.co.uk *PVC protective bedding-cadaver bags*

▶ Syntagm, 10 Oxford Road, Abingdon, Oxfordshire, OX14 2DS Tel: (01235) 522859 Fax: (01235) 554449 E-mail: william.hudson@syntagm.co.uk *User system design & training services*

▶ Syntec, Unit 1 Parkside, Ravenscourt Park, London, W6 0UU Tel: (020) 8834 7544 Fax: (020) 8762 0604 E-mail: syntec_projects@blueyonder.co.uk *Syntec''s skill base encompasses shop fitting, retail refurbishment, commercial refurbishment and bespoke joinery.*

▶ Syntec Manufacturing Ltd, 6 Mid Road, Blairlinn Industrial Estate, Cumbernauld, Glasgow, G67 2TT Tel: (01236) 739696 Fax: (01236) 727955 E-mail: sales@syntecchemicals.com *Quality cleaning & maintenance product manufrs*

Syntech Europe Ltd, 351 Wigan Road, Bolton, BL3 5QU Tel: (01204) 659899 Fax: (01204) 659941 E-mail: andrew@syntech-europe.com *Electronic assembly services*

Syntema South West, Unit 13 Hither Green, Clevedon, Avon, BS21 6XU Tel: (01275) 342777 Fax: (01275) 340820 E-mail: emma@syntemasouthwest.co.uk *Wood & metal coatings for industry*

Syntena & North East Ltd, Unit B8, Tyne Tunnel Trading Estate, North Shields, Tyne & Wear, NE29 7XB Tel: 0191-258 4564 Fax: 0191-258 2568 *Specialist coating*

▶ Synthetic Polybulk UK, Unit 4 Brandon House, 23-25 Brandon Street, Hamilton, Lanarkshire, ML3 6DA Tel: (01698) 527122 Fax: (01698) 527127 E-mail: jim.mccreadie@polybulk.com *Manufacturers of High Quality FIBC bags from a network of global production sites.*Main markets served - Fertiliser, Feed,Seeds, Chemicals, Plastic etc*

Synthite Ltd, Alyn Works, Denbigh Road, Mold, Clwyd, CH7 1BT Tel: (01352) 752521 Fax: (01352) 700182 *Formaldehyde & paraformaldehyde producers*

Synthotec Ltd, Sandys Road, Malvern, Worcestershire, WR14 1JJ Tel: (01684) 571900 Fax: (01684) 571909 E-mail: sales@synthotec.com *Precision injection moulders for bearings industry*

Synthotech Elastomers Ltd, Mangham Road, Barbot Hall Industrial Estate, Rotherham, South Yorkshire, S61 4RJ Tel: (01709) 363705 Fax: (01709) 369165 E-mail: info@synthotech-rubber.co.uk *Manufacturers of rubber products, seals & gaskets from prototype development to high or low volume injection & compression moulding. Specialists in diaphragms, rubber to metal bonding, anti-vibration products, silicone & viton moulding, liquid silicone moulding*

Syntonic Construction Ltd, 63-65 Penge Road, London, SE25 4EJ Tel: (020) 8778 7838 Fax: (020) 8659 5418 E-mail: neal.etchells@btconnect.com *Building & construction contractors*

Syntron Europe Ltd, Birchwood Way, Cotes Park Industrial Estate, Somercotes, Alfreton, Derbyshire, DE55 4QQ Tel: (01773) 605078 Fax: (01773) 605078 E-mail: chris.toner@sercelengland.com *Seismic cable maintenance, repair & geophysical equipment manufrs*

▶ Syon Lodge, Unit C, Riding Court Farm, Riding Court Road, Datchet, Slough, SL3 9JT Tel: (01753) 540722 Fax: (01753) 549649 *Joiners*

Company Information

Sypol Ltd, Elsinore House, Buckingham Street, Aylesbury, Buckinghamshire, HP20 2NQ Tel: (01296) 415715 Fax: (01296) 397106 E-mail: helpme@sypol.com *Health & safety consultants*

Syport Systems, 5 Moorlands Avenue, Kenilworth, Warwickshire, CV8 1HR Tel: (01926) 864910 E-mail: info@syport.co.uk *Computer consultant services*

Syrian Arab Airlines, 27 Albemarle Street, London, W1S 4BJ Tel: (020) 7493 2851 Fax: (020) 7493 2119 *Airlines*

Sys Dynamics Ltd, Unit 3, Burley Road, Angel Court, Leeds, LS3 1BS Tel: 0113-244 2176 Fax: 0113-244 2168 *Computer systems, networking, web design & training*

Sysco Audio Equipment, The Rickyard, Eashing Lane, Godalming, Surrey, GU7 2QA Tel: (01483) 429491 Fax: (01483) 429094 E-mail: mail@systems.co.com *Audio Visual Systems - Designers & Installers*

Sysco Services, PO Box 437, Harpenden, Hertfordshire, AL5 2BP Tel: (01582) 486000 Fax: (01582) 486086 E-mail: mail@desingteaminc.co.uk *Aerospace recruitment agents*

► Syscom Business Computing Ltd, Blackpool Technology Centre, Faraday Way, Blackpool, FY2 0JW Tel: (01253) 316333 Fax: (01253) 316338 E-mail: sales@syscom.co.uk *Computer maintenance systems services*

Syscom Group Ltd, Hampshire House, High Street, Kingswinford, West Midlands, DY6 8AW Tel: (01384) 400600 Fax: (01384) 400601 E-mail: info@syscom.plc.uk *Computer software house*

Syscom Motion Solution Ltd, Unit 19 Barnsley Business & Innovation Centre, Innovation Way, Barnsley, South Yorkshire, S75 1JL Tel: (01226) 771630 Fax: (01226) 771696 E-mail: info@automation.co.uk Principal Export Areas: Worldwide *Motion control solution providers*

Syscomm Ltd, Syscomm House, 2 Park Road, Kenilworth, Warwickshire, CV8 2GF Tel: (01926) 856000 Fax: (01926) 851158 E-mail: sales@syscomm.co.uk *Computer & network services*

Syscon Ltd, PO Box 119, North Shields, Tyne & Wear, NE30 2YD Tel: 0191-296 5542 Fax: 0191-296 5595 E-mail: info@shotel.co.uk *Hotel computerisation service*

► Sysmax Ltd, Innovation Centre, Exploration Drive, Bridge of Don, Aberdeen, AB23 8GX Tel: (01224) 827217 Fax: (01224) 827218

Sysnet Ltd, Avon Court, Cowbridge Road, Bridgend, Mid Glamorgan, CF31 3SR Tel: (01656) 647111 Fax: (01656) 651038 E-mail: enquiries@sysnetltd.co.uk *Software developers*

Sysnet Computer Consultants, Newton House, 457 Sauchiehall Street, Glasgow, G2 3LG Tel: 0141-333 1020 Fax: 0141-572 1732 *Computer consultants*

Systech UK Ltd, Willow House, Kingswood Business Park, Albrighton, Wolverhampton, WV7 3AU Tel: (01902) 373276 Fax: (01902) 373081 E-mail: john@systechuk.com *Coating & control equipment*

System 2000 Group Ltd, 39-41 Wood End Lane, Erdington, Birmingham, B24 8AN Tel: 0121-350 2000 Fax: 0121-377 6300 *Industrial door repairs & shop fronts manufrs*

► System 2000 UK Ltd, 507 Bradford Road, Batley, West Yorkshire, WF17 8LL Tel: (01924) 422000 Fax: (01924) 422118 E-mail: sales@system2000.co.uk *Aquarium products electronics*

System 3 Ltd, Denton Hall Farm Road, Denton, Manchester, M34 2SY Tel: 0161-337 3000 Fax: 0161-337 0222 *Manufacture of insulating glass units*

System 3R, Redvale House, New Road, Princes Risborough, Buckinghamshire, HP27 0JN Tel: (01844) 274455 Fax: (01844) 348800 E-mail: info.uk@system3r.com *Tooling system distributors*

System 910 Hydraulics Ltd, 7 The Old Granary, The Street, Boxgrove, Chichester, West Sussex, PO18 0ES Tel: (01243) 539789 Fax: (01243) 530307 E-mail: system910@mistral.co.uk *Manufacturers of hydraulic equipment systems*

System Access Europe Ltd, Tower 42 International Financial Centre, 25 Old Broad Street, London, EC2N 1HQ Tel: (020) 7588 8887 Fax: (020) 7588 8989 *Produce trading systems*

System Air GMPH, 20b Westside Centre, London Road, Stanway, Colchester, CO3 8PH Tel: (01206) 543311 Fax: (01206) 760497 E-mail: sales@matthews-yates.co.uk *Ventilation equipment suppliers*

System Automation Leicester Ltd, Claymill Buildings, Claymill Road, Leicester, LE4 9JJ Tel: 0116-246 0151 Fax: 0116-246 1772 E-mail: andy.austin@system-auto.demon.co.uk *Control engineers*

► System Control Specialists Ltd, 12 Swan Units, Heron Road, Sowton Industrial Estate, Exeter, EX2 7LL Tel: (01392) 444304 Fax: (01392) 444533 *Control panel manufrs & energy monitoring systems*

System Devices Ltd Automation Di, 17 Beeston Court, Stuart Road, Manor Park, Runcorn, Cheshire, WA7 1SS Tel: (01928) 571977 Fax: (01928) 571988 E-mail: sales@systemdevices.co.uk *SCARA robots & ethernet based io systems*

► System Electrical Engineering Ltd, System House, Merthyr Tydfil Industrial Park, Pentrebach, Merthyr Tydfil, Mid Glamorgan, CF48 4DR Tel: (01443) 694030 Fax: (01443) 694039

System Enterprises Ltd, Unit 21, Hartley Fold, Hartley, Kirkby Stephen, Cumbria, CA17 4JA Tel: (0845) 6430556 E-mail: info@systementerprises.com *Video Production, Video Conversion, DVD Authoring.*

► System Fixers, The Heathers, Mildenhall, Marlborough, Wiltshire, SN8 2LR Tel: (08700) 733150 E-mail: mds@the-sf.com *Your enterprise can benefit from our long experience in the computer and business environment as trouble shooters and problem solvers - we can provide answers to lighten your load for all your computer needs - from networking to internet management*

continued

System Hydraulics Ltd, Unit 5 Long Island Park, Carlisle, CA2 5AS Tel: (01228) 511444 Fax: (01228) 514206 *Hydraulic & pneumatics power packs*

System Hygiene Ltd, Altham Business Park, Altham, Accrington, Lancashire, BB5 5YT Tel: (01282) 777999 Fax: (01282) 777900 E-mail: sales@systemhygiene.co.uk *Cleaning & maintenance products retailers*

System Integration (UK) Ltd, Unit 1, Reddicap Trading Estate, Sutton Coldfield, West Midlands, B75 7BU Tel: (01283) 224222 Fax: (01283) 819615 E-mail: sales@simail.co.uk *Computer consultants*

System Link (U K) Ltd, First Floor Holgate House, Holgate Court, 4-10 Western Road, Romford, RM1 3JF Tel: (01708) 733422 Fax: (01708) 730446 *Computer software sales*

► System Lynx Ltd, Holland House, Bath Street, Walsall, WS1 3BZ Tel: (01922) 622044 Fax: (01922) 709235 *Computer software developers*

System Marketing Ltd, 249-251 Merton Road, London, SW18 5EB Tel: (020) 8874 8285 Fax: (020) 8874 9325 E-mail: sales@system-marketing.co.uk *Picture hangings manufacturers & distributors*

► System & Network Training, Robert Denholm House, Bletchingley Road, Nutfield, Redhill, RH1 4HW Tel: (01737) 821590 Fax: (01737) 821590 E-mail: sales@s-nt.co.uk *Systems & Network Training Ltd provide technical, instructor led training. Courses are available on a public schedule basis or as one company courses. Our standard courses are not based around achieving specific certifications instead they are based on the skills most likely to be required in the workplace. As well as offering standard courses we can also provide tailor made courses.*

System One Ltd, Lavant House, 39 Lavant Street, Petersfield, Hampshire, GU32 3EL Tel: (01730) 267000 Fax: (01730) 266676 E-mail: sales@systemone.co.uk *Software developers*

System One Signs, Unit 24 H T M Business Park, Abergele Road, Rhuddlan, Rhyl, Clwyd, LL18 5UZ Tel: (01745) 590880 Fax: (01745) 590880 *Sign manufrs*

System Panels Ltd, 104 Dudley Road East, Oldbury, West Midlands, B69 3EB Tel: 0121-552 4418 Fax: 0121-552 4018 E-mail: sales@marwel.com *Control panel & systems, automatic manufrs*

System Plast Ltd, Unit 3-4, Churchlands Business Park, Ufton Road, Harbury, Leamington Spa, Warwickshire, CV33 9GX Tel: (01926) 614314 Fax: (01926) 614914 E-mail: info@systemplastuk.com *Conveyor component suppliers*

System Red Ltd, Prospidnick, Helston, Cornwall, TR13 0RY Tel: (01326) 563300 Fax: (01326) 565680 E-mail: sales@systemred.co.uk *Database programmers*

System Signs, 7 Greystone Road, Carlisle, CA1 2DJ Tel: (01228) 545558 Fax: (01228) 545558 E-mail: admin@systemsigns.co.uk *General sign manufrs*

System Signs Ltd, Unit 6a Canons Yard Industrial Estate, Station Road, Wootton Bassett, Swindon, SN4 7SP Tel: (01793) 852996 Fax: (01793) 852455 E-mail: info@system-signs.com *Sign service, supply & installation specialists in exhibition graphics*

System Solutions, P O Box 3768, Bracknell, Berks, RG42 7YL Tel: 01344890008 Fax: 01344 890009 E-mail: sales@system-solutions.co.uk *Computer repair, hire & resell*

System Solutions Norwich, 19 Mahoney Green, Rackheath, Norwich, NR13 6JY Tel: (01603) 722590 Fax: (01603) 721308 E-mail: c.turner@systemsolutions.co.uk *Computer repairers*

► System Wise, 107 Saughtonhall Drive, Edinburgh, EH12 5TS Tel: 0131-313 0707 Fax: 0131-313 0808 E-mail: info@systemwise.co.uk *IT consultants & support*

► Systematic Creative Interiors Ltd, Red Shute Hill Industrial Estate, Red Shute Hill, Hermitage, Thatcham, Berkshire, RG18 9QL Tel: (01635) 201789 Fax: (01635) 200996 E-mail: sale@systematicinteriors.co.uk *Refurbishment contractors*

Systematic Multi Head Co.Ltd, Trend Grey House, Tomlow Road, Southam, Warwickshire, CV47 8HX Tel: (01926) 810678 Fax: (01926) 810618 E-mail: sales@systematic-drill-head.co.uk *Drill head manufrs*

Systematic Servicing Equipment Ltd, Field Works, Broadway Road, Willersey, Broadway, Worcestershire, WR12 7PH Tel: (01386) 852342 Fax: (01386) 858556 E-mail: sales@systematic-servicing.co.uk *Waste handling equipment supply & repairers*

Systematic Servicing Equipment Ltd, Field Works, Broadway Road, Willersey, Broadway, Worcestershire, WR12 7PH Tel: (01386) 852342 Fax: (01386) 858556 E-mail: sales@systematic-servicing.co.uk *Shot blasting contractors*

Systematics Printed Circuits Ltd, Unit 7 R.J. Mitchell Centre, Spitfire Quay, Hazel Road, Woolston, Southampton, SO19 7GB Tel: (023) 8068 5677 Fax: (023) 8068 5625 E-mail: pcbsales@systematicsprintedcircuits.com *Printed circuit manufrs*

Systemation Euro Ltd, Mansion Close, Moulton Park Industrial Estate, Northampton, NN3 6RU Tel: (01604) 491107 Fax: (01604) 493931 E-mail: sales@systemationeuro.com *Electronic component taping service & device programming service*

Systemax Communications Ltd, Unit 7 Westerham Trade Centre, The Flyers Way, Westerham, Kent, TN16 1DE Tel: (01959) 563133 Fax: (01959) 563008 *Data cabling & telephone systems installers*

Systeme Evolutif Ltd, Third Floor, 9 Cavendish Place, London, W1G 0QD Tel: (020) 7636 6060 E-mail: info@evolutif.co.uk *Software testing services*

Systemec, Radford Court Industrial Estate, Nottingham, NG7 3DY Tel: (0870) 4289180 Fax: (0870) 4289186 E-mail: mail@systemec.co.uk *Display case suppliers*

Systemform Services, 8 Northfield Point, Northfield Avenue, Kettering, Northamptonshire, NN16 9HU Tel: (01536) 411414 Fax: (01536) 411416 *Printers*

► Systemlogic Ltd, 2 Pell Street, Swansea, SA1 3ES Tel: (01792) 461577 Fax: (01792) 464411 *Professional services & computer software*

Systems Advisers Group UK Ltd, Enterprise House, Donaldson Crescent, Kirkintilloch, Glasgow, G66 1XF Tel: 0141-578 2237 Fax: 0141-578 2306 E-mail: sales@systemsadvisers.com *Microsoft business solutions providers*

Systems Audits Inspections Ltd, 51 Delph New Road, Delph, Oldham, OL3 5BY Tel: (01457) 870946 Fax: (01457) 870946 E-mail: philiptaylor@sai-online.co.uk *Quality assurance management*

Systems & Communications Ltd, 10 Moreland Close, Alton, Hampshire, GU34 2SA Tel: (01420) 88482 Fax: (01420) 544754 *Telecommunication & computer consultants*

Systems Communications & Networks (Scn) Ltd, High Trees, 15A Salisbury Road, Blandford Forum, Dorset, DT11 7HN Tel: (01258) 480121 Fax: (01258) 455366 E-mail: infa@scnltd.com *Communications trainers*

Systems Controls & Instruments UK Ltd, Manx House, Bousley Rise, Ottershaw, Chertsey, Surrey, KT16 0JX Tel: (01932) 875225 Fax: (01932) 875227 E-mail: info@sciuk.co.uk *Manufacturer & distributor of commercial, residential controls & control systems for air-conditioning*

Systems Created Ltd, Old Chapel, White Horse Road, East Bergholt, Colchester, CO7 6TU Tel: (01206) 299228 Fax: (01206) 299232 *Computer systems & consultants*

Systems For Dentists Ltd, 90 High Street, Gosforth, Newcastle upon Tyne, NE3 1HB Tel: 0191-285 9192 Fax: 0191-285 9192 *Software for dental surgery*

Systems In Micro, 47 Gainsborough Street, Sudbury, Suffolk, CO10 2ET Tel: (01787) 313317 Fax: (01787) 372226 E-mail: admin@sysim.co.uk *Software programmers*

Systems & Information Resources Ltd, 4 Hostle Park, Ilfracombe, Devon, EX34 9HW Tel: (01271) 867555 Fax: (01271) 867999 E-mail: info@softekltd.com *Computer software consultancy & development*

Systems Integration Electronics, 14 Seabeach Lane, Eastbourne, East Sussex, BN22 7NZ Tel: (01323) 647649 E-mail: sales@seacall.org.uk *Radio communications equipment distributors*

Systems Integrators Ltd, 31 Wick Road, Teddington, Middlesex, TW11 9DN Tel: (020) 8614 8070 Fax: (020) 8614 8040 E-mail: enquiries@sys-int.co.uk *Control systems*

Systems Intelligence Ltd, 21 Decimus Park, Kingstanding Way, Tunbridge Wells, Kent, TN2 3GP Tel: (01892) 509940 Fax: (01892) 509941 E-mail: sales@vitechsecurity.co.uk *Security system installers*

Systems Plus, 14 Kintyre, Antrim, BT41 2AN Tel: (028) 9448 7497 Fax: (028) 9448 7497 *Computer systems & software*

The Systems Practice plc, 134-135 High Street, Southampton, SO14 2BR Tel: (023) 8048 0001 Fax: (023) 8048 0002 E-mail: sales@tspplc.com *Software developers*

The Systems Practice P.L.C., Parkside Business Park, Curstead Way, Golborne, Warrington, WA3 3PY Tel: (01942) 270222 Fax: (01942) 275220 E-mail: janet.houghton@tspplc.com *Computer consultants*

Systems & Software Ltd, 85 Alvechurch Road, Birmingham, B31 3PG Tel: 0121-604 7001 Fax: 0121-604 7002 *Computer software company*

Systems Storage, 125 Back Road, Linton, Cambridge, CB1 6UJ Tel: (01223) 892433 Fax: (01223) 893864 E-mail: alfhughes@aol.com

Systems Support Of Cambridge, Great Chesterford Court, Great Chesterford, Saffron Walden, Essex, CB10 1PF Tel: (01799) 531777 Fax: (01799) 531778 *Applemac equipment resellers & computer consultants*

Systems Technology Consultants Ltd, Bedford Street, Stoke-on-Trent, ST1 4PZ Tel: (01782) 286300 Fax: (01782) 280036 E-mail: sytech@ebstar.co.uk *IT forensic investigations*

► Systems Transport Services Ltd, Unit 1a, Court Lane, Iver, Buckinghamshire, SL0 9HL Tel: (01753) 653023 Fax: (01753) 655305 E-mail: transportsts@aol.com

► Systems Valley Ltd, 72 New Bond Street, London, W1S 1RR Tel: (0845) 2579530 Fax: (0845) 2579530 E-mail: info@systemsvalley.com *It strategies*

► Systemsoft Communications Ltd, Lilford Lodge, Lilford, Peterborough, PE8 5SA Tel: (01832) 272049 Fax: (01832) 270028 E-mail: stan.bell@systemssoft.co.uk *Computer software developers*

Systemware Services Ltd, Unit 220, Fort Dunlop, Fort Parkway, Birmingham, B24 9FD Tel: 0121-749 8050 Fax: 0121-749 8075 E-mail: swhitehouse@ssl-uk.com *Manufacturers & distributors of ERP software /ERP Systems*Manufacturing Software and Distribution Software*

Systima Technology Ltd, 7 Prospect Business Centre, Prospect Road, Cowes, Isle of Wight, PO31 7AD Tel: (01983) 248810 Fax: (01983) 248812 E-mail: Shane@systima-technology.co.uk *Systima Technology are a dynamic Website Design and Development company based on the Isle of Wight.**Amongst the many services we offer are Website Design, Database Development, Search Engine Optimisation, Internet Consultancy, E-Commerce Systems and Payment Gateways, IT Network Solutions and Brand Development. We work alongside our clients to enhance their branding and Internet Marketing*

continued

Syston Rolling Shutters Ltd, 33 Albert Street, Syston, Leicester, LE7 2JB Tel: 0116-260 8841 Fax: 0116-264 0846 E-mail: sales@syston.com *Door & shutter manufrs*

► Sytel Ltd, 1-2 Cromwell Court, New Street, Aylesbury, Buckinghamshire, HP20 2PB Tel: (01296) 381200 *Computer software development*

Sytems (Telecom) Ltd, Unit 111 BMG Industrial Estate, Wakefield Road, Liversedge, West Yorkshire, WF15 6BS Tel: (01924) 402333 Fax: (01924) 402334 *Second hand telephone equipment dealers*

T A B Diamond Tools Ltd, 66 Alston Drive, Bradwell Abbey, Milton Keynes, MK13 9HB Tel: (01908) 320770 Fax: (01908) 320770 *Diamond tipped tool manufrs*

T A B Sheet Fabrications Ltd, Unit 3 Galliford Road Industrial Estate, Heybridge, Maldon, Essex, CM9 4XX Tel: (01621) 858848 Fax: (01621) 583847 E-mail: info@tabfab.co.uk *Metalwork fabricators, ductwork, heating & ventilation manufacturers. Also welding TIG/MIG*

► T A Brennan, Dreadnought, Hazel Road, Southampton, SO19 7GA Tel: (023) 8044 5908 Fax: (023) 8068 5704

T A Computer Consultants, 41 Oakmead Road, St. Osyth, Clacton-on-Sea, Essex, CO16 8NW Tel: (01255) 821979 E-mail: help@tacomputers.co.uk *Computer consultants*

► T A D Builders Ltd, Llwynhendy Farm, Llanelli, Dyfed, SA14 9SE Tel: (01554) 752884 Fax: (01554) 745005

T A D Precision Ltd, The Mount Toft, Cambridge, CB3 7RL Tel: (01223) 263421 Fax: (01223) 264135 E-mail: terryeasey@hotmail.co.uk *Precision sheet metalworkers*

T & A Dale, Underhill Farm, Shatterford, Bewdley, Worcestershire, DY12 1TH Tel: (01299) 861285 *Farmers*

T A Durant Ltd, Bidford House, High St, Bidford On Avon, Alcester, Warwickshire, B50 4BH Tel: (01789) 772353 Fax: (01789) 490320 *Jewellery manufrs*

T & A Envelopes Ltd, 10 Moray Court, Kimberley, Nottingham, NG16 2TL Tel: 0115-938 4674 Fax: 0115-945 8348 E-mail: t_a.envelopes@mac.com *Printers of envelopes*

T A Flavell & Son Ltd, 11 Mandale Road, Thornaby, Stockton-on-Tees, Cleveland, TS17 6AW Tel: (01642) 674536 Fax: (01642) 618249 E-mail: dave@taflavell.co.uk *Diesel fuel injection pumps & equipment*

T A G Brand, The Barn, 13-17 Margett Street, Cottenham, Cambridge, CB24 8QY Tel: (01954) 250100 Fax: (01954) 250200 E-mail: info@tagbrand.co.uk *Graphic & exhibition designers & advertising packing services*

T A G Forklift Trucks, Barlow Street, Worsley, Manchester, M28 3BQ Tel: 0161-799 6507 Fax: 0161-799 9010 *Forklift truck hire, installation, maintenance, training*

► T A G Scaffolding, Stanley Street, Glasgow, G41 1JA Tel: 0141-429 2204 Fax: 0141-429 6703

T A Green, 73 High Street, Wincanton, Somerset, BA9 9JZ Tel: (01963) 34221 Fax: (01963) 31301

T A Group Ltd, Blackhouse Industrial Estate, Peterhead, Aberdeenshire, AB42 1BW Tel: (01779) 478515 Fax: (01779) 479722 *Repair industrial instruments*

► T A Henn & Son Ltd, 38-41 Princess Street, Wolverhampton, WV1 1HD Tel: (01902) 428486 Fax: (01902) 420406 E-mail: info@exclusiveessentials.co.uk *Watch & jewellery merchants*

T A Industries Ltd, Gibson Road, Caenby Corner Estate, Hemswell Cliff, Gainsborough, Lincolnshire, DN21 5TL Tel: (01427) 668436 Fax: (01427) 668101 *Compressed air equipment sales, service & supply*

► T A Jervis & Co. Ltd, Holywell Lane, Lightmoor, Telford, Shropshire, TF4 3QJ Tel: (01952) 505778 Fax: (01952) 504520

T & A Joinery, Oakwood House, 36 Wood Lane, Partington, Manchester, M31 4ND Tel: 0161-777 6277 Fax: 0161-777 6277 *Joinery manufrs*

T A Kirkpatrick & Co Ltd, Beltenmont, Kirkpatrick Fleming, Lockerbie, Dumfriesshire, DG11 3NQ Tel: (01461) 800275 Fax: (01461) 800340 E-mail: info@takirkpatrick.com *Structural steelwork manufrs*

► T A Knox Shopfitters Ltd, Thorn Works, Bankfield Road, Woodley, Stockport, Cheshire, SK6 1RH Tel: 0161-430 3308 Fax: 0161-494 0677

T A L Computer Services Ltd, 1 Egham Business Village, Crabtree Road, Egham, Surrey, TW20 8RB Tel: (01784) 434350 Fax: (01784) 470599 E-mail: talcs@talcs.co.uk *Network consultancy services*

► T A L L Security Print Ltd, Unit 2 Pembroke Court, Manor Park, Runcorn, Cheshire, WA7 1TJ Tel: (01928) 579200 Fax: (01928) 579294

T A L Shooting & Scuba Diving, 8 St. Catherines Parade, Fairmile Road, Christchurch, Dorset, BH23 2LQ Tel: (01202) 473030 Fax: (01202) 479600 E-mail: sales@go-diving.co.uk *Fire arms maintenance & repairers*

► T A Law Stonework Contractors, The Bield, Ravenstonedale, Kirkby Stephen, Cumbria, CA17 4NQ Tel: (01539) 623215 Fax: (01539) 623436 E-mail: enquires@masonry.co.uk *Stone masons*

► T & A Logistics Newcastle Ltd, 8 Holystone Grange, Stonelea, Holystone, Newcastle upon Tyne, NE27 0UX Tel: (07968) 725110 Fax: 0191-215 1300 E-mail: sales@talogistics.co.uk *sameday/ nextday courier services*warehousing*general haulage services*air courier service*next day european services to most major cities*

T A M Computer Equipment, 40 Hunter Drive, Bletchley, Milton Keynes, MK2 3LR Tel: (01908) 366929 Fax: (01908) 649009 *Computer repairers*

T A M Engineering, Leverington Common, Leverington, Wisbech, Cambridgeshire, PE13 5JG Tel: (01945) 410494 Fax: (01945) 410476 *Aluminium & steel fabricators*

T A M Leisure Ltd, 180 Kingston Road, New Malden, Surrey, KT3 3RD Tel: (020) 8949 5435 Fax: (020) 8336 1418 E-mail: sales@tamleisure.co.uk *Trailer & caravan fitting distributors*

▶ T A & N White Ltd, Park Road Industrial Estate, Consett, County Durham, DH8 5PY Tel: (01207) 504755 Fax: (01207) 580659 E-mail: info@whitescommercialvehicles.co.uk *Sell used commercial vehicles, trucks, vans & specialist vehicles*

T A P Film & Video Ltd, 39 Hillmarton Road, London, N7 9JD Tel: (020) 7700 2212 Fax: (020) 7700 2624 *Film video equipment suppliers*

T A Plastics Ltd, Tudhoe Industrial Estate, Spennymoor, County Durham, DL16 6TL Tel: (01388) 814858 Fax: (01388) 819534 E-mail: sales@taplastics.co.uk *Plastics fabricators & distributors*

T A (Printers) Ltd, 43-45 Milford Road, Reading, RG1 8LG Tel: 0118-957 5442 Fax: 0118-958 3899 E-mail: taprinters@i12.com *Lithographic printers*

T A Ronan & Co., 2d Askew Road, London, W12 9BH Tel: (020) 8749 3051 Fax: (020) 8749 5618 *Electrical & civil engineers*

T A Savery & Co. Ltd, Bracebridge Street, Birmingham, B6 4PF Tel: 0121-380 4514 Fax: 0121-380 4507 E-mail: sales@savery.co.uk *Hydraulic equipment manufrs*

T A V, Thurston Road, Northallerton, North Yorkshire, DL6 2NA Tel: (01609) 760011 Fax: (01609) 783111 E-mail: sales@tavltd.co.uk *Screws & barrels manufrs*

▶ T A Walker Ltd, 168a Loughborough Road, Mountsorrel, Loughborough, Leicestershire, LE12 7AX Tel: (01509) 416602 Fax: (01509) 620064

▶ T A Wells Co Ltd, 268 Hamworth Road, Hounslow, TW3 3UB Tel: (020) 8569 5577

T Alarms, Little Adelaide Farm, Lower Road, East Farleigh, Maidstone, Kent, ME15 0JN Tel: (01622) 729439 Fax: 01622 729439 *Alarm installation & supplier*

T Alun Jones & Son, Danycapel, Dryslwyn, Carmarthen, Dyfed, SA32 8SD Tel: (01558) 668383 Fax: (01558) 668024 *Agricultural machinery retailers*

T B A P.L.C., 174-178 North Gower Street, London, NW1 2NB Tel: (020) 7380 0953 Fax: (020) 7387 9004 E-mail: gen@tbaplc.co.uk *Sales & marketing agency, production, event management*

▶ T & B Book Crafts, 2 Summer Place, Edinburgh, EH3 5NR Tel: 0131-556 7857

T & B Containers Ltd, Broadgate, Wrangle, Boston, Lincolnshire, PE22 9DY Tel: (01205) 270200 Fax: (01205) 270594 *Box manufrs*

T & B Contractors Ltd, Place Farm, Wheathampstead, St. Albans, Hertfordshire, AL4 8SB Tel: (01582) 833633 Fax: (01582) 833899 E-mail: post@tandb-contractors.co.uk *Building contractors*

▶ T B Dunn & Co., Albert House, 308 Albert Drive, Glasgow, G41 5RS Tel: 0141-429 1700 Fax: 0141-420 1397

T B Engineering Ltd, Network House, Perry Road, Harlow, Essex, CM18 7NS Tel: (01279) 418300 Fax: (01279) 418100 *Gear cutters & manufrs*

T B Group Ltd, The Arch, Walney Road, Barrow-in-Furness, Cumbria, LA14 5UT Tel: (01229) 870077 Fax: (01229) 811101 E-mail: brady@brady.furness.co.uk *Warehousing*

T B P Tools Ltd, 106-108 Lombard Street, Birmingham, B12 0QR Tel: 0121-622 1762 Fax: 0121-622 1174 E-mail: tbp@btconnect.com *Press tools, jigs, fixtures manufrs*

T B S Engineering, 11 Maylan Road, Earlstrees Industrial Estate, Corby, Northamptonshire, NN17 4DR Tel: (01536) 262697 Fax: (01536) 401053 *Pipework fabricators*

T B S Haulage, Mercia Way, Foxhills Industrial Estate, Scunthorpe, South Humberside, DN15 8RE Tel: (01724) 858999

▶ T B Staircases, Unit 1b Millenium Business Unit, Dawlish Business Park, Dawlish, Devon, EX7 0NH Tel: (01626) 866435 Fax: (01626) 866445 E-mail: tb.staircases@virgin.net *Specialising in the manufacture of high quality, made-to-measure timber staircases. Supplying to Trade, Residential and Builders. We offer excellent customer service with advice on design and building regulations and free estimates. Delivery and fitting service available if required.*

T B T UK Ltd, Gorsey Lane, Coleshill, Birmingham, B46 1JU Tel: (01675) 463350 *Deep hole drilling machine manufrs*

T & B Welding Products (UK) Ltd, Unit 1B, Ravenstor Road, Wirksworth Industrial Estate, Wirksworth, Matlock, Derbyshire, DE4 4FY Tel: (01629) 823779 Fax: (01629) 824961 *Mig, tig welding & plasma cutting torches manufrs*

▶ T B Williamson, Unit 39 Mayfield Industrial Estate, Dalkeith, Midlothian, EH22 4AD Tel: 0131-654 2900 Fax: 0131-654 2909

T Bacon, Spink Hall Farm, Spink Hall Lane, Stocksbridge, Sheffield, S36 1FL Tel: 0114-288 2556 Fax: 0114-288 2556 *Building merchants*

▶ T Baden Hardstaff Ltd, Hillside, Gotham Road, Kingston-on-Soar, Nottingham, NG11 0DF Tel: 0115-983 1234 Fax: 0115-983 1225

T Baden Hardstaff Ltd, Hillside, Gotham Road, Kingston-on-Soar, Nottingham, NG11 0DF Tel: 0115-983 1234 Fax: 0115-983 1225 *Transport company*

▶ T Barry Haulage, Broadway Trading Estate, Broadway Lane, South Cerney, Cirencester, Gloucestershire, GL7 5UH Tel: (01285) 860665 Fax: (01285) 862137

T Blackshaw, Conway St Depot, Conway Street, Stockport, Cheshire, SK5 7PS Tel: 0161-480 6040 Fax: 0161-474 7225 E-mail: sales@tomblackshaw.com *Roofing materials merchants*

T Bland, Sandars Road, Heapham Road Industrial Estate, Gainsborough, Lincolnshire, DN21 1RZ Tel: (01427) 610116 Fax: (01427) 810287 E-mail: t.bland@virgin.net *Specialist welding engineers*

▶ T Bourne & Son Ltd, Draper Street, Tunbridge Wells, Kent, TN4 0PG Tel: (01892) 528271

▶ T Brown Group Ltd, 24 High Street, Ewell, Epsom, Surrey, KT17 1SJ Tel: (020) 8394 1166 Fax: (020) 8393 9947

T Burden, New Workshop, Wood Lane, North Wheatley, Retford, Nottinghamshire, DN22 9BQ Tel: (01427) 880094 Fax: (01427) 880094 *Agricultural engineers*

T C Ltd, PO Box 130, Uxbridge, Middlesex, UB8 2YS Tel: (01895) 252222 Fax: (01895) 273540 E-mail: sales@tc.co.uk *Thermocouple cable accessories* Also at: Chesterfield

T C C Data Management, Humber Road, Barton-upon-Humber, South Humberside, DN18 5BW Tel: (01652) 661063 Fax: (01652) 636952 E-mail: tom.monks@birse.co.uk *Provide cost effective scanning solutions*

T C D Ltd, 31 Sinclair Road, London, W14 0NS Tel: (020) 7603 1325 Fax: (020) 7603 1536 *General international merchants*

T C & D Technical Services Ltd, Kirkcroft Farm, Thorpe Hesley, Rotherham, South Yorkshire, S61 2RP Tel: 0114-246 9410 Fax: 0114-257 7935 *Industrial cleaners & painters*

T C Dolman Construction Ltd, Broad Street, Bilston, West Midlands, WV14 0BZ Tel: (01902) 492792 Fax: (01902) 403618 *General builders*

▶ T C Fabrications Ripley Ltd, Whiteley Road, Ripley, Derbyshire, DE5 3QL Tel: (01773) 513911 Fax: (01773) 512811 E-mail: dave@tcfabs.co.uk *Sheet metal & medium fabrication engineers*

T C Hillier, 17 High Street, Oxted, Surrey, RH8 9LW Tel: (01883) 712355 Fax: (01883) 714966 *Agricultural & horticultural sales & repair*

T C J Designs, 16 Stonegate, York, YO1 8AS Tel: (01904) 611366 Fax: (01904) 611399 *Jewellery retailers*

▶ T C L Transport Engineers Ltd, Elmfield Business Park, Lotherton Way, Garforth, Leeds, LS25 2JY Tel: 0113-286 3322 Fax: 0113-286 4422 *Road tankers manufrs*

T C M S Ltd, St. Shads Industrial Estate, Brearley Street, Hockley, Birmingham, B19 3NP Tel: 0121-333 5824 Fax: 0121-333 5829 E-mail: tcmsmidland@ukonline.co.uk *Cleaning contractors*

T C Morgan, Caecwm, Huntington, Kington, Herefordshire, HR5 3PQ Tel: (01544) 370277 Fax: (01544) 370277 E-mail: tcmorganconst@aol.com *Steel fabricators & contruction services*

▶ T C Munro, The Hall, George Street, Falkirk, FK2 7EY Tel: (01324) 623729 Fax: (01324) 620693 E-mail: info@tcmunro.co.uk *Sale & erecting of greenhouses & garden sheds*

T C P Construction, River Road, Barking, Essex, IG11 0DG Tel: (020) 8594 9228 Fax: (020) 8594 9227 *Sign contractors & services*

T C Plastic Fabrications Ltd, Hawkmill Industrial Estate, Little Green Lane, Small Heath, Birmingham, B9 5BE Tel: 0121-773 2044 Fax: 0121-766 6623 E-mail: tom@tcplastics.wanadoo.co.uk *Plastic fabricators & tank manufrs*

T C Plating Co. Ltd, Unit 6b Ada St Workshops, 8 Andrews Road, London, E8 4QN Tel: (020) 7249 2603 Fax: (020) 7923 3640 *Silver-plate manufrs*

▶ T C Power Ltd, Unit 23 Priory Tec Park Saxon Way, Priory Park, Hessle, North Humberside, HU13 9PB Tel: (01482) 629550 Fax: (01482) 350670 E-mail: sales@turbinecontrols.com

T C Repair & Supply, Sheddingdean Industrial Centre, Marchants Way, Burgess Hill, West Sussex, RH15 8QY Tel: (01444) 242564 Fax: (01444) 236683 E-mail: info@tcrepair.com *Tank cleaning services*

T & C Robinson, Tattershall Road, Billinghay, Lincoln, LN4 4BN Tel: (01526) 860436 Fax: (01526) 861352 E-mail: sales@saddleforce9.co.uk *Saddlery waterproof cover manufrs*

T & C Robinson, 4 St Marys Street, Stamford, Lincolnshire, PE9 2DE Tel: (01780) 755378 Fax: (01780) 755378 E-mail: sales@no1saddlers.co.uk *Leather goods suppliers*

T C S Media (North) Ltd, Camellia House, 76 Water Lane, Wilmslow, Cheshire, SK9 5BB Tel: (01625) 536795 Fax: (01625) 536796 E-mail: staff@tcsnorth.com *Advertising services*

T C S (UK) Limited, Penmore House, Hasland Road, Chesterfield, Derbyshire, S41 0SY Tel: (01246) 279066 Fax: (01246) 274115 E-mail: dave@tcsukltd.com *TCS (UK) Limited has been established since 1994 with experience in various industries. We offer numerous services such as periodic inspection, portable appliance testing, electrical installations work, and thermographic services. High quality and flexible service guaranteed.*

▶ T C Threads Ltd, King Edward Street, Hucknall, Nottingham, NG15 7JR Tel: 0115-968 0089 Fax: 0115-968 0346 E-mail: sales@tcthreads.ltd.uk *Sell embroidery thread & accessories*

T C W Services Controls Ltd, Bradshaw Works, Bradshaw Road, Honley, Holmfirth, HD9 6DT Tel: (01484) 662865 Fax: (01484) 667574 E-mail: sales@tcw-services.co.uk *Gas safety equipment manufrs*

▶ T & C Williams (Builders) Ltd, 5-11 Norton Lees Lane, Sheffield, S8 9BA Tel: 0114-255 7387

T Choithram & Sons (London) Ltd, Old Marconi Factory, Lancelot Road, Wembley, Middlesex, HA0 2BG Tel: (020) 8903 8311 Fax: (020) 8900 1426 *Packers of pulses*

T Christien, 46 Strawberry Vale, Twickenham, TW1 4SE Tel: (020) 8892 3621 Fax: (020) 8891 5946 E-mail: terry@cartoonology.com *Animated cartoons designers & producers for business*

T Clarke plc, Stanhope House, 116-118 Walworth Road, London, SE17 1JY Tel: (020) 7358 5000 Fax: (020) 7701 6265 E-mail: info@tclarke.co.uk *Electrical contractors*

▶ T Clarke & Sons Joinery Ltd, The Workshop, Slippery Gowt Lane, Wyberton, Boston, Lincolnshire, PE21 7AA Tel: (01205) 354629 Fax: (01205) 358214 E-mail: sales@tclarkejoinery.co.uk

T Cole & Son, 18 Meadowbank Road, Carrickfergus, County Antrim, BT38 8YF Tel: (028) 9336 0844 Fax: (028) 9336 0855 E-mail: sales@tcoleandson.co.uk *Weighing equipment distributors*

T Craine, 2 Barn Court, Thicketford Road, Bolton, BL2 2LN Tel: (01204) 525830 *Saddlery manufrs & retail*

T Crossling & Co. Ltd, Portrack Grange Road, Stockton-on-Tees, Cleveland, TS18 2PF Tel: (01642) 616996 Fax: (01642) 616231 E-mail: sales@crossling.co.uk *Plumbers & engineers merchant*

▶ T D C Aberdeen Ltd, Unit 5, Bankhead Avenue, Bucksburn, Aberdeen, AB21 9ET Tel: (01224) 710077 Fax: (01224) 710088 E-mail: info@tdcaberdeen.co.uk *Electrical, electronic mechanical engineering*

T D C I, Sopwith Close, Drayton Fields Industrial Esta, Daventry, Northamptonshire, NN11 8EA Tel: (01327) 312570 Fax: (01327) 312721 E-mail: info@tdci.eu.com *Computer consultants*

T D C Services, T D C House, Ferry Hill, Ewloe, Deeside, Clwyd, CH5 3AW Tel: (01244) 534521 Fax: (01244) 533562 E-mail: sales@tdcservices.co.uk *Industrial cleaning equipment*

T & D Cruickshanks, Canal Street, Kirkintilloch, Glasgow, G66 1QY Tel: 0141-776 2043 Fax: 0141-777 7646 E-mail: tandd.cruickshanks@virgin.net *Blacksmiths & light structural engineers*

T D Distribution (UK) Ltd, 169 New Chester Road, Wirral, Merseyside, CH62 4RB Tel: 0151-643 1171 Fax: 0151-643 1483 E-mail: info@tddistribution.com *Industrial paint suppliers*

▶ T & D Electronics, 5 Liscombe Road, Dunstable, Bedfordshire, LU5 4PL Tel: (01582) 672134 E-mail: enquiries@tnd-electronics.co.uk *Repairs To All TV, VCR, Hi-Fi And Digibox Equipment. sky Installations. Freeview Aerials Fitted. Tuning-In Service. All Available 7 Days A Week.*

T D Fitchett, Redland Industrial Estate, Station Hill, St. Georges, Telford, Shropshire, TF2 9JX Tel: (01952) 620434 Fax: (01952) 610510 *Triumph motorcar spares retailers & manufrs*

▶ T D G, PO Box 1, Kirkcaldy, Fife, KY1 2SB Tel: (01592) 647405

▶ T D G, Caton Road, Lancaster, LA1 3PE Tel: (01524) 35024 Fax: (01524) 36758 E-mail: france@tdg.co.uk

T D G European Chemical Division, Picow Farm Road, Runcorn, Cheshire, WA7 4UW Tel: (01928) 580588 Fax: (01928) 565968 *Haulage & warehousing contractors*

T D G European Chemicals, Euro Terminal, Westinghouse Road, Trafford Park, Manchester, M17 1PY Tel: 0161-932 6900 Fax: 0161-932 6990 E-mail: businessenquiries@tdg.co.uk *Road transport, haulage & freight services*

T D G Novacold, South View Road, Willand, Cullompton, Devon, EX15 2RU Tel: (01884) 820008 Fax: (01884) 821372 *Storage & distribution of frozen goods services*

T D G Storage UK, Chancel Lane, Pinhoe, Exeter, EX4 8JS Tel: (01392) 467135 Fax: (01392) 466233 E-mail: joneske@tdg.co.uk *Temperature controlled storage services*

T D G Storage UK Ltd, Wisbech Road, King's Lynn, Norfolk, PE30 5LQ Tel: (01553) 761166 Fax: (01553) 767447 E-mail: wayt@tdg.co.uk *Temperature controlled storage services*

▶ T D G Storage UK, 339&361 Prescot Road, Old Swan, Liverpool, L13 3BS Tel: 0151-259 4505 Fax: 0151-228 3634 E-mail: breenk@tdg.co.uk *Temperature controlled storage services*

▶ T D G UK Storage, 350 Renfrew Road, Glasgow, G51 4SP Tel: 0141-445 2933 Fax: 0141-445 1038

T D G UK Storage, Stock Office, Portland Road, Retford, Nottinghamshire, DN22 7NR Tel: (01777) 702616 Fax: (01777) 860521 E-mail: wayt@tdg.co.uk *Temperature controlled storage* Also at: Branches throughout the U.K.

▶ T D Heating & Pipework Ltd, Sneyd Street, Stoke-on-Trent, ST6 2NZ Tel: (01782) 264279 Fax: (01782) 204692

T D I Engineering, Block 7 Unit 2 Moorpark Industrial Estate, Moorpark Place, Stevenston, Ayrshire, KA20 3JT Tel: (01294) 471769 *Steel fabricators*

T D Jenkinson, 119 Constitution Street, Edinburgh, EH6 7AE Tel: 0131-554 6079 Fax: 0131-554 6079 *Joinery manufrs*

T D Joinery, Unit 65 Millmead Industrial Estate, Millmead Road, London, N17 9UU Tel: (020) 8808 8215 *Joinery*

T D K Electronics, T D K House, 5-7 Queensway, Redhill, RH1 1YB Tel: (01737) 773773 Fax: (01737) 781360 *Electronic & optical component manufacturers & sales*

T D K Electronics Europe Ltd, Confort House, 5-7 Queensway, Redhill, RH1 1YB Tel: (01737) 781372 Fax: (01737) 773810 *Electrical components suppliers*

T D K Semi Conductor Co., 758-760 Great Cambridge Road, Enfield, Middlesex, EN1 3RN Tel: (020) 8443 7061 Fax: (020) 8443 7022 E-mail: neil.harrison@tsc.tdk.com *Semiconductor manufrs*

T D K Systems Europe Ltd, 126 Colindale Avenue, London, NW9 5HD Tel: (020) 8938) 1000 Fax: (020) 8905 8606 E-mail: info@tdksys.com Sales Contact: J. Robson *Wireless communications, PC interface cards & Bluetooth wireless technology systems*

T D Ladd & Son, Belle Vue, Clynderwen, Dyfed, SA66 7NQ Tel: (01437) 563217 Fax: (01437) 563217 *Machinery, plumbing merchants & agricultural hardware*

▶ T D Mckane & Son, 15 Drumquin Road, Castlederg, County Tyrone, BT81 7PX Tel: (028) 8167 0870 Fax: (028) 8167 0870

T D O C Ltd, 63-71 Roe Road, Northampton, NN1 4PH Tel: (01604) 233777 Fax: (01604) 234437 *Office furniture suppliers*

T & D Plastics Ltd, 2 Trinity Road North, West Bromwich, West Midlands, B70 6NB Tel: 0121-553 5605 Fax: 0121-553 1897 *Plastic vacuum forming manufrs*

▶ T D R Mechanical Services Ltd, Tansey Green Road, Brierley Hill, West Midlands, DY5 4TL Tel: (01384) 263463 Fax: (01384) 76245

T D R Transmissions, 5 Hunsley Street, Sheffield, S4 8DY Tel: 0114-262 6050 Fax: 0114-243 1826 E-mail: sales@tdrtrans.demon.co.uk *Gear box sales & reconditioning specialists*

T D S Exhibition Design, 29 Grosvenor Way, Droitwich, Worcestershire, WR9 7SR Tel: (01905) 778379 Fax: (01905) 778379 *Exhibition stand designers*

T & D Security Systems, 103 Glasgow Road, Bathgate, West Lothian, EH48 2QN Tel: (0800) 3890219 Fax: (01506) 650611 E-mail: sales@tdsecurity.co.uk *CCTV & burglar alarm installers*

T D T Technology Ltd, Unit 20 Woodside Park, Rugby, Warwickshire, CV21 2NP Tel: (01788) 570411 Fax: (01788) 567632 E-mail: sales@tdt-technology.co.uk *Sales & service duplomatic indexing turrets & mc tool accessories*

▶ T Darby Electrical Ltd, Clocktower Buildings, Shore Road, Warsash, Southampton, SO31 9GQ Tel: (01489) 559955 Fax: (01489) 559993

T Denman & Sons Melton Mowbray Ltd, Cardigan House, Burton Street, Melton Mowbray, Leicestershire, LE13 1AW Tel: (01664) 569991 Fax: (01664) 410451 E-mail: enquiries@tdenman.co.uk *Builders & contractors*

▶ T Denne & Sons Ltd, Hanover Mill, The Forstal, Mersham, Ashford, Kent, TN25 6NU Tel: (01233) 720871 Fax: (01233) 721200 *Agricultural merchants*

T Denne & Sons Ltd, Whitehill, Bilting, Ashford, Kent, TN25 4HB Tel: (01233) 812237 Fax: (01233) 813327 E-mail: p.den@btinternet.com *Agricultural merchants*

T Dixon & Son, Newbiggin-on-Lune, Kirkby Stephen, Cumbria, CA17 4NT Tel: (01539) 623229 Fax: (01539) 623229 *Agricultural merchants*

▶ T Donohoe Builders Ltd, 19-21 Chamberlain Street, Londonderry, BT48 6LR Tel: (028) 7126 7244 Fax: (028) 7137 1550

T Dunwoody & Partners, Dunwoody House, 396 Kenton Road, Harrow, Middlesex, HA3 9DH Tel: (020) 8621 2100 Fax: (020) 8621 2111 E-mail: admin@dunwoody.uk.com *Consulting engineers & building services*

T E C, Trinity Bus Park, Turner Way, Wakefield, West Yorkshire, WF2 8EF Tel: (01924) 387979 Fax: (01924) 387989 *Semi conductor manufrs*

T E C International Ltd, Molborough House, Molborough Road, Lancing, West Sussex, BN15 8UF Tel: (01903) 851920 Fax: (01903) 851910 E-mail: paulw@tecint.co.uk *Consultants to the transport trade*

▶ T E C Marine Mouldings Ltd, Prout Industrial Estate, Point Road, Canvey Island, Essex, SS8 7TJ Tel: (01268) 680606 Fax: (01268) 684592 *Boat builders & repairers*

T.E.D. (Recruitment) Ltd, 2nd Floor, 277-279 Bethnal Green Road, London, E2 6AH Tel: (020) 7613 5555 Fax: (020) 7613 1191 E-mail: info@tedrecruitment.com *Technical recruitment agency*

T & E Fabrications Ltd, Mucklow Hill, Halesowen, West Midlands, B62 8DL Tel: 0121-585 7600 Fax: 0121-585 7601 E-mail: teltd@btconnect.com *Carpet display stand manufrs*

T E Hirst, Unit 1-2 Norristhorpe Lane, Liversedge, West Yorkshire, WF15 7AZ Tel: (01924) 401852 Fax: (01924) 412181 *General fabricators*

T E Hughes & Son Warrington Ltd, Crossley Street, Warrington, WA1 2PF Tel: (01925) 634348 Fax: (01925) 234405 *Engineers merchants*

▶ T E I Ltd, Phoenix House, Forstal Road, Aylesford, Kent, ME20 7AU Tel: (01622) 792870 Fax: (01622) 792481 E-mail: blackwoodi@tei.co.uk

T E K Group, Millennium House, 30 Junction Road, Sheffield, S11 8XB Tel: 0114-263 1000 Fax: 0114-263 1991 *Management consultants mergers*

T E K Seating Ltd, 7 Spa Industrial Park, Longfield Road, Tunbridge Wells, Kent, TN2 3EN Tel: (01892) 515028 Fax: (01892) 529751 E-mail: sales@tekseating.co.uk *TEK, the UK's largest independent, after-market vehicle seating company, supplies a comprehensive range of seating for the commercial, construction, agricultural and marine markets from some of the world's leading seat manufacturers. For a reliable, individual service, TEK has all the answers.* Also at: Sheffield

T E L Engineering Ltd, Newby Road, Hazel Grove, Stockport, Cheshire, SK7 5DA Tel: 0161-456 6545 Fax: 0161-456 3810 E-mail: mail@trolexengineering.co.uk Principal Export Areas: Asia Pacific, Central Asia, Middle East, Africa, Central/East Europe & West Europe *Slip ring & cable reeling drum manufrs*

▶ T E Leece & Son Ltd, Main Road, Colby, Isle of Man, IM9 4LR Tel: (01624) 832051 Fax: (01624) 834111

▶ T E Mears Ltd, Feltham Hill Road, Feltham, Middlesex, TW13 7ND Tel: (020) 8890 2853

T & E Neville Ltd, Neville House, 301 Marsh Road, Luton, LU3 2RZ Tel: (01582) 573496 Fax: (01582) 490216 E-mail: enquiries@nevilleconstruction.co.uk *Building construction workers*

T E Penny & Co. Ltd, Gosforth Close, Sunderland Road Industrial Estate, Sandy, Bedfordshire, SG19 1RB Tel: (01767) 681717 Fax: (01767) 680260 *Thermographic printers*

T E R Instruments Ltd, 2-6 Peel Lane, Astley, Tyldesley, Manchester, M29 7QX Tel: (01942) 882275 Fax: (01942) 897958 E-mail: info@ter.co.uk *Instrument calibration services*

T E S Ltd, Lancaster House, Bow Lane, Leyland, PR25 4YA Tel: (01772) 901901 Fax: (01772) 901902 E-mail: info@tes.ltd.uk *Communication solution providers, specialising in two way radio*

Company Information

T & E Signs, Unit 4b Nalken House Eley Estate, Nobel Road, London, N18 3BH Tel: (020) 8345 7007 Fax: (020) 8345 7117 *Sign making*

▶ T E Solutions, Unit 44 Canal Bridge Enterprise Centre, Ellesmere Port, CH65 4EH Tel: 0151 3562010 *Sewing machines repairers*

T E Stone Ltd, 82-84 West Street, St. Philips, Bristol, BS2 0BP Tel: 0117-955 5144 Fax: 0117-941 2233 *Engineers' fastener distrbutors*

T E Watson & Son, Front Street, Blyth, Northumberland, NE24 4HN Tel: (01670) 823357 Fax: (01670) 823357 *Steel fabrications*

T Eccleston & Son Leigh Ltd, Welch Hill Street, Leigh, Lancashire, WN7 4DU Tel: (01942) 672993 Fax: (01942) 261964 *Sheet metalwork engineers*

T Edson & Sons Ltd, Main Road, Plumtree, Nottingham, NG12 5NB Tel: 0115-937 2247 Fax: 0115-937 2486E-mail: sales@edsons.co.uk *Joinery manufrs*

T F C Cable Assemblies Ltd, Excelsior Park, Wishaw, Lanarkshire, ML2 0ER Tel: (01698) 355017 Fax: (01698) 350559 E-mail: info@tfcasm.co.uk *Electrical contractors*

▶ T F D (Scotland) Ltd, 2 Rennie Place, College Milton, East Kilbride, Glasgow, G74 5HD Tel: (01355) 268110 E-mail: info@tfdscotland.co.uk *Windows & conservatories*

T F Keller & Sons Ltd, 24 Cattle Market St, Norwich, NR1 3DY Tel: (01603) 624681 Fax: (01603) 663790 E-mail: info@modelmarque.com *Model retailers & distributors*

▶ T F L, Goland Road, Ballygawley, Dungannon, County Tyrone, BT70 2LA Tel: (07767) 640774 Fax: (028) 8556 7089 E-mail: hblake@tfl.eu.com *Enclosures & Cabins for communications & electrical equipment for cable, cell sites, Rail ect*

T F M Engineering, 1 Ghyll Mill, Beehive Lane, New Hutton, Kendal, Cumbria, LA8 0AJ Tel: (01539) 733881 Fax: (01539) 721616 *Atv trailers & equipment manufrs*

▶ T F S, 127 Cabin Lane, Oswestry, Shropshire, SY11 2PF Tel: (07811) 768841 E-mail: nostromo127@hotmail.com *garden landscaping services*

T F & S L Textiles Ltd, 114 Raleigh Street, Nottingham, NG7 4DJ Tel: 0115-978 0515 Fax: 0115-978 5825 *Yarn merchants*

T F Sammon Plant Hire Ltd, 138 Downhills Park Road, London, N17 6BP Tel: (020) 8881 3572 Fax: (020) 8881 3572 E-mail: csammon@tiscali.co.uk *Plant hire, JCB's, diggers, excavation, site clearing.*

T & F Steel Designs, Ross Street, Brierfield, Nelson, Lancashire, BB9 5LQ Tel: (01282) 612663 Fax: (01282) 612663 *Steel fabricators*

T F X Automotive Ltd, St. Clements Road, Nechells, Birmingham, B7 5AE Tel: 0121-322 2500 Fax: 0121-322 2501 *Manufacturers of control cables*

▶ T Findlay Ltd, 1 Mansion Street, Cambuslang, Glasgow, G72 7JN Tel: 0141-641 6412

▶ T Frost (Bawtry), Home Farm Barn, Winkburn, Newark, Nottinghamshire, NG22 8PQ Tel: (01636) 636981 Fax: (01636) 636643 E-mail: sales@tfrost.co.uk *Racing saddlers, manufacturers of fine horse clothing & racing colours*

T G & A L Evans, Cross Inn Hall, Llanfihangel-Ar-Arth, Pencader, Dyfed, SA39 9JX Tel: (01559) 384304 *Mobile saw milling*

T G Aviation Ltd, Manston Airport, Manston, Ramsgate, Kent, CT12 5BN Tel: (01843) 823656 Fax: (01843) 822024 E-mail: info@tgaviation.com *Aviation & flying training*

T G B Cleaning Supplies Ltd, 370 Northolt Road, Harrow, Middlesex, HA2 8ES Tel: (020) 8423 2155 Fax: (020) 8423 6409 E-mail: tgb@tgb.co.uk *Hygiene & industrial cleaning supplies*

▶ T G Baker (Sound) Ltd, 173-175 Glasgow Road, Clydebank, Dunbartonshire, G81 1LQ Tel: 0141-941 3399 Fax: 0141-952 6003

T G Builders Merchants, Tattenhall Road, Tattenhall, Chester, CH3 9BD Tel: (01829) 770421 Fax: (01829) 770879 E-mail: admin@tggroup.co.uk *Builders & agricultural merchants* Also at: Ellesmere, Northwich & Oswestry

▶ T G Can Technology, 34 Burners Lane, Kiln Farm, Milton Keynes, MK11 3HB Tel: (01908) 561444

T G Contractors Holbeach Ltd, 21 Western Avenue, Holbeach, Spalding, Lincolnshire, PE12 7QD Tel: (01406) 422500 Fax: (01406) 422784 *Building & civil engineers*

▶ T G Cruse, Nettwood Farm, Nett Road, Shrewton, Salisbury, SP3 4HB Tel: (01980) 620369 Fax: (01980) 620821

T G Engineering, Grove Street, Cheltenham, Gloucestershire, GL50 3LZ Tel: (01242) 235403 Fax: (01242) 226637 *Spark erosion machines services*

T & G Engineering Co. Ltd, Unit 14 Camphill Industrial Estate, Camphill Road, West Byfleet, Surrey, KT14 6EW Tel: (01932) 353228 Fax: (01932) 349692 E-mail: sales@tgengineering.co.uk *Precision engineers*

T G I Great Britain, 16 Swinton La, St.Johns, Worcester, WR2 4JT Tel: (01905) 748222 Fax: (01905) 748220 E-mail: charlesbone@btinternet.com *Design & pre-press for printing*

T & G Irrigation, 175 Westgate Road, Belton, Doncaster, South Yorkshire, DN9 1QA Tel: (01427) 874200 Fax: (01427) 875333 E-mail: david@oakdale.uk.com *Irrigation contractors service*

T G Lewis Ltd, 15 Staveley Way, Brixworth Industrial Estate, Brixworth, Northampton, NN6 9EU Tel: (01604) 881966 Fax: (01604) 882318 *Textile slitting & leather trimmings manufrs*

T G Lynes Ltd, 115 Brancroft Way, Enfield, Middlesex, EN3 7QE Tel: (0845) 0716071 Fax: (020) 7278 1560 E-mail: sales@tglynes.co.uk *Heating equipment stockists*

T G M Resource, Technology House, Chasewater Court, Corbett Road, Chasewater Heaths Business Park, Burntwood, Staffordshire, WS7 3GL Tel: (01543) 458714 Fax: (01543) 458542 *Computer supplies repairs & upgrades*

▶ T G Martin & Co., Bradshaw Street, Heywood, Lancashire, OL10 1NZ Tel: (01706) 621666 Fax: (01706) 622002 E-mail: sales@embosco.com *Embossing manufrs*

T G S, 4 Armstrong Court, Armstrong Way, Yate, Bristol, BS37 5NG Tel: (01454) 322033 Fax: (01454) 322077 E-mail: tgsbristol@btconnect.com *Sign manufrs*

T G S Coach Works, Balaclava Industrial Estate, Balaclava Road, Bristol, BS16 3LJ Tel: 0117-965 9965 *Commercial vehicle body building*

T G S Doors Ltd, Unit 4 Manor Complex, Kirkby Bank Road, Knowsley Industrial Park, Liverpool, L33 7SY Tel: 0151-548 9890 Fax: 0151-549 2119 *Security doors*

▶ T G Services, Unit 5a Vicarage Farm Business Park, Winchester Road, Fair Oak, Eastleigh, Hampshire, SO50 7HD Tel: (023) 8069 5554 Fax: (01489) 860103 E-mail: enquiries@hotandcool.co.uk *Plumbing and heating specialists in Hampshire. We are happy to undertake installations, servicing, and repairs. We are Corgi and Oftec regestered- we deal with all natural gas, LPG gas and Oil work.*

T G Sussex, Ivy Arch Road, Worthing, West Sussex, BN14 8BX Tel: (01903) 215515 Fax: (01903) 215211 *Precision engineering sub contractor*

T G Welding Ltd, Unit 4 Stone La Industrial Estate, Wimborne, Dorset, BH21 1HB Tel: (01202) 881267 Fax: (01202) 849523 E-mail: tgwelding@yahoo.com *Steel fabricators*

T & G Woodware Ltd, Old Mill Road, Portishead, Bristol, BS20 7BX Tel: (01275) 841841 Fax: (01275) 841800 E-mail: info@tg-woodware.com *Wooden kitchen utensil distributors*

T Gill & Son (Norwich) Ltd, Hall Road, Norwich, NR4 6DR Tel: (01603) 623161 Fax: (01603) 624397 E-mail: gills@tgillnorwich.freeserve.co.uk *Building contractors*

T Good & Sons Ltd, 36 Vulcan Way, New Addington, Croydon, CR0 9UG Tel: (01689) 848211 Fax: (01689) 841069 E-mail: dave@tgood.co.uk *Structural steelwork & stockholders*

▶ T Guy Ltd, Guys Industrial Estate, Tollgate Road, Burscough, Ormskirk, Lancashire, L40 8TG Tel: (01704) 893304 Fax: (01704) 893603

T H Companies Ltd, 1 Moat Farm Business Center, Turkey Cock Lane, Stanway, Colchester, CO3 8ND Tel: (01206) 212825 Fax: (01206) 212824 E-mail: sales@thcompanies.co.uk *Electrical air conditioning engineers*

T H Dick & Co Ltd, Church Row, Cleveland St, Hull, HU8 7BD Tel: (01482) 329652 Fax: (01482) 589986 E-mail: info@thdick.co.uk Principal Export Areas: Worldwide *Iron castings manufrs*

T H E Section Bending Co. Ltd, Houghton Road, North Anston Trading Estate, North Anston, Sheffield, S25 4JJ Tel: (01909) 550080 Fax: (01909) 550114 E-mail: sales@thebending.co.uk *Section bending services*

T H F Joinery, Express Way, Hambridge Lane, Newbury, Berkshire, RG14 5TU Tel: (01635) 42588 Fax: (01635) 46681 *Joinery manufrs*

T H Fabrications Ltd, Unit 22 Healey New Mills, Healey Road, Ossett, West Yorkshire, WF5 8NF Tel: (01924) 266599 Fax: (01924) 266599 *Steel fabricators*

T H Findings Ltd, 42 Hylton Street, Birmingham, B18 6HN Tel: 0121-554 9889 Fax: 0121-551 7588 *Jewellery findings wholesalers*

T H G Engineering Services (Chepstow) Ltd, Rivendell, Rockwood Road, Chepstow, Gwent, NP16 5DT Tel: (01291) 624134 *Maintenance services*

T H Holroyd Ltd, Unit 15, Phoebe Lane Mills, Halifax, West Yorkshire, HX3 9EX Tel: (01422) 354793 Fax: (01422) 354255 *Thermal insulation specialists & asbestos removers*

T H Horn Ltd, Copthorne Farm, Woods Lane, Eagland Hill, Preston, PR3 6BB Tel: (01995) 600150 *Agricultural engineers*

T H Jordan Ltd, 3 Millar Street, Belfast, BT6 8JZ Tel: (028) 9045 0866 Fax: (028) 9073 2587 E-mail: sales@thjordanltd.com *General & commercial printers*

▶ T H Kenyon Gatwick Ltd, 1 Building 583b, Perimeter Road South, London Gatwick Airport, Gatwick, West Sussex, RH6 0PQ Tel: (01293) 544300 Fax: (01293) 567786

T H Kenyon & Sons plc, Kenyon House, 14a Hockerill Street, Bishop's Stortford, Hertfordshire, CM23 2DW Tel: (01279) 858700 Fax: (01279) 653454 *Building refurbishment contractors & decorating services*

T H March & Co. Ltd, 10-12 Ely Place, London, EC1N 6RY Tel: (020) 7405 0009 Fax: (020) 7404 4629 E-mail: insurance@thmarch.co.uk *Insurance brokers*

T H Martin Ltd, 112 Walter Road, Swansea, SA1 5QQ Tel: (01792) 466410 Fax: (01792) 641887 E-mail: ianmartin@thmartin.com *Financial advisers*

T H P E Ltd, 7 Beighton Street, Sutton-in-Ashfield, Nottinghamshire, NG17 4EG Tel: (01623) 556660 Fax: (01623) 409500 E-mail: thpesales@supanet.com *Hydraulic, pneumatic, electromechanical systems & component services*

T & H Plant Repair Ltd, Oxcroft Bank, Moulton Chapel, Spalding, Lincolnshire, PE12 0XT Tel: (01406) 380029 Fax: (01406) 380336 *Plant equipment repairs services*

T H Quirk (Plant Hire), Cess Road, Martham, Great Yarmouth, Norfolk, NR29 4RF Tel: (01493) 748178 Fax: (01493) 740201 *Contractors plant hire*

T H S Plastics, 5 Claymore, Tame Valley Industrial Estate, Wilnecote, Tamworth, Staffordshire, B77 5DQ Tel: (01827) 282999 Fax: (01827) 262047 E-mail: sales@ths.plastics.co.uk *UPVC window & door manufrs*

▶ T H S Tools Group, Salisbury House Unit 4, Centurion Business Park, Bessemer Way, Rotherham, South Yorkshire, S60 1FB Tel: (01709) 724000 Fax: (01709) 724014 E-mail: guy.farmer@thstools.co.uk *Buying group*

▶ T H UK Online Marketing, Bedford Heights, Brickhill Drive, Bedford, MK41 7PH Tel: (01234) 219119 Fax: (01234) 271862 E-mail: resources@thuk.co.uk *Web development, design, email marketing, fax broadcasting*

T H White Ltd, Newton, Thornbury, Bristol, BS35 1LG Tel: (01454) 417007 Fax: (01454) 414126 *Agricultural engineers*

T H White Ltd, Tetbury Road, Cirencester, Gloucestershire, GL7 1US Tel: (01285) 653354 Fax: (01285) 885175 *Franchise dealership*

T H White Ltd, Nursteed Road, Devizes, Wiltshire, SN10 3EA Tel: (01380) 722381 Fax: (01380) 729147 E-mail: enquiries@thwhite.co.uk *Lorry mounted crane distributors*

T H White Ltd, Ross Road, Huntley, Gloucester, GL19 3EX Tel: (01452) 830303 Fax: (01452) 830984 *Agricultural engineers*

T H White Ltd, Sherston Works, Knockdown, Tetbury, Gloucestershire, GL8 8QY Tel: (01454) 238181 Fax: (01454) 238772 *Agricultural engineers*

T H White Installation Ltd, 3 Nursteed Road Trading Estate, William Road, Devizes, Wiltshire, SN10 3EW Tel: (01380) 726656 Fax: (01380) 725707 E-mail: thwhite@bigwig.net *Security & fire system installation engineers* Also at: Branches through out the U.K.

T Halliday Engineering Ltd, Orchard Road, Hamworth Road Industrial Estate, Sunbury-on-Thames, Middlesex, TW16 5BZ Tel: (01932) 787862 Fax: (01932) 787839 E-mail: keng@btclick.com *Precision engineers*

T Hendry, 40 Benedict Square, Peterborough, PE4 6GD Tel: (01733) 577617 *Welding services*

T Holland Jewellery Ltd, 5 Warstone Mews, Birmingham, B18 6JB Tel: 0121-236 4658 Fax: 0121-236 4658 *Jewellery manufrs*

T I A Robotic Tooling Solutions, Unit 4C Derby Business Park, Canal Street, Derby, DE1 2RJ Tel: (01332) 204850 Fax: (01332) 204851 E-mail: info@tatem.co.uk Sales Contact: S. Tatem *Robotic tooling manufrs*

T I Engineering, 1 Bookers Lane, Earnley, Chichester, West Sussex, PO20 7JG Tel: (01243) 673659 Fax: (01243) 673659 *Steel fabricators*

▶ T I Group, Glover Industrial Estate, Spire Road, Washington, Tyne & Wear, NE37 3ES Tel: 0191-451 5700 Fax: 0191-451 5730

T I Group Automotive Systems Ltd, Unit 110 Tenth Avenue, Deeside Industrial Park, Deeside, Clwyd, CH5 2UA Tel: (01244) 280488 Fax: (01244) 283640 *Fuel systems manufrs*

▶ T I Group Automotive Systems UK Ltd, Halesfield 9, Telford, Shropshire, TF7 4ET Tel: (01952) 651000 Fax: (01952) 651166 E-mail: mdebono@uk.tiauto.com Principal Export Areas: Worldwide *TI Automotive is the Worlds leading manufacture of small diameter mild steel tubing, with 153 sites worldwide. TI Automotive has a dedicated sales, marketing and distribution unit based at Telford, Shropshire. This centre aims to exceed customer expectations in terms of cost, quality and delivery.*

▶ T I Protective Coatings, Unit 6, Lodge Bank, Crown Lane, Horwich, Bolton, BL6 5HY Tel: (01204) 468080 Fax: (01204) 695188 E-mail: sales@ticoatings.co.uk *Contractors for blasting & coating bridges & structures.*

▶ T I S Insulations, 9 The Pines, Kingswood, Hull, HU7 3GT Tel: (01482) 829888 Fax: (07970) 318994 E-mail: pete@tisinsulation.com *Thermal, Cryogenic & Acoustic Insulation Contractors for the Power Generation, Petro-Chem, Pharmaceutical, Marine & Food/Hygiene industries. All employees hold a current CCNSG safety passport. Full sheet metal working service. Company established since 1985.*

T I S Software Ltd, Regatta Place, Marlow Road, Bourne End, Buckinghamshire, SL8 5TD Tel: (01628) 532565 Fax: (01628) 532514 E-mail: info@tissoft.co.uk *Software suppliers*

T I S Tooling, Unit 16 Abbey Court, Corporation Road, Leicester, LE4 5PW Tel: 0116-261 1220 Fax: 0116-261 2224 E-mail: sales@tistooling.co.uk *Industrial tool distributors*

T I Security Ltd, Enterprise Industrial Estate, Aberford Road, Barwick in Elmet, Leeds, LS15 4EF Tel: 0113-281 2106 Fax: 0113-281 3279 *Security systems installers*

T & I Services UK Ltd, 3 Furtho Manor Farm, Northampton Road, Old Stratford, Milton Keynes, MK19 6NR Tel: (0845) 6008150 Fax: (01908) 265461 E-mail: enquiries@tiservicesuk.com *T & I Services is a provider of globalisation and linguistic services. Our comprehensive and integrated products include multilingual content management solutions, translation, conference interpreting, translation memory and a variety of internationalisation and localisation services. Since its foundation in 1997, by Lucinda Mobaraki, T & I Services has enabled the implementation of global business communication for numerous blue chip companies and Public Service entities. We maintain our headquarters in the U.K., as well as offering support from more than 16 offices in Asia, Europe and North America.*

T & I Stockman Ltd, 19 Holwell Road, Brixham, Devon, TQ5 9NE Tel: (01803) 882385 E-mail: info@stockmanfuneralservice.co.uk *Funeral directors in the South Devon Torbay area including Totnes, Marldon, Newton Abbot, Teignmouth and Bovey Tracy. Funeral services including pre-payment plans and our own service chapel*

T Ireson, Gas Lane, Cricklade, Swindon, SN6 6BY Tel: (01793) 750044 Fax: (01793) 750044 *Vehicle component manufrs*

T J A S Joinery, 42 Parcel Terrace, Derby, DE1 1LY Tel: (01332) 293687 Fax: (01332) 372353 *Joinery manufrs*

T J Agricultural Ltd, Bridge Farm, Holt Lane, Ashby Magna, Lutterworth, Leicestershire, LE17 5NJ Tel: (01455) 202414 Fax: (01455) 202414 *Agricultural services*

T J Avent, Unit 14a Innsworth Technology Park, Innsworth Lane, Gloucester, GL3 1DL Tel: (01452) 530041 Fax: (01452) 530040 *Extrusion tool manufrs*

T J Blackburn & Son, Victoria, Ableton Lane, Severn Beach, Bristol, BS35 4PR Tel: (01454) 632905 Fax: (01454) 632905 *Gates & railings*

T J Browne Ltd, 61 Ashford Road, Swindon, SN1 3NS Tel: (01793) 695752 Fax: (01793) 695752 E-mail: tim_browne@talk21.com *Domestic house extensions*

▶ T & J Building Services Ltd, 144 Curzon Street, Long Eaton, Nottingham, NG10 4FS Tel: 0115-875 2317 E-mail: tandjbuilding@ntlworld.com *General building work & design*

T J Commercials, 10 Doons Road, Cookstown, County Tyrone, BT80 9LL Tel: (028) 8675 1760 Fax: (028) 8675 1760 *Commercial repairs*

T J Cottis Transport, 17 Rawreth Industrial Estate, Rawreth Lane, Rayleigh, Essex, SS6 9RL Tel: (01702) 200119 Fax: (01268) 780026 *Transportation contractors*

T J Dobson, Tattersall Street, Oldham, OL9 6EY Tel: 0161-624 1958 Fax: 0161-624 1958 *T.J. Dobson (Ladder Centre) has been established since 1969. It is a family business & specialises in wooden & aluminium ladders of all sorts including extension, loft, roof & step ladders. We are happy to take national enquiries & will deliver throughout the North West*

T J Electrical Engineers & Contractors Ltd, Unit 3 Squirrels Lodge, Hards Lane, Peterborough, PE6 8RL Tel: (01778) 349680 Fax: (01778) 349683 E-mail: sales@tjelectrical.co.uk *Electrical contractors*

T & J Engineering Ltd, Unit 12a Boston Place, Coventry, CV6 5NN Tel: (024) 7668 8713 Fax: (024) 7668 8713 *Precision engineers*

▶ T J Evers Ltd, New Road, Tiptree, Colchester, CO5 0HQ Tel: (01621) 815787 Fax: (01621) 818085

T J Fashion, 10-14 Bridge St, Oldbury, W. Midlands, B69 4BT Tel: 0121-565 5785 Fax: 0121-565 5785 *Jacket manufrs*

T & J Fire Ltd, 5 Martinfield Business Centre, Martinfield, Welwyn Garden City, Hertfordshire, AL7 1HG Tel: (01707) 326093 Fax: (01707) 376280 E-mail: sales@tjfire.co.uk *Fire fighting equipment suppliers*

T J Foster Properties Ltd, Shear House, Petersfield Avenue, Slough, SL2 5DQ Tel: (01753) 531477 Fax: (01753) 526933 E-mail: foster@btconnect.com *Building services contractors*

▶ T J French, Stonebriggs, Cronberry, Cumnock, Ayrshire, KA18 3LP Tel: (01290) 425164 Fax: (01290) 420900

▶ T J French, Stonebriggs, Cronberry, Cumnock, Ayrshire, KA18 3LP Tel: (01290) 425164 Fax: (01290) 420900

T J H Precision Plastics Ltd, 6 Davy Road, Clacton-on-Sea, Essex, CO15 4XD Tel: (01255) 220736 Fax: (01255) 476446 E-mail: tjh@angliannet.co.uk *Plastic injection moulder manufrs*

T & J Joinery, New Barnes Cottage, Stourport Road, Bewdley, Worcestershire, DY12 1QD Tel: (01299) 822743 Fax: (01299) 877502 *Joinery manufrs*

T J K Harries, Lletty Dryw, Felinfoel, Llanelli, Dyfed, SA14 8NX Tel: (01554) 758777 Fax: (01554) 758777 E-mail: lletydryw@tiscali.co.uk *Farming & agricultural contractors*

T J Mckenna & Son Ltd, 54 Reclain Road, Dungannon, County Tyrone, BT70 3BS Tel: (028) 8775 8600 Fax: (028) 8775 8981 *Agricultural machinery manufrs*

T J Marshall Ltd, 11 Marsh Lane, Addlestone, Surrey, KT15 1UL Tel: (01932) 848088 *Amusement machines suppliers*

T J Mechanical Handling (manea) Ltd, 12 East Street, Manea, March, Cambridgeshire, PE15 0JJ Tel: (01354) 680007 *Materials handling equipment manufrs*

▶ T J Morgan (Barry) Ltd, Ty Verlon Industrial Estate, Cardiff Road, Barry, South Glamorgan, CF63 2BE Tel: (01446) 740376 Fax: (01446) 720164

T J Mouldings, Spring Lane South, Malvern, Worcestershire, WR14 1AT Tel: (01684) 562792 Fax: (01684) 560081 *Injection & blow moulding manufrs*

T J Offset Ltd, 6 The Mead Business Centre, Mead Lane, Hertford, SG13 7BJ Tel: (01992) 504438 Fax: (01992) 501891 E-mail: info@tjoffset.co.uk *Lithographic printers & designers*

T J Penny, Hammondstreet Road, Cheshunt, Waltham Cross, Hertfordshire, EN7 6PQ Tel: (01707) 875878 *Commercial vehicle repairer*

T. & J. Plastics Ltd, 23 Cedar Close, Iver Heath, Iver, Buckinghamshire, SL0 0QX Tel: (01753) 652610 Fax: (01753) 652610 E-mail: tandjplast@aol.com *Injection moulders toolmakers*

T & J Printers Ltd, Sturmi Way, Village Farm Industrial Estate, Pyle, Bridgend, Mid Glamorgan, CF33 6BZ Tel: (01656) 744288 Fax: (01656) 741804 E-mail: tandjprinters@btconnect.com *General & commercial printers*

▶ T J Riley (Plant & Transport) Ltd, Beveridge Lane Industrial Esta, Ellistown, Coalville, Leicestershire, LE67 1FB Tel: (01530) 264050

T J Services Ltd, 38 Briery Acres, Stainburn, Workington, Cumbria, CA14 1XQ Tel: (01900) 65139 Fax: (01900) 607374 E-mail: sales@tjservicessd.co.uk *Racking systems distributors*

T J Smith, 9-9a Forge Lane, Headcorn, Ashford, Kent, TN27 9QG Tel: (01622) 891025 *Furniture manufrs*

T J Smith & Son Grinding Services Ltd, 17 Clifton Street, Sheffield, S9 2DQ Tel: 0114-244 8335 Fax: 0114-244 8335 E-mail: sales@precision-grinding.co.uk *Grinding services*

T J Thomson & Son Ltd, Millfield Works, Grangefield Road, Stockton-on-Tees, Cleveland, TS18 4AE Tel: (01642) 672551 Fax: (01642) 672556 E-mail: postbox@tjthomson.co.uk *Steel processors*

T J Turner & Son, Withy Road Industrial Estate, Withy Road, Bilston, West Midlands, WV14 0RX Tel: (01902) 404851 Fax: (01902) 662924 *Haulage & scrap merchant*

▶ T J & W M Cardy Ltd, Lodge Farm House, The Green, Fornham All Saints, Bury St. Edmunds, Suffolk, IP28 6JX Tel: (01284) 728432

T & J White, High Onn House, High Onn, Church Eaton, Stafford, ST20 0AX Tel: (01952) 691223 *Agricultural contractors*

T J Williams, Wimbourne Road, Barry, South Glamorgan, CF63 3DH Tel: (01446) 729200 Fax: (01446) 739281 E-mail: sales@tjwelectrical.co.uk *Manufacturers of pressure, vacuum, standard test, chemi seal & tank contents gauges. Stockists & repairers of pressure & temperature gauges & most types of industrial instruments. Specialist design company. On off special gauges*

▶ T Jolly Services Ltd, Unit G Central Industrial Estate, St. Marks Street, Bolton, BL3 6NR Tel: (07738) 486426 Fax: (01204) 365361 E-mail: john.taylor@tjolly.co.uk *AC plumbing & heating installations & maintenance services*

T Jones & Son, 27 Leg Street, Oswestry, Shropshire, SY11 2NN Tel: (01691) 652822 *Saddlery & riding equipment supplier*

T J'S Sign Co. Ltd, Unit C4, Portland Business Park, Portland Road, Hove, East Sussex, BN3 5RY Tel: (01273) 431134 Fax: (01273) 431135 E-mail: sales@tjsignco.com *Illuminated & computer generated sign making services*

T K A Body Stampings Ltd, Wolverhampton Road, Cannock, Staffordshire, WS11 1LY Tel: (01543) 466664 Fax: (01543) 466665 E-mail: info@tkbs.thyssenkrupp.com Principal Export Areas: Worldwide *Press specialists*

▶ T K Builders, Foundry Yard, Bellingham, Hexham, Northumberland, NE48 2DA Tel: (01434) 220800 Fax: (01434) 220800

▶ T K Drake, 30 London Street, Swaffham, Norfolk, PE37 7DG Tel: (01760) 725665 Fax: (01760) 720518 E-mail: contracting@tkdrake.co.uk

T K Engineering & Gear Cutting Ltd, Forest Mills, Denman Street East, Nottingham, NG7 3PZ Tel: 0115-970 0978 Fax: 0115-942 2928 *Gear manufacturers & cutters*

T K Fabrications, Stone Hall, Down Hall Road, Matching Green, Harlow, Essex, CM17 0RA Tel: (01279) 730093 Fax: (01279) 730135 *Plastics machinists*

T K Graphics Screen Printing, 12 Beauchamp Industrial Park, Watling Street, Wilnecote, Tamworth, Staffordshire, B77 5BZ Tel: (01827) 262449 Fax: (01827) 285458 E-mail: tomtkgraphics@aol.com *Screen printing services*

T K H Rubber Linings, 81 Musgrave Road, Birmingham, B18 5HH Tel: 0121-515 1800 Fax: 0121-554 3900 E-mail: tkh@btconnect.com *Rubber liner lining systems manufrs*

T K M Engineering, 32 Priory Road, Romford, RM3 9AT Tel: (01708) 377723 Fax: (01708) 377022 E-mail: sales@tkmlondon.co.uk *Precision turned part manufrs*

T K O Procurement Services Ltd, Unit 18 Hassocks Workshop, Stroudley Rd, Basingstoke, Hants, RG24 8UQ Tel: (01256) 819000 Fax: (01256) 842100 E-mail: tony.osborn@btconnect.com *Procurement of electronic components*

▶ T K P Electronics Ltd, Unit H5 Britannia Centre For Enterprise, Pengam Road, Pengam, Blackwood, Gwent, NP12 3SP Tel: (01443) 831052 Fax: (01443) 831052

▶ T K P Surfacing Ltd, Unit 5, Argyle Commercial Centre, Argyle Street, Swindon, SN2 8AR Tel: (01793) 430014

T K Rewinds, 21 Airfield Road, Christchurch, Dorset, BH23 3TG Tel: (01202) 476641 Fax: (01202) 480450 *Electric motor rewind & repair, pump repair & maintenance services*

T K Stapling Supplies, Radnor Cliff, Folkestone, Kent, CT20 2JL Tel: (07074) 782753 Fax: (01303) 226845 E-mail: info@tk-supplies.co.uk *Industrial mailing & stapling services*

▶ T Kane, 67 Strabane Road, Newtownstewart, Omagh, County Tyrone, BT78 4JZ Tel: (028) 8166 1600 Fax: (028) 8166 2711

T King & Son Groundwork Ltd, Summerfield, Gentles Lane, Passfield, Liphook, Hampshire, GU30 7RY Tel: (01428) 751129 Fax: (01428) 751569 *Groundwork contractors*

T Knipe Ltd, Sawmills, Church Road, Allithwaite, Grange-over-Sands, Cumbria, LA11 7QH Tel: (01539) 532404 Fax: (01539) 535313 *Joinery manufacture & timber merchants*

▶ T L B Homes, 40 Royle Green Road, Manchester, M22 4NG Tel: 0161-945 5777 Fax: 0161-945 5536

T L C, 1 Dock Road, Connah's Quay, Deeside, Clwyd, CH5 4DS Tel: (01244) 814066 Fax: (01244) 818502 E-mail: sales@t-m-c.com *Liquid crystal manufrs*

▶ T L C Print Management Ltd, 4 Gadwey House, Lingt Street, High Wycombe, Buckinghamshire, HP11 2QU Tel: (01494) 522605 E-mail: lotte2005@btconnect.com *Specialists in the management of design & print projects*

▶ T L Concrete Products, D Station Street Business Park, Station Street, Cinderford, Gloucestershire, GL14 2LG Tel: (01594) 827190 *Ready mix concrete manufrs*

T L Fire Security Systems, 59 Hawthorn Road, Birmingham, B44 8QT Tel: 0121-384 1557 Fax: 0121-384 1557 *Fire Security Systems Installation*

T L J Automatics, Unit 21 Small Business Centre, Penmaen Road, Pontllanfraith, Blackwood, Gwent, NP12 2DZ Tel: (01495) 220745 Fax: 01495 232701 *Pub games & juke box hire services*

T L M Construction Fasteners Ltd, 13 Davy Road, Astmoor Industrial Estate, Runcorn, Cheshire, WA7 1PZ Tel: (01928) 576193 Fax: (01928) 581308 E-mail: sales@tlmfasteners.co.uk *Industrial construction fastener distributors*

▶ T & L Marquee Hire, Barn Lane, Milton Malsor, Northampton, NN7 3AG Tel: (01604) 859748 Fax: (01604) 859748 *Marquee hire also flooring, stage, linings, starlight lining, marquee lighting, heating & furniture hire*

▶ T L O Electrical Contractors Ltd, Woodhouse Lane, Tamworth, Staffordshire, B77 3AE Tel: (01827) 52208 Fax: (01827) 60913

T L P Consultancy Ltd, Robert Denholm House, Bletchingley Road, Nutfield, Redhill, RH1 4HW Tel: (01737) 824000 Fax: (01737) 824001 *Computer consultants*

T L S Ltd, Detling Aerodrome, Detling, Maidstone, Kent, ME14 3HU Tel: (01622) 631699 Fax: (01622) 631736 *Vehicle leasing*

T Leighton & Sons, Unit 1a Albion Trading Estate, Mossley Road, Ashton-under-Lyne, Lancashire, OL6 6NQ Tel: 0161-330 4933 Fax: 0161-343 7025 E-mail: tlsbox@aol.com *Carton merchants*

▶ T Livingstone & Sons Builders Ltd, Hillwood, Cameron, St. Andrews, Fife, KY16 8PD Tel: (01334) 840268 Fax: (01334) 840288

T M & A, 4 Hunter Drive, Kilburn, Belper, Derbyshire, DE56 0ND Tel: (01332) 880159 Fax: (01332) 880103 E-mail: tmooreassociates@onetel.com *Temporary & permanent clear span building solutions*

T M A Data Management Ltd, Surrey House, 34 Eden Street, Kingston upon Thames, Surrey, KT1 1ER Tel: (020) 8481 3988 Fax: (020) 8546 9794 E-mail: info@tma.co.uk *IT consultants*

T M Arlidge, New Road, Whaley Bridge, High Peak, Derbyshire, SK23 7JG Tel: (01663) 734230 Fax: (01663) 734230 *Cabinet manufrs*

T M B International Ltd, Platt Industrial Estate, Maidstone Road, Platt, Sevenoaks, Kent, TN15 8TB Tel: (01732) 887456 Fax: (01732) 886345 E-mail: emmac@tmbmailing.com *Providing a comprehensive range of in-house mailing services, TMB International offers a professional approach to projects of any size. Whether data processing, ink jetting, laser printing, collating, envelope enclosing or polythene wrapping, TMB will successfully meet your requirements, and deadlines.*

▶ T M B Systems Ltd, Unit 10 Silver Business Park, Airfield Way, Christchurch, Dorset, BH23 3TA Tel: (01202) 488771 Fax: (01202) 488772 E-mail: paul@tmbonline.co.uk *Supply & installation of telecoms wi-fi equipment*

T M Barker & Son, High Lane, Beadlam/Nawton, Nawton, York, YO62 7SP Tel: (01439) 770367 *Farm services*

T M C Marine Consultants Ltd, Lloyds Wharf, Mill Street, London, SE1 2BD Tel: (020) 7237 2617 Fax: (020) 7231 8069 E-mail: info@tmcmarine.co.uk *Marine consultants & naval architects*

T M E Ltd, 11 Church Street, Walton-On-Thames, Surrey, KT12 2QP Tel: (01932) 232123 Fax: (01932) 232110 E-mail: info@tme-ltd.com *Computer consultants*

T M Engineers Midlands Ltd, Oak Lane, Kingswinford, West Midlands, DY6 7JW Tel: (01384) 400212 Fax: (01384) 296019 E-mail: sales@tmengineers.co.uk *Heavy & Large Fabrication*Large Precision Machining*Custom Built Equipment*Materials handling equipment & precision engineers.*Design and build to customers requirments.*Test rigs - Design and Manufacture*

T M Fabrications, Unit 2, Dale St, Accrington, Lancashire, BB5 0AP Tel: 01254 351668 *Welding fabricators*

▶ T M Fabrications, Hicks Road, Markyate, St. Albans, Hertfordshire, AL3 8LG Tel: (01582) 842000 Fax: (01582) 842017 E-mail: tm-fabrications@btconnect.com *Steel fabricators*

T M G (Europe) Ltd, Whitestones House, 2 Kidderpore Avenue, London, NW3 7SB Tel: (01322) 861959 Fax: (0870) 7525490 E-mail: info@tmgeurope.co.uk *Offer wide ranging maritime consultancy*

▶ T M Garden & Landscapes Services, 5 Billington Gardens, Billington, Clitheroe, Lancashire, BB7 9LU Tel: (01254) 822665 E-mail: tommymarsh2000@yahoo.co.uk *We carry out all aspects of landscaping from design to construction. All work carried out by Myerscough College trained staff.Commercial and domestic projects welcome.*

T M Gibson, Jorrocks Works, Hamsterley Hall, Hamsterley Mill, Rowlands Gill, Tyne & Wear, NE39 1NJ Tel: (01207) 542369 Fax: (01207) 544013 E-mail: admin@tmgibson.co.uk *Cabinet manufrs*

T M I Foods Ltd, Lodge Way, Lodge Farm Industrial Estate, Northampton, NN5 7US Tel: (01604) 583421 Fax: (01604) 587392 E-mail: sales@tmifoods.co.uk *Food processing cook meats*

T M J Power Rewinds Ltd, Unit G3 Newington Industrial Estate, London Road, Newington, Sittingbourne, Kent, ME9 7NU Tel: (01795) 843476 Fax: (01795) 843476 *Power rewind repairers*

T M Logistics, Edgar House, Berrow Green Road, Martley, Worcester, WR6 6PQ Tel: (01886) 888241 Fax: (01886) 888196 *Road transport*

T M Lusby & Son, Willowdene, Main Road, Saltfleetby, Louth, Lincolnshire, LN11 7SS Tel: (01507) 338604 Fax: (01507) 338750 *Agricultural merchants*

T M P Northern Ltd, 281 Beckenham Road, Beckenham, Kent, BR3 4RL Tel: (020) 8676 0011 Fax: (020) 8676 0783 E-mail: sales@tmp-ltd.co.uk *Air conditioning installators*

T M P Worldwide Ltd, 53-64 Chancery Lane, Chancery House, London, WC2A 1QY Tel: (020) 7406 5000 Fax: (020) 7406 5001 *Advertising agents*

T M P Worldwide, Kinnaird, 1 Pall Mall, London, SW1Y 5AU Tel: (020) 7451 9400 Fax: (020) 7451 9401 *Consultant to management-executive search*

T M Plastics, 4-6 Fairoak Court, Whitehouse Industrial Estate, Runcorn, Cheshire, WA7 3DX Tel: (01928) 710788 Fax: (01928) 710094 E-mail: tmplastics@tmplastics.co.uk *Plastics engineering manufrs*

T M R, Canal Street, Brierley Hill, West Midlands, DY5 1JJ Tel: (01384) 75531 Fax: (01384) 573353 E-mail: sales@tmrracking.com *Steel fabricators & epoxy painting*

T M Robinson & Sons, Heads Nook, Brampton, Cumbria, CA8 9DW Tel: (01228) 670318 *Agricultural contractors*

T M S Ltd, 7 Central Park Avenue, Central Avenue, Larbert, Stirlingshire, FK5 4RX Tel: (01324) 550760 Fax: (0871) 2225035 *Computer hardware suppliers & services*

T M S Electrical Contractors, Guildford Road, Bucks Green, Rudgwick, Horsham, West Sussex, RH12 3JF Tel: (01403) 822266 Fax: (01403) 822890 E-mail: andywalder@tmselectrical.com *Electrical contractors*

▶ T M S Gas Services, 18 Marshall Close, Spixworth, Norwich, NR10 3NX Tel: (01603) 710500

T M S Systems, Park Works, Main Road, Kingsley, Bordon, Hampshire, GU35 9LY Tel: (01420) 489313 Fax: (01420) 487218 E-mail: info@tms-systems.co.uk *Pre-stressing systems manufacturers for concrete*

T M S UK Ltd, Knightswood Terrace, Blantyre, Glasgow, G72 9BQ Tel: (01698) 711103 Fax: (01698) 711103 E-mail: enquiries@tmsuk.org *Repairers of manual handling equipment*

T M Services Ltd, 5 Charterhouse Square, London, EC1M 6PX Tel: (020) 7867 8600 Fax: (020) 7867 8787 E-mail: tmservices@tmworldwide.co.uk *Oil & gas management consultants*

T & M Supplies, Barton Street, North Tawton, Devon, EX20 2HL Tel: (01837) 82601 Fax: (01837) 89082 E-mail: tswhite@talk21.com *Thermal insulators manufrs*

T M T Engineering Co., 11a Portway, Warminster, Wiltshire, BA12 8QG Tel: (01985) 216015 Fax: (01985) 216015 *Mould manufrs*

T M T Powder Coatings Ltd, 62 Hammonds Drive, Eastbourne, East Sussex, BN23 6PW Tel: (01323) 642215 Fax: (01323) 649963 E-mail: tmt.powder@virgin.net *Powder coating services*

T M Taylor & Sons, 110 St James Street, Newport, Isle of Wight, PO30 5HB Tel: (01983) 522802 *Jewellers*

T M (UK), Climpy Industrial Park, Climpy Road, Forth, Lanark, ML11 8EW Tel: (01555) 812600 Fax: (01555) 812753 *Steel stockholders*

T M Wood, Hollydale, Buildwas Road, Ironbridge, Telford, Shropshire, TF8 7BN Tel: (01952) 432292 Fax: (01952) 432736 E-mail: tmwood@enta.net *Contractors' plant sales*

▶ T McKie, Deans Park, Irongray Road, Dumfries, DG2 0HS Tel: (01387) 720826

▶ T Mcmillan Ltd, Lyon Road, Linwood, Paisley, Renfrewshire, PA3 3BD Tel: (01505) 337410 Fax: (01505) 337411

▶ T McNally Electricians Ltd, Unit 1 B, Motherwell Business Centre, Coursington Road, Motherwell, Lanarkshire, ML1 1PW Tel: (01698) 253046

▶ T Maguire & Co. (Contractors) Ltd, 3 Clarel Avenue, Birmingham, B8 1AF Tel: 0121-327 2726

▶ T Mann Ltd, 343 Eastwood Road North, Leigh-on-Sea, Essex, SS9 4LT Tel: (01702) 528437 Fax: (01702) 421344

▶ T Mannion & Co. Ltd, 26 Barrow Road, Cambridge, CB2 2AS Tel: (01223) 353372

T Moxon, Icknield Street, Beoley, Redditch, Worcestershire, B98 9AL Tel: (01527) 585073 Fax: (01527) 585073 *Agricultural engineers*

T N C Precision Engineering Ltd, 5 Kendall Court, Hurricane Way, Wickford, Essex, SS11 8YB Tel: (01268) 764631 Fax: (01268) 570978 E-mail: tncprecision@aol.com *Precision engineers*

T N Lawrence & Sons Ltd, 208 Portland Road, Hove, East Sussex, BN3 5QT Tel: (01273) 260260 Fax: (01273) 260270 E-mail: artbox@lawrence.co.uk *Artists materials retailers & manufrs*

T N Robinson Ltd, 5 Priestley Business Centre, Priestley Street, Warrington, WA5 1TF Tel: (01925) 650501 Fax: (01925) 418614 E-mail: sales@tnr.com *Electrical wholesalers*

T N S Concrete Products, Normanby Road, Scunthorpe, South Humberside, DN15 6AD Tel: (01724) 720814 *Specialist concrete manufrs*

T N S Knitwear, Majid House, 37-49 Devonshire St North, Manchester, M12 6JR Tel: 0161-273 4406 Fax: 0161-272 8207 E-mail: info@tnsknitwear.com *Textile manufrs*

T N S Media Intelligence, PA Newcentre, 292 Vauxhall Bridge Road, London, SW1V 1AE Tel: (020) 7963 7600 E-mail: tnsmi_sales@tnsofres.com *Broadcasting information services*

T N Sneath & Sons, Cross Lanes, Pinchbeck, Spalding, Lincolnshire, PE11 3SN Tel: (01775) 640373 Fax: (01775) 640125 E-mail: richard@tn-sneath.co.uk *Agricultural & grounds maintenance contractors*

T N T Express, Abeles Way, Atherstone, Warwickshire, CV9 2RY Tel: (01827) 303030 Fax: (01827) 301301 E-mail: steve.doig@tnt.co.uk *Parcel delivery & courier services*

T N T Express, Abeles Way, Atherstone, Warwickshire, CV9 2RY Tel: (01827) 303030 Fax: (01827) 301301 *Parcel delivery & carrier services*

T N T Express, Hall Road, Aylesford, Kent, ME20 7TR Tel: (01622) 716601 Fax: (01622) 716040 *Express parcel carriers*

▶ T N T Express, Wimblebury Road, Littleworth, Cannock, Staffordshire, WS12 2HW Tel: (01543) 426333 Fax: (01543) 877655

▶ T N T Express, Unit 5 12 Cromwell Road Industrial Estate, Bredbury, Stockport, Cheshire, SK6 2RF Tel: (0800) 777222 Fax: 0161-406 8788

▶ T N T Fashion Group, Earn Avenue, Righead Industrial Estate, Bellshill, Lanarkshire, ML4 3LW Tel: (01698) 844602 Fax: (01698) 845087

▶ T N T Logistics, Pilsley Road, Danesmoor, Chesterfield, Derbyshire, S45 9BX Tel: (01246) 862452 Fax: (01246) 865578

▶ T N T Transport Systems, G E C Business Park, Blackburn Road, Clayton Le Moors, Accrington, Lancashire, BB5 5YG Tel: (01254) 382171 E-mail: admin@tntlaw.co.uk

▶ T N V Construction Ltd, Kingsbury Works, Kingsbury Road, London, NW9 8UP Tel: (020) 8200 9099

▶ T Naughton Ltd, New Bank Street, Manchester, M12 4TN Tel: 0161-273 7115

▶ T Norman Price Dudley Ltd, 73 Dixons Green, Dudley, West Midlands, DY2 7DJ Tel: (01384) 253875 Fax: (01384) 211524

T O C Ltd, Brandon Road, Binley, Coventry, CV3 2AN Tel: (024) 7645 0020 Fax: (024) 7663 5722 E-mail: sales@toc-ltd.co.uk *Precision engineers*

T & O Engineering Ltd, 10 Willow Wood Road, Meopham, Gravesend, Kent, DA13 0QT Tel: (01732) 822560 Fax: (01732) 822560 E-mail: peter4tno@aol.com *Swimming pool covers*

▶ T O Jones & Sons Ltd, Glenview, Llanybydder, Dyfed, SA40 9RL Tel: (01570) 480092 Fax: (01570) 481077

T O T Shirts, Banksia Road, London, N18 3BF Tel: (020) 8887 7900 Fax: (020) 8345 6095 E-mail: paul@t-o-t-shirts.co.uk *Screen printed and embroidered merchandise . We can supply garemtns or can contract print on supplied items. From design to delivery all servcies completed in house.*Call now for competitive quote.*

T O Tomlins Ltd, Halfway House, Station Lane, Halfway House, Shrewsbury, SY5 9DB Tel: (01743) 884235 Fax: (01743) 884424 *Civil engineers*

▶ T Oconnor, D 795 London Road, Grays, Essex, RM20 3LH Tel: (01708) 890885 Fax: (01708) 890815 E-mail: sales@toconnor.co.uk *Sales, installation & removals services of heavy security equipment*

T O'Donaghue Ltd, 31-35 Kirby Street, London, EC1N 8TL Tel: (020) 7242 8001 Fax: (020) 7405 1076 E-mail: tod@todjewellers.com *Jewellery manufrs*

▶ T P A Design Co. Ltd, 33a St Lukes Road, Maidenhead, Berkshire, SL6 7DN Tel: (01628) 412388 Fax: (01628) 412390 E-mail: sales@tpadesign.co.uk *Architectural specialists*

T P Activity Toys, Severn Road, Stourport-on-Severn, Worcestershire, DY13 9EX Tel: (01299) 872800 Fax: (01299) 827163 E-mail: enquiries@tptoys.com *Outdoor toys* Also at: Malvern

▶ T P Aspinall & Sons Ltd, Middleton Business Park, Middleton Road, Middleton, Morecambe, Lancashire, LA3 3PW Tel: (01524) 852883 Fax: (01524) 853303 E-mail: enquiries@aspinall.co.uk *T.P. Aspinall & Sons Limited is a customer focused innovative solutions driven engineering company which designs, manufactures and installs specialised equipments, products and services conforming to the requirements of our customers.*

T P Broombys Ltd, Currock Road, Carlisle, CA2 4AX Tel: (01228) 538511 Fax: (01228) 531488 *Builders merchants*

T P Cooke, 1 Kym Road, Bicton Industrial Park, Kimbolton, Huntingdon, Cambridgeshire, PE28 0LW Tel: (01480) 860138 Fax: (01480) 860138 E-mail: tpcookeengineering@btinternet.com *Precision subcontract engineering services*

T P Electronics, White House Drakes View, Staddon Heights, Plymouth, PL9 9SP Tel: (01752) 482722 Fax: (01752) 482744 E-mail: info@tpelectronics.co.uk *Marine equipment manufrs*

T P Fabrications, Bolton Road, Birmingham, B10 0AU Tel: 0121-773 3798 Fax: 0121-773 3798 *Welding/steel fabrications*

T P Fay (Kirkby) Ltd, 1 Spinney Close, Kirkby, Liverpool, L33 7XZ Tel: 0151-546 6232 Fax: 0151-549 1477 E-mail: sales@tpfay.co.uk *Heating element manufrs*

T P G Storage, 7 Hudsons Way, Canvey Island, Essex, SS8 9FE Tel: (01268) 696336 Fax: (01268) 514048 *Industrial shelving installers*

▶ T P Keville Construction Ltd, 83 Paget Road, Leicester, LE3 5HN Tel: 0116-251 4622 Fax: 0116-251 9081

T P L Logistics Management, Lakeside House, Hindhead Road, Haslemere, Surrey, GU27 3PJ Tel: (01252) 737939 Fax: (01252) 733474 E-mail: info@tpl-logistics-management.co.uk *Logistics consultancy appointments & board management*

T P L Management Consultancy Ltd, Leigh House, Leigh Lane, Farnham, Surrey, GU9 8HP Tel: (01252) 737939 Fax: (01252) 733474 E-mail: info@tpl-logistics-management.co.uk *Logistics consultants*

T P M Services, 39 Downland Drive, Crawley, West Sussex, RH11 8QZ Tel: (07836) 795835 Fax: (01293) 413084 *Waste recycling*

T P Niven, Woodhead, Palnackie, Castle Douglas, Kirkcudbrightshire, DG7 1PG Tel: (01556) 600276 Fax: (01556) 600330

T P P Interiors Ltd, Rysted Lane, Westerham, Kent, TN16 1EP Tel: (01959) 563575 Fax: (01959) 561032 E-mail: des@tppinteriors.co.uk *Suspended ceilings & partitions installation*

▶ T P Powder Coating Ltd, Unit 318 Fauld Industrial Estate, Fauld, Tutbury, Burton-on-Trent, Staffordshire, DE13 9HS Tel: (01283) 520548 Fax: (01283) 520549 E-mail: sales@tppowder.co.uk *Powder coating manufrs*

T P Precision Engineers Ltd, Unit 9, Betchworth Works, Ifield Road, Charlwood, Horley, Surrey, RH6 0DX Tel: (01293) 862645 Fax: (01293) 863283 *Precision engineering*

T & P Productions, Unit 5 Parkwood Court, Rotherwas Industrial Estate, Hereford, HR2 6NU Tel: (01432) 270554 Fax: (01432) 341172 *Hydraulic cylinder manufrs*

T P Pumps Ltd, Pathfields Business Park, South Molton, Devon, EX36 3LH Tel: (01769) 579487 Fax: (01769) 574600 E-mail: sales@tppumps.co.uk *Retail water pumps*

Company Information

T P S Automotives, Hoobrook Trading Estate, Worcester Road, Kidderminster, Worcestershire, DY10 1HY Tel: (01562) 744492 Fax: (01562) 746442 E-mail: tps.auto@lineone.net *Road tanker vehicle builders*

T P S Consultants, Centre Tower, Whitgift Centre, Croydon, CR9 0AU Tel: (020) 8256 4000 Fax: (020) 8256 4116 E-mail: sales@tpsconsult.ltd.uk *Multidisciplinary design practice & services*

T P S Fronius, 1 The Omni Business Centre, Omega Park, Alton, Hampshire, GU34 2QD Tel: (01420) 546855 Fax: (01420) 546856 E-mail: alton@tps-fronius.co.uk *Welding technology centre*

▶ T P S Print Ltd, 5 Tunnel Avenue, London, SE10 0SL Tel: (020) 8269 1222 Fax: (020) 8269 1223

T P S Technitube UK Ltd, T P S Building, Blatchford Road, Horsham, West Sussex, RH13 5QR Tel: (01403) 269471 Fax: (01403) 265443 E-mail: sales@tpsuk.co.uk *Valves & tube fittings distributors*

▶ T P S Tools, 1 Lea End Cottages Lea End Lane, Hopwood, Alvechurch, Birmingham, B48 7AY Tel: 0121-445 6297 Fax: 0121-445 6297 *Pressed tool manufrs*

▶ T & P Services, All Saints Road, Wednesbury, West Midlands, WS10 9LL Tel: 0121-568 8277 Fax: 0121-568 8266

▶ T P T Construction Ltd, Redstone Road, Narberth, Dyfed, SA67 7ES Tel: (01834) 861354 Fax: (01834) 861434

T P Tiling, 36 Draper Way, Leighton Buzzard, Bedfordshire, LU7 4UD Tel: (07821) 894855 E-mail: tpickup@tiscali.co.uk *T P Tiling aims to offers a personal and professional service for fixing wall and floor tiles in the commercial and domestic market. See examples off my work on my website, www.tptiling.co.uk*

T & P Tooling Co., Mardyke Works, St Marys Lane, North Ockendon, Upminster, Essex, RM14 3PA Tel: (01708) 224220 Fax: (01708) 224220 *Tool manufrs*

T Pearson & Son, 153-157 Eardley Road, London, SW16 6BB Tel: (020) 8769 2325 *Scrap metal merchants*

T Pickles Farms Ltd, South Farm, Dowbridge, Kirkham, Preston, PR4 2YL Tel: (01772) 683032 Fax: (01772) 683157 *Retailing of dairy produce*

T Potter (1982) Ltd, 63 Whitehill Road, Glenrothes, Fife, KY6 2RP Tel: 0141-429 1500 Fax: (01592) 774666 E-mail: thos.potter@btinternet.com *Bolt, nut & fastener distributors*

T Q Education & Training Ltd, Bonsall Street, Long Eaton, Nottingham, NG10 2AN Tel: 0115-972 2611 Fax: 0115-973 1520 E-mail: info@tq.com *Teaching & training equipment manufrs*

T Q Environmental P.L.C., Unit 10, Flanshaw Way, Wakefield, West Yorkshire, WF2 9LP Tel: (01924) 380700 Fax: (01924) 361700 E-mail: sales@tqplc.com *Gas detection & environmental monitoring products manufrs*

T Q S Services Ltd, Unit 3 Hartley Park Farm Business Centre, Selborne Road, Alton, Hants, GU34 3HD Tel: (01420) 511727 Fax: (01420) 511728 *Computer resellers & installers*

T R A Engineering New Mills Ltd, Hague Bar, High Peak, Derbyshire, SK22 3AT Tel: (01663) 743541 Fax: (01663) 743541 *Precision engineers*

▶ T R A K Residential Ltd, Seymour House, Whiteleaf Road, Hemel Hempstead, Hertfordshire, HP3 9DE Tel: (01442) 838450 Fax: (01442) 838501

▶ T R B Ltd, Rhodfa TRB, St. Asaph Business Park, St. Asaph, Clwyd, LL17 0JB Tel: (01745) 586500 Fax: (01745) 584111 E-mail: info@trb-ltd.co.uk *Telecommunication systems & equipment manufrs*

T R Bullworthy, Gatehouse Farm, High Street, Culworth, Banbury, Oxfordshire, OX17 2BG Tel: (01295) 768373 Fax: (01295) 768351 E-mail: bullworthy@btconnect.com *Garage equipment services & suppliers*

T R C International Ltd, 36 Acorn Industrial Park, Crayford Road, Dartford, DA1 4AL Tel: (01322) 521784 Fax: (01322) 524804 E-mail: contracts@trcgroup.co.uk *Roofing contracting & manufrs*

T R C Midlands Ltd, Mount Pleasant Street, West Bromwich, West Midlands, B70 7DL Tel: 0121-500 6181 Fax: 0121-500 5075 E-mail: info@totalroofcontrol.co.uk *Roofing contractors*

T R Clark, Crawl Farm, Crawl Lane, Clandown, Radstock, BA3 2XH Tel: (01761) 413120 Fax: (01761) 413120 *Livestock dealers*

▶ T R Commissioning Ltd, 11-13 High Street, Caterham, Surrey, CR3 5UE Tel: (01883) 347374 Fax: (01883) 342887 *Air conditioning designers commissioning engineers*

T R Controls Ltd, 12a Oak Industrial Park, Chelmsford Road, Dunmow, Essex, CM6 1XN Tel: (01371) 876187 Fax: (01371) 876287 E-mail: alan@trcontrols.co.uk *Encoder manufrs*

T & R Direct, 275 Ashley Road, Poole, Dorset, BH14 9DS Tel: (01202) 712800 Fax: (01202) 739347 E-mail: Lee@trdirect.co.uk *Cheap house insurance, cheap car*insurance, cheap lorry insurance,*cheap travel insurance, cheap shop*insurance, cheap brass band insurance and cheap motorbike*insurance.*

T R Engineering, Islwyn, Poplar Grove, Llanrwst, Gwynedd, LL26 0ED Tel: (01492) 641487 Fax: (01492) 641487 *Steel fabricators*

T R Engineering Ltd, Unit 6 Hadrians Way, Glebe Farm Industrial Estate, Rugby, Warwickshire, CV21 1ST Tel: (01788) 552983 Fax: (01788) 552983 E-mail: sales@treng.co.uk *Precision turned parts manufrs*

▶ T R Fabrications Ltd, Houghton Road North Anston Estate, North Anston Trading Estate, North Anston, Sheffield, S25 4JJ Tel: (01909) 568777 Fax: (01909) 550630 *Steel fabricators*

T R Fastenings Ltd, Unit 1 TR Business Park, 8A Trench Road, Newtownabbey, County Antrim, BT36 4TY Tel: (028) 9084 2621 Fax: (028) 9083 7436 Principal Export Areas: Worldwide *Building/ industrial fastener manufrs*

T R Fastenings Ltd, Waterside Park, Golds Hill Way, Tipton, West Midlands, DY4 0WP Tel: (0800) 7315553 Fax: (0800) 525230 E-mail: sales@trfastenings.com Principal Export Areas: Worldwide

▶ T R G Recruitment Services Ltd, 5th Floor, 4 St. Pauls Churchyard, London, EC4M 8AY Tel: (020) 7236 8181 Fax: (020) 7236 8181 E-mail: cv@thetrggroup.co.uk *TRG provide front of the house & switchboard staffing solutions, including fully managed outsourced services. TRG specialise in front of house & switchboard manning & management, with over 30 years experience in the City of London*

T & R Group Ltd, 15-16 Woodbridge Meadows, Guildford, Surrey, GU1 1BJ Tel: (01483) 568281 Fax: (01483) 504961 E-mail: sales@transformers.co.uk *Manufacture electrical power equipment*

▶ T R Handley Ltd, Lilac House, Crosby Garrett, Kirkby Stephen, Cumbria, CA17 4PR Tel: (01768) 371929 Fax: (01768) 371929

T R L Ltd, Crowthorne House, Nine Mile Ride, Wokingham, Berkshire, RG40 3GA Tel: (01344) 773131 Fax: (01344) 770356 E-mail: info@tr1.co.uk Principal Export Areas: Asia Pacific, Central Asia, Middle East, Africa, Central/East Europe, West Europe, North America & Central America *Transport consultants, environmental assessments & civil engineering*

T R L Technology Ltd, Shannon Way, Ashchurch, Tewkesbury, Gloucestershire, GL20 8ND Tel: (01684) 278700 Fax: (01684) 850406 E-mail: d_hall@trltech.co.uk *Satellite & terrestial communications systems*

T R M Electronics, 86 Moss Road, Southport, Merseyside, PR8 4JQ Tel: (01704) 563777 Fax: (01704) 565219 E-mail: keith@trminternational.com *TRM DESIGNS & MANUFACTURES Programmable Control Systems from it's base in Southport, U.K. Motion control & Temperature control are our focus for a wide range of industries: Catering Equipment, CNC Machining of Wood, Metal and Plastics. Machine control for Welding, Bending, Shearing. X-Y table applications. Most are Customisable, and we supply FREE programmable software to control basic applications. Send us your requirements for a free no-obligation quote.*

T R M Scotland Ltd, 29 Cardowan Drive, Stepps, Glasgow, G33 6HE Tel: 0141-779 9991 Fax: 0141-779 9991 *Dictating machine services*

T R M Southern Ltd, 132 London Road, Waterlooville, Hampshire, PO7 5SU Tel: (023) 9225 5686 Fax: (023) 9225 5700 E-mail: services@trm-southern.co.uk *Repair & supply office machinery*

T R Noble, Summerfield Farm, Hawsker, Whitby, North Yorkshire, YO22 4LA Tel: (01947) 602677 Fax: (01947) 602677 *Farming & agricultural merchants*

T R P Sealing Systems Ltd, 24 Netherwood Road, Rotherwas Industrial Estate, Hereford, HR2 6JU Tel: (01432) 279366 Fax: (01432) 273017 E-mail: admin@trpsealing.com *Precision rubber mouldings manufrs*

T & R Pine, 90 Hamilton Road, Felixstowe, Suffolk, IP11 7AD Tel: (01394) 285550 Fax: (01394) 285550 E-mail: sales@tandrpine.co.uk *Furniture retailers*

T R Precision Engineering Co. Ltd, 1 Wattville Road, Smethwick, West Midlands, B66 2NT Tel: 0121-565 1384 Fax: 0121-565 2946 E-mail: trprecision@btconnect.com *Precision engineers*

T R Price & Son, Unit F3 Dudley Central Trading Estate, Hope Street, Dudley, West Midlands, DY2 8RS Tel: (01384) 237629 *Packing case & pallet manufrs*

T & R Prints, Unit 3, 55 St. Peters Road, Dunstable, Bedfordshire, LU5 4HY Tel: (01582) 660768 Fax: (01582) 660768 E-mail: tandrprints@yahoo.co.uk *Commercial screen printing services*

T & R Rentals, 109 Southway, Westborough, Guildford, Surrey, GU2 8DQ Tel: (01483) 573029 *Film hire & rental tv & video repairs*

T R Rickard, Corminnow, High Street, St. Austell, Cornwall, PL26 7TE Tel: (01726) 72675 *Coal & animal feed*

T R S Cash & Carry Ltd, 2 Southbridge Way, Southall, Middlesex, UB2 4BY Tel: (020) 8843 5400 Fax: (020) 8574 5254 *Cash & carry*

T R S International Foods Ltd, Argall Avenue, London, E10 7AS Tel: (020) 8556 2117 Fax: (020) 8556 6151 *Food distributors*

T R S U, 1 Cranside Avenue, Bristol, BS6 7RA Tel: (07748) 740874 E-mail: ben@trsu.com *Marketing services*

T R Smith & Sons Ltd, Station Road, Sutton-in-Ashfield, Nottinghamshire, NG17 5GB Tel: (01623) 555009 Fax: (01623) 442303 *Builders*

T. & R. Test Equipment Ltd, 15-16 Woodbridge Meadows, Guilford, Guildford, Surrey, GU1 1BJ Tel: (01483) 207428 Fax: (01483) 235759 E-mail: sales@trtest.com *Test equipment (high & medium voltage) & engineering*

T R Vowden Farrier, The Forge, Luton, Chudleigh, Newton Abbot, Devon, TQ13 0BW Tel: (01626) 865484 *Farrier*

T R W Automotive Ltd, New Road, New Inn, Pontypool, Gwent, NP4 0TL Tel: (01495) 754040 Fax: (01495) 752802 *Car brake manufrs*

T R W Automotive, Technical Centre, Stratford Road, Shirley, Solihull, West Midlands, B90 4GW Tel: 0121-627 4141 Fax: 0121-627 3584 E-mail: rob.miller@trw.com *Research, development & testing services*

T R W Automotive Electronics, 45 College Road, Perry Barr, Birmingham, B44 8DU Tel: 0121-356 0351 Fax: 0121-344 3396 *Automotive electronics manufrs*

T R W Automotive Electronics, Eastern Avenue, Burnley, Lancashire, BB10 2AR Tel: (01282) 855500 Fax: (01282) 412436 *Automotive electronics*

T R W Fabrication & Welding, 1 Milnthorpe Road, Holme, Carnforth, Lancashire, LA6 1PS Tel: (01524) 782647 *Fabrication & welding*

T R W Fastening Systems, Buckingham Road, Aylesbury, Buckinghamshire, HP19 9QA Tel: (01296) 717000 Fax: (01296) 717100 E-mail: gil.swash@trw.com Principal Export Areas: Worldwide *Motor vehicle component manufrs*

T R W Systems Ltd, Mercantile Road, Houghton Le Spring, Tyne & Wear, DH4 5PH Tel: 0191-512 3700 Fax: 0191-512 3661 E-mail: *Motor industry manufrs*

T R W Systems Ltd, Resolven, Neath, West Glamorgan, SA11 4HN Tel: (01639) 665000 Fax: (01639) 665350 *Car steering systems manufrs*

T R W Systems Ltd, Rainhill Road, Washington, Tyne & Wear, NE37 3HP Tel: 0191-419 4477 Fax: 0191-419 4191 *Valve manufrs*

T & R Williamson Ltd, 36 Stonebridgegate, Ripon, North Yorkshire, HG4 1TP Tel: (01765) 607711 Fax: (01765) 607908 E-mail: sales@trwilliamson.co.uk *Paint Manufrs*

T. R. Y. Ltd, 94 Halstead Street, Leicester, LE5 3RD Tel: 0116-262 9504 Fax: 0116-262 3421 E-mail: try147@hotmail.com Principal Export Areas: West Europe *Clothing distributors*

T Roberts & Sons, Trout Farm, Llanfyllin, Powys, SY22 5LZ Tel: (01691) 648420 Fax: (01691) 648420 *Agricultural equipment maintenance services*

▶ T Robertson & Sons, Whinpark Quarry, Mount Pleasant, Newburgh, Cupar, Fife, KY14 6DG Tel: (01337) 840212 Fax: (01337) 841078

T Rogers, 1a Broughton Street, London, SW8 3QJ Tel: (020) 7720 2789 Fax: (020) 7627 3318 E-mail: trogersco@aol.com *Storage, packing & removal*

T S Anderson Ltd, 15 Ashton Road, Glasgow, G12 8SP Tel: 0141-334 1418 Fax: 0141-337 2342 *Commercial property agents*

T S Barrows & Son, Hamlyn Lodge, Station Road, Ollerton, Newark, Nottinghamshire, NG22 9BN Tel: (01623) 823600 E-mail: info@hamlynlodge.com *Antique restoration & cabinet makers*

▶ T S D Cleaning Services, 361 Whitton Avenue East, Greenford, Middlesex, UB6 0JT Tel: (020) 8902 9887 E-mail: info@tsdcleaning.co.uk *TSD Cleaning is a London based Professional Cleaning Company which offers various cleaning services including:End of Tenancy cleaning,Carpet& Upholstery cleaning, Window cleaning, Communal Parts cleaning.*

T S D Precision Ltd, Unit 11 Lion Industrial Park, Northgate Way, Walsall, WS9 8RL Tel: (01922) 457620 Fax: 01922 455443 *Toolmakers of die-casting mould & die*

T S Designs Ltd, PO Box 102, Macclesfield, Cheshire, SK11 9EP Tel: (01477) 571357 Fax: (01477) 571881 *Engineers of security products*

T S E Ltd, 57 Pingle Drive, Bicester, Oxfordshire, OX26 6WD Tel: (01869) 244030 Fax: (01869) 244045 *Cashmere knit wear*

T S E (Catering Equipment) Ltd, Valmar Trading Estate, Valmar Road, Camberwell Green, London, SE5 9NP Tel: (020) 7274 4577 Fax: (020) 7978 8141 *Catering equipment manufrs*

T S G Ltd, Rumbridge Street, Totton, Southampton, SO40 9DR Tel: (023) 8030 4300 Fax: (023) 8066 7763 E-mail: sales@tsg.com *IT reseller*

T.S.G Plastics Caerphilly Ltd, Pontygwindy Industrial Estate, Douglas Works, Caerphilly, Mid Glamorgan, CF83 3HU Tel: (029) 2086 8513 Fax: (029) 2088 8815 E-mail: dave.hunter@tsgplatics.co.uk Principal Export Areas: Africa *Manufacturers of plastic & plastic injection mouldings*

T S Hattersley & Son Ltd, 63 Weymouth Road, Eccles, Manchester, M30 8TH Tel: 0161-789 1374 Fax: 0161-787 8632 E-mail: info@hattersleys.org *Lacrosse stick distributors & manufrs*

▶ T S I Luckins Ltd, Cherryholt Road, Stamford, Lincolnshire, PE9 2EP Tel: (01780) 750500 Fax: (01780) 750567 E-mail: info@luckins.co.uk *Data services*

T S I S Engineering Ltd, 14 Waterloo Place, London, SW1Y 4AR Tel: (020) 7930 1562 Fax: (020) 7939 6569 E-mail: tsis.eng@onetel.net *Engineering consultants & agents*

▶ T S I Structures Ltd, Ashgrove, Fakenham Road, Morton on the Hill, Norwich, NR9 5SP Tel: (01603) 870399 Fax: (01603) 871855

T S Industrial Products Ltd, 75 Somers Road, Rugby, Warwickshire, CV22 7DG Tel: (01788) 543387 Fax: (01788) 541311 E-mail: sales@tsindustrial.co.uk *Specialist electrical distributors*

T S International Freight Forwarders Ltd, Halesfield 19, Telford, Shropshire, TF7 4QT Tel: (01952) 586467 Fax: (01952) 680048 E-mail: info@tsinternational.com *Import & export & road haulage service*

T S International Packing Ltd, Unit C1 Halesfield 19, Telford, Shropshire, TF7 4QT Tel: (01952) 586820 Fax: (01952) 585958 E-mail: connect@tsipacking.co.uk *Export packing manufrs*

T S J Industrial Supplies Ltd, 44-50 Heaton Street, Cleckheaton, West Yorkshire, BD19 3TN Tel: (01274) 870804 Fax: (01274) 870805 E-mail: andrew@tsji.demon.co.uk *Industrial power transmission equipment distributors*

T S K Manufacturers Ltd, 27 Whitechapel Road, London, E1 1DU Tel: (020) 7247 6701 Fax: (020) 7377 6897 *Clothing manufrs*

T S K Manufacturers Ltd, 27 Whitechapel Road, London, E1 1DU Tel: (020) 7247 6701 Fax: (020) 7377 6897 *Clothing manufrs*

T & S Kitching, Dreamland Farm, Stainton, Kendal, Cumbria, LA8 0LQ Tel: (01539) 560168 *Agricultural contractors*

T S L Technology Ltd, The Station Mill, Station Road, Alresford, Hampshire, SO24 9DE Tel: (01962) 735707 Fax: (01962) 735502 E-mail: enquiries@tsltechnology.com *Consulting engineers to oil industry*

▶ T S M Ltd, 66 Babbacombe Road, Babbacombe, Torquay, TQ1 3SW Tel: (01803) 312081 Fax: (01803) 312051 E-mail: tsmltd@tiscali.co.uk *Designers, suppliers*

continued

& fixers of natural stone products. Granite Worktops. Marble Bathrooms.

T S M Ltd, Sensor House, Wrexham Technology Park, Wrexham, Clwyd, LL13 7YP Tel: (01978) 291800 Fax: (01978) 291888 E-mail: tsm@esi-tec.com *Resistive strain gauge systems manufrs*

T S & M E Darlington & Daughters, 47a Lancaster Fields, Crewe, CW1 6FF Tel: (01270) 250710 Fax: (01270) 250710 E-mail: sales@mrsdarlingtons.com *Preserves manufrs*

T S O Ltd, Publications Centre, 51 Nine Elms Lane, London, SW8 5DR Tel: (020) 7873 8787 Fax: (0870) 600 5533 E-mail: customer.services@tso.co.uk *Publishing & parliamentary services*

T & S Overseas Ltd, PO Box 248, Rochdale, Lancashire, OL11 4YA Tel: (01706) 350406 Fax: (01706) 526809 *Household textile machinery & can making machinery manufrs*

▶ T & S Packaging, Unit 1-4 West Stone, Berry Hill Industrial Estate, Droitwich, Worcestershire, WR9 9AS Tel: (01905) 773837 Fax: (01905) 773837 E-mail: mail@tspackaging.co.uk *Manufacturers of Plastic Thermoformed products. including Display trays, blister packs, Clampacks and Box inserts*

T S Refrigeration, 21 Whitwick Way, Leicester, LE3 9TG Tel: 0116-251 9907 Fax: 0116-251 9907 *Refrigeration & air conditioning services*

T S S & P Ltd, Twickenham Trading Estate, Rugby Road, Twickenham, TW1 1DU Tel: (020) 8607 0500 Fax: (020) 8607 0547 *Promotional clothing manufrs*

T S S Technology Ltd, 214 Moss Lane, Bramhall, Stockport, Cheshire, SK7 1BD Tel: 0161-439 0005 Fax: 0161-439 0006 E-mail: sales@colorconsultancy.com *Supply colour measurement equipment*

T & S Services, 32 Wimblington Road, Doddington, March, Cambridgeshire, PE15 0TJ Tel: (01354) 740025 *Agricultural contractors*

▶ T & S Technologies Ltd, 6 Tollgate Road, Stone, Dartford, DA2 6BS Tel: (01474) 824503 *Services that we can provide:-**Network support *Hardware support *Software support *training *Web Site Authoring *Website Submission Services *Website Hosting *Advice *Training *Disaster Recovery *Backup Solutions *Hardware configurations *Network Installations *Software installations*

T S Technology, Langwood, 87 Langley Road, Watford, WD17 4PW Tel: (01923) 221155 Fax: (01923) 218625 E-mail: sales@tstechnology.co.uk *Distributors or agents of deburring & mould polishing equipment. Also machine tool accessories, machine tool spindle tooling merchants or agents & metal finishing/polishing plant/ equipment/suppliers*

T Sargent, 9 Coulter Close, Cuffley, Potters Bar, Hertfordshire, EN6 4RR Tel: (01707) 874349 Fax: (01707) 876289 *Structural steel work & specialised welding*

T Shirt Products, Somers Road, Rugby, Warwickshire, CV22 7DG Tel: (0845) 0714405 Fax: (0845) 0714406 E-mail: sales@tsp-tshirts.co.uk *Textile printers & embroiderers services*

▶ T Sloyan & Sons (Builders), 19-21 Lightbody Street, Liverpool, L5 9UY Tel: 0151-207 2064

▶ T Snape & Co. Ltd, Boltons Court, Preston, PR1 3TY Tel: (01772) 254553 Fax: (01772) 204697 E-mail: sales@tsnapeprinters.co.uk

T Stensby & Co. Ltd, 1 Shudehill, Manchester, M4 2AF Tel: 0161-834 6589 Fax: 0161-834 6589 E-mail: sales@stensby.co.uk *Gun, rifle & revolver manufrs*

T Stephenson & Son Ltd, 5 Market Place, Prescot, Merseyside, L34 5SB Tel: 0151-426 5161 Fax: 0151-430 7738 E-mail: stephensonprint@btclick.com *Printers*

▶ T Sutcliffe & Co. Ltd, Weston Street, Bolton, BL3 2AL Tel: (01204) 535221 Fax: (01204) 380681 E-mail: sales@sutcliffegarages.co.uk

T Sutcliffe & Co. Ltd, Weston Street, Bolton, BL3 2AL Tel: (01204) 535221 Fax: (01204) 380681 *Sectional & portable buildings*

T & T Ltd, Jarvis Brook Goods Yard, Crowborough, East Sussex, TN6 3DS Tel: (01892) 663392 Fax: (01892) 662094 *Contractors plant hire*

T T Audio Plastics Ltd, Unit 17, St. Margarets Way, Stukeley Meadows Industrial Estate, Huntingdon, Cambridgeshire, PE29 6EB Tel: (01480) 412345 Fax: (01480) 412533 E-mail: admin@ttap.co.uk *Injection mouldings manufrs*

T T Buildings Ltd, Kingsley Road, Bideford, Devon, EX39 2PF Tel: (01237) 475679 Fax: (01237) 421526 E-mail: sales@ttbuildings.co.uk *Farm buildings*

T T C Engineering Ltd, Unit 13, Chalwyn Industrial Estate, Old Wareham Road, Poole, Dorset, BH12 4PE Tel: (01202) 738181 *Powder coating, stove enameling & steel fabrication services*

T T C Lifting Gear Ltd, Newlyn Road, Cradley Heath, West Midlands, B64 6BE Tel: (01384) 564059 Fax: (01384) 410587 *Suppliers of lifting gear*

T T Carpets & Ceilings, The Red Barn, Harmony Hill, Milnthorpe, Cumbria, LA7 7QA Tel: (01539) 562898 Fax: (01539) 564404 E-mail: enquires@ttcarpets.fsnet.co.uk *Ceilings & carpet manufrs*

▶ T T Catering Solutions Ltd, Unit 3-4 Swan Park, Kettlebrook Road, Tamworth, Staffordshire, B77 1AG Tel: (01827) 54400 Fax: (01827) 315016 E-mail: tedblake@ttcatsol.co.uk *Catering equipment supply services*

T & T Consultancy, Advantage House, Trentham Business Quarter, Stoke-on-Trent, ST4 8GQ Tel: (01782) 644141 Fax: (01782) 646142 E-mail: enquries@tandt.com *Training consultancy*

T T Electronics, East Field Industrial Estate, Glenrothes, Fife, KY7 4NX Tel: (01592) 662200 Fax: (01592) 662299 *Electronic component supplier & manufrs*

T T Electronics Welwyn Components Ltd, Welwyn Electronics Park, Bedlington, Northumberland, NE22 7AA Tel: (01670) 822181 Fax: (01670) 829465 E-mail: info@welwyn-tt.com *Welwyn Components provides leading edge technology and cost effective manufacturing services for*

continued

continuation
Resistive Components and custom Hybrid Circuits for a broad range of applications in the Automotive, Industrial, Avionics /Defence, Telecom, and Medical Markets.

▶ T T Enterprises, Knighton, Canada Hill, Newton Abbot, Devon, TQ12 6AF Tel: (01626) 208928 *Computer maintenance & repair*

▶ T T F (Scotland) Ltd, 4 Block 3 12 King's Haugh, Peffermill Road, Edinburgh, EH16 5UY Tel: 0131-652 0030 Fax: 0131-661 0550 E-mail: admin@ttf-aircon.com

T T F (Scotland) Ltd, 4 Block 3 12 King's Haugh, Peffermill Road, Edinburgh, EH16 5UY Tel: 0131-652 0030 Fax: 0131-661 0550 E-mail: admin@ttf-aircon.com *Install & service air conditioning*

T & T Fabrications Ltd, 8 Atlas Works, Norwich Road, Lenwade, Norwich, NR9 5SW Tel: (01603) 872277 Fax: (01603) 870413 *Sheet metal fabrication & metalwork*

T & T Furnishings, Coldharbour Lane House, 108 Coldharbour Lane, Hayes, Middlesex, UB3 3HD Tel: (020) 8569 0162 Fax: (020) 8848 0294 *Reproduction furniture*

T T I, 2 Cliveden Office Village, Lancaster Road, Cressex Business Park, High Wycombe, Buckinghamshire, HP12 3YZ Tel: (01494) 460000 Fax: (01494) 460090 E-mail: sales.london@uk.ttiinc.com *Electronic equipment distributors*

T T I Electrical Ltd, Tti House Millers Yard, Long Lane, London, N3 2QG Tel: (020) 8343 1661 Fax: (020) 8343 1771 E-mail: sales@tti-group.co.uk *Electrical supply wholesalers*

T T I Group Ltd, Bamfurlong Industrial Park, Staverton, Cheltenham, Gloucestershire, GL51 6SX Tel: (01452) 712023 Fax: (01452) 714418 *Heat treatment of metal*

T T I Nitriding Services Ltd, Hortonwood 40, Telford, Shropshire, TF1 7YU Tel: (01952) 677372 Fax: (01952) 677370 E-mail: info@nitriding.co.uk *Heat treatment services*

T T Pumps Ltd, Onneley Works, Newcastle Road, Woore, Crewe, CW3 9RU Tel: (01630) 647200 Fax: (01630) 642100 E-mail: response@ttpumps.com *Pump manufrs*

▶ T T S Shipping Ltd, Charter House, 14 Park Road, Melton Mowbray, Leicestershire, LE13 1TT Tel: (01664) 410441 Fax: (01664) 410208 E-mail: admin@tts.co.uk

▶ T & T Steeplejacks Ltd, Snowdon House, Snowdon Road, Middlesbrough, Cleveland, TS2 1DY Tel: (01642) 247972 Fax: (01642) 247972

T T UK Ltd, Windsor Road, Bedford, MK42 9SU Tel: (01234) 342566 Fax: (01234) 352184 E-mail: info@tt-uk.com *Trenchless technology equipment*

T T V Facilities Ltd, Unit 12A 12G, Airport Industrial Estate, Newcastle Upon Tyne, NE3 2EF Tel: 0191-214 2300 Fax: 0191-214 2301 E-mail: info@ttv.org.uk *Audio visual equipment hire*

T T W Services Ltd, Suite 3, The Octagon, Brighton Marina Village, Brighton, BN2 5WB Tel: (01273) 699003 E-mail: ttw@winman.co.uk *Computer consultants*

T Trevethicks, Gregory Street, Nottingham, NG7 2NP Tel: 0115-978 3467 Fax: 0115-978 3467 *Boat repairers & manufrs*

T U V Product Service, Snitterfield Road, Bearley, Stratford-upon-Avon, Warwickshire, CV37 0EX Tel: (01789) 731155 Fax: (01789) 731264 E-mail: mbrain@tuvps.co.uk *Electromagnetic compatibility (EMC) testing services*

T U V Rheinland Group UK, 24 Bennetts Hill, Birmingham, B2 5QP Tel: 0121-634 8000 Fax: 0121-634 8080 E-mail: safety@uk.tuv.com *Test, inspection & certification services*

T V A Installations Stockport Ltd, Waterloo House, Hopes Carr, Stockport, Cheshire, SK1 3BL Tel: 0161-480 2265 Fax: 0161-480 6720 E-mail: tva@btconnect.com *Television aerial erectors & digital satellite systems*

T V F plc, 59-69 Queens Road, High Wycombe, Buckinghamshire, HP13 6AH Tel: (01494) 450641 Fax: (01494) 465378 *Fire protection consultants*

T V Kenealy, The Yard, Harthall Lane, Pimlico, Hemel Hempstead, Hertfordshire, HP3 8SE Tel: (01923) 266341 Fax: (01923) 291107 *Commercial body shop*

T V P Ltd, Unit 5, First Avenue, Globe Business Park, Marlow, Buckinghamshire, SL7 1YA Tel: (01628) 473121 Fax: (01628) 477563 E-mail: sales@tvp.ltd.uk *Contract packers & direct mailing*

T V R Power Ltd, 339 Bedworth Road, Longford, Coventry, CV6 6BN Tel: (024) 7636 6177 Fax: (024) 7636 5428 E-mail: dom@tvr-power.co.uk *High performance engine manufrs*

T V Times, Kings Reach Tower, Stamford Street, London, SE1 9LS Tel: (020) 7261 7000 Fax: (020) 7261 7888 *Magazine publishers*

▶ T W Bell Belsay Ltd, Burnside Garage, Grange Road, Stamfordham, Newcastle upon Tyne, NE18 0PF Tel: (01661) 886207

T W Bowler Ltd, Shadyoak, Marple Road, Stockport, Cheshire, SK2 5HF Tel: 0161-487 3363 Fax: 0161-487 3527 E-mail: sales@bowlers-stockport.co.uk *General & heavy haulage*

T W Bracher & Co. Ltd, Royal George Street, Stockport, Cheshire, SK3 8AS Tel: 0161-480 2005 Fax: 0161-477 1673 E-mail: sales@tw-bracher.co.uk *Hat component manufrs*

▶ T W E Haulage, Thorpe Mead, Banbury, Oxfordshire, OX16 4RZ Tel: (01295) 262299 Fax: (01295) 262255

T W Eaton & Co. Ltd, 247 Noel Street, Nottingham, NG7 6AR Tel: 0115-978 4084 Fax: 0115-942 2631 *Textile cutting machine spare parts & manufrs*

T W Engineering Ltd, Angular House, Quarry Hill Road, Ilkeston, Derbyshire, DE7 4DA Tel: 0115-932 3223 Fax: 0115-930 6221 E-mail: tw@tweng.co.uk *Precision engineers*

T W Fabrications, Green Acres, Duns Tew Road, Middle Barton, Chipping Norton, Oxfordshire, OX7 7DG Tel: (01869) 347014 Fax: (01869) 347014 *Steel fabrication*

T W G Packaging, King Edward Industrial Estate, Gibraltar Row, Liverpool, L3 7HJ Tel: 0151-227 1045 Fax: 0151-236 2114 E-mail: mygpackaging@compuserve.com *Stationers & printing services*

T W Generators, 2 Long Marston Road, Marsworth, Tring, Hertfordshire, HP23 4NF Tel: (01296) 668420 Fax: (01296) 662064 E-mail: sales@twgenerators.co.uk *Diesel electric generator manufrs*

T W Holden & Son, Yew Tree Farm, Chipping Road, Chaigley, Clitheroe, Lancashire, BB7 3LX Tel: (01995) 61300 Fax: (01995) 61300 *Joinery manufrs*

T W Howarth & Co. Ltd, 31-35 Chiltern Street, London, W1U 7PN Tel: (020) 7935 2407 Fax: (020) 7224 2564 E-mail: sales@howarth.uk.com *Wood wind instrument dealers*

T W I Ltd, Granta Park, Great Abington, Cambridge, CB1 6AL Tel: (01223) 899000 Fax: (01223) 892794 E-mail: twi@twi.co.uk *Engineering consultants*

T W International Ltd, T W House, Oxford Road, Calne, Wiltshire, SN11 8RS Tel: (01249) 822100 Fax: (01249) 821919 E-mail: sales@twinternational.com *Electronic tool manufrs*

▶ T W Joinery South Wales Ltd, Heol Ffaldau, Brackla, Bridgend, Mid Glamorgan, CF31 2HQ Tel: (01656) 667745 Fax: (01656) 650887 *Joinery service*

T W L Force Systems, 15 Old Farm Lane, Fareham, Hampshire, PO14 2DB Tel: (01329) 665186 Fax: (01329) 668177 E-mail: sales@twlforce.co.uk *Non-destructive test equipment/systems manufrs*

T W Logistics Ltd, The Old Ship Yard, Gainsborough, Lincolnshire, DN21 1NQ Tel: (01427) 614551 Fax: (01427) 613770 *Road transport, haulage & freight services*

T W Metals Ltd, Unit 43 Nursling Industrial Estate, Majestic Road, Nursling, Southampton, SO16 0AF Tel: (023) 8073 9333 Fax: (023) 8073 9601 E-mail: enquiries@twmetals.co.uk *Metal pipe tube, sheet, bar, extrusions distributors*

▶ T W Moore & Son, Criton Industrial Estate, Stanford Road, Orsett, Grays, Essex, RM16 3DH Tel: (01375) 892333 Fax: (01375) 892555

▶ T W Mouldings, Brook Farm, Thrapston Road, Ellington, Huntingdon, Cambridgeshire, PE28 0AE Tel: (01480) 891899 Fax: (01480) 890768 E-mail: sales@tw-mouldings.co.uk

T W Page & Son Ltd, 7 Buxton Road, Frettenham, Norwich, NR12 7NQ Tel: (01603) 898071 Fax: (01603) 898049 E-mail: admin@twpage.co.uk *Well borers & water engineers, pumps & water treatments*

T W Parker (Paper) Ltd, Farriers Way, Bootle, Merseyside, L30 4XL Tel: 0151-523 7308 Fax: 0151-530 1318 *Self-adhesive label manufrs*

▶ T W Patterns, Stoke Row, Coventry, CV2 4JP Tel: (024) 7644 9571

T W Relph & Sons Ltd, Moore House, Yanwath, Penrith, Cumbria, CA10 2LA Tel: (01768) 864308 Fax: (01768) 890916 E-mail: johnwrelph@hotmail.com *Agricultural suppliers*

▶ T W Sampson & Co., Churchill House Lenton Lane, Nottingham, NG7 2NR Tel: 0115-986 8800 Fax: 0115-986 7909

T W Stamping Ltd, 112-117 Charles Henry Street, Birmingham, B12 0SJ Tel: 0121-622 2600 Fax: 0121-622 2700 E-mail: sales@guestsstamping.co.uk *Hot brass stamping services*

T W Steam & Heating Services Ltd, Unit 7-8 Rennys Lane, Durham, DH1 2RS Tel: 0191-384 1400 Fax: 0191-386 4251 *Heating engineers & steel fabricators*

T W Taylor & Co., Whitehouse Enterprise Centre, Whitehouse Road, Newcastle upon Tyne, NE15 6EP Tel: 0191-274 3013 Fax: 0191-274 3013 *Decorative plastics manufrs*

T W Ward CNC Machinery Ltd, Savile Street, Sheffield, S4 7UD Tel: 0114-276 5411 Fax: 0114-270 0786 E-mail: sales@wardcnc.com *Machine tool suppliers*

T W Wiseman Joinery, 116b Albert Road, Southsea, Hampshire, PO4 0JS Tel: (023) 9282 8186 *Joinery manufrs*

T Ward Shipping Ltd, 3 Johns Place, Leith, Edinburgh, EH6 7EL Tel: 0131-554 1231 Fax: 0131-553 3631 E-mail: shipping@tward.co.uk *Freight forwarders & ships agents* Also at: Grangemouth, Grimsby, Immingham & The Clyde

▶ T Wills & Son, Bridge Hill, Kirkbride, Wigton, Cumbria, CA7 5JB Tel: (01697) 351227 Fax: (01697) 351424

T Wilson & Sons, The Barracks, Abbeytown, Wigton, Cumbria, CA7 4SY Tel: (01697) 361628 Fax: (01697) 361622 *Agricultural engineers*

T Y M Seals & Gaskets, A Hopton Park, London Road, Devizes, Wiltshire, SN10 2EY Tel: (01380) 734510 Fax: (01380) 734511 E-mail: admin@tym.co.uk *Silicone rubber hose, gaskets & mouldings manufrs*

▶ T&K Summerson, stockgill close, Gamston, Nottingham, NG2 6SA Tel: 0115-981 5153 E-mail: info@tkgardenservices.co.uk *Estate/ Letting Agents Garden Maintenance Services, Garden Maintenance,Pressure Wash Services, Grass Cutting , Hedge , Shrub and Bush Trimming , Holiday Garden Care Services , Low maintenance Gravel Gardens , Gutter Cleaning*

▶ T&T, 199-201 Green Lane, Stoneycroft, Liverpool, L13 6RH Tel: 0151-220 1616 Fax: 0151-220 1616 E-mail: sales@ttpowertools.co.uk *Power tool & plant repair*

▶ T1 Commercial, PO Box 5783, Westcliff-on-Sea, Essex, SS1 9BX Tel: (01702) 305856 E-mail: enquiries@t1-commercial.com *Consultants, Agents and Brokers. Sourcing and supplying all types of commercial flooring. Carpet Tile Specialists. Wood, Laminates, Carpet and Granite all sourced from leading*

continued

companies and Mills. End of Lines and surplus stocks obtainable.

T2 Business Solutions, Melrose Hall, Cypress Drive, St. Mellons, Cardiff, CF3 0YZ Tel: (029) 2079 9133 Fax: (029) 2081 9515 E-mail: enquiries@t2business.co.uk *Welcome to t2 business solutions**We provide incredibly dynamic and highly flexible Training, Coaching and Business Support solutions, which all share one common goal - Delivering quantifiable value to our clients.* *

▶ T2 Technical Services Ltd, PO Box 611, Hull, HU5 3ZW Tel: (0845) 2264661 Fax: (0845) 2264665 E-mail: info@t2technical.co.uk *Portable appliance testing services*

T2 Technologies, 4-5 Market Street, Newport, Gwent, NP20 1FU Tel: (01633) 212133 Fax: (01633) 212473 E-mail: enquiries@t2technologies *Website design & development also e-commerce design & development*

▶ T3 Magic, Unit 2 Lochside Court, Irongray Road, Dumfries, DG2 0HS Tel: (01387) 721170 E-mail: info@t3magic.com *Distributors of hair products*

T3 Therapy To Takeaway, 7/Nunhold Business Centre, Dark Lane, Hatton, Warwick, CV35 8XB Tel: (01926) 843714 Fax: (01926) 843739 E-mail: info@t3therapy.co.uk *Health food & health supplements retailers*

▶ t3money Ltdd, 27 Hadley Way, Winchmore Hill, London, N21 1AL Tel: (07984) 467103 *Website giving details on how to improve personal finance. Trade secrets on casino"s, risk free betting, eaby and the stock markets.*

Tab Business Machines & Equipment Ltd, 2-3 London Road, London, SE1 6JZ Tel: (020) 7620 3366 Fax: (020) 7633 0206 E-mail: sales@tab.uk.com *Office stationers suppliers*

Tab Fabs Ltd, Unit 4 Lower Wield, Alresford, Hampshire, SO24 9AJ Tel: (01256) 389123 Fax: (01256) 389188 *Steel fabricators*

Tab Logix Ltd, 200 Milton Park, Abingdon, Oxfordshire, OX14 4TF Tel: (01235) 864818 Fax: (01235) 861275 Principal Export Areas: Worldwide *Storage warehousing contractors*

Tab Refractory Construction & Maintenance Co. Ltd, Unit 7 Parkdale Industrial Estate, Wharf Street, Warrington, WA1 2HT Tel: (01925) 230222 Fax: (01925) 230430 E-mail: tabrcm@aol.com *Refractory lining contractors*

Tabelek (Control Systems) Ltd, Jubilee Road, Waterlooville, Hampshire, PO7 7RE Tel: (023) 9261 0016 Fax: 023 9261 0016 *Hampshire based company engaged in the manufacture of electricity distribution and control apparatus. Tabelek Control Electronics Control Systems Ltd offers Control Systems, Control Systems, Electric and Instrumentation, Electrical.*

▶ Taberner Plant Hire Ltd, Bell House Lane, Anslow, Burton-on-Trent, Staffordshire, DE13 9PA Tel: (01283) 564017 Fax: (01283) 512243

Table Makers, 155 St. John's Hill, London, SW11 1TQ Tel: (020) 7223 2075 Fax: (020) 7223 7296 E-mail: sales@tablemakers.co.uk *Table manufrs*

Table Place Ltd, 1 Thistleton Road, Market Overton, Oakham, Leicestershire, LE15 7PP Tel: (01572) 767636 Fax: (01572) 767932 *Makers & retailers of classic furniture* Also at: Huntingdon & Kenilworth

Table Toppers, 34 Highview Gardens, Upminster, Essex, RM14 2YZ Tel: (01708) 640495 *China & glassware hire*

Tablesport Ltd, Unit 4 Surney Farm, Long Buckby Wharf, Long Buckby, Northampton, NN6 7PP Tel: (01327) 842546 Fax: (01327) 842737 *Service Amusements Machines*

The Tabletop Group, Pool Potteries, Pool Street, Church Gresley, Swadlincote, Derbyshire, DE11 8EQ Tel: (01283) 213800 Fax: (01283) 817969 E-mail: *Kitchen & household pottery*

▶ Tabounchik Trading, 1a Maxim Cottages, Hophurst Lane, Crawley Down, Crawley, West Sussex, RH10 4LJ Tel: (01342) 717188 E-mail: tabounchik@fsmail.net *importer of Russian white, pink,green and black marble and granite stone.High quality and low prices.*Also semi-precious stones*

Tabs Technicom UK P.L.C., Stockholm Road, Suttonfields Industrial Estate, Hull, HU7 0XW Tel: (01482) 825558 Fax: (01482) 825557 *Building systems manufrs*

Tabs Training Ltd, Brunel House, Mitchell Road, Salisbury, SP2 7PY Tel: (01722) 338668 Fax: (01722) 332052 E-mail: sales@tabsltd.co.uk *Computer training consultants*

Tabs Training Ltd, Brunel House, Mitchell Road, Salisbury, SP2 7PY Tel: (01722) 338668 Fax: (01722) 332052 E-mail: sales@tabsltd.co.uk *Accountants*

Tabuchi Electric UK Ltd, Tabuchi House, Robson Avenue, Teesside Industrial Estate, Stockton-on-Tees, Cleveland, TS17 9LS Tel: (01642) 750750 Fax: (01642) 750108 *Transformer manufrs*

Tac, Gronant Buildings, 14 South Penrallt, Caernarfon, Gwynedd, LL55 1NS Tel: (01286) 671123 Fax: (01286) 678890 E-mail: admin@teledwyr.com *Trade association - television production*

Tac Satchwell, Europa House, 310 Europa Boulevard, Westbrook, Warrington, WA5 7XR Tel: (01925) 401000 Fax: (01925) 401166 *Heating & ventilation system service*

Tachodisc, 19 Kingsland Grange, Woolston, Warrington, WA1 4RW Tel: (01925) 820088 Fax: (01925) 831300 E-mail: info@tachodisc.co.uk *Tachograph suppliers & manufrs*

Tachograph Analysis Consultants, 23 Westway, Maghull, Liverpool, L31 2PQ Tel: 0151-531 1004 Fax: 0151-531 1122 E-mail: nigelkirkwood@digital-tachograph.com *Tachograph consultants*

Tack A Round Saddlery Ltd, 41A High Street, Billingshurst, West Sussex, RH14 9PP Tel: (01403) 783862 Fax: (01403) 786069 E-mail: sales@tackaround.co.uk *Saddlery retailers*

▶ Tack N Jibe, Flat 1, 2 Linden Road, Bexhill-on-Sea, East Sussex, TN40 1DN Tel: (07917) 341778 *We provide a custom printing and embroidery service to all.*We use high quality garments because quality is as important to us as it is to you.*We specialise in the boating and sailing markets but can cater for all.*NO MINIMUM ORDER.*Just ask, its free .....*

▶ Tack Rack, Unit 17 Midland Mills, Station Road, Cross Hills, Keighley, West Yorkshire, BD20 7DT Tel: (01535) 631100 Fax: (01535) 631100 *Equestrian equipment manufrs*

▶ Tack Shack, 44 Calder Road, Mirfield, West Yorkshire, WF14 8NR Tel: (01924) 491119 Fax: (01924) 503777 *Suppliers of equestrian supplies*

Tackburn Ltd, Unit 11A Imex Business Centre, Oxleason Road, East Moons Moat, Redditch, Worcestershire, B98 8LG Tel: (01527) 68559 Fax: (01527) 68559 *Fixings & wall ties*

▶ Alan Tackle, 10 Bridge Road, Southampton, SO19 7GQ Tel: (023) 8044 6222 *Fishing tackle manufrs*

Tackle & Gun, 3 East Well, High Street, Tenterden, Kent, TN30 6AH Tel: (01580) 764851 *Fishing tackle, guns & equestrian equipment suppliers*

Tacklestore Ltd, Unit S3 Chittening Industrial Estate, Chittening, Bristol, BS11 0YB Tel: 0117-938 1600 E-mail: sales@tacklestore.net *Lifting equipment retailers*

Tacktick Marine Electrical, 22 North Street, Emsworth, Hampshire, PO10 7DG Tel: (01243) 379331 Fax: (01243) 379199 E-mail: sales@tacktick.com *Marine electronic production & distributors*

Tackwood Transport, Foundry Way, Little End Road Industrial Estate, Eaton Socon, St. Neots, Cambridgeshire, PE19 8TR Tel: (01480) 214340 Fax: (01480) 406468 E-mail: ts@tackwoodservices.co.uk *Tackwood services are a family run business that has been operating in St Neots since 1971. We offer a range of services from our purpose built warehouse, ideally situated close to the A1 comprising of offices, maintenance and warehouse facilities.*

Tacp Landscape Architects, 10 Park Grove, Cardiff, CF10 3BN Tel: (029) 2022 8966 Fax: (029) 2039 4776 E-mail: cardiff@tacp.uk.com *Landscape architects*

Tactical Controls Ltd, Unit 4 Parkland Business Centre, Chartwell Road, Lancing, West Sussex, BN15 8UE Tel: (01903) 750800 Fax: (01903) 750678 E-mail: email@tacticalcontrols.co.uk *Temperature controller manufrs*

▶ Tactical MarComms, 16 Blythe Road, Corfe Mullen, Wimborne, Dorset, BH21 3LR Tel: (01202) 699967 Fax: (01202) 699967 E-mail: eddie.palmer@tacticalmarcomms.com *Industrial business to business marketing services*

Tadberry Evedale Printers Ltd, Unit 2-4 1a Philip Walk, London, SE15 3NH Tel: (020) 7732 2226 Fax: (020) 7358 0006 E-mail: colin@tadberry-evedale.co.uk *Printers suppliers & quality colour printers*

Tadley Engineering Ltd, Oak Tree Works, Silchester Road, Tadley, Hampshire, RG26 3PX Tel: 0118-981 0621 Fax: 0118-981 0787 E-mail: info@tadleyengineering.co.uk *Precision sheetmetal fabrication electronics & presswork specialists*

Tadpole Cartesia plc, Waterloo House, Waterloo Street, Clifton, Bristol, BS8 4BT Tel: 0117-923 8853 Fax: 0117-923 8834 *Computer systems & software developers*

Tadpole Contracts Ltd, The Old Bakery, High Street, Great Bardfield, Braintree, Essex, CM7 4RF Tel: (01371) 810817 Fax: (01371) 810024 *I T consultants*

Tadware Ltd, 31 Hill Field, Oadby, Leicester, LE2 4RW Tel: 0116-271 6137 Fax: 0116-271 6137 E-mail: tadnet@globalnet.co.uk *Test programmer (financial)*

Tadweld Ltd, Station Estate, Station Road, Tadcaster, North Yorkshire, LS24 9SG Tel: (01937) 832865 Fax: (01937) 835823 E-mail: info@tadweld.co.uk *Fabrication engineers*

Taecomm, Penrallt, Cwmbach, Whitland, Dyfed, SA34 0DR Tel: (07770) 555011 Fax: (01994) 448709 *Electronic point sale & professional sound systems*

▶ Taeno Design Consultants, The Mill, Home Farm, Ardington, Wantage, Oxfordshire, OX12 8PD Tel: (01235) 833785 Fax: (01235) 833860 *Taeno is a product development consultancy. We work with manufacturers to make their products more competitive by reducing costs, adding customer value or increasing market life*

▶ Taf Tyre Products, Littleton House, Littleton Road, Ashford, Middlesex, TW15 1UU Tel: (01784) 420505 Fax: (01784) 259707 E-mail: tas@tas-tyreproducts.com *Manufacturers & suppliers of corporate work wear*

▶ Taft International Transport, Weatherfield Lodge, Each End, Ash, Canterbury, Kent, CT3 2BZ Tel: (01304) 813406 Fax: (01304) 813404 E-mail: sales@roadhaulageuk.com

Tag, Unit 1 Derby Road Business Park, Burton-on-Trent, Staffordshire, DE14 1RW Tel: (01283) 531855 Fax: (01283) 741411 E-mail: sales@taglesuire.co.uk *Sports, leisure & work wear distributors*

Tag, 29 Clerkenwell Road, London, EC1M 5TA Tel: (020) 7251 4571 Fax: (020) 7253 5355 E-mail: info@tagmedia.co.uk *Typesetter & reprographic printers*

Tag Farnborough Airport Ltd, Farnborough Airport, Farnborough, Hampshire, GU14 6XA Tel: (01252) 379000 Fax: (01252) 379051 E-mail: ops@tagfarnborough.com *Aircraft engineers & maintenance.*

Tag Guard Ltd, Unit 2 Blendworth Farm House, Blendworth, Waterlooville, Hampshire, PO8 0AG Tel: (023) 9259 8218 Fax: (023) 9259 8918 E-mail: sales@tag-guard.co.uk *Electronic security tagging equipment distributors*

Tag Instantprint Ltd, 182 London Road, Kingston Upon Thames, Surrey, KT2 6QW Tel: (020) 8546 6833 Fax: (020) 8547 1441 E-mail: taginstantprint@aol.com *Office stationers printers*

Tag Learning Ltd, 25 Pelham Road, Gravesend, Kent, DA11 0HU Tel: (01474) 357350 Fax: (01474) 537887 *Education software suppliers*

Tag Plastic Extrusions Ltd, 21 Marsh Green Road North, Marsh Barton Trading Estate, Exeter, EX2 8NY Tel: (01392) 479036 Fax: (01392) 432835 *Plastic extrusion manufrs*

▶ Tag Training Services, 20 Leyland Drive, Kingsthorpe, Northampton, NN2 8QA Tel: 07974 972913 Fax: 0870 1351199 *We can offer quality cost effective training training throughout the uk.on a variety of truck types Including Counterbalance,Reach,Pivot Steer,Narrow Aisle,MEWPS and many more.*

▶ Tag Company UK Ltd, Duval House, High Street Harmondsworth, Harmondsworth, West Drayton, Middlesex, UB7 0BT Tel: (020) 8283 4999 E-mail: info@tagcompany.com *TAG Company International is a full service EAS company offering users a true, quality alternative. TAG features state-of-the-art 58 kHz Acousto-Magnetic (AM) and 8.2 MHz Swept Radio Frequency (RF) EAS systems and tags, Internet-based EAS (for remote service and data-mining), and Advanced/Smart Tagging.*

Taggart & Co. Ltd, 38-44 Main Street, Ballymoney, County Antrim, BT53 6AP Tel: (028) 2766 2130 Fax: (028) 2766 6129 *Building materials suppliers*

Taggart Motor Group, 528-540 Windmillhill Street, Motherwell, Lanarkshire, ML1 2AQ Tel: (01698) 266133 Fax: (01698) 262693 E-mail: enquiries@taggarts.co.uk *Motor distributors* Also at: Bellshill, Dunfermline & Glasgow

▶ TAGit, 21 Mead Road, Willesborough, Ashford, Kent, TN24 0BS Tel: (07946) 333292 *Tagit produce custom printed key tags, asset tags, pet tags, identity cards, business cards, medical tags, fobs, room key tags in small quantities at affordable prices*

▶ Tagster, Unit 30, 63 Jeddo Road, London, W12 9EE Tel: (0870) 0605528 Fax: (020) 8735 0150 E-mail: sales@tagster.co.uk *Supply key tags & security key cabinets*

Tahanni Ltd, Unit 37 Wessex Trade Centre, Ringwood Road, Poole, Dorset, BH12 3PG Tel: (01202) 746900 Fax: (01202) 723111 E-mail: info@tahanni.com *Precision engineers suppliers & manufrs*

▶ Tailor Made Conservatories Windows & Doors, Barlby Road, Selby, North Yorkshire, YO8 5BJ Tel: (01757) 705866 *UPVC & timber conservatories, windows & doors*

Tailor Made Telecom Ltd, Bridge House, 7 & 9 Church Road, Bristol, BS5 9JJ Tel: 0117-955 9830 Fax: 0117-955 9840 E-mail: info@tmtelecom.co.uk *Telecommunications specialists*

▶ Tailored Fire & Security, 8 Saville Street, Bolton, BL2 1BY Tel: (01204) 385022 Fax: (01204) 385033 E-mail: sales@tfs-ltd.com *Install cctv, security access control & alarm systems*

▶ Tailored Fire & Security (Manchester) Ltd, Unit 1 Fifth Street, The Village, Trafford Park, Manchester, M17 1JX Tel: 0161-872 3282 Fax: (0870) 240 7176 E-mail: sales@redetec.co.uk *Redetec - Data and server rack Fire Protection systems; Computer Fire Protection, Using FM200, Novec1230, Point and Vesda high sensitivity fire detection, Fire Detection and Suppressioin all in one 2U x 19" rack chassis.*Redetec also has IP connectivity, with MIB and SNMP, Telnet and Webpage condition & alarm management.*

Tailored Panels, Unit 4 Minster Park, Grundymore Estate West Moors, Wimborne, Dorset, BH21 6QW Tel: (01202) 871998 Fax: (01202) 861215 E-mail: tailored-panel@hotmail.com *Air compressors, industrial power & hand tools suppliers*

▶ Tailored Trailers and Bottled Gas Supplies, Oakenshaw Gas Centre, Dyehouse Road, Oakenshaw, Bradford, West Yorkshire, BD12 7BX Tel: 01274 416116 Fax: 01274 694222 E-mail: web@tailoredtrailers.co.uk *Trailers, standard modified & custom built & trailers services*

▶ Tailored Transport Solutions Ltd, 12 Amos Crescent, Scunthorpe, South Humberside, DN16 1RA Tel: (01724) 339169 E-mail: bobby76_373@hotmail.com *Transport/ courier services avaliable 24/7 any distance. Full goods in transit cover provided.*

Tailormade Software, Poolside, 43 Pool Lane, Brocton, Stafford, ST17 0TY Tel: (01785) 660005 Fax: (01785) 660005 E-mail: sales@tailormadesw.co.uk *Software development*

▶ John Tainton, 2 Broomhills Industrial Estate, Rayne Road, Braintree, Essex, CM7 2RG Tel: (01376) 528992 Fax: (01376) 528993 E-mail: southernsales@johntainton.co.uk *Steel stockholder supplier flattened mild steel sheets & plates*

John Tainton, Hoo Farm Industrial Estate, Worcester Road, Kidderminster, Worcestershire, DY11 7RA Tel: (01562) 740477 Fax: (01562) 68765 E-mail: jtsales@johntainton.co.uk *Steel decoiling services*

▶ John Tainton, Blackvein Industrial Estate, Cross Keys, Newport, Gwent, NP11 7PX Tel: (01495) 279247 Fax: (01495) 279243 E-mail: jtcksales@johntainton.co.uk *Specialist supplier of flattened mild steel sheets & plates*

▶ John Tainton, 5 Cromwell Road, Bredbury, Stockport, Cheshire, SK6 2RF Tel: 0161-406 1006 Fax: 0161-406 6614 E-mail: northernsales@johntainton.co.uk *Steel plate manufrs*

▶ Taipale Automotive UK, New Quay Road, Lancaster, LA1 5QN Tel: (01524) 840804 Fax: (01524) 36450 E-mail: esapirttijarvi@aol.com *Specialist manufacturer of Flex-EL APH underfloor heating/ drying foils. Main application is in vehicle floor, doors, walls, steps and exit/entrance areas.*Product is only 0.2mm thin, light weight and maintenance free.*

continued

Taisei Europe Ltd, 19 Hanover Sq, London, W1S 1HY Tel: (020) 7316 4000 Fax: (020) 7316 4001 *Construction & civil engineers*

▶ K.J. Tait Engineers, 15 Woodside Terrace, Glasgow, G3 7XH Tel: 0141-332 9676 Fax: 0141-332 0995E-mail: glasgow@kjtait.com *Engineers*

Taj Crafts, 2 Wellesley Avenue, Iver, Buckinghamshire, SL0 9AY Tel: (01753) 653900 E-mail: tajcrafts@btopenworld.com *Craft & yarn suppliers*

Takbro Ltd, Unit 5 Albert Drive, Burgess Hill, West Sussex, RH15 9TN Tel: (01444) 245601 Fax: (01444) 872316 E-mail: mail@takbro.co.uk *Terminal tag distributors*

Takbro Ltd, 59 Church Street, Walshaw, Bury, Lancashire, BL8 3BN Tel: (01204) 887001 Fax: (01204) 545400E-mail: sales@takbro.co.uk *Cable accessories suppliers & manufrs*

Take Five Beverages, 271 Camp Road, St. Albans, Hertfordshire, AL1 5NR Tel: (01727) 851826 Fax: (01727) 869068 E-mail: sales@take-five.co.uk *Beverage distribs*

Take One Ltd, Unit 1, Moor Barn, Sheldon Lane, Bakewell, Derbyshire, DE45 1QR Tel: (01629) 814610 Fax: (01629) 814610 E-mail: info@takeoneltd.com *Manufacturers of personalised melamine table mats,coasters, trays & chopping boards etc. for both the commercial & domestic market, since 1984.*

Take One Media, Unit 4 Century Point, Halifax Road, High Wycombe, Buckinghamshire, HP12 3SL Tel: (01494) 888500 Fax: (01494) 436914 *Direct marketing services*

Takeuchi Mfg (UK) Ltd, Unit E2B, John Boyd Dunlop Drive, Kingsway Business Park, Rochdale, Lancashire, OL16 4NG Tel: 01706 657722 E-mail: sales@takeuchi-mfg.co.uk *Mini excavator distribution*

▶ Takisawa Ltd, Meir Road, Redditch, Worcestershire, B98 7SY Tel: (01527) 522211 Fax: (01527) 510728 E-mail: sales@takisawa.com Principal Export Areas: Worldwide *Machine tool*

Taktec Ltd, 158 Kristiansand Way, Letchworth Garden City, Hertfordshire, SG6 1TY Tel: (01462) 486985 Fax: (01462) 486985 *CNC machine tool & repair agents*

▶ Taktomat, 15, Rushley Drive, Sheffield, S17 3EL Tel: 0114-262 0480 Fax: 0114-262 0480

▶ Taktyle Science Europe Ltd, Bentwaters Parks, Rendlesham, Woodbridge, Suffolk, IP12 2TW Tel: (01394) 420741 Fax: (01394) 420664 *Textile signs*

▶ Tal Freeway Ltd, Wellington Road, Gateshead, Tyne & Wear, NE11 9JL Tel: 0191-460 5037 Fax: 0191-460 9477

Talana Plastics Ltd, 28 Standard Way, Fareham, Hampshire, PO16 8XG Tel: (01329) 822940 Fax: (01329) 231034 E-mail: enquiries@talanaplastics.com *Plastic moulding including injection manufrs*

▶ A.C. Talbot - Appliance Repairs, 3 Carisbrooke Crescent, Barrow-in-Furness, Cumbria, LA13 0HU Tel: (01229) 835263 Fax: (0871) 2110099 E-mail: andee.talbot@tiscali.co.uk *Repair non integrated washing machines, electric cookers, fridges*

Talbot Components, Unit 1 Talbot Way, Shavington Park, Market Drayton, Shropshire, TF9 3SJ Tel: (01630) 653551 Fax: (01630) 654425 E-mail: sales@talbotcomp.co.uk *Filter specialists*

Talbot Designs Ltd, 225 Long Lane, Finchley, London, N3 2RL Tel: 0845 8510136 Fax: (020) 8349 0294 E-mail: sales@talbotdesigns.co.uk *Established in 1947, Talbot Designs is able to produce to order an enormous range of bespoke and custom designed plastic fabrications.*We manufacture items using all the standard thermoplastics; acrylic, polycarbonate, PETG, PVC and high impact polystyrene. Talbot Designs is also one of the UK's leading acrylic plastic dome and bubble suppliers, with a huge range of stock acrylic domes available for next day delivery.*Our highly experienced team can handle any complex fabrication or moulding projects, even those with tight deadlines. That is one of the many reasons we have so much repeat business and our clients return time and time again.*"Only limited by imagination" is our motto - so call us today with your fabrication requirement, however challenging it may be!*

Talbot Office Products Equipment Ltd, 5 Gunnery Terrace, The Royal Arsnal, Woolwich, London, SE18 6SW Tel: (020) 7231 7020 Fax: (020) 7231 8087 *Office equipment agents*

Talbot Plan Printing Co., 47 Wyle Cop, Shrewsbury, SY1 1XJ Tel: (01743) 343740 Fax: (01743) 343740 E-mail: d.chidlow@btconnect.com *Drawing office equipment distributors*

Talbot Plastics, Talbot House, Ross Road, Reading, RG1 8EL Tel: 0118-957 4211 Fax: 0118-950 2335 Principal Export Areas: Worldwide *Polythene bags carriers & sack manufrs*

Talbot Plating Co. Ltd, Victoria Works, River Way, Barrowford, Nelson, Lancashire, BB9 6EL Tel: (01282) 618107 Fax: (01282) 692381 *Electroplating services*

Talbot Textiles & Upholstery Supply Co. Ltd, 16-18 Dargan Cresent, Belfast, BT3 9JP Tel: (028) 9078 1521 Fax: (028) 9077 8610 E-mail: ronnie@talbottexile.co.uk *Upholstery suppliers* Also at: Glasgow

Talbot Tool Co. Ltd, Grip Works, Crowhurst Road, Brighton, BN1 8AT Tel: (01273) 508881 Fax: (01273) 540544 E-mail: sales@talbot-tool.co.uk *Drill jig bush manufrs*

Talbots Birmingham Ltd, 56-60 Princip Street, Birmingham, B4 6LN Tel: 0121-333 3544 Fax: 0121-333 3520 E-mail: sales@talbotsbirm.co.uk *Jewellery pad manufrs*

Talbotts Biomass Energy Ltd, Tollgate drive, Tollgate Industrial Estate, Stafford, ST16 3HS Tel: (01785) 213366 Fax: (01785) 256418 E-mail: sales@talbotts.co.uk *Manufacturers waste to energy systems*

Talent & Production Services, Oakla,, East Grinstead, Salisbury, SP5 3RY Tel: (01722) 712921 Fax: (01722) 712992 *TV programming agents*

▶ Talent Television, Lion House, 72-75 Red Lion Street, London, WC1R 4NA Tel: (020) 7421 7800 Fax: (020) 7421 7811

Talent Weighing S & S Ltd, 3j Anchor Bridge Way, Dewsbury, West Yorkshire, WF12 9QS Tel: (01924) 438127 Fax: (01924) 438129 E-mail: info@talentweighing.co.uk Principal Export Areas: Worldwide *Talent Weighing manufacture, service, repair and calibrate all types of industrial weighing scales and systems covering the UK. We are an independent company formed in 1982 supplying weighing scales and weighing equipment including platform weigh scales, axle weighers, axle weigh pads, medical weigh scales including baby scales, chair scales and wheelchair scales. In addition to stand alone basic products we also manufacture and supply intrinsically safe weighing scales and special weighing equipment. Talent Weighing are a Quality Assured company to BS EN ISO 9002 and offer a complete after sales service which includes maintenance contracts covering not only our own equipment but other manufacturers weighing scales.*

Talentum Development Ltd, Beal Lane, Shaw, Oldham, OL2 8PF Tel: (01706) 844714 Fax: (01706) 882612 E-mail: info@talentum.co.uk *Fire detection systems, flame & spark detection designers & manufrs*

▶ Talisker Distillery, Carbost, Isle Of Skye, IV47 8SR Tel: (01478) 614300 *Whisky*

Tality, St. Johns Innovation Centre, Cowley Rd, Cambridge, CB4 0WS Tel: (01223) 421025 Fax: (01223) 421031 E-mail: hr-uk@tality.com *Electronic product designers*

▶ Talk Events UK Ltd, Unit 6, 229 Torrington Avenue, Coventry, CV4 9HN Tel: (024) 7646 2444 Fax: (0845) 6126013 E-mail: info@talkevents.com *Audio visual services*

Talk Group, Suite 57, Century House, Leeds, LS14 1BS Tel: (0870) 7550300 Fax: (0870) 7550305 E-mail: info@talkgroup.co.uk *Mobile phones, business numbers, IVR & voicemail*

▶ Talk Marketing Ltd, Stockton Business Centre, Brunswick Street, Stockton-on-Tees, Cleveland, TS18 1DW Tel: (01642) 345133 Fax: (01642) 345135 E-mail: talkmarketing@fsbdial.co.uk *Full service marketing consultancy offering, marketing & communications strategies,public relations, telemarketing & sales & marketing training, plus exciting new marketing product, streaming video email.*

Talk Paper Ltd, 1 Canada Road, Byfleet, West Byfleet, Surrey, KT14 7JL Tel: (01932) 335577 Fax: (01932) 335580 *Office papers merchants*

Talk Talk Clothing Ltd, Unit 1, Spitfire Close Coventry, Coventry, CV5 6UR Tel: (024) 7667 6713 Fax: (024) 7671 5204 *Clothing manufrs*

Talk Telecom Ltd, Unit 35 City Industrial Park, Southern Road, Southampton, SO15 1HG Tel: (023) 8071 8730 Fax: (023) 8071 8738 *Mobile phones & vehicle tracking wholesale & distributors*

▶ Talkback Thames, 20-21 Newman Street, London, W1T 1PG Tel: (020) 7861 8000 Fax: (020) 7861 8001 E-mail: sales@talkback.co.uk *Audio visual producers*

Talke Chemical Co. Ltd, Radnor Works, 1 Back Lane, Congleton, Cheshire, CW12 4PP Tel: (01260) 273357 Fax: (01260) 298175 E-mail: sales@talkechem.co.uk *Paint, timber & metal preservative manufrs*

▶ Talking Balloons, Mcgregors Way, Chesterfield, Derbyshire, S40 2WB Tel: (01246) 270555 Fax: (01246) 270566 E-mail: sales@talkingballoons.com *Printing balloons*

▶ Talking Chalk Ltd, Eastwood House, Chalk Lane, East Horsley, Leatherhead, Surrey, KT24 6TH Tel: (0845) 6586914 Fax: (020) 7681 1332 E-mail: information@talkingchalk.co.uk *Management Consultant, specialising in HR. Leadership assessment & development, team building, organisation development. Employee surveys.*

Talking Headsets Ltd, Woodlands, The Bridle Lane, Hambrook, Chichester, West Sussex, PO18 8UG Tel: (01243) 573226 Fax: (01243) 574318 E-mail: info@talkingheadsets.co.uk *Talking Headsets offer a wide range of revolutionary alternatives in hearing protection & conservation. We combine our extensive knowledge of hearing protection with the need to communicate, sometime in hostile noisy environments, to offer the right solutions to your problems. We have the latest, most sophisticated passive & electronic hearing protection, communications headsets, two-way radios & wireless DUPLEX Bluetooth communications solutions currently available on the market. Coupled with our 18 yrs of experience in the hearing protection/ communications industry you can be sure we have best the solution for you. We cater for Military, Industrial, Public Services, Marine and Aviation users along with a wide range of products suitable for use in consumer markets. Brands include MSA Sordin, A-KABEL, TELEX along with our own OEM products. Our wide range of Military, SWAT, Tactical, Airsoft headsets & accessories fulfil the requirements of some of the most demanding users in the world*

Talking Phones, Linotype House, L & M Business Park, Norman Road, Altrincham, Cheshire, WA14 4ES Tel: (0845) 4503435 *Telecommunication equipment suppliers*

Talking Technology Ltd, Technology House, 11 Palmerston Road, Sutton, Surrey, SM1 4QL Tel: (020) 8770 9343 Fax: (020) 8770 9143 E-mail: sales@talktech.co.uk *Telecommunication systems distributors & installers*

Talking T's, 1 149b Histon Road, Cambridge, CB4 3JD Tel: (01223) 304104 Fax: (01223) 304110 E-mail: sales@t-shirts.co.uk *T-shirt printing/embroidery services*

▶ TALKPROPERTY.NET Ltd T/A talkproperty, 89 Coningham Road, London, W12 8BS Tel: 07910 969619 E-mail: osp@talkproperty.net *Project Management services for residential building and refurbishment work. Acting for the client we co-ordinate the professionals involved in the design and building process from concept through to completion.*

continued

▶ Tall Poppy, 11-12 Merchants Crescent, Wharf Street Victoria Quays, Sheffield, S2 5SY Tel: 0114-272 7077 Fax: (0871) 6618601 E-mail: info@tall-poppy.com *Marketing advice, services & support*

Tallboat Plant Hire Ltd, Pedmore Road, Brierley Hill, West Midlands, DY5 1TQ Tel: (01384) 78002 Fax: (01384) 77846 *Contractors plant hire, leasing & rental*

▶ Tallboy Media Ltd, London House, 243-253 Lower Mortlake Road, Richmond, Surrey, TW9 2LS Tel: (020) 8948 9516 Fax: (020) 8940 2007 E-mail: info@tallboy.co.uk *Video production & media training services*

Tallett Charter Surveyors, 18 Long Ashton Road, Long Ashton, Bristol, BS41 9LD Tel: (01275) 540200 Fax: (01275) 540203 E-mail: tallett@tallett.co.uk *Chartered surveyors & property agents*

▶ Talmont Control Systems Ltd, 192 Fletchamstead Highway Industrial Estate, Fletchamstead Highway, Coventry, CV4 7BB Tel: (024) 7667 3355 Fax: (024) 7667 3356 E-mail: talmont.control@yahoo.co.uk *Control panel manufrs*

▶ Talon Business Support Ltd, Unit 33-36 Fountain Business Centre, Ellis Street, Coatbridge, Lanarkshire, ML5 3AA Tel: (01236) 431171 Fax: (01236) 431172 E-mail: sales@talonsys.co.uk *Computer software*

Talon Lifting, Unit 2 Brook Forge, Hightown Road, Cleckheaton, West Yorkshire, BD19 5JS Tel: (01274) 871242 Fax: (01274) 869716 *Lifting gear manufrs*

Talos Ltd, Prospect House, 20 High Street, Brasted, Westerham, Kent, TN16 1RG Tel: (01959) 561124 Fax: (01959) 561402 E-mail: info@quantus.co.uk *Computer networking & accounting software services*

Taltrees Stoves, Taltrees Centre, Worcester Road, Newnham Bridge, Tenbury Wells, Worcestershire, WR15 8JA Tel: (01584) 781361 Fax: (01584) 781363 *Heater requirement services*

▶ Talulah & Fox, 27 Barnham Road, Barnham, Bognor Regis, West Sussex, PO22 0ER Tel: (01243) 551733 E-mail: info@talulahandfox.co.uk *We create unique hats & headpieces*

Tam Fabrications Ltd, Unit 5 Rexmore Way, Liverpool, L15 0HX Tel: 0151-734 0018 *Steel fabricators*

Tam International North Sea Ltd, 1 Abbotswell Road, Aberdeen, AB12 3AB Tel: (01224) 875105 Fax: (01224) 890038 E-mail: info@tam-northsea.com *Inflatable packer manufrs*

▶ Tam O' Shanter Crystal & Awards, 116 Russell Drive, Wallacetown, Ayr, KA8 8JN Tel: (01292) 287765 Fax: E-mail: donald@tamoshanter-crystal.com *General engravers services*

Tam Transformers Ltd, Durban Road, Bognor Regis, West Sussex, PO22 9QT Tel: (01243) 861122 Fax: (01243) 830870 E-mail: tam@tamtransformers.co.uk *Design & manufacturers of laminated, ferrite, toroidal, transformers & chokes from .1va to 30KVA single & three phase*

Tama (UK), P O Box 157, Cannock, Staffordshire, WS11 9WL Tel: (01543) 274100 Fax: (01543) 277112 E-mail: info@tama-uk.fsnet.co.uk *Pneumatic punching machines manufacturers & distributors*

Tamar, Unit A, Long Acre, Saltash, Cornwall, PL12 6LZ Tel: (01752) 840036 Fax: (01752) 842326 E-mail: tamar.industrial@virgin.net *Janitorial & safety suppliers*

Tamar Crop Services Ltd, Howton Farm, Pillaton, Saltash, Cornwall, PL12 6QY Tel: (01579) 350001 Fax: (01579) 351420 E-mail: enquiries@tamarcropservices.co.uk *Agronomy services*

Tamar Inflatables, Unit 4b, Restormel Industrial Estate, Lostwithiel, Cornwall, PL22 0HG Tel: (01208) 873777 Fax: (01208) 873774 E-mail: mail@liferafts-inflatables.com *Liferafts & inflatable boats*

Tamar Inflatables, Unit 4b, Restormel Industrial Estate, Lostwithiel, Cornwall, PL22 0HG Tel: (01208) 873777 Fax: (01208) 873774 E-mail: ce.banyard@btconnect.com *Marine safety services*

Tamar Labels Ltd, Woodlands, Tavistock, Devon, PL19 8JE Tel: (01822) 833330 Fax: (01822) 834484 E-mail: sales@tamarlabels.co.uk *Label manufrs*

Tamar Specialist Brushes, Exeter, EX2 8WW Tel: (01392) 491818 Fax: (01392) 491818 E-mail: enquiries@tamarbrushes.co.uk *Chimney sweeping systems/equipment suppliers*

Tamar Trading Co. Ltd, 15 Bodmin Street, Holsworthy, Devon, EX22 6BB Tel: (01409) 253555 Fax: (01409) 254996 E-mail: sales@tamartrading.com *Builders' merchants*

▶ Tamar Valley Products Ltd, The Creamery Barn Close, Langage Business Park, Plympton, Plymouth, PL7 5HQ Tel: (01752) 340888 Fax: (01752) 348777 E-mail: info@tamaricecream.co.uk

Tamark Engineering Ltd, 924 Borough Road, Birkenhead, Merseyside, CH42 6QW Tel: 0151-201 7907 Fax: 0151-334 7407 E-mail: sales@tamarkengineering.co.uk Principal Export Areas: Worldwide *Repair and service of all makes of ultrasonic cleaning equipment.New ultrasonic cleaning equipment supplied.Manufacturer of Hilsonic ultrasonic cleaners/ultrasonic generators and transducer bars*

The Tambour Company Ltd, Warren Road, Green Lane Business Park, Featherstone, Pontefract, West Yorkshire, WF7 6EL Tel: (01977) 600026 Fax: (01977) 600991 Principal Export Areas: Worldwide *Tambour, rolling & office furniture shutters*

Tambour Doors Ltd, 21 Marston Lane, Marston, Northwich, Cheshire, CW9 6DL Tel: (01606) 42423 Fax: (01606) 48118 *Door installers & repairers*

Tambour Shades, 21 Rose Valley, Brentwood, Essex, CM14 4HZ Tel: 01277 223960 *Lampshade distributors & manufrs*

Tameside Metal Components, Dove House, Thorncliffe Wood, Hollingworth, Hyde, Cheshire, SK14 8NJ Tel: (01457) 766300 Fax: (01457) 766300 *Shop fitting manufrs*

Tameside Refrigeration & Air Conditioning Ltd, 2 Gate Centre Bredbury Park Way, Bredbury Park Industrial Estate, Bredbury, Stockport, Cheshire, SK6 2SN Tel: 0161-406 8995 Fax: 0161-406 8997 *Air conditioning engineers*

Tameside Scale Services, Winton Street, Ashton-under-Lyne, Lancashire, OL6 8NL Tel: 0161-339 6501 Fax: 0161-339 6501 *Scales & weighing equipment manufrs*

Tameside Sewing Machine Services, 266a Stamford St West, Ashton-under-Lyne, Lancashire, OL6 7NJ Tel: 0161-308 3112 *Sewing machine services, repairs & sales*

▶ Tameside Tools, Unit 17-18 Alpha Court, Windmill La Industrial Estate, Denton, Manchester, M34 3RB Tel: 0161-337 3400 Fax: 0161-337 3401 *Power tools & accessory distributors*

Tamla Of Dearne Valley Ltd, 77A Kilnhurst Road, Rawmarsh, Rotherham, South Yorkshire, S62 5QQ Tel: (01709) 527600 Fax: (01709) 527600 *Manufacturer of country clothing*

▶ Tamlite Lighting, Warwick House, Station Road, Kenilworth, Warwickshire, CV8 1JJ Tel: (01926) 858126 *Electric lamps & light bulbs*

Tamlite Lighting, Pipers Road, Park Farm Industrial Estate, Redditch, Worcestershire, B98 0HU Tel: (01527) 517777 Fax: (01527) 517666 E-mail: jrallden@tamlite.co.uk *Industrial & commercial lighting & fire alarms fitters*

Tamo Ltd, 195 Horton Road, West Drayton, Middlesex, UB7 8HP Tel: (01895) 859700 Fax: (01895) 859888 E-mail: info@tamo.co.uk *Valve distributors, agents & stockholders*

Tampoprint UK Ltd, Oaklands Park, Wokingham, Berkshire, RG41 2FD Tel: 0118-973 0500 Fax: 0118-973 0725 E-mail: sales@tampoprint.co.uk *Supply of pad printing machines*

▶ Tams Group Ltd, Blyth Pottery, Uttoxeter Road, Longton, Stoke-On-Trent, ST3 1QQ Tel: (01782) 339199 Fax: (01782) 339194 E-mail: uksales@tams.co.uk

Tams Packaging Ltd, Sopers Road, Cuffley, Potters Bar, Hertfordshire, EN6 4TP Tel: (01707) 876777 Fax: (01707) 872233 E-mail: tams.packaging@talk21.com *Based at the northern most point on the M25. Packaging design, Cardboard engineering. Manufacturers of Plain & Printed cartons, cardboard boxes, cases, containers. Carton die cutting & glueing services to the trade. Litho printing & foil blocking. All carton styles including Crash lock, 4 corner, Blister cards, Box & lids, Presentation packs, Promotional items. Inserts & Fitments, Divisions & Dividers, Greetings cards. Solid board, corrugated board & Litho laminated cartons. Check out our website - tamspackaging.com*

▶ Tamtec Electronics, Stafford Park 12, Telford, Shropshire, TF3 3BJ Tel: (01952) 299399 Fax: (01952) 299300 *Electronics manufrs*

Tamura Europe Ltd, Hopton Park, London Road, Devizes, Wiltshire, SN10 2EY Tel: (01380) 731700 Fax: (01380) 731703 E-mail: business@tamura-europe.co.uk *Transformer & power supply manufrs*

Tamworth Auto Electrics Ltd, Unit 6-7 Mariner, Tamworth, Staffordshire, B79 7UL Tel: (01827) 67539 Fax: (01827) 57473 *Auto-electronic engineering services*

Tamworth Ceilings Partitions & Interiors, 152 Lichfield Road, Tamworth, Staffordshire, B79 7SF Tel: (01827) 52738 *Suspended ceilings & office partitions installation services*

Tamworth Glass Fibre, Pooley Lane, Pooley Hall Farmhouse, Polesworth, Tamworth, Staffordshire, B78 1JA Tel: (01827) 331010 Fax: (01827) 330027 E-mail: m.hopkins267@ntlworld.com *Glass fibre custom moulders*

Tamworth Heat Treatment Ltd, 7 Darwell Park, Mica Close, Tamworth, Staffordshire, B77 4DR Tel: (01827) 318030 Fax: (01827) 318039 *Heat treatment services & surface engineering services*

▶ Tamworth Laser Marking Services, Unit 66, William Tolson Enterprise Park, Mill Lane, Fazeley, Tamworth, Staffordshire, B78 3QD Tel: (01827) 251550 Fax: (01827) 288835 E-mail: sales@tamworthlasermarking.co.uk *Laser marking & engraving of all metals services*

▶ Tamworth Pest Control, 70 Camhouses, Wilnecote, Tamworth, Staffordshire, B77 4HJ Tel: (01827) 898229 E-mail: tamworthpestcontrol@msn.com

Tamworth Steel Stockholders Ltd, Gagarin, Apollo, Tamworth, Staffordshire, B79 7TA Tel: (01827) 61531 Fax: (01827) 310078 E-mail: sales@tamworth-steel.co.uk *Black & bright steels*

▶ Tana Water UK Ltd, Unit 6, Bilton Industrial Estate, Lovelace Road, Bracknell, Berkshire, RG12 8YT Tel: (01344) 869900 Fax: (01344) 869911 E-mail: contact@tanawater.co.uk *Mainstead drinking water dispensers suppliers & manufrs*

Tanabe Seiyaku, C P House, 97-107 Uxbridge Road, London, W5 5TL Tel: (020) 8566 0356 Fax: (020) 8566 0376 E-mail: sales@tanabe.co.jp *Pharmaceuticals*

Tanaka Seiki Europe Ltd, 18 Ptarmigan Place, Townsend Drive, Nuneaton, Warwickshire, CV11 6RX Tel: (024) 7635 1153 Fax: (024) 7632 8717 E-mail: tanaka@freezone.co.uk *Coil winding machinery distributors*

Tanaz International Ltd, 336 Humberstone Lane, Leicester, LE4 9JP Tel: 0116-274 0853 Fax: 0116-246 0346 *Textiles manufrs*

Tanby Swimming Pools & Hot Tubs, 620-622 Limpsfield Road, Warlingham, Surrey, CR6 9DS Tel: (01883) 622335 Fax: (01883) 626775 E-mail: martin@tanby.freeserve.co.uk *Swimming pool, spa & sauna constructors & maintenance*

Tancred Solutions, 32b High Causeway, Whittlesey, Peterborough, PE7 1AJ Tel: (01733) 350925 Fax: (01733) 350832 E-mail: info@tancredsolutions.com *Experienced in improvement programs, crisis management, relationship management, dispute resolution, professional speaking, corporate training, managing problems, and fund raising. We also offer a professional accountancy practice, fully equipped to cater for all your needs whether you're a sole trader or a company. We can also offer full company secretarial support, company formation, fund-raising, start-up advice, planning, and we give our first accountancy consultation free of charge.*

Tandberg Data, Davenport House, Bowers Way, Harpenden, Hertfordshire, AL5 4HX Tel: (01582) 769071 Fax: (01582) 769025 *Tape storage manufacturers*

Tandem Consultancy, Top Executive Suite, 55 West Street, Chichester, West Sussex, PO19 1RU Tel: (01243) 778822 Fax: (01243) 779951 E-mail: creatorbiz@tandemuk.com *Chartered marketing consultants*

Tandem Design, The Cottage, Eastgate Street, Southampton, SO14 3HB Tel: (023) 8063 2159 Fax: (023) 8033 2352 E-mail: studio@tandem-design.co.uk *Experienced Graphic Design consultancy specialising in branding, packaging and corporate literature.*

Tandon Europe, 4th Floor Long Wing, Grosvenor House Prospect Hill, Redditch, Worcestershire, B97 4DQ Tel: (01527) 599900 Fax: (01527) 599911 E-mail: aneile@tandon.com *Computer memory distribution*

Tandon Textile Merchants, 445 Moseley Road, Birmingham, B12 9BX Tel: 0121-440 0848 Fax: 0121-446 4563 *Textile merchants*

Tanera Camans, 39 Lochy Road, Inverlochy, Fort William, Inverness-Shire, PH33 6NW Tel: (01397) 705119 *Sports sticks manufrs*

Tanfield Group plc, Vigo Centre, Birtley Road, Washington, Tyne & Wear, NE38 9DA Tel: 0191-417 2170 Fax: (0845) 1557756 E-mail: sales@tanfieldgroup.com *Precision metalworkers & fabricators & electrical vehicles*

▶ Tanfield Metal Spinners, 6 Parsons Road, Parsons Industrial Estate, Washington, Tyne & Wear, NE37 1HB Tel: 0191-419 3377

Tanfield Towbars, Blatchford Road, Horsham, West Sussex, RH13 5QR Tel: (01403) 269100 Fax: (01403) 251199 *Towing equipment & trailer distributors Also at: Brighton, Oldham, Peterborough & Witham*

Tangent, 1 Lilac Cottage, Northchapel, Petworth, West Sussex, GU28 9HL Tel: (01428) 707844 Fax: (01428) 707845 E-mail: david@thetangent.net *Graphic & interior design consultancy*

▶ Tangent Electrical Ltd, Wheel Wright Yard, 2 The Street, Hatfield Peverel, Chelmsford, CM3 2EA Tel: (01245) 382552 Fax: (01245) 382135

▶ Tangent Furniture, 36-42 New Inn Yard, London, EC2A 3EY Tel: (0870) 9904150 Fax: (0870) 9904199 E-mail: enquiries@tangentsales.co.uk *Office furniture manufrs*

▶ Tangent Printers, 52 London Road, London, SW17 9HP Tel: (020) 8648 9418

Tangerine Confectionery Ltd, Clifton Road, Blackpool, FY4 4QB Tel: (01253) 761201 Fax: (01253) 792006 *Manufacturer of confectionery*

▶ Tango Mercado, 16 Church Lane, Dingley, Market Harborough, Leicestershire, LE16 8PG Tel: (01858) 535319 E-mail: dcturner2@aol.com *Dance School specialising exclusively in Argentine Tango*

Tango Rail, Bilport Lane, Wednesbury, West Midlands, WS10 0NT Tel: 0121-502 6600 Fax: 0121-502 0303 *Steel fencing suppliers*

▶ Tango Security Ltd, 74 Heron Wood Road, Aldershot, Hampshire, GU12 4BH Tel: (01252) 650677 Fax: (01252) 320286 E-mail: tangosec@aol.com *Static security providers*

Tangram Ltd, Lane House, Main Road, Fyfield, Abingdon, Oxfordshire, OX13 5LN Tel: (01865) 390380 Fax: (01865) 390001 *Marketing consultants*

Tangye Ltd, Royal Works, Atlas Street, Clayton Le Moors, Accrington, Lancashire, BB5 5LW Tel: (01254) 615100 Fax: (01254) 615199 E-mail: sales@allspeeds.co.uk *Manufacturers of hydraulic equipment & jacks*

Tanist Computer Systems Ltd, Penbury, Pendrift, Blisland, Bodmin, Cornwall, PL30 4JT Tel: (01208) 851166 Fax: (01208) 850044 *Computer consultants*

Tanita International Ltd, The Barn Philpots Close, West Drayton, Middlesex, UB7 7RY Tel: (01895) 438577 Fax: (01895) 438511 *Scales services*

Tank Cleaners (Glasgow) Ltd, Robslee Drive, Giffnock, Glasgow, G46 7TY Tel: 0141-638 0906 Fax: 0141-638 9014 E-mail: simon@mitchellthomson.fsnet.co.uk *Industrial tank cleaning*

The Tank Exchange, Lewden House, Barnsley Road, Dodworth, Barnsley, South Yorkshire, S75 3JU Tel: (01226) 203852 Fax: (01226) 299424 *Tank stockholders of all types*

Tank Storage & Services Ltd, Unit 9 Spring Rise, Falconer Road, Haverhill, Suffolk, CB9 7XU Tel: (01440) 712614 Fax: (01440) 712615 E-mail: admin@tankstorage.co.uk *Chemical & janitorial suppliers*

▶ Tankard Of Bradford, 758 Aireworth Road, Keighley, West Yorkshire, BD21 4DH Tel: (01535) 663566 Fax: (01535) 663544

Tanker & General Ltd, Hedley Avenue, West Thurrock, Grays, Essex, RM20 4EL Tel: (01375) 370660 Fax: (0870) 8723134 E-mail: mgeary@tankergeneral.com *Commercial vehicle welders & body building services*

Tankersley Properties, 6 Henshall Street, Barnsley, South Yorkshire, S70 1XX Tel: (01226) 286361 Fax: (01226) 286361 *Joinery & glazing manufrs*

▶ Tankfreight Ltd, South Shore Road, Grangemouth, Stirlingshire, FK3 8TT Tel: (01324) 665340 Fax: (01324) 483436

Tankline Water Treatment Equipment, 16 Babington Road, Hornchurch, Essex, RM12 4AR Tel: (01708) 450234 Fax: (07971) 113276 E-mail: sales@tank-line.co.uk *Renovate cold water storage tanks*

Tanks Direct, Richmond Lodge, Bond Street, Hedon, Hull, HU12 8NY Tel: (07803) 182400 Fax: (01482) 899454 E-mail: john@networkpacific2000.freeserve.co.uk *Second hand oil & fuel tanks, storage tanks, pressure vessels manufrs*

Tanks & Vessels Industries, Bankwood Lane Industrial Estate, Bankwood Lane, New Rossington, Doncaster, South Yorkshire, DN11 0PS Tel: (01302) 866003 Fax: (01302) 864990 E-mail: sales@tanksandvessels.com *Tank stockists/tank fabricator/pump & pipework supplier*

Tankson Textiles, 173 Rolfe Street, Smethwick, West Midlands, B66 2AS Tel: 0121-558 1733 *Ladies, gents, kids garment manufrs*

Tanmill Ltd, 8 Meadow Lane, Bilston, West Midlands, WV14 9NQ Tel: (01902) 880991 Fax: (01902) 887477 *Plastic & steel fabricators*

Tannas Office Supplies Ltd, 76 High Road, London, NW10 2PU Tel: (020) 8459 0521 Fax: (020) 8459 8603 E-mail: info@tannas.co.uk *Office stationers, printers & office suppliers*

▶ Tanner Business Centre, Waterside Mill, Chew Valley Road, Greenfield, Oldham, OL3 7NH Tel: (01457) 872273 Fax: (01457) 870133 E-mail: info@tannerbrothers.co.uk *Incontinence products, pads, bed protection- disposable & washable, gloves- latex, vinyl & stretch synthetic*

Tanner Foods Ltd, Oxford Lane Dairy, Sible Hedingham, Halstead, Essex, CO9 3LE Tel: (01787) 460276 Fax: (01787) 465223 *UHT milk manufrs*

Tannoy Group Ltd, Rosehall Industrial Estate, Coatbridge, Lanarkshire, ML5 4TF Tel: (01236) 420199 Fax: (01236) 428230 E-mail: enquiries@tannoy.com *Commercial & residential audio equipment distributors*

Tanoga Ltd, Cradock Rd, Luton, LU4 0JF Tel: (01582) 502882 Fax: (01582) 581781 E-mail: info@tanoga.com *Precision toolmakers & engineers*

Tanside Ltd, Back Lane Farm, High London Lane, Winfarthing, Diss, Norfolk, IP22 2EF Tel: (01953) 861444 Fax: (01953) 861440 E-mail: tansideltd@btconnect.com *Belts & buckles manufrs*

▶ T'Ansons Combustion Engineering Services Ltd, Canal Forge, Newcastle Road, Stone, Staffordshire, ST15 8LB Tel: (01785) 819050 Fax: (01785) 819123

Tansun Ltd, 1 Ridgacre Road, West Bromwich, West Midlands, B71 1BW Tel: 0121-580 6200 Fax: 0121-580 6222 E-mail: quartzinfo@tansun.co.uk *Solarium & leisure equipment manufrs*

Tant Laboratories Ltd, 17 Twyford Business Centre, London Road, Bishop's Stortford, Hertfordshire, CM23 3YT Tel: (0870) 8770100 Fax: (01279) 713170 E-mail: sales@tantlabs.com *Optical services*

Tantalize Ltd, 186 Seven Sisters Road, London, N7 7PX Tel: (020) 7263 2404 Fax: (020) 7263 2559 *Fabric manufrs*

▶ Tantastic Tanning, 63 Chingford Mount Road, London, E4 8LU Tel: (020) 8527 3727 *Tanning salon*

Tantec UK Ltd, P O Box 9593, Tamworth, Staffordshire, B78 3HS Tel: (01827) 284244 Fax: (01827) 286311 E-mail: chris@merciasystems.co.uk *Electrical Surface Treatment & Static Control Systems.*

Tantofex Ltd, The Bathroom Works, National Avenue, Hull, HU5 4HS Tel: (01482) 346461 Fax: (01482) 445886 *Bathroom manufrs*

Tanton Ltd, Lodge Farm, Bowl Road, Charing, Ashford, Kent, TN27 0HB Tel: (0870) 7461300 Fax: (0870) 7461900 E-mail: sales@tanton.ltd.uk *Suppliers of Electric Fencing for Horses, Ponies and all livestock. Pest Control equipment and Pet Training and Containmnet systems.*

Tanton Signs, 2 Ladycroft Way, Orpington, Kent, BR6 7BX Tel: (01689) 859642 Fax: (01689) 859642 *Sign writers*

▶ Tantronics Ltd, Goyt Mill, Upper Hibbert Lane, Marple, Stockport, Cheshire, SK6 7HX Tel: 0161-427 1100 Fax: 0161-427 5100 E-mail: info@tantronics.co.uk *Suppliers of ansmann chargers*

Tapcast Ltd, Russet House, Appletree Lane, Inkberrow, Worcester, WR7 4JA Tel: (01386) 792196 Fax: (01386) 793087 E-mail: steve.neal@tapcast.co.uk *Business & home computer services*

Tapco Homecare Services, Commercial Unit, Pool House Estate, Bancroft Road, Reigate, Surrey, RH2 7RP Tel: (020) 8398 6663 Fax: (01737) 247265 E-mail: info@tapco.uk *Dry rot damp & property maintenance*

Tapekraft Ltd, Unit C Castlehills Court, Howard Road, Eaton Socon, St. Neots, Cambridgeshire, PE19 8ET Tel: (01480) 216161 Fax: (01480) 216162 E-mail: enquiries@tapekraft.co.uk *Adhesive tape & labels converters & distributors*

▶ Tapes-Direct, Unit 1, New Road Nurseries, Great Barford, Bedford, MK44 3LH Tel: (01234) 871117 Fax: (01234) 871191 E-mail: sales@tapes-direct.co.uk *Direct supply of high quality adhesive tapes at discounted prices*

Tapestream Duplication, Unit 4 Hampers Grn Indust Estate, Petworth, West Sussex, GU28 9NR Tel: (01798) 344108 Fax: (01798) 342116 *Audio-visual production agents*

Tapestry Audio Visual, Nordic House, Baltic Quay, Grangemouth, Stirlingshire, FK3 8TX Tel: (0845) 2308999 Fax: (01324) 489349 E-mail: sales@tapestryav.net *Audio-visual hire & sales*

Tapeswitch Ltd, Unit 38 Drumhead Road, Chorley North Industrial Estate, Chorley, Lancashire, PR6 7BX Tel: (01257) 249777 Fax: (01257) 246600 E-mail: sales@tapeswitch.co.uk *Industrial machine guard manufrs*

Tapflo UK Ltd, B The Apex Centre, Church Lane, Colden Common, Winchester, Hampshire, SO21 1TN Tel: (01962) 717131 Fax: (01962) 717130 E-mail: mick@tapflo-demon.co.uk *Manufacturers of pumps*

F.H. Tapley & Sons, The Smithy, Moss Lane, Cheswardine, Market Drayton, Shropshire, TF9 2RE Tel: (01630) 661376 Fax: (01630) 661376 *Steel building construction , suppliers & manufrs*

Taplin International Ltd, Unit 3 Lower William Street, Southampton, SO14 5QE Tel: (023) 8023 2304 Fax: (023) 8023 2305 E-mail: mail@switchcraft.info *Electrical, marine equipment manufrs*

Tapmatic Engineers' Merchants, 7d Millers Close, Fakenham, Norfolk, NR21 8NW Tel: (01328) 863676 Fax: (01328) 856118 E-mail: info@tapmatic.co.uk *Distributors of tapping heads, tapping fluids, synchroflex heads, precision tooling, steel collets (QC), rubber collets, Mainigley machine taps, drill-taps, SU-matic multiheads and angle heads, Llambrich keyless drill chucks, Deschner hydraulic dampers & shock absorbers, Comato grooving systems, Drabus fraction drills, Unist minimal spray units.*

Charles Tapp Builders' Merchants, 111 Southgate Road, London, N1 3JQ Tel: (020) 7359 9118 Fax: (020) 7359 9118 *Builders merchants*

Tappelectric Ltd, 2 Dragon Court, Crofts End Road, Bristol, BS5 7XX Tel: 0117-951 8274 Fax: 0117-951 3751 E-mail: info@tappelectric.co.uk *Electrical contractors*

Tapper Interiors Ltd, Vantage Business Park, Bloxham Road, Banbury, Oxfordshire, OX16 9UX Tel: (01295) 221240 Fax: (01295) 221241 *Suspended ceilings & office partition manufrs*

▶ Tappin Storage & Removals, 209 Askew Road, London, W12 9AZ Tel: (020) 8749 4434 Fax: (020) 8749 4434

Tapping Services, 18-19 Broad Lanes, Bilston, West Midlands, WV14 0RY Tel: (01902) 404882 Fax: (01902) 403692 *Industrial fasteners & tapping manufacturer*

Taprex, 2-6 Victor Road, Harrow, Middlesex, HA2 6PU Tel: (020) 8863 4698 *Sales & hire of humidifiers dehumidifiers portable & installed air con*

Taprogge U K Ltd, Unit 6, Hurlbutt Road, Heathcote Industrial Estate, Warwick, CV34 6TD Tel: (01926) 336614 Fax: (01926) 336617 E-mail: taprogge@taprogge.co.uk Principal Export Areas: Worldwide *Water filter, filtration systems specialists*

▶ TAPS WORLD UK, 1 MELLINGTON AVE, EAST DIDSBURY, MANCHESTER, MANCHESTER, M20 5WE Tel: 07753 299525 E-mail: L1HUS@AOL.COM *WHOLESALERS OF BATHROOM AND KITCHEN TAPS IN THE UK*

▶ Tapsell Lifting Equipment, Sandy La Industrial Estate, Stourport-on-Severn, Worcestershire, DY13 9QB Tel: (01299) 827262 Fax: (01299) 828272 E-mail: sales@tapsell.com *Lifting equipment manufrs*

Tar Skips & Transport Ltd, Rear of 97 King William Street, Amblecote, Stourbridge, West Midlands, DY8 4EY Tel: (01384) 390711 Fax: (01384) 828060 E-mail: peggy.tristram@btconnect.com *Skip contractors*

Tara Personal Care Ltd, 28 Ryde Avenue, Hull, HU5 1QB Tel: (01482) 444999 Fax: (01482) 473395 Principal Export Areas: Worldwide *Manufacturers of cosmetics bath salts*

Tara Signs Ltd, St. Peters Place, Western Road, Lancing, West Sussex, BN15 8SB Tel: (01903) 750710 Fax: (01903) 754008 E-mail: admin@tarasigns.com *Plastic & illuminated sign manufrs*

Tarantella Ltd, Richmond House, Lawnswood Business Park, Redbers Close, Leeds, LS16 6RD Tel: 0113-251 2000 Fax: 0113-368 6001 *Software developers & technical services*

Tarcal, Unit 15A, Pershore Trading Estate, Pershore, Worcestershire, WR10 2DD Tel: (01386) 556312 Fax: (01386) 556058 *Specialist fabricators for motorsport industry*

Tardis Communications Ltd, PO Box 446, Aylesbury, Buckinghamshire, HP21 7RJ Tel: (01296) 338747 Fax: (01296) 422014 E-mail: info@tardiscoms.co.uk *Radio components distributors & manufrs*

Tarff Valley Ltd, Tarff Station House, Ringford, Castle Douglas, Kirkcudbrightshire, DG7 2AN Tel: (01557) 820247 Fax: (01557) 820249 *Agricultural merchants*

Tarff Valley Ltd, Main Street, Glenluce, Newton Stewart, Wigtownshire, DG8 0PL Tel: (01581) 300555 Fax: (01581) 300553 *Agricultural merchant*

Target Achievement Ltd, Mercury Park, Amber Close, Amington, Tamworth, Staffordshire, B77 4RP Tel: (01827) 309709 Fax: (01827) 309719 E-mail: sales@maydown.co.uk *Computer consultants*

Target Animations & Lighting, Fairlands, Main Road, Westerfield, Ipswich, IP6 9AA Tel: (01473) 255670 Fax: (0871) 9943275 *Animation display & design & christmas lights manufrs*

Target Badges, 134 Watnall Road, Hucknall, Nottingham, NG15 7NH Tel: 0115-956 0047 Fax: 0115-956 0047 E-mail: info@targetbadges.co.uk *Leading manufacturers of personalised badges, exhibition and promotional badges, signage, key fobs, desk and doorplates and much more. No minimum order. Quick turnaround. Very competitive prices. Free quotations, information pack and samples available.*

▶ Target Communications PR Ltd, Pump Farm Cottage, 1 Ongar Road, Kelvedon Hatch, Brentwood, Essex, CM15 0LA Tel: (01277) 365344 Fax: (01277) 366668 E-mail: events@targetgroupuk.com *Event management company running network events, product launches as well as business to business exhibitions and seminars*

Target Fastenings Ltd, Holpur House, 5 Albert Road, Crowthorne, Berkshire, RG45 7LT Tel: (01344) 777189 Fax: (01344) 779038 E-mail: sales@targetfixings.com *Industrial fastener distributors & stockholders*

Company Information

Target Fluid Services, Millhouse Centre, 118 Commercial Road, Totton, Southampton, SO40 3ZW Tel: (023) 8087 2142 Fax: (023) 8066 6882 E-mail: target.fluid@btinternet.com *Hydraulic & pneumatic control system manufrs*

Target Furniture Ltd, 1 Ardington Road, Northampton, NN1 5LP Tel: (01604) 622405 Fax: (01604) 628578 *Furniture manufrs*

Target Furniture Ltd, Studland Road, Northampton, NN2 6PZ Tel: (01604) 792929 Fax: (01604) 792500 E-mail: sales@targetfurniture.co.uk *Contract furnishings manufrs*

Target Group plc, Target House, 5-19 Cowbridge Road East, Cardiff, CF11 9AB Tel: (029) 2030 1401 Fax: (029) 2030 1400 E-mail: marketing@targetgroup.net *Software development consultants*

Target Plastics Ltd, 138-140 Nathan Way, London, SE28 0AU Tel: (020) 8312 9090 Fax: (020) 8312 9191 E-mail: admin@targetplastics.co.uk *Plastic injection moulders*

Target Promotions Ltd, 170 Handcroft Road, Croydon, CR0 3LE Tel: (020) 8665 6992 Fax: (020) 8665 5606 E-mail: sales@targetpromotions.co.uk *Graphic production*

Target Signs, Unit 27 Baltic Works, Effingham Road, Sheffield, S9 3QA Tel: 0114-243 6600 Fax: 0114-243 6633 *Sign manufrs*

▶ Target Talent, 23 Castalia Square, London, E14 3NG Tel: (0845) 0097030 Fax: (0871) 7143355 E-mail: info@ttrec.co.uk *Specialising in Sales & Marketing Jobs in London. Search Vacancies, Upload your CV, Play Games & Read the News. or email us info@ttrec.co.uk*

Target Transfers Ltd, Anglia Way, Braintree, Essex, CM7 3RG Tel: (01376) 326351 Fax: (01376) 345876 E-mail: info@targettransfers.com *Manufacturers of heat applied transfers*

Target Transmission, Kilby's Yard, 25-27 Bacon Lane, Edgware, Middlesex, HA8 5AR Tel: (020) 8381 2863 Fax: (020) 8381 2863 *Repair gearboxes*

Target Trophy & Engraving Centre, 312a Lytham Road, Blackpool, FY1 6EY Tel: (01253) 348798 Fax: (01253) 348798 E-mail: sales@targettrophies.co.uk *Engravers*

Target Worldwide Express Ltd, 6 Woodlands Park, Ashton Road, Newton-le-Willows, Merseyside, WA12 0HF Tel: (01925) 247000 Fax: (01925) 575700 E-mail: enquiries@targetexpress.co.uk *Parcel couriers* Also at: Branches throughout the U.K.

Roger Targett, Nympsfield, Stonehouse, Gloucestershire, GL10 3TX Tel: (01453) 860861 Fax: (01453) 860861 *Glider repair & light aircraft maintenance*

▶ Targetti UK, Units 1-4, 11-29 Fashion Street, London, E1 6PX Tel: (020) 7377 2005 Fax: (020) 7377 0043 E-mail: office@targetti.co.uk *Lighting manufrs*

Tarion Communication Services Ltd, 27 Almond Grove, Hempstead, Gillingham, Kent, ME7 3SE Tel: (01634) 378428 Fax: (01634) 262595 *Network installing*

▶ Tariq Plastic, Unit 9B Stag Industrial Estate, Oxford Street, Bilston, West Midlands, WV14 7HZ Tel: (01902) 401263 Fax: (01902) 409364

Tarkett Ltd, Dickley Lane, Lenham, Maidstone, Kent, ME17 2QX Tel: (01622) 854000 Fax: (01622) 854500 E-mail: uksales@tarkett.com *Tarkett is one of the leading manufacturers of resilient floorcoverings in the UK, offering a comprehensive range of vinyl and linoleum products under the Tarkett brand. The product portfolio includes slip resistant floorcoverings, heavy duty floorcoverings, natural wood and stone effect design tiles, sports floors, wetroom systems, static control products and linoleum. For the latest product information click on the web link now.*

Tarlow Engineering Ltd, Unit 22 Acorn Industrial Park, Crayford Road, Dartford, DA1 4AL Tel: (01322) 550328 Fax: (01322) 522998 E-mail: tarlow@mistral.co.uk *Toolmakers & precision engineers*

▶ Tarmac Ltd, Upper Cruiks, Inverkeithing, Fife, KY11 1HH Tel: (01383) 413241 Fax: (01383) 413244 *Aggregates, stone & ashfelt & concrete specialists*

▶ Tarmac Ltd, New Bigging Quarry, Carnwath, Lanark, ML11 8NE Tel: (01555) 840361 *Sand & gravel suppliers*

▶ Tarmac Central Ltd, Pant Quarry, Halkyn, Holywell, Clwyd, CH8 8BP Tel: (01352) 780441 Fax: (01352) 781207 *Ash felts & aggregates*

▶ Tarmac Central Ltd, Dene Quarry, The Hill, Cromford, Matlock, Derbyshire, DE4 3QS Tel: (01629) 822104 Fax: (01629) 826185 *Quarry specialists*

▶ Tarmac Central Ltd, Hoveringham, Nottingham, NG14 7JY Tel: 0115-966 4292 Fax: 0115-966 5288

▶ Tarmac Centre Ltd, Harrison Street, Rotherham, South Yorkshire, S61 1EE Tel: (01709) 740700

Tarmac Motors Ltd, Foundry Lane, Widnes, Cheshire, WA8 8YZ Tel: (0870) 6006969 Fax: (01744) 885673 *Concrete & mortar ready mixed producers*

▶ Tarmac Northern Ltd, Ravelrigg Quarry, Kirknewton, Midlothian, EH27 8EF Tel: 0131-449 5523 Fax: 0131-451 5771 *Tarmac specialists*

Tarmac Northern Ltd, Lingerfield, Scotton, Knaresborough, North Yorkshire, HG5 9JN Tel: (01423) 796800 Fax: (01423) 796808 E-mail: info@tarmac-northern.co.uk *Concrete & mortar distributor & manufrs*

Tarmac Northern Ltd, Drumshoreland Road, Pumpherston, Livingston, West Lothian, EH53 0LH Tel: (01506) 853606 *Ready mixed concrete plant*

▶ Tarmac Northern Ltd, 40a Boghill Road, Newtownabbey, County Antrim, BT36 4QS Tel: (028) 9083 3879 Fax: (028) 9083 9494 *Asphalts distributors*

Tarmac Precast Concrete Ltd, Barholm Road, Tallington, Stamford, Lincolnshire, PE9 4RL Tel: (01778) 381000 Fax: (01778) 348041 E-mail: tall@tarmac.co.uk *Concrete manufrs* Also at: Hoddesdon, Lenwade & Wishaw

▶ Tarmac Precast Concrete Ltd, Thornfalcon Works, Henlade, Taunton, Somerset, TA3 5DN Tel: (01823) 442000 Fax: (01823) 443786 *Pre-cast concrete manufrs*

Tarmac Southern, Durnford Quarry, Long Ashton, Bristol, BS41 9DW Tel: (01275) 392510 Fax: (01275) 392205 *Stone suppliers*

Tarmac Southern Ltd, Holborough Road, Snodland, Kent, ME6 5PJ Tel: (0845) 6007888 Fax: (01634) 248295 E-mail: info@tarmac-southern.co.uk *Public works contractors*

▶ Tarmac Top Floor, Chainbridge Lane, Lound, Retford, Nottinghamshire, DN22 8RU Tel: (01777) 816616 Fax: (01777) 816617 *Flooring & stairs*

▶ Tarmac Topblock Ltd, Hangar 1 Ford Airfield Industrial Estate, Ford, Arundel, West Sussex, BN18 0HY Tel: (01903) 723333 Fax: (01903) 711043 *Concrete products, construction materials*

Tarmac Topmix Ltd, Belford Industrial Estate, Station Road, Belford, Northumberland, NE70 7DT Tel: (01668) 213839 *Concrete & mortar ready mixed suppliers*

Tarmac Topmix Ltd, Cornelly Quarry, Heol-Y-Splot, South Cornelly, Bridgend, Mid Glamorgan, CF33 4RD Tel: (01656) 740771 Fax: (01656) 748248 *Ready mixed concrete manufrs*

Tarmac Topmix Ltd, Unit N Babraham Rd, Sawston, Cambridge, CB2 4LH Tel: 01223 834421 *Ready mixed concrete manufacturer*

Tarmac Topmix Ltd, Rover Way, Cardiff, CF24 2RX Tel: (029) 2046 0308 Fax: (029) 2049 7232 E-mail: tonyford@tarmac.com *Ready mixed concrete suppliers*

Tarmac Topmix Ltd, PO Box 5, Chester Le Street, County Durham, DH3 2ST Tel: (01539) 727932 *Ready mix tarmac production & delivery*

Tarmac Topmix Ltd, Warren Lane, Stanway, Colchester, CO3 0NN Tel: (01473) 210707 Fax: (01206) 330437 *Ready mix concrete manufrs*

Tarmac Topmix Ltd, Tufthorn Business Park, Tufthorn Avenue, Coleford, Gloucestershire, GL16 8PP Tel: (01594) 836621 Fax: (01594) 837450 *Ready mix concrete suppliers*

Tarmac Topmix Ltd, John Street, Derby, DE1 2LU Tel: (01332) 384389 *Concrete manufrs*

Tarmac Topmix Ltd, Constarry Road, Kilsyth, Glasgow, G65 9HY Tel: (01236) 821500 *Concrete manufrs*

Tarmac Topmix Ltd, High Craighall Road, Glasgow, G4 9UD Tel: 0141-353 2515 Fax: 0141-353 2515 *Ready mix concrete manufrs*

Tarmac Topmix Ltd, Corporation Road, Newport, Gwent, NP19 0GA Tel: (01633) 280866 Fax: (01633) 290894 *Ready Mix concrete manufr*

Tarmac Topmix Ltd, Private Road 5, Nottingham, NG4 2JU Tel: 0115-961 4931 *Ready mixed concrete*

Tarmac Topmix Ltd, Sharpstones Lane, Bayston Hill, Shrewsbury, SY3 0AN Tel: (01743) 873479 Fax: (01743) 874505 *Ready mixed concrete supplies*

Tarmac Topmix Ltd, Govan Road, Fenton Industrial Estate, Stoke-on-Trent, ST4 2RS Tel: (01782) 263107 Fax: (01782) 413692 *Concrete producers*

Tarmac Toppave Ltd, 38 Hatch Pond Road, Nuffield Industrial Estate, Poole, Dorset, BH17 0JZ Tel: (01202) 642400 Fax: (01202) 642405 E-mail: sales@toppave.com *Block paving manufrs*

Tarmac Western Ltd, Viking Place, Off Rover Way, Cardiff, CF24 2RX Tel: (029) 2046 5969 Fax: (029) 2046 4407 E-mail: info@tarmac-western.co.uk *Concrete manufrs*

Tarmac Western Ltd, PO Box 1, Kington, Herefordshire, HR5 3LQ Tel: (01544) 388959 Fax: (01544) 231406 E-mail: info@tarmac-western.co.uk *Quarry*

Tarmac Western Ltd, Railway Terrace, Terrace Road, Pinvin, Pershore, Worcestershire, WR10 2DP Tel: (01386) 555389 Fax: (01386) 556014 *Tarmac manufrs*

Tarmac Western, Morfe Bank, Corus Works, Port Talbot, West Glamorgan, SA13 2NG Tel: (01639) 883052 Fax: (01639) 884435 *Slag producers*

Tarn Pure, 2-4 Copyground Lane, High Wycombe, Buckinghamshire, HP12 3HE Tel: (01494) 535576 Fax: (01494) 464175 E-mail: info@tarn-pure.com *Electronic water purification*

Tarnac Ltd, Cairneyhill Quarry, Caldercruix, Airdrie, Lanarkshire, ML6 8NX Tel: (01236) 842351 Fax: (01236) 843950 *Aggregates & coating materials*

▶ Tarnwalk (U K) Ltd, 34 Hiltingbury Road, Chandlers Ford, Eastleigh, Hampshire, SO53 5SS Tel: (023) 8026 5912

Taroni Bros, Unit 14 Rocky La Trading Estate, William Henry Street, Birmingham, B7 5ER Tel: 0121-333 3330 Fax: 0121-333 6080 *Car & lorry dismantlers*

Tarpaulin Repair Services, Three Ways, Walkers Lane, Whittington, Worcester, WR5 2NN Tel: (01905) 767077 Fax: (01905) 767077 *Tarpaulin repairers*

Tarpey-Harris Ltd, Flamstead House, Denby Hall Business Park, Denby, Ripley, Derbyshire, DE5 8NN Tel: (01332) 883950 Fax: (01332) 883951 E-mail: steve.jones@tarpey-harris.co.uk *Toolmakers & machining specialists*

Tarporley Gates, Moorcroft, Clotton, Tarporley, Cheshire, CW6 0EG Tel: (01829) 781444 *Gates & fencing manufrs*

Tarporley Tractors, Rode Street, Tarporley, Cheshire, CW6 0EF Tel: (01829) 733487 Fax: (01829) 733606 *Repairers of agricultural machinery*

A. Tarr Ltd, Meadow Business Centre, Uckfield Road, Ringmer, Lewes, East Sussex, BN8 5RW Tel: (01273) 814131 Fax: (01825) 762154 E-mail: sales@atarr.co.uk *Mattress spring coiling & wire forming machine suppliers*

Tarrant S C S Ltd, 1st Floor Victoria Court, St. Pancras, Chichester, West Sussex, PO19 7GD Tel: (01243) 839992 Fax: (01243) 839993 E-mail: rita.brown.tarrant@breathemail.net *Steeplejacks & lightning conductor engineers*

▶ Tarrs Icecream Ltd, 2 Sandown Road, Brislington, Bristol, BS4 3PN Tel: 0117-977 7290 Fax: 0117-977 7290 *Ice cream manufrs*

Tarsus Group plc, Commonwealth House, Chalkhill Road, London, W6 8DW Tel: (020) 8846 2700 Fax: (020) 8846 2801 E-mail: sales@tarsus-exhibitions.com *Exhibition organisers*

Tartan Buttonhole Co., 24 Young Avenue, Dumfries, DG2 0DJ Tel: (01387) 255130 E-mail: sales@tartanflowers.co.uk *Buttonhole products*

Tartan Hose, 44 Newry Road, Kilkeel, Newry, County Down, BT34 4DU Tel: (028) 4176 5717 Fax: (028) 4176 3241 E-mail: tartanhose@btconnect.com *Production of kilt stockings & tartan hose*

Tartan Manufacturing Ltd, 35 Soho Mills Industrial Estate, Wooburn Green, High Wycombe, Buckinghamshire, HP10 0PF Tel: (01628) 810119 Fax: (01628) 810177 *Sheet metal workers*

▶ Tartan Plant Ltd, Stirling Road, Larbert, Stirlingshire, FK5 3NJ Tel: (01324) 622956

Tarvail Ltd, Unit K4, Riverside Industrial Estate, Riverside Way, Dartford, DA1 5BS Tel: (01322) 226064 Fax: (01322) 289959 E-mail: office@tarvail.com *Pipework fabricators*

Tarvet Electronics Ltd, 1 Ferry Toll Road, Rosyth, Dunfermline, Fife, KY11 2XF Tel: (01383) 414777 Fax: (01383) 415888 *Electronic component distributors*

▶ TAS Legal Services, 12 Whiteley Close, Dane End, Ware, Hertfordshire, SG12 0NB Tel: (07813) 042428 E-mail: enquiry@tas-legal.co.uk *The one stop shop for all your legal requirements*

▶ Tasc Digital Control Systems, 1280 Century Way, Thorpe Park, Leeds, LS15 8ZB Tel: 0113-201 8998 Fax: 0113-201 8999

▶ TASC Fire Protection Services Ltd, 24B Orgreave Crescent, Dore House Industrial Estate, Sheffield, S13 9NQ Tel: (0870) 7705130 Fax: (0870) 7705131 E-mail: enquiries@tasc-groupltd.co.uk *Diamond drilling & fire protection*

Tascom International Ltd, 1 Mars House, Calleva Park, Aldermaston, Reading, RG7 8LA Tel: 0118-982 0400 E-mail: bill.white@tascom.co.uk *Manufacturers & suppliers of custom power supplies*

Tascomp Ltd, Newburgh Court, Belasis Hall Technology Park, Billingham, Cleveland, TS23 4EE Tel: (01642) 370656 Fax: (01642) 370012 E-mail: sales@tascomp.co.uk *Software for industrial automation applications suppliers*

▶ Tash Jacks, Oakland, The Street, Shorne, Gravesend, Kent, DA12 3EA Tel: (01474) 823666 Fax: (01474) 823777 E-mail: info@tashjacks.com *Suppliers for hair extension & wigs*

Tasha Sleigh Beds, Forstal Farm, Goudhurst Road, Lamberhurst, Tunbridge Wells, Kent, TN3 8AG Tel: (01892) 890769 Fax: (01892) 890769 *Antiques specialists & children's bed manufrs*

Tashglen Ltd, 3 Mountington Park Close, Harrow, Middlesex, HA3 0NW Tel: (020) 8907 9428 Fax: 020) 8909 1661 E-mail: tashglen@compuserve.com *Exporters*

Task Communications Ltd, 259 Church Road, Benfleet, Essex, SS7 4QN Tel: (01268) 793240 Fax: (01268) 881010 E-mail: sales@taskcomms.co.uk *Telecommunication systems & equipment distributors*

Task Computer Logic Ltd, 70 Skene Street, Aberdeen, AB10 1QE Tel: (0870) 7410292 Fax: (0871) 7333523 E-mail: seals@etcl.co.uk *Software developers*

Task Computer Systems, Breakspeare, College Road, London, SE21 7NB Tel: (020) 8693 5103 Fax: (020) 8299 2540 *Computer systems & software developers*

Task Lighting Ltd, 1 Low Farm Place, Moulton Park Industrial Estate, Northampton, NN3 6HY Tel: (01604) 644875 Fax: (01604) 790016 E-mail: sales@tasklighting.co.uk *Industrial lighting distributors*

Task Systems Ltd, W H House, 32 Bethnal Green Road, London, E1 6HZ Tel: (020) 7729 5088 Fax: (020) 7729 4709 E-mail: marketing@tasksystems.co.uk *Office furniture manufacturer & distributor*

Task Welding Ltd, 8a Culverin Square, Limberline Road, Hilsea, Portsmouth, PO3 5BU Tel: (023) 9269 0868 *Precision welders*

Taskers UK Ltd, 4 Roman Ridge Road, Sheffield, S9 1GB Tel: 0114-243 0927 Fax: 0114-242 5507 E-mail: sales@taskersuk.com *Hydraulic & lubrication specialists*

▶ Taskforce Software Ltd, 158 Sturminster Road, Bristol, BS14 8AT Tel: (01458) 835097 E-mail: info@taskforce-software.co.uk *Computer software*

Taskmaster Ltd, Morris Road, Leicester, LE2 6BR Tel: 0116-270 4286 Fax: 0116-270 6992 E-mail: info@taskmasteronline.co.uk *Educational supplies manufrs*

Tasktron Ltd, 3 Wintonlea, Monument Way West, Woking, Surrey, GU21 5EN Tel: (01483) 776060 Fax: (01483) 721389 E-mail: sales@crc.uk.com *Office equipment maintenance*

Taskwear Clothing, Albert School, Church Lane, Marple, Stockport, Cheshire, SK6 7AR Tel: 0161-449 9449 Fax: 0161-426 0906 E-mail: eeworkwear@hotmail.com *Workwear manufrs*

Tass Cable Management, Unit 1 Leonard House, 38a Rosemary Lane, Blackwater, Camberley, Surrey, GU17 0LT Tel: (01276) 600775 Fax: (01276) 600 622 E-mail: floorboxuk@msn.com *Cable management supplies*

Tassia Ltd, 167 Hermitage Road, London, N4 1LZ Tel: (020) 8880 1833 Fax: (020) 8880 1933 E-mail: tassia@btinternet.com *Leather & travel goods suppliers*

Tastebuds Vending Ltd, PO Box 243, Upminster, Essex, RM14 2RU Tel: (0845) 0958245 Fax: (0845) 0958246 E-mail: sales@tastebudsvending.com *TasteBuds Vending offer vending machines from a sale only basis for DIY sites through to a fully managed and operated vending service.**We also offer*

continued

Wholesale Vending Products to the trade and public.

Tastees Food Products, 20 Victoria Industrial Estate, Victoria Road, London, W3 6UU Tel: (020) 8993 1289 Fax: (020) 8993 1579 E-mail: tast33s@aol.com *Catering sandwiches distributors & manufrs*

Tasteful Vending (Southern) Ltd, Unit 2, Shirley, Solihull, West Midlands, B90 4FZ Tel: (08707) 517519 Fax: (08707) 517716 E-mail: sales@tasteful-vending.co.uk *Vending machine operators*

▶ Tasty Bites, 116 St. Marys Road, Garston, Liverpool, L19 2JG Tel: 0151-494 3145 Fax: 0151-494 3145 *Cafe*

Tata Ltd, 18 Grosvenor Place, London, SW1X 7HS Tel: (020) 7235 8281 Fax: (020) 7235 8727 E-mail: tata@tata.co.uk *Export & import agents*

Tata Consultancy Services, 12 Rutland Square, Edinburgh, EH1 2BB Tel: 0131-229 9725 Fax: 0131-228 3637 *Consultants*

▶ TATA - Phoenix Distribution Ltd, PO Box 41, Birmingham, B31 2TN Tel: 0121-472 4862 Fax: 0121-482 4158 E-mail: anthony.miles@pheonixdist.com *The TATA range of vehicles are available in both 2 & 4 wheel drive options. The TATA TL pick-up comes in single & double cab formats. The Safari is a genuine all round family 4 x 4*

Tate Engineering, Tate Estate, Kingsdown Road, Swindon, SN25 6SF Tel: (01793) 820503 Fax: (01793) 820504 E-mail: tate.engineering@virgin.net *General & precision engineers*

Tate Fastforms Ltd, Wingate House, Wingate Road, Luton, LU4 8PU Tel: (01582) 586700 Fax: (01582) 586725 E-mail: enquiries@tateconsumables.co.uk *Business forms & suppliers epos consumables*

▶ Tate Fencing Ltd, 1 Chase Wood Works, Frant Road, Frant, Tunbridge Wells, Kent, TN3 9HG Tel: (01892) 750230 Fax: (01892) 750130 E-mail: sales@tate-fencing.co.uk *Fencing & general timber products*

▶ Tate Fencing, Yellowcoat Mills, Hastings Road, Flimwell, Wadhurst, East Sussex, TN5 7PR Tel: (01580) 879900 Fax: (01580) 879677 *Fencing distributor & manufrs*

Tate Fire & Security Protection, 3 Cheddar Business Park, Wedmore Road, Cheddar, Somerset, BS27 3EB Tel: (01934) 744111 Fax: (01934) 744304 E-mail: sales@tatefire.co.uk *Fire alarm & security systems suppliers*

Tate & Lyle, 167 Regent Road, Kirkdale, Liverpool, L20 8DD Tel: 0151-933 1010 Fax: 0151-933 7434 E-mail: reception.athel@tateandlyle.com *Animal feed manufrs*

Tate & Lyle Citric Acid, Denison Road, Selby, North Yorkshire, YO8 8EF Tel: (01757) 703691 Fax: (01757) 701468 *Citric acid manufrs*

Tate & Lyle Sugars, Thames Refinery, Factory Road, London, E16 2EW Tel: (020) 7476 4455 Fax: (020) 7511 5507 E-mail: CEO@qudos.com *Sugar refiners*

Tate & Lyle Sugars, Thames Refinery, Factory Road, London, E16 2EW Tel: (020) 7476 4455 Fax: (020) 7511 5507 E-mail: CEO@qudos.com *Cane sugar process technology services*

Tate Publishing Ltd, Millbank, London, SW1P 4RG Tel: (020) 7887 8869 Fax: (020) 7887 8878 E-mail: tgpl@tate.org.uk *Books, prints, cards & social stationery suppliers*

Tate Refrigeration Ltd, Unit 7 Glan Llwyd, Tyn Y Bonau Road Industrial Estate, Pontarddulais, Swansea, SA4 8SF Tel: (01792) 885585 Fax: (01792) 883351 *Refrigeration & air conditioning services*

Robert Tate Signs Ltd, 15 East Campbell Street, Glasgow, G1 5DT Tel: 0141-552 7610 Fax: 0141-553 1725 *Sign manufrs*

Tatenhill Aviation Ltd, Tatenhill Airfield, Newborough Road, Needwood, Burton-on-Trent, Staffordshire, DE13 9PD Tel: (01283) 575283 Fax: (01283) 575650 *Aircraft rental & maintenance*

Tates, 4 Knightwood Court, Shuttleworth Close, Gapton Hall Industrial Estate, Great Yarmouth, Norfolk, NR31 0NQ Tel: (01493) 604197 Fax: (01493) 652816 E-mail: enquiries@tatesengineering.com *Sheet metalworkers*

Tatetone Ventilation Systems, 4 Bridgewater Close, Reading, RG30 1JT Tel: 0118-950 8914 Fax: 0118-950 8913 E-mail: enquiries@tateoneltd.co.uk *Ductwork designers, manufacturers & installers*

Tatham Steels Ltd, Duke Avenue, Stamley Green Industrial Estate, Cheadle Hulme, Cheadle, Cheshire, SK8 6QZ Tel: 0161-485 8535 Fax: 0161-485 7804 E-mail: tathem@bmsteel.co.uk *Steel stockholders*

Tatlow Signs Ltd, Unit 1 2 Gate Street, Blackburn, BB1 3AQ Tel: (01254) 667666 Fax: (01254) 503101 E-mail: sales@tatlowsigns.co.uk *Sign manufrs*

Tatra Plastics Manufacturing, Station Road, Norwood Green, Halifax, West Yorkshire, HX3 8QD Tel: 0845 5314245 Fax: (01274) 690283 E-mail: extrusions@tatra.co.uk Principal Export Areas: Worldwide *Tatra plastics was founded in 1963 and specialises in the manufacture of plastic tube and profile extrusions, injection moulding, telecom products, railway pads and aids, all in a wide range of engineering thermoplastic materials. We also produce the Click and Fix range of plastic panelling products. Tatra have been providing a competitive, quality service for over 40 years and will endeavour to do so well into the future. Our in house expertise enables us to offer total solutions to our customers for the most demanding product specifications, from initial concept through to finished product. We produce a range of tubes and profiles in ABS,Acrylic,PVC,HDPE,Polypropylene,Noryl, Polycarbonate,Polythene,Polyethylene,Styrene, Rigid & flexible co-extrusions. Please contact us for all your PVC, Plastic Extrusion and Injection Moulding requirements*

Tattersalls, 46 Warner Street, Accrington, Lancashire, BB5 1HN Tel: (01254) 232244 Fax: (01254) 386454 *Office supplies*

Tatung UK Ltd, Stafford Park 10, Telford, Shropshire, TF3 3AB Tel: (01952) 290111 Fax: (01952) 290390 E-mail: service@tatung.co.uk *Colour monitors manufrs*

▶ Tau Interactive, 65 The Parkway, Cottingham, Hull, HU12 9RE Tel: (08452) 600805 E-mail: info@tauinteractive.co.uk *Network Installation, Modifications & Upgrades. Structured cabling - CAT5, Fibre Optic. Wireless Solutions. Covering Schools & Businesses nationwide. Get in touch for your free quotation.*

Taunton Leisure, 110 Fore Street, Exeter, EX4 3JF Tel: (01392) 498793 Fax: (01392) 496965 *Camping equipment suppliers*

Taunton Lifting Services, Capland, Hatch Beauchamp, Taunton, Somerset, TA3 6TR Tel: (01823) 481111 Fax: (01823) 480682 *Lifting equipment hirers & retailers*

Taunton Motor Co. Ltd, 35-39 Priory Bridge Road, Taunton, Somerset, TA1 1QD Tel: (01823) 278171 Fax: (01823) 338201 E-mail: info@tauntonmotorcompany.co.uk *Approved volvo dealership*

▶ Taunton Plumbing & Heating, Unit 6, Venture 11, Priorswood Industrial Estate, Taunton, Somerset, TA2 8DG Tel: (01823) 278887 *Heating systems*

Taunton Textiles, Yarde Pl, Taunton, Somerset, TA1 1UR Tel: 01823 324444 Fax: 01823 324444 *Bedding & linen distribution & manufrs*

▶ Taurus Beds, 167a Finchley Road, London, NW3 6LB Tel: (020) 7372 1166 Fax: (020) 7328 7274 E-mail: admin@tauruspinebeds.co.uk *Beds retailers*

▶ Taurus Colour Laboratories, 6 Kelvin Business Centre, Kelvin Way, Crawley, West Sussex, RH10 9SF Tel: (01293) 553427 Fax: (01293) 553429 E-mail: LES@TAURUSCOLOURLABS.CO.UK *Taurus is a successful professional photographic laboratory based in Crawley serving the needs of many large companies both local and national.Over the last 18 years Taurus has been producing high quality photographic and exhibition services often to meet unbelievable deadlines in order to assist our clients with their requirements. All our work is done in-house and is undertaken by experienced Professional technicians with many years experience in the trade.*

Taurus Engineering, Commerce Way, Lancing, West Sussex, BN15 8TA Tel: (01903) 761188 Fax: (01903) 767268 E-mail: sales@taurusengineering.co.uk *Screen printing trade engineering services*

Taurus Leather Ltd, Montague House, 436 Leeds Road, Robin Hood, Wakefield, West Yorkshire, WF3 3BG Tel: 0113-282 3508 Fax: 0113-282 9805 *Leather goods manufrs*

▶ Taurus Logistics, New Portreath Road, Redruth, Cornwall, TR16 4HN Tel: (01209) 314772 Fax: (01209) 314773

Taurus Packaging, Meadow Lane, Little Houghton, Northampton, NN7 1AH Tel: (01604) 891707 Fax: (01604) 891708 E-mail: tauruspackaging@hotmail.com *Packaging materials & equipment*

▶ Taurus Print & Design Ltd, 6 Wintersells Road, Byfleet, West Byfleet, Surrey, KT14 7LF Tel: (01932) 355511

Tav Engineering Ltd, Unit 13-14 Priory Industrial Park, Airspeed Road, Christchurch, Dorset, BH23 4HD Tel: (01425) 270444 Fax: (01425) 276766 E-mail: tavengineering@crydom.com Principal Export Areas: Middle East, Africa, Central/East Europe, West Europe, North America & South America *Manufacturers of level control equipment*

Tavea Electrical Goods, Rear of 21 Finkle Street, Thirsk, North Yorkshire, YO7 1DA Tel: (01845) 524627 Fax: (01845) 525060 E-mail: shubebbard@tavea.co.uk *Electrical & music entertainment services*

▶ Taverham Conservatories, 61 Holt Road, Norwich, NR6 6XS Tel: (01603) 426502 Fax: (01603) 418337 *Double glazing, windows & conservatories supply & fitting services*

Tavishelm Tools Ltd, 10-12 Stacey Avenue, London, Greater London, N18 3PL Tel: 020 88039747 *Mould manufrs*

Tavnitan Ltd, 11 James Watt Close, Drayton Fields Industrial Esta, Daventry, Northamptonshire, NN11 8RJ Tel: (01327) 703888 Fax: (01327) 703666 E-mail: sales@tavnitan.co.uk *Feed machinery spare part manufrs*

▶ Tavoy Investments Ltd, 25 Bartel Close, Leverstock Green, Hemel Hempstead, Hertfordshire, HP3 8LY Tel: (0845) 2261978 Fax: (0845) 2261978 *Lovableskin.co.uk supply skincare products covering all beauty treatments and all skin types to give you an ageless, velvety, fresh and smooth skin*

Taw Engineering North West Ltd, 194 Price Street, Birkenhead, Merseyside, CH41 3PR Tel: 0151-647 6198 Fax: 0151-666 1347 E-mail: taw.engineering@virgin.net *Weights specialised manufacturers & precision engineers*

▶ Taw Valley Crafts Ltd, 1 Baron Court, Baron Way, Roundswell Business Park, Barnstaple, Devon, EX31 3TB Tel: (01271) 378296 Fax: (01271) 374118 E-mail: sales@teatrays.com *Bespoke joinery services*

▶ Taw Valley Telecoms Ltd, 63 High Street, Barnstaple, Devon, EX31 1JB Tel: (01271) 336336 Fax: 0870 4607798 E-mail: martin@tawvalleytelecoms.co.uk *Inbound /Outbound Call Centre. DRTV, Telemarketing,Media Response Handling,Virtual Receptionist,Out Of Hours, Messaging Services.*

Michael Tawn & Sons, The Barn, Hannath Rd, Tydd Gote, Wisbech, Cambs, PE13 5ND Tel: 01945 420770 *Air gun suppliers*

▶ Tawny Wood Outdoor Play, The Owls, Clayford Road, Kilgetty, Dyfed, SA68 0RR Tel: (01834) 813227 Fax: (01834) 813227 E-mail: tawnywood@yahoo.co.uk *Wooden play centres, climbing frames & swing sets manufrs*

Taws Printers Ltd, 1 Hortonwood, Telford, Shropshire, TF1 7GN Tel: (01952) 281281 Fax: (01952) 281282 E-mail: info@taws.co.uk *Total print service*

▶ Tax & Figures, Hamilton House, 111 Marlowes, Hemel Hempstead, Hertfordshire, HP1 1BB Tel: (01442) 450480 E-mail: robert@taxandfigures.com *We offer a fast and friendly accounting and tax service to owner managed businesses at an affordable cost.*

▶ Taxcafe, 214 High Street, Kirkcaldy, Fife, KY1 1JT Tel: (01592) 560081

▶ Taxi insurance from WYN Group Insurance Services, WYN House, 4 Eve Road, Woking, Surrey, GU21 5JT Tel: 01483 722266 E-mail: info@wyngroup.co.uk *Taxi Insurance from WYN Group Insurance Services for Private Hire Insurance, Public Hire Insurance and Taxi Fleet Insurance*

▶ Taxivan.Com, 350 Roman Road, London, E3 5QW Tel: (020) 8981 8043 E-mail: info@taxivan-uk.com *we also supply a man and van removal service for within london and U.K. wide.In the past we have also gone into Europe but also mainly into Ireland the land of our fathers.our rates can be fixed or on an hourly rate,with no hidden extras Thankyou*

▶ Taxmemo, Censeo House, 6 St. Peters Street, St. Albans, Hertfordshire, AL1 3LF Tel: (01727) 848998 E-mail: advice@taxmemo.net *Tax consultants*

▶ Tay Boats, Newlands View, Scone, Perth, PH2 6NW Tel: (01738) 551890

Tay Forth Machinery Ring, Newhill Farm, Glenfarg, Perth, PH2 9QN Tel: (01577) 830616 Fax: (01577) 80663 E-mail: admin@tayforth.co.uk *Agricultural contractors*

▶ Tayban Developments Ltd, Unit 9b Locomotion Industrial Estate, Chorley New Road, Horwich, Bolton, BL6 5UE Tel: (01204) 691313 Fax: (01204) 691777

Tayblast Services Ltd, Corrosion Centre, Lunan Bay, Montrose, Angus, DD10 9TG Tel: (01241) 830513 Fax: (01241) 830533 E-mail: colinkennedy@tayblast.com *Shot blasting contractors*

Taybroh Alloys & Stainless Steels Ltd, Unit 2 Eastington Trading Estate, Stonehouse, Gloucestershire, GL10 3RY Tel: (01453) 828991 Fax: (01453) 828988 E-mail: sales@taybrohalloys.co.uk *Stainless steel & aluminium stockholders*

Taybur Power Washes, 33 Craven Street, Bury, Lancashire, BL9 7PP Tel: 0161-763 6219 Fax: 0161-763 6219 *High pressure water jetting manufrs*

Taycare Medical Ltd, 351 Tong Road, Leeds, LS12 4QG Tel: 0113-231 1800 Fax: 0113-231 1805 E-mail: ben.taylor@taycare.com *Manufacture surgical footwear*

Tayco Engineering, Unit 6 Sherwood Industrial Estate, Bonnyrigg, Midlothian, EH19 3LW Tel: 0131-654 9655 Fax: 0131-654 9656 E-mail: graham@tayco.co.uk *Manufacturers, stockholders of assembly & sling wire ropes*

▶ Taycraft, 6 Strathmore Avenue, Coupar Angus, Perthshire, PH13 9ED Tel: (01828) 628477 E-mail: lachie_mackintosh@yahoo.com *Manufacture clan crest promotional items*

John Taylo Engineering Ltd, Swift Farm, Hensting La, Fishers Pond, Eastleigh, Hants, SO50 7HH Tel: 023 80600012 Fax: 023 80696233 *Tool making*

▶ Taylor, 150 Turner Lane, Ashton-under-Lyne, Lancashire, OL6 8SZ Tel: 0161-343 1294 Fax: 0161-339 9477 E-mail: info@taylorssupplies.com *Bar equipment*

A. Taylor & Son (Leeds) Ltd, Weaver Street, Leeds, LS4 2AY Tel: 0113-263 9036 Fax: 0113-231 0286 E-mail: sales@ataylor.co.uk *Steel plate fabricators & machinists*

Taylor Agencies, Narrow Gates Stable Cottage, Main Street, St. Boswells, Melrose, Roxburghshire, TD6 0AX Tel: (01835) 823555 *Giftware importers & agents*

Taylor Alden Ltd, 92-94 Toynbee Road, London, SW20 8SL Tel: (020) 8543 3866 Fax: (020) 8543 2841 E-mail: pr@tayloralden.co.uk *Public relations & marketing consultants* Also at: Newbury

Armand Taylor & Co. Ltd, Tuskite Works, Pitsea Hall Lane, Pitsea, Basildon, Essex, SS16 4UL Tel: (01268) 552167 *Electrical bobbin manufrs*

Taylor Barnard Container Services Ltd, Eling Wharf, Totton, Southampton, SO40 9LH Tel: 023 80871444 *Container manufrs*

Taylor & Braithwaite Ltd, Dyke Nook, Sandford, Appleby-in-Westmorland, Cumbria, CA16 6NS Tel: (01768) 341400 Fax: (01768) 341488 E-mail: principal@t-and-b.co.uk *Agricultural engineers*

▶ Taylor Bros Bristol Ltd, 13-25 Wilder Street, Bristol, BS2 8PY Tel: 0117-924 5452 Fax: 0117-942 7652

Taylor Bros Holdings Ltd, Taylor Building, 247 Crompton Ware, Bolton, BL2 2RY Tel: (01204) 380726 Fax: (01204) 380720 E-mail: info@taylorbros-uk.com *Electronic systems engineers*

Taylor Bros Oldham Ltd, Lee Street, Oldham, OL8 1EE Tel: 0161-652 3221 Fax: 0161-626 1736 E-mail: karen.taylorbrs@btinternet.com *Telecommunication systems manufrs*

Taylor & Brown Ltd, 29 Enterprise Way, Thornton Road Industrial Estate, Pickering, North Yorkshire, YO18 7NA Tel: (01751) 477171 Fax: (01751) 477644 *Steel fabricators*

▶ Taylor Building Services, 22 Cleveden Road, Glasgow, G12 0PX Tel: 0141-337 6588

Carl Taylor Plant Hire, 10 Garth Grove, Hirwaun, Aberdare, Rhondda Cynon Taff, CF44 9SD Tel: (01685) 813801 Fax: (01685) 813801 E-mail: taylorplant@btconnect.com *Based in South Wales with 40 years experience in the Plant Hire Industry specialising in Wheeled Excavators, (Rubber Ducks), Plant Hire, Tracked Excavators, up to 20 tonne rubber excavators, Long Reach Excavators up to 18 metre reach, JCB Hire, Low Loader Hire up to 65 tonne category 2, Tipper Hire, Midi Hire Excavators, Mini Hire Excavators. All aspects of ground work undertaken, full range of attachments for all excavators i.e.: Grabs, Grapples, Hydraulic Breakers, Shears, Pulverisers. Working for main contractors across the U.K*

Taylor Catering Foods, Exeter Road, Ottery St. Mary, Devon, EX11 1LH Tel: (01404) 814312 *Frozen food wholesalers*

Chris Taylor Production Engineering, 35 James Carter Road, Mildenhall, Bury St. Edmunds, Suffolk, IP28 7DE Tel: (01638) 510589 Fax: (01638) 515086 *Instrument engineering services*

Taylor Clarke Partnership Ltd, 4 Fitzroy Place, Glasgow, G3 7RH Tel: 0141-221 1707 Fax: 0141-221 6266 E-mail: info@taylorclarke.co.uk *Development coaches & consultants*

▶ Taylor Construction Ltd, 66C Hawthorn Road, Bognor Regis, West Sussex, PO21 2DD Tel: (01243) 829000 Fax: (01243) 829333

Taylor Construction Plant Ltd, Unit 2, Broadmeadows, Harburn, West Calder, West Lothian, EH55 8RT Tel: (01621) 850777 Fax: (01621) 843330 E-mail: mail@tcp.eu *Construction plant or equipment suppliers*

Taylor Crane Co. Ltd, 6 York St, Aberdeen, AB11 5DD Tel: (01224) 211188 Fax: (01224) 212803 *Crane hire*

Taylor Davis Ltd, Moat Road, West Wilts Trading Estate, Westbury, Wiltshire, BA13 4JF Tel: (01373) 864324 Fax: (01373) 858021 E-mail: sales@taylor-davis.co.uk *Metal & plastic containers supplier*

Taylor Durant Ltd, 2A London Avenue, North End, Portsmouth, PO2 9BU Tel: (023) 9266 8586 *Control panel manufrs*

Taylor Dynamic Controls, Unit W4 Blaby Industrial Park, Winchester Avenue, Blaby, Leicester, LE8 4GZ Tel: 0116-278 4100 Fax: 0116-278 4200 E-mail: sales@taylordynamics.com *Electronic control system counters*

Taylor Edwards & Co., Royal Buildings, Mosley Street, Manchester, M2 3AN Tel: 0161-907 3488 *Utility gas*

Taylor Electronics Manchester Ltd, 287 Chester Road, Manchester, M15 4EY Tel: 0161-834 5050 Fax: 0161-834 5051 *Neon signs manufrs*

F.A. Taylor & Co. Ltd, Faraday House, 17 Essendene Road, Caterham, Surrey, CR3 5PB Tel: (01883) 347016 Fax: (01883) 341499 *Electrical contractors*

Taylor Fencing, 4 Coton Carriage Works, Heath End Road, Nuneaton, Warwickshire, CV10 7JB Tel: (024) 7635 3313 Fax: (024) 7635 3313 *Fencing work*

Taylor Forge Ltd, Unit 3 Lime Grove, Balsall Heath, Birmingham, B12 8SY Tel: 0121-446 4196 Fax: 0121-446 4793 *Manufacturing blacksmiths*

Taylor Forgings, Effingham Road, Sheffield, S4 7ZB Tel: 0114-275 9155 Fax: 0114-272 8440 E-mail: sales@taylorforgings.com *Stainless steel stockholders*

Taylor & Francis Group P.L.C., 4 Park Square, Milton Park, Abingdon, Oxfordshire, OX14 4RN Tel: (020) 7583 9855 Fax: (020) 7017 6336 E-mail: enquiries@tandf.co.uk *Book publishers* Also at: Andover

Taylor Fuel Control, Unit 4a New England Estate, Off Pindar Road, Hoddesdon, Hertfordshire, EN11 0BZ Tel: (01992) 451101 Fax: (01992) 444954 *Fuel tank & pump services manufrs*

George Taylor (Engineering) Ltd, Block 5, Burns Road, Chapelhall Industrial Estate, Chapelhall, Airdrie, Lanarkshire, ML6 8QH Tel: (01236) 761114 Fax: (01236) 754327 E-mail: sales@gteng.co.uk *Precision engineers*

Taylor & Goodman Ltd, 7 Cradock Road, Reading, RG2 0LB Tel: 0118-987 1773 Fax: 0118-931 4945 E-mail: sales@taylorgoodman.co.uk *Electric motor, pump & transformer services* Also at: Bristol, Chelmsford, Eastbourne, Ilford & Redditch

Taylor Group, 25 St. Marys Road, Dundee, DD3 9DL Tel: (01382) 826763 Fax: (01382) 832238 E-mail: info@tgdiecasting.co.uk *Manufacturers of pressure die castings including zinc base*

Henry Taylor Tools Ltd, Peacock Estate, Liversey Street, Sheffield, S6 2BL Tel: 0114-234 0282 Fax: 0114-285 2015 E-mail: sales@henrytaylortools.co.uk *Wood carving tool manufrs*

Taylor Hobson, P O Box 36, Leicester, LE4 9JQ Tel: 0116-276 3771 Fax: 0116-274 1350 E-mail: sales@taylor-hobson.com Principal Export Areas: Worldwide *Manufacturers of surface roughness gauges; measuring equipment*

▶ Taylor Homes Scotland Ltd, 3 Woodhall Road, Wishaw, Lanarkshire, ML2 8PY Tel: (01698) 385777 Fax: (01698) 384275

Taylor Hydraulics & Mechanical Services, 36 Long Ridge, Brighouse, West Yorkshire, HD6 3RZ Tel: (01484) 717552 Fax: (01484) 717552 *Hydraulic & mechanical engineers*

Taylor Investments UK Ltd, 72 Commercial Road, Hereford, HR1 2BP Tel: (01432) 354439 Fax: (01432) 352799 *Software development, PC rentals & upgrades*

Taylor J Electric Contractors Ltd, 590 Tonge Moor Road, Bolton, BL2 3BJ Tel: (01204) 592145 Fax: (01204) 598471 E-mail: jh@jtaylorelectrical.co.uk *Electrical contractors*

▶ Taylor Jackson & Associates, Unit 2 Hepton Court, Leeds, LS9 6PW Tel: 0113 2489777

▶ Taylor James Photographic Services Ltd, 123-125 Curtain Road, London, EC2A 3BX Tel: (020) 7739 4488 Fax: (020) 7739 5958 E-mail: info@taylorjames.com *Taylor James is a high end Photographic Retouching house. We offer additional services inc. drum scanning, artworking, fine art printing,proofing,data storage.*

John Taylor Poston & Co. Ltd, 19-21 Great Queens Street, London, WC2B 5BE Tel: (020) 7242 0471 Fax: (020) 7831 8692 E-mail: gqs@toye.demon.co.uk *Jewellery, silverware, trophies & badges* Also at: Manchester

Taylor Kerr Couplings Ltd, Disraeli House, 12 Aylesbury End, Beaconsfield, Buckinghamshire, HP9 1LW Tel: (01494) 679500 Fax: (01494) 679505 E-mail: info@teekaycouplings.com *Pipework contractors & consultants* Also at: Milton Keynes

Taylor Kightley Engineering, 1 Pond Wood Close, Moulton Park Industrial Estate, Northampton, NN3 6RT Tel: (01604) 645871 Fax: (01604) 671939 E-mail: sales@tke.co.uk *Precision engineers*

Taylor & Kilduff, 80 Main Road, West Huntspill, Highbridge, Somerset, TA9 3QX Tel: (01278) 788464 Fax: (01278) 792496 *Steel fabricators*

▶ Taylor Lane Timber Frame Ltd, Chapel Road, Rotherwas Industrial Estate, Hereford, HR2 6LD Tel: (01432) 271912 Fax: (01432) 351064 E-mail: tl@taylor-lane.co.uk *Manufacturers of timber frames*

Taylor Lowestoft Ltd, Newcombe Road, Lowestoft, Suffolk, NR32 1XA Tel: (01502) 572753 Fax: (01502) 572753 *Engineers' suppliers*

▶ Taylor M.E. Ltd, Unit 3 Canal Court Business Centre, Infirmary Street, Carlisle, CA2 7AN Tel: (01228) 527584 E-mail: sales@taylor-me.co.uk

▶ Taylor Made, 1 Cornford Road, Blackpool, FY4 4QQ Tel: (01253) 761579 Fax: (01253) 698401 *Taylor made furniture*

Taylor Made Fabrication, 6 Pipers Industrial Estate, Pipers Lane, Thatcham, Berkshire, RG19 4NA Tel: (01635) 873737 Fax: (01635) 874747 E-mail: info.request@taylormadefabrication.co.uk *Sheet metalwork*

Taylor Made Golf Ltd, Spectrum House, Jays Close, Basingstoke, Hampshire, RG22 4BS Tel: (01256) 408600 Fax: (01256) 465562 *Golf club & ski equipment*

▶ Taylor Made Machinery Ltd, 3A Canal Wharf, Station Road, Langley, Slough, SL3 6EG Tel: (01753) 591433 Fax: (01753) 591441 E-mail: sales@tmm-uk.com *Based in Langley Berkshire Taylor Made Machinery Ltd build automated tray denesting, product feeding, counting and collating machines for the food, confectionery, medical and pharmaceutical industries.*

Taylor Made Pine, The Old Workshops, Longbridge Deverill, Warminster, Wiltshire, BA12 7DP Tel: (01985) 840012 Fax: (01985) 840781 *Pine manufrs*

Taylor Made Training Ltd, 132 Station Road, Glenfield, Leicester, LE3 8BR Tel: 0116-232 4800 Fax: 0116-232 4811 E-mail: mailbox@taylormadetraining.co.uk *Computer solutions centre & computer reseller*

▶ Taylor Made Windows London, Unit 22 Roxwell Trading Park, Argall Avenue, London, E10 7QY Tel: (020) 8558 6688

Taylor Maid Blinds, The Engine House, The Close, Ardington, Wantage, Oxfordshire, OX12 8PT Tel: (01235) 831599 Fax: (01235) 831599 *Window blind manufrs*

▶ Taylor Manufacturing Ltd, 21 Denmark Street, Fraserburgh, Aberdeenshire, AB43 9EY Tel: (01346) 519399 Fax: (01346) 515781 E-mail: enquiries@taylormfg.co.uk

Taylor Maxwell Holdings Ltd, Taylor Maxwell House, The Promenade, Bristol, BS8 3NW Tel: 0117-973 7888 Fax: 0117-970 6652 E-mail: info@taylor.maxwell.co.uk *Brick merchants* Also at: Branches throughout the UK

Taylor Maxwell South East, Brewery Court, 43-45 High Street, Theale, Reading, RG7 5AH Tel: 0118-930 6888 Fax: 0118-930 2888 *Brick distributors*

Taylor Maxwell Timber, The Promenade, Clifton Down, Bristol, BS8 3NJ Tel: 0117-974 1382 Fax: 0117-974 1402 E-mail: tmtbristol@tmttimber.co.uk *Timber merchants*

▶ Taylor Mechanical Services, Unit 6, Marybank Lane, Dundee, DD2 3DY Tel: (01382) 612863 Fax: (01382) 623134

Taylor Metals, 244 Bernard Street, Glasgow, G40 3NX Tel: 0141-556 1903 Fax: 0141-556 1903 *Metal merchant & steel plate stockists*

Taylor & Co (Mineral Waters) Ltd, 215 London Road, Staines, Middlesex, TW18 4JF Tel: (01784) 459923 Fax: (01784) 441595 E-mail: admin@taylordrinks.co.uk *Drink distributor*

Taylor Nelson Sofres plc, 66 Wilson Street, London, EC2A 2JX Tel: (020) 7868 6500 Fax: (020) 7868 6501 *Market researchers*

Taylor Nelson Sofres, West Gate, London, W5 1UA Tel: (020) 8967 0007 Fax: (020) 8967 4060 *Information services & market researchers*

Taylor Nelson Sofres plc, 66 Wilson Street, London, EC2A 2JX Tel: (020) 7868 6500 Fax: (020) 7868 6501 E-mail: christine.davidson@tnsofres.com *Market researchers*

▶ Nigel Taylor Ltd, Ramsden Road, Rotherwas Industrial Estate, Hereford, HR2 6LR Tel: (01432) 269266 Fax: (01432) 269990 *Ductwork design installation services*

Norman Taylor & Sons, 21 Market Place, Oldham, OL1 3AB Tel: 0161-624 7940 *Jewellery sales & repairs*

▶ P.A. Taylor Plans, The Sand Quarry, Hougher Wall Road, Audley, Stoke-On-Trent, ST7 8JA Tel: (01782) 721111 Fax: (05600) 766363 *Building surveyors*

Taylor & Pickles Ltd, Bushell St Mills, Bushell Street, Preston, PR1 2SP Tel: (01772) 251520 Fax: (01772) 561610 E-mail: info@taylorandpickles.co.uk *Corporate & architectural sign makers*

Taylor Precision Plastics Ltd, Mile Oak Industrial Estate, Maesbury Road, Oswestry, Shropshire, SY10 8GA Tel: (01691) 679516 Fax: (01691) 670538 E-mail: sales@plasticbearings.co.uk *Plastics bearing suppliers & manufrs*

Taylor Pressform Ltd, 21 Rigby Close, Heathcote Industrial Estate, Warwick, CV34 6TH Tel: (01926) 339507 Fax: (01926) 451306 *Steel presswork services*

▶ Taylor Robinson Ltd, Fire Protection House, Woolley Colliery Road, Darton, Barnsley, South Yorkshire, S75 5JA Tel: 0161-764 8674 Fax: (01226) 388206

Ron Taylor Studio, 152 North High Street, Musselburgh, Midlothian, EH21 6AR Tel: 0131-653 2700 Fax: 0131-653 2700 E-mail: rontaylor@easynet.co.uk *Photographers*

Taylor & Russell Ltd, Stonebridge Mill, Preston Road, Longridge, Preston, PR3 3AN Tel: (01772) 782295 Fax: (01772) 785341 *Field fabricators & general engineers*

Company Information

S. & H.C. Taylor Ltd, Devon House, Tan Lane, Exeter, EX2 8EG Tel: (01392) 421500 Fax: (01392) 423889 *Manufacturing opticians*

S.J. Taylor, Longmeadow Farm, Wappenham Rd, Syresham, Brackley, Northants, NN13 5HQ Tel: 01280 850084 *Food distribution*

S. & M. Taylor, Lower Ozzings Farm, Shelley, Huddersfield, HD8 8NA Tel: (01484) 863492 *Agricultural*

Samuel Taylor Ltd, Arthur Street, Lakeside, Redditch, Worcestershire, B98 8JY Tel: (01527) 522687 Fax: (01527) 500869 E-mail: sales@samueltaylor.co.uk *Electrical contact manufrs*

▶ Taylor Scaffolding Ayr Ltd, 15a Crown Street, Ayr, KA8 8BY Tel: (01292) 610945 Fax: (01292) 610945

Taylor Shaw, Albert St, Lockwood, Huddersfield, HD1 3QG Tel: (01484) 532425 Fax: (01484) 512426 E-mail: sales@taylor-shaw.co.uk *Industrial valve manufrs.*

Taylor & Son (Joinery) Ltd, 42 A Vicarage Road, Halesowen, West Midlands, B62 8HU Tel: 0121-559 3955 Fax: 0121-559 5412 *Windows & doors joinery manufrs*

Taylor & Sons Ltd, Briton Ferry, Neath, West Glamorgan, SA11 2JA Tel: (01639) 813251 Fax: (01639) 812342 *Taylor and Sons Ltd. Provide extensive fabrication, machining, painting and foundry services from four factories in based in Cardiff and Neath. "Our aim is to provide a quality service to all market sectors and all budgets. Our quality and service is not compromised by value of order or size of client. We value enquiries form £100 to £1,000,000. Our quality is regularly audited by SGS Yardsley and is currently accredited to ISO 9001 2000 with design. *Taylor and Sons Ltd welcome any audits carried out by client internal audit systems and are pleased to provide references on request.*

Taylor Steel Midlands Ltd, Autobase Industrial Estate, Tipton Road, Tividale, Oldbury, West Midlands, B69 3HU Tel: 0121-601 5081 Fax: 0121-601 5069 E-mail: info@taylor-steel-midlands.co.uk *Steel stockholders*

Taylor Studwelding Systems Ltd, Commercial Road, Dewsbury, West Yorkshire, WF13 2BD Tel: (01924) 452123 Fax: (01924) 430059 E-mail: sales@taylor-studwelding.com *Taylor Studwelding Systems Limited is a specialist in the design, manufacture and supply of studwelding equipment and studs. From simple hand held units right through to C.N.C fully automated systems, we can provide turnkey solutions to your studwelding requirement.*

▶ Taylor Systems, Lane End Court, 2a Lane End Road, Bembridge, Isle of Wight, PO35 5UE Tel: (01983) 875222 Fax: (01983) 875222 *Computer maintenance & repair services*

Thomas Taylor (Bowls) Ltd, 217 Bernard Street, Glasgow, G40 3NB Tel: 0141-554 5255 Fax: 0141-551 0594 E-mail: info@taylor-bowls.co.uk *Bowls (flat & crown) manufrs*

Taylor Tiles Holdings Ltd, Plasmarl Industrial Estate, Beaufort Road, Swansea Enterprise Park, Swansea, SA6 8JG Tel: (01792) 797712 Fax: (01792) 791103 E-mail: info@taylortiles.co.uk *Ceramic products distributors*

Taylor Tool Hire & Garden Ware, Nailbridge, Drybrook, Gloucestershire, GL17 9JW Tel: (01594) 542853 Fax: (01594) 544773 E-mail: njt@taylortoolhire.co.uk *Garden machinery suppliers*

Taylor Tunnicliff Ltd, Normacot Road, Stoke-on-Trent, ST3 1PA Tel: (01782) 501174 Fax: (01782) 328807 *Parametric equipment manufrs*

Taylor Valves Ltd, Dowker Works, Dowker Street, Milnsbridge, Huddersfield, HD3 4JX Tel: (01484) 651177 Fax: (01484) 645854 *Steam valve suppliers*

Taylor & Watson Ltd, Wentworth Road, Penistone, Sheffield, S36 6ET Tel: (01226) 762035 Fax: (01226) 370216 E-mail: taylorwatson65@hotmail.com *Fabrication engineers with shearing, press brake & rolling facilities*

Taylor & Whiteley Ltd, Riverside House,, Queen Square Business Park, Huddersfield Road, Honley, Holmfirth, HD9 6QZ Tel: (01484) 662059 Fax: (01484) 665373 *Precision engineers*

Taylor & Whitlock, 170 Dukes Ride, Crowthorne, Berkshire, RG45 6DS Tel: (01344) 780212 Fax: (01344) 780212 E-mail: sales@twj.co.uk *Jewellery repairers & manufrs*

Taylor & Woodland Ltd, 5 Tree Works, Bakers Lane, West Hanningfield, Chelmsford, CM2 8LD Tel: (01277) 841792 Fax: (01277) 841793 *Wholesale bakers*

Taylor Woodrow, 2 Princes Way, Solihull, West Midlands, B91 3ES Tel: 0121-600 8000 Fax: 0121-600 8001 *Provision of in house requisites*

Taylor Woolhouse, Greasbrough Road, Rotherham, South Yorkshire, S61 4QQ Tel: (01709) 379500 Fax: (01709) 379600 E-mail: rotamill@aol.com *Bulk storage equipment & handling*

▶ Taylored Systems, Newton House Farm, Main Street, Levisham, Pickering, North Yorkshire, YO18 7NL Tel: 0845 0573265 Fax: 0871 6618352 E-mail: info@tayloredsystems.co.uk *Computer systems support*

Taylorfab Precision Engineers, Unit 5 Greenwood Court, Ramridge Road, Luton, LU2 0TN Tel: (01582) 737279 Fax: (01582) 735616 *Capstan machinists precision production engineers*

Taylormade Castings Ltd, Cobridge Road, Stoke-on-Trent, ST1 5JP Tel: (01782) 261537 Fax: (01782) 261262 E-mail: tmcstoke@ukonline.co.uk *Ferrous & non-ferrous castings manufrs*

Taylormade Designs, Unit 14 Silver Business Park, Airfield Way, Christchurch, Dorset, BH23 3TA Tel: (0870) 8015622 Fax: (0870) 8015624 E-mail: james@taylormadedesigns.co.uk *Printed & Embroidered, Clothing & Merchandise Solutions. All kinds of clothing from t-shirts and polo shirts to outdoor jackets and corporate wear. We also offer a full bespoke design*

continued

service too. Our prices and service levels are the best in the industry. "You are as important to us as your order is to you !"

Taylormade Induction Ltd, Unit 6 Station Road, Bakewell, Derbyshire, DE45 1GE Tel: (01629) 815122 Fax: (01629) 814776 E-mail: sales@ihstaylormade.com *Induction furnace manufrs*

Taylors, 95 Victoria Rd, Bradmore, Wolverhampton, WV3 7HA Tel: (01902) 621882 Fax: 01902 621882 E-mail: taylorsppe@blueyonder.co.uk *Personal protective clothing distributors*

▶ Taylors Bakery & Confectioners, Front Street, Shotton Colliery, Durham, DH6 2LT Tel: 0191-526 1369 Fax: 0191-526 1369

Taylors Engineering, Nether Works, Nethergate Street, Bungay, Suffolk, NR35 1HE Tel: (01986) 892422 Fax: (01986) 892422 *General engineering services*

Taylors Eyre & Smith Ltd, The Bell Foundry, Freehold Street, Loughborough, Leicestershire, LE11 1AR Tel: (01509) 212241 Fax: (01509) 263305 E-mail: office@taylorbells.co.uk *Bells, fittings & frames installers*

Taylor's Garden Buildings, Ashwellthorpe Industrial Estate, Ashwellthorpe, Norwich, NR16 1ER Tel: (01508) 489260 Fax: (01508) 481622 *Garden sheds, summerhouses, log cabins, playhouses suppliers & manufrs*

Taylors Industrial Services Ltd, Hareness Circle, Altens Industrial Estate, Aberdeen, AB12 3LY Tel: (01224) 872972 Fax: (01224) 872697 E-mail: taylors_industrial_services@btinternet.com *Waste management*

▶ Taylors Keighley Ltd, 60 Cavendish Street, Keighley, West Yorkshire, BD21 3RL Tel: (01535) 603693 Fax: (01535) 603693 E-mail: info@taylorsshoes.co.uk *Taylor"s Shoes (UK) was established in 1935 and has offered its customers excellent service since then.*Some of the best brands of shoes along with a perfect fitting service makes Taylor"s Shoes the best shoe shop in Keighley.*Ladies Shoes brands include: Gabor, Lotus, Hotters, Equity, Ara, Rhodes, Morlands.*Mens Shoes brands include: Grensons, Loakes, Hotters, Lotus, Camel Active.*Children"s shoes from: Clarks, Norvic, Primigi (professionally fitted by our fully qualified staff).**

Taylors Print, 12 Gildart Street, Liverpool, L3 8ET Tel: 0151-207 2096 Fax: 0151-298 1198 *Screen printers*

Taylors Removals Ltd, The Potters, 13 Central Way, Cwmbran, Gwent, NP44 5HT Tel: (01633) 276555 Fax: (01633) 290888 *Removal specialists*

▶ Taylors Transport, 123 Nutty Lane, Shepperton, Middlesex, TW17 0RQ Tel: (01932) 788597 Fax: (01932) 785116

Taylowe Ltd, Malvern Road, Furze Platt, Maidenhead, Berkshire, SL6 7RF Tel: (01628) 413333 Fax: (01628) 413397 E-mail: taylowereception@taylowe.com *Digital artwork & reprographic imaging service providers*

▶ Taymore, Block 4A Unit 8, Larkhall Industrial Estate, Larkhall, Lanarkshire, ML9 2PA Tel: (01698) 884000 Fax: (01698) 886888 *Property repairs*

▶ Tayreed Co., Airfield Industrial Estate, Errol, PH2 7TB Tel: (01821) 642466 Fax: (01821) 642827

Tayside Aviation, Riverside Drive, Dundee, DD2 1UH Tel: (01382) 668838 Fax: (01382) 644531 *Flying training centre*

▶ Tayside Cable Technologies Ltd, Scottway, Pearce Avenue, West Pitkerro Industrial Estat, Broughty Ferry, Dundee, DD5 3RX Tel: (01382) 739351

▶ Tayside Compressor Services, Lindegaard Building, 1 Kilspindie Street, Dunsinane Industrial Estate, Dundee, DD2 3EW Tel: (01382) 813263 Fax: (01382) 819075

▶ Tayside Contracts, Brioch Road, Crieff, Perthshire, PH7 3SG Tel: (01764) 652115 Fax: (01764) 655418

▶ Tayside Contracts, Contracts House, 1 Soutar Street, Dundee, DD3 8SS Tel: (01382) 812721 Fax: (01382) 889572

▶ Tayside Contracts, Kirriemuir Road, Forfar, Angus, DD8 3TH Tel: (01307) 462616 Fax: (01307) 466990

▶ Tayside Contracts, Collace Quarry, Collace, Perth, PH2 6JB Tel: (01821) 650222 Fax: (01821) 650440

▶ Tayside Contracts, Feus Road, Perth, PH1 2UQ Tel: (01738) 630044 Fax: (01738) 630515

▶ Tayside Contracts, 4 Glenearn Road, Perth, PH2 0BE Tel: (01738) 624051 Fax: (01738) 444246

▶ Tayside Contracts Sign Shop, Signal Box Road, Blairgowrie, Perthshire, PH10 6ER Tel: (01250) 876091 Fax: (01250) 870293 E-mail: signshop@tayside-contracts.co.uk *Design & manufacture of signs & vehicle livery*

Tayside Diesel Engineering Ltd, Fowler Road, Broughty Ferry, Dundee, DD5 3RU Tel: (01382) 735960 Fax: (01382) 735969 E-mail: sales@tdedundee.co.uk *Diesel engine sales & service*

Tayside Education Link, Barns of Claverhouse, Dundee, DD4 9RA Tel: (01382) 505683 *Provide educational equipment*

Tayside Grain Co. Ltd, 6 St. Catherines Road, Perth, PH1 5SE Tel: (01738) 623121 Fax: (01738) 630419 *Agricultural merchants*

Tayside Plumbing & Building Supplies Ltd, 1 Dens Road, Dundee, DD3 7SR Tel: (01382) 229401 Fax: (01382) 202447 E-mail: office@tayside-plumbing.co.uk *Plumbing suppliers*

Tayside Pressure Washers, 89 Airlie Street, Alyth, Blairgowrie, Perthshire, PH11 8EE Tel: (01828) 632329 Fax: (01828) 632314 *Pressure washers suppliers*

Tayside Sheet Metal Ltd, 8 Angus Works, Neish Street, Dundee, DD3 7JN Tel: (01382) 828822 Fax: (01382) 828833 E-mail: vent@taysidesheetmetal.freeserve.co.uk *Ventilation ductwork systems & sheet metal fabrication*

Tayto Ni Ltd, Tandragee Castle, Tandragee, Craigavon, County Armagh, BT62 2AB Tel: (028) 3884 0249 Fax: (028) 3884 0085 E-mail: sales@tayto.com *Manufacturers of potato crisps & snacks*

Tayto (NI) Ltd, 6 Pit Hey Place, West Pimbo, Skelmersdale, Lancashire, WN8 9PS Tel: (01695) 726228 Fax: (01695) 50197 E-mail: maurice@rowanfsbusiness.co.uk *Snack food product manufrs*

▶ TAZZA D'ORO, UNIT 20, PARK ROYAL BUSINESS CENTRE, 9-21 PARK ROYAL ROAD, LONDON, NW10 7LQ Tel: 0208 9654505 Fax: 0208 9654121 E-mail: tazzadoro@btconnect.com

▶ TBS, 2 Harlaw Centre Howe Moss CR, Kirkhill Industrial Estate, Dyce, Aberdeen, AB21 0GN Tel: (01224) 729580 Fax: (01224) 729581 E-mail: tbsoring@aol.com *Manufacturers seals & o-rings*

TBS Engineering Ltd, Longhill, Elmstone Hardwicke, Cheltenham, Gloucestershire, GL51 9TY Tel: (01242) 680680 Fax: (01242) 680909 E-mail: laurie.gardiner@tbseng.co.uk *Battery making equipment manufrs*

▶ TBS Engineering (UK) Ltd, 63Market Street, Hollinsworth, Hyde, Cheshire, SK14 8HR Tel: (01457) 835585 Fax: (01457) 764627 E-mail: sales@tbsengineering.net *Full nation-wide 24 hour boiler maintenance, repairs, service*

TBS (South Wales) Ltd, Triumph Works, The Willows, Merthyr Tydfil, Mid Glamorgan, CF48 1YH Tel: (01685) 384041 Fax: (01685) 352202 E-mail: sales@triumph-tbs.com *Office furniture manufrs*

▶ TC Components, Castletown Windmill, 1 Arbory Road, Castletown, Isle of Man, IM9 1HA Tel: (01624) 829689 Fax: (01624) 829686 E-mail: tcatiom@hotmail.com *Semi-conductor products distribs*

▶ TC Fluid Control Ltd, Broadgate, Broadway Business Park, Oldham, OL9 9XA Tel: 0161-684 7488 Fax: 0161-684 7487 E-mail: info@tc-fluidcontrol.com *Valves & steam instrumentation*

TC Harrison, Oxney Road, Peterborough, PE1 5YN Tel: (01733) 425555 Fax: (01733) 425556 *Commercial vehicle distributors*

TCB-Arrow Ltd, Watchmoor House, Watchmoor Road, Camberley, Surrey, GU15 3AQ Tel: (01276) 679394 Fax: (01276) 679055 E-mail: sales@tcbarrow.co.uk *Injection mouldings, plastic mouldings thermoplastic mouldings, plastic mouldings, insert moulding, rubber moulding, LSR moulding, silicone cables, silicone moulding, ignition leads, ignition components, ignition cable, Thermo-plastic moulding, Camberley, Surrey, US, USA, Malaysia, Southeast, South east, Injection moulding, Automotive, Defence, Food Processing, Medical, Printing, DIY, Plastics, Tool design, Tool manufacture, rubber, LSR, Liquid Silicone Rubber, Plastic, Moulding, Molding*

TCE Ltd, Newstead Industrial Estate, Trentham, Stoke-On-Trent, ST4 8HX Tel: (01782) 643278 Fax: (01782) 657766 E-mail: tce@tcelabels.co.uk *Label manufacturers, badges (personalised) & general engravers*

▶ TCE Solutions Limited, 25 Dyers Court, Bollington, Macclesfield, Cheshire, SK10 5GG Tel: 0845 2572710 E-mail: Sales@tcesolutions.co.uk *TCE Solutions offer a wide range of SAP and Project Management courses.**We also offer on-site training, which is tailored to suit your company"s requirements. * *Our courses range from Financials to Customer Relationship Management, Introduction to Project Management to Risk and Issue Workshops and many more!****

▶ TCH Safety, Jasmine Cottage, Middle Street, East Harptree, Bristol, BS40 6AZ Tel: 01761 221874 E-mail: info@tchsafety.co.uk *Health & Safety Solutions provided by qualified and competent practitioners.**TCH Safety Consultants specialise in supporting small businesses. We differ from other consultancies because we will actually do the work for you. We'll help you to comply with legislation with the minimum of fuss, leaving you to focus on your work. By enlisting our services you get your own Health and Safety Manager at a fraction of the cost of employing one full time. **

▶ TCH Safety Consultants, Cobblers Cottage, Packet Lane, Rosudgeon, Penzance, Cornwall, TR20 9QD Tel: 01736 762016 Fax: 01736 762016 E-mail: info@tchsafety.co.uk *Health & Safety Solutions provided by qualified and competent practitioners.**TCH Safety Consultants specialise in supporting small and large businesses alike. We'll help you to comply with legislation with the minimum of fuss, leaving you to focus on your work. *Although based in Cornwall, we cover the entire UK, please contact us to see what we can do for your business. **

▶ TCPIP Ltd, 78 Wrentham Street, Birmingham, B5 6QP Tel: 0121-622 5000 Fax: 0121-622 5159 E-mail: sales@tcpip.ltd.uk *Audio visual installation*

▶ TCS Cellworks, Park Leys, Botolph Claydon, Buckingham, MK18 2LR Tel: (01296) 714630 Fax: 01296 713122 E-mail: office@tcscellworks.co.uk *Manufacturer & supplier of cell based reagents for academic & industrial R&D**

TCS Computer Services Ltd, The Brewhouse 19 Old Bexley Business Park, Bourne Road, Bexley, Kent, DA5 1LR Tel: (01322) 559840 Fax: (01322) 550010 E-mail: rodney.gent@tcscs.co.uk *Custom Software Development, Systems Integration, Website Development, Report Writing, Technical Documentation and Business Intelligence Suppliers*

▶ TD Textiles Direct, Wilson Road, Huyton, Liverpool, L36 6JG Tel: 0151-489 2121 *Supply bed linen, duvets, curtains and other soft furnishings direct to the public. Buy online or from one of their stores located across the UK.*

▶ TD Thermal Ltd, Cedar House, 17 Springwood Drive, Stone, Staffordshire, ST15 8TU Tel: 01785 615076 Fax: 01785 615076 E-mail: sales@tdthermal.co.uk *a specialist supplier of industrial electric heating elements, temperature sensors and controllers.*

T-Data, 57 Skylark Way, Shinfield, Reading, RG2 9AD Tel: 0118-988 8810 Fax: (07092) 312381 E-mail: info@t-data.co.uk

▶ TDB Events, The Laurels, Comberton, Ludlow, Shropshire, SY8 4HE Tel: 01584 831215 Fax: 01584 831215 E-mail: drive@f1-simulator.co.uk *Entertainment equipment suppliers*

TDG plc, 25 Victoria Street, London, SW1H 0EX Tel: (020) 7222 7411 Fax: (020) 7222 2806 E-mail: businessenquiries@tdg.co.uk *Logistics & storage*

▶ TDG, Condor Glen, Holytown, Motherwell, Lanarkshire, ML1 4UY Tel: (01698) 505800 Fax: (01698) 505220

▶ TDG UK Ltd, Bromford Gate, Bromford Lane, Erdington, Birmingham, B24 8DW Tel: 0121-327 2883 Fax: 0121-327 2551

TDG UK Ltd, High Street, Coleshill, Birmingham, B46 3BP Tel: (01675) 467447 Fax: (01675) 467585 *Distribution & warehousing* Also at: Branches throughout the U.K.

TDG UK Ltd, West Carr Lane, Hull, HU7 0BS Tel: (01482) 839839 Fax: (01482) 839565 *Public warehouse keepers services* Also at: Goole, Harrogate, Liverpool, Manchester, Warrington & West Horton

TDG UK Ltd, New Market Green, Leeds, LS9 0RW Tel: 0113-249 5604 Fax: 0113-249 1832 E-mail: greenwoodf@tdg.co.uk *Temperature controlled storage services*

TDG UK Ltd, Knockmore Industrial Estate, Moira Road, Lisburn, County Antrim, BT28 2EJ Tel: (028) 9260 2133 Fax: (028) 9260 2786 *Warehouse agents*

▶ TDG UK Ltd, Skimpot Road, Luton, LU4 0JD Tel: (01582) 572387 Fax: (01582) 847235 E-mail: wayt@tdg.co.uk *Temperature controlled warehousing & distribution*

▶ TDG UK Ltd, 29-30 Berth, Tilbury Docks, Tilbury, Essex, RM18 7DU Tel: (01375) 844266 Fax: (01375) 844335 *Temperature controlled storage services*

TDK Groundworks, 140 Grantham Road, Waddington, Lincoln, LN5 9NU Tel: (01522) 722332 Fax: (01522) 722280 *Drainage systems service*

Tdo, 15 Maddox Street, London, W1S 2QQ Tel: (020) 7629 5661 Fax: (020) 7629 7500 E-mail: post@timesdrawingoffice.co.uk *Reprographic services & photographic services*

Tdoc Projects Ltd, Suite 308, The White Studios, Templeton on the Green, Glasgow, G40 1DA Tel: 0141-637 3124 Fax: 0141-556 1212 E-mail: sales@tdoc.net *Developers of document control*

▶ Tea Korrs Event Planning And Management, 159 Mellish Street, London, E14 8PJ Tel: 078 65054464 E-mail: teakorrs@gmail.com *Tea Korrs Event Planning And Management offers professional, fun and luxurious event planning service. We specialize in Social events so if you have a birthday, anniversary, wedding or any other special occasion we are here for you. *We have exciting new ideas and a large list of vendors which will satisfy your every request.*We offer full event management so that you can enjoy your special day without a worry.*Call us to arrange an appointment. Our first visit is free of charge. We will discuss your budget, ideas and requirements and provide you with a quote free of charge. Then you can decide whether you want to hire us. It's as simple as that.**

Teacher Marks Ltd, 23 Princes Street, London, W1B 2LX Tel: (020) 7493 4422 Fax: (020) 7497 7773 E-mail: offices@teachermarks.co.uk *Property consultants & surveyors*

▶ Teachernet, Sanctuary Buildings, Great Smith Street, London, SW1P 3BT Tel: (0870) 0002288 Fax: (01928) 794248

▶ The Teaching Post, Chartwell Square, Victoria Plaza, Southend-on-Sea, SS2 5SP Tel: (01702) 619300

Teacraft Ltd, PO Box 190, Bedford, MK42 7EE Tel: (01234) 852121 Fax: (01234) 853232 E-mail: info@teacraft.com *Providers of tea technology*

Teagle Machinery Ltd, Blackwater, Truro, Cornwall, TR4 8HQ Tel: (01872) 560592 Fax: (01872) 561166 E-mail: sales@teagle.co.uk *Agricultural machinery manufrs*

▶ Teahan Abnormal Load Escort Services, 49 Cobbett Close, Enfield, Middlesex, EN3 6QT Tel: (07944) 136886 Fax: (01992) 851590 E-mail: info@abnormalloadescort.com *A nationwide escort & route survey service for the abnormal load industry. Based in North London near juction 25 of the M25, we are closely located to the city as well as the ports of Dartford, Purfleet, Tilbury, Harwich & Dover. We are also a certified member of the Abnormal Load Escort Network (ALEN). We are located approx. 20 minutes from Stratford in the East End of London, the site for the olympic village and stadium. *We have extensive experiance working with abnormal loads which includes 2nd manning and trailer steering.*

Teal Engineering, Breckland Business Park, Norwich Road, Watton, Thetford, Norfolk, IP25 6UP Tel: (01953) 885312 Fax: (01953) 883666 E-mail: info@tealengineering.co.uk *Plastics mould toolmakers & injection mouldings*

Teal & Mackrill Ltd, Lockwood Street, Hull, HU2 0HN Tel: (01482) 328053 Fax: (01482) 219266 *Protective coating paint manufrs*

Teal Patents Ltd, 2 Chelmsley Wood Industrial Estate, Waterloo Avenue, Birmingham, B37 6QQ Tel: 0121-770 4017 Fax: 0121-770 0385 E-mail: enquiries@tealwash.com *Vehicle hand wash equipment*

Teal Signs Ltd, 545 Stanningley Road, Leeds, LS13 4EN Tel: 0113-255 6363 Fax: 0113-236 0593 E-mail: sales@tealsigns.co.uk *Sign makers*

Tealwood Company, 1 Seagull Lane, Emsworth, Hampshire, PO10 7QH Tel: (01243) 371524 Fax: (01243) 378123 E-mail: sales@tealwood.co.uk *Engravers & screen printers*

Team 2000, The Heath, Runcorn, Cheshire, WA7 4SU Tel: (01928) 511333 Fax: (01928) 511334 E-mail: info@team-2000.co.uk *IT recruitment*

Team Colours, The Maltings, Roydon Road, Stanstead Abbotts, Ware, Hertfordshire, SG12 8HG Tel: (01920) 871453 Fax: (01920) 872278 E-mail: sales@teamcolours.co.uk *Team sports wear manufrs*

Team Corporation UK Ltd, 11 Old Ladies Court, High Street, Battle, East Sussex, TN33 0AH Tel: (01424) 777004 Fax: (01424) 777005 E-mail: sales@teamcorporation.co.uk *Hydraulic vibration test systems & solutions suppliers & manufrs*

Team Decorating Co., Unit 4 Beggarlee Park, Engine Lane, Newthorpe, Nottingham, NG16 3RN Tel: (01773) 760060 Fax: (01773) 760081 E-mail: teamdecorating@tiscali.co.uk *Pad printing machines, ink, pads, plates, and consumable supplier. Agents for ITW Morlock, ITW United Silicone, Madag hot stamping machines.*

Team Flitwick, Buncefield Terminal, Green Lane, Hemel Hempstead, Hertfordshire, HP2 7HZ Tel: (01442) 430480 Fax: (01442) 430460 *Fuel oil & lubricants distributors*

Team Group Technologies, Stammerham Business Centre, Capel Road, Rusper, Horsham, West Sussex, RH12 4PZ Tel: (01306) 713410 Fax: (01306) 713408 E-mail: sales@teamgt.co.uk *Suppliers & maintainers of photocopiers, printers, fax & duplicators.*

Team Management PC Hire Ltd, 3 Hermitage Court, Wapping High Street, London, E1 9PL Tel: (020) 7702 9242 Fax: (020) 7702 9747 E-mail: tanya@pchire.com *PC hire services*

Team National Ltd, Triumph House, Birmingham Road, Millisons Wood, Coventry, CV5 9AZ Tel: (01676) 526000 Fax: (01676) 522966 E-mail: sales@teamnational.co.uk *Air conditioning & heating engineers*

Team Overseas Ltd, Meridian House, Nazeing Glass Works Estate, Nazeing New Road, Broxbourne, Hertfordshire, EN10 6SX Tel: +44 (01992) 788233 Fax: +44 (01992) 788695 E-mail: sales@teamoverseas.com *Export merchants*

Team Relocations, 20 Thistle St La North West, Edinburgh, EH2 1EA Tel: 0131-260 3360 Fax: 0131-260 3361 *Relocation consultants*

Team Relocations plc, Drury Way, Brentpark, Neasden, London, NW10 0JN Tel: (020) 8784 0100 Fax: (020) 8451 0061 *International removal contractors*

Team Rewinds Ltd, Don Street, Princes Way North, Team Valley Trading Estate, Gateshead, Tyne & Wear, NE11 0TU Tel: 0191-482 3374 Fax: 0191-482 6222 E-mail: sales@teamrewindsltd.co.uk *Rewind motors supply & electrical*

▶ Team Security Systems Ltd, Windsor Court, Clarence Drive, Harrogate, North Yorkshire, HG1 2PE Tel: (01423) 534680 Fax: (0800) 2980760 E-mail: sales@teamsecuritysystems.co.uk *Electrified perimeter products, alarm systems suppliers*

Team Services Ltd, Riverside Road, Pottington, Barnstaple, Devon, EX31 1TE Tel: (01271) 374019 Fax: (01271) 375977 E-mail: sales@teamservices.co.uk *Electrical & mechanical contractors & engineers*

▶ Team Services, Unit 8 Caen View, Swindon, SN5 8WQ Tel: (01793) 878989 Fax: (01793) 878989

Team Simoco Ltd, Field House, Uttoxeter Old Road, Derby, DE1 1NH Tel: (01332) 375500 Fax: (01332) 375501 E-mail: marketing@teamsimoco.com *Digital radio system agents*

Team Spirit Software Ltd, Warwick House, 48 Collingwood Road, Witham, Essex, CM8 2DZ Tel: (01376) 519413 Fax: (01376) 520471 E-mail: sales@teamspiritsoftware.co.uk *Human resource software solutions*

▶ Team Sports Distribution, 755a Lea Bridge Road, London, E17 9DZ Tel: (020) 8521 8700 Fax: (020) 8520 5280 *Cricket equipment manufrs*

Team Strides, 6 Fleet Road, Fleet Holbeach, Holbeach, Spalding, Lincolnshire, PE12 7AX Tel: (01406) 425999 Fax: (01406) 425717 E-mail: sales@teamstrides.co.uk *Trophy manufrs*

Team Technology (South West) Ltd, Riverside Road, Pottington Business Park, Barnstaple, Devon, EX31 1TE Tel: (01271) 370420 Fax: (01271) 375977 E-mail: sales@teamtechnologysw.co.uk *Fire alarm installers* Also at: Exeter

▶ Team Tots Clothing Ltd, Unit 3 Oak House Moorgreen Industrial Park, Engine Lane, Newthorpe, Nottingham, NG16 3QU Tel: (01773) 717653 Fax: (01773) 717653 *Manufacturers of children's wear*

Team Weighing Co., 12 Rowley Avenue, Sidcup, Kent, DA15 9LA Tel: (020) 8302 9965 Fax: (01322) 286515 E-mail: mike@teamweighing.fsnet.co.uk Principal Export Areas: Worldwide *Manufacturers of weighing systems*

Team Z X 1, Millbrook Business Park, Jarvis Brook, Crowborough, East Sussex, TN6 3JZ Tel: (01892) 669828 Fax: (01892) 669832 E-mail: info@team-zx1.com *Oil lubricant suppliers*

▶ TeamAbroad Avon, 1 The Cloisters, Church Lane, Glastonbury, Somerset, BA6 9NL Tel: (01458) 834195 E-mail: info@TeamAbroad-Avon.com *Overseas property, 50,000 properties in 11 countries, please call us (01458 834195) or visit our website (www.TeamAbroad-Avon.com). We will find a property for you!*

▶ Teampro Music, 16 Wick Drive, Wickford, Essex, SS12 9AS Tel: (01268) 573273 E-mail: sales@teampromusic.co.uk *Sale of Musical Instruments and accessories.*

Teams Roofing Ltd, Wylam Close, Stephenson Industrial Estate East, Washington, Tyne & Wear, NE37 3BE Tel: 0191-419 2233 Fax: 0191-416 2210 E-mail: enquiries@teamsroofing.com *Industrial & architectural roofing sheeting & cladding*

▶ Teams Southern Ltd, 30 The Half Croft, Syston, Leicester, LE7 1LD Tel: 0116-269 1940 Fax: 0116-269 8901

▶ Teamsafe Training, 42 Kings Drive, Berrylands, Surbiton, Surrey, KT5 8NQ Tel: (020) 8399 3404 Fax: (020) 8390 9727 E-mail: troke@teamsafe.co.uk *Training Services,Health & Safety manual handling, coshh, risk assessment, personal safety, violence & aggression, conflict resolution*

Teamsped Ltd, Unit 4 Waterfall La Trading Estate, Cradley Heath, West Midlands, B64 6PU Tel: 0121-561 3886 Fax: 0121-561 3959 E-mail: john@teamsped.co.uk *Freight forwarders*

Teamtalk Satellite Ltd, Media House, Mann Island, Liverpool, L3 1DG Tel: 0151-236 4124 Fax: 0151-236 9907 E-mail: sue.henney@teamtalk.com *News & email services*

▶ Teamtogs, 4/Heritage Cottages, Harper Lane, Shenley, Radlett, Hertfordshire, WD7 9HA Tel: (0845) 8385982 Fax: (01727) 826622 E-mail: info@team-togs.com *Corporate styling staff uniforms manufrs*

Teamvise Ltd, Unit 5 & 6, Flitwick Industrial Estate, Flitwick, Bedford, MK45 1UF Tel: (01525) 718080 Fax: (01525) 718882 E-mail: daniel.king@toolstars.co.uk *Handtool distributors*

Teamwork Fabricating Ltd, C Cuxton Industrial Estate, Station Road, Cuxton, Rochester, Kent, ME2 1AJ Tel: (01634) 290551 Fax: (01634) 290021 *Lifting gear engineering services*

Teamwork Handling Ltd, Allerthorpe Business Park, Pocklington, York, YO42 1NS Tel: (01759) 322400 Fax: (01759) 303265 E-mail: magnus@teamwork-handling.co.uk *Mail handling & direct mail services*

Teamwork & Teamplay, Unit 16-17, Ashley Heath Industrial Estate, Ringwood Road, Three Legged Cross, Wimborne, Dorset, BH21 6UZ Tel: (01202) 590009 Fax: (01202) 828593 E-mail: mail@splatltd.co.uk *Corporate team building services & multi activity centre*

Teamwork Trophey Centre, St. Marks Road, St. James Industrial Estate, Corby, Northamptonshire, NN18 8AN Tel: (01536) 263487 Fax: (01536) 263487 *Producers, suppliers & engravers of trophies*

A.J. Tear & Co. Ltd, 76 Overstone Road, Northampton, NN1 3JS Tel: (01604) 639280 Fax: (01604) 633832 E-mail: sales@glanmar.co.uk *Furniture upholsterers & manufrs*

▶ Tear Away Leisure, Unit 6-7 Dowland Business Park, Harrison Way, Manby, Louth, Lincolnshire, LN11 8UX Tel: (01507) 327887 *Inflatable & bouncy castle suppliers*

S. Teasdale (Hospital Equipment) Ltd, Unit 1 & 2, Brighton Road, Stockport, Cheshire, SK4 2BE Tel: 0161-219 0080 Fax: 0161-219 0081 *Operating table mattresses manufrs*

Tebbs Engineering Development Ltd, 7 Maltings Close, Cranfield, MK43 0BY Tel: (01234) 750099 Fax: (01234) 750896 E-mail: martin@tebbseng.co.uk *Process control systems manufrs*

Tebrax Ltd, International House, Cray Avenue, Orpington, Kent, BR5 3RY Tel: (01689) 897766 Fax: (01689) 896789 E-mail: brackets@tebrax.co.uk *Shelving aluminium bracket manufrs*

▶ Tec Clothing Manufacturers, 534 Stoney Stanton Road, Coventry, CV6 5FS Tel: (024) 7666 8310

▶ Tec Pak, Unit 7, Uddens Trading Estate, Wimborne, Dorset, BH21 7LQ Tel: (01202) 870060 *Packaging distribution*

▶ Tec Transnational, 48 Fentham Road, Hampton-in-Arden, Solihull, West Midlands, B92 0AY Tel: (01926) 851403 Fax: (01675) 442222 E-mail: mail@tectransnational.com *Implement quality systems & provide support training*

▶ Tec UK, Royal Oak Way North Unit A, Daventry Distribution Centre, Royal Oak Industrial Estate, Daventry, Northamptonshire, NN11 8LR Tel: (01327) 300400 Fax: (01327) 879679 E-mail: tecuk@aol.com

Tecalemit Garage Equipment Co. Ltd, Eagle Road, Plympton, Plymouth, PL7 5JY Tel: (01752) 219111 Fax: (01752) 219128 E-mail: sales@tecalemit.co.uk *Garage servicing equipment suppliers*

Tecan Ltd, Tecan Way, Granby Industrial Estate, Weymouth, Dorset, DT4 9TU Tel: (01305) 765432 Fax: (01305) 780194 E-mail: info@tecan.co.uk *Small metal components manufrs*

Tecapet Ltd, Unitec House, Albert Place, London, N3 1QB Tel: (020) 8349 4299 Fax: (020) 8349 0252 E-mail: tecapet@aol.com *Importers & exporters*

Teccom Ltd, Howbury Centre, Crayford, Dartford, DA1 4RQ Tel: (0845) 8900844 E-mail: info@teccom.ltd.uk *Teccom Ltd - Security & Environmental Technology. West End & Kent operations. Installations, Maintenance, Testing & Commissioning. CCTV, Covert, GeoVision Digital Recording Systems, Addressable Fire Alarms & Conventional, Access Control &* Door Entry, Electrical Installation & Emergency Lighting. Air Conditioning Services, HVAC, Splits, Installation*

▶ Teccon Ltd, Dexion House, Attleborough Fields Industrial Estate, Attleborough Fields, Nuneaton, Warwickshire, CV11 6RX Tel: 02476 322880 Fax: 02476 328425 E-mail: sales@tecconltd.co.uk *Storage Warehousing available from Teccon Ltd based in Nuneaton, Warwickshire. Click the links below to visit our website or contact us via our profile page.*

Tecfacs Ltd, 6 Oaklands Business Centre, Oaklands Park, Wokingham, Berkshire, RG41 2FD Tel: 0118-977 6645 Fax: 0118-989 4461 E-mail: sales@tecfacs.com *Computer systems consultants*

Tecform Engineering, 34 Soho Mills, Wooburn Green, High Wycombe, Buckinghamshire, HP10 0PF Tel: (01628) 524989 Fax: (01628) 524989 E-mail: sales@tecform.co.uk *Wire erosion machining services*

Tech Ltd, The Granery, Leacon Farm, Leacon Lane, Charing, Ashford, Kent, TN27 0EN Tel: (01634) 290308 Fax: (01233) 714040 E-mail: johnbridges1@btconnect.com *Electronic service engineers*

Tech Cadcam, Minster House, Western Way, Bury St. Edmunds, Suffolk, IP33 3SP Tel: (01284) 754781 Fax: (01284) 750344 E-mail: sales@techcadcam.net *Engineering software suppliers*

Tech Folium Ltd, Triumph Trading Park, Speke Hall Road, Speke, Liverpool, L24 9GQ Tel: 0151-486 4300 Fax: 0151-486 3335 Principal Export Areas: Worldwide *Polyethylene film manufrs*

▶ Tech Home, 43 Church Street, Weybridge, Surrey, KT13 8DG Tel: (01932) 820521 Fax: (01932) 841205 *Audio visual equipment retailers & installers*

Tech Hose, Unit 14 Tarsmill Court, Rotherwas Industrial Estate, Hereford, HR2 6JZ Tel: (01432) 270466 Fax: (01432) 351548 E-mail: sales@tech-hose.co.uk *Hose fittings distributors & manufrs*

Tech Mat Convertors Ltd, Alder Court, Springwood Way, Tytherington Business Park, Macclesfield, Cheshire, SK10 2XG Tel: (01625) 610441 Fax: (01625) 613199 E-mail: nigels@techmat.co.uk *High pressure water jet cutting services*

Tech Op Ltd, 268 London Road, Cheltenham, Gloucestershire, GL52 6HS Tel: (01242) 570999 Fax: (01242) 588955 E-mail: sales@techop.co.uk *Computer consultants*

Tech Optics Ltd, 6 Tannery Road, Tonbridge, Kent, TN9 1RF Tel: (01732) 770466 Fax: (01732) 770476 E-mail: sales@techoptics.com *Fibre optics components distributors*

Techbake Ltd, Ham Farm, Southwick, Fareham, Hants, PO17 6AU Tel: 023 92215521 Fax: 023 92214521 *Commercial bakery equipment*

Techcast Foundries Ltd, Pigott House, Parkway Avenue, Sheffield, S9 4WA Tel: 0114-272 9741 Fax: 0114-278 1585 E-mail: sales@techcast.co.uk *Casting (non-ferrous metal) manufrs*

Techclean Services Ltd, V D U House, Old Kiln Lane, Farnham, Surrey, GU10 2JH Tel: (01428) 713713 Fax: (01428) 713798 E-mail: info@techclean.co.uk *Computer cleaning services*

Techclean Services, 102 Queslett Road East, Sutton Coldfield, West Midlands, B74 2EZ Tel: 0121-353 0074 Fax: 0121-693 0074 E-mail: birmingham@techclean.co.uk *Computer & telephone cleaning*

▶ Techdivision, 118 St. Margarets Road, Twickenham, TW1 2AA Tel: (020) 8891 3010 Fax: (020) 8288 2591 E-mail: info@techdivision.co.uk *Fast, responsive computer support & systems for small businesses*

▶ Techfield Software, 4 Banksfield Grove, Yeadon, Leeds, LS19 7LN Tel: (01943) 884478 Fax: (01943) 884478

Techfix Products Ltd, Unit 10 Two Woods Industrial Estate, Talbots Lane, Brierley Hill, West Midlands, DY5 2YX Tel: (01384) 77551 Fax: (01384) 77552 E-mail: sales@techfixproducts.com *Fixing systems distributors*

Techfore Turned Parts Ltd, Unit 32r The Washford Industrial Estate, Heming Road, Redditch, Worcestershire, B98 0DH Tel: (01527) 514218 Fax: (01527) 514200 *Turned parts manufrs*

▶ Techform Packaging Supplies, Unit 43-51, Limestone Cottage Lane, Sheffield, S6 1NJ Tel: 0114-234 9912 Fax: 0114-234 9973 *Cutlery packagers*

▶ Techies Ltd, Triumph Way, Woburn Road Industrial Estate, Kempston, Bedford, MK42 7QB Tel: (01234) 299000 Fax: (01234) 299009 E-mail: sales@techies.co.uk *Computer consultants*

▶ Techknol Developments Ltd, Station Approach Industrial Estate, Station Approach, Oakham, Leicestershire, LE15 6QW Tel: (01572) 724445 Fax: (01572) 723484 E-mail: info@techknolpower.co.uk

Techman Engineering Ltd, Techman House, Broombank Park, Chesterfield Trading Estate, Sheepbridge, Chesterfield, Derbyshire, S41 9RT Tel: (01246) 261385 Fax: (01246) 453734 E-mail: enquiries@techman-engineering.co.uk *Precision Engineering Oil Down Hole drilling Tools Bespoke services*

Techmarkets Ltd, Fourth Avenue, Trafford Park, Manchester, M17 1DB Tel: 0161-876 4125 Fax: 0161-876 4146 E-mail: techmarkets@btconnect.com *Plastic furniture fittings manufrs*

Techmate Ltd, 10 Bridgeturn Avenue, Old Wolverton, Milton Keynes, MK12 5QL Tel: (01908) 322222 Fax: (01908) 319941 *Import & distribute lab wear*

Techna International, Unit 1 Metro Centre, Dwight Road, Watford, WD18 9HG Tel: (01923) 222227 Fax: (01923) 219700 E-mail: sales@techna.co.uk *Electrical materials distributors*

Technacryl Ltd, Shakenhurst, Cleobury Mortimer, Kidderminster, Worcestershire, DY14 9AR Tel: (01299) 832406 Fax: (01299) 832676 *Acrylic fabricators & moulders*

Technal, Units 2-4 Hudswell Road, Hunslet, Leeds, LS10 1AG Tel: 0113-296 1400 Fax: 0113-296 1414 E-mail: leeds@technal.co.uk *Aluminium extrusion suppliers*

Technal Viking, J The Lodden Centre, Wade Road, Basingstoke, Hampshire, RG24 8FL Tel: (01256) 724900 Fax: (01256) 724949 E-mail: sales@technal.co.uk *Aluminium system suppliers*

Technart Ltd, Unit 45 City Industrial Park, Southern Road, Southampton, SO15 1HG Tel: (023) 8022 2409 Fax: (023) 8021 1403 E-mail: prepress@technart.co.uk *Commercial printers*

Technaseal Concrete Repairing Services, 11 Marriott Close, Heigham Street, Norwich, NR2 4UX Tel: (01603) 667106 Fax: (01603) 612636 E-mail: info@technasel.co.uk *Concrete engineers*

Techneat Engineering Ltd, 2a Henry Crabb Road, Littleport, Ely, Cambridgeshire, CB6 1SE Tel: (01353) 862044 Fax: (01353) 862644 E-mail: info@techneat.co.uk *Techneat Engineering Limited was established in 1984. Services cover a wide range of agricultural engineering but particular expertise is offered in the manufacture of spraying machinery, applicators and accessories. A diverse product range includes equipment for agriculture, amenity, sports turf, forestry and industrial use. We also have modern facilities for fabrication in mild steel, stainless steel and aluminium. In 1997 a rotational moulding machine was installed - providing the ability to manufacture polyethylene sprayer tanks and other components.*

▶ Techni Grind Preston Machining Ltd, Unit 62 Red Scar Industrial Estate, Longridge Road, Ribbleton, Preston, PR2 5ND Tel: (01772) 797589 Fax: (01772) 797682 E-mail: sales@tgmeng.co.uk

Techni Grind Preston Machining Ltd, Unit 62 Red Scar Industrial Estate, Longridge Road, Ribbleton, Preston, PR2 5ND Tel: (01772) 797589 Fax: (01772) 797682 E-mail: sales@tgmeng.co.uk *Cutting tool engineers*

Techniblinds Ltd, 16 Plumpton Way, Carshalton, Surrey, SM5 2DG Tel: (020) 8669 1122 Fax: (020) 8669 2244 E-mail: info@techniblinds.co.uk *Blind & curtain suppliers & manufacturers & installers*

▶ Techniblock Ltd, Kingsway Industrial Park, Kingsway Park Close, Derby, DE22 3FP Tel: (01332) 293977 Fax: (01332) 364488

Technic Electric Ltd, Unit 5 Lulworth Business Centre, Nutwood Way, Totton, Southampton, SO40 3WW Tel: (023) 8066 7486 Fax: (023) 8066 3830 E-mail: sales@technic.co.uk *Electronic services*

Technic Wood Products Ltd, Cambrian Industrial Estate East Side, Coedcae Lane, Pontyclun, Mid Glamorgan, CF72 9EW Tel: (01443) 222110 *Furniture frame manufrs*

▶ Technicair Ltd, Unit 3 Rough Farm Industrial Estate, Atherstone on Stour, Stratford-upon-Avon, Warwickshire, CV37 8DX Tel: (01789) 450015 Fax: (01789) 450014 E-mail: nick@technicair.prestel.co.uk *Air conditioning & ventilation engineering services*

Technical Asset Management Ltd, Falcon House City Park, Watchmead, Welwyn Garden City, Hertfordshire, AL7 1AT Tel: (01707) 333555 Fax: (01707) 390893 E-mail: sales@tam-uk.com *Computer reseller*

▶ Technical Assist Ltd, Unit A3 (2), Copley Mill, Huddersfield Road, Stalybridge, Cheshire, SK15 2QF Tel: (0800) 0196850 Fax: (0870) 7623362 E-mail: info@technicalassist.com *IT & computer services*

Technical Casino Services Ltd, Unit 9 Mulberry Business Centre, Quebec Way, Rotherhithe, London, SE16 7LE Tel: (020) 7394 4000 Fax: (020) 7231 7414 E-mail: tcsuk@tcsgroup.com *Casino equipment suppliers*

Technical Concepts Ltd, The Neutralle Centre, 4 Eastman Way, Stevenage, Hertfordshire, SG1 4UH Tel: (0870) 5686824 Fax: (01438) 311200 *Air freshener manufrs*

Technical Control Systems Ltd, Treefield Industrial Estate, Gildersome, Leeds, LS27 7JU Tel: 0113-252 5977 Fax: 0113-238 0095 E-mail: enquiries@tcspanels.co.uk *Control panel manufrs*

Technical Convertors Ltd, Unit 5 Third Way, Avonmouth, Bristol, BS11 9HL Tel: 0117-982 8808 Fax: 0117-938 4868 E-mail: sales@technicalconverters.co.uk *Coating, laminating & slitting services*

Technical Data Systems Ltd, Unit A, Watchmoor Trade Centre, Watchmoor Road, Camberley, Surrey, GU15 3AJ Tel: (01276) 684835 Fax: (0870) 1607050 E-mail: sales@tdsltd.co.uk *Computer software suppliers*

▶ Technical Demolition Services, 17 Hamilton Square, Birkenhead, Merseyside, CH41 6AX Tel: 0151-666 1272 Fax: 0151-666 1624 E-mail: techdem@btinternet.com *Demolition contractors*

Technical Earth Ltd, Unit 5f Atlas Business Centre, Oxgate Lane, London, NW2 7HJ Tel: (020) 8450 0303 Fax: (020) 8450 0330 E-mail: info@techearth.com *Audio engineers*

Technical & Engineering Services Ltd, 2A Saywood Close, Chesham, Buckinghamshire, HP5 3DP Tel: (01494) 771503 Fax: (01494) 771503 E-mail: tesagy@btconnect.com *Technical, engineering & scientific recruitment*

Technical Fabrications, Unit 28 Rowfant Business Centre, Wallage Lane, Rowfant, Crawley, West Sussex, RH10 4NQ Tel: (01342) 717523 Fax: (01342) 715392 *Stainless steel fabricators/ welding services*

Technical Filtration Systems Ltd, Croft House, Sandbeck Way, Wetherby, West Yorkshire, LS22 7DP Tel: (01937) 588222 Fax: (01937) 588345 E-mail: mail@tfs-ltd.co.uk *Filtration accessories distributors*

Technical Glass Ltd, Kelvin Way, West Bromwich, West Midlands, B70 7LB Tel: 0121-553 3334 Fax: 0121-553 3336 E-mail: sales@technicalglass.net *Toughened glass safety manufrs*

Technical Help to Exporters, 389 Chiswick High Road, London, W4 4AL Tel: (020) 8996 7474 Fax: (020) 8996 7048 E-mail: the@bsi-global.com *Help companies understand responsibilities for products*

Technical Inspection Services UK Ltd, 11 Somerset Road, Clevedon, Avon, BS21 6DP Tel: (01275) 871130 Fax: (01275) 875917 E-mail: info@tis-uk.co.uk *Non-destructive testing & inspectors*

Technical Instrument Casting Co., Kings Hill Industrial Estate, Bude, Cornwall, EX23 8QN Tel: (01288) 353150 Fax: (01288) 353783 E-mail: office@tic-castings.co.uk Produce castings

Technical & Maintenance Services Ltd, 18 Pepper Road, Calverton, Nottingham, NG14 6LH Tel: 0115-965 3036 Fax: 0115-965 5274 E-mail: brian.burbidge@talk21.com Ceramic engineering services

▶ Technical Medical Services, 8 Merlin Way, Quarry Hill Industrial Estate, Ilkeston, Derbyshire, DE7 4RA Tel: 0115-932 3242 Fax: 0115-944 1618 E-mail: tmsderby@aol.com Medical equipment sales

Technical Models Ltd, Unit 10 Crosland Industrial Estate, Stockport Road West, Bredbury, Stockport, Cheshire, SK6 2BR Tel: 0161-494 9022 Fax: 0161-430 8406 E-mail: enquiries@technical-models.co.uk Industrial model & test rig makers

Technical Moulding Projects, Unit 5d Watlington Industrial Estate, Cuxham Road, Watlington, Oxfordshire, OX49 5LU Tel: (01491) 613539 Fax: (01491) 612096 E-mail: tmp@techmouldproj.demon.co.uk Took-makers & plastic injection mouldings manufrs

Technical Network Ltd, 81-82 Darlington Street, Wolverhampton, WV1 4JD Tel: (01902) 311313 Fax: (01902) 427235 E-mail: sales@netrec.co.uk Recruitment consultants

Technical Paint Services, 27 Southcote Road, Bournemouth, BH1 3SH Tel: (01202) 295570 Fax: (0845) 2301255 E-mail: sales@technicalpaintservices.com Paint manufrs

Technical Photo Systems Ltd, 22-28 Napier Place, Wardpark North, Cumbernauld, Glasgow, G68 0LL Tel: (01236) 739668 Fax: (01236) 738376 E-mail: alan@tpsmedical.co.uk X-ray photographic film distributors

▶ Technical Press Supplies Ltd, Unit 65 Greenway Business Centre Harlow Business Park, Greenway, Harlow, Essex, CM19 5QE Tel: (0845) 8501818 Fax: (01279) 408140 Machine tool accessory manufrs

▶ Technical Print Services Ltd, Brentcliffe Avenue, Carlton Road, Nottingham, NG3 7AG Tel: 0115-987 3771

Technical Progress Ltd, 96 Telford Road, Cumbernauld, Glasgow, G67 2NJ Tel: (01236) 453266 Fax: (01236) 458274 E-mail: sales@technicalprogressltd.co.uk Computer maintenance

▶ Technical Project Services Ltd, Unit 2d Walsden Industrial Estate, Rochdale Road, Todmorden, Lancashire, OL14 6UD Tel: (01706) 810770 Fax: (01706) 810771

Technical Resin Bonders Ltd, 12 Clifton Road, Huntingdon, Cambridgeshire, PE29 7EN Tel: 0845 5314225 Fax: (01480) 414992 E-mail: sales@trbonders.co.uk One of the original companies in the UK to manufacture honeycomb sandwich panels, Technical Resin Bonders has expanded and diversified its Cellite and Matrix range of panel systems, to include fully bonded assemblies and composite structures. Supplying general engineering, rail, aerospace, defence, marine and motor racing industries.*By tailoring the separate elements of honeycomb core, skin materials and adhesive to suit individual criteria the resulting construction can be used for numerous applications where high stiffness and low weight are particular requirements. Components can be assembled into complex shaped modules and structures and finished with equipment and services. Panels and assemblies can be built to meet a multitude of environmental and service conditions including the latest regulations for fire, smoke and toxicity.

Technical Service Consultants Ltd, The Rope Walk, Schofield Street, Heywood, Lancashire, OL10 1DS Tel: (01706) 620600 Fax: (01706) 620445 E-mail: sales@tsc-ltd.demon.co.uk Microbiology consumables

▶ Technical Services, 6-9 Cleveland Road, Gosport, Hampshire, PO12 2JG Tel: (023) 9258 8059 Fax: (023) 9258 9556 E-mail: enquiries@techsoundsystems.co.uk Hire & Installation of sound & lighting systems for events, concerts, conferences etc. Event power, radiocommunications and Production Services.

Technical Services Shropshire Ltd, Unit 8, Bicton Business Park, Isle Lane, Bicton Heath, Shrewsbury, SY3 8DY Tel: (01743) 851313 Fax: (01743) 851211 E-mail: info@tsshropshire.co.uk Security installation contractors

Technical Services UK Ltd, Highfield Works, Intake Road, Bradford, West Yorkshire, BD2 3JR Tel: (01274) 637851 Fax: (01274) 637852 Motor vehicle component

Technical Software Consultants Ltd, 6 Mill Square, Featherstone Road, Wolverton Mill, Milton Keynes, MK12 5RB Tel: (01908) 317444 Fax: (01908) 220959 E-mail: info@tscinspectionsystems.com Consulting engineers

The Technical Support Service, Forrest Rd, Stirling, FK8 1UJ Tel: 01786 478694 Fax: 01786 447672 Computer consultants

Technical Systems Ltd, Long View, Simms Lane, Reading, RG7 2JP Tel: 0118-933 3700 Technical systems installers & manufacturers of electron beam accelerators

▶ Technical Textiles Executive, Batchworth Lock House, 99 Church Street, Rickmansworth, Hertfordshire, WD3 1JJ Tel: 01923 498001 E-mail: info@technicaltextiles.co.uk The Technical Textiles Executive is a membership organisation of leading UK technical textile companies. With strong links to academia, government and other industries.

Technical Transport Equipment Ltd, 87 Styal Road, Gatley, Cheadle, Cheshire, SK8 4JQ Tel: 0161-491 3150 Fax: 0161-491 3150 Refrigeration parts

Technical Treatments Ltd, Station Works, Rye Lane, Dunton Green, Sevenoaks, Kent, TN14 5HD Tel: (01732) 462656 Fax: (01732) 742602

continued

E-mail: enquiries@technical-treatments.co.uk Plastic Bottles Manufacturer for Industrial Multipurpose. Sizes ranging from 15mm to 25L in natural HDPE - LDPE, produced in narrow and wide Necks. Products can be despatched within 24 hours from Stock; ensuring quick turnarounds for urgent requirements!

▶ Technical Vending Services, T V S House, Nash Road, Beachampton, Milton Keynes, MK19 6EA Tel: (01908) 263600 Fax: (01908) 263600 E-mail: info@technicalvendingsupport.com Maintenance vending services

Technical Welding Services, Corporation Road, Rochdale, Lancashire, OL11 4HJ Tel: (01706) 655402 Fax: (01706) 657735 E-mail: sales@technicalwelding.co.uk Specialist welding and engineering company located in the north west. we specialise in the Manufacture and Refurbishment of Extruder Screws and Extruder Barrels for the Plastics, rubber and Food/Feed industries. Extruder screws, Extruder Barrels, Auger Screws, Auger barrels, General welding and Fabrication.

▶ Technically Yours Ltd, 20 Thompson Road, Newhaven, East Sussex, BN9 0RT Tel: (01273) 611178 System & software support services

Technicast Moulds, Unit 1 Garnett Close, Watford, WD24 7GN Tel: (01923) 246530 Fax: (01923) 255983 E-mail: isoo4e2893@blueyonder.co.uk Injection mould/die toolmakers, metal melting

Technician Service Centre, Main Street, Chapelhall, Airdrie, Lanarkshire, ML6 8SF Tel: (01236) 756552 Fax: (01236) 756542 E-mail: techcentre@ea.n-lanark.sch.uk Technician service centre

▶ Techniclean Supply Co., Gomm Road, High Wycombe, Buckinghamshire, HP13 7DJ Tel: (01494) 459233 Industrial cleaning equipment distributors

Technicopy, Woodford Business Development Centre, London, E18 1AB Tel: (020) 8989 9281 Photocopiers & faxes repairs & suppliers

Technicraft Anglia Ltd, Wilford Bridge Road, Melton, Woodbridge, Suffolk, IP12 1RB Tel: (01394) 385213 Fax: (01394) 387914 E-mail: technicraft@technicraft.co.uk Sheet metalwork engineers or fabricators

Technidrive Solutions, 89 Moy Road, Armagh, BT61 8DR Tel: (028) 3751 8111 Fax: (028) 3752 8181 E-mail: sales@technidrive.co.uk Gear box resellers

Technifix Catering Equipment, Nigg Station, Arabella, Tain, Ross-Shire, IV19 1QH Tel: (01862) 863231 Fax: (01862) 863343 E-mail: sales@technifix.com Electrical & gas repairs

Techniflow Hand Dryers Ltd, 6a Uddens Trading Estate, Staplehill, Wimborne, Dorset, BH21 7LQ Tel: (01425) 479866 Fax: (01202) 893700 E-mail: info@handriers.co.uk Suppliers of quality vandal-proof hand/hair dryers to companies,schools,hospitals,restaurants,pubs, fitness centres and local authorities

Techniform Graphics Ltd, 172 Bexley Road, London, SE9 2PH Tel: (020) 8850 9191 Fax: (020) 7703 6001 E-mail: sales@techniformgraphics.co.uk Sign manufrs

Techniform Sales Ltd, 14 250 Milkwood Road, London, SE24 0HG Tel: (020) 7274 1999 Fax: (020) 7274 0199 Storage & shelving distributors

Technijet, Old Station Yard, Kirkby Lonsdale, Carnforth, Lancashire, LA6 2HP Tel: (01524) 273000 Fax: (01524) 272161 Industrial cleaning suppliers

Technik Ltd, 2 4 Riverpark, Billet Lane, Berkhamsted, Hertfordshire, HP4 1HL Tel: (01442) 871117 Fax: (01442) 870891 E-mail: terry@technik.com Multi media reprographics specialists

Technik Exhibit Solutions Ltd, Unit 14 Boxted Farm Business Park, Berkhamsted Road, Hemel Hempstead, Hertfordshire, HP1 2SG Tel: (01442) 220130 Fax: (01442) 251412 E-mail: sales@techniksolutions.co.uk Exhibition stand design & construction

Technik Motors Ltd, 2a Langdale Avenue, Mitcham, Surrey, CR4 4AE Tel: (020) 8648 8162 Fax: (020) 8648 8162 Car body services

Technip Offshore Ltd, Enterprise Drive, Westhill Industrial Estate, Westhill, Aberdeenshire, AB32 6TQ Tel: (01224) 744044 Fax: (01224) 271271 Sub-sea contractors

Tech-Ni-Plant Ltd, Unit 4 Holt Court North Heneage, Street West Aston Science Park, Birmingham, B7 4AX Tel: 0121-359 8545 Fax: 0121-333 4950 Surface treatment centre

▶ Technipol Metal Finishing Services, Unit 7 Howdon Lane, Wallsend, Tyne & Wear, NE28 0AL Tel: 0191-262 6664 Fax: 0191-262 6664 E-mail: technipol@hotmail.co.uk fettling,grinding,Mechanical polishing of non ferrous metals,Stainless Steel Specialists,*

Technique Ltd, 8 Saturn House, Calleva Park, Aldermaston, Reading, RG7 8HA Tel: 0118-982 9244 Fax: 0118-982 9255 E-mail: info@technique-ltd.co.uk IT consultancy

Technique Ceilings, 46 Weston Road, Doncaster, South Yorkshire, DN4 8NF Tel: (01302) 855552 Fax: (01302) 850347 Ceiling & partitions contractors

Technique Engineering, 1 Gilmans Industrial Estate, Billingshurst, West Sussex, RH14 9EZ Tel: (01403) 784678 Fax: (01403) 784978 E-mail: info@technique-engineering.com Lifting gear designers & manufrs

Technique Training, Midland Court, Barlborough Links, Chesterfield, Derbyshire, S43 4UL Tel: (01246) 813703 Fax: (01246) 571090 E-mail: mark@techniquetraining.co.uk Electrical, mechanical, control & data training services

Techniques Surfaces (UK) Ltd, Wood Lane, Erdington, Birmingham, B24 9QL Tel: 0121-382 8060 Fax: 0121-377 8928 E-mail: info@ts-uk.com Metal heat, corrosion prevention, hard facing surface treatment manufrs

▶ Techniquip Ltd, The Old Brewery Estate, Norton Fitzwarren, Taunton, Somerset, TA2 6RN Tel: (01823) 351255 Fax: (01823) 324824 E-mail: sales@techniquip.co.uk Flow, pressure & level instrumentation distributor

Technirack Systems Ltd, Unit 18 Avenue One, Witney, Oxfordshire, OX28 4XZ Tel: (01993) 893602 Fax: (01993) 893601 Storage system services

Technisol Ltd, Unit B14 Little Heath Industrial Estate, Old Church Road, Coventry, CV6 7NB Tel: (024) 7668 0088 Fax: (024) 7658 1144 E-mail: sales@technisolltd.co.uk Electronic control units manufrs

Technisteel, 47 Kenilworth Drive, Oadby, Leicester, LE2 5LT Tel: 0116-271 1889 Fax: 0116-271 1889 E-mail: rjadams@technisteel.co.uk Display manufrs

Technitool Engineers, 5 William Street, Northampton, NN1 3EW Tel: (01604) 626790 Fax: (01604) 233425 E-mail: technitools@talk21.com Toolmakers

▶ Technival Ltd, Hillhouse Community Workshop, Argyle Crescent, Hamilton, Lanarkshire, ML3 9BQ Tel: (01698) 286966 E-mail: info@technival.co.uk Provide technical & validation services

▶ Techno Associates, 382, Sykes Road, Slough, SL1 4SP Tel: (01753) 572800 Fax: (01753) 572800

▶ Techno Consultancy (UK) Ltd, 200 Norman Crescent, Hounslow, TW5 9JW Tel: (0870) 2850765 Fax: (0870) 2860766 Website design services & optimisation

Techno Lift, 121 Barfillan Drive, Glasgow, G52 1BD Tel: 0141-882 4403 Fax: 0141-882 5353 Lifting gear distributors

Techno Trade, 167 West Street, Fareham, Hampshire, PO16 0EF Tel: (01329) 234199 Fax: (01329) 220232 Electrical tools & hardware suppliers

Technocover, Whittington Road, Oswestry, Shropshire, SY11 1HZ Tel: (01691) 653251 Fax: (01691) 658222 E-mail: sales@jonesofoswestry.com Galvanized manhole covers & steel lintels

Technocover Ltd, Henfaes Lane, Welshpool, Powys, SY21 7BE Tel: (01938) 555511 Fax: (01938) 555527 E-mail: terry.batten@technocover.co.uk Quality access cover designers & manufrs

▶ Techno-Craft (UK) Ltd, 16 The Mount, Guildford, Surrey, GU2 4HS Tel: (020) 7430 0777 Fax: (020) 7430 1777 IT solutions for banks

Technocurve, Unit 52 Enterprise Centre, Bryn Road, Aberkenfig, Bridgend, Mid Glamorgan, CF32 9BS Tel: (0845) 0515014 Fax: (0870) 0940776

▶ Technoglass Stained Glass Designers, 15 Crookstonhill Path, Glasgow, G52 3LR Tel: 0141-882 9001 Fax: 0141-882 9001

Technograph Microcircuits Ltd, Railway Triangle Industrial Estate, Walton Road, Portsmouth, PO6 1TN Tel: (023) 9232 1654 Fax: (023) 9237 5353 E-mail: info@technographmicro.com Microcircuit manufrs

Technographics UK, Polymark House, Abbeydale Road, Wembley, Middlesex, HA0 1LQ Tel: (020) 8991 0011 Fax: (020) 8998 8080 E-mail: sales@technographics.co.uk Heat fusible transfer manufrs

Technol 2000 Ltd, 5-7 Chester Road, Northwich, Cheshire, CW8 1EZ Tel: (01606) 784044 Fax: (01606) 784055 E-mail: info@technol.co.uk Computer retailers

Technol Window Repairs, 100 Braeside Road, Greenock, Renfrewshire, PA16 0QX Tel: (01475) 639989 Fax: (01475) 635301 Repair & refurbish windows, doors & crittall window distributor

Technolog Group Ltd, Technolog House, Ravenstor Road, Matlock, Derbyshire, DE4 4FY Tel: (01629) 823611 Fax: (01629) 824283 E-mail: technolog@technolog.com Data logger manufrs

Technologies Group Ltd, Hampstead Avenue, Mildenhall, Bury St. Edmunds, Suffolk, IP28 7AS Tel: (01638) 713631 Fax: (01638) 712271 E-mail: sales@tech-group.co.uk Supplier of IT products & services

Technology Blueprint Ltd, 45b High Street, St. Neots, Cambridgeshire, PE19 1BN Tel: (01480) 356226 Fax: (01480) 356227 E-mail: support@propco.co.uk Software solutions development

Technology For Business plc, 1-2 Kingdom Close, Fareham, Hampshire, PO15 5TJ Tel: (01489) 609000 Fax: (01489) 609999 E-mail: sales@tfbplc.co.uk Computer programmers

Technology Design Ltd, Wharton Park House, Nat Lane, Winsford, Cheshire, CW7 3BS Tel: (01606) 590123 Fax: (01606) 591253 E-mail: sales@technologydesign.com Principal Export Areas: Asia Pacific, Africa, Central/East Europe, West Europe & North America Non-destructive test equipment

The Technology Forge, Top Floor Pegholme, Wharfebank Business Centre, Otley, Leeds, LS21 3JP Tel: (01943) 464844 Fax: (01943) 464833 E-mail: sales@technologyforge.com Computer systems & software developers

Technology Helpdesk, Unit 3, Turnbull Way, Livingston, West Lothian, EH54 8RB Tel: (01506) 436700 Fax: (01506) 436703 E-mail: sales@technologyhelpdesk.co.uk Technology consultants

Technology Management Ltd, 1 Sunray Avenue, Whitstable, Kent, CT5 4ED Tel: (01227) 276590 Database designers, builders & testers services

▶ Technology Management & Consultancy, 3 Amethyst Close, Rainworth, Mansfield, Nottinghamshire, NG21 0GH Tel: (01623) 799204 Fax: (0871) 6611093 E-mail: enquiries@techmcl.co.uk IT management consultancy services

Technology Management (Midlands) Ltd, The Old Rectory, 57 Waterloo Road, Wolverhampton, WV1 4QH Tel: (01902) 578300 Fax: (01902) 578301 E-mail: admin@tecman.co.uk IT consultants

Technology Offshore Onshore Ltd, Woodcroft House, Crow Hill Drive, Mansfield, Nottinghamshire, NG19 7AE Tel: (01623) 654254 Fax: (01623) 420821 E-mail: kcutt@techoffshore.com Quality assurance inspection

▶ Technology Plus Services Ltd, 28, Newcomen Road, Tunbridge Wells, Kent, TN4 9PA Tel: (01892) 615315 Fax: (01892) 615316

Technology Project Services International Ltd, 1 Warwick Row, London, SW1E 5ER Tel: (020) 7963 1234 Fax: (020) 7963 1299 E-mail: mail@tps.co.uk Suppliers of consultants & engineers

▶ Technology Resourcing, Unit 29, Surrey Technology Centre, Occam Road, Guildford, Surrey, GU2 7YG Tel: (01483) 302211 Fax: (01483) 301222 E-mail: recruit@tech-res.co.uk Technical Recruitment company specialising in the recruitment of Technology & Engineering professionals, for both permanent staff appointments and contract /consultancy assignments, throughout the UK.

Technology Services, W2 Warrington Business Park, Long Lane, Warrington, WA2 8TX Tel: (01925) 444621 Fax: (01925) 492221 Electronic contract manufacturing services

Technology Services Group, Temple Point, Colton, Leeds, LS15 9JL Tel: 0113-237 5700 Fax: 0113-237 5701 E-mail: sales.north@tsgleeds.co.uk Computer systems reseller

Technology Services Group Edinburgh, Pentland Estate, Straiton, Edinburgh, EH20 9QW Tel: 0131-448 2400 Fax: 0131-448 0064 E-mail: enquiries@tsg.com IT sales & support services

Technology Shop, 10 Railway Street, Malton, North Yorkshire, YO17 7NR Tel: (01653) 600002 Fax: (01653) 690721 E-mail: shop@the-technology-shop.com Computer solutions services

Technology Sources Ltd, 2 Signet Court, Swann Road, Cambridge, CB5 8LA Tel: (01223) 516469 Fax: (01223) 729916 E-mail: info@softsim.com Computer consultants

Technology Supplies Ltd, Phoenix House, Tern Hill, Market Drayton, Shropshire, TF9 3PX Tel: (01630) 637301 Fax: (01630) 637302 E-mail: info@technologysupplies.co.uk Educational equipment & suppliers

Technology Tamed Ltd, Hadleigh Business & Learning Centre, Crockatt Lane, Hadleigh, Ipswich, IP7 6RH Tel: (01473) 826180 Computer consultancy & training

▶ Technology Ventures Maritime Ltd, Suite B 29 Harley Street, London, W1G 9QR Tel: (020) 7016 2664 Fax: (07092) 013175 E-mail: info@kinetec.uk.com Our factory produces a range of uninterruptible power supplies

▶ Technology Ventures Scotland Ltd, Atrium Court, 50 Waterloo Street, Glasgow, G2 6HQ Tel: 0141-572 1600 Fax: 0141-572 1608

▶ Technology Zoo Ltd, 31 Kenway Collier Row, Romford, RM5 3EH Tel: (01708) 507716 E-mail: help@techzoo.co.uk On-site computer repairs, upgrades & sales for busniess and home users.

Technolube Lubrication Systems, Unit 17 Calder Workshops, Gibbet Street, Halifax, West Yorkshire, HX1 4JQ Tel: (01422) 320784 Fax: (01422) 346047 Lubrication systems & equipment

Technomatic, Horizon 1, Studio Way, Borehamwood, Hertfordshire, WD6 5WH Tel: (020) 8327 5000 Fax: (0870) 5133919 Computer, monitor & printer dealers

Technoset Ltd, Unit 3A, Roman Way, Rugby, Warwickshire, CV21 1DB Tel: (01788) 560522 Fax: (01788) 541196 E-mail: sales@technoset.com Precision turned parts manufrs

Technosign Ltd, Unit 3 35a Stanbridge Road, Leighton Buzzard, Bedfordshire, LU7 4PZ Tel: (01525) 382111 Fax: (01525) 382382 Sign contractors

Technostart Ltd, 1a Clifton Avenue, London, E17 6HL Tel: (020) 8503 2778 Fax: (020) 8523 3054 E-mail: sales@technostart.co.uk Automotive bearings distributors

▶ Techno-trim, Unit 3 Fengate Trade Park, Fengate, Peterborough, PE1 5XA Tel: (01733) 552121 Fax: (01733) 552122 E-mail: info@technotrim.com Supply components, machines for ink cartridge recycling market

Technova Precision, Unit 8a Paragon Way, Bayton Road Industrial Estate, Coventry, CV7 9QS Tel: (024) 7636 7246 Fax: (024) 7636 1979 E-mail: will@technovaprecision.com Spindle rebuilding services, workheads, wheelheads, tailstocks & ballscrews

▶ Techobox Ltd, 20 Nicholas Street, Manchester, M1 4EJ Tel: 0161-228 1010 Fax: 0161-228 0707 E-mail: sales@techobox.com Computer repair services

Techpoint Services, 133 Mains Lane, Poulton-le-Fylde, Lancashire, FY6 7LD Tel: (01253) 895999 Fax: (01253) 895999 E-mail: sales@diplidata.co.uk Compact disc manufrs

Techshare Ventilation Systems, 39 Leaplish, Washington, Tyne & Wear, NE38 0RB Tel: 0191-417 2424 Fax: 0191-415 1686 E-mail: sales@techshare.co.uk Fume extraction engineers

Techsil Ltd, Unit 30 Bidavon Industrial Estate, Waterloo Road, Bidford-on-Avon, Alcester, Warwickshire, B50 4JN Tel: (01789) 773232 Fax: (01789) 774239 E-mail: sales@techsil.co.uk Silicone distributors & manufrs

▶ Techsure Computer Maintenance, Bolton Enterprise Centre, Washington Street, Bolton, BL3 5EY Tel: (01204) 363399 Fax: (01204) 363369 Computer maintenance services

Techtrol Ltd, Gregson Road, Stockport, Cheshire, SK5 7SS Tel: 0161-476 6955 Fax: 0161-476 2674 E-mail: mailbox@techtrol.co.uk Principal Export Areas: Worldwide Techtrol Limited are specialist manufacturers of solid waste incineration systems, animal carcass, hospital/ clinical & industrial incinerators used by the world's leading hospitals, universities and research companies as well as Government departments and private sector contractors. In addition we manufacture bin washing equipment, waste fired combustion equipment, cremation furnaces & gas cleaning/scrubbing plant. Using computer aided design, experience and innovative technology our incinerators provide

continued

continuation an economical solution whilst providing the highest environmental standards.

▶ Teckchek Europe Ltd, 1a Church Road, Croydon, CR0 1SG Tel: (020) 8401 1188 Fax: (020) 8401 0808 E-mail: dbeer@ikmnet.com *Computer diagnostics testing for recruiting*

Tecker Ltd, Kernow House, Tregoniggie Industrial Estate, Falmouth, Cornwall, TR11 4SN Tel: (01326) 378774 Fax: (01326) 378775 E-mail: mail@tecker.co.uk *Process engineering*

Tecknit Europe Ltd, Swingbridge Road, Grantham, Lincolnshire, NG31 7XT Tel: (01476) 590600 Fax: (01476) 591600 E-mail: tecknit.sales@twp-europe.co.uk Principal Export Areas: Worldwide *Radio frequency interference shield manufrs*

Teckno Developments Ltd, Great Gutter Lane, Willerby, Hull, HU10 6DL Tel: (01482) 657996 Fax: (01482) 651089 E-mail: sales@tecknodev.com *Welded plastic packaging manufrs*

Teckno Plastics, 43 Ryecroft Rd, Frampton Cotterell, Bristol, BS36 2HN Tel: 01454 777622 *Plastics moulding*

Tecmach Ltd, PO Box 29, St. Albans, Hertfordshire, AL1 5NU Tel: (01727) 860355 Fax: (01727) 844062 E-mail: sales@tecmach.co.uk *Manufacturers of lifts (scissor)*

Tecman Speciality Materials, Eastgate House, Moreton Road, Longborough, Moreton-in-Marsh, Gloucestershire, GL56 0QJ Tel: (01451) 830044 Fax: (01451) 830230 *Adhesive tape converters & distributors or agents*

▶ Tecnia, 63 Cromwell Road, Norwich, NR7 8XJ Tel: (01603) 488434 Fax: (0870) 1211941 E-mail: info@TECNiA.co.uk *Computer hardware & software support services*

Tecnica Europe Ltd, Suite 2 Baxall Business Centre, Adswood, Stockport, Cheshire, SK3 8LF Tel: 0161 480 5700 Fax: 0161 447 4476 *Control and Process Valves - Instruments.*Design/build Control Systems**

Tecni-Cable Ltd, 54 Merryfields, Mark, Highbridge, Somerset, TA9 4NB Tel: (01278) 641930 Fax: 0870 7669578 E-mail: sales@tecni-cable.co.uk *Tecni-Cable small diameter stainless & galvanised steel wire rope solutions. Wire ropes plastic coated & covered in PVC, nylon & polypropylene. Specialists in miniature stainless wire ropes, architectural balustrading & shopfitting display cables. High quality Talurit swage aluminium, copper & stainless fittings, swaging, pressing & cutting tools from Talurit & Felco. Rapid nationwide and international delivery. Please visit our e-commerce site for full product listings.*

Tecnicon Precision, Unit 20 Euro Business Park, New Road, Newhaven, East Sussex, BN9 0DQ Tel: (01273) 510952 Fax: (01273) 513579 *Inspect & manufacture industrial equipment*

▶ Tecni-form, Unit 11, Whitebridge Estate, Whitebridge Lane, Stone, Staffordshire, ST15 8LQ Tel: (01785) 286476 *JCB parts suppliers*

▶ Tecnik Railing, The Studio, 133 Grange Road, Ilford, Essex, IG1 1EZ Tel: (07947) 376267 *Tecnik railing offers sophisticated stainless steel balustrade soloutions with a professional dedicated team*

▶ Tecnisis Ltd, Unit 3 Martlesham Creek Industrial Estate, Sandy Lane, Martlesham, Woodbridge, Suffolk, IP12 4SD Tel: (01394) 389098 Fax: (01394) 389062 E-mail: sales@tecnisis.co.uk *Bespoke test equipment software developers*

▶ Tecno Incollaggi UK Ltd, 4 Warren Court, Stapleford, Nottingham, NG9 8EY Tel: (07866) 477542 Fax: 0115-875 2670 E-mail: info@tecnoinc.co.uk *Adhesive application systems*

▶ Tecno Vibrazioni S.R.l, 83 Highgate Road, Sileby, Loughborough, Leicestershire, LE12 7PN Tel: (01509) 813401 Fax: (0870) 2364114 E-mail: info@tecno-feeders.co.uk *Vibrator & rotary sorting machines*

Tecnograv (Angelsea) Ltd, Llangefni Trading Estate, Llangefni, Gwynedd, LL77 7UZ Tel: (01248) 750363 Fax: (01248) 725100 *Printing accessories manufrs*

Tecnon Orbichem Ltd, 12 Calico House, Clove Hitch Quay, London, SW11 3TN Tel: (020) 7924 3955 Fax: (020) 7978 5307 E-mail: sales@orbichem.com *Marketing consultants in chemicals*

▶ Tecnovision, 33 Ashville Way, Whetstone, Leicester, LE8 6NU Tel: 0116-275 3262 Fax: 0116-275 3821

▶ Teco Building Products, Wellington Road, Portslade, Brighton, BN41 1DN Tel: (01273) 439132 Fax: (01273) 410074 E-mail: buying@tecoproducts.co.uk *Metal fabricators*

Teco Electric Europe Ltd, Teco Building Centrepoint, Marshall Stevens Way, Trafford Park, Manchester, M17 1PP Tel: 0161-877 8025 Fax: 0161-877 8030 E-mail: enquiries@teco.co.uk Principal Export Areas: Africa *Manufacturers of electric motors*

TECO Europe Ltd, 60 Savile Street East, Sheffield, S4 7UQ Tel: 0114-275 9020 Fax: 0114-270 0875 E-mail: sales@tecoglas.com *Glass plant engineers & contractors*

Tecomak Ltd, Valley Industries, Tonbridge Road, Hadlow, Tonbridge, Kent, TN11 0AH Tel: (01732) 852250 Fax: (01732) 852251 E-mail: sales@tecomak.co.uk *Fume covers maintenance*

Teconnex Ltd, Bronte Works, Chesham Street, Keighley, West Yorkshire, BD21 4LG Tel: (01535) 691122 Fax: (01535) 691133 E-mail: sales@teconnex.com *Vee & band type clamp manufacturers. In addition, pipe clamp manufrs*

Tecproof Ltd, 266 Dansom Lane North, Hull, HU8 7RS Tel: (01482) 215886 Fax: (01482) 215886 *Powercoating services*

▶ Tecs Catering Equipment, 329 Alder Road, Poole, Dorset, BH12 5BH Tel: (01202) 536322

Tecseal Ltd, 4 East Chorley Business Centre, East Way, Chorley, Lancashire, PR6 0BJ Tel: (01257) 249933 Fax: (01257) 249944 *Silicones & sealants distributors*

Tecserv, Unit 7, Parsons Green Estate, Boulton Road, Stevenage, Hertfordshire, SG1 4QG Tel: (01438) 750905 Fax: (01438) 315270 E-mail: macserv-fcm@btconnect.com *Industrial & commercial floor cleaning equipment specialists*

▶ Tecstream O M G Ltd, Fernie Road, Market Harborough, Leicestershire, LE16 7PH Tel: (01858) 433624 Fax: (01858) 431042 E-mail: sales@tecstreamomg.com *Design house*

Tectime Data Systems Ltd, Copthall House, Nelson Place, Newcastle, Staffordshire, ST5 1EZ Tel: (01782) 799567 Fax: (01782) 799447 E-mail: info@tectime.com *Data collection systems suppliers & manufrs*

Tecton Timber Products, Abbey Road, Hempsted, Gloucester, GL2 5HU Tel: (01452) 381146 Fax: (01452) 381147 E-mail: paul@tecton.freeserve.co.uk *Timber beam manufrs*

Tectonic Ltd, Meridian Business Park, 1A Jupitor Court, Dominus Way, Leicester, LE19 1RP Tel: 0116-282 0567 Fax: 0116-282 0599 E-mail: info@tectonic.com *Computer systems & software sales*

Tectonics, 1 Prospect Road, Alresford, Hampshire, SO24 9QF Tel: (01962) 736316 Fax: (01962) 735098 E-mail: sales@tectonicsuk.co.uk *Tectonics Ltd. have been supplying fitters and distributors of kitchen and bedroom componentry for over 20 years. Our reputation has been built on the quality of our products, our outstanding service, innovation in the manufacturing process, intelligent use of technology and speed and flexibility in reacting to our customer's needs. We offer more than 30 ranges of kitchen and bedroom door designs available in standard or special sizes (our PVC ranges are available in over 30 colours).*

Tectonics Ltd, 10 Caker Stream Road, Alton, Hampshire, GU34 2QA Tel: (01420) 83910 Fax: (01420) 541196 E-mail: sales@tectonics.co.uk *Furniture component manufrs*

Tector Visual Systems, Woodhill Road, Collingham, Newark, Nottinghamshire, NG23 7NR Tel: (01636) 892246 Fax: (01636) 893317 E-mail: sales@graffelectronics.co.uk *Maintainers of graph electronic machines*

Tectrade Computers Ltd, Unit A1, Godalming Business Centre, Godalming, Surrey, GU7 1XW Tel: (01483) 521910 Fax: (01483) 861449 E-mail: sales@tectrade.co.uk *Computer business services*

Tecumseh Power International Ltd, 152-154 Commercial Road, Staines, Middlesex, TW18 2QP Tel: (01784) 460684 Fax: (01784) 453563 E-mail: tecumsehukltd@btinternet.com *Lawnmower engine manufrs*

Tecweld Ltd, Noble Square Industrial Estate, Brynmawr, Ebbw Vale, Gwent, NP23 4BS Tel: (01495) 310796 Fax: (01495) 312383 *Heavy engineering manufrs*

Tedbar Tinker Hire, 53 Carlisle Street, Sheffield, S4 7LJ Tel: 0114-275 3666 Fax: 0114-275 4183 E-mail: sales@tedbartinkerhire.co.uk *Power & pneumatic tool sales & hire*

Teddington Controls Ltd, Daniels Lane, St. Austell, Cornwall, PL25 3HG Tel: (01726) 74400 Fax: (01726) 67953 E-mail: info@tedcon.com *Automatic control system manufrs* Also at: Sunbury-on-Thames

Teddington Engineered Solutions, Heol Cropin, Dafen, Llanelli, Dyfed, SA14 8QW Tel: (01554) 744500 Fax: (01792) 885843 E-mail: sales@tes.uk.com *Manufacturers of metal expansion joints & metal bellows*

▶ Teddington Photo Centre, 54 Broad Street, Teddington, Middlesex, TW11 8QY Tel: (020) 8943 5232 Fax: (020) 8943 5376 *Photo retail*

Teddington Studios Ltd, Broom Road, Teddington, Middlesex, TW11 9NT Tel: (020) 8977 3252 Fax: (020) 8943 4050 E-mail: sales@pinewoodgroup.com *Television studio & transmission centre*

Tedford Rigging & Rafts, Unit 24 Ormeau Business Park, 8 Gromac Avenue, Belfast, BT7 2JA Tel: (028) 9032 6763 Fax: (028) 9023 4566 E-mail: info@tedfords.co.uk *Sail makers & riggers, life raft services*

Tedwood Storage Systems Ltd, 1489 Melton Road, Queniborough, Leicester, LE7 3FP Tel: 0116-269 3838 *Partitioning constructors*

▶ Tee Kay Shipping Glasgow Ltd, 183 St Vincent Street, Glasgow, G2 5QD Tel: 0141-222 9000 Fax: 0141-243 2100 E-mail: sales@teekayshipping.com

▶ Teeac Associates, Unit 205 Camberwell Business Centre, Lomond Grove, London, SE5 7HN Tel: (020) 7708 2396 Fax: (0870) 7656230 E-mail: info@teeac.com *Book-keeping, Accounts, Taxation, Payroll Bureau, Business Start-up, Company Formation, Business Name & Trade Mark Registration*

Teejay Workwear Ltd, Dy2 Dean Clough Office Park, Halifax, West Yorkshire, HX3 5AX Tel: (01422) 369754 Fax: (01422) 383223 E-mail: sales@teejayworkwear.co.uk *Industrial workwear manufrs*

Tee-Kay Packaging, Fengate, Peterborough, PE1 5XG Tel: (01733) 311867 Fax: (01733) 311017 E-mail: robert@tee-kay.co.uk *Corrugated box manufrs*

Teemo Designs Ltd, Roman Bank, Cherry Holt Road, Bourne, Lincolnshire, PE10 9LQ Tel: (01778) 421421 Fax: (01778) 393135 E-mail: teemo@globalnet.co.uk *Bedroom furniture manufrs*

Teemore Engineering, Teemore, Derrylin, Enniskillen, County Fermanagh, BT92 9BL Tel: (028) 6774 8377 Fax: (028) 6774 8978 *Agricultural engineers*

▶ TeePee Electronics, TeePee House, 61 Wavell Gardens, Slough, SL2 2EL Tel: (01753) 570546 Fax: (01753) 570546 E-mail: pulsarteepee@yahoo.co.uk *Taxi meters sales*

Tees Components Ltd, North Skelton, Skelton-in-Cleveland, Saltburn-by-the-Sea, Cleveland, TS12 2AP Tel: (01287) 650621 Fax: (01287) 652642 E-mail: sales@teescomponents.co.uk *Horizontal boring*Vertical boring*Milling*Turning*Precision machining*Sub-contract machinists*Engineers*

Tees Fire Systems, 8 Stonehouse Street, Middlesbrough, Cleveland, TS5 6HR Tel: (01642) 800006 Fax: (01642) 800007 E-mail: sales@teesfire.co.uk *Fire detection*

Tees Insulation Ltd, 138 Lynn Street, Hartlepool, Cleveland, TS24 7LX Tel: (01429) 265433 Fax: (01429) 863149 E-mail: info@teesgroup.com *Asbestos removal ductwork & thermal services*

Tees Tarpaulins Ltd, Skinner Street, Stockton-on-Tees, Cleveland, TS18 1EG Tel: (01642) 607772 Fax: (01642) 607633 *Tarpaulin manufrs*

Tees Valley Fire Protection Ltd, Unit 11 Nestfield Industrial Estate, Darlington, County Durham, DL1 2NW Tel: (01325) 365555 Fax: (01325) 365555 *Fire protection equipment suppliers*

▶ Tees Valley Measurement, Cannon Street, Middlesbrough, Cleveland, TS1 5JJ Tel: (01642) 223535 Fax: (01642) 210317 *Calibration & metrology services*

Teeschem Manufacturing Co. Ltd, Salters Lane, Sedgefield, Stockton-on-Tees, Cleveland, TS21 3EE Tel: (01740) 620853 Fax: (01740) 622898 E-mail: admin@teeschem_mfg.co.uk *Chemical blenders & mixing services*

Teescraft Engineering Ltd, Unit Longfield, South Church Enterprise Park, Bishop Auckland, County Durham, DL14 6XB Tel: (01388) 777339 Fax: (01388) 776242 E-mail: info@teescraft.com *Toolmakers & precision machinists*

Teesdale Crane Hire, 23 Leekworth Gardens, Middleton In Teesdale, Barnard Castle, County Durham, DL12 0TE Tel: (01833) 640395 Fax: (01833) 640395 *Crane hire, sales & service*

Teesdale Garden Crafts, Unit 5 Industrial Estate, Stainton Grove, Barnard Castle, County Durham, DL12 8UJ Tel: (01833) 631772 *Garden furniture manufrs*

Teesdale Trenchman, The Lendings, Barnard Castle, County Durham, DL12 9AB Tel: (01833) 638370 Fax: (01833) 631439 E-mail: orders@trenchermen.co.uk *Smoked food & imported delicacies distributors*

Teeside Education Support Services, Horsehouse, Leyburn, North Yorkshire, DL8 4TS Tel: (01969) 640364 Fax: (01969) 640383 E-mail: info@readindsoftware.com *Computer software distributors*

Teeside Tertiary College, Longlands Campus, Douglas St, Middlesbrough, Cleveland, TS4 2JW Tel: (01642) 298942 Fax: (01642) 245313 *Further education*

Teesside & Cleveland Trophies, 32 Borough Road, Middlesbrough, Cleveland, TS1 5DW Tel: (01642) 240176 Fax: (01642) 240176 *Trophy manufrs*

Teesside Industrial Fasteners Ltd, 6 Douglas Close, Preston Farm Industrial Estate, Stockton-on-Tees, Cleveland, TS18 3SB Tel: 01642 675630 *Bolt, nut & fastener stockists*

Teesside Training Enterprise Ltd, Middlesbrough Road East, South Bank, Middlesbrough, Cleveland, TS6 6TZ Tel: (01642) 462266 Fax: (01642) 460873 E-mail: info@tte.co.uk *Training in instrument & control, leadership skills & safety management*

Teesside Warehousing Ltd, Fleck Way, Teesside Industrial Estate, Stockton-on-Tees, Cleveland, TS17 9JZ Tel: (01642) 762534 Fax: (01642) 765777 E-mail: lisa.pluves@vectoris.co.uk *Warehouse keepers & shipping agents*

Teffont Business Systems Ltd, 9 Falcons Gate, Dean Road, Yate, Bristol, BS37 5NH Tel: (01454) 318128 Fax: (01454) 321686 E-mail: sales@teffont.co.uk *Fax machine sales & services*

Tefloturn Ltd, 29 Old Post Road, Briston, Melton Constable, Norfolk, NR24 2NB Tel: (01263) 860001 Fax: (01263) 860055 E-mail: mick@tefloturn.co.uk Principal Export Areas: Worldwide *Plastics machining services*

▶ Tefnut Builders Ltd, 3 Vale Grove, London, N4 1PY Tel: (020) 8802 3978 Fax: (020) 8809 1877

Tega Office, 58 Stockholm Road, Hull, HU7 0XW Tel: (01482) 831032 Fax: (01482) 831331 E-mail: sales@tega.co.uk *Lighting & sound equipment hire & sales*

Tege Fresh Fries Ltd, Central Business Exchange, 90 Midsummer Boulevard, Milton Keynes, MK9 2RJ Tel: 01908 843627 *Vending machine manufrs*

Tegrel Ltd, Tundry Way, Blaydon-on-Tyne, Tyne & Wear, NE21 5TT Tel: 0191-414 6111 Fax: 0191-414 0660 E-mail: sales@tegrel.co.uk *Sheet metalwork engineers and fabricators, variable message signs, MCC, stainless steel, aluminium enclosures*

Teign Valley Glass, The Old Pottery, Pottery Road, Bovey Tracey, Newton Abbot, Devon, TQ13 9DS Tel: (01626) 835285 Fax: (01626) 835315 E-mail: info@houseofmarbles.com *Manufacture traditional board games & glassware*

Teignbridge Propellers Ltd, Great Western Way, Forde Road, Newton Abbot, Devon, TQ12 4AW Tel: (01626) 333377 Fax: (01626) 360783 E-mail: sales@teignbridge.co.uk *Marine propellers & stern gear manufrs*

▶ Teignmouth Maritime Services Ltd, 8 Ivy Lane, Teignmouth, Devon, TQ14 8BT Tel: (01626) 772197 Fax: (01626) 772197 E-mail: info@tmsmaritime.co.uk *Marine & civil intrusion services*

Teignmouth Quay Co Holdings Ltd, Old Quay, Teignmouth, Devon, TQ14 8ES Tel: (01626) 774044 Fax: (01626) 776240 E-mail: teignmouth@abports.co.uk *Dock owners & warehousemen*

Teijeiro Juan Music Co. Ltd, 5 The Campsbourne, London, N8 7PN Tel: (020) 8348 9191 Fax: (020) 8348 0562 E-mail: enquiries@juanteijeiro.com *Music instruments distributors*

▶ Tej Heating Plymouth Ltd, 247 Victoria Road, Plymouth, PL5 2DQ Tel: (01752) 351411 Fax: (01752) 351808

▶ Tejay Sportswear Ltd, 67 Grace Road, Leicester, LE2 8AD Tel: 0116-283 9427 Fax: 0116-244 0193 E-mail: sales@tejay.co.uk

Tek Ltd, Unit 14, Tyseley Industrial Estate, Seeleys Road, Birmingham, B11 2LQ Tel: 0121-766 5005 Fax: 0121-766 5010 E-mail: sales@tek.ltd.uk *Solar shading Manufacturers of acoustic products, acoustic consultancy services Noise reduction*

Tek Associates Ltd, 23 Stephenson Road, St. Ives, Cambridgeshire, PE27 3WJ Tel: (01480) 495496 Fax: (01480) 496228 E-mail: lenscothfield@tekassociates.com *Electronic manufrs*

▶ Tek Computers, 16 Lancer Close, Christchurch, Dorset, BH23 2TU Tel: (0870) 1994344 Fax: (0870) 1991324 E-mail: admin@tek-computers.com *It repairs & re-sell computers services*

Tek Machinery Ltd, 9 Stadium Court, Barbot Hall Industrial Estate, Parkgate, Rotherham, South Yorkshire, S62 6EW Tel: (01709) 820820 Fax: (01709) 382504 E-mail: info@tekmachinery.co.uk *Plastics machinery suppliers*

▶ Tek Neek, Unit 10, Glenfield Park, Philips Rd, Blackburn, BB1 5PS Tel: (01254) 583008 Fax: (01254) 682965 *Sheet metalwork/ metalinking & punching services*

Tek Personnel Consultants Ltd, Bells Square, Sheffield, S1 2FY Tel: 0114-252 5730 Fax: 0114-252 5731 E-mail: enquiries@tekpersonel.co.uk *Recruitment agency*

Teka Products Ltd, 177 Milton Park, Milton, Abingdon, Oxfordshire, OX14 4SE Tel: (01235) 861916 Fax: (01235) 832137 E-mail: sales@teka.co.uk *Sink distributors & kitchen appliance manufrs*

▶ Tekcomp Ltd, 17-18 Shipyard Estate, Brightlingsea, Colchester, CO7 0AR Tel: (01206) 303555 Fax: (01206) 303595 E-mail: info@tekcomp.co.uk *CAD, CAM & CIM plastic mouldings*

Tekdata Distribution Ltd, Technology House, Crown Road, Stoke-on-Trent, ST1 5NJ Tel: (01782) 274255 Fax: (01782) 665511 E-mail: sales@tekdata.co.uk *Computer network accessories distributors*

Tekeda Telecom, Cygnet Court, Hawthorn Street, Wilmslow, Cheshire, SK9 5EL Tel: (01625) 416200 Fax: (01625) 539042 E-mail: enq@takeda-telecom.co.uk *Telecommunications installation services*

Tekfoam Foam Products, 3 Bleach Works, Whitebirk Road, Blackburn, BB1 3HY Tel: (01254) 663839 Fax: (01254) 663839 *Foam products*

Tekhniseal Ltd, Unit 1 Priestley Road, Worsley, Manchester, M28 2LY Tel: 0161-794 6063 Fax: 0161-794 4773 E-mail: tekhniseal@btconnect.com *Mechanical seal manufrs*

▶ Tekksupport, 5 Kinghorn Court, Golspie, Sutherland, KW10 6SJ Tel: (01408) 633695 E-mail: info@tekksupport.co.uk *Tekksupport provide a stress free solution to all your computer needs. We provide a friendly, reliable and cost effective service for both home and business users.*

Tekmar Electronics Ltd, Wincombe Business Park, Shaftesbury, Dorset, SP7 9QJ Tel: (01747) 855348 Fax: (01747) 851004 E-mail: tekmargroup@aol.com *Production equipment, sales & marketing specialists*

Tekmat Ltd, Ryan House, Trent Lane, Castle Donington, Derby, DE74 2PY Tel: (01332) 853443 Fax: (01332) 853424 E-mail: sales@tekmat.co.uk *Engineers cutting tools*

▶ Teknek Manufacturing Ltd, Inchinnan Business Park, Newmains Avenue, Inchinnan, Renfrew, PA4 9RR Tel: 0141-568 8100 Fax: 0141-568 8101 E-mail: sales@teknek.com Sales Contact: P. Stevenson *Sub contract electronics manufacturer, including machining, sheet metal fabrication, finishing, product marking, product painting and injection moulding.*

▶ Teknical Electrical, 3 St. Andrews Crescent, Windsor, Berkshire, SL4 4EW Tel: (0845) 8385983 Fax: (01753) 852703 E-mail: info@teknical-electrical.co.uk *NICEIC approved Electrical Contractor serving West London/M4 corridor areas*

Teknigrafiks, Unit 110 Bradley Fold Trading Estate, Radcliffe Moor Road, Bradley Fold, Bolton, BL2 6RT Tel: (01204) 389686 Fax: (01204) 531597 E-mail: sales@teknigrafiks.co.uk *Services to advertising agencies, exhibition design & build, displays*

Teknion Distribution Services, 22-24 Cloughgate Industrial Estate, Cross Street, Heywood, Lancashire, OL10 1PW Tel: (01706) 669988 Fax: (01706) 669989 E-mail: info@teknion.co.uk *Importing & distributors*

Tekno Computer Systems Ltd, 41 Bartlett Street, Caerphilly, Mid Glamorgan, CF83 1JS Tel: (029) 2088 5421 Fax: (029) 2088 5235 E-mail: info@tekno.co.uk *Computer suppliers & maintenance*

Tekno Fuel Sports Drinks, Crest Complex, Courteney Road, Gillingham, Kent, ME8 0RX Tel: (01634) 233272 E-mail: graham@teknofuel.co.uk *Sports drinks wholesaler*

▶ Teknocom Ltd, 49 Perth Road, Ilford, Essex, IG2 6BX Tel: (020) 8518 9090 Fax: (020) 8518 9091

Teknoflex Ltd, Quarry Lane Industrial Estate, Quarry Lane, Chichester, West Sussex, PO19 8PE Tel: (01243) 784516 Fax: (01243) 832832 E-mail: sales@teknoflex.com *Teknoflex - for flexible circuit solutions. We design, manufacture and assemble flexible, flex-rigid and multilayer printed circuits boards*

Teknomat UK Ltd, Unit 27, Wornal Park, Menmarsh Road, Worminghall, Aylesbury, Buckinghamshire, HP18 9PH Tel: (01844) 339828 Fax: (01844) 339829 *Coffee machine manufrs*

Teknos (UK) Ltd, Unit E1 Heath Farm, Banbury Road, Swerford, Chipping Norton, Oxfordshire, OX7 4BN Tel: (01608) 683494 Fax: (01608) 683487 E-mail: sales@teknos.co.uk *Protective coatings*

Company Information

Teknoserv (U.K.) Ltd, Culford House Unit 7, 1/7 Orsman Road, London, N1 5RA Tel: (020) 7729 3676 Fax: (020) 7729 5184 E-mail: sorab@teknoserv.freeserve.co.uk *Textiles import & export merchants*

▶ Tekpak (UK), Unit 203, 57 Great George Street, Leeds, LS1 3AJ Tel: (0845) 0537622 Fax: 0113-242 9176 E-mail: andrew.jackson@tekpak.co.uk *Machinery & factory automation services*

Tekpro Ltd, Laundry Loke, North Walsham, Norfolk, NR28 0BD Tel: (01692) 403403 Fax: (01692) 404955 E-mail: sales@catchpole.co.uk *Sampling & testing equipment & agricultural material suppliers*

Tekron Hard Metals Ltd, 6 Marsh Green Close, Biddulph, Stoke-on-Trent, ST8 6TA Tel: (01782) 522563 Fax: (01782) 516452 E-mail: tekrontool@madasafish.com *Distributors of tungsten carbide tools*

Tektonic Ltd, 118, Hastings Road, Battle, East Sussex, TN33 0TQ Tel: 07092 046259 Fax: 07092 046259 E-mail: enquiries@tektonic.co.uk *Established in 2004, we have over years experience in the IT support industry. Specialising in Networking, Internet Technology, Bespoke Programming, IT Hardware Management, Software Compliance and Training. We cover all the mainstream SoHo technologies from Peer to Peer all the way through to multi-server Windows environments with Exchange capabilities. We make IT work for you.*

▶ Tektonisk (UK) Ltd, Palmerston House, 814 Brighton Road, Purley, Surrey, CR8 2BR Tel: (08707) 606282 Fax: (020) 8655 8501 E-mail: pg@tektonisk.com *Service company specialising in Vendor Data Management for the Process Industries, including gathering, validation and delivery of equipment information.*

Tektura Wallcoverings, One Heron Quay, London, E14 4JA Tel: (020) 7536 3300 Fax: (020) 7536 3322 E-mail: sales@tektura.com *Textile & vinyl wall coverings & fabrics*

▶ Tel C Ltd, 109-111 Pope Street, Birmingham, B1 3AG Tel: 0121-200 1031 E-mail: sales@thecctvshop.com

Telco Lifts, 5 Culmore Business Centre, Culmore Road, London, SE15 2RQ Tel: (020) 7635 5851 Fax: (020) 7639 1065 *Lift engineers*

Telco Lighting Ltd, Unit C Paynetts, Paynetts Lane, Cranbrook Road, Goudhurst, Cranbrook, Kent, TN17 1DY Tel: (01580) 212229 Fax: (01580) 212038 E-mail: telcolight@aol.com *Commercial lighting supply & manufrs*

Telco Security Locks Ltd, Connaught Road, Bournemouth, BH7 6NA Tel: (01202) 420444 Fax: (01202) 432073 E-mail: sales@telcolocks.fsnet.co.uk *Security lock manufrs*

Telco Sensors Ltd, The Stables, Waen Farm, Nercwys, Mold, Flintshire, CH7 4EW Tel: (0870) 9917058 Fax: (0870) 9917059 E-mail: sales@telco-sensors.co.uk *Manufacturers & distributors of photoelectric cells & controls*

Tele Connect Ltd, 12 Rosevale Road, Parkhouse Industrial Estate West, Newcastle, Staffordshire, ST5 7EF Tel: (01782) 563443 Fax: (01782) 566227 *Cable assembly & harness (electrical) manufrs*

Tele Control Ltd, Unit 21 Three Point Business Park, Charles Lane, Haslingden, Rossendale, Lancashire, BB4 5EH Tel: (01706) 226333 Fax: (01706) 226444 E-mail: sales@tele-control.co.uk *Electrical energy controllers*

Tele Radio Limited, Beechfield House, Lyme Green Business Park, Winterton Way, Macclesfield, Cheshire, SK11 0LP Tel: 01625 509125 Fax: 01625 440022 E-mail: sales@teleradiouk.com *RADIO REMOTE CONTROLS FOR WINCHES, CRANES & HOISTS*

Teleca Ltd, 137 Barlow Moor Road, Manchester, M20 2PW Tel: 0161-447 6900 Fax: 0161-447 6901 *Computer software developers*

Telecall Ltd, 1 Stratfield Park, Elettra Avenue, Waterlooville, Hampshire, PO7 7XN Tel: (023) 9225 0525 Fax: (023) 9226 5299 E-mail: sales@telecall.uk.com *Telephone system installers*

Telecetera Computer Consultants, Carden Close, Worcester, WR1 2AR Tel: (01905) 612220 Fax: (01905) 612226 E-mail: info@telecetera.co.uk *Software consultants*

Telecom Ltd, 12 Richmond Tce, Gateshead, Tyne & Wear, NE8 1RN Tel: 0191-477 2961 Fax: 0191 497 5226 *Network services*

▶ Telecom 2000, 3 Minster Park, Collingwood Road, Verwood, Dorset, BH31 6QF Tel: (01202) 895111 Fax: (01202) 861444 *Telecommunications & electrical contractors*

Telecom Green Ltd, Highfield Drive, Eaglescliffe, Stockton-on-Tees, Cleveland, TS16 0DL Tel: (0870) 7200028 Fax: (0870) 7200029 E-mail: rob.govier@telecomgreen.co.uk *Removers & recyclers of used telecomms equipment*

▶ Telecom New Zealand, PO Box 49729, London, WC2B 6WY Tel: (0845) 2414282 E-mail: tnzinfo@callhome.co.nz *At Telecom New Zealand we are dedicated to providing you with high quality, low cost, clearly priced calls to help you keep in touch with your friends and loved ones for less.***

Telecom Security N W Ltd, Rear of, 28 Bridge Street, Hindley, Wigan, Lancashire, WN2 3LQ Tel: (01942) 203891 Fax: (01942) 204880 E-mail: sales@telecomelectrical-uk.co.uk *Electrical contractors*

Telecom Solutions International, 23-27 Endsleigh Road, Redhill, RH1 3LX Tel: (0870) 6060380 Fax: (01377) 647801 E-mail: info@tsigroup.co.uk *Telephone marketing & maintenance services*

Telecom Supply Line Ltd, Units 1&2, Treelyn Park, Welbeck Way, Woodston, Peterborough, PE2 7WH Tel: (01733) 390929 Fax: (01733) 391059 E-mail: sales@telecomsupplyline.ltd.uk *Telecommunication Infrastructure distributors*

Telecommunications Users' Association, 7 Sylvan Court, Southfields Business Park, Basildon, Essex, SS15 6TD Tel: (0870) 2202071 Fax: (0870) 2202075E-mail: tua@dial.pipex.com *Independent telecommunication services*

▶ Telecomplus, Windmill Hill Drive, Bletchley, MK3 7RE Tel: 0800 0935854 E-mail: sales@telecomplus4u.co.uk *The Utility Warehouse Discount Club is operated by Telecom plus PLC, a major British company whose shares are listed on the London Stock Exchange. We provide our customers with massive savings on their home, office and mobile phone charges as well as on other services such as gas and electricity.*

▶ Telecoms Bridgend Ltd, Unit 9D, Garth Drive, Brackla Industrial Estate, Bridgend, Mid Glamorgan, CF31 2AQ Tel: (0800) 0933652 E-mail: info@telecomsbridgend.co.uk *Provide telecommunications services to business customers*

Telecoms Personnel Ltd, 2-6 Curtain Road, London, EC2A 3NQ Tel: (020) 7247 0001 Fax: (020) 7247 0003 E-mail: personnel@telecoms.uk.net *Telecommunication staff agency*

Telecoms UK (South) Ltd, Telegraph Cottage, Christchurch Road, Ringwood, Hampshire, BH24 3AS Tel: (01425) 461700 *Telecommunications equipment & systems suppliers*

Teleconnect Systems, Melford Pl, St Peters Rd, Hockley, Essex, SS5 6AA Tel: 01702 206606 Fax: 01702 206606 *Telecommunications repairs*

▶ Telecor UK, 21 Coopers Court, Newport Pagnell, Buckinghamshire, MK16 8JS Tel: (01908) 211782 Fax: (01908) 216946 E-mail: chris.jones@telecor.co.uk *Intercom system manufrs*

Telectra Ltd, Units B3-B7, New Yatt Business Centre, New Yatt, Witney, Oxfordshire, OX29 6TJ Tel: (01993) 868866 Fax: (01993) 868894 E-mail: contact@telectra.com *Advanced solid-state lighting solutions*

Teledyne Reynolds Industries Ltd, Navigation House, Canal View Road, Newbury, Berkshire, RG14 5UR Tel: (01635) 262200 Fax: (01635) 30920 E-mail: trlsales@teledyne.com *High voltage connectors & cable assemblies manufrs*

▶ Telefax Holdings Ltd, St. Augustines Business Park, Estuary Close, Whitstable, Kent, CT5 2QJ Tel: (01227) 791901 Fax: (01227) 266280 E-mail: info@telefaxdatasystems.co.uk *Computer software developers*

▶ Teleflex Fluids Systems Europe, Euroflex Centre, Foxbridge Way, Normanton Industrial Estate, Normanton, West Yorkshire, WF6 1TN Tel: (01924) 898188 Fax: (01924) 898008 E-mail: enquiry@teleflex.com Principal Export Areas: Asia Pacific, Central Asia, Middle East, Africa, Central/East Europe & West Europe *Design/manufacture/distributor of Teflon/PTFE hoses, assembly manufacturers of thermoplastic tubing, corrugated automotive hose/turbo hose/ braking systems/clutch hose fluid transfer/ monolayer tubing/multilayer tubing/smoothbore/ tape wrapped/food industry/pharmaceutical industry/codant hose/nylon hose/jetting R7/R8 paint spray/polyamide/pa/distribution design/CAD facilities/hygienic/chlorine/gas hose/marine hose/ stainless steel braided fuel hose*

▶ TeleFone Resources (UK) Ltd, Unit 7G, N17 Studios, 784-788 Tottenham High Road, Tottenham, London, N17 0DA Tel: (020) 8803 5050 Fax: (020) 8887 0455 E-mail: sales@telresuk.com *For any of your Telecommunication requirements, NLTS Ltd are suppliers of new & refurbished telephone systems & all additionals.*Products supplied: Mitel SX50, SX2000, 30/3300 IP*Avaya, INDeX, Alchemy, Lucent Definity.*Panasonic KXT/KXTD/ KXTDA*Ericsson BP50/250 & MD1*Siemens HiPath, HiCom, ISDX, REALITIS*Meridian Norstar, Modular Meridian Option*..... and many more.*We provide an installation, Engineering & Maintenance Service.*Voice & Data Cabing *(analogue & CAT5e)*Office Equipment / Machines. *Least Cost Routing (LCR)**

Telefonix, 3 Albany Court, Albany Park, Camberley, Surrey, GU16 7QR Tel: (01252) 333888 Fax: (01252) 376167 E-mail: info@systems-supported.com *Telecommunications contractors*

Telegan Protection Ltd, 3-5 Holmethorpe Avenue, Redhill, RH1 2LZ Tel: (01737) 763800 Fax: (01737) 782727 E-mail: sales@teleganprotection.com *Fire protection engineers*

Teleki, 20 Oxhay Court, Oxhay View, Newcastle, Staffordshire, ST5 0SA Tel: (01782) 662099 E-mail: info@teleki-electronics.co.uk *Web site design services*

▶ Telekinetix Ltd, 38 Park Road North, Bedford, MK41 7RH Tel: (01234) 307571 Fax: 01234 328330 E-mail: sally@kinetixevents.co.uk *Kinetix Events specialises in the management and publicity of academic and professional conferences, seminars, workshops and exhibitions. Services include: full conference organisation, event marketing and publicity, online submission of abstracts/papers, online registration and the production and printing of proceedings.*

▶ Telemarketing Co. Ltd, 26-27 Regency Square, Brighton, BN1 2FH Tel: (01273) 765000 Fax: (01273) 765111 E-mail: info@ttmc.co.uk

Telematic Ltd, Pondwicks Road, Luton, LU1 3LH Tel: (01582) 429464 Fax: (01582) 459669 E-mail: admin@telematic.com *Lightning & surge protection devices*

Telemere Group Ltd, 128 Greenstead Road, Colchester, CO1 2SN Tel: (01206) 867188 Fax: (01206) 503444 E-mail: david.johnson@telemere.co.uk *Computer consultants*

Telenova Ltd, 144 Regina Road, Southall, Middlesex, UB2 5PP Tel: (020) 8571 5073 *Door entry systems parts manufrs*

Telenzo Carpets Ltd, 2-4 Southgate, Elland, West Yorkshire, HX5 0BW Tel: (01422) 371226 Fax: (01422) 377452 *Suppliers of carpets*

Telephone Connexions Ltd, Marconi Road, Burgh Road Industrial Estate, Carlisle, CA2 7NA Tel: (01228) 514369 Fax: (01228) 594369 E-mail: sales@telephoneconnexions.co.uk *Sales,Installation & Maintenance of telecommunications systems, voice & data networks, cabling infrastructure, IT systems, componenets , software and support. Provision Of Network services including lines with reduced rentals and call charge packages, leased lines, private circuits, broadband, bespoke virtual private networking packages, voice over internet protocol solutions, internet service provision. Certified Structured cabling solutions including Category 6,fibre optics, Wireless networks both local and wide area up to 50km, ADSL, SDSL, VDSL high bandwidth Low cost inter building links and much much more!*

Telephone Lines Ltd, 304 High Street, Cheltenham, Gloucestershire, GL50 3JF Tel: (01242) 583699 Fax: (01242) 690033 E-mail: info@telephonelines.net *Telephone manufrs*

▶ Telephone Recorders Direct Ltd, 462 London Road, Isleworth, Middlesex, TW7 4ED Tel: (020) 8326 8282 E-mail: salesmanager@telephonerecordersdirect.com *An on-line shop designed to help businesses to record their telephone calls. The site contains helpful tips on call recording including legalities and glossaries, and information sheets.*

Telephone Service Centre, 43 Wessex Estate, Ringwood, Hampshire, BH24 1XD Tel: (07970) 661519 Fax: (01425) 477589 E-mail: telephoneserv@aol.com *Telephone equipment repairers*

Telephone Services Ltd, Phonex House, 18 Suffolk Street, Pendleton, Salford, M6 6DU Tel: 0161-737 7055 Fax: 0161-737 7055 *Telephone equipment supply & installers*

Teleplan, Roman House 12 Cowdray Centre, Mason Road, Colchester, CO1 1BX Tel: (01206) 785000 Fax: (01206) 785008 E-mail: enquiries@teleplan-int.com *Computer maintenance services*

Teleport Ltd, The Pound, Cookham, Maidenhead, Berkshire, SL6 9QE Tel: (01628) 810100 Fax: (01628) 810300 E-mail: sales@teleport.co.uk *Computer reseller suppliers*

Telepresence Ltd, Lochside, Longhaven, Peterhead, Aberdeenshire, AB42 0PA Tel: (01779) 812277 Fax: (01779) 812391 *Robotics & remote control suppliers*

Telequip Ltd, 5 Acorn Business Centre, Northarbour Road, Portsmouth, PO6 3TH Tel: (023) 9221 5215 Fax: (08707) 770778 E-mail: postmaster@telequip.co.uk *Telecommunications*

Telerate Ltd, 122 Leadenhall Street, London, EC3V 4QH Tel: (020) 7832 9000 Fax: (0870) 4451440 E-mail: infoeurope@telerate.com *Financial advisers*

Telerelay Sales Ltd, Park Drive Industrial Estate, Braintree, Essex, CM7 1AW Tel: (01376) 321216 Fax: (01376) 347910 E-mail: sales@telerelay.sagehost.co.uk *Relay manufrs*

Telesat Communications, 84 Sleaford Road, Boston, Lincolnshire, PE21 8EU Tel: (01205) 369934 Fax: (01205) 369934 E-mail: telesat@totalise.co.uk *Electronic installators*

Telescan Computer Services, PO Box 1, Thornton-Cleveleys, Lancashire, FY5 1SH Tel: (01253) 829292 *Budget software suppliers*

▶ Tele-Sheds, Shelton Drive, Southport, Merseyside, PR8 2TE Tel: (01704) 571215 E-mail: sales@telesheds.co.uk *Shed manufrs*

Teleshore UK Ltd, Unit 3 Llanhilleth Industrial Estate, Llanhilleth, Abertillery, Gwent, NP13 2RX Tel: (01495) 212232 Fax: (01495) 211109 E-mail: info@teleshore.com *Health & safety supplies for cemeteries & crematoriums*

Telesis Systems Ltd, 20 Stryd Y Castell, Ruthin, Clwyd, LL15 1DR Tel: (01824) 704040 Fax: (01824) 704020 *Software developers*

Telesiseagle Ltd, Dolphin Street, Colyton, Devon, EX24 6LU Tel: (01297) 551313 Fax: (01297) 551319 E-mail: sales@telesiseagle.co.uk Principal Export Areas: Worldwide *Product Identification and Traceability Technology. Permanent, programmable, PROSCRIPT® Lasers and PINSTAMP® Marking Systems, Diode-Pumped and Fiber Laser Marking Systems.*

Telesound Ltd, 31 Hall Green Close, Malvern, Worcestershire, WR14 3QY Tel: (01684) 572506 E-mail: sales@telesound.co.uk *Control systems manufrs*

Teletec International, Cranfield Innovation Centre, University Way, Cranfield, Bedford, MK43 0BT Tel: (01234) 756027 Fax: (01234) 756028 *Telecommunication systems manufrs*

Teletech U K Ltd, 225 Bath Street, Glasgow, G2 4GZ Tel: 0141-420 2500 Fax: 0141-420 2590 E-mail: info@teletech.com *Call centre*

Teletronics Ltd, Unit C3-C5, Formal Industrial Estate, Treswithian, Camborne, Cornwall, TR14 0PY Tel: (01209) 716360 Fax: (01209) 716285 *Telecommunication equipment manufrs*

Television Installation Services (Mansfield) Ltd, Old Mill Lane Industrial Estate, Mansfield Woodhouse, Mansfield, Nottinghamshire, NG19 9BG Tel: (01623) 425800 Fax: (01623) 650767 E-mail: sales@tisnet.co.uk *Electronics & communication systems installation services*

Television Systems, Vanwall Road, Maidenhead, Berkshire, SL6 4UB Tel: (01628) 676200 Fax: (01628) 676299 E-mail: sales@televisionsystems.ltd.uk Principal Export Areas: Worldwide *Manufacturers of broadcasting equipment*

Telewest Communications Cable Ltd, 1 Genesis Business Park, Albert Drive, Woking, Surrey, GU21 5RW Tel: (01483) 750900 Fax: (01483) 750901 E-mail: info@ntl.co.uk *Telecommunication systems*

Telfac Services & Supply, 23 Treesmill Drive, Maidenhead, Berkshire, SL6 3HR Tel: (01628) 671111 Fax: (01628) 674928 E-mail: sales@telfacofficesupplies.co.uk *Office suppliers & stationers*

▶ Telford Computer Training, The Rock, Telford, Shropshire, TF3 5DA Tel: 01952 504202 E-mail: jenny_urey@hotmail.com *Qualified IT Tutor*Working with Adults in the Community**...one to one business or college run classes in the community...***

Telford Copper Cylinders, Haybridge Road, Wellington, Telford, Shropshire, TF1 2NW Tel: (01952) 262300 Fax: (01952) 253452 E-mail: sales@telford-group.com *Domestic hot water cylinders manufrs*

Telford Crane Hire Ltd, Halesfield 22, Telford, Shropshire, TF7 4QX Tel: (01952) 586304 Fax: (01952) 587848 E-mail: sales@telfordcrane.co.uk *The Company that's guaranteed to give you a lift...Established in 1981, Telford & Heartlands Crane Hire are based in Telford however we also cover Mid Wales, Birmingham, Liverpool, Shropshire, Gloucestershire and surrounding areas. We proved a 24 hour service...round the clock. At Telford and Heartlands Crane Hire service is our strength. C.I.T.B. approved operators. We can supply Lorry mounted telescopic cranes 16-80 tonnes capacity. All terrain cranes 25-80 tonnes capacity. Iron fairies 10-12 tonnes capacity, Contract lifts, Mobile crane hire, Crane hire, Telescopic crane hire, Machinery transportation hire, Four wheel crane, Six wheel crane. HIAB lorry loaders up to 26 tons capacity. Transport. Machinery installations. Give us a call for any information or technical details you may require. We are just a phone call away.*

Telford Crane Hire Ltd, Halesfield 22, Telford, Shropshire, TF7 4QX Tel: (01952) 586304 Fax: (01952) 587848 E-mail: sales@telfordcrane.co.uk *Contractors & plant hire services*

Telford Electronics, Hoo Farm, Hoo, Telford, Shropshire, TF6 6DJ Tel: (01952) 605451 Fax: (01952) 677978 E-mail: telfordelectronics@btinternet.com *Surplus electronics suppliers*

Telford Group Ltd, Enterprise House, Stafford Park 1, Telford, Shropshire, TF3 3BD Tel: (01952) 290800 Fax: (01952) 291303 E-mail: info@telfordgroup.co.uk *Power tools & welding equipment suppliers, repairers & trainer*

Telford Mechanical Handling, The Woodlands, Bridge Road, Benthall, Broseley, Shropshire, TF12 5QS Tel: (01952) 884242 Fax: (01952) 884242 E-mail: paul@conaglen.fsbusiness.co.uk *Conveyor systems, belt*

Telford Pest Control, 11 Pasteur Drive, Leegomery, Telford, Shropshire, TF1 6PQ Tel: (01952) 223706 *Pest control services*

Telford Polishers Ltd, Charlton Forge Church Street, Oakengates, Telford, Shropshire, TF2 6BY Tel: (01952) 614441 Fax: (01952) 612229 E-mail: sales@cmfc.freeserve.co.uk *Metal finishing/polishing/fabricators*

Telford Process Engineering Ltd, Business Development Centre, Stafford Park 4, Telford, Shropshire, TF3 3BA Tel: (01952) 293231 Fax: (01952) 201246 E-mail: dryers.ovens@tpe.co.uk *Dryers & coolers*

Telford Rewinds Ltd, Unit 5, Halesfield 18, Telford, Shropshire, TF7 4PP Tel: (01952) 580703 Fax: (01952) 580703 *Electric motor repair/rewind services*

Telford Tanks Ltd, Unit 3c Central Works, Peartree Lane, Dudley, West Midlands, DY2 0QU Tel: (01384) 212167 Fax: (01384) 457757 *Oil storage tank manufrs*

Telford Threadgauge Ltd, Unit 1 Halesfield 18, Telford, Shropshire, TF7 4PP Tel: (01952) 588858 Fax: (01952) 588616 *Gauge & instrument manufrs*

Telford Tower & Scaffolding Ltd, Unit F7 Castle Trading Estate, Snedshill, Telford, Shropshire, TF2 9NP Tel: (01952) 612814 Fax: (01952) 613006 *Scaffolding hire & erecting services*

Telguard, 2 Ockley Court Farm Cottages, Coles Lane, Ockley, Dorking, Surrey, RH5 5LS Tel: (01306) 710120 Fax: (01306) 713769 E-mail: sales@telguard.co.uk *Manufacturer & distributor of telephone based secure entry systems*

Teligent Ltd, Mark House, Mark Road, Hemel Hempstead, Hertfordshire, HP2 7UE Tel: (01442) 283800 Fax: (01442) 283806 E-mail: info@teligent.co.uk *Develop value added network services*

Telinet Ltd, 52 Southwark Bridge Road, London, SE1 0AR Tel: 0207 771 7700 *Telecommunication equipment & services*

Telist Engineering Services, 5 Millside Industrial Estate, Lawson Road, Dartford, DA1 5BW Tel: (01322) 291291 Fax: (01322) 291291 *Precision engineers*

Tell Products Ltd, 93 Cobbold Road, London, NW10 9SU Tel: (020) 8459 6873 Fax: (020) 8830 4977 *Manufacturing chemists*

Tellima Technology Ltd, Unit 1g Denby Dale Industrial Park, Wakefield Road, Denby Dale, Huddersfield, HD8 8QH Tel: (01484) 866806 Fax: (01484) 866816 E-mail: sales@tellima.co.uk *Software & hardware providers*

Telling Lime Products, Primrose Avenue, Wolverhampton, WV10 8AW Tel: (01902) 789777 Fax: (01902) 398777 E-mail: m.wood@telling.co.uk *Thermal structural cladding contractors*

▶ Tellure Rota, PO Box 29, Ashton-under-Lyne, Lancashire, OL5 9NB Tel: (01457) 832556 Fax: (01457) 838406 E-mail: sales@aut.co.uk *Manufacturers of general purpose & stainless steel. Also wheel distributors*

▶ Telma Retarder Ltd, 25 Clarke Road, Bletchley, Milton Keynes, MK1 1LG Tel: (01908) 642822 Fax: (01908) 641348 E-mail: telma@telma.co.uk *Electro-magnetic suppliers*

▶ Telmar C N C, Unit 3 Warrier Park, Chandler's Ford, Eastleigh, Hampshire, SO53 4NF Tel: 023 80266366

Telnet, 1 Stoney Court, Hotchkiss Way, Binley Industrial Estate, Coventry, CV3 2RL Tel: (024) 7665 0702 Fax: (024) 7665 0773 E-mail: sales@telnet.uk.com *Electronic test & measurement equipment distributors*

Telonic Instruments Ltd, Toutley Industrial Estate, Toutley Road, Wokingham, Berkshire, RG41 1QN Tel: 0118-978 6911 Fax: 0118-979 2338 E-mail: info@telonic.co.uk *Power supply distributors or agents*

Telprint Ltd, 14 Spring Road Industrial Estate, Lanesfield Drive, Wolverhampton, WV4 6UA Tel: (01902) 403355 Fax: (01902) 353802 E-mail: admin@telprint.co.uk *Commercial printing services*

Telsis Direct Ltd, 16 Barnes Wallis Road, Segensworth East, Fareham, Hampshire, PO15 5TT Tel: (01489) 885877 Fax: (01489) 885826 E-mail: sales@telsis.com *General telecommunications*

Telsol Ltd, Grove Lodge, 4 West Park Drive East, Leeds, LS8 2EF Tel: 0113-226 0666 Fax: 0113-226 0999 E-mail: enquiries@telsol.co.uk *Animal health product manufrs*

Telspec plc, Lancaster Parker Road, Rochester, Kent, ME1 3QU Tel: (01634) 687133 Fax: (01634) 684984 E-mail: net@telspec.co.uk *Telecommunication systems manufrs*

Teltron Ltd, Unit 14, 98 Victoria Road, London, NW10 6NB Tel: (020) 8453 1224 Fax: (020) 8963 0310 *Scientific instrument manufrs*

Telwise Ltd, 7 Little Forge Road, Park Farm, Redditch, Worcestershire, B98 7SF Tel: (01527) 519930 Fax: (01527) 519939 E-mail: telwise@telwiseuk.com *Telecommunication equipment & telephone systems installers and maintainers - products include Voip systems,mailbox and auto attendant systems*

Teme Valley Engineering, 1-3 Rosemary Lane, Leintwardine, Craven Arms, Shropshire, SY7 0LP Tel: (01547) 540321 Fax: (01547) 540486 *Aluminium fabricators*

Teme Valley Tractors Ltd, Castle Works, Wigmore, Leominster, Herefordshire, HR6 9UJ Tel: (01568) 770208 Fax: (01568) 770207 E-mail: bsmart@temevalley.co.uk *Sellers & maintainers of tractors*

▶ Temp Space, 5 Beechmore Road, London, SW11 4ET Tel: (0800) 3287554 E-mail: enquiries@temp-space.co.uk *Temporary buildings, temporary storage service*

▶ Tempa Pano UK, Unit 5, Centre 21 Industrial Estate, Bridge Lane, Woolston, Warrington, WA1 4AW Tel: 0845 4941730 Fax: (01925) 810386 E-mail: info@tempapano.co.uk *Tempa Pano UK offer complete enclosure solutions with high quality, enhanced safety, at lower costs. They constantly focus on the changing requirements and future demands of all their customers. Tempa Pano's wide product range offers a host of multiple benefits that relate to many applications that arise in LV Distribution and the Control of Electricity. With continued investment in the latest technological advances in production, product innovation, and highly skilled engineering personnel, they have become a principal manufacturer and exporter of Electrical and Electronic Enclosures. Tempa Pano UK are in working partnerships with many blue chip companies and their design teams, with a large part of the business being custom built enclosures. They offer excellent customer service, technical support, flexibility and reliability.*Tempa Pano are well respected in international markets with their own subsidiaries in the UK, France, Romania, Bulgaria, and Russia.*

Tempatron Ltd, 5 Darwin Close, Reading, RG2 0TB Tel: 0118-931 4062 Fax: 0118-931 0175 E-mail: info@tempatron.co.uk *Electronic products manufrs*

Temperature Applied Sciences Ltd, Unit 15 Martlets Way, Goring-by-Sea, Worthing, West Sussex, BN12 4HF Tel: (01903) 506903 Fax: (01903) 506911 *Environmental chamber & humidity cabinet manufrs*

Temperature Control Ltd, 2a Chorlton Street, Manchester, M16 9HN Tel: 0161-872 5722 Fax: 0161-872 8306 E-mail: jeff@temperature-control.co.uk *Air conditioning installers*

▶ Temperature Controlled Express, Bryn Y Plentyn Farm, Middleton, Oswestry, Shropshire, SY11 4LP Tel: (01691) 657229

Temperature Electronics Ltd, 388-400 Manchester Road, Rochdale, Lancashire, OL11 4NW Tel: (01706) 633438 Fax: (01706) 524609 E-mail: sales@tel-uk.com *Temperature controller manufrs*

Tempest Refrigeration & Air Conditioning Services Ltd, 4-4a Rabone Lane, Smethwick, West Midlands, B66 3JH Tel: 0121-558 3531 Fax: 0121-558 3531 *Commercial refrigeration services*

▶ Templar Consulting Limited, 7 Lidgett Park Avenue, Roundhay, LEEDS, LS8 1EN Tel: 0113 2179261 E-mail: info@templar-consulting.co.uk *IT Project and Change Management Consultancy helping clients to deliver successful programmes and projects either on an individual project basis or on a corporate basis.*

▶ Temple Graphics & Hardware Supplies, 25 Temple Gardens, Rochester, Kent, ME2 2NQ Tel: (01634) 718924 Fax: (01634) 718924 E-mail: barry.hyder@btinternet.com *Architectural ironmongers services*

Temple Health Foods, 17 Temple Fortune Parade, London, NW11 0QS Tel: (020) 8458 6087 Fax: (020) 8209 0059 *Health foods retailers*

Temple Leathergoods, 45 Shaw Street, Colne, Lancashire, BB8 0DD Tel: (01282) 866367 Fax: (01282) 866367 *Leather goods manufrs*

Temple Security Ltd, Temple House, 83-93 Staines Road, Hounslow, TW3 3JB Tel: (020) 8607 7500 Fax: (020) 8607 7510 E-mail: sales@templesecurity.co.uk *Security services* Also at: Branches throughout the U.K.

Temple Taunton Co Ltd, 55 Lockfield Avenue, Enfield, Middlesex, EN3 7JJ Tel: (020) 8344 9840 Fax: (020) 8344 9850 *Distributing copper wire*

▶ Templeman Associates Ltd, Unit 2, North Lynn Business Village, Bergen Way, North Lynn Industrial Estate, King's Lynn, Norfolk, PE30 2JG Tel: (01553) 776148 Fax: (01553) 778320

continued

E-mail: templemanassociates@yahoo.co.uk *Architectural consultants*

Templemead Ltd, 5 Ascot Road, Shotley Bridge, Consett, County Durham, DH8 0NU Tel: (01207) 581237 Fax: (01207) 581237 *Building contractors & suspended ceilings*

Temple's Ltd, Kemp House, 152-160 City Road, London, EC1V 2NX Tel: (020) 7566 3939 Fax: (020) 7566 3935 E-mail: info@templesltd.co.uk *Company registration agents*

▶ Templestone Fire Surrounds Ltd, Station Wharf, Castle Cary, Somerset, BA7 7PE Tel: (01963) 350242 Fax: (01963) 350258 E-mail: sales@templestone.co.uk *Templestone traditionally handcarve naturalstone fire surrounds or architectural stonework. We provide a free site visit to most of the uk with our own fitting teams and designers we can do as much or as little as our customers require from us. From help with construction & design to the fitting and removal if needed.We also have reconstituted styles of surround that can also be altered in certain dimensions if necessary.A family owned company who value highly our service and helpfullness to our clients. Guaranteed satisfaction from 0% of our existing clientel.*

▶ Tempo Europe Ltd, Suit 8 Brecon House, William Brown Close, Llantarnam Industrial Park, Cwmbran, Gwent, NP44 3AB Tel: (01633) 225600 Fax: (01633) 627711 E-mail: tempo@klauke.txtron.com Principal Export Areas: Worldwide *Telecommunication test equipment*

▶ Temposoft UK, 59-60 Thames Street, Windsor, Berkshire, SL4 1TX Tel: (01753) 272040 Fax: (01753) 272049 E-mail: info@temposoft.com *Software developers*

▶ Tempsford Stained Glass, Tempsford, Sandy, Bedfordshire, SG19 2AW Tel: (01767) 640235 Fax: (01767) 641124

▶ Temptation Alley, 361 Portobello Road, London, W10 5SA Tel: (020) 8969 1295 Fax: (020) 7727 4432 E-mail: info@temptationalley.com *The Treasure Trove of TRimmings*Tassels Tie Backs Fringes Braids*Fabrics Fillings Beads Sequins*Bouttons Zipps Haberdashery etc*over 15000 products in stock*trade and retail supplied*

Tempur Mattress Mmanufacturers, Caxton Point, Printing House Lane, Hayes, Middlesex, UB3 1AP Tel: (020) 8589 7000 Fax: (020) 8589 7001 *Pressure relieving bed manufrs*

Tempus Computers Ltd, St Pauls House, St Pauls Square, Birmingham, B3 1RB Tel: 0121-233 3100 Fax: 0121-233 4560 E-mail: sales@tempa.co.uk *Computer & computer software manufrs*

▶ Tempus Lifestyle, 41 High Street, Tarring, Worthing, West Sussex, BN14 7NR Tel: 0845 226 9170 E-mail: enquiries@tempuslifestyle.co.uk *Lifestyle and Personal Concierge Services*

Temtex Ltd, Building 74, Second Avenue, Pensnett Trading Estate, Kingswinford, West Midlands, DY6 7PP Tel: (01384) 270444 Fax: (01384) 271666 E-mail: enquiries@temtex.co.uk *Specialist packaging*

▶ Ten Ten Systems, Abbey Square, Chester, CH1 2HU Tel: (01244) 408990 Fax: (01244) 408991 E-mail: enquiries@1010systems.co.uk *IT network services*

The Tenable Screw Co. Ltd, Tenable House, Torrington Avenue, Coventry, CV4 9HN Tel: (024) 7669 4422 Fax: (024) 7647 0029 E-mail: sales@tenable.co.uk *Precision turned parts manufrs*

Tenable Screw Company Ltd, 16 Deer Park Road, London, SW19 3UB Tel: (020) 8542 6225 Fax: (020) 8543 5789 E-mail: sales@tenable.co.uk Sales Contact: N. Schlaefli *TENABLE is a sub-contract engineering company producing bespoke precision machined components for customers worldwide in the Aerospace, Automotive, Communications, Defence, Electrical & Electronic, Medical & Leisure industries. PRODUCTS include:- Connectors, pins, sockets, terminals, terminal blocks, screws, inserts and bushes. We have 265 turning MACHINES producing turned parts from 0.5 to 42mm diameter :- Cam single spindle autos :- Tornos, Strohm CNC sliding & fixed heads: Citizen,Star,Bumotec. Coil fed Escomatics Rotary transfer machines : Hydromats, Variomatics, Eubamas, Vertomats, Multispindles: Tornos, Wickman MATERIALS : Brass, Steel, Copper, Nickel Silver & Aluminium We are LOCATED at London (H.O.) Marlborough in Wiltshire & Coventry in West Midlands. We have been established for 66 years, employ 100+ people & turnover approx seven million pounds.*

The Tenable Screw Co. Ltd, Elcot Lane, Marlborough, Wiltshire, SN8 2AE Tel: (01672) 512900 Fax: (01672) 513915 E-mail: sales@tenable.co.uk *Precision turned parts manufrs*

Tenants Inks & Coatings Suppliers, Ruspidge Road, Cinderford, Gloucestershire, GL14 3AW Tel: (01594) 822375 Fax: (01594) 826251 E-mail: salessupport@tg-tics.com *Pigment dispersion manufrs*

Tenants Tar Distillers, 9 Airport Road West, Belfast, BT3 9ED Tel: (028) 9045 5135 Fax: (028) 9046 0077 E-mail: ttd@ctni.co.uk *Bitumen product manufrs*

Tenby Coachworks Ltd, The Green, Tenby, Dyfed, SA70 8EU Tel: (01834) 842016 Fax: (01834) 843283 *Motor body builders*

Tenby & Penny Co. Ltd, 38a Beulah Road, London, E17 9LQ Tel: (020) 8520 7706 Fax: (020) 8521 1632 E-mail: tenbypenny@supanet.com *Leaded light manufrs*

▶ Tended Net Computer Services, 79 Kyrkeby, Letchworth Garden City, Hertfordshire, SG6 2PG Tel: (01462) 670225 Fax: (01462) 670225 E-mail: roy.stapleton@tendednet.com *Home user computer support and small business computer specialist.*Specialist remote IT/IS department for your startup or small business.*We operate a no fix no fee repair system for home users.*

Tendring District Council, Town Hall, Station Road, Clacton-on-Sea, Essex, CO15 1SE Tel: (01255) 425501 Fax: (01255) 253118 E-mail: edu@tendringdc.gov.uk *Local government*

Tendring Hundred Water Services Ltd, Mill Hill, Manningtree, Essex, CO11 2AZ Tel: (01206) 399200 Fax: (01206) 399212 E-mail: info@thws.co.uk *Water suppliers*

Tenencia Aerospace Design, Hangar 6, Coventry Airport, Coventry, CV8 3AZ Tel: (024) 7688 2695 E-mail: info@tenencia.co.uk *Aerospace manufrs*

Tenet Technology Ltd, North Heath Lane, Horsham, West Sussex, RH12 5UX Tel: (01403) 273173 Fax: (01403) 273123 E-mail: tenet@tenetsystems.com *Computer solutions house*

▶ TENFOUR writing, 65 The Beckers, Rectory Road, London, N16 7QU Tel: 07971 669206 E-mail: chris@tenfourwriting.co.uk *TENFOUR writing helps companies and organisations create a personality through words. Content for websites, and copywriting for literature, articles, marketing and media materials.*

Tenga Engineering Co. Ltd, Britannia House, Queensway, New Milton, Hampshire, BH25 5NN Tel: (01425) 622567 Fax: (01425) 622789 *New & used machine tool suppliers*

Tenkay Electronics Ltd, Lancing Business Park, Marlborough Road, Lancing, West Sussex, BN15 8TN Tel: (01903) 855455 Fax: (01903) 761942 E-mail: sue.brown@tenkay.co.uk *Tenkay Electronics specialise in providing a complete manufacturing service to the Electronic and Electrical Industries. Full Material Procurement, Assembly, Test and Packaging. Surface Mount and Conventional PCB Assembly Cable Preparation, Cable Harnessing and wiring looms Electronic and Electrical Panel and Cabinet Wiring Approved to BS EN ISO 9001:2000 Production facilities in Asia*

▶ Tenkey Ltd, Elgan House, Ashfield Road Norton, Bury St. Edmunds, Suffolk, IP31 3NJ Tel: (01359) 244250 Fax: (01359) 244250 E-mail: stewart@tenkey.co.uk *Transport and Warehouse Consultants*

Tenmat Ltd, Ashburton Road West, Trafford Park, Manchester, M17 1RU Tel: 0161-872 2181 Fax: 0161-872 7596 E-mail: info@tenmat.com *Composite engineering services*

▶ Tennant Group Ltd, The Midway, Nottingham, NG7 2TS Tel: 0115-985 2222 Fax: 0115-988 5330 E-mail: info@tennantgroup.co.uk *Manufacture rubber safety equipment & clothing*

Tennant Motor Services (Leeds) Ltd, Parkspring Coachworks Garage, Swinnow Lane, Leeds, LS13 4LZ Tel: 0113-256 3411 Fax: 0113-236 0430 *Motor engineering services*

Tennant PVC, The Midway, Nottingham, NG7 2TS Tel: 0115-988 1300 Fax: 0115-988 5310 E-mail: sales@tennantpvc.co.uk *Manufacturers of plastic welded goods & loose leaf binders*

Tennant PVC Ltd, Unit A Meadow Grove, Meadow Lane, Nottingham, NG2 3HF Tel: 0115-934 0950 Fax: 0115-934 0955 E-mail: sales@tennantpvc.co.uk *Ring binders*

Tennant UK Ltd, Gladstone Road, Northampton, NN5 7RX Tel: (01604) 583191 Fax: (01604) 751517 E-mail: europe@tennantco.com *Floor scrubbing & sweeping machine manufrs*

▶ Tennant UK Ltd, Mount Street, New Basford, Nottingham, NG7 7HX Tel: 0115-973 8080 Fax: 0115-973 8090 E-mail: sales@tennantsuk.com *Road signs, number plates & reflective material distributors*

Tennants Consolidated Ltd, 69 Grosvenor Street, London, W1K 3JW Tel: (020) 7493 5451 Fax: (020) 7495 6736 *Chemical & food ingredients manufrs*

Tennants Distribution, Gelderd Road, Birstall, Batley, West Yorkshire, WF17 9LY Tel: (01924) 474447 Fax: (01924) 477842 E-mail: sales.leeds@tennantsdistribution.com *Chemical distributors*

Tennants Distribution, Ryders Green Road, West Bromwich, West Midlands, B70 0AX Tel: 0121-557 9751 Fax: 0121-557 8144 E-mail: sales.westbromwich@tennantsdistribution.com *Chemical distribution*

Tennants Textile Colours, 31-43 Ravenhill Rd, Belfast, BT6 8DP Tel: (028) 9045 1396 Fax: (028) 9045 8944 E-mail: sales@tennantstextilecolours.com *Pigment manufacturers to the textiles trade*

Tenneco Automotive UK Ltd, Wharfdale Road, Tyseley, Birmingham, B11 2DF Tel: 0121-707 8000 Fax: 0121-609 3035 E-mail: sales@tenneco.com Principal Export Areas: North America, Central America & South America *Estate agents*

Tenn-elcon Ltd, Algernon Industrial Estate, Shiremoor, Newcastle Upon Tyne, NE27 0BL Tel: 0191-251 4065 Fax: 0191-252 3205 *High quality electroplating services*

Jeremy Tenniswood, 36 St. Botolphs Street, Colchester, CO2 7EA Tel: (01206) 368787 Fax: (01206) 367836 E-mail: info@militaria.co.uk *Militaria retailer & wholesaler*

▶ Tennsport Sports Equipment, 372 St. Albans Road, Watford, WD24 6PQ Tel: (01923) 227987 E-mail: tenn66jm@aol.com *Sports equipment distributor*

Tenon P.L.C., Sumner House, St. Thomass Road, Chorley, Lancashire, PR7 1HP Tel: (01257) 518000 Fax: (01257) 518001 E-mail: chorley@tenongroup.com *Accountants & business advisors services* Also at: London W1, Manchester & Wigan

Tenon, Salisbury House, 31 Finsbury Circus, London, EC2M 5SQ Tel: (020) 7628 2040 Fax: (020) 7638 0217 E-mail: info@tenongroup.com *Chartered accountants & business development consultants* Also at: Chelmsford, Guildford & Swindon

Tensid UK plc, 70a Wheatash Road, Addlestone, Surrey, KT15 2ES Tel: (01932) 564133 Fax: (01932) 562046 E-mail: info@tensid.com *Graffiti removal & protection product services*

Tensile Forgings, Portersfield Road, Cradley Heath, West Midlands, B64 7BN Tel: (01384) 566758 *Manufacturers of shackles*

▶ Tensys Ltd, St. Swithins Yard, 1 Walcot Street, Bath, BA1 5BG Tel: (01225) 321950 Fax: (01225) 321969 E-mail: peter.arnold@tensys.com *Tensys Dynamics solve fluid flow based engineering design problems, utilising Computational Fluid Dynamics (CFD) for virtual product development. Our objective is to help you develop a practical and cost effective solution using the most appropriate tools, saving you time, money and reducing risk.*

Tent Hire, 105a Pargeter Street, Walsall, WS2 8QR Tel: (01922) 634808 Fax: (01922) 647788 *Camping supplies services*

Tents & Marquees Ltd, Haughton Farm, Haughton, Shrewsbury, SY4 4GB Tel: (01743) 709246 Fax: (01743) 709106 E-mail: info@tentsandmarquees.com *Marquee & furniture hire services*

▶ Tenways Engineering Services Ltd, 31 St. Marys Road, London, NW11 9UE Tel: (020) 8922 5468 Fax: (020) 8201 8022 E-mail: sales@tenwayseng.co.uk *Air conditioning equipment & accessories & control*

Tenza Technologies Ltd, Carlton Park Industrial Estate, Saxmundham, Suffolk, IP17 2NL Tel: (01728) 602811 Fax: (01728) 605282 E-mail: enquiries@tenzatech.com Principal Export Areas: Worldwide *Manufacture document enclosed wallets book cover material labels*

▶ TEP UK Ltd, 8 King Edward Street, Oxford, OX1 4HS Tel: (07921) 706641 E-mail: info@tepuk.com *Textile products*

Tepe Fashions, 126 Stratford Road, Sparkhill, Birmingham, B11 1AJ Tel: 0121-766 5635 Fax: 0121-753 5635 *Clothing manufrs*

Tepede Graphics Ltd, Laura House, Jengers Mead, Billingshurst, West Sussex, RH14 9NZ Tel: (01403) 786867 Fax: (01403) 786687 *Creation of digital printing materials manufrs*

▶ Tepnel Life Sciences P.L.C., Unit 2,, Kelvin Campus, West Of Scotland Science Park, Glasgow, G20 0SP Tel: 0141-946 8889 Fax: 0141-946 4195 E-mail: jhillier@tepnel.com *Biomedical research*

Teqnet Ltd, 5 Windsor Court, Clive Road, Redditch, Worcestershire, B97 4BT Tel: (01527) 592100 Fax: (01527) 592113 *Computer Networking & Communications*

Tequila International Holdings Ltd, 82 Charing Cross Road, London, WC2H 0QB Tel: (020) 7557 6101 Fax: (020) 7557 6111 E-mail: info@tequila-uk.com *Marketing consultants*

Tera (UK) Ltd, Park Farm Business Centre, Fornham St. Genevieve, Bury St. Edmunds, Suffolk, IP28 6TS Tel: (01284) 753263 Fax: (01284) 753257 E-mail: sales@tera-uk.com *Software developers*

Terapin Curtain Systems, 2 Glenavy Road, Upper Ballinderry, Lisburn, County Antrim, BT28 2EU Tel: (028) 9265 1007 Fax: (028) 9265 2019 E-mail: info@terapin.com *Tilt cover & tarpaulin manufrs*

Terasaki Europe Ltd, 80 Beardmore Way, Clydebank, Dunbartonshire, G81 4HT Tel: 0141-565 1600 Fax: 0141-952 9246 E-mail: marketing@terasaki.com *Circuit breaker manufrs*

Terbergmatec UK Ltd, Highgrounds Way, Rhodesia, Worksop, Nottinghamshire, S80 3AF Tel: (01909) 484000 Fax: (01909) 489000 *Commercial vehicle bodybuilders*

Tercet Precision Ltd, Millarston Industrial Estate, Paisley, Renfrewshire, PA1 2XR Tel: 0141-887 4153 Fax: 0141-887 4586 E-mail: sales@tercet.co.uk *Precision turned parts manufrs* Also at: Kilwinning

▶ Tercon Ltd, 6 Barnack Trading Centre, Novers Hill, Bedminster, Bristol, BS3 5QE Tel: 0117-963 9039 Fax: 0117-966 7074

Terecast Ltd, 25 Hylton Street, Birmingham, B18 6HJ Tel: 0121-554 1722 Fax: 0121-551 5301 E-mail: terecast@aol.com *Jewellery manufrs*

▶ Terence Wright Associates Ltd, 100 Fore Street, Barton, Torquay, TQ2 8DN Tel: (0870) 0420195 Fax: 01803 322410 E-mail: terry.wright@twa-ltd.co.uk *Terence Wright Associates Ltd specialises in meeting the increasing demand from organisations to implement effective continuity planning strategies.**TWA services include:**= Risk identification and assessment*= Business threat analysis*= Business impact analysis*= Development of continuity and recovery strategies*= Plan development*= Plan auditing and testing*= Asbestos management**TWA Limited is formed of a network of experienced consultants and business partners, such as Strategy Planning Associates and Safix; who deliver the company's range of services to the business community on a national basis. TWA is an authorized distributor for Strategy and LGO (Life Goes On) continuity planning software.**

Terex Demag UK Ltd, Unit 324 Heyford Park, Camp Road, Upper Heyford, Bicester, Oxfordshire, OX25 5HA Tel: (01869) 232443 Fax: (01869) 232840 E-mail: phil.harvey@terex-demag.com Principal Export Areas: Worldwide *Crane distributors*

Terex Equipment Ltd, Newhouse Industrial Estate, Motherwell, Lanarkshire, ML1 5RY Tel: (01698) 732121 Fax: (01698) 734046 *Manufacturer of articulate, rigid and scraper trucks from 25 to 100 tons.*

Terex Halco, PO Box 25, Halifax, West Yorkshire, HX3 9TW Tel: (01422) 399900 Fax: (01422) 330186 E-mail: halco@halcodrilling.com *Manufacturers of rock drilling equipment*

Terex Pegson Ltd, Mammoth Street, Coalville, Leicestershire, LE67 3GN Tel: (01530) 518600 Fax: (01530) 518618 E-mail: sales@bl-pegson.com *Crushing equipment manufrs*

Terex UK Ltd, Central Boulevard, Prologis Park, Coventry, CV6 4BX Tel: (024) 7633 9400 Fax: (024) 7633 9500 E-mail: enquiries@terexce.com *Construction machinery*

▶ Terfware All Terrain Mountain Boarding Apparel, 4 Lopes Road, Dousland, Yelverton, Devon, PL20 6NX Tel: (01822) 854354 *All terrain mountain boarding apparel, gear, info, forum, news, reviews, movies & more*

Teritex Sportswear, Teritex Factory, Boughton, Newark, Nottinghamshire, NG22 9ZD Tel: (01623) 861381 Fax: (01623) 835301 E-mail: info@teritex.com *Sportswear manufrs*

Termate Ltd, Leone Works, John Street, New Bassford, Nottingham, NG7 7HL Tel: 0115-978 4652 Fax: 0115-970 2106 E-mail: sales@termate.com *Terminal block manufrs*

Terminal Tackle UK Ltd, 4 Friday Street, Leighton Buzzard, Bedfordshire, LU7 1AN Tel: (01525) 370779 Fax: (01525) 370779 E-mail: terminal4tackle@hotmail.com *Fishing tackle suppliers*

Terminex Pest & Vermin Control, 53 Gloucester Drive, London, N4 2LJ Tel: (020) 7503 8234 Fax: (020) 7503 8234 E-mail: enquiries@terminex.co.uk *Pest control*

▶ Termrim Construction Ltd, 1 Pellon Place Dyson Wood Way, Bradley Business Park, Huddersfield, HD2 1GT Tel: (01484) 547525 E-mail: enquiries@termrim.co.uk

Ternent Pre-Cast, Whitehall Estate, 123a Barras Garth Road, Leeds, LS12 4JB Tel: 0113-231 9099 *Concrete products manufrs*

Ternex Ltd, Ayot Green Sawmill, 27 Ayot Green, Ayot St. Peter, Welwyn, Hertfordshire, AL6 9BA Tel: (01707) 324606 Fax: (01707) 334371 E-mail: sales@ternex.co.uk *Saw mill & joinery timber*

Terotest Ltd, 33 Station Road, Ashwell, Baldock, Hertfordshire, SG7 5LG Tel: (01462) 742499 Fax: (01462) 742497 E-mail: info@terotest.com *Automatic test equipment distributors*

Terra Eco Systems, Bracknell Sewage Treatment, Hazelwood Lane, Binfield, Bracknell, Berkshire, RG42 5NE Tel: 0118-964 0301 Fax: 0118-964 0333 *Waste disposal contractors*

▶ Terra Mould, Barkham Grange, Barkham Street, Barkham, Wokingham, Berkshire, RG40 4PJ Tel: 0118-976 1040 Fax: 0118-976 1040 E-mail: steve@terra-mould.co.uk *Industrial moulders*

Terra Nitrogen UK Ltd, Florence House, Radcliffe CR, Thornaby, Stockton-on-Tees, Cleveland, TS17 6BS Tel: (01642) 637000 Fax: (01642) 637104 E-mail: webmasteruk@uk.terraindusties.com *Fertilizer & chemicals manufrs*

Terra Therma Co, Home Farm, Toddington Road, Tebworth, Leighton Buzzard, Bedfordshire, LU7 9QD Tel: (01525) 875166 Fax: (01525) 875166 *Thermoplastic sheet line heater manufrs*

▶ Terracarbon Ltd, The Garage, Hingham Road, Hackford, Wymondham, Norfolk, NR18 9HF Tel: (01953) 851535 Fax: (01953) 851328

The Terraces Hotel, 4 Melville Terrace, Stirling, FK8 2ND Tel: (01786) 472268 Fax: (01786) 450314 E-mail: sales@terraceshotel.co.uk *Hotel & conference facility service providers*

▶ TerraDat Geophysics Ltd, Unit 2, Ocean Ho, Hunter St, Cardiff, CF10 5FR Tel: (0870) 7303050 Fax: (0870) 7303051 E-mail: info@terradat.co.uk *TerraDat Geophysics provides non-invasive geophysical surveys for site investigations ranging from contaminated land, geotechnical & unexploded ordnance through to inshore & archaeological investigations. Specialists in seismics, microgravity, magnetics, resistivity, ground conductivity & crosshole geophysics. Rapid mobilisation UK & overseas*

Terrafirma Ceramica Ltd, 119 Northfield Avenue, London, W13 9QR Tel: (020) 8840 2844 Fax: (020) 8840 2054 *Retail tile outlet supplier*

Terrafix Ltd, Unit 23c Newfields Industrial Estate, High Street, Stoke-on-Trent, ST6 5PD Tel: (01782) 577015 Fax: (01782) 835667 E-mail: sales@terrafix.co.uk *Automatic vehicle location system manufrs*

▶ Terrain Aeration Services Ltd, Aeration House 20 Millfields, Haughley, Stowmarket, Suffolk, IP14 3PU Tel: (01449) 673783 Fax: (01449) 614564 E-mail: terrainaeration@aol.com *Aeration of soil, turf & trees*

Terralift UK Ltd, 18 The Grove, Market Deeping, Peterborough, PE6 8AW Tel: (01778) 380005 Fax: (01778) 348835 E-mail: sales@terralift.ie *Fertilizer manufr*

Terram Ltd, Mamhilad, Pontypool, Gwent, NP4 0YR Tel: (01495) 757722 Fax: (01495) 762383 E-mail: info@terram.com *Geosynthetics manufrs*

Terrane Promotions, Terrane House, Whisby Way Industrial Estate, Lincoln, LN6 3LQ Tel: (01522) 697000 Fax: (01522) 697154 E-mail: sales@terrane.co.uk *Embroidery & screen printing manufrs*

Terranova, Bennet Road, Reading, RG2 0QX Tel: 0118-986 6577 Fax: 0118-931 4114 E-mail: sales@terranovagroup.co.uk *Mobile cranes, industrial transport & commercial workshop facilities*

Terrapart International Ltd, Blacksmith's Yard, Broad Hinton, Swindon, SN4 9PB Tel: (01793) 731990 Fax: (01793) 731791 E-mail: accounts@terrapart.com *Construction equipment spare part suppliers*

Terrapin Ltd, Bomnd Avenue, Bletchley, Milton Keynes, MK1 1JJ Tel: 0115-907 2700 Fax: 0115-972 2203 E-mail: sales@terrapin-ltd.co.uk *Terrapin provide fully functioning, 'walk in' building solutions in 5 senses. Permanent buildings for life, enabling buildings to facilitate your main project, expansion buildings to help you as you grow, expedient buildings for re-structuring your business, temporary buildings for just as long as you need.*

Terrill Bros (Founders) Ltd, 2 Guildford Road Industrial Estate, Hayle, Cornwall, TR27 4QZ Tel: (01736) 752168 Fax: (01736) 756215 E-mail: sales@terrill-bros.co.uk *Specialists in small scale repetition, and 'jobbing' requirements, we manufacture castings in reliably short lead-times, at consistently high quality levels, for both frequently and infrequently required batches.*Stainless steels are the bulk of output, but our range of materials/expertise varies from nickel based*

continued

*alloys, super austenitic steels, duplex and 'super' duplex steels, all the way through to low alloy and basic carbon steels.*Markets served include pumps, valves, and general components for the food, pharmaceutical, and petrochemical industries as well as many other demanding environments.*Our size ranges up to approx.500Kg, but more typically falls between 5 and 100Kg.*

▶ Terrington Data Management, IT Centre, Innovation Way, York Science Park, Heslington, York, YO10 5DG Tel: 0870 8508023 Fax: 01904 567719 E-mail: sales@terringtondm.com *Data management, data collection, pdas & handheld terminals software*

Terry Chemicals Ltd, Beckside Road, Dalton-in-Furness, Cumbria, LA15 8DZ Tel: (01229) 466373 Fax: (01229) 466604 *Janitorial chemical suppliers*

▶ Terry Clinker Health and Safety Services, Hillview, Picts Hill, Langport, Somerset, TA10 9AA Tel: (01458) 253963 Fax: (01458) 253963 E-mail: healthandsafety@terry-clinker-online.co.uk *Providing a cost effective health and safety management service for small to medium Businesses. Services including Company Safety *Policies, Risk Assessments, Reviews, Portable Appliance PAT Testing, Staff Induction Training.*

Terry Gregory Metal Fabrications Ltd, 599 Kingston Road, London, SW20 8SA Tel: (020) 8542 9941 Fax: (020) 8543 6091 E-mail: metal@terrygregory.freeserve.co.uk *Ferrous & non-ferrous metal fabricators*

▶ Terry Mark Ltd, 6 Brentfield Road, Dartford, DA1 1YJ Tel: (01322) 289700 Fax: (01322) 271548

▶ Terry Milner Proccesing Ltd, Unit 4-5, Bath Lane, Leeds, LS13 3BD Tel: 0113-236 3686 Fax: 0113-236 3391

Terry Radiators, Bay 2, 198 Derby Road, Chesterfield, Derbyshire, S40 2EP Tel: (01246) 234401 *Motor vehicle radiator manufrs*

Terry Rushton Associates, 49 Twyford Avenue, London, N2 9NR Tel: (020) 8442 1234 Fax: (020) 8442 1234 E-mail: telrush@aol.com *Electrical contractors & engineers*

▶ Terry & Thomas Construction Ltd, 34 Redfern Road, Birmingham, B11 2BH Tel: 0121-707 7566 Fax: 0121-707 7566

▶ Terry Trott, The Studio, 24 School Lane, Bapchild, Sittingbourne, Kent, ME9 9NL Tel: (01795) 472833 Fax: (01795) 475941 E-mail: info@terrytrottphotography.co.uk *Commercial & advertising photography service*

Tertio Ltd, 1 Angel Square, Torrens Street, London, EC1V 1PL Tel: (01225) 478000 Fax: (01225) 478001 *Software computer systems consultants*

Tertio Ltd, 3000 Manchester Business Park, Manchester, M22 5TG Tel: 0161-266 1016 Fax: 0161-266 1396 *Supplier of network systems*

Tes Europe Ltd, Sandyland, North End, Wisbech, Cambridgeshire, PE13 1PE Tel: (01945) 474809 Fax: (01945) 589591 E-mail: tes_europe@freenet.co.uk *Based in Wisbech, Cambridgeshire, tes(europe)ltd design, manufacture, install and commission Control Systems and Power Distribution systems for customers worldwide. tes(europe)ltd manufacture both Control Systems and Power Distribution Systems to customer specifications, or where these are non-existent, liase with the customer's technical representitives in order to produce exactly what is required. ISO 9001 compliant, tes(europe)ltd provides an excellent service in both the technical advice given and the supply of the correct Control System or Power Distribution System for your needs.*

tesa UK Ltd, Yeomans Drive, Blakelands, Milton Keynes, MK14 5LS Tel: 0845 4941752 Fax: (01908) 211555 E-mail: ukenquiry@tesa.com *tesa® has a worldwide reputation as a leading manufacturer and supplier of self-adhesive tapes and solutions to many industries, the professional trades and consumers. With over 125 years experience, our core competences are the development of adhesives and coating technology and tesa®'s aim is to provide innovative product solutions to improve our customers' processes. More than 6,000 tapes developed and marketed in over 100 countries mean our customers can rely on a tesa® adhesive tape solution for their applications supported by high levels of service. Focusing on industrial sectors such as Automotive, Transportation, Paper, Newsprint, Building and Construction, Corrugators, Electronics, Flexographic Printing and Security and Identification, tesa® offers a range of adhesive tapes specially tailored for the many and often demanding applications these sectors have to offer. All tesa® tapes meet the highest quality standards and have been awarded ISO 9001:2000, ISO/TS 16949 and ISO 14001 certification.*

▶ Tesam Distribution Ltd, Pinnacle House, Shrewsbury Avenue, Peterborough, PE2 7BJ Tel: (01733) 236277 Fax: (01733) 236278

▶ Tesco Distribution, Kilbegs Road, Antrim, BT41 4NN Tel: (028) 9444 7100 Fax: (028) 9444 7153

▶ Tesco Distribution, Caputhall Road, Deans, Livingston, West Lothian, EH54 8AS Tel: (01506) 771100 Fax: (01506) 771143

▶ Tesco Distribution, Deer Park Road, Moulton Park Industrial Estate, Northampton, NN3 6RX Tel: (01604) 447900 Fax: (01604) 447934

Tesco Stores Ltd, Tesco House, Delamare Road, Cheshunt, Waltham Cross, Hertfordshire, EN8 9SL Tel: (01992) 632222 Fax: (01992) 630794 *Bathrooms & tile retailers*

Tescom UK Ltd, 21-22 Great Sutton Street, London, EC1V 0DY Tel: (020) 7022 6700 Fax: (020) 7022 6701 E-mail: info@tescom-intl.com *Software testers*

▶ Tescos, Tesco Warehouse, Collett, Didcot, Oxfordshire, OX11 7PN Tel: (01235) 707100 Fax: (01235) 707157

Tesla Engineering Ltd, Water Lane, Storrington, Pulborough, West Sussex, RH20 3EA Tel: (01903) 743941 Fax: (01903) 745548 E-mail: tesla@tesla.co.uk *Magnet manufrs*

Tesla Transformers Ltd, Carrington Business Park, Manchester Road, Carrington, Manchester, M31 4ZU Tel: 0161-776 4080 Fax: 0161-776 4446 E-mail: sales@tesla-transformers.com *Transformer manufrs*

Tesma UK Ltd, 3 Commercil Quay, 88 Commercial Street, Edinburgh, EH6 6LX Tel: 0131-554 4466 Fax: 0131-554 3843 E-mail: administration@gibsongas.co.uk *Ship owners & operators*

Tessella Support Service plc, Chadwick House Warrington Road, Birchwood Park, Birchwood, Warrington, WA3 6AE Tel: (01925) 286800 Fax: (01925) 286808 E-mail: sales@tesella.com *Computer consultants*

Tessenderlo Fine Chemicals Ltd, Macclesfield Road, Leek, Staffordshire, ST13 8LD Tel: (01538) 399100 Fax: (01538) 399025 E-mail: sales@tessenderlofinechemicals.com *Chemical distributors*

Tessenderlow UK Ltd, West Bank Dock Estate, Widnes, Cheshire, WA8 0NY Tel: 0151-424 4281 Fax: 0151-423 6757 *Chemical manufrs*

▶ Test Devices, 21 Sedling Road, Wear Industrial Estate, Washington, Tyne & Wear, NE38 9BZ Tel: 0191-419 2345 Fax: 0191-419 2345 E-mail: sales@trnlcd.co.uk *Aerospace*

Test Diesel Services, Atlantic Works, Oakley Road, Southampton, SO16 4LL Tel: (023) 8078 9817 Fax: (023) 8077 8253 E-mail: service@testdieselservices.co.uk *Specialists in diesel fuel injection, turbocharger & electrical repair for marine, industrial, commercial and automotive engines.*

Test Plugs Ltd, 12 Falklands Road, Haverhill, Suffolk, CB9 0EA Tel: (01440) 704201 Fax: (01440) 763121 E-mail: sales@test-plugs.com *Gauges, thermometers & test plugs*

Test Safe Ltd, Bretby Business Park, Ashby Road, Bretby, Burton-on-Trent, Staffordshire, DE15 0YZ Tel: (01283) 229873 Fax: (01283) 553094 E-mail: sales@test-safe.co.uk *Electrical testing services*

Test Valley, Watt Road, Salisbury, SP2 7UD Tel: (01722) 414800 Fax: (0870) 2240449 *Packaging material merchants*

Test Valley Ceilings & Partitioning, 16 Gover Road, Southampton, SO16 9BR Tel: (023) 8086 4546 Fax: (023) 8049 5831 E-mail: gary.fawson@ntlworld.com *Suspended ceilings suppliers*

Test Valley Engineers Ltd, Stoneymarsh, Michelmersh, Romsey, Hampshire, SO51 0LB Tel: (01794) 368308 Fax: (01794) 368693 E-mail: sales@test-valley.co.uk *Structural steelwork engineers & steel fabricators*

Test Valley Engineers Ltd, Stoneymarsh, Michelmersh, Romsey, Hampshire, SO51 0LB Tel: (01794) 368308 Fax: (01794) 368693 E-mail: sales@test-valley.co.uk *Flexible ducting & hose systems*

▶ Test Valley Gardencare, Nether Wallop Business Park, Bent Street, Nether Wallop, Stockbridge, Hampshire, SO20 8EJ Tel: (0845) 4668200 Fax: (0845) 4668600 E-mail: info@test-valley-gardencare.co.uk *Landscape contractors, tree surgeons, grassland maintenance contractors, groundworks*

▶ Test Valley Mobility, 9 Greatbridge Business Park, Budds Lane, Romsey, Hampshire, SO51 0HA Tel: (01794) 521217 Fax: (01794) 521218 E-mail: admin@testvalleymobility.co.uk *Lifting equipment for disabled*

Testbank Ship Repair & Boiler Co. Ltd, Western Avenue, Western Docks, Southampton, SO15 0HH Tel: (023) 8078 7878 Fax: (023) 8078 7826 E-mail: admin@testbank.co.uk *Ship repair services*

Tested Spring Co. Ltd, 20 Hainge Road, Tividale, Oldbury, West Midlands, B69 2NG Tel: 0121-557 2308 Fax: 0121-557 4031 E-mail: sales@testedspring.com *Spring manufrs*

Testlink Ltd, Poole, Dorset, BH16 5SJ Tel: (01202) 621100 Fax: (01202) 625577 E-mail: sales@testlink.co.uk *Electronic testing services*

Testo Ltd, Newman Lane, Alton, Hampshire, GU34 2QJ Tel: (01420) 544433 Fax: (01420) 544434 E-mail: caterer@testo.co.uk *Testo is a world leader in the development and manufacture of high quality measurement instruments, with over 50 years of experience. Testo offers an extensive range of instruments for the food processing industry including:**Non-contact infrared thermometers** Contact probe thermometers** Humidity meters**pH meters**Data loggers**Cooking oil quality testers.*Testo offers a wide range of instruments to help keep you HACCP compliant, giving you extra reassurance that your methods are safe. Again and again, the company has set new standards in the field of measurement technology with constant investments in new ideas. Testo also offers service and calibration to national standards, including UKAS.*To find out more please visit www.testo.co.uk/food*

▶ Testometric Co. Ltd, Unit 1 Lincoln Business Park, Lincoln Close, Rochdale, Lancashire, OL11 1NR Tel: (01706) 654039 Fax: (01706) 646089 E-mail: info@testometric.co.uk Principal Export Areas: Africa *Manufacturers of universal strength testing machines covering tensile, compression & flexural tests for all materials.*

Testrade Ltd, Unit 22 Olds Close, Watford, WD18 9RU Tel: (01923) 720222 Fax: (01923) 720444 E-mail: sales@testrade.co.uk *Non-destructive test equipment sales*

Testrite Ltd, Woodfield Works, Old Lane, Halifax, West Yorkshire, HX3 6TF Tel: (01422) 366963 Fax: (01422) 345431 E-mail: sales@testrite.co.uk *Textile testing equipment manufrs*

Tetbury Joinery, Priory Industrial Estate, London Road, Tetbury, Gloucestershire, GL8 8HZ Tel: (01666) 504250 Fax: (01666) 504660 E-mail: tetbury.joinery@btconnect.com *Joinery manufrs*

▶ The Tetbury Stone Company Ltd, Week Farm, Combe Hay, Bath, BA2 8RF Tel: (01225) 836149 Fax: 01225 836149 E-mail: luke.pearce@tetburystone.co.uk *Internal and External stone flooring, fireplaces and masonry.*

Tetley Specialist Printers, 11 Wakelins End, Cookham, Maidenhead, Berkshire, SL6 9TQ Tel: (01628) 520047 Fax: (01628) 520047 *Corporate promotional gift distributors*

▶ Tetra Pak Processing UK Ltd, Swan House Peregrine Business Park, Gomm Road, High Wycombe, Buckinghamshire, HP13 7DL Tel: (0870) 4426400 Fax: (0870) 4426401 E-mail: processing.uk@tetrapack.com *Dairy engineering*

Tetrad plc, Hartford Mill, Swan Street, Preston, PR1 5PQ Tel: (01772) 792936 Fax: (01772) 798319 E-mail: sales@tetrad.co.uk *Furniture manufrs*

▶ Tetras Interiors Ltd, 55 Lincoln Road, Poole, Dorset, BH12 2HT Tel: (01202) 566480 Fax: (01202) 386403 E-mail: tetrasinteriors@aol.com *Furniture, boardrooms, suspended ceilings & partitioning refurbishment manufrs*

Tetroc Chambar Ltd, 3 Telford Road, Ferndown Industrial Estate, Wimborne, Dorset, BH21 7QN Tel: (01202) 871143 Fax: (01202) 897045 E-mail: sales@tetroc.com *Machine tool distributors & general engineers*

Tetrosyl Ltd, Bevis Green Works, Mill Road, Walmersley, Bury, Lancashire, BL9 6RE Tel: 0161-764 5981 Fax: 0161-797 5899 E-mail: info@tetrosyl.com *Car care products & lubricants manufrs*

Teva UK, Unit 3 Leeds Business Park, 18 Bruntcliffe Way, Morley, Leeds, LS27 0JG Tel: 0113-238 0099 Fax: 0113-201 3936 E-mail: morleyreception@tevauk.co.uk *Generic & contract pharmaceutical manufrs*

Teva UK Ltd, Albert Basin, Ivax Quays, Albert Basin, London, E16 2QJ Tel: (0870) 5020304 Fax: (0870) 5323334 E-mail: richard.daniel@ivax.co.uk *Pharmaceutical manufrs*

Teversham Engineering Ltd, Hall Farm, Church Road, Teversham, Cambridge, CB1 9AP Tel: 01223 293904 *Stove enamelling & powder coating & sub contract engineering*

Teviot Town & Country Supplies, 22 Oliver Cresent, Hawick, Roxburghshire, TD9 9BQ Tel: (01450) 371699 Fax: (01450) 371699 *Agricultural merchants*

Teviotdale Bakery, 369 South Road, Dundee, DD2 2RT Tel: (01382) 622361 Fax: (01382) 622076 E-mail: sales@teviotdale-bakery.co.uk *Distribute baked products*

Tewkesbury Marina Ltd, Bredon Road, Tewkesbury, Gloucestershire, GL20 5BY Tel: (01684) 293737 Fax: (01684) 293076 E-mail: sales@tewkesbury-marina.co.uk *Yacht builders, brokers & berthing*

▶ Tewkesbury Printing Co. Ltd, Unit 16, Shannon Way, Ashchurch, Tewkesbury, Gloucestershire, GL20 8ND Tel: (01684) 850666

Tews Engineering Ltd, 34 Lavant Street, Petersfield, Hampshire, GU32 3EF Tel: (01730) 268531 Fax: (01730) 262141 E-mail: admin@tews.uk.com *Sub contract engineers*

Tewtrell Ltd, Limekiln Lane, Birmingham, B14 4SP Tel: 0121-430 2161 Fax: 0121-430 2741 E-mail: sales@tewtrell.com *Printing trade solvents & chemicals supplies*

Tex Holdings plc, Claydon Industrial Park, Great Blakenham, Ipswich, IP6 0NL Tel: (01473) 830144 Fax: (01473) 832545 E-mail: cap@tex-holdings.co.uk *Holding company*

Tex Industrial Plastics Ltd, Wetherby Road, Derby, DE24 8HL Tel: (01332) 363249 Fax: (01332) 292186 E-mail: sales@tex-plastics.co.uk Purchasing Contact: C Riley - Barnstaple Branch Sales Contact: D. Flowers - Derby Branch *Plastics & injection moulding manufacturers.*

Tex Steel Tubes Ltd, Claydon Business Park, Gipping Road, Great Blakenham, Ipswich, IP6 0NL Tel: (01473) 830030 Fax: (01473) 831664 E-mail: wsctst@texholdings.demon.co.uk Principal Export Areas: Worldwide *Engineering company*

▶ Tex Styles, 41 Northfield Park, Hayes, Middlesex, UB3 4NU Tel: (020) 8384 2036 Fax: (020) 8384 1088

Texane Ltd, Valley Way, Market Harborough, Leicestershire, LE16 7PS Tel: (01858) 462040 Fax: (01858) 410029 E-mail: sales@taxane.com *Manufacturers of solid polyurethane & vulkollan wheels, tyres & components*

Texapin Ltd, 85 Lockfield Avenue, Enfield, Middlesex, EN3 7PY Tel: (020) 8805 2275 Fax: (020) 8443 3389 E-mail: andywells@texapin.co.uk *Laminate distributor*

Texcel Technology plc, Parkside Works, Thames Road, Crayford, Dartford, DA1 4SB Tel: (01322) 621700 Fax: (01322) 557733 E-mail: sales@texceltechnology.com *Electronic designers & manufrs*

Texecom Ltd, 559A Wilbraham Road, Manchester, M21 0AE Tel: 0161-862 9482 Fax: 0161-881 5147 E-mail: enq@texe.com *Security products manufrs*

Texecom Ltd, Slackcote Lane, Delph, Oldham, OL3 5TW Tel: (01457) 821100 Fax: (01457) 871058 *Plastic injection moulders*

Texel, PO Box 19, Todmorden, Lancashire, OL14 8FB Tel: (01706) 815262 Fax: (01706) 815262 *Second hand textile machines*

Texel (UK) Ltd, Unit 9, 21 Wadsworth Road, Greenford, Middlesex, UB6 7LQ Tel: (020) 8998 9605 Fax: (020) 8566 7797 E-mail: texel@onetel.com *Industrial machinery exporters*

Texellent Solutions, Unit 13b Stephenson Court Fraser Road, Priory Business Park, Bedford, MK44 3WJ Tel: (01234) 832540 Fax: (01234) 832541 E-mail: admin@texellent.co.uk *Software suppliers*

Texere Yarns, College Mill, Barkerend Road, Bradford, West Yorkshire, BD1 4AU Tel: (01274) 722191 Fax: (01274) 393500 E-mail: info@texereyarns.co.uk *Yarn products (mail order & internet based) suppliers*

Texicare Ltd, Unit 6, Lansil Industrial Estate, Caton Road, Lancaster, LA1 3PQ Tel: (01524) 39666 Fax: (01524) 841963 E-mail: stevenh@texicare.co.uk *Workwear & laundry services*

Texicoat Surface Preparation & Treatment Ltd, Derrydown Lane, St. Mary Bourne, Andover, Hampshire, SP11 6BS Tel: (01264) 738800 *Laser cutting services*

Texkimp Ltd, Manchester Road, Northwich, Cheshire, CW9 7NN Tel: (01606) 40345 Fax: (01606) 40366 E-mail: info@texkimp.co.uk *Creels for unwinding manufrs*

▶ Texol Technical Solutions plc, Myrekirk Road, West Gourdie Industrial Estate, Dundee, DD2 4SX Tel: (01382) 618400 Fax: (01382) 400573 E-mail: info@texol.co.uk *Gas Generator Products: Nitrogen, Hydrogen ZeroAir, DryAir*

Texon International Ltd, 16A Firtree Lane, Groby, Leicester, LE6 0FH Tel: (0870) 2255845 Fax: (0870) 225443 E-mail: enquiries@texon.com *Footwear material manufacturers & distributors*

Texon Nonwoven Ltd, Skelton Industrial Estate, Skelton-in-Cleveland, Saltburn-by-the-Sea, Cleveland, TS12 2LH Tel: (01287) 650551 Fax: (01287) 650788 E-mail: enquiries@texon.com *Footwear insoles & cleaning cloth fabrics*

▶ text2insure, 17th Floor, 30 St Mary Axe, London, EC3A 8BF Tel: (020) 7150 9995 E-mail: linkmaster@text2insure.co.uk

Textile Bonding Ltd, Textile Bonding Limited, Midland Road, Higham Ferrers, Rushden, Northamptonshire, NN10 8ER Tel: (01933) 410100 Fax: (01933) 410200 E-mail: sales@textilebonding.co.uk *Manufacturers of automotive interior trim*

▶ Textile Innovations Ltd, 14 Swan Court, Paradise Street, Oxford, OX1 1JB Tel: (01865) 201108 Fax: (01865) 201108 E-mail: mtemirov@yandex.ru *Distributors of merino wool, wool tops, knitting yarns, acrylic tow.*

Textile Services Association Ltd, 7 Churchill Court, 58 Station Road, North Harrow, Harrow, Middlesex, HA2 7SA Tel: (020) 8863 7755 Fax: (020) 8861 2115 E-mail: info@tsa-uk.org *Laundry, dry cleaning & textiles*

Textile Team Ltd, Textile House, Cline Road, London, N11 2LX Tel: (020) 8361 0111 Fax: (020) 8361 7531 *Clothing & textile manufrs*

Textino Cleaning Materials, Hulme Hall Lane, Manchester, M40 8YD Tel: 0161-223 0647 Fax: 0161-205 8401 E-mail: manchester.090@depot.co.uk *Janitorial wholesalers*

▶ Text-Messaging 4 Business, 6 Station Road, London, NW4 4PZ Tel: (0870) 7606836 Fax: (0870) 7606836 E-mail: fambizzari@yahoo.co.uk *A web-based service that provides text-messaging facilities with global reach for businesses around the world.*

Textone International Ltd, Atlas Works, Sedburgh Road, Halifax, West Yorkshire, HX3 9HB Tel: (01422) 320234 Fax: (01422) 357341 E-mail: sales@textone.co.uk *Laser & inkjet cartridges suppliers*

Textra Fabric Importers, Sheephouse Barn, Reading Road, East Hendred, Wantage, Oxfordshire, OX12 8HR Tel: (0870) 2414949 Fax: (08702) 414950 E-mail: sales@textra.co.uk *Textile & fabric designers & converters*

TF Automation, Hillam Road, Bradford, West Yorkshire, BD2 1QN Tel: (01274) 308005 Fax: (01274) 394518 E-mail: sales@tfautomation.co.uk *Pneumatic equipment distributors*

▶ TFC The Furniture Co. Ltd, Swingbridge Road, Grantham, Lincolnshire, NG31 7XT Tel: (01476) 577760 Fax: (01476) 575199 *Manufacturing & imports indoor & outdoor furniture*

▶ TFG Subs, Saturn Centre, Wolverhampton, WV4 6JX Tel: 0845 125 9520 *Golf ball manufrs*

▶ TFM, Trafalgar Close, Chandler's Ford, Eastleigh, Hampshire, SO53 4BW Tel: (023) 8026 2288 Fax: (023) 8026 0760 *Sign installation*

▶ TFS Systems Ltd, Station Road Industrial Estate, Station Road, Clowne, Chesterfield, Derbyshire, S43 4AB Tel: (01246) 570870 Fax: (01246) 570704

TG Carbide Precision Ltd, Unit 3 & 5, Hemmells, Basildon, Essex, SS15 6ED Tel: (01268) 546060 Fax: (01268) 546070 E-mail: carbideprecision@tiscali.co.uk *Precision toolmakers manufrs*

TG Engineering Plastics Ltd, Britannia Mills, Stoney Battery, Huddersfield, HD1 4TL Tel: (01484) 655221 Fax: (01484) 644779 E-mail: tom.tgeng@btconnect.com *Injection mouldings manufrs*

TG Silencers, Lower Sherriff Street, Rochdale, Lancashire, OL12 6TG Tel: (01706) 646144 Fax: (01706) 759947 *Exhaust silencer manufrs*

Thacker Barrows Ltd, Conduit Road, Norton Canes, Cannock, Staffordshire, WS11 9TE Tel: (01543) 279056 Fax: (01543) 276079 E-mail: sales@thackerbarrows.co.uk *Metal wheelbarrow manufrs*

Thackraycare Ltd, Unit 1 The Links, Bakewell Road, Orton Southgate, Peterborough, PE2 6ZX Tel: (0800) 590916 Fax: (01733) 392849 *Surgical appliance fitters or dispensers*

Thai Airways International P.L.C., 41 Albemarle Street, London, W1S 4BF Tel: (020) 7491 7953 Fax: (020) 7409 1463 *Internationaql airline*

Thain's Bakery, 341 George Street, Aberdeen, AB25 1EE Tel: (01224) 638698 Fax: (01244) 627102 *Bakery products manufrs*

▶ ThaiStyle(UK) Ladies Apparel, 23 Fleet Street, Torquay, TQ1 1DB Tel: (0845) 6440241 Fax: (0845) 2269949 E-mail: jim@thaistyle.co.uk *Clothing manufrs*

Thales Avionics Ltd, 88 Bushey Road, London, SW20 0JW Tel: (020) 8946 8011 Fax: (020) 8946 3014 *Aircraft management systems*

Thales Computers, Cornwell Business Park, 31 Salthouse Road, Brackmills Industrial Estate, Northampton, NN4 7EX Tel: (01604) 700221 Fax: (01604) 700112 E-mail: sales@thalescomputers.co.uk *Supplies*

continued

computer software & hardware mainly for defence purposes

Thales E Transactions Ltd, Unit 3-6 Milford Trading Estate, Blakey Road, Salisbury, SP1 2UD Tel: (01722) 332255 Fax: (01722) 322464 E-mail: sales@thales-e-transactions.com *Eftpos terminal manufrs*

Thales Land & Joint Systems, Newton Road, Crawley, West Sussex, RH10 9TS Tel: (01293) 518855 Fax: (01293) 446340 E-mail: jon.bye@uk.thalesgroup.com *Suppliers of air traffic control software*

Thales Optics, Glascoed Road, St. Asaph, Clwyd, LL17 0LL Tel: (01745) 588000 Fax: (01745) 584258 E-mail: alan.jenson@thales.co.uk *Optical parts manufrs*

▶ Thales Optronics, 1 Linthouse Road, Glasgow, G51 4BZ Tel: 0141-440 4000 Fax: 0141-440 4001 E-mail: sales@optronics.co.uk

Thales Optronics, 1 Linthouse Road, Glasgow, G51 4BZ Tel: 0141-440 4000 Fax: 0141-440 4001 E-mail: sales@optronics.co.uk Principal Export Areas: Worldwide *Opto-electronic components*

Thales Training & Simulation, Gatwick Road, Crawley, West Sussex, RH10 9RL Tel: (01293) 562822 Fax: (01293) 563366 Principal Export Areas: Worldwide *Training simulator suppliers*

Thales UK Ltd, Manor Royal, Crawley, West Sussex, RH10 9PY Tel: (01293) 528787 Fax: (01293) 542818 E-mail: admin@thales-defence.co.uk *Defence electronics manufrs*

Thales Underwater Systems Ltd, Dolphin House, Ashurst Drive, Stockport, Cheshire, SK3 0XB Tel: 0161-491 4001 Fax: 0161-491 1796 E-mail: info@thales-is.com *Control, business & information system company* Also at: Great Yarmouth

Thales Underwater Systems, Ocean House, Throop Road, Templecombe, Somerset, BA8 0DH Tel: (01963) 370551 Fax: (01963) 372200 E-mail: sales@tms-ltd.com *Detector & sonar equipment manufrs*

Thama Holdings Ltd, Sharrocks Street, Wolverhampton, WV1 3RP Tel: (01902) 457575 Fax: (01902) 457797 *Electric heaters manufrs*

Thame Engineering Co. Ltd, Field End, Thame Road, Long Crendon, Aylesbury, Buckinghamshire, HP18 9EJ Tel: (01844) 208050 Fax: (01844) 201699 E-mail: sales@thame-eng.com *Work holding manufrs*

Thame Farmers Auction Mart Ltd, The Cattle Market, North Street, Thame, Oxfordshire, OX9 3FP Tel: (01844) 217437 Fax: (01844) 261765 E-mail: jonquil@thame-market.co.uk *Cattle auctioneers*

Thames Accounting Centre, Systems House, Desborough Business Park, High Wycombe, Buckinghamshire, HP12 3BG Tel: (01494) 451752 Fax: (01494) 464403 E-mail: alex@thames.uk.com *Copy bureau*

Thames Card Technology Ltd, Thames House, Arterial Road, Rayleigh, Essex, SS6 7UQ Tel: (01268) 775555 Fax: (01268) 777660 E-mail: info@thamesgroup.co.uk *Plastic Card Manufacturers*Plastic Card Personaliser*Plastic Card Distributer*Smart Card Manufacturer*Identity Card Manufacturer*Telephone Card Manufacturer*Loyalty Card Manufacturer*Credit Card Manufacturer*Lenticular Card manufacturer*Charge Card Manufacturer *Credit, membership & smart card manufrs*

▶ Thames Ceilings Ltd, Greensands, Reading Road, East Hendred, Wantage, Oxfordshire, OX12 8JE Tel: (01235) 443690 Fax: (01235) 443699 E-mail: sales@thamesceilings.ltd.uk *Ceiling contractors*

Thames Cleaning Co. Ltd, 14 Hatherley Road, Sidcup, Kent, DA14 4BG Tel: (020) 8302 6633 Fax: (020) 8300 7779 E-mail: jenny.mclaren@thamescleaning.co.uk *Office cleaning & support services providers*

Thames Contract, Longreach Road, Barking, Essex, IG11 0JR Tel: (020) 8591 1555 Fax: (020) 8591 8889 E-mail: thames.c@virgin.net *Curtain walling & glazing contractors*

Thames Crane Services Ltd, 327 Heyford Park, Camp Road, Upper Heyford, Bicester, Oxfordshire, OX25 5HA Tel: (01869) 232001 Fax: (01869) 232004 *Crane & access hire*

Thames Cryogenics Ltd, Gooch Drive, Southmead Industrial Park, Didcot, Oxfordshire, OX11 7PR Tel: (01235) 815777 Fax: (01235) 815333 E-mail: sales@thamescryogenics.com *Cryogenic controls & pipe work manufrs*

▶ Thames Electronics, 244 Battersea Bridge Road, London, SW11 3AA Tel: (020) 7924 5536 Fax: 020 7924 5537 E-mail: service@thameselectronics.co.uk

▶ Thames Fishing Tackle Ltd, Unit 11 Bartleet Road, Redditch, Worcestershire, B98 0DQ Tel: (01527) 501633 Fax: (01527) 501744 *Fishing tackle suppliers*

Thames Fixings & Fasteners Ltd, Collett, Southmead Industrial Estate, Didcot, Oxfordshire, OX11 7TA Tel: (01235) 511711 Fax: (01235) 511710 E-mail: enquires@thamesfixings.co.uk *Fixings & ironmongery distributors*

Thames Forge Ltd, Fullers Yard, Sheephouse Road, Maidenhead, Berkshire, SL6 8HA Tel: (01628) 622423 Fax: (01628) 622423 *Ironwork, gates & balustrade manufrs*

▶ Thames Gas Maintenance, 56 Gloucester Road, London, SW7 4UB Tel: (020) 8870 8500

▶ Thames Group, Green Lane, Burghfield Bridge, Burghfield, Reading, RG30 3XN Tel: 0118-958 4499 Fax: 0118-959 6442 E-mail: sales@thamesgrp.com *Fibre glass moulding services*

Thames Hose & Couplings Ltd, Units 1-2 Canal Industrial Park, Canal Road, Gravesend, Kent, DA12 2PA Tel: (01474) 356485 Fax: (01474) 320392 E-mail: thc.sales@btconnect.com *Hose distributors* Also at: Dartford

Thames & Hudson, Esavian House, 181a High Holborn, London, WC1V 7QX Tel: (020) 7845 5000 Fax: (020) 7845 5050 E-mail: sales@thameshudson.co.uk *Book publishers*

Thames Information Systems Ltd, 11b Greenwich South Street, London, SE10 8NJ Tel: (020) 8858 6651 Fax: (020) 8305 1090 E-mail: info@tisl.co.uk *Computer consultants*

Thames Laboratories, The Granary, Brook Farm, Thrapston Road, Ellington, Huntingdon, Cambridgeshire, PE29 0AE Tel: (01480) 891800 Fax: (01480) 890008 E-mail: info@thameslabs.co.uk *Specialist consultancy*

Thames Loose Leaf, 289 Kiln Road, Benfleet, Essex, SS7 1QS Tel: (01702) 551155 Fax: (01702) 559068 E-mail: sales@thameslooseleaf.co.uk *Encapsulation services/plastic binder manufrs*

Thames Lubricants Ltd, Garner Street, Stoke-on-Trent, ST4 7DE Tel: (01782) 844388 Fax: (01782) 848437 E-mail: sales@thameslubricants.co.uk *High quality lubricating oil & grease producers*

Thames Manufacturing Co. Ltd, 29 Mansfields, Writtle, Chelmsford, CM1 3NH Tel: (01245) 422062 Fax: (01245) 422062 *Clocks & security guard patrol monitoring systems*

Thames Materials Ltd, Unit 324, Trumpers Way, Hanwell, London, W7 2QA Tel: (020) 8840 7233 Fax: (020) 8840 7978 E-mail: info@thamesmaterials.com *Demolition recycled & primary aggregates*

Thames Offset Printers, Unit 14 Epsom Business Park, Kiln Lane, Epsom, Surrey, KT17 1JF Tel: (01372) 745758 Fax: (01372) 741942 E-mail: thamesoff@aol.com *Lithographic printers*

▶ Thames Restek Ltd, 8 16 Ministry Wharf, Wycombe Road, Saunderton, High Wycombe, Buckinghamshire, HP14 4HW Tel: (01494) 563377 Fax: (01494) 564990 E-mail: sales@thamesrestek.co.uk

Thames Side Mayward Ltd, Unit 17 Stadium Way, Tilehurst, Reading, RG30 6BX Tel: 0118-945 8200 Fax: 0118-945 8225 E-mail: sales@thames-side.co.uk *Load cell manufrs*

Thames Side-Maywood Ltd, 2 Collumbers Drive, Summet Avenue, Southwood, Farnborough, Hampshire, GU14 0NZ Tel: (01252) 555811 Fax: (01252) 375394 E-mail: sales@thames-side.co.uk *Manufacturers of "industrial weighing load cells, force transducers and "Crash Wall" load cells"*

Thames Steel & Equipment Ltd, Turkey Cottage, Curload, Stoke St. Gregory, Taunton, Somerset, TA3 6JE Tel: (01823) 698881 Fax: (01823) 698988 E-mail: douglas.billington@lineone.net *Sell security fencing*

Thames Stockholders Ltd, Unit 5w Redburn Industrial Estate, Woodall Road, Enfield, Middlesex, EN3 4LQ Tel: (020) 8805 3282 Fax: (020) 8804 8164 *Non-ferrous metal stockholders*

Thames Valley Catering Equipment, 11 Strawberry Hill, Bloxham, Banbury, Oxfordshire, OX15 4NW Tel: 01295 677058 E-mail: simonwratten@btinternet.com *Industrial catering equipment services*

Thames Valley Chamber Of Commerce, 121 Clare Road, Stanwell, Staines, Middlesex, TW19 7QP Tel: (01784) 242478 Fax: (01784) 242472 E-mail: heathrow@thamesvalleychamber.co.uk *Chamber of commerce & industry*

Thames Valley Chamber Of Commerce & Industry, Foyer Building, Crest Road, High Wycombe, Buckinghamshire, HP11 1UD Tel: (01494) 445909 Fax: (01494) 440156 E-mail: wycombe@thamesvalleychamber.co.uk *Chamber of commerce & industry*

Thames Valley Chamber Of Commerce & Industry Ltd, 467 Malton Avenue, Slough, SL1 4QU Tel: (01753) 870500 Fax: (01753) 870515 E-mail: sales@thamesvalleychamber.co.uk *Chamber of commerce & industry*

Thames Valley Chamber Of Commerce & Industry Ltd, 467 Malton Avenue, Slough, SL1 4QU Tel: (01753) 870500 Fax: (01753) 870515 E-mail: sales@thamesvalleychamber.co.uk *Chamber of commerce & industry*

Thames Valley Chamber Of Commerce & Industry Ltd, 467 Malton Avenue, Slough, SL1 4QU Tel: (01753) 870500 Fax: (01753) 870515 E-mail: sales@thamesvalleychamber.co.uk *Commercial & office training services*

Thames Valley Cleaning Contractors (Reading) Ltd, Unit 5A, Bridgewater Close, Reading, RG30 1JT Tel: 0118-959 9141 Fax: 0118-953 3838 E-mail: thamesvalleyclng@aol.com *Office cleaning contractors*

Thames Valley Commercial, 6 Lupton Road, Thame, Oxfordshire, OX9 3SE Tel: (01844) 358200 Fax: (01844) 358201 *Property maintenance*

Thames Valley Copiers, 53 Besselsleigh Road, Wootton, Abingdon, Oxfordshire, OX13 6DX Tel: (01865) 736606 Fax: (01865) 736607 *Photocopiers suppliers & distributors*

Thames Valley Electrical Control Systems Ltd, Cannington Farm, Cannington Lane, Uplyme, Lyme Regis, Dorset, DT7 3SW Tel: (01297) 443172 Fax: (01297) 445005 E-mail: tvecs@aol.com *Electrical engineering & contractors*

▶ Thames Valley Maintenance Oxford Ltd, Unit 1 Thrupp Lane, Radley, Abingdon, Oxfordshire, OX14 3NS Tel: (01235) 529999 Fax: (01235) 537299

Thames Valley Pneumatic Ltd, Delta Way, Egham, Surrey, TW20 8RX Tel: (01784) 434999 Fax: (01784) 434499 E-mail: tvpltd@hotmail.com *Pneumatic tool repair services*

Thames Valley Pressings Ltd, Transteel Layton Road, Brentford, Middlesex, TW8 0QJ Tel: (020) 8847 3636 Fax: (020) 8758 1236 E-mail: info@tvpressings.co.uk *Metal pressings, toolmaking, welding, plating specialists*

▶ Thames Valley Refrigeration, 24 Victoria Road, Tilehurst, Reading, RG31 5AD Tel: 0118-942 8505 Fax: 0118-376 9110 E-mail: j@thamesvalleyrefrigeration.com *Refrigeration services, contractors, engineers & commercial sales*

Thames Valley Saw Services Ltd, Gravel Lane, Drayton, Abingdon, Oxfordshire, OX14 4HY Tel: (01235) 550088 Fax: (01235) 553150 E-mail: sales@tvss.co.uk *Saw maintenance & saw distributors*

Thames Valley Temperature Control, Unit 6 Harriar Park, South Mead Industrial Estate, Didcot, Oxham, Oxfordshire, OX11 7PL Tel: (01235) 811922 Fax: (01235) 812600 *Air-conditioning services & installers*

Thames Valley Textiles, Oddington Grange, Weston-on-the-Green, Bicester, Oxfordshire, OX25 3QW Tel: (01865) 331009 Fax: (01865) 331721 E-mail: info@tvt1.co.uk *Manufacturers of Banners*

Thames Valley Tiles, Bagshot Road, Bracknell, Berkshire, RG12 9SE Tel: (01344) 420585 Fax: (01344) 420585 *Ceramic wall & floor tile sales*

Thames Valley University, St Mary's Road, London, W5 5RF Tel: (020) 8231 2221 Fax: (020) 8231 2360 E-mail: learning.advice@tvu.ac.uk *Thames Valley University's London School of Tourism, Hospitality and Leisure has always had an international reputation for its courses and was the first University in the country to receive the highest grades for its hospitality and culinary arts courses from the Training Skills Council and the Quality Assurance Agency. The Academy of Culinary Arts, The Association Culinaire Francaise, The Craft Guild of Chefs and The Master Chefs of Great Britain all recognise the School of Tourism, Hospitality and Leisure as a centre of excellence, quality and innovation, and it recently achieved COVE status (a Centre of Vocational Excellence) together with many other accolades.*

Thames Valley Visuals, Providence House, Forest Road, Binfield, Bracknell, Berkshire, RG42 4HP Tel: (01344) 867166 Fax: (01344) 868006 E-mail: enquiries@thamesvalleyvisuals.co/uk *Sells & installs audio-visual equipment*

Thames Wire Production Ltd, Unit 11A Worton Hall, Worton Road, Isleworth, Middlesex, TW7 6ER Tel: (020) 8560 4936 Fax: (020) 8569 8145 E-mail: thameswire@btconnect.com *Architectural metalworkers*

Thamesdown Bearing Services, 3 Beechcroft Road, Swindon, SN2 7RD Tel: (01793) 724554 Fax: (01793) 724404 E-mail: thamesdown.bearings@wyko.co.uk *Bearing distributors*

Thamesdown Coatings Ltd, Unit 33 Whitehill Industrial Estate, Whitehill Lane, Wootton Bassett, Swindon, SN4 7DB Tel: (01793) 729421 *Powder coatings services*

Thamesdown SDC, Frankland Road, Blagrove, Swindon, SN5 8YU Tel: (01793) 428700 Fax: (01793) 511125 E-mail: sales@tsfltd.co.uk *CD & DVD replication manufrs*

▶ Thameside Freight Services Ltd, Unit A, 124 New Road, Rainham, Essex, RM13 8RS Tel: (01708) 559871

Thameside Gates & Railings, Coopers Close, Staines, Middlesex, TW18 3JY Tel: (01784) 464655 Fax: (01784) 466417 *Gates & railings*

Thameside Lifting Ltd, Europa Park, London Road, Grays, Essex, RM20 4DB Tel: (01375) 392333 Fax: (01375) 366889 *Specialists in Lifting Equipment, Hire & Sales, Testing & Repair.*

Thamesmead Business Services Ltd, 29 Pomeroy Street, London, SE14 5BW Tel: (020) 7639 0348 Fax: (020) 7639 3646 E-mail: info@thamesmeadonline.co.uk *Cleaning & hygiene suppliers*

Thane Dispersions Ltd, Spedding Road, Fenton Industrial Estate, Stoke-on-Trent, ST4 2ST Tel: (01782) 412217 Fax: (01782) 744769 E-mail: enquiries@thane.uk.com *Colours for plastics manufrs*

Thanet Coatings Ltd, Unit 4 Patricia Way, Pysons Road Industrial Estate, Broadstairs, Kent, CT10 2LF Tel: (01843) 861861 Fax: (01843) 866366 *Screen printing suppliers*

Thanet Disco Centre, 16 North Foreland Road, Broadstairs, Kent, CT10 3NN Tel: (01843) 864001 Fax: (01843) 865666 E-mail: julie.jackson10@btiternet.com *Sound & lighting sales & installation services*

Thanet Plastics, 1 Wilton Road, Haine Industrial Park, Ramsgate, Kent, CT12 5HG Tel: (01843) 590950 Fax: (01843) 590948 E-mail: sales@thanetplastics.co.uk *Based in Ramsgate Kent, covering the whole of the UK, we are a manufacturer of PVC, paper over board and polypro Ring binders, pockets, wallets, identity wallets, book jackets, diary covers promotional items, sleeves, ticket holders, document wallets, clipboards, general stationery holders, and packaging. We also offer a tampo printing, hot foil blocking, screen printing service and vac forming. In addition we offer a full design and sampling service to custom produce to the exact customer requirements.*

Thanet-Ware Kent Ltd, Ellington Works, Princes Road, Ramsgate, Kent, CT11 7RZ Tel: (01843) 591076 Fax: (01843) 586198 *Architectural & general metalworkers*

Tharsus Vision Ltd, Unit 8/9, Spencer Road, Blyth, Northumberland, NE24 5TG Tel: (01670) 367030 Fax: (01670) 352012 E-mail: sales@directmessage.co.uk *Precision sheet metalworkers*

Tharsus Welding & Sheet Metal Co. Ltd, Glen Street, Hebburn, Tyne & Wear, NE31 1NG Tel: 0191-483 2816 Fax: 0191-428 0063 E-mail: sales@tharsus.co.uk Principal Export Areas: Worldwide *Sheet metalwork contractors*

▶ That Pc, 4 Wolseley Close, Plymouth, PL2 3BY Tel: (01752) 558000 Fax: (01752) 558008

Thatcham Angling Centre, 4 Sagecroft Road, Thatcham, Berkshire, RG18 3DZ Tel: (01635) 871450 *Fishing & angling equipment suppliers*

▶ That's My Baby, 14-15 Orbit Centre, Ashworth Road, Bridgemead, Swindon, SN5 7YG Tel: (01793) 432111 Fax: (01793) 436724 E-mail: info@thatsmybaby.biz *Nursery goods*

That'Z Entertainment, Market Place, Romford, RM1 3AB Tel: (01708) 744338 Fax: (01708) 744338 *Computer software & games*

Thaumaturgy UK Ltd, PO Box 37, Nelson, Lancashire, BB9 4BE Tel: (01254) 680223 Fax: (01254) 682378 E-mail: thaumaturgy@dial.pipex.com Chemical manufrs Also at: Sutton Coldfield

▶ theACCOUNTANCYjob.com, PO Box 2448, Slough, SL1 1ZB Tel: 0870 8701193 Fax: 0870 8701194 E-mail: coz.dauncey@theACCOUNTANCYjob.com TheACCOUNTANCYjob.com is a specialist job board for the accountancy industry, part of The TipTopJob Group. The site deals with varied accountancy related roles, from, trainee positions to part and newly qualified accountants to professional accountant jobs. Job seekers can add a CV to the database, set up email alerts and search and apply for jobs for free online. To find your next accountancy job or to use the site to advertise your vacancies or to find a new employee, visit the website www.theACCOUNTANCYjob.com.

▶ Andy Theaker Ltd, 49 Wordsworth Road, Stockport, Cheshire, SK5 6JH Tel: 0161-221 1296 Fax: 0161-221 1178

Theaker recycling Ltd, Heanor Road, Loscoe, Heanor, Derbyshire, DE75 7JT Tel: (01773) 710071 Fax: (01773) 710077 E-mail: office@theakerrecycling.co.uk Pallet suppliers & wood recycling services

Theale Fireplaces Reading Ltd, Bath Road, Sulhamstead, Reading, RG7 5HJ Tel: 0118-930 2232 Fax: 0118-932 3344 E-mail: sales@thealefireplaces.com Fire places manufrs

Theatrical Pyrotechnics Ltd, The Loop, Manston Airport, Manston, Ramsgate, Kent, CT12 5DE Tel: (01843) 823545 Fax: (01843) 822655 E-mail: pyrotec@manstona.fsnet.co.uk Pyrotechnic manufrs

▶ The-Big-Move.Com, 60 Wyken Way, Wyken, Coventry, CV2 3HG Tel: (0700) 5102727 E-mail: info@the-big-move.com For FREE "Quote" Give us a call now or visit us on our website and fill out the online quote page and we will reply within 24hrs with your free quote.. Phone lines open from 8am-8pm Monday to Friday

Thebigword, 4-12 Morton Street, Leamington Spa, Warwickshire, CV32 5SY Tel: (0870) 7488060 Fax: (0870) 7488061 E-mail: sales@thebigword.com Translators and dtp

▶ theCATERINGjob.com, PO Box 2448, Slough, SL1 1ZB Tel: 0870 8701193 Fax: 0870 8701194 E-mail: coz.dauncey@thecateringjob.com TheCATERINGjob.com is a specialist job board for the catering and hospitality industry, part of The TipTopJob Group. The site deals with varied catering and hospitality related roles, from, chefs, kitchen staff and waiters to event managers and corporate event organisers. Job seekers can add a CV to the database, set up email alerts and search and apply for jobs for free online. To find your next catering or hospitality job or to use the site to advertise your vacancies or to find a new employee, visit the website www.theCATERINGjob.com.

Thecomputerservice.Co.Uk, Unit 2f Carmilles Business Centre, Bradford Road, Birstall, Batley, West Yorkshire, WF17 9JX Tel: (01924) 471949 Fax: (01924) 471949 E-mail: info@thecomputerservice.co.uk Computer repairs services

▶ theCONSTRUCTIONjob.com, PO Box 2448, Slough, SL1 1ZB Tel: 0870 8701193 Fax: 0870 8701194 E-mail: coz.dauncey@theconstructionjob.com *TheCONSTRUCTIONjob.com is a specialist job board for the construction industry, part of The TipTopJob Group. The site deals with varied construction related roles. Job seekers can add a CV to the database, set up email alerts and search and apply for jobs for free online. To find your next construction job or to use the site to advertise your vacancies or to find a new employee, visit the website www.theCONSTRUCTIONjob.com.*

thecrimpcompany.com, 145 Edge Lane, Liverpool, L7 2PG Tel: 0870 8506136 E-mail: sales@thecrimpcompany.com thecrimpcompany.com are on-line suppliers of Electricians tools, cable accessories, cable management, crimp connectors and crimp tooling. *We stock a FULL range of high quality Crimp Terminals suitable for use with our Crimp Tools to ensure a quality Crimp result for the professional, DIY and Industry.*Our huge stocks include Electricians Tools, Cable Connectors, Cable Ties, Cable Management, Crimp Terminals, Crimp Tools, Cable Glands, Cable Joints and Earthing Products and Heatshrink Products.*

▶ theGRADUATEjob.com, PO Box 2448, Slough, SL1 1ZB Tel: 0870 8701193 Fax: 0870 8701194 E-mail: coz.dauncey@theGRADUATEjob.com *TheGRADUATEjob.com is a specialist job board for all graduate related vacancies, part of The TipTopJob Group. The site deals with graduate jobs in all types of companies and includes graduate schemes and programmes as well as standard trainee jobs. Job seekers can add a CV to the database, set up email alerts and search and apply for jobs for free online. To find next job as a graduate or to use the site to advertise your vacancies or to find a new employee, visit the website www.theGRADUATEjob.com.*

Thelcastle Ltd, Unit 14, Newhaven Business Park, Barton Lane, Eccles, Manchester, M30 0HH Tel: 0161 7880345 Pneumatic conveying equipment manufrs

Thelkane Industrial Chimneys Ltd, Copse Road, Fleetwood, Lancashire, FY7 6RP Tel: (01253) 875121 Fax: (01253) 772106 Chimney manufrs

▶ Thelma's, 47 Vyse Street, Hockley, Birmingham, B18 6HF Tel: 0121-523 9020 Waxing for jewellery manufrs

▶ theLogic Limited IT Services, 65 Sycamore Gardens, Kirkmuirhill, Lanark, ML11 9SX Tel: (0789) 1997294 E-mail: info@thelogic.co.uk theLogic Limited IT Services offers pc and network support for small businesses on fixed prices.

▶ Thelwell Consultants Ltd, The Innovation Centre, Brunswick Street, Nelson, Lancashire, BB9 0PQ Tel: (01282) 877097 Fax: (01282) 877098 E-mail: info@tcreative.co.uk Graphic Design, corporate identity, literature design, flash and HTML websites, exhibition design and marketing

▶ The Theme Team Production Music, The Theme Team, 1 Leigh Rd, Gravesend, Kent, DA11 7PS Tel: (01474) 320460 E-mail: info@thethemeteam.biz The Theme Team*Composers for Film, Television and Interactive media*

Theme Traders Ltd, The Stadium, Oaklands Road, London, NW2 6DL Tel: (020) 8452 8518 Fax: (020) 8450 7322 E-mail: mailroom@themetraders.com Events organisers

▶ Thenewyou Net Ltd, Butterflies 19 Alston Mews, Thatcham, Berkshire, RG19 3XF Tel: (01635) 862239 We are a leading UK distributor for Pregnancy Tests, Ovulation Tests and Fetal Dopplers.*Fetal Dopplers are available to Rent or Buy.

▶ Theocrest Ltd, Cavans Way, Binley Industrial Estate, Binley Industrial Estate, Coventry, CV3 2SF Tel: (024) 7644 5758 Fax: (024) 7645 6438 E-mail: brian@theocrest.co.uk Manufacturers of control panels & equipment

▶ Theocus, Mitton Manor Garage, Bredon Road, Tewkesbury, Gloucestershire, GL20 5DA Tel: (01684) 298400 Fax: (01684) 298400 E-mail: Theocus@hotmail.co.uk Providing a high quality French Polishing and Upholstery service in the Gloucestershire area using both modern and traditional methods in a choice of fabric. Also able to provide services for boat and caravan upholstery.

▶ Theoffice4u, Crusader House, 145-157 St. John Street, St. John, London, EC1V 4PY Tel: (020) 7553 9725 E-mail: theteam@theoffice4u.co.uk

Theoplastic Ltd, 3 & 45 Barking Industrial Park, Alfreds Way, Barking, Essex, IG11 0TJ Tel: (020) 8591 5534 Fax: (020) 8591 9022 E-mail: theoplastic@aol.com Plastic fabricators

▶ thepass.org, 55 Roman Road, Glasgow, G61 2SG Tel: 0141 5700289 Fax: 0141 5700283 E-mail: postmaster@thepass.org Driving test and road safety information for new and learned drivers in the United Kingdom.

thepowerStore.co.uk, Unit 22, 70 Queen Elizabeth Avenue, Hillington Business Park, Hillington, Glasgow, G52 4NQ Tel: (0870) 8705522 Fax: (0870) 8705525 E-mail: sales@thepowerstore.co.uk Electronics distribution services

Theraposture Ltd, Unit 11 Warminster Business Park, Furnax Lane, Warminster, Wiltshire, BA12 8PE Tel: (01985) 847788 Fax: (01985) 847700 Bed & mattress manufrs

Therapy Equipment Ltd, 1 Cranborne Industrial Estate, Cranborne Road, Potters Bar, Hertfordshire, EN6 3JN Tel: (01707) 652270 Fax: (01707) 652622 E-mail: sales@therapyequipment.co.uk Manufacturer of healthcare equipment

▶ Therapy Resources, 16 Canal Warf, Chesterfield, Derbyshire, S41 7RY Tel: 01246 551421

Therm Tech Ltd, Unit 4a Kayley Industrial Estate, Richmond Street, Ashton-under-Lyne, Lancashire, OL7 0AU Tel: 0161 339 3049 Fax: 0161 343 3305 E-mail: thermtech@msn.com Therm Tech Ltd are based in Ashton Under Lyne, Lancashire. We provide state-of-the-art energy saving solutions for companies throughout the UK. From heat recovery and recycling systems to industrial superheaters, activated carbon technology and bespoke fabrications we will help your business to streamline energy consumption and cost. We are a compact business that combines the latest technology with a timeless dedication to quality.

Therm Tech Engineering Ltd, PO Box 30, Stockport, Cheshire, SK12 1BD Tel: (01625) 878831 Fax: (01625) 878832 E-mail: economisers@thermtech.fsnet.co.uk Boiler economiser systems suppliers

Therm Tempered Ltd, Unit E1 E2 Coedcae Lane Industrial Estate, Coedcae Lane, Pontyclun, Mid Glamorgan, CF72 9HG Tel: (01443) 228122 Fax: (01443) 233500 E-mail: sale@therm.co.uk Glass suppliers

Thermac Hire, Astra Park, Parkside Lane, Leeds, LS11 5SZ Tel: 0113-270 9555 Fax: 0113-270 9666 E-mail: sales@thermac.com Hire & Sales & Servicing of Decontamination Units, Negative Pressure Units, Vacuums for Hazardous Waste, Injection Machines. Consumable Sales - incorporating tools, signs, tapes, chemicals, asbestos bags, polythene, coveralls & full range of PPE. Respiratory Sales, Testing & Servicing of a full range of Powered, Half Face and Disposable Masks. 79. DOP & Electrical testing of NPU's, Fume Cabinets etc.

Thermaco Ltd, Unit 5, Spring Lane North, Malvern, Worcestershire, WR14 1BU Tel: (01684) 566163 Fax: (01684) 892356 E-mail: sales@thermaco.co.uk Gas & electrical control distributors, agents

Thermacom Ltd, Green Lane, Burghfield Bridge, Reading, RG30 3XN Tel: 0118-950 0606 Fax: 0118-956 0039 E-mail: sales@thermagroup.com Principal Export Areas: Worldwide Thermagroup are UK and International suppliers of compressors. We specialise in both refrigerated and remanufactured compressors. Also at: Southampton

Thermafabrications Ltd, New Craven Gate, Leeds, LS11 5NF Tel: 0113-245 7510 Fax: 0113-244 9430 Ductwork engineers & fabricators

Thermaglow Ltd, North Market Road, Winterton-On-Sea, Great Yarmouth, Norfolk, NR29 4BH Tel: (01493) 393555 Fax: (01493) 393860 E-mail: sales@thermaglow.co.uk Domestic/industrial electric heating elements

Thermal Designs UK Ltd, Broadway, Market Lavington, Devizes, Wiltshire, SN10 5RQ Tel: (01380) 816079 Fax: (01380) 813394 E-mail: sales@tdiuk.com Manufacturers & marketers of industrial passive fireproofing materials

Thermal Detection Ltd, Unit 6 Orde Wingate Way, Stockton-on-Tees, Cleveland, TS19 0GA Tel: (01642) 602878 Fax: (01642) 618307 E-mail: tdl@thermal-detection.com Principal Export Areas: Worldwide Manufacturers of resistance temperature detectors

Thermal Dynamics Ltd, Unit 2 Transfer Bridge Indust Estate, County Road, Swindon, SN1 2EG Tel: (01793) 431539 Fax: (01793) 420667 Manufacturers of frost heave prevention equipment

Thermal Energy Construction Ltd, Trent Lane, Castle Donington, Derby, DE74 2NP Tel: (01332) 810999 Fax: (01332) 855175 E-mail: info@thermalenergy.co.uk Cooling tower inspection service

Thermal Exchange Ltd, 15 Chiswick Road, Leicester, LE2 7SX Tel: 0116-254 6652 Fax: 0116-255 9176 E-mail: sales@thermalexchange.co.uk Principal Export Areas: Worldwide Established in 1982, Thermal Exchange Ltd is an International supplier of closed loop process cooling systems for industrial, medical and scientific applications. Design & Build: ISO9001, CAD/CAM facility incorporating fabrication, powder coating, assembly and final test. Products: refrigerated chillers, airblast water coolers, circulators, oil cooling, coolant chilling, liquid/liquid heat exchangers, air/liquid exchangers, heat sinks, Peltier units, OEM build. Features: 1-1000kW, low noise/vibration, fault diagnostics, +/- 0.1C control, non-ferrous circuits, deionised compatible, 50/60Hz operation, RS232 output, 19" rack mount. Applications: welding equipment, induction, mould cooling, lasers, X-ray, reaction vessels, electron microscopes, MRI, semiconductor, analytical instruments

▶ Thermal Hazard Technology, 1 North House, Bond Avenue, Bletchley, Milton Keynes, MK1 1SW Tel: (01908) 646800 Fax: (01908) 645209 E-mail: info@thermalhazardtechnology.com Thermal safety of chemicals, batteries & calorimeter services

Thermal Hire Ltd, Unit A Bedewell Industrial Park, Hebburn, Tyne & Wear, NE31 2HQ Tel: 0191-428 0423 Fax: 0191-428 0061 E-mail: enquiries@thermalhire.com Heat treatment services

▶ Thermal Imaging & NICEIC Electrical Inspections, Riverside Mansions Flat 112, Milk Yard, London, E1W 3TA Tel: (0797) 1268030 Fax: (020) 7480 6578 Thermal imaging, power analysis & harmonic analysis surveys. NICEIC electrical inspection & reporting, part P government inspections

▶ Thermal Innovations Ltd, 8 Douglas Road, Leslie, Fife, KY6 3JZ Tel: (01592) 562415 Fax: (01592) 562415 E-mail: mclement@thermal-innovations.co.uk Thermographic surveys nationwide. Electrical,mechanical,insulation,and water ingress specialists

Thermal Memory, The Deanery, 6 Dodd Croft, Rochdale, Lancashire, OL16 4QX Tel: (01706) 522611 E-mail: enquiries@shrinkfit.co.uk Military, Aerospace spiralwrap AS41088 PAN6480 efwarp cable protection accessories heat-shrinkable tubing and heat shrink sleeving for defence, ms23053, MIL-DTL-23053, VG95343, DEF-STAN, UL, CSA millitary, naval marine, PTFE-Teflon PANAVIA 6627 and PAN6628 conduit efwarp accessories with High Voltage cable and wire 3kv to 50kv UL AWM3239 XLHDPE 105 degrees, cenagrade anti-traking specialty wires.

Thermal Solutions, 3 Orchard Avenue, Poole, Dorset, BH14 8AH Tel: (01202) 715792 Fax: (01202) 718134 E-mail: sales@thermalsolutions.co.uk Air conditioning equipment suppliers

Thermal Spray Material Services Ltd, Brook Street Business Centre, Brook Street, Tipton, West Midlands, DY4 9DD Tel: 0121-520 0720 Fax: 0121-520 3002 E-mail: thermalsprayuk@aol.com Principal Export Areas: Worldwide Alloy component & metal spraying distributors

Thermal Transfer (Northern) Ltd, Thermal Transfer House, 2 Railway Street, Glossop, Derbyshire, SK13 7AG Tel: (01457) 854341 Fax: (01457) 868357 E-mail: ttglossop@compuserve.co.uk Air conditioning, heating & clean air rooms services Also at: Basingstoke, Birmingham, East Kilbride, Edinburgh, Leeds & Swindon

Thermal Transfer (U K) Ltd, Scottish Enterprise Technology Park, Rankine Avenue, East Kilbride, Glasgow, G75 0QF Tel: (01355) 234567 Fax: (01355) 266466 Heating & ventilation installers & services Also at: Basingstoke, Edinburgh, Manchester & Welling

Thermalair Ltd, 6 Lundy Court, Rougham Industrial Estate, Rougham, Bury St. Edmunds, Suffolk, IP30 9ND Tel: (01359) 271444 Fax: (01359) 271445 E-mail: enquiries@thermalairltd.co.uk HVAC engineers

Thermalec Products Ltd, Kingsley Close, Lee Mill Industrial Estate, Ivybridge, Devon, PL21 9GD Tel: (01752) 313343 Fax: (01752) 313353 E-mail: sales@thermalec.com Principal Export Areas: Worldwide Swimming pool heater manufrs

▶ Thermalfloor Underfloor Heating Systems Ltd, School Road, Tnepher Friartor, Perth, PH2 8DF Tel: (08450) 620400 Fax: (01828) 628130

▶ Thermaltran, Label House, 14 Summerfield Road, Kettering, Northamptonshire, NN15 6EN Tel: (01536) 392900 E-mail: Sales@thermaltran.co.uk Suppliers of direct thermal & thermal transfer self adhesive labels.Labels on reels suitable for datamax, zebra etc. Very competitive prices.

Thermaset Ltd, Apollo, Lichfield Road Industrial Estate, Tamworth, Staffordshire, B79 7TA Tel: (01827) 55777 Fax: (01827) 53713 Powder coating manufrs

▶ Thermashield Insulation Ltd, 30 Cumbernauld Road, Stepps, Glasgow, G33 6EW Tel: 0141-779 4815 Fax: 0141-779 2044

Thermatech Timber Structures Ltd, Bucklers Lane, St. Austell, Cornwall, PL25 3JN Tel: (01726) 71733 Fax: (01726) 71744 Timber manufrs

Thermatic Maintenance Ltd, 3 Sovereign Enterprise Park, King William Street, Salford, M50 3UP Tel: 0161-872 3724 Fax: 0161-848 0516 E-mail: dave.oakley@thermatic.co.uk Heating & ventilation & air conditioning installers Also at: Leeds & Salford

Thermaton Imaging (Thermal Imaging Services), 59 Queens Avenue, Meols, Wirral, Merseyside, CH47 0LS Tel: 0151-632 5192 Fax: 0151-632 5192 E-mail: povall@ic24.net Thermal imaging survice suppliers

Thermatool Europe Ltd, Thermatool House, Crockford Lane, Basingstoke, Hampshire, RG24 8NA Tel: (01256) 335533 Fax: (01256) 467224 E-mail: thermatooleurope@ttool.co.uk High frequency tube welding

Thermax Construction, Unit 3 Dover Court, Dover Road, Latchford, Warrington, WA4 1NW Tel: (01925) 242450 Fax: (01925) 242455 E-mail: malcolmferguson@parflothermax.co.uk Fabrication & installation of service & process pipe work

Thermeon Europe Ltd, Russ Hill Farm, Russ Hill, Charlwood, Horley, Surrey, RH6 0EL Tel: (01293) 864300 E-mail: sales@thermeoneurope.com Car rental software supplier & services

▶ Thermetal Furnaces, 1 Building 38, Thornleigh Trading Estate, Dudley, West Midlands, DY2 8UB Tel: (01384) 214888 Fax: (01384) 214778 Furnace makers

Thermex Ltd, Merse Road, North Moons Moat Industrial Estate, Moons Moat North Industrial Estate, Redditch, Worcestershire, B98 9HL Tel: (01527) 62210 Fax: (01527) 60138 E-mail: enquiry@thermex.co.uk Principal Export Areas: Worldwide Heat exchanger, transfer equipment manufrs

Thermit Welding GB Ltd, 87 Ferry Lane, Rainham, Essex, RM13 9YH Tel: (01708) 522626 Fax: (01708) 553806 Aluminothermic welding equipment manufrs

Thermo Designs Ltd, 64 Duff Street, Edinburgh, EH11 2HW Tel: 0131-313 3131 Fax: 0131-313 2772 Metal work manufrs

Thermo Devices Ltd, Floats Road, Roundthorn Industrial Estate, Manchester, M23 9NF Tel: 0161-286 5100 Fax: 0161-286 5093 E-mail: sales@tdl.endress.com Principal Export Areas: Worldwide Thermocouple manufrs

Thermo Electron Ltd, 5 Ringway Centre, Edison Road, Basingstoke, Hampshire, RG21 6YH Tel: (01256) 817282 Fax: (01256) 817292 E-mail: info@thermols.com Microbiological laboratory equipment distributors

Thermo Electron, Units 12-16, Sedgway Business Park, Common Road, Witchford, Ely, Cambridgeshire, CB6 2HY Tel: (01353) 666111 Fax: (01353) 666001 Electro chemistry manufrs

Thermo Electron, Grange Lane, Beenham, Reading, RG7 5PR Tel: 0118-971 2121 Fax: 0118-971 2835 E-mail: admin@thermormp.co.uk Dosimeters & manufacturers of radiation monitors

Thermo Electron, 2a Swift Park, Old Leicester Road, Rugby, Warwickshire, CV21 1DZ Tel: (01788) 820300 Fax: (01788) 820419 E-mail: sales.wi.uk@dermofisher.com Metal detectors

Thermo Electron, 2a Swift Park, Old Leicester Road, Rugby, Warwickshire, CV21 1DZ Tel: (01788) 820300 Fax: (01788) 820419 E-mail: tewi@thermo.com Principal Export Areas: Central/East Europe & West Europe Suppliers of process scientific analysers & instrumentation

Thermo Electron Co Operation, Unit 24 Birches Industrial Estate, East Grinstead, West Sussex, RH19 1UB Tel: (01342) 327211 Fax: (01342) 315074 E-mail: john.wolstenholme@thermo.com Scientific instrument manufrs.

Thermo Fisher Sceientific, Unit A2, Swift Park, Old Leicester Road, Rugby, Warwickshire, CV21 1DZ Tel: (01788) 820319 Fax: (01788) 820301 E-mail: saleswiuk@thermofisher.com Weighing & belt conveyor scale systems suppliers

Thermo Fisher Scientific, 1 St Georges Court, Hanover Business Park, Broadheath, Altrincham, Cheshire, WA14 5TP Tel: 0161-942 3000 Fax: 0161-942 3001 E-mail: info@thermoinformatics.com Information management systems

Thermo Fisher Scientific, Shepherd Road, Gloucester, GL2 5HF Tel: (01452) 337800 Fax: (01452) 415156 Gauging electronic measurement equipment manufrs

Thermo Logistics, 3 21-23 Emery Road, Bristol, BS4 5PF Tel: 0117-971 7001 Fax: 0117-971 7113 E-mail: thermologistics@btconnect.com Plate heat exchanger cleaning, service & repairers

Thermo Onix Ltd, Factory 1, Ion Path, Road Three, Winsford, Cheshire, CW7 3GA Tel: (01606) 548700 Fax: (01606) 548711 E-mail: eurosales@thermoonix.com Process gas analysis equipment manufrs

Thermobile UK Ltd, 12 Buckingham Close, Bermuda Industrial Estate, Nuneaton, Warwickshire, CV10 7JT Tel: (024) 7635 7960 Fax: (024) 7635 7969 E-mail: sales@thermobile.co.uk Industrial heating import

Thermocable (Flexible Elements) Ltd, Pasture Lane, Clayton, Bradford, West Yorkshire, BD14 6LU Tel: (01274) 882359 Fax: (01274) 882229 E-mail: info@thermocable.com Flexible heating elements manufrs

Thermocold Mechanical Services Ltd, Unit 11 Albion Business Park, Spring Road, Smethwick, Warley, West Midlands, B66 1LY Tel: 0121-525 5887 Air conditioning services & refrigeration

▶ Thermocool Ltd, 14 Millcroft Road, Rutherglen, Glasgow, G73 1EN Tel: 0141-647 9871 Fax: 0141-643 0850

Thermocrete, Mortimer Street, Bradford, West Yorkshire, BD8 9RL Tel: (01274) 544442 Fax: (01274) 484448 E-mail: thermocretehq@aol.com Manufacture & installation of chimney lining materials

Thermodiffusion Ltd, Hill Place, London Road, Southborough, Tunbridge Wells, Kent, TN4 0PY Tel: (01892) 511533 Fax: (01892) 515140 E-mail: thermodiffusion@btconnect.com *Industrial & commercial heating engineers*

Thermodisc Thermostats, Castle House, Old Road, Leighton Buzzard, Bedfordshire, LU7 2RG Tel: (01525) 375655 Fax: (01525) 378075 E-mail: thermodiscuk@btconnect.com *Thermostatic control manufrs*

▶ Thermodynamix Ltd, 3 Princes Park, Princesway, Team Valley Trading Estate, Gateshead, Tyne & Wear, NE11 0NF Tel: 0191-440 7000 Fax: 0191-440 7001 *Specialists in metalwork*

Thermofast Print Ltd, 2 Mills Road, Sudbury, Suffolk, CO10 2XX Tel: (01787) 880268 Fax: (01787) 880278 E-mail: sales@thermofast.co.uk *Thermographic printing services*

Thermofelt (Contracts) Ltd, Kingswood House, 31-39 Miles Road, Mitcham, Surrey, CR4 3DA Tel: (020) 8646 9300 E-mail: thermofeltcontracts@woodcote.com *Partition manufrs*

Thermoforce Ltd, Wakefield Road, Cockermouth, Cumbria, CA13 0HS Tel: (01900) 823231 Fax: (01900) 825965 E-mail: sales@thermoforce.co.uk *Thermal activators & horticultural equipment manufrs*

Thermoform Ltd, The Larches Moor Farm Road, Airfield Industrial Estate, Ashbourne, Derbyshire, DE6 1HD Tel: (01335) 343757 Fax: (01335) 300096 E-mail: enquiries@thermoform-limited.co.uk *Bespoke manufacturers of vacuum & p ressure, thermoformed plastic packaging - trays blisters, clams etc*

Thermofrost Cryo P.L.C., Robert Fawkes Ho, Rea Street South, Birmingham, B5 6LB Tel: 0121-666 4700 Fax: 0121-622 7268 E-mail: admin@thermofrostcryo.co.uk *Refrigeration & airconditioning wholesalers*

Thermofrost Cryo plc, Ernest Avenue, London, SE27 0DA Tel: (020) 8670 3663 Fax: (020) 8761 8081 E-mail: info@thermofrostcryo.co.uk *Refrigeration & air-conditioning distributors* Also at: Birmingham

Thermographics Measurements Ltd, Riverside Buildings, Dock Road, Connah's Quay, Deeside, Clwyd, CH5 4DS Tel: (01244) 818348 Fax: (01244) 818502 E-mail: sales@t-m-c.com *Manufacturer of a wide range of irreversible and reversible temperature measurement products including self adhesive thermometer labels, liquid crystals, themochromic pigments, thermal paints and colour change crayons.*

Thermograve Ltd, 171 Scudamore Road, Leicester, LE3 1UQ Tel: 0116-291 9000 Fax: 0116-291 9001 E-mail: info@thermograve.co.uk *Point of sale displays*

Thermoguard Ltd, 275 Oldham Road, Manchester, M40 7PS Tel: 0161-202 2861 Fax: 0161-202 4484 E-mail: sales@thermoguard.co.uk *Intumescent protective coating manufrs*

Thermomax Ltd, Balloo Industrial Estate, Bangor, County Down, BT19 7UP Tel: (028) 9127 0411 Fax: (028) 9127 0572 E-mail: sales@thermomax.com *Manufacturers of electric controllers, solar controllers & vacuum tube solar collectors*

Thermometric Ltd, 10 Dalby Court, Gadbrook Business Centre, Rudheath, Northwich, Cheshire, CW9 7TN Tel: (01606) 49007 Fax: (01606) 48924 *Scientific instrument manufrs*

Thermon Electrical Heating Equipment, Seventh Avenue, Team Valley Trading Estate, Gateshead, Tyne & Wear, NE11 0JW Tel: 0191-499 4900 Fax: 0191-499 4901 E-mail: sales@thermon.com *Heat tracing specialist designers & manufrs*

Thermor Russell, Station Road, Auchtermuchty, Cupar, Fife, KY14 7DP Tel: (01337) 828871 Fax: (01337) 828972 E-mail: sales.water@thermolfisher.com *Ph meter & sensor manufrs*

Thermoscreens Ltd, St. Marys Road, Nuneaton, Warwickshire, CV11 5AU Tel: (024) 7638 4646 Fax: (024) 7638 8578 E-mail: sales@thermoscreens.com *Air curtain manufrs*

Thermosel Solutions Ltd, Calico Lane, Furness Vale, High Peak, Derbyshire, SK23 7SW Tel: (01663) 748220 Fax: (01663) 741685 *Expansion joints & flexible connectors for pipelines*

Thermosensing Ltd, 30-31 Devonshire Place, Brighton, BN2 1QB Tel: (01903) 214466 Fax: (01903) 214477 *Manufacturers of control panels & ph electrodes*

▶ Thermoserve Ltd, 359 Bright Road, South Croydon, Surrey, CR2 6ER Tel: (020) 8681 7330

Thermoshield Window Services Ltd, 11 Purdeys Way, Rochford, Essex, SS4 1ND Tel: (01702) 541841 Fax: (01702) 541729 E-mail: sales@thermoshield.co.uk *Window, door & conservatory manufacturers & installers*

Thermotech Building Maintenance Ltd, Northminster Business Park, Northfield Lane, Upper Poppleton, York, YO26 6QU Tel: (01904) 788900 Fax: (01904) 788990 *Shop fitting manufrs*

Thermoteknix Systems Ltd, Teknix House, 2 Pembroke Avenue, Waterbeach, Cambridge, CB5 9QR Tel: (01223) 204000 Fax: (01223) 204010 E-mail: sales@thermoteknix.co.uk *Infra red thermal imaging*

Thermotor Ltd, Beacon House, Station Road, East Preston, Littlehampton, West Sussex, BN16 3AA Tel: (01903) 850650 Fax: (01903) 850428 E-mail: sales@thermotor.co.uk *Design & manufacture intelligent traffic signs & systems*

Thermovac Plastics Ltd, Unit 1 Low Mill Lane, Ravensthorpe Industrial Estate, Dewsbury, West Yorkshire, WF13 3LN Tel: (01924) 499268 Fax: (01924) 491440 E-mail: sales@thermovacplastics.co.uk *Vacuum formers & general fabricators*

Thermsave Welding, 9 Wavertree Park Gardens, Low Moor, Bradford, West Yorkshire, BD12 0UY Tel: (01274) 424478 Fax: (01274) 424479 E-mail: thermsavewelding@blueyonder.co.uk *Boiler maintenance & welding repairs*

ThermTec Ltd, Rectory Farm, Martham, Great Yarmouth, Norfolk, NR29 4RE Tel: 01493 748666 Principal Export Areas: Asia Pacific, Central Asia & Africa *Immersion heaters, heating elements & water heater manufrs*

Thermwatch Ltd, 1 Bridge Court, Fishergate, Norwich, NR3 1UF Tel: (01603) 760255 Fax: (01603) 761276 E-mail: enquiries@thermwatch.co.uk *Environmental products*

Thermwood Europe Ltd, Unit 3, Evans Business Centre, Belmont Industrial Estate, Durham, DH1 1SE Tel: 0191-383 2883 Fax: 0191-383 2884 E-mail: sales@thermwood.co.uk *CNC routing machine manufrs*

Thesaurus Computer Services Ltd, Bank House, 171 Midsummer Boulevard, Milton Keynes, MK9 1EB Tel: (01908) 246500 Fax: (01908) 246555 E-mail: marketing@i-tcs.com *Software support services*

Thessco Ltd, Royds Mill, Windsor Street, Sheffield, S4 7WB Tel: 0114-272 0966 Fax: 0114-275 2655 E-mail: metals@thessco.co.uk *Precious metal manufrs*

▶ Thetford Door Services, 21 Edith Cavell Close, Thetford, Norfolk, IP24 1TJ Tel: (01842) 764730 Fax: (01842) 764643 *Industrial doors manufrs*

Thetford International Limited, Rymer Point, Bury Road, Thetford, Norfolk, IP24 2PN Tel: (01842) 890500 Fax: (01842) 890077 E-mail: sales-serv@thetford-int.co.uk Purchasing Contact: Portlock Sales Contact: Stevens *Design, manufacture & servicing of waste compaction and associated equipment. Portable & static compactors are available with a variety of hoppers, chutes & side or rear loading attachments to suit every waste environment*

▶ TheTravel-Shop, 224 Lower Addiscombe Road, Croydon, CR0 7AB Tel: (020) 8654 3046 E-mail: admin@thetravel-shop.co.uk *thetravel-shop.co.uk is a secure online bookings portal that provides discount theatre tickets, theatre tickets with meal deals, theatre breaks in london''s west end and stratford upon-avon, attraction breaks to legoland windsor, alton tower and many more..., hotel reservation portal that provides competitive hotel rates in the UK and throughout europe, event breaks, holidays from the main uk holiday operators, car hire service in over 85 countries and travel insurance.*

Thew, Arnott & Co. Ltd, Newman Works, 270 London Road, Wallington, Surrey, SM6 7DJ Tel: (020) 8669 3131 Fax: (020) 8669 7747 E-mail: sales@thewarnott.co.uk *Natural raw materials for industry*

▶ Thewoodcarver.Co.Uk, Firthview, Culbo, Culbokie, Dingwall, Ross-Shire, IV7 8JX Tel: (01349) 877546 E-mail: info@thewoodcarver.co.uk *Woodcarver*

▶ Thi Projects, Unit 15 Penketh Business Park, Cleveleys Road, Great Sankey, Warrington, WA5 2TJ Tel: (01925) 415333 Fax: (01925) 415444 E-mail: thipltd@btconnect.com *Electrical trace heating & thermal insulation distributors*

Thick Film Microcircuits Ltd, Unit 4 Wickford Way, London, E17 6JD Tel: (020) 8531 7226 Fax: (020) 8527 5521 E-mail: sales@thickfilm.co.uk *Electronic component manufrs*

Thiel Technics UK, 66 Tonacliffe Road, Whitworth, Rochdale, Lancashire, OL12 8SS Tel: (01706) 868822 Fax: (01706) 343402 E-mail: sales@thiel-technics.co.uk *Storage & handling systems*

▶ Thimble & Threads, 31a Milton Street, Saltburn-by-the-Sea, Cleveland, TS12 1DN Tel: (01287) 626061 E-mail: rachel.sleeman@ntlworld.com *Clothing Alterations. High standard of work. Service discounted for bulk orders. We repair damaged stock for market traders etc. Dry cleaner contracts undertaken etc. Mail orders also taken.*

Thin Air, Griffin Farm House, Bowden Hill, Lacock, Chippenham, Wiltshire, SN15 2PP Tel: (01249) 730099 Fax: (01249) 730066 E-mail: sales@racewear.co.uk *Race wear suppliers*

▶ Thin Joint Technology Ltd, 15 Manfred Street, Erskine Industrial Estate, Liverpool, L6 1AU Tel: 0151-260 2000 Fax: 0151-260 6745 E-mail: alan@clan.co.uk *manufacturer & supplier of tools & materials for Aircrete blockwork*

Thing Ama Jigs Ltd, 136 Oyster Lane, Byfleet, West Byfleet, Surrey, KT14 7JQ Tel: (01932) 340764 Fax: (01932) 351280 *Metalworkers, general engineers*

▶ Things Fashions Ltd, 64-66 Wallis Road, London, London, E9 5LH Tel: (020) 8985 4767

▶ Think Print, Cameron Court, Winnington Hall, Winnington, Northwich, Cheshire, CW8 4DU Tel: (01606) 784567 Fax: (01606) 784777

▶ Think Smart Finance Ltd, 778 High Road, London, N12 9QR Tel: (020) 8445 5428 *Independent mortgage and life assurance broker. We can help you no matter where you are in the UK.*

▶ Think Tank Group, 1st Floor, 368 York Road, Leeds, LS9 9EB Tel: (0870) 3609600 E-mail: me@thethinktankgroup.co.uk *The Think Tank Group provides rental property in Leeds. With Houses, Flats and Apartments to rent in the Leeds City Centre and in the Outskirts, we can provide you with a high quality home to Rent.*

▶ Think4 Ltd, Block P1 Unit, Heywood Distribution Park, Pilsworth Road, Heywood, Lancashire, OL10 2TT Tel: (0870) 1644446 Fax: (01706) 620000 *Think4 supplies consumers and businesses with a vast spectrum of IT and technology products encompassing systems, components, peripherals and consumables. We focus on supplying the latest products available at competitive prices with prompt delivery.*

Think-Cl International Ltd, 8 Progress Business Centre, Whittle Parkway, Slough, SL1 6DQ Tel: (01628) 666242 Fax: (01628) 559812 E-mail: jermary.britton@think-global-group.com *Exhibition designers*

▶ ThinkWell, 78 Laitwood Road, London, SW12 9QJ Tel: (020) 8675 6454 *ThinkWell provides online interactive self-help for people suffering from mild depression, stress and anxiety. Our core service consists of the provision of self-help programmes based on CBT (Cognitive Behavioural Therapy) with interactive tools to help evaulate progress and improvement in mood and mental health.*

Thircon Ltd, Hambleton Steel Works, York Road, Thirsk, North Yorkshire, YO7 3BT Tel: (01845) 522760 Fax: (01845) 524146 *Steel building constructors*

Third Axis Ltd, Unit N Oldham Central Trading Park, Coulton Close, Oldham, OL1 4EB Tel: (0161) 628 4447 Fax: (0161) 633 0833 E-mail: axiseds@compuserve.com *Moulding manufacturers*

▶ Third Eye Services, 104 Mount View Road, London, N4 4JX Tel: (020) 8341 4133 Fax: (020) 8341 4133E-mail: sales@thirdeyeservices.co.uk *Third Eye Services - Specialist IT testing consultancy managing performance and penetration testing, application stress tests, pen tests, security consultancy, IT consulting and project management.*

Third Generation, 24 Metford Ground, Bristol, BS6 7LG Tel: 0117-935 0690 Fax: 0117-935 0690 *Sport equipment distributors*

▶ Thirsk Fabrications, Thirsk Industrial Park, York Road, Thirsk, North Yorkshire, YO7 3BX Tel: (01845) 525923 Fax: (01845) 524420

Thistle Ltd, Morebath, Tiverton, Devon, EX16 9BZ Tel: (0870) 9005449 Fax: (08709) 005449 E-mail: enquires@agridata.co.uk *Computer software*

Thistle Bearings & Engineering Products Ltd, 38 Singer Road, Kelvin Industrial Estate, East Kilbride, Glasgow, G75 0XS Tel: (01355) 225491 Fax: (01355) 242502 E-mail: sales@thistlebearings.co.uk *Bearing distributors & agents*

Thistle East Midlands Airport, Castle Donington, Derby, DE74 2SH Tel: (01332) 850700 Fax: (01332) 850823 E-mail: east.midlandsairport@thistle.co.uk *Hotel, restaurant, conference & leisure facilities*

▶ Thistle Electronics, 3 Union Street, Kelso, Roxburghshire, TD5 7DR Tel: (01573) 228950 Fax: (01573) 228951

Thistle Euston, 43-48 Cardington Street, London, NW1 2LP Tel: (0870) 3339107 Fax: (0871) 3769117 E-mail: euston@thistle.co.uk *Conference facilities & hotel*

Thistle Generators Ltd, Faraday House Coalburn Road, Fallside, Bothwell, Glasgow, G71 8DA Tel: (01698) 814888 Fax: (01698) 802592 E-mail: mailroom@thistlegenerators.com *Suppliers, installers & maintenance of generators*

Thistle Hotel, Brands Hatch, Fawkham, Longfield, Kent, DA3 8PE Tel: (01474) 854900 Fax: (01474) 854990 E-mail: brandshatch@thistle.co.uk *Hotel & conference facilities*

Thistle Hotel, The Luton Arndale Centre, Luton, LU1 2TR Tel: (01582) 734199 Fax: (01582) 402528 E-mail: luton@thistle.co.uk *Hotel & conference facilities*

▶ Thistle Marine Peterhead Ltd, Baltic Place, Peterhead, Aberdeenshire, AB42 1TF Tel: (01779) 477210 Fax: (01779) 471804 E-mail: sales@thistlemarine.co.uk *Design, manufacturing, installation of hydraulic deck equipment*

Thistle Newcastle, Neville Street, Newcastle upon Tyne, NE1 5DF Tel: 0191-232 2471 Fax: 0191-232 1285 E-mail: newcastle@thistle.co.uk *Hotel & conference facilities*

Thistle Reprographics Ltd, 55 Holburn Street, Aberdeen, AB10 6BR Tel: (01224) 213400 Fax: (01224) 213444

▶ Thistle Scientific Ltd, Goldie Road, Bothwell Park Industrial Estate, Uddingston, Glasgow, G71 6PB Tel: (01698) 338844

Thistle Seafood Ltd, The Harbour, Harbour Street, Boddam, Peterhead, Aberdeenshire, AB42 3AU Tel: (01779) 478991 Fax: (01779) 471014 E-mail: mail@thistleseafoods.com *Thistle Seafoods Ltd, a privately owned family business, is one of the top fish processing firms in the UK, specialising in frozen fish fillets and added-value fish products. Based in Peterhead, Aberdeenshire, the main part of their business is supplying frozen seafood products to retailers and foodservice companies.*

Thistle Special Beltings, Bridge of Mondynes, Fordoun, Laurencekirk, Kincardineshire, AB30 1LD Tel: (01569) 740204 Fax: (01569) 740322 E-mail: mail@thistle.uk.com *Glass fibre & rubber mouldings manufrs*

▶ Thistle Sporting Goods, 25 Knightswood Terrace, Blantyre, Glasgow, G72 9BQ Tel: (01698) 829280 Fax: (01698) 829280 E-mail: jacbag@btinternet.com *Suppliers of bagpipe cases, kilt carriers, sporrans & tartan bags*

▶ Thistle Structures Ltd, Thistle House, Cartmore Industrial Estate, Lochgelly, Fife, KY5 8LL Tel: (01592) 780202 Fax: (01592) 781908 *Steel fabrics*

Thistle Swindon Hotel, Fleming Way, Swindon, SN1 1TN Tel: (01793) 528282 Fax: (01793) 541283 E-mail: swindon@thistle.co.uk *Conference facilities & hotel*

Thistle Tools Ltd, Unit 6a, Sandwich Industrial Estate, Sandwich, Kent, CT13 9LN Tel: (01304) 612696 Fax: (01304) 619207 *Precision engineers*

Thistle Vent Ltd, 7 Strathclyde Street, Glasgow, G40 4JR Tel: 0141-554 6669 Fax: 0141-554 6669 *Ventilation engineers*

Thistlebrook Ltd, 14-16 Chase Street, Luton, LU1 3QZ Tel: (01582) 453753 Fax: (01582) 481825 *Dry lining specialists*

▶ THK UK, 1 Harrison Close, Knowlhill, Milton Keynes, MK5 8PA Tel: (01908) 303050 Fax: (01908) 303070 E-mail: sales.uk@thk.co.uk *THK U.K. is the number one source for precision LM Guides , ball splines, ball screws, cross roller rings, actuators, link balls, rod ends and more. THK have developed various types of Linear Motion Systems utilising experiences and technical know how accumulated over many years. THK can provide both high performance and cost effective application solutions. With recent innovations in Caged Ball technology, THK is leading the way into the 21st century. Supported by a localised team of sales engineers, fully qualified to discuss design requirements on site, endorsed by a resident team of internal sales staff and a technical support group, THK offers unrivalled service to the linear market. With market leading products, top level support, direct OEM dealing and national distribution - THK is all you need.*

Thom & Cook Ltd, Units 1-2 Bricklayers Arms Distribution Centre, Mandela Way, London, SE1 5SP Tel: (020) 7231 1114 Fax: (020) 7237 5139 E-mail: sales@dixonandroe.co.uk *Paper merchants*

Thomas Armstrong Ltd, Pickhill, Thirsk, North Yorkshire, YO7 4JQ Tel: (01845) 567282 Fax: (01845) 567606 *Concrete block manufrs*

Thomas Armstrong Concrete Blocks Ltd, Whinfield House, Whinfield Industrial Estate, Rowlands Gill, Tyne & Wear, NE39 1EH Tel: (01207) 544214 Fax: (01207) 541800 *Concrete block manufrs*

▶ Thomas Armstrong Construction Ltd, 8 Foss Way, Walkerville Industrial Estate, Catterick Garrison, North Yorkshire, DL9 4SA Tel: (01748) 834849 Fax: (01748) 834297 E-mail: aggregates@thomasarmstrong.co.uk

Thomas Armstrong Timber Ltd, Workington Road, Flimby, Maryport, Cumbria, CA15 8RY Tel: (01900) 68226 Fax: (01900) 870800 E-mail: timber@thomasarmstrong.co.uk *Timber components*

Thomas Automatics Co. Ltd, Bishop Meadow Road, Loughborough, Leicestershire, LE11 5RE Tel: (01509) 267611 Fax: (01509) 266836 E-mail: sales@thomas-a.co.uk *Change giving machine manufrs*

Thomas Automatics, 11 Springfield Terrace, Port Talbot, West Glamorgan, SA12 8HN Tel: (01639) 871213 *Juke box & games machines rental*

Thomas & Betts Ltd, 5 Sheepcoats, Springfield Business Park, Chelmsford, CM2 5AE Tel: (01245) 453000 Fax: (01245) 453001 E-mail: enquiries@existalite.co.uk *Emergency & safety lighting suppliers & manufrs*

▶ Thomas & Betts Holdings UK, Wilford Road, Nottingham, NG2 1EB Tel: 0115-964 3837 Fax: 0115-986 0538 E-mail: martin.critchley@tnb.com *Cable tie manufacturers & heat shrinkable products*

Thomas Birkhead & Son, Yew Tree Mills, Holmbridge, Holmfirth, HD9 2NN Tel: (01484) 691510 Fax: (01484) 691515 *Worsted cloth finishers & dyers manufrs*

Thomas Blake & Co., The Byre House, Fearby, Ripon, North Yorkshire, HG4 4NF Tel: (01765) 689042 Fax: (01765) 689042 *Cosmetic products manufrs*

Thomas Bower & Son Ltd, 111 Broomfield Avenue, Palmers Green, London, N13 4JR Tel: (020) 8882 1888 *Stationers' sundries*

Thomas Bros, Lowlands, Nash, Newport, Gwent, NP18 2DA Tel: (01633) 276316 Fax: (01633) 276316 *Agricultural contractors & sports field reinstatement*

Thomas Bros Leeds Ltd, Stanningley Field Close, Leeds, LS13 4QG Tel: 0113-256 7210 Fax: 0113-256 9199 E-mail: info@tbleeds.com *Engineers pattern makers*

Thomas Brown(Stockport) Ltd, Stanbank Street, Stockport, Cheshire, SK4 1PY Tel: 0161-480 3452 Fax: 0161-480 6207 *Fabric & wallpaper book manufrs*

▶ Thomas Building Plans, 18 Shiels Drive, Bradley Stoke, Bristol, BS32 8EA Tel: (0845) 1590089 E-mail: info@thomasbuildingplans.co.uk *Building Plans & Architectural Design of Home extensions, Loft Conversions & alterations leading to Planning Permission/Building reg. Approval. Many referrences available, please visit our web site.*

Thomas C Wild, Vulcan Works, Tinsley Park Road, Sheffield, S9 5DP Tel: 0114-244 2471 Fax: 0114-244 2052 E-mail: info@tc-wild.co.uk *Steel forging manufrs*

Colin Thomas Electronics, 138 Port Tennant Road, Swansea, SA1 8JQ Tel: (01792) 469885 Fax: (01792) 522221 *Electronics repairs & developers*

Thomas Corrie, Balmaclellan, Castle Douglas, Kirkcudbrightshire, DG7 3QE Tel: (01644) 420265 *Agricultural suppliers*

Craig Alan Thomas Ltd, 3rd Floor, 5 Covent Garden, Liverpool, L2 8UD Tel: 0151-227 2287 Fax: 0151-236 2165 E-mail: sales@atcraig.com *Timber agents*

Thomas Danby College, 5 Roundhay Road, Leeds, LS7 3BG Tel: 0113-249 4912 Fax: 0113-240 1967 E-mail: info@thomasdanby.ac.uk *Leeds Thomas Danby based in Leeds, offers catering training courses.*

▶ Thomas Doran Parkanaur Trust, 57 Parkanaur Road, Dungannon, County Tyrone, BT70 3AA Tel: (028) 8776 1272 Fax: (028) 8776 1257 E-mail: parkanaurmanorhouse@hotmail.com *Hotel conference venue*

▶ Thomas Doran Parkanaur Trust, 57 Parkanaur Road, Dungannon, County Tyrone, BT70 3AA Tel: (028) 8776 1272 Fax: (028) 8776 9428 E-mail: info@parkupholstery.plus.com *Manufacture of Orthopaedic Chairs, Domestic & Contract Soft Furniture, Reupholstery and Made-To-Order*

▶ Thomas Dornan (Printers) Ltd, Millgate, Hollings, Oldham, OL8 4JL Tel: 0161-624 4959

Thomas Dudley Group Ltd, PO Box 28, Dudley, West Midlands, DY1 4SN Tel: 0121-557 5411 Fax: 0121-557 5345 E-mail: info@thomasdudley.co.uk *Cistern manufacturers & iron founders*

E.D. Thomas Ltd, 113 Fordwater Road, Chertsey, Surrey, KT16 8HB Tel: (01932) 566963 *Commercial repairs*

Edward Thomas & Son Ltd, Usk Sawmills, Sennybridge, Brecon, Powys, LD3 8RS Tel: (01874) 636321 *Saw mill & timber treatment manufrs*

▶ Thomas Edwards, Heavers House, Chapel Street, Ryarsh, West Malling, Kent, ME19 5JU Tel: (01732) 875771 Fax: (01732) 841043 E-mail: t1jce@aol.com *Interior polishing & restoration specialists*

continued

▶ indicates data change since last edition

Thomas Engineering, Manning Road, Bourne, Lincolnshire, PE10 9HW Tel: (01778) 422720 Fax: (01778) 425530 E-mail: gecrane@totalise.co.uk *Precision engineers*

Thomas Engineering, Units 8-10, Brinell Way, Harfreys Industrial Estate, Great Yarmouth, Norfolk, NR31 0LU Tel: (01493) 650107 Fax: (01493) 415605 E-mail: admin@stuga.co.uk *Machine tool manufrs*

Thomas Ford Smithfield, Hereford House, 23 Smithfield Street, London, EC1A 9LF Tel: (020) 7248 5868 Fax: (020) 7248 6330 E-mail: sales@thomasford.biz *Butchers suppliers*

▶ Thomas Fox & Co. Ltd, 3 Rhodes Way, Watford, WD24 4YA Tel: (01923) 811700 Fax: (01923) 811710 E-mail: helpdesk@thomasfox.co.uk *General & specialised haulage*

Frank Thomas Ltd, Station Road, Finedon, Wellingborough, Northamptonshire, NN9 5NT Tel: (01933) 682260 Fax: (01933) 682261 *Motor cycle clothing suppliers*

Thomas Graham, 19 Kinneil Road, Bo'Ness, West Lothian, EH51 0AY Tel: (01506) 829090 Fax: (01506) 829075 *Crane hire*

Thomas & Green Ltd/Konos Gmbh, 81 Orchard Way, Burmell, Cambridge, CB25 0EQ Tel: 07768 682210 Fax: 01638 605146 E-mail: richard.start@ntlworld.com *Thomas and Green Ltd are an established paper converting company producing private label coffee filters, absorbent food packaging, and products for food, medical and dental industries. Further information is available on our website and samples and quotations will be supplied on request.*

▶ Thomas Guy Ltd, Tollgate Road, Burscough, Ormskirk, Lancashire, L40 8LD Tel: (01704) 893304 Fax: (01704) 893603

Thomas H Gee & Co. Ltd, 271 Summer Lane, Birmingham, B19 2PX Tel: 0121-359 1279 Fax: 0121-359 7686 E-mail: sales@thomashgee.co.uk *Electroplating services & metal finishing products*

Thomas Hamlin & Co., 64 Monmouth Street, Bridgwater, Somerset, TA6 5EJ Tel: (01278) 422452 Fax: (01278) 424036 *Motor & general engineers*

Thomas Harwood & Son Ltd, 131 Church Street, Little Lever, Bolton, BL3 1BW Tel: (01204) 708888 Fax: (01204) 701700 E-mail: traffic@thomasharwood.co.uk *Centrally located for all major motorway networks, Thomas Harwood & Son Ltd guarantees delivery of your goods nationwide door-to-door same day, next day! Using our own fleet of articulated & rigid curtainsided vehicles, you can be assured of a distribution service that is dedicated & handled with the professional care you would expect from us. For further information on our full range of distribution services, vehicles, availability & rates please contact our traffic desk direct on 01204 708888 or alternatively e-mail us at traffic@thomasharwood.co.uk. "Distribution with a difference"*

Thomas HG & Co. Ltd, 78 Steward Street, Birmingham, B18 7AF Tel: 0121-454 0677 Fax: 0121-454 0677 E-mail: markf@thomashgee.co.uk *Electroplating services*

▶ J. Thomas (Southern) Ltd, Bankside House, Henfield Road, Small Dole, Henfield, West Sussex, BN5 9XQ Tel: (01273) 494848 Fax: (01273) 497804 E-mail: cranes@jthomas.co.uk *Mobile telescopic crane hire providers*

James Thomas Engineering Ltd, Navigation Complex, Navigation Road, Worcester, WR5 3DE Tel: (01905) 363600 Fax: (01905) 363601 E-mail: sales@jamesthomas.co.uk Principal Export Areas: Worldwide *Lighting manufrs*

Thomas & Jones Ltd, 101c Palm Grove, Prenton, Merseyside, CH43 1TQ Tel: 0151-653 6070 Fax: 0151-653 5040 *Canned food catering & distributors*

▶ Thomas Kelly & Sons, 5 Picton Road, Wavertree, Liverpool, L15 4LD Tel: 0151-733 9966 Fax: 0151-733 9966

Thomas Komoly, 20 Hawthorn Grove, Wilmslow, Cheshire, SK9 5DE Tel: 01625 252804 E-mail: tomi@labconsultant.co.uk *Consultant for new laboratories or modernisation, working with Architects and Facility Managers.*

Thomas L Wilkins Ltd, 2-4 Johnson Street, Leicester, LE1 4DN Tel: 0116-251 8996 Fax: (0870) 1659258 E-mail: sales@tlwilkins.co.uk *Die stampers & embossers*

▶ Thomas Laird, Woodilee Industrial Estate, Woodilee Road Lenzie, Lenzie, Glasgow, G66 3UU Tel: 0141-776 2843

Thomas Lane & Co. Ltd, Hope St Works, Hazel Grove, Stockport, Cheshire, SK7 4EL Tel: 0161-483 9666 Fax: 0161-456 4440 E-mail: fabwork@t-lane.demon.co.uk *Fabrication engineers*

Thomas Long & Sons Ltd, Park House, Mile End Road, Colwick, Nottingham, NG4 2DW Tel: 0115-961 8888 Fax: 0115-940 0118 E-mail: enquiries@thomaslonggroup.co.uk *Building & transport contractors*

Thomas Lowe & Sons Corn Merchants Ltd, 36 Pine View, Winstanley, Wigan, Lancashire, WN3 6DF Tel: (01942) 211909 *Corn merchants*

Thomas Mcgilvray & Son Ltd, Wemyss Road, Dysart, Kirkcaldy, Fife, KY1 2XZ Tel: (01592) 655993 Fax: (01592) 655177 E-mail: sales@mcgilvray-printers.co.uk *Printers & stationers*

▶ Thomas Menzies Builders Ltd, Hayfield Place, Hayfield Industrial Estate, Kirkcaldy, Fife, KY2 5DH Tel: (01592) 264712 Fax: (01592) 200498

▶ Thomas Muckle & Sons, Bridge Street, Cragside, Morpeth, Northumberland, NE65 7SG Tel: (01669) 620321 Fax: (01669) 620505 E-mail: enquiries@thomasmuckle.co.uk *Shop fitting services*

▶ Nicki Thomas, Studridge Lane, Hedgerow, Booker, Speen, Princes Risborough, Buckinghamshire, HP27 0SA Tel: (01494) 488665 Fax: (0870) 1623908

continued

E-mail: nicki.thomas@storecompact.co.uk *Website design*

Thomas Norman, Unit 1 Moreton Industrial Estate, London Road, Swanley, Kent, BR8 8DE Tel: (01322) 611600 Fax: (01322) 611609 E-mail: info@thomasnorman.co.uk *Carrier bag & packaging manufrs*

▶ Peter Thomas & Associates, 113 High Street, Codicote, Hitchin, Hertfordshire, SG4 8UA Tel: (01438) 821408 E-mail: sales@ptadesign.com *Design consultancy*

Thomas Plant (Birmingham) Ltd, Plumbob House Valepits Road, Garretts Green Trading Estate, Birmingham, B33 0TD Tel: 0121-604 6000 Fax: 0121-604 2222 E-mail: info@kitchencraft.co.uk *Import & distribution of kitchenware*

Thomas Proctor & Son Ltd, Dukesway, Team Valley Trading Estate, Gateshead, Tyne & Wear, NE11 0NW Tel: 0191-491 3027 Fax: 0191-491 3028 E-mail: sales@thomasproctor.co.uk *Hygiene & welding, lubricants, lubrication equipment distributors* Also at: Carlisle & Middlesbrough

▶ Thomas R Callan, 22 Smith Street, Ayr, KA7 1TF Tel: (01292) 267681 E-mail: info@trcallan.com

Thomas Removals, 50 Salop Road, Wrexham, Clwyd, LL13 7AF Tel: (0800) 7834581 Fax: (01978) 366478 E-mail: info@thomas-removals.co.uk *Removals & storage contractors*

Thomas Roberts & Co., 13 Chapel Street, Menai Bridge, Gwynedd, LL59 5HW Tel: (01248) 712478 *Joinery & funeral directors services*

Thomas Shaw & Son (M/C) Ltd, Star Works, Holt Town, Manchester, M40 7FQ Tel: 0161-273 7686 Fax: 0161-274 3699 E-mail: tommy.shaw@virgin.net *Manufacturers of industrial conveyors & wire goods*

Thomas Sherriff & Co. Ltd, Wagonway Road, Alnwick, Northumberland, NE66 2NP Tel: (01665) 603555 Fax: (01665) 510558 *Agricultural engineers*

Thomas Sherriff & Co. Ltd, Eccles Service Station, Coldstream, Berwickshire, TD12 4LX Tel: (01890) 840550 *Agricultural engineers*

Thomas Sherriff & Co. Ltd, 150-162 Galashiels Road, Stow, Galashiels, Selkirkshire, TD1 2RA Tel: (01578) 730282 Fax: (01578) 730284 *Agricultural engineers*

▶ Thomas Sinden Construction Ltd, Unit 12, Brooke Trading Estate, Lyon Road, Romford, RM1 2AT Tel: (01708) 764111

Thomas & Son, Darren Road, Ystalyfera, Swansea, SA9 2LL Tel: (01639) 842158 *Soft drink manufacturers*

▶ Thomas & Sons Ltd, Harlequin Avenue, Brentford, Middlesex, TW8 9EW Tel: (020) 8568 0231 Fax: (020) 8847 4842

Thomas Sports Equipment Ltd, Pinfold Lane Industrial Estate, Bridlington, North Humberside, YO16 6XS Tel: (01262) 678299 Fax: (01262) 602063 E-mail: sales@thomas-sports.com *Parachute equipment manufrs*

Thomas Swan & Co., Crookhall, Consett, County Durham, DH8 7ND Tel: (01207) 505131 Fax: (01207) 590467 E-mail: sales@thomas-swan.co.uk *Speciality chemicals manufrs*

Thomas Telford Services Ltd, Thomas Telford House, 1 Heron Quay, London, E14 4JD Tel: (020) 7987 6999 Fax: (020) 7538 4101 E-mail: sales@t-telford.co.uk *Technical publishers*

Thomas Transport Ltd, Coppards Lane, Northiam, Rye, East Sussex, TN31 6QR Tel: (01797) 252387 Fax: (01797) 252625 *Commercial vehicle repairers*

Tudor Thomas Design, 1a Fawe Street, London, E14 6PD Tel: (020) 7987 8145 Fax: (020) 7515 4970 E-mail: tudor@tudorthomas.com *Bespoke furniture manufrs*

Vicki Thomas Associates, 195 Tollgate Road, London, E6 5JY Tel: (020) 7511 5767 Fax: (020) 7473 5177 *Gift design consultants*

Thomas Walker Pensions Trust Ltd, 39 St Paul's Square, Birmingham, B3 1QY Tel: 0121-236 5565 Fax: 0121-236 6725 E-mail: sales@thomaswalker.co.uk *Garment fastener manufrs* Also at: Leeds

Welford Thomas Ltd, Unit 35 Thornleigh Trading Estate, Dudley, West Midlands, DY2 8UB Tel: (01384) 451340 Fax: (01384) 451345 E-mail: wellford.bodies@btinternet.co.uk *Commercial body builders*

Thomas & Whitley, 3 Wortley Moor La Trading Estate, Leeds, LS12 4HX Tel: 0113-279 8880 Fax: 0113-231 0479 E-mail: sales@thomasandwhitley.co.uk *Control panel manufrs*

Thomas, Wilch & High Ltd, Europa Way, Martineau Lane, Norwich, NR1 2EN Tel: (01603) 620644 Fax: (01603) 768334 E-mail: enquiries@thomaswilchandhigh.co.uk *Rewind electric motors services*

Thomas & Wilson Ltd, 903 Fulham Road, London, SW6 5HU Tel: (020) 7384 0111 Fax: (020) 7384 0222 E-mail: sales@thomasandwilson.com *Fibrous plaster manufrs*

Thomas Wright, 6 Barge Street, St. Thomas's Road, Huddersfield, HD1 3LG Tel: (01484) 534245 Fax: (01484) 435023 E-mail: bradford@thorite.co.uk *Compressed air equipment suppliers & manufrs*

▶ Thomass Bakery, Broughton Road, Dalton-In-Furness, Cumbria, LA15 8RN Tel: (01229) 462370 *Bakery*

Thomas's Bakery, 84 Southgate, Elland, West Yorkshire, HX5 0EP Tel: (01422) 372335 Fax: (01422) 377798 *Bakers*

Thomas's Forge, The Forge, Fownhope, Hereford, HR1 4NJ Tel: (01432) 860262 Fax: (01432) 860262 *Steel fabricators*

Thomfab Engineering Services, Unit 1 Blackhill Industrial Estate, Findon, Aberdeen, AB12 4RL Tel: (01224) 781615 Fax: (01224) 781615 E-mail: duncan@thomfab.com *Specialist fabricators*

Brian Thompson, Barrock End, Hethersgill, Carlisle, CA6 6HT Tel: (01228) 675614 Fax: (01228) 675614 *Drainage services*

▶ Thompson Bros Stockport, Riverside Works, 18a Crescent Road, Stockport, Cheshire, SK1 2QG Tel: 0161-480 2424 Fax: 0161-429 0924

Thompson Builders Merchants Ltd, Bilton Road, Chelmsford, CM1 2UB Tel: (01245) 266754 Fax: (01245) 359070 E-mail: info@thompson-online.co.uk *Builders merchant services* Also at: Goodmayes

Thompson & Campbell Ltd, Unit 2 Whitedykes Industrial Estate, Cromarty, Ross-Shire, IV11 8YB Tel: (01381) 600536 Fax: (01381) 600767 *Rifle makers, gunsmiths & precision engineering services*

Thompson & Capper Ltd, Hardwick Road, Astmoor Industrial Estate, Runcorn, Cheshire, WA7 1PH Tel: (01928) 573734 Fax: (01928) 580694 E-mail: info@tablets2buy.com *Tablet & capsule contract manufrs*

Thompson Consultants Ltd, The Mow Barton, Northend, Clutton, Bristol, BS39 5QS Tel: (01761) 453673 Fax: (01761) 452707 E-mail: sales@thompson-consultants.co.uk *Computer consultants*

Thompson Contact Lenses Ltd, Ring Road, West Park, Leeds, LS16 6QL Tel: 0113-230 4304 Fax: 0113-274 5645 E-mail: sales@thompsonlenses.co.uk *Manufacture contact lenses*

E.G. Thompson (Bulk Carriers) Ltd, Suite 7 Bonnington Bond, 2 Anderson Place, Edinburgh, EH6 5NP Tel: 0131-555 5222 Fax: 0131-557 4742 *Offshore drilling management*

E.H. Thompson & Son (London) Ltd, Hallsford Bridge Industrial Estate, Stondon Road, Ongar, Essex, CM5 9RB Tel: (01277) 365500 Fax: (01277) 365550 E-mail: ehthompsons@btconnects.com *Precision turned parts manufrs*

▶ Thompson Electrical Cambridge Ltd, 15 Barnwell Business Park, Barnwell Drive, Cambridge, CB5 8UZ Tel: (01223) 212162 Fax: (01223) 242131

Thompson Fertiliser Sales, Cornfield Cottage, Thorpe Bassett, Malton, North Yorkshire, YO17 8LU Tel: (01944) 758091 Fax: (01944) 758621 E-mail: thom-fert@supanet.com *Fertiliser suppliers*

Thompson Food Co. Ltd, 9-11 Blount Street, London, E14 7RL Tel: (020) 7790 3408 Fax: (020) 7790 5162 E-mail: thompsondairy@aol.com *Dairy products*

Thompson Friction Welding Ltd, Hereward Rise, Halesowen, West Midlands, B62 8AN Tel: 0121-585 0888 Fax: 0121-585 0810 E-mail: sales@thompson-friction-welding.co.uk *Specialists in friction welding machine services*

▶ Thompson & Hudson Wire Machinery, Atlas Mill Road, Brighouse, West Yorkshire, HD6 1ES Tel: (01484) 715129 Fax: (01484) 717026 E-mail: info@thompsonandhudson.co.uk Principal Export Areas: Worldwide *Manufacturers of wire straightening, cutting & wire working machines*

John Thompson Associates Ltd, Compton House, 20 Selsdon Road, South Croydon, Surrey, CR2 6PA Tel: (020) 7378 6884 Fax: (020) 8680 9773 E-mail: compton@tal-hwt.co.uk *Management & executive selection agents*

▶ Thompson Joinery Ltd, Kettle Lane, Creeting St. Mary, Ipswich, IP6 8LL Tel: (01449) 722489 Fax: (01449) 722489

Thompson & Leigh Ltd, Unit 1 Bourne Industrial Park, Bourne Road, Crayford, Dartford, DA1 4BZ Tel: (01322) 557729 Fax: (01322) 522455 E-mail: david@t-leigh.sagehost.co.uk *Plumbing suppliers*

Thompson (Metals) Ltd, Winterton Road, Scunthorpe, South Humberside, DN15 0BA Tel: (01724) 843831 Fax: (01724) 847786 E-mail: thompsonmetals@fsnet.co.uk *Scrap metal merchants & skip hire*

Thompson Packaging, Unit 5, Kenyons Farm, Gough Lane, Walton Summit, Preston, PR5 6AR Tel: (01772) 620768 Fax: (01772) 620764 E-mail: info@arranmarketing.co.uk *Carrier Bags Plain & Printed - HDPE - LDPE - Paper Bags- Till Rolls - Toilet Rolls - Kitchen rolls - Clear Polythene bags All, Sizes, Gauges - Food Containers - Lay Flat Tube - Padded Envelopes - Tape - Grip seal - Zip Top - Vacuum Bags -Refuse Sacks - Bubble Wrap - Cleaning Products - AND MUCH MORE!!!*

Thompson & Parkes Ltd, Oldington Trading Estate, Kidderminster, Worcestershire, DY11 7QP Tel: (01562) 745881 Fax: (01562) 515578 *Builders merchants*

Thompson Plastics Group Ltd, Bridge Works, Hessle, North Humberside, HU13 0TP Tel: (01482) 646464 Fax: (01482) 644446 E-mail: info@thompson-plastics.co.uk *Caravan fittings & plastic vacuum formed product manufrs*

Thompson Plumbase, 10 Chapel Street, Redruth, Cornwall, TR15 2DE Tel: (01209) 215676 Fax: (01209) 213222 *Plumbing & heating equipment merchants* Also at: Bridgwater, Exeter, Plymouth, St. Austell & Taunton

R.E. Thompson & Co. (Vacuum) Ltd, Evingar Road, Whitchurch, Hampshire, RG28 7EU Tel: 01256 893325 Fax: 01256 893623 E-mail: sales@rethompson.co.uk *R E Thompson, based in Hampshire offer precision cnc machining services including milling and turning to industry across the UK and overseas specialising in the aerospace and defence sectors.*

R.J. Thompson, 50 Whalfedale Avenue, Dacre, Harrogate, North Yorkshire, HG2 0AU Tel: (07973) 522404 Fax: (01423) 780001 *Kitchen fitting services*

Richard Thompson Joinery Ltd, South Back Lane, Tollerton, York, YO61 1PU Tel: (01347) 838387 Fax: (01347) 838943 *Joinery manufrs*

Thompson & Robinson, Capel Hall Lane, Trimley St. Martin, Trimley St. Martin, Felixstowe, Suffolk, IP11 0RB Tel: (07791) 167338 Fax: (01394) 448008 *Pine furniture manufrs*

Thompson Shipping Ltd, 66 Totternhoe Road, Eaton Bray, Dunstable, Bedfordshire, LU6 2BD Tel: (01525) 223071 Fax: (01525) 851482 E-mail: jim@fahawkins.com *Export packers & freight forwarders*

Thompson & Son (Millwall) Ltd, Cuba Street, Isle of Dogs, London, E14 8LF Tel: (020) 7987 1844 Fax: (020) 7987 4416 *Press & Hydraulic engineers* Also at: New Cross

Thompson Strategy Works, 18 Arnold Road, Stoke Golding, Nuneaton, Warwickshire, CV13 6JG Tel: (07976) 807055 Fax: (07971) 091513 E-mail: nigel@thompsonsw.co.uk *Thompson Strategy Works provides specialist sales & marketing consultancy, business support and training solutions to industrial businesses in the areas of; *** Business Growth & performance improvement *** Marketing & Sales Strategy *** Sales and Marketing training *** Management Workshops **In addition, we are the leading UK consultancy for The Sales Activator® - a unique sales coaching and development system used by many of the UK"s leading sales organisations.***

Thompson Tackle, 2b Hitchin Road, Arlesey, Bedfordshire, SG15 6RP Tel: (01462) 835269 *Fishing tackle & pet food retailers*

Thompson Transport, Unit 19 J B J Business Park, Northampton Road, Blisworth, Northampton, NN7 3DW Tel: (01604) 859066 Fax: (01604) 859006 *Courier services*

F.H. Thompson-Felling & Sons Ltd, Poplar Sawmills, Factory Road, Blaydon-on-Tyne, Tyne & Wear, NE21 5RX Tel: 0191-499 0444 Fax: 0191-499 0220 E-mail: sales@fhthompson.co.uk *Timber importers & saw millers* Also at: Felling

Thompsons, Boxwood Street, Blackburn, BB1 9TW Tel: (01254) 691348 Fax: (01254) 695122 *Removal contractors*

Thomson Ltd, Monk Fryston Park, Betteras Hill Road, Hillam, Leeds, LS25 5PF Tel: (01977) 686100 Fax: (01977) 686149 E-mail: main@thomson-group.co.uk *Mechanical engineers & environmental cleaners*

Thomson Bros, D2 Up A Ringway, Bounds Green Industrial Estate, London, N11 2UD Tel: (020) 8361 1222 Fax: (020) 8361 1666 E-mail: enquiries@thomsonbrothers.com *Kitchens manufrs*

▶ Thomson Construction, 3 Old Farm Road, Ayr, KA8 9ST Tel: (01292) 267477

The Thomson Corporation P.L.C., 1st Floor, 180 Wardour Street, London, W1A 4YG Tel: (020) 7437 9787 Fax: (020) 7734 0561 *Holding company*

Thomson & Douglas Ltd, Kingston Place, Kingsmuir, Forfar, Angus, DD8 2RG Tel: (01307) 466952 Fax: (01307) 462270 E-mail: tdj@freenetname.co.uk *Building contractors & joinery manufrs*

Thomson Engineering, 66 Whitehill Road, Glenrothes, Fife, KY6 2RP Tel: 01592 774345 *Waste skip manufrs*

Thomson Financial Ltd, Aldgate House, 33 Aldgate High Street, London, EC3N 1DL Tel: (020) 7369 7000 Fax: (020) 7369 7240 *Computerised financial information providers and publishers of magazines and journals relating to the capital markets.*

▶ Thomson Henry J Haulage Contractor, Kirkwood, Inverurie, Aberdeenshire, AB51 7LQ Tel: (01330) 833570 Fax: (01330) 833650

Thomson & Jardine Joiners, Lanefoot, Rotchell Gardens, Dumfries, DG2 7SL Tel: (01387) 265032 Fax: (01387) 264635 *Joinery manufacturers*

Thomson & Joseph Ltd, 119 Plumstead Road, Norwich, NR1 4JT Tel: (01603) 439511 Fax: (01603) 700243 E-mail: enquiries@tandj.co.uk *Chemical merchants*

Thomson Lockhart (Engineering) Ltd, 5 Simonsburn Road, Loreny Industrial Estate, Kilmarnock, Ayrshire, KA1 5LE Tel: (01563) 527398 Fax: (01563) 522710 E-mail: info@thomsonlockhart.com *Welded fabricators*

Thomson McFarlane Ltd, West Brent, Forties Road Industrial Estate, Montrose, Angus, DD10 9PA Tel: (01674) 677077 Fax: (01674) 677999 *Steel stockholders*

Thomson Net G Ltd, 1 Hogarth Business Park, Burlington Lane, London, W4 2TJ Tel: (020) 8994 4404 Fax: (020) 8994 5611 *Multi-media training company*

Thomson Partners Ltd, 14 Sandyford Place, Glasgow, G3 7NB Tel: 0141-248 3666 Fax: 0141-248 3404 *Executive search & selection consultants*

Thomson Pettie, Canal Bank Estate, Seabegs Road, Bonnybridge, Stirlingshire, FK4 2BP Tel: (01324) 815747 Fax: (01324) 819072 *Engineering & architectural metalworkers*

▶ Thomson Pettie Ltd, Whiteshaw Engr Works, Carluke, Lanarkshire, ML8 5EJ Tel: (01555) 771062 *Steel tubes*

Thomson Pettie Chew Products, Unit 37 Trent Valley Trading Estate, Station Road, Rugeley, Staffordshire, WS15 2HQ Tel: (01889) 574274 Fax: (01889) 578193 *Tube manipulators*

▶ Thomson Print & Packaging Ltd, 3 West Telferton, Edinburgh, EH7 6UL Tel: 0131-657 4066 Fax: 0131-657 4033

Thomson Reuters (Scientific) Ltd, 77 Hatton Gardens, London, EC1N 8JS Tel: (020) 7433 4000 Fax: (020) 7433 4001 E-mail: ts.info.emea@thomson.com Principal Export Areas: Worldwide *Research & development (industrial/contract) engineering services, patent specialists services & scientific consultants.*

Thomson Sawmills, The Sawmill, Holt Road, Felthorpe, Norwich, NR10 4DB Tel: (01603) 754442 Fax: (01603) 755409 E-mail: ENQUIRIES@THOMSON-SAWMILLS.CO.UK *Timber merchants*

Thomson Scientific Sales & Services Ltd, 3 Cults Business Park, Station Road, Cults, Aberdeen, AB15 9PE Tel: (01224) 863131 Fax: (01224) 863133 E-mail: tsss@talk21.com *Laboratory suppliers*

▶ Thomson & Wallace Ltd, 25 Shuna Place, Glasgow, G20 9ED Tel: 0141-945 0433 *Sheet metalwork engineers or fabricators*

Thomson's Suspended Ceilings, Balquharn Farm, Alva, Clackmannanshire, FK12 5NZ Tel: (01259) 763427 Fax: (01259) 769865 E-mail: fionathmsn@aol.com *Suspended ceiling suppliers*

Thong In Cheek, 59 Sunderland Street, Macclesfield, Cheshire, SK11 6HN Tel: (01625) 422860 E-mail: enquiries@thongincheek.com *Lingerie retailers*

Thor Hammer Co. Ltd, Highlands Road, Shirley, Solihull, West Midlands, B90 4NJ Tel: 0121-705 4695 Fax: 0121-705 4727 E-mail: info@thorhammer.com *Soft faced hammer & mallet manufrs*

Thor Overseas Ltd, Ramsgate Road, Margate, Kent, CT9 4JY Tel: (01843) 227681 Fax: (01843) 298813 E-mail: mailbox@thor-int.co.uk *Chemical exporters & manufrs*

Thor Specialities UK Ltd, Wincham Avenue, Wincham, Northwich, Cheshire, CW9 6GB Tel: (01606) 818800 Fax: (01606) 818801 E-mail: info@thor.com *Biocides chemical products textile & cosmetic preserves manufrs*

Thor UK Plastics Ltd, Unit B & C Ranalah Estate, New Road, Newhaven, East Sussex, BN9 0EH Tel: (01273) 611444 Fax: (01273) 611113 E-mail: sales@thoruk.co.uk *Plastics fabricators*

Thorcom Network Services Ltd, Unit 4 96b Blackpole Trading Estate We, St, Worcester, WR3 8TJ Tel: (01905) 756700 Fax: (01905) 755777 E-mail: sales@thorcom.co.uk *Mobile communication systems manufrs*

Thorite, Thorite House, Laisterdyke, Bradford, West Yorkshire, BD4 8BZ Tel: (01274) 663471 Fax: (01274) 668296 E-mail: info@thorite.co.uk *Air compressor distributors & installation services*

Thorite Ltd, 55 Lowfields Road, Leeds, LS12 6BS Tel: 0113-244 4554 Fax: 0113-242 4700 E-mail: leeds@thorite.co.uk *Pneumatics distributors*

Thorite - Sheffield, Thorite Air Centre, 5 Bamforth Street, Hillsborough, Sheffield, S6 2HD Tel: 0114-233 1128 Fax: 0114-233 1140 E-mail: sheffield@thorite.co.uk *Industrial air compressors systems & installations, pneumatics*

Thorlux Lighting P.L.C., Merse Road, North Moons Moat, Redditch, Worcestershire, B98 9HH Tel: (01527) 583200 Fax: (01527) 584177 E-mail: marketing@thorlux.co.uk *Electric light fittings manufrs*

▶ Thorn Air Conditioning, Unit 27, Vastre Industrial Estate, Newtown, Powys, SY16 1DZ Tel: (01686) 623100 Fax: (01686) 623200 *Air conditioning designers*

Thorn Cycles, 91-93 St. John Street, Bridgwater, Somerset, TA6 5HX Tel: (01278) 441526 E-mail: sales@sjcycles.com *Cycle manufacturer & distributor*

▶ Thorn Joinery, 115 College Street, Irthlingborough, Wellingborough, Northamptonshire, NN9 5TU Tel: (01933) 653991 Fax: (01933) 653991 E-mail: thornjoinery@msm.com *Bespoke furniture, kitchens, conservation doors, windows*

Thorn Lighting Ltd, Silver Screens, Elstree Way, Borehamwood, Hertfordshire, WD6 1FE Tel: (0870) 1610710 Fax: (020) 8732 9801 *Lighting manufrs*

Thornavon Ltd, Unit 4 Brook Street Business Centre, Brook Street, Colchester, CO1 2UZ Tel: (01206) 796888 Fax: (01206) 796889 E-mail: thornavon@tiscali.co.uk *Noise control equipment engineers*

Thornbridge Sawmills Ltd, Laurieston Road, Grangemouth, Stirlingshire, FK3 8XX Tel: (01324) 612121 Fax: (01324) 612100 *Timber importers & saw millers*

Thornbury Clothing Co., 25 Thornbury Road, Birmingham, B20 3DE Tel: 0121-356 6777 Fax: 0121-344 4050 *Textile merchants & manufrs*

Thornbury Manufacturing Ltd, Darklake View, Estover, Plymouth, PL6 7TL Tel: (01752) 696697 Fax: (01752) 696698 E-mail: sales@tml-ltd.com *Plastic injection mouldings precision metal pressings & assembly services*

Thornbury Refrigeration Co., 34 Mill Lane, Witham, Essex, CM8 1BP Tel: (01376) 520391 Fax: (01376) 515095 *Commercial refrigeration wholesalers*

Thornbush Components & Tooling, 156 Woodland Drive, Hove, East Sussex, BN3 6DE Tel: (01273) 383972 Fax: (01273) 881771 E-mail: greenlee@thornbush.co.uk *Cables ties suppliers*

▶ Thorncraft Motorcycles, 258a Whalley New Road, Blackburn, BB1 9SR Tel: (01254) 264230 Fax: (01254) 680156 E-mail: sales@thorncraft.co.uk *Motorcycle parts sales & accessories suppliers*

Thorndon Security & Electrical Services, Cornerway 40a, Well Lane, Galleywood, Chelmsford, CM2 8QY Tel: (01245) 281880 Fax: (01245) 475233 *Burglar alarm installers*

Sandra Thorndyke, 12a Wellesley Road, Tharston, Norwich, NR15 2PD Tel: (01508) 532394 Fax: (01508) 532394 *Contract workwear equipment services*

▶ Thorne Air Conditioning, 35 Mere View Industrial Estate, Yaxley, Peterborough, PE7 3HS Tel: (01733) 240200 Fax: (01733) 244554

Thorne & Derrick, Units 9-10 Birchills Trading Estate, Emery Road, Bristol, BS4 5PF Tel: 0117-977 4647 Fax: 0117-977 5582 E-mail: southernsales@thorneandderrick.co.uk *Cable jointing & cable accessories suppliers*

Thorne & Derrick, Units 5 & 6 Gear House, Saltmeadows Road, Gateshead, Tyne & Wear, NE8 3AH Tel: 0191-490 1547 Fax: 0191-477 5371 E-mail: sales@thorneandderrick.co.uk *Power cable fittings and accessories, trace heating, tools and strapping systems.*Nationwide trace heating services - design/supply/install.*Specialist LV MV HV cable accessories distributor.*

E.H. Thorne (Beehives) Ltd, Beehive Works, Louth Road, Wragby, Market Rasen, Lincolnshire, LN8 5LA Tel: (01673) 858555 Fax: (01673) 857004 E-mail: sales@thorne.co.uk *Beekeeping equipment & candlemaking suppliers*

Thorne Engineers Ltd, Millfield Industrial Estate, York, YO19 6NA Tel: 01904 448890 *General engineers*

H.L. Thorne & Co. Ltd, Hainge Road, Tividale, Oldbury, West Midlands, B69 2PA Tel: 0121-557 6155 Fax: 0121-557 3747 E-mail: info@thorneltd.co.uk *Scrap metal merchants*

Thorne Hydraulics Ltd, Unit 24 Frontier Works, 12 King Edward Road, Thorne, Doncaster, South Yorkshire, DN8 4HU Tel: (01405) 816067 Fax: (01405) 741060 *Hydraulic ram repair specialists*

Thorne International Boiler Services Ltd, Broad Lanes, Bilston, West Midlands, WV14 0RQ Tel: (01902) 404223 Fax: (01902) 404224 E-mail: info@tibsltd.com *Manufacturers & service of boilers*

▶ Thorne Offset Ltd, Unit 4 Mercy Terrace, London, SE13 7UX Tel: (020) 8690 8233 Fax: (020) 8690 9860

Thorne Printing & Publishing Co. Ltd, 272 Friern Barnet Lane, London, N20 0NH Tel: (020) 8446 9910 Fax: (020) 8445 5864 E-mail: thorneprinting@aol.com *Commercial & general printers*

Thornell Veneers Ltd, Rushey Lane, Birmingham, B11 2BL Tel: 0121-707 7077 Fax: 0121-706 6165 *Wood veneered panel manufacturers & door specialists*

▶ Paul Thorney, 17 Bridgeman Rd, Oswestry, Shropshire, SY11 2JP Tel: (01691) 654610 E-mail: PlThrn@aol.com *Gems of Brilliance UK is THE source for loose diamonds.Providing for retail,trade and private investors worldwide*

Thornford Transmissions, Unit 4 Station Approach, Yetminster, Sherborne, Dorset, DT9 6LH Tel: (01935) 872500 Fax: (01935) 872779 *Gearbox distributors*

Thornhill Fibres Ltd, North Street, Rotherham, South Yorkshire, S60 1LG Tel: (01709) 370707 Fax: (01709) 830300 *Cellulose fibre manufrs*

▶ Thornhill Galleries, 3, 19 Osiers Road, London, SW18 1NL Tel: (020) 8874 2101 Fax: (020) 8877 0313 E-mail: sales@thornhillgalleries.co.uk *Suppliers of superb quality marble, wood & stone antique fireplaces*

Thornhill Holdings Ltd, 77 South Audley Street, London, W1K 1DX Tel: (020) 7629 0662 Fax: (020) 7629 7332 E-mail: thornhill@thornhill.co.uk *Investment management services*

Thornhill Service UK Ltd, Springvale Indust Estate, Park Springs Road, Grimethorpe, Barnsley, South Yorkshire, S72 7PT Tel: (01226) 710000 Fax: (01226) 717172 E-mail: sales@thornhill-ltd.co.uk *Heat exchanger servicing*

Thornleigh Fabrications Ltd, Unit 25, Thornleigh Trading Estate, Dudley, West Midlands, DY2 8UB Tel: (01384) 238574 Fax: (01384) 238086 *Steel fabricators*

Thornpark Ltd, B1-B2 Pegasus Court, Ardglen Road, Whitchurch, Hampshire, RG28 7BP Tel: (01256) 896161 Fax: (01256) 896162 E-mail: sales@thornpark.co.uk *Wire erosion & precision engineers*

▶ Thorns Catering Hire Equipment, 1 Newhaven Business Park, Barton Lane, Eccles, Manchester, M30 0HH Tel: 0161-788 9064 Fax: 0161-788 9103 *Catering equipment hire services*

Thorns Furniture & Catering Hire plc, C 125 Brantwood Road, London, N17 0DX Tel: (020) 8801 4444 Fax: (020) 8801 4445 E-mail: contact@thorns.co.uk *Catering equipment hire*

A.A. Thornton & Co., 235 High Holborn, London, WC1V 7LE Tel: (020) 7405 4044 Fax: (020) 7405 3580 E-mail: aat@aathornton.com Purchasing Contact: J. Barnes Sales Contact: J. Barnes Principal Export Areas: Worldwide *Patent & trade mark agents/attorneys. Also patent & (European) attorneys*

Thornton Heath Dry Cleaners, 92 Brigstock Road, Thornton Heath, Surrey, CR7 7JA Tel: (020) 8683 2589 Fax: (020) 8240 0081 E-mail: thdiy-ltd@ukgateway.net *Builders merchants Also at: London SW16*

Thornton Industries (UK) Ltd, Thornton Ho, Dock La, Shipley, W. Yorkshire, BD17 7BE Tel: (01274) 598694 Fax: (01274) 531577 E-mail: sales@tiukltd.net *Food processing equipment manufrs*

Thornton International, Unit 1-3 Denver Industrial Estate, 44 Ferry Lane, Rainham, Essex, RM13 9YH Tel: (01233) 740009 Fax: (01708) 557353 E-mail: thornton.international@btinternet.com Principal Export Areas: Worldwide *Stainless steel tanks, chemical storage*

Thornton Kelley & Co. Ltd, Spring Place Mills, Northorpe, Mirfield, West Yorkshire, WF14 0QT Tel: (01924) 493128 Fax: (01924) 495119 E-mail: david@thorntonkelley.co.uk *Yarn manufacturers, staple & multifilament in all fibres for weaving, sewing tufting & knitting, twisting, winding, beaming & dyeing, commission processing also undertaken*

Thornton & Ross Ltd, Linthwaite, Huddersfield, HD7 5QH Tel: (01484) 842217 Fax: (01484) 847301 E-mail: mail@thorntonross.com *Pharmaceutical manufrs*

Thorntons plc, Head Office, Thornton Park, Somercotes, Alfreton, Derbyshire, DE55 4XJ Tel: (01773) 540550 Fax: (01773) 540757 E-mail: tplccustserve@thorntons.co.uk *Manufacturer of confectionery*

Thornwood Designs, 6 Top Factory, Cringle Lane, Stoke Rochford, Grantham, Lincolnshire, NG33 5EF Tel: (01476) 530600 Fax: (01476) 577544 E-mail: info@lampstyle.com *Woodturning & furniture restoration services*

Thorogood Associates Ltd, Dralda House, 24-28 Crendon Street, High Wycombe, Buckinghamshire, HP13 6LS Tel: (01494) 684200 Fax: (01494) 684223 *Computer consultants*

Thorogood Timber plc, Colchester Road, Ardleigh, Colchester, CO7 7PQ Tel: (01206) 233100 Fax: (01206) 233115 E-mail: sales@thorogood.co.uk *Timber merchants, millers & machinists*

Thoroughbred Covers, 20 East Causeway Vale, Leeds, LS16 8LG Tel: 0113-261 0695 Fax: 0113 2310835 *Car cover manufrs*

▶ Thoroughclean Services, 4 Deemouth Business Centre, South Esplanade East, Aberdeen, AB11 9PB Tel: (01224) 891570 Fax: (01224) 891540 E-mail: sales@thoroughclean.co.uk *Office Cleaning Services, janitorial supplies*

Thorowgood Ltd, The Saddlery, Fryers Road, Bloxwich, Walsall, WS3 2XJ Tel: (01922) 711676 Fax: (01922) 711654 E-mail: enquiries@thorowgood.co.uk *Saddle manufrs*

Thorp Modelmakers Ltd, Whitmore Lane, Sunningdale Village, Ascot, Berkshire, SL5 0NS Tel: (01344) 876776 Fax: (01344) 876583 E-mail: thorp@atomltd.com *Scale model makers*

Thorpe Contracts Ltd, Worksop Road, Thorpe Salvin, Worksop, Nottinghamshire, S80 3JX Tel: (01909) 501414 Fax: (01909) 770767 *Conveyor belt buyers & suppliers*

Thorpe Horse Boxes, Tendring Road, Thorpe-le-Soken, Clacton-on-Sea, Essex, CO16 0AA Tel: (01255) 862411 Fax: (01255) 862340 E-mail: sales@thorpehorseboxes.com *Horse box manufrs*

Thorpe Packaging Ltd, Ripley Drive, Normanton Industrial Estate, Normanton, West Yorkshire, WF6 1QT Tel: (01924) 898802 Fax: (01924) 898803 E-mail: peter@thorpepackaging.sagehost.co.uk *Packaging merchants*

Richard Thorpe Fire Safety Services, Melbreak, Hazel Road, Ash Green, Aldershot, Hampshire, GU12 6HR Tel: (01252) 316330 E-mail: sales@richardthorpefire.co.uk *Fire safety equipment retailers*

Thorpes Of Great Glen Ltd, Church Road, Great Glen, Leicester, LE8 9FE Tel: 0116-259 3888 Fax: 0116-259 2016 E-mail: thorpes@bespoke-joinery.co.uk *Furniture manufrs*

Thorworld Industries Ltd, Unit 37, Station Lane Industrial Estate, Old Whittington, Chesterfield, Derbyshire, S41 9QX Tel: (01246) 260981 Fax: (01246) 260493 E-mail: info@thorworld.co.uk *Loading bay equipment suppliers & manufrs*

Thos Kelly & Co., Dromore Street, Ballynahinch, County Down, BT24 8AG Tel: (028) 9756 2380 Fax: (028) 9756 1564 *Wallpaper & paint distributors*

Thos P Headland (Machine Tools) Ltd, Unit 4 Blackwater Close, Fairview Industrial Park, Manor Way, Rainham, Essex, RM13 8UA Tel: (01708) 523916 Fax: (01708) 550042 E-mail: machines@tphmachinetools.co.uk *Machine tool merchants*

Thos Winnard & Sons Ltd, Sandbeck Way, Hellaby Industrial Estate, Rotherham, South Yorkshire, S66 8QL Tel: (01709) 542342 Fax: (01709) 701189 *Brake drums manufrs*

▶ Thou Art In Hampstead Ltd, 106 Mill Lane, London, NW6 1NF Tel: (020) 7431 0701 Fax: (020) 8444 4446 E-mail: info@thouartinhampstead.co.uk *Art supply & picture framing service*

▶ Thought Consultancy Ltd, 15 High Bridge, Newcastle upon Tyne, NE1 1EW Tel: 0191-269 3420 Fax: 0191-269 3429 E-mail: enquiries@thought.co.uk *Website design & development services*

▶ Thought Technologies Ltd, Suite 28, 2 Upper York Street, Bristol, BS2 8QN Tel: 0117-924 8277

▶ Ben Thow Ltd, Spires Business Units, Mugiemoss Road, Bucksburn, Aberdeen, AB21 9NY Tel: (01224) 699466 Fax: (01224) 699468

Thow Blockmakers, 13 Old Glamis Road, Dundee, DD3 8JB Tel: (01382) 823824 Fax: (01382) 823825 *Sack printing block manufrs*

Harry Thow & Co., 11 Crown Street, Ayr, KA8 8AG Tel: (01292) 264115 Fax: (01292) 282531 E-mail: h.thow@connectfree.co.uk *Glazing contractors*

Thread & Pipe Services Ltd, 26 Elliott Road, Bournemouth, BH11 8JZ Tel: (01202) 576789 Fax: (01202) 579816 E-mail: sales@threadandpipe.com *Hydraulic equipment distributors*

▶ Thread-bare, 72 Berecroft, Harlow, Essex, CM18 7SB Tel: (07736) 833632 E-mail: clare@thread-bare.co.uk *Greeting card maker*

Threaded Fastener Supplies Ltd, 72 & 73 Heming Rd, Washford, Redditch, Worcs, B98 0EA Tel: (01527) 518533 Fax: (01527) 518527 E-mail: threaded.fastener@virgin.net Purchasing Contact: M. Brace Sales Contact: M. Brace *Fastener (industrial) distributors/agents/ stockholders & screws, machine*

Richard Threadgill Associates, Tetra, 28a Grafton Square, London, SW4 0DB Tel: (020) 7207 1710 Fax: (020) 7622 2734 E-mail: richard@richardthreadgillassociates.co.uk *Architectural model manufrs*

Threading Systems Ltd, Unit 11 Park Road, Dukinfield, Cheshire, SK16 5LL Tel: 0161-330 7277 Fax: 0161-330 6384 *Manufacture of threading systems*

Threadmaster Gauges Ltd, Princes Dr Industrial Estate, Coventry Road, Kenilworth, Warwickshire, CV8 2FD Tel: (01926) 852428 Fax: (01926) 850047 E-mail: sales@threadmastergauges.co.uk *Screw & plain gauge manufrs*

Threadneedle Asset Management Ltd, 60 St Mary Axe, London, EC3A 8JQ Tel: (020) 7621 9100 Fax: (020) 7626 1266 *Investment management services*

Threadrive Components Ltd, The Gloucesters, Crompton Close, Basildon, Essex, SS14 3AY Tel: (01268) 288880 Fax: (01268) 288879 E-mail: sales@threadrive.co.uk *Specialist in the supply of screwdriver tooling for the aviation and aerospace industry. Also specialist stockists of the Nord-Lock bolt securing system.*

▶ Threads-Europe, 8 Lea Drive, Wimboldsley, Middlewich, Cheshire, CW10 0LX Tel: (01270) 526397 Fax: (01270) 526397 E-mail: julian@threads-europe.com *we supply metal polishing kits and supplies also lathe cutting tools and other types of tooling*

Thredgards Ltd, Milne House, Ward Street, Alloa, Clackmannanshire, FK10 1ET Tel: (01259) 218181 Fax: (01259) 212777 E-mail: david.haswell@thredgards.com *Plastic injection moulders*

▶ Three Bears Babywear, Cartwright Street, Wolverhampton, WV2 3BT Tel: (01902) 870838 Fax: (01902) 352005 *Children's wear manufrs*

Three Bears Playthings, Steward House, Rothbury, Morpeth, Northumberland, NE65 7TL Tel: (01669) 620315 Fax: (01669) 621900 E-mail: wwwthreebearsplay@aol.com *Educational equipment suppliers*

▶ Three Counties Computers, 14 Woodsage Drive, Gillingham, Dorset, SP8 4UF Tel: (01747) 823994 E-mail: sales@threecountiescomputers.co.uk

Three Counties Concrete Ltd, Grove House Yard, Tewkesbury Road, Upton-upon-Severn, Worcester, WR8 0PW Tel: (01684) 594464 Fax: (01684) 594940 *Ready mix concrete manufrs*

Three Counties Fire Protection, 43 Station Road, Foxton, Cambridge, CB22 6SA Tel: (01223) 510878 Fax: 01223 510878 *Fire fighting equipment distributor*

Three Counties Fixings Ltd, 6 Capital Place, Harlow, Essex, CM19 5AS Tel: (01279) 451631 Fax: (01279) 451617 E-mail: tcfltd@msn.com *Distributors or agents of l building systems*

Three Counties Fluid Power, Unit 26 Albany Trading Estate, Albany Street, Newport, Gwent, NP20 5NQ Tel: (01633) 853956 Fax: (01633) 852832 E-mail: sales@threecounties.homestead.com *Pneumatic control/equipment systems*

Three Counties Fluid Power, Unit 26 Albany Trading Estate, Albany Street, Newport, Gwent, NP20 5NQ Tel: (01633) 853956 Fax: (01633) 852832 E-mail: sales@threecounties.homestead.com *Pneumatic valve fittings*

▶ Three Counties Property Maintenance, Aylward Drive, Stevenage, Hertfordshire, SG2 8UR Tel: (01438) 748208 Fax: (01438) 759299 E-mail: info@threecountiespropertymaintenance.co.uk *Property maintenance from small house to large residential tower blocks*

Three Counties Refrigeration Ltd, PO Box 42, Saffron Walden, Essex, CB10 2BQ Tel: (01799) 523811 Fax: (01799) 523800 *Air conditioning suppliers & installers services*

Three D Sports, The Runnings, Cheltenham, Gloucestershire, GL51 9NJ Tel: (01242) 241819 Fax: (01242) 222994 E-mail: sales@3dsports.co.uk *Specialist cricket equipment suppliers*

Three Pears Ltd, 6 Station Road Industrial Estate, Station Road, Rowley Regis, West Midlands, B65 0JY Tel: 0121-559 5351 Fax: 0121-559 5353 E-mail: edunn@btconnect.com *Toiletries, perfume, pharmaceutical & household wholesalers* Also at: Birmingham & Wednesfield

Three R Display Ltd, 28 Whiteley Croft Rise, Otley, West Yorkshire, LS21 3NR Tel: (01943) 466553 Fax: (01943) 466552 E-mail: threer@btconnect.com *Shop fixtures manufrs*

Three Spires Finishing Systems Ltd, 45 Lanes Close, Kings Bromley, Burton-on-Trent, Staffordshire, DE13 7JS Tel: (01543) 473069 Fax: (01543) 473069 E-mail: info@threespiresfinishing.co.uk *To provide design, manufacture, installation and commissioning of paint finishing plant. Pre-treatment, Wet dip or spray, Powder coating, Electro-coating, Ovens (batch or conveyorised), Conveyors, Plant modifications and re-locations, spares and service contracts (burners, instrumentation calibration, etc)for new and existing plant and equipment.*

Three Star Plastics, Unit B Spencer Avenue, London, N13 4TR Tel: (020) 8881 4179 Fax: (020) 8881 4179 *Plastic products manufrs*

Three Valleys Water plc, PO Box 48, Hatfield, Hertfordshire, AL10 9HL Tel: (01707) 268111 Fax: (01707) 277333 *Public water service*

ThreeBond Europe SAS, 5 Newmarket Court, Kingston, Milton Keynes, MK10 0AS Tel: (01908) 285000 Fax: (01908) 285001 E-mail: mark.beeson@threebond.co.uk *Manufacturers of adhesives*

3663, Unit 12, Severnbridge Industrial Estate, Symondscliffe Way, Caldicot, Gwent, NP26 5YA Tel: (0870) 3663661 Fax: (0870) 3663669 *3663 First for Foodservice is the UK's leading foodservice company with sales of over £1 billion a year. We deliver quality ingredients, finished products and equipment to the catering industry.*

3663, Hickling Road, Kingswood Lakeside, Cannock, Staffordshire, WS11 8JH Tel: (0870) 3663461 Fax: (01543) 405503 *3663 First for Foodservice is the UK's leading foodservice company with sales of over £1 billion a year. We deliver quality ingredients, finished products and equipment to the catering industry.*

3663, Lee Mill Industrial Estate, Central Avenue, Ivybridge, Devon, PL21 9EW Tel: (0870) 3663601 Fax: (01752) 632 036 *3663 First for Foodservice is the UK's leading foodservice company with sales of over £1 billion a year. We deliver quality ingredients, finished products and equipment to the catering industry.*

3663, Langdon Road, Prince Of Wales Dock, Swansea, SA1 8QY Tel: (0870) 3663231 Fax: (0870) 3663239 *3663 First for Foodservice is the UK's leading foodservice company with sales of over £1 billion a year. We deliver quality ingredients, finished products and equipment to the catering industry.*

Threeways Manufacturing, Unit 2a Larpool La Industrial Estate, Whitby, North Yorkshire, YO22 4LX Tel: (01947) 821831 Fax: (01947) 821831 *Fitted furniture manufrs*

Threlfall Ltd, near Moss Farm Gulf Lane, Cockerham, Lancaster, LA2 0ER Tel: (01253) 799198 Fax: (01253) 790043 E-mail: enquiry@nearmossfarm.co.uk *Land drainage services*

Threshold Floorings Ltd, Marston Gate, South Marston Park, Swindon, SN3 4TQ Tel: (01793) 764301 Fax: (01793) 765319 E-mail: sales@thresholdflr.co.uk *Entrancing flooring dust barrier matting manufrs*

Thringstone News, 20-22 Main Street, Thringstone, Coalville, Leicestershire, LE67 8NA Tel: (01530) 222355 Fax: 01530 222533 *Aquarium & pond supplies*

Thrislington (NI) Ltd, Unit 38 Mallusk Enterprise Park, Mallusk Drive, Newtownabbey, County Antrim, BT36 4GN Tel: (028) 9084 1200 Fax: (028) 9084 4120 E-mail: thrislington@nireland.com *Partitioning contractors*

Thrislington Products Ltd, Durham Way South, Aycliffe Industrial Park, Newton Aycliffe, County Durham, DL5 6SW Tel: (01325) 301333 Fax: (01325) 301444 E-mail: sales@thrislington.co.uk *Steel demountable partition manufrs*

▶ Thrower & Hammond Ltd, Delta Close, Norwich, NR6 6BG Tel: (01603) 424210 Fax: (01603) 424201

▶ Thrower Signs, 54 Linersh Wood Close, Bramley, Guildford, Surrey, GU5 0EQ Tel: (01483) 894257 Fax: (01483) 890329 E-mail: simon@throwersigns.co.uk *Sign makers & sign writers*

▶ Thruxton Motor Sports Centre, Unit 29, Thruxton, Andover, Hampshire, SP11 8PW Tel: (01264) 882222 Fax: (01264) 882201 E-mail: sales@thruxtonracing.co.uk *Organize driving events, driving experience on a race circuit*

Thruxton Press Ltd, Thruxton Down House, Thruxton, Andover, Hampshire, SP11 8PR Tel: (01264) 889552 Fax: (01264) 889622 E-mail: publications@brunton.co.uk *Lithographic origination, plate makers printers & publishers*

Thule Ltd, Five C Business Centre, Concorde Drive, Clevedon, Avon, BS21 6UH Tel: (01275) 340404 Fax: (01275) 340686 E-mail: sales@thule.co.uk Principal Export Areas: Africa *Cycle carriers, roof boxes, roof racks & ski racks for cars*

▶ Thumbprint Animation, 120 Whitelands Avenue, Chorleywood, Rickmansworth, Hertfordshire, WD3 5RG Tel: (01923) 285754 Fax: (01923) 283903 E-mail: info@thumbprintanimation.co.uk *Thumbprint provides high end 3D graphics and 2D post for film, television and visualization industries.*

▶ Thumbprint (Cirencester) Ltd, Wilkinson Road, Love Lane, Cirencester, Gloucestershire, GL7 1YT Tel: (01285) 656927 Fax: (01285) 659134 E-mail: frank@thumbprint.uk.net *Digital printing services*

▶ Thumbprint Design, 37 St. Leonards Street, Stamford, Lincolnshire, PE9 2HL Tel: (07949) 330316 E-mail: enquiry@thumb-print.co.uk *Thumbprint Design offers graphic and web design services at competitive rates.*

▶ Thunder Communications, Perth, PH1 5ND Tel: (01738) 587907

Thunder Engineering, 1 Garfield Street, Leicester, LE4 5GF Tel: 0116-253 1105 Fax: 0116-253 1105 *Precision engineers*

Thurlaston Instrument Services, 5 Church Street, Thurlaston, Leicester, LE9 7TA Tel: (01455) 888484 E-mail: sales@thurlaston.com *Industrial electronic suppliers*

Thurlow Nunn, Cromer Road, Holt, Norfolk, NR25 6EU Tel: (01263) 713206 Fax: (01263) 713207 *Vauxhall dealers & body shop repair service providers*

Thurlow Nunn Standen Ltd, Lisle Lane, Ely, Cambridgeshire, CB7 4AE Tel: (01353) 662871 Fax: (01353) 663480 E-mail: agsales@tnsgroup.co.uk *Agricultural engineers*

Thurlow Nunn Standen Ltd, 61 The Street, Melton, Woodbridge, Suffolk, IP12 1PN Tel: (01394) 382801 Fax: (01394) 384330 E-mail: adrianbrown@tnsgroup.co.uk *Agricultural & horticultural suppliers*

Thurlow Tools, 79a Westbury Avenue, London, N22 6SA Tel: (020) 8889 1217 *Toolmakers & precision engineers*

Thurnham Contracts, Coldharbour Farm, Cold Harbour Lane, Thurnham, Maidstone, Kent, ME14 3LS Tel: (01622) 880427 Fax: (01622) 880698 *Office designers & refurbishers*

Thurrock Flue Co, Sandy Lane, West Thurrock, Grays, Essex, RM20 4BH Tel: (01708) 864908 Fax: (01708) 869200 *Concrete products supply & manufrs*

Thurrock Fork Lift Trucks, 43 King Edwards Road, South Woodham Ferrers, Chelmsford, CM3 5PQ Tel: (01245) 323256 *Fork lift trucks maintenance*

Thurroclean, Thompson Road, Trafford Park, Manchester, M17 1SE Tel: 0161-848 0821 Fax: 0161-848 0359 E-mail: info@tt-group.co.uk *Tanker cleaning & repairers*

Thurston, 110 High Street, Edgware, Middlesex, HA8 7HF Tel: (020) 8952 2002 Fax: (020) 8952 0222 E-mail: thurston@eaclare.co.uk *Bowls, bingo & indoor game snooker table manufrs*

Thurston, Clare House, 46-48 St. Anne Street, Liverpool, L3 3DW Tel: 0151-482 2700 Fax: 0151-298 1134 E-mail: thurston@eaclare.co.uk *Billiard snooker & pool table manufrs* Also at: Birmingham & Edgware

Albert Thurston Ltd, 3 Frog Island, Leicester, LE3 5AG Tel: 0116-262 7515 Fax: 0116-251 3607 E-mail: sales@albertthurston.com Principal Export Areas: Worldwide *Manufacturers of leather & imitation leather/garment belts & men's fashion braces & garment accessories. Also webbing strap manufrs*

Thurston Building Systems, Quarry Hill Industrial Estate, Hawking Croft Road, Horbury, Wakefield, West Yorkshire, WF4 6AJ Tel: (01924) 265461 Fax: (01924) 280246 E-mail: sales@thurstongroup.co.uk Principal Export Areas: Central/East Europe & West Europe *Manufacturers of portable, prefabricated & complete systems*

Thurston Engineering Ltd, Hallsford Bridge Industrial Estate, Stondon Road, Ongar, Essex, CM5 9RB Tel: (01277) 362135 Fax: (01277) 365076 E-mail: sales@thurstonengineering.co.uk *Engine reconditioners*

Thurton Foundries Ltd, Loddon Rd, Thurton, Norwich, NR14 6AN Tel: (01508) 480301 Fax: (01508) 480303 E-mail: sales@thurtonfoundries.co.uk Purchasing Contact: M. Newton Sales Contact: I. Capps *Thurton Foundries Ltd, based in Norwich are manufactures of Castings in Grey Iron, Ductile Iron, Aluminium, Brass, Bronze, Zinc & Lead.* Metals cast here are:-*Grey Iron From 0.5kg to 6000kg. BS EN 1561 1997 Grades 150 to 300. Capacity 25 tonnes per week.* Ductile Iron From 0.5kg to 1500kg BS EN 1563 1997 Grades 350/22 to 900/2* Capacity 10 tonnes per week.* aluminium All BS 1490 grades in particular LM4,6,13,25 and 31. Capacity 3 tonnes per week.* Brass All BS1400 1985 Grades in particular SCB1, 3 DCB3. Capacity 4 tonnes per week.* Bronze All BS1400 1985. In particular PB1,2,LG1,2HTB1,2. Capacity 4 tonnes per week.* Lead Pure and with Antimony. Capacity 10 tonnes per week.* Within the foundry we also manufacture Die Castings. We produce our own cast iron dies using Solidworks 2006 for CAD and Edgecam for the CAM. Metals cast in this cell are Aluminium LM6 and LM25.* Our facilities include a full machining and inspection service.*

Thwaites Ltd, Welsh Road Works, Leamington Spa, Warwickshire, CV32 7NQ Tel: (01926) 422471 Fax: (01926) 337155 E-mail: name@thwaitesdumpers.co.uk *Dumper & digger manufrs*

▶ Thymus Solutions Ltd., 59, Bispham Rd, Park Royal, London, London, NW10 7HB Tel: 0208 998-9292 Fax: 0208 998-9292 E-mail: anthony@tsl.in *Thymus provides a variety of information capture and outsourcing services including: document scanning, forms processing, document imaging, data processing services, data conversion, data entry services, optical character recognition (OCR), intelligent character recognition (ICR), electronic publishing, digital publishing, imaging services, indexing services, and PDF conversion. We also offer consulting services to provide clients with turnkey document capture and management solutions and/or web based document management services.*

▶ Thyson Technology Ltd, 264 Manchester Road, Warrington, WA1 3RB Tel: (01925) 575600 Fax: (01925) 575660

▶ Thyssen, 26 Anderson Place, Edinburgh, EH6 5NP Tel: 0131-555 3471 Fax: 0131-553 3984 *Installs maintenance & repairs, elevators, lifts & escalators*

▶ Thyssen, 26 Anderson Place, Edinburgh, EH6 5NP Tel: 0131-555 3471 Fax: 0131-553 3984

Thyssen & Krupp Automotive, 2200 Talbot Road, Fareham, Hampshire, PO15 5RY Tel: (01329) 844231 Fax: (01329) 844218 *Car component manufrs*

Thyssen Krupp Automotive Systems UK Ltd, Seven Stars Industrial Estate, Wheeler Road, Whitley, Coventry, CV3 4LB Tel: (024) 7621 7700 Fax: (024) 7621 7701 *Automotive component suppliers*

Thyssen Lifts & Esculators Ltd, 4Th Floor Maple House, High Street, Potters Bar, Hertfordshire, EN6 5BS Tel: (01707) 672000 Fax: (01707) 672011 *Lifts & escalators*

ThyssenKrupp Accessibility, 62 Boston Road, Leicester, LE4 1AW Tel: 0116-234 4310 Fax: 0116-236 4134 E-mail: info@TKAccessibility.com *Manufacturers and suppliers of wheelchair platform lifts to meet with DDA requirements for use in public buildings and affordable seated stairlifts for all stair types.*

ThyssenKrupp Aerospace Ltd, Kiltonga Industrial Estate, Belfast Road, Newtownards, County Down, BT23 4TJ Tel: (028) 9184 4100 Fax: (028) 9184 4199 *Aluminium & stainless steel stockholders*

▶ Thyssenkrupp Elevator UK Ltd, 48 Malling Street, Lewes, East Sussex, BN7 2RH Tel: (01273) 483430 Fax: (01273) 483431 *Install lifts & elevators*

Thyssenkrupp Elevator UK Ltd, Traffic Street, Nottingham, NG2 1NF Tel: 0115-986 8213 Fax: 0115-986 1549 *Lift & escalator manufrs*

Thyssenkrupp Elevator UK Ltd, 183-185 Lower Richmond Road, Richmond, Surrey, TW9 4LN Tel: (020) 8487 1445 Fax: (020) 8487 9494 E-mail: twickenham.office@tke-uk-thyssenkrupp.com *Lift engineers, suppliers & installers*

Thyssenkrupp Krause Ltd, 2 Wells Place, Gatton Park Business Centre, Redhill, RH1 3LG Tel: (01737) 284000 Fax: (01737) 284111 E-mail: sales@krause.co.uk *Engineering*

Thyssenkrupp Materials Handling Equipment, Nene House, Sopwith Way, Drayton Fields Industrial Esta, Daventry, Northamptonshire, NN11 8PB Tel: (01327) 301199 Fax: (01327) 300681 E-mail: david@tkmh.co.uk *Bulk materials handling equipment manufrs*

Thyssenkrupp Stainless UK Ltd, Unit F Elliott Way, Holford, Birmingham, B6 7AP Tel: 0121-331 3600 Fax: 0121-331 3621 E-mail: b.newitt@acciaiterni.co.uk *Stainless steel finishing/polishing services*

Thyssenkrupp V D M UK Ltd, VDM House, 111 Hare Lane, Claygate, Esher, Surrey, KT10 0QY Tel: (01372) 467137 Fax: (01372) 466388 Principal Export Areas: Africa *Nickel alloy producers*

Tib Co., Castlebridge Office Village, Kirtley Drive, Nottingham, NG7 1LD Tel: 0115-948 6500 Fax: 0115-948 6595 E-mail: sales@tibco.com *Computer consultants*

Tibard Limited, Tibard House, Broadway, Dukinfield, Cheshire, SK16 4UU Tel: 0161-342-1000 Fax: 0161-343 2016 E-mail: sales@tibard.co.uk *Tibard offer a fully managed uniform service, ranging from the direct purchase of garments to chef's wear rental and laundry services on a nationwide scale. Tibard's ethos is flexibility, we are able to design and manufacture bespoke garments or offer 'off the peg' items at competitive prices. With over 30 years of experience with fabrics and garments*

continued

Tibard Laundry Services Ltd, Holden Street, Ashton-under-Lyne, Lancashire, OL6 9JB Tel: 0161-330 5106 Fax: 0161-339 9995 *Linen & garment hire services*

Tibbett & Britten, 10 Mossbell Road, Motherwell Food Park, Bellshill, Lanarkshire, ML4 3NW Tel: (01698) 748766 Fax: (01698) 743849 *Distributors of biscuits & snack foods*

Tibbett & Britten Group P.L.C., Centennial Park, Centennial Avenue, Elstree, Borehamwood, Hertfordshire, WD6 3TL Tel: (020) 8327 2000 Fax: (020) 8327 2199 E-mail: info@tandb.co.uk *Warehouse & distributon contractors* Also at: Branches throughout the U K

Tibbett & Britten Group P.L.C., Laverstoke Road, Allington, Maidstone, Kent, ME16 0LE Tel: (01622) 671400 Fax: (01622) 692495 *Contract distribution services*

▶ Tibe & Britten P.L.C., Camerons Wood, Nettlehill Road, Houstoun Industrial Estate, Livingston, West Lothian, EH54 5DL Tel: (01506) 474000

▶ Tichler & Co, The Office at TIMBERS, Hatching Green, Harpenden, Herts, AL5 2JP Tel: 01582 768072 *"GETTING BUSINESS FINANCED"* We provide informed and independent advice on- and help with -the entire process of obtaining business or commercial finance.**Our services include an initial no obligation evaluation, business plans through to using our knowledge of the market to locate funders to quote for your business.*

Ticino Desinex Ltd, 69 Fleet Road, Fleet, Hampshire, GU51 3PJ Tel: (01252) 621185 Fax: (01252) 811223 *Printed circuit consultants, design, develop & assemble*

Ticket Systems (UK) Ltd, 176 Hurwyn Avenue, Ruislip, Middlesex, HA4 6HJ Tel: (01895) 231575 Fax: (01895) 231575 *Ticket machine manufrs*

▶ Tickets To See.com, Lockheed House, Green Lane Business Park, London, SE9 3TL Tel: 0870 199 9742 E-mail: ken.peach@ticketstosee.com *We supply, wimbledon tennis tickets, rugby six nations tickets,football tickets, theatre tickets, concert tickets, football, ship football, wimbledon,tennis tickets,cricket, rugby, all events,ascot,arsenal tickets,manchester united,chelsea,fulham,liverpool,spurs and more.*

▶ Tickhill Agriculture & Equestrian, Roydene, Bawtry Road, Tickhill, Doncaster, South Yorkshire, DN11 9HA Tel: (01302) 743827 E-mail: cmlhoey@yahoo.co.uk *All types of lawnmower and agricultural equipment serviced and repaired. Competitive fixed price quotes*

Tickhill Plant Hire, Apy Hill Lane, Tickhill, Doncaster, South Yorkshire, DN11 9PD Tel: (01302) 742383 Fax: (01302) 750924 *Plant hire contractors*

Tickle & Reynolds, 83 Heavitree Road, Exeter, EX1 2ND Tel: (01392) 272836 Fax: (01392) 422691 E-mail: ebr@tandr.freeserve.co.uk *Analysts' chemists*

Ticona UK Ltd, Stafford Park 12, Telford, Shropshire, TF3 3BJ Tel: (01952) 292747 Fax: (01952) 292383 E-mail: don.shattuck@ticona.co.uk *Plastics compounders & distribs*

Tideland Signal Ltd, Unit B Kendal House, Victoria Way, Burgess Hill, West Sussex, RH15 9NF Tel: (01444) 872240 Fax: (01444) 872241 E-mail: sales@tidelandsignal.ltd.uk Principal Export Areas: Worldwide *Manufacturers of navigational aid, solar systems, radar beacon & buoys*

Tidenhan Saddlery & Horse Feed, Stroat Farm, Stroat, Chepstow, Gwent, NP16 7LR Tel: (01594) 529226 *Saddler & riding wear*

Tideside Ltd, 5 Bow Exchange, Yeo Street, London, E3 3QR Tel: (020) 7987 4652 Fax: (020) 7987 8612 E-mail: enquiries@tideside.co.uk *Air conditioning engineers*

Tidewater Marine North Sea Ltd, Souter Head Road, Altens Industrial Estate, Aberdeen, AB12 3LF Tel: (01224) 293000 Fax: (01224) 293001 E-mail: info@tdw.com *Ship owners*

▶ Tidey & Webb Ltd, Broomers Corner, Shipley, Horsham, West Sussex, RH13 8PX Tel: (01403) 741673 Fax: (01403) 741674

Tidmas Townsend Ltd, 208-210 Seaside, Eastbourne, East Sussex, BN22 7QS Tel: (01323) 734240 Fax: (01323) 416894 *Paper & polythene bag merchants & florist*

▶ Tie The Knot, 4 Albert Road, London, N4 3RW Tel: (07956) 245585 *wedding services, chair decor, handmade invitations, lighting, organza, napkin holders & designer table plans*

Tie Rack Ltd, 49 Regent Arcade, Regent Street, Cheltenham, Gloucestershire, GL50 1JZ Tel: (01242) 574228

Tie Rack Corporate Neckwear Ltd, Capital Interchange Way, Brentford, Middlesex, TW8 0EX Tel: (020) 8230 2300 Fax: (020) 8230 2350 E-mail: corpsales@tie-rack.co.uk *Corporate tie & scarf manufrs*

Tie Rack Corporate Neckwear Ltd, Capital Interchange Way, Brentford, Middlesex, TW8 0EX Tel: (020) 8230 2300 Fax: (020) 8230 2301 *Clothing wholesaler*

Tie & Scarf Co. Ltd, Warth Park, Radcliffe Road, Bury, Lancashire, BL9 9NB Tel: 0161-761 5151 Fax: 0161-762 0202 E-mail: tieandscarf@chaytow.com *Tie & scarf manufrs*

▶ Tie Warehouse, Unit 4, The Old Rectory Business Centre, Springhead Road, Northfleet, Gravesend, Kent, DA11 8HN Tel: (0800) 1974254 *Ties suppliers*

Tiernan Automation Ltd, 308a Melton Road, Leicester, LE4 7SL Tel: 0116-266 4000 Fax: 0116-261 0090 E-mail: sales@t-automation.fsnet.co.uk *Sheet metalwork engineers, laser cutting, sheet metal manufrs*

▶ Tierra Data Rescue, 1 Barondale Cottages, Newbattle, Dalkeith, Midlothian, EH22 3LX Tel: (0845) 0940027 Fax: (0845) 0940028 E-mail: gill@tierra.co.uk *Data recovery*

Tiertex Ltd, 67 Palatine Rd, Didsbury, Manchester, M20 3LJ Tel: 0161-446 2251 Fax: 0161-446 2589 E-mail: contact@tiertex.co.uk *Computer systems & software development*

Tierway Systems Ltd, 17 Grenville Meadows, Lostwithiel, Cornwall, PL22 0JS Tel: (01208) 871114 Fax: (01208) 871114 *Aircraft instrumentation & consultants*

Tietoenator UK Ltd, Berwick House, 8-10 Knoll Rise, Orpington, Kent, BR6 0EL Tel: (01689) 836909 Fax: (01689) 833780 E-mail: info@tietoenator.com *Computer consultants*

▶ Tiger Coatings UK Ltd, 21 Pettyfields Close, Knowle, Solihull, West Midlands, B93 9EG Tel: (01564) 778866 Fax: (01564) 778866 *Powder coatings manufrs*

Tiger Communications Ltd, 77-79 Christchurch Road, Ringwood, Hampshire, BH24 1DH Tel: (01425) 461566 Fax: (01425) 461484 E-mail: sales@tigercomms.com *Telephone call logging equipment*

▶ Tiger Consultants Ltd, Tiger House, 86 Lind Road, Sutton, Surrey, SM1 4PL Tel: (020) 8395 8922 Fax: (020) 8395 8923 E-mail: info@tigerconsultants.co.uk *Technology & business process specialists*

▶ Tiger Digital Ltd, 31 Merchants House, Collington Street, Greenwich, London, SE10 9LX Tel: (0870) 1909745 Fax: (0870) 1909745 E-mail: helpme@tigerdigital.net *Technology Procurement Centre - free solution finder for best match Internet/IT/technology services.*

Tiger Hire, Crossing Gate Farm, Thorpe Lane, Eagle, Lincoln, LN6 9DY Tel: (01522) 869641 Fax: (01522) 869641 E-mail: tigerhire@fsbdial.co.uk *Catering equipment hirers*

Tiger Information Sytems, Unit 4E, Newton Court, Wavertree Technology Park, Liverpool, L13 1EJ Tel: 0151-252 0600 Fax: 0151-252 0900 E-mail: mail@tiger-sys.com *Epos providers*

Tiger Moth Designs, Greenfields Studios, Halnaker, Chichester, W. Sussex, PO18 0NQ Tel: 01243 528508 *Contract furniture makers, designers & fitters*

Tiger Racing Ltd, The Echo New Toll Service Station, Wisbech Road, Thorney Toll, Wisbech, Cambridgeshire, PE13 4AX Tel: (01733) 271131 Fax: (01733) 271131 *Producers of sports cars*

Tiger Supplies Ltd, 1 Driberg Way, Braintree, Essex, CM7 1NB Tel: (01376) 345554 Fax: (01376) 345502 E-mail: sales@tiger-supplies.co.uk *Supplier of all building trade requirements*

Tiger Timber Ltd, 36 Station Road, Chertsey, Surrey, KT16 8BE Tel: (01932) 560812 Fax: (01932) 570411 *Timber & builders merchants*

Tiger Tools Ltd, PO Box 11, Wokingham, Berkshire, RG40 4RG Tel: 0118-973 4284 Fax: 0118-973 0597 E-mail: info@headtorches.com *Lamp & torch suppliers, manufrs. Also sell headtorches, high performance head lamps, car lamps and Luxeon LED Headtorches.*

Tiger Toroids, Unit 5, Pulham Market Hall, Station Road, Pulham Market, Diss, Norfolk, IP21 4XF Tel: (01379) 650580 Fax: (01379) 608871 E-mail: tigertoroids@btinternet.com *Transformer design & production manufrs*

▶ Tigerbytes Computers, 120 Castle Street, Hinckley, Leicestershire, LE10 1DD Tel: (01455) 611116 *Computer hardware retailers*

▶ Tiger-Designs, Boundary House, Pipers Lane, Northchapel, Petworth, West Sussex, GU28 9JA Tel: 0870 4460310 Fax: 0870 1349048 E-mail: sales@boundarygroup.com *Tiger-Designs is the leading provider of professional airbrush temporary body art equipment in the UK and Europe.*

Tigerridge Consultancy Services Ltd, 4 Bonneys, The Street, Eversley, Hook, Hampshire, RG27 0PJ Tel: 0118-973 6875 Fax: (0845) 2303635 E-mail: sales@tigerridge.co.uk *Provider of it consultancy*

▶ Tigersmart Marketing, Unit 2b Everoak Industrial Estate, Bromyard Road, Tattenhoe, Milton Keynes, MK4 3BN Tel: (01908) 330770 E-mail: info@tigersmartmarketing.co.uk *TigerSMART Marketing offers strategic guidance and operational sales and marketing support to start-up companies and small to medium-sized enterprises. We provide business and marketing planning, market research, marketing performance measurement, lead generation and copywriting. We also provide support with managing marketing projects. We have particular experience in professional healthcare products and services, including medical and surgical products, dental consumables, infection control, and medical software. In addition, we also provide marketing support to clients with interests in air hygiene products, lone worker devices and couture bridalwear. This allows us to transfer our marketing skills, knowledge and experience across a diversity of market sectors and company types to provide our clients with the most appropriate marketing support for their business.*

Tigges UK Ltd, Unit 13, Road 32, Telford, Shropshire, TF1 7EU Tel: (01952) 670173 Fax: (01952) 670190 E-mail: tigges@icom-web.com *Stainless steel fastener manufrs*

Jack Tighe Coatings Ltd, Sandall Stones Road, Kirk Sandall Industrial Estate, Doncaster, South Yorkshire, DN3 1QR Tel: (01302) 880360 Fax: (01302) 880370 *Specialised coatings contractors*

Tight Lines, 164 Milnrow Road, Shaw, Oldham, OL2 8AY Tel: (01706) 881459 Fax: (01706) 881459 *Fishing tackle retailers*

Tigna Portable Buildings, Unit 47-2, Gilwilly Road, Gilwilly Industrial Estate, Penrith, Cumbria, CA11 9BL Tel: (01768) 891595 Fax: (01768) 891512 E-mail: sales@tigna.co.uk *Joinery manufrs*

Tigon Corporate Debt Recovery Services, The Old School House, Stanley, Crook, County Durham, DL15 9AN Tel: (01388) 767306 Fax: (01453) 823520 E-mail: gtomaszko@turnstoneuk.co.uk

Tigra Solutions Ltd, 16 Queens Road, Farnborough, Hampshire, GU14 6DN Tel: (01252) 816699 Fax: (01252) 812375 E-mail: info@tigra-solutions.co.uk *Computer networkers*

Tiki International (Plastics) Ltd, Velator Industrial Estate, Braunton, Devon, EX33 2DX Tel: (01271) 812442 Fax: (01271) 816570 E-mail: tiki@tikisurf.force9.co.uk *Wet-suit & surfboards*

Tikkity Boo, 10 Maryport Road, Cardiff, CF23 5JX Tel: (029) 2075 7048 E-mail: sales@tikkityboo.co.uk

Tilbrooks Landscape Ltd, 3 High Street, Tuddenham, Bury St. Edmunds, Suffolk, IP28 6SQ Tel: (01638) 712766 Fax: (01638) 715362 E-mail: info@tilbrooks.co.uk *Landscape & fencing contractors*

Tilbury Douglas Projects Ltd, 395 George Road, Erdington, Birmingham, B23 7RZ Tel: 0121-344 3900 Fax: 0121-344 4801 E-mail: enquiries@tilbury.co.uk *Building contractors*

Tilbury Metals Ltd, Old Reservoir Road, Portsmouth, PO6 1SU Tel: (023) 9221 0008 Fax: (023) 9220 1184 *Non-ferrous scrap metal merchants*

Tilcon South Ltd, Mortar Division, Church Ward House, Kemble Drive, Swindon, SN2 2TA Tel: 0117-941 4973 *Mortar plans for the building industry*

Tilda Ltd, Coldharbour Lane, Rainham, Essex, RM13 9YQ Tel: (01708) 717777 Fax: (01708) 717700 E-mail: sales@tilda.com *Tilda Ltd based in Rainham, Essex are food manufacturers. They offer basmati, long grain and speciality gourmet rice as well as Indian sauces and chutneys.*

Tilden Modular Building Systems Ltd, Stable Block, Coombe Lodge, Blagden, Bristol, BS40 7RG Tel: (01454) 413111 Fax: (01761) 462892 E-mail: info@tilden.co.uk *Design & supply pre-engineered buildings*

Tile & Bath Select Ltd, 73 Park Street, Aylesbury, Buckinghamshire, HP20 1DU Tel: (01296) 336181 Fax: (01296) 336191 *Ceramic tiles retailers*

▶ Tile Express, Unit 2 Fordview Estate, New Road, Rainham, Essex, RM13 8ET Tel: (01708) 555592 Fax: (01708) 551902 *Tile distributor*

Tile In Style UK, Hill House, Whitehall Road, Leeds, LS12 6HY Tel: 0113-243 9162 Fax: 0113-243 9135 E-mail: tis_uk_ltd@btinternet.com *European ceramic tile centre*

▶ Tile & Stone Gallery, Unit 3 Western Way, Bury St. Edmunds, Suffolk, IP33 3SP Tel: (01284) 706230 Fax: (01284) 765685 *Ceramic tiles wholesalers*

Tile Supply Solutions Ltd, Thornescroft, West Street, Wiveliscombe, Taunton, Somerset, TA4 2JP Tel: (01984) 624757 Fax: (0845) 2800105 E-mail: simon@tilesupplysolutions.com *Tile source supplies, limestone, slate, marble, sandstone, granite, travertine, mosaics, quartzite, lava stone, porcelain, ceramic, basalt, glass, metal & tumbled stone tiles and work tops in natural stone , stair cases etc.*

Tilecraft Services Ltd, 11 Scotts Road, Paisley, Renfrewshire, PA2 7AN Tel: 0141-887 4051 Fax: 0141-889 5247 E-mail: info@tilecraftservices.co.uk *Ceramic tiling contractor*

▶ Tilen Electrics Ltd, Eden Grove, Swallownest, Sheffield, S26 4TP Tel: 0114-287 2046 Fax: 0114-287 8613

Tiles UK Ltd, 1-13 Montford St Off Langworthy Road, Salford, M50 2XD Tel: 0161-872 5155 Fax: 0161-848 7948 E-mail: info@tilesuk.com *Tile merchants*

Tilewind Ltd, Carcroft Industrial Estate, Adwick Le St, Doncaster, South Yorkshire, DN6 7BD Tel: 01302 721205 *Steel fabricators*

Tilgear Tool Merchants, 69 Station Road, Cuffley, Potters Bar, Hertfordshire, EN6 4HY Tel: (01707) 873434 Fax: (01707) 870383 E-mail: orders@tilgear.uk *Precision tool merchants*

Tiling Co., Unit 1, Hampson Mill Lane, Bury, Lancashire, BL9 9TZ Tel: 0161-766 4710 Fax: 0161-796 3190 E-mail: ttc.northwest@thetilingcompany.co.uk *Ceramic tiling sub-contractors*

▶ Tiling For UK, 9 Meadwell Road, Leicester, LE3 1SU Tel: 0116-255 1863 Fax: 0116-255 1863 E-mail: tilingforuk@tiscali.co.uk *CERAMIC WALL AND FLOOR TILING*SLATE TILING*LAMINATE FLOORING*

Tilita Rosettes, 267 Hillbury Road, Warlingham, Surrey, CR6 9TL Tel: (01883) 622121 Fax: (01883) 622124 E-mail: tilita@bigfoot.com *Crane & hoist hirers*

Tilke Engineering, Bell House Lane, Anslow, Burton-on-Trent, Staffordshire, DE13 9PA Tel: (01283) 563756 Fax: (01283) 541525 *Agricultural steel frame builders*

Geoff Till Electrical Contractors Ltd, 19 Sherwood Road, Aston Fields Industrial Estate, Bromsgrove, Worcestershire, B60 3DR Tel: (01527) 871123 Fax: (01527) 873075 E-mail: info@gtelec.co.uk *Access platform hire*

John Till Printers, 32 Woodside Close, Walsall, WS5 3LU Tel: 0121-357 3267 Fax: 0121-357 3267 E-mail: info@johntill.co.uk *Printers & stationers*

Till Track, 14 Laughton Avenue, West Bridgford, Nottingham, NG2 7GJ Tel: 0115-923 1065 Fax: 0115-914 7376 *Cash registers supply, installation & maintenance*

Till & Whitehead Ltd, Park House, 37 Ings Road, Osmondthorpe Lane, Leeds, LS9 9HG Tel: 0113-249 6641 Fax: 0113-248 8968 E-mail: leeds@tillwite.com *Architectural ironmongers & builders hardware suppliers*

Till & Whitehead Ltd, Ellesmere Street, Manchester, M15 4JX Tel: 0161-827 3901 Fax: 0161-827 3915 E-mail: sales@tillwite.com *Engineers & building contractors*

Till & Whitehead, 65 Brindley Road, Astmoor Industrial Estate, Runcorn, Cheshire, WA7 1PF Tel: (01928) 581200 Fax: (01928) 580859 E-mail: info@tillwite.com *Distribution of engineering supplies & safety equipment*

Tillerman Beads, Baltimore Marina, Stackhills Road, Todmorden, LANCS, OL14 5QW Tel: (01706) 810158 Fax: (01706) 810158 E-mail: sales@tillmerman.co.uk *Tillerman Beads offers lampwork beads by British glass artist Mike Poole who creates unique, handcrafted glass beads that are one of a kind, for collecting,* *continued*

making into jewellery or displaying as art glass beads. Each glass bead is made of Moretti, Effetre or other fine art glass which is crafted into individual and elegant beads to wear or simply enjoy. Each bead or set of beads is an original work of glass bead art, no two sets are alike

Tillery Valley Foods, Unit 2-3 Cwmtillery Industrial Estate, Cwmtillery, Abertillery, Gwent, NP13 1LZ Tel: (01495) 211555 Fax: (01495) 212935 E-mail: info@tvf-online.co.uk *Food production services*

▶ Tilleys Sweets Ltd, Springfield, Oundle Road, Thrapston, Kettering, Northamptonshire, NN14 4PQ Tel: (01832) 732151

Tilling Engineering Ltd, 1 Dale House, Craven Road, Broadheath, Altrincham, Cheshire, WA14 5HJ Tel: 0161-926 9995 Fax: 0161-926 9995 E-mail: clive.tilling@tillingeng.co.uk *Pharmaceutical equipment manufrs*

Tillomed Laboratories Ltd, 3 Howard Road Industrial Estate, Eaton Socon, St. Neots, Cambridgeshire, PE19 8ET Tel: (01480) 402400 Fax: (01480) 402402 *Tillomed Laboratories Ltd specialises in the licensing, marketing & supply of generic & branded pharmaceutical products to hospitals, wholesalers & pharmacists nationwide, in a cost-effective & efficient way*

Tilloreys Soft Drinks, Creeches Lane, Walton, Street, Somerset, BA16 9RR Tel: (01458) 841534 Fax: (01458) 840740 E-mail: tilloreysdrinks@btconnect.com *Manufacturers & distributors of soft drinks Bag in Box*

Tills Horse Transport, Meadowside, Chartway Street, Kingswood, Maidstone, Kent, ME17 3QA Tel: (01622) 843675 Fax: (01622) 843675 *Horse transporters*

▶ Tills Innovations, Thingoe Cottage, The Street, Great Barton, Bury St. Edmunds, Suffolk, IP31 2QP Tel: (01284) 787479 Fax: (01284) 787507 E-mail: enquiries@tills-innovations.com *Waterscape & landscaping services*

Tilney Holdings Ltd, Royal Liver Building, Pier Head, Liverpool, L3 1NY Tel: 0151-236 6000 Fax: 0151-236 1252 E-mail: enquries@tilney.com *Investment managers*

Tilsley & Lovatt Ltd, Newstead Industrial Trading Estate, Stoke-on-Trent, ST4 8HT Tel: (01782) 657331 Fax: (01782) 644600 E-mail: sales@tilsleyandlovatt.co.uk *Diesel, mechanical & electrical engineers services*

▶ Tilt A Dor Ltd, 16 Balloo Drive, Bangor, County Down, BT19 7QY Tel: (028) 9146 8899 Fax: (028) 9127 1103 E-mail: sales@tilt-a-dor.co.uk *Manufacturers of roller shutter garage doors, insulated roller doors*

Tilt Measurement Ltd, Horizon House Baldock Industrial Estate, London Road, Baldock, Hertfordshire, SG7 6NG Tel: (01462) 894566 Fax: (01462) 895990 E-mail: sales@tilt-measurement.com *Tilt transducer manufrs*

Tim Bingham, 28 Main Street, Sutton-on-Trent, Newark, Nottinghamshire, NG23 6PF Tel: (01636) 821246 Fax: (01636) 821719 E-mail: sales@binghamgroundservices.co.uk *Installation & repair of synthetic cricket pitches, sports pitches etc*

▶ Tim Cowell, Clayhill Farm, Marden Rd, Cranbrook, Kent, TN17 2LP Tel: (01580) 715111 Fax: (01580) 714718 E-mail: webmaster@manufacturingjobs.co.uk *Job vacancy jobsite for manufacturing jobs UK wide. MRL offers a wide range of manufacturing jobs and engineering jobs throughout the UK*

▶ Tim Gittoes, Station Yard, Llandrindod Wells, Powys, LD1 5BE Tel: (01597) 823255 *Agricultural parts services*

Timac, Unit 8 Stratton Business Park, Edworth, Biggleswade, Bedfordshire, SG18 8QB Tel: (01767) 312849 Fax: (01767) 601388 E-mail: timac.engineering@freenet.co.uk *Engineering subcontract services*

Timac UK Ltd, Bath Road Industrial Estate, Bath Road, Chippenham, Wiltshire, SN14 0AB Tel: (01249) 467100 Fax: (01249) 660232 *Fertilisers, soil conditioners & animal feeds*

Timack NW Ltd, Premier Mill, Begonia Street, Darwen, Lancashire, BB3 2DP Tel: (01254) 775401 Fax: (01254) 703318 E-mail: sales@timack.co.uk *Furniture & seating manufrs*

Timbacraft Ltd, Shandon, Helensburgh, Dunbartonshire, G84 8HP Tel: (01436) 810391 Fax: (01436) 811308 *Ship, boat repairs & marine engineering*

▶ Timber Blind Co., 37a Broadway Parade, London, N8 9DB Tel: (020) 8341 3603 Fax: 020 83413603 *Wooden blinds manufrs*

Timber Box Co., Main Road, Ketsby, Louth, Lincolnshire, LN11 8QW Tel: (01507) 466250 Fax: (01507) 466250 *Joinery*

Timber Centre, Hatches Lane, Salisbury, SP1 2NZ Tel: (01722) 414900 Fax: (01722) 414909 *Bulk importers & wholesalers of wood*

▶ Timber Coaters, 187 Pensby Road, Heswall, Wirral, Merseyside, CH61 6UB Tel: (07778) 461644 Fax: 0151-342 5205 E-mail: timbercoaters@aol.com *Mobile timber coatings service*

▶ Timber Design Bedrooms, Unit 20 Riverside Mill, Lune Street, Padiham, Burnley, Lancashire, BB12 8DG Tel: (01282) 777926 Fax: (01282) 777926 E-mail: tdsshopfitting@aol.com *Shop fitters*

Timber Dryers Ltd, 36-38 River Road, Barking, Essex, IG11 0DN Tel: (020) 8594 7752 Fax: (020) 8594 1089 E-mail: sales@blumsom.co.uk *Timber drying contractors*

▶ Timber & Garden Supplies Scotland Ltd, Cally Industrial Estate, Blairgowrie Road, Dunkeld, Perthshire, PH8 0EP Tel: (01350) 727070 Fax: (01350) 727647 *Timber & garden suppliers*

Timber Line DIY, 1 Nicholson Buildings, South Shields, Tyne & Wear, NE33 5BD Tel: 0191-428 6645 Fax: 0191-428 0789 E-mail: sales@timberline.co.uk *Sheds & fencing construction*

Timber Marketing Corporation Ltd, Old House Mews, London Road, Horsham, West Sussex, RH12 1AF Tel: (01403) 255255 Fax: (01403) 210214 E-mail: tmchorsham@tmcorp.co.uk *Timber merchants*

Timber Seventy Three Ltd, Stourvale Trading Estate, Banners Lane, Halesowen, West Midlands, B63 2AX Tel: (01384) 410799 Fax: (01384) 411080 *Wooden pallets & export packaging*

Timber Store UK Ltd, Newton Road, Kingskerswell, Newton Abbot, Devon, TQ12 5ES Tel: (01803) 872400 Fax: (01803) 874072 *Timber, trade & public, suppliers*

Timber Technicians, Salterford Farm, Whinbush Lane, Calverton, Nottingham, NG14 6PE Tel: 0115-965 3399 *Cabinet makers & designers*

Timber & Tile Products Ltd, Springhill Road, Carnbane Industrial Estate, Newry, County Down, BT35 6EF Tel: (028) 3026 2609 Fax: (028) 3026 4400 E-mail: ejpurdy@timberandtilesproducts.com *Light & non-ferrous metal fabricators*

▶ Timber To Go, Newport Road, Coventry, CV6 4BQ Tel: (024) 7668 8886 Fax: (024) 7668 8869 E-mail: sales@timbertogo.com *An excellent value, reliable, supplier of quality dry timber. Chipboard/decking screws, timber & timber products, plywood, timber preservatives, chipboard, decking, chipboard, fencing, flooring timber, joinery, medium density fibreboard, plywood import, timber roof trusses, timber merchants, plywood or wood wall panelling.*

Timber Trade Federation Ltd, Clareville House, 26-27 Oxendon St, London, SW1Y 4EL Tel: (020) 7839 1891 Fax: (020) 7930 0094 E-mail: ttf@ttf.co.uk *Trade associations*

▶ Timber Workshop (Design) Ltd, Hidden Spring Vineyard, Vines Cross Road, Horam, Heathfield, East Sussex, TN21 0HG Tel: (01435) 813634 Fax: (01435) 813542 E-mail: info@timberworkshop.co.uk

▶ Timber-Cabins.Co.Uk, Red Mayes Farm, Limewalk, Long Sutton, Spalding, Spalding, Lincolnshire, PE12 9HG Tel: (01406) 363978 Fax: (01406) 365689 E-mail: enquires@timber-cabins.co.uk *Timber suppliers*

Timbercraft Cabinet Displays, Abercorn House York Farm Business Centre, Watling Street, Towcester, Northamptonshire, NN12 8EU Tel: (01327) 830663 Fax: (01327) 830963 E-mail: sales@displaycases.co.uk *Display cabinets & cases manufrs*

Timbergarden, Unit 31 Lancaster Way Business Park, Ely, Cambridgeshire, CB6 3NW Tel: (01353) 668333 Fax: (01353) 668440 *Garden supplies*

Timberkraft, Scrambledfields Yard, Higher Halstock Leigh, Higher Halstock Leigh, Yeovil, Somerset, BA22 9QX Tel: (07970) 688297 Fax: (01935) 891007 *Sectional building manufrs*

▶ Timberline Pine Ltd, 1-2 Kingswalk, Winchester, Hampshire, SO23 8AF Tel: (01962) 861133 Fax: (01962) 884231 E-mail: sales@timberlinepine.co.uk *We are a pine and oak retail company selling dining, bedroom and occasional furniture including made to measure bookcases. We offer a free specialised service wherby we will visit customers at home within a 30 mile radious, showing them brochures, discussing sizes as well as colours*

Timberman Woodworking Machinery, Gelli Garage, Bronwydd Arms, Carmarthen, Dyfed, SA33 6BE Tel: (01267) 232621 Fax: (01267) 222616 E-mail: sales@timberman.co.uk *Woodwork & power tool maintenance & suppliers*

Timbertec Joinery UK Ltd, Union Lane, Headley, Kings Clear, Newbury, Berkshire, RG20 4ST Tel: (01635) 268663 Fax: (01635) 268411

Timbertops Equestrian Supplies, Jackson Lane, Wentbridge, Pontefract, West Yorkshire, WF8 3HZ Tel: (01977) 620374 Fax: (01977) 621039 E-mail: sue@sue-clark.co.uk *Animal agency*

▶ Timberwise (UK) Ltd, PO Box 4198, Cardiff, CF14 8BG Tel: (0800) 991100 E-mail: cardiff@timberwise.co.uk *Our services include: Surveying, Woodworm, Dry & Wet Rot, Rising Damp, Cavity Wall Tie, Timber Engineering, Bird Control, Structural Repair, Basement Waterproofing, Condensation, and Penetrating Damp.*

▶ Timberwise UK plc, Chester Enterprise Centre, Hoole Bridge, Chester, CH2 3NE Tel: (01244) 321366 Fax: (01565) 621000 E-mail: chester@timberwise.co.uk *Our services include: Surveying, Woodworm, Dry & Wet Rot, Rising Damp, Cavity Wall Tie, Timber Engineering, Bird Control, Structural Repair, Basement Waterproofing, Condensation, and Penetrating Damp.*

▶ Timberwise (UK) Ltd, 19 Eagle Close, Birdwood Park, Fareham, Hants, PO16 8QX Tel: (0800) 991100 Fax: (01329) 510186 E-mail: hants@timberwise.co.uk *Our services include: Surveying, Woodworm, Dry & Wet Rot, Rising Damp, Cavity Wall Tie, Timber Engineering, Bird Control, Structural Repair, Basement Waterproofing, Condensation, and Penetrating Damp.*

▶ Timberwise UK plc, Kirkfields Business Centre, Kirk Lane, Yeadon, Leeds, LS19 7ET Tel: 0113-250 4402 Fax: 0113-250 9931 E-mail: leeds@timberwise.co.uk

▶ Timberwise (UK) Ltd, 1 Norman Road, Thurmaston, Leicester, LE4 8EL Tel: (0800) 991100 Fax: 0116-269 3678 E-mail: leics@timberwise.co.uk *Our services include: Surveying, Woodworm, Dry & Wet Rot, Rising Damp, Cavity Wall Tie, Timber Engineering, Bird Control, Structural Repair, Basement Waterproofing, Condensation, and Penetrating Damp.*

▶ Timberwise (UK) Ltd, Unit B16, Brunswick Business Centre, Brunswick Business Park, Sefton Street, Liverpool, L3 4BD Tel: (0800) 991100 Fax: 0151-284 6837 E-mail: liverpool@timberwise.co.uk *Our services include: Surveying, Woodworm, Dry & Wet Rot, Rising Damp, Cavity Wall Tie, Timber Engineering, Bird Control, Structural Repair,* *continued*

Basement Waterproofing, Condensation, and Penetrating Damp.

▶ Timberwise UK plc, 3 CWRT Roger Mostyn, Builder Street, Llandudno, Gwynedd, LL30 1DS Tel: (01492) 535065 Fax: (01492) 864004 E-mail: llandudno@timberwise.co.uk *Our services include: Surveying, Woodworm, Dry & Wet Rot, Rising Damp, Cavity Wall Tie, Timber Engineering, Bird Control, Structural Repair, Basement Waterproofing, Condensation, and Penetrating Damp.*

Timberwise UK plc, 1 Drake Mews, Gadbrook Park, Northwich, Cheshire, CW9 7XF Tel: (01606) 333636 Fax: (01606) 334664 E-mail: hq@timberwise.co.uk *Building conservation services including Basement waterproofing, basement water control, damp proofing and timber preservation.* Also at: Branches throughout the U.K.

▶ Timberwise (UK) Ltd, Bank House, 4 Wharf Road, Sale, Cheshire, M33 2AF Tel: (0800) 991100 Fax: 0161-972 0077 E-mail: sale@timberwise.co.uk *Our services include: Surveying, Woodworm, Dry & Wet Rot, Rising Damp, Cavity Wall Tie, Timber Engineering, Bird Control, Structural Repair, Basement Waterproofing, Condensation, and Penetrating Damp.*

▶ Timberwise UK plc, 4 Finchwell Close, Sheffield, S13 9DF Tel: 0114-256 1411 Fax: 0114-256 1422 E-mail: sheffield@timberwise.co.uk *Property care services*

Timberwise UK, Coombe Works, Coombe, Sherborne, Dorset, DT9 4AU Tel: (01935) 812600 Fax: (01935) 814436 E-mail: hq@timberwise.co.uk *Timber & damp treatment contactors*

▶ Timberwise UK plc, 47 The Green, Cheadle, Stoke-on-Trent, ST10 1XS Tel: (01782) 599921 Fax: 0161 962 7610 E-mail: stoke@timberwise.co.uk *Our services include: Surveying, Woodworm, Dry & Wet Rot, Rising Damp, Cavity Wall Tie, Timber Engineering, Bird Control, Structural Repair, Basement Waterproofing, Condensation, and Penetrating Damp.*

▶ Timberwise (UK) Ltd, 6 Rose Hill, Sutton, Surrey, SM1 3EU Tel: (0800) 991100 Fax: (020) 8641 4343 E-mail: sutton@timberwise.co.uk *Our services include: Surveying, Woodworm, Dry & Wet Rot, Rising Damp, Cavity Wall Tie, Timber Engineering, Bird Control, Structural Repair, Basement Waterproofing, Condensation, and Penetrating Damp.*

▶ Timberwise (UK) Ltd, Wilwood, Smith Hill, Bishopsteignton, Teignmouth, Devon, TQ14 9QT Tel: (0800) 991100 Fax: (01935) 814436 E-mail: devon@timberwise.co.uk *Our services include: Surveying, Woodworm, Dry & Wet Rot, Rising Damp, Cavity Wall Tie, Timber Engineering, Bird Control, Structural Repair, Basement Waterproofing, Condensation, & Penetrating Damp.**

▶ Timberwise (UK) Ltd, 7 Gooch Way, Worle, Weston-super-Mare, Avon, BS22 7YH Tel: (0800) 991100 Fax: (01935) 814436 E-mail: weston@timberwise.co.uk *Our services include: Surveying, Woodworm, Dry & Wet Rot, Rising Damp, Cavity Wall Tie, Timber Engineering, Bird Control, Structural Repair, Basement Waterproofing, Condensation, and Penetrating Damp.*

Timbmet Ltd, PO Box 39, Oxford, OX2 9PP Tel: (01865) 862223 Fax: (01865) 860342 E-mail: marketing@timbmet.com *Machining, door products, sheet materials soft & hardwoods components manufrs*

Timbmet Rochdale Ltd, The Klondike, Chichester Street, Rochdale, Lancashire, OL16 2AU Tel: (01706) 863800 Fax: (01706) 750484 E-mail: sales@timbmet.com *Hardwood distributors*

▶ Timcal Graphite and Carbon, PO Box 269, Congleton, Cheshire, CW12 3WP Tel: (01260) 276009 Fax: (01260) 289057 E-mail: info@uk.timcal.com *Timcal produces highly conductive carbon black pigments for plastics, fuel cells and battery applications, and graphite powder and dispersions for conductive, lubricant, automotive, mobile energy and refractory uses.*

Timco Designs Ltd, Normans Cross, Forton, Chard, Somerset, TA20 4HD Tel: (01460) 239569 Fax: (01344) 628581 *Contract drawing services*

▶ Timcon Design, Unit 2, Fleets Lane, Rylstone, Skipton, North Yorkshire, BD23 6NA Tel: (01756) 730548

Time Ltd, 6 Brook St Mill, Brook Street, Macclesfield, Cheshire, SK11 7AW Tel: (01625) 615768 Fax: (01625) 614605 E-mail: ron@timescctv.co.uk *CCTV designers & consultants*

Time, Moulton Park Business Centre, Redhouse Road, Moulton Park, Northampton, NN3 6AQ Tel: (01604) 670555 Fax: (01604) 497501 E-mail: info@recruitingtime.co.uk *We are a specialist FMCG recruiter supporting sales, marketing and commercial roles.*

Time 24 Ltd, Robimatic House, 19 Victoria Gardens, Burgess Hill, West Sussex, RH15 9NB Tel: (01444) 257655 Fax: (01444) 259000 E-mail: sales@time24.co.uk *Cable harness & assembly company*

▶ Time 24 Ltd, Empire Works, Parcel Terrace, Derby, DE1 1LY Tel: (01332) 200880 Fax: (01332) 349801 E-mail: enquiries@time24derby.co.uk *Specialists in turnkey design*

▶ Time 4 U, 10 Market Street, Woodstock, Oxfordshire, OX20 1SX Tel: (01993) 810450 Fax: (01993) 810450 E-mail: sales@time4u.co.uk *Home Management, Caretaking, Keyholding, interior design, painting/decorating,gardening. Office diary administration, golf away days, corporate and social. Relocation of property etc.,*

Time Business Systems Ltd, Unit 13 Silver Business Park, Airfield Way, Christchurch, Dorset, BH23 3TA Tel: (01202) 479999 Fax: (01202) 474741 E-mail: sales@time-business.co.uk *Digital photocopying sales & services*

Time Computer Systems Ltd, School Brow, Warrington, WA1 2TA Tel: (01925) 419797 *Computer systems & software sales*

Time Computers, Unit 2 Coypool Retail Park, Coypool Road, Plympton, Plymouth, PL7 4TB Tel: (01752) 338882 Fax: (01752) 339497 E-mail: info@thecomputershop.com *Computer resellers*

Time Couriers, 36 East Avenue, Bournemouth, BH3 7DA Tel: (01202) 764765 E-mail: sales@timecouriers.co.uk *Courier services*

Time & Data Systems International Ltd, Sentinel House, Nuffield Road, Nuffield Industrial Estate, Poole, Dorset, BH17 0RE Tel: (01202) 666222 Fax: (01202) 679730 E-mail: info@tdsi.co.uk *Access control systems manufrs*

▶ Time for Design, 8 Lichfield Road, Stone, Staffordshire, ST15 8PY Tel: (01785) 819764 E-mail: dme@timefordesign.co.uk *Webdesign service on a personal and business level, offering exclusive site designs at afordable prices!Fantastic web hosting packages also available at very competitive rates.*

Time Electronics Ltd, Unit 11, Sovereign Way, Tonbridge, Kent, TN9 1RH Tel: (01732) 355993 Fax: (01732) 770312 E-mail: mail@timeelectronics.co.uk *Electronic measuring system manufrs*

Time Engineers Ltd, Unit 3, Manor Way, Rainham, Essex, RM13 8RH Tel: (01708) 555464 Fax: (01708) 555765 *Gear box manufrs*

▶ Time Express Swiss Couriers Ltd, Unit 20, Trident Industrial Estate, Blackthorne Road, Colnbrook, Slough, SL3 0AX Tel: (01753) 686830

Time & Frequency Solutions Ltd, 25 Eastways, Witham, Essex, CM8 3AL Tel: (01376) 514114 Fax: (01376) 516116 E-mail: sales@timefreq.com Purchasing Contact: L. Walker Principal Export Areas: Worldwide *Time & Frequency Solutions have the widest and most advanced range of cost-effective precision time synchronisation and frequency synchronisation solutions for global applications. The range includes time and frequency standards and master clocks; modular timing systems; bus-level timing boards; serial and frequency distribution systems; frequency monitors; time displays including LED and analogue clocks; network time protocol (NTP) servers; dual redundant and triple redundant changeover systems. We provide synchronisation solutions in all industries where accurate time and frequency is required, e.g. secure military communications, railway signalling, financial transaction time-stamping, utilities billing, airport terminals and air traffic control, telecommunications network synchronisation, and so on. We have over 30 years experience in the time and frequency industry, and take pride in ensuring our products meet three critical factors; flexibility, compatibility and reliability.*

Time Global Ltd, 21 Cornwall Rd, St. Albans, Herts, AL1 1SQ Tel: (01727) 847454 Fax: (01727) 847453 E-mail: sales@timeglobal.co.uk *Computer parts reseller*

▶ Time Instruments, Jenna Way, Interchange Park, Newport Pagnell, Buckinghamshire, MK16 9QJ Tel: (01908) 449200 Fax: (01908) 220145 E-mail: sales@time-instruments.co.uk

Time Life International Ltd, Brettenham House, Lancaster Place, London, WC2E 7TL Tel: (020) 7499 4080 Fax: (020) 7322 1147 *Publishers*

Time Medical & Scientific Network, Unit 6, North End Industrial Estate, Bury Mead Road, Hitchin, Hertfordshire, SG5 1RT Tel: (01462) 422112 Fax: (01462) 422042 E-mail: sales@timemedical.co.uk *Educational posters, medical simulators, physics & chemistry equipment suppliers*

Time & Motion, 1 Beckside, Beverley, North Humberside, HU17 0PB Tel: (01482) 881574 *Antique clock repairers*

Time Products UK Ltd, 23 Grosvenor Street, London, W1K 4QL Tel: (020) 7416 4160 Fax: (020) 7416 4161 *Importers & luxury watches*

Time Products UK Ltd, Chartwell Drive, Wigston, Leicestershire, LE18 2EZ Tel: (0870) 8508200 Fax: (0870) 8508201 E-mail: info@sekonda.co.uk *Tools for electronic industry & watch distributors*

Time Recorder Services, 47 Phillipps Avenue, Exmouth, Devon, EX8 3JE Tel: (01395) 271676 Fax: 01395 271676 E-mail: admin@timerecord.co.uk *Sale, repair, rental of clocking in machines*

Time Recorder Services, 69a Richardshaw Lane, Stanningley, Pudsey, West Yorkshire, LS28 7EL Tel: 0113-257 7920 Fax: 0113-257 7920 E-mail: info@timerecord.co.uk *Industrial time recorder repair & sales*

Time Systems, 210 Broadgate Lane, Horsforth, Leeds, LS18 5BS Tel: 0113-258 7856 Fax: 0113-258 6612 E-mail: salests@aol.com *Largest independent manufacturer and distributor of clocking in machines and time systems in the UK with unbeatable prices. From basic card operated time clocks to P.C controlled swipe card time and attendance systems including access control and HR software. Our new range includes biometric time and attendance, including hand geometry and fingerprint recognition solutions to prevent employees clocking in and out of each other. All our solutions are guaranteed to save your company time and money or your money back. They will also increase payroll efficiency and increase building security. Next day delivery ancillary items like: Clock cards, time clock ribbons, clocking machines, time stamps, clock card racks, swipe cards and fobs. Nationwide installation and training available on all systems along with maintenance contracts*

Time Systems UK Ltd, Systems House, Wavendon, Milton Keynes, MK17 8AA Tel: (01908) 281000 Fax: (01908) 281291 E-mail: sales@timesystemsuk.com *Manufacturers of time & attendance systems*

Time Technology Ltd, Brook House, Mint Street, Godalming, Surrey, GU7 1HE Tel: (01483) 863000 Fax: (01483) 425075 E-mail: sales@time-technology.co.uk *IBM content & document management specialists*

▶ Timebus Travel, Boleyn Drive, St. Albans, Hertfordshire, AL1 2BP Tel: (01727) 866248 *Traditional classic red london buses for private hire*

Timeframe Software Ltd, The Pump House, Queens Avenue, Christchurch, Dorset, BH23 1BZ Tel: (01202) 499414 Fax: (01202) 482535 E-mail: info@timeframe.co.uk *Computer systems*

Timeguard Ltd, Victory Park, 400 Edgware Road, London, NW2 6ND Tel: (020) 8450 8944 Fax: (020) 8452 5143 E-mail: csc@timeguard.com *Time switch manufrs*

Times of Wigan Ltd, Bridge St, Wigan, Lancashire, WN3 4EY Tel: 01942 234852 *Sub-contract CNC & conventional machining*

Timesco of London, 3 Carnival Close, Basildon, Essex, SS14 3WN Tel: (01268) 297700 Fax: (01268) 297800 E-mail: info@timesco.com *Surgical medical instrument manufrs*

Timeslice Ltd, William Gaitskill House, 23 Paradise St, London, SE16 4QD Tel: (020) 7231 0073 Fax: (020) 7237 9806 E-mail: sales@timeslice.co.uk *Computer software publishers & distribs*

Timestep Electronics, PO Box 2001, Dartmouth, Devon, TQ6 9HN Tel: (01803) 833366 E-mail: sales@time-step.com *Satellite communications equipment manufrs*

Timet (U K) Ltd, PO Box 57, Swansea, SA1 1XD Tel: (01792) 870330 Fax: (01792) 874569 *Titanium rod manufrs*

Timet UK Ltd, Kynoch Works, Witton, Birmingham, B6 7UR Tel: 0121-356 1155 Fax: 0121-356 5413 E-mail: eurosales@timet.com *Titanium & titanium alloy producers* Also at: Swansea

▶ Timetra Ltd, 535 Main Street, Bellshill, Lanarkshire, ML4 1DG Tel: (01698) 746091 Fax: (01698) 843439

▶ Timezone Digital Storage Ltd, Rivacre Business Centre, Mill Lane, Ellesmere Port, CH66 3TH Tel: 0151-339 2070 E-mail: info@timezonedigital.com *Document management solution provider*

Timken Aerospace Uk Ltd, PO Box 667, Wolverhampton, WV2 4UH Tel: (01902) 719300 Fax: (01902) 719301 E-mail: talkbox@timken.com *High precision aerospace bearing manufrs*

Timken (Coventry) Ltd, Progress Close, Leofric Business Park, Binley, Coventry, CV3 2TF Tel: (024) 7623 3233 Fax: (024) 7629 6991 *Ball bearing manufrs*

Timloc Building Products, Rawcliffe Road, Goole, North Humberside, DN14 6UQ Tel: (01405) 765567 Fax: (01405) 720479 E-mail: sales@timloc.co.uk *Ventilators, domestic applications*

Timmick Precision Engineering, 17 Arkwright Court, Astmoor, Runcorn, Cheshire, WA7 1NX Tel: (01928) 563009 Fax: (01928) 563009 *Precision engineers*

Derek Timms Seals Ltd, 90 Evelyn Road, Birmingham, B11 3JJ Tel: 0121-773 7666 Fax: 0121-766 5590 E-mail: *Seal & packing distributors*

Timms Electrics, 40 Malmains Way, Beckenham, Kent, BR3 6SB Tel: 020 86505772 *Electrical suppliers*

▶ Timpson Engraving, Unit 4 Sutton Oak Drive, St. Helens, Merseyside, WA9 3PH Tel: (01744) 815350 Fax: (01744) 815671

▶ TIMSA, Association House, 99 West Street, Farnham, Surrey, GU9 7EN Tel: (01252) 739154 Fax: (01252) 739140 E-mail: timsa@associationhouse.org.uk *Insulation services*

Timsons Ltd, Bath Road, Kettering, Northamptonshire, NN16 8NQ Tel: (01536) 411611 Fax: (01536) 411666 E-mail: admin@timsons.com *Printing machinery manufrs*

Timstar Laboratory Supplies Ltd, Linea House Marshfield Bank Employment Park, Marshfield Bank, Crewe, CW2 8UY Tel: (01270) 250459 Fax: (01270) 250601 E-mail: sales@timstar.co.uk *Chemical merchants*

▶ Timtech Services, 15 Chudleigh Road, Harrogate, North Yorkshire, HG1 5NP Tel: (0771) 3711063 E-mail: jatimbrell@hotmail.com *Concrete floor surfaces company*

▶ Timuna Sea Ltd, 121 Cannon Workshops, 3 Cannon Drive, London, E14 4AS Tel: (020) 7719 9444 *Diving equipment manufrs*

R. Tincknell & Son Ltd, PO Box 9, Wells, Somerset, BA5 1TQ Tel: (01749) 683150 Fax: (01749) 583160 *Agricultural engineers*

R. Tincknell & Son Agricultural Ltd, Glastonbury Road, Wells, Somerset, BA5 1TQ Tel: (01749) 683150 Fax: (01749) 683160 *Agricultural engineering services* Also at: Branches throughout the South West

Tindall Engineering Ltd, Abryll House, Oldham, OL1 3TF Tel: 0161 6200666 *Multi-point locking systems & high security suppliers*

Tindall Precision Engineers, 11 Peacock Square Blenheim Way, Northfields Industrial Estate, Market Deeping, Peterborough, PE6 8LW Tel: (01778) 344970 Fax: (01778) 344970 *Precision engineering services*

Tindon Engineering Ltd, Unit 4 Little Snoring Airfield, Thursford Road, Little Snoring, Fakenham, Norfolk, NR21 0JL Tel: (01328) 878809 Fax: (01328) 878004

E.W. Tinegate Ltd, Lodge Road Saw Mills, 94 Lodge Road, Hockley, Birmingham, B18 5QZ Tel: 0121-554 1311 Fax: 0121-515 4464 *Timber merchants & panel sawing*

Tingewick Pottery Ltd, Upper Street, Tingewick, Buckingham, MK18 4QJ Tel: (01280) 848250 Fax: (01280) 848250 *Manufacturers of ceramic table lamps*

Tinico Alloys Ltd, Unit 1 North Drive, Greasborough Road, Rotherham, South Yorkshire, S60 1QF Tel: (01709) 376844 Fax: (01709) 828210 E-mail: tinicoltd@aol.com *Scrap metal merchants*

Tinius Olsen Ltd, Unit 6, Perrywood Business Park, Honeycrock Lane, Salfords, Redhill, RH1 5DZ Tel: (01737) 765001 Fax: (01737) 764768 E-mail: sales@tiniusolsen.co.uk *Tensile test equipment manufrs*

Tinsley Bridge (Exports) Ltd, P O Box 89, Sheffield, S9 2DZ Tel: 0114-221 1111 Fax: 0114-243 1331 E-mail: general@tinsleybridge.co.uk *Spring manufrs*

Eliza Tinsley & Co. Ltd, Unit 12, Cinder Road, Chasetown Industrial Estate, Burntwood, Staffordshire, WS7 8XD Tel: (01543) 683595 Fax: (01543) 674620 *Industrial chain manufrs*

▶ Tinsley Robor Labels, 12 Arndale Road, Wick, Littlehampton, West Sussex, BN17 7HD Tel: (01903) 731212 Fax: (01903) 738204 E-mail: sales@agilabels.com *Label printers*

▶ Tinting Express Ltd, New Estate House, Old School Lane, Fremington, Barnstaple, Devon, EX31 3AZ Tel: (01271) 322857 Fax: (01271) 326346 E-mail: sales@tintingexpress.co.uk *Supply & installation window films*

▶ Tinto Construction Ltd, 32 Main Street, Symington, Biggar, Lanarkshire, ML12 6LJ Tel: (01899) 308438

▶ Tinto Engineering Ltd, Argyle Crescent, Hillhouse Industrial Estate, Hamilton, Lanarkshire, ML3 9BQ Tel: (01698) 421212

The Tintometer Ltd, Lovibond House, Solar Way, Solstice Park, Amesbury, Salisbury, SP4 7SZ Tel: (01980) 664800 Fax: (01980) 625412 E-mail: sales@tintometer.com Purchasing Contact: L. Tryhorn Sales Contact: S. Cooper Principal Export Areas: Worldwide *Manufacturers of WATER TESTING products - applications include dinking water, waste water, industrial water treatment & swimming pools/leisure. *Manufacturers of transmission & reflectance COLOUR MEASURING instruments - for laboratory & on-line use. Applications include foods, beverages, edible oils, petroleum oils, pharmaceuticals, paints, textiles, etc.*Providers of COLOUR ANALYSIS SERVICES - UKAS/ ISO17025 certified laboratory.*

Tintometer Ltd, Palmers Way, Trenant Industrial Estate, Wadebridge, Cornwall, PL27 6HB Tel: (01208) 812719 Fax: (01208) 812719 *Optical glass manufrs*

Tintplush Ltd, 16 The Crunnis, Bradley Stoke, Bristol, BS32 8AD Tel: 0117-987 2482 Fax: 0117-987 2482 *Gold plating services & jewelleery manufrs*

Tiny Tots Ashford Ltd, 18 Elwick Road, Ashford, Kent, TN23 1PF Tel: (01233) 623511 Fax: (01233) 610636 E-mail: enquiries@tinytotsashford.co.uk *Baby wear & nursery equipment suppliers*

▶ Tioga Ltd, St. Thomas House, Mansfield Road, Derby, DE1 3TN Tel: (01332) 360884 Fax: (01332) 360885

Tioxide Europe Ltd, Moortown Road, Nettleton, Market Rasen, Lincolnshire, LN7 6AA Tel: (01472) 852037 Fax: (01472) 852037 *Landfill quarry site agents*

Tip N Lift UK Ltd, Boss Hall Road, Ipswich, IP1 5BN Tel: (01473) 747222 Fax: (01473) 740381 E-mail: tipnlift@aol.com *Lorry mounted cranes*

Tip Top Accident Repairs Ltd, Worcester Road, Kidderminster, Worcestershire, DY10 1HY Tel: (01562) 822081 Fax: (01562) 825922 *Car body repairers*

▶ Tipografic, Unit 1B, Squires Gate Industrial Estate, Squires Gate Lane, Blackpool, FY4 3RN Tel: (01253) 404142 Fax: (01253) 402882 E-mail: iesthomas@tipgrafic.co.uk *Printers manufrs*

▶ Tippabush Ltd, 5 Rookery Close, Louth, Lincolnshire, LN11 0GF Tel: (01507) 608331 E-mail: info@tippabush.co.uk *Tippabush Website Design provide simple cost effective web design and internet marketing services (including pay-per-click campaign management)for start-up and small businesses.*

Tipper Engineering Ltd, Hall Lane, Walsall Wood, Walsall, WS9 9AS Tel: (01543) 452266 Fax: (01543) 452288 *Stainless & alloy steel bolt & nut manufrs*

Tipper Hire, 36-44 London Lane, London, E8 3PR Tel: (020) 8985 6758 Fax: (020) 8986 3518 E-mail: tipperhireuk@btconnect.com *Tipper vehicle hire contractors*

Walter Tipper Ltd, Dovefields, Uttoxeter, Staffordshire, ST14 8HR Tel: (01889) 565151 Fax: (01889) 567318 E-mail: info@tippersbm.co.uk *Builders merchants* Also at: Birmingham,Kidderminster, Lichfield, Tamworth & Wolverhamton

▶ Tippetts Trimmings & Smallwares Ltd, 103 Knighton Fields Road West, Leicester, LE2 6LH Tel: 0116-283 5104 Fax: 0116-283 4207 E-mail: p.warren@btopenworld.com *Suppliers of garment accessories, labels designed & printed*

Tipro Keyboards UK Ltd, Unit 19/20, Kingston Farm Industrial Units, Down Hall Road, Matching Green, Harlow, Essex, CM17 0RB Tel: (01279) 732360 Fax: (01279) 732369 E-mail: sales@tiprokeyboards.co.uk *Data processing keyboard manufrs*

Tipton & Mill Steels Ltd, Hobart Road, Tipton, West Midlands, DY4 9LQ Tel: 0121-557 7251 Fax: 0121-557 7258 E-mail: sales@tipton-steels.co.uk *Steel plate stockholders*

Tipton Transport Ltd, Eagle Industrial Estate, Bagnall Street, Great Bridge, Tipton, West Midlands, DY4 7BS Tel: 0121-557 3201 Fax: 0121-520 1092 E-mail: sals@palletforce.com *A member of the PalletFORCE distribution network- palletised distribution, timed, next day, economy, tail loft, Ireland and services to mainland Europe. Through its expanding shareholder member depot network, full and part loads, warehouse and logistics services are available.*

Tipton Welding Service, Brick Kiln Street, Tipton, West Midlands, DY4 9BP Tel: 0121-557 1282 Fax: 0121-557 1282 *Welding equipment repairers*

Tiptree Precision Engineering, Galliford Road Industrial Estate, Heybridge, Maldon, Essex, CM9 4XD Tel: (01621) 856733 Fax: (01621) 851355 E-mail: tipeng@aol.com *Toolmakers & precision engineers*

Alec Tiranti Ltd, 3 Pipers Court, Berkshire Drive, Thatcham, Berkshire, RG19 4ER Tel: 0118-930 2775 Fax: (0845) 1232101 E-mail: enquiries@tiranti.co.uk *Manufacturers & suppliers of sculptors tools materials & equipment* Also at: London W1

Raymond Tisdale & Co. Ltd, Common Lane, Kenilworth, Warwickshire, CV8 2EL Tel: (01926) 852227 Fax: (01926) 850844 *Packing cases & pallet services*

Titan Advanced Ltd, Titan Works, Claremount Road, Halifax, West Yorkshire, HX3 6NT Tel: (01422) 330265 Fax: (01422) 343295 E-mail: sales@titangroup.co.uk Principal Export Areas: Central/East Europe & North America *Hydraulic equipment & systems manufrs*

Titan Containers (UK) Ltd, Suite 1, 1 Cecil Court, London Road, Enfield, Middlesex, EN2 6DE Tel: (020) 8362 1444 Fax: (01707) 664407 E-mail: uk@titancontainer.com *Shipping container hire leasing & sales*

Titan Distribution (UK) Ltd, North Florida Road, Haydock Industrial Estate, St. Helens, Merseyside, WA11 9UB Tel: (01942) 715333 Fax: (01942) 715111 E-mail: enquiries@titandistributionuk.com *Manufacturers of tyres*

Titan Enterprises Ltd, Unit 2 5a Coldharbour Business Park, Sherborne, Dorset, DT9 4JW Tel: (01935) 812790 Fax: (01935) 812890 E-mail: sales@flowmeters.co.uk *Flow meter, indicator & measurement systems manufrs*

Titan Environmental Ltd, Seapatrick Road, Seapatrick, Banbridge, County Down, BT32 4PH Tel: (028) 4062 6260 Fax: (028) 4062 6259 E-mail: sales@titanenv.com *Plastic & polyethylene storage tank manufrs*

Titan Environmental Ltd, 37 Seagoe Industrial Estate, Portadown, Craigavon, County Armagh, BT63 5QD Tel: (028) 3833 0668 Fax: (028) 3835 0171 E-mail: sales@titanenv.com *Manufacturers of med-large plastic containers*

Titan Fabrications Ltd, 14 Thames Street, Louth, Lincolnshire, LN11 7AD Tel: (01507) 603264 Fax: (01507) 609080 E-mail: sales@titanltd.co.uk *Steel fabricators*

Titan Fluid Power Ltd, Titan Works, Claremount Road, Halifax, West Yorkshire, HX3 6NT Tel: (01422) 398288 Fax: (01422) 398287 E-mail: sales@titangroup.co.uk *Hydraulic components*

Titan Fluid Power Ltd, Titan Works, Claremount Road, Halifax, West Yorkshire, HX3 6NT Tel: (01422) 398288 Fax: (01422) 398287 Principal Export Areas: Worldwide *General hydraulic engineers*

Titan Forge Ltd, 3 Shaftesbury Road, London, E10 7DA Tel: (020) 8558 9000 Fax: (020) 8558 8614 *Wrought iron sections*

Titan Garden Buildings Ltd, Titan Works, Blacksmith Lane, Chilworth, Guildford, Surrey, GU4 8NQ Tel: (01483) 451009 Fax: (01483) 451258 E-mail: info@titangardenbuildings.com *Timber garden sheds*

Titan Holdings Ltd, 334 Meanwood Road, Leeds, LS7 2JF Tel: 0113-262 4612 Fax: 0113-262 6557 E-mail: sales@titanhc.co.uk *Hydraulic cylinder manufrs*

Titan Motorsport & Automotive Engineering, Harley Industrial Park, Paxton Hill, St. Neots, Cambridgeshire, PE19 6TA Tel: (01480) 474402 Fax: (01480) 405668 E-mail: sales@titan.uk.net *Specialists in the design and manufacture of componets for both motorsport and automotive industries.**Suppliers of engine, steering, drivetrain, suspension and chassis components.**

Titan Pollution Control, West Portway, Andover, Hampshire, SP10 3LF Tel: (01264) 352444 Fax: (01264) 366446 E-mail: sales@titanpc.co.uk *Waste water management*

Titan Sports, 10 Ark Royal Way, Lairdside Technology Park, Birkenhead, Merseyside, CH41 9HT Tel: 0151-650 0110 Fax: 0151-647 3438 E-mail: sales@titansports.co.uk *Snooker & pool equipment restorers & suppliers*

Titan Steel Wheels Ltd, Bridge Road, Cookley, Kidderminster, Worcestershire, DY10 3SD Tel: (01562) 850561 Fax: (01562) 851576 E-mail: sales@titansteelwheels.com Principal Export Areas: Worldwide *Wheel (steel) manufrs*

Titanic Off Licence, Russell Lane, London, N20 0BB Tel: (020) 8368 9339 *Off licence*

Titanium Engineering Ltd, Unit 42 Great Western Industrial Estate, Great Western Close, Birmingham, B18 4QF Tel: 0121-523 6932 Fax: 0121-523 5991 E-mail: *Metal finishing equipment manufrs*

▶ Titan-Lite Motorsport, 36 Coleshill Ind Est, Station Rd, Coleshill, Birmingham, B46 1JP Tel: 01675 - 466060 Fax: 01675 - 467675 E-mail: info@titan-lite.com *The most durable and desirable range of motorsport oil, water and air coolers in the world!*

▶ Titchmarsh Engineering, Primrose Cottage, East Cottingwith, York, YO42 4TH Tel: (01759) 319222 *We offer a complete service for Architectural Metalwork Commisions*

Titex Tools Ltd, 1 The Courtyard, Buntsford Drive, Bromsgrove, Worcestershire, B60 3DJ Tel: (01527) 839450 Fax: (01527) 839482 E-mail: titex-prototyp@titex.com *Engineers' cutting tool manufrs*

Tithe Joinery, Upper Hammonds Farm, Ripley Lane, West Horsley, Leatherhead, Surrey, KT24 6JL Tel: (01483) 283689 Fax: (01483) 282365 *Joiners*

Tithegrove Ltd, Fairview House, 43 Bath Road, Swindon, SN1 4AS Tel: 0870 4282822 Fax: 0871 2267808 E-mail: admin@tithegrove.co.uk *Building & civil engineering contractors*

Titheringtons Ltd, 75 Strand Road, Bootle, Merseyside, L20 4BB Tel: 0151-922 4422 Fax: 0151-933 0502 E-mail: sales@sharmaplc.com *Sports & promotional bag manufrs*

Titman Tip Tools Ltd, Valley Road, Clacton-on-Sea, Essex, CO15 6PP Tel: (01255) 220123 Fax: (01255) 221422 E-mail: sales@titman.co.uk *Drill bits & router bits for the woodworking industry manufrs*

Titon Hardware Ltd, International House, Peartree Road, Stanway, Colchester, CO3 0JL Tel: (01206) 713800 Fax: (01206) 543126 E-mail: sales@titon.co.uk *Manufacturer and distributor of ventilation systems and window and door hardware.*

Titon Hardware, 11 Piperell Way, Haverhill, Suffolk, CB9 8PH Tel: (01440) 762223 Fax: (01440) 706808 *Window ventilator & hardware manufrs*

John Wallis Titt & Co. Ltd, Manor Road, Frome, Somerset, BA11 4BQ Tel: (01373) 463594 Fax: (01373) 451382 *Agricultural dairy & water engineers*

Titus International plc, Ridgeway Industrial Estate, Iver, Buckinghamshire, SL0 9HW Tel: (01753) 654680 Fax: (01753) 655385 E-mail: ryanhammond@titusint.com *Furniture fittings*

Titus Pumps Ltd, 3 Chiphouse Road, Bristol, BS15 4TR Tel: 0117-940 6293 Fax: (0870) 7877472 E-mail: sales@tituspumps.co.uk *Dispenser pump manufacturers, including lotion and bulk dispensers, finger sprays. We supply the dispensers to get product out of the bottle.*

▶ Titus Wilson & Son, Kent Works, 1 Burneside Road, Kendal, Cumbria, LA9 4RL Tel: (01539) 720244 Fax: (01539) 726677

▶ Titusfield Ltd, 5 Coningsby Road, Bretton, Peterborough, PE3 8SB Tel: (01733) 269270

Tiverton Fabrications Ltd, Tiverton Business Park, Tiverton Way, Tiverton, Devon, EX16 6TG Tel: (01884) 255701 Fax: (01884) 253047 *Stainless steel fabricators*

Tiviot Prints Ltd, Lymefield Mill, Broadbottom, Hyde, Cheshire, SK14 6AG Tel: (01457) 763297 Fax: (01457) 765499 E-mail: info@tiviotprintsltd.demon.co.uk *Screen printers & textile printing services*

▶ Ti-Visual Ltd, 4 Greenfields, Upton, Chester, CH2 1LN Tel: (01244) 382287 Fax: 0870 1357161 E-mail: info@ti-visual.co.uk *Ti-Visual is a creative services agency, offering technical illustration, information graphics and design for publications, exhibitions, conferences and presentations to industry.*

Tivoli Manufacturing Ltd, Howfield Lane, Chartham, Canterbury, Kent, CT4 7HG Tel: (01227) 731156 Fax: (01227) 730137 *Fairground equipment manufacturer*

▶ Tivolis Design, Islington Business Centre, 3/5 Islington High Street, London, N1 9LQ Tel: (020) 7745 2375 Fax: (020) 7745 2376 E-mail: sales@tivolisdesign.co.uk *High quality designer & standard heated towel rails manufrs*

▶ Tivox, 280 Bawtry Road, Wickersley, Rotherham, South Yorkshire, S66 1JY Tel: (01709) 544005 Fax: (01709) 531215 E-mail: sales@tivox.co.uk *Safety fencing suppliers*

▶ TJ International Ltd, Trecerus Industrial Estate, Padstow, Cornwall, PL28 8RW Tel: (01841) 532691 Fax: (01841) 532862

TJ Joinery, Rospeath Lane, Crowlas, Penzance, Cornwall, TR20 8DU Tel: (01736) 740000 Fax: (01736) 740000 *Joinery works*

Tjaden Ltd, 62a Chatsworth Road, London, E5 0LS Tel: (020) 8533 7234 Fax: (020) 8533 7234 *Audio & electrical contractors*

▶ TK Direct (Light Haulage) Coventry, 20 Springfield Crescent, Bedworth, Warwickshire, CV12 8NX Tel: (07970) 151944 Fax: (024) 7673 1422 E-mail: info@tkdirect.co.uk *Light Haulage Distribution throughout the U.K. over short or long haul, delivering one-off or regular delivery and collection service up to 5m in length and 1.6m in height (that's 8 std pallets or euros) up to 1.4 tonnes in weight.** We are located in the Coventry area, ideally placed for easy access off the M1, M6, M40 and all other major routes.** We'll turn up and*provide a smooth and *reliable service aided by Satellite Navigation and insurance covering your Goods In Transit.**

TKA Distribution Ltd, 11 Church Meadows, Bocking, Braintree, Essex, CM7 5SL Tel: (01376) 340170 Fax: (01376) 349163 E-mail: trevor@tkadistribution.co.uk *transport*1 pallet to 26 pallet same day next day*part loads full loads*same day courier service *shows and exhibitions*

TL Computer Systems Ltd, 40 Holton Road, Barry, South Glamorgan, CF63 4HD Tel: (01446) 747702 Fax: (01446) 744699 E-mail: mail@tlsystems.co.uk *Computer consultants*

TLC, Conwy Marina, Ellis Way, Conwy, Gwynedd, LL32 8GU Tel: (01492) 580820 Fax: (01492) 580820 *Boat repairers & engineering services*

▶ TLC Electrical Distributors Ltd, 9-11 South Street, Hucknall, Nottingham, NG15 7BS Tel: 0115-963 4794 Fax: 0115-964 2812 E-mail: sales@tlcelec.co.uk *Offer a full range of electrical products which you can order online*

TLC International Ltd, 180 Okehampton Cresent, Welling, Kent, DA16 1DB Tel: (020) 8304 7545 Fax: (020) 8303 4561 *Importers of pet products*

▶ TLC Safety, 198 Bellmead Lane, Newport, Isle of Wight, PO30 2JN Tel: (07841) 236269 E-mail: forwardto@tlcsafety.co.uk *Safety Consultant*

TLC Signs, Fairfax House, Deeping St.James Road, Deeping Gate, Peterborough, PE6 9AP Tel: (01778) 349282 E-mail: sales@tlcsigns.co.uk *Signs makers*

TLW Fasteners Ltd, 115 Lodgefield Road, Halesowen, West Midlands, B62 8AX Tel: 0121-602 4040 Fax: 0121-602 4040 *Bolt & nut manufrs*

▶ TM Courier, 52 Chester Road, Stevenage, Hertfordshire, SG1 4LE Tel: (01438) 237667 E-mail: info@tmcourier.co.uk *TM COURIER offers sameday deliveries, whether it be local or national. Fully insured for peace of mind. Charged only for loaded mileage.*

▶ Tma, Unit 9 Shepley Industrial Estate North, Audenshaw, Manchester, M34 5DR Tel: 0161-320 4050 Fax: 0161-320 7001 *Exhaust systems manufrs*

TMC, 113 Sandringham Road, Birmingham, B42 1PX Tel: 0121-356 3327 *Recruitment consultants*

TMC, Crease Drove, Crowland, Peterborough, PE6 0BN Tel: (01733) 211339 Fax: (01733) 211444 E-mail: tmc@crowlandcranes.co.uk *Lifting equipment supplier*

TMC Technology UK Co., Ltd, 12 Wedgwood Court, Stevenage, Hertfordshire, SG1 4QR Tel: (01438) 842300 Fax: (01438) 842308 E-mail: sales@tmc-uk.com *Computer equipment distributors*

▶ TMCS, 2 Swanwick Road, Leabrooks, Alfreton, Derbyshire, DE55 1LJ Tel: (01773) 540348 *Computer hardware suppliers*

TMD Technologies Ltd, Intercraft House, Swallowfield Way, Hayes, Middlesex, UB3 1AW Tel: (020) 8573 5555 Fax: (020) 8569 1839 E-mail: wecare@tmd.co.uk *Microwave component manufacturers*

▶ TMD-UK Ltd, 28B High Street, Sunninghill, Ascot, Berkshire, SL5 9NE Tel: (0870) 9906001 Fax: (0870) 9906002 E-mail: service@tmd-uk.co.uk *Supply telecom products & services*

▶ Tme Training Ltd, 5 Lower Actis, Glastonbury, Somerset, BA6 8DP Tel: (01458) 832607 *We provide Fire Warden,Fire Marshal and Fire Safety Training for all staff.*Fire Risk Assessment is another service we provide*

Tmec UK Ltd, 6 Sidenhill Close, Shirley, Solihull, West Midlands, B90 2QD Tel: 0121-733 8726 Fax: 0121-733 8726 E-mail: enquiries@tmec.co.uk *Flexible plastic packaging*

Tmi, 50 High Street, Henley-in-Arden, West Midlands, B95 5AN Tel: (01527) 851741 Fax: (01527) 851777 E-mail: sales@tmi.co.uk *Training & associated products*

▶ TML International Ltd, Unit 8 Water Line Estate, Whitby, North Yorkshire, YO21 1UY Tel: (01904) 700500 Fax: (01904) 700600 E-mail: rayw@tregwaremanufacturing.co.uk *Vacuum cleaner disposable filter bags specialists*

TML Precision Engineers, Potash Lane, Hethel, Norwich, NR14 8EY Tel: (01953) 601700 Fax: (01953) 603505 E-mail: info@tmlcnc.com *Sub contract machining services*

▶ TMP & Associates Ltd, Sedgecombe House, Garfield Road, Camberley, Surrey, GU15 2JG Tel: 01276 684007 Fax: 01276 684010 E-mail: mike@tmpandass.com *recruitment, Search, Selection *All sectors*Staff, Managers and Directors*No success; no fee*Search & selection by experieced line managers and directors*

▶ TMP Projects, P.O. Box 6, Port Talbot, West Glamorgan, SA12 8EA Tel: (01639) 883884 Fax: (01639) 883906 E-mail: sales@tmpprojects.com *TMP Projects Ltd is the leading supplier of high efficiency industrial mixing and aeration systems, utilising the globally patented Turbulator Mixing Head. Our equipment is used in all industries & business sectors. Other equipment we supply includes a wide range of stainless steel vessels, fans and drying equipment. Our unique mixing system will increase product throughput while reducing maintenance, spares requirements and running costs.*

TMS Associates Ltd, 168 Clare Road, Cardiff, CF11 6RX Tel: (029) 2025 8900 Fax: (029) 2025 8255 E-mail: h.g.patel@ntlworld.com *Software development service*

TMS Corporate Awards, 2-4 Kathleen Road, Southampton, SO19 8EX Tel: (023) 8043 8866 Fax: (023) 8068 5604 E-mail: tms@trophyman.co.uk *Advertising business gift designers*

TMS Insight (Data Capture) Ltd, 1 Chads Close, Dudley, West Midlands, DY3 2LJ Tel: (01384) 214950 Fax: (01384) 212683 E-mail: andrew.haywood@tmsinsight.com *Portable electronic data capture solutions*

▶ TMS Scheduling, 15 Lotus, Lakeside, Tamworth, Staffordshire, B77 2RZ Tel: 01827 285886 Fax: 01827 288638 E-mail: stockton@caplan13.fsnet.co.uk *We are Architectural Ironmongers based in Tamworth providing Quality Products In A Competitive World. Suppliers of Hinges, Door Closers, Locks, Cylinders, Levers, Pull Handles etc., to the Construction Industry & general public as well as specifiers to Architects.*

TMS Services, 7 Brunel Way, Fareham, Hampshire, PO15 5TX Tel: (01489) 564707 Fax: (01489) 575229 E-mail: sales@ansti.com *Turnkey testing systems supplier*

▶ TMSC Ltd, 13 Helions Road, Steeple Bumpstead, Steeple Bumpstead, Haverhill, Suffolk, CB9 7DU Tel: (01440) 730211 E-mail: sales@tmsc.co.uk *Computer software developers*

TMT Toolmakers, Units 1, 3 & 7 Bilton Industrial Estate, Stockmans Close, Birmingham, B38 9TS Tel: 0121-459 0292 Fax: 0121-459 2141 *Injection mould toolmakers*

Tmwsecretarial Services, Tesla House, 37 Hartland Road, Reading, RG2 8AB Tel: (0845) 2011635 Fax: (0845) 2011925 E-mail: info@tmwsecretarial.com *Virtual Assistant secretarial services company providing administrative services to businesses worldwide.*

TNS Research & Consultancy Ltd, 4-5 Bonhill Street, London, EC2A 4SR Tel: (020) 7891 1200 Fax: (020) 7891 1299 *Market research services*

TNT, Telford Road, Durranhill Industrial Estate, Carlisle, CA1 3NW Tel: (01228) 525645 Fax: (01228) 547991 E-mail: paul.beatie@tntlogistics.co.uk *Road transport contractors*

TNT Fireworks (UK) Ltd, Dinton Woods Storage Site, Catherine Ford Road, Dinton, Salisbury, SP3 5HB Tel: (01722) 716900 Fax: (01722) 716901 *Fireworks*

TNT Freight Management, Unit 5 & 6 Park Way Trading Estate, Cranford Lane, Hounslow, TW5 9QA Tel: (020) 8814 7000 Fax: (020) 8814 7078 E-mail: info@uk.tntfreight.com *International freight forwarders & customs brokers*

TNT Logistics Ltd, Parkside Lane, Leeds, LS11 5TD Tel: 0113-276 2244 Fax: 0113-276 2928

▶ TNT Newsfast Ltd, Olivers Place, Fulwood, Preston, PR2 9WT Tel: (01772) 561259 Fax: (01772) 791995

TNT Post UK Ltd, 1 Globeside Business Park, Fieldhouse Lane, Marlow, Buckinghamshire, SL7 1HY Tel: (01628) 771232 Fax: (01628) 816600 *Leaflet distribution services* Also at: Manchester

To Catch A Dream Ltd, The Ginnel, Harrogate, North Yorkshire, HG1 2RB Tel: (01423) 503060 Fax: (01423) 528111 E-mail: info@tocatchadream.net *Beds, bedding & blankets retailers*

Toa Corporation, Unit 2 Hook Rise South Industrial Park, Hook Rise South, Surbiton, Surrey, KT6 7LD Tel: (0870) 7740987 Fax: (0870) 7770839 E-mail: info@toa.co.uk *Manufactures of public address & voice alarm products*

Toad plc, National Control Centre, Drake Road, Mitcham, Surrey, CR4 4HQ Tel: (020) 8710 7770 Fax: (020) 8710 7708 E-mail: info@toad.co.uk *Vehicle security specialist services*

Tobel Sheetmetal Ltd, Diplocks Way, Hailsham, East Sussex, BN27 3JF Tel: (01323) 442244 Fax: (01323) 440408 E-mail: sales@tobel.co.uk *Sheet metalworkers*

Tobias Solutions, Westways, Otterbourne Rd, Shawford, Winchester, Hants, SO21 2DG Tel: (01962) 715354 Fax: (01962) 715354 E-mail: colin@tobias-solutions.co.uk *Project management & consultancy to the plastic injection moulding sector*

Toby Electronics Ltd, Beaumont Road, Banbury, Oxfordshire, OX16 1TU Tel: (01295) 271777 Fax: (01295) 271744 E-mail: info@toby.co.uk *Electronic component distributor*

▶ Tocco Photos on Canvas, PO Box 67, York, YO61 1WU Tel: (0845) 6426526 E-mail: info@toccoinside.co.uk *Professionally stretched canvases using photographic & digital images. Choose images from our online gallery or send us your own photographs.*

Toco Sport Ltd, PO Box 128, Aberdeen, AB12 3LW Tel: (01224) 895700 Fax: (01224) 896057 *Sportswear retailers*

Today Interiors Holdings Ltd, Hollis Road, Grantham, Lincolnshire, NG31 7QH Tel: (01476) 574401 Fax: (01476) 590208 E-mail: info@today-interiors.co.uk *Wall covering & fabric suppliers* Also at: London SW3

Todays Interiors Ltd, Mode Uk, 64 High Street, Uttoxeter, Staffordshire, ST14 7JD Tel: (01889) 568576 Fax: (01889) 569836 E-mail: lynne.kelly2@ntlworld.com *We are now based in Mode uk which is a furniture shop specialising in classic and modern deisigner furniture. Todays Interiors are specialists in custom made and ready made curtains blind and soft furnishings. We stock fabrics by Romo, Villa Nova, Nono, Presigious. And wallpaper by Nono and Romo. We supply to the public and contract. We provide a free local measuring and consultation.*

Todd Doors Ltd, 112-116 Church Road, Northolt, Middlesex, UB5 5AE Tel: (020) 8845 2493 Fax: (020) 8845 7579 E-mail: info@todd-doors.co.uk *Domestic door manufrs*

Todd & Duncan, Lochleven Mills, Kinross, KY13 8DH Tel: (01577) 863521 Fax: (01577) 864533 E-mail: sales@todd-duncan.com *Woollen yarn spinners & dyers*

▶ Todd Engineering Ltd, 6 Prospect House, Prospect Road, Burntwood, Staffordshire, WS7 0AL Tel: (01543) 677749 Fax: (01543) 677749 E-mail: sales@todengineering.co.uk

Todd Herbert, Percys Lane, York, YO1 9TP Tel: (01904) 628676 Fax: (01904) 653328 E-mail: graham@htodd.co.uk *Electrical contractors*

J. Todd (A F C L) Ltd, The Forge, Great Warley Street, Great Warley, Brentwood, Essex, CM13 3JF Tel: (01277) 222645 Fax: (01277) 224522 *Horse shoe manufrs*

Todd & Reed, 32a Lily Road, London, E17 8HY Tel: (020) 8558 0722 Fax: (020) 8558 0722 *Clothing manufrs*

Todd Research Ltd, Robjohns Road, Chelmsford, CM1 3DP Tel: (01245) 262233 Fax: (01245) 269409 E-mail: xray@toddresearch.co.uk *X-ray apparatus manufrs*

Todds Of Lincoln Ltd, Centenary House, Whisby Way, Lincoln, LN6 3LQ Tel: (01522) 884000 Fax: (01522) 884411 E-mail: sales@toddslinc.co.uk *Office equipment suppliers*

Tofco CPP Ltd, Meadowfield, Ponteland, Newcastle Upon Tyne, NE20 9SD Tel: (01661) 860001 Fax: (01661) 860002 E-mail: info@tofco.co.uk Principal Export Areas: Middle East *Electrical cut-outs*

Ian Tofte Voice & Data Communications, 32 Bronte Close, Aylesbury, Buckinghamshire, HP19 8LF Tel: (01296) 487982 Fax: (01296) 488050 E-mail: itofte@tiscalli.co.uk *Data communication agents*

Toft-Johnston (Construction) Ltd, Kingsley House, Apedale Road, Chesterton, Newcastle, Staffordshire, ST5 6BH Tel: (01782) 566531 Fax: (01782) 564795 E-mail: admin@toftjohnston.co.uk *Building contractors & civil engineers*

Toga Plant Hire Ltd, 67-71 Kingsland Road, London, E2 8AG Tel: (020) 7729 1471 Fax: (020) 7729 1592 *Small plant machine hire*

Togged-Up, 2 Wellgate, Clitheroe, Lancashire, BB7 2DP Tel: (01200) 427630 Fax: (01200) 424873 E-mail: linda@tusport.co.uk *School wear & sports equipment distributors*

Toghill Jewellers, 16 Hockley Street, Birmingham, B18 6BL Tel: 0121-554 2727 *Manufacturers of jewellery*

▶ Toile Solutions, 1 Starr Road, Henham, Bishop's Stortford, Hertfordshire, CM22 6AW Tel: (01279) 850277 Fax: (0870) 1635365 E-mail: sales@toilesolutions.com *Website design solutions*

▶ Toilet Hire, 1 Bottings Industrial Estate, Curdridge, Southampton, SO30 2DY Tel: (01489) 790020 Fax: (01489) 790030 *Portable toilet hire & sales*

Toilets Plus Ltd, 34 London Road, Wymondham, Norfolk, NR18 9JD Tel: (01953) 601345 Fax: (01953) 601344 E-mail: sales@toilets.co.uk *Portable toilet suppliers*

Tokai Carbon UK Ltd, Roway Lane, Oldbury, West Midlands, B69 3EJ Tel: 0121-552 5577 Fax: 0121-552 6748 E-mail: john@tokaicarboneurope.com *Graphite component manufrs*

▶ Tokheim UK Ltd, 1-3 Baker Road, Broughty Ferry, Dundee, DD5 3RT Tel: (01382) 598000 Fax: (01382) 598001

Tokheim UK Ltd, 1-3 Baker Road, Broughty Ferry, Dundee, DD5 3RT Tel: (01382) 598000 Fax: (01382) 598001 E-mail: sales@dundee.tokheim.com Principal Export Areas: Worldwide *Tokheim is the market leader in the design, manufacture and servicing of petroleum retailing solutions. With the skills and capability to drive your business forward, Tokheim is dedicated to working with you and committed to building strong business partnerships. Tokheim not only supply high-quality petroleum retailing solutions with our extensive range of dispensers, accompanied by our unbeaten payment solutions, but also recognise the need for delivering high-quality forecourt maintenance. Our highly skilled network of remote engineers is on hand to maintain and repair all manner of faults found on today's modern forecourt. At Tokheim we are dedicated to delivering improved quality of service year on year. Whether you are building a service station from the ground up or renovating and upgrading an existing forecourt, Tokheim service specialists are on-hand to work in partnership with you to deliver the best all round solution.*

Toko UK Ltd, Ward Royal Parade, Alma Road, Windsor, Berkshire, SL4 3HR Tel: (01753) 602222 Fax: (01753) 602255 *Electronic component manufrs*

The Tokyo Electric Power Company, Incorporated, Masaki Chiba, Berkeley Square House, London, W1J 6BR Tel: (020) 7629 5271 Fax: (020) 7629 5282 *Tokyo generate electric research services*

Tokyo Electron Europe Ltd, Crawley Business Quarter, Fleming Way, Crawley, West Sussex, RH10 9QL Tel: (01293) 655800 Fax: (01293) 655888 *Semiconductor production machinery & equipment manufrs*

Tokyo Fabric Printing UK Ltd, Overtons Building, Friar Street, Wednesbury, West Midlands, WS10 0RE Tel: 0121-502 6297 Fax: 0121-505 7277 E-mail: j.s.sandhu@tokyofabrics.co.uk *Fabric suppliers for upholstery*

Tokyo Leasing UK plc, 6th Floor, Valiant House, London, EC3A 5DQ Tel: (020) 7283 6100 Fax: (020) 7283 6102 *Leasing company*

Tokyo TV Ltd, Kennington Avenue, Kingswood, Bristol, BS15 1SH Tel: 0117-975 4374 Fax: 0117-975 4374 E-mail: blestwoe@lineone.net *Electro mechanical engineering*

Tolbest Ltd, 10 Aston Court, Kingsland Grange, Woolston, Warrington, WA1 4SG Tel: (01925) 825335 Fax: (01925) 825336 E-mail: info@tolbest.co.uk *Water leakage detection & control services*

Tolent Construction Ltd, Ravensworth House, Fifth Avenue, Team Valley Trading Estate, Gateshead, Tyne & Wear, NE11 0HF Tel: 0191-487 0505 Fax: 0191-487 2990

▶ Tolent Construction Ltd, 5 Christie Way, Christie Fields, Manchester, M21 7QY Tel: 0161-445 1100 Fax: 0161-445 5623 E-mail: jthorpe@tolent.co.uk *Building contractors*

Toll House Jewellery, Crown Buildings, Halifax Road, Ripponden, Sowerby Bridge, West Yorkshire, HX6 4DA Tel: (01422) 823846 Fax: (01422) 823846 *Jewellery manufrs*

Tolland Glass & Windows, 11 Tudor Parade, Well Hall Road, London, SE9 6SX Tel: (020) 8850 9236 Fax: (020) 8294 0036 *Glazing contractors double glazing suppliers*

W.H. Tolley & Son Ltd, Caddywell, Torrington, Devon, EX38 7EL Tel: (01805) 622315 Fax: (01805) 624702 E-mail: wht.hq@virgin.net *Foundation contractors*

▶ Tollgate Labels, Hyders Farm, Bonnetts Lane, Ifield, Crawley, West Sussex, RH11 0NY Tel: (01293) 551520 Fax: (01293) 551530 E-mail: sales@tollgatelabels.co.uk *Manufacturer of self-adhesive labels located in Sussex, England. Specialising in the manufacture of high quality self-adhesive labels and asset tags, on behalf of both end-user & trade customers*

Tollgate Products Ltd, Heslop, Halesfield 21, Telford, Shropshire, TF7 4NX Tel: (01952) 520130 Fax: (01952) 586605 E-mail: sales@tollgateproducts.co.uk Principal Export Areas: Worldwide *Toilet cubicle hardware manufrs*

Tollgate Security Ltd, 16 Claverton Buildings, Bath, BA2 4LD Tel: (01225) 444328 E-mail: sales@tollgatesecurity.co.uk *Intruder alarms installation*

Tollhurst, 1 North St, Bromley, BR1 1RB Tel: 020 84641179 *Joinery manufacturers*

Tolman & Co. Ltd, 30 Hogshill Street, Beaminster, Dorset, DT8 3AD Tel: (01308) 862351 *Heating & plumbing engineers*

Tolta Pumps Ltd, Unit 10, Bangors Road, Pennygillam Way, Launceston, Cornwall, PL15 7ED Tel: (01566) 773310 Fax: (01566) 779165 E-mail: sales@harburro.co.uk *Supply & install pumps for water filtration*

Toltec Systems, Exchange Quay, Salford, M5 3EQ Tel: 0161-876 4447 Fax: 0161-876 4448 E-mail: sales-uk@etoltec.com *Toltec are a unique technology business solution provider, specialising in three key areas of business including ICT Consultancy, Professional ICT Support and providing the ability to Purchase Goods and Services Online*

▶ Toltech Internet Solutions, Mansion House, 1 Ardgowan Square, Greenock, Renfrewshire, PA16 8NG Tel: (01475) 716726 Fax: (01475) 727854 E-mail: info@toltech.co.uk *Search Engine Specialists based in Scotland near Glasgow. We manage Internet Marketing campaigns for single business owners to large corporations providing Web Development, Internet Marketing, Search Engine Submissions, Pay Per Click campaigns, email Newsletters and a variety of internet related activities*

Tolway East Ltd, 1 Nuffield Close, Cambridge, CB4 1SS Tel: (01223) 425425 Fax: (01223) 420200 *Construction fixings & fast supplier*

Tolwood Ltd, Coatham Avenue, Aycliffe Industrial Park, Newton Aycliffe, County Durham, DL5 6DB Tel: (01325) 300777 Fax: (01325) 300399 E-mail: info@tolwood.co.uk *Fastener & pierce nut manufrs*

Tolworth Tools Ltd, 46B Fife Rd, Kingston upon Thames, Surrey, KT1 1SU Tel: (020) 8546 2683 Fax: (020) 8546 2683 *Plastics mould & tool manufrs*

Toly Products (UK) Ltd, Watkin Road, Wembley, Middlesex, HA9 0NL Tel: (020) 8902 3161 Fax: (020) 8900 2975 E-mail: info@toly.com *Compact case manufrs*

Tom C Saville Ltd, 9 Nottingham Road, Trowell, Nottingham, NG9 3PA Tel: 0115-930 8800 Fax: 0115-930 3336 *Fishing & angling equipment*

▶ Tom Croft Bolton Ltd, 6 Albert Street, Farnworth, Bolton, BL4 9HN Tel: (01204) 861368 Fax: (01204) 794391

▶ Tom Evans Audio Design Ltd, St. Margarets Park Main Entrance, Pengam Road, Aberbargoed, Bargoed, Mid Glamorgan, CF81 9FW Tel: (01443) 833570 Fax: (01443) 839977 E-mail: sales@audiodesign.co.uk *Audio equipment manufrs*

▶ Tom Hannah Agencies Ltd, Walkinshaw Works, Walkinshaw Street, Johnstone, Renfrewshire, PA5 8AB Tel: (01505) 321131 Fax: (01505) 329281 E-mail: sales@hannahssweets.co.uk *Sell sweets*

▶ Tom James Of London Ltd, 15-17 Christopher Street, London, EC2A 2BS Tel: (020) 7247 5246 Fax: (020) 7247 6153

Tom Jones Boatbuilders Ltd, Romney Lock Boathouse, Romney Lock, Windsor, Berkshire, SL4 6HU Tel: (01753) 860699 Fax: (01753) 856982 *Boatyard, restorations & repairs*

▶ Tom Jukes Graphics Ltd, Units 5-6 First Avenue, Westfield Industrial Estate, Midsomer Norton, Radstock, BA3 4BS Tel: (01761) 416023

▶ Tom Lee, Unit 6 Littleton Trading Estate, Littleton Lane, Shepperton, Middlesex, TW17 0NF Tel: 01932 569939 Fax: 01932 569939 E-mail: info@media-construction.co.uk *Fabrication, Design, Construction, Business, Self-Build, GRP, Film Props, Vehicles, Promotional*

Tom Morrow Ltd, 1 Anderson Avenue, Aberdeen, AB24 4LR Tel: (01224) 485567 Fax: (01224) 488607 *Tarpaulin supplier, digital printing & hold all bag manufrs*

Tom Morrow Tarpaulins Inverness Ltd, 14 Henderson Road, Inverness, IV1 1SN Tel: (01463) 220862 Fax: (01463) 243110 E-mail: enquiries@tommorrowtarpaulins.co.uk *Tarpaulin manufrs* Also at: Aberdeen

Tom Smith Parts Ltd, Old Hakin Road, Walwyns Castle, Haverfordwest, Dyfed, SA62 3EL Tel: (01437) 890414 Fax: (01437) 890256 E-mail: sales@tomsmithparts.co.uk *Agricultural machinery suppliers*

▶ Tom Super (Printing Supplies) Ltd, 23-31 Castle Street, Hamilton, Lanarkshire, ML3 6BU Tel: (01698) 286401

Tom Taylor & Son, Fish Dock Road, Grimsby, South Humberside, DN31 3PD Tel: (01472) 354604 Fax: (01472) 267071 *Protective clothing stockists*

Tomah Engineers Ltd, 104 Fitzwalter Rd., Sheffield, S2 2SP Tel: 0114-272 1199 Fax: 0114-276 8675 E-mail: tomaheng@aol.com *General engineers & roll makers*

Tomalin Associates, 12 Bardfield Centre, Great Bardfield, Braintree, Essex, CM7 4SL Tel: (01371) 811299 Fax: (01371) 811283 E-mail: sales@tomalinassociates.com *Newsletter & magazine distributors*

Tombi, Unit 20, Limberline Industrial Estate, Limberline Spur, Hilsea, Portsmouth, PO3 5DY Tel: (023) 9269 0215 Fax: (023) 9269 1095 *Steel & welding fabricators*

Tombs & Bliss, Unit K, Chosen View Road, Kingsditch Trading Estate, Cheltenham, Gloucestershire, GL51 9LT Tel: (01242) 525957 Fax: (01242) 525957 *Stove enamellers*

Tomhead Ltd, 2a Ramsden Road, Rotherwas Industrial Estate, Hereford, HR2 6NP Tel: (01432) 358420 Fax: (01432) 354448 E-mail: info@tomhead.co.uk *Storage & warehousing*

▶ Tomintoul Distillery, Kirkmichael, Ballindalloch, Banffshire, AB37 9AQ Tel: (01807) 590274 *Distillery, whisky*

Tomita (U K) Ltd, Fortway House, Banbury, Oxfordshire, OX16 4SP Tel: (01295) 277317 Fax: (01295) 278889 E-mail: sales@tomita.co.uk *Machinery parts distributors*

Tomkins Buckle, Brockhurst CR, Walsall, WS5 4QG Tel: (01922) 723003 Fax: (01922) 723149 E-mail: sales@fhtomkins.com *General presswork manufrs*

Tomlander Ltd, Paston Road, Sharston, Manchester, M22 4TF Tel: 0161-902 0226 Fax: 0161-945 5203 E-mail: tomlander@msn.com *Pipework fabricators*

G.H. Tomlin & Co. Ltd, 11 Sandon Industrial Estate, Sandon Way, Liverpool, L5 9YN Tel: 0151-207 7216 Fax: 0151-298 2347 E-mail: mark@tomlinsighns.com *Sign & rubber stamp manufrs*

Tomlin Hydraulics Ltd, Vicarage Farm Road, Peterborough, PE1 5TP Tel: (01733) 558833 Fax: (01733) 897801 E-mail: tomlinhydraulics@btconnect.com *Hydraulic manufrs*

Tomlin International, Europa Trading Centre, London Road, Grays, Essex, RM20 4DB Tel: (01375) 372952 Fax: (01375) 372952 *Commercial vehicle repairs*

▶ Tomlinson Building Ltd, 329 Tyburn Road, Birmingham, B24 8HJ Tel: 0121-327 2660 Fax: 0121-327 3110 E-mail: sales@tomlinsonbuilding.co.uk

G.F. Tomlinson Building Ltd, 14 City Road, Derby, DE1 3RQ Tel: (01332) 342202 Fax: (01332) 295936 E-mail: building@gftomlinson.co.uk *Building contractors*

G.F. Tomlinson Group Ltd, 16 City Road, Derby, DE1 3RQ Tel: (01332) 296565 Fax: (01322) 381510 E-mail: office@gftomlinson.co.uk *Building & civil engineers services*

Tomlinson & Partners, 66 Eastgate, Cowbridge, South Glamorgan, CF71 7AB Tel: (01446) 773151 Fax: (01446) 775267 E-mail: adt@tomlinsonconsulting.co.uk *Consulting civil engineers*

Tomlinson Tube & Instrument Ltd, Unit 4C Waterloo Industrial Estate, Waterloo Road, Bidford-on-Avon, Alcester, Warwickshire, B50 4JH Tel: (01789) 778966 Fax: (01789) 490239 E-mail: keith@tomlinson-tube.co.uk *Tomlinson Tube and Instrument - an ISO9000 registered company - manufacture, to customer order, a large range of high quality needles and other surgical instruments from fine stainless steel tubing and wire.*

Tomlinson & White (Contracts) Ltd, Smithy Avenue, Clay Cross, Chesterfield, Derbyshire, S45 9NX Tel: (01246) 250060 Fax: (01246) 250004 *Civil engineers*

▶ Tommy Tucker Vending, 5c Dunslow Road, Eastfield, Scarborough, North Yorkshire, YO11 3UT Tel: (01723) 584390 Fax: (01723) 582350 E-mail: info@tommytuckervending.co.uk *Vending machine manufrs*

Tomoe Valve Ltd, Estuary Road, Queensway Meadows Industrial Estate, Newport, Gwent, NP19 4SP Tel: (01633) 636800 Fax: (01633) 636801 *Performance butterfly & plastic valves manufrs*

Tomorrows World, 29 Paragon Street, Hull, HU1 3NA Tel: (01482) 324887 Fax: (01482) 325854 *Computer component suppliers*

Tomorrows World, 555 Shields Road, Newcastle Upon Tyne, NE6 4QL Tel: 0191-240 0555 E-mail: info@cpswbay.co.uk *Car audio & security installation services & phone car kits retailers*

Tom-Pac (G.B.) Ltd, PO Box 8450, Prestwick, Ayrshire, KA9 1RG Tel: (01292) 471196 Fax: (01292) 471196 E-mail: tompacgb@btconnect.com *Lubricant & gland packing distributors*

Tompion Oil Co. Ltd, Healey Road, Ossett, West Yorkshire, WF5 8LS Tel: (01924) 273295 *Oil & grease (lubricating) suppliers*

▶ Tompkins & May Partnership, Kingsmill Business Park, Chapel Mill Road, Kingston upon Thames, Surrey, KT1 3GZ Tel: (020) 8974 7270 E-mail: sales@tomkinsmay.com

▶ Tomps Plaster Supplies Ltd, 220 New Road, Sutton Bridge, Spalding, Lincolnshire, PE12 9QE Tel: (01406) 351001 Fax: (01406) 351513 E-mail: sales@tomps.com *Suppliers of mould making materials*

Tomrods Ltd, Manse Lane, Knaresborough, North Yorkshire, HG5 8LF Tel: (01423) 867333 Fax: (01423) 867834 E-mail: sales@tomrods.co.uk *Steel stockholders*

Toms Office Technology Ltd, 26 Adelaide Road, Leamington Spa, Warwickshire, CV31 3PL Tel: (01926) 425842 Fax: (01926) 832017 E-mail: sales@tomsoffice.co.uk *Office equipment distributors & stationery suppliers*

▶ Toms Tool Chest, Foxpit House, Harrington, Workington, Cumbria, CA14 5RX Tel: (01946) 830716 Fax: (01946) 833317 E-mail: TomsToolChest@aol.com *On-line sales of tools, boxes, chests, cabinets & assortments*

▶ Tom's Toys, 22 Manor Road, Newton Longville, Milton Keynes, MK17 0AJ Tel: (01908) 376951 *Long established wooden toy and rocking horse maker. Many of the wooden toys featured in our web site are only available from us. We have done all the hard work so that you can buy from us with confidence. Direct to you. Three ranges of rocking sheep, Mary, Ba Ba and Jacob. To complement our range of sheep we manufacture a rocking Old English Sheepdog.*

Tomsetts Distribution Ltd, North Quay Road, Newhaven, East Sussex, BN9 0AB Tel: (01273) 513347 Fax: (01273) 516042 E-mail: enquiries@tomsetts.com *Road transport services & storage*

Tomy Yujin Europe Ltd, St Nicholas House, St Nicholas Road, Sutton, Surrey, SM1 1EH Tel: (020) 8722 7300 E-mail: office@tomy.co.uk *Toy suppliers*

Tonbridge Fencing Ltd, Court Lane Farm, Court Lane, Hadlow, Tonbridge, Kent, TN11 0DP Tel: (01732) 852596 Fax: (01732) 852593 E-mail: info@tonbridgefencing.co.uk *Established in 1955, Tonbridge Fencing Ltd, based in the South East (Home Counties), manufacture, supply and supply and erect a wide range of timber and steel fencing and gates. We also supply and erect automatic gates and doors, access systems and video and audio access systems. We undertake works for schools; industrial premises; government establishments; utilities; domestic and private premises.*Whilst manufacturing in our own steel yard or timber workshop specialist bespoke items such as sliding gates and railings, etc, we also supply and erect fences and gates from the following companies:- Expamet: Fencing Supplies: Heras fencing: IAE: Jacksons Fencing: Charles Ransfords & Sons: Singer & James: Theilco Gratings: Orsogril: Tornado: Werra: Gunnebo: Zaun Ltd: CLD: Bekaert: BFT: ADI-Gardener.*Examples of fences erected are: security: steel palisade: mesh: sports and perimeter: acoustic: vertical bar railing: closeboard: timber palisade: bow top and chainlink.*

Tonbridge Rod & Line, 17a Priory Road, Tonbridge, Kent, TN9 2AQ Tel: (01732) 352450 Fax: (01732) 352450 *Fishing tackle retailers*

▶ Tonder & Tonder, Bryants Farm, Kiln Road, Dunsden, Reading, RG4 9PB Tel: 0118-946 3704 Fax: 0118-946 3801 E-mail: sales@tonderandtonder.com *Manufacturers of egyptian cotton bed linen*

▶ Tone Scaffolding Services, 87-91 Beddington Lane, Croydon, CR0 4TD Tel: (020) 8684 3771 Fax: (020) 8684 3772 E-mail: chris.burch@tonescaffolding.co.uk *Scaffold contractor/erector, hire & sales of scaffold plant*

▶ ToneTel Telecom, 86 Cabell Road, Guildford, Surrey, GU2 8JQ Tel: 01483 578456 Fax: 01483 871528 E-mail: sales@tonetel.co.uk *Business telephone systems*

Tong Engineering Ltd, Ashby Road, Spilsby, Lincolnshire, PE23 5DW Tel: (01790) 752771 Fax: (01790) 753611 E-mail: sales@tongpeal.com *Agricultural engineers*

Neville Tong, Tudor Lodge, Scotter, Gainsborough, Lincolnshire, DN21 3UR Tel: (01724) 762650 E-mail: jone.tong@btopenworld.com *Sheeting specialists*

Tonge Bridge Timber Sales UK Ltd, Turner Bridge Works, Windley Street, Bolton, BL2 2DF Tel: (01204) 417676 Fax: (01204) 417583 E-mail: sales@tongebridgetimber.co.uk *Timber machining services*

Tonge Fold Engineers Ltd, Ainsworth Lane, Bolton, BL2 2PP Tel: (01204) 521917 Fax: (01204) 521917 *Engine reconditioners & rebuilders*

▶ Tongling, 6 Camellia Drive, Priorslee, Telford, Shropshire, TF2 9UA Tel: (01952) 200032 Fax: (01952) 291938 E-mail: sales@tlflooring.co.uk

▶ Tonic Construction Ltd, The Coach House, Queen Court, West Tockenham, Swindon, SN4 7PJ Tel: (01793) 741234

▶ Tonis Bakery, 164 Queensway, Milton Keynes, MK2 2SW Tel: (01908) 648944 *Bakery*

R. & S. Tonks, Boothen Green, Campbell Road, Stoke-On-Trent, ST4 4BJ Tel: (01782) 848235 Fax: (01782) 747049 E-mail: headoffice@rstonks.co.uk *Exhibition stands*

Tonrose Ltd, Unit 1 Petre Road, Clayton le Moors, Accrington, Lancashire, BB5 5TZ Tel: (01254) 239900 Fax: (01254) 239111 E-mail: welcome@tonrose.com *Textile merchants*

▶ Tonwell Builders Ltd, 1 Union Street, Ramsbottom, Bury, Lancashire, BL0 9AN Tel: (01706) 821000 Fax: (01706) 821500 E-mail: sales@tonwell.com

Tony Bone Crash Repairs, Grace Road Central, Marsh Barton Trading Estate, Exeter, EX2 8QA Tel: (01392) 252277 *Resprayers & panel beaters*

Tony Cullimore Services, Berkeley Heath, Berkeley, Gloucestershire, GL13 9EW Tel: (01453) 810220 Fax: (01453) 811987 *Agricultural merchants*

Tony Graham & Co, 33-35 Whistley Road, Potterne, Devizes, Wiltshire, SN10 5QY Tel: (01380) 729445 Fax: (07005) 802576 E-mail: tony@tonygraham.co.uk *Tony Graham & Co provide repair and maintenance services for period properties, specialising in buildings constructed prior to 1840. Tony Graham's professional qualifications BEng (Hons), MSc. (Bldg Conserv.) with distinction and his experience in the conservation of domestic property enable them to provide expert friendly assistance on projects of all sizes - from mending broken door furniture to carrying out structural repairs. In additional to care of historic fabric, services include structural considerations, legislation consultancy and conservation of classical architecture.*

Tony Green, 96 Nottingham Road, Gotham, Nottingham, NG11 0HH Tel: 0115-983 1414 Fax: 0115-983 1414 *Kitchen & bedroom furniture manufrs*

Tony Hudson, Moor Farm Buildings, Moor Lane, Murton, York, YO19 5XD Tel: (01904) 481891 Fax: (01904) 481930

▶ Tony Huggins Builders, 53 Draycott Road, Chiseldon, Swindon, SN4 0LT Tel: 01793 740054 Fax: 01793 740054 *We are Swindon based building contractors, over the years, Tony Huggins Builders have expanded and we are now able to offer our clients a 'start to finish' building service.**

Tony Ling Property Investments, Empire House, Empire Way, Wembley, Middlesex, HA9 0EW Tel: (020) 8970 2130 Fax: (020) 8970 2105 *Property investments*

▶ Tony Patti Entertainments, Sunrise Radio, Merrick Road, Southall, Middlesex, UB2 4AU Tel: 07961 908650 E-mail: tonypatti@sunriseradio.com *The largest mobile disco in the UK. Specialist DJ for Asian weddings and functions. Most respected and well established Asian DJ in the UK.*

▶ Tony's Removals, 2 Wheeldale Avenue, Redcar, Cleveland, TS10 5HF Tel: (01642) 511994 E-mail: tonys.removals@ntlworld.com *Light removals mainly local but can do distance work, available at short notice, Old furniture Removed and diposed of also licenced to remove and dispose of junk LEGALY.**

Tony's Tackle Shop, 211 Seaside, Eastbourne, East Sussex, BN22 7NP Tel: (01323) 731388 Fax: (01323) 647247 E-mail: tonytackle@aol.com *Fishing tackle retailers*

Tony's Textiles, 56 Newborough, Scarborough, North Yorkshire, YO11 1ET Tel: (01723) 371171 Fax: (01723) 371171 *Beds, bedding & blankets retailers*

Tooby, Hereford Road, Ledbury, Herefordshire, HR8 2PR Tel: (01531) 635656 *Agricultural machinery sales & services*

Toogood Industrial Ltd, Unit H7, Haysbridge Business Centre, Brickhouse Lane, South Godstone, Godstone, Surrey, RH9 8JW Tel: (01342) 844188 Fax: (01342) 844220 E-mail: office@toogood.co.uk *Chain drives, bearings & conveyor distributors*

▶ Toogood Plastics, Pritchetts Way, Rookley, Ventnor, Isle of Wight, PO38 3LT Tel: (01983) 721511 Fax: (01983) 721522

John Tooke & Partners, 1a Montford Place, London, SE11 5DE Tel: (020) 7582 0255 Fax: (020) 7820 0297 E-mail: lloyd@john-tooke.co.uk *Consulting structural engineers*

Tool Care Hire (Devon) Ltd, 19 Marsh Green Road, Marsh Barton Trading Estate, Exeter, EX2 8NY Tel: (01392) 250379 Fax: (01392) 274658 *Tool & plant hirer*

Tool Centre, 104 King Street, Blackburn, BB2 2DT Tel: (01254) 57282 Fax: (01254) 678992 *Tool shop supplier*

Tool Connection Ltd, Unit 2, Kineton Road, Southam, Warwickshire, CV47 0DR Tel: (01926) 815999 Fax: (01926) 815888 E-mail: lesleyscott@lasertools.co.uk *Tool distributors*

▶ The Tool & Fixing Co. Ltd, Unit 18, Arden Business Centre, Arden Road, Alcester, Warwickshire, B49 6HW Tel: (01789) 400000 Fax: (01789) 400088 E-mail: TOOLS@UK192.COM

▶ The Tool & Gauge Co., Flat E, 200 Iverson Road, London, NW6 2HL Tel: (020) 7372 1973 Fax: (020) 7813 3345 E-mail: thetoolngaugeco@aol.com *Engineering tool distributors*

Tool & Instruments Engineering Ltd, Archenfield Road, Ross-On-Wye, Herefordshire, HR9 5AZ Tel: (01989) 563002 Fax: (01989) 562068 *Precision machinists*

Tool Production & Design Co. Ltd, Borman, Apollo, Tamworth, Staffordshire, B79 7TA Tel: (01827) 66767 Fax: (01827) 53670 *Automation system manufrs*

Tool Repair Services, Unit 51 The Sir Robert Peel Mill, Mill Lane, Fazeley, Tamworth, Staffordshire, B78 3QD Tel: (01827) 286322 Fax: (01827) 259101 E-mail: toolrepairs@hotmail.com *Pneumatic tool & repairs*

Tool-auctions-online, 13 Waveney Road, Lowestoft, Suffolk, NR32 1BT Tel: (01502) 564120 Fax: (01502) 564120 E-mail: kevin@tool-auctions-online.co.uk *DIY suppliers*

Toolbase Envrionmental, Waterloo Road, Romford, RM7 0AN Tel: (01708) 768766 Fax: (01708) 768773 E-mail: admin@toolbase.co.uk *Asbestos removal contractors*

▶ Toolbox Buddy, Regus House, George Curl Way, Southampton, SO18 2RZ Tel: 0800 023 4948 E-mail: enquiries@toolboxbuddy.co.uk *We're the competent and trustworthy solution to your maintenance, repair and improvement needs around the*home and workplace.*From changing a light bulb, to putting up a shelf, to tiling a bathroom*Toolbox Buddy is the small job specialist - *providing service that makes you smile!*Plumbing, Electrical, Carpentry, Decorating and much more - ASK US!*For fast action call now!**

Toolbox Supplies Ltd, 13 Hams Road, Lydney, Gloucestershire, GL15 5PE Tel: (01594) 841104 Fax: (01594) 841105 *Plumbing & tools distribution*

Toolbox (UK) Ltd, At Hurco, Hallifax Road, Cressex Business Park, High Wycombe, Buckinghamshire, HP12 3SN Tel: (01494) 558333 Fax: (01494) 558388 *Manufacturers of CAD/CAM systems*

Toolcom Supplies Ltd, Pitreavie Business Park, Pitreavie Business Park, Dunfermline, Fife, KY11 8UQ Tel: (01383) 728970 Fax: (01383) 620079 E-mail: sales@toolcom.co.uk *Engineers, suppliers, bolt & nut distributors*

Toolcraft Plastics Swindon Ltd, 2 Argyle Commercial Centre, 1-5 Argyle Street, Swindon, SN2 8AR Tel: (01793) 641040 Fax: (01793) 615483 E-mail: help@toolcraft.co.uk *Family company offering rapid, inexpensive product design & development, sla models, steel/ aluminium injection mould tools, injection moulding to 300mm², vacuum forming to 610mm² 0.3-6mm thick and foil/pad printing, ultrasonic welding & assembly.*

Nigel Tooley Ltd, PO Box 91, Ashtead, Surrey, KT21 1YX Tel: (01372) 278620 E-mail: coincabinet@btconnect.com *Birthday & anniversary gifts, corporate gifts, corporate birthday cards, retirement cards, collectors coins and printed place cards, menus & table number cards*

Tooling 2000 Ltd, 41 Western Road, Birmingham, B18 7QE Tel: 0121 2422000 *Press tools manufrs*

▶ Tooling & Developments Ltd, Waterside Road, Hamilton Indutrsial Park, Leicester, LE5 1TL Tel: 0116-246 1808 Fax: 0116-246 1659 *Automotive radiators*

Tooling Direct Ltd, Salford House, 535 Lichfield Road, Birmingham, B6 7SP Tel: 0121-327 1952 Fax: 0121-327 1954 E-mail: sales@tooling-direct.com *Machine tool merchants*

Tooling International Ltd, Unit 8 Speedwell Trading Estate, Kings Road, Tyseley, Birmingham, B11 2AT Tel: 0121-771 0611 Fax: 0121-773 6588 E-mail: til@enterprise.net *Fastener tooling manufrs*

Sam Tooling Ltd, 60 Newland Street, Coleford, Gloucestershire, GL16 8AL Tel: (01594) 835542 Fax: (01594) 837293 *Special purpose machines manufrs*

Toolmaster (Oxford) Ltd, 148 Oxford Road, Cowley, Oxf, OX4 2EA Tel: (01865) 712152 Fax: (01865) 747380 E-mail: sales@toolmaster.co.uk *Retail tool shop*

Toolmasters Technical Ltd, Instanta Work, Charles Street, West Bromwich, West Midlands, B70 0AZ Tel: 0121-520 1889 Fax: 0121-520 1890 E-mail: sales@toolmasters.co.uk *Deep hole boring & honing specialists*

Toolmatic Tool Design, 36 Hall Street, Birmingham, B18 6BS Tel: 0121-236 1417 Fax: 0121-233 9240 *Cutting tool & jigs & fixtures manufrs*

Toolmax General Engineering Ltd, St Martins Trade Park, Nickel Close, Winchester, Hampshire, SO23 7RJ Tel: (01962) 855515 Fax: (01962) 827790 *General engineering services*

Tooloy (T S) Ltd, Sizers Court Trading Estate, Henshaw Lane, Yeadon, Leeds, LS19 7DP Tel: 0113-250 4717 Fax: 0113-239 1207 E-mail: paul@tooloytsltdco.co.uk *Cutting tool distributors & manufrs*

Toolpak plc, Rhosddu Industrial Estate, Old Rhosrobin, Rhosrobin, Wrexham, Clwyd, LL11 4YL Tel: (01978) 291771 Fax: (01978) 290068 E-mail: sales@toolpak.co.uk *Welding & power tool distributors*

Toolroom Technology Ltd, Unit 1a & 1b, Haddenham Business Park, Thame Road, Haddenham, Buckinghamshire, HP17 8LJ Tel: (01844) 296650 Fax: (01844) 296651 E-mail: solutions@ttl-3d.co.uk *Computer engineers & suppliers*

Toolsharp Engineering Ltd, Westland Square, Westland Road, Leeds, LS11 5SS Tel: 0113-276 0855 Fax: 0113-271 5294 E-mail: toolsharp@btconnect.com *Special purpose machinery engineers & design services*

Toolspec Manufacturing Co. Ltd, Unit E, Sedgwick Road, Luton, LU4 9DT Tel: (01582) 572626 E-mail: toolspec@psilink.co.uk *Tube manipulators & fabricators*

Tooltec Industrial & Cleaning Supplies, Unit C2 Forge Meadow, Canterbury Road, Hawkinge, Folkestone, Kent, CT18 7JA Tel: (01303) 894799 Fax: (01303) 894799 *Industrial products suppliers*

Tooltek Supplies Ltd, Spyvee Street, Hull, HU8 7JJ Tel: (01482) 229628 Fax: (01482) 229630 E-mail: info@tooltek.co.uk *Hand tool stockists & engineers supplies*

Toolturn Engineering Ltd, 8 Brunel Way, Fareham, Hampshire, PO15 5TX Tel: (01489) 578878 Fax: (01489) 578859 E-mail: sales@toolturn.com *Precision machining specialists*

▶ Toomeys, 3 Mill Court, Mill Lane, Newbury, Berkshire, RG14 5RE Tel: (01635) 33206

▶ Toosey Print, 87 Spring Road, St. Osyth, Clacton-on-Sea, Essex, CO16 8RU Tel: (01255) 820264 E-mail: sales@tooseyprint.com *Business supplies printers*

▶ Tooth Whitening 4 All, 7 Mill Chase Road, Wakefield, West Yorkshire, WF2 9SL Tel: (07768) 315921 E-mail: sales@toothwhitening4all.com *We are a global supplier of Tooth Whitening kits, Mouth Trays, Lazer Whitening and Carbamide Peroxide from as little as £5.99*

Top Banana, The Studio, Broome, Stourbridge, West Midlands, DY9 0HA Tel: (01562) 700404 Fax: (01562) 700930 E-mail: info@top-b.com *Post production television facilities services*

▶ Top Banana Team Ltd, The Old Castle, Farleigh Hungerford, Bath, BA2 7RW Tel: (01225) 752445 E-mail: info@topbananateam.com *We are bursting with ideas and proven solutions to increase your sales and meet your conference needs be it national or international.*

▶ Top Class Disco's, 1 Salisbury Terrace, Stockton-on-Tees, Cleveland, TS20 2DS Tel: (01642) 863851 *We are a mobile disco operating in the teesside area.We have been operating for sometime now.Our music covers 60's to present day and can cover all types of functions.Some of our regular clients are The swan at Billingham,Genesis Singles Club Billingham.Our aim is to please.So why not give us a call for a price.*

Top Coat Finishers, Station Road, Ecclesfield, Sheffield, S35 9YR Tel: 0114-245 5867 *Powder coating suppliers*

▶ Top End Computers, Wearde, Saltash, Cornwall, PL12 4AT Tel: (01752) 844881 E-mail: alan@topendcomputers.co.uk *Computer maintenance & repair services*

Top Flight UK, 16-19 Trafalgar Way, Bar Hill, Cambridge, CB3 8SQ Tel: (01954) 786600 Fax: (01954) 786645 *Sports goods distributors*

Top Floor Ltd, 100 Cobham Road, Ferndown Industrial Estate, Wimborne, Dorset, BH21 7PQ Tel: (01202) 876339 Fax: (01202) 891047 E-mail: sales@topfloor.co.uk *Partitioning & shelving & office furniture distributors*

Top Frost International Ltd, 35 Malden Way, New Malden, Surrey, KT3 6EB Tel: (020) 8942 9424 Fax: (020) 8336 1214 E-mail: info@topfrost.co.uk *Frozen food importers & exporters*

Top Gear Ltd, 80 Leicester Road, Mountsorrel, Loughborough, Leicestershire, LE12 7AN Tel: 0116-237 6606 E-mail: cars@topgear.uk.com *Manual & automatic transmission services*

Top Gear Clothing, 69 Waterloo Road, Smethwick, West Midlands, B66 4JS Tel: 0121-555 8765 Fax: 0121-555 8765 *Childrens sports & leisure wear*

Top Gear St Albans Ltd, 152 London Road, St. Albans, Hertfordshire, AL1 1PQ Tel: (01727) 850537 Fax: (01727) 856557 E-mail: info@topgear.co.uk *Stainless steel car exhausts manufrs*

▶ Top Gun Tools & Fixings, Amy Johnson Way, Blackpool, FY4 2RP Tel: (01253) 400900 Fax: (01253) 400900 E-mail: sales@topgun.co.uk *Suppliers of tools & fixings to the construction industry*

▶ Top Hex, 43 The Glades, Huntingdon, Cambridgeshire, PE29 6JS Tel: (01480) 456200 Fax: (01480) 456221 E-mail: info@tophex.co.uk *PIC based controllers design & supply*

▶ Top Language Jobs, 770-780 Great Cambridge Road, Enfield, Middlesex, EN1 3RN Tel: (020) 8363 3334 *The No. 1 specialist website for multilingual and bilingual jobs in the UK and Ireland. This is where all the leading job agencies and employers in London and throughout the UK and Ireland promote their permanent, temporary and contract bilingual jobs. We cover junior to executive level positions across the full range of industry sectors.*

Top Man Access & Handling, 22 Lenside Drive, Bearsted, Maidstone, Kent, ME15 8UE Tel: (01622) 730540 Fax: (01622) 730540 E-mail: sales@topmanaccess.co.uk *Access equipment distributors*

Top Man Retail, 214 Oxford St, London, W1C 1DD Tel: (020) 7636 7700 Fax: (020) 7291 2907 E-mail: oxford.circus.reception@arcadiagroup.co.uk *Clothing outlet*

Top Marks Fencing, 7 Leas Road, Mansfield Woodhouse, Mansfield, Nottinghamshire, NG19 8JH Tel: (01623) 636635 *Fence erecting suppliers & fitters*

▶ Top Marquees, Ratcher Way, Forest Town, Mansfield, Nottinghamshire, NG19 0FS Tel: (01623) 415944 Fax: (01623) 415945 E-mail: sales@topmarquees.co.uk *Marquee manufrs*

Top 'N' Tails, 19 Cross Tree Centre, Braunton, Devon, EX33 1AA Tel: (01271) 814733 Fax: (01271) 814824 *Pet retailers*

▶ Top Nosh Express, 210 Radlett Road, Colney Street, St. Albans, Hertfordshire, AL2 2EN Tel: (01923) 850880

Top Notch Ltd, Kingsley, Summercourt, Newquay, Cornwall, TR8 5AG Tel: (01872) 510652 Fax: (01872) 510652 *Joinery manufrs*

▶ Top Notch Joinery Ltd, Harold Park Farm, Harold Park, Nazeing, Waltham Abbey, Essex, EN9 2SF Tel: (01992) 892240 Fax: (01992) 892665

▶ Top Office Products, Greenway Centre, Doncaster Road, Bristol, BS10 5PY Tel: 0117-959 1111 Fax: 0117-959 1112 E-mail: topofficeproducts@btconnect.com *Office equipment manufrs*

Top Oil Products Ltd, Eastway, London, E9 5NR Tel: (020) 8548 3636 E-mail: online*@aol.com *Oil products packers*

▶ Top Printers Ltd, Unit 11 Bridge Park, Harrow Road, London, NW10 0RG Tel: (020) 8961 0925 Fax: (020) 8961 9193 E-mail: sales@topprinters.co.uk

Top Security Alarm Systems, 1 Hall Lane, Prescot, Merseyside, L34 5UN Tel: (0800) 378226 Fax: 0151-289 5532 *Security installators*

Top Security Fencing UK Ltd, 55 High Street, Bridgnorth, Shropshire, WV16 4DX Tel: (01746) 763299 Fax: (01746) 766374 E-mail: topsec@btconnect.com *Fencing manufrs*

Top Table, 31 Whiteley Village, Whiteley Way, Whiteley, Fareham, Hampshire, PO15 7LJ Tel: (01489) 580258 Fax: (01489) 580258 E-mail: whitley@lifstyle.co.uk *Home wear manufrs*

Top Table Ltd, White Woods, Brasted Chart, Westerham, Kent, TN16 1LS Tel: (01959) 561363 Fax: (01959) 561363 *Catering equipment services*

Top Table Catering Hire, 13 Bessemer Close, Cardiff, CF11 8DL Tel: (029) 2023 2408 E-mail: toptable@cf11.fsnet.co.uk *Catering equipment hire*

Top Table Catering Hire, 6 Yeoman Close, Kidderminster, Worcestershire, DY10 1NU Tel: (01562) 637557 Fax: (01562) 743028 *Catering equipment hire*

Top Table Hire, Dairy Farm, Eydon Road, Woodford Halse, Daventry, Northamptonshire, NN11 3RG Tel: (01327) 260575 Fax: (01327) 261843 E-mail: sales@toptablehire.com *Decorative tableware hire*

▶ Top Tack, Unit 23 Rope Walk Shopping Centre, Rope Walk, Rye, East Sussex, TN31 7NA Tel: (01797) 222333 *Equestrian tackle retailer*

Top Technology Benches Ltd, 20-21 Tooks Court, Cursitor Street, London, EC4A 1LB Tel: (020) 7242 9990 Fax: (020) 7405 2863 E-mail: ttv@toptechnology.co.uk *Venture capital*

▶ Top Telephones, Green Farm, Oak Road, Thurston, Bury St. Edmunds, Suffolk, IP31 3SN Tel: (01359) 231936 E-mail: sales@toptelephones.co.uk *Installers and maintainers of new & obselete systems in East Anglia. Also serving residential customers installing extension sockets & fault proving etc.*

Top Trop Aquatics, 123 Caerleon Rd, Newport, Gwent, NP19 7BZ Tel: (01633) 254496 Fax: (01633) 254496 *Aquatic retailer*

Top TS Kent Ltd, Unit 35 Blenheim Close, Pysons Road Industrial Estate, Broadstairs, Kent, CT10 2YF Tel: (01843) 863737 Fax: (01843) 863684 E-mail: cotts@aol.com *T-shirt & sweatshirt screen printers*

▶ Top Weigh Ltd, Scale House, Jeffrey Estate, Rockcliffe, Carlisle, CA6 4BH Tel: (01228) 672400 Fax: (01228) 672402 *Scale & weighing machine manufrs*

Topaz Blue Ltd, Middlesex Building, Elstree Aerodrome, Elstree, Borehamwood, Hertfordshire, WD6 3AW Tel: (020) 8207 1007 Fax: (020) 8207 0307 E-mail: sales@topazblue.com *Uniform/Corporate Clothing/Promotional wear.*

Topaz Business Systems Ltd, Pella House, 54-56 Moor Street, Gloucester, GL1 4NJ Tel: (01452) 332211 Fax: (01452) 332212 E-mail: solutions@topazuk.com *Photocopier suppliers*

Topaz China, Heaths Passage, Warren Street, Stoke-on-Trent, ST3 1QD Tel: (01782) 599827 Fax: (01782) 599827 *Chinaware manufrs*

▶ Topaz Courier Services, 8 Wolverham Road, Ellesmere Port, CH65 5BU Tel: 0151-201 3629 Fax: 0151-201 3629 *UK mainland 24hr sameday courier service collect from the cheshire & wirral areas*

Topaz Hair Cosmetics Ltd, The House Of Topaz, Guilden Sutton Lane, Guilden Sutton, Chester, CH3 7EX Tel: (01244) 312606 Fax: (01244) 317482 E-mail: glenn@topazhaircosmetics.co.uk *Hair cosmetics*

Topaz Refrigeration & Air Conditioning, 113 Main Road, Marchwood, Southampton, SO40 4UZ Tel: (023) 8086 5202 Fax: (023) 8066 7562 *Refrigeration & air conditioning repairs*

▶ Topbond Ltd, Oyster Quey, Castle Road, Sittingbourne, Kent, ME10 3EU Tel: (01795) 414050 Fax: (01795) 472022 E-mail: user@topbond.co.uk

▶ Top-Cat Business Systems, 2 Ansley Road, Houghton, Huntingdon, Cambridgeshire, PE28 2DQ Tel: (01480) 460291 E-mail: tim@top-cat.com *Your own bespoke, ecommerce website just £995...**Using our powerful, integrated ecommerce system 'OfficeTrio' (http://www.officetrio.com) we can build your ready-to-trade website in under a week. Top UK designers, superb support, fully-managed service from design to SEO.*

▶ Topclass Executive Private Hire, 1st Floor Co-op Stores, The Street, Woolpit, Bury St. Edmunds, Suffolk, IP30 9RU Tel: (07949) 372949 E-mail: info@topclass-executive.co.uk *Our aim is your satisfaction. We can undertake any of your executive car travel requirments, phone or email today.*

▶ Topclass Wedding Gowns, 1st Floor Co-op Stores, The Street, Woolpit, Bury St. Edmunds, Suffolk, IP30 9RU Tel: (01359) 241422 E-mail: topclassgowns@aol.com *Try our online shopping facility for great savings off shop prices or visit our showroom, phone today.*

Topcliffe Crane & Recovery, Station Road, Topcliffe, Thirsk, North Yorkshire, YO7 3SG Tel: (01845) 577330 Fax: (01845) 577007 *Crane hire*

Topcon GB Ltd, 25 Breakfield, Coulsdon, Surrey, CR5 2HS Tel: (020) 8668 2233 Fax: (020) 8668 8322 E-mail: sales@topcon.co.uk *Survey & laser equipment (building industry)*

Topcon (Great Britain) Ltd, Unit 17 Swift Business Centre, Keen Road, Ocean Park, Cardiff, CF24 5JR Tel: (029) 2047 0776 Fax: (029) 2047 0779 E-mail: cardiff@topcon.co.uk *Surveying equipment hire, sales & repairers*

Topcon Great Britain Ltd, Topcon House, Kennet Side, Newbury, Berkshire, RG14 5PX Tel: (01635) 551120 Fax: (01635) 551170 *Optical equipment manufrs*

▶ Topdraw Visual Services, 12 Clinton Close, Grange Park, Swindon, SN5 6BP Tel: (01793) 877034 E-mail: info@topdrawvs.co.uk *A multi faceted design agency specialising in exhibition stand design*

Topfit Ltd, 1 Aston Road North, Birmingham, B6 4DS Tel: 0121-608 6711 Fax: 0121-608 2008 E-mail: sales@e-shopfittings.com *Shop fittings suppliers*

Topfit Ltd, 156 Old Church Road, Clevedon, Avon, BS21 7TU Tel: (01275) 340042 Fax: (01275) 872733 E-mail: sales@topfithealth.co.uk *Health product distributors*

▶ Topform Visual Communication Ltd, 2 The Courtyard, Lamdin Road, Bury St. Edmunds, Suffolk, IP32 6NU Tel: (01284) 747399 Fax: (01284) 747401 E-mail: sales@topformonline.co.uk *We provide design and print services for all printed media, as well as web-design services.*

▶ TopHat IT Services, 80B St. James's Street, Brighton, BN2 1PA Tel: (01273) 311224 E-mail: enquiries@tophatit.com *Computer services for small businesses*

▶ The Topiary Organisation, 42, The Briars, Foxholes, Hertford, SG13 7TR Tel: 01992 419426 Fax: 01992 419426 E-mail: info@topiary.org.uk *Topiary Org. The UK directory of independent suppliers offering topiary plants, baytrees, bay trees for sale and hire by locality and online.*Buy topiary plants and baytrees online or hire topiary and baytrees online.*

Topical Television, 61 Devonshire Road, Southampton, SO15 2GR Tel: (023) 8071 2233 Fax: (023) 8033 9835 *Audio-visual production & presentation services*

Topical Time Ltd, 5 Bleeding Heart Yard, London, EC1N 8SJ Tel: (020) 7405 2439 Fax: (020) 7831 4254 E-mail: topicaltime@btconnect.com *Clock & watch importers & dealers*

Topknot Furniture & Kitchen Co. Ltd, 290 Leverington Common, Leverington, Wisbech, Cambridgeshire, PE13 5JG Tel: (01945) 410117 Fax: (01945) 410979 E-mail: sales@topknot-furniture.co.uk *Furniture manufrs*

▶ Topknots Hair Design Ltd, The Waterfront, Eastbourne, East Sussex, BN23 5UZ Tel: (01323) 471147 E-mail: gio-gary@talk21.com *first class hairdesigners with top class service and all the products you may need to look after you new style at home*

▶ Topley & Fisher, Station Road, Hatton, Derby, DE65 5DU Tel: (01283) 812350 Fax: (01283) 812080 E-mail: topleyandfisher@btconnect.com *Precision toolmakers*

Topline Catering, Old Mills Indust Estate, Old Mills, Paulton, Bristol, BS39 7SU Tel: (01761) 415154 Fax: (01275) 333308 E-mail: mail@toplinecatering.co.uk *Catering services*

▶ Topline Dance Shoes Ltd, Havers Road, Norwich, NR3 2DU Tel: (01603) 788359 Fax: (01603) 400144 *Dance shoe manufrs*

Topline Electronics Ltd, 8a Ropemaker Park, Diplocks Way, Hailsham, East Sussex, BN27 3GU Tel: (01323) 440760 Fax: (01323) 844508 E-mail: toplineltd@compuserve.com *Electronic equipment consultants*

Topline Fabrications, Crown Works, Clayton Road, Hayes, Middlesex, UB3 1DU Tel: (020) 8813 5353 Fax: (020) 8561 3114 *Steel work fabricators*

Topline Furniture, Unit 3 Oakfield Industrial Estate, Eynsham, Witney, Oxfordshire, OX29 4TN Tel: (01865) 880799 Fax: (01865) 880744 E-mail: sales@toplinefurniture.co.uk *Head board manufrs*

Topline Instruments Co., 7 Craven Avenue, Southall, Middlesex, UB1 2DJ Tel: (020) 8867 9701 Fax: (020) 8867 9702 *Surgical instrument manufrs*

Toplink Envelopes Ltd, Marsh Lane, Temple Cloud, Bristol, BS39 5AZ Tel: (01761) 453865 Fax: (01761) 453866 E-mail: mail@toplink.co.uk *Envelope printers*

Toplix Envelopes, 20-22 Benson Road, Poole, Dorset, BH17 0GB Tel: (01202) 684685 Fax: (01202) 666182 E-mail: wessex@multiplex.co.uk *Suppliers & printers of envelopes*

▶ Topmarx Ltd, Culverlands Business Park Chardland House, Winchester Road, Shedfield, Southampton, SO32 2JF Tel: (01329) 834400 Fax: (01329) 836789

Topmix Mortars, Holesmouth, Bristol, BS11 9BN Tel: 0117-938 0111 Fax: 0117-982 8519 *Concrete (ready mixed) & mortars*

Topmix Tarmac Ltd, Tunnel Industrial Estate, London Road, Grays, Essex, RM20 3HH Tel: (01708) 864732 Fax: (01708) 860220 *Concrete & mortar ready mixed*

Topper Cases Ltd, St. Peter's Hill, Huntingdon, Cambridgeshire, PE29 7DX Tel: (01480) 457251 Fax: (01480) 452107 E-mail: sales@toppercases.co.uk Principal Export Areas: Worldwide *Manufacturers of cases*

Topper International Ltd, Kingsnorth Industrial Estate, Wotton Road, Ashford, Kent, TN23 6LN Tel: (01233) 629186 Fax: (01233) 645897 E-mail: info@toppersailboats.com *Sailing boat manufrs*

Topps Tile, 2 Kittybrewster Retail Park, Bedford Road, Aberdeen, AB24 3LJ Tel: (01224) 488111 Fax: (01224) 488222 *Tile suppliers*

▶ Tops 2 Toes, 2 Eaton Road, West Derby, Liverpool, L12 7JJ Tel: 0151-256 6446 *Baby wear & accessory suppliers*

▶ Tops Lotto, 64 Sherwood Street, Newton, Alfreton, Derbyshire, DE55 5SE Tel: (01773) 782215 E-mail: lozhaney@hotmail.com *play the lottery 88 times a week for only 5 GBPor even free if you want!*

▶ Topsham Clocks, 28 Fore Street, Topsham, Exeter, EX3 0HD Tel: (01392) 876694 *Watch & clock repairers*

Topside Group Ltd, Daimler Drive, Cowpen Lane Industrial Estate, Billingham, Cleveland, TS23 4JD Tel: (01642) 566611 Fax: (01642) 561196 *Facade engineers*

Topslot Shop Fittings Systems Ltd, Unit 37, Aneurin Bevan Avenue, Brynmenyn Industrial Estate, Brynmenyn, Bridgend, CF32 9SZ Tel: (01656) 721900 Fax: (01656) 721926 *Shop fittings manufrs*

Topspeed Consultants Ltd, 90 Reeds Avenue, Earley, Reading, RG6 5SR Tel: 0118-961 0848 Fax: 07971618391 E-mail: info@topspeed.co.uk *Computer consultant*

Toptower Ltd, Access House, Bromsgrove Road, Halesowen, West Midlands, B63 3HJ Tel: 0800 197 3662 Fax: 0121-585 7989 E-mail: neil@toptower.co.uk *Based in Halesowen, Birmingham, servicing the whole of the U.K., Toptower Limited manufacture scaffold towers for use in the DIY and industrial sectors. *The manufactured range is extensive; Steel towers, aluminium towers, folding towers, steel builders trestles, portable fume extractors, post hole borers and post rammers providing both the professional and the D.I.Y. enthusiast with the quality equipment they need at the right price. *We also factor a comprehensive range of tools to the tool hire and construction industries such as Earlex wallpaper strippers and Earlex SprayPort HVLP paint sprayers, Porta Nailer wooden flooring nailers, Tyrol Roughcasters, a complete range of ladders, steps and stagings to solve almost any access problem, suction lifters, building props, trench struts, Strongboy props, floor tile lifters and carpet kickers, Line marking Machines. *We hold large stocks of equipment which means we can supply quickly to satisfy the needs of our customers.*

▶ Toptown Printers Ltd, Vicarage Lawn, Barnstaple, Devon, EX32 7BN Tel: (01271) 371271 E-mail: sales@toptown.co.uk

▶ Tor Multimix, Unit 10 Thomas Way Industrial Estate, Glastonbury, Somerset, BA6 9LU Tel: (01458) 830630 *Ready mixed concrete suppliers*

Tor Plastics Ltd, Unit 5 - 7, Dyehouse Lane, Glastonbury, Somerset, BA6 9LZ Tel: (01458) 832826 Fax: (01458) 834597 E-mail: chris@cpcenginerring.fsnet.co.uk *Plastic injection moulders*

Tor Systems Ltd, 58-60 Longton Road, Stoke-on-Trent, ST4 8YZ Tel: (01782) 644755 Fax: (01782) 644346 E-mail: djordan@torsystems.co.uk *Software for bookings & ticketing suppliers*

Toray Europe Ltd, 7 Old Park Lane, London, W1K 1AD Tel: (020) 7663 7700 Fax: (020) 7872 8071 *Plastics coating processors*

▶ Torbay Blinds Ltd, Broomhill Way, Torquay, TQ2 7QL Tel: (01803) 617300 Fax: (01803) 616200 E-mail: info@torbayblinds.co.uk *Blind suppliers*

Torbay & Brixham Shipping Agents, The Quay, Brixham, Devon, TQ5 8AS Tel: (01803) 882214 Fax: (01803) 882579 E-mail: sales@tbsa.co.uk *Ships agents*

▶ Torbay Decorating Co. Ltd, Melville House, Melville Street, Torquay, TQ2 5SS Tel: (01803) 201464 Fax: E-mail: mail@torbaydecorating.co.uk

Torbay Posters, 93 Union Street, Torquay, TQ1 3DW Tel: (01803) 294777 Fax: (01803) 294777 *Silk screen printers*

Torbay Power Tools & Equipment, 2a Barton Hill Road, Torquay, TQ2 8JH Tel: (01803) 324095 Fax: (01803) 324095 *Power tools , hand tools & fasteners distributors*

▶ Torbay Security Solutions, 46 Bitton Avenue, Teignmouth, Devon, TQ14 8HD Tel: (01626) 776161 Fax: (01626) 772583 E-mail: enquiries@torbaysecuritysolutions.co.uk *Torbay Security Solutions, Devon, one stop for all your security needs. British Locksmith Institute trained. Systems meet British and European standards and are supplied and installed by experienced and qualified staff*

Torbay Signs, Ashfield Road, Torquay, TQ2 6HE Tel: (01803) 605981 Fax: (01803) 605913 *Sign makers*

Tordoff Engineering Ltd, 118-120 Havelock Street, Kettering, Northamptonshire, NN16 9QA Tel: (01536) 483864 Fax: (01536) 513157 *Precision engineers*

Torex Ltd, Innovation House, Alcester, Warwickshire, B49 6HA Tel: (01789) 766755 Fax: 01789 766788 E-mail: sales@swl.co.uk *Computer software*

Torex, Telfer House, Range Road, Witney, Oxfordshire, OX29 0YN Tel: (0870) 0509900 Fax: (0870) 0509901 E-mail: retail-info@torex.co.uk *Retailers of systems integrators*

Torex Hospitality, Houghton Hall Park, Houghton Regis, Dunstable, Bedfordshire, LU5 5YG Tel: (01582) 869600 Fax: (01582) 869601 E-mail: info@torexretail.com *EPOS systems manufrs*

Torex Retail, Manor Farm Courtyard, 57-61 Main Street, Frolesworth, Lutterworth, Leicestershire, LE17 5EE Tel: (01455) 202727 Fax: (01455) 202728 E-mail: info@torexretail.com *Software development retailers*

▶ Torex Retail Ltd, Imperial House, Imperial Way, Coedkernew, Newport, Gwent, NP10 8UH Tel: (01633) 811822 Fax: (01633) 811820 E-mail: dthomas@torex.co.uk *Warehouse management systems suppliers*

Torex Services Ltd, 7 Brixham Enterprise Estate, Rea Barn Road, Brixham, Devon, TQ5 9DF Tel: (01803) 854616 Fax: (01803) 855936 *Computer repairs & maintenance*

Torfaen County Borough Council Children's Information Service Edu, County Hall, Croesyceiliog, Cwmbran, Gwent, NP44 2WN Tel: (01633) 648305 Fax: (01633) 648088

continued

continuation
E-mail: info@invest-in-torfaen.org *Business support & inward investment services*

Toricourt Ltd, 38 Westbury Road, Southampton, SO15 4JP Tel: (023) 8051 0982 Fax: (023) 8078 0363 E-mail: info@spectruminteriors.co.uk *Paint spraying services*

Torin Ltd, Drakes Way, Swindon, SN3 3JB Tel: (01793) 524291 Fax: (01793) 486570 E-mail: sales@torin-sifan.com *Fans & blowers suppliers & manufrs*

▶ Torith Ltd, Macadam Place, Dundee, DD2 3QR Tel: (01382) 815731

Torix Solutions Ltd, 60 Brimmers Hill, Widmer End, High Wycombe, Buckinghamshire, HP15 6NP Tel: (01494) 714411 Fax: (01494) 712999 E-mail: info@torix.co.uk *Computer support services*

Tormax UK Ltd, Tormax HS Unit 21 Mole Bus Park, Randalls Road, Leatherhead, Surrey, KT22 7BD Tel: (01372) 377711 Fax: (01372) 378044 E-mail: tormax@langleysystems.co.uk *Automatic doors & shopfronts*

Tormo Ltd, 7 Devonshire Business Park, Chester Road, Borehamwood, Hertfordshire, WD6 1NA Tel: (020) 8207 5777 Fax: (020) 8207 5888 E-mail: sales@tormo.co.uk *Miniature cut thread screws distributors*

Tornado Boats International Ltd, Dairycoates Industrial Estate, Wiltshire Road, Hull, HU4 6PA Tel: (01482) 353972 Fax: (01482) 572475 E-mail: sales@tornado-boats.com *Rigid-hull inflatable boats manufrs*

Tornado Cutting Tools, 38a Kenilworth Drive, Oadby, Leicester, LE2 5LG Tel: 0116-271 8686 Fax: 0116-271 8686 *Tool & cutter regrinding services*

Tornado Express, Suite 220, London, E15 2SP Tel: (020) 8519 7800 Fax: (020) 8519 0603 *Courier service*

Tornado Fixings Ltd, Donisthorpe Street, Leeds, LS10 1PL Tel: 0113-242 4342 Fax: 0113-246 0272 E-mail: sales@tornado-fixings.co.uk *Industrial fixing suppliers*

Tornado Wire Ltd, 4b Waterloo Road, Bidford-on-Avon, Alcester, Warwickshire, B50 4JH Tel: (01789) 778766 Fax: (01789) 490508 E-mail: sales@tornadowire.co.uk *Fencing distributors & manufrs* Also at: Crieff & Millom

Tornado Wire Ltd, Unit 4 Devonshire Road, Millom, Cumbria, LA18 4JF Tel: (01229) 774572 Fax: (01229) 775145 *Fencing manufrs*

Tornos Technologies UK Ltd, Tornos House, Garden Road, Coalville, Leicestershire, LE67 4JQ Tel: (01530) 513100 Fax: (01530) 814212 E-mail: sales@tornos.co.uk *Machine tool manufrs*

Toroid Technology Ltd, 50 Mill Lane, Purley Way, Croydon, CR0 4AA Tel: (020) 8686 8646 Fax: (020) 8686 7177 E-mail: toroids@toroid-tech.com *Transformers*

▶ Toroidal Engineering Co., Queach Holdings, Leys Hill, Walford, Ross-on-Wye, Herefordshire, HR9 5QU Tel: (01989) 566710 E-mail: paul@tec.uk.com *Manufacturers of Toroidal transformers, 15va to 6kva. Single/3 phase. Inductors, chokes, Audio transformers signal,balanced, mains, and output are a speciality.*

Sylvester Torpey & Sons Ltd, Birchall Street, Liverpool, L20 8PD Tel: 0151-944 1044 Fax: 0151-944 1575 E-mail: sales@torpey.co.uk *Injection moulders*

Torplan Ltd, 216 Heaton Moor Road, Stockport, Cheshire, SK4 4DU Tel: 0161-443 1881 Fax: 0161-431 0786 E-mail: sales@torplan.co.uk *Copy shop & secretarial services*

▶ Torpoint Ferry, 2 Ferry Street, Torpoint, Cornwall, PL11 2AX Tel: (01752) 812233 Fax: (01752) 816873

Torque Control Ltd, 60 Alstone Lane, Cheltenham, Gloucestershire, GL51 8HE Tel: (01242) 261233 Fax: (01242) 221115 E-mail: torquecontrolltd@btinternet.com Principal Export Areas: Africa *Blind fastening distributors*

Torque Tension Systems Ltd, 5 Stephenson Court, Barrington Industrial Estate, Bedlington, Northumberland, NE22 7DQ Tel: (01670) 530411 Fax: (01670) 531991 E-mail: enquiries@tts-ltd.com *Hydraulic bolt manufrs*

Torqueleader, Tannery Lane, Bramley, Guildford, Surrey, GU5 0AJ Tel: (01483) 892772 Fax: (01483) 898536 E-mail: sales@torqueleader.co.uk *Torqueleader lead the world in the manufacture of Torque Wrenches, Torque Screwdrivers, Torque Tool accessories and Torque Calibration equipment which are used in a wide range of industrial applications where fixture integrity is critical including the Automotive, Aerospace, Electronics, Computer Assembly, White Goods, Defence and Telecoms Industries Manufactured to ISO 6789:2003, Torqueleader products offer durability, repeatability and reliability to you the Torque Tool user. We are also, at Torqueleader, an UKAS Accredited Calibration Laboratory (No: 0632). From Assembly Operations to Final Inspection and Quality Control there will be a Torqueleader product to meet your needs Torqueleader also offer a full After Sales Service, Technical Support and Torque Training Our commitment to Export is second-to-none and Torqueleader products are sold and used throughout the World.*

Torqueleader, Tannery Lane, Bramley, Guildford, Surrey, GU5 0AJ Tel: (01483) 892772 Fax: (01483) 898536 E-mail: sales@torqueleader.co.uk Sales Contact: D. Jackson Principal Export Areas: Worldwide *Leading the World in Torque Technology Tools. That, Measure Torque/Tools that Apply a Pre-set Torque/Torque Calibration Equipment/Mechanical & Digital Tools/UKAS laboratory. MHH Engineering Co Ltd is the manufacturer of the Torqueleader range of Torque tools-Torque Wrenches/Torque screwdrivers & Torque Calibration equipment.High precision torque tools for the manufacture & repair of Vehicles/ Mobile phones/Aircraft & Satellites. Air-conditioning installation,Electronics assembly,Quality Control checks & many other* *continued* *Engineering & Manufacturing applications.Discover the latest advances in Torque technology including Torque & Angle Digital Torque Wrenches & PETA Electronic Torque Analyser which produces SPC results & Calibration Certificates to ISO 6789:2003. Click on the hyperlink to our web site & learn about Torque in our Torque Information Zone with handy Torque unit conversion program. Find instruction manuals for Torqueleader products & read articles about Torque control in your industry.*

Torquemeters Ltd, West Haddon Rd, Ravensthorpe, Northampton, NN6 8ET Tel: (01604) 770232 Fax: (01604) 770778 E-mail: info@torquemeters.com Sales Contact: Chris Flavell Principal Export Areas: Worldwide *Torque meter manufrs*

Torr Printers, Unit 2 Greg Street, Stockport, Cheshire, SK5 7BS Tel: 0161-480 9821 Fax: 0161-477 0305 E-mail: norman@torrprint.fsnet.co.uk *Lithographic general printer manufrs*

Torras Paper Ltd, Creator House, Maidstone Road, Kingston, Milton Keynes, MK10 0BD Tel: (01908) 288000 Fax: (01908) 288001 E-mail: info@torraspapel.es *Paper agents*

Torre Feeds, Camboree House, Exton, Exeter, EX3 0PN Tel: (01392) 874488 Fax: (01392) 876278 E-mail: torre.feeds@talk21.com *Agricultural merchants*

Torres Engineering & Pumps Ltd, 448 Brightside Lane, Sheffield, S9 2SP Tel: 0114-249 3377 Fax: 0114-242 5885 E-mail: ken_torres@torrespumps.co.uk *Pump manufrs*

▶ Torridge Transport Ltd, School Lane, Torrington, Devon, EX38 7AJ Tel: (01805) 623477 Fax: (01805) 622727

Torr-Tech Ltd, Unit 20 B-C St Helen Industrial Estate, Bishop Auckland, County Durham, DL14 9AZ Tel: (01388) 450005 Fax: (01388) 450039 E-mail: sales@torr-tech.co.uk *Manufacturers of transformers*

▶ Tortank Ltd, Marlin House, Kings Road, Immingham, South Humberside, DN40 1AW Tel: (01469) 510777

Torton Bodies Ltd, Pilot Works, Holyhead Road, Oakengates, Telford, Shropshire, TF2 6BB Tel: (01952) 612648 Fax: (01952) 620373 E-mail: sales@torton.com Principal Export Areas: Worldwide *One stop shop for the design, build, hire, transport, refurbishment of mobile exhibition/hospitality units, trailers, motorised articulated & hydraulic demount designs available*

Torus Design Ltd, 13/6 Bernard Street, Edinburgh, EH6 6PW Tel: 0131-555 6804 Fax: 0131-555 6804 E-mail: contact@torusdesign.co.uk *torus design ltd offers innovative design solutions for a variety of projects including bridges, domestic and industrial/commercial structures and ancillary steelwork design/fabrication drawings*

Torus Production Services Stage & T V, 28-30 Wood Wharf, London, SE10 9BT Tel: (020) 8293 4909 Fax: (020) 8293 4933 *Recording studios*

▶ Torwood Timber Systems Ltd, Royston House, Royston Road, Deans Industrial Estate, Deans, Livingston, West Lothian, EH54 8AH Tel: (01506) 414105

▶ Toshiba Carrier UK Ltd, United Technologies House, Guildford Road, Fetcham, Leatherhead, Surrey, KT22 9UT Tel: (01372) 220220 Fax: (01372) 220221 *Air conditioning suppliers & distributors* Also at: Birmingham, Bristol, Manchester & Wembley

Toshiba EIS, Charnwood House, 13 Ocean Way, Cardiff, CF24 5TE Tel: (029) 2025 0900 Fax: (029) 2025 0901 *Photocopier & fax suppliers*

Toshiba Electronics (Europe) Ltd, Riverside Way, Camberley, Surrey, GU15 3YA Tel: (01276) 694600 Fax: (01276) 694800 E-mail: infobox@teu.toshiba.co.uk *Electronic component manufrs*

Toshiba of Europe Ltd, Audrey House, Ely Place, London, EC1N 6SN Tel: (020) 7242 7295 Fax: (020) 7421 7626 *Holding company for UK*

Toshiba Information Systems (UK) Ltd, Toshiba Court, Weybridge Business Park, Addlestone Road, Weybridge, Surrey, KT15 2UL Tel: (01932) 841600 Fax: (01932) 852455 E-mail: contact@toshiba-tiu.co.uk *Portable computers, copiers & telephone systems manufrs*

Toshiba International (Europe) Ltd, Albany House, 71-79 Station Road, West Drayton, Middlesex, UB7 7LT Tel: (01895) 427400 Fax: (01895) 449493 E-mail: info@til.toshiba-global.com *Industrial turbines & components suppliers*

Toshiba Medical Systems Ltd, Gatwick Road, Crawley, West Sussex, RH10 9AX Tel: (01293) 653700 Fax: (01293) 653770 *Medical imaging equipment*

Toshiba TEC Europe UK Operations, 1 Siskin House, Marlins Meadow, Croxley Business Park, Watford, WD18 8TY Tel: (01923) 233688 Fax: (01923) 233698 E-mail: administrator@toshibatec-eu.co.uk *Manufacturers of bar code systems*

Tota Crontol Systems, 2 High St, Tattenhall, Chester, CH3 9PX Tel: (01829) 770900 Fax: (01829) 770900 *Telecommunications systems manufrs*

Total Access UK Ltd, Units 5b/C, Raleigh Hall Indust Estate, Eccleshall, Stafford, ST21 6JL Tel: (01785) 850333 Fax: (01785) 850339 E-mail: sales@totalaccess.co.uk *Industrial rope access consultants*

Total Air Tool Services Ltd, The Old Sawmill, Harvest Hill Lane, Allesley, Coventry, CV5 9DD Tel: (024) 7640 3624 Fax: (024) 7640 4675 E-mail: total@totalairtools.co.uk *Pneumatic tools & equipment systems distributors*

Total Bitumen Ltd, Chain Caul Way, Preston Riversway, Ashton-on-Ribble, Preston, PR2 2TZ Tel: (01772) 729302 Fax: (01772) 724713 *Bitumen merchants & manufrs*

Total Blinds Ltd, Apex House, Builder St West, Llandudno, Gwynedd, LL30 1HH Tel: (01492) 875460 Fax: (01492) 871118 *Roller, vertical & Venetian blind manufrs*

Total Butler Ltd, Seven Brethren Bank, Sticklepath, Barnstaple, Devon, EX31 2AS Tel: (01271) 345977 Fax: (01271) 346756 E-mail: barnstaple.depot@totalbutler.co.uk *Oil distributors* Also at: St. Austell

Total Butler, Farnham Road, Bishop's Stortford, Hertfordshire, CM23 1TB Tel: (01279) 467646 Fax: (01279) 504303 *Heating oil & lubricant suppliers*

Total Butler, County House, Bayshill Road, Cheltenham, Gloucestershire, GL50 3BA Tel: (0845) 6027283 Fax: (01242) 229498 E-mail: rm.gb-mb-cssteam@totalbutler.co.uk *Petroleum company* Also at: Huntingdon, King's Lynn & Norwich

Total Butler Ltd, Fengate, Peterborough, PE1 5XB Tel: (01733) 568223 Fax: (01733) 564733 *Oil distributors*

Total Butler Ltd, Sandy Lane, Sudbury, Suffolk, CO10 7HL Tel: (01787) 371511 Fax: (01787) 370780 *Heating oils, road fuels & lubricants*

Total Butler, Haybrook, Halesfield 9, Telford, Shropshire, TF7 4QW Tel: (01952) 680168 Fax: (01952) 588351 *Oil distributors*

Total Cleaning Equipment Ltd, 223-225 Ilderton Road, London, SE15 1NS Tel: (020) 7732 0191 Fax: (020) 7732 0194 E-mail: tcelimited@aol.com *Industrial cleaning equipment distributors* Also at: Ipswich

Total Computer & Network Support Ltd, Business & Innovation Centre, 9 Aston Science Park, Love Lane, Birmingham, B7 4BJ Tel: 0121-693 6224 Fax: 0121-693 6225 *Computer networking services*

Total Computer & Office Supplies Ltd, 100 Squirrels Heath Road, Harold Wood, Romford, RM3 0LU Tel: (01708) 780300 *Computer office suppliers*

Total Computers & Accessories Ltd, Westfield House, Bratton Road, Westbury, Wiltshire, BA13 3EP Tel: (01373) 864627 Fax: (01373) 824952 E-mail: sales@tcaonline.co.uk *Computer solutions*

Total Computing, 1a Sterling Industrial Estate, Kings Road, Newbury, Berkshire, RG14 5RQ Tel: (01635) 523860 Fax: (01635) 524860 *Computer services*

Total Concept Partitions Ltd, Unit 12 Anthonys Way, Medway City Estate, Rochester, Kent, ME2 4NW Tel: (01634) 290077 Fax: (01634) 297977 E-mail: info@totalconceptpartitions.co.uk *Internal refurbishment suppliers*

▶ Total Containments Solutions, 3 Moss Industrial Estate, St. Helens Road, Leigh, Lancashire, WN7 3PT Tel: (01942) 679600 Fax: (01942) 679700 E-mail: sales@tcsltd.org.uk *Manufacture fume cupboards*

▶ Total Control School Of Motoring, 52 The Crofts, Hatch Warren, Basingstoke, Hampshire, RG22 4RF Tel: (07863) 204687 Fax: (0871) 6612585 E-mail: sales@tcsm.co.uk *Basingstoke,Kingsclere,Whitchurch,Tadley, Oakley.Overton,Hook,DrivingLessons,School of Motoring,Driving Standards Agency,DSA Approved,Instructor,driving lesson,crash course driving lesson,aa driving lesson,intensive driving lesson,basingstoke,bsm,british school of motoring,driving test,driving schools,*driving theory test,driving instructor,driving licence,driving course,driving school uk,driving tuition,pass plus,theory test,mock theory test,online theory test,learn direct,aa,intensive driving course,intensive driving school,Car,Test,Hazard Preceptio,Theory Test,Intensive Course,Pass Plus.*

Total Control Systems, Upton House, Hartlebury Trading Estate, Hartlebury, Kidderminster, Worcestershire, DY10 4JB Tel: (01299) 250010 Fax: (01299) 254999 E-mail: sales@totalcontrol.co.uk *System solutions for progressive distribution businesses*

Total E And P UK P.L.C., Crawpeel Road, Altens, Aberdeen, AB12 3FG Tel: (01224) 297000 Fax: (01224) 298999 *Oil & gas exploration production company*

▶ Total Electrical Ltd, Unit 7 Rose Way, Rochford, Essex, SS4 1LY Tel: (01702) 547744 Fax: (01702) 547741

Total Electrical Distributors, Crawford Street, Newport, Gwent, NP19 7AY Tel: (01633) 214348 Fax: (01633) 254328 *Suppliers of electrical components* Also at: Bridgend & Swansea

▶ Total Electronic Systems Ltd, 36-38 Nuffield Road, Nuffield Industrial Estate, Poole, Dorset, BH17 0RT Tel: (01202) 686100 Fax: (01202) 686100

▶ Total Energy Controls, Unit 1 Crystal Business Centre, Sandwich, Kent, CT13 9QX Tel: (01304) 619816 Fax: (01304) 619819 *Control systems manufrs*

▶ Total Energy Saving Techniques, The Lodge, 18 Wakefield Road, Brighouse, West Yorkshire, HD6 1PE Tel: (01484) 717788 Fax: (01484) 717788 *Energy management system manufrs*

▶ Total Engineering Vibration Analysis, 2 Andrews Court, Andrews Way, Barrow-in-Furness, Cumbria, LA14 2UE Tel: (01229) 835500 Fax: (01229) 834400

Total Environmental Network Ltd, 9-11 Monmouth Street, Bridgwater, Somerset, TA6 5EQ Tel: (01278) 444643 Fax: (01278) 444718 E-mail: admin@total-environmentalnetwork.co.uk *Air conditioning system services contractors*

▶ Total Epos Solutions, Woodstock Road, Belfast, BT6 9DL Tel: (028) 9046 1166 Fax: (028) 9046 1166 *Cash registers suppliers & repairers*

▶ Total Equine (UK), 46 Bridge Street, Heywood, Lancashire, OL10 1JF Tel: (01706) 620003 *Saddlery & harnesses retailers*

Total Equipment, 140 Bell Hill Road, Bristol, BS5 7NF Tel: 0117-967 3333 Fax: (01275) 852121 *Garage equipment suppliers*

Total Events & Security Services Ltd, Mercian Park, Felspar Road, Amington, Tamworth, Staffordshire, B77 4DP Tel: (01827) 723800 Fax: (01827) 723816 E-mail: gavin.traynor@te-ss.co.uk *At Total Events & Security Services we specialise in Manned Guarding, Mobile Patrols, Key Holding & Alarm Response. We are an NSI Silver Accredited company providing SIA Licenced Security Officers*

▶ Total Fabrication UK Ltd, Unit 1, Albemarle Road, Taunton, Somerset, TA1 1BE Tel: (01823) 330707 Fax: (01823) 330717 E-mail: office@totalfabricationservise.fsnet.uk *Steel fabrication services*

▶ Total Fabrications Ltd, Unit 3 & 4 Kingston Industrial, 81-86 Glover Street, Birmingham, B9 4EN Tel: 0121-772 5234 Fax: 0121-772 5231 E-mail: sales@trussing.com *Aluminum fabricators*

Total Finishing Solutions, 67-70 Mott Street, Birmingham, B19 3HE Tel: 0121-233 3505 Fax: 0121-233 9207 E-mail: wesley.jenkinson@totalfinishingsolutions.co.uk *Electroplaters* Also at: Oldbury

Total Fire Protection, 73 Greenham, Bretton, Peterborough, PE3 9YS Tel: (01733) 700722 *Total installation and service of fire extinguishers, fire alarms and emergency lighting, with an excellent opportunity to cover all aspects of your fire protection.*

Total Frequency Control Ltd, Units 3-4 Mill Lane, Storrington, West Sussex, RH20 4NF Tel: (01903) 740000 Fax: (01903) 742208 E-mail: sales@tfc.co.uk *Inductor radio frequency manufrs*

Total Gas Services, 199 Station Road, Kingsheath, Birmingham, B14 7TB Tel: 0121-269 7980 Fax: 0121-251 2920 E-mail: info@gasservices.co.uk *Heating installations*Gas appliance maintenance & repairs.*24Hour callout.*

▶ Total Gutter Maintenance Ltd, Darlington Road, Northallerton, North Yorkshire, DL6 2NW Tel: (01609) 783303 Fax: (01609) 783305 E-mail: k.blair@totalgutters.co.uk *Gutter and drain cleaning;cleaning of roofs and side cladding; treatment of cut edge corrosion; supply of gutter surface treatments and fitting of Unifold gutter lining system; specialist roofing works*

▶ Total Haulage Ni Ltd, 1 Bay View Industrial Park, Dargan CR, Belfast, BT3 9JP Tel: (028) 9077 1121 Fax: (028) 9077 9274

▶ Total Home Build, 1 Broomhill Lane, Birmingham, B43 5LB Tel: 0121-358 1056 Fax: 0121-358 1056

Total Home Entertainment International, Unit 1 Rosevale Business Park, Newcastle, Staffordshire, ST5 7QT Tel: (01782) 561000 Fax: (01782) 565400 *Distributors of computer software*

Total Home Environment, Swallow House, Cotsworld Business Village, London Road, Moreton-in-Marsh, Gloucestershire, GL56 0JQ Tel: (0845) 2600123 Fax: (01608) 652490 E-mail: info@beamvac.co.uk *Sell & install central vacuum systems & heat ventilation systems*

▶ Total Hygiene Ltd, Bank House, 182-186 Washway Road, Sale, Cheshire, M33 6RN Tel: 0161-969 1199 Fax: 0161-973 2711 E-mail: info@total-hygiene.co.uk

Total Hygiene Supplies, 3 Bedlay Place, Annathill, Coatbridge, Lanarkshire, ML5 2QR Tel: (01236) 870088 Fax: (01236) 870088 *Cleaning products distributors*

Total Industrial Cleaning, 16 Morden Road, Stechford, Birmingham, B33 8SR Tel: 0121- 243 4975 E-mail: contact@totalindustrialcleaning.co.uk *we specialise in all aspects of commerical cleaning including hotels,petrol stations,shopping centres,car parks and offices.out of hours and overnight cleans available.*

▶ Total Install Ltd, Unit 3, Hanworth Trading Estate Hampton, Feltham, Middlesex, TW13 6DH Tel: (020) 8898 5644 Fax: (020) 8898 5642 E-mail: info@totalinstall.co.uk *Furniture installations*

▶ Total IT Ltd, Unit 6, Chase Park, Daleside Road, Nottingham, NG2 4GT Tel: 0115-924 0020 Fax: 0115-947 6176 *IT providers of software & hardware*

Total Laminate Systems Ltd, 11 Nimrod Way, East Dorset Trade Park, Wimborne, Dorset, BH21 7SH Tel: (01202) 877600 Fax: (01202) 861638 E-mail: sales@total-laminate.co.uk *Laminated furniture & panels manufrs*

Total Lift Care Ltd, Suite 6 The Shakespeare Centre, 45-51 Shakespeare Street, Southport, Merseyside, PR8 5AB Tel: (01704) 549600 Fax: (01704) 545090 E-mail: info@totalliftcare.com *Lift maintenance company*

Total Logistics, Leigh Park, Fulflood Road, Havant, Hampshire, PO9 5AX Tel: (023) 9247 4123 Fax: (023) 9247 0467 E-mail: sales@appliedlogistics.co.uk *Storage warehousing contractors & expert packers*

▶ Total Maintenance Solutions, Unit 94 Silverbriar, Business & Innovation Centre, Sunderland Enterprise Park, Sunderland, SR5 2TQ Tel: 0191-516 6489 Fax: 0191-516 6499 E-mail: sales@online-tms.com *TMS provide a single point supplier solution which reduces maintenance costs, controls downtime, provides resource & also reduces the volume of suppliers & invoices needed to run your maintenance & engineering contracts. For one solution for maintenance, electrical/mechanical, software fabrication, pipework, cleaning, safety, production equipment, material handling, noise, vibration, calibration, conveyors, machine protection, guards or machine spares contact TMS*

Total Media Communications, Unit 6, Berkshire Business Centre Berkshire Drive, Thatcham, Berkshire, RG19 4EW Tel: (01635) 869297 Fax: (01635) 869342 *Supply & install computer communication networks*

▶ Total Merchandise Ltd, Standen House, Fishponds Lane, Holbrook, Ipswich, IP9 2QZ Tel: (01702) 540043 Fax: (01473) 327537 E-mail: sales@totalmerchandise.co.uk *Promotional merchandise suppliers*

▶ Total Mould & Insert, Edison Road, St. Ives, Cambridgeshire, PE27 3LF Tel: (01480) 484711 Fax: (01480) 484710 E-mail: sales@totalmould.co.uk *Manufacturers of injection, compression & transfer moulds for the rubber industry including full CAD design facility for all types of machines. Comprehensive capacity for the manufacture of turned parts & pressings*

Total Needs Network, 18 Briars Close, Farnborough, Hampshire, GU14 0PB Tel: (01252) 378286 Fax: (01252) 375227 E-mail: info@total-needs.com *IT support*

The Total Package Ltd, The Granary, Birling, West Malling, Kent, ME19 5JF Tel: (01732) 526910 Fax: (01732) 526939 E-mail: info@thetotalpackage.co.uk *Computer consultants*

Total Packing Services Ltd, Unit 1, Newton Park, Andover, Hampshire, SP10 3SH Tel: (01264) 334243 Fax: (01264) 334119 *Contract packing services*

▶ Total PC Solutions Ltd, 44 Lynton Road, Benfleet, Essex, SS7 2QQ Tel: (01702) 554077 E-mail: support@total-pc-solutions.com *Software solution suppliers*

▶ Total Photography, 38 High Street, Brandon, Suffolk, IP27 0AQ Tel: (01842) 819570 Fax: (01842) 819570 E-mail: totalrobmcdonald@yahoo.co.uk *WEDDING & PORTRAIT PHOTOGRAPHY,*1 HOUR FILM PROCESSING, *FRAMES, ALBUMS & CAMERAS STOCKED,*NEW FOR 2006 LARGE RANGE OF CAMERA PHONES.DIGITAL PRINTS WHILE U WAIT*

Total Plastics Ltd, Heming Road, Washford East, Redditch, Worcestershire, B98 0EA Tel: (01527) 500292 Fax: (01527) 501188 E-mail: totalplastics@proweb.co.uk *Badges and nameplate manufacturers*

Total Polyfilm Ltd, Unit 95, Seedlee Road, Walton Summit Industrial Estate, Bamber Bridge, Preston, PR5 8AE Tel: (01772) 322229 Fax: (01772) 314276 *Pallet stretch wrap film manufrs*

▶ Total Production Services, No. 2 Penrhos, Hollist Lane, Easebourne, Midhurst, West Sussex, GU29 9AD Tel: (01730) 810191 Fax: (01730) 810182 E-mail: sales@total-production-services.co.uk *Contact us for all your entertainment and production needs. Lighting, Sound, Stage hire and sales. Spare lamps, Adhesive tapes, Health and Safety signs*

▶ Total Quality Management Solutions Ltd, 1 Overthwart Crescent, Worcester, WR4 0JW Tel: (01905) 29753 Fax: (01905) 723548 E-mail: tqm.solutions@virgin.net *Quality management services*

▶ Total Quality Staff Ltd, Gorray House, 758-760 Great Cambridge Road, Enfield, Middlesex, EN1 3RN Tel: (020) 8443 7014 Fax: (020) 8443 7044 E-mail: info@tqs.co.uk *Total Quality Staff (TQS) have been supplying temporary staff to large and small businesses in Kent and London for over 10 years.*

▶ Total Reclaims Demolition, Kissingstone House, Radford Road, Nottingham, NG7 7EB Tel: 0115-942 1975 Fax: 0115-942 2049 E-mail: info@totalreclaims.co.uk

Total Refrigeration Ltd, Unit 2A, East Tame Business Park, Talisot Road, Hyde, Cheshire, SK14 4EJ Tel: 0161-366 2504 Fax: 0161-366 2517 E-mail: sales@totalrefrigeration.co.uk *Total Refrigeration Ltd, based in Hyde, Cheshire, is a major supplier of commercial refrigeration. Total can supply you with the 'one stop shop' solution for all your refrigeration needs. Their products range from branded ice cream freezers to bakery cabinets.*

▶ Total Register Machines, Unit 17 International Business Park, Charfleets Road, Canvey Island, Essex, SS8 0SG Tel: (01268) 680764 Fax: (01268) 680091 E-mail: sales@totalregistermachines.com *Printing processors*

Total Restraint Systems Ltd, Unit 4 Hurricane Close, Old Sarum, Salisbury, SP4 6LG Tel: (01722) 326080 Fax: (01722) 334437 E-mail: post@totalrestarint.com *Motor sport equipment manufrs*

Total Security, 7 The Greys, March, Cambridgeshire, PE15 9HN Tel: (01354) 652936 *Security alarms installers*

▶ Total Security Installations Ltd, 3 Datapoint Business Centre, 6 South CR, London, E16 4TL Tel: (020) 7511 5555 Fax: (020) 7511 1384 E-mail: sales@tsi.uk.com

▶ Total Security Northern, 3 Conyers Avenue, Chester le Street, County Durham, DH2 2HQ Tel: 0191-387 3117 Fax: 0191-387 3117 E-mail: totalnorthern@hotmail.com *Security services*

▶ Total Services - Grounds Maintenance, Mercian Park, Felspar Road, Amington, Tamworth, Staffordshire, B77 4DP Tel: (01827) 723806 Fax: (01827) 723816 E-mail: info@total-services.co.uk *Hard & Soft Landscaping - Reach Pole Window Cleaning - General Grounds Maintenance - Annual Maintenance Contracts - Single Projects -*

Total Solutions Ltd, 11 Sealand Road, Sealand, Chester, CH1 6BS Tel: (01244) 881818 Fax: (01244) 881991 E-mail: totalsols@aol.com *Design special purpose equipment manufrs*

Total Sound Ltd, 3B Oxford House, Oxford Road, Llandudno, Gwynedd, LL30 1DH Tel: (01492) 877070 Fax: (01492) 877098 E-mail: totalsound2000@yahoo.co.uk *Audio link system manufrs*

Total Spectrum Ltd, 11 Intec 2, Wade Road, Basingstoke, Hampshire, RG24 8NE Tel: (01256) 814114 Fax: (01256) 814115 E-mail: sales@totalspectrum.co.uk *With over 10 years experience, Total Spectrum are considered to be the UK's leading & most diverse supplier of both "off the shelf" CD/DVD packaging & creative packaging solutions, to the Multimedia Entertainment Markets. Our product range includes, all formats of DVD & CD cases, Tins, Gel, CD/DVD Flexi Trays, Spiders, CD/DVD pockets, Polyprop & PVC Presentation Folders, CD/DVD replication, Calendar Cases, Vacuum Formed Packs & bespoke packaging solutions. Product can be delivered from as little as one carton, through to full bulk packed, direct containers. For a full in depth over view of our products/services, please either view our web site, or call us directly on 01256 814114.*

Total Systems plc, 394 City Road, London, EC1V 2QA Tel: (020) 7294 4888 Fax: (020) 7294 4999 E-mail: sales@totalsystems.co.uk *Software house*

▶ Total Tiling Services, 1 Coteroyd Avenue, Morley, Leeds, LS27 7TU Tel: 0113-259 7316 Fax: 0113-259 7316 E-mail: total2@btinternet.com

▶ Total Trade Services, Unit 1, Cefndy Road Employment Park, Cefndy Road, Rhyl, Clwyd, LL18 2HJ Tel: (01745) 360336

Total UK Ltd - Lindsey Oil Refinery, Eastfield Road, North Killingholme, Immingham, North Lincolnshire, DN40 3LW Tel: (01469) 563300 Fax: (01469) 563766 *Refiners of crude oil*

Total Ventilation Solutions Ltd, Unit 10, Midland Oak Trading Estate, Marlissa Drive, Coventry, CV6 6HQ Tel: (024) 7666 2255 Fax: (024) 7666 2255 *Ventilation & ductwork contractors*

▶ Total Waste Management, Vatster, Gott, Shetland, ZE2 9SG Tel: (01595) 840431 Fax: (01595) 840703 *Waste management systems, offshore, onshore*

Total Welding Supplies Ltd, Unit 12-13, St. Johns Road, Kirkdale, Liverpool, L20 8PR Tel: 0151-933 7213 Fax: 0151-944 1177 E-mail: totalwelding@btconnect.com *Welding equipment distributors*

Totaljobs Group Ltd, 57 Rathbone Place, London, W1T 1JU Tel: (020) 7769 9200 Fax: (020) 7769 9201 E-mail: info@totaljobs.com *Totaljobs.com is now recognised as one of the leading recruitment websites in the UK with over 1,000 customers advertising over 60,000 vacancies at any one time. Thousands of organisations have chosen totaljobs.com to help fill vacancies from large multinational organisations to smaller business with just a local recruitment need. The website provides access to a huge pool of candidates with a great variety of skills, from a wide range of industry sectors. Over 1 million job seekers turn to totaljobs.com every month - and this audience was the first to be independently audited in 2004 in order to prove how diverse it is - people from all walks of life, in all areas of the UK.**Totaljobs.com is also the founder of 'The Network' - Europe's largest network of job sites. The Network covers 28 Countries and attracts 10.5 million jobseekers between its sites.* *

▶ Totally 2cv, Pucknell Farm, Dores Lane, Braishfield, Romsey, Hampshire, SO51 0QJ Tel: (023) 8067 6002 E-mail: Newportcv@btinternet.com *Specialising in the repair, servicing & restoration*

▶ Totally Inbound, European Communication Centre, Vicarage Farm Road, Fengate, Peterborough, PE1 5TX Tel: 0845 117 7000 Fax: (01733) 704080 E-mail: info@totallyinbound.co.uk *Totally Inbound are a state of the art 24-7 outsourced call centre offering live call handling and answering services to the business community. Specialists in charity lines, engineer callouts, media response, order entry, remote reception and virtual offce services. All services are available with an integrated IVR platform.*

▶ Totally Insured Group Ltd, Unit 4, Abbey Walk Church Street, Romsey, Hampshire, SO51 8JQ Tel: (0870) 2408891 E-mail: info@totallyinsuredgroup.co.uk *We specialise in life insurance, mortgage protection insurance and critical illness cover. We can also provide other financial services such as pensions and investments through our associate company Winchester IFA Ltd.* **Winchester IFA Limited is an appointed representative of IN Partnership - the trading name of The On-Line Partnership Limited which is authorised and regulated by the Financial Services Authority.**

▶ Totally Ratted Productions, 95 Ewart Road*Forest Fields, Forest Fields, Nottingham, NG7 6HG Tel: 0115 8330457 E-mail: productions@totallyratted.com *Guitar & Bass tuition, music theory tuition, music recording and production, custom songwriting, multimedia composition, CD artwork and design*

Totalprint Ltd, Station Road, Gedney Hill, Spalding, Lincolnshire, PE12 0NP Tel: (01406) 330122 Fax: (01406) 330123 E-mail: info@totalprintltd.co.uk *Sub contractors*

Totem Signs, 31b Albion Road, Edinburgh, EH7 5QJ Tel: 0131-476 3777 Fax: 0131-467 7446 E-mail: info@totemsigns.com *Sign manufrs*

Totes Isotoner UK Ltd, Eastman House, Radford Cresent, Billericay, Essex, CM12 0DN Tel: (01277) 630277 Fax: (01277) 630276 *Ladies & gents fashion accessories & umbrella suppliers*

Totnes Radiators, Burke Road, Totnes, Devon, TQ9 5XL Tel: (01803) 863123 Fax: (01803) 863123 E-mail: admin@carradiator.co.uk *Motor radiator & number plate manufrs*

Toton Plant Hire Ltd, Private Road 4, Colwick Industrial Estate, Nottingham, NG4 2JT Tel: 0115-940 1302 Fax: 0115-940 1312 E-mail: sales@totonplant.co.uk *Contractors' plant hire & operator training*

Totrax Ltd, Rectory Farm, Mere Booth Road, Langrick, Boston, Lincolnshire, PE22 7AD Tel: (01205) 280578 Fax: (01205) 280520 E-mail: sales@totrax.co.uk *Tyre & wheel services*

Tots & Teens Ltd, Unit B Cumberland Business Park, 17 Cumberland Avenue, London, NW10 7RT Tel: (020) 8965 8158 Fax: (020) 8961 6184 E-mail: contex@babybright.co.uk *Babywear manufrs*

Tots Tunnel, 89 Commerce Street, Glasgow, G5 8EP Tel: 0141-418 0494 Fax: 0141-418 0494 *Babies wear & nursery goods & childrens wear wholesalers*

Totternhoe Lime & Stone Co. Ltd, Lower End, Totternhoe, Dunstable, Bedfordshire, LU6 2BU Tel: (01525) 220300 Fax: (01525) 221895 E-mail: tottenhoelime@btclick.com *Lime producers*

▶ Totton & Eling Tennis Centre Ltd, Aikman Lane, Totton, Southampton, SO40 8FT Tel: (023) 8066 7532 E-mail: info@tennis-service.net *8-court, floodlit tennis centre - adult & junior coaching services*

Totton Pumps, Rushington Business Park, Chaple Lane, Totton, Southampton, SO40 9AH Tel: (023) 8066 6685 Fax: (023) 8066 6880 E-mail: info@totton-pumps.com *Pump manufrs*

Totton Timber Co. Ltd, Maynard Road, Totton, Southampton, SO40 3DB Tel: (023) 8086 0077 Fax: (023) 8087 3168 E-mail: sales@tottontimber.com *Timber merchants supplier's*

Totty, Park House, Bradford Road, Chain Bar, Cleckheaton, West Yorkshire, BD19 6BW Tel: (01274) 866600 Fax: (01274) 866737 *General building contractors*

Toty Building Services Ltd, Park House, Woodland Park, Bradford Road, Chain Bar, Cleckheaton, West Yorkshire, BD19 6BW Tel: (01274) 866700 Fax: (01274) 866737 E-mail: info@toty-building.co.uk *Public works building contractors* Also at: Cleckheaton

Toucan Engineering Ltd, 40 Staindale, Cleverland Park, Guisborough, Cleveland, TS14 8JU Tel: (07944) 161643 E-mail: info@2cancycle.com *Manufacturer of sustainable developed products*

Toucan Graphic Design Ltd, 25 Southernhay East, Exeter, EX1 1NS Tel: (01392) 438463 Fax: (01392) 495415 E-mail: designers@toucandesign.co.uk *Award winning graphic & web design company*

▶ Toucan Graphics, 20 Calderhall Avenue, East Calder, Livingston, West Lothian, EH53 0DJ Tel: (01506) 204700 Fax: (01506) 204700 E-mail: info@toucangraphics.com *Website design services*

▶ Toucan Telemarketing Ltd, Buxton Road, Bosley, Macclesfield, Cheshire, SK11 0PS Tel: (01260) 223123 Fax: (01260) 223312 E-mail: info@toucantelemarketing.co.uk *We offer a business to business telemarketing service specialising in appointment making with costs to suit all budgets and company sizes from individuals to corporate**

▶ Touch of a Button, Aztec House, 137 Moldsey Avenue, West Molesey, Surrey, KT8 2RY Tel: (07976) 375911 Fax: (0870) 9778819 E-mail: enquires@touchofabutton.co.uk *Smart technology services*

▶ Touch Alternative Health, PO Box 4462, London, W1A 7NX Tel: 020 7935 2205 Fax: 020 7935 2008 E-mail: getintouch@londontouch.com *A personalised health and beauty centre for complementary and alternative medicine, pampering, beauty and lifestyle treatments in London UK.*

Touch Finder, 10 Burnell Road, Sutton, Surrey, SM1 4EE Tel: (020) 8770 3700 Fax: (020) 8661 9295 E-mail: info@touchfinder.co.uk *Touch screens & web site software*

Touch I.T Mobile, 27 Goldsmith Avenue, Romford, RM7 0EX Tel: (07071) 222856 E-mail: admin@touchit.co.uk *ACT! consultants & IT training specialists. Qualified trainers*

▶ Touch Marketing & Design, Unit 21 Trident Park, Trident Way, Blackburn, BB1 3NU Tel: (01254) 602260 Fax: (01254) 602260 E-mail: info@touchmarketing.co.uk *Innovative marketing solutions company*

Touch Panel Products Ltd, Short Way, Thornbury, Bristol, BS35 3UT Tel: (01454) 417307 Fax: (01454) 413708 E-mail: sales@touchpanels.co.uk *Specialist membrane switch manufrs*

Touch Print Ltd, 49 Maple Avenue, Bulwark, Chepstow, Gwent, NP16 5RG Tel: (01291) 621401 Fax: (01291) 621403 E-mail: sales@touchprint.co.uk *Retailer of industrial printers*

▶ Touch The Sky Ltd, Mulberry Business Centre, 323 Goring Road, Goring-by-Sea, Worthing, West Sussex, BN12 4NX Tel: 01903 507744 E-mail: lucienne.sharpe@touchthesky.uk.com *Touch The Sky provides a videoconferencing solution for special needs therapy and other related services to the education sector*

Touch Systems Ltd, 261 Lyndon Road, Solihull, West Midlands, B92 7QP Tel: 0121-248 2448 Fax: 0121-248 2450 E-mail: sales@touchsystems.co.uk *Computer software writing house*

Touchline Flags, 4 Seven House, 36-40 Town End, Caterham, Surrey, CR3 5UG Tel: (01883) 331550 Fax: (01883) 331555 *Referees equipment*

Touchline Promotions Ltd, 17 Rayleas Close, London, SE18 3JN Tel: (020) 8856 1115 Fax: (020) 8319 3035 E-mail: touchproms@aol.com *Advertising & promotional incentives*

▶ Touchpoint Media Ltd, Frodsham Business Centre, Bridge Lane, Frodsham, WA6 7FZ Tel: (01928) 736610 Fax: (01928) 736611

Touchstar Technologies Ltd, 7 Commerce Way, Trafford Park, Manchester, M17 1HW Tel: 0161-874 5050 Fax: 0161-874 5088 E-mail: enq@touchstar.com *Hand-held touch-screen computer manufrs*

Touchstone, 1 Triton Square, London, NW1 3DX Tel: (020) 7121 4700 Fax: (020) 7121 4740 E-mail: charlie.davies@touchstone.co.uk *IT software resellor for microsoft*

Touchstone, 1 Triton Square, London, NW1 3DX Tel: (020) 7121 4700 Fax: (020) 7121 4740 *IT service providers*

Touchstone C T A, 89 Barnham Road, Barnham, Bognor Regis, West Sussex, PO22 0EQ Tel: (01243) 553479 E-mail: malcolm@tcta.co.uk *Computer consultants*

Touchstone Lighting Components, Unit 21-22, Emerald Way, Stone Business Park, Stone, Staffordshire, ST15 0SR Tel: (01785) 817123 Fax: (01785) 817120 E-mail: sales@touchstonelighting.co.uk *Light fitting components*

▶ Touchstone Tiles Ltd, 1 Ealing Road Trading Estate, Ealing Road, Brentford, Middlesex, TW8 0QY Tel: (020) 8758 2233 Fax: (020) 8758 2244 E-mail: sales@touchstonetiles.co.uk *Suppliers of all kinds of tiles and associated products. Marble, granite, limestone, slate, ceramics, mosiacs & porcelean tiles. Adhesives, trims and sealers available.*

Touchwood, Sluice Farm, Sandy Lane, Martlesham, Woodbridge, Suffolk, IP12 4SD Tel: (01394) 385522 Fax: (01394) 389555 E-mail: touchwood@zoom.co.uk *Furniture manufrs*

Touchwood Carpenters, Covered Yard, 11a King Street, Lancaster, LA1 1JN Tel: (01524) 381048 Fax: (01524) 381048 *Pine furniture manufrs*

Touchwood Joinery (London) Ltd, Railway Arch, 384-385 Denmark Road, London, SE5 9JR Tel: (020) 7733 3003 Fax: (020) 7737 5247 *Joinery manufrs*

Tough Furniture, Stokewood Road, Craven Arms Business Park, Craven Arms, Shropshire, SY7 8NR Tel: (01588) 674340 Fax: (01588) 674341 *Specialist furniture manufrs*

Tough Glass Ltd, 158 Harbour Road, Kilkeel, Newry, County Down, BT34 4AU Tel: (028) 4176 3444 Fax: (028) 4176 3252 E-mail: johna@toughglass.com *Curved & flat toughened safety glass manufrs*

▶ Tough Packaging Ltd, Unit 4 River Close North, Teaninich Industrial Estate, Alness, Ross-Shire, IV17 0PB Tel: (01349) 882734 Fax: (01349) 884488 E-mail: sales@bagsonline.co.uk *Packaging services*

▶ Tough Security Systems Ltd, 60 Munro Place, Glasgow, G13 2UW Tel: 0141-434 1400

Tough Surveys Ltd, 27 Ferry Road, Teddington, Middlesex, TW11 9NN Tel: (020) 8977 4494 Fax: (020) 8977 7546 E-mail: johntough@ctinternet.com *Yacht, ship & boat builders*

Toughglaze UK Ltd, 12 Chandos Road, London, NW10 6NF Tel: (020) 8838 4400 Fax: (020) 8838 3322 E-mail: info@toughglaze.com *Glass processor & toughners*

Tour & Andersson, Unit 3 Nimbus Park Porz Avenue, Houghton Hall Park, Houghton Regis, Dunstable, Bedfordshire, LU5 5XR Tel: (01582) 866377 Fax: (01582) 865655 E-mail: samuel.coe@tourandersson.co.uk *Manufacturer of hydronic balancing values.* Also at: Stourport

▶ Touraco Ltd, 6 Robert Leonard Industrial Site, Aviation Way, Southend-on-Sea, SS2 6GG Tel: (01702) 547800 Fax: (01702) 547788 E-mail: info@touraco.co.uk *Manufactures & printers of presentation folders*

Toveglen Ltd, Unit 1 Drakes Lane, Boreham, Chelmsford, CM3 3BE Tel: (01245) 360435 Fax: (01245) 362322 E-mail: mbladon@toveglen.co.uk *Plastering & dry lining contractors*

Tow B Fabs, Unit 5-6 Kents Avenue, Hemel Hempstead, Hertfordshire, HP3 9XH Tel: (01442) 256764 Fax: (01442) 256764 *Towing equipment manufrs*

Tow Bar & Trailer Equipment, 44 Camp Road, Farnborough, Hampshire, GU14 6EP Tel: (01252) 540319 *Towing bracket distributors & camping equipment accessories*

Tow Path Ltd, Unit 150 Medway Enterprise Centre, Enterprise Close, Medway City Estate, Rochester, Kent, ME2 4SY Tel: (01634) 296644 Fax: (01634) 724152 *General engineering & machining services*

▶ Towable Access, 11a Ramshill Road, Scarborough, North Yorkshire, YO11 2LN Tel: (01723) 370399 Fax: (01723) 370399 E-mail: Rick_Nightingale@hotmail.com *Access platform hire*

The Towel House Co. Ltd, 120 Glover Street, Birmingham, B9 4EY Tel: 0121-766 6644 Fax: 0121-771 0446 E-mail: info@polehousecompany.co.uk *Metal fabrications*

▶ Towel Rails (UK) Ltd, Unit 8, Cape Industrial Estate, Coal Hill Lane, Farsley, Pudsey, W. Yorkshire, LS28 5NA Tel: 0113-204 7540 Fax: 0113-204 7959

Towell & Scott Ltd, Homefield Farm, Sherford, Kingsbridge, Devon, TQ7 2AT Tel: (01548) 531325 Fax: (01548) 531777 E-mail: mail@towell-scott.co.uk *Giftware, plastic tableware & greeting cards manufrs*

▶ Tower Bakery Ltd, Shore Road, Perth, PH2 8BH Tel: (01738) 563333 *Bakery*

Tower Ceramics, 91 Parkway, London, NW1 7PP Tel: (020) 7485 7192 Fax: (020) 7267 9571 *Ceramic & porcelain tile importers & distributors*

Tower Chemicals Ltd, First Avenue, Grangefield Industrial Estate, Pudsey, West Yorkshire, LS28 6QN Tel: 0113-256 8111 Fax: 0113-256 9111 E-mail: sales@towerchemicals.co.uk *Chemical manufrs*

▶ Tower Conversions, 70 Espedair Street, Paisley, Renfrewshire, PA2 6RW Tel: 0141-887 1081

Tower Demolition Ltd, 264 Hanworth Road, Hounslow, TW3 3TY Tel: (020) 8569 5152 Fax: (020) 8569 4337 E-mail: mail@tower-demolition.co.uk *Demolition contractors*

Tower Digital Ltd, 312 Central Drive, Blackpool, FY1 6LE Tel: (01253) 400011 Fax: (01253) 400022 E-mail: info@towerdigital.co.uk *Computer hardware suppliers*

Tower Doors Ltd, 107 Coltness Lane Queenslie Indust Estate, Glasgow, G33 4DR Tel: 0141-774 6162 Fax: 0141-774 6163 *Timber door manufrs*

Tower Glass Ltd, Yeomans Industrial Park, Yeomans Way, Bournemouth, BH8 0BJ Tel: (01202) 518555 Fax: (01202) 539015 E-mail: sales@towerglass.co.uk *Glass processing & silvering services*

Tower Hill Merchants plc, 92-94 Tooley Street, London, SE1 2TH Tel: (020) 7407 8161 Fax: (020) 7407 2949 E-mail: thm@towerhillmchts.co.uk *Export merchants & sugar brokers*

Tower Insurance Co. Ltd, Jubilee Building, 1 Victoria Street, Douglas, Isle Of Man, IM99 1BF Tel: (01624) 673446 Fax: (01624) 663864 *Insurance company*

Tower Machine Tools Ltd, Mayflower Close, Chandler's Ford, Eastleigh, Hampshire, SO53 4AR Tel: (023) 8026 0266 Fax: (023) 8026 1012 E-mail: towermctools@compuserve.com *Muratec & wiedemanns cnc turret punch presses distributors*

Tower Media Solutions, 25 Holywell Row, London, EC2A 4XE Tel: (020) 7247 0876 Fax: (020) 7247 5717 E-mail: helpdesk@towermedia.co.uk *Design origination & print*

Tower Mints Ltd, 1-21 Carew Street, London, SE5 9DF Tel: (020) 7733 7268 Fax: (020) 7274 0151 E-mail: info@towermint.co.uk *Personalise chocolate coins*

▶ Tower Press Ltd, 2 Alton Road, South Warnborough, Hook, Hampshire, RG29 1RT Tel: (01256) 861886 Fax: (01256) 861887 E-mail: sales@tower-press.co.uk

Tower Scaffolding South West, Unit 7 Milber Trading Estate, Newton Abbot, Devon, TQ12 4SG Tel: (01626) 331446 Fax: (01626) 335515 E-mail: tower.info@btopenworld.com *Scaffolding contractors*

Tower Signs, 2 Railway Yard, Railway Street, Ballymena, County Antrim, BT42 2AF Tel: (028) 2565 8306 Fax: (028) 2565 8306 *Sign manufrs*

Tower Structures Marketing Ltd, 44 Westbourne Terrace, London, W2 3UH Tel: (020) 7402 4452 Fax: (020) 7706 8643 *Steel constructors*

Tower Systems Furniture Ltd, 45 Garman Road, London, N17 0UR Tel: (020) 8885 4422 Fax: (020) 8801 9822 *Office furniture manufrs*

Tower Tool Co. Ltd, Tower Manfactory, Radnor Road, Wigston, Leicestershire, LE18 4XY Tel: 0116-277 6520 Fax: 0116-277 6388 E-mail: myles@tower-tool.demon.co.uk *Manufacturers of moulds for the rubber industry*

Tower Welding Ltd, 7 Abbey Trading Estate, London, Greater London, SE26 5TW Tel: 020 86599900 *Steel fabricators*

Tower Welding Alloys Ltd, 5 Malham Road Industrial Estate, London, Greater London, SE23 1AH Tel: 020 82915533 *Welding equipment distributors*

Towergate Marine Underwriting, 91-92 High Street, Lymington, Hampshire, SO41 9AP Tel: (01590) 671560 Fax: (01590) 679893 E-mail: tmu@towergate.co.uk *Insurance underwriters*

Towerglens Ltd, Dock Lane Industrial Estate, Turner St, Dudley, West Midlands, DY1 1SD Tel: (01384) 455025 Fax: (01384) 451300 E-mail: sales@towerglens.com *Control panel manufrs*

Towerip Ltd, Unit 1-2 162 Leabrook Road, Tipton, West Midlands, DY4 0DY Tel: 0121 5020469 *Foundry & mechanical engineers*

Towerite Environmental Consultants, Old Road, Lamport, Northampton, NN6 9HF Tel: (01604) 686772 Fax: (01604) 686773 E-mail: info@towerite.co.uk *Air & water environmental services*

Towermaster Ltd, Braintree Enterprise Centre, 46 Springwood Drive, Braintree, Essex, CM7 2YN Tel: (01376) 324809 Fax: (01376) 552296 E-mail: sales@towermaster.co.uk *Floodlighting tower & column manufrs*

▶ Towers Contractors Ltd, 1 Towers Court, Duckworth Street, Blackburn, BB2 2JQ Tel: (01254) 694746

Towers Perrin, 71 High Holborn, London, WC1V 6TP Tel: (020) 7170 2000 Fax: (020) 7170 2222 *Management consultants*

Towers Perrin, 71 High Holborn, London, WC1V 6TP Tel: (020) 7170 2000 Fax: (020) 7170 2222 *Actuaries & management consultants* Also at: Newbury & St. Albans

Towers Recruitment Services, Chiltern Chambers, St Peters Avenue, Caversham, Reading, RG4 7DH Tel: 0118-946 1200 Fax: 0118-946 3318 E-mail: jobs@towers.co.uk *Technical staff recruitment services*

Towers & Sanders, Unit 1 Bellingham Trading Estate, Franthorne Way, London, SE6 3BX Tel: (020) 8695 6400 Fax: (0845) 2575992 E-mail: info@scaffold-tower.co.uk

Towersleep Ltd, King Edward Street, Grimsby, South Humberside, DN31 3JW Tel: (01472) 355371 Fax: (01472) 242915 E-mail: sales@towersleep.co.uk *Mattress & divans manufrs*

John Towle & Son Ltd, Cleveland Chambers, New Cleveland Street, Hull, HU8 7ER Tel: (01482) 223876 Fax: (01482) 224968 *Building contractors*

Towler Engineering Ltd, 34 Oxford Road, Clacton-on-Sea, Essex, CO15 3TB Tel: (01255) 423723 Fax: (01255) 434484 *Engineers*

Town Bent Products Ltd, Unit 10-11 Daisyhill Industrial Estate, Ashworth Street, Rishton, Blackburn, BB1 4JW Tel: (01254) 876644 Fax: (01254) 876646 E-mail: townbent.products@virgin.net *Metal pressings manufrs*

▶ Town & Country, 7a Hill Avenue, Amersham, Buckinghamshire, HP6 5BD Tel: (01494) 722088 Fax: (01494) 434912 E-mail: sales@townandcountry.com

▶ Town & Country, Home Farm Works, Clifton Road, Deddington, Banbury, Oxfordshire, OX15 0TP Tel: (01869) 337070

Town & Country, 53 Bouncers Lane, Prestbury, Cheltenham, Gloucestershire, GL52 5JB Tel: (01242) 239531 *Pest control services*

Town & Country, Whitwick Business Park, Stenson Road, Whitwick, Leicester, LE67 4JP Tel: (01530) 830990 Fax: (01530) 830877 E-mail: info@townandco.com *Leather goods manufrs*

▶ Town & Country, Water Eaton Lane, Penkridge, Stafford, ST19 5QE Tel: (01785) 714600 Fax: (01785) 711221 E-mail: andycoombs@townandcountry.uk.com *Commercial and Domestic Removals**Professional,competitive and always on time!*

▶ Town & Country, Water Eaton Lane, Penkridge, Stafford, ST19 5QE Tel: (01785) 714600 Fax: (01785) 711221 E-mail: andycoombs@townandcountry.uk.com

▶ Town & Country Carpets, 20 Mostyn Avenue, Llandudno, Gwynedd, LL30 1YY Tel: (01492) 872400 E-mail: siliven@aol.com *Flooring retailer*

▶ Town & Country Catering, Unit 6, Buriton Business Park, Weston, Petersfield, Hampshire, GU32 3NJ Tel: (01730) 260048

Town & Country Gates & Railings, Unit 6e Waterloo Industrial Estate, Gorsey Mount Street, Stockport, Cheshire, SK1 3BU Tel: 0161-429 7325 Fax: 0161-480 4388 E-mail: philbohen@aol.com *Wrought iron workers*

Town & Country Pine, Photique House, 1 South Road, Erdington, Birmingham, B23 6EA Tel: 0121-382 9002 *Pine furniture manufr*

Town & Country Pine, 24 Hanover Buildings, Southampton, SO14 1JU Tel: (023) 8083 7353 Fax: (023) 8070 3385

▶ Town & Country Removals Ltd, Unit 3, 100 Church Street, Staines, Middlesex, TW18 4YA Tel: (01784) 464188 Fax: 01784 464484 E-mail: info@townandcountryremovals.net *Removal, storage and shipping services, local moves, long distance moves, Ireland and Overseas. Storage facility *Members of The British Association of Removers.*

Town & Country Signs Ltd, 125 Poplar High Street, London, E14 0AE Tel: (020) 7515 8383 Fax: (020) 7538 8657E-mail: info@tcsigns.co.uk *Sign installers & manufrs*

▶ Town & Country Turf, Howards Nursey, Handcross Road, Lower Beeding, Horsham, West Sussex, RH13 6NX Tel: (01403) 892634 Fax: (01403) 892635 E-mail: sales@tcturf.co.uk *Landscape product suppliers*

Town & County Engineering Services Ltd, Warden Tree Lane, Pinchbeck, Spalding, Lincolnshire, PE11 3UG Tel: (01775) 725678 Fax: (01775) 767205 E-mail: sales@townandcounty.uk.com *Belting, conveyor & engineering supplies*

Town End Leeds plc, Silver Court, Intercity Way, Leeds, LS13 4LY Tel: 0113-256 4251 Fax: 0113-239 3315 E-mail: sales@dyes.co.uk *Producer and supplier of colours for industry.. products inc. natural and synthetic food colours, liquid flavours and associated food ingredients. All products comply to quality standards.*

▶ Town Hall Exchange, Town Hall Buildings, Castle Street, Farnham, Surrey, GU9 7ND Tel: (01252) 720600 Fax: (01252) 720601 E-mail: farnham@redstone-bc.com *Serviced offices managed office space to rent, lease*

Town Head Farm Cottages, Town Head Farm, Great Asby, Appleby-in-Westmorland, Cumbria, CA16 6EX Tel: (01768) 351499 Fax: 01768 353771 E-mail: sales@westmorlandfurniture.co.uk *Furniture manufacturers, distributors & wholesalers*

Town House : Country House, 56 Byron St, Glasgow, G11 6LZ Tel: 0141-357 2250 Fax: 0141-339 9005 *Interior designers & furnishers*

Town Joinery, Garth Road, Morden, Surrey, SM4 4NJ Tel: (020) 8330 7451 Fax: (020) 8330 7336 E-mail: sales@townjoinery.co.uk *Joiners, built in & bespoke furniture*

Town Mills Textiles Ltd, 19-20 New Mill Street, Dudley, West Midlands, DY2 8PB Tel: (01384) 253683 Fax: (01384) 455044 E-mail: townmillslimted@hotmail.com *Clothing manufrs*

Town Street Jewellers, 69 Town Street, Armley, Leeds, LS12 3HD Tel: 0113-231 9991 Fax: 0113-231 9991 *Jewellery retail & trophy manufrs*

Towne Lifting & Testing, Pennine Avenue, North Tees Industrial Estate, Stockton-on-Tees, Cleveland, TS18 2RJ Tel: (01642) 611035 Fax: (01642) 611036 *Ships rigging & lifting gear suppliers*

Townend Precision Presswork, Unit 12 Ladbroke Park Industrial Estate, Millers Road, Warwick, CV34 5AN Tel: (01926) 490023 Fax: (01926) 402052 *Presswork specialists*

Townhead Electroplating Services, Unit E3 Fieldhouse Industrial Estate, Fieldhouse Road, Rochdale, Lancashire, OL12 0AA Tel: (01706) 647802 E-mail: townheadelectroplating@yahoo.com *Metal finishers & electroplaters*

Townley Hughes & Co. Ltd, Unit 7 Meadow La Industrial Park, Ellesmere Port, CH65 4TY Tel: 0151-357 1800 Fax: 0151-357 2117 E-mail: townleyhughes@aol.com *Design heating & ventilation engineers*

Townley Office Equipment, Unit 4 Malham Road, London, SE23 1AG Tel: (020) 8291 1999 Fax: (020) 8291 9177 *Stationary product distributors*

Townroe Ltd, 80 Rockingham Street, Sheffield, S1 4EB Tel: 0114-272 3361 Fax: 0114-275 7934 *Electroplaters*

Towns & Carnie Ltd, The Ward, Huntly, Aberdeenshire, AB54 4QU Tel: (01466) 792413 Fax: (01466) 792413 *Animal health food specialists*

Townscape Products Ltd, Fulwood Road South, Sutton-in-Ashfield, Nottinghamshire, NG17 2JZ Tel: (01623) 513355 Fax: (01623) 440267 E-mail: sales@townscape-products.co.uk *Street furniture manufrs*

D.H. Townsend & Co. Ltd, Unit 1, St Andrews Industrial Estate, Bridport, Dorset, DT6 3DL Tel: (01308) 423305 Fax: (01308) 427913 E-mail: dhtownsendeng@aol.com *Agricultural & general engineering*

Townsend Print Services Ltd, Sterling Court Leyland Business Park, Centurion Way, Farington, Leyland, PR25 3GR Tel: (01772) 622322 Fax: (01772) 624466 E-mail: sales@townsendprint.co.uk *Printers*

Townson Tractors Ltd, West End, Kendal Road, Hellifield, Skipton, North Yorkshire, BD23 4HE Tel: (01729) 850374 Fax: (01729) 850315 E-mail: sales@townsontractors.co.uk *Agricultural machinery retail repairs*

Towone Trailers, 40 Havelock Street, Hessle Road, Hull, HU3 4JH Tel: (01482) 225645 Fax: (01482) 585979 *Road trailer suppliers*

Towrite Electric Vehicles (Harborough) Ltd, Albert Road, Market Harborough, Leicestershire, LE16 7LU Tel: (01858) 433548 Fax: (01858) 434209 E-mail: sales@towrite.co.uk *Electric vehicles & trailers manufrs*

Towrite Fabrications Ltd, Albert Road, Market Harborough, Leicestershire, LE16 7LU Tel: (01858) 467805 Fax: (01858) 434209 E-mail: sales@towrite.co.uk *Manufacturers of road trailers & electric vehicles*

Towy Works Ltd, The Quay, Carmarthen, Dyfed, SA31 3JR Tel: (01267) 236601 Fax: (01267) 238189 *Building materials merchants*

Tox Pressotechnik Ltd, Unit 35, Stafford Business Village, Dyson Way, Staffordshire Technology Park, Stafford, ST18 0TW Tel: (01785) 887903 Fax: (01785) 887027 E-mail: sales@tox-uk.com *Hydraulic cylinder manufrs*

Toy Trading Ltd, 7 North St Industrial Estate, Droitwich, Worcestershire, WR9 8JB Tel: (01905) 794979 Fax: (01905) 774503 E-mail: sales@toytrading.net *Engineers distributors*

Toye & Co. P.L.C., 19-21 Great Queen Street, London, WC2B 5BE Tel: (020) 7242 0471 Fax: (020) 7831 8692 E-mail: gqf@toye.demon.co.uk *Cooperate identity products*

Toye Kenning & Spencer Ltd, Regalia House, Newtown Road, Bedworth, Warwickshire, CV12 8QR Tel: (024) 7631 5634 Fax: (024) 7664 3018 E-mail: sales@toye.com *Civil & military regalia* Also at: Bridgend, Edinburgh, Glasgow & Manchester

Toye Kenning Spencer Stadden, 77 Warstone Lane, Birmingham, B18 6NL Tel: 0121-236 3253 Fax: 0121-236 7217 E-mail: sales@toyebirm.demon.co.uk *Badge & button manufrs*

Toymaster Ltd, 725 Ormskirk Road, Wigan, Lancashire, WN5 8AT Tel: (01942) 214864 Fax: (01942) 205463 E-mail: info@webtouchsolutions.co.uk *Online marketing services*

Toyo Tyre, 4 Express Business Park, Shipton Way, Rushden, Northamptonshire, NN10 6GL Tel: (01933) 411144 Fax: (01933) 410945 E-mail: info@toyo.co.uk *Tyre distributors*

Toyoda Gosei Fluid Systems UK Ltd, Rockingham Road, Market Harborough, Leicestershire, LE16 7QE Tel: (01858) 439800 Fax: (01858) 410191 *Brake & clutch component manufrs*

Toyoda Mitsui Europe, Matrix House, Loughborough Motorway Trading Estate, Gelders Hall Road, Shepshed, Loughborough, Leicestershire, LE12 9NH Tel: (01509) 501730 Fax: (01509) 501730 E-mail: sales@toyoda-mitsui.com *Machine tool manufrs*

Toyota (G B) plc, Great Burgh, Burgh Heath, Epsom, Surrey, KT18 5UX Tel: (01737) 363633 Fax: (01737) 367700 E-mail: info@toyota.com *Motor cars & commercial vehicle retailers*

Toyota Industrial Equipment Northern Ltd, Pioneer Way, Castleford, West Yorkshire, WF10 5QG Tel: (01977) 712000 Fax: (01977) 712001 E-mail: we.deliver@uk.toyota-industries.eu *Provider of forklift trucks, warehouse equipment and supporting services.*

▶ Toyota & Lexus Specialists Ltd, 63 Connaught Road, Sutton, Surrey, SM1 3PJ Tel: (020) 8286 2201 E-mail: info@toyotalexusspecialists.co.uk *Toyota & lexus parts, servicing & repairs*

Toyota Material Handling UK, Unit 1-5, Sheetglass Road, Culler Drive, Queenborough, Kent, ME11 5JS Tel: 0870 850 1400 *Material Handling Distributor - Forklifts, Warehouse Equipment & Supporting Services*

Toyota Material Handling UK, 705-707 Stirling Road, Trading Estate, Slough, SL1 4SY Tel: 0870 850 1400 E-mail: we.deliver@uk.toyota-industries.eu *Material Handling Distriobutor - Forklifts, Warehouse Equipment & Supporting Services*

Toyota Motor Manufacturing UK Ltd, Deeside Industrial Park, Deeside, Clwyd, CH5 2TW Tel: (01244) 282121 Fax: (01244) 282901 *Motor manufrs*

Toyota Motor Manufacturing UK Ltd, Toyota Motor Manufacturing (Uk) Ltd, Derby, DE1 9TA Tel: (01332) 282121 Fax: (01332) 282801 E-mail: info@toyotauk.com *Vehicle manufrs*

Toyota Motor Marketing Europe, Alexandra Dock North, Grimsby, South Humberside, DN31 3TD Tel: (01472) 347477 Fax: (01472) 348426 *Car exporters*

Toys N Togs, 94 Boundary Road, Hove, East Sussex, BN3 7GB Tel: (01273) 880808 Fax: (01273) 882298 E-mail: zwindle40uk@yahoo.co.uk *Toys & nursery distributors*

▶ Toystat, 18 Gravelly Industrial Park, Birmingham, B24 8HZ Tel: 0121-327 9744 Fax: (0870) 0434484 E-mail: sales@toystat.co.uk *Wholesales of toys & stationary*

TP Fay Ltd, 57 Admin Road, Knowsley Industrial Park, Liverpool, L33 7TX Tel: (0870) 3505058 Fax: (0870) 3505059 E-mail: sales@tpfay.co.uk Purchasing Contact: D. Fay Sales Contact: D. Fay *Manufacturers of heating elements, immersion heaters & electric water heaters*

TP Refrigeration, 2 George Street, Leighton Buzzard, Bedfordshire, LU7 3JX Tel: (01525) 376629 Fax: (01525) 851200 E-mail: tprefrig@aol.com *Air conditioning installers*

▶ TPH Locksmiths, 27 Shustoke Road, Solihull, West Midlands, B91 2NR Tel: 0121 7041999 E-mail: tomhartop@msn.com *24 Hour Emergency Locksmiths & Boarding up Service*

Tpi Plastic Sheeting Supplies, Scott Lidgett Road, Stoke-on-Trent, ST6 4NQ Tel: (01782) 837141 Fax: (01782) 575154 E-mail: info@tpi-polythene.co.uk *Polythene bag manufrs*

TPOS Ltd, Mitre House, Lodge Road, Long Hanborough Business Park, Witney, Oxfordshire, OX29 8LP Tel: (01993) 883688 Fax: (01993) 883611 *Computer software developers*

TPS Fronius, 108 Highfields Road, Bilston, West Midlands, WV14 0LD Tel: (01902) 495686 Fax: (01902) 496461 *Welding supplies distributors automated & manual welding systems*

TPS Fronius Ltd, 5 Simonsburn Road, Kilmarnock, Ayrshire, KA1 5LE Tel: (01563) 529435 Fax: (01563) 523510 E-mail: sales@tps-fronius.co.uk *Welding supplies distributors automated & manual welding systems*

TQ Limited, 22 South Street, Rochford, Essex, SS4 1BQ Tel: (01702) 530051 E-mail: go@toolquotes.com *TQ is a product developement company with expertise in concept creation, mechanical engineering (UK based), electroniocs hardware and software development, toolmaking and compoonent/complete product manufacturing in China for UK and world markets.*

TQC Ltd, Hooton Street, Nottingham, NG3 2NJ Tel: 0115-950 3561 Fax: 0115-948 4642 E-mail: sales@tqc.co.uk *Designers and manufacturers of assembly and test equipment for special purpose applications. Working for over 25 years in all industries including automotive and medical /pharmaceutical. From design and development and consultancy work to large system installations. Leak testing machines and leak detection systems, sole UK distributor for Nolek leak test instruments. Specialist knowledge of leak test fixture and seal design. Assembly and test solutions including fully automated, semi-automatic, linear and rotary systems, bespoke pick and place mechanisms to robot integration. Custom built engineering solutions supplied to customer specifications using inhouse facilities. GAMP experience, fully managed projects, experienced engineering staff.*

▶ TQS Ltd, The Stables, Station Road West, Oxted, Surrey, RH8 9EE Tel: (01883) 732002 Fax: (01883) 724638 E-mail: davidforester@tqsltd.co.uk *Development of packaged & bespoke application software*

▶ TR CAD Services Ltd, 12 Oakfield Road, Carterton, Oxfordshire, OX18 3QN Tel: 01993 214132 Fax: 01993 774329 E-mail: nigel.tozer@ntlworld.com *TR CAD Services ltd offer a Design and Drawing service covering Engineering mainly in the Plastics Industry Using 2D Draughting and 3D Modelling Software,and any other Drawings in General*

TR Fastenings, Trifast House, Bolton Close, Bellbrook Industrial Estate, Uckfield, East Sussex, TN22 1QW Tel: (01825) 764711 Fax: (01256) 461281 *Industrial fastener suppliers*

TR Fastenings Ltd, Trifast House, Bellbrook Industrial Estate, Uckfield, East Sussex, TN22 1QW Tel: (0800) 7315553 Fax: (0800) 525230 E-mail: sales@trfastenings.com Principal Export Areas: Worldwide *A recognised market leader in fastener distribution, manufacturing & vendor managed inventory systems. Offering same day despatch, comprehensive stock ranges include: nuts, bolts washers, machine screws, high tensile products, sheet metal fasteners, fasteners for plastics, micro diameter fasteners, security fasteners, thread-locking fasteners, nylon fasteners etc. Materials include, steel, stainless steel, brass, plating finishes include zinc, zinc/yellow, nickel, black etc* Also at: Branches throughout the U.K.

Trac Heaton Ltd, Mount Pleasant Street, West Bromwich, West Midlands, B70 7DL Tel: 0121-553 1510 Fax: 0121-500 5846 E-mail: info@tracheaton.com *Special purpose tooling manufrs*

Trac International Ltd, Unit 12 Kirkhill Industrial Estate, Howe Moss Drive, Dyce, Aberdeen, AB21 0GL Tel: (01224) 725800 Fax: (01224) 725801 E-mail: info@tracinternational.com *Rope access*

Trace Group plc, 224-232 St John Street, London, EC1V 4QR Tel: (020) 7825 1000 Fax: (020) 7825 1001 E-mail: sales@tracegroup.com *Software writers & suppliers*

Tracel Ltd, Sand Road Industrial Site, Great Gransden, Sandy, Bedfordshire, SG19 3AJ Tel: (01767) 677521 Fax: (01767) 677952 *Precision engineers* Also at: Branches throughout the U.K.

Traceman Fire Protection Consultants, 27 Leinster Road, Swinton, Manchester, M27 5YQ Tel: 0161-793 8448 Fax: 0161-794 2129 E-mail: enquiries@traceman.co.uk *Specialist in electrical services, fire protection, trace heating, detection & frost protection*

Tracerco, Coxwald Way, Belasis Hall Technology Park, Billingham, Cleveland, TS23 1LB Tel: (01642) 370620 Fax: (01642) 370704 E-mail: tracerco@massey.com *Oil & gas suppliers*

Tracey John Welding Ltd, Block 12, 5 Clydesmill Drive, Clydesmill Industrial Estate, Glasgow, G32 8RG Tel: 0141-641 7500 Fax: 0141-641 9738 E-mail: john@john-tracey-welding.co.uk *Specialist welding services, all disciplines*

▶ William Tracey Ltd, Dunniflats Depot, Lugton, Kilmarnock, Ayrshire, KA3 4EA Tel: (01505) 850343 Fax: (01505) 850102 E-mail: dunniflats@wmtracey.co.uk *Waste disposal company*

Trachem Fluid Solutions, 10 Victoria Road, Adwick-le-Street, Doncaster, South Yorkshire, DN6 7AZ Tel: (01302) 723111 Fax: (01302) 727744 E-mail: sales@oil-store.co.uk *Lubricant distributors*

Track Maintenance Equipment Ltd, Witham Wood, Marley Lane, Haslemere, Surrey, GU27 3PZ Tel: (01428) 651114 Fax: (01428) 644727 E-mail: sales@tmeltd.co.uk *Railway lighting & railway track maintenance suppliers & manufrs*

Track Right, Bridge Farm, Cuckfield Road, Burgess Hill, West Sussex, RH15 8RE Tel: (01444) 246370 Fax: (01444) 246370 *Saddlery specialists*

Trackcard Ltd, Rassler Wood House, Henley Road, Marlow, Buckinghamshire, SL7 2EN Tel: (01628) 890036 Fax: (01628) 478215 E-mail: sales@trackcard.co.uk *Card payment systems*

▶ Trackday Gift Experiences, PO Box 169, Wymondham, Norfolk, NR18 0WL Tel: (0870) 9103786 E-mail: info@trackday-gift-experiences.com *The UK's Specialist in Driving Gift Experiences - We differ from other Gift Experience web sites because we specialise in Car Track Days and Driving Experiences.*

Tracker Network Ltd, Otter House 5 Cowley Business Park, High Street, Cowley, Uxbridge, Middlesex, UB8 2AD Tel: (01895) 234567 Fax: (01895) 234117 E-mail: info@tnuk.co.uk *Vehicle security system manufrs*

Trackit Systems Ltd, Trival House, Unit 3 Hawthorne Park, Coal Road, Leeds, LS14 1PQ Tel: 0113-306 0306 Fax: 0113-276 0685 *Bar code system manufrs*

Trackline Presentation Services, 68 Alton Street, Crewe, CW2 7QB Tel: (01270) 665750 Fax: (01270) 665750 E-mail: enquires@trackline.com *Video sound track producers*

Tracks Cad Systems Ltd, London Road, Wokingham, Berkshire, RG40 1PD Tel: (01344) 455046 Fax: (01344) 860547 E-mail: sales@trackscad.co.uk *Plotter & printer suppliers*

▶ Tracks & Poles & Things, The Old Windmill, Mill Lane, Parbold, Lancashire, WN8 7NW Tel: (01257) 462787 Fax: (01257)462787 E-mail: sales@tracksandpoles.com *Curtain tracks & poles suppliers*

▶ Tracline UK Ltd, Bennett House, 1 High Street, Edgware, Middlesex, HA8 7TA Tel: (020) 8952 7770 Fax: (020) 8951 5149 E-mail: sales@tracline.co.uk *Educational aids equipment suppliers*

Tracs International Ltd, Falcon House, Union Grove Lane, Aberdeen, AB10 6XU Tel: (01224) 321213 Fax: (01224) 321214

Tract Ltd, Mckay Trading Estate, Station Approach, Bicester, Oxfordshire, OX26 6BF Tel: (01869) 326300 Fax: (01869) 323430 E-mail: info@tract.ltd.uk *Office furniture manufrs*

Traction Batteries South East, Chilton Industrial Estate, 11 Addison Road, Sudbury, Suffolk, CO10 2YW Tel: (01787) 880011 Fax: (01787) 880770 E-mail: sales@traction-batteries.co.uk *Suppliers & service industrial batteries*

Traction Electrical Services, Withymoor Farm, Day House Lane, Hillesley, Wotton-under-Edge, Gloucestershire, GL12 7QY Tel: (01453) 843526 Fax: (01453) 844145 E-mail: tracelec@freenetname.co.uk *Battery charger manufrs*

Traction Equipment (Stafford) Ltd, Glover Street, Stafford, ST16 2NY Tel: (01785) 223355 Fax: (01785) 211074 E-mail: call@tractionequipment.co.uk *Traction equipment hire & retailers*

Tractor Service, 548 Galleywood Road, Chelmsford, CM2 8BX Tel: (07889) 461892 Fax: (01245) 492471 *Agricultural machinery, buy, sell & service*

Tractor Spares Ltd, Strawberry Lane, Willenhall, West Midlands, WV13 3RN Tel: (01902) 633614 Fax: (01902) 605685 E-mail: tractorsparesltd@aol.com *Industrial tractor spares suppliers*

Tractormatic Agricultural Services, 61 Waterloo Road, Lisburn, County Antrim, BT27 5NW Tel: (028) 9266 3133 Fax: (028) 9266 3136 *Spare tractor part manufrs*

Trad Group Ltd, Pelican Wharf, Imperial Street, London, E3 3ED Tel: (020) 8980 1155 Fax: (020) 8981 3019 E-mail: enquiries@trad.co.uk *Scaffolding contractors*

Trada Technology Ltd, Stocking Lane, Hughenden Valley, High Wycombe, Buckinghamshire, HP14 4ND Tel: (01494) 569600 Fax: (01494) 565487 E-mail: information@trada.co.uk *Researchers & consultant services*

Trade Advertising Services, The Bungalow Manor Lane, Unit 11 K U S Industrial Estate, Hawarden, Deeside, Clwyd, CH5 3DP Tel: (01244) 520351 Fax: (01244) 536363 E-mail: tradeadvertising@aol.com *Screen printers*

Trade Association Management Ltd, Tamesis House, 35 St. Philips Avenue, Worcester Park, Surrey, KT4 8JS Tel: (020) 8330 6446 Fax: (020) 8330 7447 E-mail: mmta@tamgroup.co.uk *Trade association*

Trade Blinds, 104 Oak Road, Sittingbourne, Kent, ME10 3PR Tel: (01795) 428793 *Blind distributors*

▶ The Trade Centre, Lawlor House The Pinnacles Harlow Essex, Cawley Hatch, Harlow, Essex, CM19 5AN Tel: (01279) 433321 Fax: (01279) 433326 E-mail: lauren@tradesuk.com *Conference room hire & construction industry training services*

▶ Trade Conservatories 2 U Ltd, 36 Temple Way, Heybridge, Maldon, Essex, CM9 4PX Tel: (01621) 852200 Fax: (0845) 1303872 E-mail: sales@tradeconservatories2u.co.uk *Suppliers of high quality conservatories*

Trade Counter Ltd, Unit D Trading Estate Road, London, NW10 7LU Tel: (020) 8385 2753 Fax: (020) 8965 9765 E-mail: ptc@netcomuk.co.uk *Warehousing & dispatch services*

Trade Cutting Formes Ltd, Unit 14b, Tanfield Lea Industrial Estate North, Tanfield Lea, Stanley, County Durham, DH9 9UU Tel: (01207) 230598 Fax: (01207) 290945 E-mail: sales@tcf-ltd.co.uk *Quality laser cutting forms*

▶ Trade Displays UK, Saval Lane, Coalpit Road, Newry, Co. Down, BT34 2RQ Tel: (028) 3083 3757 Fax: (0709) 2357124 E-mail: info@tradedisplays.co.uk *We offer a unique range of fabric banners and displays inc. Flex Display, T Flag, tablecloths, large backdrops for POS and events, indoor and outdoor, fast service and strict quality assurance*

Trade Effluent Monitoring Equipment, 2a Croft Street, Cheltenham, Gloucestershire, GL53 0EE Tel: (01242) 228745 Fax: (01242) 228745 *Water equipment suppliers*

Trade Flooring Ltd, 8 St. James Mill Road, Northampton, NN5 5JW Tel: (01604) 751721 Fax: (01604) 755506 E-mail: sales@tflcarpets.co.uk *General flooring contractors Also at: Kettering*

Trade Gaps Ltd, Kitchen Farm, Skipton Old Road, Colne, Lancashire, BB8 7ER Tel: (01282) 843740 Fax: (01282) 841776 E-mail: sales@tradegaps.com *Clothing distributors*

Trade Glass Supplies Ltd, Unit 2, Lythgoes Lane, Warrington, WA2 7XE Tel: (01925) 411488 Fax: (01925) 231420 E-mail: tradeglass@aol.com *Double glazing manufrs*

Trade Grade Products Ltd, 10 Victory Close Woolsbridge Indust Estate, Verwood, Wimborne, Dorset, BH21 6SX Tel: (01202) 820177 Fax: (01202) 814011 E-mail: sales@theglue.co.uk *Adhesive distributors & agents*

Trade Mark Advice & Service Bureau, Fulwood House, 12 Fulwood Place, London, WC1V 6HR Tel: (020) 7242 2535 Fax: (020) 7405 8113 E-mail: info@beckgreener.com *Beck Greener was established in 1867, making it one of the oldest intellectual property firms in the world. They provide a comprehensive service in relation to patents, trade marks, designs, copyright and related rights. Their offices are in the heart of London's historic legal district, within walking distance of the London Patent Office and The High Court.*

Trade Mark Advice & Service Bureau, Fulwood House, 12 Fulwood Place, London, WC1V 6HR Tel: (020) 7242 2535 Fax: (020) 7405 8113 E-mail: info@beckgreener.com *Solicitors*

Trade Mark Consultants Co. Ltd, 54 Hillbury Avenue, Harrow, Middlesex, HA3 8EW Tel: (020) 8907 6066 Fax: (020) 8907 0743 E-mail: info@trademarkco.co.uk *Trade mark attorneys*

▶ Trade Meter Supplies Ltd, I-Centre House, Hamilton Way, Mansfield, Nottinghamshire, NG18 5BR Tel: (01623) 600677 Fax: (01623) 422003 E-mail: info@trademetersupplies.co.uk *Kamstrup stockiest distributor, water, energy, gas meters*

Trade Paint Supplies Ltd, Grove Road, Northfleet, Gravesend, Kent, DA11 9AX Tel: (01474) 560382 Fax: (01474) 362926 E-mail: sales@tradepaintsupplies.ltd.uk *Paint & protective coatings suppliers*

Trade Point Systems Ltd, Phoenix House, 2A Amity Grove, London, SW20 0LJ Tel: (020) 8944 1003 Fax: (020) 8971 6767 E-mail: info@tradepointsys.co.uk *Computer software developers*

Trade Set Forms Ltd, Unit 1, Building 329, Rushock Trading Estate, Droitwich Road, Rushock, Droitwich, Worcestershire, WR9 0NR Tel: (01299) 251076 Fax: (01299) 251077 E-mail: info@tradesetforms.com *Business form printers*

Trade Signs, 150 London Road, Bedford, MK42 0PS Tel: (01234) 211782 Fax: (01234) 340200 E-mail: sales@tradesigns229.ffnet.co.uk *Sign manufrs*

▶ Trade Skills 4 U, 3 Metana House, Priestley Way, Crawley, West Sussex, RH10 9NT Tel: (01293) 529777 E-mail: enquires@tradeskills4u.co.uk

▶ Trade Solutions, Trading House, 9 Cecil Road, Stretford, Manchester, M32 9BZ Tel: 0161 2863001 *Business consultancy offering advice on all business related issues including Strategy, Market Analysis, Marketing and Sales, Operations and Human Resources. We also take our service one step further and actually implement solutions or strategies if you want us to. We are completely flexible and will work with you to achieve your business goals.*

Trade Supplies, Unit 208, The Commercial Centre, Picket Piece, Andover, Hampshire, SP11 6LU Tel: (01264) 334108 Fax: (01264) 337727 *Ventilation equipment supplier*

Trade Supplies, Trade House, Freestone Road, Bristol, BS2 0QN Tel: 0117-972 8230 Fax: 0117-972 8231 *Ventilation equipment & air conditioning distributor*

Trade Systems, 48-56 Hawks Road, Kingston Upon Thames, Surrey, KT1 3EE Tel: (020) 8549 5281 Fax: (020) 8541 5637 E-mail: sales@tradesystems.co.uk *Storage & shop fitting equipment*

Trade Wind Technology Ltd, The Old Stores, 11 North Street, Tillingham, Southminster, Essex, CM0 7TR Tel: (01621) 779037 Fax: (01621) 779034 E-mail: sales@t-w-t.co.uk Principal Export Areas: Worldwide *Trade Wind Technology was formed in September 1998 to offer computer consultancy specialising in database systems in particular Unify, Microsoft Access, SQL and Informix; database design and administration, as well as bespoke development and support using database technologies. We also offer web site support. Our clients include many well-known and established companies ranging in size from small businesses to public utilities. We operated mostly in the South East, although we have clients from outside this area. Our aim is to provide an excellent service and as an independent company we are able to give independent advice. We are particularly valuable to small businesses that do not have an IT department, but occasionally need help with their computer systems. Tel. 01621 779037*

▶ Trade Windows (Bristol), F St Vincents Trading Estate, Feeder Road, Bristol, BS2 0UY Tel: 0117-972 1041 Fax: 0117-977 1133

▶ Tradecall, 4 Bracknell Road, Camberley, Surrey, GU15 4BG Tel: (01276) 501755 Fax: (01276) 501755 E-mail: dave@the-roofer.co.uk *Roofing services*

▶ Tradelane Limited, 1 Victoria Avenue, Birmingham, B1 1BD Tel: 0121 6322240 Fax: 0121 6322241 E-mail: info@tradelane.co.uk

▶ Tradeline Works, 241 Hornbeams, Harlow, Essex, CM20 1PN Tel: (01279) 869316 Fax: (01279) 869605 E-mail: tradelineworks@yahoo.co.uk *We carry out gas & electricity testing on appliances & building circuits for domestic & commercial premises, we also issue landlord certificates & homebuyers reports. We cover all of London & the Home Counties tel 07760 100674 anytime*

Tradelink Direct Ltd, Marwick Road, March, Cambridgeshire, PE15 8PH Tel: (01354) 657650 Fax: (01354) 657400 *Double glazing manufrs*

Trade-Link (EC) Ltd, 5 Carlton Gardens, Ealing, London, W5 2AN Tel: (020) 8998 1090 Fax: (020) 8810 5871 E-mail: tradelinkec@clara.net *Oil & petrochemical industry suppliers*

Trademark Interiors, 8 March Monte Gate, Hemel Hempstead, Hertfordshire, HP2 7BF Tel: (01442) 260022 Fax: (01442) 232244 E-mail: info@tmark.co.uk ***Trademark is a well established office interiors business supplying small and large clients throughout the UK. A wide range of the latest design and build services are offered including;**Office, and executive desking*Reception desking*Office, boardroom and table seating*Soft furnishings*Glass Partition*Partitioning*Office storage*Storage Wall*Audio visual*Bespoke Furniture*Building Control Approval*Space Planning*Installation Teams*Lease Purchase**Trademark Interiors also offer design, installation and project management services as a full solution provider.**Browse the web site at www.tmark.co.uk and take a look at extensive the extensive range of office furniture and services.**

continued

Trader Tiles, Unit 2 Progress Business Park, Orders Lane, Kirkham, Preston, PR4 2TZ Tel: (01772) 681140 Fax: (01772) 681140 *Ceramic products retailers*

Traders Coffee Ltd - Traders of Surbiton, 274 Ewell Road, Surbiton, Surrey, KT6 7AG Tel: (020) 8390 0311 Fax: (020) 8390 8280 E-mail: admin@coffeebay.co.uk *Traders Coffee Ltd offers coffee related products to meet industry requirements. Their products range from a wide selection of coffee beans to coffee carts and espresso machines. They are based in Surbiton, Surrey and look forward to dealing with your requests.*

▶ Trades Team Ltd, Greenlaw, Castle Douglas, Kirkcudbrightshire, DG7 2LH Tel: (01556) 504951

Tradesigns Signs & Nameplates, 1124 Pershore Road, Stirchley, Birmingham, B30 2YG Tel: 0121-471 1381 Fax: 0121-471 1381 *Sign manufrs*

▶ Tradesmen Recommended, Unit 10B, Dinting Lane Industrial Estate, Glossop, Derbyshire, SK13 7NU Tel: (01457) 856270 Fax: (01457) 862214 E-mail: enquiries@tradesmen-recommended.co.uk *Free online service to property/building owners who want to find trustworthy & reliable tradesmen*

▶ Tradestar UK Ltd, 6 Scott Close, Bicester, Oxfordshire, OX26 2FB Tel: 01869 240560 Fax: 01869 240916 E-mail: info@tradestar.net *Tradestar was formed in 1989. Our long experience enables us to deliver translations which are quick,inexpensive and above all of high Quality. Technical translation, legal translation, translation into French, German, Italian, Spanish or any other language. We also provide DTP, Interpreting and Web-site localisation.*

Tradestock Ltd, Poole Works, Poole, Wellington, Somerset, TA21 9HW Tel: (01823) 661717 Fax: (01823) 666543 E-mail: sales@tradestockltd.co.uk *Melamine laminate manufrs*

▶ Tradeteam Ltd, Eddison Road, Hams Hall Distribution Park, Coleshill, Birmingham, B46 1TT Tel: (01675) 468500 Fax: (01675) 467541 E-mail: phil.storer@tradeteam.com

▶ Tradeteam Ltd, Stockingswater Lane, Enfield, Middlesex, EN3 7PZ Tel: (020) 8216 6900 Fax: (020) 8216 6929

▶ Tradeteam Ltd, Scottish Distribution Centre, Dale Avenue, Cambuslang, Glasgow, G72 7DX Tel: 0141-646 3500 Fax: 0141-646 3530

Tradewinds Merchandising Co. Ltd, Lynton Road, London, N8 8SL Tel: (020) 8341 9700 Fax: (0845) 2309006 E-mail: sales@tradewinds.eu.com *Tee shirt printers*

Tradewinds UK Ltd, 2 Lombard Way, Banbury, Oxfordshire, OX16 4TD Tel: (01295) 278866 Fax: (01295) 278855 E-mail: twuk@tradewindworldwide.co.uk *Importers of bicycle parts*

Tradex Instruments Ltd, C Davis Road, Chessington, Surrey, KT9 1TY Tel: (020) 8391 0136 Fax: (020) 8397 1924 E-mail: info@tradexinstruments.com *Gear manufacturers or cutters*

Trading Hedingham and Beds, Wash Farm, Queen St, Sible Hedingham, Halstead, Essex, CO9 3RH Tel: (01787) 462228 *Bed retailers*

Trading House International Ltd, 80 South Audley Street, London, W1K 1JH Tel: (020) 7491 9002 Fax: (020) 7491 9005 E-mail: tradinghouse@freenet.co.uk *Chemical exporters*

The Trading Post, Hallmark Farm, Ashford Road, St. Michaels, Tenterden, Kent, TN30 6SP Tel: (01233) 850522 Fax: (01233) 850522 *Protective clothing suppliers*

The Trading Standards Institute, Suite 3-5 Hadleigh Business Centre, London Road, Hadleigh, Benfleet, Essex, SS7 2BT Tel: (0870) 8729000 Fax: (0870) 8729025 E-mail: institute@tsi.org.uk *Membership based organisations & unions*

Trading Style, Unit 2, Pemberton Business Centre, Richmond Hill, Pemberton, Wigan, Lancashire, WN5 8AA Tel: (01942) 621942 Fax: (01942) 620909 E-mail: info@tradingstyle.co.uk *Based in the North West but supplying customers throughout the UK. Customer Service, Competitive Pricing, Quality Products and Account Facilities are just a few of the reasons why you should click through and look at the site. We supply PPE, Hi Vis, Workwear and Officewear. All of which can be personalised with your company name Logo or other messages. Don't hesitate to contact us either by email or phone(We will pay for the call) and we will respond to your enquiry promptly.*

Trading Technologies UK Ltd, 1st Floor, 36 Poultry Street, London, EC2R 8AJ Tel: (020) 7600 2121 Fax: (020) 7600 3344 E-mail: support@tradingtechnologies.com *Sell software*

Trading Transactions Ltd, Shepherds Hill, London, N6 5RG Tel: (020) 8341 3474 Fax: (020) 8347 8552 *Fashion agents, exporters & contractors*

▶ Trading365.co.uk, 2 Cromwell Road, Cheshunt, Herts, EN7 6AS Tel: 07092 021212 Fax: 07092 021212 E-mail: info@trading365.co.uk *Trading365.co.uk. DVD"s, CD"s, MP3 Players, Mobile Phones, you name it, we"ve got it ! or if we haven"t then use our request service where we will source the item for you at a great price !**Simply email : info@trading365.co.uk*

Traditional Carpets, 44 Warstock Road, Birmingham, B14 4ST Tel: 0121-436 6900 Fax: 0121-436 6901 E-mail: enquiries@traditionalcarpets.co.uk *Supply & fit traditional carpets & accessories*

Traditional Cookers, 28 London Road, Horndean, Waterlooville, Hampshire, PO8 0BY Tel: (023) 9259 9227 Fax: (023) 9259 8997 E-mail: sales@trad-cookers.co.uk *Traditional cooker suppliers*

Traditional Design, Unit 7 Waterside Mill, Waterside, Macclesfield, Cheshire, SK11 7HG Tel: (01625) 425292 *Kitchen designers*

▶ The Traditional Furniture Co., Unit 1, Tholthorpe Business Park, Tholthorpe, York, YO6 1SS Tel: (01347) 830000 E-mail: info@thetfc.co.uk *Furniture retailer*

Traditional Homes & Interiors, 16 Market Street, Portadown, Craigavon, County Armagh, BT62 3LD Tel: (028) 3835 2081 Fax: (028) 3835 0182 *Suppliers of curtains, gifts & occasional furniture*

▶ Traditional Joinery, Unit 1, Redding Industrial Estate, Redding, Falkirk, FK2 9TT Tel: (01324) 718400 *Joinery & building*

Traditional Lift Products Ltd, Unit 2 The Brambles, Lees Road, Knowsley Industrial Park, Liverpool, L33 7RW Tel: 0151-548 2121 Fax: 0151-548 2269 *Lift component manufrs*

▶ The Traditional Paint Co., 1 North End, Bury Mead Road, Hitchin, Hertfordshire, SG5 1RT Tel: 0845 8903434 Fax: 01462 421337 E-mail: traditionalpaint@yahoo.co.uk *Suppliers of lime wash*

▶ Traditional Print, Chapel Road, Ridgewell, Halstead, Essex, CO9 4RU Tel: (01440) 788866 Fax: (01440) 788877

Traditional Shipwright Services Ltd, Westons Point Boat Yard, Turks Lane, Sandbanks Road, Parkstone, Poole, Dorset, BH14 8EW Tel: (01202) 748029 E-mail: paulk0611@aol.com *Boat building & restoration services*

▶ The Traditional Signwriting & Signmaking Company, 3 Berryfield Road, London, SE17 3QE Tel: (020) 7708 3271 Fax: (020) 7701 9766 E-mail: james@signwriting-london.co.uk *In house signwriting & signmaking company*

Traditional Structures Contracts Ltd, Landywood Lane, Cheslyn Hay, Walsall, WS6 7AJ Tel: (01922) 414145 Fax: (01922) 416958 *Building steel frame constructors or fabricators*

▶ Traditional Values Ltd, 10-14 West Street, Southend-on-Sea, SS2 6HJ Tel: (01702) 300087 Fax: (01702) 390766 E-mail: info@traditional-values.co.uk *CAD design, stationery, furniture, printing equipment suppliers*

Traditional Woodworking Co. Ltd, Unit 11 North St Trading Estate, Brierley Hill, West Midlands, DY5 3QF Tel: (01384) 262405 Fax: (01384) 483707 *Furniture frame manufrs*

▶ Tradpin Construction Ltd, 14 Hemnall Street, Epping, Essex, CM16 4LW Tel: (01992) 561234

Traesko Furniture, 89-91 Joel Street, Northwood, Middlesex, HA6 1LU Tel: (01923) 820341 Fax: (01923) 826711 *Furniture retailer*

Trafag UK Ltd, 12 Josselin Court, Josselin Road, Burnt Mills Industrial Estate, Basildon, Essex, SS13 1QF Tel: (01268) 727172 Fax: (01268) 727572 E-mail: enquiries@trafag.co.uk *Temperature & pressure control equipment manufrs ISO 9001*

Trafalgar Cases Ltd, Stanhope Works, Primrose Hill, Kings Langley, Hertfordshire, WD4 8HS Tel: (01923) 261155 Fax: (01923) 268064 E-mail: sales@trafalgarcases.com *Manufacturers of corrugated plywood boxes*

Trafalgar Chemicals Ltd, Wylds Road, Bridgewater, Bridgwater, Somerset, TA6 4BH Tel: (01278) 431330 Fax: (01278) 431323 E-mail: trafalgersales@ambersil.co.uk *Automotive cleaning chemical suppliers*

Trafalgar Engineering Co., Station Road, Station Mills, Cottingham, North Humberside, HU16 4LL Tel: (01482) 843558 *Precision engineers*

Trafalgar Equipment, Commercial Street, Ystrad Mynach, Hengoed, Mid Glamorgan, CF82 7DY Tel: (01443) 812491 Fax: (01443) 816501 E-mail: trafalgarclean@aol.com *Cleaning chemicals & equipment*

Trafalgar Fabrications Co., Canon House, Harvest Lane, Sheffield, S3 8EF Tel: 0114-275 2521 Fax: 0114-275 2521 *Fire escape fabrications*

Trafalgar House Engraving, 4 Trafalgar Street, Brighton, BN1 4EQ Tel: (01273) 603498 Fax: (01273) 680181 *Nameplate engravers*

▶ Trafalgar Press, 20 Robert Cort Industrial Estate, Britten Road, Reading, RG2 0AU Tel: 0118-975 0899 Fax: 0118-975 3220 E-mail: sales@trafpress.co.uk

▶ Trafalgar Scientific, 4 Selbury Drive, Oadby, Leicester, LE2 5NG Tel: 0116-271 9010 Fax: 0116-271 4665 E-mail: sales@trafalgarscientific.co.uk *Laboratory equipment distributors*

Trafalgar Square Collectors Centre, 7 Whitcomb Street, London, WC2H 7HA Tel: (020) 7930 1979 Fax: (020) 7930 1152 *Medal dealer*

Trafalgar Textile Co. Ltd, Greenbrook Works, Lowerhouse Lane, Burnley, Lancashire, BB12 6ND Tel: (01282) 772923 Fax: (01282) 772923 *Springs & general engineers*

Traffco Engineers Pattern Co, Midland Road, Scunthorpe, South Humberside, DN16 1DQ Tel: (01724) 842753 Fax: (01724) 865569 *Moulds for precast concrete*

▶ Traffic Barrier Supplies, Fen Lane, Long Bennington, Newark, Nottinghamshire, NG23 5ED Tel: (01400) 282600

Traffic & Commercial Signs Ltd, Unit 14 Merryhills Enterprise Park, Park Lane, Wolverhampton, WV10 9QF Tel: (01902) 307879 Fax: (01902) 728976 *Sign manufacturers & erectors*

Traffic Safety Supplies (U K) Ltd, Tait Road Industrial Estate, Croydon, CR0 2DP Tel: (020) 8684 6643 Fax: (020) 8684 6532 *Traffic sign manufrs*

Traffic Sign Contracting Ltd, P O Box 102, Burton-on-Trent, Staffordshire, DE13 0BN Tel: (01283) 515595 Fax: (01283) 515915 *Sign manufacturer*

▶ Traffic Signals Civils, 43 Sandilands Street, Glasgow, G32 0HT Tel: 0141-778 9670 Fax: 0141-778 9670 *Traffic signal installation*

Trafford Lifting Services Ltd, Unit 2-3 Naval Street, Manchester, M4 6AX Tel: 0161-205 9716 Fax: 0161-205 8569 *Materials handling*

Trafford Rubber Additives Ltd, Alma Works, Station Street, Dukinfield, Cheshire, SK16 4SE Tel: 0161-339 8693 Fax: 0161-343 2965 E-mail: info@trafford-rubber-additives.co.uk *Rubber chemical manufrs*

▶ Trafford Rubber Products Ltd, Greengate Works, Broadoak Business Park, Ashburton Road West, Trafford Park, Manchester, M17 1RW Tel: 0161-873 7172 Fax: 0161-848 9762 E-mail: traffordrubber@beeb.net Principal Export Areas: Worldwide *Manufacturers of high quality rubber compounds for the Roller Covering, Tank Lining and Hose Markets. Custom Compounding in Slab or Sheet form. Suppliers to the Electrical, Telecom and Marine Industry. Safety Products for Insulation and Fire Protection.*

Trafford Signs Ltd, First Avenue, Trafford Park, Manchester, M17 1TS Tel: 0161-872 7103 Fax: 0161-848 8565 E-mail: traffordsigns@btconnect.com *Signwriting manufrs*

Trafford Timber & Damp-Proofing Specialists Ltd, 1086 Chester Road, Stretford, Manchester, M32 0HL Tel: 0161-972 5777 Fax: 0161-972 5888 E-mail: admin@traffordtds.fsworld.co.uk *Timber & damp proving specialists*

▶ Trafford Trailer Repairs, Stretford Motorway Estate, Stretford, Manchester, M32 0ZH Tel: 0161-865 6225 Fax: 0161-865 6226 *Commercial vehicle repairers*

Traigo Kitchens & Furniture, Pasture Lane, Gaddesby, Leicester, LE7 4XD Tel: (01664) 840423 Fax: (01664) 840833 *Kitchen & furniture manufr*

Trailer Engineering, Central Avenue, Cradley Heath, West Midlands, B64 7BY Tel: (01384) 564765 Fax: (01384) 410782 E-mail: info@trailerengineering.co.uk *Manufacturers of fuel & water bowsers*

▶ Trailer Express Ltd, Park House, 5-9 Park Street, Birkenhead, Merseyside, CH41 1ET Tel: 0151-647 0101 Fax: 0151-647 0708

Trailer Tilts Ltd, 15A Walton Avenue, Felixstowe, Suffolk, IP11 8HH Tel: (01394) 673635 Fax: (01394) 673635 *Tarpaulins manufacturers & importers & wholesalers*

Trailer & Transport Ltd, Trailer House, West Quay Road, Southampton, SO15 1GZ Tel: (023) 8033 3111 Fax: (023) 8033 3600 *Trailer sales & hire*

Trailers Distribution Services, Unit 2 Charnley Fold Lane, Bamber Bridge, Preston, PR5 6AA Tel: (01772) 315557 Fax: (01772) 315939 E-mail: trailers.ltd@btinternet.com *Cinema equipment distributors*

▶ Trailertech Services Ltd, Unit 7 Plaxton Park, Cayton Low Road, Eastfield, Scarborough, North Yorkshire, YO11 3BQ Tel: (01723) 584897 Fax: (01723) 585235 *Small easy access vehicle sales*

▶ Train 4 It Ltd, 275-285 High Street, London, E15 2TF Tel: (020) 8519 9243 Fax: (020) 8519 9243

Train A Lift Ltd, Tal Centre, Charter Avenue, Coventry, CV4 8AF Tel: (024) 7646 9027 Fax: (024) 7646 2005 E-mail: sales@train-a-lift.co.uk *Fork lift truck operator training schools*

Train & Grow Ltd, 73 Green Lane, Cookridge, Leeds, LS16 7ET Tel: 0113-226 4303 Fax: 0113 2264303 E-mail: enquiries@trainandgrow.com *Accredited NLP Practitioner and Master Practitioner courses. Also bespoke NLP in business courses, such as NLP for Sales, Advanced Presentation Skills and NLP for HR. Contact us for details.*

Train & Kemp, 10 Kennington Park Place, London, SE11 4AS Tel: (020) 7582 1276 Fax: (020) 7582 5728 E-mail: mail@trainandkemp.co.uk *Civil & structural engineers*

The Training Foundry, City Campus, Pond Street, Sheffield, S1 1WB Tel: 0114-225 5888 Fax: 0114-225 5889 E-mail: itfoundry@shu.ac.uk *Software package training for business*

Training For The Millennuim, Rocheway, Rochford, Essex, SS4 1DQ Tel: (01702) 543680 Fax: (01268) 690133 E-mail: tftmrochford@yahoo.co.uk *Computer training services*

Training Partnership Ltd, 450 Babbacombe Road, Torquay, TQ1 1HW Tel: (01803) 290222 Fax: (01803) 290333 E-mail: info@thetrainingpartnershipltd.com *International work experience & language training*

Training World, 22 Larchwood Close, Romford, RM5 3QX Tel: (01708) 746948 Fax: (01708) 739041 E-mail: info@trainingworld.co.uk *Training services*

▶ Trainingeye, St Albans Road, Watford, WD24 4AS Tel: (08707) 201108

▶ Trak Construction Ltd, Seymour House, Whiteleaf Road, Hemel Hempstead, Hertfordshire, HP3 9DE Tel: (01442) 838500

Trak Microwave Ltd, Dunsinane Avenue, Dunsinane Industrial Estate, Dundee, DD2 3QF Tel: (01382) 833411 Fax: (01382) 833599 *Microwave components & sub-systems manufrs*

Trak Precision Grinders Ltd, St. Georges Way, Bermuda Industrial Estate, Nuneaton, Warwickshire, CV10 7JS Tel: (024) 7634 7117 Fax: (024) 7637 4808 E-mail: enquiries@trakltd.co.uk *Aircraft landing gear manufrs*

▶ Traker Engineering Ltd, Garth Works, Taffs Well, Cardiff, CF15 7RN Tel: (029) 2081 1088 Fax: (029) 2081 3520 E-mail: info@traker-eng.co.uk Principal Export Areas: Africa *Metal box/container (electric/adaptable) manufacturers. Also pressings, sheet metal & steel fabricators*

Traktools, Old Buckenham, Old Buckenham, Attleborough, Norfolk, NR17 1PG Tel: (07860) 251375 Fax: (01953) 861126 E-mail: track.tools@virin.net *Machine tool suppliers*

Tramar Trading Ltd, Trinity Buoy Wharf, 64 Orchard Place, London, E14 0JW Tel: (020) 7093 1155 Fax: (020) 7093 1133 E-mail: info@tramartrading.co.uk *Our business is an exclusive marketing of natural stone products, travertine, limestone, marble across UK.We supply stone products to distributors, wholesalers, contractors.*Our company is based* continued *in London. We import all our products directly from Turkey.*

Tramontana Bros, Foxglove Cottage, Mamble, Kidderminster, Worcestershire, DY14 9JL Tel: (01299) 832422 Fax: (01299) 832026 *Shot blasting contractors*

Tramspread Agricultural Machinery, Hobbies Lane, Mendlesham, Stowmarket, Suffolk, IP14 5SZ Tel: (01449) 766133 Fax: (01449) 766155 E-mail: tramspread@yahoo.co.uk *Agricultural equipment distribution & manufrs*

Tranasco Co. Ltd, Unit 28 Greenhill Industrial Estate, Coatbridge, Lanarkshire, ML5 2AG Tel: (01236) 424400 Fax: (01236) 424477 *Stone tile manufrs & installers*

Tranex Telecommunications Ltd, 29 High Street, Rothwell, Kettering, Northamptonshire, NN14 6AD Tel: (01536) 711028 Fax: (01536) 713082 E-mail: radiosales@tranex.co.uk *Radio communication equipment suppliers, sales & services*

Tranex Translation & Typesetting, 10 Barley Mow Passage, London, W4 4PH Tel: (020) 8747 1486 Fax: (020) 8995 0163 E-mail: nagitranex2@aol.com *Translation & typesetting services*

Tranfood Meat Co. Ltd, 1 Abbey Street, Birkenhead, Merseyside, CH41 5JG Tel: 0151-666 1660 Fax: 0151-647 4172 *Food packaging manufrs*

Tranilamp Ltd, 69-70 Eastern Way, Bury St. Edmunds, Suffolk, IP32 7AB Tel: (01284) 767055 Fax: (01284) 701921 E-mail: sales@tranilamp.co.uk *Indicator lamp & transformer manufrs*

▶ Tranquility, 21 Hartfield Road, Forest Row, East Sussex, RH18 5DY Tel: (01342) 825865 E-mail: linda@l-kernahan.freeserve.co.uk *Allergy & environmental toxin investigation*

Tranquility Aquatics & Reptile Centre Ltd, 46-47 George Street, Brighton, BN2 1RJ Tel: (01273) 621691 Fax: (01273) 626908 *Aquatics & reptile retailers*

▶ Trans Bridge Freight Services Ltd, 384 Heywood Old Road, Middleton, Manchester, M24 4SB Tel: 0161-655 0100 Fax: 0161-655 0111

Trans European Technology, 132 Goswell Road, London, EC1V 7DY Tel: (020) 7553 9950 Fax: (020) 7608 3588 E-mail: sales@tet.co.uk *IT solution provider*

Trans European Trailer Services Holbeach, 2a Avenue Road, Grantham, Lincolnshire, NG31 6TA Tel: (01476) 570077 Fax: (01476) 577799 *Trailer services throughout europe*

▶ Trans Food Ltd, 22 Wainman Road, Woodson, Peterborough, PE2 7BU Tel: (01733) 238668 Fax: (01733) 238818 *Bakery products specialists*

Trans Pennine Bearing Co., 48 Listerhills Road, Bradford, West Yorkshire, BD7 1HT Tel: (01274) 732366 Fax: (01274) 391503 *Bearing manufrs*

Trans Pennine Garage Equipment, 11 Twitch Hill, Horbury, Wakefield, West Yorkshire, WF4 6NA Tel: (01924) 266355 Fax: (01924) 263572 *Garage equipment retail & services*

▶ Trans Plant Mastertrain, Schovella, Cliff Road, Gorran Haven, St. Austell, Cornwall, PL26 6JN Tel: (01392) 426242 Fax: (01392) 205006 E-mail: geoff_fox@hotmail.com *A wide range of training is offered to individuals and companies working in all industrial and commercial sectors. Our main training base is in Exeter but we are able to supply on-site training throughout the UK and, in some cases, overseas. Training includes goods vehicle (LGV/HGV) - all categories, trailer techniques, load security, dangerous goods (ADR), forklift truck, industrial counterbalance, rough terrain, telescopic handler, sideloader, cranes (mobile, static, lorry-mounted, ship-mounted), hydraulic loader, slinger/signaller, Appointed Persons (Cranes), excavator, dumper, tractor and trailer, loading shovel, mobile elevating work access platform, skips, safety awareness (construction, etc), abrasive wheels, manual handling, basic plant maintenance, vocational instructor, Dangerous Goods Safety Adviser, NVQs in Driving Goods Vehicle, Transporting Goods by Road, Warehouse and Distribution.**

Trans Tronic, Whitting Valley Road, Old Whittington, Chesterfield, Derbyshire, S41 9EY Tel: (01246) 264260 Fax: (01246) 455281 E-mail: sales@trans-tronic.co.uk *Electrical coil winder, transformer & toroidal transformer manufrs*

Trans World Couriers Ltd, 3 Bricklayers Arms Distribution Centre, Mandela Way, London, SE1 5SR Tel: (020) 7231 3131 Fax: (020) 7237 3048 E-mail: sales@twc.uk.com *Courier services*

Trans World Shipping, Thurrock Park Way, Tilbury, Essex, RM18 7HW Tel: (01375) 488222 Fax: (01375) 488233 E-mail: tws@bernardgroup.plc.co.uk *Freight forwarders*

Transaction Network Services UK Ltd, Unit 2 The Boulevard, Welwyn Garden City, Hertfordshire, AL7 1EL Tel: (01707) 362200 Fax: (01707) 371764 *ATM transactions service providers*

TransAirVac International Ltd, PO Box 491, Newcastle, Staffordshire, ST5 0TW Tel: (01782) 710282 Fax: (01782) 710126 E-mail: office@transairvac.com *Distributors of blowers & compressed air*

Transalliance UK Ltd, Stonehouse Lane, Purfleet, Essex, RM19 1NX Tel: (01708) 869111 Fax: (01708) 867386 E-mail: hnpurfleet@btconnect.com *Road transport, haulage & freight services*

▶ Transaltionpro, Wolseley Road, London, E7 9PE Tel: (020) 7870 1068 *translation agency offers quality and efficiency french englsih spanish*

Transam Distributors Ltd, 13 Furnace Road, Muirkirk, Cumnock, Ayrshire, KA18 3RE Tel: (01290) 661515

Transam Microsystems Ltd, 2 Bakers Yard, Bakers Row, London, EC1R 3HT Tel: (020) 7837 4050 Fax: (020) 7837 3804 E-mail: transam@transam.co.uk *Computer systems consultancy services*

Transatlantic Plastics Ltd, Unit 6 Lulworth Business Centre, Nutwood Way, Totton, Southampton, SO40 3WW Tel: (023) 8086 9999 Fax: (023) 8066 6622 E-mail: sales@transpack.co.uk *Packaging material/goods/products manufrs*

Transbelt Ltd, 36 Howe Street, Bootle, Merseyside, L20 8NG Tel: 0151-922 1314 Fax: 0151-922 3983 E-mail: transbelt@btconnect.com *Conveyor belting manufrs* Also at: Manchester & Woodford Green

Transbelt Ltd, 46 The Acorn Centre, Barry Street, Oldham, OL1 3NE Tel: 0161-620 0493 Fax: 0161-627 0084 E-mail: sales@transbelt.co.uk *Conveyor & transmission manufrs*

▶ Transbuild Building Contractors Ltd, 37a Kenilworth Drive, Oadby, Leicester, LE2 5LT Tel: 0116-271 0897 Fax: 0116-272 0454

Transbus International Ltd, Hydepark Industrial Estate, Mallusk, Newtownabbey, County Antrim, BT36 8NP Tel: (028) 9034 2006 Fax: (028) 9034 2678 E-mail: phaveron@walexander.co.uk *Bus manufrs*

Transcendata Europe Ltd, 4 Carisbrooke Court, Buckingway Business Park, Anderson Road, Cambridge, CB24 4UQ Tel: (01954) 234300 Fax: (01954) 234349 E-mail: sales@transcendata.com *Engineering software manufrs*

▶ Transcom Communications UK Ltd, 69-71 Cutlers Road, South Woodham Ferrers, Chelmsford, CM3 5WA Tel: (01245) 324347 Fax: (01245) 328597 *Communication agents*

Transcomm UK Ltd, Heathrow Boulevard, 280 Bath Road, West Drayton, Middlesex, UB7 0DQ Tel: (020) 8990 9090 Fax: (020) 8990 9110 E-mail: customer.services@transcomm.uk.com *Transcomm provides business critical wireless data solutions that help organisations run their business more profitably and efficiently, making up-to-the-minute information available whenever and wherever it is needed, securely and reliably.*

▶ Transcool Ltd, Gilmans Industrial Estate, Billingshurst, West Sussex, RH14 9EZ Tel: 01403 786326 *Transmitting system engineers*

▶ Transdek UK Ltd, PO Box 76, Retford, Nottinghamshire, DN22 8ST Tel: (01777) 705958 Fax: (01777) 706756 E-mail: info@transdek.com *Designers of manual handling loading systems*

Transdrive Engineering Services Ltd, Units 18-20, Moss Lane Indust Estate, Royton, Oldham, OL2 6HR Tel: (01706) 881940 Fax: (01706) 882436 E-mail: sales@transdrive.co.uk *Power transmission engineers*

Transenigma Ltd, 33 Soundwell Road, Bristol, BS16 4QQ Tel: 0117-956 4429 Fax: 0117-956 4430 E-mail: info@transenigma.co.uk *IT consultant*

▶ Transeuropa Ferries, Ferry Terminal, Ramsgate, Kent, CT11 9FT Tel: (01843) 595522 Fax: (01843) 594663

Transfair Llanllyr Spring Water Co., Llanllyr, Talsarn, Lampeter, Dyfed, SA48 8QB Tel: (01570) 470788 Fax: (01570) 471074 *Spring water bottling manufrs*

Transfit, 572 Wilmslow Road, Manchester, M20 3DB Tel: 0161-367 7559 Fax: 0161-491 6124 E-mail: sales@transfit.com *Car hi-fi installation & securities*

Transfix Gearboxes, 8 The Maple Industrial Estate, Wentworth Road, Mapplewell, Barnsley, South Yorkshire, S75 6DT Tel: (01226) 381000 Fax: (01226) 381000 *Gearbox reconditioners*

Transflo Instruments Ltd, Station Road, Staplehurst, Tonbridge, Kent, TN12 0QD Tel: (01580) 895000 Fax: (01580) 895050 *Fuel management systems for fleets*

▶ Transfoam Ltd, Unit 18, Cape Industrial Estate, Coal Hill Lane, Farsley, Pudsey, West Yorkshire, LS28 5NA Tel: 0113-256 6390

Transforge UK Ltd, 19 Edmondthorpe Road, Wymondham, Melton Mowbray, Leicestershire, LE14 2AD Tel: (01572) 787504 Fax: (01572) 787565 *Steel fabricators*

▶ Transform Building Services Ltd, 6 Lockyer House, Waterman St, London, SW15 1EE Tel: 020 8789 8780 Fax: 020 8789 8811 E-mail: contact@transformltd.co.uk *Residential and commercial building and refurbishment company. Bathroom installation, kitchen installation, painting and decorating, general building work, carpentry, plumbing.*

▶ Transform ebusiness Ltd, Fortissat House, Newmill-Canthill Road, Shotts, Lanarkshire, ML7 4NS Tel: (07793) 973873 E-mail: imacg@transform-ebusiness.com *E business consultants*

Transformation Tubes, 118 Winkworth Road, Banstead, Surrey, SM7 2QR Tel: (01737) 373483 Fax: (01737) 370590 E-mail: transtubes@aol.com *Lighting goods distributor*

▶ Transformer Equipment Ltd, Unit 9 Crystal Business Centre, Sandwich Industrial Estate, Sandwich, Kent, CT13 9QX Tel: (01304) 612551 Fax: (01304) 613630 E-mail: luke@transformers.freeserve.co.uk Principal Export Areas: Worldwide *Started by Mr. L.H. Cooper in 1948, supplying high quality transformers to the MOD, Electronics and Communications industries.*With approval by the BBC, BT, MOD, Siemens-Plessey, GEC Marconi, and works in the main to the MOD'S Standards of DEF.5214.*Compliance to EN 60 742, BS 3535, BT etc.*- Mains transformers, 10 kva <100amps or 10,000V*- Specialists in Auto, Audio, Isolating and Charger Transformers*- 3 Phase transformers*- Fast track prototyping*- full design service*- customised projects*- Built to DEF, BT, BS3535, EN60 742.*Our in house production and computer-aided design systems allied to many years experience, allow the company to offer a service of individual design or of course, a capacity to work strictly to customers' own drawings.*All items individually made and 100% tested for greater accuracy and uniformity.*

Transformer Manufacturing Co. Ltd, Riverside Industrial Estate, Mill Lane, Maldon, Essex, CM9 4LD Tel: (01621) 843322 Fax: (01621) 843355 E-mail: sales@tmc.co.uk *Manufacturers of transformers*

▶ Transformer Systems, 9 Easy Road, Leeds, LS9 8QS Tel: 0113-216 8392 Fax: 0113-216 9491 E-mail: info@transformersystems.co.uk *Suppliers & installers of racking, garment handling, mezzanine floor*

Transformotor Ltd, Unit 43 Coneygre Industrial Estate, Tipton, West Midlands, DY4 8XU Tel: 0121-557 4491 Fax: 0121-557 3175 *Electrical plant repairers*

Transfra Graphics Ltd, Stadium Place, Leicester, LE4 0JS Tel: 0116-234 0440 Fax: 0116-235 1881 E-mail: sales@transfragraphics.com *Narrow width transfer printers*

Transglobal Air, 11 Skyways Business Park, Exeter Airport, Silverton, Exeter, EX5 4HX Tel: (01392) 362122 Fax: (01392) 362092 E-mail: exeter@transglobalgroup.com *Freight forwarders*

Transglobal Distribution Ltd, PO Box 26, Radlett, Hertfordshire, WD7 9ZY Tel: (01923) 853319 Fax: (01923) 853319 E-mail: transglobaldistribut@lycos.com *Overseas library suppliers*

Trans-Global Engineering Ltd, Camlock Works, 13-15 Bridlington Road, Hunmanby, Filey, North Yorkshire, YO14 0LR Tel: (01723) 892122 Fax: (01723) 891554 E-mail: trans@beckgroup.co.uk *Explosion proof door manufrs*

Transhock Distribution Ltd, Unit 1, Industrial Estate, Arden Road, Saltley, Birmingham, B8 1DL Tel: 0121-322 4200 Fax: 0121-327 6239 E-mail: transhock@aol.com *Shock absorber distributors*

Transigns Display Ltd, Warish Hall, Warish Hall Road, Takeley, Bishop's Stortford, Hertfordshire, CM22 6NZ Tel: (01279) 871566 Fax: (01279) 871967 *Advertising display equipment*

Transit Retail Services, Manor Farm, Wibtoft, Lutterworth, Leicestershire, LE17 5BB Tel: (01455) 220221 Fax: (01455) 220208 E-mail: enquiries@trs-uk.co.uk Principal Export Areas: Central/East Europe & West Europe *Charity shop*

Transition Computing Ltd, 12 Challenge House, Sherwood Drive, Bletchley, Milton Keynes, MK3 6DP Tel: (0870) 0110999 Fax: (08700) 514550 E-mail: enquiries@transitioncomputing.com *Bespoke software developers services*

Transition International Ltd, Hi-Temp Works, 480 Penistone Road, Sheffield, S6 2FU Tel: 0114-244 7447 Fax: 0114-233 3071 E-mail: david@transition-international.com *Metal producers*

Transition Support Ltd, Vantage Point Business Village, 7/4, Mitcheldean, Gloucestershire, GL17 0DD Tel: (01594) 546151 Fax: (01594) 546153 E-mail: mail@transition-support.com *Consulting, training and publishing services specializing in quality management, business excellence, process management and ISO 9000*

▶ Trans-K9 Kennel & Dog Transit Products, High Carminnows, Dalry, Castle Douglas, Kirkcudbrightshire, DG7 3TB Tel: 0845 3308849 E-mail: info@transk9.co.uk *Dog Transit Boxes, Quad Bike Boxes, Dog Trailers, Maintenance Free Kennels and Equipment*

▶ Transland International, Ocean Park, Birkenhead, Merseyside, CH41 1NE Tel: 0151-653 4540 Fax: 0151-653 4547 E-mail: sales@translandgroup.ie

▶ Translation Agency TGV24, Crimond Croft, Whitehouse, Alford, Aberdeenshire, AB33 8DL Tel: (01577) 862702 E-mail: tgv24@e3internet.com

▶ Translation French Engish Spanish, 2 Wolseley Road, London, E7 9PE Tel: (020) 78701068

Translift Freight Ltd, Womersley Road, Knottingley, West Yorkshire, WF11 0DN Tel: (01977) 672301 Fax: (01977) 607071 *Road transport/haulage/freight services*

Translift Holdings plc, 22 Padgets Lane, Redditch, Worcestershire, B98 0RB Tel: (01527) 527411 Fax: (01527) 510177 E-mail: sales@translift.co.uk Principal Export Areas: Worldwide *Fork lift trucks manufrs*

▶ Translinc Ltd, Jarvis House, 157 Sadler Road, Lincoln, LN6 3RS Tel: (01522) 503400 Fax: (01522) 552997 E-mail: sales@translinc.co.uk *Contract Hire of Vehicles and Plant**Passenger Transport Services by Road*

Transmac Valves Ltd, Unit 4 Building 26, First Avenue, Pensnett Trading Estate, Kingswinford, West Midlands, DY6 7TB Tel: (01384) 288265 Fax: (01384) 288096 *Air conditioning*

Transmag Power Transformers Ltd, 66-72 Lower Essex Street, Birmingham, B5 6SU Tel: 0121-622 3217 Fax: 0121-622 3217 E-mail: sales@transmag-transformers.co.uk *Transformer & electrical coil winder manufrs*

Transmail Ltd, Unit 21 Concorde Road, Norwich, NR6 6BJ Tel: (01603) 404217 Fax: (01603) 483944 E-mail: sales@transmail.co.uk *Polythene envelopes, bands & wallets*

▶ Transmanche, Passenger Terminal, Beach Road, Newhaven, East Sussex, BN9 0BG Tel: (01273) 612875 Fax: (01273) 612864 E-mail: sales@transmancheferries.com

Transmark FCX Ltd, Heaton House, Riverside Drive, Hunsworth Lane, Bradford, West Yorkshire, BD19 4DH Tel: (01274) 700000 Fax: (01274) 700152 E-mail: jhill@heaton-valves.co.uk Principal Export Areas: Worldwide *Valve distributors*

Transmission Bearings UK Ltd, 6 Falcon Park, Basildon, Essex, SS14 3AL Tel: (01268) 533002 Fax: (01268) 522891 *Bearings, seals, v-belts & power transmission distributors*

Transmission Components Ltd, 2 Jubilee Trading Centre, Jubilee Road, Letchworth Garden City, Hertfordshire, SG6 1NE Tel: (01462) 672222 Fax: (01462) 480001 E-mail: gwhite@transmissioncomponents.com *Specialist in power take offs, worldwide & distributors, agents*

Transmission Design & Supply Co. Ltd, Unit 1A, Marlborough Street, Burnley, Lancashire, BB11 2HW Tel: (01282) 435143 Fax: (01282) 435160 *Transmission designers & suppliers*

Transmission Development Co GB Ltd, 26 Dawkins Road, Poole, Dorset, BH15 4HF Tel: (01202) 675555 Fax: (01202) 677466 E-mail: sales@transdev.co.uk Purchasing Contact: I. Osborne *Manufacturers of industrial/mechanical power transmission equipment, pulleys & rubber & timing belting. In addition, distributors, agents & stockists of transmission* continued

continuation
belting & chain drives. Also conveyor chains & gear cutters/manufrs*
Transmission & Engineering Services, Unit 17 Springfield Road, Grantham, Lincolnshire, NG31 7BL Tel: (01476) 591500 Fax: (01476) 590336 *Castors, wheels & high precision lock nuts distributors*
Transmission Of Power Ltd, 37 Sketchley Meadows, Hinckley, Leicestershire, LE10 3ES Tel: (01455) 616538 Fax: (01455) 250237 *Power transmission equipment, electrical engineering & installations, special purpose machine building & design, manufacturer of control panels, suppliers of industrial chemicals, fabricated guard systems, manufacturer of jigs & fixtures*
J.R. Transmissions, 35a Queens Road, Farnborough, Hampshire, GU14 6JP Tel: (01252) 548337 Fax: (01252) 370442 *Gear box reconditioners*
Transmit Containers Ltd, Bessemer Way, Harfreys Industrial Estate, Great Yarmouth, Norfolk, NR31 0LX Tel: (01493) 650792 Fax: (01493) 443500 *Offshore container services* Also at: Aberdeen
Transmitton Ltd, Coalfield Way, Ashby-de-la-Zouch, Leicestershire, LE65 1JD Tel: (01530) 258000 Fax: (01530) 258008 E-mail: sales@transmitton.co.uk *Integrated control agents*
▶ Transmon Engineering, 131 Barkby Road, Leicester, LE4 9LG Tel: 0116-274 1077
Transnational Corporation Ltd, Portland House, 4 Albion Street, Cheltenham, Gloucestershire, GL52 2LG Tel: (01242) 529424 Fax: (01242) 222834 E-mail: services@transnationalltd.com *Debt collection services* Also at: Belfast, Dublin, Glasgow, Liverpool, London & Manchester
Transnorm Systems Ltd, 4 Ashchurch Business Centre, Alexandra Way, Ashchurch, Tewkesbury, Gloucestershire, GL20 8TD Tel: (01684) 291100 Fax: (01684) 291550 E-mail: sales@transnorm.co.uk *Materials handling systems*
Transocean, Crawpeel Road, Altens Industrial Estate, Aberdeen, AB12 3LG Tel: (01224) 427700 Fax: (01224) 427800 *Oil well drilling contractors*
Transome Partition Systems, 9 Ducketts Mead, Canewdon, Rochford, Essex, SS4 3QS Tel: (01702) 258720 Fax: (01702) 258582 *Partitions & cubicles distributors*
Transpaint UK Ltd, 114 B M K Industrial Estate, Wakefield Road, Liversedge, West Yorkshire, WF15 6BS Tel: (01924) 503200 Fax: (01924) 500912 E-mail: transpaint@ltlbusiness.com *Commercial vehicle finishing service*
▶ Transpan Scotland Ltd, 53 Cornfield Road, Turriff, Aberdeenshire, AB53 4BP Tel: (01888) 563059
▶ Transparent Assets Limited, 29 Harley Street, London, W1G 9QR Tel: 0207 612 4287 E-mail: info@transparentassets.com *Wireless monitoring and diagnostics of physical assets.**We deploy our wireless sensors, vibration analysis and provide manufacturing industry with a service to predict failure of the equipment before it occurs.*
Transparent Box Co. Ltd, 22 Back Lane, Stonesby, Melton Mowbray, Leicestershire, LE14 4PT Tel: (01664) 464227 Fax: (01664) 464001 E-mail: info@transparentbox.co.uk *Manufacturers of clear PVC packaging*
Transpeed Removals, Unit 2B, Gatwick Business Park, Kennel Lane Kennel Lane Kennel Lane, Hookwood, Horley, Surrey, RH6 0AY Tel: (01293) 774672 Fax: (01293) 822564 E-mail: sales@transpeed-removals.co.uk *Industrial & domestic removal company*
▶ Transplant Services, 2 Blacker Road, Mapplewell, Barnsley, South Yorkshire, S75 6BW Tel: (01226) 388878 Fax: (01226) 388450
Transport 4 Print Ltd, Avila, 13 Silkmore Lane, Stafford, ST17 4JN Tel: (01785) 601504 E-mail: t4p@ntlworld.com *Specialist transport to the printing industry. European transport. Digital presses, image seters, guillotines, small offset litho. Friendly competent drivers with engineering experience. Full insurance cover. Competitive rates. Call 01785 601504*
Transport Distribution Ltd, Dock Gate 2, Felixstowe, Suffolk, IP11 3SW Tel: (01394) 675601 Fax: (01394) 674278 *Freight forwarding agents* Also at: Orpington
Transport Enterprises Ltd, Unit 11, Swannington Road, Broughton Astley, Leicester, LE9 6TU Tel: (01455) 285295 Fax: (01455) 285283 *Commercial vehicle body builders*
Transport Fabrications Ltd, Appleton Road, Acaster Malbis, York, YO23 2UZ Tel: (01904) 744622 Fax: (01904) 744633 E-mail: stuarttransfab1@aol.com *Commercial vehicle repairs & conversions*
Transport & Plant Services, Hoobrook Trading Estate, Worcester Road, Kidderminster, Worcestershire, DY10 1HY Tel: (01562) 822446 Fax: (01562) 746442 *Commercial vehicle repairers*
Transport Training Services, 16 Whitburn Drive, Bury, Lancashire, BL8 1EH Tel: 0161-764 3949 Fax: 0161-763 5690 E-mail: sales@transporttraining.co.uk *Forklift trucks operation trainers*
▶ Transport (U K) Ltd, Hydrauch Estate, St Andrews Rd, Avonmouth, Bristol, BS11 9HW Tel: 0117-982 9816 Fax: 0117-982 1243
▶ Transporter, Bexhill Road, Eastbourne, East Sussex, BN22 7JH Tel: (0781) 7332392 Fax: *Freelance courier, based in East Sussex, operating nationwide, personal 24/7 service*
Transportomatic, Tollgate Drive, Tollgate Industrial Estate, Stafford, ST16 3HS Tel: (01785) 258500
Transpower Drives Ltd, 4 Bridle Close, Finedon Road Industrial Estate, Wellingborough, Northamptonshire, NN8 4RN Tel: (01933) 441101 Fax: (01933) 443326 E-mail: sales@transpower.co.uk *Bearing distributors*
Transpower Engineering Ltd, 1 Lion Works, Palatine Street, Denton, Manchester, M34 3LY Tel: 0161-336 7111 Fax: 0161-336 5822 *Transformer manufrs*
▶ Transram Europe, 11 Kendal Road, Sompting, Lancing, West Sussex, BN15 9SF Tel: (01903) 754967 Fax: (01903) 754234 E-mail: transram@ntlworld.com *Crane assisted transport services*
Transtar, Glasgow, G52 4BL Tel: 0141-810 9644 Fax: 0141-810 8642 E-mail: sales@transtargear.co.uk *Fluorescent & discharge lighting control gear manufacturers & suppliers*
Transtar Metals Ltd, Transtar (Europe) House, 1 Meredews, Letchworth Garden City, Hertfordshire, SG6 1WH Tel: (01462) 687650 Fax: (01462) 684642 E-mail: sales@transtarmetals.com *Aerospace metals stockholders*
Transtec Computers Ltd, 39 North Bar Street, Banbury, Oxfordshire, OX16 0TH Tel: (01295) 756100 Fax: (01295) 276133 *Manufacture & sell computer hardware*
Transtec International, 39, Westbrook Trading Estate, Westbrook Road, Trafford Park, Manchester, M17 1AY Tel: 0161-772 1844 Fax: 0161-772 1845 E-mail: info@transtecinternational.com *Mechanical power transmission products distributors*
▶ Transtech Removals, Westinghouse Industrial Estate, Trafford Park, Manchester, M17 1DF Tel: 0161-877 5622 Fax: 0161-877 5623
Transtel Communications Ltd, Baileys House, Stoke Poges Lane, Slough, SL1 3PB Tel: (01753) 691869 Fax: (01753) 505639 E-mail: admin@transtel.com *Software development services*
Transterra Ltd, 2 Copperfields Orchard, Kemsing, Sevenoaks, Kent, TN15 6QH Tel: (01732) 761687 Fax: (01732) 761687 *Financial newsletter publishers*
Transtherm Ltd, 12 Banner Park, Wickmans Drive, Coventry, CV4 9XA Tel: (024) 7647 1120 Fax: (024) 7647 1125 E-mail: sales@transtherm.ltd.uk *Transtherm Cooling Industries specialises in the design & manufacture of air blast water coolers, dry air blast coolers, air blast box coolers, closed/open circuit cooling towers, pump stations, air to air plate/tubular heat exchangers, adiabatic coolers, air cooled steam condensers, refrigeration condensers & air heating & cooling coils. Rapid response to your needs is ensured by the computerised selection of products and this, together with the experience of our engineers, ensures that the optimum solution is provided for each application*
▶ Transversal Sheet Metal Co. Ltd, Maypole Fields, Halesowen, West Midlands, B63 2QB Tel: (01384) 411135 Fax: (01384) 413674
Transware Computer Services Ltd, 218 Eagle Tower, Montpellier Drive, Cheltenham, Gloucestershire, GL50 1TA Tel: (01242) 583583 Fax: (01242) 523258 E-mail: transware@btinternet.com *Software development warehouse industry*
▶ Transwave Converters, 30 Redfern Road, Tyseley, Birmingham, B11 2BH Tel: (0844) 7700272 Fax: (0844) 7700292 E-mail: transwave@powercapacitors.co.uk *Manufacturers of single-to-three-phase converters*
Trans-Web Ltd, Manchester Street, Oldham, OL9 6EF Tel: 0161 6270022 *Webbing lifting slings manufrs & distributors*
▶ Transworld Properties Ltd, 10 Eastern Avenue, Peterborough, PE1 4PJ Tel: (01733) 709807 Fax: (01733) 752548 E-mail: sales@overseas-properties.uk.com *Property consultants, overseas*
Transworld Publishers, 61-63 Uxbridge Road, London, W5 5SA Tel: (020) 8579 2652 Fax: (020) 8579 5479 E-mail: info@transworld-publishers.co.uk *Publishers*
▶ Transworld Transport Ltd, Pitt Street, Widnes, Cheshire, WA8 0TG Tel: 0151-423 6168 Fax: 0151-420 0902
Trant Construction Ltd, Rushington Business Park, Rushington Lane, Totton, Southampton, SO40 9LT Tel: (023) 8066 5544 Fax: (023) 8066 5500 E-mail: construction@trant.co.uk *Civil engineering construction & building*
▶ Tranter Ltd, Unit 50, Monckton Road Industrial Estate, Wakefield, West Yorkshire, WF2 7AL Tel: (01924) 298393 Fax: (01924) 291596 E-mail: sales@tranterphe.com Principal Export Areas: Worldwide *Heat exchangers*
Tranter Fire & Security Systems Ltd, 118 Bull Head Street, Wigston, Leicestershire, LE18 1PB Tel: 0116-288 8555 Fax: 0116-288 8855 *Install fire & security systems*
Tranters Ltd, Markeaton Printing Works, Payne Street, Derby, DE22 3AZ Tel: (01332) 341982 Fax: (01332) 292707 E-mail: trantersales@btconnect.com *Business forms manufrs*
Trantor Ltd, Green Hedges Bungalow, Pontadawe Road, Neath, West Glamorgan, SA10 7YL Tel: (01639) 633072 *Computer consultants*
▶ Trantsport Ltd, Units 1 & 2, Florida Close, Hot Lane Industrial Estate, Burslem, Stoke On Trent, ST6 2DJ Tel: (01782) 833388 Fax: (01782) 833389 E-mail: traffic@trantsport.co.uk *Transport & warehousing services*
▶ Tranzlink Storage District, 13 Canyon Road, Netherton Industrial Estate, Wishaw, Lanarkshire, ML2 0EG Tel: (01698) 377000 Fax: 08456 343223 E-mail: sales1@somethingsensible.com *Pallet distribution company throughout the UK, Ireland and Europe.*
Trapese Group, Millbrook House, 141 Milton Road, Weston-super-Mare, Avon, BS22 8AA Tel: (01934) 413547 Fax: (01934) 413418 E-mail: sales@soutencomputersystems.co.uk *Computer software consultants*
Trapex Hardware Ltd, Pindar Road, Hoddesdon, Hertfordshire, EN11 0DE Tel: (01992) 462150 Fax: (01992) 446736 E-mail: info@trapex.com *Architectural ironmongery manufs*
Trapp Forge, Trapp Lane, Simonstone, Burnley, Lancashire, BB12 7QW Tel: (01282) 771025 Fax: (01282) 779500 E-mail: trapp_forge@btconnect.com *Blacksmiths & fabricators manufrs*
Trase UK Ltd, 311 Gloucester Road, Cheltenham, Gloucestershire, GL51 7AR Tel: (01242) 690600 Fax: (01242) 528681 E-mail: sales@trase.co.uk *Computer repairers*
Trasfor Electric Ltd, Belwell House, 1A Belwell Lane, 4 Oaks, Sutton Coldfield, West Midlands, B74 4AA Tel: 0121-323 3339 Fax: 0121-323 3301 E-mail: andrew.jackson@trasfor.co.uk *Electric motor & gearbox distributors*
▶ Trattles & Rushforth Security Ltd, Faraday House, Sopwith Close, Preston Farm Industrial Estate, Stockton-on-Tees, Cleveland, TS18 3TT Tel: (01642) 604534 Fax: (01642) 677815 E-mail: ashleyday@trattles.com
Trauffler, Unit 1, 307 Merton Road, London, SW18 5JS Tel: (020) 7251 0240 Fax: (020) 8874 8627 E-mail: sales@trauffler.com *China & glass importers & wholesalers*
▶ Travail Employment Group Ltd, 7 St. Johns Hill, Shrewsbury, SY1 1JD Tel: (01743) 235532 Fax: (01743) 236327 E-mail: shrewsbury@travailshrewsbury.co.uk *Travail Employment Group - Recruitment of Temporary & Permanent Staff*Office, Commercial, Industrial, Skilled and Technical, Catering, Drivers, Executive, Hospitality, Sales and Retail.* **Travail Interim Appointments provide Interim Managers such as CEO"s, Managing Director,*Financial Director, General and Divisional Managers, and all levels of Directors, *Managers, Professionals and Engineers.* *We have offices in Aberystwyth, Mold, Chester, Newtown, Shrewsbury, Telford, The Wirral & Wrexham***
Travel Lines Ltd, 3 Church Street, Shoreham-By-Sea, West Sussex, BN43 5DQ Tel: (01273) 464662 Fax: (01273) 464693 E-mail: info@travel-lines.co.uk *Conference travel organisers*
Travel Management Systems Ltd, 33 Dee View Rd, Connah's Quay, Deeside, Clwyd, CH5 4AY Tel: (01244) 811777 E-mail: davidweigh@lineone.net *Computer consultants*
Travel Port, Galileo House Unit 10, Hurricane Way, Slough, SL3 8US Tel: (01753) 288000 Fax: (01753) 288001 E-mail: info@galileo.uk.com *Providers & distributors of software for travel agents*
Travel Trade, Ludgate House, 245 Blackfriars Road, London, SE1 9UY Tel: (020) 7921 8005 Fax: (020) 7921 8032 E-mail: enquiries@cmpinformation.com *Paper publishers*
▶ Travel Wright, 2 Masons Way, Barnoldswick, Lancashire, BB18 6DU Tel: (01282) 815111 Fax: (01282) 850044 E-mail: info@travelwright.co.uk *Airport transfer service*
▶ Travelbooker.org, 50 Mill Street, Kingston upon Thames, Surrey, KT1 2RF Tel: (020) 8546 0661 *Special low rates on holidays and flights. We particularly offer discounts on luxury hotels and caribbean cruises. We will also book your car hire and insurance. All your travel needs in one click.*
▶ The Travellers' Friend Limited, 3 Barttelot Court, Barttelot Road, Horsham, West Sussex, RH12 1AU Tel: 01403 255977 Fax: 01403 217919 E-mail: sales@travellersfriend.com *We are a fully accredited and successful business travel agency offering a comprehensive range of services and facilities and specialising in the SME market. We are obsessed with service and attention to detail and seek cost effective value for money travel solutions for commercial clients. Please call to see what we can do for you.*
Travellers Tales UK Ltd, Canute Court, Toft Road, Knutsford, Cheshire, WA16 0NL Tel: (01565) 757300 Fax: (01565) 757308 E-mail: emma@t-tales.com *Designers of computer games*
Travelling Light Birmingham, Squires Croft Business Centre, Sutton Coldfield, West Midlands, B76 2RY Tel: 0121-313 3598 Fax: 0121-313 0446 E-mail: sales@travellinglightbirmingham.co.uk *Lighting engineers*
Travelling Wire, Unit 3 Teknol House, Victoria Road, Burgess Hill, West Sussex, RH15 9LH Tel: (01444) 239920 Fax: (01444) 239920 E-mail: twire@btconnect.com *We are a precision engineering company specialising in E.D.M. Wire Erosion, C.N.C. Spark Erosion & E.D.M. Fast Drilling & Boring; Jig Grinding; Surface Grinding; Turning & C.A.D. Programming*
▶ TravellingPhotos.com, 1 Station Road, Lewes, East Sussex, BN7 2YY Tel: (07880) 730096
Travelocity Business Ltd, Edward House, Stockport, Cheshire, SK1 3DQ Tel: (0845) 7110011 Fax: 0161-968 9300 E-mail: hotels@first-option.co.uk *Hotel reservation services*
Travelon International Ltd, Unit 7 The Oxgate Centre, Oxgate Lane, London, NW2 7JA Tel: (020) 8450 2345 Fax: (020) 8450 4224 E-mail: office@travelon-international.co.uk *Luggage importers, agents & distributors* Also at: Manchester
Travelstock Packaging Ltd, 20 & 21 The Arches, South College St, Aberdeen, AB11 6JX Tel: (01224) 582657 Fax: (01224) 584303 E-mail: sales@travelstockpackaging.co.uk *Paper packaging merchants*
Travelstyle, 32 Chatley Street, Manchester, M3 1HX Tel: 0161-832 4865 Fax: 0161-832 6145 *Travel bag importer*
▶ Travhydro Ltd, R B R House, Hawksworth Road, Central Park, Telford, Shropshire, TF2 9TU Tel: (01952) 210163 Fax: (01952) 210157 *Storage manufrs*
Travik Chemicals Ltd, Grindon Way, Heighington Lane Business Park, Newton Aycliffe, County Durham, DL5 6SH Tel: (01325) 307000 Fax: (01325) 307070 E-mail: info@travik.co.uk *Chemicals manufrs*
Harry Travis (Rishworth) Ltd, New Market, Otley, West Yorkshire, LS21 3AE Tel: (01943) 462530 Fax: (01943) 462530 *Agricultural supplies & hardware*
Travis Perkins plc, Sydenham Wharf, Lower Bristol Road, Bath, BA2 3EE Tel: (01225) 446110 Fax: (01225) 442796 E-mail: bath@travisperkins.co.uk *Timber building materials suppliers*
Travis Perkins plc, The Quay, Fen Lane, Beccles, Suffolk, NR34 9BH Tel: (01502) 712421 Fax: (01502) 711110 *Builders & timber & plumbers merchants* Also at: Wreningham
Travis Perkins plc, 67 Shortmead Street, Biggleswade, Bedfordshire, SG18 0BD Tel: (01767) 313020 Fax: (01767) 601774 E-mail: biggswade@travisperkins.co.uk *Builders merchants*
Travis Perkins, 1 South Road, Hockley, Birmingham, B18 5LT Tel: 0121-554 3396 Fax: 0121-554 6811 *Builders plumbers & timber merchants*
Travis Perkins plc, Fairfield Street, Bradford, West Yorkshire, BD4 9QP Tel: (01274) 681065 Fax: (01274) 688843 *Builders merchants*
Travis Perkins plc, New Road, Stoke Gifford, Bristol, BS34 8QW Tel: 0117-969 5811 Fax: 0117-923 6284 *Builders merchants* Also at: Branches throughout the U.K.
Travis Perkins plc, Kelston Road, Bristol, BS10 5EP Tel: 0117-950 4700 Fax: 0117-950 4500 *Builders & plumbers merchants*
Travis Perkins plc, Havyat Road Trading Estate, Havyat Road, Wrington, Bristol, BS40 5PA Tel: (01934) 862439 Fax: (01934) 863617 *Builders merchants*
▶ Travis Perkins plc, Navigation Road, Chelmsford, CM2 6HX Tel: (01245) 490000 Fax: (01245) 359055 *Builder merchants*
Travis Perkins plc, Gloucester Road, Cheltenham, Gloucestershire, GL51 8TP Tel: (01242) 521477 Fax: (01242) 584437 *Building materials merchants service* Also at: Branches throughout the U.K.
Travis Perkins plc, Station Road, Chesterfield, Derbyshire, S41 9ET Tel: (01246) 450338 Fax: (01246) 453263 *Builders merchants*
Travis Perkins plc, Mayors Avenue, Dartmouth, Devon, TQ6 9NG Tel: (01803) 832216 Fax: (01803) 835694 *Building materials to the trade & retail customer*
▶ Travis Perkins plc, Sandown Road, Derby, DE24 8SR Tel: (01332) 361377 Fax: (01332) 381597 *Builders merchants*
Travis Perkins plc, Recreation Lane, Felixstowe, Suffolk, IP11 9DQ Tel: (01394) 278999 Fax: (01394) 273486 *Builders, plumbers & timber merchants*
Travis Perkins plc, 24-42 Palmerston Road, Harrow, Middlesex, HA3 7RR Tel: (020) 8861 1750 Fax: (020) 8861 3556 *Builder merchants*
Travis Perkins plc, Belle Vue Way, Hartlepool, Cleveland, TS25 1JZ Tel: (01429) 221133 Fax: (01429) 863357 E-mail: sales@travisperkings.co.uk *Builders merchants*
Travis Perkins plc, Thurman Street, Ilkeston, Derbyshire, DE7 4BY Tel: 0115-932 4278 Fax: 0115-944 1338 *Builders & plumbers merchants*
Travis Perkins plc, Shore St, Inverness, IV1 1NT Tel: (01463) 231171 Fax: (01463) 710315 *Builders merchants*
Travis Perkins plc, Long Leys Road, Lincoln, LN1 1DU Tel: (01522) 527113 Fax: (01522) 567905 *Building materials merchants* Also at: Horncastle & Market Rasen
Travis Perkins, 43 Spindus Road, Speke Hall Industrial Estate, Liverpool, L24 1YB Tel: 0151-486 1660 Fax: 0151-486 3031 *Builders & plumbers merchants* Also at: Manchester
Travis Perkins plc, Chamberlayne Road, London, NW10 3NB Tel: (020) 8964 9000 Fax: (020) 8969 0702 E-mail: enquiries@travisperkins.com *Builders merchants* Also at: London NW9 & NW10
Travis Perkins plc, 205 Balham High Road, London, SW17 7BQ Tel: (020) 8673 0181 Fax: (020) 8673 6818 *Builders' merchants*
Travis Perkins plc, 26 Sangley Road, London, SE6 2JN Tel: (020) 8698 1081 Fax: (020) 8461 1229 *Timber & builders merchants*
Travis Perkins plc, 61-63 Pimlico Road, London, SW1W 8NF Tel: (020) 7730 6622 Fax: (020) 7730 6012 *Builders merchants supplier* Also at: Branches throughout London & the South-East
Travis Perkins plc, Boyn Valley Road, Maidenhead, Berkshire, SL6 4EE Tel: (01628) 770577 Fax: (01628) 625919 *Timber & builders merchants service*
Travis Perkins plc, 7 Seph Way, York Road Industrial Park, Malton, North Yorkshire, YO17 6YF Tel: (01653) 692444 Fax: (01653) 600453 E-mail: malton@travisperkins.co.uk *Builders & plumbers merchants*
Travis Perkins plc, Bond Street, Malvern, Worcestershire, WR14 1TQ Tel: (01684) 568401 Fax: (01684) 892745 E-mail: malvern@travisperkins.co.uk *Builders & timber merchants*
Travis Perkins plc, Liverpool Road, Eccles, Manchester, M30 0UG Tel: 0161-789 2631 Fax: 0161-787 7579 E-mail: andycorrigan@travisperkins.co.uk *Timber & builders merchants* Also at: Branches throughout the UK
Travis Perkins plc, Lodge Way House, Lodge Way, Northampton, NN5 7UG Tel: (01604) 752424 Fax: (01604) 758718 E-mail: careers@contemporary.co.uk *Timber & builders merchants*
▶ Travis Perkins, Blackhouse Circle, Blackhouse Industrial Estate, Peterhead, Aberdeenshire, AB42 1BN Tel: (01779) 471500 Fax: (01779) 471237 E-mail: gavin.davidson@travisperkins.co.uk *Builders merchants*
Travis Perkins plc, Livsey Street, Rochdale, Lancashire, OL16 1SS Tel: (01706) 657325 Fax: (01706) 648026 E-mail: rochdale@travisperkins.co.uk *Builders merchants & ironmongers timber*
Travis Perkins plc, Lissadel Street, Salford, M6 6BR Tel: 0161-736 8751 Fax: 0161-737 9744 *Timber & builders merchants & tool hire services* Also at: Berry & Stockport

Travis Perkins plc, Greenland Works, Coleford Road, Sheffield, S9 5NN Tel: 0114-244 1081 Fax: 0114-243 5276 E-mail: david.lee@travisperkins.co.uk *Builders merchants*

Travis Perkins plc, Manchester Road, Whitehill Industrial Estate, Whitehall Industrial Estate, Stockport, Cheshire, SK4 1NY Tel: 0161-480 0881 Fax: 0161-477 3658 *Builders & plumbers merchants* Also at: Northampton

Travis Perkins plc, 45 Stourbridge Road, Stourbridge, West Midlands, DY9 7DG Tel: (01384) 422314 Fax: (01384) 422860 E-mail: stourbridge@travisperkins.co.uk *Building materials merchants*

Travis Perkins plc, Heathside House, Brighton Road, Tadworth, Surrey, KT20 6BE Tel: (01737) 362111 Fax: (01737) 370476 E-mail: burghheath@travisperkins.co.uk *Builders merchants*

Travis Perkins plc, 205 High Street, West Wickham, Kent, BR4 0LX Tel: (020) 8777 8326 Fax: (020) 8777 8567 E-mail: sean.patterson@travisperkins.co.uk *Builders merchants*

Travis Perkins plc, Pickerings Road, Halebank, Widnes, Cheshire, WA8 8XE Tel: 0151-424 1444 Fax: 0151-424 7770 E-mail: widnes@travisperkins.co.uk *Building material merchants* Also at: Liverpool

Travis Perkins Trading Co. Ltd, Rowlandson Street, Grimsby, North East Lincolnshire, DN31 3LL Tel: (01472) 345471 Fax: (01472) 242760 *Builders & plumbers merchants* Also at: Branches throughout the UK

Travis Perkins Trading Co. Ltd, Bluebridge Industrial Estate, 11 Second Avenue, Colchester Road, Halstead, Essex, CO9 2HA Tel: (01787) 477882 Fax: (01787) 473761 *Builders & timber merchants*

▶ Travisbead, 611 South Eighth Street, Milton Keynes, MK9 3DE Tel: (01908) 231401 E-mail: info@travisbead.com *Graphic design & web design*

▶ Travology Limited, Business and IT Consultants, High Bank, Old Forge Lane, Horney Common, Uckfield, East Sussex, TN22 3EL Tel: 0871 871 2662 E-mail: enquiries@travology.ltd.uk *Leading Independent Business & Technology Consultancy Specialising in Dynamic Packaging Solutions and Selling and Reservations Systems.**

Trawlpac Sea Foods Ltd, Craigshaw Place, West Tullos Industrial Estate, Aberdeen, AB12 3AH Tel: (01224) 871093 Fax: (01224) 872266 E-mail: trawlpac@aol.com *Fish processors*

Trax, Unit 1a Severn Farm Industrial Estate, Welshpool, Powys, SY21 7DF Tel: (01938) 554297 Fax: (01938) 554597 E-mail: sales@traxjh.com Principal Export Areas: Worldwide *Manufacturers of wheel balance weights*

Trax Circuits, Unit 15a Ellough Industrial Estate, Ellough, Beccles, Suffolk, NR34 7TD Tel: (01502) 711626 Fax: (01502) 711626 E-mail: traxcircuits@electronicrepairs.co.uk *Electronic engineers*

Trax Hydraulics North West Ltd, Unit 3, Langley Road, Burscough Industrial Estate, Burscough, Ormskirk, Lancashire, L40 8JR Tel: (01704) 892411 Fax: (01704) 896593 *Hydraulic engineers*

Trax Portable Access, Dukeries Industrial Estate, Claylands Avenue, Worksop, Nottinghamshire, S81 7DJ Tel: (0870) 240 2381

Trax UK Ltd, Suite 4B Christchurch House, Beaufort Court, Medway City Estate, Rochester, Kent, ME2 4FX Tel: (01634) 724724 Fax: (01634) 290524 E-mail: sales@trax-uk.co.uk *Software developers*

▶ Traxsys, Embankment Way, Ringwood, Hampshire, BH24 1EU Tel: (01425) 463100 Fax: (01425) 463111 E-mail: sales@penny-gilescp.co.uk *Manufacture of high quality trackball & computer input devices*

Traymaster Ltd, New Road, Catfield, Great Yarmouth, Norfolk, NR29 5BQ Tel: (01692) 582100 Fax: (01692) 582211 *Agricultural compost machinery manufrs*

▶ Tread Safe Southern, 2a Wyncombe Road, Bournemouth, BH5 2JU Tel: (01202) 426400 Fax: (0870) 9509288 *Matting & anti slip materials suppliers*

Treadfast Tyres Ltd, Dudley Road, Halesowen, West Midlands, B62 8EB Tel: 0121-550 2566 Fax: 0121-504 0858 *Tyre retailers*

▶ Treadstone Technology, Galleon House, 4-10 Guildford Road, Chertsey, Surrey, KT16 9BJ Tel: (01932) 567527 Fax: (01932) 570772 E-mail: info@treadstone.co.uk *Bespoke packaging supplier*

Treasko, Centurion House, 136-142 London Road, St. Albans, Hertfordshire, AL1 1PQ Tel: (01727) 837773 Fax: (01727) 836562 *Pine furniture manufrs & retailers*

Treasure & Son Ltd, Temeside, Ludlow, Shropshire, SY8 1JW Tel: (01584) 872161 Fax: (01584) 874876 E-mail: mail@treasure&son.co.uk *Conservation builders*

Treasures, 6 Brendon Road, Watchet, Somerset, TA23 0AU Tel: (01984) 634903 Fax: (01984) 634903 E-mail: laurence.welbourne@btopenworld.com *Computer software developers*

Treasures Of Woodchurch, 1-3 The Green, Woodchurch, Ashford, Kent, TN26 3PE Tel: (01233) 860249 *Antique pine furniture*

R.C. Treatt & Co. Ltd, Northern Way, Bury St. Edmunds, Suffolk, IP32 6NL Tel: (01284) 702500 Fax: (01284) 703809 E-mail: marketing@rctreatt.com *Distributors & agents of aromatic raw material & flavour manufrs*

▶ Treble M Colour Output, Production House, 205 Garnett Street, Bradford, West Yorkshire, BD3 9HA Tel: (01274) 393937 Fax: (01274) 393940

Treble Nine Signs, 8 Whittingham Road, Halesowen, West Midlands, B63 3TE Tel: 0121-550 1581 Fax: 0121-550 1581 E-mail: russ@treble-nine-signs.freeserve.co.uk *Sign manufrs*

▶ Treble R Fabrications, 42 Crossgate Road, Park Farm Industrial Estate, Redditch, Worcestershire, B98 7SN Tel: (01527) 510401 Fax: (01527) 503325 *Water defense systems manufrs*

Trebor Bassett, Brimington Road, Chesterfield, Derbyshire, S41 7UN Tel: 0114-250 3358 Fax: (01246) 233820 *Sweet manufrs*

Trebor Bassett Ltd, Monkhills Works, Ferrybridge Road, Pontefract, West Yorkshire, WF8 2JS Tel: (01977) 701431 Fax: (01977) 705491 *Sweet factory manufrs*

Trecarn Engineering, 1 Ivanhoe Industrial Estate, Tournament Way, Ashby-de-la-Zouch, Leicestershire, LE65 2UU Tel: (01530) 412802 Fax: (01530) 417515 *Hose clip & clamping product distributors*

▶ Tree Care Services Ltd, 29a Castle Mews, Salisbury, SP1 1TT Tel: (01722) 332250 Fax: (01722) 334947 E-mail: mailto@treecareservices.co.uk *Arboriculture, Site Clearance, Plant & Chipper Hire,*

▶ Tree Of Life Coaching, 15 Hillier Close, New Barnet, Barnet, Hertfordshire, EN5 1BD Tel: (020) 8440 4925 E-mail: david@treeoflifecoaching.co.uk *Tree of Life Coaching specialises in coaching people around career and business issues, and mentoring new and aspiring coaches. The website includes case studies, tools, tips and articles for site visitors on issues such as problem solving, goal setting, stress management and the work/life balance.*

Peter Tree Electrical Ltd, 79 Horley Road, Redhill, RH1 5AS Tel: (01737) 762168 Fax: (01737) 771435 E-mail: petertree@petertreeltd.co.uk *Electrical sub contractors*

▶ Tree Tops Forestry, The Old School House, Coniston Cold, Skipton, North Yorkshire, BD23 4EA Tel: (01756) 749626 Fax: (01756) 749626 E-mail: jonathan@treetopsforestry.fsbusiness.co.uk *Professional tree surgeons,*Tree Felling & Forestry contractors.*Established 1973*

Tree Tops Play Equipment, 78 London Road, Canterbury, Kent, CT2 8LS Tel: (01227) 761899 *Playground equipment manufrs*

▶ Treefellar Scotland, 6 Brodick Avenue, Kilwinning, Ayrshire, KA13 6RJ Tel: (01294) 554472 Fax: (01294) 542825 E-mail: admin@treefellar.co.uk *Tree care specialists services*

▶ Treehouse Furniture Ltd, 174 Penarth Road, Cardiff, CF11 6NL Tel: (029) 2023 0796 Fax: (029) 2023 0796 E-mail: ralph@intothewoods.co.uk *Wooden furniture manufrs*

▶ treehousebuilders.co.uk, 60 Court Leet, Coventry, CV3 2JR Tel: (07879) 224260 E-mail: chris@treehousebuilders.co.uk *Building tree houses, summer houses, garden furniture and play equipment, and other one-off pieces!*

▶ Treetop Design, Lisnaskea, Enniskillen, County Fermanagh, BT92 0FS Tel: (028) 6772 4285 Fax: (028) 6772 4285 *Cabinet manufrs*

▶ Treeway Fencing Ltd, 9 Cannock Wood Industrial Estate, Cannock Wood Street, Cannock, Staffordshire, WS12 0PL Tel: (01543) 425893 Fax: (01543) 423654 E-mail: sales@treeway.co.uk

Tre-Fad Engineering, Unit 3, Cwmbraw Industrial Estate, Ebbw Vale, Gwent, NP23 5AE Tel: (01495) 350077 *Steel fabricators & welders*

Trefoil Steel Co. Ltd, Rotherfield Works, Deadmans Hole Lane, Sheffield, S9 1QQ Tel: (01709) 830701 Fax: (01709) 830737 E-mail: sales@trefoilsteel.com *Stainless steel & iron casting manufrs*

Treforest Foundry Ltd, 16 Windsor Road, Pontypridd, Mid Glamorgan, CF37 1BY Tel: (01443) 402075 Fax: (01443) 486182 E-mail: enquiries@treforest-foundary.com *Iron castings manufrs*

Treforest Glass, Units 9 & 10, Upper Boat Industrial Park, Pontypridd, Mid Glamorgan, CF37 5BP Tel: (01443) 841313 Fax: (01443) 841221 E-mail: enquiries@treforestglass.co.uk *Emergency shop front glazing service*

Trefriw Woollen Mills Ltd, Trefriw, Gwynedd, LL27 0NQ Tel: (01492) 640462 Fax: (01492) 641821 E-mail: info@trefriw-woollen-mills.co.uk *Manufacturers of welsh tapestry*

Tregartha Dinnie, Chancery House, 199 Silbury Boulevard, Milton Keynes, MK9 1JL Tel: (01908) 306500 Fax: (01908) 306505 *Public relations & graphic design event management*

Tregawne, PO Box 48, Pershore, Worcestershire, WR10 3YE Tel: (01386) 861800 Fax: (01386) 861900 E-mail: sales@tregawne.freeserve.co.uk *Exclusive silver giftware manufrs*

Tregenza Richard, 72 Otley Road, Guiseley, Leeds, LS20 8BN Tel: 0113-270 2421 Fax: 0113-277 9868 E-mail: fasteners@tregenza.co.uk *Nut & bolt merchants*

Tregoning Ford, Tollgate, St. Breock, Wadebridge, Cornwall, PL27 7HT Tel: (01208) 893000 Fax: (01208) 815320 E-mail: sales@tregoningford.co.uk *New & used car sales*

▶ Tregrehan Garden, Tregrehan House, Par, Cornwall, PL24 2SJ Tel: (01726) 814389

Tregunna's Metal Finishing Services, Hatton Row, London, NW8 8PP Tel: (020) 7262 5678 Fax: (020) 7724 2354 E-mail: sales@hattanmetalcraft.co.uk *Chrome plating manufrs*

▶ Treibacher Schleifmittel UK, Claremont House, 12-14 Claremont Road, West Byfleet, Surrey, KT14 6DY Tel: (01932) 347499 Fax: (01932) 354081 *Abrasives products manufrs*

Trek Diagnostic Systems Ltd, Imberhorne Lane, East Grinstead, West Sussex, RH19 1QX Tel: (01342) 318777 Fax: (01342) 318666 E-mail: info@trekds.com *Microbiological manufacturers of medical diagnostic kits*

▶ Trek Highway Services Ltd, 7a Burrell Way, Thetford, Norfolk, IP24 3RW Tel: (01842) 821991 Fax: (01842) 821992

Trelawney Engineering, Old Yard Workshop, Vansittart, Windsor, Berkshire, SL4 1SE Tel: (01753) 850300 E-mail: info@trelawneyengineering.co.uk *Sheet metalwork engineers*

Trelawny SPT Ltd, 13 Highdown Road, Leamington Spa, Warwickshire, CV31 1XT Tel: (01926) 883781 Fax: (01926) 450352 E-mail: sales@trelawny.co.uk *Descaling equipment manufrs*

Trellborg Forsheda Pipe Seals, 4 Station Yard, Station Road, Bakewell, Derbyshire, DE45 1GE Tel: (01629) 813835 Fax: (01629) 814658 E-mail: jwest@forsheda.com *Pipe seals & technical support* Also at: Aldershot

Trelleborg Applied Technology, Halfpenny Lane, Knaresborough, North Yorkshire, HG5 0PP Tel: (01423) 862677 Fax: (01423) 868340 E-mail: sales@unitex.co.uk *Manufacturers of bespoke engineering components and custom mouldings, utilising high specification polyurethane (Vulkollan), designed for outstanding performance and abrasion resistance. Quality engineered polyurethane products including sheet, film, gaskets, scraper and squeegee blades for all industries*

Trelleborg Automotive (U K) Ltd, Holbrook Lane, Coventry, CV6 4QX Tel: (024) 7629 3300 Fax: (024) 7629 3390 E-mail: diane.whitworth@trelleborg.com *Rubber to metal bonded products*

Trelleborg Beadle, Unit 30 Bergen Way, Hull, HU7 0YQ Tel: (01482) 839119 Fax: (01482) 879418 E-mail: lesley.kidd@trelleborg.com Principal Export Areas: Worldwide *Protective products manufrs*

▶ Trelleborg Cealing Solutions (Rotherham), Bradmarsh Busines Park, Rotherham, South Yorkshire, S60 1BX Tel: (01709) 789800 Fax: (01709) 374819 E-mail: enquiries@orkotmarine.com *Industrial & marine bearing manufrs*

Trelleborg Cealing Solutions UK, Unit 6 Dyffryn Industrial Estate, Pool Road, Newtown, Powys, SY16 3RD Tel: (01686) 617000 Fax: (01686) 624875 *Mechanical seal manufrs*

Trelleborg Fillite Ltd, Goddard Road, Astmoor Industrial Estate, Runcorn, Cheshire, WA7 1QF Tel: (01928) 566661 Fax: (01928) 572380 E-mail: enquiries@fillite.com *Lightweight silicate filler manufrs*

Trelleborg Industrial Avs, 1 Hoods Close, Leicester, LE4 2BN Tel: 0116-267 0300 Fax: 0116-267 0301 E-mail: auto@trelleborg.com *Suspension components & anti-vibration mountings manufrs*

Trelleborg Sealing Solutions, 1 Cranbrook Way, Shirley, Solihull, West Midlands, B90 4GT Tel: 0121-744 1221 Fax: 0121-733 2442 E-mail: tssuk@trelleborg.com Principal Export Areas: Worldwide *Marketing for seal company*

Trelleborg Stanton Ltd, 853 London Road, Grays, Essex, RM20 3LG Tel: (01708) 685685 Fax: (01708) 685686 E-mail: sales@stanton-uk.com *Motor vehicle component manufrs*

Trelleborg Wheel Systems (UK) Ltd, Resolution Road, Flagstaff 42, Ashby-de-la-Zouch, Leicestershire, LE65 1DW Tel: (01530) 565656 Fax: (01530) 565630 E-mail: info.tws.uk@trelleborg.com *Agricultural Tyres*

Trelleborg Woodville, Hearthcote Road, Swadlincote, Derbyshire, DE11 9DX Tel: (01283) 222145 Fax: (01283) 222911 E-mail: john.blackham@trelleborg.com *Polymer & rubber product manufrs*

▶ Trellevorg Celing Solutions, Ashchurch, Tewkesbury, Gloucestershire, GL20 8JS Tel: (01684) 852211 Fax: (01684) 852210

Trellidor Ltd, Unit 20 Bloomfield Park, Bloomfield Road, Tipton, West Midlands, DY4 9AH Tel: 0121-557 0303 Fax: 0121-557 0353 E-mail: sales@trellidor.co.uk *Security company*

Trelowarren Pottery Ltd, Mawgan, Helston, Cornwall, TR12 6AF Tel: (01326) 221366 E-mail: trelowarren.pottery@virgin.net *Studio pottery retailers*

Trelrapak Cheese & Powder Systems Ltd, Coldharbour Business Park, Sherborne, Dorset, DT9 4JW Tel: (01935) 818800 Fax: (01935) 818818 *Design & manufacture process systems for cheese & dairy food*

Tremco Illbruck Production Ltd, 393 Edinburgh Avenue, Slough, SL1 4UF Tel: (01753) 691696 Fax: (01753) 822640 *Weatherproofing materials manufrs* Also at: Wigan

Tremelling Pattern Co., 3 Lisle Road, High Wycombe, Buckinghamshire, HP13 5SH Tel: (01494) 533897 Fax: (01494) 472777 *Engineering pattern makers*

Tremlett Ski Craft Ltd, Odhams Wharf, Topsham, Exeter, EX3 0PD Tel: (01392) 873680 Fax: (01392) 876277 *Ship builders*

▶ Tremorfa Ltd, 5 Cyprus House, Pascal Close, St. Mellons, Cardiff, CF3 0LW Tel: (029) 2033 0000 Fax: (029) 2033 0029 E-mail: enquiries@tremorfar.com

▶ Trench Ltd, Unit 5, C M T Industrial Estate, Broadwell Road, Oldbury, West Midlands, B69 4BQ Tel: 0121-544 7011 Fax: 0121-544 7721 *Manufacturing*

▶ Trench Less Installations Ltd, 15 York Street, Wolverhampton, WV1 3RN Tel: (01902) 689110 Fax: (01902) 653478 E-mail: underground@tiltd99.freeserve.co.uk *Specialist Horizontal Directional Drilling sub contractors providing a high quality No-Dig pipe, cable and duct installation service to utility companies and contractors nationwide.*

Trench Packaging Ltd, Unit C, New Farm, Froyle Lanw, South Warnborough, Hook, Hampshire, RG29 1SH Tel: (01256) 861333 Fax: (01256) 861334 E-mail: sales@trenchpack.co.uk *Packaging suppliers*

Trench UK Ltd, South Drive, Hebburn, Tyne & Wear, NE31 1UW Tel: 0191-483 4711 Fax: 0191-430 0633 E-mail: sales@trench-uk.com *High voltage insulators & transformers*

▶ Trenchco Ltd, 400 Edgware Road, London, NW2 6ND Tel: (020) 8208 3234 Fax: (020) 8450 9958 *Ground work contractors*

Trenchex Garden Machinery, Dove Fields Industrial Estate, Uttoxeter, Staffordshire, ST14 8ER Tel: (01889) 565155 Fax: (01889) 563140 E-mail: enquiries@trenchax.com *Garden machinery suppliers*

Trend Consulting Ltd, Swan Business Centre, Fishers Lane, London, W4 1RX Tel: (020) 8747 2400 Fax: (020) 8747 2401 E-mail: barrett@trend.co.uk *Computer consultants*

Trend Machinery & Cutting Tools Ltd, Unit 6, Odhams Trading Estate, Watford, WD24 7TR Tel: (01923) 249911 Fax: (01923) 236879 E-mail: stamperm@trendm.co.uk *Routing cutters & machine manufrs*

Trend Marine Products Ltd, Sutton Road, Catfield, Great Yarmouth, Norfolk, NR29 5BG Tel: (01692) 581307 Fax: (01692) 582993 E-mail: enquiry@trendmarine.com *Marine windows*

Trend Refrigeration Ltd, Holt Lane, Liverpool, L27 2YB Tel: 0151-487 9278 Fax: 0151-487 9254 *Refrigeration & air conditioning sales, installation & repairs*

Trend U K, Unit 75 Questor, Powder Mill Lane, Dartford, DA1 1JA Tel: (0870) 1218326 Fax: (0870) 1218328 *Computer consultants, maintenance solutions & recovery*

▶ Trendell Simpson Of Dundee Ltd, 3 Lintrathen Street, Dundee, DD3 8EF Tel: (01382) 825629 Fax: (01382) 832316

Trendell's Print Ltd, Critchmere Lane, Haslemere, Surrey, GU27 1PR Tel: (01428) 643269 Fax: (01428) 656057 E-mail: john@trendells.co.uk *Commercial printers*

▶ Trendgrey Construction Ltd, Coventry Bridge Meadow, Tomlow Road, Stockton, Southam, Warwickshire, CV47 8HX Tel: (01926) 814161

Trendpam Machinery Ltd, Unit 24, Barwell Business Park, Leatherhead Road, Chessington, Surrey, KT9 2NY Tel: (020) 8391 4411 Fax: (020) 8397 7811 *Plastics machinery & plant distribs*

Trendrail Ltd, Units 10 & 11, Brindley Road, Reginald Road Industrial Estate, St. Helens, Merseyside, WA9 4HY Tel: (01744) 851100 Fax: (01744) 851122 *Manufacturers of railway electrical equipment & light engineers*

Trends Furniture Centre, 499 London Road, Camberley, Surrey, GU15 3JE Tel: (01276) 22942 Fax: (01276) 675620 *Furniture retailers*

Trendsetter Home Furnishings Ltd, Brook Mill, Hollins Road, Oldham, OL8 4JY Tel: 0161-627 4458 Fax: 0161-627 0649 *Continental quilt & pillow manufrs*

Trent Aero Engineering Ltd, 9 Argosy Road, East Midland Int Airport, Castle Donington, Derby, DE74 2SA Tel: (01332) 812348 Fax: (01332) 812954 E-mail: sales@trentaero.co.uk *Aircraft sheet metalwork engineers*

▶ Trent Aluminium Systems, Unit K3 Prospect Close, Lowmoor Business Park, Kirkby-in-Ashfield, Nottingham, NG17 7LF Tel: (01623) 755666 Fax: (01623) 759222 E-mail: trentalu@btconnect.com *Aluminium shop fronts manufrs*

Trent Concrete Ltd, Private Road 3, Colwick Industrial Estate, Nottingham, NG4 2BG Tel: 0115-987 9747 Fax: 0115-987 9948 E-mail: admin@trentconcrete.co.uk *Architectural concrete cladding manufrs*

▶ Trent Instruments Ltd, Unit B, Brookside Road, Ruddington, Nottingham, NG11 6AT Tel: 0115-984 8244 Fax: 0115-945 6101 E-mail: sales@trentinstruments.co.uk *Supplier, pressure gauges & air horns, associate railway equipment*

Trent Joinery Manufacturing, Grassthorpe Road, Sutton-on-Trent, Newark, Nottinghamshire, NG23 6QX Tel: (01636) 822524 Fax: (01636) 822524 *Joinery manufrs*

Trent Pottery A Funiture Ltd, Regent Street, Narborough, Leicester, LE19 2DS Tel: 0116-286 4911 Fax: 0116-286 7286 E-mail: sales@pubfurnitureuk.co.uk *Trent Pottery, Leicester, is a well established business formed in 1960. They have a proven history in supplying contract quality furniture to the pub, bar, club, hotel and restaurant trade and have both the experience and range to offer you the very best selection of furniture for your individual needs. They offer a large assortment of pub chairs, hotel furniture, stools and tables for bar, cafe, restaurant and hotel including banquet, stacking and conference chairs.*

Trent Scales Ltd, Eagle Road, Ilkeston, Derbyshire, DE7 4RB Tel: 0115-944 1141 *Manufacturers of weigher/weighing sysystems including (batch), (electronic) & (industrial), also weigh/count (combined) machines. Service repair and calibration to ISO9002.*

Trent Shopfitters, Gateway House, Beechdale Road, Nottingham, NG8 3EZ Tel: 0115-942 5151 Fax: 0115-942 5656 *Shop fitters & joinery contractors*

Trent Trophies & Engraving, 63 George Street, Newcastle, Staffordshire, ST5 1JT Tel: (01782) 619828 Fax: (01782) 619828 *Engravers of trophies*

Trent Valley Bearings & Pneumatics Ltd, Transmission House, 1 South Street, Long Eaton, Nottingham, NG10 1ER Tel: 0115-973 2234 Fax: 0115-946 0817 E-mail: sales@trent-valley.co.uk *Bearing & power transmission distributors*

▶ Trent Valley Plumbing & Building Ltd, 113 Trent Boulevard, West Bridgford, Nottingham, NG2 5BN Tel: 0115-982 2332 Fax: 0115-982 0119

Trentex Engineering Ltd, Garner Street, Stoke-on-Trent, ST4 7AX Tel: (01782) 207171 Fax: (01782) 207272 E-mail: sales@trentex.co.uk *Precision machining & fabricators*

Trentgate Anglia Ltd, 35 Eastern Way, Bury St. Edmunds, Suffolk, IP32 7AB Tel: (01284) 753500 Fax: (01284) 706389 E-mail: sales@trentgate.co.uk *Lithographic platemakers*

Trentham Fencing & Contractors Ltd, 17-19 Church Lane, Stoke-on-Trent, ST4 4QB Tel: (01782) 644165 Fax: (01782) 644490 E-mail: sales@trenthamfencing.co.uk *Supply & erection of fencing & gates*

▶ Trenton Construction Co. Ltd, 2 Marychurch Road, Stoke-on-Trent, ST2 9BJ Tel: (01782) 264908 Fax: (01782) 205186

Trenton Millway Holdings Ltd, Marston Road, St Neots, St. Neots, Cambridgeshire, PE19 2HF Tel: (01480) 473693 Fax: (01480) 406225 E-mail: sales@trentonbox.co.uk *Printed carton manufrs*

▶ Trenton Technical Services Ltd, 6 Botley Road, Hedge End, Southampton, SO30 2HE Tel: (01489) 796243 Fax: (01489) 797503 E-mail: sales@trentontechnical.com *Trenton Technical Services offer a range of electronics test, repair and maintenance solutions to cater for all your requirements. From one-off 'ad-hoc' repairs to comprehensive electronics maintenance contracts, we can facilitate all manner of equipment repairs for clients, large and small, throughout the South of England.*

▶ Trentwood Timber Supplies Ltd, Victoria Street, Stoke-on-Trent, ST4 6HD Tel: (01782) 616407 Fax: (01782) 712565 E-mail: timber@trentwood.fsbusiness.co.uk *Suppliers of timber, pallets & ISPM15 compliant packing cases*

Trescher Fabrications Ltd, Ra1 & 2, Bermondsey Trading Estate, London, SE16 3LL Tel: (020) 7231 8692 Fax: (020) 7252 3303 E-mail: sales@trescherfabrications.co.uk *Fab & weld in steel, structural, fire escapes, staircase manufrs*

Tresises, Stanley Street, Burton-on-Trent, Staffordshire, DE14 1DY Tel: (01283) 568276 Fax: (01283) 511207 *Colour printing services*

Treske Ltd, Station Works, Thirsk, North Yorkshire, YO7 4NY Tel: (01845) 522770 Fax: (01845) 522692 E-mail: info@treske.co.uk *Furniture manufrs*

Trespaphan UK Ltd, Unit 608 Delta Business Park, Swindon, SN5 7XL Tel: (01793) 344000 Fax: (01793) 344001 *Polypropylene film manufrs*

Tressanda Printers, 362 Tamworth Road, Long Eaton, Nottingham, NG10 3AT Tel: 0115-973 2388 Fax: 0115-946 1148 E-mail: sales@tressanda.com *Trade printers*

Tressler Coachworks Ltd, Unit 44 Bell Lane, Bellbrook Industrial Estate, Uckfield, East Sussex, TN22 1QL Tel: (01825) 762262 Fax: (01825) 767446 *Car body repair services*

Trestan Finishers Ltd, Unit B, 26 Hazel Road, Southampton, SO19 7GA Tel: (023) 8043 3081 E-mail: info@trestanfinishers.co.uk *Stove enamelling powder coating services*

Treston Ltd, 5b Bone Lane, Newbury, Berkshire, RG14 5SH Tel: (01635) 521521 Fax: (01635) 37452 E-mail: salesuk@treston.com *Workbenches, mobile benches, trolleys, parts storage bins, parts storage cabinets and industrial office screens are just some of the products we manufacture for our range of industrial furniture and storage systems. These products are also available to ESD specification and in particular; ESD workbenches and ESD trolleys as well as ESD small parts storage systems are our area of expertise. Please learn more about our products on this site or feel free to contact us for further information.*

Treval Engineering Ltd, Crossways, Cray Avenue, Orpington, Kent, BR5 4AA Tel: (01689) 834301 Fax: (01689) 890660 E-mail: info@treval.co.uk *Steel fabricators*

Treves (U K) Ltd, Farnham Lane, Farnham, Knaresborough, North Yorkshire, HG5 9JR Tel: (01423) 798800 Fax: (01423) 798827 E-mail: enquiries@treves.co.uk *Car head rests manufrs*

▶ Treviscoe Builders Merchants, The Old Cooperage, Little Treviscoe, St. Austell, Cornwall, PL26 7QP Tel: (01726) 822388 Fax: (01726) 823383 E-mail: sales@treviscoe.com *An independant merchant located in the heart of Cornwall*

Trevon Industrial Finishers, Whitewalls Industrial Estate, Regent Street, Colne, Lancashire, BB8 8LJ Tel: (01282) 861786 Fax: (01282) 863829 *Powder coating & metal finishers*

Trevor Iles Ltd, Valley Mills, Valley Road, Bradford, West Yorkshire, BD1 4RU Tel: (01274) 728837 Fax: (01274) 734351 E-mail: sales@trevoriles.co.uk *Janitorial products suppliers*

Trevor James & Co., Worldwind House Ashmill Business Park, Ashford Road, Lenham, Maidstone, Kent, ME17 2GQ Tel: (01622) 859590 Fax: (01622) 859596 E-mail: sales@worldwind.co.uk *Musical instrument manufrs*

Trevor K Deakin, Unit 11 High Street Industrial Estate, Long Lane, High Street, St. Austell, Cornwall, PL26 7SU Tel: (01726) 824616 Fax: (01726) 822101 *Glass fibre moulders*

▶ Trevor Ward, 19 Tandragee Road, Newry, County Down, BT35 6QE Tel: (028) 3026 5613 Fax: (028) 3026 6610

Trevus Tools, Park View Works, Park Street, Stalybridge, Cheshire, SK15 2BT Tel: 0161-338 8398 Fax: 0161-338 8398 *Light engineers*

Trew Gates Ltd, Unit 4 Trefor Work Shops, Trefor, Caernarfon, Gwynedd, LL54 5LD Tel: (01286) 660418 Fax: (01286) 660687 E-mail: sales@trewgates.com *Gate manufrs*

Trewick Coachworks Ltd, Benton Square Indust Estate, Wesley Drive, Newcastle upon Tyne, NE12 9UN Tel: 0191-266 3581 Fax: 0191-270 0597 E-mail: repairs@trewicks.co.uk *Car repairers*

Treworrick Engineering Ltd, 22b Albert Drive, Burgess Hill, West Sussex, RH15 9TN Tel: (01444) 232513 Fax: (01444) 248565 E-mail: sales@treworrick.co.uk *Small & medium precision engineering services*

Treyone Woodcraft, Horningtops, Liskeard, Cornwall, PL14 3PX Tel: (01503) 240922 Fax: (01503) 240933 E-mail: enquiries@treyone.co.uk *Kitchen manufrs*

Tri Ard Stainless Fasteners Ltd, 1 Manor Industrial Estate, Pleck Road, Walsall, WS2 9XX Tel: (01922) 612230 Fax: (01922) 614044 *Industrial fastener distributors*

Tri Ark, Burnham Business Park, Springfield Road, Burnham-on-Crouch, Essex, CM0 8TE Tel: (01621) 781144 Fax: (01621) 781155 E-mail: sales@tri-ark.com *Air operated diaphragm pumps & spares distributors*

Tri Controls Systems Ltd, Colham Green House, Colham Green Road, Uxbridge, Middlesex, UB8 3QQ Tel: (01895) 257500 Fax: (01895) 256510

Tri Development Ltd, Loomer Road, Newcastle, Staffordshire, ST5 7LB Tel: (01782) 561526 Fax: (01782) 561584 E-mail: tridevltd@btconnect.com *Steel fabricators*

Tri Fen Engineering, Unit 28 Boston Industrial Estate, Power Station Road, Rugeley, Staffordshire, WS15 2HS Tel: (01889) 577871 Fax: (01889) 585093 *Manufacturers & suppliers security gates & fencing*

Tri Med Services Ltd, 1-2 Ossian Mews, London, N4 4DT Tel: (020) 8348 4666 Fax: (020) 8348 5666 E-mail: london@tri-med.com *Purchasing agents service*

▶ Tri Pac Logistics, 3 49-51 Nurseries Road, Baillieston, Glasgow, G69 6UL Tel: 0141-773 2942 Fax: 0141-773 2507 E-mail: enquiries@tripaclogistics.co.uk *Packaging material manufrs*

Tri Systems Ltd, 59 Mansell Street, London, E1 8AN Tel: (020) 7264 0440 Fax: (020) 7264 0450 E-mail: info@trisystems.co.uk *IT consultants*

TRI Technology Ltd, 15 Cowlairs, Southglade Business Park, Hucknall Road, Nottingham, NG5 9RA Tel: 0115-977 0707 Fax: 0115-977 0606 E-mail: enquiries@tritechnology.co.uk *Transformer manufacturers & pc reassembly*

Tri Wire Ltd, Good Hope Close, Normanton, West Yorkshire, WF6 1TR Tel: (01924) 223744 Fax: (01924) 220098 E-mail: sales@nexanstriwire.com *Copper wire manufrs*

Triac Air Conditioning Ltd, Shrubbery House, 47 Prospect Hill, Redditch, Worcestershire, B97 4BS Tel: (01527) 591199 Fax: (01527) 596284 *Air conditioning installation, service & design, chillers*

Triad Creative Marketing, Randolph House, 37-41 Longshut Lane West, Stockport, Cheshire, SK2 6RX Tel: 0161-480 2482 Fax: 0161-480 8926 E-mail: mail@triadcreative.com *Advertising & marketing consultants*

Triad Fabrications, Globe Works, Queensway, Rochdale, Lancashire, OL11 2QY Tel: (01706) 655099 Fax: (01706) 658712 E-mail: admin@triadfabs.com *Sheet metal workers*

Triad Group P.L.C., Weyside Park, Catteshall Lane, Godalming, Surrey, GU7 1XE Tel: (01483) 860222 Fax: (01483) 860198 E-mail: mail@triad.plc.uk *Computer software development services*

Triad Phoenix Engineering Ltd, Wigwam Lane, Hucknall, Nottingham, NG15 7TA Tel: 0115-963 4020 Fax: 0115-963 4020 *Engineering*

▶ Trialout Ltd, Unit 7 Cornwall Street, Parr Industrial Estate, St. Helens, Merseyside, WA9 1QT Tel: (01744) 616222 Fax: (01744) 616333

Trianco Heating Products Ltd, Thorncliffe, Chapeltown, Sheffield, S35 2PH Tel: 0114-257 2349 Fax: 0114-257 1419 E-mail: info@trianco.co.uk *Domestic boiler manufrs*

Triangle Development Services Ltd, 8 Cross & Pillory Lane, Alton, Hampshire, GU34 1HL Tel: (01420) 547500 Fax: (01420) 547501 *Software developers*

▶ Triangle Digital Support Ltd, 64a Market Place, Thirsk, North Yorkshire, YO7 1LW Tel: (01845) 527437 Fax: (0870) 7059860 E-mail: business@triangledigital.com *Computer board level manufrs*

Triangle Electronic Controls Ltd, Unit 3 Knowles Estate, Knowles Road, Clevedon, Avon, BS21 7XS Tel: (01275) 878770 Fax: (01275) 878771 *Electronic design & assembly*

Triangle Fire Protection Ltd, White Cliffs Business Park, Honeywood Road, Whitfield, Dover, Kent, CT16 3EH Tel: (01304) 828182 Fax: (01304) 829000 *Fire equipment services*

Triangular Business Systems, 1 Marlston Court, Rough Hill, Marlston-cum-Lache, Chester, CH4 9JT Tel: (01244) 683450 Fax: (01244) 674949 E-mail: enquiries@triangularsystems.co.uk *Computer consultants & networks*

Triarom Ltd, Triarom House, Birch Street, Windermere, Cumbria, LA23 1EG Tel: (01539) 444639 Fax: (01539) 448701 E-mail: sales@triarom.co.uk *Computer suppliers*

Tribal Asset Management Ltd, Unit E Gillette Close, Staffordshire Technology Park, Stafford, ST18 0LQ Tel: (0870) 0601040 Fax: (0870) 0607040 E-mail: info@tribalassetmanagement.co.uk *Computer software house*

Tribal Automation Ltd, 6 Lodge Forge Trading Estate, Cradley Road, Cradley Heath, West Midlands, B64 7RW Tel: (01384) 562563 Fax: (01384) 562563 *Vibratory bowl feeders*

▶ Tribal Education Ltd, St. Leonards House, St. Leonards Gate, Lancaster, LA1 1NN Tel: (01524) 384050 E-mail: info.education@tribalgroup.co.uk *Bespoke software suppliers*

▶ Tribeka, 134 The Harlequin, Watford, WD17 2UB Tel: (01923) 630259 *Computer software services*

Tribologic Ltd, C/O Mechanical Engineering Dept, The University Of Leeds, Woodhouse Lane, Leeds, LS2 9JT Tel: 0113-233 2159 Fax: 0113-343 2160 E-mail: info@tribologic.co.uk *Industrial engineering consultants*

Tribolube Ltd, Unit 4 Woodside, Thornwood, Epping, Essex, CM16 6LH Tel: (01992) 577551 Fax: (01992) 577553 *Lubricating systems distributors*

Tribune Business Systems Ltd, 30 City Road, London, EC1Y 2AY Tel: (020) 7870 0000 Fax: (020) 7870 0011 E-mail: info@tribune.co.uk *IT consultancy services*

Tribune Graphics Ltd, Unit 11 New Road Industrial Estate, Grace Road, Sheerness, Kent, ME12 1DB Tel: (01795) 580261 Fax: (01795) 663318 E-mail: mail@tribunegraphics.co.uk *Sign manufrs*

▶ Tricare Homes Ltd., Soothill Manor, 294 Soothill Lane, Batley, West Yorkshire, WF17 6EU Tel: (01924) 284201 Fax: (01924) 471297

R.E. Tricker Ltd, St. Michaels Road, Northampton, NN1 3JX Tel: (01604) 630595 Fax: (01604) 624978 E-mail: sales@trickers.com *Boot & shoe manufrs*

Trickey Of Ewell, Blenheim Road, Epsom, Surrey, KT19 9AH Tel: (01372) 747727 Fax: (01372) 729103 E-mail: online@trickeys.fsnet.co.uk *Wholesale stationery distributors*

▶ Tricks 4 Treats Pet Dog Training, 54 Goldfinch Road, Creekmoor, Poole, Dorset, BH17 7TD Tel: 01202 773581 Fax: 08702 860899 E-mail: jo@tricks4treats.co.uk *Pet Dog Training Classes held at the Creekmoor Community Centre.*Puppy Socialisation, Novice, Intermediate and One 2 One offered. Please call for further information, or visit our site.*

Trico Ltd, Skewfields, Pontypool, Gwent, NP4 0XZ Tel: (01495) 767700 Fax: (01495) 767877 E-mail: sales@tricoproducts.com *Motor accessories manufrs*

Trico Services Ltd, The Old Powder Mill, Powder Mill Lane, Dartford, DA1 1NT Tel: (01322) 276777 Fax: (01322) 276776 *Powder coaters & stove enamellers*

Trico VE Ltd, 76 Windmill Hill, Colley Gate, Halesowen, West Midlands, B63 2BZ Tel: (01384) 569555 Fax: (01384) 565777 E-mail: anjella@trico-ve.co.uk *Sign & panel manufrs*

Tricodent Ltd, 8 Teknol House, Victoria Road, Burgess Hill, West Sussex, RH15 9LH Tel: (01444) 247752 Fax: (01444) 239800 E-mail: tricodent@tricodent.com *Dental laboratory equipment*

▶ Tricogen Laboratories Ltd, Whitworth Avenue, Aycliffe Industrial Park, Newton Aycliffe, County Durham, DL5 6YN Tel: (01325) 300778 Fax: (01325) 301655

TricoInternational (Shipping) Ltd, Unit 4, Building C Woodgreen Business Centre, Clarendon Road, London, N22 6TP Tel: (020) 8888 8787 Fax: (020) 8889 5445 E-mail: trico@tricoshipping.com *International forwarding agents*

▶ Tricom, Unit 4, Turner Street, Dudley, West Midlands, DY1 1TX Tel: (01384) 456560 *Specialist fitting room call systems*

Tricom Telecom, 9 Thorne Way, Kirton, Boston, Lincolnshire, PE20 1JP Tel: (01205) 724889 Fax: (01205) 724852 E-mail: tricom.telecom@fsbdial.co.uk *Telecom equipment suppliers & installers*

Tricomed Surgical Ltd, 10 Tenterden Road, Croydon, CR0 6NN Tel: (020) 8656 1924 Fax: (020) 8656 7026 E-mail: tricomed@btconnect.com *Surgical instrument distributors, agents & maintenance*

Tricon Ltd, 60 High Craithall Road, Port Dundas, Glasgow, G4 9UD Tel: 0141-332 1551 Fax: 0141-332 8545 *Control systems distributors*

Tricon Freight Services, Shuttleworth Close, Great Yarmouth, Norfolk, NR31 0NQ Tel: (01493) 659311 Fax: (01493) 653657 E-mail: triconfrt@aol.com Principal Export Areas: Worldwide *Freight forwarding agents* Also at: Norwich

Tricore Ltd, Blackburn Industrial Estate, Kinellar, Aberdeen, AB21 0RX Tel: (01224) 790338 Fax: (01224) 790660 E-mail: info@tricore.co.uk *Rock bits sales & rentals services*

Tricorne Leather, 13 Bell Lane, London, NW4 2BP Tel: (020) 8203 6774 Fax: (020) 8203 6145 *Leather skin distributors*

Tricostar, 11 Limes Court, Conduit Lane, Hoddesdon, Hertfordshire, EN11 8EP Tel: (01992) 442800 Fax: (01992) 442810 E-mail: info@tricostar.com *Software distributors & designers*

Tricrest Precision Toolmakers Ltd, 7 Poplar Drive, Witton, Birmingham, B6 7AD Tel: 0121-331 4078 Fax: 0121-331 4073 E-mail: tricrest@wwwuk.net *Injection mould toolmakers*

Tridac Ltd, Elton House, Bushey Hall Road, Bushey, WD23 2HJ Tel: (01923) 242398 Fax: (01923) 250864 *Dental equipment manufrs*

Trident Alarms, 23 Hawksmoor Dr, Perton, Wolverhampton, WV6 7TL Tel: 01902 743494 Fax: 01902 688557 *Installation*

Trident Commercials, Hermitage Lane, Aylesford, Kent, ME20 7PX Tel: (01622) 720020 Fax: (01622) 720082 *Commercial vehicle repair & service*

▶ Trident Dental Laboratory, Rose Lane, Liverpool, L18 8AG Tel: 0151-724 4656 Fax: 0151-724 6855

Trident Engineering Consultants, Gatehouse Offices Babcock Park, Porterfield Road, Renfrew, PA4 8DJ Tel: 0141-561 2202 Fax: 0141-561 2259 E-mail: trident@trident-engineering-consultants.co.uk *Consulting engineers*

Trident Exhibitions Ltd, West Devon Business Park, Brook Lane, Tavistock, Devon, PL19 9DP Tel: (01822) 614671 Fax: (01822) 614818 E-mail: info@trident-exhibition.co.uk *Exhibition & conference organisers*

▶ Trident Fire Alarm Systems Ltd, Unit GM Wilsons Park, Monsall Road, Manchester, M40 8WN Tel: 0161-205 1661 Fax: 0161-205 1771 *Fire alarm systems installers*

Trident Fire Protection Company Ltd, Henfold Lane, Newdigate, Dorking, Surrey, RH5 5AF Tel: (01306) 886166 Fax: (01306) 631430 E-mail: cbta@arabact.co.uk *Fire protection equipment manufrs* Also at: Ashton-under-Lyne

Trident Group UK Ltd, 14-15 Yeldon Court, Finedon Road Industrial Estate, Wellingborough, Northamptonshire, NN8 4SS Tel: (01933) 228228 Fax: (01933) 229922 E-mail: sales@tridentgroupuk.com *Pneumatic fastening systems stapling & nailing*

Trident (Hull) Ltd, Unit H 330-338 Wincolmlee, Kingston Upon Hull, Hull, HU2 0QE Tel: (01482) 213134 Fax: (01482) 213272 E-mail: john@tridentltd.Karoo.co.uk *Engravers services*

Trident Interiors, 7 The Glade, Croydon, CR0 7QG Tel: (020) 8656 1207 Fax: (020) 8655 1992 E-mail: contacts@tridentinteriors.co.uk *Office refurbishes*

Trident Microsystems Ltd, Perrywood Business Park, Honeycrock Lane, Redhill, RH1 5JQ Tel: (01737) 780790 Fax: (01737) 771908 E-mail: sales@trident-uk.co.uk Principal Export Areas: Worldwide *Liquid crystal display panel distributors or agents*

Trident Recycling Ltd, Suite 4, 19 Marine Crescent, Kinning Park, Glasgow, G51 1HD Tel: 0141-420 3131 Fax: 0141-420 3166 E-mail: mail@trident-recycling.co.uk *recyclers,granulators and balers of commercial and industrial*plastic waste of all kinds in all forms including rigid plastic and film.*

Trident Sections Ltd, Unit 33 Dawley Trading Estate, Dawlings Lane, Kingswinford, West Midlands, DY6 7AP Tel: (01384) 401700 Fax: (01384) 292785 *Steel section manufrs*

▶ Trident Systems Consulting Ltd, 6-7, Hockley Hill, Birmingham, B18 5AA Tel: 0121-523 5333 Fax: 0121-523 2111

Trident Trailers Ltd, 27A Upper Fant Road, Maidstone, Kent, ME16 8BP Tel: (01622) 678811 Fax: (01622) 678262 E-mail: enquiries@trident-trailers.co.uk *Trailer suppliers & hire*

Trident Windows & Blinds, 193 South Farm Road, Worthing, West Sussex, BN14 7TW Tel: (01903) 202022 Fax: (01903) 200199 *Windows fabricating*

Tridonic Ltd, Thomas House Hampshire International Business Park, Crockford L, Chineham, Basingstoke, Hampshire, RG24 8LB Tel: (01256) 374300 Fax: (01256) 374200 E-mail: enquiries@uk.tridonic.co.uk *Lighting equipment distributors*

Trifab Steel Fabrication Co. Ltd, Unit 2 Lakeland Business Centre, Parish Lane, Pease Pottage, Crawley, West Sussex, RH10 5NY Tel: (01293) 511263 Fax: (01293) 512899 E-mail: a7bsl@aol.co.uk *Fabricators, sheet metal workers & welders service*

Trifast P.L.C., Trifast House, Bellbrook Park, Uckfield, East Sussex, TN22 1QW Tel: (01825) 769696 Fax: (01825) 767882 *Nuts & bolt manufrs*

Trifibre Containers International, Mill Road, Newbourne, Woodbridge, Suffolk, IP12 4NP Tel: (01473) 811865 Fax: (01473) 811873 E-mail: mukesh@trifibre.co.uk Purchasing Contact: R. Parker Sales Contact: R.C. Parker Principal Export Areas: Worldwide *Manufacturers of cases, instrument cases & transit containers*

▶ Trifix Electronic Service, Unit C33 Houghton Enterprise Centre, Lake Road, Houghton le Spring, Tyne & Wear, DH5 8BJ Tel: 0191-512 6715 Fax: 0191-512 6714 E-mail: trifix@farmore.net *Repair of industrial electronic equipment. Fanuc drives, Nachi servo amps, Robot teach pendants.*

Triflite Cases, 14 The Studio, Oldbury Business Centre, Cwmbran, Gwent, NP44 3JU Tel: (01633) 869142 Fax: (01633) 869155 E-mail: brad@triflite-cases.co.uk Purchasing Contact: M. Truman Sales Contact: D. Bisiker Principal Export Areas: Worldwide *Flight case manufrs*

Triform Moulds Ltd, Oakridge Road, High Wycombe, Buckinghamshire, HP11 2PF Tel: (01494) 445354 Fax: (01494) 448200 *Plastics moulding toolmakers*

▶ Trifusion Ltd, 105 The Broadway, London, NW7 3TG Tel: (020) 8959 6677 Fax: (020) 8959 9206

Trigon Snacks Ltd, Atherton Road, Liverpool, L9 7AQ Tel: 0151-523 8700 Fax: 0151-521 5370 E-mail: sales@trigon-snacks.com *Peanut products manufrs*

Trilectric Ltd, 262-270 Field End Road, Ruislip, Middlesex, HA4 9NB Tel: (020) 8866 1611 Fax: (020) 8866 1655 E-mail: mainreception@trilectric.co.uk *Electrical contractors services*

Trills, Enterprise House, 21 Sherwood Road, Bromsgrove, Worcestershire, B60 3DR Tel: (01527) 874920 Fax: (01527) 876857 E-mail: enquiries@trills.co.uk *Ceiling & partition contractors & internal refurbishment services*

▶ Trilo-Byte, 53 Cayley Promenade, Rhos on Sea, Colwyn Bay, Clwyd, LL28 4EP Tel: (07780) 713382 E-mail: info@trilo-byte.co.uk *Computer services*

Trilobyte Design Ltd, Mersa House, Haroldslea Drive, Horley, Surrey, RH6 9DT Tel: (01293) 774747 E-mail: info@trilobytedesigns.co.uk *Computer aided design (CAD) services*

Trilogy, 189 Castleblany Road, Keady, Armagh, BT60 3HY Tel: (028) 3753 0950 Fax: (028) 3753 0950 *Sign manufrs*

Trilogy Broadcast, 26 Focus Way, Walworth Industrial Estate, Andover, Hampshire, SP10 5NY Tel: (01264) 384000 Fax: (01264) 334806 E-mail: sales@trilogycomms.com *Television equipment manufrs*

Trilogy Publishing, Aries House, 43 Selkirk Street, Cheltenham, Gloucestershire, GL52 2HJ Tel: (01242) 222132 Fax: (01242) 235103 E-mail: sales@trilogypublishing.com *Software writers*

Trilogybrookes Printing, Ashbourne Way, Shirley, Solihull, West Midlands, B90 4QU Tel: 0121-745 9600 Fax: 0121-745 6200 E-mail: tkeatet@trilogymediagroup.com *Business print suppliers*

▶ Trim A Tree, Wharley Farm, College Road, Cranfield, Bedford, MK43 0AH Tel: (0800) 7831665 Fax: (0800) 7831665 E-mail: info@trimatree.co.uk *Tree surgery & garden services*

Trim Acoustics, Unit 38 Redburn Industrial Estate, Woodall Road, Enfield, Middlesex, EN3 4LE Tel: (020) 8443 0099 Fax: (020) 8443 1919 E-mail: sales@trimacoustics.co.uk *Acoustic treatment services*

▶ Trim Profiles Ltd, C Fleming Way, Coronation Road, Cressex Business Park, High Wycombe, Buckinghamshire, HP12 3TS Tel: (01494) 440352 Fax: (01494) 448933 *Laser profile cutting, general fabrication prototype work, mild steel*

▶ Trim Tech Trade Ltd, Avenue Industrial Estate, Southend Arterial Road, Harold Wood, Romford, RM3 0BY Tel: (01708) 378269 Fax: (01708) 707751

Trim Technology & Services Ltd, 9-14 Colliery Lane, Exhall, Coventry, CV7 9NW Tel: (024) 7664 6000 Fax: (024) 7664 6001 E-mail: sales@trim-technology.com *Soft trim products designers & manufrs*

Trim Tone Ltd, 8 Coastguard Way, Christchurch, Dorset, BH23 3NR Tel: (01202) 482514 E-mail: trimtone@onetel.net.uk *Electro-medical equipment & beauty equipment manufacturers*

▶ Trim Wizard, 3 Trelawne Drive, Cranleigh, Surrey, GU6 8BS Tel: (07748) 963904 E-mail: andy@trimwizard.co.uk *Smart repairs & auto electrical work, bumper scuffs, interior trim*

Trimat Ltd, Narrowboat Way, Hurst Business Pk, Brierley Hill, W. Midlands, DY5 1UF Tel: (01384) 473400 Fax: (01384) 261010 E-mail: sales@trimat.co.uk Principal Export Areas: Worldwide *A specialist manufacturer of industrial & marine brake linings supplying to the original equipment & replacement spares markets. Products include woven brake lining, industrial friction materials & clutch*

Trimate Fabrications, Unit 10 Mearclough Works, Walker Lane, Sowerby Bridge, West Yorkshire, HX6 2AR Tel: (01422) 834665 Fax: (01422) 834665 E-mail: trimate@totalise.co.uk *Steel fabricators*

▶ Trimerix Ltd, Unit 31 Lincoln Road, Cressex Business Park, High Wycombe, Buckinghamshire, HP12 3RL Tel: (01494) 447712 E-mail: info@trimerix.co.uk *Design & development consultancy*

▶ Trimet Engineering, 14 Tullylagan Road, Cookstown, County Tyrone, BT80 9AY Tel: (028) 8676 9937 Fax: (028) 8676 3484

Trimetals Ltd, Sunrise Business Park, Higher Shaftesbury Road, Blandford Forum, Dorset, DT11 8ST Tel: (01258) 459441 Fax: (01258) 480408 E-mail: trimetals@btconnect.com *Storage units*

Trimfix Mouldings Ltd, 11 Leigh Road, Ramsgate, Kent, CT12 5EU Tel: (01843) 585698 Fax: (01843) 594351 *Plastic injection moulding manufrs*

Trimite Ltd, Albert Road, St. Philips, Bristol, BS2 0YA Tel: 0117-971 6115 Fax: 0117-971 7090 *Manufacturing*

Trimite Ltd, 38 Welbeck Road, Glasgow, G53 7RG Tel: 0141-881 9595 Fax: 0141-881 9333 E-mail: glasgow.sales@trimite.com *Paint manufrs*

Trimite Ltd, Arundel Road, Uxbridge, Middlesex, UB8 2SD Tel: (01895) 251234 Fax: (01895) 256489 E-mail: info@trimite.com *Paints & powder coatings manufrs*

Trimline Valves Ltd, 6 Dales Park Drive Worsley Road, Swinton, Manchester, M27 0FP Tel: 0161-727 8128 Fax: 0161-727 9060 E-mail: harrycope@trimlinevalveslimited.co.uk *Valve distributors*

Trimplex, Mulberry Way, Belvedere, Kent, DA17 6AN Tel: (020) 8312 0400 Fax: (020) 8312 1400 E-mail: saftytread@btconnect.com *Constructional engineers services*

Trimplex Ltd, Darby Way, Narborough, Leicester, LE19 2GP Tel: 0116-286 6611 Fax: 0116-275 0216 E-mail: valplas@freeuk.com Principal Export Areas: Central/East Europe & West Europe *Manufacturers of plastic extrusions*

▶ Trimseal Mastiq Applicators, Eastcote, Brixham Road, Paignton, Devon, TQ4 7BD Tel: (01803) 524511 Fax: (01803) 524511 *Joint sealers*

Trimtex Clothing Co. Ltd, Unit 63 Ada Street Workshops, 8 Andrews Road, London, E8 4QN Tel: (020) 7254 8888 Fax: (020) 7254 8889 E-mail: pauljmay@onetel.com *Clothing wholesalers & manufrs*

Trinder Brothers, 3 Beaver Units, Quarry Lane Industrial Estate, Chichester, West Sussex, PO19 7NY Tel: (01243) 783504 Fax: (01243) 783504 *Car repairer & re spraying services*

▶ Trinem Consulting, 10 Montrose Terrace, Edinburgh, EH7 5DL Tel: 0131-652 8190 Fax: 0131-652 3512 E-mail: info@trinem.com *Advanced IT solutions, specialise in the delivery & implementations of configuration management systems*

▶ Tring Bathrooms, 4-6 Miswell Lane, Tring, Hertfordshire, HP23 4BX Tel: (01442) 827295 Fax: (01442) 824148

Tring Metal Polishing, Unit 13 Brook Street, Tring, Hertfordshire, HP23 5EF Tel: (01442) 824151 *Metal polishing services*

Trinity Aerospace Engineering Ltd, Bilton Road, Kingsland Industrial Park, Basingstoke, Hampshire, RG24 8LJ Tel: (01256) 840276 Fax: (01256) 840278 E-mail: sales@trinityaero.co.uk *Aircraft maintenance & component manufrs*

▶ Trinity Construction Services, Old Barn, Mountnessing Road, Blackmore, Ingatestone, Essex, CM4 0NX Tel: (01277) 822600 Fax: (01277) 822900 E-mail: sales@style2000.co.uk

Trinity Controls Ltd, 41 Eton Wick Road, Eton Wick, Windsor, Berkshire, SL4 6LU Tel: (01753) 840022 Fax: (01753) 832808 *Control panels*

▶ Trinity Electrical Services Ltd, St Johns House, Clyde Street, Bingley, West Yorkshire, BD16 4LD Tel: (01274) 551161

Trinity Engineering Northampton Ltd, 15 Horsley Road, Northampton, NN2 6LJ Tel: (01604) 719803 Fax: (01604) 716670 E-mail: alan@trinityengnorth.co.uk *Sheet metal fabricators & engineers*

Trinity Expert Systems, 1 The Oaks, Westwood Way, Westwood Business Park, Coventry, CV4 8JB Tel: (024) 7642 0100 Fax: (024) 7642 0111 E-mail: info@tesl.com *IT solution consultants services*

Trinity Fire Ltd, Unit 8 Caburn Enterprise Park, The Broyle, Ringmer, Lewes, East Sussex, BN8 5NP Tel: (01273) 812208 Fax: (01273) 813259 *Fire extinguisher sales & services*

Trinity Fish Products Ltd, 4 Trinity Street, Grimsby, North East Lincolnshire, DN31 3AN Tel: (01472) 354963 Fax: (01472) 361320 E-mail: trinityfp@hotmail.com *Fish processors*

Trinity Graphic Ltd, Hawthorn Avenue, Hull, HU3 5JD Tel: (01482) 227431 Fax: (01482) 223152 E-mail: trinityg@globalnet.co.uk *Process engravers*

▶ Trinity Joinery, La Rue De La Hougette, St. Clement, Jersey, JE2 6LD Tel: (01534) 853567 Fax: (01534) 857191 *Custom made joinery services*

Trinity Mirror P.L.C., 6 Heritage Court, Lower Bridge Street, Chester, CH1 1RD Tel: (01244) 861500 Fax: (01244) 861560 *Printers*

▶ Trinity Protection Systems Ltd, Old Mill House, Oil Mill Lane, Clyst St. Mary, Exeter, EX5 1AG Tel: (01392) 874455 Fax: (01392) 875546 E-mail: info@trinityprotection.co.uk *Fire & security systems supply & service*

Trinity Publication Ltd, 1ST Floor Edward House, Edward Street, Birmingham, B1 2RA Tel: 0121-233 8712 Fax: 0121-233 8715 E-mail: techsupport@micromart.co.uk *Computer sales publications*

▶ Trinity Sales & Marketing Ltd, Harwell Innovation Centre, 173 Curie Avenue, Harwell Intnl Business Centre, Didcot, Oxfordshire, OX11 0QG Tel: (01235) 838590 Fax: (01235) 838591 E-mail: info@trinitysalesandmarketing.co.uk *Suppliers of engine parts*

Trinity Wholefoods, 3 Trinity Street, Hastings, East Sussex, TN34 1HG Tel: (01424) 430473 E-mail: trintywholesales@phonecoop.coop *Organic products retailers*

Trinkle Irrigation Watering Systems, Reeves Hall, Coombe Lane, Bovey Tracey, Newton Abbot, Devon, TQ13 9PH Tel: (01626) 832977 Fax: (01626) 835369 *Garden irrigation system suppliers*

Trintools Ltd, 6 Cranford Way, Smethwick, West Midlands, B66 2RU Tel: 0121-558 0886 Fax: 0121-558 2986 E-mail: sales@trintools.co.uk *Die toolmaker specialists*

Trio, Treetops House, Gillotts Lane, Henley-On-Thames, Oxfordshire, RG9 1PT Tel: (01491) 579118 Fax: (01491) 412211 *Servo electric motor controller manufrs*

Trio Hire Direct Ltd, 1 Summerson Court, Summerson Road, Bleak Hall, Milton Keynes, MK6 1LE Tel: (01908) 222700 Fax: (01908) 222842 E-mail: info@trio-waste.co.uk *Commercial vehicle sales & hire service*

Trio Jewellery, 197 Warstone Lane, Birmingham, B18 6JR Tel: 0121-200 1367 Fax: 0121-212 0982 *Jewellery manufrs*

Trio Motion Technology Ltd, Shannon Way, Tewkesbury, Gloucestershire, GL20 8ND Tel: (01684) 292333 Fax: (01684) 297929 E-mail: sales@triomotion.com *Automatic control equipment manufrs*

▶ Trio Packaging Ltd, Unit 8 Station Road, Ampthill, Bedford, MK45 2QP Tel: (01525) 841313 Fax: (01525) 841515

▶ Trio Scaffoldings, 400 Edgware Road, London, NW2 6ND Tel: (020) 8452 3337 Fax: (020) 8208 0621

Trio Skips & Hooks Ltd, Ashville Road, Gloucester, GL2 5DA Tel: (01452) 331022 Fax: (01452) 331566 E-mail: info@trio-waste.co.uk *Manufacturers of container handling equipment*

Trio Systems, 14 Hampton Road, Twickenham, TW2 5QB Tel: (020) 8893 4455 Fax: (020) 8893 4456 E-mail: sales@triosystems.co.uk *Office suppliers*

Trio Tools Rainham Ltd, New Road, Rainham, Essex, RM13 8HA Tel: (01708) 555111 Fax: (01708) 555114 E-mail: sales@triotools.fsbusiness.co.uk *Tungsten carbide tool manufrs*

Triogen Ltd, Triogen House, 117 Barfillan Drive, Glasgow, G52 1BD Tel: 0141-810 4861 Fax: 0141-810 5561 E-mail: sales@triogen.com *Manufacturers of ozone generators, ultra-violet systems*

Trios Ironing Laundry Services, Rear of, 87 Shakespeare Drive, Westcliff-on-Sea, Essex, SS0 9AA Tel: (01702) 351418 *Ironing & clothing repairers*

Tripack, Beels Road, Stallingborough, Grimsby, South Humberside, DN41 8DN Tel: (01469) 577075 Fax: (01469) 577076 *Wire tie importers*

Tri-Pack Plastics Ltd, Estate Road No. 1, South Humberside Industrial Estate, Grimsby, South Humberside, DN31 2TB Tel: (01472) 355038 Fax: (01472) 266930 E-mail: mail@tri-pack.co.uk *Manufacturers of corrugated plastic containers*

Tripenta Ltd, Unit 8, Willersey Industrial Park, Broadway, Worcestershire, WR12 7RR Tel: (01386) 858398 Fax: (01386) 858743 E-mail: tripenta@aol.com *Plastics materials suppliers*

Triplar Ltd, Baron Avenue, Earls Barton, Northampton, NN6 0JE Tel: (01604) 812999 Fax: (01604) 812992 E-mail: office@triplar.co.uk *Shopfitters*

Tri-Plas Mouldings Ltd, Unit 1, 3 & 7 Bilton Industrial Estate, Stockmans Close, Birmingham, B38 9TS Tel: 0121-459 0292 Fax: 0121-459 2141 *Plastic injection mouldings manufrs*

▶ Triple A Lift Refurbishments, 4 Athlone Road, Warrington, WA2 8JJ Tel: (01925) 232090 *Elevators refurbishers*

Triple Crown CHS, 43 High Street, Middleton Cheney, Banbury, Oxfordshire, OX17 2NX Tel: (01295) 712269 Fax: (01295) 713191 *Cleaning materials supplies*

Triple Engineering Yorkshire Ltd, Unit 7 Humberside Way, Barnsley, South Yorkshire, S71 3RN Tel: (01226) 770058 Fax: (01226) 731246 *Engineering manufrs*

Triple S Fabrications Ltd, Brooklands Business Centre, Taylor Lane, Loscoe, Heanor, Derbyshire, DE75 7TA Tel: (01773) 763246 Fax: (01773) 763246 E-mail: triplesfabsltd@aol.com *Experts in all types of steel fabrications in any individual requirement or design - staircases, smoke shelter, smoking, balustrades, workstations, ducting, fire escapes, railing, gates, machining*We also supply an on site mobile maintenance service to any location. memorial bench*

▶ Triple S Municipal, 4 Orchard Way, Haywards Heath, West Sussex, RH16 1UX Tel: (01444) 457211 *Used road Sweepers, Sales and Spares from Triple S Municipal. Support for Johnston, Elgin, Madvac and Scarab machines. Good quality machines always in stock, along with a full range of Johnston sweeper spares.*

▶ Triple S Recruitment Ltd, Heath Business Technical Park, Runcorn, Cheshire, WA7 4QX Tel: (01928) 576925 E-mail: info@boxpeople.co.uk *Recruitment and HR Consultancy providing help and assistance to successful businesses in the Widnes and Runcorn area to source new permanent only employees.*

Triple T Engineering Ltd, Hackworth Industrial Park, Shildon, County Durham, DL4 1HF Tel: (01388) 774444 Fax: (01388) 774444 E-mail: sales@triple-t-eng.co.uk *Sub contract mechanical engineering services*

Triple X Components Machining Ltd, Masons Road, Stratford-upon-Avon, Warwickshire, CV37 9NF Tel: (01789) 200400 Fax: (01789) 414063 E-mail: machining@triplexcm.com *Precision machinist services & precision engineers* Also at: Hereford

Triplefast International Ltd, Unit 13 Monmer Close Industrial Estate, Willenhall, West Midlands, WV13 1JR Tel: (01902) 636399 Fax: (01902) 609880 E-mail: sales@triplefast.co.uk *Manufacturers, stockist and suppliers of high integrity, fully traceable threaded fasteners for the power generation and heavy engineering industries*

TripleTrack Business Systems Ltd, 25 Market Place, Warminster, Wiltshire, BA12 9BB Tel: (01985) 214260 Fax: (01985) 215806 E-mail: enquiries@tbs-net.com *Training*

Tripoint Ltd, 1090 Guillat Avenue, Kent Science Park, Sittingbourne, Kent, ME9 8GU Tel: (01795) 434000 Fax: (01795) 434001 E-mail: admin@tripoint.co.uk *Computer software developers*

▶ Tripos Consultants, 44 Brown Lane, Barton-in-Fabis, Nottingham, NG11 0AD Tel: 0115-983 1127 Fax: 0115-983 0987 E-mail: info@triposconsultants.co.uk *Tripos is a provider of bespoke management and commercial skills training for a wide range of organisations. The consultants also advise on the design and introduction of performance management /appraisal processes.*

Tripos Tools Ltd, Upper Interfields, Malvern, Worcestershire, WR14 1UT Tel: (01886) 833377 Fax: (01886) 833579 *Precision engineers services*

Tripp Batt & Co. Ltd, Hepworth Road, Stanton, Bury St. Edmunds, Suffolk, IP31 2BT Tel: (01359) 250268 Fax: (01359) 251603 *Agriculture engineers*

Tripp's Trophies, 49 Long Row, Felinfoel, Llanelli, Dyfed, SA15 4LW Tel: (01554) 772995 Fax: (01554) 772995 E-mail: trippstrophies@btopenworld.com *Sport trophies, glass ware & engraving services*

▶ Tripstamp Ltd, 56 Pound Farm Road, Chichester, West Sussex, PO19 7PU Tel: (01243) 538912 Fax: (01243) 538910

Trireme Object Technology International Ltd, Regents House, Heaton Lane, Stockport, Cheshire, SK4 1BS Tel: 0161-225 3240 E-mail: clive@trireme.com *Computer software training*

Trisoft Ltd, Accent Park, Bakewell Road, Orton Southgate, Peterborough, PE2 6XS Tel: (01733) 372700 Fax: (01733) 372729 *Software developers*

Trisport Ltd, 38 Amber Close, Tamworth Business Park, Amington, Tamworth, Staffordshire, B77 4RP Tel: (01827) 56544 Fax: (01827) 53181 E-mail: salesinfo@trisportgolf.com Principal Export Areas: Worldwide *Injection moulding spikes & tees*

Trist Draper Hydraulics, Unit 6f Redbrook Business Park, Wilthorpe Road, Barnsley, South Yorkshire, S75 1JN Tel: (01226) 281140 Fax: (01226) 243223 E-mail: sales@tristdraper.co.uk *Hydraulic hose & fittings distributors*

Trist Draper Hydraulics, Unit 16, Merdock Road, Manton Lane Industrial Estate, Bedford, MK41 7PD Tel: (01234) 212661 Fax: (01234) 270421 E-mail: sales.bedford@trysisdraper.com *Hydraulic hose & fittings distributors* Also at: Aylesbury, Barnsley & Newcastle upon Tyne

Tristar Machinery & Plant Ltd, Londonderry Works, George Street Industrial Estate, Seaham, County Durham, SR7 7SL Tel: 0191-581 3244 Fax: 0191-581 0273 *Used machine tools & equipment*

Tristar (UK) Ltd, 229-231 Dunstable Road, Luton, LU4 8BN Tel: (01582) 652525 Fax: (01582) 402789 E-mail: hic10@hotmail.com *Black refuse sack manufacturers & importers*

Tri-State Electronics, Unit 4, Bumpers Enterprise Centre, Bumpers Farm Industrial Estate, Chippenham, Wiltshire, SN14 6QA Tel: (01249) 464650 Fax: (01249) 445414 E-mail: mikenickless@msn.com *Sub-contract electronic services*

Tristian Ltd, 11 Hastings Rd, Croydon, CR0 6PH Tel: (020) 8655 3373 Fax: (020) 8655 3336 *Joinery*

Tri-Stor Products Ltd, 23 Weetwood Drive, Sheffield, S11 9QL Tel: 0114-236 3052 Fax: 0114-236 4429 E-mail: pdconstantine@aol.com *Storage systems & mezzanine flooring manufrs*

Tritan Engineering Ltd, Bondgate, Green Lane, Ripon, North Yorkshire, HG4 1QQ Tel: (01765) 601608 Fax: (01765) 606800 *Engineering*

Tritec Systems Ltd, Riverview House, London Road, Old Basing, Basingstoke, Hampshire, RG24 7JL Tel: (01256) 477778 Fax: (01256) 477776 E-mail: sales@tritec.co.uk *Control systems software company*

Tritech Alkast, Castle Park Road, Whiddon Valley Industrial Esta, Barnstaple, Devon, EX32 8PA Tel: (01271) 376521 Fax: (01271) 326155 E-mail: *Aluminium investment & lost wax casting manufrs*

Tritech Computer Services Ltd, Forge House, Mill Road, Liss, Hampshire, GU33 7DX Tel: (01730) 893789 Fax: (01730) 894589 E-mail: sales@tritech.org.uk *Lease administration software*

Tritech International Ltd, Peregrine Road, Westhill Business Park, Westhill, Aberdeenshire, AB32 6JL Tel: (01224) 744111 Fax: (01224) 741771 E-mail: sales@tritech.co.uk *Sub-sea systems & sonar manufrs*

Tritech Precision Products Ltd, Bridge Road North, Wrexham Industrial Estate, Wrexham, Clwyd, LL13 9PS Tel: (01978) 661111 Fax: (01978) 661392 E-mail: info@tritech-precision-products.co.uk Principal Export Areas: Worldwide *Casting manufrs*

Tritech Security & Electrical Services, 22 Muriel Street, Barrhead, Glasgow, G78 1QB Tel: 0141-881 1100 Fax: 0141-881 4449

Tritel Ltd, Unit 1 Bolney Grange Business Park, Hickstead, Haywards Heath, West Sussex, RH17 5PB Tel: (01444) 871188 Fax: (01444) 871199 E-mail: sales@tritel.co.uk *Suppliers & stockists of all kinds of tapes; specialising in adhesive*

Triten International Ltd, Shawfield Road, Barnsley, South Yorkshire, S71 3HS Tel: (01226) 702300 Fax: (01226) 702311 E-mail: triten@triten.co.uk *Wear resistant materials manufrs*

Triton plc, Shepperton Business Park, Caldwell Road, Nuneaton, Warwickshire, CV11 4NR Tel: (024) 7634 4441 Fax: (024) 7634 9828 E-mail: reception@triton.plc.uk *Bathroom fittings & accessories, shower units manufrs*

Triton Boat Fitters, Eliza Ann Street, Eccles, Manchester, M30 0GL Tel: 0161-787 9200 Fax: 0161-787 8225 E-mail: sales@tritonboatfitters.co.uk *Bolt factory fitters*

Triton Chemical Manufacturing Co. Ltd, Unit 5 Lyndean Industrial Estate, 129 Felixstowe Road, London, SE2 9SG Tel: (020) 8310 3929 Fax: (020) 8312 0349 E-mail: info@triton-chemicals.com *Damp proof chemical manufrs*

Triton Controls Ltd, 2 Randolph Industrial Estate, Evenwood, Bishop Auckland, County Durham, DL14 9SJ Tel: (01388) 833000 Fax: (01388) 833680 E-mail: info@tritoncontrols.co.uk *Electronic & electrical equipment services*

Triton Electronics Ltd, Bigods Hall, Bigods Lane, Dunmow, Essex, CM6 3BE Tel: (01371) 872812 Fax: (01371) 876065 E-mail: sales@tritonel.com *Design, manufacturers electronic, mechanical instruments*

▶ Triton Tooling, Unit 11 Harmill Industrial Estate, Grovebury Road, Leighton Buzzard, Bedfordshire, LU7 4FF Tel: (01525) 376007 Fax: (01525) 372007 *Friction stair welding tools manufrs*

▶ Triton Workshop Systems, Pontygwindy Industrial Estate, Caerphilly, Mid Glamorgan, CF83 3HU Tel: (02920) 888815

Tritools, 15 Albert Road, Aldershot, Hampshire, GU11 1SZ Tel: (01252) 310429 Fax: (01252) 324428 *Press tool manufacturers & pressings, general presswork*

▶ Trity Protection Systems, Unit C15B Holly Farm Business Park, Honiley, Kenilworth, Warwickshire, CV8 1NP Tel: (01926) 485080 Fax: (01926) 485090 *Commercial fire alarm system manufrs*

Triumph International Ltd, Arkwright Road, Groundwell Industrial Estate, Swindon, SN25 5BE Tel: (01793) 722200 Fax: (01793) 728341 *Women's & men's underwear & leisurewear distributors*

Triumph Needle Co. Ltd, 14 Albion Street, Wigston, Leicestershire, LE18 4SA Tel: 0116-222 9222 Fax: 0116-222 9220 E-mail: triumphneedle@btclick.com *Sewing machine parts manufrs*

Triumph Precision Engineering, Unit 29 The Acorn Centre, Barry Street, Oldham, OL1 3NE Tel: 0161-626 0550 *Precision engineers*

Triumph Technologies, Unit A, Station Yard, Thame, Oxfordshire, OX9 3UH Tel: (01844) 261666 Fax: (01844) 261666 E-mail: technical@triumphtech.co.uk *Computer consultants*

Triune Precision Engineering Co. Ltd, Spring Lane, Malvern, Worcestershire, WR14 1AJ Tel: (01684) 573331 Fax: (01684) 893201 *Pressure, gravity & investment die manufrs*

Triwarm Ltd, Unit E, Hamstead Industrial Estate, Austin Way, Great Barr, Birmingham, B42 1DU Tel: 0121-525 0500 Fax: 0121-525 6800 E-mail: sales@tri-warm.co.uk *Toughened glass & sealed unit manufrs*

Triwonder Signs, Unit 4, Tannery Road, Tonbridge, Kent, TN9 1RF Tel: (01732) 770444 Fax: (01732) 363888 *Sign manufrs*

▶ Triyoga UK Ltd, 6 Erskine Road, London, NW3 3AJ Tel: (020) 7483 3344 Fax: (020) 7483 3346 E-mail: info@triyoga.co.uk

TRM Packaging Ltd, Red Cat Lane, Burscough, Ormskirk, Lancashire, L40 0SY Tel: (01704) 892811 Fax: (01704) 895546 E-mail: sales@trmpack.co.uk *Corrugated box & container manufrs* Also at: Skelmersdale

TRM (Southern) Ltd, 19 Willow Gdns, North Baddesley, Southampton, SO52 9FY Tel: (023) 8073 3824 Fax: (023) 8041 0992 *Audio engineers & dictaphone repairs*

Troax UK Ltd, Enterprise House, Murdock Road, Dorcan, Swindon, SN3 5HY Tel: (01793) 542000 Fax: (01793) 618784 E-mail: info@troax.co.uk *Industrial partitioning & machine guarding manufrs*

Trodell Plant Ltd, Ightham Sandpit, Borough Green Road, Ightham, Sevenoaks, Kent, TN15 9JB Tel: (01732) 882662 Fax: (01732) 885675 *Excavation & plant hirers*

Trodham Plant Ltd, Liphook Road, Hollywater, Bordon, Hampshire, GU35 9AF Tel: (01428) 751588 Fax: (01428) 751550 E-mail: trodham@aol.com *Plant hire & repairers*

Trog Associates Ltd, PO Box 243, South Croydon, Surrey, CR2 6WF Tel: (020) 8786 3614 Fax: (020) 8405 8049 E-mail: gostwrighter@dslpipex.com *Computer software*

continued

rogen UV Technology Ltd, 5 De-Salis Court, Hampton Lovett Industrial Estate, Droitwich, Worcestershire, WR9 0QE Tel: (01905) 771117 Fax: (01905) 772270 E-mail: uksales@trojanuv.com *Water treatment plant*

roika Contracting Ltd, 850 Herries Road, Sheffield, S6 1QW Tel: 0114-269 0900 Fax: 0114-234 4885 E-mail: sales@troikaam.co.uk *Architectural plaster mouldings & designs*

rojan Aluminium Ltd, 7 Burton Close, Falcon Road Industrial Estate, Norwich, NR6 6AY Tel: (01603) 426024 Fax: (01603) 417882 E-mail: sale@trojanaluminium.co.uk *Manufacturers of aluminium framed windows & doors*

rojan Asphalt Mixers Ltd, 34 Hill La Industrial Estate, Markfield, Leicestershire, LE67 9PN Tel: (01530) 245232 Fax: (01530) 244063 E-mail: info@bitmen.co.uk *Trojan Asphalt Mixers Limited has been established for almost 20 years and are now the market leaders within the UK, as well as exporting to other countries. Trojan can supply six standard models of mixers, ranging from the 12cwt 'Scorpion' to the four ton 'Chieftan', offering improved safety features, built-in quality and reliability through advanced engineering technology.*

rojan Garage Equipment Services Ltd, 3 Orchard Court, Armstrong Way, Yate, Bristol, BS37 5GW Tel: (01454) 326161 Fax: (01454) 326363 E-mail: trojanges@btconnect.com *Garage equipment sales & service*

rojan Mixers, 1191 Stratford Road, Hall Green, Birmingham, B28 8BX Tel: 0121-777 5555 Fax: 0121-777 5555 E-mail: trojanmixers@hotmail.com *Water treatment plant manufrs*

rojan Plastics Ltd, Ramsden Mills, Britannia Road, Huddersfield, HD3 4QG Tel: (01484) 648181 Fax: (01484) 657098 E-mail: sales@trojanplastics.co.uk *Bath & shower tray manufrs*

rojan Signs Ltd, 11 Lyon Road, Hersham Industrial Estate, Walton-On-Thames, Surrey, KT12 3PU Tel: (01932) 232400 Fax: (01932) 987687 E-mail: troy@trojansigns.com *Sign manufrs*

rojan Special Fasteners Ltd, 18 Fortnum Close, Tile Cross, Birmingham, B33 0LG Tel: 0121-789 8586 Fax: 0121-789 8006 E-mail: sales@trojanspecialfastenersltd.co.uk *Manufacturers of fasteners (industrial) & (special specification) & bolts & nuts, non-standard. Also nu t tapping services. In addition, nuts: castle; full; lock; slotted; slotted thick; specialised; bright steel, bar turned*

Trojan Woodworking, Bourne Road, Pode Hole, Spalding, Lincolnshire, PE11 3LW Tel: (01775) 767786 Fax: (01775) 767786 *Furniture designers & makers*

▶ Trolley Jack Services, 11 Smith Street, Falkirk, FK2 7NB Tel: (01324) 634526 Fax: (01324) 622176

Trolley Maintenance Services Ltd, Chelworth Lodge, Cricklade, Swindon, SN6 6HP Tel: (01793) 759184 Fax: (01793) 759469 E-mail: info@trolleymaintenance.co.uk *Trolley & truck maintenance services*

Trolley Watch UK, 18 Alderley Road, Bournemouth, BH8 8SA Tel: (01202) 247111 E-mail: lmoss@cwcom.net *Trolley retrieval*

Trollull Ltd, 17-18 Brunel Gate, West Portway Industrial Estate, Andover, Hampshire, SP10 3SL Tel: (01264) 333443 Fax: (01264) 334428 E-mail: trollull@trollull.co.uk *Scouring pad & steel wool product manufrs*

Tromans Bros, 6 Troman Industrial Estate, 212 Halesowen Road, Netherton, Dudley, West Midlands, DY2 9PD Tel: (01384) 569495 Fax: (01384) 569495 *Metal polishers for all metals*

▶ Tron Systems Ltd, Tron House, Quarrywood Court, Livingston, West Lothian, EH54 6AX Tel: (01506) 400450 E-mail: sales@tronsystems.co.uk *Computer consultants*

Troon Marine Services Ltd, Harbour Road, Troon, Ayrshire, KA10 6DJ Tel: (01292) 316180 Fax: (01292) 316180 *Marine engineers*

▶ James Troop, 4 Davy Road, Astmoor Industrial Estate, Runcorn, Cheshire, WA7 1PZ Tel: (01928) 566170 Fax: (01928) 577314 E-mail: sales@jamestroop.co.uk *Diesel, gas & dual fuel engineers,Remote monitoring of prime movers, generator & pump specialists, spare parts. 24/7*

Tropair Engineering Ltd, Building 528, Biggin Hill Airport, Biggin Hill, Westerham, Kent, TN16 3BN Tel: (01959) 576767 Fax: (01959) 540033 E-mail: tropairmail@aol.com *Air conditioning engineers*

Trophies & Engraving, 43 Valley Mount, Harrogate, North Yorkshire, HG2 0JG Tel: (01423) 507319 Fax: (01423) 507319 E-mail: sales@trophies-and-engraving.co.uk *Engraving services*

Trophies & Engraving Services, 651 Stockport Road, Manchester, M12 4QA Tel: 0161-224 7879 *Engraving services*

Trophies Of Radstock, Unit 15 Old Mills Industrial Estate, Old Mills, Paulton, Bristol, BS39 7SU Tel: (01761) 418488 Fax: (01761) 418488 *Supply & engrave trophies*

Trophy Centre Ltd, 266 High Street, Ayr, KA7 1NB Tel: (01292) 610638 *Sports trophies manufrs*

The Trophy Centre Ltd, 18 Kilmarnock Road, Glasgow, G41 3NH Tel: 0141-649 3843 Fax: 0141-649 3843 *Trophies suppliers*

Trophy Centre, 12 Reynolds Street, Warrington, WA4 1PP Tel: (01925) 444365 Fax: (01925) 444365 *Trophy engravers & manufrs*

▶ Trophy Distributors, 4 West Gate Park, Tintagel Way, Aldridge, Walsall, WS9 8ER Tel: (01922) 455545 Fax: (01922) 459966 E-mail: info@trophydistributors.co.uk *Trophy distributors*

Trophy Distributors UK Ltd, Queensway Trading Estate, 16/17 Bartholomew Row, Birmingham, B5 5JU Tel: 0121-236 7843 Fax: 0121-236 3229 E-mail: sales@trophydistributors.co.uk *Sports trophy components distribs*

The Trophy Shop, 48 Victoria Street, Perth, PH2 8JT Tel: (01738) 632245 E-mail: sales@perth-trophy-shop.com *Trophies, awards & engravable gifts plus a full engraving service specialists*

Trophy Sportswear, 7a Forest La, London, E15 1HA Tel: (020) 8534 1687 *Sportswear manufacturer*

Trophy World, 12 Bourtree Pl, Hawick, Roxburghshire, TD9 9HW Tel: 01450 372174 *Shoe repairs*

Trophy World Awards Engraving, 50 Albert Street, Dundee, DD4 6QQ Tel: (01382) 461004 Fax: (01382) 461004 *Trophy engraving & manufs*

Trophyman Supplies Ltd, Olympic Works, 2-4 Kathleen Road, Southampton, SO19 8EX Tel: (023) 8043 8888 Fax: (023) 8068 5604 E-mail: sales@trophyman.co.uk *Sports trophy manufrs*

Tropi Quaria, 27-29 Anglesea Road, Southampton, SO15 5QH Tel: (023) 8077 3120 Fax: (023) 8077 3120 *Tropical aquarium suppliers*

Tropical Engineering, Unit 8, Saunders Drive, Cowes, Isle of Wight, PO31 8HU Tel: (01983) 280456 Fax: (01983) 281844 E-mail: office@tropicalengineering.co.uk *Boat repairers*

Tropical Interior Landscapes, 2 The Old Fire Station, Albion Street, Birmingham, B1 3EA Tel: 0121-233 9804 Fax: 0121-233 9802 *Floral display contractors*

Tropicana Health & Fitness, Unit 38 Forge Lane, Minworth, Sutton Coldfield, West Midlands, B76 1AH Tel: 0121-351 3110 Fax: (0845) 3450917 E-mail: sales@tropicanahealthandfitness.com *Health food supplements*

Trotman Publishing & Empower Group Ltd, 2 The Green, Richmond, Surrey, TW9 1PL Tel: (020) 8486 1150 Fax: (020) 8486 1151 E-mail: management@trotman.co.uk *Publishers of educational books*

▶ Trotman & Taylor, 40 Deer Park, Ivybridge, Devon, PL21 0HY Tel: (01752) 698410 Fax: (01752) 698410 E-mail: enquiries@trotmantaylor.com *Architectural services*

Trouble Shooter Electronics Ltd, Pear Patch, Walnut Tree Lane, Maidstone, Kent, ME15 9RQ Tel: (01622) 743196 Fax: (01622) 743196 E-mail: troubleshooter@btconnect.com *Repair & service to machine's control systems*

Trounce Ltd, New St Marks Works, St Marks Lane, Manchester, M8 4FW Tel: 0161-740 2159 Fax: 0161-721 4768 E-mail: sales@trounce.co.uk *Flag, banner & bunting manufrs*

Troup Bywaters & Anders, 51 Praed Street, London, W2 1NR Tel: (020) 7565 5666 Fax: (020) 7565 5744 *Building consulting engineers*

▶ Trousseau Ltd, 284a North Road, Gabalfa, Cardiff, CF14 3BN Tel: 029 20610099 E-mail: admin@trousseaultd.co.uk

▶ Trout Ltd, Trout Road, West Drayton, Middlesex, UB7 7TE Tel: (01895) 443247 Fax: (01895) 442024 E-mail: sales@trouttool.co.uk *Engineering services*

▶ Troutline Fishing Supplies, 80 Stoneybeck, Bishop Middleham, Ferryhill, County Durham, DL17 9BN Tel: (07917) 016359 E-mail: sales@troutline.co.uk *A new and exciting place to buy all types of fly fishing equipment. We can supply from Snowbee, Fladen, Cortland and many more at some unbeatable prices. Rods, Reels, Lines, Flies we have it all at www.troutline.co.uk*

Trouvay & Cauvin Ltd, Broadgate, Oldham Broadway Business Park, Chadderton, Oldham, OL9 9XA Tel: 0161-684 7488 Fax: 0161-684 7487 E-mail: sales@trouvay-cauvin.co.uk *Valves & piping specialist*

▶ Trovum Computer Consultants, 49 Calderfield Close, Stockton Heath, Warrington, WA4 6PJ Tel: (01925) 600435 Fax: (01925) 600435

Trowell Plant Sales Ltd, 111 Station Road, Selston, Nottingham, NG16 6FF Tel: (01773) 580878 Fax: (01773) 580881 E-mail: tpsl@btconnect.com *Contractors plant export merchants*

Trowtronics UK Ltd, Unit 41 South Hampshire Industrial Park, Totton, Southampton, SO40 3SA Tel: (023) 8066 0055 Fax: (023) 8066 0012 E-mail: trowtronics.@aol.conf.au *Printed circuit assembly services*

Trox UK Ltd, Caxton Way, Thetford, Norfolk, IP24 3SQ Tel: (01842) 754545 Fax: (01842) 763051 E-mail: sales@troxuk.co.uk *Manufacturers & distributors of air movement products*

Troy Components Ltd, Troy Industrial Estate, Jill Lane, Sambourne, Redditch, Worcestershire, B96 6ES Tel: (01527) 892941 Fax: (01527) 893310 *Motor components engineers*

TRP, Pride Parkway, Sleaford Business Park, Sleaford, Lincolnshire, NG34 8GL Tel: (01529) 300111 Fax: (01529) 300310 E-mail: info@trp.uk.com *Specialised farm equipment*

Tru Group Ltd, Broad Lane, Gilberdyke, Brough, North Humberside, HU15 2TB Tel: (01430) 441528 Fax: (01430) 441904 E-mail: sales@trugroup.co.uk *Plastics injection mouldings manufrs*

Tru Tools, 74 Heming Road, Redditch, Worcestershire, B98 0EA Tel: (01527) 523157 Fax: (01527) 510170 *Precision toolmakers*

Truarc, 2 Eastgate, Lowfields Business Park, Elland, West Yorkshire, HX5 9DN Tel: (01422) 375191 Fax: (01422) 311685 *Pipework fabricators*

Trubloc Ltd, Concrete Works, Carew Airfield, Milton, Tenby, Dyfed, SA70 8SX Tel: (01646) 651531 *Concrete block manufrs*

Trucast Ltd, Marlborough Road, Ryde, Isle of Wight, PO33 1AD Tel: (01983) 567611 Fax: (01983) 567618 E-mail: info@doncasters.com *Casting manufrs*

Truck & Bus Services, The Homestead Garage, Gresford Road, Llay, Wrexham, Clwyd, LL12 0NU Tel: (01978) 855506 *Commercial repairer*

Truck Care, 3 Holmer Road, Hereford, HR4 9SD Tel: (01432) 342679 Fax: (01432) 265414 E-mail: truckcaregl@aol.com *Truck services*

Truck Masters Handling, Norwich Livestock, Hall Road, Norwich, NR4 6EQ Tel: (01603) 458817 Fax: (01603) 452789 E-mail: mail@truckmasters.co.uk *Industrial rough terrain forklift distributors*

Truck Tac Ireland, 32 Camaghy Road, Galbally, Dungannon, County Tyrone, BT70 2NT Tel: (028) 8775 8736 Fax: (028) 8775 8926 *Road haulage & commercial vehicle repairs*

Truck Tec, 1 Clark Way, Bellshill Industrial Estate, Bellshill, Lanarkshire, ML4 3NX Tel: (01698) 339090 Fax: (01698) 339080 E-mail: sales@trucktecltd.co.uk *Commercial vehicle bodybuilders & repairers*

Truck & Trailer Components Ltd, Unipart House, Garsington Road, Cowley, Oxford, OX4 2PG Tel: (01865) 383999 Fax: (0800) 361677 E-mail: ttc@unipart.co.uk *Truck & trailer component distributors*

Truck & Trailer Equipment Ltd, 37-39 Hawes Lane, Rowley Regis, Warley, West Midlands, B65 9AL Tel: 0121-559 7711 Fax: 0121-559 5637 E-mail: sales@trucktrailerequip.co.uk *Truck & trailer equipment suppliers*

▶ Truck Training UK (Warrington) Ltd, The Old Barn, Bellhouse Lane, Moore, Warrington, WA4 6TR Tel: (01925) 740404 Fax: (01925) 740404 E-mail: info@trukwarrington.com *The leading supplier of quality HGV/LGV driving tuition in Warrington & Bolton.*

Truck Transmissions Ltd, Davyfield Road, Blackburn, BB1 2LU Tel: (01254) 690100 Fax: (01254) 690222 E-mail: sales@trucktransmissionsltd.co.uk *Recondition transmissions for trucks*

Truck-Alignment Ltd, Anchor & Hope Lane, London, SE7 7RY Tel: (020) 8858 3781 Fax: (020) 8858 5663 E-mail: admin@vipgroupltd.co.uk *Commercial vehicle & accident repairers*

▶ Truckcraft Bodies Ltd, Cooper Street Works, Cooper Street, Dukinfield, Cheshire, SK16 4JB Tel: 0161-830 0011 Fax: 0161-830 0022 *Commercial vehicle body builders & repairers*

Truckfix Leeds, Harper Farm, Whitehall Road, Leeds, LS12 6JU Tel: 0113-231 1788 Fax: 0113-279 6874 *Commercial vehicle repairs*

Truck-Lite Co. Ltd, Waterfall Lane, Cradley Heath, West Midlands, B64 6QB Tel: 0121-561 7000 Fax: 0121-561 1415 E-mail: birminghamsales@truck-lite.com *Motor vehicle components & accessories*

Truckman Ltd, Chosen View Road, Cheltenham, Gloucestershire, GL51 9LT Tel: (01242) 580033 Fax: (01242) 580044 E-mail: sales@truckman.co.uk *Glass fibre hardtops manufrs*

Truckmasters Handling Ltd, Boston Road, Wainfleet St. Mary, Skegness, Lincolnshire, PE24 4HA Tel: (01754) 880481 Fax: (01754) 880601 E-mail: mail@truckmasters.co.uk *Fork lift distributors* Also at: Norwich & Wisbech

Truckmasters (Handling) Ltd, Boston Road, Wainfleet, Skegness, Lincolnshire, PE24 4HA Tel: (01754) 882182 Fax: (01754) 880197 E-mail: stores@truckmasters.co.uk *Fork truck repair, sales & parts*

▶ Truckmixer UK Ltd, 1 Stainsby Close, Holmewood Industrial Estate, Chesterfield, Derbyshire, S42 5UG Tel: (01246) 854339 Fax: (01246) 854339 *Manufacture of truck mounted concrete mixers*

▶ Trucks Ltd, Carleton House, Ashley Crescent, Southampton, SO19 9NA Tel: (023) 8044 4434

Trucks R Us, Sovereign House, Farthing Road, Ipswich, IP1 5AP Tel: (01473) 744117 Fax: (01473) 748850 E-mail: sales@trucks-are-us.co.uk *Trucks R Us Based in Ipswich Suffolk TRUCKS R US specialise in used Commercial Vehicle sales and Plant Sales. We also deal in new and used motorhomes Based in East Anglia Trucks R Us sell anywhere in the UK. Offering all leading manufacturers including MERCEDES - FORD - DAF - SCANIA - RENAULT - MITSABUSHI - VOLVO - FUNMOVER - KENTUCKY CAMPERS - JCB -FIAT - ISUZU - NISSAN - TOYOTA - VOLKSWAGEN - RIMORE - VAUXHALL - HITACHI - MAN - MAZDA - FOURWINDS CAMPERS Trucks R Us also sell a large range of used Plant including Forklifts, Telehandlers, Diggers, Excavators, Mini Diggers and Dumpers Please contact us for more information on our large selection of new and used MOTORHOMES, CAMPER VAN and CAMPERS Motorhomes and Campers now available for HIRE Please ring for details*

▶ TruckSmart Ltd, Lancaster New Road, Cabus, Preston, PR3 1AD Tel: 01524 791999 Fax: 01524 792999 E-mail: sales@trucksmart.co.uk *HGV maintenance workshop*

Truckstop Hawkes, Unit 9 Brook Street, Redditch, Worcestershire, B98 8NG Tel: (01527) 68279 Fax: (01527) 60026 E-mail: info@truckstophawkes.co.uk *Commercial vehicle body fittings*

Truclass Ltd, Stallings Lane, Kingswinford, West Midlands, DY6 7HU Tel: (01384) 400919 Fax: (01384) 400719 *Industrial boiler repairs*

Trucut Technologies UK Ltd, Flavell Works, Garratt Street, Brierley Hill, West Midlands, DY5 1JU Tel: (01746) 764900 Fax: (01384) 481195 E-mail: sales@chartway.co.uk *Small turned parts manufrs*

True Craft Furniture Ltd, Bath Lane, Leeds, LS13 3BB Tel: 0113-236 1100 Fax: 0113-236 0301 E-mail: furniture@true-craft.freeserve.co.uk *Furniture manufrs*

▶ True Sounds, 14 Mason Road, Norwich, NR6 6RF Tel: 01603 483450 E-mail: info2@truesounds.net *Record shop & Online store for all types of dance music.*Inc Techno, Electro, breakbeat, hiphop, funk & reggae.*

True Systems Ltd, Systems House, 127 High Street, Teddington, Middlesex, TW11 8HH Tel: (020) 8977 5151 E-mail: sales@truesystems.co.uk *Computer software developers*

Truecut Co, 33 Dulverton Road, Birmingham, B6 7EQ Tel: 0121-327 2815 Fax: 0121-327 2832 *Turned part manufrs*

▶ Trueform Engineering Ltd, Unit 4 Pasadena Close, Pump Lane, Hayes, Middlesex, UB3 3NQ Tel: (020) 8561 4959 Fax: (020) 8589 0545 E-mail: sales@trueform.co.uk *Install & manufacturer bus stops & bus shelters*

Trueform Engineering Ltd, Unit 4 Pasadena Close, Pump Lane, Hayes, Middlesex, UB3 3NQ Tel: (020) 8561 4959 Fax: (020) 8848 1397 E-mail: sales@trueform.co.uk *Trueform's comprehensive manufacturing facilities can cope with virtually all requirements. State of the art technology and CAD-DAM design, CNC punching and folding, precision engineering, welding and fixing combine to produce quality precision and medium weight fabrications to a high standard of accuracy time after time.*

Trueline Engineering Services Ltd, Unit 15 King Street Trading Estate, Middlewich, Cheshire, CW10 9LF Tel: (01606) 836961 Fax: (01606) 836528 *Steel & aluminium fabricators*

Truepart Ltd, Decoy Bank, Doncaster, South Yorkshire, DN4 5JD Tel: (01302) 344919 Fax: (01302) 327191 E-mail: info@wst.co.uk *Vehicle spare part merchants*

▶ Trueprint Litho, Unit A9 Continental Approach, Westwood Industrial Estate, Margate, Kent, CT9 4JG Tel: (01843) 220200 Fax: (01843) 292646

Truflow Hydraulic Components Ltd, Unit F5 Lockside, Anchor Brook Industrial Park, Aldridge, Walsall, WS9 8BZ Tel: (01922) 745488 Fax: (01922) 745399 E-mail: truflow@bt.co.uk *Distributors & stockholders of hose & tube fittings & hydraulics*

▶ Truframe Ltd, Unit 3, K L M Hudson Road, Saxby Road Industrial Estate, Melton Mowbray, Leicestershire, LE13 1BP Tel: (01664) 410140

▶ Tru-Gen Ltd, Linwood Grange, Martin Moor, Metheringham, Lincoln, LN4 3BQ Tel: (01526) 378154 Fax: (01526) 378637 E-mail: arther@tru-gen.fsnet.co.uk *Aviation ground power spares & repairs*

▶ Trugs Florist, 18 South Street, Exeter, EX1 1DZ Tel: (01392) 422592 Fax: (01392) 422522 E-mail: sales@trugs.co.uk *Floral suppliers*

Truk Mark, 391 Holywood Road, Belfast, BT4 2LS Tel: (028) 9065 8837 Fax: (028) 9065 7225 E-mail: devansco@btinternet.com *Computerised signwriting services*

Trulaw Fabs Ltd, 338 Summer Lane, Birmingham, B19 3QL Tel: 0121-359 1191 Fax: 0121-359 4855 *Metal finishing & electroplating*

Tru-Line Ltd, Unit 16, Victoria Street, Middlesbrough, Cleveland, TS1 5QZ Tel: (01642) 232411 Fax: (01642) 217457 *Suspended ceilings*

Tru-Lon Printed Circuits (Royston) Ltd, Newark Close, York Way Industrial Estate, Royston, Hertfordshire, SG8 5HL Tel: (01763) 248922 Fax: (01763) 249281 E-mail: info@tru-lon.co.uk *PCB printed circuit manufrs*

▶ Truly Scrumptious, 85 New Road, Porthcawl, Mid Glamorgan, CF36 5DH Tel: (01656) 788080 Fax: 01656 788080 E-mail: lorraine@trulyscrumptiousonline.co.uk *Wedding designers offering bridal wear design services*

Trumac Groups Ltd, Brook Lane, The Ham, Westbury, Wiltshire, BA13 4HB Tel: (01373) 821600 Fax: (01373) 826808 *Commercial vehicle bodybuilders*

Trumbar Truck Care Ltd, 57 Victoria Road, Diss, Norfolk, IP22 4JD Tel: (01379) 652161 Fax: (01379) 641500 *Motor vehicle repair services*

Truperm Pleating Co. Ltd, Williams Street, Gorton, Manchester, M18 7AH Tel: 0161-223 3185 Fax: 0161-231 6813 *General platters*

▶ Truplas Ltd, Vine Road, Johnston, Haverfordwest, Dyfed, SA62 3NZ Tel: (01437) 890999 Fax: (01437) 899388

Truro Canvas, Malpas Road, Truro, Cornwall, TR1 1QH Tel: (01209) 820945 Fax: (01872) 240011 *Sun shades, tents & textile manufrs*

Truro Portable Buildings, Longdowns Industrial Estate, Longdowns, Penryn, Cornwall, TR10 9NA Tel: (01209) 860269 Fax: (01209) 860020 E-mail: sales@truro-portable-buildings.co.uk *Portable timber building manufrs*

Truro Tractors Ltd, Treburley, Launceston, Cornwall, PL15 9PU Tel: (01579) 371133 Fax: (01579) 371010 *Agricultural engineering services*

Truscanian Ltd, St. Martins Industrial Estate, Engine Street, Oldbury, West Midlands, B69 4NL Tel: 0121-552 3011 Fax: 0121-552 4672 *Non-ferrous founders & engineers*

Truscott Catering Equipment Ltd, 54c South Nelson Road, South Nelson Industrial Estate, Cramlington, Northumberland, NE23 1WF Tel: (01670) 714440 Fax: (01670) 715585 *Service & repair of catering equipment*

Trusprings Ltd, Lodge Mill, Lodge Street, Wardle, Rochdale, Lancashire, OL12 9JR Tel: (01706) 648550 Fax: (01706) 377130 *Spring manufrs*

▶ Truss 2 Frame, Catfoss Industrial Estate, Bewholme Lane, Brandesburton, Driffield, North Humberside, YO25 8ES Tel: (01964) 544777 Fax: (01964) 544888 *Timber frames & roof trusses*

▶ Truss Form Ltd, Hollin Bridge, Burnley Road East, Rossendale, Lancashire, BB4 9JR Tel: (01706) 212238 Fax: (01706) 223522

Trust Co. P.L.C., 2-3 Namrik Mews, Hove, East Sussex, BN3 2TF Tel: (01273) 735999 Fax: (01273) 736999 E-mail: info@trustco.co.uk *Computer systems & software developers*

Trust Alarms, 3 Pool Hall Syke, Dewhirst Road, Rochdale, Lancashire, OL12 0AS Tel: (01706) 357050 *Electrical alarms - installation and design*

▶ Trust Deal, 295 Haggerston Road, London, E8 4EN Tel: (020) 7254 3567 Fax: (020) 7254 3567

The Trust Partnership, 6 Trull Farm Buildings, Trull, Tetbury, Gloucestershire, GL8 8SQ Tel: 01284 841900 Fax: 01285 841576 E-mail: Belinda@TheTrustPartnership.com *The Trust Partnership has 15 years experience of administering charitable trusts and corporate social responsibility programmes. **Companies*

continued

continuation
and trusts are inundated with requests for support. We evaluate and respond to the incoming mail (or phone calls), and then manage the decision making process to save Trustees and committee members time, and money.

Trustclean Ltd, Queens Court, Doncaster, South Yorkshire, DN5 9QH Tel: (01302) 783193 Fax: (01302) 781556 E-mail: info@trustclean.co.uk *Food hygiene & specialist cleaning contractors*

Trustmark Solutions, Trustmark House, Alpha Court, Monks Cross Drive, Huntington, York, YO32 9WN Tel: (0870) 1210321 Fax: (0870) 1210320 *Software consultants & resellers*

▶ TrustSign UK Ltd, Unit 6, Nightingale Way, Alsager, Stoke-on-Trent, ST7 2GH Tel: (01270) 873942 Fax: (0870) 1300263 E-mail: sales@trustsign.co.uk *A leading provider of Digital Certificate technology, TrustSign UK enables enterprises of all sizes to secure their internal and external communication channels. Establishing compliance with regulatory and legal requirements such as HMCE 700-63 rules for electronic invoicing, TrustSign delivers a focused portfolio of business critical x.509 Digital Certificate solutions. Bringing added value to all Internet communication channels the TrustSign range of certificates, consultancy services and managed services not only increases overall business security but provides the high level of trust and assurance enterprise customers now insist upon.*

▶ Trustyle UK Ltd, Trustyle, Unit 50, Woodside, Thornwood, Epping, Essex, CM16 6LJ Tel: (01992) 578112 Fax: (01992) 572831 E-mail: enquiries@trustyle.co.uk *Providing corporate clothing & high quality work wear*

▶ Truswell Haulage Ltd, Cairn Lodge, Douglas, Lanark, ML11 0RJ Tel: (01555) 851844 Fax: (01555) 851392

▶ Truswell Haulage, Surbiton Street, Sheffield, S9 2DN Tel: 0114-244 9568 Fax: 0114-242 6630

▶ Trutek Fasteners Ltd, Leigh Street, Sheffield, S9 2PR Tel: 0114-242 3333 Fax: 0114-242 3300 *Industrial fasteners distributors*

Trutex plc, Jubilee Mill, Taylor Street, Clitheroe, Lancashire, BB7 1NL Tel: (01200) 421202 Fax: (01200) 421209 E-mail: info@trutex.com *School wear manufacturers & suppliers*

Tru-Thread Ltd, Station Road, Coleshill, Birmingham, B46 1HT Tel: (01675) 462193 Fax: (01675) 462841 E-mail: admin@tru-thread.co.uk *Thread gauge calibration & manufrs*

Trutorq Actuators, 1 The Anchorage, Gosport, Hampshire, PO12 1LY Tel: (023) 9251 1123 Fax: (023) 9250 2272 E-mail: leon@trutorq-actuators.com *Valve manufrs*

Truturn Precision Engineering (Charfield) Ltd, Units L2-L3, Bath Road Trading Estate, Lightpill, Stroud, Gloucestershire, GL5 3QF Tel: (01453) 752888 Fax: (01453) 753888 E-mail: truturn@truturn.co.uk *Precision engineers*

TRW Aeronautical Systems Lucas Areospace, 4 Bruce Street, Belfast, BT2 7LA Tel: (028) 9044 5800 Fax: (028) 9044 5801 *Aeronautical system manufrs*

Try Homes Southern Ltd, Bridge House, 27 Bridge Street, Leatherhead, Surrey, KT22 8HL Tel: (01372) 385170 Fax: (01372) 385199 E-mail: customerservice@tryhomes.co.uk *Housing development*

▶ Try Temps Ltd, Unit A2 Imex Business Park, Kings Road, Tyseley, Birmingham, B11 2AL Tel: 0121-693 3311 Fax: 0121-693 3355 E-mail: sales@trytemps.co.uk *Try Temps supplies temporary and permanent staff in the following Areas: Engineering Automotive Distribution and Service Companies*The first two permanent placements are charged at 10 percent of the commensurate salary*

Tryac Electrical Engineers, Unit 3 Isaac Newton Way, Grantham, Lincolnshire, NG31 9RT Tel: (01476) 576434 Fax: (01476) 578416 *Manufacturers of electrical domestic & farming equipment*

Tryang Jig & Gauge Co., Unit 3-4 Wynford Industrial Estate, Wynford Road, Birmingham, B27 6JP Tel: 0121-706 8050 Fax: 0121-765 4294 E-mail: mikedavis@tryang.fsbusiness.co.uk *Precision engineers*

Tryax Ltd, 10 Jubilee Trading Centre, Jubilee Road, Letchworth Garden City, Hertfordshire, SG6 1NE Tel: (01462) 481295 Fax: (01462) 685275 E-mail: sales@tryax.com *CNC milling machines manufrs*

Tryco Designs Ltd, 8 Orchard Street, Norwich, NR2 4PP Tel: (01603) 627157 Fax: (01603) 665412 E-mail: trycodesigns@ukgateway.net *Drawing office & reprographic services CAD bureaux* Also at: Great Yarmouth

Tryg-Baltica International, 69-70 Mark Lane, London, EC3R 7HJ Tel: (020) 7709 1000 Fax: (020) 7709 1001 *Insurance providers*

▶ Tryline Rugbywear, Unit 101, Greenwich Commercial Centre,, 49, Greenwich High Road, London, SE10 8JL Tel: (020) 8694 6888 Fax: (020) 8694 6888 E-mail: trylinerugbywear@aol.com *Rugby clothing manufacturer*

Trylon, Bury Close, Higham Ferrers, Rushden, Northamptonshire, NN10 8HQ Tel: (01933) 411724 Fax: (01933) 350357 E-mail: info@trylon.co.uk *Plastic & crafts material suppliers*

Trymdata Computer Systems, 157 Redland Road, Bristol, BS6 6YE Tel: (0845) 2308075 *SAGE software & training service*

Tryst, Kippen Station, Kippen, Stirling, FK8 3JA Tel: (01786) 870295 *Plaque designers*

Tryst Engineering Ltd, Fairfield Works, West Wycombe Road, High Wycombe, Buckinghamshire, HP11 2LR Tel: (01494) 442497 Fax: (01494) 465829 E-mail: tryst@ndirect.co.uk *General engineering services*

Tryus Transport Ltd, 1 Delph Industrial Estate, Delph Road, Brierley Hill, West Midlands, DY5 2UA Tel: (01384) 265237 Fax: (01384) 262474 *Road transport/haulage, freight services*

TS Direct, 473a King Street, Stoke-on-Trent, ST3 1EU Tel: (01782) 335962 Fax: (01782) 335962 *Sectional buildings*

▶ Tsa Advet Ltd, Unit B1, Evans Business Centre, Deeside Industrial Park, Deeside, Flintshire, CH5 2JZ Tel: (01244) 287060 Fax: (01244) 281703 E-mail: derek.whatling@tsaadvet.co.uk *Document management, control & archiving services*

▶ Tsakos Shipping London Ltd, 18 Buckingham Gate, London, SW1E 6LB Tel: (020) 7802 8300 Fax: (020) 7592 9990

Tsana Ltd, 41 Baldwin Way, Swindon, Dudley, West Midlands, DY3 4PF Tel: (01384) 400566 E-mail: sales@tsana.com *Process improvement consultants*

▶ TSC Foods Ltd, Units 3-4, Arkwright Way, Queensway Industrial Estate, Scunthorpe, South Humberside, DN16 1AL Tel: (01724) 272900 Fax: (01724) 272901

▶ TSC Graphics Ltd, 28 Factory Lane, Croydon, CR0 3RL Tel: (020) 8686 6553

TSD Wakefield, Keys Road, Mixs Hill, Somercoates, Alfreton, Derbyshire, DE55 7FQ Tel: (0870) 6090111 Fax: (01773) 521015 E-mail: sales@wakefields.co.uk *Material flows storage systems*

TSG Ltd, High Street, Broom, Alcester, Warwickshire, B50 4HN Tel: (01789) 778900 Fax: (01789) 772272 *Computer software & systems developers*

TSG Ltd, 1 Gosforth Park Way, Salters Lane, Newcastle upon Tyne, NE12 8ET Tel: 0191-256 1166 Fax: 0191-256 1167 E-mail: sales@tsg.com *Computer systems & software distributors*

▶ Tshirt Rebel, PO Box 63, Pontypool, Torfaen, NP4 6WH Tel: (01495) 758781 E-mail: service@tshirtrebel.com *Over 50,000 products including hundreds of tshirts, skinny ribs, hoodies, vests & muscle tops, polo shirts, sports kits, team kits, casual wear, outwear, plus.... hardwearing industrial clothing, safety/reflective, specialist catering/chef clothing, childrens & babies clothing, many promotional items, teddies, coasters, mousemats, keyrings, magnets...... All of our items can be personalised or decorated to your specification by our in house production team if required. Fast, Friendly & Reliable*

TSL Extrusions, Elton Park Business Centre, Hadleigh Rd, Ipswich, IP2 0HN Tel: 0845 4940747 Fax: (01473) 236044 E-mail: sales@tubeway.co.uk Purchasing Contact: A.G. Duncan *Manufacturers of extruded rigid & flexible PVC profiles to customer specification. Manufacture & supply of hardware & DIY products, sold under the Easyfix tradename, to retail outlets, including such products as: Rigid Angles, Channels, Clip-on, Draught Excluders, Secondary Double Glazing, Aluminium Profiles, Acrylic Sheeting, Self Adhesive Products, Sticky Pads, Sticky Feet, Metal Carpet edge, Laminate Floor edge, Electrical Trunking, Tile Edge & Bath Seals*

▶ TSL Vanguard Ltd, Psalters Lane, Steel Street, Holmes, Rotherham, South Yorkshire, S61 1DF Tel: (0870) 6096009 Fax: (0870) 6096010 E-mail: ian.liversidge@btconnect.com

TSR Disco Equipment, 74 Albany Road, Coventry, CV5 6JU Tel: (024) 7667 9929 Fax: (024) 7671 5147 E-mail: sales@t-s-r.co.uk *Audio professional visual display services*

TSS (International) Ltd, 1 Garnet Close, Greycaine Industrial Estate, Watford, WD24 7JZ Tel: (01923) 470800 Fax: (01923) 470838 E-mail: tssmail@tssuk.co.uk *Marine survey equipment manufrs*

Tsubakimoto UK Ltd, Osier Drive, Annesley, Nottingham, NG15 0DX Tel: (01623) 688700 Fax: (01623) 688729 E-mail: sales@tsubaki.co.uk *Manufacturers of chains including conveyor, industrial*

▶ TT Software Ltd, PO Box 476, Guernsey, GY1 6BB Tel: (01481) 700202 E-mail: sales@ttsoftware.gg *TT Software supplies payroll and personnel software to Guernsey, Jersey and the Isle of Man.*

TT Visuals, 205 Royal College Street, London, NW1 0SG Tel: (020) 7419 9555 Fax: (020) 7419 9556 E-mail: ttvisuals@mac.com *Editing & camera facilities & duplication*

TTAB Connectors Ltd, Ynysboeth Industrial Estate, Abercynon, Mountain Ash, Mid Glamorgan, CF45 4SF Tel: (01443) 740331 Fax: (01443) 741676 Principal Export Areas: Worldwide *Connectors manufrs*

T-Tech Tooling Ltd, 70 Prince Of Wales Lane, Yardley Wood, Birmingham, B14 4JZ Tel: 0121-474 2255 Fax: 0121-474 2066 E-mail: sales@t-tech.co.uk *Manufacture solid thread cutting tools & special cutting tools*

T-T-Electric, Unit 7A, Waterloo Park Industrial Estate, Upper Brook Street, Stockport, Cheshire, SK1 3BP Tel: 0161-480 0037 Fax: 0161-476 4390 E-mail: john.legg@t-t-electric.com *Specialist electric motor manufrs*

TTF Air Conditioning Ltd, 5 Tower Road, Washington, Tyne & Wear, NE37 2SH Tel: 0191-416 4525 Fax: 0191-416 4650 E-mail: cg-ttssales@jci.com *Industrial refrigeration & air conditioning services*

Tti Group Ltd, 39-43 Bilton Way, Luton, LU1 1UU Tel: (01582) 486644 Fax: (01582) 481148 E-mail: sales@ttigroup.co.uk *Surface coating, surface engineering, hot isostatic pressing & heat treatment services, metal including on-site* Also at: Blackburn, Cheltenham, Leeds, Letchworth, Luton, Tipton, Watford & West Bromwich

TTL Sales & Distribution Ltd, Units 1-3 CMS Business Park, Station Lane, Featherstone, Pontefract, West Yorkshire, WF7 6EQ Tel: (01977) 600064 Fax: (0870) 7449959 E-mail: sales@ttlonline.co.uk *Manufacturing & distribution lighting & light controls*

▶ TTR UK Ltd Telecomms Technology Recruitment, Britannia House, Leagrave Road, Luton, LU3 1RJ Tel: (01582) 736963 Fax: (01582) 876839 E-mail: sales@ttr.co.uk *Telecoms recruitment company*

▶ TTS, Celect House, 12a Fairbairn Road, Livingston, West Lothian, EH54 6TS Tel: (01506) 464448 Fax: (01506) 464430 E-mail: web@ttsce.co.uk *Consultant engineers*

Tube Care Inspection Ltd, Bessemer Way, Harfreys Industrial Estate, Great Yarmouth, Norfolk, NR31 0LX Tel: (01493) 601548 Fax: (01493) 656097 E-mail: sales@tubecare.co.uk *Tubular inspection services*

▶ Tube Engineers Ltd, Ardgraft Works, Newtoft Business Park, Newtoft, Market Rasen, Lincolnshire, LN8 3WA Tel: (01673) 862286 Fax: (01673) 885562 E-mail: sales@tubeengineers.co.uk *Tube manipulation*

Tube Fins Ltd, N Riverside Industrial Estate, Atherstone Street, Fazeley, Tamworth, Staffordshire, B78 3SD Tel: (01827) 251234 Fax: (01827) 286612 E-mail: bob@tubefins.co.uk *Heat exchanger tube manufrs*

Tube Form Technology Ltd, Unit D, Waterside Estate, 25-27 Willis Way, Poole, Dorset, BH15 3TD Tel: (01202) 686970 Fax: (01202) 686996 *Tube manipulation specialists*

Tube Gear Ltd, Unit B1 Springhead Enterprise Park, Springhead Road, Northfleet, Gravesend, Kent, DA11 8HB Tel: (01474) 321954 Fax: (01474) 321988 E-mail: sales@tube-gear.com *Automotive industry tube fitting distributors*

Tube & Marine Products Bingley Ltd, Albion Garage, Keighley Road, Bingley, West Yorkshire, BD16 2RD Tel: (01274) 567534 Fax: (01274) 567539 E-mail: sales@tmpeng.co.uk *Stainless steel catering equipment supply & manufrs*

Tube Tec, Spurryhillock Industrial Estate, Broomhill Road, Stonehaven, Kincardineshire, AB39 2NH Tel: (01569) 762211 Fax: (01569) 768065 E-mail: sales@tubetec.co.uk *Thread protective coating manufrs*

Tube Tech (International) Ltd, Rawreth Industrial Estate, Rawreth Lane, Rayleigh, Essex, SS6 9RL Tel: (0870) 2414999 Fax: (01268) 786998 E-mail: info@tubetech.com *UK & overseas emergency response services*

▶ Tube & Wire Display Ltd, Middle Mill, Oxford Street East, Ashton-under-Lyne, Lancashire, OL7 0NE Tel: 0161-339 4877 Fax: 0161-343 2596 *Specialists in manufacturing points of sale displays*

Tubeclamps Ltd, Unit A2, Cradley Business Park, Cradley Heath, West Midlands, B64 7DW Tel: (01384) 565241 Fax: (01384) 410490 E-mail: sales@tubeclamps.co.uk *Tube clamp manufrs*

Tubeclip Ltd, Unit 9-11 British Estate Business Park, 132 Bath Road, Reading, RG30 2EU Tel: 0118-957 2281 Fax: 0118-958 4630 E-mail: tubeclip@btconnect.com *Tube fittings manufrs*

Tubeformers Engineering Ltd, Units 11-15 Strawberry Lane Industrial Estate, Strawberry Lane, Willenhall, West Midlands, WV13 3RS Tel: (01902) 630300 Fax: (01902) 630066 *Tube fabricators & manipulators*

Tubeline, 13 Stockwell Drive, Mangotsfield, Bristol, BS16 9DN Tel: 0117-970 2448 Fax: 0117-956 6649 E-mail: sales@tubeline.co.uk *Tyre & inner tube suppliers*

Tubend Manufacturers, Stanley Street, Sowerby Bridge, West Yorkshire, HX6 2AH Tel: (01422) 833461 Fax: (01422) 835319 E-mail: tubenduk@aol.com *Tube manipulation services*

Tubeolight Signcraft C I, 1 Landes Du Marche, La Grande Route De St. Pierre, St. Peter, Jersey, JE3 7AY Tel: (01534) 485591 Fax: (01534) 485592 E-mail: sales@signtechjersey.co.uk *Sign manufrs*

Tuberex Exhausts Systems Ltd, Airfield Industrial Estate, Hixon, Stafford, ST18 0PF Tel: (01889) 271212 Fax: (01889) 272112 *Automotive exhaust system manufrs*

Tubes Fittings Valves Ltd, Bath Lane, Mansfield, Nottinghamshire, NG18 2BZ Tel: (01623) 643235 Fax: (01623) 420920 E-mail: sales@tubefiitingsvalves.co.uk *Valves tube fitting & distributors*

Tubestyle Products Ltd, New John Street, Halesowen, West Midlands, B62 8HT Tel: 0121-561 5522 Fax: 0121-561 5834 *Tubular furniture manufrs*

Tubetech Ltd, Arundel Road, Uxbridge, Middlesex, UB8 2RP Tel: (01895) 233268 Fax: (01895) 231933 *Tube bending.*

Tubewise Furniture, The Roundhouse, Harbour Road, Par, Cornwall, PL24 2BB Tel: (01726) 817625 Fax: (01726) 816405 *Furniture makers*

Tubros Engineering Ltd, Stanley Street, Workington, Cumbria, CA14 2JD Tel: (01900) 64444 Fax: (01900) 603292 *General engineers*

Tubular Furniture Ltd, Unit F1-F3, Coedcae Industrial Estate, Pontyclun, Mid Glamorgan, CF72 9HG Tel: (01443) 229326 Fax: (01443) 230493 E-mail: sales@tubular-furniture.co.uk *Contract & office seating manufrs*

Tubular Scaffolding Ltd, 1081 Duke St, Glasgow, G31 5NX Tel: 0141-554 3801 Fax: 0141-554 3801 *Scaffolding contractors* Also at: Irvine

Tuc, Congress House, 23-28 Great Russell Street, London, WC1B 3LS Tel: (020) 7636 4030 Fax: (020) 7636 0632 E-mail: info@tuc.org.uk *Trade union organisation*

▶ Tuchan Tolmie, Avalon, Station Road, Conon Bridge, Dingwall, Ross-Shire, IV7 8BJ Tel: (01349) 861356 Fax: (01349) 865393

Tuchkin Enterprises Ltd, PO Box 88, Hatfield, Hertfordshire, AL9 5DU Tel: (01707) 278436 Fax: (01707) 269347 E-mail: tuchkin@ntlworld.com *Industrial mineral processing manufrs*

Edwin Tucker & Sons Ltd, Teign Road, Newton Abbot, Devon, TQ12 4AA Tel: (01626) 334002 Fax: (01626) 330153 E-mail: info@tuckersmaltings.com *Maltsters*

▶ Tucker Hammett Electrical, 4 Progress Way, Mid Suffolk Business Park, Eye, Suffolk, IP23 7HU Tel: (01379) 873009 Fax: (01379) 873179

John Tucker & Son, Lockyers Farm, Mudgley, Wedmore, Somerset, BS28 4TY Tel: (01934) 712594 Fax: (01934) 712594 *Ditch & rhine maintenance & plant hire*

Tommy Tucker Ltd, Barnham House, Aurillac Way, Hallcroft Industrial Estate, Retford, Nottinghamshire, DN22 7PX Tel: (01777) 70514 Fax: (01777) 860859 E-mail: sales@mgagency.demon.co.uk *Popcorn & fun food manufrs*

A.B Tuckey, Church Street, Stockton, Southam, Warwickshire, CV47 8JG Tel: (01926) 812134 Fax: (01926) 810354 *Agricultural contractors*

Tuckey Print Ltd, 79 Moseley Road, Birmingham, B12 0HL Tel: 0121-773 7411 Fax: 0121-766 7339 E-mail: sales@tuckeyprint.co.uk *Refined commercial digital and lithographic printers and print finishing with over 150 years combined industry experience. Click the links below to visi our website or contact us via our profile page.*

Tudol International Ltd, Colette Court, 125 Sloane Street, London, SW1X 9AU Tel: (020) 7730 996 Fax: (020) 7824 8691 E-mail: mail@tudol.co.uk *Property services & radiator sales*

Tudor, 3 Ellesmere Business Park, Oswestry Road, Ellesmere, Shropshire, SY12 0EW Tel: (01691) 623424 Fax: (01691) 624479 E-mail: nevilletudor@virgin.net *Pressed metal components, brackets, hydraulic pumps & rams specialists*

Tudor, 2 Kirkwall Grove, Stoke-on-Trent, ST2 7PH Tel: (01782) 538777 Fax: (01782) 538777 *Ceramic transfer wholesalers*

▶ Tudor Associates Ltd, Stallington Hall Farm, Stallington Road, Blythe Bridge, Stoke-On-Trent, ST11 9QJ Tel: (01782) 388439 Fax: (01782) 399737 E-mail: rosiepatterson@hotmail.com *Mortgage & associated insurance brokerage*

Tudor Blinds, 5 Win Business Park, Canal Quay, Newry, County Down, BT35 6PH Tel: (028) 3082 5900 Fax: (028) 3082 5588 *Blind manufrs*

Tudor Bros (Flooring) Ltd, Unit 5 Warrior Business Centre, Fitzherbert Road, Farlington, Portsmouth, PO6 1TX Tel: (023) 9232 1244 Fax: (023) 9221 9267 E-mail: tudorbros@aol.com *Flooring contractor specialists*

Tudor Business Forms Ltd, 2 Meridian Centre, Vulcan Way, New Addington, Croydon, CR0 9UG Tel: (01689) 844888 Fax: (01689) 844999 E-mail: sales@tudorofficesupplies.co.uk *Computer stationery & contract stationers*

▶ Tudor Leaded Light Co., 9a Pinner Road, Watford, WD19 4EF Tel: (01923) 236932 Fax: (01923) 238210 E-mail: peter@tudorleadedlight.co.uk *Leaded light, glass contractors*

Tudor Press, 209 Oxford Road, Reading, RG1 7PX Tel: 0118-957 4197 Fax: 0118-957 5212 *General printer*

▶ Tudor Signs, 6 CWRT Y Coed, Brackla, Bridgend, Mid Glamorgan, CF31 2ST Tel: (01656) 650901 Fax: (01656) 650901 *Sign makers*

Tudor Storefitters Ltd, 17 Southfield, Welwyn Garden City, Hertfordshire, AL7 4ST Tel: (01707) 333048 Fax: (01707) 372626 E-mail: tudor999@aol.com *Shop fitters*

Tudor Stud Farm Equestrian Centre, Tudor Stud Farm, Chinnor road, Bledlow Ridge, High Wycombe, Buckinghamshire, HP14 4AA Tel: 01494 481056 Fax: 01494 481056 E-mail: tracey-tudorstudfarm@hotmail.co.uk *35 acre livery yard.*Indoor school.*Outdoor menage.*Solarium.*Plenty of hacking.*Large stables (19ft x 14ft).*24 hour security*

Tudorstone Building Materials Ltd, Daneshill Road, Lound, Retford, Nottinghamshire, DN22 8RB Tel: (01777) 816589 Fax: (01777) 817115 *Stone & concrete products manufrs*

▶ Tudorstone Stone Products, The Dale, Stoney Middleton, Hope Valley, Derbyshire, S32 4TF Tel: (01433) 639005 Fax: (01433) 639656 E-mail: darlstone@ukonline.co.uk *Stone walling & masons*

Tuf Treads Dyfed Ltd, Coalbrook Road, Pontyberem, Llanelli, Dyfed, SA15 5HU Tel: (01269) 870134 Fax: (01269) 870443 *Tyre fitters & retreaders*

Tuf Work & Safety Wear, 26 North Road, Yate, Bristol, BS37 7PA Tel: (01454) 335050 Fax: (01454) 335001 E-mail: sales@tuf.com *Safety & protective wear sales*

Tuffa Bobbin Co., 10 Greycaines Industrial Estate, Bushey Mill Lane, Watford, WD24 7GG Tel: (01923) 222248 Fax: (01923) 817024 E-mail: sales@tuffabobbin.com *Textile machinery manufrs*

Tuffnell Glass, Unit 2b, 35 Eastgate North, Driffield, North Humberside, YO25 6DG Tel: (01377) 240745 Fax: (01377) 240746 E-mail: sales@tuffnellglass.co.uk *Scientific & artistic glass blowers, bead makers manufrs*

Tuffnells Parcel Express, Caswell Road, Brackmills Industrial Estate, Northampton, NN4 7PW Tel: (01604) 768765 Fax: (01604) 766116 *Road transport, haulage & freight services*

Tuffnells Parcel Express Ltd, P Yew Tree Trading Estate, Kilbuck Lane, Haydock, St. Helens, Merseyside, WA11 9UX Tel: (01942) 721313 Fax: (01942) 721498 *Parcel deliveries*

▶ Tuffnells Parcels Express Ltd, Azalea Road, Rogerstone, Newport, Gwent, NP10 9SA Tel: (01633) 891010 Fax: (01633) 891044 E-mail: nick.walters@tuffnells.co.uk *UK & international parcel carrier*

Tufthane Ltd, Falkland Close, Charter Avenue Industrial Estate, Coventry, CV4 8AU Tel: (024) 7646 0600 Fax: (024) 7669 4313 E-mail: admin@tufthane.com Principal Export Areas: Worldwide *Manufacture cast & moulded polyurethane components*

Tufting & Process Machinery Ltd, Commercial Mill, St. Pauls Court, Oswaldtwistle, Accrington, Lancashire, BB5 3HP Tel: (01254) 391400 Fax: (01254) 391332 E-mail: tpm@achinery.fslife.co.uk *Textile machinery manufrs*

Tufts & Whitton, 14 Old Norwich Road, Marsham, Norwich, NR10 5PS Tel: (01263) 732401 Fax: (01263) 734791 E-mail: mike@tuftswhitton.co.uk *Control panel manufrs*

▶ TUK Ltd, Unit 4, Wimbledon Stadium Business Centre, Riverside Road, London, SW17 0BA Tel: (020) 8946 6688 Fax: (020) 8879 7410 E-mail: stephen@tuk.co.uk *A long established supplier of data and telecoms cabling systems,*

continued

continuation
specialising in IDC connection strips, connection boxes, tools and accessories, modular/RJ type plugs and sockets, category 5, 5e and 6 cabling and more

Tuke & Bell, Galaxy Point, Patent Drive Moorcroft Park, Wednesbury, West Midlands, WS10 7XD Tel: 0121-506 7330 Fax: 0121-506 7333 E-mail: reception@tukeandbell.co.uk *Sewage treatment equipment manufrs*

Tulgrove Ltd, Jameson Road, Aston, Birmingham, B6 7SJ Tel: 0121-327 2296 Fax: 0121-328 5612 E-mail: tulgrove@tulgrove.co.uk *Presswworkers & welded assemblers*

Tulip Ltd, Mantle Lane, Coalville, Leicestershire, LE67 3DU Tel: (01530) 836501 Fax: (01530) 510708 *Meat manufrs*

Tulip Ltd, Beveridge Way, Hardwick Narrows Estate, King's Lynn, Norfolk, PE30 4NB Tel: (01553) 771937 Fax: (01553) 777139 *Processors of cooked meats* Also at: King's Lynn

Tull Properties Ltd, Bath Road, Box, Corsham, Wiltshire, SN13 8AA Tel: (01225) 744321 Fax: (01225) 744333 E-mail: office@tullprop.com *Property development company*

Tullett Liberty Number 3 Ltd, Cable House, 54-62 New Broad Street, London, EC2M 1JJ Tel: (020) 7827 2520 Fax: (020) 7827 2859 E-mail: enquiries@tullett.com *International money brokers*

Tullford Marketing, 37 Europa Way, Martineau Lane, Norwich, NR1 2EN Tel: (01603) 629649 Fax: (01603) 630186 E-mail: andrew@tullford.co.uk *Designers manufacturers and printers of pavement signs. Specialist printers of sticker and vinyl graphics.*

Tullibardine, Castleton Road, Auchterarder, Perthshire, PH3 1JS Tel: (01764) 662696 Fax: (01764) 662011 *Agricultural engineers*

Tullis Russell, Markinch, Markinch, Glenrothes, Fife, KY7 6PB Tel: (01592) 753311 Fax: (01592) 755872 E-mail: papermakers@trg.co.uk *Paper manufrs* Also at: Solihull

Tullis Russell Coaters Ltd, Church Street, Bollington, Macclesfield, Cheshire, SK10 5QF Tel: (01625) 573051 Fax: (01625) 575525 E-mail: enquiries@trcoaters.co.uk *Coated paper processors & converting services*

Tullis Russell Coaters Ltd, Brittains Paper Mills, Commercial Road, Hanley, Stoke-on-Trent, ST1 3QS Tel: (01782) 202567 Fax: (01782) 202157 E-mail: enquiries@trcoaters.co.uk Sales Contact: C. Butler Principal Export Areas: Worldwide *Decalcomania paper & coated paper & board manufrs*

▶ Tulloch Civil Engineering Ltd, Grigorhill Industrial Estate, Nairn, IV12 5HX Tel: (01667) 455014 Fax: (01667) 455128

▶ Tulloch of Cummingston, Minulay, Cummingston, Elgin, Morayshire, IV30 5XY Tel: (01343) 835622

John Tulloch Ltd, Rogers Road, Selkirk, TD7 5DT Tel: (01750) 20586 Fax: (01750) 22586 E-mail: office@johntulloch.co.uk *Knitwear manufrs*

▶ Tullos Training Ltd, Craigshaw Drive, West Tullos Industrial Estate, Aberdeen, AB12 3AL Tel: (01224) 872316 Fax: (01224) 894677 E-mail: info@tullostraining.co.uk *Training in engineering*

Tullyraine Quarries Ltd, 122 Dromore Road, Banbridge, County Down, BT32 4EG Tel: (028) 4066 2481 Fax: (028) 4066 2748 E-mail: enquiries@tullyrainequarries.co.uk *Quarry masters & road surfacing contractors*

Tullys Sewing Machines & Accessories, 5 Holmeside, Sunderland, SR1 3JG Tel: 0191-565 7995 Fax: 0191-565 7209 E-mail: tullysew@aol.com *Sewing machine repairs & services*

▶ Tumble Forge, 76 Bethesda Road, Tumble, Llanelli, Dyfed, SA14 6LG Tel: (01269) 841612 Fax: (01269) 832107 E-mail: sales@tumbleforge.co.uk *Fabrication*

▶ Tumble Tyres & Exhausts, B4 Llannon Road, Upper Tumble, Llanelli, Dyfed, SA14 6BT Tel: (01269) 845022 Fax: (01269) 845022

Tunbridge Wells Glass Works, 10-12 Tunnel Road, Tunbridge Wells, Kent, TN1 2BT Tel: (01892) 533141 Fax: (01892) 544215 E-mail: jan@twgw.co.uk *Glass merchants, replacement windows & doors services*

Tunedata Ltd, 21 Bournes Row, Hoghton, Preston, PR5 0DR Tel: (01254) 853174 Fax: (01254) 853174 E-mail: john.abbott@btinternet.com *Computer consultancy*

Tunewell Transformers, 2 Maple Park, Essex Road, Hoddesdon, Hertfordshire, EN11 0EX Tel: (01992) 801300 Fax: (01992) 801301 E-mail: sales@tunewell.com *Neon transformers*

Tungate Forms & Labels Ltd, Brookhouse Way, Cheadle, Stoke-on-Trent, ST10 1SR Tel: (01538) 755755 Fax: (01538) 756062 *Label & form manufrs*

Tungscarb Products Ltd, 5 Bodmin Road, Coventry, CV2 5DB Tel: (024) 7661 4498 Fax: (024) 7660 2173 E-mail: sales@tungscarbproduct.co.uk *Tungsten carbide products manufrs*

▶ Tungsten Alloys Manufacturing Ltd, Unit C2 Poplar Way, Catcliffe, Rotherham, South Yorkshire, S60 5TR Tel: (01709) 363633 Fax: (01709) 838089 E-mail: sales@tungsten-alloys.co.uk *Tungsten alloys manufrs*

Tungsten Die Co., 32 Cogan Street, Barrhead, Glasgow, G78 1EJ Tel: 0141-876 1516 Fax: 0141-876 1516 *Precision engineers, manufacturing dies*

Tungsten Die Services, 54 Ledger La, Wakefield, West Yorkshire, WF1 2PH Tel: 01924 835523 Fax: 01924 835523 *Tungsten carbide wire drawing dies*

Tungsten Manufacturing Ltd, 22-28 Cambridge Street, Aylesbury, Buckinghamshire, HP20 1RS Tel: (01296) 394566 Fax: (01296) 394566 E-mail: sales@tungsten.co.uk Principal Export Areas: Worldwide *Technology development of tungsten products*

▶ Tunics 2 U, 1076 Tollcross Road, Glasgow, G32 8UN Tel: 0141-764 0055 Fax: 0141-764 0055 E-mail: tunic.makers@ntlworld.com *Clothing manufrs*

Tunika Safety Products, Tannery House, Nelson Street, Bolton, BL3 2JW Tel: (01204) 366713 Fax: (01204) 366714 E-mail: sales@tunikasafety.co.uk *Protective & safety clothing manufrs*

Derek Tunnah Design Ltd, 3 Witney Way, Boldon Business Park, Boldon Colliery, Tyne & Wear, NE35 9PE Tel: 0191-519 1437 Fax: 0191-519 1484 E-mail: mail@derek-tunnah.co.uk *Engineering consultants*

Tunnel Engineering Services UK Ltd, Heywood Street, Oldham, OL4 2HA Tel: 0161-626 6005 Fax: 0161-627 0993 E-mail: info@tesuk.co.uk *Tunnelling machine equipment manufrs*

Tunnicliff Engineering Co. Ltd, 30 Derby Road, Hinckley, Leicestershire, LE10 1QF Tel: (01455) 637220 Fax: (01455) 637220 *Sheet metal work & machine shop services*

Thomas Tunnock Ltd, 34 Old Mill Road, Uddingston, Glasgow, G71 7HH Tel: (01698) 813551 Fax: (01698) 815691 E-mail: sales@tunnock.co.uk *Chocolate biscuits manufrs*

Tunstall Group Ltd, Whitley Lodge, Whitley Bridge, Goole, North Humberside, DN14 0HR Tel: (01977) 661234 Fax: (01977) 662570 *Electronic communication systems manufrs*

Tuplin Ltd, Unit 7-8 Bridge Industrial Estate, Balcombe Road, Horley, Surrey, RH6 9HU Tel: (01293) 433433 Fax: (01293) 433438 E-mail: sales@tuplin.co.uk *Export freight packers*

Tuplin Stansted Ltd, Unit 4 Birchanger Industrial Estate, Stansted Road, Bishop's Stortford, Hertfordshire, CM23 2TH Tel: (01279) 656461 Fax: (01279) 652520 *Export packers & freight forwarders*

Tupman & Hainey Ltd, Louisa Street, Worsley, Manchester, M28 3GA Tel: 0161-790 2664 Fax: 0161-703 8435 *Sheet metalworkers*

Turbex Ltd, Unit 1, Riverwey Industrial Park, Newman Lane, Alton, Hampshire, GU34 2QL Tel: (01420) 544909 Fax: (01420) 542264 E-mail: sales@turbex.co.uk Purchasing Contact: S Laker Sales Contact: S.J. Hancock *Turbex offers a very wide choice of Component Cleaning Machines, backed up by expert advice, on cleaning agents, component handling methods and process specifications. We supply single and multi stage spray washing machines, single and multi stage ultrasonic cleaning machines, tunnel washers, mould cleaning machines, dunking/agitation, basket rotation, jet turbulation, cascade deionising rinsing, hot air drying, spray lance cleaning, oil skimming, oil emulsion separation, steam extraction and filtration systems. At TURBEX we are able to provide total product support for all your component cleaning requirements, based on the concept of long term partnerships.*

Turbine Blading Ltd, Station Road, Shipston-on-Stour, Warwickshire, CV36 4BL Tel: (01608) 661805 Fax: (01608) 662249 E-mail: paul.levitch@ps.ge.com *Turbine blade manufrs*

Turbine Controls Ltd, 52 Kenilworth Drive, Oadby Industrial Estate, Oadby, Leicester, LE2 5LG Tel: 0116-271 7248 Fax: 0116-271 7250 E-mail: mk@turbinecontrolsltd.com *Turbine control systems manufrs*

▶ Turbine Services Ltd, Phoenix Business Park, Paisley, Renfrewshire, PA1 2BH Tel: 0141-849 6123 Fax: 0141-849 7023 E-mail: info@turbineserviceslimited.com

Turbine Support Ltd, 7 Dodnor Park, Newport, Isle of Wight, PO30 5XE Tel: (01983) 826252 Fax: (01983) 826253 E-mail: sales@turbine-support.com *Dynamic balancing gas turbines services*

Turbo Engineering Ltd, Unit 14, Prince Consort Industrial Estate, Hebburn, Tyne & Wear, NE31 1EH Tel: (0845) 4941706 Fax: 0191-483 6745 E-mail: dominic.rutherford@btinternet.com *Non-standard bolt & nut manufrs*

Turbo Force Ltd, Unit 21 Old Mill Industrial Estate, Bamber Bridge, Preston, PR5 6SY Tel: (01772) 697979 Fax: (01772) 697989 E-mail: sales@turboforce.co.uk *Turbo charger manufrs*

Turbo Power Services Ltd, Unit 2 Waldron Court, Prince William Road, Loughborough, Leicestershire, LE11 5GD Tel: (01509) 240020 Fax: (01509) 240030 E-mail: steve@turbopowerservies.com *Turbine maintenance & repair services*

Turbo Systems, 1 Gillett Street, Hull, HU3 4JA Tel: (01482) 325651 Fax: (01482) 211434 E-mail: mmoss@turbo-systems.com *Manufacturers of food, cosmetic & pharmaceutical processing equipment*

Turbo Technics Ltd, 2 Skitty Close, Brackmills, Northampton, NN4 7PL Tel: (01604) 764005 Fax: (01604) 769668 E-mail: enquiries@turbotechnics.com *Transport turbo charger manufrs*

▶ Turfmech Machinery Ltd, Hanger 5, New Road, Hixon, Stafford, ST18 0PF Tel: (01889) 271503 Fax: (01889) 271321 E-mail: sales@turfmech.co.uk *Plant & turf machinery suppliers*

▶ Turfonline, Westminster Chambers, 106 Lord Street, Southport, Merseyside, PR8 1LF Tel: (01704) 501555 Fax: (01704) 501333 E-mail: jenny.knight@turfland.co.uk *Turf order online, next day delivery's nationwide*

Turgelplan Ltd, 38-39 Somerset House, Somerset Road, London, SW19 5JA Tel: (020) 8947 8655 Fax: (020) 8947 8382 *Interior designer, contractors & linen embroiderers*

Turk Launches Ltd, Town End Pier, 68 High Street, Kingston Upon Thames, Surrey, KT1 1HN Tel: (020) 8546 2434 Fax: (020) 8546 5775 E-mail: operations@turks.co.uk *Passenger & party boat hire*

▶ Turkey Property Search, 11 St. Davids Crescent, Penarth, South Glamorgan, CF64 3LZ Tel: (029) 2071 1898 E-mail: s.burston1@ntlworld.com *Property search consultants for property for sale or to rent in Turkey*

Turkington Engineering Ltd, 14 Tullylagan Road, Cookstown, County Tyrone, BT80 9AY Tel: (028) 8676 3372 Fax: (028) 8676 3484 E-mail: tls@lineone.net *Pig & poultry housing manufrs*

Turkish Airlines, 125 Pall Mall, London, SW1Y 5EA Tel: (020) 7766 9300 Fax: (020) 7976 1733 E-mail: turkishairlines.uk@btinternet.com *Air flights*

Turkish Chamber Of Commerce & Industry, Bury House, 33 Bury Street, London, SW1Y 6AU Tel: (020) 7321 0999 Fax: (020) 7321 0989 E-mail: info@tbcci.org *Chambers of commerce*

▶ Turkish Estates Link Limited, 28 Skylines Village, Limeharbour, London, E14 9TS Tel: 0207 9872707E-mail: contact@turkishestateslink.com *London Based international estate agency selling residential and commercial properties in Turkey*

▶ Turks Head Inn, 49 Chapel Street, Penzance, Cornwall, TR18 4AF Tel: (01736) 363093 Fax: (01736) 360215 E-mail: info@turksheadpenzance.co.uk *Bar & restaurant*

▶ Turland Joinery Tewkesbury Ltd, Unit 1 Northway Lane, Tewkesbury, Gloucestershire, GL20 8JG Tel: (01684) 293245 Fax: (01684) 299444

Turley Associates Ltd, 43 Park Place, Leeds, LS1 2RY Tel: 0113-386 3800 Fax: 0113-244 3650 E-mail: leeds@rta.co.uk *Planning & development consultants*

Turley Associates Ltd, The Chancery, 58 Spring Gardens, Manchester, M2 1EW Tel: 0161-831 1300 Fax: 0161-831 1301 E-mail: enquiries@turley.co.uk *Consultants & chartered town planners*

▶ Turley Bros, 7 Corcreechy Road, Newry, County Down, BT34 1LP Tel: (028) 3026 6421 Fax: (028) 3025 0542

▶ Turn Key Air Conditoning Ltd, Unit S, Network Centre, Hebburn, Tyne & Wear, NE31 1SF Tel: 0191-496 3990 Fax: 0191-496 3991 E-mail: enquires@tkac.co.uk *Air conditioning equipment suppliers*

▶ Turnberg Homes Ltd, 18 Allerdyce Drive, Great Weston Retail Park, Glasgow, G15 6RY Tel: 0141-944 6544 Fax: 0141-944 9494

Turnbridge Engineering Ltd, Hanworth Court, Hanworth Road, Low Moor, Bradford, West Yorkshire, BD12 0SG Tel: (01274) 693699 Fax: (01274) 693944 E-mail: admin@turnbridge.co.uk *CNC machine services*

Turnbull & Co. Ltd, 95 Southgate, Sleaford, Lincolnshire, NG34 7RQ Tel: (01529) 303025 Fax: (01529) 413364 *Builders merchants*

Turnbull (Electro Platers) Ltd, Factory BT 75-4, North Seaton Industrial Estate, Ashington, Northumberland, NE63 0YB Tel: (01670) 854383 Fax: (01670) 854593 *Electroplating services*

Turnbull Scott & Co. Ltd, 5 Spring Lakes, Deadbrook Lane, Aldershot, Hampshire, GU12 4UH Tel: (01252) 343949 Fax: (01252) 343939 E-mail: enquiries@turnbullscott.co.uk *Holding company*

Turnbull & Scott Engineers Ltd, Glenfield Park One, Philips Road, Blackburn, BB1 5PF Tel: (01254) 586460 Fax: (01254) 586490 E-mail: sales@turnbull-scott.co.uk *Manufacturers of thermolier space heaters*

Turnbulls Truro Ltd, 97 Kenwyn Street, Truro, Cornwall, TR1 3BX Tel: (01872) 245155 Fax: (01872) 245150 *Car security & audio security installers*

Turncircuit Ltd, 13 Chaucer Bus Park, Watery Lane, Kemsing, Sevenoaks, Kent, TN15 6PW Tel: (01732) 763140 Fax: (01732) 763511 *Precision engineers*

Turnell & Odell Ltd, 61-65 Sanders Road, Finedon Road Industrial Estate, Wellingborough, Northamptonshire, NN8 4NL Tel: (01933) 222061 Fax: (01933) 440073 E-mail: sales@toengineering.co.uk *Precision engineers & CNC engineering services*

Turner & Co., Hamlin Way, Hardwick Narrows Industrial Estate, King's Lynn, Norfolk, PE30 4NG Tel: (01553) 692822 Principal Export Areas: Worldwide *Specialists in strapping machines*

Turner, 8-9 171 Church Hill Road, Thurmaston, Leicester, LE4 8DH Tel: 0116-269 7714 Fax: 0116-269 7717 E-mail: enquiries@mturnerservices.co.uk *Metal fabricators*

Turner & Co., 240 Sebert Road, London, E7 0NP Tel: (020) 8534 1843 Fax: (020) 8519 0057 *Monumental memorials*

Turner Aluminium Castings Ltd, 1 Robinson Close, Telford Way Industrial Estate, Kettering, Northamptonshire, NN16 8PU Tel: (01536) 525270 Fax: (01536) 412367 *Diecastings, aluminium & alloy & CNC machining*

Turner Aviation Ltd, Spiersbridge Terrace, Thornliebank, Glasgow, G46 8JQ Tel: 0141-638 2265 Fax: 0141-638 9694 E-mail: enquiries@turner-aviation.co.uk *Aircraft component over haulers* Also at: Aberdeen

Turner & Coates Ltd, PO Box 91, Salford, M6 6XG Tel: (0845) 8909870 Fax: (0845) 8909871 E-mail: info@turnerandcoates.com *Engineering & quality management consultants* Also at: Altrincham

Turner Construction Devon Ltd, Blue Ball Lodge, Stockland, Honiton, Devon, EX14 9DB Tel: 01404 881599 *Building work specialists*

Turner Contracting Services Ltd, 95 Rhyddwen Road, Craig Cefn Parc, Swansea, SA6 5RG Tel: (01792) 842732 Fax: (01792) 842732 *Civil engineers*

Turner Djesel Ltd, Unit 1a Dyce Industrial Park, Dyce, Aberdeen, AB21 7EZ Tel: (01224) 723925 Fax: (01224) 723927 E-mail: burtbutchart@turner-diesel.co.uk *Engine control services*

E. Turner Sons, 32 Cathedral Road, Cardiff, CF11 9UQ Tel: (029) 2022 1002 Fax: (029) 2038 8206 *Construction*

Edward W. Turner & Son, Logistics House, 80 Regent Road, Liverpool Freeport, Bootle, Merseyside, L20 1BL Tel: 0151-922 1888 Fax: 0151-933 3488 E-mail: eddie.magnall@dfwltd.com *Shipping*

▶ Turner Engineering (Farnborough) Ltd, Unit 6, Sandhurst, Berkshire, GU47 9DB Tel: 01252 860021

Turner Grain Engineering Ireland Ltd, 1 Station Road, Moira, Craigavon, County Armagh, BT67 0NE Tel: (028) 9261 1590 Fax: (028) 9261 2797 *Feed mill design & construction*

Turner Hire Drive Ltd, 65 Craigton Road, Glasgow, G51 3EQ Tel: 0141-440 1900 Fax: 0141-307 1213 *Scaffolding contractors*

▶ Turner Hire & Sales Ltd, Fitzwilliam House, Thames Street, Rotherham, South Yorkshire, S60 1LU Tel: 0114-258 1682 Fax: (01709) 830166

Turner Hydraulics, Old Station Yard, Magor, Caldicot, Gwent, NP26 3HT Tel: (01633) 881966 Fax: (01633) 881991 E-mail: ian@turnerhydraulics.co.uk *Hydraulic engineers* Also at: Magor

Turner & Jarvis Ltd, Dunton Road, Broughton Astley, Leicester, LE9 6NA Tel: (01455) 282028 Fax: (01455) 285347E-mail: turnjarvis@aol.com *Knitwear manufrs* Also at: Hinkley

John L. Turner Transport & Hydraulic Engineers, 41 Cumberworth Lane, Upper Cumberworth, Huddersfield, HD8 8PD Tel: (01484) 606798 Fax: (01484) 608512 *Hydraulic engineers*

Turner Langdale Ltd, 115 Beddington Lane, Croydon, CR0 4TD Tel: (020) 8689 5122 Fax: (020) 8689 3745 E-mail: sales@turnerlangdale.co.uk *Printer wrap manufrs*

Turner Machine Tools, 23 Waterloo Park, Bidford-on-Avon, Alcester, Warwickshire, B50 4JG Tel: (01789) 772921 Fax: (01789) 778614 E-mail: info@turner-riveters.co.uk Principal Export Areas: Worldwide *Riveting machine manufrs*

Turner Maintenance Ltd, Bessemer Road, Norwich, NR4 6DQ Tel: (01603) 626609 Fax: (01603) 626090 *Painting & building contractors* Also at: Sudbury

Turner Packaging Ltd, Horndon Business Park, West Horndon, Brentwood, Essex, CM13 3HW Tel: (01277) 810846 Fax: (01277) 810191 E-mail: service@turnerpack.co.uk *Packaging manufrs*

Peter Turner Fork Lifts Ltd, Wistons Lane, Elland, West Yorkshire, HX5 9DT Tel: (01422) 378900 Fax: (01422) 372492 E-mail: sales@peterturner-forklifts.co.uk *Forklift trucks training, supply & service*

Turner Power Train Systems Ltd, Racecourse Road, Wolverhampton, WV6 0QT Tel: (01902) 833000 Fax: (01902) 833750 E-mail: page_kevin_g@cat.com *Drivetrain manufrs*

▶ Turner & Pritchard, 9 Block C Tuffley Park, Lower Tuffley Lane, Gloucester, GL2 5DP Tel: (01452) 522488 Fax: (01452) 303653

Turner Removal Services, Huyton Road, Adlington, Chorley, Lancashire, PR7 4JR Tel: (01254) 56182 Fax: (01257) 484324 *Removal & storage specialists*

▶ Richard Turner Ltd, 101 Coupe Lane, Old Tupton, Chesterfield, Derbyshire, S42 6HA Tel: (01246) 861738 Fax: (01246) 863587 E-mail: info@ropeaccessuk.com *Industrial rope access contractors*

Sam Turner & Sons Ltd, Darlington Road, Northallerton, North Yorkshire, DL6 2XB Tel: (01609) 772422 Fax: (01609) 770653 E-mail: clothing@sam-turner.co.uk *Agricultural & horticultural hardware merchants*

▶ Turner Specialist Cleaning, Stopford Road, St. Helier, Jersey, JE2 4LZ Tel: (07797) 733183 *Carpet & curtain cleaning*

Stuart Turner Ltd, Market Place, Henley-on-Thames, Oxfordshire, RG9 2AD Tel: (01491) 572655 Fax: (01491) 573704 E-mail: sales@stuart-turner.co.uk *Pump manufrs*

Turner Sunblinds, Forrest Street, Blackburn, BB1 3BB Tel: (01254) 57763 Fax: (01254) 272101 *Sunblind manufrs*

Turner Tools Ltd, 15 Armstrong Close, St. Leonards-on-Sea, East Sussex, TN38 9ST Tel: (01424) 853055 Fax: (01424) 851085 E-mail: turnertools@turnertools.com *Machine tool supplies*

Turner & Townsend, 111 Charles Street, Sheffield, S1 2ND Tel: 0114-272 9025 Fax: 0114-275 3760 E-mail: she@turntown.co.uk *Construction consultants & quantity surveyors*

Turner & Townsend, Victoria House, Pearson Way, Thornaby, Stockton-on-Tees, Cleveland, TS17 6PT Tel: (01642) 611116 Fax: (01642) 612414 E-mail: tee@turntown.co.uk *Construction & management consultants services* Also at: Branches throughout the UK

Turner Vehicle Bodies Ltd, Carseview Road, Forfar, Angus, DD8 3BT Tel: (01307) 462142 Fax: (01307) 466070 *Refrigerated vehicle body manufacturers & converters*

W.A. Turner Ltd, Broadwater Lane, Tunbridge Wells, Kent, TN2 5RD Tel: (01892) 515215 Fax: (01892) 510028 E-mail: sales@waturner.co.uk *Sausage & pies manufacturers & frozen food processors*

Turner & Wilson Ltd, Road Three, Winsford Industrial Estate, Winsford, Cheshire, CW7 3PD Tel: (01606) 861191 Fax: (01606) 861231 E-mail: sales@turnerwilson.com *Stainless steel flue lining manufrs*

Turnercraft Cabinet Makers, 5 Furlong Parade, Stoke-on-Trent, ST6 3AX Tel: (01782) 837618 Fax: (01782) 837618 *Furniture manufrs*

Turners Bar Fitters & Joiners Ltd, Martins Mill, Pellon Lane, Halifax, West Yorkshire, HX1 5QJ Tel: (01422) 354984 Fax: (01422) 342770 *Bar & shop fitters*

▶ Turners Dairies, Myrtle Grove Farm, Myrtle Grove, Patching, Worthing, West Sussex, BN13 3XL Tel: (01903) 871520 Fax: (01903) 871524 *Dairy product manufrs*

Turners Of Felixstowe, 56 St Andrews Road, Felixstowe, Suffolk, IP11 7BT Tel: (01473) 610830 Fax: (01394) 273670 *Soft furnishing manufrs*

Turners Fine Foods, Spelmonden Farm, Spelmonden Road, Goudhurst, Cranbrook, Kent, TN17 1HE Tel: (01580) 212818 Fax: (01580) 212241 *Fine food manufrs*

▶ Turners Hoole Ltd, 53 Liverpool Old Road, Much Hoole, Preston, PR4 4GA Tel: (01772) 613434 Fax: (01772) 617666

Company Information

Turners Industrial Cleaning Systems Ltd, Leyden Works, Leyden Road, Stevenage, Hertfordshire, SG1 2BP Tel: (01438) 352802 Fax: (01438) 314188 E-mail: turners.carole@talk21.com *Office cleaning contractors*

Turners Removals, 7 The Courtyard, Crawley Road, Faygate, Horsham, West Sussex, RH12 4SE Tel: (01293) 852030 Fax: (01293) 852031 E-mail: turnersremovals@aol.com *Business & industrial removals services*

▶ Turners Soham Ltd, 1 Allerton Bywater Business Park, Newton Lane, Allerton Bywater, Castleford, West Yorkshire, WF10 2AL Tel: (01977) 603395 Fax: (01977) 603679

Turners Soham Ltd, Fordham Road, Newmarket, Suffolk, CB8 7NR Tel: (01638) 720335 Fax: (01638) 720940 E-mail: carol.chapman@turners-distribution.com *Road transport contractors & cold storage*

Turner's Tackle & Bait, 4a Station Road, Faringdon, Oxfordshire, SN7 7BN Tel: (01367) 241044 *Fishing tackle suppliers*

Turney Wylde Construction, Tyne View Terrace, Wallsend, Tyne & Wear, NE28 6SG Tel: 0191-295 8600 Fax: 0191-295 8601 *Building & plastering contractors.*

Turnfield Engineering, Unit D Bowyer Street, Birmingham, B10 0SA Tel: 0121-773 2923 Fax: 0121-766 8773 *Press tool manufrs*

Turnils (U K) Ltd, The Washington Centre, Washington Street, Dudley, West Midlands, DY2 9SB Tel: (01384) 233233 Fax: (01384) 239339 E-mail: sales@turnils.com *Canopy, awning & sunblind distributors*

Turnip House Knitwear, 24 Trassey Road, Newcastle, County Down, BT33 0QB Tel: (028) 4372 6754 Fax: (028) 4372 6754 E-mail: info@turniphouse.com *Clothing*

Turnkey, 114-116 Charing Cross Road, London, WC2H 0JR Tel: (020) 7419 9999 Fax: (020) 7856 7089 *Recording equipment manufrs*

Turnkey, 114-116 Charing Cross Road, London, WC2H 0JR Tel: (020) 7419 9999 Fax: (020) 7379 0093 *Recording equipment retailers*

▶ Turnkey Computer Technology Ltd, Thornton Lodge, East Kilbride Road, Clarkston, Glasgow, G76 9HW Tel: 0141-644 5444 Fax: 0141-644 5446 *Software house & hardware reseller*

Turnkey Instruments Ltd, Units 1-2 Dalby Court, Gadbrook Business Centre, Rudheath, Northwich, Cheshire, CW9 7TN Tel: (01606) 44520 Fax: (01606) 331526 E-mail: shop@turnkey-instruments.com *Dust control & monitoring system manufrs*

Turnkey Products Ltd, 1-2 Dalby Court, Gadbrook Business Centre, Rudheath, Northwich, Cheshire, CW9 7TN Tel: (01606) 445200 Fax: (01606) 331526 E-mail: shop@turnkey-products.com *Enclosures & electronic contract manufacturing*

Turnmil Engineering, Riverside Industrial Estate, Glanamman, Ammanford, Dyfed, SA18 1LQ Tel: (01269) 825684 Fax: (01269) 824650 E-mail: ceri@turnmil.co.uk *Special purpose machinery manufacturers & press tools etc.*

Turnock Ltd, Reaymer Close, Walsall, WS2 7QZ Tel: (01922) 710422 Fax: (01922) 710428 *Tunion range manufrs*

Turnomatic Ltd, Unit C8 Angel Road Works, Advent Way, London, N18 3AH Tel: (020) 8807 0661 Fax: (020) 8807 6134 E-mail: enquiry@turnomaticltd.com *Turned parts manufrs*

▶ Turnpike Press Ltd, Unit A1 Valley Link Estate, Meridian Way, Enfield, Middlesex, EN3 4TY Tel: (020) 8805 8850 Fax: (020) 8805 8851

Turnquest, Regent House, Bath Avenue, Wolverhampton, WV1 4EG Tel: (01902) 810075 Fax: (01902) 810078 E-mail: info@turnquest.co.uk *Supply & install of handrail & balustrade*

Turnshire Engineering Ltd, Unit 3, Acacia Close, Cherry Court Way, Leighton Buzzard, Bedfordshire, LU7 8QE Tel: (01525) 851202 Fax: (01525) 851202 *Mechanical engineers*

Turnstile Systems 2000 Ltd, Unit F4 Phoenix Trading Estate, London Road, Thrupp, Stroud, Gloucestershire, GL5 2BX Tel: (01453) 883590 E-mail: bert@turnstile.uk.com *Turnstile installers & manufrs*

Turnstyle Ltd, Claypole Lane, Dry Doddington, Newark, Nottinghamshire, NG23 5HZ Tel: (01400) 282342 Fax: (01400) 282353 *Pine bed manufacturer*

Turnstyle Designs, Baron Way, Roundswell Business Park, Barnstaple, Devon, EX31 3TB Tel: (01271) 325325 Fax: (01271) 328248 E-mail: sales@turnstyledesigns.com *Door knobs designers & manufrs*

Turnstyle Wood Turners, Leicester Street, Melton Mowbray, Leicestershire, LE13 0PP Tel: (01664) 562460 Fax: (01664) 562460 *Woodturners and pattern makers*

Turntech Precision Engineers, Unit 33 Liberty Close, Woolsbridge Industrial Estate, Three Legged Cross, Wimborne, Dorset, BH21 6SY Tel: (01202) 822040 Fax: (01202) 829146 E-mail: sales@turntech-precision.co.uk *Subcontract machinists*

Turnwell Engineering, 4 Heritage Way, Corby, Northamptonshire, NN17 5XW Tel: (01536) 260043 Fax: (01536) 260043 *Precision engineers*

Turnwright Ltd, 12 & 19 Barking Industrial Park, Alfreds Way, Barking, Essex, IG11 0TJ Tel: (020) 8591 2862 Fax: (020) 8594 6999 E-mail: sales@turnwright.freeserve.co.uk *Hospital bed & bed spares manufrs*

Turpin Barker Armstrong, 1 Westmead Road, Sutton, Surrey, SM1 4LA Tel: (020) 8661 7878 Fax: (020) 8661 0598 E-mail: tba@turpinba.co.uk *Insolvency practitioners, accountants & financial advisors* Also at: Sutton

Turpin Distribution Services Ltd, Pegasus Drive, Stratton Business Park, Biggleswade, Bedfordshire, SG18 8TQ Tel: (01767) 604800 Fax: (01767) 601640 E-mail: turpin@turpin-distribution.com *Academic journal, book distributors & online publishers*

Turpin Smale Foodservice Consultancy, Blackfriars Foundry, 156 Blackfriars Road, London, SE1 8EN Tel: (020) 7620 0011 Fax: (0870) 141 0397 E-mail: chris.brown@turpinsmale.co.uk

continued

Leading UK Catering Consultants - Peter Smale and Chris Brown - own this independent and well established consultancy. New project feasibility studies, catering tenders, operations audits and solid, practical advice on all aspects of the catering industry. Specialists in improving quality standards and financial contribution by strategic reviews, market tendering and in-house advice. Clients include:- Clubs - Royal Automobile Club Conference centres - Scottish Exhibition & Conference Centre Companies - Rolls Royce Councils - Enfield Borough Council Government - Ministry of Defence Hotels - Chester Grosvenor Leisure Attractions - Historic Royal Palaces Museums - Natural History Museum Palaces - Buckingham Palace Restaurants & Bars - Corney & Barrow Retailers - Tchibo Shows - Balmoral Show Societies - Royal Horticultural Society Theatres & Venues - Shakespeare's Globe Universities - University of Sussex

Turpins Packaging Systems Ltd, Kennedy Way, Clacton-on-Sea, Essex, CO15 4AB Tel: (01255) 423402 Fax: (01255) 473312 E-mail: sales@sleevit.com *Tamper evident packaging machinery*

Alan Turrell Furniture, Ffrwdy Drain, Llandeilo, Dyfed, SA19 6SA Tel: (01558) 822383 Fax: (01558) 822383 *Furniture manufrs*

Turrier Scales Ltd, Units 3-4, Vernon Trading Estate, New John Street, Halesowen, West Midlands, B62 8HT Tel: 0121-559 1127 Fax: 0121-561 1046 *Industrial scale manufrs*

▶ Turriff Academy, Victoria Terrace, Turriff, Aberdeenshire, AB53 4EE Tel: (01888) 563216 Fax: (01888) 568966

▶ Turriff Contractors Ltd, Cornfield Road, Turriff, Aberdeenshire, AB53 4BP Tel: (01224) 494148

Turriff Timber Products, Markethill Industrial Estate, Turriff, Aberdeenshire, AB53 4QY Tel: (01888) 563929 Fax: (01888) 563929 *Portable buildings, timber house kit manufrs*

The Turtle Partnership, Hofer House, 185 Uxbridge Road, Hampton, Middlesex, TW12 1BN Tel: (020) 8941 6994 Fax: (020) 8941 4730 E-mail: mike@turtleweb.com *Software developerst & support (lotus messaging)*

Turtle & Pearce Ltd, 30 Borough High Street, London, SE1 1XU Tel: (020) 7407 1301 Fax: (020) 7378 0267 E-mail: sales@flags-turtle.co.uk *FLAGMAKERS GROUP**A collective of three of the most established and respected names in the business, Able Flags, George Tutill and Turtle & Pearce, have been supplying flags since the early 19th century. Although investing heavily in modern methods of manufacture, Flagmakers still continue to produce flags using original techniques such as appliqué and hand painting. Over time, Flagmakers have continually added new and innovative products to their portfolio. From fibreglass flagpoles to the fashionable new flexi-poles and flags and from digitally printed corporate PVC banners to display bunting in a variety of substrates. Flagmakers - First for Flags, PVC & Exhibition Banners, Bunting, Hand Wavers, Sashes, Flagpoles and Banner Frames. Offices in London, Weybridge, New Milton, Dundee.*

Turtle Wax Ltd, East Gillibrands, Skelmersdale, Lancashire, WN8 9TX Tel: (01695) 722161 Fax: (01695) 716621 E-mail: enquiries@turtlewax.com *Car care manufrs*

▶ Turton Construction Ltd, Sovereign Works, Gelderd Road, Birstall, Batley, West Yorkshire, WF17 9PY Tel: (01924) 477324

Turton Manufacturing Ltd, Unit 3 The Furlong, Berry Hill Industrial Estate, Droitwich, Worcestershire, WR9 9AH Tel: (01905) 796166 Fax: (01905) 796199 E-mail: sales@turtonslimited.com *Protective clothing manufrs*

▶ Turton Plating Services, 9 Quarry Road, Chorley, Lancashire, PR6 0LR Tel: (01257) 264532 Fax: (01257) 241654

Turton Retail Systems, 18 Hillside Avenue, Bromley Cross, Bolton, BL7 9NG Tel: (01204) 307589 Fax: (01204) 307589 E-mail: sales@turtonretail.co.uk *Price marking equipment sales*

Turton Safety Ltd, 1 Britannia Park, Trident Drive, Wednesbury, West Midlands, WS10 7XB Tel: 0121-567 4100 Fax: 0121-567 4141 E-mail: sales@turton.co.uk *Protective clothing & safety product distributors*

Turvey & Co., 14 Glasgow Road, Edinburgh, EH12 8HZ Tel: 0131-334 0707 Fax: (0870) 0555651 E-mail: pam@turfys.com *Wig makers & suppliers*

▶ Tuscany Contract Fabrics, Century Park, Garrison Lane, Birmingham, B9 4NZ Tel: (07976) 616052 E-mail: tuscany_contract_fabrics@imageblinds.co.uk *Suppliers of blinds fabrics*

▶ Tuskala, Clarendon Business Centre, 38 Clarendon Road, Eccles, Manchester, M30 9EF Tel: 0161-789 5153 Fax: 0161-788 9470 E-mail: sales@tuskala.com *Computer resellers*

Tusting & Burnett (1938) Ltd, Pavenham, Bedford, MK43 7NX Tel: (01234) 826136 Fax: (01234) 824328 *Leather producers*

Tutbury Crystal Glass Ltd, Burton Street, Tutbury, Burton-on-Trent, Staffordshire, DE13 9NR Tel: (01283) 813281 Fax: (01283) 813228 E-mail: info@tutburycrystal.co.uk *Lead crystal glassware manufrs*

Tuthill Controls Group, Diplocks Way, Hailsham, East Sussex, BN27 3JS Tel: (01323) 841510 Fax: (01323) 845848 *Manufacturers of control cables*

Tuthill Linkage Ltd, Unit 41 Suttons Industrial Park, Reading, RG6 1AZ Tel: 0118-929 9900 Fax: 0118-966 5978 E-mail: dneave@tuthill.com *Rod ends & ball joint manufrs*

Tuthill Temperley, Wardington House, Wardington, Banbury, Oxfordshire, OX17 1SD Tel: (01295) 750513 Fax: (01295) 750036 E-mail: george.tuthill@wardington.com *Cider apple harvesting machinery manufrs*

Tuthill Vacuum Systems, Pennine Business Park, Pilsworth Road, Heywood, Lancashire, OL10 2TL Tel: (01706) 362400 Fax: (01706) 362444 E-mail: uksales@tuthill.com *Vacuum pump manufrs*

George Tutill Ltd, 9 Higham Road, Chesham, Buckinghamshire, HP5 2AF Tel: (01494) 783938 Fax: (01494) 791241 E-mail: info@flags-tutill.co.uk *FLAGMAKERS GROUP**A collective of three of the most established and respected names in the business, Able Flags, George Tutill and Turtle & Pearce, have been supplying flags since the early 19th century. Although investing heavily in modern methods of manufacture, Flagmakers still continue to produce flags using original techniques such as appliqué and hand painting. Over time, Flagmakers have continually added new and innovative products to their portfolio. From fibreglass flagpoles to the fashionable new flexi-poles and flags and from digitally printed corporate PVC banners to display bunting in a variety of substrates. Flagmakers - First for Flags, PVC & Exhibition Banners, Bunting, Hand Wavers, Sashes, Flagpoles and Banner Frames. Offices in London, Weybridge, New Milton, Dundee.*

Tutill Nicol Ltd, 1 Richmond Street, Liverpool, L1 1EE Tel: 0151-709 3319 Fax: 0151-707 8785 *Commercial stationers*

Tutin Garment Labels, 3 Imperial Works, Imperial Road, Nottingham, NG6 9GB Tel: 0115-975 7722 Fax: 0115-975 7744 E-mail: roger@tutin-labels.co.uk *Garment label printers*

Tutor Academy, 19 Marnland Grove, Bolton, BL3 4UJ Tel: (07006) 374147 E-mail: info@tutoracademy.co.uk *Come and visit Tutor Academy, the number one source for private tuition. Our agency matches the most suitable, experienced and qualified tutors with the needs of the student. One-to-one and online tuition are available in all academic subjects and foreign languages at your home, or the tutor's home, anywhere in the UK.**Tutor Academy gives you the best chance of finding the most suitable tutor, and a far greater chance than the resources of just one client could achieve. We have more experience, know-how and resources to ensure this is the case, can offer massive price reductions and offers that non-web based agencies find hard to supply.**Visit us now at**http://www.tutoracademy.co.uk**Thanks*

▶ Tutor Hall Ltd, 52 Braunston Gate, Leicester, LE3 5LG Tel: 0116-254 6798

Tutorpro Ltd, 10 High Street, Wellington, Somerset, TA21 8RA Tel: (01823) 661669 Fax: (01823) 661668 E-mail: general@tutorpro.com *Training software writers*

▶ Tutors 4 Computers, 25 Lower Bartons, Fordingbridge, Hampshire, SP6 1JB Tel: (07919) 094523 E-mail: Tutors4Computers@hotmail.co.uk *One-to-one computer tuition in your own home. Especially suitable for Senior Citizens but available to all. From £15 per hour.*

Tutte & Thomas, J 1 Liners Industrial Estate, Pitt Road, Southampton, SO15 3FQ Tel: (023) 8022 5343 Fax: (023) 8023 3446 E-mail: tutte.thomas@virgin.net *Wholesale footwear distribs*

▶ Tutti Bambini UK Ltd, Unit 18, New Southgate Industrial Estate, Lower Park Road, London, N11 1QD Tel: (0870) 8890390 Fax: (0870) 8890391 E-mail: webmaster@tuttibambini.co.uk *Suppliers of baby products & nursery furniture*

▶ The Tutu Shop, 2-4 Pendarves Street, Beacon, Camborne, Cornwall, TR14 7SQ Tel: (01209) 716833 E-mail: sales@thetutushop.co.uk *Tutu shop, fancy dress & club wear*

Tuv UK Quality Assurance Ltd, Surrey House, Surrey Street, Croydon, CR9 1XZ Tel: (020) 8686 3400 Fax: (020) 8680 4035 E-mail: london@tuv-uk.com *Inspection certificating engineers*

Tuxford & Tebbutt, 46-56 Thorpe End, Melton Mowbray, Leicestershire, LE13 1RB Tel: (01664) 502900 Fax: (01664) 502901 *Cheese manufrs*

TV Department Ltd, 3 Altrincham Road, Wilmslow, Cheshire, SK9 5ND Tel: (01625) 538835 Fax: (01625) 522898 *TV production for adverts*

▶ TV One, V Continental Approach, Westwood Industrial Estate, Margate, Kent, CT9 4JG Tel: (01843) 873311 Fax: (01843) 873301 E-mail: web@vinemicros.com *Video hardware manufacturers*

TV One, V Continental Approach, Westwood Industrial Estate, Margate, Kent, CT9 4JG Tel: (01843) 873311 Fax: (01843) 873301 E-mail: web@vinemicros.com Principal Export Areas: Worldwide *Conference production services*

▶ Tva Transformers Ltd, Unit 20/29, Teesway, North Tees Industrial Estate, Stockton-on-Tees, Cleveland, TS18 2RS Tel: (01642) 612444 Fax: (01642) 633997 E-mail: info@tvatransformers.co.uk *Current instrument transformer manufacturers*

▶ TV-BAY Ltd, PO Box 6090, Newbury, Berkshire, RG14 2BB Tel: (01635) 237237 Fax: (01635) 529966 E-mail: info@tv-bay.com *Broadcast, film & pro video equipment sale, wanted & hire*

▶ Tvedt Group Ltd, Alma House, 38 Crimea Road, Aldershot, Hampshire, GU11 1UD Tel: (01252) 318388 Fax: 01252 336894 E-mail: enquiries@tvedt.co.uk

TVI Home Appliance Centre, Unit 6 Peartree Lane, Dudley, West Midlands, DY2 0QU Tel: (01384) 571879 Fax: (01384) 482575 E-mail: tvi1@btconnect.com *Electrical retailers*

TVM Systems, 2 Newgate Court, Paradise Street, Coventry, CV1 2RU Tel: (024) 7625 7875 Fax: (024) 7625 6433 E-mail: sales@tvm-systems.co.uk *Computer maintenance & repairs*

TVM Workplace Improvements Ltd, PO Box 6, Wigan, Lancashire, WN6 8EF Tel: (01257) 254488 E-mail: sales@nofumes.co.uk *Workplace improvement dust extraction equipment*

TWC, The Drill Hall, 262 Huddersfield Road, Thongsbridge, Holmfirth, HD9 3JL Tel: (0800) 9171918 Fax: (01484) 685210 E-mail: claire_fisher@btconnect.com *TWC The Window Company Limited has become one of the U.K's leading & most respected replacement window companies. our claim to be the innovative window company is well supported by the many patents & patent applications that*

continued

have been submitted in respect of the materials, designs & construction used in our products. Our windows weather it be a Casement, Tilt & turn or Vertical Sliding Sash are fully sculptured inside & out and are available not just in White, but also over 1500 different colours. Fully concealed gaskets are as standard eliminating the unsightly black rubber seal usually associated with PVC-u windows. For a complimentary Brochure on any of our products including Windows, Doors & Conservatories please phone Free on 0800 917 1 918 or visit or Website www.twcthewindowcompany.net

▶ TWD Hosting Limited, 76 Oak Street, Shaw, Oldham, OL2 8EJ Tel: 01706 881126 E-mail: sales@twdhosting.co.uk *We supply website solutions to businesses - from new businesses to large existing companies... Experts in CMS"s, eCommerce and business promotion... We offer extreme support and it"s in plain English!*

▶ Tweedie Evans Consulting, First Floor, 55 High Street, Wells, Somerset, BA5 2AE Tel: (01749) 677760 Fax: (01749) 679345 E-mail: info@tecon.co.uk *TEC delivers practical long term solutions for contaminated land management, brownfield regeneration and geotechnical design*

Tweedy & Holt, Suite D106, Dean Clough Office Park, Halifax, West Yorkshire, HX3 5AX Tel: (01422) 363161 Fax: (01422) 355290 E-mail: sales@tweedyandholt.co.uk *Transport & distribution consultants* Also at: Peterborough

Tweeny, Kingfisher House, Wheel Park, Westfield, Hastings, East Sussex, TN35 4SE Tel: (07004) 893369 Fax: (01424) 751444 E-mail: sales@tweeny.co.uk *Domestic food waste unit manufrs*

Twelco Fabrications Ltd, Old Airfield, Belton Road, Sandtoft, Doncaster, South Yorkshire, DN8 5SX Tel: (01724) 710844 Fax: (01724) 710188 E-mail: twelcofabltd@aol.com *Security units & steel fabricators*

▶ Twelfth Man Marketing, 38 Garth Road, Bangor, Gwynedd, LL57 2SE Tel: (020) 7871 1781 E-mail: info@twelfth-man.com *Twelfth man marketing provides creative marketing strategies to both b2b and b2c markets. From market research, focus groups, and consumer psychology, to branding and positioning, campaign development and management.*

Twemlow & Co Manufacturing Ltd, 1-2 St. Peters Church Walk, Nottingham, NG1 2JR Tel: 0115-950 5997 *Jewellery manufacturers & repairers*

▶ Twenty Four Seven, 1 Marsel House, Stephensons Way, Ilkley, West Yorkshire, LS29 8DD Tel: (01943) 604777 Fax: (01943) 604800 E-mail: enquiries@247recruitment.org.uk *Supply of Locums & GP's throughout the UK.*

▶ Twenty Four Seven, 1 Marsel House, Stephensons Way, Ilkley, West Yorkshire, LS29 8DD Tel: (01943) 604777 Fax: (01943) 604800 E-mail: education@247recruitment.org.uk *Education consultancy working with teachers and schools throughout the UK*

▶ Twenty Seven, 34 Inchview Terrace, Edinburgh, EH7 6TQ Tel: 0131-467 6989 E-mail: enquiries@twenty-seven.co.uk *Twenty-Seven, exclusive hand made wedding stationery. Choose from the designs on our online gallery and request a free sample invitation. If you have your own idea - or would like your stationery to match your individual colour scheme - please call us to chat about it. A bespoke service is also available. Seating plans, table numbers & guest books available.*

Twenty Twenty Displays Ltd, Unit 25, Tregoniggie Industrial Estate, Falmouth, Cornwall, TR11 4SN Tel: (01326) 372520 Fax: (01326) 377243 E-mail: info@twentytwentydisplays.com *Design exhibition & sign manufrs* Also at: Nottingham

▶ Twentyfourseven Design & Print, The New Media Centre, Old Road, Warrington, WA4 1AT Tel: (01925) 240247

▶ Twentytwo Design, 1 Down Close, Portishead, Bristol, BS20 8BX Tel: (01275) 842768 E-mail: info@twentytwo.co.uk *Freelance graphic designers*

Twickenham Plating Group Ltd, 12-13 Balena Close, Poole, Dorset, BH17 7DB Tel: (01202) 692416 Fax: (01202) 600628 E-mail: info@pender.co.uk *Electroplaters*

Twickenham Plating Group Ltd, 7-9 Edwin Road, Twickenham, TW1 4JJ Tel: (020) 8744 1800 Fax: (020) 8744 2001 E-mail: info@twickenham.co.uk *Electroplating services*

Twide-Paragon Ltd, Glasshouse Fields, London, E1W 9JA Tel: (020) 7790 2333 Fax: (020) 7790 0201 E-mail: paragon@twigroup.co.uk *Roof lights, glazing & security glass manufrs*

C. Twigg & Son, Hope Street, Rotherham, South Yorkshire, S60 1LH Tel: (01709) 373146 Fax: (01709) 362747 E-mail: btwigg@btconnect.com *Motor bodywork specialists*

▶ William Twigg (Matlock) Ltd, 26 Bakewell Road, Matlock, Derbyshire, DE4 3AX Tel: (01629) 56651 Fax: (01629) 56123 E-mail: sales@twiggs.co.uk *Steel stockholders, fabrication engineers & general merchants*

▶ Twighlightzone, Green Pastures, Kentisbury, Barnstaple, Devon, EX31 4NN Tel: (0845) 2268145 Fax: (0845) 2268145 E-mail: frankie@twighlightzone.com *It services & support*

Twin Engineering Ltd, First Avenue, Bletchley, Milton Keynes, MK1 1DX Tel: (01908) 367018 Fax: (01908) 367093 E-mail: david.twin@btconnect.com *Welding &fabrication*

▶ Twin Services Ltd, 70-72 Skinner Street, Stockton-on-Tees, Cleveland, TS18 1EG Tel: (01642) 606067 Fax: (01642) 618551 E-mail: mail@twinservices.co.uk *Building Services Engineers*Providing Heating, Water services, ventilation, air conditioning, electrical work, plumbing etc.*

Twinbridge Engineering Co., Langley Place, Burscough Industrial Estate, Ormskirk, Lancashire, L40 8JS Tel: (01704) 892959 Fax: (01704) 894892 E-mail: sales@twinbridge.co.uk *Precision & general engineers*

Twinfix Ltd, 201 Cavendish Place, Birchwood, Warrington, WA3 6WU Tel: (01925) 811311 Fax: (01925) 852955 E-mail: gjk@twinfix.com *Roof glazing product suppliers*

Twinjet Aircraft Sales Ltd, Essex House, Proctor Way, Luton, LU2 9PE Tel: (01582) 452888 Fax: (01582) 400098 E-mail: jets@twinjet.co.uk *Aircraft leasing, chartering & sale services*

▶ Twinkle Clean, Bexleyheath, Kent, DA7 9DH Tel: (0870) 0669919 E-mail: clean@twinkleclean.com *Cleaning services*

▶ Twinkle Nights, 79 Bennetts Castle Lane, Dagenham, Essex, RM8 3YB Tel: (020) 8599 0741

Twinstar Chemicals Ltd, Cunningham House, Westfield Lane, Harrow, Middlesex, HA3 9ED Tel: (020) 8907 2944 Fax: (020) 8927 0683 E-mail: *Chemical distributors*

Twisted Fish Ltd, 1 Stan Hill, Charlwood, Horley, Surrey, RH6 0EP Tel: (01293) 863763 Fax: (01293) 863201 *Computer reseller & consultants*

Twisted Octopus Ltd, 4 Spring Gardens, Watery Lane, Wooburn Green, High Wycombe, Buckinghamshire, HP10 0NZ Tel: (01628) 523159 Fax: (01628) 523159 E-mail: sales@twistedoctopus.com *Design for Print Branding Web Design Multimedia Copywriting Photography Art Direction Advertising Exhibitions Packaging Print Management*

Twistlink Ltd, Stadon Road, Anstey, Leicester, LE7 7AY Tel: 0116-236 1860 Fax: 0116-236 6423 E-mail: sales@fabmania.com *Manufacturers of all types of braid, cord, bootlaces, woven tape, webbing and elastics. Our web site illustrates over 1500 items in stock, our make to order service offers speed and flexibility on design and colour.*

▶ Twistyfish, 38 Overnhill Road, Bristol, BS16 5DP Tel: (07729) 290896 E-mail: sales@twistyfish.co.uk *Kite surfing & extreme sport related t -shirt manufrs*

▶ Two & A Half, 9 Queens Road, Enfield, Middlesex, EN1 1NE Tel: (020) 8363 6709 Fax: (020) 8363 6709 E-mail: enquiries@twoandahalf.co.uk *Designers of hand made garden water sculptures*

Two Bee's, Minkstone Works, Normacot Road, Stoke-on-Trent, ST3 1PR Tel: (01782) 313280 Fax: (01782) 313055 *General joiners & manufrs*

Two Guys, 27a Burnaby Close, Basingstoke, Hampshire, RG22 6UJ Tel: (01256) 464981 Fax: (01256) 464356 *Fishing tackle retail*

▶ Two Heads Global Design Ltd, Kit Lane, Checkendon, Reading, RG8 0TY Tel: (01491) 681061 Fax: (01491) 682095 E-mail: victoria@2heads.tv *Exhibitions *Interiors *Marcomms *Digital media**

Two Star Fashions Ltd, 53 Hatter Street, Manchester, M4 5FU Tel: 0161-832 5318 Fax: 0161-839 9779 *Clothing manufacturers for children & women*

Two Wests & Elliott Ltd, Carrwood Road, Chesterfield, Derbyshire, S41 9RH Tel: (01246) 451077 Fax: (01246) 260115 E-mail: sales@twowests.co.uk *Greenhouse equipment manufacturers & retailers*

Twyford Bathrooms Ltd, Lawton Road, Alsager, Stoke-on-Trent, ST7 2DF Tel: (01270) 879777 Fax: (01270) 873864 Principal Export Areas: Worldwide *Manufacturers of bathroom suites*

Twyford Cookers Ltd, Units 31-32 Three Elms Trading Estate, Bakers Lane, Hereford, HR4 9PU Tel: (01432) 355924 Fax: (01432) 272664 E-mail: sales@twyford-cookers.com *AGA cookers renovators*

Twyman Engineering Ltd, Unit J, Troon Way Business Centre, Leicester, LE4 9HA Tel: 0116-276 5953 Fax: 0116-276 5953 *Machining services*

Twyver Ltd, Unit 9 Chancel Close, Gloucester, GL4 3SN Tel: (01452) 525096 Fax: (01452) 356555 E-mail: dslater@twyverswitchgear.co.uk *Electrical engineers services* Also at: Branches throughout the U.K.

Tyack Export Sales Services, 52 Davies Road, West Bridgford, Nottingham, NG2 5JA Tel: 0115-981 1633 Fax: 0115-969 6030 E-mail: martin@exportsales.net *Export selling services*

Tychon Partnership, West Point, 78 Queens Road, Bristol, BS8 1QX Tel: 0117-907 5595 Fax: 0117-925 4556 *Property investment company*

Tyckam Engineering Ltd, 18 Levellers Lane, Eynesbury, St. Neots, Cambridgeshire, PE19 2JL Tel: (01480) 218282 Fax: (01480) 218282 *Engineering subcontract services*

Tyco, Jarrold Way, Bowthorpe Employment Area, Norwich, NR5 9JD Tel: (01603) 201201 Fax: (01603) 201333 E-mail: tycocontrolsystems.uk@tycoint.com *Control gear manufrs*

▶ Tyco Electronic Product Group, 160 Billet Road, London, E17 5DR Tel: (020) 8919 4000 Fax: (020) 8919 4040

Tyco Electronics, Kinmel Park, Bodelwyddan, Rhyl, Clwyd, LL18 5TZ Tel: (01745) 584545 Fax: (01745) 584780 E-mail: admin@pinacl.com *Data communication systems manufrs*

Tyco Electronics, Head Office, Faraday Road, Swindon, SN3 5HH Tel: (01793) 528171 Fax: (01793) 572516 E-mail: PICUK@tycoelectronics.com Purchasing Contact: J O'Brien Sales Contact: V Collier Principal Export Areas: Worldwide *Tyco Electronics is the world's largest passive electronic components manufacturer; a leader in cutting-edge wireless, fibre optic and complete power systems technologies and a provider of premise wiring components and systems. We provide advanced technology products from over forty well known and respected brands. Based on the interconnect and wire and cable technology leadership of AMP and Raychem,*

continued

Tyco Electronics has added a full complement of leading component brands to offer customers an unparalleled portfolio of connectors, relays, circuit breakers, cables, components, resistors, motors and a myriad of others across 25 product segments. Our ability to serve your requirements is realised through a strong R&D program, expertise in materials science, product design and process engineering, and our network of experienced application engineers, sales representatives and customer service personnel. We want to make your next generation of products successful.

Tyco Electronics, Head Office, Faraday Road, Swindon, SN3 5HH Tel: (01793) 528171 Fax: (01793) 572516 E-mail: passivesales@tycoelectronics.com *Electronic component manufrs*

Tyco Electronics Ltd Bowthorpe Emp, Unit 8 A Freshfield Industrial Estate, Stevenson Road, Brighton, BN2 0DF Tel: (01273) 692591 Fax: (01273) 601741 E-mail: craig.sutton@bowthorpe-emp.com *Manufacturers & suppliers of surge arresters*

Tyco Electronics Identifications, Chapel Farm Industrial Estate, Cwmcarn/Cross Keys, Cross Keys, Newport, Gwent, NP11 7ZB Tel: (01495) 273519 Fax: (01495) 272979 E-mail: sales@tycoelectronics.com *Tyco Electronics is the world's largest passive electronic components manufacturer; a leader in cutting-edge wireless, fibre optic and power systems technologies and a provider of premise wiring components and systems. We provide advanced technology products from over forty well known and respected brands. Tyco Electronics is a world class supplier of identification solutions, providing labels for every industry and application from industrial and commercial, to printing systems, software and technical support. We offer a variety of labels ranging from blank labels to high specification customised labels, fascias and membrane switch applications. A wide variety of manufacturing processes are used, including silk-screen, flexographic, letterpress, hot foil, direct laser engraving and thermal transfer. These processes combined with advanced material, ink and selected adhesives enable us to offer a solution for almost every industrial labelling application.*

Tyco Fire and Intergrated Solutions Ltd, Tyco Park, Grimshaw Lane, Newton Heath, Manchester, M40 2WL Tel: 0161-205 2321 Fax: 0161-455 4459 *Fire protection safety services*

Tyco Fire & Integrated Solutions, Tyco Park, Grimshaw Lane, Manchester, M40 2WL Tel: 0161-455 4475 Fax: 0161-455 4532 E-mail: wfs.doors.uk@tycoint.com *Manufacturers of industrial, security & fire doors*

Tyco Fire & Integrated Solutions, Molly Avenue, Mapperley, Nottingham, NG3 5FW Tel: 0115-955 1199 Fax: 0115-955 1919 E-mail: spectorlumunex.uk@tycoint.com *Emergency & public communications systems manufrs*

Tyco Fire & Intergrated Solutions, Unit 4 Bradley Hall Trading Estate, Standish, Wigan, Lancashire, WN6 0XQ Tel: (01257) 427164 Fax: (01257) 427490 E-mail: wfs.wigan.uk@tycoint.com *Manufacturers of industrial doors*

Tyco Fire & Intigrated Solutions, Unit 1A Howemoss Drive, Kirkhill Industrial Estate, Dyce, Aberdeen, AB21 0GL Tel: (01224) 255900 Fax: (01224) 255905 *Flow measurement sales & consultants*

▶ Tyco Health Care UK Ltd, Ashwood Crockford Lane, Chineham Business Park, Chineham, Basingstoke, Hampshire, RG24 8EH Tel: (01256) 708880 E-mail: info@kendallhq.com *Medical supply company*

Tyco Networks (UK) Ltd, Wheatley Hall Road, Doncaster, South Yorkshire, DN2 4NB Tel: (01302) 812712 Fax: (01302) 364738 Principal Export Areas: Africa, Central/East Europe, West Europe & North America *AC & fractional horse power electric motor manufrs*

Tyco Plastics Ltd, Armytage Road, The Industrial Estate, Brighouse, West Yorkshire, HD6 1PT Tel: (01484) 714313 Fax: (01484) 720452 E-mail: info@tycoplastics.com *Manufacturers of packaging*

Tyco Plastics Ltd, Unit 2 Westland Square, Leeds, LS11 5SS Tel: 0113-270 3737 Fax: 0113-270 0778 *Polyethylene converters & manufrs*

Tyco Plastics Ltd, Unit 2 Westland Square, Leeds, LS11 5SS Tel: 0113-270 3737 Fax: 0113-270 0778 *Packaging products manufrs*

Tyco Valves & Controls Distribution (UK) Ltd, Wellheads Terr, Wellheads Industrial Estate, Aberdeen, AB22 7GF Tel: (01224) 722562 Fax: (01224) 771607 E-mail: sales_aberdeen@tyco-valves.com *Valves training maintenance & manufrs*

Tyco Valves & Controls Distribution (UK) Ltd, Crosby Road, Market Harborough, Leicestershire, LE16 9EE Tel: (01858) 467281 Fax: (01858) 434728 E-mail: uk_sales@tyco-valves.com Principal Export Areas: Worldwide *Distributors & stockholders for valves*

Tyco Valves & Controls Distribution UK Ltd, White Moss Business Park, Moss Lane View, Skelmersdale, Lancashire, WN8 9TN Tel: (01695) 554800 Fax: (01695) 554835 E-mail: dny@tyco-valves.com *Boiler & heating equipment manufrs*

Tyf Adventure Ltd, 1 High Street, St. Davids, Haverfordwest, Dyfed, SA62 6SA Tel: (01437) 721611 Fax: (01437) 721692 E-mail: sales@tyf.com *Adventure equipment retailers*

Tyke Rollers Ltd, 1c Victoria Court, Colliers Way, Clayton West, Huddersfield, HD8 9TR Tel: (01484) 868331 Fax: (01484) 868332 E-mail: sales@tykerollers.com *Industrial rollers supply & manufrs*

Tyler Bros Sutton In Ashfield Ltd, Hunt Close, Lowmoor Business Park, Kirkby-in-Ashfield, Nottingham, NG17 7ER Tel: (01623) 758286 Fax: (01623) 756144 E-mail: admin@tybro.co.uk *Precision engineers*

▶ Tyler Packaging Ltd, Fosse Way, Chesterton, Leamington Spa, Warwickshire, CV33 9JY Tel: (01926) 651451 Fax: (01926) 651691 E-mail: info@tylerpackaging.co.uk *High performance manufrs*

Philip Tyler Polymers Ltd, Globe House, Love Lane, Cirencester, Gloucestershire, GL7 1YG Tel: (01285) 885330 Fax: (01285) 659774 E-mail: sales@philiptylerpolymers.co.uk *Plastic scrap & waste recycling*

Tyler Storage Ltd, 2 Compton Drive, Poole, Dorset, BH14 8PW Tel: (01202) 733344 Fax: (01202) 730228 *Storage equipment distributors*

Tylex Bropad Ltd, Ballingdon Hill Industrial Estate, Ballingdon Hill, Sudbury, Suffolk, CO10 2DX Tel: (01787) 371158 Fax: (01787) 311044 E-mail: tylex.polystyrene@btinternet.com *We design & manufacture anything in expanded polystyrene (EPS), polystyrene sheet, polystyrene, expanded polyethylene and flexible foams for display or transit packaging, EPS blocks, corners, edge protectors, loose fill, trays, all made to your specifications. We also offer cardboard and packaging products, bubble wrap, tapes etc. Please feel free to call.*

Tylex Products Ltd, Ashton Works, Cunliffe Road, Blackpool, FY1 6SD Tel: (01253) 765046 Fax: (01253) 791676 E-mail: tylex.polystyrene@btinternet.com *Polystyrene packaging manufrs*

Tyne Electro Diesel Ltd, Units 5-7, Noble St Industrial Estate, Newcastle upon Tyne, NE4 7PD Tel: 0191-226 1286 Fax: 0191-226 1438 E-mail: sales@tyneelectrodiesel.co.uk *Repair fuel injection equipment*

Tyne Gangway Structures Ltd, Howdon Lane, Wallsend, Tyne & Wear, NE28 0AL Tel: 0191-262 3657 Fax: 0191-262 1498 E-mail: info@tynegangway.co.uk *Ships fittings manufrs*

▶ Tyne Insulation Supplies, Firwood Industrial Estate, Thicketford Road, Bolton, BL2 3TR Tel: (01204) 302220 Fax: (01204) 302230 *Insulation suppliers*

Tyne Slipway & Engineering, Commercial Road, South Shields, Tyne & Wear, NE33 1RP Tel: 0191-455 4893 Fax: 0191-456 6396 *Ship repair*

Tyne Tees Packaging Ltd, Grindon Way, Heighington Lane Business Park, Newton Aycliffe, County Durham, DL5 6DQ Tel: (01325) 311114 Fax: (01325) 311301 E-mail: sales@tyneteespackaging.co.uk *Corrugated packaging manufrs*

Tyne Tees Power Tool Co., 96 Heaton Road, Newcastle upon Tyne, NE6 5HL Tel: 0191-265 9054 Fax: 0191-276 5872 *Repair services*

Tyne Tools, 17 Deer Park Road, Moulton Park Industrial Estate, Northampton, NN3 6RX Tel: (01604) 647020 Fax: (01604) 790668 *Toolmakers & services*

▶ Tyne Tube Ltd, Nile Street, South Shields, Tyne & Wear, NE33 1RH Tel: 0191-455 1144 Fax: 0191-455 4339 E-mail: enquiries@tynetubeservices.co.uk *Steel tube/pipeline fitting stockholders*

Tyne Tunnel Engineering Ltd, B3 Narvik Way, Tyne Tunnel Trading Estate, North Shields, Tyne & Wear, NE29 7XJ Tel: 0191-258 0585 Fax: 0191-296 1745 E-mail: enquiries@ttengineering.co.uk *Sheet metal fabricators & pipe work*

Tyne Valley TV Ltd, Unit 1 10 Front Street, Prudhoe, Northumberland, NE42 5HJ Tel: (01661) 832383 Fax: (01661) 832383 *Television rental services*

Tyne & Weir Timber, Lanesley Sawmill, Lanesley, Gateshead, Tyne & Wear, NE11 0EX Tel: 0191-491 3988 Fax: 0191-491 4054 *Pallet manufrs*

Tynedale Farm Services, Townfoot, Longtown, Carlisle, CA6 5LY Tel: (01228) 792377 Fax: (01228) 792377 *Agricultural merchants*

Tynedale Farm Services, John Peel Theatre, Station Road, Wigton, Cumbria, CA7 9BA Tel: (01697) 342060 Fax: (01697) 344067 *Agricultural merchants*

Tyneside Safety Glass, Kingsway North, Team Valley Trading Estate, Gateshead, Tyne & Wear, NE11 0JX Tel: 0191-487 5064 Fax: 0191-487 0358 E-mail: sales@safetyglass.co.uk *Safety glass manufrs*

Tynetec Ltd, Cowley Road, Blyth Industrial Estate, Blyth, Northumberland, NE24 5TF Tel: (01670) 352371 Fax: (01670) 362807 E-mail: sales@tynetec.co.uk *Electronic communication manufrs*

Tyne-Tees Filtration Ltd, Blue House Point Road, Portrack Industrial Estate, Stockton-On-Tees, Cleveland, TS18 2QL Tel: (01642) 617401 Fax: (01642) 617404 E-mail: enquiries@ttf-uk.com *Filter bag & sleeve manufrs*

Tynok Ltd, Midland Ho, Vicarage Road West, Woodsetton, Dudley, W. Midlands, DY1 4NP Tel: (01902) 887270 Fax: (01902) 880428 *Furnace manufrs*

Type Help, Unit 2 Triangle Ho, 2 Broomhill Rd, London, SW18 4HX Tel: 020 88752450 Fax: 020 88752422 *IT support*

▶ Type In Motion Ltd, 169 High Street, Boston Spa, Wetherby, West Yorkshire, LS23 6BH Tel: (01937) 844815 Fax: (01937) 845327 E-mail: enquiries@typeinmotion.co.uk *Offers corporate identity, web development, interactive design*

Typecast Machinery, 39 North Howard Street, Belfast, BT13 2AP Tel: (028) 9024 2366 Fax: (028) 9023 7735 *Printer equipment distributors*

Typerite Ltd, Upper Dromore Road, Warrenpoint, Newry, County Down, BT34 3PN Tel: (028) 4177 2111 Fax: (028) 4175 2022 E-mail: info@typerite.com *Manufacturer of printing consumables*

Typewriter & Equipment Co. Ltd, Teco House, High Street, Lye, Stourbridge, West Midlands, DY9 8LU Tel: (01384) 424416 Fax: (01384) 423423 E-mail: info@tecoltd.co.uk *Office stationary & furniture suppliers*

Typex Group, Newcastle House, Albany Court, Newcastle Business Park, Newcastle Upon Tyne, NE4 7YB Tel: 0191-256 4400 Fax: 0191-226 0252 E-mail: info@typex.com *Networking software & hardware service*

Typhoon Ltd, K Colindale Business Park, Carlisle Road, London, NW9 0HN Tel: (020) 8200 5688 Fax: (020) 8205 5088 *Exporters & importers of oriental products*

▶ Typing For Business, Ridge Mount, Middlewich Road, Wistaston, Nantwich, Cheshire, CW5 6PB Tel: (01270) 252065 E-mail: info@typingforbusiness.co.uk *Typing for Business offers a Virtual Secretarial Service including: Word Processing, Audio Transcriptions, both digital and analogue, all types of Typing and more, much, much more.*

The Typing Factory Romscot UK, 12 Renfield Street, Glasgow, G2 5AL Tel: 0141-221 1242 Fax: 0141-248 4652 E-mail: christian@typingfactory.com *We provide full package of high quality, low cost, secretarial services including typing/transcription, translation, printing, mass-mailing, data entry, PC maintenance, corporate design, web design, web programming, web hosting & software programming*

Typing Workshop, 60 Shirley Road, Croydon, CR0 7EP Tel: (020) 8655 3503 Fax: (020) 8655 3588 *Secretarial services*

▶ Tyre Crumb Limited, Long Acre, Long Lane, Bovingdon, Hertfordshire, HP3 0NE Tel: 07747 633338 Fax: 01442 833130 E-mail: Sales@TyreCrumb.com *Tyre recycling & rubber crumb supplier. Rubber Crumb supplied from horse menage (15-20mm, 0.05% metal impurity)to 3mm call for price (ex-works) and availability*

▶ John Tyre & Sons, 81 George Street, Dunoon, Argyll, PA23 8BP Tel: (01369) 702343 Fax: (01369) 702257 E-mail: johntyreandsons@aol.com *Metal fabrication*

Tyre Maintenance Supplies Ltd, 49 Springvale Industrial Estate, Cwmbran, Gwent, NP44 5BB Tel: (01633) 873512 Fax: (01633) 876096 *Tyre repair materials suppliers*

▶ Tyre Mountain, Unit 1 New Zealand Road, Stockport, Cheshire, SK1 4AG Tel: 0161 4809991 Fax: 0161 4808347 E-mail: Info@tyremountain.co.uk *We sell the full range of car & van tyres*

Tyre Team Ltd, Rutherglen, Wycombe Road, Saunderton, Princes Risborough, Buckinghamshire, HP27 9NP Tel: (01844) 273373 Fax: (01844) 273262 *Car & truck tyre distributors*

Tyre Vulcanising Heywood Ltd, 86-90 Chorlton Road, Manchester, M15 4AN Tel: 0161-226 2342 Fax: 0161-226 2342 *Tyre vulcanizes*

▶ Tyre Zone, K Trinity Trading Estate, Tribune Drive, Sittingbourne, Kent, ME10 2PG Tel: (01795) 430043 Fax: (01795) 439740 E-mail: sale@tyrezone.net *Tyre distributors*

▶ Tyre-Finder (ITBUK), Inhurst Avenue, Waterlooville, Hampshire, PO7 7QS Tel: (0845) 2301966 Fax: (0845) 2301966 E-mail: info@tyre-finder.co.uk *Suppliers classic & vintage tyres & tubes for car & commercial vehicle*

Tyrell Corporation Ltd, 17-19 Foley Street, London, W1W 6DW Tel: (020) 7343 5500 E-mail: sales@tyrell.co.uk *Professional media, film broadcasting*

Tyrella Rosettes Ltd, 3 4 Ewart Street Workshops, 2 Ewart Street, Saltney Ferry, Chester, CH4 0BL Tel: (01244) 680204 Fax: (01244) 671410 E-mail: sales@tyrella.com *Rosettes manufrs*

Tyremart Agricultural Ltd, Main Road, Long Bennington, Newark, Nottinghamshire, NG23 5DJ Tel: (01400) 283820 Fax: (01400) 283137 E-mail: sales@tyremart.co.uk *Tyremart (Agricultural) Ltd are part of the ADR group of companies which stock, distribute and sell ADR, COLAERT & ATW ranges of Axles, Suspensions, Wheel Units, Spring Drawbars and associated equipment.*

Tyresales Tyreplus Autoservice, Oxleasow Road, Redditch, Worcestershire, B98 0RE Tel: (01527) 528090 Fax: (01527) 501411 *Tyres, exhausts & shock absorbers*

▶ Tyresonline.NET, Units 8&9 Sandpits Ind Est, Summerhill Street, Birmingham, B1 2PD Tel: 0870 746 4742 Fax: 0870 747 9139 E-mail: sales@tyresonline.net

Tyreways Ltd, Church Street, Uttoxeter, Staffordshire, ST14 8AA Tel: (01889) 564216 Fax: (01889) 564213 *Tyre & accessory retailers* Also at: Walsall

Tyrework Ltd, 343 Hatton Road, Feltham, Middlesex, TW14 9QS Tel: (020) 8751 3211 Fax: (020) 8884 0189 *Tyre repair*

▶ Tyrol Sales Co., 3 Fordview Estate, New Road, Rainham, Essex, RM13 8ET Tel: (01708) 526146 Fax: (01708) 525905 E-mail: tyrolsales@cwcom.net *Rough cast render hand tools*

Tyrolit Ltd, Eldon Close, Crick, Northampton, NN6 7UD Tel: (01788) 823738 Fax: (01788) 823089 *Abrasive manufrs*

Tyrone Brick Ltd, Coalisland Road, Dungannon, County Tyrone, BT71 6LA Tel: (028) 8772 3421 Fax: (028) 8772 7193 E-mail: sales@tyrone-brick.co.uk *Brick manufrs*

Tyrone Constitution, 25-27 High Street, Omagh, County Tyrone, BT78 1BD Tel: (028) 8224 2721 Fax: (028) 8224 3549 *Newspaper & printing*

▶ Tyrone Fabrication Ltd, 87 Goland Road, Ballygawley, Dungannon, County Tyrone, BT70 2LA Tel: (028) 8556 7200 Fax: (028) 8556 7089 *Metal enclosures manufacturers*

Tyrone Printing Co., Unit 179, Moygashel Mills, Moygashel, Dungannon, County Tyrone, BT71 7HB Tel: (028) 8772 2274 Fax: (028) 8772 6164 *General printers*

Tyrrell Services, 29 Cavendish Road, Woking, Surrey, GU22 0EP Tel: (01483) 776684 Fax: (01483) 776684 *Service & repair catering equipment*

Tyser & Co. Ltd, 12-20 Camomile Street, London, EC3A 7PJ Tel: (020) 7623 6262 Fax: (020) 7397 4852 *Insurance brokers*

▶ Darren Tyson, The Maltings, School Lane, Amersham, Buckinghamshire, HP7 0ES Tel: (01494) 729705 Fax: (01494) 729705 E-mail: enquiries@darrentysonfurniture.co.uk *Manufacturers of furniture*

Darren Tyson Furniture, 10 Lane End Road, High Wycombe, Buckinghamshire, HP12 4JF Tel: (01494) 445090 *Furniture manufrs*

Tyson H Burridge Ltd, Old Coach Works, Distington, Workington, Cumbria, CA14 5XJ Tel: (01946) 830333 Fax: (01946) 830777 E-mail: sales@haulagecumbria.co.uk *Road transport, haulage, freight & warehousing*

▶ Tyson L & Sons, Elland Road, Sowerby Bridge, West Yorkshire, HX6 4DB Tel: (01422) 823582 Fax: (01422) 823363

Tyson Sewing Machines Ltd, 4 High Street, Southall, Middlesex, UB1 3DA Tel: (020) 8574 1587E-mail: sales@tysonsewingmachines.co.uk *Sewing machines retailers*

▶ Tytan Jetting Ltd, Unit 1 Broomiesburn Road, Ellon, Aberdeenshire, AB41 9RD Tel: (01358) 729444 Fax: (01358) 729333 E-mail: enquires@tytan.co.uk *Pumps & cutting systems*

Tytherley Nurseries, Dean Road, West Tytherley, Salisbury, SP5 1NR Tel: (01794) 341213 *Horticultural nursery*

Tyzack Associates Ltd, Medius House, 2 Sheraton Street, London, W1F 8BH Tel: (020) 7758 4000 Fax: (020) 7758 4001 E-mail: info@tyzackassociates.com *Executive search services*

▶ Tyzack Machine Knives Ltd, PO Box 89, Sheffield, S9 2DZ Tel: 0114-221 1064 Fax: 0114-221 1090 E-mail: sales@tyzack.com *Manufacturer of guillotine shear blades, slide ways machine knives*

U B H International Ltd, Orrell Lane, Burscough, Ormskirk, Lancashire, L40 0SL Tel: (01704) 898500 Fax: (01704) 898518 E-mail: tanks@ubh.co.uk *Tank container & pressure vessel manufrs*

U B S Investment Bank, 100 Liverpool Street, London, EC2M 2RH Tel: (020) 7567 8000 Fax: (020) 7568 4800 *Merchant bankers*

U C B Celltech Ltd, 208 Bath Road, Slough, SL1 3WE Tel: (01753) 534655 Fax: (01753) 536632 *Prescription pharmaceutical product manufrs*

U C B Starkeys Technicast Ltd, 45 Kingston Way, Stockholm Road, Hull, HU7 0XW Tel: (01482) 825203 Fax: (01482) 878094 E-mail: enquiries@bi-group.com *Round & profile iron bar manufrs*

▶ U C I Logistics Ltd, Unit 131, Heathhall Industrial Estate, Heathhall, Dumfries, DG1 3PH Tel: (01387) 265268

U C M S, Brook Road, Wimborne, Dorset, BH21 2BJ Tel: (01202) 840111 Fax: (01202) 840204 *Computer services*

▶ U C M Timber Speciality Ltd, Roylance Buildings, 90-92 Waters Green, Macclesfield, Cheshire, SK11 6LH Tel: (01625) 616433 Fax: (01625) 511015 E-mail: sales@mercantile.uk.com *Import agents for timber products*

▶ U C M Valeting, Orchard Cottage, Church Road, Ardley, Bicester, Oxfordshire, OX27 7NP Tel: (0700) 5982193 E-mail: mark@ucmvaleting.com *Covering Bucks & Oxon we provide our customers with a first class service time & again! With valets starting from as little as £20.00 you can''t go wrong!*

U C P Ltd, 117 Baltimore Road, Birmingham, B42 1AA Tel: 0121-358 0400 Fax: 0121-358 3683 E-mail: info@ucp.co.uk *Cycle components & accessories & general engineering services*

U D O Mayfair, 28 North Audley Street, London, W1K 6JH Tel: (020) 7499 6216 Fax: (020) 7495 6136 E-mail: mayfair@servicepointuk.com *Printing & photocopying services*

U Deserve a Medal, Tawel, Ely Valley Road, Coed Ely, Tonyrefail, Porth, Rhondda Cynon Taff, CF39 8PX Tel: (01443) 671174 E-mail: Enquiries@u-deserve-a-medal.co.uk *Traditionally, medals have been associated with sporting achievements, but U Deserve a Medal can provide a personalised custom medal to fit any occasion, be it an award, an event or just as an unusual gift.*

U E S Ltd, Newark Road South, Glenrothes, Fife, KY7 4NS Tel: (01592) 773275 Fax: (01952) 773753 *Asbestos removal contractors*

U F C Ltd, Synergy House, Guildhall Close, Manchester Science Park, Manchester, M15 6SY Tel: 0161-232 5500 Fax: 0161-232 5501 E-mail: info@ultrafine.co.uk *Custom synthesis & contract researchers*

U F G Storage Systems, 1a Lalleford Road, Luton, LU2 9JG Tel: (01582) 414173 Fax: (01582) 414173 *Installers of storage equipment*

▶ U G Foods UK Ltd, Unit B 10 Aladdin Workspace, Long Drive, Greenford, Middlesex, UB6 8UH Tel: (020) 8575 6353 Fax: (020) 8578 6354

U G S Ltd, Milford House, Priory End, Hitchin, Hertfordshire, SG4 9AL Tel: (01462) 440222 Fax: (01462) 440522 E-mail: betty.waterhouse@ugs.com *Computer software development services*

U Group Ltd, 1277 Coventry Road, Yardley, Birmingham, B25 8BP Tel: 0121-764 6400 Fax: 0121-764 7380 E-mail: admin@ugroupltd.com *U Group (formerly known as Unicorn Spirit Measures) has been established over 40 years. They are based in Yardley, Birmingham. Manufactures and supply spirit measures, bottle skips, bar trays, bottle brackets etc.*

Co U Help Ltd, 32 Beech Hill, Haywards Heath, West Sussex, RH16 3RX Tel: (01444) 440551 Fax: (01444) 441698 E-mail: info@compuhelp.co.uk *Computer consultants*

▶ U K A E A, Dounreay, Thurso, Caithness, KW14 7TZ Tel: (01847) 802121 *Nuclear research*

U K C Distribution Ltd, Unit 3, Tan La, Exeter, EX2 8EG Tel: (01392) 491919 Fax: (01392) 494567 *IT trade*

U K C Hospitality, Tanglewood, Giles Lane, Canterbury, Kent, CT2 7LX Tel: (01227) 828000 Fax: (01227) 828019 E-mail: hospitality-enquiry@kent.ac.uk *Conference facilities & organisers*

U K Cabling Ltd, 7 South View Road, Walton, Peterborough, PE4 6AG Tel: (01733) 321555 Fax: (01733) 322995 E-mail: sales@ukcabling.com *Data cabling installation & specialised cables manufrs*

U K Equipment Ltd, 48 Suttons Park Avenue, Reading, RG6 1AZ Tel: 0118-966 9121 Fax: 0118-966 4369 *Automotive equipment*

U K F Stainless Ltd, 12 Buntsford Park Road, Bromsgrove, Worcestershire, B60 3DX Tel: (01527) 578686 Fax: (01527) 837792 *Stainless steel stockholders*

▶ U K Logistic Solutions, Unit 23 Parsonage Ind Est, Forest Hall Road, Stansted, Essex, CM24 8TY Tel: 01279 817001 Fax: 01279 817004 E-mail: uklogistics@btconnect.com *National & International Express Transport Services. From letters to Freight at a competetive Rate.*

▶ U K P Ltd, Unit 12, Lawson Hunt Industrial Park, Guildford Road, Broadbridge Heath, Horsham, West Sussex, RH13 3JR Tel: (0870) 7707228 Fax: (0870) 7707229 E-mail: sales@ukp.co.uk *Electrical insulating paper, films & laminates manufrs*

U K R Transmissions Ltd, 249 Cotmanhay Road, Ilkeston, Derbyshire, DE7 8NE Tel: 0115-932 4572 Fax: 0115-944 0585 E-mail: sales@ukrtrans.co.uk *Industrial transmission specialists*

U K Solenoid Ltd, 115 London Road, Newbury, Berkshire, RG14 2AH Tel: (01635) 45991 Fax: (01635) 37807 E-mail: sales@uksol.co.uk *Control gear (electric) manufacturers. Also switches including isolating, control & enclosed For any sales enquiry please contact us via our direct sales line: 01635 262626*

U K Tapes Ltd, 5 Cooper Drive, Springwood Industrial Estate, Braintree, Essex, CM7 2RF Tel: (01376) 349090 Fax: (01376) 348989 E-mail: sales@uktapes.com *Specialist tape manufrs*

U L G Northumbrian Ltd, Gables House, 62 Kenilworth Road, Leamington Spa, Warwickshire, CV32 6JX Tel: (01926) 452464 Fax: (01926) 452465 E-mail: ulg@ulg.co.uk *Rural development services*

U M E C UK Ltd, Business Centre, Barham Court, Teston, Maidstone, Kent, ME18 5BZ Tel: (01622) 618780 Fax: (01622) 618782 E-mail: sales@umec.co.uk *Electronic component suppliers*

U Mole Ltd, Unit 11 Hardwick Road Industrial Estatepark, Hardwick Road, Great Gransden, Sandy, Bedfordshire, SG19 3BJ Tel: (01767) 677503 Fax: (01767) 677827 E-mail: info@umole.co.uk *Trench less no dig equipment provider*

U N C (International) plc, Mayflower Close, Chandlers Ford Industrial Esta, Chandlers Ford, Eastleigh, Hampshire, SO53 4AR Tel: (023) 8026 9866 Fax: (023) 8025 3198 E-mail: sales@umc.co.uk *Ship repairers & diving contractors*

▶ U P B Ltd, Whitehouse Distribution Centre, White House Road, Ipswich, IP1 5NX Tel: (01473) 742233 Fax: (01473) 743800 *Livestock farmers*

U P M Kymmene Ltd, 2 Victoria Street, Altrincham, Cheshire, WA14 1ET Tel: (0870) 6000876 Fax: (0870) 6060876 *Paper agents* Also at: Edinburgh & Manchester

U P M Kymmene Ltd, Weighbridge Road, Deeside Industrial Park, Deeside, Clwyd, CH5 2LL Tel: (01244) 284137 Fax: (01244) 285019 E-mail: info@upm-kymmene.com *Manufacture news print*

U P S Ltd, Newcastle House, Castle Boulevard, Nottingham, NG7 1FT Tel: (0845) 7877877 Fax: 0115-971 6049 *Courier services*

▶ U P S Direct, 6 Camross Drive, Shrewsbury, SY1 3XH Tel: (01743) 243833 Fax: (01743) 340555 E-mail: ghollis@upsdirect.com *UPS services generating sets install maintain power protection equipment suppliers*

U P S Installations Nl Ltd, 25B Somerville Road, Clady, Strabane, County Tyrone, BT82 9QZ Tel: (028) 7188 2257 *UPS installers*

▶ U Q G Ltd, 99-101 Cambridge Road, Milton, Cambridge, CB24 6AT Tel: (01223) 425601 Fax: (01223) 420506 E-mail: sales@uqgoptics.com Principal Export Areas: Worldwide *Optical engineering manufrs*

U R S A Automatic Gates & Traffic Barriers Ltd, Unit 24 Howard Court, Nerston Industrial Estate, East Kilbride, Glasgow, G74 4QZ Tel: (0845) 4300800 Fax: (01355) 234617 E-mail: sales@ursagates.co.uk *Electric gates,automatic gates, security gates,automatic security gates,barrier gates,traffic barriers,stainless steel barriers, automatic traffic barriers automatic parking systems ,automatic bollards,parking bollards ,electric bollards,manual bollards, road blockers,high security road blockers.*

U R S A UK Ltd, Crest House, 102-104 Church Road, Teddington, Middlesex, TW11 8PY Tel: (020) 8977 9697 Fax: (020) 8977 9456 E-mail: ursauk@uralita.com *Insulation materials*

▶ U R S Corporation Ltd, 243 West George Street, Glasgow, G2 4QY Tel: 0141-226 3611 Fax: 0141-248 3773 *Engineering consultancy*

U R S Corporation Ltd, St Georges House, 5 St Georges Road, London, SW19 4DR Tel: (020) 8944 3300 Fax: (020) 8944 3301 E-mail: europeaninformation@urscorp.com *Engineering & environmental consultants* Also at: Branches throughout the U.K.

▶ U R U Computer, 2 Nobel Square, Burnt Mills Industrial Estate, Basildon, Essex, SS13 1LS Tel: (01268) 728111 E-mail: sales@uru.uk.com *Computer systems consultants*

U S Filters Electrocatalytic Products, 9 Norman Way, Severn Bridge Industrial Estate, Portskewett, Caldicot, Gwent, NP26 5YN Tel: (01291) 426500 Fax: (01291) 426501 E-mail: sales@elcat.co.uk Sales Contact: P. Barton Principal Export Areas: Worldwide *Manufacturers of anode (plating), cathodic*

continued

protection systems, chlorination plant, corrosion control/monitoring systems, electrolytic chlorination (water sterilisation) & electrochemical deposition platers/plating services

U S G (U K) Ltd, 1 Swan Road, South West Industrial Estate, Peterlee, County Durham, SR8 2HS Tel: 0191-586 1121 Fax: 0191-586 0097 E-mail: sales@usg-europe.com *Suspended ceiling components manufrs*

U S I Ltd, Unit 1 Steadman Place, Riverside Business Park, Irvine, Ayrshire, KA11 5DN Tel: (01294) 222444 Fax: (01294) 222456 *Computers for the electronics industry repair upgrade circuit boards suppliers*

U S I Group Ltd, The Tube, 86 North Street, Manchester, M8 8RA Tel: (0845) 3734200 Fax: (0845) 3734300 E-mail: sales@usiltd.com *Buying & selling clearance branded stocks*

▶ U S I UK Ltd, 1 Steadman Place, Riverside Business Park, Irvine, Ayrshire, KA11 5DN Tel: (01294) 222444 Fax: (01294) 222456 *Repair & upgrade computer motherboards*

U S Steel Kosice UK Ltd, 46-54 High Street, Ingatestone, Essex, CM4 0DG Tel: (01277) 355155 Fax: (01277) 354649 E-mail: info@ussk.co.uk *Steel mill*

U T I Ltd, Skyway 14, Calder Way, Colnbrook, Slough, SL3 0BQ Tel: (01753) 681212 Fax: (01753) 764450 *Air freight forwarders* Also at: Glasgow & Manchester

U T I Worldwide (U K) Ltd, Reading Cargo Centre, Hyperion Way, Rose Kiln Lane, Reading, RG2 0JS Tel: 0118-986 9595 Fax: 0118-987 6074 *Freight forwarders services*

U T S Johnsons Removals Storage, Unit 1 Parker Industrial Estate, Mansfield Road, Derby, DE21 4SZ Tel: (01332) 371452 Fax: (01332) 298803 E-mail: moves@johnsons-rs.co.uk *Removal & storage contractors*

U T T Ltd, Ashton Close, Beaumont Leys, Leicester, LE4 2BN Tel: 0116-233 8884 Fax: 0116-233 8885 E-mail: sales@utt-ltd.co.uk *Tungsten carbide tool manufrs*

▶ U W G Ltd, 1 Chalk Hill House, 19 Rosary Road, Norwich, NR1 1SZ Tel: (01603) 767438 Fax: (01603) 767441 *Off shore equipment services*

U2 Sports Cars Ltd, Rowley Wood Lane, Hartwell, Northampton, NN7 2QT Tel: (01604) 863504 Fax: (01604) 863807 *Race car constructors*

Ubbink (U K) Ltd, Borough Road, Brackley, Northamptonshire, NN13 7TB Tel: (0845) 4563499 Fax: (01280) 705332 E-mail: info@ubbink.co.uk *Ubbink UK Ltd have been manufacturing and supplying high quality, high performance products to the construction industry for over 30 years and have probably the most comprehensive range of building products available today.*Ubbink is committed to sustainability; not only are our products designed to provide solutions which are environmentally friendly and energy efficient, but we are focussed on reducing the environmental impact of every part of our business. We select our materials meticulously, employ energy efficient manufacturing processes and work to reduce waste and carbon emissions throughout our organisation.*

▶ Ubermagic, 78 Western Road, Leigh-on-Sea, Essex, SS9 2PW Tel: (01702) 470573 E-mail: support@ubermagic.co.uk *We specialise in printing & stretching your photos onto canvas or printing them as a poster. Why not turn your photographs into Pop Art or into a stylish collage.*

Ubiquity Software Corporation, Suite B Building 3 The Eastern Business Park, Wern Fawr Lane, St. Mellons, Cardiff, CF3 5EA Tel: (029) 2081 7500 Fax: (029) 2081 7501 *Software house*

Ucl Coatings, Peartree Lane, Dudley, West Midlands, DY2 0QY Tel: (01384) 262747 Fax: (01384) 480262 *Paint spraying contractors*

UCM Timber P.L.C., 3rd Floor, Suffolk House, College Road, Croydon, CR9 1TH Tel: (020) 8680 9900 Fax: (020) 8681 8776 E-mail: sales@ucmtimber.co.uk *Hardwood agents*

Ucontrol Ltd, Units 24-25, Strawberry Lane Industrial Estate, Strawberry Lane, Willenhall, West Midlands, WV13 3RS Tel: (01902) 601441 Fax: (01902) 602503 E-mail: infr@ucontroll.com *Electric control gear manufrs*

▶ Ucs Civils Ltd, Rand, Market Rasen, Lincolnshire, LN8 5NJ Tel: (01673) 859200 Fax: 01673 859201

Uct Ltd, Abbot Street, London, E8 3DP Tel: (020) 7254 1650 Fax: (020) 7518 0302 E-mail: info@uctltd.com *Computer consultants*

Udare Ltd, Unit 2 Hampstead West, 224 Iverson Road, London, NW6 2HL Tel: (020) 7372 2220 Fax: (020) 7328 8803 *Fashion manufrs*

Uddeholm Steel Stockholders, European Business Park, Taylors Lane, Oldbury, West Midlands, B69 2BN Tel: 0121-552 5530 Fax: 0121-544 3036 E-mail: sales@uddeholm.co.uk *Leading producer of tool steels, high performance steels & strip steels.*

Udny Edgar & Co. Ltd, 314 Balham High Road, London, SW17 7AA Tel: (020) 8767 8181 Fax: (020) 8767 7709 *Mosaic & ceramic tile importers*

Ufcc, 9 Withcote Avenue, Leicester, LE5 6SW Tel: 0116-241 6776 *Fibre optics installation*

Ufone Precision Engineers Ltd, Unit 21 Thornleigh Trading Estate, Dudley, West Midlands, DY2 8UB Tel: (01384) 233288 Fax: (01384) 252931 E-mail: enquiries@ufone-eng.com *Sub-contract machining services*

Ugitech UK Ltd, Units 14-15 Erdington Industrial Park, Chester Road, Birmingham, B24 0RD Tel: 0121-382 9494 Fax: 0121-386 1328 E-mail: sales@uginesavoie.usinor.com *Stainless steel bars*

Ugo Foods Group Ltd, 1 Hertsmere Industrial Park, Warwick Road Borehamwood, Borehamwood, Hertfordshire, WD6 1GT Tel: (020) 8207 0100 Fax: (020) 8207 1245 E-mail: info@ugogroup.com *Pasta & noodle manufrs*

▶ U-Install Irrigation, 39 Morrison Court, Stevenston, Ayrshire, KA20 4JS Tel: (07866) 492651 E-mail: tony@u-installirrigation.co.uk *Vibratory mole plough & trencher hire*

UJOB - UK Employment Vacancies, PO Box 139, Thornton-Cleveleys, Lancashire, FY5 4WU Tel: (0870) 7668565 E-mail: ujob@ujob.co.uk *1000's UK Job Vacancies across all sectors and UK/EIRE locations.Free CV builder service. Candidates can also upload CV's and apply directly to jobs. Register for EMAIL JOB ALERTS and receive job details direct to your inbox on a daily basis. Recruiters post job vacancies FREE.*

▶ UK Access Solution Ltd, Kelvin Way, West Bromwich, West Midlands, B70 7JY Tel: 0121-500 5055

UK Accreditation Service Ltd, 21-47 High Street, Feltham, Middlesex, TW13 4UN Tel: (020) 8917 8400 Fax: (020) 8917 8500 E-mail: info@ukas.com *Calibration & testing services*

▶ UK Air, 3000 Aviator Way, Manchester Airport, Manchester, M41 0TN Tel: 0161-266 1116 E-mail: ian.wilde@flyukair.com *UK Based worldwide air charter and aircraft positioning company*

UK Analytical Ltd, Lower Ground Floor, Dison Building, Buslingthorpe Lane, Leeds, LS7 2DG Tel: (0113) 2392 572 Fax: (0113) 2392 575 E-mail: uka@kirkstall.fsbusiness.co.uk *Research laboratory*

▶ UK Animal Livestock, Unit D2, Whitwood Enterprise Park, Whitwood Lane, Whitwood, Castleford, W. Yorkshire, WF10 5PX Tel: (01977) 667222 Fax: (01977) 667333

▶ UK Ansa-Call Limited, Marsh Farm Business centre, Bowling Alley, Crondall, Farnham, Surrey, GU10 5RJ Tel: 01252 850444 Fax: 0845 8800161 E-mail: beth@ansa-call.com *We provide professional contact services including brochure request handling, virtual receptionist services, CRM call handling, outbound telemarketing incl. lead generation, data cleansing and appointment setting. UK Ansa-Call own one of the largest B2B database in the UK containing records on over 1.8m businesses. This data is the most competitively priced in the UK with lists starting from just £80 per 00 records. Each list supplied is profiled to your exact selection criteria.*

▶ UK ATC, Royal Observatory Edinburgh, Blackford Hill, Edinburgh, EH9 3HJ Tel: 0131-668 8100 *Metalworking services*

▶ UK Automotive Finance Ltd, 3 Alfred St Garage, Alfred Street, Newton-le-Willows, Merseyside, WA12 8BH Tel: (01925) 227777 Fax: (01925) 226655 E-mail: dave@ukautomotivefinance.co.uk *UK Automotive Finance supply all your fleet needs from small pool cars*to executive limousines and the small site van up to 38t units. We combine*our buying power and fleet knowledge with our wide range of finance*packages to supply the best package to suit your requirements based on *cost, period, vehicle specification, corporate image and vehicle support.*Whether you require one vehicle or a fleet of cars and commercial vehicles*we look to provide good service and satisfaction.*

▶ UK Awnings, 8- 10 Ruxley Lane, Epsom, Surrey, KT19 0JD Tel: (020) 8394 0011 Fax: (020) 8394 0022 E-mail: info@uk-awnings.com *Patio awnings supplied & installed*

▶ UK Bathroom Interiors, 3/4 Old Laundry, Fishergreen, Ripon, North Yorkshire, HG4 1NL Tel: (0845) 2008526 E-mail: mark@ukbathroominteriors.com *UK based suppliers of contemporary bathroom furniture & fixtures*

▶ UK Biometrics, Henson Group, Comet Row, Killingworth, Newcastle upon Tyne, NE12 6RZ Tel: 0191-216 0550 Fax: 0191-216 0550 E-mail: info@ukbiometrics.co.uk *Finger print security systems & solutions supplies & manufrs*

▶ UK Blending Ltd, 9 Davy Road, Clacton-on-Sea, Essex, CO15 4XD Tel: (01255) 225002 Fax: (01255) 225003 E-mail: sales@uk-blending.com *Manufacturer of powdered food ingredients including sweet and savoury blends (bakery mixes, seasonings, marinades and chicken breadings. Contract packing from 500g - 25kg)*

▶ UK Blinds, 48 Moorside Crescent, Drighlington, Bradford, West Yorkshire, BD11 1HS Tel: 0113-285 2895

▶ UK Business Print Ltd, 15 Hendersyde Park, Kelso, Roxburghshire, TD5 7TU Tel: (01573) 224889 Fax: (01573) 223854 E-mail: sales@ukbrand.com *Business suppliers*

UK C M G, Suite A1, Kebbell House, Delta Gain, Watford, WD19 5BE Tel: (020) 8421 5330 Fax: (020) 8421 5457 E-mail: ukcmg@ukcmg.org.uk *Computer consultants*

UK Cables Ltd, London Distribution Centre, Westlands Industrial Estate, Millington Road, Hayes, Middlesex, UB3 4AZ Tel: (020) 8561 9111 Fax: (020) 8561 6777 *Electric cable distributors*

▶ UK Car Source, Martland Mill Garage, Martland Mill Lane, Martland Mill, Wigan, Lancashire, WN5 0LZ Tel: (07802) 422346 Fax: (01942) 248099 E-mail: dave@ukcarsource.co.uk *Vehicle supply*

▶ UK Care Products, Petre Street, Sheffield, S4 8LJ Tel: 0114-243 3377 Fax: 0114-243 3377 E-mail: mail@options4health.co.uk *Medical equipment suppliers*

UK Centre For Economic & Environmental Development, 48 Broadway, Peterborough, PE1 1SB Tel: (01733) 311644 Fax: (01733) 312782 E-mail: info@ukceed.org *Research institute*

▶ UK Circuits & Electronic Solutions Ltd, Stockfield Road, Chadderton, Oldham, OL9 9LG Tel: 0161-627 4050 Fax: 0161-633 4077 E-mail: sales@ukcircuits.co.uk *Printed circuit board assembly specialists*

UK Coal plc, Harworth Park Industrial Estate, Blyth Road, Harworth, Doncaster, South Yorkshire, DN11 8DB Tel: (01302) 751751 Fax: (01302) 752420 *Coal mining*

UK Computer Maintenance Ltd, Unit 13 The Glennmore Center, Waterwell Business Park, Quedgley, Gloucester, GL2 2 AP Tel: 0870 0261234 Fax: 0870 0262345 E-mail: Sales@ukcm.co.uk *Computer*

continued

continuation
maintenance and repair. Portable Appliance testing. Website development ,creation and hosting. Computer peripherals and equipment. Computer networking and cabling. Printer and notebook repair. VOIP.

UK Contracts Warwick Ltd, Thorn Way, Long Itchington, Southam, Warwickshire, CV47 9PF Tel: (01926) 813308 Fax: (01926) 813349 E-mail: ukcontracts@connectfree.co.uk *Joiners*

▶ UK County Couriers Ltd, 21 Malvern Drive, Ilford, Essex, IG3 9DP Tel: (0870) 4460810 Fax: (0870) 4460740 E-mail: ukcountycouriers@btinternet.com *Sameday: Quick response collections and immediate deliveries by dedicated vehicle throughout the UK and Europe. Custom: Tailor made solutions to your courier and transport problems - if it can be done, we can do it. International: Next day delivery to most of Europe. Expressed delivery to the rest of the world. Direct delivery service also available for the fastest possible delivery times. Nextday: A full range of timed delivery options. Distribution: Specialists in one-off, short lead-in national distribution projects. Storage: NEW - 00 square feet of storage is now available for high value motorcycle/vehicles. Nationwide collection/ delivery for safe storage is available in a CCTV, access controlled area, all at very competitive rates.*

▶ UK Deliveries (Birmingham) Ltd, Duddeston Mill Trading Estate, Duddeston Mill Road, Saltley, Birmingham, B8 1AP Tel: 0121-333 3640 Fax: 0121-333 3640 E-mail: ukdels@btconnect.com

▶ UK Diamond Tools, Tyrells Hall, Fowlmere Road, Shepreth, Royston, Hertfordshire, SG8 6QS Tel: (01763) 260430 Fax: (01763) 260430 E-mail: queries@schereltd.co.uk *Internet sales service*

UK Digital Storage Ltd, 91 Station Road, Forest Hall, Newcastle upon Tyne, NE12 8AQ Tel: 0191-280 0001 Fax: 0191-290 0001 E-mail: dbryce@ukdigitalstorage.com *UK digital storage documents & management systems services*

▶ UK Direct Couriers, Unit 10B, Gatehouse Trading Estate, Lichfield Road, Brownhills, Walsall, WS8 6JZ Tel: (01543) 372225

UK Distributors Footwear Ltd, Churchill Way, Fleckney, Leicester, LE8 8UD Tel: 0116-240 3485 Fax: 0116-240 2762 E-mail: footwear@ukdistributors.co.uk *Footwear wholesale distributors*

▶ UK Dynamo, The Innovation Centre, Epinal Way, Loughborough, Leicestershire, LE11 3EH Tel: (01509) 228864 E-mail: mc@ukdynamo.com *Commercial website development*

UK Electrical Links, 9 Marion Road, Furnace Green, Crawley, West Sussex, RH10 6QQ Tel: (0870) 7437802 Fax: (01293) 537436 E-mail: ajm@elec.co.uk *Internet directory publishers*

UK Estimating Support Ltd, First Floor, 125-129 Witton Street, Northwich, Cheshire, CW9 5DY Tel: 0845 644 5327 Fax: 0845 644 5328 E-mail: office@estimatingsupport.co.uk *Send Your Electrical Estimates, Mechanical Estimates to UK Estimating Support Ltd. We use SEC Electrical Estimating Software and Mechanical Estimating Software to produce your Electrical and Mechanical Estimates. We are Members of: ECA and HVCA. The Estimating Software produces a variety of Reports, to download a sample Electrical and Mechanical Estimate or PDF Brochure visit our Website. "Our Mechanical and Electrical Estimators are Professional, Experienced and Care about Winning Your Work" Electrical Estimating Service, Mechanical Estimating Service, Bid Management Software and Services, Building Engineering Services, Electrical Mechanical building services, CAD Drawing Service, Project Management - Bid Support, Electrical Contractor software. Construction Estimating Software, Electrical, Consultants - Estimating, Consultants - Mechanical, Documentation - Operating and Maintenance, Electrical manuals, Consulting Electrical Engineers, Electrical Estimating Services, Electrical Estimating Software, Operations and Maintenance manuals, Electrical Contractors Software.*

UK Exchangers Ltd, Unit 13 StileBrook Road, Olney, Buckinghamshire, MK46 5EA Tel: (01234) 244320 Fax: (01234) 714978 E-mail: sales@uk-exchangers.com *Plate head exchangers for industrial food, dairy, refrigeration & marine application.*

UK Filters Ltd, 3b High Street, Cheshunt, Waltham Cross, Hertfordshire, EN8 0BX Tel: (01992) 468804 *Electrostatic filter manufrs*

UK Fire International Ltd, PO Box 7708, Market Harborough, Leicestershire, LE16 8ZR Tel: (01536) 772261 Fax: *Manufacture fire fighting equipment*

UK Fire International Ltd, The Safety Centre, Mountergate, Norwich, NR1 1PY Tel: (01603) 727000 Fax: (01603) 727073 E-mail: norwich@ukfire.co.uk Principal Export Areas: Asia Pacific, Central Asia, Middle East, Africa, Central/East Europe & West Europe *Fire extinguishers*

UK Fire Protection Rentals Ltd, Alscott Mill, Alscott, Telford, Shropshire, TF6 5EE Tel: (01952) 250750 Fax: 0121-270 6575 E-mail: enquiries@ukfireprotection.com *Fire protection equipment, sales, service & rental*

UK FITTED KITCHENS, 10 Rosemary Road, Norwich, NR7 8ER Tel: (0800) 075 8100 E-mail: uk.fittedkitchens@fsmail.net *From Budget to Bespoke, UK FITTED KITCHENS offer you unbeatable quality and price, so whatever your budget we can help you achieve the kitchen of your dreams. With Free computer aided home design plus fixed price estimate means that for peace of mind contact UK FITTED KITCHENS on 0800 075 80 or visit our Norwich Showroom open 7 days a week on the ring road between ASDA and B&Q*

▶ UK Fly Control, Parkwood Estate, East Somerset Way, Wells, Somerset, BA5 1UT Tel: (01749) 673688 Fax: (01749) 673681 E-mail: candy@arkayltd.co.uk *Highest quality fly control equipment manufrs*

▶ UK Forks, Central House, Beckwith Knowle, Otley Road, Beckwithshaw, Harrogate, North Yorkshire, HG3 1UD Tel: (0800) 123101 Fax: (01423) 565657 E-mail: info@ukforks.com *UKForks, the industry's No.1 specialist rental provider of telescopic handlers, rough terrain straight mast fork lifts and attachments.*You can be assured that when it comes to your material handling requirements, UKForks is here to lift the load - providing you with the latest top quality equipment, technical expertise and first class support. In essence, we will bring you one step closer to achieving your project targets.*As a key integral business of Vp plc with over 50 years experience and expertise in the specialist field of plant hire, we continue to invest in new equipment and have a strategic distribution network throughout the country, meaning that you can be assured every piece of equipment you hire is the most reliable and safest available on the market today.*Furthermore, you will receive first class customer support and a full back up service that is second to none. National coverage for all your hire and service needs from one central number 0800 123 1*

UK Freephone, PO Box 800, South Ockendon, Essex, RM15 4WH Tel: (0870) 7485835 Fax: (0870) 7485329 E-mail: info@ukfreephone.co.uk *Business to business telecoms services suppliers*

▶ UK Fun, Martland Mill Garage, Martland Mill Lane, Martland Mill, Wigan, Lancashire, WN5 0LZ Tel: (01942) 217422 Fax: (01942) 248099 E-mail: dave@uk-fun.co.uk *Events equipment suppliers*

▶ UK Gse, 8 Midland Court, Central Park, Lutterworth, Leicestershire, LE17 4PN Tel: (01455) 558847 Fax: (01455) 558424

▶ UK HAIR SUPPLIES, 11 Denholme Avenue, Stockton-on-Tees, Cleveland, TS18 3QE Tel: (01642) 871716 E-mail: deborahmd@ntlworld.com *UK Hair Supplies sell hair extension equipment,human hair, silky straight, Keratin Glue Sticks, Fusion wand, digital unit, micro needles. weaving, training kits, human hair , glue gun, keratin, fusion system, shrinkies, micro rings, widest range of hair colours available, eyelash extension kits and training, acrylic nail extension kits and training, pre bond hair extension kits, hot keratin glue pots, keratin re bond flakes.pre bonded hair*

▶ UK Househunter, 343 Kenilworth Road, Basingstoke, Hampshire, RG23 8JW Tel: (01256) 422205 Fax: (01256) 422205 E-mail: ukhous@ukhousehunter.com *Sell your home, house, property on UK Househunter and save thousands. An alternative to the estate agent, saving homeowners around £4,000 with a cost-effective and simple way to sell their home. Don't move home without us!*http:// www.ukhousehunter.com*

▶ UK Hydroponic Suppliers Association, The Tower, Daltongate Business Centre, Daltongate, Ulverston, Cumbria, LA12 7AJ Tel: (07785) 788020 *The trade association for the United Kingdom Hydroponic Industry. Offering a central voice and a valuable on-going store locator on the website.*

▶ UK Industrial Roof & Cladding Ltd, Coombs Road, Halesowen, West Midlands, B62 8AE Tel: 0121-559 4250 Fax: 0121-559 4450 E-mail: ukroofclad@yahoo.co.uk

UK Industrial Supplies Ltd, Unit G Motorway Distribution Centre, Avonmouth Way West, Avonmouth, Bristol, BS11 9YT Tel: 0117-923 5653 Fax: 0117-982 0505 E-mail: admin@ukindsup.co.uk *Protective clothing & hose distributors*

▶ UK Land Solutions, Field House, 7 Victoria Avenue,, Westgate-on-Sea, Kent, CT8 8BG Tel: (01843) 834938 *Land sourcing agents to developers and self-builders.*

UK Landscape, 88 Moring Road, London, SW17 8DL Tel: (020) 8682 0624 E-mail: sales@uklandscape.net *Software, web design & online gallery*

▶ UK Locate and Trace Group, P O Box 76, Bolton, BL1 4WQ Tel: 08701 624961

▶ UK Lottery Online, Unit 142 Roslyn Road, South Tottenham, London, N15 5JJ Tel: (020) 8800 7271 Fax: (020) 8800 7277 E-mail: info@uk-lotteryonline.co.uk *We have great pleasure to welcome you to Virtual World Direct and the e-Lottery Syndicate System.**You can massively increasing your chances of scooping a jackpot in two of the world's richest, tax-free, lump-sum lotteries - and your chances of earning a substantial residual income*

▶ UK Magic - Magic Supplies & Services (Magicians & Entertainers), 1 Wakeford Cottages, Selden Lane, Worthing, West Sussex, BN11 2LQ Tel: (01903) 211785 Fax: (01903) 211519 E-mail: info@natzler.com *Entertainment agency & publisher*

▶ UK Maintenance Contractors, 497A Bolton Road, Ashton-in-Makerfield, Wigan, Lancashire, WN4 8TJ Tel: (01942) 716800 Fax: (01942) 712588

UK Marble Ltd, 21 Burcott Road, Hereford, HR4 9LW Tel: (01432) 352178 Fax: (01432) 352112 E-mail: sales@ukmarble.co.uk *Granite & marble suppliers & masons*

UK Marketing (1998) & Co Ltd, 4 Wicklow St, Middlesbrough, Cleveland, TS1 4RG Tel: 01642 456789 *Badges & emblems*

▶ The UK Office Ltd, 11 Faulkners Way, Leighton Buzzard, Bedfordshire, LU7 2SS Tel: (01525) 382050 Fax: (0845) 299 1922 E-mail: tuko@theukoffice.com *Suppliers of broadcast & media communications equipment including; DTV video encoders; E1/IP audio, voice and data multiplexers; MPEG-2/4, H.264 & Windows Media video encoders & servers; Broadcast Localizing technology; Uncompressed HD Transport; Wireless Microwave Radios.*

UK Offshore Operators Association Ltd, 232 Vauxhall Bridge Road, London, SW1V 1AU Tel: (020) 7802 2400 Fax: (020) 7802 2401 E-mail: info@ukooa.co.uk *Trade association*

UK Oils Birmingham Ltd, 115-119 Wainwright Street, Birmingham, B6 5TG Tel: 0121-328 8770 Fax: 0121-326 9770 E-mail: uk.oils@btconnect.com *Based in Birmingham, we are an independent Oil waste merchant. Our services include: Liquid waste disposal, Oil waste recycling, Oil waste disposal, Liquid waste removal, Marine fuel oil waste recovery, Site clearance contractors, Hazardous waste transportation, Waste oil collection systems, Hazardous waste disposal, Waste oil collection services, Waste treatment, oil and water separation, Waste disposal management services, Industrial waste disposal, Industrial waste processors, Liquid waste management, Waste collection services, Industrial liquid waste, and other services.**Please contact us on 0121 3288770*

▶ UK On-Line Shop, Administration Centre, Unit 1, Bell Road, Walsall, WS5 3JW Tel: 0121-357 9865 Fax: E-mail: ukon@bgtcom.co.uk *Mail order services*

▶ UK Operators Ltd, The Pin Mill, New Street, Charfield, Wotton-under-Edge, Gloucestershire, GL12 8ES Tel: (01453) 843121 Fax: (01453) 843079 E-mail: reception@ukoperators.co.uk

UK Packaging, 36-38 Nansen Road, Leicester, LE5 5FX Tel: 0116-273 4141 Fax: 0116-273 8181 E-mail: fardinsattar@hotmail.com *Packaging*

UK Packaging Supplies Ltd, 100 Brantwood Road, London, N17 0XY Tel: (020) 8801 8144 Fax: (020) 8365 0847 E-mail: sales@ukplc.co.uk *Corrugated carton distributors*

▶ UK Pavement Light Construction Luton Ltd, 18 Summers Road, Luton, LU2 9HS Tel: (01582) 724854 Fax: (01582) 455484 E-mail: info@ukpavementlight.co.uk *Pavement light, repairs, re-sealed, fire escapes & cellar flaps*

▶ UK Payroll, Gilbert Wakefield House, 67 Bewsey Street, Warrington, WA2 7JQ Tel: (01925) 631330 Fax: (01925) 638440 E-mail: info@uk-payroll.net *A comprehensive payroll service including bureau (outsourcing) for businesses and contractor pay solutions.*

▶ UK Plant & Diamond Drilling Ltd, 3 Church Street, New Pitsligo, Fraserburgh, Aberdeenshire, AB43 6NP Tel: (01771) 653447

UK Point Of Sale Group Ltd, Emery Court, The Embankment Business Park, Heaton Mersey, Stockport, Cheshire, SK4 3GL Tel: 0161-431 4400 Fax: 0161-431 4411 E-mail: info@ukpos.com *Point of sale display systems manufrs*

UK Power Systems Ltd, Hunmanby Industrial Estate, Hunmanby, Filey, North Yorkshire, YO14 0PH Tel: (01723) 892999 Fax: (01723) 892674 E-mail: sales@ukpowersystems.com *Generator installation services, maintenance & hire*

UK Precision Ltd, Unit 8 Newbery Centre, Airport Business Park, Exeter, EX5 2UL Tel: 01392 444066 Fax: 01392 444077 E-mail: info@ukprecision.co.uk *Qualtech Engineering Ltd & Yalesystems Ltd merged to become UK Precision Ltd. UK Precision is a sub-contract precision engineering company based in Chard & Exeter specialising in the supply of high quality machined components using the latest CNC technology. We have experience in many sectors including Motorsport, Medical, Marine, Defence, Hydraulics, Electronic and Rail. From simple washers to medical implant technology, we are proud to offer the ultimate professional service.*We have a solid reputation built on trust, innovation and professionalism. We don"t just produce parts, we provide an engineering support service to help you develop the best component solution for your needs. We believe that we have the skills to play a dynamic part in your success.*We have extensive experience of working in a wide variety of materials including Monel, Titanium, Stainless Steel, Steel, Aluminium and Plastics, providing customised parts for a variety of industrial and commercial uses.*

UK Prevention (Nottingham) Ltd, 53 York Dr, Princes Meadows, Nottingham, NG8 6PP Tel: 0115-942 5999 *Fire prevention equipment suppliers*

▶ UK Pumps Ltd, Knowsley Road, Haslingden, Rossendale, Lancashire, BB4 4RR Tel: (01706) 221979 Fax: (01706) 215620 E-mail: ukpumpsltd@hotmail.com *Concrete pumping contractors, hire & sale of concrete pumps*

UK Racing Castings, Unit 1-2 Argent Business Park, Argent Road, Queenborough, Kent, ME11 5JP Tel: (01795) 585454 Fax: (01795) 585488 E-mail: sales@uk-racing-castings.co.uk *Sand casting foundry manufrs*

▶ UK Recon, 9 Salkeld Street, Glasgow, G5 8HE Tel: 0141-429 7338 Fax: 0141 429 7338 E-mail: ukrecon@fsmail.net *Recondition cylinder heads & engines & all aspects of engine repairs*

▶ UK Sales Jobfinders Ltd, Saffron Walden, Essex, CB11 4JL Fax: (01799) 541117 E-mail: info@salesjobsfinder.co.uk *Sales Force Personnel Recruitment Agencies*

▶ UK Seating Direct, 47 Albert Street, Aberdeen, AB25 1XT Tel: 0870 6092106 Fax: 0870 6092105 E-mail: info@ukseatingdirect.co.uk *Seating retailers*

UK Shelving Ltd, Northwick Road, Canvey Island, Essex, SS8 0PS Tel: (01268) 515247 Fax: (01268) 510829 *Metal shelving suppliers*

▶ UK Shelving Ltd, Faraday Building, 136-144a Queen Victoria Street, London, EC4V 4BU Tel: (020) 7357 6489 Fax: (01268) 510829 E-mail: sales@ukshelving.co.uk *Shelving & racking manufrs*

UK Shopfront Shutters Ltd, Bridge Road, Southall, Middlesex, UB2 4AB Tel: (020) 8571 5553 Fax: (020) 8574 7066 E-mail: ukshopfronts@aol.com *Shop front shutter*

▶ UK Sign Co., Unit 9a Beauchamp Industrial Park, Watling Street, Wilnecote, Tamworth, Staffordshire, B77 5BZ Tel: (01827) 262277 E-mail: sales@uksigncompany.com *Sign makers & vehicle graphics*

UK Site Fix Ltd, 1 Spring Gardens, Frome, Somerset, BA11 2NU Tel: (01373) 452207 Fax: (01373) 452207 E-mail: jonhowell@tinyworld.co.uk *Steel fabricators*

UK Software Ltd, Innovation Centre, Millenium Way, Thanet, Broadstairs, Kent, CT10 2WA Tel: (01843) 609345 Fax: (01843) 609351 E-mail: sales@uksoftware.ltd.uk *Software suppliers*

UK Sportgear International Ltd, UK House, Freer Street, Nuneaton, Warwickshire, CV11 4PR Tel: (0870) 4031400 Fax: (0870) 4031399 E-mail: info@ukgear.com *Sports clothing suppliers*

UK Spring Supplies, 7 Elmwood, Sawbridgeworth, Hertfordshire, CM21 9NL Tel: (01279) 723666 Fax: (01279) 723729 E-mail: larryelmwood@aol.com *Circlip spring & wireshape manufrs*

▶ UK Stairparts, 18 Bowlers Croft, Basildon, Essex, SS14 3EE Tel: (01268) 284000 Fax: (01268) 534800 *Manufacturers of spindles, newels, handrails etc.*

UK Steel Export Ltd, Blackvein Industrial Estate, Cross Keys, Newport, Gwent, NP11 7PY Tel: (01495) 270033 Fax: (01495) 273190 E-mail: ukstlexp@aol.com *Steel exporters*

▶ UK Stone, Trench Farm, Red Hall Lane, Nr. Overton, Wrexham, LL13 0NA Tel: 01352 744973 Fax: 01352 750294 E-mail: info@ukstone.co.uk *Granite worktops and natural stone*

UK Systems Inc Ltd, 1a Grantham Road, Bingham, Nottingham, NG13 8BX Tel: (01949) 877020 Fax: (01949) 877771 E-mail: sales@uksl.com *Software vendor & consultants services*

UK Technology, 2 Hillside Cottages, Shirenewton, Chepstow, Gwent, NP16 6RU Tel: (01291) 641477 *Water management consultants*

UK Telcom, UK House, Springfield Road, Hayes, Middlesex, UB4 0LG Tel: (020) 8573 5052 Fax: (020) 8561 7758 *Electric cable manufrs*

uk therapist, 9 Kingsmill Industrial Estate, Cullompton, Devon, EX15 1BS Tel: 01884 33489 Fax: 01884 34519 E-mail: jane@uktherapist.co.uk *Recruitment website for Allied Health Professionals, Physiotherapists and Occupational Therapists*

UK Time Ltd, 1000 Great West Road, Brentford, Middlesex, TW8 9DW Tel: (020) 8326 6900 Fax: (020) 8326 6999 E-mail: sales@timex.com *Timex watches wholesale dealers & distributors*

▶ UK Trade & Investment, Kingsgate House, 66-74 Victoria Street, London, SW1E 6SW Tel: 020 7215 8000 E-mail: info@uktradeinvest.gov.uk *UK Trade & Investment is the Government organisation that helps UK-based companies succeed in an increasingly global economy. Its range of expert services are tailored to the needs of individual businesses to maximise their international success. We provide companies with knowledge, advice and practical support. UK Trade & Investment also helps overseas companies bring high quality investment to the UK's vibrant economy - acknowledged as Europe's best place from which to succeed in global business. We provide support and advice to investors at all stages of their business decision-making. UK Trade & Investment offers expertise and contacts through a network of international specialists throughout the UK, and in British Embassies and other diplomatic offices around the world. For further information please visit www.uktradeinvest.gov.uk or telephone +44 (0)20 7215 8000.*

UK Tyre Exporters Ltd, 131 Scrubs Lane, London, NW10 6QY Tel: (020) 8969 7796 Fax: (020) 8960 7863 E-mail: uktyres108@aol.com *Tyre exporters & recyclers*

▶ UK Windscreens, 44 Grassington Crescent, Liverpool, L25 9RU Tel: 0151 2844471 E-mail: info@ukwindscreens.co.uk *Windscreen Repair and Replacement in the Liverpool & North West area, Competitive Prices, Insuranc Billing, Windsceens, Heated rear windows, Bodyglass, Stone chips, Remove and Refit*

UK Worldwide Engineering Ltd, 21 Westhall Park, Warlingham, Surrey, CR6 9HS Tel: (01883) 624137 Fax: (01883) 624137 E-mail: brigil@compuserve.com *Coil winding machine manufrs*

▶ Uk250 Ltd, 2 Alpha House, Farmer Ward Road, Kenilworth, Warwickshire, CV8 2ED Tel: (01926) 863004 Fax: (01926) 863005 E-mail: info@uk250.co.uk *UK250.co.uk - online web directory, web guide with a selection of the best UK websites in 250 categories from Arts to Weekend Breaks.*

▶ UK-CentralHeating.com, Unit 29, Humphries Court, Whitley Road, Manchester, M40 7GB Tel: 0871 4744351 Fax: 0871 2360251 E-mail: sales@uk-centralheating.com *Domestic central heating systems providers*

Ukerna, Atlas Centre, Fermi Avenue, Chilton, Didcot, Oxfordshire, OX11 0QS Tel: (01235) 822200 Fax: (01235) 822399 *Computer software developers*

UKI Partnerships, Green Flag House, Cote Lane, Pudsey, West Yorkshire, LS28 5GF Tel: 0113-236 3236 Fax: 0113-257 3111 E-mail: rcroucher@directline.com *Breakdown repair & recovery services & insurance*

▶ UKL LONDON, Units 3-4 Dover House Industrial Estate, Witley, Godalming, Surrey, GU8 5QZ Tel: (01428) 682424 Fax: 01428 684900 E-mail: ukl@ucs-group.co.uk *Importers/ Wholesaler/distributors of Fruit of the Loom,Hanes,Stedman,Gildan,*Kustom Kit, and other leading t-shirts & sweatshirts*

UKO2, 1 Lamerton Way, Wilmslow, Cheshire, SK9 3UN Tel: (020) 7726 7123 E-mail: severine@netbooster.co.uk

▶ Ukp Accessories, Bank House, Bott Lane, Walsall, WS1 2JQ Tel: (01922) 640598 Fax: (01922) 611885 E-mail: enquires@ukpaccessories.com *Clothing trimmings distributors*

Company Information

▶ Ukrainian Information Service Ltd, 200 Liverpool Road, London, N1 1LF Tel: (020) 7607 6266 Fax: (020) 7607 6737

▶ uksaltwaterflies.com, 15 Bay View Terrace, Porthleven, Helston, Cornwall, TR13 9JQ Tel: (01326) 562753 E-mail: sales@uksaltwaterflies.com *Providers of fly fishing products*

Jennifer Ulisse Ltd, Warwick House, Monument Way West, Woking, Surrey, GU21 5ET Tel: (01483) 721614 Fax: (01483) 770644 E-mail: sales@jenniferulisse.com *Gift importers & sellers*

▶ Ullapool Construction Ltd, North Road, Ullapool, Ross-Shire, IV26 2XL Tel: (01854) 612244 Fax: (01854) 612911

Ullman International, 1 Stable Court Beechwoods, Elmete Lane, Leeds, LS8 2LQ Tel: 0113-201 8844 Fax: 0113-201 8855 *Textile agents*

Ullmann & Bamforth Ltd, York House, 67 Bradford Road, Brighouse, West Yorkshire, HD6 1ST Tel: (01484) 714033 Fax: (01484) 721339 E-mail: sales@ullmann-bamforth.co.uk *Man-made fibre & yarn merchants*

Fred E. Ullmann, 20-24 Kirby Street, London, EC1N 8TS Tel: (020) 7242 7810 Fax: (020) 7242 0205 *Jewellery manufrs*

Ulster Carpet Mills Ltd, Castleisland Factory, Garvaghy Road, Portadown, Craigavon, County Armagh, BT62 1EE Tel: (028) 3833 4433 Fax: (028) 3833 3142 *Carpet manufrs*

Ulster Carpet Mills Ltd, 322 King Street, London, W6 0RR Tel: (020) 8741 1100 Fax: (020) 8741 1640 E-mail: uclondon@ulstercarpets.com *Manufacturers of Axminster, Wilton & tufted carpets*

▶ Ulster Castings Ltd, 2-4 Bridge St, Comber, Newtownards, County Down, BT23 5AT Tel: (028) 9187 2372 Fax: (028) 9187 0088 E-mail: jneedham@ulstercastings.com *Light alloy casting & engineering services*

Ulster Ceramics, 29 Garvagh Road, Swatragh, Maghera, County Londonderry, BT46 5QE Tel: (028) 7940 1260 Fax: (028) 7940 1739 E-mail: ulsterceramics@btinternet.com *Manufacture ceramics*

Ulster Electro Finishes Ltd, 78 Ballyrashane Road, Coleraine, County Londonderry, BT52 2LJ Tel: (028) 7034 3022 Fax: (028) 7035 5985 E-mail: uefltd@aol.com *Electroplating plant & material suppliers*

Ulster Engineering Ltd, Cogry Mill, Cogry Road, Doagh, Ballyclare, County Antrim, BT39 0PU Tel: (028) 9335 2526 Fax: (028) 9335 2302 E-mail: sales@ulster-engineering.co.uk *Manufacturers & designers of industrial shredders*

Ulster Factors Ltd, 7 North Street, Belfast, BT1 1NH Tel: (028) 9032 4522 Fax: (028) 9023 0336 E-mail: wjm@ulsterfactors.com *Financial Factoring/Accounts Recievable Finance*

Ulster Fire Extinguishers Service, 58 Greystone Road, Antrim, BT41 1JZ Tel: (028) 9446 1524 Fax: (028) 9442 9515 *Servicing & supplying fire prevention equipment*

Ulster Industrial Explosives Ltd, Unit 1 Kilroot Park, Carrickfergus, County Antrim, BT38 7PR Tel: (028) 9335 1444 Fax: (028) 9335 1474 E-mail: info@uielimited.com *Explosive manufacturers & suppliers*

Ulster Livestock Care, 13 Ballygonny Road West, Moneymore, Magherafelt, County Londonderry, BT45 7NS Tel: (028) 8673 7500 Fax: (028) 8673 6426 *Agricultural merchants*

Ulster Weavers Apparel Ltd, 245 Castlewellan Road, Main Road, Moygashel, Banbridge, County Down, BT32 3SG Tel: (028) 4062 4490 Fax: (028) 4062 1100 E-mail: info@moygashel.com *Linen manufrs*

Ulster Weavers Home Fashions, Unit 1-6 St Helens Business Park, Holywood, County Down, BT18 9HQ Tel: (028) 9032 9494 Fax: (028) 9032 6612 E-mail: sales@ulsterweavers.com *Linen manufrs*

Ultima Business Systems Ltd, 448 Basingstoke Road, Reading, RG2 0LP Tel: 0118-902 7500 Fax: 0118-902 7400 E-mail: sales@ultimabusiness.com Principal Export Areas: Worldwide *Computer resellers*

▶ Ultimate Angling Centre, 118 Cambridge Road, Hitchin, Hertfordshire, SG4 0JN Tel: (01462) 440600 Fax: (01462) 434500 *Fishing tackle retailers*

▶ Ultimate Bite Ltd, 8 Eagle Road, Bristol, BS4 3LJ Tel: (07976) 730219 Fax: (07976) 730219 E-mail: mark.hall@ul.co.uk *Catering contract services*

▶ Ultimate Cleaners (Industrial) Ltd, Unit 9, Cousin Street, Dudley Road, Wolverhampton, WV2 3DG Tel: (01902) 451451 E-mail: sales@ultimateindustrial.co.uk *Wholesale & retail supply of personal protective equipment*

▶ Ultimate Days Ltd, PO Box 54, Pickering, North Yorkshire, YO18 7WZ Tel: (0845) 0652201 E-mail: sales@ultimatedays.com *Ultimate days specialises in corporate hospitality with a difference. Choosing Ultimate Days Hospitality will ensure the superior distinction is foremost in your client's mind.*

▶ Ultimate Decking, Breckbarn Cottage, Weston Road, Ringland, Norwich, NR8 6JL Tel: 01603 881171 Fax: 01603 880851 E-mail: Decking@paulmillbank.co.uk *Supplier of hardwood decking*

Ultimate Discount Heating, 28 Rushgrove Avenue, London, NW9 6QS Tel: (020) 8205 6688 Fax: (020) 8205 8899 *Heating suppliers*

Ultimate Ducting Sales, Unit 14 Riverside Court, Don Road, Sheffield, S9 2TJ Tel: 0114-242 5377 Fax: 0114-261 0495 *Ducting distributors*

Ultimate Hair Co., 104 Eastgate Centre, Basildon, Essex, SS14 1AG Tel: (01268) 282008 *Hairdressers equipment & suppliers*

Ultimate Hair Co., 15-17 Queens Road, Southend-On-Sea, SS1 1LT Tel: (01702) 433334 *Hairdressers equipment & suppliers*

Ultimate Hairdressing & Beauty Supplies, 10 George Road, Guildford, Surrey, GU1 4NP Tel: (01483) 566255 Fax: (01483) 574333 *Hairdressing products distributors*

▶ Ultimate It Ltd, 42a High Street, Egham, Surrey, TW20 9DP Tel: (01784) 477474 *Computer system consultants*

▶ Ultimate Loft Ladders, 28 Moore Close, Dartford, DA2 6NN Tel: (0800) 0157755 E-mail: sales@ultimateloftladders.co.uk *We specialise in fitting both aluminium and timber loft ladders. We also offer a loft flooring, insulation and lighting service. We cover London, Kent, Essex, Sussex, and Surrey (Southern England). Please call us on our freephone number for our brochure and price list or to check whether we cover your area.**We also offer a nationwide supply only service on all of our ladders.*

Ultimate Office Interiors, 307 Mariners House Queens Dock Commercial Centre, Norfolk Street, Liverpool, L1 0BG Tel: 0151-708 7700 Fax: 0151-708 7701 E-mail: liverpool@unilock.co.uk *Partition & interior contractors & suppliers*

Ultimate Signs, Business House, 1 Calow Lane, Hasland, Chesterfield, Derbyshire, S41 0AL Tel: (01246) 222555 Fax: (01246) 271030 E-mail: ian@ultimate-signs.com *Sign makers*

▶ Ultimate Storage Equipment Ltd, Unit 2, Northside Industrial Park, Whitley Bridge, Goole, North Humberside, DN14 0GH Tel: (0800) 0284377 Fax: (0800) 0284388 E-mail: info@useltd.co.uk *Suppliers of new and used warehouse storage equipment and sundries.*

▶ Ultimation Machines Ltd, Laundry Way, Capel, Dorking, Surrey, RH5 5LG Tel: (01306) 712205 Fax: (01306) 713182 *Manufacturers of wire forming & welding machines*

Ultra Clean, Hillside Cottage, Croesau Bach, Oswestry, Shropshire, SY10 9AY Tel: (01691) 670837 Fax: (01691) 670837 E-mail: philevo@btinternet.com *Contract cleaning, carpet & upholstery cleaning*

Ultra Contract Services, Camford Way, Luton, LU3 3AN Tel: (01582) 490000 Fax: (01582) 597038 E-mail: mail@ultracs.co.uk *Electrical & building shop fitters*

Ultra Dynamics Ltd, 2 Upperfield Road, Kingsditch Trading Estate, Cheltenham, Gloucestershire, GL51 9NY Tel: (01242) 707900 Fax: (01242) 707901 E-mail: sales@ultradynamics.demon.co.uk *Railway re-traders for marshalling yards*

▶ Ultra Electronics Ltd, 419 Bridport Road, Greenford, Middlesex, UB6 8UA Tel: (020) 8813 4444 Fax: (020) 8813 4568 E-mail: information@ultra-scs.com *Electronic manufrs*

Ultra Electronics Ltd, Armitage Road, Rugeley, Staffordshire, WS15 1DR Tel: (01889) 503300 Fax: (01889) 572929 E-mail: enquiries@pmes.com *Electronic systems manufrs*

Ultra Electronics Command & Control Systems, Knaves Beech Business Centre, Loudwater, High Wycombe, Buckinghamshire, HP10 9UT Tel: (01628) 530000 Fax: (01628) 524557 E-mail: info@ueccs.co.uk *Computer manufrs*

Ultra Electronics Electrics, Kingsditch Lane, Cheltenham, Gloucestershire, GL51 9PG Tel: (01242) 221166 Fax: (01242) 221167 E-mail: admin@ultra-electronics.com *Aerospace & defence electrical equipment*

Ultra Finishing Ltd, Heasandford Trading Estate, Burnley, Lancashire, BB10 2BE Tel: (01282) 436934 Fax: (01282) 428915 E-mail: sales@ultra-group.co.uk *Bathroom accessories & fitting manufrs*

Ultra Furniture, Churchill House Building 66, Third Avenue, Pensnett Trading Estate, Kingswinford, West Midlands, DY6 7GA Tel: (01384) 400240 Fax: (01384) 405048 E-mail: admin@ultra-furniture.co.uk *Lounge furniture manufrs*

Ultra Hard Products, Heath Farm Cottage, Cockaynes Lane, Alresford, Colchester, CO7 8DA Tel: (01206) 827121 *Industrial diamond manufrs*

Ultra Labels, 3 57a Gwendolen Road, Leicester, LE5 5FL Tel: 0116-273 7643 Fax: 0116-273 7643 *Computer cut vinyl letter & labels*

▶ Ultra Precision Engineering, 149 Camford Way, Luton, LU3 3AN Tel: (01582) 595365 Fax: (01582) 597385

Ultra Precision Products Ltd, Homefield Road, Haverhill, Suffolk, CB9 8QP Tel: (01440) 706030 Fax: (01440) 762828 E-mail: info@ultraprecision.co.uk *Precision engineers & precision turned parts*

▶ Ultra Tough Ltd, Unit J Field Way, Greenford, Middlesex, UB6 8UN Tel: (020) 8575 5050 Fax: (020) 8575 7033

Ultra Vision International Ltd, Commerce Way, Leighton Buzzard, Bedfordshire, LU7 4RW Tel: (01525) 381112 Fax: (01525) 370091 E-mail: lenses@ultravision.co.uk *Contact lens manufrs*

Ultrafine Technology Ltd, Unit 14 Brook Lane Business Centre, Brook Lane North, Brentford, Middlesex, TW8 0PP Tel: (020) 8569 9920 Fax: (020) 8569 9649 E-mail: sales@ultrafinetechnology.co.uk *Endoscope manufrs*

Ultralife Batteries UK Ltd, 18 Nuffield Way, Abingdon, Oxfordshire, OX14 1TG Tel: (01235) 542642 Fax: (01235) 535766 E-mail: drichards@ultralife.co.uk *Manufacturers of specialist batteries*

Ultralift Lifting Equipment, 4 Shipyard Road, Selby, North Yorkshire, YO8 8BN Tel: (01757) 213850 Fax: (01757) 700681 *Steel fabrications*

Ultramatrix Production Services Ltd, Farfield Works, Birds Green, Romsley, Bridgnorth, Shropshire, WV15 6HJ Tel: (01746) 780360 Fax: (01746) 780933 *Tent frame & pole manufrs*

Ultramedic Ltd, Wavertree Boulevard South, Liverpool, L7 9PF Tel: 0151-228 0354 Fax: 0151-252 1673 *Medical test equipment suppliers*

Ultrarad Technical Services Hull Ltd, Holderness House, Staithes Road, Hedon, Hull, HU12 8DX Tel: (01482) 324495 Fax: (01482) 620016 E-mail: uts.hull@virgin.net *Ship surveys & non destructive testing services*

Ultrascan Non-Destructive Testing Ltd, Unit 39, Canal Bridge Enterprise Centre, Meadow Lane, Ellesmere Port, CH65 4EH Tel: 0151-357 3069 Fax: 0151-355 2490 E-mail: scantek@ultrascan-ndt.com *Non-destructive testing service*

continued

Ultraseal Birmingham, 64 Maney Hill Road, Sutton Coldfield, West Midlands, B72 1JS Tel: 0121-355 7582 Fax: 0121-355 7582

▶ Ultraseal Wakefield, 10 Hyman Walk, South Elmsall, Pontefract, West Yorkshire, WF9 2TR Tel: (07717) 537003 E-mail: enquiries@ultraseal-wakefield.co.uk *Distributor and installer of Ultraseal products in the Wakefield area*

Ultrasoft Technologies Ltd, 29 Knoll Park Road, Chertsey, Surrey, KT16 9LR Tel: (01932) 570057 Fax: (01932) 570103 E-mail: enquiry@ultrasoft-tech.co.uk *Computer software*

Ultrasonic Cleaning Services UK Ltd, 10 Pepper Road, Leeds, LS10 2EU Tel: 0113-271 5807 Fax: 0113-271 5722 E-mail: sales@ucs-uk-ltd.co.uk *Ultrasonic sub contract cleaning services for flexgraphic printing rollers and paint stripping sub contracting services*

Ultrasound Technologies Ltd, Lodge Way, Severn Bridge Industrial Estate, Portskewett, Caldicot, Gwent, NP26 5PS Tel: (01291) 425425 Fax: (01291) 427093 E-mail: ultratech@doppler.co.uk *Medical vascular, vet, electronic equip manufrs*

Ultraspection Ltd, 13 St. Josephs Close, Olney, Buckinghamshire, MK46 5HD Tel: (01234) 714092 Fax: (01234) 714192 E-mail: ultraspection@btinternet.com *Non-destructive test services* Also at: Cadnam

Ultrassage, Unit 25, Moor Lane Trading Estate, Sherburn in Elmet, Leeds, LS25 6ES Tel: (01977) 680000 *Direct sales*

Ultratech Services, 73C Stevens Road, Stourbridge, West Midlands, DY9 0XW Tel: (01384) 373926 Fax: (01384) 393785 E-mail: ultratech@btinternet.com *Filter distributors/agents*

▶ Ultronics NDT Ltd, 14 Exeter Close, Chippenham, Wiltshire, SN14 0YG Tel: (01249) 465571 Fax: (01249) 660574 E-mail: davidclark@ultronicsndt.co.uk *Ultrasonic transducer manufrs*

Ulysses Ltd, Unit A Troon Way Business Centre, Humberstone Lane, Leicester, LE4 9HA Tel: 0116-276 9152 Fax: (0845) 1300259 E-mail: info@ulysses.uk.com *IT support & computer services*

Umbrella Manufacturing & Repairing Co. Ltd, 68h Sapcote Trading Centre, Wyrley Road, Birmingham, B6 7BN Tel: 0121-328 9292 Fax: 0121-328 9292 *Umbrella & promotional umbrellas manufrs*

Umbro International Ltd, Umbro House, 5400 Lakeside, Cheadle, Cheshire, SK8 3GQ Tel: 0161-492 2000 Fax: 0161-492 2001 E-mail: sales@umbro.com *Sportswear suppliers* Also at: Aylesmere & Ellesmere Port

Umeco plc, Concorde House, 24 Warwick New Road, Leamington Spa, Warwickshire, CV32 5JG Tel: (01926) 331800 Fax: (01926) 312680 *Services to aerospace industry*

Umist Ventures Ltd, The Fairbairn Building, Manchester, M60 1QD Tel: 0161-200 3057 Fax: 0161-200 3052 *Technology transfer*

Umney Brothers, Midland Structures Estate, Ampthill Road, Bedford, MK42 9JJ Tel: (01234) 348671 Fax: (01234) 348671 *Wooden chair frame manufrs*

Umoe Schat Harding Ltd, Mumby Road, Gosport, Hampshire, PO12 1AE Tel: (023) 9258 1331 Fax: (023) 9258 2565 E-mail: sales@schat-harding.co.uk *Marine safety equipment manufrs*

▶ Umtali Ltd, 51 Arundel Road, Woodley, Reading, RG5 4JR Tel: 0118-944 1111 Fax: (0871) 2360368 E-mail: info@umtali.co.uk *Specialists in providing corporate style services*

Unbar Rothon Ltd, 2 Radford Crescent, Billericay, Essex, CM12 0DR Tel: (01277) 632211 Fax: (01277) 630151 E-mail: prothon@unbarrothon.co.uk *Food seasonings, flavourings & colours*

Unbrako, 12-14 Tower Street, BIRMINGHAM, B19 3RR Tel: 0121 333 4610 Fax: 0121 333 4525 E-mail: unbrako.uk@spstech.com Principal Export Areas: Africa *High strength socket screw & industrial fastener manufrs*

▶ Uncle Roy's, 2 Holm Street, Moffat, Dumfriesshire, DG10 9EB Tel: (01683) 221076 Fax: (01683) 221076 *Food processors & products manufrs*

Uncle Tom's Dolls Houses Factory, 49 Ansty Road, Wyken, Coventry, CV2 3FG Tel: 0247 6278104 Fax: 0247 6278104 E-mail: info@dollshouses.atspace.com *Manufacturers of dolls houses*

Under Pressure, Unit 8 Eastlands, Coal Park Lane, Southampton, SO31 7GW Tel: (01489) 589891 Fax: (01489) 589785 E-mail: info@underpressure.uk.com *Industrial cleaning equipment distributors*

▶ Underbridge Leisure, 32 Pryme Street, Anlaby, Hull, HU10 6SH Tel: (01482) 659459 Fax: (01482) 749649 E-mail: sales@underbridgeleisure.karoo.co.uk *Hire & sale outdoor leisure products, bouncy castles, slides, hot tubs*

▶ Underfloor Heating, Norris House Elton Park Business Centre, Hadleigh Road, Ipswich, IP2 0HU Tel: (01473) 280444 Fax: (01473) 231850

▶ Underfloorheatingshop, 66 Rea Street, Birmingham, B5 6LB Tel: 0121-622 4334 Fax: 0121-622 5768 E-mail: manager@underfloorheatingshop.co.k *Under floor heating product supplies & service*

Underground Location Systems Uls Ltd, 66 Hall Lane, North Walsham, Norfolk, NR28 9DU Tel: (01692) 404494 Fax: (01692) 404494 E-mail: jw@correlators.co.uk *Underground installation & maintenance services*

▶ Underground Moling Services Ltd, Units 2, Middlefield Industrial Estate, Falkirk, FK2 9HQ Tel: (01324) 625143 Fax: (01324) 624091 E-mail: sales@undergroundmoling.co.uk

▶ Underground Surveys, Unit G14 Warrington Business Park, Long Lane, Warrington, WA2 8TX Tel: (01925) 444664 Fax: (01925) 444663 E-mail: info@undergroundsurveys.co.uk

Underhill Building Services, Valley Road, Plymouth, PL7 1RF Tel: (01752) 283280 Fax: (01752) 344410 *Fabrication engineers*

Underlay Direct, 1 Woodlea Gardens, Sauchie, Alloa, Clackmannanshire, FK10 3BD Tel: (07768) 588714 Fax: (01259) 218097 E-mail: sales@underlaydirectscotland.co.uk *Underlay supplier throughout uk*

Underpin & Makegood (Contracting) Ltd, 37 Millmarsh Lane, Enfield, Middx, EN3 7UY Tel: (020) 8805 4000 Fax: (020) 8805 4222 E-mail: david@underpin.com *Civil engineering contractors*

Undersea Ltd, 1 Forelle Centre, 30 Black Moor Road, Ebblake Industrial Estate, Verwood, Dorset, BH31 6BB Tel: (01202) 822025 Fax: (01202) 826626 E-mail: enquiries@undersea-ltd.demon.co.uk *Manufacturers of charging panels for air nitrox & tri mix personal filters. Charging & all types of adapters*

▶ Underwater Pool Repair Services Ltd, 448-450 Manchester Road East, Little Hulton, Manchester, M38 9NS Tel: 0161-799 1222 Fax: 0161-702 9958 *Repairs for swimming pool*

▶ Underwood Construction Ltd, Commercial House, Fontwell Avenue, Eastergate, Chichester, West Sussex, PO20 3RY Tel: (01243) 545115 Fax: (01243) 545116

▶ Uneek Fashions, Unit C, 27 Burleys Way, Leicester, LE1 3BE Tel: 0116-262 6662

▶ Uneek Freight Services Ltd, Amberley Way, Hounslow, TW4 6BH Tel: (020) 8569 4949 Fax: (020) 8569 5101 E-mail: info@uneekfreight.com *International Freight Forwarders*Worldwide Courier*Air & Se Export*Air & Sea Import*

▶ Unger UK Ltd, 9 Planetary Industrial Estate, Planetary Road, Willenhall, West Midlands, WV13 3XA Tel: (01902) 306644 Fax: (01902) 306644 E-mail: ungeruk@ungerglobel.uk *Cleaning material manufrs*

Ungerer Ltd, Sealand Road, Chester, CH1 4LP Tel: (01244) 371711 Fax: (01244) 380185 E-mail: ungereruk@ungerer.co.uk *Flavour & fragrance compounds manufrs*

Uni Credito Italiano, 17 Moorgate, London, EC2R 6PH Tel: (020) 7606 9011 Fax: (020) 7606 3920 E-mail: info@unicredit.co.uk *Banking services*

Uni Fire Seurities, 9 Moor St Trading Estate, Brierley Hill, West Midlands, DY5 3SS Tel: (01432) 353400 Fax: (0800) 0723868 E-mail: admin@uni-fire.co.uk *Fire alarm & extinguisher suppliers*

Uni Lever, Carrow Works, Bracondale, Norwich, NR1 2DD Tel: (01603) 660166 Fax: (01603) 692099 E-mail: sales@unilever.com *Food product manufrs*

▶ Uni PC, 168, Woodhouse Lane, Leeds, LS2 9H Tel: 0113-242 9778 Fax: 0113-242 9842

Uni Seal (South Coast) Co. Ltd, 28 Balena Close, Poole, Dorset, BH17 7EB Tel: (01202) 602800 Fax: (01202) 658651 *Double glazed unit manufrs*

Uni Seat Northern Contracts Ltd, Firlands Mills, South Parade, Pudsey, West Yorkshire, LS28 8AD Tel: 0113-255 9606 Fax: 0113-256 5088 *Entertainment & leisure seating manufrs*

Uni Trunk Ltd, Altona Road, Lisburn, County Antrim, BT27 5QB Tel: (028) 9262 5100 Fax: (028) 9262 5101 E-mail: lisburn@unitrunk.co.uk *Electrical cable trunking systems manufrs*

▶ Uni Trunk, Titan2 Coxwell Avenue, Wolverhampton Science Park, Wolverhampton, WV10 9RT Tel: (01902) 717786 Fax: (01902) 714105 *Cable management specialists*

Unibend Engineering, Kirkdale Works, Spring Place, Whitworth, Rochdale, Lancashire, OL12 8JY Tel: (01706) 853239 *Tube manipulation & bending services* Also at: Facit

Unibind Systems Ltd, 3 Oak Court, Betts Way, Crawley, West Sussex, RH10 9GG Tel: (01293) 530182 Fax: (01293) 529272 E-mail: sales@unibindsystems.co.uk *Document binding systems distributors*

Unibond, Apollo Court, 2 Bishops Square Business Park, Hatfield, Hertfordshire, AL10 9EY Tel: (01707) 289041 Fax: (01707) 289099 *Consumer adhesive distributors & manufrs*

▶ UNIC Cranes Europe Ltd, Unit 10, Ridgeway, Drakes Drive, Long Crendon, Aylesbury, Buckinghamshire, HP18 9BF Tel: (01844) 202071 Fax: (01844) 202075 E-mail: sales@unic-cranes.co.uk *Sale of mini cranes, designed for lifting in restricted access*

Unic International (UK), Colwick Road, Nottingham, NG2 4BG Tel: 0115-947 4000 Fax: 0115-950 6666 E-mail: info@unic.co.uk *Waste management products & can crusher services*

Unicar Leeds Ltd, 90 Kirkstall Road, Leeds, LS3 1LT Tel: 0113-245 1444 Fax: 0113-243 5532 E-mail: enquiries@unicar.co.uk *Motor vehicle audio engineers*

Unichem Ltd, 24 Marsh Green Road, Marsh Barton Trading Estate, Exeter, EX2 8LZ Tel: (01392) 434941 Fax: (01392) 425781 *Pharmaceutical wholesalers & distribution*

Unichem plc, Kingsway, Fforestfach, Swansea, SA5 4HA Tel: (01792) 561561 Fax: (01792) 589493 *Pharmaceutical wholesalers*

Unichem (Warehousing) Ltd, Unichem House, Cox Lane, Chessington, Surrey, KT9 1SN Tel: (020) 8391 2323 Fax: (020) 8974 1707 *Pharmaceutical wholesalers*

Uniclip Ltd, Royston Road, Byfleet, Surrey, KT14 7NY Tel: (01932) 355277 Fax: (01932) 351285 E-mail: info@uniclipengland.com *Manufacturer of UNEX hose clips*

Unico Ltd, North Main Street, Carronshore, Falkirk, FK2 8HT Tel: (01324) 573410 Fax: (01324) 573401 E-mail: sales@unicodirect.com *'Falkirk-based Unico Ltd supply cleaning materials and hygiene products including soap, handtowel and toilet tissue dispensers.*

Unico UK Ltd, Garamonde Drive, Wymbush, Milton Keynes, MK8 8LF Tel: (01908) 260000 Fax: (01908) 260360 E-mail: drives@unico.co.uk

Unicolour Ltd, Tandem Works, Wakefield Road, Waterloo, Huddersfield, HD5 0AN Tel: (01484) 516974 Fax: (01484) 510667 E-mail: dyes@unicolour.co.uk *Dyestuff merchants*

Unicom Group, Enterprise Way, Edenbridge, Kent, TN8 6EW Tel: (01732) 865238 Fax: (01732) 866820 E-mail: info@uni-com.uk.com *Safety & security products*

Unicores Ltd, Unit F Bull Street, Brierley Hill, West Midlands, DY5 3NQ Tel: (01384) 70542 Fax: (01384) 74380 *Transformer core manufrs*

▶ Unicorn Ltd, 1 Park Works Canal Bridge Enterprise Centre, Meadow Lane, Ellesmere Port, CH65 4EH Tel: 0151-355 5151 Fax: 0151-357 1733 E-mail: pumps@unicornltd.fsnet.co.uk *Mechanical engineers*

Unicorn Building & Maintenance Ltd, Biltam Farm, Stan Hill, Charlwood, Horley, Surrey, RH6 0EP Tel: (01293) 862775 Fax: (01293) 863205 *Building repairs, maintenance, extensions & alterations*

Unicorn Containers Ltd, 5 Ferguson Drive, Lisburn, County Antrim, BT28 2EX Tel: (028) 9266 7264 Fax: (028) 9262 5616 E-mail: sales@unicorn-containers.com *Vending machine manufrs*

▶ Unicorn Events Ltd, Unicorn House, 5 Russell Grove, Westbury Park, Bristol, BS6 7UD Tel: 0117-942 9151 Fax: (0845) 2805151 E-mail: info@unicornevents.com

Unicorn Metals, 3 Belper Road, Kilburn, Belper, Derbyshire, DE56 0LQ Tel: (01332) 882000 Fax: (01332) 880141 *Non-ferrous metal stockholders & steel*

Unicorn Mucksuckers, 41 High Street, Clophill, Bedford, MK45 4AA Tel: (01525) 860255 Fax: (01525) 861635 E-mail: info@uti.co.uk *Industrial vacuum unit manufrs*

Unicorn Office Products Ltd, Unit 25 Station Road Workshops, Station Road, Bristol, BS15 4PJ Tel: 0117-907 6662 Fax: 0117-907 6663 E-mail: sales@unicornonline.net *Office products retailers, printing services*

Unicorn Print & Design, 143 North Street, Romford, RM1 1ED Tel: (01708) 765017 Fax: (01708) 733491 E-mail: unicorndie@aol.com *Printers & hot foilers services*

Unicorn Products Ltd, South Barn, Crockham Park, Crockham Hill, Edenbridge, Kent, TN8 6UP Tel: 0115-985 3500 Fax: (01732) 782801 E-mail: assist@unicorngroup.com *Sports equipment manufrs*

Unicorn Sheet Metal Works, Unit 28, Point Pleasant Industrial Estate, Wallsend, Tyne & Wear, NE28 6HA Tel: 0191 2622882 E-mail: sales@unicornlasercutting.co.uk *Sheet metal fabricators*

▶ Unicorn Trails, 2, Acorn Centre, Chestnut Avenue, Biggleswade, Bedfordshire, SG18 ORA Tel: 01767 600606 E-mail: david@unicorntrails.com *Unicorn Trails offer horse riding holidays, is a full service travel agency offering friendly independent advice on veterinary-approved rides. Lifetime experiences even if you can"t ride or need more experience for your dream holiday.*

Unicut, 6 Tewin Court, Welwyn Garden City, Hertfordshire, AL7 1AU Tel: (01707) 331227 Fax: (01707) 390382 E-mail: sales@unicutprecision.com *Precision turned parts & milling vertical mill*

Uniex Freight Services, Lodge Way, Thetford, Norfolk, IP24 1HE Tel: (01842) 751751 Fax: (01842) 751665 E-mail: freight@uniex.co.uk *Shipping & freight forwarding agents* Also at: Dover, Felixstowe & Nottingham

Unifab Engineering Ltd, Pelham Road, Cleethorpes, South Humberside, DN35 7JT Tel: (01472) 230149 Fax: (01472) 230149 *Manufacturers of food processing equipment*

Unified Solutions Ltd, 883-884 Plymouth Road, Slough, SL1 4LP Tel: (01753) 775050 Fax: (01753) 775020 E-mail: info@unified.co.uk *Computer recruitment & support*

Unifiller (U K) Ltd, 2 Bridge Mills Rochdale Road, Edenfield, Ramsbottom, Bury, Lancashire, BL0 0RE Tel: (01706) 828802 Fax: (01706) 829986 E-mail: sales@unifiller.com *Bakery plant & equipment agents suppliers*

Unifire & Security, Unit 3 Station Yard, Bromfield, Ludlow, Shropshire, SY8 2BT Tel: (01584) 856868 Fax: (020) 7754 9148 E-mail: peter@uni-fire.co.uk *Fire extinguishing equipment suppliers*

Unifix Ltd, Bridge House, Grove Lane, Smethwick, West Midlands, B66 2QT Tel: 0121-609 0099 Fax: 0121-626 0587 E-mail: marketing@unifix.com *Suppliers of fixings & fasteners*

Uniflo Systems Ltd, 9 Neptune Industrial Estate, Neptune Close, Medway City Estate, Rochester, Kent, ME2 4LT Tel: (01634) 716117 Fax: (01634) 290235 E-mail: sales@uniflo.co.uk *Air conditioning equipment & ventilation units*

The Uniform Co., Unit 2 Imperial Works, Fountayne Road, London, N15 4QL Tel: (020) 8801 5011 *Clothing manufrs*

Uniform Express Ltd, Unit C7 South Way, Bounds Green Industrial Estate, Bounds Green Road, London, N11 2UL Tel: (020) 8368 0114 Fax: (020) 8361 0624 E-mail: mail@uniformexpress.co.uk *Promotional clothing manufrs*

▶ Uniform Sportswear Distributors, 35 Ash House Lane, Little Leigh, Northwich, Cheshire, CW8 4RG Tel: (01606) 892783 Fax: (01606) 892549 E-mail: usdltd@enterprise.net *Uniform clothing manufrs*

Uniform World Ltd, 57 Boulton Road, Handsworth, Birmingham, B21 0RB Tel: 0121-523 4538 Fax: 0121-523 4538 *Trousers manufrs*

Unify Corp (UK) Ltd, Malt House, Hummer Road, Egham, Surrey, TW20 9BD Tel: (01784) 487940 Fax: (01784) 487941 E-mail: info@unify.com *Computer software*

Unigears Ashford Ltd, Unit 8 Henwood Business Centre, Henwood Industrial Estate, Ashford, Kent, TN24 8DH Tel: (01233) 642798 Fax: (01233) 650725 E-mail: sales@unigears.co.uk *Gear cutting & gear box manufrs*

▶ Uniglobe Prestige Travel, 28a New Street, St. Neots, Cambridgeshire, PE19 1AJ Tel: (01480) 404680 Fax: (01480) 405656 E-mail: sales@prestigetravel.biz *Travel Management and Agents*

Unigold Computer Maintenance, 34 Stringers Avenue, Guildford, Surrey, GU4 7NW Tel: (01483) 459045 Fax: (01483) 459046 E-mail: enquiries@unigold2000.co.uk *Computer services*

Unigraph UK Ltd, 287 Pitsmoor Road, Sheffield, S3 9AS Tel: 0114-275 2801 Fax: 0114-275 9769 E-mail: sales@unigraph.uk *Photocopying machine distributors*

Unigraphics Solutions, Knoll Road, Camberley, Surrey, GU15 3SY Tel: (01276) 702000 Fax: (01276) 702100 *IT software solution services*

▶ Uniheat Oxford Ltd, 33-37 Stockmore Street, Oxford, OX4 1JT Tel: (01865) 242708 Fax: (01865) 798347

Unijet Products Ltd, Unit 4 The Ham, Brentford, Middlesex, TW8 8EZ Tel: 020 85608978 *Precision engineers*

Unijig Ltd, Bowling Back Lane, Bradford, West Yorkshire, BD4 8UF Tel: (01274) 656750 Fax: (01274) 668375 E-mail: sales@unijig.co.uk *Precision engineers*

Unilathe Ltd, Ford Green Business Park, Ford Green Road Smallthorne, Stoke-on-Trent, ST6 1NG Tel: (01782) 533300 Fax: (01782) 532013 E-mail: sales@unilathe.co.uk *General engineers*

Unilever Best Foods Ltd, London Road, Purfleet, Essex, RM19 1SD Tel: (01708) 863300 Fax: (01708) 684786 *Food products manufrs*

Unilever Bestfoods UK Ltd, Croespenmaen Industrial Estate, Kendon, Crumlin, Newport, Gwent, NP11 3AG Tel: (01495) 248555 Fax: (01495) 247657 E-mail: enquiries@ubfoodsuk.com *Food manufrs*

Unilever Frozen Food & Ice Cream, Martin Score, Lowestoft, Suffolk, NR32 1JG Tel: (01502) 573131 Fax: (01502) 504840 *Food processors*

Unilever Overseas Holdings Ltd, PO Box 68, London, EC4P 4BQ Tel: (020) 7822 5252 Fax: (020) 7822 5898 E-mail: press-office.london@unilever.com Principal Export Areas: Worldwide *Holding company for group involved in fast moving consumer goods*

Unilever UK Walls's Ltd, Station Avenue, Walton-On-Thames, Surrey, KT12 1NT Tel: (01932) 263000 Fax: (01932) 263152 *Frozen food processors & product manufrs*

▶ Uni-Lite International Ltd, Unit 7 Colemeadow Road, North Moors Moat, Redditch, Worcestershire, B98 9PB Tel: (01527) 584344 Fax: (01527) 584345 E-mail: sales@uni-lite.com *Manufacturers of torches & rechargeable batteries*

▶ Unilock Group, Unit 7 E, Enterprise Way, Vale Park, Evesham, Worcestershire, WR11 1GU Tel: (01386) 765155

Unilvever, Coal Road, Seacroft, Leeds, LS14 2AR Tel: 0113-222 5000 Fax: 0113-222 5362 *Aerosols manufrs*

Unimach Machine Tools Ltd, Folgate Road, North Walsham, Norfolk, NR28 0AJ Tel: 01692 409706 *Steel working machine manufrs*

▶ Unimar Ltd, 5 Perivale Industrial Park, Horsenden La South, Greenford, Middlesex, UB6 7RL Tel: (020) 7870 5695 Fax: (020) 8810 7766 E-mail: info@unimarltd.co.uk

Unimaster Components, 9 Arnhem Road, Newbury, Berkshire, RG14 5RU Tel: (01635) 528692 E-mail: sales@unimaster.co.uk *Hydraulic hose assembly services*

Unimatco Ltd, Bulstrode, Oxford Road, Gerrards Cross, Buckinghamshire, SL9 8SZ Tel: (01753) 886105 Fax: (01753) 889378 E-mail: sales@unimatco.co.uk *Charity exporter merchants*

Unimatic Engineers Ltd, 130 Granville Road, London, NW2 2LN Tel: (020) 8922 1000 Fax: (020) 8922 1066 E-mail: sales@unimatic.com *Distributors of bearings, linear electric motors*

Unimax, Unit 2, Acan Business Park, Garrard Way, Telford Way Industrial Estate, Kettering, Northamptonshire, NN16 8TD Tel: (01536) 419200 Fax: (01536) 419222 E-mail: sales@unimaxswitch.com *Safety switch supplier distributor & manufrs*

▶ Unimax Switch, Unit 2 Acan Business Development Park, Garrard Way, Telford Way Industrial Estate, Kettering, Northamptonshire, NN16 8TD Tel: (01536) 419200 Fax: (01536) 419222 E-mail: sales@unimaxswitch.com *Electronic switches manufrs*

Unimerco Ltd, Nanscawen Road, Fradley, Lichfield, Staffordshire, WS13 8LH Tel: (01543) 267777 Fax: (01543) 267778 E-mail: info@unimerco.com *Cutting tool manufrs*

Unimet Enamellers Ltd, 183-185 Cardiff Road, Reading, RG1 8HD Tel: 0118-959 5528 *Stove enamelling services*

Unimetal Ltd., Bay 6B, Tractor Spares Industrial Estate, Strawberry Lane, Willenhall, West Midlands, WV13 3RS Tel: (01902) 366035 Fax: (01902) 601221 E-mail: billallen@btconnect.com *Castings suppliers*

Union Fabrications, Unit 12 & 13 Garden Mill Industrial Estate, Derby Road, Kingsbridge, Devon, TQ7 1SA Tel: (01548) 852922 Fax: (01548) 852922 *Metal fabricators*

▶ Union Glass Centres Ltd, 1 Armada Street, Plymouth, PL4 8LS Tel: (01752) 664418 Fax: (01752) 225195 E-mail: info@unionglass.co.uk *Glass & glazing supply services*

Union Grain Storage Ltd, Kirmans Marsh Farm, Marsh Lane, Orby, Skegness, Lincolnshire, PE24 5JA Tel: (01754) 810222 *Grain storage services*

Union Industries, Whitehouse Street, Leeds, LS10 1AD Tel: 0113-244 8393 Fax: 0113-242 1307 E-mail: sales@unionindustries.co.uk Principal Export Areas: Worldwide *Manufacturers of industrial net fabric, tarpaulin, flags & banners. In addition, plastic & industrial dividing curtain manufrs. Also aircraft spraying*

▶ Union Ink Co. Ltd, 28 Eldon Way, Paddock Wood, Tonbridge, Kent, TN12 6BE Tel: (01892) 834555 Fax: (01892) 834666

Union Papertech Ltd, Simpson Clough Mill, Ashworth Road, Heywood, Lancashire, OL10 4BE Tel: (01706) 364121 Fax: (01706) 624944 *Paper manufrs*

Union Pumps Union Pumps, Green Road, Penistone, Sheffield, S36 6BJ Tel: (01226) 763311 Fax: (01226) 766535 E-mail: bkearsley@unionpump.textron.com *Pump manufrs*

Union Steel Products Ltd, Row End, Berrow Green Road, Martley, Worcester, WR6 6PQ Tel: (01886) 888828 Fax: (01886) 888853 *Speciality & electric grade steel*

Union Steel Tubes, Wellington House, Wellington Industrial Estate, Bilston, West Midlands, WV14 9EE Tel: (01902) 881222 Fax: (01902) 880500 E-mail: enquiries@unionsteel.co.uk *Steel tube stock holder*

Union Transport Group plc, Imperial House, 21-25 North Street, Bromley, BR1 1SJ Tel: (020) 8290 1234 Fax: (020) 8402 7770 E-mail: utg.plc@uniontransport.co.uk *Shipping & freight forwarding*

Union Veneers, 20 Rigg Approach, London, E10 7QN Tel: (020) 8556 8866 Fax: (020) 8539 1382 *Wood veneers*

Unipac, Greenock Road, Slough, SL1 4QQ Tel: (01753) 773000 Fax: (01753) 773111 E-mail: sales@unipac.biz Principal Export Areas: Worldwide *Bottle cap lining material manufrs*

Unipart Automotive Ltd, Windsor Road, Bedford, MK42 9SU Tel: (01234) 350601 Fax: (01234) 261647 *Car component traders & retailers*

Unipart Automotive Ltd, Unit 5 - 7, Shepcote Enterprise Park 2, Europa Drive, Sheffield, S9 1XT Tel: 0114-243 0301 Fax: 0114-261 7745 E-mail: bb.sheffieldnorth.m@unipart.co.uk *Specialist motor factors* Also at: Chesterfield, Mansfield & Worksop

Unipart Eberspacher Exhaust Systems, Durbar Avenue, Coventry, CV6 5LZ Tel: (024) 7663 8663 Fax: (024) 7666 1084 E-mail: enquiries@unipart.co.uk *Exhaust systems manufacturers*Steel Fuel Tank Manufacturers*Fuel Filler Neck Manufacturers*Engine Pipework*Tube Manipulation*Furnace Brazing*Robotic Welding*Fabrication*

▶ Unipart Logistics, Unipart House, Garsington Road, Cowley, Oxford, OX4 2PG Tel: (01865) 383793 Fax: (01865) 383669 E-mail: lyn_mcdowell@unipart.co.uk *Unipart Logistics is the logistics & service management division of the Unipart Group of Companies & is one of EuropeÆs leading service providers of logistics to the automotive, technology,telecommunications, aerospace, rail, leisure & retail sector*

Unipath Ltd, Priory Business Park, Bedford, MK44 3UP Tel: (01234) 835000 Fax: (01234) 835001 E-mail: info@unipath.com *Manufacturers of pregnancy & ovulation kits* Also at: Basingstoke

▶ Uniplex Computer Systems Ltd, Unit 32 Harmill Industrial Estate, Grovebury Road, Leighton Buzzard, Bedfordshire, LU7 4FF Tel: (01525) 217321 Fax: (01525) 217328 E-mail: info@uniplex.co.uk *Software house*

Uniplex (UK) Ltd, 11 Furnace Hill, Sheffield, S3 7AF Tel: 0114-272 6858 Fax: 0114-272 7288 E-mail: sales@uniplex-uk.com *Medical equipment sales & service & repairs*

Unipol Plastic Sheeting Supplies, Prospect House, Taylor Business Park, Risley, Warrington, WA3 6HP Tel: (01925) 768001 Fax: (01925) 768008 E-mail: sales@unipoluk.com *Polycarbonate sheeting*

Unipools Leisure Construction Ltd, 621 Watford Way, Mill Hill, London, NW7 3JN Tel: (020) 8959 8686 Fax: (020) 8959 2037 E-mail: info@unipools.com *Water filtration system distributors*

Uniprize Machine Tools Ltd, A3 Bankfield Industrial Estate, Sandy Lane, Stockport, Cheshire, SK5 7SE Tel: 0161-429 6161 Fax: 0161-429 0606 E-mail: uniprize@uniprize.freeserve.co.uk *Machine tool manufacturers*

▶ Unipro Computer Systems, Top Cart Shed, Chilgrove Farm, Chilgrove, Chichester, West Sussex, PO18 9HU Tel: (01243) 535399 E-mail: sales@up.com *Computer maintenance & repair services*

Uniq plc, 1 Chalfont Park, Gerrards Cross, Buckinghamshire, SL9 0UN Tel: (01753) 276000 Fax: (01753) 276071 E-mail: info@uniqplc.com *Convenience foods*

Uniq Prepared Foods Smedleys, Wardentree Lane, Pinchbeck, Spalding, Lincolnshire, PE11 3UY Tel: (01775) 710789 Fax: (01775) 710504 E-mail: enquiries@uniq.com *Chilled salads manufrs*

Uniqema, Pool Lane, Bromborough Pool, Wirral, Merseyside, CH62 4UF Tel: 0151-643 3200 Fax: 0151-645 9197 *Oleo chemical suppliers*

Unique Advantage Coaching, 11 Babylon Lane, Bishampton, Pershore, Worcestershire, WR10 2NN Tel: (0845) 6442424 Fax: (0870) 1328311 E-mail: enquiries@uniqueadvantage.co.uk *Professional Executive Business and Personal Coaching for Performance, Effectiveness and Transition. An innovative mix of methods and programmes, creating cost effective results for large organisations, small businesses and private clients. Risk Free start programmes.*

Unique Bedding-parties, The Warehouse, 4-5 Mason St, Consett, County Durham, DH8 5DD Tel: 01207 592300 *Textiles & home furnishing*

▶ Unique Building Contractors, 20 Ivydale Road, Plymouth, PL4 7DF Tel: (01752) 228344 Fax: (01752) 250619

Unique Car Mats UK Ltd, 2 Hassall Road, Skegness, Lincolnshire, PE25 3TB Tel: (01754) 761334 Fax: (01754) 767355 E-mail: info@uniqueproductsuk.com *Car mat & accessory manufrs*

Unique Concepts Licensing Ltd, Regus House, Falcon Drive, Cardiff, CF10 4RU Tel: (029) 2050 4029 Fax: (029) 2050 4129 *Pewter model manufrs*

▶ Unique Consulting Solutions Ltd, 32 New Road, Lymm, Cheshire, WA13 9DY Tel: (01925) 753899 Fax: (01925) 758815 E-mail: trevor@uniqueconsulting.co.uk *Business planning service*

▶ Unique Crafts, Oldham Road, Middleton, Manchester, M24 1QZ Tel: 0161-653 4477 Fax: 0161-653 4488

Unique Design Systemation, Manor Farm, Pickstock, Shifnal, Shropshire, TF10 8AH Tel: (01952) 550037 Fax: (01952) 551183 E-mail: bob@unique-design.co.uk *Supply of automated assembly equipment air tools*

Unique Design Systems Modular, Manor Farm, Pickstock, Newport, Shropshire, TF10 8AH Tel: (01952) 550037 Fax: (01952) 550037 E-mail: barryb.uds.ltd@fsmail.net

Unique Dutch Light Co. Ltd, Bent Spur Road, Kearsley, Bolton, BL4 8PD Tel: (01204) 571800 Fax: (01204) 862412 E-mail: enquiries@elite-greenhouses.co.uk *Commercial glasshouse manufrs*

▶ Unique Enamelling Services, Bee Mill, Preston Road, Ribchester, Preston, PR3 3XJ Tel: (01254) 878265 Fax: (01524) 792299 E-mail: enqiuries@ues-ltd.co.uk *Enamelling of baths, sinks & metal antique restoration services*

▶ Unique Finishing Equipment Ltd, Unit 10u St. Albans Enterprise Centre, Long Spring, Porters Wood, St. Albans, Hertfordshire, AL3 6EN Tel: (01727) 899900 Fax: (01727) 899901 E-mail: info@uniquefinishing.co.uk *Print finishing services*

▶ Unique Fire Safety Solutions, Suite 39, 792 Wilmslow Road, Didsbury, Manchester, M20 6UG Tel: (07969) 664105 E-mail: sales@uniquefiresafety.com *Fire Safety Advice, Fire safety risk assessments, DIY fire safety risk assessments, Fire Extinguisher And Fire marshall training, CAD drawings for premises, fire log books*

▶ Unique Fun Casino, 57 Kilmiston Drive, Fareham, Hampshire, PO16 8EG Tel: (01329) 513624 Fax: (01329) 513624 E-mail: debraann.foxell@btconnect.com *Bring the thrills and excitement of a real Casino to all your events. Roulette, Blackjack, & Poker tables with Professional & friendly Croupiers for all your Corporate entertainment, Weddings, Parties, Charity Fund Raising, Summer Balls, Dinner Dances or any other events. Our professional and personal approach will guarantee you a very successful, but most important of all, an enjoyable event. Most competitive prices. Book now for an evening with a difference!**

Unique Graphics, 136 Lauriston Road, London, E9 7LH Tel: (020) 8986 9686 Fax: (020) 8533 0238 E-mail: mail@justpostcards.co.uk *Printing & distribution of cards*

Unique Id Ltd, 1 Barnes Wallis Court, Wellington Road, Cressex Business Park, High Wycombe, Buckinghamshire, HP12 3PS Tel: (01494) 511022 Fax: (01494) 511033 E-mail: sales@barcodecentral.co.uk *Bar code systems suppliers*

▶ Unique Integrated Systems, 3c Selby Place, Stanley Industrial Estate, Skelmersdale, Lancashire, WN8 8EF Tel: (01695) 50332 Fax: (01695) 50644

▶ Unique Metal & Glass Co. Ltd, First Stage House, Brimington Road North, Whittington Moor, Chesterfield, Derbyshire, S41 9BE Tel: (01246) 208789 Fax: (01246) 208791 E-mail: umg@metal-glass.com *Architectural products manufrs*

Unique Scaffolding Ltd, Kangley Bridge Road, London, SE26 5AU Tel: (020) 8778 8483 Fax: (020) 8676 8439 *Scaffolding contractors*

Unique Technical Services, 62 Willesden Lane, London, NW6 7SX Tel: (020) 8232 8889 Fax: (020) 8568 6777 *Photocopier servicing*

Unique Windows Ltd, Perry Road, Harlow, Essex, CM18 7NR Tel: (01279) 420385 Fax: (01279) 420387 E-mail: sales@uniquewindowsltd.co.uk *Window manufrs*

Uniroof International, Worth Corner, Turners Hill Road, Crawley, West Sussex, RH10 7SL Tel: (01293) 889888 Fax: (01293) 883369 E-mail: export@uniroof.com *Waterproofing manufrs*

Unirose Ltd, Mount Ephraim Farm, Freight Lane, Cranbrook, Kent, TN17 3PG Tel: (01580) 714477 Fax: (01580) 713534 *Wooden presentation box manufrs*

Uniross Batteries, Uniross House, Old Mill Road, Portishead, Bristol, BS20 7BX Tel: (0870) 2206988 Fax: (01275) 846999 E-mail: sales@uniross.com *Battery charger distributors*

Unisant (Holdings) Ltd, PO Box 65, Cradley Heath, West Midlands, B64 5PP Tel: 0121-559 5136 Fax: 0121-561 4265 E-mail: syoung@bdprofiles.co.uk *Manufacturers flanges*

Uniseed Engineering Ltd, Shepherds Grove Industrial Estate, Stanton, Bury St. Edmunds, Suffolk, IP31 2AR Tel: (01359) 250469 Fax: (01359) 252245 *Steel fabricators*

Unisem (Europe) Ltd, Pen Y Fan Industrial Estate, Croespenman, Crumlin, Newport, Gwent, NP11 3XT Tel: (01495) 244111 Fax: (01495) 244828 E-mail: enquiries@atlantic1.co.uk *Semi-conductor package assembly & test services*

▶ Uniserve Consulting Ltd, Berger House, 38 Berkeley Square, London, W1J 5AE Tel: (020) 7493 9323 Fax: (020) 7493 9324 *Computer systems consultants*

Unison Engine Components, 1 Bentley Wood Way, Network 65 Business Park, Hapton, Burnley, Lancashire, BB11 5TG Tel: (01282) 831199 Fax: (01282) 422989 *Gas components repairers, designers & manufrs*

Unisport, D1-D2, 3-19 Victorian Grove, London, N16 8EN Tel: (020) 7241 6104 *Clothing manufrs*

Unispray Powder Coatings, Unit 185 Thorp Arch Trading Estate, Thorp Arch, Wetherby, West Yorkshire, LS23 7BJ Tel: (01937) 541267 Fax: (01937) 541267 *Powder coating services*

Unistrut Holdings Ltd, Unistrut House, Edison Road, Bedford, MK41 0HU Tel: (01234) 220400 Fax: (01234) 216004 E-mail: cmathews@tyco-bspd.com *Safety harness, cable & metal framing manufrs*

Company Information

Unistyle Plastics, Unit 6 Ranton Park, Martindale, Cannock, Staffordshire, WS11 7XL Tel: (01543) 500554 Fax: (01543) 578444 E-mail: unistyleplastics@btconnect.com *Sheet plastic fabrications*

▶ Unisurf Engineering Ltd, Barnard Road, Bradford, West Yorkshire, BD4 7ED Tel: (0870) 7508833 Fax: (0870) 7508844 E-mail: info@unisurf-eng.co.uk *Precision engineers to printing industry*

Unisys Group Services Ltd, Bakers Court, Bakers Road, Uxbridge, Middlesex, UB8 1RG Tel: (01895) 237137 Fax: (01895) 862092 E-mail: sales@unisys.com *Information technology consultants* Also at: Branches throughout the U.K.

▶ Unit 17 Ltd, BBIC, 17 Innovation Way, Barnsley, South Yorkshire, S75 1JL Tel: (07919) 424954 Fax: (01226) 249590 E-mail: studio@unit17.co.uk *Promotional & corporate film production*

Unit 22 Model Makers, 7 Cubitt Street, London, WC1X 0LN Tel: (020) 7278 3872 Fax: (020) 7837 8372 E-mail: mail@unit22.co.uk *Architectural model makers*

Unit Construction, 41 Cardinal Close, Tonbridge, Kent, TN9 2EN Tel: (01732) 355250 Fax: (01892) 355984 *Steel fabricators*

▶ Unit Design Ltd, Sycamore Trading Estate, Squires Gate Lane, Blackpool, FY4 3RL Tel: (01253) 349965 Fax: (01253) 349081

Unit Design, 9d Portaferry Road, Newtownards, County Down, BT23 8NN Tel: (028) 9181 7160 Fax: (028) 9181 3172 E-mail: info@unitdesign-ni.co.uk *Fitted kitchen & bedroom manufrs*

Unit F, F Liver Industrial Estate, Long Lane, Walton, Liverpool, L9 7ES Tel: 0151-525 3344 Fax: 0151-525 3113 E-mail: liverpool@williamwilson.co.uk *Plumbing & heating equipment merchants*

The Unit Joinery Co., 8-12 Totman Crescent, Rayleigh, Essex, SS6 7UY Tel: (01268) 774802 Fax: (01268) 774183 *Laboratory furniture manufacturers & installers*

Unit Line Ltd, 1 The Avenue, West End Road, High Wycombe, Buckinghamshire, HP11 2QQ Tel: (01494) 440045 Fax: (01494) 438898 E-mail: sales@unitline.com *Joinery manufrs*

Unit Metal Construction Co. Ltd, Dale Street, Bilston, West Midlands, WV14 7JY Tel: (01902) 491436 Fax: (01902) 491665 E-mail: unitmetal@btconnect.com *Sheet metalworkers*

Unit Sidecars Ltd, Wethersfield Road, Sible Hedingham, Halstead, Essex, CO9 3LB Tel: (01787) 461000 Fax: (01787) 461000 E-mail: sales@unitsidecars.co.uk *Sidecar manufrs*

Unit Superheater Engineering Ltd, Unit Works, 2-8 Morfa Road, Swansea, SA1 2ET Tel: (01792) 654091 Fax: (01792) 456198 E-mail: eng@unit.co.uk *Petro-chemical power station contractors*

▶ Unit Two Security Ltd, 17 Hareleeshill Road, Larkhall, Lanarkshire, ML9 2EX Tel: (01698) 881885

Unita Packaging Ltd, Unit 15 Bloomsgrove Industrial Estate, Ilkeston Rd, Nottingham, NG7 3JG Tel: 0115-978 6172 Fax: 0115-978 6776 E-mail: sales@unita.co.uk *Paper & polythene bag manufacturing.*

Unitas Software, 1 Kingsgate Street, Coleraine, County Londonderry, BT52 1LB Tel: (02870) 320732 Fax: (02870) 321333 E-mail: info@unitassoftware.com *Financial software & procurement solutions*

▶ Unitech Electrical Ltd, Unit 4 Castlehill Industrial Estate, Carluke, Lanarkshire, ML8 5UF Tel: (01555) 752211 Fax: (01555) 772822

Unitech Engineering Co. Ltd, Prospect Road, Burntwood, Staffordshire, WS7 0AL Tel: (01543) 675800 Fax: (01543) 687070 E-mail: info@unitech.uk.com *Catering & food processing equipment suppliers*

Unitech Engineering Services Ltd, The Old Dairy, Ball Hill, Newbury, Berkshire, RG20 0NY Tel: (01635) 253997 Fax: (01635) 255180 E-mail: unitech@unitech-engineering.co.uk *Control panel component manufrs*

United Abrasives Ltd, Unit 1 Charles Street, Walsall, WS2 9LZ Tel: (01922) 625544 Fax: (01922) 626345 E-mail: unitedabrasives@btconnect.com *Abrasive belt manufrs*

United Advertising Publications Plc, Link House, 25 West St, Poole, Dorset, BH15 1LL Tel: (01202) 445000 Fax: (01202) 445000 E-mail: enquiries@exchangeandmart.co.uk *Book & magazine publishers*

United Agri Products Ltd, London Road, Dunkirk, Faversham, Kent, ME13 9LR Tel: (01227) 753713 Fax: (01227) 753719 *Agricultural chemical suppliers*

United Agri Products, 23-24 Ilton Business Park, Ilton, Ilminster, Somerset, TA19 9DU Tel: (01460) 55129 Fax: (01460) 55171 *Chemical farm supplies*

United Agri Products Ltd, Balboughty Farm, Perth, PH2 6AA Tel: (01738) 555400 Fax: (01738) 555401 *Agro chemicals*

United Agri Products Ltd, Fresh Winds Farm, Long Lane, Telford, Shropshire, TF6 6HD Tel: (01952) 260012 Fax: (01952) 260337 *Agrochemicals*

United Agriproducts Ltd, Robsheugh Farm, Milbourne, Newcastle upon Tyne, NE20 0JQ Tel: (0870) 4114666 Fax: (0870) 4114667 *Agricultural chemicals suppliers*

United Air Systems, 32 Alexandra Road, Clevedon, Avon, BS21 7QH Tel: 01275 341322 *Ventilation equipment suppliers*

United Auctions, Stirling Auction Market, Kildean, Stirling, FK9 4UB Tel: (01786) 473055 Fax: (01786) 450393 *Livestock auctioning*

United Biscuits (UK), 54 Church Street, Caldewgate, Carlisle, CA2 5TG Tel: (020) 8234 5000 Fax: (01228) 535900 *Biscuit & snacks manufrs*

United Biscuits UK Ltd, Crossley Road, Manchester, M19 2SD Tel: 0161-432 0202 Fax: 0161-443 1896 *Biscuit manufrs*

United Box, Airlie, Kirriemuir, Angus, DD8 5NY Tel: (01575) 530229 Fax: (01575) 530388 *Potato box distributors & manufrs*

United Bright Bar Co. Ltd, Station Road, Four Ashes, Wolverhampton, WV10 7DG Tel: (01902) 791010 Fax: (01902) 790044 E-mail: sales@unitedbrightbar.co.uk *Steel bar manufrs*

United Business Media GP No 3 Ltd, Ludgate House, 245 Blackfriars Road, London, SE1 9UY Tel: (020) 7921 5000 Fax: (020) 7528 2772 *Business publishers* Also at: Birmingham & Manchester

United Business Media GP No 3 Ltd, Ludgate House, 245 Blackfriars Road, London, SE1 9UY Tel: (020) 7921 5000 Fax: (020) 7528 2772 *Newspaper, book & magazine publishers*

United Closures And Plastics Ltd, Salhouse Road, Norwich, NR7 9AL Tel: (01603) 423131 Fax: (01603) 407942 *Manufacturers of plastic caps*

▶ United Coatings Ltd, Unit 28 The Parkwood Centre, Aston Road, Waterlooville, Hampshire, PO7 7HT Tel: (023) 9223 2758 Fax: (023) 9223 2759 E-mail: neil@unitedcoatingltd.com *Electroplating services*

United Crane Services Ltd, Niagara Works, Beeley Wood Rd, Sheffield, S6 1NH Tel: 0114-285 2801 Fax: 0114-232 5626 E-mail: unitedcranes@aol.com *Crane manufrs*

United Dairy Farmers, 15 Dargan Road, Belfast, BT3 9LS Tel: (028) 9037 2237 Fax: (028) 9037 2222 E-mail: info@utdni.co.uk *Marketing milk & dairy products*

▶ United Demolition Ltd, 13B Hopetoun Lane, Bathgate, West Lothian, EH48 1PP Tel: (01506) 815800

▶ United Diesel Ltd, Unit 6 Leaton Industrial Estate, Bomere Heath, Shrewsbury, SY4 3AP Tel: (01939) 291155 Fax: (01939) 290791 E-mail: Keith@uniteddiesel.co.uk *Family business specializing in remanufacturing diesel injectors*

▶ United Distillers & Vintners, Lagavulin Distillery, Port Ellen, Isle of Islay, PA42 7DZ Tel: (01496) 302400 Fax: (01496) 302733

▶ United Distillers & Vintners, Menstrie Bond, Menstrie, Clackmannanshire, FK11 7EP Tel: (01259) 761351

▶ United Distillers & Vintners, Pencaitland, Tranent, East Lothian, EH34 5ET Tel: (01875) 342000 Fax: (01875) 342001

▶ United Egg Ltd, Unit 18, Llandough Trading Estate, Penarth Road, Cardiff, CF11 8RR Tel: (029) 2070 5701 Fax: (029) 2070 5366 E-mail: info@unitedegg.co.uk *Egg processors*

▶ United Excelsior, 2 Woodside Industrial Estate, Pedmore Road, Dudley, West Midlands, DY2 0RL Tel: (01384) 267770 Fax: (01384) 482127 E-mail: enquiries@exlcr.co.uk *Washroom panelling systems services*

United Fashions Ltd, Irvinebank Rd, Darvel, Ayrshire, KA17 0HS Tel: 01560 321717 Fax: 01560 323323 *Clothing manufacturers*

United Fillings Ltd, 27 Vine Street, Billingborough, Sleaford, Lincolnshire, NG34 0QE Tel: (01529) 240207 Fax: (01529) 240204 E-mail: cushions@unitedfillings.co.uk *Cushions for upholstery industry*

United Fish Industries (U K) Ltd, Gilbey Road, Grimsby, South Humberside, DN31 2SL Tel: (01472) 263333 Fax: (01472) 263451 *Fish meal & fish oil manufrs*

United Fish Products Ltd, Greenwell Place, East Tullos Industrial Estate, Aberdeen, AB12 3AY Tel: (01224) 854444 Fax: (01224) 854333 *Fish meal/fish oil suppliers*

United Fish Products Ltd, Greenwell Place, East Tullos Industrial Estate, Aberdeen, AB12 3AY Tel: (01224) 854444 Fax: (01224) 854333 *Trade association*

United Flags & Flagstaffs Ltd, Boarshaw Road, Middleton, Manchester, M24 2WH Tel: 0161-653 6381 Fax: 0161-655 3383 E-mail: sales@unitedflags.co.uk *Flags & flagpole manufrs*

United Fork Trucks (1992) Ltd, Unit 30, Malmesbury Road, Kingsditch Trading Estate, Cheltenham, Gloucestershire, GL51 9PL Tel: (01242) 577092 Fax: (01242) 577092 E-mail: cheltenham@unitedforktrucks.co.uk *Fork lift truck dealers* Also at: Bromsgrove

United Fork Trucks 1992 Ltd, 1 Eurolink Commercial Park, Symmonds Drive, Sittingbourne, Kent, ME10 3SY Tel: (01795) 472498 Fax: (01795) 479730 E-mail: sittingbourne@unitedforktrucks.co.uk *Manufacture & sales of fork lift trucks*

▶ United Freight Distributuion Ltd, 2 Ashley Drive, Bothwell, Glasgow, G71 8BS Tel: (01698) 802802 Fax: (01698) 802800

▶ The United Industrial Convertors Ltd, 25 Bell End, Rowley Regis, West Midlands, B65 9LU Tel: 0121-559 9293

United Kingdom Mutual War Risks Association Ltd, International House, 26 Creechurch Lane, London, EC3A 5BA Tel: (020) 7283 4646 Fax: (020) 7929 3918 *Marine insurance company*

United Lift Trucks London, Old London Road, Copdock, Ipswich, IP8 3JF Tel: (01279) 417155 *Fork lift trucks retailers*

United Marine Aggregates Ltd, Uma House, Shopwhyke Road, Chichester, West Sussex, PO20 2AD Tel: (01243) 817200 Fax: (01243) 817216 E-mail: info@umag.co.uk *Aggregate producers* Also at: Branches throughout the U.K.

United Moulders Ltd, Farnham Trading Estate, Farnham, Surrey, GU9 9NY Tel: (01420) 86616 Fax: (01252) 721250 E-mail: sales@uml.co.uk Principal Export Areas: Worldwide *Injection moulders mainly life jacket inflators manufrs*

United Oil Products Ltd, Unit 2 Wonastow Road Industrial Estate East, Monmouth, Gwent, NP25 5JB Tel: (01600) 772110 Fax: (01600) 772660 E-mail: unitedoil@hotmail.com *Greasy & antibody products manufrs*

United Optical Ltd, 44-46 Corporation Street, Belfast, BT1 3DE Tel: (028) 9024 1351 Fax: (028) 9032 3594 E-mail: unitedoptical@lineone.net *Optical lens manufrs*

United Optical Ltd, 44-46 Corporation Street, Belfast, BT1 3DE Tel: (028) 9024 1351 Fax: (028) 9032 3594 *Optical glass manufrs*

United Optical Industries Ltd, 583 Moseley Road, Birmingham, B12 9BL Tel: 0121-442 2222 Fax: 0121-449 9993 E-mail: sales@bog.co.uk *Manufacturing opticians & ophthalmic distributors*

▶ United Pallet Repairs, Unit 11, Black Rock Mills, Waingate, Linthwaite, Huddersfield, HD7 5NS Tel: (01484) 847363 Fax: (01484) 847363

United Paper Merchants Ltd, 15 Linfield Industrial Estate, Linfield Road, Belfast, BT12 5LA Tel: (028) 9032 7303 Fax: (028) 9043 8702 E-mail: sales@united-paper.com *Paper merchants*

United Parcels Service (UPS) Ltd, Gresham Road, Nuneaton, Warwickshire, CV10 7QR Tel: (0845) 7877877 Fax: (024) 7664 2188 E-mail: callcentre@europe.ups.com *Road transport/haulage/freight services*

United Parts, Station Farm, Station Road, Kirton Lindsey, Gainsborough, Lincolnshire, DN21 4BD Tel: (01652) 648931 Fax: (01652) 640769 E-mail: jimg@unitedparts.co.uk *Construction plant machinery spare part distributors*

▶ United Refrigeration Ltd, Cluster Industrial Estate, Rodney Road, Southsea, Hampshire, PO4 8ST Tel: (023) 9281 4774 Fax: 023 92814776 E-mail: info@unitedrefrigeration.co.uk *Refrigeration & air conditioning services & installation*

▶ United Refrigeration Ltd, Lindberg Road, Ferndown Industrial Estate, Wimborne, Dorset, BH21 7SP Tel: (01202) 855855 Fax: (01202) 855995 E-mail: ukbranch04@uri.com *Refrigeration & aircom wholesales*

▶ United Safety, Unit 25b Station Lane Industrial Estate, Station Lane, Old Whittington, Chesterfield, Derbyshire, S41 9QX Tel: (01246) 268990 Fax: (01246) 268889 E-mail: unitedsafety@tiscali.co.uk *Based in Derbyshire with over 40 years combined experience in the industry, with a nationwide customer base of local authorities, industry & the general public. We specialise in all types of ppe, hygiene, safety & janitorial goods. We have a well stocked trade counter with workwear, industrial, hi viz, corporate & leisure wear. You will find all manner of gloves, safety footwear, skin care, protective clothing, masks, ear, eye and head protection, paper products, detergents and janitorial supplies, brushes, safety signs etc. You can view and purchase a small selection of our products on line at*http://stores.ebay.co.uk/ UNITED-SAFETY-LTD were you can also view our exceptional customer feedback which really speaks for its self!*Feel free to contact us for advise or a quote - our dedicated staff will be more than happy to help. We ship all over the United Kingdom at highly competitive prices - you will wonder how we do it - just be glad we do!!!*

United Salvage Ltd, 5 Quay Middle, King George Dock,, Hull, HU9 5PR Tel: (01482) 224181 Fax: (01482) 324669 E-mail: svitzersalvage@svitzer.co.uk *Tug operators & marine salvage*

United Springs Ltd, Mandale Park, Norman Road, Rochdale, Lancashire, OL11 4HP Tel: 01706 644551 Fax: 01706 630516 E-mail: amay@united-springs.co.uk Principal Export Areas: Worldwide *Manufacturer of torsion springs, compression springs, clock springs, extension springs, wireforms and pressings.*

United Steel Services Leeds Ltd, 282 Cutler Heights Lane, Bradford, West Yorkshire, BD4 9HU Tel: (01274) 654254 Fax: (01274) 688208 E-mail: united@steels.co.uk *Steel stockholders*

United Storage Systems Ltd, United House, The Street, Takeley, Bishop's Stortford, Hertfordshire, CM22 6QR Tel: (01279) 871787 Fax: (01279) 871636 E-mail: sales@unitedstorage.co.uk *Suppliers of racking & shelving systems & mezzanine floors*

United Supplies Ltd, United House, 6 Regent Road, Aberdeen, AB11 5NS Tel: (01224) 581321 Fax: (01224) 573141 *Customs & excise bonded warehouse*

United Trade & Services Ltd, 256 Water Road, Wembley, Middlesex, HA0 1HX Tel: (020) 8810 6444 Fax: (020) 8810 6455 E-mail: united.trade@btinternet.com *Finance agents & property investors*

United Tyre Ltd, 1 Barkley Square, Clifton, Bristol, BS8 1HL Tel: 0117-929 9291 Fax: 0117-921 4650 *Tyre wholesalers*

United Utilities Operational Services Highland Ltd, Dawson House, Great Sankey, Warrington, WA5 3LW Tel: (01925) 234000 Fax: (01925) 233360 E-mail: enquiries@unitedutilities.com *Multi-utility company*

United Welding Supplies Ltd, Unit 32, The Cam Centre, Wilbury Way, Hitchin, Hertfordshire, SG4 0TW Tel: (01462) 437991 Fax: (01462) 421274 E-mail: sales@unitedwelding.co.uk *Welding supplies & equipment services* Also at: Norwich

▶ United Windows & Glazing Ltd, Mill Lane, Billinghay, LN4 4ES Tel: (01526) 861285 Fax: (01526) 861584 E-mail: unitedkel@dekker.demon.co.uk *Window & doors manufrs*

▶ Uniteg Overseas Solvents Ltd, Business & Technology Centre, Bessemer Drive, Stevenage, Hertfordshire, SG1 2DX Tel: (01438) 310037 Fax: (01438) 310001 E-mail: uniteg@btopenworld.com *Blend & supply maintenace chemicals for Railways/Aircraft/ Haulage and all forms of transport.Also chemicals for industry in general.*

Unitek Computers, Unitek House, Oxford Road, Tatling End, Gerrards Cross, Buckinghamshire, SL9 7BB Tel: (01753) 890500 Fax: (01753) 891916 E-mail: sales@chilternelectronics.co.uk Principal Export Areas: Central/East Europe *Computer dealers & hardware*

UniTek Technologies, 6 Wadsworth Road, Perivale Industrial Estate, Greenford, Middlesex, UB6 7JJ Tel: (0870) 9005100 Fax: (0870) 9005300 E-mail: info@unitek.co.uk *IT systems hardware & software suppliers*

Uniter Group Ltd, Unit 3, Uniter House, Radford Way, Billericay, Essex, CM12 0DX Tel: (0845) 8112000 Fax: (0845) 8112001 *Facsimile distributors*

▶ Unitor Refrigeration Equipment, Sovereign Way, Dock Road, Birkenhead, Merseyside, CH41 1DL Tel: 0151-670 5150 Fax: 0151-670 5159 *Refrigeration equipment manufrs*

Unitor UK Ltd, Kelvin House, 40 Kelvin Road, Wallasey, Merseyside, CH44 7JW Tel: 0151-630 3869 Fax: 0151-637 0151 E-mail: sales@unitor.com *Marine services/ship safety*

Unitrans International Ltd, Woodfield House, Hatmi Lane, Brenchley, Tonbridge, Kent, TN12 7AE Tel: (01892) 723270 Fax: (01892) 724188 E-mail: robert-fogg@unitrans.fsnet.co.uk *Universal air freight forwarders*

Unitron Systems & Developments Ltd, 76A Jameson House, High Street, Broseley, Shropshire, TF12 5EX Tel: (01952) 883817 Fax: (01952) 883672 *Internet service provider*

Unitrunk Cable Systems, Unit 2 Orbital Way, Denton, Manchester, M34 3QA Tel: 0161-336 1177 Fax: 0161-336 1188 *Electrical engineers*

▶ Unity Art, 18 Nelson Road, Hastings, East Sussex, TN34 3RZ Tel: (01424) 201158 Fax: (01424) 201158 E-mail: enquiries@unitydesignandprint.com *Design for print and full website design service. Corporate identity, logos, brochures, posters an flyers. FREE delivery within 20 mile radius of Hastings. Call 01424 201158 or email enquiries@unitydesignandprint.com for a FREE no-obligation quote.*

Unity Biscuits Ltd, Units 7-8 Saltley Industrial Centre, Adderley Road, Saltley, Birmingham, B8 1AW Tel: 0121-327 5588 Fax: 0121-328 2974 *Manufacturer of biscuits*

Unity Coach Painters, Unit 16 Sandybridge La Industrial Estate, Shafton, Barnsley, South Yorkshire, S72 8PH Tel: (01226) 781800 *Coach painters*

Unity Engineering Services, Unit 18 Wansdyke Workshops, Unity Road, Keynsham, Bristol, BS31 1NH Tel: 0117-986 6241 Fax: 0117-986 6241 *Fabrication & welding manufrs*

Unity Plating Co. Ltd, Mount Pleasant Street, Oldham, OL4 1HH Tel: 0161-287 8714 Fax: 0161-287 8715 E-mail: enquiries@unity.zuunet.co.uk *Electroplaters*

Univar Ltd, International House, Zenith, Paycocke Road, Basildon, Essex, SS14 3DW Tel: (01268) 594400 Fax: (01268) 594481 E-mail: exports@univareurope.com *We are the world's leading chemical distributor and can offe a wide range of speciality chemicals and colours globally*

Univar Northern Ireland Ltd, 2 Malone Road, Belfast, BT9 5BN Tel: (028) 9068 1434 Fax: (028) 9038 1880 *Chemical distributors*

Univer Manufacturing Co. Ltd, Station Road, Bradford, West Yorkshire, BD1 4SF Tel: (01274) 725777 Fax: (01274) 725111 E-mail: enquiries@univer.co.uk Principal Export Areas: Central Asia & North America *Pneumatic equipment & hydraulic cylinder manufrs*

Univercell Battery Co. Ltd, Unit 9b Stafford Park 12 Telford, Shropshire, TF3 3BJ Tel: (01952) 293388 Fax: (01952) 290473 E-mail: sales@univercell-batteries.co.uk *Special battery pack manufrs*

Universal 2000 Ltd, Bedford Rd, Houghton Conquest, Bedford, MK45 3LS Tel: (01234) 740922 Fax: (01234) 742505 *Construction equipment exporters*

Universal A V Services, Guy Street, Bradford, West Yorkshire, BD4 7BB Tel: (01254) 351359 Fax: (01274) 200281 *Audio visual hire services*

Universal Access & Power Plants Ltd, 14 Pony Road, Cowley, Oxford, OX4 2RD Tel: (01865) 450000 Fax: (01865) 451111 E-mail: sales@universalhire.co.uk *Scaffold tower hire, leasing & rental*

Universal Aerial Platforms, Swinbourne Road, Burnt Mills Industrial Estate, Basildon, Essex, SS13 1GZ Tel: (01268) 722700 Fax: (01268) 722706 E-mail: basildon@universalplatforms.com *Access platform hire/leasing/rental*

Universal Air Tool Co. Ltd, Unit 8 Lane End Industrial Park, Lane End, High Wycombe, Buckinghamshire, HP14 3BY Tel: (01494) 883300 Fax: (01494) 883237 E-mail: sales@universal.co.uk *Pneumatic hand tools distributors*

Universal Alloys & Metals Ltd, Lowe House, 1 Ranmoor CR, Sheffield, S10 3GU Tel: 0114-230 8855 *Metal alloys distributor*

Universal Applications, 2 Clarkes Road, Wigston, Leicestershire, LE18 2BG Tel: 0116-288 8038 Fax: 0116-288 8036 *Engineering consultants*

Universal Applied Coatings Ltd, Parish Lane, Pease Pottage, Crawley, West Sussex, RH10 5NY Tel: (01293) 514943 Fax: (01293) 552619 *Metal finishers*

▶ Universal Arches Ltd, 103 Peasley Cross Lane, St. Helens, Merseyside, WA9 3AL Tel: (01744) 612844 Fax: (01744) 694250 E-mail: sales@universalarches.com *Upvc bending co*

▶ Universal Augers Ltd, Brook Road, Bicton Industrial Park, Kimbolton, Huntingdon, Cambridgeshire, PE28 0EY Tel: (01480) 861440 Fax: (01480) 861446 E-mail: info@universal-augers.com *Drilling tool manufrs*

Universal Balancing Ltd, Unit 12 Douglas Road Industrial Estate, Douglas Road, Kingswood, Bristol, BS15 8PD Tel: 0117-907 7403 Fax: 0117-907 7402 E-mail: sales@unibal.co.uk *Universal Balancing Ltd. Provide a worldwide customer base balancing solutions. Their product range is comprehensive and uses the latest technology and principles. If you require a standard machine or have a bespoke application Universal Balancing can provide a comprehensive competitive proposal tailored to your exact needs.*

Universal Balancing, Station Street, Cradley Heath, West Midlands, B64 6AJ Tel: (01384) 567550 Fax: (01384) 413997 E-mail: jblomer@unifabrcations.co.uk *Steel fabricators & balancing machines*

Universal Boltforgers, Unit 28 Dudley Road West, Tividale, Oldbury, West Midlands, B69 2PJ Tel: 0121-522 5950 Fax: 0121-520 5333 E-mail: office@universal-boltforgers.co.uk *Bolt & nut manufrs*

Universal Button Co. Ltd, 10-12 Witan Street, London, E2 6JX Tel: (020) 7739 5750 Fax: (020) 7739 1961 *Metal & plastic badge & button manufrs*

Universal Carbon Fibres Ltd, Station Mills, Station Road, Wyke, Bradford, West Yorkshire, BD12 8LA Tel: (01274) 600600 Fax: (01274) 711666 E-mail: info@ucfltd.co.uk *Advanced materials high performance & fire resistant*

▶ Universal Chemicals, Yardley Road, Knowsley Industrial Park, Liverpool, L33 7SS Tel: 0151-549 1071 Fax: 0151-546 8803 *Chemical manufacture*

Universal Components Ltd, Universal House, Pennywell Road, Bristol, BS5 0ER Tel: 0117-955 9091 Fax: 0117-955 6091 E-mail: info@universal-aluminium.co.uk *Aluminium extrusions for glazing & sign industries, design & manufrs*

▶ Universal Computers, 1 St. Georges Close, Sheffield, S3 7HJ Tel: 0114-278 6222 Fax: 0114-278 6222 *Computer hardware suppliers*

▶ Universal Computers Technology Ltd, Unit 304 K2 Heathfield Way, Kings Heath Industrial Estate, Northampton, NN5 7QP Tel: (01604) 588635 Fax: (01604) 588606

Universal Container Services Ltd, Boundary Trading Park, Liverpool Road, Irlam, Manchester, M44 6QJ Tel: 0845 4941757 Fax: 0161-775 9079 E-mail: sales@universal-containers.com *Universal Container Services is a leading Container Sales, Container Hire Container Repair and Site Accommodation Specialist. With several depots located in key areas, universal Container Services are able to offer high quality new and Used Shipping Containers for sale or Hire in any size from 6foot to 45foot, delivered anywhere in England and Wales . Universal also Manufacture all Portable accommodation and site welfare units such as offices, Mess Rooms, Drying Rooms portable toilet blocks and much more. Weather you Require A reefer container, Standard Shipping container, Flat Rack Open top or any Portable site accommodation unit, Universal Container Services will provide High Quality product and service at affordable prices.*

▶ Universal Contract Management, Unit 16 Thornton Industrial Trad Est, Milford Haven, Dyfed, SA73 2RR Tel: 01646 690115

Universal Cooling Ltd, Unit 1a West End Business Park, Oswaldtwistle, Accrington, Lancashire, BB5 4WE Tel: (01254) 396005 Fax: (01254) 396055 E-mail: sales@universalcooling.co.uk *Air conditioning & refrigeration systems*

Universal Crop Protection Ltd, Park House, Maidenhead Road, Cookham, Berkshire, SL6 9DS Tel: (01628) 526083 Fax: (01628) 810457 E-mail: enquiries@unicrop.com *Agricultural chemical distributors*

Universal Display Fittings Co. Ltd, 51 Mortimer Street, London, W1W 8JH Tel: (020) 7580 9471 Fax: (020) 7436 9732 E-mail: info@universaldisplay.co.uk *Display fittings manufrs*

Universal Engine Power Ltd, 9 Flitch Industrial Estate, Chelmsford Road, Dunmow, Essex, CM6 1XJ Tel: (01371) 875331 Fax: (01371) 874777 E-mail: sales@unipower.uk.com *Stone restoration*

Universal Engineering, Unit 10 Mid Wynd, Dundee, DD1 4JG Tel: (01382) 223592 Fax: (01382) 202506 E-mail: sales@universalengtool.co.uk *Cutting tool distributors*

Universal Engineering Workholding Ltd, New Street, Netherton, Huddersfield, HD4 7EZ Tel: (01484) 663018 Fax: (01484) 663758 E-mail: sales@uew.co.uk *Power chuck & cylinder distributors & specialist work holding manufrs*

Universal Envelopes Ltd, 5 Bourne Road, Bexley, Kent, DA5 1LG Tel: (01322) 529529 Fax: (01322) 529829 *Envelope manufrs*

Universal Express Ltd, 139-141 Hamilton Road, Felixstowe, Suffolk, IP11 7BL Tel: (01394) 282867 Fax: (01394) 286767 E-mail: info@universalexpress.co.uk *Freight forwarders*

Universal Fabrications, Mansfield Road, Edwinstowe, Mansfield, Nottinghamshire, NG21 9NJ Tel: (01623) 824212 Fax: (01623) 824212 *Fabricators*

▶ Universal Fabrications (Coventry) Ltd, Whitacre Road Ind Estate, Nuneaton, Warwickshire, CV11 6BX Tel: 024 76370272

Universal Fabrications North West Ltd, Star Iron Works, Taurus Street, Oldham, OL4 2BN Tel: 0161-620 0550 Fax: 0161-620 0247 E-mail: sales@universal-fabrications.co.uk *Sheet metalworkers & fabricators*

Universal Fibre Optics (Old Co) Ltd, 6 Home Place, Coldstream, Berwickshire, TD12 4DT Tel: (01890) 883416 Fax: (01890) 883062 E-mail: info@universal-fibre-optics.com Principal Export Areas: Worldwide *Manufacture of optical fibre and fibre optic lighting systems and components.*

Universal Fixings Ltd, Unit 1 2 Balds Lane, Jubilee Business Park, Lye, Stourbridge, West Midlands, DY9 8SH Tel: (01384) 422284 *Cable management systems*

Universal Flooring Accessories Ltd, Interserve House, Ruscombe Park, Twyford, Reading, RG10 9JU Tel: 0870 770 4330 Fax: 0118 934 3667 E-mail: info@uniflooring.co.uk *Universal flooring Accessories was established to produce high quality flooring accessories at extremely competitive prices. We offer full support to Trade Wholesalers with large stock availability for next day nationwide distribution.*

Universal Flooring Contractors, 7a George Road, Erdington, Birmingham, B23 7QE Tel: 0121-377 8808 Fax: 0121-377 8184 E-mail: sales@universal-flooring.co.uk *Industrial epoxy resin flooring specialists*

Universal Forwarding, Freight Village, Newcastle Int Airport, Woolsington, Newcastle upon Tyne, NE13 8BH Tel: 0191-214 0800 Fax: 0191-214 0811 E-mail: info@universal-forwarding.co.uk *International freight forwarding*

Universal Glass Co, 8-16 Camelon Street, Glasgow, G32 6AF Tel: 0141-764 0444 Fax: 0141-764 0044 E-mail: universalglass@btinternet.com *Mirror manufrs*

Universal Glazing Ltd, Unit 12 Silver Court, Intercity Way, Leeds, LS13 4LY Tel: 0113-257 2021 Fax: 0113-239 3317 E-mail: universal@unit12.fsnet.co.uk *Patent glazing systems manufrs*

Universal Grinding Services Ltd, Unit 1/2, Kings Road Works, Kings Road, New Haw, Addlestone, Surrey, KT15 3BG Tel: 01932 346806 Fax: 01932 350978 E-mail: ugsltd@btconnect.com *Precision grinding services and CNC machining*

Universal Guards Servicing Ltd, Turnpike Close, Grantham, Lincolnshire, NG31 7XU Tel: (01476) 565858 Fax: (01476) 590296 E-mail: sales@lightguards.com *Press brake guard manufrs*

▶ Universal Hardware Supplies Direct Ltd, 1ADillwyn Road, Sketty, Swansea, SA2 9AQ Tel: (01792) 205050 Fax: (01792) 202255 E-mail: info@u-h-s.co.uk *Retailers of architectural ironmongery*

▶ Universal Heating Supplies, 97 Heaton Park Road, Newcastle Upon Tyne, NE6 5NR Tel: 0191-209 9399 E-mail: enquires@universalheating.co.uk *Plumbing, gas & electric fires, showers & bathrooms*

Universal Hydraulic Power, Unit 6 Arden Business Park, Enterprise Close, Medway City Estate, Rochester, Kent, ME2 4LY Tel: (01322) 555452 Fax: (01634) 290871 E-mail: unihose@fastnet.co.uk *Hose distributors* Also at: Ashford (Kent), Crayford & Maidstone

Universal Hydraulics Ltd, Carrwood Road, Chesterfield, Derbyshire, S41 9QB Tel: (01246) 451711 Fax: (01246) 450399 E-mail: sales@universalhydraulics.co.uk *Hydraulic engineers*

Universal Instrument Services Ltd, Cambridge Road, Whetstone, Leicester, LE8 6PA Tel: 0116-275 0123 Fax: 0116-275 0262 E-mail: sales@uiscal.co.uk *Electronic instrument recalibration services*

▶ Universal IT (UK) Ltd, Unit 11, TewinRoad Business Centre, Garden Court, Welwyn Garden City, Hertfordshire, AL7 1BH Tel: (01707) 322320 Fax: (01707) 322032

Universal Joineries (Newcastle) Ltd, Fisher Street, Newcastle Upon Tyne, NE6 4NH Tel: 0191-262 8554 Fax: 0191-263 6018 *Joinery*

▶ Universal Lifting Services, Green End, Gamlingay, Sandy, Bedfordshire, SG19 3LB Tel: (01767) 651800 Fax: (01767) 650066 E-mail: info@universallifting.com *Fabrication & welding services*

Universal Locks, 894 Plymouth Road, Slough, SL1 4LP Tel: (01753) 696630 Fax: (01753) 568461 E-mail: info@universalsecurity.co.uk *Locksmiths, safe engineers & shutter installations*

Universal Manufacturing Supplies, 25 Whitehorse Street, Baldock, Hertfordshire, SG7 6QB Tel: (01462) 892277 Fax: (01462) 892277 *Industrial fasteners distributors*

Universal Moulding Co., 500 Ipswich Rd, Slough, SL1 4EP Tel: (01753) 570023 Fax: (01753) 535005 E-mail: andy@alltechmoulds.co.uk *Injection & plastic moulding manufrs,product design,mould manufacture,assembly,small and large batch production and low cost tooling.*

Universal Packaging Ltd, Units 3-4, Capitol Industrial Centre, Fulmar Way, Wickford, Essex, SS11 8YW Tel: (01268) 561400 Fax: (01268) 572900 E-mail: admin@uplgroupltd.com *Corrugated case containers manufrs*

Universal Packing Specialists Ltd, Unit 7 Space Waye, Feltham, Middlesex, TW14 0TH Tel: (020) 8893 1180 Fax: (020) 8893 2214 E-mail: sales@universalpacking.co.uk *Export packing services*

Universal Play Ltd, 4 Derwent Close, Tangmere, Chichester, West Sussex, PO20 2FQ Tel: (01243) 784722 Fax: (01243) 784742 E-mail: universal.play@primex.co.uk *Childrens playground equipment suppliers, designers & installers*

Universal Power Systems, Weldon Road, Loughborough, Leicestershire, LE11 5RN Tel: (01509) 261100 Fax: (01509) 261148 E-mail: sales@upsltd.co.uk *Uninterruptible power supply manufrs*

Universal Press Ltd, Bridge House, Chilton Foliat, Hungerford, Berkshire, RG17 0TG Tel: (01488) 682328 Fax: (01488) 681899 E-mail: adviser@universal-press.co.uk *Printers*

▶ Universal Products Ltd, Struan Drumore Road, Killearn, Glasgow, G63 9NX Tel: (01360) 550111 Fax: (01360) 550222 E-mail: info@universalstorage.co.uk *Distributors of racking & shelving products*

Universal Products Leicester Ltd, 46 Main Street, Kirby Muxloe, Leicester, LE9 2AU Tel: 0116-239 3625 Fax: 0116-239 3625 *Motor vehicle accessories manufrs*

Universal Rentals (UK) Ltd, Unit 31, Spaces Business Centre, Ingate Place, London, SW8 3NS Tel: (020) 7720 8787 Fax: (020) 7627 4586 E-mail: info@universalrentals.co.uk *Computer rentals services*

Universal Rewinds Ltd, 273 Wincolmlee, Hull, HU2 0PZ Tel: (01482) 226238 Fax: (01482) 586654 E-mail: rewinds@lineone.net *Electric motor rewinding services & electrical contractors*

Universal Rubber Co., The Old Bakery, 2 Tithe Barn Road, Stafford, ST16 3PQ Tel: (01785) 252793 Fax: (01785) 225379 *Rubber products manufrs*

Universal Sealants UK Ltd, Kingston House, Pattinson North, Washington, Tyne & Wear, NE38 8QA Tel: 0191-416 1530 Fax: 0191-415 4377 E-mail: info@usluk.com *Specialist bridge expansion joint contractors*

Universal Seals & Bearings Ltd, Waterloo Indust Park, Upper Brook Street, Stockport, Cheshire, SK1 3BP Tel: 0161-429 0287 Fax: 0161-477 2940 *Oil seal & o-ring distributors*

Universal Securities CCTV Ltd, 47a/49 Newbold Road, Chesterfield, Derbyshire, S41 7PL Tel: (01246) 555893 Fax: (01246) 239997 *Security cameras, alarms etc.*

▶ Universal Security Systems Ltd, Mint Business Park, 41 Butchers Road, London, E16 1PW Tel: (020) 7511 8080

▶ Universal Security UK Ltd, Unit 120 City Business Park, Somerset Place, Plymouth, PL3 4BB Tel: (01752) 511222 Fax: (01752) 202426 E-mail: sales@unisecltd.co.uk *Security installation services*

Universal Sheet Metal Co., Dunlop Road, Hunt End Industrial Estate, Redditch, Worcestershire, B97 5XP Tel: (01527) 402202 Fax: (01527) 403030 E-mail: usm@usmlimited.co.uk *Stainless steel sheet metal workers*

Universal Sheetmetal Works, 317 Blucher Road, London, SE5 0LH Tel: (020) 7703 4575 *Ductwork manufrs*

▶ Universal Showcards, 23 Stonefield Way, Ruislip, Middlesex, HA4 0YF Tel: (020) 8841 4551 Fax: (020) 8845 0737 E-mail: info@universal-sc.co.uk *Printer finishers*

Universal Silk Screen Printers, Unit 5 Leeside Works, Stanstead Abbotts, Ware, Hertfordshire, SG12 8JL Tel: (01920) 877274 Fax: (01920) 877114 *Universal based in Stanstead Abbotts are sign manufacturers, screen printers and vehicle livery contractors for Stanstead Abbotts, Hertford, Ware, Stevenage and Harlow.*

Universal Sound, 25 Brancaster Lane, Purley, Surrey, CR8 1HJ Tel: (020) 8660 0990 *Music production services*

Universal Steel, 9 Lindholme Gardens, Owlthorpe, Sheffield, S20 6TD Tel: (07870) 575523 Fax: 0114-248 4139 E-mail: peterjwatters@tiscali.co.uk *Servicing all of the UK, UNIVERSAL EISEN UND STAHL GMBH are one of Europe's leading stockists of steel plate in carbon, alloy & stainless grades. Plate cutting up to 300mm thick and additional testing to customer specification are done in-house and deliveries made within 7 days to any UK destination. Specialists in Abrasion Resistant steel plate - 400HB Wearplate /500HB Wearplate /X120Mn12 (12 - 14% Manganese Plate), High Strength steel plate - S690QL / S890QL /S960QL /S700MC /RQT701, Boiler, Pressure Vessel Plate: P265GH /P295GH / P355NL1 /P460NL1 /ASME SA516-60 /A516-70, Chrome Molybdenum plate - ASTM A387 grade 5 /11 /12 /22 /13CrMo4-5 /10CrMo9-10 / 12CrMo19.5 /16Mo3, Structural Steel Plate - S235JRG2 /S275JR /S355J2+N /S460NL / 355EMZ /C45 /C60 /42CrMo4 /16MnCr5. Specialists in heavy steel plate - up to 4m wide and 16m long. Peter Watters is UK Sales Director and your point of contact for any UK business.*

Universal Steels Ltd, 52 Peasehill Road, Rosyth, Dunfermline, Fife, KY11 2GB Tel: (01383) 418720 Fax: (01383) 411505 *Steel merchants & fabricators*

▶ Universal Supplies Clydesdale Ltd, Hozier Street, Carluke, Lanarkshire, ML8 5DW Tel: (01555) 772474 Fax: (01555) 772426 E-mail: sales@uscltd.co.uk Purchasing Contact: D. Perry Sales Contact: I. Perry Principal Export Areas: Worldwide *Hydraulic system engineering design services; hydraulic control system design; cylinders, hydraulic, ind dustrial*

Universal Supplies UK Ltd, South Street, Retford, Nottinghamshire, DN22 6JJ Tel: (01777) 706600 Fax: (01777) 706600 *Safety equipment protective clothing retailers*

▶ Universal Technologies, Stanton Lane, Potters Marston, Leicester, LE9 3JR Tel: (01455) 273663 Fax: (01455) 273993 E-mail: sales@universaltechno-cctv.com *Closed circuit television equipment suppliers*

Universal Thermosensors Ltd, Units 10-11 Castle Road Technical Centre, Castle Road, Murston, Sittingbourne, Kent, ME10 3RG Tel: (01795) 470924 Fax: (01795) 476733 E-mail: sales@universal-thermosensors.co.uk *Thermocouple manufrs*

Universal Tool (Gloucester) Co. Ltd, Unit 16-18, Bamfurlong Industrial Park, Staverton, Cheltenham, Gloucestershire, GL51 6SX Tel: (01452) 712597 Fax: (01452) 857540 E-mail: mike@inona-uk.com *Precision engineers*

Universal Towel Co. Ltd, 1 Spa Industrial Park, Longfield Road, Tunbridge Wells, Kent, TN2 3EN Tel: (01892) 518822 Fax: (01892) 518118 E-mail: info@u-t-c.co.uk *Washroom services supplier*

Universal Trade Services Ltd, 32 Marylebone High Street, London, W1U 4PR Tel: (020) 7224 5801 Fax: (020) 7935 3237 E-mail: director@utslimited.com *Gas turbine spare part suppliers*

Universal Transmission Services, Unit 16 Worcester Road, Hoobrook Enterprise Centre, Kidderminster, Worcestershire, DY10 1HB Tel: (01562) 861651 *Gear box (reconditioned) rebuilders & suppliers*

Universal Tyres & Spares Ltd, Unit 18 Crown Trading Centre, Clayton Road, Hayes, Middlesex, UB3 1DU Tel: (020) 8569 0090 Fax: (020) 8569 0509 *Motor tyre dealers & exporters* Also at: Acton, Iver, Langley & Southall

Universal Vulcanising Services, Unit 4 Moss Lane, Little Hoole, Preston, PR4 4SX Tel: (01772) 614343 Fax: (01772) 614848 *Conveyor belt suppliers*

Universal Weighing Services, 1 Winders Corner, Barlborough, Chesterfield, Derbyshire, S43 4WH Tel: (01246) 813333 *Weighing machine manufrs*

▶ Universal Worktops, Prospect Road, Crook, County Durham, DL15 8JN Tel: (01388) 768500 Fax: (01388) 768703 E-mail: sales@universalworktops.com *Worktop & kitchen suppliers & manufrs*

The Universities Press (Belfast) Ltd, Alanbrooke Road, Belfast, BT6 9HF Tel: (028) 9070 4464 Fax: (028) 9079 3295 *Printers*

University of Derby Buxton, Devonshire Campus, 1 Devonshire Road, Buxton, Derbyshire, SK17 6RY Tel: (01298) 71100 Fax: (01298) 27261 E-mail: enquiriesudb@derby.ac.uk *The University of Derby based in Buxton offers a variety of undergraduate, postgraduate and part-time courses.*

▶ University of Edinburgh, Kings Buildings, Mayfield Road, Edinburgh, EH9 3JL Tel: 0131-650 5619

▶ University Of Leeds Farms Ltd, Financial Services, 11-84 Ec Stoner Building, Leeds, LS2 9JT Tel: 0113-234 0206 Fax: 0113-343 4058 E-mail: consulting@leeds.ac.uk *Research & development, laboratory testing services & expert witness*

University Of Plymouth, Drake Circus, Plymouth, PL4 8AA Tel: (01752) 600600 *University*

University Of Wales Institute Cardiff, Western Avenue, Cardiff, CF5 2SG Tel: (029) 2041 6070 Fax: (029) 2041 6286 E-mail: info@uwic.ac.uk *Educational establishment*

▶ Uniwire Ltd, Unit 21 Glan Yr Afon Industrial Estate, Llanbadarn Fawr, Aberystwyth, Dyfed, SY23 3JQ Tel: (01970) 611326 Fax: (01970) 615868 *Barbed wire & stock fence manufrs*

▶ Unix Recruitment Ltd, Brightside Business Centre, 60 Lonnen Road, Wimborne, Dorset, BH21 7AX Tel: (01202) 888021 E-mail: richard@unixrecruitment.co.uk *Unix Recruitment Ltd is an IT recruitment agency specialising in recruitment for UNIX IT professionals. We recruit for many organisations within market sectors such as, Banking & Finance, Trading Support, Telecoms, Manufacturing, Media, ISP"s, Software Houses, Government, Pharmaceuticals, Data Storage, SAN Manufacturing & Vendors and IT Solution Companies concentrating on UNIX IT recruitment with a global reach for local and international We have over 7 years UNIX recruitment experience and have gained a unique pro-active perspective within this exciting, demanding market sector. Having extensive UNIX knowledge we have a clear understanding of our clients needs and can identify suitable applicants quickly & effectively. Therefore do not send through irrelevant applications. We recruit in a professional manner with a personal touch and offer a fast, effective, and reliable UNIX recruitment service."clients."*

▶ Unlimited Knits, 1a Darlton Drive, Arnold, Nottingham, NG5 7JS Tel: 0115-926 3999 Fax: 0115-926 3888 *Knitwear suppliers*

Unlimited Service, Rickett Street, London, SW6 1RU Tel: (020) 7386 6150 *IT consultants*

Unomedical Ltd, 26-27 Thornhill Road, Redditch, Worcestershire, B98 9NL Tel: (01527) 587700 Fax: (01527) 592111 E-mail: redditch@unomedical.com *Surgical instruments manufrs*

Unox UK, Unit 3 Marsh Farm Business Centre, Bowling Alley, Crondall, Farnham, Surrey, GU10 5RJ Tel: (01252) 851522 Fax: (01252) 851492 E-mail: info@unoxuk.com *Specialist importer of Combination Steam,Bakery and Bake-Off Ovens and Ceramic Grills.*

Unravel Mills Ltd, Broomfield Mill Street, Preston, PR1 1NQ Tel: (01772) 259065 Fax: (01772) 881398 E-mail: sales@unravelmills.co.uk *Registered charity & pattern book manufrs*

▶ UNSA UK Ltd, Number One The Beehive, Lions Drive, Shadsworth Business Park, Blackburn, BB1 2QS Tel: (01254) 699469 Fax: (01254) 699569 *Packaging equipment manufrs*

Unsco, Manor Road, Kiveton Park Station, Sheffield, S26 6PB Tel: (01909) 770431 Fax: (01909) 772848 E-mail: galdrich@unsco.com *Specialist steel*

▶ UP Consulting Ltd, 186 Allesley old Road, Coventry, CV5 8GJ Tel: (0870) 0678803 Fax: (0870) 0671850 E-mail: mail@upconsulting.co.uk *We aid companies with Employment Law {minimising employee law suites & pay outs due to non-compliance}, Forming HR policies, procedures & practice, Absenteeism and long term sick policy, Practice and procedures formulation, Formulation of individual employment contracts, Disciplinary procedures {dismissing fairly & reasonably}, Keeping you informed of employment law updates {i.e. April, 2005}, Health and Safety issues, Employee handbook formulation specific to your organisation, Discrimination & Equal opportunities policy, Performance management - setting targets/ measurements and monitoring, Appraisal procedures, Recruitment and retention strategies, Outsourced HR Consultancy and Succession and manpower planning. As well as Business Strategy, Sales & Marketing, Business Planning and Technology for Businesses.***

Up Country Autoproducts UK Ltd, Norwich Road, Halesworth, Suffolk, IP19 8QJ Tel: (01986) 875171 Fax: (01986) 875260 E-mail: sales@upcountry4x4.co.uk *Welding fabricators & machinists*

▶ Up Front Security Ltd, 307 West George Street, Glasgow, G2 4LF Tel: 0141-221 5448 Fax: 0141-221 5449

Up The Pole Ltd, 56 Meadow Road, Catshill, Bromsgrove, Worcestershire, B61 0JL Tel: (01527) 833873 Fax: (01527) 836578 *Flag, banners & table flags manufrs*

Update, Quadrant House, The Quadrant, Brighton Road, Sutton, Surrey, SM2 5AS Tel: (020) 8652 3500 *Update is a UK journal of continuing clinical education for family practioners.*

Update Products Ltd, The Westway, Alvechurch Road, Birmingham, B31 3PU Tel: 0121-477 7777 Fax: 0121-477 6880 *Metal fabricators*

Upfield Engineering, Rutherfords Business Park, Marley Lane, Battle, East Sussex, TN33 0TY Tel: (01424) 775373 Fax: (01424) 777164 E-mail: enquiries@upfieldengineering.co.uk *Mechanical & precision engineers*

▶ Upgrade, 13 Fore Lane Avenue, Sowerby Bridge, West Yorkshire, HX6 1BQ

Upgrade Bikes Ltd, PO Box 2518, Horsham, West Sussex, RH13 8RA Tel: (01403) 711611 Fax: (01403) 710753 *Bicycle wholesalers & manufrs*

Company Information

Upgraders Computer Systems, 23 Ivatt Way, Peterborough, PE3 7PG Tel: (01733) 703269 Fax: (01733) 750767 E-mail: sales@upgraders.co.uk *Computer network services*

▶ Upholstery Fabrics UK, 7 Eaton Close, Stockwood, Bristol, BS14 8PR Tel: 01275 830213 E-mail: enquires@upholsteryfabricsuk.co.uk

Upholstery Services, 51 Mansfield Road, Sheffield, S12 2AG Tel: 0114-265 4546 *Re-upholstery foam rubber manufrs*

▶ Upholstery Techniques Ltd, Stanway Grounds, Stanway, Cheltenham, Gloucestershire, GL54 5DR Tel: (01242) 621414 Fax: (01242) 621471

▶ Uplift Power Platforms, Unit 1 8 Flanshaw Way, Wakefield, West Yorkshire, WF2 9LP Tel: (01924) 383833 Fax: (01924) 383832

Upm Machinery Sales Ltd, 5 Elder Way, Waterside Drive, Langley, Slough, SL3 6EP Tel: (01753) 548801 Fax: (01753) 544115 E-mail: royf@upm.co.uk *Plastics ancillary equipment*

Uponor Ltd, Berristow Lane, Blackwell, Alfreton, Derbyshire, DE55 5JD Tel: (01773) 811112 Fax: (01773) 812343 E-mail: marketing@uponor.co.uk *Plastic pipe manufrs*

Uponor Housing Solutions Ltd, Snapethorpe, Rugby Road, Lutterworth, Leicestershire, LE17 4HN Tel: (01455) 550355 Fax: (01455) 550366 E-mail: hsenquiries@uponor.co.uk *Plastic tubes & underfloor heating systems*

Upoxy Research Ltd, Newbattle Industrial Estate, Dalkeith, Midlothian, EH22 4AD Tel: 0131-663 1111 Fax: 0131-663 7220 E-mail: mail@upoxy.co.uk *Automotive refinish paint manufrs*

▶ Upper Deck Loft Conversions, 81J Clotherholme Road, Ripon, North Yorkshire, HG4 2DN Tel: 01765 604596 *We carry out loft conversions in both modern trussed lofts and traditional lofts from design to completion*

Upper & Lower Leisurewear, Leylands House, Molesey Road, Walton-On-Thames, Surrey, KT12 3PW Tel: (01932) 241174 Fax: (01932) 244947 E-mail: sales@upperandlower.co.uk *T-shirt printing specialists*

Upright International, Unit F1, Halesfield 4, Telford, Shropshire, TF7 4AP Tel: (01952) 685200 Fax: (01952) 685255 E-mail: mdavey@uprighteuro.com *Alloy tower/ hydraulic work platforms distribs* Also at: Branches throughout the U.K.

Bill Upsall Ltd, Charlotte Street, South Shields, Tyne & Wear, NE33 1PX Tel: 0191-455 6305 Fax: 0191-455 6305 E-mail: phil@billupsalltrophies.fslife.co.uk *Sports goods & trophies, glass & engraving*

Upstairs Downstairs Chester Ltd, 23 Chester Street, Saltney, Chester, CH4 8BL Tel: (01244) 679566 Fax: (01244) 680857 E-mail: ud_stairs1984@yahoo.co.uk *Kitchen & bathroom installation & distributors*

▶ Upthejunction.Com, 3 Saxon Road, Hoylake, Wirral, Merseyside, CH47 3AE Tel: 0151-632 2451 E-mail: info@upthejunction.com *Search engine placement & marketing consultants*

Upton Farm Services, Tewkesbury Road, Upton-Upon-Severn, Worcester, WR8 0PU Tel: (01684) 591071 *Agricultural engineers*

Upton Metal Works, Magdalene Road, Torquay, TQ1 4AF Tel: (01803) 814326 Fax: (01803) 200598 *Metalworker agents*

Upton Oil Co. Ltd, Blandford Road North, Upton, Poole, Dorset, BH16 6AA Tel: (01202) 622257 Fax: (01202) 632578 E-mail: uptonoil.co@btinternet.com *Fuel oil distributors*

Upton & Scott, Huntspill Road, Highbridge, Somerset, TA9 3DE Tel: (01278) 783279 Fax: (01278) 783279 *Precision engineers*

Upton Vending Ltd, Vivars Way, Canal Road, Selby, North Yorkshire, YO8 8BE Tel: (01757) 291515 Fax: (01757) 294600 E-mail: sales@uptonvending.co.uk *Vending machine agents*

▶ Uptown Events, PO Box 1492, London, North London, NW11 6WL Tel: 0870 1226971

Upu Industries Ltd, 1 Quillyburn Business Park, Banbridge Road, Dromore, County Down, BT25 1BY Tel: (028) 9269 9020 Fax: (028) 9269 9029 E-mail: info@steve-orr.com *Agricultural*

▶ The UPVC Cleaning Company Ltd, PO BOX 559, Edgware, Middlesex, HA8 4BM Tel: 0800 1973033 E-mail: enquiries@upvc-cleaning.co.uk *Specialist upvc cleaners for the residential & commercial sectors, one-off or contract. we clean windows, doors, conservatories, fascias, soffits, cladding and guttering. free estimates or site surveys, fully insured. FACT ! we clean what the window cleaners wont touch.*

Urad Saddlery & Leathercare Products, Unit 4 Cavans Way, Binley Industrial Estate, Coventry, CV3 2SF Tel: (024) 7645 4244 Fax: (024) 7645 4245 *Saddlery distributor*

▶ The Urban Decor Shop, PO Box 245, Barnstaple, Devon, EX32 9WZ Tel: (01271) 323634 E-mail: info@theurbandecorshop.com *Household furniture & accessories*

Urban Design & Developments Ltd, Units 4-5, Incomol Business Park, Derby Road, Chesterfield, Derbyshire, S45 9AG Tel: (01246) 862319 Fax: (01246) 863192 E-mail: streetstructures@aol.com *We are one of the UK's leading specialist manufacturers and installers of glazed canopies. Our objective is to offer excellence in all our services whilst maintaining value for money."We specialise in the design, manufacture and installation of Canopies, Walkways, Bus Shelters, Vertical glazing and all types of decorative steelwork."The majority of projects we undertake are bespoke, and our clients benefit from our involvement at the early stages of design to advise on costs and best practice methods." "We supply structures in a variety of materials and we offer the choice of tailor made options which can be due to budget, location, visual requirements or a wide range of other influences."Materials commonly used include, Galvanised Steel, Stainless Steel, Decorated Mild Steel, Safety Glass, Polycarbonate, Aluminium, Cast Iron and a full compliment of paint finishes in any RAL or BS colour of your choice."*

continued

▶ Urban Elements, Glebe Farm, Cross Street, Barrow-upon-Humber, North Lincolnshire, DN19 7AL Tel: (01469) 533253 Fax: (01469) 533253 E-mail: info@urbanelements.co.uk *Design, manufacture & supply contemporary street furniture & lighting*

Urban Haylo, 77 Whyke Lane, Chichester, West Sussex, PO19 7PD Tel: (01243) 783755 Fax: (01243) 783653 *Jewellery manufrs*

▶ Urban Hygiene Ltd, Skynet Business Park, Robin Hood Airport, Doncaster, South Yorkshire, DN9 3GA Tel: (01302) 623193 Fax: (01302) 623167 E-mail: enquiries@urbanhygiene.co.uk *Anti graffiti removal liquids manufrs*

▶ Urban Icon, 1 Drill Hall Business Centre, East Parade, Ilkley, West Yorkshire, LS29 8EZ Tel: (01943) 605861 Fax: (01943) 605862 *Hairdressing accessory suppliers*

Urban Initiatives, Adam House, 1 Fitzroy Square, London, W1T 5HE Tel: (020) 7380 4545 Fax: (020) 7380 4546 E-mail: info@urbaninitiatives.co.uk *Urban designers*

Urbanhurst UK Ltd, Twyford Business Centre, London Road, Bishop's Stortford, Hertfordshire, CM23 3YT Tel: (01279) 755590 Fax: (01279) 652644 *Cylinder head specialists*

▶ Urbansoul Design, Kingfisher Centre, Futures Park, Bacup, Lancashire, OL13 0BB Tel: (01706) 877899 Fax: (01706) 877899 E-mail: info@urbansouldesign.co.uk *Graphic designers*

Urbis Lighting Ltd, 1-5 Telford Road, Basingstoke, Hampshire, RG21 6YW Tel: (01256) 354446 Fax: (01256) 841314 E-mail: sales@urbislighting.com *Street furniture & lighting manufrs*

URENCO (Capenhurst) Ltd, Capenhurst, Chester, CH1 6ER Tel: 0151-473 4000 Fax: 0151-473 4384 E-mail: cad@cap.urenco.co.uk *Carbon fibre tube/electric motor manufrs*

▶ Uretek UK Ltd, Peel House, Peel Rd, Skelmersdale, Lancs, WN8 9PT Tel: (01695) 50525 Fax: (01695) 555212 E-mail: sales@uretek.co.uk *Leading the world in Repair Technologies. For over 25 Years The Uretek resin injection techniques have led the world in offering the most advanced and accurate systems for concrete slab lifting and stabilisation. Recent research and innovation has resulted in the unique Uretek Deep Injection soil stabilisation method.*

Urethane Industrial Products Ltd, Evingar Industrial Estate, Ardglen Road, Whitchurch, Hampshire, RG28 7BB Tel: (01256) 892830 Fax: (01256) 896899 E-mail: urethaneindustrial@hotmail.com *Manufacturers rollers*

▶ Uro Frames, 357 Oldham Road, Ashton-under-Lyne, Lancashire, OL7 9NE Tel: 0161-343 7220 E-mail: sales@uroframes.com

Urofoam Ltd, Duddon Road, Askam-in-Furness, Cumbria, LA16 7AN Tel: (01229) 467901 Fax: (01229) 467272 *Foam products manufrs*

Urolite Ltd, 4 Northwold Road, London, N16 7HR Tel: (020) 7241 6093 E-mail: info@urolite.co.uk *Window fitters*

▶ Uropa Promotional Items, 132 Soho Road, Birmingham, B21 9LN Tel: 0121-554 6850 Fax: 0121-554 1922 E-mail: enquiries@uropainternational.co.uk *Source & supply goods for the promotional gifts & incentives market*

▶ Urquhart & Co., Rhevackin, Kiltarlity, Beauly, Inverness-Shire, IV4 7HT Tel: (01463) 741564

▶ Urquhart & Co, 9 Lotland Street, Inverness, IV1 1ST Tel: (01463) 223500 Fax: (01463) 226060

Urquhart Dykes & Lord, 30 Welbeck Street, London, W1G 8ER Tel: (020) 7487 1550 Fax: (020) 7487 1599 E-mail: email@udl.co.uk *Chartered patent attorneys* Also at: Bradford & Leeds

Urquhart Dykes & Lord, Amen Corner, St Nicholas Chambers, Newcastle upon Tyne, NE1 1PE Tel: 0191-261 8573 Fax: 0191-222 1604 E-mail: newcastle@udl.co.uk *Patent trade mark agents & attorneys*

Simon Urquhart Ltd, Orchardbank Industrial Estate, Forfar, Angus, DD8 1TD Tel: (01307) 462584 Fax: (01307) 465229 *Scrap metal merchants*

Urschel International Ltd, Tiber Way, Meridian Business Park, Leicester, LE19 1QP Tel: 0116-263 4321 Fax: 0116-263 4300 E-mail: international@urschel.com *Food processing machinery manufrs*

▶ Us 4 Slush Ltd, 8C Canford Business Park, Magna Road, Poole, Dorset, BH21 3AP Tel: (01202) 572104 E-mail: sales@us4slush.com *Manufacturers of slush drink syrup, slush drinks machine sales & service*

Us Marine & Industrial Pump Repair, Site 20 Grangefield Industrial Estate, Richardshaw Lane, Pudsey, West Yorkshire, LS28 6QW Tel: 0113-256 3721 Fax: 0113-255 9820 E-mail: sales@usmarine.co.uk *Industrial & marine pump repairers*

USB-FlashDrive.com, Nash House, Datchet Road, Slough, SL3 7LR Tel: (01753) 491470 Fax: (01753) 539801 E-mail: sales@usb-flashdrive.co.uk *USB flash drive manufrs*

▶ Used Car Expert, 107-111 Fleet Street, London, EC4A 2AB Tel: (0870) 4442920 Fax: (0870) 4442921 E-mail: action@usedcarexpert.com *Used car expert & used car buying guides*

Used Fork Lifts, 107 Perry Street, Billericay, Essex, CM12 0NH Tel: (01277) 624608 Fax: (01277) 656108 *Forklift distributors*

Use-It Computers, 7 High Street, Rishton, Blackburn, BB1 4JZ Tel: (01254) 877009 Fax: (01254) 885281 *Computer systems & networking retailers*

Usel Supported Employment, 182-188 Cambrai Street, Belfast, BT13 3JH Tel: (028) 9035 6600 Fax: (028) 9035 6611 E-mail: sales@usel.co.uk *Sheltered employment services for blind & disabled people*

▶ User 2 Computers, 4 South Clerk Street, Edinburgh, EH8 9JE Tel: 0131-662 9955 Fax: 0131-662 9944 E-mail: sales@user2.net *Computer retail & service*

Usk Valley Fluid Power, Unit 16 Mill Street Industrial Estate, Mill Street, Abergavenny, Gwent, NP7 5HE Tel: (01873) 857225 Fax: (01873) 858790 E-mail: sales@uskvalleyfp.co.uk *Hose & filter distributors*

▶ Uson Ltd, Western Way, Bury St. Edmunds, Suffolk, IP33 3SP Tel: (01284) 760606 Fax: (01284) 763049 E-mail: info@uson.co.uk *Leak & flow test systems*

▶ Uson Ltd, Western Way, Bury St. Edmunds, Suffolk, IP33 3SP Tel: (01284) 760606 Fax: (01284) 763049 E-mail: info@uson.co.uk *Leak detectors, air/gas; manufacturer of leak detector & chromatography equipment*

Ustigate Ltd, Unit 4, Norfolk Road Industrial Estate, Gravesend, Kent, DA12 2PS Tel: (01474) 363012 Fax: (01474) 359046 E-mail: sales@ustigate.co.uk *Water display fountains manufrs*

Uswitch.Com, Portland House, Stag Place, London, SW1E 5BH Tel: (0800) 0930607 Fax: (020) 7233 5933 E-mail: sales@uswitch.com *Comprehensive, impartial, comparison service that helps consumers choose the most suitable credit card, personal loan and utilities service available from all UK providers based on their current circumstances.*

▶ Utg Ltd, Unit 6, Halifax Court, Dunston, Gateshead, Tyne & Wear, NE11 9JT Tel: 0191-460 3903 Fax: 0191-413 8222 E-mail: utg@utgltd.wanadoo.co.uk *Tiepin gear suppliers*

Utility Options, 78 Northgate Street, Chester, CH1 2HR Tel: (0800) 1950123 Fax: (01352) 781813 E-mail: enquiries@utility-options.co.uk *Electricity, gas & telecomm consultants*

The Utility Warehouse, PO Box 407, Huntingdon, Cambridgeshire, PE29 2ZG Tel: (0845) 1242201 Fax: (0870) 7773753 *Provider of the cheapest fixed-line*

▶ The Utility Warehouse Discount Club, 110 Crossways Road, Knowle Park, Bristol, BS4 2SU Tel: 0117-977 9275 *Save money on your utility bills."UK's cheapest gas and electricity."Great mobile deals,including sim only."Internet."Home phone with free calls, and telephone line."*

Utility Week, Quadrant House, The Quadrant, Sutton, Surrey, SM2 5AS Tel: (020) 8652 3500 *Published by the Reed Utility Information Services (RUIS), Utility Week is the only weekly news magazine covering the electricity, gas, telecoms & water undustries.*

Utopia Computers Ltd, 29-31 High Glencairn Street, Kilmarnock, Ayrshire, KA1 4AE Tel: (01563) 574280 Fax: (01563) 574280 E-mail: sales@utopiacomputers.co.uk *Computer components sales & repair*

▶ Utopia Mortgage Solutions, The Bearings, Bowbridge Road, Newark, Nottinghamshire, NG24 4BZ Tel: (01636) 593990 Fax: (08700) 501222 E-mail: craig@utopia4mortgages.co.uk *Mortgages,Advice, remortgages,capital raising,right to buy,adverse or bad credit mortgages,self certificate,insurances for life, buildings and contents and accident sickness and unemployment*

▶ Utopia Valley - Natural Healthcare Intelligent Selfcare, Concorde House, Grenville Place, London, NW7 3SA Tel: (0870) 6091280 *Health care*

▶ Uts Scotland Ltd, Anniesland Industrial Estate, Glasgow, G13 1EU Tel: 0141-959 4477

Uttley & Thompson Electronics Ltd, 90 Abbey Street, Accrington, Lancashire, BB5 1EE Tel: (01254) 384850 Fax: (01254) 395474 E-mail: uttleyandthompson@farmore.net *Control panel component manufrs*

George Utz Ltd, Grange Close, Clover Nook Industrial Estate, Alfreton, Derbyshire, DE55 4QT Tel: (01773) 543170 Fax: (01773) 543180 E-mail: info@uk.georgutz.com *Comprehensive range of plastic containers*

▶ UV Refinish Technology Ltd, 15 Jasmine Road, Great Bridgeford, Stafford, ST18 9PT Tel: 01785 281171 Fax: 01785 281171 E-mail: mproctor@uv-refinishtechnology.co.uk *Suppliers to the SMART Repair market of UV Smart repair systems which include fillers, primers, clear coats, UV clear coat with direct adhesion to polished alloy wheels which cures in 2 minutes, mixing tinters and consumables.*

Uvitec Ltd, 36a Union Lane, Cambridge, CB4 1QB Tel: (01223) 568060 Fax: (01223) 306198 E-mail: uvi@uvitec.co.uk *Suppliers of equipment for bio labs*

▶ UXB (UK) Ltd, Challacombe Close, Landkey, Barnstaple, Devon, EX32 0NG Tel: (01271) 831439 Fax: (01271) 831442 E-mail: pjh@uxb.com

Uxbridge Engineering Co. Ltd, Robinswood, Dukes Kiln Drive, Gerrards Cross, Buckinghamshire, SL9 7HD Tel: (01753) 889511 Fax: (01753) 880118 E-mail: enquiries@uxbridge-eng.demon.co.uk *Air conditioning & heating contractors*

▶ Uxbridge Press Ltd, 129 High Street, Uxbridge, Middlesex, UB8 1DL Tel: (01895) 850058 Fax: (01895) 850805 E-mail: info@drayton.co.uk

Uxbridge Skip Hire Ltd, Harvil Road, Harefield, Uxbridge, Middlesex, UB9 6JW Tel: (01895) 257639 Fax: (01895) 810329 E-mail: sales@uxbridgeskiphire.co.uk *Waste disposal & skip hire services*

Uynit 2, 1 Green Lane, Wardle, Nantwich, Cheshire, CW5 6BN Tel: (01829) 261010 Fax: (01829) 260884 E-mail: timber@rowlinson.co.uk *Timber importers*

V A C Contracting Ltd, 3 Barton Industrial Estate, Faldo Road, Barton-le-Clay, Bedford, MK45 4RP Tel: (01582) 883980 Fax: (01582) 883981 *Air conditioning installation*

V A Electronic Design Ltd, Unit 16 Canongate Venture, 5 New Street, Edinburgh, EH8 8BH Tel: 0131-556 4668 Fax: 0131-556 4669 *Electronic equipment manufrs*

V A G Finance Ltd, Finance House, Orchard Bray, Edinburgh, EH4 1PF Tel: 0131-332 2451 Fax: 0131-332 1301 *Motor vehicle insurance*

▶ V A G Systems Computer Engineers, 112 Wincolmlee, Hull, HU2 0PZ Tel: (01482) 60906 E-mail: info@vagsystems.co.uk *Computer repairers & suppliers*

V A Heating Ltd, 30-38 Yeaman Street, Stoke-on-Trent, ST4 4AP Tel: (01782) 845633 Fax: (01782) 745371 *Heating appliance distributors*

V A I Industries UK Ltd, Warren Road, Scunthorpe North Lincolnshire, DN15 6XH Tel: (01724) 280360 Fax: (01724) 864405 E-mail: j.harris@fuchsuk.com *Steelworks plant equipment manufrs*

▶ V.A.L. Ltd, Swallow Mill, Swallow Street, Stockport, Cheshire, SK1 3HJ Tel: 0161-480 6780 Fax: 0161 476 6279 E-mail: info@val-ltd.co.uk *Printers*

V A Marriott Ltd, Handford Road, Ipswich, IP1 2BA Tel: (01473) 255041 Fax: (01473) 232176 E-mail: info@marriottbuilders.co.uk *Building contractors*

V A T Vacuum Products Ltd, Edmund House, Rugby Road, Leamington Spa, Warwickshire, CV32 6EL Tel: (01926) 452753 Fax: (01926) 452758 E-mail: uk@vatvalve.com *Vacuum valves manufrs*

▶ V A Tech Reyrolle Ltd, 15 Bessemer Drive, Kelvin Industrial Estate, East Kilbride, Glasgow, G75 0QX Tel: (01355) 570970 Fax: (01355) 570971 *Metalworking & fabrication services*

V A Turner & Son, The Chestnuts, High Street, Barcombe, Lewes, East Sussex, BN8 5BA Tel: (01273) 400339 Fax: (01273) 401615 *Publi address equipment contractors*

V A Whitley & Co. Ltd, Milward House, Fir Street, Heywood, Lancashire, OL10 1NW Tel: (01706) 364211 Fax: (01706) 366828 E-mail: mine@vawhitley.co.uk *Catering foods, packaging & equipment manufrs*

V B C Group, 16 Regent Park, Park Farm Industri Estate, Wellingborough, Northamptonshire, NN8 6GR Tel: (01933) 679500 Fax: (01933) 679250 E-mail: sales@vbcgroup.com *Specialist welding manufrs*

V B Fabrications Ltd, Barnswood Farm, Rushton Spencer, Macclesfield, Cheshire, SK11 0RA Tel: (01260) 226261 Fax: (01260) 226544 E-mail: vic@milkingequipment.com *Dairy & agricultural equipment manufrs*

V B Johnson & Partners, 304-310 St. Albans Road Watford, WD24 6PW Tel: (01923) 227236 Fax: (01923) 231134 E-mail: watford@vbjohnson.co.uk *Chartered quantity surveyors* Also at: Normanton

▶ V B Pro, I C S House, Hall Road, Heybridge, Maldon, Essex, CM9 4LA Tel: (01621) 857758 E-mail: timt@vb-pro.co.uk *Dot Net Web Architecture & SQL Server Database Experts*

▶ V B Trophies, Unit 1 Lumen Road, Royston, Hertfordshire, SG8 7AF Tel: (01763) 244116 Fax: (01763) 250850 E-mail: sales@vbgroup.co.uk *Top quality trophy & awards for all events to fit any budget*

▶ V C Consulting, Suite 6, 146 Hagley Road, Birmingham, B16 9NX Tel: 0121-454 2334 Fax: 0121-454 5026 E-mail: info@vc-consulting.co.uk *VC Consulting helps companies grow more rapidly - by finding new customers and raising business finance. S whether you're a new start-up, an SME or well established, if you have decided to build your business we can help. Your goals might be to find and target more customers. You could be launching a new product. You might need a reliable business plan and an introduction to lenders. Or, you may want us to help you gain access to grant funding. That is exactly what we do, but our involvement doesn't end there.ßßW don't just develop innovative marketing plans and raise finance - we will also help you put your ideas into practice!*

V C Digital Ltd, 44 Bridge Road, Crosby, Liverpool, L23 6SG Tel: 0151-931 2226 Fax: 0151-931 3136 *Drawing office materials suppliers*

V C E Ltd, Unit 3 Hamilton Street, Carluke, Lanarkshire, ML8 4HA Tel: (01555) 772567 Fax: (01555) 770530 *Valve repairers & refurbishing services*

V C I Office Furniture, 183 Brighton Road, South Croydon, Surrey, CR2 6EG Tel: (020) 8680 524 Fax: (020) 8680 7081 E-mail: vci@btconnect.com *Suppliers of quality office furniture*

V & C Installation Ltd, 24 Severnside Industrial Estate, Sudmeadow Road, Gloucester, GL2 5HS Tel: (01452) 415236 Fax: (01452) 309324 E-mail: paulvye@btconnect.com *Ductwork fabricators & installers*

V C Saunders Engineering Ltd, 20 Weir Road, London, SW19 8UG Tel: (020) 8947 5262 Fax: (020) 8944 1812 *Car accessories manufrs*

V.C.W. Engineering Ltd, Unit 8 Ailwin Road, Morto Hall industrial Estate, Bury St. Edmunds, Suffolk IP32 7DS Tel: (01284) 768371 Fax: (01284) 768371 E-mail: brucewhiteman@aol.com *Press tool manufrs*

▶ V Celebrate, 181 Streatfield Road, Harrow, Middlesex, HA3 9DA Tel: (020) 8204 7807 Fax: (020) 8204 7807 *Cakes decoration services*

V D M Sales, Unit 22 Mackley Industrial Estate, Henfield Road, Small Dole, Henfield, West Sussex, BN5 9XR Tel: (01273) 494066 Fax: (01273) 494147 *Sale of garment rails to the retail industry*

▶ V E Pinington & Sons Ltd, Aldrens Lane, Lancaster, LA1 2DE Tel: (01524) 65148

V E S Andover Ltd, Eagle Close, Chandler Ford Industrial Estate, Eastleigh, Hampshire, SO53 4NF Tel: (0870) 2404340 Fax: (0870) 2404550 E-mail: vesltd@ves.co.uk *Air Handling & ventilator services*

V E S Pest Control, Netherside, Bradwell, Hope Valley, Derbyshire, S33 9JL Tel: (01433) 621199 Fax: (01433) 621714 E-mail: ves@legend.co.uk *Pest control products suppliers*

▶ V E S Precision Ltd, 10 Cropmead Industrial Estate, Crewkerne, Somerset, TA18 7HQ Tel: (01460) 270600 Fax: (01460) 270601 E-mail: enquiries@vesprecision.com *Subcontractors to the Aerospace Industry. Design & manufacture of machine knives for the*

continued

continuation
food packaging industry. Design & manufacturing facility utilising AutoCAD supported by Edgecam and CNC turning, milling, wire & spark erosion, grinding plus CMM inspection facility.
V F Intimates Ltd, Block L Westways Business Park, Porterfield Road, Renfrew, PA4 8DJ Tel: 0141-885 4730 Fax: 0141-885 4731 Import & distribution of ladies under garments
V & F Sheetmetal Co. Ltd, Unit 22-25, Mitchell Close, Segensworth East, Fareham, Hampshire, PO15 5SE Tel: (01489) 577786 Fax: (01489) 889008 E-mail: sales@vandf.co.uk Precision sheet metal fabrications and presswork for the Lighting, Heating, Electronics, Audio and allied trades. CNC punching and CNC bending via 3D software and the latest equipment. Small batches to large volume production. Components manufactured in steel, Zintec, galv. aluminium, stainless steel, copper and brass from 0.4mm to 5mm thick.
V G Mathers Ltd, Cottown Garage, Kintore, Inverurie, Aberdeenshire, AB51 0XQ Tel: (01467) 642742 Fax: (01467) 642842 E-mail: vic.mathers@tesco.net Road transport, haulage & freight services
V G Scinta Ltd, Maunsell Road, St. Leonards-On-Sea, East Sussex, TN38 9NN Tel: (01424) 851291 Fax: (01424) 851489 E-mail: sales@vgscinta.com High vacuum equipment & components
V G Signs, 46 Seaforth Road, Leeds, LS9 6AJ Tel: 0113-248 8737 Fax: 0113-248 8737 Sign makers
V G Willox & Building Contractor Ltd, Roadside Croft, Crimond, Fraserburgh, Aberdeenshire, AB43 8QD Tel: (01346) 532981 Fax: (01346) 532851
▶ V H E Construction P.L.C., Phoenix House, 6 Hawthorn Park, Coal Road, Leeds, LS14 1PQ Tel: 0113 273 9200 Fax: 0113 273 9202 E-mail: s.maloney@construction.vhe.co.uk VHE provides contaminated land remediation techniques for brownfield site reclamation including bioremediation, soil washing, soil stabilisation & modification, together with excavation & disposal, enabling the regeneration & redevelopment of former industrial sites throughout the UK
V H F Engineering Ltd, Point West Virage Park, Green Lane, Cannock, Staffordshire, WS11 0NH Tel: (01543) 571631 Fax: (01543) 462303 E-mail: sales@vhfengineering.co.uk Engineering & hydraulic manufrs
▶ V H I UK Ltd, Raines House, Denby Dale Road, Wakefield, West Yorkshire, WF1 1HR Tel: (0870) 1206170 Fax: (0870) 1206171 E-mail: office@vhi-UK.com Design & manufacture of stainless steel refractory anchors
V H M Systems Ltd, 80-86 Chapel Street, Thatcham, Berks, RG18 4QN Tel: (01635) 861707 Wheel manufrs
V H S Hire Store, 1180 Aldridge Road, Great Barr, Birmingham, B44 8PE Tel: 0121-360 8500 Fax: 0121-366 6875 Tool hire
▶ V H S Holdings Ltd, 7 College Park Drive, Westbury-On-Trym, Bristol, BS10 7AN Tel: 0117-950 0202 Fax: 0117- 377 7842 E-mail: vgr@vhsholdings.com Website marketing, design, website optimisation for search engine ranking. Cost Per Click management skills
V H S Hydraulic Components, Unit 1, Block A, Waleswood Road, Wales Bar, Sheffield, S26 5PY Tel: (01909) 772666 Fax: (01909) 773226 E-mail: sales@hydraulic-components.net VHS Hydraulic Components was established in the mid nineties, primarily specialising in the supply of commercial vehicle hydraulics such as PTO pumps, gearboxes, 12 & 24 volt DC mini power packs and control valve systems. *In recent years the company has developed substantially in the industrial hydraulic market and are now able to offer, through an experienced, reliable and friendly team of staff, a full hydraulic service to include full system design, manufacture and distribution of hydraulic components & systems to include industrial power packs with electric, diesel or petrol drives for a variety of applications.
V I L Resins Ltd, Union Road, Bolton, BL2 2DT Tel: (01204) 388800 Fax: (01204) 362775 E-mail: enquiries@vilresins.com Synthetic resin manufrs
V I P-polymers, 15 Windover Road, Huntingdon, Cambridgeshire, PE29 7EB Tel: (01480) 411333 Fax: (01480) 450430 E-mail: sales@vip-polymers.com Moulders & extruders to customer specification manufrs
V I Precision Grinders Ltd, Pingemead Farm, Pingewood, Reading, RG30 3UR Tel: 0118 9866546 Grinding precision & surfaces
V I Software, St. Michaels Square, Ashton-under-Lyne, Lancashire, OL6 6XN Tel: 0161-343 1322 Fax: 0161-343 1355 E-mail: robert@visoftware.co.uk Software house manufrs
V Installations Mechanical Handling Ltd, Saxon Business Park, Stoke Prior, Bromsgrove, Worcestershire, B60 4AD Tel: 01527 833248 Mechanical handling engineers installation, servicing & maintenance
V J G Jewlery, 6 Warwick Lane, Warwick Street, Worthing, West Sussex, BN11 3DP Tel: (01903) 239574 Fax: (01903) 239574 E-mail: inquries@vjg-jewlery.co.uk Jewellery manufrs
V J Imports Ltd, Unit 14,, Welch Hill St, Leigh, Lancs, WN7 4DU Tel: 01942 673281 E-mail: vjimports@fsmail.net Brazilian pine furniture importer in the North West. Cash and Carry and wholesale. Beds and bedroom furniture in solid pine. Delivery can be negotiated. Additional products from time to time eg dining sets, metal beds etc.
V J Technology Ltd, Technology House Cobbswood Industrial Estate, Brunswick Road, Ashford, Kent, TN23 1EN Tel: (01233) 637695 Fax: (01233) 664361 Fastener & fixing manufrs
V Jackson, 103 Fairview Road, Stevenage, Hertfordshire, SG1 2NP Tel: (01438) 722016 Groundwork consultants
V K F Renzel, 20e Harris Business Park, Hanbury Road, Stoke Prior, Bromsgrove, Worcestershire, B60 4BD Tel: (01527) 878311 Fax: (01527) 878411 E-mail: sales@vkf-renzel.co.uk Point of sale display suppliers
V L B Products Ltd, 12 Birch Road East Industrial Estate, Birch Road East, Birmingham, B6 7DB Tel: 0121-328 4575 CNC machinists/auto turned parts
V L Test Systems Ltd, 3/4 Middle Slade, Buckingham Indust Estate, Buckingham, MK18 1WA Tel: (01280) 822488 Fax: (01280) 822489 E-mail: vltukltd@aol.com Automotive safety test equipment suppliers
V M C Ltd, Trafalgar Works, Station Road, Chertsey, Surrey, KT16 8BE Tel: (01932) 563434 Fax: (01932) 566598 E-mail: info@vmclimited.co.uk Vacuum metallising & spray painting
▶ V & M Day Ltd, 94 Water Road, Reading, RG30 2NN Tel: 0118-957 3117 Fax: 0118-950 3631
V M G Bakeries Ltd, 90-94 Glentanar Road, Glasgow, G22 7XA Tel: 0141-336 6999 Fax: 0141-336 6191 Bakers
V M R Publicity, 241 Redcatch Road, Knowle, Bristol, BS4 2HQ Tel: 0117-972 0505 Fax: 0117-972 0606 E-mail: vmrviv@aol.com Silk screen & graphic printers
V M S Ltd, Blenheim Road, Pocklington Industrial Estate, York, YO42 1NR Tel: (01759) 305030 Fax: (01759) 305816 E-mail: admin@vmsl.co.uk Network installations & training consultancy
V M S Enterprises Ltd, 50c Chatterton Road, Bromley, BR2 9QE Tel: (020) 8313 1111
V P plc, Beckwith Knowle, Otley Road, Beckwithshaw, Harrogate, North Yorkshire, HG3 1UD Tel: (01423) 533400 Fax: (01423) 565657 E-mail: enquiries@vpplc.com Contractors tool hire & plant hire services Also at: Branches throughout the U.K.
V & P Engineering, Wakefield Road, Brighouse, West Yorkshire, HD6 1PE Tel: (01484) 719360 Fax: (01484) 400093 Tool manufrs
V P Equipment Ltd, Longford Business Centre Orchard Lea, Winkfield Lane, Windsor, Berkshire, SL4 4RU Tel: (01753) 623336 Fax: (01753) 623337 E-mail: graeme.crowder@vpe.co.uk Electronics suppliers
V & P Fox Engravers, 23 Cecil Court, London, WC2N 4EZ Tel: (020) 7836 2902 Fax: (020) 7379 8676 E-mail: foxlox s@aol.com Master locksmiths & engravers
V P Welding Ltd, VP Square, Storeys Bar Road, Peterborough, PE1 5YS Tel: (01733) 552888 Fax: (01733) 311972 Stainless steel fabricators
▶ V Pack Sales Ltd, Tollgate Road, Burscough, Ormskirk, Lancashire, L40 8LD Tel: (01704) 895008
V Power Ltd, Hollins Mill, Rochdale Road, Todmorden, Lancashire, OL14 6SA Tel: (01706) 815008 Food equipment
V R M, Dorset Avenue, Thornton-Cleveleys, Lancashire, FY5 2DE Tel: (01253) 852461 Fax: (01253) 852461 Shop fittings manufrs
V R Plastics Ltd, 1 Brookhill Road, Brookhill Industrial Estate, Pinxton, Nottingham, NG16 6NT Tel: (01773) 580505 Fax: (01773) 580496 E-mail: vrpinxton@vrscottgroup.com Injection moulders (plastic) manufrs
▶ V R S Auto Electrics, 254 Humber Road, Coventry, CV3 1BH Tel: (024) 7644 7850 Fax: (024) 7644 8100 E-mail: vrsauto@AOL.COM MOTS ,RADIO DECODES ,DASH BOARDS ,MILEAGE CORRECTION , AIR CONDITIONING ,MOT REPAIRS , ALTERNATORS , STARTER MOTORS , ALL CAR REPAIRS AND SERVICING brakes steering welding
V S A Products Ltd, Hardwick Trading Estate, Rollesby Road, King's Lynn, Norfolk, PE30 4JS Tel: (01553) 761521 Fax: (01553) 691464 E-mail: vsa-enquiries@btconnect.com Adhesive tape manufrs
▶ V S P Ltd, 4 Malling Walk, Bottesford, Scunthorpe, North Lincolnshire, DN16 3SS Tel: (01724) 335005 Fax: (01724) 338981 E-mail: enquiries@vspuk.com Import and distribution of vinyl sheet piles.
V & S Plymouth Ltd, Black Friars Distillery, Southside Street, Plymouth, PL1 2LQ Tel: (01752) 665292 Fax: (01752) 220062 E-mail: shaun@plymouthgin.com Principal Export Areas: Worldwide Distillers
V S R Co., Unit 13A, Shrub Hill Industrial Estate, Worcester, WR4 9EL Tel: (01905) 452800 Fax: (01905) 731811 E-mail: sales@v-s-r.co.uk VSR equipment manufacturer & on-site services
▶ V & S Scaffolding Services Ltd, Unit 10A Warehams Lane, Hertford, SG14 1LA Tel: (01992) 558464
V S W Atomtech Ltd, Unit 4 Heather Close, Lyme Green Business Park, Macclesfield, Cheshire, SK11 0LR Tel: (01625) 500108 Fax: (01625) 500801 Manufacturers of scientific instruments
V Ships Ltd, Gate House, 1 Farringdon Street, London, EC4M 7NS Tel: (020) 7489 0088 Fax: (020) 7489 0529 E-mail: ships@vships.com Ship brokers
▶ V Signs, Unit 27, Evesham Road, Fladbury, Pershore, Worcestershire, WR10 2QS Tel: (01386) 861700 Fax: (01386) 861700 Sign manufrs
V T Aerospace Ltd Ltd, 15 Cobham Road, Ferndown Industrial Estate, Wimborne, Dorset, BH21 7PE Tel: (01202) 893500 Fax: (01202) 895331 E-mail: airwork@bta.co.uk Principal Export Areas: Worldwide Aircraft components
V T L Automotors Ltd, Ellen Holme, Luddendenfoot, Halifax, West Yorkshire, HX2 6EL Tel: (01422) 882561 Fax: (01422) 883323 Development, sale & manufacture of automotive components
V T M U K Ltd, 8 Corinium Centre, Raans Road, Amersham, Buckinghamshire, HP6 6JQ Tel: (01494) 738600 Fax: (01494) 738610 E-mail: admin@vtm.co.uk Sales Contact: P. Rafferty VTM supplies electronic components to businesses throughout the UK and the rest of the world We make every effort to understand the needs of our customers, and are happy to assist with any technical issues.
▶ V & T Mcphie, Woodside Cottage, Linlithgow, West Lothian, EH49 6NB Tel: (01506) 847278 Fax: (01506) 840995
V T Marine Products Ltd, Hamilton Road, Cosham, Portsmouth, PO6 4PX Tel: (023) 9253 9750 Fax: (023) 9253 9764 Marine ride control systems manufrs
V T S Doeflex, 3 St. Annes Boulevard, Redhill, RH1 1AX Tel: (01737) 771221 Fax: (01737) 772461 E-mail: sales@vtsdoeflex.co.uk Plastic sheet manufrs
V T Software Solutions, Unit 4Thornbury Office Park, Midland Way, Thornbury, Bristol, BS35 2BS Tel: (01454) 874002 Fax: (01454) 874001 E-mail: enquire@vtsoftwaresolutions.com Fleet, asset & housing repairs management software solutions
V T Technology Ltd, Park Road, Holmewood, Chesterfield, Derbyshire, S42 5UY Tel: (01246) 850828 Fax: (01246) 854083 E-mail: vehicletrim@tmat.com Noise control mat manufrs
V Tech SMT, Bandeath Industrial Estate, Throsk, Stirling, FK7 7NP Tel: (01786) 813999 Fax: (01786) 813998 E-mail: sales@vtech-smt.co.uk
▶ V Tech SMT, Bandeath Industrial Estate, Throsk, Stirling, FK7 7NP Tel: (01786) 813999 Fax: (01786) 813998 E-mail: sales@vtech-smt.co.uk
▶ V & W Animatronics, Unit 2, Cockles Lane, Weymouth, Dorset, DT4 9LT Tel: (01305) 768959 Fax: (01305) 768959 E-mail: info@animatronica.co.uk Animatronic figures for museums & theme park manufrs
V W Panels Ltd, 302 Ampthill Road, Bedford, MK42 9QS Tel: (01234) 352021 Fax: (01234) 305390 E-mail: enquiries@vwpanels.co.uk Accident repair service
V W R International Ltd, Hunter Boulevard, Magna Park, Lutterworth, Leicestershire, LE17 4XN Tel: (01455) 558600 Fax: (01455) 558586 E-mail: uk.sales@uk.vwr.com Chemical & fine chemical manufrs
V X I Power Ltd, Westminster Industrial Estate, Station Road, North Hykeham, Lincoln, LN6 3QY Tel: (01522) 500511 Fax: (01522) 500515 E-mail: sales@vxipower.com Principal Export Areas: Worldwide Power supply manufrs
V X L Instruments Ltd, Rayner House, 23 Higher Hillgate, Stockport, Cheshire, SK1 3ER Tel: 0161-429 7767 Fax: 0161-429 7477 E-mail: warranty@vxl.net Computer terminal manufrs
V_Tech Engineering, Mandy Cottage, Maidenhead Road, Billingbear, Wokingham, Berkshire, RG40 5RT Tel: (01344) 867228 Fax: (01344) 482244 E-mail: v_techuk@yahoo.co.uk Vacuum engineering
▶ V1 Creative Media Ltd, 2 Highview Way, Midanbury, Southampton, SO18 4FG Tel: (023) 8067 1352 Fax: (0870) 7626063 E-mail: info@v1creativemedia.co.uk We specialize in 3D Visualization and Image manipulation. **3D Modelling Marketing Renders Visualisation Photomontages Animation Logo Design Photo Manipulation Poster Design And much more..*
V10 Polymers Ltd, Rockcliffe Works, Paterson Street, Blackburn, BB2 3SP Tel: (01254) 680384 Fax: (01254) 674933 E-mail: david@holtplastics.co.uk Waste plastics reclamation
▶ V11 Fold, 81 Weston Street, London, SE1 3RS Tel: (020) 7403 9770 Fax: (020) 7232 0578 E-mail: info@vii-fold.com Tie manufrs
▶ V2 Display Solutions Ltd, Unit 15, Victoria Business Centre, Neilston Street, Leamington Spa, Warwickshire, CV31 2AZ Tel: (01926) 739088 Fax: (01926) 739088 E-mail: veetoo@ntlworld.co.uk V2 specialises in the production and installation of retail and exhibition displays. We produce and fit vinyls, banners, graphics, signage, POS items, bespoke display cabinets and complete exhibition stands.
V4Technical Ltd, 1 Quay Point, Station Road, Woodbridge, Suffolk, IP12 4AL Tel: (01394) 382400 UK based web development for small to National companies with in the UK.
▶ V50 Co. Ltd, 8 Albyon Terrace, Aberdeen, AB10 1YP Tel: (01224) 626699 E-mail: info@v50.co.uk Internet consultancy
VacAir Superstore, Unit 2 Latchmore Industrial Park, Lowfields Road, Leeds, LS12 6dn Tel: 0113-208 8501 Fax: 0113-208 8400 E-mail: sales@vacair-superstore.com VacAir Superstore has an international reputation as a leading supplier offering the UK's widest choice of vacuum pumps , side channel blowers, and low pressure compressors available, all at the lowest cost to the customer.*We are the UK's leading supplier for replacement spare parts for vacuum pumps.*Becker vacuum pumps, Rietschle vacuum pumps, Busch pumps, Orion pumps,*Edwards, Leybold, Nash, Elmo, Siemens, Gast and many more are all available.*We offer a repair service, either through our workshop (OEM trained engineers), or on site. All fully guaranteed.*Through our technical sales we can evaluate any application to offer not only the most cost effective solutions but also the best solutions from an application and production/maintenance point of view. Our technical service also means we can offer pump units for applications still in the design process or for bespoke solutions.*Trial vacuum pumps and vacuum pump hire is available.
Vaccar Ltd, Beaulieu Park, Staunton, Coleford, Gloucestershire, GL16 8PB Tel: (01600) 716216 Fax: (01600) 785183 E-mail: info@vaccar.com Milking machine components & milking systems
Vacflo, Unit 14, Bingswood Industrial Estate, Whaley Bridge, High Peak, Derbyshire, SK23 7LY Tel: (01663) 719519 Fax: (01663) 719519 E-mail: mail@vacflo.com Pipe/tube manipulations
▶ Vacflow Pumps, Unit 10 Horbury Bridge Mills, Bridge Road, Horbury, Wakefield, West Yorkshire, WF4 5RW Tel: (01924) 274518 Fax: (01924) 279405 Vacuum pump engineers, repairs & servicing
Vacform Group Derbyshire Ltd, Unit B1 Stainsby Close, Holmewood Industrial Estate, Holmewood, Chesterfield, Derbyshire, S42 5UG Tel: (01246) 855811 Fax: (01246) 854963 E-mail: info@vac-form.com Conductive packaging suppliers
Vacform Group Yorkshire Ltd, Unit 8b Felnex Close, Leeds, LS9 0SR Tel: 0113-248 9994 Fax: 0113-249 1211 E-mail: sales@vacuum-forming-plus.co.uk Plastics vacuum forming services
Vacman Specialist Cleaning, Budmhor, Portree, Isle of Skye, IV51 9DJ Tel: (01478) 613111 Fax: (01478) 613321E-mail: info@vacman.co.uk Office cleaning contractor services
▶ Vacplas Mouldings Ltd, 4 Willow Park Business Centre, Lower Barnes Street, Clayton le Moors, Accrington, Lancashire, BB5 5SW Tel: (01254) 875588 Fax: (01254) 875599
▶ Vacsax Ltd, Western Wood Way, Plympton, Plymouth, PL7 5BG Tel: (01752) 337000
Vactec Derby Ltd, Eagle Road, Quarry Hill Industrial Estate, Ilkeston, Derbyshire, DE7 4RB Tel: 0115-930 4806 Fax: 0115-930 4806 Plastic mouldings
Vacu Lug Traction Tyres Ltd, Gonerby Hill Foot, Grantham, Lincolnshire, NG31 8HF Tel: (01476) 593095 Fax: (01476) 513809 E-mail: info@vaculug.com Tyre retreaders Also at: Sales depots throughout the U.K.
Vacua Therm Sales Ltd, 5 Parkburn Court, Parkburn Industrial Estate, Hamilton, Lanarkshire, ML3 0QQ Tel: (01698) 825169 Fax: (01698) 824265 Furnace engineers
Vacucom Ltd, Unit 4B, Aspect Court, Cannel Row, Silverdale Enterprise Park, Silverdale, Newcastle, Staffordshire, ST5 6SS Tel: (01782) 660007 Fax: (01782) 660009 E-mail: sales@vacucom.co.uk Vacuum component, pump & industrial robot component distributors
Vacuum Engineering Services Ltd, St. Modwen Road, Stretford, Manchester, M32 0ZE Tel: 0845 5314240 Fax: 0161-866 8861 E-mail: info@vac-eng.com Manufacturers of leak detector test systems, (including air/gas) & complete/packaged vacuum systems. In addition, leak detection services
Vacuum Formers Ltd, Brunswick Mill, Pickford Street, Macclesfield, Cheshire, SK11 6JN Tel: (01625) 428389 Fax: (01625) 619808 E-mail: info@vacuumformers.co.uk Sales Contact: A. MacDonald Plastic cutting/guillotining services, plastic thermoforming processors or services & plastic vacuum formed products manufacturers or services. We also offer a fabrication service
Vacuum Forming Scotland, Newmains Avenue, Inchinnan, Renfrew, PA4 9RR Tel: 0141-812 5075 Fax: 0141-812 5058 E-mail: info@vacfs.co.uk Plastics vacuum forming toolmakers
Vacuum Hospital, 4 Mckeown Street, Lisburn, County Antrim, BT28 1BD Tel: (028) 9266 1126 Vacuum repair services
Vacuum Impregnated Products Ltd, Hew Cut Lane, Woolston, Warrington, WA1 4AG Tel: (01925) 817213 Fax: (01925) 823862 E-mail: sales@viproducts.co.uk Welding & switchgear contact materials
Vacuum Lifting, Rowallan, Kilmarnock, Ayrshire, KA3 2LW Tel: (01563) 540400 Fax: (01563) 520139 E-mail: sales@vacuumliftinguk.co.uk Vacuum lifting equipment & fork lift truck attachment manufrs
Vacuum Scientific Services Ltd, 44 Ellesmere Street, Manchester, M15 4JY Tel: 0161-833 9108 Fax: 0161-835 1443 E-mail: sales@vacuum-scientific.com Scientific equipment manufrs
Vacuum Systems Ltd, Unit 11 Lexden Lodge Industrial Estate, Crowborough Hill, Crowborough, East Sussex, TN6 2NQ Tel: (01892) 665633 E-mail: krizek@vacsys.co.uk Scientific instrumentation & laboratory services
Vacuumatic, Brunel Way 8, Severalls Industrial Park, Colchester, CO4 9QX Tel: (01206) 841100 Fax: (01206) 841166 E-mail: sales@vacuumatic.com Optical counter and paper sheet counting and batching machine, marking systems for web products
▶ Vacuumbags2u.co.uk, 115 Sedlescombe Road North, St. Leonards-on-Sea, East Sussex, TN37 7EJ Tel: (01424) 729800 E-mail: silverhillapp@btconnect.com Spare parts & consumables for vacuums
▶ Vader Cleaning Service, 49 Carrigard, Dundrum, Newcastle, County Down, BT33 0SG Tel: (07814) 977145 E-mail: gmurf2001@yahoo.com Window cleaning, powerwashing, builders cleans
Vai UK Ltd, 7 Fudan Way, Thornaby, Stockton-on-Tees, Cleveland, TS17 6ER Tel: (01642) 662100 Fax: (01642) 606569 E-mail: contact@vai.co.uk Design engineers
▶ Vaillant Ltd, Unit D1, Lowfields Business Park, Elland, West Yorkshire, HX5 9DG Tel: (01422) 376070 Fax: (01422) 311986
Vaillant Ltd, Vaillant House, Trident Close, Medway City Estate, Rochester, Kent, ME2 4EZ Tel: (01634) 292300 Fax: (01634) 290166 Boiler maintenance, service & distributors
▶ Sandrine Vaillant, Old Vallis Cottage, Vallis Road, Frome, Somerset, BA11 3EN Tel: (0777) 9668707 Fax: (01373) 474945 E-mail: sandrine.vaillant@btinternet.co.uk I offer a quick efficient secretarial service to local businesses. Audio & copy typing, filing, mailing lists, translation French/English, proof-reading, presentations, graphic design and internet-based search...Work from home/overnight delivery. Excellent work at reasonable rates
▶ Vaioni Group Ltd, 39 Salford University Business Park, Leslie Hough Way, Salford, M6 6AJ Tel: (0870) 1600650 Fax: (0870) 1600651 E-mail: richard.chapman@vaioni.com Computer hardware & software support services
Vak Systems T G A Ltd, Redmoor Lane, New Mills, High Peak, Derbyshire, SK22 3LL Tel: 01663 745575 Industrial vacuum manufrs
Val D'Or Ltd, 24 Hatton Gardens, London, EC1N 8BQ Tel: (020) 7405 5102 Fax: (020) 7405 7373 Jewellery manufrs

Company Information

▶ Val d'Or Language Tuition, 30 A Dixon Street, Swindon, SN1 3PL Tel: (01793) 514150 E-mail: valou@madasafish.com *French and Spanish tuition for young children,Gcse and A"Level examination preparation.*Tuition for adults for business and pleasure.**

Val Spicer, The Sugar Mill, Harford Bridge, Tavistock, Devon, PL19 9LR Tel: (01822) 617610 Fax: (01822) 617610 Principal Export Areas: Central/East Europe & West Europe *Suppliers of foam products*

Val U Blinds, 17 Pilmuir Street, Dunfermline, Fife, KY12 7AJ Tel: (01383) 739476 Fax: (01383) 739476 *Window blind retailers & manufrs*

▶ Val Williams, Winnington Hall, Winnington, Northwich, Cheshire, CW8 4DU Tel: (01606) 48715 E-mail: val.williams@nissimo.co.uk *Body Massage for health at Winnington Hall. Relieve stress/tension. Ease muscular aches/pains. Promote better joint movement. Boost blood circulation/immune system. Detoxify the body. Promote general well-being. Full Body Treatment/Back & Shoulders/Indian Head Massage.*

Valan Wax Products Ltd, Unit 14 Alfred Court Saxon Business Park, Hanbury Road, Stoke Prior, Bromsgrove, Worcestershire, B60 4AD Tel: (01527) 876541 Fax: (01527) 570054 *Wax for the casting industry.*

Valance Glass Fibre Co. Ltd, Unit 8 Netherwood Indsl Estate, Atherstone, Warwickshire, CV9 1JA Tel: (01827) 715619 Fax: (01827) 715619 *Glass fibre mouldings manufrs*

Valance Glass Fibre Co. Ltd, Unit 8 Netherwood Indsl Estate, Atherstone, Warwickshire, CV9 1JA Tel: (01827) 715619 Fax: (01827) 715619 *Sewage plant manufrs*

Valbruan UK Ltd, 36a Walworth Road, Andover, Hampshire, SP10 5LH Tel: (01264) 333390 Fax: (01264) 333315 *Stainless steel stockholders* Also at: Birmingham & Salford

Valco Cincinnati, Unit 7-8 Hortonwood 32, Telford, Shropshire, TF1 7YN Tel: (01952) 677911 Fax: (01952) 677945 E-mail: sales@valco.co.uk *Adhesive application equipment*

Vald Birn (UK) Ltd, Cambois, Blyth, Northumberland, NE24 1SW Tel: (01670) 818111 Fax: (01670) 855511 E-mail: sales@valdbirn.co.uk *Sand, grey & spheroidal castings*

Valden Hire Services Ltd, 5 St Clements Road, Nechells, Birmingham, B7 5AF Tel: 0121-327 8920 Fax: 0121-327 7606 *Plant & tool hire*

Vale Blinds, 27 Main Street, Bottesford, Nottingham, NG13 0EP Tel: (01949) 845399 Fax: (01949) 845399 *Blind manufrs*

Vale Brothers Ltd, Long Street, Walsall, WS2 9QG Tel: (01922) 624363 Fax: (01922) 720994 E-mail: sales@valebrothersvalebrothers.co.uk *Rubber mouldings & saddlery products*

▶ Vale Building Services Ltd, Sundeala, Cardiff Road, Taffs Well, Cardiff, CF15 7PR Tel: (029) 2081 3183 Fax: (029) 2081 3512

Vale Contractors (South Wales) Ltd, Unit 45 Tumulus Way, Llandow Trading Estate, Llandow, Cowbridge, South Glamorgan, CF71 7PB Tel: (01446) 793562 Fax: (01446) 795231 E-mail: sale@valecontractors.co.uk *Vale Contractors based in South Wales are experienced in the following aspects of Civil Engineering: Drainage Public Street Works Reinforced Concrete Environmental Improvements Groundworks Retaining Walls Highway Maintenance River Work Traffic Calming Projects Parks Sports Grounds Electricity Generation Projects We are a family business established for over 25 years and the range of work we undertake is vast ranging from those complicated jobs that you trust us with to the quality high profile schemes you associate us with. We are experienced to know that problems do occur but our philosophy is to sort them out and work with the client. We list among our clients: Local Authorities, Hydro Aluminium Alupres, Biffa Waste Services Ltd, Persimmon Homes (Wales) Ltd, Costain Civil Engineering, Charles Church Wales, Airparks Ltd, Barratts, Richards Construction, R.T. Contractors, Tyco Fire & Integrated Services.*

Vale Furniture Warehouse, 83 Laurelvale Road, Tandragee, Craigavon, County Armagh, BT62 2LE Tel: (028) 3884 9921 Fax: (028) 3884 9921 *Furniture retailers*

Vale Of Glamorgan Travel, 53 Coed Mieri, Tyla Garw, Pontyclun, Mid Glamorgan, CF72 9UW Tel: (0870) 0436026 Fax: (0870) 0436127 E-mail: sales@valeofglamtravel.co.uk *Personal travel consultants*

Vale Labels, Unit P Creech Business Park, Creech St. Michael, Taunton, Somerset, TA3 5PX Tel: (01823) 443902 Fax: (01823) 444188 E-mail: info@valelabels.co.uk *Label printers*

Vale Of Mowbray Ltd, 5-6 Mowbray Terrace, Leeming Bar, Northallerton, North Yorkshire, DL7 9BL Tel: (01677) 422661 Fax: (01677) 424986 E-mail: sales@valeofmowbray.com *Pork pie & sausage manufrs*

Vale Nameplates, Winster Grove, Great Barr, Birmingham, B44 9EJ Tel: 0121-360 8785 Fax: 0121-366 6003 E-mail: pat@valenameplates.co.uk *Nameplate (plastic) manufrs*

Vale Textile Services, Vale Road, Llandudno Junction, Gwynedd, LL31 9SH Tel: (01492) 581167 Fax: (01492) 593015 *Commercial laundry services*

Thomas Vale Construction Ltd, Foundation House, Paddock Road, Caversham, Reading, RG4 5BY Tel: 0118-947 8444 Fax: 0118-946 1086 E-mail: general@thomasvale.com *Building contractors*

▶ Vale (UK) Ltd, Kitling Road, Knowsley Industrial Park South, Knowsley, Prescot, Liverpool, L34 9JA Tel: 0151-546 4684

▶ Vale Veneers, 29 Poplar Road, Aylesbury, Buckinghamshire, HP20 1XN Tel: (01296) 433151 E-mail: info@valeveneers.co.uk *Mail order service*

Vale Weavers Ltd, Caldervale Mill, Barrowford, Nelson, Lancashire, BB9 7BL Tel: (01282) 617692 Fax: (01282) 696530 *Textile weaving manufrs*

▶ Vale of Wigan Ltd, Rear Mill, Wood Street, Wigan, Lancashire, WN3 4HL Tel: (01942) 246553 *Joinery manufacturers of conservatories & staircases*

Valedene, 12 Lillington Avenue, Leamington Spa, Warwickshire, CV32 5UJ Tel: (01926) 339707 Fax: (01926) 316071 *Fence & barrier suppliers*

Valenbeck Ltd, Bailey Industrial Estate, Ellison Street, Jarrow, Tyne & Wear, NE32 3JU Tel: 0191-483 2290 Fax: 0191-483 3574 E-mail: sales@valenbeck.co.uk *Cardboard box manufrs*

Valent Ltd, 49 Longford Road, Chorlton-Cum-Hardy, Manchester, M21 9WP Tel: 0161-881 3503 Fax: 0161-860 5519 *Industrial roofing systems*

Valentine Audio Visual, 6 Myrtle Avenue, Kirkintilloch, Glasgow, G66 4HP Tel: 0141-578 9950 Fax: 0141-578 9960 E-mail: SALES@VALENTINE-AV.CO.UK *Audio visual equipment, sales, hire, audio visual installation*

▶ Valentine Press Ltd, Valentine House, Pembroke Business Centre, Gardiners Lane South, Basildon, Essex, SS14 3AP Tel: (01268) 282555

Valentine Tools, 6 Royce Road, Crawley, West Sussex, RH10 9NX Tel: (01293) 428555 Fax: (01293) 428559 E-mail: sales@valentinetools.co.uk *Engineer suppliers*

▶ Valentines Property Maintenance Ltd, 19 A Rock Street, Brighton, BN2 1NF Tel: (01273) 693522

Valeport Ltd, St. Peters Quay, Totnes, Devon, TQ9 5EW Tel: (01803) 869292 Fax: (01803) 869293 E-mail: sales@valeport.co.uk *Manufacturers of hydrological & oceanographic instruments*

▶ Valet Magic, 6 High Street, Stanwell, Staines, Middlesex, TW19 7JS Tel: (01753) 680395 Fax: (01753) 680395 E-mail: info@valetmagic.com *Detailing valeting company, fully mobile, insured, private & commercial*

▶ Valetmaster Mobile Car Valeting Service, Unit 8, Westerleigh Road, Pucklechurch, Bristol, BS16 9RB Tel: 07966 022209 E-mail: robert01@fsmail.net *Valet car services*

Valetpro, 3 Summervale Road, Tunbridge Wells, Kent, TN4 8JA Tel: (07950) 023767 E-mail: greg@valetpro.co.uk *Valeting equipment supplier*

Valgram Stainless Steel Ltd, Unit 28 Parkrose Industrial Estate, Middlemore Road, Smethwick, West Midlands, B66 2DZ Tel: 0121-555 6241 Fax: 0121-555 5650 *Stainless steel stockholders*

Valiant Lamps Ltd, European I Park, Knowles Lane, Bradford, West Yorkshire, BD4 9AD Tel: (0870) 4450000 Fax: (0870) 4450001 E-mail: wholesale@europeanlampgroup.com *Lighting distributors*

Valiant Sails, 7 Fullbridge, Maldon, Essex, CM9 4LE Tel: (01621) 853558 Fax: (01621) 853566 E-mail: osc@chandler.eu.com *Sail makers*

Valiant Trading Co., 63 Paxford Road, Wembley, Middlesex, HA0 3RJ Tel: (020) 8904 9999 *Brass wear import & distribution*

▶ Validata Ltd, 23 Harewood Road, Allestree, Derby, DE22 2JP Tel: (01332) 552425 E-mail: enquiries@validata-eng.co.uk *Design and manufacture of test rigs, prototypes, instrumentation and sensors. Provision to engineering R&D organisations of mechanical and aerothermal design, testing and dev services.*

Validation Centre, Unit 9 Sinclair Court, Great Yarmouth, Norfolk, NR31 0NH Tel: (01493) 443800 Fax: (01493) 443900 E-mail: sales@tvcalx.co.uk *Data logging & welding inspection testing*

Valkris Communications, Deunant, Capel Curig, Betws-y-Coed, Gwynedd, LL24 0DS Tel: (01690) 720263 Fax: (01690) 720263 E-mail: admin@valkris.co.uk *Radio communications equipment distributors*

Valla Cranes, Unit 5 Sidings Court, Henry Boot Way, Hull, HU4 7DY Tel: (01482) 351546 Fax: (01482) 351091 E-mail: E.Finn@valla-cranes.co.uk *Valla manufacture range of mobile cranes that are ideally suited to working in confined areas. Lifting capacities from 2 to 90 ton. Power options include diesel, electric & LPG.*

Valldata Services Ltd, Halifax Road, Bowerhill, Melksham, Wiltshire, SN12 6UB Tel: (01225) 354200 Fax: (01225) 709689 E-mail: sales@valldata.co.uk *Direct marketing services*

Vallectric Ltd, Sweet Street, Leeds, LS11 9DB Tel: 0113-242 3800 Fax: 0113-242 4960 E-mail: info@vallectric.co.uk *Electrical & mechanical contractors* Also at: Hull

▶ Vallectric Hull Ltd, Unit 2, The Shine, St. Mark Street, Hull, HU8 7FB Tel: (01482) 324521 Fax: (01482) 587371

Valley Arms Co., Bolero Camp, Park Road, Ruthin, Clwyd, LL15 1NB Tel: (01824) 704438 Fax: (01824) 704438 *Fire arms dealer*

▶ Valley Builders Ltd, 214 London Road, East Grinstead, West Sussex, RH19 1HE Tel: (01342) 311377 Fax: (01342) 300251 E-mail: sales@valleybuildersltd.co.uk *Aspects of residential, commercial, conservation & insurance works*

Valley Canoe Products Ltd, Private Road 4, Colwick Industrial Estate, Nottingham, NG4 2JT Tel: 0115-961 4995 Fax: 0115-961 4970 E-mail: ceakayak@globalnet.co.uk *Glass fibre moulding manufacturers & boat builders*

Valley Electronics, 15 Bridge End, Hebden Bridge, West Yorkshire, HX7 5DR Tel: (01422) 885088 Fax: (01422) 885088 E-mail: v.tronics@freeuk.com *Electronic maintenance sevice*

Valley Engraving Ltd, 91-92 High Street, Clydach, Swansea, SA6 5LN Tel: (01792) 842374 Fax: (01792) 846130 *Engraving sign specialists*

Valley Farm Foods Ltd, Zenith House, North Holme Road, Louth, Lincolnshire, LN11 0HQ Tel: (01507) 600976 Fax: (01507) 607839 E-mail: sales@valleyfarmfoods.com Principal Export Areas: Worldwide *Food*

Valley Fashions Ltd, Unit 2g 10-14 Hollybush Gardens, London, E2 9QP Tel: (020) 7729 7642 *Womens wear & childrens wear manufrs*

Valley Fastners, 65 Hay Hall Road, Birmingham, B11 2AU Tel: 0121-693 0031 Fax: 0121-693 0032 E-mail: sales@siemensvdo.com *Industrial fastener, bolt & screw distributors*

Valley Instruments, Churchfield Court, 14 Bewcastle Road, Nottingham, NG5 9PJ Tel: 0115-967 0025 Fax: 0115-967 0025 E-mail: valley.ins@fsbdial.co.uk *Repair industrial instruments*

▶ Valley Joinery, Unit 23 Baldock Industrial Estate, London Road, Baldock, Hertfordshire, SG7 6NG Tel: (01462) 490404 Fax: (01462) 490210 *Specialised joinery*

▶ Valley Management & Maintenance Ltd, Eastern House, Porthcurno, Porthcurno, Penzance, Cornwall, TR19 6JT Tel: (01736) 810477 Fax: (01736) 810477

Valley Pest Control Ltd, 1f Station Road, Hemyock, Cullompton, Devon, EX15 3SE Tel: (01823) 680932 Fax: (01823) 681247 *Pest controllers*

▶ Valley Pine & Gifts, 135 Enbrook Valley, Folkestone, Kent, CT20 3NE Tel: (01303) 245552 *Pine furniture manufrs*

▶ The Valley Printing Co. Ltd, Harden Beck Mill, Harden, Bingley, West Yorkshire, BD16 1BL Tel: (01535) 272861 Fax: (01535) 275332

Valley Reinforcements Ltd, Endle Street, Southampton, SO14 5FZ Tel: (023) 8022 6126 Fax: (023) 8033 8832 E-mail: andy@vrconstruction.f2s.com *Building steel frame constructors or fabricators*

Valley Screenprint Co., Units 1-2, Browells Lane, Feltham, Middlesex, TW13 7EQ Tel: (020) 8890 8271 Fax: (020) 8890 8485 E-mail: post@vspcm.demon.co.uk *Self-adhesive label manufrs* Also at: Manchester

Valley Signs, 2 Farnworth Park Industrial Estate, Queen Street, Farnworth, Bolton, BL4 7BY Tel: (01204) 795444 Fax: (01204) 792033 *Sign screen printers*

Valley Spring Co. Ltd, Pottery Lane East, Chesterfield, Derbyshire, S41 9BH Tel: (01246) 451981 Fax: (01246) 454327 E-mail: sales@valleyspring.com *Springs manufacturers; springs, compression;springs titanium; springs nickel (alloy)*

Valley Systems Ltd, 26 Moorfields Close, Staines, Middlesex, TW18 3LU Tel: (01784) 457645 Fax: (01784) 438777 E-mail: trushton@magsol.co.uk *Security access control engineers, installers or services*

▶ Valley Windows Ltd, The Old Spray Shop, Woodside Trading Estate, Usk, Monmouthshire, NP15 1SS Tel: (01291) 675470 Fax: (01291) 675472 E-mail: ian@valleywindows.co.uk *Suppliers & installers of windows, doors & conservatories*

Valleys Woodcraft Ltd, Unit 1-2 Cwmdraw Industrial Estate, Newtown, Ebbw Vale, Gwent, NP23 5AE Tel: (01495) 350758 Fax: (01495) 307054 E-mail: sales@valleyswoodcraft.com *Instrument case & presentation box manufrs*

Valli & Valli Ltd, Unit 8 Hedging Lane Industrial Estate, Hedging Lane, Wilnecote, Tamworth, Staffordshire, B77 5HH Tel: (01827) 283655 Fax: (01827) 280553 E-mail: sales@valiandvali.co.uk *Brass door fittings manufrs*

Vallis Press Ipi Ltd, 1 Thames View, Newtown Road, Henley-on-Thames, Oxfordshire, RG9 1HG Tel: (01491) 576553 Fax: (01491) 410512 *General printers*

Vallourec Mannesmann Oil & Gas UK Ltd, 4 Prospect Place, Westhill, Aberdeenshire, AB32 6SY Tel: (01224) 279340 Fax: (01224) 279341 E-mail: info@vmog.co.uk *Seamless casing manufacturers & casing & tubing services*

Vallourec UK Ltd, George House, 121 High Street, Henley-in-Arden, West Midlands, B95 5AU Tel: (01564) 792277 Fax: (01564) 795818 E-mail: sales@vallourec.co.uk *Manufacturers of steel tubes*

▶ Valmec Lift Trucks Ltd, Units 16-17, Pontcynon Industrial Estate, Abercynon, Mountain Ash, Mid Glamorgan, CF45 4EP Tel: (01443) 740488 Fax: (01443) 742736 *Food technology consultants*

Valor Heating, Wood Lane, Erdington, Birmingham, B24 9QP Tel: 0121-373 8111 Fax: 0121-373 8181 E-mail: sales@valor.co.uk *Manufacture gas & electric fires*

Valpar Industrial Ltd, 13 Balloo Drive, Bangor, County Down, BT19 7QY Tel: (028) 9145 4544 Fax: (028) 9145 7512 E-mail: info@valpar.co.uk *Flexible hose & tubing suppliers*

Valrene Ltd, 234 Highfield Road, Washwood Heath, Birmingham, B8 3QR Tel: 0121-327 5388 Fax: 0121-328 3197 *Painting & decorating*

Valro Manufacturing Ltd, Units 2-4, The Grove, Parkgate Industrial Estate, Knutsford, Cheshire, WA16 8XP Tel: (01565) 650204 Fax: (01565) 650755 E-mail: enquiries@valro.co.uk *Electronic equipment design manufrs*

Valsan Ceramics Ltd, Unit 7c Whitebridge Industrial Estate, Whitebridge Lane, Stone, Staffordshire, ST15 8LQ Tel: (01785) 818626 Fax: (01785) 812114 *Ceramic lighting manufrs*

Valsan UK Ltd, 1-3 Durban Park, Bognor Regis, West Sussex, PO22 9RJ Tel: (01243) 833500 Fax: (01243) 833503 E-mail: sales@valsanuk.com *Brass & ceramic household decorative products*

The Valspar UK Holding Corporation Ltd, Unit 2-3 Avenue One, Witney, Oxfordshire, OX28 4XR Tel: (01993) 707400 Fax: (01993) 775579 *Coating & varnish manufrs* Also at: Wythenshawe

Valtec Controls Ltd, Halifax Works, St. Marys Lane, Tewkesbury, Gloucestershire, GL20 5SF Tel: (01684) 292383 Fax: (01684) 294498 E-mail: valtec.controls@btinternet.com *Manufacturers of servo drive positioning systems & control systems*

Valtone Woodcraft, 2 Goodly Hill, Pershore, Worcestershire, WR10 3HE Tel: (01386) 554759 Fax: (01386) 553686 E-mail: valtonewoodcraft@btconnect.com *Hardwood joiners*

Valu Plan Furnishing, 11 Scotch Street, Ulster Gazette Shopping Centre, Armagh, BT61 7PU Tel: (028) 3752 2166 Fax: (028) 3752 2166 *Blind & curtain retailers & manufrs*

Value House Aquatics, Units 3-7 Brethren Bank, Barnstaple, Devon, EX31 2AZ Tel: (01271) 328462 Fax: (01271) 328462 *Aquarium suppliers*

Value In Approach, Imex Busines Centre, Shobnall Road, Burton-On-Trent, Staffordshire, DE14 2AU Tel: (01283) 567505 Fax: (01283) 505805 *Computer training & business consultants*

▶ ValueUK.Com, Boxer Place, Leyland, PR26 7QL Tel: (01772) 424455 Fax: (0870) 7772845 E-mail: rb@valueuk.com *Media & storage supplies*

▶ Valutech Ltd, 79-80 Shrivenham Hundred Bus, Park, Watchfield, Swindon, SN6 8TZ Tel: (01793) 787080 Fax: (01793) 786683 E-mail: terry.pudwell@mikrolive.co.uk *IT & electronics for businesses, education & consumers*

Valve Center, 2 Bold Business Centre, Bold Lane, St. Helens, Merseyside, WA9 4TX Tel: (01925) 290660 Fax: (01925) 227463 E-mail: sales@valvecenter.co.uk *Distributors of actuators*

Valve Componets Ltd, 6 Singer Road, East Kilbride, Glasgow, G75 0XS Tel: (01355) 263884 Fax: (01355) 245146 E-mail: sales@vcl.uk.com *Valve internal & actuator kit manufrs*

Valve Grove, Unit 15 16 Withy Road Industrial Estate, Withy Road, Bilston, West Midlands, WV14 0RX Tel: (01902) 498560 Fax: (01902) 498474 *Oil waste recycling*

▶ Valve & Process Solutions, Unit 11 Pottery La West, Chesterfield, Derbyshire, S41 9BN Tel: (01246) 220070 Fax: (0870) 220969 E-mail: sales@vandpsolutions.com *Process equipment distributors*

Valve Services Ltd, Station Road, South Shields, Tyne & Wear, NE33 1ED Tel: 0191-454 6185 Fax: 0191-454 6185 *Valve sales & repairers*

Valve Solutions Ltd, Units 6-7, Enterprise Court, Micklefield, Leeds, LS25 4BU Tel: 0113-287 6888 Fax: 0113-287 6999 *Valve manufrs*

Valvekits Ltd, Brookside Way, Huthwaite, Sutton-in-Ashfield, Nottinghamshire, NG17 2NL Tel: (01623) 446700 Fax: (01623) 440214 E-mail: valvekits@valvekits.co.uk *Valve reconditioning & repair services*

Valvelink UK Ltd, 17 Cotswold Green, Stonehouse, Gloucestershire, GL10 2ES Tel: (01453) 822222 Fax: (01453) 821111 *Industrial valve suppliers*

Valvestock, 2 Fielder Drive, Fareham, Hampshire, PO14 1JG Tel: (01329) 283425 Fax: (01329) 822741 E-mail: enquiries@valvestock.co.uk Purchasing Contact: A. Pill Sales Contact: Cole *Valvestock is one of the major specialist valve distributors in the United Kingdom. We have invested in an in-house operation for either electrical or pneumatic valve/actuator packages with its own fully equipped instrumentation workshop with full electric, pneumatic and hydraulic facilities to enable the testing of each individual product before despatch* Also at: Birmingham & Warrington

Valvetech Ltd, Unit 9, Brookside Industrial Estate, Sawtry, Huntingdon, Cambridgeshire, PE28 5SB Tel: (01487) 833080 Fax: (01487) 833081 E-mail: sales@valvetech.co.uk *Valve distributors including plastic & stainless steel*

Valvil Services, 533 Rayleigh Road, Benfleet, Essex, SS7 3TN Tel: (01268) 745333 Fax: (01268) 745333 *Sign makers*

Valvoline Oil Co., Dock Road, Birkenhead, Merseyside, CH41 1DR Tel: 0151-652 1551 Fax: 0151-653 8900 E-mail: sales@valvolineuk.com *Motor oil manufrs*

Van Bodies Lancs Ltd, East Gate, White Lund Trading Estate, White Lund Industrial Estate, Morecambe, Lancashire, LA3 3DY Tel: (01524) 34422 Fax: (01524) 381432 E-mail: vanbodies@btconnect.com *Specialist Commercial Vehicle Body Building Taxi Conversions/Camper Conversions across the UK. Please call our experts with your requirements.*

▶ Van & Deliver, 3 Warkton Close, Chilwell, Nottingham, NG9 5FR Tel: 0845 1214484 E-mail: enquiries@van-and-deliver.co.uk *Van & Deliver are a Nottingham based courier company. Our aim is to provide a quality service to all our customers whatever the size of job, at an affordable price. We are a member of the largest network of independant transport companies in the UK. That means we have access to thousands of vehicles, which are based at hundreds of sies in every major city in the country. We will deliver your goods in a way that reflects your product!!**

Van Der Graaf UK Ltd, 23 The Metro Centre, Peterborough, PE2 7UH Tel: (01733) 391777 Fax: (01733) 391044 E-mail: paul@vandergraaf.co.uk Principal Export Areas: Africa *Conveyor belt components manufrs*

Van Der Lande Industries, 59 Marsh Lane, Hampton-in-Arden, Solihull, West Midlands, B92 0AJ Tel: (01675) 443801 Fax: (01675) 443169 E-mail: roger.peart@vanderlande.co.uk *Conveyor systems & handling equipment sales & maintenance services*

▶ David Van Edwards, The Smokehouse, 6 Whitwell Road, NORWICH, NR1 4HB Tel: (01603) 629899 E-mail: lutes@vanedwards.co.uk *Suppliers of lutes & bows*

▶ Van Elle Ltd, Windsor Terrace, Springwell, Gateshead, Tyne & Wear, NE9 7QN Tel: 0191-417 8332 Fax: 0191-417 8334 E-mail: info@van-elle.co.uk

Van Elle Ltd, Kirkby Lane, Pinxton, Nottingham, NG16 6JA Tel: (01773) 580580 Fax: (01773) 862100 E-mail: info@van-elle.co.uk *Geotechnical engineering contractors.*

▶ Van Ellis Ltd, F Lambs Farm Business Park, Basingstoke Road, Swallowfield, Reading, RG7 1PQ Tel: 0118-988 9290 Fax: 0118-988 9294

Van Gadgets, 137 Heston Road, Hounslow, TW5 0RD Tel: (0870) 3833388 Fax: (020) 8572 8510 E-mail: sales@vangadgets.co.uk *Commercial vehicle accessories distribution & sales*

▶ Van Gaver Electrical Co. Ltd, 50 Bridgford Road, West Bridgford, Nottingham, NG2 6AP Tel: 0115-981 2820 Fax: 0115-945 5632 E-mail: mail@vangaverelectrical.co.uk

▶ Van Hee Recruitment, William Street, Gateshead, Tyne & Wear, NE10 0JP Tel: 0191-438 6161 Fax: 0191-495 0141 E-mail: traffic@vanhee.co.uk *Your Partner in Personnel Services! We specialise in recruiting for offshore and onshore workers in the metal and oil & gas industries.*

▶ Van Laun A E Ltd, 226 London Road, Portsmouth, PO2 9JQ Tel: (023) 9269 9081 Fax: (023) 9265 1798

Van Leeuwen Tubes Ltd, Unit 7 Provincial Park, Nether Lane, Ecclesfield, Sheffield, S35 9ZX Tel: 0114-257 7577 Fax: 0114-257 0639 E-mail: sales@vanleeuwen.nl Principal Export Areas: Worldwide *Steel stockholders*

Van Locks Ltd, 76 Portland Street, Manchester, M1 4GU Tel: 0161-236 1231 Fax: 0161-236 2885 E-mail: vanlock@talk21.com *Security vehicle system distributors*

Van Oord UK Ltd, Lockside Place, Newbury, Berkshire, RG14 5QS Tel: 01635 529101 *Dredging & marine contractors*

▶ Van Renselar, 1 Rydal Drive, West Wickham, Kent, BR4 9QH Tel: (020) 8462 1022 E-mail: art@van-renselar.com *Art services*

Van Son Ink UK Ltd, 71 Alston Drive, Bradwell Abbey, Milton Keynes, MK13 9HG Tel: (01908) 317717 Fax: (01908) 221005 E-mail: vanson@compuserve.com *Printing ink distributors*

Van Tongeren International Ltd, Van Tongeren House, 84a High Street, Godalming, Surrey, GU7 1DU Tel: (01483) 428082 Fax: (01483) 417741 E-mail: van-tong@netcomuk.co.uk *Gas cleaning & scrubbing plant manufrs*

Van Zelm Chem, 82 Williams St, Grays, Essex, RM17 6DZ Tel: (01375) 374612 Fax: (01375) 404007 E-mail: sales@vanzelm.co.uk *Chemicals, cleaning equipment*

▶ Vanandman.com, 33 Shaldon Drive, Morden, Surrey, SM4 4BE Tel: (0870) 8505282 E-mail: garyij@hotmail.com *Removals*

▶ Vanax, 1 Mordaunt Street, Glasgow, G40 3JZ Tel: 0141-550 8881 Fax: 0141-550 8889 E-mail: sales@vanax.co.uk *Van lining & accessory fitting service*

▶ Vandalite, Dunkirk Mills, Dunkirk Street, Halifax, West Yorkshire, HX1 3TB Tel: (01422) 354254 Fax: (01422) 356066 *Lighting manufrs*

Vanden Powder Coatings Ltd, 79 Manchester Road, Westhoughton, Bolton, BL5 3QD Tel: (01942) 818953 Fax: (01942) 840678 *Stove enamellers & powder coaters*

Robert Vanderpump & Co. Ltd, Clarks Farm Road, Danbury, Chelmsford, CM3 4PH Tel: (01245) 225966 Fax: (01245) 225866 E-mail: vanderpump@btconnect.com *Export merchants & shippers*

Vanderquest Ltd, 7 Latimer Road, Teddington, Middlesex, TW11 8QA Tel: (020) 8943 2818 Fax: (020) 8943 4812 E-mail: nick@vanderquest.co.uk *DVD & broadcast video duplication service*

Vandex (UK) Ltd, PO Box 200, Guildford, Surrey, GU2 4WD Tel: (0870) 2416264 Fax: (0870) 2416274 E-mail: info@vandex.co.uk *Manufacturers & distributors of basement waterproofing, concrete repair & concrete protection products*

Vandgard Anti Climb Guards, PO Box 51, Edenbridge, Kent, TN8 6WY Tel: (01797) 229872 *Security fencing manufrs*

Vangard Ltd, Schofield Street, Royton, Oldham, OL2 6PT Tel: 0161-652 1249 Fax: 0161-678 6790 *Metal fabricators*

Vange Scaffolding & Engineering Co. Ltd, 14 Brunel Road, Benfleet, Essex, SS7 4PS Tel: (01268) 792701 Fax: (01268) 795542 E-mail: vangenicky@aol.com *Provision of scaffolding & access services*

Vanguard Contracts Ltd, 2 Birch Court, Blackpole East, Worcester, WR3 8SG Tel: 01905 759700 Fax: 01905 759711 E-mail: sales@vanguardcontracts.co.uk *As a specialist Interiors Contractor, Vanguard Contracts offers a complete turnkey fit-out service to a range of clients within the retail, leisure, public and industrial sectors. We are specialist providers of interior design solutions, including mezzanine floors, shopfitting, office partitioning and commercial fit-out*

Vanguard Couriers Ltd, 6 Bendall Mews, London, NW1 6SN Tel: (020) 7258 1818 Fax: (020) 7723 8274 E-mail: courierslondon@aol.com *Courier service*

Vanguard Fishing Tackle, 25 Widebar Gate, Boston, Lincolnshire, PE21 6SR Tel: (01205) 369994 Fax: (01205) 359327 *Fishing tackle merchants*

Vanguard Foundry Ltd, Bott Lane, Lye, Stourbridge, West Midlands, DY9 7AW Tel: (01384) 422557 Fax: (01384) 423338 E-mail: jwilletts@vanguargfoundry.co.uk *Spheroidal graphite iron castings*

Vanguard Microelectronics Ltd, 2 The Stocks, Cosgrove, Milton Keynes, MK19 7JD Tel: (01908) 563399 Fax: (01908) 263003 E-mail: sales@sunrise.co.uk *Semi-conductor component distributors*

▶ Vanguard Oil & Gas Consultants Ltd, 7 Sunert Road, Milltimber, AB13 0JQ Tel: (01224) 862186 Fax: (01224) 867651

▶ Vanguard Processin Equipment Ltd, Vanguard, Spafield, Slaithwaite, Huddersfield, HD7 5BX Tel: (01484) 847388 Fax: (01484) 847688 *Food processing equipment distributors*

Vanguard Shutters Ltd, Vanguard Works, Coldhurst Street, Oldham, OL1 2DN Tel: 0161-652 3498 Fax: 0161-627 2697 E-mail: sfyfe@dovervanguard.co.uk *Roller shutter manufrs*

Vanguard Wire Products, Victoria Wire Works, Raglan Street, Halifax, West Yorkshire, HX1 5QY Tel: (01422) 353339 Fax: (01422) 364532 E-mail: info@thinkg.co.uk Principal Export Areas: Central/East Europe & West Europe *High volume wire manufrs*

▶ Vanilla Heaven, 4 Northfield Avenue, Lincoln, LN2 2FB Tel: (01522) 753781 E-mail: sales@global-gadgets.com *Alarm systems for homes, cars & motorbikes & gadgets & latest crazes*

Vanitorials Ltd, 8 Armstrong Road, Manor Trading Estate, Benfleet, Essex, SS7 4PW Tel: (01268) 752224 Fax: (01268) 792444 *Janitorial supplies*

Vanity Pine, 186 Marsh Lane, Preston, PR1 8RT Tel: (01772) 252187 Fax: (01772) 563253 *Pine furniture manufacturer & retailer*

▶ Vanity-Pure Design Ltd, 24 Hampshire Road, Derby, DE21 4EG Tel: 01332 727317 Fax: 01332 727317 E-mail: h.dunmore@vanity-puredesign.co.uk *We specialise in offering 3D Modeling & Visualisation, Graphic and Web-page design.**We can transform you 2D sketches or drawings into stunning 3D virtual models with texturs, surroundings and people.***

Vann Draper Electronics, Barrow-on-Trent, Derby, DE73 7HL Tel: (01283) 704706 Fax: (01283) 704707 E-mail: admin@vanndraper.co.uk *Instrument manufrs*

E. Vanner, 63 Radnor Drive, Southport, Merseyside, PR9 9RS Tel: (01704) 226384 *Watch & clock material dealers*

Vanners Silks, Weavers Lane, Sudbury, Suffolk, CO10 1BB Tel: (01787) 372396 Fax: (01787) 310674 E-mail: rcroft@vanners.com *Silk fabric weavers*

▶ Vannypeco Consulting, Corsham Street, London, N1 6DR Tel: (020) 7490 4009 Fax: (020) 7490 8070

Vanriet UK Ltd, W Riverside Industrial Estate, Atherstone Street, Fazeley, Tamworth, Staffordshire, B78 3RW Tel: (01827) 288871 Fax: (01827) 250810 E-mail: sales@vanriet.co.uk *Pallet handling equipment, systems & conveyor system manufrs*

Vanstead, Unit 6 Manor Farm Road, Birmingham, B11 2HT Tel: 0121-707 4929 Fax: 0121-707 2155 E-mail: office@vanstead.com *Air freight shippers & forwarders*

▶ Vantage Electronics Ltd, 4 Carlo Court, Finchampstead, Wokingham, Berkshire, RG40 4RF Tel: 0118-973 1186 Fax: 0118-973 1192

Vantage Micro Systems Ltd, 2 Airfield Park, Cheddington Lane, Long Marston, Tring, Hertfordshire, HP23 4QR Tel: (01296) 668966 Fax: (01296) 662798 E-mail: sales@vantageit.co.uk *IT products suppliers*

Vantage Power Drives Ltd, 244 Bromford Lane, West Bromwich, West Midlands, B70 7HX Tel: 0121-500 5525 Fax: 0121-553 2629 *Engineers*

▶ Vantage Training Ltd, 4 Trent Lane, East Bridgford, Nottingham, NG13 8PF Tel: (01949) 21212 Fax: 0870 7406607 E-mail: info@vtl.co.uk *Vtl offer over 0 customisable software courses, with 1-1 training or groups of up to 8. You can choose to learn on-site or at one of our training venues. * Vtl also have a long history of application development for Office automation solutions, including complex databases and spreadsheets.**

Vantana Blinds, Church Street, Glenrothes, Fife, KY7 5NF Tel: (01592) 610500 *Window blind suppliers*

Vanton Pumps Ltd, Unit 6 Radnor Park Industrial Centre, Back Lane, Congleton, Cheshire, CW12 1JJ Tel: (01260) 277040 Fax: (01260) 280605 E-mail: vanton@btinternet.com *Manufacturer of pumps, including acid, chemical & corrosion resistant*

Vantrunk Building Services Ltd, Goddard Road, Astmoor Industrial Estate, Runcorn, Cheshire, WA7 1QF Tel: (01928) 564211 Fax: (01928) 580157 E-mail: sales@vantrunk.co.uk Principal Export Areas: Worldwide *Manufrs of cable management systems*

Vanwest Ltd, Unit 2 High Street, Lenches Bridge, Pensnett, Kingswinford, West Midlands, DY6 8XD Tel: (01384) 400255 Fax: (01384) 400258 *Specialist handrail manufrs*

Vapac Humidity Control Ltd, Station Road, Edenbridge, Kent, TN8 6EG Tel: (01732) 863447 E-mail: peter.dewdney@eton_williams.com *Humidifier & control system distributors & manufrs*

Vapor Tek Ltd, Fairclough Street, Bolton, BL3 2AF Tel: (01204) 521795 Fax: (01204) 364576 E-mail: information@vapor-tek.co.uk *Corrosion prevention & protection manufrs*

Vapormatic Company Limited, P O Box 58, Exeter, EX2 7NB Tel: (01392) 435461 Fax: (01392) 438445 E-mail: sales@vapormatic.com *Tractor spares manufrs*

Vapormatt Ltd, Monarch Centre, Venture Way, Priorswood Industrial Est, Taunton, Somerset, TA2 8DE Tel: (01823) 257976 Fax: (01823) 336446 E-mail: sales@vapormatt.com *Vapormatt Ltd are UK manufacturers of blast/shot blast cleaning equipment & cleaning/washing (industrial) equipment. Also manufacturers of vapour blast plant, abrasive powder/grains & abrasive products (industrial finishing). Deburring equipment, grit blasting abrasive materials, shot peening equipment & industrial degreasing plant/degreasers. Sand blasting equipment, abrasive plastic materials/finishing media manufacturers. We have a global network of agents & distributors to service international requirements.*

Vapour Safe Ltd, Rosscliffe Rd, Ellesmere Port, CH65 3AS Tel: 0151-356 3955 *Cleaning industry equipment manufrs*

George Varcas & Partners, Windshield, Brimpton Common, Reading, RG7 4RU Tel: 0118-981 4983 Fax: 0118-981 7138 E-mail: paul@varcas.co.uk *Air conditioning & refrigeration contractors*

Varcol Electrical Services Ltd, Cornwall Street, Manchester, M11 2WQ Tel: 0161-223 9696 Fax: 0161-223 0976 E-mail: sales@varcol.co.uk *Control panel manufrs*

▶ Vardells Ltd, Staden Lane Business Park, Ashbourne Road, Buxton, Derbyshire, SK17 9RN Tel: (01298) 767600 Fax: (01298) 767619 E-mail: vardells@vardells.com *Computer maintenance & repair services*

Vargus Tooling UK Ltd, Halesfield 4, Telford, Shropshire, TF7 4AP Tel: (01952) 583222 Fax: (01952) 583383 E-mail: sales@vargustooling.co.uk *Indexable tooling specialists*

Vari Labels, 44a Waldeck Road, Dartford, DA1 1UA Tel: (01322) 293186 Fax: (01322) 442225 *Self-adhesive label manufrs*

Varian Ltd, 28 Manor Road, Walton-On-Thames, Surrey, KT12 2QF Tel: (01932) 898000 Fax: (01932) 228769 *Analylitic & scientific instruments*

Variant Systems UK Ltd, Unit S1 The Old Brickyard, Ashton Keynes, Swindon, SN6 6QR Tel: (01285) 861870 Fax: (01285) 862110 E-mail: s.ascroft@variantsystems.co.uk *Roll & dairy containers*

Varichem Co. Ltd, Blaenant Industrial Estate, Blaenavon Road, Brynmawr, Ebbw Vale, Gwent, NP23 4BX Tel: (01495) 312388 Fax: (01495) 312167 E-mail: info@varichem.co.uk *Chemical manufrs*

Varipack Ltd, Unit L, Durgates Industrial Estate, Wadhurst, East Sussex, TN5 6DF Tel: (01892) 784567 Fax: (01892) 783477 *PVC binders & stationery*

Varipart Engineering, Florence Mill Business Park, Whalley New Road, Blackburn, BB1 9SR Tel: (01254) 264394 Fax: (01254) 675555 E-mail: sales@varipartengineering.co.uk *Precision engineers*

▶ Varis Engineering, 10-12 West Road, Greshop Industrial Estate, Forres, Morayshire, IV36 2GW Tel: (01309) 671211 Fax: (01309) 671241 *Manufacture mariners distillery engineer work water treatment plant*

Varitronix UK Ltd, 3 Milbanke Court, Milbanke Way, Bracknell, Berkshire, RG12 1RP Tel: (01344) 303077 Fax: (01344) 300099 E-mail: sales@varitronixuk.ltd.uk *Liquid crystal display manufrs*

Varivane Industries Ltd, William Road, Nursteed Industrial Estate, Devizes, Wiltshire, SN10 3EW Tel: (01380) 723624 Fax: (01380) 728367 E-mail: varivane.industries@btinternet.com *Sheet metalwork fabricators*

Varley & Gulliver Ltd, Alfred Street, Sparkbrook, Birmingham, B12 8JR Tel: 0121-773 2441 Fax: 0121-766 6875 E-mail: sales@v-and-g.co.uk *Steel & aluminium fabricators*

H. Varley Ltd, Unit 82, The Wenta Business Centre, Colne Way, Watford, WD24 7ND Tel: (01923) 249334 Fax: (01923) 245513 E-mail: sales@varley.co.uk *Industrial wheels & castors*

Varley Pumps Ltd, 1 Kimpton Road, Luton, LU1 3LD Tel: (01582) 731144 Fax: (01582) 402563 E-mail: varleysales@haywardtyler.com *Pumps: lubricating oil; gear; positive displacement*

Varley Trophies, 78 Beaumont Road, Plymouth, PL4 9BP Tel: (01752) 665984 Fax: (01752) 229567 E-mail: chris@howe11.fsbusiness.co.uk *Sports trophies & engravers*

Varlin Ltd, Rookery Farm, West Charlton, Charlton Mackrell, Somerton, Somerset, TA11 7AL Tel: (01458) 224080 Fax: (01458) 224090 E-mail: sales@varlin.co.uk *Storage, racking & shelving distributors*

▶ Varo (UK), 75 School Lane, Hartford, Northwich, Cheshire, CW8 1PF Tel: (01606) 786860 Fax: (01606) 784566 *Power tool suppliers*

▶ Varta Microbattery GmbH, 16 Progress Business Centre, Whittle Parkway, Slough, SL1 6DQ Tel: (01628) 607930 Fax: (01628) 607939 E-mail: uksales@varta.com *Manufacturer & supplier of batteries*

Vartex (Textiles) Ltd, 54 Totara Park House, 34-36 Great Inn Road, London, WC1X 8HR Tel: (020) 7580 3866 Fax: (020) 7831 1515 E-mail: vtextiles@btclick.com *Textile merchants*

Vary-Lite, 20-22 Fairway Drive, Greenford, Middlesex, UB6 8PW Tel: (020) 8575 6666 Fax: (020) 8575 0424 E-mail: info@vari-lite.eu.com *Commercial & theatrical lighting*

▶ Vasahus Ltd, Unit 4A, Wiston Business Park, London Road, Ashington, Pulborough, West Sussex, RH20 3DJ Tel: (01903) 891990 Fax: (01903) 892031 E-mail: info@vasahus.biz

Vaseco Ltd, Bromley House, Barlow Drive, Woodford Park Industrial Park, Winsford, Cheshire, CW7 2JZ Tel: (01606) 590000 Fax: (01606) 590100 E-mail: sales@vaseco.com *Scientific equipment manufrs*

▶ Vast Trading, Titus House, 29 Saltaire Road, Shipley, West Yorkshire, BD18 3HH Tel: 01274 609609 Fax: 01274 531966 E-mail: mark@vasttrading.co.uk *Vast Trading is a UK importer of Toys, Novelty Goods, Relaxation and massage products*

Vaughan Agri, Yellowham Wood, Dorchester, Dorset, DT2 8FA Tel: (01305) 849000 Fax: (01305) 849222 *Agricultural engineers*

Vaughan Engineering Group Ltd, Aercon Works, 556 Antrim Road, Newtownabbey, County Antrim, BT36 4RF Tel: (028) 9083 7441 Fax: (028) 9034 2469 E-mail: info@vaughan-group.co.uk *Mechanical & electrical engineers*

▶ Vaughan Jones Socket Screws Ltd, Unit 352 Thorp Arch Trading Estate, Thorp Arch, Wetherby, West Yorkshire, LS23 7BJ Tel: (01937) 843298 Fax: (01937) 843501 E-mail: enquiries@vaughanjones.co.uk *Vaughan Jones is a special fastener manufacturer, offerering slotted and socket screws, nuts, washers, bushes, and all manner of turned parts.*

▶ Vaughan Logistics Ltd, Dukeries Industrial Estate, Claylands Avenue, Worksop, Nottinghamshire, S81 7BQ Tel: (01909) 486371

Vaughan Mechanical Services (Scotland) Ltd, Aercon Works, East Mains Industrial Estate, Broxburn, West Lothian, EH52 5ND Tel: (01506) 853506 Fax: (01506) 854006 E-mail: vel@vaughan-group.co.uk *Air conditioning, ductwork fabrication & engineers* Also at: Newtownabbey

Stewart Vaughan & Co. Ltd, Unit 21 Riverside Business Park, Lyon Road, London, SW19 2RL Tel: (020) 8544 9199 Fax: (020) 8540 8884 *Transmission belting & conveyor belting distributors*

Vauxhall Motors Ltd, North Road, Ellesmere Port, CH65 1AL Tel: 0151-355 3777 Fax: 0151-350 2911 *Car manufrs*

Vauxhall Motors Ltd, Griffin House, Osborne Road, Luton, LU1 3YT Tel: (01582) 721122 Fax: (01582) 427400 *Car manufrs*

Vaz Finishers, 25 Mallet Road, London, SE13 6SP Tel: (020) 8852 0711 *Stove enamellers*

VBS Support Ltd, Gala House, 3, Raglan Road, Birmingham, B5 7RA Tel: (0870) 7534020 Fax: (0870) 7534022 E-mail: info@vbs.co.uk *Software support consultants*

Vbug, 4 Park Parade, Park Road, Farnham Royal, Slough, SL2 3AU Tel: (01753) 649680 Fax: (01753) 647222 E-mail: sales@vbug.co.uk *Provide computer developers services*

VCS Clearpoint Ltd, Salop Street, Daybrook, Nottingham, NG5 6HD Tel: 0115-967 1234 Fax: 0115-967 1154 E-mail: clearpoint@demon.co.uk *Lithographic printers*

VcsTimeless, 249 Upper Third Street, Witan Gate West, Milton Keynes, MK9 1DS Tel: 01908 350550 Fax: 01908 350551 E-mail: contact@vcstimeless.com *Electronic processing systems*

VDC, 86 Oxford Road, Clacton-on-Sea, Essex, CO15 3TG Tel: (01255) 221884 Fax: (01255) 429242 *Sign makers*

Ve Track Ltd, 7 Westerloch Crescent, Lerwick, Shetland, ZE1 0RP Tel: (01595) 696201 Fax: (01595) 696897 E-mail: graeme@vetrack.com *Drive right vehicle data monitors sales, installation & data management*

Vecom Stainless Finishers Ltd, Unit 7, Claycliffe Business Park, Cannon Way, Barnsley, South Yorkshire, S71 1HT Tel: (0845) 2309704 Fax: (0845) 2309604 E-mail: sales@vecom.co.uk *Whether its pre polishing of stainless steel sheet for refrigerators and buildings to electropolishing of medical and pharmaceutical equipment, pickling of duplex reactor vessels to cleaning of revolving doors and the supply of speciality cleaning products we can be of service.*

Vecstar Furnaces, Unit 11-12 Dunston Trading Estate, Foxwood Road, Chesterfield, Derbyshire, S41 9RF Tel: (01246) 260094 Fax: (01246) 450213 E-mail: enquiries@vecstar.co.uk Principal Export Areas: Worldwide *Electric, heat treatment & laboratory furnaces*

Vectis Optical Laboratories Ltd, 81a High Street, Newport, Isle of Wight, PO30 1BG Tel: (01983) 525272 Fax: (01983) 525272 *Optical lenses manufrs*

Vectis Transport Ltd, Riverway Industrial Estate, Newport, Isle Of Wight, PO30 5UX Tel: (01983) 523515 Fax: (01983) 526225 E-mail: vectis@redfunnel.co.uk *Road transport services*

Vector Data Systems UK Ltd, Ho, Newark Road, Peterborough, PE1 5FL Tel: (01733) 296866 Fax: (01733) 296868 E-mail: plowdens@anteonuk.com *Computer systems integrator*

Vector Electronics Ltd, Aco House, Rembrandt Way, Aycliffe Industrial Park, Newton Aycliffe, County Durham, DL5 6BD Tel: (01325) 319182 Fax: (01325) 319182 *Transformers & wound components*

Vector Instruments, 115 Marsh Road, Rhyl, Clwyd, LL18 2AB Tel: (01745) 350700 Fax: (01745) 344206 E-mail: admin@windspeed.co.uk *Meteorological instrument manufrs*

▶ Vector International Ltd, Unit 31, Wellheads Crescent, Wellheads Industrial Estate, Aberdeen, AB21 7GA Tel: (01224) 775242 E-mail: sales@vector-supplies.ltd.uk *Pipes & tubes manufrs*

Vector International Ltd, Unit 31, Wellheads Crescent, Wellheads Industrial Estate, Aberdeen, AB21 7GA Tel: (01224) 775242 Fax: (01224) 772212 E-mail: sales@vector-supplies.ltd.uk *Gauges, valves & pumps distributors*

Vector Microsystems Ltd, Unit 41, Claydon Industrial Park, Ipswich, IP6 0NL Tel: (01473) 833999 Fax: (01473) 833222 *Computer manufrs*

▶ Vector Programming, Unit 2, 81 Sterte Avenue West, Poole, Dorset, BH15 2AL Tel: (01202) 671060 E-mail: info@vector-programming.co.uk *We specialise in supplying programs and engineering solutions for Multi-axis NC machining centres to the Aerospace and Automotive Industries. **

Vector Seating Ltd, Raleigh Road, Bedminster, Bristol, BS3 1QU Tel: 0117-953 2000 Fax: 0117-953 2005 E-mail: sales@vector-seating.co.uk *Office chair manufrs*

▶ The Vector Studio, 44 High Oakham Close, Sutton-in-Ashfield, Nottinghamshire, NG17 4JS Tel: (07931) 934479 E-mail: thevectorstudio@hotmail.com *Graphic design for advertising & marketing services*

▶ Vector Surveys, 24 Edwin Street, London, E16 1QA Tel: (020) 7474 3991 Fax: (020) 7474 3991 E-mail: pjwarr@btopenwolrd.com *Land & building measured surveys, architectural design services*

Vectra Group Ltd, Europa House, 310 Europa Boulevard, Westbrook, Warrington, WA5 7YQ Tel: (01925) 444648 Fax: (01925) 444701 E-mail: info@vectragroup.co.uk *Safety engineering & management services*

Vee Bee Ltd, Old Wharf Road, Stourbridge, West Midlands, DY8 4LS Tel: (01384) 378884 Fax: (01384) 374179 E-mail: veebee-filtration@veebee.co.uk *Oil filters manufacturers*

Vee Clutch Plates, Mill Lane, Brighouse, West Yorkshire, HD6 1PN Tel: (01484) 721409 Fax: (01484) 400203 E-mail: vee@clutch.fsbusiness.co.uk *Clutch manufrs*

Company Information

Veeanco Ltd, 20-22 Dunston Trading Estate, Foxwood Road, Chesterfield, Derbyshire, S41 9RF Tel: (01246) 452152 Fax: (01246) 455940 E-mail: sales@veeanco.com *Marine engineers*

Veeco Instruments Ltd, Nanotech House Buckingway Business Park, Anderson Road, Swavesey, Cambridge, CB24 4UQ Tel: (01954) 233900 Fax: (01954) 231300 E-mail: info@veeco.co.uk *Scientific instruments manufrs*

Veefix Auto Centre, Stephenson Way, Crawley, West Sussex, RH10 1TN Tel: (01293) 545980 *Garage, mot & repairs station*

Veejay Knitwear, 62-68 Highcross Street, Leicester, LE1 4NN Tel: 0116-253 7732 Fax: 0116-251 9618 *Knitwear manufrs*

W. Veenstra & Co. (UK) Ltd, Unit 1, 57 Bushey Grove Road, Bushey, WD23 2JW Tel: (01923) 637893 Fax: (01923) 248055 E-mail: brandone@btconnect.com *Tube bending machine distributors*

▶ Veerman's Shed Centre, 130 High Street, Tranent, East Lothian, EH33 1HJ Tel: (01875) 613090 Fax: (01875) 617492 E-mail: email@veermans.co.uk *Sheds, summerhouses, playhouses & pet housing*

▶ Vega Controls Ltd, Kendal House, Victoria Way, Burgess Hill, West Sussex, RH15 9NF Tel: (01444) 870055 Fax: (01444) 870080 E-mail: info@uk.vega.com *Level & pressure instrument manufrs*

Vega Nutritionals Ltd, 41 Central Avenue, West Molesey, Surrey, KT8 2QZ Tel: (020) 8939 3480 Fax: (0845) 2267400 E-mail: sales@vegavitamins.co.uk Principal Export Areas: Worldwide *Vitamins suppliers*

Vege, Unit 2 Meltham Lane, Chesterfield, Derbyshire, S41 7LG Tel: (01246) 272227 Fax: (01246) 229991 *Distributors of engines*

Vegem Ltd, PO Box 9, Leeds, LS27 0QN Tel: 0113-253 0451 Fax: 0113-252 1161 E-mail: enquiries@vegem.co.uk *Motor components suppliers.*

Veggie World Co. Ltd, 150-152 Queen's Way, Bletchley, Milton Keynes, MK2 2RS Tel: (0870) 7449976 Fax: (0870) 7449978 E-mail: sales@veggie-world.com *Vegetarian food wholesalers*

Vehicle Body Services, 56 Arthur Street, Redditch, Worcestershire, B98 8JY Tel: (01527) 529188 Fax: (01527) 514317 *Motor vehicle accident repairs*

Vehicle Build, 4 George Baylis Road, Berry Hill Industrial Estate, Droitwich, Worcestershire, WR9 9RB Tel: (01905) 826083 Fax: (01905) 826093 *Commercial motor body builders*

Vehicle Cleaning Products, Unit 1997 Lea Valley Business Centre, 1 Hawley Road, London, N18 3SB Tel: (020) 8367 4609 E-mail: sales@vcp.gbr.cc *We have been supplying valeting chemicals and sundries for 25 years and have built up a reputation for quality and value.*

▶ Vehicle Consulting - (S&B), 17 Menzies Avenue, Basildon, Essex, SS15 6SX Tel: 0845 0535719 Fax: 0845 0535720 E-mail: brian@vehicleconsulting.com *Vehicle Consulting offer personal, commercial, fleet and executive car hire and rental.*

Vehicle Movements (North East) Ltd, Sandy Lane, North Gosforth, Newcastle Upon Tyne, NE3 5HE Tel: 0191-236 1101 Fax: 0191-236 1143 E-mail: vehiclemovements@murrayhogg.co.uk *Car transporter contractors*

Vehicle Security, 159 Balby Rd, Doncaster, S. Yorkshire, DN4 0RG Tel: 01302 311390 Fax: 01302 310114 *Buy & Install Systems*

Vehicle Security Systems, 292-294 St. Helens Road, Bolton, BL3 3RP Tel: (01204) 660822 Fax: (01204) 660820 E-mail: info@vehiclesecuritysystems.co.uk *Security systems*

Vehicle & Tail Lift Repairs, 2 Churchward, Didcot, Oxfordshire, OX11 7HB Tel: (01235) 818922 Fax: (01235) 510236 *Vehicle & tail lift repairers*

Vehicle & Tail Lift Repairs, 4 Monarch Works, Elswick Road, Fenton Industrial Estate, Stoke-on-Trent, ST4 2SH Tel: (01782) 845386 Fax: (01782) 846175 E-mail: vtrstoke@vtrgroup.co.uk *Tailboard lifting gear repair services*

▶ Vehicle Test Consulting Ltd, C-Mac House, Windmill Lane, Denton, Manchester, M34 3AP Tel: 0161-335 0670 Fax: 0161-335 0692 E-mail: vtc@cl-group.com *Vehicle test consultants*

Vehicle Window Centre, Unit 2-3 Ashley Estate, Carr Wood Road, Castleford, West Yorkshire, WF10 4SR Tel: (01977) 604977 Fax: (01977) 603466 E-mail: sales@horsebox.co.uk *Manufacturers of horsebox windows, horsebox doors, horsebox lockers, also for catering vehicles, ice cream vehicles, racecar transporters, etc*

▶ VehicleOptions (Wales), Redwither Business Centre, Redwither Business Park, Wrexham, LL13 9XR Tel: (01978) 664516 Fax: (01978) 661494 E-mail: nickcarlton@vehicleoptions.biz *VehicleOptions is now probably the largest and most successful independent vehicle leasing brokerage in the UK, with a "Network" of over 30 strategically located offices with direct access to the manufacturers; the majority of top contract hire companies and powerful quotation systems; hundreds of dealerships and thousands of new and nearly vehicles.*

Vehicletrademaster, PO Box 5347, Northampton, NN3 7YT Tel: (08702) 405445 Fax: (08702) 405445 E-mail: vtmoffice@btinternet.com *Buy a new or used vehicle or sell your own vehicle from only £11.99 until it is sold online with vehicletrademaster, find your next vehicle with our quick search vehicle finder.*

▶ Vein Removal Cornwall, Flat 1 Galleon Court, 14 Fore Street, Fowey, Cornwall, PL23 1AQ Tel: (01726) 832823 E-mail: vivienne.barker@btinternet.com *Specialists in the removal of red, spider, thread veins & tattoo*

Veitchi (Scotland) Ltd, Unit 7, Hareness Circle, Altens Industrial Estate, Aberdeen, AB12 3LY Tel: (01224) 896333 Fax: (01224) 890354 E-mail: aberdeen@veitchi.com *Flooring contractors*

▶ Veitchi Scotland Ltd, 15 Bouverie Street, Rutherglen, Glasgow, G73 2RY Tel: 0141-647 0661 Fax: 0141-613 1575 *Flooring manufrs*

Veka P.L.C., Farrington Road, Rossendale Road Industrial Estate, Burnley, Lancashire, BB11 5DA Tel: (01282) 716611 Fax: (01282) 718490 E-mail: salesenquiry@veka.com *Window upvc extrusion manufrs*

Veker Extrusions Ltd, Shaftmoor Lane, Hall Green, Birmingham, B28 8SP Tel: 0121-777 5000 Fax: 0121-777 5015 E-mail: enquiries@vekex.com *Manufacturers of gaskets & extruded rubber products*

Veker Extrusions Ltd, Shaftmoor Lane, Hall Green, Birmingham, B28 8SP Tel: 0121-777 5000 Fax: 0121-777 5015 E-mail: paul@vekex.com *Rubber extrusion manufrs*

Velcro Ltd, 1 Aston Way, Middlewich, Cheshire, CW10 0HS Tel: (01606) 738806 Fax: (01606) 738814 E-mail: uksales@velcro.co.uk *Without a doubt the VELCRO® brand product range is one of the most versatile fastening systems available on the market. With a proven track record across a range of industries, including automotive, industrial, medical, construction and electrical, there is always a fastening solution to suit your needs.*

The Velocette Motor Cycle Co., Meriden Works, Birmingham Road, Millisons Wood, Coventry, CV5 9AZ Tel: (01676) 522066 Fax: (01676) 522331 *Classic motor cycle parts manufrs*

Velspar, 95 Aston Church Road, Birmingham, B7 5RQ Tel: 0121-322 6900 Fax: 0121-322 6901 E-mail: infoeurope@powderstore.com *Powder coatings manufrs*

Veltshaw Builders Ltd, Pentney Road, Main Road, Narborough, King's Lynn, Norfolk, PE32 1TE Tel: (01760) 337424 Fax: (01760) 337511

Velux Company Ltd, Woodside Way, Glenrothes East, Glenrothes, Fife, KY7 4ND Tel: (01592) 772211 Fax: (01592) 771839 E-mail: enquiries@velux.co.uk *Roof window manufrs*

▶ VEN Systems Ltd, 25 Wingmore Road, London, SE24 0AS Tel: (07718) 159555 Fax: (020) 7837 8443 E-mail: info@venplaster.co.uk *Polished plastering specialists*

Vencel Resil Ltd, Infinity House, Anderson Way, Belvedere, Kent, DA17 6BG Tel: (020) 8320 9100 Fax: (020) 8320 9110 E-mail: sales@vencel.co.uk *Insulations manufrs* Also at: Belvedere, Glasgow, Howden & Whitecroft

Venchem Ltd, Knotts Lane, Colne, Lancashire, BB8 8AA Tel: (01282) 861198 Fax: (01282) 860020 E-mail: sales@venchem.co.uk *Chemical (fine organic chemical) manufrs*

▶ Venco, Jenning Street, Hull, HU8 7AN Tel: (01482) 585101

Venda & Sons Engineering Ltd, Unit 31 Kings Grove, Maidenhead, Berkshire, SL6 4DP Tel: (01628) 773315 Fax: (01628) 773315 E-mail: sales@venda-engineering.co.uk *Precision engineers*

Venda Valet Ltd, Unit 3-4 Neville Street Industrial Estate, Neville Street, Chadderton, Oldham, OL9 6LD Tel: 0161-633 3793 Fax: 0161-628 3805 *Vending machine distributors*

Vendcare Nationwide Services Ltd, Avenue 3, Station Lane Trading Estate, Witney, Oxfordshire, OX28 4BQ Tel: (01993) 703959 Fax: (01993) 776045 E-mail: sales@vendcare.com *Vending machine suppliers*

Vendingworld Services Ltd, Court Lodge Farm, Warren Road, Chelsfield, Orpington, Kent, BR6 6ER Tel: (01689) 873107 Fax: (01689) 835787 E-mail: info@vendingworld.co.uk *Vending machines & ingredient distributors*

Vendredi Screen Print, 23 Airfield Road, Christchurch, Dorset, BH23 3TG Tel: (01202) 470570 Fax: (01202) 470570 E-mail: vendredi@btconnect.com *Screen printers & vinyl graphics service*

▶ Vendsafe Ltd, 19 Elim Court Gardens, Crowborough, East Sussex, TN6 1BS Tel: (01892) 655752 E-mail: vendsafe@fsmail.net *specialist in strip and clean of all types of vending machines, to a sterile and totally clean condition*

Veneer Workshop Ltd, 37a South Street, Portslade, Brighton, BN41 2LE Tel: (01273) 422332 Fax: (01273) 418220 E-mail: mail@veneerworkshop.co.uk *Veneer board manufrs*

Venetian Blind Services, 78 Bleerick Drive, Antrim, BT41 1HX Tel: (028) 9073 9309 Fax: (028) 9442 8866 *Blind maintenance & suppliers*

Venex Technical Developments Ltd, Unit 3, Mount Pleasant Farm, Moorend Road, Yardley Gobion, Towcester, Northamptonshire, NN12 7UF Tel: (01908) 543158 Fax: (01908) 543052 E-mail: chris@venex.biz *Reprographic paper coaters*

Venhill Engineering Ltd, 21 Ranmore Road, Dorking, Surrey, RH4 1HE Tel: (01306) 885111 Fax: (01306) 740535 E-mail: info@venhill.co.uk *Flexible control cable manufrs*

▶ Venice Marble Ltd, 254 Kilburn High Road, London, NW6 2BX Tel: (020) 7372 3191 Fax: (020) 7372 3196

Vent Axia Ltd, Fleming Way, Crawley, West Sussex, RH10 9YX Tel: (01293) 526062 Fax: (01293) 551188 E-mail: info@vent-axia.com *Ventilating/ exhaust & axial fan manufrs*

Vent Duct, The Hollies, Campton Road, Meppershall, Shefford, Bedfordshire, SG17 5PB Tel: (01462) 815018 Fax: (01462) 817045 *Ventilation ductwork manufrs*

R.S. Vent, 28 Swan Road, Washington, Tyne & Wear, NE38 8JJ Tel: 0191 4165737 *Extractor system manufrs*

Vent Services Ltd, 4 Old Airfield Industrial Estate, Cheddington Lane, Long Marston, Tring, Hertfordshire, HP23 4QR Tel: (01296) 660000 Fax: (01296) 660111 *Ventilation services*

Ventair Ltd, Wednesbury Trading Estate, Darlaston Road, Wednesbury, West Midlands, WS10 7JN Tel: 0121-502 5518 Fax: 0121-556 6737 *Air conditioning manufrs*

▶ Ventana Ltd, Unit 5 Bawtry Business Park, Off Station Road, Bawtry, Doncaster, South Yorkshire, DN10 6QD Tel: (01302) 714400 Fax: (01302) 714433

Ventana UK Ltd, Gainsborough House, 33 Throgmorton Street, London, EC2N 2BR Tel: (020) 7861 9550 Fax: (01494) 677840 E-mail: enquiries@ventana.co.uk *Meeting & conference facilitators*

Ventco Fan Stockists, 1 Bull Lane, Pill, Bristol, BS20 0EF Tel: (01275) 372340 Fax: (01275) 372340 *Ventilation equipment sales*

Ventec Systems Ltd, Units D1-D4 St. Catherines Business Complex, Broad Lane, Leeds, LS13 2TD Tel: 0113-239 4170 Fax: 0113-239 4190 E-mail: admin@ventec.co.uk *Install & maintain fire protection & detection systems*

Vented Services Telford Ltd, Unit A6 Hortonwood 10, Telford, Shropshire, TF1 7ES Tel: (01952) 677788 Fax: (01952) 677789 E-mail: addessee@vented-services.co.uk *Air conditioners*

Ventek Ltd, Unit 5, Starcrest Industrial Estate, Talbots Lane, Brierley Hill, West Midlands, DY5 2YT Tel: (01384) 79414 Fax: (01384) 79434 E-mail: sales@ventek.co.uk *Heating & ventilation engineers, ventilation or service. Also local exhaust ventilation (IEV) testing.*

Ventfix Fabrications Ltd, Unit 54-55 Youngs Industrial Estate, Aldermaston, Reading, RG7 4PW Tel: 0118 9816246 *Steel & welding fabricators*

Ventilate Ltd, Solent Industrial Estate, Shamblehurst Lane, Hedge End, Southampton, SO30 2FX Tel: (01489) 782262 Fax: (01489) 781822 E-mail: info@peelfabs.co.uk *Peel Fabrications(Southampton) Ltd are a top quality Ductwork Manufacturers who have been established for over 30 years, and are situated in Hedge end, Southampton, just off Junction 7 of the M27. We have our own Contracting Department who take all necessary site dimensions, produce detailed working drawings, and co-ordinate all site work. We are on the approved list of Ductwork Contractors for Hampshire County Council, Isle of Wight County Council, Southampton City Council, University of Southampton, Royal Berkshire and Battle Hospitals NHS Trust, and Southampton University Hospital NHS Trust. We can offer a complete First Class Personal Service to all our clients, whether the project is large or small. Although based in Southampton, we normally cover the area bordered by the M4, but we have also undertaken projects as far afield as South Wales, Cornwall, Kent, Cambridgeshire, the Midlands, and even as far as Scotland*

Ventilation Gear Co. Ltd, 9 Morjon Drive, Birmingham, B43 6JH Tel: 0121-358 7592 Fax: 0121-358 2364 *Electrical window gearing fitters*

Ventilation & Heating Sales, Unit 5 Whitequarries Industrial Estate, Winchburgh, Broxburn, West Lothian, EH52 6PZ Tel: (01506) 830033 Fax: (01506) 830022 *Ventilation distributor*

▶ Ventilation & Hygiene Specialists, Unit 2 Wilson Street, Thornaby, Stockton-on-Tees, Cleveland, TS17 7AR Tel: (01642) 675755 Fax: (01642) 675760

Ventilation Services Co., 6 Callender Place, Stoke-on-Trent, ST6 1JL Tel: (01782) 575140 Fax: (01782) 832796 *Ventilation systems*

Vention Hire Centre, 74 Cannock Road, Willenhall, West Midlands, WV12 5RZ Tel: (0800) 7310589 Fax: (01922) 402085 *Contractors plant hire*

Ventitherm Ltd, 121 Park Road, London, W4 3EX Tel: (020) 8994 5583 Fax: (020) 8994 8221 *Heating & air conditioning*

Ventrac Sheet Metal Ltd, 20 Nimmo Drive, Glasgow, G51 3SX Tel: 0141-440 2221 Fax: 0141-425 1550 E-mail: john@ventrac.co.uk *Sheet metalwork engineers*

▶ Ventrolla Thames Valley, Friar Park Stables, Badgemore, Henley-On-Thames, Oxfordshire, RG9 4NR Tel: (01491) 412141 Fax: (01491) 412341 E-mail: info@ventrollathamesvalley.com *Renovate sash windows*

Ventronic Imports Co., Unit 9 Derby Road Industrial Estate, Hounslow, TW3 3UH Tel: (020) 8572 1201 Fax: (020) 8572 1195 E-mail: sales@californiapro.com *Skate & skate supplies importers & wholesalers*

▶ Ventura (Jazz Band), Seafire Close, York, YO30 4UU Tel: (0776) 9504794 E-mail: yorkjazz@fmail.co.uk *Live jazz and blues for every occasion. From parties and functions to corporate events and weddings. Ventura have played at prominent jazz clubs across Yorkshire, and have years of solid experience. Line up includes: saxophone, flute, piano and bass as a trio line up, adding drums for a quartet and trumpet or guitar for a quintet. Our style is classic dinner jazz, swing and blues including tunes made famous by the likes of Sinatra, Nat Cole, Ella Fitzgerald and so on. Please contact us today for demo pack and prices.*

Venture Chemicals, Unit 2 Spring Lane Industrial Estate, Ashmore Lake, Willenhall, West Midlands, WV12 4HW Tel: (01902) 368585 Fax: (01902) 366356 *Industrial cleaning material manufrs*

Venture Dairy Services, Dobles Lane Industrial Estate, Holsworthy, Devon, EX22 6HN Tel: (01409) 254413 Fax: (01409) 254304 E-mail: sales@venturedairyservices.co.uk *Milking machines distributors*

▶ Venture Fire Consultancy, Windowplan House, Knight Road, Rochester, Kent, ME2 2AH Tel: (01634) 719025 Fax: (01634) 719025 E-mail: office@venturefire.co.uk *Fire safety & protection equipment suppliers & safety consultancy*

Venture Health Care Ltd, Aston Grange, Oaker, Matlock, Derbyshire, DE4 2JJ Tel: (01629) 733860 *Selling incontinent products to NHS*

Venture Lifting Services Ltd, 52 Grove Road, Newbury, Berkshire, RG14 1UL Tel: (01635) 40150 Fax: (01635) 40195 *Crane hire*

▶ Venture Logistics & Distribution, Venture House, Bilton Way, Lutterworth, Leicestershire, LE17 4JA Tel: (01455) 555400

Venture Oilfield Services Ltd, 11 Faraday Road, Southfields, Glenrothes, Fife, KY6 2RU Tel: (01592) 772176 Fax: (01592) 775455 E-mail: mail@ventureoil.com *Drilling equipment repairs*

Venture Packaging Inovations Ltd, Sketchley La Industrial Estate, 14 Waterfield Way, Burbage, Hinckley, Leicestershire, LE10 3ER Tel: (01455) 251457 Fax: (01455) 613645 E-mail: sales@vpi.org.uk *Printed folding cartons & specialist packaging services*

Venture Tape Europe, 5-6 Faraday Close, Drayton Fields Industrial Estate, Daventry, Northamptonshire, NN11 8RD Tel: (01327) 876555 Fax: (01327) 876444 E-mail: jaeanne@venturetape.co.uk *Industrial adhesive tapes*

Venture Wales, Venture House, Navigation Park, Abercynon, Mountain Ash, Mid Glamorgan, CF45 4SN Tel: (01443) 742888 Fax: (01443) 742444 E-mail: abercynon@venturewales.com *Enterprise agents*

Venturpak Ltd, 11-16 & 19-22 Willow Road, Pen-Y-Fan Industrial Estate, Crumlin, Newport, Gwent, NP11 4EG Tel: (01495) 241700 Fax: (01495) 241710 E-mail: office@venturpak.co.uk *Packaging & contract packaging manufrs*

▶ Venue Reservations, 13 Bishopsgate, London, EC2N 3BA Tel: (020) 7334 3922 Fax: (020) 7334 3911 E-mail: enquiries@venuereservations.co.uk *Venue searching for a private party or corporate event?"Let us do the finding for you. Our expert team has a comprehensive database of more that 150 venues around the UK. We are dedicated to working closely with you, finding the right place for your particular requirements.*We have three comprehensive ways to help you find the perfect venue: *Contact our Business Development Manager who will personally visit you to discuss your requirements. *Call our Venue Finding Team on 020 7334 3922. The team has a highly comprehensive knowledge of over a hundred venues in the UK and will gladly provide you with detailed information about our Venues. *Search our directory on the website. The directory lists a broad range of our venues.*

▶ Venue Select, Heythrop Park, Endstone, Chipping Norton, Oxfordshire, OX7 5UE Tel: (0870) 3502577 Fax: (08703) 502587 E-mail: info@venue-select.co.uk *Corporate event management including conference planning, team building activities, training & assessment, corporate hospitality & entertainment, incentive travel schemes & product launches.*

▶ Venus Computers & Communications Ltd, 66 Ridgeways, Harlow, Essex, CM17 9HG Tel: (01279) 422211

Venus Fashions, Unit 5, 5 Tavistock Road, London, W11 1AT Tel: (020) 8880 2929 *Fashion manufrs*

Venus Fashions, Roundthorn Rd, Oldham, OL4 1AX Tel: 0161-627 2057 Fax: 0161-626 0241 *Ladies & men's clothing manufacturer*

Venus Services, The Old Rectory, Church Street, Southwell, Nottinghamshire, NG25 0HG Tel: (01636) 814633 Fax: (01636) 815403 E-mail: audley@btopenworld.com *Plant hire & manufrs*

Veoilawater Solutions & Technologys, Marlow International, Parkway, Marlow, Buckinghamshire, SL7 1YL Tel: (01494) 887700 Fax: (01628) 897001 E-mail: sales.uk@veoliawater.com *Water treatment plant manufrs*

Veolia Enviromental Services, Brookside Depot, Buxton Road, Frettenham, Norwich, NR12 7NQ Tel: (01603) 890960 Fax: (01603) 890061 E-mail: broodland@veolia.co.uk *Refuse collection*

Veolia Enviromental Services plc, Norwood Industrial Estate, Ellisons Road, Killamarsh, Sheffield, S21 2DR Tel: 0114-247 9000 Fax: 0114-247 9018 E-mail: info@onyxgroup.co.uk *Total waste management*

Verbatim Ltd, Prestige House, 23-26 High St, Egham, Surrey, TW20 9DU Tel: (01784) 439781 Fax: (01784) 470760 E-mail: info@verbatim-europe.com *Manufacturers of computer accessories & consumables*

▶ Verbo Computers Ltd, 11 Station Road, Northfleet, Gravesend, Kent, DA11 9DY Tel: (01474) 353277 *IT & pc sales & services*

Verco Office Furniture Ltd, Chapel Lane, High Wycombe, Buckinghamshire, HP12 4BG Tel: (01494) 448000 Fax: (01494) 464216 E-mail: sales@verco.co.uk *Office furniture manufrs*

Verdandi Ltd, Verdandi House, Chapel Grove, Addlestone, Surrey, KT15 1UG Tel: (01932) 852888 Fax: (01932) 841954 E-mail: info@verdandi.co.uk *Project management consultants*

▶ Verdi Business Forms Ltd, Harold Court House, Church Road, Harold Wood, Romford, RM3 0JX Tel: (01708) 377311 Fax: (01708) 377327 E-mail: enquiries@verdi.co.uk *Suppliers of bespoke printed stationery*

Verdict Aerospace Components Ltd, 3 Chilten Hill, Chalfont St. Peter, Gerrards Cross, Buckinghamshire, SL9 9YZ Tel: (01753) 890922 Fax: (01753) 890933 E-mail: info@verdictaerospace.com *Precision engineers*

▶ Verdict Solutions, 109A Oyston Mill, Strand Road, Preston, PR1 8UR Tel: (01772) 722007 E-mail: info@verdictsolutions.co.uk *Services Include: Webdesign, E-commerce, Search Engine Optimisation & Hosting**Also offline services including marketing, graphic design, corporate identity and leaflet design and print.**Call us for a quote: 01772 722007*

Verdigris Ltd, Unit A 44 Askew CR, London, W12 9DP Tel: (020) 8749 7881 Fax: (020) 8740 6310 *Copper labels*

Vere Engineering Ltd, 17 Jameson Road, Birmingham, B6 7SJ Tel: 0121-327 3630 Fax: 0121-327 3050 *Presswork/toolmakers*

Verichrome Plating Services Ltd, Larkhall Industrial Estate, Larkhall, Lanarkshire, ML9 2PG Tel: (01698) 886060 Fax: (01698) 886060 E-mail: may@verichrome.com *Electroplating services*

Vericroe Ltd, Kinnoull Road, Dunsinane Industrial Estate, Dundee, DD2 3XR Tel: (01382) 813838 Fax: (01382) 832721

Verifeye (UK) Ltd, 1 Branksome Business Centre, Cortry Close, Poole, Dorset, BH12 4BQ Tel: (023) 8028 4727 Fax: (01202) 733366 E-mail: sales@verifeye.co.uk *Digital surveillance installers & manufrs*

▶ Verify, c/o Knox & Eames, Greys Green, Rotherfield Greys, Henley-on-Thames, Oxfordshire, RG9 4QG Tel: 0118-957 4046 Fax: 0118-958 4100 E-mail: office@verify24plus.com *Verify offer a full range of global investigation and security support services, for both corporate and private clients.**

Verifyne Plastic Products Ltd, Lever Mill, Slater Street, Blackburn, BB2 4PA Tel: (01254) 675639 Fax: (01254) 673787 E-mail: enquiries@verifyne-plastics.co.uk *Plastics injection moulders*

Verine Ltd, 52 Broton Drive Trad Estate, Halstead, Essex, CO9 1HB Tel: (01787) 472551 Fax: (01787) 476589 E-mail: sales@verine.co.uk *Gas, electric fires & appliance manufrs*

Veriplast, Pikelaw Place, West Pimbo, Skelmersdale, Lancashire, WN8 9PX Tel: (01695) 721221 Fax: (01695) 726324 *Polystyrene cup manufrs*

▶ VeriSIM Ltd, Forsyth House, Rosyth Europarc, Rosyth, Dunfermline, Fife, KY11 2UU Tel: (01383) 428059 Fax: (01383) 428060 *IT software development*

Veritas DGC Ltd, Crompton Way, Crawley, West Sussex, RH10 9QN Tel: (01293) 443000 Fax: (01293) 443010 E-mail: info@veritasdgc.com *Seismic survey services*

Verity Time Co. Ltd, PO Box 188, Tring, Hertfordshire, HP23 6YU Tel: (01442) 828585 Fax: (01442) 826945 E-mail: info@veritytime.co.uk *Watch importers*

Verivide, Quartz Close, Enderby, Leicester, LE19 4SG Tel: 0116-284 7790 Fax: 0116-284 7799 E-mail: enquiries@verivide.com *Visual & colour assessment equipment manufrs*

Verleywood Ltd, Unit 1 Plot 5 Warrenwood Industrial Estate, Stapleford, Hertford, SG14 3NU Tel: (01992) 501218 *Joinery manufrs*

▶ Vermex Ltd, 16 Low Poppleton Lane, York, YO26 6AZ Tel: (01904) 798676 Fax: (01904) 782365 E-mail: enquiries@vermexpestcontrol.co.uk *Pest controllers*

Vermicon Pest Control, 3 Middleburn Cottages, Kirkness, Cardenden, Lochgelly, Fife, KY5 0HH Tel: (01592) 868900 Fax: (01592) 868900 *Pest control*

Vermikil Pest Control Services Ltd, PO Box 3049, Romford, RM3 7BQ Tel: (0800) 0568834 Fax: (0800) 0568835 E-mail: contacts@vermikil.com *Prevention and control of rodents, non-rodent mammals, flying & crawling insects and birds including the use of BIRDS of PREY as a natural deterrent.*

▶ Verminator Pest Control, Crossford, Dunfermline, Fife, KY12 8NU Tel: (07774) 034856 E-mail: andymks@fsmail.net *vermin and pest controler based in fife.All pests controled from the woodland to the barn.*

▶ Vernet Solutions Ltd, Wick Avenue, Wheathampstead, St. Albans, Hertfordshire, AL4 8PZ Tel: (0845) 4656655 *Telecommunications, consultancy*

Vernham Labels Ltd, 6 Mayfield Avenue Industrial Park, Fyfield Road, Weyhill, Andover, Hampshire, SP11 8HU Tel: (01264) 773501 Fax: (01264) 773065 E-mail: malcolm@vernhamlabels.co.uk *Vernham labels Ltd is a specialist label company supplying both national and local companies with long and short run work from plain up to six colours on a variety of substrates, with adhesives and inks to suit the customers needs. With an understanding that the packaging often sells the product, we are totally committed to supplying quality and a personal service while ensuring that orders are delivered on time.*

Vernier Springs and Pressings Ltd, Edward Street, Redditch, Worcestershire, B97 6HA Tel: (01527) 582950 E-mail: roger@verniersprings.com *Manufacturers of springs & pressings*

Vernon Computer Forms, 5 Spring Mill Business Centre, Avening Road, Nailsworth, Stroud, Gloucestershire, GL6 0BS Tel: (01453) 834466 Fax: (01453) 834554 E-mail: sales@vernoncf.co.uk *Print management service*

Vernon Developments, Unit B, Mucklow Hill Trading Estate, Phase 2, Halesowen, West Midlands, B62 8DQ Tel: 0121-501 1171 Fax: 0121-550 6181 *Commercial vehicle components*

Vernon Swimming Pools, Thistley Hall, Widdington, Saffron Walden, Essex, CB11 3ST Tel: (01799) 541470 Fax: (01799) 541701 *Swimming pools suppliers*

Vernon's Fuse Co, 22 Trinity Trading Estate, Tribune Drive, Sittingbourne, Kent, ME10 2PG Tel: (01795) 471234 Fax: (01795) 476996 *Electrical component packaging service*

Vero Software, The Mill, Brimscombe Port, Brimscombe, Stroud, Gloucestershire, GL5 2QG Tel: (01453) 732900 Fax: (01453) 887444 *Computer software suppliers*

▶ Vero Technologies Ltd, Unit 25 Solent Industrial Estate, Shamblehurst Lane, Hedge End, Southampton, SO30 2FY Tel: (01489).776930 Fax: (01489) 776938 E-mail: sales@verotl.com *Manufacturers of proto typing products for electronics*

▶ Verona Kitchens Ltd, 24 Grasgarth Close, London, W3 9HS Tel: (020) 8993 1540 Fax: (020) 8993 1540 E-mail: sales@veronakitchens.co.uk *Our Complete, all-inclusive service takes care off all the planning and design. Eliminates the hassle of having to find reliable builders, joiners,*

continued

*electricians and plumbers. The result a quality kitchen designed around your needs**

Verona Originals Ltd, 89-91 New Road, Whitechapel, London, E1 1HH Tel: (020) 7375 1666 Fax: (020) 7274 3025 E-mail: ray@raifashions.com *Children's wear exporters & manufrs* Also at: Derby & Leicester

Veronica Preserved Plants, 131 Ballysnod Road, Larne, County Antrim, BT40 3NP Tel: (028) 2827 4016 Fax: (028) 2827 4016 *Floral & plant displays*

▶ Verrall & Parks, 225-227 Seaside, Eastbourne, East Sussex, BN22 7NR Tel: (01323) 737633 Fax: (01323) 745789 E-mail: sales@verrallandparks.co.uk *Plumbing & heating engineers*

Penfold Verrall Ltd, The Chalk Pit, Mile Oak Road, Portslade, Brighton, BN41 2RB Tel: (01273) 412224 Fax: (01273) 412563 E-mail: info@penfoldverrall.com *Plant hire & haulage contractors & site clearance services*

Versaduct Sheet Metal Ltd, Edwin Avenue, Hoo Farm Industrial Estate, Kidderminster, Worcestershire, DY11 7RA Tel: (01562) 824913 Fax: (01562) 823809 *Sheet metalwork & air conditioning manufrs*

Versapak International, The Versapak Centre, Centurion Way, Erith, Kent, DA18 4AF Tel: (020) 8333 5353 Fax: (020) 8312 2051 E-mail: catsales@versapak.co.uk *Envelope printing*

▶ Versatile Ltd, Units 1-11, Prince of Wales Industrial Estate, Abercarn, Newport, Gwent, NP11 5AR Tel: (01495) 247233

Versatile Controls Ltd, Unit R1 Innsworth Technology Park, Innsworth Lane, Gloucester, GL3 1DL Tel: (01452) 731447 Fax: (01452) 731621 E-mail: sales@versatilecontrols.co.uk *Hydraulic, pneumatic & stainless steel valves*

Versatile Fittings Ltd, Bicester Road, Aylesbury, Buckinghamshire, HP19 8AU Tel: (01296) 483481 Fax: (01296) 437596 E-mail: info@versatile-fittings.co.uk *Manufacturers of shop fittings*

Versatile Kent Ltd, 94 Dover Road, Folkestone, Kent, CT20 1LA Tel: (01303) 850219 Fax: (01303) 220929 E-mail: info@versatile-kent.co.uk *Suspended ceiling & partitioning contracting services*

Versatile Precision Tools Ltd, Victoria Road, Ulverston, Cumbria, LA12 0BZ Tel: (01229) 582366 Fax: (01229) 580871 E-mail: mail@vptools.co.uk *Precision engineers & toolmakers services*

Versatility Embroiderers, Lullington Hall, Coton Road, Lullington, Swadlincote, Derbyshire, DE12 8EJ Tel: (01827) 373403 Fax: (01827) 373403 E-mail: sales@versatility.freeserve.co.uk *Embroidery & printing services*

▶ Verseveld P.L.C., Coningesby House, 24 St. Andrews Street, Droitwich, Worcestershire, WR9 8DY Tel: (01905) 797999 Fax: (01905) 798958 E-mail: marc@verseveldplc.com *Manufacture of quality raw & cooked meat & poultry*

Version One Ltd, London House, London Road South, Poynton, Stockport, Cheshire, SK12 1YP Tel: (01625) 856500 Fax: (01625) 856501 E-mail: info@versionone.co.uk *Software house services*

Versital Ltd, Victoria Mill, Bradford Road, Bolton, BL3 2HF Tel: (01204) 380780 Fax: (01204) 392831 E-mail: np@langnp.demon.co.uk *Marble manufrs*

▶ Versotech Ltd, 81D Main Street, Calderbank, Airdrie, Lanarkshire, ML6 9SG Tel: (01236) 753875 Fax: (01236) 754497 E-mail: info@versotech.co.uk *Specialist electrical & civil engineers*

▶ Versyns Ventures Ltd, Versyns House, Vale Road, Mayfield, East Sussex, TN20 6BD Tel: (01435) 874800 Fax: (01435) 873631 E-mail: chrislilly@versynsventures.com *Finance & venturing boutique, 'Rainmakers' in the high-tech & telecoms sector*

Vertec Engineering, 4 Pitmedden Road, Dyce, Aberdeen, AB21 0DP Tel: (01224) 772969 Fax: (01224) 772528 E-mail: info@vertec-eng.co.uk *Designers & manufacturers of fire protected containers*

Vertec Printing Services Ltd, 1 Swan Road, Westminster Industrial Estate, London, SE18 5TT Tel: (020) 8319 5252 Fax: (020) 8319 5275 E-mail: info@vertec-print.co.uk *Lithographic printers*

Vertex Financial Services Holdings Ltd, Allen Jones House, Jessop Avenue, Cheltenham, Gloucestershire, GL50 3SH Tel: (01242) 547000 Fax: (01242) 547016 *Outsourcing & software for the financial services industry*

▶ Vertex Law LLP, 39 Kings Hill Avenue, Kings Hill, West Malling, Kent, ME19 4SD Tel: (0870) 0844040 Fax: (0870) 0844041 E-mail: contact@vertexlaw.co.uk *Corporate & commercial lawyers*

Vertex Moulding Ltd, 4 Shornecliffe Industrial Estate, North Close, Folkestone, Kent, CT20 3UH Tel: (01303) 253198 Fax: (01303) 253198 E-mail: vml01@vml01.fsnet.co.uk *Plastic injection moulding manufrs*

Vertex Precision Engineering Ltd, 7 Armoury Road, Lufton Trading Estate, Yeovil, Somerset, BA22 8RL Tel: (01935) 477310 Fax: (01935) 706212 E-mail: vertex@vertexeng.demon.co.uk *Specialist sheet metalworkers*

Vertex Systems Ltd, 47 Holmlea Road, Goring, Reading, RG8 9EX Tel: (01491) 872812 *Software developers*

Vertical Access Ltd, Tame Bank,, Unit E211 Warmco Industry Park, East Gate,, Manchester Road,, Mossley, Ashton-under-Lyne, Lancashire, OL5 9AY Tel: (01457) 838722 Fax: (01457) 833881 E-mail: info@verticalaccess.co.uk *Industrial rope access specialists whose services include latchway installations, inspections and testing, , coring, ground anchors and soil nails, geotechnical contracts, devegetaion, confined spaces and banner installations. Link up approved and constructionline member. We also offer IRATA and Safe Working at Height training courses to all levels **

Vertical Cabinet Co. Ltd, Hithercroft Road, Wallingford, Oxfordshire, OX10 9DG Tel: (01491) 839966 Fax: (01491) 835656 E-mail: sales@ver.co.uk *Refrigeration equipment manufrs*

▶ Vertical Solutions, Juniper Gardens, Shenley, Radlett, Hertfordshire, WD7 9LA Tel: (01923) 839393 Fax: (01923) 839394 E-mail: admin@vsolutions.uk.com *Computer consultants*

Vertical Systems, 14 Hemmells, Basildon, Essex, SS15 6ED Tel: (01268) 416155 Fax: (01268) 541287 E-mail: peter.healey@tarsc.net *Computer suppliers*

Vertical Tec, Unit 14 Ash Industrial Estate, Flex Meadow, Harlow, Essex, CM19 5TJ Tel: (020) 7383 3388 Fax: (01279) 413388 E-mail: sales@verticaltec.co.uk *Blind manufrs*

Vertical Technology Ind Rope Access Specialists, Unit 15 Wren Centre, Westbourne Road, Emsworth, Hampshire, PO10 7SU Tel: (01243) 377599 Fax: (01243) 377227 E-mail: admin@vertical-technology.com *Industrial roped access*

Vertical Transportation Ltd, Grovebury Road, Leighton Buzzard, Bedfordshire, LU7 4RU Tel: (01525) 850027 Fax: (01525) 851357 *Plant hire & tower crane manufrs*

Vertik-al Ltd, Yardley Brook Industrial Park, Lea Ford Road, Shard End, Birmingham, B33 9TX Tel: 0121-608 7171 Fax: 0121-693 7787 E-mail: vertikalltd@aol.com *Powder coating services*

Verus Instruments Ltd, Clare House, Pinewood Road, High Wycombe, Buckinghamshire, HP12 4DA Tel: (01494) 558206 Fax: (01494) 558383 E-mail: sales@verus.co.uk *Moisture meter & calibrating equipment manufrs*

▶ vervel, 20 Laurier Road, London, NW5 1SG Tel: (0795) 8461843 Fax: (0870) 4434036 E-mail: info@vervel.com *Supply chain management consultancy specialising in purchasing and supplier management*

Verwin Plumbing & Heating Ltd, Maisonette, 223b London Road, Reading, RG1 3NY Tel: 0118-966 6049 Fax: 0118-935 2686 *Heating engineers*

Verwood Precision Services, 3 Holloways Ebblake Industrial Estate, Bessemer Close, Ebblake Industrial Estate, Verwood, Dorset, BH31 6AZ Tel: (01202) 829310 Fax: (01202) 814994 E-mail: verwoodprecision@talktalk.net *Precision engineering specialists*

▶ Very PC Ltd, 399 Langsett Road, Sheffield, S6 2LJ Tel: 0114-234 3656 Fax: 0114-234 3656 E-mail: sales@very-pc.co.uk *Computer equipment & computer related services*

Veryan Ltd, Wellhouse Road, Beech, Alton, Hampshire, GU34 4AH Tel: (01420) 543131 Fax: (01420) 543232 E-mail: solutions@veryan.com *Computer training services database & website for education*

Veryards Ltd, 18a High St, Llandaff, Cardiff, CF5 2DZ Tel: (029) 2055 2444 Fax: (029) 2055 4447 E-mail: admin@veryards.com *Consulting engineers* Also at: Rossett & Stockport

▶ Ves Andover Ltd, Unit D, Deacon Trading Estate, Eastleigh, Hampshire, SO50 6RS Tel: (023) 8064 4806

Vesco Services Ltd, 6B Middlefield Road, Falkirk, FK2 9AG Tel: (01324) 611166 Fax: (01324) 621166 E-mail: sales@vescovalves.co.uk *Valve repair & refurbishment services*

▶ Vestas-Celtic Wind Technology Ltd, PO Box 9263, Campbeltown, Argyll, PA28 6WA Tel: (01586) 555000 Fax: (01586) 555111 *Wind turbine tower manufrs*

Vestatec Automotive Engineering, Unit 3-4 Chase Park, Daleside Road, Nottingham, NG2 4GT Tel: 0115-911 6767 Fax: 0115-912 6767 E-mail: admin@vestatec.co.uk *Automotive engineering*

▶ Vestguard UK Ltd, Sevenacres, Barnhall Road, Tolleshunt Knights, Maldon, Essex, CM9 8HD Tel: (0845) 6016660 Fax: (01621) 814316 E-mail: info@vestguard.com *Sale of specialised protective equipment*

Vesuvius Flogates, British Steel Complex, Lackenby Works, Middlesbrough, Cleveland, TS6 7RW Tel: 01642 440054 Fax: 01642 465966 *Refractory materials installers*

Vesuvius UK Ltd, Unit 10 Wednesbury Trading Estate, Wednesbury, West Midlands, WS10 7JN Tel: 0121-502 6000 Fax: 0121-556 7401 *Refractory materials distributors* Also at: Manchester & Sheffield

▶ Vetas UK Ltd, Unit 16 Robinsons Industrial Estate, Shaftesbury Street, Derby, DE23 8NL Tel: (01332) 365300 Fax: (01332) 602455 E-mail: vetas100@hotmail.com *Fashion jewellery & accessories wholesalers*

Vetco Gray Controls Ltd, Harness Road, Altens Industrial Estate, Aberdeen, AB12 3LE Tel: (01224) 872211 Fax: (01224) 894840 *Oil & gas supplies*

Vetco Grey, 2 High Street, Nailsea, Bristol, BS48 1BS Tel: (01275) 810100 Fax: (01275) 851467 E-mail: paul.roberts@vetco.com *Subsea control systems manufrs*

Veterinary Immunogenics, Carleton Hill, Carleton, Penrith, Cumbria, CA11 8TZ Tel: (01768) 863881 Fax: (01768) 891389 *Equine biological production*

Veterinary Instrumentation, Broadfield Road, Sheffield, S8 0XL Tel: (0845) 1309596 Fax: (0845) 1308687 E-mail: info@vetinst.co.uk *Veterinary instrumentation suppliers*

Vetoquinol Ltd, Buckingham Industrial Park, Great Slade, Buckingham, MK18 1UA Tel: (01280) 814500 Fax: (01280) 825462 E-mail: sales@vetoquinol.co.uk *Vet pharmaceuticals*

Vetraform Ltd, Unit 19-20, Halesfield 18, Telford, Shropshire, TF7 4PP Tel: (01952) 587631 Fax: (01952) 582596 E-mail: alex@vetraform.co.uk *Precision engineers to industry*

Vetrotex UK Ltd, Units 1-2 Thames Park, Lester Way, Wallingford, Oxfordshire, OX10 9TA Tel: (01491) 833280 Fax: (01491) 833280 *Glass fibre & glass fibre fabric distributors*

▶ Vetter UK Ltd, Barford Road, Little Barford, St. Neots, Cambridgeshire, PE19 6WB Tel: (01480) 402900 Fax: (01480) 402572 E-mail: vetteruk@laingorourke.com *Internal external stone masonry & cladding contractors*

VF Northern Europe Ltd, Park Road East, Calverton, Nottingham, NG14 6GD Tel: 0115-965 6565 Fax: 0115-965 7742 *Clothing distributors*

▶ VHGC, Unit 2 Aston Street, Shifnal, Shropshire, TF11 8DT Tel: (01952) 461107 Fax: (01952) 463030

▶ VHO, Suite 24 Basepoint Business Centre, Rivermead Drive, Swindon, SN5 7EX Tel: 01793 608701 Fax: 01793 608704 E-mail: vivienne@vhorg.co.uk *Telemarketing, lead and appointment generation. Campaign planning, data cleansing and qualification.*Experienced in most sectors but specialise in IT.**

▶ VI Sigma, 60 White Lion Street, London, N1 9PH Tel: (020) 7837 7830 Fax: (020) 7837 7840 *Clothing manufrs*

Vi Spring Ltd, Ernesettle Lane, Plymouth, PL5 2TT Tel: (01752) 366311 Fax: (01752) 355109 E-mail: info@vispring.co.uk *Mattress manufrs*

Via Lighting, 95 St. Peters Street, Syston, Leicester, LE7 1HL Tel: 0116-260 0866 Fax: 0116-260 0944 E-mail: website@vialaghting.co.uk *Lampshade frames & wirework manufrs*

Viacom Networks Italia Ltd, 2nd Floor UK House, London, W1D 1DS Tel: (020) 7478 5240 Fax: (020) 7478 5250 E-mail: info@viacom.com *Holding company*

▶ Viamaster International Ltd, Valley Farm Way, Leeds, LS10 1SE Tel: 0113-270 0033 Fax: 0113 270 0065 E-mail: mail@viamaster-intl.com *Full load and express groupage operator, specialising in transport to & from Italy and Spain.*

▶ Viamaster International Ltd, Valley Farm Way, Leeds, LS10 1SE Tel: 0113-270 0033 Fax: 0113 2707723 E-mail: hroberts@viamaster.co.uk *Warehousing, general and temperature sensitive, container handling for import and export loads, insurance assessment facility, hazardous, out-of-gauge, steel, 24hr security*

Vianen Ventilation Systems, Coten House, 59-63 Coten End, Warwick, CV34 4NU Tel: (01926) 496644 Fax: (01926) 493977 E-mail: info@vianen.co.uk *Kitchen canopies, ultraviolet canopies, ventilated ceilings, stainless steel grease filters, recessed light fittings, service distribution units, waterwash canopies, stainless steel splashbacks*

▶ VIAPACK-UK, 29 Halliday Drive, Leeds, LS12 3PA Tel: (07774) 219192 Fax: 0113-263 1646 E-mail: paveluk@orange.net *Sale/Service/Parts,for manual and automatic bagging machines,From, VIAPACK, PAVEL, SKYROBE, COVERTEX, PERFROLE, and Convoyor systems the specialist at your service.*

▶ Viatech Ltd, Unit 16A, Klondyke Industrial Estate, Rushenden Road, Queenborough, Kent, ME11 5HN Tel: (01795) 666601 *Steel fabrication*

Viaton Industries Ltd, Brassington, Wirksworth, Matlock, Derbyshire, DE4 4ES Tel: (01629) 540373 Fax: (01629) 540289 E-mail: sales@viaton.co.uk *Barites aggregate producers & iron oxide pigments*

▶ Viatris, Building 2000, Cambridge Research Park, Beach Road, Waterbeach, Cambridge, CB5 9PD Tel: (01223) 205999

Vibracoustics Ltd, Unit 1 Brook House, Cross Street, Syston, Leicester, LE7 2JG Tel: 0116-260 5700 Fax: 0116-260 5707 E-mail: mail@vibracoustics.com *Rubber, metal air, sprint coil designers, manufacturers & suppliers*

Vibrair Materials Handling Equipment, Virginia Mills, 187 Higher Hillgate, Stockport, Cheshire, SK1 3JG Tel: 0161-480 8991 Fax: 0161-474 7737 *Powder handling equipment manufrs /dust extraction & dust collection*

Vibro Automation Ltd, Acton Av, Long Eaton, Nottingham, NG10 1GA Tel: 0115-946 8361 Fax: 0115-946 8362 *Vibratory bowl feeder equipment manufrs*

Vibronoise Ltd, 62 Talbot Rd, Old Trafford, Manchester, M16 0PN Tel: 0161-428 3100 Fax: 0161-428 1198 E-mail: info@virbronoise.co.uk *Noise/vibration control consultants*

Vic Haines, Racecourse Road, Pershore, Worcestershire, WR10 2EY Tel: (01386) 553288 Fax: (01386) 554615 *Road transport services*

Vic Smith Ltd, 4-5 Dennis Parade, Winchmore Hill Road, London, N14 6AA Tel: (020) 8882 8292 Fax: (020) 8882 8800 E-mail: sales@vicsmithbeds.co.uk *Bed & pine furniture retailers*

▶ Vicaas Ltd, Milkwood Road, London, SE24 0JF Tel: (020) 7274 1145

Vicary Plant Spares, Station Road, North Kilworth, Lutterworth, Leicestershire, LE17 6HY Tel: (01858) 880219 Fax: (01858) 881034 *Industrial machine repairs*

Viceroy Trading Co. Ltd, 67 St. Johns Road, Hemel Hempstead, Hertfordshire, HP1 1QG Tel: (01442) 239770 Fax: (01442) 239124 E-mail: vtcltd@tesco.net *Safety equipment & disposable protective clothing distributor & manufrs*

Vicforge Air Systems Ltd, Lufton 2000, Yeovil, Somerset, BA22 8HS Tel: 01935 428387 *Air conditioning, heating, ventilation*

Vickers Electronics Ltd, Alliance House, Westpoint Enterprise Park, Trafford Park, Manchester, M17 1QS Tel: (0870) 7420808 Fax: (0870) 7480808 E-mail: info@vickers-electronics.co.uk *Energy management contractors*

Vickers Co Formations, 1 High St Mews, London, SW19 7RG Tel: (020) 8944 2067 Fax: (020) 8241 9879 E-mail: enquiries@vickersinformation.co.uk *Company formations, seals, searches, registers & registration agents*

J.J. Vickers & Sons Ltd, Unit 9, 35 Revenge Road, Lordswood, Chatham, Kent, ME5 8DW Tel: (01634) 201284 Fax: (01634) 201286 E-mail: sales@jjvickers.co.uk *Sports optics distributors*

▶ indicates data change since last edition

Vickers Laboratories Ltd, Grangefield Industrial Estate, Richardshaw Road, Pudsey, West Yorkshire, LS28 6QW Tel: 0113-236 2811 Fax: 0113-236 2703 E-mail: info@vicklabs.co.uk *Chemical manufrs*

▶ Vickers Self Drive Ltd, 16B Vickers Industrial Estate, Mellishaw Lane, Morecambe, Lancashire, LA3 3EN Tel: (01524) 845550 Fax: (01524) 845515 E-mail: enquiries@vickersselfdrive.com *Vickers Self Drive offer a fleet of fully serviced and well maintained small commercial vehicles. Hire a transit van for just £50 per day - with unlimited mileage, insurance and breakdown cover! Short term and long term contract rates are also great value for money.*

Vickers & Son (Plumbers' Merchants) Ltd, Greenfield Place, Vale Road, Rhyl, Clwyd, LL18 2BP Tel: (01745) 345300 Fax: (01745) 344288 E-mail: sales@vickers-rhyl.co.uk *Plumbers merchants*

Vico Engineering Services, Compstall Mills Estate, Andrew Street, Compstall, Stockport, Cheshire, SK6 5HN Tel: 0161-427 3644 Fax: 0161-426 0215 E-mail: info@vico-engineering.co.uk *Brick production plant & equipment merchants*

Vicomte Bernard De Romanet Ltd, 212 Fordham Road, Newmarket, Suffolk, CB8 7LG Tel: (01638) 721145 Fax: (01638) 720330 *Wine & spirit importers*

Vicon Industries Ltd, 17 Brunel Way, Fareham, Hampshire, PO15 5TX Tel: (01489) 566300 Fax: (01489) 566322 E-mail: sales@vicon.co.uk *CCTV security maintenance manufrs*

▶ Vicon Industries Ltd, Whitworth Court, Manor Park, Runcorn, Cheshire, WA7 1TA Tel: (01928) 530420 Fax: (01928) 530421 *CCTV manufrs*

Vicsteels Ltd, Suite 20 London House, 266 Fulham Road, London, SW10 9EL Tel: (020) 7795 2345 Fax: (020) 7795 0460 E-mail: vicsteels@aol.com *Nickel merchants*

Victor Buyck Ltd, 20 Kingswood Creek, Wraysbury, Staines, Middlesex, TW19 5EN Tel: (01784) 483006 Fax: (01784) 483008 E-mail: sales@buyck.be *Steel fabricators*

Victor Engineering Co., 6d Arndale Road, Wick, Littlehampton, West Sussex, BN17 7HD Tel: 01903 716650 *Press tool manufacturers & general presswork*

Victor Europe Ltd, Victor House, Eagle Technology Park, Queensway, Rochdale, Lancashire, OL11 1TQ Tel: (01706) 648485 Fax: (01706) 648483 E-mail: sales@victoreurope.com *Plastic injection molding machines & cnc machine tools supplier*

▶ Victor Green & Company Ltd, 16-16a Baldwins Gardens, London, EC1N 7RJ Tel: (020) 7269 9200 Fax: 020 7269-9210 E-mail: victor@victorgreen.co.uk *Retrieval and assessment of patent and technical literature for infringement, validity, novelty and state-of-the-art subject matter searches; Name searches; Registered design searches; Patent status enquiries and file histories.*

▶ Victor Printing Co. Ltd, 3a Bridge Road, Felixstowe, Suffolk, IP11 7SL Tel: (01394) 274402 Fax: (01394) 276087

Victor Stationery Ltd, 4 Marshalls Road, Belfast, BT5 6QU Tel: (028) 9040 1555 Fax: 028 90704872 E-mail: sales@victorstationery.com *Stationery manufrs*

Victor Tandberg & Co. Ltd, Bridge House, Restmor Way, Wallington, Surrey, SM6 7AH Tel: (020) 8773 1431 Fax: (020) 8715 1119 E-mail: sales@victortandberg.co.uk *Board & paper agents*

Victoria P.L.C., Worcester Road, Kidderminster, Worcestershire, DY10 1HL Tel: (01562) 749300 Fax: (01562) 749649 *Carpet manufrs*

Victoria Aquatics, 45 Victoria Road, Carlisle, CA1 2UE Tel: (01228) 535602 Fax: (01228) 535602 *Tropical fish marine coldwater plant ponds pumps manufrs*

▶ Victoria Bakery, 83 High Street, Barnet, Hertfordshire, EN5 5UR Tel: (020) 8449 0790 Fax: (020) 8440 1206 *Bakery*

▶ Victoria Cartridge Creations, 67 Lower Parliament Street, Nottingham, NG1 3BB Tel: 0115-911 5100 Fax: 0115-911 5100 E-mail: sales@victoriagartlidge.co.uk *Giftware suppliers*

Victoria Communications, Victoria Buildings, Bank Avenue, Morley, Leeds, LS27 9JF Tel: 0113-252 2233 Fax: 0113-252 1846 E-mail: gregg@viccom.co.uk *Copying & duplicating suppliers*

▶ Victoria Electrical & Building Services Ltd, 82-84 Victoria Road, Glasgow, G42 7AA Tel: 0141-423 6122 Fax: 0141-422 1133

Victoria Fabrications Ltd, Station Road, Whittington Moor, Chesterfield, Derbyshire, S41 9ES Tel: (01246) 450605 Fax: (01246) 455987 *Steel fabricators & structural engineers*

Victoria Fan & Engineering Supplies Ltd, Audley Street Works, Audley Street, Mossley, Ashton-under-Lyne, Lancashire, OL5 9HW Tel: (01457) 835391 Fax: (01457) 833378 E-mail: sales@victoriafans.co.uk *Fan manufacturers*

Victoria Foods (Bristol) Ltd, 39 Marsh Common Road, Pilning, Bristol, BS35 4JY Tel: (01454) 618618 Fax: (01454) 202713 E-mail: victoria.foods@virgin.net *Wholesale food distribution services*

Victoria Health Foods, Unit 23 Broadwalk Shopping Centre, Station Road, Edgware, Middlesex, HA8 7BD Tel: (020) 8905 6931 Fax: (020) 8905 6931 *Health foods & supplier*

▶ Victoria House, 71-73 Victoria Road, Polegate, East Sussex, BN26 6BX Tel: (01323) 487178 Fax: (01323) 487178 E-mail: tdrnathan@hotmail.com *Residential care home*

▶ Victoria Jones Ltd, Wandsworth Bridge Road, London, SW6 2UH Tel: (020) 7610 6969 Fax: (020) 7610 9191 E-mail: info@vjones.com *Furniture, paintings & sculptures suppliers*

Victoria Linen Co., 2 Hargreaves St Mill, Hargreaves Street, Haslingden, Rossendale, Lancashire, BB4 5RQ Tel: (01706) 220020 Fax: (01706) 220020 E-mail: brochure@victorialinen.co.uk *Custom made bed linen*

Victoria Medical & General Cleaning Services Ltd, Victoria House, Skeltons Lane, London, E10 5BZ Tel: (020) 8556 0141 Fax: (020) 8558 9437 *Office, clinic & hospital cleaners service*

Victoria Mouldings, 8 Emley Moor Business Park, Leys Lane, Emley, Huddersfield, HD8 9QY Tel: (01924) 840611 Fax: (01924) 840611 *Fibreglass mouldings manufrs*

Victoria Precision (Birmingham) Co., Manchester Street, Aston, Birmingham, B6 4HL Tel: 0121-359 3821 Fax: 0121-359 6704 *Press tool manufrs*

Victoria Production Engineering Ltd, Oldham Street, Denton, Manchester, M34 3SA Tel: 0161-320 1800 Fax: 0161-320 1810 E-mail: sales@victoriaproduction.co.uk *General engineering services*

Victoria Sawmill & Country Store, The Old Sawmills, Hawkerland Road, Colaton Raleigh, Sidmouth, Devon, EX10 0HP Tel: (01395) 568060 Fax: (01395) 567902 E-mail: admin@victoria-sawmills.co.uk *Timber stockists*

▶ Victoria Transport, Commercial St, Macduff, Banffshire, AB44 1SB Tel: (01261) 833157

Victorian Brass Bedstead Co., Hoe Copse, Cocking, Midhurst, West Sussex, GU29 0HL Tel: (01730) 812287 E-mail: toria@netcomuk.co.uk *Bed restoration*

Victorian Model Workshop, The Ferrers Centre, Melbourne Road, Staunton Harold, Ashby-de-la-Zouch, Leicestershire, LE65 1RU Tel: (01332) 864436 E-mail: info@modelworkshop.co.uk *Mechanical model manufrs*

Victorian Saddles, 117 Halifax Road, Rochdale, Lancashire, OL12 9BA Tel: (01706) 644490 Fax: (01706) 644490 E-mail: sales@victoriansaddles.co.uk *Leather saddle retail & riding kit*

Victorian Wood Works Contracts Ltd, 54 River Road, Creekmouth, Barking, Essex, IG11 0DW Tel: (020) 8507 5996 Fax: (020) 8507 1149 E-mail: sales@victorianwoodworks.co.uk *Wood flooring manufrs*

Victoriana, Station Road, Petersfield, Hampshire, GU31 4AH Tel: (01730) 264009 Fax: (01730) 264009 *Furniture retail & distributors*

Victory Boatbuilders, Lower Boat House North Pondside, The Historic Dockyard, Chatham, Kent, ME4 4TY Tel: (01634) 813057 Fax: (01634) 813057 E-mail: sales@havengore.com *Boat restoration & promotion*

Victory Imaging, Forest Buildings, 41 Creswell Road, Clowne, Chesterfield, Derbyshire, S43 4PN Tel: (01246) 570771 Fax: (01246) 570772 E-mail: sales@victory-imaging.co.uk *Digital imaging specialists*

▶ Victory Lighting, Quay West, Salamander Quay, Harefield, Uxbridge, Middlesex, UB9 6NZ Tel: (01895) 821821 Fax: (01895) 821822 *Electric light bulbs & lamps*

Victory Workwear Ltd, 5 Holder Road, Aldershot, Hampshire, GU12 4RH Tel: (01252) 352800 Fax: (01252) 352805 *Work wear & janitorial equipment distributors* Also at: Harrow & Isle Of Wight

Videcom Travel Systems Ltd, Newtown Road, Henley-on-Thames, Oxfordshire, RG9 1HG Tel: (01491) 578951 Fax: (01491) 579368 E-mail: sales@videcom.com *Computer systems for travel industry*

Video 125, High Street, Sunninghill, Ascot, Berkshire, SL5 9NG Tel: (01344) 628565 Fax: (01344) 623302 E-mail: sales@video125.co.uk *Mail order video & production service providers*

Video Arts Group Ltd, 6-7 St. Cross Street, London, EC1N 8UA Tel: (020) 7400 4800 Fax: (020) 7400 4900 E-mail: sales@videoarts.co.uk *Training video producers & distributors* Also at: Birmingham, Leeds & Manchester

Video Display Europe, Unit 5 Old Forge Trading Estate, Dudley Rd, Stourbridge, W. Midlands, DY9 8EL Tel: (01384) 894777 Fax: (01384) 895788 E-mail: sales@vdceuro.com *Cathode ray tube sales & manufrs*

▶ Video Highway (Europe) Ltd, Cheltermill House, Water Lane, Newark, Nottinghamshire, NG24 1HA Tel: (0870) 7746226 Fax: (0870) 7746336 E-mail: sales@videohighway.co.uk *Video Highway provides professional video conferencing solutions as well as reselling video conferencing products and presentation equipment.*

Video House Productions, 32 Ash Street, Fleetwood, Lancashire, FY7 6TH Tel: (01253) 770510 Fax: (01253) 776729 E-mail: gilly@slater.co.uk *Video & television productions*

Video Makes Money Ltd, 140 Wythenshawe Road, Northenden, Manchester, M23 0PF Tel: 0161-902 9000 Fax: 0161-945 9900 *Videos & CD & DVDS manufrs*

Video Promotions International, Stoneleigh, Fryerning, Ingatestone, Essex, CM4 0NP Tel: 01277 353734 Fax: 01277 353734 *Audio*

Video Tec Ltd, Unit 132 Bradley Hall Trading Estate, Standish, Wigan, Lancashire, WN6 0XQ Tel: (01257) 428601 Fax: (01257) 428606 E-mail: admin@vtecltd.co.uk *CCTV systems & installers*

Videoactive Ltd, Mill House, Higher Wych, Malpas, Cheshire, SY14 7JR Tel: (01948) 780564 Fax: (01948) 780566 E-mail: enquiries@videoactive.co.uk *Audio visual services (corporate & conferences)*

▶ VideoComm Technologies, Broughton Grange, Headlands, Kettering, Northamptonshire, NN15 6XA Tel: 0870 2401237 Fax: 0870 1340035 E-mail: enquiries@vidcomm.co.uk *Marketing technology business*

Videofone Productions, 49 Wellington Road, Hampton, Middlesex, TW12 1JY Tel: (020) 8977 9112 Fax: (020) 8943 1147 *Video producers*

Videographics Presentation Services, 18a Lansdown Road, Swindon, SN1 3NE Tel: (01793) 527226 Fax: (01793) 481236 *Audio visual hire & production services*

Videoquest 2004 Ltd, 27 Masson Avenue, Ruislip, Middlesex, HA4 6QT Tel: (020) 8842 2783 Fax: (020) 8842 2784 E-mail: videoquestltd@btconnect.com *Telecommunication systems installers*

Videor Technical GmbH, 14 Campbell Court, Bramley, Tadley, Hampshire, RG26 5EG Tel: (0870) 7749944 Fax: (0870) 7749955 E-mail: info@videortechnical.com *Closed circuit television manufrs*

Videotheque, 54 Rosebank Crescent, Exeter, EX4 6EH Tel: (01392) 214064 *Audio visual hire*

Videotron Ltd, 441-443 Cranbrook Road, Ilford, Essex, IG2 6EW Tel: (020) 8554 7617 Fax: (020) 8554 0110 E-mail: phobbs@videotronltd.freeserve.co.uk *Video equipment suppliers*

▶ Vidox Video Productions Ltd, Unit 1b Dane John Works, Gordon Road, Canterbury, Kent, CT1 3PP Tel: (01227) 781155 E-mail: info@vidox.co.uk *Producers of audio-visual & multimedia dvd's*

▶ Viemac Ltd, Apple Tree Close, Halstead, Essex, CO9 2TL Tel: 01787 472513 Fax: 01787 472513 E-mail: info@viemac.co.uk *Auto electrical specialists. We supply and install the best vehicle security systems, audio and accessories available.*

Viessmann Ltd, Hortonwood 30, Telford, Shropshire, TF1 7YP Tel: (01952) 675000 Fax: (01952) 675040 E-mail: info-uk@viessmann.com *Heating equipment manufrs*

▶ Viet UK, 36 The Street, Didmarton, Badminton, Avon, GL9 1DS Tel: (01454) 238530 Fax: (01454) 238877 **Supply, Installation & Service of:*Wide Belt sanding machines.*High quality & precision sanding equipments.*Sanding, Calibrating and Finishing woodworking Machines.*Sanding Lines & Special Sanding and Polishing equipments.**

▶ View Creative Ltd, Riverside Park, Benarth Road, Conwy, Gwynedd, LL32 8UB Tel: (01492) 576743 Fax: (01492) 576742 E-mail: talk@viewcreative.co.uk *Graphic design services*

View Point Internet Ltd, Venture House Arlington Square, Downshire Way, Bracknell, Berkshire, RG12 1WA Tel: (01344) 300100 Fax: (01344) 742950 E-mail: sales@viewpoint.net.uk Principal Export Areas: Worldwide *Internet software development services*

View Pulse, 6 Tarranbrae, Willesden Lane, London, NW6 7PL Tel: (020) 7372 7595 Fax: (020) 7372 4067 *Buying house*

▶ View Right Visual Systems Ltd, Unit 10 Paper Mill End Industrial Estate, Birmingham, B44 8NH Tel: 0121-356 4441 Fax: 0121-356 4400 E-mail: pcallow@btconnect.com *Audio visual services*

▶ View2IT Ltd, 4, Edge Close, Weybridge, Surrey, KT13 0SZ Tel: 01932 851016 E-mail: info@view2it.co.uk *Providing complete IT solutions, from home Internet configuration and PC repair to corporate networks, VPN connections and data cabling with price plans to suite levels of requirements.*

Viewlocity Software Ltd, 165 Burwood Road, Walton-on-Thames, Surrey, KT12 4AT Tel: (01932) 260340 Fax: (01932) 260341 *Chain optimisation suppliers*

▶ Viewtouch Ltd., COf Hilton Studios, Park Lane, Lichfield, Staffordshire, WS14 0EU Tel: (0870) 7605756 Fax: (0870) 1309350 E-mail: info@viewtouch.co.uk *Online internet services providers*

▶ The Vigilante Gardener, 149 Pavilion Road, Worthing, West Sussex, BN14 7EG Tel: (01903) 200853 E-mail: stuart@tvglandscaping.co.uk *Garden maintenance & landscaping services*

Viglen Technology Ltd, 7 Handley Page Way Colney Street, Colney Street, St. Albans, Hertfordshire, AL2 2DQ Tel: (01923) 858700 Fax: (01727) 201888 E-mail: marketing@viglen.co.uk *Personal computer manufrs*

Vigo Carpet Gallery Ltd, 6A Vigo Street, London, W1S 3HF Tel: (020) 7439 6971 Fax: (020) 7439 2353 E-mail: vigo@btinternet.com *Hand knotted carpets*

Vigo Computer Systems Ltd, Hewell Lane, Malt Shovel Barn, Tardebigge, Bromsgrove, Worcestershire, B60 1LL Tel: 0121-447 7222 Fax: 0121-447 7333 E-mail: support@vigosoftware.co.uk *Software house consultants*

Vigurs Torquay Ltd, Vigurs Yard, Forest Road, Torquay, TQ1 4JS Tel: (01803) 327535 Fax: (01803) 316940 E-mail: info@virgus.co.uk *Motor body repairers*

Vijay Fashions Ltd, 120 Broughton Street, Manchester, M8 8AN Tel: 0161-834 7711 Fax: 0161-833 0933 E-mail: ianq@vijayfashions.co.uk *Clothing wholesalers*

Viking Ltd, Chatsworth House, Portland Close, Houghton Regis, Dunstable, Bedfordshire, LU5 5AW Tel: (01582) 603600 Fax: (01582) 471114 E-mail: accounts@vikingltd.co.uk *Cables & connectors for telecomms industry*

Viking Arms Ltd, New York Mill, New York Industrial Estate, Harrogate, North Yorkshire, HG3 4BW Tel: (01423) 780810 Fax: (01423) 781500 E-mail: info@vikingarms.com *Gunsmiths*

Viking Computer Services, 10 Slingsby Grove, York, YO24 1LS Tel: (01904) 708022 E-mail: vikingcs@hotmail.com *Computer hardware & software repairers*

Viking Extrusions Ltd, 4 Ivy Arch Road, Worthing, West Sussex, BN14 8BX Tel: (01903) 205532 Fax: (01903) 205534 E-mail: sales@vikext.co.uk *Precision rubber silicone extrusions manufrs*

▶ Viking Heating, 119 Brompton Park, Brompton on Swale, Richmond, North Yorkshire, DL10 7JR Tel: (01748) 818622 E-mail: enquiries@vikingheating.co.uk *Oil heating service & repairs*

Viking Industrial Products Ltd, 1 Coronation Business Centre, Hard Ings Road, Keighley, West Yorkshire, BD21 3ND Tel: (01535) 610373 Fax: (01535) 616231 E-mail: sales@vikingtapes.co.uk *Packaging palletwrap & adhesive tapes, packaging*

▶ Viking International, 26-32 Millbrae Road, Langside, Glasgow, G42 9TU Tel: 0141-632 3222 *Automotive components manufrs*

Viking Johnson, 46-48 Wilbury Way, Hitchin, Hertfordshire, SG4 0UD Tel: (01462) 443322 Fax: (01462) 443311 E-mail: sales@vikingjohnson.com *Pipeline fittings manufrs*

Viking Optical Ltd, Blyth Road, Halesworth, Suffolk, IP19 8EN Tel: (01986) 875315 Fax: (01986) 874788 E-mail: viking@vikingoptical.co.uk *Magnifier, binocular & telescope distributors*

Viking Plant Hire Ltd, 2 Dewing Road, Rackheath Industrial Estate, Norwich, NR13 6LN Tel: (01603) 720771 Fax: (01603) 721779 E-mail: viking-plant@virgin.net *Plant hire, sales & service contractors*

Viking Pump Ltd, Viking House, Dannemore Drive, Sheffield, S9 5DF Tel: 0114-244 7701 Fax: 0114-243 2614 *Pump maintenance & repair services*

Viking Saddlery, Dean Court Farm, Lower Dean, Buckfastleigh, Devon, TQ11 0LT Tel: (01364) 644064 E-mail: info@vikingsaddlery.force9.co.uk *Saddlery repair & retail services*

Viking Services, Glenfoot, Abernethy, Perth, PH2 9LS Tel: 01738 850631 *High pressure washers sell & service*

Viking Shipping Services Ltd, Ousegate, Selby, North Yorkshire, YO8 8BL Tel: (01757) 702688 Fax: (01757) 701601 E-mail: sales@vikingshipping.co.uk *Based in Selby, North Yorkshire, Viking Shipping operates an extensive warehousing and handling facility. All types of palletised, bagged or bulk goods can be accommodated. The products arrive on site via road of wharf for transit or longer term storage and re-distribution. Vessel chartering, deep sea FCL and LCL movements, Nationwide UK distribution, packing and re-packing and freight forwarding facilities including European Transport, Worldwide Shipping & Airfreight are just some of the services offered by this long established company.*

Viking Signs, Unit 2 Alma Park Road, Grantham, Lincolnshire, NG31 9SE Tel: (01476) 590261 Fax: (01476) 590261 E-mail: sales@vikingsigns.co.uk *Sign manufrs*

Viking Stainless Products, Unit 9 Castlelaurie Industrial Estate, Falkirk, FK2 7XF Tel: (01324) 636298 Fax: (01324) 634818 *Stainless steel fabricators*

Viking Trailers Ltd, Taylor Holme Industrial Estate, Bacup, Lancashire, OL13 0LE Tel: (01706) 875139 Fax: (01706) 875277 E-mail: sales@vikingtrailers.co.uk *Airport/ industrial trailers*

▶ Vikoma (International) Ltd, 88 Place Road, Cowes, Isle of Wight, PO31 7AE Tel: (01983) 296021 Fax: (01983) 200561 *Oil spill response equipment manufrs*

Vilene Interlinings, PO Box 3, Elland, West Yorkshire, HX5 9DX Tel: (01422) 327900 Fax: (01422) 327999 E-mail: vilenesales@freudenberg-nw.com *Interlining manufrs*

Village Gears Ltd, Duke Street, Wednesfield, Wolverhampton, WV11 1TH Tel: (01902) 725565 Fax: (01902) 727313 *Gear manufacturers & cutters*

Village Joinery Works, 242a North Deeside Road, Peterculter, Aberdeenshire, AB14 0UQ Tel: (01224) 735706 Fax: 01224 735706 *Furniture joinery*

Village Knitware, 115 Kildoag Rd, Londonderry, BT47 3TH Tel: (028) 7139 7845 *Knitwear manufrs*

Village Leathers, 18 The Market, The Piazza, London, WC2E 8RB Tel: (020) 8965 2722 Fax: (020) 8965 2722 E-mail: sales@villageleathers.com *Leather belt & embraces*

Village Saddlery, 182 Chester Road, Warrington, WA4 6AR Tel: (01925) 629629 Fax: (01925) 629628 *Saddlery retailer*

Village World Ltd, Manor Orchard, Staplegrove, Taunton, Somerset, TA2 6EQ Tel: (01823) 326767 Fax: (01823) 326917 E-mail: info@villageworld.co.uk *Home furniture manufrs*

Villamead, 203 Inkerman Street, Birmingham, B7 4SA Tel: 0121-359 7498 Fax: 0121-359 7498 E-mail: villamead@aol.com *Aluminium stockholders*

▶ Villarebec, 8 Dawlish Drive, Southport, Merseyside, PR9 9RA Tel: (01704) 506697 E-mail: dot@villarebec.com *Private holiday Villa with heated swimming pool in Orlando Florida. Ideal location for Walt Disney World and all other florida attractions.*

▶ Villas To Go, Kenburgh Court, 131-137 South Street, Bishop's Stortford, Hertfordshire, CM23 3HX Tel: (01279) 464464 Fax: (01279) 759168

Villavent Ltd, Avenue Two, Station Lane, Witney, Oxfordshire, OX28 4YL Tel: (01993) 778481 Fax: (01993) 779962 E-mail: sales@villavent.co.uk *Ventilation suppliers & distributors*

Vimto, Laurel House Woodlands Park, Ashton Road, Newton-le-Willows, Merseyside, WA12 0HH Tel: (01925) 294080 Fax: (01925) 294090 *Distributors of soft drinks*

Vinalith Ltd, Valley House, Cray Avenue, Orpington, Kent, BR5 3RZ Tel: (01689) 878211 Fax: (01689) 833946 E-mail: sales@vinalith.co.uk *Lithographic printers*

Vinall Covers, 64 Hammonds Way, Totton, Southampton, SO40 3HF Tel: (023) 8086 9411 Fax: (023) 8086 9411 E-mail: kbh47@hotmail.com *Boat cover makers*

Vinatec Signs & Nameplates, 244 Bentley Road, Doncaster, South Yorkshire, DN5 9QP Tel: (01302) 822777 Fax: (01302) 822777 E-mail: sales@vinatec.co.uk *Sign makers*

▶ Vincehire Ltd, Bowenhurst Farm, Mill Lane, Crondall, Farnham, Surrey, GU10 5RP Tel: (01252) 852311 Fax: (01252) 852311 E-mail: vincehire@talk21.com *Hires & sales of temporary fencing, barriers*

Vincent Processes Ltd, Turnpike Industrial Estate, Turnpike Road, Newbury, Berkshire, RG14 2NT Tel: (01635) 40295 Fax: (01635) 37680 E-mail: carlsmith@vincentprocesses.co.uk *Product process developers*

Vincent Rickards, Unit 22 Blackworth Industrial Estate, Highworth, Swindon, SN6 7NA Tel: (01793) 765251 Fax: (01793) 765251 E-mail: vincerickards@onetel.com *Specialist cabinet & case makers*

Vincent Timber Ltd, 8 Montgomery Street, Birmingham, B11 1DU Tel: 0121-772 5511 Fax: 0121-766 6002 E-mail: gdw@vincenttimber.co.uk *Timber merchants & importers*

Vincents Shopfitters Ltd, Priory Works, Newton Street, Newton Saint Faith, Norwich, NR10 3AD Tel: (01603) 891050 Fax: (01603) 890689 E-mail: post@vincents.co.uk *Shop fitters & fly screen manufrs*

Vinci Services Ltd, Ditton Road, Widnes, Cheshire, WA8 0WE Tel: 0151-422 3800 Fax: 0151-423 3934 *Engineers* Also at: Stockton-on-Tees

Vine Water Services, 96 Chichester Rd, Seaford, E. Sussex, BN25 2DT Tel: 01323 894967 Fax: 01323 892535 *Water equipment & services*

Vinnell & Son, 6 West Street, Great Gransden, Sandy, Bedfordshire, SG19 3AT Tel: (01767) 677267 *Architectural joinery manufrs*

Vinola Knitwear, 191 Ross Walk, Leicester, LE4 5HH Tel: 0116-268 1461 Fax: 0116-266 5280 *Knitwear manufrs*

Vintage Archives, LT Braxted Hall, Witham Road, Little Braxted, Witham, Essex, CM8 3EU Tel: (01376) 501311 Fax: (01376) 504982 E-mail: mail@vintagearchives.co.uk *Storage (archive & commercial record) services*

Vintage Engine Technology Ltd, Fullers Hill, Little Gransden, Sandy, Bedfordshire, SG19 3BP Tel: (01767) 651794 Fax: (01767) 651794 *Aircraft engine restoration services*

▶ VintageView UK, 16 Lower Park Road, New Southgate, London, N11 1QD Tel: (0870) 7659225 Fax: (0870) 7052939 E-mail: info@vintageview.co.uk *Innovative Wine Storage & Racking System. Displays wine bottles with the label forward; show the label not the cork!*

Vintec Laboratories, Bucknalls Lane, Watford, WD25 9XX Tel: (01923) 661144 Fax: (01923) 661115 E-mail: vinteclabs@aol.com *Analytical & consulting chemists*

Vintellect Ltd, Fetcham Park House, Lower Road, Fetcham, Leatherhead, Surrey, KT22 9HD Tel: (01372) 371093 E-mail: info@vintellect.co.uk *UK's leading experts on wine preservation, wine education (tutored and e-learning), wine consulting*

Vinten Broadcast Ltd, Western Way, Bury St. Edmunds, Suffolk, IP33 3TB Tel: (01284) 752121 Fax: (01284) 750560 E-mail: contact@vinten.com *Camera support equipment manufrs*

Vinter Sign, Rear Of 37 Chipstead Valley Rd, Coulsdon, Surrey, CR5 2RB Tel: 020 86609603 Fax: 020 86609640 *Signs makers*

The Vinyl Cut, Newmill Farm, Stonehaven, Kincardineshire, AB39 3YJ Tel: (0845) 0565589 Fax: (01569) 740102 *Sign makers*

Vinyl Graphics Flags Banners, 109 Bell Hill Road, Flat, Bristol, BS5 7LY Tel: 0117-935 3705 Fax: 0117-940 1446 E-mail: sales@vinylgraphicsonline.co.uk *Sign manufrs*

▶ Vinyl Signs, 85 Clos Myddlyn, Beddau, Pontypridd, Mid Glamorgan, CF38 2JT Tel: (01443) 201871 Fax: (01443) 208474 E-mail: sales@vinylsign.biz *Vinyl signs, heavy duty pvc banners, safety signs & security signs suppliers*

▶ Violet Farm Foods Ltd, Units 10-11, Uddens Trading Estate, Wimborne, Dorset, BH21 7LQ Tel: (01202) 891006 Fax: (01202) 896281 E-mail: sales@vff.co.uk *Chilled, Frozen and Ambient catering deliverys*

Viomedex Ltd, Gordon Road, Buxted, Uckfield, East Sussex, TN22 4LH Tel: (01323) 446130 Fax: (01825) 733407 E-mail: vx@viomedex.com *Project management & assistance of contract manufrs*

Vipa Designs, 26 Digby Drive, Melton Mowbray, Leicestershire, LE13 0RQ Tel: (01664) 567890 Fax: (01664) 565314 E-mail: enquiries@vipadesigns.co.uk *Jewellery manufrs*

▶ Vipamedia Ltd, 12 Norton Road, Woodley, Reading, RG5 4AH Tel: 0870 1453858 Fax: 0870 1453858 E-mail: davidj@vipamedia.com *Software development, web design and management, bespoke software solutions, computer user support, business productivity consultancy, marketing consultancy, printing services, Portfolio Publishing software developers, Hewlett Packard Partners, network installation, computer training - A one stop shop for computer solutions for home users, small businesses and large corporates - Vipamedia is the solution provider for IT for the user.*

Viper Metal Products Ltd, Oldmixon Cresent, Weston-super-Mare, Avon, BS24 9AX Tel: (01934) 621912 Fax: (01934) 614347 E-mail: tony@viparmetal.co.uk *Sheet metalworkers*

▶ Viper Performance, Registered Office: 21 Kiniths Way, Birmingham, B62 9HJ Tel: 0121 6028359 E-mail: pitstoptuning@blueyonder.co.uk *Viperperformance are specialists in high quality Silicone hoses,*Alloy tubing & hose clamps for Intercooler , induction and other pipe work requirements.**We sell a large range of:*Silicone Turbo hoses, Silicone water & coolant hoses,*High pressure Silicone hoses, Silicone Elbows & Reducers. Silicone Vacuum Tubing,*Mirror Polished Alloy Elbows & Straights, and stainless steel hose clips.**Viper Performance Silicone hoses are designed for high performance engines *and will withstand the most demanding applications. **Our Silicone hoses are all hand crafted in the UK to strict quality controls,*and are the highest quality on the market.**We sell to retail and trade customers.**

Vipond Fire Protection Ltd, 10 Glenfield Road, Kelvin Industrial Estate, East Kilbride, Glasgow, G75 0RA Tel: (01355) 237588 Fax: (01355) 263399 E-mail: admin.uk@vipondltd.co.uk *Active fire protection system installers*

▶ Vipul Dave, 72 Portswood Road, Southampton, SO17 2FW Tel: 0845 8382737 Fax: 0845 8382736 E-mail: info@motordriven.co.uk *contract hire & leasing *new & used **WHY BUY WHEN YOU CAN CONTRACT HIRE **Contract Hire & Leasing *Cars & Commercials*New & Used Vehicles*Independent *Fleet Management*Work or Home Delivery**We at motor driven believe in making it easy for your*business or yourself in obtaining a new vehicle.*We are independent and able to find the best option *for you. The advice we give is free and will save you time,*money and effort. **Why buy when you can hire, it will free up capital to invest in *your company and people. It would be great to talk to you *directly either by telephone or email. **We can save thousands off the running cost of your fleet*

Virage, Cambridge Business Park, Cowley Road, Cambridge, CB4 0WZ Tel: (01223) 488540 Fax: (01223) 488541 E-mail: info@virage.com *Software engineers*

▶ Virani Food Products Ltd, 10-14 Stewarts Road, Finedon Road Industrial Estate, Wellingborough, Northamptonshire, NN8 4RJ Tel: (01933) 230500 Fax: (01933) 230510

Virgin Atlantic Airways Ltd, The Office, Manor Royal, Crawley, West Sussex, RH10 9NU Tel: (01293) 616161 Fax: (01293) 561721 E-mail: sales@virgin-atlantic.com *Airline*

▶ Virgin Balloon Flights, Jesson House, Stafford Park 1, Telford, Shropshire, TF3 3BD Tel: (01952) 212750 Fax: (01952) 292020 E-mail: sales@virginballoonflights.co.uk *Balloon trip services*

Virgin Balloon Flights, Jesson House, Stafford Park 1, Telford, Shropshire, TF3 3BD Tel: (01952) 212750 Fax: (01952) 292020 *Balloon flight services*

Virgin Books Ltd, Thames Wharf Studios, Rainville Road, London, W6 9HA Tel: (020) 7386 3300 Fax: (020) 7386 3360 *Book publishers*

▶ The Virgin Cosmetics Company, 55 Drovers Way, Bradford, West Yorkshire, BD2 1JZ Tel: 01274 306430 E-mail: nicola@ashton2602.f2s.com *As your Virgin Cosmetics Consultant I can assist you with choosing the products that are right for you. If you like what you see, the best way to try and buy our gorgeous products is at home and amongst friends at a Virgin Vie Class. Not only do you get expert advice, a free make-over and a chance to play with all our new products but as Hostess you can get all your favourite products for FREE. **I work with a range of beautiful cosmetics, skincare from Switzerland, make-up from Milan and bath and body treats you won"t be able to resist! As well as earning excellent commission, selling these award winning products, I also enjoy the benefits of our exciting incentives and promotions, where you can earn anything from diamond earrings to a BMW.*If you would like to know a little bit more about the opportunities available with the Virgin Cosmetics Company, then please call me I will be happy to chat you through it without obligation.**

▶ Virgin Cosmetics Co, 26 Thurrock Lakeside Shopping Centre, West Thurrock, Grays, Essex, RM20 2ZF Tel: (01708) 680601 Fax: (01708) 680603

Viridian Envirosolutions Ltd, Unit 81, Thomas Way, Lakesview International Business Park, Hersden, Canterbury, Kent, CT3 4JZ Tel: (01227) 713999 Fax: (01227) 713607 E-mail: info@viridian.biz *Environmental management*

Viridian Group Ltd, 120 Malone Road, Belfast, BT9 5HT Tel: (028) 9066 8416 Fax: (028) 9068 9117 E-mail: sales@viridiangroup.co.uk *Utilities suppliers* Also at: Branches throughout Northern Ireland

▶ Viridor Waste Management, Pilsworth Quarry & Landfill, Pilsworth Road, Pilsworth, Bury, Lancashire, BL9 8QZ Tel: 0161-797 1828

Viridor Waste Managment, Thames House, Wood Lane, Slough, SL1 9EB Tel: (01753) 512832 Fax: (01753) 536230 *Waste disposal*

Viridor Waste Management Ltd, Great Western House, Station Approach, Taunton, Somerset, TA1 1QW Tel: (01823) 721400 Fax: (01823) 334027 *Waste disposal contractors & waste recyclers* Also at: Bristol, Exeter, Newton Abbot, Par, Plymouth, Poole & Torbay

▶ Viridor Waste Management Ltd, 42 Kings Hill Avenue, Kings Hill, West Malling, Kent, ME19 4AJ Tel: (01732) 229200 *Waste disposal & landfill services*

Virilium Co. Ltd, 9 Colne Way Court, Colne Way, Watford, WD24 7NE Tel: (01923) 233133 Fax: (01923) 251037 *Dental equipment manufrs*

Virkonnen Ltd, 17a High Street, Reigate, Surrey, RH2 9AA Tel: (01737) 223233 Fax: (01737) 243061 E-mail: sales@virkonnen.co.uk *Safety consultants*

Virtalis, Chester House, 79 Dane Road, Sale, Cheshire, M33 7BP Tel: 0161-969 1155 Fax: 0161-969 1166 E-mail: info@vrweb.com *Virtual reality specialists*

▶ Virtio, Alba Centre, Alba Campus, Livingston, West Lothian, EH54 7EG Tel: (01506) 402410 *Virtio powers dramatic gains in software development productivity by delivering high-performance pre-silicon software simulations of complete handheld and wireless embedded devices and systems to shorten product development time.*

▶ Virtual Archive, Riverbank House, 1 Putney Bridge Approach, London, SW6 3JD Tel: (020) 7736 9002 Fax: 0207 6106162 E-mail: alex@vasat.co.uk *Virtual Archive provides a complete electronic document management solution including the provision of Application Design and Consultancy, Document Management Software, Multi-format Document Scanning, Outsourced Document Management and Training, Post Implementation Support and Maintenance.**In addition, the business has considerable experience managing the creation of Electronic Data Rooms to facilitate and control*

continued

*the legal due diligence phase of Acquisition and Divestment projects.**

▶ Virtual Assistant, 11 Farquhar Road, Port Glasgow, Renfrewshire, PA14 5AS Tel: (07732) 213368 E-mail: info@thevirtualassistant.me.uk *Virtual Assistant services offering external administrative support to small businesses as and when they need it, cutting down on the need and expense of employing temporary staff. I can help with a wide variety of tasks at your convenience.*

Virtual Image, 184 Reddish Road, Stockport, Cheshire, SK5 7HS Tel: 0161-480 1915 Fax: 0161-612 2965 E-mail: virimage@cs.com *Computer software developers*

▶ Virtual Lifestyles, Virtual House, 280 Marlow Bottom, Marlow, Buckinghamshire, SL7 3PT Tel: 01628 474742 E-mail: info@virtual-lifestyles.com *Digital audio, cctv, video & sound installation engineers*

▶ Virtual Office Bureau Limited, 4 Twyfords, Crowborough, East Sussex, TN6 1YE Tel: 01892 653325 Fax: 01892 665861 E-mail: virtualofficebureau@yahoo.co.uk *Provision of Secretarial/Admin services. Including all typing from copy to audio and also shorthand. Mostly remote but can attend on site, ie. to take Minutes at Meetings.*

Virtual Reality Marketing Ltd, PO Box 26, Moreton-in-Marsh, Gloucestershire, GL56 0ZD Tel: (01608) 652676 Fax: (01608) 652533 *Computer software manufrs*

▶ Virtual Secretarial Services, 235 The Broadway, Sunderland, SR4 9HB Tel: (07986) 854995 Fax: 0191-534 3657 E-mail: info@virtual-secretarialservices.com *VSS offers audio and digital transcription services, word processing and typing of manuscripts, dissertations, theses etc (discount available for students), web design, presentations and more, available 24/7 very cheap rates.*

▶ Virtual Systems Solutions Ltd, 2 Sable Court, Southfields Business Park, Basildon, Essex, SS15 6SR Tel: (01268) 582950 Fax: (01268) 582951 E-mail: jcampbell@vssolutions.co.uk *IT solutions, communications, networking & storage solutions*

▶ Virtual Tapestry Ltd, Dulcote, Dulcote, Wells, Somerset, BA5 3NU Tel: (0870) 7456334 Fax: (0870) 7456334 E-mail: linda@virtualtapestry.co.uk *From small, brochure-style websites, to full e-commerce facilities*

Virtusec.Com, 5 Abbotsford Court, Kelso, Roxburghshire, TD5 7SQ Tel: (07765) 246124 Fax: (01573) 224731 E-mail: info@virtusec.com *Secretarial services*

▶ Virus & Adware Removal, Woodpeckers, 19 Wildcroft Drive, Wokingham, Berkshire, RG40 3HY Tel: 0118-977 5957 Fax: 0118-977 5957 E-mail: aardy@btinternet.com *Computer software consultancy services*

Visa Hand Tools Ltd, Gibson House, Barrowby Lane, Garforth, Leeds, LS25 1NG Tel: 0113-286 9245 Fax: 0113-286 6859 E-mail: enq@visatools.co.uk *Manufacturers of Quality Fibreglass Handled Forestry and Fencing Equipment including Axes, Logsplitters, Wedges, Sledge Hammers, Ball Pein Hammers, Walling, Scutch, Brick and Slaters Hammers. All Fibreglass tools are manufactured in the UK.*

▶ Visa Press Ltd, Campbell Court, Bramley, Tadley, Hampshire, RG26 5EG Tel: (01256) 882131

Viscose Closures Ltd, Unit 1 Fleming Way, Crawley, West Sussex, RH10 9JY Tel: (01293) 519251 Fax: (01293) 540005 E-mail: sales@viscose.co.uk *Suppliers of shrink labels & sleeveing manufrs*

Viscount Butchers Products Ltd, 10-30 Robinson Street East, Grimsby, South Humberside, DN32 9AE Tel: (01472) 345847 Fax: (01472) 354787 E-mail: sales@visprod.co.uk *Butcher & bakers suppliers*

▶ Viscount Interiors, 5 Thorley Hall Stables, Thorley, Bishop's Stortford, Hertfordshire, CM23 4BE Tel: (01279) 654309 Fax: (01279) 654309 E-mail: sales@viscountinteriors.co.uk *Office products & furniture equipment suppliers*

Vishal Fashions Ltd, 137 Harrison Road, Leicester, LE4 6NP Tel: 0116-268 2944 Fax: 0116-268 2944 *Casual clothing manufrs*

Vishay Ltd, Pallion Trading Estate, Sunderland, SR4 6SU Tel: 0191-514 4155 Fax: 0191-567 8662 E-mail: paul.robson@vishay.com *Electronic component manufrs*

Vishay Ltd, Units 6-7, Marshall Road, Hillmead, Swindon, SN5 5FZ Tel: (01793) 521351 Fax: (01793) 525163 *Passive electronic components distributers & manufrs*

Vishay Measurements Group UK Ltd, 1 Cartel Units, Stroudley Road, Basingstoke, Hampshire, RG24 8FW Tel: (01256) 462131 Fax: (01256) 471441 E-mail: email@measurementsgroup.co.uk Principal Export Areas: Worldwide *Manufacturers of load cells, strain gauge systems & transducers (force measurement)*

Visi Group Ltd, Ram House, Chalky Lane, Chessington, Surrey, KT9 2NF Tel: (01372) 748749 Fax: (01372) 748148 *Software developers*

Visibility Europe Ltd, 3Rd Floor, 1 Ashley Road, Altrincham, Cheshire, WA14 2DT Tel: 0161-927 2500 Fax: 0161-928 9700 *Computer software house*

Visible Productions Ltd, Jubilee Yard, Queen Elizabeth St, London, SE1 2LP Tel: (020) 7403 9333 Fax: (020) 7403 5225 *Video production*

Visilume Ltd, Unit 30 Moor Park Industrial Estate, Tolpits Lane, Watford, WD18 9SP Tel: (01923) 211131 Fax: (01923) 211432 E-mail: sales@visilume.co.uk *Safety equipment suppliers*

▶ Visintini-Jones, Capel Barn, Capel Road, Orlestone, Ashford, Kent, TN26 2EH Tel: (01233) 733617 Fax: (01233) 733511 E-mail: rayjones@talktalk.net *On behalf of buyers/sellers: Oil and refined products - D2, Jet fuel, Gasoline, M0 etc.*

Vision Aids Ltd, PO Box 4370, Epping, Essex, CM16 5FA Tel: (01992) 573550 Fax: (01992) 573580 *CCTV equipment manufrs*

Vision Assurance Systems, Basepoint Business & Innovation Centre, Caxton Close, Andover, Hampshire, SP10 3FG Tel: (01264) 326309 E-mail: sales@visionassurancesystems.com *Image processing equipment supply & manufrs*

Vision Blinds, The Quest, Ampthill Road, Houghton Conquest, Bedford, MK45 3JP Tel: (01234) 741633 Fax: (01234) 741981 *Blind manufrs*

Vision Blinds Stockport, 38b Gorton Road, Stockport, Cheshire, SK5 6AE Tel: 0161-432 2771 Fax: 0161-432 8291 E-mail: sales@vision-blinds.com *Interior, exterior blinds & canopies manufrs*

▶ Vision Colour Print Ltd, 132 Wakefield Road, Drighlington, Bradford, West Yorkshire, BD11 1DR Tel: 0113-287 9962 Fax: 0113-385 6606 E-mail: studio@visioncolourprint.com

Vision Computers, 84 King Street, Alfreton, Derbyshire, DE55 7DD Tel: (01773) 834666 E-mail: sales@visioncomputers.fsnet.co.uk *Computer repairers*

▶ Vision Computing, Treleigh Industrial Estate, Jon Davey Drive, Redruth, Cornwall, TR16 4AX Tel: (01209) 315566

The Vision Corporation, PO Box 3010, Wokingham, Berkshire, RG41 5FY Tel: 0118-978 4483 Fax: 0118-978 4283 E-mail: sales@vision-corporation.co.uk *Printer suppliers*

▶ Vision Express (UK) Ltd, 81-83 Russell Way, Metrocentre, Gateshead, Tyne & Wear, NE11 9XX Tel: 0191-460 0644 Fax: 0191-460 0097 *Optical specialists*

Vision Fire & Security, Vision House Focus 31, Mark Road, Hemel Hempstead Industrial Estate, Hemel Hempstead, Hertfordshire, HP2 7BW Tel: (01442) 242330 Fax: (01442) 249327 *Public address, general alarm systems & equipment designers & manufrs*

Vision Labs Ltd, 2 Foley Grove, Foley Business Park, Kidderminster, Worcestershire, DY11 7PT Tel: (01562) 820333 Fax: (01562) 820500 *Optical lens manufrs*

▶ Vision Light Plastics Ltd, 2-7 Decoy Road, Worthing, West Sussex, BN14 8ND Tel: (01903) 823339 Fax: (01903) 206868 E-mail: sales@visionlight.co.uk *Fabricated plastic products manufrs*

▶ Vision Litho, 70 Wood End Green Road, Hayes, Middlesex, UB3 2SL Tel: (020) 8561 8726 E-mail: visionlitho@mac.com *Printers*

Vision Mix, The Old Dairy, Broadfield Road, Sheffield, S8 0XQ Tel: 0114-250 1007 Fax: 0114-250 1006 *Video facilities services*

▶ Vision Office Automation plc, Caxton House, Watermark Way, Foxholes Business Park, Hertford, SG13 7TZ Tel: (01992) 509555 Fax: (01992) 509666 E-mail: vision@visionplc.co.uk *At Vision we supply, install and maintain Canon"s comprehensive range of multifunctional office devices*

Vision Options Ltd, York House, 22 Old Shoreham Road, Brighton, BN1 5DD Tel: (01273) 385000 Fax: (01273) 549549 E-mail: voptions@aol.com *LED sign manufrs*

▶ Vision Photographic Ltd, Unit 1 Slader Business Park, Witney Road, Nuffield Industrial Estate, Poole, Dorset, BH17 0GP Tel: (01202) 667670 Fax: (01202) 668670 E-mail: info@visionphoto.co.uk *Photography advertising, commercial*

▶ Vision Print Imaging Products, 29 Ivatt Way, Peterborough, PE3 7PH Tel: (01733) 334477 Fax: (01733) 330083

Vision Printers Ltd, 25 Colne Valley Business Park, Huddersfield, HD7 5QG Tel: (01484) 847307 Fax: (01484) 846581 E-mail: sales@visionprint.com *Print & design services*

▶ Vision Printers Ltd, Vision House, 1 Silverdale Lane, Tunbridge Wells, Kent, TN4 9LA Tel: (01892) 545006 Fax: (01892) 538069 E-mail: sales@vision-printers.co.uk *Local printers graphic design, pre-press & finishing services*

Vision Screen Services, Bridge Cottage, Church Road, Rawreth, Wickford, Essex, SS11 8SH Tel: (01268) 765374 Fax: (01268) 765374 *Audio visual equipment suppliers*

Vision Security Consultants, 22 Radley Road, Wallasey, Merseyside, CH44 2BU Tel: 0151-630 1603 *Alarm system installers*

Vision Sheet Metal Works, 3 Block 3, Inveresk Industrial Estate, Musselburgh, Midlothian, EH21 7UL Tel: 0131-665 7193 Fax: 0131-665 7193 *Sheet metal manufrs*

Vision Signs & Ceilings, 151-153 New Road, Portsmouth, PO2 7QS Tel: (023) 9267 2525 Fax: (023) 9262 4462 E-mail: sales@visionsigns.com *Sign makers & corporate signage*

▶ Vision Software Solutions Ltd, 49 Westfields, St Albans, St. Albans, Hertfordshire, AL3 4LS Tel: (01727) 817220 E-mail: sales@vision-software.co.uk *Computer software suppliers*

▶ Vision Sound & Light, 18 Barlow Park, Broughty Ferry, Dundee, DD5 3UB Tel: (01382) 480900 Fax: (01382) 480901 E-mail: info@visionsound.co.uk *Audio visual services*

Vision UK, PO BOX 501, DARTFORD, DA4 0LG Tel: 01322 866313 Fax: 01322 864816 E-mail: info@vision-uk.co.uk *Vision supply Vehicle Reversing Aids, Vehicle Reversing Cameras, Vehicle Parking Sensors, Rear view cameras*

Vision Visual Solutions Ltd, 1 Solent Industrial Estate, Shamblehurst Lane, Hedge End, Southampton, SO30 2FX Tel: (01489) 781000 Fax: (01489) 781100 E-mail: sales@vvsltd.co.uk *Sign contractors*

Vision Visual Solutions Ltd, 1 Solent Industrial Estate, Shamblehurst Lane, Hedge End, Southampton, SO30 2FX Tel: (01489) 781000 Fax: (01489) 781100 E-mail: sales@vvsltd.co.uk *Sign makers*

▶ Vision Warehouse, Unit 35 Stadium Business Centre, North End Road, Wembley, Middlesex, HA9 0AT Tel: (020) 8903 8185 Fax: (020) 8903 8566 E-mail: info@visionuk.co.uk *Manfacturing VHS Cassettes and DVD's*

▶ Vision (Yorkshire) Ltd, Unit 2a, Shaw Lane Industrial Estate, Ogden Road, Doncaster, South Yorkshire, DN2 4SE Tel: (01302) 328600 Fax: (01302) 760741 *Manufacturers of windows & doors*

▶ vision40 finance, 7 Whymark Avenue, Woodgreen, London, N22 6DJ Tel: (07958) 630576 Fax: (020) 8352 3472 E-mail: tanwa@vision40finance.com *International Project funding for emerging markets, $6 Millions and above*

▶ Visions Of Africa, Bolney Place, Cowfold Road, Bolney, Haywards Heath, West Sussex, RH17 5QT Tel: (0845) 3450065 Fax: (0871) 2223913 E-mail: info@visionsofafrica.co.uk

Visionsec Building Service, Kings Road, Basingstoke, Hampshire, RG22 6DJ Tel: (01256) 336286 Fax: (01256) 471977 *Security services*

Visionstyle Leisure, Houldsworth Mill, Houldsworth Street, Reddish, Stockport, Cheshire, SK5 6DA Tel: 0161-442 7082 Fax: 0161-442 1939 E-mail: sales@visionstyle.co.uk *Headwear *Importers*Clothing accessory**The home of a wide range of exciting promotional headwear, leisurewear, bags and umbrellas.**We pride ourselves on new innovations and offer many products exclusive in the UK. All of our products are also available as customised, bespoke designs with an experienced design and production team ready to advise you. **Whatever you choose you''ll be in good company. Some of the world''s most prestigious brands are on our products. So mix with Ford, Harrods, Lotus, Manchester United, McLaren F1, Mothercare and Rolls Royce.**

▶ Visiontech Solutions Ltd, 31 Kingsmead Avenue, Mitcham, Surrey, CR4 1ES Tel: (020) 8679 2108 Fax: (020) 8679 2108 E-mail: info@visiontech.co.uk *Electrical installations*

▶ Visitech Design, Fiscal House, 2 Havant Road, Emsworth, Hampshire, PO10 7JE Tel: (07802) 361662 Fax: (01247) 389883 E-mail: alan@visitechdesign.com *Product design services*

▶ Visqueen Building Products, Albion House, 4 Compton Way, Witney, Oxfordshire, OX28 3AB Tel: (01993) 848800 Fax: (01993) 776233

Visqueen Building Products South Wales Ltd, Maerdy Industrial Estate, Rhymney, Tredegar, Gwent, NP22 5PY Tel: (01685) 840672 Fax: (01685) 842580 E-mail: admin@visqueenbuilding.co.uk *High performance building films suppliers*

Visscher Caravelle UK Ltd, 5-9 Erica Road, Stacey Bushes, Milton Keynes, MK12 6HS Tel: (01908) 220101 Fax: (01908) 220911 *Car mats & accessories manufrs*

Visser & Smit Hanab UK, Unit 1a Orion Way, Kettering Business Park, Kettering, Northamptonshire, NN15 6NL Tel: (01536) 314700 Fax: (01536) 314709 E-mail: info@vsh-uk.com *Civil engineering*

▶ Vista Blinds, 150 Sandy Row, Belfast, BT12 5EY Tel: (028) 9024 3615 Fax: (028) 9086 1433 *Blind distributors*

▶ Vista Engineering, 16 Baronald Street, Rutherglen, Glasgow, G73 1AH Tel: 0141-613 3144 Fax: 0141-613 3031 *Reinforcement & brickwork support*

Vista Engineering Ltd, Carrbrook Works, Shallcross Mill Road, Whaley Bridge, High Peak, Derbyshire, SK23 7JL Tel: (01663) 736700 Fax: (01663) 736710 *Wall tie manufrs*

Vista Labels Limited, Vista House, Hempshaw Lane, Stockport, Cheshire, SK1 4NB Tel: 0161-477 5151 Fax: 0161-477 9203 E-mail: sales@vistalabels.com Purchasing Contact: R. Clarke Sales Contact: T. Grice *Vista Labels Ltd based in Stockport in Cheshire are specialists in all aspects of labels and labelling in the UK. We offer a bespoke service for self adhesive labels for all industries including food and drink, pharmaceuticals, automotive, DIY products, cosmetics, promotional labels and computer labels. We also specialise in plain or blank thermal labels and ribbons and hot foil blocking. Vista has responded to an increasing demand for high quality labels in small to medium batch quantities with the installation of an Etipol Combi 270 letterpress printing machine. By also using the latest Macintosh technology we can provide in house design and artwork, ultimately producing films and plates to go straight to press. We have been established since 1974 and our company culture is to exceed your expectations, please see our website or online brochure for more information.*

▶ Vista Optics Ltd, Cheshire Science Centre, Gorsey Lane, Widnes, Cheshire, WA8 0RP Tel: (0870) 0111620 Fax: (0870) 0111630 E-mail: sales@vista-optics.com *Optical raw material*

Vista Products, 219 Kings Road, Tyseley, Birmingham, B11 2AA Tel: 0121-707 3242 Fax: 0121-706 5666 *Spiral staircase manufrs*

Vista Signs, 267 Nottingham Road, Nottingham, NG7 7DA Tel: 0115-942 1511 Fax: 0115-942 2462 E-mail: sales@vista-signs.co.uk *Sign manufrs*

Vista Visuals UK, Unit 4 Old Mill Industrial Estate, Bamber Bridge, Preston, PR5 6SY Tel: (01772) 696725 Fax: (01772) 696726 E-mail: danny@vistavisuals.co.uk *Manufacturers of presentation equipment*

Vista Ward Banknotes, 5 Greenfields Way, Burley in Wharfedale, Ilkley, West Yorkshire, LS29 7RB Tel: (01943) 865709 Fax: (01943) 865609 *Banknote & coins collectables*

Vista-Brunswick Ltd, 105 Glenfrome Road, Bristol, BS2 9XA Tel: 0117 9551491 *Metal window frame manufrs*

Vistar Night Vision Ltd, 24 Doman Road, Camberley, Surrey, GU15 3DF Tel: (01276) 708800 Fax: (01276) 708807 E-mail: info@vistar.co.uk *Marine night vision equipment*

Visteon, Basildon Plant, Christopher Martin Road, Basildon, Essex, SS14 3HG Tel: (01268) 705300 Fax: (01268) 533970 E-mail: sales@visteon.com *Automotives components manufrs*

Visual Blinds, Hollings Road, Bradford, West Yorkshire, BD8 8PJ Tel: (01274) 723772 Fax: (01274) 722567 E-mail: sales@visualblinds.co.uk *Blind manufrs*

▶ Visual Communications, 209 Lynchford Road, Farnborough, Hampshire, GU14 6HF Tel: (01252) 540044 Fax: (01252) 516616 E-mail: tara@vis-com.net *Interior & exterior shop & office refurbishment*

Visual Computer Technologies Ltd, Unit 207 Solent BSNS Centre 3, Millbrook Road West, Southampton, SO15 0HW Tel: (023) 8077 9162 Fax: (023) 8078 8222 E-mail: sales@focused.co.uk *Apple mac & pc sales repair manufrs*

▶ Visual Data Concepts, Home Farm, Minety, Malmesbury, Wiltshire, SN16 9PL Tel: (01666) 861015 Fax: (01666) 861181 *Computer software services*

Visual Identity, 19 Shenley Pavilions, Chalkdell Drive, Shenley Wood, Milton Keynes, MK5 6LB Tel: (01908) 867171 Fax: (01908) 867170 E-mail: creativity@visualidentity.co.uk *Design & communications company*

▶ Visual Image Signs, Staple Close, West Quantoxhead, Taunton, Somerset, TA4 4DF Tel: (01984) 639211 Fax: (01984) 639511 E-mail: postmaster@visualimagesigns.co.uk *Sign manufrs*

Visual Impact Ltd, Unit M5, Southpoint Industrial Estate, Foreshore Road, Cardiff, CF10 4SP Fax: (029) 2049 6175 E-mail: cardiff@visuals.co.uk *Audio visual equipment & accessory suppliers*

Visual Impact, Wakes End Farm, Wakes End, Eversholt, Milton Keynes, MK17 9FB Tel: (01525) 280518 E-mail: info@visualimpact.uk *Commercial & industrial photographers*

Visual Impact Signs, Breach Road, West Thurrock, Grays, Essex, RM20 3NR Tel: (01708) 865566 Fax: (01708) 865566 *Sign writers*

Visual Information Systems, Unit 8 Canal Business Park, Dumballs Road, Cardiff, CF10 5FE Tel: (029) 2025 2020 Fax: (07967) 057997 *Close circuit television installer*

Visual Packaging Ltd, 100 Albert Road, (Opposite Outram Road), London, N22 7AH Tel: (020) 8888 6622 Fax: (020) 8888 1121 *Bag manufrs in polypropylene, polythene & cellophane*

The Visual Partnership, 35 Purdeys Way, Purdeys Industrial Estate, Rochford, Essex, SS4 1ND Tel: (01702) 546539 Fax: (01702) 542490 *Mannequin suppliers*

▶ Visual Security Solutions, 16, Ilton Business Park, Ilton, Ilminster, Somerset, TA19 9DU Tel: (01460) 259573 Fax: (01460) 259574

▶ Visual Service Centre, Unit 1 Derby Trading Estate, Stores Road, Derby, DE21 4BE Tel: (01332) 291119 Fax: (01332) 291119 E-mail: info@visualservicecentre.co.uk *Specialists in plasma, lcd, dlp & rear projection screen repairs*

▶ Visual Sounds Ltd, 891 Old Lode Lane, Solihull, West Midlands, B92 8JF Tel: 0121-242 3279 E-mail: enquiries@visualsounds.co.uk *Plasma, Home cinema installers based in the midlands*

Visual Surveillance Systems Ltd, 18 Station Road, Drighlington, Bradford, West Yorkshire, BD11 1JU Tel: 0113-285 2324 Fax: 0113-285 3026 *Surveillance installers*

Visual Systems, Unit 11 Brickfields Industrial Park, Kiln Lane, Bracknell, Berkshire, RG12 1NQ Tel: (01344) 427161 Fax: (01344) 860282 E-mail: sales@visualsystems.co.uk *Audio visual equipment suppliers*

▶ Visual Technology Solutions Ltd, Church Hatch, Market Place, Ringwood, Hampshire, BH24 1AW Tel: (0870) 7542269 Fax: (0870) 7542279 *Software development manufrs*

Visual Testing Services Ltd, PO Box 424, Peterborough, PE3 9DH Tel: (01733) 267285 Fax: (01733) 261356 E-mail: insight@vtservices.co.uk *Robotic cameras, inspections of hazardous, inaccessible areas*

▶ Visualeze Design, Annandale Road, London, SE10 0DB Tel: (020) 8488 6856 E-mail: kelly@visualeze.net *Website design studio & internet marketing consultancy*

▶ Visualfeast, Unit 501 Tea Trade Wharf, 26 Shad Thames, London, SE1 2AS Tel: (020) 7089 9484 Fax: (0870) 0514471 E-mail: events@visual-feast.co.uk *Visualfeast is an event design company who create set designs for product launches, parties, conferences and other events that require a high level of design presentation.*

▶ Visualfiles Computer Systems, Rownhams, Southampton, SO16 8LS Tel: (023) 8073 8539 Fax: (023) 8079 9768 *Software developers*

▶ Visualisation Services, 18 Hodder Avenue, Liverpool, L31 9PQ Tel: 0151-520 1128 E-mail: simon@manning65.freeserve.co.uk *3d Computer Graphic Imaging for Architectural and Interior Design.*

▶ Visualize Digital, The Studio, 8 Westgate Road, Faversham, Kent, ME13 8HF Tel: 01795 538128 E-mail: info@visualizecreative.co.uk *Based in the Southeast of England, we supply illustration, design and interpretation services for clients in England, Europe and Canada. Our clients range from large national institutions to local companies and charities, and specialise in Heritage and Environmental interpretation.**We have considerable experience within our team of illustrators and designers which allows us to offer a specialist range of services specifically geared to our client's requirements. We are enthusiastic about what we do and enjoy the challenge of meeting your brief. There are no salesmen and you will only ever talk to a designer or project manager who will be fully briefed on your requirement.**

▶ Visualize Printers, E Sutherland Houses, Sutherland Road, London, E17 6BU Tel: (020) 8527 6225 Fax: (020) 8523 4219

▶ Visual-Q Ltd, The Corner House, Willow Walk, Englefield Green, Egham, Surrey, TW20 0DQ Tel: (0870) 2401059 Fax: (01784) 472143 E-mail: tgates@visual-q.co.uk *Retailer of health & safety consultancy & products*

▶ Visuals 3D, 26 School Brow, Romiley, Stockport, Cheshire, SK6 3AT Tel: 0161-430 2623 E-mail: info@visuals-3d.co.uk *Visuals 3d is a 3d computer visualisation company*

▶ Visvount Town & Country Homes, Shepperton Marina, Felix Lane, Shepperton, Middlesex, TW17 8NS Tel: (01932) 230077 E-mail: mail@vtch.co.uk

Vita Cortex Ni Ltd, Dunmurry Industrial Estate, Dunmurry, Belfast, BT17 9HU Tel: (028) 9061 8625 Fax: (028) 9061 9479 E-mail: info@vitacortex.co.uk *Polyurethane cushioning manufrs*

Vita Health Foods, 565 Lea Bridge Road, London, E10 7EQ Tel: (020) 8539 3245 *Health shop*

Vita Liquid Polymers Ltd, Harling Road, Wythenshawe, Manchester, M22 4SZ Tel: 0161-998 3226 Fax: 0161-946 0118 E-mail: sales@vita-liquid.co.uk *Flame retardant compounds manufrs*

Vitabiotics Health Foods, 1 Apsley Way, London, NW2 7HF Tel: (020) 8955 2600 Fax: (020) 8955 2601 *Multi vitamin & mineral distributors*

Vitagrow Fertilisers Ltd, PO Box 161, Southport, Merseyside, PR9 8GH Tel: (01704) 507777 Fax: (01704) 507222 E-mail: sales@vitagrow.co.uk *Fertiliser manufrs*

Vital Office Products, Brokers House, 2A Ada Street, London, E8 4QU Tel: (020) 7923 2277 Fax: (020) 7923 4646 *Computer accessories distributors*

Vital Pharmaceuticals Ltd, 68 Wellington Court, 55-67 Wellington Road, St. Johns Wood, London, NW8 9TA Tel: (020) 7586 7070 Fax: (020) 7586 5757 E-mail: vitalpharm@aol.com *Pharmaceutical import & export merchants*

Vital Signs, 1-15 Union Street, Cookstown, County Tyrone, BT80 8NN Tel: (028) 8676 5551 E-mail: sales@vitalsigns.org.uk *Sign manufrs*

Vital Signs & Graphics Ltd, 326 Great Cheetham Street East, Salford, M7 4UJ Tel: 0161-792 7557 Fax: 0161-792 7677 E-mail: sales@vitalsignsandgraphics.co.uk *Sign designers, manufacturers & installers*

Vitalabs Europe Ltd, 18 Old Saintfield Road, Carryduff, Belfast, BT8 8EY Tel: (028) 9081 2323 Fax: (028) 9081 2454 E-mail: info@vitalabseurope.com *Health care product services*

Vitalighting Ltd, 4 Sutherland Court Moor Park Industrial Centre, Tolpits Lane, Watford, WD18 9NA Tel: (01923) 896476 Fax: (01923) 897741 E-mail: sales@vitalighting.com *Manufacturers of light fittings*

Vitaline Pharmaceuticals (UK) Ltd, Unit 8, Ridgeway, Drakes Drive, Long Crendon, Aylesbury, Buckinghamshire, HP18 9BF Tel: (01844) 202044 Fax: (01844) 202077 E-mail: info@vitaline.co.uk *Pharmaceutical distributors*

Vitality Group Ltd, Garman Road, London, N17 0QN Tel: (020) 8493 1100 Fax: (020) 8885 8203 E-mail: cashandcarry@vitalitygroup.co.uk *Wholesalers of toiletries, medicines & household goods*

Vitalograph Ltd, Maids Moreton House, Vitalograph Business Park, Maids Moreton, Buckingham, MK18 1SW Tel: (01280) 827100 Fax: (01280) 823302 E-mail: sales@vitalograph.co.uk *Medical instrumentation manufrs*

▶ Vitamin UK, PO Box 98, Manchester, M20 6PZ Tel: (0800) 0568148 Fax: 0161-445 4939 E-mail: info@vitaminuk.com *Vitamins, herbal remedies, aromatherapy oils distributors*

Vitamol Ltd, Rycroft St, Ashton-under-Lyne, Lancashire, OL7 0BN Tel: 0161-342 1400 Fax: 0161-343 1872 E-mail: r.winter@vitamol.co.uk *Based in Manchester, England, Vitamol supply bespoke rubber moldings and thermoplastic moldings throughout the world. Products manufactured by Vitamol include sealing applications, braking components, wiring harness, insulators, bump stops, mudflaps, interior trim parts and exterior trim parts, over-moulded and bonded mouldings. Vitamol have experience in the manufacture of braking system sealing applications where tight tolerance and high quality standards are required. In addition to moulding of parts, assembly and packaging can be performed. Vitamol's customer portfolio covers a wide range of markets including Automotive OEMs, Automotive tier 1, Building products, industrial pipeline sealing, leisure industry, electrical & domestic applications and many more. Vitamol have many years of experience in custom moulding, if you have a requirement for a rubber and /or thermoplastic application Vitamol can assist you in to production through the design & development phase*

Vitax Ltd, Owen Street, Coalville, Leicestershire, LE67 3DE Tel: (01530) 510060 Fax: (01530) 510299 E-mail: info@vitax.co.uk *Horticultural chemical & fertilisers product manufrs*

Vitcas Ltd, 16 Clothier Road, Brislington, Bristol, BS4 5PS Tel: 0117 9117895 Fax: 0117 9711152 E-mail: info@vitcas.com *British Manufacturer of Refractory Materials,Refractory Cement,Fire Cement,Fire Bricks,Refractory Castable,Plastic Mouldable,Chemical Resistant Cements,Zircon Product,High Alumina Mortars,Silica Mortars,Vitcas Heatproof Screed,Vitcas Heat Resistant Plaster,Outdoor Pizza Oven,Mouldable Firebricks,Ceramic Fiber Adhesive,Ceramic Fiber Blanket,Fire Clay,Heat Resistant Tile Adhesive,Black Premium Firecement, Refractory Glaze Wash,White Pipe Jointing Compound,Zircon Paint etc.*

Vitec, Oldham Road, Middleton, Manchester, M24 2DB Tel: 0161-653 8231 Fax: 0161-654 8942 E-mail: vitec@kay-metzeler.co.uk *Manufacturers of acoustic insulation materials, foam & glazing tape*

Vitec Group plc, 1 Wheatfield Way, Kingston upon Thames, Surrey, KT1 2TU Tel: (020) 8939 4650 Fax: (020) 8939 4680 E-mail: info@vitecgroup.com *Holding companies*

Vitec Group Communications Ltd, 7400 Beach Drive, Cambridge Research Park, Cambridge, CB25 9TP Tel: (01223) 815000 Fax: (01223) 815001 E-mail: vgc.uk@vitecgroup.com *Manufacturers of digital voice communications systems*

Vitech Scientific Ltd, Unit 14 Huffwood Trading Estate, Partridge Green, Horsham, West Sussex, RH13 8AU Tel: (01403) 710479 Fax: (01403) 710382E-mail: sales@vitech.co.uk *Scientific instrument distributors*

Vitelec Electronics Ltd, Station Road, Bordon, Hampshire, GU35 0LG Tel: (01420) 488661 Fax: (01420) 488014 E-mail: sales@vitelec.co.uk Principal Export Areas: Worldwide *Cable assembly manufrs*

Vitesse plc, Excelda House, 15 Tennis Street, London, SE1 1YD Tel: (020) 7357 7888 Fax: (020) 7357 8855 E-mail: sales@vitesse.plc.uk *Office suppliers*

▶ Vitesse Labelling Products Ltd, Unit 6 Countess Street, Ashton-under-Lyne, Lancashire, OL6 6UE Tel: 0161-343 3883 Fax: 0161-339 0229 E-mail: vitesselabellingproductsltd@ic24.net *Manufacturers of Printed & Plain Labels. All Products including Thermal Transfer/ Direct,Computer,Laser,Security Labels. Printer Ribbons.*Specialists in quick turnround.*

Vitesse Mailing, 17 Wellington Road, London, E10 7QF Tel: (020) 8558 8006 Fax: (020) 8558 8084 E-mail: aziz@vitessemailing.com *Direct mail company*

▶ Vitesse Printing Company Ltd, 18-19 Crimscott Street, London, SE1 5TE Tel: (020) 7274 0120 Fax: (020) 7252 0635 E-mail: sales@vitesseprint.co.uk

Vitra Ltd, 30 Clerkenwell Road, London, EC1M 5PG Tel: (020) 7608 6200 Fax: (020) 7499 1967 E-mail: info_uk@vitra.com *Office furniture manufrs*

Vitrition UK Ltd, 7 Victoria Spring Business Park, Wormald Street, Liversedge, West Yorkshire, WF15 6RA Tel: (01924) 410400 Fax: (01924) 410500 E-mail: jo.pollard@btconnect.com *Suppliers of food ingredients & contract manufacturing services*

▶ Vitrolife UK Ltd, 26 Heriot Watt Research Park, Riccarton, Currie, Midlothian, EH14 4AP Tel: 0131-449 4956

▶ Vittoria Fabrication, Unit 4&5 Vittoria Street, Smethwick, West Midlands, B66 2ND Tel: 0121-565 4343 Fax: 0121-555 5792 *Fabrication & haulage*

Viva Imaging Ltd, Photographic House, Northgate, Nottingham, NG7 7BE Tel: 0115-978 4527 Fax: 0115-978 3791 E-mail: sales@vivaimaging.co.uk *Photographic services*

Viva Science Ltd, Unit 31, Stroud Business Centre, Stonehouse, Gloucestershire, GL10 3RQ Tel: (01453) 821972 Fax: (01453) 827928 *Medical equipment design manufrs*

Vivair Ltd, South View House, 252 High Street, Croydon, CR0 1NF Tel: (020) 8225 1120 Fax: (020) 8260 0054 E-mail: laura.davies@dialaflight.co.uk *Travel agents*

▶ Vivalda Ltd, Unit 27, Bergan Way, Sutton Field Industrial Estate, Hull, HU7 0YQ Tel: (01482) 310865 Fax: (01482) 824946 E-mail: sales@vivalda_hull.co.uk *Insulated & composite panels & cladding suppliers*

▶ Vivatech, Shambria, Woodvill Road, Leatherhead, Surrey, KT22 7BP Tel: (01372) 377362 Fax: (01372) 373927 E-mail: viva.tech@virgin.net *Computer hardware*

Vivelle (U.K.) Ltd, Victoria House, Croft Street, Widnes, Cheshire, WA8 0NQ Tel: 0151-423 6273 Fax: 0151-495 1438 E-mail: vivelle@globalnet.co.uk *Manufacturer of plush fabrics*

Vivian & Holt Kitchen Design Centre, 52a Lymington Road, New Milton, Hampshire, BH25 6PY Tel: (01425) 619963 Fax: (01425) 611114 E-mail: admin@qualitydesignedkitchens.com *Fitted kitchens & appliances designers & suppliers*

Vivid Gaming Ltd, Hilton House, Marston Brewery, Shobnall Road, Burton-on-Trent, Staffordshire, DE14 2BW Tel: (01283) 500066 Fax: (01283) 845432 E-mail: sales@vivid-gaming.com *Amusement machines manufrs*

▶ Vivid Image Ltd, Unit 4, Bamfords Yard, Bamford Lane, Turvey, Bedford, MK43 8DL Tel: (01234) 881515 E-mail: sales@viplimited.co.uk *Graphic design services of brochures, leaflets etc*

▶ Vivid Trading, Mere Farm Bell, Bell Lane, Saham Toney, Thetford, Norfolk, IP25 7HD Tel: (01953) 883264 E-mail: vividmail@hotmail.com *Vivid trading service*

Vivid Views, Aberlan House, Blackburn Industrial Estate, Kinellar, Aberdeen, AB21 0RX Tel: (01224) 798307 Fax: (01224) 790986 E-mail: info@vividviews.co.uk *Multimedia CD production*

▶ Vivista Ltd, Methuen Park, Chippenham, Wiltshire, SN14 0TW Tel: (01249) 443777 Fax: (07002) 929999

Vivitech Ltd, Westgate Lodge, Low Street, North Wheatley, Retford, Nottinghamshire, DN22 9DS Tel: (01427) 881277 Fax: (01427) 883018 E-mail: info@vivitech.co.uk *Industrial control systems designers*

Vivitext Designers, The Old School, Old Hunstanton Road, Hunstanton, Norfolk, PE36 6HZ Tel: (01485) 534566 Fax: (01485) 534828 E-mail: viv@vivitext.co.uk *Graphic design*

Vixen Surface Treatments Ltd, Jay Avenue, Teesside Industrial Estate, Stockton-on-Tees, Cleveland, TS17 9LZ Tel: (01642) 769333 Fax: (01642) 769441 *Manufacturers of shot & blast cleaning equipment*

Vixon Computer Systems, 29-33 Grimsby Road, Cleethorpes, South Humberside, DN35 7AQ Tel: (01472) 362672 Fax: (01472) 350806 E-mail: vixsoft@vixsoft.co.uk *Computer software developers*

Viz Biz Design, 4 24 Ings Road, Wakefield, West Yorkshire, WF1 1DZ Tel: (01924) 377888 Fax: (01924) 385573 E-mail: vizbiz@btconnect.com *Sign manufrs*

Vizio Ltd, Moor Farm Road, Airfield Industrial Estate, Ashbourne, Derbyshire, DE6 1HD Tel: (01335) 300310 Fax: (01335) 300377 E-mail: sales@vizio.co.uk *Washroom, janitorial, hygiene & catering products & services*

▶ Viziononline, 1 Red Place, London, W1K 6PL Tel: 0207 6478699 Fax: 0207 6478699 E-mail: henry@viziononline.co.uk *Web design consultants*

VKHP, 5 Newcomen Road, Tunbridge Wells, Kent, TN4 9PA Tel: (01892) 521841 Fax: (01892) 533149 E-mail: tw@vkhp.co.uk *Civil structural & consulting engineers*

▶ VM UK Ltd, Unit 7 Rough Farm Industrial Estate, Atherstone on Stour, Stratford-upon-Avon, Warwickshire, CV37 8DX Tel: (01789) 459262 Fax: (01789) 459262

▶ VMAL, Unit B3 Connaught Business Centre, London, NW9 6JL Tel: (0845) 1082356 Fax: (0845) 1082357 E-mail: info@vmal.co.uk *Web print & sign design*

VMS UK, 120-126 Holme Lane, Sheffield, S6 4JW Tel: 0114-285 2595 Fax: 0114-231 4145 E-mail: vms@vms.fsbusiness.co.uk *Computing & photocopying services*

▶ Vnet Web Solutions, 46 Clensmore Street, Kidderminster, Worcestershire, DY10 2JS Tel: (01562) 66610 Fax: (01562) 829026 E-mail: vnet@veldonn.co.uk *Internet specialists*

▶ Voakes Of Whixley, Whixley Grange, Boroughbridge Road, Whixley, York, YO26 8AY Tel: (01423) 339988 E-mail: enquiries@voakespies.co.uk *Pie distributors*

Voakes Of Whixley, Whixley Grange, Boroughbridge Road, Whixley, York, YO26 8AY Tel: (01423) 339988 Fax: (01423) 339988 *Pie manufrs*

▶ Vocal Coach Studio, Berry Hill, Mansfield, Nottinghamshire, NG18 4HZ Tel: 01623 474464 E-mail: business@vocalcoachstudio.co.uk

Vocality International Ltd, Lydling Barn Lydling Farm, Puttenham Lane, Shackleford, Godalming, Surrey, GU8 6AP Tel: (01483) 813120 Fax: (01483) 813121 E-mail: sales@vocality.com *Satellite multiplexed services*

Vocalvale Ltd, 2 Yarmouth Road, Hemsby, Great Yarmouth, Norfolk, NR29 4NJ Tel: (01493) 732575 Fax: (01493) 730795 *Alarms installations*

Voco Systems Ltd, 75 The Grove, London, W5 5LL Tel: (020) 8579 8587 Fax: (020) 8840 0018 *Broadcasting equipment manufrs*

Vocom Ltd, Unit 6 Budbrooke Indust Est, Budbrooke Rd, Warwick, CV34 5HG Tel: 01926 493322 Fax: 01926 492870 *Telecommunications*

Voest Alpine Stahl Ltd, Albion Place, London, W6 0QT Tel: (020) 8600 5800 Fax: (020) 8741 3099 E-mail: officelondon@vosetalpine.com *Steel producers & further processing*

Voestalpine Elmsteel Ltd, Dodwells Bridge Industrial Estate, Jacknell Road, Hinckley, Leicestershire, LE10 3BS Tel: (01455) 620300 Fax: (01455) 620320 *Precision tube cutting services*

Voestalpine Polynorm Plastics Ltd, PO Box 9, St. Helens, Merseyside, WA10 6FE Tel: (01744) 743333 Fax: (01744) 743300 *Plastic thermoformed & moulding manufrs*

Vogal Industrial Installations, Regent House, Shrewsbury Avenue, Peterborough, PE2 7WH Tel: 01733 370789 *Plant & machinery installation contractors*

▶ Vogelsang, Unit 10/12, Quakers Coppice, Crewe, CW1 6EW Tel: (01270) 216600 Fax: (01270) 216699 E-mail: sales@vogelsang.co.uk

▶ Denise Vogt, 9 Valley Rise, Leeds, LS13 1HA Tel: 0113-255 2034 E-mail: contact@urtranslated.com *Specialists in German and English translation services to business. *Contact US and UR Translated.*

Vogue Management Services Ltd, Unit 8-10 Strawberry La Industrial Estate, Strawberry Lane, Willenhall, West Midlands, WV13 3RS Tel: (0870) 4030107 Fax: (0870) 4030108 E-mail: info@vogue-uk.co.uk *Bathroom accessories suppliers & manufrs*

Vogue Plastics Machinery Ltd, The Old Sawmill, Elizabeth Street, Macclesfield, Cheshire, SK11 6QL Tel: (01625) 613200 E-mail: js@vogueplastics.com *Selling used machinery*

Voice Connect Ltd, 10-12 Firtree Lane Trading Estate, Groby, Leicester, LE6 0FH Tel: 0116-232 2622 Fax: 0116-232 2433 E-mail: info@voiceconnect.co.uk *Unified messaging*

▶ Voice & Data, Unit4 Devonshire Business Centre, Cranborne Road, Potters Bar, Hertfordshire, EN6 3JR Tel: (01707) 291190 Fax: (0870) 4604233 E-mail: info@voiceanddata.co.uk *Telecommunications*

Voice Products Ltd, Innovation House, Alexander Bell Centre, Hopkinson Way, Andover, Hampshire, SP10 3UR Tel: (0870) 0503870 Fax: (0870) 0503872 E-mail: info@voiceproducts.co.uk *Installers of voice & data solutions*

▶ Voice Squad, 62 Blenheim Gardens, London, NW2 4NT Tel: (020) 8450 4451 E-mail: voices@voicesquad.com *Voice-over agency*

Voiceport Ltd, 49-51 York Road, Brentford, Middlesex, TW8 0QP Tel: (020) 8568 0462 Fax: (020) 8568 4151 E-mail: info@windmillstudios.net *Audio-visual hire services*

Voicescript, 31 Rickford Road, Nailsea, Bristol, BS48 4QB Tel: 01275 791184 E-mail: enquiries@voicescript.co.uk *We offer fast, afforable transcription for all market sectors, including conference services, research and medical. All typists 70+ wpm, UK-based.*

Voith Fabrics Blackburn, Cartmell Road, Blackburn, BB2 2SZ Tel: (01254) 55101 Fax: (01254) 581320 E-mail: info@voith.com *Felt & fabric manufrs* Also at: Sevenoaks

Voith Fabrics Stubbins Ltd, Stubbins Vale Mill, Stubbins Vale Road, Bury, Lancashire, BL0 0NT Tel: (01706) 822951 Fax: (01706) 283401 *Fabric forming services*

Voith Turbo Ltd, 6 Beddington Farm Road, Croydon, CR0 4XB Tel: (020) 8667 0333 Fax: (020) 8667 0403 E-mail: turbo.uk@voith.com *Hydraulic equipment systems distributors*

Voith Turbo Ltd, Meir Road, Park Farm North, Redditch, Worcestershire, B98 7SY Tel: (01527) 516666 Fax: (01527) 516777 E-mail: info@hlhydraulic.demon.co.uk *Hydraulic power unit manufrs*

Vokera Ltd, Stubs Beck Lane, West 26 Business Park, Cleckheaton, West Yorkshire, BD19 4TT Tel: (01274) 866112 Fax: (01274) 86555 *Heat appliance manufrs*

Vokera Ltd, Borderlake House, Unit 7 & 8, Riverside Industrial Estate, London Colney By Pass, London Colney, St. Albans, Hertfordshire, AL2 1HG Tel: (01442) 281400 Fax: (01442) 450565 E-mail: enquiries@vokera.co.uk *Manufacturers of Domestic Gas Fired Boilers*

Vokes Ltd, Henley Park, Normandy, Guildford, Surrey, GU3 2AF Tel: (01483) 569971 Fax: (01483) 235384 E-mail: sales@vokes.com *Filtration technology & engineering*

Vokins At Home, Denton Island, Newhaven, East Sussex, BN9 9BB Tel: (01273) 612485 Fax: (01273) 612230 E-mail: info@vokinsathome.com *Beds, bedding & blankets retailers*

B. Voles & Son Ltd, 279 Chiswick High Road, London, W4 4PU Tel: (020) 8994 0984 Fax: (020) 8747 8918 E-mail: mail@voles.co.uk *Electrical contractors*

Volex, Butts Mill, Butts Street, Leigh, Lancashire, WN7 3AD Tel: (01942) 672393 Fax: (01942) 677395 E-mail: sales@volexwiring.com *Electrical cable assemblies & harness manufrs*

▶ Volex Group P.L.C., 124 St James Business Centre, Linwood Road, Paisley, Renfrewshire, PA3 3AT Tel: 0141-849 1818

Volex Group plc, Dornoch House, Kelvin Close, Birchwood, Warrington, WA3 7JX Tel: (01925) 830101 Fax: (01925) 830141 *Holding company*

Volga-Dnepr UK Ltd, Endeavour House, Coopers End Road, London Stansted Airport, Stansted, Essex, CM24 1HA Tel: (01279) 661166 Fax: (01279) 661103 E-mail: dennis.gliznoutsa@volga-dnepr.co.uk Principal Export Areas: Worldwide *Cargo specialists*

▶ Volker Stevin Ltd, 152-154 Coles Green Road, London, NW2 7HD Tel: (020) 8438 6380 Fax: (020) 8438 6414 E-mail: info.london@volkerstevin.co.uk *Civil engineers*

VolkerBrooks Ltd, Whitegate, White Lund Industrial Estate, Morecambe, Lancashire, LA3 3BY Tel: (01524) 599400 Fax: (01524) 599401 E-mail: info.vb@volkerstevin.co.uk *Steel fabrication, formwork & crawler crane hire*

VolkerSteel Foundations Ltd, Springwell Road, Springwell, Gateshead, Tyne & Wear, NE9 7SP Tel: 0191-417 3545 Fax: 0191-416 2894 E-mail: info.ss@volkerstevin.co.uk *Steel piling contractors & stockists*

Volkl Tennis (UK) Ltd, Unit38 Chadkirk Business Park, Vale Road, Romiley, Stockport, Cheshire, SK6 3NE Tel: 0161-484 5151 Fax: 0161-427 8000 *Tennis racquet distributors*

Volkobind Engineering Company Ltd, Unit 1 Tansey Green Trading Estate, Tansey Green Road, Brierley Hill, West Midlands, DY5 4TA Tel: (01384) 79746 Fax: (01384) 75737 E-mail: sales@volkobind.co.uk *General engineers & press tool manufrs*

Vollmer UK Ltd, Orchard Park Industrial Estate, Town Street, Sandiacre, Nottingham, NG10 5BP Tel: 0115-949 1040 Fax: 0115-949 0042 E-mail: admin@vollmer-uk.com *Manufacturers of bandsawing servicing equipment*

Voltech Instruments Ltd, 148 Harwell International Business Centre, Harwell, Didcot, Oxfordshire, OX11 0RA Tel: (01235) 834555 Fax: (01235) 835016 E-mail: sales@voltech.co.uk Principal Export Areas: Worldwide *Electronic test equipment manufrs*

Voltek Automation, Churchill Way, Nelson, Lancashire, BB9 6RT Tel: (0870) 7454971 Fax: (0870) 7454972 E-mail: sales@voltek.co.uk *Electronic security systems*

Voltex Electronics Ltd, Octagon House, Bradford Road, Sandbeds, Keighley, West Yorkshire, BD20 5LY Tel: (01274) 510668 Fax: (01274) 510669 E-mail: sales@voltexelectronics.com *Cable management systems manufrs*

Volts Vehicle Auto Electrical Blandford Dorset, 9 Chettle, Chettle City, Blandford Forum, Dorset, DT11 8DB Tel: (01258) 830624 E-mail: volts@billynet.co.uk *Blandford Vehicle Auto Electrics Electrician Electricail Electronics Wiltshire Dorset diagnostics diagnostic engineer 01258 830624 volts.org.uk*

Volume Design Associates, The Studio, 22 Kings Road, High Wycombe, Buckinghamshire, HP11 1SA Tel: (01494) 459989 Fax: (01494) 459089 E-mail: info@vda.co.uk *Internet site design & creation services*

Volume Ventalation Ltd, The Old Quarry, Springwell Lane, Rickmansworth, Hertfordshire, WD3 8UX Tel: (01923) 770331 Fax: (01923) 290313 E-mail: sales@volvent.com *Ventilation & extraction services*

Volvina Ltd, 1-3 Duke Street, Northampton, NN1 3BE Tel: (01604) 633044 Fax: (01604) 629868 E-mail: volvina@curtains-uk.com *Curtain & blinds manufrs*

Volvo Aero Services, The Mill, Abbey Mill Business Park, Lower Eashing, Godalming, Surrey, GU7 2QJ Tel: (0870) 2422436 Fax: (01483) 523799 *Aircraft equipment sales*

Volvo Construction Equipment Ltd, Portobello Road, Birtley, Chester le Street, County Durham, DH3 2RR Tel: 0191-410 9863 Fax: 0191-410 7617 *Retailers, service providers & repairers of earth moving goods*

Volvo Construction Equipment, First Avenue, Minworth, Sutton Coldfield, West Midlands, B76 1BA Tel: 0121-351 7711 Fax: 0121-313 1480 *Car parts & maintenance*

Volvo Group UK Ltd, Wedgnock Lane, Warwick, CV34 5YA Tel: (01926) 401777 Fax: (01926) 490991 E-mail: recruitment@newskies.com *One of Europe's largest Volvo dealership for commercial vehicles, sell, repair & service new & used trucks, sell parts for all makes & offer a full range of finance & warranty packages*

Volvo Truck, Pytchley Lodge Road Industrial Estate, Pytchley Lodge Road, Kettering, Northamptonshire, NN15 6JJ Tel: (01536) 516311 Fax: (01536) 412386 *One of Europe's largest Volvo dealerships for commercial vehicles, sell, repair & service new & used trucks, sell parts for all makes & offer a full range of finance & warranty packages* Also at: Kempstown, Leicester & Peterborough

Volvo Truck & Bus Scotland Ltd, 9 Fifty Pitches Place, Glasgow, G51 4GA Tel: 0141-810 2777 Fax: 0141-810 2788 E-mail: enquiries@volvoscot.co.uk *Commercial vehicle distributors*

▶ Volvo Truck & Bus South, Delaware Drive, Tongwell, Milton Keynes, MK15 8JH Tel: (01908) 210525 Fax: (01908) 840064 E-mail: sales@vtbsouth.co.uk *Truck & bus service & repair, truck rental, vehicle recovery, mobile service, technical department, MOT testing & preparation. Parts services, parts delivery, emergency parts ordering (V.O.R), warranty cover, non-Volvo parts, workshop consumables*

Volvo Truck South Ltd, Station Road, Stoney Stanton, Leicester, LE9 4LU Tel: (01455) 273260 Fax: (01455) 272092 *One of Europe's largest Volvo dealerships for commercial vehicles, sell, repair & service new & used trucks, sell parts for all makes & offer a full range of finance & warranty packages*

Von Roll UK Ltd, Unit 6, Lawrence Way, Dunstable, Bedfordshire, LU6 1BD Tel: (01582) 500500 Fax: (01582) 476456 E-mail: wire@vonroll.com *Manufacturers of wire (insulated, copper & enamelled) & copper strip*

Vopak Terminal Teeside Ltd, Seal Sands, Middlesbrough, Cleveland, TS2 1UA Tel: (01642) 546767 Fax: (01642) 543600 *Bulk liquid chemical storage contractors*

Vordale Ltd, Irthlingborough Road, Little Addington, Kettering, Northamptonshire, NN14 4AS Tel: (01933) 652330 Fax: (01933) 651592 *Engineering services*

Vortex Communications Ltd, 75 The Grove, London, W5 5LL Tel: (020) 8579 2743 Fax: (020) 8840 0018 E-mail: info@vtx.co.uk *Broadcast equipment manufrs*

Vortex Computers Ltd, 13-15 St. Michaels Square, Ashton-under-Lyne, Lancashire, OL6 6LF Tel: 0161-343 5555 Fax: 0161-343 7777 E-mail: sales@vortex.manc.co.uk *Computer maintenance & repairs*

Vortex Hydra UK Ltd, Kingmoor Industrial Estate, Kingmoor Road, Carlisle, CA3 9QJ Tel: (01228) 510800 Fax: (01228) 510808 E-mail: vh_sales_uk@vortexhydra.com *Roof tile machine manufrs*

Vortex T Shirts Ltd, 2 Grange Lane Industrial Estate, Carrwood Road, Barnsley, South Yorkshire, S71 5AS Tel: (01226) 202329 Fax: (01226) 249748 E-mail: sales@vortexuk.com *Garment decoration printing & embroidery manufrs*

Vortok International, 6-7 Haxter Close, Roborough, Plymouth, PL6 7DD Tel: (01752) 700601 Fax: (01752) 702353 E-mail: sales@vortok.co.uk *Railway maintenance products*

▶ Vos Logistics Cargo, Oxnam Road, Jedburgh, Roxburghshire, TD8 6NN Tel: (01835) 864972 Fax: (01835) 863953 E-mail: cmercer@voslogistics.com

▶ Vosper International Ltd, 7 Killermont View, Glasgow, G20 0TZ Tel: 0141-945 5529 E-mail: design@vosper.co.uk

Vossloh-Schwabe (UK) Ltd, 42 Tanners Drive, Blakelands, Milton Keynes, MK14 5BW Tel: (01908) 517800 Fax: (01908) 517817 E-mail: sales@vsuk.vossloh.com *Lamp holders & lighting components distributors*

Votex Hereford Ltd, Redhill Depot, Ross Road, Hereford, HR2 8BH Tel: (01432) 274361 Fax: (01432) 352743 E-mail: sales@votex.co.uk *Agricultural machinery manufrs*

Vox Solutions Ltd, 8 Adlington Court, Birchwood, Warrington, WA3 6PL Tel: (0870) 7770660 Fax: (0870) 0113552 E-mail: sales@voxsolutions.co.uk *Communication equipment distribution*

▶ Voxar Ltd, Bonnington Bond, 2 Anderson Place, Edinburgh, EH6 5NP Tel: 0131-472 4792

▶ Voyager Computers, 90a Frankwell, Shrewsbury, SY3 8JR Tel: 01743 341755 E-mail: voyagercomputers@hotmail.com *Computer upgrades and repairs. We are also experts in configuring P.C"s to specification.*

▶ Voyager Foods, B Sunrise Enterprise Park, Ferryboat Lane, Sunderland, SR5 3RX Tel: 0191-549 5700 Fax: 0191-549 3418

▶ Voyager Site Services, Ashton Clough Road, Liversedge, West Yorkshire, WF15 6JX Tel: (07870) 588297 E-mail: voyagersiteservices@aol.com *Structural steel fabrication*

Voyager Yachts Ltd, Southdown Quay, Millbrook, Torpoint, Cornwall, PL10 1HG Tel: (01752) 823329 Fax: (01752) 822354 *Boat builders*

▶ VP Commercial Ltd, 22 Timor Grove, Stoke-on-Trent, ST4 8RR Tel: (01782) 646660 Fax: 01782 646672 E-mail: vp@vp-com.co.uk *Vending & Procurement of Shopfitting and Catering Equipment.*Specialist in the Bakery Fresh Food Retail Market.*

Vpe, 7 Verwood Industrial Estate, Blackhill, Verwood, Dorset, BH31 6HA Tel: (01202) 827205 Fax: (01202) 827207 E-mail: sales@vpeltd.co.uk *Manufacturers of plastic tubes, pipes & profiles*

VPM Ltd, Birch House, Fraser Road, Erith, Kent, DA8 1QX Tel: (01322) 430043 Fax: (01322) 430044 E-mail: comptonshaun@aol.com *Toolmakers*

VPoint TV Ltd, 1 First Avenue, Sherwood Rise, Nottingham, NG7 6JL Tel: 0115-969 3636 Fax: 0115-969 3434 E-mail: mail@vpoint.tv *Video production & edititors*

Vredestein (UK) Ltd, Unit D, Whittle Close, Park Farm Industrial Estate, Wellingborough, Northamptonshire, NN8 6TY Tel: (01933) 677770 Fax: (01933) 675329 E-mail: customer.uk@vredestein.com *Tyre distributors*

▶ V-Seal Ltd, Mill Lane, Halifax, West Yorkshire, HX3 6TR Tel: (01422) 300009 Fax: (01422) 363025

▶ VSG, 1 Linthouse Road, Glasgow, G51 4BZ Tel: 0141-440 4140

▶ Vsiblehealth, Cheviot Way, Verwood, Dorset, BH31 6UG Tel: (01202) 813572 *We at visiblehealth are dedicating in supplying the best health and beauty products around today.*

▶ VSI-Thinking, Royal Stuart Workshops Unit 8, Adelaide Place, Cardiff, CF10 5BR Tel: (029) 2033 1188 Fax: (029) 2025 1400 E-mail: jon@vsi-thinking.com *VSI-thinking are web solution developers providing e-business solutions. **We develop web based business applications for content management, business information systems and value added services. **Our web sites have a proven track record of success and awards. Our Neilson Active Holidays web site as winner of the 'Best marine web site' and 'Best contribution to the marine industry', at the London Olympia Boat Show 2003. **VSI Thinking has a blue chip client base including companies as diverse as Thomas Cook, AVIS, Neilson, Appeals Service Judicary and SPC International. **

Vstore Ltd, Unit 6, Maxwell Road, Peterborough, PE2 7HU Tel: (01733) 238448 Fax: (01733) 238142 E-mail: ken@vstore.co.uk *Mobile phones & accessories services*

VT Halmatic Ltd, Hamilton Road, Cosham, Portsmouth, PO6 4PX Tel: (023) 9253 9600 Fax: (023) 9253 9601 E-mail: info@halmatic.com *Commercial & military boat builders*

▶ VTC Vehicle Tecnology, Media House, Capricorn Park, Blakewater Road, Blackburn, BB1 5QH Tel: (01254) 667330 Fax: (01254) 667341 E-mail: cevans@vtcctv.com *Interactive plant security, mobile CCTV, lone worker systems*

VTEC Industry Europe, Eagleside House, Chantry Street, Andover, Hampshire, SP10 1DE Tel: (01264) 336901 Fax: (01264) 355768 E-mail: sales@vtec.co.uk *Computer memory suppliers*

VTS Royalite, Cliftonhall Road, Newbridge, Midlothian, EH28 8PW Tel: 0131-333 3369 Fax: 0131-333 5161 E-mail: sales@vtsroyalite.co.uk *Thermoplastic sheet manufrs*

Vue, 187 Cross Street, Sale, Cheshire, M33 7JG Tel: 0161-962 4356 Fax: 0161-973 5060 E-mail: sales@vue-cctv.co.uk *Closed circuit television retailers*

▶ Vulcan Aluminium Ltd, 37A Copenhagen Road, Hull, HU7 0XQ Tel: (01482) 830500

Vulcan Engineering Ltd, Troutbeck Road, Sheffield, S7 2QA Tel: 0114-249 3333 Fax: 0114-249 3322 E-mail: service@vulcan-eng.com *Seal distributors & manufrs*

Vulcan Europe, 9 New Star Road, Leicester, LE4 9JD Tel: 0116-246 0055 Fax: 0116-246 1142 E-mail: sales@vulcaneurope.com Principal Export Areas: Worldwide *Foundry equipment manufrs*

Vulcan Industrial Fasteners Ltd, Unit 6, Emerald Way, Stone Business Park, Stone, Staffordshire, ST15 0SR Tel: (01785) 818494 Fax: (01785) 818399 E-mail: sales@vulcanfasteners.co.uk *Industrial fastener distributors & agents*

Vulcan Plastics Ltd, Hosey Hill, Westerham, Kent, TN16 1TZ Tel: (01959) 562304 *Roof & light window manufrs*

Vulcan Refractories Ltd, Brookhouse Industrial Estate, Cheadle, Stoke-on-Trent, ST10 1PN Tel: (01538) 752238 Fax: (01538) 753349 E-mail: sales@vulcan-refractories.co.uk *Heating element & refractory manufrs*

Vulcan Stove Enamelling Ltd, Station Road, East Preston, Littlehampton, West Sussex, BN16 3AA Tel: (01903) 770287 Fax: (01903) 783426 *Powder coating services*

▶ Vulcan Tanks Ltd, Cotes Park Lane, Cotes Park Industrial Estate, Somercotes, Alfreton, Derbyshire, DE55 4NJ Tel: (01773) 835321 Fax: (01773) 836578 E-mail: sales@vulcantanks.co.uk *Storage tank manufacturer, supplier & erector*

Vulcana Gas Appliances Ltd, 30 Bridge Road, Haywards Heath, West Sussex, RH16 1TX Tel: (01444) 415871 Fax: (01444) 441433 E-mail: vulcanagas@pavilion.co.uk *Commercial gas heating equipment manufrs*

▶ Vulcascot Ltd, Gatwick Gate Industrial Estate, Lowfield Heath, Crawley, West Sussex, RH11 0TG Tel: (01293) 560130 Fax: (01293) 537743 E-mail: sales@vulcascot.co.uk *Manufacturers of cable protectors, industrial laminates & plastics*

Vulcascot Ltd, Braintree Road, Ruislip, Middlesex, HA4 0XX Tel: (020) 8841 4211 Fax: (020) 8841 3544 *Plastics sheet material stockholders* Also at: Bristol & Leicester

Vulkan Industries Ltd, Archer Road, Armytage Road Industrial Estate, Brighouse, West Yorkshire, HD6 1XF Tel: (01484) 712273 Fax: (01484) 721376 E-mail: sales@vulkan.co.uk *Industrial manufacturers of flexible couplings*

Vultron International Ltd, Unit 2 City Park Industrial Estate, Gelderd Road, Leeds, LS12 6DR Tel: 0113-263 0323 Fax: 0113-279 4127 E-mail: vultronuk@aol.com Principal Export Areas: Worldwide *Suppliers of electronic display boards*

VWS Westgarth Ltd, Orbital House, 3 Redwood Crescent, East Kilbride, Glasgow, G74 5PR Tel: (01355) 588038 Fax: (01355) 588001 *Manufacturers of water treatment plants & desalination & equipment*

▶ Vycon Products Ltd, Western Road, Kilmarnock, Ayrshire, KA3 1NG Tel: (01563) 574481 Fax: (01563) 533537 E-mail: sales@vycon.co.uk *Manufacture customized packaging*

▶ Vydas International Marketing, Swan House, Passfield Business Centre, Lynchborough Road, Passfield, Liphook, Hampshire, GU30 7SB Tel: (01428) 751822 Fax: (01428) 751833 E-mail: info@vydas.co.uk *Specialist sensors distributors*

Vye's Hove Ltd, 17-26 Carlton Terrace, Portslade, Brighton, BN41 1XF Tel: (01273) 412191 Fax: (01273) 415659 *Motor crash & paint repairs*

▶ indicates data change since last edition

Vygon UK Ltd, Bridge Road, Cirencester, Gloucestershire, GL7 1PT Tel: (01285) 657051 Fax: (01285) 650293 E-mail: vygon@vygon.co.uk *Disposable medical products distributors*

George Vyner Ltd, PO Box 1, Holmfirth, HD9 7YP Tel: (01484) 685221 Fax: (01484) 688538 *Account book publishers & distributors*

Vyner Litho Plates, 4 Kingside, Ruston Road, London, SE18 5BX Tel: (020) 8854 5544 E-mail: vyners@compuserve.com *Lithographic plate manufrs*

Vysal Lighting Ltd, Five Acres, Morse Close, Malmesbury, Wiltshire, SN16 9UW Tel: (01666) 822059 Fax: (01666) 822422 E-mail: vysal@vysal.com *Light fittings & under floor heating manufrs*

▶ Vytran UK Ltd, 8 Kew Court Pynes Hill, Rydon Lane, Exeter, EX2 5AZ Tel: (01392) 445777 Fax: (01392) 445009 *Sales & support of optical fibre recoaters & splicers*

VZS Seagoe Advanced Ceramics, 35-38 Cavendish Way, Glenrothes, Fife, KY6 2SB Tel: (01592) 630505 Fax: (01592) 773192 E-mail: sales@vzs-seagoe.com *Industrial ceramic product manufrs*

W + S Measuring Systems Ltd, Queens House, The Square, Corwen, Clwyd, LL21 0DG Tel: (01490) 413550 Fax: (01490) 413014 E-mail: info.uk@globalencoder.com *Sensors & encoders manufrs*

▶ W A A Eddie Ltd, Blochairn Road, Glasgow, G21 1HL Tel: 0141-333 1919 Fax: 0141-333 0909 E-mail: sales@waaeddie.co.uk *Fresh fish*

W A Banham & Sons Ltd, The Pipeworks, Eye Road, Hoxne, Eye, Suffolk, IP21 5BA Tel: (01379) 668268 Fax: (01379) 668268 *Demolition contractors*

W & A Baxter, 269 Gunters Bridge, Petworth, West Sussex, GU28 9JJ Tel: (01798) 342561 Fax: (01798) 342275 *Building contractors*

▶ W A Billing, 53 Catley Road, Sheffield, S9 5JF Tel: 0114-242 4233 Fax: 0114-242 4266 E-mail: sales@wabilling.co.uk *Aluminium Fabrications and manufacture of Press Tools for long life and ease of use*

W A C Mccandless Engineering Ltd, 95-99 Limestone Road, Belfast, BT15 3AB Tel: (028) 9035 1811 Fax: (028) 9074 6015 E-mail: sales@wacmccandless.com *Engineering parts distributors*

W A Carr Engineering Ltd, 60 Broad Oaks, Sheffield, S9 3HJ Tel: 0114-256 2222 Fax: 0114-256 2474 *General engineers*

W A Daw & Son, Hans Farm, Ruckinge, Ashford, Kent, TN26 2PX Tel: (01233) 732311 *Agriculture*

W A Deacon & Sons Ltd, 1 High Street, Lavenham, Sudbury, Suffolk, CO10 9PY Tel: (01787) 247389 Fax: (01787) 248581

W A Durose & Son, Lordspiece, Stanton, Ashbourne, Derbyshire, DE6 2DD Tel: (01335) 324316 *Agricultural contractors*

W A Ellwood Signs, 1 Ferry Lane, Rainham, Essex, RM13 9YH Tel: (01708) 521703 Fax: (01708) 521703 *Neon signs manufrs*

W A Engineering (Nuneaton) Ltd, Carlyon Road, Carlyon Road Industrial Estate, Atherstone, Warwickshire, CV9 1LQ Tel: (01827) 715188 Fax: (01827) 717168 E-mail: sales@waengineering.co.uk *Precision & cnc engineers*

W A Fairhurst & Partners, 88 Queens Road, Aberdeen, AB15 4YQ Tel: (01224) 321222 Fax: (01224) 323201 E-mail: sales@fairhurst.co.uk *Consulting engineers*

W A Fairhurst & Partners, 1 Arngrove Court, Newcastle upon Tyne, NE4 6DB Tel: 0191-221 0505 Fax: 0191-221 0949 E-mail: newcastle@fairhurst.co.uk *Consultants construction & civil engineers*

W A Farm Supplies Ltd, The Group Office Wallett Court, Southenden Road, Headcorn, Ashford, Kent, TN27 9LN Tel: (01622) 890835 Fax: (01622) 890830 *Agricultural services*

W A Fox Knitting Co Ltd, Unit 12-13 Premier Works, Canal Street, Wigston, Leicestershire, LE18 4PL Tel: 0116-277 2592 *Knitwear trimmings, knitted collars, cuffs & sportswear manufrs*

W A Hare & Son Ltd, 94 Main Street, Kelfield, York, YO19 6RG Tel: (01757) 248188 Fax: (01757) 248999 E-mail: sales@wahare.com *Building contractors/joinery manufrs*

▶ W A Humphreys International Transport Ltd, Unit 8 Ely Valley Industrial Estate, Pontyclun, Mid Glamorgan, CF72 9DZ Tel: (01443) 226582 Fax: (01443) 237647

W A Humphries Ltd, 65 Hunters Vale, Birmingham, B19 2XH Tel: 0121-554 0125 Fax: 0121-554 0155 *Silver plate manufrs*

W A Hutton & Co. Ltd, 37 School Lane, Stockport, Cheshire, SK4 5DE Tel: 0161-431 5500 Fax: 0161-442 1318 E-mail: sales@wahutton.co.uk *Office equipment suppliers*

▶ W A Jaines & Son Ltd, Warwick Road, Fairfield Industrial Estate, Louth, Lincolnshire, LN11 0YB Tel: (01507) 606497 Fax: (01507) 600505

W A Mcgarrie & Son Ltd, Friarton Road, Perth, PH2 8BB Tel: (01738) 631194 Fax: (01738) 633814 E-mail: office@mcgarrie.net *Sheet metalworkers balustrades*

W.& A.Ross Ltd, 55 Days Road, St Phillips, St. Philips, Bristol, BS2 0QS Tel: 0117-955 8855 Fax: 0117-935 0518 E-mail: sales@rossofficesupplies.co.uk *Commercial & legal stationers*

W A S O 2000, 15 Park Avenue, Cheadle Hulme, Cheadle, Cheshire, SK8 6EU Tel: (0870) 9027979 Fax: 0161-428 1790 E-mail: sales@waso.co.uk *Incar audio & entertainment*

W A S P Hockey, 5 Healey New Mills, Healey Road, Ossett, West Yorkshire, WF5 8NF Tel: (01924) 278053 Fax: (01924) 278053 E-mail: sales@wasphockey.co.uk *Field hockey sports goods manufrs*

W A Simpson Marine Ltd, 1 Logie Avenue, Dundee, DD2 2AS Tel: (01382) 566670 Fax: (01382) 668661 E-mail: admin@wasimpsonmarine.com *Boat builders & glass fibre moulders services*

W A Skinner & Co UK Ltd, Dorset Way, Byfleet, West Byfleet, Surrey, KT14 7LB Tel: (01932) 344228 Fax: (01932) 348517 *Fencing contractors*

▶ W A Willson Ltd, 24 Church Street, Hoo, Rochester, Kent, ME3 9AL Tel: (01634) 251096 Fax: (01634) 253845

▶ W Accountancy Ltd, 369 Hertford Road, Enfield, Middlesex, EN3 5JW Tel: (020) 8804 0478 Fax: (020) 8804 0221 E-mail: c.wheatley@waccountancy.co.uk *Accountancy & taxation services*

W Accountancy Ltd, Victoria Rdknaphill, Knaphill, Woking, Surrey, GU21 2AA Tel: (01483) 797901 Fax: (01483) 797899 E-mail: m.wood@waccountancy.co.uk *Accountancy, taxation & business consultancy*

▶ W Allen Bolton Ltd, James Street, Westhoughton, Bolton, BL5 3QR Tel: (01942) 818888 Fax: (01942) 818886

W Andrews (Signs), 17 Rees House, Burnhall Industrial Estate, Fleetwood, Lancashire, FY7 8RS Tel: (01253) 826862 Fax: (01253) 826862 *Sign makers*

W B Alloy Products Ltd, 37 Dalsetter Avenue, Glasgow, G15 8TE Tel: 0141-944 5500 Fax: 0141-944 9000 *Welding electrode manufrs*

▶ W B B Minerals Ltd, Levenseat Quarry, Fauld House, Bathgate, West Lothian, EH47 9AD Tel: (01270) 752752 Fax: (01501) 772621 *WND*

W B B Minerals Ltd, North Devon Works, Peters Marland, Torrington, Devon, EX38 8QE Tel: (01805) 602200 Fax: (01805) 602201 *Ball clay extraction & processing services*

▶ W B Bradford Measham Ltd, 45 High Street, Measham, Swadlincote, Derbyshire, DE12 7HR Tel: (01530) 272870 Fax: (01530) 271521

▶ W B Chadbourn Scaffolding & Industrial Screens Ltd, Unit 9 Curriers Close, Charter Avenue Industrial Esta, Coventry, CV4 8AW Tel: (024) 7646 2742 Fax: (024) 7646 4652 E-mail: jackie@chadbourn.co.uk *Specialist asbestos licensed scaffolding*

W B Engineering, 13 Paynes Lane, Rugby, Warwickshire, CV21 2UH Tel: (01788) 565225 Fax: (01788) 565225 *Steel fabricators*

▶ W B Floor Machines, Unit 7 Burns Way, Holmbush Potteries Indust Estate, Faygate, Horsham, West Sussex, RH12 4ST Tel: (01293) 852122 Fax: (0870) 7707208 E-mail: info@wbfloormachines.co.uk *Cleaning equipment suppliers*

▶ W B Formwork Co 1990, Atlas Works, Robinson Street, Stalybridge, Cheshire, SK15 1TH Tel: 0161-338 4543 Fax: 0161-338 8269

W B J Ltd, Metrology House, Dukinfield Road, Hyde, Cheshire, SK14 4SD Tel: 0161-367 9898 Fax: 0161-367 9700 E-mail: admin@wbj.co.uk *Gauge repair/engineers' table makers*

W B Muddeman & Son Ltd, The Scope Complex, Wills Road, Totnes, Devon, TQ9 5XN Tel: (01803) 862058 Fax: (01803) 866273 E-mail: su4555@eclipse.co.uk *Wholesale jewellers & importers*

▶ W B Power Services Ltd, Manners Avenue, Manners Industrial Estate, Ilkeston, Derbyshire, DE7 8EF Tel: 0115-930 0359 Fax: 0115-944 4433 E-mail: sales@wbpsltd.co.uk

W B Power Source Ltd, Brandon Way, West Bromwich, West Midlands, B70 8JB Tel: 0121-525 4441 Fax: 0121-525 4446 *Traction batteries*

W B S Consulting, Grove Business Centre, Grove Technology Park, Wantage, Oxfordshire, OX12 9FF Tel: (01235) 227434 Fax: (01235) 227435 E-mail: enquiries@wwbsgroup.com *Business improvement service*

W B Swift Ltd, Leafland Street, Halifax, West Yorkshire, HX1 4LX Tel: (01422) 358073 Fax: (01422) 330360 E-mail: wbswift@nildram.co.uk *Textile engineers*

W Ball & Son Holdings Ltd, Albion Works, Burr Lane, Ilkeston, Derbyshire, DE7 5JD Tel: 0115-932 2403 Fax: 0115-944 0630 E-mail: sales@baltex.co.uk *Warp knitted fabric manufrs*

W Barker & Sons, Broughton Nook, School House Lane, Abbots Bromley, Rugeley, Staffordshire, WS15 3BT Tel: (01283) 840266 Fax: (01283) 840562 *Live stock contractor*

W Baybutt Ltd, Plantation Road, Burscough Industrial Estate, Ormskirk, Lancashire, L40 8JT Tel: (01704) 892905 Fax: (01704) 892262 *Road haulage & warehousing services*

W Bertram & Sons Ltd, Walpole Street, South Shields, Tyne & Wear, NE33 5EF Tel: 0191-455 6727 Fax: 0191-455 6727 *Boiler repairs & steel fabricators*

W Brewin & Co Ltd, Eastern Boulevard, Leicester, LE2 7BE Tel: 0116-254 6372 Fax: 0116-254 2856 *Hosiery manufrs*

W Brown & Sons, Wreigh View, Thropton, Morpeth, Northumberland, NE65 7NA Tel: (01669) 620349 Fax: (01669) 621541 *Builders*

W Bryer & Sons Ltd, 25a Hatton Garden, London, EC1N 8BN Tel: (020) 7404 9090 Fax: (020) 7404 9191 *Wholesale jewellers-silversmiths*

W Burkinshaw, Bath Steel Works, Penistone Road, Sheffield, S6 3AJ Tel: 0114-272 3777 Fax: 0114-272 3777 *Forging manufrs*

W Button & Co. Ltd, Larchfield Works, Larchfield Road, Leeds, LS10 1QP Tel: 0113-270 4287 Fax: 0113-277 6975 E-mail: wbuttonco@aol.com *Woodworkers*

W C A Leisure Machines Ltd, 4 Newnham Road, Plympton, Plymouth, PL7 4AN Tel: (01752) 336651 Fax: (01752) 340892 *Servicing & supplying of amusement machines*

W C Commercials Ltd, Stanbridge Road, Great Billington, Leighton Buzzard, Bedfordshire, LU7 9JH Tel: (01525) 851797 Fax: (01525) 851798 E-mail: wccom@fsbdial.co.uk *Commercial vehicle repairers*

W C Evans & Sons, Limes Avenue, London, SE20 8QR Tel: (020) 8676 0047 Fax: (020) 8676 8268 E-mail: wcevans.ltd@btinternet.com *Metal engineering & building contractors*

▶ W C F Fuels North West, Station Goods Yard, Warton Road, Carnforth, Lancashire, LA5 9EU Tel: (01524) 733669 Fax: (01524) 720077 E-mail: sales@wcfnorthwest.co.uk *Oil distribution*

W C Hunkin & Sons, 1 Passage Lane, Fowey, Cornwall, PL23 1JS Tel: (01726) 832874 Fax: (01726) 832001 *Boat builders*

▶ W C L (Holdings) Ltd, 12 Foxley Hill Road, Purley, Surrey, CR8 2HB Tel: (020) 8763 9903 Fax: (020) 8763 9913 E-mail: wclholdings@aol.com *Building contractor*refubishment*alterations & extensions*

W C Martin & Co Ltd, Cumbernauld House, Cumbernauld, Glasgow, G67 3JG Tel: (01236) 868000 Fax: (01236) 868111 *Electrical contractors*

W C Munsch & Co., Unit Ag2 3 Clarence Business Park, Clarence Road, Bollington, Macclesfield, Cheshire, SK10 5JZ Tel: (01625) 573971 Fax: (01625) 573250 E-mail: sales@wcmunsch.co.uk *Rubber product distribs*

W C S Computer Services, Sovereign House, 53 Broadwater Street West, Worthing, West Sussex, BN14 9BY Tel: (01903) 209320 Fax: (01903) 232767 E-mail: admin@wcscomputers.com *Computer retailers*

W C S Environmental Ltd, Home Close Stables, Station Road, Iron Acton, Bristol, BS37 9TA Tel: (01454) 227122 Fax: (01454) 227190 *Water control services*

W C Stopher, Homeview, Halesworth Road, Redisham, Beccles, Suffolk, NR34 8NF Tel: (01986) 781253 *Agricultural contractors*

W C Thornton & Son Ltd, Brook House, Garstang Road, Bilsborrow, Preston, PR3 0RD Tel: (01995) 640212 Fax: (01995) 641063 *Agricultural merchants*

W Campbell, 11 Kedar Bank, Mouswald, Dumfries, DG1 4LU Tel: (01387) 830239 *Agricultural contractors*

W Campbell & Son Ltd, Harpings Road, Hull, HU5 4JG Tel: (01482) 444422 Fax: (01482) 444424 *Steel fabrication contractors*

▶ W Carter, Alconbury Airfield, Alconbury, Huntingdon, Cambridgeshire, PE28 4WX Tel: (01480) 453355 Fax: (01480) 454265

W Carters (Haulage) Ltd, Sub Station Road, The Dock, Felixstowe, Suffolk, IP11 3JB Tel: (01394) 676623 Fax: (01394) 673560 *Road transport, haulage & freight services*

W Christie & Co. Ltd, 22 Crownpoint Road, Glasgow, G40 2BS Tel: 0141-951 1265 Fax: 0141-556 1444 E-mail: sales@wchristie.co.uk *Marine & catering equipment distributors*

W Christie (Industrial) Ltd, Christie House, Meadow Bank Road, Rotherham, South Yorkshire, S61 2NF Tel: (01709) 550088 Fax: (01709) 550030 E-mail: sales@wchristie.com *Total Torque Solutions. Sales, hire & calibration of torque tools for industry wide bolt tightening applications. Range includes precision pneumatic, hydraulic & electric torque tools. ISO 9001 & UKAS quality management certified.*

W Clarke, 98 Cardiff Road, Llandaff, Cardiff, CF5 2DT Tel: (029) 2056 2058 Fax: (029) 2056 2180 E-mail: wmcllandaff@aol.com *Church furnishers & restoration specialists*

W Coates & Sons Nottingham Ltd, Montpelier Road, Nottingham, NG7 2JW Tel: 0115-978 5103 Fax: 0115-978 5103 *Rope & twine manufrs*

W Collins, Cupola Works, Masbrough Street, Rotherham, South Yorkshire, S60 1EX Tel: (01709) 382556 *Scrap metal merchants*

▶ W Coy & Son Ltd, Unit 5, Langar Industrial Estate, South Harby Road, Nottingham, NG13 9HY Tel: (01949) 860216

W & D, Belmont House, Coopers Lane, Christchurch, Coleford, Gloucestershire, GL16 7AL Tel: (01594) 835839 Fax: (01594) 835839 *Amusement machine operators*

▶ W D A Machine Knives, Orgreave Road, Sheffield, S13 9LQ Tel: 0114-269 3311 Fax: 0114-269 4411 E-mail: sales@wdaknives.co.uk *Manufacture of Machine Knives for the Packaging, Print and Food industries.*Serrated Knives for Vertical Form Filling Machines*

W D Bishop & Sons Ltd, 9 Park Road, London, N8 8TE Tel: (020) 8348 0149 Fax: (020) 8340 0929 *Locksmiths & security engineers*

▶ W D Cooper, Progress Drive, Cannock, Staffordshire, WS11 0JE Tel: (01543) 503192 Fax: (01543) 572719

W D L (Contracting) Ltd, Stuart Quarry, Penderyn, Aberdare, Mid Glamorgan, CF44 9JY Tel: (01685) 811525 Fax: (01685) 814326 E-mail: accounts@wdlewisaberdare.co.uk *Civil engineering*

W D Lewis & Sons, 90-92 Bridge Street, Lampeter, Dyfed, SA48 7AG Tel: (01570) 422540 Fax: (01570) 423644 E-mail: sales@wdlewis.co.uk *Agricultural merchants*

W D M, North View, Soundwell, Bristol, BS16 4NX Tel: 0117-956 7233 Fax: 0117-957 0351 *Mechanical engineers & engineering contractors*

W D M Engineers Ltd, Units 4-6, Pontygwindy Industrial Estate, Caerphilly, Mid Glamorgan, CF83 3HU Tel: (029) 2086 7750 Fax: (029) 2086 9938 *Precision production engineers*

W D M Software Ltd, Greensfield Business Centre, Mulgrave Terrace, Gateshead, Tyne & Wear, NE8 1PQ Tel: 0191-478 6666 Fax: 0191-478 1283 E-mail: info@wdmsoft.co.uk *Software house writers*

W D P Co., 37 Park Road, Bromley, BR1 3HJ Tel: (020) 8464 9011 Fax: (020) 8464 8977 E-mail: wdpco@aol.com *Computer dealers*

W & D Peddie Ltd, 284 High Street, Perth, PH1 5QS Tel: (01738) 621449 Fax: (01738) 629232 *Steel merchants*

▶ W D Pulley's, 54 Cuckoo Road, Birmingham, B7 5SY Tel: 0121-327 5133 Fax: 0121-327 2756 E-mail: birminghamsales@afc-uk.com *Conveyor system manufrs*

W D S Watford, Hagden Lane, Watford, WD18 7DJ Tel: (01923) 226606 Fax: (01923) 242799 E-mail: sales@wdsltd.co.uk *Work holding systems manufrs*

▶ W D Smurthwaite & Sons, Sotherby Road, South Bank, Middlesbrough, Cleveland, TS6 6LP Tel: (01642) 462222 Fax: (01642) 463333

W D Stant Ltd, 37a Rivulet Road, Wrexham, Clwyd, LL13 8DY Tel: (01978) 266123 Fax: (01978) 361954 E-mail: sales@wdstant.co.uk *Building contractors*

W D Stirling Ltd, Drummond House, Gainsborough Drive, Sherborne, Dorset, DT9 6DS Tel: (01935) 817399 *Property holding & owning company*

W Dooher, 4 Loughan Road, Dunamanagh, Strabane, County Tyrone, BT82 0QE Tel: (028) 7139 8084 Fax: (028) 7139 8084 *Steel fabricators*

W Downing, 79 Spencer Street, Birmingham, B18 6DE Tel: 0121-236 7353 Fax: 0121-200 2429 *Die sinking & badge manufrs*

W Drake Bradford Ltd, Bolling Road, Bradford, West Yorkshire, BD4 7BG Tel: (01274) 733541 Fax: (01274) 740892E-mail: info@wdrake.co.uk *Engine re-manufrs*

W Durston Ltd, Progress House, Hospital Hill, Chesham, Buckinghamshire, HP5 1PJ Tel: (01494) 793244 Fax: (01494) 792966 *Rolling mill manufacturers for jewellery trade*

W E A Group Ltd, Unit 4 Hales Road Industrial Estate, Hales Road, Leeds, LS12 4PL Tel: 0113-279 9442 Fax: 0113-279 0703 E-mail: info@wae-group.co.uk *Sign manufrs*

W E Allard Ltd, 64 Winpenny Road, Parkhouse Industrial Estate E, Parkhouse Industrial Estate Ea, Newcastle, Staffordshire, ST5 7RH Tel: (01782) 563653 Fax: (01782) 273856 *Industrial reconditioned engines rebuilders*

▶ W & E Associates, 21 Broad Ground Road, Redditch, Worcestershire, B98 8YP Tel: (01527) 525189 Fax: (01527) 525189

W E Atkins & Sons, Abbey Fields, Rocester, Uttoxeter, Staffordshire, ST14 5JX Tel: (01889) 590922 Fax: (01889) 591700 *Agricultural consultants & technical service providers*

W E Bates Ltd, Bath Meadow Cottage, Gaydon Road, Bishops Itchington, Southam, Warwickshire, CV47 2QZ Tel: (01926) 613222 Fax: (01926) 614222 E-mail: sales@w-e-bates.co.uk *Stainless steel tube manufrs*

W E C S Precision Ltd, Blenheim Road, Longmead Industrial Estate, Epsom, Surrey, KT19 9BE Tel: (01372) 741633 Fax: (01372) 740539 E-mail: npooles@wecsprecision.com *Precision engineers*

W E Collier & Sons Ltd, 12 Soham Road, Fordham, Ely, Cambridgeshire, CB7 5LD Tel: (01638) 720045 Fax: (01638) 721442 *Horse transporters*

W E Couplings Ltd, 2 Grimeford Industrial Estate, Grimeford Lane, Anderton, Chorley, Lancashire, PR6 9HL Tel: (01257) 475101 Fax: (01257) 482424 E-mail: info@we-couplings.com *Hose assembly manufrs*

▶ W E Cox & Sons Ltd, 95 Stewart Road, Bournemouth, BH8 8PA Tel: (01202) 395863 Fax: (01202) 395863

W E Deane Ltd, Mayesbrook House, River Road, Barking, Essex, IG11 0EU Tel: (020) 8532 6400 Fax: (020) 8532 6497 E-mail: info@deanefreight.com *Shipping & forwarding agents*

W E Harrison Sheffield Ltd, 33 Regent Terrace, Sheffield, S3 7QA Tel: 0114-272 0561 Fax: 0114-272 0564 E-mail: weh@quista.net *Lightning conductors & flagpole suppliers*

▶ W E & I Wright Ltd, Garage, High Stoop, Tow Law, Bishop Auckland, County Durham, DL13 4HJ Tel: (01388) 730297 Fax: (01388) 730130

W E Instrumentation Ltd, Unit 15 Chamberlayne Road, Bury St. Edmunds, Suffolk, IP32 7EY Tel: (01284) 704805 Fax: (01284) 762932 E-mail: sales@we-instrumentation.co.uk Principal Export Areas: Worldwide *Process instrumentation controllers*

W E Mann, The Maids Head, Lynn Road, East Winch, King's Lynn, Norfolk, PE32 1NP Tel: (01553) 840965 E-mail: deemann@ntlworld.com *Bar equipment & accessory suppliers*

W E Rawson Ltd, Castlebank Mills, Portobello Road, Wakefield, West Yorkshire, WF1 5PS Tel: (01924) 373421 Fax: (01924) 290334 *Technical felts & upholstery manufrs*

W E Rudd Ltd, Unit 23 Louis Pearlman Centre, Goulton Street, Hull, HU3 4DL Tel: (01482) 327792 *Wholesale tobacconists & vending operators*

W E Scorgie & Son, Balrownie Smithy, Menmuir, Brechin, Angus, DD9 7RG Tel: (01356) 660229 Fax: (01356) 660229 *Agricultural engineers*

W E Services Ltd, 1 Shillingford Close, Appleton, Warrington, WA4 5QB Tel: (01925) 263490 Fax: (07092) 304593 E-mail: wayne@weservices.wanado.com *General engravers*

W E Wilde & Co. Ltd, Unit 12 Cropper Row, Alton Road, Ross-on-Wye, Herefordshire, HR9 5LA Tel: (01989) 565100 Fax: (01989) 764326 E-mail: wilde.coltd@virgin.net *Farm equipment parts & accessories retailers*

W F Ltd, Upper Gallery, Station Approach Industrial Estate, Pulborough, West Sussex, RH20 1AQ Tel: (01798) 875312 Fax: (01798) 875570 E-mail: wf@wf-online.com *Electrical wholesalers*

W F Arber & Co. Ltd, 459 Roman Road, London, E3 5LX Tel: (020) 8980 2067 *Printers & commercial stationers*

▶ W F Button & Son Ltd, Button House, Pix Farm Lane, Hemel Hempstead, Hertfordshire, HP1 2RY Tel: (01442) 879440 Fax: (01442) 879442 E-mail: sales@wfbutton.co.uk *Demolition contractors*

W F Chinn Ltd, Marsh Lane, Crediton, Devon, EX17 1ES Tel: (01363) 772639 Fax: (01363) 772639 E-mail: wfchinn@lineone.net *Sausage manufrs*

▶ W F Clayton & Co., Sackville Road, Bangor, Gwynedd, LL57 1LE Tel: (01248) 353665 Fax: 01248 370958

W F Denny, F Tudor Road, Broadheath, Altrincham, Cheshire, WA14 5RZ Tel: 0161-927 4949 Fax: 0161-927 4940 E-mail: wfdennyenquiries@btconnect.com *Paper/polythene/foil packaging distribs*

W F E Ltd, Crossley Road, Crossley Road, Heaton Chapel, Stockport, Cheshire, SK4 5BD Tel: 0161-432 0281 Fax: 0161-431 3575 E-mail: wfel@hs.utc.com *Aluminium fabricators*

W F Electrical, Unit 6 Westerton Road, East Mains Industrial Estate, Broxburn, West Lothian, EH52 5AU Tel: (01506) 858833 Fax: (01506) 855257 E-mail: edinbugh.industrial@hagemeyerservicecentre.co.uk *Electric control gear suppliers*

W F Electrical plc, 50-51 Burnt Mill, Elizabeth Way, Harlow, Essex, CM20 2HU Tel: (01279) 417171 Fax: (01279) 450902 *Electrical goods wholesaler & distributors*

W F Electrical plc, 1 Trinity Centre, Park Farm Industrial Estate, Wellingborough, Northamptonshire, NN8 6ZB Tel: (01933) 679009 Fax: (01933) 400264 *Electrical wholesalers*

W F Electrical Distributors, 313-333 Rainham Road South, Dagenham, Essex, RM10 8SX Tel: (020) 8517 7000 Fax: (020) 8595 0519 E-mail: peter.warsap@hagemeyer.co.uk *Distributors of electrical products & installation materials*

W F Electrical Wholesalers Plc, Snowdrop Lane, Haverfordwest, Dyfed, SA61 1JB Tel: (01437) 764141 Fax: (01437) 760479 *Electrical wholesalers*

W F Flavell (Patternmakers), Avon Industrial Estate, Rugby, Warwickshire, CV21 3UY Tel: (01788) 575967 Fax: (01788) 575967 *Engineers' pattern makers*

W F Foster & Son, 62a Fordwater Road, Chertsey, Surrey, KT16 8HL Tel: (01932) 563019 Fax: (01932) 567010 *Scrap iron & metal merchants*

▶ W F Frost Services Ltd, Arundel Business Centre, 49 Station Road, Harold Wood, Romford, RM3 0BS Tel: (01708) 377002 Fax: (01708) 377149

▶ W F Giles & Sons Ltd, Dockham Road, Cinderford, Gloucestershire, GL14 2AL Tel: (01594) 823144

▶ W F Hall & Son Ltd, Wern Road, Goodwick, Dyfed, SA64 0AA Tel: (01348) 872272 Fax: (01348) 872991 E-mail: sales@wfhalltransport.co.uk

W F Joy & Co. Ltd, Unit 1a Parnall Industrial Estate, Parnall Road, Bristol, BS16 3JF Tel: 0117-958 5865 Fax: 0117-958 5865 *Sheet metalwork & aluminium fabricators*

W F O L C Ltd, Unit 6 Woking Business Park, Albert Drive, Woking, Surrey, GU21 5JY Tel: (01483) 727571 Fax: (01483) 725066 *Electric supplies wholesale dealers* Also at: Branches throughout the UK

W F S Ltd, 30 Main Road, Weston, Crewe, CW2 5NA Tel: (01270) 252001 Fax: (01270) 213131 E-mail: contact@wfsltd.co.uk *Agricultural merchants*

W F Wades, 12 Falcon Business Centre, Falcon Close, Burton-on-Trent, Staffordshire, DE14 1SG Tel: (01283) 541621 Fax: (01283) 510382 *Electrical equipment wholesalers*

W Farthing & Sons, Fulton Road, Benfleet, Essex, SS7 4PZ Tel: (01268) 794103 Fax: (01268) 756094 *Ornamental ironwork manufrs*

W Fayers & Sons, 15 Margaret Road, Barnet, Hertfordshire, EN4 9NR Tel: (020) 8370 6400 Fax: (020) 8370 6415 *Builders' merchants*

W Fayers & Sons Ltd, 76 Alfred Road, Buckhurst Hill, Essex, IG9 6DR Tel: (020) 8504 6625 Fax: (020) 8505 0626 *Building merchants*

W Fischer & Sons Luton Ltd, 4a William Street, Luton, LU2 7RE Tel: (01582) 404022 Fax: (01582) 400455 *Hat & materials importers & merchants*

W Forrest & Son Paisley Ltd, 241 Biggar Road, Newarthill, Motherwell, Lanarkshire, ML1 5LY Tel: (01698) 860149 Fax: (01698) 860920 *Animal bi products rendering plant*

W France Successors, Luck Lane, Huddersfield, HD1 4QU Tel: (01484) 426032 Fax: (01484) 426032 *Joinery services*

▶ W Freeman & Son Ltd, Dunton Wharf, Lichfield Road, Curdworth, Sutton Coldfield, West Midlands, B76 9EN Tel: (01675) 470777 Fax: (01675) 470743

W G Ball Ltd, Longton Mill, Anchor Road, Stoke-on-Trent, ST3 1JW Tel: (01782) 312286 Fax: (01782) 598148 E-mail: sales@wgball.com *Colour & glazed (ceramic) manufrs*

W G Banham & Sons, Springlea, Half Moon Lane, Redgrave, Diss, Norfolk, IP22 1RU Tel: (01379) 898438 Fax: (01379) 898438 *Agricultural general engineers, repairs & services*

W G Bingham & Co. Ltd, New Warehouse, Manby Road, Immingham, South Humberside, DN40 2LH Tel: (01469) 573945 Fax: (01469) 576057 E-mail: imminghamsales@sorsky.com *Safety equipment stockists* Also at: Hull

W G Crotch Ornamental Plaster Work, 10 Tuddenham Avenue, Ipswich, IP4 2HE Tel: (01473) 250349 Fax: (01473) 213180 E-mail: annetaylorwgcrtch@yahoo.co.uk *Fibrous plaster*

W G Dodds & Son, The Sawmill Bowesfield Industrial Estate, Bowesfield Lane, Stockton-on-Tees, Cleveland, TS18 3HJ Tel: (01642) 674827 Fax: (01642) 644809 E-mail: sales@wgdodds.co.uk *Fence & shed manufrs*

W G Fabrications Ltd, 69 High Street, Princes End, Tipton, West Midlands, DY4 9JF Tel: 0121-520 0024 Fax: 0121-520 0089 *Steel fabricators*

W G & H Horsley, Ashville, Main Street, Newton on Derwent, York, YO41 4DA Tel: (01904) 608742 Fax: (01904) 608755 *Haulage & storage contractors*

W G H Wire Drawers Ltd, Imperial Works, 217 Oxford Street, Bilston, West Midlands, WV14 7HY Tel: (01902) 354142 Fax: (01902) 354250 *Non-ferrous & ferrous materials supplier*

W G Harrison Ltd, Dysart Road, Grantham, Lincolnshire, NG31 7LF Tel: (01476) 402041 Fax: (01476) 566999 *Lithographic & thermographic printers*

W G Heath Electrical Services Ltd, 8 Pomphlett Farm Industrial Estate, Broxton Drive, Plymouth, PL9 7BG Tel: (01752) 480300 Fax: (01752) 480303 E-mail: heath@wgplymouth.ffnet.co.uk *Electrical contractors*

▶ W G K London Ltd, Old Bovingdon Airfield, Whelpley Hill, Chesham, Buckinghamshire, HP5 3RR Tel: (01442) 831856 Fax: (01442) 831857

W G Keyte & Sons Ltd, Daux Road, Billingshurst, West Sussex, RH14 9SP Tel: (01403) 782276 *Bearings manufrs*

▶ W G Mackenzie, 4 Pinefield Parade, Elgin, Morayshire, IV30 6AG Tel: (01343) 541665 Fax: (01343) 540016

W & G Metalwork Ltd, Sugarbrook Mill, Buntsford Hill, Stoke Pound, Bromsgrove, Worcestershire, B60 3AR Tel: (01527) 870752 Fax: (01527) 579930 *Fire escape designers*

W G Office Supplies Ltd, Unit 3 Crayford Industrial Estate, Swaisland Drive, Crayford, Dartford, DA1 4HS Tel: (01322) 526527 Fax: (01322) 556249 E-mail: sales@wgo.co.uk *Commercial stationers* Also at: Lowestoft & Romford

W G & P D Gilson, 8 Burdett Road, Southend-on-Sea, SS1 2TN Tel: (01702) 467030 Fax: (01702) 467030 *Fish merchants & distributors*

W G Phillips, Rosemount, Princes Gate, Narberth, Dyfed, SA67 8TF Tel: (01834) 860244 Fax: 01834 860244 *Agricultural contractors*

W.G. Photo, Southdownview Road, Worthing, West Sussex, BN14 8NJ Tel: (01903) 200528 Fax: (01903) 200528 E-mail: mike@wgphoto.co.uk *Industrial & advertising photographers*

W G Pinsent Ltd, Unit B5 Star Business Centre, Marsh Way, Rainham, Essex, RM13 8UP Tel: (01708) 552943 Fax: (01708) 630890 *Butcher sundry suppliers*

W G Plastics Ltd, 55 Knights Hill Square, London, SE27 0HP Tel: (020) 8761 2464 Fax: (020) 8761 2464 *Plastic injection moulders & makers*

W & G Pollard Ltd, Jacob Street, Accrington, Lancashire, BB5 1HU Tel: (01254) 391628 Fax: (01254) 382897 *Sheet metalworkers & fabricators*

▶ W G Silverton & Co. Ltd, Meeting House Lane, Baldock, Hertfordshire, SG7 5BP Tel: (01462) 491800 Fax: (01462) 490740

W G Spink & Sons, 1 Harrow Road, Hereford, HR4 0EH Tel: (01432) 272575 Fax: (01432) 342361 *Glazing contractors*

W G Walker & Co Ayr Ltd, Hawkhill Works, Somerset Road, Ayr, KA8 9NF Tel: (01292) 263122 Fax: (01292) 611691 E-mail: enquiries@wgwalker.co.uk *Mastic asphalt contractors*

▶ W Gadsby & Son Ltd, Huntworth Business Park, Bridgwater, Somerset, TA6 6TS Tel: (01278) 437123 Fax: (01278) 458561 E-mail: sales@gadsby.co.uk *Basket ware supplier & manufrs*

W Gilchrist & Co., 65a London Road, Sevenoaks, Kent, TN13 1AU Tel: (01732) 457666 Fax: (01732) 457246 *Suppliers of filters*

W Glen & Son, Errol, Perth, PH2 7TE Tel: (01821) 642878 Fax: (01821) 642878 *Farming*

W Goddard, Baths Road, Bromley, BR2 9RB Tel: (020) 8460 9600 Fax: (020) 8460 9601 E-mail: goddardstamps@btinternet.com *Rubber stamp manufrs*

W Gordon Scott & Co., Unit 14 Ies Centre, Horndale Avenue, Aycliffe Industrial Park, Newton Aycliffe, County Durham, DL5 6DS Tel: (01325) 300643 Fax: (01325) 300643 *Fire extinguisher suppliers*

▶ W Green Son & Waite Ltd, Invicta Works, Chalk Pit Avenue, Orpington, Kent, BR5 3JP Tel: (01689) 831361 Fax: (01689) 875191

W H B Logistics Ltd, Old Wolverton Road, Milton Keynes, MK12 5NL Tel: (01908) 222121 Fax: (01908) 222929 E-mail: sp@whb-international.com *Transport, shipping & forwarding agents*

W H B Stevenson, 19 Alder Hill Avenue, Leeds, LS6 4JQ Tel: 0113-278 4751 Fax: 0113-295 7864 E-mail: design@whbs.net *Computer consultants*

▶ W H Barley Transport & Storage Ltd, Old Wolverton Road, Old Wolverton, Milton Keynes, MK12 5NL Tel: (01908) 227222 Fax: (01908) 227370 E-mail: sales@whbarley.co.uk *W H Barley (Transport And Storage) Limited, a Milton Keynes based general haulage company, providing a first class logistics solution for warehouse and pallet distribution services to customers based in Bucks, Beds and across the UK. Utilising our own comprehensive fleet, the Palletline Network and the Transport Association we provide a complete distribution solution for single pallets, full loads or any volume in between. Services include; express, overnight, economy, tail-lift, and timed deliveries/collections across the UK, Ireland and Europe, as well as comprehensive warehouse and storage solutions. Over 35 years in the distribution and logistics industry have resulted in our total focus on customer care, with every employee committed to meeting customer deadlines and schedules.*

W H Bence Coachworks Ltd, Great Western Business Park, Armstrong Way, Yate, Bristol, BS37 5NG Tel: (01454) 310909 Fax: (01454) 321665 *Coach builders*

W H Bowker Ltd, Holme Road, Bamber Bridge, Preston, PR5 6BP Tel: (01772) 628800 Fax: (01772) 628801 E-mail: enquiries@bowker.co.uk *Road transport, haulage & freight services*

▶ W H Bowker International Ltd, Littlefair Road, Hull, HU9 5LP Tel: (01482) 706557 Fax: (01482) 706533 E-mail: info@bowkertransport.co.uk

▶ W H Catchpole Ltd, Bestwood Works, Drove Road, Portslade, Brighton, BN41 2PA Tel: (01273) 439227

▶ W H Clarke Engineering Ltd, Oxcroft Industrial Estate, Clowne Road, Stanfree, Chesterfield, Derbyshire, S44 6AG Tel: (01246) 241046 Fax: (01246) 241047 E-mail: sales@steelfabs.co.uk

W H Collier Ltd, Brick Works, Church Lane, Marks Tey, Colchester, CO6 1LN Tel: (01206) 210301 Fax: (01206) 212540 *Hand made facing bricks*

W H Constable & Co. Ltd, 16 Barnwell Business Park, Barnwell Drive, Cambridge, CB5 8UZ Tel: (01223) 211888 Fax: (01223) 416888 *Glass merchants*

W.H Crossley Ltd, Newby Road Industrial Estate, Newby Road, Hazel Grove, Stockport, Cheshire, SK7 5DA Tel: 0161-456 3767 Fax: 0161-483 0602 *Sheet metalwork engineers or fabricators & sheet metalwork precision fine limit engineers or fabricators*

W H Dale Ltd, Main Street, Thornton Curtis, Ulceby, South Humberside, DN39 6XW Tel: (01469) 531229 Fax: (01469) 530611 E-mail: sales@whdale.co.uk *Structural steelwork fabricators & tank installations*

W H Darby Co Ltd, 16 Well Street, Birmingham, B19 3BJ Tel: 0121-554 9817 Fax: 0121-523 3585 E-mail: info@whdarby.co.uk *HIGH QUALITY CRAFTSMANSHIP AND SERVICE SPANNING THREE CENTURIES. Your best guarantee of prompt, high quality services the reputation we have developed over three centuries. From the earliest days, the company has run on the foundations of craftsmanship and service, and we remain true to these traditions today. Still in family ownership, the company has faithfully maintained the standards of quality, attention to detail and service that were set two centuries ago. We have built on these foundations and have developed complimentary skills to become one of the foremost names in manufacturing Medals, badges, insignia and other presentational products, backed up by standards of service others find hard to match.*

W H Davis Ltd, Langwith Road, Langwith Junction, Mansfield, Nottinghamshire, NG20 9SA Tel: (01623) 742621 Fax: (01623) 744474 E-mail: management@whdavis.co.uk *Railway rolling stock services*

▶ W H Dunn & Co., 10 William Street, South Shields, Tyne & Wear, NE33 1PQ Tel: 0191-456 7503 Fax: 0191-454 5520

W H Evans, Melinllecheiddior, Garndolbenmaen, Gwynedd, LL51 9EZ Tel: (01766) 530635 Fax: (01766) 530635 *Agricultural foodstuffs*

W & H Fabrications Ltd, Scatcherd Works, Morley, Leeds, LS27 9BE Tel: 0113 2534633 *Heating & ventilation engineers*

W H Flinn Ltd, 77 Albony Road, Manchester, M21 0BN Tel: 0161-881 9591 Fax: 0161-862 9180 E-mail: whflinn@btconnect.com *Electrical wholesalers*

W H Fluidpower Ltd, Unit 9, Rossbank Road, Rossmoor Industrial Estate, Ellesmere Port, CH65 3AN Tel: (0151) 355 2211 Fax: (0151) 355 2277 E-mail: whfluidpower@ukonline.co.uk *Hydraulic & pneumatic components distributors*

W H Foster & Sons Ltd, Stourdale Road, Cradley, Cradley Heath, West Midlands, B64 7BG Tel: (01384) 415170 Fax: (01384) 415185 E-mail: sales@whfoster.co.uk *Laminated plastics fabricators*

W H Gayton, Gaytons Bakery, Maypole Lane, Grendon, Atherstone, Warwickshire, CV9 2BS Tel: (01827) 712538 Fax: (01827) 713340 *Bakery*

W H Greaves & Son Electroplating Ltd, 2 Lock Street, Sheffield, S6 3BJ Tel: 0114-232 3272 Fax: 0114-232 3273 *Electroplating, powder coating & stove enamelling*

W H Halmshaw Ltd, Pioneer Works, Goulton St, Hull, HU3 4AS Tel: (01482) 589689 Fax: (01482) 325084 E-mail: info@halmshaws.co.uk *Plumbers' merchants & glass stockists*

W H Hannaford, 100 Chester Road, Watford, WD18 0RE Tel: (01923) 223669 Fax: (01923) 223669 *General welding*

W H Hendy & Sons, Units 1-5, Station Road Industrial Estate, Wiveliscombe, Taunton, Somerset, TA4 2LX Tel: (01984) 623386 Fax: (01984) 624343 *Sewage & sludge pumps services*

W H Hillerby & Sons Ltd, Ballast Hill, Blyth, Northumberland, NE24 2AU Tel: (01670) 352423 Fax: (01670) 356795 *Roofing contractors*

W H Hodder & Sons, Forge Yard, Lymden Lane, Stonegate, Wadhurst, East Sussex, TN5 7EE Tel: (01580) 201501 Fax: (01580) 201502 *General builders & heating engineers*

W H Horton, West Street, Tamworth, Staffordshire, B79 7JE Tel: (01827) 52810 Fax: (01827) 66122 E-mail: info@whhorton.co.uk *Plumbing & builders merchants*

W H Hulley, 26 Ebenezer Street, Sheffield, S3 8SR Tel: 0114-272 1205 Fax: 0114-276 5621 E-mail: sales@hulley-ladders.co.uk *Ladder makers*

W H Humphreys & Son Ltd, 1 Sydney Road, Watford, WD18 7XX Tel: (01923) 226206 Fax: (01923) 210355 E-mail: sales@humphreys-moving.com *Overseas removal contractors*

W H I Tapestry Shop, 85 Pimlico Road, London, SW1W 8PH Tel: (020) 7730 5366 *Needlepoint retailers*

W H Ireland Ltd, 11 St James's Square, Manchester, M2 6WH Tel: 0161-832 2174 Fax: 0161-833 0935 E-mail: laurie.beavers@wh-ireland.co.uk *Stock & share brokers*

W H James & Son Ltd, Cross House, Crymych, Dyfed, SA41 3UJ Tel: (01239) 831233 Fax: (01239) 831415 *Agricultural equipment retailers*

W H K (Walton) Ltd, Walton Business Centre, 44-46 Terrace Road, Walton-on-Thames, Surrey, KT12 2SD Tel: (01932) 247979 Fax: (01932) 245948 E-mail: colin@whk.co.uk *Electrical & mechanical contractors & engineers*

W H Kemp, Cory Way, West Wilts Trading Estate, Westbury, Wiltshire, BA13 4QT Tel: (01373) 823322 Fax: (01373) 824411 E-mail: sales@whkemp.co.uk *Cable harness manufrs*

W H Kirkwood Ltd, 27 Hope Street, Greenock, Renfrewshire, PA15 4AW Tel: (01475) 721248 Fax: (01475) 888465 E-mail: info@whkirkwood.co.uk *Building & public work contractors*

▶ W & H Leslie Ltd, Enterprise Drive, Westhill Industrial Estate, Westhill, Aberdeenshire, AB32 6TQ Tel: (01224) 740203 Fax: (01224) 742041

W H M Engineering Ltd, 24 Earl Haig Road, Hillington Industrial Estate, Glasgow, G52 4JU Tel: 0141 8834422 *Steel fabricators services*

▶ W H Malcolm Ltd, 201 Castlebank Street, Glasgow, G11 6DZ Tel: 0141-334 9841

W H Malcolm Ltd, 865 South Street, Glasgow, G14 0BX Tel: 0141-435 5299 Fax: 0141-435 5298 E-mail: contact@whm.co.uk *Road transport/haulage/freight services*

▶ W H Malcolm Ltd, Nethermains Road, Kilwinning, Ayrshire, KA13 6PY Tel: (01294) 551321 Fax: (01294) 552803 E-mail: admin@malcolmgroup.co.uk

▶ W H Malcolm Ltd, Newhouse Industrial Estate, Motherwell, Lanarkshire, ML1 5RY Tel: (01698) 834007 Fax: (01698) 832133

▶ W H Malcolm Ltd, Newton Picot Depot, Gatenby, Northallerton, North Yorkshire, DL7 9NG Tel: (01677) 424096 Fax: (01677) 423124

▶ W H Malcolm Ltd, Burnbrae Drive, Linwood, Paisley, Renfrewshire, PA3 3BU Tel: (01505) 324321 Fax: (01505) 333215

W H Marren Ltd, Temple Bar, Willenhall, West Midlands, WV13 1SD Tel: (01902) 605208 Fax: (01902) 601014 *Scrap metal merchants*

▶ W H Oddie Ltd, 129 Scotland Road, Nelson, Lancashire, BB9 7XR Tel: (01282) 602181 Fax: (01282) 602303 *Bakery product retailer*

W H P Labels Ltd, 48 Smith Street, Birmingham, B19 3EN Tel: 0121-523 0007 Fax: 0121-523 2221 E-mail: rhwhp@aol.com *General lithographic printing services*

W H Palmer & Sons, Archers Fields, Burnt Mills Industrial Estate, Basildon, Essex, SS13 1DH Tel: (01268) 520078 Fax: (01268) 521673 *Pre-cast concrete products*

W H Pettit & Co Long Eaton Ltd, Bonsall Street, Long Eaton, Nottingham, NG10 2AH Tel: 0115-973 2577 Fax: 0115-946 1212 *Sheet metalworkers & fabricators*

W H Povoas Ltd, Radnor Street, Stretford, Manchester, M32 8LP Tel: 0161-865 1086 Fax: 0161-864 3584 E-mail: sales@whpovoas.co.uk *Engineers' suppliers*

W H Ricketts & Sons, Forge Works, Ffynnon Gynydd, Hereford, HR3 5LX Tel: (01497) 847250 Fax: (01497) 847329 *Steel fabricators*

W H Rowe & Son Ltd, Quayside Road, Southampton, SO18 1DH Tel: (023) 8022 5636 Fax: (023) 8022 5146 E-mail: sales@whrowe.com *Aluminium casting engineering & powder coating services*

W H Sallis & Sons, Llechryd, Cardigan, Dyfed, SA43 2QL Tel: (01239) 682220 *Agricultural merchants*

W H Scott & Son, Unit 2 Elmbank Channel Commercial Park, Queens Road, Belfast, BT3 9DT Tel: (028) 9076 6700 Fax: (028) 9076 6701 E-mail: sales@gunnebo.se *Lifting gear manufrs*

W H Scuffham Refrigeration Engineers, 95 West Street, Boston, Lincolnshire, PE21 8RE Tel: (01205) 310163 Fax: (01205) 310165 *Air conditioning & refrigeration contractors*

▶ W H Simmonds & Son Ltd, The Old House, West Street, Wrotham, Sevenoaks, Kent, TN15 7AR Tel: (01732) 883079 Fax: (01732) 884055 E-mail: info@whsimmonds.co.uk

W H Smith & Sons Tools Ltd, Water Orton Lane, Minworth, Sutton Coldfield, West Midlands, B76 9BG Tel: 0121-748 7777 Fax: 0121-749 6213 E-mail: info@whs-tools.com *Plastics injection moulders & toolmakers with additional services i.e. design & prototyping, plastics painting & printing, PCB assembly, leather/PVC covering & finishing*

▶ W H Snow Ltd, 17 Mansfield Street, Liverpool, L3 3EG Tel: 0151-207 0571

W H Tinsley & Sons Ltd, Wem Industrial Estate, Soulton Road, Wem, Shrewsbury, SY4 5SD Tel: (01939) 232301 Fax: (01939) 235110 *Wrought iron specialist manufrs*

▶ W & H (U K) Ltd, 6 Stroud Wood Bus Centre, Park St, St. Albans, Hertfordshire, AL2 2NJ Tel: (01727) 874990

W H Whittingham & Sons Ltd, 84-86 West Street, Rochford, Essex, SS4 1AS Tel: (01702) 544146 Fax: (01702) 542326 *Motor vehicle repairs & sales*

W H Wilmot Ltd, 62 Albion Street, Birmingham, B1 3EA Tel: 0121-236 1729 Fax: 0121-233 4957 E-mail: sales@whwilmot.com *Watch bracelet manufrs*

W Hall Ltd, Hydepark Industrial Estate, Cloughmore Road, Newtownabbey, County Antrim, BT36 4WW Tel: (028) 9084 1444 Fax: (028) 9034 2466 E-mail: sales@whall.co.uk *Fork lift trucks retail & repairers*

W Hall & Son Holywell Ltd, Greenfield Road, Greenfield, Holywell, Clwyd, CH8 7QB Tel: (01352) 711444 Fax: (01352) 714793 *Carbonated mineral water manufacturers & wholesalers of beers wines & spirits*

W Hallam Castings Ltd, Coulman Road Industrial Estate, Thorne, Doncaster, South Yorkshire, DN8 5JU Tel: (01405) 813006 Fax: (01405) 813786 E-mail: sales@hallamcastings.co.uk *High pressure diecastings*

W Hanson Silsden Ltd, Hainsworth Road, Silsden, Keighley, West Yorkshire, BD20 0LY Tel: (01535) 652347 Fax: (01535) 652347 E-mail: woodturners@btinternet.com *Repetition wood turners*

W Hanson Timber & Builders Merchants Ltd, Uxbridge Road, Southall, Middlesex, UB1 3EQ Tel: (020) 8571 3161 Fax: (020) 8574 3816 E-mail: sales@w-hanson.co.uk *Timber merchants & builders merchants* Also at: Harrow & Hounslow

W Haycock, Leys Bank, North Leys, Ashbourne, Derbyshire, DE6 1DQ Tel: (01335) 342395 Fax: (01335) 342395 *Clock manufacturer & makers of historic machinery*

W Hayden & Son Ltd, Webb Street, Bilston, West Midlands, WV14 8XL Tel: (01902) 402341 Fax: (01902) 491832 *Site clearance & excavation*

W Hogg Joinery, 1 Back Bowman Street, Darlington, County Durham, DL3 0HG Tel: (01325) 351838 *Joinery manufrs*

W Howkins & Co., 65-67 Newnham Avenue, Bedford, MK41 9QJ Tel: (01234) 261143 E-mail: sales@whowkins.co.uk *English timber merchants*

W Hume & Son, Hillside House, Norham, Norham, Berwick-upon-Tweed, TD15 2JZ Tel: (07753) 937070 Fax: (01289) 382435 *Agricultural contractors*

▶ W I & A Gilbert Road Contractors, Easter Kersland, Dalry, Ayrshire, KA24 4JA Tel: (01294) 834433 Fax: (01294) 833343

continued

W I G Engineering Ltd, Barnfield, Chesterton, Bicester, Oxfordshire, OX26 1TE Tel: (01869) 320515 Fax: (01869) 320513
E-mail: wig@oxford38.fsnet.co.uk *Structural steel engineers*

W I S, Kings Castle Business Parke, The Drove, Bridgwater, Somerset, TA6 4AG Tel: (01278) 439128 Fax: (01278) 439129 *Work wear & protective clothing supplier*

W I S International, Chancery House, 53/64 Chancery Lane, London, WC2A 1RA Tel: 020 8743 5492 Fax: 020 8181 6910
E-mail: wis-int@btclick.com *Theft-Fraud Investigations. Due Diligence analysis. Pre-employment.Contractors litigation & reputation reports.Corporate-competitive intelligence.Counterfeit,passing off & grey market.Full Investigation service.*

W I T Systems, Unit1 7 Business Development Centre, Main Avenue, Treforest Industrial Estate, Pontypridd, Mid Glamorgan, CF37 5UR Tel: (01443) 844565 Fax: (01443) 842925
E-mail: info@wit-systems.net *IT consultants*

▶ W & J Allardyce Commercials Ltd, Hillside Garage, Longridge, Bathgate, West Lothian, EH47 8AN Tel: (01501) 770218 Fax: (01501) 771425
E-mail: william.allardyce@btopenworld.com *Mechanical spares, sales & vehicle sales*

W J Brown Agricultural Services Ltd, Dunecht, Westhill, Aberdeenshire, AB32 7BS Tel: (01330) 860870 Fax: (01330) 860870 *Plant engineers*

W & J Cruickshank & Co., 31 Telford Street, Wick, Caithness, KW1 5EQ Tel: (01955) 602674 Fax: (01955) 602674 *Soft drinks manufrs*

W & J Dunlop, College Mains Road, Dumfries, DG2 0NU Tel: (01387) 263733 Fax: (01387) 254326 E-mail: admin@dunlops.com *Veterinary products wholesalers* Also at: Aberdeen

W J Evans Precision Ltd, Lint House, Linthouse Lane, Wednesfield, Wolverhampton, WV11 3EA Tel: (01902) 731116 *Engineers pattern makers suppliers*

W J Fish, 47 Brearley Street, Hockley, Birmingham, B19 3NS Tel: 0121-359 2252 Fax: 0121-359 2252 *Souvenir & fancy goods manufrs*

W J Ginniff, 161 Ballygowan Road, Banbridge, County Down, BT32 3QS Tel: (028) 4066 2285 Fax: (028) 4066 2285 *Excavation contractors*

W J Gowar & Co. Ltd, Rheidol Mews, London, N1 8NU Tel: (020) 7226 3644 Fax: (020) 7226 2969 *Brass radiator grille manufrs*

W J Gresham & Son, Commonside, Old Leake, Boston, Lincolnshire, PE22 9PR Tel: (01205) 870279 Fax: (01205) 870954 *Joinery contractors & cabinet makers*

W J Groundwater Ltd, 9 Park Road, Bushey, WD23 3EE Tel: (020) 8950 7256 Fax: (020) 8950 5207 E-mail: info@wjgl.com *Dewatering equipment manufrs* Also at: Chester

W J & H Crozier, 19 Outlack Road, Armagh, BT60 2AN Tel: (028) 3752 2202 Fax: (028) 3752 2283 *Stone quarry bitmac plant & civil engineers*

W J Hall & Co., 10a Old Bridge Way, Shefford, Bedfordshire, SG17 5HQ Tel: (01462) 851044 Fax: (01462) 851044
E-mail: info@hallprecision.co.uk *Precision engineers*

▶ W J Harte Construction Ltd, 1 Hamilton Road, Bothwell, Glasgow, G71 8AT Tel: (01698) 854033 Fax: (01698) 854667
E-mail: admin@wjharte.co.uk

W J Hatt Ltd, Foxcovert Farm, Goring Heath, Reading, RG8 7SL Tel: (01491) 680424 Fax: (01491) 680425 E-mail: wjhatt@aol.com *General contractors*

W J Haysom & Son, St Adhelms Quarry, Swanage, Dorset, BH19 3LN Tel: (01929) 439217 Fax: (01929) 439215
E-mail: haysom@purbeckstone.co.uk *Masonry contractors & quarry operators*

W J Higgins & Son, Middlegate Farm, Pitney, Langport, Somerset, TA10 9AQ Tel: (01458) 250475 Fax: (01458) 251010 *Agricultural contractors*

W.J.Horrod Ltd, 1 Leaway, Off Lea Bridge Road, London, E10 7QW Tel: (020) 8539 8746
E-mail: sales@wjhorrod.co.uk *Asphalt & bitumen equipment manufrs*

▶ W J Jenkins & Sons Tipton Ltd, Pound Garage, Bridge Road, Tipton, West Midlands, DY4 0JW Tel: 0121-557 6085 Fax: 0121-520 6815
E-mail: wjjenkinsandsons@tiscali.co.uk

W J King Garages Ltd, Albany Park Garage, 10-16 Steynton Avenue, Bexley, Kent, DA5 3HP Tel: (020) 8300 4466 *Petrol distributors*

W J L Engineering, 30-31 Sapcote Trading Centre, Powke Lane, Cradley Heath, West Midlands, B64 5QR Tel: (01384) 567782 Fax: (01384) 412692 E-mail: wjlengineering@btconnect.com *Manufacturer of non-standard & special nuts & bolts*

▶ W J Lafford Ltd, 21 Harmondsworth Road, West Drayton, Middlesex, UB7 9JJ Tel: (01895) 442441 Fax: (01895) 421596
E-mail: alexis@memorialsculpture.com *Monumental masons & sculptors*

W J Law Plant & Transport Ltd, 171 Moira Road, Lisburn, County Antrim, BT28 1RW Tel: (028) 9266 6602 Fax: (028) 9260 3663 *Road transport, haulage & freight services*

▶ W J M & Co Builders Ipswich Ltd, 3a North Hill Road, Ipswich, IP4 2PW Tel: (01473) 212796 Fax: (01473) 287490

▶ W J Mclaughlin & Sons, 76 Sloughan Road, Drumquin, Drumquin, Omagh, County Tyrone, BT78 4QW Tel: (028) 8283 1270 Fax: (028) 8283 1623

W J Marine Analytical Services Ltd, Unit 4, Marine Park, Tapton Hall Industrial Estate, Great Yarmouth, Norfolk, NR31 0NL Tel: (01493) 600600 Fax: (01493) 652099
E-mail: wjmarine@btinternet.com *Specialists to offshore industry*

W J Morray Engineering Ltd, Anglia Way, Braintree, Essex, CM7 3RG Tel: (01376) 322722 Fax: (01376) 323277
E-mail: sales@morray.com *Moray engineering design & manufrs*

W J Nelson & Son Ltd, Fashoda Street, Belfast, BT5 5EX Tel: (028) 9045 6020 Fax: (028) 9073 8312 E-mail: wjnsafe@aol.com *Protective clothing manufacturers, rubber product merchants & safety*

W J Nigh & Sons, 1 Station Approach, Shanklin, Isle of Wight, PO37 7AS Tel: (01983) 863291 Fax: (01983) 866283
E-mail: sales@wjnigh.co.uk *Giftware wholesalers*

W J O Rees, King Heriot, Solva, Haverfordwest, Dyfed, SA62 6XN Tel: (01437) 721313 *Agricultural contractors*

▶ W J Olds Ltd, 365 Park Road, Birmingham, B18 5SR Tel: 0121-554 6068

▶ W.J O'Neill Interiors, 132 Hamilton Road, Glasgow, G32 9QR Tel: 0141-764 1591 Fax: 0141-764 2309 *Joiners*

W J P Engineering Plastics Ltd, Albert Works, Albert Avenue, Bobbers Mill, Nottingham, NG8 5BE Tel: 0115-929 9555 Fax: 0115-929 0422
E-mail: sales@wjpengineeringplastics.co.uk *PTFE machinists, products, components & fittings suppliers*

▶ W J Pearce & Sons, High Street, Chew Magna, Bristol, BS40 8PW Tel: (01275) 332417 Fax: (01275) 332417
E-mail: suepearce2003@yahoo.co.uk *Butchers*

W J Rendell Ltd, Ickleford Manor, Ickleford, Hitchin, Hertfordshire, SG5 3XE Tel: (01462) 432596 Fax: (01462) 420423 *Contraceptive pessaries manufrs*

W J Richardson Glazing Ltd, 46 Glebe Way, West Wickham, Kent, BR4 0RL Tel: (020) 8777 6330 Fax: (020) 8777 4453 *Double glazing & glass contractors*

▶ W J S Thomson, Riverside Industrial Estate, Newton Stewart, Wigtownshire, DG8 6EY Tel: (01671) 403467 Fax: (01671) 403642

W J Sait (Bristol) Ltd, 87-89 Church Road, Redfield, Bristol, BS5 9JR Tel: 0117-955 5898 Fax: 0117-955 5898 *Hairdresser suppliers*

▶ W & J Scaffolding Ltd, Ennerdale Road, Shrewsbury, SY1 3LD Tel: (01743) 442204

W & J Scaffolding Ltd, Construction House, Toll End Road, Tipton, West Midlands, DY4 0HW Tel: 0121-522 4454 Fax: 0121-522 4457
E-mail: tipton@wjscaffolding.co.uk *Scaffolding contractors*

W J Shields & Sons, Hall Farm, Main Street, Shipton by Beningbrough, York, YO30 1AA Tel: (01904) 470263 Fax: (01904) 471872 *Agricultural engineers*

▶ W J Simms Ltd, 14-16 Beddington Farm Road, Croydon, CR0 4XB Tel: (020) 8684 4288

W J Smith Metal Stockists Ltd, Ashmore Lake Way, Willenhall, West Midlands, WV12 4LF Tel: (01902) 607336 Fax: (01902) 634905 *Steel stockholders*

W J & W Lang Ltd, 1 Seedhill, Paisley, Renfrewshire, PA1 1JL Tel: 0141-889 3134 Fax: 0141-889 3182
E-mail: sales@langwetblue.co.uk *Leather tanning services*

W J Webb & Co. Ltd, 35 Broadgate, Whaplode Drove, Spalding, Lincolnshire, PE12 0TN Tel: (01406) 330467 Fax: (01406) 330887
E-mail: webb1@which.net *Rubber moulding manufrs*

▶ W J Wicks & Sons, Bigadon Lane, Buckfastleigh, Devon, TQ11 0DT Tel: (01364) 643237 Fax: (01364) 642054 *Fencing contractors*

W K D Storage Systems Ltd, 3-4 Bourne Industrial Estate, Wrotham Road, Borough Green, Sevenoaks, Kent, TN15 8DF Tel: (01732) 882042 Fax: (01732) 885763
E-mail: sales@wkdstorage.co.uk *Storage equipment systems*

▶ W K Edwards, Ketley Road, Kingswinford, West Midlands, DY6 8DA Tel: (01384) 270936 Fax: (01384) 291488

▶ W K Engineering Services, Tweed Road, Clevedon, Avon, BS21 6RR Tel: (01275) 349700 Fax: (01275) 349722 E-mail: info@wk.com

W K Howarth, 3 Blyth Road, Halesworth, Suffolk, IP19 8EN Tel: (01986) 874417 Fax: (01986) 875518 *Lamp shade manufrs*

▶ W K K Electrical Services, 35 The Cutts, Dunmurry, Belfast, BT17 9HN Tel: (028) 9030 8881 Fax: (028) 9030 8882

W K L Glass, High House Farm, Barling Road, Barling Magna, Southend-on-Sea, SS3 0LZ Tel: (01702) 217539 Fax: (01702) 217539 *Aluminium products manufrs*

W & K Rossiter, 79 Aldwick Road, Bognor Regis, West Sussex, PO21 2NW Tel: (01243) 828017 Fax: (01243) 828017
E-mail: trophieswk@yahoo.co.uk *Sports trophies retail & engraving services*

▶ W K T Global Logistics Ltd, Unit 2 & 8, Capitol Industrial Centre, Fulmar Way, Wickford, Essex, SS11 8YW Tel: (01268) 560843

W K Thomas & Co. Ltd, Mount House, Mount Road, Chessington, Surrey, KT9 1HY Tel: (020) 8391 2211 Fax: (020) 8391 2980
E-mail: info@wkthomas.com *Disposable catering equipment manufrs*

W K W Precision Engineering Co. Ltd, Shaw Royd Works, Shaw Lane, Halifax, West Yorkshire, HX3 9HD Tel: (01422) 351720 Fax: (01422) 330017 E-mail: sales@wkw-eng.co.uk *Gear manufrs*

▶ W Kelly & Co., 38 Derryleckagh Road, Newry, County Down, BT34 2NL Tel: (028) 3026 5461

W Kelly & Sons, 2 Islington Square, Liverpool, L3 8DD Tel: 0151-207 3050 Fax: 0151-207 3050 *Cabinet furniture manufrs*

W Kennedy, The Holmes, Holmes Lane, Bacup, Lancashire, OL13 8BS Tel: (01706) 876438 Fax: (01706) 852217 *Manufacturing engineers & machinery merchants*

▶ W Kirk Ltd, London Road, Adlington, Macclesfield, Cheshire, SK10 4NL Tel: (01625) 879990

W Kitchen Galgate Ltd, Mainstone Works, Galgate, Lancaster, LA2 0JJ Tel: (01524) 751210 Fax: (01524) 752532 *Precision engineers*

W Knight & Co Roadworks Ltd, Lissett Road, Maidenhead, Berkshire, SL6 1AZ Tel: (01628) 673014 *Civil engineering contractors*

W L Bussell & Co. Ltd, 30 Hope Street, Weymouth, Dorset, DT4 8TU Tel: (01305) 785633 Fax: (01305) 768657
E-mail: sales@bussells.co.uk *Boat builders & yacht chandlers*

W L D Textiles, Lansdowne Terrace, York, YO10 3EA Tel: (01904) 413453 Fax: (01904) 413453 *DIY & furniture wholesalers*

W L Dingley & Co, Buckle Street, Honeybourne, Evesham, Worcestershire, WR11 7QE Tel: (01386) 830242 Fax: (01386) 833541 *Fertiliser manufrs*

W L Gore & Associates UK Ltd, Mariner Drive, Dundee Technology Park, Dundee, DD2 1JA Tel: (01382) 561511 Fax: (01382) 561007 *Electronic products suppliers & manufrs*

W L Jones Engravers Ltd, North Lonsdale Road, Ulverston, Cumbria, LA12 9DJ Tel: (01229) 583856 Fax: (01229) 580847 *Manufacturing industrial engravers*

▶ W L M Consulting Ltd, 21 Swan Way, Church Crookham, Fleet, Hampshire, GU51 5TU Tel: (01252) 621255
E-mail: enquiry@wlmconsulting.com *WLM Consulting Ltd: Life Coaching and Therapy Services: Female coach based in Surrey/ Hampshire offering self development coaching, professional and personal life support to help people live their best life. Inspirational self help through coaching, build your self esteem, lose your limiting beliefs, personal training for your inner self/mind, specialist in personal change/ improvement using techiniques of coaching, questioning, hypnosis, NLP*

W L P C Ltd, Unit 19 Manor Complex, Kirkby Bank Road, Knowsley Industrial Park, Liverpool, L33 7SY Tel: 0151-549 1781 *Powder coating services*

W L Sirman & Son Ltd, 145 Goldsworth Road, Woking, Surrey, GU21 6LS Tel: (01483) 768020 Fax: (01483) 740545 *Electrical contractors*

W L Straughan & Son Ltd, Bedlington Lane Farm, Bedlington, Northumberland, NE22 6AA Tel: (01670) 823042 Fax: (01670) 827230
E-mail: enqs@wlstrayghan.co.uk *Environmental contractors*

W L West & Sons Ltd, Selham, Petworth, West Sussex, GU28 0PJ Tel: (01798) 861611 Fax: (01798) 861633 *Timber merchants & sawmills service*

W Laird, Nethan Street, Motherwell, Lanarkshire, ML1 3TF Tel: (01698) 249249 Fax: (01698) 249385 E-mail: enquiries@williamlaird.co.uk *Powered access sales & services*

W Lane Ltd, Forty Foot Road, Middlesbrough, Cleveland, TS2 1HG Tel: (01642) 242871 Fax: (01642) 242046
E-mail: w.lane@parson-crossland.co.uk *Metal castings manufrs* Also at: Hertford

W Lees Walsall Ltd, Hatherton Works, Leamore Lane, Walsall, WS3 2BJ Tel: (01922) 476435 Fax: (01922) 407118 E-mail: sales@wlees.co.uk *Leather belts & mens braces*

W M Arnold Boroughbridge Ltd, Station Yard, Boroughbridge, York, YO51 9BL Tel: (01423) 322871 Fax: (01423) 324380
E-mail: sales@wmarnold.demon.co.uk *Crane services*

▶ W M B Installations Ltd, The Yard, Dorchester Road, Swinton, Manchester, M27 5NU Tel: 0161-793 6019 Fax: 0161-727 7067

▶ W M Black & Sons Building Contractors Ltd, 540 Gorgie Road, Edinburgh, EH11 3AL Tel: 0131-443 3400 Fax: 0131-443 7775

W M Camping Ltd, Herne Road, Herne Bay, Kent, CT6 7LH Tel: (01227) 712222 Fax: (01227) 712222 E-mail: sales@wmcamping.co.uk *Camping equipment suppliers*

W M Codd Ltd, Marsh Lane, Barton-upon-Humber, South Humberside, DN18 5HB Tel: (01652) 632578 Fax: (01652) 660484 *Steel fabricators & erectors*

W M D Catering Equipment, Unit 22-23, Prince Of Wales Industrial Estate, Abercarn, Newport, Gwent, NP11 5AR Tel: (01495) 241848 Fax: (01495) 240401
E-mail: rebecca@wmdcatering.co.uk *Retail catering equipment*

▶ W M Donald Ltd, Marlaine, Netherley, Stonehaven, Kincardineshire, AB39 3QN Tel: (01569) 730590 Fax: (01569) 731315

▶ W M Donnelly & Co. Ltd, Myre House, 15 Law Place, Nerston, Glasgow, G74 4QL Tel: (01355) 221718 Fax: (01355) 909001

▶ W M Friel Ltd, Somervell Street, Cambuslang, Glasgow, G72 7EB Tel: 0141-646 1444 Fax: 0141-646 2200

W M Herdman Manufacturing Co. Ltd, Orchard Road, Finedon, Wellingborough, Northamptonshire, NN9 5JG Tel: (01933) 680416 Fax: (01933) 681369 *Blind & curtain manufrs*

W & M Horner, Bolton by Bowland, Clitheroe, Lancashire, BB7 4PQ Tel: (01200) 441284 Fax: (01200) 440069
E-mail: shearinguk@hotmail.co.uk *Sheep shearing equipment wholesalers*

W M Kenyon Macclesfield Ltd, 73 Great King Street, Macclesfield, Cheshire, SK11 6PN Tel: (01625) 422074 Fax: (01625) 617712 *Steel stockholders*

W M Mcewen Miller, George Street, Wick, Caithness, KW1 4DG Tel: (01955) 603188 Fax: (01955) 602479 *Coal merchants*

▶ W M Robinson (Bilsborrow) Ltd, Craigmore, Bilsborrow Lane, Bilsborrow, Preston, PR3 0RN Tel: (01995) 640379

W M Rollings Ltd, 49 Brook Street, Wrexham, Clwyd, LL13 7LR Tel: (01978) 364956 Fax: (01978) 359659
E-mail: wmrollings@aol.com *Motor factor manufrs*

W M S Development Services P.L.C., 45 Beech St, London, EC2Y 8AD Tel: (020) 7614 4828 Fax: (020) 7614 4801 *IT services & recruitment*

W M S Displays Ltd, Unit 2/3, Southways Industrial Estate, Coventry Road, Hinckley, Leicestershire, LE10 0NJ Tel: (01455) 619966 Fax: (01455) 619988 E-mail: info@wmsdisplays.com *Shop fitting services*

W M Shutters Ltd, Springhill Trading Estate, Aston Street, Shifnal, Shropshire, TF11 8DR Tel: (01952) 272265 Fax: (01952) 272331
E-mail: sales@wmshutters.com *Aluminium shutters manufr*

W M Spence Ltd, PO Box 344, Bradford, West Yorkshire, BD3 9TH Tel: (01274) 661824
E-mail: enquiries@wmspence.co.uk *Sheet metalwork engineers*

W M Stephen Bakers Ltd, 20 Duncan Cresent, Dunfermline, Fife, KY11 4BT Tel: (01383) 626637 *Bakers*

W & M Watson, Unit 1a Clyde Industrial Estate, Glasgow, G73 1PP Tel: (01506) 852324 Fax: (01506) 855210 *Carton & packaging merchants*

W M Young Transport Ltd, School House Farm, Beamhurst, Uttoxeter, Staffordshire, ST14 5EA Tel: (01889) 507279 Fax: (01889) 563266

W Maccarthy & Sons Ltd, Unit 1 Block 1, Woolwich Dockyard Industrial Estate, Woolwich Church St, London, SE18 5PQ Tel: (020) 8316 4321 Fax: (020) 8316 5566
E-mail: box.maccarthy@virgin.net *Cardboard box manufrs*

W Mcmullin & Sons, 27 Desborough Lane, Plymouth, PL4 9PJ Tel: (01752) 660874 Fax: (01752) 660874
E-mail: wmcmullinandsons@btconnect.com *Removal contractors & storage*

W Madden Insulation, Swinnow View, Leeds, LS13 4TZ Tel: 0113-257 9818 Fax: 0113-257 7586 E-mail: sales@wmadden.demon.co.uk *Builders, plumbers & timber merchants*

W Marfitt Kitchens & Bedrooms, 108a Upper Aughton Road, Southport, Merseyside, PR8 5EX Tel: (01704) 563701 Fax: (01704) 562313 *Kitchen & bedroom manufrs*

▶ W Martin Oliver, Carrsgate, Bardon Mill, Hexham, Northumberland, NE47 7EX Tel: (01434) 344555

W Metcalfe Leamington Ltd, Rugby Road, Cubbington, Leamington Spa, Warwickshire, CV32 7NU Tel: (01926) 335175 Fax: (01926) 337623 *Timber merchants*

W N Lindsay Ltd, Gladsmuir Granary, Gladsmuir, Tranent, East Lothian, EH33 1EJ Tel: (01875) 852151 Fax: (01875) 852926
E-mail: enquiries@wnlindsay.com *Grain merchants & warehousemen*

W N Thomas & Sons Ltd, Stoke Gardens, Slough, SL1 3QA Tel: (01753) 524575 Fax: (01753) 694765
E-mail: info@thomasmetalrecycling.co.uk *Metal recyclers*

W O M International, Cherrycourt Way, Leighton Buzzard, Bedfordshire, LU7 4AA Tel: (01525) 375033 Fax: (01525) 383552
E-mail: services@wom-int.com *Dust control mats manufrs*

W.O.S. - UK Contractors, 6A Bell Flats, 280-286 High Road, Willesden, London, NW10 2EX Tel: (0870) 896 4010 Fax: (0870) 762 3512
E-mail: info@ukbuildingcontractors.com *Experienced specialist building contractors in the UK (London and the South West), World Opportunities & Services - UK specialise in construction, property maintenance and refurbishment including specialist building projects. We do also have our *Recruitment/ Employment Section, specialized in Construction Industry and Engineering Services.**Professional Building Services:***W.O.S. - UK Building Services provides a professional service, quality workmanship and value for money that our blue chip client base demand. Our large and varied workforce has the flexibility and experience to undertake projects ranging from minor repairs and maintenance to major refurbishments, specialist projects and construction works. *We have teams of fully trained RICS qualified Surveyors to carry out site surveys and inspections and ensure fair pricing and accurate specification.*

W Oliver Allen & Sons, Loe Bar Road, Porthleven, Helston, Cornwall, TR13 9EN Tel: (01326) 562222 Fax: (01326) 562222
E-mail: woallen@porth-leven.com *Agricultural & sports net manufrs*

W Oliver Exorna Ltd, Hillmans Way, Coleraine, County Londonderry, BT52 2EB Tel: (028) 7035 6501 Fax: (028) 7035 3674 *Furniture manufrs*

W P A Furnaces & Engineering Projects Ltd, 24 Monmer Close Industrial Estate, Willenhall, West Midlands, WV13 1JR Tel: (01902) 631155 Fax: (01902) 602615 *Electric furnace manufrs*

W P B Computer Supplies Ltd, Longacres House, Lower Stock Road, West Hanningfield, Chelmsford, CM2 8UY Tel: (01277) 841343 Fax: (01277) 840372
E-mail: s.flint@wpbnet.com *Computer components manufrs*

W P B Machining Services Ltd, 21 Offerton Industrial Estate, Stockport, Cheshire, SK2 5TH Tel: 0161 4778500 *Machining services*

W & P Blinds, Unit M2 The Paddocks, 347 Cherry Hinton Road, Cambridge, CB1 8DH Tel: (01223) 243030 Fax: (01223) 243030
E-mail: info@wandpblinds.co.uk *Blind manufrs*

W P C Software Ltd, 9 Wellsway, Keynsham, Bristol, BS31 1HS Tel: 0117-908 1484 Fax: 0117-940 2060 E-mail: wpc@wpcsoft.com *Software developers*

W P Ceiling Co. Ltd, 85 Mansfield Avenue, Barnet, Hertfordshire, EN4 8QF Tel: (020) 8449 9603 Fax: (020) 8449 2754
E-mail: rpayne7812@aol.com *Suspended ceilings contractors*

W & P Food Service Ltd, Tannochside Drive, Uddingston, Glasgow, G71 5PD Tel: (01698) 803000 Fax: 01698 803031 *Dried goods distributors*

W & P Forgings Ltd, 11 Hedon Road, Hull, HU9 1LL Tel: (01482) 323089 Fax: (01482) 324735 E-mail: info@wp-forging.co.uk *Drop & press forging manufrs*

W P Gallagher, 22 Blagden Lane, Huddersfield, HD4 6JZ Tel: (01484) 422644 *Groundwork's & civil engineering contractors*

W P L Ltd, 1-2 Aston Road, Waterlooville, Hampshire, PO7 7UX Tel: (023) 9224 2600 Fax: (023) 9224 2624
E-mail: admin@wpl-limited.co.uk *WPL Limited, provides a range of innovative solutions for commercial grease management, designed for environments where grease, oil and fat can cause blockages in waste pipes or drain runs. *Utilising patented bio-technology, WPL provides short and long-term off the shelf or tailor-made solutions which are cost effective and have minimal impact on the environment.*

W P Lang Ltd, Railway Road, Airdrie, Lanarkshire, ML6 9AB Tel: (01236) 752515 Fax: (01236) 753888 *Joinery manufrs*

W P M Europe, Unit 1-2 Sam Brown Industrial Units, Dog & Gun Lane, Whetstone, Leicester, LE8 6LJ Tel: 0116-275 2393 Fax: 0116-275 3095 E-mail: mharriman@wpm.com *Printing machine manufrs*

▶ W P M R Ltd, 69 Trinity Street, Leamington Spa, Warwickshire, CV32 5YN Tel: (01926) 338845 Fax: (01926) 336613 *Preservation services, damp proofing, property services-commercial & domestic maintenance, pest control-flying & crawling insects*

W P Notcutt Ltd, Homewood Farm, Newark Lane, Ripley, Woking, Surrey, GU23 6DJ Tel: (01483) 223311 Fax: (01483) 479594 E-mail: sales@notcutt.com *Rubber moulding compounds suppliers*

W P S Logistics Ltd, The Old Power Ho, Rhossdu Industrial Estate, Wrexham, Clwyd, LL11 4YL Tel: (01978) 261043 Fax: (01978) 312695 *Pallet reconditioners*

W P Thompson & Co., Eastcheap House, Central Approach, Letchworth Garden City, Hertfordshire, SG6 3DS Tel: (01462) 682139 Fax: (01462) 676775 E-mail: letchworth@wpt.co.uk *Patent agents/ attorneys; patent (European) attorneys & trade mark agents/attorneys* Also at: Hull, Letchworth & London WC1

W P Thompson & Co., 55 Drury Lane, London, WC2B 5SQ Tel: (020) 7240 2220 Fax: (020) 7240 8505 E-mail: london@wpt.co.uk *Patent & trade mark agents*

▶ W Parker & Sons, 6 Pierce Lane, Fulbourn, Cambridge, CB21 5DL Tel: (01223) 880464 Fax: (01223) 881694 E-mail: sales@wparkerandson.co.uk *Joinery manufrs*

W Parrot & Sons, Unit 17 Whitegate Industrial Estate, Whitegate Road, Wrexham, Clwyd, LL13 8UG Tel: (01978) 358070 Fax: (01978) 357392 *Precision engineers*

W Peters & Son Ltd, 16 High St, Turriff, Aberdeenshire, AB53 4DT Tel: (01888) 563589 Fax: (01888) 563936 E-mail: info@wpeters.co.uk *Commercial printers & editorial services*

W Pettigrove, Chadwell Cottage, Owlswick, Princes Risborough, Buckinghamshire, HP27 9RJ Tel: (01844) 345751 Fax: (01844) 345751 *Fairground amusements*

W Pollard & Son Ltd, 19 Kirk Road, Nottingham, NG3 6GX Tel: 0115-950 4791 Fax: 0115-950 4791 *Road contractors*

▶ W Portsmouth & Co. Ltd, 69 Havelock Road, Luton, LU2 7PW Tel: (01582) 731517 Fax: (01582) 401920 E-mail: mail@wportsmouth.co.uk

W Powell & Son Ltd, 35-37 Carrs Lane, Birmingham, B4 7SX Tel: 0121-643 0689 Fax: 0121-631 3504 E-mail: sales@william-powell.co.uk *Gun makers & dealers & country clothing*

▶ W Pringle & Sons, The Garage Hamburg Cottages, Lawhill Road, Carluke, Lanarkshire, ML8 5HF Tel: (01555) 770550 Fax: (01555) 770556

W R Advertising Ltd, Black Lake, West Bromwich, West Midlands, B70 0PL Tel: 0121-525 2626 Fax: 0121-525 2955 E-mail: sales@wradvertising.co.uk *Sign manufrs*

▶ W R Associates, Panstar House, 13-15 Swakeleys Road, Uxbridge, Middlesex, UB10 8DF Tel: (01895) 622922 Fax: (01895) 639300 E-mail: michelle@wr-associates.co.uk *Consultant Engineers for Mechanical and Electrical Building Services. Designing all services including, heating. lighting, air-con, drainage, BMS. Also act as Planning Supervisors*

W R Clark & Co Engineers Ltd, Bridge St Industrial Estate, Bridge Street, Clay Cross, Chesterfield, Derbyshire, S45 9NU Tel: (01246) 862325 Fax: (01246) 250033 *Engine component & spare parts manufrs*

▶ W R D Worldwide Music Ltd, 282 Camden Road, London, NW1 9AB Tel: (020) 7267 6762 Fax: (020) 7482 4029 E-mail: info@wrdmusic.com *WRD are an online and offline manufacturer and distributor of Ballroom & Latin CDs, books and DVDs. We wholesale to other companies and also sell directly to the public.*

The W R Davidge Planning Practice, PO Box 463, Peterborough, PE8 6HU Tel: (01780) 763901 Fax: (01733) 235051 E-mail: davidge.planning@virgin.net *Town planning consultants*

W.R Engraving Name Plate Manufacturers, 12a Green Lane Industrial Estate, Green Lane, Letchworth Garden City, Hertfordshire, SG6 1HP Tel: (01462) 686845 Fax: (01462) 686845 *Industrial engravers*

W R Forktrucks, 1 Thorold St, Grimsby, South Humberside, DN31 3AE Tel: 01472 250186

W R Hardy, 153 East High Street, Forfar, Angus, DD8 2EQ Tel: (01307) 466635 Fax: (01307) 468820 *Gunsmiths & fishing tackle suppliers*

W R Moulds (UK) Ltd, Aurillac Way, Hallcroft Road, Hallcroft Industrial Estate, Retford, Nottinghamshire, DN22 7SS Tel: (01777) 708432 Fax: (01777) 860383 E-mail: enquries@wrmoulds.co.uk *Plastic mould hire*

W R Newland & Sons Ltd, 129 Croydon Road, Caterham, Surrey, CR3 6PE Tel: (01883) 344622

W R Outhwaite & Son Ropemakers, Burtersett Road, Hawes, North Yorkshire, DL8 3NT Tel: (01969) 667487 Fax: (01969) 667576 E-mail: sales@ropemakers.com *Rope & braid product manufrs*

W R P Construction, Southway House, Southway Drive, Bristol, BS30 5LW Tel: 0117-961 9111 Fax: 0117-961 9222 E-mail: sales@frictionservices.co.uk *Brake & clutch lining/facing, friction materials manufrs* Also at: Exeter

W R R, 5 The Arianne Business Centre Blackburn Road, Townsend Industrial, Houghton Regis, Dunstable, Bedfordshire, LU5 5DZ Tel: (01582) 665718 Fax: (01582) 664490 E-mail: wroberts@wrr-uk.com *Shot blasting contractors & fire protection contractors services*

W R R Pedley & Co. Ltd, Ann Street, Willenhall, West Midlands, WV13 1EW Tel: (01902) 366060 Fax: (01902) 603411 *Pressings & welded fabrication manufrs*

W R Refrigeration Ltd, 8 Buckingham Court, Springfield, Chelmsford, CM2 6XW Tel: (01245) 463405 Fax: (01245) 463411 *Refrigeration engineers*

W R Refrigeration Ltd, 1 Calow Lane, Hasland, Chesterfield, Derbyshire, S41 0AL Tel: (01246) 272281 Fax: (01246) 550153 *Refrigeration engineers*

W R Refrigeration Ltd, Shor Street, Evesham, Worcestershire, WR11 3AU Tel: (01386) 40359 Fax: (01386) 40359 *Commercial refrigeration repair & installers*

W R Refrigeration Ltd, 47 Colvilles Place, Kelvin Industrial Estate, East Kilbride, Glasgow, G75 0PZ Tel: (01355) 237237 Fax: (01355) 241888 *Refrigeration equipment service*

▶ W R Refrigeration Ltd, Austin Fields, King's Lynn, Norfolk, PE30 1PH Tel: (01553) 773259 Fax: (01553) 767756

W R Refrigeration Ltd, 96 Nepshaw La South, Gildersome, Morley, Leeds, LS27 7JQ Tel: 0113-238 0038 Fax: 0113-238 0708

W R Refrigeration Ltd, Frog Island, Leicester, LE3 5BG Tel: 0116-251 1060 Fax: 0116-242 5766 *Refrigeration installers*

W R Refrigeration Ltd, 2 Woolram Wygate, Spalding, Lincolnshire, PE11 1NX Tel: (01775) 768978 Fax: (01775) 768713 E-mail: chriscocks@wrspalding.com *Refrigeration engineers*

W R Roberts & Sons, 60-64 Chapel Street, Wincham, Northwich, Cheshire, CW9 6DA Tel: (01606) 45849 Fax: (01606) 41281 E-mail: robertsscrap@talk21.com *Scrap metal merchants*

▶ W R S, Systems House, St. Cross Lane, Newport, Isle Of Wight, PO30 5BZ Tel: (01983) 533888 Fax: (01983) 530163 E-mail: sales@wrssystems.co.uk *Suppliers of epos systems & cash registers*

W R S Alarms, 103 High Street, Yatton, Bristol, BS49 4DR Tel: (01934) 834013 Fax: (01934) 876142 E-mail: admin@wrsalarms.com *Security alarms installation*

▶ W R Simmers Ltd, Backmuir, Keith, Banffshire, AB55 5PE Tel: (01542) 882543 Fax: (01542) 886065 *Structural engineers*

W R Suckling & Sons, 6 Chapel Street, Steeple Bumpstead, Haverhill, Suffolk, CB9 7DQ Tel: (01440) 730227 *Agricultural contractors*

W R Tooling Ltd, Armytage Road Industrial Estate, Armytage Road, Brighouse, West Yorkshire, HD6 1QF Tel: (01484) 719642 Fax: (01484) 716854 E-mail: info@wrtooling.co.uk *Die & plastic mould toolmakers*

W R Winton Ltd, Richmond House, Forsyth Road, Woking, Surrey, GU21 5SB Tel: (01483) 770121 Fax: (01483) 715630 E-mail: info@winton-antlia.com *Blast furnace slag distribs*

▶ W.R Woolgar Furnisher Removels, 12 Heathfield Road, Handsworth, Birmingham, B19 1HB Tel: 0121-554 4963

W R Wright & Sons Ltd, 110-118 Cherry Lane, Liverpool, L4 8SF Tel: 0151-270 2904 Fax: 0151-226 8833 E-mail: sales@wrwright.co.uk *Wholesale butchers' suppliers*

W Raybould & Sons Ltd, Croxstalls Close, Walsall, WS3 2XT Tel: (01922) 479196 Fax: (01922) 494616 E-mail: sales@raybould.co.uk *Manufacturers of spurs & brass founders*

W Reeves Badges Ltd, 34-35 Tenby Street, Birmingham, B1 3EE Tel: 0121-236 3731 Fax: 0121-236 3731 E-mail: sales@reevesbadges.co.uk *Established in 1910. Vitreous enamelled badge manufacturers. Metal badges, sports badges, promotional badges, badges to specification, Motor Vehicle badges. Quick turn around. Repair & restoration of enamelled badges.*

W. Ridley & Co. Ltd, 12-16 Bean Street, Hull, HU3 2PQ Tel: (01482) 224691 Fax: (01482) 587098 E-mail: info@wridley.co.uk *Corrugated case, paper & polythene packaging manufrs*

W Robinson & Sons Ec Ltd, 35-41 Fowler Road, Hainault Industrial Estate, Ilford, Essex, IG6 3WR Tel: (020) 8559 6000 Fax: (020) 8559 6001 E-mail: info@pump.co.uk *Pump repairers & retailers*

W & S Allely Ltd, PO Box 58, Smethwick, West Midlands, B66 2RP Tel: 0121-558 3301 Fax: 0121-555 5194 E-mail: sales@allely.co.uk *Non-ferrous metal & stainless steel stockholders* Also at: Chippenham, Consett, Rochdale & Rochester

▶ W S Atkins Scotland, 50 Melville Street, Edinburgh, EH3 7HF Tel: 0131-225 9301 Fax: 0131-225 9837

W S Barrett & Son Ltd, Riverside Industrial Estate, Marsh Lane, Boston, Lincolnshire, PE21 7PJ Tel: (01205) 362585 Fax: (01205) 310831 E-mail: info@wsbarrett.co.uk Principal Export Areas: Central/East Europe & West Europe *Trucks & Trolley Manufacturers*

▶ W S Biggin & Son, 1 Hanger Hill, Creswell, Worksop, Nottinghamshire, S80 4AA Tel: (01909) 720245 Fax: (01909) 723487 *Construction services*

W S Britland & Co. Ltd, Tilmanstone Depot, Pike Road, Eythorne, Dover, Kent, CT15 4DH Tel: (01304) 831583 Fax: (01304) 831983 E-mail: britland.dover@dial.pipex.com *Steel & pipework manufrs*

W S D S Business Systems Ltd, 5 Chapel Road, Portslade, Brighton, BN41 1PF Tel: (01273) 420011 Fax: (01273) 420022 E-mail: sales@wsds-works.co.uk *Furniture wholesalers & retailers*

W S Dunsire & Sons Ltd, 40 Birkhill Road, Stirling, FK7 9JS Tel: (01786) 462954 Fax: (01786) 450008 E-mail: sales@wsdunsire.com *Joinery manufacturers & builders*

▶ W S Engineering Ltd, Park Works, Park Road, Leek, Staffordshire, ST13 8SA Tel: (01538) 373131 Fax: (01538) 384862 E-mail: info@wseng.co.uk *Engineering products & services*

W S G Operating Co. Ltd, New Walton Pier Co Ltd, Walton on the Naze, Essex, CO14 8ES Tel: (01255) 670970 Fax: (01255) 850383 E-mail: sales@wsgscales.com *Personal weighing machine operators*

W S Hardware, Stafford Road, Coven Heath, Wolverhampton, WV10 7PS Tel: (01902) 782200 Fax: (01902) 782500 E-mail: sales@ws-hardware.co.uk *Metal products & house signs to garden centres & wholesalers*

W S Henderson & Son Ltd, Bute Street, Salford, M50 1DU Tel: 0161-736 1511 Fax: 0161-745 8159 E-mail: motorrepairs@wshendersons.freeserve.co.uk *Industrial electric motor repairs*

W S I Expert Net Solutions, 54 Gleneagles Road, Bloxwich, Walsall, WS3 3UJ Tel: (07855) 413370 Fax: (07813) 964997 E-mail: jon@wsiexpertnetsolutions.com

W S I Internet Consulting & Education, 99 Oxford Road, Abingdon, Oxfordshire, OX14 2AB Tel: (01235) 206859 Fax: E-mail: brian@wsione-stopwebsolutions.co.uk *Web design*

W S Jenkins & Co. Ltd, Tariff Road, London, N17 0EN Tel: (020) 8808 2336 Fax: (020) 8365 1534 E-mail: sales@wsjenkins.co.uk *Wood finishing manufrs*

W S Moore, 160 Malpas Road, Newport, Gwent, NP20 5PN Tel: (01633) 855902 Fax: (01633) 855902 *Monumental masons & stone merchants*

W S P Consulting Engineers, 4-5 Lochside View, Edinburgh, EH12 9DH Tel: (01382) 225308 Fax: (01382) 206029 E-mail: david.gray@wspgroup.com *Consulting engineers*

W S P Group P.L.C., Buchanan House, 24-30 Holborn, London, EC1N 2HS Tel: (020) 7314 5000 Fax: (020) 7314 5111 E-mail: info@wspgroup.com *Engineering consultants services*

W S Robinson & Sons London Ltd, 324a Limpsfield Road, South Croydon, Surrey, CR2 9BX Tel: (020) 8651 2010 *Trimmings merchants*

▶ W S S Associates Ltd, 23 Austin Friars, London, EC2N 2QP Tel: (020) 31707837 E-mail: accounts@wss-associates.com *Accountancy recruitment, specialising in the Property sector. The type of positions we recruit for include Service charge accountants, Property Management Accountants, Client Accountants. We also recruit for all Corporate accounting positions.*

W S S Windsor, 58 St. Leonards Road, Windsor, Berkshire, SL4 3BY Tel: (01753) 864483 Fax: (01753) 621102 E-mail: sales@wsswindsor.com *Engravers*

W S Shearing & Sons, Southfield Holdings, Amesbury Road, Weyhill, Andover, Hampshire, SP11 8ED Tel: (01264) 772974 *Hay & straw merchants*

▶ W S Steele Communications Ltd, Unit 505 Oakbank Industrial Estate, Garscube Road, Glasgow, G20 7LU Tel: 0141-353 3393 Fax: 0141-353 3396 E-mail: info@wssteele.com *Metal work services*

▶ W S Traffic Ltd, 3 Rosewood Drive Crews Hill, Enfield, Middlesex, EN2 9BT Tel: (020) 8363 0700 *Installation & maintenance of traffic signals*

W S Westin Group Ltd, Phoenix Mill, Leeds Road, Huddersfield, HD1 6NG Tel: (01484) 421585 Fax: (01484) 432420 E-mail: sales@westin.co.uk *Cooker hoods, extractors manufrs*

W S Wood Machinery, 9 36 Hornock Road, Coatbridge, Lanarkshire, ML5 2QA Tel: (01236) 432700 Fax: (01236) 432909 *Woodworking machinery retailers*

W Sails, 51 Southsea Avenue, Leigh-on-Sea, Essex, SS9 2AX Tel: (01702) 714550 Fax: (01702) 714550 *Sail makers & marine supplies*

▶ W. Salsbury Ltd, 22a-24 Newnham Street, Bedford, MK40 3JR Tel: (01234) 354286 *Servicers/suppliers of cigarette vending machines*

▶ W Sharples & Sons Ltd, Unit 38a Lune Industrial Estate, Lancaster, LA1 5QP Tel: (01524) 849836 Fax: (01524) 388299 E-mail: info@wrightandco-nw.co.uk

W Smart & Son Ltd, 44 Park Road, Rushden, Northamptonshire, NN10 0RG Tel: (01933) 312038 Fax: (01933) 318891 *Shoe repair components & moulders*

▶ W Smith, Murrayfield Road, Leicester, LE3 1UW Tel: 0116-231 3007 Fax: 0116-231 3005

W Speirs & Sons Ltd, 4 Portland Avenue, The Industrial Estate, Irvine, Ayrshire, KA12 8JD Tel: (01294) 275434 Fax: (01294) 312008 *Sheet metalwork fabricators*

W Spurr & Sons, 6 Wakefield Commercial Park, Bridge Road, Horbury, Wakefield, West Yorkshire, WF4 5NW Tel: (01924) 274746 Fax: (01924) 274746 *Steel engineering*

W Stone & Sons, 20 Lodge Causeway, Bristol, BS16 3JB Tel: 0117-965 3125 Fax: 0117-965 3125 *General engineers*

▶ W Sweeting & Sons Ltd, Washbrook, Hill Road, Sandford, Winscombe, Avon, BS25 5RJ Tel: (01934) 822588 Fax: (01934) 820564

W T Armatur UK Ltd, Singleton Court Business Centre, Wonastow Road Industrial Estate (West), Monmouth, Gwent, NP25 5JA Tel: (01600) 712178 Fax: (01600) 712179 *Sales & marketing for industrial valves*

W T Clark & Co (Brushes) Ltd, P O Box 2, Birmingham, B46 1HX Tel: (01675) 463085 Fax: (01675) 467455 *Industrial brush manufrs*

W & T Clayson, Henbury Close, Henbury, Elham, Canterbury, Kent, CT4 6NL Tel: (01303) 840233 Fax: (01303) 840160 *Agricultural contractors*

▶ W T Construction Poole Ltd, Selbys Yard, Huntick Road, Lytchett Matravers, Poole, Dorset, BH16 6BB Tel: (01202) 620541 Fax: (01202) 620543

▶ W T Endacott Ltd, 21 East Street, Okehampton, Devon, EX20 1AT Tel: (01837) 52888 Fax: (01837) 54381

W T H Precision Tooling Ltd, 236 Berwick Avenue, Slough, SL1 4QT Tel: (01753) 521483 Fax: (01753) 694778 *Precision toolmakers*

W T I Fasteners Ltd, Unit 10 Huntingdon Court, Westminster Industrial Estate, Measham, Swadlincote, Derbyshire, DE12 7DS Tel: (01530) 273100 Fax: (01530) 273007 E-mail: admin@wireinserts.com *Helical wire thread inserts & thread repair kit manufrs*

W T I Fasteners Ltd, Unit 10 Huntingdon Court, Westminster Industrial Estate, Measham, Swadlincote, Derbyshire, DE12 7DS Tel: (01530) 273100 Fax: (01530) 273007 E-mail: admin@wireinserts.com *Manufacturers of threaded inserts & fasteners*

W T Johnson & Sons Huddersfield Ltd, Bankfield Mills, Moldgreen, Huddersfield, HD5 9BB Tel: (01484) 549965 Fax: (01484) 448106 E-mail: office@wtjohnson.co.uk *Piece dyers & finishers*

W T Knowles & Sons Ltd, Ash Grove Sanitary Pipe Works, Elland Road, Elland, West Yorkshire, HX5 9JA Tel: (01422) 372833 Fax: (01422) 370900 E-mail: martin@wtknowles.co.uk *Drain pipe & chimney pot manufrs*

W T L International, Tunstall Road, Bosley, Macclesfield, Cheshire, SK11 0PE Tel: (01260) 223284 Fax: (01260) 223589 E-mail: sales@wtl-int.com Principal Export Areas: Worldwide *Environmentally friendly products from sustainable organic natural resources for diverse applications including, filtration media, renewable fuels, cat litter & animal bedding, wood plastic composites, burn out media, & cosmetics. Also provides contract blending, packing, warehousing services.*

W T Mather Ltd, Lockett Road South Lancashire Industrial Estate, South Lancashire Industrial Es, Ashton-in-Makerfield, Wigan, Lancashire, WN4 8DE Tel: (01942) 711615 Fax: (01942) 271290 E-mail: sales@wt-mather.co.uk *Jams & mincemeat suppliers*

W T Parkes Upholstery, Regency Works, 1a Shakleton Road, Coventry, CV5 6HT Tel: (024) 7669 1199 *Upholstery specialists*

W T Products Ltd, Unit 3 Cedar Terrace, Leeds, LS12 1TQ Tel: 0113-279 7345 Fax: 0113-231 0725 E-mail: wtproducts1@btconnect.com *Dust control monitor systems manufrs*

W T Rowley & Sons, 37 Cannon Street, Shrewsbury, SY2 5HQ Tel: (01743) 356020 *Plumbing & heating engineers*

W Tabern & Sons Ltd, Duncan Street, St. Helens, Merseyside, WA10 3TF Tel: (01744) 24763 Fax: (01744) 24764 *Road transport haulage & freight services*

W Taylor & Sons, 2a Warfield Road, Feltham, Middlesex, TW14 8AD Tel: (020) 8890 2153 Fax: (020) 8893 1271 E-mail: w.taylor@aol.com *Precision, general engineers*

W Thacker & Sons Ltd, Field Gate, Walsall, WS1 3DJ Tel: (01922) 622302 Fax: (01922) 647790 *Sheet metal pressings manufrs*

W Thatcher, Borron Street, Stockport, Cheshire, SK1 2JD Tel: 0161-480 3438 Fax: 0161-476 5361 *Bakers wholesale manufrs*

W Thompson & Son Ltd, 2 Nobel Road, London, N18 3BH Tel: (020) 8807 7576 Fax: (020) 8807 9517 E-mail: wthompsons@lineone.net *Wood machinists & turnkey manufrs*

W Todd & Sons, Mintsfeet Road North, Kendal, Cumbria, LA9 6LZ Tel: (01539) 724311 Fax: (01539) 720277 *Riding wear manufrs*

W Trout & Son, Boat House, Ferry Road, Topsham, Exeter, EX3 0JJ Tel: (01392) 873044 Fax: (01392) 875176 E-mail: wtrout1@tiscali.co.uk *Boat yard services*

▶ W U C S Industrial, Tokoloshe, Long Marston Road, Welford on Avon, Stratford-upon-Avon, Warwickshire, CV37 8EG Tel: (01789) 750913 Fax: (01789) 751345 E-mail: sales@wucsltd.co.uk *Industrial electrical engineers*

W V H Welding Services, 6 Midas Industrial Estate, Longbridge Way, Cowley, Uxbridge, Middlesex, UB8 2YT Tel: (01895) 233501 *Welding consultants*

▶ W V Training, 27 King St Trading Estate, Middlewich, Cheshire, CW10 9LF Tel: (01606) 841954 Fax: (01606) 558200 E-mail: mickwvt@fsmail.net *Training consultants,confined space,breathing apparatus,fire,chemical spillage*

▶ W Vallance, Hoddom Road, Ecclefechan, Lockerbie, Dumfriesshire, DG11 3BY Tel: (01576) 300279

W W Computer Systems, Mowbray House, 58-70 Edgware Way, Edgware, Middlesex, HA8 8DJ Tel: (020) 8958 1347 Fax: (020) 8958 1348 E-mail: simone@wwcomputers.co.uk *Computer consultants*

W W E Semiconductors Ltd, The Beeches, Grange Rd, Uckfield, E. Sussex, TN22 1QU Tel: (01825) 746900 Fax: (01825) 746911 *Obsolete semiconductors*

W & W Engineers Ltd, Farndon Road, Market Harborough, Leicestershire, LE16 9NP Tel: (01858) 466166 Fax: (01858) 464921 *Steel fabricators*

W W Fixings Ltd, Marston Road, Wolverhampton, WV2 4LA Tel: (01902) 310031 Fax: (01902) 429017 E-mail: sales@wwfix.co.uk *Power tool distributors*

W W Grew & Co. Ltd, Stafford Street, Wednesbury, West Midlands, WS10 7JX Tel: 0121-556 3337 Fax: 0121-556 8171 E-mail: info@wwgrew.com *Precision turned parts manufrs*

W & W H Pettit, Lawnswood Cowbit Road, Spalding, Lincolnshire, PE12 6AA Tel: (01775) 723411 Fax: (01775) 713064 *Agricultural consultants*

▶ W W Installations, 19 Gregorys Mill Street, Worcester, WR3 8BA Tel: (01905) 723113

W W Martin Thanet Ltd, Dane Park Road, Ramsgate, Kent, CT11 7LT Tel: (01843) 591584 Fax: (01843) 596333 E-mail: brian.pratt@wwmartin.co.uk *General building contractors*

W W P Consultants Ltd, 5-15 Cromer Street, London, WC1H 8LS Tel: (020) 7833 5767 Fax: (020) 7833 5766 E-mail: info@wwp-london.co.uk *Mechanical, Electrical & Public Health Consulting Engineers*

▶ W W Pert Construction Ltd, Broomfield Industrial Estate, Broomfield Road, Montrose, Angus, DD10 8SY Tel: (01674) 673883 Fax: (01674) 678533

▶ W W Pipetech Ltd, 12 Dock Road, Connah's Quay, Deeside, Clwyd, CH5 4DS Tel: (01244) 830164 Fax: (01244) 830214 E-mail: sales@pipetech.org.uk

W W S Tarpaulins Ltd, 22 Bryggen Road, The Old Station Yard, Galton Road, King's Lynn, Norfolk, PE32 1LQ Tel: (01553) 777304 Fax: (01553) 849888 E-mail: info@wwstarpaulins.co.uk *Tarpaulin manufacturers & repairers*

W Walters, Rope Walk, Ilkeston, Derbyshire, DE7 5HX Tel: 0115-932 4982 *Shed manufrs*

W Watson & Sons, 165 High Street, Perth, PH1 5UP Tel: (01738) 639861 Fax: (01738) 634662 E-mail: watsonsofperth@aol.com *Retail china & cutlery giftware*

▶ W Westerman 1981 Ltd, 158 By-Pass Road, Chilwell, Nottingham, NG9 5HQ Tel: 0115-925 5100 Fax: 0115-943 0833 E-mail: sales@westermanhomes.co.uk

W Yeomans Ltd, 11 Midland Way, Barlborough, Chesterfield, Derbyshire, S43 4XA Tel: (01246) 571270 Fax: (01246) 571271 E-mail: mailbox@wyeomans.com *Retail clothing, footwear & camping suppliers*

W Young & Son Ltd, 6-8 Godstone Road, Purley, Surrey, CR8 2DA Tel: (020) 8660 1158 Fax: (020) 8763 2021 *Builders merchants*

W2O Environment, 58 Cecil Road, Northampton, NN2 6PQ Tel: (01604) 478415 Fax: (01604) 478415 E-mail: wolfram@w2oenvironment.net *Environmental consulting training & research for the leather industry*

W3 Dot Wigtown, 16 Albert St, Newton Stewart, Wigtownshire, DG8 6EJ Tel: (01671) 404492 Fax: (01671) 402139 *Computer manufacturer, networking & retail*

▶ W3 Web Designs Ltd, 10 Millfield, Whitland, Dyfed, SA34 0QN Tel: (01994) 241454 Fax: (01994) 241454 E-mail: admin@w3designs.co.uk *Affordable web design services*

W4 Ltd, Unit B, Ford Lane Industrial Estate, Arundel, West Sussex, BN18 0DF Tel: (01243) 553355 Fax: (01243) 553540 E-mail: enquiries@w4limited.com *Caravan, camping & marine accessories manufrs*

▶ Wac Tackle, 5 Anstice Square, Madeley, Telford, Shropshire, TF7 5BD Tel: (01952) 586786 Fax: (01952) 620497 *Fishing tackle retailers*

Wackenhut U K Ltd, 875 Sidcup Road, London, SE9 3PP Tel: (020) 8850 4647 Fax: (020) 8850 0612 *Security services* Also at: Branches throughout the U.K.

▶ Wackiki, 7 Upper Mealough Road, Belfast, BT8 8LR Tel: 02890 817612 Fax: 02890 817613 E-mail: adam@wackiki.com *Sound & lighting hire & installation*

▶ Wackygraphics.Com, 1 Jays Close, Basingstoke, Hampshire, RG22 4BS Tel: (01256) 346794 E-mail: sales@wackygraphics.com *Manufacture of quality signs, vehicle graphics, 'stickers' & building signs /graphics all at affordable prices. Design & fitting service available.*

Wacs Trade Centre, Bond House, Goodwood Road, London, SE14 6BL Tel: (020) 8692 5864 Fax: (020) 8692 1322 E-mail: sales@wacstradecentre.com *Office cleaning supplies, car cleaning supplies, steam machines, industrial vacuum cleaners, how to clean automotive upholstery, pressure washers, bleach, kitchen cutlery, pest control, vacuum cleaners, floor machines, ladders, janitorial suppliers, hoovers & cleaning chemicals*

Wadco International, Unit 3 15 Nimrod Way, Wimborne, Dorset, BH21 7SH Tel: (01202) 890103 Fax: (01202) 890101 E-mail: sales@wadcointernational.ltd.uk *Export procurement*

William Waddell Ltd, 30 Russell Street, Wishaw, Lanarkshire, ML2 7AN Tel: (01698) 355034 Fax: (01698) 374970 *Bakery machinery manufacturers & light engineering*

▶ Waddicor Associates, Beech House, Grasby Road, North Kelsey Moor, Market Rasen, Lincolnshire, LN7 6HJ Tel: (01652) 678321 Fax: (01652) 678317 E-mail: info@waddicor.com *Electronic design consultancy*

▶ Waddie & Co. Ltd, Dewar Square, Deans Industrial Estate, Livingston, West Lothian, EH54 8SA Tel: (01506) 419393

Waddington Buildings Ltd, Station Road, Brompton on Swale, Richmond, North Yorkshire, DL10 7SH Tel: (01748) 812323 Fax: (01748) 812145 *Steel buildings*

Henry Waddington Ltd, The Stores, Halton West, Skipton, North Yorkshire, BD23 4LL Tel: (01729) 850206 Fax: (01729) 850658 *Agricultural merchants*

▶ Waddington & Ledger Ltd, Lowfields Way, Lowfields Business Park, Elland, West Yorkshire, HX5 9DA Tel: (01422) 315000 Fax: (01422) 315031 E-mail: sales@wlprint.co.uk

Waddingtons Cartons Ltd, Cockburn Fields, Middleton Grove, Leeds, LS11 5LX Tel: 0113-276 0730 Fax: 0113-276 0165 E-mail: enquiries@myholdings.co.uk Principal Export Areas: Worldwide *Food carton & packaging suppliers*

John Waddon (1967) Ltd, 1 Sedgemount Industrial Estate, Bristol Road, Bridgwater, Somerset, TA6 4AR Tel: (01278) 422280 Fax: (01278) 444266 E-mail: sales@waddons.co.uk *Tarpaulin manufrs*

Wade, Delta Road, Parr, St. Helens, Merseyside, WA9 2ED Tel: (01744) 451616 Fax: (01744) 26791 E-mail: enquiries@deltafluidproducts.com *Compression fittings manufrs*

Bernard F. Wade Ltd, PO Box 1865, Sheffield, S36 8BY Tel: (01226) 370860 Fax: (01226) 370836 E-mail: berniebolt@talk21.com *Nuts & bolts distributors for automotive trade*

Wade Building Services Ltd, Groveland Road, Tipton, West Midlands, DY4 7TN Tel: 0121-520 8121 Fax: 0121-557 7061 E-mail: sales@wade-bs.co.uk *Steel lintel scaffolding & fencing* Also at: Widnes

Wade Ceramics Ltd, Royal Victoria Pottery, Westport Road, Burslem, Stoke-On-Trent, ST6 4AG Tel: (01782) 577321 Fax: (01782) 575195 E-mail: alan.keenan@wade.co.uk *Ceramics products manufrs*

Wade Computing Services Ltd, 263 Buxton Road, Stockport, Cheshire, SK2 7NR Tel: 0161-456 0104 Fax: 0161-483 9119 E-mail: sales@wadecomputing.co.uk *Computer hardware/pegasus accounting software distributors*

Wade Precision Engineering, Unit 39 Penley Industrial Estate, Penley, Wrexham, Clwyd, LL13 0LQ Tel: (01948) 830268 Fax: (01948) 830268 *Precision engineers*

Wade Spring Ltd, Bennett Street, Long Eaton, Nottingham, NG10 4HL Tel: 0115-946 3000 Fax: 0115-946 1361 E-mail: mchiltern@wade-spring.com *Furniture & bedding springs manufrs*

Wade Upholstery, Bridge Street, Sandy Acre, Nottingham, NG10 5BH Tel: 0115-939 4500 Fax: 0115-949 0465 *Upholsterers manufrs* Also at: Bramcote, Gainsborough, Leeds, Nottingham & Sandiacre

Wadebridge Computers Ltd, Laura House, Fair Park Road, Wadebridge, Cornwall, PL27 7NT Tel: (01208) 815956 Fax: (01208) 815968 E-mail: wadcom@btconnect.com *Computer services*

▶ Wader Labelling Systems Ltd, 26 Carham Road, Hoylake, Wirral, Merseyside, CH47 4FF Tel: 0151-632 3464 Fax: 0151-632 5151

▶ Waders Welding & Fabrication Ltd, Elliott Road, Love Lane Industrial Estate, Cirencester, Gloucestershire, GL7 1YS Tel: (01285) 640725 Fax: (01285) 641698 E-mail: garywaders@tiscali.co.uk *Welder & fabrication*

W.F. Wades, Unit 11, Garrick Industrial Centre, Irving Way, London, NW9 6AQ Tel: (020) 8203 0055 Fax: (020) 8203 6570 *Electric equipment wholesalers*

Wades of Wednesbury Ltd, Webb Street, Coseley, Bilston, West Midlands, WV14 8XL Tel: (01902) 496491 Fax: (01902) 491982 *Scrap metal merchants*

Wadeworld Trade Ltd, 50 Burnhill Road, Beckenham, Kent, BR3 3LA Tel: (020) 8663 3577 Fax: (020) 8663 3212 E-mail: info@wadetrade.com *Business education & courses*

▶ Wadey Builders, Leigh Road, Betchworth, Surrey, RH3 7AW Tel: (01306) 611467 Fax: (01306) 611519

▶ Wadham Fencing, 9 Rylands Farm Industrial Estate, Bagley Road, Wellington, Somerset, TA21 9PZ Tel: (01823) 662429 Fax: (01823) 666675 E-mail: enquires@wadhamfencing.co.uk *Domestic or commercial fencing manufrs*

Wadkin Ltd, Franks Road, Hilltop Industrial Estate, Bardon, Coalville, Leicestershire, LE67 1TT Tel: (01530) 513500 Fax: (01530) 513513 E-mail: info@wadkin.com *Woodworking machinery and supplies including education*

Wadland Bros, Lower Hampt, Luckett, Callington, Cornwall, PL17 8NT Tel: (01579) 370234 Fax: (01579) 370234 *Sectional buildings manufrs*

Wadsworth Electronics Ltd, Central Avenue, West Molesey, Surrey, KT8 2QB Tel: (020) 8268 7000 Fax: (020) 8268 6565 E-mail: info@wadsworth.co.uk *Distributor of computer network & security products* Also at: Birmingham, Bristol & Warrington

Wadsworth Security Products, Unit 1 Epsom Downs Metro Centre, Waterfield, Tadworth, Surrey, KT20 5EZ Tel: (01737) 360512 Fax: (01737) 370475 *Lock distributors*

Waeco UK Ltd, Unit D1 Roman Hill Trading Estate, Broadmayne, Dorchester, Dorset, DT2 8LY Tel: (01305) 854000 Fax: (01305) 854288 E-mail: enquiries@waeco.co.uk *Coolin distributors*

Waen Agricultural Sales, Waen, Llanbedr Dyffryn Clwyd, Ruthin, Clwyd, LL15 1SR Tel: (01824) 705571 Fax: (01824) 705243 E-mail: lindadyer@waenagriculturalsales.fsnet.co.uk *Agricultural engineers*

Wafer Technology Ltd, 34 Maryland Road, Tongwell, Milton Keynes, MK15 8HJ Tel: (01908) 210444 Fax: (01908) 210443 E-mail: sales@wafertech.co.uk *Semi-conductor material manufrs*

Waffell Ltd, 111 Sadler Road, Doddington Road, Lincoln, LN6 3RS Tel: (01522) 888444 Fax: (01522) 888400 E-mail: sales@totalbikebits.com *British motorcycle parts distributors*

Wafios-Metoma Ltd, 21 Colemeadow Road, North Moons Moat, Redditch, Worcestershire, B98 9PB Tel: (01527) 65396 Fax: (01527) 67570 E-mail: sales@wafios-metoma.com *Distributors & agents of wire, nail & spring production machinery*

Wagenaar Generators Ltd, Gilfach-Y-Rhiw, Abergwili, Carmarthen, SA32 7ER Tel: (01267) 237078 Fax: (01267) 234113 E-mail: johndenver@amgenerators.com *Generating sets diesel driven, emergency, standby used & reconditioned suppliers*

▶ Wagg Jex & Co. Ltd, Harvest House, Wisbech Road, King's Lynn, Norfolk, PE30 5JL Tel: (01553) 772963 Fax: (01553) 769184

Waggonworks Trailers & Towing Equipment, 1 White Cottage, Marshside, Canterbury, Kent, CT3 4EJ Tel: (01227) 860650 Fax: (01227) 860650 *Trailer manufacturers & components*

▶ Wagner Biro Ltd, Bankside House, 107-112 Leadenhall Street, London, EC3A 4AF Tel: (020) 7398 1590 Fax: (020) 7398 1599 E-mail: info@waagnerbiro.co.uk *Construction engineers*

Wagon Automotive, Tysley Plant, Saville House, Redfern Park Way, Birmingham, B11 2BF Tel: 0121-706 0330 Fax: 0121-706 1929 *Pressings & welded assemblie services*

Wagon Automotive Wantage Plant, Main Street, East Challow, Wantage, Oxfordshire, OX12 9SY Tel: (01235) 770770 Fax: (01235) 770017 E-mail: wantage@wagonautomotive.com *Automotive component manufrs*

Wagstaff Foundries Ltd, Poyle Trading Estate, 7 David Road, Colnbrook, Slough, SL3 0DB Tel: (01753) 683356 Fax: (01753) 683358 E-mail: andrew@asp-wagstaff.co.uk *Iron founders*

Wagstaff Office Interiors, Unit 12-15 Wharfeside, Rosemont Road, Wembley, Middlesex, HA0 4PE Tel: (020) 8432 1000 Fax: (020) 8432 1111 E-mail: interiors@wagstaffgroup.co.uk *Office equipment suppliers* Also at: London SE11 & WC1

Wain Bros Ltd, 774 Leek Road, Stoke-on-Trent, ST1 6AE Tel: (01782) 202180 Fax: (01782) 213127 *Pre-cast concrete manufrs*

Wain Shiell & Son Ltd, 12 Saville Row, London, W1S 3PQ Tel: (020) 7734 1464 Fax: (020) 7439 0093 *Woollen merchants*

Wainhomes South West Ltd, Owlsfoot Business Centre, Sticklepath, Okehampton, Devon, EX20 2PA Tel: (01837) 841000

Wainwright Bros & Co. Ltd, Lambourn House, 7 Western Road, Romford, RM1 3LD Tel: (01708) 756622 Fax: (01708) 756633 E-mail: freight@wainwrightgroup.com *Freight forwarders & forwarding agents*

John Wainwright Systems Ltd, Third Avenue, Midsomer Norton, Radstock, BA3 4XD Tel: (01761) 414700 Fax: (01761) 414722 E-mail: post@jwsltd.co.uk *Designers & manufacturers of access control systems*

Wainwright Print Finishers Ltd, Unit 6 Redfern Industrial Estate, Dawson Street, Market Street, Hyde, Cheshire, SK14 1RD Tel: 0161-368 9797 Fax: 0161-367 8732 *Printing trade finishing services*

▶ Wainwright Transport, 19 Wood Street, Ashby-de-la-Zouch, Leicestershire, LE65 1EL Tel: (01530) 412057 Fax: (01530) 415824

G W Waite Ltd, North Lonsdale Road, Ulverston, Cumbria, LA12 9DN Tel: (01229) 582046 Fax: (01229) 583893 E-mail: sales@gwwaite.com *Family Company (estab. 1946) offering complete in house service including, Tooling, Progressive and second operation Presswork, welded and riveted sub assemblies in ferrous and non ferrous metals, automatic zinc plating facility. Accredited to ISO 9001:2000.*

▶ Waite Property, St. Julians Avenue, St. Peter Port, Guernsey, GY1 1WB Tel: (01481) 722121 Fax: (01481) 722100

▶ Waitings Drainage & Pipeline Contractors, Moss Road, Cliburn, Penrith, Cumbria, CA10 3AL Tel: (01931) 714270 Fax: (01931) 714508 E-mail: info@waitings.co.uk *Drainage & pipe line*

Waivis Co. Ltd, 14 Minerva Road, London, NW10 6HJ Tel: (020) 8965 6818 Fax: (020) 8965 6287 E-mail: info@waivis.co.uk *Rolling shutters for office furniture manufacturers.*

Wake Industries Ltd, Basin Lane, Tamworth, Staffordshire, B77 2AH Tel: (01827) 65864 Fax: (01827) 53326 E-mail: info@wakeindustries.co.uk *Tubular furniture manufrs*

Wakefield Cash Registers, 250 Bradford Road, Wakefield, West Yorkshire, WF1 2BA Tel: (01924) 366753 *Cash registers & weighing scales repair & suppliers*

Wakefield Engineering Services, 44 Grove Park, Calder Grove, Wakefield, West Yorkshire, WF4 3BZ Tel: (01924) 277726 Fax: (01924) 281730 E-mail: derek@weserv.fsbusiness.co.uk *Servicing the Sheet Metalworking Industry Sales - Service - Repairs*

Wakefield Inspection Services Ltd, 14-20 Pall Mall, Liverpool, L3 6AL Tel: 0151-236 0752 Fax: 0151-236 0140 E-mail: wif@wakefieldinspection.com *Cotton controllers*

Wakefield Interiors, 7 Monton Ave, Eccles, Manchester, M30 9HS Tel: 0161-788 7126 *Ceilings & partitions*

Wakefield Joinery, Unit 8, Heacham, King's Lynn, Norfolk, PE31 7BT Tel: (01485) 571313 Fax: (01485) 571313 *Joinery manufrs*

Wakefield Taffarello Associates, 54 Old Street, London, EC1V 9AL Tel: (020) 7250 0500 Fax: (020) 7250 1553 E-mail: wta@wtadspr.demon.co.uk *Advertising & public relations agency*

▶ Tom Wakefield, Holly Tree Cottage, Woodmancote, Cirencester, Glos, GL7 7EF Tel: (0776) 6604866 Fax: E-mail: info@furryfeetstudios.com *Multimedia CD/DVD's Animation, Web Design, Logo Design, Photography and all aspects of Graphic Design*

Waker UK Ltd, 99 Bellshill Road, Uddingston, Glasgow, G71 7NT Tel: (01698) 801010 Fax: (01698) 808068 *Porter cabins & modular buildings suppliers*

▶ Wal, Unit D3 The Point Office Park, Weaver Road, Lincoln, LN6 3QN Tel: (01522) 692284 Fax: (01522) 694731 E-mail: cs@wal-filters.co.uk *Water filters & stationary distributors*

Walbrad Wool Trading Co., White Rose Mill, Holdsworth Road, Halifax, West Yorkshire, HX3 6SN Tel: (01422) 241001 Fax: (01422) 246331 E-mail: info@cashmere-fibre.co.uk *Wool waste merchants*

Dave Walch Ltd, 121 Percival Lane, Runcorn, Cheshire, WA7 4UY Tel: (01928) 574681 Fax: (01928) 577790 E-mail: dave@anodisersruncorn.com *Anodising electroplating services*

Walcon Ltd, Cockerell Close, Segensworth West, Fareham, Hampshire, PO15 5SR Tel: (01489) 579977 Fax: (01489) 579988 E-mail: sales@walconmarine.com *Design & construction of yacht harbours*

Walcott House Ltd, Lyneham, Chipping Norton, Oxfordshire, OX7 6QQ Tel: (01993) 832940 Fax: (01993) 832950 *Design service for hanging systems & curtain poles*

A. & G. Walden Bros Ltd, 34 Wimbledon Avenue, Brandon, Suffolk, IP27 0NZ Tel: (01842) 811776 Fax: (01842) 814603 E-mail: trucks@walden.co.uk *Walden's manufacture an extensive range of Materials Handling products, the range includes Sack Trucks, Chair Carrying Sack Trucks,Heavy Duty Sack Trucks, Three Way Sack Trucks, Folding Sack trucks, Star Wheel Sack Trucks, Stair Climbing Sack Trucks, Platform Trucks, High Sided Platform trucks, Nesting Platform trucks, Box Trucks, Table Trolleys, Steel Shelf Trolleys, Order Picking Trolleys, Nesting Order Picking Trolleys, Trolleys with Steps, Panel and Board trolleys, Small Panel Trolleys, Upright Panel*

continued

Trolleys, Turntable Trucks, Two Tonne Turntable Trucks, Heavy Duty Turntable Trucks, One Tonne Trailers, Piano Skates, Furniture Skates, Pallet Skates, Pipe Skates, Drum Handling, Drum Trolleys, Drum Stands, Cylinder Trucks, Cylinder Trolleys, Cylinder Stands, Cylinder Racks, Pallet trucks, High lift Pallet Trucks, Safety steps High Safety Steps, Garment Rails, Tyre Trolleys, Mobile Ramps, Cycle Racks, Cycle Stands

Waldham Precision Engineering Ltd, 2 Lennox Road, Bilton Industrial Estate, Basingstoke, Hampshire, RG22 4AP Tel: (01256) 359898 Fax: (01256) 844043 E-mail: sales@waldhamprecision.co.uk Principal Export Areas: Asia Pacific & Central Asia *Precision engineers*

▶ Waldmann Lighting Ltd, Holme Well Road, Middleton, Leeds, LS10 4TQ Tel: 0113 2775662 Fax: 0113 2775775 E-mail: enquiries@waldmannlighting.co.uk *Manufacturer's for light in the workplace, task lighting ,office*

Waldridge Engineering, Greenham Business Park, Greenham, Wellington, Somerset, TA21 0LR Tel: (01823) 672444 *Steel fabricators services*

Wales Foam, Unit 3 Rocky Park, Tenby, Dyfed, SA70 7LH Tel: (01834) 844333 Fax: (01834) 844346 E-mail: info@walesfoam.com *Foam company*

▶ Wales Telecom, Y Manor 6, Victoria Parade, South Beach, Pwllheli, Gwynedd, LL53 5AL Tel: (01758) 613078 E-mail: info@wales-telecom.co.uk *Wales Telecom are business and domestic telephone, broadband, wireless/wap and satellite providers*

Wales Water Gardening, Croesyceiliog, Cwmbran, Gwent, NP44 2BZ Tel: (01633) 871144 Fax: 01633 873722 *Aquarium services & distribution*

Walford E A Chelmsford, Navigation Road, Chelmsford, CM2 6HD Tel: (01245) 262426 Fax: (01245) 352301 *Safety glass replacement services*

Walford Metal Spinning Co. Ltd, 13 Morris Road, Nuffield Industrial Estate, Poole, Dorset, BH17 7RS Tel: (01202) 678848 Fax: (01202) 678848 *Metal spinnings manufrs*

Walgrave Electrical Services Ltd, 13 North Portway Close, Round Spinney, Northampton, NN3 8RQ Tel: (01604) 490100 Fax: (01604) 490101 E-mail: walgrave@skynet.co.uk *Power engineer*

Walk Easy Ltd, Unit 3, Hadstock Road Industrial Estate, Hadstock Road, Linton, Cambridge, CB21 4XM Tel: (01223) 892623 Fax: (01223) 893880 E-mail: sales@walkeasy.ltd.uk *Personal attack alarm manufrs*

Walk Easy Sales, 2 Vicarage Field, Broom Street, Great Cornard, Sudbury, Suffolk, CO10 0JT Tel: (01787) 311559 E-mail: enquiries@walkeasy.co.uk *Surgical appliance wholesalers*

Walkbury Electronics Ltd, 30 The Metro Centre, Peterborough, PE2 7UH Tel: (01733) 404830 Fax: (01733) 404839 E-mail: sales@walkbury.co.uk *Assembly for electronics*

▶ Walkden Warehousing Ltd, 3 Orion Trading Estate, Tenax Road, Trafford Park, Manchester, M17 1JT Tel: 0161-848 7684 Fax: 0161-877 5373

Walker, 6a Digby Drive, Melton Mowbray, Leicestershire, LE13 0RQ Tel: (01664) 410354 Fax: (01664) 410354 *Sign & label suppliers*

Walker Aec Ltd, 16c Dawkins Road, Poole, Dorset, BH15 4JY Tel: (01202) 685135 Fax: (01202) 677415 E-mail: sales@walkeraec.com *Specialis precision engineers*

Brian Walker, Westwood, Fovant, Salisbury, SP3 5JW Tel: (01722) 714370 Fax: (01722) 714853 *Cabinet makers & antique restoration*

▶ Walker Bros (Elland) Ltd, Ainleys Industrial Estate, Huddersfield Road, Elland, West Yorkshire, HX5 9JP Tel: (01422) 310767 Fax: (01422) 377837 E-mail: sales@wbelland.com *Design & manufacture of shop fitting & point of sale display metalwork.*Manufacture of lamp guards, furniture components and welding lugs.*Sub-contract design & manufacture of pressed, punched, fabricated and painted metal components, assemblies and finished products.*

Walker Bros Services, Hurst Street, Bury, Lancashire, BL9 7ES Tel: 0161-761 7776 Fax: 0161-761 1666 *Chemical janitorial manufrs*

▶ Walker Catering Supplies Ltd, Sherwood House, Bloomsgrove Industrial Estate, Nottingham, NG7 3JG Tel: 0115-979 0110 Fax: 0115-979 1393 E-mail: info@walkercateringsupplies.com *Catering equipment suppliers*

Walker Chair Care, 107 Bradford Road, Dewsbury, West Yorkshire, WF13 2ET Tel: (01924) 465588 Fax: (01924) 459688 E-mail: sales@walkerchaircare.co.uk *Upholsterers*

▶ Walker & Connell Ltd, Hastings Square, Darvel, Ayrshire, KA17 0DS Tel: (01560) 320237 Fax: (01560) 322209

Walker Construction UK Ltd, Park Farm Road, Park Farm Industrial Estate, Folkestone, Kent, CT19 5DY Tel: (01303) 851111 Fax: (01303) 259439 E-mail: sales@walker-construction.co.uk *Building industry services*

Walker Crane Services Ltd, Trading Estate, Motherwell Way, Grays, Essex, RM20 3XD Tel: (01708) 867251 Fax: (01708) 863636 E-mail: info@walkercranes.co.uk *Lorry mounted & hydraulic cranes*

Walker Crips Groups plc, Finsbury Tower, 103-105 Bunhill Row, London, EC1Y 8LZ Tel: (020) 7253 7502 Fax: (020) 7253 7500 E-mail: client.services@wbwcservices.co.uk *Stock & share brokers*

David Walker Engineering Services, St Lawrence Industrial Estate, Manston Road, Ramsgate, Kent, CT11 0QZ Tel: (01843) 589954 Fax: (01843) 589954 *Engineering services*

Walker Engineering (Essex) Ltd, Unit 2A North Hill Business Park, North Hill, Horndon-On-The-Hill, Stanford-Le-Hope, Essex, SS17 8QA Tel: (01375) 361428 Fax: (01375) 361428 E-mail: walkereng@btconnect.com *Mould manufrs*

Walker Eurosalt Ltd, 6 Northern Road, Belfast, BT3 9AL Tel: (028) 9074 8551 Fax: (028) 9075 4937 E-mail: info@chem-vite.co.uk *Salt merchants*

Walker Filtration Ltd, Spire Road, Glover East, Washington, Tyne & Wear, NE37 3ES Tel: 0191-417 7816 Fax: 0191-415 3748 E-mail: sales@walkerfiltration.co.uk *Filter manufrs*

Walker Fire, Unit 1 Brock House, Brocks Way, East Mains Industrial Estate, Broxburn, West Lothian, EH52 5NB Tel: (01506) 858108 Fax: (01506) 858002 E-mail: uk@walkerfire.com *Fire fighting equipment service company*

Walker Fire, 10 The Quad, Mercury Court, Chester, CH1 4QP Tel: (01244) 371345 Fax: (01244) 370396 E-mail: uk@walkerfire.com *Fire protection engineers & installation service*

Walker Fire, 2 Roman Way, Longridge Road, Ribbleton, Preston, PR2 5BB Tel: (01772) 693777 Fax: (01772) 693760 E-mail: uk@walkerfire.com *Fire fighting equipment distributors*

Walker Freight Services Ltd, 8-9 Blackthorne Cresent, Colnbrook, Slough, SL3 0QR Tel: (01753) 683288 Fax: (01753) 681917 E-mail: sales@walker-freight.com *International freight forwarders*

George Walker & Co., 81-83 Glasgow Road, Dumbarton, G82 1RE Tel: (01389) 733933 Fax: (01389) 742305 E-mail: admin_dept@georgewalker.co.uk *Messengers-at-arms & sheriff officers*

George Walker Ltd, Fosse Way Sawmills, Fosse Way, Syston, Leicester, LE7 1NH Tel: 0116-260 8330 Fax: 0116-269 7450 E-mail: info@george-walker.co.uk *Timber merchants*

George Walker & Sons F R Ltd, Station Road, Mallaig, Inverness-Shire, PH41 4PY Tel: (01687) 462305 Fax: (01687) 462178 *Fish merchants*

Walker Group Scotland Ltd, Westerwood House, Royston Road, Deans, Livingston, West Lothian, EH54 8AH Tel: (01506) 413101 Fax: (01506) 414843 E-mail: info@walkergroup.co.uk

Walker & Hartle Ltd, Derby Road, Ripley, Derbyshire, DE5 3HS Tel: (01773) 743334 Fax: (01773) 743334 *Joinery manufrs*

Walker Holding Ltd, 33-34 Liliput Road, Brackmills Industrial Estate, Northampton, NN4 7DT Tel: (01604) 760529 Fax: (01604) 675641 E-mail: sales@walkerpack.co.uk *Contract packers*

Walker & Holmes Ltd, Linton Street, Bradford, West Yorkshire, BD4 7EZ Tel: (01274) 728655 Fax: (01274) 723678 E-mail: walkerholmesltd@aol.com *Dust & fume extraction plant manufrs*

Walker & Howell Ltd, Forge Road, Whaley Bridge, High Peak, Derbyshire, SK23 7HY Tel: (01663) 732471 Fax: (01663) 733927 E-mail: sales@walkerandhowell.co.uk *Engineers' suppliers*

Ian Walker, 58 Ettington Cl, Wellesbourne, Warwick, CV35 9RJ Tel: (01789) 840341 Fax: (01789) 840341 *Livestock*

Walker Interiors Ltd, East Park Street, Morley, Leeds, LS27 0PW Tel: 0113-253 7566 Fax: 0113-387 8601 E-mail: walkerintltd@aol.com *Suspended ceilings manufrs*

▶ Walker & Kitching Ltd, Sandall Stones Road, Kirk Sandall Estate, Kirk Sandall, Doncaster, South Yorkshire, DN3 1QR Tel: (01302) 880044

Walker Machinery, Lindsay Farm, High Cogges, Witney, Oxfordshire, OX29 6UN Tel: (01993) 772255 Fax: (01993) 771007 E-mail: sales@walkermachinery.fsnet.co.uk *Used plant & equipment distributors*

▶ Walker Macleod Ltd, 8-36 Bulldale Street, Glasgow, G14 0NU Tel: 0141-954 0297 Fax: 0141-950 1351 E-mail: sales@walkermacleod.co.uk *Sheet metal fabricators*

Walker May Halifax Ltd, 7 The Market Business Centre, Hanson Lane, Halifax, West Yorkshire, HX1 5PF Tel: (01422) 347483 Fax: (01422) 342096 E-mail: walkermay@btclick.com *Demolition contractors & stone merchants*

Walker Metalwork (Elland) Ltd, Castle Mills, Elland, West Yorkshire, HX5 0RY Tel: 01422 310011 *Steel fabricators*

Walker & Partners Ltd, Inkersall Road Industrial Estate, Speedwell Industrial Estate, Staveley, Chesterfield, Derbyshire, S43 3JN Tel: (01246) 472147 Fax: (01246) 473913 E-mail: sales@walkerandpartners.co.uk *Contractors, process plant & machinery distributors*

▶ Walker Precision Engineering Ltd, 4 Fullarton Drive, Glasgow East Investment Park, Glasgow, G32 8FA Tel: 0141-641 9641 Fax: 0141-646 2060 *Precision engineering*

Walker Products, Unit 71 Kage Buildings, Pye Bridge Industrial Estate, Pye Bridge, Alfreton, Derbyshire, DE55 4NU Tel: (01773) 609257 Fax: (01773) 609257 *Steel fabricators*

Walker Rewinds, Unit 4 Station Road Industrial Estate, Madeley, Telford, Shropshire, TF7 5EF Tel: (01952) 582594 Fax: (01952) 582594 *Industrial electric motor repairers*

Roy Walker Pine, Lindens Farm, North Road, Newark, Nottinghamshire, NG23 6QL Tel: (01636) 822173 Fax: (01636) 822229 E-mail: sale@roywalkerpine.com *Pine furniture manufrs*

Walker Rubber & Plastics Ltd, Unit 22, Farthing Road, Ipswich, IP1 5AP Tel: (01473) 749131 Fax: (01473) 240917 E-mail: sales@walker-rubber.co.uk *Industrial rubber products*

Walker Rubber & Plastics Ltd, Last House, 21-23 Burnet Road, Sweetbriar Industrial Estate, Norwich, NR3 2BS Tel: (01603) 487371 Fax: (01603) 406502 E-mail: sales@walker-rubber.co.uk *Manufacturers of Rubber Extrusions, Mouldings and Fabrications. We also supply: Adhesives, Belting, Clips, Cork, Couplings, Ducting, Felt, Fenders, Fittings, Gaskets, Hoses, Matting, 'O' Rings, PVC Curtains, PTFE, Sheet, Sponge, Strip, Tube, Washers, Wall Defenders.* Also at: Ipswich

Walker S Nonsuch Ltd, Calverley Street, Stoke-on-Trent, ST3 1QS Tel: (01782) 321525 Fax: (01782) 599449 E-mail: walkersnonsuch@walkers-nonsuch.co.uk *Confectionery manufrs*

▶ Walker Security Systems Ltd, Unit 17 Anniesland Business Park, Netherton Road, Glasgow, G13 1EU Tel: 0141-959 7300 Fax: (0845) 2250700 E-mail: sales@walkersecurity.co.uk *Security systems installation, maintenance and service.*

Walker Signs, Cook Lane, Heckmondwike, West Yorkshire, WF16 9JG Tel: (01924) 407918 Fax: (01924) 404058 E-mail: enquiries@walkersigns.co.uk *Sign manufrs*

Walker Singleton Commercial Ltd, Property House, Lister Lane, Halifax, West Yorkshire, HX1 5AS Tel: (01422) 430000 Fax: (01422) 430010 E-mail: comm@walkersingleton.co.uk *Chartered surveyors*

Walker & Smith, Lanes Mills, 403 Bradford Road, Batley, West Yorkshire, WF17 5LY Tel: (01924) 474469 Fax: (01924) 474460 E-mail: sales@walker-smith.co.uk *Textile opening machinery manufrs*

Walker Sound Ltd, 8 Somerset Road, Southsea, Hampshire, PO5 2NL Tel: (023) 9273 0259 *Sound hire company*

Steven Walker & Sons Ltd, Portersfield Road, Cradley Heath, West Midlands, B64 7BE Tel: (01384) 569087 Fax: (01384) 633727 E-mail: sales@swsltd.co.uk *Bolt manufrs*

Walker Timber Ltd, Carriden Sawmills, Bo'Ness, West Lothian, EH51 9SN Tel: (01506) 823331 Fax: (01506) 822590 E-mail: mail@walkertimber.com *Timber importers & timber frame manufrs*

▶ Tony Walker Interiors, Whitehall Court, 14 Telford Road, Edinburgh, EH4 2BA Tel: 0131-343 6151 Fax: 0131-332 4366 E-mail: enquiries@tonywalker.co.uk *Home & commercial interior designers*

Walker Training, Park Farm Road, Park Farm Industrial Estate, Folkestone, Kent, CT19 5DY Tel: (01303) 850186 Fax: (01303) 850908 E-mail: walkertraining@hotmail.com *We provide courses such as Confined Spaces, New Roads and Street Works Act (1991)(NRSWA) Operative & Supervisor, Site Managers, Personal Track Safety (PTS) Initial & Refresher and many more. Call for details and full list of courses.*

▶ W. Walker Transport, Granitehill Road, Aberdeen, AB16 7AX Tel: (01224) 698844 Fax: (01224) 685967 E-mail: steve@williamwalkertransport.co.uk *Road transport/haulage/freight & hazardous load transport contractors*

Walker Wade, Security House, Cleckheaton, West Yorkshire, BD19 3TT Tel: 01274 852261 *Roller shutters*

▶ Walkers, 361 Argyll Street, Dunoon, Argyll, PA23 7RN Tel: (01369) 706003

▶ Walkers Bros Cockermouth Ltd, 6 Market Place, Cockermouth, Cumbria, CA13 9NQ Tel: (01900) 823302 Fax: (01900) 823302

Walkers Chocolate Emporium, 6 High Street, Ilfracombe, Devon, EX34 9DF Tel: (01271) 867193 *Hand made chocolate retailers & manufrs*

▶ Walkers International Movers Ltd, 33-34 Liliput Road, Brackmills Industrial Estate, Northampton, NN4 7DT Tel: (01604) 704030

▶ Walkers Manchester, Crabtree Lane, Manchester, M11 4GU Tel: 0161-223 7814 Fax: 0161-231 7212 E-mail: info@walkersmcr.com *Screen printers & point of sale specialists. Digital capabilities.*

▶ Walkers Of Shrewsbury Ltd, 51 Mardol, Shrewsbury, SY1 1PP Tel: (01743) 241411 *Fishing tackle retailers*

Walkers Snack Foods Ltd, Leacroft Road, Birchwood, Warrington, WA3 6WA Tel: (01925) 283500 Fax: (01925) 283555 E-mail: nrdc.reception@intl.pepsico.com *Snack food distributors*

Walkers Yacht Chandlery, 1 Brunel Road, Leigh-on-Sea, Essex, SS9 5JL Tel: (01702) 421321 Fax: (01702) 421321 *Boat & engine sales & service*

Walkerworld Steel Fabricators, 451 Stanton Road, Burton-on-Trent, Staffordshire, DE15 9RS Tel: (01283) 515439 Fax: (01283) 517554 *Onsite welding & rectification*

Walki Ltd, Ray Lane, Barnacre, Preston, PR3 1GG Tel: (01995) 604227 Fax: (01995) 605222 E-mail: wawgar@upm-kymmene.com *Paper & board converters, barrier packaging & extrusion coating*

▶ Walkplace Ltd, The Byre, Lower End Farm, Leafield, Witney, Oxfordshire, OX29 9QG Tel: (01993) 878550 Fax: (01993) 878036

▶ Wall 2 Wall Painting & Decorating, 16 Hob Green Road, Stourbridge, West Midlands, DY9 9EX Tel: (01562) 887413 E-mail: wall2_wall@yahoo.co.uk *We are a Painting and Decorating company who are prepared to travel and work on all kinds of properties whether its residentail, industrial or commercial. we have teams of skilled tradesmen at your disposal to help your job run quickly and smoothly.*

Wall Engineering Co. Ltd, Cromer Road, North Walsham, Norfolk, NR28 0NB Tel: (01692) 403701 Fax: (01692) 406610 E-mail: info@wallengineering.co.uk *Structural engineers & cladding contractors*

▶ Wall To Wall Security Door Systems, Units 8-10 Western Business Park, Coombs Road, Halesowen, West Midlands, B62 8AE Tel: 0121-561 1912 Fax: 0121-561 5232

Wallace, Cameron & Co. Ltd, 26 Netherhall Road, Netherton Industrial Estate, Wishaw, Lanarkshire, ML2 0JG Tel: (01698) 354600 Fax: (01698) 354700 E-mail: sales@wallacecameron.com *First aid dressings suppliers*

▶ Wallace Couriers Ltd, 286 Muswell Hill Broadway, London, N10 2QR Tel: (020) 8352 3634 Fax: (07785) 789024 E-mail: paulwallace@blueyonder.co.uk *Courier services*

Wallace Of Kelso Ltd, Bowmont Street, Kelso, Roxburghshire, TD5 7EA Tel: (01573) 224131 Fax: (01573) 226145 E-mail: info@wallaceofkelso.co.uk *Agrochemical distributors*

▶ Wallace Screen Print Ltd, 7 Ballard Business Park, Cuxton Road, Rochester, Kent, ME2 2NY Tel: (01634) 724772 Fax: (01634) 727490 E-mail: sales@wprintgroup.co.uk *Printing services*

Wallace Sheetmetal & Fabrication Ltd, Old Jam Works Lane, Station Road, Wigton, Cumbria, CA7 9AX Tel: (01697) 342918 Fax: (01697) 344617 E-mail: mail@wallacesheetmetal.co.uk *Fabrication & sheetmetal work manufrs*

▶ Wallace & Tiernan, Priory Works, Five Oak Green Road, Tonbridge, Kent, TN11 0QL Tel: (01732) 771777 Fax: (01732) 771800 E-mail: sales@wallace-tiernan.com *Water treatment plant & equipment manufrs*

▶ Wallace Whittle & Partners, 166 Great Western Road, Aberdeen, AB10 6QE Tel: (01224) 285300 Fax: (01224) 285301 E-mail: aberdeen@wallacewhittle.com *Consulting engineers*

▶ Wallace Whittle & Partners, Broughton Street Lane, Edinburgh, EH1 3LY Tel: 0131-524 5800 Fax: 0131-557 5801 E-mail: sales@wwpltd.co.uk *Electrical engineer consultants*

Wallass & Co. Ltd, Lumb Lane Mills, Lumb Lane, Bradford, West Yorkshire, BD8 7GA Tel: (01274) 724215 Fax: (01274) 724839 E-mail: sales@wallass.com *Fabric manufrs*

F.W. Wallen & Sons Ltd, Welkin Road, Lower Bredbury, Stockport, Cheshire, SK6 2BH Tel: 0161-494 9766 Fax: 0161-406 7580 E-mail: info@egertonstationery.co.uk *Stationers*

Les Wallen Manufacturing Ltd, Lambda Works, 45A Whitehall Road, Ramsgate, Kent, CT12 6DE Tel: (01843) 582864 Fax: (01843) 590726 E-mail: lee@wallen-antennae.co.uk *Radio communications services*

▶ Waller Building Services, Pheasants Farm, Sheppey Way, Bobbing, Sittingbourne, Kent, ME9 8QX Tel: (01795) 424435 Fax: (01795) 424812 E-mail: info@wallerservices.com

Waller Eurosel, 43 Bridgeman Terrace, Wigan, Lancashire, WN1 1TT Tel: (01942) 234897 Fax: (01942) 496276 E-mail: info@waller-eurosel.co.uk *Wraparound case packaging machinery*

Waller Transport Services Ltd, Brewery Yard, 6 Landseer Road, Ipswich, IP3 0AZ Tel: (01473) 254717 Fax: (01473) 250582 E-mail: ipswichtraffic@wallertransport.co.uk *Never lost for a lorry. Always a load. Return load specialists, established 1974*

Wallhurst Metals Ltd, 97 Holborn Hill, Birmingham, B6 7QX Tel: 0121-327 3597 Fax: 0121-327 3597 *Cable scrap & metal merchants*

Wallingford Computing Services Ltd, 142 Wantage Road, Wallingford, Oxfordshire, OX10 0LU Tel: (01491) 835959 Fax: (01491) 838071 E-mail: barry.harris@btconnect.com *Computer consultants & sales*

Wallington Sewing Machines, 108e Manor Road, Wallington, Surrey, SM6 0DW Tel: (020) 8647 1830 *Sewing machine reconditioners & new sales*

Wallis Ltd, 47 Homesdale Road, Bromley, BR2 9TN Tel: (020) 8464 3377 Fax: (020) 8464 5847 E-mail: gen@wallisb.kier.co.uk *Refurbishment contractors*

Wallis Barfield, 2 Midland Avenue, Netherfield, Nottingham, NG4 2LG Tel: 0115-961 7038 Fax: 0115-961 1482 *Toilet cubicles*

Wallis Office Furniture Ltd, 8-18 Fowler Road, Hainault Industrial Estate, Ilford, Essex, IG6 3UT Tel: (020) 8500 9991 Fax: (020) 8500 1949 E-mail: sales@wallisoffice.com *Office chair manufrs*

Wallminster Ltd, 24 Charles II Street, St. James's, London, SW1Y 4QU Tel: (020) 7976 1840 Fax: (020) 7976 1850 E-mail: info@tankcontainers.co.uk *Flexi-tank sales & tank containers*

Wallop Woodcrafts (Master Pattern Makers), Unit 3, Hollom Down Road, Lopcombe Corner, Salisbury, SP5 1BP Tel: (01264) 781766 Fax: (01264) 782793 E-mail: nick@wallopwoodcrafts.co.uk *Wallop Woodcrafts (Master Patternmakers): specialises in Patterns, Moulds, Models and Tooling in Timber and Fibreglass for the GRP, GRG, RTM, Vacuum Forming and Cast Resin Industries. Wallop Woodcrafts, Master Patternmakers are Wood Pattern Makers and Fibreglass Mould Makers based in Wiltshire, UK.*

Wallpaper Warehouse, 7 Fforest Business Centre, Queensway, Fforestfach, Swansea, SA5 4DH Tel: (01792) 578090 Fax: (01792) 421100 E-mail: divinahill1@hotmail.com *Business products wallpaper retailer*

▶ Walls Bakery, Springfields, Walls, Shetland, ZE2 9PG Tel: (01595) 809308 *Bakery products*

Walls & Ceilings International Ltd, 31 Tything Road, Kinwarton, Alcester, Warwickshire, B49 6ES Tel: (01789) 763727 Fax: (01789) 400312 E-mail: sales@walls-and-ceilings.co.uk *Plastering beads & accessories manufrs*

Walls Pre Pack Ltd, 37 Avenue Road, Bilston, West Midlands, WV14 9DJ Tel: (01902) 883333 *Pre-packing nails & screw suppliers*

▶ Wallshield Southern Ltd, Suite 283, 34 Buckingham Palace Road, London, SW1W 0RH Tel: (0845) 4081107 E-mail: enquiries@protectyourwalls.co.uk *Wall protection provider*

Wallwik UK, 86 Sulivan Court, Peterborough Road, London, SW6 3DB Tel: 0845 094 0501 Fax: 0845 094 0801 E-mail: paul.rydzyk@wallwik-uk.com *Wallwik is a new DIY system to remove wallpaper. Wallwik is the quicker, easier and cleaner than other method of stripping wallpaper. Wallwik can even remove multiple layers of wallpaper at once.*

Wallwork Heat Treatment Birmingham Ltd, Sydenham Road, New Shires Industrial Estate, Birmingham, B11 1DQ Tel: 0121-771 2467 Fax: 0121-628 1555 E-mail: enquiries@wallworkht.com *Metal & vacuum heat treatment services* Also at: Bury

Walmer Batteries & Signs, 36 North Barrack Road, Walmer, Deal, Kent, CT14 7DU Tel: (01304) 372164 Fax: (01304) 372233 E-mail: walmerbatteries@hotmail.com *Battery distributors or agents service*

Walmley Removals & Transport, 270 Great Lister Street, Birmingham, B7 4DB Tel: 0121-359 8558 Fax: 0121-359 6889 E-mail: sales@whitesremovals.co.uk *Removal contractors*

▶ Walmotts Gas Service Engineers, D L O Stores, Alexandra Road, Grantham, Lincolnshire, NG31 7AS Tel: (01476) 594451 Fax: (01476) 591349

▶ Walney, The Keys, Latchford Mews, Wheathampstead, Hertfordshire, AL4 8BB Tel: 0870 733 0011 Fax: 0870 733 0016 E-mail: sales@redhotradiators.co.uk *Cast Iron, aluminium, tubular steel & bathroom radiators manufrs*

▶ Walnut Club, Main Road, Hathersage, Hope Valley, Derbyshire, S32 1BB Tel: (01433) 651155 Fax: (01433) 651155 E-mail: info@thewalnutclub.com *Derbyshire & Peak Districts first all organic restaurant and wine bar, Michelin star aspiring with famous chef Nicolas Wilson.**

Walnut Tree Workshop, The Old Dairy, Woodgreen Road, Breamore, Fordingbridge, Hampshire, SP6 2AB Tel: (01725) 512165 *Cabinet manufrs*

Walrus Office Group Ltd, Barton Fields Centre, Church Broughton, Derby, DE65 5AP Tel: (01283) 733339 Fax: (01283) 733399 E-mail: info@walrus.co.uk *Office stationary services*

Maurice Walsah & Co. Ltd, Drumaness Industrial Estate, Old Park Road, Drumaness, Ballynahinch, County Down, BT24 8SE Tel: (028) 9756 2842 Fax: (028) 9756 2592 E-mail: info@mauricewalsh.com *Manufacturers of light steel products*

The Walsall Box Co. Ltd, Bank Street, Walsall, WS1 2ER Tel: (01922) 628118 Fax: (01922) 723395 E-mail: mail@thewalsallbox.co.uk *Plain, printed, rigid & covered boxes & carton manufrs*

Walsall Brake Services Ltd, Middlemore Lane West, Aldridge, Walsall, WS9 8BG Tel: (01922) 744625 Fax: (01922) 744626 *Commercial vehicle component distributors*

Walsall Brickcutting Ltd, 7 Field Gate, Walsall, WS1 3DJ Tel: (01922) 642499 Fax: (01922) 639135 *Brick cutters*

Walsall Die & Tool Co. Ltd, Unit 2 Woodall Street, Walsall, WS3 3HG Tel: (01922) 492989 Fax: (01922) 492989 *Die sinking & tool making*

Walsall Die & Tool Company Ltd, Gatehouse Trading Estate, Lichfield Road, Brownhills, Walsall, WS8 6JZ Tel: (01543) 378887 Fax: (01543) 452246 E-mail: sales@belcot.co.uk Principal Export Areas: Worldwide *Press tool manufrs*

Walsall Furnace Construction Services Ltd, 272 West Bromwich Road, Walsall, WS5 4NN Tel: (01922) 637388 Fax: (01922) 637388 *Furnace construction maintenance & repairers*

Walsall Gold Blocking Service, John Street, Walsall, WS2 8AF Tel: (01922) 630031 Fax: (01922) 722855 *Gold blocking pad printing services*

Walsall Metropolitan Borough Council, Suffolk Place, Walsall, WS2 7AY Tel: (01922) 653818 Fax: (01922) 722114 *PVCu window & door manufacturers & fabricators*

Walsall Metropolitan Borough Council All Enquiries Walsall Boroug, Civic Centre, Walsall, WS1 1DQ Tel: (01922) 654709 Fax: (01922) 615737 *Support of urban & economic regeneration*

Walsall Pressings Co. Ltd, Wednesbury Road, Walsall, WS1 4JW Tel: (01922) 721152 Fax: (01922) 721106 E-mail: post@walpres.co.uk Principal Export Areas: Worldwide *Manufacturers of pressings*

Walsall Print Co. Ltd, Midland Road, Walsall, WS1 3QL Tel: (01922) 721272 Fax: (01922) 625950 E-mail: info@walsall-print.co.uk *Lithographic printers*

Walsall Riding Saddle Co. Ltd, Crosby House, Garden Street, Walsall, WS2 8EF Tel: (01922) 624768 Fax: (01922) 641438 E-mail: sales@exsell.com *Equestrian equipment manufrs*

Walsall Transformers Ltd, 246 Green Lane, Walsall, WS2 8HS Tel: (01922) 722933 Fax: (01922) 721222 E-mail: sales@walsall-transformers.co.uk *Transformer & wound components manufrs*

▶ Walsall Van Hire, 305-317 Wednesbury Road, Pleck, Walsall, WS2 9QJ Tel: 01922 639652 E-mail: andrew@walsallvanhire.co.uk *Walsall van hire, based 2 minutes from junction 9 of M6. Competitive prices guaranteed!!*

▶ Walsh Construction North West Ltd, 216 Belmont Road, Bolton, BL1 7AZ Tel: (01204) 303108

Walsh Demolition, 257 Moorland Road, Cardiff, CF24 2LJ Tel: (029) 2046 0645 Fax: (029) 2046 0645 *Total site clearance & demolition*

J. Walsh Spinnings, Unit 2, 58 Caroline Street, Hockley, Birmingham, B3 1UF Tel: 0121-233 3258 Fax: 0121-233 3258 *Metal spinners, spinnings, metal product design, development services, metal filter components & general engineers*

Walsh & Jenkins plc, Power House, Powerscroft Road, Sidcup, Kent, DA14 5EA Tel: (020) 8308 6300 Fax: (020) 8308 6340 E-mail: bags@walsh-jenkins.co.uk *Printed packaging*

R.L. Walsh & Sons (Coventry) Ltd, 17 Lythalls Lane, Coventry, CV6 6FN Tel: (024) 7668 7241 Fax: (024) 7666 2870 E-mail: office@rlwalsh.co.uk *Automotive component manufrs*

▶ S. Walsh & Sons Ltd, Sleepers Farm, 1 Riverview, Chadwell St. Mary, Grays, Essex, RM16 4DH Tel: (01375) 846909 Fax: (01375) 856368 *Haulage services*

▶ Walshaw Buildings Ltd, Unit 14 Dunscar Industrial Estate, Blackburn Road, Egerton, Bolton, BL7 9PQ Tel: (01204) 301671 Fax: (01204) 308782 E-mail: sales@dunscartimber.co.uk

Company Information

Walter Bailey Par Ltd, St Andrews Road, Par, Cornwall, PL24 2LX Tel: (01726) 812245 Fax: (01726) 812246 *Agricultural potato & coal merchants*

Walter Group Ltd, Walters House, 12 Merlin Centre, Lancaster Road, High Wycombe, Buckinghamshire, HP12 3TB Tel: (01494) 795100 Fax: (01494) 461107 E-mail: terry@aquila-innovations.co.uk *Design consultancy*

Walter Hill Plant Ltd, Maze Street, Bristol, BS5 9TQ Tel: 0117-955 5151 Fax: 0117-941 3685 *Pump maintenance & distribution*

▶ Walter J Parsons (Electrical Engineers) Ltd, 15 Heath Mill Lane, Birmingham, B9 4AE Tel: 0121-772 4524 Fax: 0121-766 8069 E-mail: dave@walterjparsons.com

▶ Walter Lambert & Sons Ltd, Edgar Street, Nelson, Lancashire, BB9 8HA Tel: (01282) 612354 Fax: (01282) 615104

Walter Lilly & Co. Ltd, Waddon House, 283 Stafford Road, Croydon, CR0 4NN Tel: (020) 8730 6200 Fax: (020) 8730 6247 E-mail: info@walter-lilly.co.uk *Building & construction contractors*

Walter Maschinenbau GmbH, B13 Holly Farm Business Park, Honiley, Kenilworth, Warwickshire, CV8 1NP Tel: (01926) 485047 Fax: (01926) 485049 E-mail: info.uk@walter-machines.com *Cutting tool manufrs*

Walter Meirer (UK) Ltd, Highlands Road, Shirley, Solihull, West Midlands, B90 4NL Tel: (0871) 6630664 Fax: (0871) 6631664 E-mail: uk.climate@waltermeier.com *Air conditioning distributors* Also at: Bristol, Leeds, Stockport & Uxbridge

Walter Melville Ltd, Fanshaws Lane, Brickendon, Hertford, SG13 8PG Tel: (01992) 511285 Fax: (01992) 511286 E-mail: melville_trimmings@yahoo.co.uk *Elastic webbing & buckle manufrs*

▶ Walter Moss & Son Ltd, Market Street, Coalville, Leicestershire, LE67 3DX Tel: (01530) 831351 Fax: (01530) 832546 E-mail: construction@waltermoss.co.uk

Walter Newbury Partners Ltd, Grangewood House, Grangewood Street, London, E6 1EZ Tel: (020) 8472 0526 Fax: (020) 8472 8875 E-mail: walternewbury@totalise.co.uk *Book binders distributor & manufrs*

Walter Phillips Materials Ltd, Unit 3 Ratcliffe Street, Stockport, Cheshire, SK1 3ES Tel: 0161-429 0309 Fax: 0161-477 7884 E-mail: brolly@clara.net *Umbrella importers & stockists*

Walter Roofing Contractors Ltd, Paper Mill End, Aldridge Road, Great Barr, Birmingham, B44 8NH Tel: 0121-331 4441 Fax: 0121-356 8271 *Industrial waste disposal & skip hire*

Walter Smith Nelson Ltd, Wenning Street, Nelson, Lancashire, BB9 0LE Tel: (01282) 698142 Fax: (01282) 619109 E-mail: wsmith@provider.co.uk *Textile by-products & cleaning & polishing cloth suppliers*

Walter Wright, 29 Albion Road, Luton, LU2 0DS Tel: (01582) 721616 Fax: (01582) 725055 E-mail: enquiries@walterwright.com *Millinery designers*

C.T. Walters (Electrical) Ltd, Unit 4, Park End, Works Industrial Estate, Brackley, Northamptonshire, NN13 5LX Tel: (01869) 810047 Fax: (01869) 811103 E-mail: ctwalters@lineone.net *Electrical contractors services*

Walters Group, Walters House, 12 Merlin Centre, Lancaster Road, High Wycombe, Buckinghamshire, HP12 3TB Tel: (01494) 453700 Fax: (01494) 461107 E-mail: sales@waltersmicro.co.uk *Printed circuit board assembly services*

▶ Walters Hexagon, 4 Grange Park, Newtownabbey, County Antrim, BT36 4LA Tel: (028) 9083 8924 Fax: (028) 9083 8924 E-mail: admin@waltershexagon.com *Fasteners manufrs*

▶ Walters Houghton, St. Ives Way, Factory Road, Sandycroft, Deeside, Clwyd, CH5 2QS Tel: (01352) 733882 Fax: (01352) 733822 E-mail: info@waltershoughton.com *Sachets manufrs*

J. Walters & Co. Ltd, 47 & 49 Howard Street, Birmingham, B19 3HL Tel: 0121-236 5937 *Packing case makers*

Walters OEP Ltd, 15 -17 Wroslyn Road Industrial Estate, Wroslyn Road, Freeland, Witney, Oxfordshire, OX29 8SN Tel: (01993) 886200 Fax: (01993) 886210 E-mail: info@oep.co.uk *Manufacturers of transformers*

Walters Office World Ltd, 19 Royce Road, Peterborough, PE1 5YB Tel: (01733) 707000 Fax: (01733) 708000 E-mail: info@walters.co.uk *Office equipment suppliers*

Stephen Walters & Sons Ltd, Sudbury Silk Mills, Sudbury, Suffolk, CO10 2XB Tel: (01787) 372266 Fax: (01787) 880126 E-mail: sales@stephenwalters.co.uk *Silk fabrics manufrs*

▶ Waltham Litho Ltd, Unit 6, Raven Road Industrial Estate, London, E18 1HB Tel: (020) 8504 1035 Fax: (020) 8504 9365

Waltham Paper Co. Ltd, County Ho, County Industrial Estate, Boars Tye Road, Silver End, Witham, Essex, CM8 3PW Tel: (01425) 622550 Fax: (01277) 261789 *Printers' suppliers*

Walther Couplings, 29 Akeman Street, Tring, Hertfordshire, HP23 6AN Tel: (01442) 891929 Fax: (01442) 890812 E-mail: sales@walther-couplings.com *Couplings manufrs*

Walther Trowal Ltd, Spedding Road, Fenton Industrial Estate, Fenton, Stoke-on-Trent, ST4 2SN Tel: (01782) 412111 Fax: (01782) 744267 E-mail: enquires@metaret.co.uk *Component finishing ceramic abrasives*

▶ Walton Clutch, 2a Beech Road, Walton, Liverpool, L4 5UU Tel: 0151-525 5505 Fax: 0151-525 5505 *Gear box manufrs*

Walton Coachworks (Kingswood) Ltd, Kingswood Station, Kingswood, Tadworth, Surrey, KT20 6EB Tel: (01737) 355050 Fax: (01737) 373327 *Motor crash repair services*

▶ Walton Dental Arts Ltd, Kinawley, 3 Station Road, Leatherhead, Surrey, KT22 7AA Tel: (01372) 377154 Fax: (01372) 362369 E-mail: sales@waltondentalarts.co.uk

▶ Walton Designs Ltd, 41 St Helens Way, Thetford, Norfolk, IP24 1HG Tel: (01842) 752522 Fax: (01842) 754060 E-mail: sales@waltondesignsltd.co.uk *Manufacturers of the rack & pinion drawing boards*

Walton Heat Treatment Ltd, 143 Hersham Road, Walton-on-Thames, Surrey, KT12 1RR Tel: (01932) 241975 Fax: (01932) 241975 *Heat treatment services*

Walton Hire, Knowle Lane, Buckley, Clwyd, CH7 3JA Tel: (01244) 543365 Fax: (01244) 541200 *Small power tool hire, retailers & repairs*

Jeffrey Walton Jewellery, 62 Albion Street, Leeds, LS1 6AD Tel: 0113-244 3198 Fax: 0113-242 3751 *Jewellery manufrs*

John Walton Machine Tools Ltd, Smithy Carr Lane, Brighouse, West Yorkshire, HD6 2HL Tel: (01484) 712507 Fax: (01484) 710549 E-mail: cyoung@chucks.co.uk *Machine tool accessories distributors*

Walton Plating Ltd, 118 Ashley Road, Walton-on-Thames, Surrey, KT12 1HN Tel: (01932) 221206 Fax: (01932) 246699 E-mail: enquiries@waltonplating.co.uk *Electroplaters & anodises*

Walton Press, 7 Adlams Central Park, Wirrall Park Road, Glastonbury, Somerset, BA6 9XE Tel: (01458) 834292 Fax: (01458) 834271 E-mail: sandy@waltonpress.co.uk *General printers*

Walton Tyres, 48 Davenport Drive, Woodley, Stockport, Cheshire, SK6 1PU Tel: 0161-406 6700 *Tyre fitters & distribs*

Waltons Of Radcliffe Sales Ltd, Unit 14 Bradley Fold Trading Estate, Radcliffe Moor Road, Bradley Fold, Bolton, BL2 6RT Tel: (01204) 393633 Fax: (01204) 363196 E-mail: sales@waltons-of-radcliffe.com *Manufacturers of sheet metalworking machinery*

WAM Engineering Ltd, Unit 14, Alexandra Way, Ashchurch Business Centre, Tewkesbury, Gloucestershire, GL20 8NB Tel: (01684) 299100 Fax: (01684) 299104 E-mail: shev@wameng.com *Bulk materials handling equipment. Also conveyor systems, screw & dust filtration*

Wampfler Co Ltd, Unit B4, Altrincham Business Park, Stuart Road, Broadheath, Altrincham, Cheshire, WA14 5GJ Tel: 0161-929 6032 Fax: 0161-928 9126 E-mail: wampfler.uk@wampfler.com *Energy supply safety and product handling systems manufrs*

The Wandsworth Group Ltd, Albert Drive, Sheerwater, Woking, Surrey, GU21 5SE Tel: (01483) 713400 Fax: (01483) 740384 E-mail: info@wandsworthgroup.com *Electric wiring accessories manufrs* Also at: London NW10

▶ Wannells, Unit 1, Highfield Barns, Clyst Road, Topsham, Exeter, EX3 0BY Tel: (01392) 874281 Fax: E-mail: mail@wannells.com *Electrical contractors*

Wannop & Fox Ltd, South Pallant House, 8 South Pallant, Chichester, West Sussex, PO19 1TH Tel: (01243) 778844 Fax: (01243) 788349 E-mail: wannopfox@compuserve.com *Solicitors*

Wansbeck Teaching Tapes, 3 Bankside, Morpeth, Northd, NE61 1XD Tel: (01670) 505455 Fax: (01670) 518011 E-mail: wansbeck@btinternet.com *Educational equipment & supplies*

Wansdyke Security Ltd, PO Box 179, Corsham, Wiltshire, SN13 9TL Tel: (01225) 810225 Fax: (01225) 810625 E-mail: sales@wansdyke.co.uk *Secure data & document storage*

Wantage Engineering Co. Ltd, 6 W & G Industrial Estate, Faringdon Road, East Challow, Wantage, Oxfordshire, OX12 9TF Tel: (01235) 764161 Fax: (01235) 764163 E-mail: sales@wantageengineer.f9.co.uk *Steel fabricators*

Wantzen Ltd, Anton House, South Park, Sevenoaks, Kent, TN13 1EB Tel: (01732) 458185 Fax: (01732) 458188 E-mail: info@wantzen.co.uk *Printing machine distributors*

Wanzl Ltd, Europa House, Heathcote Lane, Heathcote, Warwick, CV34 6SP Tel: (01926) 451951 Fax: (01926) 451952 *Shop fitters*

Warbeck Engineering Services, 12 Regent Road, Liverpool, L3 7DS Tel: 0151-236 9494 Fax: 0151-236 9988 E-mail: warbreckengineering.servicesltd@virgin.net *Ship repairers*

Warbla Forge, Lowtown, Pudsey, West Yorkshire, LS28 9AY Tel: 0113-255 2538 Fax: 0113-290 9112 *Fabricators, automatic gates & rails suppliers*

Warbrick International, Cranford Court, King Street, Knutsford, Cheshire, WA16 8BW Tel: (01565) 652616 Fax: (01565) 633159 E-mail: sales@warbrick.co.uk *Manufacturers agent & distributor wire & cable*

▶ Warburtons Ltd, Unit An Badentoy CR, Portlethen, Aberdeen, AB12 4YD Tel: (01224) 780808 Fax: (01224) 780808 *Bread makers*

Warburtons Ltd, Sholto Cresent, Righead Industrial Estate, Bellshill, Lanarkshire, ML4 3LX Tel: (01698) 741066 Fax: (01698) 741015 *Bakery*

▶ Warburtons Ltd, Billington Road, Burnley, Lancashire, BB11 5BX Tel: (01282) 456311 Fax: (01282) 455804 E-mail: info@warburtons.co.uk *Bakery products*

▶ Warburtons Ltd, Express Way, Wakefield Europort, Normanton, West Yorkshire, WF6 2TZ Tel: (01924) 244100 *Bakers*

▶ Warburtons Ltd, Glebe Street, Shaw, Oldham, OL2 7SF Tel: (01706) 847744 Fax: (01706) 882162 E-mail: recruitment@cisilion.com *Bakery*

▶ Warburtons Ltd, 3 Christleton Court, Manor Park, Runcorn, Cheshire, WA7 1ST Tel: (01928) 579088 Fax: (01928) 579089 *Distribution for the bakery*

Warburtons (Fylde) Ltd, 21 Caunce Street, Blackpool, FY1 3LA Tel: (01253) 407700 Fax: (01253) 27046 *Bakery suppliers*

Warco Machine Tools Ltd, Warco House, Fisher Lane, Chiddingfold, Godalming, Surrey, GU8 4TD Tel: (01428) 682929 Fax: (01428) 685870 E-mail: warco@warco.co.uk *Machine tools*

Ward & Co. Ltd, Unit 18, Maze St, Barton Hill Trading Estate, Bristol, BS5 9TE Tel: 0117-955 3385 Fax: 0117-955 7518 E-mail: sales@ward-signs.co.uk *Sign manufrs*

▶ Ward Aerial Installations Ltd, 181 Woodhouse Road, London, N12 9AY Tel: (020) 8368 0077 E-mail: office@wardaerials.co.uk

Ward Alan, Unit B Enderley Street, Newcastle, Staffordshire, ST5 2BS Tel: (01782) 713713 Fax: (01782) 740700 *Household furniture retailers*

Alan Ward UK, Unit 9, Brookfield Drive, Bridgtown, Cannock, Staffordshire, WS11 0JN Tel: (01543) 506509 Fax: (01543) 573800 *Car paint manufrs*

Ward Bekker Ltd, Three Winds, Madge Hill, Kinnersley, Severn Stoke, Worcester, WR8 9JN Tel: (01905) 371200 Fax: (01905) 371049 *Weighing machine & industrial vibrator manufrs*

▶ Ward Building Services Ltd, 223 Clepington Road, Dundee, DD3 7SZ Tel: (01382) 884123 Fax: (01382) 884248

Donald Ward Ltd, Moira Road, Woodville, Swadlincote, Derbyshire, DE11 8DG Tel: (01283) 217192 Fax: (01283) 212515 *Scrap metal dealers*

Ward Engineering, 15 Acacia Close, Leighton Buzzard, Bedfordshire, LU7 4QE Tel: (01525) 851337 Fax: (01525) 374776 E-mail: wardeng@onetel.com *General & precision engineers*

Ward Executive Ltd, High Street, Epsom, Surrey, KT19 8EH Tel: (020) 8332 0555 Fax: (020) 8405 7701 E-mail: ward@wardexec.co.uk *Executive search & selection services*

Ward Fabrication Ltd, Brick Street, Cleckheaton, West Yorkshire, BD19 5EH Tel: (01274) 861123 Fax: (01274) 852664 *Road tanker manufacturers & repair services*

Geoff Ward, Glantanat Isaf, Llangedwyn, Oswestry, Shropshire, SY10 9LQ Tel: (01691) 780278 *Farming contracting*

Ward Holdings Ltd, 2 Ash Tree Lane, Chatham, Kent, ME5 7BZ Tel: (01634) 855111 Fax: (01634) 577172 E-mail: inbox@ward-homes.co.uk *Holding company*

Ward Insulated Panels Ltd, Sherburn, Malton, North Yorkshire, YO17 8PQ Tel: (01944) 710591 Fax: (01944) 710777 E-mail: wbc@wards.co.uk *Manufacturers & suppliers of cladding panels*

Ward International Consulting Ltd, Funtley Court, 19 Funtley Hill, Fareham, Hampshire, PO16 7UY Tel: (01329) 280280 Fax: (01329) 221010 E-mail: admin@wardint.co.uk *Transport consultants*

Jamie Ward Furniture, 7 Combroke Grove, Hatton Park, Warwick, CV35 7TG Tel: (07970) 422867 E-mail: jamie@jamieward.com *Designer/maker of bespoke furniture*

▶ John Ward, 48 Albert Road, Sheffield, S8 9QW Tel: 0114-281 1475 E-mail: drumsrdangerous@blueyonder.co.uk *Hand made drums (percussion instruments) made to order. "I give a log a voice!"Each one a unique thing of beauty suitable for the expert or novice. Absolutely no power tools used.*

John Ward Welding, Lythalls Lane, Coventry, CV6 6FL Tel: (024) 7666 3200 Fax: (024)7666 3200 E-mail: john@ward-welding.co.uk *High quality welding services*

Ward Lester Display Co. Ltd, 187 Angel Place, Fore Street, London, N18 2UD Tel: (020) 8803 2425 Fax: (020) 8807 7986 E-mail: sfarthing@wardlester.co.uk *Point of sale advertising*

Mike Ward Associates, The Rodgelands, Bank Lane, Abberley, Worcester, WR6 6BQ Tel: (01299) 896654 Fax: (01299) 896955 *Petroleum industry consultants*

Peter Ward Engineering, Sheaf Bank, Gleadless Road, Sheffield, S2 3DA Tel: 0114-255 0633 Fax: 0114-255 5371 E-mail: info@peterwardengineering.net *Steel fabricators*

Peter Ward Homes Ltd, Suite A Annie Reed Court, Annie Reed Road, Beverley, North Humberside, HU17 0LF Tel: (01482) 861484 Fax: (01482) 863227 E-mail: ward@peterwardhomes.co.uk *Property developers*

Ward Philipson Group Ltd, Dunston Industrial Estate, Halifax Road, Gateshead, Tyne & Wear, NE11 9HW Tel: 0191-460 5915 Fax: 0191-460 8540 E-mail: info@wardphilipson.co.uk *Office suppliers, lipographics & phonegraphic printers* Also at: Newcastle & Sunderland

▶ Ward Plant Ltd, West Mains Farm, Newbigging, Carnwath, Lanark, ML11 8NB Tel: (01555) 840497

Ward Roofing, Cleatham Road, Kirton Lindsey, Gainsborough, Lincolnshire, DN21 4JR Tel: (01652) 641950 Fax: (01652) 648161 E-mail: reception@wardroofing.co.uk *Roofing contractors*

Wardah Electrics Ltd, 207 Strathmartine Road, Dundee, DD3 8PH Tel: (01382) 815844 Fax: (01382) 810115 E-mail: sales@wardahelectrics.com *Electrical & industrial engineers*

▶ Wardell Shopfitters Ltd, 2 Cowton Way, Eaglescliffe, Stockton-on-Tees, Cleveland, TS16 0RE Tel: (01642) 789184 Fax: (01642) 789084 E-mail: sales@wardellshopfitters.co.uk *Shop fitters for design, manufacture & installation*

Warden Bros Newtownards Ltd, 43-45 High Street, Newtownards, County Down, BT23 7HS Tel: (028) 9181 2147 Fax: (028) 9182 0226 E-mail: wardenbros@aol.com *Hardware & furniture merchants*

▶ Warden Construction Ltd, Unit 4 Fishergate Court, Fishergate, Preston, PR1 8QF Tel: (01772) 270100 Fax: (01772) 270102 E-mail: info@warden.co.uk

Warden Group, 464 Dunstable Road, Luton, LU4 8DR Tel: (01582) 573030 Fax: (01582) 508751 E-mail: admin@wardenplastics.co.uk *Plastic extrusion & injection moldings specialists*

Wardfire, 6 The Galloway Centre, Hambridge Lane, Newbury, Berkshire, RG14 5TL Tel: (01635) 552999 Fax: (01635) 552566 E-mail: sales@wardfire.co.uk *Fire protection & health & safety*

Wardle & Keach, Mill Lane, Kislingbury, Northampton, NN7 4BD Tel: (01604) 891133 Fax: (01604) 891155 E-mail: sales@wardleandkeach.co.uk *Removal & storage specialists*

Wardlock Educational Co. Ltd, 1 Christopher Road, East Grinstead, West Sussex, RH19 3BT Tel: (01342) 318980 Fax: (01342) 410980 E-mail: orders@wleducat.freeserve.co.uk *Educational book publishers*

Wardons Metal Co. Ltd, Unit D4 Riverside Industrial Estate, Riverside Way, Dartford, DA1 5BS Tel: (01322) 276711 Fax: (01322) 288278 E-mail: wardons@jacobwhite-hospquip.co.uk *Sheet metalworkers*

Wardpark Gardner, 30 Winchester Avenue, Denny, Stirlingshire, FK6 6QE Tel: 01324 825136 *Catering equipment manufrs*

Wardray Premise Ltd, 3 Hampton Court Estate, Summer Road, Thames Ditton, Surrey, KT7 0SP Tel: (020) 8398 9911 Fax: (020) 8398 8032 E-mail: sales@wardray-premise.com *Radiation protection & x-ray accessories manufrs*

Ward's Flexible Rod Co. Ltd, 22 James Carter Road, Mildenhall, Bury St. Edmunds, Suffolk, IP28 7DE Tel: (01638) 713800 Fax: (01638) 716863 E-mail: sales@wardsflex.co.uk *Drain & sewer cleaning equipment manufrs*

Wards Of Helston, 27 Meneage Street, Helston, Cornwall, TR13 8AA Tel: (01326) 572244 Fax: (01326) 572243 *Florists*

Wards Welding & Fabrications, Cranfield Road, Woburn Sands, Milton Keynes, MK17 8UR Tel: (01908) 586505 Fax: (01908) 587505 E-mail: steve@wardsweldingandfsnet.co.uk *Abattoir plant engineers, fabricators & manufrs*

Wards Woodcraft Furnishings, Termon Business Park, Quarry Road, Sixmilecross, Omagh, County Tyrone, BT79 9AL Tel: (028) 8076 0952 Fax: (028) 8076 0986 *Joiners*

Wardtec Ltd, Unit 92, Heming Road, Washford, Redditch, Worcestershire, B98 0DH Tel: (01527) 520594 Fax: (01527) 502235 E-mail: ward-tec@btconnect.com *Pressworkers & machinists*

Ware Motorama Ltd, Silverhook House, Bates Road, Romford, RM3 0JH Tel: (01708) 330500 Fax: (01708) 330504 E-mail: 520@wipers.co.uk *Car parts*

Ware Sheet Metal Ltd, Units 3-6, Charlton Mead Lane, Hoddesdon, Hertfordshire, EN11 0DJ Tel: (01992) 466483 Fax: (01992) 469604 E-mail: sales@waresheetmetal.co.uk *Manufacturers of fine limit sheet metal*

Thomas Ware & Sons Ltd, Coronation Road, Southville, Bristol, BS3 1RN Tel: 0117-966 4021 Fax: 0117-966 3885 E-mail: thomas.ware@btconnect.com *Leather tanners*

W.H. Ware & Sons Ltd, Barns Ground, Ken Road, Clevedon, Avon, BS21 6ST Tel: (01275) 874327 Fax: (01275) 335480 E-mail: christinewilliams@waresbinding.com *Book binders & print finishers*

▶ Ware247 Ltd, 16 Castle Grove Drive, Leeds, LS6 4BR Tel: (0845) 3457859 E-mail: sales@ware247.co.uk *Servers & all types memory for cameras, phones, psp & computer*

Warefence Ltd, Clare Terrace, Carterton, Oxfordshire, OX18 3ES Tel: (01993) 847227 Fax: (01993) 840551 E-mail: info@warefence.co.uk *Fencing contractors*

Wareham Window Centre Ltd, 4 Warren Way, Holton Heath Trading Park, Poole, Dorset, BH16 6NJ Tel: (01929) 553218 Fax: (01202) 622866 E-mail: sales@warehamwindows.co.uk *Window manufacturers & suppliers*

Warehouse Direct, Dorman Street, Manchester, M11 1NY Tel: 0161-223 2032 Fax: 0161-220 8189

Warehouse Direct Industrial Ltd, PO Box 928, Woking, Surrey, GU23 7ZN Tel: 08707 700709 Fax: 08707 700659 E-mail: sales@wdil.co.uk *Warehouse Direct specialises in supplying quality Loading Bay products, at low low prices.*

▶ WarehouseEquipment.co.uk, 58 Gleneagles Ave, Leicester, LE4 7GB Tel: 0116-266 4478 Fax: 0116-266 4478 E-mail: sales@warehouseequipment.co.uk *Distributors of storage, handling and distribution equipment.*mezzanine flooring, pallet racking, roll cages, stillages, scales and trucks and trolleys*

▶ Waring Industrial Electrical, 6 Lower Beestow, Mossley, Ashton-under-Lyne, Lancashire, OL5 9QF Tel: 0161-303 1409 E-mail: waringelectrical@aol.com *Electrical, electronic & mechanical engineers*

J. Waring & Son (Wrea Green) Ltd, Wrea Green, Preston, PR4 2NB Tel: (01772) 682924 Fax: (01772) 671071 E-mail: jwaring@ukonline.co.uk *Agricultural & industrial building manufrs*

Waring & Woodfellows, Esgriar Saw Mills, Llanfair Clydogau, Lampeter, Dyfed, SA48 8LL Tel: (01570) 493450 Fax: (0870) 1254632 E-mail: info@woodfellows.com *Furniture designers & cabinet makers*

Warings Construction Group Holdings Ltd, Gatcombe House, Hilsea, Portsmouth, PO2 0TU Tel: (023) 9269 4900 Fax: (023) 9269 4948 *Building & civil engineering contractors*

C. Wark & Sons, 6 West Road, Irvine, Ayrshire, KA12 8RE Tel: (01294) 273999 Fax: (01294) 273222 *Joiners & joinery manufrs*

Warkworth Treatment Works, Warkworth, Morpeth, Northd, NE65 0UB Tel: (01665) 711386 Fax: (01665) 713309 E-mail: david.richardson@mwl.co.uk *Water treatment equipment & service*

Warley Construction Co. Ltd, Swinbourne Road, Burnt Mills Industrial Estate, Basildon, Essex, SS13 1LD Tel: (01268) 726020 Fax: (01268) 725285 E-mail: info@warleyconstruction.co.uk *Structural steelwork fabricators*

Warley Galvanizers, Station Street, Cradley Heath, West Midlands, B64 6AJ Tel: (01384) 566548 Fax: (01384) 566624 *General galvanisers to the trade*

Warley Painters Ltd, Winchester Works, Malt Mill Lane, Halesowen, West Midlands, B62 8JF Tel: 0121-561 5665 Fax: 0121-561 5556 E-mail: wp@warleypaint.co.uk *Refurbishment & painting & decorating service*

Warley Polishing Ltd, James Scott Road, Halesowen, West Midlands, B63 2QT Tel: (01384) 634036 Fax: (01384) 411025 E-mail: sales@warleypolishing.co.uk *Metal finishing & polishing services*

Warmac Ltd, Bear House, 7 Tootal Grove, Salford, Manchester, M6 8DN Tel: (0870) 0500739 Fax: (0870) 0552670E-mail: info@warmac.co.uk *Pressuring equipment manufrs*

Warman CNC, 214 Moseley Street, Birmingham, B5 6LE Tel: 0121-622 4045 Fax: 0121-666 6539 E-mail: warmancnc@aol.com *Production precision machinists*

The Warman Group Ltd, 7 The Wharf, Bridge Street, Birmingham, B1 2JS Tel: 0121-605 1111 Fax: 0121-605 0111 E-mail: enquiries@warmangroup.com *Public relations consultants*

▶ Warmbac Wetsuits, Adlams Central Park Wirral Park, Wirrall Park Road, Glastonbury, Somerset, BA6 9XE Tel: (01458) 835567 Fax: (01458) 835567 E-mail: Dug@devwebdesigns.co.uk *Wetsuits, caving equipment manufrs*

▶ Warmfloor Heating (Ireland) Ltd, Unit E11 Gortrush Industrial Estate, Great Northern Road, Omagh, County Tyrone, BT78 5LU Tel: (028) 8225 2288 Fax: (028) 8225 9515 E-mail: mail@warmfloor.ie

▶ WarmFloors Ltd, 8 Roundhill Avenue, Cottingley, Bingley, West Yorkshire, BD16 1PH Tel: (01274) 568536 Fax: (01274) 568538 E-mail: sales@warmfloorsonline.com *Under floor heating suppliers*

Warmflow Engineering Co. Ltd, Lissue Industrial Estate, Moira Road, Lisburn, County Antrim, BT28 2RF Tel: (028) 9262 1515 Fax: (028) 9262 1199 E-mail: mail@warmflow.co.uk *Oil fired boiler manufrs*

Warmglade Ltd, 2 College Farm, Church Street, Whaddon, Royston, Hertfordshire, SG8 5RU Tel: (01223) 208788 *Steel fabrication, staircases & bicycle sheds Manufacturing*

Warmup P.L.C, Unit 702, Tudor Estate, Abbey Road, London, NW10 7UW Tel: (0845) 3452288 Fax: (0845) 3452299 E-mail: sales@warmup.co.uk *Electrical under-tile heating*

Warner Bros Distributors Ltd, Warner House, 98 Theobalds Road, London, WC1X 8WB Tel: (020) 7984 5200 Fax: (020) 7984 5001 *Film distributors*

Warner Glass Croydon Ltd, 431 Brighton Road, South Croydon, Surrey, CR2 6YG Tel: (020) 8660 9271 Fax: (020) 8668 0374 *Glass merchants & glaziers*

Warner Howard Group Ltd, Woodgrange Avenue, Harrow, Middlesex, HA3 0XD Tel: (020) 8927 0100 Fax: (020) 8927 0101 E-mail: sales@warnerhoward.co.uk *Hand dryer*

▶ Warner Land Surveys, Beaumont House, 59 High Street, Theale, Reading, RG7 5AL Tel: 0118-930 3314 Fax: 0118-930 1859 E-mail: wlsl@warnerlandsurveys.com *3D laser scanning & dimensional control, Petro-Chem & 3D critical interface engineering, major construction projects, topographical & measured building surveys, monitoring & deformation surveys*

Warner Textile Machinery, Magna Road, Wigston, Leicestershire, LE18 4ZH Tel: 0116-278 7578 Fax: 0116-278 7588 E-mail: wtm@warnertextilemachinery.co.uk Principal Export Areas: Worldwide *Manufacturers of stockinette fabric for cleaning and polishing. Suppliers of quality cleaning cloths suitable for the valeting industry.*

Warnes Mail Marketing Ltd, 577 Kingston Road, London, SW20 8YA Tel: (020) 8687 3800 Fax: (020) 8545 2701 E-mail: sales@warnes.co.uk *Direct mail marketing services*

▶ Roger Warnes Transport Ltd, Station Road, Leziate, King's Lynn, Norfolk, PE32 1EJ Tel: (01553) 841087

▶ Warnock Plant Hire Ltd, West Rogerton, East Kilbride, Glasgow, G74 4NU Tel: (01355) 242992 Fax: (01355) 249424

Warp Systems Ltd, Debmarc House, 193 London Road, Staines, Middlesex, TW18 4HR Tel: (01784) 492222 Fax: (01784) 460100 *Internet networking consultants services*

Warr Bros, Nab Works, Long Lane, Pott Shrigley, Macclesfield, Cheshire, SK10 5SD Tel: (01625) 574634 Fax: (01625) 576372 E-mail: sales@bowlandmanchester.co.uk *Pre cast concrete product manufrs*

▶ Warrawee Duck Farm, Pollards Moor Road, Copythorne, Southampton, SO40 2NZ Tel: 023 80811457 E-mail: nicky.janaway@warraweeduckfarm.co.uk *Duck farm producing fertile duck eggs, eating eggs & ducks*

Warren Ltd, Ackender Road, Alton, Hampshire, GU34 1JT Tel: (01420) 85401 Fax: (01420) 89808 *Removal & storage specialists*

Warren Engineering, 18A Station Close, Potters Bar, Hertfordshire, EN6 1TL Tel: (01707) 642870 Fax: (01707) 642870 *Sub-contract engineers*

Warren Engineering Ltd, Birkbeck Road, Sidcup, Kent, DA14 4DB Tel: (020) 8300 5111 Fax: (020) 8308 9977 E-mail: warrenengineering@supanet.com *Civil engineers*

Warren Engineering, B4-B5 Unit Northway Trading Estate, Northway Lane, Tewkesbury, Gloucestershire, GL20 8JH Tel: (01684) 298000 Fax: (01684) 295981 E-mail: warrenengineering@aol.com *Stainless steel tube fabricators*

Warren Evans, 158a Camden Street, London, NW1 9PA Tel: (020) 7284 1132 Fax: (020) 7267 6604 E-mail: info@warrenevans.com *Manufacturers of beds*

Warren F Electrical Ltd Electric Engineers, 10c6 Skerne Road Aycliffe Indust Estate, Aycliffe, Newton Aycliffe, County Durham, DL5 6EP Tel: (01325) 310322 Fax: (01325) 301075 *Electrical contractors*

Warren Farm, Southport Old Road, Liverpool, L37 0AN Tel: (01704) 833630 Fax: (01704) 873820 *Saddlery & riding wear*

Frank Warren Ltd, Terrace Street, Oldham, OL4 1HQ Tel: 0161-287 8118 Fax: 0161-287 5226 E-mail: sales@fwarren.co.uk *Electrical & engineering equipment wholesalers*

Warren Insulation, Blackthorne Road, Colnbrook, Slough, SL3 0DU Tel: (01753) 687272 Fax: (01753) 681623 E-mail: heathrow@warren.co.uk *Fire seals & barriers insulation distributors*

Warren Insulation plc, Unit 8c, Harding Way, St. Ives, Cambridgeshire, PE27 3WR Tel: (01480) 467972 Fax: (01480) 464993 E-mail: headoffice@warren.co.uk *Distributors of insulation & related materials*

John Warren Furniture Ltd, 4-6 New Inn, Broadway, London, EC2A 3PZ Tel: (020) 8986 3366 Fax: (020) 7729 8770 E-mail: sales@jwfltd.co.uk *Furniture makers*

Warren Labels, 6 Ullswater Road, Kettering, Northamptonshire, NN16 8UD Tel: (01536) 410842 Fax: (01536) 417070 E-mail: bunnyjsh@warrenlabels.fsnet.co.uk *General printers & label specialists*

Warren Measurement Systems, 15 Berwick Way, Kettering, Northamptonshire, NN15 5XF Tel: (01536) 310722 Fax: (01536) 310722 E-mail: sales@warrenmeasurement.co.uk *Machine tool measuring systems*

▶ Michael Warren Design, 275 Goldhawk Road, London, W12 8EU Tel: (07957) 195895 E-mail: mail@michaelwarrendesign.com *London"s newest talent in product design*

Warren P & Co. Ltd, The Garage, Frimley Green Road, Frimley Green, Camberley, Surrey, GU16 6LD Tel: (01252) 835436 Fax: (01252) 835711 *Car repairs cycle sales & repairers*

▶ Warren Photographic, Warren House, Albury Heath, Guildford, Surrey, GU5 9DB Tel: (01483) 203354 E-mail: us@warrenphoto.freeserve.co.uk *Specialised photography & digital enhancement services*

Warren Point Ltd, Pixmore House, Pixmore Centre, Pixmore Avenue, Letchworth Garden City, Hertfordshire, SG6 1JG Tel: (01462) 483733 Fax: (01462) 786103 *Computer-based system consultants*

Warren Precision Engineering, 4 Shield Industrial Estate, Manor House Avenue, Southampton, SO15 0LF Tel: (023) 8032 2618 Fax: (023) 8032 2619 *Precision engineers*

R.C. Warren Packers Ltd, Unit C Valley Park, Tolpits Lane, Watford, WD18 9LT Tel: (01923) 770747 Fax: (01923) 770731 E-mail: twarren@warrenpackers.co.uk *Contract packing*

Warren & Tarry Ltd, Glenbarr Avenue, Bradgate Street, Leicester, LE4 0AE Tel: 0116-262 6056 Fax: 0116-262 6056 *Machine engravers*

Warrender Products, 284 Chepstow Road, Newport, Gwent, NP19 8NN Tel: (01633) 278336 Fax: (01633) 666986 *Self adhesive product manufrs*

Warrenpoint Harbour Authority, The Docks, Warrenpoint, Newry, County Down, BT34 3JR Tel: (028) 4177 3381 Fax: (028) 4177 3962 E-mail: info@warrenpointharbour.co.uk *Harbour authority*

Warrington Chain Ltd, Howley Quay, Howley Lane, Warrington, WA1 2DZ Tel: (01925) 630820 Fax: (01925) 631947 E-mail: sales@warringtonchain.co.uk *Lifting gear services*

Warrington Chamber Of Commerce, International Business Centre, Delta CR, Westbrook, Warrington, WA5 7WQ Tel: (01925) 715150 Fax: (01925) 715159 E-mail: info@warrington-chamber.co.uk *Chamber of commerce*

Warrington Civils & Lintels, Wilson Patten Street, Warrington, WA1 1HN Tel: (01925) 255700 Fax: (01925) 416520 E-mail: warrington@civilandlintels.co.uk *Buildbase is one of the UK's fastest growing builders merchants. All of our branches are long established companies which have been serving local trades people for many years, with knowledge and experience to match. We believe strongly in understanding the needs of trades professional and our business has been developed specifically to meet those demands. Massive stocks, top quality products, competitive pricing, reliable delivery, specialist staff and exceptional customer service.*

Warrington Fire Research Centre, 101 Marsh Gate La, Stratford, London, E15 2NQ Tel: (020) 8519 8297 Fax: (020) 8519 3029 *Fire testing & surveying*

▶ Warrington Lock & Safe, 8 Whitfield Avenue, Paddington, Warrington, WA1 3NF Tel: (01925) 851398 Fax: (01925) 851398 E-mail: suzi@warringtonlocks.co.uk *Locksmiths*

▶ Warrington Self Storage, Athertons Quay, Warrington, WA5 1AH Tel: (01925) 417007 *Store anything from personal possesions, business documents, furniture, classic cars, office equipment, boats, tools and machinery to building materials. At our secure, monitored self storage site in central Warrington, Cheshire.*

Warrington Timber Co. Ltd, 1 Bowood Court, Winwick Quay, Warrington, WA2 8QZ Tel: (01925) 232687 Fax: (01925) 230167 *Timber merchants*

Warringtonfire Global Safety, Holmesfield Road, Warrington, WA1 2DS Tel: (01925) 655116 Fax: (01925) 655419 E-mail: info@wfrc.co.uk *Fire safety consultants*

▶ Warriors World Ltd, Unit 12, Pembroke Business Centre, Gardiners Lane South, Basildon, Essex, SS14 3HY Tel: (07970) 004098 E-mail: sales@warriorsworld.co.uk *Martial art & sporting equipment suppliers*

Warthog plc, 10 Eden Place, Cheadle, Cheshire, SK8 1AT Tel: 0161-608 1200 Fax: 0161-610 3033 E-mail: info@warthog.co.uk *Computer games developers*

Wartsila UK Ltd, Peterseat Drive, Altens Industrial Estate, Aberdeen, AB12 3HT Tel: (01224) 871166 Fax: (01224) 871188 E-mail: enquiries@wartsila.com *Generating sets & motor service providers*

Wartsila UK Ltd, Riverside Business Centre, River Lawn Road, Tonbridge, Kent, TN9 1EP Tel: (01732) 783571 E-mail: uk.marine@wartsila.com *Diesel engineers*

Warwick Brassfounders & Engineering Co. Ltd, 14-16 Haden Street, Birmingham, B12 9BH Tel: 0121-440 0901 Fax: 0121-440 6725 *Turned parts manufrs*

Warwick Bros Alresford Ltd, The Dean, Alresford, Hampshire, SO24 9BN Tel: (01962) 732681 Fax: (01962) 735385 E-mail: info@warwicktrailers.co.uk *Agricultural & commercial trailers*

Warwick Buildings Ltd, Southam Road, Long Itchington, Southam, Warwickshire, CV47 9QL Tel: (01926) 815757 Fax: (01926) 815162 E-mail: sales@warwickbuildings.com *Timber sectional buildings manufrs*

Warwick Ceilings, 10 Blackall Industrial Estate, Hamberts Road, South Woodham Ferrers, Chelmsford, CM3 5UW Tel: (01245) 325533 Fax: (01245) 323363 E-mail: info@warwick.gb.com

Warwick Container Systems (UK) ltd, Stoneleigh Visual Centre, Queensway, Leamington Spa, Warwickshire, CV31 3JT Tel: (01926) 314120 Fax: (01926) 885719 E-mail: post@warwickcontainer.demon.co.uk *Intermediate bulk container manufrs*

Warwick Design Consultants Ltd, Unit 12, Waterloo Park, Bidford-on-Avon, Alcester, Warwickshire, B50 4JG Tel: (01789) 490591 Fax: (01789) 490592 E-mail: wdc@warwickdesign.com *Industrial design consultants*

▶ Warwick Dipple Design, First Floor, No 6 Somers Road, Somers Road Industrial Estate, Rugby, Warwickshire, CV22 7DE Tel: (01788) 535105 Fax: (01788) 571581 E-mail: studio@wddesign.co.uk *Design, production service, corporate identity, marketing material*

Warwick Engineering, 3 River Gardens, Feltham, Middlesex, TW14 0RD Tel: (020) 8844 2268 Fax: (020) 8751 0509 *Sheet metalwork engineers*

Warwick & Esplen Ltd, Telfords Yard, London, E1W 2BS Tel: (020) 7480 7614 Fax: (020) 7265 0950 E-mail: info@hadleyshipping.com *Ship managers*

Warwick Evans Optical Co. Ltd, 22 Palace Road, London, N11 2PS Tel: (020) 8888 0051 Fax: (020) 8888 9055 E-mail: sales@keystonevision.com *Vision screening instrument distributors*

Warwick Fraser, Unit 9 Alfold Business Centre, Loxwood Road, Alfold, Cranleigh, Surrey, GU6 8HP Tel: (01403) 753069 Fax: (01403) 752469 E-mail: sales@warwickfraser.co.uk *Computer room solutions*

Warwick I C Systems Ltd, Warwick House, Woodhouse Road, Horsley Woodhouse, Ilkeston, Derbyshire, DE7 6AY Tel: (01332) 781882 Fax: (01332) 781410 E-mail: sales@warwickicsystems.com *Software house*

Warwick Industrial Supplies, Emscote Mill, Wharf Street, Warwick, CV34 5LB Tel: (01926) 497350 Fax: (01926) 403777 E-mail: sales@warwicksupplies.com *Engineers tools, PPE & footwear distributors*

Warwick Interiors, 4 Melbourne Industrial Estate, Watts Street, Chadderton, Oldham, OL9 9LQ Tel: 0161-624 1000 Fax: 0161-624 2247 E-mail: sales@warwickinteriors.co.uk *Bathrooms*

▶ Warwick Machine Tool, Honiley Road, Kenilworth, Warwickshire, CV8 1NQ Tel: (01676) 534534 Fax: (01676) 534548 E-mail: sales@ona-edm.co.uk *Machine tool manufrs*

P. & S. Warwick, Unit 48 Sapcote Trading Centre, 374 High Road, London, NW10 2DJ Tel: (020) 8451 2385 Fax: (020) 8830 1161 *Clothing manufrs*

Warwick Street Metal Works Ltd, 77 Warwick Street, Birmingham, B12 0NH Tel: 0121-773 5181 Fax: 0121-766 7104 *Non ferrous scrap metal merchants*

Warwick Wireless Ltd, Lychgate Lane, Aston Flamville, Hinckley, Leicestershire, LE10 3AQ Tel: (01455) 233616 Fax: (01455) 233179 E-mail: sales@radiotelemetry.co.uk *Radio modems, radio telemetry & wireless video systems manufrs*

Warwickshire Fire Protection, 17 Sanders Road, Coventry, CV6 6DH Tel: (024) 7636 4729 Fax: (024) 7636 4729 *Fire protection equipment*

Warwickshire Ignition Services Ltd, 5 Colletts Drive, Cheltenham, Gloucestershire, GL51 8JQ Tel: (01242) 523500 Fax: (01242) 524117 *Auto-electrical specialists & factors*

Warwickshire Investment Partnership, Shire Hall, Warwick, CV34 4SX Tel: (01926) 412830 Fax: (01926) 410268 E-mail: wips@warwickshire.gov.uk *Business support*

Warwickshire Pine, 263 Tile Hill Lane, Coventry, CV4 9DW Tel: (024) 7667 5328 Fax: (024) 7667 5328 *Pine furniture & joinery manufrs*

Wasco Circuits, Wasco House, Willow Lane, Lancaster, LA1 5NA Tel: (01524) 69900 Fax: (01524) 67544 E-mail: front.office@nht.co.uk *Printed circuit board manufrs*

Wasdell Packaging Machines Ltd, Upper Mills Trading Estate, Stonehouse, Gloucestershire, GL10 2BJ Tel: (01453) 828383 Fax: (01453) 828687 E-mail: reception@wasdell.co.uk *Pharmaceutical product packers*

Alan Wasden Ltd, Niloc Works, Penistone Road, Sheffield, S6 2FW Tel: 0114-234 8824 Fax: 0114-232 1246 Principal Export Areas: Worldwide *Manufacturers of hand tools & power tool accessories, under the duracut, niloc & paramo brands. We also provide forging, powder coating & finishing services.*

Wash Shop, 1 Hartford Way, Sealand Industrial Estate, Chester, CH1 4NT Tel: (01244) 520916 Fax: (01244) 526022 *Car wash*

Washbourn & Garrett Ltd, Ashcroft Road, Knowsley Industrial Park North, Liverpool, L33 7TW Tel: 0151-546 2901 Fax: 0151-548 5562 E-mail: enquiries@washbourngarrett.co.uk *Futniture manufrs*

Washburn Fabrications Ltd, Riffa Business Park, Harrogate Road, Leathley, Otley, West Yorkshire, LS21 2RZ Tel: 0113-284 1111 Fax: 0113-284 2842 *Fabricators*

Washford Engineering Ltd, Unit 41, Crossgate Road, Park Farm Industrial Estate, Redditch, Worcestershire, B98 7SN Tel: (01527) 525390 Fax: (01527) 510241 E-mail: enquiries@washfordengineering.co.uk *Precision engineers*

Washford Finishings, 9 Washford Industrial Estate, Bartleet Road, Redditch, Worcestershire, B98 0DQ Tel: (01527) 525936 Fax: (01527) 526433 *Powder coating services*

Washington Components Ltd, Prestex House, Hertburn Industrial Estate, Hertburn, Washington, Tyne & Wear, NE37 2SF Tel: 0191-416 9676 Fax: 0191-417 7087 E-mail: sales@washingtoncomponents.co.uk Principal Export Areas: Worldwide *Engineering component manufrs*

Washington Direct Mail Ltd, Fourth Avenue, Team Valley, Gateshead, Tyne & Wear, NE11 0JS Tel: 0191-482 4291 Fax: 0191-491 0109 E-mail: wdm@wdml.co.uk *Direct mail & polywrapping digital printing*

Washington Mills Electro Minerals Ltd, Mosley Road, Trafford Park, Manchester, M17 1NR Tel: 0161-848 0271 Fax: 0161-872 2974 E-mail: sales@washingtonmills.co.uk Principal Export Areas: Worldwide *Abrasive grains & powders refractory manufrs*

Washington Powder Coatings Ltd, 13 Bridgewater Road, Hertburn Industrial Estate, Washington, Tyne & Wear, NE37 2SG Tel: 0191-416 4085 Fax: 0191-415 7825 *Powder coating services*

Washington Precision Engineering (NSE) Ltd, 6 Tilley Road, Crowther Industrial Estate, Washington, Tyne & Wear, NE38 0AE Tel: 0191-416 1564 Fax: 0191-415 3712 E-mail: info@wp-eng.co.uk *Precision engineers*

▶ Washington Print, 24 Beswick Street, Manchester, M4 7HR Tel: 0161-273 8600 Fax: 0161-274 3708

Washington & Riley Ltd, 1 William Clowes Street, Stoke-on-Trent, ST6 3AR Tel: (01782) 834363 Fax: (01782) 834366 E-mail: info@washingtonandriley.ltd.uk *Architectural hardware, ironmongers & metalwork distributors*

▶ Washtec UK Ltd, 14a Oak Industrial Park, Chelmsford Road, Dunmow, Essex, CM6 1XN Tel: (01371) 878800 Fax: (01371) 878810 E-mail: sales@washtec-uk.com *Manufacturers of vehicle cleaning/washing systems*

▶ Wasp Barcode Technologies, 20 Churchill Square, Kings Hill, West Malling, Kent, ME19 4YU Tel: (0845) 4301971 Fax: (0845) 6001973 *Make & design barcodes & software & hardware*

Wasp It, Unit 2 Cefn Coed Business Park, Nantgarw, Cardiff, CF15 7QQ Tel: (01443) 657100 Fax: (01443) 848331 E-mail: info@wasp-it.co.uk *Computer consultants*

Wasp Joinery & Construction Ltd, Eastington Trading Estate, Eastington, Stonehouse, Gloucestershire, GL10 3RZ Tel: (01453) 824289 Fax: (01453) 824289 *Pallet & case manufrs*

▶ WASP Managed Services, 88 Gracechurch Street, London, EC3V 0DN Tel: (020) 7283 0088 Fax: (020) 7337 6370 *Computer systems consultants*

Wasp Metal Polishing Ltd, Unit 4 Beaver Industrial Estate, Southmoor Lane, Havant, Hampshire, PO9 1JW Tel: (023) 9245 0011 Fax: (023) 9245 0011 E-mail: director@waspmetalpolishing.com *Metal polishing services*

Wasp Supplies Ltd, Richardson Bottoms, Progress Way, Chalton, Luton, LU4 9TR Tel: (01582) 566560 Fax: (01582) 566056 E-mail: sale@waspsupplies.co.uk *Specialist distributor of welding equipment, abrasives & power tools*

Wass Quadrant Printers Ltd, 2 Rodney Street, London, N1 9JH Tel: (020) 7278 7897 Fax: (020) 7837 1119 E-mail: print@wassquadrant.com *Colour printers*

▶ T. Wassell, Unit 5 Field Road Industrial Estate, Bloxwich, Walsall, WS3 3JW Tel: 01922 408883 *Welders*

Wassen International Ltd, Unit 14 Mole Business Park, Randalls Road, Leatherhead, Surrey, KT22 7BA Tel: (01372) 379828 Fax: (01372) 376599 E-mail: info@wassen.com *Vitamin & health food products manufrs*

▶ Waste Wise UK Ltd, 19 Middle Street, Isham, Kettering, Northamptonshire, NN14 1HL Tel: (08700) 174091 Fax: (08700) 174092 E-mail: robin.archer@ukonline.co.uk *Waste Recycling, Nationwide Skip Hire, Waste Collection Services, Wait & load Waste Collections*

▶ Wastecycle Ltd, Private Road 4, Colwick Industrial Estate, Nottingham, NG4 2JT Tel: 0115-940 3111 Fax: 0115-940 4141 E-mail: sales@wastecycle.co.uk *Wastecycle are the leading Waste Management and Recycling company in the UK. Wastecycle have adopted a new approach to Waste Management by recycling rather than landfilling waste materials. We can offer a total waste management service and a modern Material Recycling Facility to maximise your Waste Savings.*

Wastefile UK, Radford House, Stafford Park 7, Telford, Shropshire, TF3 3BQ Tel: (01952) 292000 Fax: (01952) 299984 E-mail: admin@wastefile.com *Waste management services*

▶ Watch PR, 29 Gibbon Road, Kingston upon Thames, Surrey, KT2 6AD Tel: 020 8286 0654 E-mail: enquiries@watchpr.com *Watch PR is a cost-effective public relations agency that delivers high impact, value for money media programmes in the technology, business to business, business to consumer,new media and charity sectors.*

Watchdogs Security Alarms, 47 Great Meadow, Shaw, Oldham, OL2 7PX Tel: (01706) 840077 *Burglar & intruder alarm systems*

Watchers Binoculars & Telescopes, Devonshire Place, Kents Bank Road, Grange-over-Sands, Cumbria, LA11 7HF Tel: (01539) 535910 E-mail: watcherswildlife@aol.com *Wild life country shop*

▶ Watchesuk Com, Atlantic Square, 24 Station Road, Witham, Essex, CM8 2TL Tel: (01376) 500501 Fax: (01376) 500777

Watchfront Electronics, 27 Charterhouse Close, Bracknell, Berkshire, RG12 0XF Tel: (020) 7517 4900 Fax: (020) 7517 4903 E-mail: sales@watchfront.co.uk *Electronic hardware & software design consultants*

▶ Watchkeeper Security, Guggleton Farm, Station Road, Stalbridge, Sturminster Newton, Dorset, DT10 2RQ Tel: 01258 817743 Fax: 01747 841556 E-mail: info@watchkeepersecurity.co.uk *Manufacturers of WatchKeeper boat security systems, GPS boat tracking systems and marina acess and boat ID equipment*

Watchwise Ltd, 20 North River Road, Great Yarmouth, Norfolk, NR30 1SG Tel: (01493) 842216 Fax: (01493) 857703 E-mail: ngraver@watchwise.co.uk *Manufacturers of furniture frames*

▶ Watco Refrigeration Ltd, Unit 1 Hardengreen Industrial Estate, Dalkeith, Midlothian, EH22 3NX Tel: 0131-561 9502 Fax: 0131-561 9503

Watco Refrigeration Ltd, Unit 1 Hardengreen Industrial Estate, Dalkeith, Midlothian, EH22 3NX Tel: 0131-561 9502 Fax: 0131-561 9503 E-mail: info@watco-refridgeration.co.uk *Catering equipment & air conditioning suppliers & installers*

Water Active Ltd, PO Box 627, Watford, WD23 2JW Tel: 01923 235050 Fax: 01923 252220 E-mail: info@wateractive.co.uk *Publisher of the UK"s number one A3 water industry publication.*

Water Of Ayr, Dalmore, Stair, Mauchline, Ayrshire, KA5 5PA Tel: (01292) 591204 *French chalk producers & agents*

Water Hall Group plc, Paralel House, 32 London Road, Guildford, Surrey, GU1 2AB Tel: (01483) 452333 Fax: (01483) 452322 *Waste management landfill*

▶ Water Industry Commissioner For Scotland, Ochil House, Springkerse Business Park, Stirling, FK7 7XE Tel: (01786) 430200 Fax: (01786) 462018 E-mail: sales@watercommissioner.co.uk

The Water Mill Press Ltd, 33-35 Pitcliffe Way, Upper Castle Street, Bradford, West Yorkshire, BD5 7SG Tel: (01274) 738833 Fax: (01274) 738844 E-mail: sales@watermillpress.co.uk *Label manufrs*

▶ Water Out UK, PO Box 139, Upminster, Essex, RM14 2YD Tel: (0500) 510052 Fax: (01708) 507212 E-mail: floodlines@aol.com *Flooded buildings, building shell quick drying*

Water Plant Ltd, Cowgrove, Wimborne, Dorset, BH21 4EL Tel: (01202) 885977 Fax: (01202) 885977 E-mail: info@waterplantltd.co.uk *Water course maintenance*

▶ Water Quality Centre, Spencer House, Manor Farm Road, Reading, RG2 0JN Tel: 0118-923 6214 Fax: 0118-923 6373 E-mail: info@materialstesting.co.uk *Testing service for non-metallic materials*

▶ The Water Services Group Ltd, Suite 7, MSP House, Fourth Way, Wembley, Middlesex, HA9 0TW Tel: (0845) 2300180 Fax: (020) 8372 3442 E-mail: info@water-serv.com *A Total service provider for all aspects of underwater inspection, maintenance, rehabilitation and construction*

▶ Water Side, Unit 14-15, The Griffon Centre, Vale of Leven Industrial Estat, Dumbarton, G82 3PD Tel: (01389) 755500

▶ Water Smart, Unit 15 Coppull Enterprise Centre, Mill Lane, Coppull, Chorley, Lancashire, PR7 5BW Tel: (01257) 793355 Fax: (01257) 793366 *Supply & installation of mains- fed, plumbed in water coolers*

▶ Water Smart (NW) Ltd, Unit 5 Imex Spaces, Glenfield Business Park, Philips Road, Blackburn, BB1 5PF Tel: (0845) 4506984 Fax: (01257) 793366 E-mail: watersmart@btinterent.com *Water cooler installations*

Water Soft Ltd, 35 Meadow Rise, Blackmore, Essex, CM4 0QY Tel: (01277) 822771 Fax: (01277) 822771 *Water treatment*

Water Softening Services, Meadows End House, 22 Bridge Meadow, Denton, Northampton, NN7 1DA Tel: (01604) 890805 *Water softener engineer*

Water Sports, 6A Barfield Road, West Mersea, Colchester, CO5 8QT Tel: (01206) 384296 *Boat equipment & accessories*

Water Support Services, 18a High West Street, Dorchester, Dorset, DT1 1UW Tel: (01305) 266614 Fax: (01305) 267017 E-mail: info@water-support.co.uk *Water management services including leak detection, pipe repair*

Water Systems, 3 Sunnylaw Road, Bridge of Allan, Stirling, FK9 4QD Tel: (01786) 834676 Fax: (01786) 833988 *Mineral water suppliers*

▶ Water Tech Systems 2000 Ltd, Unit 1, Lowesmoor Trading Estate, Worcester, WR1 2SF Tel: (01905) 22113

Water Techniques Maintenance Ltd, 5 Devoil Close, Guildford, Surrey, GU4 7FG Tel: (01483) 565544 Fax: (01483) 454400 E-mail: sales@watertechniques.co.uk *Fountain (water display) consultants & designers*

Water Technology Ltd, Powke Lane Industrial Estate, Blackheath, Rowley Regis, West Midlands, B65 0AH Tel: 0121-561 3144 Fax: 0121-561 3329 E-mail: water.tech@virgin.net *Cooling towers & industrial water softening equipment manufrs*

Water Treatment Technology, PO Box 2333, Sudbury, Suffolk, CO10 7FW Tel: (01787) 313993 Fax: (01787) 311693 E-mail: sales@h2owtt.com *Water treatment services*

Water UK Ltd, 1 Queen Annes Gate, London, SW1H 9BT Tel: (020) 7344 1844 Fax: (020) 7344 1866 E-mail: sales@water.org.uk *Trade association*

Water Waiter Ltd, Telford Way, Telford Way Industrial Estate, Kettering, Northamptonshire, NN16 8UN Tel: (01536) 310444 *Water coolers*

▶ Water Warehouse Ltd, Unit 32 Nailsworth Mills Estate, Avening Road, Nailsworth, Stroud, Gloucestershire, GL6 0BS Tel: (01453) 837400 Fax: (01453) 837401 *Water cooler manufrs*

Water Weights, Unit 7 Gapton Hall Industrial Estate, Vanguard Road, Great Yarmouth, Norfolk, NR31 0NT Tel: (01493) 442591 Fax: (01493) 442535 E-mail: marketing@imes-group.com *Water weights hire & testing services*

Water World Ltd, Chester High Road, Burton, Neston, CH64 8TF Tel: 0151-336 3616 Fax: 0151-336 7718 *Water gardens*

▶ Waterbeds Direct, 7 Talbot Row, Euxton, Chorley, Lancashire, PR7 6HS Tel: (0808) 1001419 E-mail: sales@waterbedsdirect.co.uk *Waterbeds*

Waterbury Bathroom Accessories Ltd, 60 Adams Street, Birmingham, B7 4LT Tel: 0121-333 6062 Fax: 0121-333 6459 E-mail: sales@waterbury.co.uk *Bathroom accessories suppliers*

Watercare Specialists Ltd, Unit 2 Beech Tree Park, Bidford-on-Avon, Alcester, Warwickshire, B50 4JF Tel: (01789) 778177 Fax: (01789) 490001 *Water treatment services*

Waterchem Ltd, Unit 2c, Derwent Close, Worcester, WR4 9TY Tel: (01905) 23669 Fax: (01905) 729959 E-mail: info@waterchem.co.uk *Water treatment services*

Watercoolers (UK) Ltd, Unit 4 Brickfields Industrial Estate, Finway Road, Hemel Hempstead, Hertfordshire, HP2 7QA Tel: (01442) 211121 Fax: (01442) 211171 E-mail: sales@mainlinewater.co.uk *Water coolers retailers & manufrs*

Watercut Profiles Ltd, Unit 3, Murdock Road, Bicester, Oxon, OX26 4PP Tel: (01869) 327888 Fax: (01869) 249410 E-mail: sales@watercut.co.uk Principal Export Areas: Asia Pacific, Middle East, Africa & North America *Water jet (high pressure) cutting, precision cutting, profile cutting & stainles*

▶ WaterEconomiser.Com, 79 Chichester St, Belfast, BT1 4JE Tel: 028 90656552 E-mail: mail@watereconomiser.com *Water Manager, Water Miser, Urinal flush control device. Automatic faucets, flushes, water saving devices, water savers. WATER ECONOMISER*

Waterfall & O'Brien, 138 Forest Road, Fishponds, Bristol, BS16 3SN Tel: 0117-958 3448 Fax: 0117-958 6776 *Analytical chemists*

Waterfield Odham & Associates Ltd, 22 London Road, Riverhead, Sevenoaks, Kent, TN13 2BT Tel: (01732) 465444 Fax: (01732) 452550 E-mail: engineer@woaltd.co.uk *Consulting engineers*

Waterfit Ltd, 293 Birmingham New Road, Dudley, West Midlands, DY1 4SJ Tel: 0121-520 7987 Fax: 0121-557 0357 E-mail: enquires@waterfit.co.uk *Non-ferrous metal founders*

▶ Waterflo Ltd, Kenyon Business Park, Pilkington Street, Bolton, BL3 6HL Tel: (01204) 385252 Fax: (01204) 385253 E-mail: info@waterflo.co.uk *Industrial & domestic water cooler retailers*

Waterforce, Southport Delivery Office Southport Business Park, Wight Moss, Southport, Merseyside, PR8 4ZZ Tel: (0800) 0933267 E-mail: info@pressure-washing.me.uk *high/low pressure cleaning of ornamental stonework,industrial and domestic cleaning of buildings and glass constructions, plant and machinary*

Waterford Wedgwood Australia Ltd, Barlaston, Stoke-on-Trent, ST12 9ES Tel: (01782) 204141 Fax: (01782) 204402 E-mail: sales@wedgwood.co.uk *Hotel bone china manufacturers/retail* Also at: London

Waterford Wedgwood UK P.L.C., Barlaston, Stoke-On-Trent, ST12 9ES Tel: (01782) 204141 Fax: (01782) 204402 E-mail: customer.care@wedgwood.com *Crystal fine china & ceramic manufrs*

Waterfront Systems Ltd, Thornhill Lodge, Thornhill, Stalbridge, Sturminster Newton, Dorset, DT10 2SH Tel: (01963) 364307 Fax: (01963) 364306 *CCTV manufrs*

Waterhouse Building Refurbishment & Interiors, 98 Bradford Road, East Ardsley, Wakefield, West Yorkshire, WF3 2JL Tel: (01924) 822274 Fax: (01924) 823951 E-mail: info@waterhouse-ideas.co.uk *Building contractors - refurbishment specialists*

D. Waterhouse & Co., Lambert Works, Luton St, Keighley, W. Yorkshire, BD21 2LE Tel: (01535) 642539 Fax: (01535) 642539 *Machine tool maintenance & services*

Waterhouse E J & Sons Ltd, Kings Lane, Chipperfield, Kings Langley, Hertfordshire, WD4 9ER Tel: (01923) 267444 Fax: (01923) 261883 *Building contractors*

Peter Waterhouse Contractors, 26C Coronation Road, Crosby, Liverpool, L23 5RQ Tel: 0151-924 1964 Fax: 0151-924 1964 *Joiners*

Waterhouse Pressings Ltd, Unit 4f Snaygill Industrial Estate, Keighley Road, Skipton, North Yorkshire, BD23 2QR Tel: (01756) 794577 Fax: (01756) 701481 *High volume precision pressings*

Waterjet Profiles Ltd, Units 9, Ryder Way, Basildon, Essex, SS13 1QH Tel: (01268) 591491 Fax: (01268) 729726 E-mail: sales@waterjet-profiles.co.uk Principal Export Areas: Worldwide *Water jet (high pressure) cutting services*

▶ Waterless Detailers (Derby) Ltd, 20 Victoria Drive, Woodville, Swadlincote, Derbyshire, DE11 8DY Tel: (07970) 607166 E-mail: derby@waterlessdetailers.co.uk *specialists in vehicle valeting .we DONT use water*

▶ The Waterless Valeting Co. Edinburgh, 1A Lansdowne Crescent, Edinburgh, EH12 5EQ Tel: 0131-225 3220 E-mail: brian.anderson22@btopenworld.com *Car valerting services*

Waterlife Aquatic Exotic Plant & Pet Centre, 476 Bath Road, Longford Near Heathrow, West Drayton, Middlesex, UB7 0ED Tel: (01753) 685696 Fax: (01753) 685437 E-mail: sales@waterlife.co.uk *Tropical fish dealers & manufrs*

Waterlife Studio, Booker Garden Centre, Clay Lane, Booker, Marlow, Buckinghamshire, SL7 3DH Tel: (01494) 526865 E-mail: sales@thewaterlifestudio.co.uk *Aquatics suppliers*

Waterline Ltd, Jenna House, 6 Mollins Court, Cumbernauld, Glasgow, G68 9HP Tel: (0870) 5561560 Fax: (01236) 453868 E-mail: sales@waterline.co.uk *Kitchen & bedroom product distribs*

▶ Waterline Equipment Company, Everite Works, Derby Road, Widnes, Cheshire, WA8 9ND Tel: 0151-495 3505 Fax: 0151-495 3522 E-mail: geoff@waterline-uk.com *Pipe lining equipment manufrs*

▶ Waterlock Business Development, The Studios, The Street, Stourmouth, Canterbury, Kent, CT3 1HZ Tel: (01227) 720007 Fax: (01227) 720001 E-mail: wbd@waterlock.co.uk *Waterlock is a provider of business development services primarily to the construction and landscape industries.**We concentrate on helping our clients to improve the areas of their business that involve finding, pricing and winning work.**With over 20 years of hands-on sales, marketing and contracting experience at all levels, we offer a practical and proven approach to winning more work for you.**Our CFSystem database is an ideal tool to help you manage your business development at all levels. **We also provide cost planning and advisory services for end user clients where our practical knowledge can prove invaluable.**Sales-Marketing-Tender preparation-Client Consultancy-*CFSystem-Training-IT Support and development**www.waterlock.co.uk***

Waterloo Design & Print Plc, Reliance House, Birmingham St, Halesowen, West Midlands, B63 3HW Tel: 0121-550 1795 Fax: 0121-501 1514 E-mail: admin@waterloo.uk.com *Printers of business supplies manufrs*

Waterloo Motor Trade Ltd, Main Street, Hull, HU2 0JX Tel: (01482) 328308 Fax: (01482) 212398 E-mail: sales@waterloo-mt.co.uk *Motor factors & engineers* Also at: Beverley, Bridlington & Springbank

Waterlow Publishing Information Services Ltd, Paulton House, 8 Shepherdess Walk, London, N1 7LB Tel: (020) 7490 0049 Fax: (020) 7253 1308 E-mail: marketing@waterlow.com *Specialist information publishers*

Waterlow Secretaries Ltd, 6-8 Underwood Street, London, N1 7JQ Tel: (020) 7250 3350 Fax: (020) 7608 0867 E-mail: companyservices@waterlow.com *Legal services*

▶ Waterman Gore Ltd, Cumbrae House, 15 Carlton Court, Glasgow, G5 9JP Tel: 0141-429 3386 Fax: 0141-429 6299

▶ Waterman Group, Unit 2 11 Canning St Lane, Edinburgh, EH3 8ER Tel: 0131-221 7020 Fax: 0131-221 7099 E-mail: s.g.burke@waterman-group.co.uk *We provide a fully comprehensive, multi-disciplinary infrastructure consultancy service to public and private sector clients which includes design, inspection and supervision of all areas of highway, bridge, water and underground infrastructure, from the early development planning stage through to construction and long term maintenance. We are also equipped to provide full transportation and geotechnical studies including planning support. Additional skills include air quality assessment, traffic noise monitoring and flood risk analysis.*

Waterman Offshore Ltd, Peters Works, Wouldham, Rochester, Kent, ME1 3XL Tel: (01634) 865341 Fax: (01634) 687447 E-mail: enquiries@watermanoffshoreltd.co.uk *Steel fabricators*

Watermans, 50 Parsons Street, Banbury, Oxfordshire, OX16 5NB Tel: (01295) 269210 Fax: (01295) 269210 *Jewellers manufrs*

Watermarc Chemical Services, Unit 38 Nine Mile Point Industrial Estate, Cwmfelinfach, Ynysddu, Newport, Gwent, NP11 7HZ Tel: (01495) 200005 Fax: (01495) 200844 *Industrial water treatment services*

Watermark Business Forms Ltd, 353 Stratford Road, Shirley, Solihull, West Midlands, B90 3BW Tel: 0121-733 1633 Fax: 0121-733 1683 E-mail: sales@watermark.print.com *Forms printers*

Watermark Systems UK Ltd, 18 Cotton Brook Road, Derby, DE23 8YJ Tel: (01332) 366000 Fax: (01332) 372006 E-mail: sales@watermark-uk.com *Aluminium & stainless steel metal fabricators*

Watermill Products Ltd, Fairview Industrial Estate, Hurst Green, Oxted, Surrey, RH8 9BD Tel: 01883 715425 *Power shower pumps manufrs*

Watermiser Ltd, Tower Works, 4-8 Stoneygate Road, Newmilns, Ayrshire, KA16 9AJ Tel: (01560) 320762 Fax: (01560) 323093 E-mail: info@watermiser.co.uk *Cooling tower manufrs*

Watermota Ltd, Cavalier Road, Heathfield Industrial Estate, Newton Abbot, Devon, TQ12 6TQ Tel: (01626) 830910 Fax: (01626) 830911 E-mail: mike@watermota.co.uk *Marine engineers*

▶ The Waterpoint, 2 Argyle Street, Stonehouse, Larkhall, Lanarkshire, ML9 3LL Tel: (01698) 793933 Fax: (01698) 793933 E-mail: sales@thewaterpoint.com *Water coolers & coffee machine manufrs*

▶ WaterPromotions, PO Box 27, Richmond, Surrey, TW10 6XN Tel: (020) 8948 5551 *Custom labeled spring water and energy drinks. Our water is bottled at source in England. Labels can be fully personalised. Low minimums, quick turnarounds.*

▶ Waterproof World, 113 Cowper Road, Hemel Hempstead, Hertfordshire, HP1 1PF Tel: (01442) 401300 Fax: 0114-240 1301 E-mail: info@waterproofworld.co.uk *Quality children's outdoor clothes for babies, toddlers & kids suppliers*

Waters, 730-740 Centennial Park, Centennial Way, Elstree, Borehamwood, Hertfordshire, WD6 3S Tel: (020) 8238 6100 Fax: (020) 8207 7070 E-mail: jobs@corpworld.co.uk *Chromatography equipment suppliers*

Waters & Robson Abbeywell Ltd, Abbey Well, 12 Coopies Lane, Morpeth, Northumberland, NE61 6JF Tel: (01670) 513113 Fax: (01670) 515821 E-mail: enquiries@abbey-well.co.uk *Mineral water producers*

Waters & Stanton plc, 22 Main Road, Hockley, Essex, SS5 4QS Tel: (01702) 206835 Fax: (01702) 205843 E-mail: sales@wsplc.com *Amateur radio communications specialists, tv & radio*

▶ Watersavers Water Treatment Equipment, Earl Road, Rackheath Industrial Estate, Rackheath, Norwich, NR13 6NT Tel: (01603) 720999 Fax: (01603) 721499 E-mail: sales@watersavers-norwich.co.uk *Auto save flushing control manufrs*

▶ Waterscape Solutions Ltd, 41 Sandford, Ringwood, Hampshire, BH24 3BS Tel: (01425) 482906 Fax: (01425) 472380 E-mail: info@waterscapesolutions.co.uk *Install all types of irrigation systems & drainage*

Waterseal Waterbar & Sealant Ltd, 1 Weston Cour Stokesley Industrial Estate, Stokesley, Middlesbrough, Cleveland, TS9 5GA Tel: (01642 717717 Fax: (01642) 717718 *Civil engineers services*

Watershed Design, 31 Freegrove Road, Islington, London, N7 9RG Tel: (020) 7700 1759 Fax: (020) 7700 1692 E-mail: peter@watershed-uk.com *Graphic designers*

Watershed Media Centre, 1 Canons Road, Bristol, BS1 5TX Tel: 0117-927 6444 Fax: 0117-921 3958 E-mail: admin@watershed.co.uk *Media centre, arts projects, cinema & conference facilities*

Watershed Packaging Ltd, Westpoint, Westland Square, Leeds, LS11 5SS Tel: 0113-277 0606 Fax: 0113-277 7174 E-mail: sales@watershed-packaging.co.uk *Printed adhesive tape manufrs*

Watershed Packaging Ltd, 30 Chapman Way, Tunbridge Wells, Kent, TN2 3EF Tel: (01892) 515777 Fax: (01892) 510852 E-mail: enquiries@kent.watershed-packaging.co uk *Self adhesive labels manufrs*

▶ Watershed Plastics Ltd, Unit 7, Bowburn South Industrial Estat, Bowburn, Durham, DH6 5AD Tel: 0191-377 8020

Waterside Aquatics & Koi Centres, West Park Road, Copthorne, Crawley, West Sussex, RH10 3HG Tel: (01342) 712332 Fax: (01342) 712332 *Aquatic sales service*

Watersmeet, Metal & Ores Industrial Estate, 138 Hanbury Road, Stoke Prior, Bromsgrove, Worcestershire, B60 4JZ Tel: (01527) 832292 Fax: (01527) 832949 E-mail: sales@watersmeetltd.co.uk *Gift manufrs*

Waterstar, Chester House, Westgate, Bishop Auckland, County Durham, DL13 1PG Tel: (01388) 517513 E-mail: john.mccutheon@waterstar.co.uk *Computer consultants*

Waterton Engineering Co. Ltd, 2 Raymond Avenue, Chadderton, Oldham, OL9 7HW Tel: 0161-624 0004 Fax: 0161-624 8276 *Sheet metalworkers, presswork & laser profiling services*

Waterways, 85 Brereton Avenue, Cleethorpes, South Humberside, DN35 7RP Tel: (01472) 342475 Fax: (01507) 354513 *Aquarium & pond suppliers*

Waterways Pet Centre, Milton Ernest Garden Centre, Radwell Road, Milton Ernest, Bedford, MK44 1SH Tel: (01234) 823567 Fax: (01234) 823567 E-mail: info@waterways-direct.com *Retailer of pet & aquatic accessories*

Waterwise Aquarium & Pond Supplies, The Water Garden Centre, 144 Coggeshall Road, Marks Tey, Colchester, CO6 1HR Tel: (01206) 212310 Fax: (01206) 213084 *Aquatic suppliers*

▶ Wates Construction Ltd, Network House, Basing View, Basingstoke, Hampshire, RG21 4HG Tel: (01256) 301750 Fax: (01256) 358166

▶ Wates Construction Ltd, Royds Hall Road, Leeds, LS12 6AJ Tel: 0113-231 1880 Fax: 0113-231 9994

Wates Construction Ltd, 1260 London Rd, Norbury, London, SW16 4EG Tel: (020) 8764 5000 Fax: (020) 8679 7611 E-mail: info@wates.co.uk *General contractors*

Watford Coatings Ltd, Park House, Greenhill CR, Watford, WD18 8QU Tel: (01923) 235640 Fax: (01923) 449229 E-mail: sales@watfordcoatings.co.uk *Industrial paint sprayers*

Watford Electronics, Finway, Dallow Road, Luton, LU1 1WE Tel: (0870) 0270900 Fax: (0870) 0270901 E-mail: info@watford.co.uk *Computer & accessory sales*

Watford Express Ltd, Unit 20 Peerglow Industrial Est, Olds Approach, Tolpits La, Watford, WD18 9SR Tel: (01923) 771383 Fax: (01923) 771383 *Road transport, haulage & freight services*

Watford Printers Ltd, 58 Vicarage Road, Watford, WD18 0EW Tel: (01923) 223885 Fax: (01923) 221757 E-mail: wpl@btconnect.com *General printing services*

Watford Refrigeration & Air Conditioning Ltd, Wiggenhall Industrial Estate, Watford, WD18 0FT Tel: (01923) 227726 Fax: (01923) 233525 E-mail: sales@wataref.co.uk *Refrigeration engineers, design, installation services*

Watford Sheltered Workshops Ltd, Century Park, Dalton Way, Watford, WD17 2SF Tel: (01923) 220256 Fax: (01923) 245311 E-mail: richard@watfordworkshop.co.uk *Assemblers & packaging services for industry*

Watford & West Herts Chamber Of Commerce, The Business Centre, Colne Way, Watford, WD24 7AA Tel: (01923) 442442 Fax: (01923) 445050 E-mail: sales@watford-chamber.co.uk *Chamber of commerce services*

continued

Wath Rubber & Plastics Ltd, Pump House, Station Road, Wath-upon-Dearne, Rotherham, South Yorkshire, S63 7DQ Tel: (01709) 876900 Fax: (01709) 877998 E-mail: info@wath.co.uk *Hydraulic hose manufrs*

Watker Sealants, 14 Brown La West, Leeds, LS12 6BH Tel: 0113-242 1745 Fax: 0113-247 1745 E-mail: paulinecorbet@aol.com *Sealant application services*

Watkins Hire, Churwell Vale, Shaw Cross Business Park, Dewsbury, West Yorkshire, WF12 7RD Tel: (01924) 439733 Fax: (01924) 439732 E-mail: hire@watkinshire.co.uk *Hire/leasing/ rental of boilers, portable buildings & tanks*

▶ Watkins & Sole, Unit 5 Garonor Way, Portbury, Bristol, BS20 7XE Tel: (01275) 376370 Fax: (01275) 376371

▶ Watkinson Construction, 10 Briar Close, Borrowash, Derby, DE72 3GB Tel: (01332) 662232E-mail: watkinson.builders@ntlworld.com

▶ Watkinson Industrial, 78 River Road, Barking, Essex, IG11 0DS Tel: (020) 8507 9642

Watkinson Lifting & Transportation Ltd, Invincible Works, Marriner Road, Keighley, West Yorkshire, BD21 5LW Tel: (01535) 600151 Fax: (01535) 692249 E-mail: sales@watkinsons.com *Road transport & haulage services*

Watkiss Automation Sales Ltd, Watkiss House, 1 Blaydon Road, Sandy, Bedfordshire, SG19 1RZ Tel: (01767) 681800 Fax: (01767) 691769 E-mail: sales@watkiss.com *Collator machine manufrs*

Watling JCB Ltd, Dog & Gun Lane, Whetstone, Leicester, LE8 6LJ Tel: 0116-286 3621 Fax: 0116-286 3171 E-mail: watjcb@atlas.co.uk *Contractors' plant distribs*

Watmoor Engineering Co. Ltd, Dawley Road, Hayes, Middlesex, UB3 1EE Tel: (020) 8573 6877 Fax: (020) 8573 1880 E-mail: barry.robins@btclick.com *Engineering services*

Daniel Watney, 25 Hosier Lane, London, EC1A 9DW Tel: (020) 7246 5000 Fax: (020) 7248 7001 E-mail: info@danwat.com *Chartered surveyors*

Watpower International Ltd, PO Box 1389, London, W5 1JJ Tel: (020) 8810 9148 Fax: (020) 8810 5509 E-mail: info@watpower.co.uk *Export management, marketing & development services*

▶ Watret & Co. Ltd, 65-67 Park Street, St. Albans, Hertfordshire, AL2 2PE Tel: (01727) 873765

Wats On Lighting & Sound Ltd, Upper House, Presteigne, Powys, LD8 2HG Tel: (01544) 260114 Fax: (01544) 267686 *Lighting & sound equipment suppliers, retailers & manufrs*

▶ Watson & Co., Kiln Lane, Stallingborough, Grimsby, South Humberside, DN41 8DS Tel: (01469) 572728 Fax: (01469) 578410 *Transport & haulage services*

A.J. Watson (Electrical Services) Ltd, Browning Street, Hoddlesden, Darwen, Lancashire, BB3 3NE Tel: (01254) 760048 Fax: (01254) 760034 E-mail: info@agele.co.uk *Construction of control panels*

Watson Brook, 119a High Street, Tewkesbury, Gloucestershire, GL20 5JY Tel: (01684) 291155 Fax: (01684) 291166 E-mail: sales@watsonbrook.co.uk *Hardwood flooring installation services*

Watson Bros Ltd, 30-34 Wilson Place, East Kilbride, Glasgow, G74 4QD Tel: (01355) 233144 Fax: (01355) 233850 E-mail: colin@turnersrollerdoors.com *Roller shutter & fire door manufrs*

C.J. Watson, Hilton Chambers, Roushill, Shrewsbury, SY1 1PN Tel: (01743) 362898 Fax: (01743) 362898 *Hand engraver*

Watson Construction Group Ltd, Westwood, West Calder, West Lothian, EH55 8PN Tel: (01506) 871561 Fax: (01506) 871770 E-mail: info@watsongroup.co.uk *Building construction services*

Watson Diesel Ltd, Elm Grove, London, SW19 4HE Tel: (020) 8879 3854 Fax: (0870) 4441386 E-mail: sales@watsondiesel.com *Diesel fuel injection engineers*

Edgar Watson Ltd, Trent Lane, Nottingham, NG2 4DT Tel: 0115-950 3891 Fax: 0115-859 118 *Timber merchants* Also at: Basford

▶ Watson Electrical, Unit 1 Engine Shed Lane, Skipton, North Yorkshire, BD23 1UP Tel: (01756) 799661 Fax: (01756) 790332

Watson Engineering, 12 Upper Gough Street, Birmingham, B1 1JG Tel: 0121-643 1922 Fax: 0121-633 4019 *Precision turned parts manufrs*

▶ George Watson (Construction) Ltd, Station Road, Hipperholme, Halifax, West Yorkshire, HX3 8HW Tel: (01422) 202695 Fax: (01422) 204469

Watson Group Ltd, Tudor House, Highlands Road, Shirley, Solihull, West Midlands, B90 4ND Tel: 0121-705 4624 Fax: 0121-711 1086 E-mail: jean@wapwatson.com *Giftware manufrs*

Watson Hallam, Burlington House, 369 Wellingborough Road, Northampton, NN1 4EU Tel: (01604) 230823 Fax: (01604) 230923 *Civil engineers*

▶ Helen Watson, PO Box 565, East Grinstead, West Sussex, RH19 1WQ Tel: (07799) 645907 E-mail: jobs@networking4you.net *Jobs from home*

Herbert Watson Freight Services Ltd, Mirwell House, Carrington Lane, Sale, Cheshire, M33 5NL Tel: 0161-905 0410 Fax: 0161-905 0420 E-mail: phil@herbertwatson.co.uk *International freight forwarder*

Watson & Hillhouse Ltd, Whitehouse Road, Ipswich, IP1 5NT Tel: (01473) 748652 Fax: (01473) 240090 E-mail: info@w-h.co.uk *Piling equipment specialists hire/sales*

Watson John Joinery Ltd, Usworth Road Indust Estate, Hartlepool, Cleveland, TS25 1PD Tel: (01429) 222023 Fax: (01429) 222630 E-mail: sales@johnwatson-joinery.co.uk *Joinery manufrs*

Watson Joinery, 11 Station Road, Thurlby, Bourne, Lincolnshire, PE10 0HD Tel: (01778) 422537 Fax: (01778) 394079 *Joinery contractors manufrs*

▶ Watson & Lewis Ltd, 5 Cullen Way, London, NW10 6JZ Tel: (020) 8961 3000 Fax: (020) 8965 1990 *Electroplating services*

Watson & May Ltd, 38b Pitshanger Lane, London, W5 1QY Tel: (020) 8997 3203 Fax: (020) 8997 3188 E-mail: wat.may@virgin.net *Electrical contractors*

▶ Watson Norie Ltd, Wincomblee Road, Walker, Newcastle upon Tyne, NE6 3PL Tel: 0191-262 7411 Fax: 0191-263 0496 E-mail: headoffice@watsonnorie.co.uk *Electrical & instrumentation installation contractors* Also at: Grangemouth & Scunthorpe

P.J. Watson Ltd, 63-66 Hatton Garden, London, EC1N 8LE Tel: (020) 7831 3333 Fax: (020) 7831 7100 E-mail: info@pjwatson.co.uk *Jewellery*

▶ Peter Watson, 57 Euston Grove, Crow, Ringwood, Hampshire, BH24 1FB Tel: (07866) 737655 E-mail: tasminservices@tiscali.co.uk *Watsons Couriers and Light Haulage,"We provide a fast , efficient, and friendly Uk sameday service. We are fully insured, and our G.I.T value is £ 15000,00.We are based in Bournemouth, and can go anywhere in the UK. We look forward to you call.*

Watson Petroleum Ltd, Causeway End, Brinkworth, Chippenham, Wiltshire, SN15 5DN Tel: (01782) 816932 *Fuel & lubricant deliveries*

Watson Petroleum Ltd, Vector House, Sileby Road, Barrow upon Soar, Loughborough, Leicestershire, LE12 8LX Tel: (01509) 815777 Fax: (01509) 816363 *Fuel oils & lubricants service*

Watson Petroleum Ltd, Hunters Lane, Rugby, Warwickshire, CV21 1EA Tel: (01788) 572401 Fax: (01788) 540010 *Fuel oil distributors*

Watson Productions Ltd, Gothic House, Bank Lane, Totnes, Devon, TQ9 5EH Tel: (01803) 863033 Fax: (01803) 864219 *Audio visual equipment services*

Watson Signs, Unit 1 Dunaverig, Ruskie, Thornhill, Stirling, FK8 3QW Tel: (01786) 850501 Fax: (01259) 720022 E-mail: Admin@watsonsigns.co.uk *Signs, awnings & canopies*

Watson Steel Structures Ltd, PO Box 9, Bolton, BL6 4BL Tel: (01204) 699999 Fax: (01204) 694543 *Structural steelwork engineers* Also at: Bristol

▶ Walter Watson Ltd, 2 Edison House, Fullerton Road, Glenrothes, Fife, KY7 5QR Tel: (01592) 612500 Fax: (01592) 612900 E-mail: info@walter-watson.co.uk *Structural fabrication services*

▶ Watsons, Breach Barns Lane, Waltham Abbey, Essex, EN9 2AD Tel: (01992) 651900 Fax: (01992) 651900 E-mail: sales@watsonsbuilders.co.uk *Ceiling contractors, partitions & complete refurbishments*

▶ Watsons Dairy, Bere Farm, Heath Road, Soberton, Southampton, SO32 3QH Tel: (01329) 832127 Fax: (01329) 834502 *Dairy processors*

▶ Watt A Dog Grooming, 5 Hasman Terrace, Cove Bay, Aberdeen, AB12 3GD Tel: (01224) 874841 E-mail: jenifer@watt-a-dog.co.uk *Professional dog grooming*

▶ Bruce Watt, Hilltop, Harrowby, Grantham, Lincolnshire, NG31 9HA Tel: (01476) 590333 E-mail: hilltoppds@o2.co.ik *Architectural, planning and design service.*

Watt & Dewar, 62-68 New Row, Dunfermline, Fife, KY12 7EF Tel: (01383) 724146 Fax: (01383) 622966 *Wholesale retailers*

Watt Fences, Broken Brea Farm, Easby, Richmond, North Yorkshire, DL10 7EY Tel: (01748) 822666 Fax: (01748) 822666 *Fence manufrs*

Watt Gilchrist Ltd, Ring Road, West Park, Leeds, LS16 6RA Tel: 0113-288 3200 Fax: 0113-275 1690 E-mail: info@gilchrist.co.uk *Design, artwork & reprographics*

Watt Industrial Tyres Ltd, Church Road, Lydney, Gloucestershire, GL15 5EN Tel: (01594) 847100 Fax: (01594) 847181 E-mail: cliverickards@watts-polymers.co.uk *Industrial tyre manufrs*

J. & W. Watt Ltd, London Road, Carlisle, CA1 2NN Tel: (01228) 522311 Fax: (01228) 511926 E-mail: office@wattstorage.com *Storage, warehousing & distribution services*

Watties Welders & Fabricators, New Cottage Rosemill, Bridgefoot, Dundee, DD3 0PW Tel: (01382) 812794 Fax: (01382) 884114 E-mail: info@wattieswelders.com *Welding engineers*

Watts 4 X 4 Centre, 122 Scarborough Road, Bridlington, North Humberside, YO16 7NU Tel: (01262) 606782 Fax: (01262) 604629 E-mail: wattsmix@aol.com *Concrete manufrs*

Captain O.M. Watts, 7 Dover Street, London, W1S 4LD Tel: (020) 7493 4633 Fax: (020) 7495 0755 E-mail: captianwatts@marineforce.com *Yacht chandlers*

Charles Watts Engineering Ltd, 94-102 Somers Road, Rugby, Warwickshire, CV22 7DH Tel: (01788) 543152 Fax: (01788) 575986 E-mail: sales@charleswatts.co.uk *General engineers & steel fabricators*

Watts Clift Holdings Ltd, Westgate, Aldridge, Walsall, WS9 8DJ Tel: (01922) 743360 Fax: (01922) 743362 *Holding company & metal stockholders*

Watts Construction Ltd, Unit 1 & 2 Beacon Road Works, Beacon Road, Chatham, Kent, ME5 7BP Tel: (01634) 409149 Fax: (01634) 403005 E-mail: wattsgroupltd@btconnect.com *Sheet metal engineers*

E.J. Watts Engineering Group, Faldo Road, Barton-le-Clay, Bedford, MK45 4RJ Tel: (01582) 881601 Fax: (01582) 881075 E-mail: info@ejwatts.co.uk *E J Watts Engineering Group (est 1963) in Luton, Bedfordshire, operates from a 28,000 sq ft factory. Leading UK Suppliers of Pressings, Tube Bending and Tube Welding Services, Sheet Metal Work, Tapping, Sawing, Deburring, Guillotining, CNC Machining and Flow Drilling. Robotic Welding and manual MiG welding to TiG, Projection & Spot Welding to Brazing and Soldering. Press work, Tube forming and Welded Assemblies, Engineering and Subcontract Engineering Services, and Component Manufacturers. We produce a large and varied array of Components such as LCD TV stands, Tubular Car Seat frames, Scaffold Brackets, Cable management systems, Shop fittings, Point of Sale Stands, Office Furniture, and Car & Telecoms Components, to name but*

continued

a few. From low to high production runs, sample and prototype work, to full production tooled parts. All tools and jigs, samples and prototypes are designed and made in house, minimising cost to give excellent value and fast lead times. ISO 9001 : 2000 credited.

Watts Engineering Services, 22d Orgreave Crescent, Sheffield, S13 9NQ Tel: 0114 2880667 *Plant maintenance & repair services*

Watts Group Of Companies, Althorpe House, High Street, Lydney, Gloucestershire, GL15 5DD Tel: (01594) 847400 Fax: (01594) 847401 E-mail: info@watts-group.co.uk *Tyre distributors*

Watts Industrial Tyres plc, 9a Brindley Road, Bayton Road Industrial Estate, Coventry, CV7 9EP Tel: (024) 7664 5222 Fax: (024) 7636 7111 *Supplier of industrial tyres*

Watts Industrial Tyres plc, 9 Spencer Street, Grimsby, South Humberside, DN31 3AA Tel: (01472) 362589 Fax: (01472) 352772 *Supplier of tyres for all industries*

Watts Industrial Tyres plc, Unit 7 Brickfields, Liverpool, L36 6HY Tel: 0151-481 4500 Fax: 0151-481 4501 E-mail: liverpool@watts_tyres.co.uk *Supplier of tyres for all industries*

Watts Industrial Tyres plc, Albion Road, West Bromwich, West Midlands, B70 8AX Tel: 0121-553 5451 Fax: 0121-500 5079 E-mail: westbrom@watts.co.uk *Tyres, forklift trucks applications manufrs*

Watts Industries UK Ltd, Grosvenor Business Centre, Enterprise Way, Vale Park, Evesham, Worcestershire, WR11 1GA Tel: (01386) 446997 Fax: (01386) 41923 E-mail: sales@wattsindustries.com *Valves & vessel distributors*

Watts & Partners, 2-12 Montgomery Street, Belfast, BT1 4NX Tel: (028) 9024 8222 Fax: (028) 9024 8007 E-mail: mail.belfast@watts.co.uk *Consultants to the property & construction industry*

▶ Watts & Partners, 60 Fountain Street, Manchester, M2 2FE Tel: 0161-831 6180 Fax: 0161-834 7750 E-mail: mail.manchester@watts.co.uk *Consultants to the property & construction industry*

Watts & Stone, Castle Balfour Demesne, Lisnaskea, Enniskillen, County Fermanagh, BT92 0LT Tel: (028) 6772 1282 Fax: (028) 6772 1106 E-mail: sales@wattsandstone.co.uk *Uniform work wear & sportswear manufrs*

Watts Systems Ltd, Church Street, Old Basford, Nottingham, NG6 0GA Tel: 0115-970 5566 Fax: 0115-970 6688 *Suspended ceilings partitioning & office furniture*

▶ Watts Transport, The Moat, Buckland, Buntingford, Hertfordshire, SG9 0QB Tel: (01763) 271653 Fax: (01763) 273319

Watts Tyre & Auto Centres, Unit 301, Dean Road, Bristol, BS11 8AT Tel: 0117-982 4896 Fax: 0117-982 4896 *Suppliers of tyres for all industrial applications*

Watts Urethane Products Ltd, Church Road, Lydney, Gloucestershire, GL15 5EN Tel: (01594) 847150 Fax: (01594) 843586 E-mail: sales@wattsgroup.co.uk *Polyurethane moulding services*

W. Clifford Watts Ltd, 118-122 Scarborough Road, Bridlington, East Yorkshire, YO16 7NU Tel: (01262) 675383 Fax: (01262) 604629 E-mail: wcliffordwatts@aol.com *Sand/gravel/ stone quarry owners*

Wattshop Computer Systems, 5-7 Dunning Street, Stoke-on-Trent, ST6 5AP Tel: (01782) 575280 E-mail: craig@wattshop.com *Computer services*

Wattson Shopfitters Ltd, 4-6 Countess Wear Road, Countess Wear, Exeter, EX2 6LG Tel: (01392) 258781 Fax: (01392) 420866 E-mail: wattson@theshopfitters.co.uk *Shop fitters*

Waugh Road Services Ltd, Wesley Way, Benton Square Industrial Estate, Newcastle Upon Tyne, NE12 9TA Tel: 0191-266 1046 Fax: 0191-215 0754 *Road transport/haulage/freight services*

William Waugh Edinburgh Ltd, Custom House, 11 West Harbour Road, Edinburgh, EH5 1PH Tel: 0131-552 7758 Fax: 0131-552 7758 E-mail: recycle@williamwaugh.co.uk *Metal merchants & scrap metal recyclers*

▶ William Waugh & Sons (Builders) Ltd, Broadford, Auldgirth, Dumfries, DG2 0RT Tel: (01387) 740216 Fax: (01387) 740586

▶ Wave Accounting Solutions Limited, 15 Lara Close, Throop, Bournemouth, BH8 0HB Tel: 07970 476709 E-mail: gordon@waveaccountingsolutions.co.uk *Bournemouth based accountancy services.*

▶ Wave Contemporary Jewellery, 18a Finkle Sti, Kendal, Cumbria, LA9 4AB Tel: (01539) 729805 Fax: (01539) 48067 E-mail: info@wavejewellery.co.uk *Jewellery retailer & manufrs*

▶ Wave Interiors, Unit 1, Baron Road, Blackpool, FY1 6JU Tel: (01253) 401601

▶ Wave Marketing & Design, Upper Hey House, Barkisland, Halifax, West Yorkshire, HX4 0EQ Tel: (01422) 820787 Fax: (01422) 820790 E-mail: sales@wavemad.co.uk *Advertising, publicity & exhibition stand designers & producers*

▶ WaveFX - Video & Multimedia Production, The Barn, 19 Edward Street, Cambridge, CB1 2LS Tel: (07779) 240169 E-mail: jamie@wavefx.co.uk *Multimedia presentations, video editing & filming for corporate media*

▶ Waveney Electrical Services, 115 Whapload Road, Lowestoft, Suffolk, NR32 1UL Tel: (01502) 561139 Fax: (01502) 560720

Waveney Engineering Ltd, 12a Crankill Road, Ballymena, County Antrim, BT43 5JF Tel: (028) 2564 4700 Fax: (028) 2565 9533 E-mail: sales@waveneyengltd.co.uk *General engineers*

Waveney Fork Trucks Ltd, Whapload Road, Lowestoft, Suffolk, NR32 1UL Tel: (01502) 569106 Fax: (01502) 508273 E-mail: info@waveneylifttrucks.co.uk *Fork lift truck specialists*

Waveney Laundry Ltd, Clonavon Road South, Ballymena, County Antrim, BT43 5BJ Tel: (028) 2564 2131 Fax: (028) 2564 3123 E-mail: mail@waveneylaundry.com *Laundry, dry cleaning & textile rental*

▶ Waveney Publishing Ltd, Waveney House, 45-47 Stour Street, Birmingham, B18 7AJ Tel: 0121-454 9441 Fax: 0121-454 9529 *Educational print & design, yearbooks, homework planners, student diaries, prospectuses and many other print & marketing products.*

Waveney Security Ltd, 1 Southend Road, Bungay, Suffolk, NR35 1DN Tel: (01986) 895588 Fax: (01986) 892288 E-mail: suffolk@waveneysecurity.co.uk *Security installation*

Waveney Truck Parts Ltd, 172-174 Mile Cross Lane, Norwich, NR6 6RY Tel: (01603) 400774 Fax: (01603) 418427 E-mail: sales@waveneytruckparts.co.uk *Commercial vehicle spares* Also at: Bungay

▶ Waveplus Systems Ltd, Broadhaven Cottage, Honeysuckle Lane, Headley Down, Bordon, Hampshire, GU35 8JA Tel: (01428) 713 430 E-mail: enquiries@waveplus.co.uk *Lotus Notes & Lotus Domino software and bespoke application design. Products for Lotus Notes & Domino to improve communication and business processes.*

The Waverley Beer TBS Ltd, Unit 3A, Saxon Way, Wincanton Business Park, Wincanton, Somerset, BA9 9RT Tel: (01963) 34264 Fax: (01963) 435204 E-mail: admin@waverleytbs.co.uk *Licensed bar suppliers*

Waverley Engineering Ltd, Waverley Street, Coatbridge, Lanarkshire, ML5 2BE Tel: (01236) 429099 Fax: (01236) 602710 E-mail: sales@waverleyfabs.co.uk *Fabricating engineers*

Waverley Housing Ltd, 27 North Bridge Street, Hawick, Roxburghshire, TD9 9BD Tel: (01450) 364200 Fax: (01450) 375905 *Property management services*

▶ Waverley Press (Aberdeen) Ltd, 12 Wellheads Crescent, Wellheads Industrial Estate, Aberdeen, AB21 7GA Tel: (01224) 775000 E-mail: admin@waverleypress.co.uk

Waverly Cutting Tools, 55 Abbotswell Road, Aberdeen, AB12 3AD Tel: (01224) 879714 Fax: (01224) 872385 *Carbide tooling suppliers*

▶ WaveZone Ltd, 834 Stockport Rd, Manchester, M19 3AW Tel: (0845) 1668443 Fax: 0161-257 3248 E-mail: info@wavezone.co.uk *Wireless networking, remote access, mobility solutions, web/email hosting/networking/Microsoft consultancy/broadband*

Wavin Ni Ltd, Rathdown Close, Lissue Industrial Estate, Lisburn, County Antrim, BT28 2RB Tel: (028) 9262 1577 Fax: (028) 9262 1969 E-mail: sales@wavin.ie *Plastic pipe & fittings distributors*

Wavin Plastics Ltd, Parsonage Way, Chippenham, Wiltshire, SN15 5PN Tel: (01249) 766600 Fax: (01249) 443286 E-mail: sales@wavin.co.uk *Plastic materials pipeline systems manufrs*

▶ Waxall Wood Finishes, Unit 1 Kilroot Park, Carrickfergus, County Antrim, BT38 7PR Tel: (028) 9336 5690 Fax: (028) 9336 5690 E-mail: enquiries@waxall.co.uk *All types of wooden finishing undertaken*

William Way (New Malden) Ltd, 74-76 Coombe Road, New Malden, Surrey, KT3 4QU Tel: (020) 8942 9498 Fax: (020) 8949 8712 *Builders' merchants*

▶ The Way2Lay Lay Betting Service, 16 Athol Street, Barrow-in-Furness, Cumbria, LA14 2QT Tel: (01229) 870079 E-mail: cleyden1@aol.com *The Way2Lay Lay Betting Service offering daily selections results and systems.All selections are proofed.A honest successful service.*

Wayahead Tackle Ltd, Off Back Market Street, Hindley, Wigan, Lancashire, WN2 3AD Tel: (01942) 525868 Fax: (01942) 525860 *Fishing tackle supplier*

▶ Waycon Precast Ltd, Western Wood Way, Plympton, Plymouth, PL7 5BQ Tel: (01752) 335777 Fax: (01752) 336777 *Foundation contractors*

Wayfarer Service Division, Workshop, 112 Gloucester Road, Croydon, CR0 2DE Tel: (020) 8404 1234 Fax: (020) 8689 9465 *Ticket machine manufrs*

Wayfarer Transit Systems Ltd, 10 Willis Way, Fleets Industrial Estate, Poole, Dorset, BH15 3SS Tel: (01202) 670671 Fax: (01202) 339369 E-mail: sales@wayfarer.co.uk *Bus ticket suppliers*

▶ Wayfinder UK Ltd, Rayhome House, Walshaw Road, Bury, Lancashire, BL8 1PY Tel: 0161-797 4490 E-mail: info@wayfinderconsulting.co.uk *Sign design consultancy*

Waygate Engineering Co Ltd, Stadium Place, Leicester, LE4 0JS Tel: 0116-235 2240 E-mail: rjbwaygate@aol.com *Plastics machining specialists*

▶ WayGoose, 45 Skylines Village, Limeharbour, London, E14 9TS Tel: (020) 7537 0700 Fax: (020) 7515 4545 E-mail: info@waygoose.com *Recruitment consultancy*

Waymatic Ltd, 15 Bridgewater Way, Windsor, Berkshire, SL4 1RD Tel: (01753) 869218 Fax: (01753) 830519 E-mail: waymatic@btconnect.com *Weighing & weigh cell systems, metal detector test pieces manufrs*

Waymouth Northumbria Ltd, 11 Ennerdale Road, Riverside Business Park, Blyth, Northumberland, NE24 4RT Tel: (01670) 545000 Fax: (01670) 545333 E-mail: enquiries@waymouth.co.uk *Precision engineers.*

Wayne Bassford, 12 Kepler, Lichfield Road Industrial Estate, Tamworth, Staffordshire, B79 7XE Tel: (01827) 55000 *Motor vehicle repairers*

▶ Wayne Dresser Ltd, Unit 15 Butlerfield Industrial Estate, Bonnyrigg, Midlothian, EH19 3JQ Tel: (01875) 822500

▶ Wayne Paulo Photo-Stock, 14 Neville Avenue, Thornton-Cleveleys, Lancashire, FY5 3BG Tel: (01253) 864598 E-mail: wayne@photo-stock.co.uk *Photographic*

continued

continuation
services and prints for sale and publication and the development of DVD"s learning photography "Get the Picture...series for sale

▶ Ways & Means, Findel House, Excelsior Road, Ashby-de-la-Zouch, Leicestershire, LE65 1NG Tel: (0845) 6060911 Fax: (01530) 419150

The Ways & Means Trust Ltd, 2 Paddock Road, Caversham, Reading, RG4 5BY Tel: 0118-948 1944 Fax: 0118-946 1176 E-mail: mail@waysandmeans.org.uk *Contract packers*

Wayside Engineering Services Limited, Rhosddigre, Llandegla, Wrexham, Clwyd, LL11 3AU Tel: (01978) 790269 Fax: (01978) 790478 E-mail: graham.dillon@btinternet.com *Wayside Engineering based in Wrexham established since 1980 contracting to the building and civil engineering trades. Our services include Fabrication and Welding in Mild, Stainless and Alloys. Mobile Welding is also available. Supply and fixing of Industrial Flooring, Access Ladders, Staircases, Balustrading and Handrailing systems. Fire Escapes, Spiral Staircases, Platforms, Small Structures, Supply of Structural Steels. Wrought Iron Work, Gates, Electric/ Automatic opening Gates, Balustrades, Security Services, Security Grills. Fencings, Railings, Bollards, Barriers, P2 Parapet Road Barriers, Predestrian Railings Finishings can be done in Powder Coating, Galvanising or Paint. We have expertise in numerous industries inclusing local councils, schools, MOD, water treatment plants, telecom, power stations and the railway industry with many more, please see our website for further examples of our work please contact mobile number 07977432351.*

Wayside Water Gardens, Doncaster Road, Oldcotes, Worksop, Nottinghamshire, S81 8HT Tel: (01909) 731367 Fax: (01909) 730511 E-mail: sales@waysidewatergardens.co.uk *Water garden specialists*

▶ Wayvik Ltd, South Road, Ellesmere Port, CH65 4LD Tel: 0151-355 5558 Fax: 0151-356 7022 E-mail: info@wayvik.com *Sales & refurbishment of new & used chemical process equipment*

Waywood Cabinet Makers, Butts Green, East End, Chadlington, Chipping Norton, Oxfordshire, OX7 3LT Tel: (01608) 676433 Fax: (01608) 676291 E-mail: sales@waywood.co.uk *Furniture manufrs*

Waywood Products, 27 Brownlow Business Centre, Ulster Street, Lurgan, Craigavon, County Armagh, BT67 9AN Tel: (028) 3834 8153 Fax: (028) 3834 8153 *Metal spinning & metal polishers*

Wayzgoose Holdings Ltd, Wayzgoose Ltd, East Road, Sleaford, Lincolnshire, NG34 7EH Tel: (01529) 304505 Fax: (01529) 307257 E-mail: enquiries@wayzgoose.co.uk *Commercial litho printers*

WB Hydraulic Services, 45 Boston Road, Leicester, LE4 1AW Tel: 0116-235 2606 E-mail: bill@wbhydserv.freeserve.co.uk *Hydraulic power pack systems manufrs*

▶ WB Mechanical Services Ltd, 34 Dursley Road, Blackheath, London, SE3 8PD Tel: (020) 8319 4457 E-mail: wbmsltd@aol.com *MECHANICAL SERVICES FOR PLUMBING AND HEATING,FROM REFERBISHMENTS TO FULL INSTALLATION INDUSTRIAL AND COMMERCIAL.FULLY TRAINED PLUMBERS AND FITTERS*

WB Office Equipment Ltd, 16 Mandervell Road, Oadby, Leicester, LE2 5LQ Tel: 0116-271 1033 Fax: 0116-271 1022 *Office equipment & furniture distributors*

WBM, 34-35 Whitburn Street, Bridgnorth, Shropshire, WV16 4QN Tel: (01746) 761358 Fax: (01746) 764163 E-mail: wbm.calibration@tiscali.co.uk *Calibration of measuring equipment*

WBR Design Ltd, 126 High Street West, Glossop, Derbyshire, SK13 8HJ Tel: (01457) 857664 Fax: (01457) 851580 E-mail: wbr@wbrdesign.com *Consulting engineers & designers*

Wci Pollution Control Ltd, Unit 1 Old Brewery Road, Wiveliscombe, Taunton, Somerset, TA4 2PW Tel: (01984) 623404 Fax: (01984) 624449 E-mail: wcipc@aol.com *Water & waste water treatment plant*

▶ WCL Ltd, 1 Oaks Drive, Newmarket, Suffolk, CB8 7SX Tel: (01638) 666006 Fax: (01638) 667245 E-mail: wcl.enquiries@uk.taylorwoodroe.com

WCR, 169 Irvine Road, Kilmarnock, Ayrshire, KA1 2LA Tel: (01563) 535962 Fax: (01563) 511337 *Cash register repairs & retailers*

▶ WCS, 70 Pendennis Park, Bristol, BS4 4JN Tel: (07966) 504290 E-mail: enq@wcsmaintenance.co.uk *Quality Assurance and workmanship are our pride.We provide all aspects of property maintenance, service and repair. From kitchens to bathrooms, roof replacement /repair, UPVC guttering, plastering,ceramic tiling, etc. etc.*

▶ WCW Media, Westbrook Road, Trafford Park, Manchester, M17 1AY Tel: (0870) 4608707 Fax: 0161-877 9090 E-mail: sales@wcwmedia.com *The Source of Quality Media. Blank Media - DVD,DVD-R, DVD+R, DVD RAM, CD, Optical, Ram and accessories. We also supply Epsom and Canon compatible Ink.*

Wd-40 Co. Ltd, PO Box 440, Milton Keynes, MK11 3LJ Tel: (01908) 555400 Fax: (01908) 266900 E-mail: sales@wd40.co.uk *Oil*

▶ Wdit Solutions Ltd, Unit 20 Bumpers Enterprise Centre, Vincients Road, Bumpers Farm, Chippenham, Wiltshire, SN14 6QA Tel: (01249) 709000 Fax: (01249) 467050 E-mail: sales@wdit.biz *IT solutions for small business*

WDS, Richardshaw Road, Grangefield Industrial Estate, Pudsey, West Yorkshire, LS28 6LE Tel: 0113-290 9852 Fax: (0845) 6011173 *General engineers* Also at: Shipley & Watford

▶ We Do Powder Coating Ltd, Unit B3 Troon Way Business Centre, Humberstone Lane, Leicester, LE4 9HA Tel: 0116-276 0061 *Powder coating services*

We 'R' Storage Ltd, Richmond Street, West Bromwich, West Midlands, B70 0DD Tel: 0121-520 3532 Fax: 0121-522 3862 E-mail: johnlee@werstorage.freeserve.co.uk *Storage, warehousing, archive & self access*

Weald Ltd, High Street, Buxted, Uckfield, East Sussex, TN22 4LA Tel: (01825) 732000 Fax: (01825) 732722 E-mail: tony@wealdpackaging.freeserve.co.uk *Packaging (specialist) suppliers*

Weald Polyproducts Ltd, Unit 1, Heron Bussiness Park, White Field Avenue, Sundon Park, Luton, LU3 3BB Tel: (01582) 508517 Fax: (01582) 570188 E-mail: sales.wheels@btconnect.com *Polystyrene packaging manufrs* Also at: Tonbridge

Weald Print Solutions Ltd, Unit 3, Daux Rd, Billingshurst, W. Sussex, RH14 9SJ Tel: (01403) 783176 Fax: (01403) 785461 E-mail: info@wealdprintsolutions.co.uk *General printers*

Weald Refrigeration, 5 Vestry Industrial Estate, Vestry Road, Sevenoaks, Kent, TN14 5EL Tel: (01732) 452050 Fax: (01732) 452122 E-mail: sales@wealdrefrigeration.com *Cooling cabinet manufrs*

▶ Wealden Engineering Services Ltd, The Coach House, Harts Green, Sedlescombe, Battle, East Sussex, TN33 0RS Tel: (01424) 870500 Fax: (0870) 4604089 E-mail: patrick@wealden-services.com *Exporters, Export Agents, Procurement Agents & global sourcing of OEM spare parts.*

Wealden Saddlery, Buckhurst Farm, Merriments Lane, Hurst Green, Etchingham, East Sussex, TN19 7RG Tel: (01580) 860860 Fax: (01580) 860860 E-mail: wealdensaddlery@btconnect.com *Specialists in the supply & fitting of new & secondhand riding saddles*

Wealdpark Ltd, Sutton Road, St. Helens, Merseyside, WA9 3DJ Tel: (01744) 22567 Fax: (01744) 451339 E-mail: sales@wealdpark.co.uk *Turned parts manufrs*

Wealth Management Software P.L.C., 45 Beech Street, London, EC2Y 8AD Tel: (020) 7614 4800 Fax: (020) 7614 4801 *Computer programming software*

Wealth Of Nations World-Wide Ltd, Crouches Farm, Furnace Lane, Horsmonden, Tonbridge, Kent, TN12 8LX Tel: (01892) 724724 Fax: (01892) 724726 E-mail: info@wealthofnations.co.uk *Womens fashion suppliers*

Wear Cote 1980 Ltd, Unit 32 Cambridge Yard, Cambridge Road, London, W7 3UP Tel: (020) 8567 1911 Fax: (020) 8579 9185 E-mail: wearcote@hotmail.com *Electroless (nickel) plating services*

Wear Dockyard Ltd, South Docks, Sunderland, SR1 2EE Tel: 0191-567 4749 Fax: 0191-510 0765 *Ship repairers, converters & marine engineers*

Wear Fine, School Street, Rochdale, Lancashire, OL12 0NY Tel: (01706) 650545 Fax: (01706) 359774 *Casual wear manufrs*

Wear Valley Aerosols Ltd, Unit 7b Hatfield Way, South Church Enterprise Park, Bishop Auckland, County Durham, DL14 6XF Tel: (01388) 772250 Fax: (01388) 772263 E-mail: sales@gpaerosols.co.uk *Aerosol contract filler specialising in bag-on-valve aerosols*

Weardale Joinery, Queensbury, Sedling Plain, Wearhead, Bishop Auckland, County Durham, DL13 1PW Tel: 01388 537434 *Joinery manufacturers*

Weardale Steel (Wolsingham) Ltd, Durham Road, Wolsingham, Bishop Auckland, County Durham, DL13 3HX Tel: (01388) 527201 Fax: (01388) 527838 E-mail: les.graham@weardalecastings.co.uk *Steel & iron foundry engineers*

Weare Peter 1984 Ltd, 112-116 Hazelwick Road, Crawley, West Sussex, RH10 1NH Tel: (01293) 525673 Fax: (01293) 614054 *Lock fitting & installation specialist services & security systems distributors*

Wearhouse Ltd, 32 North Street, Taunton, Somerset, TA1 1LW Tel: (01823) 333291 Fax: (01823) 334699 *Outdoor camping equipment*

Wearnes Cambion Ltd, Mill Bridge, Castleton, Hope Valley, Derbyshire, S33 8WR Tel: (01433) 621555 Fax: (01433) 621290 E-mail: sales@cambion.com *Electronic component designers & manufrs*

Wearparts UK Ltd, Oaks Industrial Estate, Gilmorton Road, Lutterworth, Leicestershire, LE17 4HA Tel: (01455) 553551 Fax: (01455) 550907 E-mail: sales@wearparts.com *Impact, wear & heat resisting component producers*

Wearside Electronics, 32 Wilson Street North, Sheepfolds Industrial Estate, Sunderland, SR5 1BB Tel: 0191-514 4199 Fax: 0191-514 1324 E-mail: jimjohnson@edward-thompson.com *Bingo machine manufacturers/concessionaires*

Wearwell Group Ltd, Gargarin, Lichfield Road, Tamworth, Staffordshire, B79 7TR Tel: (01827) 310553 Fax: (01827) 66139 E-mail: sales@wearwell.co.uk *Protective clothing manufrs*

▶ Weast, 297 Osier CR, London, N10 1RD Tel: (020) 8815 9988 Fax: (0870) 1330866 E-mail: sales@weast.co.uk *Computer hardware suppliers*

Weather Call, Avalon House, 57-63 Scrutton Street, London, EC2A 4PJ Tel: (020) 7613 6000 Fax: (020) 7613 5005 E-mail: weathercall@itouch.co.uk *IT consultants*

▶ Weatherbreak, Unit 27 Scott Road Industrial Estate, Luton, LU3 3BF Tel: (01582) 585500 Fax: (01582) 580994 E-mail: info@weatherbreak.co.uk *Double glazing suppliers, conservatories, doors, windows*

Weathercare Blinds, 33a Stevenson Road, Ipswich, IP1 2EY Tel: (01473) 221803 Fax: (01473) 280940 *Blinds manufrs*

Weatherford, Crawpeel Road, Altens Industrial Estate, Aberdeen, AB12 3LG Tel: (01224) 380280 Fax: (01224) 380088 *Oil & gas exploration services* Also at: Aberdeen & Great Yarmouth

▶ Weatherford Manufacturing, Unit 1b-2b Blackness Industrial Centre, Blackness Road, Altens Industrial Estate, Aberdeen, AB12 3LH Tel: (01224) 380110 Fax: (01224) 380060 E-mail: sales@weatherford.co.uk *Tool rentals*

▶ Weatherford UK, Aberdeen Science & Energy Park, Claymore Drive, Bridge of Don, Aberdeen, AB23 8GD Tel: (01224) 423423 Fax: (01224) 423200 *Metalwork*

Weatherford (UK), Gapton Hall Road, Gapton Hall Industrial Estate, Great Yarmouth, Norfolk, NR31 0NL Tel: (01493) 441155 Fax: (01493) 657403 E-mail: bdk@eu.wetherford.com *Precision engineers*

▶ Weatherford UK Ltd, 76-78 Charlotte Street, London, Greater London, W1T 4QW Tel: 020 74624930

▶ Weatherguard Systems, Cardenden, Lochgelly, Fife, KY5 0AU Tel: (01592) 782828

Mark Weatherhead Ltd, Helions Road, Steeple Bumpstead, Haverhill, Suffolk, CB9 7DU Tel: (01440) 730377 Fax: (01440) 730777 *Agricultural engineers services*

Mark Weatherhead Ltd, Garden Walk, Royston, Hertfordshire, SG8 7HT Tel: (01763) 242361 Fax: (01763) 245106 *Agricultural engineering services* Also at: Hardwick

Weatherite Electrical Ltd, Weatherite House, Westgate Park, Tintagel Way, Aldridge, Walsall, WS9 8EX Tel: (01922) 741600 Fax: (01922) 741601 E-mail: sales@weatherite-electrical.com *Control panel manufacturing & electrical installers*

▶ Weatherseal Holdings Ltd, 8 Darrows Industrial Estate, John Brannan Way, Bellshill, Lanarkshire, ML4 3HD Tel: (01698) 845468 Fax: (01698) 844807

▶ Weatherseal Holdings Ltd, New Business Park, Newhouse Road, Grangemouth, Stirlingshire, FK3 8LL Tel: (01324) 666934 Fax: (01324) 666204

Weathershield Ltd, 82 Curries Close, Canley, Coventry, CV4 8AW Tel: (024) 7647 4447 Fax: (024) 7646 1977 *Double glazed windows manufrs*

▶ Weatherstrong Timber Framed Buildings, Henfield Road, Cowfold, Horsham, West Sussex, RH13 8DU Tel: (01403) 865666 E-mail: andrwpar9@aol.com *Manufacturer of Timber buildings such as Sheds Summerhouses Workshops Garages and Home offices*

Weatherwise Canopies & Covers, Thorpe Lane, Banbury, Oxfordshire, OX16 4UT Tel: (01295) 253097 Fax: (01295) 253097 E-mail: weatherwise@fsbdial.co.uk *Fork lift truck canopy manufrs*

Weavabel Labels & Tags, 3 Focus Business Park, Focus Way, Yeadon, Leeds, LS19 7DB Tel: 0113-239 1122 Fax: 0113-250 6848 *Labeling of fabrics*

Weaver plc, 86-92 Worcester Road, Bromsgrove, Worcestershire, B61 7AQ Tel: (01527) 575588 Fax: (01527) 575258 E-mail: info@weaver.plc.uk *Construction group & main contractor*

Weaver Demolition Ltd, Farrington Fields, Farrington Gurney, Bristol, BS39 6UU Tel: (01761) 452391 Fax: (01761) 453644 E-mail: mike@weaverdemolition.com *Demolition contractors*

Weaver Mabbs Engineering Ltd, 31a North Street, Emsworth, Hampshire, PO10 7DA Tel: (01243) 371416 Fax: (01243) 376343 E-mail: sales@weavermabbs.co.uk *Sub-contract machining services*

Mike Weaver Communications Ltd, Unit 6 Fullwood Close, Aldermans Green Industrial Estate, Coventry, CV2 2SS Tel: (024) 7660 2605 Fax: (024) 7660 2609 *Communications two way radio systems retail & hire service*

R.V. Weaver, Rectory Road, Grays, Essex, RM17 6BD Tel: (01375) 390820 Fax: (01375) 393333 *Refuse chute manufrs*

Weavo Fencing Products Ltd, Station Works, Hatch Beauchamp, Taunton, Somerset, TA3 6SH Tel: (01823) 480571 Fax: (01823) 480175 E-mail: sales@weavo.co.uk *Fencing manufrs*

▶ Web Age Ltd, The Walled Garden, Sundrum, Ayr, KA6 5LA Tel: (01292) 571460 Fax: (01292) 571470 *Internet services*

▶ Web Alive (UK) Ltd, 25 Chalk Farm Road, London, NW1 8AG Tel: (0871) 4346400 Fax: (0871) 4346401 E-mail: fraser.henderson@webalive.co.uk *Software for self build websites*

Web Applications, Hollinwood Business Centre, Albert Street, Oldham, OL8 3QL Tel: 0161-682 6565 Fax: 0161-682 6969 E-mail: kamal@webappuk.com *Application provider for the travel industry*

▶ Web Construction Ltd, Bishops Court Gardens, Bishops Court Lane, Clyst St. Mary, Exeter, EX5 1DH Tel: (01392) 872100 Fax: (01392) 872101

▶ Web Design - Edinburgh UK, Mclelland House, 33 East London Street, Edinburgh, EH7 4BN Tel: (0870) 7606313 Fax: (0871) 4330373 E-mail: enquires@the3gcompany.co.uk *Website designers*

Web Fabrications Ltd, Gledholt Business Park, Allen Row, Paddock, Huddersfield, HD1 4SB Tel: (01484) 545333 Fax: (01484) 422194 *Acoustic engineers & general fabricators services*

▶ Web Warehouse Ltd, Unit 12, Strathclyde Business Centre, 416 Hamilton Road, Cambuslang, Glasgow, G72 7XR Tel: (0845) 1260325 E-mail: info@web-warehouse.net *Website services*

▶ Webaddons, Ardlyn, Linton Bank Drive, West Linton, Peeblesshire, EH46 7DT Tel: (07817) 156829

Webasto Roof Systems Ltd, Unit 7 Kingsbury Business Park, Kingsbury Road, Sutton Coldfield, West Midlands, B76 9DL Tel: 0121-313 5600 Fax: 0121-351 4905 E-mail: customer.service@webasto.co.uk *Powder coating services. Webasto Metal Finishing, formerly known as T W Coatings, has built up a formidable reputation for delivering the highest quality metal finishing. The speed of the operation, the committed customer service, the accurate delivery, the value for money and the*

continued

excellent end product are the ingredient of a service that's hard to beat.

Allan H. Webb & Co. Ltd, Colne Lodge, Longbridge Way, Uxbridge, Middlesex, UB8 2YG Tel: (01895) 239387 Fax: (01895) 234429 E-mail: enquiries@ahw-ux.co.uk *Technical publications service* Also at: Stonehouse

Webb Display Services Ltd, Canalside Harris Business Park, Hanbury Road, Stoke Prior, Bromsgrove, Worcestershire, B60 4DJ Tel: (01527) 837306 Fax: (01527) 575230 E-mail: graphics@webbdisplay.co.uk *Exhibition, graphic & display contractors*

Webb Elec Ltd, 27 Owen Road Industrial Estate, Willenhall, West Midlands, WV13 2PY Tel: 0121-526 5070 Fax: 0121-568 7208 E-mail: sales@webb-elec.co.uk *Electric motor repairs & rebuilders*

Webb Engineering Worcester Ltd, Unit 11f Shrub Hill, Worcester, WR4 9EL Tel: (01905) 29775 Fax: (01905) 726324 *Sub-contract engineers*

G. Webb Haulage Ltd, Station Road, Longstanton, Cambridge, CB4 5DS Tel: (01954) 260691 Fax: (01954) 261211 E-mail: sales@gwebb.uk.com *Bulk road haulage contractors services* Also at: Ipswich

Gerry Webb Transport Services Ltd, 4 Shelson Parade, Ashford Road, Feltham, Middlesex, TW13 4QZ Tel: (020) 8867 0000 Fax: (020) 8867 0088 E-mail: gerrywebbtpt@talk21.com *Road transport, haulage, freight service providers*

Webb Hydraulic Equipment, Acton Place Industrial Estate, Acton, Sudbury, Suffolk, CO10 0BB Tel: (01787) 312563 Fax: (01787) 880618 E-mail: info@extrareach.co.uk *Hydraulic service & supply specialists*

I.S.G. Webb Ltd, Unit 2 Progress Estate, Bircholt Road, Maidstone, Kent, ME15 9YH Tel: (01622) 670281 Fax: (01622) 683528 E-mail: project.office@isgwebb.com *Cabling system manufrs* Also at: Birmingham, London & Manchester

▶ J Webb Plant Hire, 14 Cripps Avenue, Peacehaven, East Sussex, BN10 8AL Tel: (01273) 582459 Fax: (01273) 587080 E-mail: info@jwebbplanthire.co.uk *Operated & self drive excavators, low loaders & crane lorries suppliers*

A.P. Webb Plant Hire, Tilcon Avenue, Stafford, ST18 0YJ Tel: (01785) 241335 Fax: (01785) 255178 *Contractors' plant hire*

Todd Webb & Co. Ltd, Unit 5 Ryehill Close, Lodge Farm Industrial Estate, Northampton, NN5 7UA Tel: (01604) 581430 Fax: (01604) 586081 E-mail: toddwebb@tiscali.co.uk *Uniforms, staff wear & promotional gifts distributors & manufrs*

Webb Truck Equipment, Acton Place, Melford Road, Acton, Sudbury, Suffolk, CO10 0BB Tel: (01787) 377368 Fax: (01787) 880618 E-mail: sales@web-extrareach.co.uk *Commercial vehicle body/skip manufrs*

Webb & Wells Ltd, 9 Chilford Court, Rayne Road, Braintree, Essex, CM7 2QS Tel: (01376) 550044 Fax: (01376) 550022 E-mail: sales@webbwells.co.uk *Electronic cable manufrs*

Webber & Harrison, Unit 270 Ricardo Way, Lymington, Hampshire, SO41 8JU Tel: (01590) 689009 Fax: (01590) 689006 E-mail: allanwebber@btconnect.com *Reproduction furniture manufrs*

Webber Office Solutions Inc Blare It Out Biographi, 117 Marsh Road, Rhyl, Clwyd, LL18 2AB Tel: (01745) 337066 Fax: (01745) 337072 E-mail: sales@officerus.com *Contract office furniture suppliers*

Webbro Ltd, Whinfield Drive, Aycliffe Industrial Estate, Aycliffe Industrial Park, Newton Aycliffe, County Durham, DL5 6AU Tel: (01325) 313781 Fax: (01325) 300762 *Precision engineers & toolmakers*

Webbs Power Tools Ltd, 146 Boldmere Road, Sutton Coldfield, West Midlands, B73 5UD Tel: 0121-355 3939 Fax: 0121-355 4747 E-mail: sales@webbs-site.co.uk *Tool hire*

Webbs Spare Parts, 127-129 High Street, Stevenage, Hertfordshire, SG1 3HS Tel: (01438) 312669 Fax: (01438) 729867 E-mail: web21.stevenage@autonetplus.co.uk *Motor spares suppliers*

Webbs Woodwork Ltd, 1 Queens Passage, Chislehurst, Kent, BR7 5AP Tel: (020) 8467 7900 Fax: (020) 8467 7900 *Furniture retailers*

▶ WebCad, The Barn, HodgeHill Farm, Blakedown, Kidderminster, Worcestershire, DY10 3NR Tel: 01562 515318 Fax: 0709 2394102 E-mail: sales@webcad2005.co.uk *Cad Drafting , Cad Conversion , Printing , Scanning , Printing , Operating and Maintenance Manuals pdf*

Webcom Puters, 22 Station Road, Teignmouth, Devon, TQ14 8PE Tel: (01626) 779636 Fax: (01626) 779636 *Computer maintenance & repairs*

▶ Webcredible Ltd, 99 Mansell Street, London, E1 8AX Tel: (020) 7423 6320 Fax: 0207 481 2569 E-mail: info@webcredible.co.uk *Internet services*

▶ Webease, The Old Fountain, 12 Dennis Green, Gamlingay, Sandy, Bedfordshire, SG19 3LQ Tel: (01767) 650730 E-mail: ricsale@webeaseuk.co.uk *Search engine promotion provider*

Weber Automatic Assembly Systems Ltd, 3 Landscape Close, Weston Business Park, Weston-On-The-Green, Oxfordshire, OX25 3SX Tel: (01869) 343688 Fax: (01869) 343699 E-mail: sales@weberautomation.com *Riveting & automated screwdriving machines manufrs*

Weber S B D, Old Paper Mill, Ballyclare, Co. Antrim, BT39 9EB Tel: (028) 9335 2999 Fax: (028) 9332 3232 *External insulation manufrs*

Weber Shandwick, 58 Queens Road, Aberdeen, AB15 4YE Tel: (01224) 806600 Fax: (01224) 208823 E-mail: jrmacdonald@webershandwick.com *Public relations consultants*

Webex Sports Ltd, 5 Parade, Exmouth, Devon, EX8 1RS Tel: (01395) 260000 Fax: (01395) 260111 *Sports equipment manufrs & distributors*

Webfresh Design, 40 Castlegate Drive, Bradford, West Yorkshire, BD10 8BW Tel: 0845 8382527 E-mail: info@webfreshdesign.co.uk *Bradford based Webfresh Design specialises in CSS Web Design, Web Optimisation and E-commerce to help businesses throughout Leeds, Bradford, Harrogate, Huddersfield and the rest of the UK succeed online.*

ebgibb Welding & Fabrications, Unit 11 Bluebird Industrial Estate, Park Lane, Wolverhampton, WV10 9QQ Tel: (01902) 722040 Fax: (01902) 722040 E-mail: shane@webgibb.u-net.com *Fabrication welding steel construction*

ebheads Interactive - London Website Design Agency, The Stables, Old Park Ride, Theobolds Park, Waltham Cross, Hertfordshire, EN7 5HY Tel: (020) 7287 7060 E-mail: info@webheads.co.uk *Web design agency*

Webkit, 4 Thomas Street, St. Pauls, Bristol, BS2 9LL Tel: (0870) 7606932 E-mail: andy@wk1.net *Design and construct internet based databases. Experts in secure and user friendly feature rich data stores, applied across a range of industries. We can develop individual solutions to specific problems and consult clients where necessary. Also developed resource sharing applications for clients with multiple sites and customers.*

'ebley & Scott Ltd, Frankly Industrial Park, Tay Road, Rednal Rubery, Birmingham, B45 0PA Tel: (0121) 453 1864 Fax: (0121) 457 7846 E-mail: guns@webley.co.uk *Air gun manufacturers & sporting goods importers*

Weblight Lighting Contractors, 5 Central City Industrial Estate, Red Lane, Coventry, CV6 5RY Tel: (024) 7668 6620 Fax: (024) 7668 6080

/eblight Lighting Contractors, Unit 14 Park Court, Sullivans Way, St. Helens, Merseyside, WA9 5GZ Tel: (01744) 455711 Fax: (01744) 455710 E-mail: sales@weblight.co.uk *Electrical maintenance & lighting restoration services*

▶ Webmart Scotland, 16 Naughton Road, Wormit, Newport-on-Tay, Fife, DD6 8PE Tel: (01382) 542777 Fax: (01382) 542777

/ebmaster Ltd, Units 5-6 Astra Industrial Centre, Royle Barn Road, Rochdale, Lancashire, OL11 3DT Tel: (01706) 656122 Fax: (01706) 764400 E-mail: sales@webmasterltd.co.uk *Label stock manufrs*

▶ Webnet Ltd, 41 Tintern Avenue, Tyldesley, Manchester, M29 7WL Tel: (01942) 516162 Fax: (01942) 730484 E-mail: sales@yourhomedirect.co.uk *Fire & smoke detectors suppliers*

Webnet Systems, 141 Church Street, Malvern, Worcestershire, WR14 2AN Tel: (01684) 574990 Fax: (01684) 574412 *Computer services*

Vebron Marling Ltd, Hareholme Mill, Bacup Road, Rawtenstall, Rossendale, Lancashire, BB4 7JL Tel: (01706) 214001 Fax: (01706) 830003 E-mail: sales@andrewwebron.com *Cloth & fabric filters, filter bags, needle felt mechanical felt manufrs*

Vebs Ltd, Ashborne House Waterperry Court, Middleton Road, Banbury, Oxfordshire, OX16 4QG Tel: (01295) 277272 Fax: (01295) 264070 E-mail: enquiries@websint.com Principal Export Areas: Central/East Europe, West Europe, North America, Central America & South America *Environmental consultants*

▶ Webs Solution Ltd, Parkgate House, Park Gate, Bradford, West Yorkshire, BD1 5BS Tel: (0797) 7105629 Fax: (01274) 822096 E-mail: sales@webssolution.com *Web site designing, ecommerce, database, content management or flash services*

Webscribe Ltd, PO Box 464, Berkhamsted, Hertfordshire, HP4 2UR Tel: (01442) 876000 Fax: (01442) 872279 E-mail: jenny@webscribe.co.uk *Direct marketing computer services*

Web-Services.Com, Forge Farm, Cropedy, Banbury, Oxfordshire, OX17 1QF Tel: (01295) 758474 Fax: (01295) 758474 *Computer consultants*

Websight Solutions, 254 Kingsley Avenue, Kettering, Northamptonshire, NN16 9EZ Tel: (01536) 518587 Fax: (0870) 1224871 E-mail: sales@websight-solutions.com *Website design, online systems, data driven systems, e-commerce solutions, domain registration, hosting, email services, multimedia solutions, online marketing*

▶ Website Northern Ireland, 156 Keady Road, Armagh, BT60 3AE Tel: (07719) 546222 E-mail: dconlon@websiteni.com *Website Design and Development*

▶ The WebsiteGirl, Chester House, Chester Road, gillingham, Kent, ME7 4AF Tel: 01634 322819 E-mail: info@thewebsitegirl.co.uk *Providing ecommerce solutions, website design, flash animation.*We build online stores using the highly acclaimed Actinic software.*

▶ Websitepro, Balmoral House, Rochdale, Lancashire, OL16 3EL Tel: (01706) 524572 E-mail: info@websitepro.co.uk *Website design, e-commerce & database solutions*

▶ Websites For You, 38 Howard Road, Portsmouth, PO2 9PS Tel: (023) 9271 0311 Fax: (023) 9271 0311 E-mail: trevor@websitesforyou.co.uk *Website Design, Hosting Packages, Domain Search*

▶ Websitescostuless, PO Box 14592, Kinross, KY13 8YE Tel: (07709) 366206 *Websites from only £59.99 including 12 months domain name and hosting. Visit our website now and see how great we are. You'll be happy you did!*

Webster Bros, Walworth Enterprise Centre, Duke Close West Way, Andover, Hampshire, SP10 5AR Tel: (01264) 323842 Fax: (01264) 323842 *Shirt & collar manufrs*

▶ Webster Contracts Ltd, Kingsmuir, Forfar, Angus, DD8 2NS Tel: (01307) 466161

▶ David Webster Ltd, Field House, Station Approach, Harlow, Essex, CM20 2FB Tel: (01279) 645100 Fax: (01279) 645101 E-mail: info@dwltd.co.uk *Lighting installation*

Webster Drives Ltd, Folds Road, Bolton, BL1 2SE Tel: (01204) 382121 Fax: (01204) 386100 *Power take-off unit manufrs*

Webster & Horsfall Ltd, Fordrough, Birmingham, B25 8DW Tel: 0121-772 2555 Fax: 0121-772 0762 E-mail: sales@websterandhorsfall.co.uk *Manufacturers of galvanised wire, stainless steel wire, wire (fine), wire (oil tempered) & wire (steel). Also wire straightening/cutting services*

▶ Webster Richard & Co., 30 Leigh Road, Eastleigh, Hampshire, SO50 9DT Tel: (023) 8032 2312 Fax: (023) 8061 1698 E-mail: mail@rwco.co.uk *Conveyance solicitors*

W.K. Webster & Co. Ltd, 10 Fen Church Avenue, London, EC3M 5BN Tel: (020) 8300 7744 Fax: (020) 8309 1266 E-mail: info@wkwebster.com *Marine insurance settlement agents*

William Webster, 107 Buchanan Street, Glasgow, G1 3HF Tel: 0141-248 5469 *Engravers, jewellery manufrs*

▶ Websters Ltd, 40 Crossdene Road, Crosshouse, Kilmarnock, Ayrshire, KA2 0JU Tel: (01563) 534540 Fax: (0845) 1232561

Websters Burn Ltd, Whitings Lane, Burn, Selby, North Yorkshire, YO8 8LG Tel: (01757) 270233 Fax: (01757) 270459 *Timber merchants & joinery manufrs*

Websters Hemming & Sons Ltd, 274 Stoney Stanton Road, Coventry, CV6 5DJ Tel: (024) 7668 8300 Fax: (024) 7663 7671 *Brick manufrs*

Websters Insulation Ltd, Crowtree Farm, Crowtree Bank, Thorne Levels, Doncaster, South Yorkshire, DN8 5TF Tel: (01405) 812682 Fax: (01405) 817201 E-mail: info@webstersinsulation.com *Polyurethane spray foam insulation contractors*

Webster-Wilkinson Ltd, Unit A, Halesfield 10, Telford, Shropshire, TF7 4QP Tel: (01952) 585701 Fax: (01952) 581901 E-mail: sales@webster-wilkinson.com *Ceramic insulator manufr*

▶ WebsynergiDesign, Suite 23, 57 Frederick Street, Birmingham, B1 3HS Tel: 0121 2706505 E-mail: info@websynergidesign.co.uk *Web design agency, logo design, marketing*

Webtec Products Ltd, Nuffield Road, St. Ives, Cambridgeshire, PE27 3LZ Tel: (01480) 397444 Fax: (01480) 466555 E-mail: sales@webtec.co.uk *Hydraulic test equipment manufrs*

▶ Webtones, 17 Main Street, Saxelby, Melton Mowbray, Leicestershire, LE14 3PQ Tel: (0845) 6443089 Fax: (0870) 7625228 *Webtones Ltd provides cutting edge web design solutions to business across the UK, please view our website to view examples of our work*

Wecando Flooring Specialists Lincoln Ltd, Lincoln Road, Nettleham, Lincoln, LN2 2NE Tel: (01522) 595770 Fax: (01522) 595887 E-mail: wecandoflg@aol.com *Flooring contractors*

Weco Engineering Ltd, Griston Road, Watton, Thetford, Norfolk, IP25 6DL Tel: (01953) 881142 Fax: (01953) 882795 *Steel fabricators*

Wedberry Safe Co. Ltd, Premier House, Tennyson Drive, Pitsea, Basildon, Essex, SS13 3BT Tel: (01268) 556724 Fax: (01268) 558755 *Safe installation contractors*

▶ Duncan Weddell Web Services, Duncanlaw, Gifford, Haddington, East Lothian, EH41 4PQ Tel: (01620) 810343 E-mail: info@duncanweddell.co.uk *Website design, promotion and hosting for rural business.*

Wedderspoon Processes Ltd, Eassie Station, Eassie, Forfar, Angus, DD8 1SG Tel: (01307) 840396 Fax: (01307) 840404 *Agricultural engineering services*

▶ Wedding & Party Magicians & Entertainers, 1 Wakeford Cottages, Selden Lane, Worthing, West Sussex, BN11 2LQ Tel: 01903 211785 E-mail: weddingmagicians@btinternet.com *Entertainment agency*

▶ Weddings Abroad, 15 High Street, Chasetown, Burntwood, Staffordshire, WS7 3XE Tel: (01543) 686884 Fax: 01543 686884 E-mail: helen@perfect-weddings.net *We specialise in arranging weddings abroad and offer professional help and advise on every aspect of your overseas wedding. *We also offer a tailor-made honeymoon service, offering some of the most romantic locations worldwide.*

▶ Weddings Direct, 23 Compton Rise, Withington, Cheltenham, Gloucestershire, GL54 4DB Tel: (01242) 890430 E-mail: sales@weddings-direct.co.uk *UK wedding directory, listing local suppliers*

Wedge Chemicals Ltd, 34 Selsdon Road, South Croydon, Surrey, CR2 6PB Tel: (020) 8680 6960 Fax: (020) 8688 4053 E-mail: sales@wedgechemicals.co.uk *Industrial chemical distribution*

Wedge Engineering Ltd, 16 Darlington Close, Sandy, Bedfordshire, SG19 1RW Tel: (01767) 683527 Fax: (01767) 683529 E-mail: wedgeeng@btconnect.com *Sheet metal fabricators*

Wedge Group Galvanising Ltd, 359 Canal Road, Bradford, West Yorkshire, BD2 1AN Tel: (01274) 221555 Fax: (01274) 221566 *Corrosion protection* Also at: Bradford, Glasgow, Liverpool, Newport, Peterborough, Saffron Walden & Worksop

Wedge Roofing Centres, Belfont Trading Estate, Mucklow Hill, Halesowen, West Midlands, B62 8DR Tel: 0121-550 2729 Fax: 0121-585 5258 *Roofing material distributors*

Wedge Roofing Centres Ltd, Unit 16, Salamons Way, Rainham, Essex, RM13 9UL Tel: (01708) 555213 Fax: (01708) 550255 *Roofing material suppliers*

▶ Wedgewood Homes, Tower Industrial Estate, London Road, Wrotham, Sevenoaks, Kent, TN15 7NS Tel: (01732) 824744 Fax: (01732) 824745

Wedgwood A V Ltd, 16 Glentworth Road, Skegness, Lincolnshire, PE25 2TG Tel: (01754) 769967 Fax: (01754) 768036 E-mail: generalmanager@wedgwood-group.com *Audio visual equipment computers & internet*

Wednesbury Fabrications, 1 Upper Chapel Street, Tividale, Oldbury, West Midlands, B69 2PG Tel: 0121-557 5171 Fax: 0121-557 7003 *Sheet metalwork engineers & general fabrications*

Wednesbury Precision Tool Ltd, 7 Conduit Road, Norton Canes, Cannock, Staffordshire, WS11 9TJ Tel: (01543) 274901 Fax: (01543) 277557 *Press toolmakers manufrs*

Wednesfield Refrigeration Services Ltd, 262 Penn Road, Wolverhampton, WV4 4AD Tel: (01902) 345111 Fax: (01902) 620346 E-mail: sales@wednesfieldrefrigeration.co.uk *Refrigeration service, maintenance, commercial & sales*

Wednesfield Shotblasting Ltd, Planetary Road, Willenhall, West Midlands, WV13 3SW Tel: 01902 731781 *Shot blasting & heat treatment services*

▶ Wee Badgers Badges, PO Box 3821, Glasgow, G46 6JY Tel: 0141-649 1207 Fax: 0141-649 1207 E-mail: info@weebadgers.com *Promotional products manufrs*

WEEE Labels.com, Unit 4, City Estate,, Corngreaves Road, Cradley Heath, West Midlands, B64 7EP Tel: 0870 7773645 Fax: 0870 7773644 E-mail: sales@weeelabels.com *A division of Customark Identification we are a one stop shop for all your label needs in complying with new Waste Electrical and Electronic Equipment (WEEE) Legislation. Manufacturing a selection of cost effective standard off-the-shelf WEEE Label products and bespoke designs that will last the life cycle of your electronic equipment / products.**Situated in the heart of the Black Country Customark sell a range of WEEE labels at standard sizes but can also design and make to your own requirements. This can be from intergrating the WEEE logo onto your existing label design to selling you plain labels, thermal printers and ribbons so that you can print your own onsite*

Weeks Computing Services, 6 Langley Street, London, WC2H 9JA Tel: (020) 7379 3548 Fax: (020) 7240 8870 E-mail: office@weekscomputing.com *Market research data processing bureau*

Weeks Restoration & Conservation, 7 Hurst Road, Eastbourne, East Sussex, BN21 2PJ Tel: (01323) 439899

Weetabix Ltd, Factory 1, Earlstree Industrial Estate, Earlstree Road, Corby, Northamptonshire, NN17 4AZ Tel: (01536) 722181 Fax: (01536) 401532 *Breakfast cereal manufrs*

Weetabix Food Co Ltd, Weetabix Mills, Burton Latimer, Kettering, Northamptonshire, NN15 5JR Tel: (01536) 722181 Fax: (01536) 725361 E-mail: foodservice@weetabix.com *Nestled deep in the heart of the English countryside, The Weetabix Food Company has been creating delicious breakfast cereals since 1932, using only the finest ingredients. Their main home is a 75 acre site in Kettering, Northamptonshire, from where they produce their famous range of popular cereals, including Weetabix, Alpen, Weetaflakes, Ready Brek, Weetabix Minis and Weetos.*

▶ Wefco (Gainsborough) Ltd, Brittania Works, Spring Gardens, Gainsborough, Lincolnshire, DN21 2AZ Tel: (01427) 611000 Fax: (01427) 612000 E-mail: glennb@wefco.net Principal Export Areas: Central/East Europe & West Europe *LPG containers, pressure vessels & oil storage tank manufrs*

Weg Electric Motors UK Ltd, Unit 28 29, Walkers Road, Moons Moat North Industrial Estate, Redditch, Worcestershire, B98 9HE Tel: (01527) 596748 Fax: (01527) 591133 E-mail: wegsales@wegelectricmotors.co.uk Principal Export Areas: Worldwide *WEG is a global supplier of LV MV & HV electric motors, in capacities up to 20MW, & also complete turnkey solutions including motors, drives, PLCs, switchgear, transformers & software*

Wegener Sefton, G 7 Unit Liver Industrial Estate, Long Lane, Walton, Liverpool, L9 7ES Tel: 0151-521 7070 Fax: 0151-525 2458 E-mail: howardpaul@btconnect.com *Polythene bags & plastics envelopes manufrs*

Weh (UK) Ltd, 2 Batemans Lane, Wythall, Birmingham, B47 6NG Tel: (01564) 825100 Fax: (01564) 825105 E-mail: instatest@lineone.net *Pressure test equipment manufrs*

Weigh Control Systems Ltd, 2 Felton Mill, Felton, Morpeth, Northumberland, NE65 9HL Tel: (01670) 787177 Fax: (01670) 787179 *Industrial weighing system suppliers*

Weighfab Ltd, Unit 3, 35 Catley Rd, Sheffield, S9 5JF Tel: 0114-261 1132 Fax: 0114-261 1132 *Weighbridge manufrs*

Weighing Technology Services Ltd, 4 Selbury Drive, Oadby Indust Estate, Oadby, Leicester, LE2 5NG Tel: 0116-271 3228 Fax: 0116-271 3229 E-mail: enquires@wts-ltd.co.uk *Weighing machine sales, refurbishment, service & repair*

Weighload Systems Ltd, Watling Street Works, Watling St, Brownhills, Walsall, WS8 7JT Tel: (01543) 453494 Fax: (01543) 453167 Purchasing Contact: H. Degville Sales Contact: G. Price Principal Export Areas: Worldwide *Crane safety/overload protection systems manufrs*

Weighsafe, Meadow Croft, Denaby Lane, Old Denaby, Doncaster, S. Yorkshire, DN12 4JX Tel: (01709) 584752 Fax: (01709) 571197 *Crane repairs*

Weightlifter Bodies Ltd, Grange Lane North, Scunthorpe, South Humberside, DN16 1BN Tel: (01724) 872444 Fax: (01724) 853647 *Commercial vehicle body/trailer builders*

Weightron (U K) Ltd, Weightron House, Brimington Road North, Chesterfield, Derbyshire, S41 9AN Tel: (01246) 260062 Fax: (01246) 260844 E-mail: info@weightroncb.co.uk *Electronic & mechanical scale manufrs*

Weighwell Engineering, 23 Orgreave Place, Sheffield, S13 9LU Tel: 0114-269 9955 Fax: 0114-269 9256 E-mail: sales@weighwell.co.uk *Industrial weighing systems & weighbridge for railways manufrs*

Weighwright Weighing Equipment, 55a Putnoe Lane, Bedford, MK41 9AE Tel: (01234) 313883 Fax: (01234) 313883 E-mail: info@scalemart.co.uk *Weighing equipment*

Weil Bros & Stern Raw Cotton, 5 Abbots Quay, Monks Ferry, Birkenhead, Merseyside, CH41 5LH Tel: 0151-650 1000 Fax: 0151-650 0655 E-mail: cotton@weilstern.com *Cotton merchants*

Weilburger Schramm Coatings UK Ltd, Stuart Road, Manor Park, Runcorn, Cheshire, WA7 1SF Tel: (01928) 570900 Fax: (01928) 579235 *Industrial paint manufrs*

Weiler Beehive Europe Ltd, Unit 60 Beeches Industrial Estate, Waverley Road, Yate, Bristol, BS37 5QR Tel: (01454) 320900 Fax: (01454) 326262 E-mail: sales@weilerinc.co.uk *Food processing machinery suppliers*

Weiler-Knight (UK) Ltd, 17 Glebe Road, Groby, Leicester, LE6 0GT Tel: 0116-287 6963 Fax: 0116-287 8099 E-mail: mel.knight@pipemedia.co.uk *Classic car dealers & restorers*

Andrew Weir Shipping Ltd, Dexter House, 2 Royal Mint Court, London, EC3N 4XX Tel: (020) 7265 0808 Fax: (020) 7481 4784 E-mail: aws@aws.co.uk *Ship management*

Weir Engineering Services, PO Box 4, Barton-upon-Humber, South Humberside, DN18 5BN Tel: (01652) 632702 Fax: (01652) 633112 E-mail: steemturbines@weir.co.uk *Pump & turbine services & compressors* Also at: Sandy

Weir Engineering Services Ltd, 149 Newlands Road, Glasgow, G44 4EX Tel: 0141-637 7141 Fax: 0141-637 7358 E-mail: sales@weir.co.uk *Pump manufrs*

Weir Engineering Services, Winnington Avenue, Northwich, Cheshire, CW8 4FT Tel: (01606) 782255 Fax: (01606) 871631 E-mail: sales@upl.weir.co.uk *Pump servicing agents*

Gerald Weir Enterprises Woodcraft Ltd, 7 Vermont Road, Ipswich, IP4 2SR Tel: (01473) 252606 Fax: (01473) 214621 *Furniture & antiques manufr*

▶ Weir Group plc, 149 Newlands Road, Glasgow, G44 4EX Tel: 0141-637 7111 Fax: 0141-637 2221 E-mail: admin@weir.co.uk

Weir Group P.L.C., 20 Waterloo Street, Glasgow, G2 6DB Tel: 0141-637 7111 Fax: 0141-221 9789 E-mail: investor-relations@wg.weir.co.uk *Holding company*

Weir Lge Process, Keith House, 2 Redheughs Rigg, Edinburgh, EH12 9DQ Tel: 0131-317 8787 Fax: 0131-452 3333 E-mail: sales@lgeprocess.com Principal Export Areas: Worldwide *Process plant contractors, designers & consultants*

▶ Weir & Mcquiston Scotland Ltd, 16 Netherdale Road, Netherton Industrial Estate, Wishaw, Lanarkshire, ML2 0ER Tel: (01698) 372113 Fax: (01698) 356924

Weir Minerals Europe Ltd, Halifax Road, Todmorden, Lancashire, OL14 5RT Tel: (01706) 814251 Fax: (01706) 815350 E-mail: sales.uk@weirminerals.com Principal Export Areas: Worldwide *War man pump founders*

▶ Weir Street Light Engineering Co. Ltd, Weir Street, Blackburn, BB2 2AN Tel: (01254) 59544 Fax: (01254) 698767

Weircliffe International Ltd, St Andrews Road, Exeter, EX4 2AG Tel: (01392) 272132 Fax: (01392) 413511 E-mail: sales@weircliffe.com *Magnetic tape bulk erase manufrs*

Weird Dimensions, 33a Lowman Road, London, N7 6DE Tel: (020) 7607 2176 Fax: (020) 7609 6848 *Model manufrs*

Weirgrove Automation Ltd, Lords Mill, Oakridge Road, High Wycombe, Buckinghamshire, HP11 2PA Tel: (01494) 448387 Fax: (01494) 530734 E-mail: weirgrove@weirgrove.co.uk *Programmable software control systems*

Weishaupt UK Ltd, Stoke Gardens, Slough, SL1 3QD Tel: (01753) 512345 Fax: (01753) 512585 E-mail: sales@weishaupt.idps.co.uk *Oil & gas burner manufrs*

John Weiss & Son Ltd, 89 Alston Drive, Bradwell Abbey, Milton Keynes, MK13 9HF Tel: (01908) 318017 Fax: (01908) 318708 E-mail: sales@johnweiss.com *Surgical instrument manufrs*

Weiss UK Ltd, 27 Manchester Drive, Leegomery, Telford, Shropshire, TF1 6XY Tel: (01952) 240953 Fax: (01952) 244442 E-mail: info@weiss.uk.com *Automation equip, cam driven pick & place machines suppliers*

D.H.J. Weisters Ltd, Anchor Mill, Darwen, Lancashire, BB3 0AH Tel: (01254) 873333 Fax: (01254) 873659 E-mail: customer-services@weisters.co.uk *Scarf & necktie fabric manufrs* Also at: Macclesfield

Weland Ltd, Hardley Industrial Estate, Hardley, Southampton, SO45 3NQ Tel: (023) 8084 9747 Fax: (023) 8084 9054 E-mail: info@weland.co.uk *Weland AB is a family-owned manufacturing company. Work shops and head office are situated at Smålandsstenar. Since the start-up back in 1947 Weland AB has experienced a considerable expansion of its business activities. But even if the company has grown to its present size the objective is still the same - to be flexible and offer the same service to all our customers no matter big or small. But not only, also spiral staircases for indoor and outdoor applications, straight flight staircases, railings and other goods of steel. In the course of recent years we have added, on a contracting basis, laser cutting and other manufacturing methods to our scope of business nowadays representing a considerable share in our activities.*

Welbeck Catering Spares, 20 Bushey Hall Road, Bushey, WD23 2ED Tel: (01923) 801555 *Electric and Gas Components for the catering appliances*

Welbeck House Ltd, Unit D Long Eaton Industrial Estate, Field Farm Road, Long Eaton, Nottingham, NG10 3FZ Tel: 0115-946 9333 Fax: 0115-983 6322 *Upholstered furniture manufrs*

Welbeck Pharmaceuticals & Hospital Supplies Ltd, 37 Marylebone High Street, London, W1U 4QE Tel: (020) 7486 0254 Fax: (020) 7486 1054 *Pharmaceutical wholesalers*

Company Information

Welbeck Tiles Ltd, Workshop, 2-3 Trereife Park, Penzance, Cornwall, TR20 8TB Tel: (01736) 333106 Fax: (01736) 762000 E-mail: info@welbecktiles.com *Tile manufrs*

Welburn Precision Engineering Ltd, Barrys Lane, Scarborough, North Yorkshire, YO12 4HA Tel: (01723) 366453 Fax: (01723) 500729 *General & precision engineers*

▶ Welburn Transport, Hackett Street, Tipton, West Midlands, DY4 0JJ Tel: 0121-557 1776 Fax: 0121-520 6783

Welby Health Care Ltd, Units 16-17 Evans Business Centre, 53-58 South Avenue, High Blantyre Industrial Estate, Glasgow, G72 0XB Tel: (0845) 2572173 Fax: (0870) 4714144 E-mail: info@welbyhealthcare.co.uk

▶ Welch & Phillips Ltd, 17 New St, Wem, Shrewsbury, SY4 5AE Tel: (01939) 232762

Robert Welch Designs Ltd, Lower High Street, Chipping Campden, Gloucestershire, GL55 6DY Tel: (01386) 840522 Fax: (01386) 841111 *Industrial designers*

Welch Transport Ltd, Granta Terrace, Stapleford, Cambridge, CB2 5DL Tel: (01223) 843011 Fax: (01223) 843979 E-mail: ianlawton@welchgroup.co.uk *Road transport haulage freight services*

▶ Welchs Transport Ltd, High Street, Henlow, Bedfordshire, SG16 6BS Tel: (01462) 812888 Fax: (01462) 817217

▶ Welch's Transport Ltd, 6 Industrial Estate, Crittall Road, Witham, Essex, CM8 3DE Tel: (01376) 512295 Fax: (01376) 511772 E-mail: sales@welchgroup.co.uk

Welco, 2 Parklands, Rednal, Birmingham, B45 9PZ Tel: (0800) 9549001 Fax: (0845) 6888900 E-mail: sales@welco.co.uk *Storage & handling equipment manufrs*

Welcom Software Ltd, The Exchange, Station Parade, Harrogate, North Yorkshire, HG1 1TS Tel: (0845) 4565859 Fax: E-mail: info@welcom.co.uk *Welcom Software is a computer software house that has specialised in the development, implementation and support of commercial lending software, credit management software and retail software, including a point of sale software package.* Also at: Aberdeen & Farnborough

▶ Welcom Telecom Ltd, G4 The Old Convent, Beeches Green, Stroud, Gloucestershire, GL5 4AD Tel: (0870) 7777011 Fax: (0870) 7777016 E-mail: info@welcometelecom.co.uk *UK businesses telephone call service*

Welcome Computer Systems Ltd, The Pytchley Unit, Victors Barns, Brixworth, Northampton, NN6 9DQ Tel: (0845) 4582121 Fax: (0845) 4582020 E-mail: sales@welcome-computers.co.uk *Computer Systems Ltd, based in Spratton, Northamptonshire, supply a range of computer solutions to the hotel industry. These solutions aim to bolster the security and efficiency of hotel systems. Solutions include EPoS systems for manging bookings. There are many solutions available which can be tailored to any business size.*

▶ Welcome Fireplace Co Ltd, 44 Seaward Street, Glasgow, G41 1HJ Tel: 0141-429 8242 Fax: 0141-429 1067

Welcome Windows Ltd, Wembley Works, Hemingfield Road, Wombwell, Barnsley, South Yorkshire, S73 0LY Tel: (01226) 340240 Fax: (01226) 340327 *Manufacture double glazed windows & doors*

Weld Lag (Preston) Ltd, Unit 11 Oysten Mill, Strand Road, Preston, PR1 8UR Tel: (01772) 768858 Fax: (01772) 768865 E-mail: enquiries@weldlag.co.uk *Industrial thermal insulation & asbestos removal*

▶ Weld Tec, 16 Castleroddy Road, Omagh, County Tyrone, BT79 7UA Tel: (028) 8164 7831

Weld-AC Supplies Ltd, Unit 3 Arden Works, Fenton Road, Kings Cross, Halifax, West Yorkshire, HX1 3PP Tel: (01422) 346536 Fax: (01422) 364994 E-mail: sales@weldac.co.uk *Welding equipment suppliers*

Weldametal Services Ltd, 10-12 Winfield Street, Dunstable, Bedfordshire, LU6 1LS Tel: (01582) 665246 Fax: (01582) 661443 E-mail: weldametal@aol.com *Heating pipework & metal fabricators*

Weldatube Mechanical Services Ltd, 74 Fryerning Lane, Ingatestone, Essex, CM4 0NN Tel: (01277) 353306 Fax: (01277) 354903 E-mail: keepincall@btopenworld.com *Mechanical repair & installation*

Weldcraft Engineering, Hayeswood Farm, Hayeswood Road, Timsbury, Bath, BA2 0FQ Tel: (01761) 472722 Fax: (01761) 479062 *Engineers*

▶ Welded Metal Products, 157 Howe Circle, Newport, Gwent, NP19 9GS Tel: (01633) 282605 E-mail: weldedmetal.products@virgin.net *WROUGHT IRON GATES & RAILINGS,SCHOOL RAILINGS ,BALUSTRADING,SECURITY GRILLS,WEATHERVANES,AND OTHER IRON & STEEL GARDEN FEATURES SIGN HANGERS ETC....WELDED METAL PRODUCTS, ARE BASED IN NEWPORT ,GWENT ,SOUTH WALES,UK*

Welded Presswork (1982) Ltd, Stafford Road, Darlaston, Wednesbury, West Midlands, WS10 8SZ Tel: 0121-526 2022 Fax: 0121-526 4905 E-mail: enquiries@weldedpresswork.co.uk *Pressings & steel fabricators, laser cutting & powder coating services*

▶ Welder Equipment Services Ltd, Redfield Road, Lenton Lane Industrial Estate, Nottingham, NG7 2UJ Tel: 0115-986 8181 Fax: 0115-985 1936 *hire of professional MIG TIG MMA SUB-ARC welding,PLASMA and POSITIONING, equipment to industry*

Weldex Ltd, Kingsway South, Team Valley Trading Estate, Gateshead, Tyne & Wear, NE11 0JL Tel: 0191-497 3410 Fax: 0191-497 3411 E-mail: weldex@responsive-engineering.com *Weldex is recognised as a specialist welding company that provides customers with competitive advantage by the expert application of technically advanced welding processes. With exceptional facilities including a clean room, services include: Precision Welding and Fabrication, Repair and Recovery Welding,*

continued

Production Welding, Inlays and Overlays, Welding Consultancy and On-site maintenance Welding. Weldex is part of the Responsive Engineering group of companies.

Weldgrip, 2d Redbrook Business Park, Wilthorpe Road, Barnsley, South Yorkshire, S75 1JN Tel: (01226) 785553 Fax: (01226) 731563 E-mail: info@weldgrip.com *Reinforcing & welded mesh manufrs*

Welding Alloys Ltd, The Way, Fowlmere, Royston, Hertfordshire, SG8 7QS Tel: (01763) 207500 Fax: (01763) 207501 E-mail: sales@welding-alloys.com *Welding equipment/welding wire manufrs*

Welding Alloys N W, Station Road, Sandycroft, Deeside, Clwyd, CH5 2PT Tel: (01244) 520588 Fax: (01244) 535635 *Welding suppliers*

Welding Engineering Services Ltd, Unit 2, Barking Industrial Park, Alfreds Way, Barking, Essex, IG11 0TJ Tel: (020) 8591 5777 Fax: (020) 8594 0622 *Welding & cutting suppliers*

Welding Engineers Ltd, 2a Orange Lane, Montrose, Angus, DD10 8ND Tel: (01674) 674825 Fax: (01674) 671314 E-mail: enquiries@weldingengineers.co.uk *Industrial door setters*

Welding Engineers (Glasgow) Ltd, 38 Dalness Street, Glasgow, G32 7RF Tel: 0141-778 8461 Fax: 0141-763 0152 E-mail: sales@weldingengineers.co.uk *Industrial door manufrs*

Welding Engineers (Hertford) Ltd, Unit 1, Lower Road, Great Amwell, Ware, Hertfordshire, SG12 9TA Tel: (01920) 468634 Fax: (01920) 487463 E-mail: hertford@weldingengineers.co.uk *Door repair & maintenance services* Also at: Glasgow, Manchester & Montrose

Welding Engineers (Mersey) Ltd, Units 2-4 Navigation Trading Estate, Bower Street, Newton Heath, Manchester, M40 2AR Tel: 0161-205 2797 Fax: 0161-205 4032 E-mail: enquiries@liftgates.co.uk *Supply, install & repair industrial doors & gates service*

Welding Fabrication Services, Unit 10 Rollingmill Business Park, Rollingmill Street, Walsall, WS2 9EQ Tel: (07875) 405253 Fax: (01922) 474686 *Welded fabrication manufrs*

▶ Welding Plant Repairs, 1 Britannia Park Industrial Estate, North Road, Stoke-on-Trent, ST6 2PZ Tel: (01782) 266664 Fax: (01782) 280180 E-mail: matt@weldsupplies.net *Grinding, abrasive products*

Welding Repairs & Supplies Co. Ltd, Brandon Way, West Bromwich, West Midlands, B70 8JW Tel: 0121-553 6581 Fax: 0121-553 2953 E-mail: weldingrepair@aol.com *Distributor of welding equipment, protective clothing & consumables*

Welding Services Dundee Ltd, 2 Eagle Mills, Brown Constable Street, Dundee, DD4 6QZ Tel: (01382) 223760 Fax: (01382) 225085 *Metal fabricators*

Welding Services (Weldon) Ltd, Trevithick Road, Willowbrook South Industrial E, Corby, Northamptonshire, NN17 5XY Tel: (01536) 266623 Fax: (01536) 403159 E-mail: weldingservices@aol.com *Welding engineers*

Welding & Site Services Ltd, Unit 18 Twin Lakes Industrial Park, Bretherton Road, Croston, Leyland, PR26 9RF Tel: (01772) 601300 Fax: (01772) 601496 E-mail: sales@welding-services.co.uk *Steel fabricators*

Welding Supplies UK Ltd, 7a Sketchley Meadows, Hinckley, Leicestershire, LE10 3EN Tel: (01543) 572544 Fax: (01543) 466156 E-mail: sales@weldingsupplies-uk.co.uk *Welding supplies distributors or agents*

Welding Tool Supplies, Cromer House, Caxton Way, Stevenage, Hertfordshire, SG1 2DF Tel: (01438) 726991 Fax: (01438) 350022 *Welding equipment suppliers & services*

▶ Welding Units UK Ltd, Mill Lane, Rainford, St. Helens, Merseyside, WA11 8LR Tel: (01744) 884881 Fax: (01744) 883302 E-mail: sales@weldingunits.com *Design & manufacture of flanges*

Weldit, 25-27 Bilton Way, Luton, LU1 1UU Tel: (01582) 727840 Fax: (01582) 727841 *Metal stockholders*

Weldmet Ltd, Unit 8, 55 Weir Road, Wimbledon, London, SW19 8UG Tel: (020) 8947 1244 Fax: (020) 8947 6080 E-mail: sales@weldmet.co.uk *Welding equipment/supplies & distributors*

Weldon Engineering Ltd, Unit 4B Climpy Industrial Park, Climpy Road, Forth, Lanark, ML11 8EW Tel: (01555) 812233 Fax: (01555) 812454 E-mail: sales@weldon-engineering.com *Steel fabricators*

▶ Weldon Plant Ltd, Lammas Road, Weldon North, Corby, Northamptonshire, NN17 5JF Tel: (01536) 260833 Fax: (01536) 261800 E-mail: sales@weldonplant.co.uk *Earthmoving and Civil Engineering Contractor*

Weldright Fabrications, Old Coal Yard, Green Lane West, Garstang, Preston, PR3 1NJ Tel: (01995) 604166 Fax: (01995) 600889 E-mail: garstangtruckbodys@hotmail.com *Fabricators*

Weldrite Steel Fabricators, Providence Works, Norton Street, Miles Platting, Manchester, M40 8EH Tel: 0161-203 4541 Fax: 0161-205 1980 E-mail: weldriteuk@aol.com *Steel fabricators*

Weldsafe, New Albion Estate, Yoker, Glasgow, G13 4DJ Tel: 0141-952 2200 Fax: 0141-941 3777 E-mail: weldsafeltd@btconnect.com *PPE welding & safety suppliers*

Weldspares-OKI Ltd, Unit 50 Melford Court, Hardwick Grange, Warrington, WA1 4RZ Tel: (01925) 813288 Fax: (01925) 817223 E-mail: sales@weldspares-oki.com *Welding accessories & consumables*

Weldspeed Ltd, Protea Way, Pixmore Avenue, Letchworth Garden City, Hertfordshire, SG6 1JT Tel: (01462) 481616 Fax: (01462) 482202 E-mail: sales@weldspeed.co.uk *Welding suppliers & distributors*

Weldtec Welding Services, Mackleys Industrial Estate, Henfield Road, Small Dole, Henfield, West Sussex, BN5 9XE Tel: (01273) 493493 Fax: (01273) 493493 E-mail: weldtecwelding@aol.com *Sheet metal workers & welders*

Weldtite Products Ltd, Unit 9, Harrier Road, Humber Bridge Industrial Estate, Barton-Upon-Humber, South Humberside, DN18 5RP Tel: (01652) 660000 Fax: (01652) 660066 E-mail: sales@weldtite.co.uk *Cycle accessory manufrs*

Weldwork Ltd, Central Way, Feltham, Middlesex, TW14 0XJ Tel: (020) 8890 4141 Fax: (020) 8751 5793 E-mail: info@cmf.co.uk *Metal construction services*

Weleda U K Ltd, Heanor Road, Ilkeston, Derbyshire, DE7 8DR Tel: 0115-944 8200 Fax: 0115-944 8210 E-mail: weledauk@compuserve.com *Toiletries manufrs*

Welfix Fasteners & Fixing Devices, 192 Monkmoor Road, Shrewsbury, SY2 5BH Tel: (01743) 344766 Fax: (01743) 350875 *Fixings & fastenings distributors*

Welglaze Ltd, Watermill Industrial Estate, Aspenden Road, Buntingford, Hertfordshire, SG9 9JS Tel: (01763) 271811 Fax: (01763) 273108 E-mail: sales@welgaurd.co.uk *Aluminium window manufrs*

Welham Diesel Injection Co. Ltd, Hawarden Avenue, Coleman Road, Leicester, LE5 4NL Tel: 0116-276 6831 Fax: 0116-246 0635 Principal Export Areas: Worldwide *Diesel fuel injection reconditioner*

Welin Fire Insulation, Unit 14a Millpark Industrial Estate, Cannock, Staffordshire, WS11 7XU Tel: (01543) 469220 Fax: (01543) 468129 *Fireproofing installation contractors*

Welin Lambie Ltd, Brittania House, Old Bush Street, Brierley Hill, West Midlands, DY5 1UB Tel: (01384) 78294 Fax: (01384) 265100 E-mail: admin@welin-lambie.co.uk *Marine winch & lifeboat launchers manufrs*

Well Laid Table, Green Acres, Whaplode Drove, Spalding, Lincolnshire, PE12 0SP Tel: (01406) 330206 Fax: (01406) 330206 *Catering equipment & linen hire*

Well Service, West Brent, Forties Road Industrial Estate, Hillside, Montrose, Angus, DD10 9ET Tel: (01674) 677177 Fax: (01674) 677277 E-mail: sales@wellservice.com *Oilfield equipment manufrs*

Well Tied Ltd, 6 Llwynderw Drive, West Cross, Swansea, SA3 5AP Tel: (01792) 405151 *Cavity wall ties installers*

▶ Well Wicked Limited, Southover, Hurst Lane, Egham, Surrey, TW20 8QJ Tel: 01344 844439 E-mail: Martinpcraven@BTinternet.com *Experiences, Gifts and Gadgets for all the family*

Wellan Studios Printers)Ltd, Unit 1, Grange Valley Road, Batley, West Yorkshire, WF17 6GG Tel: (01924) 473481 Fax: (01924) 477353 E-mail: sales@wellanstudios.com *Screen process printers*

Welland Engineering Ltd, 31a Cranmore Lane, Holbeach, Spalding, Lincolnshire, PE12 7HT Tel: (01406) 490660 Fax: (01406) 490444 E-mail: sales@generating-sets.com *Manufacturers & distributors of generating sets*

Welland Flooring Co Corby Ltd, Weldon Road, Corby, Northamptonshire, NN17 1UZ Tel: (01536) 265195 Fax: (01536) 261323 E-mail: sales@wellandflooring.co.uk *Flooring specialists & contractors*

Welland Supplies, Blenheim Way, Northfields Industrial Estate, Market Deeping, Peterborough, PE6 8LD Tel: (01778) 380371 Fax: (01778) 346916 E-mail: sales@welland-supplies.co.uk *Industrial supply company offering free daily deliveries.*

Welland Timber Products Ltd, Geddington Road, Corby, Northamptonshire, NN18 8ET Tel: (01536) 201992 Fax: (01536) 401178 E-mail: info@wellandtimber.co.uk *Timber building & joinery specialists, suppliers & contractors*

Wellbrite Plating Co., 24 Lansdown Place Lane, Cheltenham, Gloucestershire, GL50 2LB Tel: (01242) 523790 *Electroplaters*

Weller Packaging Ltd, Birchbrook Industrial Park, Lynn Lane, Shenstone, Lichfield, Staffordshire, WS14 0DJ Tel: (01543) 482100 Fax: (01543) 482140 E-mail: sales@wellerpackaging.co.uk *Packaging merchants*

Weller Patents Development, 1-8 Grand Parade Mews Rear of, 96-110 Upper Richmond Road, London, SW15 2SP Tel: (020) 8788 6684 Fax: (020) 8788 4669 *Manufacturers of test & quality control equipment*

Sam Weller & Sons Ltd, Pickwick Mill, Thongsbridge, Holmfirth, HD9 3JL Tel: (01484) 683201 Fax: (01484) 689700 E-mail: info@samwellerltd.co.uk *Manufacturers of cotton fabric, decatising wrapper, hessian sack, polypropylene bags & industrial fabric. Also filter bags & sleeves*

Weller Tools, 815 Warwick Road, Tyseley, Birmingham, B11 2EL Tel: 0121-707 3303 Fax: 0121-707 3303 *Precision engineers*

Wellfare Electrical Co. Ltd, 116-118 Sutton Road, Southend-on-Sea, SS2 5ER Tel: (0800) 2943632 Fax: (01702) 468482 *Independent electrical retailer*

Wellfast Industrial Supplies Ltd, 157-159 New John Street, Halesowen, West Midlands, B62 8HT Tel: 0121-559 3805 Fax: 0121-559 9836 E-mail: david@page6745.freeserve.co.uk *Industrial safety clothing shoes fasteners*

Wellfield Precision Tooling Co. Ltd, Lower Philips Road, Whitebirk Industrial Estate, Blackburn, BB1 5QN Tel: (01254) 260002 Fax: (01254) 680517 E-mail: sales@wellfieldprecision.co.uk *Precision engineers*

Wellform Ltd, Unit E14, Cumberland Road Trading Estate, Loughborough, Leicestershire, LE11 5DE Tel: (01509) 264000 Fax: (01509) 611891 *Gate manufrs*

Wellgate Door Systems, Ladyship Centre, Old Lane, Halifax, West Yorkshire, HX3 5QN Tel: (01422) 320520 Fax: (01422) 320499 E-mail: sales@wellgate-doors.co.uk *Industrial & fast acting door manufrs*

Wellgates, Unit 6 Junction 7 Business Park, Blackburn Road, Clayton Le Moors, Lancashire BB5 5JW Tel: (01254) 395379 Fax: (01254) 395379 *Manufacture & install security gates & turnstiles*

Wellhead Electrical Supplies Ltd, Unit 4d Wellhead CR, Wellheads Industrial Estate, Aberdeen, AB21 7GA Tel: (01224) 723606 Fax: (01224) 723606 E-mail: sales@wellheads.co.uk *Electric suppliers, agents & distributors*

▶ Wellhouse Consultants, 404 The Spa, Melksham, Wiltshire, SN12 6QL Tel: (01225) 708225 Fax: (01225) 707126 E-mail: graham@wellho.net *Training service*

Welling Sewing Centre, 104-106 Welling High Street, Welling, Kent, DA16 1TJ Tel: (020) 8304 0470 Fax: (020) 8298 1582 *Sell sewing machines, dress fabrics & haberdashery*

Wellingborough Town Centre Patnership Ltd, 18-19 Spring Lane, Wellingborough, Northamptonshire NN8 1EY Tel: (01933) 270795 Fax: (01933) 222202 E-mail: info@wellingboroughchamber.co.uk *Business advisors*

▶ Wellington Angling Centre, 18 High Street, Wellington, Somerset, TA21 8RA Tel: (01823) 666343 Fax: (01823) 666343 *Fishing tackle manufrs*

Wellington Country Sports, 24 High Street, Wellington, Somerset, TA21 8RA Tel: (01823) 662120 Fax: (01823) 667970 E-mail: sales@wellingtoncountrysports.co.uk *Outdoor pursuits clothing distributors*

Wellington Park Ltd, Wellington Park, Church Road Leyland, PR25 3AB Tel: (01772) 432881 Fax: (01772) 453151 *Hire rooms for conference*

Wellington Pharmacy, 39 Knightsbridge, London, SW1X 7NL Tel: (020) 7235 2653 Fax: (020) 7235 0158 E-mail: wellington1@btconnect.com *Veterinary & human medicines wholesale & distributors*

Wellington Signs Ltd, 66 Winchester Road, Southampton, SO16 6UL Tel: (023) 8078 0780 Fax: (023) 8036 0361 *Screen printers*

W. Wellington & Son Ltd, Old Station Yard, Industrial Estate, Kingsbridge, Devon, TQ7 1EF Tel: (01548) 852166 Fax: (01548) 852066 *Removal & storage specialists*

Wellington Welding Supplies Ltd, Pottington Road, Barnstaple, Devon, EX31 1JH Tel: (01271) 325333 Fax: (01271) 325334 *Industrial welding supplies*

Wellman P.L.C., Newfield Road, Oldbury, West Midlands, B69 3ET Tel: 0121-601 3000 Fax: 0121-543 0010 *Holding company or group*

Wellman Automation, 6 Appleby Glade Industrial Estate, Ryder Close, Swadlincote, Derbyshire, DE11 9EU Tel: (01283) 550052 Fax: (01283) 550064 E-mail: wellman-automation@btconnect.com *Electrical panel manufrs*

Wellman Booth, 2 Kirkfields Industrial Centre, Kirk Lane, Yeadon, Leeds, LS19 7LX Tel: 0113-387 9730 Fax: 0113-250 6180 E-mail: sales@wellmanbooth.co.uk *Designers & manufacturers of special purpose cranes*

Wellman Defence, Airport Service Road, Portsmouth, PO3 5PG Tel: (023) 9266 4911 Fax: (023) 9269 7864 E-mail: enquiries@wellmandefence.co.uk *Hydrogen generator & purification equipment manufrs*

Wellman Hunt Graham Ltd, Astley Street, Dukinfield, Cheshire, SK16 4QT Tel: 0161-331 4400 Fax: 0161-331 4434 *Heat exchanger designers & manufrs*

▶ Wellow Park Developments Ltd T/A Wellow Park Wind, 27 Beresford Street, Mansfield, Nottinghamshire, NG18 2PH Tel: (01623) 422872

Wells Associates, Brundish Lodge, Brundish, Woodbridge, Suffolk, IP13 8BU Tel: (07768) 866958 Fax: (01986) 798731 E-mail: info@wells-associates.com *Gas & electricity management service*

Wells Envelopes, 3 Paycocke Close, Basildon, Essex, SS14 3HS Tel: (01268) 284442 Fax: (01268) 271177 E-mail: wellsenv@yahoo.co.uk *Stationary over printers service*

Wells Fabrications & Developments Ltd, Unit 39a Wyrley Trading Estate, Wyrley Road, Birmingham, B6 7DB Tel: 0121-327 3354 Fax: 0121-327 3418 E-mail: ian.godwin@btconnect.com *Steel fabricators*

Wells Hire Centre, Underwood Business Park, Wookey Hole Road, Wells, Somerset, BA5 1TU Tel: (01749) 674410 Fax: (01749) 671599 E-mail: shannonp@netcomuk.co.uk *Plant-tool hire & sales*

Wells Masonry Services Ltd, Ilsom Farm, Ilsom, Tetbury, Gloucestershire, GL8 8RX Tel: (01666) 504251 Fax: (01666) 502285 E-mail: sales@wells-group.co.uk *Stone masons*

▶ Paul Wells Consultants, 32 Catharine Close, Chafford Hundred, Grays, Essex, RM16 6QH Tel: (01375) 484044 E-mail: paulwellsconsult@btinternet.com *We are an Office Interiors Recruitment Company, servicing the Office Furniture, Fit-Out, Design & Build and A&D markets.*

▶ Wells Poultry Housing, The Bungalow, Windsor Road, Brynmawr, Ebbw Vale, Gwent, NP23 4JA Tel: (01495) 313838 E-mail: info@chicken-house.co.uk *Poultry housing, feeders and drinkers*

Wells Rain Ltd, The Wardens, Watling Street, Leintwardine, Craven Arms, Shropshire, SY7 0LL Tel: (01547) 540498 Fax: (01547) 540500 *Irrigation engineering*

Wells & Root Ltd, Parker Drive, Leicester, LE4 0JP Tel: 0116-235 3535 Fax: 0116-235 3910 E-mail: enquiries@wellsandroot.co.uk *Air freight agents*

Wells Spiral Tubes Ltd, Prospect Works, Airedale Road, Keighley, West Yorkshire, BD21 4LW Tel: (01535) 664231 Fax: (01535) 664235 E-mail: sales@wells-spiral.co.uk *Ductwork to drainage specialists* Also at: Bury

▶ Wellsway BMW, Lower Bristol Road, Bath, BA2 3DR Tel: (01225) 448145 Fax: (01225) 420794 *Car dealers & Garage services*

Wellsway Mini, Lower Bristol Road, Bath, BA2 3DR Tel: (01225) 448555 Fax: (01225) 420794 E-mail: sales@wellswaymini.co.uk *Car dealers & Garage services*

ellvil Engineering Company Ltd, Spring Place, New Street, Luton, LU1 5DF Tel: (01582) 727171 *Sub contract precision engineers*

WellyIT, 8 Lower Westford, WELLINGTON, Somerset, TA21 0DN Tel: (07962) 174984 E-mail: ntdobson@hotmail.com *Business computing software consultancy*

elmet Coral Metals, Main Road, Unstone, Dronfield, Derbyshire, S18 4AB Tel: (01246) 414907 Fax: (01246) 411777 *Aluminium recyclers*

elo UK Ltd, Dunlop Road, Hunt End Industrial Estate, Redditch, Worcestershire, B97 5XP Tel: (01527) 546897 Fax: (01527) 545191 E-mail: welo.uk@btinternet.com *Supplier of wear & spare parts for wire erosion machines*

elprint Display Ltd, Unit A, 690 Melton Road, Thurmiston, Leicester, LE4 8BB Tel: 0116-269 8878 Fax: 0116-269 8765 E-mail: office@welprint.demon.co.uk *Print manufrs*

elsh Agricultural Office, Plas Y Ffynnon, Cambrian Way, Brecon, Powys, LD3 7HP Tel: (01874) 625123 Fax: (01874) 622737 *Civil servant services*

Welsh Boxes of Swansea Ltd, Bruce Road, Swansea Industrial Estate, Fforestfach, Swansea, SA5 4HX Tel: (01792) 586527 Fax: (01792) 585410 E-mail: sales@welshboxes.co.uk *Corrugated box manufrs*

Velsh Farm Supplies Ltd, Gorseland, North Road, Aberystwyth, Dyfed, SY23 2AR Tel: (01970) 636433 Fax: (01970) 611494 E-mail: enquiries@wfsagri.net *Agricultural farm suppliers*

Welsh Hills Bakery, Old Tramway, Hirwaun, Aberdare, Mid Glamorgan, CF44 9NY Tel: (01685) 813545 *Bakery*

Velsh Lady Preserves Ltd, Bryn, Y Ffor, Pwllheli, Gwynedd, LL53 6RL Tel: (01766) 810496 Fax: (01766) 810067 E-mail: info@welshladypreserves.com *Food manufrs*

Velslot Fencing, Common Lane, Carrington, Manchester, M31 4QJ Tel: 0161-777 6705 Fax: 0161-777 6908 *Concrete fencing manufrs*

Welsted Joinery Ltd, 31 Cutlers Road, South Woodham Ferrers, Chelmsford, CM3 5WA Tel: (01245) 329688 Fax: (01245) 329342 *Timber merchants*

Veltec Systems UK Ltd, Peak House, Works Road, Letchworth Garden City, Hertfordshire, SG6 1GB Tel: (01462) 475628 Fax: (01462) 475626 E-mail: weltec.uk@ashwell.com *PCB automatic test equipment & AOI vision systems sales & services*

Veltech International Ltd, 10 Bramley Road, St. Ives, Cambridgeshire, PE27 3WS Tel: (01480) 461611 Fax: (01480) 301010 *Environmental monitoring for poultry industry*

Welters Organisation Worldwide, D Kingmoor Park, Heathlands Estate, Carlisle, CA6 4RE Tel: (0870) 2416422 Fax: (01228) 674959 E-mail: sales@welters-worldwide.com *Stone products*

Velton Bibby & Baron Ltd, Station Road, Midsomer Norton, Radstock, BA3 2BE Tel: (01761) 416523 Fax: (01761) 413862 E-mail: enquiries@welton.co.uk *Paper packaging manufrs*

Weltonfield Narrowboats, Welton, Daventry, Northamptonshire, NN11 2LG Tel: (01327) 842282 Fax: (01327) 843754 E-mail: enquiries@weltonfield.co.uk *Boat builders manufrs*

Weltonhurst Ltd, Centurion Way Roman Road Industrial Estate, Roman Road, Blackburn, BB1 2LD Tel: (01254) 671177 Fax: (01254) 671717 E-mail: sales@weltonhurst.co.uk *Plastic blow moulding*

Weltool Engineering Co. Ltd, 25 Aston Court, Kingsland Grange, Woolston, Warrington, WA1 4SG Tel: (01925) 813449 *General engineers*

Welvent Ltd, Whisby Way, Whisby Road, Lincoln, LN6 3LQ Tel: (01522) 693008 Fax: (01522) 500429 E-mail: enquiries@welvent.com *Agricultural storage*

Welwyn Lighting Designs Ltd, Bessemer Road, Welwyn Garden City, Hertfordshire, AL7 1HH Tel: (01707) 255300 Fax: (01707) 255357 E-mail: sales@wewyn-lighting.co.uk *Light shades & lamp manufrs*

Wema, Horton Court, Horton, Bristol, BS37 6QR Tel: (01454) 316103 Fax: (01454) 310510 *Marine electronics equipment manufrs*

Wenaas UK Ltd, Wenaas Buildings, Hareness Circle, Altens Industrial Estate, Aberdeen, AB12 3LY Tel: (01224) 894000 Fax: (01224) 878789 E-mail: sales@wenaas.co.uk Principal Export Areas: Worldwide *As specialists in Workwear and Safety equipment we can ensure you use the most effective and cost efficient products. We supply all PPE, ear defenders, hard hats,safety footwear,Respiratory gear,hi viz clothing,Flame Retardant Coveralls,Eyewear,Gloves,Thermal gear, Waterproof clothing, food industry clothing e.t.c. For further information please contact sales above.*

▶ Wenaas UK Ltd, Unit 19, Morgans Business Park, Norton Canes,, Cannock, Staffs, WS11 9UU Tel: 01543 496300 Fax: 01543 496310 E-mail: midlands@wenaas.co.uk *As specialists in Workwear and Safety equipment we can ensure you use the most effective and cost efficient products. We supply all PPE, ear defenders, hard hats,safety footwear,Respiratory gear,hi viz clothing,Flame Retardant Coveralls,Eyewear,Gloves,Thermal gear, Waterproof clothing, food industry clothing e.t.c. For further information please contact sales above.*

Wenban Smith Ltd, 14 Newland Road, Worthing, West Sussex, BN11 1JT Tel: (01903) 230311 Fax: (01903) 821780 E-mail: sales@wenban-smith.co.uk *Timber merchants*

Wenda Electronics & Engineering, 47 Cobham Road, Ferndown Industrial Estate, Wimborne, Dorset, BH21 7QZ Tel: (01202) 874961 Fax: (01202) 861260 E-mail: wendasheetmetal@cwcom.net *Sheet metalwork engineers*

Wendage Pollution Control Ltd, Rangeways Farm, Conford, Liphook, Hampshire, GU30 7QP Tel: (01428) 751296 Fax: (01428) 751541 E-mail: info@wpc.uk.net *Established in 1980 with over 30 years of experience in the Sewage and Waste Water industry. Wendage Pollution Control Ltd are a family run business based in the South East of England offering a quality service, specialising in the supply, installation and maintenance of packaged sewage treatment plants and pumping stations. They are sewage & effluent treatment specialists and consultants in pollution control.*

Wendland Roof Solutions, Olympus Park Business Centre, Quedgeley, Gloucester, GL2 4NF Tel: (0870) 420 7900 Fax: (0870) 420 7901 *Conservatory roofing systems*

▶ Wendrick management Services Limited, 9 Wateredge Close, Pennington, Leigh, Lancashire, WN7 3UP Tel: 01942 261275 Fax: 01942 261275 E-mail: ecrookes@wendrick.com *Management and business training especially Supply Chain Management*

Wendt Boart (UK) Ltd, Station Road, Staplehurst, Tonbridge, Kent, TN12 0QD Tel: (01580) 890800 Fax: (01580) 890888 E-mail: sales@wbuk.wendtgroup.com Principal Export Areas: Africa *Manufacturers of diamond impregnated grinding wheels*

▶ Wendy's Cakes, 285 Sheldon Heath Road, Birmingham, B26 2TY Tel: 0121-243 7341 E-mail: wendyscakes@yahoo.co.uk *Cakes made for all occasions, design service available*

Wengain, Lisle Lane, Ely, Cambridgeshire, CB7 4AS Tel: (01353) 668181 Fax: (01353) 668102 E-mail: sales.enquiries@wengain.co.uk *Chemical distributors*

Wenglor Sensoric, Suite B Secondfloor Aspen House, 15 Medlicott Close, Corby, Northamptonshire, NN18 9NF Tel: (01536) 747299 Fax: (01536) 742301 E-mail: info.uk@wenglor.de *Sensors & proximity switches manufrs*

Wengo Information Services, 82 London Road, Biggleswade, Bedfordshire, SG18 8EB Tel: (01767) 313972 Fax: (01767) 222273 E-mail: geoffreybuzzard@compuserve.com *Computer consultancy*

Wenlock Installations Ltd, Unit 1 Holloway Street West, Dudley, West Midlands, DY3 2DZ Tel: (01902) 664472 Fax: (01902) 662261 *Steel fabricators*

Wenmore Rooflights, Unit 1A Parnall Industrial Estate, Parnall Road, Fishponds, Bristol, BS16 3JF Tel: 0117-958 5865 Fax: 0117-958 5865 *Sky light manufrs*

▶ Wensley Contracts, 100 Manor Farm Road, Birmingham, B11 2HX Tel: 0121-706 7878 Fax: 0121-707 0353

▶ Wensley Transport, Green Lane, Castleford, West Yorkshire, WF10 2RY Tel: (01977) 550259 Fax: (01977) 514239 E-mail: wensley@transport76.fsnet.co.uk *Vehicle movement*

Wensum, South Corner, Brighton Road, Lowfield Heath, Crawley, West Sussex, RH11 0PH Tel: (01293) 422700 Fax: (01293) 422701 E-mail: enquiries@wensum.co.uk *Design, manufacture & supply uniforms & corporate business wear*

Wensum Pools Ltd, Parker Drive, Fakenham, Norfolk, NR21 8RP Tel: (01328) 838835 Fax: (01328) 855725 E-mail: sales@wensumpools.co.uk *Swimming pool installers*

Wentmore Shipping & Haulage Ltd, The Lodge Barrington Hall, Dunmow Road, Hatfield Broad Oak, Bishop's Stortford, Hertfordshire, CM22 7JL Tel: (01279) 718711 Fax: (01279) 718510 E-mail: wentmore@globalnet.co.uk *Freight forwarding agents*

Wentus Ltd, 2 Business Centre, Osbournby, Sleaford, Lincolnshire, NG34 0DH Tel: 01529 455695 *Packaging manufacturers - flexible*

Wentwood Outdoor Timber Products Ltd, Abergavenny Road, Raglan, Usk, Gwent, NP15 2BH Tel: (01291) 691070 *Garden & patio furniture distributors & manufrs*

Wentworth Business Services, Pennine View, Birstall, Batley, West Yorkshire, WF17 9NF Tel: (01924) 444501 Fax: (01924) 444266 E-mail: sales@wentworthbs.co.uk *Business forms printers*

▶ Wentworth Equine Travel - Self Drive Horseboxes, Elm Villas, Crazies Hill, Wargrave, RG10 8LU Tel: 07946 451629 E-mail: sales@wentworthequinetravel.co.uk *SELF DRIVE HORSE BOX HIRE - ONLY £99.00 PER DAY. Wide range of Luxury Newly built horseboxes to suit all needs.*www.wentworthequinetravel.co.uk*

Wentworth Laboratories Ltd, 1 Gosforth Close, Sandy, Bedfordshire, SG19 1RB Tel: (01767) 681221 Fax: (01767) 691951 *Probing equipment manufrs*

Wentworth Tool & Die, Woodbine House, Wold Newton, Driffield, North Humberside, YO25 3YD Tel: (01262) 470270 Fax: (01262) 470270 E-mail: woodbinehouse@aol.com *Tool manufrs*

Wera Tools, Unit 2 McGregors Way, Turnoaks Business Park, Off Storforth Lane, Chesterfield, Derbyshire, S40 2WB Tel: (01246) 277756 Fax: (01246) 273335 *Power tool accessories manufrs*

Werecon Engineering Ltd, 403 Netherwood Road, Rotherwas Industrial Estate, Hereford, HR2 6JU Tel: (01432) 355454 Fax: (01432) 358727 *Hydraulic cylinder repairs*

Wereldhave Property Corporation plc, 39 Sloane Street, London, SW1X 9WR Tel: (020) 7235 2080 Fax: (020) 7245 9962 *Property management services*

▶ Wergs Garage Ltd, 81 Wergs Road, Wolverhampton, WV6 9BP Tel: (01902) 751656 Fax: (01902) 744748

▶ Werner Synthetics Ltd, 663 Ajax Avenue, Slough, SL1 4BG Tel: (01753) 512444

Werneth Manufacturing Co., Unit 2 Dawson Street, Redfern Industrial Estate, Hyde, Cheshire, SK14 1RD Tel: 0161-368 3079 Fax: 0161-368 3079 *Aluminium fabricators*

Wernick Group Holdings Ltd, Molineux House, Russell Gardens, Wickford, Essex, SS11 8BL Tel: (01268) 735544 E-mail: simon.doran@wernickwickford.co.uk *Retailers & hirers of portable cabins* Also at: Brownhills & Horwich

Wernick Hire Ltd, Pipe Lane, Banbury, Oxfordshire, OX16 2RP Tel: (01295) 275315 Fax: (01295) 709827 *Portable cabin hire & sale*

Wernick Hire, Shepherds Grove Industrial Estate, Stanton, Bury St. Edmunds, Suffolk, IP31 2AR Tel: (01359) 250526 Fax: (01359) 252019 E-mail: hire@wernickbury.co.uk *Portable site accommodation hire & manufrs*

Wernick Hire Ltd, Nursteed Road Trading Estate, Mill Road, Devizes, Wiltshire, SN10 3EW Tel: (01380) 727371 Fax: (01380) 721639 E-mail: hire@wernickdevizes.co.uk *Accommodation for building site offices*

Wernick Hire Ltd, Baluniefield Trading Estate, Balunie Drive, Dundee, DD4 8YZ Tel: (01382) 477108 Fax: (01382) 778741 *Portable building hire*

Wernick Hire Ltd, Wellington Road, Gateshead, Tyne & Wear, NE11 9JL Tel: 0191-461 1000 Fax: 0191-461 1001 *Portable building* Also at: Cowdenbeath & Ossett

Wernick Hire Ltd, 220 Leads Road, Hull, HU7 0DF Tel: (01482) 791990 Fax: (01482) 791960 E-mail: hire.hull@wernick.co.uk *Portable accommodation services*

Wernick Hire Ltd, Cartmore Industrial Estate, Lochgelly, Fife, KY5 8LL Tel: (01592) 783355 Fax: (01592) 783366 E-mail: hire@wenicklockgelly.co.uk *Hire & sell portable buildings services*

Wernick Hire Ltd, Leeway Industrial Estate, Newport, Gwent, NP19 4SL Tel: (01633) 281118 Fax: (01633) 282242 *Portable cabins*

Wernick Hire Ltd, B Fairfax Road, Heathfield Industrial Estate, Newton Abbot, Devon, TQ12 6UD Tel: (01626) 832999 Fax: (01626) 832393 *Portable buildings* Also at: Branches throughout the U.K.

▶ Wernick Hire Ltd, 1882190 Keyham Road, Devenport, Plymouth, PL2 1RD Tel: (01752) 567037 Fax: (01752) 567348 E-mail: hire@wernickplymouth.co.uk *Portable accommodation, modular buildings, secure stores & offices*

Wesbart UK Ltd, Daux Road, Billingshurst, West Sussex, RH14 9YR Tel: (01403) 782738 Fax: (01403) 784180 E-mail: wesbart@talk21.com *Laboratory storage systems manufrs*

Wesbroom Engineering Ltd, 173 Mersea Road, Colchester, CO2 8PN Tel: (01206) 576959 Fax: (01206) 573788 *Steel fabricators & trailers (all types) manufrs*

W. Weschenfelder & Sons Ltd, 2 North Road, Middlesbrough, Cleveland, TS2 1DD Tel: (01642) 247524 Fax: (01642) 249336 E-mail: weschies@compuserve.com *Suppliers of sausage making equipment & sausage casing manufrs*

Wesco, 114 Highfields Road, Witham, Essex, CM8 2HH Tel: (01376) 503590 Fax: (01376) 514236 E-mail: sales@wesco-uk.com *Educational equipment & suppliers*

Wesco Access Ltd, 1 Struan Place, Douglas Water, Lanark, ML11 9LW Tel: (01555) 880808 Fax: (01555) 880901 E-mail: neil@wescoaccess.com *Window cleaning & maintenance contractors*

Wescol Ltd, PO Box 41, Wolverhampton, WV1 2RZ Tel: (01902) 351283 Fax: (01902) 871937 E-mail: sales@wescol.com *Welding & cutting equipment manufrs*

Wescombe Maurice B, Silverdale Road, Hayes, Middlesex, UB3 3BN Tel: (020) 8561 0862 Fax: (020) 8561 7007 *Hydraulic fly press conversions*

Wescott Refrigeration Ltd, 188 Fenside Avenue, Coventry, CV3 5NJ Tel: (024) 7641 6677 Fax: (024) 7641 6647 *Refrigeration & air conditioning engineers services*

▶ J. Wesley (Electrical Contractors) Ltd, Units 7-10 Station Approach, Hitchin, Hertfordshire, SG4 9UP Tel: (01462) 437677 Fax: (01462) 422738 E-mail: info@wesleyservices.co.uk *Electrical contracts*

Wesley-Barrell Ltd, Ducklington Mill, Standlake Road, Ducklington, Witney, Oxfordshire, OX29 7YR Tel: (01993) 893100 Fax: (01993) 702720 E-mail: furniture@wesley-barrell.co.uk *Upholsterers manufrs*

▶ Wessco Ltd, 26 Botley Road, Hedge End, Southampton, SO30 2HE Tel: (01489) 790099 Fax: (01489) 795799 E-mail: sales@wessco.co.uk *Garage equipment suppliers*

Wessel Energy Cables, Aghafad, Longford, County Longford, Tel: 0161-763 7474 Fax: 0161-763 7373 E-mail: abbcablesales.ie@abb.com *Cable manufrs*

Wessex Badges Ltd, Unit 1, Silverhills Buildings, Decoy Industrial Estate, Newton Abbot, Devon, TQ12 5LZ Tel: (01626) 363301 Fax: (01626) 363301 E-mail: grahamstephens@tesco.net *Badge manufrs*

Wessex Belden CDT, Unit 8 Crow Arch Lane Industrial Estate, Crow Arch Lane, Ringwood, Hampshire, BH24 1PE Tel: (01425) 480804 Fax: (01425) 480805 E-mail: sales@wessexcdt.co.uk *Cable distributors*

Wessex Blinds Covers Ltd, Belvedere Trading Estate, Taunton, Somerset, TA1 1BH Tel: (01823) 366060 Fax: (01823) 366063 *Custom made blinds & canopies*

Wessex Cater Hire, 17 St. James Road, Southampton, SO15 5FB Tel: (023) 8077 5497 Fax: (023) 8077 5548 E-mail: info@wessexcaterhire.co.uk *Plates & tableware hirers*

Wessex Cleaning Equipment & Janitorial Supplies Ltd, Unit 1 Mount Pleasant Industrial Estate, Mount Pleasant Road, Southampton, SO14 0SP Tel: (023) 8023 4304 Fax: (023) 8023 7226

continued

E-mail: sales@wessexcleaning.com *Cleaning equipment & janitorial supplies*

Wessex Coin Ltd, Unit 11 Hambridge Business Centre, Hambridge Lane, Newbury Berkshire, Newbury, Berkshire, RG14 5TU Tel: (01635) 37277 Fax: (01635) 550073 E-mail: wessexcoin@btconnect.com *Amusement machines & wholesalers*

Wessex Compressor Services, B1 46 Holton Road, Holton Heath Trading Park, Poole, Dorset, BH16 6LT Tel: (01202) 624877 Fax: (01202) 625827 E-mail: office@wessexcompressors.co.uk *Air compressor distributors & maintenance contractors*

Wessex Crystal, Unit 4 Silver End Industrial Estate, Brierley Hill, West Midlands, DY5 3LA Tel: (01384) 481390 Fax: (01384) 481600 *Glass cutting & polishing services*

▶ Wessex Dental Laboratory, Unit 10 Holes Bay Park, Sterte Avenue West, Poole, Dorset, BH15 2AA Tel: (01202) 674486 Fax: (01202) 674486 E-mail: wessex.dental@virgin.net *Dentist - Philip M Laws, John Stoodle Registed Technicians*

Wessex Ducting Ltd, 11a Dawkins Road, Poole, Dorset, BH15 4JP Tel: (01202) 661222 Fax: (01202) 661888 *Ducting design contractors, manufacturers & installers*

Wessex Farm Installations, Mill Road, High Ham, Langport, Somerset, TA10 9DJ Tel: (01458) 250292 Fax: (01458) 259102 *Milking machines & equipment*

Wessex Fine Foods, 148 Tuckton Road, Bournemouth, BH6 3JX Tel: (01202) 429267 *Pie manufrs*

Wessex Fire & Safety Ltd, 8 St. Martins Avenue, Shanklin, Isle of Wight, PO37 6HB Tel: (01983) 862765 Fax: (01983) 867326 E-mail: sales@wessexfire.com *Service & sell fire equipment & fire cons*

▶ Wessex Fire & Security Ltd, Wessex House, Wincombe Lane, Shaftesbury, Dorset, SP7 8PJ Tel: (01747) 851661 Fax: (01747) 858860 E-mail: fire@wessex.org *Installation & maintenance of fire & security products*

Wessex Fixings, Unit 60 South Way, Andover, Hampshire, SP10 5AF Tel: (01264) 332332 Fax: (01264) 332550 *Fastener & fixings distribs*

Wessex Forge, Unit 5, Lodgehill Industrial Estate, Westbury-Sub-Mendip, Wells, Somerset, BA5 1EY Tel: (01749) 672984 Fax: (01749) 670150 E-mail: info@wessexforge.co.uk *Home & garden product manufrs*

Wessex Formes Ltd, 2 Lindberg Road, Ferndown Industrial Estate, Wimborne, Dorset, BH21 7SP Tel: (01202) 870754 Fax: (01202) 870764 *Cutter manufrs*

▶ Wessex Frame Buildings Ltd, Dovedale House, 16 Butts Road, Alton, Hampshire, GU34 1NB Tel: (01420) 82112 Fax: (01420) 82112 E-mail: enquiries@wessexframebuildings.co.uk *Wessex Frame Buildings are design and build contractors located in Alton, Hampshire,*

Wessex Frames, Permaframe House, Georges Ground, Frome, Somerset, BA11 4RP Tel: (01373) 455955 Fax: (01373) 467650 *Double glazing manufrs*

Wessex Funding Ltd, Jewry House, Jewry Street, Winchester, Hampshire, SO23 8RZ Tel: (01962) 877818 Fax: (01962) 890049 E-mail: wessex@tcp.co.uk *Independent insurance administrators/financial services*

Wessex Galvanisers Ltd, Tower Industrial Estate, Tower Lane, Eastleigh, Hampshire, SO50 6NZ Tel: (023) 8062 9952 Fax: (023) 8065 0289 E-mail: wessex@wedge-galv.co.uk *Hot dip galvanizing organisation, part of nation-wide Wedge Group*

Wessex Garage Doors Ltd, Bessemer Close, Ebblake Industrial Estate, Verwood, Dorset, BH31 6AZ Tel: (01202) 825451 Fax: (01202) 823242 E-mail: sales@wessexdoors.co.uk *Glass fibre moulders*

Wessex Glass Co. Ltd, 42 Stanley Hill, Bristol, BS4 3BA Tel: 0117-977 4012 Fax: 0117-977 2526 *Glazing contractors services*

Wessex Guild, 26-36 Horton Road, West Drayton, Middlesex, UB7 8JE Tel: (01895) 449595 Fax: (01895) 431665 E-mail: cmf@lineonewest.co.uk *Steel & aluminium fabricators*

Wessex Homes Group Ltd, Shillingstone Lane, Okeford Fitzpaine, Blandford Forum, Dorset, DT11 0RB Tel: (01258) 860455 Fax: (01258) 861436 E-mail: info@wessexparkhomes.co.uk *Mobile home manufrs*

Wessex Incineration Co Ltd, Bunns Lane, West Woodlands, Frome, Somerset, BA11 5ES Tel: (01373) 465707 Fax: (01373) 451114 *Incineration plant*

Wessex Industrial Doors (Yeovil) Ltd, Artillery Road, Lufton, Yeovil, Somerset, BA22 8RP Tel: (01935) 473708 Fax: (01935) 479413 E-mail: george@wessexindustrialdoors.com *Industrial door manufrs*

▶ Wessex Intumescent Supplies Ltd, 312 Botley Road Unit 11, Cherry Tree Farm, Burridge, Southampton, SO31 1BQ Tel: (01489) 885792 Fax: (01489) 579391 E-mail: info@wis-ltd.com *Suppliers of Intumescent Fireseals & Fire Protection Products, Draught, Weather & Acoustic Seals, Joinery & Glazing Seals, Conservatory Roof Seals.*ISO9001 approved company*

▶ Wessex Leisure Services Ltd, 2 South Way, Southwell Business Park, Portland, Dorset, DT5 2NL Tel: (01305) 824376 Fax: 01305 824376 *We specialise in repair and servicing of caravans and motorhomes. ALso we have a great selection of camping equipment.*

▶ Wessex Malthouse Direct, 24A East Reach, Taunton, Somerset, TA1 3EP Tel: (01823) 331111 Fax: (01823) 334503 E-mail: sales@wessexmalthouse.com *Printers & stationers*

▶ Wessex Mantles Ltd, 16 Airfield Road, Christchurch, Dorset, BH23 3TG Tel: (01202) 481555 Fax: (01202) 481555

Wessex Marine Equipment Ltd, Logistics House, 1 Park Road, Southampton, SO15 3US Tel: (023) 8063 5215 Fax: (023) 8063 5216 *We provide a full and comprehensive First Outfit and Naval Stores Service to Shipbuilders constructing new*

continued

Company Information

continuation
vessels and follow on through with life equipment, purchasing facility, full technical support and backup.

Wessex Medical Equipment Co. Ltd, Budds Lane, Romsey, Hampshire, SO51 0HA Tel: (01794) 830303 Fax: (01794) 512621
E-mail: info@wessexmedical.co.uk
Manufacturers & designers of lifting products

▶ Wessex Memorials, 2 Clump Farm Industrial Estate, Higher Shaftesbury Road, Blandford Forum, Dorset, DT11 7TD Tel: (01258) 450252 Fax: (01258) 450253
E-mail: info@wessexmemorials.co.uk *Masons*

▶ Wessex Plumbing & Heating Services Ltd, Unit 3 5b Surrey Close, Granby Industrial Estate, Weymouth, Dorset, DT4 9GD Tel: (01305) 766549 Fax: (01305) 766549
E-mail: colin-wessexplumbing@btconnect.com
Specialised Drain Cleaning

Wessex Polybags, Unit 1 Ashville Trading Estate, Royston Road, Baldock, Hertfordshire, SG7 6NN Tel: (01462) 490600 Fax: (01462) 490800
E-mail: sales@wessexpolybags.co.uk *Flexible packaging products suppliers & manufrs*

Wessex Power Technology Ltd, 189 Ashley Road, Poole, Dorset, BH14 9DL Tel: (01202) 723000 Fax: (01202) 723400
E-mail: wpt@wessexpower.co.uk *Electronic instrument distributors*

Wessex Radiator, Portsmouth Road, Bursledon, Southampton, SO31 8EP Tel: (023) 8040 2848 Fax: (023) 8040 2848 *Motor radiator repairers & manufrs*

Wessex Resins & Adhesives Ltd, Cupernham Lane, Romsey, Hampshire, SO51 7LF Tel: (01794) 521111 Fax: (0870) 7701032
E-mail: info@wessex-resins.com *Epoxy formulators*

Wessex Rope & Packaging, 6 20 Abingdon Road, Nuffield Industrial Estate, Poole, Dorset, BH17 0UG Tel: (01202) 661066 Fax: (01202) 661077 E-mail: sales@wrp-poole.co.uk
Packaging material & ratchet assembly manufacturers for the haulage industry

Wessex Servicing, 22 Maureen Close, Poole, Dorset, BH12 3HG Tel: (01202) 718818 Fax: (01202) 718818
E-mail: service@wessexservicing.co.uk
Microwaves

Wessex Steel Co. Ltd, Wessex House, 9 Station Parade, London, SW12 9AB Tel: (020) 8675 5331 Fax: (020) 8675 9525
E-mail: nigel@wessexsteel.co.uk *Steel traders*

Wessex Textiles Ltd, Blake Industrial Park, Colley Lane, Bridgwater, Somerset, TA6 5LT Tel: (01278) 450450 Fax: (01278) 450550
E-mail: sales@wessextextiles.co.uk *Uniform clothing manufrs*

Wessex Tool Co.Ltd, Wessex House, Devizes, Wiltshire, SN10 1PS Tel: (01380) 723423 Fax: (01380) 720100 *Plastics injection moulders*

▶ Wessex Tool & Die Ltd, 28 Holton Road, Holton Heath Trading Park, Poole, Dorset, BH16 6LT Tel: (01202) 620242 Fax: (01202) 620252 *Tool manufacturers & exporter*

Wessingham Gas Vessels L.P.G. Ltd, Unit 3 Blagdon Depot, Frankland Lane, Durham, DH1 5TA Tel: 0191-384 3073 Fax: 0191-383 0615
E-mail: peterburdon@wessingham.freeserve.co.uk *Suppliers of refurbished pressure vessels*

Wessington Cabins Ltd, Wessington Avenue, Calne, Wiltshire, SN11 0AP Tel: (01249) 812153 Fax: (01249) 817652
E-mail: sales@wessingtoncabins.co.uk *Portable toilet manufrs*

Wessington Cryogenics Ltd, Building 9, Philadelphia Complex, Houghton Le Spring, Tyne & Wear, DH4 4UG Tel: 0191-512 0677 Fax: 0191-512 0745
E-mail: info@wessingtoncryogenics.co.uk
Principal Export Areas: Asia Pacific, Central Asia, Africa, Central/East Europe & West Europe *Manufacturers of cryogenic equipment & liquified gas containers. Also maintenance & repair services of cryogenic tanks & pressure vessels*

W.H. Wesson (Fencing) Ltd, 126 Connaught Road, Brookwood, Woking, Surrey, GU24 0AS Tel: (01483) 472124 Fax: (01483) 472115
Fencing contractors & merchants

West 9 Coffee Ltd, Arabica House, The Pines, Broad Street, Guildford, Surrey, GU3 3VH Tel: (01483) 303641 Fax: (01483) 303615
Coffee distributors

West Alloy Ltd, Garth Road, Morden, Surrey, SM4 4LN Tel: (020) 8337 2211 Fax: (020) 8330 7640 E-mail: sales@westalloy.com Principal Export Areas: Worldwide *Injection moulders*

▶ R. West and Son, Sutton Road, PLYMOUTH, PL4 0HN Tel: (01752) 664345 Fax: (01752) 669745 E-mail: info@rwest.co.uk *Manufacturers of timber pallets & wooden packing cases*

▶ West AV Solutions, 231 Knowle Avenue, Knowle, Fareham, Hampshire, PO17 5DQ Tel: (01329) 836603 E-mail: chris@westavsolutions.com
Audio and Visual installations including AMX programming for commercial and residential applications

West Bay Small Boat Supplies, Unit 8a The Old Timber Yard, West Bay, Bridport, Dorset, DT6 4EL Tel: (01308) 459511 Fax: (01308) 459511
E-mail: westbaysmallboats@supanet.com
Chandler manufacturers & distributors

West Bay Water Sports Ltd, 10A West Bay, Bridport, Dorset, DT6 4EL Tel: (01308) 421800 Fax: (01308) 421800
E-mail: steve@anglianmailorder.com *Water sports retail outlet*

West Bromwich Central Plating Co. Ltd, Great Bridge St, West Bromwich, West Midlands, B70 0DA Tel: 0121-557 5352 *Nickel/chromium/zinc plate polishing*

West Bromwich Machine Tools, Unit 7/8 Birch Court, Crystal Drive, Smethwick, West Midlands, B66 1RB Tel: 0121-544 6503 Fax: 0121-544 6503 *Machine tools & spares distributors*

West Bromwich Pressings Ltd, Pleasant Street, Lyng, West Bromwich, West Midlands, B70 7DT Tel: 0121-525 5540 Fax: 0121-525 0581
Presswork ers

West Bromwich Sheet Metal Ltd, Unit 43n Siddons Factory Estate, Howard Street, West Bromwich, West Midlands, B70 0SU Tel: 0121-556 9120 Fax: 0121-556 9120 *Dust & extraction plant manufrs*

West Brook Resources Ltd, West Brook House, Wreakes Lane, Dronfield, Derbyshire, S18 1LY Tel: (01246) 290545 Fax: (01246) 292293
Ferro-alloy metal suppliers

West Coast Controls Ltd, Crossveggate Industrial Estate, Milngavie, Glasgow, G62 6RA Tel: 0141-956 4327 Fax: 0141-956 6639
E-mail: wcc@westcoastcontrols.co.uk *Electrical control panel manufrs*

West Coast Corrugated Ltd, Tokenspire Park, Moorgate Road, Knowsley Industrial Park, Liverpool, L33 7RX Tel: 0151-549 1002 Fax: 0151-549 1185 *Corrugated carton manufrs*

▶ West Coast Energy Ltd, 18d Liberton Brae, Edinburgh, EH16 6AE Tel: 0131-672 1888 Fax: 0131-672 1999
E-mail: mail@westcoastenergy.co.uk

▶ West Coast Radio, 3 Spen Farm Studios, Clifton Road, Blackpool, FY4 4QA Tel: (01253) 838828 Fax: (01253) 838828
E-mail: sales@westcoastradio.co.uk *Audio & visual suppliers*

▶ West Coast Smoked Foods Ltd, Stonebarn, Gilgarran, Workington, Cumbria, CA14 4RF Tel: (01946) 834475 Fax: (01946) 833996
E-mail: info@westcoastseafoods.co.uk *We offer a full range of oak smoked scottish salmon products for mail order. In addition we have a full online catalogue of our products for the wholesale and manufacturing sectors, we offer full range of frozen and smoked salmon products*

West Communications Ltd, The Estate Office, Charlestown Road, St. Austell, Cornwall, PL25 3NJ Tel: (01726) 222020 Fax: (01726) 68880 E-mail: info@west-comms.net
Telecommunications

▶ West Controls Ltd, 14 Manstone Mead, Sidmouth, Devon, EX10 9RX Tel: 01395 512816 Fax: 01395 513532
E-mail: sales@westcontrols.co.uk *West Controls Ltd brings to you over 15 years experience in instrumentation, together with the support of key suppliers we can offer a broad range of products to suit a wide variety of applications in many different industries. ** **As an independent distributor, West Controls are able to choose from many principal manufacturers to provide the best solution at the right price. We can reduce your multiple supplier headaches by becoming your single source supplier.****Our product portfolio includes Temperature, Pressure, Flow, Level & Process Control Instrumentation.*

West Cornwall Storage & Distribution Ltd, Calloose, Leedstown, Hayle, Cornwall, TR27 5ET Tel: (01736) 850146 Fax: (01736) 850148
Storage & distribution services

West Country Binders Ltd, 35 Buckingham Road, Weston-super-Mare, Avon, BS24 9BG Tel: (01934) 630950 Fax: (01934) 636615
E-mail: alistair@westcountrybinders.co.uk
Bookbinding services

West Country Business Systems Holdings Ltd, Somerset House, Magdalene Street, Glastonbury, Somerset, BA6 9EJ Tel: (01458) 833344 Fax: (01458) 835297
E-mail: sales@wcbs.co.uk *Computer software house*

West Country Cash Registers, 31 Merrivale Road, Beacon Park, Plymouth, PL2 2QG Tel: (01752) 210011 Fax: (01752) 210012 *Sales in cash registers*

West Country Crane Hire Ltd, 3 Slip North Internal P C 1310, Royal H M Dockyard, Plymouth, PL1 4SG Tel: (01752) 223344 Fax: (01752) 222229
E-mail: brian.metters@westcountrycranehire.com
Crane & road transport hire

West Country Door & Gate, Harpitt Lodge, Old Village, Willand, Cullompton, Devon, EX15 2RW Tel: (01884) 32233 Fax: (01884) 33335 *Gate manufrs*

West Country Fine Food Ltd, East Farm, Church Lane, Codford, Warminster, Wiltshire, BA12 0PJ Tel: (01985) 850524 Fax: (01985) 850690
Specialist food distributors

West Country Marketing Advertising, Unit 1 Woodend Lane Industrial Estate, Stoke Lacy, Bromyard, Herefordshire, HR7 4HQ Tel: (01885) 490500 Fax: (01885) 490585
E-mail: sales@wcma.co.uk *Badge manufrs*

West Country Security, Security House, Newham Road, Truro, Cornwall, TR1 3QG Tel: (01872) 275596 Fax: (01872) 264834 *Security alarms agents*

▶ West Country Tile Centre Ltd, Pool Indust Park, Wilson Way, Pool, Redruth, Cornwall, TR15 3RX Tel: (01209) 212909 Fax: (01209) 711992
E-mail: info@westcountrytilecentre.co.uk *We have a massive range of tiles on display as well as thousands available within a few days of order. Our range consists of both budget and the more exclusive tiles in the full range of finishes including Ceramic, Porcelain, Glass, Slate, Quarry and Victorian.***

West Country Welding Supplies Ltd, 4 Ashmead Business Centre, Ashmead Road, Keynsham, Bristol, BS31 1SX Tel: 0117-986 6006 Fax: 0117-986 1892
E-mail: sales@westcoweld.co.uk *Welding equipment suppliers*

West Cumberland Engineering Ltd, Joseph Noble Road, Lillyhall Industrial Estate, Lillyhall, Workington, Cumbria, CA14 4JX Tel: (01900) 872787 Fax: (01900) 872789
E-mail: wcel@wcel.vhe.co.uk *Welding & fabricators*

▶ West Cut, 8 Lancaster Park Industrial Estate, Bowerhill, Melksham, Wiltshire, SN12 6TT Tel: (01225) 707377 Fax: (01225) 707172
E-mail: sales@westcut-engineering.co.uk
Manufacturers, water jet profile

West Design Products Ltd, West House, Shearway Business Park, Pent Road, Folkestone, Kent, CT19 4RJ Tel: (01303) 297888 Fax: (01303) 297877
E-mail: sales@westdesignproducts.co.uk
Graphic design products

West Dorset Aquatics, Littlemoor Road, Weymouth, Dorset, DT3 6AD Tel: (01305) 835250 Fax: (01305) 835250 *Aquatic suppliers*

West End Blind Co., 152 Broadway, Cardiff, CF24 1NL Tel: (029) 2048 6774 Fax: (029) 2048 6774 *Blinds distributors & manufrs*

West End Cabinet Co., Addison Industrial Estate, Blaydon-on-Tyne, Tyne & Wear, NE21 4SJ Tel: 0191-414 4469 Fax: 0191-414 0463
E-mail: enquiries@west-end-cabinet.com *Joinery manufrs*

West End Marine, Stocks Lane, Batley, West Yorkshire, WF17 8PA Tel: (01924) 478060 Fax: (01924) 478060
E-mail: westendmarine1@aol.com *Marine Engineers*

West End Plant Display, Manor Nursery, Kilham Lane, Winchester, Hampshire, SO22 5QD Tel: (01962) 852844 *Floral & plant displays*

West End Stationers Ltd, 231 Kentish Town Road, London, NW5 2JT Tel: (020) 7485 4472 Fax: (020) 7267 5231 *Commercial stationers*

▶ West End Window Co. Ltd, Unit 8-9 Novers Hill Trading Estate, Novers Hill, Bedminster, Bristol, BS3 5QY Tel: 0117-966 7661 Fax: 0117-966 7773 E-mail: sales@westendwindows.co.uk

West Engineering Ltd, Olympus Close, Ipswich, IP1 5LN Tel: (01473) 467930 Fax: (01473) 467931 E-mail: info@westengineering.co.uk Principal Export Areas: Worldwide *Manufacturers of Spirally Welded Pipework; Spiral Wound, Flat Oval and Clipped Ductwork & fittings; Steel Piling Tube and General Metal Fabrication.*

West Engineering Ltd, Olympus Close, Ipswich, IP1 5LN Tel: (01473) 467930 Fax: (01473) 467931
E-mail: west@engineering40.fsbusiness.co.uk
Principal Export Areas: Africa *Grain & agricultural crop aeration equipment & agricultural machinery/equipment/implement manufrs*

West Engineering Services Ltd, Unit 1a Abbey Mill Business Centre, Paisley, Renfrewshire, PA1 1TJ Tel: 0141-889 2331 Fax: 0141-887 9564 *Power transmission equipment*

West Of England Friends Housing Society Ltd, PO Box 164, Bristol, BS6 6BH Tel: 0117-989 2020 Fax: 0117-924 4615 *Business advisers*

West Of England Mutual War Risks Association Ltd; Tower Bridge Court, 224 Tower Bridge Road, London, SE1 2UP Tel: (020) 7716 6000 Fax: (020) 7716 6100
E-mail: mail@westpandi.com *Marine insurance suppliers*

▶ West Hampshire Tarmacadam Ltd, Unit 14, Liberty Close, Woolsbridge Industrial Park, Three Legged Cross, Wimborne, Dorset, BH21 6SY Tel: 01202 813508 Fax: 01202 813508 E-mail: office@w-h-t.co.uk *Highway maintenance contractor utilising infrared and sealcoating expertise.*

West Hartlepool Steam Navigation Co. Ltd, Kepwick Mill, Kepwick, Thirsk, North Yorkshire, YO7 4BH Tel: (01845) 537888 Fax: (01845) 537793 E-mail: mail@whsn.co.uk *Holding company* Also at: London EC3

West Highland Dairy Sheep, Achmore, Strome Ferry, Ross-Shire, IV53 8UW Tel: (01599) 577203 Fax: (01599) 577331
E-mail: info@westhighlanddairy.co.uk *Dairy products manufacturers & trainers*

West Instruments Ltd, The Hyde, Brighton, BN2 4JU Tel: (01273) 606271 Fax: (01273) 609990 E-mail: info@westinstruments.com
Temperature control manufrs

John West Foods Ltd, Lancaster House Mercury Court, Tithebarn Street, Liverpool, L2 2GA Tel: 0151-243 6200 Fax: 0151-236 5465 *Canned foods merchants*

West Kent Cold Storage Co Ltd, Arctic House, Rye Lane, Dunton Green, Sevenoaks, Kent, TN14 5HB Tel: (01732) 748200 Fax: (01732) 740667 E-mail: gordon.fuller@wkcs.co.uk *Cold storage & warehousing*

▶ West Kent Inventory Services, Elm Tree House, Row Dow Lane, Otford, Sevenoaks, Kent, TN15 6XN Tel: (01959) 523233
E-mail: mail@westkentinventoryservices.co.uk
West Kent Inventory Services provide to Letting Agents and Landlords a comprehensive and professional inventory, check-in and check-out. Fully insured and a member of the AIIC.

▶ West Kent Windows Ltd, 6 Church Trading Estate, Slade Green Road, Erith, Kent, DA8 2JA Tel: (01322) 338158 Fax: (01322) 338159

West Leigh Ltd, 11-13 Spa Road, London, SE16 3RB Tel: (020) 7232 0030 Fax: (020) 7232 1763 E-mail: info@west-leigh.co.uk *Aluminium & steel framed window manufacturers & installers*

West London Brokers, Hale Edge North, Crabhill Lane, South Nutfield, Redhill, RH1 5NR Tel: (01737) 823286 Fax: (01737) 822656
E-mail: w.l.b@btconnect.com *Independent financial advisers*

West London Electric Acton Ltd, 9-11 High Street, London, W3 6NQ Tel: (020) 8992 2155 Fax: (020) 8992 4067 E-mail: sales@wle.co.uk
Public address systems distributors

Martin West Signs, 200 Pyotts Hill, 20 Pyotts Hill, Old Basing, Basingstoke, Hants, RG24 8AP Tel: (01256) 464005 *Signwriting & glass gilding*

▶ West Meon Pottery, Church Lane, West Meon, Petersfield, Hampshire, GU32 1JW Tel: (01730) 829434 Fax: (01730) 829434
E-mail: sales@westmeonpottery.co.uk
Manufacturers of architectural terracotta chimney pots

West Mercia Air Conditioning Ltd, 29a Tarsmill Court, Rotherwas Industrial Estate, Hereford, HR2 6JZ Tel: (01432) 358489 Fax: (01432) 358489 E-mail: sales@wmaircon.com *Air conditioning & ventilation units distributors & services*

West Mercia Fork Truck Services Ltd, 23 Hainge Road, Tividale, Oldbury, West Midlands, B69 2NR Tel: 0121-522 2211 Fax: 0121-557 2665 E-mail: sales@westmercia.co.uk *Fork lift sales, hire & repairers*

West Mercia Hydraulics, 9 Horton Court, Hortonwood 50, Telford, Shropshire, TF1 7GY Tel: (01952) 606696 Fax: (01952) 670333
E-mail: wm.telford@wyko.co.uk *Hydraulic equipment*

West Mercia Sections Ltd, Nicholls Road, Tipton, West Midlands, DY4 9LG Tel: 0121-557 9927 Fax: 0121-520 3133
E-mail: sales@westmerciasections.freeserve.co.uk *Cold rolled steel sections*

West Mercia Security, 52 Walker Avenue, Stourbridge, West Midlands, DY9 9EL Tel: (01384) 396316 Fax: (01384) 396316
Security alarms installers

West Mercia Welding Services Ltd, Mercia House Wednesfield Road, Willenhall, West Midlands, WV13 1AN Tel: (01902) 608620 Fax: (01902) 606905 E-mail: wmws@cwcom.net *Welding supplies distributors*

West Meters Ltd, Phoenix House, London Road, Corwen, Clwyd, LL21 0DR Tel: (01490) 412004 Fax: (01490) 413336
E-mail: mail@westmeters.co.uk *Thermometer manufrs*

West Midland Engines, Saltley Road, Saltley, Birmingham, B7 4TD Tel: 0121-359 4402 Fax: 0121-359 7340 *Cylinder borers/crankshaft grinders*

▶ West Midland Glass Centre Ltd, Lupin Works, Worcester Road, Kidderminster, Worcestershire, DY10 1JR Tel: (01562) 60561 Fax: (01562) 752322

West Midland Glazing Co. Ltd, 123-125 Grove Lane, Birmingham, B17 0QT Tel: 0121-426 127 Fax: 0121-428 1625 *Aluminium, timber & upvc window frames instillation services*

West Midland Grinding Ltd, 1 Brookvale Trading Estate, Moor Lane, Birmingham, B6 7AQ Tel: 0121-356 3356 Fax: 0121-344 3770 *Centre less grinding specialists services*

West Midland Mouldings Ltd, Unit 2 West Coppice Road, Walsall, WS8 7HB Tel: (01543) 378100 Fax: (01543) 378100 *Plastic injection moulding*

West Midland Office Supplies, Cherry Tree Walk, Farrier Street, Worcester, WR1 3BH Tel: (0870) 3330933 Fax: (0870) 9001449 *Office equipment & commercial stationery suppliers*

▶ West Midland Pallets, 5 Holland Park, Bentley Road South, Wednesbury, West Midlands, WS10 8LN Tel: 0121-526 2630 Fax: 0121-526 2630
E-mail: sales@1stcallwestmidlandspallets.com
Recycle & sell wooden pallets wooden crates, metal spillages

West Midland Signs, 56 Station Road, Cradley Heath, West Midlands, B64 6NU Tel: (01384) 635577 Fax: (01384) 635577 *Sign makers*

▶ West Midlands Electrical, 17 High Street, West Bromwich, West Midlands, B70 6PP Tel: 0121-525 8919 Fax: 0121-553 1259

West Midlands Food Machines, 108 Worcester Road, Kidderminster, Worcestershire, DY10 1JS Tel: (01562) 742592 Fax: (01562) 742592
Catering equipment suppliers

West Midlands Foundry Co. Ltd, Blakemore Road, West Bromwich, West Midlands, B70 8JF Tel: 0121-553 1515 Fax: 0121-500 5839
Aluminium die castors

West Midlands Hire & Haulage, Dartmouth Road, Smethwick, West Midlands, B66 1BG Tel: 0121-555 5558 Fax: 0121-555 4939
E-mail: roylangford@wmhh.co.uk *Vehicle hire services*

West Midlands Laminating Co. Ltd, 50 Midland Street, Birmingham, B9 4DG Tel: 0121-773 0722 Fax: 0121-773 0741
E-mail: sales@westmidlam.co.uk *Print finishing & laminating cutting & creasing service*

West Midlands Lighting Centre, 10-12 York Road, Erdington, Birmingham, B23 6TE Tel: 0121-350 1999 Fax: 0121-377 7490
E-mail: westlight@msn.com *Lighting specialists*

West Midlands Precision Engineering Ltd, Unit 10/14, Gainsborough Trad Estate, Rufford Road, Stourbridge, West Midlands, DY9 7ND Tel: (01384) 397071 Fax: (01384) 378628
E-mail: info@westmidlandstpreg.co.uk *Precision machined parts*

West Midlands Thermocouples, Unit 203 Telsen Industrial Centre, Thomas Street, Birmingham, B6 4TN Tel: 0121-359 0535 Fax: 0121-359 4005
Temperature instrument manufrs

West Norfolk Superlime Co. Ltd, Station Road, Hillington, King's Lynn, Norfolk, PE31 6DG Tel: (01485) 600269 Fax: (01485) 609622
E-mail: info@westnorfolk.com *Lime producers & distribs*

West One Carriers, 99 North Street, London, SW4 0HF Tel: (020) 7720 0056 *Van parcel delivery services*

West Packaging Ltd, Cornish Street, Sheffield, S6 3AA Tel: 0114-276 0555 Fax: 0114-275 7590
E-mail: info@westpack.co.uk *Corrugated case & packaging, tape manufacturers & distributors*

West Pennine Storage Equipment Ltd, West Pennine Business Park, Burnley Road, Bacup, Lancashire, OL13 8PJ Tel: (01706) 875500 Fax: (01706) 875600
E-mail: westpenninesd@aol.com *Shelving & storage, equipment & systems distributor or agents*

▶ West Pennine Trucks Ltd, Cardronna, Station Road, Knighton, Powys, LD7 1DT Tel: (01547) 528600 Fax: (01547) 520597

▶ West Point Construction, Westpoint House, Securehold Business Centre, Redditch, Worcestershire, B98 7LG Tel: (01527) 528899 Fax: (01527) 529998
E-mail: info@westpoint-construction.co.uk *Civil engineering roads & sewers groundworks plant hire remediation*

West Point Engineering & Commercial Ltd, 3 St James's Square, London, SW1Y 4JU Tel: (020) 7930 0042 Fax: (020) 7839 2875 *Engineering products exporters services*

▶ West Printing Works Ltd, Elm Grove Lane, Steyning, West Sussex, BN44 3SA Tel: (01903) 813007 Fax: (01903) 814905

West Products (Jewellery) Ltd, Hanworth Trading Estate, Hampton Road West, Feltham, Middlesex, TW13 6DH Tel: (020) 8755 2638 Fax: (020) 8755 2166
E-mail: jeff@westproducts.co.uk *Fashion jewellery manufrs*

West Riding Aluminium Ltd, Unit 1 Young Street Industrial Estate, Young Street, Bradford, West Yorkshire, BD8 9RE Tel: (01274) 499761 Fax: (01274) 481678

continued

ntinuation
E-mail: wra@eurotelbroadband.com *Aluminium systems suppliers & installers*

West Riding Crushing Services Ltd, Holme Lane, Tong, Bradford, West Yorkshire, BD4 0RJ Tel: (01274) 687852 Fax: (01274) 688695

est Riding Engravers Ltd, 60 Wellington Street, Leeds, LS1 2EE Tel: 0113-243 9156 Fax: 0113-246 0787 E-mail: sales@wre-ltd.com *Engravers, sign makers & rubber stamp manufrs*

st Riding Home Securities, 13 Cross Street, Wakefield, West Yorkshire, WF1 3BW Tel: (01924) 377158 Fax: (01924) 201448 *Alarms & locksmiths*

est Riding Toyota, Leeds Road, Huddersfield, HD2 1YY Tel: (01484) 514514 Fax: (01484) 517724 *New & used car specialist*

est Salts Medilink, Salts House, 53 Valley Road, Plymouth, PL7 1RF Tel: (01752) 346027 Fax: (01752) 346027 *Surgical equipment distributors*

WEST SAW SERVICES LTD, UNIT 15, BALTIC WORKS, EFFINGAM ROAD, Sheffield, S9 3QA Tel: 0114 2426620 Fax: 0114 2426620 E-mail: josilk@btinternet.com *Established since 1987**Sharpening of handsaws,TCT ,High-Speed-Steel,Plate saw blades and all types of cutters.**

est Of Scotland Engineering Co. Ltd, 200 Old Dumbarton Road, Glasgow, G3 8QB Tel: 0141-339 6746 Fax: 0141-357 2325 E-mail: enquiries@wose.co.uk *Hydraulic engineers service*

West of Scotland Loan Fund Ltd, East Ayrshire Council HQ, London Road, Kilmarnock, Ayrshire, KA3 7BU Tel: 01563 554603 Fax: 01563 576238 E-mail: fundmanager@wslf.co.uk *Loan finance up to £50,000 is available to small and medium sized businesses located in the West of Scotland area.**As a public sector "gap funder" businesses should ensure they have exhausted all private sector sources.**Businesses can register on-line and download the application form.*

est & Senior Ltd, Milltown Street, Radcliffe, Manchester, M26 1WE Tel: 0161-724 7131 Fax: 0161-724 9519 E-mail: david.brown@westsenior.co.uk *Pigments manufrs*

West Side Project Management, The Winding House, Narborough Wood Park, Desford Road, Enderby, LE19 4XT Tel: (0844) 8006835 Fax: (0844) 8000035 E-mail: enquiries@westside.uk.net *Mechanical project management specialists*

est Street Studios, West Street Studios, 3 West Street, Buckingham, MK18 1HL Tel: (01280) 822814 Fax: E-mail: jamie@weststreetstudios.co.uk *Computer software, compact disc & compact disc read only memory (CD-ROM) duplicating services*

est Suffolk Tool & Gauge Ltd, 63d Gorse Industrial Estate, Barnham, Thetford, Norfolk, IP24 2PH Tel: (01842) 890278 Fax: (01842) 890632 *Precision engineers*

Vest Surrey Engineering Ltd, Enterprise House, Ashford Road, Ashford, Middlesex, TW15 1XG Tel: (01784) 254085 Fax: (01784) 247785 E-mail: sales@wse.co.uk *General engineering design & manufacture special purpose machines*

Vest Sussex Engineering Co. Ltd, Wedglen Industrial Estate, Midhurst, West Sussex, GU29 9RE Tel: (01730) 810045 Fax: (01730) 810047 *Production & precision engineers*

▶ West Sussex Signs, Clovelly Road, Southbourne, Emsworth, Hampshire, PO10 8PF Tel: (01243) 377702 Fax: (01243) 376454 E-mail: sales@westsussexsigns.co.uk *Sign contractors*

▶ West Thurrock Coachworks Ltd Grays, 2 Manor Way Industrial Estate, Curzon Drive, Grays, Essex, RM17 6BG Tel: (01375) 397989 Fax: (01375) 398282 *Repair & paint vehicles*

Vest Wales Bacon, 5 Carmarthen Road, Cross Hands, Llanelli, Dyfed, SA14 6SP Tel: (01269) 842148 Fax: (01269) 842148 *Bacon & ham curers merchants & wholesalers*

Vest Wales Chamber of Commerce, Creswell Buildings, 1 Burrows Place, Swansea, SA1 1SW Tel: (01792) 653297 Fax: (01792) 648345 E-mail: info@wwcc.co.uk *Chamber of commerce*

Vest Wales Marble & Granite, Units 9-11 Industrial Estate, Church Road, Gorslas, Llanelli, Dyfed, SA14 7NN Tel: (01269) 832868 Fax: (01267) 238525 E-mail: mail@westwalesmarbleandgranite.com *Manufacturers of marble fireplaces, wooden fire surrounds, granite worktops and sellers of a wide range of gas and electric fires.*

▶ West Wales Telecom, Camrose Lass, Portfield Gate, Haverfordwest, Dyfed, SA62 3LS Tel: (01437) 760984 E-mail: admin@westwalestelecom.com *Provide telecommunication services to businesses*

Vest Wiltshire Micros, White Hart Yard, Trowbridge, Wiltshire, BA14 8BY Tel: (01225) 762759 Fax: (01225) 764120 E-mail: sales@wwmicros.co.uk *Computer retailers*

▶ West Window Interiors, 2 Straw House Cottage, Kirkby Road, Ripon, North Yorkshire, HG4 3JU Tel: (01765) 608609 E-mail: sales@westwindowinteriors.co.uk *Bespoke kitchen, bedroom, bathroom & free standing furniture*

Vest Yorkshire Drawing Office Services Ltd, Swallow Hill Mills, Tong Road, Leeds, LS12 4QG Tel: 0113-220 5400 Fax: 0113-231 0615 E-mail: enquiries@wydos.co.uk *Drawing office suppliers*

Vest Yorkshire Fabrics Ltd, 20 High Ash Drive, Leeds, LS17 8RA Tel: (0870) 4439842 Fax: 0113-225 6550 E-mail: info@stroud-brothers.demon.co.uk *Men's textile merchants & machine suppliers*

Vest Yorkshire Printing Co. Ltd, Wyprint House, Smith Way, Wakefield Road, Ossett, West Yorkshire, WF5 9JZ Tel: (01924) 280522 Fax: (01924) 280145 E-mail: sales@westyor.co.uk *Colour printers & lithography*

▶ West Yorkshire Property Development Corporation Ltd, The Drill Hall 56 Leeds Road, Ilkley, West Yorkshire, LS29 8EQ Tel: (01535) 670033 E-mail: info@verminix.co.uk *Verminix Corporation is an Environmental Services and Landscape Gardening Company. Our prices are very competitive, so why not give us a call.*

West Yorkshire Spinners Ltd, Lowertown Mills, Lowertown, Oxenhope, Keighley, West Yorkshire, BD22 9JQ Tel: (01535) 642824 Fax: (01535) 642655 *Worsted spinners*

West Yorkshire Steel Co. Ltd, Sandbeck Works, Sandbeck Industrial Estate, Wetherby, West Yorkshire, LS22 7DN Tel: 01937 584440 Fax: (0845) 658 1305 E-mail: sales@westyorksteel.com Sales Contact: D. Ellis Principal Export Areas: Worldwide *U.K. special steel stockholder and supplier of tool steel, including cold work, hot work, and plastic mould steel specifications. High speed steel. Silver steel. Ground flat stock. Toolbits. High speed steel. Steel specifications; British, European, International including BS970 BS4659 DIN Werkstoff UNS Euronorm ASTM AISI. Stainless steel, 17/4PH, duplex and super duplex grades. Austenitic, Martensitic and Feritic. Engineering steel, carbon steel, key steel, alloy steel, spring steel, cast iron, non ferrous metals. All grades can be supplied as bar, plate, sheet or cut from block. Non standard sizes can be produced as steel forgings. To supply the product you want we offer a full range of services; with automated band sawing facilities for cut steel blanks, profiled laser and flame cut plate and sheet. Material can be centreless precision ground or surface ground to your required tolerances.*

Westac Holdings Ltd, Dial House, Govett Avenue, Shepperton, Middlesex, TW17 8AG Tel: (01932) 244042 Fax: (01932) 247124 E-mail: chris@westacltd.co.uk *Export services*

Westac Power Ltd, Powerpac House, Eastern Road, Aldershot, Hampshire, GU12 4TD Tel: (01252) 341134 Fax: (01252) 345353 E-mail: sales@westac.co.uk *Generator manufrs*

Westaff UK Ltd, Friary House, 46-50 Southgate Street, Gloucester, GL1 2DR Tel: (01452) 304090 Fax: (01452) 300332 E-mail: chichester@westaff.co.uk *Employment agents* Also at: Branches throughout the U.K.

Westair Flying Services Ltd, Blackpool Airport, Blackpool, FY4 2QX Tel: (01253) 404925 Fax: (01253) 401121 E-mail: services@westair.uk.com *Air charter service, flying school & engineers*

Westaway Sails Ltd, Erme Bridge, Ivybridge, Devon, PL21 9DU Tel: (01752) 892560 Fax: (01752) 895575 E-mail: sales@westawaysails.co.uk *Sail makers manufrs*

Westbay Technology Ltd, Main Street, Baycliff, Ulverston, Cumbria, LA12 9RN Tel: (01229) 869108 Fax: (01229) 869108 E-mail: sales@westbay.ndirect.co.uk *Electronic design software*

Westbournes Steel & Pipe, 1 Clovelly Road, Southbourne, Emsworth, Hampshire, PO10 8PE Tel: (01243) 376751 Fax: (01243) 376613 *Steel fabricators*

Westbrook Communications, Unit 9 Spectrum Industrial Estate, Bircholt Road, Maidstone, Kent, ME15 9YP Tel: (01622) 661860 Fax: (08700) 056902 E-mail: southeast@westbrookuk.com *Communications & internet services*

▶ Westbrook Communications Ltd, Unit 23 City Business Park, Somerset Place, Plymouth, PL3 4BB Tel: (0845) 0039090 Fax: (0870) 0056901 E-mail: southwest@westbrookuk.com *Data communication system installers*

Westbrook Marketing Ltd, 24 The Dean, Alresford, Hampshire, SO24 9AZ Tel: (01962) 733122 Fax: (01962) 733122 E-mail: sales@westbrookmarketing.co.uk *Distributor of advertising, business & promotional merchandise*

Westbrook Welding Alloy Ltd, 5 Melford Court, Hardwick Grange, Woolston, Warrington, WA1 4RZ Tel: (01925) 839983 Fax: (01925) 839990 E-mail: sales@westbrookwelding.co.uk *Welding wire wholesales*

▶ Westbury Conservatories Ltd, 2 Martels, High Easter Road, Barnston, Dunmow, Essex, CM6 1NA Tel: (01371) 876576 Fax: (01371) 872305

Westbury Control Systems Ltd, Unit 5, Wylam Court, Telford Way, Stephenson Industrial Estate, Coalville, Leicestershire, LE67 3HE Tel: (01530) 510751 Fax: (01530) 510756 E-mail: sales@westbury-uk.com *Westbury Control Systems design and manufacture Control Panel and Control systems for industrial control and automation projects to customer specific requirements. Our systems can range from simple to complex; starters to networked control solutions for a variety of industrial applications. Westbury Control Systems are centrally located in the Midlands offering service and support through out the UK and overseas.*

Westbury Country Foods Ltd, Unit 1 Lodge Hill Industrial Estate, Station Road, Westbury Sub Mendip, Wells, Somerset, BA5 1EY Tel: (01749) 870122 Fax: (01749) 870177 *Sandwich filling manufrs*

Westbury Financial Management, Hall Farm Estate, Gadbrook Road, Betchworth, Surrey, RH3 7AH Tel: (01306) 611611 Fax: (01306) 611613 E-mail: sales@westburyfilters.co.uk *Air filters manufrs*

Westbury Homes, Glanville House, Church Street, Bridgwater, Somerset, TA6 5AT Tel: (01278) 458645 Fax: (01278) 452274 *Building contractors*

▶ Westbury Homes, Anchor Boulevard, Crossways, Dartford, DA2 6QH Tel: (01322) 421800 Fax: (01322) 421900

▶ Westbury Homes, Bartley House, Station Road, Hook, Hampshire, RG27 9JF Tel: (01256) 744000 Fax: (01256) 769388

▶ Westbury Industrial Supplies, 651 Melton Road, Thurmaston, Leicester, LE4 8EB Tel: 0116-264 0920 Fax: 0116-264 0922 *Industrial suppliers*

Westbury Park Engineering Ltd, Brook Lane, Westbury, Wiltshire, BA13 4ES Tel: (01373) 825500 Fax: (01373) 825511 E-mail: jamesbrain@westparkeng.co.uk *Structural engineers*

Westcliff Armature Winding Co., 369 Westborough Road, Westcliff-On-Sea, Essex, SS0 9TS Tel: (01702) 341854 *Electrical motor rewind services*

Westco Bilanciai Ltd, Broadgauge House, Westridge Way, Bishops Lydeard, Taunton, Somerset, TA4 3RU Tel: (01823) 433411 Fax: (01823) 433334 E-mail: sales@westcoweigh.co.uk *Industrial weighing equipment, weighbridges, pallet scales, labelling & packaging, barcode, silo, vessel, hopper, checkweighing, onboard vehicle weighing.*

Westco Group Ltd, Penarth Road, Cardiff, CF11 8YN Tel: (029) 2037 6700 Fax: (029) 2038 3573 E-mail: westco@westcodiy.co.uk *Tile floor coverings*

Westcom Computer Consultants, 6-8 Wilson Street, Workington, Cumbria, CA14 4AZ Tel: (01900) 870455 Fax: (01900) 606665 E-mail: sales@west-comm.co.uk *Computer hardware suppliers*

Westcom Engineers, Global Park, East Gates Industrial Estate, Colchester, CO1 2TW Tel: (01206) 794114 Fax: (01206) 792749 E-mail: admin@westcomeng.fsnet.co.uk *CNC engineers*

Westcombe Industries Ltd, Royce Road, Peterborough, PE1 5YB Tel: (01733) 746300 Fax: (01733) 746310 *Precision CNC machining services for small to large batches. 250mm turning and 1000mm machining centre capacities. CAD/CAM enables fast production turnaround. Fully equipped manual machine shop with CMM inspection capabilities. Small assembly work carried out.*

Westcon Convergents, 1 Clayton Manor, Victoria Gardens, Burgess Hill, West Sussex, RH15 9NB Tel: (01444) 230004 Fax: (01444) 243889 E-mail: info@cranetel.co.uk *Telecommunications distributors*

Westcon UK Ltd, 159 Edinburgh Avenue, Slough, SL1 4UE Tel: (01753) 797800 Fax: (01753) 797801 E-mail: sales@westcon.co.uk *Computer hardware distributors*

Westcountry Conveyors, 23 Lowley Road, Pennygillam Industrial Estate, Launceston, Cornwall, PL15 7PY Tel: (01566) 777940 Fax: (01566) 777659 E-mail: westconveyors@aol.com *Conveyor belt installation, repair & manufrs*

Westcountry Security Ltd, 9 Orchard Court, Heron Road, Sowton Industrial Estate, Exeter, EX2 7LL Tel: (01392) 671561 Fax: (01392) 671562 E-mail: sales@westcountrysecurity.co.uk *Security agents*

Westcountry Security Exeter Ltd, 15 Billacombe Road, Plymouth, PL9 7HN Tel: (0870) 8500432 Fax: (01752) 492591 E-mail: sales@westcountrysecurity.co.uk *Alarm systems designers & installers* Also at: Exeter

Westcountry Shotblasting Ltd, Armidale, Fenny Bridges, Honiton, Devon, EX14 3BG Tel: (07870) 606116 E-mail: blasting@btinternet.com *? Sand, Shot & Grit Blasting*? Steel, Brick, Stonework and Home Exteriors*? Timber Ageing*? Fully Mobile Service & Works Based Blasting*? Priming & Spraying Service*? Commercial, Plant & Agricultural**

Westcrete Pre-cast Concrete Ltd, Stoney Bridges, Membury Road, Axminster, Devon, EX13 5RL Tel: (01297) 32002 E-mail: sales@westcrete.fsnet.co.uk *Ready mix concrete suppliers & builders merchants*

The Westdale Press Ltd, Unit 70, Portmanmoor Road Industrial Estate, Cardiff, CF24 5HB Tel: (029) 2046 1363 Fax: (029) 2066 2608 E-mail: alan@westdale.co.uk *Lithographic printers* Also at: London NW

Westdale Products Ltd, 56 Blackpole Road, Worcester, WR3 8SQ Tel: (01905) 457959 Fax: (01905) 458047 *Metal fabricators*

Westec Office Equipment, 8 Old Town Street, Dawlish, Devon, EX7 9AL Tel: (01626) 888117 Fax: (01626) 888299 E-mail: sales@westec.uk.com *Xerox engineering system & dealer for machines*

Westek Holdings Ltd, Unit 1 Lancaster Park Industrial Estate, Bowerhill, Melksham, Wiltshire, SN12 6TT Tel: (01225) 790600 Fax: (01225) 702968 E-mail: sales@westekuk.com *Computer suppliers & manufrs*

Westend Leisure, 21 Briar Close, Newhall, Swadlincote, Derbyshire, DE11 0RX Tel: (01283) 214064 E-mail: garyandbev@tiscali.co.uk *Bouncing castle hire*

▶ Westerman Road Haulage Services, Station Road, Sutton-in-Ashfield, Nottinghamshire, NG17 5FH Tel: (01623) 441111 Fax: (01623) 440301

Westermans Welding Equipment, 2 Brook Street, Syston, Leicester, LE7 1GD Tel: 0116-269 6941 Fax: 0116-269 6942 E-mail: welding@westermans.com *Machinery manufacturers & welding equipment*

Westermo Data Communications Ltd, Talisman Business Centre, Duncan Road, Park Gate, Southampton, SO31 7GA Tel: (01489) 580585 Fax: (01489) 580586 E-mail: sales@westermo.co.uk *Suppliers of industrial data communications products*

Western Air Ltd, Bencroft View House, Studley Hill, Studley, Calne, Wiltshire, SN11 9NL Tel: (01249) 817579 Fax: (01249) 819006 *Refrigeration & air conditioning installation*

Western Automation, Unit 1 Spitfire Road, Birmingham, B24 9PR Tel: 0121-328 2000 Fax: 0121-328 7156 E-mail: sales@etfbirmingham.co.uk *Electrical & control distributors*

Western Automation, Western House, Ipswich Road, Cardiff, CF23 9AQ Tel: (029) 2048 8446 Fax: (029) 2047 1843 E-mail: sales@appliedautomation.co.uk *Hydraulic & pneumatic equipment suppliers*

Western Automation, Unit 1 Boston Court, Salford, M50 2GN Tel: 0161-877 0910 Fax: 0161-876 5243 E-mail: westernautomation@yahoo.co.uk *Automation & control electrical distributors*

Western Automation Ivac, 5 Colemans Bridge, Witham, Essex, CM8 3HP Tel: (01376) 511808 Fax: (01376) 500862 E-mail: sales@waivac.co.uk *Valve distributors including actuated, chemical & solenoid*

Western Blocks Ltd, 42 Upton Towans, Hayle, Cornwall, TR27 5BL Tel: (01736) 753128 Fax: (01736) 756857 *Pre-cast & ready mixed concrete manufrs*

Western Castors & Wheels Ltd, Mardle Way, Buckfastleigh, Buckfastleigh, Devon, TQ11 0NR Tel: (01364) 43235 Fax: (01364) 643405 E-mail: sales@western-uk.com *Castor suppliers*

Western Computer Group Ltd, Victoria House, Temple Gate, Bristol, BS1 6PW Tel: 0117-922 5661 Fax: 0117-922 6504 E-mail: applecentre@western.co.uk *Apple mac dealers*

Western Corrugated Ltd, Unit 59 60 Springvale Industrial Estate, Cwmbran, Gwent, NP44 5BE Tel: (01633) 872525 Fax: (01633) 861524 E-mail: sales@western-corr.co.uk *Corrugated fibre board manufrs*

▶ Western Event Hire, C Clarke Centre, Hennock Road North, Marsh Barton Trading Estate, Exeter, EX2 8NJ Tel: (0845) 6061062 Fax: (01392) 411952 *Catering equipment hire*

▶ Western Eye, Kinley House, 43 The Crescent, Bristol, BS9 4RP Tel: (07803) 593833 E-mail: mail@western-eye.com *Film, television & corporate video production*

▶ Western Ferries Clyde Ltd, Marine Parade, Hunters Quay, Dunoon, Argyll, PA23 8HJ Tel: (01369) 704452 Fax: (01369) 706020 E-mail: info@western-ferries.co.uk

▶ Western Foods, Units 3-4 Bridge Court, Imerington Road, Ivybridge, Devon, PL21 9EY Tel: (01752) 690371 Fax: (01752) 690371 *Barkers*

▶ Western I T Services, 1, Tindal Street, Chelmsford, CM1 1ER Tel: (01245) 284886

Western Industrial, Linhay Business Park, Eastern Road, Ashburton, Devon, TQ13 7UP Tel: (01364) 651860 Fax: (01364) 651861 E-mail: sales@westernindustrial.co.uk *Storage handling specialists*

Western Industrial Insulation, Blakeney Business Park, High Street, Blakeney, Gloucestershire, GL15 4EB Tel: (01594) 517238 Fax: (01594) 516836 *Sprayed polyurethane foam insulation*

Western Industries Co. Ltd, 5 Garage Road, Queens Drive, London, W3 0HE Tel: (020) 8992 1360 Fax: (020) 8993 7780 E-mail: w.industries@talk21.com *International sales promotion*

▶ Western Isles Kite Co., West View, Aird Timsgarry, Isle of Lewis, HS2 9JA Tel: (01851) 672771 E-mail: info@wikc.co.uk *Power kite specialists suppliers in the outer hebrides*

Western Laboratory Service Ltd, Unit 8 Redan Hill Estate, Redan Road, Aldershot, Hampshire, GU12 4SJ Tel: (0870) 7879528 Fax: (0870) 7879529 E-mail: info@wls.co.uk *Laboratory consumables suppliers*

Western Mail, Newsdesk, Havelock Street, Cardiff, CF1 1WR Tel: (029) 2058 3668 Fax: (029) 2058 3443 *Newspaper publishers*

Western Mechanical Handling UK Ltd, Celtic Road, Moss Side Industrial Estate, Callington, Cornwall, PL17 7SD Tel: (01579) 383788 Fax: (01579) 383923 *Food handling equipment manufrs*

Western Metalcraft, 79d Grove Road, Fishponds, Bristol, BS16 2BP Tel: 0117-965 3865 Fax: 0117-965 3865 *Light metal fabricators*

Western Minerals Ltd, 253 Cranbrook Road, Ilford, Essex, IG1 4TQ Tel: (020) 8554 0102 Fax: (020) 8518 2920 *Mineral merchants*

Western Models Ltd, Acre Ridge, Clayhidon, Cullompton, Devon, EX15 3TW Tel: (01823) 666767 Fax: (01823) 666757 E-mail: sales@westernmodels.com *Model car & plane manufrs*

Western Morning News Co. Ltd, 17 Brest Road, Derriford, Plymouth, PL6 5AA Tel: (01752) 765500 Fax: (01752) 765515 E-mail: plymouthfrontcounter@westcountrypublications.co.uk *Publishers*

Western Office Equipment, 53 Omaha Road, Walker Lines Industrial Estate, Bodmin, Cornwall, PL31 1ES Tel: (01208) 72042 Fax: (01208) 79642 E-mail: western@office54.fsbusiness.co.uk *Cash registers*

▶ Western Power Steering, Hanham Business Park, Memorial Road, Hanham, Bristol, BS15 3JE Tel: 0117-960 2906 Fax: 0117-960 2910 E-mail: sales@westernpowersteering.co.uk *Power steering racks, pumps, boxes worldwide supply*

Western Printers, 103 Cleveland Street, London, W1T 6PP Tel: (020) 7631 5225 Fax: (020) 7323 6512 E-mail: sales@western-printers.co.uk *General printers*

Western Refrigeration Services Ltd, 46 Aldercombe Road, Bristol, BS9 2QL Tel: 0117-968 3964 Fax: 0117-968 3964 *Air conditioning service providers*

Western Refrigeration Co. (Taunton), 53 Hamilton Road, Taunton, Somerset, TA1 2EL Tel: (01823) 272347 Fax: (01823) 272368 E-mail: sales@westfridge.sagehost.co.uk *Refrigerating & air conditioning engineers*

Western Regional Energy Agency Network, 1 Nugents Entry, Enniskillen, County Fermanagh, BT74 7DF Tel: (028) 6632 8269 Fax: (028) 6632 9771 *Energy efficiency centre*

Richard Western Ltd, The Durbans, Apsey Green, Framlingham, Woodbridge, Suffolk, IP13 9RP Tel: (01728) 723224 Fax: (01728) 724291 E-mail: sales@richard-western.co.uk Principal Export Areas: Worldwide *Agricultural machine suppliers*

Western Saw Service, Unit 37 Willan Industrial Estate, Vere Street, Salford, M50 2GR Tel: 0161-736 9608 Fax: 0161-736 9608 *Saw sharpening services*

Western Self Storage, A Phoenix Trading Estate, London Road, Thrupp, Stroud, Gloucestershire, GL5 2BX Tel: (01453) 883743 Fax: (01453) 231033 E-mail: info@westernselfstorage.co.uk *Lock-up storage contractors & services*

▶ Western Standard Corporation, 49 Florence Road, Gedling, Nottingham, NG4 2QL Tel: 0115-940 3131 Fax: 0115-940 3134 *Independent commercial and business finance brokers with over 35 years experience in the UK market.*- Commercial Mortgages*- Property Development*- Asset finance*- Invoice Finance.**When others say NO, we look to find the way to say YES!*

Western Timber & Builders Merchants - Heston, 236a Heston Road, Hounslow, TW5 0RH Tel: (020) 8570 3218 Fax: (020) 8570 3794 *Building materials merchants*

Western Tooling Ltd, 55-57 Sterte Avenue, Poole, Dorset, BH15 2AJ Tel: (01202) 677654 Fax: (01202) 677876 E-mail: sales@westerntooling.co.uk *Valves & fittings for flexi tanks, rigid tanks & containers manufrs*

Western Towing & Alarms, Unit A1 Kingsteignton Industrial Estate, Kingsteignton, Newton Abbot, Devon, TQ12 3BN Tel: (01392) 216336 Fax: (01392) 430415 E-mail: sales@westerntowing.co.uk *Towbars supplied & fitted. Trailer sales, service, spares, repairs & accessories*

Western Towing & Alarms, Unit A1 Kingsteignton Industrial Estate, Kingsteignton, Newton Abbot, Devon, TQ12 3BN Tel: (01392) 216336 Fax: (01626) 363111 E-mail: richardsaxton@aol.com *Tow bars & trailer supplier manufrs*

Western Truck Ltd, 123 Clydesdale Place, Moss Side Industrial Estate, Leyland, PR26 7QS Tel: (01772) 454124 Fax: (01772) 456075 E-mail: rr@westerntruck.co.uk *Commercial vehicle distributors*

Western Tyres Ltd, Alloys House, St.Andrews Road, Avonmouth, Bristol, BS11 9HS Tel: 0117-940 1991 Fax: 0117-923 5099 E-mail: mike@westtyre.demon.co.uk *Tyre wholesalers*

▶ Western Well Tool Ltd, Unit1 Airways Industrial Estate, Pitmedden Road, Dyce, Aberdeen, AB21 0DT Tel: (01224) 224646

Westerngeco, Schlumberger House, Buckingham Gate, London Gatwick Airport, Gatwick, West Sussex, RH6 0NZ Tel: (01293) 556000 Fax: (01293) 556080 E-mail: sales@westerngeco.com *Geophysical consultants*

Westex Carpets Ltd, Castle Mills, Northgate, Cleckheaton, West Yorkshire, BD19 3JB Tel: (01274) 861334 Fax: (01274) 873266 E-mail: info@westexcarpets.co.uk *Carpets*

Westfalia Surge Ltd, 30 Tanners Drive, Blakelands, Milton Keynes, MK14 5BN Tel: (01908) 589600 Fax: (01908) 589650 E-mail: sales@westfaliasurgeltd.com *Milking machine distributors*

Westfield Advertising Specialities Ltd, 1 Helena Street, Birmingham, B1 2RJ Tel: 0121-233 1671 Fax: 0121-236 4121 E-mail: sales@westfieldltd.co.uk *Business gift manufrs*

Westfield Caledonian Ltd, 4 Mollins Court, Cumbernauld, Glasgow, G68 9HP Tel: (01236) 786300 Fax: (01236) 786301 E-mail: info@west-cal.co.uk *Air & water monitoring consultants*

Grant Westfield Ltd, 3 Westfield Avenue, Edinburgh, EH11 2QH Tel: 0131-337 6262 Fax: 0131-337 2859 E-mail: sales@grantwestfield.co.uk *Fabricators, laminators & building interior products services*

▶ Westfield International Transport, Hortham Lane, Gaunts Earthcott, Almondsbury, Bristol, BS32 4JP Tel: (01454) 775566 Fax: (01454) 776817

Westfield Manchester Ltd, Hawthorn House, 14 Manchester Road, Wilmslow, Cheshire, SK9 1BG Tel: (01625) 548100 Fax: (01625) 548200 E-mail: westfildtexuk@aol.com *Ladies clothing*

Westfield Precision Engineering, 14 Westfield Industrial Estate, Gosport, Hampshire, PO12 3RX Tel: (023) 9250 1854 Fax: (023) 9252 7423 *Precision engineers*

Westfield Sports Cars Ltd, 1 Gibbons Industrial Park, Dudley Road, Kingswinford, West Midlands, DY6 8XF Tel: (01384) 400077 Fax: (01384) 288781 E-mail: info@westfield-sportscars.co.uk *Chassis builders & motor vehicle body*

Westfield Truro Cornwall Ltd, Kerley Paddock, Chacewater, Truro, Cornwall, TR4 8JY Tel: (01872) 560860 Fax: (01872) 561056 E-mail: info@westfieldtransport.com *Haulage contractors*

Westford Plastics & Engineering Ltd, Westford, Wellington, Somerset, TA21 0DU Tel: (01823) 662377 Fax: (01823) 663238 E-mail: l_cross@msn.com *Plastic engineers & design*

Westframe Investments Ltd, 162-164 Teignmouth Road, Torquay, TQ1 4RY Tel: (01803) 313861 Fax: (01803) 312063 E-mail: westframe@construction-ltd.fsnet.co.uk *Industrial & commercial design & construction*

▶ Westgate Design, 37 The Drive, Sevenoaks, Kent, TN13 3AD Tel: (01732) 454588 Fax: (01732) 779087 E-mail: shaun@westgatedesign.co.uk *Design consultancy*

Westgate Developments, Derby House, 11 Rosebery Road, Langley Vale, Epsom, Surrey, KT18 6AF Tel: (01372) 800404 Fax: (01372) 800407 E-mail: west-gate@ntlworld.com *Broadcasting equipment manufrs*

Westgate Factory Dividers, PO Box 21, Stafford, ST16 3DD Tel: (01785) 242171 *Window film contracts factory screening service*

Westgate Fastenings, Gapton Hall Industrial Estate, Viking Road, Great Yarmouth, Norfolk, NR31 0NU Tel: (01493) 603207 Fax: (01493) 656284 E-mail: westgatefastenings@connectfree.co.uk *Fastenings*

Westgate Fastenings, 5-6 Cumberland Place, Lowestoft, Suffolk, NR32 1UQ Tel: (01502) 560061 Fax: (01502) 517505 *Fasteners suppliers*

Westgate Group Ltd, Newchurch, Romney Marsh, Kent, TN29 0DZ Tel: (01303) 872277 Fax: (01303) 874801 E-mail: sales@wefi.co.uk *Equestrian distributors*

Westgate Solar Control, PO Box 21, Stafford, ST16 3YJ Tel: (01785) 242181 *Solar heat reflecting & control film supply install*

Westguard Safety Ltd, Unit 1 Newporte Business Park, Cardinal Close, Bishops Road, Lincoln, LN2 4SY Tel: (01522) 513512 Fax: (01522) 549658 E-mail: sales@medikit.co.uk *Protective clothing safety equipment & footwear & first aid*

Westham Food Supplies, 9 Gordon Row, Weymouth, Dorset, DT4 8LL Tel: (01305) 783608 *Fresh food suppliers*

Westhaven Properties Ltd, 1 Sherbourne Road, Acocks Green, Birmingham, B27 6AB Tel: 0121-706 6100 Fax: 0121-707 1890 *Property developers*

Westhead Welding Fabricators Ltd, 1 Glan Y Morfa Industrial Estate, Marsh Road, Rhyl, Clwyd, LL18 2AD Tel: (01745) 344461 Fax: (01745) 344769 *Steel fabricators*

Westheath Press Ltd, 55 Mott Street, Birmingham, B19 3HE Tel: 0121-236 0507 Fax: 0121-236 1088 *Lithographers & advertising printers*

Westinghouse Rail Systems Ltd, PO Box 79, Chippenham, Wiltshire, SN15 1JD Tel: (01249) 441441 Fax: (01249) 441442 E-mail: wrsl.marketing@invensys.com *Signalling & integrated controls systems*

Westinsure Webb Ltd, Alexandra House, 63 Killigrew Street, Falmouth, Cornwall, TR11 3PE Tel: (01326) 313737 Fax: (01326) 211387 E-mail: enquiries@westinsurewebb.co.uk *Insurance & investment brokers* Also at: Truro

Westlairds Ltd, Patrixbourne, The Green, Datchet, Slough, SL3 9JH Tel: (01753) 543939 Fax: (01753) 549933 E-mail: westlairds@westlairds.co.uk *Manufacturers & suppliers of instruments for quality control*

▶ Westlake Information Technology Ltd, 9 Windmill Field Denmead, Waterlooville, Hampshire, PO7 6PL Tel: (023) 9226 9594 E-mail: info@westlake-it.com *We are an independent IT Support Company providing a comprehensive range of computer services to small businesses throughout Hampshire and the surrounding counties. **

Westlakes, 440 High Road, Wembley, Middlesex, HA9 6AH Tel: (020) 8902 2392 Fax: (020) 8902 1780 E-mail: enquiries@westlakes.uk.com *Commercial stationers & computer supplies*

Westland Casting Co. Ltd, 4-5 Vaux Road, Finedon Road Industrial Estate, Wellingborough, Northamptonshire, NN8 4TG Tel: (01933) 276718 Fax: (01933) 442185 E-mail: info@westlandcastings.co.uk *Aluminium sand & gravity castings*

▶ Westland Rollers Ltd, F Trevithick Road, Willowbrook East Industrial Es, Corby, Northamptonshire, NN17 5XY Tel: (01536) 401899 Fax: (01536) 401773 E-mail: sales@westland-worldwide.de *Manufactures of precession ground rubber coated rollers*

Westlb UK Ltd, 25 Basinghall Street, London, EC2V 5HA Tel: (020) 7020 7300 Fax: (020) 7020 2002 E-mail: sales@westlb.com *Investment bankers*

Westler Foods Ltd, Amotherby, Malton, North Yorkshire, YO17 6TQ Tel: (0800) 0276336 Fax: (01653) 600187 E-mail: custserv@westler.com *Westlers is a Malton, North Yorkshire-based.rapidly evolving producer of convenience foods with a vast experience of producing a range of products for both caterers and consumers. Their product range includes convenience meals, Kono Pizza, hot dogs and burgers, fruit and vegetables, Mexican snacks, nachos and many more.*

Westley Consulting Ltd, 7 St Andrews Terrace, Bath, BA1 2QR Tel: (01225) 312261 Fax: 01225 312261 E-mail: henrybrown@btconnect.com *Business planning consultant and food product marketing adviser to UK rural and food companies, and Government agencies. Specialists in business planning, marketing strategy, food product marketing and Government grant applications.*

▶ Westley Dental Laboratories Ltd, 430 Stratford Road, Sparkhill, Birmingham, B11 4AD Tel: 0121-772 5313 Fax: 0121-772 5313

Westley Engineering Ltd, 120 Pritchett Street, Birmingham, B6 4EH Tel: 0121-333 1925 Fax: 0121-333 1926 E-mail: engineering@westleyrichards.co.uk *Contract precision pressing services*

Westley Group Ltd, PO Box No1, Doulton Road, Cradley Heath, West Midlands, B64 5QS Tel: (01384) 410111 Fax: 08701 290 865 E-mail: clair.littley@westleygroup.co.uk *Westley Group is one of Europe's largest ferrous and non-ferrous foundry & engineering groups, consisting of the following five brands: FRANCIS W BIRKETT:Low-high volume sand, gravity & shell castings, finish machined. Franberlube self-lubricated bearings & white metalling. SPUNALLOYS: Centrifugal castings in bronze, aluminium bronze, gunmetal and steel alloys up to 2000mm ø. MATHERS: Steel sand castings in carbon steel, low alloy steels, CrMo steels & nickel alloys, stainless steel, super duplex steels, ZERON® & duplex. WESTLEYS: TOTAL CASTING SERVICE offering high integrity and commercial sand castings in copper based alloys. Complete finish machining via on-site machine shop. Global and UK procurement. WALTER FRANK: Non-ferrous fire fighting fittings & equipment, pressure regulating valves (including PRV9i - see www.prv9i.com) and instantaneous fittings. Design & engineering services.*

Westley Plastics Ltd, Gawne Lane, Cradley Heath, West Midlands, B64 5QY Tel: (01384) 414840 Fax: (01384) 414849 E-mail: sales@plastics.co.uk *Manufacturers of cast nylon machinists of engineering plastics*

Westline Distributors Ltd, West Line Industrial Estate, Birtley, Chester le Street, County Durham, DH2 1AU Tel: 0191-410 2636 Fax: 0191-492 2108 E-mail: LINDA@bedegroup.net *Westline*

continued

Distributors are a specialist supplier to the construction industry and our mission is to "source and supply specialist building products for our clients in the construction industry, that save time, cut costs and assits them to achieve their business goals" whilst focusing on customer service. Westline Distributors supply Catnic Lintels , Special Lintels and Builders Steelwork as well as other specialist products. See our Product Summary for further information. We have our own Technical Department where our experienced, dedicated team can produce schedules and supply calculations on request offering a quality service which is second to none. We also have a full design service should bespoke work be required. We have depots in the North East and the Nottingham areas , which carry excellent stock ranges. We have a proven distribution network with a quick turnaround, which covers the whole of the United Kingdom.

▶ Westlink Transport, Unit 6-7 Euro Way, Blagrove, Swindon, SN5 8YW Tel: (01793) 421611 Fax: (01793) 541542 E-mail: sales@westlinkuk.co.uk

Westlock Controls Ltd, 22 Chapman Way, Tunbridge Wells, Kent, TN2 3EF Tel: (01892) 516277 Fax: (01892) 516279 E-mail: info@westlockcontrols.com *Process control, valves & actuations monitoring manufrs*

Westman Engineering Ltd, Units 15-18 Block 3, Old Mill ParkIndustrial Estate, Mansfield Woodhouse, Nottinghamshire, NG19 9BG Tel: (01623) 648740 Fax: (01623) 420376 *Sheet metal light steel fabricators*

Westman Systems Ltd, Unit 5-6 Thistle Park, Crossways Road, Bridgwater, Somerset, TA6 6LS Tel: (01278) 424717 Fax: (01278) 424718 E-mail: westman.systems@lineone.net *Manufacturers of battery chargers*

▶ Westmans Engineering, Westmans Trading Estate, Love Lane, Burnham-on-Sea, Somerset, TA8 1EY Tel: (01278) 781666 Fax: (01278) 781666

Westmid Fans, Zephyr House, Mucklow Hill, Halesowen, West Midlands, B62 8DN Tel: 0121-550 0315 Fax: 0121-585 5185 E-mail: westmidfunds@btconnect.com *Environmental equipment stockists*

▶ Westmill Foods Ltd, The Quay, Selby, North Yorkshire, YO8 4EG Tel: (01757) 293200 Fax: (01757) 293208 E-mail: sales@allinsonbaking.com *Rice packers*

Westmill Joinery, Belgravia Street, Penzance, Cornwall, TR18 2AJ Tel: (01736) 362579 *Joinery manufrs*

Westminster Controls Ltd, Unit 3 Pym Street, Leeds, LS10 1PG Tel: 0113-288 4500 Fax: 0113-246 0791 E-mail: info@westminstercontrols.com *Control systems specialists*

▶ Westminster Hotel, 16 Leinster Square, London, W2 4PR Tel: (020) 7221 9131 Fax: (020) 7221 4073 E-mail: reservations@thewestminsterhotel.com *The Westminster is located in a quiet garden square in Bayswater/Notting Hill close to Paddington Station(Heathrow Express terminal)and is perfectly situated for anyone visiting London for business or pleasure. All rooms are en-suite, furnished in a modern way and have wired modem-connections for easy access to the Internet. Other Guest room facilities include remote controlled colour TV with satellite channels, radio, direct dial telephone, trouser press with iron, hairdryer and a welcome tray with tea and coffee making facilities. Every morning the hotel provides a generous Continental Buffet Breakfast or a choice of full English Breakfast to all Guests and in the evening dinner and snacks are served in 'Conrads Bar'. We offer everything you would expect from a 3star central London hotel plus a friendly atmosphere making all our Guests feel very welcome. ***

Westminster Joinery, Bowcombe Meadows Business Park, Bowcombe Road, Newport, Isle of Wight, PO30 3HZ Tel: (01983) 825355 *Joinery manufrs*

Westminster Motor Insurance Association Ltd, 21 Buckingham Palace Road, London, SW1W 0PN Tel: (020) 7834 3976 Fax: (020) 7834 4898 *Insurance company*

Westminster Partitions & Joinery Ltd, Unit F, Printing House Lane, Hayes, Middlesex, UB3 1AP Tel: (020) 8848 0126 Fax: (020) 8848 8845 E-mail: info@partition.co.uk *Partition contractors*

Westminster Pharmaceutical Paramedics Supplies, 17 Duncan Road, Gillingham, Kent, ME7 4LA Tel: (01634) 852728 Fax: (01634) 856410 *Pharmaceuticals manufrs*

Westminster Plastic Fabrication Ltd, Wynstead, Parkgate Road, Saughall, Chester, CH1 6JS Tel: (01244) 881884 Fax: (01244) 880111 E-mail: westpack@tiscali.co.uk *Conveyor belting suppliers & fitters & plastic fabrications*

▶ Westminster Sonus, Westminster House, Herschel Centre, Church Street, Slough, SL1 1PJ Tel: (01753) 553325 Fax: (01753) 553867 E-mail: crn@westminstersonus.com *Conference & language services*

▶ Westmorland Fire & Security Ltd, Beezon Chambers, Sandes Avenue, Kendal, Cumbria, LA9 6BL Tel: (01539) 724919 Fax: (01539) 740589 E-mail: service@westmorlandsecurity.co.uk *CCTV, access control, gas suppression systems manufrs*

The Westmorland Gazette Newspaper, 1 Wainwright Yard, Kendal, Cumbria, LA9 4DP Tel: (01539) 720555 Fax: (01539) 723618 E-mail: gazette@kendal.newsquest.co.uk *Newspaper*

Westmorland Glass Kendal Ltd, Shap Road, Kendal, Cumbria, LA9 6LX Tel: (01539) 730000 Fax: (01539) 740076 *Glass merchants & glaziers*

Westmorland Truck Bodies Ltd, 19 Cumberland St, Hull, HU2 0QB Tel: (01482) 329062 Fax: (01482) 329062 *Coach builders & paint sprayers*

Westmount Picture Framing, 116A Westmount Road, London, SE9 1UT Tel: (020) 8850 5220 *Picture framing services*

Westok Ltd, Horbury Junction Industrial Estate, Calder Vale Road, Horbury, Wakefield, West Yorkshire, WF4 5ER Tel: (01924) 264121 Fax: (01924) 280030 E-mail: info@westok.co.u *Steel fabricators*

Westomatic Vending Systems Ltd, Shaldon Road, Newton Abbot, Devon, TQ12 4TZ Tel: (01626) 323100 Fax: (01626) 332828 E-mail: mailbox@westomatic.com *Vending machine manufrs*

Weston & Bolton Ltd, 118-126 Gipsy Lane, Leicester, LE4 6RL Tel: 0116-266 4441 E-mail: sales@weston-bolton.co.uk *Builders merchants*

Weston Business Forms, Unit 23-24 Solent Industrial Estate, Shamblehurst Lane, Hedge End, Southampton, SO30 2FY Tel: (01489) 780707 Fax: (01489) 780200 E-mail: sales@westonbusinessforms.co.uk *Business form printers & manufrs*

Weston Catering Products, Unit B3, Oldmixon Cresent, Weston-Super-Mare, Avon, BS24 9AY Tel: (01934) 642477 Fax: (01934) 624484 *Trailers manufrs*

Weston Designs, Unit G9 Rudford Industrial Estate, Ford Road, Arundel, West Sussex, BN18 0BD Tel: (01403) 274639 Fax: (01403) 274665 E-mail: sales@westondesigns.ndo.co.uk *Intern. & external signing & sign designers*

▶ Weston Electrical Services, Laurel House, 1 Station Road, Worle, Weston-super-Mare, Avon BS22 6AR Tel: (01934) 516500 Fax: (01934) 516400

Weston Hair & Beauty Supplies, 8 Orchard House Station Road, Worle, Weston-super-Mare, Avon BS22 6AU Tel: (01934) 520252 Fax: (01934) 520252 *Hair & beauty suppliers*

J. Weston & Partners Ltd, Cudgamoor Farm, East Putford, Holsworthy, Devon, EX22 7XR Tel: (01237) 451838 Fax: (01237) 451553 E-mail: nigel.moulder@hotmail.co.uk *Welding supplies manufrs*

Weston Sawmill & Nursery, Hatch Lane, Weston Under Lizard, Shifnal, Shropshire, TF11 8JU Tel: (01952) 850383 Fax: (01952) 850372 *Garden centre & sawmill*

Weston Of Scandinavia (UK) Ltd, Fairfax House, Causton Road, Colchester, CO1 1RJ Tel: (01206) 542544 Fax: (01206) 761869 *Carpet*

Weston, Shipley & Weston Ltd, Premier Works, Samson Road, Hermitage Industrial Estate, Coalville, Leicestershire, LE67 3FP Tel: (01530) 814062 Fax: (01530) 814064 E-mail: eberryson@aol.com *Brushes manufrs*

▶ Weston Transport Ltd, Units 1-2, 50 Woodhead Road, Chryston, Glasgow, G69 9HY Tel: 0141-779 4177

▶ Westone Masonry, Unit 4 Knightcott Industrial Estate, Banwell, Avon, BS29 6JN Tel: (01934) 824488 Fax: (01934) 824499

Westone Products Ltd, 8 Hampstead Gate, 1a Frognal, London, NW3 6AL Tel: (020) 7431 900 Fax: (020) 7431 9002 E-mail: sales@westoneproducts.com *Oral hygiene products manufrs*

Westons Development, Pickering Street, Maidstone, Kent, ME15 9RT Tel: 01622 740418 Fax: 01622 743911 E-mail: dbwestons@aol.com *Contract packaging/plastic vacuum forming*

Westpark Fabrications Ltd, Unit 4 Waterfield Mill, 4 Balmoral Road, Darwen, Lancashire, BB3 2EW Tel: (01254) 760136 Fax: (01254) 762116 *Steel fabricators & wire goods manufrs*

Westpile Ltd, Dolphin Bridge House, Rockingham Road, Uxbridge, Middlesex, UB8 2UB Tel: (01895) 258266 Fax: (01895) 271805 E-mail: john.gedge@westpile.co.uk *Piling contractors, bored, driven & piled retaining walls*

▶ Westpoint Homes Ltd, 3 Arthur Street, Clarkston Glasgow, G76 8BQ Tel: 0141-644 2223 Fax: 0141-644 5059

▶ Westpoint Industries, 105 Boundary Street, Liverpool, L5 9YJ Tel: 0151-427 1973 E-mail: westpoint@netvigator.com *Manufacturer & distributor of medical machines & probes*

▶ Westport Manufacturing Ltd, Unit 15 Solway Trading Estate, Maryport, Cumbria, CA15 8NF Tel: (01900) 814225 Fax: (01900) 818581

▶ Westridge Construction Ltd, Junction Road, Bodiam, Robertsbridge, East Sussex, TN32 5UP Tel: (01580) 830600 Fax: (01580) 830700 E-mail: marketing@westridgeconstruction.co.uk *Education, healthcare, residential & commercial project contractors services*

Westronics Ltd, 11-12 Marcus Close, Tilehurst, Reading, RG30 4EA Tel: 0118-942 6726 Fax: 0118-945 1481 E-mail: sales@westronics.co.uk *Burglar, fire & security installers*

Westrow Control Systems, 33 Westrow Gardens, Ilford, Essex, IG3 9NF Tel: (020) 8590 2798 Fax: (020) 8220 2442 E-mail: sales@westrowcontrolsystems.co.uk *Building of control panels for industrial doors*

Westructure Timber Frames Ltd, Wichita Works, Water Lane, Exeter, EX2 8BU Tel: (01392) 411211 Fax: (01392) 411211 *Timber frame manufrs*

Westrup (UK) Ltd, 30 North Street, Wetherby, West Yorkshire, LS22 6NN Tel: (01937) 581365 Fax: (01937) 586904 E-mail: info@westrup.co.uk *Agricultural engineers*

▶ West-Side Computers, First Floor, Harris Road, 159 Victoria Road, Swindon, SN1 3BU Tel: (01793) 784848 Fax: (0870) 4582556 E-mail: enquiries@westside.uk.com *Computer PC IT network hardware and software supply support and maintenance - offices in Swindon Wiltshire, Basingstoke Hampshire and Oxfordshire*

Westside Engineering Site Services Ltd, Westside House, Pontugwindy Industrial Estate, Caerphilly, Mid Glamorgan, CF83 3HU Tel: (029) 2086 0123 Fax: (029) 2085 1122 *Boiler installation & machinery engineers*

Westside I T Solutions, 125 Murray Road, Sheffield, S11 7GH Tel: (07745) 121208 E-mail: rob@westside-it.net *Pc repair broadband & home network setup*

stside Polythene Ltd, Ribble Works, Wakefield Road, Bispham, Blackpool, FY2 0DL Tel: (01253) 358742 Fax: (01253) 500120 E-mail: info@westsidepolythene.co.uk *Polythene carrier bag manufrs*

stside Welding and Engineering Ltd, 9 Broadfield Place, Welwyn Garden City, Hertfordshire, AL8 6LJ Tel: 01707 332872 Fax: 01707 332872 E-mail: westsideweld@hotmail.co.uk *Westside Welding and Engineering are a mobile welding company based in Hertfordshire and offer their welding services Nationwide. Westside Welding carry out on site mobile welding to construction plant, concrete and asphalt plant and heavy earthmoving equipment, which involves steel repairs and machine modifications for contractors and machinery dealers. Westside Welding specialise in construction plant maintenance and repair, asphalt plant maintenance and repair, concrete plant maintenance and repair and process plant maintenance. Westside Welding also offer the following services: on site welding and fabricating, steel erecting, steel pipe work installations, plant erections and plant repairs. Westside Welding have a large client base including Tarmac, Cemex, Hanson, Liebherr and Aggregate Industries. Westside Welding and Engineers cover all of the country, 7 days a week.*

ststar Industries, 77 Cricklade Road, Swindon, SN2 1AB Tel: (01793) 512686 Fax: (01793) 512686 *Cable harnessing manufrs*

estward Building Services Ltd, Burraton Road, Saltash, Cornwall, PL12 6LU Tel: (01752) 844600 Fax: (01752) 854254 E-mail: sales@westwoodbuildingservices.com *Tool distributors & agents*

Westward Energy Services, Energy House, Alloy Industrial Estate, Pontardawe, Swansea, SA8 4EN Tel: (01792) 862424 Fax: (01792) 830354

estward Mouldings Ltd, The New Factory, Delaware Road, Gunnislake, Cornwall, PL18 9AS Tel: (01822) 832120 Fax: (01822) 833938 E-mail: enquiry@fleetscale.co.uk *GRP mouldings*

estward Paper Sales, Cofton Road, Marsh Barton Trading Estate, Exeter, EX2 8QW Tel: (01392) 272096 *Paper & board merchants*

Westward Quest Ltd, Ardara, Clachan Seil, Oban, Argyll, PA34 4TL Tel: (01852) 300379 Fax: (01852) 300379 E-mail: rob@westwardquest.co.uk *Sail training & recreational sailing providers*

Westward Training & Personnel, 34 Rolle Street, Exmouth, Devon, EX8 2SH Tel: (01392) 490167 Fax: (01395) 279297 E-mail: wtp.training@btconnect.com *Training providers*

estway Business Services, 2 St. Marys Way, Baldock, Hertfordshire, SG7 6JF Tel: (01462) 490900 Fax: (01462) 490411 *Office stationery suppliers*

estway Composites, Unit H The Factory, Dippenhall, Farnham, Surrey, GU10 5DW Tel: (01252) 820200 Fax: (01252) 820217 E-mail: enquiries@westway.co.uk *Glass reinforced plastic moulders*

estway Pipeline Supplies, 8 Woodward Road, Knowsley Industrial Park North, Liverpool, L33 7UZ Tel: 0151-548 0010 Fax: 0151-549 1545 *Pipe & fittings stockholders*

estway Precision Engineering Ltd, Henty Road, Southampton, SO16 4GF Tel: (023) 8078 9229 Fax: (023) 8070 2967 *CNC machinists*

estwell Developments Ltd, Whitewall Road, Frindsbury, Rochester, Kent, ME2 4DZ Tel: (01634) 726148 Fax: (01634) 727081 E-mail: info@westwelldevelopments.fsnet.com *Engineers*

estwells Electrical Contractors, 311 Clipsley Lane, Haydock, St. Helens, Merseyside, WA11 0JG Tel: (01744) 23482 Fax: (01744) 28780 E-mail: george@westwells.co.uk *Catering equipment repairers*

estwhite Engineering Services, 32 Boston Road, Gorse Hill Industrial Estate, Leicester, LE4 1AU Tel: 0116-235 7522 Fax: 0116-235 7522 *Precision engineers*

estwind International Ltd, 23 Robjohns Road, Chelmsford, CM1 3AG Tel: (01245) 261201 Fax: (01245) 293615 E-mail: paper@wwi.org *Paper export agents*

estwind Oak Buildings Ltd, Laurel Farm, Yatton, Bristol, BS49 4QA Tel: (01934) 877317 Fax: (01934) 877317 E-mail: sales@westwindoak.com *Oak building manufrs*

estwire Harnessing Ltd, Unit 10 Headlands Trading Estate, Headlands Grove, Swindon, SN2 7JQ Tel: (01793) 537217 Fax: (01793) 421039 E-mail: graham@westwire.demon.co.uk Purchasing Contact: T. Humphrey Sales Contact: S. Poulter *Westwire design, develop and manufacture cable harnesses, wiring looms and either open loom or encapsulated form. We also manufacture coaxial cables, coiled cables and box wiring. Contact us for our design and CAD drawing facilities. Enquiries may be sent to trevor@westwire.demon.co.uk*

Westwood Associates Ltd, Hampden House, Hampden Road, Chalfont St. Peter, Gerrards Cross, Buckinghamshire, SL9 9DP Tel: (01753) 887161 Fax: (01753) 891214 Principal Export Areas: Central/East Europe & West Europe *Computer resellers*

Westwood Automation Ltd, Bell Close, Newnham Industrial Estate, Plympton, Plymouth, PL7 4JH Tel: (01752) 202113 Fax: (01752) 202117 *Engineer fabricators*

Westwood Bolt & Nut Co. Ltd, Claypit Lane, West Bromwich, West Midlands, B70 9UP Tel: 0121 5532405 *Bolt & nut merchants & manufrs*

▶ Westwood Classic Design Ltd, Unit 1C, Woodland Industrial Estate, Eden Vale Road, Westbury, Wiltshire, BA13 3QS Tel: (01373) 827676 Fax: (01373) 858014 E-mail: info@westwoodclassicdesign.co.uk *Westwood design bespoke kitchens, bathrooms, bedrooms*

continued

▶ Westwood Dawes, 54 Cuckoo Road, Aston, Birmingham, B7 5SY Tel: 0121-327 5133 Fax: 0121-327 7256 E-mail: wd.pulleys@afc-uk.com *Design & supply & manufacture of conveying products*

Westwood Fencing, Bathpool, Taunton, Somerset, TA1 2DX Tel: (01823) 337150 Fax: (01823) 351991 *Wood fencing manufrs*

Westwood Furniture, Sugworth Farm Unit 12, Borde Hill Lane, Haywards Heath, West Sussex, RH16 1XP Tel: (01444) 410211 Fax: (01444) 410211 E-mail: sales@westwoodfurniture.co.uk *Furniture manufrs*

Westwood Meters & Timers Ltd, Torre Station Yard, Newton Road, Torquay, TQ2 5DD Tel: (01803) 297179 Fax: (01803) 299080 E-mail: sales@electricmeters.co.uk *Electrical meter engineers*

▶ Westwood Press Ltd, Margate Road, Broadstairs, Kent, CT10 2PR Tel: (01843) 862864

▶ Westwood Printers, Unit C3, Willowbridge Way, Whitwood, Castleford, West Yorkshire, WF10 5NP Tel: (01977) 604647

Wesurail Ltd, 21-22 Auster Road, Clifton Moor, York, YO30 4XA Tel: (01904) 692544 Fax: (01904) 692566 E-mail: admin@wesurail.com *Train washes & controlled emission toilets*

Wet Pets Aquatic Centre, Fiskerton Road, Southwell, Nottinghamshire, NG25 0TH Tel: (01636) 816910 *Aquatic pets & accessories*

Wetherby Engineering Co. Ltd, Britannia Mills, Portland St, Bradford, West Yorkshire, BD5 0DW Tel: (01274) 827216 Fax: (01274) 390527 E-mail: sales@wetherby-engineering.co.uk *General engineers*

Wetherby Shade Card Co. Ltd, Grangefield Industrial Estate, Pudsey, West Yorkshire, LS28 6QJ Tel: 0113-257 7381 Fax: 0113-239 3217 E-mail: info@wetherby-shade-card.co.uk *Pattern card & pattern book makers*

Wetherells Contracts Ltd, 9 The Crescent, Selby, North Yorkshire, YO8 4PD Tel: (01757) 702161 Fax: (01757) 704026 *Contract furnishing manufrs*

Wetherford Wellserv, Crawpeel Road, Altens Industrial Estate, Aberdeen, AB12 3LG Tel: (01224) 410000 Fax: (01224) 380060 *Wire line operators*

▶ The Wetsuit Factory, 24 Bay Tree Hill, Liskeard, Cornwall, PL14 4BG Tel: (01579) 343573 Fax: (01579) 342062 E-mail: sales@thewetsuitfactory.com *Manufacturers & importers of wetsuits, surfboards & body boards*

Wetton Cleaning Services Ltd, 278-280 St James's Road, London, SE1 5JX Tel: (020) 7237 2007 Fax: (020) 7252 3277 E-mail: wcs@wetton.co.uk *Office cleaning contractors*

Wevax Ltd, Prospect Close, Lowmoor Business Park, Kirkby-in-Ashfield, Nottingham, NG17 7LF Tel: (01623) 754268 Fax: (01623) 723447 *Cardboard & corrugated box manufrs*

Wexco Ltd, Earlswood Trading Estate, Poolhead Lane, Earlswood, Solihull, West Midlands, B94 5EW Tel: (01564) 703624 Fax: (01564) 703066 E-mail: sales@wexco.co.uk *Thread roll & cutting tool manufrs*

▶ Wexham Developments 93, 2c Amity Road, Reading, RG1 3LJ Tel: 0118-966 1977 Fax: 0118-966 1981 *Test equipment manufrs*

Wexham Developments 93, Unit 8 Youngs Industrial Estate, Paices Hill, Aldermaston, Reading, RG7 4PW Tel: 0118- 981 0411 Fax: 0118-981 0811 E-mail: wexdev@compserve.com *Testing instruments (construction)*

Wey Adhesives Ltd, Unit 45 Murrell Green Business Park, London Road, Hook, Hampshire, RG27 9GR Tel: (01256) 766661 Fax: (01256) 766667 E-mail: sales@weyadhesives.com *Adhesive & associated equipment distribs*

▶ Weybridge Construction, 1 Tristar Bus Centre, Star Road, Partridge Green, Horsham, West Sussex, RH13 8RY Tel: (01403) 713111

Weyers Bros Ltd, Unit 1 Knight House, Lenthall Road, Loughton, Essex, IG10 3UD Tel: (020) 8508 3886 Fax: (020) 8508 7122 E-mail: john.weyers@weyers.co.uk *Precision engineers*

▶ Weyfringe Labelling Systems, Longbeck Road, Marske-by-the-Sea, Redcar, Cleveland, TS11 6HQ Tel: (01642) 490121 Fax: (01642) 490385 E-mail: sales@weyfringe.co.uk Principal Export Areas: Worldwide *Manufacturers and distributors of barcode labelling systems including label printers - label applicators - labelling software - barcode readers - barcode verifiers - adhesive labels and thermal transfer ribbons. Weyfringe also design and build custom labelling solutions.*

Weymouth Precision Engineers Ltd, 4 Kent Close, Granby Industrial Estate, Weymouth, Dorset, DT4 9TF Tel: (01305) 785375 Fax: (01305) 781602 E-mail: enquiries@weymouthprecision.co.uk *Precision engineers*

Weymouth Same Day Express Couriers, Unit 10 Links Estate, Surrey Close, Granby Industrial Estate, Weymouth, Dorset, DT4 9TY Tel: (01305) 782058 Fax: (01305) 766156 *Same day couriers*

Weymouth Scrap Co., 20 Cambridge Road, Granby Industrial Estate, Weymouth, Dorset, DT4 9TJ Tel: (01305) 785538 Fax: (01305) 777595 *Scrap iron & steel merchants*

▶ WFCA Integrated Ltd, Cobden House, 25 London Road, Tunbridge Wells, Kent, TN1 1DA Tel: (01892) 511085 Fax: (01892) 512180 E-mail: info@wfca.co.uk *Advertising, design, media, marketing agency*

WGC Ltd, 7 Academy Buildings, Fanshaw Street, London, N1 6LQ Tel: (020) 7729 2980 Fax: (020) 7729 5828 E-mail: sales@wgc-group.co.uk *European recruitment agency services*

WGM Engineering Ltd, 1 Abbey Mill Business Centre, Paisley, Renfrewshire, PA1 1TJ Tel: 0141-889 1009 Fax: 0141-848 6257 E-mail: info@wgmltd.com *Pump repair services*

▶ WH Smith Retail Ltd, Holford Way, Holford, Birmingham, B6 7AX Tel: 0121-344 4455 Fax: 0121-356 7186

WH Smith Retail Ltd, Greenbridge Road, Swindon, SN3 3LD Tel: (01793) 616161 Fax: (01793) 426410 E-mail: info@whsmithonline.com *Stationery retail & distribution centre*

Whale Engineering, Unit 9 Eldin Industrial Estate, Edgefield Road Loanhead, Loanhead, Midlothian, EH20 9DX Tel: 0131-440 4290 Fax: 0131-440 0272 *Steel fabricators*

Whale & Martin, 156 Broadgate, Weston Hills, Spalding, Lincolnshire, PE12 6DQ Tel: (01406) 380731 Fax: (01406) 380984 *Cabinet makers*

Whale Tankers Ltd, Ravenshaw, Solihull, West Midlands, B91 2SU Tel: 0121-704 5700 Fax: 0121-704 5701 E-mail: whalemail@whale.co.uk Principal Export Areas: Worldwide *Cleaning equipment suppliers, jet type, high & ultra high pressure for metals*

Whaleys Bradford Ltd, Harris Court, Bradford, West Yorkshire, BD7 4EQ Tel: (01274) 576718 Fax: (01274) 521309 E-mail: whaleys@btinternet.com *Textiles*

Jim Whalley Batteries, 1 Homestead Cottage, Playhatch, Reading, RG4 9QR Tel: 0118-947 9953 Fax: 0118-947 3345 *Battery distributors*

Whalley John Ltd, 5 Stort Valley Industrial Estate, Stansted Road, Bishop's Stortford, Hertfordshire, CM23 2TU Tel: (01279) 654181 Fax: (01279) 654424 E-mail: john@whalley-integrale.ukclara.com *Motor vehicle repairers*

▶ Wharf Systems, 37 Ullin Street, London, E14 6PN Tel: 020 75179943 E-mail: admin@wharfsystems.com

Wharfdale Telecom, 5 Park Terrace, Otley, West Yorkshire, LS21 1HH Tel: (01943) 465987 Fax: (01943) 463012 *Telecommunications*

▶ Wharfebank Contract Associates, The Workshop, Wharfe Bank Terrace, Tadcaster, North Yorkshire, LS24 9AN Tel: (01937) 530048 Fax: (01937) 832676

▶ Wharfedale Construction Ltd, Moor Knoll Lane, East Ardsley, Wakefield, West Yorkshire, WF3 2DX Tel: (01924) 822185 Fax: (01924) 827832

Wharfedale International Ltd, I A G House, Ermine Business Park, Huntingdon, Cambridgeshire, PE29 6XU Tel: (01480) 431737 Fax: (01480) 431767 E-mail: info@wharfedale.co.uk *Loud speaker manufrs*

Wharfedale Tractors Ltd, Riffa Business Park, Harrogate Road, Otley, West Yorkshire, LS21 2XB Tel: 0113-284 1117 Fax: 0113-284 3110 *Tractor supplies*

▶ Wharton Construction Ltd, Kellaw Road, Darlington, County Durham, DL1 4YA Tel: (01325) 288742 E-mail: enquiries@whartonconstructionltd.co.uk

Wharton Electronics, Unit 15 Thame Park Business Centre, Wenman Road, Thame, Oxfordshire, OX9 3XA Tel: (01844) 260567 Fax: (01844) 218855 E-mail: info@wharton.co.uk *Clock & time code system manufrs*

Wharton Landscapes, Esh Winning, Durham, DH7 9PT Tel: 0191-373 3213 Fax: 0191-373 4975 *Landscaping & fence contractors*

▶ What No Safety Services Ltd, Thornaby, Cecil Avenue, Salisbury, SP2 8EE Tel: 01722 326390 Fax: 01722 326390 E-mail: abarrett@whatnosafety.co.uk *Health and Safety Consultancy operating in the Wessex Region.*All training, advice and risk assessments undertaken**

Whatley & Co (Pewsley) Ltd, Avonside Works, Pewsey, Wiltshire, SN9 5AS Tel: (01672) 562404 Fax: (01672) 563091 E-mail: whatley.pewsey@lineone.net *Vehicle body repairs/waterwork engineers*

Whatman International Ltd, Springfield Mill, Sandling Road, Maidstone, Kent, ME14 2LE Tel: (01622) 676670 Fax: (01622) 677011 E-mail: info@whatman.com *Holding company*

▶ What's in the Box?, 93 Derby Road, Bramcote, Nottingham, NG9 3GW Tel: (0845) 0524200 Fax: (0845) 0524300 E-mail: sales@printer-stuff.co.uk *Printers, electronic & office equipment specialists*

Whattam Refrigeration, The Warehouse, George Court, York, YO31 7PG Tel: (01904) 630795 Fax: (01904) 634859 *Refrigeration, air conditioning sales & services*

Wheal Jane Enterprises Ltd, Old Mine Offices, Wheal Jane, Baldhu, Truro, Cornwall, TR3 6EE Tel: (01872) 560200 Fax: (01872) 562020 E-mail: carnon@wheal-jane.co.uk *Carnon Contracting is a Mining /Civil Engineering, and specialist drilling and Piling company formed in 1988 to market the expertise of the workforce of Cornwall's last tin mines, South Crofty and Wheal Jane.*

Wheale Thomas Hodgins plc, Berkeley Square House, 13 Berkeley Square, Bristol, BS8 1HB Tel: 0117-927 2311 Fax: 0117-927 2315 E-mail: wth@wth.co.uk *Staff recruitment agents*

▶ Wheatherford Dis Manufacturing UK Ltd, 1 James Chalmers Road, Kirkton Industrial Estate, Arbroath, Angus, DD11 3LR Tel: (01241) 434400 Fax: (01241) 434555

Wheatley Associates, 9 Main Street, Witchford, Ely, Cambridgeshire, CB6 2HG Tel: (01353) 664605 E-mail: enquiries@wheatley-associates.net *Computer training & consultancy*

Wheatley Associates, Technology Park, Broad Road, Bacton, Stowmarket, Suffolk, IP14 4HN Tel: (01449) 781001 E-mail: info@wheatley-associates.co.uk *Software developers & consultants*

Wheatley Dyson & Son Ltd, 1 Quarry Court, Beacon Hill Road, Halifax, West Yorkshire, HX3 6AQ Tel: (0800) 6342010 Fax: (0800) 0424329 E-mail: sales@wheatley-dyson.co.uk *Office products suppliers*

Wheatley Pallet Services Ltd, Sandall Stones Road, Kirk Sandall, Doncaster, South Yorkshire, DN3 1QR Tel: (01302) 885803 Fax: (01302) 884218 E-mail: wpspallet@aol.com *Pallet & fencing manufacturers & pallet repairs. Also wooden cases*

Wheatley Plastics Ltd, Reynolds Mill, Newbridge Lane, Stockport, Cheshire, SK1 2NR Tel: 0161-477 2800 Fax: 0161-480 6611 E-mail: wheatley.plastics@btconnect.com *Injection mouldings manufrs*

▶ Wheatley Printers Ltd, C2 Phoenix Trading Estate, London Road, Thrupp, Stroud, Gloucestershire, GL5 2BX Tel: (01453) 731001 Fax: (01453) 731418

Wheatley & Sons Ltd, 25a Arnison Road, East Molesey, Surrey, KT8 9JQ Tel: (020) 8979 5762 Fax: (020) 8941 7388 *Building contractors (general)*

▶ Wheatsheaf Press, Print Works, Lacey Green, Wilmslow, Cheshire, SK9 4BQ Tel: (01625) 530530 Fax: (01625) 535898 E-mail: print@wheatsheaf.u-net.com

Wheatsheaf Technical Ltd, 3 Haycliffe Avenue, Off Moore Avenue, Bradford, West Yorkshire, BD7 4HY Tel: (01274) 577789 Fax: (0870) 912 8057 E-mail: t.rijneveld@xs4all.nl *Food & bakery machinery specialists*

Wheel Masters, Tufthorn Industrial Estate, Stepbridge Road, Coleford, Gloucestershire, GL16 8PJ Tel: (01594) 835678 Fax: (01594) 835789 E-mail: sales@wheelsuk.co.uk *Wheel distributors & manufrs*

▶ The Wheel Surgery, 67, Nutfield Road, Merstham, Redhill, RH1 3ER Tel: (01737) 644123 Fax: (01737) 644123 *Refurbish alloy wheels*

Wheelabrator Group, 43-44 Gravelly Industrial Park, Tyburn Road, Birmingham, B24 8TG Tel: 0121-326 6481 Fax: 0121-328 0256 E-mail: uk-info@wheelabrator.co.uk *Manufacturers of abrasive plastic materials & finishing media*

Wheelbase Engineering Ltd, Lower Eccleshill Road, Darwen, Lancashire, BB3 0RP Tel: (01254) 819399 Fax: (01254) 776920 E-mail: sales@wheelbase.net *Chassis modification specialists*

▶ Wheelchair Care Ltd, Unit 2, Greshop Industrial Estate, Forres, Morayshire, IV36 2GW Tel: (01309) 676677 Fax: (01309) 674479 E-mail: enquiries@wheelchaircare.co.uk *Mobility daily living aid dealers*

Alan E. Wheeler & Son, Unit 90, Condover Industrial Estate, Condover, Shrewsbury, SY5 7NH Tel: (01743) 718226 Fax: (01743) 718224 E-mail: sales@vacuumlifting.com *Manufacturers of lifting (vacuum) equipment*

Chris Wheeler Construction Ltd, Church Farm, Burbage, Marlborough, Wiltshire, SN8 3AT Tel: (01672) 810315 Fax: (01672) 810309 E-mail: cw.cw@btinternet.com *Fencing contractors*

Wheeler & Clinch Ltd, 75-99 Nathan Way, West Thamesmead Business Park, London, SE28 0BQ Tel: (020) 8854 4261 Fax: (020) 8854 6341 E-mail: whclinch@aol.com *Mould manufacturers & toolmakers for plastics*

Wheeler & Co. (Concrete Products) Ltd, Old Pit Yard, Clandown, Radstock, BA3 3DA Tel: (01761) 432296 Fax: (01761) 472220 *Concrete block manufrs* Also at: Timsbury

Wheeler Fabrications Ltd, Orchard House, Sherbourne Road, Balsall Heath, Birmingham, B12 9DJ Tel: 0121-440 2345 Fax: 0121-440 4008 E-mail: wheelerfabs@btconnect.com *Sheet metal prototypes*

Wheeler, Hickson & Co., 10-11 Lower John Street, London, W1F 9EB Tel: (020) 7437 0186 Fax: (020) 7439 4994 E-mail: info@wheelerhickson.co.uk *Woollen manufacturers' agents*

Wheeler International, 33 Riverside Walk, Tamerton Foliot, Plymouth, PL5 4AQ Tel: (01752) 702077 Fax: (01752) 702077 E-mail: tonywheeler@btconnect.com *Engineering consultants*

Wheeler & Jupp, 11b Holywell Hill, St. Albans, Hertfordshire, AL1 1EU Tel: (01727) 868127 Fax: (01727) 840931 E-mail: sales@wheelerandjupp.com *Structural & civil consulting engineers*

M & D Wheeler Ltd, Avondale Business Centre, Woodland Way, Kingswood, Bristol, BS15 1AW Tel: 0117-960 3358 Fax: E-mail: m.d.wheeler@btinternet.com *BSL loaded bare board test. Surface mount BGA soldering hot-air rework. None-contact dimensional measurement. Vanwell functional test maintenance repair. Service and support of Vanwell and BSL systems.*

▶ Wheeler Monitoring, The Corner House, Faringdon Road, Abingdon, Oxfordshire, OX14 1BH Tel: (01235) 525803 Fax: (01235) 525803 E-mail: info@wheelermon.co.uk *Electronic design*

Wheeler & Oliver, 22 Cooperage Green, Royal Clarence Marina, Gosport, Hampshire, PO12 1FY Tel: (023) 9252 0091 Fax: (023) 9252 0189 E-mail: info@wheelerandoliver.com *All sorts of leather goods, leather goods manufrs*

Richard Wheeler Associates, 130 High Street, Hungerford, Berkshire, RG17 0DL Tel: (01488) 684944 Fax: (01488) 685233 E-mail: sales@rwaconsultants.com *Human resources consultancy search/selection*

Wheeler's (Westbury) Ltd, 31D Link Road, West Wilts Trading Estate, Westbury, Wiltshire, BA13 4JB Tel: (01373) 823755 Fax: (01373) 858045 E-mail: info@wheelers-westbury.co.uk *Mechanical & electrical contractors*

Wheelhouse Ltd, 9-21 Bell Road, Hounslow, TW3 3NS Tel: (020) 8570 3501 Fax: (020) 8570 6666 E-mail: davidh@wheelhouse.ltd.uk *General wholesale merchants & retail outlet* Also at: Twickenham

Wheelie Bin Direct Ltd, 22 Hainge Road, Tividale, Oldbury, West Midlands, B69 2NH Tel: 0121-557 1302 Fax: (0870) 2420175 E-mail: info@wheeliebindirect.co.uk *Waste container manufrs*

Wheels Van & Truck Rentals, 7 St. Albans Road, Barnet, Hertfordshire, EN5 4LN Tel: (020) 8441 1818 Fax: (020) 8440 1921 *Commercial van & truck hire* Also at: Barking, Enfield, London E10, N1, NW10 & Waltham Cross

Company Information

Wheelton Health Care, 11 Dalton Court, Commercial Road, Darwen, Lancashire, BB3 0DG Tel: (01254) 777977 Fax: (01254) 777978 E-mail: info@wheeltonhealthcare.net *Homeopathic remedies mail order services*

Wheelwash Ltd, Leslie Road, Woodford Park Industrial Estate, Winsford, Cheshire, CW7 2RB Tel: (01606) 592044 Fax: (01606) 592045 E-mail: sales@wheelwash.com *Wheelwash are a growing company with solid foundations, with over 15 years worldwide experience behind us since developing the ever popular patented wheelwash drive through bath, we aim to provide a solution by understanding the site requirements before recommending the most suitable product from our range for wheel and chassis washing for your site equipment and commercial vehicles. We operate throughout the world with our head office based in Cheshire, UK and offices in many other locations. A large flexible rental fleet and full manufacturing support allows us to react quickly and professionally. Our after sales support includes provision maintenance, a robust warranty, full spares service and technical support.*

P. Whelan Ltd, 113 New Bridge Street, Newcastle Upon Tyne, NE1 2SW Tel: 0191-261 2677 Fax: 0191-261 1248 E-mail: info@whelanconstruction.co.uk *Building contractors/developers*

▶ Wheldon Contracts & Services Ltd, 127 High Street, Newport Pagnell, Buckinghamshire, MK16 8SE Tel: (01908) 211127 Fax: (01908) 612008 E-mail: sales@wheldons.co.uk

Where To Go Ltd, 180 Pentonville Road, London, N1 9LB Tel: (020) 7278 4393 Fax: (020) 7837 5838 E-mail: whatson@whatsoninlondon..co.uk *Book & magazine publishers*

Whesco Ltd, Aughton, Collingbourne Kingston, Marlborough, Wiltshire, SN8 3SA Tel: (01264) 850136 Fax: (01264) 850136 E-mail: mail@whesc-ltd.co.uk *Electrical contractors*

Whessoe Oil & Gas Ltd, Brinkburn Road, Darlington, County Durham, DL3 6DS Tel: (01325) 390000 Fax: (01325) 390001 Principal Export Areas: Worldwide *Storage tank contractors*

▶ Whest Audio, Acton Business Centre, School Road, London, NW10 6TD Tel: (020) 8965 4535 Fax: (020) 7681 1089 *Audio manufrs*

Which Magazine, 2 Marylebone Road, London, NW1 4DF Tel: (020) 7770 7000 Fax: (020) 7770 7600 *Books & magazines publishers*

▶ Whichlist.com, Tapton Park Innovation Centre, Brimington Road, Chesterfield, Derbyshire, S41 0TZ Tel: (01246) 297179 Fax: (01246) 297180 E-mail: sales@whichlist.com *Whichlist.com have been in the mailing list industry for over 20 years and have used all of our knowledge and experience to supply our customers with the most accurate , selective and comprehensive mailing lists available. Mailing Lists of contacts, addresses and telephone numbers allow a company to identify it's total market prospects, the profile of which are probably "look alikes" of current customers. We are currently owners of three major databases, including the largest business database in the UK*

Whiddon Valley Engineering Ltd, Units 4 & 5, Castle Park Road, Whiddon Valley Industrial Estate, Barnstaple, Devon, EX32 8PA Tel: (01271) 376288 Fax: (01271) 323474 E-mail: wve@btconnect.com *Production engineers*

Whipp & Bourne, Switchgear Works, Manchester Road, Rochdale, Lancashire, OL11 2SS Tel: (01706) 632051 Fax: (01706) 674236 *Switchgear manufrs*

Whippendell Electrical Ltd, 477-479 Whippendell Road, Watford, WD18 7PU Tel: (01923) 228201 Fax: (01923) 228007 E-mail: sales@whippendell-electrical.co.uk *Electrical control gears* Also at: Nelson & Telford

Whippendell Electrical Ltd, 477-479 Whippendell Road, Watford, WD18 7PU Tel: (01923) 228201 Fax: (01923) 228007 E-mail: kevin@wippendale-marine.co.uk *Switchgear manufrs*

Whippendell Precision, 477-479 Whippendell Rd, Watford, WD18 7PU Tel: (01923) 221622 Fax: (01923) 816004 *Specialising in the aerospace and high tolerance component industries. We are highly experienced in CNC turning and milling to produce small and medium batches of complex parts and components. We work with Aluminium, mild steels, plastics and brass. We offer complete solutions, including prototype and Proof of Concept work, working with you to develop your products. We pride ourselves on delivering on time high quality parts and components.*

Whipple Engineering Co. Ltd, Manor Farm, Caldecott, Wellingborough, Northamptonshire, NN9 6AR Tel: (01933) 461711 *General engineers*

Whirlowdale Trading Co. Ltd, Canklow Meadows Industrial Estate, West Bawtry Road, Rotherham, South Yorkshire, S60 2XL Tel: (01709) 829061 Fax: (01709) 378947 E-mail: sales@whirlowdale.com *Export packing & pallet manufrs*

Whirlwind Fire Extinguisher Maintenance, Whirlwind Rise, Dudmoor Lane, Christchurch, Dorset, BH23 6BQ Tel: (01202) 475255 Fax: (01202) 475255 *Fire alarm maintenance & suppliers*

▶ Whirlwind Technologies Ltd, 1 Poplar Street, (Off Buck Street), Leigh, Lancashire, WN7 4HL Tel: (01942) 671300 Fax: (01942) 262042 E-mail: info@whirltech.co.uk *Develop & supply an innovative system that clean & clear pipes*

Whirly Bird Services Ltd, Montrose Way, Dyce, Aberdeen, AB21 0JF Tel: (01224) 771423 Fax: (01224) 773789 E-mail: mail@whirlybird.co.uk *Helicopter survival suit services*

Whispair, Unit 31 Romsey Industrial Estate, Greatbridge Road, Romsey, Hampshire, SO51 0HR Tel: (01794) 523999 Fax: (01794) 519151 E-mail: info@whispaire.co.uk *Manufacturer distributor of heating & cooking equipment*

The Whistle Fish Gallery, Unit 1 Barncoose Industrial Estate, Barncoose, Redruth, Cornwall, TR15 3RQ Tel: (01209) 202424 Fax: (01209) 202434 E-mail: sales@milkwoodpublishing.com *Greeting cards publishing services*

▶ Whistler Technology Xchange, Phoenix House, Oak Tree Lane, Mansfield, Nottinghamshire, NG18 4LF Tel: (01623) 425880 Fax: (01623) 425881 *Distributor of electrical components*

Whistler's Farm, 4 Lorenzo Drive, Liverpool, L11 1BW Tel: 0151-256 0340 Fax: 0151-256 0653 *Ham curing*

Whiston Industries Ltd, Oak Street, Cradley Heath, West Midlands, B64 5JY Tel: (01384) 560606 Fax: (01384) 638182 E-mail: bob.whiston@whistonindustries.com Principal Export Areas: Worldwide *Press Toolmakers for automotive body panels, Tool and Die Manufacture.Transfer,Progression and Line Dies.World Class Tool & Die Design and Manufacture.Large CNC Milling Machines.*

Whit Products Ltd, Factory Road, Tipton, West Midlands, DY4 9DJ Tel: 0121-557 7651 Fax: 0121-557 5334 *Food packers*

Whitaker & Co Denholme Ltd, Denholme Gate, Bradford, West Yorkshire, BD13 4EW Tel: (01274) 833611 Fax: (01274) 833782 *Window manufrs*

J. Whitaker & Sons Ltd, Endeavour House, 189 Shaftesbury Avenue, London, WC2H 8TJ Tel: (020) 7420 6000 Fax: (020) 7836 6781 *Directory publishers & booksellers*

Whitaker & Sawyer Ltd, Unit 17 Midas Business Centre, Wantz Road, Dagenham, Essex, RM10 8PS Tel: (020) 8593 7204 Fax: (020) 8595 7353 E-mail: info@wsbrushes.co.uk *General & industrial brush manufrs*

Whitaker Technical Plastics Ltd, Redwood Court, Tytherington Business Park, Macclesfield, Cheshire, SK10 2XH Tel: (01625) 612571 Fax: (01625) 612594 E-mail: g_whitaker@btconnect.com *Plastic compound manufrs*

▶ Thomas Whitaker (Eastburn) Ltd, Unit 11 A Sandylands Business Centre, Carleton New Road, Skipton, North Yorkshire, BD23 2AA Tel: (01756) 797579 Fax: (01756) 797580 E-mail: contact@twelimited.plus.com *Specialist joinery manufacturers kitchens bedrooms & staircases*

Whitaker Transmissions, 2 Heys Lane, Oswaldtwistle, Accrington, Lancashire, BB5 3BJ Tel: (01254) 382791 Fax: (01254) 239062 *Belting manufrs*

Whitakers Chocolates Skipton Ltd, 85 Keighley Road, Skipton, North Yorkshire, BD23 2NA Tel: (01756) 792531 Fax: (01756) 700225 E-mail: sales@whitakerschocolates.com *Chocolate manufrs*

Whitakers Equestrian Services Ltd, 3 Hikers Way, Drakes Drive, Long Crendon, Aylesbury, Buckinghamshire, HP18 9RW Tel: (01844) 202151 Fax: (01844) 202152 E-mail: sales@polyjumps.com *Rubber flooring & plastic show jumps & veterinary consumables manufrs*

Whitby Angling Supplies, 65 Haggersgate, Whitby, North Yorkshire, YO21 3PP Tel: (01947) 603855 *Retail fishing tackle distributors*

C. Oliver Whitby & Sons Ltd, Hospital Fields, Fulford Road, York, YO10 4FS Tel: (01904) 655106 Fax: (01904) 627663 E-mail: wcoliver@aol.com *Removal & storage specialists*

Whitby & Chandler Ltd, Green Road, Penistone, Sheffield, S36 6PH Tel: (01226) 370380 Fax: (01226) 767138 E-mail: enquiries@whitby-chandler.co.uk *Gasket manufrs*

Whitby Morrison Ltd, Fourth Avenue, Western Road Industrial Estate, Crewe, CW1 6TT Tel: (01270) 581318 Fax: (01270) 250220 *Ice cream van manufrs*

Whitby Tanks Ltd, Custom House, 1 Old Market Place, Whitby, North Yorkshire, YO21 3BT Tel: (01947) 606237 Fax: (01947) 602876 E-mail: sales@whitbytanks.co.uk *Whitby Tanks are based in Whitby, North Yorkshire and specialise in the sale and hire of new and used tanks and vessels for the chemical, pharmaceutical and food industries. They offer a comprehensive service for the installation and commissioning for all tanks and add-ons. Their products include custom built tanks, fuel management systems, pumps and accessories, vessels and many more.*

▶ Whitbybird, 60 Newman Street, London, W1T 3DA Tel: (020) 7631 5291 Fax: (020) 7323 4645 *Engineering services*

Whitchem Ltd, 23 Albert Street, Newcastle, Staffordshire, ST5 1JP Tel: (01782) 711777 Fax: (01782) 717290 E-mail: enquiries@whitchem.co.uk *Cement colour distributors & chemical merchants*

Whitchurch Building Supplies, College Road, Cardiff, CF14 2NZ Tel: (029) 2062 5422 Fax: (029) 2061 6840 *Building materials merchants*

▶ Whitchurch Business Centre, Green End, Whitchurch, Shropshire, SY13 1AD Tel: (01948) 660550 Fax: (01948) 660560 E-mail: james.archer@whitchurchbc.co.uk *Fully managed and serviced offices are available for rent in a prestigious list building in the heart of Whitchurch town centre. We offer a full range of services: Office accommodation to suit most budgets; Mail address; telephone answering services; Meeting Room facilities; Voice mail facilities; Email and internet access; Fax & Photocopying service; Secretarial and administrative support*Telephone 01948 660550 for more information**

▶ White & Co plc, Pitreavie Business Park, Pitreavie Business Park, Dunfermline, Fife, KY11 8UT Tel: (01383) 739933 Fax: (01383) 621577

White, Usher Street, Ludworth, Durham, DH6 1NE Tel: (01429) 820487 Fax: (01429) 821508

▶ White & Co plc, 2 St. Peters Technical Park, St. Peter, Jersey, JE3 7ZN Tel: (01534) 484002 Fax: (01534) 485448

▶ White, 5 Kirby Street, London, EC1N 8TS Tel: (020) 7242 7472 *Jewellery manufrs*

White & Co. Ltd, 50a Main Road, Hackleton, Northampton, NN7 2AB Tel: (01604) 870982 Fax: (01604) 870529 E-mail: shoes@whiteeb.co.uk *Shoe & boot manufrs* Also at: Daventry

▶ White & Co. plc, Dundas Spur, Portsmouth, PO3 5NL Tel: (023) 9266 3221 Fax: (023) 9265 0114

Arthur White Dryers Ltd, 16 Upper Brook Street, Oswestry, Shropshire, SY11 2TB Tel: (01691) 657960 Fax: (01691) 670462 E-mail: awdryers@moulson-chemplant.co.uk *Process plant*

White Bros Ltd, Gosforth Industrial Estate, Newcastle Upon Tyne, NE3 1XD Tel: 0191-213 0455 Fax: 0191-284 1351 E-mail: enquiries@whitebros.co.uk *Stainless steel metalworkers*

White Bros, Rear 2 & 3, Ruskin Road, Stanford-le-Hope, Essex, SS17 0LF Tel: (01375) 672259 Fax: (01375) 361028 E-mail: whitebros1950@aol.com *Scrap metal merchants*

White Building Services, 172 Southworth Road, Newton-le-Willows, Merseyside, WA12 0BT Tel: (01925) 225141 Fax: (01925) 226457 E-mail: mail@whitebuildingservices.co.uk *Building services contractors*

▶ White Cat, 7 Micheldever Gardens, Whitchurch, Hampshire, RG28 7JY Tel: (01256) 892952 E-mail: kimbyatt@whitecatdesign.biz *Graphic designers*

White Cross Plant Ltd, 135 Engineer Road, West Wilts Trading Estate, Westbury, Wiltshire, BA13 4JW Tel: (01373) 824422 Fax: (01373) 825234 *From its Wiltshire base White Cross Plant can supply and install concrete batching plants throughout the UK. With the in-house design team we can engineer plants to suit customers' individual requirements. We are also happy to undertake the refurbishment of existing plants, which could involve the replacement of aggregate hoppers, the supply of additional silo capacity and up-grading conveyor systems. Over many years of successful trading with the major concrete producers, as well as independant concrete products manufacturers, we have not only gained considerable experience of our clients' needs, but are confident that no problem is nsurmountable. From initial site survey through to plant commissioning our engineers are always on hand to ensure customer satisfaction.*

White Cross Ring Co. Ltd, Battye Street, Bradford, West Yorkshire, BD4 8AG Tel: (01274) 669933 Fax: (01274) 660137 E-mail: jason@whitecrossring.co.uk *Section bending services tube manipulators*

D.C. White & Partners Ltd, Highfield, Pilcot Hill, Dogmersfield, Hook, Hampshire, RG27 8SX Tel: 0845 4941739 Fax: (01252) 815625 E-mail: blair.white@dcwhite.co.uk *DC White & Partners, located in north east Hampshire, offers over 30 years of expertise in mechanical/ structural engineering consultancy If it can break it will break, usually at the worst possible time! But why did it break, and how can we stop it happening again? We can provide these answers within realistic timescales to minimise the impact upon your business. Vibration, fatigue, explosions, bad design are just a few of the problems that our engineers encounter and mitigate on a daily basis. Our consultants use everything from hand calculations to the latest powerful software, combined with experience from across the engineering sector to provide practical solutions to engineering problems. We specialise in complex finite element analysis and computer aided design to solve a variety of clients problems. Using software such as Abaqus, Mathcad and Solidworks we are able to assist you with optimising your designs and finding solutions for equipment failure.*

D.P. White & Co., 58 Hackenden Cl, East Grinstead, West Sussex, RH19 3DS Fax: (01342) 335747 *D.O. White & Co. based in East Grinstead, West Sussex offers conveyor systems, bolts and nuts, gaskets, industrial fasteners and transformers.*

White Drift Translations Ltd, 2 Stanley Street, Llanelli, Dyfed, SA15 2EU Tel: (01554) 757700 Fax: (01554) 757222 E-mail: info@whitedrift.com *White Drift Translations Limited - Talking your language in theirs. A small investment in the services of highly qualified, native speaking translators and interpreters who have expertise in your specialist area pays big returns. Let us make the world yours. Language Translation Services. Over 100 languages from all over the World - Arabic, African, Asian, Brazilian, Chinese, Croatian, Czech, Danish, Dutch, English, Finnish, Flemish, French, German, Hindi, Hungarian, Italian, Norwegian, Polish, Portuguese, Russian, Spanish, Welsh, and many many more. Translating, Interpreting, Voice Overs, etc*

White Eagle Foundry Ltd, 199 Cuckfield Road, Hurstpierpoint, Hassocks, West Sussex, BN6 9RT Tel: (01273) 832062 Fax: (01273) 833628 E-mail: wef@wef.co.uk *Non-ferrous sandcasters & metal polishers*

White & Etherington Ltd, New Farm Road, Alresford, Hampshire, SO24 9QE Tel: (01962) 732783 Fax: (01962) 735422 *Timber merchants & fencing contractors*

▶ White & Fensome Building Contractors, 2 Hewlett Road, Luton, LU3 2RP Tel: (01582) 594766 Fax: (01582) 594866

White Grove Group plc, Central House, Halesfield 19, Telford, Shropshire, TF7 4QT Tel: (01952) 685300 Fax: (01952) 581612 E-mail: sales@whitegrove.co.uk *Office furniture dealers*

White Hart Optical Co. Ltd, Redburn Road, Newcastle upon Tyne, NE5 1PQ Tel: 0191-286 0441 Fax: 0191-271 0721 *Manufacturing opticians*

▶ White Heather Taxis Ltd, Brackencroft, Auchtercairn, Gairloch, Ross-shire, IV21 2BS Tel: 01445 712608 Fax: 01445 712608 E-mail: whiteheathertaxis@btinternet.com *Taxis & Private Hire. Limousine Hire: Funeral and Wedding Service.*Highland Tours. Train, Ferry*

continued

and Rail Links. 25hr service. Premier Highland Service, serving the highlands of Scotland.

White House Linen Specialists, 102 Waterford Road, London, SW6 2HA Tel: (020) 7629 3521 Fax: (020) 7629 8269 E-mail: john@the-white-house.co.uk *Linen & textile merchants & china, silver & crystal*

▶ White House Press Ltd, Units 14-16 The Marin Harbour Road, Lydney, Gloucestershire, GL15 5ET Tel: (01594) 842015 Fax: (01594) 841880

White House Products Ltd, Kelburn Business Pk, Port Glasgow, Renfrewshire, PA14 6TD Tel: (01475) 742500 Fax: (01475) 742888 E-mail: info@whp.co.uk Sales Contact: D. MacMillan Principal Export Areas: Worldwide *Hydraulic equipment & component distributors, fitters & agents. Also, hydraulic pumps*

James White & Son (Engineering) Co. Ltd, Commercial Road, Reading, RG2 0RU Tel: 0118-987 3421 Fax: 0118-975 0521 E-mail: mark@jameswhite.freeserve.co.uk *Sheet metalworkers*

John White & Son (Weighing Machines) Ltd, 6 Back Dykes, Auchtermuchty, Cupar, Fife, KY14 7DW Tel: (01337) 827600 Fax: (01337) 827444 E-mail: enquiries@johnwhiteandson.com *Weigh manufacturers & weighing equipment calibratin services* Also at: Glasgow

John White Trophies, 115 Lindon Road, Walsall, WS8 7DD Tel: (01543) 379070 Fax: (01543) 379070 E-mail: john.white@virgin.net *Sports trophy engravers*

White Knight Express Couriers, 38 Whitebean Close, Paignton, Devon, TQ3 3GA Tel: (01803) 664822 *Deliveries*

L. White & Sons, 34 Newbury Lane, Oldbury, West Midlands, B69 1HF Tel: 0121-511 1096 Fax: 0121-511 1096 *Joiners*

White Light (Electrics) Ltd, 20 Merton Industrial Park, Jubilee Way, Wimbledon, London, SW19 3WL Tel: (020) 8254 4800 Fax: (020) 8254 4801 E-mail: info@whitelightgroup.co.uk *Theatrical lighting services*

White Lightning Solutions, 97 Brighton Road, Godalming, Surrey, GU7 1PW Tel: (01483) 429040 Fax: (01483) 429030

White Lodge Saddlery, White Lodge, Middle Road Tiptoe, Lymington, Hampshire, SO41 6FX Tel: (01590) 682396 Fax: (01590) 681717 E-mail: sales@whitelodgesaddlery.co.uk *Saddlers & riding equipment suppliers*

White Milne & Co., Baird Avenue, Dundee, DD2 3XG Tel: (01382) 814822 Fax: (01382) 813751 E-mail: sales@whitemilne.co.uk *Engineering & electrical goods*

Paul White Ltd, 69 Upper Accomodation Road, Leeds, LS9 8LS Tel: 0113-248 9898 Fax: 0113-248 4863 E-mail: leeds@paulwhiteltd.co.uk *Giftware stationary & greeting card distributors*

White Rabbit Enterprises Ltd, 94 Creynolds Lane, Monkspath, Solihull, West Midlands, B90 4ER Tel: 0121-744 3297 Fax: 0121-733 2876 E-mail: whiterabbitltd@solihull2.demon.co.uk *Television & theatre production*

White Reclamation Ltd, New Hall Farm, Liverpool Road, Eccles, Manchester, M30 7LJ Tel: 0161-789 3268 Fax: 0161-707 5909 E-mail: mail@thewhitegroup.co.uk *Scrap iron & steel merchants*

▶ Ron White Fixing, 25 571 Finchley Road, London, NW3 7BN Tel: (0800) 1075113 Fax: (020) 7856855 E-mail: ronwhitefixing@ntlworld.com *Window & door maintenance & repair services*window an door online shop**

White Rose Computer Supplies, Unit 10, Elvington Industrial Estate, York, YO41 4AR Tel: (01904) 608775 Fax: (01904) 608163

White Rose Formations, Sovereign House, 7 Station Road, Kettering, Northamptonshire, NN15 7HH Tel: (01536) 414088 Fax: (01536) 481278 E-mail: office@wrfinternational.demon.co.uk *Company formations & company searches services*

▶ White Rose Packaging, Unit 23-24 Latchmore Industrial Park, Low Fields Road, Leeds, LS12 6DN Tel: 0113-246 0410 Fax: 0113-234 3136 E-mail: sales@whiterosepackaging.co.uk *Manufacturer of corrugated cases*

▶ White Rose Pallets, Butterbowl Works, Ring Road, Lower Wortley, Leeds, LS12 5AJ Tel: 0113-289 0499

White Rose Saddlery, Wiger Mews, Langton Road Norton, Malton, North Yorkshire, YO17 9QG Tel: (01653) 697440 Fax: (01653) 697440 E-mail: enquiries@whiterosesaddlery.com *Saddlery retail & manufrs*

▶ Ruth White Yoga Products Ltd, Building 188 Firs Street, New Greenham Park, Newbury, Berkshire, RG19 6HW Tel: (01635) 277494 Fax: (01635) 277497 E-mail: sales@ruthwhiteyoga.com *Retailers of yoga & wellbeing products*

The White Sea & Baltic Company Ltd, Arndale House, Otley Road, Leeds, LS6 2UU Tel: 0113-230 4774 Fax: 0113-230 4770 E-mail: sales@whitesea.co.uk *Chemical traders & distributors*

White & Street International Ltd, Unit 17-18, Enfield Industrial Estate, Redditch, Worcestershire, B97 6BN Tel: (01527) 67881 Fax: (01527) 69966 E-mail: enquiries@whiteandstreet.com Principal Export Areas: Worldwide *Manufacturer of machinery for the plastics & cable manufacturing industries*

T.H. White Ltd, London Road, Marlborough, Wiltshire, SN8 2RN Tel: 01672 512328 *Agricultural engineers* Also at: Branches throughout the U.K.

Thomas White (Leicester) Ltd, Marlborough Drive, Fleckney, Leicester, LE8 8UR Tel: 0116-240 4005 Fax: 0116-240 4006 E-mail: enquiries@thomaswhitelimited.co.uk *Proximity switch manufrs*

▶ White UK Ltd, Heanor Gate Indust Estate, Heanor, Derbyshire, DE75 7SJ Tel: (01773) 534888 Fax: (01773) 534999 E-mail: sales@whiteukltd.co.uk *CCTV, projectors, audio visual equipment, cable network retailer*

White Waghorn Ltd, 9 High Street, Stevenage, Hertfordshire, SG1 3BG Tel: (01438) 726393 E-mail: info@whitewaghorn.co.uk *Computer consultants services*

White Water The Canoe Centre, Shepperton Marina, Felix Lane, Shepperton, Middlesex, TW17 8NS Tel: (01932) 247978 Fax: (01932) 241368 E-mail: whitewater@canoecentre.demon.co.uk *Canoeing specialists, retail*

▶ White Water Charters, Penarth Marina, Penarth, Vale of Glamorgan, CF64 1TZ Tel: (07970) 936443 E-mail: info@whitewatercharters.co.uk *White Water Charters is a fishing boat charter providing boat trips out of Penarth and Milford Haven, where you can go fishing for cod, bass, pollack, conger eels, rays and shark fishing, or enjoy wildlife trips off the coast of South and West Wales.***

White Young Green, 27-31 Cumberland Street, Bristol, BS2 8NL Tel: 0117-924 4144 Fax: 0117-924 4145 E-mail: bristol@wyg.com *Consulting engineers*

White Young Green, 12 St. Andrews Crescent, Cardiff, CF10 3DD Tel: (029) 2023 1141 Fax: (029) 2072 7649 E-mail: cardiff@wyg.com *Consulting engineers*

White Young Green, Wallington House, Starbeck Avenue, Newcastle upon Tyne, NE2 1RH Tel: 0191-232 3043 Fax: 0191-261 0986 E-mail: newcastle@wyg.com *Consulting engineers & project managers*

White Young Green, Regatta House, Clippers Quay, Salford, M50 3XP Tel: 0161-872 3223 Fax: 0161-872 3193 E-mail: manchester@wyg.com *Consulting engineers*

White Young Green Ltd, The Mill Yard, Nursling Street, Nursling, Southampton, SO16 0AJ Tel: (0870) 6091084 E-mail: southampton@wyg.com Principal Export Areas: Worldwide *Consulting engineers*

White Young Green Consulting, Family House, 4 Bedford Business Park, Croydon, CR0 2AP Tel: (020) 8649 6600 Fax: (020) 8649 6629 *Consulting engineers*

White Young Green Consulting, Family House, 4 Bedford Business Park, Croydon, CR0 2AP Tel: (020) 8649 6600 Fax: (020) 8649 6629 E-mail: londoncroydon@wyg.com *Environmental consultants*

White Young Green Consulting Ltd, Arndale Court, Headingley, Leeds, LS6 2UJ Tel: 0113-278 7111 Fax: 0113-278 3487 E-mail: enquiries@wyg.com *Engineering & environmental consultants* Also at: Billingham, Cockermouth, Grimsby, Leeds, London, Manchester, Purley, Runcorn & Stevenage

White Young Green Environmental Northern Ireland Ltd, 1 Locksley Business Park, Montgomery Road, Belfast, BT6 9UP Tel: (028) 9078 1090 Fax: (028) 9070 6050 *Consulting engineers*

Whitechapel Bell Foundry Ltd, 34 Whitechapel Road, London, E1 1DY Tel: (020) 7247 2599 Fax: (020) 7375 1979 E-mail: sales@whitechapelbellfoundry.co.uk *Church bell founders suppliers*

▶ Whitecode Ltd, Highfield House, 2 West Hill, Dartford, DA1 2EW Tel: (01322) 289977 Fax: (01322) 289988

Whitecroft Designs Ltd, 53 High Street, Stourbridge, West Midlands, DY8 1DE Tel: (01384) 443644 Fax: (01384) 443696 E-mail: acutler@btconnect.com *Exhibition stand designers*

Whitecroft Lighting Ltd, Burlington Street, Ashton-under-Lyne, Lancashire, OL7 0AX Tel: (0870) 5087087 Fax: (0870) 5084210 E-mail: sales@lightshow.co.uk *Lighting manufrs (commercial industrial specialist)*

Whitecross Engineering Ltd, Columbia House, Columbia Drive, Worthing, West Sussex, BN13 3HD Tel: (01903) 690807 Fax: (01903) 690807 *Air conditioning, refrigeration, mechanical & electrical building services*

▶ Whitefield Distribution Ltd, F Birch Industrial Estate, Whittle Lane, Heywood, Lancashire, OL10 2SX Tel: (01706) 361970 Fax: (01706) 361997

▶ Whitefield Fabrications Ltd, Kirklees St, Bury, Lancashire, BL8 3NJ Tel: 01204 887700

▶ Whiteford Crocker Ltd, Park House, 28 Outland Road, Plymouth, PL2 3DE Tel: (01752) 550711 Fax: (01752) 560029 E-mail: mail@whitefordcrocker.com *We deal with personal injury compensation claims, conveyancing (buying and selling freehold and leasehold homes) family law (divorce, finance and children), wills and probate (including estates tax and inheritance). Civil disputes and commercial property (including commercial leases and partnerships) and related services. ***

Whitefurze Ltd, Burnsall Road Industrial Estate, Burnsall Road, Coventry, CV5 6BT Tel: (024) 7671 7755 Fax: (024) 7671 7474 *Plastic house & garden ware manufrs*

▶ Whitegold Taxis, 4 Inglenook Court, Maltby, Rotherham, South Yorkshire, S66 7NZ Tel: (01709) 812222 Fax: 01709 769560 E-mail: larjimoh@yahoo.com *Business/ Management Consultants-- **-business planning*-business Strategy formulation & implimentation*-market research*-Business advisory services to new start-up companies, partnerships, sole traders etc*-Project management *-Change management advise and implimentation*-communication audit*-Sales and marketing plan/strategy formulation and implimentation*-Idea and Knowledge management services**

Whitegrove Group P.L.C., Units 5-7, Goodwood Road, Boyatt Wood Industrial Estate, Eastleigh, Hampshire, SO50 4NT Tel: (023) 8064 2643 Fax: (023) 8064 2647 *Stationery office equipment suppliers*

▶ Whitehall Fabrications Ltd, Whitehall House, Bruntcliffe Lane, Morley, Leeds, LS27 0LZ Tel: 0113-222 3000 Fax: 0113-222 3001 E-mail: sales@whitehall-uk.com *Kitchen worktops, manufrs*

Whitehall Printing Co Avon Ltd, Gordon Road, Whitehall, Bristol, BS5 7DL Tel: 0117-951 7311 Fax: 0117-935 4378 E-mail: enquiries@whitehallprinting.co.uk *Commercial Printing*

Whitehall Recruitment Ltd, 37-41 High Street, Edenbridge, Kent, TN8 5AD Tel: (01732) 864777 Fax: (01732) 865777 E-mail: info@whitehall.uk.com *Recruitment consultants for the chemical & scientific industries*

Whitehall Security Services, 137-139 High Street, Beckenham, Kent, BR3 1AG Tel: (020) 8658 3933 Fax: (020) 8663 3467 E-mail: sales@whitehallsecurity.com *Detective agency & security services*

Whitehead, Unit 4 Coomber Way, Croydon, CR0 4TQ Tel: (020) 8684 4507 Fax: (020) 8683 3100 E-mail: info@pfwhitehead.com *Road haulage services*

Whitehead Alloys Ltd, 4 Buck Street, Middlesbrough, Cleveland, TS2 1LW Tel: (01642) 223606 Fax: (01642) 246137 E-mail: whiteheadalloys@btconnect.com *Secondary aluminium suppliers*

Whitehead Engineering, Unit 6 Haydon Industrial Estate, Radstock, BA3 3RD Tel: (01761) 432305 Fax: (01761) 435329 E-mail: info@whiteheadengineering.co.uk *Poultry processing equipment manufrs*

Whitehead Gardner Tooling Ltd, Unit 2, Spring Gardens Industrial Estate, Romford, RM7 9LD Tel: (01708) 756023 Fax: (01708) 733219 E-mail: enquiries@whiteheads.co.uk *Injection mould making*

Whitehead Man G K R & Associates, Queensbury House, 3 Old Burlington Street, London, W1S 3AE Tel: (020) 7534 0000 Fax: (020) 7290 2050 E-mail: mail@wmann.com *Specialist recruitment consultants*

Whitehead & Wood Ltd, Brindley Close, Network 65 Business Park, Hapton, Burnley, Lancashire, BB11 5TD Tel: (01282) 446000 Fax: (01282) 446044 E-mail: service@wwcom.co.uk *Whitehead & Wood specialise in providing innovative product presentation across a variety of substrates. Visit www.shadecard.com for SHADE CARD and SAMPLE CARD With our extensive knowledge and experience of creative product presentation we have the ability to design and produce innovative concepts in product sampling for the flooring and fabric industries. From CAD and surface graphics we print and convert board and cut and affix product using a bespoke automated production line. Effective design, quality of print and reliability of product affixing are key in a market ready for fresh ideas and where innovation can also mean cost savings. With UK operational and sales facilities plus manufacturing capabilities in China, we are in a unique position to offer a strategic and integrated service which includes concepting, visualising, packaging constructional design and sampling, artwork, repro, origination, colour printing, shade cards and packaging.*

▶ Whitehead Woodward & Co., Gleniffer, Hoseley Lane, Marford, Wrexham, Clwyd, LL12 8YE Tel: (01978) 855478 Fax: 0161-237 3595 E-mail: fwhitehead@wwsolicitors.co.uk *Solicitors*

Whitehill Woodworking Machinery, 6 Union Street, Luton, LU1 3AN Tel: (01582) 736881 Fax: (01582) 488987 E-mail: david@whitehill-tools.com *Woodworking machine tool manufrs*

Whitehouse Consultants Ltd, 29 Harcourt Road, Dorney Reach, Maidenhead, Berkshire, SL6 0DT Tel: (01628) 630459 Fax: (01524) 411037 E-mail: sales@whitehouse-consult.co.uk *Computer consultants*

Whitehouse Cox & Co. Ltd, 1 Morton Court Lockside, Anchor Brook Industrial Park, Aldridge, Walsall, WS9 8BZ Tel: (01922) 458881 Fax: (01922) 458889 E-mail: customerservice@whitehouse-cox.co.uk *Made-up leather goods manufrs*

Whitehouse Electrical Ltd, Brickheath Road, Wolverhampton, WV1 2SR Tel: (01902) 451961 Fax: (01902) 870971 E-mail: peter@coswhielec.co.uk *Electrical installation engineers*

Whitehouse Engineering Co. Ltd, 14 Trench Road, Newtownabbey, County Antrim, BT36 4UU Tel: (028) 9084 8311 Fax: (028) 9034 2773 E-mail: info@whitehouse-eng.com *Sheet metalwork engineers & fabricators*

Whitehouse Furniture Ltd, Whytehouse Farm, Greenway, Rock, Kidderminster, Worcestershire, DY14 9SJ Tel: (01299) 832466 Fax: (01299) 832576 E-mail: sales@whitehousefurniture.co.uk *Educational, office & hotel furniture manufrs*

Whitehouse Machine Tools Ltd, 7 Princes Drive Industrial Estate, Coventry Road, Kenilworth, Warwickshire, CV8 2FD Tel: (01926) 852725 Fax: (01926) 850620 E-mail: sales@wmtcnc.com *Machine tool merchants*

Whitehouse Plastics Ltd, Unit 4 Tiber Way, Glebe Farm Industrial Estate, Rugby, Warwickshire, CV21 1ED Tel: (01788) 541042 Fax: (01788) 552314 E-mail: sales@whitehouseplastics.co.uk *Manufacturing plastic extrusions to the highest quality from many different thermo plastic materials. We can offer a full design and consultancy services at the onset of new projects*

▶ Whiteinch Demolition Ltd, Caledonia Street, Clydebank, Dunbartonshire, G81 4EX Tel: 0141-951 4000 E-mail: info@whiteinchasbestos.com

Whiteland Engineering Ltd, Torrington Lane, Bideford, Devon, EX39 4BH Tel: (01237) 472203 Fax: (01237) 472205 E-mail: info@whitelandengineering.co.uk *Special purpose machinery manufrs*

Whiteleaf Ltd, Po Box 2, Princes Risborough, Buckinghamshire, HP27 9DP Tel: (01844) 261199 Fax: (01844) 342337 E-mail: sales@whiteleaffurniture.co.uk *Furniture manufrs*

Whitelegg Machines Ltd, Horsham Road, Beare Green, Dorking, Surrey, RH5 4LQ Tel: (01306) 713200 Fax: (01306) 711865 E-mail: sales@whitelegg.com *Coil winding machinery manufrs*

Whiteley Ltd, Pool In Wharfedale, Otley, West Yorkshire, LS21 1RP Tel: 0113-284 2121 Fax: 0113-284 2272 *Insulating paper & board manufrs*

Benjamin Whiteley & Sons Ltd, Park Road, Mills, Elland, West Yorkshire, HX5 9HX Tel: (01422) 372272 Fax: (01422) 375651 *Property Managers*

Whiteley Electronics Ltd, Victoria Street, Mansfield, Nottinghamshire, NG18 5RW Tel: (01623) 415600 Fax: (01623) 420484 E-mail: e-mail@whiteleyelectronics.com *Public address & passenger information systems manufrs*

Whiteley Electronics Ltd, Grove Road, Cosham, Portsmouth, PO6 1LX Tel: (023) 9232 6223 Fax: (023) 9237 6327 *Electronic assembly services*

▶ The Whiteley H A T Co. Ltd, Unitb 1, Bramingham Business Park, Enterprise Way, Luton, LU3 4BU Tel: (01582) 493393 Fax: (01582) 491838 E-mail: sales@whiteley-hat.co.uk *Manufacturers & distributors of high quality fashionable hats*

Whiteley Read Engineering Ltd, Gateway Indust Estate, Rotherham, South Yorkshire, S62 6JL Tel: (01709) 710661 Fax: (01709) 710961 E-mail: sales@whitely-read.co.uk *Pressure vessels designers & manufrs*

▶ Whiteley-Brooks Engineering Ltd, 3 Herald Way, Binley Industrial Estate, Coventry, CV3 2NY Tel: (024) 7645 5938 Fax: (024) 7663 6950

▶ Whitelock & Co. Ltd, 308-310 Bournemouth Road, Poole, Dorset, BH14 9AR Tel: (01202) 763214 Fax: (01202) 752443 E-mail: enquiries@whitelock.co.uk

Whitemountain Quarries, 26 Ballycarngannon Road, Lisburn, County Antrim, BT27 6YA Tel: (028) 9263 9750 Fax: (028) 9263 9751 E-mail: info@lagan-group.com *Building & construction*

Whites Ltd, 4 Bond Gate Chambers, Bond Gate, Nuneaton, Warwickshire, CV11 4AL Tel: (024) 7635 0909 Fax: (024) 7635 0909 E-mail: knight@pipemedia.co.uk *Picture framing & fine restorers manufrs*

Whites Accident Repair Centre, 10 Imperial Way, Croydon, CR0 4RR Tel: (020) 8686 0055 Fax: (020) 8688 1102 *Motor body builders*

Whites Of Braunston, 38 High Street, Braunston, Oakham, Leicestershire, LE15 8QU Tel: (01572) 722517 Fax: (01572) 755900 *Agricultural machinery dealers*

Whites Burners Ltd, 9 Ilfracombe Gardens, Whitley Bay, Tyne & Wear, NE26 3ND Tel: 0191-252 9933 Fax: 0191-252 9955 *Oil & gas commercial & domestic, service & maintenance engineers*

Whites Concrete Ltd, Ravensthorpe Road, Thornhill Lees, Dewsbury, West Yorkshire, WF12 9EF Tel: (01924) 464283 Fax: (01924) 459183 E-mail: whites@longley.uk.com *Pre-cast concrete product manufrs*

Whites Conservatories & Garden Buildings, Reigate Road, Buckland, Reigate, Surrey, RH2 9RE Tel: (01737) 240579 Fax: (01737) 240579 E-mail: sales@whitesconservatories.co.uk *For 50 years, Compton has built an enviable reputation with thousands of customers for manufacturing top quality concrete garages and sectional buildings at outstanding value for money prices. Our vast product range includes:- Banbury Concrete Garages Apex Spar Concrete Garages Flat Spar Concrete Garages Apex Brick Concrete Garages Apex Rockstone Concrete Garages Timber Garages Motorcycle Concrete Garages Concrete Sheds Concrete Workshops & Buildings Compton's ranges of both domestic and commercial Concrete Buildings include:- Extra High Concrete Garages (Suitable for Minibuses, Vans and other High Vehicles etc) Secure Stores Battery Garages Clubhouses Bin Stores Semi Industrial Buildings Workshop & Offices*

Whites Electronics Ltd, 35j Harbour Road, Inverness, IV1 1UA Tel: (01463) 223456 Fax: (01463) 224048 E-mail: sales@whelects.demon.co.uk *Metal detection equipment manufrs*

▶ Whites Estate Agents Ltd, 339 Wellingborough Road, Northampton, NN1 4ER Tel: (01604) 233600 E-mail: webmarketing@whitesestateagents.co.uk *Whites Estate Agents sell residential property in Northampton and surrounding villages.*We also provide advice on planning on land and commercial sites throughout northamptonshire, Bedfordshire and Cambridgeshire. This can be Free to the owner**

Whites Material Handling Ltd, 10-12 Dixon Road, Bristol, BS4 5QW Tel: 0117-972 0006 Fax: 0117-972 3296 E-mail: enquiries@whitesmh.co.uk *Fabrication of attachments/construction industry*

White's Removals & Transport Ltd, 257 Great Lister Street, Birmingham, B7 4DB Tel: 0121-359 3571 Fax: 0121-359 6889 E-mail: enquiries@whitesremovals.co.uk *UK & overseas removal contractors*

▶ Whites Of Skendleby, 1, Fordington Water Works, Fordington, Alford, Lincs, LN13 0HQ Tel: (01790) 753904 Fax: (01790) 752565

Whites Of Skendleby, Skendleby, Spilsby, Lincolnshire, PE23 4QE Tel: (07774) 658100 Fax: (01754) 890270 E-mail: diggerdjw@aol.com *Agricultural engineers*

▶ Whites Transport Ltd, Laundry Road, Minster, Ramsgate, Kent, CT12 4HY Tel: (01843) 821377 Fax: (01843) 822530 E-mail: sales@whitestransport.co.uk

Whitestone Management Ltd, Whitestone House, Rover Way, Cardiff, CF24 2RX Tel: (029) 2045 1725 Fax: (029) 2045 1526 *Whitestone continues to build upon its strong reputation and is fast becoming one of the leading contractors in South Wales. With over a decade of first hand experience as commercial building contractors we are ideally suited to cater for all your development needs whatever the project value or scale.*

Whitewater UK Ltd, 2 Beech Road, Purley on Thames, Reading, RG8 8DS Tel: 0118-984 5565 Fax: 0118-961 5626 E-mail: tech@whitewater.net *Water treatment*

Whitewedge Systems Ltd, 42 Jacklyns Lane, Alresford, Hampshire, SO24 9LG Tel: (01962) 734165 Fax: (01962) 734214 E-mail: nick.stone@www.sys.co.uk *Interim management services*

Whitfield & Son Ltd, Marsh Trees House, Marsh Parade, Newcastle, Staffordshire, ST5 1BT Tel: (01782) 622666 Fax: (01782) 622655 E-mail: sales@whitson.co.uk *Raw materials supplier for the ceramic industry*

T.D. Whitfield & Sons Ltd, Oak Lea Mills, Meadow Rd, Apperley Bridge, Bradford, W. Yorkshire, BD10 0LY Tel: (01274) 613106 Fax: (01274) 617688 *Textile waste merchants*

Whitfire Shavings & Sawdust Supplies Ltd, Heatherfield Works, Church Lane, Farington Moss, Leyland, PR26 6RD Tel: (01772) 335178 Fax: (01772) 629843 *Sawdust & wood shavings contractors*

Whitford Plastics Ltd, Christleton Court, Manor Park, Runcorn, Cheshire, WA7 1ST Tel: (01928) 571000 Fax: (01928) 571010 E-mail: sales@whitfordww.co.uk *Fluoropolymer coating manufrs*

▶ Whithouse Products, Kelburn Business Park, Port Glasgow, Renfrewshire, PA14 6TD Tel: (01475) 742500 Fax: (01475) 742888 *Hoses, pumps, gauges & filters*

Whiting & Wilson, 540 Burnley Road, Rossendale, Lancashire, BB4 8NE Tel: (01706) 830974 Fax: (01706) 830974 *Jewellery manufrs*

Whitland Engineering Ltd, West Street, Whitland, Dyfed, SA34 0AE Tel: (01994) 240442 Fax: (01994) 240937 E-mail: whitland.engineering@btinternet.com *Whitland Engineering provides project management, engineering services inclusive of mechanical and electrical design, stainless steel fabrication and installation operating throughout the UK.*

Whitley Willows Ltd, Addlecroft Lane, Lepton, Huddersfield, HD8 0NH Tel: (01484) 600800 *Textile manufrs*

Whitman Laboratories Ltd, Bedford Road, Petersfield, Hampshire, GU32 3DD Tel: (01730) 266522 Fax: (01730) 261500 *Cosmetic manufrs*

Whitmar Blinds, 9a Stour Valley Close, Upstreet, Canterbury, Kent, CT3 4DB Tel: (01227) 860440 Fax: (01227) 860440 *Window blind manufrs*

Whitmarley Engineering Co. Ltd, Ivy Road, Stirchley, Birmingham, B30 2NX Tel: 0121-458 7491 Fax: 0121-433 4137 E-mail: enquiries@whitmarley.fsnet.co.uk *Wire work pressings*

Whitminster International Ltd, Dudbridge Road, Stroud, Gloucestershire, GL5 3HF Tel: (01453) 762266 Fax: (01453) 762277 E-mail: mailroom@whitminster.co.uk *Paper converting machine manufrs*

▶ Whitmont Press, 2B Mount Pleasant Road, London, SE13 6RB Tel: (020) 8690 2696

Whitmores Timber Co. Ltd, Main Road, Claybrooke Magna, Lutterworth, Leicestershire, LE17 5AQ Tel: (01455) 209121 Fax: (01455) 209041 E-mail: info@whitmores.co.uk *Hardwoods & sawmilling services*

▶ Whitnell Plant, School Farm Buildings, School Road, Langham, Colchester, CO4 5PB Tel: (01206) 272834 Fax: (01206) 272104 E-mail: sales@whitnell.co.uk *Civil engineering*

Whiton Tools Ltd, Parsonage Street, Oldbury, West Midlands, B69 4PH Tel: 0121-552 6065 Fax: 0121-544 7684 *Toolmakers*

Whitstable Marine, Sea Wall, Whitstable, Kent, CT5 1BX Tel: (01227) 262525 Fax: (01227) 772750 E-mail: sales@thedinghystore.co.uk *Maring equipment retailers*

Whittaker Bros Ltd, 31 Firs Street, Dudley, West Midlands, DY2 7DW Tel: (01384) 252112 Fax: (01384) 232541 *Electrical engineers & contractors*

Whittaker Fleet Care Ltd, Bordesley Street, Birmingham, B5 5PN Tel: 0121-643 6211 Fax: 0121-643 8299 E-mail: info@wfleetcare.com *Fleet maintenance services*

Gerald Whittaker Signs, The Workshop Iron Hill, Hollycombe, Liphook, Hampshire, GU30 7LP Tel: (01428) 722260 Fax: (01428) 722260 *Sign manufrs*

Whittaker Office Supplies Ltd, Weldon Road, Loughborough, Leicestershire, LE11 5TE Tel: (01509) 235888 Fax: (01509) 610511 E-mail: smart@whittaker-os.co.uk *Office equipment & commercial stationery suppliers*

R.W. Whittaker (Pallets) Ltd, Booth Street, Middleton Junction, Manchester, M24 1SF Tel: 0161-643 1718 Fax: 0161-643 0556 E-mail: robwhit@palcase.fastnet.co.uk *Pallet makers & repairers*

Richard Whittaker Ltd, Unit 28 Transpennine Industrial Estate, Gorrels Way, Queensway, Rochdale, Lancashire, OL11 2QR Tel: (01706) 341700 Fax: (01706) 341357 E-mail: sales@richard-whittaker.com *Starch products, contract packers*

Whittall Warehouses Ltd, The Old Court House, Back Lane, Hereford, HR4 8SG Tel: (01544) 318788 Fax: (01544) 318165 E-mail: whittall@wwlgroup.co.uk *Warehouse keepers*

▶ Whitten Ltd, Unit 4, 39 Willow Lane, Mitcham, Surrey, CR4 4NA Tel: (020) 8640 3888 E-mail: whittenmetalworks@btconnect.com *Steel fabricators*

Whitten Timber Ltd, Eagle Wharf, Peckham Hill Street, London, SE15 5JT Tel: (020) 7732 3804 Fax: (020) 7635 3555 *Family run business since 1919. Specialising in all aspects of timber needs.*

Whittingham Design & Manufacturing Co. Ltd, Chapel Works, Chapel Green, Willenhall, West Midlands, WV13 1QY Tel: (01902) 607272 Fax: (01902) 637884 *Machine tool manufrs*

Whittinghams, 119 Garstang Road, Claughton-on-Brock, Preston, PR3 0PH Tel: (01995) 640302 Fax: (01995) 640790 *Agricultural dealers*

Whittington Tool Hire, 73 Mason Road, Birmingham, B24 9EH Tel: 0121-382 5770 Fax: 0121-373 4542 *Tool hire & sales*

▶ indicates data change since last edition

Whittle Movers Ltd, Charnley Fold Lane, Bamber Bridge, Preston, PR5 6AA Tel: (01772) 626565 Fax: (01772) 627770 E-mail: mail@whittle.co.uk *World-wide removals & storage*

Whittle Painting, 170a Monton Road, Eccles, Manchester, M30 9GA Tel: 0161-787 7667 Fax: 0161-787 8841 E-mail: sales@whittlepaintinggroup.co.uk *Painting contractors*

Whittle Painting Group Ltd, Daybrook House, Merchant Street, Nottingham, NG6 8GT Tel: 0115-977 0311 Fax: 0115-977 1472 E-mail: sales@whittlegroup.co.uk *Painting contractors industrial & commercial*

Whittle Valve Repairs Ltd, Unit 3 Tower Enterprise Park, Great George Street, Wigan, Lancashire, WN3 4DP Tel: (01942) 493495 E-mail: sales@whittle-valves.co.uk *Valve repairers, reconditioning & refurbishers*

Whittles Publishing Services, Roseleigh House, Latheronwheel, Latheron, Caithness, KW5 6DW Tel: (01593) 741240 Fax: (01593) 741360 E-mail: info@whittlespublishing.com *Publishing & publishing services*

Whittlesey Catering Hire Ltd, Unit 15 Springwater Business Park, Station Road, Whittlesey, Peterborough, PE7 2EU Tel: (01733) 203491 Fax: (01733) 203491 E-mail: sales@cateringhireuk.com *Catering equipment hire*

Whittlesey Engineering Co. Ltd, Fenland District Industrial Estate, Station Road, Whittlesey, Peterborough, PE7 2EY Tel: (01733) 203766 Fax: (01733) 350808 *Production engineers & precision machinists*

Whitton Precision Ltd, Bridge Works, Durnsford Road, London, SW19 8DR Tel: (020) 8946 6431 Fax: (020) 8947 1292 E-mail: whittonprecision@btconnet.com *Press toolmakers & precision pressings*

Whitwell & Sons, 1 Laycock Gate, Blackpool, FY3 8AT Tel: (01253) 395172 Fax: (01253) 395176 *Fabrication manufrs*

▶ Whitwick Engineering Coalville Ltd, 117 London Road, Coalville, Leicestershire, LE67 3JE Tel: (01530) 510770 Fax: (01530) 510068

Whitworth Holdings Ltd, Victoria Mills, London Road, Wellingborough, Northamptonshire, NN8 2DT Tel: (01933) 443444 Fax: (01933) 222523 E-mail: enquiries@whitworthbros.ltd.uk *Holding company*

Whitworth Co Partnership, 18 Hatter Street, Bury St. Edmunds, Suffolk, IP33 1NE Tel: (01284) 760421 Fax: (01284) 704734 E-mail: sales@wcp-architects.com *Chartered architects & surveyors*

Whitworths Ltd, Orchard House, Irthlingborough, Wellingborough, Northamptonshire, NN9 5DB Tel: (01933) 653000 Fax: (01933) 652525 E-mail: sales@whitworths.co.uk *Dried fruit packers*

▶ Who Media Ltd, 18 Bircham Tofts, Bircham Tofts, King's Lynn, Norfolk, PE31 6QT Tel: (01904) 781526 *Web site design, production and marketing*

Wholebake Ltd, Tyn Llidiart Industrial Estate, Corwen, Clwyd, LL21 9RR Tel: (01490) 412297 Fax: (01490) 412053 E-mail: wholebake@aol.co.uk *Cereal bar manufrs*

Wholefoods Bedford, 1 Thurlow Street, Bedford, MK40 1LR Tel: (01234) 219618 Fax: (01234) 213929 *Health store*

▶ Wholesale Italian Charms UK, 2 Waverly Court, Rowlands Road, Worthing, West Sussex, BN11 3JD Tel: (0799) 0553775 Fax: (01903) 217119 E-mail: info@carla-mar.co.uk *We are U.K importers and wholesalers of Low Cost Italian Charms. Suitable for Market Traders, Independant Retailers and Party Plan. Our Italian Charms are available from 20p each. Retail displays are also stocked. Bracelets & Keyrings also available.*

Wholesale Lighting, 34-41 White Lion Street, London, N1 9PQ Tel: (020) 7278 8993 Fax: (020) 7833 4762 E-mail: sales@ryness.co.uk *Electrical contractors* Also at: London EC4, NW1, SW1, W1 & W2

▶ Wholesale Mortgages, Lluest Pentre, Pentre Lane, Rhuddlan, Rhyl, Clwyd, LL18 6HY Tel: (01745) 590006 Fax: (01745) 590016 *Mortgage & Insurance advice*

▶ Wholesale Movie TV Music Gifts Ltd, 1St Floor, 1 Chapel Street, Bridlington, North Humberside, YO15 2DR Tel: (01262) 677730 Fax: (01262) 675702 *Gift website*

Wholesale Newspaper Services Ltd, Altnagelvin Industrial Estate, Trench Road, Londonderry, BT47 2ED Tel: (028) 7132 0700 Fax: (028) 7132 0701 E-mail: info@wns.co.uk *Daily, regional newspaper & magazine distributors*

Wholesale Nutrition Ltd, Aztec House, Delta Business Park, Salterns Lane, Fareham, Hampshire, PO16 0JL Tel: 0800 174545 Fax: (01329) 289222 *Food supplement sales*

Wholesale Stationers (Devon) Ltd, Brunel Road, Brunel Industrial Estate, Newton Abbot, Devon, TQ12 4PB Tel: (01626) 365007 Fax: (01626) 367269 E-mail: sales@wholesalestationers.co.uk *Stationery wholesalers*

Wholesale Tropicals, 220 Bethnal Green Road, London, E2 0AA Tel: (020) 7739 5356 Fax: (020) 7729 2444 E-mail: tjones@xln..co.uk *Aquatic centre*

Wholesale Welding Supplies Ltd, 1 The Orbital Centre, Icknield Way, Letchworth Garden City, Hertfordshire, SG6 1ET Tel: (01462) 482200 Fax: (01462) 482202 E-mail: wws@wholeweld.co.uk *Welding suppliers*

Wholistic Research Co., Five House Farm, Sandon Road, Therfield, Royston, Hertfordshire, SG8 9RE Tel: (0845) 4303100 Fax: (01763) 287467 E-mail: info@wholisticresearch.com *Mail order health equipment suppliers*

WHS Halo, Water Orton Lane, Minworth, Sutton Coldfield, West Midlands, B76 9BW Tel: 0121-749 3000 Fax: 0121-749 2511 E-mail: info@whs-halo.co.uk *Plastic material manufrs*

▶ Whyte, Hindstones Farm, New Aberdour, Fraserburgh, Aberdeenshire, AB43 6LY Tel: (01346) 561219 Fax: (01346) 561484

▶ Whyte and McKay Ltd, Golfview Terrace, Invergordon, Ross-Shire, IV18 0HP Tel: (01349) 852451 Fax: (01349) 854104 *Distillers*

Whyte Group Ltd, Marlborough House, 298 Regents Park Road, London, N3 2UA Tel: (020) 8346 5946 Fax: (020) 8349 4589 E-mail: sales@whytechem.co.uk *Chemical distributors & manufrs*

Whyte & Mackay, Dalmore House, 310 St. Vincent Street, Glasgow, G2 5RG Tel: 0141-248 5771 Fax: 0141-221 1993 *Distillers*

▶ Whyte & MacKay Ltd, Golfview Terrace, Invergordon, Ross-Shire, IV18 0HP Tel: (01349) 852451 *Spirits*

Wichita Co. Ltd, Ampthill Road, Bedford, MK42 9RD Tel: (01234) 350311 Fax: (01234) 350317 E-mail: clutch@wichita.co.uk *Clutches, brake units & couplings manufrs*

Wick Hill Ltd, Rivercourt, Albert Drive, Woking, Surrey, GU21 5RP Tel: (01483) 227600 Fax: (01483) 227700 E-mail: info@wickhill.co.uk *IT & security specialists*

▶ Wicked the Candle Shop, Newmarket Buildings, Postern Gate, Bridgnorth, Shropshire, WV16 4BX Tel: 01746 767651 E-mail: wickedthecandleshop@uk2.net *Candle manufrs*

Wickens Engineering Ltd, 1 Shire Business Park, Wainwright Road, Worcester, WR4 9FA Tel: (01905) 456780 Fax: (01905) 456073 E-mail: info@wickens.co.uk *Structural steelwork engineers*

Wickers World Hot Air Balloon Co., The Hawthorns, Tolldish Lane, Great Haywood, Stafford, ST18 0RA Tel: (01889) 882222 Fax: (01889) 881122 E-mail: sales@wickersworld.co.uk *Arial advertising & pleasure flights*

Wickersley Angling Centre, Unit 3 Denby Way, Maltby, Rotherham, South Yorkshire, S66 8HR Tel: (01709) 540998 Fax: (01709) 540998 *Fishing tackle suppliers*

Wickes Building Supplies Ltd, Newcraighall Road, Edinburgh, EH15 3HS Tel: 0131-669 6161 Fax: 0131-669 4366 *Supplies heating & plumbing goods*

Wickham Auto Wash Ltd, Norton Road, Stevenage, Hertfordshire, SG1 2BB Tel: (01438) 314041 Fax: (01438) 740140 E-mail: all@wickham-autowash.co.uk Sales Contact: T.A. Stokes Principal Export Areas: Worldwide *Washing systems, wheel washing equipment retailers & manufrs*

Wickham Industries Ltd, Ledston Luck Enterprise Park, Leeds, LS25 7BF Tel: 0113-287 2002 Fax: 0113-287 3020 E-mail: info@wickhamindustries.co.uk *Chemical products manufrs*

Wickham Laboratories, Winchester Road, Wickham, Fareham, Hampshire, PO17 5EU Tel: (01329) 832511 Fax: (01329) 834262 E-mail: mail@wickhamlabs.co.uk *Analytical laboratory services*

Wickman Coventry Ltd, Automatic House Discovery Way, Leofric Business Park, Binley, Coventry, CV3 2TD Tel: (024) 7654 7900 Fax: (024) 7654 7420 E-mail: sales@wickman.co.uk *Machine tool manufrs*

Wick's Ltd, Unit 18L Ring Road, Burntwood Business Park, Burntwood, Staffordshire, WS7 3JQ Tel: (01543) 672488 Fax: (01543) 685211 *Industrial workwear & children's wear manufrs*

Wicks & Martin Ltd, Bromyard Industrial Estate, Bromyard, Herefordshire, HR7 4HT Tel: (01885) 483636 Fax: (01885) 483692 E-mail: mike@wicksandmartin.co.uk Sales Contact: G.T. Williams *Manufacturers of mechanical control cables for automotive, aerospace, agricultural & all other industries. Bowden-type cable are produced for throttle, handbrake, clutch & similar applications, as well as wire rope assemblies up to 6mm diameter*

Steve Wicks Built-in Furniture, Unit 4, 133-139 Church Rd, Hadleigh, Essex, SS7 2EJ Tel: (020) 8980 8332 Fax: (020) 8980 8332 *Built-in furniture manufrs*

▶ Steve Wicks Transport, 19 Crescent Grove, Hartshill, Stoke-On-Trent, ST4 6EN Tel: (01782) 768871 Fax: (01782) 768871 E-mail: stevewickstransport@hotmail.com *Light haulage & courier service*

Wicksteed Engineering Ltd, Hove Road, Rushden, Northamptonshire, NN10 0JB Tel: (01933) 318555 Fax: (01933) 410103 E-mail: mail@wicksteed.com *Heat exchanger tube extracting manufrs*

Wicksteed Leisure Ltd, Digby St, Kettering, Northamptonshire, NN16 8YJ Tel: (01536) 517028 Fax: (01536) 410633 E-mail: sales@wicksteed.co.uk *Playground, sports equipment, safety surfacing & outdoor leisure furniture manufacturers*

Wida Group, 2 Brookside Road, Ruddington, Nottingham, NG11 6AT Tel: 0115-921 4797 Fax: 0115-984 5097 E-mail: info@widagroup.com *Website design, hosting & e-commerce*

▶ Widd Signs, Maserati House, Geldered Road, Leeds, LS12 1AS Tel: 0113-279 4144 Fax: 0113-279 7935 E-mail: sales@widdsigns.co.uk *Signage, full design, manufacture, installation & project management services*

Widd Signs, 194 Armley Road, Leeds, LS12 2NB Tel: 0113-279 4144 Fax: 0113-279 7935 E-mail: admin@widdsigns.co.uk *Signs manufrs*

Widdop Bingham & Co. Ltd, Broadgate, Broadway Business Park, Chadderton, Oldham, OL9 9XE Tel: 0161-688 1200 Fax: 0161-682 6808 E-mail: sales@widdop.co.uk *Clock & gift importers & distributors service* Also at: Manchester

Widdop De Courcy Ltd, Prospect Works, Allerton Road, Allerton, Bradford, West Yorkshire, BD15 7AF Tel: (01274) 495709 Fax: (01274) 547396 E-mail: sales@widdops.com *Industrial brush manufrs*

▶ Widdowson Group, The Mill Lane, Glenfield, Leicester, LE3 8DX Tel: 0116-231 1188 Fax: 0116-287 9898

Widdowson-Dalebrook Engineers Ltd, Basford Road, Crewe, CW2 6ES Tel: 01270 661111 *Precision turned parts manufrs*

▶ Wide Blue Yonder, 20 Purbrook Road, Tadley, Hampshire, RG26 4PR Tel: (07976) 274018 E-mail: info@wideblueyonderweb.co.uk *We are a web design company, specialising in sites for small businesses. We can register domain names, design/host your site and configure email for your business. All packages include free hosting for 1 year, basic search engine optimisation and regular updates.*

Wide Range Engineering Services Ltd, Coventry Road, Acan Way, Narborough, Leicester, LE19 2FT Tel: 0116-275 0100 Fax: 0116-275 0086 E-mail: sales@wres.co.uk *Distributors/ agents of bearings; hydraulic components/ fittings; power tool/accessories & power transmission equipment (industrial/mechanical)*

Wide Range Services Ltd, Alexandra Dock, Hull, HU9 1TA Tel: (01482) 898261 Fax: (01482) 587271 E-mail: sales@wrshull.co.uk *Ship container repairers*

▶ Wide World Services, 16 Millers Yard, Mill Lane, Cambridge, CB2 1RQ Tel: (01223) 576044 E-mail: james_williams:wideworld.co.uk *Underground survey, asset location, leakage detection*

Wideacre Metal Gates Ltd, 15 Buttress Way, Smethwick, West Midlands, B66 3DL Tel: 0121-558 4263 Fax: 0121-558 5735 E-mail: gailkaren@msn.com *Steel & timber fencing manufrs*

Widenoble Services Ltd, Tower House Unit 25 Baldock Industrial Estate, London Road, Baldock, Hertfordshire, SG7 6NG Tel: (01462) 895431 Fax: (01462) 895096 E-mail: eileen@widenoble.freeserve.co.uk *Precision engineers, milling & turning services*

Widewell Communications, 49 Lulworth Drive, Plymouth, PL6 7DT Tel: (01752) 721226 Fax: (01752) 721236 E-mail: enquire@widewell.co.uk *Telephone systems installation*

Widget World, Unit F9 Blackpole Trading Estate East, Blackpole Road, Worcester, WR3 8SG Tel: (01905) 754520 Fax: (01905) 759488 E-mail: gas@widgetworld.freeserve.co.uk *Industrial gas suppliers*

Widnes Tank Container Services Ltd, Ditton Road, Widnes, Cheshire, WA8 0NE Tel: 0151-424 6742 Fax: 0151-423 4210 E-mail: info@widnestcs.co.uk *Tank & container repairs*

▶ Widnes Windows, 140 Birchfield Road, Widnes, Cheshire, WA8 9ED Tel: 0151-424 3332 Fax: 0151-420 4603 E-mail: info@widneswindows.co.uk *Window, conservatory & roofline installers*

Widney Leisure Ltd, 5 Alfred Court Saxon Business Park, Hanbury Road, Stoke Prior, Bromsgrove, Worcestershire, B60 4AD Tel: (01527) 577800 Fax: (01527) 577900 E-mail: sales@widney-leisure.co.uk *Liquefied petroleum gas fires*

Widney Pressings, Scotswood Road, Newcastle upon Tyne, NE15 6BZ Tel: 0191-273 9117 Fax: 0191-272 3492 E-mail: awingfield@bodyinwhitepressings.co.uk *Pressed component manufrs*

Wieland Electric Ltd, 1 The Riverside Business Centre, Walnut Tree Close, Guildford, Surrey, GU1 4UG Tel: (01483) 531213 Fax: (01483) 505029 E-mail: info@wieland.co.uk *Electric connector manufrs*

Wielander & Schill UK Ltd, Unit 13 Hurricane Close, Old Sarum, Salisbury, SP4 6LG Tel: (01722) 422270 Fax: (01722) 410511 E-mail: info@wielanderschill.co.uk *Supply car body shop equipment*

Wienerberger Ltd, Smoke Jack Brickworks, Horsham Lane, Wallis Wood, Dorking, Surrey, RH5 5QH Tel: (01306) 627481 Fax: (01306) 627561 *Brick manufrs*

▶ Wig Advice.co.uk, Trentham, Stoke-on-Trent, ST4 8TU Tel: (01782) 644287 E-mail: sallywigshelp@tiscali.co.uk *One of Britains" top wig technicians, working in films and television, offers GOOD, HONEST advice to people on all matters relating to wigs.*

Wigan Aluminium Windows Co. Ltd, 7 Bridge Mills Rochdale Road, Edenfield, Ramsbottom, Bury, Lancashire, BL0 0RE Tel: (01706) 822993 Fax: (01706) 822436 *Window manufrs*

Wigan Borough Partnership Ltd, Wigan Investment Centre, Waterside Drive, Wigan, Lancashire, WN3 5BA Tel: (01942) 705705 Fax: (01942) 705272 E-mail: kmulligan@wbp.org.uk *Business support & trainers*

▶ Wigan Bouncy Castles, 75 Skull House Lane, Appley Bridge, Wigan, Lancashire, WN6 9DJ Tel: (01257) 251042 Fax: (01257) 251042 E-mail: hire@bouncey.co.uk *All our bouncy castles are available for hire on a half /full day basis from only £40. All are less than 1 year old, full tested with certificates, and are regularly cleaned*

Wigan Storage Systems Ltd, 1 Edale Drive, Standish, Wigan, Lancashire, WN6 0LN Tel: (01257) 424345 Fax: (01257) 423958 E-mail: sales@wiganstorage.co.uk *Storage equipment supply & installers, racking & shelving*

Wigan Tool & Die Co. Ltd, Unit 1, Great George Street, Wigan, Lancashire, WN3 4DP Tel: (01942) 324866 Fax: (01942) 820618 E-mail: enquiries@wigantoolanddie.co.uk *Mould makers & precision engineers*

Wigan Trailer Centre Ltd, Cricket St Business Park, Cricket Street, Wigan, Lancashire, WN6 7TP Tel: (01942) 248373 Fax: (01942) 821317 E-mail: info@wtcltd.co.uk *Trailer manufacturers & vehicle body builders*

Wiggett Construction Group Ltd, Viking House, 449 Middleton Chadderton, Oldham, OL9 9LB Tel: 0161-626 3010 Fax: 0161-627 1373 E-mail: info@wiggett.co.uk *Building contractors*

F. Wiggins (Meakins), 106 Brook Farm Road, Saxmundham, Suffolk, IP17 1WL Tel: (07887) 751801 *Optical filter manufrs*

▶ Wiggins Transport Ltd, Horton Road, Staines, Middlesex, TW19 6AQ Tel: (01753) 683324

Wigglesworth Company.Ltd International Merchants, 69 Southwark Bridge Road, Wigglesworth House, London, SE1 0NG Tel: (020) 7403 1919 Fax: (020) 7403 3232 E-mail: enquiries@wigglesworthfibres.com *Fibre merchants*

Wiggly Wigglers Ltd, Lower Blakemere Farm, Blakemere, Hereford, HR2 9PX Tel: (01981) 500391 Fax: (01981) 500108 E-mail: wiggly@wigglywigglers.co.uk *Worms & worm composting distributors*

Wigham-Richardson Ship Brokers Ltd, 36 Spital Square, London, E1 6DY Tel: (020) 7730 5200 Fax: (020) 7377 1495 E-mail: wigrich@btclick.com *Ship brokers*

▶ Wighill Park Guns, Wighill Park Nurseries, Wighill Park, Tadcaster, North Yorkshire, LS24 8BW Tel: (01937) 833757 Fax: (01937) 530563 E-mail: info@wighillparkguns.co.uk *An extensive range of air guns, air rifles, scopes and gun cabinets from this UK specialist offerin excellent advice, honesty and after sales servic*

▶ Wight Aerials, 34 North Street, Ventnor, Isle of Wight, PO38 1NJ Tel: (07973) 511614 E-mail: sales@wightaerials.com *digital aerials and satellite television services*

Wight Business Services, 3 Daish Way, Newport, Isle of Wight, PO30 5XB Tel: (01983) 822229 Fax: (01983) 521899 E-mail: wbs@freenet.co.uk *Office equipment repairs, services & wholesalers*

▶ Wightcat, 14 Carisbrooke Road, Newport, Isle o Wight, PO30 1BL Tel: (01983) 527525 Fax: (01983) 527579 E-mail: sales@wightcat.com *Craft shop & wedding stationary*

▶ Wightcat Wedding Services, Medina Avenue, Newport, Isle of Wight, PO30 1EL Tel: (01983) 248214 E-mail: weddings@wightcat.com *Wightcat Wedding Services for*Exclusive Wedding Stationery.*Bespoke designs, special papers, foil printed with Gold or Silver, other colours available.*Line drawing of your Church or Wedding venue.***

▶ Wightfibre Composite Components, 58 Lanes End, Totland Bay, Isle of Wight, PO39 0AL Tel: (01983) 754748 Fax: (01983) 754748

Wightman Metals, Ringway, Bounds Green Industrial Estate, London, N11 2UD Tel: (020) 8368 1660 Fax: (020) 8368 9570 *Steel stockholders*

Wightman & Parrish Ltd, Station Road Industrial Estate, Hailsham, East Sussex, BN27 2QA Tel: (01323) 440444 Fax: (01323) 846027 E-mail: sales@w-p.co.uk *Janitorial supply services*

Wightman Stewart Ltd, Oldham Road, Sowerby Bridge, West Yorkshire, HX6 4EH Tel: (01422) 823801 Fax: (01422) 824031 E-mail: info@wightmanstewart.co.uk *CNC machine tools sales & services*

Wigmore Managements Ltd, 65 Wigmore Street, London, W1U 1BQ Tel: (020) 7935 0192 Fax: (020) 7935 3074 *Property investment company*

Wigmore Products, 18 Lower Street, Pulborough, West Sussex, RH20 2BL Tel: (01903) 893355 Fax: (01798) 875004 *Men's toiletries importers*

Wigpool, 46 Walkers Road, Moons Moat North Industrial Es, Redditch, Worcestershire, B98 9HE Tel: (01527) 64086 Fax: (01527) 62319 *Repetition turned part manufrs*

▶ Wigtopia, Unit 106, 9 St Johns Street, Colchester, CO2 7NN Tel: (01206) 570976 E-mail: sales@wigtopia.co.uk *Hairpieces or wigs manufrs*

Wika Instruments Ltd, 4 Gatton Park Business Centre, Wells Place Merstham, Redhill, RH1 3LG Tel: (01737) 644008 Fax: 01737 644403 E-mail: info@wika.co.uk *Gauge & transmitter manufrs*

▶ Wil Lec Electrical Contractors Ltd, 246 Corporation Road, Grimsby, South Humberside, DN31 2QB Tel: (01472) 241881 Fax: (01472) 241884

Wilan Technologies Ltd, Wilan, Thimbleby, Horncastle, Lincolnshire, LN9 5RB Tel: (01507) 525008 Fax: (01507) 525008 E-mail: info@wilan-technologies.ltd.uk *Computer consultancy*

Wiland Wines Ltd, Regent House, Ellis Street, Anstey, Leicester, LE7 7FG Tel: 0116-236 3479 Fax: 0116-234 0262 *Partitioning & suspended ceilings*

Wilbar Components Ltd, Martindale Industrial Estate, Hawks Green, Cannock, Staffordshire, WS11 7XN Tel: (01543) 578873 Fax: (01543) 570450 E-mail: enquiries@wilbar.co.uk *Hydraulic component manufrs*

Wilbar Engineers, Patterson Street, Blaydon-on-Tyne, Tyne & Wear, NE21 5TL Tel: 0191-414 5697 Fax: 0191-499 0174 E-mail: wilbarengineer@aol.com *General engineers*

Wilco International Ltd, 1 America Square, London, EC3N 2LS Tel: (020) 7418 4500 Fax: (020) 7418 4504 E-mail: reception@adpwilco.co.uk *Software house*

Wilco Manufacturing Ltd, Tyseley Industrial Estate, Seeleys Road, Birmingham, B11 2LQ Tel: 0121-772 6212 Fax: 0121-772 2871 E-mail: martinlane@wilcomanufacturing.co.uk *Automatic repetition turned parts manufrs*

▶ Wilcom Services, 6 Amersham Road, Chalfont St. Peter, Gerrards Cross, Buckinghamshire, SL9 0NY Tel: (01494) 876600 Fax: (01494) 876600

Wilcomatic Ltd, 123 Beddington Lane, Croydon, CR0 4YL Tel: (020) 8649 9760 Fax: (020) 8680 9791 E-mail: sales@wilcomatic.co.uk *Motor car & commercial vehicle washing equipment* Also at: Bristol, Edinburgh, Leicester & Warrington

Wilcon Connooly Ltd, Thomas Wilson House, Tenter Rd, Moulton Park, Northampton, NN3 6QJ Tel: (01604) 790909 Fax: (01604) 790467 E-mail: wilcosconnoolly@wilcon.co.uk *House builder*

Wilcox Desk Top Equipment, Unison House, 46 George Street, Kidderminster, Worcestershire, DY10 1PY Tel: (01562) 824470 Fax: (01562) 829867 E-mail: sales@wilcoxdesktop.co.uk *Office equipment suppliers, stationers*

Wilcox Reproductions Ltd, D Lea Road, Waltham Abbey, Essex, EN9 1AS Tel: (01992) 760707 Fax: (01992) 788021 *Furniture reproduction*

Robert Wilcox (Abrasives) Ltd, 19 Desborough Avenue, High Wycombe, Buckinghamshire, HP11 2RS Tel: (01494) 530533 Fax: (01494) 524532 *Abrasive materials specialists*

▶ indicates data change since last edition

min Wild & Son, 55 Price Street, Birmingham, 6JZ Tel: 0121-359 2303 Fax: 0121-359 2303 *n makers*

R. Wild (Plastic Moulders) Ltd, 67 St. Mary's ad, Market Harborough, Leicestershire, 16 7DS Tel: (01858) 463074 Fax: (01858) 1732 *Plastic mouldings manufrs*

ld Goose Carvings, Unit 2E Delaware Road lustrial Estate, Delaware Road, Gunnislake, rnwall, PL18 9AR Tel: (01822) 833764 x: (01822) 833801 nail: info@buycarvings.com *Furniture manufrs*

ld Insight Ltd, 5 Cambridge Road, Ely, mbridgeshire, CB7 4HJ Tel: (01353) 665304 x: (01353) 610466 nail: enquiries@wildinsight.co.uk *Underwater trumentation engineers*

Manufacturing Group Ltd, PO Box 103, mingham, B5 5SJ Tel: 0121-643 9611 x: 0121-766 5278 E-mail: csd@wild.uk.com *ecision pressings*

Moor Quarry Products, Cinetic Quarries, ndy Lane, Wildmoor, Bromsgrove, orcestershire, B61 0QR Tel: 0121-453 3121 x: 0121-457 8558 nail: jwcineticsands@aol.com *Suppliers undry & building sands*

Park Leisure Ltd, Wild Park Brailsford, ailsford, Ashbourne, DE6 3BN Tel: (01335) 0485 Fax: (01335) 361019 mail: enquiries@wildparkleisure.com *Leisure rvices*

Strawberry Interactive Multimedia Ltd, 1 artland Avenue, Shrewsbury, SY2 5UW l: (01743) 354386 Fax: (01743) 354386 *oftware developers*

Thang, 337 Derby Road, Liverpool, Bootle, erseyside, L20 8LQ Tel: 0151-933 3289 ax: 0151-922 4865 mail: admin@wildthang.co.uk *Screen printed & nbroidered work wear leisure wear, caps, shirts manufrs.*

Things, 12 Denmark Road, Exeter, EX1 1SL el: (01392) 493775 Fax: (01392) 413538 nail: info@wildthingsgifts.com *Costume wellery & giftware manufrs*

Thymes, 2 Hughenden Yard, High Street, arlborough, Wiltshire, SN8 1LT Tel: (01672) 16373 Fax: (01672) 516373 *Organic food uppliers*

ild West Jerky UK, Units 2-3, Eireastadh, rowlista, Isle of Lewis, HS2 9JG Tel: (0870) 415948 Fax: (0870) 7415948 -mail: info@wildwestjerky.co.uk *Beef jerky JSA) products distributor*

ild Wood & Rose, 110 Johnson Road, merson Green, Bristol, BS16 7JG el: 0117-957 1420 Fax: 0117-970 2285 -mail: shop@wildwoodrose.com *Luxury bath & ody products manufrs*

an Sign Services Ltd, Unit 5, Plot 7f Claymore, me Valley Industrial Estate, Tamworth, affordshire, B77 5DQ Tel: (01827) 283400 ax: (01827) 283808 -mail: sales@wildan-signs.co.uk *Sign ontractors & manufrs*

ildblood Electrical Contractors, Station Road, eathfield, East Sussex, TN21 8LB Tel: (01435) 64655 Fax: (01435) 865772 -mail: sales@wildblood.com

bore & Gibbons, 361 Liverpool Road, London, 1 1NL Tel: (020) 7607 7312 Fax: (020) 7609 062 E-mail: sales@wildbore.co.uk *Trade mark ttorneys*

cat Taconic, School Close, Burgess Hill, West ussex, RH15 9RD Tel: (01444) 247756 ax: (01444) 248416 -mail: sales@wildcat-taconic.com *Conveyor elt manufrs*

Wilde & Co. Ltd, 66-72 Devon Street, irmingham, B7 4SL Tel: 0121-380 0300 ax: 0121-359 5438 -mail: enquiries@johnwilde.co.uk Principal xport Areas: Worldwide *Coffin furniture manufrs*

e UK Ltd, Brindley Lodge, Adcroft Street, tockport, Cheshire, SK1 3HZ Tel: 0161-474 479 Fax: 0161-474 7492 -mail: info@wildeandpartners.co.uk *Civil & mechanical engineering consultancy*

Vilden Services Ltd, 131 Belswains Lane, lemel Hempstead, Hertfordshire, HP3 9UZ el: (01442) 212941 Fax: (01442) 251164

Vildfire, Space 219, 99 Warwick Street, eamington Spa, Warwickshire, CV32 7RJ el: (0845) 4309101 -mail: info@wildfirecoaching.com *Talent Management: Helping people tap into their unlimited talent for their own careers, team cohesion and performance and managing change. This is on-the-job and you see results ast through direct training plus one-to-one and eam coaching.*

Vilding Butler Construction Ltd, Wessex Way, Vinchester, Hampshire, SO21 1WP Tel: (01962) 17850

ding Engineering Services Ltd, High Street, Great Cheverell, Devizes, Wiltshire, SN10 5XZ Tel: (01380) 812918 Fax: (01380) 813997 *Manufacturers & suppliers of precision machined parts*

ding Partnership, The Malt House, Eardisley, Hereford, HR3 6NH Tel: (01544) 327405 Fax: (01544) 327902 E-mail: allen@wildingpartnership.co.uk *Rug manufrs*

dings Professional Systems Ltd, 14 Dunlop Road, Hadleigh Road Industrial Estat, Ipswich, P2 0UG Tel: (01473) 219819 Fax: (01473) 219955 E-mail: wildings@wildings.com *Computer support*

dman Transport (Bedford) Ltd, Postley Road, Kempston, Bedford, MK42 7BU Tel: (01234) 854244 Fax: (01234) 841362 E-mail: roy@wildmantransport.com *Road transport contractors*

don Engineering Worcester Ltd, White Ladies Close, Worcester, WR1 1QA Tel: (01905) 522014 *Precision engineers*

Wildoo Ltd, 1 Nursery Close, Dunstable, Dunstable, Bedfordshire, LU6 1XQ Tel: (0870) 9771550 Fax: (0870) 1991614 E-mail: info@wildoo.co.uk *Sales agency*

Wildtrax Electronics Ltd, Unit 11A Southcourt Road, Worthing, West Sussex, BN14 7DF Tel: 0845 5314279 Fax: (01903) 212003 E-mail: howard@wildtrax.com *Wildtrax Electronics Ltd is a specialist in SMT assemblies. We have grown considerably and built up a reputation for quality and efficiency. We maintain a flexible approach to allow us to get the job done when the customer needs it. Our experience in Surface Mount placement is quite immense. Between our four main operator/ programmers we have around 40 years of experience to call on. We welcome international enquiries. **Services available: **Prototype Assembly, Surface Mount Assembly, Conventional 'Through Hole' Assembly (via one of our partner companies), Automatic Visual Inspection, Functional Test (where possible), Epoxy Encapsulation. **We can also offer a full or partial procurement service*

Wiles Group Ltd, Walmgate Road, Greenford, Middlesex, UB6 7LN Tel: (020) 8758 7700 Fax: (020) 8758 7722 E-mail: sales@wilesgreenworld.co.uk *Business computer & design & stationary suppliers*

John Wiley & Sons Ltd, The Atrium Southern Gate, Terminus Road, Chichester, West Sussex, PO19 8SQ Tel: (01243) 779777 Fax: (01243) 775878 E-mail: rlong@wiley.co.uk *Publishers*

▶ Wilf Noble, Sneaton Lane, Ruswarp, Whitby, North Yorkshire, YO22 5HL Tel: (01947) 824061 Fax: (01947) 820524

Wilfab UK Repair Services, Unit 2 Holmes Lane, Rotherham, South Yorkshire, S61 1AZ Tel: (01709) 553132 Fax: (01709) 553132 *Lifting equipment & fabrication*

Wilfast Ltd, Masters House, 13 High Street, Clophill, Bedford, MK45 4AB Tel: (01525) 861999 Fax: (01525) 861919 E-mail: wilfast@kbnet.co.uk *Industrial fastener distributors*

Wilfield Shopfitting & Exhibitions, 53-59 New Tythe Street, Long Eaton, Nottingham, NG10 2DL Tel: 0115-946 6960 Fax: 0115-946 6969 E-mail: sales@wilfield.com *Shop fittings manufrs*

Wilfred Hutchinson & Son, Husthwaite, York, YO61 4PB Tel: (01347) 868352 *Furniture manufrs*

Wilfred Lord Ltd, Oak Mill, Mellor St, Rochdale, Lancashire, OL12 6UY Tel: (01706) 341311 Fax: (01706) 861810 *Painting contractors* Also at: Leeds, Widnes & Wigan

Wilfrid Smith Group plc, Elm House, Medlicott Close, Corby, Northamptonshire, NN18 9NF Tel: (01536) 460020 Fax: (01536) 462400 E-mail: info@wilfrid-smith.co.uk *Chemical & fine chemical merchants*

▶ Wilgrove Express Forms Ltd, Unit 4-5 Endeavour Way, Croydon, CR0 4TR Tel: (020) 8665 7665 Fax: (020) 8689 6500

Wilhams Insulation Export Division Ltd, 117 Bohemia Road, St. Leonards-on-Sea, East Sussex, TN37 6RL Tel: (01424) 201000 Fax: (01424) 201000 E-mail: sales@wilhams.-insulation.co.uk *Insulation specialists thermal, acoustic & fire*

Wilkes Iris Ltd, Widco Works, 80a London Road, Bexhill-on-Sea, East Sussex, TN39 3LE Tel: (01424) 217630 Fax: (01424) 215406 *Iris diaphragm manufrs*

Wilkes Lighting Ltd, Lyric House, 113-115 Tong Road, Leeds, LS12 1QJ Tel: 0113-231 9076 Fax: 0113-231 9078 E-mail: mick.wilkes@virgin.net *Lamp & lighting specialists*

P.J. Wilkes Plastics Ltd, Unit 12A Izons Industrial Estate, Oldbury Road, West Bromwich, West Midlands, B70 9BS Tel: 0121-525 4224 Fax: 0121-525 2242 E-mail: pjw@pjwsigns.freeserve.co.uk *Acrylic display signs manufrs*

Wilkes Security Products Ltd, Tipton Road, Tividale, Oldbury, West Midlands, B69 3HY Tel: 0121-520 9666 Fax: 0121-520 9667 *Luggage lock manufrs*

▶ Wilkie Electronics, 16 Muirhall Terrace, Perth, PH2 7ES Tel: (01738) 621492 *Research & development services*

Wilkin & Sons Ltd, Tiptree, Colchester, CO5 0RF Tel: (01621) 815407 Fax: (01621) 814555 E-mail: tiptree@tiptree.com *Jam manufrs*

▶ Wilkinson, Unit 1 28 St. Johns Walk, Colchester, CO2 7AL Tel: (01206) 767662 *Retailers of home & garden products*

▶ Wilkinson, 14 The Chilterns, High Wycombe, Buckinghamshire, HP13 5ES Tel: (01494) 471608 *Hardware store*

Wilkinson, 81 High Street, Redcar, Cleveland, TS10 3DE Tel: (01642) 492471 E-mail: enquiries@wilko.co.uk *Home & Garden Store*

Wilkinson, 31-57 The Lower Parade, Sutton Coldfield, West Midlands, B72 1XX Tel: 0121-321 3387

▶ Wilkinson Estates, 1 High Street, Maidenhead, Berkshire, SL6 1JN Tel: (01628) 777075 Fax: (01628) 788007 E-mail: post@wilkinsons.co.uk *The complete property lettings, sales and management service for Maidenhead, Cookham, Marlow and surrounding areas. Financial Services and International Property*

H.L. Wilkinson & Co. Ltd, 49-51 Central Street, London, EC1V 8AB Tel: (020) 7253 5241 Fax: (020) 7250 1562 E-mail: info@hlwilikinson.co.uk *Textile merchant-converters*

▶ Wilkinson Hardware Stores Ltd, 14-18 Nutter Road, Thornton-Cleveleys, Lancashire, FY5 1BG Tel: (01253) 859326 *Home & garden retailers*

John Wilkinson (Machinery & Tools) Ltd, 27 Arthur Street, Edinburgh, EH6 5DA Tel: 0131-554 1641 Fax: 0131-553 7961 E-mail: sales@wilkinsonmachinery.com *Machinery merchants*

Wilkinson Joinery Ltd, Market Hill, Wigton, Cumbria, CA7 9EY Tel: (01697) 342344 Fax: (01697) 342718 *Joinery manufrs*

Wilkinson Mobile Catering Systems Ltd, Unit 1, Global Way,, Lower Eccleshill Road,, Darwen, Lancashire, BB3 0RP Tel: 01254 706348 Fax: 01254 701335 E-mail: sales@wilkinsoncatering.co.uk *Manufacturers of catering trailers & motorised catering units*

Patrick Wilkinson Saddlers Ltd, 108 Walkergate, Beverley, North Humberside, HU17 9BT Tel: (01482) 870800 Fax: (01482) 883376 *Saddlerys & tack manufrs*

Wilkinson Richmond, Unit E11 Countess Avenue, Cheadle Hulme, Cheadle, Cheshire, SK8 6QS Tel: 0161-485 1655 Fax: 0161-486 6097 *Stationery & greeting card suppliers*

Wilkinson Sails, Swale Marina, Conyer, Teynham, Sittingbourne, Kent, ME9 9HN Tel: (01795) 521503 Fax: (01795) 521503 E-mail: wilkinsonsails@yahoo.co.uk *Sail makers*

Wilkinson & Scott Ltd, 58 Nelson Street, Bradford, West Yorkshire, BD5 0DZ Tel: (01274) 724059 Fax: (01274) 305389 E-mail: anne@mac56.com *Dyestuff & chemical agents distributors*

Wilkinson & Son, 14a Hall Street North, Boothtown, Halifax, West Yorkshire, HX3 6TS Tel: (01422) 349630 Fax: (01422) 349630 *Metal spinning manufrs*

Wilkinsons Furniture, Adlington Industrial Estate, Adlington, Macclesfield, Cheshire, SK10 4NL Tel: (01625) 870070 Fax: (01625) 870070 *Furniture importers & distributors*

Wilks Bros, Murthly, Perth, PH1 4HG Tel: (01738) 710381 Fax: (01738) 710581 *Agricultural engineers*

Leslie Wilks Associates, 1 Sunnyside, Claygate Road, Laddingford, Maidstone, Kent, ME18 6BQ Tel: (01892) 730863 Fax: (01892) 730864 E-mail: info@leslie-wilks.co.uk *Structural engineering consultants*

Wilks (Rubber Plastics Manufacturing) Co. Ltd, Woodrolfe Road, Tollesbury, Maldon, Essex, CM9 8RY Tel: (01621) 869609 Fax: (01621) 868863 E-mail: sales@wilks.co.uk *Manufacturers of upvc boat supplies & decking*

Will Gray, The Magic Castle, 88 Church Lane, Whitwick, Coalville, Leicestershire, LE67 5DJ Tel: (01530) 457465 Fax: (0871) 7333318 E-mail: magic@willgray.co.uk *Will Gray (member of the Leicester Magic Circle and the International Brotherhood of Magicians) will bring his own unique brand of magic and comedy to your event. This talented award winning magician will amaze and astound you with his eye popping magic. You've probably seen this type of magic on television but now you can experience it right in front of your eyes and even in your own hands. Impress your guests with this unique form of entertainment and have them talking about it for weeks. **Whether you are celebrating a birthday, engagement or anniversary or just having a get together, why not let magic provide the ideal entertainment. Will's light hearted and entertaining performance is professional yet friendly and involves the audience to ensure they have a truly magical and memorable experience. **

▶ Will Recruit, Kingswood House, The Avenue, Cliftonville, Northampton, NN1 5BT Tel: (0870) 0468686 E-mail: info@willrecruit.com *We are UK-based international recruitment consultants working to help clients find scarce talent, and individuals to make the right career moves, in the following areas:*** Oil, gas, petroleum and power industries* Engineering and construction professions* Business process outsourcing - IT solutions architecture and strategy development.* Senior project and programme management, in various industries.**We identify and recruit senior professionals in principal and management positions for our clients and help our candidates find new jobs. Our success can be measured by our clients choosing to work with us on an ongoing basis and our candidates recommending us to others - and others to us. We believe that the success of a business usually depends on the quality of its professional staff - and that the right person will make the difference.*

Willacy Oil Services Ltd, Whittle Close, Engineer Park, Deeside, Clwyd, CH5 2QE Tel: (01244) 520122 Fax: (01244) 520283 E-mail: sales@willacyoil.com *Based on the North Wales Border near Deeside, Willacy Oil Services Limited have been established since 1989. Operating globally, Willacy offers a wide range of services to the petrochemical and tank cleaning industry. These services include, contracting, offering full contracting services to oil refineries, manufacturing, for the design and build of a range of equipment for use around the globe and, project engineering, for the complete design and build of static sludge handling plant. Our total sludge management solutions include sludge quantification, using the patented Sludge Profiler for Oil Tank (SPOT), online mechanical sludge removal, sludge processing/oil recovery and secondary treatment options.*

Willand Engineering Co Halifax Ltd, Hopwood Lane, Halifax, West Yorkshire, HX1 5EL Tel: (01422) 369000 Fax: (01422) 380821 *Stainless steel fabrication*

Willard Conservation, Leigh Road, Chichester, West Sussex, PO19 8TS Tel: (01243) 776928 Fax: (01243) 533845 E-mail: willard@willard.dial.iql.co.uk *Electrical contractors*

Willard Handling Systems Ltd, Eagle Iron Works, Bromley Street, Hull, HU2 0PQ Tel: (01482) 223746 Fax: (01482) 213404 E-mail: user@whs.co.uk *Fork lift truck hire, distributors, servicing & training* Also at: Scunthorpe

Willard Skip Hire Ltd, 4 Folgate Road, North Walsham, Norfolk, NR28 0AJ Tel: (01692) 405820 Fax: (01692) 500058 *Skip & mini-skip hire*

Willas Engineering Ltd, 9-10 Village Farm Road, Village Farm Industrial Estate, Pyle, Bridgend, Mid Glamorgan, CF33 6BL Tel: (01656) 745000 Fax: (01656) 745175 E-mail: ian@willas.co.uk *Mechanical engineers*

G.B. Willbond Ltd, Deakins Placed, Radford, Nottingham, NG7 3FT Tel: 0115-841 8888 Fax: 0115-841 8876 E-mail: thogg@willbond.co.uk *Heating & plumbers' merchants*

Willbros (Overseas) Ltd, The Old Rechtory, Barkston, Grantham, Lincolnshire, NG32 2NB Tel: (020) 8549 4471 Fax: (020) 8974 8536 E-mail: arthur.west@willbros.com *Engineers & constructors*

Willcocks Engineering Avon Ltd, Pizey Avenue, Clevedon, Avon, BS21 7TS Tel: (01275) 873035 Fax: (01275) 870209 E-mail: willcocksavon@btconnect.com *Precision engineers*

Willenhall Fasteners Holdings Ltd, Frederick William Street, Willenhall, West Midlands, WV13 1NE Tel: (01902) 630760 Fax: (01902) 636447 E-mail: sales@willenfast.co.uk *Distributors agents stockholders of nut, industrial fasteners, tools & sealants*

Willenhall Locks Ltd, Stringes Lane, Willenhall, West Midlands, WV13 1LF Tel: (01902) 636041 Fax: (01902) 636733 E-mail: sales@willenhall-locks.co.uk *Lock manufrs*

Willenhall Shearing Co, Leve Lane, Willenhall, West Midlands, WV13 1PS Tel: (01902) 605126 Fax: (01902) 631919 *Shearing (steel sheet) services & steel stockholders*

Willenhall Tube & Forging, Bloxwich Lane Indust Estate, Bloxwich Lane, Walsall, WS2 8TF Tel: (01922) 725505 Fax: (01922) 720131 E-mail: enquiries@willenhalltube.co.uk *Tube manipulators*

Willerby Holiday Homes Ltd, Imperial House, 1251 Hedon Road, Hull, HU9 5NA Tel: (01482) 707808 Fax: (01482) 711482 E-mail: sales@willerby.com *Holiday home manufrs*

Willeringhaus & Co. Ltd, The Mill, 23 Saunders Copse, Mayford, Woking, Surrey, GU22 0NS Tel: (01483) 723158 Fax: (01483) 723158 E-mail: willeringhaus.co@talk21.com *Woven labels manufrs*

Willers & Sons, Centenary Works, Button End, Harston, Cambridge, CB22 7NX Tel: (01223) 870360 Fax: (01223) 870360 *Building contractors*

Willesden Supplies, Unit 39 Sapcote Trading Estate, 70 Budden Hill Lane Willesden, London, NW10 3EA Tel: (020) 8459 4440 Fax: (020) 8459 8448 *Plumbing systems & plumbers*

D.S. Willetts (Stainless) Ltd, Murdoch Road, Bilston, West Midlands, WV14 7HG Tel: (01902) 404221 Fax: (01902) 405705 E-mail: sales@dswilletts.co.uk *Stainless steel profile cutters*

Willey & Bunker Ltd, Park Avenue Industrial Estate, Sundon Park Road, Luton, LU3 3BP Tel: (01582) 574382 Fax: (01582) 490043 E-mail: willey&bunker@itnet.co.uk *Joinery , shop fitting & furniture spraying services*

Willey & Dalley, Palace Gate, Exeter, EX1 1JA Tel: (01392) 272694 Fax: (01392) 271220 E-mail: willeyanddalley@exe52.wanadoo.co.uk *Plumbers & electricians*

▶ Willfield Developments, 14a Enfield Road, Brentford, Middlesex, TW8 9NX Tel: (020) 8569 9490 Fax: (020) 8847 5992 E-mail: willfield@btinternet.com

▶ William Anderson & Son Ltd, 34 Loanbank Quadrant, Glasgow, G51 3HZ Tel: 0141-440 2881 Fax: 0141-445 1480

William Arnold Tarpaulins Ltd, 30 Thames Road, Barking, Essex, IG11 0HZ Tel: (020) 8594 1500 Fax: (020) 8594 7773 E-mail: www.tarpaulins.co.uk *Tarpaulin manufrs*

▶ William Austin Engineering Services Ltd, Arden House, 341-343 Kenilworth Road, Balsall Common, Coventry, CV7 7DL Tel: (01676) 533666 Fax: (01676) 535536

William Ball, London Road, Grays, Essex, RM20 4WB Tel: (01375) 375151 Fax: (01375) 393355 E-mail: sales@wball.co.uk *Kitchen, bedroom & study furniture manufrs*

William Beckett Plastics Ltd, Unit 5a, Tinsley Industrial Park, Shepcote Way, Sheffield, S9 1TH Tel: 0114-243 4399 Fax: 0114-256 0196 E-mail: sales@beckettplastics.co.uk *Manufacturers of specialised plastic packaging*

William Birch Engineers Ltd, Milton Street, Salford, M7 1UX Tel: 0161-834 9675 Fax: 0161-833 2268 E-mail: sales@william-birch.co.uk *Web process machinery manufrs*

▶ William Black & Son Ltd, 7 Clerk Street, Brechin, Angus, DD9 6AF Tel: (01356) 623103 Fax: (01356) 623105

William Boyer & Sons Transport Ltd, Trout Road, West Drayton, Middlesex, UB7 7SN Tel: (01895) 445141 Fax: (01895) 442027 *Gravel merchants* Also at: Colnbrook & Harefield

William Burrows Printers Ltd, Tansey Green Road, Brierley Hill, West Midlands, DY5 4TL Tel: (01384) 79678 Fax: (01384) 79678 *General & commercial printers*

▶ William Clegg, 105 Main Road, Fenwick, Kilmarnock, Ayrshire, KA3 6DY Tel: (01560) 600673

William Cook, Cross Green Approach, Leeds, LS9 0SG Tel: 0113-249 6363 Fax: 0113-249 1376 E-mail: sales@william-cook.co.uk *Steel castings manufrs*

▶ William Cook Holbrook Precision Ltd, Station Road, Halfway, Sheffield, S20 3GD Tel: 0114-251 0410 Fax: 0114-251 0096 E-mail: admin@william-cook.co.uk *Steel casting manufrs*

William Coutts, Howemuir, Blackhills, Peterhead, Aberdeenshire, AB42 3LJ Tel: (01779) 476086 Fax: (01779) 476947 *Road transport, haulage & freight services*

▶ William Culross & Son Ltd, Queen Street, Coupar Angus, Blairgowrie, Perthshire, PH13 9DF Tel: (01828) 627266 Fax: (01828) 627146

William Daniels UK Ltd, Unit 1c Beacon Industrial Estate, Hull Road, Withernsea, North Humberside, HU19 2EG Tel: (01964) 614081 Fax: (01964) 614341 E-mail: sales@williamdaniels.co.uk *Pharmaceutical supply distribution*

▶ William Downer & Iw, York Road, Totland Bay, Isle of Wight, PO39 0HB Tel: (01983) 752187 Fax: (01983) 754614

William E Naylor & Son, Queen Street, Driffield, North Humberside, YO25 6QJ Tel: (01377) 253597 Fax: (01377) 240302 E-mail: info@wenaylor.co.uk *Joinery manufrs*

Company Information

William G. Fuller & Co. Ltd, 43 Earl Street, Hastings, East Sussex, TN34 1SG Tel: (01424) 426094 Fax: (01424) 444763 E-mail: sales@fullermedical.co.uk *Hospital equipment manufrs*

William G Search Ltd, Whitehall Road, Leeds, LS12 6EP Tel: 0113-263 9081 Fax: 0113-231 0267 E-mail: info@wgsearch.co.uk *Plant hire contractors & light engineering services* Also at: Liverpool, Manchester, Nottingham & Sheffield

▶ William Grant & Sons Distillers Ltd, Girvan Distillery, Grangestone Industrial Estate, Girvan, Ayrshire, KA26 9PT Tel: (01465) 710637 Fax: (01465) 714214

William Hackett Chains Ltd, Alnwick Station, Alnwick, Northumberland, NE66 2NP Tel: 01665 604200 *Lifting equipment distributors*

William Hackett Chains Ltd, Maypole Fields, Halesowen, West Midlands, B63 2QE Tel: (01384) 569431 Fax: (01384) 639157 E-mail: info@williamhackett.co.uk *Chain & hoist manufrs*

William Halstead & Co Dudley Hill Ltd, Stanley Mills, Edward Street, Bradford, West Yorkshire, BD4 9RS Tel: (01274) 682921 Fax: (01274) 685698 E-mail: sales@williamhalstead.co.uk *Mohair & worsted manufrs*

▶ William Hamilton & Sons Contractors Ltd, Dovesdale Farm, Stonehouse, Larkhall, Lanarkshire, ML9 3PR Tel: (01698) 792211 Fax: (01698) 792212

William Hayes Ltd, Bankfield Works, Haley Hill, Halifax, West Yorkshire, HX3 6ED Tel: (01422) 365034 Fax: (01422) 345497 E-mail: enquiries@williamhayes.co.uk *Packaging merchants*

William Henry Martin Ltd, Allfield Court, Condover, Shrewsbury, SY5 7AP Tel: (01743) 874550 Fax: (01743) 874650 *Machinery manufrs*

William Hill plc, Greenside House, 50 Station Road, London, N22 7TP Tel: (020) 8918 3600 Fax: (020) 8918 3726 E-mail: name.@williamhill.co.uk *Holding company*

William Hinsley Engineers Ltd, 1 Croft Street, Sowerby Bridge, West Yorkshire, HX6 2AJ Tel: (01422) 839968 *Sheet metal workers*

▶ William Hughes Civil Engineering Ltd, Bodffordd, Llangefni, Gwynedd, LL77 7DZ Tel: (01248) 750193 Fax: (01248) 723709 E-mail: admin@williamhughes.com

William Hunter & Sons (Ironfounders) Ltd, Halton House, Millrigg Road, Wiston, Biggar, Lanarkshire, ML12 6HT Tel: (01899) 850500 Fax: (01899) 850566 *Iron & steel casting manufrs*

▶ William James Shoes Ltd, Sartoris Road, Rushden, Northamptonshire, NN10 9TL Tel: (01933) 317497

William Jones Clifton Ltd, 32 Lower Essex Street, Birmingham, B5 6SN Tel: 0121-622 8900 Fax: 0121-622 8909 E-mail: sales@jonesclifton.com *Rubber stamp manufrs* Also at: Branches throughout the U K

William Jones Packaging, Unit B5 South Point, Foreshore Road, Cardiff, CF10 4SP Tel: (029) 2048 6262 Fax: (029) 2048 1230 E-mail: sales@wjpackaging.co.uk *Polyethylene carrier bag merchant*

▶ William Kirk Ltd, Adlington Industrial Estate, London Road, Adlington, Macclesfield, Cheshire, SK10 4NL Tel: (01625) 879990 Fax: (01625) 879807

William Lennon & Co. Ltd, The Bank, Stoney Middleton, Hope Valley, Derbyshire, S32 4TD Tel: (01433) 630451 Fax: (01433) 630954 E-mail: sales@williamlennon.co.uk *Safety footwear distributors & manufrs*

William Lillico & Sons Ltd, The Forstal, Beddow Way, Aylesford, Kent, ME20 7BT Tel: (01622) 718487 Fax: (01622) 882475 E-mail: post@lillico.co.uk *Agricultural merchants & agents* Also at: Dorking, Lewes, Midhurst, Sevenoaks & Tunbridge Wells

William Loxley Ltd, 1 Weoley Avenue, Birmingham, B29 6PP Tel: 0121-472 0834 Fax: 0121-472 0834 E-mail: williamloxley@blueyonder.co.uk *Monumental masons & marble workers*

▶ William McClure & Sons, 49 Bank Street, Irvine, Ayrshire, KA12 0LL Tel: (01294) 279123

William Mciver & Son, 1 Hawthorn Terrace, Bishop Middleham, Ferryhill, County Durham, DL17 9AX Tel: 0191-377 1001 Fax: 0191-377 1002 E-mail: enquiries@wmmcivorandson.com *Agricultural merchants*

▶ William Marjoribanks, Rose Bank, Main Street, St. Boswells, Melrose, Roxburghshire, TD6 0AU Tel: (01835) 822787 Fax: (01835) 822809

William Martin Ltd, The Studio, Tubney Warren Barn, Tubney, Abingdon, Oxfordshire, OX13 5QJ Tel: (01865) 390258 Fax: (01865) 390234 E-mail: info@wmproductions.co.uk *Video, design & events*

William Mellard & Son, River Works, Campbell Road, Stoke-on-Trent, ST4 4RN Tel: (01782) 744777 Fax: (01782) 744512 E-mail: sales@mellard.co.uk *Steel stockholders*

▶ William Miller Plumbers, 70 Shakespeare Street, Glasgow, G20 8TJ Tel: 0141-946 8244 Fax: 0141-946 2502 *Plumbers*

▶ William Nicol Aberdeen Ltd, 27-29 Barclayhill Place, Portlethen, Aberdeen, AB12 4PF Tel: (01224) 782100 Fax: (01224) 782681

▶ William Nimmo & Co. Ltd, Tennant House, 21 Tennant Street, Leith, Edinburgh, EH6 5NA Tel: 0131-554 2431

William O'Hanlon & Co Ltd, Mochdre Industrial Estate, Mochdre, Newtown, Powys, SY16 4LE Tel: (01686) 611800 Fax: (01686) 611802 E-mail: info@williamohanlon.co.uk *Furnishing textile converter*

William Oliver North Shields Ltd, Little Bedford Street, North Shields, Tyne & Wear, NE29 6NW Tel: 0191-257 5011 Fax: 0191-296 3140 E-mail: sales@worr.co.uk *Sheet metalworkers*

▶ William Paton Ltd, West Avenue, Phoenix Retail Park, Paisley, Renfrewshire, PA1 2FB Tel: 0141-840 6040

▶ WM Paton & Sons Ltd, Unit 1, 42 Waggon Road, Ayr, KA8 8BA Tel: (01292) 313311

WM Print Ltd, 45-47 Frederick Street, Walsall, WS2 9NE Tel: (01922) 643008 Fax: (01922) 720149 E-mail: cooper@wmprint.co.uk *Printing services*

William R Pinchin, Unit 22, Ravenswood Industrial Estate Shernhall Street, London, E17 9HQ Tel: (020) 8521 5590 Fax: (020) 8509 2070 E-mail: williamrpinchin@aol.com *Joinery manufrs*

William Rainford, Leckwith Road, Bootle, Merseyside, L30 6YF Tel: 0151-525 5991 Fax: 0151-530 1676 *Industrial sand producers*

William S Graham & Sons Dewsbury Ltd, Ravens Ing Mills, Ravensthorpe, Dewsbury, West Yorkshire, WF13 3JF Tel: (01924) 462456 Fax: (01924) 457985 *Carpet yarn manufrs*

▶ William Selwood Pumps & Plant Hire Ltd, 2236 London Road, Glasgow, G32 8YF Tel: 0141-778 5155 Fax: 0141-778 8652

▶ William Shanks Construction, 139 Greengairs Road, Greengairs, Airdrie, Lanarkshire, ML6 7SY Tel: (01236) 830417 Fax: (01236) 830742

William Shaw Scholes Ltd, 273 Whitechapel Road, Scholes, Cleckheaton, West Yorkshire, BD19 6HN Tel: (01274) 873157 Fax: (01274) 874777 *Musical instruments*

William Sinclair Holdings Public Ltd Company, Firth Road, Lincoln, LN6 7AH Tel: (01522) 537561 Fax: (01522) 560648 E-mail: info@william-sinclair.co.uk *Compost, fertiliser & pot distributors & manufrs*

William Sinclair Horticulture Ltd, Malvern Road, Knottingley, West Yorkshire, WF11 8EG Tel: (01977) 677676 Fax: (01977) 607138 E-mail: fyba@william-sinclair.co.uk *Manufacturers of horticultural sundries*

William Sinclair & Sons Stationers Ltd, PO Box 1, Otley, West Yorkshire, LS21 1QF Tel: (01943) 461144 Fax: (01943) 850017 E-mail: sales@silvine.com *Stationery manufrs*

▶ William Skinner & Son, Highfield, St. Quivox, Ayr, KA6 5HQ Tel: (0845) 0519060 Fax: (01292) 671133

William Smith Ltd, 7 Faraday Street, Dryburgh Industrial Estate, Dundee, DD2 3QQ Tel: (01382) 813814 Fax: (01382) 814222 E-mail: info@smithshoes.co.uk *Footwear distributors & retailers*

William Stead, 67-68 Hatton Garden, London, EC1N 8JY Tel: (020) 7242 5330 Fax: (020) 7242 6160 *Precious stone merchants*

▶ William Sword Ltd, Groveside Bakeries, 8 Limekilns Road, Cumbernauld, Glasgow, G67 2TX Tel: (01236) 725094 Fax: (01236) 730472 *Bakery*

William T. Wood Machinery Ltd, Bentoria Works, 395 Petre Street, Sheffield, S4 8LJ Tel: 0114-256 2200 Fax: 0114-256 1965 E-mail: sales@dronmctools.demon.co.uk *Machinery second-hand retailers*

▶ William Thompson & Son (Dumbarton) Ltd, Birch Road, Dumbarton, G82 2RN Tel: (01389) 762271 Fax: (01389) 742217

William Tilston, 3a-3c The Borders Industrial Park, River Lane, Saltney, Chester, CH4 8RJ Tel: (01244) 678786 Fax: (01244) 683935 *Building contractors*

William Turner Master Cutlers, Savanna, Holywell Bay, Newquay, Cornwall, TR8 5PQ Tel: (01637) 830925 Fax: (01637) 831032 *Cutlery manufrs*

William W Cope, Unit 34 Camp Hill Industrial Estate, John Kempe Way, Birmingham, B12 0HU Tel: 0121-766 8874 Fax: 0121-771 2866 E-mail: martingeer@williamcope.co.uk *Marking & engraving machine manufrs*

William W Kerr, Mosshill, Ayr, KA6 6AJ Tel: (01292) 267376 Fax: (01292) 289645 *Agricultural engineers*

William Walton & Sons, 152 Stamford Street Central, Ashton-under-Lyne, Lancashire, OL6 6AD Tel: 0161-330 1506 *Cake decorations, wedding ornaments; cake boards most shapes*

William Way Godstone Ltd, 38-42 High Street, Godstone, Surrey, RH9 8LW Tel: (01883) 742757 Fax: (01883) 742757 *Building materials merchants*

William West, 8 Kingside, Ruston Road, London, SE18 5BX Tel: (020) 8316 6966 E-mail: sales@williamwest.co.uk

William Whiteley & Sons (Sheffield) Ltd, Unit 1 Lakeside Rother Valley Wa, Holbrook Industrial Estate, Holbrook, Sheffield, S20 3RW Tel: 0114-251 4999 Fax: 0114-251 2919 E-mail: sales@whiteley.co.uk *Scissor manufrs*

▶ William Wilson Ltd, Caxton Place, Mitchelston Industrial Estate, Kirkcaldy, Fife, KY1 3LT Tel: (01592) 653295 Fax: (01592) 655179

▶ William Woodsend Ltd, Palatine Street, Castle Boulevard, Lenton, Nottingham, NG7 1GH Tel: 0115-947 6792

▶ William Yuille, Grangeston, Girvan, Ayrshire, KA26 9PY Tel: (01465) 713527

▶ Williams, Cowlairs, Nottingham, NG5 9RA Tel: 0115-975 5888 Fax: 0115-974 4777

▶ Williams, Old Barn Farm, Rosliston Road, Walton-on-Trent, Swadlincote, Derbyshire, DE12 8LR Tel: (01283) 711635 Fax: (01283) 711405 E-mail: fandjwilliams@btconnect.com *Steel fabricators*

A.J. & B.J. Williams (Martley) Ltd, Hillend Sawmills, Martley, Worcester, WR6 6QL Tel: (01886) 888601 Fax: (01886) 888481 *Conservatories*

▶ Williams Accountants, 27 Torrington Avenue, Stafford, ST17 0HZ Tel: (01785) 608179 Fax: (01785) 608179 E-mail: williams.accountants@ntlworld.com *Williams Accountants LLP offer practical help and advice for small businesses, sole traders and partnerships. The following are a few of the services we provide:Statutory accounts / Management accounts /Bookeeping /Personal / Business tax advice /VAT /Payroll /Internal auditing /Business planning/Budgeting /Cash flow forecasting.**Call us to discuss how we can help your business achieve its potential.*

Williams Associates, 9 Carlton Cresent, Southampton, SO15 2EZ Tel: (023) 8033 9959 Fax: (023) 8033 3582 E-mail: wilassoc@hants09.freeserve.co.uk *Investigation services*

▶ Williams Associates (Southern) Ltd, Prospect House, Prospect Road, Cowes, Isle Of Wight, PO31 7AD Tel: (01983) 292000 Fax: (01983) 292550 E-mail: williamsassock@fsbdial.co.uk

Williams & Brown, Unit 11 Ketlan Court, River Lane, Saltney, Chester, CH4 8RH Tel: (01244) 678302 Fax: (01244) 681519 E-mail: williamsandbrownsigns@btopenword.com *Sign making for estate agents*

Williams De Broe plc, PO Box 515, London, EC2N 2HD Tel: (020) 7588 7511 Fax: (020) 7588 1702 *Stock broker*

Williams Dennis Ltd, Unit C 6 Wharncliffe Street, Barnsley, South Yorkshire, S70 6BP Tel: (01226) 207600 Fax: (01226) 207600 *Hairdressing & beauty warehouse*

Dennis Williams Ltd, Off Abb Scott Lane, Huddesfield Road, Bradford, West Yorkshire, BD12 0TU Tel: (01274) 675636 Fax: (01274) 694043 *Hairdressing accessories & requisites distributors*

Dennis Williams Ltd, Unit 2 Fotherby Street, Grimsby, South Humberside, DN31 3AH Tel: (01472) 240810 Fax: (01472) 240810 *Hairdressing wholesalers*

Williams Distributors, 108-110 Burghley Road, Peterborough, PE1 2QE Tel: (01733) 564252 Fax: (01733) 555275 *Hand & power tool distributors*

E. Williams Plating Ltd, Unit 3, The Dean, Alresford, Hampshire, SO24 9BQ Tel: (01962) 733199 Fax: (01962) 735146 E-mail: enquiries@ewp-hants.co.uk *Electroplaters & metal finishers*

▶ Williams Electrical Services Northern, 11 Gilpin Street, Sheffield, S6 3BL Tel: 0114-249 3012 Fax: 0114-249 3013 E-mail: business@williamselectrical.com

Williams Engineers Ltd, Unit X Birch House, Birch Walk, Fraser Road, Erith, Kent, DA8 1QX Tel: (01322) 431333 Fax: (01322) 439501 E-mail: williamspes@btconnect.com *Precision engineers*

Williams Fasteners Ltd, 8 Tees Court, Wallis Road, Skippers Lane Industrial Estate, Middlesbrough, Cleveland, TS6 6DX Tel: (01642) 460261 Fax: (01642) 440966 *Bolts, nuts & industrial fastener distributors*

Williams Fasteners, 3 Burton Close, Norwich, NR6 6AZ Tel: (01603) 483447 Fax: (01603) 482145 E-mail: darren.ray@williamsfasteners.com *Industrial fastener distributors*

Williams Fasteners, Unit 4a, Shepcote Way, Tinsley Industrial Estate, Sheffield, S9 1TH Tel: 0114-256 5200 Fax: 0114-256 5210 E-mail: sales@williamsfasteners.com *Bolt & nut merchants* Also at: Coalville, Hull, Manchester & Norwich

Glyn Williams & Associates, Ladywood, Droitwich, Worcestershire, WR9 0AJ Tel: (01905) 757700 Fax: (01905) 757800 *Computer software*

▶ Williams Hall Ltd, St. George's House, 14 George Street, Huntingdon, Cambridgeshire, PE29 3BD Tel: (01480) 426515 Fax: (0871) 9942705 E-mail: info@williamshall.co.uk *Williams Hall are specialist accountancy and finance recruitment consultants covering the East Anglia and South Lincolnshire regions. Covering recruitment from Trainee Accountants to Finance Directors and beyond we take a personal approach to working with both our candidates and clients.*

Williams Harris Optical Supplies, 4 Stanley Green Road, Poole, Dorset, BH15 3AF Tel: (01202) 686622 Fax: (01202) 674020 *Optical manufrs*

Williams Ian Computer Software Consultancy, 12 High Green, Norwich, NR1 4AP Tel: (01603) 300301 *Computer software*

Ifor Williams Trailers Ltd, The Smithy, Cynwyd, Corwen, Clwyd, LL21 0LB Tel: (01490) 412527 Fax: (01490) 412770 E-mail: sales@iwt.co.uk Principal Export Areas: Central/East Europe & West Europe *Manufacturers of trailers including agricultural, horse box, road & tipping. Also manufacturers of pick-up truck canopies & trailer spare parts/wearing parts*

Williams Industrial Services Ltd, Unit 5, Hyde Park, Commercial Centre, Newtownabbey, County Antrim, BT36 4PY Tel: (028) 9083 8999 Fax: (028) 9084 2211 E-mail: sales@wis-ni.com *Instrumentation & electrical suppliers*

Williams Instruments, 29E Station Road, Desborough, Desborough, Kettering, Northamptonshire, NN14 2RL Tel: (01536) 762674 Fax: (01536) 761973 E-mail: pumppackage@btconnect.com *Pump stockholders & distributors*

J.J. Williams (Gaskets) Ltd, 1 Beresford Road, Whitstable, Kent, CT5 1JP Tel: (01227) 265522 Fax: (01227) 770146 E-mail: enquiries@jjwilliams.co.uk Purchasing Contact: J. Williams Sales Contact: J. Williams *JJ Williams Gaskets Ltd in Kent are one of the leading manufacturers of washers and gaskets in the UK. JJ Williams have been producing machined and stamped components since 1822. Stampings available in Vulcanised fibre; Natural rubber; Synthetic rubber; Leatheroid; Nylon; PTFE; Leather; Plastics; Non-asbestos jointings; Polyester; Nomex; Engineering felts; Cork; Press papers; SRBP; SRBF; Papers; Latty applications; Components available - o Nylon ; Acetal ; PTFE ;Vulcanised fibre ; PVC ; SRBP; SRBF; All types of electrical insulators; Our success results from utilising absolute state of the art technology and machinery combined with generations of experience. JJ Williams operate under ISO 9001:2000 Certificate No. Q05939, giving customers complete quality assurance*

▶ Williams, Jenkins & Co. Ltd, 3 Hannah Street, Porth, Rhondda Cynon Taff, CF39 9PU Tel: (01443) 688046 Fax: (01443) 688046 E-mail: info@williamjenkins.info *South Wales located Accountants with 20+ years experience in VAT, VAT Returns, TAX, Self Assessment, PAYE, New Company Formation etc.*

Williams Lea, Clifton House, 75-77 Worship Street, London, EC2A 2EJ Tel: (020) 7772 4400 Fax: (020) 7772 4468 E-mail: sales@williamslea.com *Printing services*

Williams Lea UK Ltd, Foxbridge Way, Normanton Industrial Estate, Normanton, West Yorkshire, WF6 1TN Tel: (01924) 890000 Fax: (01924) 245444 E-mail: info@williamslea.com *Management organisation specialising in print*

Williams Machinery, 173 Nine Mile Ride, Finchampstead, Wokingham, Berkshire, RG40 4JD Tel: 0118-973 7004 Fax: 0118-973 7004 E-mail: bdwilliams@tinyworld.co.uk *Tube bending & tube end forming machinery manufacturers & agents*

N.L. Williams Group Ltd, Westside Industrial Es Jackson Street, St. Helens, Merseyside, WA9 3AT Tel: (01744) 26526 Fax: (01744) 22551E-mail: enquiries@safetysurfacing.uk. *Metal finishing, anti-corrosion specialists & surface preparation*

O.J. Williams Ltd, Station Road, St. Clears, Carmarthen, SA33 4BN Tel: (01994) 230355 Fax: (01994) 231585 E-mail: enquiries@ojwilliams.co.uk *Fuel & p*

Williams & Oakey Engineering Co. Ltd, Radsto Road, Midsomer Norton, Radstock, BA3 2A Tel: (01761) 412013 Fax: (01761) 417174 E-mail: mail@williams-oakey.co.uk *Precision engineers*

Williams Office Concept Ltd, 1 Arthur Street, De DE1 3EF Tel: (01332) 371311 Fax: (01332) 364797 *Office equipment distributors*

Owen Williams Ltd, 41 Whitcomb Street, Londo WC2H 7DT Tel: (020) 7839 1072 Fax: (020) 7827 2439 *Civil structural geotec engineers* at: Barrow in Furness, Cambridge, Rickmansworth & Winchester

Owen Williams Railways Ltd, Meridian, 85 Smallbrook, Queensway, Birmingham, B5 4H Tel: 0121-654 7059 Fax: 0121-654 7242 E-mail: meridianoffice@owenwilliams.co.uk *Consulting engineers* Also at: Birmingham

▶ Williams Plant Hire Ltd, Aberbechan Wharf, Newtown, Powys, SY16 3AW Tel: (01686) 630244 Fax: (01686) 630557

Williams Plant Hire Ltd, Henfaes Lane, Welshp Powys, SY21 7BE Tel: (01938) 552337 Fax: (01938) 555650 *Contractors' plant hire* at: Newtown

Rowland Williams & Co. Ltd, 106 Cherry Lane, Liverpool, L4 8SF Tel: 0151-256 6565 Fax: 0151-256 1616 *Motor spirit distributors*

S.F. Williams & Co. Ltd, Essex Works, Kenway, Southend-On-Sea, SS2 5DX Tel: (01702) 445851 E-mail: sales@sfw.co.uk *Paper back aluminium foil manufrs*

Williams & Shaw Ltd, Agar House, 31 Ballynahi Road, Carryduff, Belfast, BT8 8BB Tel: (028) 9081 3075 Fax: (028) 9081 4135 E-mail: info@williams-shaw.co.uk *Mechanica electrical consultants*

▶ Williams Shipping Transport Ltd, Manor Hous Avenue, Southampton, SO15 0LF Tel: (023) 8052 9555 Fax: (023) 8052 9444

Williams Shipping Transport Ltd, Manor House Avenue, Southampton, SO15 0LF Tel: (023) 8070 1314 Fax: (023) 8077 2422 E-mail: enquires@willams-shipping.co.uk *Fre forwarders, haulage & container hire crane vehicles*

Williams & Co Southampton Ltd, Victoria Street, Southampton, SO14 5QZ Tel: (023) 8022 04 Fax: (023) 8063 8930 E-mail: sales@williams-eng.co.uk *Williams & has been in the business of manufacturing g since 1960. Our clients include manufacturer the aerospace, nuclear, military and medical industrial markets. Types of gear cutting undertaken include spur and helical gears, worms and wormwheels, involute splines, ch sprockets, timing belt pulleys, internal gears, straight sided serrations. We also specialise CNC milling, CNC turning, grinding, lapping honing, whilst maintaining a vigorous quality control department conforming to BS EN ISO 9002 requirements.*

▶ Williams Tanker Service Ltd, Howley Park Ro East, Morley, Leeds, LS27 0BS Tel: 0113-28 7990 Fax: 0113-289 7574

Williams Technical Services Ltd, 36 Station Roa North Harrow, Harrow, Middlesex, HA2 7SE Tel: (020) 8863 2492 Fax: (020) 8863 1524 *Electric power/hand tool distribs*

Thomas Williams (Euxton) Ltd, Springfield, Wiga Road, Euxton, Chorley, Lancashire, PR7 6LB Tel: (01257) 262642 *Sand & gravel suppliers*

W. Williams & Son (Bread Street) Ltd, Unit 15-1 High Cross Center, Fountayne Road, London, N15 4QN Tel: (020) 8885 8440 Fax: (020) 88 9294 E-mail: sales@williamsltd.co.uk *Haberdashery & craft distribs* Also at: Glasgo

Williams Weddings, 17 Albany Way, Bristol, BS30 8UA Tel: 0117-949 0297 Fax: 0117-949 0297 *Video & wedding stationery producers*

▶ Williams Window Fabrication Ltd, Unit 6, Sou Elgin Place, Clydebank, Dunbartonshire, G81 1XP Tel: 0141-941 3050

Williamson & Co., Hill Street Works, Hill Street, Elgin, Morayshire, IV30 1AL Tel: (01343) 542 Fax: (01343) 548107 *Metal merchants*

H. Williamson & Sons Ltd, Main Street, Scallowa Shetland, ZE1 0TR Tel: (01595) 880645 Fax: (01595) 880535 E-mail: mail@hwilliamson.co.uk *Marine electronics engineers*

▶ Williamson Kitchens, 60 Union Street, Keith, Banffshire, AB55 5DP Tel: (01542) 888088 Fax: (01542) 888088 *Manufacturers of kitcher*

Williamson Leisure, Wroxham Barns, Tunstead R Hoveton, Norwich, NR12 8QU Tel: (01603) 784118 E-mail: info@wroxham-barns.co.uk *Funfair rides & vintage slot machines*

Williamson Pumps, Aviation House, The Street, Poynings, Brighton, BN45 7AQ Tel: (01273) 857752 Fax: (0845) 2263639 E-mail: info@williamsonpumps.co.uk *Manufacturers of pumps, peristaltic pumps*

R. Williamson, Brick Kiln Road, Hevingham, Norwich, NR10 5NN Tel: (01603) 754771 *Building material manufrs*

T.D. Williamson (UK) Ltd, Faraday Road, Dorcan Way, Swindon, SN3 5HF Tel: (01793) 603600 Fax: (01793) 603601 E-mail: pigging@tdw.co. *Pipeline integrated surveyors*

Williamson's Electrical Co. Ltd, 44b The Gardens London, SE22 9PZ Tel: (020) 8693 1634 Fax: (020) 8693 5964 *Electrical installation contractors*

The Willing Wire Company Ltd, Middlemore Lane Walsall, WS9 8SP Tel: (01922) 452814 Fax: (01922) 743248 E-mail: mail@willing-wire.com *Bright drawn st & wire manufrs*

Willingale Tubes Ltd, Chilton Industrial Estate, Windham Road, Sudbury, Suffolk, CO10 2XD Tel: (01787) 375300 Fax: (01787) 880108 E-mail: info@willingale-tubes.com *Tubing manipulation services*

▶ indicates data change since last edition

ington Crop Services, Woodend, Rattlesden Road, Drinkstone Green, Bury St. Edmunds, Suffolk, IP30 9TL Tel: (01449) 736602 Fax: (01449) 737352 E-mail: info@willingtoncropservices.co.uk *Agricultural consultants*
is Ltd, 78-86 Dublin Road, Belfast, BT2 7BY Tel: (028) 9024 2131 Fax: (028) 9032 1087 *Insurance advisors*
. Willis & Co. Ltd, 25-29 Robert St, Northampton, NN1 3BL Tel: (01604) 631826 Fax: (01604) 631826 E-mail: canto_ltd@btinternet.com *Training organisation for special needs for adults*
hony Willis Shopfitters Ltd, 55 Grosvenor Street, Cardiff, CF5 1NJ Tel: (029) 2034 5582 Fax: (029) 2023 7260 E-mail: mail@anthonywillis-shopfitters.co.uk *Shop & office fitters*
lis & Bates, Reservoir Road, Halifax, West Yorkshire, HX2 0ES Tel: (01422) 361228 Fax: (01422) 340480 E-mail: sales@bairstowbrothers.co.uk *Specialist engineers & metal pressings & spinning manufrs*
lis Engineering NI Ltd, 14 Silverwood Industrial Estate, Lurgan, Craigavon, County Armagh, BT66 6LN Tel: (028) 3834 8444 Fax: (028) 3831 6333 *Structural & steel engineers*
lis European, Dock Meadow Drive, Wolverhampton, WV4 6LE Tel: (01902) 490895 Fax: (01902) 490896 E-mail: info@williseuropean.com *Engineers & manufrs*
lis Gambier, 121 Radwinter Road, Saffron Walden, Essex, CB11 3HY Tel: (01799) 510170 Fax: (01799) 510171 *Importers of bedroom furniture*
Willis News Ltd, Unit 5 22 Pakenham Street, London, WC1X 0LB Tel: (020) 7427 2233 Fax: (020) 7713 8115 *Distribution of newspapers, magazines & subscriptions*
lis Overseas Investments Ltd, 10 Trinity Square, London, EC3P 3AX Tel: (020) 7488 8111 Fax: (020) 7488 8223 *Insurance brokers*
Willis Tackle Products, The Rye, Eaton Bray, Dunstable, Bedfordshire, LU6 2BQ Tel: (01525) 221968 *Fishing tackle suppliers*
llmott Dixon Construction Ltd, Willmott Dixon House, Park Street, Hitchin, Hertfordshire, SG4 9AH Tel: (01462) 442200 Fax: (01462) 442204 E-mail: construction.hitchin@willmottdixon.co.uk *Building contractors*
llmott Dixon Construction Ltd, Unit 3 Cliffe Park, Bruntcliffe Road, Morley, Leeds, LS27 0RY Tel: 0113-238 3283 Fax: 0113-238 0268 E-mail: construction.leeds@willmottdixon.co.uk *Building contractors*
llmott Dixon Construction Ltd, Spirella Building, Bridge Road, Letchworth Garden City, Hertfordshire, SG6 4ET Tel: (01462) 671852 Fax: (01462) 681852 E-mail: head.office@willmottdixon.co.uk *Building & property maintenance contractors*
llmotts Transport Ltd, Willmotts Business Park, Waterlip, Shepton Mallet, Somerset, BA4 4RN Tel: (01749) 880333 Fax: (01749) 880337 E-mail: enquiries@willmottsbusinesspark.co.uk *Commercial warehousing*short or long-term lease of storage & industrial property*
illochrome Ltd, Westside, Jackson Street, St. Helens, Merseyside, WA9 3AT Tel: (01744) 738488 Fax: (01744) 23039 *Electroplaters*
live Willoughby & Associates, 4 New Burlington Place, London, W1S 2HS Tel: (020) 7437 6171 Fax: (020) 7437 0846 E-mail: clive.willoughby@fifieldglyn.com *Commercial property consultants*
illow Agricultural Engineers, Willow Farm, Newchurch, Romney Marsh, Kent, TN29 0DY Tel: (01303) 874490 Fax: (01303) 874763 *Agricultural engineers*
illow Bay Boats, Low House Farm, Cleabarrow, Windermere, Cumbria, LA23 3NA Tel: (01539) 442741 E-mail: sales@willowbayboats.co.uk *Boat building & designers*
illow Communications Ltd, Kilvey Road, Brackmills Industrial Estate, Northampton, NN4 7BQ Tel: (01604) 877001 Fax: (01604) 877100 E-mail: mail@wcl.biz *Sound & public address systems*
Willow Concepts Ltd, Heath Mill Road, Wombourne, Wolverhampton, WV5 8AP Tel: (01902) 893860 *Promotional goods & clothing.*
Willow Joinery, 5 Low March Indust Estate, Low March, Daventry, Northamptonshire, NN11 4SD Tel: (01327) 878419 Fax: (01604) 661251 *Joiners*
Willow Models, 4 Willow Grove, Golcar, Huddersfield, HD7 4RX Tel: (01484) 658832 Fax: (01484) 658832 E-mail: sales@willowmodels.com *Model making services*
Willow Sportswear Ltd, 70 Harden Lane, Wilsden, Bradford, West Yorkshire, BD15 0EU Tel: (01535) 275854 Fax: (01535) 275854 E-mail: willowsportswear@hotmail.com *Sportswear mail-order*
Willow Stove Enamellers, Unit 11 Eagle Trading Estate, Willow Lane, Mitcham, Surrey, CR4 4UY Tel: (020) 8646 7169 Fax: (020) 8646 7169 *Powder coating services & suppliers*
Willow Wings, 16 Houston Road, Rugby, Warwickshire, CV21 1BS Tel: 07746 738952 E-mail: nikknack0@yahoo.co.uk *Willow Wings, manufacturer of show jumps, poles, hanging gates, hanging planks, brush fillers, etc. We pride ourselves in offering quality products at competitive prices.*
Willowcrete Manufacturing Co., Deptford Terrace, Sunderland, SR4 6DF Tel: 0191-565 9528 Fax: 0191-564 0934 E-mail: jeff.broomfield@willowcrete.com *Fencing manufrs & contractors*
The Willows, Hessay, York, YO26 8JU Tel: (01904) 738206 Fax: (01904) 738206 E-mail: info@willowsfishery.co.uk *A tranquil and scenic carp & coarse fishery on the outskirts of York. Free onsite parking with disabled access. Refreshments available and onsite toilet.*
▶ Willows Construction Services, 9 Ashton Road, Golborne, Warrington, WA3 3TS Tel: (01942) 528300 *Gas pipelines*
▶ Willows Of London Ltd, 17 St. Johns Terrace, London, E7 8BX Tel: (020) 8345 6727 Fax: (020) 8257 7980 E-mail: peter@willowsoflondon.clara.co.uk *Bookkeeping, accountancy and office administration for small businesses, either at your premises or "takeaway"*
Willpack Case Mnfrs, Unit 1a Blackheath Trading Estate, Cakemore Road, Rowley Regis, West Midlands, B65 0QN Tel: 0121-559 4949 Fax: 0121-559 4545 E-mail: sales@willpack.net
Willprint Screen Process Printers, 7 Pomeroy Drive, Oadby, Leicester, LE2 5NE Tel: 0116-271 0574 Fax: 0116-271 0550 E-mail: sales@willprints.co.uk *Screen printers & sign manufrs*
Arnold Wills & Co. Ltd, Station Road, Uppingham, Oakham, Leicestershire, LE15 9TZ Tel: (01572) 822261 Fax: (01572) 821059 E-mail: enquiries@arnoldwills.co.uk *Belts, braces, leather goods & fashion accessories manufrs*
▶ Benjamin H.W. Wills, Argoed Uchaf Farm, Sunnyview, Argoed, Blackwood, Gwent, NP12 0AJ Tel: (07980) 019849 E-mail: theartist@bhww.co.uk
Wills Engineered Polymers Ltd, Dunball Park, Dunball, Bridgwater, Somerset, TA6 4TP Tel: (01278) 686800 Fax: (01278) 686848 E-mail: *Sealing ring manufrs*
Wills (Engineers) Ltd, Woodside Lane, Sheffield, S3 9PB Tel: 0114-272 4334 Fax: 0114-272 4334 *CNC machinists*
Wills Mill, mobile sawmilling and timber, The Woodshed, Home Farm, Baynards Park, Cranleigh, Surrey, GU6 8EQ Tel: 01483 548000 Fax: 01483 548000 E-mail: will@wills-mill.co.uk *We are a small sawmill and tree work company that offers a wide range of tree surgery, woodland management, mobile sawmilling, local timber, timber framing and wood machining services. We specialise in: Moving and sawing timber on sensitive sites using low impact, environmentally friendly techniques. Providing sawn local timber from native and exotic species. Rugged structures and outdoor furniture.*
Wills & Reynolds, 20 Henry Street, Northampton, NN1 4JE Tel: (01604) 638868 *Joinery manufrs*
Wills Ridley, Kernick Industrial Estate, Unit One, Annear Road, Penryn, Cornwall, TR10 9EW Tel: (01326) 376015 Fax: (01326) 376212 E-mail: info@wills-ridley.com *Marine hydraulic engineers*
Willsden Steel Ltd, Airfield Business Park, Elvington, York, YO41 4AU Tel: (01904) 608773 Fax: (01904) 608754 *Steel sheet stockholders*
▶ Willsons Printers (Newark) Ltd, Highlander House, Cross Street, Newark, Nottinghamshire, NG24 1PP Tel: (01636) 702334 Fax: (01636) 701396 E-mail: andy@willsons.com *Print management*
▶ Willstone Construction & Joinery Co. Ltd, Clowance Wood Farm, Clowance Wood, Praze-An-Beeble, Camborne, Cornwall, TR14 0NW Tel: (01209) 831001 Fax: (01209) 831001 E-mail: tracy@willstoneconstruction.co.uk *Property developers, Renovations, New Build, Joinery Manufactures and Suppliers*
▶ Willyn Contracts Ltd, Common Lane, Watnall, Nottingham, NG16 1HD Tel: 0115-938 9606 Fax: 0115-938 4027
▶ Wilmac Construction, Woodhill Road, Sandon, Chelmsford, CM2 7SG Tel: (01245) 475082
▶ Wilmacourt Ltd, 1 Riverbank Enterprise Centre, Broad Street, Dewsbury, West Yorkshire, WF13 3SA Tel: (01924) 465014 Fax: (01925) 451551
Wilman Equipment Ltd, Baker Street, Bradford, West Yorkshire, BD2 4NX Tel: (01274) 636977 Fax: (01274) 636714 *Material storage handling engineers*
Wilman Marine Ltd, 510 Victoria Road, Feltham, Middlesex, TW13 7DR Tel: (020) 8890 4000 Fax: (020) 8751 4128 E-mail: wilmanuniversal@msn.com *Marine & brewery engineers*
Wilman Universal Industries, Green Lane, Hounslow, TW4 6DF Tel: (020) 8570 4455 Fax: (020) 8572 2389 E-mail: sales@universaldispensesystems.com *Catering equipment manufrs*
Wilmat Handling Company Ltd, 43 Steward Street, Birmingham, B18 7AE Tel: 0121-454 7514 Fax: 0121-456 1792 E-mail: info@wilmat-handling.co.uk *Manufacturers of pedestrian controlled battery powered forklift trucks*
Wilmat Handling Company Ltd, 43 Steward Street, Birmingham, B18 7AE Tel: 0121-454 7514 Fax: 0121-456 1792 E-mail: info@wilmat-handling.co.uk *Materials handling manufs*
Wilmond Engineering Co. Ltd, 45 Bury Mead Road, Hitchin, Hertfordshire, SG5 1RX Tel: (01462) 459495 Fax: (01462) 420102 E-mail: sales@wilmond.co.uk *Trailer & tow bar services & distributors*
Wilmot Packaging Ltd, Rutherford Way, Swindon Village, Cheltenham, Gloucestershire, GL51 9TU Tel: (01242) 245151 Fax: (01242) 245155 *Carton manufrs*
Wilmshurst Bros Ltd, North Wing New England House, New England Street, Brighton, BN1 4GH Tel: (01273) 683255 Fax: (01273) 683255 E-mail: wilmshurstbros@yahoo.co.uk *Indoor & outdoor blinds & security blind repairers & manufrs*
Wilmslow, Omega Works Stuart Road, Bredbury Park Industrial Estate, Bredbury, Stockport, Cheshire, SK6 2SR Tel: 0161-406 0666 Fax: 0161-406 0777 E-mail: enquiries@wimslowplant.com *Contractors' plant hirers*
Wilmurten Manufacturing Co. Ltd, Manorway Industrial Estate, Bridge Road, Grays, Essex, RM17 6BJ Tel: (01375) 373984 Fax: (01375) 391867 E-mail: wilmurten@aol.com *Rubber mouldings manufrs*
Wilo Salmson Pumps Ltd, Centrum 100, Burton-on-Trent, Staffordshire, DE14 2WJ Tel: (01283) 523000 Fax: (01283) 523099 E-mail: sales@wilo.co.uk *Manufacturers of pumps*
Wilplan Training Ltd, Unit 2, Lake End Court, Taplow Road, Taplow, Maidenhead, Berkshire, SL6 0JQ Tel: (07808) 171295 Fax: (01628) 663740 E-mail: info@wilplantraining.co.uk *Security Industry Training Consultants providing quality courses required for application of the SIA Licence.**Door Supervisors*BJT For security guards*Conflict managment for all staff including NHS, Security, *Physical Intervention & Self defence.*First Aid Courses & More.**With over 20 years experience in the licenced retail and security business we pride ourself in providing quality courses. *Ex military trainers.*
▶ Wilprint Group Ltd, Ipswich Road, Cardiff, CF23 9XX Tel: (029) 2049 8484
Wilsanco Plastics Ltd, Killyman Road Industrial Estate, Killyman Road, Dungannon, County Tyrone, BT71 6LN Tel: (028) 8772 3131 Fax: (028) 8772 7318 E-mail: mailbox@wilsanco.com *Plastic container manufrs*
Wilsecure Installations, 292 Dewsbury Road, Leeds, LS11 6JT Tel: 0113-271 6097 Fax: 0113-270 4259 E-mail: sales@tindsdaletv.co.uk *Burglar alarm installators*
Wilson Air Pneumatics, Unit 1 Southall Enterprise Centre, Bridge Rd, Southall, Middx, UB2 4AE Tel: (020) 8893 5050 Fax: (020) 8893 5011 *Air compressor agents & vacuum pump maintenance/repair services*
Wilson Alarms, Ruyton XI Towns, Shrewsbury, SY4 1WX Tel: (0845) 2306966 Fax: (0845) 2306967 E-mail: enquiries@wilson-alarms.co.uk *CCTV, alarms installation & distributors*
▶ Wilson Alexander, Queen Caroline House, 3 High, Windsor, Berkshire, SL4 1LD Tel: (01753) 850540 Fax: 01753 850490 E-mail: info@wilsonalexander.com *Established specifically to partner with life science manufacturing organisations, to identify and select the most talented and inspired manufacturing professionals, Wilson Alexander aims to help you gain competitive advantage through manufacturing operations. We are able to offer Executive Search and Interim Management services.**We specialise in working with life science companies, including:**Animal Health, Bio-Pharmaceuticals, Biotechnology, Chemicals, Contract Manufacturing, Crop Science, Diagnostics, Ethical Pharmaceuticals, Generics, Manufacturing Equipment, Medical Devices, Medical Products, Over-the-Counter Medicines, Personal Care Products, Scientific Products and Vaccines.**Our aim is to help improve the performance of your business, by attracting talented individuals to your organisation who will add value through leadership, process improvement and operational excellence.**See www.wilsonalexander.com to learn more on contact us directly by telephone or email.*
▶ Wilson Andrew H Electrical Ltd, Hatston Industrial Estate, Scotts Road, Kirkwall, Orkney, KW15 1RE Tel: (01856) 873015
Wilson Bowden Group Services Ltd, Wilson Bowden House, Leicester Road, Ibstock, Leicestershire, LE67 6WB Tel: (01530) 260777 Fax: (01532) 262805 *Residential house builders*
Wilson Bros (Chickenley) Ltd, Chickenley Mills, Dewsbury, W. Yorkshire, WF12 8ND Tel: (01924) 463252 Fax: (01924) 463439 E-mail: chris@wilsonbros.demon.co.uk *Fibre reclaimers & wool blends*
Wilson Bros Sheffield Ltd, 35 Kirk Street, Sheffield, S4 7JX Tel: 0114-272 6179 Fax: 0114-276 5889 *Dust & fume extractors & sheet metal workers contractors*
Charles Wilson Engineers Ltd, 63 High Street, Harpenden, Hertfordshire, AL5 2SL Tel: (01582) 763122 Fax: (01582) 462697 E-mail: hire@cwplant.co.uk *Plant hire contractors*
▶ WILSON CLEANING SERVICES, 20 RISHWORTH CLOSE, Stockport, Cheshire, SK2 5NG Tel: 0161 483 0571 *OFFICE COMMERCIAL INDUSTRIAL AND RESIDENTIAL CLEANING SERVICES CONTRACT AND ONE OFFS*
Wilson & Collins Ltd, Balthane Industrial Estate, Balthane, Ballasalla, Isle of Man, IM9 2AJ Tel: (01624) 822854 Fax: (01624) 824995 *General & structural engineers services*
Wilson Connolly Lancashire, Bradley Lane, Standish, Wigan, Lancashire, WN6 0XN Tel: (01257) 425511 Fax: (01257) 426674 *Building Contractors*
Wilson Connolly Midlands, Century House, The Lakes, Northampton, NN4 7SJ Tel: (01604) 887220 Fax: (01604) 887221 E-mail: midlands@wilsonconnolly.co.uk *Home construction*
Wilson Connolly Scotland Ltd, 2 Garbett Road, Livingston, West Lothian, EH54 7DL Tel: (01506) 405700 Fax: (01506) 405701 E-mail: scotland@wilsonconnolly.co.uk *Estate development company* Also at: Aberdeen
Wilson Construction Ltd, Saltcoats House, Cutlers Road, South Woodham Ferrers, Chelmsford, CM3 5WA Tel: (01245) 428282 Fax: (01245) 428283 E-mail: info@wilson-construction.com *Groundwork & civil engineering contractors*
Wilson Electric Motor Sales Ltd, 12-18 Radstock Street, Battersea, London, SW11 4AT Tel: (01622) 687128 Fax: (020) 7924 1887 *Electrical contractors*
Wilson Electrical Distributors, Unit 6 Waterside, Hamm Moor Lane, Addlestone, Surrey, KT15 2SN Tel: (01932) 848020 Fax: (01932) 820600 E-mail: sales@wilsonelectrical.com *Electrical wholesalers & distributors* Also at: London SW19
Wilson Electrical Distributors Ltd, 2 Balfour Business Centre, Balfour Road, Southall, Middlesex, UB2 5BD Tel: (020) 8574 4218 Fax: (020) 8843 1048 E-mail: chris@lmob.co.uk *Electrical installers*
Wilson & Garden, 38 Tollpark Road, Wardpark East, Cumbernauld, Glasgow, G68 0LW Tel: (01236) 853120 Fax: (01236) 853123 E-mail: info@wgltd.com *Manufacturers of visual communication equipment*
Wilson & Garden Ltd, 2 Carrington Road, Spalding, Lincolnshire, PE11 1LY Tel: (01775) 712332 Fax: (01775) 712332 *Educational products manufrs*
George Wilson Industries Ltd, 1 First Avenue, Minworth, Sutton Coldfield, West Midlands, B76 1BA Tel: 0121-313 7000 Fax: 0121-313 7001 E-mail: malcolm.w@gwi-ltd.co.uk Principal Export Areas: Worldwide *Gas meters & gas regulator suppliers*
Wilson Glass & Mirror, Weston Road, Norwich, NR3 3WG Tel: (01603) 415400 Fax: (01603) 415401 E-mail: wilsonglass@btconnect.com *Glass sealed units laminated manufrs*
Wilson Gunn, Chancery House, 53-64 Chancery Lane, London, WC2A 1QU Tel: (020) 7242 2631 Fax: (020) 7242 0075 E-mail: gee@wilsongunn.com *Accountants*
▶ Wilson Gunn Mccaw, 5th Floor, Blackfriars House, Manchester, M3 2JA Tel: 0161-827 9400 Fax: 0161-832 4905 E-mail: wgm@wilsongunn.com *Trade & service mark attorneys*
Wilson Gunn Skerrett, Charles House, 148 Great Charles Street, Birmingham, B3 3HT Tel: 0121-236 1038 Fax: 0121-233 2875 E-mail: skerrett@wilsongunn.com *Patent & trade mark agents*
Hunter Wilson & Partners Ltd, The Sawmill, Rigg, Gretna, Dumfriesshire, DG16 5JL Tel: (01461) 338454 Fax: (01461) 338468 E-mail: sales@hunterwilson.co.uk *Machine round timber manufrs*
Ian Wilson, 2 Edinborough Road, Lanark, ML11 7RS Tel: (01555) 660666 Fax: (01555) 663901 E-mail: info@smiddywroughtiron.com *Horse shoes suppliers & manufrs*
Ian Wilson, 11 East Main Street, Harthill, Shotts, Lanarkshire, ML7 5QW Tel: (01501) 753206 Fax: (01501) 752580 E-mail: nielsenscotland@compuserve.com *Chemical distributors*
Wilson Insurance Broking Group Ltd, Wilson House, 1-3 Waverley Street, Nottingham, NG7 4HG Tel: 0115-942 0111 Fax: 0115-942 0459 E-mail: info@wilorg.co.uk *Insurance brokers*
James Wilson Ltd, Broom Road Business Park, Broom Road, Poole, Dorset, BH12 4PA Tel: (01202) 731731 Fax: (01202) 736736 E-mail: enquiries@james.wilson-ltd.com *Aeronautical design & engineering services*
James Wilson & Sons, 33 Brown Street, Glasgow, G2 8PF Tel: 0141-221 3590 Fax: 0141-248 3673 *Engineers' suppliers & tool merchants*
▶ James Wilson (Transport) Ltd, Springfield Garage, Muirkirk, Cumnock, Ayrshire, KA18 3QU Tel: (01290) 661244
Ken Wilson Associates, 52 Union Road, Inverness, IV2 3JY Tel: (01463) 237375 Fax: (01463) 237666 E-mail: enquiries@kwa.uk.net *Consulting/civil & structural engineers*
Ken Wilson Associates, 25 Collingwood Street, Newcastle upon Tyne, NE1 1JE Tel: 0191-261 7171 Fax: 0191-232 0146 E-mail: debra@kwa.co.uk *Recruitment agency*
▶ Wilson Kennett Partnership, College House 2 College Street, Harlow Hill, Harrogate, North Yorkshire, HG2 0AH Tel: (01423) 531183 Fax: (01423) 531184 E-mail: wkp@wkpartnership.co.uk
Wilson Knowles & Sons, 6 Chapel Lane, Heckmondwike, West Yorkshire, WF16 9JT Tel: (01924) 402208 Fax: (01924) 406895 E-mail: sales@wilsonknowlesandsons.co.uk *Textile machinery manufrs*
Wilson Leisure, 27 St. Peters Road, Buckie, Banffshire, AB56 1DJ Tel: (01542) 833592 Fax: (01542) 833592 *Coin operated equipment maintenance & hire*
Wilson Lendrum & Weir Ltd, Derrychara Road, Enniskillen, County Fermanagh, BT74 6JF Tel: (028) 6632 2720 Fax: (028) 6632 2212 *Motor vehicle accessories manufrs*
M.J. Wilson Group, Wrotham Road, Meopham, Gravesend, Kent, DA13 0QB Tel: (01474) 812406 Fax: (01474) 814265 E-mail: northdinst@freeuk.com *Industrial instrument distributors*
Wilson Machinery International Ltd, Roseberry House, Old Church Road, East Hanningfield, Chelmsford, CM3 8BG Tel: (01245) 403040 Fax: (01245) 403028 E-mail: sales@wilsonmachinery.demon.co.uk Principal Export Areas: Worldwide *Machine tool merchants*
Wilson & Mansfield Ltd, Headley House, Headley Road, Grayshott, Surrey, GU26 6TU Tel: (01428) 601140 Fax: (01428) 607851 E-mail: david@wmjuice.co.uk *Essential oil & fruit juice importers*
Wilson Metals Ltd, Ifton Colliery, St. Martins, Oswestry, Shropshire, SY11 3DA Tel: (01691) 778363 Fax: (01691) 778363 E-mail: wilson@pedigreecomputers.co.uk *Scrap metal merchants*
Wilson Packaging Products, 38 Hatherley Road, Manchester, M20 4RU Tel: 0161-434 0454 Fax: 0161-448 1070 E-mail: wilsonpackaging@btconnect.com *Packaging product distributors*
Wilson Process Systems Ltd, Waterworks Road, Hastings, East Sussex, TN34 1RT Tel: (01424) 722222 Fax: (01424) 720730 E-mail: sales@wps.co.uk *Electronic contract & printed circuit manufrs*
R. Wilson & Co. (Platers) Ltd, Zachrome Works, Sheffield Road, Whittington Moor, Chesterfield, Derbyshire, S41 8NH Tel: (01246) 450387 Fax: (01246) 455875 E-mail: office@zachrome.com *Chrome platers*
Scott Wilson Pavement Engineering Ltd, 12 Regan Way Faraday Building, Nottingham Science & Technology Park, Chilwell, Nottingham, NG9 6RZ Tel: 0115-907 7000 Fax: 0115 907 7001 E-mail: enquiry@swpe.co.uk *Consulting engineers*

Sid Wilson (Newcastle) Ltd, 3-5 Tundry Way, Chainbridge Road Industrial Estate, Blaydon-On-Tyne, Tyne & Wear, NE21 5SJ Tel: 0191-414 3344 Fax: 0191-414 5962 E-mail: sidwilsonsweets@aol.com *Wholesale confectioners, stationers & toys*

Wilson & Sons (Engineering) Ltd, Morley Road, Staple Hill, Bristol, BS16 4QB Tel: 0117-956 9769 Fax: 0117-957 1670 E-mail: admin@wilsons-engineering.co.uk *Precision engineers*

T.C. Wilson Ltd, Unit 3-4, Kelsey Cl, Attleborough Fields Ind Estate, Nuneaton, Warwickshire, CV11 6RS Tel: (024) 7632 9914 Fax: (024) 7634 2486 *Point of sale display producers*

Wilson Textiles Ltd, 22 Milnpark Street, Glasgow, G41 1BB Tel: 0141-429 0715 Fax: 0141-420 1627 *Textile merchants*

Wilson Tool & Engineering Co Essex Ltd, 2-4 Parsons Road, Manor Trading Estate, Benfleet, Essex, SS7 4PY Tel: (01268) 752836 Fax: (01268) 565323 E-mail: sales@wilson-tool.co.uk *Precision engineering specialists*

Wilson Tool International Ltd, Stirling Road, South Marston Industrial Estat, Swindon, SN3 4TQ Tel: (01793) 831818 Fax: (0800) 373758 E-mail: sales@wilsontool.eu *Total solutions provider for the sheet metals industry*

Wilson UK Ltd, Unit 3 Bloxwich Lane Industrial Estate, Bloxwich Lane, Walsall, WS2 8TF Tel: (01922) 725800 Fax: (01922) 649888 E-mail: uksales@wilsononline.com Purchasing Contact: G. Homer Sales Contact: J. Mark Principal Export Areas: Worldwide *Design, installation & distribution of fluid handling & powder finishing equipment. Supply & distribution to the offshore oil and gas industry, incorporating supply chain management, protective clothing and pipes valves and fittings.*

Wilsons Of Clifton Ltd, 97 Hitchin Road, Shefford, Bedfordshire, SG17 5JB Tel: (01462) 811000 Fax: (01462) 817475 *Powered access platform hirers*

▶ Wilsons Deliveries, Hallam Fields Road, Ilkeston, Derbyshire, DE7 4AZ Tel: 0115-944 7007 Fax: 0115-944 7013

▶ Wilsons Drop Kerbs, Ger-Y-Mynydd, Seiriol Road, Penmaenmawr, Gwynedd, LL34 6HB Tel: (01492) 623170 E-mail: wilsonsdropkerbs@hotmail.co.uk *Specialists in fitting drop kerbs for vehicle access*

Wilsons Glass Ltd, 6 St Marys Lane, Upminster, Essex, RM14 2QT Tel: (01708) 224215 Fax: (01708) 224215 *Glass merchants*

Wilsons Hydraulic Services Ltd, 142 Clydeholm Road, Clydeside Industrial Estate, Glasgow, G14 0QQ Tel: 0141-569 1066 Fax: 0141-954 3986 E-mail: sales@wilsonhydraulics.co.uk *Garage Service equipment maintenance contractors*

Wilsons Safety Supplies Ltd, Gibson Street, Amble, Morpeth, Northumberland, NE65 0LR Tel: (01665) 712572 Fax: (01665) 713096 E-mail: dennis@wilson-safety.co.uk *Safety clothing wholesalers*

Wilsons & Co. (Sharrow) Ltd, Sharrow Mills, Sheffield, S11 8PL Tel: 0114-266 2677 Fax: 0114-267 0504 E-mail: snuff4you@aol.com *Tobacco products manufrs*

▶ Wilsons Washrooms, 588a Glasgow Road, Clydebank, Dunbartonshire, G81 1NH Tel: 0141-941 3913 Fax: 0141-941 3907 E-mail: info@wilsonwashrooms.com *Provide a comprehensive washroom facility solution*

Wilsport, 5 Fleming Close, Wellingborough, Northamptonshire, NN8 6UF Tel: (01933) 403404 Fax: (01933) 405070 E-mail: edw@wilsport.freeserve.co.uk *Sportswear manufacturers & leisurewear*

Wilstead Patterns & Castings, Brickyard House, Mill Lane, Arlesey, Bedfordshire, SG15 6RF Tel: (01462) 835559 *Non-ferrous metal castings & pattern making services*

Wiltan Ltd, Pontnewynydd Industrial Estate, Pontnewynydd, Pontypool, Gwent, NP4 6YW Tel: (01495) 750711 Fax: (01495) 753730 E-mail: sales@wiltan.co.uk *We are the UK's number 1 manufacturers & supplier specialising in all types of strip wound magnetic cores in cold rolled grain orientated steel & nickel iron to British, international & customer specific standards.*

▶ Wilton Conservatories Ltd, Wilton House, Wilton, Salisbury, SP2 0BZ Tel: (01722) 742700

▶ Wilton Engineering Services, Port Clarence Road, Port Clarence, Middlesbrough, Cleveland, TS2 1RZ Tel: (01642) 546611 Fax: (01642) 546622 E-mail: info@wiltonengineering.co.uk *Metal fabrication manufrs*

▶ Wilton Graphics Ltd, Harnham Trading Estate, Netherhampton Road, Salisbury, SP2 8NW Tel: (01722) 320300

▶ Wilton Plaster Mouldings, Wimbledon Avenue, Brandon, Suffolk, IP27 0NZ Tel: (01842) 811117 Fax: (01842) 811991 *Suppliers, manufacturers & installers of plaster moulding products*

Wilts Wholesale Electrical Co. Ltd, Kennet Way, Canal Road Industrial Estate, Trowbridge, Wiltshire, BA14 8BL Tel: (01225) 777300 Fax: (01225) 777001 E-mail: info@wilts.co.uk *Wholesale electrical suppliers*

▶ Wiltshire Accident Repair Centre, Hopton Estate, London Road, DEVIZES, Wiltshire, SN10 2EY Tel: 01380 735035 Fax: 01380 728532 E-mail: info@wiltshireaccident.com *Vehicle accident repair specalists for cars and vans, from major accident reconstruction to minor blemishes. Insurance company approved. Company management facility available. 24 hr recovery service*

Wiltshire & Avon Cash Registers Ltd, 80 West Street, Old Market, St. Philips, Bristol, BS2 0BW Tel: 0117-955 5708 Fax: 0117-954 0904 *Cash register sales & services*

Wiltshire (Bristol) Ltd, First Avenue, Portbury West, Bristol, BS20 7WP Tel: (01275) 375555 Fax: (01275) 375590 E-mail: enquiries@wiltshire-print.co.uk *Lithographic printers*

▶ Wiltshire Building Conservation, 33-35 Whistley Road, Potterne, Devizes, Wiltshire, SN10 5QY Tel: (01380) 729902 Fax: (0700) 5802576 *Conservation of historic buildings*

▶ Wiltshire Couriers.co.uk, Abercarn, Newtown, Heytesbury, Warminster, Warminster, Wiltshire, BA12 0HN Tel: 01985 840321 Fax: 01985 840321 E-mail: info@wiltshirecouriers.co.uk

▶ Wiltshire Farm Foods, Unit 3, 147 Stockton Street, Middlesbrough, Cleveland, TS2 1BU Tel: (01642) 643999 Fax: (01642) 648017 *Frozen meal delivery service*

G.R. Wiltshire & Co., Smoke Hall Lane, Winsford, Cheshire, CW7 3BE Tel: (01455) 202666 Fax: (01606) 555511 E-mail: sales@smeetimber.com *Structural hardwood merchants & marine applications*

▶ Wiltshire Glass & Windows, Unit 6 Parkers Close, Downton Industrial Estate, Salisbury, SP5 3RB Tel: (01725) 513030 Fax: (01725) 510145

Wiltshire Printing Co Croydon Ltd, 131 Love Lane, Mitcham, Surrey, CR4 3YA Tel: (020) 8648 0061 Fax: (020) 8648 6547 *General printers*

▶ Wiltshire Recovery, Hopton Park Industrial Estate, Hopton Road, Devizes, Wiltshire, SN10 2EY Tel: (01380) 735055 Fax: (01380) 730252 E-mail: admin@wiltshire-recovery.com *24 hr recovery service 7 Days a week service including Heavy Recovery.*

▶ Wiltshire Roofing & Building, 157 Bath Road, Longwell Green, Bristol, BS30 9DD Tel: 0117-377 5315 E-mail: katyryan@blueyonder.co.uk

Wimbledon Automatics, 182 Hartfield Road, London, SW19 3TQ Tel: (020) 8540 7780 *Automatic transmissions*

Wimbledon Bathrooms, 32 The Downs, Wiimbledon, London, SW20 8JA Tel: (020) 8946 7521 Fax: (020) 8946 7521 *Bathroom design and installation*

Wimbledon Builders Merchants Ltd, Gap Road, London, SW19 8JA Tel: (020) 8947 9933 Fax: (020) 8944 1622 *Builders merchants*

Wimbledon Copy Bureau, 257-261 Haydons Road, London, SW19 8TY Tel: (020) 8542 8342 Fax: (020) 8715 8959 E-mail: colour@wcb.co.uk *Photocopying services*

Wimbledon Metal Co. Ltd, 105-107 Brighton Road, Surbiton, Surrey, KT6 5NF Tel: (020) 8399 2178 *Scrap metal merchants*

Wimbledon Sewing Machine Co.Ltd, 292-312 Balham High Road, London, SW17 7AA Tel: (020) 8767 4724 Fax: (020) 8767 4726 E-mail: wimbledonsewingmachinecoltd@btinternet.com *International industrial sewing machine dealers*

Wimbock U K, Aspen Way, Yalberton Industrial Estate, Paignton, Devon, TQ4 7QR Tel: (01803) 407006 Fax: (01803) 407006 E-mail: wimbockuk@btconnect.com *Wimbock UK based in Paignton, Devon are a supplier of ventilation systems including kitchen extractor hoods, ceiling ventilators and air outlets.*

Wimborne Engineering, 58 Cobham Road, Ferndown Industrial Estate, Wimborne, Dorset, BH21 7QH Tel: (01202) 893043 E-mail: knud@moldtecknik.co.uk *Injection mould professional toolmakers manufrs*

Wimborne Engraving Co., Wimborne Industrial Estate, Mill Lane, Wimborne, Dorset, BH21 1LN Tel: (01202) 886373 Fax: (01202) 886373 *Engraving services*

▶ Wimborne Furniture, 52 King Street, Wimborne, Dorset, BH21 1EB Tel: (01202) 849635 Fax: 01202 849635 E-mail: info@wimbornefurniture.com *Furniture retailer specialising in providing high quality solid oak*

Wimborne Leather Co., Unit 2b, Sunrise Business Park, Blandford Forum, Dorset, DT11 8ST Tel: (01258) 455397 Fax: (01258) 480610 *Leather furniture & upholstery manufrs*

Wimborne Welding Supplies Ltd, Unit 16J Chalwyn Industrial Estate, Old Wareham Road, Parkstone, Poole, Dorset, BH12 4PE Tel: (01202) 722606 Fax: (01202) 722606 *Industrial gas & welding distribs*

Wimhall Ltd, Creswell Road, Clowne, Chesterfield, Derbyshire, S43 4LT Tel: (01246) 810619 *Filling station*

George Wimpey South West Ltd, Omicron Windmill Hill Business Park, Whitehill Way, Swindon, SN5 6PA Tel: (01793) 898200 Fax: (01793) 898207 *Building contractors*

Wimpole Garages Ltd, Portland Street South, Ashton-under-Lyne, Lancashire, OL6 7RE Tel: 0161-330 9551 Fax: 0161-339 0141 *Accident repair centre services*

Wimpole International Ltd, 113 Colney Heath Lane, St. Albans, Hertfordshire, AL4 0TN Tel: (01727) 868057 Fax: (01727) 847116 E-mail: wimpoleint@mcmail.com *Medical equipment exporters*

George Wimpy West Yorkshire Ltd, Sandpiper House, Peel Avenue, Calder Park, Wakefield, West Yorkshire, WF2 7UA Tel: (01924) 241500 Fax: (01924) 241580 *House builders*

Win plc, 1 Cliveden Office Village, Lancaster Road, Cressex Business Park, High Wycombe, Buckinghamshire, HP12 3YZ Tel: (01494) 750500 Fax: (01494) 750820 E-mail: enquiries@winplc.com *Paging, information services & text messaging systems manufrs*

▶ Wincan Computer Systems, 13 Cherry Street, Woking, Surrey, GU21 6EE Tel: (01483) 762226 Fax: (01483) 762226 E-mail: info@wincaneurope.com *Computer software*

▶ Wincanton Group Ltd, Faraday Avenue, Hams Hall Distribution Park, Coleshill, Birmingham, B46 1AL Tel: (01675) 433333 Fax: (01675) 433366

Wincanton Group Ltd, Middle Bank, Doncaster, South Yorkshire, DN4 5JU Tel: (01302) 507100 Fax: (01302) 507114 *Administration for distributors*

▶ Wincanton Group Ltd, Caledonian Mill, Leith Docks, Edinburgh, EH6 6NZ Tel: 0131-554 0803

▶ Wincanton Logistics Ltd, Newbridge Road, Little Stanney, Chester, CH2 4RA Tel: 0151-356 6323

Wincanton Logistics Ltd, Central Way, Feltham, Middlesex, TW14 0XQ Tel: (020) 8831 1500 Fax: (020) 8831 1518 *Distribution services for sainsbury* Also at: Branches throughout the U.K.

▶ Wincanton Logistics Ltd, Wellington Parkway, Magna Park, Lutterworth, Leicestershire, LE17 4XW Tel: (01455) 550444 Fax: (01455) 559060

▶ Wincanton Logistics Ltd, Aston Lane North, Preston Brook, Runcorn, Cheshire, WA7 3GA Tel: (01928) 703500 Fax: (01928) 703555

▶ Wincanton Logistics Ltd, Northway Trading Estate, Northway Lane, Tewkesbury, Gloucestershire, GL20 8JH Tel: (01684) 278500 Fax: (01684) 278501

▶ Winch Solutions, Unit 1 Low Bank Road, Ashton-In-Makerfield, Wigan, Lancashire, WN4 9RN Tel: (01257) 473572 Fax: (01257) 473572 E-mail: admin@winchsolutions.co.uk *Winches & accessories suppliers*

Winch, Tony, Chapel Farm, Chapel Lane, Westhumble, Dorking, Surrey, RH5 6AY Tel: (01306) 742373 *Joiners*

Winchcombe Power Tools, 299 Wimpson Lane, Southampton, SO16 4PY Tel: (023) 8039 9957 Fax: (023) 8078 1719 *Power tools retailers & repairers*

A. Winchester & Sons, 9 Great Queen Street, Dartford, DA1 1TJ Tel: (01322) 221388 Fax: (01322) 227659 E-mail: dartfordskips@aol.com *Waste transfer station*

▶ Winchester Electro Optics, Unit 20a Home Farm Rural Industries, East Tytherley Road, Lockerley, Romsey, Hampshire, SO51 0JT Tel: (01794) 340005 Fax: (01794) 340005 E-mail: info@w-e-o.co.uk *Electronic & optical designers & manufrs*

▶ Winchester Events Ltd, 272 Back Street, Winchester, Hampshire, SO23 7NN Tel: (01962) 889159 Fax: (01962) 884946 E-mail: sales@winchesterevents.co.uk *Conference & events services*

Winchester Procurement Ltd, Unit 7 Winnall Indust Estate, Moorside Road, Winchester, Hampshire, SO23 7FX Tel: (01962) 840008 Fax: (01962) 840009 E-mail: sales@winprop.co.uk *Procurement agents & consultants specialising in engineering, laboratory & medical equipment manufrs*

Winchmaster Lifting Equipment, 6 South Orbital Trading Park, Hedon Road, Hull, HU9 1NJ Tel: (01482) 223663 Fax: (01482) 218285 E-mail: sales@winchmaster.co.uk Principal Export Areas: Worldwide *Winch distributors, cable pulling winches & motor vehicle recovery equipment. Winchmaster are specialists in providing disabled/handicapped person vehicle winch systems. AC Recovery Winches, AC Lifting Winches, DC Recovery Winches, DC Lifting Winches, Hydraulic Winches, Hand Winches, Chain Hoists, Cable Puller, Web Strapping & Parts*

Wincilate Ltd, Quarry Offices, Aberllefenni, Upper Corris, Machynlleth, Powys, SY20 9RT Tel: (01654) 761602 Fax: (01654) 761418 E-mail: slate@wincilate.co.uk *Slate quarrying & prefabrication*

Wincro Metal Industries Ltd, 3 Fife Street, Sheffield, S9 1NJ Tel: 0114-242 2171 Fax: 0114-243 4306 E-mail: sales@wincro.com *Stainless Steel Building Products*

Wind River UK Ltd, Unit 10 Viscount Way, South Marston Industrial Estate, Swindon, SN3 4TN Tel: (01793) 831831 Fax: (01793) 831808 *Embedded computer systems manufrs*

Windboats Marine Ltd, Grange Walk, Wroxham, Norwich, NR12 8RX Tel: (01603) 782236 Fax: (01603) 784106 E-mail: windboats@aol.com *Boat builders*

Windcrest (HSP Electronics) Ltd, Unit 8 Abbey Manufacturing Estate, Mount Pleasant, Wembley, Middlesex, HA0 1NR Tel: (020) 8795 0333 Fax: (020) 8795 0444 E-mail: windcrest@aol.com *Intercom unit manufrs*

Oscar Windebank & Son Ltd, The Bassetts, Box, Corsham, Wiltshire, SN13 8ER Tel: (01225) 742929 *Timber merchants*

Winder Boats, Kensington Street, Keighley, West Yorkshire, BD21 1PW Tel: (01535) 604980 Fax: (01535) 605371 E-mail: guy@winderboats.freeserve.co.uk *Boat builders & repairs*

Windglass Windows Ltd, 536 Kingston Road, London, SW20 8DT Tel: (020) 8540 8848 Fax: (020) 8540 8065 E-mail: windows.windglass@virgin.net *Glazing contractors services*

Winding Technology, Moorland House, Midway, South Crosland, Huddersfield, HD4 7DA Tel: (01484) 663389 Fax: (01484) 666783 E-mail: coil@winding.demon.co.uk *Coil winding machinery manufrs*

Windlelm Ltd, 130 Western Road, Hove, East Sussex, BN3 1DA Tel: (01273) 770681 Fax: (01273) 321387 *Export merchants & property developers*

▶ Windles Printers, Meadow View, Drakes Drive, Long Crendon, Aylesbury, Buckinghamshire, HP18 9EQ Tel: (01844) 201683 Fax: (01844) 201695

Windmill Business Systems Ltd, Cattells Mill Road, Willingham, Cambridge, CB4 5LA Tel: (01954) 261661 Fax: (01954) 261661 E-mail: info@windmillweb.net *Computer consultants*

Windmill Buying Services Ltd, 4 Derby Street, Norwich, NR2 4PU Tel: (01603) 632008 Fax: (01603) 612236 E-mail: wwindmill@compuserve.com Principal Export Areas: Worldwide *Buying & purchasing (overseas) specialists*

▶ Windmill Demolition Co. Ltd, Windmill Lane, Denton, Manchester, M34 2JF Tel: 0161-320 9119

Windmill Feeds & Saddlery, Mill Lane, Lewes Road, Cross in Hand, Heathfield, East Sussex, TN21 0TA Tel: (01435) 864383 Fax: (01435) 864383 *Animal feed suppliers*

Windmill Graphics, PO Box 11, Stroud, Gloucestershire, GL5 5BH Tel: (01453) 87375 Fax: (01453) 873699 E-mail: sales@windmillgraphics.co.uk *Lithographic printers*

Windmill Sofas, 1 Picks Cottage Factory Unit, Sewardstone Road, London, E4 7RA Tel: (02 8805 5084 Fax: (020) 8524 2444 *Furniture upholstery manufrs*

Windmill Tapes & Labels, 6 Mackenzie Industrial Estate, Bird Hall Lane, Stockport, Cheshire, SK3 0SB Tel: 0161-495 3959 Fax: 0161-428 1603 E-mail: sales@windmilltapes.co.uk *Print & plain packaging tape & labels manufrs*

Windmill Windows, 115 Red Bank Road, Blackpo FY2 9HZ Tel: (01253) 594065 Fax: (01253) 500474 E-mail: sales@windmillwindows.co.uk *Plastic windows & door installation services*

Windmore Concrete Products, Windmore Green, Creca, Annan, Dumfriesshire, DG12 6RP Tel: (01461) 500350 Fax: (01461) 500350 *Concrete product suppliers*

▶ Wind-O-Kleen, 3 Queens Avenue, Glazebury, Warrington, WA3 5NE Tel: (01925) 765092 Fax: (01925) 479173 E-mail: manager@wind-o-kleen.com *Window cleaning contractors*

Windor Controls Ltd, Unit 58 Hillgrove Business Park, Nazeing, Waltham Abbey, Essex, EN9 2HB Tel: (01992) 893737 Fax: (01992) 893130 E-mail: barryrichards@windorcontrols.co.uk *CCTV, automatic door & access control syste suppliers*

Window Box Co., 3 Bridle Road, Woodford, Stockport, Cheshire, SK7 1QH Tel: 0161-439 6585 Fax: 0161-439 6585 *Wooden window bo manufrs, containers & watering services*

The Window Cleaning Co., 57 Shelton Street, Wilnecote, Tamworth, Staffordshire, B77 5DB Tel: (01827) 282892 E-mail: thewincleaningco@aol.com *Domestic Commercial window cleaning for Tamworth, Sutton Coldfield and surrounding villages*

Window Craft (Nuneaton) Ltd, Whitacre Road, Nuneaton, Warwickshire, CV11 6BY Tel: (024) 7638 4896 Fax: (024) 7638 4896 *Window fra & plate glass manufrs*

Window & Door Security Systems Ltd, Building 6 Third Avenue, Pensnett Trading Estate, Kingswinford, West Midlands, DY6 7XU Tel: (01384) 288321 Fax: (01384) 288212 E-mail: sales@windowanddoorsecurity.co.uk *Suppliers & installers of security products,such as Grilles,Barriers,Roller Shutters,Collapsable Gates. Also Specialist Window Films CONTAC FREEPHONE 0800 028 4299*

▶ Window Fitters Mate, Unit 27 Riverside Estate, Sir Thomas Longley Road, Medway City Estat Rochester, Kent, ME2 4DP Tel: (01634) 71771 Fax: (01634) 717714

▶ Window Gard Ltd, The Waterhouse Business Centre, 2 Cromar Way, Chelmsford, CM1 2QE Tel: (0870) 3218250 Fax: (0870) 3218270 E-mail: hq@windowgard.co.uk *Glass (security) manufrs*

The Window Glass Company Bristol Ltd, 11 Emer Road, Bristol, BS4 5PF Tel: 0117-977 9292 Fax: 0117-977 9299 E-mail: mail@windowglass.co.uk *Aluminium shop front manufrs*

Window Machinery Sales Ltd, Unit 3c Hadrians Way, Glebe Farm Industrial Estate, Rugby, Warwickshire, CV21 1ST Tel: (01788) 577577 Fax: (01788) 567938 *PVCu window fabrication machinery service*

The Window Makers Ltd, 1 Larchwood Business Centre, Havant, Hampshire, PO9 3QL Tel: (023 9265 1700 Fax: (023) 9269 5422 E-mail: sales@leadingwindows.co.uk *Window manufrs*

Window Shades, Claremont Building, Old Clatterbridge Road, Wirral, Merseyside, CH63 4JB Tel: (01978) 263000 Fax: (01978) 263222 *Blind & curtain suppliers*

▶ Window Warehouse, Bowen Industrial Estate, Aberbargoed, Bargoed, Mid Glamorgan, CF81 9EP Tel: (01443) 879275 Fax: (01443) 839442

▶ Window Widget, Unit 1, Venture Business Centre Madleaze Road, Gloucester, GL1 5SJ Tel: (01452) 300912 Fax: (01452) 300912 *Manufacturers of window frames*

Window World Of Kent, 24 Juniper Close, Ashford Kent, TN23 3JY Tel: (01233) 642322 Fax: (087 1656459 E-mail: e-breeze@windows-world.fsnet.co.uk *PVCu windows & doors suppliers*

▶ Window World Services, Unit 3, Crystal Drive, Smethwick, W. Midlands, B66 1QG Tel: 0121-544 1176

Window World Wholesale, Marl Road, Knowsley Industrial Park, Liverpool, L33 7UH Tel: 0151-546 0333 Fax: 0151-546 0333 *Venetian & vertical blinds*

▶ Windowblend Double Glazing, 6 Poplar Road, Broadmeadow Industrial Estate, Dumbarton, G82 2RQ Tel: (01389) 761624 Fax: (01389) 761625 E-mail: enquiries@leonardbuilders.co.uk *Windo doors & conservatories*

▶ Windowcharm, Kent Road, Sheffield, S8 9RN Tel: (01709) 379092 Fax: 0114-255 8142 *Blind curtain manufrs*

Windowlink Ltd, Station Road, Minety, Malmesbury Wilts, SN16 9QY Tel: (0870) 7701640 Fax: (01666) 860889 *Software*

Windowmaker, Madleaze Trading Estate, Madleaze Road, Gloucester, GL1 5SG Tel: (01452) 42334 Fax: (01452) 300193 E-mail: mail@swiftsheild.co.uk *Double glazed products manufrs*

Windows Direct Merseyside Ltd, Hastings House, Sandford Street, Birkenhead, Merseyside, CH41 1AR Tel: 0151-666 1414 Fax: 0151-666 1515 E-mail: sales@windowsdirect.org *Window & door manufrs*

Windows & Doors U Fit, Manor Way, Kinmel Bay, Rhyl, Clwyd, LL18 5BE Tel: (01745) 354540 Fax: (01745) 354540 E-mail: sales@conservatories-northwales.co.uk *Window manufrs*

ɔws & SQL Programmers Ltd, 31 Leconfield ad, London, N5 2RZ Tel: (020) 7359 0099 x: (020) 7359 0110 mail: services@winsql.com *Software velopment*

ndowscreens UK, PO Box 181, Upminster, sex, RM14 1GX Tel: (01708) 222273 x: (01708) 641898 mail: info@flyscreensuk.co.uk *Fly screen ppliers*

ndowseal & Distinctive Windows, Bradford ɔad, Winsford, Cheshire, CW7 2PD l: (01606) 594734 Fax: (01606) 598038

ndowworld Ltd, Unit G, Belgrave Industrial entre, Ross Walk, Leicester, LE4 5HH l: 0116-261 0078

rush Guns Ltd, PO Box 127, Witney, fordshire, OX28 6FX Tel: (01993) 703035 x: (01993) 771014 *Gunsmith services*

ndrush Maidenhead, Bath Road, Taplow, aidenhead, Berkshire, SL6 0AH Tel: (01628) 2100 Fax: 01628 682111 mail: maidenhead.retailsales@windrush.co.uk *lkswagen Retailer*Trade parts specialist*0s of w & Volkswagen approved used rs,*competitive finance arranged, any-make rt-exchanges welcome and nationwide elivery.*Fully fitted service workshop.*

rush Valley Joinery Ltd, The Barn, Sawpit ane, Little Rissington, Cheltenham, oucestershire, GL54 2NB Tel: (01451) 820100 ax: (01451) 820100 *Joinery manufrs*

Windsmoor Group, Windsmoor Ho, Lawrence d, London, N15 4EP Tel: (020) 8800 8022 ax: (020) 8809 6747 *Ladies' retailers* Also at: ondon W1

indsor Bronzite Solicitors, 43 Bargates, hristchurch, Dorset, BH23 1QD Tel: 0870 020555 Fax: 0870 4020556 mail: info@windsorbronzite.co.uk *A modern d progressive firm, maintaining the tradition d friendly manner of a high street practice. We ecialise in PROPERTY · PROFESSIONAL EGLIGENCE · ACCIDENT CLAIMS EMPLOYMENT LAW · COMPANY & OMMERCIAL · WILLS & PROBATE **We offer REE initial consultations and a No Win No Fee ervice.*

dsor Creative Communications, Anglesey odge, Farnborough Road, Aldershot, ampshire, GU11 3BJ Tel: (0845) 4503407 ax: (0845) 4503409 -mail: windsor@windsor-creative.com *dvertising & marketing agents*

dsor Developments, Waddington Street, ldham, OL9 6QH Tel: 0161-624 6252 *Pine rniture manufrs*

dsor Engineering Ltd, Unit 10 Eastgate Park, rkwright Way, Scunthorpe, South Humberside, N16 1AE Tel: (01724) 867418 Fax: (01724) 81708 -mail: scunthorpesales@windsorkomatsu.co.uk *ork lift trucks hire & supply*

dsor Food Machinery, Units 1-6 Mountain Farm, larsh Road, Hamstreet, Ashford, Kent, N26 2JD Tel: (01233) 733737 Fax: (01233) 33392 -mail: sales@windsorfoodmachinery.com *Vindsor Food Machinery Ltd, Ashford, Kent, are eaders and specialists in the field of supplying neat processing equipment to the retail, dustrial and catering industries. Second-hand nd equipment leasing services are also vailable. Their products range from bandsaws o sausage fillers.*

dsor House Natural Water Co Ltd, Park Road, msworth, Hampshire, PO10 8NY Tel: (01243) 76156 Fax: (01243) 379100 *Water bottlers*

Vindsor Kitchens, 39 Martley Gardens, Hedge nd, Southampton, SO30 2XB Tel: 01489 95489 E-mail: sales@windsorkitchens.com *Carpentry services, total design & planning of itchens, floors*

dsor Life Assurance Co. Ltd, Windsor House, elford Centre, Town Centre, Telford, Shropshire, F3 4NB Tel: (0870) 8873333 Fax: (0870) 091111 E-mail: sales@windsor-life.com *Assurance & pension services*

Vindymains Farm Ltd, Windymains Farm, lumbie, East Lothian, EH36 5PA Tel: (01875) 33602 *Timber merchants*

Vine and Spirit International Ltd, 9th Floor Hyde louse, Edgware Road, Hendon, London, W9 6LH Tel: (020) 8975 1023 Fax: (020) 8975 025 E-mail: sales@wineandspirit.com *Wine & spirit importers & exporters*

Vine Cave, Hetton, Skipton, North Yorkshire, BD23 6LT Tel: (01756) 730415 Fax: (01756) 730363 *Wine retailers*

e Corner Ltd, Unit 4, British Coal Enterprise Park, Brunel Close, Harworth, Doncaster, South Yorkshire, DN11 8SG Tel: (01302) 744916 Fax: (01302) 751233 E-mail: info@winecorner.co.uk *Wine storage*

VineBag.co.uk, 4 Melcombe Gardens, Harrow, Middlesex, HA3 9RH Tel: (0701) 0704731 E-mail: sales@winebag.co.uk *We design, print and manufacture customised environmentally friendly jute bags. We work closely with our customers to match the bags to their specifications and providing an excellent service whilst ensuring that the goods are of very high quality and very competetively priced. No bag is too small or too big for us to make !!!*

es Precision Engineers, The Old Dairy, Egg Pie Lane, Weald, Sevenoaks, Kent, TN14 6NP Tel: (01732) 740542 Fax: (01732) 464440 E-mail: sales@winesweb.com *EDM precision engineering & die sinking services*

eware, PO Box 3135, Littlehampton, West Sussex, BN16 3LP Tel: (01903) 786148 Fax: (01903) 786371 E-mail: admin@wineware.co.uk *Wine accessories suppliers*

Winfield Construction, Marshall House, Heanor Gate Road, Heanor, Derbyshire, DE75 7RG Tel: (01773) 762555 Fax: (01773) 762444

nfield Engineering Ltd, Alma Park Road, Grantham, Lincolnshire, NG31 9SE Tel: (01476) 567105 Fax: (01476) 566505 *Fabrication & welding engineers*

nfield Gears Ltd, 80a Windsor Road, Bexhill-on-Sea, East Sussex, TN39 3PE Tel: 01424 733599 *Gear manufrs*

▶ Winfoware Technologies, 786 London Road, Thornton Heath, Surrey, CR7 6JB Tel: (020) 8683 3193 Fax: (020) 8683 3193

▶ Wingate Electrical plc, 70 Jessie Street, Glasgow, G42 0PG Tel: 0141-422 1800 Fax: 0141-422 1822

▶ Wingate Electrical plc, Unit C 25 Copperfield Street, London, SE1 0EN Tel: (020) 7401 3856 Fax: (020) 7928 1547

Wingate Signs Ltd, 23 Pilsworth Way, Bury, Lancashire, BL9 8RE Tel: 0161-767 9383 Fax: 0161-796 3827 E-mail: wingatesigns@btinternet.com *Manufacture signs*

Wingates Ltd, Unit 3 East Way, Rivergreen Industrial Estate, Sunderland, SR4 6AD Tel: 0191-510 1717 Fax: 0191-510 1188 E-mail: info@wingatesltd.co.uk *Hand made furniture manufrs*

▶ Winged Bull Aviation, 5, Norway House, 22 Cockspur Street, Trafalgar Square, London, SW1Y 5BN Tel: 0870 850 3395 Fax: 0870 850 3396 E-mail: fly@bullwings.com *Business, Executive & Private aircraft charter: *Leasing of aircraft for Cargo & passenger flights. *Based in Farnborough Airport, UK*

▶ Wing-Graphics.com, P.O. BOX 61, Leighton Buzzard, Bedfordshire, LU7 0UW Tel: 01296 682445 Fax: 01296 682445 E-mail: jason@wing-graphics.com *Wing-Graphics.com*An independent production studio based in the village of Wing, Beds and run by graphic designer Jay Purcell.**We specialise in providing Design, Video Production & Promotional services to people working in Music, Art, Film, Literature and anything creative.**We can provide a no-obligation quote for your project, or work within your budget.*

Wingham Engineering Co. Ltd, Unit 8 Building 2, Sandwich Industrial Estate, Sandwich, Kent, CT13 9LY Tel: (01304) 612284 Fax: (01304) 620012 E-mail: sales@quickway-wingham.co.uk *Building system/unit manufrs*

Wingrove & Edge Ltd, The Tannery, West Hill, Milborne Port, Sherborne, Dorset, DT9 5HL Tel: (01963) 250620 Fax: (01963) 250627 E-mail: email@whitmore-bacon.co.uk *Leather finishers*

Wings Knitwear Co., 32-35 Walsall Road, Willenhall, West Midlands, WV13 2EG Tel: (01902) 606867 Fax: (01902) 633365 *Knit wear manufrs*

▶ WinIT Consultancy Ltd, West Mills, Newbury, Berkshire, RG14 5HG Tel: (0870) 2000635 Fax: (0870) 2000755 E-mail: robin@winitconsultancy.co.uk *Software programming*

Winken (Marking) Ltd, Eyre Street, Birmingham, B18 7AA Tel: 0121-456 3141 Fax: 0121-456 3151 *Embossed metal nameplate manufrs*

▶ Winkhaus UK Ltd, 2950 Kettering Parkway, Kettering Venture Park, Kettering, Northamptonshire, NN15 6XZ Tel: (01536) 316000 Fax: (01536) 416516 *Manufacturers of metal fabrications*

K.D. Winkle, 46-47 Retreat Street, Wolverhampton, WV3 0JT Tel: (01902) 428738 *Food manufrs*

Winkler International Ltd, Po Box 104, Peacehaven, E. Sussex, BN10 7WD Tel: (01273) 585010 Fax: (01273) 587981 E-mail: john.winkler@winkler.co.uk *Training in specialists pricing*

Winlaton Hygiene Supplies, 2 Banks Court, Transbritannia Enterprise Park, Blaydon-on-Tyne, Tyne & Wear, NE21 5NH Tel: 0191-414 0708 Fax: 0191-414 0708 E-mail: whssales@btconnect.com *Janitorial suppliers*

Winn & Coales Denso Ltd, Denso House, 33-35 Chapel Road, London, SE27 0TR Tel: (020) 8670 7511 Fax: (020) 8761 2456 E-mail: mail@denso.net *Anti corrosion tapes & coatings*

Winn Tools Ltd, Kendricks Road, Wednesbury, West Midlands, WS10 8LY Tel: 0121-526 2075 Fax: 0121-526 5095 *Tungsten carbide tool manufrs*

Winnard Workwear, 129 Edenfield Road, Rochdale, Lancashire, OL11 5AE Tel: (01706) 352947 E-mail: slocw@yahoo.co.uk *Suppliers of quality embroidered work wear*

Winnersh Plant Hire Ltd, 580 Reading Road, Winnersh, Wokingham, Berkshire, RG41 5HA Tel: 0118-979 2828 Fax: 0118-979 0333 E-mail: info@winnershplant.co.uk *Contractors plant hire*

Winning Blend Ltd (T/U Welsh Pantry), Unit 1 Riverside Industrial Park, Treforest Industrial Estate, Treforest, Pontypridd, Mid Glamorgan, CF37 5TG Tel: (01443) 843587 Fax: (01443) 842304 E-mail: sales@welshpantry.com *Pasties, pies & sausage roll manufrs*

Winning Golf, Winning Golf, 5 Carden Place, Aberdeen, AB10 1UT Tel: (0845) 4505090 Fax: (01224) 652969 E-mail: info@winninggolf.net *Golf improvement & corporate golf events & teambuilding*

Winpack Ltd, Unit A1 Lattersey Hill Trading Estate, Benwick Road, Whittlesey, Peterborough, PE7 2JA Tel: (01733) 208799 Fax: (01733) 204007 *Contract packers*

Winpenny Photography, 3 Wesley Street, Otley, West Yorkshire, LS21 1AZ Tel: (01943) 462597 Fax: (01943) 850861 E-mail: webmaster@winpennyphoto.co.uk *Commercial photographers*

David Winrow Marketing, PO Box 9, Northwich, Cheshire, CW9 7TP Tel: (01606) 41241 Fax: (01606) 47847 E-mail: sales@winrow.co.uk *Commercial information specialists*

Winsford Fabrications, Road 5, Winsford Industrial Estate, Winsford, Cheshire, CW7 3SH Tel: (01606) 597305 Fax: (01606) 597308 *Steel & pipework fabricators*

Harris Winsford, Wharton Rd, Wharton Bridge, Winsford, Cheshire, CW7 3BB Tel: (01606) 557321 Fax: (01606) 559115 *Pork & bacon distributors*

Winslow Adaptics Ltd, Unit 5 Brecon Enterprise Park, Brecon, Powys, LD3 8BT Tel: (01874) 625555 Fax: (01874) 625500 E-mail: sales@winslowadaptics.com *Connector socket manufrs*

Winstanley & Co. Ltd, Racecourse Road, Pershore, Worcestershire, WR10 2DG Tel: (01386) 552278 Fax: (01386) 556531 E-mail: winstanleyco@compuserve.com Principal Export Areas: Worldwide *Fabricators & engineers*

Winstanley Metal Fabrications Ltd, 501 Old York Road, London, SW18 1TF Tel: (020) 8874 9043 Fax: (020) 8874 9044 *Light structural steelwork fabricators services*

Winstanley & Watkins, 104 Duke Street, Liverpool, L1 5AG Tel: 0151-709 0808 Fax: 0151-709 3060 E-mail: info@wwprint.co.uk *Printers*

Winsted Ltd, Units 7 & 8 Lovett Road, Hampton Lovett Industrial Estate, Droitwich, Worcestershire, WR9 0QG Tel: (01905) 770276 Fax: (01905) 779791 E-mail: harry@winsted.co.uk *Console furniture manufrs*

Winston & Allan Ltd, Unit 5-6 Nutwood Trading Estate, Limestone Cottage Lane, Sheffield, S6 1NJ Tel: 0114-231 4744 Fax: 0114-232 3967 E-mail: sales@winstonandallan.co.uk *Press toolmakers & presswork manufrs*

Winston Fabrications, Dale Road Trading Estate, Dale Road, Shildon, County Durham, DL4 2RE Tel: (01388) 777989 Fax: (01388) 776296 E-mail: anthony@winstonfabrications.co.uk *Sheet metal fabricators, powder coatings*

▶ Winstones Ice Cream Ltd, Green Acres, Rodborough Common, Stroud, Gloucestershire, GL5 5BX Tel: (01453) 873270 Fax: (01453) 872030 E-mail: info@winstonesicecream.co.uk

▶ Winstonmead London, Bentalls House, Bentalls, Basildon, Essex, SS14 3BS Tel: (01268) 595959 Fax: (01268) 532319 E-mail: sales@winstonmead.co.uk *Stationery distributors*

Winstons Sport & Casual Wear, 2-4 Bridge Road, Orpington, Kent, BR5 2BH Tel: (01689) 837975 Fax: (01689) 603512 E-mail: stevewinstons@aol.com *Sportswear manufrs*

▶ Wintegra, International House, Stanley Boulevard, Hamilton Intnl Technology Park, Blantyre, Glasgow, G72 0BN Tel: (01698) 404889

John Winter & Co. Ltd, Washer Lane Works, Halifax, West Yorkshire, HX2 7DP Tel: (01422) 364213 Fax: (01422) 330493 E-mail: sales@johnwinter.co.uk *Foundry & dental suppliers*

R. Winter Tooling, 7 Stirling Park, Laker Road, Rochester, Kent, ME1 3QR Tel: 01634 666627 Fax: 01634 666637 E-mail: focus@rwintertooling.com *Engineers pattern & vacuum forming toolmakers*

Winter & Co UK Ltd, Stonehill, Stukeley Meadows Industrial Estate, Huntingdon, Cambridgeshire, PE29 6ED Tel: (01480) 377177 Fax: (01480) 377166 E-mail: sales@winteruk.com *Book covering materials distributors*

Winterborne Zelston Fencing Ltd, Bridge Cottage, Winterborne Zelston, Blandford Forum, Dorset, DT11 9EU Tel: (01929) 459245 Fax: (01929) 459011 E-mail: rbower@wzfencing.fsnet.co.uk *Fencing contractors*

Winterbotham,Darby & Co.Limited, Granville House Gatton Park, Business Centre, Redhill, RH1 3AS Tel: (01737) 646646 Fax: (01737) 646600 E-mail: wdarby@windar.co.uk *Food importers & distributors*

Winterfield Safes, The Hall, Newton Le Willows, Bedale, North Yorkshire, DL8 1SW Tel: (01677) 450774 Fax: (01677) 450774 E-mail: helen@winterfieldsafes.co.uk *Winterfield Safes Ltd offer the largest selection of safes online today. We supply safes for the Home or Office including Fireproof safes, Security safes, Cash safes, Gun safes and Hotel safes. All safes come direct from the manufacturer so we can pass on the huge savings straight to you the customer. We aim to be the most competitively priced on the web today. We offer fast free delivery to ground floor mainland UK. **If you are a business can you really afford to not look after your irreplaceable computer media? Why not keep it locked away in a fire resistant data safe for peace of mind? Maybe you need a safe at home for all those important documents like passports, cheque books, wills and deeds plus of course any items of value such as jewellery? Then why not check out the great range of security safes on our website.***

Wintergreen Trading Co. Ltd, PO Box 415, Southampton, SO31 9ZQ Tel: (01489) 607300 Fax: (01489) 607600 *Refrigeration equipment exporters*

▶ Winterlift Ltd, Fairhills Industrial Estate, Woodrow Way, Irlam, Manchester, M44 6ZQ Tel: 0161-775 4400 Fax: (0845) 1309003 E-mail: andrew.winter@btinternet.co.uk *Contract lifting & crane hire specialists*

Winterthur Life UK Holdings Ltd, Winterthur Way, Basingstoke, Hampshire, RG21 6SZ Tel: (01256) 470707 Fax: (01256) 472682 E-mail: enquiries@winterthur-life.co.uk *Life assurance & pension services*

Winterton Leisurewear Ltd, Regent Road, Countesthorpe, Leicester, LE8 5RF Tel: 0116-277 9789 Fax: 0116-278 4395 E-mail: info@magicfit.co.uk *Leisurewear manufrs*

Winterwarm UK Ltd, Unit H3, Taylor Industrial Estate, Risley, Warrington, WA3 6BL Tel: (01925) 765799 Fax: (01925) 762996 E-mail: enquiries@winterwarm.com *Gas fired suspended unit heaters suppliers*

Winther,Browne & Company Ltd, 75 Bilton Way, Enfield, Middlesex, EN3 7ER Tel: (020) 8344 9050 Fax: (020) 8344 9051 E-mail: sales@wintherbrowne.co.uk *Decorative moulding manufrs*

Wintrust Securities Ltd, 21 New Street, Bishopsgate, London, EC2M 4HR Tel: (020) 7523 5230 Fax: (020) 7523 5233 E-mail: info@wintrust.co.uk *Merchant bankers*

▶ Wintur Project Services Ltd, 9 Selborne Gardens, Perivale, Greenford, Middlesex, UB6 7PD Tel: (0845) 0450920 Fax: (0845) 0450921 E-mail: sales@fortunes-forever.com *Introducing unique mail order business information programs that are jam-packed with powerful and time proven tips, tactics, strategies, and secrets you can use to potentially get off the*

continued

right foot and really get to build a super profitable mail order business that can dominate your market.

▶ Winwood Products, Somerton House, Hazell Drive, Newport, Gwent, NP10 8FY Tel: (0845) 3732733 Fax: (0845) 3732735 E-mail: info@winwood-products.com *Agent & distributor of lumber & wood-based panel products*

Winyard Engineering Ltd, 2-3 Cresswell Close, Pinchbeck, Spalding, Lincolnshire, PE11 3TY Tel: (01775) 725285 Fax: (01775) 710620 E-mail: sales@wfpe.co.uk Principal Export Areas: Africa *Manufacturers of food processing plant & machinery & filling machine*

Wipak UK Ltd, Unit 3 Buttington Cross Enterprise Park, Buttington, Welshpool, Powys, SY21 8SL Tel: (01938) 555255 Fax: (01938) 555277 E-mail: sales@wipak.com *Sachet packaging machine manufrs*

Wirac Automation Ltd, 5 Parker Court, Dunston, Gateshead, Tyne & Wear, NE11 9EW Tel: 0191-460 1177 Fax: 0191-460 1079 E-mail: wirac@aol.com *Electrical control boxes manufrs*

Wire All Products, 42 New Road, Rochester, Kent, ME1 1DX Tel: (01634) 812984 Fax: (01634) 409636 E-mail: sales@wireall.co.uk *Electronic sub-contract manufrs*

Wire Belt Co. Ltd, Castle Road, Sittingbourne, Kent, ME10 3RF Tel: (01795) 421771 Fax: (01795) 428905 E-mail: sales@wirebelt.co.uk *Industrial conveyor systems manufrs*

▶ Wire Cut Technologies Ltd, 115 Saturn Way, Hemel Hempstead, Hertfordshire, HP2 5PD Tel: (01442) 401856 Fax: (01442) 401856 E-mail: dshew@wire-cut.co.uk *Wire erosion Toolmaking Edm Wire cutting Jigs and fixtures Spark Erosion*

Wire Erosion Co. Ltd, Units 8-9, Springfield Business Centre, Oldends Lane, Stonehouse, Gloucestershire, GL10 3SX Tel: (01453) 827771 Fax: (01453) 827761 *Spark/wire erosion machining services*

▶ Wire Fittings Designs Ltd, Unit 6 Victoria Avenue Industrial Estate, Swanage, Dorset, BH19 1AU Tel: (01929) 422762 Fax: (01929) 427661 E-mail: sales@wirefittings.co.uk *Display manufrs*

The Wire House, Unit 13, 72 Farm Lane, London, SW6 1QA Tel: (020) 7385 5490 Fax: (020) 7385 5490 *Florist sundries*

Wirebird Ltd, 39 Aquatical House, Bell Lane, London, E1 7LU Tel: (020) 7650 2390 Fax: (020) 7377 2912 *Infrastructure support & IT*

Wirecloth Sales & Development Ltd, 11a East View, Grappenhall, Warrington, WA4 2QH Tel: (01925) 268417 Fax: (01925) 604861 E-mail: wireclothsales@aol.com *Wire mesh & knitted wire mesh manufrs*

Wired Media Ltd, Broad Plain, Bristol, BS2 0JP Tel: 0117-930 4365 Fax: 0870-169 7625 E-mail: info@wiredmedia.co.uk *Internet services, website design & content management*

▶ Wired UK, 107 Maddison House, 226 High Street, Croydon, CR9 1DF Tel: (0774) 2023084 Fax: (0906) 4062563 E-mail: info@wireduk.net *Commercial Catering Equipment Engineers**Specialising in repairs and Serving**Lincoln Inpinger Conveyor Ovens*Henny Penny Pressure Fryers HP600*Henny Penny Holding Cabinets*Garland Solid Tops*Rational CPC Ovens*Falcon Ovens and Ranges*Florigo Ranges*Lincat Repairs Servicing*Hobart Dishwashers*Middelby Conveyor Ovens*Moffat Hot Cupboards*Comenda Dishwashers*Brasilia Espresso Machines *Pressure Boilers For Inspection*Pitco Fryalator*Waste Disposal IMC and Hobart*Meiko Dishwashers*Convotherm Combi Ovens*

Wireguard Ltd, Crabtree Manorway South, Belvedere, Kent, DA17 6AW Tel: (020) 8320 6181 Fax: (020) 8311 6435 *Wire products & fabrications*

Wireless Alarms, 17 Church Road, Great Bookham, Leatherhead, Surrey, KT23 3PG Tel: (01372) 450960 Fax: (01372) 450961 *Alarms distributors*

▶ Wireless CCTV, Mitchell Hey Mills, College Road, Rochdale, Lancashire, OL12 6AE Tel: (01706) 631166 Fax: (01706) 631122 E-mail: sales@wcctv.com *Manufacturers of re-deployable wireless cctv surveillance systems*

▶ Wireless Fibre Systems Ltd, Adaptive House, Quarrywood Court, Livingston, West Lothian, EH54 6AX Tel: (01506) 407832 E-mail: info@wirelessfibre.co.uk *Communication services*

Wiretech International Ltd, 194 Fletchamstead Highway Industrial Estate, Fletchamstead Highway, Coventry, CV4 7BB Tel: (024) 7667 3366 Fax: (024) 7671 3030 *Wire & spark erosion specialists*

Wirex Metal Baskets, Marston Road, Hoddesdon, Hertfordshire, EN11 0AD Tel: (01992) 469585 Fax: (01992) 441940 *Manufacturers of industrial wire goods/products & wire baskets*

▶ Wiring Solutions Ltd, 21 High Street, Glinton, Peterborough, PE6 7LS Tel: (01733) 253910

Wirral Blinds, 79 Mill Lane, Wallasey, Merseyside, CH44 5UB Tel: (0800) 0286330 Fax: 0151-638 8163 *Blind resellers*

Wirral Chamber Of Commerce & Industry Ltd, 16 Grange Road West, Birkenhead, Merseyside, CH41 4DA Tel: 0151-647 8899 Fax: 0151-650 0440 E-mail: mail@wirralchamber.u-net.com *Chamber of commerce*

▶ Wirral Continuous Ltd, 26 Thursby Rd., Croft Business Park, Wirral, Merseyside, CH62 3PW Tel: 0151-334 0895

▶ Wirral Fospray Ltd, Hawarden Business Park, Clwyd Close Manor Lane, Hawarden, Deeside, Clwyd, CH5 3NS Tel: (01244) 520202 Fax: (01244) 520363 E-mail: sales@wirralfospray.com *Wirral Fospray Ltd was founded some 26 years ago, and is a privately owned company based in North Wales. We are one of the largest suppliers of metal treatment chemicals in the finishing industry. We formulate, manufacture, distribute and technically support all our chemical solutions.*

Wirral Fospray Ltd, Old Tramway, Stoke-on-Trent, ST4 3PX Tel: (01782) 334077 Fax: (01782) 596608 *Specialty fabric manufrs*

Company Information

Wirral Metals Ltd, 2 Carlton Road, Birkenhead, Merseyside, CH42 9NQ Tel: 0151-652 2115 E-mail: sales@wirralmetals.com *Non-ferrous scrap metal merchants*

Wirral Pine Centre, 315 Chester Road, Little Sutton, Ellesmere Port, CH66 3RF Tel: 0151-339 5520 Fax: 0151-339 5520 *Pine furniture reseller*

Wirral Sign Service, Thorndale Business Centre, Wallasey Road, Wallasey, Merseyside, CH44 2AG Tel: 0151-638 6382 Fax: 0151-638 6382 E-mail: info@wirralsigns.co.uk *Sign manufrs*

Wirral Textile Motifs Ltd, 117 Royden Road, Wirral, Merseyside, CH49 4LX Tel: 0151-678 6076 Fax: 0151-678 6076 E-mail: motifs@btopenworld.co.uk *Embroidery services*

Wirs Ltd, Church Lane, Wolverhampton, WV2 4AL Tel: (01902) 712525 Fax: (01902) 429016 E-mail: sales@wirs.co.uk *Welding & cutting equipment hire* Also at: Stoke-on-Trent

Wirth Engineering, Birch House, Fraser Road, Erith, Kent, DA8 1QX Tel: (01322) 434345 Fax: (01322) 434346 *CNC & conventional turning*

Wisbech Computer Services Ltd, 107 Norwich Road, Wisbech, Cambridgeshire, PE13 2BB Tel: (01945) 464146 Fax: (01945) 464680 E-mail: sales@wisbech.com *Payroll software house*

Wisbech Fabrications Ltd, Unit 3, 62 Weasenham Lane, Wisbech, Cambridgeshire, PE13 2RU Tel: (01945) 466477 Fax: (01945) 466456 E-mail: wisfabltd@aol.com *Steel & aluminium manufacturing engineering services*

▶ Wisdom Fireplaces, 1014 Stockport Road, Manchester, M19 3WN Tel: 0161-248 8108 Fax: 0161-248 8108 E-mail: enquiries@wisdomfireplaces.co.uk *Reproduction georgian, victorian, edwardian & art nouveau fireplaces suppliers*

Wisdom Information Technolgolist Ltd, 6 Flemring Road, Livingston, West Lothian, EH54 7BN Tel: (01506) 497490 Fax: (01506) 497494 E-mail: admin@wisdomit.co.uk *IT support, services & maintenance*

Wise Handling Ltd, Haworth Road, Cullingworth, Bradford, West Yorkshire, BD13 5DU Tel: (01535) 272033 Fax: (01535) 275774 E-mail: sales@wiseboathoists.co.uk *Materials handling manufrs*

▶ Wise Owl Book Keepers, 15 Bridus Mead, Blewbury, Didcot, Oxfordshire, OX11 9PJ Tel: (01235) 850691 Fax: (0871) 7334308 E-mail: andrew@wiseowlbookkeepers.co.uk *Bookkeeping service - payroll,VAT,management accounts, bank reconciliation using Sage, Quickbooks etc. Your office or ours, online or by post. We do the books. You do the business.*

▶ Wise Productions UK Ltd, 3 Star Works, Salter Street, London, NW10 6UN Tel: (020) 8960 5111 Fax: (020) 8960 5151 E-mail: sales@wiseproductions.co.uk

Wise Speke, Commercial Union House, 39 Pilgrim Street, Newcastle upon Tyne, NE1 6RQ Tel: 0191-279 7300 Fax: 0191-279 7301 E-mail: gavin.martin@wise-speke.co.uk *Stockbrokers*

Wise Systems Ltd, 7a High Street, Corsham, Wiltshire, SN13 0ES Tel: (01249) 717000 Fax: (01249) 717002 E-mail: info@wisesystems.co.uk *Computer systems consultants*

Wise Weigh, 33-34 Retail Market, Coventry, CV1 3HT Tel: (024) 7652 5034 E-mail: berylbrozj3@supernet.co.uk *Health food retailers*

Wise Worksafe, 3 Parr Road, Stanmore, Middlesex, HA7 1PZ Tel: (020) 8381 1811 Fax: (020) 8381 1827 *Protective clothing suppliers also safety & hygiene products*

Robert Wiseman Dairies Ltd, Craigshaw Drive, West Tullos, Aberdeen, AB12 3XB Tel: (01224) 896969 Fax: (01224) 871948 E-mail: rwiseman@wiseman-dairies.co.uk *Milk powdered processed products manufrs*

▶ Robert Wiseman Dairies Ltd, 3 Noremac Way, Bellshill Industrial Estate, Bellshill, Lanarkshire, ML4 3NY Tel: (01698) 749356 Fax: (01698) 746739 *Dairy producers*

Robert Wiseman Dairies, Rolle Road, Torrington, Devon, EX38 8AU Tel: (01805) 622018 Fax: (01805) 624970 E-mail: claire.turner@robertwisemans.co.uk *Dairy producers*

Wish Tower Hotel, King Edwards Parade, Eastbourne, East Sussex, BN21 4EB Tel: (01323) 722676 Fax: (01323) 721474 E-mail: info@wishtower.co.uk *Conference & syndicate facilities*

▶ Wishaw Printing Co., 84 Stewarton Street, Wishaw, Lanarkshire, ML2 8AG Tel: (01698) 357223 Fax: (01698) 351277

▶ Wishbone Technology Ltd, 6 Bolebridge Mews, Bolebridge Street, Tamworth, Staffordshire, B79 7PA Tel: (01827) 319988 *Computer maintenance & repair services*

▶ Wisla Narrow Fabrics, Unit 1 Littlemoss Road, Droylsden, Manchester, M43 7EF Tel: 0161-301 4747 Fax: 0161-301 5757 E-mail: ekweb@aol.com *Manufacturer of industrial webbings*

Wiswell Bros, 96 Clipsley Lane, Haydock, St. Helens, Merseyside, WA11 0UB Tel: (01744) 602236 Fax: (01744) 602236 *Joinery manufrs*

Wit Press, Ashurst Lodge, Lyndhurst Road, Ashurst, Southampton, SO40 7AA Tel: (023) 8029 3223 Fax: (023) 8029 2853 E-mail: witpress@witpress.com *Publisher of engineering research*

Witan Pressings Ltd, Unit 3, Alexander Mill, Gibb Street, Long Eaton, Nottingham, NG10 1EE Tel: 0115-946 1545 Fax: 0115-946 0874 E-mail: witan-pressings@btconnect.com *General presswork & toolmaking services*

Witcombs Removals, 45 Wentworth Way, Birmingham, B32 2UZ Tel: 0121-426 6703 Fax: 0121-426 5294 E-mail: sales@witcombs-removals.co.uk *Office removal & storage specialists*

Witham Glass Works, 1 Wilton Street, Hull, HU8 7LG Tel: (01482) 329183 Fax: (01482) 211959 *Mirror manufrs*

Witham Oil & Paint (Lowestoft) Ltd, Stanley Road, Oulton Broad, Lowestoft, Suffolk, NR33 9ND Tel: (01502) 563434 Fax: (01502) 500010 E-mail: kathy.rowlands@withamoil-lowestoft.co.uk *Specialist & industrial paint manufrs*

Witham Saddlery, 63b Newland Street, Witham, Essex, CM8 1AA Tel: (01376) 512366 Fax: (01376) 512366 *Saddlery retail*

▶ Witham Valley Civil Engineering Ltd, Slippery Gowt Lane, Wyberton, Boston, Lincolnshire, PE21 7AA Tel: (01205) 311021 Fax: (01205) 359376

Witherby & Co. Ltd, 32-36 Aylesbury Street, London, EC1R 0ET Tel: (020) 7253 5413 Fax: (020) 7336 7493 E-mail: briandoors@witherbys.co.uk *Stationers & printers*

Witheridge Post Office & Stores, 17 West Street, Witheridge, Tiverton, Devon, EX16 8AA Tel: (01884) 861684 Fax: (01884) 860329 *Furniture restoration*

▶ Witherley Services Ltd, Witherley House, Hazelway, Nuneaton, Warwickshire, CV10 7QG Tel: (024) 7635 1188

P. Withers Agricultural, Moat End Farm House, Hindlip Lane, Claines, Worcester, WR3 8SA Tel: (01905) 458159 *Agricultural engineers*

Withers & Rogers, 75 Colmore Row, Birmingham, B3 2AP Tel: 0121-245 3900 Fax: 0121-245 3930 E-mail: admin@withersrogers.com *Patent & trademark agents*

Withey Contracts Ltd, Waburn House, Adams Close, Kempston, Bedford, MK42 7JE Tel: (01234) 844600 Fax: (01234) 844601 E-mail: info@withey.co.uk *Shop fitters & joinery manufrs*

Withington Health Foods, 486 Wilmslow Road, Manchester, M20 3BG Tel: 0161-445 6696 *Health foods & products*

Withnall Design Consultants, Trinity House, Church Lane, Croughton, Brackley, Northamptonshire, NN13 5LS Tel: (01869) 810590 Fax: (01869) 810590 E-mail: withnall@btopenworld.com *Industrial design consultants, expert witnesses & engineering services*

Withy Grove Stores Ltd, 35-39 Withy Grove, Manchester, M4 2BJ Tel: 0161-834 0044 *Safe & office furniture factors*

Witter Towbars, 11 Drome Road, Deeside Industrial Park, Deeside, Clwyd, CH5 2NY Tel: (01244) 284500 Fax: (01244) 284577 E-mail: sales@witter-towbars.com *Towing brackets & equipment manufrs*

Wittey Machinery Ltd, Unit 17 Haddenham Aerodrome Industrial Estate, Dollicott, Haddenham, Aylesbury, Buckinghamshire, HP17 8LJ Tel: (01844) 344723 Fax: (01844) 342004 *Plastics extrusion machine manufrs*

Witton Chemical Co. Ltd, Southgate Avenue, Mildenhall, Bury St. Edmunds, Suffolk, IP28 7AT Tel: (01638) 716001 Fax: (01638) 717658 E-mail: sales@witton.com Principal Export Areas: Worldwide *Polyurethane chemicals & pharmaceutical manufrs*

Witton Kramer Products, 72 Cakemore Road, Rowley Regis, West Midlands, B65 0QT Tel: 0121-698 3100 Fax: 0121-698 3241 E-mail: info@brookcrompton-blackheath.co.uk *Brake & thruster manufrs*

Wittons Carpets Ltd, Olive Mill, Olive Lane, Darwen, Lancashire, BB3 3DJ Tel: (01254) 702211 *Retail*

▶ Wittur Ltd, 11 Broncoed Business Park, Wrexham Road, Mold, Clwyd, CH7 1HP Tel: (01352) 707470 Fax: (01352) 707471 E-mail: sales@lifteknic.co.uk *Lift maintenance*

Witzenmann UK Ltd, Righead Industrial Estate, Bellshill, Lanarkshire, ML4 3LW Tel: (01698) 749660 Fax: (01698) 740774 *Flexible hose manufrs*

Witzig's Ltd, Unit 5, George Edwards Road Industrial Estate, Fakenham, Norfolk, NR21 8NL Tel: (01328) 864941 Fax: (01328) 864943 E-mail: info@witzigs.co.uk *Indoor games, sports & goods manufrs*

Wizard Ltd, Wizard House, Cambridge Road, Teddington, Middlesex, TW11 8DR Tel: (020) 8943 0121 Fax: (020) 8977 9074 E-mail: barry@wizardtoys.com *Toy manufrs*

Wizard Systems, Lingley House, Commissioners Road, Rochester, Kent, ME2 4EE Tel: (01634) 718181 Fax: (01634) 715031 *Alarm installation*

Wizard UK, 8 Tanners Yard, 239 Long La, London, SE1 4PT Tel: (020) 7940 4654 Fax: (020) 7407 7969 *Computer software development*

Wizards Ltd, Alpha House, Ashridge Road, Chesham, Buckinghamshire, HP5 2RE Tel: (01494) 837515 Fax: (01494) 837013 E-mail: info@wizards.co.uk *Computer system consultants*

Wizardsoft Ltd, 88a High Street, Billericay, Essex, CM12 9BT Tel: (01277) 634771 Fax: (01277) 634770 E-mail: enquiries@wizardit.co.uk *IT support & consultants*

▶ Wiznet Services, 1 Michaels Way, Sling, Coleford, Gloucestershire, GL16 8LZ Tel: 01594 834515 E-mail: info@Wiznet-Services.co.uk *Wiznet Services are able to provide Competent fully Qualified Driving Instuction, Pass Plus, Motorway lessons and many other types of Driving Instruction. We are also able to suply Computers, Printers, Consultancy, Support, large or small networks and consumables for Home or Business. We will advise you of the best systems to meet your requirements.*

Wiztek, P C Upgrade Centre, 8 Bond St, Redruth, Cornwall, TR15 2QB Tel: (01209) 314296 E-mail: wiztek@hotmail.com *Computers*

Wizzbitz Ltd, 792 Wilmslow Road, Didsbury, Manchester, M20 6UG Tel: (08701) 657310 E-mail: customerservice@wizzbitz.com *Wizzbitz Limited offers a wide range of Dell products. We stock a wide range of Dell spares for any faulty or broken internal parts. We also supply full Dell systems new and refurbished. We can source any parts which aren"t listed. We also provide a computer repair /updating service, we provide a free collection and return service."*

▶ WizzLink Ltd, 23 Avondale Avenue, Esher, Surrey, KT10 0DB Tel: (020) 8339 0508 Fax: (020) 8398 0206 E-mail: simon.kim@wizzlink.com *High Speed Hotel Internet Equipment*

▶ Wizzy Design Ltd, Unit 300 J C Albyn Complex, Burton Road, Sheffield, S3 8BZ Tel: 0114-281 3332 Fax: (0870) 1394643 E-mail: wizzy@wizzy.co.uk *Web design services*

WJC Ltd (Plating Jigs), John Street, Brierfield, Nelson, Lancashire, BB9 5NX Tel: (01282) 613985 Fax: (01282) 698677 E-mail: sales@wjc.co.uk *Family owned WJC have over 30 years experience in the design and manufacture of Dip Moulded products and Plating Jigs. We offer an uncompromising service that is supported by our dedicated and experienced workforce. With our modern, well-equipped dipping facility we can provide a fast and worry free transition from concept to successful delivery of your product. We operate throughout the UK and welcome enquiries from Mainland Europe. Please Call to discuss your requirements on 01282 613 985.*

WJJ Supplies Ltd, Unit 2 Greenfield Farm Industrial Estate, Congleton, Cheshire, CW12 4TR Tel: (01260) 218187 Fax: (01260) 218186 E-mail: sales@wjjsupplies.co.uk *Protective clothing distributors*

WMH Transmissions Ltd, Lichfield Road Industrial Estate, 24 Cavendish, Tamworth, Staffordshire, B79 7XH Tel: (01827) 310311 Fax: (01827) 307118 E-mail: sales@wmh-trans.co.uk *HIWIN UK AGENT. *STOCKIST AND MANUFACTURER OF TRANSMISSION EQUIPMENT.*

▶ Wmsafety Services Ltd, Unit 4 Great Barr Business Park, Baltimore Road Great Barr, Great Barr, Birmingham, B42 1DY Tel: 0121-241 6713 Fax: 0121-241 6713 E-mail: susan.bannon@wmsafetyservices.info *Health & Safety Consultants and*Planning Supervisors*

Woburn Chemicals Ltd, Chesney Wold, Bleak Hall, Milton Keynes, MK6 1LQ Tel: (01908) 670081 Fax: (01908) 670084 E-mail: sales@woburnchemicals.co.uk *Chemical distributors*

Wogen Group Ltd, 4 The Sanctuary, Westminster, London, SW1P 3JS Tel: (020) 7222 2171 Fax: (020) 7222 5862 E-mail: wogen@wogen.co.uk *Titanium*

Wohr Parking Sytems, Aston Works, Back Lane, Aston, Bampton, Oxfordshire, OX18 2DQ Tel: (01993) 851791 Fax: (01993) 851793 E-mail: sales@woehr.de *Mechanical car parking systems manufrs*

Wok Master Foods Ltd, 14 Birch Lane, Manchester, M13 0NN Tel: 0161-225 3072 Fax: 0161-248 0989 *Chinese food manufrs*

Woking Forge Ltd, 126A High Street, Old Woking, Woking, Surrey, GU22 9JN Tel: (01483) 760313 Fax: (01483) 756332 *Wrought ironworkers/gate automation*

▶ Woking Print & Publicity Ltd, The Print Works, St. Johns Lye, Woking, Surrey, GU21 7RS Tel: (01483) 884884 Fax: (01483) 884880

Woking Sheet Metal & Coachworks Ltd, 141 Goldsworth Road, Woking, Surrey, GU21 6LT Tel: (01483) 761898 Fax: (01483) 755605 E-mail: woking.sheetmetal@btinternet.com *Metal electrical cabinet manufrs*

Wokingham Times, Unit 5 Anville Court, 44 Denmark Street, Wokingham, Berkshire, RG40 2BB Tel: 0118-936 6180 Fax: 0118-936 6190 E-mail: editorial@wokingham-times.co.uk *Newspaper publishers*

▶ Wold Pottery, 79 High Street, Loftus, Saltburn-By-The-Sea, Cleveland, TS13 4HG Tel: (01287) 640100 *Pottery manufrs*

▶ Wolds Engineering Services Ltd, Unit 1d Pocklington Industrial Estate, Pocklington, York, YO42 1NR Tel: (01759) 303877 Fax: (01759) 306952 E-mail: johnoxley@btconnect.com *Bearing, castors, belts, pulleys, lubricants & work wear manufrs*

▶ Wolds Trailers, Millington Heights, Millington, York, YO42 1UB Tel: 01759 368225 Fax: 01759 369906 E-mail: millingtonheights@hotmail.com *Manufacturers of agricultural trailers*

Woldsway Foods Ltd, Ashby-by-Partney, Spilsby, Lincolnshire, PE23 5RG Tel: (01754) 890641 Fax: (01754) 890444 E-mail: sales@woldsway.co.uk *Food processors*

Wolf Filtration Ltd, 81 Burlington Street, Ashton-under-Lyne, Lancashire, OL6 7HJ Tel: 0161-339 1604 Fax: 0161-343 1434 E-mail: sales@wolffiltration.co.uk *Filter bag & sleeve manufrs*

Wolf Garden Ltd, Crown Business Park, Dukestown, Tredegar, Gwent, NP22 4EF Tel: (01495) 306600 Fax: (01495) 303344 E-mail: info@wolf-garden.co.uk *Distributors of gardening tools*

▶ Wolf Heating Uk Ltd, 8 Brunel Court, Rudheath Way, Gadbrook Business Park, Northwich, Cheshire, CW9 7EG Tel: 01606 354371 Fax: 01606 44805 E-mail: info@wolfheatinguk.co.uk

The Wolf Safety Lamp Co. Ltd, Saxon Road Works, Heeley, Sheffield, S8 0YA Tel: 0114-255 1051 Fax: 0114-255 7988 E-mail: info@wolf-safety.co.uk *Electrical explosion proofs & light fittings equipment manufrs*

Wolf Systems Ltd, Shilton Industrial Estate, Shilton, Coventry, CV7 9QL Tel: (0870) 7339933 Fax: (0870) 7339944 E-mail: mail@wolfsystem.co.uk *Roof truss systems designers*

▶ Wolfe Designs Ltd, 125 Clydesdale Place, Moss Side Industrial Estate, Moss Side, Leyland, PR26 7QS Tel: (01772) 456191 Fax: (01772) 622464 E-mail: daviddesouza@btconnect.com *Manufacturers of lighting, cooling, heating & access products*

▶ Wolfestone Translation, Metropole Chambers, Salubrious Passage, Swansea, SA1 3RT Tel: (0845) 0000083 Fax: 0845 000 0083 E-mail: sales@wolfestone.co.uk *Wolfestone Translation offers high quality translation and interpreting services for all sectors and at competitive prices. Our commitment to quality means that we only utilise native/first language speakers. We also pride ourselves on the efficiency, reliability and speed of our service.*

Wolff Olins Brand Consultants, 10 Regents Wh All Saints Street, London, N1 9RL Tel: (020) 7713 7733 Fax: (020) 7713 0217 E-mail: enquiries@wolff-olins.com *Branding consultants*

Wolfin Textiles Ltd, 359 Uxbridge Road, Hatch Pinner, Middlesex, HA5 4JN Tel: (020) 8428 9911 Fax: (020) 8428 9955 E-mail: cotton@wolfintextiles.co.uk *Industria cotton textiles merchants*

▶ Wolfram 74, 148 Tooley Street, London, SE1 2TU Tel: (020) 7357 9581 *Office furnitu distributors*

Wolfson Microelectronics plc, Westfield Road, Edinburgh, EH11 2QB Tel: 0131-272 7000 Fax: 0131-272 7001 E-mail: info@wolfsonmicro.com *Integrated c distributors/agents/suppliers*

▶ WolfsonEMC, Cardiff University, Queens Building, Newport Road, Cardiff, CF24 3AA Tel: (029) 2087 5936 Fax: (07898) 199422 E-mail: richard@WolfsonEMC.co.uk *Electromagnetic compatibility service*

Wollens Ltd, Wirrall Park Road, Glastonbury, Somerset, BA6 9XE Tel: (01458) 832244 Fax: (01458) 834926 E-mail: info@wollens.prestel.co.uk *Builders plumbers merchants*

Wolseley P.L.C., Park View 1220, Arlington Business Park, Theale, Reading, RG7 4GA Tel: 0118-929 8700 Fax: 0118-929 8701 *Hol company*

Wolseley Build Centre Ltd, 12 Cross Lane, Wallasey, Merseyside, CH45 8RQ Tel: 0151- 6031 Fax: 0151-639 0367 E-mail: s79-wallasey@wolseley.co.uk *Builde merchants*

Wolseley Centers Ltd, Boroughbridge Road, Ri North Yorkshire, HG4 1SL Tel: (01765) 6906 Fax: (01765) 694516 *Plumbing/heating/build distribs* Also at: Branches throughout the U.K

Wolseley Centre, Willow Lane, Lune Industrial Estate, Lancaster, LA1 5NA Tel: (01524) 672 Fax: (01524) 844101 *Timber & builders merchants* Also at: Leicester

Wolseley (U K) Ltd, Overton Road, Kirkcaldy, F KY1 2DU Tel: (01592) 653555 Fax: (01592) 650228 E-mail: kirkcaldytsb@woolsely.co.uk *Wholesale ironmongers* Also at: Dundee & Inverness

Wolseley UK P.L.C., Furthergate Industrial Park Hutton Street, Blackburn, BB1 3BY Tel: (012 682692 Fax: (01254) 682440 E-mail: blackburn.k87@wolseley.co.uk *Plasti materials stockholders*

Wolsey, Abbey Meadows, Leicester, LE4 5AD Tel: 0116-262 6755 Fax: 0116-253 0154 E-mail: sales@wolsey.com *Sock, knitwear, underwear sleepwear wholesalers* Also at: Dumfries & London W1

Wolstenholme Ltd, Clough Bank Works, Downg Drive, Sheffield, S4 8BT Tel: 0114-244 5600 Fax: 0114-244 6556 E-mail: sales@wolstenholme.co.uk *Special machine knife manufrs*

Wolstenholme Bidco Ltd, Springfield House, Lov Eccleshill Road, Darwen, Lancashire, BB3 0I Tel: (01254) 873888 Fax: (01254) 703430 E-mail: sales@wolstenholme-int.com *Global manufacturers and suppliers of metallic pigments, metallic finished inks, slurries and dispersions. Distributors of MFX® Colour Software and manufacturers of the MFX® Si Base Ink.*

Wolstenholmes Valves, Ainsworth Vale Mill, Vale Street, Bolton, BL2 6QF Tel: (01204) 528609 Fax: (01204) 361964 E-mail: sales@wolstenholmes-valves.co.uk *Valve manufacture & refurbishment*

Wolters Kluwer UK Ltd, 145 London Road, Kingston Upon Thames, Surrey, KT2 6SR Tel: (0870) 2415726 Fax: (020) 8547 2638 E-mail: info@wolterkluwer.co.uk Purchasing Contact: T Hendron *Publishers of business & professional information services, offering onl loose-leaf, software, training,seminars & consultancy solutions*

Wolverhampton Abrasives, Orgreave Drive, Sheffield, S13 9NR Tel: (0800) 0853085 Fax: 0114-254 0913 E-mail: gritsales@aol.co *Abrasive product distributors & manufrs*

Wolverhampton Electro Plating Ltd, Wood Lane, Wolverhampton, WV10 8HN Tel: (01902) 397 Fax: (01902) 785372 E-mail: enquiries@anochrome-group.co.uk *Electroplating services*

Wolverhampton Glass & Windows, Pelham Stree Wolverhampton, WV3 0BJ Tel: (01902) 77383 Fax: (01902) 423294 *Window & door installat services*

Wolverhampton Grinding Company Ltd, Rosehill Willenhall, West Midlands, WV13 2AR Tel: (01902) 606442 Fax: (01902) 636137 E-mail: sprint@btclick.com *Precision grinders*

Wolverhampton Handling Ltd, Unit 10 Planetary Industrial Estate, Planetary Road, Willenhall, West Midlands, WV13 3XQ Tel: (01902) 7264 Fax: (01902) 864744 E-mail: sales@wolverhamptonhandling.co.uk *Gravity conveyor, roller idler, drums pulley an complete bespoke handling schemes*

Wolverhampton Mobility, 210 Newhampton Road West, Wolverhampton, WV6 0RW Tel: (01902 744824 E-mail: info@wolverhamptonmobility.co.uk *Mobility products & disability aid suppliers*

Wolverhampton Plastics Holdings Ltd, Sharrocks Street, Wolverhampton, WV1 3RP Tel: (01902 455116 Fax: (01902) 455200 E-mail: wton.plastics@virgin.net *Sign makers engravers*

Wolverhampton Pressings Co. Ltd, Whetstone House, Fordhouse Road, Wolverhampton, WV10 9EA Tel: (01902) 307799 Fax: (01902) 721026 E-mail: sales@ralphmartindale.com *General pressings manufrs*

▶ Wolverine Proctor & Schwartz, 3 Langlands Avenue, East Kilbride, Glasgow, G75 0YG Tel: (01355) 575350 Fax: (01355) 575351 Sal Contact: S. Scouller Principal Export Areas: Worldwide *Manufacturers of drying equipment including chemical, continuous band, food industry, industrial plant or equipment & fluid bed. In addition, manufacturers of ovens (foo*

contin

nuation
dustry) & cereal food processing plant & achinery. Also, exhaust gas (industrial) ollution treatment control equipment

erley Press & Studio Ltd, 39-43 Temple Bar, illenhall, West Midlands, WV13 1SH l: (01902) 604130 Fax: (01902) 637746 *ommercial printers & graphic designers*

erson X-Ray & Electro-Medical Ltd, Walsall reet, Willenhall, West Midlands, WV13 2DY el: (01902) 637333 Fax: (01902) 605482 -mail: enquiries@wolversonx-ray.co.uk *X-ray quipment, accessory manufacturers & stributors* Also at: Dunmow & Manchester

bourne, Ounsdale Road, Wombourne, olverhampton, WV5 8EB Tel: (01902) 324222 ax: (01902) 894081 mail: info@wombourne-printers.co.uk *Printers brochures & forms*

bourne Patterns Ltd, Heath Mill Close, ombourne, Wolverhampton, WV5 8EX el: (01902) 893415 Fax: (01902) 324011 *ngineers' pattern makers*

onderFalls, Manderley, Auldgirth, Dumfries, G2 0SA Tel: 01387 740685 Fax: 01387 740697 -mail: ian@wonderfalls.co.uk *Suppliers of ontemporary natural slate and copper indoor ater features.*

onderWorks, Redemption House, 53 Theobald reet, Borehamwood, Herts, WD6 4RT Tel: 020 953 7733 Fax: 020 8953 3388 -mail: info@wworks.co.uk *Events Management, edding Planning, Chocolate Fountain Rentals, eminars & Conferences, Concerts*

ontner Smith (Stocktakers & Gaugers) Ltd, 9 oringfield Road, Bexleyheath, Kent, DA7 6DX el: (01322) 523186 -mail: tonylast@wontnersmith.co.uk *tocktaking to the On-Licensed Trade (Pubs, lubs, Bars etc.).*Periodic Stocktaking. aluations for Changeover and Year-Ends. Full rinted results produced on site if required.*

berry Engineering & Marine Co, 21 Parvis oad, West Byfleet, Surrey, KT14 6HD el: (01932) 352070 Fax: (01932) 353479 *Plant aintenance & marine engineers*

d, 2 Sea View Road, Colwyn Bay, Clwyd, L29 8DG Tel: (01492) 534000

d Ash Formes Ltd, Kingsfield Ways, ingsheath, Northampton, NN5 7QN el: (01604) 752242 Fax: (01604) 751727 *Cutter anufrs*

d Ash Formes Ltd, Kingsfield Ways, ingsheath, Northampton, NN5 7QN el: (01604) 752242 Fax: (01604) 751727 *Press nives*

d Auto Holdings Ltd, Cromwell Works, Colne oad, Huddersfield, HD1 3ES Tel: (01484) 28261 Fax: (01484) 434933 -mail: sales@woodauto.co.uk *Auto-electrical omponent manufrs* Also at: Bracknell, Tamworth Yatton

d Auto Supplies, 4B Locksley Drive, Belfast, T10 0BH Tel: (028) 9060 5880 Fax: (028) 9060 376 *Motor auto electrical parts*

ard J. Wood, 13-17 Hayes Lane, Stourbridge, Vest Midlands, DY9 8QJ Tel: (01384) 892775 ax: (01384) 892662 *Metalwork engineers*

od Brothers Ltd, Unit 10 Fairways Business entre, Airport Service Road, Portsmouth, O3 5NU Tel: (023) 9266 4492 Fax: (023) 9267 865 E-mail: sales@woodbrothers.co.uk *Joinery manufacturers & internal building specialist*

od Bros Furniture Ltd, London Road, Ware, ertfordshire, SG12 9QH Tel: (0845) 1303303 ax: (01920) 464388 -mail: sales@oldcharm.co.uk *Furniture manufrs*

Wood Ltd, 10 Chapel Lane, Lowgate, Hull, U1 1SB Tel: (01482) 223429 Fax: (01482) 15146 E-mail: user@cliffwoodltd.co.uk *Wholesale electrical supplies agents*

. Wood Medical Ltd, Units 6-7, 1 Kirkhill Place, irkhill Industrial Estate, Dyce, Aberdeen, B21 0GU Tel: (01224) 723388 Fax: (01224) 70670 E-mail: admin@dmwood-medical.com *Medical & first aid supply services*

Wood Scotland, Grampian House, Virginia treet, Aberdeen, AB11 5AU Tel: (01224) 11900 Fax: (01224) 212828 -mail: reception.aberdeen@sctland.co.uk *Office quipment suppliers*

od Group Accessories & Components, Unit 22 Vellheads Industrial Centre, Wellheads rescent, Dyce, Aberdeen, AB21 7GA el: (01224) 255810 Fax: (01224) 255818 rincipal Export Areas: Worldwide *Turbine eengineering*

Vood Group Heavy Industrial Turbines, Unit D Vorcester Trading Estate, Worcester, WR3 8HR el: (01905) 459570 Fax: (01905) 754651 *Engineering suppliers*

Vood Group Hit, 9 Deerdykes Court South, umbernauld, Glasgow, G68 9HW Tel: (01236) 68180 Fax: (01236) 458872 *Repair & maintenance of gas turbines*

od Group Light Industrial Turbines Ltd, Kirkhill Drive, Kirkhill Industrial Estate, Dyce, Aberdeen, B21 0EU Tel: (01224) 413000 Fax: (01224) 70008 E-mail: sales@wglit.com *Gas turbine repair & maintenance*

od Group Pressure Control Ltd, Blackhouse Circle, Blackhouse Industrial Estate, Peterhead, Aberdeenshire, AB42 1BN Tel: (01779) 474293 ax: (01779) 474298 *Valve repair & offshore maintenance*

od Group Production Technology Ltd, Maersk House, Greenbank Road, East Tullos Industrial Estate, Aberdeen, AB21 3BR Tel: (01224) 340000 Fax: (01224) 216775 *Pressure gauge distributors*

od Harris, 1 Cleeve Court, Leatherhead, Surrey, KT22 7RJ Tel: (01372) 362990 Fax: (01372) 362920 *Uniform clothing suppliers*

od Harris Ltd, 47-53 Cannon Street, London, C4M 5SH Tel: (020) 7489 8189 Fax: (020) 7236 7686 *Uniforms suppliers*

Vood & Son Ltd, Kirkby Mills Industrial Estate, irby Mills, Kirkbymoorside, York, YO62 6NL el: (01751) 433434 Fax: (01751) 433094 -mail: sales@johnwoods.co.uk *Agricultural engineers*

J. Wood & Son, 24 Dove Way, Kerkby Mills Industrial Estate, Kirkby Morside, York, YO62 6QR Tel: (01751) 433434 Fax: (01751) 433094 E-mail: admin@johnwoods.co.uk *Agricultural & horticultural machinery services* Also at: Dunnington & Pickering

John D. Wood International Ltd, 19 Berkeley Street, London, W1J 8ED Tel: (020) 7629 9050 Fax: (020) 7493 9815 E-mail: property@johndwood.com *Property surveying & commercial investment agents*

K.J. Wood Beveller, 34 Slades Road, Golcar, Huddersfield, HD7 4NE Tel: (01484) 653283 Fax: (01484) 653283 *Woodwork machinists*

Wood & Loines Ltd, Unit 5 Portersfield Road, Cradley Heath, West Midlands, B64 7BN Tel: (01384) 411581 Fax: (01384) 413660 E-mail: sales@wood-loines.com *Engineers pattern makers for automotive industry*

Wood Mac Ltd, Vale Street, Todmorden, Lancashire, OL14 5HG Tel: 01706 814224 *Woodworking machinery agents*

Wood Machines Ltd, 1 Galley Hill Industrial Estate, London Road, Swanscombe, Kent, DA10 0AA Tel: (01322) 385566 Fax: (01322) 384449 E-mail: mail@uemcoltd.com *Specialist machinery manufrs*

Wood Mackenzie Global Consultants, 74-77 Queen Street, Edinburgh, EH2 4NF Tel: 0131-243 4400 Fax: 0131-243 4653 E-mail: sales@woodmac.com

Wood Mitchell Printers Ltd, Festival Way, Stoke-on-Trent, ST1 5TH Tel: (01782) 202440 Fax: (01782) 202402 E-mail: rmitchell@wood-mitchell.co.uk *Colour printers*

Wood & Mott Ltd, 29 Morses Lane, Brightlingsea, Colchester, CO7 0SD Tel: (01206) 303929 Fax: (01206) 304925 E-mail: ernie@wood-and-mott.co.uk *Reproduction & bespoke furniture manufrs*

▶ Wood N Garden, Main Street, Perth, PH2 7LX Tel: (01738) 860006 Fax: (01738) 860008 E-mail: enquiries@woodngarden.co.uk *WOOD N GARDEN IS LOCATED IN GLENCARSE AND DUE TO ITS CLOSE PROXIMITY TO BOTH PERTH AND DUNDEE (JUST OFF THE A90) IS WELL SITUATED TO PROVIDE SCOTLAND AND THE REGION WITH GOOD QUALITY WOODEN GARDEN MATERIALS. WE ARE SUPPLIERS OF SAWN TIMBER FENCING MATERIALS, FENCE PANELS, DECKING, GARDEN AND DRIVEWAY GATES, WOODEN SHEDS AND SUMMERHOUSES, CHILDREN"S PLAY EQUIPMENT, WOODEN GARDEN FURNITURE, PLANTERS, LOG BORDER ROLLS, RABBIT HUTCHES/RUNS, DOG KENNELS, BIRD TABLES AND MANY OTHER WOODEN GARDEN PRODUCTS.*

▶ Wood N Things, 5 James Street, Brigg, South Humberside, DN20 8LS Tel: (01652) 650054 Fax: (01652) 650054

R.A. Wood Adhesive Tapes Ltd, Unit 2 Waterside Business Centre, Wolverhampton Road, Cannock, Staffordshire, WS11 1SN Tel: (01543) 578331 Fax: (01543) 572301 *Adhesive tape converters*

Richard Wood Packaging Ltd, Guys Industrial Estate Tollgate Road, Burscough, Ormskirk, Lancashire, L40 8TG Tel: (01704) 893073 Fax: (01704) 895276 E-mail: woodpackaging@aol.co.uk *Corrugated box, case & container manufrs*

Wood & Richardson Ltd, Royden House, 156 Haxby Road, York, YO31 8JN Tel: (01904) 622712 Fax: (01904) 620352 E-mail: sales@woodrichardson.co.uk *Litho & digital printers*

Russell Wood Ltd, 30 Great Guildford St, London, SE1 0HS Tel: (020) 7928 0505 Fax: (020) 7928 8931 E-mail: russellwoodltd@btinternet.com *Investment management services*

Wood Shop, 130 New Road, Skewen, Neath, West Glamorgan, SA10 6HL Tel: (01792) 812360 Fax: (01792) 321359 E-mail: woodshop@woodshopjoinery.co.uk *Joinery & household maintenance manufrs*

Wood & Son, 3 Barrack Road, Guildford, Surrey, GU2 9RU Tel: (01483) 504012 Fax: (01483) 504012 *Fabricators, welders & steel stockists*

▶ Wood & Son, 24 Wilton Park Road, Shanklin, Isle of Wight, PO37 7BT Tel: (01983) 866313

Wood, Son & Fleming Ltd, 12 Nascot Street, Watford, WD17 4RB Tel: (01923) 253911 Fax: (01923) 243921 *Textile manufrs*

Wood & Stirling, Claughton Industrial Estate, Brockholes Way, Claughton-on-Brock, Preston, PR3 0PZ Tel: (01995) 640664 Fax: (01995) 640065 E-mail: craig@woodandstirling.co.uk *Paper converting machines manufrs*

T. Wood Ltd, Canal Street, Stockport, Cheshire, SK1 3BZ Tel: 0161-480 5012 Fax: 0161-474 7266 E-mail: info@waterloo-sheetmetal.co.uk *Sheet metalworkers*

Timothy Wood Ltd, Units 1-2, Bradley Mills Industrial Estate, Huddersfield, HD1 6PQ Tel: (01484) 440000 Fax: (01484) 440011 *Industrial ironmongers*

▶ Wood View Builders Ltd, 12 Carron Place, Kelvin Industrial Estate, East Kilbride, Glasgow, G75 0YL Tel: (01355) 612560

W.J. Wood & Son Ltd, 1 Fleethall Road, Purdeys Industrial Estate, Rochford, Essex, SS4 1NF Tel: (01702) 544554 Fax: (01702) 530573 E-mail: sales@tyres.uk.com *Motor tyre factors*

Wood Wool, 22 Broach Road, Sandy Lane Industrial Estate, Stourport-on-Severn, Worcestershire, DY13 9QB Tel: (01299) 828059 Fax: (01299) 826975 *Wood packaging*

▶ Wood For You, Unit 1b, Treburley Industrial Units, Launceston, Cornwall, PL15 9PU Tel: (01579) 370786 E-mail: kevin@wood-4-you.co.uk *Garden structure*

George Woodall & Sons Ltd, 35 & 37 Market Place, Malton, North Yorkshire, YO17 7LP Tel: (01653) 692086 Fax: (01653) 691488 E-mail: shop@gwoodall.com *Canvas goods manufrs*

Woodall Services Ltd, Station Road, Coleshill, Birmingham, B46 1HT Tel: (01675) 466020 Fax: (01675) 465745 E-mail: enquiries@woodalltransport.co.uk *Road transport, haulage & freight services*

Woodall Steels Ltd, Town Works, Washington Street, Dudley, West Midlands, DY2 9PH Tel: (01384) 456888 Fax: (01384) 457755 *Steel stockholders*

A. & B. Woodberry Ltd, 156 Crow Lane, Romford, RM7 0ES Tel: (01708) 737979 Fax: (01708) 737918 E-mail: abwoodberry@go-plus.net *Metal furniture makers & fabricators*

Woodberry Bros & Haines Ltd, Commerce Way, Walrow, Highbridge, Somerset, TA9 4AJ Tel: (0870) 0600555 Fax: (01278) 781337 E-mail: info@wbhltd.com *Household furniture suppliers*

Woodberry Chillcott & Co. Ltd, Unit 17 Court Road Industrial Estate, Cwmbran, Gwent, NP44 3AS Tel: (01633) 869311 Fax: (01633) 874676 E-mail: cwmbran@woodberrychillcott.co.uk *Tools, fasteners & steel distributor*

Woodberry Chillcott & Co. Ltd, 6 Spinnaker Road, Hempsted, Gloucester, GL2 5FD Tel: (01452) 418341 Fax: (01452) 300362 E-mail: sales@woodberrychillcott.co.uk *Tools, fasteners & steel distributors*

Woodberry Chillcott & Co. Ltd, Unit 6 Langage Industrial Estate, Eastern Wood Road, Plympton, Plymouth, PL7 5ET Tel: (01752) 343421 Fax: (01752) 346947 E-mail: plymouth@woodberrychillcott.co.uk *Tools, fasteners & steel distributors*

Woodberry Chillcott & Co. Ltd, 5 Mountbatten Business Park, Jackson Close, Portsmouth, PO6 1UR Tel: (023) 9238 8031 Fax: (023) 9237 3615 E-mail: portsmouth@woodberrychillcott.co.uk *Tools, fasteners & steel distributors*

Woodbourne Garage, 1 Cuckmere Way, Brighton, BN1 8GB Tel: (01273) 561581 Fax: (01273) 555694 *MOT's &mechanical repair services*

Woodbridge Foam (UK) Ltd, Caxton Road, Elms Industrial Estate, Bedford, MK41 0EJ Tel: (01234) 211333 Fax: (01234) 272047 *Foam manufrs*

Woodburn Engineering Ltd, Rosganna Works, Trailcock Road, Carrickfergus, County Antrim, BT38 7NU Tel: (028) 9336 6404 Fax: (028) 9336 7539 E-mail: tony@woodburnengineeringltd.co.uk *Steel fabricators*

Woodchip Computers, 15 Walker Close, Glusburn, Keighley, West Yorkshire, BD20 8PW Tel: (01535) 636981 Fax: (0870) 7061967 E-mail: sales@woodchipcomputers.co.uk *Computer consultants*

▶ Woodcote Building Services Ltd, Acton Street, Long Eaton, Nottingham, NG10 1FT Tel: 0115-946 5252 Fax: 0115-946 8262

Woodcraft Of Burston Ltd, Station Buildings, Station Road, Burston, Diss, Norfolk, IP22 5UB Tel: (01379) 741090 Fax: (01379) 741095 E-mail: apires6939@aol.com *Furniture manufrs*

Woodcraft & Design, 202 High Street, London Colney, St. Albans, Hertfordshire, AL2 1JQ Tel: (01727) 823154 Fax: (01727) 823154 E-mail: info@woodcraftdesign.co.uk *Furniture manufrs*

▶ Woodcraft Designs, 121 The Pannier Market, South Street, Torrington, Devon, EX38 8HD Tel: (01805) 625444 E-mail: info@woodcraftdesigns.co.uk *Design & build quality furniture & kitchens using traditional methods*

▶ Woodcraft Fencing, Mold Road, Cefn-y-Bedd, Wrexham, Clwyd, LL12 9YG Tel: (01978) 769330 Fax: (01978) 756490 E-mail: woodcraft_fencing@yahoo.co.uk *Manufacture & supply of wooden fencing panels*

Woodcraft Industries & DIY, 191 London Road, Glasgow, G40 1PA Tel: 0141-552 1437 Fax: 0141-552 1437 *Diy shop & joinery manufrs*

Woodcraft Joinery Ltd, Units 28 & 29 Delph Road Trading Estate, Delph Road, Brierley Hill, West Midlands, DY5 2TW Tel: (01384) 265888 Fax: (01384) 481949 E-mail: info@woodcraftjoinery.co.uk *Design & Build, Refurbishment,*Shopfitters & Bespoke joinery manufactures*

Woodcraft Joinery, Wheal Rose, Scorrier, Redruth, Cornwall, TR16 5DA Tel: (01209) 821883 Fax: (01209) 821883 *Door, window & stair manufrs*

▶ Woodcraft Supplies, 163-165 Deanston Drive, Glasgow, G41 3LP Tel: 0141-649 3838 Fax: 0141-649 9181 E-mail: info@woodcraftsupplies.co.uk

Woodcraft Windows, 104 Hull Road, Hessle, North Humberside, HU13 9NB Tel: (01482) 644315 *Wooden window frame manufrs*

Woodcrafts, 25 Bayton Road Industrial Estate, Bayton Road, Exhall, Coventry, CV7 9EL Tel: (024) 7636 1022 Fax: (024) 7664 4299 E-mail: pdl@btconnect.com *Pattern & model manufrs*

Woodcroft Engineering Ltd, Rugby Road, Brandon, Coventry, CV8 3GG Tel: (024) 7654 2285 Fax: (024) 7654 2615 E-mail: info@weltd.co.uk *Precision engineers*

The Woodcutter, Receptional 7, Station Square, High Street, Flitwick, Bedford, MK45 1DP Tel: (01525) 715520 *Furniture manufrs*

▶ Wooden Choice Ltd, 127 Manchester Road, Worsley, Manchester, M28 3JT Tel: 0161-703 7919 E-mail: info@woodenchoice.co.uk *Wooden Choice offers an extensive range of traditional and educational wooden toys for your child and baby. Bikes, trains, dolls, rocking horses and role-playing games are all available.*

▶ Wooden Door Co., Unit 10 Oystons Mill, Strand Road, Preston, PR1 8UR Tel: (01772) 430055 Fax: (01772) 430066 *Sells doors*

▶ The Wooden Flagpole Co., The Croft, West Street, Wiveliscombe, Somerset, TA4 2JP Tel: 01984 624794 Fax: 01984 624532 E-mail: mark.stoddart@btconnect.com *Tradional, hand made wooden flagpoles, various sizes available.*

▶ Wooden Garden, 9 Moffathill, Airdrie, Lanarkshire, ML6 8PY Tel: (01236) 602715

▶ Wooden Heart Designs, Chapel Barn Yard, Deptford, Wylye, Warminster, Wilts, BA12 0QQ Tel: (01985) 248286 Fax: (01985) 248286

▶ Wooden House Design & Media, Upton House, Baldock Street, Royston, Hertfordshire, SG8 5AY Tel: 01763 247288 E-mail: kelly@woodenhouse.com *Award winning graphic design consultancy specialising in corporate identity, advertising, print graphics, web design and TV promos.*

continued

Wooden Workshop Ltd, 454 Hornsey Road, London, N19 4EE Tel: (020) 7263 8070 Fax: (020) 7272 1668 E-mail: enquiries@wwltd.freeserve.co.uk *Futon manufrs*

Woodend Fabrications Ltd, Manchester Road, Mossley, Ashton-under-Lyne, Lancashire, OL5 9AT Tel: (01457) 834880 Fax: (01457) 838261 *Steel fabricators*

Woodentops, 26 High Street, Dereham, Norfolk, NR19 1DR Tel: (01362) 699656 Fax: (01362) 699656 *Pine furniture suppliers*

Woodentops, 31 Norfolk Street, King's Lynn, Norfolk, PE30 1AL Tel: (01553) 765928 Fax: (01553) 765928 *Furniture retailers*

▶ Wooderson Packaging Ltd, Alexander House, Christy Court, Basildon, Essex, SS15 6TL Tel: (01268) 548200 Fax: (01268) 541878 E-mail: info@woodersonpackaging.co.uk *Flexible packaging manufrs*

Woodfield, Station Yard, Station Road, Bluntisham, Huntingdon, Cambridgeshire, PE28 3PA Tel: (01487) 843031 Fax: (01487) 843342 *Machinery exporters*

▶ Woodfield Engineering Services Ltd, Unit 2, Woodfield House, Gravel Lane, Banks, Southport, Merseyside, PR9 8BY Tel: (01704) 220729 Fax: (01704) 220515 E-mail: woodfieldservice@btconnect.com *Supply of fabricated, machined components & assemblies*

Woodfield Systems Ltd, The Wharf, Crown Quay Lane, Sittingbourne, Kent, ME10 3JJ Tel: (01795) 421551 Fax: (01795) 421554 *Steel fabricators*

Woodfield Systems Ltd, Tyler Way, Swalecliffe, Whitstable, Kent, CT5 2RS Tel: (01227) 793351 Fax: (01227) 793625 E-mail: sales@akerkvaerner.com *Marine loading arm manufrs*

Woodfit Ltd, Kem Mill, Kem Mill Lane, Whittle-le-Woods, Chorley, Lancashire, PR6 7EA Tel: (01257) 266421 Fax: (01257) 264271 E-mail: sales@woodfit.com *Furniture fitting distributors*

Woodflakes Of Daventry Ltd, Unit 1, Hollandstone Farm, High Street, Flore, Northamptonshire, NN7 4LP Tel: (01327) 343344 Fax: (01327) 342470 E-mail: woodflakes@interface99.fsbusiness.co.uk *Wood shavings & animal bedding supply & distribute*

Woodford Computer Consultants, Little Fairwood, Fairwood Road, Dilton Marsh, Westbury, Wiltshire, BA13 4EL Tel: (01373) 824966 Fax: (01373) 825966 E-mail: woodford@fairwood.co.uk *Computer consultancy services*

Woodford Engineering, Unit 1A, The Bridge, Narberth, Dyfed, SA67 8QA Tel: (01834) 861368 Fax: (01834) 861368 *Commercial vehicle service & repairers*

Woodford Sheet Metal Ltd, 14 Wham Street, Heywood, Lancashire, OL10 4QU Tel: (01706) 364295 Fax: (01706) 621996 E-mail: woodford-sm@lineone-net.co.uk *Heating & ventilation engineers*

Woodfurn, Unit 6 Easter Court, Woodward Avenue, Yate, Bristol, BS37 5YS Tel: (01454) 313684 Fax: (01454) 313731 *Wood furniture manufrs*

Woodgate & Partners Ltd, Brishing Court Barn, Brishing Lane, Boughton Monchelsea, Maidstone, Kent, ME17 4NF Tel: (01622) 744666 Fax: (01622) 741747 *Corporate insurance brokers*

▶ Woodgate-Loydor Ltd, Elmfield Avenue, Teddington, Middlesex, TW11 8BS Tel: (020) 8977 3491

▶ Woodgates Chartered Certified Accountants, 100, London Road, Leicester, LE2 0QS Tel: 0116-254 3718 Fax: 0116-275 6575

Woodgrain Joinery, 3 Roan Close, Dungannon, County Tyrone, BT70 1NE Tel: (028) 3754 8070 Fax: (028) 3754 8070 *Joinery manufrs*

A.N. Woodhams & Co. Ltd, 95 Worship Street, London, EC2A 2LX Tel: (020) 7377 9966 Fax: (020) 7375 0942 E-mail: woodhams@btinternet.com *Tea merchants*

Woodhead Connectivity Ltd, Unit 9 Rassau Industrial Estate, Rassau, Ebbw Vale, Gwent, NP23 5SD Tel: (01495) 350436 Fax: (01495) 350877 E-mail: contact@whdhd.co.uk *Electrical connector manufrs*

Woodhead R.S.R Springs Commercial Vehicle Spares, 41 Rothersthorpe Avenue, Rothersthorpe Avenue Industrial Estate, Rothersthorpe Avenue Industrial Estat, Northampton, NN4 8JH Tel: (01604) 675777 Fax: (01604) 675808 E-mail: sales@serckintertruck.co.uk *Commercial vehicle parts & steel springs*

Uriah Woodhead & Son Ltd, Valley House, Valley Road, Bradford, West Yorkshire, BD1 4RY Tel: (01274) 727528 Fax: (01274) 726574 *Builders' merchants*

Woodheads Seeds Ltd, Island Farm, Little Airmyn, Selby, North Yorkshire, YO8 8PT Tel: (01757) 617000 Fax: (01757) 618888 E-mail: woodheads@zoom.co.uk *Seed merchants*

Woodheart Joinery Manufacturers, 2a Catton Road, Arnold, Nottingham, NG5 7JD Tel: 0115-967 0195 Fax: 0115-967 4068 *Joinery manufrs*

Woodhill Engineering, St Andrews House, West Street, Woking, Surrey, GU21 6EB Tel: (01483) 717600 Fax: (01483) 717630 E-mail: info@woodhill.co.uk *Engineering consultants*

Woodhouse Environmental Services, 18 Yardley Road, Hedge End, Hedge End, Southampton, SO30 0HQ Tel: 0808 100 1630 Fax: (01489) 790100 E-mail: info@woodhouseservices.co.uk *Air ventilation services*

Woodhouse UK plc, Harrison Way, Leamington Spa, Warwickshire, CV31 3HL Tel: (01926) 314313 Fax: (01926) 883778 E-mail: enquires@woodhouse.co.uk *Manufacturer & installation of street furniture, street lighting*

Company Information

▶ Woodhouse Upholstery, Unit 24 Bookers Way, Todwick Road Industrial Estate, Dinnington, Sheffield, S25 3SH Tel: (01909) 565879 Fax: (01909) 560685 E-mail: enquiries@woodhouse-contracts.co.uk *Refurbish upholstery*

Woodhull Roofing Ltd, Unit S3 Olton Wharf, Richmond Road, Solihull, West Midlands, B92 7RN Tel: 0121-707 3111 Fax: 0121-708 1222 E-mail: woodhull.roofing@ic24.net *Roofing contractors*

▶ Woodland Commercial Ltd, 292 Worton Road, Isleworth, Middlesex, TW7 6EL Tel: (020) 8560 0010 Fax: (020) 8560 1470 E-mail: info@woodlandcommercial.co.uk *Building contractors*

▶ Woodland Export Packaging UK, 52 Cobden Street, Salford, M6 6WF Tel: 0161-736 2032 Fax: 0161-736 1733 E-mail: sales@woodlandsxp.com *Export packaging fitting cases*

Woodland Flyscreen & Bird Exclusion Products, 73a Kennel Ride, Ascot, Berkshire, SL5 7NU Tel: (01344) 886459 Fax: (01344) 886459 *Pest control products manufrs*

Woodland Furniture Co., Woodlands, Gwersyllt, Wrexham, Clwyd, LL11 4NW Tel: (01978) 755666 Fax: (01978) 758222 E-mail: john@bostock55.freeserve.co.uk *Office furniture manufrs*

▶ Woodland Grange, Management Development & Conference Centre, Old Milverton Lane, Leamington Spa, Warwickshire, CV32 6RN Tel: (01926) 336621 Fax: (01926) 450648 E-mail: sales@wgrange.com *Training, management development & conference centre services*

Woodland Improvement & Conservation Ltd, Newent Lane, Huntley, Gloucester, GL19 3HG Tel: (01452) 832100 Fax: (01452) 831039 E-mail: sales@woodimp.co.uk *Forest tree nurserymen*

Woodland International Transport, Anglia Cargo Terminal, Priors Way, Coggeshall, Colchester, CO6 1TL Tel: (01376) 565100 Fax: (01376) 565101 E-mail: info@woodlanduk.com *Freight forwarders* Also at: Barnsley, Hoddesdon & Leeds

▶ Woodland International Transport, 2 Woodland House, Hall Dene Way, Seaham Grange Industrial Estate, Seaham, County Durham, SR7 0PU Tel: 0191-521 9780 Fax: 0191-521 9797

Woodland Leather, 27-33 Bethnal Green Road, London, E1 6LA Tel: (020) 7729 9494 Fax: (020) 7729 2555 E-mail: woodland_leather@btconnect.com *Wholesale retailers of suede & leather wear*

WOODLAND LINE, INGLENOOK COTTAGE, MILL LANE, HORSEMANS GREEN, WHITCHURCH, SHROPSHIRE, SY13 3DT Tel: 01948 830334 Fax: 01948 830334 E-mail: ingrid.geoff@tesco.net *Professional joinery services provided by traditionally-trained craftsman. From shopfitting through to building renovation a full range of joinery services can be provided. Commercial joinery items of all types can be provided including bespoke offices and office furniture tailored to each particular client's needs. Exhibition stands can also be constructed. Kitchens and all other kinds of fitted furniture can also be produced.*

▶ Woodland Park C T S G, Lower Road, Bookham, Leatherhead, Surrey, KT23 4EF Tel: (01372) 451040 Fax: (01372) 451040

▶ Woodland Site Services Ltd, Unit 20 Optima Park, Thames Road, Dartford, DA1 4QX Tel: (01322) 555085 Fax: (01322) 520545 E-mail: enquiries@woodlands-ss.co.uk *Electrical service suppliers*

Woodland Timber Products, Haughmond Hill Upton Magna, Haughmond, Uffington, Shrewsbury, SY4 4RW Tel: (01743) 709383 Fax: (01743) 709366 *Timber fence manufrs*

Woodlands Fashions, 33 Commercial Road, London, E1 1LD Tel: (020) 7247 0506 Fax: (020) 7247 7666 E-mail: sales@jeniceleather.co.uk *Leather garments distribs*

Woodlands Generators, Crab Apple Way, Vale Park, Evesham, Worcestershire, WR11 1GP Tel: (01386) 760256 Fax: (01386) 442740 E-mail: sales@woodlands-generators.com *Generator generating set, power supply (load bank) test equipment suppliers*

Woodlands Joinery, The Barn Weir Courtney Yard, Blackberry Lane, Lingfield, Surrey, RH7 6NG Tel: (01342) 835856 Fax: (01342) 835856 E-mail: woodlands.joinery@ntlword.co.uk *Joinery manufrs*

Woodlands Park Dairy, Woodlands, Wimborne, Dorset, BH21 8LX Tel: (01202) 822687 Fax: (01202) 826051 E-mail: sales@woodlands-park.co.uk *Specialist dairy manufrs*

Woodlands Tarpaulins, 8 Middle Lickhurst, Bleasdale Road, Whitechapel, Preston, PR3 2ER Tel: (01995) 640779 Fax: (01995) 640277 *Tarpaulin maintenance or repair*

Woodlark Interiors, Moorhurst Lane, Copse Farm, Holmwood, Dorking, Surrey, RH5 4LJ Tel: (01306) 713009 Fax: (01737) 841098 *Fitted kitchens & joinery*

Edward Woodley & Sons Ltd, Newton Road, Higham Ferrers, Rushden, Northamptonshire, NN10 8HR Tel: (01933) 353373 Fax: (01933) 358275 E-mail: ewoodley@globalnet.co.uk *Leather manufacturers & merchants*

Woodley Engineering Stockport Ltd, Whitefield Road, Bredbury, Stockport, Cheshire, SK6 2QR Tel: 0161-430 7488 Fax: 0161-406 6061 *Steel cutting punch manufrs*

Woodleys Joinery Ltd, Exeter Road, Newton Poppleford, Sidmouth, Devon, EX10 0BJ Tel: (01395) 568666 Fax: (01395) 568122 *Joiners*

Trevor Woodliffe, Treveen House, Meltonby, York, YO42 1PN Tel: (01759) 304202 Fax: (01759) 304202 *Agricultural contractors*

Woodline Floors Ltd, Unit 3, Brook Farm, Horsham Road, Cowfold, Horsham, West Sussex, RH13 8AH Tel: (01403) 860000 Fax: (0870) 8400040 E-mail: sales@woodlinefloors.co.uk *Flooring importers*

▶ Woodman Construction Management Ltd, 50 Victoria Road, Burgess Hill, West Sussex, RH15 9LH Tel: 01444 233413 Fax: 01444 871231 E-mail: clientservices@woodman.co.uk *Construction management & office furniture suppliers*

Woodman Hill Ltd, Imperial Way, Watford, WD24 4YX Tel: (01923) 233977 Fax: (01923) 235941 E-mail: sales@woodmanhill.co.uk *Chemical packers & fillers*

Woodmet Anodisers Ltd, Globe Lane, Dukinfield, Cheshire, SK16 4RQ Tel: 0161-339 1943 Fax: 0161-343 1610 *Aluminium fabricators*

Woodnewton Pottery, 43 Main Street, Woodnewton, Peterborough, PE8 5EB Tel: (01780) 470866 Fax: (01780) 470127 E-mail: sales@studiopottery.co.uk *Pottery retailers & manufrs*

Woodrich Design Ltd, Shaw Barn, Whitesmith, Lewes, East Sussex, BN8 6JD Tel: (01825) 872066 Fax: (01825) 872894 *Furniture & kitchen manufrs*

Woodrow Business Centre, 65-66 Woodrow, London, SE18 5DH Tel: (020) 8854 1194 Fax: (020) 8317 0394 E-mail: info@woodrowbusinesscentre.com *Serviced offices*

▶ Woodrow Construction Islay Ltd, Glenegedale, Isle of Islay, PA42 7AS Tel: (01496) 300003 Fax: (01496) 300111

Woodrow Universal Ltd, Junction Mills, Skipton Road, Cross Hills, Keighley, West Yorkshire, BD20 7SE Tel: (01535) 633364 Fax: (01535) 634439 E-mail: sales@woodrowuniversal.co.uk *Industrial & apparel fabric manufrs*

Woodrows of Salisbury, Stephenson Road, Churchfields Industrial Estate, Salisbury, SP2 7NP Tel: (01722) 328401 Fax: (01722) 412782 *Builders' merchants trade suppliers*

Woodruffs Bakery Buffet Service, 4 Deacon Road, Southampton, SO19 7PZ Tel: (023) 8044 8124 *Bakery*

Woodrush Distribution, Unit 6 Greenfield Road, Pulloxhill, Bedford, MK45 5EY Tel: (01525) 717199 Fax: (01525) 717606 E-mail: sales@woodrush.co.uk *Warehousing & distributors*

▶ Woods Building Services Ltd, Woods House, River Way, Harlow, Essex, CM20 2DP Tel: (01279) 444630

▶ Woods Design & Print, Bumpers Way, Bumpers Farm, Chippenham, Wiltshire, SN14 6NG Tel: (01249) 460630 Fax: (01249) 460631 *Design & Print.*

Woods Dorchester, 34-35 High East Street, Dorchester, Dorset, DT1 1HN Tel: (01305) 262666 Fax: (01305) 250073 E-mail: woodsdor@globalnet.co.uk *Removal, storage specialist & home furnishers*

Woods Dyke Boat Yard, Lower Street, Horning, Norwich, NR12 8PF Tel: (01692) 630461 Fax: (01692) 631415 E-mail: sales@woodsdyke-boatyard.co.uk *Boat repair & boat hire*

Woods Electromech Ltd, Unit 4 Parc Ty Glas, Llanishen, Cardiff, CF14 5DU Tel: (029) 2075 7071 Fax: (029) 2075 8934 E-mail: dawoods@btclick.com *Electrical engineers*

Woods Engineering, Dunn Farm, Littleham, Bideford, Devon, EX39 5HR Tel: (01237) 473338 Fax: (01237) 473338 *Agricultural engineers*

Herbert Woods, Broads Haven, Bridge Road, Potter Heigham, Great Yarmouth, Norfolk, NR29 5JD Tel: (01692) 670711 Fax: (01692) 670734 E-mail: mail@broads.co.uk *Boat hire leasing rental*

▶ Woods & Hughes (Bolts & Screws) Ltd, Unit 9, Hill Top Industrial Estate, Shaw Street, West Bromwich, West Midlands, B70 0TX Tel: 0121-505 7551 Fax: 0121-505 7652 E-mail: sales@socketscrews.co.uk *Bolt & nut distributors manufacturers hexagon bolts & sets*

Woods Packaging, Unit D4 Whitwood Enterprise Park, Whitwood Lane, Whitwood, Castleford, West Yorkshire, WF10 5PX Tel: (01977) 604050 Fax: (01977) 604400 E-mail: sales@woods-packaging.co.uk *Packaging materials distributors*

▶ Woods Of Perth Ltd, 113-119 Glover Street, Perth, PH2 0JF Tel: (01738) 622244 Fax: (01738) 635234 E-mail: info@woodsofperth.co.uk

R.J. Woods Engineering & Materials Consultancy, 86 Stanley Green Road, Poole, Dorset, BH15 3AG Tel: (01202) 671169 Fax: (01202) 671169 *Engineers*

Woods Radio Frequency Services Ltd, Bullocks Farm, Bullocks Lane, Takeley, Bishop's Stortford, Hertfordshire, CM22 6TA Tel: (01279) 870432 Fax: (01279) 871689 *Woodwork machinery manufrs*

Wood's Timber Co Ltd, Witham, Hull, HU9 1BG Tel: (01482) 320466 Fax: (01482) 212799 *Timber importers & saw millers*

Woods Transport Ltd, 6 Climax Works, Garnet Road, Leeds, LS11 5JY Tel: 0113-276 1116 Fax: 0113-276 1116 *Road transport & haulage services*

▶ Woods of Wales, Henfaes Lane, Welshpool, Powys, SY21 7BE Tel: (01938) 554789 Fax: (01938) 554921 E-mail: sales@woodsofwalesffnet.co.uk *Timber products& timber*

Woods & Woods, 311-323 Muswell Hill Broadway, London, N10 1BY Tel: (020) 8444 6055 Fax: (020) 8365 3106 *Wood & leather furniture suppliers*

▶ Woodscope Jordan Ltd, Hope Carr Way, Leigh, Lancashire, WN7 3DE Tel: (01942) 602266 Fax: (01942) 602277 E-mail: woodscopejordan@aol.com *Joinery & construction services*

Woodseats Engineering, 3 Canal Works, Cadman Street, Sheffield, S4 7ZG Tel: 0114-279 6143 Fax: 0114-279 6143 E-mail: sales@woodseatsengineering.com *Press workers & light engineering*

Woodside Air Conditioning Ltd, 81 Woodside Business Park, Shore Road, Birkenhead, Merseyside, CH42 1EP Tel: 0151-650 2369 Fax: 0151-650 2375 E-mail: desau@merseymail.com *Construction*

Woodside Engineers (Cwmbran) Ltd, Forgehammer, 22 Woodside Road, Cwmbran, Gwent, NP44 3AA Tel: (01633) 484448 Fax: (01633) 484448 *Precision machinists*

Woodside Festoon Lighting Ltd, Light House, Lancashire Hill, Stockport, Cheshire, SK4 1RR Tel: 0161-480 6448 Fax: 0161-474 1823 *Lighting manufrs*

▶ Woodside Group Ltd, Unit 10 Imperial Park, Rawreth Lane, Rayleigh, Essex, SS6 9RS Tel: (01268) 785111 Fax: (01268) 785666 E-mail: sales@woodsidegroup.co.uk

Woodside Haulage Ltd, 61 Carrickfergus Road, Ballynure, Ballyclare, County Antrim, BT39 9QJ Tel: (028) 9335 2255 Fax: (028) 9334 0427 E-mail: info@woodsides.com *Road transport, haulage & freight services*

▶ Woodside Haulage (G B) Ltd, Unit 280 Carnfield Place, Walton Summit Industrial Estate, Bamber Bridge, Preston, PR5 8AN Tel: (01772) 323381 Fax: (01772) 627020 E-mail: info@woodside-haulage.co.uk

Woodside Joinery Ltd, 33 Crossways, London Road, Sunninghill, Ascot, Berkshire, SL5 0PL Tel: (01344) 876625 Fax: (01344) 876625 E-mail: sales@woodsidejoinery.co.uk *Joinery manufrs*

Woodside Pneumatics Ltd, Stirling Road Industrial Estate, Dykehead Road, Airdrie, Lanarkshire, ML6 7UJ Tel: (01236) 756171 Fax: (01236) 751210 E-mail: sales@woodside-compressors.co.uk *Dryers & air compressors*

Woodside Precast Concrete Ltd, Dawes Lane, Scunthorpe, South Humberside, DN15 6UW Tel: (01724) 281872 Fax: (01724) 280866 E-mail: info@caststone.co.uk *Manufacturers of precast concrete & architectural cast stone*

Woodside Press Ltd, 22a Islington Road, Bristol, BS3 1QB Tel: 0117-985 5500 Fax: 0117-963 9969 *General printers*

Woodsome Tool & Electric Co. Ltd, Tape Lane, Hurst, Reading, RG10 0DN Tel: 0118-934 1142 Fax: (01488) 71820 *Hydraulic lifting manufrs*

Woodsons Of Aberdeen Ltd, Goval House, Dyce, Aberdeen, AB21 0HT Tel: (01224) 722884 Fax: (01224) 722859 E-mail: sales@woodsons.co.uk *Marine electronic equipment distributors*

▶ Woodspray Timber Preservation Services, 21 Hillhead Road, Toomebridge, Antrim, BT41 3SF Tel: (028) 7965 1794 Fax: (028) 7965 1795 E-mail: info@woodsprayltd.com *Pre-finish spray specialists of**- Doors *- Windows *- Skirtings *- Architraves *- Stairs *- Flooring *- Walls and Ceiling finishes*

Woodstock, 127 Wandsworth Bridge Road, London, SW6 2TT Tel: (020) 7371 8484 Fax: (020) 7731 3676 *Furniture retailers*

Woodstock Computer Solutions Ltd, Malvern, Oakhanger, Bordon, Hampshire, GU35 9JJ Tel: (01420) 474722 E-mail: roly@wcsweb.co.uk *Software consultants & developers*

▶ Woodstock Designs Ltd, Manor House, Ryehill, Hull, HU12 9NH Tel: (01964) 621100

Woodstock Felt Roofing Ltd, 1 Elmsfield House, Worcester Road, Chipping Norton, Oxfordshire, OX7 5XS Tel: (01608) 644644 Fax: (01608) 646658 E-mail: wfr001@aol.com *Felt roofing contractors*

Woodstock Furniture Ltd, 4 William Street, London, SW1X 9HL Tel: (020) 7245 9989 Fax: (020) 7245 9981 *Furniture manufrs*

▶ Woodstock Homes, 14 Redland Park, Bristol, BS6 6SB Tel: 0117-974 1021 Fax: 0117-974 4113 E-mail: sales@woodstockhomes.co.uk *Bristol based Woodstock Homes specialises in building small groups of well-specified new homes, usually within established communities across South Wales and the South West*

Woodstock Interiors 2000, Garth Works, Taffs Well, Cardiff, CF15 7YF Tel: (029) 2081 0363 Fax: (029) 2081 0363 E-mail: derick.kingston@ntlworld.com *Joinery furniture manufrs*

Woodstock Joinery Co., 9A Windermere Road, London, N19 5SG Tel: (020) 7281 4866 Fax: (020) 7263 4888 *Window frames*

Woodstock Joinery Ltd, 3 Romar Court, West Denbigh, Bletchley, Milton Keynes, MK1 1RH Tel: (01908) 647369 Fax: (01908) 646545 *Joinery*

Woodstock Leabank Office Furniture, Corrie Way, Bredbury, Stockport, Cheshire, SK6 2ST Tel: 0161-494 1242 Fax: 0161-494 4409 E-mail: sales@woodstockleabank.co.uk *Office furniture wholesalers*

Woodstock Neckwear Ltd, Telford Road, Glenrothes, Fife, KY7 4NX Tel: (01592) 771777 Fax: (01592) 631717 *Neck tie & men's accessories distributors* Also at: London

Woodstyle, Swinnow View, Leeds, LS13 4TZ Tel: 0113-255 9098 Fax: 0113-220 9727 *Shop fittings design & manufrs*

Woodtec, 38 Festival Drive, Loughborough, Leicestershire, LE11 5XJ Tel: (01509) 219246 Fax: (01509) 260117 E-mail: sales@woodtec2.co.uk *Concrete formwork & pattern manufrs*

▶ Woodtek Industries Ltd, 105 Creagh Road, Castledawson, Magherafelt, County Londonderry, BT45 8EY Tel: (028) 7946 9088 Fax: (028) 7946 9033 E-mail: sales@woodtekindustries.com *Wood turning*

Walter Woodthorpe Ltd, Manifirs House, London Road, Kirton, Boston, Lincolnshire, PE20 1JE Tel: (01205) 722050 Fax: (01205) 722818 *Solid fuel distributors*

▶ Woodview Light Transport Ltd, Ransome Road, Northampton, NN4 8AD Tel: (01604) 766201 Fax: (01604) 701210

▶ Woodward Food Service, Carsegate Road North, Inverness, IV3 8EA Tel: (01463) 236521 Fax: (01463) 243720

Woodward Grosvenor & Co. Ltd, Green Street, Kidderminster, Worcestershire, DY10 1HR Tel: (01562) 820020 Fax: (01562) 820042 E-mail: sales@woodward.com *Carpet manufrs*

▶ Woodward Peet Engineering Services Ltd, 21 Offerton Industrial Estate, Hempshaw Lane, Stockport, Cheshire, SK2 5TH Tel: 0161-474 1348 Fax: 0161-480 9261 *Engineering services*

Woodward Services, 14 Eldon Road, Reading, RG1 4DL Tel: 0118-926 6664 *Computer prin[ter] repairs*

Woodwards Food Service, Craigshaw Drive, W[est] Tullos Industrial Estate, Aberdeen, AB12 3A[...] Tel: (01224) 291744 Fax: (01224) 291765 *C[old] storage facilities*

▶ Woodware Repetitions Ltd, 47 Mowbray Stre[et] Sheffield, S3 8EN Tel: 0114-272 6060 Fax: 0114-279 7475 *Wood merchants*

Woodwars of Wigan Ltd, Stephen's Way, Goos[e] Green, Wigan, Lancashire, WN3 6PQ Tel: (01942) 230026 Fax: (01942) 826026 *Tr[...] dealers*

Woodway Engineering Ltd, Lower Road, Barna[...] Shilton, Coventry, CV7 9LD Tel: (024) 7684 [...] Fax: (024) 7662 1796 E-mail: woodway@btconnect.com *Warning lighting & siren manufrs*

Woodway Farm Machinery, Woodway Farm, Lit[tle] Lane, Princes Risborough, Buckinghamshire HP27 9NW Tel: (01844) 345375 Fax: (01844) 274081 *Farm machinery equipment agents*

Woodway Packaging Ltd, 25-27 Mallard Close, Earls Barton, Northampton, NN6 0JF Tel: (01604) 812678 Fax: (01604) 810678 *Polythene & general packaging distributors*

Woodwork, 108 London Road, Southborough, Tunbridge Wells, Kent, TN4 0PS Tel: (01892) 533273 Fax: (01892) 619655 E-mail: simon@wwths.demon.co.uk *Pine kitc[hen] furniture, bespoke kitchen & bedroom fitters manufrs*

The Woodwork Dust Control Company Ltd, Wo[...] Road, Brill, Aylesbury, Buckinghamshire, HP18 9UB Tel: (01844) 238833 Fax: (01844) 238899 E-mail: woodworkdust@ukonline.co.[uk] *Dust extraction plant manufrs*

Woodworking Machinery Ireland, 72-74 Waterlo[o] Road, Lisburn, County Antrim, BT27 5NW Tel: (028) 9266 0034 Fax: (028) 9266 0979 *Woodwork machinery sales*

Woodworking Machinery Services & Repairs, 3[...] Merlewood, Dickleburgh, Diss, Norfolk, IP21 [...] Tel: (01379) 741412 Fax: (01379) 741412 *Woodworking machine maintenance repair services*

The Woodworks, 5 Landscape Road, Weston-On-The-Grn, Bicester, Oxfordshire, OX25 3SX Tel: (01869) 343010 Fax: (01869) 343797 E-mail: info@woodworksweb.co.uk *Cabinet makers*

▶ Woodworks, Unit 2 Moorside, Colchester, CO1 2TJ Tel: (01206) 862929 Fax: (01206) 862686

Woodworks, 41-43 North Valley Road, Colne, Lancashire, BB8 9AQ Tel: (01282) 721843 Fax: (01282) 860664 E-mail: sales@matkinson.co.uk *Joinery manu[frs]*

Woody's Pine Emporium, 34-40 Derby Road, Ipswich, IP3 8DN Tel: (01473) 717064 Fax: (01473) 713480 E-mail: info@woodyspine.co.uk *Pine furniture distributors*

Woody's Timber & Building Supplies Ltd, Kirkha[m] Road, Freckleton, Preston, PR4 1HY Tel: (01772) 683737 Fax: (01772) 686104 *Distributing farm suppliers*

▶ Wool Duvets, Jasmine House, Saxlingham Road, Blakeney, Holt, Norfolk, NR25 7PB Tel: (01263) 741799 E-mail: enquiries@woolduvets.co.uk *UK mail order suppliers of wool or cashmere duvets & pillows, cashmere & lambs wool throws*

Wool 'N' Things, Broadway, Totland Bay, Isle of Wight, PO39 0AS Tel: (01983) 752434 Fax: (01983) 752434 *Wool, haberdashery & craft suppliers*

Wool Testing Authority Europe Ltd, Oakwood Warehouse, City Road, Bradford, West Yorkshire, BD8 8JY Tel: (01274) 732396 Fax: (01274) 760419 *Wool testing services*

Woolbro (Distributors) Ltd, Prospect Ho, Victoria Rd, Morley, Leeds, LS27 9DB Tel: 0113-252 4349 Fax: 0113-238 0142 *Fancy goods importers*

▶ Wooldridge & Simpson Ltd, The Gables, Woodstock Road, Yarnton, Kidlington, Oxfordshire, OX5 1PH Tel: (01865) 370700 Fax: (01865) 370598

Wooler Ltd, North Way, Andover, Hampshire, SP10 5AZ Tel: (01264) 324181 Fax: (01264) 333554 *General sub-contract engineers*

Woolexpo Ltd, 19 Bruton Place, London, W1J 6[...] Tel: (020) 8274 0565 Fax: (020) 7629 2513 E-mail: chris@woolexpo.biz *Cashmere accessories & fabric specialists*

Woolf Ltd, 1 Procter Street, London, WC1V 6DW Tel: (020) 7492 0202 Fax: (020) 7492 0203 E-mail: enquiries@woolfltd.com *Construction Management /Project management consultan[ts] contractors/engineers/planners.*

Woolf Engineering, Pennybridge Industrial Estate Ballymena, County Antrim, BT42 3HB Tel: (02[8]) 2564 7938 Fax: (028) 2564 5102 E-mail: info@woolfengineering.com *General Engineers*

Woollacott Gears Ltd, Llay Hall Industrial Estate, Cefn-Y-Bedd, Wrexham, Clwyd, LL12 9YG Tel: (01978) 761848 Fax: (01978) 762340 *CN[C] lathes & machining centres gear cutting & full component manufrs*

▶ J.P. Woollacott Ltd, 10 Ash Hill Road, Torquay TQ1 3HZ Tel: (01803) 213235 Fax: (01803) 213247 E-mail: jpw@email.com *Plumbing, heating & gas engineers*

Woollen & Co. Ltd, Old Lane, Halfway, Sheffield, S20 3GZ Tel: 0114-276 4411 Fax: 0114-248 9980 E-mail: woollens@hotmail.co.uk *Sign makers*

Woollen Mill, 179 High Street, Edinburgh, EH1 1[...] Tel: 0131-225 8023 Fax: 0131-220 3103 E-mail: info@woollenmill.co.uk *High quality jackets & jumpers distributors*

Woollen Spinners (Huddersfield) Ltd, Wellington Mills, Lindley, Huddersfield, HD3 3HR Tel: (01484) 322200 Fax: (01484) 644829 E-mail: wshuddes@aol.com *Carpet yarn spinners*

Woolley GMC Engineering Co. Ltd, 18 Crondal Road, Exhall, Coventry, CV7 9NH Tel: (024) 7636 2371 Fax: (024) 7636 8171 *Production engineers*

n Woolley Ltd, Moseley Press, The Orchard, ston, West Midlands, WV14 0EB Tel: (01902) 1601 Fax: (01902) 401257 *Design, print & tionary*
oolleys World Of Computers, 80 Salters Road, alsall, WS9 9JB Tel: (01543) 453411 x: (01543) 453411 *Computer maintenance & air services*
nans Electrostatics, Sudbury Road, Bures, ffolk, CO8 5JT Tel: (01787) 227392 x: (01787) 227597 nail: woolmansfloors@aol.com *Anti-static terials suppliers*
nough Ac Ltd, 7 Parmiter Industrial Centre, rmiter Street, London, E2 9HZ Tel: (020) 8980 13 Fax: (020) 8980 9814 *Leather table liners upholsterers*
sery Cheese, The Old Dairy, Up Sydling, rchester, Dorset, DT2 9PQ Tel: (01984) 3359 Fax: (01300) 341991 nail: woolsery.cheese@virgin.net *Cheese anufrs*
oolton Powerwash, 62 Charterhouse Road, oolton, L25 8SU Tel: 0151 421 0799 nail: ianbryson1@hotmail.com *Driveway and tio Professional Cleaning /Pressure Washing.*
olyhats.com, 30 Westonfields, Totnes, Devon, 9 5QU Tel: 07077 400681 nail: admin@woolyhats.com *Woolyhats.com ll Winter hats, gloves and scarves to people of ages at knock down wholesale prices. All of r hats, gloves and scarves are made from the est materials to a very high standard and are itable for extreme weather conditions which ake them ideal for wearing on the slopes whilst ing or just protecting you from the everyday eather conditions.*
ter & Williams Ltd, Jubilee Road, High ycombe, Buckinghamshire, HP11 2PG l: (01494) 525372 Fax: (01494) 463469 *neered panel manufrs*
ton Bridge Industries Ltd, 10 Medina Court, ctic Road, Cowes, Isle of Wight, PO31 7XD l: (01983) 280707 Fax: (01983) 280785 *Boat uilders & repairers*
ester Tools & Fixings Ltd, Unit 10A Shrub Hill dustrial Estate, Shrub Hill Road, Worcester, R4 9EL Tel: (01905) 723421 Fax: (01905) 116 E-mail: sales@worcestertool.co.uk *Power ols, hand tools, fixings & ironmongery stributors*
orcester Urban Scuba, The Stables, Upper ttenhall, Worcester, WR7 4RU Tel: (07971) 2679 E-mail: info@urbanscuba.com *All scuba urses, PADI courses, IAHD course, equipment pair and hire. Worcester"s Scuba centre*
ester Ventilation Systems Ltd, PO Box 190, oitwich, Worcestershire, WR9 7DE l: (01905) 794422 Fax: (01905) 794488 mail: mail@worcester-vent.co.uk *Industrial ntilation & dust extraction manufrs*
orcestershire Marble, Button Bridge, Kinlet, ewdley, Worcestershire, DY12 3AW l: (01299) 841206 Fax: (01299) 841516
estershire Metal Holdings Ltd, Trentham ouse, 40 Red Lion Street, Alvechurch, rmingham, B48 7LF Tel: 0121-445 3316 ax: 0121-447 7053 *Holding company*
estershire Steels Co., Unit 20 Enfield dustrial Estate, Redditch, Worcestershire, 97 6BY Tel: (01527) 67777 Fax: (01527) 64225 mail: worcestershire.steels@virgin.net *Bright & ack steel stockholders*
ckhadt UK Ltd, Ash Road North, Wrexham dustrial Estate, Wrexham, Clwyd, LL13 9UF l: (01978) 661261 Fax: (01978) 660130 mail: mail@wockhardtuk.co.uk Principal Export eas: Worldwide *Pharmaceuticals products anufrs*
l and Page, 45 Lime Grove, Hoole, Chester, H2 3HW Tel: (01244) 312489 mail: edit@wordandpage.co.uk *Editing, layout, esign and typesetting of text & pictures; econdary activities include font design, anslation (esp. Finnish, Germanic languages, ld Norse, Latin, Greek). Specialist area is cademic publications, but business documents c. also welcome. Limitations: only work on omputer (no hard copy except for reference); o self-publishers or novels, memoirs etc. We e VAT-registered. Advanced and Registered ember of Society for Editors and Proofreaders. stablished 1996.*
l Link Ltd, 121a Godolphin Road, London, 12 8JN Tel: (020) 8749 3388 Fax: (020) 8749 398 E-mail: sales@wordlink.demon.co.uk *Direct arketing services*
l Processing Services, 107 Dashwood Avenue, igh Wycombe, Buckinghamshire, HP12 3EB l: (01494) 538090 Fax: (01494) 538088 -mail: info@wordproc.co.uk *Word processing & hotocopying services*
ord2Word Translation Services, 1 Grosvenor ardens, Woodford Green, Essex, IG8 0AR el: 0207 1935665 -mail: info@word2word.co.uk *We provide a fast nd competative translation service for all types f Documents.*We work with Local Councils and any Goverment organisations.*For a free quote all us now.*
dcrafts, Unit 9 The Beaver Centre, Putney oad West, Freemans Common, Leicester, E2 7TD Tel: 0116-255 8422 Fax: 0116-255 524 E-mail: info@wordcrafts.co.uk *Computer raphic services*
dflow, 32-38 Scrutton Street, London, C2A 4RQ Tel: (020) 7377 1182 Fax: (020) 377 2942 E-mail: help@wordflow.co.uk *omputer & office consumable suppliers*
dley Production Ltd, The Warehouse, 1 High t, Penarth, South Glamorgan, CF64 1EY el: (029) 2070 0590 Fax: (029) 2070 0550 -mail: sales@wordleyproduction.com *roduction company*
ordleys, 9 Bennington Street, Cheltenham, loucestershire, GL50 4ED Tel: 01242 525208 ax: 01242 525208
ds That Sell, 45 Sherrardspark Road, Welwyn arden City, Herts, AL8 7LD Tel: 01707 887989 ax: 07050 663664 -mail: mel@wordsthatsell.co.uk *Copywriting nd Marketing consultancy, specialising in highly ffective direct marketing techniques, especially ales letters, catalogues & leaflets.*

▶ Words Worth, Benfleet Water Tower, 335 Benfleet Road, Benfleet, Essex, SS7 1PW Tel: (01268) 756261 Fax: (01268) 750706 *For 15 years WordsWorth has been providing companies of all sizes and in many different industries with Public Relations support as an affordable and effective alternative to advertising.***
Wordsmith & Co., Farnham Royal, Slough, SL2 3WZ Tel: (01753) 645636 Fax: (01753) 669402 E-mail: dn@wordsmith-and-co.demon.co.uk *Publishing*
Wordsworth UK Ltd, Grimshaw Lane, Middleton, Manchester, M24 2AE Tel: 0161-653 9006 Fax: 0161-653 2613 *Contract packers & toiletries manufrs*
Work Group Support Systems, The Studio, Craigleth Road, Edinburgh, EH4 2EB Tel: 0131-477 7775 Fax: 0131-332 7467 E-mail: n.hill@wgss.co.uk *Software reseller*
Work In Style Ltd, Keighley Business Centre, South Street, Keighley, West Yorkshire, BD21 1AG Tel: (01535) 667625 Fax: (01535) 610488 E-mail: sales@workinstyle.com *Hospital garment & textile manufrs*
▶ Work Permit Consultants, Mount Ephraim, Tunbridge Wells, Kent, TN4 8AS Tel: 01892 543939 Fax: 01892 527653 E-mail: enquiry@workpermitconsultants.com *Work Permit and immigration specialist advisors. Regulated by the OISC to provide expert immigration advice.*
Work Place Safety Management Ltd, Unit 11A, Whitwick Business Centre, Whitwick Business Park, Stenson Road, Coalville, Leicestershire, LE67 4JP Tel: (01530) 276535 Fax: (01530) 276536 *Dust extraction installation service*
The Work Shop, 7 High Street, Ringwood, Hampshire, BH24 1AB Tel: (01425) 489393 Fax: (01425) 489402 E-mail: sales@thework-shop.net *A new recruitment agency specialising in permanent recruitment, placing local people in local jobs.*
Work Space, Chequers Street, Wigan, Lancashire, WN1 1HN Tel: (01942) 230512 Fax: (01942) 238800 *Nursery ware & soft furnishings manufrs*
▶ Work Tool Hire Ltd, 43 Commercial Road, Port Talbot, West Glamorgan, SA13 1LN Tel: (01639) 898888 Fax: (01639) 884377
▶ The Work Wear Department, 4, 93 West Main Street, Broxburn, West Lothian, EH52 5LE Tel: (01506) 859333 Fax: (01506) 859333
▶ Work Wear Warehouse, Duncrue CR, Belfast, BT3 9BW Tel: (028) 9077 7114 Fax: (028) 9077 3115 E-mail: sales@garmentgraphixs.co.uk *Personalised work wear & promotional clothing suppliers*
Work & Weather Wear, 44 High Street, Biggar, Lanarkshire, ML12 6BJ Tel: (01899) 221076 Fax: (01899) 221450 *Outdoor clothing, workwear & camping supplies*
▶ Workforce, Forth Family Centre, Castle Road, Rosyth, Dunfermline, Fife, KY11 2AS Tel: (01383) 420000 Fax: (01383) 415500
Workforce (Employment) Ltd, Force Group House, 31-33 Albion Street, Stoke-on-Trent, ST1 1QF Tel: (01782) 221900 Fax: (01782) 281047 E-mail: enquiry@workforce-employment.co.uk *Employment agency*
▶ Workforce Systems, Unit 13 Nortex Business Centre, 105 Chorley Old Road, Bolton, BL1 3AS Tel: (01204) 842225 Fax: (01204) 497197 E-mail: sales@workforce.co.uk *Computer consultancy*
Working Boats UK Ltd, 12 High Street, Fordington, Dorchester, Dorset, DT1 1JZ Tel: (01305) 257488 Fax: (01305) 257488 E-mail: chris@working-boats.co.uk *Boat builders*
Working Images, The Old Stables, Kingston House Estate, Kingston Bagpuize, Abingdon, Oxfordshire, OX13 5AX Tel: (07831) 843338 Fax: (01865) 375855 E-mail: chris@working-images.co.uk *Photographers, commercial or industrial*
▶ Working Space Solutions, 32 Selbourne Road, Weston-super-Mare, Avon, BS23 4LU Tel: 0117-925 1899 Fax: 0117-925 1913 E-mail: workingspace@btopenworld.com *Shelving storage & office partitions*
Working Wall Ltd, 97A Addison Road, Enfield, Middlesex, EN3 5LA Tel: (01992) 558800 Fax: (020) 8272 5417 *Audio-visual equipment & suppliers*
Working Wood Ltd, Unit 1 New Cut, Wellington Street, Newmarket, Suffolk, CB8 0HT Tel: (01638) 669256 *Hand made furniture, music instruments & boats manufrs*
Work-Kit Ltd, Unit 18c Rovex Business Park, Hay Hall Road Tyseley, Birmingham, B11 2AG Tel: 0121-706 4341 Fax: 0121-707 4831 E-mail: mail@work-kit.fsnet.co.uk *Workwear & safety wear suppliers*
Workleen, Rushes Road, Petersfield, Hampshire, GU32 3AR Tel: (0800) 7836484 Fax: (01730) 260633 *Protective clothing, footwear distributors*
Workmates Building Trade, 3 The Schoolhouse, Second Avenue, Trafford Park, Manchester, M17 1DZ Tel: 0161-877 8080 Fax: 0161-877 8088 E-mail: paul.hallsworth@danielowen.co.uk *Employment agency specialising in construction*
Workmates (Building Trades) Ltd, Hadwyn House, Field Road, Reading, RG1 6AP Tel: 0118-952 1000 Fax: 0118-950 8181 E-mail: adrian.tigg@workmates.co.uk *Employment agency specialising in construction*
Workmates Maintenance Recruitment Ltd, 6 Queen Street, London, EC4N 1SP Tel: (020) 7248 7000 Fax: (020) 7248 6060 E-mail: steve.tombs@workmates.co.uk *Employment agency specialising in construction*
▶ Workplace Office Furniture Ltd, 47 Albert Street, Aberdeen, AB25 1XT Tel: (01224) 639325 Fax: (01224) 648830 *Sales & distribution of office furniture*
Workrest Blades, 3 Wattville Road Industrial Estate, Wattville Road, Smethwick, West Midlands, B66 2NT Tel: 0121-558 4339 Fax: 0121-558 3666 E-mail: neal@workrestblades.co.uk *Machine tools manufrs*
▶ The Workroom Ltd, 28 Waterside, 44-48 Wharf Road, London, N1 7UX Tel: (020) 7608 0840 Fax: (020) 7608 0850 E-mail: admin@workroom.co.uk *We are The*

continued

Workroom, a communication and design agency - the room with a view on how to create, invigorate and revitalize brand identity and marketing communications. We work for Reckitt Benkiser, The Scouts, New Scientist, Soil Association, Medical Research Council and others. Our clients get rigorous thinking, strategy, ideas, energy and a collaborative approach which delivers results. That's why 70% of our business comes from people we have worked with before. We'd love to share a view on your business or brand.
Works Design Ltd, The Co-Op Centre, 11 Mowll Street, London, SW9 6BG Tel: (020) 7820 8501 Fax: (020) 7820 8502 E-mail: sales@worksdesign.co.uk *Works Design, established in 1988, provides Product and Engineering Design services. Styling, innovation, engineering, production drawings. Products from industrial equipment to consumer goods. Visit our web site or ask for our brochure.*
▶ Workscape Ltd, 1-2 Westpoint Business Park, Bumpers Farm, Chippenham, Wiltshire, SN14 6RB Tel: (01249) 447200 Fax: (01249) 447400 *Office Designers.*
▶ Worksmart Solutions, 41 Tickford Street, Newport Pagnl, Newport Pagnell, Buckinghamshire, MK16 9AW Tel: (01908) 613613 E-mail: sales@worksmart.co.uk *Computer software developers*
Worksop Galvanizing Ltd, Claylands Avenue, Worksop, Nottinghamshire, S81 7BQ Tel: (01909) 486384 Fax: (01909) 482540 E-mail: worksop@wedge-galv.co.uk *Hot dip galvanising organisation, part of nation-wide Wedge Group* Also at: Bradford
Workspace Office Solutions Ltd, 1 Swanick Court, Alfredton, Ripley, Derbyshire, DE5 57AF Tel: (01773) 523080 Fax: (01773) 523099 E-mail: email@pentos-plc.co.uk *Office furniture systems manufrs* Also at: London W1
Workstation Technologies Ltd, 21 Sovereign Road, Kings Norton Business Centre, Birmingham, B30 3HN Tel: 0121-486 1234 Fax: (0870) 9901918 E-mail: info@wtluk.com *Computer systems manufrs*
Worktown Office Supplies Ltd, 1 Park Court, Premier Way, Abbey Park, Romsey, Hants, SO51 9AQ Tel: (01794) 525065 Fax: (01794) 525025 E-mail: orders@worktown.com *Office equipment furniture*
Workware & Business Casuals, Unit 26 Snedshill Industrial Estate, Snedshill, Telford, Shropshire, TF2 9NH Tel: (01952) 615976 Fax: (01952) 614440 E-mail: enquiries@myworkwear.co.uk *Workwear supply services*
Workware Protective Equipment, Tannery House, Tannery Road, Harraby Green Business Park, Carlisle, CA1 2SS Tel: (01228) 591091 Fax: (01228) 590026 E-mail: sales@workware.co.uk *Protective clothing importers*
Workwear Express Ltd, The Image Centre, Wesley Place, Coxhoe, Durham, DH6 4LG Tel: 0191-377 9318 Fax: 0191-377 9001 E-mail: info@workwearexpress.com *Work wear equipment*
▶ Workwear Trading, Unit 5, Bone Lane, Newbury, Berkshire, RG14 5SH Tel: 01635 527301 Fax: 01635 522811 E-mail: info@tradingsolutions.co.uk *Workwear Trading offers high quality Fristads work clothing at competetive prices. We also sell safety shoes & boots. Overalls, high Vis & Flame retardent garments. We also offer an embroidery & Print service.*
▶ Workwear World, 445 Honeypot Lane, Stanmore, Middlesex, HA7 1JJ Tel: (020) 8206 2004 Fax: (020) 8206 2005 E-mail: sales@workwearworld.co.uk *Workwear clothing retailers & manufrs (embroidered or screen printed with company logos)*
World Beta Standard Equestrian Products, Unit 12, Ennerdale Road, Kitty Brewster Industrial Estate, Blyth, Northumberland, NE24 4RT Tel: (01670) 357300 Fax: (01670) 357301 E-mail: sales@falpro.com *Equestrian goods importers*
World of Brass, 9 Hebble Close, Bolton, BL2 3FS Tel: (0845) 260 9009 Fax: (0845) 260 9008 E-mail: info@worldofbrass.co.uk *Choose from a range of door furniture, door handles, door knobs, door locks and latches, cabinet fittings, window furniture, bathroom fittings, electrical light switches and sockets, and designer architectural hardware products. All produced to the highest quality in solid brass, chrome, stainless steel, aluminium and black iron. From the classic to the contemporary, whatever your style or budget, World of Brass has something that's perfect for you to express your individuality.*
World of Catering, 684-692 Lea Bridge Road, London, E10 6AW Tel: (020) 8556 5038 Fax: (020) 8558 9410 E-mail: *Air conditioning, refrigeration & catering equipment distributors*
▶ World Courier, Sea Containers House, 20 Upper Ground, London, SE1 9PD Tel: (020) 7717 1400 Fax: (020) 7928 7105 E-mail: contact@worldcourier.com *Courier services (air) including overseas*
World Of Fishes, 31 North End, London Road, East Grinstead, West Sussex, RH19 1QJ Tel: (01342) 410636 Fax: (01342) 317085 E-mail: sales@worldoffishes.com *Aquarium & pond suppliers*
World Of Fragrance, Units 1-3 Mile End, Brandon, Suffolk, IP27 0NG Tel: (01842) 815551 Fax: (01842) 814481 E-mail: wofs@prince4828.fsworld.co.uk *Fragrance & giftware*
▶ World Freight Centre Ltd, 26 Bond, Europa Way, Trafford Park, Manchester, M17 1WF Tel: 0161-848 0066 Fax: 0161-848 0055 E-mail: sales@worldfreightcentre.com
▶ World of Garden Leisure, 30 Broadway, Sheerness, Kent, ME12 1TP Tel: (01795) 663444
World Language Consultants Ltd, 88 Bermondsey Street, London, SE1 3UB Tel: (020) 7357 6981 Fax: (020) 7357 7755 E-mail: worldlanguages@btconnect.com *Language translation services*

World Leisurewear Ltd, 46 High Steet, Cowes, Isle Of Wight, PO31 7RR Tel: (01983) 291744 Fax: (01983) 297252 E-mail: sales@worldleisurewear.com *Clothing manufrs*
▶ World Management Services Ltd, 71 Station Road, Ellon, Aberdeenshire, AB41 9AR Tel: (01358) 720334
World Markets Co. P.L.C., 525 Ferry Road, Edinburgh, EH5 2AW Tel: 0131-315 2000 Fax: 0131-315 2999 *Investment information services*
▶ World Nuclear Association, 22a St. James's Square, London, SW1Y 4JH Tel: (020) 7451 1520 Fax: (020) 7839 1501 E-mail: wna@world-nuclear.org *Promoting nuclear energy*
▶ World Precision Instruments Ltd, Astonbury Farm Business Centre, Aston, Stevenage, Hertfordshire, SG2 7EG Tel: (01438) 880025 Fax: (01438) 880026 E-mail: wpiuk@wpi-europe.com *Biomedical instrumentation manufrs*
World Of Sewing, 56-64 Camden Road, Tunbridge Wells, Kent, TN1 2QP Tel: (01892) 536314 Fax: (01892) 520810 E-mail: sales@sewing-world.co.uk *Multi-brand independent sewing machine specialists*
World Transport Agency Ltd, 19-21 Schneider Close, Felixstowe, Suffolk, IP11 3BQ Tel: (01394) 673247 Fax: (01394) 673721 E-mail: arb@wta.co.uk *Freight forwarders*
World Transport Agency Ltd, Thameside House Kingsway Business Park, Oldfield Road, Hampton, Middlesex, TW12 2HD Tel: (020) 8941 7373 Fax: (020) 8941 8138 *Freight forwarders* Also at: Birmingham, Felixstowe, Hull, Liverpool & Manchester
World Transport Agency Ltd, Room 215-217, Building 308, World Freight Terminal, Manchester Airport, Manchester, M90 5PZ Tel: 0161-436 5656 Fax: 0161-499 1145 *General freight agents*
World Visual Ltd, 35 Lower Richmond Road, London, SW14 7EZ Tel: (020) 8876 4444 Fax: (020) 8392 9200 E-mail: info@worldvisual.co.uk *Designs*
World Of Water Ltd, Wood Lane, Timperley, Altrincham, Cheshire, WA15 7PJ Tel: 0161-903 9944 Fax: 0161-903 9666 *Aquatic centre retailers*
World Of Water, West Street, Coggeshall, Colchester, CO6 1NT Tel: (01376) 563836 Fax: (01376) 563598 E-mail: sales@worldofwater.com *Pond & water feature distribution*
World Of Water, Turners Hill Road, Worth, Crawley, West Sussex, RH10 4PE Tel: (01293) 883237 Fax: (01293) 883231 E-mail: crawley@worldofwater.com *Pond supplies*
World Of Water, Mulbrooks, Hailsham, East Sussex, BN27 2RH Tel: (01323) 442400 Fax: (01323) 848400 *Aquatics supplier*
World Of Water, 93 Great Bridge Road, Romsey, Hampshire, SO51 0HB Tel: (01794) 515923 Fax: (01794) 830846 *Water gardens retailers*
World Of Water (Nottingham), Woodlands, Lowdham Lane, Woodborough, Nottingham, NG14 6DN Tel: 0115-966 3333 Fax: 0115-966 5030 *Aquatic centre*
World Welding Alloys Ltd, Unit 18 Shrivenham Hundred Business Park, Majors Road, Watchfield, Swindon, SN6 8TZ Tel: (01793) 783880 Fax: (01793) 782977 E-mail: info@welding.fsnet.co.uk *Welding equipment distributors*
World Wide Direct Mail Ltd, Unit 4, Clipper Close, Medway City Estate, Strood, Rochester, Kent, ME2 4QR Tel: (01634) 723135 Fax: (01634) 713399 E-mail: paul.barford@btconnect.com *Direct mail advertising contractors*
▶ World Wide Fishing Flies, 5 Gillfoot Avenue, Smithfield, Egremont, Cumbria, CA22 2QE Tel: (01946) 820593 Fax: (01946) 820593 E-mail: mark@worldwidefishingflies.co.uk *Quality hand tied flies for the Discerning Game Fly Fisherman.*Full Custom Tying Service.*Free Worldwide Shipping.*
World Wide Food Machinery Ltd, Ten Acres, Barton Street, Ashby-cum-Fenby, Grimsby, South Humberside, DN37 0RU Tel: (01472) 827132 Fax: (01472) 220207 E-mail: sales@worldwidefoodmachinery.co.uk *Food preparation machinery refurbishers*
World Wide Time Share Hypermarket, Woodland Point, Wootton Mount, Bournemouth, BH1 1PJ Tel: (0870) 4431466 Fax: (0870) 4431477 E-mail: sales@timeshare-hypermarket.com *Worldwide Timeshare Hypermarket has been trading in Timeshare resale's for over five years and has acquired an excellent reputation for customer care by providing a highly professional service, combining one of the biggest timeshare week databases with a long waiting list of buyers eager for specific weeks when they become available. Being full members of the Organization for Timeshare in Europe (OTE) and ensuring all legal obligations are adhered to as well as holding monies deposited in an Escrow account and having no registration fees, no national press advertising costs and no commissions to pay ensures your transaction is secure and good value for money. Dealing with all aspects of Time share including, Time Share resale, time share rental, selling time shares, time share exchange, Time share purchase, rci timeshare and worldwide Timeshare destinations including Spain, England, Florida, Cyprus, Madeira, Malta, Grand Canaria and Tenerife to name a few.*
The World of Wood, Ganol Bldgs, Sarn, Pwllheli, Gwynedd, LL53 8HG Tel: (01758) 730544 Fax: (01758) 730544 *Furniture makers & restorers*
▶ Worldcare Wales Ltd, Ffordd Maelgwyn, Tremarl Industrial Estate, Llandudno Junction, Gwynedd, LL31 9PL Tel: (01492) 593080 E-mail: john@worldcarewaste.fsnet.co.uk *Waste management & skip hire services*
Worldmark, 4 Redwood CR, East Kilbride, Glasgow, G74 5PA Tel: (01355) 249191 Fax: (01355) 230875 E-mail: info@donprint.com *Labelling*

Company Information

Worldmark, 4 Redwood CR, East Kilbride, Glasgow, G74 5PA Tel: (01355) 249191 Fax: (01355) 230875 E-mail: info@donprint.com *Self-adhesive computer label manufrs*

Worlds Apart Ltd, Unit 4 Union Court, 18-20 Union Road, London, SW4 6JP Tel: (020) 7622 0171 Fax: (020) 7622 7975 E-mail: info@worldsapart.co.uk *Toy & kite manufrs*

▶ Worlds Apart, Unit C Aldow Enterprise Park, Manchester, M12 6AE Tel: 0161-274 3737 Fax: 0161-274 3738 E-mail: sales@t-shirtprinter.com *Screen printing services*

World's End Couriers, Unit 6b Farm Lane Trading Estate, Farm Lane, London, SW6 1QJ Tel: (020) 7381 8991 Fax: (020) 7385 4468 *Courier & international services*

Worlds End Waste, Pensbury Place, London, SW8 4TP Tel: (020) 8874 8130 Fax: (020) 7720 9159 *Waste disposal*

World's Fair Ltd, Albert Mill, Albert Street, Oldham, OL8 3QL Tel: 0161-683 8000 Fax: 0161-683 8001 E-mail: wfair@worldsfair.co.uk *Publishers & exhibition organisers*

Worldwide Catering Ltd, 8 Failsworth Industrial Estate, Morton Street, Failsworth, Manchester, M35 0BN Tel: 0161-684 7774 Fax: 0161-684 7343 *Fruit & vegetable distributors*

▶ Worldwide Corporate Services, 5 Angelica Way, Whiteley, Fareham, Hampshire, PO15 7HY Tel: (0700) 5946936 E-mail: info@worldcorporate.co.uk *Your own Offshore company formation online using our electronic incorporation service. Our offshore company formation service is totally automated and puts you in control through our web site. Worldwide Corporate Services is the UKs leading offshore company registration agent.*

▶ Worldwide Dispensers, Merton Industrial Park, Lee Road, London, SW19 3WD Tel: (020) 8545 7500 Fax: (020) 8545 7502 E-mail: sales@dsswd.com *Plastic tap & dispenser manufrs*

Worldwide Exhibition Specialists Ltd, 1 York House, Langston Road, Loughton, Essex, IG10 3TQ Tel: (020) 8508 2224 Fax: (020) 8502 4969 E-mail: info@worldwidexpo.co.uk *Exhibition transportation logistics*

▶ Worldwide Granite Ltd, Unit 1 Esgors Farm, High Road, Thornwood, Epping, Essex, CM16 6LY Tel: (01992) 571144 Fax: (01992) 571133 *We manufacture granite kitchen work tops at competive prices, we also supply and fit cladding, bathrooms, hotel receptions and floors*

Worldwide Ideas Ltd, Ideas House Station Estate, Eastwood Close, London, E18 1RT Tel: (020) 8530 7171 Fax: (020) 8530 7365 E-mail: sales@worldwideideas.co.uk *Advertising gifts manufrs*

Worldwide PC UK Ltd, 88-90 Manningham Lane, Bradford, West Yorkshire, BD1 3ES Tel: (01274) 745515 E-mail: gary@wwpc.co.uk *Computer hardware & software distributors*

Worldwide Solutions Ltd, Unit 5, Alfred Court, Saxon Business Park, Hanbury Road, Stoke Prior, Bromsgrove, Worcestershire, B60 4AD Tel: (01527) 870849 Fax: (01527) 874499 E-mail: enquiries@wwsolutions.co.uk *Distributor of bar code scanning & data collection equipment*

Worldwide Tropicals, 75 Commerce Street, Glasgow, G5 8EP Tel: 0141-427 1066 Fax: 0141-429 4448 *Importer & sales of tropical fish*

The Worldwide Wood Co., 154 Colney Hatch Lane, London, N10 1ER Tel: (020) 8365 2157 Fax: (020) 8365 3965 E-mail: sales@solidwoodflooring.com *Solid wood flooring dealers*

Worleyparsons Europe Ltd, Parkview, Great West Road, Brentford, Middlesex, TW8 9AZ Tel: (020) 8758 9477 Fax: (020) 8710 0220 E-mail: info@worleyparsons.com *Project management consultants*

Worlifts Ltd, 90 Roebuck Lane, West Bromwich, West Midlands, B70 6QX Tel: 0121-460 1113 Fax: 0121-525 1022 E-mail: sales@worlifts.co.uk Principal Export Areas: Worldwide *Hydraulic suppliers*

Wormald Lintott, Hewett Road, Great Yarmouth, Norfolk, NR31 0NN Tel: (01493) 440500 Fax: (01493) 442639 E-mail: wormaldsafetyandservice.uk@tycoint.com *Fire & safety services*

Wormells Roofing Centre, Regent Street, Coventry, CV1 3EL Tel: (024) 7622 0755 Fax: (024) 7652 5463 E-mail: coventry@wedge-roofing-centres.com *Roofing centre*

Wornald Auto Refinishers, Units 9-10 Park Drive Business Center, Wakefield, West Yorkshire, WF3 3ET Tel: (01924) 822444 *Commercial vehicle repair services*

Worrall Locks Ltd, Erebus Works, Albion Road, Willenhall, West Midlands, WV13 1NH Tel: (01902) 605038 Fax: (01902) 633558 E-mail: sales@worrall-locks.co.uk *Lock manufrs*

▶ Ben Worsley, 14 Foster Avenue, Beaumont Park, Huddersfield, HD4 5LN Tel: (01484) 326669 Fax: (01484) 326669 E-mail: info@ben-worsley.com *Tailoring, medal mounting, regimental ties & blazer badges manufrs*

Worsley Paper Ltd, 5 Barshaw Park, Leycroft Road, Beumont Leys, Leicester, LE4 1ET Tel: (0870) 2410474 Fax: (0870) 2402630 E-mail: info@worsleypaper.co.uk *Paper merchants*

Worsley-Brehmer Ltd, Norman Road, Altrincham, Cheshire, WA14 4ES Tel: 0161-926 8464 Fax: 0161-927 7277 *Print finishing suppliers*

Worson Die Cushions Ltd, Linel Works, 89-91 Rolfe St, Smethwick, West Midlands, B66 2AY Tel: 0121-558 0939 Fax: 0121-558 0017 *Press die cushions manufrs*

Worster & Hounslow, 2 Oaklands Avenue, Watford, WD19 4LW Tel: (01923) 239762 Fax: (01923) 225762 *Electrical contractors*

▶ Worswick Engineering Ltd, Philips Road, Blackburn, BB1 5SG Tel: (01254) 261351 Fax: (01254) 682208 E-mail: sales@worswick.com *Manufacturers of* continued *ingot casting machines & gravity diecasting equipment*

Worth Installations Ltd, Bramwell House, Park Lane, Keighley, West Yorkshire, BD21 4QX Tel: (01535) 210510 Fax: (01535) 691508 E-mail: sales@worthcomms.co.uk *Telecommunications installers*

▶ Worth Scaffolding Co., Rookfield, Crawley Road, Faygate, Horsham, West Sussex, RH12 4SA Tel: (01293) 852619 Fax: (01293) 852620

▶ Worth Solutions Ltd, 66 Leonard Street, London, EC2A 4LW Tel: (020) 7739 3861 *Software consultants*

Worthing Aquatics, High Street, Angmering, Littlehampton, West Sussex, BN16 4AW Tel: (01903) 778922 Fax: (01903) 778902 *Aquarium & pond suppliers*

Worthing Chamber of Commerce & Industry Ltd, 7 Richmond Road, Worthing, West Sussex, BN11 1PN Tel: (01903) 203484 Fax: (01903) 203289 E-mail: mail@worthingchamber.co.uk *Chamber of commerce*

▶ Worthing & District TV Ltd, 147 Tarring Road, Worthing, West Sussex, BN11 4HE Tel: (01903) 201925 Fax: (01903) 208420

Worthing Removals & Storage Co P & H Ltd, Ivy Arch Road, Worthing, West Sussex, BN14 8BX Tel: (01903) 204280 Fax: (01903) 824245 E-mail: sales@worthingremovals.co.uk *Removal contractors & storage contractors*

▶ Worthington Armstrong UK Ltd, 401 Princesway, Team Valley Trading Estate, Gateshead, Tyne & Wear, NE11 0TU Tel: 0191-487 0606 Fax: 0191-491 4085

▶ Worthington Brown Designs, 24 Huddersfield Road, Holmfirth, HD9 2JS Tel: (01484) 688808 Fax: (01484) 688818 E-mail: bt@worthingtonbrown.co.uk *Marketing agency*

▶ Worthington Sharpe Ltd, MSEC Zochonis Building, University of Manchester, Oxford Road, Manchester, M13 9PL Tel: 0161-275 1891 Fax: 0161-275 1919 E-mail: info@worthingtonsharpe.com *Worthington Sharpe Ltd. is a team of professional engineers that provide an innovative and practical mechanical engineering design and product development service.*

Worthside Engineering, Dalton Lane, Keighley, West Yorkshire, BD21 4JU Tel: (01535) 605698 Fax: (01535) 610302 *Heating & ventilation engineers*

Wortley Standards Ltd, Forge Lane, Wortley, Sheffield, S35 7DN Tel: 0114-288 2423 Fax: 0114-288 2423 E-mail: wortley@globalnet.co.uk *Calibrating services*

WotWot.com, Armstrong House, 4-6 First Avenue, Doncaster Finningley Airport, Hayfield Lane, Doncaster, South Yorkshire, DN9 3GA Tel: (0870) 1657305 Fax: (0870) 1657319 E-mail: enquiries@envico-online.com *Safety equipment storage products suppliers*

Wound Products Ltd, Brooklands House, Brooklands Approach, North Street, Romford, RM1 1DX Tel: (01708) 729000 Fax: (01708) 733373 E-mail: sales@woundproducts.com *Transformer manufrs*

Woven Electronics Componants Ltd, Burcombe Lane, Wilton, Salisbury, SP2 0ES Tel: (01722) 744242 Fax: (01722) 744079 E-mail: woven@wovenelectronics.co.uk *Cable assemblies manufrs*

Wovina Woven Labels, 1 & 3 Omaha Road, Bodmin, Cornwall, PL31 1ER Tel: (01208) 73484 Fax: (01208) 78158 E-mail: sales@wovina.com *Woven label manufacturers & embroiderers*

▶ WP Internet Services, 14 Lovatt Close, Tilehurst, READING, RG31 5HG Tel: 07875 297424 E-mail: info@wpinternetservices.co.uk *Broadband Internet services and alternative Telephone service provider. Advice to small business on web and IT matters.*

▶ WPD Contracts, 67a Willowfield Road, Eastbourne, East Sussex, BN22 8AP Tel: (01323) 419866 Fax: (01323) 419867 E-mail: richard@duffy.powernetbtclick.co.uk *Electrical contractors*

▶ WPM Group, Mindenhall Court, High Street, Stevenage, Hertfordshire, SG1 3BG Tel: (01438) 311486 Fax: (01438) 311487 E-mail: enquiries@wpm-group.com *Project management training & consultancy services*

▶ WPR Media Limited, 75 Stonegate Road, Meanwood, Leeds, LS6 4HZ Tel: 0113 2788908 E-mail: editorial@wprmedia.co.uk *Publishers of Materials Handling World Magazine that covers all areas of the supply chain*

▶ WPT (UK) Ltd., One Canada Square, 28th Floor, Canary Wharf, London, E14 5DY Tel: 020 7956 8697 Fax: 020 7956 8666 E-mail: info@wpt-uk.com *Waste Paper Trade*

Wragby C B & Electrical, Market Place, Wragby, Market Rasen, Lincolnshire, LN8 5QU Tel: (01673) 857064 Fax: (01673) 857064 *CB radio electrical sales*

Wragg Bros Ltd, Robert Way, Wickford, Essex, SS11 8DQ Tel: (01268) 732607 Fax: (01268) 768499 E-mail: wragg.bros@btclick.com *Metal fabricators*

Wragg Bros Engineering Ltd, Keys Road, Nixs Hill Industrial Estate, Alfreton, Derbyshire, DE55 7FQ Tel: (01773) 832288 Fax: (01773) 520776 *Engineering sub-contract services & general engineering*

Wraight's Of Dover, Edgar Road, Dover, Kent, CT17 0ES Tel: (01304) 201289 Fax: (01304) 213264 *Industrial coatings*

Wraith Accommodation P.L.C., Accommodation House, Main Street, Torksey, Lincoln, LN1 2EE Tel: (01427) 718000 Fax: (01427) 718921 E-mail: sales@wraith.co.uk *Business accommodation hirers*

▶ Wraith Engineering, Unit 43 Station Road Workshops, Station Road, Kingswood, Bristol, BS15 4PJ Tel: 0117-910 9919 Fax: 0117-981 1279 E-mail: sales@wraith-engineering.co.uk *Specialist suppliers of compressor spares & marine equipment*

Wrangbrook Engineering, Sheepwalk Lane, Upton, Pontefract, West Yorkshire, WF9 1LL Tel: (01977) 648748 *Lawnmower & blade spares*

Wrap Film Systems Ltd, Hortonwood 45, Telford, Shropshire, TF1 7FA Tel: (01952) 678800 Fax: (01952) 678801 E-mail: sales@wrapfilm.com *Wrap Film Systems Ltd, a division of Benedetti International plc, is Europe's leading cling film and foil convertor to the catering and hospitality industry. With 30 years experience we are shaping the future of dispensing film and foil with our award winning Wrapmaster refillable dispenser and new Benedetti disposable dispenser.*

Wrapex Ltd, Unit 6 Lodge Causeway Trading Estate, Lodge Causeway, Bristol, BS16 3JB Tel: 0117-965 7000 Fax: 0117-958 6886 E-mail: sales@wrapex.co.uk *Aluminum foil & cling film manufrs*

Wrapid Contract Services Ltd, Astley Park Industrial Estate, Chaddock Lane, Astley, Manchester, M29 7JY Tel: (01942) 894132 Fax: (01942) 894983 *Packaging services*

Wrapid Holdings Ltd, 250 Thornton Road, Bradford, West Yorkshire, BD1 2LB Tel: (01274) 220220 Fax: (01274) 736195 E-mail: mail@wrapid.co.uk *Packerging suppliers.*

Wrapid Holdings Ltd, 250 Thornton Road, Bradford, West Yorkshire, BD1 2LB Tel: (01274) 220220 Fax: (01274) 736195 E-mail: mail@wrapid.co.uk *Wrapping machine merchants*

Wraps UK, 2 Nimrod Way, East Dorset Trade Park, Wimborne, Dorset, BH21 7SH Tel: (01202) 880204 Fax: (01202) 842632 E-mail: sales@wrapsuk.com *Shrink packaging equipment manufrs*

Wratten Joinery, Aylesford Cottage, Guildford Road, Normandy, Guildford, Surrey, GU3 2AS Tel: (01483) 235324 Fax: (01483) 232131 *Bespoke unit specialists, sash windows & staircases*

Wraxall Power Transmission Equipment, The Lodge Dunchurch Trading Estate, London Road, Dunchurch, Rugby, Warwickshire, CV23 9LN Tel: (01788) 817522 Fax: (01788) 817852 E-mail: sales@wraxall.com *Power transmission equipment*

Christopher Wray (Lighting Emporium) Ltd, 600 Kings Road, London, SW6 2YW Tel: (020) 7736 8434 Fax: (020) 7751 8699 E-mail: sales@christopherwray.com *Decorative lighting fittings*

Wrayram Engineers Ltd, 403 Netherwood Road, Rotherwas Industrial Estate, Hereford, HR2 6JU Tel: (01432) 355454 Fax: (01432) 358727 E-mail: enquiries@wrayram.com *Hydraulic cylinder manufrs*

Wraysbury Dive Centre, Station Road, Wraysbury, Staines, Middlesex, TW19 5ND Tel: (01784) 488007 Fax: (01784) 488007 E-mail: info@learntodive.co.uk *Diving training & equipment hire & retail*

WRC plc, Frankland Road, Blagrove, Swindon, SN5 8YF Tel: (01793) 865000 Fax: (01793) 865001 E-mail: solutions@wrcplc.co.uk *Environmental & water treatment consultants*

Wreake Valley Craftsmen Ltd, Rearsby Road, Thrussington, Leicester, LE7 4UD Tel: (01664) 424380 Fax: (01664) 424287 E-mail: info@wreakevalley.com *Contract furniture suppliers*

Wrefords Transport, Ransome Road, Northampton, NN4 8AD Tel: (01604) 761429 Fax: (01604) 768764 E-mail: sales@swwreford.co.uk *Road transport contractors*

Wrekin Construction Co Ltd, Lamledge Lane, Shifnal, Shropshire, TF11 8BE Tel: (01952) 468000 Fax: (01952) 468001 E-mail: info@wrekin.co.uk *Wrekin Construction, Building, Build, Construction, Civil Engineering, UK Office Developments, UK Engineering, UK Engineers, Investor in People, UK Civil Engineering, Factory Building, Office Building, Office Developments, Rail, British Railways UK*

Wrekin Construction Co. Ltd, Enterprise Road, Raunds, Wellingborough, Northamptonshire, NN9 6JE Tel: (01933) 624404 Fax: (01933) 623496 E-mail: raunds@wrekin.co.uk *Civil engineers*

▶ Wrekin Fabrication Ltd, Walcot, Telford, Shropshire, TF6 5ER Tel: (01952) 740222 Fax: (01952) 740331 E-mail: enquires@wrekinfabs.co.uk *Steel fabrication*

Wrekin Pneumatics Telford Ltd, Park Road, Dawley Bank, Telford, Shropshire, TF4 2BE Tel: (01952) 505566 Fax: (01952) 504703 E-mail: wrekin@interramp.co.uk *Air compressor distributors*

Wrekin Shell Mouldings Ltd, Unit D1 & D2, Halesfield 21, Telford, Shropshire, TF7 4NX Tel: (01952) 580946 Fax: (01952) 582546 E-mail: wsm@dynafluid.com *Non-ferrous metal castings manufacturers & precision machinists*

Wrekin Steel Ltd, Unit A4 Hortonwood 10, Telford, Shropshire, TF1 7ES Tel: (01952) 677600 Fax: (01952) 677900 *Steel stockholders*

Wrekin Windows Ltd, Units D1-D4, Stafford Park 4, Telford, Shropshire, TF3 3BA Tel: (01952) 290733 Fax: (01952) 290956 E-mail: les.burks@wrekin-windows.co.uk *UPVC window manufrs*

Wren Ltd, Harrier House, Aviation Way, Southend Airport, Southend-on-Sea, SS2 6UN Tel: (01702) 548044 Fax: (01702) 541463 E-mail: sales@wrenpack.co.uk *Printers of solid board cartons & other printed board materials*

Wren Industrial & Marine Fabrications Ltd, 24 Sandon Way, Liverpool, L5 9YN Tel: 0151-207 0023 Fax: 0151-207 3916 *Light & non ferrous metal fabricators*

Jonathan Wren & Co. Ltd, 34 London Wall, London, EC2M 5RU Tel: (020) 7309 3550 Fax: (020) 7309 3552 E-mail: career@jwren.com *Recruitment consultants services for investment banking & accountancy*

Wren Media Ltd, Lodge Farm, Gulls Green Road, Fressingfield, Eye, Suffolk, IP21 5SA Tel: (01379) 586787 Fax: (01379) 586755 E-mail: post@wrenmedia.co.uk *Media communications audio & print work producers*

Wren Metal Co. Ltd, Russell Street, Chadderton, Oldham, OL9 9LD Tel: 0161-624 9835 Fax: 0161-627 2746 *Sheet metalwork engineers & fabricators*

Wren Press Stationary Ltd, Unit 1 Chelsea W[...] 15 Lots Road, London, SW10 0QJ Tel: (02[...] 7351 5887 Fax: (020) 7352 7063 E-mail: orders@wrenpress.com *Stationery engraving services*

▶ Wrenco (Contractors)Limited, Sefton Lane Industrial Estate, Liverpool, L31 8DN Tel: 0151-520 2323 E-mail: ho@wrenco.co[...]

Wrencon Ltd, Baron House, Hillcommon, Taun[...] Somerset, TA4 1DS Tel: (01823) 400021 Fax: (01823) 400051 *Quality services at competitive rates, for domestic, commercia[...] industrial sites. We provide free quotations[...] size jobs. See our website for examples of[...] services and previous jobs*

WRES Ltd, 25 Whitney Road, Nuffield Industri[...] Estate, Poole, Dorset, BH17 0GL Tel: (012[...] 674480 Fax: (01202) 660776 *Welding spec[...]*

Wrexham Blinds, The Workshopd, Maes Y Garnedd, Tafarn-Y-Gelyn, Llanferres, Mold, Clwyd, CH7 5SE Tel: (01978) 359788 Fax: (01352) 810234 *Blind manufrs*

Wrexham County Borough Council, The Guild[...] Wrexham, Clwyd, LL11 1AY Tel: (01978) 2[...] Fax: (01978) 292106 E-mail: business@wrexham.gov.uk *Propert[...] development*

▶ Wrexham Metal Finishing, Unit 250a Redwi[...] Business Park, Redwither Business Park, Wrexham, Clwyd, LL13 9UE Tel: (01978) 664888 Fax: (01978) 664888 *Metal finisher[...] powder coating services*

Wrexham Mineral Cables Ltd, Plot 4 Wynnsta[...] Technology Park, Ruabon, Wrexham, Clwy[...] LL14 6EN Tel: (01978) 810789 Fax: (01978[...] 821502 E-mail: sales@wrexhammineralcable.com *Cables, mineral insulated*

Wrexham Pallet Services, Rhosddu Industrial Estate, Main Road, Rhosrobin, Wrexham, C[...] LL11 4YL Tel: (01978) 261043 Fax: (01978[...] 312695 *Pallet suppliers*

Wrexham Power Tool Services, Five Fords Ga[...] Bridge Road, Wrexham Industrial Estate, Wrexham, Clwyd, LL13 9PS Tel: (01978) 6[...] Fax: (01978) 664644 *Electric pneumatic po[...] tools suppliers & repair*

Wrexham Rubber & Fabrications Ltd, Unit 226[...] Redwither Complex, Wrexham Industrial Es[...] Wrexham, Clwyd, LL13 9UE Tel: (01978) 661869 Fax: (01978) 664566 *Industrial rub[...] fabricators*

WRG Partition Systems, 22 Bartleet Road, Redditch, Worcestershire, B98 0DQ Tel: (01[...] 502299 Fax: (01527) 502288 E-mail: wrgpartitions@aol.com *Industrial partitioning systems*

WRH Marketing UK Ltd, 6 Stanstead Courtyar[...] Parsonage Road, Takeley, Bishop's Stortfor[...] Hertfordshire, CM22 6PU Tel: (01279) 6356[...] Fax: (01279) 445666 E-mail: productinfo@wrh-marketing-uk.com *Conveyor systems & stacking machine mar[...]*

Wright & Co., Bramston Street, Brighouse, We[...] Yorkshire, HD6 3AA Tel: (01484) 715166 Fax: (01484) 715166 *Manufacturer of biscu[...] brandy snaps*

Wright Air Systems Ltd, 11 Regent Street, Rochdale, Lancashire, OL12 0HQ Tel: (017[...] 343980 Fax: (01706) 525771 E-mail: was@ame-services.co.uk *Dust & fu[...] extraction*

Wright Aluminium Systems Ltd, Unit 9, Prince Consort Industrial Estate, Hebburn, Tyne & Wear, NE31 1EH Tel: 0191-430 0835 Fax: 0191-483 3062 *Aluminium fabricators*

Wright Bros, Farley, Matlock, Derbyshire, DE4 [...] Tel: (01629) 582687 Fax: (01629) 582687 E-mail: tax@farmersweekly.net *Agricultural contractors*

Wright Brothers (Clayton) Ltd, Victoria Works, Barnard Road, Bradford, West Yorkshire, BD4 7DY Tel: (01274) 587777 Fax: (01274) 394629 *Contractors' plant/crane/skip hire*

Wright Bros Partnership Ltd, Waverley Road, Sheffield, S9 4PL Tel: 0114-244 1807 Fax: 0114-243 9277 *Heating engineers*

Wright Bus Ltd, Galgorm Industrial Estate, Fen[...] Road, Galgorm, Ballymena, County Antrim, BT42 1PY Tel: (028) 2564 1212 Fax: (028) 2[...] 9703 E-mail: sales@wright-bus.com *P.S.V b[...] builders*

Charles Wright & Sons Ltd, Church Road, Old Leake, Boston, Lincolnshire, PE22 9NU Tel: (01205) 870434 Fax: (01205) 871240 *Agricultural merchants*

Wright Cottrell & Co., 76 Gravelly Industrial Pa[...] Birmingham, B24 8TL Tel: 0121-328 2200 Fax: 0121-328 2233 *Dental suppliers* Also a[...] Branches throughout the U.K.

David Wright (Electrical) Ltd, Unit 9 Progress Business Park, Orders Lane, Kirkham, Pres[...] PR4 2TZ Tel: (01772) 682331 Fax: (01772) 686770 E-mail: davidwright9@btconnect.co[...] *Electrical appliance refurbishers*

Wright Electric Company Ltd, 35 Clarendon Avenue, Trowbridge, Wiltshire, BA14 7BW Tel: (01225) 761188 Fax: (01225) 761188 E-mail: sales@wrightelec.demon.co.uk *Manufacturers of rectifier (electrical), power supply, custom built & ACDC military applications*

Wright Engineering Co. Ltd, Masons Road, Stratford-upon-Avon, Warwickshire, CV37 9[...] Tel: (01789) 292939 Fax: (01789) 297458 E-mail: sales@wright-eng.co.uk *Hose coupli[...] garage forecourt equipment manufrs*

Wright Engineering Co Nottingham Ltd, Colwickwood Works, Colwick Road, Nottingh[...] NG2 4BG Tel: 0115-950 2284 Fax: 0115-94[...] 4967 E-mail: wright@wright-engineers.co.uk *Mechanical & precision engineers*

Wright Engineering Rainham Ltd, Imperial Trad[...] Estate, Lambs La North, Rainham, Essex, RM13 9XL Tel: (01708) 554618 Fax: (01708[...] 553395 E-mail: wright0458@aol.com *Gener[...] engineers*

Wright Guard Security Systems & Electrical, 2 [...] Columbia Avenue, Mansfield, Nottinghamshi[...] NG18 3LD Tel: (01623) 645808 *Burglar alar[...] systems & electrical contractors*

Health Group Ltd, Dunsinane Avenue,
sinane Industrial Estate, Dundee, DD2 3QD
(01382) 833866 Fax: (01382) 811042
ail: administrator@wright-dental.co.uk
icial tooth (for dental profession) manufrs
at: Birmingham, Glasgow, Leeds, London,
chester & Newcastle
ght Healthy, Ashburner Street, Bolton,
1TQ Tel: (01204) 386700
ail: wrighthealthy@aol.com *Health food*
ducers
Machinery Ltd, Stonefield Way, Ruislip,
dlesex, HA4 0JU Tel: (020) 8842 2244
(020) 8842 1113
ail: sales@wright.co.uk *Packaging*
chinery equipment distribution manufrs
ght & Maclennan Ltd, Camps Industrial
ate, Kirknewton, Midlothian, EH27 8DF
(01506) 881486 *Metalworking & fabrication*
vices
right Ltd, Woodland Works, Woodlands
d, Thundridge, Ware, Hertfordshire,
12 0SP Tel: (01920) 461235 Fax: (01920)
423E-mail: maxwrightlimited@btinternet.com
omatic switchgear electronic systems
nufrs
l Wright Ltd, PO Box 469, High Wycombe,
kinghamshire, HP14 3GL Tel: (01491)
274 *Industrial electrical contractors*
Vright Merchandising, 185 Weedon Road,
thampton, NN5 5DA Tel: (07000) 226397
(01604) 456129
ail: tshirts@mickwright.com *Merchandising*
nts (promotional clothing) Also at: London
ght & Owen Ec Ltd, 16 Watson Place,
nouth, PL4 9QN Tel: (01752) 222133
(01752) 226909
Plastics Ltd, Fernie Road, Market
borough, Leicestershire, LE16 7PH
(01858) 465661 Fax: (01858) 431831
ail: sales@wplastic.co.uk *Plastics injection*
uldings manufrs
ght Projects Ltd, 79 Back Sneddon Street,
sley, Renfrewshire, PA3 2BT Tel: 0141-887
7 Fax: 0141-887 7598
Rain Irrigation, 4 Christchurch Road,
gwood, Hampshire, BH24 3SB Tel: (01425)
251 Fax: (01425) 472258
ail: sales@wrightrain.com *Irrigation, slurry &*
t suppression manufrs
& Round Ltd, PO Box 157, Gloucester,
1LW Tel: (01452) 523438 Fax: (01452)
631
ail: wright-and-round@interactive-sciences.
k *Brass band music publishers*
Ruffell (Joinery), Plough Road Centre, Great
tley, Colchester, CO7 8LG Tel: (01206)
601 Fax: (01206) 251443 *Timber*
ineering & trussed rafter specialists
Sign Service, 1 Greenside, Pudsey, West
kshire, LS28 8PU Tel: 0113-255 7259
: 0113-255 7259
ail: jon808@btclick.com *Sign contractors*
ght Signs, 4 Teal Business Park, Dodwells
d, Hinckley, Leicestershire, LE10 3BZ
(01455) 616151 Fax: (0845) 8906151
ail: sales@asg.co.uk *Sign manufrs*
ght & Smith Ltd, 26 Whiston Road,
enhoe, Northampton, NN7 1NL Tel: (01604)
277 Fax: (01604) 890641
ht & Son (Holdings) Ltd, Main Street,
ntain Road, Hull, HU2 0LA Tel: (01482)
845 Fax: (01482) 323636
ail: enquiry@wrightgroup.co.uk *Holding*
pany
Transport Services, 6 Council Houses,
rham Hill, Sparham, Norwich, NR9 5QT
(01603) 872022 Fax: (01603) 872022
ilage & road transport
Way Cleaning & Maintenance Services,
serts End, 11a Bosserts Way, Highfields
decote, Cambridge, CB23 7PA Tel: (01954)
405 Fax: (01954) 212406
ail: wright-way@btconnect.com *Office*
ning contractors
orm Ltd, Church Road, Redgrave, Diss,
folk, IP22 1RJ Tel: (01379) 898400
: (01379) 898405
ail: sales@wrightform.com *Metal engineering*
vices
ghts Blinds, Highfield House, Fulwood Row,
wood, Preston, PR2 5RU Tel: (01772)
836 Fax: (01772) 798353 *Blind manufrs*
s Engineering, 7 Tardygate Mill, Coote Lane,
tock Hall, Preston, PR5 5JD Tel: (01772)
070 Fax: (01772) 337070 *Wrought ironwork*
s Flooring Contractors, 78a Sabine Road,
don, SW11 5LW Tel: (020) 7223 5970
: (020) 7228 4616 *Flooring contractors*
s Garage Ullesthorpe Ltd, Claybrooke Road,
sthorpe, Lutterworth, Leicestershire,
7 5AD Tel: (01455) 209171 *Jig work*
s Hose Clips Ltd, Unit 15 Portway Close,
entry, CV4 9UY Tel: (024) 7647 0377 *Classic*
restoration
s Of Lymm Ltd, Warrington Lane, Lymm,
eshire, WA13 0SA Tel: (01925) 752226
: (01925) 757569
ail: info@wrightsoflymm.co.uk *Traditional*
writers, decorators & gilder suppliers
s Plastics Ltd, Brandon Way, West
mwich, West Midlands, B70 8JH
0121-580 3080 Fax: 0121-580 3081
ail: sales@wrightsplastics.co.uk *Plastic*
uum formed products
s Property Services, Unit 317 Tedco Bus
tre, Viking Industrial Park, Jarrow, Tyne &
ar, NE32 3DT Tel: 0191-428 3362
: 0191-428 3314
ail: homeshields@hotmail.co.uk *Building &*
fing
s Sandbach Ltd, 9 Old Middlewich Road,
dbach, Cheshire, CW11 1DP Tel: (01270)
416 Fax: (01270) 760278
ail: sales@wrightsprinters.com *General*
ters
ghts Tools & Supplies, 98a Creek Road,
ch, Cambridgeshire, PE15 8RD Tel: (01354)
778 Fax: (01354) 650646 *Tool retailers*
ways Ltd, Beveridge Lane, Ellistown,
lville, Leicestershire, LE67 1FB Tel: (01530)
183 Fax: (01530) 263186
ail: info@wrightwaysltd.co.uk *Demolition*

continued

contractors & asbestos removal service providers

▶ Wrigmers Baits, Unit 3 Exeter Street, Teignmouth, Devon, TQ14 8JJ Tel: (01626) 777302

Wrington Precision Automatics, 19 Blue Water Drive, Elborough, Weston-Super-Mare, Avon, BS24 8PF Tel: (01934) 823525 Fax: E-mail: pill@wrington.co.uk *Manufacturers of precision turned parts*

▶ The Wrington Vale Medical Practice, Ladymead Lane, Churchill, Winscombe, Avon, BS25 5NH Tel: (01934) 852362 E-mail: martin@wringtonvaleconstruction.co.uk *bespoke carports, verandas, specialist stone work extensions, and follies. civic award winning*

Write On Signs, Kilda Road, Perth, PH1 3FL Tel: (01738) 630007 Fax: (01738) 449191 E-mail: info@write-on-signs.com *Sign manufrs*

▶ The Write Track, Head Office, 107 Herons Wood, Harlow, Essex, CM20 1RT Tel: 01279 639356 E-mail: GetOn@TheWriteTrack.biz *Comprehensive copywriting, editing and desktop publishing services: professional expertise for all your marketing collateral, newsletters, policies and procedures, Web sites and B2B documentation.*

▶ write4me.co.uk, St Martin's Studios, Greenbank Road, Ashton VIllage, Sale, Cheshire, M33 5PL Tel: 0845 054 8585 *www.write4me.co.uk uses top specialist writers to provide anything written. Word perfect for business, fun or families. We guarantee prices and deadlines on a single project basis.*

Writing Machine, 19 City Business Centre, Hyde Street, Winchester, Hampshire, SO23 7TA Tel: (01962) 841250 Fax: (01962) 870558 E-mail: sales@writingmachine.com *Marketing & copywriting consultants services*

Wrought Art, 7 Gordon Road, Derby, DE23 6WR Tel: (01332) 340563 Fax: (01332) 200234 *Architectural ornamental ironwork & steel fabrications*

Wrought Iron Shop, 136 Prescot Road, Fairfield, Liverpool, L7 0JB Tel: 0151-252 0460 Fax: 0151-252 0460 *Wrought iron manufrs*

▶ Wrought Ironwork Nottingham, 1A Bailey Street, Stapleford, Nottingham, NG9 7BD Tel: (07976) 293162 E-mail: wrought.iron@ntlworld.com *Steel fabrication*

Wroughton Developments, 14 Barcelona Cresent, Wroughton, Swindon, SN4 9EE Tel: (01793) 812292 Fax: (01793) 812292 *General engineering*

WRTL Exterior Lighting, 2 Waterside Park, Golds Hill Way, Tipton, West Midlands, DY4 0PU Tel: 0121-521 1234 Fax: 0121-521 1250 E-mail: sales@wrtl.co.uk *Industrial & commercial light suppliers*

Wrythe Properties Ltd, 56 St. James Road, Carshalton, Surrey, SM5 2DU Tel: (020) 8647 9100 Fax: (020) 8669 9655 *Sub-contract precision engineers*

▶ WSG Packaging Ltd, 7 Smiths Forge, North End Road, Yatton, Bristol, BS49 4AU Tel: (01934) 877272 Fax: (01934) 877287 *Wholesale packaging distributors*

▶ WSi Ltd, Units 1-3, Beezon Road Trading Estate, Kendal, Cumbria, LA9 6BW Tel: (01539) 790604 Fax: (01539) 790601 E-mail: sales@wsi-sign.co.uk *Sign survey, design, manufacture & installation*

▶ WSI Core Solutions, 65 Hendon Way, London, NW2 2LX Tel: (020) 8458 2928 Fax: (0871) 6616581 E-mail: sally@wsicoresolutions.com *Develop and maintain websites, provide e-business solutions such as online learning systems, online communications, internet marketing and internet consultancy and support.*

WSI Smart Web Systems, 2 Naunton Way, Leckhampton, Cheltenham, Gloucestershire, GL53 7BQ Tel: (01242) 570330 Fax: (01242) 570330 E-mail: tony@hodderonline.com *Devise & implement online business strategies*

WSP, Colston Avenue 33, Bristol, BS1 4UA Tel: 0117-930 2000 Fax: 0117-929 4624 E-mail: admin@wspgroup.com *Consulting engineers*

WSP International Ltd, First Point, Buckingham Gate, London Gatwick Airport, Gatwick, West Sussex, RH6 0NT Tel: (01293) 602600 Fax: (01293) 602699 E-mail: info@wsp-int.com *Consulting engineers*

▶ WT Flockhart Ltd, 17c, Water-Ma-Trout, Helston, Cornwall, TR13 0LW Tel: (01326) 561971 E-mail: sales@flockhart-heating.co.uk

▶ Wudo Ltd, 2 Stanley Road, Hertford, SG13 7LQ Tel: (01992) 504014 Fax: (01992 537388 E-mail: rachelwu@lineone.net *Agents for chinese factories including natural stones (kirb, setts & slabs) ceramic times, bath & mixers*

Wulfruna Col Co., Minerva Wharf, Horseley Field, Wolverhampton, WV1 3DT Tel: (01902) 453517 *Wholesale & retail coal merchants*

Wulfruna Locksmith Ltd, Security Centre, 198 Penn Road, Wolverhampton, WV4 4AA Tel: (01902) 337267 Fax: (01902) 337267 *Locksmith services*

Wulstan Design & Controls Ltd, 98c Blackpole Trading Estate, Worcester, WR3 8TJ Tel: (01905) 458555 Fax: (01905) 454325 E-mail: malcolm@wulstandesigns.fsbusiness.co.uk *Mechanical engineering design services*

Wunderman Ltd, Fourth Floor, Greater London House, Hampstead Road, London, NW1 7QP Tel: (020) 7611 6666 Fax: (020) 7611 6668 *Direct marketing consultants*

Wup Doodle, The Street, Hepworth, Diss, Norfolk, IP22 2PS Tel: (01359) 254001 Fax: (01953) 688378 E-mail: info@wupdoodle.com *CNC Wood Machining, 3-Axis router, Edge Banding, Hole Boring, Sanding, Sawing & Nesting services for full furniture production. Wooden & MDF components for interior designers, set design, shopfitters, architects, etc. We manufacture clients designs from 'one-off' prototypes to large, repeat runs. *CAD drawing facility. Panel saw cutting service. Contract Furniture manufacture. Kitchen Unit manufacturer also Kitchen Unit Doors. Supply of materials (MDF, Laminates, Solid Wood, Plywood, etc) also can source fixings, handles, etc & we will arrange transport throughout the UK.*

Wurth (UK) Ltd, 1 Centurion Way, Erith, Kent, DA18 4AE Tel: (0870) 5987841 Fax: (0870) 5987842 E-mail: info@wurth.co.uk *Commercial vehicle component & spare parts distributors or agents*

▶ WV Entertainment Limited, C/O The Suite, 3 Goldthorn Avenue, Wolverhampton, WV4 5AA Tel: 07939 930781 *We specialise in music promos & corporate videos*

▶ WW Scaffolding, Unit 9-10 Capital Industrial Centre, Willow Lane, Mitcham, Surrey, CR4 4NA Tel: (020) 8648 1444 Fax: (020) 8640 3440

▶ Wwe Solutions, Erskine Square, Hillington Industrial Estate, Glasgow, G52 4BJ Tel: 0141-585 9255 Fax: 0141-585 9254 E-mail: sales@wwesol.co.uk *Bearings, electric motors, gearboxes, pneumatics & pumps suppliers*

WWF Paper Sales UK, Brunswick House, Regent Park 299 Kingston Road, Leatherhead, Surrey, KT22 7LU Tel: (01372) 385100 Fax: (01372) 386366 E-mail: sales@wwfpapersales.co.uk *Paper merchants*

▶ www.321Deco.co.uk, 14 Bridgeway Centre, Wrexham Industrial Estate, Wrexham, LL13 9QS Tel: (01978) 661572 Fax: (01978) 661572 E-mail: sd@ukmemory.com *Great Reproduction Art Deco, Nouveau, and gift ideas.*

▶ www.a1quads.co.uk, Maesybont, Llanelli, SA14 7SR Tel: (0870) 3215908 Fax: (0870) 3215908 E-mail: oddjob@a1quads.co.uk *quads hire sales repair spares, quad biking in west wales pay and go using one of our quads or atv"s fun activity days corperate days and party"s bookings taken groups welcome*

▶ www.aircon4less.co.uk, 8 Cannon Lane, Pinner, Middlesex, HA5 1HR Tel: 0845 257 4358 E-mail: admin@aircon4less.co.uk *Air conditioning at unbelievable prices ! Wall splits from £259, Ceiling cassettes from £769.*

▶ www.allpower2computers.co.uk, PO Box 7327, Colchester, CO6 3WB Tel: 0845 4308732 Fax: 01206 247094 E-mail: softwaresales@allpower2computers.co.uk *We sell Brand New Home & Business Software, 2nd User Laptops and PC Accessories plus Collectable "OO" Trains at very competitive prices.*

▶ Www.Boat-Stands.Co.Uk, Unit 3 Millview Barn, Off Grange Road, Bursledon, Southampton, SO31 8GD Tel: (023) 8045 2100 E-mail: info@boat-stands.com *Motor boat & yacht stands, supports & cradles manufrs*

▶ www.bouncycastlerus.co.uk, Unit B7 Sanderson Center, Lees Lane, Gosport, Hampshire, PO12 3UL Tel: (07835) 767940 E-mail: info@bouncycastlerus.co.uk *Bouncy Castle Hire for Gosport, Fareham, Portsmouth, Eastleigh, Southampton, Lee on the Solent, Hampshire & The South Coast. Book Your Bouncy Castle today, Bouncy Castles in most sizes.*

▶ www.broadbandbuyer.co.uk, Unit 8, Cromwell Business Centre, Howard Way, Interchange Park, Newport Pagnell, Buckinghamshire, MK16 9QS Tel: (01908) 888327 Fax: (01908) 614521 E-mail: sales@broadbandbuyer.co.uk *Providers of broadband & wireless networking hardware*

▶ www.caelectrocomps.co.uk, 36 Park Lane, Bishop's Stortford, Hertfordshire, CM23 3NH Tel: (01279) 656051 Fax: (01279) 656051 E-mail: chris@caelectrocomps.co.uk *Relays, radio frequency suppliers*

▶ www.champagneentertainments.co.uk, 23 Mersey Way, Thatcham, Berkshire, RG18 3DL Tel: 01635 863135 Fax: 01635 863135 E-mail: rjlowrie@aol.com *Champagne entertainments provide a high calibre of service from intimate private party to a large corporate function, offering a wide range of facilities & packages.*

▶ www.debttrack.com, 40 Garswood Street, Ashton-in-Makerfield, Wigan, Lancashire, WN4 9AF Tel: (01942) 292432 E-mail: enquires@debttrack.com

▶ www.emmalove.com, Bridle Lane, Streetly, Sutton Coldfield, West Midlands, B74 3PT Tel: (0797) 1425195 E-mail: design@interiorlove.co.uk *For the latest in Brisith art and design visit our friendly site. We regularly update with new and exciting artists from all over the UK. Many artists can work to commission. Paintings, scupltures and conceptual art are amongst are recent additions.*

▶ www.eurocote.co.uk, 2 Alamein Close, Broxbourne, Hertfordshire, EN10 7TF Tel: (01992) 471000 Fax: (01992) 463805 E-mail: eurocote@btconnect.com

▶ www.farmmodels.co.uk, The Old Manor Farmhouse, Lower Road, Edington, Westbury, Wiltshire, BA13 4QW Tel: (01380) 831459 Fax: (01380) 830659 E-mail: office@farmmodels.co.uk *Models & die cast toys manufrs*

▶ www.firesafetyconsultants.co.uk, 5 Pardovan Holdings, Philpstoun, Linlithgow, West Lothian, EH49 6QZ Tel: (01506) 671707 Fax: (0700) 6313561 E-mail: sbrooker@firesafetyconsultants.co.uk *S Brooker & Associates offer fire safety, thermal imaging and engineering consultancy services. Their Head Office is in Central Scotland. S Brooker & Associates are Fire Engineering and Fire Investigation Specialists offering support to the nuclear, petrochemical, marine, offshore and computer industries.*

▶ www.fullcoloursigns.biz, Unit 3 Granville Court, Leighton Street, Nottingham, NG3 2FU Tel: 0115-841 8416 Fax: 0115-841 8417 E-mail: sales@fullcoloursigns.biz *BUY ONLINE full range of digitally printed Banners Signs & Display Ideas*FREE POSTERS with most products*

▶ www.getpaidontime.co.uk, 1 Mill Lane, Westhoughton, BOLTON, BL5 2DN Tel: 01942 817905 E-mail: training@getpaidontime.co.uk *Credit Management Training & Consultancy - Nationwide. *We provide a range of courses & services to enhance your credit control/ collections function.*

▶ www.greetingcards-online.co.uk, Barley Sheaf School House, Holland Fen, Lincoln, LN4 4QH Tel: (01205) 280469 Fax: (01205) 280469 E-mail: enquiries@greetingcards-online.co.uk *Greeting cards for both retail & corporate sales*

▶ www.headphone-deals.com, 94 Chopin Road, Basingstoke, Hampshire, RG22 4JW Tel: 01256 418993

▶ www.herbalcare4u.com, 65 Mayfield Park South, Fishponds, Bristol, BS16 3NF Tel: 0117 9586577 E-mail: danielle.saunders@kingitsolutions.com *This site has high quality products aimed to help with weight loss, weight gain, weight management, healthy skin, inner nutrition, sports nutrition, increased levels of energy, a balanced digestive system, better immune system and much more. *The products have been extensively tested by top scientists to ensure their top quality. These products are being sold in over 60 countries and have therefore passed many regulations to ensure their safety and validity. They really work and the results are fantastic! I haven"t been ill since taking these products and I"ve dropped in weight by five pounds so far!*

▶ www.hotelstobuy.co.uk, 46 Trefusis Road, Falmouth, Cornwall, TR11 4QQ Tel: 01326 313295 E-mail: admin@hotelstobuy.co.uk *Directory of hotels, B&Bs and guest houses for sale in the UK, plus advice about buying and running a successful accommodation business.*

▶ www.icbaby.com, 85 Bruce Avenue, Worthing, West Sussex, BN11 5LB Tel: (0870) 2406575 E-mail: Jane@icbaby.com *Nursery products & baby goods suppliers*

▶ www.koolkonsoles.com, Manchester, M1 Tel: 07980 641938 E-mail: koolkonsoles@luckymail.com *Xbox & ps2, modchips & chipping services*

▶ www.letsspendless.org, John Clarke Centre, Middlesbrough, Cleveland, TS6 6UZ Tel: (07739) 509097 *Sale of refurbished computers, monitors & software*

▶ www.liquidatedstocklots.com, 2 Blackburn House, Bedford Road, Aspley Guise, Milton Keynes, MK17 8DH Tel: (01908) 583847

▶ www.Nutritionzone.co.uk, Unit 5, Mill Road Industrial Estate, Linlithgow Bridge, Linlithgow, West Lothian, EH49 7QY Tel: (01506) 848968 E-mail: admin@nutrtionzone.co.uk *www.nutritionzone.co.uk for the very latest health and nutrition products. Everything from Patch-it Detox patches, Tonalin slimming products, vitamins, herbal extracts, Omega oils, eczema and dermatitis products to standard vitamins. You probably won"t find these brands in any health food shops. Our store is completely secure so you can be sure you are in safe hands. We despatch orders the very next day and at present all - Shipping in the UK is FREE*

▶ www.oldpine.co.uk, Salisbury Road, Breamore, Fordingbridge, Hampshire, SP6 2EA Tel: (01725) 512132 E-mail: info@oldpine.co.uk *Specialising in old & antique pine furniture*

▶ www.painterssupply.co.uk, 5 Chelford Road, Macclesfield, Cheshire, SK10 3LG Tel: 01625 502121 Fax: 01625 508261 E-mail: info@painterssupply.co.uk *Suppliers of paint, wood stains & wallpapers*

▶ www.pembrokedesign.com, 41 Church Street, Pembroke Dock, SA72 6AR Tel: (01646) 687240 *Make your own 3D Magic Eye Pictures *from your favourite picture, photograph or logo . You can then add them to your web sites, greeting cards, clothing and your advertising. Even make screen savers etc.*Until a very few years ago the only way to provide someone with a realistic 3-dimensional picture, involved making them look at a specially prepared image through red/ green specs. But this technique has now been superseded by the SIRDS or 'Magic Eye" method. This enables a 3-dimensional picture to be presented withou the use of any special equipment. It is currently being used in the generation of a wide variety of images in many different media. Viewed raw, SIRDS or stereograms, provide a rock solid, specs-free 3-d illusion.*

▶ www.qrcmodels.co.uk, 18 Conglass Drive, Inverurie, Aberdeenshire, AB51 4LB Tel: (07815) 746035 E-mail: info@qrcmodels.co.uk

www.rutherfordsofcoldstream.co.uk, Pinnaclehill Industrial Estate, Kelso, Roxburghshire, TD5 8DW Tel: (01573) 226255 Fax: (01573) 228255 E-mail: enquiries@dmi.gb.net *Spare Parts Supplied & Fitted for Rutherfords of Coldstream, John Rutherford & Sons, JR Grain Handling Equipment.*20/4 Grain Cleaners, 30/6 Grain Cleaners, Grain/Stone Separators, Barley De-awners, Heavy Duty Sieve Units, Dust Extraction Fan Units, Chain & Flight Conveyors, Deep Flight Conveyors, Flow & Return Conveyors, Belt Conveyors, Conveyor Accessories, Mechanical Intake Units, Grain Ducting & Accessories, Belt & Bucket Elevators, Grain Samplers, Etc*

▶ www.saundersallotment.co.uk, 88 Dunkeld Road, Gosport, Hampshire, PO12 4NJ Tel: (023) 92 586619 E-mail: berylsau@saundersallotment.co.uk *An allotment garden in Hampshire.*

▶ www.simply-recruit.com, Baltic Works, Baltic Street, Hartlepool, Cleveland, TS25 1PW Tel: (01833) 638110 Fax: (01833) 630389 E-mail: sarahjane@simply-recruit.com *Agencies very welcome to place all candidates on web site - feel free to look **Simple, fast and cost effective solution to labour shortage*We have an extensive database of willing unskilled European workers keen to improve their financial circumstances through honest, hard and fair work in the United Kingdom.**Our networking and advertising throughout the European Union, particularly the new accession states of including Czech republic, Estonia, Cyprus, Latvia, Hungary, Malta and Poland is producing a stream of hard working honest determined potential employees all delighted t be given the chance to work in the UK.**

▶ WWW Solutions, 19 ROOKWOOD AVENUE, NEW MALDEN, SURREY, KT3 4LY Tel: 0871 874 0266 Fax: 0871 874 0268 E-mail: contact@wwwsolutions.ws *Professional Domain Registration, Hosting, Web Design and*

continued

Company Information

continuation
*Marketing Solutions for Your Business.*Specialising in servicing SME"s and SOHO"s we offer:*Full Service, Self Service and Self Build.*All our services are:*Great Quality - Great Value - Great Service.*We make it as Simple as ABC for You*

▶ www.tallulahbay.co.uk, 65 Carless Close, Gosport, Hampshire, PO13 9PN Tel: (023) 923 66177 E-mail: tarina@tallulahbay.co.uk *DIY website*

▶ www.teng.co.uk, 83 Manor Road, Darwen, Lancashire, BB3 2SN Tel: (01254) 707443 E-mail: enquiries@toolshack.biz *Suppliers of Teng Tools automotive products , including socket sets, roller cabinets, tool boxes, spanners,tool kits ,ratchets ,air tools and measuring equipment.*

▶ www.thameslabs.co.uk, The Granary, Suite 2, Brook Farm, Thrapston Road, Ellington, Huntingdon, Cambridgeshire, PE28 0AE Tel: (01480) 891800 Fax: (01480) 890008 E-mail: john@thameslabs.co.uk *Asbestos consultancy*

▶ www.TheToolman.co.uk, Dodnor Industrial Estate, Newport, Isle Of Wight, PO30 5XA Tel: (01983) 526344 Fax: (01983) 821547 E-mail: mark@thetoolman.co.uk *Power tools manufrs*

www.throwitaway.com, 211 Winchester Road, Basingstoke, Hampshire, RG21 8YH Tel: (07887) 993202 E-mail: sales@throwitaway.com *Suppliers of Printed Napkins and Disposables. Keenest prices and no minimum runs*

▶ www.topgun.co.uk, 18 Derby Road, Blackpool, FY1 2JF Tel: (01253) 296000 Fax: (01253) 296001 E-mail: topgun@nildram.co.uk *Nails & nailing equipment*

▶ www.webmozaic.com, 16 Moss Lane, Elworth, Sandbach, Cheshire, CW11 3JN Tel: 01270 750180 E-mail: info@webmozaic.com *Professional webhosting and design for SME"s. We concentrate on what your website has to do for your business. **

▶ wwwireforks, Truman Brewery, 91 Brick Lane, London, E1 6QL Tel: 0207 1736273 E-mail: jim@wireforks.com *WWWIREFORKS IS A NEW COMPANY. A NEW COLLABORATION, IN FACT. WE DESIGN AND BUILD HI-SPEC WEBSITES FOR ANY COMPANY THAT ASPIRES TO AN INTELLIGENT AND CONSCIENTIOUS ONLINE PRESENCE. WE ARE COMPACT, EFFICIENT AND HIGHLY RECOMMEND OURSELVES. WE HAVE THE WEB SKILLS IN FLASH, JAVASCRIPT, SQL, XML, PHP, HTML AND MOST IMPORTANTLY DESIGN.*

Wyards Removals, Knightsdale Road, Ipswich, IP1 4NE Tel: (01473) 463708 Fax: (01473) 744447 E-mail: sales@wyardsremovals.co.uk *Removals & storage specialists*

Wyatt Ltd, Unit 3, Whittington Buissness Park, Oswestry, Shropshire, SY11 4ND Tel: (01691) 662592 Fax: (01691) 658346 E-mail: wyattltd@aol.com *Effluent treatment plants manufrs*

Wyatt & Ackerman Ltd, 30 North Street, Bedminster, Bristol, BS3 1HW Tel: 0117-966 1675 Fax: 0117-966 1775 E-mail: sales@wyattandackerman.co.uk *Packaging, stationary & printing materials manufrs*

Wyatt Bros (UK) Ltd, Waymills Industrial Estate, Whitchurch, Shropshire, SY13 1TT Tel: (01948) 662526 Fax: (01948) 667560 E-mail: info@wyattbros.com *Pump distributors*

▶ Wyatt Engineering, Darrow Wood Farm, Shelfanger Road, Diss, Norfolk, IP22 4XY Tel: (01379) 640200 Fax: (01379) 640200

Gordon Wyatt Ltd, 236 Tithe Street, Leicester, LE5 4BN Tel: 0116-276 7719 Fax: 0116-246 0360 *Ladies' dress & suit wholesalers*

John Wyatt Ltd, Braithwaite Street, Leeds, LS11 9XE Tel: 0113-244 4151 Fax: 0113-242 3186 E-mail: enquiries@johnwyattltd.co.uk *Vegetable oil & animal fat merchants*

Wyatts, 62 Footshill Road, Bristol, BS15 8EZ Tel: 0117-967 1836 Fax: 0117-935 2106 E-mail: info@wyatts-butchers.co.uk *Air conditioning service providers*

Wyatts Blinds, Deans Farm, Stratford sub Castle, Salisbury, SP1 3YP Tel: (01722) 335985 Fax: (01722) 340492 *Blind suppliers*

Wybone Ltd, Mason Way, Hoyland, Barnsley, South Yorkshire, S74 9TF Tel: (01226) 744010 Fax: (01226) 350105 E-mail: sales@wybone.co.uk *Street furniture manufrs*

Wych Tree Technology, 22 Afan Valley Road, Neath, West Glamorgan, SA11 3SN Tel: (01639) 645016 E-mail: sw@wychtree.com *Software consultants*

Wychem Ltd, Bury Road, Stradishall, Newmarket, Suffolk, CB8 8YN Tel: (01440) 820338 Fax: (01440) 820399 *Chemical manufrs*

Wycis Engineering Co. Ltd, 1 Wheatear, Perry Road, Witham, Essex, CM8 3YY Tel: (01376) 516247 Fax: (01376) 514721 E-mail: wycis@btinternet.com *Hydraulic engineers.*

Wyck Hill House Hotel, Wyck Hill, Stow on the Wold, Cheltenham, Gloucestershire, GL54 1HY Tel: (01451) 831936 Fax: (01451) 832243 E-mail: sales@nichehotels.com *Hotel & conference facilities*

Wyckham Blackwell Group Ltd, Old Station Road, Hampton-In-Arden, Solihull, West Midlands, B92 0HB Tel: (01675) 442233 Fax: (01675) 442227 E-mail: info@wyckham-blackwell.co.uk *Prefabricated trusses agents*

Wycliff Services Ltd, Godwin Road, Earlstrees Industrial Estate, Corby, Northamptonshire, NN17 4DS Tel: (01536) 406500 Fax: (01536) 406800 E-mail: johnh@wycliff-services.co.uk *Mechanical & electrical engineers*

Wycombe Models & Engineering, Gomm Road, High Wycombe, Buckinghamshire, HP13 7DJ Tel: (01494) 447941 Fax: (01494) 461959 *Cutting tool distributors*

Wycombe Panels Ltd, Coronation Road, Cressex Business Park, High Wycombe, Buckinghamshire, HP12 3RP Tel: (01494) 530473 Fax: (01494) 461815

continued

E-mail: sales@wycombepanels.co.uk *Veneered wood manufrs*

▶ Wye Technology UK Ltd, 6 Mitcheldean Enterprise Workshops, Brook Street, Mitcheldean, Gloucestershire, GL17 0SL Tel: (01594) 544806 Fax: (01594) 544609 E-mail: wyetecukltd@aol.com *Electronic equipment contracts manufrs*

Wye Valley Aviation Ltd, Orchard House, Bridstow, Ross-on-Wye, Herefordshire, HR9 6AJ Tel: (01989) 763134 Fax: (01989) 768242 *Balloon flights*

Wye Valley Demolition, Lloyd George House, Fordshill Road, Rotherwas, Hereford, HR2 6NS Tel: (01432) 361670 Fax: (01432) 361689 E-mail: info@wyevalleygroup.co.uk *Demolition contractors*

Wye Valley Engineering Ltd, Unit 260 Netherwood Road Rotherwas Indust Estate, Rotherwas Industrial Estate, Hereford, HR2 6JU Tel: (01432) 266507 Fax: (01432) 341645 E-mail: enquries@durabase.co.uk *General fabricators*

Wye Valley Precision Engineering (Holdings) Ltd, Station Approach, Ross-On-Wye, Herefordshire, HR9 7AQ Tel: (01989) 763519 Fax: (01989) 766662 E-mail: sales@wye-valley.co.uk *Precision rubber moulders*

Wye Valley Printers, Units 8 & 9, Foley Trading Estate, Hereford, HR1 2SF Tel: (01432) 268286 Fax: (01432) 356322 E-mail: sales@wyevalleyprinters.co.uk *General colour printing specialists & note pads manufrs*

Wye Valley Reclemation, Llyod George House, Fordshill Road, Rotherwas Industrial Estate, Hereford, HR2 6NS Tel: (01432) 353606 Fax: (01432) 340020 E-mail: info@wyevalleygroup.co.uk *Skip contractors*

Wye Valley Tractors Ltd, Tanyard Lane, Ross-on-Wye, Herefordshire, HR9 7BH Tel: (01989) 562486 Fax: (01989) 566030 E-mail: wvt1@aol.com *Agricultural engineers & exporters*

▶ Wyedean Wholefoods, 28 High Street, Chepstow, Gwent, NP16 5LJ Tel: (01291) 630002 Fax: (01291) 630002 *Health food retailers*

Wyedean Wholefoods, 18 Newerne Street, Lydney, Gloucestershire, GL15 5RF Tel: (01594) 841907 Fax: (01594) 841907 *Whole foods (health shop) food & supplements suppliers*

Wyeth Laboratories, Bath Road, Taplow, Maidenhead, Berkshire, SL6 0AP Tel: (01628) 604377 Fax: (01628) 666368 *Pharmaceutical*

Wyeval Audio-Visual Sales, 16 Tarsmill Court, Rotherwas, Hereford, HR2 6JZ Tel: (01432) 272113 Fax: (01432) 272113 *Audio visual equipment suppliers*

Wyevale Garden Centres Ltd, Dunstable Road, Caddington, Luton, LU1 4AN Tel: (01582) 457313 Fax: (01582) 480716 *Horticultural sundries*

▶ Wygar Construction Co. Ltd, 22 Broadway North, Walsall, WS1 2AJ Tel: (01922) 614535 Fax: (01922) 723405 E-mail: info@wygar.co.uk

Wyke Electrical Control Ltd, Unit 1, St Marks Square, Hull, HU3 2DQ Tel: (01482) 328630 Fax: (01482) 320674 *Electrical control specialists*

Wyke Plastics Plastic Moulders, Bradford Road, Brighouse, West Yorkshire, HD6 4BW Tel: (01484) 710414 Fax: (01484) 711649 *Injection & plastic moulding manufrs*

Wyke Printers Ltd, Gothenburg Way, Hull, HU7 0YD Tel: (01482) 831290 Fax: (01482) 878244 E-mail: info@wyke-printers.co.uk *Lithographic printers*

Wykebeck Recoveries, Selby Road, Leeds, LS9 0EW Tel: 0113-248 4735 Fax: 0113-249 5122 *Car & van recovery services*

Wykeham Farrance International Ltd, Chiltern House, Unit 4B, Knaves Beech Business Centre, Loadwater, High Wycombe, Buckinghamshire, HP10 9QY Tel: (01628) 521000 Fax: (01628) 530300 E-mail: sales@wfi.co.uk *Soil testing equipment manufrs*

Wyken Tools Ltd, Unit 3, Bodmin Road, Coventry, CV2 5DZ Tel: (024) 7662 1515 Fax: (024) 7662 1472 E-mail: jezwykentools@aol.com *Precision engineers*

Wykes International Ltd, 434 Thurmaston Boulevard, Leicester, LE4 9LD Tel: 0116-276 8282 Fax: 0116-274 2506 E-mail: sales@wykes.co.uk *Elastic yarn manufrs*

Wyko Group Ltd, Amber Way, Halesowen, West Midlands, B62 8WG Tel: 0121-508 6000 Fax: 0121-508 6464 E-mail: marketing@wyko.co.uk *Industrial products & services nationwide* Also at: Branches throughout the U.K.

Wyko Industrial Distribution Ltd, Venture Way, Priorswood Industrial Estate, Taunton, Somerset, TA2 8DE Tel: (01823) 271221 Fax: (01823) 289675 E-mail: scantron@scantron-net.co.uk *Non contact measurement equipment services*

Wyko Seals Ltd, Hereward Rise, Halesowen Industrial Park, Halesowen, West Midlands, B62 8AN Tel: 0121-501 2021 Fax: 0121-501 3014 E-mail: sales@dichta.com Principal Export Areas: Africa *Bearings & seals distributors*

Wyko Tubes, Vauxhall Street, Queens Cross, Dudley, W. Midlands, DY1 1TA Tel: (01384) 237816 Fax: (01384) 457463 E-mail: sales@wyko-tubes.co.uk *Welded tubes & cylinders manufrs*

Wyles Hardy & Co. Ltd, Ley Hill Road, Bovingdon, Hemel Hempstead, Hertfordshire, HP3 0NW Tel: (01442) 832234 Fax: (01442) 834342 E-mail: enquiries@wyleshardy.com *Plant machinery valuers & auctioneers*

Peter Wylie, 26 Noel Street, London, W1F 8GY Tel: (020) 7734 6140 Fax: (020) 7734 4904 E-mail: ptrwylie@aol.com *Sales agency*

Wyman Dillon Ltd, Silverhill, Rudgeway, Bristol, BS35 3NS Tel: (01454) 200000 Fax: (01454) 200002 E-mail: mail@wymandillon.co.uk *Database marketing services*

Wyman Gordon Ltd, Houstoun Road, Houstoun Industrial Estate, Livingston, West Lothian, EH54 5BZ Tel: (01506) 446200 Fax: (01506) 446300 *Heavy engineers*

Wymark Ltd, Runnings Road Ind Estate, Cheltenham, Gloucestershire, GL51 9NQ Tel: 01242 520966 *Automatic lubricants & rust prevention equipment suppliers*

▶ Wymbs Engineering Ltd, Clarence Road, Bollington, Macclesfield, Cheshire, SK10 5JZ Tel: (01625) 575154 Fax: (01625) 573109 E-mail: info@wymbsengineering.com *Food Processing Plant and Machinery, Food Processing Equipment available from Wymbs Engineering Ltd based in Macclesfield, Cheshire. Click the links below to visit our website or contact us via our profile page.*

▶ Wymondham Recovery Services, Valleyside Industrial Estate, Station Road, Wymondham, Norfolk, NR18 0NN Tel: (01953) 602376

Wyndeham Graphics Ltd, Unit 3-4 Maverton Road, London, E3 2JE Tel: (020) 8983 0022 Fax: (020) 8981 9802 *Pre-press*

Wyndeham Heron & Co. Ltd, The Bentalls Complex, Colchester Road, Heybridge, Maldon, Essex, CM9 4NW Tel: (01621) 877777 Fax: (01621) 877776 *Heat set web offset printers*

Wyndeham Impact Ltd, Units L1-L3, Impact House, Grafton Way, West Ham Industrial Estate, Basingstoke, Hampshire, RG22 6HY Tel: (01256) 479816 Fax: (01256) 324671 E-mail: impact@wyndeham.co.uk *Web offset printers*

Wyndham Granger, Butts Road, Southwick, Brighton, BN42 4EJ Tel: (01273) 592244 Fax: (01273) 870210 E-mail: thegrangepress@msn.com *Printers*

Wyndham Plastics Ltd, Ogmore Terrace, Bridgend, Mid Glamorgan, CF31 1SU Tel: (01656) 652869 Fax: (01656) 669915 E-mail: steve@wyndham-plastics.co.uk *Point of sale & shop fitting fabricators*

Wyndham Plastics & Glass, Unit 8 Horsefair Road, Waterton Industrial Estate, Bridgend, Mid Glamorgan, CF31 3TN Tel: (01656) 667767 Fax: (01656) 669915 E-mail: steve@wyndham-plastics.co.uk *Mirror, glass & acrylics processors*

Wynn Ceilings, 200 The Broadway, London, NW9 7EE Tel: (020) 8202 0368 Fax: (020) 8202 2167 *Suspended ceilings systems contractors*

Wynne Jones Laine & James, 22 Rodney Road, Cheltenham, Gloucestershire, GL50 1JJ Tel: (01242) 515807 Fax: (01242) 224183 E-mail: patenedagents@wynne-jones.com *Chartered patent agents services* Also at: Cardiff

▶ Wynns Road Haulage Services, 2 High Street, Eccleshall, Stafford, ST21 6BZ Tel: (01785) 850411 Fax: (01785) 851866

Wynnstay & Clwyd Farmers P.L.C., The Roe, St. Asaph, Clwyd, LL17 0LB Tel: (01745) 582527 Fax: (01745) 584538 *Agricultural suppliers*

Wynnstay Group plc, 1 Maesyllan, Llanidloes, Powys, SY18 6DF Tel: (01686) 412696 Fax: (01686) 412696 *Agricultural & garden suppliers*

Wynnstay Group P L C, Eagle House, Llansantffraid, Powys, SY22 6AQ Tel: (01691) 828512 Fax: (01691) 828690 E-mail: info@wynnstayplc.co.uk *Agricultural merchants & millers*

Wynnstay Group plc, Llanidloes Road, Newtown, Powys, SY16 1ET Tel: (01686) 626379 Fax: (01686) 626679 *Agricultural merchants*

Wynnstay Group plc, Park Road, Ruthin, Clwyd, LL15 1NQ Tel: (01824) 704900 Fax: (01824) 705846 *Agricultural merchants*

Wynnstay Group plc, Severn Road, Welshpool, Powys, SY21 7AY Tel: (01938) 552591 Fax: (01938) 556279 *Agricultural merchants*

Wynnstay Hotel, 43 Church Street, Oswestry, Shropshire, SY11 2SZ Tel: (01691) 655261 Fax: (01691) 670606 E-mail: sales@wynnstayhotel.com *Hotel & conference facilities*

Wynnstay Stores, Watergate Street, Llanfair Caereinion, Welshpool, Powys, SY21 0RG Tel: (01938) 810525 Fax: (01938) 810256 *Agricultural merchants*

Wynnstruments Ltd, Wynn House, Lansdown Estate, Cheltenham, Gloucestershire, GL51 8PL Tel: (01242) 232266 Fax: (01242) 231131 E-mail: sales@wynn.co.uk *Electric motor & marine windscreen wiper manufrs*

▶ Wyre Electric, 31 Gilgal, Stourport-on-Severn, Worcestershire, DY13 9AJ Tel: (07973) 742085 Fax: (01299) 871765

▶ Wyre Heating Ltd, Unit 3 Lisle Avenue, Kidderminster, Worcestershire, DY11 7DE Tel: (01562) 751832 Fax: (01562) 748383

Wyre Repairs Ltd, J Boyn Valley Industrial Estate, Boyn Valley Road, Maidenhead, Berkshire, SL6 4EJ Tel: (01628) 674691 Fax: (01628) 674691 E-mail: info@wyrerepairs.co.uk *Electric motor repair specialists*

▶ Wyre Wall Coverings, Scorton Avenue, Blackpool, FY3 7HD Tel: (01253) 316587 E-mail: wyrewall@btinternet.com *We supply an exelent sevice to both Domestic and Commercial areas of plastering eg,plasterboarding external rendering,internal finishes,mf ceiling and wall systems,architectural plastering and many more.If you may have any questions we are happy to help.*MR STEVEN MCGOVERN*

Wyresdale Concrete Products, Bradshaw Lane, Stakepool, Preston, PR3 6AJ Tel: (01253) 790364 *Concrete products manufrs*

▶ Wyretech Ltd, 6-7 Sketchley Meadows, Hinckley, Leicestershire, LE10 3EN Tel: (01455) 238877 Fax: (01455) 238877 E-mail: enquiries@wyretech.co.uk *Manufacturing & distribution of electrical equipment*

▶ Wyse Assist, Prospect House, 25 High Street, Chesham, Buckinghamshire, HP5 1BG Tel: (01494) 790600 Fax: (01494) 790696 E-mail: helpdesk@wyseassist.com *WYSE ASSIST - a market leader in the provision of quality, cost effective on-line credit and business information.**We have access to over 4 million UK companies, both incorporated and unincorporated, in addition to a comprehensive database of international organisations. **Our credit reports are simple to use; available on-line 24 hours a day; excellent value for money;instantly accessible via our website and updated daily.**

Wyse Technology (U K) Ltd, 1 The Pavilions, Ruscombe Park, Twyford, Reading, RG10 9 Tel: 0118-934 5345 Fax: (01734) 340749 E-mail: sales@wyse.com *Microcomputer & peripheral equipment*

Wytkin Services, Waterswallows Industrial Par Waterswallows Road, Buxton, Derbyshire, SK17 7JB Tel: (01298) 70069 Fax: (01298) 70069 E-mail: Wytkinservices@aol.com *Engineering & crane hire*

Wyvale Associates Ltd, Wilson Street, Southampton, SO14 5AY Tel: (023) 8063 8 Fax: (023) 8033 3138 *Powder coating & gl*

Wyvern Business Systems, Wyvern House, Netherwood Road, Rotherwas Industrial Es Hereford, HR2 6JJ Tel: (01432) 271233 Fax: (01432) 263550E-mail: buyer@wbs.uk *Computer dealers & manufrs*

Wyvern Furniture Ltd, Units 13-15, Hartlebury Trading Estate, Hartlebury, Kidderminster, Worcestershire, DY10 4JB Tel: (01299) 251 Fax: (01299) 251836 *Upholstery manufrs*

Wyvern Handling & Storage Equipment Ltd, P Box 5483, Stourport-on-Severn, Worcesters DY13 3BG Tel: (01299) 829300 Fax: (0129 825799 E-mail: sales@wyvernhandling.co.u *Storage equipment distributors*

Wyvern Marlborough Ltd, Wyvern Buildings, 1 Grove Trading Estate, Dorchester, Dorset, DT1 1SU Tel: (01305) 268981 Fax: (01305) 264717 *Fireplace manufrs & retail showroo Retail telephone number - (01305) 268981*

Wyvern Mouldings Ltd, Unit 6 Britannia Busine Park, Britannia Way Enigma Bus Park, Mal Worcestershire, WR14 1GZ Tel: (01684) 56 Fax: (01684) 560862 E-mail: info@wyvernmouldings.co.uk *Thermoplastic injection moulders*

Wyvern Optical Ltd, 87 Narborough Road, Leicester, LE3 0LF Tel: 0116-254 8431 E-mail: wyvern1947@aol.com *Optical manu*

Wyvern Sheet Metal & Fabrications Ltd, Three Springs Trading Estate, Vincent Road, Worcester, WR5 1BW Tel: (01905) 357830 Fax: (01905) 357830 E-mail: sales@wyvernsheetmetal.wanadoo. *Sheet metal works fabricators or engineers*

Wyze Security Systems, 296 Stag Lane, Lond NW9 0EG Tel: (020) 8998 3057 Fax: (020) 1027 *Engineer alarms*

X B R Electronics Ltd, Campbell Road, Eastle Hampshire, SO50 5AE Tel: (023) 8061 321 Fax: (023) 8061 3215 E-mail: sales@xbrelectronics.com *Electroni repair equipment*

▶ X D S Ltd, Cornishway West, Galmington Trading Estate, Taunton, Somerset, TA1 5N Tel: (01823) 325999

X Electrical, 4 Station Buildings, Fife Road, Kingston upon Thames, Surrey, KT1 1SW Tel: (020) 8546 1233 Fax: (020) 8549 1233 *Electrical reseller*

X J F Plastics Ltd, Unit 1 & 2, Southfield Lane Industrial Estate, Whitwell, Worksop, Nottinghamshire, S80 4SB Tel: (01909) 724 Fax: (01909) 724582 E-mail: enquiries@xjfplastics.co.uk *Plastic rotational moulders, product & tool design*

X K O Group P.L.C., Clyde House, 16 Milburn Avenue, Oldbrook, Milton Keynes, MK6 2W Tel: (01908) 295400 Fax: (01908) 393633 *Mini-computers & software distribs*

X K S Ltd, Unit 19 St. Asaph Business Park, Glascoed Road, St. Asaph, Clwyd, LL17 0L Tel: (01745) 584953 Fax: (01745) 583047 *I company*

X L B Signs, 5 Hayes Metro Centre, Springfiel Road, Hayes, Middlesex, UB4 0LE Tel: (02 8561 5664 Fax: (020) 8561 5665 *Sign mak*

X L Systems, 1 Leas Road, Warlingham, Surre CR6 9LN Tel: (01883) 622778 Fax: (01883) 626991 E-mail: sales@xls.co.uk *Radio data modem suppliers*

▶ X Met, 106 107, Newhouse Industrial Estate Newhouse, Motherwell, Lanarkshire, ML1 5 Tel: (01698) 733533 Fax: (01698) 734617 *products manufrs*

X Press Tools Ltd, Station Yard, Thame, Oxfordshire, OX9 3UH Tel: (01844) 214603 Fax: (01844) 214601 *Press tools manufrs*

X R Fasteners Ltd, Unit 85 86 Imperial Trading Estate, Lambs La North, Rainham, Essex, RM13 9XL Tel: (01708) 526274 Fax: (01708 525981 *Industrial fastener distributors*

X Ray Accessories Ltd, 16 Rudolph Road, Bus WD23 3DY Tel: (020) 8950 2223 Fax: (020) 8950 5015 *X-ray accessories manufrs*

X T & A T Computers Ltd, 77c St Pancras, Chichester, West Sussex, PO19 7LS Tel: (01243) 533367 Fax: (01243) 536018 E-mail: sales@xtat.co.uk *Small computer systems sales & repairs*

X Tech Stainless Steel Fabrications Ltd, Unit A Trecenydd Industrial Estate, Caerphilly, Mid Glamorgan, CF83 2RZ Tel: 029 20886639 *Stainless steel fabricators & erectors*

X Tek Systems Ltd, Unit 5 Icknield Way Indust Estate, Icknield Way, Tring, Hertfordshire, HP23 4JX Tel: (01442) 828700 Fax: (01442 828118 E-mail: sales@xtek.co.uk Principal Export Areas: Worldwide *Manufacturer x-ray inspection systems*

▶ X2 (UK) Ltd, The Gatehouse, Fradley Distribution Park, Wood End Lane, Lichfield Staffordshire, WS13 8NE Tel: (01543) 2545

X2m Ltd, 2 The Acorns, Redehall Road, Small Horley, Surrey, RH6 9QJ Tel: (0870) 770462 Fax: (0870) 7704626 E-mail: info@x2muk.c *X2M are retailers of USB flash storage devi with advanced synchronization and data management software. Displays Outlook en Internet Explorer Favourites, Wallpaper and wherever you go, on any computer. Send/ receive emails from almost anywhere and synchronizes all your changes back again*

▶ X5 Ltd, Unit 6, 77 London Road, Newbury, Berkshire, RG14 1JN Tel: (0870) 2863666 Fax: (0870) 2863866 E-mail: sales@x5.ltd.u *Safety equipment suppliers*

Xact Prepack, Lawco House, 60 Vauxhall Roa Liverpool, L3 6DL Tel: 0151-4793070 Fax: 0 4793022 E-mail: info@xactprepack.co.uk *Leading specialist providers of high quality coding and marking systems and packaging*

con

uation
stems. We supply solutions for a range of
ustries including construction,
armaceuticals, automotive, agriculture, paper
d timber.

mtec Ltd, 2 Swinstead Road, Corby Glen, antham, Lincolnshire, NG33 4NU Tel: (01476) 0874 Fax: (01476) 550284 nail: info@xamtec.com *Computer intenance services*

Employee Trustee Company Ltd, 420 ames Valley Park Drive, Thames Valley Park, ading, RG6 1PU Tel: (0870) 2416181 x: (0870) 2426282 E-mail: info@xansa.com *mputer systems, business & IT consultants* o at: Branches throughout the U.K.

ntium Consulting, 34 Buckingham Palace ad, London, SW1W 0RH Tel: (020) 7354 54

Ltd, Gaddesden Place, Great Gaddesden, mel Hempstead, Hertfordshire, HP2 6EX : (01442) 350000 Fax: (01442) 350010 nail: sales@xara.com *Software developers*

Engineering Ltd, Fleetwood Road, Lune eet, Padiham, Burnley, Lancashire, 12 8DG Tel: (01282) 680000 Fax: (01282) 0888 E-mail: sales@xavier-eng.co.uk *ecision turned parts manufrs*

Press, Unit D6 Barwell Business Park, atherhead Road, Chessington, Surrey, 9 2NY Tel: (020) 8391 4707 Fax: (020) 8397 02 E-mail: xavierpress@talk21.com *General nters & point of sale services*

re Equipment Ltd, 3 Starley Court, Hotchkiss y, Binley Industrial Estate, Coventry, 3 2RL Tel: (024) 7644 4412 Fax: (024) 7663 03 E-mail: xcalibre-equipt@btconnect.com *nufacturers of diamond core drilling chinery*

alibur Sign Writers, 241 Torquay Road, ignton, Devon, TQ3 2HW Tel: (01803) 666125 x: (01803) 666126 *Signs & print manufrs*

apewithus, Southbridge House, Southbridge ace, Croydon, CR0 4HA Tel: (0870) 6093484 nail: sales@xcapewithus.com *Online Hotel okings through Europe and America*

Printers, 8 Cowley Mill Trading Estate, ngbridge Way, Cowley, Uxbridge, Middlesex, 8 2YG Tel: (01895) 256332 Fax: (01895) 0902 E-mail: info@xcardtechnology.com *minating services to the trade*

GB Ltd, Barbara House, Cross Green proach, Leeds, LS9 0SG Tel: 0113-391 8230 x: 0113-391 8239 E-mail: sales@x-cel.com *sket manufrs*

nange Group, The Gallery Office, Chewton ndip, Radstock, BA3 4NT Tel: (0845) 601 92 *xchangegroup provides expert support in ance, IT and marketing for ambitious mpanies. We give practical strategic advice d donãt shy away from implementing it.**We t straight to the core of the challenges you e: we unpack the issues, develop the way ward, and help you achieve your goals.**Our egrated approach offers specialist individuals, wide range of services and the latest IT stems. Whether your management team eds strengthening or a project needs support, ãll guarantee expert input.**

hange International, 17-18 Britton Street, ndon, EC1M 5NQ Tel: (020) 7490 4455 x: (020) 7490 4456 nail: sales@xchangeuk.com *Computer ftware manufrs*

bec Labels, Halesfield 17, Telford, Shropshire, 7 4PW Tel: (01952) 587777 Fax: (01952) 0111 *Printing label manufrs*

core Ltd, 59 Highbury Gardens, Seven Kings rd, Ilford, Essex, IG3 8AF Tel: (07800) 0908 E-mail: sales@xecore.co.uk *Our EPOS ail, hospitality and back office server is a hly configurable package solution tailored for ique businesses and provides customer cused services to serve, capture and analyse ta for improved marketing. Bespoke software lution is also available using our unique XT delling approach that caters for your unique siness. Web development and hosting.*

n Network Services Ltd, Anchorage Court spian Road, Atlantic Street, Broadheath, rincham, Cheshire, WA14 5HH Tel: 0161-929 82 Fax: 0161-929 5264 mail: sales@xenon-uk.co.uk *Micro-computer alers* Also at: Bristol, Daventry, Hemel mpstead, Irmston, Isle of Man, Leeds & ingstone

ous Systems Ltd, The Anchorage, Central dbrook, Lydbrook, Gloucestershire, GL17 9SB : (01594) 862000 Fax: (01594) 862001 mail: sales@xenopus.co.uk *Computer services*

va, 310 Science Park, Milton Road, mbridge, CB4 0WG Tel: (01223) 423413 x: (01223) 423458 mail: sales@xenova.co.uk *Pharmaceutical search & testing services*

web Drying Systems Ltd, 158 Church Lane, cking, Braintree, Essex, CM7 5SG : (01376) 346426 mail: p_eagle@xericweb.com *Web dryers for xographic printing, speciality coatings. signers & manufrs including standard, custom mbination infrared, UV-curing systems, nvection dryers, air flotation dryers, pingement dryers, conveyor ovens, clean om dryers, and other specialised systems lored to meet specific customer needs*

Capital Europe plc, Bridge House, Oxford ad, Uxbridge, Middlesex, UB8 1HS : (01895) 251133 *Photocopying facilities*

Document Imaging Services, Beech House, ntage Point Business Village, Mitcheldean, oucestershire, GL17 0DD Tel: (01594) 592750 x: (01594) 592710 mail: document.imaging.helpdesk@document. .uk *Document imaging*

Ltd Technical Centre, PO Box 17, Welwyn rden City, Hertfordshire, AL7 1BU : (01707) 353535 Fax: (01707) 353424 *ormation technology technical support*

(U K) Ltd, Cheadle Place, Stockport Road, eadle, Cheshire, SK8 2JX Tel: 0161-931 3750 x: 0161-931 3751 *Photocopier manufrs*

Xerxes Belts, Troy Mills, Troy Road, Horsforth, Leeds, LS18 5NQ Tel: 0113-258 6675 Fax: 0113-239 0127 E-mail: sales@xerxes-belts.co.uk *Fashion belt manufrs*

X-GL Systems Ltd, 24 Hunters Reach, Waltham Cross, Hertfordshire, EN7 6HQ Tel: (01992) 638763 Fax: (0870) 0521734 E-mail: sales@xgl.com *Software developers*

Xicon Education Ltd, Bank House, 1 Bank Street, Warrington, WA1 2AP Tel: (01925) 240342 Fax: (01925) 244894 E-mail: info@xicon.com *Database consultants*

Xilinx Ltd, Benchmark House, 203 Brooklands Road, Weybridge, Surrey, KT13 0RH Tel: (01932) 820821 Fax: (0870) 7350601 E-mail: sales@xilinx.com *Computer chips & components*

▶ Xing Chao Ltd, 42 Milner Street, Preston, PR1 6BN Tel: (01772) 883937 Fax: 01772 883937 E-mail: info@xingchaoltd.com

Xing Xing, 2 Acton Hill Mews, Acton, London, W3 9QN Tel: (020) 8896 7618 Fax: (020) 8993 0785 E-mail: info@xingxingltd.com *Xing Xing are manufacturers and suppliers to the catering and hospitality industries with an extensive range of unusual shape vitrified porcelain tableware, 18/10 high quality stainless steel cutlery in modern patterns. Buffet ware, chafing dishes and juice dispensers for hotel use. Bespoke designs of crockery can be produced to order. Full colour catalogues and prices are available by contacting us and all our products can be seen in our London showroom. We deliver most items immediately from UK stock. Samples available on request.*

▶ Xinit Systems Ltd, 7 Skylines Village, Limeharbour, London, E14 9TS Tel: (020) 7538 8230 Fax: (020) 7538 8246 *Computer hardware & software suppliers*

X-Innovation Ltd, Unit 5 Springwater Business Park, Crews Hole Road, Bristol, BS5 8AN Tel: 0117-941 2291 Fax: 0117-941 2292 E-mail: nickt@x-innovations.demon.co.uk *X-ray systems*

Xirtek, Matrix House, Langley Road, Chippenham, Wiltshire, SN15 1BT Tel: (01249) 767710 Fax: (01249) 766767 E-mail: info@matrixeng.co.uk

Xixin Ltd, Hartington House, Bilton Way, Luton, LU1 1UU Tel: (01582) 400340 Fax: (01582) 481498 E-mail: sales@xixin.co.uk *Electrical metal enclosures manufrs*

▶ XJ Services, Heritage Way, Corby, Northamptonshire, NN17 5XW Tel: (01536) 201888 E-mail: tim@xjservices.co.uk *Jaguar Specialists in all models 1960 to present.*Caring, individual, personal service from Jaguar enthusiasts.*New and Used parts always available for most models.*Servicing, Other repairs, MOT repairs, Welding, AC repairs.*Established 1988*

XL Marking Systems, Unit 405 Thorp Arch Trading Estate, Thorp Arch, Wetherby, West Yorkshire, LS23 7BJ Tel: (01937) 844014 Fax: (01937) 842137 *Marking systems distributors*

XL Plating Co, 99-103 Ryecroft Street, Gloucester, GL1 4NB Tel: (01452) 525400 *Electro/chrome platers*

XL Scales Ltd, Units 7-8 Trafalgar Industrial Estate, Sovereign Way, Downham Market, Norfolk, PE38 9SW Tel: (01366) 384554 Fax: (01366) 385300 E-mail: contact@xlscales.com *Scales distribs*

XL Tools Ltd, Unit 3, Aylesham Industrial Estate, Brighouse Road, Bradford, West Yorkshire, BD12 0NQ Tel: 01274 693505 Fax: 01274 694023 *Manufacturer's of plastic injection moulds,diecasting and rubber moulds*

XM Services, Baldovie Road, Dundee, DD4 8UQ Tel: (01382) 734488 Fax: (01382) 734489 E-mail: sales@xmservices.co.uk *Engineering services*

▶ Xma Ltd, 44 Nottingham South & Wilford Industrial Estate, Nottingham, NG11 7EP Tel: 0115-846 4000 Fax: 0115-981 0180 E-mail: sales@bsfitness.co.uk *Computer supplies & equipment reseller*

Xmark Media Ltd, Old Village Hall, The Street, Effingham, Leatherhead, Surrey, KT24 5JS Tel: (01372) 750555 Fax: (01372) 750666 E-mail: mobilex@zetnet.co.uk *Exhibition organisers & direct marketing services*

Xograph Imaging Systems, Xograph House, Hampton Street, Tetbury, Gloucestershire, GL8 8LD Tel: (01666) 501501 Fax: (01666) 501502 E-mail: enquiry@xograph.com *Medical imaging specialists*

Xos Ltd, Panorama Business Village, 1-3 Blairtummock Place, Glasgow, G33 4EN Tel: 0141-766 2860 Fax: (0870) 7558864 E-mail: danrhoda@xosltd.co.uk *Xerox equipment supply & service nationwide*

▶ XP Computers, Rivendell, 46A Queens Road, Hertford, SG13 8AZ Tel: (07801) 142365 Fax: (0870) 7058640 E-mail: enquiry@xpcomputers.co.uk *Computer maintenance & repair*

▶ Xperience, Xperience House, 25 Paterson Road, Finedon Road Industrial Estate, Wellingborough, Northamptonshire, NN8 4BZ Tel: (01933) 231100 Fax: (01933) 231111 *IT software services*

Xperience Peg Associates Ltd, Belmont House, Lambdon Road, London, SW20 0LW Tel: (020) 8880 4440 Fax: (020) 8880 4442 E-mail: sales@xperience-group.co.uk *Computer software resellers*

Xperience Support Ltd, 11 Ferguson Drive, Knockmore Hill Industrial Park, Lisburn, County Antrim, BT28 2EX Tel: (028) 9267 7533 Fax: (028) 9267 2887 E-mail: info@xperience-group.com *Computer systems consultants*

Xpert Systems Ltd, 910 Birchwood Boulevard, Birchwood, Warrington, WA3 7QN Tel: (01925) 851111 Fax: (01925) 811182 *Computer network systems*

Xpertec Engineering Software Ltd, 19 Paddock End, Waterlooville, Hampshire, PO7 6UW Tel: (023) 9224 1546 Fax: (023) 9226 3770 E-mail: dbreach@xpertec.co.uk *Software engineers*

Xpose Media Ltd, Unit 3 Mona Industrial Park, Gwalchmai, Holyhead, Gwynedd, LL65 4RJ Tel: (01407) 720222 Fax: (01407) 720066 E-mail: sales@angleseysigns.co.uk *Sign Manufrs*

▶ Xposition, Hollyhock Cottage, Buttle Lane, Shepton Beauchamp, Ilminster, Somerset, TA19 0LG Tel: (01460) 249396 Fax: (01460) 249396 E-mail: info@xposition.co.uk *Consultancy to small businesses & not-for-profit organisations*

▶ Xpress Business Services, Unit 30-31 The Bell Centre, Newton Road, Crawley, West Sussex, RH10 9FZ Tel: (01293) 616848 Fax: (01293) 511666 E-mail: sales@xpress-services.co.uk *Printers*

▶ Xpress Data Systems, 10 Prenton Village Road, Prenton, Merseyside, CH43 3AD Tel: (07833) 972194 E-mail: neil@xpress-data.co.uk *Computerised management information systems*

▶ Xpress Print, Graphix House, Wellington Circle, Altens, Aberdeen, AB12 3JG Tel: (01224) 878799 Fax: (01224) 878713

▶ Xpress Relocation Ltd, Dane Road, Bletchley, Milton Keynes, MK1 1JQ Tel: (01908) 374999

Xpress Scaffold Systems, Batham Gate Road, Fairfield, Buxton, Derbyshire, SK17 7HS Tel: (01298) 73136 Fax: (01298) 23630

▶ Xpresscds Tape & CD Manufacturers, The Converted Barn, Thorn Road, Marden, Tonbridge, Kent, TN12 9LN Tel: (01622) 832302 E-mail: info@xpresscds.co.uk *CD and DVD duplication and replication. Fast and friendly professional service including artwork, packaging and delivery at lowest prices.*

▶ XPT Solutions, One St. Colme Street, Edinburgh, EH3 6AA Tel: 0131-220 8253 Fax: 0131-220 8201

▶ Xrio Ltd, Beacon Lodge, Texas Street, Morley, Leeds, LS27 0HG Tel: (0845) 6443226 Fax: (0845) 6443227 E-mail: sales@xrio.com *Distribution of load balancing products*

X-Rite Ltd, The Acumen Centre, First Avenue, Poynton, Stockport, Cheshire, SK12 1FJ Tel: (01625) 871100 Fax: (01625) 871444 *Colour measuring instrument manufrs*

XRN Engineering Ltd, Unit 2-3, A V S Trading Park, Chapel Lane, Milford, Godalming, Surrey, GU8 5HE Tel: (01483) 861777 Fax: (01483) 425841 E-mail: xrn.eng@btinternet.com *British classic cars spares & engine reconditioning services*

Xta Electronics Ltd, Riverside Business Centre, Worcester Road, Stourport-on-Severn, Worcestershire, DY13 9BZ Tel: (01299) 879977 Fax: (01299) 879969 E-mail: sales@xta.co.uk *Professional audio equipment manufrs*

Xtal Security Systems Ltd, 191 Replingham Road, London, SW18 5LY Tel: (020) 8877 9802 Fax: (020) 8877 3427 E-mail: info@xtalsecurity.com *Security alarms installers*

▶ Xtel Communications (UK) Ltd, Commerce Court, Challenge Way, Bradford, West Yorkshire, BD4 8NW Tel: (0800) 8499066 Fax: (0800) 8499096 E-mail: sales@xtelcomms.net *Supply & install new telephone systems*

Xtex Polythene Ltd, Spring Mills, Main Street, Wilsden, Bradford, West Yorkshire, BD15 0DX Tel: (01535) 272871 Fax: (01535) 275702 E-mail: sales@xtec.co.uk *Pallet covers, polyethylene bags & polyethylene film manufrs*

▶ Xtp international, Adamson House, Towers Business Park, Wilmslow Road, Didsbury, Manchester, M20 2YY Tel: 0161-955 4227 Fax: 0161-445 8225 E-mail: stevew34@hotmail.com *Xtp International work solely with the learning skills council to provide recognized qualifications for security professionals on & off site. Xtp work with every element of training people from police officers to parking attendants.*

▶ Xtral Ltd, Pelham Works, Pelham Street, Wolverhampton, WV3 0BJ Tel: (01902) 425040

▶ Xtralite Rooflights Ltd, Unit 9, Spencer Road, Blyth, Northumberland, NE24 5TG Tel: (01670) 354157 Fax: (01670) 354875 E-mail: sales@xtralite.co.uk *Roof lighting manufrs*

▶ Xtreme Business Solutions Ltd, Unit 3 Westhill Business Centre, Arnhall Business Park, Westhill, Aberdeen, AB32 6UF Tel: (01224) 744666 Fax: (01224) 330566 E-mail: sales@xtremesolutionsltd.com *Installation of data cabling*

Xtreme Engineering Limited, 335 Blandford Road, Poole, Dorset, BH15 4HP Tel: (01202) 682051 Fax: (01202) 682051 E-mail: sales@xtreme-engineering.co.uk *Designers, manufacturers and installers of Finishing systems including Spraybooths, Paint Kitchens, Flash-off and auxilliary finishing equipment. Our standard product range includes low maintenance Pumpless waterwash spraybooths, low noise high efficient Paint arrester spraybooths and waterwash waste removal systems.*

▶ Xtreme Technology, 87 Hawthorn Road, Bognor Regis, West Sussex, PO21 2BE Tel: (01243) 825255 Fax: (01243) 825255

▶ xum music service, 28 Floriston Court, Northolt, Middlesex, UB5 4JX Tel: (07704) 345414 E-mail: info@xum-music.co.uk

▶ Xyligo Softwares, 7 Roebuck Court, Didcot, Oxfordshire, OX11 8UT Tel: 01235 519500 E-mail: dgallacher@xyligo.com *Xyligo Softwares offers a professional website design service to small to medium sized businesses, at less than half the cost of some other providers.*

▶ Xyratex, Langstone Technology Park, Langstone Road, Havant, Hampshire, PO9 1SA Tel: (023) 9249 6000 Fax: (023) 9249 6001 E-mail: info@uk.xyratex.com *Storage & network technology*

Xytron, Unit 4 Twyford Court, Twyford Road, Hereford, HR2 6JR Tel: 0800 8818900 Fax: (01432) 342742 E-mail: info@xytron.co.uk *Xytron - The data recovery specialists. Manufacturer approved, clean room facility, Xytron recover data from, hard drives, Laptop, Desktop, Server, RAID, Smart media, CD/DVD, Memory stick, in fact all storage and systems are routinely recovered. On site data recovery services allow the recovery of data where*

continued

confidentiality and security are required. Xytron data recovery labs have invested in bio metric security and secure servers, your recovered data is very secure. Our dedicated engineers are waiting to help you now, please call 0800 881 8900 for solutions. Password data recovery services for hard drives and associated software. Disaster recovery solutions are available now from Xytron data recovery labs, free 24HR diagnosis. No data No fee policy. Recovered data is verified before it is shipped back to you, you only pay for what you require.

Xyz Printers, 1 Londesborough Road, Market Weighton, York, YO43 3AZ Tel: (01430) 872315 Fax: (01430) 874046 *Commercial & general printers*

▶ Y anchor, 19 Earsdon Terrace, West Allotment, Newcastle Upon Tyne, NE27 0DY Tel: 0191 2159738 *The Ultimate in security ground anchors.Motorcycles,Jetskis,*Caravans, Trailerboats. direct from the manufacturer*

Y & B Plating Ltd, 6 Priestley Way, Crawley, West Sussex, RH10 9NT Tel: (01293) 528974 Fax: (01293) 552877 *General electroplaters*

▶ Y C M Group, Welton Top, Beverley Road, Welton, Brough, North Humberside, HU15 1QR Tel: (0800) 1954303 Fax: (01482) 665441 E-mail: info@ycmgroup.com *Private and Commercial Landscape design and construction. Approved contractors to local Goverment.*At YCM Group we have a team of highly qualified and experienced Design consultants complemented by a professional and dedicated team of operatives.**Brought together to offer a perfect team to help you realise a dream landscape from initial concepts to Computer aided 3D walk throughs, implementation or project management. **We have the solutions to the many questions, concerns and challenges facing our clients. We differ from the usual landscape design consultants by being able to draw on over 40 years combined experience in industry and the private sector with many blue chip clients.**We are constantly pushing our suppliers for better quality and value for money as well as supplying and sourcing cutting edge fittings, lighting and bespoke items. **

Y C Plastics Ltd, Unit 2, Litchard Industrial Estate, Bridgend, Mid Glamorgan, CF31 2AL Tel: (01656) 647774 Fax: (01656) 647323 E-mail: sales@ycplastics.co.uk Principal Export Areas: Worldwide *Vacuum forming plastics services*

Y C R Cash Registers, 100 Embankment Road, Plymouth, PL4 9HY Tel: (01752) 251901 Fax: (01752) 600880 *Cash register distributors*

Y Constantine, 12-13 Greville Street, London, EC1N 8SB Tel: (020) 7242 7171 Fax: (020) 7242 7172 *Jewellery manufrs*

▶ Y D C Ltd, Littleworth Road, Esher, Surrey, KT10 9PD Tel: (01372) 476000 Fax: (01372) 476111 *Yoghurt distributors*

Y D P Ltd, 151 Knox Road, Wellingborough, Northamptonshire, NN8 1HX Tel: (01933) 229335 Fax: (01933) 223975 E-mail: info@ydpltd.co.uk *Computer software*

Y D T Medical Ltd, 92 Hartley Down, Purley, Surrey, CR8 4EB Tel: (020) 8763 9777 Fax: (020) 8763 9444 E-mail: ydtlimited@aol.com *Suppliers of medical equipment for the veterinary profession*

▶ Y.F. P.C. Repairs, 70 Water Meadows, Crabtree Park, Worksop, Nottinghamshire, S80 3DB Tel: 01909 481275 E-mail: giannis@pcgiannis.com *Shop On-Line Computer Parts, Software, Laptops, LCD TFT TV etc...*

Y J L Construction Ltd, Lovell House, 616 Chiswick High Road, London, W4 5RX Tel: (020) 8982 4200 Fax: (020) 8994 9558 *Building contractors* Also at: Branches throughout the U.K.

Y K K Europe Ltd, 61 Central Street, London, EC1V 8AN Tel: (020) 7017 8555 Fax: (020) 7017 8585 E-mail: enquiries@ykkeurope.com *Fasteners manufrs*

▶ Y O G Marine Computer Systems, Suite 19, 46 Warwick Way, Westminster, London, SW1V 1RY Tel: (0870) 8733750 Fax: (0870) 8733760 E-mail: info@yog-it.co.uk *Marine computer manufrs*

Y P H Welding Supplies, Unit 1 Stubbins Lane, Claughton-on-Brock, Preston, PR3 0QH Tel: (01995) 604057 Fax: (01995) 604018 E-mail: alan@yphltd.co.uk *Distributors, importers & exporters of welding equipment & supplies*

Y P S Valves Ltd, Richardshaw Road, Grangefield Industrial Estate, Pudsey, West Yorkshire, LS28 6QW Tel: 0113-256 7725 Fax: 0113-236 1987 E-mail: info@yps-valves.co.uk *Stainless steel gate globe & check valves distributors*

Y Ryte Ltd, 5 Runnings Road, Kingsditch Trading Estate, Cheltenham, Gloucestershire, GL51 9NQ Tel: (01242) 515826 Fax: (01242) 584877 E-mail: sales@y-ryte.co.uk *Rubber stamp manufacturers & supplier of marking devices*

Y S L Videowall Hire Ltd, Unit 11 Concorde Park, Amy Johnson Way, York, YO30 4WT Tel: (01904) 693535 Fax: (01904) 691114 E-mail: info@yslvideowallhire.co.uk *Video wall equipment hire service*

Y2k Maintenance Ltd, 1 The Business Park, Chichester Road, Romiley, Stockport, Cheshire, SK6 4BL Tel: 0161-494 9333 Fax: 0161-494 9555 E-mail: russell@y2kaircon.co.uk *Air conditioning installers*

▶ Y3k Systems Ltd, The Bearings, Bowbridge Road, Newark, Nottinghamshire, NG24 4BZ Tel: (01636) 708342 Fax: (01636) 708343 E-mail: info@y3k.info *Computer consultants*

Yacc, Old Vicarage, Old Vicarage Lane, Monk Fryston, Leeds, LS25 5EA Tel: (01977) 687980 Fax: (01977) 687998 E-mail: sales@yacc.co.uk *Computer consultants*

▶ Yacht Charters Asia, Halden House, High Halden, Ashford, Kent, TN26 3BT Tel: (0870) 1615098 E-mail: tom@yachtchartersasia.com *Yacht Charters Asia are a yacht charter agency specializing in charters in the Asia Pacific region. We have an easy to use search facility that makes choosing boats from several different operators easy.*

Company Information

Yacht Marina Ltd, Naburn Marina, Naburn, York, YO19 4RW Tel: (01904) 621021 Fax: (01904) 611950 E-mail: info@yachtservice.co.uk *Boat distributors*

Yacht Shipping Ltd, Bowling Green House, 1 Orchard Place, Southampton, SO14 3PX Tel: (023) 8022 3671 Fax: (023) 8033 0880 E-mail: info@ysl.wainwrightgroup.com *Yacht shipping & transportation services*

YachtScan Ltd, 52 Gifford Terrace Road, Plymouth, PL3 4JE Tel: 0845 873 6335 Fax: 07790 320492 E-mail: info@yachtscan.co.uk *Professional Marine Surveys for Sail and Power vessels, wood, steel and GRP/FRP construction. Surveys for pre purchase, insurance, damage and repair. IIMS qualified and fully insured.*

Yaffe Martin International, Arrow Mill, Queensway, Rochdale, Lancashire, OL11 2QN Tel: (01706) 717800 Fax: (01706) 717801 E-mail: info@martinyaffee.com *Toy merchants*

S. Yaffy Protective Clothing, 310 Main Street, Glasgow, G40 1LW Tel: 0141-554 2202 Fax: 0141-556 4347 E-mail: admin@yaffy.co.uk *Protective clothing manufrs*

Yajima UK Ltd, Unit 17, Rassau Industrial Estate, Rassau, Ebbw Vale, Gwent, NP23 5SD Tel: (01495) 307190 Fax: (01495) 308677 E-mail: adams@yajima-uk.co.uk *Automated welding systems manufrs*

Yale Europe, Flagship House, Reading Road North, Fleet, Hampshire, GU51 4WD Tel: (01252) 770700 Fax: (01252) 770890 *Materials handling equipment manufrs*

Yale Materials Handling UK, Unit 2 Red Rooster Industrial Estate, Tintagel Way, Aldridge, Walsall, WS9 8ER Tel: (01922) 742460 Fax: (01922) 742469 E-mail: sales@yale-uk.com *Fork lift trucks* Also at: Branches throughout the U.K.

Yale UK, 143 Rimrose Road, Bootle, Merseyside, L20 4XQ Tel: 0151-933 8300 Fax: 0151-933 5465 *Fork lift hire, sales & repairers*

Yamada Europe Co. Ltd, Festival Drive, Ebbw Vale, Gwent, NP23 8XS Tel: (01495) 300900 Fax: (01495) 300909 *Automotive parts manufrs*

Yamaha Kemble Music U K Ltd, Sherbourne Drive, Tilbrook, Milton Keynes, MK7 8BL Tel: (01908) 366700 Fax: (01908) 368872 *Musical instrument distributors*

Yamazaki Machinery UK Ltd, Badgeworth Drive, Worcester, WR4 9NF Tel: (01905) 755755 Fax: (01905) 755001 E-mail: info@mazaklaser.co.uk

▶ Yampy Solutions Ltd, The Courtyard, 3 Abbey Street, Dudley, West Midlands, DY3 2ND Tel: (01384) 255000 *IT services*

Yanco Ltd, Monks Ferry, Birkenhead, Merseyside, CH41 5LH Tel: 0151-650 8600 Fax: 0151-650 2277 E-mail: buyers@yanco.co.uk *International buying agencies*

▶ Yankee Candles Europe, 1 Bristol Distribution Park, Hawkley Drive, Bradley Stoke, Bristol, BS32 0BF Tel: (01454) 454500 Fax: (01454) 454510 *Candles & accessories distributors*

Yankel Importers, Wirral, Merseyside, CH44 Tel: (0870) 7433396 *The UK"s leading importers of pure Dead Sea Mineral Mud for therapeutic use.*Suppliers to spas, salons, therapists, health centres and individual clients.*

Yannedis Ltd, Riverside House Woodford Trading Estate, Southend Road, Woodford Green, Essex, IG8 8HQ Tel: (020) 8550 8833 Fax: (020) 8551 0026 E-mail: sales@yannedis.com *Door hardware manufrs* Also at: Branches throughout the South East

Yansport Safety Wear Ltd, Frederick Street, Walsall, WS2 9NE Tel: (01922) 721721 Fax: (01922) 723710 *Football, cricket, leisure & safety wear work clothing suppliers*

Yardbury Engineering & Oil Filled Products Ltd, Greenhole Place, Bridge of Don Industrial Estate, Aberdeen, AB23 8EU Tel: (01224) 826677 Fax: (01224) 826310 E-mail: admin@yardbury.com *Oilfield equipment repairs & manufrs*

Yardbury Kinetics Ltd, Castle Way, Castlepark Industrial Estate, Ellon, Aberdeenshire, AB41 9RG Tel: (01358) 722255 Fax: (01358) 725205 E-mail: a.huntley@yardburykinetics.com *Hydraulic engineers*

Yardene Engineering Ltd, 3 Daux Road, Billingshurst, West Sussex, RH14 9SJ Tel: (01403) 783558 Fax: (01403) 783104 E-mail: sales@yardene.co.uk *Railway signalling equipment manufrs*

Yardi Apb, 201-249 Avebury Boulevard, Milton Keynes, MK9 1AX Tel: (01908) 308400 Fax: (01908) 550022 E-mail: personnel@apb.co.uk *Computer software*

Yardley Holland Ltd, 154 Stafford Street, Walsall, WS2 8EA Tel: (01922) 633877 Fax: (01922) 634868 *Tubes & fittings merchants*

▶ Yardscrapers UK, 82 Cheetham Meadow, Leyland, PR26 7UA Tel: (01772) 434484 Fax: (01772) 434484 E-mail: maxiscrape@aol.com *Agricultural farmers*

Yarl Hydracentre Ltd, Scarth Road, Sowerby Wood Industrial Estate, Barrow-In-Furness, Cumbria, LA14 4RF Tel: (01229) 845560 Fax: (01229) 845561 E-mail: yarl@hydracentre.com *Hydraulic equipment manufrs, sales & engineering* Also at: Carlisle & Workington

Yarmouth Bearing & Transmissions, 7 James Court, Faraday Road, Great Yarmouth, Norfolk, NR31 0NF Tel: (01493) 655505 Fax: (01493) 653640 E-mail: yarmouth.bearings@wyko.co.uk *Bearing distributors*

Yarmside Fabrications Ltd, Durham Lane, Eaglescliffe, Stockton-on-Tees, Cleveland, TS16 0PS Tel: (01642) 782920 Fax: (01642) 786060 *Steel fabricators*

Yarwood Editorial Services, 9 Willow Walk, Needham Market, IP6 8DT Tel: 01449 720558 E-mail: yarwood-editorial-services@phonecoop.coop *Editor with over 15 years" publishing management experience offering comprehensive freelance support to trade and public sector publishers, book packagers, and corporate clients. Services provided include: abstracting; copy-editing; copywriting; indexing; on-screen editing; project management; proofreading; rewriting; structural editing; sub-editing; and writing. Please contact Kim on*

continued

yarwood-editorial-services@phonecoop.coop for further details.

▶ Yashar Bish, 96 Gloucester Road, Brighton, BN1 4AP Tel: (01273) 671900 Fax: (01273) 671900 E-mail: kim@yashar-bish.com *Hand woven rugs, carpets & textiles from turkey, afghanistan & persia manufrs*

Yaskawa Electric UK Ltd, 1 Hunt Hill, Cumbernauld, Glasgow, G68 9LF Tel: (01236) 735000 Fax: (01236) 458182 *Electronic component manufrs*

▶ Yate Express Stationers, 250 Longs Drive, Yate, Bristol, BS37 5XR Tel: (01454) 880080 Fax: (01454) 880081 E-mail: y.e.s@blueyonder.co.uk *Suppliers of Photo Printers,Commercial Stationery,High Quality Shredders,Desking and Office Seating*

Yateley Industries For The Disabled Ltd, Mill Lane, Yateley, Hampshire, GU46 7TF Tel: (01252) 872337 Fax: (01252) 860620 *Hand block/screen textile printers*

Yates, 80 Dollman Street, Birmingham, B7 4RP Tel: 0121-333 7091 Fax: 0121-333 7092 E-mail: akyates@btconnect.com *Profile cutting*

Yates Concrete Products, 177 Agbrigg Road, Wakefield, West Yorkshire, WF1 5BU Tel: (01924) 200997 *Concrete manufrs*

David Yates Studio, 409 Hempshaw Lane, Offerton, Stockport, Cheshire, SK1 4QA Tel: 0161-476 0464 E-mail: davidyates409@aol.com *Photographer*

▶ Yates Electrical, 30 Clearmount Avenue, Newmilns, Ayrshire, KA16 9ER Tel: (01563) 573783 Fax: (01560) 323482 E-mail: sales@a-r-removals.vze.com *Electrical services*

Yates Estate Ltd, 205 Walworth Road, London, SE17 1RL Tel: (020) 7703 3255 Fax: (020) 7701 6062 E-mail: property@yatesestate.co.uk *Property managers*

Gordon Yates Ltd, Palladium House, 1-4 Argyll Street, London, W1F 7TA Tel: (020) 7494 4466 Fax: (020) 7494 4499 *Secretarial recruitment*

▶ Yates Landscaping Ltd, 6 Hawthorne Business Park, Hawthorne Street, Warrington, WA5 0BT Tel: (01925) 638883 Fax: (01925) 638883 E-mail: yateslandscaping@tiscali.co.uk *Hard & Soft Landscaping - Scheduled Maintenance - Private & Public Gardens & Grounds - Commercial & Domestic Landscaping - Industrial Estates - Urban Renewal Schemes - Planting - Countryside Access***

Peter Yates Leathergoods Ltd, Unit M2 Lockside, Anchor Brook Industrial Park, Aldridge, Walsall, WS9 8BZ Tel: (01922) 453800 Fax: (01922) 453808 E-mail: sales@peteryatesleathergoods.co.uk *Leather goods manufrs*

Yates Print Finishers, 7 Saffron Way, Leicester, LE2 6UP Tel: 0116-283 9456 E-mail: margaret@yatesltd.fsnet.co.uk *Wire-o binding & finishers*

William Yates Ltd, White Rose Works, 61 Eyre Lane, Sheffield, S1 3GF Tel: 0114-272 3518 Fax: (0845) 0958686 E-mail: sales@chimoholdings.co.uk *Cutlery manufrs*

Yazaki (Europe) Ltd, Second Floor St. Katherines House, St. Marys Wharf, Mansfield Road, Derby, DE1 3TC Tel: (01332) 202023 Fax: (01332) 204023 *Wiring harness distributors*

▶ YCARTwedding Stationary, 1B Union Street, Greenock, Renfrewshire, PA16 8JH Tel: (07951) 145871 E-mail: tracy@ycart.co.uk *Creative personalised & unique wedding stationary & handmade cards*

Ye Old Court Yard, 29 South Street, Newtownards, County Down, BT23 4JT Tel: (028) 9182 0044 *Garden furniture manufrs*

Yeadon Hydraulics Ltd, Sizers Court, Off Henshaw Lane, Yeadon, Leeds, LS19 7DP Tel: 0113-250 3296 Fax: 0113-250 5624 E-mail: johnhall@dynamicshydraulics.com *Hydraulic engineers, installation & service*

Year In Industry, Unit 27a Weltech Centre, Ridgeway, Welwyn Garden City, Hertfordshire, AL7 2AA Tel: (01707) 871504 Fax: (01707) 377453 E-mail: admin@yini.org.uk *Industrial placements service to industry*

Yearn Glass & Co., 55 Wallis Road, London, E9 5LH Tel: (020) 8533 3307 Fax: (020) 8533 7189 E-mail: sales@yearnglass.co.uk *Domestic mirror manufrs*

Yearnhome Joinery Ltd, 11 Orchid Court, Ty Canol, Cwmbran, Gwent, NP44 6JP Tel: (01633) 866703 Fax: (01633) 866703 E-mail: yearnhomejoinery@aol.com *Joinery manufrs*

Yehlex UK, 321f Mayoral Way, Team Valley Trading Estate, Gateshead, Tyne & Wear, NE11 0RT Tel: 0191-491 5502 Fax: 0191-491 5503 E-mail: sales@yehlex.co.uk *Sports goods equipment distributors*

▶ Yeldray Agencies, Langley Drive, Birmingham, B35 7AD Tel: 0121-730 2000 *Gift & toy wholesalers*

Yello Telecommunications Management Ltd, 23 Meadvale Road, Leicester, LE2 3WN Tel: 0116-224 4000 Fax: 0116-224 4010 E-mail: enquiries@yello.co.uk *Telecommunication services*

Yellowpatter Sussex Ltd, Chantry Lane, Storrington, West Sussex, RH20 4TA Tel: (01903) 745741 Fax: (01903) 742668 E-mail: sales@yellowpatter.co.uk Principal Export Areas: Worldwide *Stainless steel enclosures manufrs*

Yellowstone Electronic Solutions Ltd, 17 Lyneham Road, Luton, LU2 9JS Tel: (01582) 722011 Fax: (01582) 654440 E-mail: sales@yellowstone.co.uk *Computer network services*

Yelrom Designs, 6 Oundle Drive, Ilkeston, Derbyshire, DE7 5DX Tel: (07976) 068235 E-mail: info@evolution-media.co.uk *Website & graphic design services*

Yeoman Aggregates Ltd, Stone Terminal, Horn Lane, London, W3 9EH Tel: (020) 8896 6820 Fax: (020) 8896 6811 *Limestone aggregate suppliers* Also at: Branches throughout the U.K.

▶ Yeoman (Morven) Ltd, Rhugh Garbh Depot, Barcaldine, Oban, Argyll, PA37 1SE Tel: (01631) 720489 Fax: (01631) 720639 *Quarrying*

Yeoman Upholstery plc, Enterprise Way, Flitwick, Bedford, MK45 5BS Tel: (01525) 713771 Fax: (01525) 717877 E-mail: peter@yeomanupholstery.co.uk *Furniture manufrs*

Yeomans Army Stores, 5-7 Rodgers Lane, Alfreton, Derbyshire, DE55 7FF Tel: (01773) 831486 Fax: (01246) 551024 E-mail: mailbox@yeomansoutdoors.co.uk *Camping equipment & outdoor wear retailers*

▶ Yeomans Army Stores, 146 Parade, Leamington Spa, Warwickshire, CV32 4AG Tel: (01926) 451276 *Outdoor & camping equipment suppliers*

Yeomans Army Stores, 6 Jubilee Buildings, Sutton-in-Ashfield, Nottinghamshire, NG17 1DE Tel: (01623) 511339 *Camping & outdoor suppliers*

Yeomans Outdoor Centre, 5 Keighley Road, Skipton, North Yorkshire, BD23 2LP Tel: (01756) 797733 *Camping & outdoors equipment suppliers*

Yeomans Outdoors, 3 Victoria Square, Ashbourne, Derbyshire, DE6 1GG Tel: (01335) 342468 *Clothing manufrs*

Yeomans Outdoors, 84-86 St. Peters Street, Derby, DE1 1SR Tel: (01332) 384684 E-mail: enquiries@yeomansoutdoors.co.uk *Camping equipment suppliers*

Yeomans Outdoors, 1b Oxford Street, Ripley, Derbyshire, DE5 3AG Tel: (01773) 748044 *Camping equipment retailers*

Yeovil Circuits Ltd, 1 Armoury Road, Lufton Trading Estate, Lufton, Yeovil, Somerset, BA22 8RL Tel: (01935) 428313 Fax: (01935) 431446 E-mail: yeovil.circuits@eclipse.co.uk *Flexible printed circuit manufrs*

Yeovil Hydraulics, 14 Gazelle Road, Lynx Trading Estate, Yeovil, Somerset, BA20 2PJ Tel: (01935) 472233 Fax: (01935) 431211 E-mail: enquiries@yeovilhydraulics.co.uk *Yeovil Hydraulics based in Yeovil Somerset can cater For all your hydraulic needs... we carry stock to suit all your requirements. Suppliers of Univer® for unbeatable service & innovation. " Pumps, valves & accessories " Flexible valve islands " Telescopic pneumatic cylinders " Induction, brazing & pipe manipulation " Clean line cylinders (available in stainless steel) " Hydraulic power units " Hose assemblies while you wait " Fluid & air power centre All types of oils, pneumatics, vaccuum parts, CETOP valves (CETOP3, CETOP5, CETOP7), hydraulic valves, industrial hose. Testing and Certification up to 15,000 PSI of Hosing Assemblies. Manufactured Burst Tester (Uniburst) Uniburst 1000, Uniburst 1250, Uniburst 1300 bottle testing equipment from injection moulding systems. " Loose hose fittings or complete assemblies " All different materials available*

Yeovil Woodworking, Buckland Road, Pen Mill Trading Estate, Yeovil, Somerset, BA21 5HA Tel: (01935) 474190 Fax: (01935) 474355 *Joinery manufrs*

Yeoward Shipping Ltd, The Logistics Office, Port of Liverpool, Liverpool, L21 1JR Tel: 0151-928 8173 Fax: 0151-928 8174 E-mail: yeowardshipping@btconnect.com *Ships agents & forwarding agents*

Yes City Ltd, 12 Carthusian Street, London, EC1M 6EZ Tel: (020) 7600 4600 Fax: (020) 7600 7424 E-mail: richard.amphlett@yescity.biz *Marketing agents*

▶ Yes Graphic Design & Print, 73 Birkmyre Road, Glasgow, G51 3HG Tel: 0141-445 8644 Fax: 0141-445 8655

Yes Response Ltd, Unit 15 Brookside Business Park, Brookside Road, Uttoxeter, Staffordshire, ST14 8AU Tel: (01889) 561400 Fax: (01889) 568264 E-mail: dhanley@yesresponse.co.uk *Marketing agency & fulfillment house services*

Yesterdays Pine Co, 7 Terry Dicken Industrial Estate, Station Road, Stokesley, Middlesbrough, Cleveland, TS9 7AE Tel: (01642) 711101 Fax: (01642) 711101 *Pine furniture supplier & manufrs*

Yesterdays Of Wolston, 2 Warwick Road, Wolston, Coventry, CV8 3HB Tel: (024) 7654 4818 Fax: (024) 7654 5510 E-mail: yesterdaysemail@aol.com *Furniture suppliers*

▶ Yesteryear Railwayana, Stabling Cottage, Goodwin Road, Ramsgate, Kent, CT11 0JJ Tel: (01843) 587283 Fax: (01843) 587283 E-mail: info@yesrail.co.uk *Printers of railway books & railway history material*

▶ Yeti's PR, Marketing & Design, 21 The Courtyard, London Road, Gloucester, GL1 3PS Tel: (01452) 300683 E-mail: andy@10yetis.co.uk *Affordable PR, marketing & Design services for small businesses*

Yetman Sausages, 52-54 Hazelwick Road, Crawley, West Sussex, RH10 1LZ Tel: (01293) 525235 *Sausage manufrs*

Yew Tree Joinery, Yew Tree House, Hill Road, Sandford, Winscombe, Avon, BS25 5RJ Tel: (01934) 820585 Fax: (01934) 820585 *Joinery manufrs*

Yewdale Bridge, Wickford Enterprise Centre, Enterprise Way, Wickford, Essex, SS11 8DH Tel: (01268) 570900 Fax: (01268) 732509 E-mail: sales@yewdalebridge.com *Design, manufacture and wholesale of the DEFIANT, VITESSE, MOVATRACK, KESTREL and HARRIER brands of blinds, curtains, curtain tracts, insect screens and anti-ligature products. Professional help and training services available.*

Yha Adventure Shops P.L.C., 90-98 Corporation Street, Birmingham, B4 6XS Tel: 0121-236 7799 Fax: 0121-236 4118 E-mail: birmingham@yhaadventure.com *Mountain camping & hiking equipment*

▶ YMA Associates Ltd, 22 Chelmarsh Close, Redditch, Worcestershire, B98 8SQ Tel: (01527) 585090 Fax: (0870) 0521898 E-mail: ksenquiries@yma-associates.com *It consultants*

YMT Ltd, Brympton Way, Lynx West Trading Estate, Yeovil, Somerset, BA20 2HP Tel: (01935) 428375 Fax: (01935) 432684 E-mail: sales@ymtltd.co.uk *Machine tool suppliers*

Yo6 Computing, White Lodge, Tollerton Road, Huby, York, YO61 1HX Tel: (0845) 6441440 Fax: (0871) 2205371 E-mail: enquiries@yo6.co.uk *Software engi*

▶ Yogabuds Ltd, 47 Algers Road, Loughton, Essex, IG10 4NG Tel: 020 8508 3653 *Yoga is committed to developing yoga as part of mainstream education in*primary and speci needs schools, resulting in more children receiving the*benefits. This can only happe training more specialist teachers. You*will n a qualification to teach and that qualificatior needs to be*accredited to be meaningful. T accreditation, from Edexcel, is the BTEC*- Advanced Diploma for Teaching Yoga to Children.*

Yokogawa Ltd, Stuart Road, Manor Park, Run Cheshire, WA7 1TR Tel: (01928) 597100 Fax: (01928) 597101 E-mail: info@uk.yokogawa.com *Electronic measuring equipment*

Yokogawa Marex Ltd, 34 Medina Road, Cowe Of Wight, PO31 7DA Tel: (01983) 296011 Fax: (01983) 291776 E-mail: sales@ymx.yokogawa.com Principa Export Areas: Worldwide *Supervisory contr systems manufrs*

Yokogawa UK Ltd, Solar House, Mercury Park Wycombe Lane, Wooburn Green, High Wycombe, Buckinghamshire, HP10 0HH Tel: (01628) 535640 Fax: (0870) 2384342 E-mail: christine.amos@uk.yokogawa.co.uk *Emergency & safety shutdown systems ma*

Yokogowa Measurement Technologies Ltd, So House, Murcary Park, Wickham Lane, Woo Green, Buckinghamshire, HP10 0HH Tel: (01628) 535830 Fax: (01628) 535839 E-mail: info@uk.yokogowa.com *Instrumenta & measurement*

Yokota UK, Low Common Road, Dinnington, Sheffield, S25 2RJ Tel: (01909) 552471 Fax: (01909) 552472 E-mail: info@yokota.c *Suppliers of 'Yokota', 'Toku' & 'Red Rooster airtools for automotive & industrial productic applications. Full range of industrial torque controlled production & assembly tools. On the first choices of the motor industry. Also 'Action' industrial impact sockets & adaptors*

▶ Yonder Mountain, Maunview, 2 Old Mill Clos Forest Town, Mansfield, Nottinghamshire, NG19 0EA Tel: (01623) 625545 E-mail: ron.koch@yonder-mountain.co.uk *Website authoring & hosting email & compu configuration*

York Assemblies Ltd, 374 Thurmaston BLVD, Leicester, LE4 9LE Tel: 0116-246 3240 *Engineering machine shops*

York Blind Co., Heworth House Studio, Melrosegate, York, YO31 0RP Tel: (01904) 416389 Fax: (01904) 416389 *Soft furnishing supplier & manufrs*

York Box, 31 Auster Road, Clifton Moor, York, YO30 4XA Tel: (01904) 610651 Fax: (01904 691458 *Cardboard boxes manufrs* Also at: Leeds

York Brick Cutting Co, Broad Oak Cottage, Da Lane, Kexby, York, YO41 5LJ Tel: (01904) 607123 Fax: (01904) 607500 E-mail: sales@yorkbrick.co.uk *Brick cutters artificial stone suppliers*

▶ Caroline York Ltd, Broad House, Broad Lan Bracknell, Berkshire, RG12 9BJ Tel: (01344 450504 E-mail: info@carolineyork.co.uk *Retailers of curtains, blinds & soft furnishing*

York City Leather Co., Unit 7, Roland Court Industrial Estate, Huntington Road, York, YO32 9PW Tel: (01904) 765461 Fax: (0190 765461 E-mail: lenyclyork@line1.net *Leathe goods merchants & manufrs*

▶ York City Printers Ltd, Unit 4, Birch Park, Huntington Road, York, YO31 9BL Tel: (019 620490

▶ York Coffee Systems, Unit 1, Acaster Indust Estate, Acaster Malbis, York, YO23 2TX Tel: (01904) 702016 Fax: (01904) 702016 E-mail: admin@yorkcoffeesystems.com *Suppliers of high quality brand name tea & coffee vending machines*

York Coin Leisure, Units 4 & 9 Roland Court, Huntington, York, YO32 9PW Tel: (01904) 750445 Fax: (01904) 767844 E-mail: yorkcoin@leisure72.fsbusiness.co.u *Suppliers of amusement machines, pool tab fruit machines covering North Yorkshire.*

York Distribution Ltd, 23-24 Auster Road, York, YO30 4XA Tel: (01904) 693969 Fax: (01904 693255 E-mail: sales@ydl.co.uk *Computer*

York Glassware Services Ltd, 9 The Crescent, YO24 1AW Tel: (01904) 651493 Fax: (0190 611932 E-mail: mail@ygs.net *Laboratory equipment suppliers & manufrs*

York Handmade Brick Co. Ltd, Winchester Hou Forest Lane, Alne, York, YO61 1TU Tel: (01 838881 Fax: (01347) 838885 E-mail: sales@yorkhandmade.co.uk *Brick s & manufrs*

York International Ltd, Gardiners La South, Basildon, Essex, SS14 3HE Tel: (01268) 24 Fax: (01268) 246001 E-mail: sales@york.co *Air conditioning systems, refrigeration instal & retailers services*

▶ York International, 37 Deerdykes View, Cumbernauld, Glasgow, G68 9HN Tel: (012 786000

▶ York International Ltd, 4 Zealley Estate, Gre Way, Kingsteignton, Newton Abbot, Devon, TQ12 3TD Tel: (01626) 333734 Fax: (01626 335220

▶ York International Ltd, Arden House, Marsh Lane, Hampton-in-Arden, Solihull, West Midlands, B92 0AJ Tel: (01675) 443341 Fax: (01675) 442402

York Linings International Ltd, Millfield Industri Estate, Wheldrake, York, YO19 6NA Tel: (01 449777 Fax: (01904) 449888 E-mail: yorkhq@yli-ltd.demon.co.uk *Refract contractors*

York Metrology Ltd, 6 Highmeres Road, Leices LE4 9LZ Tel: 0116-246 0250 *Measuring equipment calibration manufrs*

York Model Making & Display Ltd, Unit 13, The Commercial Centre, Stockton On The Fores York, YO32 9LE Tel: (01904) 400358 Fax: (01904) 400358

con